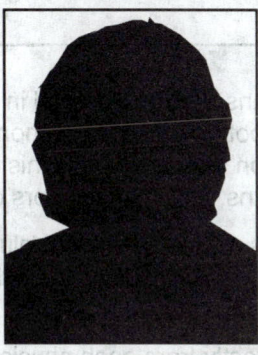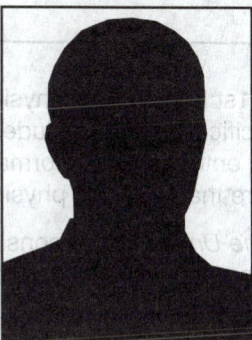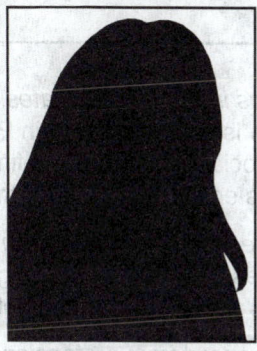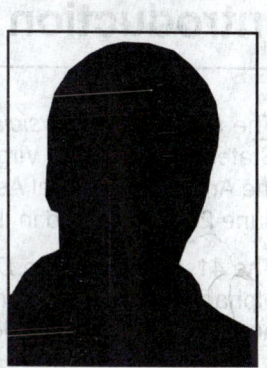

41st Edition

Directory

of

Physicians

in the United States

AMERICAN MEDICAL ASSOCIATION

Introduction

The *Directory of Physicians in the United States,* 41st Edition, lists physicians who are located in the United States, Puerto Rico, Virgin Islands, and certain Pacific Islands. It includes both members and nonmembers of the American Medical Association (AMA). The final entry date for information that appears in this edition was June 2008. Included in this edition are data for more than 900,000 physicians, including Doctors of Osteopathy.

The 41st edition of the *Directory of Physicians in the United States* consists of four volumes. Volume 1 is the alphabetical index. Volumes 2, 3, and 4 are the geographical register, arranged alphabetically within each state and city. A Guide to Codes and an Explanation of Codes appear in each part of the *Directory.*

The listings have been prepared from professional information obtained directly from each physician and verified information supplied in part by medical schools, state licensing and other federal agencies, and the American Board of Medical Specialties. The compilation, organization, and publication of physician data are continuing programs, and it is the aim of the AMA to achieve a high degree of accuracy. Users of this *Directory* are invited to inform the AMA's Division of Survey and Data Resources of any existing inaccuracies or updates to information listed.

Updates to physician listings can be directed to the following department:

American Medical Association
Division of Survey and Data Resources
Attn: Data Verification Unit
515 North State Street
Chicago, IL 60654
312 464-5759
312 464-4880 (Fax)

The Association wishes to thank all who cooperated in furnishing information for this edition.

Information regarding certification from a member board of the American Board of Medical Specialties® (ABMS) is proprietary data maintained in a copyrighted database compilation owned by ABMS. © 2008 American Board of Medical Specialties. All rights reserved.

Important Notice: The *Directory of Physicians in the United States* is compiled and published by the American Medical Association as a reference source of demographic and professional information on individual physicians in the United States. The *Directory* or any of its data, listings, or other constituent elements may not be republished, resold, or duplicated, in whole or in part, for commercial or any other purposes, or for purposes of compiling mailing lists or any other lists of physicians. The use of the *Directory* to establish independent data files or compendiums of statistical information is prohibited.

AMA Physician Masterfile

Established by the American Medical Association (AMA) in 1906, the Physician Masterfile was initially developed as a record-keeping device supporting membership and mailing activities. Since then, the Physician Masterfile has expanded to include significant education, training, and professional certification information on virtually all Doctors of Medicine (MDs) and Doctors of Osteopathic Medicine (DOs) in the United States, Puerto Rico, Virgin Islands, and certain Pacific Islands.

The AMA Division of Survey and Data Resources is dedicated to effectively and accurately collecting, analyzing, and managing data within the Physician Masterfile, which serves as a primary resource for professional medical organizations, universities and medical schools, research institutions, governmental agencies, and other health-related groups. Use of the Physician Masterfile by agencies and organizations concerned with verifying physicians' credentials and health manpower planning is fundamental to the AMA's mission to strengthen the medical profession and ensure quality health care for the American public.

The Physician Masterfile includes information on members and nonmembers of the Association and graduates of international medical schools who live in the United States. A record is established when individuals enter medical schools accredited by the Liaison Committee on Medical Education (LCME) or, in the case of international medical graduates (IMGs), upon entry into a postgraduate residency training program accredited by the Accreditation Council for Graduate Medical Education (ACGME). IMGs are also identified when they obtain a license from one of the 68 licensing jurisdictions. As a physician's training and career develop, additional professional certification information is added to the Masterfile record.

The AMA's database comprises current and historical data for more than 940,000 residents and physicians and approximately 77,000 students in the United States. This figure includes approximately 243,000 graduates of foreign medical schools who reside in the United States and who have met the educational and credentialing requirements necessary for recognition and approximately 62,000 doctors of osteopathy. Each AMA Physician Masterfile record includes the physician's name, medical school and year of graduation, gender, birthplace, and birthdate. Additional data (residency training, state licensure, board certification, geographical location and address, type of practice, present employment, and practice specialty) are added from primary data sources or from surveying the physicians directly as their training and career develop.

Masterfile records are never removed even in the case of a physician's death. The AMA maintains information on more than 170,000 deceased physicians. These data are shared with other organizations and agencies who credential physicians and are used to identify individuals who attempt to fraudulently assume the credentials of deceased physicians.

Physicians' records are subject to change and are updated continually through the extensive data collection activities performed within SDR. The Census of Physicians (PPA census) consists of targeted mailings sent to as many as 250,000 physicians each year. Physicians are presented with their Masterfile information and asked to report any data discrepancies or submit updates to their information. Although information collected from the annual PPA census contributes to much of the information maintained in the AMA Physician Masterfile, primary source data are also obtained from the organizations identified below.

- American Board of Medical Specialties (ABMS): ABMS-member board certification and subcertification status
- Accreditation Council for Graduate Medical Education (ACGME): ACGME-accredited residency programs and GME teaching institutions
- Education Commission for Foreign Medical Graduation (ECFMG): international medical graduates who have been certified or have applied for certification by the ECFMG
- Group Practices: group practice location and physician affiliation
- Liaison Committee on Medical Education: US medical school matriculation and graduation data
- National Residency Matching Program: residents matched to ACGME-accredited programs
- State and Specialty Medical Societies: membership information
- State licensing boards: physicians' initial and active licensure status
- United States Postal Service Address Correction System (ACS): address updates generated through ACS change of address and nondelivery processing
- United States Drug Enforcement Administration (DEA): federal controlled substance registration and status

AMA Physician Masterfile (continued)

Over the years, various studies have been conducted to assess the quality of the Physician Masterfile. More recent studies comparing selected variables have demonstrated that the Masterfile continues to be one of the most comprehensive and accurate sources of physician data in the United States.

The AMA Board of Trustees has mandated guidelines for the release of AMA data. The AMA respects and is committed to protecting the privacy of personal information of its members, customers, and business partners. The AMA's Privacy Statement explains how the AMA collects, uses, shares, and safeguards personal information and is available online at http://www.ama-assn.org/ama/pub/category/7454.html. Under these guidelines—which are intended to safeguard the confidentiality of physicians' records and the AMA's proprietary rights—physician data are available for manpower research and other specific purposes.

The Division of Database Products and Licensing maintains the list of authorized companies who supply information from the AMA Physician Masterfile to researchers and to firms and institutions interested in providing goods and services to physician and group practices. For more information on AMA Database Licensing, direct your inquiries to the following individuals:

Peter Ellis
(312) 464-4876
E-mail: peter.ellis@ama-assn.org

Andrea McNeal
(312) 464-5167
E-mail: andrea.mcneal@ama-assn.org
(312) 464-5801 (fax)

The physician information contained in the AMA Directory of Physicians in the United States does not meet the primary source requirements for physician credentialing as outlined by accrediting organizations such as the National Committee for Quality Assurance (NCQA) or the Joint Commission.

The AMA seeks to achieve a high degree of accuracy in the organization and publication of physician data. Direct any changes to information to the Division of Survey and Data Resources at the following address:

American Medical Association
Division of Survey and Data Resources
Attn: Data Verification Unit
515 North State Street
Chicago, IL 60654
312 464-5759
312 464-4880 (Fax)

Guide to Codes in Geographical Register

EXAMPLE of listing: **DOE, John Robt.** 1220 N MAIN St 43210   #048–02–1968 ▲ L1971 **OBG PD** *020†85‡

(Note: ■ May appear in place of the address. The symbols #, *, and † act as data separators, not indicators of footnoted or other information.)

43210	#048–02–1968	▲	L1971	OBG	PD	*020	†85	‡
Postal Zip Code	Medical School and Year of Graduation	Osteopathic Physician	Year of License	Primary Specialty	Secondary Specialty	Type of Practice	American Specialty Board	Physician's Recognition Award

Local Address — Preferred Professional Address (address at which physicians receive medically related material).

Privacy Protected — ■—Indicates contact information is privacy protected by request of physician and/or AMA.

Postal Zip Code — 43210—Indicates Postal Zip Code Number.

Medical School — #048–02—First three digits indicate state (or foreign country) of medical school location; next two digits indicate specific medical school. See list of US, Canadian, and foreign medical schools in Volumes 1–4.

Year of Graduation — 1968—Year the physician graduated from the medical school listed.

Osteopathic Physician — ▲—Indicates Osteopathic Physician Member of AMA. Osteopathic physicians who are not AMA members do not appear in this directory.

Year of License — L1971—Year of license in state of present professional mailing address.

Primary Self-Designated Practice Specialty — OBG—Indicates primary or major field of specialty practice as designated by the physician. See Explanation of Codes.

Secondary Self-Designated Practice Specialty — PD—Indicates secondary field of specialty practice as designated by the physician. See Explanation of Codes.

Type of Practice — *020—Indicates the type of physician's practice as follows:

012—Resident—All Years	071—Retired
020—Direct Patient Care	072—Semiretired
030—Administrative Activities	074—Temporarily not in practice
040—Medical Teaching	075—Inactive for other reasons
050—Medical Research	100—No Classification
062—Non-Patient Care	

(For definitions of these terms, see Explanation of Codes in Volumes 1–4.)

American Specialty Board Certification — †85—Indicates that the physician has successfully completed an approved educational program and evaluation process resulting in certification by one of the 24 member boards of the American Board of Medical Specialties®. See Explanation of Codes.

Physician's Recognition Award — ‡—Indicates that the physician held a Physician's Recognition Award current as of June 2008. See Explanation of Codes.

Explanation of Codes

Intended Use of AMA Physician Masterfile Codes for Self-designation of Practice Specialties/Areas of Practice

Self-designated practice specialties/areas of Practice (SDPS) listed on the AMA Physician Masterfile have historically related to the record-keeping needs of the American Medical Association and do not imply "recognition" or "endorsement" of any field of medical practice by the Association. SDPS refers to a self-designated specialty which is not equivalent to nor does it imply ABMS® Board Certification. The fact that a physician chooses to designate a given specialty/area of practice on our records does not necessarily mean that the physician has been trained or has special competence to practice the SDPS.

Codes for Self-designation of Practice Specialties by Specialty/Areas of Practice

AR	Abdominal Radiology	ESN	Endovascular Surgical Neuroradiology (Radiology)	MGP	Molecular Genetic Pathology (Pathology)
AS	Abdominal Surgery			OMO	Musculoskeletal Oncology
ADM	Addiction Medicine	ES	Endovascular Surgical Neuroradiology (Neurological Surgery)	MSR	Musculoskeletal Radiology
ADP	Addiction Psychiatry			NPM	Neonatal-Perinatal Medicine
AMF	Adolescent Medicine (Family Medicine)	EP	Epidemiology	NEP	Nephrology
AMI	Adolescent Medicine (Internal Medicine)	FPS	Facial Plastic Surgery	NDP	Neurodevelopmental Disabilities (Pediatrics)
ADL	Adolescent Medicine (Pediatrics)	FM	Family Medicine		
ACA	Adult Cardiothoracic Anesthesiology (Anesthesiology)	FOP	Forensic Pathology	NDN	Neurodevelopmental Disabilities (Psychiatry & Neurology)
		PFP	Forensic Psychiatry		
OAR	Adult Reconstructive Orthopedics	GE	Gastroenterology	N	Neurology
AM	Aerospace Medicine	GP	General Practice	NS	Neurological Surgery
A	Allergy	GS	General Surgery	NMN	Neuromuscular Medicine (Neurology)
AI	Allergy & Immunology	FPG	Geriatric Medicine (Family Medicine)	NMP	Neuromuscular Medicine (Physical Medicine & Rehabilitation)
ALI	Clinical Laboratory Immunology (Allergy & Immunology)	IMG	Geriatric Medicine (Internal Medicine)		
		PYG	Geriatric Psychiatry	NP	Neuropathology
PTH	Anatomic/Clinical Pathology	GYN	Gynecology	RNR	Neuroradiology
ATP	Anatomic Pathology	GO	Gynecological Oncology	NUP	Neuropsychiatry
AN	Anesthesiology	HS	Hand Surgery	NO	Neurotology (Otolaryngology)
BBK	Blood Banking/Transfusion Medicine	HNS	Head & Neck Surgery	NC	Nuclear Cardiology
ICE	Clinical Cardiac Electrophysiology	HEM	Hematology (Internal Medicine)	NM	Nuclear Medicine
CTR	Cardiothoracic Radiology	HMP	Hematology (Pathology)	NR	Nuclear Radiology
CD	Cardiovascular Disease	HO	Hematology/Oncology	NTR	Nutrition
PCH	Chemical Pathology	HEP	Hepatology	OBS	Obstetrics
CAP	Child Abuse Pediatrics	HPM	Hospice & Palliative Medicine	OBG	Obstetrics & Gynecology
CHP	Child and Adolescent Psychiatry	HPA	Hospice & Palliative Medicine (Anesthesiology)	OM	Occupational Medicine
CHN	Child Neurology			OPH	Ophthalmology
CBG	Clinical Biochemical Genetics	HPE	Hospice & Palliative Medicine (Emergency Medicine)	OMF	Oral & Maxillofacial Surgery
CCG	Clinical Cytogenetics			ORS	Orthopedic Surgery
CG	Clinical Genetics	HPF	Hospice & Palliative Medicine (Family Medicine)	OSS	Orthopedic Surgery of the Spine
DDL	Clinical and Laboratory Dermatological Immunology	HPI	Hospice & Palliative Medicine (Internal Medicine)	OTR	Orthopedic Trauma
				OMM	Osteopathic Manipulative Medicine
ILI	Clinical and Laboratory Immunology (Internal Medicine)	HPO	Hospice & Palliative Medicine (Obstetrics & Gynecology)	OFA	Foot and Ankle, Orthopedics
				OTO	Otolaryngology
PLI	Clinical and Laboratory Immunology (Pediatrics)	HPP	Hospice & Palliative Medicine (Pediatrics)	PME	Pain Management
				PMM	Pain Medicine
CMG	Clinical Molecular Genetics	HPR	Hospice & Palliative Medicine (Physical Medicine & Rehabilitation)	APM	Pain Medicine (Anesthesiology)
CN	Clinical Neurophysiology			PMN	Pain Medicine (Neurology)
CLP	Clinical Pathology	HPN	Hospice & Palliative Medicine (Psychiatry & Neurology)	PMP	Pain Medicine (Physical Medicine & Rehabilitation)
PA	Clinical Pharmacology				
CRS	Colon & Rectal Surgery	HPD	Hospice & Palliative Medicine (Radiology)	PPN	Pain Medicine (Psychiatry)
CHS	Congenital Cardiac Surgery (Thoracic Surgery)			PLM	Palliative Medicine
		HOS	Hospitalist	PDA	Pediatric Allergy
CS	Cosmetic Surgery	IG	Immunology	PAN	Pediatric Anesthesiology (Anesthesiology)
CFS	Craniofacial Surgery	ID	Infectious Disease		
CCA	Critical Care Medicine (Anesthesiology)	IM	Internal Medicine	PDC	Pediatric Cardiology
		IC	Interventional Cardiology	PCS	Pediatric Cardiothoracic Surgery
CCM	Critical Care Medicine (Internal Medicine)	LM	Legal Medicine	CCP	Pediatric Critical Care Medicine
		MFM	Maternal & Fetal Medicine	PDD	Pediatric Dermatology
OCC	Critical Care Medicine (Obstetrics & Gynecology)	MG	Medical Genetics	PE	Pediatric Emergency Medicine (Emergency Medicine)
		MDM	Medical Management		
PCP	Cytopathology	MM	Medical Microbiology	PEM	Pediatric Emergency Medicine (Pediatrics)
D	Dermatology	ON	Medical Oncology		
DMP	Dermatopathology	ETX	Medical Toxicology (Emergency Medicine)	PDE	Pediatric Endocrinology
DS	Dermatologic Surgery			PG	Pediatric Gastroenterology
DBP	Developmental-Behavioral Pediatrics	PDT	Medical Toxicology (Pediatrics)	PHO	Pediatric Hematology/Oncology
DIA	Diabetes	PTX	Medical Toxicology (Preventive Medicine)	PDI	Pediatric Infectious Disease
DR	Diagnostic Radiology			PN	Pediatric Nephrology
EM	Emergency Medicine	MGG	Molecular Genetic Pathology (Medical Genetics)	PO	Pediatric Ophthalmology
END	Endocrinology, Diabetes and Metabolism			OP	Pediatric Orthopedics

x

PDO	Pediatric Otolaryngology	**SME**	Sleep Medicine	
PP	Pediatric Pathology	**SMI**	Sleep Medicine (Internal Medicine)	
PDP	Pediatric Pulmonology	**SMO**	Sleep Medicine (Otolaryngology)	
PDR	Pediatric Radiology	**SMP**	Sleep Medicine (Pediatrics)	
RPM	Pediatric Rehabilitation Medicine	**SMN**	Sleep Medicine (Psychiatry & Neurology)	

PDO Pediatric Otolaryngology
PP Pediatric Pathology
PDP Pediatric Pulmonology
PDR Pediatric Radiology
RPM Pediatric Rehabilitation Medicine
PPR Pediatric Rheumatology
NSP Pediatric Surgery (Neurology)
PDS Pediatric Surgery (Surgery)
PTP Pediatric Transplant Hepatology
UP Pediatric Urology
PD Pediatrics
PHM Pharmaceutical Medicine
PHL Phlebology
PM Physical Medicine & Rehabilitation
PS Plastic Surgery
PSH Plastic Surgery within the Head & Neck
PSO Plastic Surgery within the Head & Neck (Otolaryngology)
PSP Plastic Surgery within the Head & Neck (Plastic Surgery)
GPM Preventive Medicine
PRD Procedural Dermatology
PRO Proctology
P Psychiatry
PYA Psychoanalysis
PYM Psychosomatic Medicine
PHP Public Health and General Preventive Medicine
PCC Pulmonary Critical Care Medicine
PUD Pulmonary Disease
RO Radiation Oncology
RP Radiological Physics
R Radiology
REN Reproductive Endocrinology and Infertility
RHU Rheumatology
SP Selective Pathology

SME Sleep Medicine
SMI Sleep Medicine (Internal Medicine)
SMO Sleep Medicine (Otolaryngology)
SMP Sleep Medicine (Pediatrics)
SMN Sleep Medicine (Psychiatry & Neurology)
SCI Spinal Cord Injury Medicine
ESM Sports Medicine (Emergency Medicine)
FSM Sports Medicine (Family Medicine)
ISM Sports Medicine (Internal Medicine)
OSM Sports Medicine (Orthopedic Surgery)
PSM Sports Medicine (Pediatrics)
PRS Sports Medicine (Physical Medicine & Rehabilitation)
CCS Surgical Critical Care (Surgery)
HSO Surgery of the Hand (Orthopedics)
HSP Surgery of the Hand (Plastic Surgery)
HSS Surgery of the Hand (Surgery)
SO Surgical Oncology
TS Thoracic Surgery
TRS Trauma Surgery
THP Transplant Hepatology (Internal Medicine)
TTS Transplant Surgery
UME Undersea & Hyperbaric Medicine (Emergency Medicine)
UM Undersea & Hyperbaric Medicine (Preventive Medicine)
UCM Urgent Care Medicine
U Urology
VIR Vascular and Interventional Radiology
VM Vascular Medicine
VN Vascular Neurology
VS Vascular Surgery

In addition to the above, the following specialty designations are also used:

OS Other (i.e., a specialty other than those appearing above)
US Unspecified

Combined Specialties:

EFM Emergency Medicine/Family Medicine
IMD Internal Medicine/Dermatology
MEM Internal Medicine/Emergency Medicine
IEC Internal Medicine/Emergency Medicine\Critical Care Medicine
IFP Internal Medicine/Family Medicine
MDG Internal Medicine/Medical Genetics
MN Internal Medicine/Neurology
INM Internal Medicine/Nuclear Medicine
MPD Internal Medicine/Pediatrics
MPM Internal Medicine/Physical Medicine & Rehabilitation
IPM Internal Medicine/Preventive Medicine
MP Internal Medicine/Psychiatry
NNM Neurology/Nuclear Medicine
NRN Neurology/Diagnostic Radiology/ Neuroradiology
NPR Neurology/Physical Medicine & Rehabilitation
PDM Pediatrics/Dermatology
EMP Pediatrics/Emergency Medicine
PMG Pediatrics/Medical Genetics
PPM Pediatrics/Physical Medicine & Rehabilitation
CPP Pediatrics/Psychiatry/Child & Adolescent Psychiatry
FPP Psychiatry/Family Medicine
PYN Psychiatry/Neurology

Note: No code appears for those physicians who have not designated a practice specialty. The code **TY** appears for those physicians in a transitional year of accredited graduate medical education.

Type of Practice

The Type of Practice code is indicated by a numeric code and reflects the physician's **primary** type of practice as follows:

012   **Resident—All Years**   Includes any physician in supervised practice of medicine among patients in a hospital or in its outpatient department, with continued instruction in the science and art of medicine by the staff of the facility. Also includes any physician in advanced training in the clinical divisions of medicine, surgery, and other specialty fields preparing for practice in a given specialty. Fellows are included as residents for record-keeping purposes.

020   **Direct Patient Care**   Physicians engaged in seeing patients—also includes patient services by such physicians as pathologists and radiologists.

030   **Administrative Activities**   Physicians in administrative activities in a hospital, other health facility, agency, clinic, group, or any other organization by which they are salaried as an executive or administrative staff member.

040   **Medical Teaching**   Physicians with teaching responsibilities in medical schools, hospitals, nursing schools, colleges, universities, or other educational institutions in which they are salaried as an administrative staff member.

050	**Medical Research**	Physicians conducting research—includes activities (whether funded or unfunded) performed to develop new medical knowledge, potentially leading to publication.
062	**Other Medical Activities (Non-Patient Care)**	Physicians employed by insurance companies, corporations, voluntary organizations, medical societies, associations, grants, and foreign countries, and engaged in activities such as institutional review boards, audit committees, credentialing, community service, lectures, and voluntary activities.
071–075	**Inactive Categories**	Physicians who are retired (071), semiretired (072), temporarily not in practice (074), or inactive for other reasons (075).
100	**No Classification**	Physicians who did not provide information on their type of practice.

Certification from a Member Board of the American Board of Medical Specialties®*

The intent of the certification of physicians by the Member Board of the American Board of Medical Specialties (ABMS) is to provide assurance to the public that a physician specialist certified by a Member Board of the ABMS has successfully completed an approved educational program and evaluation process that includes an examination designed to assess the knowledge, skills, and experience required to provide quality patient care in that specialty. This *Directory* lists the **initial** certificate issued to diplomates.

Medical specialty certification in the United States is a voluntary process. While medical licensure sets the minimum competency requirements to diagnose and treat patients, it is not specialty specific. Board certification demonstrates a physician's exceptional expertise in a particular specialty and/or subspecialty of medical practice and a physician's commitment and expertise in consistently achieving superior clinical outcomes in a responsive, patient-focused setting.

Certification by an ABMS Member Board involves a rigorous process of testing and peer evaluation that is designed and administered by specialists in the specific area of medicine. At one time, physicians were awarded certificates that were not time limited and, therefore, did not have to be renewed. Later, a program of periodic recertification (every six to 10 years) was initiated to ensure that physicians engaged in continuing education and examination to keep current in their specialty.

In 2006, ABMS's 24 Member Boards adopted a new gold standard for recertification with a continuous ABMS Maintenance of Certification (MOC) program for all specialties. MOC uses evidence-based guidelines and national standards and best practices in combination with customized continuing education so that physicians demonstrate their leadership in the national movement for healthcare quality. MOC also requires proof of continuing education and experience in between testing for recertification.

Through ABMS's Maintenance of Certification (MOC) process, board-certified physicians in 24 medical specialties build six core competencies for quality patient care in their medical specialty. These competencies were first adopted by the Accreditation Council for Graduate Medical Education (ACGME) and ABMS in 1999.

Six Core Competencies

- Patient Care—Provide care that is compassionate, appropriate, and effective treatment for health problems and to promote health.

- Medical Knowledge—Demonstrate knowledge about established and evolving biomedical, clinical, and cognate sciences and their application in patient care.

- Interpersonal and Communication Skills—Demonstrate skills that result in effective information exchange and teaming with patients, their families, and professional associates (e.g., fostering a therapeutic

Explanation of Codes (continued)

relationship that is ethically sounds, uses effective listening skills with nonverbal and verbal communication; working as both a team member and at times as a leader).

- Professionalism—Demonstrate a commitment to carrying out professional responsibilities, adherence to ethical principles, and sensitivity to diverse patient populations.

- Systems-based Practice—Demonstrate awareness of and responsibility to larger context and systems of healthcare. Be able to call on system resources to provide optimal care (e.g., coordinating care across sites or serving as the primary case manager when care involves multiple specialties, professions, or sites).

- Practice-based Learning and Improvement—Able to investigate and evaluate their patient care practices, appraise and assimilate scientific evidence, and improve their practice of medicine.

American Specialty Boards

Board Code	Board Name	Board Code	Board Name
90	American Board of Thoracic Surgery	85	American Board of Surgery
15	American Board of Dermatology	40	American Board of Orthopaedic Surgery
95	American Board of Urology	60	American Board of Physical Medicine and Rehabilitation
16	American Board of Emergency Medicine	20	American Board of Internal Medicine
10	American Board of Colon and Rectal Surgery	18	American Board of Family Medicine
75	American Board of Psychiatry and Neurology	03	American Board of Allergy and Immunology
50	American Board of Pathology	30	American Board of Obstetrics and Gynecology
55	American Board of Pediatrics	45	American Board of Otolaryngology
28	American Board of Nuclear Medicine	65	American Board of Plastic Surgery
35	American Board of Ophthalmology	70	American Board of Preventive Medicine
80	American Board of Radiology	25	American Board of Neurological Surgery
05	American Board of Anesthesiology	19	American Board of Medical Genetics

Physician's Recognition Award

In 1968 the AMA House of Delegates established the AMA Physician's Recognition Award (PRA) to encourage physicians to participate in continuing medical education (CME) and to acknowledge when individual physicians complete CME activities. Activities that meet education standards established by the AMA can be designated *AMA PRA Category 1 Credit*™ by educational institutions accredited to provide CME to physicians. These typically include state medical societies, medical specialty societies, medical schools, and hospitals. Other activities, usually independent or physician directed learning, may be reported for *AMA PRA Category 2 Credit*™.

AMA PRA certificates are awarded in lengths of 1, 2, or 3 years, with the following requirements:

1-year certificate–50 credits
- 20 credits, *AMA PRA Category 1 Credits*™
- 30 credits, *AMA PRA Category 1 or 2 Credits*

2-year certificate–100 credits
- 40 credits, *AMA PRA Category 1 Credits*
- 60 credits, *AMA PRA Category 1 or 2 Credits*

3-year certificate–150 credits
- 60 credits, *AMA PRA Category 1 Credits*
- 90 credits, *AMA PRA Category 1 or 2 Credits*

At least 50% of the credits submitted must be within the physician's specialty or area of practice. The AMA also offers the PRA with Commendation, a certificate that recognizes physicians who regularly demonstrate a high level of commitment to their continuing education and requires a greater amount of credit. More information is available at www.ama-assn.org/go/pra.

It is important to note that the AMA continues to support voluntary reporting of CME. Additionally, a physician may participate in CME and choose not to apply for the PRA. The double-dagger symbol (‡) in this *Directory* indicates that the physician held a PRA certificate as of May 2008.

Information that a physician has the PRA certificate is included in Doctor Finder, the list of physicians provided on the AMA Homepage. The certificate is accepted by a number of state licensing boards as evidence that a physician has completed the continuing education requirement for medical relicensure. The Joint Commission accepts an AMA-approved PRA application form as an acceptable record of physician's continuing medical education activities.

General Information

Address Unknown Physicians whose addresses are temporarily unknown are listed only in the alphabetical index of physicians in the *Directory*. "Address Unknown" will appear after the names of these physicians. Information will be listed in both the alphabetical and geographical indexes for physicians if their cities and states are known.

Military Mail The US Postal Service requires all overseas military mail to include new addressing formats. Both APO and FPO mail have the following new designations:

AE	Mail going to Europe, the Middle East, Africa, and Canada
AP	Mail going to the Pacific
AA	Mail going to areas in the Americas other than Canada

Physician Statistics Annual summary statistics on the distribution of physicians in the United States are available from the Association in the annual *Physician Characteristics and Distribution in the US* volume published by the AMA Division of Survey and Data Resources.

Pacific Islands Physicians who are residing on certain Pacific Islands will have "PI" printed after the island/city name in the alphabetical index of physicians. All demographic data, including the professional mailing address, will appear in the "Pacific Islands" section of the *Directory*.

Temporary Foreign Physicians who are temporarily residing in a foreign country are not listed.

State Codes The following abbreviations are used in the alphabetical index of physicians to indicate the states in which physicians are located.

AK	Alaska	NE	Nebraska
AL	Alabama	NH	New Hampshire
AR	Arkansas	NJ	New Jersey
AZ	Arizona	NM	New Mexico
CA	California	NV	Nevada
CO	Colorado	NY	New York
CT	Connecticut	OH	Ohio
DC	District of Columbia	OK	Oklahoma
DE	Delaware	OR	Oregon
FL	Florida	PA	Pennsylvania
GA	Georgia	PR	Puerto Rico
HI	Hawaii	RI	Rhode Island
IA	Iowa	SC	South Carolina
ID	Idaho	SD	South Dakota
IL	Illinois	TN	Tennessee
IN	Indiana	TX	Texas
KS	Kansas	UT	Utah
KY	Kentucky	VA	Virginia
LA	Louisiana	VI	Virgin Islands
MA	Massachusetts	VT	Vermont
MD	Maryland	WA	Washington
ME	Maine	WI	Wisconsin
MI	Michigan	WV	West Virginia
MN	Minnesota	WY	Wyoming
MO	Missouri	PI	Pacific Islands
MS	Mississippi	AA	US Military Postal Service
MT	Montana	AE	US Military Postal Service
NC	North Carolina	AP	US Military Postal Service
ND	North Dakota		

To Obtain Information

To obtain information regarding various health organizations and health-related activities, contact the following:

Hospitals and hospital administrators in the United States:

American Hospital Association
1 N Franklin St
Chicago, IL 60606-3421
312 422-3000
www.aha.org

Medical libraries and librarians that are members of the Medical Library Association:

Medical Library Association
65 E Wacker Place, Suite 1900
Chicago, IL 60601-7246
312 419-9094
312 419-8950 (fax)
www.mlanet.org

Medical schools, addresses, accreditation, requirements for admissions, administrative officers, department directors, administrative staff, etc:

Association of American Medical Colleges
2450 N Street NW
Washington, DC 20037-1126
202 828-0400
202 828-1125 (fax)
www.aamc.org

Canadian physicians, hospitals, and medical schools:

Canadian Medical Association
1867 Alta Vista Dr
Ottawa, Ontario, Canada K1G 5W8
800 663-7336 x2295
613 565-5471 (fax)
www.cma.ca

American Board of Medical Specialties
1007 Church Street, Suite 404
Evanston, IL 60201-5913
847 491-9091
www.abms.org

US Medical School Codes

The following is a list of medical schools in the United States and Puerto Rico, existing and extinct, arranged in state order and showing the code numbers by which schools are designated in this *Directory*. Existing schools are listed in regular type. Schools no longer in existence and schools of Osteopathic Medicine whose graduates are listed in this *Directory* are in italics. **Note:** The AMA does not accredit or approve medical schools or medical education programs. This list only represents those medical schools from which **current** *Directory* physicians have graduated.

001   **Alabama**
001-02 University of Alabama School of Medicine, Birmingham
001-06 University of South Alabama College of Medicine, Mobile

003   **Arizona**
003-01 University of Arizona College of Medicine, Tucson
003-75 *Midwestern University, Arizona College of Osteopathic Medicine, Glendale*

004   **Arkansas**
004-01 University of Arkansas College of Medicine, Little Rock

005   **California**
005-02 University of California, San Francisco, School of Medicine, San Francisco
005-06 Keck School of Medicine of the University of Southern California, Los Angeles
005-11 Stanford University School of Medicine, Stanford
005-12 Loma Linda University School of Medicine, Loma Linda
005-14 David Geffen School of Medicine, University of California, Los Angeles
005-15 University of California, Irvine, California College of Medicine, Irvine
005-16 University of California, Irvine, California College of Medicine, Irvine
005-17 University of California, Irvine, California College of Medicine, Irvine
005-18 University of California, San Diego, School of Medicine, La Jolla
005-19 University of California, Davis, School of Medicine, Davis
005-75 *College of Osteopathic Physicians and Surgeons of Los Angeles, Los Angeles (Extinct)*
005-76 *Western University of the Health Sciences, College of Osteopathic Medicine of the Pacific, Pomona (COMP)*
005-77 *Touro University College of Osteopathic Medicine, San Francisco*

007   **Colorado**
007-02 University of Colorado School of Medicine, Denver

008   **Connecticut**
008-01 Yale University School of Medicine, New Haven
008-02 University of Connecticut School of Medicine, Farmington

010   **District of Columbia**
010-01 George Washington University School of Medicine and Health Science, Washington
010-02 Georgetown University School of Medicine, Washington
010-03 Howard University College of Medicine, Washington

011   **Florida**
011-02 University of Miami, L. M. Miller School of Medicine, Miami
011-03 University of Florida College of Medicine, Gainesville
011-04 University of South Florida College of Medicine, Tampa
011-05 Florida State University College of Medicine, Tallahassee
011-75 *Nova Southeastern University, College of Osteopathic Medicine, Ft Lauderdale*

012   **Georgia**
012-01 Medical College of Georgia School of Medicine, Augusta
012-05 Emory University School of Medicine, Atlanta
012-21 Morehouse School of Medicine, Atlanta
012-22 Mercer University School of Medicine, Macon

014   **Hawaii**
014-01 University of Hawaii John A. Burns School of Medicine, Honolulu

016   **Illinois**
016-01 Rush Medical College of Rush University, Chicago
016-02 University of Chicago, Division of Biological Sciences, Pritzker School of Medicine, Chicago
016-06 Northwestern University, Feinberg School of Medicine, Chicago
016-11 University of Illinois College of Medicine, Chicago
016-42 Chicago Medical School at Rosalind Franklin University of Medicine and Sciences, North Chicago

016   **Illinois (continued)**
016-43 Loyola University of Chicago Stritch School of Medicine, Maywood
016-45 Southern Illinois University School of Medicine, Springfield
016-76 *Midwestern University, Chicago College of Osteopathic Medicine, Downers Grove*

017   **Indiana**
017-20 Indiana University School of Medicine, Indianapolis

018   **Iowa**
018-03 University of Iowa Roy J. and Lucille Carver College of Medicine, Iowa City
018-75 *Des Moines University, College of Osteopathic Medicine and Surgery, Des Moines*

019   **Kansas**
019-02 University of Kansas School of Medicine, Kansas City

020   **Kentucky**
020-02 University of Louisville School of Medicine, Louisville
020-12 University of Kentucky College of Medicine, Lexington
020-75 *Pikeville College, School of Osteopathic Medicine, Pikeville*

021   **Louisiana**
021-01 Tulane University School of Medicine, New Orleans
021-05 Louisiana State University School of Medicine in New Orleans, New Orleans
021-06 Louisiana State University School of Medicine in Shreveport, Shreveport

022   **Maine**
022-75 *University of New England, College of Osteopathic Medicine, Biddeford*

023   **Maryland**
023-01 University of Maryland School of Medicine, Baltimore
023-07 Johns Hopkins University School of Medicine, Baltimore
023-12 Uniformed Services University of the Health Sciences, Bethesda

024   **Massachusetts**
024-01 Harvard Medical School, Boston
024-05 Boston University School of Medicine, Boston
024-06 *College of Physicians and Surgeons, Boston*
024-07 Tufts University School of Medicine, Boston
024-15 *Middlesex University School of Medicine, Waltham*
024-16 University of Massachusetts Medical School, Worcester

025   **Michigan**
025-01 University of Michigan Medical School, Ann Arbor
025-07 Wayne State University School of Medicine, Detroit
025-12 Michigan State University College of Human Medicine, East Lansing
025-76 *Michigan State University College of Osteopathic Medicine, East Lansing*

026   **Minnesota**
026-04 University of Minnesota Medical School—Minneapolis, Minneapolis
026-08 Mayo Medical School, Rochester

027   **Mississippi**
027-01 University of Mississippi School of Medicine, Jackson

028   **Missouri**
028-02 Washington University School of Medicine, St Louis
028-03 University of Missouri, Columbia School of Medicine, Columbia
028-34 St Louis University School of Medicine, St Louis
028-44 *Kansas City University of Physicians and Surgeons, Kansas City*
028-45 *Mid West Medical College, Kansas City*
028-46 University of Missouri—Kansas City School of Medicine, Kansas City
028-78 *Kansas University of Medicine and Bioscience, College of Osteopathic Medicine, Kansas City*
028-79 *A. T. Still University of the Health Sciences, Kirksville College of Osteopathic Medicine, Kirksville*

030   **Nebraska**
030-05 University of Nebraska College of Medicine, Omaha
030-06 Creighton University School of Medicine, Omaha

031   **Nevada**
031-01 University of Nevada School of Medicine, Reno

032   **New Hampshire**
032-01 Dartmouth Medical School, Hanover

033   **New Jersey**
033-05 University of Medicine and Dentistry of New Jersey—New Jersey Medical School, Newark
033-06 University of Medicine and Dentistry of New Jersey—Robert Wood Johnson Medical School, Piscataway/New Brunswick
033-75 *University of Medicine and Dentistry of New Jersey, New Jersey School of Osteopathic Medicine, Stratford*

034   **New Mexico**
034-01 University of New Mexico School of Medicine, Albuquerque

035   **New York**
035-01 Columbia University College of Physicians and Surgeons, New York
035-03 Albany Medical College, Albany
035-06 University of Buffalo, State University of New York School of Medicine and Biomedical Science, Buffalo
035-08 State University of New York—Downstate Medical Center, College of Medicine, Brooklyn
035-09 New York Medical College, Valhalla
035-15 State University of New York—Upstate Medical University, Syracuse
035-19 New York University School of Medicine, New York
035-20 Joan and Sanford I. Weill Medical College of Cornell University, New York
035-45 University of Rochester School of Medicine and Dentistry, Rochester
035-46 Albert Einstein College of Medicine of Yeshiva University, Bronx
035-47 Mount Sinai School of Medicine of the City University of New York, New York
035-48 Stony Brook University Health Science Center, School of Medicine, Stony Brook
035-75 *New York College of Osteopathic Medicine of Old Westbury (NYCOM)*

036   **North Carolina**
036-01 University of North Carolina at Chapel Hill School of Medicine, Chapel Hill
036-05 Wake Forest University School of Medicine, Winston-Salem
036-07 Duke University School of Medicine, Durham
036-08 The Brody School of Medicine at East Carolina University, Greenville

037   **North Dakota**
037-01 University of North Dakota School of Medicine and Health Sciences, Grand Forks

038   **Ohio**
038-02 *Eclectic Medical College, Cincinnati*
038-06 Case Western Reserve University School of Medicine, Cleveland
038-40 Ohio State University College of Medicine and Public Health, Columbus
038-41 University of Cincinnati College of Medicine, Cincinnati
038-43 University of Toledo College of Medicine, Toledo
038-44 Northeastern Ohio University's College of Medicine, Rootstown
038-45 Wright State University Boonshoft School of Medicine, Dayton
038-75 *Ohio University, College of Osteopathic Medicine, Athens*

039   **Oklahoma**
039-01 University of Oklahoma College of Medicine, Oklahoma City
039-05 *Oral Roberts University School of Medicine, Tulsa*
039-79 *Oklahoma State University, College of Osteopathic Medicine, Tulsa*

040   **Oregon**
040-02 Oregon Health Science University School of Medicine, Portland

041   **Pennsylvania**
041-01 University of Pennsylvania School of Medicine, Philadelphia
041-02 Jefferson Medical College—Thomas Jefferson University, Philadelphia
041-07 Medical College of Pennsylvania, Philadelphia
041-09 Hahnemann University School of Medicine, Philadelphia
041-12 University of Pittsburgh School of Medicine, Pittsburgh

041 **Pennsylvania (continued)**
041-13 Temple University School of Medicine, Philadelphia
041-14 Pennsylvania State University College of Medicine, Hershey
041-15 Drexel University College of Medicine, Philadelphia
041-77 *Philadelphia College of Osteopathic Medicine, Philadelphia*
041-78 *Lake Erie College of Osteopathic Medicine, Erie*

042 **Puerto Rico**
042-01 University of Puerto Rico School of Medicine, San Juan
042-02 Ponce School of Medicine, Ponce
042-03 Universidad Central del Caribe, School of Medicine, Bayamon
042-04 *San Juan Bautista School of Medicine, Caguas*

043 **Rhode Island**
043-01 Brown Medical School, Providence

045 **South Carolina**
045-01 Medical University of South Carolina College of Medicine, Charleston
045-04 University of South Carolina School of Medicine, Columbia

046 **South Dakota**
046-01 University of South Dakota School of Medicine, Vermillion

047 **Tennessee**
047-05 Vanderbilt University School of Medicine, Nashville
047-06 University of Tennessee, Health Science Center, College of Medicine, Memphis
047-07 Meharry Medical College School of Medicine, Nashville
047-20 East Tennessee State University James H. Quillen College of Medicine, Johnson City

048 **Texas**
048-02 University of Texas Medical Branch at Galveston, Galveston
048-04 Baylor College of Medicine, Houston
048-12 University of Texas Southwestern Medical School at Dallas, Dallas
048-13 University of Texas Medical School at San Antonio, San Antonio
048-14 University of Texas Medical School at Houston, Houston
048-15 Texas Tech University Health Science Center School of Medicine, Lubbock
048-16 Texas A&M University System Health Science Center, College of Medicine, College Station
048-78 *University of North Texas Health Science Center, College of Osteopathic Medicine, Fort Worth*

049 **Utah**
049-01 University of Utah School of Medicine, Salt Lake City

050 **Vermont**
050-02 University of Vermont College of Medicine, Burlington

051 **Virginia**
051-01 University of Virginia School of Medicine Health System, Charlottesville
051-04 Virginia Commonwealth University, School of Medicine, Richmond
051-07 Eastern Virginia Medical School of the Medical College of Hampton Roads, Norfolk
051-75 *Edward Via Virginia College of Osteopathic Medicine, Blacksburg*

054 **Washington**
054-04 University of Washington School of Medicine, Seattle
054-15 *Washington College of Physicians and Surgeons, Seattle*

055 **West Virginia**
055-01 West Virginia University School of Medicine, Morgantown
055-02 Joan C. Edwards School of Medicine, Marshall University, Huntington
055-75 *West Virginia School of Osteopathic Medicine, Lewisburg*

056 **Wisconsin**
056-05 University of Wisconsin Medical School, Madison
056-06 Medical College of Wisconsin, Milwaukee

Foreign Medical School Codes

Canadian Medical Schools

The following is a list of medical schools in Canada, existing and extinct, arranged by province and showing the code numbers by which schools are designated in this *Directory*. Existing schools are listed in regular type. Schools no longer in existence whose graduates are listed in this Directory are in italics. **Note:** The AMA does not accredit or approve medical schools or medical education programs. This list only represents those medical schools from which **current** *Directory* physicians have graduated.

060   **Alberta**
060-01 University of Alberta, Faculty of Medicine, Edmonton
060-02 University of Calgary, Faculty of Medicine, Calgary

061   **British Columbia**
061-01 University of British Columbia, Faculty of Medicine, Vancouver

062   **Manitoba**
062-01 The University of Manitoba, Faculty of Medicine, Winnipeg

063   **Newfoundland**
063-01 Memorial University of Newfoundland, Faculty of Medicine, St Johns

064   **Nova Scotia**
064-01 Dalhousie University, Faculty of Medicine, Halifax

065   **Ontario**
065-01 University of Toronto, Faculty of Medicine, Toronto
065-02 *Toronto School of Medicine, Toronto (Extinct)*
065-03 *Medical Faculty of Trinity University, Toronto (Extinct)*
065-05 Queens University, Faculty of Medicine, Kingston
065-06 The University of Western Ontario, Faculty of Medicine, London
065-09 University of Ottawa, Faculty of Medicine, Ottawa
065-10 McMaster University, School of Medicine, Hamilton

067   **Quebec**
067-01 McGill University, Faculty of Medicine, Montreal
067-02 Universite de Montreal, Faculte de Medecine, Montreal
067-03 Universite Laval, Faculte de Medecine, Sainte-Foy
067-04 *Laval Universite, Medical Faculte, Montreal (Extinct)*
067-06 Universite de Sherbrooke, Faculte de Medecine, Sherbrooke

068   **Saskatchewan**
068-01 University of Saskatchewan, College of Medicine, Saskatoon

Other Foreign Medical Schools

The following is a list of other foreign medical schools, existing and extinct, arranged numerically and showing the code numbers by which schools are designated in this *Directory*. **Note:** The AMA does not accredit or approve medical schools or medical education programs. This list only represents those medical schools from which **current** *Directory* physicians have graduated.

082   **Micronesia**
082-01 Pacific Basin University School of Medicine, Pohnpei

104   **Cayman Islands**
104-01 St Matthew's University, Grand Cayman

107   **Aruba**
107-01 Xavier University School of Medicine, Granjestad

117   **Cook Islands**
117-01 St Mary's School of Medicine, Rarotonga
117-02 James Cook School of Medicine, South Seas University, Avarua

118   **Afghanistan**
118-01 Kabul Medical Institute, Faculty of Medicine, Kabul
118-02 State Medical Institute of Nangarhar, Faculty of Medicine, Jalalabad

120   **Albania**
120-01 Universiteti I Tiranes, Fakulteti I Mjekesise, Tirana

125   **Algeria**
125-01 Universite d'Alger Faculte Mixte de Medecine et de Pharmacie, Alger
125-03 Institut National d'Enseignement Superieur Sciences Medicales, Constantine
125-04 Institut National d'Enseignement Superieur Sciences Medicales, Oran
125-05 Institut National d'Enseignement Superieur Sciences Medicales de Annaba, Annaba
125-06 Institut de Sciences Medicales d'Universite, Universite de Tizi-Ouzou, Tizi-Ouzou
125-08 Institut de Sciences Medicales Sidi-Bel-Abbes, Sidi-Bel-Abbes

128   **Angola**
128-01 University de Luanda, Faculty of Medicine, Luanda

130   **Antigua**
130-01 University of Health Sciences Antigua, School of Medicina, St Johns
130-02 American University of Antigua, College of Medicine, Woods

132   **Argentina**
132-01 Universidad de Buenos Aires, Facultad de Medicina, Buenos Aires
132-02 Universidad Nacional de Cordoba, Facultad de Ciencias Medicina, Cordoba
132-03 Universidad Nacional de La Plata, Facultad de Ciencias Medicina, La Plata
132-04 Universidad Nacional de Rosario, Facultad de Medicina, Rosario
132-05 Universidad Nacional de Tucuman, Facultad de Medicina, San Miguel de Tucuman
132-06 Universidad Nacional de Cuyo, Facultad de Ciencias Medicina, Mendoza
132-07 Universidad del Salvador, Facultad de Medicina, Buenos Aires
132-08 Universidad Nacional del Nordeste, Facultad de Medicina, Corrientes
132-09 Universidad Catolica de Cordoba, Facultad de Medicina, Cordoba
132-10 Universidad Maimonides, Facultad de Medicina, Buenos Aires
132-11 Universidad Favaloro, Facultad de Medicina, Buenos Aires
132-12 Instituto Universitario de Ciencias de la Salud, Facultad De Medicina, Capital Federal
132-13 Universidad Adventista del Plata, Facultad de Ciencias Medicina, Entre Rios
132-14 Universidad Austral, Facultad de Ciencias Biomedicas, Pilar, Buenos Aires

143   **Australia**
143-01 University of Adelaide, Faculty of Medicine, Adelaide, South Australia
143-02 University of Melbourne, Faculty of Medicine, Parkville, Victoria
143-03 University of Sydney, Faculty of Medicine, Sydney, New South Wales
143-04 University of Newcastle, Faculty of Medicine, Newcastle, New South Wales
143-05 University of Queensland Medical School, Herston, Queensland
143-06 University of Western Australia Faculty of Medicine and Dentistry, Perth, Western Australia
143-07 University of New South Wales, Faculty of Medicine, Kensington, New South Wales
143-08 Monash University, Faculty of Medicine, Clayton, Victoria
143-10 University of Tasmania, Faculty of Medicine, Hobart, Tasmania
143-11 The Flinders University of South Australia School of Medicine, Bedford Park,
          South Australia

154   **Austria**
154-01 Karl-Franzens Universitaet Graz, Medizinische Fakultaet, Graz (407-27 from March 13,
          1938, to June 1945)
154-02 Leopold Franzen Universitaet Innsbruck, Medizinische Fakultaet, Innsbruck (407-28 from
          March 13, 1938, to June 1945)
154-07 Universitaet Wien, Medizinische Fakultaet, Wien (407-26 from March 13, 1938, to
          June 1945)
154-08 Medizinische Universitaet Wien, Vienna

155   **Bahrain**
155-01 Arabian Gulf University College of Medicine and Medical Science, Manama

160   **Bangladesh**
160-01 Chittagong Medical College, University of Chittagong, Chittagong (704-10 before July 1972)
160-02 Dhaka Medical College, Dhaka University, Dhaka (704-03 before July 1972)
160-03 Sir Salimullah Medical College, Dhaka
160-04 Mymensingh Medical College, Mymensingh (704-12 before July 1972)
160-05 Rajshahi Medical College, Rajshahi (704-11 before July 1972)
160-06 Sylhet Medical College, Chittagong University, Sylhet (704-13 before July 1972)
160-07 Sher-E-Bangla Medical College, Barisal (Barisal Medical College)
160-08 Rangpur Medical College, Rangpur

160   **Bangladesh (continued)**
160-09 Bangladesh Medical College, Dhaka University, Dhaka
160-10 Institute of Postgraduate Medicine and Research, Dhaka
160-11 Jahurul Islam Medical College and Hospital, Dhaka University, Kishoreganj
160-12 Institute of Applied Health Sciences, University of Science and Technology–Chittagong, Chittagong
160-13 Comilla Medical College, Chittagong University, Comilla
160-14 Zainul Haque Sikder Women's Medical College and Hospital, University of Dhaka, Dhaka
160-15 Dinajpur Medical College, Rajshahi University, Dinajpur
160-16 Medical College for Woman and Hospital, University of Dhaka, Dhaka
160-17 Khulna Medical College, Rajshahi University, Khulna

162   **Barbados**
162-01 University of the West Indies, School of Clinical Medicine and Research, Bridgetown

165   **Belgium**
165-01 Universite Libre de Bruxelles, Faculte de Medecine et de Pharmacie, Bruxelles
165-02 Rijksuniversiteit Gent, Faculteit der Geneeskunde, Gent
165-03 Universite de l'Etat a Liege, Faculte de Medecine, Liege
165-04 Katholiteke Universiteit Leuven, Faculteit der Geneeskunde, Leuven
165-05 Facultes Universitaires Notre-Dame de la Paix, Faculte de Medecine, Namur
165-06 Vrije Universiteit Brussels, Faculte der Geneeskunde en de Farmacie, Brussels
165-07 Universite Catholique de Louvain, Bruxelles
165-08 Universitaire Centrumvan Antwerpen, Faculteit Voor Geneeskunde en Farmacie, Wilrijk

166   **Belize**
166-01 Central America Health Sciences University, School of Medicine, Belize City
166-02 St Matthews University School of Medicine, San Pedro, Ambergris Caye
166-03 Grace University, Belmopan (661-01 before Aug 1999)
166-04 Hope University School of Medicine, Belmopan City, Cayo District
166-05 St. Luke's University, School of Medicine, Belmopan
166-06 Medical University of the Americas, San Pedro Town, Ambergris Caye

170   **Benin**
170-01 Universite Nationale Du Benin, Faculte des Sciences de La Sante, Cotonou

176   **Bolivia**
176-01 Universidad Boliviana Mayor de San Andres, Facultad de Ciencias, La Paz
176-02 Universidad Boliviana Mayor de San Francisco X Chuguisaca, Facultad de Ciencias, Sucre
176-03 Universidad Mayor de San Simon, Facultad de Ciencias de la Salud, Cochabamba
176-04 Universidad Privada del Valle, Facultad de Medicina, Cochabamba
176-05 Universidad Nuestra Senora de La Paz, Facultad de Medicina, La Paz
176-06 Universidad Privada del Valle, Facultad de Medicina, La Paz

187   **Brazil**
187-01 Universidade Federal de Bahia, Faculdade de Medicina, Salvador, Bahia
187-02 Universidade Federal de Rio Grande do Sul, Faculdade de Medicina, Porto Alegre, RS
187-03 Universidade Federal de Rio de Janeiro, Faculdade de Medicina, Rio de Janeiro, RJ
187-04 Universidade de Sao Paulo, Faculdade de Medicina, Sao Paulo, SP
187-05 Universidade Federal da Paraiba, Centro de Ciencias, Joao Pessoa, Paraiba
187-06 Universidade Federal de Minas Gerais, Faculdade de Medicina Belo Horizonte, Minas Gerais
187-07 Universidade Federal de Pernambuco, Centro de Ciencias, Recife, PE
187-08 Universidade Federal do Parana, Setor de Ciencias, Curitiba, Parana
187-09 Universidade do Estado da Guanabara, Faculdade de Ciencias, Rio de Janeiro, RJ
187-10 Universidade Federal do Ceara, Centro de Ciencias, Fortaleza, Ceara
187-11 Universidade de Sao Paulo, Faculdade de Medicina de Ribeiro Preto, Ribeiro Preto, Sao Paulo
187-12 Escola Paulista de Medicina, Sao Paulo, SP
187-13 Universidade Federal Fluminense, Faculdade de Medicina, Niteroi, Rio de Janeiro
187-14 Universidade Federal do Espirito Santo, Centro Biomedico, Vitoria, Espirito Santo
187-15 Universidade Federal do Maranhao, Centro de Ciencias da Saude, Sao Luiz, Maranhao
187-16 Universidade Federal do Rio Grande do Norte, Centro de Ciencias, Natal, RN
187-17 Universidade Federal de Santa Catarina, Faculdade de Medicina, Florianopolis, Santa Catarina
187-18 Escola de Medicina e Cirugia, Universidade do Rio de Janeiro, Centro de Ciencias, Rio de Janeiro, RJ
187-19 Pontificia Universidade Catolica de Sao Paulo, Faculdade de Medicina, Sorocaba, Sao Paulo

187	**Brazil (continued)**

187-20 Universidade Federal do Para, Centro de Ciencias da Saude, Belem, PA
187-21 Faculdade de Ciencias Medicina de Pernambuco, Recife, Pernambuco
187-22 Universidade Estadual do Para, Centro Ciencias Biologicas e da Saude, Campus II, CEP
187-23 Universidade Federal de Santa Maria, Centro de Ciencias, Santa Maria, Rio Grande do Sul
187-24 Fundacao Universitaria Mineira, Faculdade de Ciencias Medicas de Minas Gerais, Belo Horizonte, Minas Gerais
187-25 Fundacao Faculdade Federal de Ciencias Medicina de Porto Alegre, Porto Alegre, Rio Grande do Sul
187-26 Universidade Catolica do Parana, Centro de Ciencias, Curitiba, Parana
187-27 Fundacao Universidade do Rio Grande, Faculdade de Medicina, Rio Grande do Sul
187-28 Faculdade de Medicina do Triangulo Mineiro, Uberaba, Minas Gerais
187-29 Universidade Federal de Juiz de Fora, Faculdade de Medicina, Juiz de Fora, Minas Gerais
187-30 Universidade Estadual de Campinas, Faculdade de Ciencias Medicina, Campinas, Sao Paulo
187-31 Faculdade de Ciencias Medicina da Santa Casa de Sao Paulo, SP
187-32 Universidade Federal de Goias, Faculdade de Medicina, Goiania, Goias
187-33 Fundacao Universidade de Brasilia, Faculdade de Ciencias, Brasilia, DF
187-35 Faculdade de Medicina de Itajuba, Itajuba
187-39 Universidade do Amazonas, Faculdade de Medicina, Manaus, Amazonas
187-40 Fundacao Municipal de Ensino Superior Marilia, Faculdade de Medicina de Marilia, Marilia, Sao Paulo
187-41 Universidade de Mogidas Cruzes, Faculdade de Medicina, Mogidas Cruzes, Sao Paulo
187-42 Fundacao Universitaria Federal de Pelotas, Faculdade de Medicina, Pelotas, Rio Grande do Sul
187-43 Faculdade de Medicina de Petropolis, Petropolis, Rio de Janeiro
187-45 Universidade Gama Filho, Escola Medica do Rio de Janeiro, RJ
187-46 Escola de Medicina e Saude Publica, Salvador, Bahia
187-47 Faculdade de Ciencias Medicina de Santos, Santos, SP
187-48 Universidade Federal de Sergipe, Centro de Ciencias Biologicas, Aracaju, SE
187-49 Universidade Estadual Paulista, Faculdade de Medicina, Botucatu, Sao Paulo
187-50 Faculdade de Medicina de Taubate, Taubate, Sao Paulo
187-51 Fundacao Universidade Federal do Piaui, Centro de Ciencias, Teresina, PI
187-52 Fundacao Universidade Federal de Mato Grosso do Sul, Centro de Ciencias, Campo Grande, MS
187-53 Fundacao Universidade Federal de Uberlandia, Centro de Ciencias, Uberlandia, Minas Gerais
187-54 Escola de Medicina de Santa Casa de Misericordia de Vitoria, Vitoria, Espirito Santo
187-55 Faculdade de Medicina de Jundiai, Jundiai, Sao Paulo
187-57 Fundacao Universidade Estadual de Londrina, Centro de Ciencias, Londrina, Parana
187-58 Universidade Federal de Alagoas, Centro de Ciencias, Maceio, Alagoas
187-60 Faculdade de Medicina do Norte de Minas, Montes Claros, Minas Gerais
187-61 Fundacao Universidade Passo Fundo, Faculdade de Medicina, Passo Fundo, Rio Grande do Sul
187-62 Faculdade de Medicina de Santo Amaro, Santo Amaro, Sao Paulo
187-63 Faculdade de Ciencias Medicina "Dr J A Garcia Coutinho," Pouso Alegre, Minas Gerais
187-64 Faculdade de Medicina e Cirurgia de Pernambuco, Recife, Pernambuco
187-67 Fundacao Universitaria do ABC Faculdade de Medicina Santo Andre, Sao Paulo
187-69 Fundacao Faculdade Regional de Medicina de Sao Jose do Rio Preto, Sao Jose, Sao Paulo
187-70 Universidade Federale da Paraiba, Centro de Ciencias Biologicas e da Suade, Campina Grande, PB
187-71 Fundacao B P Nunes, Faculdade de Medicina de Campos, Campos, Rio de Janeiro
187-72 Faculdade de Medicina de Teresopolis, Teresopolis, Rio de Janeiro
187-73 Fundacao Universidade de Caxias do Sul, Centro de Ciencias, Caxias do Sul, RS
187-74 Faculdade de Medicina de Valenca, Valenca, Rio de Janeiro
187-75 Faculdade de Medicina de Vassouras, Vassouras, Rio de Janeiro
187-76 Faculdade Evangelica de Medicina do Parana, Curitiba, Parana
187-77 Escola de Ciencias Medicina de Volta Redonda, Volta Redonda, RJ
187-78 Escola de Medicina Fundacao Tech-Educ Souza Marques, Rio de Janeiro
187-79 Faculdade de Medicina Catanduva, Catanduva, Sao Paulo
187-80 Pontificia Universitaria Catolica de Rio Grande do Sul, Faculdade de Medicina, Porto Alegre, RS
187-81 Universidade Sao Francisco, Faculdade de Ciencias Medicina, Braganca Paulista, Sao Paulo
187-82 Fundacao Presidente Antonio Carlos, Faculdade de Medicina de Barbacena, Barbacena, MG
187-83 Fundacao Educ do Estadual do Para, Faculdade Estadual de Medicina do Para, Belem, Para

187   **Brazil (continued)**
187-84 Universidade Catolica de Pelotas, Centro de Ciencias da Saude e Biologicas, Pelotas, RS
187-86 Pontificia Universidade Catolica de Campinas, Faculdade de Ciencias, Campinas, SP
187-87 Faculdade de Medicina do Estado, RJ
187-88 Fundacao Universidade Regional de Blumenau, Blumenau
187-89 Universidade de Ribeirao Preto, Curso de Medicina, Ribeirao Preto

198   **Bulgaria**
198-01 Medical University of Sofia, Faculty of Medicine, Sofia
198-02 Plovdiv Medical Academy, Faculty of Medicine, Plovdiv
198-03 Varna Medical Academy, Faculty of Medicine, Varna
198-04 Higher Medical Institute—Pleven, Faculty of Medicine, Pleven
198-05 Higher Medical Institute, Stara Zagora

209   **Myanmar (Formerly Burma)**
209-01 Institute of Medicine I, Yangon
209-02 Mandalay University, Institute of Medicine, Mandalay
209-03 Institute of Medicine II, Mingaladon, Yangon

211   **Burundi**
211-01 Universite du Burundi, Faculte de Medicine du Bujumbura, Bujumbura

215   **Cambodia**
215-01 Faculte de Medecine et des Science Paramedicales, Phnom-Penh University, Cambodia

217   **Cameroon**
217-01 Universite Federale du Cameroun, Centrale Universite des Sciences de la Sante, Yaounde

220   **Sri Lanka (Formerly Ceylon)**
220-01 University of Colombo, Faculty of Medicine, Colombo
220-02 University of Peradeniya, Faculty of Medicine, Peradeniya
220-03 University of Kelaniya, Faculty of Medicine, Ragama
220-04 University of Jaffna, Faculty of Medicine, Jaffna
220-05 University of Ruhuna, Faculty of Medicine, Galle
220-06 University of Sri Jayewardenepura, Faculty of Medicine, Nugegoda

231   **Chile**
231-01 Universidad de Chile, Escuela de Pregrado, Facultad de Medicina, Santiago
231-02 Universidad de Concepcion, Facultad de Medicina, Concepcion
231-03 Pontificia Universidad Catolica de Chile, Facultad de Medicina, Santiago
231-04 Universidad Austral de Chile, Facultad de Medicina, Valdivia
231-05 Universidad de Valparaiso, Facultad de Medicina, Valparaiso
231-06 Universidad de la Frontera, Departamento de Ciencias de la Salud, Facultad de Medicina, Temuco
231-07 Universidad de Los Andes, Facultad de Medicina, Las Condes-Santiago

242   **China**
242-   (Also see 243 China effective 1971)
242-03 Capitol University of Medical Sciences, Training Centre of General Practice, (Peking Union Medical College), Beijing
242-06 *South China Medical College, Canton (Extinct)*
242-07 *Hsiangya Medical College, Changsha, Hunan (Extinct)*
242-09 *St Johns University (Pennsylvania Medicine Sch), Shanghai, Kiangsu (Extinct)*
242-10 *Cheeloo University School of Medicine, Tsinan, Shantung (Extinct)*
242-13 *Hackett Medical College for Women, Canton, Kwangtung (Extinct)*
242-15 *Women's Christian Medical College, Shanghai, Kiangsu (Extinct)*
242-16 National Shanghai Medical College, Shanghai, Kiangsu
242-17 West China Union University College of Medicine and Dentistry, Chengtu, Szechwan
242-21 Sun Yat Sen University of Medical Sciences, College of Medicine, Guangdong, Kwangtung
242-22 *Aurora University Faculty of Medicine, Shanghai, Kiangsu (Extinct)*
242-24 *Tung Teh Medical College, Shanghai, Kiangsu (Extinct)*
242-25 *Army Medical College, Nanking, Kiangsu (Extinct)*
242-26 *National Central University College of Medicine, Nanking, Kiangsu (Extinct)*
242-27 *Tung Nan Medical College, Shanghai, Kiangsu (Extinct)*
242-28 *National Tung Chi University Faculty of Medicine, Shanghai, Kiangsu (Extinct)*
242-29 National Kiangsu Medical College, Chingkiang, Kiangsu
242-30 National Kweiyang Medical College, Kweiyang, Kweichow
242-31 *Lanchow University Medical College, Lanchow, Kansu (Extinct)*
242-33 Fukien Provincial Medical College, Foochow, Fukien

242   **China (continued)**

242-34 *National Chung Cheng Medical College, Nanchang, Kiangsu (Extinct)*
242-36 Hopei Provincial Medical College, Paoting, Hopei
242-37 Kuang Hua Medical School, Canton, Kwangtung
242-39 Shansi University Medical College, Taiyuan, Shansi
242-43 Chekiang Provincial Medical College, Hangchow, Chekiang
242-44 Harbin Medical University, Harbin, Sungkiang
242-45 Second Shanghai Medical College, Shanghai, Shanghai
242-46 Shantung Provincial Medical College, Tsinan, Shantung
242-47 National Peking University Medical College, Peking, Hopei
242-48 Tientsin Medical College, Tientsin, Hopei
242-50 National Chung Shan University (Sun Yat Sen) Medical College, Canton, Kwangtung
242-51 National Defense Medical Center School of Medicine, Shanghai, Kiangsu
242-52 Wuhan Medical College, Hankow, Hupeh
242-54 North Kiangsu Medical College, Kiangsu, Nantung
242-55 Dairen Medical College, Liaotung, Dairen
242-56 Tungchi Medical College, Hupeh, Tsungnan, Wuchang
242-57 Anwhei Medical College, Anwhei, Hopei
242-58 Guangdong Province Cardiovascular Institute, Guangdong
242-59 Jining Medical College, Jining, Shangdong
242-60 Tianjin College of Traditional Chinese Medicine, Tianjin City, Tianjin
242-61 Shenyang Medical College, Shenyang, Liaoning
242-62 Ningxia Medical College, Yinchuan, Ningxia Hui, Autonomous Region
242-63 Nanjing University School of Medicine, Nanjing, Jiangsu
242-64 Shangdong College of Traditional Chinese Medicine, Jinan, Shangdong
242-65 Chengde Medical College, Chengde, Hebei
242-67 Heilongjiang University of Traditional Chinese Medicine, Harbin, Heilongjiang
242-68 Hebei College of Traditional Chinese Medicine, Shi-Jiazhuang City, Hebei
242-69 Baotou Medical College, Inner Mongolia Autonomous Region
242-70 Yunyand Medical College, Shryan, Hubei
242-71 Medical College of Hubei Institute for Nationalities, Enshi
242-72 Hubei Medical College, Xianning Branch, Xianning, Hubei
242-73 Medical Center of Fudan University, Faculty of Medicine, Shanghai
242-74 Shandong University, Shandong Medical University, Jinan, Shandong
242-75 Medical College of Nankai University, Tianjin
242-76 Medical College of Julin University, Changchun
242-77 Zhengzhou University, College of Medicine, Zhengzhou Henan

243   **China**

243-   (Also see 242 China before 1971)
243-01 Zunyi Medical College, Zunyi, Guangxi
243-02 Medical College of Yangzhou University, Yangzhou, Jiangsu
243-03 Peking Union Medical College, Beijing
243-04 Guangdong College of Medicine and Pharmacy, Guangzhou, Guangdong
243-05 Shantou University Medical College, Shantou, Guangdong
243-06 Zhangjakou Medical College, Zhangjakou, Hebei
243-08 First Military Medical University, Faculty of Medicine, Guangdong
243-09 Hubei College of Traditional Chinese Medicine, Wuhan, Hubei
243-10 Yanbian Medical College, Yanji, Jilin
243-11 Guilin School of Medicine, Guilin, Guanji
243-12 Xingxiang Medical College, Xingxiang, Henan
243-13 Binzhou Medical College, Binzhou, Shandong
243-14 Beijing University of Traditional Chinese Medicine, Faculty of Medicine, Beijing
243-15 Yuzhou University, Faculty of Medicine, Chongquing, Sichuan
243-16 Shanghai First Medical College, Shanghai (242-16 before 1971)
243-17 Chengdu College of Traditional Medicine, Chengdu, Sichuan (242-21 before 1971)
243-18 Taishan Medical College, Tai'an, Shangdong
243-19 Liaoning College of Traditional Chinese Medicine, Shenyang, Liaoning
243-20 North China Medical College for the Coal Industry, Tangshan, Hebei
243-21 Sun Yat-Sen University of Medical Sciences, Guangzhou, Guangdong
243-22 Guangzhou College of Traditional Chinese Medicine, Hangzhou, Zhejiang
243-23 Luzhou Medical College, Luzhou, Sichuan
243-24 Medical College of Nanjing University, Nanjing, Jiangsu
243-25 Kunming Medical College, Kunming, Yunnan
243-26 Zhejiang College of Traditional Chinese Medicine, Hangzhou, Zhejiang
243-27 Dali Medical College, Faculty of Medicine, Dali, Yunnan
243-28 Jilin Medical College, Jilin
243-29 Nanjing College of Traditional Chinese Medicine, Nanjing, Jiangsu (242-29 before 1971)
243-30 Guiyang Medical College, Guiyang, Guizhou (242-30 before 1971) (formerly Kweiyang)

243

China (continued)

243-31 Henan College of Traditional Chinese Medicine, Zhengzhou, Henan
243-32 Qingdao Medical College, Qingdao, Shangdong (242-32 before 1971)
243-33 Fujian Medical College, Fuzhou, Fujian Province (242-33 before 1971)
243-34 Jiangxi College of Traditional Chinese Medicine, Nanchang
243-35 Gannon School of Medicine, Ganzhou
243-36 Hebei Medical University, Shi-Jiazhuong City, Hebei (242-35 before 1971)
243-38 Henan Medical University, Zhengzhou City, Henan (242-38 before 1971)
243-39 Shanxi Medical College, Taiyuan, Shanxi (242-39 before 1971)
243-40 Lanzhou Medical College, Lanzhou, Gansu (242-40 before 1971) (Lanchow University)
243-41 Youjiang Medical College for Nationalities of Guangxi, Baise, Guangxi
243-42 Jinzhou Medical College, Jinzhou, Liaoning
243-43 Zhejiang Medical University, Hangzhou (242-43 before 1971) (Chekiang Province)
243-44 Harbin Medical University, Harbin, Heilongjiang (242-44 before 1971)
243-45 Shanghai Second Medical University, Shanghai (242-45 before 1971)
243-46 Shangdong Medical University, Jinan, Shandong (242-46 before 1971)
243-47 Peking University Medical College, Peking (242-47 before 1971) (Beijing Medical University)
243-48 Tianjin Medical College, Tianjin (Tientsin) (242-48 before 1971)
243-49 Xuzhou Medical College, Xuzhou, Jiangsu
243-50 Sun Yat-Sen University of Medical Sciences, Guangzhou, Guangdong (242-50 before 1971) (Chungshan)
243-52 Wuhan Medical College, Wuhan (Tonji Medical University) (242-52 before 1971)
243-53 Inner Mongolia Medical College, Hohhot, Inner Mongolia Autonomous Region
243-54 Nantong Medical College, Nantong, Jiangsu (242-54 before 1971) (N Kiangsu MC)
243-55 Dalian Medical College, Dalian, Liaoning (242-55 before 1971)
243-56 Tungchi Medical College, Wuhan, Hubei (242-56 before 1971)
243-57 Anhui Medical College, Hefei, Anhui (242-57 before 1971)
243-58 Second Military Medical University, Faculty of Medicine, Shanghai
243-59 Hainan University Medical Department, Haikou, Hainan Island, Guangdong
243-60 University of Yunnan Medical College, Kunming
243-61 Guangxi Medical University, Nanning, Guilin, Guangxi (Kwangsi Provincial Medical College)
243-62 Jiangxi Medical College, Nanchang, Jiangxi (Kiangsi Medical College)
243-63 Chongqing Medical University, Chongqing, Sichuan (Chungking University)
243-64 Xian Medical College, Xian, Shensi Province, Shaanxi
243-65 Hubei Medical College, Wuhan, Hubei
243-66 Xinjiang Medical College, Urumuchi, Xinjian Uygur Autonomous Region
243-67 Weifang Medical College, Weifang, Shandong
243-68 Szechwan Medical College, Chengtu
243-69 Capital University of Medical Science, Beijing City
243-70 Hwasi University Medical College, Szechwan, Chengtu (Sichuan)
243-71 Nanjing Railway Medical College, Nanjing, Jiangsu
243-72 West China University of Medical Science, Chengdu City, Sichuan (AKA 638-01)
243-73 Wuhan University Medical College, Hubei, Wuhan
243-74 Hengyang Medical College, Hengyang, Hunan
243-75 Wenzhou Medical College, Wenzhou, Zhejiang
243-76 Hunan Medical College, Changsha, Hunan (243-07 before 1953)
243-77 Guangzhou Medical College, Guangzhou, Guangdong
243-78 Suzhou Medical College, Suzhou, Jiangsu
243-79 Shanghai College of Traditional Chinese Medicine, Shanghai
243-81 Jinan University Medical College, Guangzhou, Guangdong
243-82 Guangdong Medical College, Zhanjiang, Guangdong
243-83 Bengbu Medical College, Bengbu, Anhui
243-84 Anhui College of Traditional Chinese Medicine, Hefei City, Anhui
243-85 Wannan Medical College, Wuhu, Anhui
243-86 Beijing College of Traditional Chinese Medicine, Beijing
243-92 Bethune Medical University, Changchun, Jilin
243-93 Zhenjiang Medical College, Zhenjiang, Jiansu
243-94 Third Military Medical University, Chongqing
243-95 Fourth Military University, Shaanxi
243-96 Academy of Military Medical Science, Beijing
243-97 Shanghai Railway Medical College, Shanghai
243-98 First Medical College of the Navy, Qing-Dao, Shandong
243-99 Jiamusi Medical College, Jiamusi

244

Taiwan (Formerly Formosa)

244-   (Also see 385 Formosa before 1971)
244-01 Kaohsiung (Takau) Medical College, Kaohsiung (385-01 before 1971)
244-02 National Taiwan University, College of Medicine, Taipei (385-02 before 1971)

244   **Taiwan (Formerly Formosa) (continued)**
244-03 National Defense Medical Center, Taipei (385-03 before 1971)
244-04 Taipei Medical College, Taipei (385-04 before 1971)
244-05 China Medical College, Taichung (385-05 before 1971)
244-06 Chung-shan Medical and Dental College, Taichung
244-08 National Yang Ming Medical College, Taipei
244-09 Shihezi Medical College, Shihezi, Xinjiang Uygur Autonomoug Region, Taiwan

264   **Colombia**
264-01 Universidad Nacional de Colombia, Facultad de Medicina, Bogota
264-02 Universidad de Cartagena, Division de Ciencias de la Salud, Cartagena
264-03 Universidad de Antioquia, Facultad de Medicina, Medellin
264-04 Pontificia Universidad Javeriana, Facultad de Medicina, Bogota
264-05 Universidad del Valle, Division de Ciencias de la Salud, Cali
264-06 Universidad de Caldas, Facultad de Medicina, Manizales
264-07 Universidad del Cauca, Division de Ciencias de la Salud, Popayan
264-08 Universidad Libre, Facultad de Medicina, Cali
264-09 Universidad Industrial de Santander, Division de Ciencias de la Salud, Bucanaranga
264-10 Colegio Mayor de Nuestro Senora del Rosario, Facultad de Medicina, Bogota
264-11 Escuela de Medicina Juan N Corpas, Bogota
264-12 Universidad del Norte, Facultad de Medicina, Barranquilla
264-13 Universidad de Pontificia Bolivariana, Facultad de Medicina, Medellin
264-14 Universidad Metropolitana, Facultad de Medicina, Barranquilla
264-15 Universidad Libre de Colombia, Facultad de Medicina, Barranquilla
264-16 Instituto de Ciencias de la Salud, Facultad de Medicina, Medellin
264-17 Universidad Technical de Pereira, Facultad de Medicina, Pereira
264-18 Escuela Colombiana de Medicina, Bogota
264-19 Universidad Militar Nueva Granada, Bogota
264-20 Universidad del Quindio, Escuela de Medicina, Armenia
264-21 Universidad el Bosque, Escuela Colombiana de Medicina, Santa Fe de Bogata
264-22 Universidad de la Sabana, Facultad de Medicina, Chia, Cundinamarca
264-23 Universidad Surcolombiana, Facultad de Medicina y Ciencias de la Salud, Neiva, Huila
264-24 Universidad Autonoma de Bucaramanga, Facultad de Medicina, Floridablanca, Bucaramanga
264-25 Universidad de Santander (UDES) Facultad de Medicina, Bucaramanga
264-26 Fundacion Universidad de San Martin, Facultad de Medicina, Santa Fe de Bogota
264-27 Universidad Pedagogica y Tecnica de Colombia, Tunja

266   **Congo (Formerly Zaire)**
266-01 Universite de Kinshasa, Kinshasa (University National Zaire)
266-02 Universite de Kisangani, Faculte de Medecine, Kisangani
266-03 Universite de Lubumbashi, Faculte de Medecine, Lubumbashi

270   **Costa Rica**
270-01 Universidad de Costa Rica, Facultad de Medicina, San Jose
270-02 Escuela Autonoma de Ciencias Medicas de Centro America, San Jose
270-03 Universidad Internacional de las Americas, Escuela de Medicina, San Jose
270-04 Universidad de IberoAmerica, Escuela de Medicina, San Jose

275   **Cuba**
275-01 Instituto Superior de Ciencias Medicas de La Habana, La Habana
275-02 Instituto Superior de Ciencias Medicas de Santiago de Cuba, Santiago de Cuba
275-03 Instituto Superior de Ciencias Medicas de Villa Clara, Villa Clara
275-04 Instituto Superior de Ciencias Medicas "Carlos J. Finlay," Camaguey
275-05 Centro Universidad Camilo Cienfuegos de Matanzas, Matanzas
275-06 Centro Universidad de Holguin, Holguin
275-07 Facultad de Ciencias Medicas Pinar del Rio, Pinar del Rio
275-08 Facultad de Ciencias Medicas Matamzas/University of Havana, Matamzas
275-09 Facultad de Ciencias Medicas Pinar Del Rio, University Of Havana, Pinar del Rio
275-10 Facultad de Ciencias Medicas "CS Mandulay,"Manzanilla
275-11 Facultad de Ciencias Medicas Sancti Spiritus, Sancti Spiritus
275-12 Facultad de Ciencias Medicas Guantanamo, Guantanamo

286   **Czechoslovakia**
286-01 Deutsche Univerzita Medizinische Fakulta, Praha (154-05 before 1919)
286-02 Univerzita Karlova, Fakulta of Pediatrics, Praha
286-03 Univerzita Komenskeho, Lekarska Fakulta, Bratislava
286-04 Marary Kova Univerzita V Brno, Faculty of Medicine, Brno
286-05 Univerzita Palackeho, Lekarska Fakulta, Olomouc
286-06 Univerzita P. J. Safarika, Lekarska Fakulta, Kosice

286   **Czechoslovakia (continued)**
286-07 Univerzita Karlova, Lekarska Fakulta, Hradec Kralove
286-09 Univerzita Karlova, Lekarska Fakulta, Plzen
286-11 Univerzita Karlova, Fakulta of Hygiene, Praha
286-12 Univerzita Komenskeho, Lekarska Fakulta, Martin
286-13 Univerzita Karlova v Praze, Fakulta of General Medicine, Praha

297   **Denmark**
297-01 Kobenhavns Universitet, Det Laegevidenskabelige Fakultet, Kobenhavn
297-02 Arhus Universitet, Det Laegevidenskabelige Fakultet, Arhus
297-03 Odense Universitet, Det Laegevidenskabelige Fakultet, Odense

305   **Dominica (West Indies)**
305-01 Ross University, School of Medicine and Veterinary Medicine, Roseau

306   **St Lucia (West Indies)**
306-01 Spartan Health Science University, Vieux Fort
306-02 College of Medicine and Health Sciences, Castries

308   **Dominican Republic**
308-01 Universidad Autonoma de Santo Domingo (USAD), Facultad de Ciencias Medicina de la Salud, Santo Domingo
308-02 Universidad Nacional Pedro Henriquez Urena, Escuela de Medicina, Santo Domingo
308-03 Universidad Central del Este (UCE), Escuela de Medicina, San Pedro de Macoris
308-04 Pontificia Universidad Catolica Madre y Maestra (UCMM), Facultad de Ciencias Medicina, Santiago
308-05 Instituto Technologico de Santo Domingo (INTEC), Facultad de Medicina, Santo Domingo
308-06 Universidad Nordestana (UNNE), Facultad de Ciencias Medicina, San Francisco de Macoris
308-07 *Universidad CETEC, Escuela de Medicina, Santo Domingo (Extinct)*
308-08 *Universidad CIFAS, Escuela de Medicina, Santo Domingo (Extinct)*
308-10 *Universidad Mundial Dominicina (UMD), Escuela de Medicina (World University), Santo Domingo (Extinct)*
308-11 Universidad Tecnologica de Santiago (UTESA), Escuela de Medicina, Santiago
308-12 *Universidad Eugenio Maria de Hostos (UNIREMHOS), Escuela de Medicina, Santo Domingo (Extinct)*
308-13 Universidad Iberoamericana (UNIBE), Escuela de Medicina, Santo Domingo
308-14 *Universidad Federico Henrique y Carvajal, Facultad de Medicina, Santo Domingo (Extinct)*
308-15 Universidad Internacional Eugenio Maria de Hostos, Santo Domingo
308-16 Universidad Tecnologica del Cibao (Uteci), Faculty of Medicine, La Vega

319   **Ecuador**
319-01 Universidad Central del Ecuador, Facultad de Ciencias Medicas, Escuela de Medicina, Quito
319-02 Universidad de Cuenca, Facultad de Ciencias Medicas, Cuenca
319-03 Universidad de Guayaquil, Facultad de Ciencias Medicas, Guayaquil
319-04 Universidad Catolica de Santiago de Guayaquil, Facultad de Medicina, Guayaquil
319-05 Universidad Nacional de Loja, Escuela de Medicina Humana, Loja
319-06 Universidad de Catolica de Cuenca, Facultad de Medicina y Ciencias, Cuenca
319-07 Universidad San Francisco de Quito, Colegio de Ciencias de la Salud, Quito
319-08 Pontificia Universidad Catolica del Ecuador, Quito
319-09 Universidad Tecnica de Manabi, Facultad de Ciencias de la Salud, Manabi

330   **Egypt (United Arab Republic)**
330-   (Also see 915 United Arab Republic effective 1971)
330-01 Ibrahim Pasha University, Faculty of Medicine, Cairo (915-01 after Jan 1971)
330-02 Kasr El Aini Faculty of Medicine, Cairo University, Cairo (915-02 after Jan 1971)
330-03 Faculty of Medicine, Alexandria University, Alexandria (915-03 after Jan 1971)
330-04 Abbasis Faculty of Medicine, University of Ain Shams, Cairo (915-04 after Jan 1971)

341   **El Salvador**
341-01 Universidad de El Salvador, Facultad de Medicina, San Salvador
341-03 Universidad Evangelica, Facultad de Medicina, San Salvador
341-04 Universidad Alberto Masferrer, Facultad de Medicina, San Salvador
341-05 Universidad Dr Jose Matias Delgado, Facultad de Ciencias de la Salud, Merliot
341-06 Universidad Autonoma de Santa Ana, Facultad de Medicina, Santa Ana

352   **England (United Kingdom-England-Wales)**
          352-   (Also see 917 United Kingdom-England-Wales effective 1971)
          352-01 The Medical School University of Birmingham, Birmingham
          352-02 University of Bristol, Faculty of Medicine, Bristol
          352-03 Cambridge University Medical School, Cambridge
          352-04 University of Newcastle-Upon-Tyne Medical School, Newcastle-Upon-Tyne
          352-05 University of Leeds, School of Medicine, Leeds
          352-06 University of Liverpool, Faculty of Medicine, Liverpool
          352-07 University of London, Faculty of Medicine, Charing Cross Hospital Medical School, London
          352-08 Victoria University of Manchester, Faculty of Medicine, Manchester
          352-09 Oxford University Medical School, Oxford
          352-10 University of Sheffield, Faculty of Medicine, Sheffield
          352-11 Registrable Qualification Granted by English Conjoint Board
          352-17 Registrable Qualification Granted by Society of Apothecaries of London
          352-24 University of London, St George's Hospital Medical School, London (917-24 after 1971)

363   **Estonia**
          363-01 Tartu Ulikooli Faculte de Medecine de l'Universite de Tartu, Tartu (Extinct)

366   **Ethiopia**
          366-01 Addis Ababa University, Faculty of Medicine (Haile Selassie University), Addis Ababa
          366-02 Gondar College of Medical Science, Addis Ababa University, Gondar
          366-03 Jimma Health Science Institute, Jimma

368   **Fiji**
          368-01 Fiji School of Medicine, Suva

374   **Finland**
          374-01 University of Helsinki, Laaketieteellinen Tiedekunta, Helsinki
          374-02 University of Turku, Laaketieteellinen Tiedekunta, Turku
          374-03 University of Oulu, Laaketieteellinen Tiedekunta, Oulu
          374-04 University of Kuopio, Laaketieteellinen Tiedekunta, Kuopio
          374-05 University of Tampere, Laaketieteellinen Tiedekunta, Tampere

385   **Formosa (Taiwan)**
          385-   (Also see 244 Taiwan effective Jan 1, 1971)
          385-01 Kaohsiung (Takau) Medical College, Kaohsiung
          385-02 College of Medicine National Taiwan University, Taipei
          385-03 National Defense Medical Center, Taipei
          385-04 Taipei Medical College, Taipei
          385-05 China Medical College, Taichung

396   **France**
          (U.F.R.) = Unites d'Enseignement et de Recherche Medicales
          396-01 Universite de Bordeaux II, U.F.R. de Medecine, Bordeaux
          396-02 Universite de Lille II, U.F.R. Medecine, Lille
          396-03 Universite Claude-Bernard, U.F.R. de Medecine Grange Blanche, Lyon (Lyon I)
          396-04 Universite de Montpellier I, U.F.R. de Medecine, Montpellier
          396-05 Universite de Nancy I, U.F.R. A et B Medecine, Vandoeuvreles-Nancy
          396-06 Universite de Pierre et Marie Curie (Paris VI), U.F.R. Brossais-Hotel-Dieu, Paris
          396-07 Universite Paul Sabatier, U.F.R. Medecine Toulouse-Rangeuil, Toulouse
          396-08 Universite de Louis Pasteur, U.F.R. Sciences Medecine, Strasbourg (407-18 before 1918)
          396-09 Universite de Lyon 1, UFR de Medecine Laennec, Lyon
          396-10 Universite de Rouen, U.F.R. de Medecine, Rouen
          396-11 Universite d'Aix-Marseille II, U.F.R. de Medecine, Marseille
          396-12 Universite de Paris, U.F.R. de Medecine Necker-Enfants Malades, Paris
          396-13 Universite de Paris, U.F.R. de Medecine Saint-Antoine, Paris
          396-14 Universite Claude-Bernard (Lyon 1), Faculte de Medecine Lyon-Nord, Villeurbanne Cedex
          396-15 Universite de Nantes, U.F.R. de Medecine et Techniques Medecine, Nantes
          396-16 Universite de Besancon, U.F.R. de Medecine, Besancon
          396-17 Universite de Clermont-Ferrand, U.F.R. de Medecine, Clermont-Ferrand
          396-18 Universite Sciences et Medecine de Grenoble, U.F.R. de Medecine, La Tronche
          396-19 Universite Francois-Rabelais, U.F.R. de Medecine de Tours, Tours
          396-20 Universite de Picardie, U.F.R. de Medecine, Amiens, France (Universite d'Amiens)
          396-21 Universite d'Angers, U.F.R. des Sciences Medecine et Pharmaceutiques, Angers
          396-22 Universite de Caen, U.F.R. de Medecine, Caen
          396-23 Universite de Dijon, U.F.R. de Medecine, Dijon
          396-24 Ecole Libre de Medecine, Lille
          396-25 Universite de Limoges, U.F.R. de Medecine et de Pharmaceutiques, Limoges

396 **France (continued)**
396-26 Universite de Poitiers, U.F.R. Mixte de Medecine et de Pharmaceutiques, Poitiers
396-27 Universite de Reims, U.F.R. de Medecine, Reims
396-28 Universite de Rennes I, U.F.R. Clinique et Therapeutiques Medecine, Rennes
396-30 Universite de Nice, U.F.R. de Medecine, Nice
396-31 Universite Rene Descartes (Paris V), U.F.R. Cochin-Port Royal, Paris
396-32 Universite de Paris VII, U.F.R. de Medecine Lariboisiere-St Louis Paris
396-33 Universite de Saint-Etienne, U.F.R. de Medecine, Saint-Etienne
396-34 Universite Paris Val-de-Marne, U.F.R. de Creteil, Creteil
396-35 Universite de Paris-Sud XI, Recherche de Medecine, Kremlin-Bicetre, Orsay, Paris
396-36 Universite de Paris, U.F.R. de Medecine et de Biologie Humaine, Bobigny
396-37 Universite Rene Descartes, U.F.R. de Medecine Paris-Ouest, Garches
396-38 Universite de Paris (VI) et Marie Curie, U.F.R. de Medecine Pitie-Salpetriere, Paris
396-39 Universite de Paris Sud, U.F.R. de Medecine Kremlin-Bicetre, Paris
396-40 Universite de Toulouse III, U.F.R. de Sciences Medecine de Toulouse Purpan, Toulouse
396-41 Universite de Paris VII, U.F.R. de Medecine Xavier Bichat, Paris

397 **Gabon**
397-01 Centre Universite des Sciences de la Sante, Libreville

407 **Germany**
407-   (Also see 408 Germany, East effective Jan 1, 1971)
407-   (Also see 409 Germany, West effective Jan 1, 1971)
407-01 Friedrich-Wilhelms Universitaet Medizinische Fakultaet, Berlin
407-02 Medizinische Fakultaet Rheinischen, Friedrich Wilhelms Universitaet, Bonn
407-03 Schlesische-Friedrich-Wilhelms Universitaet Medizinische Fakultaet, Breslau (759-10 effective 1945)
407-04 Medizinische Fakultaet der Universitaet Erlangen, Erlangen, Bayern
407-05 Medizinische Fakultaet der Albert Ludwigs Universitaet, Freiburgim Breisgau, Baden-Wurttemberg
407-06 Medizinische Fakultaet der Justus Liebig Universitaet, Giessen, Hessen
407-07 Medizinische Fakultaet der Georg August Universitaet, Gottingen, Niedersachsen
407-08 Medizinische Fakultaet der Universitaet Greifswald, Greifswald
407-09 Medizinische Fakultaet der Martin Luther Universitaet, Halle
407-10 Medizinische Fakultaet der Universitaet Heidelberg, Heidelberg, Baden-Wurttemberg
407-11 Medizinische Fakultaet der Friedrich Schiller Universitaet, Jena
407-12 Medizinische Fakultaet der Christian Albrechts Universitaet, Kiel, Schleswig Holstein
407-13 *Albertus Universitaet Medizinische Fakultaet, Konigsberg, Prussia (Extinct)*
407-14 Universitaet Leipzig Medizinische Fakultaet, Saxony
407-15 Medizinische Fakultaet der Philipps Universitaet, Marburg Lahn, Hessen
407-16 Medizinische Fakultaet der Ludwig Maximilians Universitaet, Munchen, Bayern
407-17 Medizinische Fakultaet der Universitaet Rostock, Rostock
407-19 Medizinische Fakultaet der Eberhard Karls Universitaet, Tubingen, Baden-Wurttemberg
407-20 Medizinische Fakultaet der Julius Maximilians Universitaet, Wurzburg, Bayern
407-21 Medizinische Fakultaet der Universitaet Hamburg, Hamburg
407-22 Medizinische Fakultaet der Universitaet Koln, Koln, Nordrhein-Westfalen
407-23 Medizinische Fakultaet der Johann Wolfgang Goethe Universitaet, Frankfurt-am-Main, Hessen
407-24 Medizinische Fakultaet der Westfalischen Landes Universitaet, Munster, Nordrhein-Westfalen
407-25 Medizinische Akademie in Dusseldorf, Dusseldorf, Nordrhein-Westfalen
407-26 Medizinische Fakultaet der Universitaet Wien, Wien (154-07 before Mar 13, 1938, and effective Jun 1, 1945)
407-27 Karl Franzens Universitaet Medizinische Fakultaet, Graz (154-01 before Mar 13, 1938, and effective Jun 1, 1945)
407-28 Leopold Franzens Universitaet Medizinische Fakultaet, Innsbruck (154-02 before Mar 13, 1938, and effective Jun 1, 1945)
407-29 *United Hungarian Universitaet Medizinische School, Halle (Extinct)*
407-30 Medizinische Fakultaet der Humboldt Universitaet, Berlin
407-32 Medizinische Fakultaet der Johannes Gutenberg Universitaet, Mainz, Rheinland Pfalz
407-33 Medizinische Fakultaet der Freien Universitaet Berlin, Berlin
407-34 Medizinische Fakultaet der Universitaet des Saarlandes, Homburg, Saarland
407-35 Klinikum Essen der Ruhr Universitaet, Bochum, Essen
407-36 Medizinische Akademie Leubeck 2nd Fakultaet Medizinische Christian Albrechts Universitaet, Kiel, Leubeck

408 **Germany, East (Former)**
408-   (Also see 407 Germany before 1971)
408-08 Erns-Moritz-Arndt Universitaet, Bereich Medizin, Greifswald (407-08 before 1971)

408 **Germany, East (Former) (continued)**

408-09 Martin Luther Universitaet, Bereich Medizin, Halle (407-09 before 1971)

408-11 Friedrich-Schiller Universitaet, Bereich Medizin, Jena (407-11 before 1971)

408-14 Karl Marx Universitaet, Bereich Medizin, Leipzig (formerly 407-14 Universitaet Leipzig Medizinische Fakultaet)

408-17 Wilhelm Peick Universitaet, Bereich Medizin, Rostock (407-17 before 1/71)

408-30 Humboldt Universitaet Berlin, Medizinische Fakultaet, Berlin (407-30 before 1971)

408-31 Medizinische Akademie "Carl-Gustav Carus," Dresden

408-32 Medizinische Akademie Erfurt, Erfurt

408-34 Medizinische Akademie Magdeburg, Magdeburg

409 **Germany, West (Former)**

409-   (Also see 407 Germany before 1971)

409-02 Rheinischen Friedrich Wilhelms Universitaet, Medizinische Fakultaet, Bonn (407-02 before 1971)

409-04 Friedrich-Alexander Universitaet, Medizinische Fakultaet, Erlangen (407-04 before 1971)

409-05 Albert-Ludwigs Universitaet, Medizinische Fakultaet, Freiburg (407-05 before 1971)

409-06 Justus-Liebig Universitaet, Fachbereich Humanmedizin, Giessen (407-06 before 1971)

409-07 Georg-August Universitaet, Medizinische Fakultaet, Gottingen (407-07 before 1971)

409-10 Ruprecht-Karl Universitaet, Medizinische Fakultaet, Heidelberg (407-10 before 1971)

409-12 Christian-Albrechts Universitaet, Medizinische Fakultaet, Kiel (407-12 before 1971)

409-15 Philipps Universitaet, Fachbereich Humanmedizin, Marburg (407-15 before 1971)

409-16 Ludwig Maximilians Universitaet, Medizinische Fakultaet, Munchen (407-16 before 1971)

409-19 Eberhard-Karls Universitaet, Medizinische Fakultaet, Tubingen (407-19 before 1971)

409-20 Universitaet Wurzburg, Medizinische Fakultaet, Wurzburg (407-20 before 1971)

409-21 Universitaet Hamburg, Medizinische Fakultaet, Krankenhaus Eppendorf, Hamburg (407-21 before 1971)

409-22 Universitaet zu Koln, Medizinische Fakultaet, Koln (407-22 before 1971)

409-23 Johann-Wolfgang-Goethe Universitaet, Medizinische Fakultaet, Frankfurt (407-23 before 1971)

409-24 Westfalische Wilhelms Universitaet, Medizinische Fakultaet, Munster (407-24 before 1971)

409-25 Universitaet Dusseldorf, Medizinische Fakultaet, Dusseldorf (407-25 before 1971)

409-32 Johannes-Gutenberg Universitaet, Medizinische Fakultaet, Mainz (407-32 before 1971)

409-33 Freie Universitaet Berlin, Medizinische Fakultaet, Berlin (407-33 before 1971)

409-34 Universitaet Saarlandes/Saarbrucken, Medizinische Fakultaet, Homburg (407-34 before 1971)

409-35 Ruhr Universitaet Bochum, Medizinische Fakultaet, Bochum (407-35 before 1971)

409-36 Medizinische Hochschule Luebeck, Luebeck (407-36 before 1971)

409-37 Universitaet Heidelberg, Fakultat fur Klinische Medizin, Mannheim

409-38 Medizinische Hochschule Hannover, Hannover

409-39 Rheinisch-Westfal Tech Hochschule, Medizinische Fakultaet, Aachen

409-40 Technischen Universitaet, Medizinische Fakultaet, Munchen

409-41 Universitaet Ulm, Medizinische Fakultaet, Ulm

409-42 Gesamthochschule Essen, Medizinische Fakultaet, Essen

409-43 Universitaet Regensburg, Fachbereich Bio-Vorklinische Medizinische, Regensburg

409-44 Universitaet Witten-Herdecke, Medizinische Fakultaet, Herdecke

409-45 Otto-Von-Guericke Universitaet, Medizinische Fakultaet, Magdeburg

405-46 Charite-Universitaet Atsmedizin, Berlin

412 **Ghana**

412-01 University of Ghana Medical School, Accra

412-02 University of Science and Technology, School of Medicine Sciences, Kumasi

412-03 St Luke School of Medicine–Ghana, Cape Coast

418 **Greece**

418-01 University of Athens, Faculty of Medicine, School of Health Science, National and Kapodistrian, Athens

418-02 Aristotle University of Thessaloniki, Medicine School, Thessaloniki

418-03 University of Patras, Medical School, Patras

418-04 University of Ioannina, Medical School, Ioannina

418-05 University of Crete, School of Health Sciences, Heraklion

418-06 University of Thraki, Medical Section, Alexandraupolis

418-07 University of Thessaly Medical School, Larissa

422 **Grenada (West Indies)**

422-01 St George's University, School of Medicine, St George's

429   **Guatemala**
429-01 Universidad de San Carlos, Facultad de Ciencias Medicas, Guatemala
429-02 Universidad Francisco Marroquin, Facultad de Medicina, Guatemala

435   **Guinea**
435-01 Universite de Conakry, Faculte de Medicine, Conakry

436   **Guyana**
436-01 University of Guyana, Faculty of Health Sciences, Georgetown
436-02 University of Guyana Medical School, Faculty of Health Sciences, Turkeyen, Demera
436-03 American International School of Medicine, Cumingsburg, Georgetown

440   **Haiti**
440-01 Universite d'Etat d'Haiti, Ecole de Medecine et de Pharmacie, Port-au-Prince
440-02 Universite Notre Dame d'Haiti, Faculte de Medecine, Port-au-Prince

451   **Honduras**
451-01 Universidad Nacional Autonoma de Honduras, Facultad de Ciencias Medicas, Tegucigalpa

462   **Hong Kong**
462-01 University of Hong Kong, Faculty of Medicine, Hong Kong
462-02 The Chinese University of Hong Kong, Faculty of Medicine, Hong Kong

473   **Hungary**
473-01 Semmelweis Orvostudomanyi Egyetem (Peter Pazmany University), Budapest
473-02 Albert Szent-Gyorgyi Orvostudomanyi Egyetem, Szeged
473-03 Pecsi Orvostudomanyi Egyetem, Pecs
473-04 Debreceni Orvostudomanyi Egyetem, Debrecen
473-05 *Magyar Kiralyi Tudomanyegyetem Orvostudomanyi Fakultas, Koloszvar (Extinct)*

484   **Iceland**
484-01 University of Iceland, Laeknadeild, Haskoli Islands, Reykjavik

495   **India (Goa)**
495-01 University of Bombay
    Affiliated medical colleges are:
      Grant Medical College, Bombay University, Bombay, Maharashtra
      Seth Gordhandas Sunderdas Medical College, Bombay University, Bombay, Maharashtra
495-02 University of Calcutta, Medical College, Calcutta, West Bengal
495-03 Guru Nanak dev University, Medical College, Amritsar, Punjab
495-04 Madras Medical College, Dr M G R Medical University, Madras, Tamil Nadu
495-05 Lucknow University, King George's Medical College, Lucknow, Uttar Pradesh
495-06 Terna Medical School, University of Mumbai, Koparkhairnare, New Bombay
495-07 Sher-I-Kashnir Institute of Medical Sciences, Deemed University, Kashmir
495-08 Punjab University, Christian Medical College, Ludhiana, Punjab
495-09 Mysore Medical College, Mysore University, Mysore, Karnataka
495-10 Guru Govind Singh Medical College, Punjab University, Faridkot, Punjab
495-11 Andhra Medical College, Andhra University, Visakhapatnam, Andhra Pradesh
495-12 Sarojini Najdu Medical College, Agra University, Agra, Uttar Pradesh
495-13 Sriram Chandra Bhanj Medical College, Utkal University, Cuttack, Orissa
495-14 Institute of Medical Sciences, Banaras Hindu University, Varansasi, Uttar Pradesh
495-15 Patna Medical College, Patna University, Patna, Bihar
495-16 Stanley Medical College, Dr M G R Medical University, Madras, Tamil Nadu
495-17 Topiwala National Medical College, University of Bombay, Bombay, Maharashtra
495-18 Assam Medical College and Hospital, Dibrugarh University, Dibrugarh, Assam
495-19 Medical College, Nagpur University, Nagpur, Maharashtra
495-20 Mahatma Gandhi Mem Medical College, Devi Ahilya Vishwavidhyalaya Indore, Madhya
    Pradesh
495-21 Osmania Medical College, University of Health Science, Hyderabad, Andhra Pradesh
495-22 Byramjee Jeejeebhoy Medical College, Gujarat University, Ahmedabad, Gujarat
495-23 Medical College, M. S. University of Baroda, Baroda, Gujarat
495-24 Darbhanga Medical College, LN Mithila University, Laheriasarai, Bihar
495-25 *Escola Medico Cirurgica de Goa Medical College, Goa (Extinct)*
495-26 JN Medical College, Nagpur University, Warda, Maharashtra
495-27 Christian Medical College, Dr M G R Medical University, Vellore, Tamil Nadu
495-28 Byramjee Jeejeebhoy Medical College, University of Pune, Pune, Maharashtra
495-29 Government Medical College, Punjab University, Patiala, Punjab
495-30 Sawai Man Singh Medical College, University of Rajasthan, Jaipur, Rajasthan
495-31 Medical College, University of Kerala, Trivandrum, Kerala

495	India (Goa) (continued)

495-32 Nilratan Sircar Medical College, University of Calcutta, Calcutta, West Bengal
495-33 Bangalore Medical College, Bangalore University, Bangalore, Karnataka
495-34 Gajra Raja Medical College, Jiwaji University, Gwalior, Madhya Pradesh
495-35 Karnataka Medical College, Karnataka University, Hubli, Karnataka
495-36 All-India Institute of Medical Sciences, Ansari Nagar, New Delhi, Delhi
495-37 Kasturba Medical College, Mysore University, Mangalore, Karnataka
495-38 RG Kar Medical College, University of Calcutta, Calcutta, West Bengal
495-39 Calcutta National Medical College, University of Calcutta, Calcutta, West Bengal
495-40 OHN Medical College, Gujarat University, Navranapura, Bombay
495-41 GSVM Medical College, Kanpur University, Kanpur, Uttar Pradesh
495-42 Madurai Medical College, Madurai University, Madurai, Tamil Nadu
495-43 Dayanand Medical College and Hospital, Punjab University, Ludhiana, Punjab
495-44 Medical College, Calicut University, Calicut, Kerala
495-45 Maulana Azad Medical College, University of Delhi, New Delhi, Delhi
495-46 Bankura Sammilani Medical College, University of Calcutta, Bankura, West Bengal
495-47 Medical College, Rani Durgavati Vishwavidhyalaya, Jabalpur, Madhya Pradesh
495-48 MP Shah Medical College, Saurashtra University, Jamnagar, Gujarat
495-49 Gandhi Medical College, Bhopal University, Bhopal, Madhya Pradesh
495-50 Guntur Medical College, University of Health Sciences, Guntur, Andhra Pradesh
495-51 Government Medical College, Kashmir University, Srinagar, Jammu & Kashmir
495-52 St John's Medical College, Bangalore University, Bangalore, Karnataka
495-53 Jawaharlal Institute of Post-grad Medical Education, Madras University, Pondicherry, Tamil Nadu
495-54 Rajendra Medical College, Ranchi University, Ranchi, Bihar
495-55 Sardar Patel Medical College, University of Rajasthan, Bikaner, Rajasthan
495-56 Government Medical College, Marathwada University, Aurangabad, Maharashtra
495-57 Kakatiya Medical College, University of Health Sciences, Warangal, Andhra Pradesh
495-58 Rangarya Medical College, University of Health Sciences, Kakinada, Andhra Pradesh
495-59 Kilpauk Medical College, Dr M G R Medical University, Madras, Tamil Nadu
495-61 Chingleput Medical College, Dr M G R Medical University, Chingleput, Tamil Nadu
495-62 Kurnool Medical College, University of Health Sciences, Kurnool, Andhra Pradesh
495-63 Kottayam Medical College, Ghandiji University, Kottayam, Kerala
495-64 SS Medical College, AP Singh University, Rewa, Madhya Pradesh
495-65 Gandhi Medical College, Vijayawada University of Health Sciences, Hyderabad, Andhra Pradesh
495-66 Thanjavur Medical College, Dr M G R Medical University, Thanjavur, Tamil Nadu
495-67 Moti Lal Nehru Medical College, University of Allahabad, Allahabad, Uttar Pradesh
495-69 PBD Sharma Medical College, Maharishi Dayanand University, Rohtak, Haryana
495-70 Sri Venkatesvara Medical College, University of Health Sciences, Tirupati, Andhra Pradesh
495-71 Sri Bhausahab Hire Medical College, North Maharashtra University, Dhule
495-72 Government Medical College, Vijayanagara Institute of Medical Sciences Gulbarga University, Bellary, Karnataka
495-73 Armed Forces Medical College, University of Pune, Pune, Maharashtra
495-74 Ravindra Nath Tagore Medical College, University of Rajasthan, Udaipur, Rajasthan
495-75 Mahatma Gandhi Memorial Medical College, Ranchi University, Jamshedpur, Bihar
495-76 NHL Municipal Medical College, Gujarat University, Ahmedabad, Gujarat
495-77 JN Medical College, Aligarh Muslim University, Aligarh, Uttar Pradesh
495-78 Gawahati Medical College, Gawahati University, Gawahati, Assam
495-79 VSS Medical College, Sambalpur University, Burla, Orissa
495-80 TD Medical College, Kerala University, Alleppey, Kerala
495-82 Miraj Medical College, Shivaji University, Miraj, Maharashtra
495-83 Government Medical College, Nagpur University, Nagpur, Maharashtra (495-19)
495-84 Baba Raghav Das Medical College, Gorakhpur University, Gorakhpur, Uttar Pradesh
495-85 Mahatma Gandhi Institute of Medical Science, Nagpur University, Wardha, Maharashtra
495-87 Silchar Medical College, Gauhati University, Silchar, Assam
495-89 Government Medical College, South Gujarat University, Surat, Gujarat
495-90 Indira Gandhi Medical College, Himachal Pradesh University, Simla, Himachal Pradesh
495-91 Medical College, Jhansi University, Jhansi, Madhya Pradesh
495-92 JLN Medical College, Ravi Shankar University, Rajpur, Madhya Pradesh
495-93 SS Medical College, AP Singh University, Rewa, Madhya Pradesh
495-94 Coimbatore Medical College, Dr M G R Medical University, Coimbatore, Tamil Nadu
495-95 Tirunelveli Medical College, Madurai University, Tirunelveli, Tamil Nadu
495-96 Lokmanya Tilak Mun Medical College, University of Mumbai, Mumbai, Maharashtra
495-97 Dr Vaishampayan Memorial Medical College, Shivaji University, Sholapur, Maharashtra
495-98 JLN Medical College, Karnataka University, Belgaum, Karnataka
495-99 JJM Medical College, Kuvempu University, Devangere, Karnataka

496 India

496-01 Mahadevappa Rampure Medical College, Gulbarga University, Gulbarga, Karnataka
496-02 Jawaharlal Nehru Medical College, University of Rajasthan, Ajmer, Rajasthan
496-03 Dr SN Medical College, University of Rajasthan, Jodhpur, Rajasthan
496-04 LLRM Medical College, Meerut University, Meerut, Uttar Pradesh (Lala Lajbut Rai Mam)
496-05 MKCG Medical College, Berhampur University, Berhampur, Orissa
496-06 Jawaharlal Nehru Medical College, Bhagalpur University, Bhagalpur, Bihar
496-07 Lady Hardinge Medical College, Delhi University, New Delhi, Delhi
496-08 North Bengal Medical College, University of North Bengal, Darjeeling, West Bengal
496-09 College of Medical Sciences, University of Delhi, New Delhi, Delhi
496-10 MLB Medical College, Bundelkhand University, Jhansi, Uttar Pradesh
496-11 Sri Krishna Medical College, Bihar University, Muzaffarpur, Bihar
496-12 Burdwan Medical College, Burdwan University, Burdwan, West Bengal
496-13 Patliputra Medical College, Ranchi University, Dhanbad, Bihar
496-14 Nalanda Medical College, Magadh University, Patna, Bihar
496-15 Goa Medical College, Goa University, Panaji, Goa Daman and Diu
496-16 Anugrah Narain Magadh Medical College, Madagh University, Gaya, Bihar
496-17 Government Medical College Jammu, Jammu University, Jammu and Kashmir
496-18 Regional Medical College, Manipur University, Imphal, Manipur
496-19 SRTR Medical College, Marathwada University, Ambajogai, Maharashtra
496-20 Dr Ambedkar Medical College, Bangalore University, Bangalore, Karnataka
496-21 MS Ramaian Medical College, Bangalore University, Bangalore, Karnataka
496-22 Kempegowda Institute of Medical Science, Bangalore University, Bangalore, Karnataka
496-23 Sri Ramachandra Medical College and Research Institute, Dr M G R Medical University, Porur, Madras
496-24 Siddhartha Medical College, University of Health Sciences, Vijayawada, AP
496-25 Rural Medical College of Pravaro Medical Trust, Pune University, Pravara
496-26 Krishna Institute of Medical Science, Shivaji University, Karad, Maharashtra
496-27 Deccan College of Medical Sciences, Osmania University, Hyderabad
496-28 Rajah Muthiah Medical College, Annamalai University, Annamalainagar
496-29 Trichur Medical College, University of Calicut, Trichur, Kerala
496-30 Dr PDM Medical College, Amravati, Maharashtra
496-31 BLDE Association's Medical College, Karnataka University, Bijapur, Karnataka
496-32 PSG Institute of Medical Sciences and Research, Bharathiar University, Tamil, Nadu
496-33 Adichunchanagiri Institute of Medical Science, Mysore University, Faculty of Medicine, Bellur
496-34 Sri Devaraj Urs Medical College, Shivaji University, Kolhapur
496-35 JSS Medical College, Mysore University, Mysore, Karnataka
496-36 Dr DY Patil Medical College, Shivaji University, Kolhapur, Maharashtra
496-37 Siddhartha Medical College, Bangalore University, Tukmur, Karnataka
496-38 Seth G S Medical College, University of Bombay, Parel, Bombay
496-39 Bangalore Medical College, Bangalore, Karnataka
496-40 Al-Ameen Medical College, Karnataka University, Bijapur
496-41 Pramukh Swami Medical College, Sardar Patel University, Karamsad, Gujerat
496-42 Bharati Vidyapeeth Medical College, Bharati Vidyapeeth Deemed University, Pune, Maharashtra
496-43 Government Medical College, Chandigarh University, Punjab
496-44 KJ Somaiya Medical College, University of Mumbai, Chembur, Bombay
496-45 Mohan Kumaramangalam Medical College, Dr MGR Medical University, Salem, Tamil Nadu
496-46 Mahatma Gandhi Mission's Medical College, Bombay University, New Bombay, Maharashtra
496-47 NDMVP Samaj Medical College, Poona University, Nashik, Maharashtra
496-48 Jawahar Medical Foundation's Annasaheb Chudaman Patil Memorial College, Dhule
496-49 NKP Salve Institute of Medical Sciences, Nagpur University, Nagpur
496-50 Mahatma Gandhi Mission's Medical College, Dr BA Marathwada University Aurangabad, Maharashtra
496-51 Dr DY Patil Education Society's Medical College, Shivaji University, Kolhapur, Marashtra
496-52 Maharashtra Institute of Medical Science and Research, Swami Ramanand Teerth University, Latur, Maharashtra
496-53 Shri Vasantrao Naik Government Medical College, Amravati University, Yavatmal, Maharashtra
496-54 Government Medical College Bhavnagar, Bhavnagar University, Bhavnagar
496-55 Rajiv Gandhi Medical College, Maharashtra University of Health Sciences, Thane
496-56 Government Medical College Nanded, Maharashtra University of Health Sciences, Nanded
496-57 Santosh Medical College, Ch Charan Singh University, Ghaziabad, Uttar Pradesh
496-58 Sher-I-Kashmir Institute of Medical Sciences, Sher-I-Kashmir Institute of Medical Sciences (Deemed University), Srinagar, Kashmir
496-59 Kasturba Medical College, Manipal Academy of Higher Education, Mangalore, Karnataka

655   **Morocco**
655-01 University Mohammed V, Faculte de Medicine et de Pharmacie, Rabat
655-03 University Hassan II, Faculte de Medicine et de Pharmacie, Casablanca

660   **Netherlands**
660-01 Universiteit van Amsterdam, Faculteit der Geneeskunde, Amsterdam
660-02 Rijksuniversiteit te Groningen, Faculteit der Geneeskunde, Groningen
660-03 Rijksuniversiteit te Leiden, Faculteit der Geneeskunde, Leiden
660-04 Rijksuniversiteit te Utrecht, Faculteit der Geneeskunde, Utrecht
660-05 Katholieke Universiteit, Faculteit der Geneeskunde, Nijmegen
660-06 Vrije Universiteit, Faculteit der Geneeskunde, Amsterdam
660-07 Erasmusuniversiteit, Faculteit der Geneeskunde, Rotterdam
660-08 Rijksuniversiteit Limburg, Faculteit der Geneeskunde, Maastricht

661   **St Kitts and Nevis**
661-01 Grace University, School of Medicine, Cades Bay (February 1985)
661-02 Medical University of the Americas
661-03 Windsor University, Basseterre
661-04 International University of the Health Sciences (IUHS), Basseterre

665   **Netherland Antilles**
665-01 Saba University School of Medicine, Saba
665-02 University of Sint Eustatius, Sint Eustatius
665-03 St James School of Medicine, St James
665-04 Xavier University School of Medicine, Bonaire

671   **New Zealand**
671-01 University of Otago, Medical School, Dunedin
671-02 University of Auckland, School of Medicine, Auckland

672   **Nepal**
672-01 Tribhuvan University, Institute of Medicine, Kathmandu
672-02 Manipal College of Medical Sciences, Kathmandu University, Pokhara, Kaski District
672-03 BP Koirala Institute of Health Sciences, Dharan, Sunsari District
672-04 College of Medical Sciences–Bharatpur, Kathmandu University, Bharatpur, Chitwan
672-05 Nepal Medical College, Attarkhel, Jorpati, Kathmandu
672-06 Nepalgunj Medical College, Kathmandu University, Nepalgunj
672-07 Kathmandu Medical College, Kathmandu University, Kathmandu

682   **Nicaragua**
682-01 Universidad Nacional Autonoma de Nicaragua, Facultad de Ciencias Medicas, Leon
682-02 Universidad de Oriente y Medicina (Southeastern Univ), Granada (Extinct)
682-03 Universidad Nacional Autonoma de Nicaragua, Facultad de Ciencias, Managua
682-04 Universidad Americana, Facultad de Ciencias Medicas, Managua

688   **Niger**
688-01 Abdou Moumouni University of Niamey, Faculty of Medical Sciences, Niamey

690   **Nigeria**
690-01 University of Ibadan, College of Medicine, Ibadan, Oyo
690-02 University of Lagos, College of Medicine, Lagos
690-03 Ahmadu Bello University, Faculty of Medicine, Zaria, Kaduna
690-04 University of Nigeria, College of Medicine, Enugu, Anambra
690-05 Obafemi Awolowo University, College of Health Sciences, Ile-Ife, Oyo
690-06 University of Benin, College of Medical Sciences, Benin City, Bendel
690-07 University of Jos, Faculty of Medical Sciences, Jos Plateau State
690-08 University of Ilorin, Faculty of Health Sciences, Ilorin, Kwara
690-09 University of Maiduguri, College of Medical Sciences, Maiduguri, Borno
690-10 University of Calabar, College of Medical Sciences, Calabar, Cross River
690-12 University of Port Harcourt, College of Health Sciences, Port Harcourt, Rivers
690-13 Danfodiyo University, College of Health Sciences, Sokoto
690-14 Ogun State University, College of Health Sciences, Ogun
690-15 Nnamdi Azikiwe University, College of Health Sciences, Nnewi
690-16 Abia State University, Faculty of Medicine, Uturu Abia State
690-17 Ebonyi State University, College of Health Sciences, Abakaliki
690-18 Ladoke Akintola University of Technology, College of Health Sciences, Osogbo
690-19 Bayero University, Faculty of Medicine, Kano

692   **North Vietnam**
         692-   (Also see 938 Vietnam, North, effective Jan 1, 1971)
         692-01 Universite de Hanoi, Faculte Mixte de Medecine et de Pharmacie, Hanoi

693   **Norway**
         693-01 Universitetet i Oslo, Det Medisinske Fakultet, Oslo
         693-02 Universitetet i Bergen, Det Medisinske Fakultet, Bergen
         693-03 Universitetet i Trondheim, Det Medisinske Fakultet, Trondheim
         693-04 Fagomradet Medisinske Universitetet i Tromso, Tromso

695   **Oman**
         695-01 Sultan Qaboos University, College of Medicine, Al Khod, Muscat

704   **Pakistan**
         704-   (Also see 160 Bangladesh effective July 1972)
         704-01 King Edward Medical College, University of Punjab, Lahore
         704-02 Dow Medical College, Karachi University, Karachi
         704-03 Dacca Medical College, Dacca (160-02 effective July 1972)
         704-04 Nishtar Medical College, Bahuddin Zakaria University, Multan
         704-05 Punjab Medical School, University of Punjab, Faisalabad
         704-06 Fatima Jinnah Medical College for Women, University of Punjab, Lahore
         704-07 *CMS Medical School, Hyderabad (Extinct)*
         704-08 Liaquat Medical College, University of Sind, Jamshoro
         704-09 Khyber Medical College, Peshawar University, Peshawar
         704-10 Chittagong Medical College, Chittagong (160-01 effective July 1972)
         704-11 Rajshahi Medical College, Rajshahi (160-05 effective July 1972)
         704-12 Lytton Medical College, Mymensingh (160-04 effective July 1972)
         704-14 Aminuddin Medical School, Qetta
         704-15 Quaid-e-Azam Medical College, Islamia University, Bahawalpur
         704-16 Sind Medical College, University of Karachi, Karachi
         704-17 Chandka Medical College, University of Sind, Larkana
         704-18 People's Medical College, Nawabshah
         704-19 Bolan Medical College, University of Baluchistan, Qetta
         704-20 Rawalpindi Medical College, University of Punjab, Rawalpindi
         704-21 Allama Iqbal Medical College, University of Punjab, Lahore
         704-22 Army Medical College, Quaid-e-Azam University, Rawalpindi
         704-23 Nawabshah Medical College for Girls, University of Sind, Nawabshah
         704-24 Ayub Medical College, University of Peshawar, Abbottabad
         704-25 Aga Khan Medical College, Aga Khan University, Karachi
         704-26 Baqai Medical and Dental College, University of Karachi, Karachi
         704-27 Karachi Medical and Dental College and A Shaheed Hospital, University of Karachi, Karachi
         704-28 Hamdard College of Medicine and Dentistry, Hamdard University, Karachi
         704-29 Ziauddin Medical College, Ziauddin University, Karachi
         704-30 Frontier Medical College, Bahria University, Abbottabad
         704-31 Kabir Medical College, the Gandhara University, Peshawar
         704-32 Islamic International Medical College, Itamdard University, Rawalpindi
         704-33 Shifa College of Medicine, Bahria University of Islamabad, Islamabad
         704-34 Isra University, Faculty of Medicine and Allied Medical Sciences, Hyderabad

715   **Panama**
         715-01 Universidad de Panama, Facultad de Medicina, Panama City
         715-02 Universidad Latina de Panama, Facultad de Medicina y de la Salud, Panama City

720   **Papua**
         720-01 University Papua New Guinea, Faculty of Medicine, Boroko

726   **Paraguay**
         726-01 Universidad Nacional de Asuncion, Facultad de Ciencias Medicas, Asuncion

737   **Peru**
         737-01 Universidad Nacional Mayor de San Marcos, Programa Academico de Medicina Humana, Lima
         737-03 Universidad Nacional de Trujillo, Programa Academico de Medicina Humana, Trujillo
         737-05 Universidad Nacional de San Agustin, Programa Academico de Medicina, Arequipa
         737-06 Universidad Peruana Cayetano Heredia, Programa Academico de Medicina, Lima
         737-08 Universidad San Luis Gonzaga, Programa Academico de Medicina Humana, Ica
         737-09 Universidad Nacional Federico Villareal, Programa Academico de Medicina Humana, Lima
         737-10 Universidad San Martin de Porres, Facultad de Medicina, Lima

737 **Peru (continued)**
737-11 Universidad Catolica de Santa Maria, Facultad de Medicina Humana, Arequipa
737-12 Universidad Nacional de Piura, Facultad de Medicina Humana, Piura
737-13 Universidad Cientifica del Sur, Facultad de Crencias de la Salud, Lima

748 **Philippines**
748-01 University of Santo Tomas, Faculty of Medicine and Surgery, Manila
748-02 University of the Philippines, College of Medicine, Manila
748-03 University of Perpetual Help Rizal, Faculty of Medicine, Las Pinas
748-07 Manila Central University, College of Medicine, Caloocan City, Manila
748-08 Far Eastern University, Dr N Reyes Medical Foundation Institute of Medicine, Manila
748-09 Matias H Aznar Memorial College of Medicine, Inc, Cebu City
748-10 University of the East, Ramon Magsaysay Memorial Medical Center, Quezon City
748-11 Cebu Institute of Medicine, Cebu City
748-12 Virgen Milagrosa Educational Institute of Medical Foundation, San Carlos City
748-13 Dr F Duque Medical Foundation College of Medicine, Lyceum Northwestern, Dagupan City
748-14 West Visayas State College, School of Medicine, Iloilo
748-15 University of Visayas, Gullas College of Medicine, Mandawe City, Cebu
748-16 St Louis University, College of Medicine, Baguio City, Benguet
748-17 Davao Medical School Foundation, Davao City, Davao del Sur
748-18 Perpetual Help College of Medicine, Binan, Laguna
748-19 Cebu Doctors College of Medicine, Cebu City
748-20 Emilio Aguinaldo College of Medicine, De LaSalle University, Dasmarinas, Cavite
748-21 Fatima College of Medicine, Valenzuela, Manila
748-22 Bicol Christian College of Medicine, Legaspi City, Albay
748-23 Philippine Muslim-Christian College of Medicine Foundation, Antipolo, Rizal
748-24 Angeles University Foundation, College of Medicine, Angeles City, Pampanga
748-25 Remedios T Romualdez Medical Foundation, College of Medicine, Tacloban City
748-26 Divine Word University, College of Medicine, Tacloban City, Leyte
748-27 Xavier University, Dr JP Rizal College of Medicine, Cagayan de Oro City
748-28 Iloilo Doctors College of Medicine, Iloilo City
748-29 University of the City of Manila, College of Medicine, Intramuros, Manila
748-30 University of the Philippines System, Institute of Health Science, Tacloban City, Leyte
748-31 St Luke's College of Medicine—William H Quasha Memorial, Quezon City
748-32 Ateneo de Zamboanga University, College of Medicine, Zamboanga City
748-33 San Beda College of Medicine, Manila
748-34 Mindanao State University, College of Medicine, Iligan City, Mindanao

759 **Poland**
759-01 College of Medicine, Jagiellonski University, Krakow
759-02 University JK Wydzial Lekarski, Lwow (154-04 before 1919, 913-89 after 1945)
759-03 Akademia Medyczna Warszawie, Warszawa
759-04 Akademia Medyczna, Poznan
759-05 University Stefana Batorego Wydzial Lekarski, Wilno (913-49 effective 1945)
759-06 Akademia Medyczna, Lublin
759-07 Akademia Medyczna, Gdansk
759-08 Pomorska Akademia Medyczna, Szczecin
759-09 Akademia Medyczna, Lodz
759-10 Akademia Medyczna we Wroclawiv, Wroclaw
759-11 Akademia Medyczna, Bialystok
759-12 Slaska Akademia, Katowice-Ligota
759-15 Military Medyczna Akademia, Lodz
759-16 Akademia Medyczna IM Ludwika Rydygiera, Bydgoszcz
759-17 Slaskiej Akademia Medyczna w Zabrze, Zabrze
759-18 Akademia Medyczna IM Karola Marcinkowskiego W Poznaniv, Faculty II, Poznon

770 **Portugal**
770-01 Universidade de Coimbra, Faculdade de Medicina, Coimbra
770-02 Universidade de Lisboa, Faculdade de Medicina, Lisboa
770-03 Universidade de Porto, Faculdade de Medicina, Porto
770-04 Universidade Nova de Lisboa, Faculdade de Ciencias Medicas, Lisboa

775 **Zimbabwe (Formerly Rhodesia)**
775-01 University of Zimbabwe, Godfrey Huggins School of Medicine, Avondale, Harare

781 **Romania**
781-01 Institutul de Medicina si Farmacie "Carol Davila," Bucuresti
781-02 Institutul de Medicina si Farmacie "Grigore T Popa," Iasi
781-03 Institutul de Medicina si Farmacie "Iuliu Hatieganu," Cluj-Napoca

781 **Romania (continued)**
781-04 Institutul de Medicina, Timisoara
781-05 Institutul de Medicina si Farmacie, Tirgu Mures
781-06 Facultatea de Medicina Generala Din Craiova, Craiova
781-07 "L Blaga" University of Sibiu, "V Papilian" School of Medicine, Sibiu
781-08 Universitatea "Ovidus," Facultatea de Medicina si Farmacie, Constanta
781-09 Universitatea de Vest "Vasile Goldis," Facultatea de Medicina, Arad
781-10 Universitatea Din Oradea, Facultatea de Medicina, Oradea
781-11 Universitatea Independenta Titu Maiorescu, Facultatea de Medicina, Bucharest
781-12 Universitatea Transilvania, Facultatea de Medicina Generala, Brasov

790 **Rwanda**
790-01 Universite Nationale de Rwanda, Faculte de Medecine, Butare

795 **Samoa**
795-01 Oceania University of Medicine, Apia

797 **Saudi Arabia**
797-01 King Saud University, College of Medicine (Univ of Riyadh), Riyadh
797-02 King Abdel Aziz University, College of Medicine and Allied Science, Jeddah
797-03 King Faisal University, College of Medicine and Medical Science, Dammam
797-04 King Saud University, College of Medicine, Abha

803 **Scotland**
803-   (Also see 919 United Kingdom-Scotland effective 1971)
803-01 University of Aberdeen, Faculty of Medicine, Aberdeen (919-01 effective January 1971)
803-02 University of St Andrews School of Medicine, Dundee (919-06 effective January 1971)
803-03 University of Edinburgh, Faculty of Medicine, Edinburgh (919-03 effective January 1971)
803-05 University of Glasgow, Faculty of Medicine, Glasgow (919-05 effective January 1971)
803-09 Registrable Qualification Granted by Scottish Conjoint Board (919-09 effective January 1971)
803-16 Polish School of Medicine, Edinburgh (Extinct)

820 **Senegal**
820-01 Universite de Dakar, Faculte de Medecine et de Pharmacie, Dakar
820-02 St Christopher's College of Medicine, Dakar

822 **Seychelles**
822-01 University of Seychelles American Institute of Medicine, Victoria

823 **Sierra Leone**
823-01 University of Sierra Leone, College of Medicine and Allied Health Sciences, Freetown

825 **Singapore**
825-01 National University of Singapore, Faculty of Medicine, Singapore

830 **Somalia**
830-01 National University of Somalia, Faculty of Medicine, Mogadishu

836 **South Africa**
836-01 University of the Witwatersrand, Medical School, Johannesburg
836-02 University of Cape Town, Faculty of Medicine, Cape Town
836-03 University of Pretoria, Faculty of Medicine, Pretoria
836-04 University of Stellenbosch, Faculty of Medicine, Tygerberg
836-05 University of Natal, Faculty of Medicine, Congella
836-06 University of the Orange Free State, Faculty of Medicine, Bloemfontein
836-07 University of South Africa, Faculty of Medicine, Medunsa
836-08 University of Transkei, Faculty of Health Sciences, Umtata

840 **South Vietnam**
840-   (Also see 941 Vietnam, South)
840-01 Faculte Mixte de Medecine et de Pharmacie Universite de Saigon, Saigon

847 **Spain**
847-01 Universidad de Barcelona, Facultad de Medicina, Barcelona
847-02 Universidad de Cadiz, Facultad de Medicina, Cadiz
847-03 Universidad de Granada, Facultad de Medicina, Granada
847-04 Universidad Complutense de Madrid, Facultad de Medicina, Madrid
847-05 Universidad de Santiago, Facultad de Medicina, Santiago de Compostela

847   **Spain (continued)**
847-06 Universidad de Zaragoza, Facultad de Medicina, Zaragoza
847-07 Universidad de Alcala de Henares, Facultad de Medicina, Madrid
847-08 Universidad de Valencia, Facultad de Medicina, Valencia
847-09 Universidad de Valladolid, Facultad de Medicina, Valladolid
847-10 Universidad de Salamanca, Facultad de Medicina, Salamanca
847-11 Universidad de Navarra, Facultad de Medicina, Pamplona
847-12 Universidad Autonoma de Barcelona, Facultad de Medicina, Barcelona
847-13 Universidad Autonoma de Madrid, Facultad de Medicina, Madrid
847-14 Universidad de la Laguna, Facultad de Medicina, La Laguna
847-15 Universidad de Oviedo, Facultad de Medicina, Oviedo
847-16 Universidad de Murcia, Facultad de Medicina, Murcia
847-17 Universidad de Pais Vasco, Facultad de Medicina, Bilbao
847-18 Universidad de Extremadura, Facultad de Medicina, Badajoz
847-19 Universidad de Cordoba, Facultad de Medicina, Cordoba
847-20 Universidad de Santander, Facultad de Medicina, Santander
847-21 Universidad de Malaga, Facultad de Medicina, Malaga
847-22 Universidad de Alicante, Facultad de Medicina, Alicante
847-23 Universidad de Sevilla, Facultad de Medicina, Sevilla
847-24 Universidad Rovira I Virgili, Facultad de Medicina y Ciencias de la Salud, Reus
847-25 Universidad de las Palmas de Gran Canaria, Centro Superior de Ciencias y de la Salud,
       Las Palmas de Gran Canaria
847-26 Universidad Miguel Hernandez, Facultad de Medicina, San Juan De Alicante

848   **Sudan**
848-   (Also see 849 before 1971)
848-01 University of Khartoum, Faculty of Medicine, Khartoum
848-02 University of Juba, College of Medicine, Juba
848-03 University of Gezira, Faculty of Medicine, Wad Medani
848-04 Ahfad University for Women, School of Medicine, Omdurman
848-05 Omdurman Islamic University, Faculty of Medicine and Health Sciences, Omdurman
848-06 University of Kordofan, Faculty of Medicine and Health Sciences, Omdurman
848-07 Academy of Medical Sciences and Technology, Faculty of Medicine, Khartoum
848-08 Shendi University, Faculty of Medicine and Health Sciences, Shendi

849   **Sudan**
849-   (Also see 848 Sudan effective 1971)
849-01 University of Khartoum, Faculty of Medicine, Khartoum (848-01 before 1971)

850   **Suriname**
850-01 Anton de Kom University van Suriname, Faculty of Medical Science, Paramaribo

858   **Sweden**
858-01 Universitetet i Lund, Medicinska Fakulteten, Lund
858-02 Karolinska Institutet, Medicinska Fakulteten, Stockholm
858-03 Universitetet i Uppsala, Medicinska Fakulteten, Uppsala
858-04 Universitetet i Umea, Medicinska Fakulteten, Umea
858-05 Universitetet i Goteborg, Medicinska Fakulteten, Goteborg
858-06 Universitetet i Linkoping, Medicinska Fakulteten, Linkoping

869   **Switzerland**
869-01 Universitat Basel, Medizinische Fakultat, Basel
869-02 Universitat Bern, Medizinische Fakultat, Bern
869-04 Centre Medical Universitaire, Faculte de Medecine, Geneve
869-05 Universite de Lausanne, Faculte de Medecine, Lausanne
869-07 Universitat Zurich, Medizinische Fakultat, Zurich

875   **Syria**
875-01 University of Damascus, Faculty of Medicine, Damascus
875-02 University of Aleppo, Faculty of Medicine, Aleppo
875-03 University of Tichreen, Faculty of Medicine, Lattakia
875-04 Al-Baath University, Faculty of Medicine, Homs

880   **Tanzania**
880-01 University of Dar-es-salaam, Faculty of Medicine, Dar-es-salaam
880-02 International Medical and Technology University, Dar-es-Salaam

891   **Thailand**
891-01 Chulalongkorn University, Faculty of Medicine, Bangkok
891-02 Mahidol University, Siriraj Hospital, Faculty of Medicine, Bangkok
891-03 Chiang Mai University, Faculty of Medicine, Chiang Mai
891-04 Mahidol University, Ramathibodi Hospital, Faculty of Medicine, Bangkok
891-05 Khon Kaen University, Faculty of Medicine, Khon Kaen
891-06 Pramongkutklao College of Medicine, Bangkok
891-07 Prince of Songkla University, Faculty of Medicine, Songkla
891-08 Srinakharinwirot University, Faculty of Medicine, Bangkok
891-09 Thammasat University, Faculty of Medicine, Prathum-Thanee
891-10 Rangsit University, Faculty of Medicine, Bangkok
891-11 Bangkok Metropolitan Administration Medical College and Vajira Hospital, Dusit, Bangkok

893   **Togo**
893-01 Universite de Benin, Faculte de Medecine, Lome

894   **Trinidad/Tobago**
894-01 University of the West Indies, Faculty of Medicine, St Augustine

895   **Tunisia**
895-01 Faculte de Medecine de Tunis, Tunis
895-02 Faculte de Medecine de Sousse, Sousse
895-03 Faculte de Medecine de Sfax, Sfax
895-04 Faculte de Medecine de Monastir, Monastir

902   **Turkey**
902-01 Uludag Universitesi, Tip Fakultesi, Bursa (Istanbul University and Bursa University)
902-03 Ankara Universitesi, Tip Fakultesi, Ankara
902-04 Ege Universitesi, Tip Fakultesi, Izmir
902-05 Hacettepe Universitesi, Tip Fakultesi, Hacettepe, Ankara
902-06 Ataturk Universitesi, Tip Fakultesi, Erzurum
902-07 Istanbul Universitesi, Cerrahpasa Tip Fakultesi, Istanbul
902-08 Dicle University, Tip Fakultesi, Diyarbakir (Diyarbakir University)
902-09 Cukurova Universitesi, Tip Fakultesi, Adana
902-10 Istanbul University, Tip Fakultesi, Istanbul
902-11 Anadolu Universitesi, Tip Fakultesi, Eskisehir
902-12 Erciyes University, Tip Fakultesi, Kayseri (Kayseri University)
902-15 Cumhuriyet Universitesi, Tip Fakultesi, Sivas
902-17 Ondokuz Mayis Universitesi, Tip Fakultesi, Samsun
902-16 Karadeniz Ternik University, Tip Fak, Trabzon
902-18 Trakya Universitesi, Tip Fakultesi, Edirne (Edirne Istanbul University)
902-19 Marmara Universitesi, Tip Fakultesi, Istanbul
902-20 Dokuz Eylul Universitesi, Tip Fakultesi, Inciralti, Izmir
902-21 Gazi Universitesi, Tip Fakultesi, Balgat, Ankara
902-22 Gulhane Askeri Tip Akademisi, Askeri Tip Fakultesi, Ankara
902-23 Akdeniz Universitesi, Tip Fakultesi, Antalya
902-24 Firat Universitesi, Tip Fakultesi, Elazig
902-25 Selcuk Universitesi, Meram Tip Fakultesi, Konya
902-26 Baskent University, faculty of Medicine, Ankara

905   **Uganda**
905-01 Makerere University Medical School, Kampala (315-01 before 1971)
905-02 Kigezi International School of Medicine, Kabale
905-03 Mbarara University of Science and Technology, Faculty of Medicine, Mbarara

912   **Union of Soviet Socialist Republics (Former)**
912-01 Second Tashkent State Medical Institute, Tashkent, Uzbekistan
912-02 "Aieti" Highest Medical School, Tiblisi, Georgia
912-03 Kirov State Medical Academy, Kirov, Russia
912-04 Bukovynian State Medical Academy, Chernovtsy, Ukraine
912-05 Gomel State Medical Institute, Faculty of Medicine, Gomel, Belarus
912-06 State Classical Academy Named for Maimonid, Moscow, Russia
912-07 Ulyanovsk State University, Medical Faculty, Institute of Medicine and Ecology, Ulyanovsk
912-08 St Petersburg Medical and Technical Institute, St Petersburg
912-09 Moscow State University–Lomonosov, Faculty of Basic Medicine, Moscow
912-10 Moscow Institute of Medico-Social Rehabilitation, Moscow
912-11 Khariv National V.N. Karazin University, School of Fundamental Medicine, Kharkiv, Ukraine

Licensing Agreement for *Directory of Physicians in the United States, 41st Edition* (four-volume set)

The American Medical Association ("AMA") grants you, the "Licensee," a perpetual non-exclusive license to use the *Directory of Physicians in the United States, 41st Edition* ("DOP"), copyrighted by the AMA, and subsequent editions of DOP for which payment is received. Licensee and its employees and agents (and patrons if Licensee is a Library) may use DOP within Licensee's facilities. Licensee may not copy, make derivative works, release, sell or lease any DOP information or otherwise authorize use of or use DOP information in any database or to create a database or to compile any mailing list or directory. If a Library, Licensee's responsibility with regard to unsupervised, in-house photocopying of the *Directory of Physicians in the United States* by Library patrons is limited to the prominent display of Copyright warnings and notices, as required by law, on each public photocopy machine. The term of this license is perpetual unless terminated for breach as provided below. If a DOP book is defective, AMA would be pleased to replace it at no charge if the DOP book is returned to the AMA within thirty (30) days from the date of acquisition. Regardless of the license granted herein, AMA shall retain title and copyright in DOP at all times. This license may not be assigned without the AMA's approval. If Licensee is a Library, Licensee agrees that DOP shall be designated as reference texts only and Licensee will not circulate DOP; and that DOP shall not leave Licensee's facilities or be part of any interlibrary loan program.

EXCEPT FOR THE THIRTY-(30) DAY LIMITED WARRANTY PROVIDED ABOVE, AMA, ITS SUPPLIERS OR AGENTS, MAKE NO WARRANTIES, EXPRESSED OR IMPLIED, WITH RESPECT TO DOP, AND DISCLAIM ANY WARRANTY OF MERCHANTABILITY OR FITNESS FOR A PARTICULAR PURPOSE. IN NO EVENT WILL AMA BE LIABLE FOR ANY DAMAGES OR LOSSES INCLUDING, BUT NOT LIMITED TO, LOST PROFITS OR OTHER INCIDENTAL OR CONSEQUENTIAL DAMAGES.

If Licensee breaches any material provisions of this license, this license to use DOP shall be terminated upon written notice to Licensee and Licensee will return DOP to AMA within three (3) days. If a court holds any provision of this Agreement to be unenforceable the enforceability of the other provisions shall not be affected. Licensee further agrees to accept reasonable modifications to this Agreement if notified in writing by AMA in order solely to comply with any court holding which would protect AMA's property rights including copyright in DOP. This Agreement: (i) is the only agreement between the parties with respect to the subject matter of this Agreement; and (ii) shall be governed by the laws of Illinois.

No modifications to this license will be accepted.

Licensing Agreement for Directory of Physicians in the United States, 41st Edition (four-volume set)

Contents

Officials for 2008–2009

496 **India (continued)**

496-60 Padmashree Dr DY Patil Medical College for Women, Maharashtra University of Health Sciences, Pune

496-61 Pandit Deendayal Upadhyay Medical College, Saurashtra University, Rajkot

496-62 VMKV Medical College, Tamilnadu Dr MGR Medical University, Tamilnadu

496-63 Academy of Medical Sciences, Kannur University, Pariyaram, Kannur

496-64 Maharashtra Institute of Medical Education and Research, Maharashtra University of Health Sciences, Talegaon-Dabhade, Pune

496-65 HN Bahuguna Garhwal University, Himalayan Institute of Medical Sciences, Dehradun

496-66 Mamata Medical College, NTR University of Health Sciences, Khamman, AP

496-67 Acharya Shri Chander College of Medical Sciences, Jammi University, Sidhra, JK

496-68 Sri Guru Ram Das Institute of Medical Science and Research, Baba Farid University of Health Sciences, Amritsar, Punjab

496-69 Vinayaka Mission Medical Center, Karaikal, Pondicherry University, Pondicherry, UT

496-70 The Institute of Road Transport Perunthurai Medical Center, Dr. MGRMU, Erode District, TN

496-71 K.A.P. Vishwanathan Government Medical College, Dr. MRG Medical University, Trichy, TN

496-72 S.V.S. Medical College, NTR University of Health Sciences, Mahboobnagar, AP

496-73 Yenepoya Medical College, Rajiv Gandhi University of Health Sciences, Mangalore

496-74 Kamineni Institute of Medical Sciences, NTR University of Health Sciences, Narketpally

496-75 Mata Gujri Memorial Medical College, B.N. Mandal University, Purnea, Bihar

506 **Indonesia**

506-01 University of Indonesia, Faculty of Medicine, Jakarta, Jawa Barat

506-02 Airlangga University, Faculty of Medicine, Surabaya, Jawa Timur

506-03 Gadjah Mada Sekip University, Faculty of Medicine, Yogyakarta

506-04 University of Sumatra Utara, Faculty of Medicine, Medan

506-05 Padjadjaran University, Faculty of Medicine, Bandung, Jawa Barat

506-06 Universitas Kristen Maranatha, Fakultas Kedokteran, Bandung, Jawa Barat

506-07 Universitas Udayana Denpasar, Fakultas Kedokteran, Bali

506-09 Christian University, Faculty of Medicine, Djakarta

506-11 Faculty of Medicine, Malang

506-12 Universitas Sam Ratulangi, Faculty of Medicine, Manado, Sulawesi Utara

506-13 Universitas Andalas, Faculty of Medicine, Padang, Sumatera Barat

506-14 Universitas Sriwijaya, Faculty of Medicine, Palembang, Sumatera Selatan

506-15 Diponegro University, Faculty of Medicine, Semarang, Jawa Tengah

506-16 Universitas Trisakti, Fakultas of Medicine, Djakarta

506-18 Hasanuddin University, Faculty of Medicine, Ujung Pandang, Sulawesi Selatan

506-19 Universitas Brawijaya, Faculty of Medicine, Malang, Java Timur

506-22 Universitas Taruma Negara, Faculty of Medicine, Jakarta

506-23 Universitas Katolik Indonesia Atamajaya, Jakarta

506-24 Universitas Islam Sumatra Utara, Faculty of Medicine, Medan, Sumatra Utara

506-25 Universitas Methodist Indonesia, Faculty of Medicine, Medan

517 **Iran**

517-01 Tehran University of Medical Sciences and Health Service, Tehran Medical School, Tehran

517-02 Shahed University, Faculty of Medicine, Tehran

517-03 Tabriz University, Faculty of Medicine (University of Azarabadegan), Tabriz

517-04 Meshed University, Medical School (Ferdowsi University), Meshed

517-05 Shiraz University, School of Medicine (Pahlavi University), Shiraz

517-06 Isfahan University, Faculty of Medicine, Isfahan

517-07 Ahwaz University, School of Medicine (Shahid Chamran University), Ahwaz

517-08 Shahid Beheshti University of Medical Sciences and Health Services, Faculty of Medicine (Jarjani Medical School), Tehran

517-09 Medical Center of Iran (Imperial Center of Iran), Tehran

517-10 West Azerbaijan University of Medical Sciences and Health Services, (Urmia University), Oroumieh

517-11 Iran University of Medical Science, Tehran

517-12 Islamic Azad University, Teheran Medical Unit, Tehran

517-13 Kerman University of Medical Science, Faculty of Medicine, Kerman

517-14 Yazd Shahid Sadoughi University of Medical Sciences, Yazd

517-15 Hamadan University of Medical Sciences, Hamadan

517-16 Kashan University of Medical Sciences, Kashan

517-17 Bakhtaran University of Medical Sciences, Bakhataran

517-18 Manzandaran University of Medical Sciences, Babol

517-19 Shahr-E-Kord University of Medical Sciences, Shahr-E-Kord

517-20 Bandar Abbas-Hormozgan University of Medical Sciences, Bandar Abbas

517-21 Zanjan University of Medical Sciences and Health Services, Zanjan

517-22 Islamic Azad University, Najef Abad Medical Faculty, Najef Abad

517-23 Ghazvin University of Medical Sciences and Health Services, Ghazvin

Foreign Medical School Codes (continued)

517   **Iran (continued)**
517-24 Zahedan University of Medical Sciences and Health Services, Zahedan
517-25 Kermanshah University of Medical Sciences and Health Services, Kermanshah
517-26 Islamic Azad University–Mashhad Branch, Faculty of Medicine, Mashhad
517-27 Islamic Azad University–Tabriz Branch, Faculty of Medicine, Tabriz
517-28 Fasa Faculty of Medical Sciences, Fasa
517-29 Guilan University of Medical Sciences, Faculty of Medicine, Rasht
517-30 Ardabil Islamic Azad University, Faculty of Medicine, Ardabil
517-31 Semnan University of Medical Sciences, Semnan
517-32 Birjand University of Medical Sciences and Health Service, Faculty of Medicine, Birjand
517-33 Shiraz University of Medical Sciences, Faculty of Medicine, Shiraz
517-34 Mazandaran University of Medical Sciences, Faculty of Medicine, Sari, Mazandaran
517-35 Golestan University of Medical Education and Health Services, Gorgan
517-36 Arak University of Medical Sciences, School of Medicine, Arak
517-37 Fatemieh University of Medical Sciences, Qom
517-38 Rafsanjan University of Medical Sciences and Health Services, Rafsanjan

528   **Iraq**
528-01 University of Baghdad, College of Medicine, Baghdad
528-02 University of Mosul, College of Medicine, Mosul
528-03 University of Basra, College of Medicine, Basra
528-04 University of Al-Mustansiriyah, Mustansiriyah Medical College, Baghdad
528-05 Kufa University, College of Medicine, Kufa
528-06 University of Salahadin, Salahadin Medical School, Erbil
528-07 Saddam University, Saddam College of Medicine, Baghdad
528-08 Dohuk College of Medicine, University of Dohuk, Dohuk

539   **Ireland**
539-01 Queens University Belfast, Faculty of Medicine, Belfast (Also see 918 United Kingdom-Northern Ireland effective 1971)
539-02 University College of Cork, National University of Ireland, Faculty of Medicine, Cork
539-03 University of Dublin, Trinity College, Faculty of Health Sciences, Dublin
539-04 University College of Dublin, National University of Ireland, Faculty of Medicine, Dublin
539-05 University College of Galway, National University of Ireland, Faculty of Medicine, Galway
539-06 Royal College of Surgeons in Ireland, Medical School, Dublin
539-07 Penang Medical College, National University of Ireland, Dublin
539-11 Registrable Qualification Granted by Apothecaries' Hall of Dublin

550   **Israel**
550-01 The Hebrew University, Hadassah Medical School, Jerusalem
550-02 University of Tel Aviv, Sackler Faculty of Medicine, Tel Aviv
550-03 Technion-Israel Institute of Technology, Faculty of Medicine, Haifa
550-04 Ben Gurion University of Negev, Faculty of Health Sciences, Beersheva

560   **Palestinian Authority**
560-01 Al Quds University, Faculty of Medicine, Abu-Dis, Jerusalam

561   **Italy**
561-01 Universita di Bologna, Facolta di Medicina e Chirurgia, Bologna
561-02 Universita degli Studi di Cagliari, Facolta di Medicina e Chirurgia, Cagliari
561-03 Universita di Milano, Facolta di Medicina e Chirurgia, Milano
561-04 Universita di Catania, Facolta di Medicina e Chirurgia, Catania
561-05 Seconda Universita degli Studi di Napoli, Facolta di Medicina e Chirurgia, Naples
561-06 Universita di Firenze, Facolta di Medicina e Chirurgia, Firenze
561-07 Universita di Genova, Facolta di Medicina e Chirurgia, Genova
561-08 Universita di Messina, Facolta di Medicina e Chirurgia, Messina
561-09 Universita di Modena, Facolta di Medicina e Chirurgia, Modena
561-10 Universita di Napoli-I, Facolta di Medicina e Chirurgia, Napoli
561-11 Universita di Padova, Facolta di Medicina e Chirurgia, Padova
561-12 Universita di Palermo, Facolta di Medicina e Chirurgia, Palermo
561-13 Universita di Parma, Facolta di Medicina e Chirurgia, Parma
561-14 Universita di Pavia, Facolta di Medicina e Chirurgia, Pavia
561-15 Universita di Perugia, Facolta di Medicina e Chirurgia, Perugia
561-16 Universita di Pisa, Facolta di Medicina e Chirurgia, Pisa
561-17 Universita di Roma-La Sapienza, Facolta di Medicina e Chirurgia, Roma
561-18 Universita di Sassari, Facolta di Medicina e Chirurgia, Sassari
561-19 Universita di Siena, Facolta di Medicina e Chirurgia, Siena
561-20 Universita di Torino, Facolta di Medicina e Chirurgia, Torino
561-21 Universita di Bari, Facolta di Medicina e Chirurgia, Bari

583   **Korea, South (continued)**
583-20 Chungbuk National University, College of Medicine, Chungbuk
583-21 In-Je College School of Medicine, Pusan
583-22 Hallym University, Faculty of Medicine, Chunchon, Kangweon-do
583-23 Inha University, College of Medicine, Hyeon-dong, Inchon
583-24 Kosin Medical College, Seo-ku, Pusan
583-25 Wonkwang University, School of Medicine, Chonbuk
583-26 Kon-kuk University, College of Medicine, Chungchungbuk-Do
583-27 Wonju Medical College, Wonju, Kanwon-Do
583-28 Dongguk University, Medical College, Kyungju-Si, Kyungbuk
583-29 Dankook University, College of Medicine, Cheonan, Choongnam-Do
583-30 Ulsan University, College of Medicine, Songpa-Ku, Seoul
583-31 Dong-A University, College of Medicine, Pusan
583-32 Eulji University, College of Medicine, Taejan

584   **Kuwait**
584-01 Kuwait University, Faculty of Medicine, Health Science Center

590   **Laos**
590-01 Ecole Royale de Medecine du Laos, Vientiane

594   **Latvia**
594-01 Latvijas Universitate Medicinas Fakultate, Riga (See 913-16 effective 1957)

605   **Lebanon**
605-01 American University of Beirut, Faculty of Medicine, Beirut
605-02 St Joseph's University, Faculty of Medicine, Beirut
605-03 Lebanese University, School of Medicine, Faculty of Medical Sciences, Beirut
605-04 Beirut Arab University, Faculty of Medicine, Beirut
605-05 University of Balamand, Faculty of Medicine and Medical Sciences, Tripoli

610   **Liberia**
610-01 University of Liberia, AM Dogliotti College of Medicine, Monrovia
610-02 St Luke School of Medicine–Liberia, Monrovia

613   **Libya Arab Republic**
613-01 Al Arab Medical University, Faculty of Medicine, Benghazi
613-02 University of Al Fateh, Faculty of Med, Tripoli

616   **Lithuania**
616-01 Vytauta Didziojo University Medical Fakelteto, Kaunas (See 913-96 effective 1950)

620   **Madagascar (Formerly Malagasy)**
620-01 *Escole de Medecine et de Pharmacie, Tananarive (Extinct)*
620-02 Universite de Madagascar, Faculte de Medecine, Establ d'Enseignement, Antananarivo

622   **Malawi**
622-01 University of Malawi, College of Medicine, Chichiri, Blantyre

624   **Malaysia**
624-01 University of Malaya, Faculty Perubatan, Kuala Lumpur
624-02 University Kebargsaan, Faculty Perubatan, Kuala Lumpur
624-03 University Sains Malaysia, Pusat Pengajain Sains Perubatan, Penang
624-04 International Medical University, Faculty of Medicine, Kuala Lumpur
624-05 International Islamic University of Malaysia, Faculty of Medicine, Pahang

625   **Mali**
625-01 Ecole Nationale de Medecine, Bamako

627   **Malta**
627-01 University of Malta, Medical School, Guardamangia

638   **Manchuria (China)**
638-01 Manchuria Medical College, Mukden (Now 243-72)
638-02 *Mukden Medical College, Mukden (Extinct)*

649   **Mexico**
649-01 Universidad Nacional Autonoma de Mexico, Facultad de Medicina, Mexico, DF
649-02 Universidad Autonoma de Nuevo Leon, Facultad de Medicina, Monterrey, Nuevo Leon

649   **Mexico (continued)**

649-03 Universidad de Guadalajara, Facultad de Medicina, Guadalajara, Jalisco
649-04 Universidad Autonoma de San Luis Potosi, Facultad de Medicina, San Luis Potosi
649-05 Escuela Medico Militar, Mexico, DF
649-06 Universidad de Yucatan, Facultad de Medicina, Merida, Yucatan
649-07 Universidad Michoacana de San Nicolas de Hidalgo, Facultad de Medicina, Morelia, Michoacan
649-08 Escuela Libre de Homeopatia de Mexico, Mexico, DF
649-09 *Escuela Libre de Homeopatia Estado de Puebla, Puebla (Extinct)*
649-10 Universidad Autonoma "Benito Juarez" de Oaxaca, Escuela de Medicina y Cirugia, Oaxaca
649-12 Universidad Autonoma de Aguascalientes, Centro Biomedico, Aguascalientes
649-13 Universidad Anahuac, Escuela de Medicina, Mexico, DF
649-14 Universidad Autonoma de Guadalajara, Facultad de Medicina, Guadalajara, Jalisco
649-16 Universidad Autonoma de Baja California, Escuela de Medicina, Mexicali, Baja Calif Norte
649-17 Escuela Nacional de Medicina y Homeopatica, Mexico, DF
649-18 Universidad Autonoma de Puebla, Facultad de Medicina, Puebla
649-19 Universidad Autonoma de Tamaulipas, Escuela de Medicina, Tampico, Tamaulipas
649-20 Universidad Veracruzana-Veracruz, Facultad de Medicina, Veracruz
649-21 Universidad Autonoma de Hidalgo, Escuela de Medicina, Pachuca, Hidalgo
649-22 Universidad Juarez del Estado de Durango, Escuela de Medicina Humana, Durango
649-23 Universidad Autonoma de Coahuila, Facultad de Medicina, Torreon, Coahuila
649-24 Universidad de Campeche, Facultad Escuela de Medicina, Campeche
649-25 Universidad de Guanajuato, Facultad de Medicina, Leon, Guanajuato
649-26 Instituto Politecnico Nacional, Escuela Superiore de Medicina, Mexico, DF
649-27 Universidad Autonoma de Chihuahua, Facultad de Medicina, Chihuahua
649-28 Universidad Autonoma del Estado de Mexico, Instituto de Ciencias, Toluca
649-29 Universidad Autonoma "Juarez" de Tabasco, Escuela de Medicina, Villahermosa
649-30 Universidad de Monterrey, Facultad de Medicina, Monterrey, Nuevo Leon
649-31 Universidad La Salle, Escuela Mexicana de Medicina, Mexico, DF
649-32 Universidad Autonoma de Zacatecas, Escuela de Medicina Humana, Zacatecas, Mexico
649-33 Universidad Autonoma de Ciudad Juarez, Escuela de Medicina, Ciudad Juarez, Chihuahua
649-34 Universidad Xochicalco, Centro de Estudios, Ensenada, Baja California Norte
649-35 Universidad del Noreste, Escuela de Medicina, Tampico, Tamaulipas
649-36 Centro de Estudios Universidad Xochicalco AA, Cuernavaca, Morelos (1980)
649-37 Centro Biomedico Cuauhnahuac Escuela de Medicina, Cuernavaca, Morelos
649-38 Universidad de Montemorelos, Escuela de Medicina, Montemorelos, Nuevo Leon
649-39 Universidad Autonoma de Guerrero, Escuela de Medicina, Acapulco, Guerrero
649-40 Universidad Auto Metro, Division de Ciencias Biologia y de la Salud, Xochimilco
649-41 Universidad Valle del Bravo, Escuela de Medicina, Ciudad Reynosa, Tamaulipas
649-42 Universidad Autonoma de Estado de Morelos, Escuela de Medicina, Cuernavaca
649-43 Universidad Popular Autonoma del est de Puebla, Escuela de Medicina, Puebla
649-44 Universidad Nacional Autonoma de Mexico, Escuela Nacional-Iztacala, Tlanepatla, Mexico, DF
649-45 Universidad Autonoma de Tamaulipas, Facultad de Medicina, Matamoros, Tamaulipas
649-46 Universidad Autonoma de Baja California, Escuela de Medicina, Tijuana, Baja California Norte
649-47 Universidad Veracruzana-Poza Rica, Escuela de Medicina, Poza Rica, Veracruz
649-48 Universidad Autonoma de Coahuila, Escuela de Medicina, Saltillo
649-50 Universidad Veracruzana-Jalapa, Facultad de Medicina, Jalapa, Veracruz
649-51 Universidad Regional del Sureste AC, Escuela de Medicina, Oaxaca de Juarez
649-52 Instituto Technologico y de Estudios Superiores de Monterrey, Escuela de Medicina "Ignacio A. Santos," Monterrey
649-53 Universidad Autonoma de Sinaloa, Escuela de Medicina, Culiacan, Sinaloa
649-54 Universidad Mexico-Americana del Norte, Escuela de Medicina, Reynosa, Tamaulipas
649-56 Universidad Autonoma de Nayarit, Escuela de Medicina Humana, Tepic, Nayarit
649-57 Universidad Veracruzana-Minatitlan, Facultad de Medicina, Minatitlan, Veracruz
649-59 Universidad de Colima, Facultad de Medicina, Colima
649-60 Universidad Autonoma de Queretaro, Facultad de Medicina, Queretaro
649-61 Centro Interdisciplinario de Ciencias de la Salud, Carretera Xochimilco Oaxtepec, DF
649-62 Universidad Nacional Autonoma de Mexico, DF
649-63 Esculela Medicos Naval, Mexico City
649-64 Universidad Panamericana, Escuela de Medicina, DF

652   **Mongolia**

652-02 Sainshand Medical College, Sainshand

654   **Montserrat (West Indies)**

654-01 American University of the Caribbean, School of Medicine, Plymouth
654-02 University of Science, Arts and Technology, Olveston

572   **Japan (continued)**

572-50 Kurume University, Faculty of Medicine, Kurume
572-51 Osaka Medical College, Takatsuki, Osaka
572-52 Tokushima University, School of Medicine, Shinkura-cho, Tokushima
572-53 Sapporo Medical College, Chuo-ku, Sapporo
572-54 Wakayama Prefectural Medical College, Wakayama
572-55 Nara Prefectural Medical College, Kasihara, Nara
572-56 Fukushima Prefectural Medical College, Fukushima
572-57 Tokai University, Faculty of Medicine, Isehara, Kanagawa
572-58 Nagoya National University, School of Medicine, Showa-ku, Nagoya
572-59 Osaka Medical University for Women, Hirakata, Osaka
572-60 Kitasato University, Faculty of Medicine, Sagamihara
571-61 Akita University, School of Medicine, Akita
572-63 Kawasaki Medical College, Kurashiki, Okayama
572-64 Kanazawa Medical College, Uchinada-machi, Kahoku-gun, Ishikawa
572-65 St Marianna Medical College, Miyamaeku, Kawasaki, Kanagawa
572-66 Miyazaki Medical College, Kiyotake-cho, Miyazaki
572-67 Shiga Medical College, Setatsukinowa-cho, Ohtsu
572-68 Hyogo Medical College, Mukokawa-machi, Nishinomiya
572-69 Kinki University, Faculty of Medicine, Minimichagawi-gun, Osaka
572-70 Saitama Medical College, Moroyama-machi, Iruma, Saitama
572-71 Dokkoyo Medical College, Mibu-machi, Shimotsuga
572-72 Jichi Medical College, Kawachi-machi, Kawachi
572-73 Teikyo University, Faculty of Medicine, Itabashi-ku, Tokyo
572-74 Yamagata University, Faculty of Medicine, Zao-Iida, Yamagata
572-75 Toyama Medical and Pharmacological University, Toyama
572-76 Boei Medical College, Tokorozawa (National Defense Medical College)
572-77 Shimane Medical College, Enya-cho, Izumo
572-78 Kochi Medical College, Oko-cho, Nangoku, Kochi
572-79 Yamanashi Medical College, Tamaho, Nakakoma, Yamanashi
572-80 Fukui Medical College, Matsuoka-cho, Yoshido, Fukei
572-81 Saga Medical College, Nabeshima, Saga
572-82 Oita Medical College, Hasama-Cho, oita
572-83 University of Occupational and Environmental Health, Sangyo Medical College, Kitakyushu
572-84 Kagawa Medical College, Miki-cho, Kita, Kagawa
572-85 Ryuku University, Faculty of Medicine, Nishihara-cho, Okinawa

575   **Jordan**

575-01 University of Jordan Faculty of Medicine, Amman
575-02 Yarmouk University, Faculty of Medicine (Jordan University of Science and Technology), Irbid

577   **Kenya**

577-01 University of Nairobi, College of Health Sciences, Nairobi
577-02 Moi University, Faculty of Health Sciences, Eldoret

582   **Korea, North**

582-07 Ham Heung Medical School, Ham Heung (583-07 before 1971)

583   **Korea, South**

583-01 Yonsei University, College of Medicine, Sudai-moon-ku, Seoul
583-02 Seoul National University, College of Medicine, Chongno-ku, Seoul
583-03 Korea University College of Medicine (Woo Sok Medical College), Chongno-ku, Seoul
583-04 Kyungpuk National University, College of Medicine, Taegu
583-05 Pyong Yang Medical College, Pyong Yang (582-05 effective 1971)
583-06 Chonnam University Medical School, Kwangju
583-07 Ham Heung Medical School, Ham Heung (582-07 effective 1971)
583-08 Ewha Womens University, College of Medicine, Seoul
583-09 Pusan National University, College of Medicine, Pusan
583-10 Catholic Medical College, Chongno-ku, Seoul
583-11 Chosun University, College of Medicine, Kwangju
583-12 Kyunghee University, College of Medicine, Dong-dae-moonka, Seoul
583-13 Hanyang University, College of Medicine, Sungdung-ku, Seoul
583-14 Choong-nam National University, College of Medicine, Taejon
583-15 Choongang University, College of Medicine, Seoul
583-16 Chonpuk National University Medical School, Jeonju
583-17 Keimyung University, College of Medicine, Taegu
583-18 Yeongnam University, College of Medicine, Taegu
583-19 Soonchunghyang College of Medicine, Choongschungnam-do

561 **Italy (continued)**

561-22 Universita di Ferrara, Facolta di Medicina e Chirurgia, Ferrara
561-23 Universita Cattolica de Sacro Cuore, Facolta di Medicina e Chirurgia, Roma
561-24 Universita di Trieste, Facolta di Medicina e Chirurgia, Trieste
561-25 Libero Universita degli Studi G d'Annunzio, Facolta di Medicina e Chirurgia, Chieti
561-26 Libero Istituto Universita di Medicina e Chirurgia dell'Aquila, Aquila
561-27 Universita di Ancona, Facolta di Medicina e Chirurgia, Ancona
561-28 Universita di Reggio Calabria, Facolta di Medicina e Chirurgia, Catanzaro
561-29 Universita degli Studi di Brescia, Facolta di Medicina, Brescia
561-30 Universita di Verona, Facolta di Medicina e Chirurgia, Verona
561-31 Universita di Napoli-II, Facolta di Medicina e Chirurgia, Napoli
561-32 Universita di Roma-Tor Vergata, Facolta di Medicina e Chirurgia, Roma
561-33 Libera Universita Campus Bio–Medico Di Roma, Facolta Di Medicina E Chirugia, Rome
561-35 Universita degli Studi di Milano-Bicocca Facolta di Medicina e Chirurgia, Monza
561-36 Universita degli Studi di Udine, Facolta diMedicina e Chirurgia, Udine

563 **Ivory Coast**

563-01 Univ d'Abidjan, Faculte de Medecine, Abidjan

566 **Jamaica (West Indies)**

566-   (Also see 950 West Indies)
566-01 University of West Indies, Faculty of Medical Science, Kingston (950-01 before 1971)

572 **Japan**

572-01 Kyoto University, Faculty of Medicine, Sakyo-ku, Kyoto
572-03 University of Tokyo, Faculty of Medicine, Bunkyo-ku, Tokyo
572-04 Fujita-Gakuen University, Kutsukake, Toyoake, Aichi
572-05 Chiba University, Faculty of Medicine, Chiba
572-06 Kanazawa University, Faculty of Medicine, Kanazawa
572-07 Kumamoto University Medical School, Kumamoto
572-08 Nagasaki University, Faculty of Medicine, Nagasaki
572-09 Okayama University, Faculty of Medicine, Okayama
572-10 Tohoku University, Faculty of Medicine, Sendai
572-11 *Tokyo Medical College (Nippon Ikadaigaku), Hongo, Tokyo (Extinct)*
572-12 Kyushu University, Faculty of Medicine, Fukuoka
572-13 Kyoto Prefectural Medical College, Kamikyo-ku, Kyoto
572-14 Asahikawa Medical College, Asahikawa
572-15 Niigata University, School of Medicine, Asahimachi-dori, Niigata
572-16 Osaka University, Faculty of Medicine, Kita-ku, Osaka
572-18 Tokyo Women's Medical College, Shinjuku-ku, Tokyo
572-19 Ehime University, Faculty of Medicine, Onsen, Ehime
572-20 Keio Gijuku University, School of Medicine, Shinjuku-ku, Tokyo
572-21 Fukuoka University, Faculty of Medicine, Jonan-Ku, Fukuoka
572-22 Hamamatsu Medical College, Hamamatsu
572-23 Tsukuba Faculty of Medicine, Sakura-mura, Niihari, Ibaraki
572-26 Showa University, Faculty of Medicine, Shinagawa-ku, Tokyo
572-27 Toho University, Faculty of Medicine, Ota-ku, Tokyo
572-28 Nihon University, Faculty of Medicine, Itabashi-ku, Tokyo
572-29 Hokkaido University, Faculty of Medicine, Kita-ku, Sapporo
572-30 Kobe University, Faculty of Medicine, Chuo-ku, Kobe
572-31 Yamaguchi Prefectural University of Medicine, Ube
572-32 Yokohama City University, Minami-ku, Yokohama
572-33 Gumma University, School of Medicine, Maebashi
572-34 Mie Prefectural University, Faculty of Medicine, Edoboshi, Tsu
572-35 Tokyo Medical & Dental University, School of Medicine, Bunkyo-ku, Tokyo
572-36 Hiroshima University, Faculty of Medicine, Minami-ku, Hiroshima
572-37 Tokyo Jikei, School of Medicine, Minato-ku, Tokyo
572-38 Nippon Medical College, Bunkyo-ku, Tokyo
572-39 Iwate Medical College, Morioka
572-40 Juntendo University, Faculty of Medicine, Bunkyo-ku, Tokyo
572-41 Shinshu University, Faculty of Medicine, Matsumoto
572-42 Kansai Medical University, Moriguchi, Osaka
572-43 Tottori University, Faculty of Medicine, Yonago
572-44 Hirosaki University, Faculty of Medicine, Hirosaki
572-45 Kagoshima University, Faculty of Medicine, Kagoshima
572-46 Gifu University, School of Medicine, Gifu
572-47 Nagoya City University, Mizuho-ku, Nagoya
572-48 Osaka City Medical School, Obeno-ku, Osaka
572-49 Tokyo Medical University, Shinjuku-ku, Tokyo

913   **Union of Soviet Socialist Republics (Former)**

913-01 First Leningrad Medicine Institute (IP Pavlova Institute), St Petersburg, Russia
913-02 Voronez Medical Institute, Voronez, Russia
913-03 Kazan State Medical Institute, Kazan, Russia
913-04 Harkov Medical Institute, Harkov, Ukraine
913-05 Kiev Medical Institute, Kiev, Ukraine
913-06 First Moscow Sechenav Medical Institute, Moscow, Russia
913-07 Odessa Medical Institute, Odessa, Ukraine
913-08 Tomsk Medical Institute, Tomsk, Russia
913-09 St Petersburg State Medical Academy, St Petersburg, Russia
913-10 Dnepropetrovsk Medical Institute, Dnepropetrovsk, Ukraine
913-11 Saratov Medical Institute, Saratov, Russia
913-12 Rostov Medical Institute, Rostov on Don, Russia
913-13 Crimea Medical Institute, Simferopol, Ukraine
913-14 Irkutskij Medicinskij Institut, Irkutsk, Russia
913-15 Second Moscow Medical Institute, Russian State Medical Institute, Moscow, Russia
913-16 Latvian Medical Academy, Riga, Latvia (594-01 before 1957)
913-17 SM Kirov Academy of Military Medicine, Faculty of Medicine, St Petersburg, Russia
913-18 Vinnica Medical Institute, Pirogova, Vinnica, Ukraine
913-19 Azerbaijan State Medical Institute, Baku, Azerbaijan
913-21 Tashkent Medical Institute, Tashkent, Uzbekistan
913-22 Kuban Medical Institute, Krasnodar, Russia
913-23 Tbilisi State Medical Institute, Tbilisi, Georgia
913-24 *Stalino Institute of Medicine, Stalino (Extinct), Ul Artema, Ukraine*
913-26 Samarkand Medical Institute, Samarkand, Uzbekistan
913-27 Orenburg Medical Institute, Orenburg, Russia
913-28 *Third Medical Institute, St Petersburg, Russia (Extinct)*
913-29 Alma-Atinskij Medical Institute, Alma Ata, Kazakhstan
913-30 Turmenskij Medical Institute, Ashabad, Turmenistan
913-31 Dagestan State Medical Academy, Mahackala, Russia
913-32 Minsk Medical Institute, Minsk, Belarus
913-33 Vitebsk Medical Institute, Vitebsk, Belarus
913-34 Kyrgyz State Medical Academy, Bishkek, Kyrgyzstan
913-35 Kursk Medical Institute, Kursk, Russia
913-36 Nizhni Novgorod State Medical Academy, Nizhni Novgorod, Russia
913-37 Samara State Medical University, Samara, Russia
913-38 Yerevan Medical Institute, Yerevan, Armenia
913-39 Perm Medical Institute, Perm, Russia
913-40 Mordovskogo University, Medical Faculty, Saransk, Russia
913-41 Sredneaziatsij/Cen Asian/Tashkent Medical Pediatric Institute, Tashkent, Uzbekistan
913-42 Ivano-Frankovsk Medical Institute, Ivano-Frankovsk, Ukraine
913-43 Grodno Medical Institute, Grodno, Belarus
913-44 Aktjubinskij Medical Institute, Aktjubinsk, Kazakhstan
913-45 Karaganda State Medical Institute, Karaganda, Kazakhstan
913-46 Semipalatinskij Medical Institute, Semipalatinsk, Kazakhstan
913-47 Vorosilovgradskij/Lugansk Medical Institute, Vorosilovgrad, Ukraine
913-48 Zaporozskij Medical Institute, Zaporoz'e, Ukraine
913-49 Vilnius University, Medical Faculty, Vilnius, Lithuania
913-50 Kishinev State Medical Institute, Kishinev, Moldava
913-51 Arhangel'skij Medicinskij Institut, Arhangel'sk, Russia
913-52 Astrakhan State Medical Academy, Astrakhan, Russia
913-53 Altajskij Medicinskij Institut, Barnaul, Russia
913-54 Amur State Medical Academy, Blagovestchensk, Russia
913-55 Celjabinsk State Medical Academy, Celjabinsk, Russia
913-56 Citinskij Medicinskij Institut, Cita, Russia
913-57 Ternopol Medical Institute, Ternopol, Ukraine
913-58 Severo-Ossetinskij Medicinskij Institut, Dzaudzikau, Russia
913-59 Stalinbad Medicinskij Institut, Stalinbad Ul Kirova, Russia
913-60 Habarovskij Medicinskij Institut, Haborovsk, Russia
913-61 Ivanovskij Medicinskij Institut, Ivanovo, Russia
913-62 Izevskij Medicinskij Institut, Udmurt, Russia
913-63 Jakutskogo Universitet, Medicinskij Fakultet, Jakutskaga, Russia
913-64 Jaroslavskij Medicinskij Institut, Jaroslavl, Russia
913-65 Tver State Medicinskij Institut, Tver (Kalinin), Russia
913-66 Kemerovskij Medicinskij Institut, Kemerovo, Russia
913-67 Krasnojarskij Medicinskij Institut, Krasnojarsk, Russia
913-69 Leningrad Pediatric Medical Institute, St Petersburg, Russia
913-70 University of Uzgorod, Faculty of Medicine, Uzgorod, Ukraine
913-71 Moscow Medicine Institute of the Ministry of Health, Moscow, Russia

913

Union of Soviet Socialist Republics (Former) (continued)

913-72 Novosibirsk Medical Institute, Novosibirsk, Russia
913-73 Omskij Medicinskij Institut, Omsk, Russia
913-74 Chkalov Medicinskij Institut, Chkalov, Russia
913-75 Molotovskij Medicinskij Institut, Molotov, Russia
913-76 Petrozavodskogo Universitet Medicinskij Fakultet, Petrozavodsk, Karel'skaja, Russia
913-77 Rjazanskij Medicinskij Institut, Akademia I. P. Pavlova, Rjazan, Russia
913-78 Smolensk State Medical Academy, Smolensk, Russia
913-79 Andizan State Medical Institute, Andizan, Uzbekistan
913-80 Stavropol'skij Medicinskij Institut, Stavropol, Russia
913-81 Sverdlovskij Medicinskij Institut, Sverdlovsk, Russia
913-82 Baskirskij Medicinskij Institut, Ufa, Russia
913-83 Vladivostokskij Medicinskij Institut, Vladivostok, Russia
913-84 Volgogradskij Medicinskij Institut, Volgograd, Russia
913-85 Tadzikskij Medicinskij Institut, Dusanbe, Tajikistan
913-86 Cernovickij Medicinskij Institut, Cernovcy, Ukraine
913-87 Stanislavskij Medicinskij Institut, Stanislav, Ukraine
913-89 Danylo Halysky Lviv State Medical University, Lviv, Ukraine
913-90 Celinogradskij Medicinskij Institut, Celinograd, Kazakhstan
913-91 Cusvasskkii Universitet I N Ul Lanov, Medicinskij Fakultet, Ceboksary, Cuvasskaja, Russia
913-92 Patrice Lumumba People's Friendship University, Medicinskij Fakultet, Moskva, Russia
913-93 Kabardino-Balkarskogo Universitet, Medicinskij Fakultet, Nal'Cik, Russia
913-94 Tartu State Medical Institute, Tartu, Estonia (see 363-01)
913-95 Tjumenskij Medicinskij Institut, Tjumen, Russia
913-96 Kaunas Medical Institute, Kaunas, Lithuania (616-01 before 1950)
913-97 Donetsk Medical Institute, Doneck, Ukraine
913-98 Poltavskij Medicinskij Stomatologiceskij Institut, Poltava, Ukraine
913-99 Moscow Medical Stomatologic Institute, Moscow, Russia

915

United Arab Republic (Egypt)

915-02 University of Cairo, Faculty of Medicine, Cairo (330-02 before 1971)
915-03 University of Alexandria, Faculty of Medicine, Alexandria (330-03 before 1971)
915-04 Ain Shams University, Faculty of Medicine, Cairo (330-04 before 1971)
915-05 University of Asyut, Faculty of Medicine, Asyut
915-06 University of Mansura, Faculty of Medicine, Mansura
915-07 Tanta Faculty of Medicine, Tanta
915-08 Al Azhar University, Faculty of Medicine, Cairo
915-09 Zagazig University, Benha Faculty of Medicine, Benha
915-10 El-Minia University, Faculty of Medicine, El-Minia
915-11 Suez Canal University, Faculty of Medicine, Ismalia
915-12 Menoufia University, Faculty of Medicine, Shibin el Kom
915-13 South Valley University, Sohag Branch, Faculty of Medicine, Sohag
915-14 Zagazig University, Faculty of Medicine, Zagazig
915-15 October 6 University, Faculty of Medicine, October 6 City

916

United Arab Emirates

916-01 Dubai Medical College for Girls, Dubai
916-02 United Arab Emirates University, Faculty of Medicine and Health Sciences, Al Ain, Abu Dubai
916-03 Gulf Medical College Ajman, Ajman

917

United Kingdom-England-Wales

917-   (Also see 352 England before 1971)
917-01 University of Birmingham, The Medical School, Birmingham (352-01 before 1971)
917-02 University of Bristol, The Medical School, Bristol (352-02 before 1971)
917-03 University of Cambridge, School of Clinical Medicine, Cambridge (352-03 before 1971)
917-04 University of Newcastle-Upon-Tyne, The Medical School, Newcastle-Upon-Tyne (352-04 before 1971)
917-05 University of Leeds, School of Medicine, Leeds (352-05 before 1971)
917-06 University of Liverpool, Faculty of Medicine, Liverpool (352-06 before 1971)
917-07 University of London, Faculty of Medicine, Charing Cross and Westminster Medical School, London (352-07 before 1971)
917-08 University of Manchester, Faculty of Medicine, Manchester (352-08 before 1971)
917-09 Oxford University Medical School, Oxford (352-09 before 1971)
917-10 University of Sheffield Medical School, Sheffield (352-10 before 1971)
917-11 Registrable Qualification Granted by English Conjoint Board (352-11 before 1971)
917-12 University of Nottingham Medical School, Nottingham
917-13 University of Leicester, School of Medicine, Leicester

917   **United Kingdom-England-Wales (continued)**
917-14 University of Southampton, Faculty of Medicine, Southampton
917-17 Registrable Qualification Granted—Society of Apothecaries, London (352-17 before 1971)
917-18 University of Wales, College of Medicine, Cardiff (946-01 before 1971)
917-19 University of London, Kings College School of Medicine and Dentistry, London (352-19 before 1971)
917-20 University of London, St Bartholomew's Hospital Medical College, London (352-20 before 1971)
917-21 University of London, United Medical and Dental Schools of Guys and St Thomas Hospitals
917-22 University of London, Westminister Medical School, London
917-23 University of London, Guys Hospital Medical School, London (See 917-07; 352-23 before 1971)
917-24 University of London, St George's Hospital Medical School, London (352-24 before 1971)
917-25 University of London, London Hospital Medical College, London (352-25 before 1971)
917-26 University of London, The Middlesex Hospital Medical School, London (352-26 before 1971)
917-28 University of London, Royal Free Hospital School of Medicine, London (352-28 before 1971)
917-29 University of London, St Mary's Hospital Medical School, London (352-29 before 1971)
917-30 University of London, University College, School of Medicine, London (352-30 before 1971)
917-31 University of London, St Bartholomew's and the Royal London School of Medicine and Dentistry, London
917-32 St Mary's Hospital Medical School, Imperial College, London
917-33 Imperial College School of Medicine at St Mary's College, London
917-34 Royal Free and Unversity College Medical School, London
917-35 Guys, King's and St Thomas School of Medicine, University of London, London
917-36 United Medical and Dental Schools of Guy's and St Thomas's, London

918   **United Kingdom-Northern Ireland**
918-   (Also see 539 Ireland before 1971)
918-01 Queen's University of Belfast, Faculty of Medicine, Belfast (539-01 before 1971)

919   **United Kingdom-Scotland**
919-   (Also see 803 Scotland before 1971)
919-01 University of Aberdeen, Faculty of Medicine, Aberdeen (803-01 before 1971)
919-02 University of Dundee, Faculty of Medicine and Dentistry, Dundee (803-02 before 1971)
919-03 University of Edinburgh, Faculty of Medicine, Edinburgh (803-03 before 1971)
919-05 University of Glasgow, Faculty of Medicine, Glasgow (803-05 before 1971)
919-06 University of St Andrew's, The Medical School, St Andrews
919-07 University of Southampton, Faculty of Medicine, Highfield, Southampton
919-09 Registrable Qualification Granted—Scottish Conjoint Board (803-09 before 1971)

924   **Uruguay**
924-01 Universidad de la Republica, Facultad de Medicina, Montevideo

935   **Venezuela**
935-01 Universidad Central de Venezuela, Escuela de Medicina "Luis Razetti," Caracas
935-02 Universidad de Los Andes, Escuela de Medicina, Merida
935-03 Universidad del Zulia, Escuela de Medicina, Maracaibo
935-04 Universidad de Caraboba, Facultad de Ciencias de la Salud, Aragua, Valencia
935-05 Universidad Centro-Occidental, Escuela de Medicina "Dr PA Ortiz," Barquisimeto
935-06 Universidad de Oriente, Escuela de Medicina, Bolivar
935-07 Universidad Central, Escuela de Medicina "Jose Mara Vargas," Caracas
935-08 Universidad de Carabobo, Faculdad de Ciencias de la Salud, Aragua
935-09 Universidad Nacional Experimental Francisco de Miranda, Programa de Medicina, Coro
935-10 Universidad Nacional Experimental "Romulo Gallegos," Facultad Medicina, San Juan de los Morros

938   **Vietnam, North**
938-   (Also see 692 North Vietnam before 1971)
938-01 Faculte Mixte de Medecine et de Pharmacie, Universite de Hanoi, Hanoi (692-01 before 1971; 942-03 after 1985)

941   **Vietnam, South**
941-   (Also see 840 South Vietnam before 1971)
941-01 Medical and Pharmaceutical University, Ho-Chi-Minh City (840-01 before 1971; 942-01 after 1983)
941-02 Universite de Hue, Faculte de Medecine, Hue (942-02 after 1983)

Foreign Medical School Codes (continued)

942 **Vietnam**
942-01 Medical and Pharmaceutical University, Ho-Chi-Minh City (840-01 before 1971)
942-02 University of Hue, Faculty of Medicine, Hue
942-03 Hanoi Medical School, Hanoi
942-04 Centre Universitaire de Formatian des Professionnels de Sante, Ho Chi Minh

946 **Wales**
946-   (Also see 917 United Kingdom-England-Wales effective 1971)
946-01 University of Wales, College of Medicine, Cardiff

950 **West Indies (Jamaica)**
950-   (Also see 566 Jamaica effective 1971)
950-01 University of the West Indies, Faculty of Medical Science, Kingston, Jamaica

951 **Yemen**
951-01 University of Sana'a, Faculty of Medicine and Health Science, Sana'a
951-02 Aden University, Faculty of Medicine, Aden

957 **Yugoslavia (Former)**
957-01 Sveucilista u Zagrebu, Medicinski Fakultet, Zagreb, Croatia
957-02 Univerziteta u Beogradu, Medicinski Fakultet, Beograd, Serbia
957-03 Univerziteta Edvarda Kardelja V. Ljubljani, Medicinski Fakultet, Ljubljana, Slovenia
957-04 Kiril & Metodij Univerziteta, Medicinski Fakultet, Skopje, Macedonia
957-05 Sveucilista "Vladimir Bakaric" Univerziteta Rijeka, Medicinski Fakultet, Rijeka, Croatia
957-06 Univerziteta u Nisu, Medicinski Fakultet, Nis, Serbia
957-07 Univerziteta u Novom Sadu, Medicinski Fakultet, Novi Sad, Serbia
957-08 Univerziteta u Sarajevu, Medicinski Fakultet, Sarajevo, Bosnia-Herzegovina
957-09 Univerziteta u Pristina, Medicinski Fakultet, Pristina, Serbia
957-10 Univerziteta u Tuzli, Medicinski Fakultet, Tuzla, Bosnia-Herzegovina
957-11 Univerziteta "Djuro Pucar Stari," Medicinski Fakultet, Banja Luke, Bosnia-Herzegovina
957-12 University of Zagreb–Split Branch, School of Medicine, Split, Croatia
957-13 University of Kragujevac, Faculty of Medicine, Kragujevac, Serbia

965 **Zambia**
965-01 University of Zambia, School of Medicine, Lusaka

ABERDEEN – MOORE

BARTISS, Michael John. 1902 N SANDHILLS BLVD, STE E 28315 #035-06-1987 L1993 **OPH PO** *020 †35
DEESE, Myra Jane. 210 MAGNOLIA SQUARE CT 28315 #036-01-1990 L1993 **FM** *020 †18
JACOBSON, Peter Lars. ■ 28315 #028-02-1977 L1978 **N** *071 †75
KLENZAK, Scott Michael. ■ 28315 #036-01-1996 L1997 **P** *020 †75
LINEBERGER, Thomas Henry. 1902 N SANDHILLS BLVD, PINEHURST MEDICAL CLINIC 28315 #036-01-1980 L1981 **IM** *020 †20
OFOSU, Charles. ■ 28315 #412-01-2001 L2006 **IM** *020 †20
SCHNELL, Edward Walter. 1902 SANDHILLS BLVD N # D 28315 #016-43-1954 L1977 **OPH** *020 †35
WALKER, David Anthony. 1902 SANDHILLS BLVD N # J 28315 #021-05-1968 L1972 **OPH** *020 †35

ADVANCE – DAVIE

ARONSON, Philip Roger. ■ 27006 #035-08-1948 L1986 **CD IM** *071 †20
BARNETT, Steven Paul. ■ 27006 #005-14-1977 L2005 **P** *020 †75
BORDERS, Kevin Jason. ■ 27006 #001-02-2004 L2006 **AN** *012
BRYSON, Tracie Ciocan. 108 DORNACH WAY 27006 #036-08-1998 L2002 **D** *020 †15
BURKS, Tamara Jean. ■ 27006 #005-12-1998 L2001 **IM** *020 †20
BURKS-BERMUDEZ, Suzanne L. ■ 27006 #011-04-1993 L1994 **IM** *020 †20
CARLE, Timothy Ryan. 146 BROOKDALE DR 27006 #036-07-2004 L2005 **FM** *100 †18
CHIU, David. ■ 27006 #023-01-1998 L2003 **AN** *020
DETRICK, Bill D. ■ 27006 #041-09-1946 L1947 **GP** *071
ELLIS, George Jos, Jr. ■ 27006 #010-01-1956 L1981 **OBG GYN** *071 †30
ELLIS, Helen Jones. ■ 27006 #051-04-1954 L1982 **GP** *071
FARAHNAKIAN, Ali. ■ 27006 #517-01-1966 L1975 **R GS** *020 ‡
GUTH, Caryl Joy. 142 BERMUDA VILLAGE DR 27006 #036-05-1962 L1962 **AN FM** *071 †05
GWYNN, Thomas L. ■ 27006 #036-05-1951 L1951 **IM** *071
HESS, Suzanne Powell. 108 DORNACH WAY 27006 #036-08-1985 L1988 **D IM** *020 †20,15
HUNSINGER, Susan Yurgel. 169 YADKIN VALLEY RD 27006 #011-03-1980 L1995 **PD** *020 †55
JACKSON, James Robt. ■ 27006 #036-07-1956 L1956 **NS** *072 †25
KING, Katherine Chung-Ho. ■ 27006 #036-05-1962 L1967 **PD NPM** *071 †55
LINTON, Eugene B. ■ 27006 #051-04-1951 L1956 **OBG** *071 †30
MAYES, John Burton. ■ 27006 #035-20-1942 **GYN** *071 †30
MORRISON, John Calvin. ■ 27006 #036-05-1970 L1970 **NM** *020 †20,28
NELSON, David Stephen. ■ 27006 #036-05-1961 L1961 **FPG GS** *072
RAHMAN, Zahid. ■ 27006 #704-09-1991 L2000 **NM** *100
REID, Charles H, Jr. ■ 27006 #036-07-1942 L1945 **IM** *071 †20
SERK, Holly Christine. ■ 27006 #019-02-2007 **PD** *012
TOLBERT, Franklin Lee. 5391 US HIGHWAY 158 27006 #051-04-1983 L1984 **FM** *020 †18
WHITLOW, Christopher T. ■ 27006 #036-05-2004 **DR** *012

AHOSKIE – HERTFORD

ALMARIO, Joselito S. 700 ACADEMY ST S 27910 #748-01-1967 L1982 **U** *020 †95
AMIN, Saad. 500 ACADEMY ST S, ROANOKE-CHOWAN HOSPITAL 27910 #704-01-1989 L2001 **IMG** *020 †20,55
BRETT, John Montgomery. ■ 27910 #051-04-1976 L1980 **EM** *071 †20
BROWN, Sherry Bernita. ■ 27910 #010-03-1993 L1996 **FM** *020 †18
CHAFIN, Timothy Brent. ■ 27910 #036-08-2000 L2004 **AN** *020 †05
CLAYTON, Melvin Louis. PO BOX 788 27910 #036-01-1973 L1973 **IM FM** *062
COOKE, Robert Glenn, III. 700 ACADEMY ST S 27910 #036-08-1991 L1996 **OBG** *020 †30
DIMKPA, Okechukwu. 500 ACADEMY ST S 27910 #913-12-1995 L2005 **IM** *020 †20
EDWARDS, Beverly Frances. 700 SUNSET ST E 27910 #036-08-1988 L1991 **PD** *020 †55
FERGUSON, Steven Wallace. 500 ACADEMY ST S 27910 #038-06-1986 L1993 **GP FPG** *020
FLEETWOOD, Joseph A, Jr. 500 ACADEMY ST S 27910 #036-05-1947 L1948 **GP** *071
FREI, Timothy E. PO BOX 340, AHOSKIE MED ASSOC 27910 #041-02-1979 L1982 **IM EM** *020 †20
GELOT, Raghuvir Baxiram. 202 NC HIGHWAY 42 W 27910 #495-23-1967 L1976 **OTO HNS** *020 †45
GURKIN, Worth Wicker, Jr. 201 COLONY AVE S, CAROLINA PEDIATRICS PA 27910 #036-08-1982 L1997 **PD** *020
HERNANDEZ, Jorge Enrique. 100 ACADEMY ST S, ROANOKE-CHOWAN HOSPITAL 27910 #011-02-1992 L2002 **AN** *020 †05
HILL, Mary Wynn. ■ 27910 #055-01-1997 L2008 **OS** *020 †20,75
JONES, Colin Douglas. 240 ACADEMY ST S, MEDICAL ARTS CENTER 27910 #036-01-1973 L1973 **FM** *100 †18
KAHN, Robert Chas. 312 ACADEMY ST S 27910 #041-01-1977 L1982 **GS** *020 †85
KARLSSON, Ulf Lennart. 301 ACADEMY ST S, AHOSKIE CANCER CENTER 27910 #858-02-1968 L1994 **RO** *020 †80
KEHAYES, Alexander Ryland. PO BOX 663 27910 #036-01-1970 L1971 **AN** *020 †05
LADAK, Hadi Kassimali. 500 ACADEMY ST S, ROANOKE CHOWAN HOSPITAL 27910 #704-02-1981 L2001 **IM FPG** *020 †20
LANG, D R, Jr. 705 SUNSET ST E, AHOSKIE MED CTR 27910 #010-03-1957 L1960 **FM GP** *020
LARABEE, Lawrence Norman. 602 ACADEMY ST S 27910 #036-05-1993 L1998 **ORS** *020 †40
MANSY, Jan Awadalla. 500 ACADEMY ST S 27910 #915-04-1994 L2001 **FM** *020 †18 ‡
MAZHAR, Iqbal. 420 PEACOCK ST 27910 #704-04-1961 L1976 **OPH** *020 †35
MISSE, Edouard. 500 ACADEMY ST S 27910 #396-04-1979 L2001 **GS** *020 †85 ‡
PIERCE, Charles Grainger. 201 COLONY AVE S 27910 #036-01-1975 L2004 **PD PDA** *020
POWELL, James Robert. 240 ACADEMY ST S 27910 #051-07-1999 L2002 **IM** *020 †20
RICHARDSON, Claudia Weave. 214 CHURCH ST E, P O BOX 928 27910 #036-08-1989 L1993 **OBG** *020 †30
SAWYER, Chas Judson, III. 240 ACADEMY ST S, MEDICAL ARTS CENTER 27910 #036-01-1963 L1963 **FM** *020 †18
STANLEY, John Hampton. 500 ACADEMY ST S 27910 #045-01-1954 L1955 **GP GPM** *020
STEWART, David Lawrence. 500 ACADEMY ST S, ROANOKE-CHOWAN HOSPITAL 27910 #036-08-1990 L2002 **EM** *020 †16
SULEMAN, Jawal. 500 ACADEMY ST S, ROANOKE-CHOWAN HOSPITAL 27910 #036-01-1995 L2002 **CD** *020 †20
TAYLOR, Julian Raleigh. 240 ACADEMY ST S 27910 #036-05-1969 L1969 **FM** *020 †18
THOMAS, Jason Joseph. 500 ACADEMY ST S, P O BOX 1385 27910 #308-13-2000 L2005 **IM** *020 †20
TIPTON, David Glen. 111 HERTFORD COUNTY HGH RD, HIGH ROAD 27910 #001-06-1985 L2004 **P** *020 †75 ‡
TULLOO, Rajeshree. 500 ACADEMY ST S 27910 #913-12-1995 L2005 **PYG** *100 †75
WRIGHT, Patricia Ann. 1313 FIRST ST W, SOLID FOUNDATION 27910 #041-09-1984 L1989 **P** *020

ALBEMARLE – STANLY

ALEXANDER, Anne Dickinson. 301 YADKIN ST 28001 #012-01-1987 L1989 **IM EM** *020 †20
ALLEN, Brian David. 923 N 2ND ST STE 205 28001 #016-11-1990 L1996 **GS** *020 †85
BALDWIN, Alison Joan. 301 YADKIN ST, MD 28001 #045-04-2005 L2007 **IM** *012
BARNUM, Lamonica Yvette. 105 YADKIN ST, STE 303 28001 #048-13-2004 L2007 **PD** *020
BARTLEY, John Harry. 440 N 9TH ST 28001 #041-12-1975 L1992 **PD** *020 †16
BEARD, David Craven. 307 YADKIN ST 28001 #036-07-1983 L1987 **CD** *020 †20
BLAKELY, Joseph John, III. 301 YADKIN ST 28001 #051-07-1985 L1991 **EM** *020
BOHNSACK, Michael Robt. 301 YADKIN ST 28001 #056-06-1981 L1984 **AN** *020 †05
BREWER, Ann R. 325 YADKIN ST, D B A PIEDMONT NEUROLOGY 28001 #036-08-1985 L1986 **N IM** *020
BRYAN, Herbie. 929 N 2ND ST, STE 205 28001 #566-01-1977 L2001 **PUD IM** *020 †20
CAMPBELL, Paul Thos. 307 YADKIN ST 28001 #041-13-1985 L1988 **CD IM** *020 †20
CLAUDIUS, Pushp K. 301 YADKIN ST, PRIMEDOC OF STANLEY, PA 28001 #495-47-1970 L1995 **IM** *020 †20
COATS, Elaine Myers. 105 YADKIN ST, STE 203 28001 #036-01-1988 L1990 **PD** *020 †55
COLES, Eugene John. ■ 28001 #033-06-1980 L1992 **DR** *020
DE TORRE, James Bowman W. 105 YADKIN ST, STE 101 28001 #036-01-1976 L1979 **ORS** *020 †40
EDDINS, George E, Jr. 301 YADKIN ST 28001 #035-20-1945 L1951 **LM CD** *071
EMERY, Mark Thomas. 929 N 2ND ST STE 101, ALBEMARLE ENT PA 28001 #036-08-1994 L2001 **OTO** *020 †45
FINNIE, John William. 945 N 5TH ST 28001 #028-34-1998 L2004 **IM** *020 †20
FORT, Wilkinson Davis. 1000 N 5TH ST 28001 #047-06-1960 L1964 **OBG** *071 †30
GAITHER, Robert Huth. 1000 N 5TH ST, W DAVIS FORT MD 28001 #010-01-1964 L1972 **GYN** *071 †30 ‡
GREEN, Francis Weatherly. ■ 28001 #036-01-1956 L1956 **IM** *071 †20
GREEN, John Lindsay. 301 YADKIN ST, RADIOLOGY DEPARTMENT 28001 #012-01-1988 L2003 **DR** *020 †80
HALL, Timothy S. 105 YADKIN ST, STE 102 28001 #048-15-1992 L1996 **OBG** *020 †30
HALL-BAKER, Everlyn. 1426 E MAIN ST 28001 #045-04-1981 L1989 **FM** *020 †18
HERRING, John Harvard. 1000 N 5TH ST, W DAVIS FORT MD 28001 #047-06-1958 L1968 **OBG** *071 †30
HINSON, Jenny Lynn. 301 YADKIN ST 28001 #036-08-2000 L2004 **MPD** *020
HUNTER, Joseph Kevin. 105 YADKIN ST 28001 #036-08-1997 L1999 **FM** *020 †18
JACOBY, Richard Michael. 1908A HILCO ST 28001 #041-13-1986 L1994 **CD IM** *020 †20
JENKINS, Larry Parker. 923 N 2ND ST STE 103 28001 #047-06-1964 L1972 **OPH GP** *020 †35 ‡
JOHNSEN, Eric Merriman. 1007 N 6TH ST 28001 #025-07-1977 L1980 **FM** *020 †18 ‡
JOHNSON, Yolanda O. 105 YADKIN ST, STE 203 28001 #012-05-1999 L2002 **PD** *020 †55
JOLLY, William Oscar, III. 305 YADKIN ST, STANLY MEDICAL PLAZA 28001 #036-01-1963 L1963 **FM** *071 †18
JONES, Karen Denise. 1426 E MAIN ST 28001 #010-03-2000 L2004 **FM** *020 †18
KARTSIMARIS, Evelina Geor. 331 N 1ST ST, GERIATRICS 28001 #759-01-2001 L2007 **END** *100
KEPP, Edward Allen. 319 YADKIN ST, REVELSTONE FAM PRACTICE 28001 #041-09-1981 L1994 **FM** *020 †18
KILDE, John David. 929 N 2ND ST STE 101, ALBEMARLE ENT 28001 #056-06-1998 L2003 **OTO** *020 †45
KILGORE, Samuel Rea. ■ 28001 #036-07-1943 L1981 **P** *071 †75
KREMERS, Karis H. 945 N 5TH ST 28001 #027-01-1980 L1990 **ON HEM** *020 †20
KRUG, James Ronald. 301 YADKIN ST 28001 #035-06-1992 L1997 **AN** *020 †05
LAWRENCE, Linda W. 301 YADKIN ST 28001 #036-05-1985 L1986 **PD** *020 †55
LEFLER, Rufus Stamey, III. 923 N 2ND ST STE 101 28001 #036-05-1978 L1979 **IM DIA** *020 †20
LEWIS, George Wm. ■ 28001 #023-07-1960 L1993 **EM** *071
LILES, Richard Vernon, Jr. 320 YADKIN ST, ALBEMARLE FAMILY MED CENTE 28001 #036-01-1957 L1957 **FM** *071 †18
LITTLE, Keenya. 929 N 2ND ST STE 201, FAMILY CTR FOR WOMANS 28001 #036-01-1999 L2003 **OBG** *020 †30
MAC, Harjit Bala. 816 N 3RD ST 28001 #495-22-1972 L1980 **PM** *020 †60
MAC, Surendrapal Singh. 816 N 3RD ST BOX 1230 28001 #495-20-1970 L1979 **ORS** *020 †40
MEHTA, Nalin Chimanlal. 815 N 3RD ST 28001 #495-22-1970 L1975 **IM ON** *020 †20
MELO-LIZARDO, Isaias E. ■ 28001 #308-01-1988 L1996 **FM** *020 †18
MINTON, Morris S, Jr. 315 YADKIN ST 28001 #048-02-1969 L1974 **D** *020 †15
MORPHEW, Peggy Kay. ■ 28001 #026-04-1985 L1994 **FM** *020 †18
MURRAY, John Patrick. 220 YADKIN ST, COMMUNITY CARE CLINIC 28001 #028-02-1966 L1986 **OTO** *020 †45
NAVARRO, Felipe. 307 YADKIN ST 28001 #005-15-1990 L2006 **CD** *020 †20
PADRTA, Jerry C, Jr. 311 YADKIN ST 28001 #001-06-1989 L2008 **GS** *020 †85 ‡
PASTORINI, Paul Richard. 923 N 2ND ST, STE 204 28001 #035-08-1981 L1986 **U** *020 †95
REDDY, Ravi Kanth T. 929 N 2ND ST, STE 105 28001 #495-21-1972 L2000 **IM GE** *020 †20
ROBERTSON, Elizabeth Shaw. 929 N 2ND ST STE 201 28001 #021-01-1989 L1996 **OBG** *020 †30
SALTZMAN, Leonard David. 317 YADKIN ST 28001 #033-05-1992 L1995 **FM** *020 †18
SAMUEL, Harold Sudhir. 111 PENNY ST 28001 #495-65-1981 L1995 **IM** *020
SAVIN, Robert Michael. 301 YADKIN ST 28001 #025-07-1973 L1993 **OBG** *020 †30
SCHMIDT, David Wm. 923 N 2ND ST, STE 102 28001 #011-04-1990 L1999 **N** *020 †75
SCHMIT, Tricia Marie. 105 YADKIN ST 28001 #030-05-1999 L2002 **PD** *020 †55
SELLERS, Frank Barkley. 220 YADKIN ST 28001 #036-05-1959 L1959 **ORS** *071 †40
SELTZER, Stephen Chas. 105 YADKIN ST 28001 #018-03-1974 L1998 **FM** *020 †18
SHEN, John. 1000 N 5TH ST 28001 #016-06-1985 L1993 **OBG** *020 †30
SKARDA, John Clayton. 301 YADKIN ST 28001 #012-01-1985 L1988 **EM FM** *020 †18
SMITH, Leroy Carter. 301 YADKIN ST, 409 WEST HARRISON STREET 28001 #028-02-1975 L1982 **GS FM** *020 †85
SMITH, Whitman E, Jr. PO BOX 1398 28002 #036-07-1957 L1957 **GS VS** *071 †85
STIBAL, Darlene May. 303C YADKIN ST 28001 #016-45-1980 L1988 **GS GP** *020 †85

■ = Address Information Privacy Protected

STODDARD, Charles Edwin. 105 YADKIN ST, STE 202 28001 #045-01-2001 L2004 NEP *020 †20

SYKES, Delia C. 301 YADKIN ST 28001 #748-10-1977 L1983 AN *020

TAYLOR, Robert Earle, Jr. 323 YADKIN ST 28001 #045-01-1985 L1988 D IM *020 †20,15

VALERI, Frank Scott. 1908A HILCO ST 28001 #041-14-1980 L1981 CD IM *020 †20

VEATCH, Philip Dean. 1908 HILCO ST, # B 28001 #012-01-1989 L1992 IM *020 †20

WALLACE, John Morris. 301 YADKIN ST 28001 #045-01-1959 L1961 PTH HMP *071 †50

WAN, Shaw Pong. 1009 N 6TH ST 28001 #020-02-1977 L2005 U *095

WATSON, Susan Carol. 105 YADKIN ST 28001 #016-42-1978 L1996 NPM PD *020 †55

WHITECAR, Paul Wayne. 301 YADKIN ST 28001 #023-12-1991 L1998 OBG *020 †30

WILLIAMS, Richard F. 945 N 5TH ST, ALBEMARLE 28001 #004-01-1988 L1992 HO *020 †20

WYNN, Ossian Barry. 301 YADKIN ST, STANLEY MEMORIAL HOSPITAL 28001 #036-01-1979 L1984 EM *020 †16

YOUNG, Terica Natasha. 105 YADKIN ST 28001 #045-01-1998 L2004 CHP *020 †75

ZUCKER, Joseph. 105 YADKIN ST, STE 101 28001 #064-01-1979 L1984 ORS *020 †40

ANDREWS – CHEROKEE

CLAYTON, Thomas Vann. 82 MEMORIAL DR 28901 #422-01-1983 L2002 FM *020 †18

DEREN, Matthew Jos. ■ 28901 #017-20-1953 L1985 AN *071 †05

FRAZER, Hugh Milton. 71 WHITAKER LN 28901 #038-40-1956 L1994 FM *020 †18

ROPER, Gary Wayne. 71 WHITAKER LN 28901 #036-01-1989 L1990 IM *020 †20 ‡

SEAL, Edna F. 415 WHITAKER LN 28901 #047-06-1982 L1985 EM *020 †18

ANGIER – HARNETT

BURNS, Keely Lynn. 511 N RALEIGH ST, STE B 27501 #054-04-1997 L2002 FM *020 †18

FOLARIN, Olalekan Tokunbo. ■ 27501 #473-04-1996 L2007 IM *020 †20

UMESI, Joseph Jack. 84 MEDICAL DR, ANGIER MEDICAL 27501 #036-08-2000 L2004 FM *020 †18

WHITE, Ann L. ■ 27501 #001-06-1997 FM *020

APEX – WAKE

AGRAWAL, Malay. 1001 W WILLIAMS ST, STE 102 27502 #016-06-1996 L2000 CD *020 †20

AGRAWAL, Mamatha. 800 W WILLIAMS ST, STE 200 27502 #016-06-1997 L2000 FM *020 †18

BARCLAY, William Robt. ■ 27502 #060-01-1946 L1951 PUD *071

BEAN, Sarah M. ■ 27539 #035-45-2002 L2006 PCP *100 †50

BEST, James Ted. 410 E WILLIAMS ST 27502 #036-01-1959 L1993 FM *071 †18

BLACKWELL, Samuel Dwight. 1011 PEMBERTON HILL RD, STE 101 27502 #011-03-1987 L1988 FM *020 †18 ‡

BOWMAN, Brian Patrick. 1021 W WILLIAMS ST 27502 #036-07-1998 L2001 PD *020 †55

BRUNER, Robert Kincaid. 1001 W WILLIAMS ST, STE 102 27502 #036-05-1987 L1989 CD IM *020 †20

BYRD, Christopher S. 212 S SALEM ST, APEX FAMILY MEDICINE 27502 #036-08-1999 L2002 FM *020 †18

CHARLTON, Warwick Anthony. 210 GREEN LEVEL RD 27523 #836-02-1981 L1985 FM *020 †18

CHIRITESCU, Micsunica E. 1091 PEMBERTON HILL RD, STE 201 27502 #781-06-1984 L2000 D *020 †20,15 ‡

DOLLINGER, Maureen Diane. 2021 SHEPHERDS VINEYARD DR, # 101 27502 #011-02-1982 L1986 FM *020 †18

FAHEY, Richard Patrick. ■ 27502 #016-42-1942 L1981 AN GP *071

FERRY, Tiffanie Spring. 1021 W WILLIAMS ST 27502 #016-11-2002 L2004 FM *020 †18

FORREST, Brian Ray. 1031 W WILLIAMS ST, STE 106 27502 #036-01-1998 L2000 FM *020 †18

FOX, Daniel Lester. ■ 27502 #036-01-2008 *012

GENTRI, John Louis. ■ 27539 #422-01-1985 L1987 IM PM *020

GREINER, Robert John. ■ 27502 #041-02-2003 L2003 PHO *012 †55

GUZZO, Joseph Anthony. 1001 W WILLIAMS ST, STE 102 27502 #035-03-1992 L1995 CD *020 †20

HERZIG, David Warren. ■ 27502 #047-06-2008 *012

HUSSAIN, Mariyam Afrouz. ■ 27539 #496-27-1990 L2001 FM *020 †18

JOHNSON, Renee Hedgepeth. 1021 W WILLIAMS ST 27502 #012-01-1989 L1992 PD *020 †55

JOHNSTON, Krystol L. ■ 27523 #048-12-1997 L1998 FM *020 †18

KEYS, Kristal Tamara. ■ 27523 #036-05-2003 L2007 AN *020

KHANDELWAL, Gautam. ■ 27539 #036-01-2002 L2007 EM *100 †16

KRAUS, John Edward, Jr. ■ 27502 #036-07-1997 L1998 P *020 †75

LAHIRI, Nandini. 1001 W WILLIAMS ST, STE 103 27502 #495-39-1992 L2000 FM *020 †18

LAWSON, Healy West. 212 S SALEM ST 27502 #051-04-1985 L1991 FM *020 †18

LEE, Clara N. ■ 27502 #008-01-1996 L2004 GS *020 †85,65

LENTZ, M Rigdon. ■ 27523 #010-02-1975 L1977 ON IM *050 †20

LOUGHLIN, Ceila Elizabeth. ■ 27502 #012-01-2002 L2005 PDP *012 †55

MILLER, Daniel Everett. ■ 27502 #055-01-2007 IM *012

MORAN, Daniel Lawrence. 1001 W WILLIAMS ST STE 104 27502 #011-02-1988 L2001 PD *020 †55

MORRIS, Peter Delaney. ■ 27502 #048-12-1981 L1988 PHP FM *050 †70,18

MOXEY, Beverton Rodino. ■ 27502 #305-01-2001 L2002 IM *100 †20

MURTHI, Nandini Rao. ■ 27502 #496-15-1994 L2002 IM *020

NIGHORN, Laura Hagelstein. ■ 27502 #048-16-1993 L2000 FM *020 †18

PANDA, Ramakanta. ■ 27502 #495-13-1978 TS *020

PARK, John Kyun. ■ 27539 #012-01-2000 L2008 REN OBG *020 †30 ‡

PEARSON, John Kent. ■ 27502 #036-07-1953 L1953 GP *071

PETERSON, Kirk Darrel. ■ 27502 #045-04-2004 L2006 DR *012

RAMSDELL, Kimberly Glass. 1031 PEMBERTON HILL RD, STE 101 27502 #038-41-1996 L1998 PD *020 †20

RAY, Doreen. ■ 27502 #047-05-2003 L2007 MPD *020 †20

SAINI, Satinder Pal Singh. ■ 27539 #496-43-1998 L2005 IMG IM *020 †20 ‡

SCARLETT, Susan Marie. ■ 27539 #036-07-1988 L1993 PD *020

SEIDEL, Hope Pollock. 1021 W WILLIAMS ST 27502 #041-02-1998 L2002 PD *020 †55

SENTHILNATHAN, Shobana. 1001 W WILLIAMS ST, STE 102 27502 #495-04-1987 L1999 IM *020 †20

SHANKAR, Yajaman C. ■ 27539 #495-09-1966 L1973 PD *020 †55

SPRINGFIELD, Claude H, IV. 800 W WILLIAMS ST STE 200 27502 #027-01-1998 L2001 FM *020 †18

STANLEY, Leanne Janene. ■ 27539 #036-07-2008 *012

STEELE, Virgil Svendsen. 1021 W WILLIAMS ST 27502 #045-01-1983 L1985 PD NTR *020 †55

SURA, Siddharth Piyush. ■ 27539 #036-01-2008 *012

TOVE, Nancy Louise. 2021 SHEPHERDS VINEYARD DR 27502 #036-01-1982 L1985 FM *020 †18

TROY, Annette Lynn. 212 S SALEM ST 27502 #041-15-2000 L2004 MPD *020 †20

TURNIER, Anne-Marie. 108B N SALEM ST STE 203 27502 #036-01-1999 L2004 CHP P *020 †75

WESTMORELAND, Tammy J. ■ 27502 #036-08-2000 GS *012

WILSON, Anita Duncan. 212 S SALEM ST, APEX FAMILY MEDICINE 27502 #051-07-2004 L2007 FM *020 †18

YADUSKY, Ronald Jos. ■ 27502 #041-02-1957 L1971 GS TS *071 †85,90

ZIMMERMAN, Sherri Arthur. 1021 W WILLIAMS ST 27502 #036-01-1991 L1994 PHO *020 †55

ARAPAHOE – PAMLICO

WOLFENBARGER, Keith Arlo. 248 NEUSE RIVER DR 28510 #019-02-1958 L1974 EM GP *020

ARCHDALE – RANDOLPH

BECK, Mark Craig. 11635 N MAIN ST 27263 #036-01-1983 L1986 FM *020 †18

BENNETT-CAIN, Andrea L. 4306 CHEYENNE DR 27263 #036-05-1999 L2002 PD *020 †55

ESCAJEDA, Richard Timothy. 10188 N MAIN ST, CORNERSTONE FAMILY PRAC 27263 #007-02-1981 L1995 IMG OBS *020 †18 ‡

JACOBUCCI, Nicola Jos. 10188 N MAIN ST, OF ARCHDALE 27263 #038-43-1980 L1997 FM *020 †18

JOHNSTON, Daniel Lee. 205 BALFOUR DR 27263 #036-01-2002 L2007 CHP *020

JUNCADELLA, Beatriz Eunic. 4306 CHEYENNE DR 27263 #036-08-2002 L2005 PD *020 †55

PINCUS, Maria Diane. 4306 CHEYENNE DR 27263 #051-07-1989 L1995 PD *020 †55

REEDY, Frank E, Jr. 4306 CHEYENNE DR 27263 #036-05-1993 L1996 PD *020 †55

SUTTLE, Evelyn Amy. 4306 CHEYENNE DR 27263 #047-06-1978 L1982 PD *020 †55 ‡

THOMPSON, William Keith. 4306 CHEYENNE DR 27263 #036-05-1969 L1969 PD *020 †55

WILLIAMS, David Robt, Jr. 4306 CHEYENNE DR 27263 #036-01-1989 L1990 PD *020 †55

WINTERS, Donald Bryant. 4306 CHEYENNE DR, ARCHDALE PEDIATRICS 27263 #030-06-1993 L1996 PD *020 †55

ARDEN – BUNCOMBE

BARTELT, Curtis Frederick. ■ 28704 #041-13-1953 L1975 FM *071 †18

BELL, John Wm, Jr. ■ 28704 #045-01-1970 L2000 EM *020 †16

BERNSTEIN, Joshua Emil. 600 JULIAN LN, STE 630 28704 #036-01-1995 L2005 MPD *020 †20,55

BUEHLER, Erich Gerhard. 77 AIRPORT RD, 77 AIRPORT ROAD 28704 #036-01-1994 L1997 FM *020 †18

BURRIS, Richard R, Jr. 2161 HENDERSONVILLE RD 28704 #036-08-1985 L1986 FM *020 †18

BUSH, Ronald Earl. 2561 HENDERSONVILLE RD, ARDEN MEDICAL CENTER 28704 #005-12-1967 L1975 IM *020 †20

BUSHORE, Sarah. ■ 28704 #047-20-2001 L2003 RNR *020 †80

CHHABRA, Sandeep. ■ 28704 #496-09-1996 L2004 CD *020 †20

CHHABRA, Shalini. ■ 28704 #495-37-1996 L2005 FPG IM *050 †20

COGBURN, Michael David. 78 LONG SHOALS RD 28704 #036-08-1982 L1985 D IM *020 †15

CYPCAR, David. 600 JULIAN LN, STE 620 28704 #056-05-1988 L1993 AI PD *020 †55,03

ELLISTON, Winston Leon. 600 JULIAN LN, STE 620 28704 #005-12-1973 L1977 A *020 †55,03

GALOS, George. ■ 28704 #035-08-1951 L1980 AN *071 †05

GILLIS, Stephanie Elaine. 2585 HENDERSONVILLE RD, STE C 28704 #036-05-2003 L2005 FM *020 †18

GOURDIN, Frederick Walter. 78 LONG SHOALS RD, PA 28704 #012-05-1975 L1998 D DS *020 †85,15

HAWES, Eric Marshall. 2585 HENDERSONVILLE RD, ASHEVILLE WOMENS MEDICAL 28704 #036-05-1995 L2002 OBG *020 †30

HILL, Stephen Thos. 2585 HENDERSONVILLE RD, ASHEVILLE WOMENS MEDICAL 28704 #055-01-1980 L1984 OBG *020 †30

HUNT, Christi Garrett. 2585 HENDERSONVILLE RD, ASHEVILLE WOMENS MEDICAL 28704 #028-34-1996 L2000 OBG *020 †30

JACKSON, Linda Hall. ■ 28704 #036-01-1967 L1987 CHP P *071 †75

JENKINS, Henry Avner, IV. 600 JULIAN LN, STE 620 28704 #012-01-1996 L2002 AI *020 †55,03

KEEGAN, Kirk A, Jr. ■ 28704 #023-01-1968 L2006 OBG MFM *030 †30 ‡

MAC KENZIE, Brian James. 32 STONEHOUSE RD, ASHEVILLE HOSPITALIST ASSO 28704 #036-05-2002 L2004 IM *020 †20

MC GRAW, Charles Jos. 600 JULIAN LN, STE 640 28704 #026-04-1978 L1997 FM FPG *020 †18

MORENO, Carmen Lucia. ■ 28704 #264-18-1985 L2004 PD PDI *020

RIMMER, Marina Valeryevna. ■ 28704 #913-02-1997 L2007 IM *020 †20

RINSLER, Stephen Saml. ■ 28704 #035-46-1967 L2007 PD ADL *071 †55

SAGBERG, Anne Elisabeth. 103 APPALACHIAN BLVD, # 216 28704 #693-01-1947 L1958 P *071

SIMMONS, Michelle Aileen. 2585 HENDERSONVILLE RD, ASHEVILLE WOMENS MEDICAL 28704 #011-03-1996 L2000 OBG *020 †30

STEPHENS, Michael David. 2161 HENDERSONVILLE RD 28704 #012-05-1988 L1995 FM *020 †18

TURK, Thomas Spencer. 2404 BARKWOOD LN 28704 #036-01-1995 L1997 FM *020 †18

VAN WYE, John Edward. 600 JULIAN LN, STE 620 28704 #005-11-1985 L1991 AI PDA *020 †55,03 ‡

WALL, Antoinette Wilkes. 7 GLENN BRIDGE RD STE D 28704 #011-02-1972 L1976 EM GP *020

WESTLY, Elizabeth Ann. 2161 HENDERSONVILLE RD, ASHEVILLE DERMATOLOGY CENT 28704 #021-01-1976 L1990 IM *020 †15

WHITAKER, Clay W. ■ 28704 #038-06-1952 L1952 OTO HNS *071 †45

WRIGHT, John R. 2585 HENDERSONVILLE RD, ASHEVILLE WOMENS MEDICAL 28704 #048-16-1995 L2002 OBG *020 †30

ASHEBORO – RANDOLPH

ACHREJA, Ranvir Singh. 155 MCARTHUR ST 27203 #495-20-1970 L1983 GS VS *020 †85

ADAMS, Harvey. 364 WHITE OAK ST 27203 #036-01-1955 L1955 GYN *071 †30

AINSWORTH, Kerry Harrison. ■ 27205 #016-06-1962 L1987 GYN OM *020 †30

■ = Address Information Privacy Protected

AKBARY, Ali. 237 N FAYETTEVILLE ST, STE B 27203 #306-01-1989 L2000 **CD** *020 †20
BETTS, Charles Saml, III. 350 N COX ST, STE 16 27203 #051-01-1967 L1973 **IM** *020 ‡
BILLMIRE, Karen Leigh. 110 W WALKER AVE, SANDHILLS CENTER 27203 #024-16-1984 L1986 **P** *020 †75
BLAKE, Sidney Allen. 350 N COX ST, STE 6 27203 #036-05-1991 L1994 **IM** *020 †20
BROOKS, Kim Chree. 138 DUBLIN SQUARE RD STE B 27203 #036-01-1992 L1996 **OBG** *020 †30
BROWN, Robert Lee. 197 NC HIGHWAY 42 N, STE B 27203 #036-08-1992 L1995 **EM** *020 †16
BUHRMAN, William Currie. 364 WHITE OAK ST, MAILING: P O BOX 4174 27203 #036-07-1983 L2000 **GS TS** *050 †05
BUTLER, Robert Hoyt. 364 WHITE OAK ST 27203 #036-05-1973 L1983 **GE IM** *020 †20
CABERWAL, Daljit Singh. 364 WHITE OAK ST 27203 #495-32-1970 L1976 **U** *020 †95
CAMERON, John Darroch. 550 WHITE OAK ST 27203 #036-01-1979 L1982 **FM** *020 †18
CARIGNAN, Peter Martin. 364 WHITE OAK ST 27203 #032-01-1998 L2002 **AN** *020 †05 ‡
CARLSTEIN, Marjorie H. 110 W WALKER AVE, RANDOLPH UNIT 27203 #036-05-1991 L1993 **CHP** *020
CHAMBERLIN, Patricia Ann. 350 N COX ST STE 12 27203 #048-02-1978 L2007 **PD** *020 †55
CHAO, Roberto. ■ 27205 #011-02-1985 L2002 **U** *020 †95
CHAUDHARY, Umbreen Javaid. 525 WHITE OAK ST 27203 #704-06-1997 L2004 **IM** *100 †20
CHODRI, Tanvir Anwar. 610 N FAYETTEVILLE ST, STE 300 27203 #704-22-1989 L2003 **PCC CCM** *020 †20
CLAIBORNE, Claudia Viola. 364 WHITE OAK ST 27203 #051-04-1996 L2000 **IM** *020 †20
COCHRAN, John L, Jr. ■ 27203 #036-05-1950 L1952 **PD** *071
CONNORS, Wayne Frederick. 610 N FAYETTEVILLE ST, STE 111 27203 #654-01-1999 L2003 **PD** *020 †55
DAVIS, George Thomas. ■ 27205 #036-01-1962 L1962 **OBG** *071
DHATT, Malkiat Singh. 542 WHITE OAK ST, STE A 27203 #495-03-1968 L1978 **CD IM** *020 †20
DIXON, Leslie Susan W. 110 W WALKER AVE 27203 #012-01-1988 L1994 **CHP** *075 †75
DUNHAM, Cynthia Byrd. 212 FOUST ST 27203 #036-01-1985 L1988 **NEP IM** *020 †20
EVANS, Richard Alan. 171 MACARTHUR ST 27203 #038-41-1993 L2001 **GS** *020 †85
EYO, Unwana Amajak. 364 WHITE OAK ST, P O BOX 3433 27203 #041-14-1997 L2003 **IM** *020 †20
FEIN, Bennett Ira. 700 SUNSET AVE 27203 #035-19-1986 L2004 **GE IM** *020 †20
FOLK, Thomas Geoffrey. 237 N FAYETTEVILLE ST, STE B 27203 #036-05-1991 L1993 **CD IM** *020 †20
FOX, Richard Franklin. 212 FOUST ST 27203 #036-01-1975 L1976 **NEP IM** *020 †20
GACCIONE, Craig Stephen. 237 N FAYETTEVILLE ST, STE A 27203 #035-09-1993 L1997 **OBG** *020 †30
GARING, Kendall Kay. 550 WHITE OAK ST 27203 #023-01-2002 L2006 **MPD** *020 †20
GIMENEZ, David Gerardo. 171 MACARTHUR ST 27203 #025-07-1990 L1995 **GS** *020 †85
GOBEL, William K. 1209 IDLEWOOD DR 27205 #036-05-1952 L1952 **FM** *071 †18
GOLDSBOROUGH, Kellie Anne. 212 FOUST ST 27203 #018-03-1997 L1998 **NEP** *020 †20
GRANTHAM, Thomas Wentworth. 200 E ACADEMY ST 27203 #036-01-1982 L1983 **P** *020
GREEN, Thomas Walton, III. 364 WHITE OAK ST, PRIMEDOC OF RANDOLPH COUNT 27203 #051-04-1998 L2001 **IM** *020 †20
GRESALFI, Thomas J, Jr. 110 W WALKER AVE 27203 #035-01-1983 L1985 **P** *020 †75
GRIFFIN, Marion Wilson. 218 FOUST ST STE D 27203 #036-01-1962 L1962 **GS VS** *071 †85
GRISSO, Greg Alan. 327 ROCK CRUSHER RD 27203 #051-04-1993 L1999 **IM** *020 †20
GULLAPALLI, Swaruparani V. 547 N FAYETTEVILLE ST, ASHEBORO PSYCHIATRIC SERVI 27203 #495-78-1967 L2004 **P** *020 †75
GUPTA, Anjali Lala. 208 FOUST ST STE A 27203 #495-45-1994 L2001 **IM** *020 †20
GUPTA, Rajesh. 208 FOUST ST STE A 27203 #495-45-1992 L1997 **GE** *020 †20
HAAK, Edward Decker, Jr. ■ 27205 #051-01-1968 L1972 **IM CD** *020
HANDLEY, Robert Osler. 220 FOUST ST 27203 #056-06-1975 L1979 **OPH** *020 †35
HANSPAL, Prithvipal Singh. 283 WHITE OAK ST 27203 #495-12-1965 L1980 **U** *020 †95
HAQUE, Imran Pasha. 610 N FAYETTEVILLE ST, STE 200 27203 #308-13-1998 L2002 **IM** *020 †20
HARSH, Renuka Shiv. 364 WHITE OAK ST 27203 #495-30-1977 L1987 **PD** *020 †55
HARSH, Shiv Kumar. 542A WHITE OAK ST, MEDICINE CENTER-P O BOX 20 27203 #495-30-1977 L1986 **CD IM** *020 †20
HASSAN, Sami. 167 MACARTHUR ST, UWHARRIE MEDICAL CENTER 27203 #036-08-1991 L1995 **IM** *020
HAVILAND, Julie C. 364 WHITE OAK ST 27203 #038-41-2000 L2004 **EM** *020
HELSABECK, Eric Haigler. 364 WHITE OAK ST 27203 #036-01-1975 L1983 **EM FM** *020 †18,16
HILL, Donald Scott. 364 WHITE OAK ST, RANOLPH HOSPITAL 27203 #036-05-1993 L1996 **EM** *020 †16
HODGES, Beth Gillen. 208 W SALISBURY ST STE A 27203 #038-45-1996 L1999 **FM** *020 †18
HODGES, Francisco M. 208 W SALISBURY ST STE A 27203 #038-45-1996 L1999 **FM** *020 †18
IRWIN, Michael Dennis. 364 WHITE OAK ST 27203 #033-06-1983 L1986 **FM** *020 †18
ISLEY, Joseph Plonk. 364 WHITE OAK ST 27203 #036-07-1978 L1999 **IM** *020 †20
JOHNSON, Mary Helen. 1073 WOODSIDE PL, ASHEBORO PED 27205 #036-05-1991 L1994 **PD** *020 †55
JOHNSTON, George Browne. ■ 27205 #041-02-1945 L1945 **GS** *071 †85
KHAN, Jaber Amjad. 550 WHITE OAK ST 27203 #038-40-1994 L1997 **FM** *020 †18
KIMMEL, Stephen Warner. 360 SUNSET AVE 27203 #036-08-1995 L1996 **FM** *020 †18
KINLAW, James Brady. 550 WHITE OAK ST 27203 #051-01-1974 L1975 **FM** *020 †18
KLOSTERMYER, Brooks V. RANDOLPH HOSPITAL 27203 #041-09-1954 L1959 **DR** *020 †80
KRASOWSKI, Robert J. 542 WHITE OAK ST, STE A 27203 #759-07-1989 L1999 **CD** *020 †20
LAROCCA, Joseph Anthony. 364 WHITE OAK ST, PRIMEDOC OF RANDOLPH 27203 #008-01-1992 L2006 **GP** *020
LEE, Keung Wai. 132 W MILLER ST, ASSOCIATES 27203 #035-06-1996 L1999 **IM** *020 †20
LENNON, Barbara Martin. ■ 27203 #036-08-1989 L1992 **PD** *020 †55
LENNON, Yates Alton. 237 N FAYETTEVILLE ST # A, CENTRAL CAROLINA WOMEN'S C 27203 #036-08-1989 L1998 **OBG** *020 †30
LEWIS, De Quincy Andrew. 713 S FAYETTEVILLE ST, STE B 27203 #045-01-2000 L2006 **HO** *020
LININGER, Michael David. 149 MACARTHUR ST 27203 #041-12-1993 L1999 **GS** *020 †85
LURIA, Alan Stuart. 220C FOUST ST, ASHEBORO OPHTHALMOLOGY 27203 #010-01-1973 L1981 **OPH** *020 †35
LUTMAN, George Benton. ■ 27205 #028-03-1964 L1972 **PTH** *071 †50
LYERLY, Ricky Duane. 364 WHITE OAK ST 27203 #036-08-1996 L2002 **DR OS** *020
MATTINGLY, Michael Thos. 220 FOUST ST, STE B 27203 #030-06-1988 L1995 **NEP** *020 †20
MAY, Sheila D. 149 MACARTHUR ST 27203 #001-02-1980 L1992 **IM** *020 †20
MC CARTY, Christine Marie. 713 S FAYETTEVILLE ST, STE B 27203 #011-04-1979 L1999 **ON HEM** *020 †20
MC FADDEN, David Morris. ■ 27203 #036-01-1971 **P** *100
MC FARLAND, Kathryn A. 237 N FAYETTEVILLE ST, STE B 27203 #026-04-1998 L2004 **IM** *020 †20
MC GUKIN, James Robt, Jr. 237 N FAYETTEVILLE ST, STE B 27203 #045-01-1986 L1988 **CD NM** *020 †20
MC RAE, Alexis Nicole. 610 N FAYETTEVILLE ST, STE 103 27203 #041-14-1998 L2001 **EM UCM** *020 †16
MC ROBERTS, Deborah Sue. 157 MACARTHUR ST 27203 #027-01-1985 L1988 **FM PD** *020 †18
MEAD, Robert J, Jr. 722 CEDAR CREEK DR 27205 #041-02-1978 L2001 **AN PD** *075 †55,03
MEYER, Robin Lynn. 237 N FAYETTEVILLE ST # A 27203 #665-01-2003 L2007 **OBG** *020
MISENHEIMER, Timothy Joe. 237 N FAYETTEVILLE ST # D 27203 #036-01-1987 L1988 **GE IM** *020 †20
MUNLEY, Brian James. 542 WHITE OAK ST, STE A 27203 #041-09-1980 L1997 **CD** *020 †20
MURKIN, Scott Alan. 197 NC HIGHWAY 42 N, STE B 27203 #047-05-1992 L1993 **FM OM** *020 †18
OSTEEN, Thomas Lee. 138 DUBLIN SQUARE RD STE A 27203 #028-02-1974 L1987 **ORS** *020 †40
OWEN, Chas Fletcher, Jr. ■ 27204 #041-01-1937 L1937 **R** *071 †80
PEKAREK, Elizabeth Mary. 110 W WALKER AVE 27203 #020-12-1986 L1989 **P** *020 †75
PENNER, Pamela A. 515 W SALISBURY ST STE D, SUMMIT FAMILY MEDICINE 27203 #025-07-1994 L2001 **FM** *020 †18
PERRY, Lawrence Edward. 138 DUBLIN SQUARE RD, STE A 27203 #035-15-1979 L1980 **FM** *020 †18
PINCUS, William Arnold. 364 WHITE OAK ST 27203 #051-07-1989 L1995 **OTO** *020 †45
POP, Liviu Eugen. 364 WHITE OAK ST 27203 #781-03-1984 L2004 **DR** *100 †80
PROCHNAU, Caroline C. 132 W MILLER ST, ASSOCIATES 27203 #036-01-1998 L2000 **IM** *020 †20
REDDING, John F, II. 550 WHITE OAK ST, WHITE OAK FAMILY PHYSICIAN 27203 #036-05-1993 L1995 **FM** *020 †18
REDDING, Rebecca Steddom. 364 WHITE OAK ST, DEPT OF QUALITY 27203 #051-01-1995 L1997 **FM** *030 †18
REVANKAR, Rajan. 542 WHITE OAK ST, STE A 27203 #495-72-1988 L1999 **CD** *020 †20
RICHARDSON, Cris Ray. 237 N FAYETTEVILLE ST, STE A 27203 #055-02-1994 L2001 **OBG** *020 †30
ROBBINS, Robert Alan. 550 WHITE OAK ST, WHITE OAK FAMILY PHYSICIAN 27203 #036-05-1992 L1995 **FM** *020 †18
ROSE, Noralea Elizabeth. ■ 27205 #036-01-1998 L2002 **EM** *020 †16
SANDHU, Jagjit Singh. 364 WHITE OAK ST 27203 #495-29-1963 L1979 **GP FM** *020
SANZENBACHER, Larry James. 364 WHITE OAK ST 27203 #038-40-1967 L1985 **GS** *020 †85
SCARLATA, Salvatore P. ■ 27205 #035-08-1943 L1974 **AN** *020
SCHEUTZOW, Mark. ■ 27205 #038-40-1993 L1997 **PMM PM** *071
SCHULTZ, Douglas Ernst. 237 N FAYETTEVILLE ST # D 27203 #035-08-1984 L1991 **CCM PUD** *020 †20
SCOTT, Robert Baird. 550 WHITE OAK ST 27203 #051-07-1979 L1981 **FM** *020 †18
SEBHAT, Berhan. 364 WHITE OAK ST 27203 #038-43-1998 L2004 **IM** *075
SHACKELFORD, Ernest D, Jr. ■ 27203 #051-04-1952 L1953 **DR NM** *071 †80
SHEVLIN, Patricia Ann. 375 SUNSET AVE, ASHEBORO FAMILY PHYSICIANS 27203 #010-01-1990 L1996 **FM** *020 †18
SIMPSON, John Larry. 350 N COX ST, STE 27 27203 #036-05-1973 L1973 **FM OM** *020 †18
SINGH, Ranbir. 542 WHITE OAK ST 27203 #495-29-1963 L1978 **ORS** *020 †40
SISCO, Lance Thayer. 138 DUBLIN SQUARE RD STE A, ORTHOPAEDIC SURGERY CENTER 27203 #011-03-1986 L2003 **ORS OSM** *020 †40
SISTASIS, Jim. 147 E ACADEMY ST, MAILING: P O BOX 4247 27203 #422-01-1993 L1999 **FM** *020 †18
SISTASIS, Rowena Maria. 147 E ACADEMY ST, MAILING: P O BOX 4247 27203 #748-01-1991 L1997 **FM** *020 †18
SKOWRONEK, David Gordon. 550 WHITE OAK ST 27203 #036-05-1974 L1974 **GP** *020
SMITH, Karla Rene. 1831 N FAYETTEVILLE ST 27203 #005-06-1999 L2002 **FM** *020 †18
SOPALA, Jerzy Antoni. 132 W MILLER ST, ASSOCIATES 27203 #759-07-1991 L2001 **IM IMG** *020 †20
STERNE, Kirsten S. 208 W SALISBURY ST STE A 27203 #038-45-1999 L2002 **FM** *020 †18
STINSON, Jeffrey Allen. 237 N FAYETTEVILLE ST, STE A 27203 #038-41-2001 L2004 **OBG** *020
STOUT, Charles Walter. 364 WHITE OAK ST 27203 #036-01-1958 L1958 **GP OTO** *020 †18
SUGGS, C Ann Howard. ■ 27203 #051-04-1947 L1950 **PD** *071
SUGUITAN, Eden A. 364 WHITE OAK ST 27203 #748-10-1967 L2002 **GE IM** *040 †20
TEAGUE, Randall Scott. 364 WHITE OAK ST 27203 #036-05-1974 L1974 **DR NM** *020 †16,80
THOMAS, Millard Brady, III. 138 DUBLIN SQUARE RD, STE A 27203 #036-08-1988 L1991 **FM** *020 †18
THOMPSON, Joe Wayne. 1535 N FAYETTEVILLE ST 27203 #036-01-1958 L1958 **FM** *020
THORNTON, William C, Jr. 350 N COX ST STE 20, OF ASHEBORO 27203 #045-01-1971 L1976 **IM GP** *020 †20
TYSON, Archie Alexander. 237 N FAYETTEVILLE ST, STE B 27203 #036-05-1984 L1985 **CD IM** *020 †20
UPPIN, Nina Basappa. 610 N FAYETTEVILLE ST, STE 200 27203 #495-98-1990 L1999 **IM** *020 †20
VINOCUR, Patricia Ann. 132 W MILLER ST C 27203 #017-20-1986 L2000 **PD** *020 †55
VYAS, Chandra Kant. 542 WHITE OAK ST, STE A 27203 #496-03-1971 L1988 **CD IM** *020 †20
WALHA, Gurmukh Singh. 542 WHITE OAK ST 27203 #495-03-1968 L1979 **ORS HS** *020 †40
WALHA, Sukhwant Kaur. 364 WHITE OAK ST 27203 #495-29-1975 L1982 **PM GP** *020
WEBB, Martin W. 212 FOUST ST 27203 #917-18-1992 L2002 **NEP** *020 †20
WEST, Charles B, Jr. 124 N PARK ST 27203 #036-05-1984 L1989 **OTO HNS** *020 †45
WHYTE, Thomas Murphy. 350 N COX ST STE 20 27203 #036-05-1985 L1986 **FM** *020 †18
WILLIAMS, David Goodwin. 364 WHITE OAK ST BOX 1048, RANDOLPH HOSPITAL INC 27203 #012-05-1971 L1975 **DR** *020 †80
WILLIAMS, James Todd. 360 SUNSET AVE 27203 #036-01-1990 L1992 **D** *020 †15
WILLIAMS, Ronald Lynn. 197 NC HIGHWAY 42 N STE B, DBA FIRSTCARE 27203 #036-01-1976 L1983 **EM** *020
WILLIFORD, Robert Earl. 230 FOUST ST 27203 #012-05-1955 L1955 **GP OS** *020 †18
WILLIS, Leanne K. 223 W WARD ST 27203 #048-14-1989 L1992 **N IM** *020 †75
WILSON, James Kirk. 364 WHITE OAK ST, MAILING: P O BOX 4174 27203 #048-14-1984 L2000 **AN** *020 †05
ZELLER, Kathleen E. 138 DUBLIN SQUARE RD STE B, RANDOLPH WOMEN'S HEALTH CA 27203 #011-02-2002 L2007 **OBG** *020

ASHEVILLE – BUNCOMBE

ABBEY, Joseph E. ■ 28804 #605-01-1947 L1954 **GS OS** *071

■ = Address Information Privacy Protected

ABBOTT, Jennifer Lynn. 118 WT WEAVER BLVD, ATTN: CAROLYN DAVIS 28804 #007-02-2002 L2003 **FM** *020 †18

ABERNETHY, William B, III. 5 VANDERBILT PARK DR 28803 #036-05-1993 L2001 **IM** *020 †20

ACKRILL, Cynthia Leigh. 115 WHITE ASH DR E 28803 #023-01-1985 L1990 **GP** *020

ADAMS, Jeffrey Gene. 222 ASHELAND AVE 28801 #041-02-1994 L2000 **MSR** *020 †80

ADCOCK, Rustan O'Neal. 206 ASHELAND AVE 28801 #032-01-2003 L2005 **FM** *020 †18

AHEARNE, Paul Michael. 14 MEDICAL PARK DR 28803 #036-07-1988 L2000 **SO** *020 †85

AHL, Ernest Theodor, Jr. RICEVILLE & TUNNEL RDS, VA MED CTR 28805 #012-05-1976 L1981 **PTH** *020 †50

AHMED, Mehr T. ■ 28805 #704-04-1986 L1991 **PM** *020 †60

AHSANUDDIN, Ashfaq A. ■ 28806 #422-01-1995 L2008 **IM** *020 †20

ALLEN, William Paul. 14 VICTORIA RD, STE 101 28801 #045-01-1979 L1996 **MG PD** *020 †55,19

ALLISON, E Jackson, Jr. 1100 TUNNEL RD, VA MEDICAL CENTER (11) 28805 #036-01-1975 L1975 **EM FM** *071 †16,18

AMBLER, Richard Brian. ■ 28801 #004-01-2007 **FP** *012

ANAND, Sanjay Kumar. 76 PEACHTREE RD, STE 300 28803 #028-46-1991 L2002 **AN** *020 †05

ANDERSON, Albert Bernard. 141 ASHELAND AVE STE 100 28801 #036-05-1982 L1983 **OPH** *020

ANDERSON, J Robert. 1 SAINT DUNSTANS RD, STE 100 28803 #036-05-1991 L2005 **FM** *020 †18

ANDERSON, Susan M. 41 OAKLAND RD STE 200, LAUREL OB/GYN 28801 #036-05-1991 L1995 **OBG** *020 †30

ANDREWS, James Keister. 147 ASHELAND AVE 28801 #036-05-1994 L1998 **IM** *020 †20

ANIXTER, William Leighton. 34 N ANN ST 28801 #010-01-1977 L1987 **P** *020 †75

ARENDALE, Stephen Sydnes. 222 ASHELAND AVE 28801 #048-04-1967 L1974 **R NM** *020 †80

ARIAIL, Jerry Nolan. 390 S FRENCH BROAD AVE 28801 #012-01-1971 L1977 **D IM** *020 †15

ARMSTRONG, Bruce Griffey. 1 DOCTORS PARK 28801 #036-05-1975 L1975 **U** *020 †95

ARMSTRONG, Robert F. 1200 RIDGEFIELD BLVD, STE 250 28806 #036-01-1993 L1998 **N** *020 †75

ARRILLAGA VARGAS, A. 509 BILTMORE AVE, STE B321 28801 #041-07-1988 L2002 **CCS** *020 †85

ARWOOD, Richard Scott. 445 BILTMORE AVE 28801 #012-05-1995 L1998 **IM** *020 †20

ASBILL, Brian Henry. 5 VANDERBILT PARK DR 28803 #045-01-1994 L2001 **CD** *020 †20

ASKEW, William A. ■ 28803 #012-01-1946 L1960 **R** *071 †80

ASSAD, Norman Abraham. 520 BILTMORE AVE, STE A 28801 #065-06-1966 L2001 **REN GYN** *020 †30

AWNY, Laila A. 1100 TUNNEL RD 28805 #915-04-1974 L1999 **IM EM** *020 †20

AYSCUE, Lanier Hasty. ■ 28803 #036-01-1989 L1994 **FM CLP** *020 †50,18

BACOT, Bruce K. 11 VANDERBILT PARK DR 28803 #048-04-1983 L1997 **PDP PDA** *020 †55

BAGLEY, Carter Snow. 1065 HENDERSONVILLE RD 28803 #051-01-1959 L1969 **OTO HNS** *071 †45

BAILEY, John Bennett. 500 CENTRE PARK DR 28805 #048-02-1975 L1979 **PD** *020 †55

BAKER, Steven Howard. 53 S FRENCH BROAD AVE 28801 #036-01-1987 L1994 **CHP** *020 †75

BALAZS, Dezso Adam. ■ 28803 #473-01-1940 L1960 **R** *071 †80

BALLANTINE, William Clayt. 1 W PACK SQ, STE 300 28801 #020-02-1990 L1993 **IM** *020 †20

BARE, Ricky Lee. 1 DOCTORS PARK 28801 #036-08-1990 L1991 **U** *020 †95

BARKER, Robert A. 333 GASHES CREEK RD, PARKWAY MEDICAL GROUP 28803 #021-06-1981 L1984 **FM** *020 †18

BARTOW, Anna Louise. 445 BILTMORE AVE, STE 407 28801 #047-06-2000 L2005 **MPD** *020

BASHINSKY, Alice Lawson. 8 MEDICAL PARK DR, ASHEVILLE EYE ASSOCIATES 28803 #036-05-2000 L2001 **OPH** *020 †35

BATE, David Soule, Jr. 8 NEW LEICESTER HWY 28806 #010-01-1979 L1980 **FM UCM** *030 †18

BATTLE, Philip Kemp. 1091 HENDERSONVILLE RD, STE 202 28803 #020-02-1977 L1980 **IM** *020

BAUMGARTEN, Alan Sol. 206 ASHELAND AVE 28801 #025-12-1983 L1984 **FM NTR** *020 †18

BAZEMORE, Webster C, Jr. 30 CHOCTAW ST, ASHEVILLE PULMONARY ASSOCI 28801 #012-05-1980 L1989 **PUD CCM** *020 †20

BEARDSLEY, Thomas Lewis. 8 MEDICAL PARK DR 28803 #036-07-1977 L1981 **OPH** *020 †35 ‡

BEAVERS, Kimberly L. 191 BILTMORE AVE 28801 #036-01-1997 L1999 **GE** *020 †20

BECK, Rainer Siegfried. 118 WT WEAVER BLVD, MAHEC FHC 28804 #409-20-1998 L2004 **FM** *020

BEKKER, Kirsten Elizabeth. 118 WT WEAVER BLVD, MAHEC FAMILY HEALTH CENTER 28804 #025-01-2006 L2008 **FP** *012

BELL, Carol Roland. 445 BILTMORE AVE, STE 505 28801 #045-01-1960 L1968 **AN** *071 †05

BELSKUS, Blanca Lilia. ■ 28805 #054-04-2005 L2008 **FM** *100

BENNETT, Mark Wilson, Jr. 428 BILTMORE AVE 28801 #036-01-1977 L1977 **FM** *020 †18

BERG, Mary Herndon. 158 ZILLICOA ST, THE PISGAH INSTITUTE, PA 28801 #036-08-1995 L1997 **P** *020

BERGER, Thomas Jay. 1100 TUNNEL RD # 112 28805 #024-07-1971 L1998 **TS** *020 †85,90

BERKWITS, Leland. 9 STUART CIR, MOUNTAIN SPINE AND REHABIL 28804 #016-06-1984 L2006 **PM PME** *020 †60 ‡

BERNER, Thomas. 190 BILTMORE AVE, STE 5 28801 #023-07-1968 L1973 **EM** *020 †16

BERNSTEIN, Ira Michael. 1100 TUNNEL RD 28805 #036-05-1970 L1970 **GE IM** *020 †20

BERNSTEIN, Lauren E. 750 ALLIANCE CT, ASHEVILLE ENDOCRINOLOGY CO 28806 #024-01-1999 L2005 **END** *020 †20

BESLEY, Richard Norton. ■ 28803 #041-02-1963 L1966 **P** *071 †75

BEYER, Michael Gordon. 304A NEW LEICESTER HWY 28806 #016-43-1995 L2005 **FM** *020 †18

BIDDLE, James Robt. 832 HENDERSONVILLE RD, ASHEVILLE INTEGRATIVE MEDI 28803 #028-03-1989 L1996 **IM NTR** *020 †20

BILBREY, Geo Marvin, Jr. 509 BILTMORE AVE 28801 #001-02-1962 L1971 **TS** *071 †85,90

BINNS, Oliver Andrew. 257 MCDOWELL ST, ASHEVILLE CARDIO & THORACI 28803 #051-01-1992 L2001 **TS GS** *020 †85,90

BIRD, Antonio Modesto. 14 S PACK SQ STE 362 28801 #035-06-1994 L1995 **P ADP** *020 †75

BITTER, Karl Ffolliott. 1 DOCTORS PARK 28801 #036-01-1963 L1963 **U** *020 †95

BIXBY-HAMMETT, Doris M. ■ 28803 #019-02-1948 L1952 **PD** *071

BLACK, Quinten Curtis. 445 BILTMORE AVE, STE G102 28801 #021-01-1998 L2003 **RO** *020 †80

BLAIR, Charles Edward. 8 NEW LEICESTER HWY 28806 #047-07-1982 L1991 **FM** *020 †18

BLINN, Lawrence Allan. 222 ASHELAND AVE 28801 #041-02-1983 L1988 **DR** *075 †80

BOBBITT, Joseph Michael. 3 DOCTORS PARK STE C 28801 #051-04-1974 L1978 **OPH** *071

BOCK, Richard Wolcott. 257 MCDOWELL ST 28803 #051-01-1986 L1995 **VS GS** *020 †85

BOERNER, Robert Martin. 520 BILTMORE AVE, ASHEVILLE CONSULTATIVE MED 28801 #036-01-1961 L1961 **ID PUD** *071 †20

BOERNER, Robert Michael. 222 ASHELAND AVE 28801 #036-01-1995 L2001 **RNR** *020 †80

BOONE, Judith. ■ 28803 #056-05-1964 L1965 **PTH** *020 †50

BORIS, Jeffrey Randall. 5 VANDERBILT PARK DR 28803 #028-02-1991 L2004 **PDC PD** *020 †55

BOTHE, Brian Michael. 1998 HENDERSONVILLE RD 28803 #005-12-1979 L2002 **PM** *020 †60

BOTTOM, Krystal S. 11 VANDERBILT PARK DR 28803 #011-03-1989 L1996 **PHO** *020 †55

BOYD, Ellen. 14 VICTORIA RD, STE 101 28801 #045-01-1975 L1978 **MG PD** *020 †55,19

BRADSHAW, William Alan. 14 MEDICAL PARK DR 28803 #048-16-1995 L2001 **GS** *020 †85

BRADT, Susan Diana. ■ 28805 #011-04-2004 L2006 **FM** *020 †18

BRAMHAM, Jane. 20 MEDICAL PARK DR 28803 #005-02-1975 L2007 **HO HEM** *020 †20 ‡

BRAUN, Simon D. 84 COXE AVE STE 2A 28801 #012-05-1977 L1982 **VIR DR** *020 †80

BRAZIL, Wilburn Oscar, Jr. 100 VICTORIA RD 28801 #021-05-1961 L1966 **U** *071 †95

BRIDGMAN, Albert Henry. VET ADMIN HOSP 28805 #021-05-1956 L1971 **VS TS** *020 †85,90

BROADHURST, Richard S. 333 GASHES CREEK RD 28803 #048-15-1986 L1998 **OM** *020 †70

BROOKS, Melissa Christine. ■ 28803 #055-01-2006 **OBG** *100

BROSNAN, Rhoda Brooker. 5 VANDERBILT PARK DR 28803 #045-01-1997 L2001 **CD** *020 †20

BROSNAN, Thomas Mock. 900 CENTRE PARK DR, STE A 28805 #045-01-1997 L2001 **OPH** *020

BROSNAN, Walter Hawkins. 900A CENTRE PARK DR 28805 #045-01-1985 L1989 **OPH** *020

BROWN, Andy Paul. PO BOX 2959 28802 #027-01-2001 L2007 **VIR** *020 †80

BROWN, Arnold. 1100 TUNNEL RD, VA MED CTR 28805 #005-06-1964 L2004 **ID IM** *030 †20

BROWN, Cynthia J Hecker. 11 VANDERBILT PARK DR 28803 #028-03-1985 L1988 **PD** *020 †55

BROWN, David Allen. 390 S FRENCH BROAD AVE 28801 #012-01-1982 L1987 **A AI** *020 †55,03

BROWN, Gretchen Godchaux. 2 MEDICAL PARK DR, STE 1000 28803 #021-05-2000 L2007 **PD** *020 †55

BROWN, James Everett. 76 PEACHTREE RD, STE 300 28803 #048-02-1976 L1978 **AN** *020 †05

BROWN, Stephen Delhman, Jr. 445 BILTMORE AVE, STE 407A 28801 #036-01-1998 L2001 **IM** *020 †20

BROWN, Walter J, III. 222 ASHELAND AVE 28801 #012-01-1985 L1990 **DR** *020 †80

BRUMMER, Jane K B. 190 BILTMORE AVE, STE 5 28801 #048-04-1988 L1989 **FM FPG** *020 †18

BRYAN, Charles W. 445 BILTMORE AVE, STE 100 28801 #048-12-1985 L1991 **HEM ON** *020 †20

BRYAN, William Blair. 7 VANDERBILT PARK DR, STE 100A 28803 #036-07-1956 L2007 **PD** *071 †55

BRYAN, Wm Alexander, III. 7 VANDERBILT PARK DR, STE 100-A 28803 #005-12-1968 L1973 **PD** *020 †55

BUECHLER, C Michael. 509 BILTMORE AVE, MSN ST JOSEPH HLTH SYS 28801 #016-06-1974 L1999 **TRS CCS** *020 †85

BUIE, Stephen Eugene. 158 ZILLICOA ST 28801 #036-01-1981 L1987 **P IM** *020 †20,75

BURKE, Margaret Ober. 7 VANDERBILT PARK DR 28803 #023-01-1985 L1989 **PM SCI** *020 †60

BURKETT, Donna Lynn. ■ 28801 #036-01-1995 L2001 **FM** *071 †18

BURKHARDT, Nathan Leslie. 129 MCDOWELL ST 28801 #047-06-1959 L1966 **ORS OS** *071 †40

BURNS, Margaret V. ■ 28804 #036-07-1937 L1948 **P** *071

BURT, Terrence Wm. 509 BILTMORE AVE 28801 #021-05-1979 L1981 **EM** *020 †16

BURTON, Harry G, III. 257 MCDOWELL ST 28803 #020-02-1974 L1981 **TS** *020 †85,90

BUSER, Steven Donald. 932 HENDERSONVILLE RD, FOREST CENTER - STE 101 28803 #036-07-1989 L1997 **P** *020 †75

BUSSEY, Frederick N, II. 1100 TUNNEL RD 28805 #016-06-1960 L1986 **GS** *030 †85

BUYS, Elizabeth Anne. 900 HENDERSONVILLE RD 28803 #017-20-1999 L2000 **OBG** *020 †30

BUZZANELL, Charles Anton. 1025 BREVARD RD, STE 3 28806 #010-02-1984 L2005 **PME** *075 †05

BYRNE, David Edward. ■ 28803 #027-01-1975 L1975 **GS** *071 †85

BYRON, Cheryl Ann Maxwell. ■ 28805 #016-06-1968 L1995 **CHP P** *074

BYRON, Robert Sill. 227 LYNN COVE RD 28804 #038-41-1964 L1968 **P** *071

CABANISS, Micki L. 1091 HENDERSONVILLE RD 28803 #035-15-1965 L1990 **OBG NPM** *071 †30

CAHAN, Steven Lee. 3 DOCTORS PARK STE B 28801 #035-19-1976 L1989 **OPH** *020 †35 ‡

CAIN, Larry Ray. 417 BILTMORE AVE, DOCTORS PARK 3H 28801 #041-12-1974 L1989 **GE** *020 †20

CALDERBANK, James Blake. 76 PEACHTREE RD, STE 300 28803 #035-01-1973 L1999 **AN IM** *020 †20,05

CALDWELL, Cecelia Rave. 11 VANDERBILT PARK DR 28803 #038-41-1984 L1987 **CCP PD** *020 †55

CALDWELL, Ronald Ranord. 200 CHARLOTTE ST 28801 #036-05-1975 L1975 **IM** *020 †20

CALLAGHAN, Wm Michael. 143 ASHELAND AVE 28801 #038-40-1981 L1985 **GPM** *020 †70,30

CALLISON, William J. ■ 28803 #047-05-1953 L1960 **ORS OS** *071 †40

CAMBLOS, Joshua F B. ■ 28803 #051-01-1943 L1948 **GS** *071 †85

CAMMARATA, Angelo Chas. 75B LIVINGSTON ST, BLUE RIDGE BONE & JOINT 28801 #041-13-1989 L1999 **HS ORS** *020 †40

CAMPBELL, Allen Barry. ■ 28803 #035-01-1961 L1968 **OBG** *071 †30

CAMPBELL, Bethany Mcbraye. 93 VICTORIA RD 28801 #001-02-2004 **OBG** *012

CANAHUATE, Alfredo. ■ 28804 #308-01-1949 L1961 **FM** *071

CANNON, Daniel Fredrick. 6 BROOKLET ST 28801 #016-02-1988 L1998 **FM** *020 †18

CANNON, Shelli Elizabeth. 333 GASHES CREEK RD, PARKWAY MEDICAL GROUP 28803 #005-12-1988 L1992 **FM** *020 †18

CANNON, William M. WESLEY DRIVE VILLA 23D 28803 #045-01-1939 L1952 **PTH** *071 †50

CAPPIELLO, David Lawrence. 129 MCDOWELL ST, BLUE RIDGE BONE & JOINT 28801 #035-20-1964 L1971 **ORS** *020 †40 ‡

CAQUIAS-GONZALEZ, Eileen. 190 BILTMORE AVE, STE 5 28801 #042-02-1995 L1996 **FM** *020 †18

CARCHMAN, Rebecca Maya. 11 VANDERBILT PARK DR 28803 #550-02-1999 L2003 **CCP** *020 †55

CARGILL, John G, III. 1 DOCTORS PARK, ASHEVILLE UROLOGICAL ASS 28801 #051-01-1982 L1988 **U** *020 †95 ‡

CARLISLE, Lauren Keely. 131 MCDOWELL ST, STE 100 28801 #021-05-1997 L2006 **PD** *020 †55

CARRATT, Evan Demetrios. 118 WT WEAVER BLVD 28804 #010-01-1990 L1995 **FM** *100

CARSON, Homer Shannon, III. 76 PEACHTREE RD, STE 300 28803 #012-01-1968 L2003 **AN** *071 †05 ‡

CARTER, Gilbert Bruce. 1100 TUNNEL RD, VETERANS ADMIN MED CTR 28805 #048-02-1971 L2005 **FM NTR** *020 †18

CARTER, John Jefferson, Jr. 158 ZILLICOA ST, PSYCHOTHERAPY & EDUCATION, 28801 #001-02-1975 L1984 **CHP P** *020 †75

CASSIDY, Scott. 1100 TUNNEL RD, MEDICAL CENTER 28805 #011-04-1977 L2001 **FM** *020 †18

CAVANAUGH, Pamela Blanks. 445 BILTMORE AVE, STE 407 28801 #001-02-1990 L1995 **IM** *020 †20

CHALLY, Margaret Kristin. ■ 28804 #023-07-1999 L2005 **EM** *020 †16

CHAND, Mridu. 445 BILTMORE AVE, STE 100 28801 #672-01-1991 L2002 **HO** *020 †20

CHANG, John Chihhsiung. 1100 TUNNEL RD 28805 #036-08-1988 L1989 **FM** *020 †18

CHANG, Paul Siuchung. 876 NEW LEICESTER HWY, STE 3 28806 #016-02-1983 L1987 **IM NTR** *020

CHAPALA, Vijaya Kumari. 111 TUNNEL RD, VA HOSP 28805 #305-01-1995 L1999 **IM** *020 †20

CHAPMAN, Jesse P, Jr. ■ 28803 #041-01-1943 L1948 **TS GS** *075 †85,90

CHAPMAN, William Edward. 1100 TUNNEL RD, VETERANS HOSP 28805 #008-02-1976 L1988 **PTH** *020 †50

CHARI, Roopa. 12 1/2 WALL ST, STE F 28801 #038-43-1992 L2008 **IM** *020 †20 ‡

CHASE, James Allan. ■ 28804 #017-20-1955 L1955 **OM** *071

CHAY, Christopher Haekang. 445 BILTMORE AVE STE 100, CANCER CARE OF WNC PA 28801 #036-01-1996 L2002 **HO** *020 †20

CHENEY, Paul R, Jr. 1 VANDERBILT PARK DR STE 2 28803 #012-05-1977 L1987 **IM** *020 †20

CHILDERS, Terry Cely. 500 CENTRE PARK DR 28805 #051-01-1980 L1985 **PD** *020 †55

CHITOUR, Lisa Nell Jordan. 24 MEDICAL PARK DR, BILTMORE OB GYN 28803 #048-04-1979 L2006 **OBG** *020 †30

CHOI, Jong Jin. 68 SWEETEN CREEK RD 28803 #583-02-1969 L2004 **PM** *020 †60 ‡

CHU, Peter Tice. 64 PEACHTREE RD 28803 #036-01-1994 L1995 **PD** *020 †55

CLARK, Kenneth J, Jr. 191 BILTMORE AVE 28801 #035-06-1971 L1978 **GE IM** *071 †20 ‡

CLAXTON, Martha A Mahanes. 7 VANDERBILT PARK DR, # 100A 28803 #051-01-1961 L1963 **PD** *071 †55

CLEMENTS, David A, II. 41 OAKLAND RD, STE 100 28801 #035-01-1994 L1998 **IM** *020 †20

CLEMENZI, Rebecca Ann. 206 ASHELAND AVE 28801 #011-03-1980 L1981 **EM FM** *020 †16,18

COBB, David Laurence, Jr. 50 DOCTORS DR, STE N-1 28801 #047-06-1995 L1996 **OBG** *020 †30

COBB, Mark Wm. 281 MCDOWELL ST, WNC DERMATOLOGICAL ASSOCIA 28803 #041-07-1981 L1999 **D DMP** *020 †15

COBLENTZ, Alice Anne. ■ 28803 #041-07-1977 L1982 **IM** *020

COHEN, Alan Roger. ■ 28804 #035-48-1980 L1981 **FM** *020 †18

COHEN, Brian Louis. 100 VICTORIA RD 28801 #036-01-2002 L2008 **U** *100

COHEN, Susan Ray. 2 MEDICAL PARK DR, STE 1000 28803 #036-01-1988 L1991 **PD** *020 †55

COLADONATO, Michael Josep. 118 WT WEAVER BLVD 28804 #051-01-2005 L2006 **FP** *012

COLE, Toby Cecil, Jr. 222 ASHELAND AVE 28801 #036-05-1991 L1996 **DR** *020 †80

COLEMAN, Bernard S. ■ 28803 #352-05-1961 **PA** *071

CONA, Costantino Dino. 222 ASHELAND AVE 28801 #035-08-1991 L1997 **DR** *020

CONDRA, Kellie Smith. 90 ASHELAND AVE 28801 #047-06-1992 L1996 **RO** *020 †80

CONQUEST, Anne Marie. 509 BILTMORE AVE, STE B321 28801 #021-05-1999 L2007 **CCS TRS** *100 †85

CONWAY, Donald Ray. 5 LIVINGSTON ST 28801 #045-01-1986 L1994 **PS GS** *020 †85,65

COOK, Jason Thomas. 118 WT WEAVER BLVD, MAHEC FAMILY PRACTICE PGM 28804 #001-02-2007 **FP** *012

COPE, Randall Kevin. ■ 28803 #018-75-2004, ▲ L2007 **IM** *020 †20

COULSON, Carol Catherine. 900 HENDERSONVILLE RD 28803 #023-01-1988 L2000 **OBS MFM** *020 †30

COUNCELL, Richard Bruce. 2 YORKSHIRE ST 28803 #036-05-1981 L1988 **OBG** *020 †30

COYLE, Margaret Mary. 7 ATHERTON WAY, P O BOX 1170 28803 #010-02-1982 L2002 **IM** *020 †20

CRANDALL, James David. 8 MEDICAL PARK DR, UNIVERSITY OF KENTUCKY 28803 #051-04-2000 L2007 **OPH** *100 †35

CRAWFORD, Joe Dean. ■ 28803 #036-05-1978 L1979 **FM IG** *020

CREWS, Harry Denniston. 10 MCDOWELL ST 28801 #023-07-1964 L1972 **IM NEP** *071 †20

CRIGLER, Norris Wolf, Jr. 222 ASHELAND AVE 28801 #036-07-1976 L1981 **DR VIR** *020 †80

CRISOLOGO, Loreto L. ■ 28803 #748-01-1950 L1974 **EM** *071

CROOK, Lynn. 1100 TUNNEL RD, VAMC PATHOLOGY (113) 28805 #045-01-1974 L1975 **CLP HEM** *020 †50

CROSBY, Edward Brown. 34 GRANBY ST 28801 #001-02-1968 L1974 **ORS** *071 †40

CROSLEY, David Clay. ■ 28803 #001-02-1986 L1988 **LM** *075

CROSS, Michael Todd. 30 CHOCTAW ST 28801 #036-01-1997 L2003 **PCC** *020 †20

CRUZ, Leonard Lee. 932 HENDERSONVILLE RD #101 28803 #011-02-1981 L1993 **P** *020 †75

CUELLAR, John Patrick, III. 76 PEACHTREE RD, STE 210 28803 #048-12-1985 L1989 **OBG** *020 †30

CUENTO, Oblendo Almendras. 8 NEW LEICESTER HWY 28806 #748-01-1965 L1990 **GS** *020 †85

CUMBIE, Brian Christopher. 750 ALLIANCE CT, ASHEVILLE ENDOCRINOLOGY 28806 #001-06-2001 L2007 **END** *020 †20,55

CUMMINGS, Charles Emmett. ■ 28803 #021-05-1958 L1962 **D** *071 †15

CUMMINGS, Charles James. 30 CHOCTAW ST 28801 #036-01-1990 L1998 **PCC** *020 †20

CUMMINGS, Lorraine Marie. 62 ORANGE ST 28801 #035-08-1990 L1994 **OBG** *020 †30

CURL, Mary Ann Wolf. 1100 TUNNEL RD, GERIATRICS & EXTENDED CARE 28805 #048-12-1999 L2002 **IMG** *020 †20

CURRAN, Gary Allan. 220 RIDGEFIELD CT, PISGAH FAM HEALTH 28806 #025-01-1994 L1996 **FM** *020 †18

CURRENS, Andrea. 900 HENDERSONVILLE RD, STE 206 28803 #020-02-1997 L2001 **OBG** *020 †30

CURRENS, John W. 285 MCDOWELL ST 28803 #020-02-1996 L2001 **OTO** *020 †45

CUTCHEN, Lisa Anne. 118 WT WEAVER BLVD 28804 #034-01-2004 L2007 **FM** *020

DALTON, Alvin Stanley, Jr. 304 SUMMIT ST, P O BOX 5819 28803 #005-12-1976 L1981 **NPM** *020 †55

DALTON, Rory Ralph. 509 BILTMORE AVE 28801 #001-02-1986 L2007 **PTH** *020 †85,50

DANNINGER, Sarah Joyce. ■ 28803 #036-01-2006 **FP** *012

DARTT, Diane F. 509 BILTMORE AVE 28801 #012-05-1995 L1996 **FM** *020 †18

DAVID, Stephen Michael. 75B LIVINGSTON ST, BLUE RIDGE BONE & JOINT 28801 #065-01-1992 L1993 **ORS** *020 †40

DAVIS, Philip Coleman. ■ 28803 #051-04-1964 L1972 **GYN** *071 †30

DEALY, Darilyn Hedden. 53 S FRENCH BROAD AVE 28801 #036-07-1979 L1985 **ID IM** *020 †20

DEAN, John Newell. 147 ASHELAND AVE 28801 #012-05-1974 L1978 **IM** *020 †20 ‡

DE BOW, Elizabeth Carol. 41 OAKLAND RD STE 125, MENTAL HEALTH ASSOCIATION 28801 #047-06-1998 L2002 **P** *020 †75

DECKER, Carrie Michele. ■ 28803 #048-15-2002 L2006 **AN** *100 †05

DEDMAN, Karen Ledwith. 260 MERRIMON AVE STE 200, COMMUNITY FAMILY PRACTICE 28801 #016-01-1981 L1983 **FM** *020 †18

DEERING, Timothy B. 191 BILTMORE AVE 28801 #035-09-1972 L1977 **GE IM** *020 †20

DEJOURNETT, Leon Martin. 11 VANDERBILT PARK DR 28803 #016-42-1986 L1994 **PD CCP** *020 †55

DELK, Christopher Wood. 509 BILTMORE AVE, MISSION HOSPITALS 28801 #051-04-2004 L2007 **EM** *020

DE MATOS, Pierre. 14 MEDICAL PARK DR 28803 #023-07-1994 L1998 **GS** *020 †85

DEMENT, Joseph Miller. 111 VICTORIA RD, ASSOCIATES SOUTHERN ORTHO 28801 #047-06-1983 L1988 **ORS** *020 †40 ‡

DEPAOLO, Charles James. 3B MCDOWELL ST, CHARLES J DE PAOLO, MD, PA 28801 #021-05-1987 L1992 **ORS** *020 †40

DEPHOUSE, Derek Holt. 64 PEACHTREE RD 28803 #045-04-1997 L2001 **PD** *020 †55

DESMOND, Timothy Patrick. 222 ASHELAND AVE 28801 #021-06-1983 L1987 **DR** *020 †80

DESROCHERS, Danielle. ■ 28806 #036-05-2004 L2007 **FM** *020 †18

DICKERSON, Bryon Anthony. 222 ASHELAND AVE 28801 #035-03-1993 L1995 **DR** *020 †80

DIEZ, Edgardo. 68 SWEETEN CREEK RD, THOMS REHABILITATION HOSPI 28803 #042-03-1988 L1992 **PM** *020 †60 ‡

DILL, Gregory O. 1854 HENDERSONVILLE RD 28803 #048-04-1989 L2003 **P** *020 †75

DISMUKES, Wm Paul, Jr. ■ 28804 #028-02-1960 L1998 **IM HEM** *071 †20

DIZNOFF, Emily Anne. 41 OAKLAND RD 28801 #012-05-2001 L2002 **FM** *020 †18

DODD, Patricia. ■ 28803 #023-01-1944 L1954 **GS** *071 †85

DODD, Richard Craig. 750 ALLIANCE CT 28806 #016-02-1978 L1981 **END IM** *020 †20

DODSON, Leigh Masten. 2 MEDICAL PARK DR, STE 1000 28803 #036-01-1999 L2001 **PD** *020 †55

DOLAN, Daniel Lynn. 9 W BAIRD MOUNTAIN RD 28804 #047-05-1955 L1977 **IM** *030 †20

DOMBY, William Roger. 30 CHOCTAW ST 28801 #051-04-1972 L1979 **PUD CCM** *020 †20

DORRIS, Hugh Duncan, Jr. 1119 HENDERSONVILLE RD, STE 200 28803 #012-01-1990 L1994 **D** *020 †15

DOSTROW, Victor Geo. ■ 28814 #027-01-1983 L2002 **N PA** *020 †75

DOUGLAS, Michael Gene. 513 MCDOWELL ST 28803 #055-02-1989 L1997 **VS** *020 †85

DOWDESWELL, Robert Horton. 509 BILTMORE AVE 28801 #045-01-1970 L1975 **PTH** *020 †50

DOWLER, Shannon Brown. 1812 HENDERSONVILLE RD 28803 #036-08-1999 L2000 **FM** *020 †18

DRAKE, Christopher T. ■ 28804 #016-02-1958 L1959 **GS** *071 †85

DRAY, Gregory Jos. 675 BILTMORE AVE STE E, ASHEVILLE MEDICAL BLDG 28803 #038-40-1973 L1980 **P** *020 †40,75

DRESSEL, Laura Erin. 118 WT WEAVER BLVD 28804 #012-01-2003 L2004 **FM** *020 †18

DUKOWICZ, Andrew C. 191 BILTMORE AVE, ASHEVILLE GASTROENTEROLOGY 28801 #034-01-2001 L2007 **GE** *020

DUNCAN, George Clovis. 119 TUNNEL RD STE D, STATE DEPT. HHS 28805 #045-01-1973 L1974 **PD OS** *071 †55 ‡

DUNKIN, Pamela Ann. 172 ASHELAND AVE STE D 28801 #028-02-1982 L1994 **P** *020 †75

DUNN, William Burwell, III. 10 MEDICAL PARK DR 28803 #045-01-1970 L1980 **PTH** *020 †50

EARLY, James Howard. 946 TUNNEL RD 28805 #048-15-1984 L2002 **FM** *020 †18

EBY, William Michael. 76 PEACHTREE RD, STE 300 28803 #051-04-1983 L1992 **AN** *020 †05

EDDINGS, Tally Harry, III. 129 MCDOWELL ST, BLUE RIDGE BONE & JOINT 28801 #012-01-1991 L1998 **ORS** *020 †40

EDWARDS, Christopher A. 14 MEDICAL PARK DR, REGIONAL SURGICAL SPECIALI 28803 #012-22-2001 L2007 **GS** *020

EDWARDS, Christopher Alan. 14 MEDICAL PARK DR 28803 #017-20-1995 L1996 **GS** *020 †85

EGERTON, Courtney D. ■ 28803 #020-02-1946 L1947 **GYN** *071 †30

EHRLICHMAN, Gloria S. ■ 28806 #042-01-1955 L1973 **PD** *071

EIZEMBER, Frances Lim. 509 BILTMORE AVE 28801 #036-07-1997 L1998 **EM** *020 †16

ELDER, Christopher L. 111 VICTORIA RD, ASSOCIATES SOUTHERN ORTHO 28801 #035-20-1997 L1998 **ORS** *020 †40

ELLINGTON, Kenneth Raynor. 509 BILTMORE AVE, MISSION HOSPITAL 28801 #036-01-1986 L1990 **AN** *020 †05

ELLIS, James Madison, Jr. 1809 ELLICOTT LN 28803 #021-05-1985 L1992 **EM** *020 †16

ELLIS, Laura Burton. 131 MCDOWELL ST STE 202 28801 #036-01-1992 L2003 **GS VS** *020

ELLISTON, Erwin Bruce. 190 BILTMORE AVE, STE 5 28801 #005-12-1972 L1973 **FM** *071 †18

ELY, Peter Kimberley. ■ 28805 #048-13-1981 L1982 **AN** *020 †05

ELY, Stephen Wilson. 257 MCDOWELL ST 28803 #051-01-1986 L1993 **GS** *020 †85,90

ENDE, John Francis. 222 ASHELAND AVE 28801 #036-01-1992 L1996 **DR** *020 †80

ENGELBRECHT, Matthew A. 1200 RIDGEFIELD BLVD, STE 250 28806 #016-43-2002 L2006 **N** *020 †75

ENGLISH, Thomas Leon. PO BOX 18267 28814 #036-07-1969 L1969 **GS PD** *020 †85

ENTMACHER, Edward Philip. 480 ELK MOUNTN SCNC HWY HI 28804 #036-01-1978 L1981 **P CHP** *020

ERRICO, Robert Andrew. 2 MEDICAL PARK DR, STE 1000 28803 #036-05-1991 L1994 **NPM PD** *020 †55

EUBANKS, Reavis Thayer. 86 VICTORIA RD 28801 #021-01-1971 L1976 **GS OS** *020 †85

EVINS, Grace Gibbes. 16 MCDOWELL ST 28801 #036-01-1995 L1996 **OBG** *020 †30

EXAR, Elliott Nicholas. 30 CHOCTAW ST 28801 #023-07-1993 L2000 **PCC** *020 †20

FADEM, Jerold Jos, Jr. 1 W PACK SQ, STE 300 28801 #011-03-1981 L2001 **IM** *040 †20

FAGAN, Ernest Blake. 118 WT WEAVER BLVD 28804 #047-05-1998 L1999 **FM** *020 †18

FARMER, Woodard Eason. 428 BILTMORE AVE 28801 #021-01-1939 L1947 **IM** *072

FEE, James Paul. 509 BILTMORE AVE 28801 #021-01-2002 L2006 **MPD** *020 †20,55

FELL, Dale Eliot. 509 BILTMORE AVE 28801 #020-12-1978 L1979 **PS** *020 †65

FEREN, Stephen David. 1100 TUNNEL RD, ASHEVILLE VAMC 28805 #012-01-1998 L2007 **SME N** *020

FERRIS, Julian Campbell. 509 BILTMORE AVE 28801 #010-01-1991 L2000 **IM PD** *020 †55,20

FERRISS, Adrienne S. 1100 TUNNEL RD, ASHEVILLE VA MEDICAL CENTE 28805 #021-05-1988 L2001 **GPM** *020 †70

FIELD, James Rista. 222 ASHELAND AVE 28801 #048-12-1995 L2000 **VIR** *020 †80

FIELDS, Robert William. 501 BILTMORE AVE 28801 #011-03-2000 L2001 **FM** *020 †18

FISHER, Ronald Paul. 190 BILTMORE AVE, STE 5 28801 #011-03-1977 L1978 **FM FPG** *020 †18

FLANDERS, Paul C. 509 BILTMORE AVE, EMERGENCY DEPT-MEMORIAL CA 28801 #012-05-1999 L2002 **EM** *020 †16

FLEEMAN, Sheri W. 222 ASHELAND AVE 28801 #012-05-1996 L2001 **DR** *020 †80

FLEMING, Saml Bryson, II. 10 MCDOWELL ST, MOUNTAIN KIDNEY AND HYPERT 28801 #036-01-1991 L1996 **NEP** *020 †20

FLETCHER, Barry Davis. ■ 28805 #067-01-1961 L1999 **PDR DR** *071 †80

FLORENCE, Thomas James. ■ 28803 #012-05-1943 L1944 **U** *071 †95

FOGLEMAN, Brigette Diane. 7 VANDERBILT PARK DR, STE 100A 28803 #036-08-2001 L2005 **PD** *020 †55

FOLGER, John R, Jr. 190 BILTMORE AVE, STE 5 28801 #036-05-1953 L2004 **FM PHP** *071 †18 ‡

FORLAW, James Russell. 1220 HENDERSONVILLE RD, THE BARIATRIC CLINIC 28803 #011-02-1956 L1996 **FM EM** *020 †18

FORTESCUE, William N, Jr. ■ 28801 #036-07-1962 L1962 **GPM** *062

FOWLER, William Bright. 675 BILTMORE AVE STE F 28803 #036-05-1956 L1956 **IM** *020 †20

FOY, David Mark. 41 OAKLAND RD 28801 #038-06-1978 L1979 **FM** *020 †18

FRANK, William Geo. ■ 28803 #010-01-1964 L1966 **P PYA** *071 †75

FRAYNE, Daniel James. 118 WT WEAVER BLVD 28804 #005-15-1999 L2002 **FM** *020 †18

FRAZER, Joe Walton, III. 190 BILTMORE AVE, STE 5 28801 #036-07-1979 L1989 **EM** *020 †16

NORTH CAROLINA
ASHEVILLE

FREDERICK, Bruce Robt. ■ 28804 #056-05-1968 L1970 **R** *071 †80
FRIEDMAN, Ronald Myron. 445 BILTMORE AVE STE 100 28801 #035-47-1977 L1996 **HO IM** *020 †20
FRISCH, Harold Michael. 509 BILTMORE AVE, STE B321 28801 #010-02-1994 L2007 **OTR ORS** *040 †40
FRYE, Karen Renee. 100 VICTORIA RD 28801 #025-01-1981 L1992 **U** *020 †95
FURDYNA, Julia Anne. 1100 TUNNEL RD, VA MEDICAL CENTER 28805 #017-20-1991 L1997 **OTO** *020 †45
FURIGAY, Paul Joseph. 304 SUMMIT ST 28803 #041-12-1998 L2004 **NPM** *020 †55
GAFFORD, Glenn David. 1100 TUNNEL RD 28805 #047-06-1978 L1986 **IM ID** *020 †20
GALLAGHER, Timothy Jos. 222 ASHELAND AVE 28801 #021-05-1969 L1976 **DR** *075 †80
GALLOWAY, J Bruce. 428 BILTMORE AVE 28801 #065-05-1944 L1949 **ORS** *071 †40
GARBARINO, Elizabeth Star. 24 MEDICAL PARK DR, BILTMORE OB GYN 28803 #047-06-2002 L2006 **OBG** *020
GARBEE, Henry Wesley. 2 MEDICAL PARK DR, STE 1000 28803 #036-05-1967 L1967 **PD GP** *020 †55 ‡
GARDNER, Elizabeth F. 1 VANDERBILT PARK DR, STE 200 28803 #012-01-1999 L2000 **IM** *020 †20
GARDNER, John Pierre. 1 VANDERBILT PARK DR, STE 200 28803 #012-01-1999 L2002 **FM** *020 †18
GARRETT, Janet Beer. 509 BILTMORE AVE 28801 #035-20-1983 L1986 **DR** *020 †80
GARROWAY, Neil W. 118 WT WEAVER BLVD 28804 #035-06-1970 L2006 **IM END** *040 †20
GARTON, Graciela R. 445 BILTMORE AVE 28801 #132-01-1981 L2002 **RO** *020 †80
GENGLER, Norman J. ■ 28804 #016-06-1949 L1987 **AN** *071 †05
GENTLING, Peter Allen. 3 DOCTORS PARK STE D 28801 #016-06-1964 L1998 **GS** *071 †85
GERDINE, Park Lambuth. ■ 28803 #012-05-1954 L1956 **GP** *071
GERGEL, Randy Steven. ■ 28804 #045-04-1982 L1987 **CHP P** *020 †75
GETTINGER, Glen Scott. 76 PEACHTREE RD, STE 300 28803 #012-05-1981 L1983 **AN IM** *020 †05
GETTYS, Joseph Miller, Jr. 222 ASHELAND AVE 28801 #012-05-1971 L2002 **DR** *020 †80
GIBBS, Fredrick Glen. ■ 28806 #019-02-1964 L1996 **IM** *072 ‡
GILMER, Summer Harrold. 93 VICTORIA RD, MAHEC OB/GYN 28801 #045-04-2005 L2006 **OBG** *012
GLANCE, Gregory Lynn. 60 LIVINGSTON ST, STE 200 28801 #036-05-1986 L1988 **IM** *020 †20
GODBOLD, Ronald Lee. 281 MCDOWELL ST 28803 #001-02-1969 L1973 **D** *020 †15
GOEBEL, Michael James. 75B LIVINGSTON ST, BLUE RIDGE BONE & JOINT 28801 #018-03-1992 L1998 **ORS OSS** *020 †40
GOLDMAN, Stephen Richard. ■ 28804 #012-05-1970 L2002 **OBG** *071 †30 ‡
GOLDSTEIN, Jeffrey Brian. 8 MEDICAL PARK DR 28803 #036-07-1994 L2000 **OPH** *020 †35
GOLDSTEIN, Meryl. 509 BILTMORE AVE 28801 #012-05-1991 L1999 **PTH** *020 †50
GOLLBERG, Harold Ronald. 7 YORKSHIRE ST STE 201 28803 #048-02-1966 L1972 **PYG P** *020
GOMEZ-URIA, Albino. VET ADMIN HOSP, DEPT MED 28805 #847-04-1961 L1966 **END IM** *071 †20
GONZALEZ, Edgardo. 1100 TUNNEL RD 28805 #308-04-1981 L1983 **P** *020
GONZALEZ, Jose Enrique. 190 BILTMORE AVE, STE 5 28801 #036-08-1998 L1999 **FM** *020 †18
GOODWIN, Mary Katherine. 93 VICTORIA RD, MAHEC WOMEN'S HEALTH CENTE 28801 #036-05-2003 L2005 **OBG** *100
GOODWIN, Thomas Carl. 190 BILTMORE AVE, STE 5 28801 #041-14-1981 L1984 **P** *020 †75
GOSFIELD, Edward, III. 7 VANDERBILT PARK DR, SPECIALISTS 28803 #041-01-1989 L2007 **PM** *020 †28,60
GOUGH, William, III. 445 BILTMORE AVE, STE 306 28801 #035-45-1976 L1980 **RHU IM** *020 †20
GOWIN, Kristin Marie. 445 BILTMORE AVE, STE 306 28801 #038-41-1990 L1999 **RHU** *020 †20
GRAF, Kenneth Walter. 509 BILTMORE AVE, STE B321 28801 #041-09-1998 L2004 **ORS** *020 †40
GRAHAM, Dwight David. 11 VANDERBILT PARK DR 28803 #020-12-1991 L2000 **PDS** *020 †85
GRAHAM, Jeffrey Brewer. 118 WT WEAVER BLVD 28804 #004-01-2002 L2003 **FM** *020 †18
GRAINGER, Wade Kenton. 1998 HENDERSONVILLE RD, STE 45 28803 #005-12-1983 L1986 **FM FPG** *020 †18
GRANERA, Sonia Lis. ■ 28803 #021-05-1994 L2001 **IM** *020 †20
GRANT, Colby Leigh. 7 VANDERBILT PARK DR, STE 100A 28803 #051-07-2003 L2006 **PD** *030 †55
GRANT, Gregory. 1998 HENDERSONVILLE RD, STE 31 28803 #021-01-1979 L1983 **OBG** *020 †30
GRANT, Patricia Rabine. 69 MCDOWELL ST 28801 #012-01-2001 L2006 **APM AN** *020 †05
GRAVATT, Benjamin Thos. 76 PEACHTREE RD, STE 300 28803 #041-12-1979 L1980 **AN** *020 †05
GREEVER, C Martin. ■ 28805 #038-43-1986 L1987 **IM PHP** *020 †20
GREGORY, Jerry Glen. 527 APPELDOORN CIR 28803 #039-01-1969 L1979 **P** *072 †75
GREGORY, Kate Welsh. 29 RAVENSCROFT DR, STE 4 28801 #047-05-1996 L2001 **P** *020 †75
GREGORY, R D, Jr. PO BOX 2959 28802 #020-02-1950 L1957 **R** *071 †80
GRIER, Michael Wm. 191 BILTMORE AVE 28801 #005-06-1969 L1975 **GE IM** *020 †20
GRIFFIN, Robert A. ■ 28804 #041-13-1951 L1952 **P** *071
GROH, Gordon Irwin. 75B LIVINGSTON ST, BLUE RIDGE BONE & JOINT 28801 #028-03-1986 L1995 **HS** *020 †40
GROH, Mark Allen. 257 MCDOWELL ST 28803 #028-46-1986 L1994 **GS** *020 †85,90
GROH, Sumandeep. 341 RED FOX CIR 28803 #028-46-1984 L1995 **PD EM** *020 †55
GROTH, John Frederick, Jr. ■ 28805 #041-01-1955 L1957 **PD** *071 †55
GUNTHER, Robert Clarence. 428 BILTMORE AVE DEPT ANES 28801 #035-19-1964 L1972 **AN** *020 †05
HAAKSMA, James Alan. 260 MERRIMON AVE, STE 200 28801 #036-01-1996 L1997 **FM** *020 †18
HADNAGY, Michael John, II. 99 MCDOWELL ST 28801 #036-08-1999 L2001 **IM** *020 †20
HALL, Jennifer Janet. ■ 28803 #012-01-2005 **FP** *012
HALL, Lorne Franklyn. ■ 28804 #010-01-1960 L1986 **OBG** *072 †30
HALL, Suzanne Ellen. 1100 TUNNEL RD, ASHEVILLE VA MED CTR 28805 #024-16-1984 L2004 **ORS** *020 †40
HAMAKER, Stanley Spencer. 35 WOODFIN ST 28801 #036-01-1982 L1983 **FM** *020 †18
HAMEL, Theresa Lyn. 500 CENTRE PARK DR 28805 #036-01-1989 L1991 **PD** *020 †55
HAMILTON, C Christian. 1100 TUNNEL RD 28805 #036-08-1986 L1989 **IM** *020
HAMILTON, William G. 190 BILTMORE AVE, STE 5 28801 #917-25-1966 L1976 **FM** *020 †18
HAMMETT, James Frank, Jr. ■ 28803 #036-05-1947 L1948 **AN GP** *071
HANAWAY, Patrick James. 63 ZILLICOA ST, GENOVA DIAGNOSTICS 28801 #028-02-1987 L1996 **FM** *020 †18
HANICH, Robert Frank. 5 VANDERBILT PARK DR 28803 #041-01-1983 L1989 **CD IM** *020 †20
HANKLEY, Daniel Walter, Jr. 75B LIVINGSTON ST, BLUE RIDGE BONE & JOINT 28801 #047-06-1996 L2001 **PM** *020 †60
HANSEN, Todd Herman. 5 VANDERBILT PARK DR 28803 #018-03-1988 L1990 **CD** *020 †20
HANSON, Stephen Martin. ■ 28803 #056-06-1948 L1950 **PTH** *071 †50
HAPKE, Edith Josephine. 428 BILTMORE AVE 28801 #407-33-1956 L1972 **PUD IM** *071
HARD, Miriam Jane. 18 CANTERBURY RD, NAVAL HOSPITAL 28805 #041-30-1986 L2005 **FM** *020 †18
HARDENBERGH, Marla J. 16 MCDOWELL ST 28801 #055-01-1998 L2007 **OBG** *100
HARKNESS, Ursula Fritzi. 900 HENDERSONVILLE RD 28803 #016-06-1997 L2006 **OBG** *020
HARLEY, Stewart Jacques. 1249 HENDERSONVILLE RD, S J HARLEY MD PA 28803 #025-01-1969 L1976 **ORS OSS** *020 †40
HARRELSON, Anna Quinn. ■ 28805 #045-04-2006 **FP** *012
HART, Andrew P. 76 PEACHTREE RD, STE 300 28803 #018-03-1984 L1987 **AN** *020 †05
HARTMAN, Moses Mc Coy. V A MED CTR, DEPT ANES 28805 #041-13-1948 L1949 **AN PD** *020
HARTMANN, Thomas Michael. 222 ASHELAND AVE 28801 #012-05-1980 L1985 **RNR DR** *020 †80
HASLAM, John Battle. 466 MERRILLS COVE RD 28803 #036-07-1965 L1965 **RO** *071 †80
HATHAWAY, Sharon C. ■ 28803 #036-07-1987 L2002 **IM** *074 †20
HATHAWAY, William Robert. 5 VANDERBILT PARK DR 28803 #056-06-1988 L1990 **CD IM** *020 †20
HAYES, John David. 1056 HAYWOOD RD STE C, OAKLAND PARK WOMEN'S HEALT 28806 #035-47-1999 L2002 **OBG** *020
HAYES, Mary Scott. 35 WOODFIN ST 28801 #045-04-2000 L2001 **FM** *020 †18
HAYNES, William Lee. 8 MEDICAL PARK DR 28803 #036-07-1987 L1988 **OPH** *020 †35
HAZLEHURST, John L. 14 MEDICAL PARK DR 28803 #036-01-1956 L1956 **GS** *071 †85
HEATH, Jill Kennedy. 223 E CHESTNUT ST, STE 4 28801 #048-16-1986 L1991 **P** *020 †75
HECK, Jeffrey Edward. 118 WT WEAVER BLVD 28804 #038-43-1979 L2004 **FM** *020 †18
HEDRICK, Mark Raymond. 60 LIVINGSTON ST, BLUE RIDGE BONE & JOINT 28801 #012-01-1988 L1994 **ORS OS** *020 †40
HELLREICH, Mark Allan. 30 CHOCTAW ST, ASHEVILLE PULMONARY ASSOCI 28801 #036-05-1981 L1984 **PUD IM** *020 †20
HELMS, Mark Edward. 509 BILTMORE AVE, MEMORIAL MISSION HOSPITAL 28801 #050-02-1978 L1993 **FM EM** *020 †18,16
HEMME, Hal S. 60 LIVINGSTON ST STE 200 28801 #035-06-1976 L1979 **IM** *020 †20
HENDERSON, John Arthur. ■ 28803 #016-11-1945 L1972 **GS** *071 †85
HENDERSON, Rex Arthur. 509 BILTMORE AVE, EMERGENCY CARE CENTER 28801 #011-02-1978 L1983 **EM** *020 †16
HENDERSON, Robt Clark, II. 93 VICTORIA RD, MAHEC WOMENS HLTH CTR 28801 #048-15-1986 L2002 **OBG GYN** *040 †30
HENRETTA, John Patrick. 513 MCDOWELL ST 28803 #051-04-1990 L1999 **VS** *020 †85
HENRY, Ozmer L, Jr. ■ 28803 #036-05-1948 L1949 **IM PUD** *071
HERRINGTON, Mary Vee. 445 BILTMORE AVE, STE 407A 28801 #047-20-1998 L2005 **IM** *020
HERSKOVITS, Elizabeth J. 118 WT WEAVER BLVD 28804 #005-02-1999 L2006 **IMG** *071 †20
HESTER, David Alan. 750 ALLIANCE CT 28806 #039-01-1973 L1978 **END DIA** *020 †20
HETZEL, David John. 509 BILTMORE AVE 28801 #056-06-1988 L1997 **GO GYN** *020 †30
HICKS, Melissa Maxine. 118 WT WEAVER BLVD 28804 #028-03-1984 L1985 **FM** *040 †18
HILL, Arthur Theodore, Jr. 428 BILTMORE AVE 28801 #036-05-1956 L1956 **IM** *071 †20
HILL, Haywood N, Jr. 445 BILTMORE AVE, STE 407A 28801 #036-05-1970 L1970 **IM** *071 †20
HILL, Ronald Chas. 1100 TUNNEL RD, CARDIOTHORACIC SURGERY 28805 #055-01-1974 L1982 **TS** *020 †85,90
HILL, Sherry Leigh. 509 BILTMORE AVE 28801 #036-01-1993 L2001 **EM** *020 †16
HILL, Vicente Jose. 509 BILTMORE AVE 28801 #035-45-1993 L2001 **EM** *020 †16
HIND, Angela Callaway. 5 DOCTORS PARK STE G, 417 BILTMORE AVENUE 28801 #036-08-1990 L1991 **IM** *020 †20
HINGSONGATES, Alyson Mich. 93 VICTORIA RD, WOMENS HEALTH CENTER 28801 #045-01-2004 L2007 **OBG** *012
HODSHON, Courtney Cumming. 93 VICTORIA RD, MAHEC WOMEN'S HEALTH CENTE 28801 #047-20-2004 L2005 **OBG** *012
HOEGERMAN, Georgeanne S. 1998 HENDERSONVILLE RD, RUTH BERNAL MD 28803 #016-11-1976 L1995 **PD ADM** *050 †55
HOER, James Brian. 445 BILTMORE AVE, STE 407 28801 #035-45-1987 L1993 **IM** *020 †20
HOLL, Blair Lyn. 190 BILTMORE AVE, STE 5 28801 #041-09-1990 L1999 **IM** *020 †20
HOLMAN, James F. 520 BILTMORE AVE STE A, SCIENCE 28801 #004-01-1970 L1981 **REN GYN** *030 †30
HOLMAN, Susan Catherine. 197 CUMBERLAND AVE 28801 #012-05-1981 L1984 **IM** *020 †20
HOLT, John Plummer. 92 CONGRESS ST 28801 #047-07-1956 L1958 **FM GP** *072
HOOKER, Michael Phillip. 76 PEACHTREE RD, STE 300 28803 #040-02-1980 L1983 **AN** *020 †05
HOOPER, Clifford Harold. 1100 TUNNEL RD 28805 #047-05-1952 L1952 **OTO** *072
HOPPING, Michael Wayne. 356 BILTMORE AVE 28801 #028-03-1978 L1982 **P** *071 †75
HORTON, Jennifer Alexis. 24 MEDICAL PARK DR, BILTMORE OB GYN 28803 #045-01-2000 L2004 **OBG** *020
HOWALD, Thomas Chas. 509 BILTMORE AVE 28801 #038-41-1969 L1974 **EM** *020 †18
HOWDEN, Nancy L. 100 RIDGEFIELD CT, SPECIALTY CENTER PA 28806 #036-01-1998 L2005 **OBG** *020 †30
HOYT, Sara Lippard. ■ 28803 #036-01-1954 L1954 **PD** *020 †55
HUBBARD, Robert Thos. ■ 28804 #041-13-1943 L1943 **FM** *071
HUFF, Olson. 980 HENDERSONVILLE RD 28803 #020-02-1962 L1966 **PD OS** *062 †55
HUFFSTUTTER, William M. 6 BROOKLET ST 28801 #047-06-1977 L1983 **CHN N** *020 †55,75
HUGHES, Jack. 286 OLD HAW CREEK RD 28805 #041-01-1943 L1943 **U** *071 †95
HULKOWER, Stephen D. 118 WT WEAVER BLVD 28804 #041-02-1981 L1986 **FM** *020 †18
HULL, James Dixon, III. ■ 28803 #016-02-1964 L1965 **GS** *071 †85
HULL, Matthew Craig. 509 BILTMORE AVE 28801 #056-06-1998 L2003 **RO** *020 †80
HUMBLE, Theodore Hamilton. 14 MEDICAL PARK DR 28803 #048-12-1982 L1990 **GS VS** *020 †85
HUME, Lara Rebecca. ■ 28803 #011-02-1996 L1999 **IM** *020 †20
HUMPHREY, David Alan. 445 BILTMORE AVE, STE 404 28801 #028-03-1993 L1995 **IM** *020 †20
HUMPHREY, Sonia L. 445 BILTMORE AVE, MISSION BARIATRICS-HEC 28801 #017-20-1994 L1996 **IM** *020 †20
HUMPHREYS, David Harding. 5 LIVINGSTON ST 28801 #038-41-1979 L1986 **PS** *020 †45,65
HUMPHREYS, Joan Heller. ■ 28804 #038-41-1980 L1986 **NS GS** *071
HUNT, Jason Daniel. 509 BILTMORE AVE 28801 #028-34-1996 L2000 **EM** *020 †16
HUTCHIN, Mark Eric. 281 MCDOWELL ST 28803 #036-01-2000 L2007 **D** *020 †15
HUTTO, Edith. ■ 28803 #045-01-1958 L1959 **D** *071
HYDE, Lee Sanford. 22 NEW LEICESTER HWY, STE A 28806 #038-06-1969 L1987 **FM IMG** *020 †18
HYDE, Rebecca Gail. 22 NEW LEICESTER HWY, STE A 28806 #027-01-1980 L1986 **FM EM** *020 †18

HYLTON, Joel W, Jr. 500 CENTRE PARK DR, MOUNTAIN AREA PEDIATRIC AS 28805 #036-01-1985 L1988 **PD** *020 †55

IBRAHIM, George Kaissar. 1100 TUNNEL RD 28805 #036-07-1987 L1990 **U** *020 †95

IBRAHIM, Stacey Neal. 509 BILTMORE AVE 28801 #036-01-1989 L1991 **PTH** *020 †50

ILARIA, Robert Leslie. 356 BILTMORE AVE, CENTER 28801 #020-02-1962 L1970 **P GP** *030 †75

ISBEY, Edward Kenneth, Jr. 8 MEDICAL PARK DR 28803 #025-07-1955 L1961 **OPH** *072 †35 ‡

ISBEY, Edward Kenneth, III. 8 MEDICAL PARK DR 28803 #036-01-1981 L1982 **OPH** *020 †35

ISENOGLE, Kenneth F. ■ 28803 #017-20-1957 L1957 **OTO** *071 †45

ISRAEL, Bruce Frederick. 53 S FRENCH BROAD AVE, STE 200 28801 #036-01-1995 L1998 **ID** *020 †20

JABER, Peter Wm. 281 MCDOWELL ST, WNC DERMATOLOGICAL ASSOC 28803 #025-01-1985 L1992 **D IM** *020 †20,15 ‡

JACKSON, Don Vernon, Jr. 20 MEDICAL PARK DR, ONCOLOGY ASSOCIATES, PA 28803 #051-01-1972 L1978 **ON HEM** *020 †20

JACKSON, Kenneth Wade, Jr. 2 YORKSHIRE ST 28803 #012-01-1997 L2004 **OBG** *020 †30

JACKSON, Mark Thomas. 500 CENTRE PARK DR, MOUNTAIN AREA PEDIATRIC AS 28805 #001-02-2000 L2002 **PD** *020 †55

JACOBS, Ronnie Lynn. 78 CRESTRIDGE DR, P O BOX 7568 28803 #036-01-1992 L1993 **IM** *020 †20

JAGODA, Frank S. 222 ASHELAND AVE 28801 #048-02-1985 L1989 **DR** *020 †80 ‡

JANSEN, Jay Carlton. 75B LIVINGSTON ST, BLUE RIDGE BONE & JOINT 28801 #017-20-1992 L1998 **OSM** *072 †40

JARRETT, Samuel David. 111 VICTORIA RD, ASSOCIATES SOUTHERN ORTHO 28801 #005-12-1999 L2002 **ORS** *020 †40

JEFFRIES, Brentley Doyle. 191 BILTMORE AVE 28801 #036-01-1985 L1988 **GE IM** *020 †20

JEFFRIES, Lydia Marie. 143 ASHELAND AVE 28801 #018-03-1986 L1987 **OBG** *020 †30 ‡

JENKINS, Oscar Ray, Jr. 5 VANDERBILT PARK DR 28803 #012-01-1986 L1992 **CD IM** *020 †20

JOE, Randall Robert. 76 PEACHTREE RD, STE 300 28803 #048-02-1995 L2003 **AN** *020 †05

JOHNSON, Alan Morse. 257 MCDOWELL ST 28803 #021-01-1980 L1988 **GS** *020 †85,90

JOHNSON, Daniel Sloan. 428 BILTMORE AVE 28801 #036-01-2002 L2006 **P** *020

JOHNSON, Herbert S. ■ 28803 #016-06-1960 L1961 **GP** *020

JOHNSON, James Andrew. 1100 TUNNEL RD, ASHEVILLE VA MEDICAL CENTE 28805 #045-01-1996 L1999 **IM** *020 †20

JOHNSON, Julia F. 118 WT WEAVER BLVD 28804 #043-01-2002 L2003 **FM** *020 †18

JOHNSON, Paul Douglas. 41 OAKLAND RD STE 200 28801 #047-06-1983 L1987 **OBG** *020 †30

JOHNSON, Randall Divan. 14 MEDICAL PARK DR 28803 #025-01-1975 L1977 **GS** *020 †85

JOHNSON, Ronald Wayne. 1 TOWN SQUARE BLVD, STE 220 28803 #045-01-1981 L1986 **FM** *020 †18 ‡

JOHNSON, Todd Clayton. ■ 28803 #036-05-1980 L1988 **PM** *071 †60

JOLLEY, Bob Ray. 80 PEACHTREE RD, STE 104 28803 #045-01-1986 L1990 **P** *020 †75

JONES, Jennifer. 86 VICTORIA RD 28801 #055-75-2000, ▲ L2005 **N** *020 †75

JONES, Lawrence Ralph. 428 BILTMORE AVE 28801 #019-02-1968 L1991 **P** *020 †75 ‡

JONES, Tony. 1 ANGLER TRL 28803 #036-01-1990 L2004 **FM** *020 †18

JOSLIN, Scott Andrew. 509 BILTMORE AVE, PRIME DOC OF ASHEVILLE 28801 #051-04-1989 L1998 **IM P** *020 †75,20

JOYNER, John T. ■ 28804 #036-05-1952 L1952 **IM HEM** *071 †20

KABASAN, Dennis Clark. 1100 TUNNEL RD 28805 #154-01-1977 L1981 **IM IMG** *020 †20

KACZMAREK, Ellen Marie. 190 BILTMORE AVE, STE 5 28801 #035-15-1981 L2002 **IM** *020 †20

KALATHIL, Meenakshi. ■ 28802 #495-04-1986 L2000 **IM** *020 †20

KALATHIL, Sumodh. ■ 28804 #495-44-1987 L1998 **GE** *020 †20

KALUZYNSKI, Thomas S. 100 FAR HORIZONS LN 28803 #036-01-1981 L1982 **IM END** *020 †20

KAMELL, Andrew William. 68 SWEETEN CREEK RD 28803 #043-01-1998 L2007 **FM PLM** *020 †18

KANDALA, Saisree. 1100 TUNNEL RD, VA MEDICAL CENTER 28805 #495-70-1994 L1999 **IM** *020 †20

KAPLAN, A N. ■ 28805 #036-05-1956 L1956 **PD PDA** *071 †55,03

KAREGEANNES, James C. 75B LIVINGSTON ST, BLUE RIDGE BONE & JOINT 28801 #036-07-1989 L1993 **ORS OAR** *020 †40

KAUFMAN, Stephen L. 1100 TUNNEL RD, VA HOSP DEPT RADIO 28805 #041-01-1967 L2002 **DR VIR** *020 †80 ‡

KEATON, Nancy Coleman. 1 VANDERBILT PARK DR, STE 240 28803 #036-08-1989 L1994 **VIR** *020 †80

KEEL, James Franklin, III. 30 CHOCTAW ST, ASHEVILLE PULMONARY ASSOCI 28801 #036-07-1974 L1978 **IM NM** *020 †20

KEENAN, Bruce Stone. ■ 28803 #041-01-1964 L1965 **PDE PD** *071 †55

KELISCHEK, Sabine. 76 PEACHTREE RD, STE 210 28803 #036-01-1990 L1994 **GYN** *020 †30

KELLY, Elizabeth Ann. 1100 TUNNEL RD, ASHEVILLE VA MEDICAL CENTE 28805 #001-06-2000 L2002 **P** *020

KENNEDY, Joseph L, III. 520 BILTMORE AVE, STE A 28801 #024-07-1990 L1993 **OBG** *020 †30

KENNEDY, Maureen E. 143 ASHELAND AVE 28801 #038-40-1990 L1994 **OBG** *071 †30

KENNEDY, Thomas Francis. 3002 TIMBER TRL 28804 #025-01-1968 L1974 **R** *071 †80

KENNERLY, R Michael. 445 BILTMORE AVE, STE 506 28801 #010-02-1972 L1975 **TS** *020 †90,85

KHOURY, Ada C. 12 1/2 WALL ST, STE Q 28801 #048-16-1988 L1989 **P ADP** *020 †75 ‡

KIEFFER, Henri L G, II. 84 COXE AVE, STE 2A 28801 #051-01-1980 L1986 **DR** *020 †80

KIEFFER, Robert Wilson. VA MEDICAL CENTER SURG SER 28805 #023-07-1978 L1987 **GS VS** *020 †85

KING, Ladene Joy. ■ 28805 #051-01-2006 **OBG** *012

KIRATZIS, Philip Stephen. 7 YORKSHIRE ST STE 201 28803 #001-02-1989 L1995 **CHP** *020

KIRBY, Lemuel Broome. 222 ASHELAND AVE 28801 #036-05-1992 L2004 **VS** *020 †85

KIRCHNER, Sandra G. ■ 28803 #035-20-1967 L1970 **PDR** *071 †80

KIRSCHKE, David Louis. 35 WOODFIN ST, BUNCOMBE COUNTY HEALTH CTR 28801 #011-03-1996 L1999 **FM** *020 †18

KITTNER, Philip Joel. 16 MCDOWELL ST 28801 #035-09-1964 L1971 **OBG** *071 †30

KLINE, Robert Stuart. 260 MERRIMON AVE, STE 200 28801 #040-02-1983 L1984 **FM** *020 †18

KOHATSU, Keith Yukihide. 1100 TUNNEL RD, DEPT RADIOLOGY VA MED CTR 28805 #016-01-1988 L1988 **R** *020 †80

KOONTZ, Jack Alexander. ■ 28803 #036-01-1964 L1964 **FM** *030 †18

KOVACH, Steven Leslie. 76 PEACHTREE RD, STE 300 28803 #048-02-1982 L1983 **AN** *020 †05

KOWA, Harald H. 509 BILTMORE AVE 28801 #011-03-1988 L1991 **PD** *020 †55

KRISEL, Chad Scott. 118 WT WEAVER BLVD, MAHEC FAMILY PRACTICE PGM 28804 #011-05-2006 L2007 **FP** *012

KROLL, Larry Le Roy. 53 S FRENCH BROAD AVE 28801 #005-12-1965 L1974 **ORS** *071 †40

KRUEGER, Alan Lee. 1100 TUNNEL RD 28805 #019-02-1967 L1978 **P GP** *020 †75

KRUPNICK, Jon Eder. 509 BILTMORE AVE, MEDICINE 28801 #045-04-1994 L1998 **EM** *020 †16

KUBITSCHEK, Kenneth R. 190 BILTMORE AVE, STE 5 28801 #048-04-1978 L1985 **IM** *020 †20

KUDVA, Vidya B. 68 SWEETEN CREEK RD 28803 #495-35-1978 L2002 **PM** *020 †60 ‡

KUEHL, William David. 509 BILTMORE AVE 28801 #018-03-1983 L1990 **CD IM** *020 †20

KUEHN, Eric Ford. 509 BILTMORE AVE 28801 #012-01-1990 L1994 **RO** *020 †80 ‡

KUHN, Charles Wilson. ■ 28804 #041-01-1954 L1955 **P** *071

KUMAR, Raj D. 1100 TUNNEL RD 28805 #495-94-1990 L2006 **IM** *020 †20

KUROWSKI, Cameron John. 206 ASHELAND AVE, ASHEVILLE FAMILY HEALTH CE 28801 #038-45-1995 L2002 **FM** *020 †18

KUTOB, Rabi Dean. 190 BILTMORE AVE, STE 5 28801 #003-01-1985 L1986 **FM** *020 †18

LACERNA, Mario Alcancia. ■ 28803 #748-07-1952 L1962 **PTH** *071 †50

LADD, James Duncan. 147 ASHELAND AVE 28801 #036-01-1983 L1990 **IM** *020 †20

LAFLEUR, Karie D. ■ 28806 #021-05-2006 **OBG** *012

LA GARDE, Douglas Chas. 11 VANDERBILT PARK DR, MISSION CHILDREN'S CLINICS 28803 #021-05-1969 L2006 **PD GE** *020 †55

LALOR, Allen Weeks. 509 BILTMORE AVE 28801 #036-01-1991 L1992 **EM** *020 †16

LAMBERT, Milton Bruce. 1100 TUNNEL RD, VA MEDICAL CENTER 28805 #056-05-1964 L1967 **ORS** *020 †40

LANDAU, Richard Lloyd. 509 BILTMORE AVE 28801 #051-04-1972 L1975 **PTH** *020 †50

LANDIS, Suzanne Elizabeth. 118 WEAVER BLVD 28804 #041-01-1978 L1984 **IM GPM** *020 †20,70

LANE, Ronald Wm. 1065 HENDERSONVILLE RD 28803 #032-01-1984 L1998 **OTO** *040 †45

LANE, Wendy Susan. 141 ASHELAND AVE, MNTN DIABETESAND ENDOCRINE 28801 #032-01-1984 L1998 **END** *020 †20

LANGFORD, Joseph Scott. 509 BILTMORE AVE 28801 #005-12-1997 L2000 **EM** *020 †16

LANGLOIS, John Philip. 68 SWEETEN CREEK RD, P.O. BOX 5779 28803 #023-07-1983 L1990 **FM** *040 †18

LANSING, Ann Meredith. 428 BILTMORE AVE 28801 #036-07-1981 L1984 **IM** *020 †20

LATESSA, Robyn Ann. 118 WT WEAVER BLVD, MAHEC 28804 #024-16-1994 L1995 **FM** *020 †18

LAUDERMAN ALMOINA, Jose A. ■ 28804 #847-06-1979 L1982 **DR** *020 †80

LAURENS, John. 445 BILTMORE AVE, STE 303 28801 #021-01-1944 L1975 **CRS** *071 †10

LAWRENCE, John Elmore. 5 VANDERBILT PARK DR 28803 #036-07-1972 L1974 **CD IM** *020 †20

LEACH, David Colvin. ■ 28804 #035-45-1969 L1970 **IM END** *020 †20

LEAKE, Arthur E, Jr. 445 BILTMORE AVE, STE 505 28801 #036-01-1966 L1966 **AN GP** *020 †05 ‡

LE BLANC, Michelle Anne. 100 RIDGEFIELD CT, SPECIALTY CENTER PA 28806 #048-14-1996 L1997 **OBG** *020 †30

LECHNER, Chris Todd. 20 MCDOWELL ST, CAROLINA HAND SURGERY ASSO 28801 #038-40-1986 L1991 **HS ORS** *020 †40

LE CROY, Charles Michael. 509 BILTMORE AVE, MEMORIAL MISSION HOSPITAL, 28801 #036-07-1989 L1990 **ORS OTR** *020 †40

LEDBETTER, John W. 509 BILTMORE AVE 28801 #036-05-1953 L1953 **N** *071

LEE, Il Sung. 123A ACTON CIR 28806 #583-10-1966 L1975 **IM GP** *020

LEETZ, Kenneth Laurence. 80 PEACHTREE RD, STE 104 28803 #012-05-1981 L1997 **P** *020 †75

LEHMAN, Nancy Carolyn. 14 S PACK SQ STE 362 28801 #045-01-1996 L2001 **P PYG** *020 †75

LENDERMAN, Mark Day. 206 ASHELAND AVE 28801 #051-01-1990 L1991 **FM** *020 †18

LENINGTON, Kenneth Taber. 80 PEACHTREE RD, STE 104 28803 #056-06-1977 L1984 **P** *020 †75 ‡

LEONARD, Jayne Bunton. 118 WT WEAVER BLVD 28804 #036-07-1990 L1991 **FM** *020 †18

LETSON, Austin Kellett. 41 OAKLAND RD, STE 200 28801 #036-01-1995 L1996 **OBG** *020 †30

LEWIS, Brian Ritchie. 118 WT WEAVER BLVD 28804 #036-01-2004 **FP** *012

LEWIS, William Lloyd. 509 BILTMORE AVE 28801 #045-01-1988 L1989 **EM** *020 †16

LI, John Chichang. 1100 TUNNEL RD, SURGICAL PROGRAM TEAM (112 28805 #026-04-1992 L2000 **GS** *020 †85

LICHTIG, Lisa Michelle. 207 CHARLOTTE ST, FAMILY TO FAMILY 28801 #025-01-1990 L1996 **FM** *020 †18

LIGON, Harold Belton. 428 BILTMORE AVE 28801 #045-01-1955 L1956 **FM GP** *071

LIM, Chang Sun. 5 VANDERBILT PARK DR 28803 #036-07-1992 L1996 **CD** *020 †20

LINCOLN, David O. 80 DEERHAVEN LN 28803 #035-06-1965 L1972 **ORS OS** *071 †40

LIND, Richard Norman. 1100 TUNNEL RD, ASHEVILLE VAMC 28805 #016-11-1977 L1990 **IM ON** *020 †20

LINDSEY, Julie Annette. 30 GARFIELD ST, STE D 28803 #045-04-1993 L1996 **P** *020 †75

LITTLETON, Frederick, Jr. 445 BILTMORE AVE, STE 407 28801 #041-01-1979 L1981 **IM** *020 †20

LITZENBERGER, Willard, Jr. 304 SUMMIT ST 28803 #020-12-1978 L1982 **NPM PD** *020 †55

LIVINGSTON, Lauren Joann. 118 WT WEAVER BLVD, MAHEC FAMILY PRACTICE PGM 28804 #036-07-2006 **FP** *012

LONG, Carol Ann. 500 CENTRE PARK DR 28805 #041-14-1985 L1988 **PD** *020 †55

LOVE, Douglas Scott. 64 PEACHTREE RD, STE 100 28803 #036-08-2000 L2003 **PD** *020 †55

LOWENBERGH, Laura W. 30 HENDERSONVILLE RD, 15 BILTMIRE CROSSING 28803 #038-40-1966 L1969 **P** *020 †75

LUCAS, Shantae Ladon. 445 BILTMORE AVE, STE 100 28801 #020-12-1991 L1998 **HO** *020 †20

LUCKE, John Chas. 1100 TUNNEL RD # 112, ASHEVILLE VA MED CTR 28805 #028-34-1985 L1992 **TS** *020 †90,85

LYLES, Evelyn Mc Master. 100 RIDGEFIELD CT, SPECIALTY CENTER PA 28806 #045-01-1981 L1985 **OBG** *020 †30

LYSKO, Jane Elizabeth. 509 BILTMORE AVE 28801 #036-01-1981 L1982 **PTH** *020 †50

LYTLE, Richard Allen, Jr. 7 VANDERBILT PARK DR, MOUNTAIN NEUROSURGICAL & S 28803 #001-02-1997 L2004 **NS** *020 †25

MACALUSO, Damien Charles. 8 MEDICAL PARK DR 28803 #005-18-1995 L2004 **OPH** *020 †35

MACDONALD, Andre John. 84 COXE AVE STE 2A, UNIVERSITY OF UTAH 28801 #836-02-1992 L2007 **RNR** *020 †80

MAC DOWELL, Brian T. 1070 TUNNEL RD, STE 100 28805 #051-01-1983 L1986 **FM** *020 †18

MACMILLAN, Douglas P. ■ 28804 #036-01-1998 L2006 **VS** *020 †85

MADDOX, Charles Deaton. 4 DOCTORS PARK STE B 28801 #012-01-1966 L1971 **IM** *020 †20

MADDOX, Wm Towers, Jr. 509 BILTMORE AVE 28801 #012-01-1977 L1982 **CD IM** *020 †20

MADISON, William M, Jr. ■ 28803 #012-05-1949 L1949 **CD IM** *071 †20

MAGNESS, Linda Kaye. ■ 28803 #020-02-1974 L1994 **R OS** *020 †80

MAILLIS, Maxwell Sherwood. ■ 28806 #016-02-1965 L1968 **CD IM** *020 †20 ‡

MAITLAND, Alexander. 1 DOCTORS PARK 28801 #008-01-1955 L1961 **U** *071 †95

MANGONE, Peter George. 60 LIVINGSTON ST, BLUE RIDGE BONE & JOINT 28801 #012-05-1993 L1999 **ORS GS** *020 †40

MARDER, Gerard. ■ 28801 #036-07-1952 L1954 **PD** *071 †55

MARNOCK, James Jerome. 942 TUNNEL RD, BLUE RDG FAM PRAC 28805 #048-14-1991 L1995 **FM** *020 †18

MARTIN, John Paul. 509 BILTMORE AVE, OCCUMED AND STAFF HEALTH 28801 #003-01-1976 L1982 **FM EM** *020 †18

MARX, William Foster, Jr. 222 ASHELAND AVE 28801 #051-01-1993 L2003 **RNR** *020 †80

MASHAW, Arsheeya. 118 WT WEAVER BLVD, MAHEC 28804 #036-05-2004 L2007 **FM** *100 †18

MAUTERER, David John. 14 MEDICAL PARK DR 28803 #023-01-1985 L1990 **GS** *020 †85

MAY, Lisa L. ■ 28801 #036-01-1993 L1995 **D** *020 †15

MAYNARD, Stuart Tyrus. 12 LOOKOUT RD E, BEVERLY HILLS 28805 #036-01-1973 L1973 **EM FM** *020 †18

MC ANALLY, Lon Wyatt, Jr. 77 MCDOWELL ST 28801 #021-05-1966 L1971 **PD** *075

MC ARTHUR, Holly Kristin. 41 OAKLAND RD, STE 200 28801 #011-03-1994 L1995 **OBG** *020 †30

MC CAIN, Trent Winslow. 30 CHOCTAW ST 28801 #036-05-1995 L1998 **PCC** *020 †20

MC CALL, William H. ■ 28804 #051-04-1938 L1938 **OPH OTO** *071

MC CARRICK, James Patrick. 30 CHOCTAW ST, ASHEVILLE PULMONARY ASSOCI 28801 #010-02-1983 L1991 **IM PCC** *020 †20

MC CLAIN, David John. 53 S FRENCH BROAD AVE 28801 #036-01-1982 L1997 **ID IM** *050 †55,20

MCCLAIN, Ferrell Ann. 501 BILTMORE AVE 28801 #539-06-2005 L2006 **FP** *012

MC COLLOUGH, William Mark. 509 BILTMORE AVE 28801 #011-03-1985 L2003 **RO** *020 †80 ‡

MC CONNELL, Mary H. 509 BILTMORE AVE 28801 #010-01-1950 L1955 **PD** *071

MC COY, Timothy Haskell. ■ 28803 #048-13-1975 L1976 **AN** *020

MC CULLOUGH, Chas T, Jr. 129 MCDOWELL ST 28801 #047-05-1961 L1971 **ORS** *020 †40

MC CUTCHEON, Frank B, Jr. 131 MCDOWELL ST, STE 200 28801 #004-01-1978 L1982 **PS** *020 †65

MC CUTCHEON, Julia Winn. 2 WALL ST, STE 108 28801 #036-01-1987 L1992 **P** *020 †75

MC DONOUGH, James Michael. 5 LIVINGSTON ST 28801 #016-06-1967 L1976 **PS** *020 †85,65 ‡

MC GHEE, Terrence Barclay. 20 MCDOWELL ST 28801 #012-01-1976 L1978 **N** *020 †75

MCGOVERN, James Jos. 5 VANDERBILT PARK DR 28803 #038-40-1990 L1997 **PDC** *020 †55

MC GUIRE, John O'Brien. 14 MEDICAL PARK DR 28803 #036-07-1971 L1978 **GS** *071 †85

MC INTOSH, John Clarke. 131 MCDOWELL ST STE 203, PED PULM & SLEEP DISORDERS 28801 #045-01-1981 L2001 **PDP PD** *020 †55

MC INTYRE, Ross Wm P. 1100 TUNNEL RD, VA MEDICAL CENTER 28805 #061-01-1970 L1979 **AN GS** *020 †05

MC KAY, Judythe Schott. 158 ZILLICOA ST 28801 #045-04-1996 L2007 **CHP** *020 †75

MC KENNA, William Raymond. 53 S FRENCH BROAD AVE 28801 #041-01-1978 L1984 **ID IM** *020 †20

MC KIBBIN, William Keith. 60 LIVINGSTON ST, BLUE RIDGE BONE & JOINT 28801 #001-02-1991 L1998 **ORS OFA** *020 †40

MC MILLAN, James Hinton. 206 ASHELAND AVE 28801 #012-01-1977 L1978 **FM FSM** *020 †18

MC MURDO, Strathmore K, Jr. 675 BILTMORE AVE STE A, STE A 28803 #014-01-1976 L1997 **DR** *020 †80

MC TAMMANY, John Robt. 1812 HENDERSONVILLE RD 28803 #036-07-1961 L1961 **FM** *071 †30

MEADOR, Toni Lynn. 222 ASHELAND AVE 28801 #036-05-1993 L1999 **DR** *020 †80

MENDELSOHN, Steven Louis. 2 MEDICAL PARK DR, STE 700 28803 #035-45-1978 L1979 **RHU IG** *020 †20

MESSERSMITH, Ann Kathryn. ■ 28804 #041-14-1986 L1988 **FM** *020 †18

MESSINO, Michael Jos. 445 BILTMORE AVE STE 100 28801 #038-40-1979 L1983 **ON HO** *020 †20

METCALF, Lawrence E. ■ 28805 #016-06-1943 L1944 **PD** *071 †55

MEYER, Christopher George. 445 BILTMORE AVE STE 306 28801 #003-01-2003 L2006 **RHU** *012 †20

MEYER, John Andrew. 76 PEACHTREE RD, STE 300 28803 #011-03-1983 L1986 **AN** *020 †05

MICHALETS, James Patrick. 1100 TUNNEL RD, VA DEPT OF PSYCHIATRY 28805 #056-05-1990 L1993 **P** *020 †75

MIDKIFF, Paul Andrew. 118 WT WEAVER BLVD, PRACTICE PROGRAM 28804 #020-12-2004 L2006 **FM** *100 †18

MILLER, Ansley Carnochan. 11 VANDERBILT PARK DR, MISSION CHILDREN'S HOSP 28803 #012-01-2004 L2007 **PD** *020 †55

MILLS, Craig A. 60 LIVINGSTON ST, STE 200 28801 #038-41-1974 L1980 **GP** *020 †20

MILTON, David Thos. 84 COXE AVE STE 2A, MAILING: P O BOX 2959 28801 #047-06-1981 L1986 **DR** *020 †80

MIMS, Dawson A, III. 417 BILTMORE AVE, PRIME DOC 5-G DOCTORS PARK 28801 #036-01-1997 L2000 **IM** *020 †20

MIMS, Susan Rupp. 11 VANDERBILT PARK DR 28803 #036-01-1994 L1995 **MPD PD** *020 †20,70,55

MINKIN, Bruce Irving. 20 MCDOWELL ST, CAROLINA HAND SURGERY 28801 #047-06-1980 L1987 **HS** *020 †40

MINNICH, Kendal Bragg. 206 ASHELAND AVE, ASHEVILLE FAMILY HEALTH 28801 #011-02-1992 L1994 **FM** *020 †18

MITCHELL, Chas Henry, IV. 191 BILTMORE AVE 28801 #023-07-1967 L1995 **PG GE** *071 †55

MITCHELL, Meredith Evelyn. 93 VICTORIA RD, MAHEC WOMEN'S HEALTH CENTE 28801 #045-01-2004 L2007 **OBG** *012

MOFFATT, Robert Carr. 86 VICTORIA RD 28801 #047-06-1957 L1965 **SO OS** *020 †85

MOID, Mohammad Imran. ■ 28803 #704-25-1990 L2003 **HO** *100 †20

MONTGOMERY, James H, III. 222 ASHELAND AVE 28801 #047-06-1978 L1985 **R IM** *020 †20,80 ‡

MONTGOMERY, Wayne Swope. 129 MCDOWELL ST DEPT ORS 28801 #025-07-1948 L1955 **ORS** *020 †40

MOORE, David Elden. 222 ASHELAND AVE 28801 #036-05-1986 L1990 **DR VIR** *020 †80

MOORE, Edward Eugene. 428 BILTMORE AVE 28801 #024-01-1942 L1947 **OPH** *071 †35

MOORE, Pierce J, Jr. 509 BILTMORE AVE 28801 #005-12-1944 L1947 **GS GP** *071

MOORE, Robert Brian. 1065 HENDERSONVILLE RD 28803 #047-20-1999 L2005 **OTO** *020 †45

MORANO, James Ugo. 1100 TUNNEL RD, DEPT OF IMAGING 28805 #027-01-1978 L1978 **VIR R** *020 †80

MOREADITH, Jeffrey H. 35 LAKEWOOD DR, ASHEVILLE HOSPITALIST GROU 28803 #036-07-1992 L1994 **MPD** *020 †55,20

MORELOCK, Sandra Yvette. 30 CHOCTAW ST, CARE ASSOCIATES, PA 28801 #047-06-1992 L1998 **PCC** *020 †20

MORETZ, Frank Hannon. 76 PEACHTREE RD, STE 300 28803 #036-01-1974 L1976 **AN** *020 †05

MORGAN, Christine Marie. 131 MCDOWELL ST, STE 100 28801 #045-01-1993 L1998 **PD** *020 †55

MORGAN, James Sill, Jr. 428 BILTMORE AVE 28801 #035-20-1982 L1988 **GE IM** *020 †20

MORGENSTERN, Eva Louise. ■ 28804 #008-02-1976 L1988 **N IM** *020 †20,75

MORRIS, Andrew James. 118 WT WEAVER BLVD 28804 #048-04-2003 L2004 **FM** *100 †18

MORRIS, Arthur Sherman. ■ 28806 #036-01-1959 L1959 **OBG** *071 †30

MORRIS, Kimberly Krepp. 701 BILTMORE AVE 28803 #011-03-1993 L1994 **FM** *020 †18

MORRISON, Roger W. 40 OAKLAWN AVE 28804 #024-01-1943 L1951 **PTH** *071 †50

MOSER, Artus Monroe, Jr. 10 MCDOWELL ST 28801 #036-01-1964 L1966 **NEP IM** *020 †20

MOUW, David Richard. 118 WT WEAVER BLVD 28804 #025-01-1983 L1986 **FM FPG** *071 †18

MULFORD, Thomas Broderick. 76 PEACHTREE RD, STE 300 28803 #023-01-1987 L2002 **AN** *020 †05

MULLENDORE, Jennifer L. 35 WOODFIN ST, BUNCOMBE COUNTY HEATH 28801 #010-02-2003 L2006 **FM** *020 †18

MULLINS, Diane Louise. 509 BILTMORE AVE 28801 #038-44-1987 L1998 **DMP PTH** *020 †50

MULLIS, Donald Lee. 111 VICTORIA RD, ASSOCIATES SOUTHERN ORTHO 28801 #011-02-1972 L1973 **ORS** *020 †40 ‡

MURCKO, Lisa Cleopatra. 5 LIVINGSTON ST 28801 #041-07-1988 L1995 **PS FPS** *020 †65

MURPHY, James Jos, Jr. VET ADMIN HOSP, DEPT RAD 28805 #008-01-1964 L1968 **R** *020 †80

MURRAY, Chas Forrest, Jr. 35 WOODFIN ST 28801 #036-01-1976 L1976 **FM** *020

MUSGROVE, Holly Christine. 206 ASHELAND AVE, ASHEVILLE FAMILY HEALTH 28801 #038-45-1995 L1996 **FM** *020 †18

MUSTOE, Margaret Hope. 64 PEACHTREE RD 28803 #005-11-1987 L1991 **PD** *020 †55

NAISANG, Forth Robt. VA MEDICAL CTR 28805 #012-05-1965 L1967 **IM** *020

NARRON, Gregory Harold. 932 HENDERSONVILLE RD, STE 101 28803 #036-08-1988 L1993 **P CHP** *020 †75

NEBLETT, Donald Thos. 20 ALL SOULS CRES 28803 #047-06-1958 L1978 **P** *072 †55

NEIMKIN, Ronald Jay. 53 S FRENCH BROAD AVE 28801 #035-20-1975 L1977 **HS ORS** *020 †40

NELSON, G Dudley. 155 LIVINGSTON ST, ABCCM MEDICAL CLINIC 28801 #035-03-1944 L1976 **FM PHP** *071

NELSON, William M. ■ 28805 #045-01-1953 L1953 **IM OS** *030

NESHAT, Amir Ali. 1220 HENDERSONVILLE RD 28803 #517-06-1960 L1974 **ON** *020 †85

NEUMANN, Jennifer Lynn. 118 WT WEAVER BLVD 28804 #033-05-2006 L2008 **FP** *012

NGUYEN, David. ■ 28806 #011-03-2007 **FP** *012

NICHOLS, Robert L. ■ 28805 #016-02-1958 L1965 **PTH NM** *071 †50

NICOLINI, Jennifer C. 60 LIVINGSTON ST STE 200 28801 #036-08-1999 L2004 **MPD** *020 †20,55

NIELAND, Melissa J. 501 BILTMORE AVE, DEPT FM 28801 #048-12-2007 **FP** *012

NOEL, Margaret Anne. 100 FAR HORIZONS LN 28803 #036-01-1983 L1984 **IM IMG** *020 †20

NOH, Jung Ja Kim. 1100 TUNNEL RD, ASHEVILLE VA MC 28805 #583-08-1968 L1980 **PM SCI** *020 †60

NOTO, Joseph Anthony. 520 BILTMORE AVE, ASHEVILLE SURGICAL ASSOC P 28801 #041-01-1961 L1970 **GS CD** *020 †85,90

NOVOSELSKY, Seth Perry. 1100 TUNNEL RD 28805 #021-05-1963 L1963 **U** *071 †95

NURRE, Lisa Denise. 29 RAVENSCROFT DR, STE 3 28801 #038-45-1994 L1995 **D** *020 †15

O'CONNOR, Patrick L. ■ 28803 #035-06-1973 L1974 **ORS** *071 †40

O'DONNELL, Brian Peter. 500 CENTRE PARK DR 28805 #016-43-1999 L2006 **PD** *020 †55

OGDEN, William Singleton. 1100 TUNNEL RD 28805 #012-01-1965 L1967 **ORS** *020 †40

OGILVIE, Walter E, III. ■ 28805 #035-01-1945 L1951 **IM** *071

OLACK, Jerome Andrew. 1100 TUNNEL RD 28805 #041-13-1967 L1978 **R NM** *020 †80

OLBRANTZ, Keith Richard. 222 ASHELAND AVE 28801 #056-05-1982 L1983 **DR** *020 †80

OLINGER, Benjamin Ray. 1065 HENDERSONVILLE RD 28803 #051-01-1960 L2001 **OTO** *071 †45

OXNER, Claudia Gertrude. ■ 28803 #045-01-1956 L1960 **AN** *071

PAGE, Donna Ann. 2 MEDICAL PARK DR, STE 1000 28803 #036-05-1988 L1996 **PD** *020 †55

PALMERI, Russell Francis. ■ 28803 #010-02-1980 L1987 **OBG** *071 †30

PARHAM, John Vernon, Jr. 1100 TUNNEL RD, VETS ADM MED CTR 28805 #027-01-1978 L1983 **AN** *020

PARKS, Norman Howard. 2 MEDICAL PARK DR, STE 1000 28803 #035-15-1963 L1977 **PD** *071 †55

PARKS, Ronald R. 20 SPRING HOLLOW CIR 28805 #023-01-1969 L2000 **P IM** *020 †18,75

PASCHAL, Barton Riley. 20 MEDICAL PARK DR, CANCER CENTERS OF NORTH CA 28803 #012-05-1976 L1980 **ON HEM** *020 †20

PASCHALL, John Spruill. 64 PEACHTREE RD 28803 #036-08-1997 L1998 **PD** *020 †55

PATE, Barry Reeves. 675 BILTMORE AVE STE H 28803 #036-01-1958 L1959 **OTO** *071

PATE, Barry Reeves, Jr. 675 BILTMORE AVE 28803 #036-05-1991 L1997 **OTO** *020 †45

PATRIE, Lewis E. 356 BILTMORE AVE 28801 #035-03-1952 L1980 **P PHP** *071 †70,75

PATTON, James Matthew. 1200 RIDGEFIELD BLVD, STE 250 28806 #012-05-1989 L1991 **N** *020 †75

PAYNE, Winston Chas. 900 CENTRE PARK DR, STE A 28805 #025-01-1967 L1974 **OPH** *020 †35

PAYTON, James Bayard. 64 MERRIMON AVE 28801 #038-41-1973 L1989 **CHP P** *020 †75

PEKAL, Wieslawa. 445 BILTMORE AVE, STE 100 28801 #035-08-1990 L1998 **HO** *020 †20

PENN, Robert Lee. 1998 HENDERSONVILLE RD, STE 45 28803 #005-12-1988 L2007 **FM** *020 †18 ‡

PERINO, Lisa Maria. 8 NEW LEICESTER HWY 28806 #016-11-1991 L2002 **FM** *020 †18

PESTOFF, Marianne Rose. 2 YORKSHIRE ST 28803 #017-20-1995 L1996 **OBG** *020 †30

PETERSON, Christopher Bri. 428 BILTMORE AVE 28801 #036-01-2002 L2006 **P** *020 †75

PETERSON, Eric Webster. 77 CHURCH ST 28801 #036-07-1971 L1971 **P** *020 †75

PETERSON, Neil P. 222 ASHELAND AVE 28801 #016-06-1979 L1982 **DR NM** *020 †80

PETERSON, Susan Wynn. 304A NEW LEICESTER HWY, LEICESTER MEDICAL CLINIC, 28806 #036-01-1995 L2001 **FM** *020 †18

PHILLIPS, Betsy Coward. ■ 28803 #036-01-1982 L1983 **IM** *075 †20

PHILLIPS, Herbert O, IV. ■ 28803 #036-01-1981 L1982 **ORS** *020 †40 ‡

PICKENS, John Palmer. 7 WALDEN RIDGE DR STE 200 28803 #047-20-1983 L1985 **OTO PS** *020 †45

PIERSON, John Duane. 119 TUNNEL RD STE D, OCTOBER ROAD 28805 #047-06-1960 L2004 **P** *020 †75 ‡

PIKUS, Harold Jason. 7 VANDERBILT PARK DR, MOUNTAIN NEUROSURGICAL & S 28803 #023-01-1991 L2001 **NS** *020 †25

PIXLEY, Jane Elizabeth. 2 MEDICAL PARK DR, STE 1000 28803 #036-05-1989 L1993 **PD** *020 †55

PLAUT, Timothy Arnold. 260 MERRIMON AVE, STE 200 28801 #036-08-1995 L1996 **FM** *020 †18

PLEMMONS, Ronald L. 495 BILTMORE AVE, OCUMED/STAFF HEALTH 28801 #036-05-1977 L1977 **OM FM** *020 †18

POLANSKY, Meredith A. 118 WT WEAVER BLVD 28804 #011-03-2004 **FP** *012

POPE, Fergus Bailey. 356 BILTMORE AVE 28801 #917-20-1963 L1969 **P OS** *071

POPLAWSKI, Tadeusz F. 11 VANDERBILT PARK DR 28803 #847-11-1985 L1996 **CHN** *020 †75

PORTER, Cedric Warren, Jr. 1 BEAVERDAM CT 28804 #035-01-1964 L1970 **OBG PHP** *020 †70,30

POSTON, Harold C, Jr. 509 BILTMORE AVE 28801 #045-01-1980 L1991 **PTH** *020 †50

■ = Address Information Privacy Protected

POWELL, Benjamin Philip. 445 BILTMORE AVE, STE 505 28801 #001-02-1971 L1979
AN *071 †05 ‡

POWELL, Jack. 428 BILTMORE AVE 28801 #005-12-1947 L1950 GS *020 †85

POWELL, James B, II. 1065 HENDERSONVILLE RD 28803 #001-02-1965 L1973
OTO FPS *020 †45

POZNER, Robert Stanley. 445 BILTMORE AVE STE 305 28801 #036-08-1984 L1987 IM *020 †20

PRESTON, Andrea Leigh. ■ 28805 #025-12-2006 FP *012

PRITCHARD, Robert Jos. 30 CHOCTAW ST 28801 #025-07-1989 L1995 PUD *020 †20

PUCKETT, James Butler. 20 MEDICAL PARK DR, ASSOCIATES 28803 #036-01-1974 L1974
IM HO *020 †20

PUGH, Basil L. 76 PEACHTREE RD STE 300, MEDOASIS, INC. 28803 #055-01-1982 L1995
AN AM *020 †05

PUGH, Rodney Vance. 76 PEACHTREE RD, STE 300 28803 #036-01-1986 L1989 AN *020 †05

PYERITZ, Eric Al. 1 UNIVERSITY HTS, UNCA STUDNT HLTH CPO 2710 28804
#041-12-1978 L1980 FM *020 †18

QUARANTA, Brian Patrick. 445 BILTMORE AVE, STE G102 28801 #033-05-1998 L2002
RO *020 †80 ‡

QUIGLEY, Steven Lawrence. 111 MCDOWELL ST, BETHESDA SURGICAL PC 28801
#010-01-1984 L2003 GS *020 †85

RAJKUMAR, Sarala. 1100 TUNNEL RD, VA MEDICAL CENTER 28805 #495-42-1998 L2006
IM *020 †20

RAMMING, Scott Anthony. 509 BILTMORE AVE, MISSION HOSPITALS 28801
#050-02-1994 L1998 EM *050 †20

RAMSEY, Jamie Lauren. ■ 28804 #012-01-2006 *012

RANKIN, Chas Albert, Jr. 509 BILTMORE AVE 28801 #041-02-1954 L1967 OBG *071

RAO, Gururaj K. VA MED CTR 28805 #495-04-1958 L1972 DR *020

RAPPAPORT, Jonathan Meier. 141 ASHELAND AVE, MOUNTAIN DIABETES AND ENDO 28801
#021-05-2000 L2006 END *020 †55

RARDIN, Duff Andrew. 86 VICTORIA RD 28801 #036-05-1986 L1990 N *020 †75 ‡

RARDIN, Thomas E, Jr. 428 BILTMORE AVE 28801 #038-06-1962 L1968 RHU IM *071

RATHBUN, John Malcolm. 158 ZILLICOA ST 28801 #041-12-1973 L2005 P *020 †55 ‡

RATHBUN, Lewis S. 428 BILTMORE AVE 28801 #024-01-1939 L1947 GYN *071 †30

RATHBURN, Stephen D. ■ 28805 #038-44-1982 L2002 AN *020 †05

RAY, Lisa Anne. 118 WT WEAVER BLVD 28804 #012-05-1992 L2001 FM *020 †18

READLING, Thos Alexander. 77 MCDOWELL ST 28801 #036-05-1960 L1960 PD *071

RENNARD, Thomas Wm. 147 ASHELAND AVE 28801 #025-01-1990 L1992 IM *020 †20

RENTZ, Simms Hunter, Jr. 304 SUMMIT ST 28803 #045-01-1983 L2004 NPM *020 †55

RERYCH, Stephen Karl. 5 DOCTORS PARK STE A, BILTMORE SURGICAL ASSOC., 28801
#035-01-1974 L1986 GS VS *020 †85

REYNOLDS, Robert Jack. 445 BILTMORE AVE 28801 #047-06-1980 L1984 IM *020

RHOLL, Vicky L. 509 BILTMORE AVE 28801 #026-04-1989 L2000 PTH *020 †50

RICE, Lucian Candler, Jr. 509 BILTMORE AVE 28801 #012-05-1970 L1973 IM *020 †20

RICE, Roberta G. ■ 28801 #026-04-1944 L1951 OS GS *071 †85

RITTER, Melita A. 76 PEACHTREE RD, STE 300 28803 #038-43-1988 L1992 AN PMM *020 †05

RIVERS, Carole Weatherly. 1100 TUNNEL RD # 116, ASHEVILLE VA MEDICAL CENTE 28805
#036-08-1992 L1993 P *020 †75

ROBERTS, Elisa Macy. 3 WALDEN RIDGE DR STE 200 28803 #035-09-1982 L1986 D *020 †15

ROBERTS, Joseph Edward. 4 DOCTORS PARK STE A 28801 #016-06-1956 L1985 P *020

ROBERTS, Kevin Jay. 3 WALDEN RIDGE DR STE 200 28803 #035-19-1980 L1986 IM P *020

ROBERTSON, Brison O, III. 41 OAKLAND RD 28801 #001-06-1980 L1981 FM *020 †18

ROBERTSON, Vida Barnwell. 12 1/2 WALL ST, STE M 28801 #036-01-2001 L2006 CHP *020

ROBINSON, Amy Danielle. 509 BILTMORE AVE 28801 #035-48-2001 L2005 OBG *020

ROBINSON, Kathy Sue. 87 CLINTON AVE, BUNCOMBE COUNTY HEALTH CEN 28806
#036-01-1989 L1995 FM *020 †18

RODGERS, James P. ■ 28801 #043-01-1986 L1987 P *020 †75

RODINE, Mary Kim. 445 BILTMORE AVE STE 501, ADM OFF 28801 #016-11-1980 L1983
IM *071 †20

ROGERS, David York. 115 1/2 MOUNT CARMEL RD 28806 #041-09-1977 L1983 FM *020 †18

ROGERS, George Carraway. ■ 28813 #023-01-1943 L1943 OBG OS *020

ROOS, Steven David. 76 PEACHTREE RD, STE 300 28803 #007-02-1984 L1987 AN *020 †05

ROS, Stephanie Teresa. ■ 28803 #011-03-2007 *012

ROSAL, Peter Hugo. ■ 28802 #038-40-2001 L2007 DR *020 †80,28

ROSENBERG, Eugene Barry. ■ 28803 #024-01-1965 L1973 DR IM *030 †80

ROSENBERG, Joel Benj. 445 BILTMORE AVE STE 305 28801 #047-01-1972 L1977 IM *020 †20

ROSS, Polly Ellison. 10 RIDGELAWN RD, WNC COMMUNITY HEALTH SVC 28806
#036-05-1989 L1990 FM *020 †18

ROTH, Kenneth. ■ 28803 #035-20-1951 L1986 IM GE *071 †20

ROTMAN, Harold Harvey. VA MED CTR, DEPT MED 28805 #065-01-1958 L1985 PUD IM *030

ROWE, Charles Thos. 222 ASHELAND AVE 28801 #051-01-1968 L1975 R *020 †80 ‡

ROWE, David Foster. 69 MCDOWELL ST, TRIDENT PAIN CENTER, PA 28801 #047-06-2000 L2005
APM *100 ‡

ROWE, John Edward. 118 WT WEAVER BLVD 28804 #050-02-1977 L1992 FM *020 †18

ROYSTER, Randolph Lewis. 445 BILTMORE AVE, STE G102 28801 #051-01-1966 L1974
RO *020 †80

RUNKLE, Andrew William. 118 WT WEAVER BLVD 28804 #041-15-1999 L2000 FM *020 †18

RUSSELL, Annemarie I. 39 EASTMOOR DR 28805 #012-01-1989 L1999 P *020 †75

RUSSELL, Jeffrey Kent. 750 ALLIANCE CT 28806 #051-01-1972 L1977 DIA END *020 †20

RUSSELL, John Hunter. 5 VANDERBILT PARK DR 28803 #051-01-1963 L1971 CD IM *071 †20

RUSSELL, Philip E. ■ 28803 #036-07-1950 L1954 IM PUD *071 †20

SABO, John Tunnel. 1100 TUNNEL RD, SURGICAL SERVICE 28805 #025-07-1985 L1985
AN PME *020 †20,05

SAENGER, Paul Lentz. 129 MCDOWELL ST, BLUE RIDGE BONE & JOINT 28801
#036-01-1976 L1976 ORS *020 †40

SALTZMAN, Carole. 24 MEDICAL PARK DR, BILTMORE OB GYN 28803 #005-11-1988 L1994
GYN *020 †30 ‡

SALYERS, Martha Jane. 35 WOODFIN ST, BUNCOMBE CNTY HLTH CTR 28801
#025-12-1982 L1984 FM *020 †18

SANCHEZ, Fernando A. 1100 TUNNEL RD, VA MEDICAL CENTER 28805 #308-02-1989 L1999
IM *020 †20

SANDLER, Adrian David. 11 VANDERBILT PARK DR 28803 #917-03-1982 L1987
ADL PD *020 †20

SANDRIDGE, David Allen. 2 YORKSHIRE ST 28803 #051-04-1965 L1966 GYN REN *071 †30

SANTIN, Amy Jo. ■ 28801 #036-01-2007 FP *012

SAUNDERS, Wade H, III. 5 VANDERBILT PARK DR 28803 #036-07-1967 L1969 CD IM *020 †20

SCHEER, Thomas Frederick. 87 FOREST RD 28803 #012-01-1979 L1992 RO *020 †80

SCHELL, Robert Eugene. ■ 28804 #047-05-1940 L1940 IM IMG *071

SCHERR, Kent John. 16 MCDOWELL ST 28801 #037-01-1996 L1997 OBG *020 †30

SCHMIDT, Troy Gregory. 129 MCDOWELL ST 28801 #012-05-2001 L2007 ORS *100

SCHMITT, Philip Julian. 428 BILTMORE AVE 28801 #010-02-1980 L1985 P CHP *020 †75

SCHNEIDER, Alexander Taro. 509 BILTMORE AVE, MISSION NEUROLOGY 28801
#020-12-1997 L2004 N *020 †75

SCHRIEFER, Walter Henry. 509 BILTMORE AVE, CAROLINA MOUNTAIN EMERGENC 28801
#051-07-1989 L1992 EM *020 †16

SCHROEDER, David Paul. 5 VANDERBILT PARK DR 28803 #038-40-1973 L1995 CD IM *020 †20

SCHROEDER, Karl Vincent. 1100 TUNNEL RD, VA MEDICAL CENTER 28805
#020-12-1984 L1986 P *020 †75

SCHULHOF, Lary Alan. 7 VANDERBILT PARK DR 28803 #017-20-1969 L1974 NS *071 †25

SCHUTTE, Harold Delano. 53 S FRENCH BROAD AVE, ASTON PARK CENTER 28801
#005-12-1962 L1963 PD *040 †55 ‡

SCHWAB, Jodi Erin. 43 OAKLAND RD 28801 #020-12-1999 L2000 FM *020 †18

SCHWARTZ, Arthur. ■ 28804 #035-20-1946 L1973 IM *071 †20

SCOTHORN, Douglas James. 11 VANDERBILT PARK DR 28803 #047-05-1997 L2006
PHO *020 †55

SCOTT, Duncan Robert, II. 1200 RIDGEFIELD BLVD, STE 155 28806 #045-01-1993 L1998
APM *020 †55

SECHLER, Joseph Wm. 2 MEDICAL PARK DR, STE 1000 28803 #011-03-1990 L2005
PD PDP *020 †55

SERFAS, David Hill. 509 BILTMORE AVE 28801 #035-20-1977 L1983 CD IM *020 †20

SEWELL, Constance Jones. 946 TUNNEL RD 28805 #036-01-1987 L1998 FM *020 †18 ‡

SEXTON, James Kermit. ■ 28804 #035-05-1959 L1959 DR NM *071 †80,28

SHAFFER, Stephen Roger. 1 N PACK SQ STE 402 28801 #036-01-1963 L1963
ORS LM *020 †40

SHARPE, Eugene Baxter. ■ 28804 #016-06-1952 L1952 R NM *071 †80

SHAVER, Glyndon B, Jr. VA HOSPITAL 28805 #047-06-1961 L1983 ORS HS *071 †40

SHEELEY, Regan Robert. 136 MIMOSA DR 28806 #045-01-1993 L1996 FM *020 †18

SHELTON, Phyllis Estelle. 509 BILTMORE AVE, 509 BILTMORE AVE 28801 #051-07-1983 L2000
EM PD *020 †55,16

SHEPHERD-NOBLE, Billie A. 260 MERRIMON AVE, STE 200 28801 #020-12-1992 L1994
FM *020 †18

SHEPPARD-LA BRECQUE, V. 11 VANDERBILT PARK DR 28803 #016-11-1987 L1997
PD *020 †55

SHERMAN, Jonathan Douglas. 7 VANDERBILT PARK DR, SPINE CENTER, P.A. 28803
#017-20-1995 L2001 NS *020 †25

SHIVERS, James Allison. 84 COXE AVE STE 2A 28801 #036-01-1971 L1971 DR NM *020 †80

SHOOK, Earl L, Jr. FF3 CROWFIELDS DR 28803 #035-09-1952 L1958 U *071 †95

SHORT, John Gregory. 222 ASHELAND AVE 28801 #051-01-1993 L2001 RNR *020 †80

SHUFORD, Fuller Adams. 191 BILTMORE AVE 28801 #036-01-1962 L1962 GE IM *071 †20

SIDDALL, John Brane. ■ 28803 #038-40-1956 L1956 AN *071 †05

SIDES, Judith L Mc Kay. ■ 28805 #024-07-1967 L1970 ADL GPM *075

SIEGERT, Claudine E. 5 DOCTORS PARK STE E 28801 #017-20-1995 L2001 GS *020 †85

SIGMON, Kiran Ruth. 900 HENDERSONVILLE RD 28801 #036-08-1996 L1997 OBG *020 †30

SIMMONS, Charles Numa. ■ 28803 #045-01-1955 L1978 R NR *071 †80

SIMON, Della Jayne. 445 BILTMORE AVE, STE 407 28801 #041-04-1998 L2001 IM *020 †20

SIMPKINS, Kenny Leon. 100 VICTORIA RD, VICTORIA UROLOGICAL ASSOC 28801
#048-02-1982 L1988 U *020 †95

SIMPSON, George A. ■ 28803 #035-20-1951 L1976 GP FOP *071

SLEATER, Joseph Patrick. 509 BILTMORE AVE 28801 #017-20-1990 L1996 DMP *020 †50

SLEIGHT, Burdette K. 84 COXE AVE STE 2A, P O BOX 2959 28801 #012-01-1991 L2007
PDR *020 †80

SLOAN, James Marshall. 942 TUNNEL RD 28805 #036-07-1956 L1956 GP IM *071 †18

SMALLWOOD, James Clayton. 900 HENDERSONVILLE RD 28803 #012-01-1975 L1983
OBG *020 †30 ‡

SMART, Leslie Albert, Jr. ■ 28806 #005-12-1954 L1962 GP *071

SMATHERS, Sesalie L. 509 BILTMORE AVE 28801 #036-01-1996 L2001 RO *020 †80

SMITH, Brian Edward. 8 MEDICAL PARK DR 28803 #012-01-1993 L1997 OPH *020 †35

SMITH, Craig Thos. ■ 28804 #035-05-1959 L1995 OTO A *071 †45

SMITH, Daniel Judson. 281 MCDOWELL ST, WNC DERMATOLOGICAL ASSOCIA 28803
#045-01-1990 L1995 D *020 †15

SMITH, Ellison Leon, Jr. 445 BILTMORE AVE, STE 306 28801 #036-01-1993 L1999
RHU *020 †20

SMITH, Everett D. 206 ASHELAND AVE 28801 #005-12-1953 L1954 GP *071

SMITH, Jason Isaac. 222 ASHELAND AVE 28801 #055-01-1995 L2000 DR *020 †80

SMITH, John Mc Neill, III. 76 PEACHTREE RD, STE 300 28803 #036-01-1980 L1981 AN *020 †05

SMITH, Kiernan Adams. 501 BILTMORE AVE 28801 #539-06-2005 L2006 FP *012

SMITH, Myron Wallace, III. 129 MCDOWELL ST 28801 #021-05-1990 L1995 ORS *020 †40

SMITH, Thomas Allen. ■ 28804 #047-06-1955 L1961 P *020

SNEED, Shelley Melinda. 41 CHILES AVE 28803 #012-01-1983 L1991 PFP P *020 †75

SNODDY, William Ray. 41 OAKLAND RD 28801 #001-02-1975 L1977 FM FPG *020 †18

SOOSAAR, Peeter Agu. 14 MEDICAL PARK DR 28803 #021-05-1987 L1992 GS *020 †85

SORENSEN, Elizabeth Anne. 39 CHOCTAW ST, VICKERY FAMILY MEDICINE 28801
#012-05-2003 L2005 FM *100 †18

SOUFAS, Marianne Clare. 260 MERRIMON AVE, STE 200 28801 #035-48-1992 L1994
FM *020 †18

SOUZA, Joseph John. 5 VANDERBILT PARK DR 28803 #056-06-1990 L1991 CD ICE *020 †20

SPEED, James Kirven. 750 ALLIANCE CT 28806 #039-01-1982 L2001 END IM *020 †20

SPENCER, Heather E. 206 ASHELAND AVE, ASHEVILLE FAMILY HEALTH 28801
#032-01-1977 L1978 EM *020 †16

SPENCER, John Paul. 111 VICTORIA RD 28801 #005-19-1972 L1976 ORS *071 †40

SPROUSE, Jason Todd. 509 BILTMORE AVE 28801 #036-01-1996 L2001 PTH *020 †50

SQUIRES, Raymond Jay, II. ■ 28803 #012-05-1969 L1972 PTH *020 †50

STAHLY, Thomas La Mar. ■ 28803 #017-20-1967 L2001 DR *020 †80

STALEY, Michael Curtis. 1 DOCTORS PARK, ASHEVILLE UROLOGICAL ASSOC 28801
#045-01-1994 L2000 U *020 †95

STALFORD, Kimberly F. 509 BILTMORE AVE 28801 #051-01-1992 L2007 P *020 †75

STANLEY, David Michael. 76 PEACHTREE RD, STE 300 28803 #025-01-1988 L1992 AN *020 †05

STANLEY, Thos Eugene, III. 76 PEACHTREE RD 28803 #036-07-1981 L1988 AN GS *020 †05

STANTON, Elizabeth. 6 ROBERTS RD, CROSSROADS TREATMENT CENTE 28803
#027-01-1982 L1989 P CHP *020 †75

STEEN, Claude E, Jr. 1710 OLD HAYWOOD RD 28806 #005-12-1944 L1959 FM *071

STEIN, Abraham Oscar. ■ 28803 #803-09-1942 L1947 P *071

STEIN, Joan. ■ 28803 #352-11-1942 P *071
STEINFELD, John Robt. 222 ASHELAND AVE 28801 #051-01-1968 L1974 DR *071 †80
STEVENS, James Conrad. 445 BILTMORE AVE STE 403 28801 #001-02-1973 L1976 GS *020 †85
STEWARD, Robert Isaac. 206 ASHELAND AVE, ASHEVILLE FAMILY HEALTH CT 28801 #051-01-1990 L2002 FM *020 †18
STEWART, Charles Robt. ■ 28803 #041-12-1943 L1944 DR *071
STEWART, John Purdy. 41 OAKLAND RD, STE 200 28801 #012-01-1977 L1987 OBG *020 †55,30
STILLSON, Jeffrey Dean. ■ 28804 #035-45-1975 L1982 IM *020 †20,16
STONE, Bradley Allen. 76 PEACHTREE RD, STE 300 28803 #038-43-1982 L1989 AN *020 †05
STRANGE, John Nelson, Jr. 1998 HENDERSONVILLE RD, STE 40 28803 #027-01-1977 L1986 GS *071 †85
STRANGES, Steven Michael. ■ 28803 #045-04-1981 L1987 NS *071 †25
SULLIVAN, Margaret Hancoc. ■ 28814 #005-02-2007 *012
SUMMERLIN, Harry H, Jr. 118 WT WEAVER BLVD 28804 #036-07-1961 L1961 FM *071 †18
SUNDERHAUS, Earl E. 119 TUNNEL RD, ASHERVILLE EYE CLNC 28805 #038-40-1963 L1968 OPH *020 †35 ‡
SUTARIA, Kalpeshkumar N. ■ 28805 #495-76-1987 L1999 IM *020 †20
SUTARIA, Leena K. ■ 28805 #495-23-1990 L1999 IM *020 †20
SWEARINGEN, George S. 35 WOODFIN ST 28801 #045-01-1984 L2006 FM *020 †18
SWEEDE, Sharon. 1100 TUNNEL RD, VAMC PC1 28805 #012-05-1979 L1980 FM ADM *020 †18
TAIT, Jeffrey. 43 OAKLAND RD 28801 #917-04-1973 L1979 FM *020 †18
TANKESLEY, Robt Mc Kinney. ■ 28803 #051-01-1943 L1943 R *071 †80
TAUBER, Stuart Davis. ■ 28804 #041-12-1960 L1961 END IM *071
TAYLOR, Reid De Jarnette. 509 BILTMORE AVE, MISSIONS HOSPITAL 28801 #011-03-1983 L1988 N *020 †75
TEAFORD, Michael Jacob. 509 BILTMORE AVE 28801 #012-01-1976 L1982 PTH *020 †50
TEMPLETON, John Douglas. 11 VANDERBILT PARK DR 28803 #021-01-1998 L2000 PD *020 †55
TEMPLETON, Virginia Hood. 100 FAR HORIZONS LN, MEMORYCARE 28803 #035-48-1998 L2001 FM *020 †18
THAKURI, Mohan Chand. 445 BILTMORE AVE STE 100, CANCER CARE OF WNC, PA 28801 #672-01-1991 L2001 HO *020 †20
THEOFRASTOUS, James Paul. 100 RIDGEFIELD CT, SPECIALTY CENTER PA 28806 #050-02-1987 L1995 OBG *075 †30
THOMPSON, Cleveland, IV. 76 PEACHTREE RD, STE 300 28803 #012-01-1991 L1998 PMM AN *020 †05
THOMPSON, Errington C. 509 BILTMORE AVE, STE B321 28801 #048-12-1987 L2005 GS TRS *020 †85
THOMPSON, James Stevens. 20 MCDOWELL ST 28801 #039-01-1970 L1976 HS ORS *040 †40
THORNBURG, Lacy Eugene. 20 MCDOWELL ST, CAROLINA HAND SURGERY ASSO 28801 #024-01-1989 L1996 HS *020 †40
THRASH, William Virgil. 147 ASHELAND AVE 28801 #012-01-1970 L1976 IM *020 †20 ‡
TOBIN, James Russell. ■ 28805 #035-15-1965 L1966 PD PHP *071 †55
TOPPLE, Sissel Kay. 333 GASHES CREEK RD, PARKWAY MEDICAL GROUP 28803 #036-01-1990 L1994 FM *020 †18
TRAMM, Jeanne Norgaard. 76 PEACHTREE RD, STE 300 28803 #016-06-1981 L1982 AN *020 †05
TRASK, Elizabeth J. 76 PEACHTREE RD, STE 300 28803 #036-08-1982 L1985 AN *020 †05
TRASK, John Donald. 6 BROOKLET ST, LAUREL OB/GYN 28801 #045-01-1978 L1985 OBG *020 †30
TRAVIS, Gerald Wayne. 3 CARSON CREEK DR, CAROLINA MOUNTAIN PSCH 28803 #020-02-1989 L1994 CHP *020 †75
TRAVIS, John Walton. PO BOX 8422 28814 #024-07-1969 L1973 GPM *050
TRAVIS, Stacy Dyer. 24 MEDICAL PARK DR, BILTMORE OB GYN 28803 #020-02-1989 L1995 OBG *020 †30
TREAKLE, Kevin Burke. 41 OAKLAND RD 28801 #051-01-1984 L1989 FM IM *020 †18
TRICHON, Benjamin Howard. 5 VANDERBILT PARK DR 28803 #016-06-1995 L2000 CD IM *020 †20
TRIPP, Marjorie Ellen. 5 VANDERBILT PARK DR 28803 #008-01-1973 L1986 PDC *020 †55
TROXLER, David Hays. 30 CHOCTAW ST 28801 #036-07-1974 L1981 PUD CCM *020 †20
TUCH-LAWSON, Ellen. 8 NEW LEICESTER HWY 28806 #051-04-1976 L1991 EM *020 †16
TURAKHIA, Bharati V. ■ 28805 #495-02-1974 L1976 DR OS *020 †80
TURK, Robert Spencer. 3 DOCTORS PARK 28801 #012-05-1956 L1964 GS *071 †85
TURNER, Jennifer Lynn. ■ 28803 #041-14-1996 L2007 GS *020 †85
TURPIN, Payton Duke. 59 COLLEGE ST, # 205 28801 #012-05-1978 L2005 IM EM *020 †16
TUTEN, Cindy J. 68 SWEETEN CREEK RD, COMPREHENSIVE REHABILITATI 28803 #011-04-1987 L2001 PM PMM *020 †60
TWARDON, Elizabeth Maria. 43 OAKLAND RD 28801 #024-01-1995 L1998 FM *020 †18
UHREN, Robert Jos, Jr. 509 BILTMORE AVE 28801 #035-15-1974 L1977 FM *020 †18
UNKS, Dennis Michael. 5 VANDERBILT PARK DR 28803 #041-12-1987 L1989 CD IM *020 †20
USEDOM, James E. 5 VANDERBILT PARK DR 28803 #016-11-1984 L1985 CD IM *020 †20
VAN BLARICOM, Lawrence S. 41 OAKLAND RD 28801 #064-01-1949 L1960 NS *071
VANCE, Amy Weaver. 41 OAKLAND RD, STE 200 28801 #045-01-1998 L2003 OBG *020 †30
VANDERBEEK, Randall B. 428 BILTMORE AVE 28801 #036-07-1963 L1963 U *071 †95
VANDERKWAAK, Timothy John. 509 BILTMORE AVE 28801 #025-07-1993 L2000 GO *020 †30
VAN DYKE, Allen H, Jr. 900 HENDERSONVILLE RD 28803 #036-05-1971 L1971 OBG EM *020 †30
VAN FRANK, Alison C. 369 MONTFORD AVE 28801 #049-01-1990 L2000 FM *020 †18
VAN KIRK, Marion Perkins. 1 VANDERBILT PARK DR, STE 150 28803 #048-13-1983 L1987 OPH *020 †35
VAN NORT, Joseph John. 509 BILTMORE AVE 28801 #041-14-1990 L1992 IM PD *020 †55,20
VAN TASSEL, Eric David. 5 VANDERBILT PARK DR 28803 #036-01-1982 L1988 CD *020 †20
VARELA, Enrique Angel. 190 BILTMORE AVE, STE 5 28801 #935-07-1978 L1993 IM *020 †20
VARGO, Jill. 445 BILTMORE AVE, STE 306 28801 #055-02-1984 L1989 RHU IM *020 †20
VASEY, Charles Gibbs. 5 VANDERBILT PARK DR 28803 #018-03-1980 L1986 CD IM *020 †20
VEGA, Christopher Steven. 509 BILTMORE AVE, CAROLINA MOUNTAIN EMGNCY 28801 #019-02-2000 L2001 EM *020
VENDEL, Lisa Marie. 8 NEW LEICESTER HWY 28806 #038-43-1994 L1995 FM *020 †18
VICKERY, David Augustus. 39 CHOCTAW ST 28801 #012-01-2001 L2002 FM *020 †18
VOLK, Mercedes A. 118 WT WEAVER BLVD 28804 #048-15-2002 L2004 FM *100 †18
VYAS, Snehal C. ■ 28803 #495-89-1977 L1984 ID *020 †20
WADE, Lorena. ■ 28801 #005-12-1996 L1999 FM *020 †18
WADE, Robert Leonard, Jr. 5 VANDERBILT PARK DR 28803 #024-05-1991 L2000 CD *020 †20
WALBURGH, Carl Eric. 11 VANDERBILT PARK DR 28803 #035-15-1971 L1993 PDS *020 †85
WALKENSTEIN, Eileen. ■ 28804 #041-07-1950 L1973 P *071 †75
WALLACE, Douglass Michael. 509 BILTMORE AVE, DEPT OF EMERGENCY MEDICINE 28801 #036-05-2001 L2005 EM *020 †16
WALLENBORN, Peter A, III. 285 MCDOWELL ST 28803 #051-01-1979 L1984 OTO *020 †45
WALLENIUS, Steven Todd. 264 HAYWOOD RD 28806 #036-01-1995 L1996 FM *020 †18
WALLER, Robert Jos. 509 BILTMORE AVE 28801 #010-02-1973 L1974 RO *020 †80
WALTER, Karen Joanne. 500 CENTRE PARK DR, MOUNTAIN AREA PEDIATRIC 28805 #005-14-1996 L1999 PD *020 †55
WALTON, Richard Frank. ■ 28803 #065-05-1961 L1977 FM PHP *074 †18
WANDER, John Chas. 333 GASHES CREEK RD, PARKWAY MEDICAL GROUP 28803 #028-34-1979 L1982 FM *020 †18
WANG, Lihuan. 1100 TUNNEL RD, ASHEVILLE VETERANS AFFAIRS 28805 #012-01-1998 L2007 DR *020 †80
WARD, David Felton. 136 MIMOSA DR 28806 #047-20-1988 L1997 AM OM *020 †70
WARREN, Sarah Kathleen. 445 BILTMORE AVE, STE 407 28801 #035-45-1993 L2001 IM *020 †20
WATKINS, Roy Wayne. 63 ZILLICOA ST, GREAT SMOKIES DIAG LAB 28801 #036-08-1986 L1989 FM *020 †18
WATSON, George S. ■ 28806 #041-13-1945 L1946 IM PM *071 †20
WATSON, Ruth A. 16 MCDOWELL ST 28801 #305-01-1989 L1999 OBG *020 †30
WATSON, Susan P. ■ 28803 #036-07-1971 L1971 AN PD *071 †55,05
WATTS, Jana Christina. 534 BILTMORE AVE 28801 #036-08-2000 L2001 FM *020 †18
WEAST, Robert Randolph. 84 COXE AVE, STE 2A 28801 #041-01-1970 L1976 DR *020 †80
WEAVER, Zebulon, III. 80 VICTORIA RD 28801 #036-01-1961 L1961 ON HEM *071
WEBB, Susan Ross. ■ 28801 #048-04-1990 L2007 P *020 ‡
WEEKS, John Wesley. ■ 28801 #036-07-1965 L1965 GYN END *071 †30
WEILBAECHER, James Edward. ■ 28803 #021-05-1958 L1975 ORS *071 †40
WEINBERGER, April Lynn. ■ 28801 #041-15-2007 FP *012
WEINRIB, Stephen Louis. 141 ASHELAND AVE 28801 #001-02-1992 L2002 END *020 †20
WEISENBERGER, Anthony Jos. 428 BILTMORE AVE 28801 #028-02-1971 L1981 P ADP *020 †75
WEIZMAN, Michael S. 43 OAKLAND RD, RAVENSCROFT FAMILY HEALTH 28801 #041-13-1997 L2000 FM *020 †18
WELGE, Barry Gene. 1100 TUNNEL RD 28805 #026-04-1972 L1973 CD IM *020 †20
WELLS, Robert Milton. VET ADMIN MED CTR, DEPT PSYCH 28805 #021-01-1954 L1979 P *071 †75
WELLS, Robert Stanley. 190 BILTMORE AVE, STE 5 28801 #039-01-1980 L1983 IM *020 †20
WESTLE, Marc B. 417 BILTMORE AVE, MAILING: P O BOX 7568 28801 #028-78-1989, ▲ L2000 IM IMG *020 †20 ‡
WESTLY, Stephen Kottemann. 1998 HENDERSONVILLE RD, RD # 25 28803 #021-01-1978 L1987 HS ORS *020 †40
WHARTON, William Wyant. 5 VANDERBILT PARK DR 28803 #051-01-1988 L1991 CD *020 †20
WHATLEY, Nancy Elizabeth. 76 PEACHTREE RD, STE 300 28803 #011-04-1987 L1997 AN *020 †05
WHITE, Dennis Patrick. 21 TURTLE CREEK DR 28803 #022-75-1995, ▲ L2004 PM *020 †60
WHITE, Terry Edward. 417 BILTMORE AVE, 4C DOCTORS PARK 28801 #028-03-1980 L1986 PM PME *075 †60 ‡
WHITEHOUSE, James Duncan. 53 S FRENCH BROAD AVE, STE 200 28801 #012-05-1993 L1997 ID IM *020 †20
WHITESIDE, Carl Thos. 70 WOODFIN PL STE 130 28801 #036-01-1969 L1969 P N *020
WIEST, Helen Hyman. 222 ASHELAND AVE 28801 #045-01-1984 L1989 DR *020 †80
WIEST, Samuel Habecker. 509 BILTMORE AVE 28801 #041-01-1982 L1985 EM FM *020 †18,16
WIGGINS, Robert E, Jr. 8 MEDICAL PARK DR, ASHEVILLE EYE ASSCS 28803 #036-01-1984 L1985 OPH PD *020 †35 ‡
WILKES, Dru Van. 1100 TUNNEL RD, VA HOSPITAL 28805 #036-05-1963 L1963 FM PD *020
WILKIE, Louis J. 1100 TUNNEL RD, VETS HOSP RAD DEPT 28805 #041-02-1953 L1982 R NM *020 †80
WILKINSON, Todd Michael. 16 MEDICAL PARK DR, ADVANCED DERMATOLOGY AND S 28803 #036-01-2004 L2006 D *012
WILLETT, Eugene S, Jr. 111 VICTORIA RD 28801 #051-04-1969 L1976 ORS *020 †40
WILLIAMS, Ameliann B. 158 ZILLICOA ST 28801 #045-04-1986 L1999 P CHP *020 †75
WILLIAMS, Charles Emery. 428 BILTMORE AVE 28801 #021-05-1963 L1974 OTO *071 †45
WILLIAMS, Nathan Edward. 445 BILTMORE AVE 28801 #030-06-1979 L1983 GYN GO *020 †30
WILLINGHAM, Sharon Givens. ■ 28806 #020-02-1981 L1987 P PME *020
WILSON, Carol. 2 MEDICAL PARK DR, STE 100 28803 #001-06-1993 L2007 PD *020 †55
WILSON, Catherine Marie. ■ 28803 #005-12-1963 L1968 GYN *071 †30
WILSON, John Leighton, Jr. 1312 PATTON AVE 28806 #026-04-1976 L1991 NTR OS *020
WOFFORD, Michael Wesley. ■ 28805 #012-01-1968 L1969 PMM *071
WOOD, Angela Scott. 93 VICTORIA RD 28801 #012-01-2004 L2005 OBG *012
WOOD, Carter Railsback. 509 BILTMORE AVE 28801 #021-06-2001 L2005 MPD *020 †20
WOOD, Kimberly Linnander. ■ 28801 #047-05-1990 L1999 IM *020 †20
WORD-SIMS, Margaret. ■ 28804 #038-40-1984 L1987 IM *020 †20
WRIGHT, Eileen M. 1312 PATTON AVE, GREAT SMOKIES MED CENTER, 28806 #011-04-1975 L1997 EM GPM *020 †16
WRIGHT, Robin Diane. 179 CHARLOTTE ST 28801 #038-45-1989 L1995 GE *020 †20
YAGER, Cornell Keith. 509 BILTMORE AVE 28801 #010-02-1984 L1994 EM IM *020 †16
YANCEY, Cynthia Brunson. 35 WOODFIN ST 28801 #027-01-1982 L1985 FM *020 †18
YARBOROUGH, Mark Alan. 1 DOCTORS PARK 28801 #045-01-1983 L1988 U *020 †95 ‡
YEATER, Richard Elwood. 501 BILTMORE AVE 28801 #665-01-2007 FP *012
YODER, Charles De Wayne. 304 SUMMIT ST 28803 #036-01-1974 L1974 PD *020 †55
YOUNG, Michael H. 86 VICTORIA RD 28801 #036-01-1975 L1978 N *020 †20,75
YOUNG, William Albert. 1 TOWN SQUARE BLVD, STE 225 28803 #021-01-1979 L2004 PS *020 †65 ‡
YOUNGBLOOD, Robert Carter. 84 COXE AVE STE 2A, ASHEVILLE RADIOLOGY ASSOCI 28801 #027-01-1984 L1991 R IM *020 †20,80
ZAFFINO, Maryshell Brosch. ■ 28803 #045-01-2008 *012
ZAHLER, Charles Gary. ■ 28804 #045-01-1963 L1973 PS *020 †85,65
ZEILENDER, Stuart Bruce. 30 CHOCTAW ST 28801 #035-15-1984 L1991 PUD CCM *020 †20
ZEPP, Melissa Kathryn. 333 GASHES CREEK RD, PARKWAY MEDICAL GROUP 28803 #019-02-1996 L2001 FM *020 †18
ZIVONY, Daniel Israel. 16 MEDICAL PARK DR 28803 #038-40-1991 L2002 D DMP *040 †55,15

ATLANTIC – CARTERET

MC GIRT, Murphy Frank, Jr. 113 YAUPON LN 28511 #036-01-1964 L1964 ORS *071 †40

7202

■ = Address Information Privacy Protected

ATLANTIC BEACH – CARTERET

CRONAN, Thomas Leo. 301 COMMERCE WAY, SEASPRAY UNIT 104 28512 #016-43-1956 L1995 FM *071 †18
GOLDBERG, David Jaime. ■ 28512 #132-01-1966 L1974 P *071
HOACHLANDER, Eldon Geo. ■ 28512 #041-13-1942 L1970 OS AN *071
LYNCH, Chas Townsend, Jr. ■ 28512 #036-07-1967 L1967 DR *020 †80
MARRIOTT, John Daughtry. ■ 28512 #036-01-1962 L1962 DR RO *020 †80,28
NOBLE, Keith C. ■ 28512 #038-06-1940 L1978 EM OS *071 †85
STACY, Shannon Marie. ■ 28512 #028-34-2006 L2007 *012
STRICKLAND, Nigel John. ■ 28512 #917-03-1959 L1976 R NR *062

AULANDER – BERTIE

ELKHOURY, Semaan Yacoub. 108 S COMMERCE ST, AULANDER FAMILY PHYSICIANS 27805 #605-01-1993 L1996 IM *020 †20
SAUNDERS, Jay Fred S. PO BOX 309 27805 #036-01-1954 L1954 FM GP *071 †18

AURORA – BEAUFORT

CALLAHAN, John Conway. 151 3RD ST 27806 #051-04-1993 L1997 FM *020 †18

AYDEN – PITT

ADAMS, Robin Denise. 137 3RD ST, PITT FAMILY PHYSICIANS 28513 #036-08-1992 L1993 FM *020 †18
BOWEN, Tracey W. 137 3RD ST 28513 #036-08-1995 L1998 MPD *020 †20
FRAZIER, Richard Ellis. ■ 28513 #036-05-1962 L1962 FM PD *071 †18
GALLOWAY, James M, Jr. 1402 W 3RD ST 28513 #036-05-1974 L1974 FM *020 †18
MOORE, Carol Ann. 4465 MAGELLAN CT 28513 #036-08-1988 L1991 FP *012
QUICK, Erica Camille. ■ 28513 #036-08-2007 OBG *012
WEAVER-LEE, Lashawn A. ■ 28513 #045-01-2004 OBG *012

BADIN – STANLY

DE REAMER, John W. ■ 28009 #036-07-1946 L1950 D *071 †15

BAHAMA – DURHAM

FRUSH, Karen S. ■ 27503 #036-07-1986 L1988 PD *020 †55
GRANGER, Christopher Bull. ■ 27503 #008-02-1984 L1990 CD IM *020 †20
JACOBS, Richard L, II. ■ 27503 #025-01-1985 L1991 AN *020 †05
MYERS, Christopher James. ■ 27503 #539-03-2001 L2007 GS *020
ROBERTS, Elizabeth M. ■ 27503 #045-01-1949 L1951 GP PHP *071

BAKERSVILLE – MITCHELL

OBEID, Robert James. PO BOX 447 28705 #028-02-1984 L1986 FM *020 †18

BALD HEAD ISLAND – BRUNSWICK

LINK, Marianne C. ■ 28461 #033-05-1964 L1965 AN IM *071
WADDELL, William Bryan. ■ 28461 #036-07-1962 L1996 EM *071 †18
WESTER, Thaddeus B. ■ 28461 #036-07-1951 L1953 PHP PD *071

BALSAM – JACKSON

BRIDGES, William Denman. ■ 28707 #027-01-1962 L1962 P *071
OHLWILER, David Austin. ■ 28707 #035-45-1954 L1957 PS *071 †65
SCHIESS, Robert John. 51 WESTVIEW DRIVE 28707 #036-05-1954 L1954 GP *071

BANNER ELK – WATAUGA

BREIDENTHAL, Ward B. ■ 28604 #028-02-1949 L1956 PD CHP *071
COOK, Roberta Anne. ■ 28604 #035-15-1977 L1996 GP *020
COOK, Steven Henry. 108 PARK AVE 28604 #035-15-1977 L1993 FM OBG *020 †18
DAVIS, Floyd. PO BOX 1705 28604 #047-06-1958 L1970 EM GS *071
HAIZLIP, Thomas Matthews. PO BOX 68, TATE CLINIC PA 28604 #036-01-1993 L1998 GS *020 †85
LUMPKIN, Martha Ray. ■ 28604 #023-07-1951 L1951 IM IMG *020
MARKGRAF, Wolfgang H. ■ 28604 #025-07-1949 L1950 OS GS *071 †85
PARSAVAND, Jacqueline B. ■ 28604 #041-07-1957 L1958 OBG *071 †30
SAFKO, Kenneth Roland. ■ 28604 #011-03-1967 L1973 OPH *071 †35
SMITH, Robert C. 1867 LEE GUALTNEY RD, ITAL 28604 #041-12-1953 L1959 IM *072
TATE, William Cummings, II. 805 SHAWNEEHAW AVE 28604 #036-01-1972 L1972 GS *020 †85
WILSON, Shelburne D, Jr. 805 SHAWNEEHAW AVE 28604 #047-05-1973 L1988 EM OS *020
WOELFEL, James Thos. HIGHWAY 184 28604 #056-06-1959 L1974 GS *071

BARNESVILLE – ROBESON

WAMPLER, Garland Earhart. MAIN ST 28319 #036-01-1956 L1956 FM *071

BAT CAVE – HENDERSON

SLOSS, Katherine Anne. PO BOX 290, 154 JEAN LUC DR 28710 #038-06-1983 L1986 FM *020 †18

BATH – BEAUFORT

BOWMAN, James Frederick. ■ 27808 #041-13-1961 L1966 ORS OSM *071 †40
GLOVER, William J. ■ 27808 #016-13-1949 L1988 GS *071 †85
MONROE, William Murchison. 228 KIRBY GRANGE AVE 27808 #036-01-1964 L1964 OPH *071 †35

BATTLEBORO – NASH

DIAMOND, John Danl. 3918 BISHOP RD 27809 #026-04-1971 L1999 FM *020 †18

BAYBORO – PAMLICO

DUNN, Ernest C, Jr. 606 MAIN ST, PAMLICO MEDICAL CENTER P 28515 #036-01-1979 L1981 FM *020
HORSTMAN, Anthony Jos. ■ 28515 #020-12-1969 L1970 AN *020 †05
HUDSON, Richard Woodard. 606 MAIN ST 28515 #036-01-1961 L1961 GP *020
LAMSAL, Suman. 606 MAIN ST, PAMLICO MEDICAL CENTER P 28515 #672-01-1993 L1999 IM *020 †20
LEE, Sue Hollowell. PO BOX 416 28515 #051-07-1983 L1990 PD *020 †55

BEAR CREEK – CHATHAM

THOMAS, Edward T. 665 BILL LAMBERT RD, GREENWAY FARM 27207 #917-19-1948 L1986 AN *071 †05

BEAUFORT – CARTERET

CROSSWELL, James J, Jr. 97 CAMPEN RD 28516 #036-05-1980 L1981 FM *020 †18
HAMBRIGHT, Rufus R. ■ 28516 #036-07-1950 L1958 OBG *071
HAYWARD, James Neil. ■ 28516 #024-07-1954 L1976 N *071 †75
KUERS, Peter Friedrich W. 106 PROFESSIONAL PRK DR #D, BEAUFORT CARE 28516 #001-02-1967 L1978 GP EM *020
LEWIS, Martin T. 301 JONES AVE 28516 #035-09-1953 L1954 GP *071
MERRICK, Margaret F. 249 SHORE DR 28516 #051-07-1980 L1999 PD *020 †55

BEECH MOUNTAIN – WATAUGA

MILLER, Murray Jos. ■ 28604 #041-09-1955 L1956 CD IM *020 †20

BELHAVEN – BEAUFORT

BEAMER, Mark Edward. 245 ALLEN ST 27810 #036-08-1991 L2002 FM *020 †18
BOYETTE, Charles Otis. 202 E WATER ST 27810 #036-01-1961 L1961 FM *020 ‡
GENZ, Roy Steffen. 202 E WATER ST, PUNGO DISTRICT HOSP 27810 #308-07-1982 L1988 EM *020 †18
JONES, Gregory Lee. 166 E WATER ST 27810 #036-01-1977 L1980 FM ORS *020 †18
URBAN, Ann Marie. 202 E WATER ST, PRIMARY CARE 27810 #023-01-1997 L2000 PD *020
WRIGHT, James Thurman. ■ 27810 #041-02-1943 L1943 GP GS *071

BELMONT – GASTON

ABBASI, Fariha. 400 PARK ST, CHARLOTTE EYE, EAR, NOSE A 28012 #041-09-1990 L1999 N *020 †75
AIZCORBE, Raul Cesar. 684 PARK ST 28012 #275-01-1952 L1964 FM *020
CHAR, Sadhana Vedavyasa. 1220 SPRUCE ST 28012 #038-43-1998 L1999 FM *020 †18
CHIN, Tanya Elizabeth. 1220 SPRUCE ST, SOUTH POINT FAMILY 28012 #032-01-2002 L2004 FM *020 †18
DYKSTERHOUSE, Andrew John. 1220 SPRUCE ST, SOUTH POINT FAMILY 28012 #045-04-2001 L2003 FM *020
FERRAND, David Nathaniel. ■ 28012 #033-05-2003 L2006 EM *020 †16
GODFREY, Joseph Lawrence. 100 GLENWAY ST, STE A 28012 #019-02-1983 L1998 P *020 †75
HOLMAN, Joseph Ralph. 1212 SPRUCE ST, STE 307 28012 #020-02-1984 L1988 OBG *020 †30
HORSLEY, William Nolen. ■ 28012 #036-07-1941 L1946 GP PD *072
HOWE, Donald Douglas. 1212 SPRUCE ST, STE 307 28012 #036-01-1970 L1970 OBG *020 †30
JACOBS, George Daniel. 1212 SPRUCE ST, STE 307 28012 #036-01-1976 L1976 OBG *020 †30
KEYZER, Helene Pauline. ■ 28012 #036-01-1991 L1996 PD *020 †55
KIRBY, Daniel Lee. 1212 SPRUCE ST, ARTHRITIS CONSULTANTS OF 28012 #011-03-1988 L1999 RHU IM *020 †20
KISH, Laurence Michael. 1223 SPRUCE ST 28012 #041-07-1994 L1996 IM *020 †20
LOCKLEAR, David Glenn. 1220 SPRUCE ST, SOUTH POINT FAMILY 28012 #036-05-1978 L1979 FM *020 †18
LYNCH, Sean Michael. 1212 SPRUCE ST, STE 307 28012 #012-01-1998 L2002 OBG *020 †30
MCCUNE, Scott Alan. 1223 SPRUCE ST, WHITESTONE FAMILY MEDICINE 28012 #038-43-1990 L1993 IM *020 †20
OWENSBY, Susan Bignall. 209 PARK ST, CAROMONT PEDIATRIC 28012 #025-12-1995 L1996 PD *020 †55
PEACH, Charles Arthur. 1212 SPRUCE ST, STE 307 28012 #012-01-1978 L1982 OBG *020 †30
QUINN, Rayford Edwin. 209 PARK ST STE 100 28012 #045-01-1973 L1973 FM *020 †18
RINEHART, David Apgar. 1220 SPRUCE ST, SOUTH POINT FAMILY 28012 #051-01-1982 L1984 FM *020 †18
ROBINSON, Karla Liana. 1220 SPRUCE ST 28012 #016-01-2002 L2005 FM *020 †18
STEPHENS, Caroline Dove. 1220 SPRUCE ST 28012 #045-01-2004 L2007 FM *020 †18
WILCOX, Sam, II. 1212 SPRUCE ST, STE 307 28012 #011-02-2001 L2005 OBG *020
WYSONG, Brian Edward. 1220 SPRUCE ST 28012 #012-01-2003 L2006 FM *020 †18

BENSON – JOHNSTON

BAKER, Crystal Dawn. 3333 NC HIGHWAY 242 N 27504 #036-08-2000 L2006 FM *020 †18

DAWKINS, Robert Gene, Jr. 70 CRAPE MYRTLE DR, STE 104 27504 #038-44-1993 L2001 **FM** *020 †18

HARMON, Revella B. 411 N PLEASANT COATS RD, R S MEDICAL ASSOCIATES, PA 27504 #024-07-1993 L2000 **FM** *020 †18

KAMDAR, Manali Kirtikumar. 1 MEDICAL DR, EASTERN CAROLINA MED CTR 27504 #496-44-2004 **IM** *012

KUNCHA, Hari Kiran. 1 MEDICAL DR, EASTERN CAROLINA MEDICAL C 27504 #496-24-1988 L2004 **PM** *020

MAC KINNON, Christopher J. 804 S MARKET ST 27504 #064-01-1985 L1996 **GP** *020

MAYNARD, Eugene H, Jr. 3333 NC HIGHWAY 242 N 27504 #036-01-1993 L1994 **FM** *020 †18 ‡

MIZELLE, Donna Grimsley. PO BOX 399, 3333 HWY 242N 27504 #036-08-2000 L2003 **FM** *020 †18

REDDY, Viswanatha K. 1 MEDICAL DR, EASTERN CAROLINA MEDICAL C 27504 #495-70-1990 L1999 **IM** *020 †20

THOMAS, Sheela K. 925 E SINGH PLZ 27504 #495-31-1980 L1995 **IM** *020 †20

VYAS, Pankaj Kirtikant. 1 MEDICAL DR 27504 #495-23-1982 L1987 **IM UCM** *020 †20

BESSEMER CITY – GASTON

BARRO, Lee Dennis. 614 GASTONIA HWY, BESSEMER FAMILIY MEDICINE, 28016 #064-01-1976 L1981 **GP** *020

KISER, Henry Lester. 720 GASTONIA HWY 28016 #036-01-1959 L1959 **PD FM** *071

STITT, Van Junius. 119 W PENNSYLVANIA AVE 28016 #036-01-1975 L1975 **FM** *020 †18

BEULAVILLE – DUPLIN

BAREFOOT, Robert Allen. ■ 28518 #036-08-1988 L1991 **FM** *020 †18

FANARJIAN, Nicole Joy. ■ 28518 #035-03-2002 L2006 **OBG** *020

GUNTER, Kathryn Snowdy. ■ 28518 #048-04-2006 **GS** *012

KEITER, William E, Jr. 116 E MAIN ST 28518 #036-01-1960 L1960 **PDA PD** *071 †55

MILLAN, Poala Galvez. 116 E MAIN ST 28518 #748-02-1990 L2001 **PD** *020 †55

PATE, Carl Danl, Jr. 119 CROSSOVER RD 28518 #036-01-1982 L1989 **PD** *020 †55

PERRY, Joan Templeton. 116 E MAIN ST 28518 #036-01-1983 L1985 **PD** *020 †55

QUINN, Marshall Kirk. 119 CROSSOVER RD, POST OFFICE 986 28518 #036-05-1983 L1984 **FM** *020 †18

REECE, Orvil Young, Jr. 116 E MAIN ST 28518 #001-02-1975 L1978 **PD** *020 †55

RIDDLE, Donald Michael. 116 E MAIN ST 28518 #036-05-1982 L1985 **PD** *020 †55

SICO-DAVIS, Christandra R. 116 E MAIN ST 28518 #748-08-1992 L1997 **PD** *020 †55

BILTMORE FOREST – BUNCOMBE

WATSON, Donald Chas. ■ 28803 #036-07-1972 L2005 **TS** *071 †85,90

BILTMORE LAKE – BUNCOMBE

DAVIS, Ryan Christopher. ■ 28715 #019-02-2000 L2007 **EM** *020

NIEVES-GONZALEZ, Orlando. ■ 28715 #649-14-1988 L2003 **FM EM** *020 †18

VO, Mary Beth D. ■ 28715 #036-07-2001 L2004 **PD** *100 †55

BLACK MOUNTAIN – BUNCOMBE

ALDRICH, Stephen Linwood. ■ 28711 #016-06-1948 L1986 **IM** *071

ARRENDELL, Cad W, Jr. ■ 28711 #039-01-1945 L1954 **GS CRS** *071 †85

BLAKE, Daniel Jackson. 201 TABERNACLE RD 28711 #036-01-1978 L1998 **P** *020 †75

BROADHURST, Laurel. 201 TABERNACLE RD, JFK-ALCOHOL AND DRUG TREAT 28711 #038-41-1987 L1995 **PHP OM** *030 †70

BURNETT, Anthony Thos. 201 TABERNACLE RD, C/O JULIAN F KEITH ADATC 28711 #036-08-1986 L1991 **P ADP** *030 †18

CARGILE, Leslie Summar J. 3164 ROUTE 70 28711 #047-20-1982 L1985 **FM** *020 †18

DOWNS, Edward Alley. ■ 28711 #010-01-1954 L1955 **IM** *071 †20

ELLIS, George John, III. ■ 28711 #024-01-1963 L1970 **END IM** *071 †20

FARRIOR, Hugh Lanier. ■ 28711 #051-04-1953 L1956 **OBG** *071 †30

FINEGAN, Robert F. ■ 28711 #016-06-1952 L1953 **AN PUD** *071 †05

FORE, William Whately. ■ 28711 #036-07-1960 L1960 **END IM** *071 †28,20

GEIGER, Joseph Kennard. ■ 28711 #041-01-1956 L1957 **PD PHP** *020 †55

GREGORY, Arlene. 411 W STATE ST 28711 #011-02-1966 L1996 **AN** *020

HEID, James K. ■ 28711 #026-04-1953 L1997 **FM GP** *071 †18

KELLY, Richard Bruce. 932 OLD US HWY 70 W, BLACK MOUNTAIN CENTER 28711 #038-43-1980 L1981 **FM** *020 †18

KOSTENKO, Susan Anne. 201 TABERNACLE RD, JULIAN F KEITH ADATC 28711 #036-05-1995 L1997 **P** *020 †75

MC CARTY, Ben. ■ 28711 #047-06-1957 L1958 **OPH OS** *071 †35

MOORE, Bertha Loving. 200 TABERNACLE RD, APT G101 28711 #035-20-1950 **PHP** *071

NAGEL, Donald Chas. 301 TABERNACLE RD, CTR 28711 #036-01-1972 L1972 **ADM FM** *071 †18

NEVILLE, Margaret C Brown. ■ 28711 #045-01-1962 L1962 **P** *071 †75

PYRON, Katharine A A. 117 SUGAR MAPLE DR, MAILING: P O BOX 460 28711 #028-03-1968 L1989 **IM** *020 †20

SCOTT, Kenneth Munro. ■ 28711 #041-01-1941 L1974 **ID DR** *071 †85

SWANTON, Caroline H. OLD HIGHWAY 70, BLACK MOUNTAIN CENTER 28711 #036-05-1961 L1961 **PD OS** *071

VALENCIA, Rodolfo Cirineo. 2 BLACK MOUNTAIN CENTER 28711 #748-01-1964 L1993 **GP IM** *075

WILSON, John Knox. ■ 28711 #041-02-1943 L1949 **PD** *071 †55

BLADENBORO – BLADEN

HARRIS, John J, Jr. ■ 28320 #047-06-1984 L2007 **AN** *062 †05

BLOUNTS CREEK – BEAUFORT

MILLER, Linda Cartner. ■ 27814 #036-08-1999 L2006 **CHP** *020

BLOWING ROCK – WATAUGA

DAVANT, Charles, Jr. 416 CHESTNUT CIR 28605 #045-01-1945 L1948 **GP** *071

DAVANT, Charles, III. 366 CHESTNUT CIR 28605 #036-01-1972 L1972 **FM FPG** *020 †18

DAVIS, John D, Jr. 366 CHESTNUT CIR 28605 #036-01-1978 L1979 **FM FPG** *020 †18

JENKINS, Jos Mc Kendrie. ■ 28605 #036-01-1974 L1974 **U** *020 †95

KILPATRICK, Russell James. PO BOX 2559, 116 JOHNS RIVER RD 28605 #036-07-1975 L1977 **D AM** *030 †15

LIESEGANG, Glen Robert. 366 CHESTNUT CIR 28605 #020-12-1983 L1987 **FM IMG** *020 †18

LITTLEJOHN, Mark Hays. ■ 28605 #016-06-1961 L1980 **DR NM** *071 †80,28

MC CUBBINS, Paul S. PO BOX 868 28605 #036-01-1958 L1958 **IM** *071

MOSS, Robert Wyman, Jr. ■ 28605 #045-01-1972 L1978 **ORS** *071 †40

PETRANY, Zoltan. ■ 28605 #067-01-1956 L1973 **R** *071 †80,28

VANCE, Thomas Doyle. ■ 28605 #036-07-1956 L1956 **FM** *071 †80

BOILING SPRINGS – CLEVELAND

DORN, Robert Marshall. 315 W COLLEGE AVE 28017 #045-04-1985 L1988 **FM** *020 †18

BOLIVIA – BRUNSWICK

ANDERSON, Kami Karen. 1620 GOLEY HEWETT RD SE #3 28422 #037-01-1994 L2003 **AN** *020 †05

BOLTON – COLUMBUS

SCHMEHL, Rolland Malcolm. ■ 28423 #005-12-1973 L1974 **AN FM** *075

WHITE, David Eugene. 213 9TH ST 28423 #010-03-1987 L2004 **FM** *020 †18 ‡

BOONE – WATAUGA

ADAMS, Gregory Lynn. 345A DEERFIELD RD STE A, ADOLESCENT MEDICINE, INC 28607 #038-40-1979 L1986 **PD GP** *020 †55

ANAGNOS, Damon Philip. 141 DOCTORS DR 28607 #036-05-1988 L1996 **HS PS** *020 †85,65

ANDERSON, Steven Robert. 194 DOCTORS DR 28607 #036-05-2002 L2007 **ORS** *020

ASHLINE, Peter Thos. 175 MARY ST, THE SANGER CLINIC 28607 #016-11-1989 L1991 **CD** *020 †20

ATKINS, William Shaffer. 150 MARKET HILLS DR 28607 #036-05-1971 L1971 **OPH** *020 †35

ATWELL, Phyllis Sage. 152 SOUTHGATE DR, STE 3A 28607 #036-01-1983 L1984 **P** *020 †75

BAUGHAM, Ila Evans. 2359 HIGHWAY 105 28607 #036-05-1979 L1982 **PD** *020 †55

BEASON, Billy James. 237 LONGVUE DR STE C 28607 #045-01-1970 L1979 **FM** *020 †18

BELL, James Murphy, Jr. 336 DEERFIELD RD, WATAUGA MEDICAL CENTER ED 28607 #051-01-1979 L1980 **EM FM** *020 †18

BELL, Joseph Taylor, II. 141 DOCTORS DR 28607 #036-01-1988 L1990 **PHL** *020 †18

BENSEN, Christopher V. 194 DOCTORS DR 28607 #036-01-1995 L2003 **ORS** *100 †40

BROWD, Carroll Rosalyn. 336 DEERFIELD RD, WATAUGA MEDICAL CENTER 28607 #011-03-2003 L2006 **EM** *020

BROWN, Forrest M, Jr. 108 DOCTORS DR, TAYLOR & SYKES 28607 #012-01-1986 L1998 **IM** *020 †20

BULLOCK, Steven Reed. 400 SHADOWLINE DR, STE 201A 28607 #047-06-1980 L2001 **DR GP** *020 †80

CABALO, Gerry. 245 WINKLERS CREEK RD, STE C 28607 #005-12-1970 L2006 **IM IMG** *020 †20,18

CARRINGER, Donald Wayne. 614 HOWARD STREET, HEALTH SERVICES 28608 #036-01-1983 L1984 **FM** *020 †18

CHARLES, Barry Michael. ■ 28607 #035-19-1974 L1997 **FM** *020

CLINE, David Michael. 237 LONGVUE DR STE B 28607 #045-01-1973 L1979 **FM** *020 †18

COOPER, Warren Paul. PO BOX 3000 28607 #016-11-1992 L2006 **GS** *020 †85

CORNELLA, Rick J. 400 SHADOWLINE DR, STE 201A 28607 #036-01-1982 L1985 **DR** *020 †80

CRANSTON, Jay Wheeler. APPALACHIAN STATE, HLTH SVCS 28608 #025-01-1967 L1998 **FM OS** *020 †18

CRITTENDEN, Jeffrey Paul. 400 SHADOWLINE DR, STE 202 28607 #012-05-1986 L1996 **N** *020 †75

CZERMAK, Charles L, Jr. 833 STATE FARM RD BX 10, DEPT OF RADIOLOGY 28607 #012-05-1966 L1974 **DR** *020 †80

DAGHER, Paul Sami. 965 STATE FARM RD, WATAUGA SURG RP 28607 #005-12-1993 L1998 **GS** *020 †85

DAILEY, Timothy Patrick. 252 E KING ST, STE 104 28607 #035-15-1992 L2003 **FM** *020 †18

DAVIS, Walter Etchells. 336 DEERFIELD RD, SEBY B JONES CANCER CENTER 28607 #036-07-1966 L1966 **ON HEM** *071 †20

DEAN, Clayton Clewis. ■ 28607 #021-01-1960 L1968 **GS** *071 †85

DERRICK, William Adam, Jr. ■ 28607 #045-01-1965 L1968 **ADL OS** *071

DE VIRGILIIS, Juan Carlos. 381 DEERFIELD RD, 381 DEERFIELD RD 28607 #132-03-1982 L2007 **P** *020 †18

DOUGLAS, Michal Erin. 212 BIRCH ST 28607 #003-01-1972 L1979 **AN** *020 †05

EDMISTEN, Timothy Dwight. 965 STATE FARM RD, WATAUGA SURGICAL GROUP, P. 28607 #036-08-1993 L1998 **GS** *020 †85

ELLIS, M Barry. 336 DEERFIELD RD 28607 #012-01-1980 L1990 **OTO FPS** *020 †45

ELLISON, Robert Stanfill. 336 DEERFIELD RD 28607 #036-05-1980 L1984 **PD** *020 †55

FISHER, Kyle Stewart. 212 BIRCH ST 28607 #047-06-1983 L1987 **AN** *020 †05

FLEMING, Stephen Godwin. 194 DOCTORS DR 28607 #036-05-1980 L1986 **ORS HS** *020 †40

FORD, Charles Wesley, Jr. 870 STATE FARM RD, STE 101 28607 #036-05-1985 L1994 **OTO A** *020 †45 ‡

FOX, Leverne S, Jr. 175 MARY ST, THE SANGER CLINIC 28607 #036-01-1980 L1981 **CD IM** *020 †20

FRAZIER, Harold N, Jr. 965 STATE FARM RD 28607 #036-05-1982 L1988 **GS VS** *020 †85

FREEMAN, John Jackson. 838 STATE FARM RD STE 2 28607 #012-01-1969 L1973 OBG *020 †30

FURMAN, Richard Warren. 965 STATE FARM RD 28607 #012-01-1966 L1968 TS GS *071 †90,85

GARNER, Jo Francis. 336 DEERFIELD RD 28607 #001-06-1976 L1981 D *020 †15 ‡

GARTH, Gregory Allen. 895 STATE FARM RD, STE 303 28607 #041-14-1981 L2003 OTO HNS *020 †45 ‡

GEIGER, Patricia Ann. ASU STUDENT HEALTH SERVICE 28608 #036-05-1978 L1981 PD ADL *020 †55

GELDMEIER, Richard Wayne. 400 SHADOWLINE DR STE 201A, WATANGA RADIOLOGICAL SERVI 28607 #047-06-1984 L1989 DR *020 †80

GEORGE, Lynn Darcy. 212 BIRCH ST 28607 #010-01-1956 L1963 AN FM *071 †05,18

GRASINGER, Cecilia Fabry. 870 STATE FARM RD STE 101 28607 #039-01-1988 L1992 OBG *020 †30

GRAY, Theodore Flint, III. 870 STATE FARM RD, ONCOLOGY, PLLC, SUITE 103- 28607 #012-05-1987 L1989 HO IM *020 †20

GRIFFITH, Robert Finch. 136 FURMAN RD, STE 7 28607 #037-01-1988 L1991 IM *020 †20

HACKER, Marye E. 336 DEERFIELD RD, ED WATAUGA MEDICAL CENTER 28607 #012-22-1986 L1993 FM *020 †18

HAIBACH, Peter Jos. 136 FURMAN RD, STE 7 28607 #011-03-1978 L1984 IM *020 †20

HARTER, Mark Richard. 237 LONGVUE DR STE A 28607 #045-01-1976 L1979 FM *020 †18

HELAK, Joseph Walter. 175 MARY ST 28607 #035-15-1975 L1983 CD IM *020 †20

HENDERSON, Anita. 950 STATE FARM RD, STE 300 28607 #050-02-1978 L1981 FM *020 †18

HERRING, William B. 194 DOCTORS DR 28607 #036-05-1953 L1953 ON HEM *071 †20

HERRING, Wm Arthur, Jr. 194 DOCTORS DR, P.A. 28607 #045-01-1965 L1972 ORS *071 †40

HOLMES, Patrick Edward. 400 SHADOWLINE DR, STE 201A 28607 #047-20-1994 L1995 VIR *020 †80

HUBBARD, John Behrens. 194 DOCTORS DR 28607 #051-07-2002 L2007 ORS *020

KADYK, Jan Marc. 194 DOCTORS DR 28607 #019-02-1969 L1976 ORS *020 †40

KRONTZ, Daniel Paul. 610 STATE FARM RD, STE A 28607 #028-01-1983 L1987 OPH *020 †35

LONAS, John Robt. 345A DEERFIELD RD 28607 #012-01-1986 L1998 PD *020 †55

LOPEZ, Tara Leigh. 336 DEERFIELD RD, EMERGENCY DEPARTMENT 28607 #011-02-2001 L2007 EM *020 †16

MARCHESE, John Richard. 166 DOCTORS DR 28607 #010-02-1961 L1970 OBG *020 †30

MASSEY, Thomas Neely. 175 MARY ST 28607 #036-05-1955 L1955 CD IM *020 †20

MC ADAMS, Suzanne Elaine. 895 STATE FARM RD STE 501 28607 #010-01-1990 L1996 N *020 †75

MIDDLEBROOK, Margaret F. 345 DEERFIELD RD STE A 28607 #036-05-1990 L2001 PD *020 †55

MILLER, Edmund Eugene. 610 STATE FARM RD, # A 28607 #016-06-1974 L1978 OPH *020 †35

MILLER, Harold. ■ 28607 #035-08-1940 L1945 GP *071

MINER, Frederick Parker C. 434 DEERFIELD FOREST PKWY 28607 #012-01-1979 L1982 EM *020 †16

MOORE, Jill Olinger. 169 DOCTORS DR 28607 #047-20-2001 L2005 D *020 †15

MOREHOUSE, Winifred V. 400 SHADOWLINE DR, STE 104 28607 #024-07-2000 L2007 MPD *020 †20,55

MURPHEY, Susan Elizabeth. 336 DEERFIELD RD 28607 #048-13-1990 L2004 FM *020 †18

MURREY, Marshall Cary. 950 STATE FARM RD, STE 300 28607 #047-06-1989 L1992 FM *020 †18

NENOW, Mark Chas. 895 STATE FARM RD, STE 303 28607 #016-01-1986 L2005 OTO A *020 †45 ‡

NEWELL, John Chilton. 194 DOCTORS DR 28607 #027-01-1984 L1990 ORS *020 †40

NGUYEN, Daniel Hien. 212 BIRCH ST 28607 #011-03-1992 L1997 AN *020 †05

NORDSTROM, Carl Robt. ASU HEALTH SERVICES 28608 #036-05-1976 L1978 FM *020 †18

OLIVER, Frederick C, Jr. ■ 28607 #045-01-1975 L1979 IM *071 †20

PALMER, John Eric. 108 DOCTORS DR 28607 #028-03-1995 L1997 IM *020 †20

PETERSON, Anne C. 838 STATE FARM RD STE 1 28607 #047-06-1997 L2002 GS *020 †85

PETERSON, Matthew Shane. 870 STATE FARM RD, STE 100 28607 #047-06-1997 L2002 OBG *020 †30

PRESSLY, Margaret Rose. 381 DEERFIELD RD 28607 #036-05-01-1990 L2006 FM *075 †18

PREWITT, Thomas Wendall. 838 STATE FARM RD, STE 1 28607 #027-01-1988 L1995 GS SO *020 †85

QUALHEIM, Robert Everett. 400 SHADOWLINE DR, STE 101 28607 #036-05-1981 L1984 NEP *020 †18,20

REED, Robert Andrew. 400 SHADOWLINE DR, STE 201A 28607 #012-05-1962 L1991 R *071

RUSHING, Dykes T, Jr. ■ 28608 #001-02-1994 L1997 PD *020 †55

SHIRLEY, Robert E L, Jr. 870 STATE FARM RD, STE 100 28607 #012-01-1969 L1975 OBG *020 †30

SMITH, Leslie Ann. 336 DEERFIELD RD, PEACHTREE INTERNAL MEDICIN 28607 #036-08-2002 L2005 IM *020 †20

SNYDER, Robert Carlson. 237 LONGVUE DR, STE D 28607 #041-12-1971 L1996 PUD IM *020

SPARKS, Margaret Kimbel. 581 MEADOWVIEW DR 28607 #020-02-1983 L2000 D DS *020 †15

STAFFORD, Sharon Kane. 336 DEERFIELD RD, WATANGA MED CTR ED 28607 #047-06-1978 L1988 EM FM *020 †20

STANLEY, Ronald Jay. 169 DOCTORS DR 28607 #036-01-1972 L1972 D *020 †15

ST CLAIR, Wesley Scott. 345 DEERFIELD RD STE A, ADOLESCENT MEDICINE, INC 28607 #012-01-1999 L2002 PD *020 †55

STEIN, Marshall Jay. 132 POPLAR GROVE CONNECTOR, NEW RIVER BHC STE B 28607 #035-46-1976 L1979 P *020

STEIN, Theodore D. ■ 28607 #165-04-1971 L1973 GP *071

STRICKLAND, Daniel M. 336 DEERFIELD RD 28607 #012-01-1976 L1992 OBG REN *020 †30

SYKES, Charles Louis, Jr. 108 DOCTORS DR 28607 #036-05-1977 L1977 IM *020 †20 ‡

TAYLOR, Russell Carl. 108 DOCTORS DR 28607 #036-01-1964 L1964 IM *020

TEETER, Robert Tennant. 126 POPLAR GROVE RD, CONNECTOR RD 28607 #036-01-1974 L1974 OBG *020 †30

THOMPSON, Otis R, Jr. ■ 28607 #036-05-1953 L1953 IM *071

TRATE, Douglas Michael. 870 STATE FARM RD, STE 102 28607 #033-05-1990 L1996 GE IM *020 †20

TRATE, T Cate. 870 STATE FARM RD, STE 102 28607 #041-13-1992 L1996 PM *020 †60

VANDIVER, Scott Lee. 212 BIRCH ST 28607 #047-06-1983 L1984 AN *020 †20,05

VILAS, Laureen Noll. 132 POPLAR GROVE RD 28607 #045-04-1989 L2004 CHP *020 ‡

WALLER, Ted James. 194 DOCTORS DR 28607 #016-06-1966 L1973 ORS *071 †40

WESTPHAL, Aaron Addison. ■ 28607 #045-45-2002 L2007 D *020 †15

WHANGER, Herbert Noel. ■ 28607 #038-06-1954 L1954 P OS *071

WHITLOCK, John Lee. 136 FURMAN RD, STE 7 28607 #023-01-1973 L1984 IM GP *020 †20

WHITTAKER, David Stanton, Jr. 169 DOCTORS DR, BOONE DERMATOLOGY CLINIC 28607 #011-03-1996 L2000 D *020 †15 ‡

WINFIELD, John Buckner. 400 SHADOWLINE DR, STE 102 28607 #035-20-1968 L1978 RHU IM *050 †20

WOLFE, Kevin Wiley. 950 STATE FARM RD, STE 200 28607 #017-20-1983 L2007 PUD IM *020 †20

WOLFF, A Donald. 336 DEERFIELD RD 28607 #036-01-1954 L1954 RO *071 †80

YANG, Gan-Hsiung. ■ 28607 #244-05-1981 L1984 P *020 †75

ZIMMERMAN, Clinton B, Jr. 345 DEERFIELD RD, STE A 28607 #036-05-1987 L1991 PD *020 †55

ZUBER, Thomas John. 336 DEERFIELD RD 28607 #036-01-1983 L1986 FM FPG *020 †18

BRASSTOWN – CLAY

YONG, Shiong Sung. ■ 28902 #244-02-1968 L1980 U *020

BREVARD – TRANSYLVANIA

BAHNSON, Frederic F. 188 MEDICAL PARK DR, STE B 28712 #036-01-1973 L1973 OTO *020 †45

BAUM, William Carman. ■ 28712 #025-01-1942 L1943 U *071 †95

BENTON, George Ruffin, III. 90 HOSPITAL DR 28712 #036-01-1973 L1973 FM FSM *020 †18

BIERRENBACH, Ricardo C. 45 N COUNTRY CLUB RD 28712 #187-86-1987 L2002 P *020

BODIE, Barry Hoyt. 4 MEDICAL PARK DR 28712 #045-01-1982 L1997 U *020 †95

CLARK, John Douglas, Jr. 90 HOSPITAL DR 28712 #036-05-1990 L1994 OBG *071

COHEN, Joseph A. ■ 28712 #035-03-1989 L1992 EM IM *020 †20

COOK, James Hosmer. 3 MEDICAL PARK DR 28712 #018-03-1963 L1972 D *020 †15

DUNKELBERG, Ray H. 123 GALLIMORE RD, MEDICAL ASSCS OF TRANSYLVA 28712 #045-01-1967 L1975 IM NEP *020 †20

FARRAR, Martha Carver. ■ 28712 #045-01-1989 L1989 P *020 †75

FARRAR, William Edmund. ■ 28712 #012-01-1958 L1958 ID IM *062 †20

FINNERTY, Frank A, Jr. ■ 28712 #010-02-1947 L1996 CD IM *071 †20

FISHER, Anthony Lee. ■ 28712 #045-01-1994 L1997 EM *020 †16

FLECK, Laura Beth. 316 CHESTNUT ST 28712 #016-06-1985 L2002 N *020 †75 ‡

FOSTER, Marshall Shane. 120 E MAIN ST, STE 105 28712 #036-05-1994 L1997 FM *020 †18

FRIEDMAN, Alan David. 317 CHESTNUT ST 28712 #001-02-1968 L1979 U *020 †95

GEBB, David Martin. 1910 ASHEVILLE HWY 28712 #011-02-1969 L1973 OBG GP *020

GOYNE, Ruth Garner. ■ 28712 #041-07-1946 L1947 GP *071

GRAHAM, Angus Woodward. 316 CHESTNUT ST 28712 #011-04-1984 L1993 OAR OSS *020 †20,40

GREGOR, Henry Frederick. 120 E MAIN ST, STE 105 28712 #051-04-1978 L1991 OBG *020 †30

HARRIS, Stephen M. 137 MOYTOY LN 28712 #024-05-1951 L1955 P ADP *072 †75

HAWK, Robert Joe. 1140 ASHEVILLE HWY 28712 #012-05-1965 L2006 GYN *020 †30

HENDEL, Robert Chas. 90 HOSPITAL DR 28712 #008-02-1972 L1979 GS *020 †20

HERNANDEZ, Carmelo Abel. 87 MEDICAL PARK DR, STE B 28712 #038-45-1997 L2001 OBG *020 †30

HOEKSTRA, Suzanne Alisa. 87 MEDICAL PARK DR, STE A 28712 #016-45-1993 L1998 GS VS *020 †85

ISSERMAN, Mark Steven. 89 MEDICAL PARK DR, STE C 28712 #041-02-1977 L1995 IM CD *020 †20

JENNINGS, Lowell E. ■ 28712 #017-20-1949 L1952 FM *071

JOHNSON, James Carl. ■ 28712 #056-06-1964 L1989 ORS *020 †40

KEELEY, James Murray. 90 HOSPITAL DR 28712 #048-02-1960 L1964 FM *020 †18

KILPATRICK, Gerald Thos. ■ 28712 #012-05-1966 L2003 PD *071 †55

KITAHATA, Luke Masahiko. ■ 28712 #572-03-1947 L1964 AN *071 †05

LEFLER, Charles Deems. 90 HOSPITAL DR 28712 #036-01-1970 L1970 IM *020 †20

LEMEL, Mark Steven. 316 CHESTNUT ST, STE 2 28712 #038-06-1986 L2004 HS ORS *020 †40

MARQUIS, James Ralph. 341 AYUGIDV CT, CONNESTEE FALLS 28712 #010-01-1956 L1997 PDR R *071 †80

MARSCHKE, Gerald Roger. 192 EAGLE POINT DR 28712 #026-04-1955 L1996 IM *020 †20

MARTIN, Gerald R. 317 CHESTNUT ST 28712 #048-02-1987 L1988 IM *020 †20

MATZKE, Debbie Sue. ■ 28712 #026-04-1978 L2006 IM *071 †20 ‡

MELTON, Emily Rogers. 187 MEDICAL PARK DR 28712 #036-08-2003 L2006 FM *020 †18

MILETI, Carmen Gabriela. 90 HOSPITAL DR 28712 #781-01-1990 L2007 IM *020 †20

MYERS, Veresa Troutman. 3 MEDICAL PARK DR, HENDERSONVILLE PEDIATRICS 28712 #036-01-1994 L1995 PD *020 †55

NASH, Allan Dale. 1664 PROBART ST 28712 #019-02-1970 L1976 IM *020 †20

O'CAIN, Charles Frank. 90 HOSPITAL DR 28712 #012-05-1973 L1980 PUD SME *020 †20

PEDERSEN, Joseph Terrance. ■ 28712 #035-15-1994 L1999 RO ON *072 ‡

POSTON, Robert Lewis. 187 MEDICAL PARK DR 28712 #036-07-1957 L1957 GP *020 †18

PUMILIA, Paul Wolff. 123 GALLIMORE RD, TRANSYLVANIA, PA 28712 #021-05-1997 L2001 IM *020 †20

RHOLL, James Cornell. 7 MEDICAL PARK DR, BLDG 7 28712 #026-04-1989 L1999 IM *020 †20

ROGERS, Andrew Lewis. 90 HOSPITAL DR 28712 #045-01-1982 L1987 OS *062 †85

ROGERS, James Speed. ■ 28712 #025-01-1945 L1948 NS *071 †25

SANDERS, James H, Jr. 5 MEDICAL PARK DR 28712 #045-01-1951 L1952 FPG ADM *071 †18

SHAW, James Robt. 123 GALLIMORE RD, MEDICAL ASSOCS OF TRANSYLV 28712 #045-01-1978 L1990 EM *020 †18

SHEA, Timothy J. 187 MEDICAL PARK DR 28712 #035-03-1995 L1998 FM *020 †18

SNETMAN, Lawrence A. 20 YUNEGA CT 28712 #011-02-1974 L2007 IM HEM *020 †20 ‡

STAMM, Carl Peter. 7 MEDICAL PARK DR, BLDG 7 28712 #035-09-1980 L1992 GE *020 †20

STEINFELD, Lowell Alvin. ■ 28712 #011-03-1964 L2003 IM CD *020 †20

ST JOHN, Thos Arthur, Jr. ■ 28712 #041-02-1974 L1999 PD NDP *020 †55

STRICKER, Dorothea G. RR 3 BOX 66 28712 #026-04-1942 L1948 OS *075

SZTYBER, Gerard. 90 HOSPITAL DR 28712 #654-01-1997 L2002 FM *020

TYSON, James Wm. 90 HOSPITAL DR 28712 #048-02-1968 L1968 FM *020 †18

VARNER, Donald R, Jr. 7 MEDICAL PARK DR, BLDG 7 28712 #036-05-1981 L1989 GE IM *020 †20

VOLATILE, Katherine M. 188 MEDICAL PARK DR STE C, LOOKING GLASS EYE CENTER P 28712 #012-05-1983 L2002 OPH *020 †35

WELLS, Ora John. 157 MEDICAL PARK DR, HENDERSONVILLE PED PA 28712 #012-01-1977 L1998 PD *020 †55

WOODWORTH, Everett Wayne. ■ 28712 #016-11-1948 L1950 GS *071 †85

BROWNS SUMMIT – GUILFORD

AMES, Richard Haight. ■ 27214 #036-07-1941 L1948 **NS** *071 †25
MOORE, Donald Wilson. 4901 E NC HIGHWAY 150 27214 #036-05-1976 L1980 **FM** *020 †18

BRYSON CITY – SWAIN

ARKANSAS, Carmen. 45 PLATEAU ST 28713 #049-01-1998 L2002 **PD** *020
BUNNOW, Thomas Lawrence. 45 PLATEAU ST, STE 250 28713 #025-07-2000 L2004
    FM *020 †18 ‡
CRIDER, Steven Snowden. 45 PLATEAU ST, STE 250 28713 #047-20-1996 L1998 **IM** *020 †20
ENGEL, Mark Allen. 45 PLATEAU ST, STE 250 28713 #040-02-1997 L2000 **FM** *020 †18
GOGGIN, Colin Warner. 45 PLATEAU ST STE 250, SWAIN MED CTR 28713 #051-01-1999 L2003
    FM EM *020 †18
HOOPER, Robert Leslie. 45 PLATEAU ST 28713 #036-05-1964 L1964 **R NR** *071 †80
KORKEILA, Petri J. ■ 28713 #374-02-1986 L1998 **IM** *020 †20
KUMAR, Jai Robert. 45 PLATEAU ST 28713 #036-07-1995 L1999 **PD** *020 †55
NORDLING, Robert Eric. LAUDA CEMETERY ROAD 28713 #030-05-1958 L1959 **GP** *020 †18
ONEILL, Penelope Herndon. 45 PLATEAU ST 28713 #045-04-1990 L1993 **PD** *020 †55
SALE, Paul Russell. ■ 28713 #020-02-1971 L1973 **GP** *020
SAM, Jennifer. 45 PLATEAU ST STE 250, DBA SWAIN MEDICAL CENTER 28713
    #005-18-2000 L2004 **FM** *020 †18 ‡
SHELL, Peter Mathes. ■ 28713 #047-06-1988 L2003 **IM** *020 †20
TOLEDO, Charles Humberto. 45 PLATEAU ST 28713 #011-03-1984 L1987 **PD** *030 †55
VAN DEUSEN, Linda Sue. 45 PLATEAU ST, STE 250 28713 #012-05-1999 L2003 **FM** *020 †18
VANMIDDLESWORTH, Frank L. 45 PLATEAU ST, STE 200 28713 #036-01-2003 L2006
    FM *020 †18
ZIMMERMAN, David Bruce. 45 PLATEAU ST STE 2, SWAIN COUNTY HOSPITAL 28713
    #038-43-1985 L1990 **FM** *020

BUIES CREEK – HARNETT

BLACKMON, Bruce B. 502 HATCHER ST 27506 #036-05-1951 L1951 **OM GP** *072
HARRIS, Robert Mark. ■ 27506 #036-01-1977 L1977 **P** *020 †75

BUNN – FRANKLIN

KUMAR, Dhruva. 285 MAIN ST, BUNN MEDICAL CENTER 27508 #495-84-1976 L1995
    FM *020 †18

BUNNLEVEL – HARNETT

BROWN, Jamey Ann. ■ 28323 #023-12-2006 L2007 **FP** *012

BURGAW – PENDER

ADAMS, James Wellington. 507 E FREMONT ST 28425 #036-05-1997 L1998 **FM** *020 †18
DIAMOND, Patrick. 308 S BENNETT ST 28425 #649-19-1988 L2001 **FM** *075
GONZALEZ, Claudia Edith. 301 S CAMPBELL ST 28425 #036-05-2000 L2002 **FM** *020 †18
NASRALLAH, Naseem Hani. 407 E FREMONT ST, SURGICAL MEDICAL CLINIC 28425
    #915-02-1965 L1974 **GS** *071 †85
PEREZ, Mark David. 506 E FREMONT ST, EMERGENCY DEPT 28425 #011-03-1994 L1997
    FM *020 †18
RALLIS, Michael Geo. 301 S MCNEIL ST 28425 #010-01-1977 L1979 **IM** *020 †20
SINGH, Brajendra Prasad. 507 E FREMONT ST 28425 #495-54-1979 L1985 **IM** *020 †20
WECKEL, Bryan Monty. 310 S BENNETT ST, BOX 1266 28425 #036-05-1998 L1999
    FM PLM *020 †18

BURLINGTON – ALAMANCE

ABERNETHY, Paul Mc Bee. 1214 VAUGHN RD 27217 #036-05-1943 L1943 **OPH** *071 †35
ADAMS, James Gilroy. 1236 HUFFMAN MILL RD, STE 2000 27215 #020-02-1991 L1994
    APM IM *020 †05
ANDERSON, Marshall Wilson. 1234 HUFFMAN MILL RD 27215 #036-01-1993 L1995
    IM *020 †20
ANDREASSI, Maureen P. 1234 HUFFMAN MILL RD 27215 #035-48-1994 L1996 **IM** *020 †20
ARMOUR, Edouard Fitzroy. 1234 HUFFMAN MILL RD, DEPT OF ORTHOPAEDICS 27215
    #047-05-1995 L2001 **OSM** *020 †40
ATTIGERE, Rekha Nagappa. 1240 HUFFMAN MILL RD 27215 #495-99-2001 L2007 **IM** *100 †20
BAILEY, Scott Allen. 3804 S CHURCH ST 27215 #055-01-2002 L2005 **PD** *020 †55
BATES, Harold Bascom. ■ 27215 #036-05-1954 L1954 **U** *071 †95
BAUGHMAN, D Joe. ■ 27215 #038-06-1957 L1957 **OS** *071
BAUMAN, Robert Paul. 1236 HUFFMAN MILL RD, PIEDMONT VASCULAR STE 130 27215
    #025-07-1977 L1984 **CD IM** *020 †20
BENNETT, Paul Scott. 1248 HUFFMAN MILL RD 27215 #036-01-1993 L1998 **OTO** *020 †45
BERRY, Jonathan Jordan. 1678 WESTBROOK AVE 27215 #041-01-1983 L1986 **CD IM** *020 †20
BHATTI, M Amjad. 1236 HUFFMAN MILL RD, STE 1500 27215 #704-01-1961 L1972
    GS CD *071 †85,90
BHATTI, M Arshad. 1236 HUFFYINGTON MILL ROAD 27216 #704-01-1964 L1971 **CD IM** *020
BHOTIKA, Seema Santosh. 1234 HUFFMAN MILL RD, KERNODLE CLINIC 27215
    #036-05-2004 L2007 **FM** *020 †18
BIGNER, Sandra H. 2039 WILLOW SPRING LN, LABCORP CYTOLOGY 27215
    #047-06-1971 L1975 **PTH** *020 †50
BIOLA, Holly Rose. 5270 UNION RIDGE RD, DUKE GERIATRICS DIVISION 27217
    #012-05-2000 L2003 **IMG** *020 †18,70
BLAIR, George Walker, Jr. ■ 27215 #041-01-1947 L1947 **IM** *071
BLOCKER, Michael Edward. 1236 HUFFMAN MILL RD, STE 2800 27215 #024-16-1994 L1996
    ID IM *020 †20
BONNEY, Warren Kent. 3804 S CHURCH ST 27215 #041-13-1992 L1998 **PD** *020 †55

BRAY, Anthony David. 1240 HUFFMAN MILL RD 27215 #036-01-1992 L2006 **FM** *020 †18
BROWN, Alycia Moore. 1236 HUFFMAN MILL RD, MEDICAL ARTS CTR STE 2500 27215
    #036-01-2000 L2001 **CHP P** *020 †75 ‡
BROWN, Jeffrey Eugene. 1234 HUFFMAN MILL RD, KERNODLE CLINIC WEST 27215
    #036-01-2000 L2003 **IM** *020
BROWNE, Geoffrey Hamet. 1240 HUFFMAN MILL RD 27215 #036-08-1991 L1996 **R** *020 †28
BULLA, Jefferson D II. 315 N GRAHAM HOPEDALE RD 27217 #036-01-1960 L1960 **GP** *071
BURNETTE, Howard Olsen. ■ 27215 #051-04-1947 L1948 **GP** *071
BYRNETT, Jeffrey Wm. 1041 KIRKPATRICK RD, STE 150 27215 #038-40-1979 L1985
    GS VS *020 †85
CALIFF, James Christopher. 1234 HUFFMAN MILL RD 27215 #036-07-1981 L1988
    ORS *020 †40
CALLWOOD, Dwayne Dennis. 1236 HUFFMAN MILL RD, STE 1000 27215 #051-04-1989 L1992
    CD *020 †20
CARROLL, Hillary Nichols. 3804 S CHURCH ST 27215 #036-05-1987 L1991 **PD** *020 †55
CARROLL, Paul Joseph. 1236 HUFFMAN MILL RD, STE 2000 27215 #036-05-1987 L1991
    AN *020
CARTER, Robert Wilson. ■ 27215 #036-05-1963 L1963 **IM CD** *071 †20
CHAPLIN, Don Clarence. 1234 HUFFMAN MILL RD 27215 #036-01-1969 L1969 **IM** *020 †20 ‡
CHEN, William Youngson. 1236 HUFFMAN MILL RD, PO BOX 209 27215 #028-34-1981 L1989
    P *020 †75
CHEREN, Isa. 319 N GRAHAM HOPEDALE RD, FL B 27217 #036-05-1988 L1991 **FM** *020 †18
CHOKSI, Janak K. 1236 HUFFMAN MILL RD, STE 120 27215 #495-23-1972 L1982
    ON HEM *020 †20
CHRYSTAL, Glenn Stuart. 1236 HUFFMAN MILL RD, HEMATOLOGY ASSOCIATES LLP 27215
    #010-01-1983 L1988 **RO ATP** *030 †80
CLARK, Joseph Madison. 1248 HUFFMAN MILL RD 27215 #036-05-1995 L1997 **OTO** *020 †45
CLARKE, Peter R H. 1234 HUFFMAN MILL RD 27215 #025-01-1983 L1986 **N** *020 †75
COOPER, Hector W. 1240 HUFFMAN MILL RD 27215 #036-01-1996 L2001 **DR** *020 †80
COPE, Brian Scott. 1236 HUFFMAN MILL RD, STE 2550 27215 #036-05-1991 L1996 **U** *020 †95
CRAWFORD, Larry Clarke. 1234 HUFFMAN MILL RD 27215 #036-05-1971 L1971 **GS** *020 †85
CRISP, Gregory Hannibal. 1236 HUFFMAN MILL RD, STE 2000 27215 #036-01-1978 L1981
    AN *020
DANIEL, Michael Page. 1041 KIRKPATRICK RD, STE 250 27215 #012-05-1985 L1992
    U GS *020 †95
DAVIS, Christopher Lee. 2260 S CHURCH ST STE 603 27215 #036-01-1980 L1982 **OS IM** *020
DAVIS, Jack B. 1914 MCKINNEY ST, B M A BURLINGTON 27217 #024-01-1948 L1952 **P** *020
DE FRANCESCO, Martin A. 1234 HUFFMAN MILL RD 27215 #041-14-1984 L1993
    OBG FM *020 †30
DINGELDEIN, Steven Andrew. 3344 S CHURCH ST 27215 #036-01-1982 L1985 **OPH** *020 †35
DU BARD, Carol Annette. 221 N GRAHAM HOPEDALE RD, PIEDMONT HEALTH
    SERVICES, 27217 #023-07-1996 L1999 **GPM** *020 †18,70
DURHAM, David Brannan. 1236 HUFFMAN MILL RD, MEDIAL ARTS BLDG 27215
    #305-01-2003 L2007 **P** *020
DUSZLAK, Carla G. 1211 MAY CT 27215 #024-16-1978 L1982 **P** *074 †75
EASON, Ernest Bernard. 1522 VAUGHN RD 27217 #036-01-1980 L1983 **IM** *020
ELLINGTON, Amzi J, Jr. ■ 27215 #041-13-1952 L1953 **OBG** *071 †30
ELLINGTON, Robert Norwood. ■ 27215 #036-07-1957 L1957 **GP** *020 †30
ELLIOTT, Robert Taylor. 1234 HUFFMAN MILL RD 27215 #045-01-1978 L1987 **GE IM** *020 †20
ELMAHI, Nadear. 1240 HUFFMAN MILL RD, ALAMANCE REGIONAL MEDICAL 27215
    #848-01-2001 L2006 **IM** *020 †20
ELSANJAK, Abdelaziz Ali. ■ 27215 #913-07-1991 L2007 **IM** *020
EVANS, Ricky Lee. 1234 HUFFMAN MILL RD 27215 #036-08-1994 L1996 **OBG** *020 †30
FATH, Kenneth Alan. 1234 HUFFMAN MILL RD, KERNODLE CLINIC INC 27215
    #038-40-1986 L1994 **CD IM** *020 †20
FISHER, Donald Eugene. 1041 KIRKPATRICK RD, PRACTICE 27215 #018-03-1996 L1999
    FM *020 †18
FLOWER, Kori Bridget. 221 N GRAHAM HOPEDALE RD 27217 #005-02-1998 L2002
    PD *020 †55
FRALIX, Teresa Ann. 221 N GRAHAM HOPEDALE RD, DREW CHC 27217 #036-07-1996 L1997
    FM *020 †18
GAMBLE, William Hedrick. 1678 WESTBROOK AVE 27215 #036-01-1976 L1977 **CD IM** *020
GANJI, Jagadeesh R. 1678 WESTBROOK AVE 27215 #495-99-1990 L2001 **CD IC** *020 †20
GERLACH, David Campbell. 1240 HUFFMAN MILL RD 27215 #047-05-1990 L1995 **IM** *020 †20
GILBERT, Richard Leslie. 1041 KIRKPATRICK RD, PRACTICE 27215 #036-08-1986 L1987
    FM *020 †18
GITTIN, Robert Glen. 1236 HUFFMAN MILL RD, HEMATOLOGY ASSOCIATES LLP 27215
    #422-01-1981 L1987 **IM** *020 †20
GOLDAR, Margarita Maria. 2322B S CHURCH ST, MARGARITA GOLDAR, PC 27215
    #308-01-1981 L2004 **PD** *020 ‡
GOLEY, Alexander Fairley. 1509 VAUGHN RD 27217 #036-01-1956 L1956 **IM** *071 †20
GRINER, Eugene Wilson, Jr. 1240 HUFFMAN MILL RD 27215 #017-20-1978 L1982
    EM FM *020 †18,16
GUPTA, Abhinav. ■ 27215 #496-09-2000 L2007 **IM** *100 †20
HARMAN, John Simon. 827 HEATHER RD, BURLINGTON UROLOGICAL ASSO 27215
    #051-04-1961 L1968 **U OS** *020 †95
HARPER, Larry Olen. 1234 HUFFMAN MILL RD 27215 #055-01-1967 L1973 **IM END** *020 †20
HARRIS, Robert Paul. 1091 KIRKPATRICK RD 27215 #036-05-1996 L2000 **OBG** *020 †30
HAVILAND, Ann E. 1234 HUFFMAN MILL RD 27215 #025-07-1980 L1984 **IM GE** *020 †20
HAYES, James Wm. GRAHAM HOPEDALE RD 27215 #036-01-1955 L1955 **ORS** *071 †40
HAZARIKA, Surovi. PO BOX 1305 27216 #495-18-1998 **IM** *012
HEADEN, Kenneth Jay. 804 S CHURCH ST 27215 #036-01-1992 L1994 **P** *020
HEARD, William Upton. 1240 HUFFMAN MILL RD, PRIMEDOC OF BURLINGTON, PA 27215
    #021-01-1992 L2003 **IM** *020 †20
HEARN, Andrew Taylor. 1248 HUFFMAN MILL RD 27215 #038-40-1990 L2006 **VS GS** *020 †85
HENDERSON, Richard Robt. 1522 VAUGHN RD 27217 #017-20-1961 L1962 **D** *020 †15
HINES, Edward Lloyd. 1236 HUFFMAN MILL RD, STE 2300 27215 #010-01-1970 L1976
    ORS HS *020 †40
HODGES, James Thos. 1234 HUFFMAN MILL RD, KERNODLE CLINIC 27215
    #036-05-1963 L1964 **ORS** *071 †40
HOOTEN, James Philmon, Jr. 1234 HUFFMAN MILL RD, KERNODLE CLINIC 27215
    #036-01-1987 L1988 **ORS** *020 †40
IVEY, William Coy. ■ 27216 #036-01-1956 L1956 **GP IM** *071
JADALI, Fayegh. 2961 CROUSE LN, STE A 27215 #409-10-1987 L1997 **IM NM** *020 †20,28
JEFFRIES, Cheryl Lynette. 316 N GRAHAM HOPEDALE RD, KERNODLE CLINIC 27217
    #036-01-1986 L1989 **IM** *020 †20

JIBRAIL, Wadi Jurjus. ■ 27216 #396-04-1958 L1967 **GP** *071
JOHNSON, David Sander. 3804 S CHURCH ST 27215 #047-06-1977 L1981 **PD** *020 †55
JOHNSON, Leslie Donald. 1240 HUFFMAN MILL RD 27215 #036-05-1969 L1969 **DR** *071 †80
JOHNSON, Sarah Elizabeth. 221 N GRAHAM HOPEDALE RD, CENTER 27217 #023-07-1996 L1998 **FM** *020 †18
JOHNSTON, John David. 1240 HUFFMAN MILL RD, PRIME DOC OF BURLINGTON, P 27215 #012-22-1999 L2001 **IM** *020 †20
JORDAN, David Alan. 1240 HUFFMAN MILL RD 27215 #036-05-1981 L1992 **DR NM** *020 †20,80
KELLY, Charles Anthony. 1234 HUFFMAN MILL RD 27215 #010-02-1993 L2002 **N** *020 †75
KELLY, Thomas Andrew. 1678 WESTBROOK AVE 27215 #035-19-1981 L1983 **CD** *020 †20
KEPHART, William K. 1236 HUFFMAN MILL RD 27215 #045-01-1992 L1997 **APM** *020 †05
KERNER, Michael Louis. 1225 HUFFMAN MILL RD, BURLINGTON IMAGING-BREAST 27215 #010-02-1975 L1993 **DR** *020 †80
KERNODLE, Charles E, Jr. ■ 27215 #036-07-1942 L1944 **GS** *071
KERNODLE, Donald R. 316 N GRAHAM HOPEDALE RD 27217 #036-07-1953 L1953 **OPH OTO** *071
KERNODLE, Dwight Talmadge. KERNODLE CLINIC 27215 #036-07-1947 L1947 **IM** *020
KERNODLE, Geo Wallace, Jr. 1234 HUFFMAN MILL RD 27215 #036-01-1981 L1983 **RHU IM** *020 †20 ‡
KERNODLE, George Wallace. 1234 HUFFMAN MILL RD, KERNODLE CLINIC 27215 #036-07-1945 L1945 **PD** *071 †55
KERNODLE, Harold B, Jr. 1234 HUFFMAN MILL RD, KEMODLE CLINIC 27215 #036-07-1969 L1969 **ORS** *020 †40
KHAN, Fozia M. 2991 CROUSE LN, NOVA MEDICAL ASSOCIATES 27215 #704-04-1991 L1997 **IM** *020 †20
KHAN, Neelam S. 2905 CROUSE LN, STE 2250 27215 #704-06-1990 L1997 **IM** *020 †20
KHAN, Saadat A. 2991 CROUSE LN, NOVA MEDICAL ASSOCIATES, L 27215 #704-04-1989 L1997 **PCC** *020 †20
KHAN, Shaukat Ali. 2905 CROUSE LN 27215 #704-01-1985 L1997 **CD** *020 †20
KINCIUS, Constance Ann. 1091 KIRKPATRICK RD 27215 #017-20-1978 L1982 **GYN** *020 †30
KLEIN, Bert Jack, III. 1234 HUFFMAN MILL RD 27215 #036-05-1996 L1997 **IM** *020 †20
KLEINMAN, Dawn Elizabeth. 1240 HUFFMAN MILL RD 27215 #036-01-1997 L1998 **D** *020 †15
KNERR, Julia Snow. 319 N GRAHAM HOPEDALE RD, HEALTH, DISAB & SUB ABUSE 27217 #035-46-1988 L2000 **P** *020 †75
KNOWLES-JONAS, Lynde. 1236 HUFFMAN MILL RD, STE 2600 27215 #041-13-1993 L1998 **OBG** *020 †30 ‡
KOWALSKI, Bruce Jay. 1234 HUFFMAN MILL RD 27215 #055-02-1991 L1997 **CD** *020 †20
KOWALSKI, David Carl. 1734 WESTBROOK AVE 27215 #055-02-1987 L1988 **D** *020 †15
LAMB, Andrew Stephen. 1234 HUFFMAN MILL RD 27215 #001-02-1984 L1992 **IM** *020 †20 ‡
LANCE, Edward D. 316 N GRAHAM HOPEDALE RD 27217 #055-01-1984 L1987 **FM OS** *020 †18
LAVINE, Philip H. 1240 HUFFMAN MILL RD 27215 #023-01-1977 L2001 **P OS** *020 †75
LEE, Dae Hee. 2142 N CHURCH ST 27217 #583-01-1970 L1976 **FM EM** *020
LESUEUR, Robert Wilson. ■ 27216 #047-07-1930 L1931 **OS GP** *020
LINDLEY, Joseph J. KERNODLE CLINIC 27215 #051-04-1951 L1952 **GS** *071 †85
LITTLE, Robert Winfield. 2505 S MEBANE ST STE A 27215 #036-01-1972 L1972 **PD** *020 †55
LONG, Eugene Monroe, II. 1234 HUFFMAN MILL RD 27215 #036-07-1963 L1963 **GYN** *071 †30
MALONEY, Nancy Jane. 1041 KIRKPATRICK RD, PRACTICE 27215 #051-04-1996 L1999 **FM** *020 †18
MANN, Philip Rogers. 803 HERMITAGE RD 27215 #051-01-1960 L1962 **FM IM** *071 †18
MASOUD, Javed. 1236 HUFFMAN MILL RD # 14 27215 #704-08-1968 L1979 **CD IM** *050
MC NIEL, Jesse Neal. ■ 27215 #004-01-1960 L1964 **P IMG** *071 †75
MC QUEEN, Chapman Teague. 1248 HUFFMAN MILL RD 27215 #036-01-1991 L1994 **OTO** *020 †45
MC QUEEN, Robert Hughes. 1678 WESTBROOK AVE 27215 #036-08-1992 L1993 **CD** *020 †20
MEBANE, Charles Thos. ■ 27215 #047-07-1970 L1977 **DR GP** *020
MEBANE, Dorothy Gaither. ■ 27215 #010-03-1973 L1982 **PD** *020
MERTZ, David Kimo. 3804 S CHURCH ST 27215 #014-01-1996 L1997 **PD** *020 †55
MICKIEWICZ, Cristina W. 319 N GRAHAM HOPEDALE RD, HUMAN SERVICES CENTER 27217 #035-19-1981 L1992 **P** *020
MILLER, Aileen Heritage. 316 N GRAHAM HOPEDALE RD, KERNODLE CLINIC EASTTOWN 27217 #055-01-1983 L1985 **END** *020 †20
MILLER, Howard Edward. 1236 HUFFMAN MILL RD, STE 2300 27215 #035-15-1974 L1979 **ORS HS** *020 †40
MILLER, James Arthur. 316 N GRAHAM, KERNODLE CLINIC EASTOWNE 27217 #036-01-1981 L1983 **FM EM** *020 †20
MILLER, Mark Frederic. 1234 HUFFMAN MILL RD, KERNODLE CLINIC 27215 #036-07-1990 L1995 **IM** *020 †20
MILLER-ANDERSON, Lydia H. 319 N GRAHAM HOPEDALE RD, FL A 27217 #038-06-1998 L1999 **P** *020 †75
MIN, John Kyunghwan. 1234 HUFFMAN MILL RD, KERNODLE CLINIC 27215 #016-06-1995 L2000 **IM** *020 †20
MINTER, Karin Thomas. 3804 S CHURCH ST 27215 #036-07-2002 L2005 **PD** *100
MOFFETT, Joel Blane. 315 N GRAHAM HOPEDALE RD 27217 #036-01-1984 L1988 **FM** *020 †18
MOFFITT, Kristen Sampson. 3804 S CHURCH ST 27215 #017-20-1986 L1988 **PD** *020 †55
MORAYATI, Shamil J. 2921 CROUSE LN 27215 #528-03-1977 L1991 **END NM** *020 †28,18
MORRISEY, Lemont. 1041 KIRKPATRICK RD, STE 100 27215 #036-05-1981 L1982 **FM** *020 †18
MUNDY, Donald Ashford. 1236 HUFFMAN MILL RD, STE 2000 27215 #060-01-1967 L1977 **AN** *020 †05
NAVARRO, Hugo Antonio. 1240 HUFFMAN MILL RD, ALAMANCE REGIONAL MEDICAL 27215 #715-01-1986 L2005 **NPM** *020 †55
NAVEIRA, Francisco Arturo. 1236 HUFFMAN MILL RD, STE 2100 27215 #042-03-1988 L1994 **APM AN** *020 †05
NEWMAN, Ann E. 5270 UNION RIDGE RD, SCOTT CLINIC 27217 #036-07-1996 L1999 **GPM** *020 †18
NORTON, Larry Everett. 315 N GRAHAM HOPEDALE RD 27217 #036-05-1980 L1990 **FM** *020 †18
OLENICK, Sarah Jones. 1240 HUFFMAN MILL RD 27215 #016-43-1989 L1994 **PTH PCP** *020 †50
OSTROWSKI, Edward S. 1240 HUFFMAN MILL RD 27215 #024-16-1978 L1983 **DR** *020 †80
OWEN, Christina Denane. ■ 27215 #036-01-2007 **FP** *012
PALMER, Scott Patrick. 1236 HUFFMAN MILL RD, STE 2000 27215 #035-15-1988 L1989 **AN** *020 †05
PANDIT, Sandeep Raj. 1236 HUFFMAN MILL RD, HEMATOLOGY ASSOCIATES LLP 27215 #495-09-1992 L2004 **IM** *020 †20
PARADIS, Paula Yvette. 221 N GRAHAM HOPEDALE RD 27217 #023-07-1991 L1998 **PD** *020 †55

PARASCHOS, Alexander. 1234 HUFFMAN MILL RD 27215 #051-04-1986 L1993 **CD IM** *020 †20
PATEL, Sona Agamsharan. 1240 HUFFMAN MILL RD 27215 #495-23-1994 L2003 **IM** *020 †20 ‡
PATEL, Utpal K.. 1240 HUFFMAN MILL RD, PRIMEDOC OF BURLINGTON 27215 #308-13-2002 L2005 **AN** *012
PATTERSON, James Benson. 1638 MEMORIAL DR, ALAMANCE DERMATOLOGY PA 27215 #036-01-1976 L1976 **D DS** *020 †15 ‡
PAUL, Bhakti Bipin. ■ 27215 #496-38-2001 L2008 **IM** *012
PEED, Douglas Warren. 1234 HUFFMAN MILL RD 27215 #036-01-1984 L1988 **IM** *020 †20
PORFILIO, William Louis. ■ 27215 #036-01-2003 L2007 **OPH** *020
POWELL, James Bobbitt. 1447 YORK CT 27215 #036-07-1964 L1964 **CLP** *030 †50
POWELL, Thomas Edward, III. ■ 27216 #036-07-1961 L1961 **CLP** *030
POWER, Jon David. 1234 HUFFMAN MILL RD 27215 #004-01-1973 L1991 **OBG** *071 †30
PRUITT, Ronald Anthony. ■ 27215 #051-04-1959 L1961 **ORS** *071 †40
QAYUMI, Maleka. 2039 WILLOW SPRING LN 27215 #495-92-1976 L1997 **PTH** *020 †50
REGISTER, Thomas Eugene. 1240 HUFFMAN MILL RD 27215 #036-01-1984 L1991 **R** *020 †80
RINKER, George Ernest. 1240 HUFFMAN MILL RD 27215 #036-05-1965 L1965 **PTH** *020 †50 ‡
RIZWAN, Saima. 1240 HUFFMAN MILL RD, PRIMEDOC OF BURLINGTON, PA 27215 #704-06-2000 L2005 **IM** *100 †20
RODRIGUEZ, Iris Milagrosa. ■ 27215 #033-05-1994 L2001 **PD** *020 †55
ROSENOW, Philip John. 1091 KIRKPATRICK RD 27215 #012-05-1970 L1979 **OBG** *020 †30
ROWE, Theodore Chas, III. 1713 S CHURCH ST 27215 #051-04-1968 L1969 **FM** *020 †70,18
RYAN, William James. 1236 HUFFMAN MILL RD, MED ARTS CTR STE 2300 27215 #021-05-1972 L1973 **P** *020 †75
SANDERS-CLIETTE, Angela P. 2039 WILLOW SPRING LN, STE C 27215 #036-01-1989 L1994 **PCP** *050 †20
SANKAR, Seeplaputhur G. 1041 KIRKPATRICK RD, STE 150 27215 #495-15-1974 L1981 **GS VS** *020 †85
SCHERMERHORN, Thomas J. 1234 HUFFMAN MILL RD, 1234 HUFFMAN MILL RD 27215 #023-12-1989 L2001 **OBG** *020 †30
SCOTT, Charles Kimrey. 3804 S CHURCH ST 27215 #036-01-1966 L1966 **PD OS** *020 †55
SCOTT, Samuel Edwin. 1234 HUFFMAN MILL RD 27215 #036-01-1963 L1963 **FM** *071 †18
SHAPLEY-QUINN, Kathleen M. 319 N GRAHAM HOPEDALE RD, HUMAN SERVICES CENTER, SUI 27217 #036-01-1993 L1998 **FM** *020 †18
SHARMA, Ranjan. 2280 S CHURCH ST, STE 202 27215 #036-08-1986 L1989 **AI** *020 †20,03
SIEGEL, Drew. 1234 HUFFMAN MILL RD 27215 #649-14-1978 L1991 **GE IM** *020 †20
SKULSKIE, Martin Usher. 1234 HUFFMAN MILL RD, KERNODLE CLINIC 27215 #001-06-1994 L1999 **GE** *020 †20
SMITH, Christopher Edmund. 1236 HUFFMAN MILL RD, STE 2300 27215 #036-07-1976 L1984 **ORS HS** *020 †40 ‡
SMITH, Jarvis Wilton, Jr. 1234 HUFFMAN MILL RD 27215 #036-05-1980 L1985 **GS VS** *020 †85
SMITH, Jeffrey Alan. 1713 S CHURCH ST 27215 #036-01-1979 L1991 **OM R** *075
SOWLES, Krichna Ferrari. 1041 KIRKPATRICK RD, STE 100 27215 #187-54-1998 L2007 **FM** *020 †18
SPANN-SCOTT, Charlene. 316 N GRAHAM HOPEDALE RD 27217 #036-08-1994 L1997 **IM** *020 †20
SPARKS, Jeffrey David. 1234 HUFFMAN MILL RD 27215 #036-07-1989 L1991 **IM** *020 †20
SPEERS, Rex Wilson. ■ 27215 #049-01-1944 L1950 **PYA CHP** *071
SPRAGUE, Jane Hooper. 1240 HUFFMAN MILL RD 27215 #036-01-1981 L1982 **AN** *020 †05
STALLWORTH, James M, Jr. ■ 27215 #045-01-1971 L1990 **AN PME** *020 †05
STEIN, Rosemary F. 2105 MAPLE AVE 27215 #308-02-1988 L1999 **PD** *020 †55
STEWART, Tara Lisa. 1734 WESTBROOK AVE 27215 #049-01-1997 L1999 **D** *020 †15
STOIOFF, Scott Cooper. 1236 HUFFMAN MILL RD 27215 #045-01-1985 L1994 **U** *020 †95
STONEBURNER, Richard G. ■ 27215 #051-04-1942 L1953 **GS OS** *071 †85
SUTTON, Edward C. ■ 27215 #041-01-1951 L1951 **GYN** *071 †30
SYDNOR, Charles Ford. 1214 VAUGHN RD, ALAMANCE EYE CENTER 27217 #051-01-1969 L1972 **OPH** *020 †35
TATE, Allen Denny, Jr. ■ 27215 #023-01-1948 L1948 **FM** *071
TEJAN-SIE, Sheikh Ahmed. 2905 CROUSE LN 27215 #690-01-1991 L2005 **IM** *020 †20
THOMAS, Mathai S. 1236 HUFFMAN MILL RD, STE 2000 27215 #036-01-1977 L1977 **AN** *020 †05
VAICKUTE, Rima. 1240 HUFFMAN MILL RD 27215 #913-49-1988 L2004 **IM** *020 †20
VAN DALEN, Robert Warren. 1091 KIRKPATRICK RD 27215 #036-07-1979 L1983 **OBG** *020 †30
VAN STAVEREN, Gijsbertus. 1236 HUFFMAN MILL RD, STE 2000 27215 #660-03-1982 L1985 **AN** *020 †05
VAUGHT, William Wayne, Jr. 1248 HUFFMAN MILL RD 27215 #016-11-1968 L1975 **OTO** *020 †45
WADE, Eugene Henrypeter. 1041 KIRKPATRICK RD, STE 100 27215 #010-03-1981 L1984 **FM EM** *020 †18
WALKER, John Barrett, III. 1234 HUFFMAN MILL RD, MEDICAL DEPARTMENT 27215 #036-05-1975 L1975 **IM** *020 †20
WALL, Jack Gardner. 1240 HUFFMAN MILL RD 27215 #036-01-1968 L1968 **R** *020 †80
WALSH, Kim Marie. 319 N GRAHAM HOPEDALE RD, HUMAN SRV CTR STE B 27217 #036-07-1987 L1989 **PHP FM** *030 †18
WARD, David Clark. 1214 VAUGHN RD, LOWER LEVEL 27217 #036-01-1987 L1989 **CHP** *020 †20
WASHINGTON, John Langtry. 1236 HUFFMAN MILL RD, STE 2900 27215 #001-02-1975 L1976 **GYN FM** *020 †18,30
WEBSTER, Megan Aileen. ■ 27215 #048-13-2007 **P** *012
WIETING, Richard John. 1240 HUFFMAN MILL RD, PRIMEDOC OF BURLINGTON, PA 27215 #422-01-1999 L2007 **IM** *020 †20
WILLCOCKSON, William S. 1240 HUFFMAN MILL RD, ALAMANCE REG MED CTR 27215 #048-02-1985 L1986 **EM** *020
WILLIAMS, Joseph Benjamin. ■ 27215 #020-12-2005 **P** *012
WOLFF, Michael Richard. 827 HEATHER RD, BURLINGTON UROLOGICAL ASSO 27215 #017-20-1983 L1983 **U** *020 †95
YBANEZ, Jane Karen. 1236 HUFFMAN MILL RD, HEMATOLOGY ASSOCIATES LLP 27215 #038-06-1998 L2004 **HO** *020 †20
ZARZAR, George Theodore. ■ 27215 #605-01-1970 L1979 **GP** *075

BURNSVILLE – YANCEY

ANTINORI, Joseph James. 14 ACADEMY ST, BURNSVILLE FAMILY MEDICINE 28714 #033-05-2000 L2003 **FM** *020 †18
CORT, David Arthur. 320 PENSACOLA RD 28714 #036-05-1970 L1970 **EM IM** *020 †20
CORT, Gretchen Stuart. ■ 28714 #036-05-2008 *012

CRAIG, David Franklin. ■ 28714 #036-01-1979 L1980 **FM EM** *020 †18
CRIVEANU, Lucia. 800 MEDICAL CAMPUS DR 28714 #781-01-1980 L1996 **PD** *020 †55
KHAN, Shehla Gul. 800 MEDICAL CAMPUS DR 28714 #704-06-1991 L1999 **IM** *020 †20
MC GAHEY, Judith Goldman. 300 DHARMA WAY 28714 #035-46-1972 L1974 **FM ADL** *071 †18
MC KAY, James H W, III. SEVEN MILE RIDGE ROAD, CELO HEALTH CENTER#200 28714
#012-05-1984 L1990 **FM IM** *020 †18
MILLER, Robert Alan. ■ 28714 #051-04-1972 L2005 **ORS** *071 †40 ‡
MITCHELL, Philip Keith. ■ 28714 #036-08-1993 L1994 **FM** *020 †18
NEWBERRY, William Marcus, Jr. ■ 28714 #012-05-1964 L1964 **IM** *030
O'BRIEN, Sudeshna Dasgupt. 71 BLUE RIDGE LN 28714 #495-02-1982 L2003 **PD** *020 †55
PEVERALL, Elizabeth M. 116 SEVEN MILE RIDGE RD, CELO HEALTH CENTER 28714
#035-01-1993 L1995 **FM** *020 †18 ‡
POLGAR, Jeffrey Robert. 800 MEDICAL CAMPUS DR 28714 #024-07-2000 L2003 **FM** *020 †18
SITNICK, Joseph Louis. ■ 28714 #041-01-1961 L1976 **R** *071 †80
STELLA, Mitsuko. ■ 28714 #011-03-1998 L2000 **FM** *020 †18
STEPHENS, Peter John T. ■ 28714 #067-01-1965 L1970 **PTH FOP** *071 †50
STEWART, Russell M, III. ■ 28714 #055-01-1971 L1971 **PUD IM** *020 †20

BUTNER — GRANVILLE

AKINLI, Ergun Mehmet. 1003 12TH ST 27509 #902-10-1965 L1977 **P** *020
ALLEN, Andree M. 1003 12TH ST, JOHN UMSTEAD HOSP 27509 #011-02-1982 L1989
P *030 †75
ALLSBROOK, Linwood R. 1003 12TH ST, CPI-JUH 27509 #020-12-1981 L1984 **CHP P** *020 †75
AMAYA, Marcelino. JOHN UMSTEAD HOSPITAL 27509 #649-01-1954 L1965 **CHP P** *071 †75
ANDERSON-BROWN, Tedra L. 1003 12TH ST, BUTNER ALCOH & DRUG TREAT 27509
#036-07-1991 L1995 **P** *020 †75
ANTOLOVIC-STANFEL, Nives. 1003 12TH ST, JOHN UMSTEAD HOSPITAL 27509
#957-01-1983 L1997 **P** *020 †75
ARRINGTON, Erica Michelle. 1003 12TH ST, JOHN UMSTEAD HOSPITAL 27509
#036-01-1999 L2002 **CHP** *020
BONNER, Niranjani Reddy. 1600 E C ST, P O BOX 3000 27509 #495-57-1972 L2003
PHP PD *030 †55 ‡
BRIGGS, Andrew Gessner. JOHN UMSTEAD HOSP 27509 #051-01-1956 L1957 **P** *071 †75
CARRERAS, Pedro. 1003 12TH ST 27509 #847-01-1948 L1964 **P** *071
CASSIDY, Frederick. 1003 12TH ST, BLDG 24 27509 #047-05-1988 L1991 **P** *020
COOPER, Armah J. 1003 12TH ST, JOHN UMSTEAD HOSPITAL 27509 #047-07-1981 L1985
P *020 †75
GAZZOLA, Luiz Renato A. 1003 12TH ST, JOHN UMSTEAD HOSPITAL AAU 27509
#187-06-1980 L2003 **P** *020 †75
GOUST, Olivier C. 1003 12TH ST 27509 #045-01-1990 L1992 **P CHP** *020 †75
GRAY, Kathryn Lynn. 1003 12TH ST 27509 #017-20-1984 L1987 **CHP P** *020 †75
HANES, Constance Margo. 1003 12TH ST, ADULT ADMISSIONS/DEPT PSYC 27509
#033-05-1989 L1995 **P** *020 †75
HESS, Deborah Kaye. 1600 E C ST, PHYSICIAN SERVICES 27509 #041-02-1982 L1985
FM *020 †18
HODGE, Angela Karen. 1003 12TH ST, ADULT ADMISSIONS HOSP 27509 #025-12-1987 L1996
P CHP *020
IRIGARAY, Pedro Jose. 1003 12TH ST 27509 #649-01-1955 L1965 **P** *071 †75
JOHNSON, Charles, Jr. 1003 12TH ST 27509 #010-03-1963 L1965 **IM END** *071 †20
JOHNSON, Charles Ross. 1003 12TH ST, ADATC 27509 #036-05-1965 L1965 **P ADP** *020
JOHNSON, Joy Mooring. 1003 12TH ST, MURDOCH CTR 27509 #036-08-1982 L1999 **IM** *020 †20
KEATING, Janet Hader. 1600 E C ST, MURDOCH CENTER 27509 #028-03-1987 L1989
FM *020 †18
KSHETRAPAL, Viney. ■ 27509 #495-34-1967 L1978 **CHP** *020
MATTOX, Barbara Gavin. 1003 12TH ST, JOHN UMSTEAD HOSPITAL 27509 #036-01-1998 L2005
P *020 †75
MC EVOY, Joseph Patrick. 1003 12TH ST, JOHN UMSTEAD HOSPITAL 27509
#047-05-1973 L1989 **PA P** *050 †75
MERCADO JR., Sergio. ■ 27509 #649-14-1999 L2003 *100
OATES, Elizabeth Woods. 1003 12TH ST, JOHN UMSTEAD HOSPITAL 27509
#016-43-1993 L2001 **P** *020 †75
OGRON, Rita Ann Wilson. PO BOX 3000, DHHS - MURDOCH DEVEL CTR 27509
#056-06-1985 L1995 **EM** *071 †16
OXLEY, Stephen Leo. 1003 12TH ST 27509 #020-12-1973 L1988 **P** *030 †75
POHL, Gary Brian. 1003 12TH ST 27509 #025-12-1989 L1993 **P** *020 †75
REDDI, Jayasree Madi. 1003 12TH ST, JOHN UMSTEAD HOSPITAL REHA 27509
#495-11-1981 L1996 **P** *020 †75
RIZK, Victor F. 1003 12TH ST, JOHN UMSTEAD HOSPITAL 27509 #915-02-1972 L1981 **OBG** *020
SAXENA, Arti. 12TH ST PSYCH 27509 #495-30-1976 L1985 **P GP** *020
SAXENA, Ganesh Kumar. 1600 E C ST, MURDOCH CENTER 27509 #495-45-1975 L1977 **P** *020
SERRANO, Maitee Soledad. ■ 27509 #649-14-1999 L2002 **FM** *100
SNYDER, Melinda Susan. 1003 12TH ST 27509 #038-40-1974 L1980 **GP EM** *020 †55
STRICKLAND, Gay. 1600 E C ST, MURDOCH CENTER 27509 #036-01-1980 L1981 **FM** *020 †18
TURPIN, Delilah Little. 1600 E C ST, MURDOCH CTR PHYS SVCS 27509 #051-01-1963 L1971
GP PD *071 †55

BUXTON — DARE

MUIZNIEKS, Ansis. ■ 27920 #035-01-1959 L1960 **IM GE** *071

CALABASH — BRUNSWICK

BLANDING, James D, Jr. 375 S MIDDLETON DR NW 28467 #020-12-1965 L2001
PTH GP *062 †50
LESZCZYNSKI, Donald B. ■ 28467 #041-14-1986 L2001 **IM** *075
PRESSLEY, Kevin Ray. 602 THOMASBORO RD SW, INTRAMED FAMILY PRACTICE & 28467
#036-05-1985 L1992 **FM** *020 †18
SAUNDERS, G La Cruise. 602 THOMASBORO RD SW, P O BOX 4608 28467
#005-18-1979 L1992 **FM** *020 †18

CAMDEN – CAMDEN

MITRA, Ranjana Neelanjana. ■ 27921 #539-06-2001 L2007 **IM** *020 †20
WILLIAMS, L Polk, Jr. PO BOX 172 27921 #036-05-1957 L1957 **GS** *071 †85

CAMERON – HARNETT

MELTZER, Morton. 448 HORSE N CARRIAGE LN, HORSE N CARRIAGE FARM 28326
#035-09-1965 L1967 **UCM P** *020 †18 ‡
ROGERS, Otto Floyd, III. ■ 28326 #017-20-1976 L1977 **EM** *020 †16
WRIGHT, Wendy Latrice. ■ 28326 #047-07-2000 L2002 **FM** *100 †18

CAMP LEJEUNE – ONSLOW

ALVIS, Jeffrey Stephen. ■ 28547 #051-01-2004 L2004 **GS** *100
ARNOLD, Ryan David. 100 BREWSTER BLVD, NAVAL HOSP CAMP LEJEUNE 28547
#021-06-2006 **FP** *012
BARRION, Joseph Pacifico. 100 BREWSTER BLVD, NH CAMP LEJEUNE NC 28547
#023-12-1995 L1999 **OPH** *020 †35
BLACKWOOD, Carol Lee. 100 BREWSTER BLVD, NAVAL HOSPITAL 28547 #050-02-1997 L2005
FM *020 †18
BOEHM, Marilyn F. 100 BREWSTER BLVD, ATTN: CREDENTIAL OFFICE 28547
#038-44-1984 L1987 **FM** *020 †18
BROOKS, John Scott. PSC BOX 20080, HEALTH SERVICE SUPPORT 28542 #023-12-1999 L2001
AM GPM *020
BUTLER, Henry Emerson, III. 100 BREWSTER BLVD, CODE 09G 28547 #035-01-1969 L2006
GS TRS *020 †85
CUPO, William Walter. 100 BREWSTER BLVD, ATTN: CREDENTIAL OFFICE 28547
#041-02-1994 L2000 **EM** *020 †16
DAIGLE, Patrick Jos. 100 BREWSTER BLVD, NAVAL HOSPITAL 28547 #021-05-1983 L1983
FP *012
DEAFENBAUGH, Bradley Keit. ■ 28547 #051-04-2005 L2005 *100
DEBEN, Sophia Esther. 100 BREWSTER BLVD, DEPT ORTHO SURG 28547 #010-01-2000 L2007
ORS *020
FISHER, Earl Elliott, Jr. 100 BREWSTER BLVD, CODE 09G 28547 #036-01-1964 L1964 **PD** *020
FLACH, Eric W. 100 BREWSTER BLVD, CODE 09G 28547 #030-06-2001 L2003 **AN** *012
GALLAGHER, James Feargal. 100 BREWSTER BLVD, NAVAL HOSPITAL 28547
#012-01-1987 L1989 **OPH** *020 †35
GARGETT, James Michael. 100 BREWSTER BLVD, CODE 09G 28547 #017-20-1971 L2002
FM *020 †18
GESSLER, Eric Michael. 100 BREWSTER BLVD, CODE 09G 28547 #023-12-1994 L1995
OTO *020 †45
GREEN, Julie. 100 BREWSTER BLVD, CDR, MC, USN 28547 #023-12-1994 L1996 **GS** *020
GREER, Joy Anna. 100 BREWSTER BLVD, ATTN PROFESSIONAL AFFAIRS 28547
#051-07-2001 L2006 **OBG** *020 †30
HACKELTON, Karissa Lynn. 100 BREWSTER BLVD 28547 #011-02-2001 L2002 **FM** *020 †18
HANCOCK, James Lee. 100 BREWSTER BLVD, NAVAL HOSPITAL 28547 #023-12-1995 L1997
EM *100 †18
HAYES, Stella Marie. 100 BREWSTER BLVD, NAVAL HOSP CAMP LEJEUNE 28547
#031-01-1993 L2007 **FM** *020 †18
HEATH, Justin. 100 BREWSTER BLVD, NAVAL HOSP CAMP LEJEUNE 28547 #005-77-2007, ▲
FP *012
HINKS, Robert Paul. 100 BREWSTER BLVD, PSC BOX 201, NAVAL HOSPITA 28547
#041-02-1982 L1984 **GS** *020 †85
HOLLIS, Ewell Maydell. PO BOX 9086 28547 #047-06-1999 L2001 *020
JASCOMB, Emori Moore. 100 BREWSTER BLVD, NAVAL HOSP CAMP LEJEUNE 28547
#023-12-1998 L2000 **FP** *012
JOHNSON, Thomas Murray. ■ 28547 #026-04-1989 L1990 **N OM** *020 †75
KING, Neil Mac Connell. 100 BREWSTER BLVD, CAMP LEJEUNE 28547 #051-07-1993 L1997
N *020
LAU, Gregory Weiyip. 100 BREWSTER BLVD, ATTN: CREDENTIAL OFFICE CO 28547
#003-01-2001 L2002 **OBG** *020
LA VAN, J T. 100 BREWSTER BLVD, NAVAL HOSPITAL 28547 #011-02-1992 L1994 **FM** *020 †18
LISSON, Scott Walker. 100 BREWSTER BLVD, NAVAL HOSPITAL 28547 #024-05-1999 L2007
U *020 †95
LY, Nam Thanh. 100 BREWSTER BLVD, NAVAL HOSPITAL 28547 #023-12-1999 L2001
PCC *020 †20
MAHER, Daniel F. 100 BREWSTER BLVD, INTERNAL MED 28547 #036-01-1996 L2002
IM *020 †20
MATTINGLY, Michael Charle. ■ 28547 #011-02-2005 L2007 **PD** *100
MOELLER, Kathleen Holt. 100 BREWSTER BLVD, NAVAL HOSPITAL 28547 #023-12-1985 L2003
DR GP *020 †80 ‡
MOELLER, Michael Scott. 100 BREWSTER BLVD, CODE 09G 28547 #023-12-1985 L1988
FM AM *020 †18
MONAGHAN, Timothy Daniel. 100 BREWSTER BLVD, CODE 09G 28547 #007-02-1983 L1984
PTH FOP *020 †50
MRUGALA, Amy Lynn. 100 BREWSTER BLVD, NH CAMP LEJEUNE NC 28547
#035-15-1997 L1999 *020 †35
NIXON, Chas Richard, II. 100 BREWSTER BLVD, CODE 09G 28547 #011-02-1986 L2001
EM *020 †16
NOLTKAMPER, Daniel F. 100 BREWSTER BLVD, CODE 09G 28547 #048-02-1990 L2002
EM *020 †16
OLESEN, Mark Clifford. 100 BREWSTER BLVD, NAVAL HOSP CAMP LEJEUNE 28547
#056-06-1983 L1984 **OM** *030 †70
PAZDERNIK, Lisa Ann. 100 BREWSTER BLVD, NAVLA HOSPITAL 28547 #019-02-1997 L1997
OBG *020 †30
PLAYFORD, Scott Alan. 100 BREWSTER BLVD, NAVAL HOSPITAL, CODE 09G 28547
#045-01-1997 L1998 **FSM** *100 †18
SANCHEZ, Cynthia Rose. 100 BREWSTER BLVD, ATTN: CREDENTIAL OFFICE 28547
#025-07-2001 L2003 **FP** *012
SORRELLS, Timothy C. ■ 28547 #001-06-1988 L1989 **PTH** *020 †50
SWIBER, Matthew John. 100 BREWSTER BLVD, NAVAL HOSP/ PROFESSIONAL A 28547
#048-14-2001 L2005 **AN** *020 †05

■ = Address Information Privacy Protected

TAYLOR, Aaron Milford. 100 BREWSTER BLVD 28547 #049-01-1995 L2007 **GS** *020 †80
TAYLOR, Stanley Douglas. 100 BREWSTER BLVD, CODE 09G 28547 #010-03-1976 L1994 **PD PDE** *075 †55
TEDESCHI, Adrienne S. 100 BREWSTER BLVD, NAVAL HOSPITAL 28547 #035-15-2003 L2007 **PD** *100
TENNYSON, Tyra Dareece. 100 BREWSTER BLVD, NAVAL HOSP CAMP LEJEUNE 28547 #048-02-2006 **FP** *012
THOMAS, Rachel Elizabeth. ■ 28547 #036-08-2005 L2006 **FP** *012
VERGARA, Jose Gerardo. 100 BREWSTER BLVD, CODE 09G 28547 #032-01-1989 L1996 **GE** *020
WELTON, Richard Chas. 100 BREWSTER BLVD, ATTN: CREDENTIAL OFFICE 28547 #028-34-1974 L1979 **RHU IM** *020 †20

CANDLER – BUNCOMBE

AGARWAL, Bal Krishan. 65 ORVIS STONE CIR, BILTMORE LAKE 28715 #495-30-1963 L2005 **CD IM** *020 †20
AGARWAL, Brij Lata. ■ 28715 #495-30-1966 L1974 **PD END** *020 †55
BRANNAN, Gordon Robt. ■ 28715 #005-12-1940 **GP** *071
BRANNAN, Winona Buchanan. ■ 28715 #005-12-1940 L1943 **OBG GP** *071
BROWN, Royce Marion. ■ 28715 #005-12-1953 L1953 **AN** *071 †05
COIN, Wendy Kathryn. 1219 SMOKEY PARK HWY 28715 #036-01-1990 L1991 **FM** *020 †18 ‡
SEDGWICK, Mary Pat. 1459C SAND HILL RD # 2239 28715 #036-08-1998 L1999 **OBG** *071
SOMMERVILLE, Lewis Cass. ■ 28715 #005-12-1954 L1955 **FM** *071 †18
STALLINGS, Thos Franklin. ■ 28715 #024-01-1954 L1954 **PD** *020 †55
WELLS, David Alexander. 1219 SMOKEY PARK HWY, HOMINY VALLE FAMILY HEALTH 28715 #036-01-1993 L1995 **FM** *020 †18

CANTON – HAYWOOD

ARDAMAN, Miles Ferdi. 1247 PANTHER BRANCH RD, PRIMEDOC PSYCHIATRIC SERVI 28716 #048-04-1994 L2005 **P** *020 †75
GOODWIN, Ernest Boyd, Jr. MIDWAY MEDICAL CLINIC 28716 #036-07-1961 L1961 **FM OM** *071 †18
HAMMEL, Steven Donald. 125 PARK ST 28716 #035-06-1994 L1997 **PD** *020 †55
KINTER, Mark Edward. 30 N MAIN ST 28716 #045-01-1991 L1999 **FM** *020 †18
LEVREAU, Marjorie Shmunes. 30 N MAIN ST 28716 #011-03-2000 L2001 **FM** *020 †18
MORRISON, Frank Crawford. ■ 28716 #036-01-1955 L1955 **GP** *072 †18
PETERSON, Robert Lee, Jr. 121 PARK ST 28716 #036-01-1982 L1983 **OBG** *020
STANLEY, Adrienne Elizabe. ■ 28716 #038-43-2007 **FP** *012
STINES, Ernest Harrison. ■ 28716 #036-05-1957 L1957 **FM** *071 †18
WALL, Stephen Jay. 125 PARK ST 28716 #048-14-1986 L1989 **PD** *020 †55 ‡

CAPE CARTERET – CARTERET

GENTRY, Barry Chance. ■ 28584 #047-06-1998 L2000 **FM** *100 †18
LOVE, Leah Kristen. ■ 28584 #023-12-2001 **FM** *020 †18
POEHLMAN, George S. 906 WB MCLEAN BLVD, EASTERN CAROLINA INTERNAL 28584 #028-03-1973 L1993 **FM** *040 †18
THOMAS, Raymond Lewis. 906 WB MCLEAN DR, MEDICINE, PA 28584 #054-04-1979 L1982 **FM** *020 †18
WARD, Joseph Major. ■ 28584 #036-07-1947 L1949 **FM OM** *071 †18

CAROLINA BEACH – NEW HANOVER

CHESHIRE, Mc Kinley, III. ■ 28428 #036-07-1983 L1984 **IM EM** *020
CHRISTIANSEN, Sara Lynn. 1328 N LAKE PARK BLVD #106, SEASIDE INT MED-BOX 311 28428 #026-08-1991 L2002 **IM** *020 †20
GARCES, David Ed. 101 HOPETOWN RD 28428 #264-04-1978 L1982 **EM FM** *020 †18,16
GLIDDEN, Horace Kay. 1403 S LAKE PARK BLVD 28428 #035-08-1960 L1977 **EM** *020 †16
RUSCETTI, Howard Dale. 1300 BRIDGE BARRIER RD 28428 #007-02-1999 L2000 **FM** *020 †18

CAROLINA SHORES – BRUNSWICK

BATEMAN, Rolland D, Jr. ■ 28467 #038-41-1950 L1950 **CD IM** *071 †20
SCHILLING, Charles D. ■ 28467 #051-01-1941 L1941 **EM GS** *071 †85

CARRBORO – ORANGE

ALKER, Alisa Patricia. ■ 27510 #036-01-2008 *012
AMANN, Kristen Elizabeth. ■ 27510 #035-06-2007 **MPD** *012
ANNIS, Cory Lyn. 127 FIDELITY ST 27510 #012-01-1992 L1994 **MPD PD** *020 †55,20
BAECHER, Laura Elizabeth. 400 DAVIE RD, #7 FIDELITY COURT CONDOMIN 27510 #035-19-2003 L2007 **OBG** *100
BATSON, Eric Peter. ■ 27510 #041-07-1979 **FM** *050
BEHLING, Karen Jutta. 127 FIDELITY ST, CARRBORO PEDIATRICS & INTE 27510 #019-02-1998 L2004 **MPD** *020 †20,55
BENJAMIN, Lee Steven. 200 WEATHERVANE DR 27510 #025-07-1997 L2002 **OS** *020 †55,16
BLANCO, Roberto Alejandro. ■ 27510 #047-05-2005 L2008 **P** *012
BLOBE, Gerard Conrad. ■ 27510 #036-07-1995 L2000 **HO ON** *020 †20
BOMBACK, Andrew S. ■ 27510 #035-01-2003 L2007 **IM** *012 †20
BRODER, Joshua Seth. 601 JONES FERRY RD 27510 #008-01-1999 L2002 **EM** *020 †16
BUNDY, David Gordon. 299 LLOYD ST, PIEDMONT HEALTH SERVICES, 27510 #025-01-1998 L2003 **PD** *020 †55
BUSBY, Stuart. ■ 27510 #017-20-2002 L2006 **N** *100
CARLOTTI, Gina Marie. ■ 27510 #041-02-2006 **FP** *012
CHEKOL, Seble Shibabaw. ■ 27510 #036-01-2008 *012
CLARK, Sandra Irene. 299 LLOYD ST, PIEDMONT HEALTH SVC INC 27510 #036-01-1990 L1995 **FM** *020 †18
COLE, Thomas Ballard. ■ 27510 #048-04-1981 L1989 **PHP** *050 †55

DANKNER, Wayne Matthew. ■ 27510 #035-09-1981 L2000 **ID PD** *020 †55
EAST, Joan E. 299 LLOYD ST 27510 #036-01-1996 L1998 **FM** *020 †18
EPNER, Ronald Alan. 313 BERRYHILL DR 27510 #035-20-1976 L1981 **ORS HS** *020 †40
FISCHER, Jonathan Eli. 301 LLOYD ST 27510 #036-01-1998 L2001 **FM** *020
FORBES, Karolyn Beth. 301 LLOYD ST 27510 #036-01-1998 L2001 **FM** *020 †18
FORT, Prem. ■ 27510 #036-01-2006 **PD** *012
FRISBY, Xenia Yvette. ■ 27510 #003-01-2004 L2007 **IM** *100 †20
GAAL, Geza Zoltan. ■ 27510 #473-01-1954 L1962 **CD IM** *020
GARDNER, Cynthia Denise. ■ 27510 #047-06-1994 L2005 **PTH** *020 †50
GOODNO, Charles Christian. 201 E POPLAR AVE, P O BOX 363 27510 #036-01-1983 L1985 **GPM** *020,70
GOVERMAN, Jeremy. ■ 27510 #550-02-2000 L2005 **PS** *012 †85 ‡
HAGELE, Dana Marie. ■ 27510 #016-01-1995 L2000 **GPM** *020 †55
HARMON, Quaker Elizabeth. ■ 27510 #065-01-1997 L2001 **FM** *100
HENSLER, Margaret Bridgid. ■ 27510 #036-01-2004 L2007 **EM** *020
HLADIK, Anne Jennifer. ■ 27510 #036-01-2008 *012
HLADIK, Gerald Allen. 105 RENEE LYNN CT, CAROLINA DIALYSIS-CARRBORO 27510 #024-05-1989 L1992 **NEP** *020 †20
IVERSON, Megan Anne. ■ 27510 #036-01-2008 *012
JACKSON, Saundra Alicia. ■ 27510 #036-01-2008 *012
JASKOLKA, Michael Stephen. 108 PRIMROSE LN, MICHAEL STEPHEN JASKOLKA D 27510 #036-01-2005 **GS** *100
JOHNSON, Krystal Brown. ■ 27510 #036-01-2005 **PTH** *012
KALMAN, Rebecca Irene. ■ 27510 #036-01-2008 *012
KLEIN, Carol Lynn. 301 LLOYD ST 27510 #041-12-1979 L1981 **FM** *030 †18
KNIERIM, Kyle Edwin. ■ 27510 #036-01-2008 *012
LAWRENCE, Kerith Davidson. 127 FIDELITY ST, CARRBORO PEDS & INTERNAL M 27510 #043-01-1998 L2000 **MPD PD** *020,55
LEA, Georgia Shattuck. ■ 27510 #012-05-2004 **N** *012
LEE, Catherine Seening. ■ 27510 #036-01-2006 L2007 **P** *012
LUCAS, Quinton Alan. ■ 27510 #036-01-2008 *012
MANOR, James Peter. 610 JONES FERRY RD 27510 #025-01-1980 L1982 **FM** *020 †18
MOORE, James Le Grand. ■ 27510 #041-02-1944 L1944 **ORS** *072 †40
MOUW, Mary S Mc Kown. 610 JONES FERRY RD, STE 102 27510 #036-01-1996 L2000 **FM** *020 †18
MUEHLBAUER, Marcus. ■ 27510 #409-43-2001 **IM** *012
OH, Daniel Seojyong. ■ 27510 #036-01-2008 *012
PRATHER, Donna Lynn. 200 N GREENSBORO ST STE D7 27510 #036-01-1978 L1979 **P** *030 †18,75
RAINES, Alexander Nathan. ■ 27510 #036-01-2008 *012
RAMANATHAN, Chandar. ■ 27510 #422-01-2004 L2007 **PDP** *012 †55
REDMANN, Beverly Joan. 200 W WEAVER ST, STE 3 27510 #056-05-1987 L1990 **CHP P** *020 †75
REECE, Jennifer Leigh. ■ 27510 #003-01-2007 **PD** *012
ROWLAND, Barbara Helen. 299 LLOYD ST, PIEDMONT HEALTH SERVICES 27510 #005-18-1978 L1988 **FM** *020 †18
RUSSELL, Dave James. ■ 27510 #007-02-2006 L2006 **OPH** *012
SADLER, Natalie J. 200 N GREENSBORO ST, STE C7A 27510 #048-14-1987 L1989 **P** *020
SALANSKY, Jessica Beth. ■ 27510 #011-04-2005 L2008 **PD** *012
SARTOR, Nichola John. 205 LLOYD ST, #101 PEDIATRICS&INT MED 27510 #025-01-1992 L1998 **MPD** *020 †55,20
SCHEUNEMANN, Leslie Page. ■ 27510 #036-01-2005 L2008 **IM** *012
SHAUGHNESSY, Gretchen Gai. ■ 27510 #011-04-2004 L2007 **ID** *012 †20
SHOLAR, Tracy Lynn. 306 ESTES DRIVE EXT, APARTMENT 8 BUILDING N 27510 #036-01-2008 *012
SMITH, David Lucas. 110 W MAIN ST STE 2H, EL FUTURO, INC 27510 #004-01-2000 L2001 **CHP** *020 †75
SMITH, Elizabeth L Uy. ■ 27510 #036-01-2008 *012
STEINER, Beat Danl. 299 LLOYD ST, PIEDMONT HLTH SERV INC 27510 #036-01-1989 L1993 **GPM** *020 †70,18
STOKES, Rene J. ■ 27510 #036-01-2008 *012
THEROUX, Deana M. ■ 27510 #043-01-1996 L2003 **PD** *020 †55
THEUER, Heather H. ■ 27510 #020-02-1990 L2003 **SP** *020 †50
THOMAS, Gayle Duddles. 301 LLOYD ST, CARRBORO COMMUNITY HEALTH 27510 #005-14-1986 L1989 **FM** *020 †18
TOBIN, Paul Christopher. 301 LLOYD ST, CARRBORO COMMUNITY HEALTH 27510 #036-01-1991 L1992 **IM PD** *020 †55,20
UCKUN, Aysin. ■ 27510 #902-05-1981 L2004 **PDE PD** *020
VAUGHAN, Daniel Patrick. ■ 27510 #025-07-1971 L1974 **FM IM** *071 †20
WALLACE, Cynthia Kay. ■ 27510 #048-04-2005 L2005 **IM** *012
WALLACE, James Grier, Jr. ■ 27510 #036-01-2007 **FP** *012
WARE, Tracy Anne. 610 JONES FERRY RD, STE 208 27510 #041-01-1987 L2002 **P** *020 †75
WATKINS, Andre'A Patrice. ■ 27510 #036-01-2008 *012
WEN, Kwun Wah. ■ 27510 #036-01-2008 *012
WILKS, Bruce E. 610 JONES FERRY RD, RAD STE#102 27510 #024-16-1980 L1985 **FM** *020 †18
YU, Rupal Lakhani. ■ 27510 #036-01-2008 *012
ZIMMER, Christopher A. ■ 27510 #051-01-1993 L1994 **IM** *100

CARTHAGE – MOORE

CAGLE, Nicole Alexandria. PO BOX 704 28327 #036-08-2004 **PD** *012
GREENWOOD, Arthur John. ■ 28327 #023-12-2003 L2005 **GS** *012
LEONARD, Thomas Robert. 304 SAUNDERS ST, MOORE FAMILY CARE, PA 28327 #017-20-1995 L1996 **FM** *020 †18
MARTIN, Geoffrey Allan. ■ 28327 #020-12-2000 L2004 **FM** *020 †16
ZOLMIAN, Hrad Haig. ■ 28327 #024-01-1940 L1942 **IM PD** *071

CARY – WAKE

ABDUL KAREEM, Farhath Sul. 1900 KILDAIRE FARM RD, WAKEMED CARY HOSPITAL 27518 #495-59-1994 L2003 **IM** *020
ABELS, Byron Clifford, Jr. 115 CRESCENT COMMONS DR, STE 200 27518 #012-05-1985 L1995 **GS** *020 †85

■ = Address Information Privacy Protected

ADAMS, David Paul. 218 ASHVILLE AVE, STE 20 27518 #036-01-1992 L1993 **FM** *020 †18
ADAMS, William Chambliss. 101 SW CARY PKWY, STE 270 27511 #051-04-1978 L1982 **PD** *020 †55
AGARWAL, Abhay K. 550 NEW WAVERLY PL, STE 105 27518 #495-01-1993 L1998 **IM CD** *030 †20 ‡
AGARWAL, Neelu. 550 NEW WAVERLY PL, STE 105 27518 #495-20-1996 L2001 **IM** *020 †20
AGHA, Bilal M. 216 ASHVILLE AVE STE 50, AGHA ARTHRITIS ASSOCIATES, 27518 #704-25-1990 L2001 **RHU** *020 †20
AMBRUZS, Josephine Marie. ■ 27519 #033-06-2007 **IM** *012
ANDERSON, Lynn Hunter. ■ 27518 #016-06-1949 L1949 **IM CD** *071 †20
ANDERSON, Zachary John. 1900 KILDAIRE FARM RD, WAKE MED CARY HOSPITAL 27518 #055-02-2002 L2005 **FM** *020 †18
ANDORN, Anne Cramer. ■ 27519 #038-40-1973 L1977 **PA P** *050 †75
ANDRAWES, Souad G. 1515 SW CARY PKWY 27511 #915-05-1975 L1988 **PD** *020 †55
ANDREWS, Aimee Rachelle. 570 NEW WAVERLY PL, STE 110 27518 #038-40-1994 L2002 **PEM** *020 †55
ANTHONY, Michael Lamar. 550 NEW WAVERLY PL, DBA CARY OBSTETRICS & 27518 #027-01-1988 L1992 **OBG** *020 †30
ARANA, Guillermo Fernando. 975 WALNUT ST STE 255, VILLAGE SQUARE OFFICE BLDG 27511 #176-03-1962 L1969 **FM PTH** *020
ARCHINAL, Ginette Anne. 101 SW CARY PKWY, STE 170 27511 #143-07-1983 L1998 **FM** *020 †18
ARTIGUES, Moira Frierson. 1020 S HILLS DR, STE 380 27513 #045-01-1995 L1996 **PFP** *020 †75
ASRANI, Sanjay Girdhari. 2000 REGENCY PKWY STE 100 27518 #496-38-1988 L2000 **OPH** *020 †35
ASSANIE, Suzie. 124 HUNTSMOOR LN 27513 #023-07-1998 L2002 **OBG** *020 †30
ATKINS, Broadus Zane. ■ 27511 #036-07-1995 L2001 **TS** *020 †85
ATKINSON, Helen Parker. ■ 27513 #036-01-1992 *075
AU, Victor Kwen-Wei. 300 KEISLER DR, STE 102 27518 #041-02-1979 L1986 **PS** *020 †65
BAER, Samantha Denise. 101 SW CARY PKWY STE 270 27511 #017-20-1992 L1999 **PD** *020 †55
BAJWA, Aisha B. 1230 SE MAYNARD RD, STE 203 27511 #704-06-1988 L2000 **APM** *020 †60
BAJWA, Waheed Khalid. 1230 SE MAYNARD RD STE 203 27511 #704-01-1979 L2000 **P** *020 †75
BAKEWELL, William E, Jr. ■ 27511 #067-01-1949 L1960 **P** *071 †75
BARRETT, Katherine Ellis. 1505 SW CARY PKWY, STE 300 27511 #036-01-1996 L2000 **OBG** *020 †30
BARRINGER, Thad J. 1135 KILDAIRE FARM RD 27511 #047-05-1953 L1957 **P** *072 †75
BARTELS, George Thomas. 204 ASHVILLE AVE STE 50 27518 #036-07-1978 L1980 **FM NTR** *020
BARUIZ, Cleothe Uytico. 106 RIDGE VIEW DR, MICHAEL STADIEM MD FAAFP 27511 #748-11-1978 L1991 **BBK IM** *020 †20
BASKETT, Debra Renee. 100 SAS CAMPUS DR, SAS INSTITUTE, INC 27513 #038-40-1990 L1993 **FM** *020 †18
BASSETT, Deborah Walgrove. 101 SW CARY PKWY, STE 270 27511 #035-15-1992 L1998 **PD** *020 †55
BAYTION, Christine Jane. ■ 27511 #038-43-1992 L2004 **IM** *020 †60
BELL, David W, IV. 307 NEW RAIL DR 27513 #036-01-1995 L1998 **CHP** *020 †75
BELL, Richard Alan. 1515 SW CARY PKWY, STE 220 27511 #036-01-1980 L1982 **PD** *020 †55
BENAVIDES, Colby Elizabet. 1505 SW CARY PKWY, STE 300 27511 #036-01-1998 L2001 **OBG** *020
BENEDICT, Frederick E. 401 KEISLER DR, DHILLON ORTHOPAEDIC & 27518 #038-41-1983 L1988 **ORS** *020 †40
BENEVIDES, Gay Marie. 570 NEW WAVERLY PL, STE 210 27518 #036-01-1996 L1997 **EM** *020 †16
BENSON, Jill Lynn. 1900 KILDAIRE FARM RD 27518 #016-11-1997 L2002 **EM UM** *020 †16
BERNSTIEN, Joel Michael. ■ 27519 #048-12-2006 **OBG** *012
BEST, Randall Mark. 212 ASHVILLE AVE, STE 10 27518 #036-01-1981 L1982 **EM** *020 †16
BHAT, Bhavna. ■ 27519 #496-17-1999 L2007 **IM** *020 †20
BILBRO, Scott Carter. 530 NEW WAVERLY PL, STE 200 27518 #036-05-1993 L1997 **IM** *020 †20
BLAND, William H. ■ 27511 #036-05-1948 L1949 **GP** *071
BLEIER, Seth Jason. 543 KEISLER DR, STE 202 27518 #051-07-2002 L2005 **EM** *020 †16
BLOOM, Carie Lee. 1001 CRESCENT GREEN DR 27518 #021-01-2000 L2002 **PD** *020 †55
BLOOM, O Josh. 3700 NW CARY PKWY 27513 #021-01-2000 L2001 **FSM** *020 †18
BLOUNT, James G, Jr. 3700 NW CARY PKWY 27513 #036-05-1998 L2000 **FM FSM** *020 †18
BOGHARA, Hareshkumar Dhir. 118 ASHLEY BROOK CT 27513 #495-23-2006 *100
BOLICK, Karen Lucovsky. ■ 27513 #036-01-1986 L1987 **AN** *050
BONPAIN, Anne Bond. 550 NEW WAVERLY PL, DBA CARY OBSTETRICS & 27518 #036-01-2001 L2002 **OBG** *020 †30
BRANNON, Gregory Jos. 530 NEW WAVERLY PL, STE 301 27518 #016-42-1988 L1993 **OBG** *020 †30
BROADDUS, Carl Ashton, Jr. ■ 27511 #051-01-1947 L1966 **TS GS** *071 †85,90
BRODY, Michael Jay. 1000 CRESCENT GREEN DR, STE 102 27518 #041-02-1995 L1998 **GE** *020 †20
BROWN, Donald Claude. 580 NEW WAVERLY PL STE 120 27518 #036-01-1974 L1974 **FM** *020 †18
BROWNING, Charles Thomas. 400 PINNER WEALD WAY, STE 102 27513 #036-01-1999 L2003 **P** *100
BRUCKERT, Joseph Walter. 1110 SE CARY PKWY, STE 203 27518 #409-25-1982 L1990 **FM** *020 †18
BRUGGERS, Barry Alan. 550 NEW WAVERLY PL, STE 200 27518 #021-05-1979 L1981 **OBG** *020 †30
BUCHANAN, Ann Marie. ■ 27518 #036-08-2002 L2004 **PD** *100
BUCHIN, David L. ■ 27518 #035-06-1966 L1979 **OS** *071 †75
BURKHART, Charles Andrew. ■ 27511 #038-40-1957 L1974 **OS GP** *071
BUSHELL, Ian Wilson. 200 KEISLER DR STE B, OF CARY 27518 #012-22-1994 L1995 **FM** *020 †18
BYRD, Terri M. 156 SHIRLEY DR 27511 #012-01-1979 L2004 **IMG** *020 †20 ‡
CALDWELL, Matthew Cowley. ■ 27513 #048-13-2003 L2007 **OPH** *020
CAPLAN, Jordan Alan. ■ 27519 #031-01-2006 L2006 **DR** *012
CAPPOLA, James Joseph, III. 1900 KILDAIRE FARM RD, WAKE MED CARY HOSPITAL 27518 #035-45-1994 L1997 **IM** *020 †20
CARROLL, Raymond Mc Kay. 1120 SE CARY PKWY, STE 100 27518 #036-01-1996 L2005 **ORS** *020 †40
CARROLL, Regina Martin. 1020 SOUTHHILL DR STE 38 27513 #028-34-1979 L2000 **P PYG** *020 †75
CASEY, Raynor C. 216 ASHVILLE AVE 27518 #036-01-1991 L1997 **OPH DIA** *020 †35
CHAO, Christopher Phillip. 975 WALNUT ST, STE 255 27511 #038-06-1998 L1999 **FM** *020 †18
CHAO, Irene S Tsang. 101 SW CARY PKWY STE 270, TRIANGLE PEDUATRIC CTR 27511 #036-01-1995 L1998 **PD** *020 †55
CHAPPELL, Jonathan D. 218 ASHVILLE AVE, STE 10 27518 #036-07-2001 L2007 **ORS** *100
CHARLSON, Mark David. 218 ASHVILLE AVE, STE 10 27518 #036-01-1997 L2004 **ORS** *020 †40
CHARLTON, Oliver P. ■ 27511 #836-01-1961 L1977 **DR** *071 †80
CHARRON, George Maurice. 401 KEISLER DR, DHILLON ORTHOPAEDIC & 27518 #021-05-1984 L1989 **ORS** *020 †40
CHATRATH, Harmeet. 1515 SW CARY PKWY STE 200, PRIMARY CARE OF CARY PLLC 27511 #495-29-1982 L1996 **IM** *020 †20
CHATTERJEE, Manjusri. 1000 CRESCENT GREEN DR, STE 100 27518 #495-02-1974 L1985 **P** *020 †75
CHIARAMONTI, Alexander. 101 SW CARY PKWY, STE 210 27511 #025-01-1976 L1977 **D** *020 †15
CHOI, Youngin Naomi. 222 ASHVILLE AVE, STE 10 27518 #016-01-1997 L2007 **FM** *020 †18
CHRISTAKOS, Arthur Chris. ■ 27511 #045-01-1955 L1964 **OBG OS** *071 †30
CLARK, Robert Earl. 200 WELLESLEY TRADE LN 27519 #048-12-1985 L1987 **D IM** *020 †15
CLAYTON, Christy Lou. 212 ASHVILLE AVE, STE 220 27518 #036-08-1986 L1990 **OBG** *020 †30
COLE, Byron Kenneth. 401 HICKORYWOOD BLVD 27519 #038-41-1960 L1972 **IM PUD** *020 †20
COLLINS, Roger Stewart. 101 SW CARY PKWY, STE 140 27511 #036-08-1998 L2005 **PS** *020
COOK, David Harry. 1219 WALNUT ST, CENTER, PA 27511 #036-08-1984 L1994 **N** *020 †75
COOK, Yvette Rose. 301 KEISLER DR STE C 27518 #020-12-1980 L1990 **N SME** *020 †75
CORK, Randy Dean. 300 ASHVILLE AVE, STE 100 27518 #012-05-1988 L1994 **R OS** *020 †80
COURSEY, Courtney Ann. ■ 27513 #035-01-2003 L2007 **DR** *012
CRITTENDEN, Susan L. 530 NEW WAVERLY PL, STE 200 27518 #036-01-1981 L1982 **IM** *020 †20
CUSHING, William Thos. ■ 27518 #305-01-1987 L2006 **FM** *020 †18
DANIELS, Jasmin Cornette. 1903 N HARRISON AVE # 101, 3C FAMILY SERV 27513 #036-01-1998 L2001 **CHP P** *020 †75
DASCAL, Joel. ■ 27511 #869-05-1973 L1979 **EM** *020 †16
DAUD, Shahnaz Kausar. 200 KEISLER DR STE B 27518 #704-06-1972 L1989 **FM** *020
DAVIS, Samuel P, III. 1900 KILDAIRE FARM RD 27518 #036-05-1993 L1999 **OTO FPS** *020 †45
DAWKINS, Jennings R, Jr. ■ 27513 #036-07-1979 L1982 **PHM IM** *050
DEIGAN, Eric Arthur. 300 ASHVILLE AVE, STE 280 27518 #065-01-1980 L1991 **OBG MFM** *020 †30
DE LISSIO, Michael Gerard. 1000 CRESCENT GREEN DR, STE 102 27518 #035-06-1980 L1987 **GE IM** *020 †20
DENKER, Michele Joy. 1020 SOUTHHILL DR, STE 320 27513 #035-06-1989 L1990 **P** *020 †75
DENNY, John Paul. 216 ASHVILLE AVE 27518 #036-07-2000 L2006 **OPH** *020 †35
DEOGUN, Gurvinder Kaur. ■ 27513 #030-05-2001 L2007 **AI** *020 †55,03
DESAI, Pratik Vipinbhai. 300 KEISLER DR, STE 204 27518 #495-23-1990 L2000 **CD** *020 †20
DESAI, Sunil J. 300 KEISLER DR, STE 204 27518 #495-76-1983 L1994 **HO IM** *020 †20
DE SIMONE, Robert Alfred. ■ 27518 #024-07-1961 L1989 **DR NM** *071 †80
DESROSIERS, Raymonde C. ■ 27513 #440-01-1980 **GS** *100
DESSAUER, Kati Elizabeth. 570 NEW WAVERLY PL, STE 130 27518 #036-01-1985 L1988 **FM** *020 †18
DORNIC, Demetrian Ivan. 3701 NW CARY PKWY, STE 101 27513 #039-01-1994 L1998 **OPH** *020 †35
DOYLE, Raymond Thos. ■ 27518 #023-07-1954 L1956 **IM** *071 †20
DUBERMAN, Eric David. 216 ASHVILLE AVE, STE 30 27518 #035-01-1985 L2001 **GS CRS** *020 †85,10
DUNN, James Ralph, Jr. ■ 27511 #023-07-1951 L1958 **GS TS** *071 †85,90
EISENBEIS, Charles F, II. 216 ASHVILLE AVE STE 20, CANCER CENTERS OF NORTH CA 27518 #016-02-1996 L2005 **HO** *020 †20
ELKORDY, Maha Abdul. 216 ASHVILLE AVE, ASSOC, CARY BRANCH 27518 #036-01-1988 L1989 **HEM** *020 †20
ELSTON, Scott Cody. 1110 KILDAIRE FARM RD 27511 #041-02-1988 L1991 **IM** *072 †20
ENOCHS, Paul Ebenezer. 300 ASHVILLE AVE, STE 200 27518 #001-06-1997 L2002 **GS** *020 †85
ESTOK, Martin, Jr. ■ 27513 #033-05-1980 L2007 **IM** *030 †20 ‡
FAHEEM, Uzma S.. 605 HALCYON MEADOW DR 27519 #704-02-1992 L2006 **P** *020 ‡
FAIRBROTHER, Scott Nield. 543 KEISLER DR, STE 202 27518 #036-08-2000 L2003 **GS** *020 †16
FAIRCHILD, Amy Dawn. 2000 REGENCY PKWY 27518 #036-01-1998 L1999 **CHP** *020 †75
FELDMAN, Brian Louis. ■ 27519 #051-07-2001 L2005 **PHO** *012 †55
FELDMAN, Natalie Sobota. ■ 27519 #051-07-2004 L2007 **EM** *100
FERRALL, Robert John. 940 SE CARY PKWY, STE 200 27518 #036-05-1988 L1995 **PD** *020 †55
FIRRINCIELI, Vincent L. 300 ASHVILLE AVE, STE 300 27518 #011-04-1998 L2003 **AI** *100 †20,03
FLAHERTY, Thomas Francis. 1515 SW CARY PKWY 27511 #048-14-1985 L1987 **PD** *020 †55
FLANAGAN, Tiffany. 212 ASHVILLE AVE, STE 220 27518 #036-01-1991 L1994 **OBG** *020 †30
FLEMING, Christopher Paul. 400 ASHVILLE AVE STE 300 27518 #038-06-1977 L1981 **OPH OM** *020 †35 ‡
FLICK, Anita Pardue. ■ 27518 #036-01-1992 *100
FLYNN, Timothy Corcoran. 200 WELLESLEY TRADE LN 27519 #028-03-1982 L1985 **D** *020 †15
FOSTER, Charlie H. 600 NEW WAVERLY PL, STE 203 27518 #036-01-1997 L2000 **FM** *020 †18
FOX, Michael Raymond. ■ 27511 #001-06-1980 L2004 **PTH** *020 †50
FULGHUM, James S, III. 400 KEISLER DR 27518 #036-01-1971 L1971 **OSS** *020 †25
FURS, Stephen Joseph. 1000 CRESCENT GREEN DR, STE 102 27518 #008-02-1990 L1994 **GE** *020 †20
GADDY, Ladson Brooks. ■ 27513 #036-01-2008 *012
GAGLIARDI, Michael D. 101 SW CARY PKWY, STE 170 27511 #041-12-1992 L2000 **FM** *020 †18
GARIMELLA, Rama Goli. 300 KEISLER DR, STE 204 CARY CARDIOLOGY 27518 #495-58-1988 L1998 **CD** *020 †20
GARSIDE, John Arthur. 1110 SE CARY PKWY 27518 #036-01-1993 L2000 **OTO** *020 †45
GAWOR, Kristina Daina. ■ 27519 #051-04-2006 **P** *012
GAYAM, Padmaja Reddy. 311 ASHVILLE AVE STE D 27518 #496-01-1990 L1997 **AI IM** *020 †20
GELBER, Richard Steven. 100 CORNERSTONE DR 27519 #035-15-1985 L2006 **PD** *020 †55
GERTZ, Edward Walter. ■ 27519 #041-12-1967 L1968 **CD IM** *075
GESSNER, Sarah Y. 212 ASHVILLE AVE, STE 10 27518 #036-01-1995 L2002 **PD** *020 †55
GIBBONS, Gregory Robert. 114 BRADY CT, GIBBONS FAMILY MEDICINE 27511 #036-01-1996 L1999 **FM** *020 †18
GIBBONS, Joyce Barbee. 114 BRADY CT, GIBBONS FAMILY MEDICINE, P 27511 #036-01-1991 L1994 **FM** *020 †18 ‡
GLOTZER, John Mark. ■ 27519 #024-01-1981 L1997 **TS GS** *020 †85,90
GODBOUT, Christopher Jon. 400 KEISLER DR, CAROLINA REHABILITATION & 27518 #038-45-1999 L2003 **PM** *020 †60

■ = Address Information Privacy Protected

GODWIN, James Edward. 580 NEW WAVERLY PL, STE 210 27518 #019-02-1991 L1993 IM *020 †20

GOEL, Renu. 102 COMMONWEALTH CT STE H 27511 #035-03-1997 L1998 P *020 †75

GOLI, China Kondala Rao. 251 KEISLER DR, STE 300 27518 #495-58-1992 L1999 IM *020 †20

GOPAL, Satish. ■ 27511 #036-07-2001 L2001 MPD *100 †20,55

GRAHAM, Mark L, II. 300 ASHVILLE AVE, STE 310 27518 #026-08-1982 L1990 HEM ON *020 †20

GRAYBEAL, Frank Russell, Jr. 101 SW CARY PKWY, STE 40 27511 #045-01-1977 L1988 DR *020 †80 ‡

GREENBERG, Lawrence H. 2000 REGENCY PKWY STE 204 27518 #550-01-1985 L1990 P *020 †75

GREGG, Cynthia Marie. 3550 NW CARY PKWY, STE 100 27513 #036-01-1988 L1995 OTO FPS *020 †45

GRIFFITHS, Dorothea Ann. ■ 27519 #017-20-1994 L1998 OBG *020

GROSS, Michael David. ■ 27519 #012-01-1979 L1981 FM OM *020

GUMBER, Subhash C. 216 ASHVILLE AVE 27518 #024-16-1990 L1995 GE *020 †20

GUTHRIE, Robin Elizabeth. ■ 27518 #036-07-2007 L2007 *012

GWINN, Michael Dale. 400 KEISLER DR 27518 #038-40-1986 L1990 PM *020 †60

HACKELING, Theresa A. 105 PAHLMEYER PL 27519 #024-07-1995 L1996 EM *020 †16

HAMAD, Mazen E. 222 ASHVILLE AVE, STE 30 27518 #875-01-1976 L1989 FM *020 †18

HAMAD, Sabah Farouk. 115 CRESCENT COMMONS DR, STE 200 27518 #036-08-1992 L2000 GS *020 †85

HANNA, Donald Paul. 1805 KILDAIRE FARM RD 27518 #025-07-1979 L1987 PS GS *020 †65,85

HANSON, Curtis A. 218 ASHVILLE AVE, STE 10 27518 #048-02-2001 L2006 ORS *020

HARDIN-LEE, Laura Kay. 212 ASHVILLE AVE, STE 10 27518 #036-01-1994 L1997 FM *020 †18

HARRIS, Timothy Edward. 218 ASHVILLE AVE, STE 10 27518 #051-01-1997 L2003 ORS *020 †40

HART, William Michael. 121 MADISON SQUARE LN 27513 #036-05-2002 L2004 FSM *020 †18

HATTAWAY, Alexander C, III. 200 ASHVILLE AVE, STE 30 27518 #036-01-1965 L1965 OTO A *071 †45

HEATER, Kaja. ■ 27519 #038-41-1982 L1986 DR *020 †80

HELTON, Mary Beth Ogle. 530 NEW WAVERLY PL, PEDIATRICS 27518 #036-08-1994 L1996 PD *020 †55

HILL, James Carver. ■ 27511 #036-01-1984 L1985 FM *071 †18

HILL, Mark Reginald. ■ 27511 #036-08-2003 L2006 EM *100 †16

HILLIARD, Geoffrey W. 2501 WESTON PKWY, STE 201 27513 #036-01-1986 L2001 PS GS *020 †65

HOROWITZ, David A. 101 SW CARY PKWY, STE 270 27511 #024-05-1979 L1984 PD *020 †55

HOYT, Elizabeth S. ■ 27511 #036-01-1966 L1966 GP *020

HREN, Catherine Madeline. 101 SW CARY PKWY 27511 #036-07-1991 L1994 D *020 †15

HULKA, Gregory Fabian. 1110 SE CARY PKWY, STE 100 27518 #036-07-1988 L1994 PDO OTO *020 †45

HUMMEL, Rachel Leah. 3700 NW CARY PKWY 27513 #028-79-2001, ▲ L2006 FM *020 †18

JACOBS, James Wm. 530 NEW WAVERLY PL, STE 200 27518 #038-40-1992 L1994 IM *020 †20

JAFFE, David Jay. 206 TOWNE VILLAGE DR 27513 #041-13-1987 L1999 CHN *020 †75,55

JANEFALKAR, Preeti Madan. 1900 KILDAIRE FARM RD 27518 #495-83-1997 L2005 IM *020

JEFFERSON, Henry Dawson, Jr. ■ 27511 #036-01-1977 L1982 FM *020 †18

JOHNSON, Katherine Barbar. ■ 27511 #016-43-2004 P *012

JOHNSON, Kenneth Roger. ■ 27518 #041-09-1956 L1957 OBG *071 †30

JOHNSON, Robert Bruce. 101 SW CARY PKWY, STE 210 27511 #036-07-1978 L1986 D *020 †15

JONES, Frederick Samuel. 580 NEW WAVERLY PL, ASSOCIATES 27518 #016-01-1979 L1986 NEP RHU *020 †20

JONES, William Burns, Jr. 1155 EXECUTIVE CIR 27511 #045-01-1955 L1960 PHP *071 †70

JORDAN, Joan T. 530 NEW WAVERLY PL STE 101 27518 #036-07-1983 L1984 IM GP *020 †20

JUDGE, Gurdev Singh. 401 KEISLER DR STE 201, ALLERGY ASTHMA SINUS CTR 27518 #495-10-1985 L1992 AI PD *020 †55,03

JUNEJA, Vijay Kumar. 103 BAINES CT, STE 200 27511 #495-29-1990 L1997 IM *020 †20 ‡

JUNG, Zehra. ■ 27513 #495-45-1993 L2005 IM *020 †20

KASULA, Aniil K. 311 ASHVILLE AVE STE C, CARY CHILDREN'S CLINIC 27518 #495-50-1990 L1995 PD *020 †55 ‡

KEARY, Frank Vincent. 505 QUEENSFERRY RD 27511 #065-09-1965 L1997 IM EM *020

KERR, Miller James. ■ 27518 #041-15-2008 *012

KHAN, Mazhar Ulhaq. ■ 27519 #704-20-1996 L2003 NM *012 †20

KIRBY, Scott Garth. 212 ASHVILLE AVE, STE 10 27518 #021-01-1974 L1991 EM IM *020 †20,16 ‡

KNAUDT, Patricia Ruth. 547 KEISLER DR STE 104 27518 #039-01-1995 L1997 P *020 †75

KOCSIS, Margaret M. 106 ROYCE DR, 106 ROYCE DRIVE 27518 #036-05-1990 L1993 PD *020 †55

KOLAR, Edward Warren, III. 1900 KILDAIRE FARM RD 27518 #041-14-1987 L1994 FM *020 †18

KONDRU, Jaisheela. ■ 27519 #495-58-1998 L2008 IM *020 †20 ‡

KONDURU, Vijaya Nirmala. 907 KILDAIRE FARM RD, WESTERN WAKE INTERNAL MEDI 27511 #495-70-1992 L1999 IM *020 †20

KOOMEN, Jacob, Jr. ■ 27511 #035-45-1945 L1958 PHP *071

KRAUS, Carl Neil. 1001 WINSTEAD DR STE 200 27513 #028-02-1995 L1995 ID *020 †20

KRUSE, Shawn Richard. ■ 27513 #026-04-2004 L2008 AN *012

KULP, Kenneth Robt. 1152 EXECUTIVE CIR, STE 200 27511 #036-01-1974 L1974 D *020 †15

KUMAR, Amit. 940 SE CARY PKWY, STE 100 27518 #024-05-1999 L2006 OPH *100 †35

LANCASTER, Alisa. 100 CORNERSTONE DR, ADOLESCENT MEDICINE 27519 #036-07-1992 L1995 PD *020 †55

LAWSON, William Thomas, Jr. ■ 27519 #036-07-2000 GS *100

LE, Tuyetdung Christine. 530 NEW WAVERLY PL, PEDIATRICS 27518 #033-06-2001 L2004 PD *020 †55

LEE, Kevin Michael. 580 NEW WAVERLY PL, STE 210 27518 #036-01-2000 L2003 NEP *020 †20 ‡

LEE, Melvin G. ■ 27518 #064-01-1980 L2007 *020

LEE, Nam Hyung. ■ 27513 #583-02-1949 L1962 PTH BBK *020 †50

LEVIN, Mina L. 530 NEW WAVERLY PL, STE 200 27518 #041-01-1975 L1977 IM *020 †20

LIGHTFOOT, Harry Mckinley. ■ 27519 #036-01-1999 L2002 GS *100 †85

LIU, Lixia. ■ 27519 #243-53-1986 L2005 PTH *020

LOPEZ-LINUS, Marchi Vor. 940 SE CARY PKWY, STE 200 27518 #036-01-1999 L2002 PD *020 †20

LU, Xinrong. ■ 27519 #243-54-1995 *100

LUBLIN, Anna. ■ 27511 #035-19-1943 L1945 PD *071 †55

MAC KENNA, Jarlath M. ■ 27518 #539-04-1969 L1973 OBG *020 †30

MAC KENZIE, Mary Theresa. 270 CORNERSTONE DR, STE 105 27519 #060-01-1986 L1997 FM *020 †18 ‡

MACOMBER, Christine Linz. ■ 27511 #024-16-1996 L2007 PD *020 †55

MACOMBER, Joshua Caldwell. 300 KEISLER DR, CARY CARDIOLOGY, PA 27518 #024-16-1996 L2007 IC CD *020 †20

MALIK, Michael. 530 NEW WAVERLY PL, STE 304 27518 #035-09-1995 L2000 GS *020 †85

MANGELSDORF, Heidi M. 101 SW CARY PKWY, STE 210 27511 #048-04-1992 L1994 D *020 †15

MANN, Charles Hayes. 601 KEISLER DR, STE 200 27518 #055-01-1966 L1981 OTO GP *020 †45

MANNELLI, Paolo. 2000 REGENCY PKWY, STE 280 27518 #561-23-1987 L2004 P *020

MARIANO, Rowena Blas. 1110 SE CARY PKWY, SPECIALIST 27518 #005-14-1999 L2003 APM *020 †60

MARION, Jeremiah R. 1110 SE CARY PKWY, STE 100 27518 #036-07-1973 L1975 OPH OS *020 †35 ‡

MARKOWITZ, Michael. ■ 27513 #016-11-1994 L2000 GPM *050 †70

MARSH, Kendra Na. ■ 27519 #047-07-2003 L2006 CD *012

MARTIN, Anita Louise. 212 ASHVILLE AVE STE 10, PEDIATRICS 27518 #036-01-1983 L1986 PD *020 †55

MARTIN, Carol Ann. 1220 SE MAYNARD RD, STE 102 27511 #036-01-1978 L2001 P OS *075

MASSARO, Arlene M. 130 PRESTON EXECUTIVE DR, STE 103 27513 #305-01-1984 L1996 PD PHO *020 †55

MAYDEW, Noemi Mariano. 550 NEW WAVERLY PL, DBA CARY OBSTETRICS & 27518 #018-03-1995 L1999 OBG *020 †30

MC BRIDE, Ann Farrar. 1001 CRESCENT GREEN DR 27518 #036-07-1982 L1986 PD *020 †55

MCCALL, Shannon Jones. ■ 27519 #036-07-2000 L2001 PTH *020 †50

MC CARTHY, Kevin Eugene. 910 STRATHORN DR, 910 STRATHORN DRIVE 27519 #041-13-1981 L2004 DR IM *020 †28,80

MC GEARY, Scott Alan. 212 ASHVILLE AVE STE 10, PEDIATRICS, PA 27518 #040-02-1977 L1987 PD ID *020 †55

MC INNIS, Terry Alice. 203 FRENCHMANS BLUFF DR, GLAXOSMITHKLINE 27513 #036-05-1987 L1999 OM *030 †70

MC KENNA, Joseph P. ■ 27513 #060-01-1963 L1995 GS *071 †85

MC NASBY, David Michael. ■ 27519 #024-07-1997 L1998 *100

MEDINA, Victor Anthony. 115 CRESCENT COMMONS DR, STE 200 27518 #030-05-1985 L1988 GS VS *020 †85

MEINBERG, Eric Grant. 218 ASHVILLE AVE, STE 10 27511 #025-01-1997 L2003 ORS *020 †40

MILES, Martha Cope. 125 EDINBURGH DR, STE 207 27511 #039-01-1988 L1992 N *020

MIN, Zhao. ■ 27519 #243-04-1984 L2008 PD *100

MINEIRO, Luiz E G. ■ 27519 #187-06-1954 L1981 EM GS *020 †85,16

MINTZER, Melanie. 110 PRESTON EXECUTIVE DR, STE 108 27513 #067-01-1980 L1984 FM GPM *020 †20

MOBAREK, Sameh Khamis A H. 300 ASHVILLE AVE, STE 301 27518 #915-04-1982 L1997 CD *020 †20

MODY, Sital Prakash. 1900 KILDAIRE FARM RD 27518 #759-06-2002 L2007 IM *020 †20

MOREAU, Karen Christina. ■ 27518 #047-06-1987 L1989 PD *020

MORENO, Ricardo Daniel. 115 CRESCENT COMMONS DR, STE 200 27518 #024-01-2000 L2005 GS *020 †85

MORESCHI, Rafael M. 105 KILMAYNE DR STE B 27511 #726-01-1972 L1981 IM CD *020 †20

MORRELL, Robert X, Jr. 400 KEISLER DR, CAROLINA REHAB ASSOCIATES 27518 #020-02-1983 L1986 PM MDM *020 †60

MORTON, Thomas Rex. ■ 27513 #036-05-1972 L1972 FM *020

MUSSELMAN, Corey Neal. 1110 SE CARY PKWY, STE 203 27518 #011-03-1991 L1993 FM *020 †18

MYLES, Herbert Louis, Jr. 570 NEW WAVERLY PL, STE 210 27518 #045-01-1998 L2004 EM *020 †16

NAIDU, Aswani Subbaram. 251 KEISLER DR STE 300 27518 #495-28-1993 L2001 IM *020 †20

NARDIELLO, John. ■ 27519 #035-48-2006 AN *012

NAYAL, Vandana. 100 CORNERSTONE DR 27519 #495-61-1989 L2006 NPM *100 †55

NEWMAN, Alexander Nance. 204 ASHVILLE AVE 27518 #036-05-1989 L1993 FM *020 †18

NGUYEN, Maitrang Le. ■ 27519 #024-16-1998 L2001 IM *020

NIEMAN, Christopher Mark. 521 WINDSTREAM WAY 27518 #038-40-2001 L2007 DR *020 †80

NUNEZ, Claudia Ynez. 256 TOWNE VILLAGE DR, WEST CARY PSYCHIATRY 27513 #011-04-1998 L2005 PYG *020 †20

NUNEZ, Pedro Juan. 256 TOWNE VILLAGE DR 27513 #011-04-1998 L2005 FM *020 †18

OLIVERIO, Michael I. 580 NEW WAVERLY PL, ASSOCIATES 27518 #055-01-1990 L1996 NEP *020 †20

O'NEAL, Kevin D. 400 ASHVILLE AVE STE 300, WESTERN WAKE EYE CTR PA 27518 #048-04-1997 L2001 OPH *020 †35 ‡

OSE, Wendy Elise Gross. ■ 27518 #036-07-1975 L1976 P *071 †75

OUTLAW, David Thomas. 224 HIGH HOUSE RD, STE 100 27513 #036-01-1996 L2000 MPD *020 †20,55

PAI, Jeevan Jagdish. 1000 CRESCENT GREEN DR, STE 102 27518 #030-05-1999 L2006 GE *100 †20

PALOMBARO, James Frank. 1900 KILDAIRE FARM RD 27518 #035-15-1989 L1998 EM *020 †16

PARIKH, Himanshu P. 401 KEISLER DR, DHILLON ORTHOPAEDIC & 27518 #495-89-1989 L1996 IM *020 †20

PARIKHDESAI, Amrita S. 103 BAINES CT 27511 #495-83-1989 L1994 IM *020 †20

PARK, Sun Mie. 1911 SNOWY OWL LN 27518 #051-01-1996 L2000 EM *020 †16

PARKS, Jeffrey David. 400 PINNER WEALD WAY, STE 102 27513 #012-01-1999 L2001 P *020

PARMAR, Shefali V. 100 CORNERSTONE DR 27519 #051-01-2002 L2005 PD *100 †55

PATEL, Balubhai N. 400 ASHVILLE AVE, STE 340 27518 #495-23-1980 L1989 NEP IM *020

PATEL, Chaitany Rasikbhai. ■ 27511 #305-01-2002 L2006 FM *100 †18

PATEL, Mehul Balubhai. ■ 27511 #035-46-2006 L2007 IM *020

PATEL, Prashant K. 103 BAINES CT 27511 #035-48-1995 L1998 IM *020 †20 ‡

PATEL, Rujuta Hetulkumar. ■ 27513 #495-76-2000 L2006 NEP *012 †20 ‡

PATEL, Sejan Bhupendra. ■ 27519 #038-40-2004 L2007 IM *100 †20

PENNELL, Jennifer Kern. 1020 SOUTHHILL DR, STE 380 27513 #038-40-1996 L1997 P *020 †75

PHAM, Lu Gia. ■ 27511 #941-01-1962 L1978 GP PD *071

PICKENS, Andrew Trice. ■ 27513 #028-34-2005 L2008 EM *012

PIKE, Michael Robt. 1000 CRESCENT GREEN DR, STE 102 27518 #035-47-1973 L1979 GE IM *020 †20

PISHARODY, Murali Dhara. ■ 27519 #016-11-2003 L2003 FP *012

PLYMYER, Matthew Ray. ■ 27518 #041-07-1987 L1993 PTH PCP *020 †50

POLAVARAM, Yuvaraju. 907 KILDAIRE FARM RD 27511 #495-70-1991 L1998 NEP *020

POOLE, Terry Wayne. 1900 KILDAIRE FARM RD 27518 #036-05-1973 L1973 GYN *071 †30

POULOS, Karen Kristine. 2000 REGENCY PKWY STE 204 27518 #036-01-1994 L1998 CHP *020 †75

PREMAKUMAR, Sanjay Kumar. 543 KEISLER DR, STE 202 27518 #036-01-2002 L2005 **EM** *020

PRITCHETT, Douglas Brian. 251 KEISLER DR, STE 201 27518 #047-05-1982 L1988 **IM** *020 †20

PUGLIESE, Wm Mc Cammon. ■ 27511 #035-03-1954 L1955 **FM IMG** *071

RABON, Fred Scott. SAS HEALTH CARE CT 27513 #045-01-1985 L1988 **FM** *020 †18

RAJBHANDARI, Dharma Devi. ■ 27519 #495-24-1970 L2002 **RO GP** *020 †80

RAJENDRAPRASAD, Makam V S. 1120 SE CARY PKWY, MEDICINE SPECIALISTS 27518 #495-99-1978 L2003 **GE** *020 †20 ‡

RAMAN, Sujatha. 530 NEW WAVERLY PL, STE 200 27518 #496-23-1999 L2004 **IM** *020 †20

RAVI, Himabindu. ■ 27519 #495-21-1995 L2003 *020

RAYBORN, Jobeth Linnette. ■ 27519 #020-02-1998 **FM** *100

REDDY, Edavally Narayan. 550 NEW WAVERLY PL STE 120 27518 #495-65-1981 L1998 **IM** *020 †20

RENCK, Gregory Richard. 102 COMMONWEALTH CT STE H 27511 #016-11-1997 L1998 **CHP P** *020 †75

RESNIK, Robert John. 930 SE CARY PKWY, STE 200 27518 #051-07-1988 L1990 **IM** *020 †20

REYNOLDS, Paul David. 110 PRESTON EXECUTIVE DR A 27513 #028-34-1981 L1990 **IM** *020 †20

RICHARD, Daniel. 600 NEW WAVERLY PL, STE 203 27518 #016-11-1996 L2004 **FM** *020 †18 ‡

RIHAL, Rabina. ■ 27513 #036-01-2007 **IM** *012

ROANE, Karen Denise. 401 KEISLER DR, DHILLON ORTHOPAEDIC & 27518 #036-08-1987 L1988 **OBG** *020 †20

ROBERTS, Joan Therese. 1110 SE CARY PKWY, STE 100 27518 #036-07-1989 L1994 **PO** *020 †35

ROGAN, Matthew Paul. ■ 27513 #035-03-1971 L1994 **OS PD** *030 †55

ROGERS, Ronald Gray. 530 NEW WAVERLY PL, STE 301 27518 #036-01-1990 L1994 **OBG** *020 †30

ROZAKIS, Mary Ann. 212 ASHVILLE AVE, STE 10 27518 #036-05-1982 L1985 **PD** *020 †55

RUTLEDGE, William Jeffrey. 100 CORNERSTONE DR, CORNERSTONE PEDIATRICS 27519 #047-05-1997 L2000 **PD** *020 †55

RYAN, Sarah D. 1515 SW CARY PKWY 27511 #025-07-1996 L2005 **PD** *020 †55

SALTER, Teresa Palmer. 101 SW CARY PKWY STE 270, TRIANGLE PEDIATRIC CENTER, 27511 #036-01-1975 L1975 **PD** *020 †55

SANITATE, Scott Steven. 1110 SE CARY PKWY, SPECIALIST 27518 #025-07-1988 L1992 **PM** *020 †60

SCHMIDT, Robert Scott. 580 NEW WAVERLY PL, STE 210 27518 #056-06-1989 L1992 **NEP** *020 †20

SCHRODER, Derek Quentin. 530 NEW WAVERLY PL, STE 200 27518 #003-01-1991 L2003 **IM** *020 †20

SCHWEICKERT, Lori Ann. 1903 N HARRISON AVE 27513 #030-06-1991 L1994 **CHP** *020 †75 ‡

SCOTT, Jessica S. 111 ADVENT CT, WAVERLY PRIMARY CARE 27518 #024-07-1993 L1995 **FM** *020 †18

SEIDEL, Geoffrey Keenan. 550 NEW WAVERLY PL, STE 200 27518 #041-02-1998 L2002 **OBG** *020 †30

SHAH, Dhirenkumar N. 300 KEISLER DR, STE 204 27518 #495-89-1982 L1991 **IM** *020 †20

SHAH, Dipen Ramesh. 600 NEW WAVERLY PL, STE 205 27518 #495-48-1997 L2005 **FM** *020 †18

SHAH, Nanda Mahendra. 519 KEISLER DR, STE 104 27518 #495-19-1978 L1998 **OBG** *020

SHAH, Priyavadan M. 300 KEISLER DR, STE 204 CARY CARDIOLOGY 27518 #495-23-1972 L1981 **CD IM** *020 †20

SHARRITS, Amie Lynn. 400 PINNER WEALD WAY, STE 102 27513 #038-44-1999 L2001 **P** *100 †15

SHEARIN, Dorothy R B. 910 REEDY CREEK RD 27513 #041-07-1954 L1955 **GP** *071 †55

SHEARIN, William Arthur. 101 SW CARY PKWY, WAKE OPHTHALMOLOGY 27511 #036-07-1962 L1962 **OPH** *071 †35

SHEIKH, Sattar Abdus. ■ 27513 #704-02-1985 L1994 **IM EM** *020 †20

SHEITMAN, Brian B. ■ 27519 #028-34-1987 L1996 **P** *020 †75

SHELTON, Monica Harris. 940 SE CARY PKWY, STE 200 27518 #036-01-1983 L1988 **PD** *020 †55

SHESHADRI, Vijay. 1130 KILDAIRE FARM RD, STE 240 27511 #038-43-1995 L1999 **OBG** *020 †30

SHOFFNER, Sylvia Piqueras. 530 NEW WAVERLY PL, STE 200 27518 #041-01-1995 L1997 **IM** *020 †20

SIEGEL, Cara Beth. 222 ASHVILLE AVE 27518 #051-04-1989 L1995 **PM** *020 †60

SIMONE, Frank Anthony. ■ 27518 #561-17-1959 **AN** *071

SINGH, Amit Kumar. ■ 27519 #036-05-2004 L2005 **IM** *100 †20

SINGH, Harminder Paul. 1120 SE CARY PKWY, MEDICINE SPECIALISTS 27518 #048-15-1991 L1996 **GE IM** *020 †20

SINGH, Paramjeet. 216 ASHVILLE AVE, CAROLINA CARY 27518 #495-90-1981 L1996 **HEM** *020 †20

SINGH, Paul Gulsharan. 400 KEISLER DR 27518 #016-42-2002 L2007 **PM** *100 †60

SLUGG, Peter Hill. ■ 27519 #016-11-1966 L1967 **IM PA** *071 †20

SMITH, Michael Kevin. 940 SE CARY PKWY, STE 200 27518 #003-01-1980 L1984 **PD** *020 †55

SMOOT, Gary Lowell. 1110 SE CARY PKWY, SPECIALIST 27518 #038-40-1987 L1991 **PM PME** *020 †60

SOHN, Ivy Ellen. 202 WHITCOMB LN 27518 #550-02-1995 L2007 **PFP** *020 †75

SOMARATNE, Ransi M. 1001 WINSTEAD DR, STE 200 27513 #035-03-1993 L1995 **CD** *020 †20

SOTO, Maryann Liwag. 212 ASHVILLE AVE STE 10, ACCENT URGEN CARAFTER HOUR 27518 #020-12-2002 L2006 **PD** *020 †55

SPECA, Joellen Christine. ■ 27518 #050-02-2001 L2008 **HO** *100 †20

SPECTOR, Jared Eli. 601 KEISLER DR # 200 27518 #048-04-1994 L2000 **OTO** *020 †45

STADIEM, Michael David. 1125 KILDAIRE FARM RD, STE 207 27511 #041-01-1976 L1979 **FM** *020 †18

STEIN, Adam David. 300 KEISLER DR STE 102, CENTER, PA 27518 #036-07-1990 L1997 **OTO** *020 †45

STEPHENSON, Sharon Rose. 550 NEW WAVERLY PL, DBA CARY OBSTETRICS & 27518 #036-01-1984 L1988 **OBG** *020 †30

STEVENS, Craig A. 106 RIDGE VIEW DR STE A, TRIANGLE FAMILY CARE PA 27511 #038-41-1989 L1994 **FM** *020 †18

STEVENS, Patience B. ■ 27511 #036-08-1986 L1990 **PD PHP** *062 †55

STONE, Robert Thomas, Jr. 105 SW CARY PKWY, STE 200 27511 #036-01-1994 L1996 **OPH** *020 †35

SUMMERS, Ronald Alan. 401 KEISLER DR, DHILLON ORTHOPAEDIC & 27518 #019-02-1992 L1998 **OSM** *020 †40

TABB, Seth Edward. 104 FOUNTAIN BROOK CIR, STE A 27511 #011-03-1990 L1992 **CHP P** *020 †75

TABRIZI, Sara N. 940 SE CARY PKWY, STE 200 27518 #036-01-2002 L2005 **PD** *100

TACKMAN, Lori Anne. 100 CORNERSTONE DR 27519 #025-12-1993 L2000 **PD** *020 †55

TAHTAWI, Samira Said. 212 ASHVILLE AVE, STE 220 27518 #024-07-1998 L2002 **OBG** *020 †30

TALBERT, Luther M. 400 ASHVILLE AVE, STE 200 27518 #051-01-1953 L1959 **REN OBG** *071 †30

TALLURI, Krishna Kumari. 100 TYNEMOUTH DR 27513 #495-70-1975 L1996 **P** *050

TELFER, James Gavin, Jr. 305 S ACADEMY ST STE A 27511 #028-02-1971 L1977 **IM FM** *020 †20

TEUNIS, Frances S. 530 NEW WAVERLY PL, STE 101 27518 #051-01-1991 L1997 **ID** *020 †20

THOMAS, Edwin Scott. 106 E PARK ST 27511 #036-01-1964 L1964 **IM PD** *071

THOMPSON, Benj Everett. ■ 27511 #036-01-1958 L1958 **GP** *071

THURBER, David Cushman, Jr. 1900 KILDAIRE FARM RD 27518 #035-45-1977 L1981 **IM** *020 †20

TODD, Karen Anne. 100 CORNERSTONE DR, ADOLESCENT MEDICINE 27519 #036-08-1992 L1995 **PD** *020 †55

TONKENS, Ross Michael. ■ 27519 #008-01-1974 L1975 **CD IM** *050 †20

TRIPP, Cecil De Wayne. ■ 27511 #036-01-1960 L1960 **D GP** *020

TYNER, Michael Anthony. 208 ASHVILLE AVE, STE 50 27518 #045-01-1983 L1990 **GS** *020 †85

ULLAH, A B M Enayet. 1601 WALNUT ST 27511 #160-01-1979 L1998 **IM** *020 †20

USHER, Bruce Warren, Jr. 300 ASHVILLE AVE, STE 301 27518 #045-01-1993 L2000 **CD** *020 †20

VAIDYA, Prabhakar Narhari. 580 NEW WAVERLY PL, ASSOCIATES 27518 #496-38-1969 L1975 **NEP IM** *020 †20

VALDEZ, Michael Campbell. 1900 KILDAIRE FARM RD, ATTN: HOSPITALIST OFFICE 27518 #422-01-2004 L2008 **IM** *020 †20

VALLABH, Vinod C. 570 NEW WAVERLY PL, STE 140 27518 #495-37-1980 L1987 **GE IM** *020 †20

VAN CLEEFF, Martin. 530 NEW WAVERLY PL, STE 200 27518 #036-05-1992 L1995 **IM** *020 †20

VANDERGRIFF, Elizabeth F. 110 PRESTON EXECUTIVE DR 27513 #048-13-1992 L1995 **FM** *020 †18

VARLEY, Rebecca Jane. ■ 27519 #048-13-2006 **PTH** *012

VICE, Carrie Hale. ■ 27518 #036-08-2001 L2004 **EM** *020 †16

VIEHMAN, Greg Edwin. 200 WELLESLEY TRADE LN 27519 #041-02-1993 L1996 **D** *020 †15 ‡

VORA, Sharad Ganpatrai. 251 KEISLER DR, STE 101 27518 #495-89-1983 L1995 **PUD CCM** *020 †20

VOYNOW, Judith Ann. ■ 27513 #041-01-1982 L1994 **PDP** *050 †55

VYAS, Hema. ■ 27519 #654-01-2001 L2007 **CHP** *100

WALTER, Steven Wayne. ■ 27519 #038-43-1983 L1984 **IM** *020 †20 ‡

WANG, Yi-Zhe. ■ 27513 #243-29-1986 L2006 **P** *020

WARD, John Thos. 105 SW CARY PKWY STE 200 27511 #039-01-1981 L1983 **OPH** *020 †35

WASE, Raymond Edward, Jr. ■ 27518 #011-03-1974 L1975 **EM OM** *020 †16

WATKINS, Robert Stuart. 580 NEW WAVERLY PL, STE 120 27518 #051-01-1980 L1993 **IM** *020 †20

WATTS, Wanda Kay. ■ 27519 #036-05-1985 L1988 **FM ADM** *020 †18

WELCH, Gerald Edwin. 300 ASHVILLE AVE, STE 305 27518 #038-40-1995 L2000 **OBG** *020 †30

WHEELAN, Sarah Jo. ■ 27513 #023-07-2003 *100

WHICKER, James Hubert. 200 ASHVILLE AVE, STE 30 27518 #036-01-1966 L1966 **OTO GS** *071 †45

WHITE, Lisa Marie. ■ 27511 #007-02-2006 **PD** *012

WILCOX, William David. 1110 SE CARY PKWY, STE 100 27518 #041-12-1970 L1977 **OPH** *020 †35

WILL, Matthew Arthur. ■ 27519 #017-20-2005 **OBG** *012

WILSON, Brett Lamond. 100 CORNERSTONE DR 27519 #036-07-1988 L1991 **PD** *020 †55

WILSON, Richard Dale. ■ 27511 #024-01-1976 L1978 **FM** *020 †18

WILSON, Stephen Millard. 611 SHERWOOD FOREST PL 27519 #036-05-1988 L1989 **IM** *020

WITUS, Carl. ■ 27511 #065-01-1936 L1979 **PD** *071 †55

WOMBLE, James Cornelius. 224 HIGH HOUSE RD STE 100 27513 #036-01-1986 L1990 **IM PD** *020 †20,55

WON, John Sunghoon. 3600 NW CARY PKWY STE 105 27513 #036-01-2002 L2006 *020

WU, Sheue-Mei. ■ 27518 #036-01-2001 L2006 **P** *100

WUBBEN, Ryan James. 543 KEISLER DR, STE 202 27518 #056-05-1997 L2001 **EM** *020 †16

YADUSKY, A J. 300 ASHVILLE AVE, STE 220 27518 #036-01-1989 L1993 **OBG** *020

YAHALOM, Gilad. ■ 27513 #660-01-2003 *100

YANAMADALA, Mamata. ■ 27519 #495-65-1999 L2008 **IMG** *012 †20

YANG, Helen Wen. 1000 CRESCENT GREEN DR, STE 202 27518 #243-38-1990 L2001 **FM** *020 †18

YANTCH-BUCHIN, Sandra Lee. ■ 27518 #033-05-1964 L1979 **PD** *071 †55

YERBY, Lemuel Gaston, III. 115 CRESCENT COMMONS DR, STE 200 27518 #012-05-1985 L1994 **GS** *020 †85

YOUNG, Cynthia Cerise. 212 ASHVILLE AVE, STE 30 27518 #018-03-2001 L2005 **FM** *020 †18

YOUNG, Matthew Monroe. 531 SE MAYNARD RD 27513 #038-41-2000 L2002 **EM** *020 †16

YOUNG, Noel Wm, Jr. 1110 SE CARY PKWY, STE 100 27518 #036-07-1963 L1963 **OPH** *020 †35

ZAIIM, Loghman. ■ 27513 #308-11-1985 L1988 **PD** *020 †55

ZHANG, Jing Jean. 600 NEW WAVERLY PL, STE 203 27518 #243-52-1986 L2002 **FM** *020 †18

ZILAVY, Dennis Lee. 530 NEW WAVERLY PL, BRANNON & ROGERS OB AND GY 27518 #056-05-1972 L1993 **OBG** *020 †30

CASHIERS – JACKSON

BASH, Vincent C, Jr. ■ 28717 #039-01-1951 L1952 **FM GS** *071

BERRYHILL, Bruce Holt. PO BOX 1945 28717 #036-01-1964 L1964 **OTO HNS** *071 †45

CHRISTIE, John Norton. ■ 28717 #036-07-1958 L1959 **IM GE** *071 †20

CHRISTOPHER, Wm E, Jr. ■ 28717 #036-05-1961 L1961 **P** *071

CHUBB, Nicholas C. PO BOX 578, 186 CEDAR CT 28717 #041-12-1951 L1952 **P** *071 †75

COOK, Robert T. ■ 28717 #004-01-1951 L1951 **DR NM** *071 †80,28

GILBERT, J C, Jr. ■ 28717 #047-06-1951 L1973 **OBG** *071 †30

HASTINGS, Edward V. ■ 28717 #056-06-1944 L1952 **PTH** *071 †50

HEFFINGTON, Mark Wm. ■ 28717 #047-06-1978 L1982 **FM** *020 †18

LEHMAN, Ronald Jay. ■ 28717 #035-19-1959 L1972 **ORS** *071 †40

LINDSAY, Thomas Fowler. PO BOX 2806, 45 SLABTOWN RD STE A 28717 #036-01-1988 L1989 **FM** *071 †18

MILCIUNAS, Lourdes Elias. PO BOX 1821, 424 TURNBERRY LN 28717 #011-02-1975 L2000 **FM** *020

■ = Address Information Privacy Protected

PRESTON, Steven Paul. ■ 28717 #011-02-1975 L1977 **NEP IM** *071 †20
STAATS, Ethan Freeman. ■ 28717 #012-05-1959 L1959 **OTO** *071 †45
WILLIAMS, Thomas Beekman. ■ 28717 #011-02-1966 L1973 **PUD IM** *071 †20

CASTALIA – NASH

LYNCH, Donald Ray, Jr. ■ 27816 #036-01-2008 *012

CASTLE HAYNE – NEW HANOVER

SPRINGER, Joseph G. ■ 28429 #038-41-1950 L1968 **GP** *071
WALDREP, Douglas Alan. 5000 LAMBS PATH WAY, MEDICAL DIRECTOR, YAHWEH C 28429 #045-01-1988 L2006 **CHP P** *020 †75 ‡

CEDAR MOUNTAIN – TRANSYLVANIA

BROWN, Eli Hinson. 750 SPANISH OAK DR - IDLE 28718 #011-02-1960 L1971 **DR NM** *020 †80

CEDAR POINT – CARTERET

BEASLEY, Charles Britton. 718 CEDAR POINT BLVD 28584 #036-01-1974 L1975 **OTO HNS** *020 †45 ‡
CARR, Edward Sleight. ■ 28584 #025-01-1942 L1951 **P** *072 †75
GOHEEN, Barbara Lynn. 718 CEDAR POINT BLVD 28584 #054-04-1997 L2002 **OTO** *020 †45
POHLMAN, Barbara Lori. 103 SHADY PATH 28584 #026-04-1981 L1996 **OM PTX** *030 †20,70
RICKABAUGH, John Clyde. 540 CEDAR POINT BLVD 28584 #036-08-1992 L1994 **FM** *020 †18
ROSSO-SALISBURY, Bianca H. 718 CEDAR POINT BLVD, WESTERN CARTERET MEDICAL C 28584 #033-05-1994 L1997 **FM** *020 †18
SABISTON, Walter Roberts. 718 CEDAR POINT BLVD 28584 #036-01-1967 L1967 **OTO GS** *020 †45
SKARDA, Karen Ruth. 540 CEDAR POINT BLVD 28584 #035-48-1978 L1993 **FM** *020 †18
WILLIS, Kerry Allen. 540 CEDAR POINT BLVD 28584 #036-01-1985 L1986 **FM** *020 †18

CERRO GORDO – COLUMBUS

CARLSON, James Lennart. 7497 ANDREW JACKSON HWY SW 28430 #056-06-1991 L2006 **FM** *020 †18

CHADBOURN – COLUMBUS

BUFFKIN, Kimberly Rebecca. ■ 28431 #036-08-2004 L2007 **EM** *020
ESKANDER, Essam Sobhy. 104 E 7TH AVE, PA 28431 #915-02-1979 L1990 **FM** *020 †18
WALTON, Geo Britain, Jr. ■ 28431 #036-07-1956 L1956 **R OS** *071 †80

CHAPEL HILL – ORANGE

ABAID, Lisa Nicole. 101 MANNING DR, DEPT OB/GYN CB 7570 27514 #011-02-2000 L2003 **OBG GO** *020 †30
ABEL, Ki Lynn. ■ 27516 #011-03-1994 L2005 **PD PEM** *020 †55
ADAMS, Christina Elaine. 101 MANNING DR, DEPT FM 27514 #010-03-2007 **FP** *012
ADAMS, James Clayton. ■ 27514 #056-05-2003 L2006 **IM** *020 †20
ADAMS, Kirkwood Floyd, Jr. 730 MARTN LTHR KNG JR BLVD, BOLIN CREEK SUITE 207 27514 #036-01-1976 L1976 **CD** *050 †20
ADAMS, Madeline Mei. ■ 27516 #051-01-2004 L2007 **IM** *020 †20
ADAMSON, Jerome Eugene. ■ 27517 #036-07-1954 L1954 **PS** *071 †65
ADELMAN, Leon Chaim. ■ 27514 #036-01-2008 *012
ADEROJU, Ademola Olubusol. UNIV OF N CAROLINA SCH OF, 3018 OLD CLINIC BLDG/CB760 27599 #047-07-2005 **IM** *012
ADIGUN, Chris G. ■ 27514 #036-01-2007 **IM** *012
ADIMORA, Adaora Alise. CB #7030, 547 BURNETT, DIV OF INFECTIOUS DISEASES 27599 #008-01-1981 L1988 **IM ID** *050 †20
ADUNKA, Oliver. 101 MANNING DR CB7070, DEPT OF OTOLARYNGOLOGY 27514 #154-07-1999 L2006 **OTO NO** *020
AFENYIANNAN, Araba N. 101 MANNING DR, BANKTRANFUSION MEDICINE 27514 #025-01-1997 L2002 **CLP BBK** *020 †50
AHLGRIM, Heidi Swygard. CB 7030, UNC-CHAPEL HILL-DEPT MED 27599 #017-20-1994 L1998 **ID** *020 †20
AH-TYE, Collette. 100 EUROPA DR STE 260 27517 #041-12-1999 L2004 **CHP** *020 †75
AITSEBAOMO, Egede J. 2340-C MBRB, CB 7126, UNIVERSITY OF NC, CHAPEL H 27599 #048-14-1997 L2001 **CD** *020 †20
AJMANI, Ajay Kumar. CAMPUS BOX 7280, DIV URHM UNCCH SCH OF MED 27599 #495-73-1983 L1992 **ALI RHU** *071 †55,20
ALEMAN, Marco Antonio. DIV OF GEN MED CB 7110, UNC CHAPEL HILL 27599 #016-11-1985 L1997 **IM** *040 †20
ALEXANDER, Joshua Jacob. UNC SCHOOL OF MEDICINE, CAMPUS BOX 7200 27599 #036-13-1990 L1995 **PD PM** *020 †55,60
ALEXANDER, Lawrence M. UNIV OF N CAROLINA SCH OF, 3314 BIOINFORMATICS BUILDI 27599 #035-19-2003 **ORS** *012
ALEXANDER, Thomas Blick. ■ 27517 #036-01-2008 *012
ALEXANDER, William James. 1414 RALEIGH RD, STE 400 27517 #027-01-1974 L1991 **IM ID** *050 †20
ALLEN, B Titus. ■ 27517 #036-07-1966 L1966 **IM END** *071 †20
ALLEN, Geoffrey Abbott. UNIV OF NO CAROLINA, CB 7220, DIV PED HEM/ONCOL 27599 #036-01-1993 L1997 **PHO** *020 †55
ALMEKINDERS, Louis C. UNIV NC/CB 7055 OPH SURG 27599 #660-07-1980 L1984 **ORS OSM** *020 †40
ALTMAN, James Ryan. ■ 27516 #045-01-2007 **IM** *012
AMBLER, Denisse M. 1829 E FRANKLIN ST 27514 #021-06-1998 L1999 **P CHP** *020 †75 ‡
AMIN, Chirag. CB 7305, 3009 OLD CLINIC BUILD 27599 #017-20-2002 L2005 **HO** *012 †20

AMIRI, Sherin. ■ 27516 #010-03-1998 L1999 **PD** *020 †55
ANDERSON, Arthur Alex. ■ 27517 #054-04-1954 L1994 **CHP P** *071 †75
ANDERSON, Charles Melvin. ■ 27516 #005-11-1982 L1984 **DR** *020 †80
ANDERSON, Christina Kay. ■ 27516 #011-04-2008 *012
ANDERSON, Jay Arthur. 101 MANNING DRIVE, CB#7010 27599 #036-01-1984 L2007 **AN PD** *020 †05 ‡
ANDERSON, Jeffrey Allan. 130 MASON FARM RD, CB #7030 27599 #055-01-2001 L2004 **ID** *100
ANDERSON, Rennae Suzette. ■ 27514 #028-02-1995 L2006 **PTH** *020 †50
ANDRAWES, Steven Nathan. ■ 27516 #036-01-2008 *012
ANGCHAISUKSIRI, Pantep. ■ 27517 #891-01-1986 L1993 **IM** *100
ANGOTTI, Frank Thomas, III. NEUROSCI HOSP, CB# 7160 10625 27599 #055-01-2007 **P** *012
ANNEX, Brian Herb. ■ 27514 #008-01-1985 L1988 **CD IM** *012
APISARNTHANARAX, Smith. 101 MANNING DR, UNIV OF NC HOSPITAL 27514 #043-01-2002 L2006 **RO** *012
ARCHDEACON, Patrick Lavin. UNC SCHOOL OF MEDICINE, 7024 BURNETT WOMACK BLDG 27599 #035-01-2001 L2006 **IM** *100 †20
ARIS, Robert Michael. UNIV OF N CAROLINA, 420 BURNETT-WOMACK CB 7020 27599 #047-05-1984 L1993 **PCC IM** *100 †20
ARMANNSSON, Ragnar. ■ 27516 #484-01-1993 L1999 **AN** *100 †05
ARMAO, Diane Mary. ■ 27514 #041-02-1990 L1997 **NP** *020
ARTIS, Avis Adriena. 300 MEADOWMONT VILLAGE CIR, STE 311 27517 #036-07-1984 L1989 **OBG** *020 †30
ASCHBRENNER, Mathew Warre. 101 MANNING DR, UNIV OF NC HOSPS 27514 #056-05-2006 **OPH** *012
ASHER, Gary Norman. 101 MANNING DR, CB #7595 27514 #550-04-2003 L2006 **FM** *100 †18
ASHKIN, Evan Arthur. 590 MANNING DR, CAMPUS BOX 7595 27599 #024-07-1988 L1998 **FM** *020 †18
ATAGA, Kenneth Isimemen. 101 MANNING DR, UNC HOSPITALS 27514 #690-06-1990 L1997 **HO** *020 †20
AUGUSTUS, Todd Matthew. ■ 27514 #036-05-2008 *012
AUSTIN, Gregory Lawrence. ■ 27599 #008-01-2000 L2004 **GE** *100 †20
AVERY, Andrew John. ■ 27514 #035-09-2007 **IM** *012
AVERY, Katrina Howard. 300 MEADOWMONT VILLAGE CIR, STE 311 27517 #036-01-1991 L1996 **OBG** *020 †30
AYLSWORTH, Arthur Selden. MANNING DR CB #7220, UNIV NC-DEPT PEDIATRICS 27599 #041-01-1967 L1974 **OS PD** *040 †55,19
AYLWARD, Gillian. 110 TIMBERHILL PL, TIMBERLYNE FAMILY 27514 #063-01-1983 L1993 **FM** *020 †18
AZAR, Henry Amin. ■ 27514 #605-01-1952 L1955 **PTH HEM** *071 †50
AZEEM, Samreen Waqar. 32405 ARCHDALE 27517 #704-20-1998 L2006 **FM** *020 †18
BAE-JUMP, Victoria Lin. ■ 27517 #051-04-2000 L2004 **OBG** *100 ‡
BAERMAN, Kathryn Jean. ■ 27517 #036-01-2001 **GS** *012
BAILEY, Ann Geryl. MANNING DR, UNC DEPT OF ANEST 27514 #016-45-1980 L1985 **AN PD** *020 †55,05
BAKER, Edward Lamar. ■ 27517 #048-04-1972 L1972 **OM** *030 †20,70
BALDWIN, Ruth Lennek. ■ 27517 #051-01-1983 L1986 **PD** *071 †55
BALLARD, David E. DEPT OF ANES, CB 7010 N 2201 UNC HOSP 27599 #034-01-1975 L1977 **AN** *020 †05
BALLARD, Yvonne Lynnette. 101 MANNING DR, UNIV OF NC HOSPS 27514 #023-01-2004 L2007 **ID** *012 †20
BANDARENKO, Nicholas, III. 101 MANNING DR, UNC HOSPITALS 27514 #036-05-1990 L1995 **BBK** *020 †50
BANKAITIS, Lee Anne. 1717 LEGION RD STE 103 27517 #001-02-1997 L2001 **FM** *020 †18 ‡
BARBARO, Ryan Pasquale. ■ 27514 #036-01-2005 *012
BARKER, Pierre Michael. 130 MASON FARM RD, CAMPUS BOX #7220 27599 #836-02-1979 L1994 **PDP** *030 †55
BARNETT, Thomas B. U NC SHO MED CB7020 27599 #035-45-1949 L1952 **PUD IM** *071 †20
BARNHILL, Larry Jarrett, Jr. CB #7160, UNC AT CHAPEL HILL 27599 #036-05-1975 L1975 **CHP P** *020 †75
BARNHOUSE, Kathleen Knesp. CB # 7595, DEPT OF FAMILY PRACTICE 27599 #025-07-2000 L2002 **FM** *100 †18
BAROT, Nishidh Amrutlal. ■ 27516 #051-07-2004 L2004 **N** *012
BARRICK, Brian Patrick. 101 MANNING DR, UNC MEM HOSP 27514 #047-05-2001 L2005 **AN** *100 †05
BARRITT, Alfred Sidney, IV. 6723 FALCONBRIDGE RD, UNIVERSITY OF NORTH CAROLI 27517 #051-01-2002 L2006 **GE** *012 †20
BARRON, Bruce A. ■ 27517 #035-19-1971 L1972 **GYN OS** *071 †30
BARTHOLOMEW, David Allen. ■ 27514 #036-01-1994 L1995 **CHP** *020 †75
BARTHOLOMEW, Neva Edens. 101 CONNER DR, STE 402 27514 #036-01-1995 L1997 **FM** *020 †18
BASHFORD, Robert Alonzo. 210 COLUMBIA PLACE WEST 27599 #036-01-1971 L1971 **CHP** *040 †30,75
BATES, Melisa Kaye. ■ 27514 #036-01-2007 **PD** *012
BATSON, Ronald Monroe. 11 THE COURTYARD 27516 #021-05-1977 L1980 **P** *020 †75
BATTIGELLI, Mario Cesare. ■ 27517 #561-06-1951 L1965 **PUD IM** *071 †70
BAUDET, Heather Georgette. ■ 27516 #036-01-2007 **PD** *012
BAUMAN, John Howard. ■ 27516 #038-06-1958 L1992 **IM** *071 †20
BEACH, Rachel Bowes. ■ 27514 #036-01-2004 **AN** *012
BEAMER, Staci Erin. ■ 27516 #036-01-2008 *012
BEAMON, Carmen Jevonne. ■ 27514 #036-01-2007 **OBG** *012
BEASLEY, Karen Rose. 101 MANNING DR, CB#7160 27514 #036-01-2003 L2005 **P** *012
BEAVEN, Anne Wood. 101 MANNING DR, DEPT OF INTERNAL MEDICINE 27514 #036-01-2000 L2003 **IM** *100 †20
BECHTOLDT, Albert A, Jr. ■ 27517 #008-01-1961 L1968 **AN** *071 †05
BECKER, Kenneth Alan. 891 WILLOW DR STE 1 27514 #033-05-1998 L2006 **D** *020 †15
BECKER, Sylvia Irene. CB 7595, MANNING DRIVE, UNC-DEPARTMENT OF FAMILY M 27599 #036-07-1997 L2001 **FM** *020 †18
BECKLEY, Robert Franklin. ■ 27517 #041-13-1941 L1942 **R OS** *071
BEGLEY, Devon Eva. 101 MANNING DR 27514 #038-41-2006 L2006 **DR** *012
BEIDLER, Stephanie K. 101 MANNING DR 27514 #016-02-2002 L2005 **GS** *100
BELHORN, Thomas H. 130 MASON FARM RD, CB 7220 27599 #036-01-1987 L1999 **PDI** *020 †55
BELL, William Edward. ■ 27514 #051-04-1955 L1955 **N PD** *071 †75,55
BELOFF, Jerome S. ■ 27514 #035-01-1943 L1944 **PD PHP** *071 †55
BENJAMIN, John Tabb. BIOINFORMATICS BUILDING, CB 7220 DEPT OF PEDIATRICS 27599 #035-01-1966 L2003 **PD HEM** *100 †55

BENNETT, Kimberly Kay. NEUROSCI HOSP, CB# 7160 10625 27599 #036-01-2007 **P** *012

BENSON, Walter Russell. ■ 27514 #036-07-1944 L1952 **PTH** *071 †50

BENTLEY, Stuart Anthony. UNIV OF N CAROLINA, CB #7525 27599 #917-07-1967 L1981 **PTH** *020 †50

BERGDOLT, Barbara Ann. 120 CONNER DR, CHAPEL HILL FAMILY MEDICIN 27514 #025-01-1994 L1997 **MPD** *020 †20,55

BERGER, Gary Sterling. 109 CONNER DR, STE 2200 27514 #035-45-1969 L1973 **GYN** *020 †30,70

BERGER, Jeffrey Stuart. ■ 27516 #550-02-2001 L2006 **CD** *012

BERGER, Robert Gary. 100 MASON FARM RD 27599 #036-01-1976 L1976 **IG** *020 †20

BERGER, Stephanie Paige. ■ 27516 #036-01-2006 L2008 **PD** *012

BERGLUND, Lisa Marie. UNIV OF N CAROLINA SCH OF, 3314 BIOINFORMATICS BUILDI 27599 #018-03-2005 **ORS** *012

BERKOWITZ, Lee Richard. 101 MANNING DR, UNC HOSPITALS 27514 #038-40-1975 L1975 **HEM IM** *030 †20

BERKOWITZ, Seth Aloisi. ■ 27516 #036-01-2008 *012

BERNARD, Stephen Alan. SCHOOL OF MEDICINE, UNIVERSITY OF NORTH CAROLI 27599 #036-01-1973 L1980 **ON IM** *020 †20

BERNSTEIN, Kyrie Lauren. 101 MANNING DR, OGMEROOM 1107-A 27514 #051-01-2002 L2003 **PD** *100

BERSTLER, Yvonne Enwan. 101 MANNING DR, DEPT OF FAMILY MED CB7595 27514 #036-05-2005 L2008 **FP** *012

BEVIN, A Griswold. 101 MANNING DR 27514 #008-01-1960 L1968 **PS HS** *071 †85,65

BHARTUR, Sheela G. 101 MANNING DR, OGMEROOM 1107-G 27514 #012-01-2003 L2006 **NM** *012

BIDGOOD, Willis D, Jr. ■ 27517 #011-03-1977 L1979 **R** *020 †80

BIEBER, Dale E. 1838 MARTN LTHR KNG JR #B-, PEDIATRICS AT CHAPEL HILL 27514 #041-14-1976 L2000 **MPD GP** *012

BIESE, Kevin James. CAMPUS BOX 7594, DEPT OF EMERGENCY MEDICINE 27599 #036-01-2002 L2006 **EM** *100 †16

BILIC, Maya. 2238 NELSON HWY, STE 100 27517 #038-41-2001 L2005 **D** *020 †15

BINZ, Nikki Marie. 101 MANNING DR, DEPT EM 27514 #036-01-2007 **EM** *012

BIRCHARD, Katherine R. 101 MANNING DR 27514 #016-42-2001 L2004 **DR** *020 †80

BIRKHEAD, Newton C. ■ 27517 #041-01-1949 L1950 **CD IM** *071

BISHAI, George Boulos. ■ 27516 #036-01-2008 *012

BITAR, Raghid Sobhi. UNIV OF N CAROLINA SCH OF, 182 WING D CB 7228 27599 #605-01-2002 L2008 **GS** *012

BLACK, Jenna Ella. 101 MANNING DR 27514 #038-41-2000 L2004 **AN** *020 †05

BLATT, Julie. 101 MANNING DR 27514 #023-07-1976 L1997 **PHO** *050 †55

BLAU, William Stephen. N2201 UNC HOSPITALS, CB #7010 27599 #036-01-1987 L1991 **AN PMM** *020 †05

BLUM, Eve. ■ 27516 #041-07-1986 L1988 **PD** *071 †55

BOAS, Zachary Petrone. ■ 27516 #036-07-2008 *012

BOEHLECKE, Brian A. UNC CHAPEL HILL CB 7020 27599 #035-06-1970 L1980 **PUD IM** *020 †20

BOEHLKE, Christopher S. ■ 27517 #026-04-2003 L2007 *100

BOGGESS, John Fletcher. 101 MANNING DR, CB# 7570 27514 #040-02-1991 L1995 **OBG** *020 †30

BOGGESS, Kim A. CB#7516, DEPT/OB GYN DIV/M-F-M 27599 #035-48-1990 L1995 **ID** *020 †20

BONDURANT, Stuart. 125 MAC NIDER BLDG, CB 7000 27599 #036-07-1953 L1953 **IM CD** *030

BOOLS, Lindsay Marie. ■ 27517 #036-01-2008 *012

BOOSEY, Shane Austin. 101 MANNING DR, OGMEROOM 1107-A 27514 #038-40-2001 L2003 **CHP** *020 †75

BORDBAR, Firooz. ■ 27517 #517-01-1957 L2003 **GYN U** *071 †30 ‡

BORDLEY, William Clayton. BOX 7225 DEPT COM PED, UNIVERSITY OF NC 27599 #023-07-1986 L1991 **PD PHP** *020 †55

BOSE, Carl Lewis. 7220 UNIVERSITY OF NC 27599 #012-05-1974 L1977 **NPM PD** *020 †55

BOTTSFORD-MILLER, Justin. 101 MANNING DR CB7600, UNC HOSPS 27514 #018-03-2006 **OBG** *012

BOUCHER, Richard Chas. 7011 THURSTON BOWLES BLDG, CB 7248 27599 #035-01-1970 L1978 **IM PUD** *020 †20

BOULDIN, Thomas Welborn. DEPT PATH, CB #7525 27599 #036-01-1974 L1979 **NP ATP** *040 †50

BOULWARE, Mark Everett. ■ 27517 #028-46-2003 L2006 **CD** *012 †20

BOWES, Watson Allen. ■ 27514 #007-02-1959 L1982 **MFM OBG** *071 †30

BOWLBY, Lynn Anne. ■ 27514 #024-07-1991 L2006 **IM** *020 †20

BOWMAN, Frederick O, Jr. 12723 MOREHEAD GOVERNR CLB 27514 #041-01-1952 L1952 **TS** *071 †85,90

BOWMAN, James A, Jr. 6330 QUADRANGLE DR, STE 100 GEN FAM HLTH 27517 #038-06-1945 L1945 **OBG** *071 †30

BOYCE, Leslie Helen. 101 MANNING DR 27514 #033-05-1990 L1997 **CHN** *020 †55,75

BOYSEN, Philip Gerald, Jr. 513 MANNING DR, CB# 7595 WLM B ACICK BLDG 27599 #041-01-1949 L1994 **AN IM** *030 †20,05

BOZYMSKI, Eugene Michael. UNC MED CTR DIV OF GASTNLG, #7032 MBRB 27599 #056-06-1960 L1966 **GE IM** *020 †20

BRABHAM, Vance Wells, IV. ■ 27517 #041-03-2001 L2008 **VS** *012

BRADFORD, Eric Speir. 112 WESTSIDE DR 27516 #036-01-1993 L2005 **IM** *020 †20

BRADFORD, Kathleen Kilroy. ■ 27517 #041-14-1990 L2004 **CCP PD** *020 †55

BRADFORD, William Tate. ■ 27514 #036-01-2008 *012

BRASHEAR, H Robt, Jr. 250 BURNETT WOMACK BLDG 27514 #005-02-1945 L1953 **ORS** *071 †40

BRASINGTON, Chadwick R. 1828 MARTN LTHR KNG JR, STE D14 27514 #045-01-1998 L1999 **OPH** *020 †35

BRAUN, Thomas Gyula. CB 7025 RM 751 CLN SCI BLD 27599 #060-01-1961 L1986 **N** *020 †75

BRECHER, Maria. ■ 27516 #016-02-1983 L1992 **PTH HEM** *020 †20

BRECHER, Mark Elliott. BRINKHOUS-BULLITT BLDG., UNC-CH, CB#7525 27599 #016-02-1982 L1992 **BBK CLP** *020 †50

BRENNAN, Michael West. 1828 MARTN LTHR KNG JR, STE D14 27514 #048-13-1978 L1982 **OPH** *020 †35

BRENNER, William Edward. 101 CONNER DR, STE 402 27514 #038-06-1962 L1969 **GYN** *071 †30

BRESLIN, Marianne S. ■ 27514 #407-25-1946 L1960 **P PYA** *071 †75

BRESSLER, Peter Bartlett. 6320 QUADRANGLE DR, STE 110 27517 #036-07-1981 L1994 **IM AI** *020 †20,03

BRICE, Jane Helen. 101 MANNING DR 27514 #036-01-1994 L1997 **EM** *020 †16

BRICKNER, Thomas Eugene. NORT CAROLINA, UNIVERSITY OF 27599 #038-43-1987 L1996 **FM FSM** *020 †18

BRIGGAMAN, Robert Alan. 101 MANNING DR 27514 #035-19-1960 L1967 **D** *050 †15

BRODEY, Benjamin Boris. ■ 27514 #024-01-1988 L2004 *020

BROMBERG, Philip Allan. U OF NC SCH MED CB # 7310, ASTHMA AND LUNG BIO 27599 #024-01-1953 L1975 **PUD IM** *020 †20

BRONSTEIN, David Marvin. ■ 27516 #036-01-1997 L1998 **FM** *020 †18

BROOM, Sarah Annis. ■ 27514 #036-01-2008 *012

BROWN, David Warren. 940 AIRPORT RD 27514 #035-45-1967 L2007 **IM** *020 †20

BROWN, James Eldon Jay. 109 1/2 E FRANKLIN ST, SERA-TEC BIOLOGICALS 27514 #065-06-1955 L1983 **OBG** *071 †30

BROWN, Minnie Marilyn. 1211 MAC NIDER BLDG, UNIV OF NC SCH MED 27599 #036-01-1996 *100

BROWNLEE, Robert C, Jr. ■ 27514 #047-05-1945 L1963 **PD** *071 †55

BRUBAKER, Beth Ann. CB 7550, 141 MACNIDER BUIL, PROGRAM ON AGING 27599 #036-01-2001 L2004 **IMG** *020

BRUBAKER, Lauren Marie. ■ 27517 #036-01-2007 **IM** *012

BRUCKSTEIN, Melvyn. ■ 27517 #035-08-1965 L1996 **IM PUD** *071 †20

BRUNDRETT, Megan Elizabet. ■ 27516 #038-45-2007 **MPD** *012

BRYAN, James A, III. 55 VILCOM CENTER DR # 140 27514 #036-01-1983 L1985 **OPH** *020 †35

BRYAN, James Alexander. 5039 OLD CLINIC BLDG, UNC HOSP CB 7110 27599 #041-01-1957 L1957 **IM HEM** *071 †20

BRYAN, Pat Chappell. 120 CONNER DR 27514 #036-01-1983 L1989 **OBG** *020 †30

BRYDON, Kim Marie. 209 SILVER CREEK TRL 27514 #019-02-1987 L1991 **P** *020 †75

BRYSKIN, Robert Boris. ■ 27599 #038-41-2002 L2007 **AN** *020 †05

BRYSON, Julia Easton. ■ 27514 #040-02-2005 **PM** *012

BUB, Michelle Karen. 101 MANNING DR, OGMEROOM 1107-A 27514 #050-02-2001 L2004 **END** *100

BUCHANAN, Ian Baird. ■ 27514 #036-01-2004 **MDM** *030

BUCHMAN, Craig Alan. 7070 UNIVERSITY OF NC, OTOLARYNGOLOGY HEAD & 27599 #011-03-1990 L2001 **OTO** *020 †45

BUCK, Scott Harding. 130 MASON FARM RD, CAMPUS BOX #7220 27599 #038-45-1984 L1987 **PDC** *020 †55

BUCKMIRE, Robert Arthur. UNIVERSITY OS NC AT CHAPEL, G0142 NEUROSCIENCES HOSPIT 27599 #051-01-1994 L2004 **OTO** *020 †45

BULLITT, Elizabeth. 101 MANNING DR, UNC HOSPITALS 27514 #007-02-1975 L1978 **NS** *020 †25

BUNCE, Leslie Anne. ■ 27516 #036-01-1985 L1988 **HEM IM** *020 †20

BUNCE, Paul Leslie. ■ 27517 #016-02-1942 L1997 **U** *071 †95

BUNZENDAHL, Hartwig H G E. UNC SCHOOL OF MEDICINE, DEPT OF SURGERY CB7228 27599 #409-10-1974 L1990 **GS** *020 †80

BURKE, Charles Thomas. 101 MANNING DR, CB 7510 27514 #004-01-1996 L2000 **VIR** *020 †80

BURKE, Jason Russell. 107 BRISTOL DR 27516 #036-01-1996 L1998 **AN PTH** *020 †05

BURNETT, Gordon Bernard. 101 MANNING DR DEPT PSYCH 27514 #919-01-1964 L1976 **P PA** *020

BURNS, Harriett Purves. ■ 27514 #036-07-2004 L2008 **MPD** *012

BURNS, Walter Woodrow, Jr. 120 CONNER DR, STE 100 27514 #036-01-1969 L1972 **GS** *020 †85

BURNS, Walter Woodrow, III. 120 CONNER DR, STE 100 27514 #036-05-1994 L1996 **GS** *020 †85

BURROWS, Kimberly Juanita. ■ 27514 #036-01-2008 *012

BUSBY-WHITEHEAD, Jan. 141 MACNIDER BLDG, CB7550 27599 #048-02-1977 L1994 **IM IMG** *040 †20

BUSHNELL, Brandon Dubose. UNIV OF N CAROLINA SCH OF, 3314 BIOINFORMATICS BUILDI 27599 #012-01-2003 L2007 **ORS** *012

BUTTS, John Davis. ■ 27599 #036-07-1972 L1973 **FOP PTH** *020 †50

BYER, Tara T. 101 MANNING DR, OGMEROOM 1107-G 27514 #036-01-2003 L2004 **D** *020 †15

BYERLEY, Julie Story. 101 MANNING DR, UNC HOSPITALS 27514 #036-07-1998 L2001 **PD** *020 †55

BYERLY, Faera Ledford. 101 MANNING DR, CB#7600 27514 #036-01-2001 L2005 **GS** *012

BYNUM, Donald K, Jr. UNIV OF N CAROLINA, 3157 BIOINFORMATICS 27599 #048-14-1976 L1982 **HS ORS** *020 †40

BYRD, Jim Franklin, Jr. ■ 27514 #048-02-2006 **GS** *012

BYRNS, Patricia Jane. 243 MACNIDER BLDG, CB 700 UNC 27599 #007-02-1985 L1990 **IM PHP** *030 †20

CAIRNS, Bruce Arthur. 101 MANNING DR, DEPT OF SURGERY, CB#7600 27514 #041-01-1989 L1999 **GS** *020 †85

CALDERON, Lilian G. ■ 27599 #649-01-1973 L1998 **PTH N** *020 †50

CALDWELL-GETTES, Ann L. ■ 27514 #021-01-1958 L1979 **IM GP** *020

CALIKOGLU, Ali Suha. UNIV N CAROLINA, CB 7039 MBRB 3341 DEPT PED 27599 #902-03-1982 L1997 **PDE** *020 †20

CALVO, Benjamin F. 3010 OLD CLINIC BLDG, DEPT OF SURGERY CB 7213 27599 #023-01-1981 L1993 **SO GS** *050 †85

CAMPBELL, Amy Suzanne. ■ 27599 #020-02-2000 L2007 **DR** *100 †80

CAMPION, Edmund Ronan. OF MEDICINE, CB#7055 UNL SCHOOL 27599 #032-01-1981 L1991 **ORS** *020 †40

CANNATO, Carrie Beth. 101 MANNING DR, UNC HOSPITALS 27514 #038-44-2002 L2005 **GPM** *012 †20

CANTRELL, Matthew Glendon. ■ 27517 #038-40-2005 L2008 **IM** *012

CAPRIO, Anthony J. CAMPUS BOX 7550, 259A MACNIDER BUILDING 27599 #035-06-2000 L2005 **IM IMG** *050 †20 ‡

CARABALLO, Damian Eduardo. 101 MANNING DR, DEPT EM 27514 #011-04-2007 **EM** *012

CARDONES, Adela Rambi Gua. ■ 27517 #748-02-1995 **D** *012

CAREY, Lisa Anne. 3009 OLD CLINIC BLDG, UNC ONCOLOGY CB7305 27599 #023-07-1990 L1997 **ON** *050 †20

CAREY, Timothy Stephen. UNC CHAPEL HILL 27599 #050-02-1976 L1983 **IM GYN** *040 †20

CARLIN, Faith. 50010 GOVERNORS DR, # 246 27517 #005-15-1984 L2007 **OBG** *020 †30

CARLOUGH, Martha C. CB 7595 MANNING DRIVE, DEPT OF FAMILY MEDICINE 27599 #041-02-1989 L1993 **FM** *075 †18

CARLSON, Lindsay Marie. ■ 27514 #036-01-2008 *012

CARPENTER, Frederick J. ■ 27514 #056-05-1953 L1954 **AN** *071 †05

CARRAWAY, Anthony Glenn. 101 MANNING DR 27514 #036-01-1984 L1985 **P** *020 †75

CARRIZOSA, Daniel Ricardo. 101 MANNING DR, OGMEROOM 1107-A 27514 #036-01-2001 L2004 **HO** *020

CARSON, Culley Clyde. 427 BURNETT, BOX 7235 WOMACK BLDG 27599 #010-01-1971 L1978 **U** *020 †95

CARSON, Shannon Stewart. 4134 BIOINFORMATICS BLDG, CB # 7020 27599 #036-01-1989 L1999 **PUD CCM** *050 †20

■ = Address Information Privacy Protected

CARTER, Alicia Lynette. 101 MANNING DR, UNE HOSPITALS 27514 #036-01-2000 L2003 **PTH** *100 †50

CARTER, Wilbur Brooks, Jr. 513 MANNING DR, CB 7595 27599 #036-01-1980 L1994 **FM** *020 †18

CASTILLO, Elizabeth. UNIV OF N CAROLINA-CHAPEL, 7040 BURNETT-WOMACK BLDG 27599 #016-11-1999 L2006 **PS** *100 †85

CASTILLO, Mauricio. 101 MANNING DR, CLINIC BLDG 27514 #429-01-1983 L1991 **DR** *020 †80

CASTOR, Cecil W, Jr. 27514 #025-01-1951 L1952 **IM RHU** *071 †20

CAVENAR, Jesse Oscar, Jr. ■ 27516 #004-01-1963 L1968 **P PYA** *040 †75

CEFALO, Robert Chas. ■ 27517 #024-07-1959 L1978 **MFM OBG** *030 †30

CERAMI, Carla Jean. ■ 27517 #035-19-1994 L1996 **PD** *100

CHAHIN, Nizar Suleiman. ■ 27517 #875-01-1992 L1997 **CN** *100 †75

CHALERMSKULRAT, Worakij. MEDICINE, UNC PULMONARY & CRITICAL C 27599 #891-04-1993 L1997 **PCC** *020 †20

CHAMPION, Margaret E Kern. ■ 27514 #055-01-1971 L1975 **P** *020 †75

CHAN, Stephanie Chien-Ru. ■ 27516 #036-01-2008 L2008 *012

CHANCE, Elizabeth Whiting. 407 E FRANKLIN ST 27514 #036-05-2006 L2006 **OTO** *012

CHANDLER, Arthur C, Jr. CB# 7040, 617 BURNETT-WOMACK BLDG 27599 #036-07-1959 L1959 **OPH** *020 †35

CHANG, Emily Hueywen. ■ 27514 #036-01-2007 **IM** *012

CHANG, Lydia Hwei. ■ 27516 #025-01-1998 L2007 **PCC** *020 †20

CHANG, Patricia Pat-Yue. 99 MANNING DR, CB#7075 BURNETT-WOMACK BLD 27514 #023-07-1995 L2002 **CD** *020 †20

CHAO, Hsia-Fu. ■ 27517 #385-03-1961 *050

CHELMINSKI, Paul Roman. 5039 OLD CLINIC BLDG CB#71, UNC DEPT OF MEDICINE 27599 #036-01-1995 L1997 **MPD** *020 †20

CHENG, Alan Chungkee. UNIV OF N CAROLINA SCH OF, 3018 OLD CLINIC BLDG CB 76 27599 #012-05-2006 **IM** *012

CHESSON, Melanie Anne. ■ 27516 #036-08-1997 L2000 **IM** *020 †20

CHIDGEY, Brooke Alison. 101 MANNING DR, UNIV OF NC HOSPS 27514 #048-13-2007 **AN** *012

CHILDERS, Jeffrey Brennon. CAMPUS BOX # 7160, UNC PSYCHIATRY-CHAPEL HILL 27599 #036-08-2001 L2005 **PFP** *012

CHINO, Junzo Paul. ■ 27514 #017-20-2004 **RO** *012

CHIOU, Peter Yenchang. ■ 27514 #033-05-2003 L2007 **DR** *012

CHITKARA, Denesh Kumar. ■ 27517 #038-40-1996 L2005 **PG** *020 †55

CHOI, Mina Nui. 300 MEADOWMONT VILLAGE CIR, HARRIS & SMITH OB/GYN 27517 #036-07-1991 L1993 **OBG** *020 †30

CHONG, Wui Kheong. UNC HOSPITALS, CB 7510 DEPT OF RAD 27599 #917-04-1980 L1997 **DR** *020 †80

CHOU, Michael Lichien. UNIVERSITY OF N CAROLINA, ASTHMA AND LUNG BIOLOGY 27599 #048-04-2004 L2007 **AI** *012 †20

CHRISTENSEN, Frank Howard. 100 EUROPA DR, STE 255 27517 #028-34-1976 L1977 **PS OPH** *020 †35 ‡

CHRISTIAN, Charles M, II. 7010 UNC HOSPITALS, N2201 NORTH WING CB 27599 #021-05-1975 L1979 **AN PME** *020 †05

CHRISTIAN, Robt Meade, Jr. 816 CHURCHILL DR, CHAPEL HILL PEDIATRICS P.A 27517 #038-06-1967 L1968 **PD GP** *020 †20

CHRISTIE, Heather Larock. ■ 27516 #021-01-2005 L2007 **FP** *012

CHRYSIS, Dionisios. AIRPORT RD 600 27514 #418-03-1985 **NPM** *100

CHRZANOWSKA, Barbara. 21 BLOOMSBURY CT 27517 #759-10-1962 L1995 **PD PDE** *020 †55

CHUANG, Alice Weitzu. 214 MACNIDER, CB #7516 27599 #047-06-1997 L2003 **OBG** *020 †30

CHUDASAMA, Shruti Laxmika. ■ 27514 #036-01-2008 *012

CIOCCA, Mario Frank, Jr. CB #7470, UNC CAMPUS HEALTH SERVICES 27599 #033-05-1993 L1996 **IM ISM** *020 †20

CIRIACO, Paola. ■ 27517 #561-17-1988 L1997 *020

CLANTON, Pamela Anne. 101 MANNING DR, UNC DIV OF GEN MED 27514 #012-01-1990 L2002 **IM** *040 †20

CLARK, Henry Toole, Jr. ■ 27514 #035-45-1944 L1944 **PHP** *030

CLARK, Richard Lee. U.N.C. MEDICAL SCHOOL, U.N.C. HOSPITALS 27599 #023-07-1966 L1973 **DR** *020 †80

CLARK, Thomas Boyle, III. UNIVERSITY OF N CAROLINA, CAMPUS BOX 7580 27599 #045-01-1983 L1984 **FOP ATP** *020 †50

CLARK, Vivian Elizabeth. 120 CONNER DR 27514 #024-05-1981 L1986 **OBG** *020 †30

CLARKE, John Paul. 101 MANNING DR, UNC HOSPITALS 27514 #035-45-1976 L1991 **DR GS** *020 †40,80

CLARKE PEARSON, Kathleen. 1838 MARTN LTHR KNG JR 27514 #036-01-1985 L1987 **PD** *020 †55

CLAYBORN, Valarie Cheri. ■ 27514 #036-01-1989 *100

CLAYTON, Nancy Carol. UNC DEPT OF PSYCHIATRY, CB 7160 27599 #036-01-1992 L1998 **P** *020 †75

CLEMMONS, David Robt. UNC SCHOOL OF MED, DEPT MED 27514 #036-01-1974 L1974 **END IM** *050 †20

CLIFFORD, Susann Levy. 1512 E FRANKLIN ST, STE 100 27514 #011-03-1993 L1997 **OBG** *020 †20

CLOTFELTER, Lucile D. 180 PROVIDENCE RD 27514 #036-01-1986 L1987 **P** *020 †75

CLYDE, Wallace Alex, Jr. 101 MANNING DR 27514 #047-05-1954 L1955 **ID PD** *050 †55

COAKLEY, Raymond Dermot. 130 MASON FARM RD # 70, DIVISION OF PULMONARY & CR 27599 #539-04-1990 L2001 **PCC** *020

COEYTAUX, Remy Rene. 55 VILCOM CENTER DR STE 11 27514 #005-11-1996 L1999 **FM** *020 †18

COHEN, Kenneth Lee. 130 MASON FARM RD, CB#7040 OPHTHALMOLOGY 27599 #016-11-1971 L1978 **OPH** *020 †35

COHEN, Myron Scott. 130 MASON FARM RD CB7030, UNC-CHAPEL HILL 27599 #016-01-1974 L1980 **ID IM** *050 †20

COHN, Jonathan Allen. 13 CHARRINGTON PL 27517 #035-20-1978 L1988 **GE IM** *050 †20

COLAVITA, Paul Dominick. ■ 27517 #036-01-2008 *012

COLE, Craig Harcourt. 101 MANNING DR 27514 #065-06-1963 **IM OS** *020

COLEMAN, Philip D, Jr. ■ 27514 #036-01-1968 L1968 **GS** *071 †85

COLEMAN, Rosalind Anne. UNIV NC, CB 7461 27599 #038-06-1969 L1978 **PD OS** *050 †55

COLEMAN, William L. CAMPUS BOX #7255 27599 #034-01-1979 L1985 **PD** *020 †55

COLES, William Henry. ■ 27514 #036-01-1962 L1962 **OS OPH** *071 †35

COLEY, Silas Bodie, Jr. 815 KENMORE RD, 815 KENMORE RD 27514 #036-01-1965 L1965 **P OS** *020 †75

COLFORD, Cristin Mulderig. CB 7110, 5039 OLD CLINIC BUILDING 27599 #036-01-2001 L2004 **IM** *020

COLINDRES, Romulo Ernesto. ■ 27514 #036-01-2000 L2003 **PD EP** *020 †55

COLINDRES, Romulo Ernesto. 348 MACNIDER CB 7155 27599 #341-01-1966 L1973 **NEP** *020 †20

COLLICHIO, Frances Ann. 3009 OLD CLINIC BUILDING, /ONCOLOGY, CB#7305 27599 #035-45-1987 L1998 **IM** *020 †20

COLLIER, Albert Milford. 101 MANNING DR # 7220, UNIV OF NC HOSPS 27514 #011-02-1963 L1968 **ID PD** *050 †55

COMEAU, Terrance Brian W. CB # 7305, 3009 OLD CLINIC BLDG 27599 #064-01-1989 L1996 **IM** *020

COMSTOCK, Lloyd Karr. ■ 27514 #036-01-1973 L2004 **FM** *020 †18

CONLEY, Wm Gustavus, III. 408 LAKESHORE LN 27514 #051-04-1960 L1961 **PD PN** *020 †55

CONNOLLY, Annamarie. 101 MANNING DR 27514 #024-07-1991 L1995 **OBG** *020 †30

COOK, Anne Bouchelle. ■ 27516 #036-01-2008 *012

COOK, Jeffrey John. 101 MANNING DR, UNC HOSPITALS, DEPARTMENT 27514 #024-16-2005 L2007 **EM** *012

COOMBS, Randall Floyd. ■ 27517 #005-06-1972 L1995 **AN** *105

COOPER, Herbert A. ■ 27516 #019-02-1964 L1974 **PHO CLP** *071 †55

CORBIE-SMITH, Giselle. WING D, CB#7240, DEPT OF SOCIAL ME 27599 #035-46-1991 L2000 **IM** *020 †20

COREY, John Daniel. 513 MANNING DR, CB 7595 27599 #036-01-1993 L1995 **FM** *020 †18

CORNWALL, Thomas Paul. 101 MANNING DR 27514 #016-06-1970 L1973 **PYA CHP** *020

COSTELLO, Frederick M. 130 MASON FARM RD, CB# 7075 27599 #054-04-2001 L2004 **IC** *012

COTTON, John Lawrence. CB# 7220, 200 MASON FARM RD 27599 #035-15-1990 L1996 **PDC** *020 †55

COUCH, Marion Joan. 7070 UNIVERSITY OF NC, OTOLARYNGOLOGY HEAD & 27599 #016-01-1990 L2003 **OTO** *020 †45

COURTWRIGHT, Andrew Mille. ■ 27517 #036-01-2008 *012

COVINGTON, Mary Margaret. UNIV OF N CAROLINA, CB #7470 27599 #048-12-1987 L1994 **IM** *020 †20

COWAN, Judith H R. CB #7470 27599 #039-01-1958 L1981 **OS P** *030 †75

COWARD, Holly Jean. 141 MACNIDER BLDG, CB 7550, DEPT OF GERIATRIC MEDICINE 27599 #035-05-1988 L2001 **IM IMG** *020 †20

COWARD, Robert Matthew. ■ 27517 #036-01-2007 **GS** *012

COWEY, Charles Lance. 101 MANNING DR, DIV OF HEMA/ONCOLOGY 27514 #048-02-2003 L2005 **HO** *012 †20

COWHERD, Stacy Mclellan. ■ 27514 #036-01-2008 *012

COX, Suellen. 5821 FARRINGTON RD, STE 101 27517 #038-06-1989 L1995 **D** *020 †15

CRAIGE, Ernest. ■ 27517 #024-01-1943 L1952 **CD IM** *075 †20

CREIGHTON, Robert A. UNC DEPARTMENT OF ORTHOPAE, 3143 BIOINFORMATICS BUILDI 27599 #051-04-1998 L2004 **OSM** *020 †40

CREIGHTON, Tara Leeanne. ■ 27517 #046-01-2005 **OBG** *012

CRIM, Courtney. 101 MANNING DR 27514 #025-01-1977 L1999 **PUD CCM** *020 †20

CROMARTIE, William James. ■ 27517 #012-05-1937 L1937 **IM ID** *071 †50,20

CROOM, Robert D, III. 101 MANNING DR, DEPT SURG 27514 #036-01-1964 L1964 **GS** *071 †85

CROSS, Alan Whittemore. 101 MANNING DR 27514 #035-01-1970 L1978 **PD GPM** *030 †55

CROSS, Robt Vander Voort. ■ 27517 #041-12-1947 L1953 **OBG** *071

CROWLEY, Andres Xavier. ■ 27517 #036-01-2008 *012

CUENCA, Nelida Alba. ■ 27517 #132-02-1957 **PHP ADL** *071 †55

CULTON, Donna Aline. ■ 27517 #036-01-2006 L2008 **D** *012

CUOMO, Christopher. 413 SUMMERWALK CIR 27517 #036-01-2002 L2005 **GS** *020

CURTIS, Thomas Edwin. 101 MANNING DR, UNC HOSPITALS 27514 #036-01-1951 L1953 **P** *071 †75

CZAJKOWSKI, Julia. 101 MANNING DR, UNIV OF NC HOSP 27514 #409-37-2005 **N** *012

DAHNERS, Laurence Earl. 3153 BIOINFORMATICS, CB#7055 27599 #003-01-1978 L1983 **ORS OTR** *040 †40 ‡

DALEY-PLACIDE, Racquel R. UNC 27599 #047-07-2002 L2005 **IMG** *100 †20

DALLDORF, Frederic G. ■ 27514 #035-20-1958 L1965 **ATP FOP** *071 †50

DALLDORF, Joanna S Stein. ■ 27516 #035-20-1958 L1965 **PD** *071 †55

DAMITZ, Lynn Ann. 7034 BURNETT-WOMACK, CAMPUS BX 7195 27599 #041-09-1993 L1999 **PS** *020 †65

DANCEL, Rex Drapete. 101 MANNING DR, UNC HOSPITALS 27514 #036-05-2004 L2006 **GPM** *012 †18

DANEK, Julia Lynn. 109 CONNER DR, STE 106 27514 #036-01-1990 L1991 **P PYA** *020 †75

DARLING, Jama Margaret. 27599 #047-06-1996 L2005 **GE** *020 †20

D'ARMINI, Andrea Maria. ■ 27517 #561-03-1987 *100

DAUGIRD, Allen J. CB#7595, MANNING DRIVE, DEPT OF FAMILY MEDICINE 27599 #036-01-1977 L1980 **FM** *020 †18

DAVALOS, Jorge. CB 7075, UNC-CHAPEL HILL 27599 #011-02-2002 L2005 **CD** *012 †20

DAVE, Sandeep S. ■ 27514 #016-06-1999 L2007 **HEM** *020 †20

DAVENPORT, Marsha L. 101 MANNING DR #020-12-1982 L1985 **PDE** *050 †55

DAVIDAI, Giora. ■ 27517 #550-02-1982 **PA** *030

DAVIDIAN, Edward Wm. ■ 27516 #036-01-1963 L1968 **AN** *071 †05

DAVIES, Kenneth Roger. 302 CAROLINA MEADOWS VILLA 27517 #025-01-1981 L1983 **AN IM** *020 †05

DAVIS, Devon Lynn. ■ 27517 #047-05-1994 L1996 **EM** *020 †16

DAVIS, Ian Jonathan. UNC SCHOOL MED C/B 7295, LINEBERGER CANCER CTR 27599 #016-06-1995 L2006 **PHO** *050 †20

DAVIS, Jonathan Charles. ■ 27517 #036-01-2008 *012

DAVIS, Karen Pamela. ■ 27516 #036-08-1983 L2001 **PD** *020 †55

DAVIS, Stephanie Duggins. CB 7220 635 BURNETT WOMACK, UNIV NC DEPT PED 27599 #036-05-1993 L1999 **PDP** *020 †20

DAWKINS, Karon. CB #7160, DEPT OF PSYCHIATRY 27599 #045-01-1986 L1993 **P** *020 †75

DAY, Deborah. ■ 27517 #010-01-1983 L1984 **IM OM** *020

D'CRUZ, O'Neill F. 3100 BIOINFORMATICS BLDG, CAMPUS BOX 7025 27599 #495-52-1984 L1991 **CHN PD** *020 †20

DEAN, Norman L. 109 TURNAGE RD, CHAPEL HILL NC 27517 #035-08-1964 L1994 **IM PUD** *020 †20

DEASON, Mindy Jean. ■ 27517 #036-01-2008 *012

DEB, Arjun. CHAPEL H, UNIVERSITY OF N CAROLINA A 27599 #495-02-1997 L2007 **CD** *100 †20

DE CHERNEY, Geo Stephen. ■ 27517 #041-13-1978 L1979 **DIA END** *050 †20

DEES, Elizabeth Claire. 3009 OLD CLINIC UNC CA, CB 7305 27599 #036-07-1993 L1999 **ON** *020 †20

DELLON, Elisabeth Potts. 200 MASON FARM RD, DIV OF PED PULM CB 7220 27514 #026-04-1999 L2004 **PDP** *100 †20,55

DELLON, Evan Samuel. 130 MASON FARM RD, CB #7080; BIOINFORMATICS B 27599 #023-07-1999 L2004 **GE** *100 †20

DELUCA, Jason Richard. 101 MANNING DR, DEPT OF PHYSICAL MED/REHAB 27514 #035-15-2005 **PM** *012

DE MAIO, Valerie J. NEUROSCIENCES HOSPITAL CB7, UNC DEPT EMERGENCY MEDICIN 27599 #060-02-2001 L2003 **EM** *020 †16

DE MARCHI, Wilhelmina J. ■ 27516 #660-06-1978 L2002 **CHP** *020 †75

DE MORE, Nancy. 3010 OLD CLINIC BLDG, CB 7213 27599 #016-42-1991 L2001 **GS** *020 †85

DENHAM, Amy Catherine. 513 MANNING DRIVE CB#7595, UNC DEPT OF FAMILY MEDICIN 27599 #036-01-1999 L2000 **GPM** *020 †18,70

DENNISTON, Clark Rohwer. 513 MANNING DR, CB 7595 27599 #010-02-1983 L1990 **FM** *020 †18

DENT, Georgette Amantha. 101 MANNING DR, UNC HOSPITALS 27514 #036-07-1981 L1983 **PTH BBK** *050 †50

DENU, Cynthia Jeanne. 7155, 340 MAC NICLER BLDG 27599 #033-05-1993 L1996 **NEP** *020 †20

D'ERCOLE, Augustine. 361 MSRB S. COLUMBIA ST, PED ENDOCRINOLOGY CB#7220 27599 #010-02-1969 L1977 **PDE NPM** *050 †55

DEREBAIL, Vimal Kumar. UNC SCHOOL OF MED, 7024 BURNETT WOMACK BLDG 27599 #012-01-2002 L2005 **NEP** *012 †20

DE ROSA, G Paul. 400 SILVER CEDAR CT 27514 #017-20-1965 L1995 **OP ORS** *030 †40

DESAI, Kinnari Paresh. ■ 27516 #042-02-2002 L2006 **OBG** *100

DESELM, Tracy Martin. 101 MANNING DR DEPT OF, CAMPUS BOX 7594 27514 #012-05-1988 L1991 **EM** *020 †16

DETWILER, Randal Kent. 347 MACNIDER BLDG, DIV OF NEPHOLOGY 27599 #038-40-1986 L1988 **NEP** *020 †20

DEVEAUGH-GEISS, Joseph. ■ 27514 #035-15-1972 L1991 **P** *050 †75

DE VRIES, David Todd. 2238 NELSON HWY, STE 100 27517 #036-01-2003 L2007 **D** *020 †15

DE WALT, Darren Andrew. UNIVERSITY OF N CAROLINA, 5039 OLD CLINIC BLDG CB711 27599 #047-05-1997 L1998 **MPD** *050 †20,55

DIAMANTIS, Stephanie Anna. ■ 27514 #035-47-2006 L2007 **D** *012

DIAZ, Luis Alberto. 130 MASON FARM RD 27599 #737-03-1969 L1999 **IG D** *050 †15

DIEHL, Christie Lynne. 101 MANNING DR, DEPT OF EMERG MED CB-7594 27514 #038-43-2006 **EM** *012

DIELEMAN, Levinus Albert. GLAXO BLDG, RM 146, UNC DIGESTIVE DISEASES 27599 #660-05-1983 L1996 *020

DILLON, Patrick Michael. 101 MANNING DR, 3009 OLD CLINIC BUILDING 27514 #036-01-2004 L2007 **HO** *012 †20

DINGFELDER, James Ray. 180 PROVIDENCE RD, STE 3 27514 #041-02-1965 L1972 **OBG GYN** *020 †30

DIRSCHL, Douglas Ray. CB # 7055, 3147 BIOINFORMATICS BLDG 27599 #040-02-1988 L2003 **ORS** *020 †40

DIXON, Robert Geo. ■ 27517 #035-15-1988 L1998 **VIR** *020 †16,80

DOAN, Phuong Linh. UNIV OF N CAROLINA SCH OF, 3018 OLD CLINIC BLDG/CB760 27599 #036-01-2003 L2006 **HO** *012 †20

DOANES, Aric Masharn. RM 354, WING C, CB 7065 27599 #012-21-1993 L2004 **TS** *020 †85

DOGRA, Sunil. UNC-CB#7010 223 BURNDLE, DEPT ANES 27599 #495-73-1978 L1994 **AN PME** *020 †05

DOIL, Catherine Renee. ■ 27514 #036-01-2008 *012

DONALDSON, Jeffrey Hugh. ■ 27517 #038-40-2001 L2006 **PS** *012

DONALDSON, Scott H. 7011 THURSTON BOWLES BLDG, CB 7248 27599 #025-01-1990 L1993 **PCC** *020 †20

DONOHUE, James Francis. 101 MANNING DR 27514 #033-05-1969 L1974 **PUD IM** *020 †20

DOOLEY, Mary Anne. CHAPEL HILL, UNIVERSITY OF NC 27599 #036-01-1983 L1988 **RHU IM** *020 †20

DORN, Spencer David. CB # 7080, UNC GASTRO & HEPATOLOGY 27599 #035-08-2002 L2005 **GE** *012 †20

DORON, Mia Wechsler. UNC HOSPITALS, DEPT OF PEDIATRICS CB 7596 27599 #036-07-1988 L1991 **NPM** *020 †55

DOSTOU, Jean M. 160 DENTAL CIR, UNC SCHOOL OF MEDICINE 27599 #043-01-1992 L1998 **END** *020 †20

DOUTOVA, Anastassia Vladi. ■ 27516 #036-01-2005 L2008 **IM** *012

DOWNS, John Preston. 5039 OLD CLINIC BLDG, CAMPUS BOX #7110 27599 #011-03-2002 L2005 **IM** *020 †20

DRAKE, Amelia Fischer. 7070 UNIVERSITY OF NC, OTOLARYNGOLOGY HEAD & 27599 #036-01-1981 L1988 **OTO** *020 †45

DREESEN, Elizabeth B. 101 ARBUTUS PL 27517 #024-01-1987 L1996 **GS** *020 †85

DROSSMAN, Douglas Arnold. 1110 BIOINFORMATICS, CB #7080 27599 #035-46-1970 L1976 **GE IM** *040 †20

DRUTZ, David J. PO BOX 3616, PACIFIC BIO ASSOC LLC 27515 #020-02-1962 L1963 **ID IM** *062 †20

DUBNER, Steven David. ■ 27516 #056-06-2003 L2004 **FOP** *012 †50

DUNCAN, Joseph Alexander. 130 MASON FARM RD, SCHOOL OF MEDICINE 27599 #048-12-2001 L2003 **ID** *100

DUNPHY, Cherie Hilborn. CB 7525 UNC 27599 #021-06-1982 L2000 **PTH HMP** *020 †50

DU PONT, Nefertiti C. ■ 27514 #048-16-1999 L2007 **OBG GO** *020

DUTTON, Jonathan Jos. 5111 BIOINFORMATICS CB7040, DEPT OPHTHAL UNC MED CTR 27599 #028-02-1977 L1983 **PS OPH** *020 †35

DUVOISIN, Roger Clair. ■ 27517 #035-09-1954 L1957 **N** *071 †75

DWANE, Richard John. 108 GALWAY DR 27517 #010-02-1962 L1989 **OBG** *020 †30

DZIEDZIC, Thomas Scott. ■ 27516 #035-09-2003 L2005 **DR** *012

EARP, Henry Shelton, III. CB #7295, THE SCH OF MED UNC CHAPEL 27599 #036-01-1970 L1971 **END IM** *020 †20

EASTERLING, William Ewart. UNC PHYSICIANS SERVICES 27514 #036-01-1956 L1956 **OBG END** *071 †30

EASTMAN, William Joseph, Jr. ■ 27517 #036-08-1993 **IM** *075

EBERST, Mary Ellen. UNIV NC SCH OF MED, CB 7594 DEPT EM 27599 #038-41-1987 L1989 **EM** *020 †20,16

ECKER, Jerome Albert, Jr. 101 MANNING DR, UNC HOSPITALS 27514 #048-13-1998 L2001 **GE** *020 †20

ECKMAN, Thomas Roy. ■ 27517 #016-06-1961 L1962 **OBG** *071 †30

EDDS, Wendy Armore. 1001 S HAMILTON RD 27517 #036-01-1996 L2001 **FM** *071 †18

EDHEGARD, Kim David. 101 MANNING DR, UNIV OF NC HOSPS 27514 #001-06-2006 L2007 **D** *012

EDKINS, Patricia Mellor. 6330 QUADRANGLE DR, STE 500 27517 #036-01-1980 L1981 **RO** *062 †80

EDUPUGANTI, Srilatha. 130 MASON FARM RD # 7030, UNC-CHAPEL HILL 27599 #021-05-1992 L1997 **ID** *020 †20

EDWARDS, John Clark. UNIVERSITY OF N CAROLINA, NEPHROLOGY DIV, DEPT OF ME 27599 #016-02-1985 L2005 **NEP** *020 †20

EGAN, Jennifer Anne. ■ 27516 #035-46-2003 L2007 **PTH** *100 †50

EGAN, Thomas M. CB 7065, 3040 BURNETT-WOMACK BLDG 27599 #065-01-1976 L1989 **TS** *020 †85,90

EIFRIG, David Eric. 513 MANNING DR, CB# 7595 WLM B ACICK BLDG 27599 #023-07-1960 L1977 **OPH** *071 †35

EISEN, Mark Joshua. 900 MARTN LTHR KNG JR BLVD, HOLISTIC FAMILY PRAC 27514 #025-01-1980 L1981 **FM OS** *020 †18

ELBABAA, Samer Kamal. ■ 27517 #575-01-1998 L2000 **NS** *012

ELDRIDGE, Frederic Louis. UNC DEPT PHYSIOLOGY 206H 27514 #005-11-1948 L1973 **PUD CD** *050 †20

ELKINS-WILLIAMS, Stephen. ■ 27516 #036-01-2008 *012

EMRICH, Lisa Anne. 11312 US HIGHWAY 15 501 N, STE 308 27517 #017-20-2000 L2004 **MPD** *020

ENGLERT, Danielle E. 101 MANNING DR, CB 7025 27514 #046-01-2003 L2007 **N** *100

ENGMANN, Cyril Mark. CB# 7596 4TH FL DEPT PEDS, UNIV OF NO CA CHAPEL HILL 27599 #917-26-1994 L2004 **NPM** *020 †55

ERDBRUEGGER, Uta. 101 MANNING DR 27514 #409-33-1996 L2001 **NEP** *100 †20

ERDEM, Nurum Filiz. 141 MAC NIDEY BLDG, CB 7550 27599 #025-01-1996 L1997 **IMG** *020 †20 ‡

ERON, Joseph J, Jr. 7215 UNIVERSITY OF NC 27599 #024-01-1984 L1992 **ID IM** *020 †20

ESCOLAR, Maria Luisa. 1450 RALEIGH RD, PMENT AND LEARNING/UNC 27517 #264-18-1986 L1998 **PD** *020 †55

ESPER, Darlene Michelle. 101 MANNING DR 27514 #048-14-2002 L2006 **OBG** *100 †30

ESPIRITU, Jennifer Marie. ■ 27516 #023-12-1998 L1998 **GPM** *012

ESTHER, Charles Richard. 130 MASON FARM RD, CAMPUS BOX #7220 27599 #012-05-1998 L1999 **PDP** *012 †20

ESTHER, Robert John. 101 MANNING DR, DEPT OF ORTHOPAEDICS, CB 7 27514 #047-05-1998 L2003 **OMO** *100

EVANS, James Philip. CB #7264, DEPT OF GENETICS 27599 #019-02-1984 L1994 **IM MG** *020 †20,19

EVERS, Michael Dollish. 4015 OLD CLINIC BLDG, DEPT OB/GYN U OF N C 27599 #025-01-2000 L2003 **OBG** *020 †30

EWEND, Matthew Glaize. 3013 BURNETT-WOMACK BLDG. 27599 #023-07-1990 L1997 **NS** *020 †25

EZZEDDINE, Serena Diana. UNIV OF N CAROLINA SCH OF, 3018 OLD CLINIC BLDG CB 76 27599 #011-02-2006 **IM** *012

FAIR, Jeffrey Haskell. 2110 BIOINFORKATICS BLDG. 27599 #036-08-1983 L1985 **GS** *020 †85

FAITH, Rickard Edward. 207 S ELLIOTT RD 27514 #011-04-1990 *100

FALK, Donald H. ■ 27516 #036-01-1986 L1987 **P** *020

FALK, Ronald J. 7023 BURNETT WOMACK UNC, CB #7155 27599 #036-01-1977 L1977 **NEP IM** *050 †20

FAN, Zheng. MEDICAL SCH WING E RM 117, DEPT OF PEDS CB 7487 27599 #243-16-1991 L2005 **MG CHN** *050 †75,19

FARBER, Mark Adam. CB #7212, 210 BURNETT-WOMACK 27599 #021-01-1991 L1996 **VS** *020 †85

FARMER, Mary Katherine. 101 MANNING DR, UNIV NC HOSP 27514 #012-01-2001 L2006 **RHU** *012 †20

FARMER, Thomas Wohlsen. UNIV OF N C SCH OF MED 27599 #024-01-1941 L1998 **N IM** *072 †20,75

FARRELL, Timothy Michael. UNIV OF NORTH CAROLINA, 320 MEDICAL WING E 27599 #033-06-1990 L1999 **GS** *020 †85

FARROW, Jenni Elizabeth. 101 MANNING DRIVE, UNIVERSITY OF NORTH CAROLI 27599 #038-41-2003 L2007 **CHP** *012

FARROW, Stephen Chas. ■ 27517 #917-20-1969 L1977 *100

FASTENBERG, Michael Eric. ■ 27514 #035-48-2005 L2006 **D** *012

FELDMAN, Zachary William. 101 MANNING DR, UNIV OF NORTH CAROLINA 27514 #036-07-2004 **CHP** *012

FELIX, Ana Cristina. DEPT OF NEUROLOGY CB#7025, UNC CHAPEL HILL 27599 #836-01-1989 L2000 **N VN** *020 †75

FELLNER, Susan K. 1300 MASON FARM RD, UNIV OF NORTH CAROLINA 27514 #011-03-1966 L1996 **NEP IM** *050 †20

FERGUSON, Karen Ann. 1829 E FRANKLIN ST, STE 300 27514 #048-13-1976 L1986 **OBG** *075 †30

FERNALD, Gerald Wallace. N C SCH MED, DEPT PED 27514 #036-01-1960 L1960 **PD ID** *040 †55

FERNANDES, Michael V. ■ 27514 #495-27-1969 L1975 **IM NEP** *050 †20

FERRELL, Paul Brent, Jr. ■ 27517 #036-01-2008 *012

FERRIS, Maria Esther. ■ 27516 #649-01-1983 L2000 **PD PHP** *020 †55

FIELDING, Julia Rose. ■ 27599 #041-12-1987 L2000 **R** *020 †80

FIELDS, April Louise. 101 MANNING DR, UNC HOSPITAL, 27514 #036-01-2006 L2008 **P** *012

FILER, William Glenn, III. ■ 27514 #028-34-2008 *012

FINGERMAN, Mitchell Evan. ■ 27516 #008-02-2004 L2008 **AN** *012

FINKEL, Alan Glen. 3114 BIOINFORMATICS BLDG, UNIVERSITY OF NC 27599 #035-06-1985 L1987 **N PMM** *020 †75

FINN, Arthur Leonard. N C MEMORIAL HOSP, DEPT MED 27599 #024-05-1958 L1970 **IM** *050 †20

FINN, J Charlie. 5821 FARRINGTON RD, STE 202 27517 #038-06-1989 L1995 **FPS OTO** *020 †45

FINN, William Francis. 345 MAC NIDER BLDG CB#7155, DEPT OF MED UNIV OF NC 27599 #035-15-1966 L1972 **NEP IM** *050 †20

FINNEGAN, Timothy Michael. 3009 OLD CLINIC BLDG, CAMPUS BOX 7305 27599 #041-15-2001 L2005 **HO** *012 †20

FINNELL, Alice Claire. ■ 27514 #035-46-1985 L1989 **IM** *020 †20

FISCHER, Janet Jordan. ■ 27514 #023-07-1948 L1952 **ID IM** *071 †20

FISCHER, Newton Duchan. ■ 27514 #048-02-1945 L1952 **OTO** *071 †45

FISCHER-PAP, Lucia T. ■ 27514 #132-01-1956 L1962 **AI** *050 †03

FISHER, Michael John. 513 MANNING DR, CB 7595 27599 #038-41-1973 L1995 **FM** *020 †18

FLANAGAN, Paul Marcus. ■ 27514 #036-01-1997 *100

FLEMING, Derek Phillip. 101 MANNING DR, DEPT OF ANESTHESIOLOGY 27514 #038-43-2006 **AN** *012

FOOTE, Margaret Jane G. 101 MANNING DR 27514 #065-06-1976 L1988 **FM** *020

FORD, Anne C. 1512 E FRANKLIN ST, STE 100 27514 #036-01-1988 L1998 **OBG IM** *020 †30

FORD, Carol Ann. CB #7220, COMMUNITY PEDIATRICS 27599 #011-03-1983 L1986 **IM PD** *050 †20,55

FORD, Hubert James. ■ 27516 #011-02-2002 L2004 **PCC** *012 †20

FORD, Peter Frederick. ■ 27516 #143-08-1997 L2005 **VS** *100 †85 ‡

FORDHAM, Christopher, III. PO BOX 7000, UNIV OF NORTH CAROLINA 27514 #024-01-1951 L1951 **IM NEP** *071 †20

■ = Address Information Privacy Protected

FORDHAM, Lynn Ansley. SCHOOL OF MEDICINE, CB 7510 DEPT OF RADIO 27599 #024-07-1989 L1993 **PDR R** *020 †80

FORRESTER, Douglas John. 101 MANNING DR, UNC HOSPITALS 27514 #012-05-1992 L1997 **AN** *020 †05

FORTE, Jamila Ifeabeni. CB# 7593, PEDIATRIC EDUCATION 27599 #036-01-2003 L2006 **PD** *020

FOSTER, Matthew Charles. CAMPUS BOX 7110, 5039 OLD CLINIC BLDG 27599 #036-01-2002 L2005 **HO** *012 †20

FOWLER, Robert Noel. ■ 27516 #065-01-1964 **FM PA** *030

FOWLER, Wesley C, Jr. 5017 OLD CLINIC BLDG, CB 7570 UNC CHAPEL HL 11 27599 #036-01-1966 L1966 **OBG GO** *020 †30

FOWLER, William Craig. 5107A BIOINFORMATICS BLDG, CB#7040 27599 #051-04-1985 L1992 **OPH** *040 †35

FOWLKES, Dana Merrinan. ■ 27516 #035-20-1977 L1983 **PTH MG** *050

FOX, Amy Elizabeth. ■ 27514 #021-01-2007 **IM** *012

FOY, Zachary Mark. ■ 27514 #036-01-2008 *012

FRACHTLING, Richard James. ■ 27514 #021-05-1986 L1994 **P** *020 †75

FRADIN, Mark Sandor. 891 WILLOW DR, STE 1 27514 #035-01-1986 L1990 **D** *020 †15

FRAIJ, Ghassan. UNIV OF N CAROLINA SCH OF, 3018 OLD CLINIC BLDG CB 76 27599 #039-01-2006 **IM** *012

FRANCE, Michael John. E, CB#7081, 320 MEDICAL WING 27599 #671-02-1994 L2004 **GS** *100

FRANTZ, Elman Grady. 101 MANNING DRIVE, CB 7220 UNC SCHOOL OF MEDI 27599 #041-14-1981 L1984 **PDC** *020 †55

FRAZIER, Harold Leon. 180 PROVIDENCE RD STE 5 27514 #036-05-1966 L2004 **P** *020 †75

FREDERICK, Laurence D, Jr. ■ 27517 #016-11-1945 L1952 **GS** *071 †85

FREDERICK, Lauretta Sue. ■ 27517 #036-07-1983 L1986 **IM** *020 †20

FREEMAN, David F. 101 MANNING DR, UNC HOSPITALS 27514 #036-05-1951 L1961 **PYA CHP** *020 †75

FREEMAN, Katherin L. 200 MASON FARM RD, STE 7220 27514 #048-04-1983 L1999 **PD PG** *040 †55

FREEMAN, Sandra. 615 E ROSEMARY ST, SANDRA FREEMAN MD 27514 #036-08-1992 L1998 **P** *020

FREIBERGER, John Jacob. ■ 27514 #048-12-1979 L2000 **AN CCM** *075 †05

FRENCH, Frank Sikes. 101 MANNING DR, UNC HOSPITALS 27514 #035-45-1956 L1961 **PD OS** *075 †55

FRICK, Donna Elliott. 109 CONNER DR, BLDG 3 27514 #036-01-1974 L1974 **P** *020 †75

FRIED, Daniel Benjamin. 101 MANNING DR, DEPT. OF RADIATION ONCOLOG 27514 #036-01-2001 L2006 **RO** *100 †80

FRIED, Floyd Alan. 428 BURNETT-WOMACK 27514 #016-02-1961 L1970 **U** *020 †95

FRIED, Michael David. 120 CONNER DR 27514 #035-19-1971 L1973 **OBG** *020 †30

FRIED, Michael Warren. UNC LIVER PROGRAM, CB#7080, DEPT OF MEDICINE 27599 #550-02-1984 L1998 **HEP GE** *020 †20

FRITZ, Marc Anthony. 4001 OLD CLINIC BLDG, CB #7570 27599 #021-01-1977 L1993 **END OBG** *050 †30

FRY, Gerald Louis. 109 CONNER DR, CHAPEL HILL SURGICAL CTR 27514 #018-03-1966 L1973 **AN** *020 †05

FULLER, Megan Kelly. ■ 27517 #048-04-2007 **GS** *012

FULLWOOD, Phillip Andrew. 121 S ESTES DR, STE 100 27514 #036-01-1990 L1993 **P** *020 †75

FULTON, Joseph J. CB 7212, 3022 BURNETTE WOMACK BLDG 27599 #035-15-1998 L2003 **GS** *100 †85

FUNKHOUSER, Wm Keith, Jr. 101 MANNING DR, UNC HOSPITALS 27514 #047-05-1979 L1996 **PTH** *020 †50

FURMAN, Jeffrey Wm. 120 CONNER DR, MEDICINE PA 27514 #038-41-1978 L1980 **FM** *020 †18

FURMAN, William Ross. 101 MANNING DR, UNC HOSPITALS 27514 #035-20-1976 L2000 **AN IM** *020,05

GABRIEL, Don Alexander. UNC SCH OF MED DEPT/HEM ON 27514 #036-01-1972 L1972 **HEM IM** *040 †20

GALA, Gary Jek. 101 ARBUTUS PL 27517 #043-01-1987 L1996 **P** *100 †85,75

GALVIN, Shannon Rebecca. 130 MASON FARM RD, INFECTIOUS DISEASES 27599 #011-02-1997 L1999 **ID** *020 †20

GANGAROSA, Lisa Marie. CB # 7080, UNIVERSITY OF NORTH CAROLI 27599 #036-07-1991 L2001 **GE IM** *020 †20

GARBUTT, James Cameron. UNC OF CHAPEL HILL CB 7160, NEURO SCI HOSP DEPT PSYCH 27599 #016-11-1975 L1980 **P ADP** *020 †75

GARFUNKEL, Joseph Morris. ■ 27517 #041-13-1948 L1984 **PD PDC** *071 †55

GARRETT, Neil Edward. 118B OLD DURHAM RD 27517 #036-05-1987 L1990 **GP** *020

GARRETT, Peter Alfred. ■ 27514 #041-12-1974 L1975 **PHP** *071 †70

GARRISON, Aaron Paul. ■ 27514 #025-07-2004 L2007 **GS** *012

GARTNER, Anne Elizabeth. 1525 E FRANKLIN ST, STE 3 27514 #036-07-1999 L2004 **CHP** *100 †75

GATES, Douglas Hart. ■ 27516 #036-01-2006 **GS** *012

GAVIN, Martin. ■ 27516 #836-02-1989 L1998 *020

GAWOR, Grzegorz Mariusz. 101 MANNING DR, UNIV OF NC 27514 #051-04-2006 **EM** *012

GAY, Cynthia Leigh. ■ 27517 #036-01-1999 L2003 **ID** *100 †20

GAYNES, Bradley Neil. CB 7160, UNIV NC 27599 #051-01-1989 L1995 **P PHP** *020 †75

GEHRIG, Paola Alvarez. CB 7570 MACNIDER BUILDING, UNIV OF NORTH CAROLINA 27599 #011-03-1993 L1997 **OBG** *020 †30

GELLER, Elizabeth Joanne. DEPT UROGYNECOLOGY, CB 7570 MACNIDER BLDG 27599 #036-01-2001 L2005 **GYN** *020 †30

GEORGES, Linda Swinson. 101 MANNING DR 27514 #012-01-1976 L1991 **AN** *020 †05

GERADTS, Joseph. ■ 27517 #016-02-1987 L2005 **ATP** *020 †50 ‡

GERBE, Ronald Wm. 109 CONNER DR STE 207 27514 #036-01-1976 L1976 **OTO** *020 †45

GERBER, David Allen. 4026 BURNETT-WOMACK BLDG, CB7211 27599 #041-12-1989 L1998 **GS TTS** *020 †85

GERKIN, Jonathan Scott. 101 MANNING DR, UNC HOSPITALS 27514 #038-45-2004 L2005 **P** *012

GETTES, Leonard Sheffer. 130 MASON FARM RD # 70, 4TH FL 27599 #041-01-1958 L1978 **CD IM** *050 †20

GHIA, Jawahar Narottamdas. 101 MANNING DR DEPT ANES 27514 #496-38-1961 L1971 **AN OS** *020 †05

GHIO, Andrew Jonathan. 104 MASON FARM RD, CRB, HSD, NHEERL, EPA 27599 #024-05-1981 L1988 **PUD IM** *020 †20

GIALLANZA, Peterson F. ■ 27599 #035-06-2003 L2007 **SME** *012

GIANGIACOMO, Annette Lynn. CAMPUS BOX 7040, 5110 BIOINFORMATICS BUILDI 27599 #028-03-2001 L2006 **OPH** *100 †35

GIBBONS, Erin Anne. ■ 27514 #036-01-2008 *012

GIBBS, Wood Beasley. ■ 27517 #036-05-2005 L2008 **IM** *012

GIBSON, Debra Luanne. 1703 LEGION RD, STE 206 27517 #036-01-2001 L2003 **P** *020

GIDUZ, Thomas Tracy. 194 FINLEY GOLF COURSE RD, STE 202 27517 #036-01-1984 L1987 **P** *020 †75

GILANI, Ajamal Masood. 3114 BIOINFORMATICS BLDG, UNC NEUROLOGY CB#7025 27599 #704-17-1988 L2002 **N** *020 †75

GILBERT, Leah Kaye. ■ 27517 #036-01-2008 *012

GILCHRIST, Michael James. UNIV OF N CAROLINA SCH OF, 3018 OLD CLINIC BLDG/CB760 27599 #051-07-2004 L2007 **IM** *100 †20

GILCHRIST, Thomas F. ■ 27517 #021-01-1962 L1962 **FOP ATP** *071 †50

GILGOR, Robert Samuel. 891 WILLOW DR 27514 #041-01-1962 L1968 **D OS** *030 †15

GILLESPIE, Barbara Sorian. 101 MANNING DR, DEPT OF MED UNC HOSP 27514 #041-15-2001 L2004 **NEP** *020

GILMAN, Andrew Lee. CB #7220 27599 #041-02-1985 L2004 **PHO PD** *020 †55

GILMORE, John H, Jr. U OF NORTH CAROLINA, DEPT OF PSYCH CB #7160 27599 #036-01-1985 L1990 **P OS** *050 †75

GINSBERG, Nicolle. 101 MANNING DR, DEPT FM 27514 #036-01-2006 **FP** *012

GIPSON, Debbie Titzer. 349 MACNIDER HALL/CB#7155, DIVISION OF NEPHROLOGY 27599 #017-20-1989 L1999 **PN** *020 †55

GIPSON, Patrick Evan. 349 MACNIDER HALL/CB #7155, HILL,DIV NEPHY & HYPERTENS 27599 #017-20-1989 L1999 **NEP** *012 †55,20

GITELMAN, Hillel Jonathan. CB 7155 OLD CLINIC, BLDG 226H 27599 #035-45-1958 L1966 **NEP IM** *071 †20

GIUSTO, John. 104 MARKET ST, THE CAROLINA CENTER FOR 27516 #010-02-1988 L1999 **PM IM** *020 †60

GIVRE, Syndee Jill. 5TH FLOOR BIOINFORMATICS, DEPT OF OPHTHALMOLOGY 27599 #035-46-1994 L2002 **OPH** *020 †35

GLASS, Paul Edwin, III. ■ 27517 #036-01-2008 *012

GLECKMAN, Aaron Morris. 101 MANNING DR 27514 #024-16-1995 L2002 **NP** *020

GLENN, James Hartman. ■ 27517 #010-01-1957 L1964 **DR NM** *071 †80

GLUCK, George Scott. UNIV OF N CAROLINA SCH OF, 3314 BIOINFORMATICS BUILDI 27599 #035-19-2006 **ORS** *012

GODLEY, Paul Alphonso. CB #7305, 3009 OLD CLINIC BLDG 27599 #024-01-1984 L1987 **ON HEM** *050 †20

GOLD, Stuart Harrison. UNC/BURNET WOMCK/CB 7220, DEPT PED 27514 #047-05-1981 L1989 **PHO PD** *020 †55

GOLDBACH, Robert Herman. 1838 MARTN LTHR KNG JR 27514 #041-09-1987 L1994 **PD** *020 †55

GOLDBERG, Richard Miles. 3009 OLD CLINIC CB#7305, UNIV OF NC 27599 #035-15-1979 L2003 **ON IM** *020 †20 ‡

GOLDEN, Keith Mitchell. UNIV OF N CAROLINA SCH OF, 3018 OLD CLINIC BLDG/CB760 27599 #051-04-2005 **IM** *012

GOLDING, Michael. 101 MANNING DR, UNC HOSPITALS 27514 #038-40-1991 L1997 **P** *020 †75

GOLDMAN, Richard Andrew, II. ■ 27516 #036-01-2008 *012

GOLDSMITH, Lowell Alan. 130 MASON FARM RD 27599 #035-08-1963 L2002 **D** *040 †15

GOLDSTEIN, Adam Oliver. UNIV OF N CAROLINA, CB7595 DEPT OF FAMILY MEDI 27599 #012-01-1987 L1990 **FM PHP** *050 †18

GOLDSTEIN, Beth Goodrich. 2238 NELSON HWY STE 100, CENTRAL DERMATOLOGY CNTR P 27517 #012-01-1986 L1990 **D** *020 †15

GOLDSTEIN, Brian P. UNC-CH SCHOOL OF MEDICINE, 4030 BONDURANT HALL, CB#70 27599 #035-19-1988 L1990 **IM MDM** *030 †20

GOLIN, Carol Elaine. ■ 27516 #036-01-1989 L1992 **IM** *020 †20

GOODMAN, Hanni Elizabeth. ■ 27514 #036-01-2007 **AN** *012

GOODMAN, Maxwell Williams. ■ 27516 #047-01-1958 L1959 **FM UM** *062

GOODMAN, Michael David. CB #7525 DEPT OF PATHOLOGY, UNIVERSITY OF N CAROLINA 27599 #005-14-1969 L2000 **ATP** *062 †50 ‡

GORDON, Christopher Josep. 101 MANNING DR, UNIV OF NC HOSPS 27514 #010-02-2007 **PTH** *012

GORE, Mitchell Ray. 101 MANNING DR, CB 7070 27514 #036-01-2006 **OTO** *012

GOURLAY, Margaret Lee. MANNING DRIVE CB 7595, UNC FAMILY PRACTICE CENTER 27599 #016-21-1998 L2002 **FM** *020 †18

GOYER, Robert Andrew. ■ 27517 #028-34-1955 L1965 **PTX** *071 †50

GRAHAM, Karen Anne. 110 CONNER DR STE 4 27514 #065-10-1993 L2000 **P** *020 †75

GRAHAM, Matthew C. 101 MANNING DR, OGMEROOM 1107-A 27514 #051-07-2003 L2006 **PTH** *100 †50

GRANGER, Bruce Todd. 940 MARTN LTHR KNG JR BLVD, JR BLVD 27514 #028-02-1989 L1992 **IM** *020 †20

GREENBERG, Rebecca Ann. 590 MANNING DR, CB 7595 27599 #033-06-1999 L2007 **FM** *100 †18

GREENE, Kevin Gary. C B 7525, BRINKHAUS-BULLITT BLDG 27599 #051-01-2004 L2006 **PTH** *012

GREENWOOD, Robert Saml. 101 MANNING DR 27514 #048-02-1968 L1977 **CHN PD** *040 †55,75

GREGANTI, Mac Andrew. 125 MACNIDER HALL, DEPT OF MED-CB #7005 27599 #027-01-1972 L1977 **IM IMG** *020 †20

GREGORY, Patricia C. 101 MANNING DRIVE, CAMPUS BOX 7200 - RM 1148 27599 #051-01-1990 L2005 **PM** *020 †60

GRIER, Nichole Danniele. 101 MANNING DR, DEPT. OF PSYCHIATRY 27514 #036-01-1998 L1999 **CHP** *020 †75

GRIGGS, Thomas Russell. DIVISION OF CARDIOLOGY, UNIVERSITY OF N.C. CB#7075 27599 #036-01-1969 L1969 **IM PTH** *020 †20

GRIMM, Ian Scott. CAMPUS BOX 7080, UNIV OF NORTH CAROLINA 27599 #041-02-1984 L1993 **GE IM** *020 †20

GRIMSON, Baird Sanford. BURNETT-WOMACK BLDG CB7040, 617 CHAPEL HILL 27599 #036-07-1969 L1969 **OPH OS** *020 †35

GRISHAM, Joe Wheeler. UNC-CH DEPT PTH CB 7525 27599 #047-05-1957 L1973 **PTH GE** *040

GROBEN, Pamela A. 130 MASON FARM RD 27599 #041-01-1977 L1982 **PTH** *020 †50

GRODER, Martin Gary. 104 S ESTES DR STE 304 27514 #035-01-1964 L1972 **P** *075 †75

GROSSMAN, Steven Howard. 101 MANNING DR 27514 #051-04-1973 L1976 **IM NEP** *050 †20

GUALTIERI, Thomas. 400 FRANKLIN SQ, 1829 E. FRANKLIN ST. 27514 #035-01-1969 L1973 **N CHP** *020 †75

GUCSAVAS, Muge. MEDICAL SCHOOL WING C, DEV GEN & MEYTABOLISM-PEDS 27599 #902-03-1983 L1996 **PD MG** *040 †55,19

GUDERIAN, Laura Jean. ■ 27514 #021-05-2003 L2006 **IM** *100 †20

GUGELMANN, Hallam Melvill. ■ 27514 #036-01-2008 *012

GUGELMANN, Richard John. 151 E ROSEMARY ST, STE 201 27514 #048-02-1971 L1976 **PD** *020 †55

GUION, Willie Kent. UNIV OF NC SCHOOL OF MED 27514 #036-01-1992 *100

GUITERAS, George Patrick. 120 CONNER DR, MEDICINE PA 27514 #036-01-1969 L1969
FM *020 †18

GULLEY, Margaret Lynn. UNC PATHOLOGY DEPT 27599 #036-01-1984 L2001
PTH HMP *050 †50

GUPTA, Anjali. 101 MANNING DR, DEPT EM 27514 #035-03-2007 EM *012

GUSH, Kimberly Ann. 300 MARKET ST STE 112 27516 #036-01-2002 L2005 PD *020 †55

GUSTKE, Erik Jonathan. CAMPUS BOX 7470, UNIV/NORTH CAROLINA-CHAPEL 27599
#036-01-1999 L2004 P *020 †75

GWYTHER, Robert Edwin, Jr. 513 MANNING DR, CB 7595 27599 #038-43-1975 L1978
FM ADM *020 †18

HADAR, Eldad J. UNIV OF N CAROLINA, CB 7060 27599 #026-04-1991 L2001 NS *020 †25

HADLER, Nortin Marvin. 3300 THURSTON BLDG, UNC DEPT MEDICINE 27599
#024-01-1968 L1974 RHU IM *050 †03,20

HADLER, Susan Caryl. UNC DENTAL SCHOOL, DIAGNOSTIC SCIENCES RM199 27514
#036-01-1985 ATP *040

HADLEY, Johanna Lynn. 101 MANNING DR 27514 #038-45-2006 FP *012

HAGGERTY, John James. CB#7160, DEPT. OF PSYCHIATRY UNC-CH 27599
#023-01-1971 L1975 P *020 †75

HAHN, Gunter Ernst. ■ 27517 #407-15-1954 L1959 IM *071

HAITHCOCK, Benjamin Earl. CB 7065, 3040 BURNETT-WOMACK BUILDI 27599
#025-12-1998 L2004 TS *100 †85

HALE, Leslie Morgan. 110 CONNER DR, STE 2 27514 #036-01-1961 L1961 OPH *020 †35

HALE, Robert Vernon. 110 CONNER DR STE 2 27514 #036-01-1967 L1967 OPH *020 †35

HALL, Buford. ■ 27517 #024-01-1945 L1948 IM CD *071 †20

HALL, Colin David. UNC SCHOOL OF MEDICINE, 705 CLLINICAL SCIENCES 27599
#803-01-1966 L1973 N *020 †75

HALL, Timothy Ralph. 205 SAGE RD, STE 100 27514 #036-01-1998 L2001 PD *020 †55

HALLADAY, Jaqualine R. 104 DAIRY GLEN RD 27516 #035-45-1991 L2001 GPM *100 †30,70

HALLE, Jan Stuart. N C MEM HOSP, DEPT RAD 27514 #024-07-1975 L1975 RO *075 †80

HALLECK, Seymour Leon. 101 MANNING DR 27514 #016-01-1952 L1972 P *040 †75

HALPERN, David Justin. UNC HOSPITALS, CB 7550, 142 MACNIDER HALL 27599
#035-20-2004 L2007 IMG *012 †20

HALVORSON, Eric Glenn. UNC, DIV OF PLASTIC SURG 27599 #036-07-1998 L2006
PS *100 †85,65

HAMBY, George Walters. 901 WILLOW DR, DOCTORS BLDG, SUITE 3 27514
#036-01-1958 L1958 P *020

HAMRICK, Allen Willard. UNIVERSITY OF NORTH CAROLI, CB #7471 STUDENT HEALTH 27599
#036-01-1987 L1994 P *020 †75

HAMRICK, Harvey James. UNC SCHOOL OF MED, CB #7593 27599 #036-01-1967 L1967
PD *030 †55

HAN, Jaok. ■ 27517 #583-04-1951 L1966 CD IM *020

HANEMANN, Michael Stephen. ■ 27516 #021-05-2001 L2003 PS *012 †45

HANNAPEL, Andrew C. 161 MANNING DR # 7595, DEPARTMENT OF FAMILY MEDIC 27514
#010-01-1992 L1998 FM *040 †18

HANSEN, Mark Krogness. ■ 27516 #026-04-1977 L1978 OS PD *030 †55

HANSON, Cherissa Lee. CB 7221 STE 20195 2ND FL, UNC AT CHAPEL HILL 27599
#048-02-2001 L2004 PD *100 †55

HANSON, Laura Catherine. UNIVERSITY OF N CAROLINA, 141 MACNIDER BLDG CB 7550 27599
#024-01-1986 L1988 IMG IM *020 †20

HARDISON, Joshua Lee. 120 CONNER DR STE 101, WHA DBA CHAPEL HILL OBGYN 27514
#036-01-1998 L2002 OBG *020 †30

HARKER, Elsje. 101 MANNING DR, UNIV OF NC HOSPS 27514 #024-05-2007 AN *012

HARNED, Herbert S, Jr. ■ 27517 #008-01-1945 L1958 PD PDC *071 †55

HARP, Joyce Beatrice. MCGAVRAN-GREENBERG HALL, CB7461 27599 #021-01-1984 L1997
END IM *020 †20

HARPER, James Robinson. UNC SCHOOL OF MEDICINE, 113 MACNIDER BULDING
CB953 27599 #036-01-1960 L1960 IM CD *020 †20

HARRELL, Diane Michelle. UNIVERSITY OF N CAROLINA S, CB #7593 27599 #011-03-2007
PD *012

HARRELL, Raymond Martin. ■ 27517 #036-01-2007 AN *012

HARRIGAN, Michael. SPITAL CB 7594, DEPT EMRG MED NEUROSCIENCE 27599
#035-15-1993 L1996 EM *020 †16

HARRILL, Annmarie Jordan. ■ 27516 #045-01-2006 PD *012

HARRINGTON, John Jos. 141 MACNIDER BLDG, UNIV OF NC 27599 #030-06-1992 L2001
CN *100 †20

HARRIS, Bradford Dean. UNIV OF NC, CHAPEL HILL, DEPT OF PEDS, CB 7221 27599
#024-05-1990 L2001 PD CCP *020 †55

HARRIS, Charles Odell. 300 MEADOWMONT VILLAGE CIR, STE 311 27517 #036-01-1979 L1980
OBG *020 †30

HARRIS, Herbert Wm. ■ 27516 #041-12-1990 L1992 P *020 †75

HARRIS, Russell P, Jr. 5039 OLD CLINIC, CB 7110, DIV OF GENERAL MEDICINE 27599
#023-07-1970 L1975 IM FM *050 †20,18,70

HARRIS, Tyndall P. ■ 27515 #036-07-1950 L1951 IM OS *071

HARRIS, William Thomas. UNIV OF N CAROLINA, 5TH FLOOR BIOINFORMATICS 27599
#048-12-1999 L2007 PDP *100 †55

HARTMAN, Lisa Mc Avey. 940 MARTN LTHR KNG JR BLVD 27514 #055-01-1997 L1998
IM *020 †20

HARTNETT, Mary E. 5110 BIONINFORMATICS BLDG, UNC-CH DEPT. OF OPH CB7040 27599
#035-03-1983 L2003 OPH *020 †35 ‡

HARTSELL, Angela Chia-Mei. 101 MANNING DR, DEPT OF PEDIATRICS 27514 #036-08-2006
PD *012

HASKELL, Barbara Ann. 101 MANNING DR 27514 #035-48-1984 L1999 FM *040 †18

HAUSER, Justin Bradley. CB 7010, DEPT OF ANESTHESIOLOGY 27599 #036-01-2001 L2005
PAN *100 †05

HAWK, James Solley. UNIV OF N CAROLINA SCH OF, 3018 OLD CLINIC BLDG CB 76 27599
#045-01-2006 IM *012

HAWKINS, David Miller. 800 EASTOWNE DR STE 106 27514 #036-07-1965 L1965 P *020 †75 ‡

HAWKINS, David Rollo. 800 EASTOWNE DR, GROUP FOR PSYCHOTHERAPY 27514
#035-45-1946 L1952 P *072 †75

HAYASHI, Paul Hideyo, Jr. RM 8011, CB 7584 BURNETT-WOMACK BLD 27599
#005-18-1987 L2006 GE *020 †20 ‡

HAYES, David Neil. ■ 27514 #036-01-1996 L2004 HO *100 †20

HAYS, Laura Marie. ■ 27517 #036-01-2008 *012

HAYSTEAD, Clare Mhairim. ■ 27514 #051-01-2000 L2005 DR *100 †80

HEATH, Stacey Maurice. 300 MEADOWMONT VILLAGE CIR, STE 311 27517 #036-08-1988 L1992
OBG *020 †30

HEETDERKS, Peter William. 112 SAN MIGUEL PL 27514 #011-02-1995 L2005 CCM *020 †20

HEIZER, William David. U NC SCH MED CB 7080 27514 #023-07-1963 L1970 GE NTR *020 †20

HELMRATH, Michael Anthony. ■ 27516 #038-41-1993 L2007 PDS *020 †85

HELTON, Margaret Rose. 513 MANNING DR, CB 7595 27599 #025-01-1987 L1990
IMG *100 †18

HENDERSHOT, Edward F. ■ 27516 #020-02-1985 L2006 ID IM *030 †20

HENDERSON, Ashley G. 4133 BIOINFORMATICS, CB #7020 27599 #048-12-1996 L1998
PCC IM *050 †20 ‡

HENDERSON, Frederick W. 101 MANNING DR, DEPT PED 27514 #036-01-1970 L1970
PD ID *050 †55

HENDERSON, Gavin Jeffrey. UNIVERSITY OF N CAROLINA S, CB #7593 27599 #036-01-2007
PD *012

HENDERSON, Richard Clark. CB# 7055, DIV OF ORTHOPAEDICS 27599 #016-02-1980 L1985
ORS OP *020 †40

HENDRICKS, Charles H. ■ 27514 #025-01-1943 L1968 OBG *071 †30

HENKE, David C. CB# 7020, 4136 BIOINFORMATIC BLDG. 27599 #036-01-1977 L1977
PUD IM *050 †20,15

HENLEY, Nancy S. 101 MANNING DR 27514 #036-01-1982 L1983 IM *030 †20

HENRY, George W. DEPT OF PEDIATRICS, UNC-CH, CAMPUS BOX 7220 27599
#036-01-1977 L1977 PDC *020 †55

HENRY, Marianna Matthews. 130 MASON FARM RD, CAMPUS BOX #7220 27599
#036-01-1977 L1977 PD *020 †55

HENRY, Steven Alonzo. ■ 27517 #045-01-1982 L1984 IM *075 †20

HERBST, Chas Arthur, Jr. UNIV N CAROLINA MEM, DEPT SURG 27514 #027-01-1967 L1973
AS GS *030 †85

HERFARTH, Hans. 130 MASON FARM RD, CB 7080 SCHOOL OF MED 27599
#409-33-1992 L2006 GE IM *100

HERION, John Carroll. ■ 27517 #024-01-1953 L1953 HEM IM *071

HERRINGTON, Robert Thos. ■ 27517 #054-04-1957 L1959 PDC PD *071 †55

HERTZ, Caryn Marjorie. 109 CONNER DR, STE 1201 27514 #035-45-1986 L1990 AN *020 †05

HICKERSON, Adam Duane. ■ 27516 #005-12-2004 GS *100

HIGGINS, Steven Patrick. ■ 27514 #036-07-2002 D *012 †20

HIGTOW, Lisa Beth. 130 MASON FARM RD, CB#7030 27599 #051-01-1998 L2001 ID *100 †20

HILL, John Benj. ■ 27517 #035-01-1952 OS *071

HILL, Michael Alan. MANNING DR, CB 7160 27599 #038-45-1982 L1985 P PYG *020 †75

HILLMAN, Anne Elizabeth. 11312 US HIGHWAY 15 501 N, STE 308 27517 #036-01-1997 L2001
MPD *020 †20,55

HINDERLITER, Alan Lee. 130 MASON FARM RD, CB# 7075 27599 #028-02-1981 L1985
CD *040 †20

HINN, Albert Richard, Jr. CB #7025 UNC, 3114 BIOINFORMATICS BLDG. 27599
#036-01-1987 L1988 N IM *020 †75

HIPP, Cecilia Giblin. ■ 27516 #036-01-1983 *074

HOBGOOD, Cherri Deserea. UNC SCHOOL OF MEDICINE, DEPT OF EMERGENCY MED 27599
#036-01-1989 L1990 EM *040 †16

HODGES, Leon Carey. ■ 27517 #011-02-1966 L2003 OS D *030 †15

HODGIN, Jeffrey Benton. ■ 27516 #036-01-2003 L2006 PTH *100 †50

HOFFMAN, Byron Jay, Jr. 101 MANNING DR 27514 #012-05-1976 L1979 IM *020 †20

HOFFMEISTER, Dean Louis. ■ 27514 #016-11-2002 L2007 DR *100 †80

HOHNEKER, John Arthur. 67 CEDAR HILLS CIR 27514 #033-06-1985 L1989 ON HEM *050 †20

HOLLINGSHEAD, Michael C. 101 MANNING DRIVE, UNC DEPARTMENT OF NEURORAD 27599
#036-01-2002 L2007 DR *100 †80

HOLT, Terrence Edward. 141 MACNIDER, PROGRAM ON AGING, CB#7550 27599
#036-01-2000 L2002 IMG *100 †20

HOMEISTER, Jonathon W. 101 MANNING DRIVE, BRINKHOUSE BULLITT BLDG, C 27599
#025-01-1992 L2005 ATP *050 †50

HONEYCUTT, Andrea Bingham. ■ 27516 #036-01-2005 L2008 IM *012

HOOLE, Axalla John, IV. CB 9500, 121 MACNIDER HALL 27599 #045-01-1964 L1972
IM *020 †20

HOOVER, Stephen Albert. ■ 27516 #036-01-2006 ORS *012

HOPKINS, John Sloan. ■ 27517 #036-01-2008 *012

HOROWITZ, Eric Neal. ■ 27517 #035-15-2003 L2003 NPM *012 †55

HOSFORD, Sandra Burson. 205 SAGE RD, CHAPEL HILL PEDIATRICS PA 27514
#036-07-1986 L1990 PD *020 †55

HOSSEINIPOUR, Mina C. 547 BURNETT WOMACK CB#7030 27599 #016-06-1995 L1999
ID *020 †20

HOUPT, Jeffrey Lyle. 51319 CHURCH 27599 #048-04-1967 L1975 P *030 †75

HOWARD, James Francis. UNIVERSITY OF N CAROLI, 3114 BIOINFORMATICS BLDG, 27599
#050-02-1974 L1979 N CN *040 †75

HOWARD-WILLIAMS, Escher L. ■ 27516 #036-01-2005 L2008 IM *012

HOWARTH, Christopher Leo. CB #7594, EMERG MED, GRD FL/NEURO HO 27599
#005-14-1987 L1991 EM *020 †16

HOWES, Brendan Luke. ■ 27516 #036-01-2004 L2008 AN *012

HOYLE, David Emory. ■ 27517 #036-01-1989 *075

HUANG, Benjamin Yubin. ■ 27516 #036-07-1999 L2002 RNR *100 †80

HUANG, David Yuyiao. 3114 BIOINFORMATICS BLDG, CB 7025 NEUROLOGY UNC CH 27599
#036-07-1997 L2002 N *050 †75

HUANG, Xuemei. 101 MANNING DR, UNC HOSPITALS 27514 #243-47-1987 L2000 N *020 †75

HUFFINES, William Davis. 314 BERRYHILL HALL 219H, UNIV OF NORTH CAROLINA 27514
#036-01-1955 L1955 PTH GP *075 †50

HUFFMAN, Katherine A. 101 MANNING DR 27514 #055-01-1977 L1979 IM NEP *020 †20

HUGHES, Bruce Bryan. 1829 E FRANKLIN ST, STE 200A 27514 #021-01-1972 L1993 P EM *020

HUGHES, Thomas Arnold. ■ 27517 #035-47-2002 L2007 RNR *012 †80

HULKA, Barbara Sorenson. 2317 HONEYSUCKLE RD 27514 #035-01-1959 L1967
GPM *030 †70

HULKA, Jaroslav Fabian. 101 MANNING DR DEPT OBG 27514 #035-01-1956 L1967
END OBG *050 †30

HULTMAN, Charles Scott. BURNETT-WOMACK BUILDING, SUITE 7038 27599
#041-12-1990 L2004 GS *020 †85,65

HUMBERSON, Jennifer Lynn. 101 MANNING DR, UNIV NC MED WING E 27514
#051-04-2003 L2005 MG *012

HUMLAN, Michele Ann. 901 WILLOW DR, STE 2 27514 #010-01-1984 L1988 PD ADL *071 †55

HUMMERT, Erin Higgins. ■ 27514 #019-02-2004 L2008 MPD *012

HUMPHREY, Holly Lain. ■ 27517 #036-01-2005 L2008 IM *012

HUMPHRIES, John Elliott. ■ 27516 #023-07-1984 L1986 HEM ON *050 †20

HUNT, Christine Marie. ■ 27514 #024-05-1982 L1988 GE IM *050 †20

HUNT, Vernon Brock. 101 MANNING DR 27514 #041-12-1971 L1994 IM *071 †20

HURSEY, Darrin Robert. ■ 27514 #025-07-2001 L2004 PCC *012

HURT, Christopher B. ■ 27514 #011-03-2003 L2006 ID *012 †20

HURWITZ, Shepard R. 400 SILVER CEDAR CT 27514 #035-01-1976 L2007 ORS *020 †40

HUTTO, Burton Roy. CB #7160, UNC DEPT OF PSYCHIATRY 27599 #045-01-1988 L1992 P *040 †75

HYSLOP, William Brian. 2016 OLD CLINIC BLDG, UNIV OF NC CB# 7510 27599 #016-11-1993 L2001 DR *020 †80

IBAZEBO, Wesley Robert. ■ 27517 #048-02-2006 PM *012

IBRAHIM, Michel Ayoub. U OF NC SCH P H 27514 #330-02-1957 PHP *030

IDRISS, Marilyn M. 205 SAGE RD, STE 100 27514 #036-07-1992 L1995 PD *020 †55

IGLESIAS, Dana Michelle. UNIV OF N CAROLINA SCH OF, DEPT OF FAMILY MED CB7595 27599 #012-21-2002 L2005 FM *100 †16

IKENBERRY, Lynn David. 727 EASTOWNE DR STE 300B 27514 #036-01-1974 L1976 P *020

INGRAM, David Lawrence. ■ 27514 #036-01-1988 L1992 AN *020

IRONS, Cary F, III. 8 THE COURTYARD 27516 #036-01-1977 L1977 P CHP *020 †75

IRVIN, William Johnson, Jr. 10 MANNING DR, UNIVERSITY OF NORTH CAROLI 27514 #051-04-2003 L2006 HO *012 †20

ISAACS, Kim Luise. OF GASTROENTEROLOGY, DIVISION 27599 #035-48-1984 L1985 GE IM *020 †20

ISENSTEIN, Arin Lynn. 101 MANNING DR, UNIV OF NC 27514 #005-02-2006 D *012

ISLEY, Timothy Chas. 141 PROVIDENCE RD, STE 230 27514 #036-01-1985 L1986 CHP *020 †75

IVESTER, Thomas Steven. 214 MACNIDER CB#7516, UNC SCHOOL OF MEDICINE 27599 #036-08-1996 L2003 OBG MFM *020 †30

IYENGAR, Sumathi Sridhar. ■ 27517 #495-33-1988 L1994 PD *020 †55

JACKSON, Cheryl Lynn. 130 MASON FARM RD, CAMPUS BOX # 7220 27599 #041-01-1987 L2004 PD *020 †20

JACKSON, Margaret Elizabe. ■ 27516 #036-01-2008 *012

JACOBSON, Sharon Lydia. 101 MANNING DR, DEPT FM 27514 #023-01-2007 FP *012

JACOBSTEIN, Roy Alan. ■ 27514 #025-01-1973 L1977 PD GP *020 †55

JAGUST, Morton. ■ 27514 #035-09-1951 L1997 FM *020 †18

JAIN, Anitha Kamla. UNIVERSITY OF N CAROLINA S, CB #7593 27599 #011-03-2007 PD *012

JAMES, A Everette. ■ 27517 #036-07-1963 L1963 R LM *071 †80,28

JAMES, Dominika Lipowska. ■ 27517 #012-01-2005 AN *012

JAMES, Jesse Cimarron. UNIV OF N CAROLINA SCH OF, 3018 OLD CLINIC BLDG/CB760 27599 #008-01-2005 GPM *012

JAMES, Olga Gennadyevna. ■ 27514 #913-54-1993 NM *012

JANG, Soyoon. 101 MANNING DR, DEPT OF NEPHROLOGY 27514 #036-01-2004 L2007 NEP *012 †20

JANNELLI, Mary Lee. 101 MANNING DR 27514 #035-48-1991 L1996 OBG *020 †30

JANOWSKY, David Steffan. UN OF N CAROLINA, DEPT OF PSYCH CB 7175 27599 #005-02-1964 L1986 P *020 †75

JANOWSKY, Esther Celia J. ■ 27514 #005-02-1965 L1987 AN *020 †05

JAQUES, Paul Francis. MEMORIAL HOSP, DEPT RADIOL 27514 #917-26-1970 L1976 DR *020 †80

JAROSCAK, Jennifer Joi. PEDIATRIC HEME/ONC-CB#7220, PEDIATRICS UNC-CHAPEL HILL 27599 #038-40-1993 L1998 PHO *020 †55

JENKINS, Sasha Nicole. ■ 27516 #036-01-2008 *012

JENNETTE, J Charles. CB 7525, DEPT OF PATH 27599 #036-01-1973 L1977 PTH NEP *020 †50

JENNETTE, John Allen. 101 MANNING DR, UNC HOSPITALS 27514 #051-04-1979 L1987 AN *020 †05

JENSEN, Eric Webb. WING C RM 245A, UNC 27599 #038-06-1969 L1976 P *020

JEONG, Seong Joo. 130 MASON FARM RD # 7 27599 #583-06-2002 L2007 PCC *012 †20

JERATH, Maya Ratna. THURSTON 3330, CB 7280 27599 #050-02-2000 L2005 IM *100 †20,03

JI, Na Young. 10625 NEUROSCIENCES HOSP, BOX 7160 DEPT OF PSYCHIATY 27599 #583-05-2000 L2007 CHP *012

JIMENEZ, Andrea Mercedes. 412 CALDWELL EXT STE A 27516 #016-11-1985 L1988 CHP P *020 †75

JOHNSON, David Randall. 141 PROVIDENCE RD, STE 230 27514 #045-01-1983 L1985 CHP P *020 †75

JOHNSON, Margaret Gould. ■ 27517 #036-01-1985 L1987 PTH *020 †50

JOHNSON, Tatum Simon. ■ 27514 #021-05-2000 L2006 DR PDR *020 †80

JOHNSON, Tiffany Grace. ■ 27514 #036-01-2005 NS *012

JOHNSTON, Helen M Presley. ■ 27517 #047-05-1935 L1942 OS *071

JOKHU, Maitriyi N. 101 MANNING DR, UNIV OF NC HOSPS 27514 #048-16-2006 AN *012

JONAS, Beth Laurie. 100 MASON FARM RD 27599 #035-15-1989 L1998 RHU *020 †20

JONAS, Daniel Eric. 5039 OLD CLINIC BLDG, CB 7110 27599 #038-40-2001 L2005 MPD *020 †20,55

JONES, Andrew Rawdon. 101 CONNER DR, STE 200 27514 #017-20-1978 L1981 ORS *020 †40 ‡

JONES, David Neil. ■ 27514 #143-11-1986 L1994 NM *020

JONES, Joseph Kempton. ■ 27516 #036-07-1946 L1950 FM *071 †18

JONES, Samuel Wayne. WOMACK BLDG. CB# 7228, CARE AND BURNS. 4008 BURNE 27599 #036-01-1995 L2006 CCS *100 †85

JONES, Thomas Mcintosh. 727 EASTOWNE DR, STE 300A 27514 #034-01-1974 L1981 CHP PD *020 †55,75

JORDAN, Joanne Marie. 100 MASON FARM RD 27599 #023-07-1981 L1984 RHU IM *050 †20

JORDAN, Judy B. ■ 27517 #048-12-1992 L1993 IM *020 †20

JOSEPH, Mark. UNIV OF N CAROLINA SCH OF, "DEPARTMENT OF SURGERY, CB 27599 #039-01-2005 GS *012

JOYNER, William S. 109 CONNER DR, STE 1101 27514 #024-01-1952 L1952 FM *071 †18

JUDGE, Amy Murray. 101 MANNING DR, DEPT OF ANESTHESIOLOGY 27514 #020-12-2006 AN *012

JULIANO, Jonathan James. 130 MASON FARM RD, DIVISION OF INF. DISEASES 27599 #036-01-2001 L2005 ID *012 †20

KAESEMEYER, Wayne Harry. ■ 27517 #036-05-1978 L1979 CD *020 †20 ‡

KAFER, Enid Rosemary. 101 MANNING DR, UNC HOSPITALS 27514 #143-03-1961 L1973 AN PUD *050 †05

KAGETSU, Naomi Jayne. 891 WILLOW DR, STE 2 27514 #035-06-1986 L1995 D *020 †15

KAHL, Christina Ross. ■ 27517 #036-07-2004 L2008 MPD *012

KAHN, Kevin Alexander. UNC HOSPITALS, 3143 BIOINFORMATICS BUILDI 27599 #045-01-1992 L1996 N *020 †20

KAHNER, Steven. ■ 27517 #010-02-1968 L1992 OBG *071 †30

KAHWATI, Leila Catherine. ■ 27514 #041-12-1996 L1997 GPM *020 †70,18

KAMMEYER, Joel Aaron. ■ 27514 #038-40-2002 L2006 FM *012

KANDULA, Leena. ■ 27514 #495-50-1995 L2005 PG *100 †55

KANDZARI, David Edward. ■ 27517 #036-07-1995 L1999 CD *020 †20

KANE, William Jos. ■ 27517 #041-13-1969 L1974 FM *030 †18

KANG, Yubin. ■ 27516 #243-58-1985 L2005 HO *012 †20

KANNARKAT, Mily Joy. ■ 27516 #051-07-2006 IM *012

KARTHEISER, Paul Harlan. 101 MANNING DR, DEPT OF PSYCHIATRY UNC HOS 27514 #036-01-1997 L1998 P *020 †75

KARTHIKEYAN, Omkar. UNIVERSITY OF N CAROLINA S, CB #7593 27599 #025-01-2007 PD *012

KARVAZY, Eszter Sarolta. CB#7470 S-H-S BLDG, JAMES A TAYLOR STUDENT HEA 27599 #473-01-1972 L1983 EM IM *074 †22

KASTHURI, Raj S. ■ 27515 #495-37-1997 L2007 HO *100 †20

KATZ, Laurence Matthew. N E GRAVELLY DR., UNC CH EMERGENCY MEDICINE 27599 #033-06-1987 L1996 EM IM *020 †20,16

KATZNELSON, Jessica Haran. UNC-CH, CB #7220 27599 #035-48-1997 L2002 PD *020 †55

KAUFER, Daniel Ian. 3114 BIOINFORMATICS BLDG, CB#7025 27599 #056-05-1988 L2003 N *020 †12

KAUFFMAN, Abraham L. ■ 27517 #352-11-1936 L1938 FM OM *071

KAUFMAN, David Gordon. UNIV OF N CAROLINA SCHOOL, DEPT OF PATH 27514 #028-02-1968 L1975 ATP *050

KAUK, Justin Ryan. UNIV OF N CAROLINA SCH OF, 3114 BIOINFORMATICS BUILDI 27599 #028-03-2006 ORS *012

KEAGY, Blair Allen. 101 MANNING DR 27514 #041-12-1970 L1971 AS *020 †90,85

KEAGY, Kathleen E Salter. 205 SAGE RD STE 100, CHAPEL HILL PEDIATRICS PA 27514 #041-12-1970 L1971 PD PDC *020 †55

KEEFE, Bernadette. 101 MANNING DR, UNC HOSPITALS 27514 #035-01-1981 L1987 OS DR *020 †80

KEENER, Jay Donovan. BIOINFORMATICS BUILDING, CB# 7055 27599 #055-01-1998 L2004 ORS *020 †40

KEHRL, Howard Richard. 104 MASON FARM RD, US EPA HUMAN STUDEIS FAC 27599 #025-01-1977 L1980 PUD IM *050 †20

KEIFER, Anne Turner. UNC HOSPITALS, CB 7010 DEPT ANES 27599 #036-01-1979 L1998 AN *020 †05

KEIFER, John Conlon. ■ 27514 #036-01-1979 L1999 AN HEM *020 †50,05

KEITH, Charles Rush. 2131 MARIONS FORD RD 27516 #019-02-1957 L1963 CHP PYA *020 †75

KEKU, John K. ■ 27514 #690-07-1982 L1993 IM *020

KELLEY, Meera. 130 MASON FARM RD, CB#7030 27599 #038-44-1990 L1993 ID *020 †20

KELLY, Hanna Lines. ■ 27516 #041-01-2000 L2003 HO *100 †20

KENT, Richard Stephen. ■ 27516 #025-18-1975 L1981 CD IM *050 †20

KETTELKAMP, Donald Benj. ■ 27514 #018-03-1955 L1956 ORS *071 †40

KEYSERLING, Harold F. 101 MANNING DR, OGME ROOM 1107A 27514 #012-01-1999 L2002 RNR *100 †80 ‡

KEYSERLING, Thomas Chas. 5039 OLD CLINIC BLDG, CB# 7110 27599 #012-05-1982 L1985 IM GPM *020 †20

KHAN, Ahmed Mosharraf. ■ 27514 #036-01-2008 *012

KHAN, Anwaar Ahmed. 300B MCGREGOR DR 27514 #704-04-1974 L2007 GE CD *020 †20 ‡

KHAN, Raza Latif. ■ 27514 #550-04-2002 L2007 SME *100 †75

KHANDANI, Amir H. UNIV OF NC DEPT RAD, CB 7510 27599 #409-22-1992 L2003 NM *020 †28

KHANDELWAL, Anjay Kumar. ■ 27516 #496-34-1999 L2007 CCS *012 †85

KHERA, Naina. 101 MANNING DR CB7600, UNC HOSPS 27514 #045-01-2006 OBG *012

KIDD, Maureen Ann. ■ 27514 #016-01-2000 L2005 GS *100

KIES, Darren David. 101 MANNING DR, UNIV OF NC HOSPS 27514 #021-01-2006 DR *012

KILLENBERG, Susan Diaz. ■ 27514 #008-02-1992 L2005 P *020 †75

KIM, Sandra Chihyun. 200 MASON FARM RD, STE 7220 27514 #025-01-1994 L2001 PG *020 †55

KIRKMAN, Henry Neil, Jr. 513 MANNING DR, CB# 7595 WLM B ACICK BLDG 27599 #023-07-1952 L1965 PD MG *071 †55,19

KIRKPATRICK, Jennifer D. ■ 27516 #048-13-2004 L2008 AN *012

KISER, Margaret Ann. 101 MANNING DR, DEPT MED 27514 #036-01-1985 L1986 NEP IM *020 †20

KISER, Michelle. ■ 27516 #036-01-2007 GS *012

KISTNER, Robert Arthur. ■ 27517 #016-43-1953 L1954 *071

KIZER, Catherine Maud. ■ 27514 #036-01-2007 IM *012

KIZER, J Stephen. CB #7005, ROOM 3025 OLD CLINIC BLDG 27599 #036-07-1970 L1970 IM IMG *050 †20

KLAUBER, Samuel. ■ 27514 #869-02-1937 L1939 GP *071

KLEIN, Caroline Marie. 3114 BIOINFORAHICS, CAMPUS BOX 7025 27599 #048-02-1994 L2003 CN *020 †75

KLEIN, David Aryeh. 110 TIMBERHILL PL 27514 #036-01-1986 L1992 FM *020 †18

KLEIN, David Mendel. ■ 27517 #010-01-1953 L1994 NS *020 †25

KLEMMER, Philip John. ■ 27514 #041-13-1972 L1998 NEP IM *020 †20

KLIPSTEIN, Christopher A. BOX 7110, DIV OF GENERAL MEDICINE 27599 #035-45-1994 L1998 IM *020 †20

KNIGHT, Ashu Sabharwal. UNIV OF N CAROLINA SCH OF, CB7593 27599 #024-05-2002 L2006 PD *100 †55

KNOWLES, Michael Ray. 7011 THRUSTON BOWLES BLDG, CB 7248 27599 #036-01-1971 L1971 IM NEP *020 †20

KNOX, Mary Ann. ■ 27517 #012-01-2007 PD *012

KOCIS, Keith Christopher. 20160 2ND FLOOR 27599 #035-15-1987 L2000 CCP PDC *020 †55

KOEPKE, John Thomas. ■ 27516 #016-01-1990 L2005 CG *020 †18,19

KOHN, Geoffrey Paul. ■ 27514 #143-08-1997 L2007 *100

KOLLN, Karen Anne. 10011 DAVID STONE DR 27517 #018-03-2003 OTO OTO *012

KOMIVES, Eugenie Marie. ■ 27514 #024-01-1985 L1986 FM *020 †18

KONDRAD, Elin Curran. 101 MANNING DR, DEPT OF FAMILY CB7595 27514 #036-01-2004 FP *012

KOOMEN, Marcia Anne. 101 MANNING DR, UNC HOSP RADIOLOGY DEPT 27514 #036-01-1984 L1985 DR *040 †80

KOPP, Vincent Jos. CB# 7010, DEPARTMENT OF ANESTHESIOLO 27599 #036-01-1982 L1983 AN PD *020 †55,05

KORUDA, Mark Jos. BX 7210, UNC-SURG CAMPUS 27599 #008-01-1981 L1988 GS *020 †85

KOTCH, Jonathan Bruce. U OF N CAROLINA CB 7400, CB 7445 ROSENAU HALL 27599 #005-11-1973 L1976 PHP PD *040 †70,55

KOVATCH, Douglas James. 101 MANNING DR, CB# 7160 27514 #041-13-2003 L2006 P *100

KOWAL, Kathleen Tammara. ■ 27517 #033-05-1984 L2007 P *012 †18

KOZLOWSKI, Tomasz. 4022 BURNETT-WOMACK BLDG, CB#7211 27599 #759-03-1985 L2005 GS *100

KRASOVICH, Janelle Lynn. 940 MARTN LTHR KNG JR BLVD 27514 #056-06-2000 L2003 IM *020 †20

KRAYBILL, Ernest Nissley. UNC HOSPITALS, CB 7600 GEN CLNCL RESRCH 27599 #041-01-1962 L1964 **NPM PD** *071 †55

KROEGER, Christopher A. ■ 27516 #005-11-1996 L2007 **GS** *100

KRONHAUS, Alan Keith. ■ 27517 #024-05-1972 L1979 **OS IM** *030

KSHIRSAGAR, Abhijit V. UNIVERSITY OF N CAROLINA, DIVISION NEPHROLOGY 27599 #012-05-1993 L1996 **IM** *020 †20

KUHN, Deborah Anne. ■ 27517 #036-07-2007 **FP** *012

KUHNS, William Jos. COLONY APTS H 4 27514 #023-07-1948 L1977 **BBK HEM** *050

KUMAR, Gaurav. ■ #495-45-1996 L2005 **RNR** *100

KURTZ, Avrom L. 101 MANNING DR, UNIV OF NC HOSPS 27514 #007-02-2006 **N** *012

KURZ, James Eckhardt, Jr. 11312 US 15 501 HWY N, STE 308 27517 #028-03-1993 L1995 **MPD IM** *020 †55,20

KWAN, Mildred. ■ 27517 #012-05-2003 **AI** *012 †20

KYLSTRA, Jan Andrew. 1828 MARTN LTHR KNG JR, STE D14 27514 #036-07-1983 L1989 **OPH** *020 †35

KYLSTRA, Kimberly. 11312 US HIGHWAY 15 501 N, STE 308 27517 #036-01-1987 L1991 **IM PD** *020 †20,55

LABBOK, Miriam Harriet. ■ 27516 #021-01-1975 L1977 **GPM NTR** *050 †70

LACHIEWICZ, Paul F. 101 MANNING DR BLDG 229H 27514 #035-20-1977 L1983 **ORS** *050 †40

LACKEY, Robert Stevenson. ■ 27517 #041-02-1948 L1948 **DR FM** *071 †80

LACOUR, Jeffrey Brian. ■ 27517 #021-05-2003 L2004 **OTO** *012

LADNER, Keith Michael. ■ 27516 #007-02-2005 **OTO** *012

LAI-GOLDMAN, Myla P. ■ 27517 #035-01-1983 L1990 **PTH CLP** *020 †50

LAIL, Jennifer Lynn. 205 SAGE RD, CHAPEL HILL PEDIATRICS PA 27514 #020-12-1978 L1980 **PD** *020 †55

LAMANNA, Roger Weed. 940 MARTN LTHR KNG JR BLVD 27514 #051-04-1974 L1975 **NEP IM** *020 †20

LAMAY, Edward Norman. ■ 27514 #036-05-1988 L1991 **EM** *020 †16

LAMBA, Jaydeep J. 101 MANNING DR, UNIV OF NC HOSPS 27514 #045-04-2003 L2004 **PCC** *012 †20

LAMBERT, Nathan Destry. 101 MANNING DR 27514 #017-20-2003 L2006 **CD** *012 †20

LAMBERTSEN, Christian J, Jr. 7624 KENNEBEC DR, MERIDIANS & PARALLES 27517 #041-01-1976 L1984 **OM FM** *020 †18

LANE, John Weston. 120 CONNER DR STE 101 27514 #036-07-1972 L1976 **OBG** *020 †30

LANG, Stephen Norman. CAMPUS BOX 7055, UNC CHAPEL HILL 27599 #016-11-1965 L1966 **ORS** *020 †40

LANNON, Carole Marie. UNIV OF N CAROLINA, UNC CB #7226 27599 #026-04-1982 L1986 **PD** *040 †20,55

LARAMORE, Andrew Pace. ■ 27514 #012-05-2007 **PTH** *012

LARSON, James Lionel, Jr. 101 MANNING DR, UNC HOSPITALS 27514 #011-03-1993 L1997 **EM** *012 †16

LASSITER, Richard Edward. 120 CONNER DR 27514 #036-01-1965 L1965 **OBG** *020 †30

LASSITER, William Edmund. ■ 27517 #024-01-1954 L1954 **NEP IM** *071 †20

LAUDATE, James Darrell. ■ 27516 #036-01-2007 **IM** *012

LAUGHON, Matthew Maxwell. UNC HOSPITALS, CB #7596, 4TH FLOOR 27599 #051-01-1998 L1999 **NPM** *020 †55

LAVELLE, John P. 101 MANNING DR, 2ND FL MAIN HOSP 27514 #539-06-1984 L2000 **U** *020 †95

LAVENHOUSE, Clifton, Jr. UNC HOSPITAL, DEPT OF EMER MEDICINE 27599 #036-01-2001 L2004 **EM** *100

LA VIA, Maria Carmela. BOX 7160, UNIV NORTH CAROLINA 27599 #045-01-1991 L2005 **CHP OS** *020 †75

LAVINE, Leroy S. ■ 27517 #035-19-1943 L1949 **ORS** *072 †40

LEE, Eugene Eunsuk. 101 MANNING DR, CB7010 223 BURNETT-WOMACK 27514 #038-44-2002 L2004 **PAN** *100 †05

LEE, Joseph K T. CAMPUS BOX 7510, UNC SCHOOL OF MED 27599 #028-02-1973 L1991 **DR R** *020 †80

LEE, Justin Allen. ■ 27516 #036-01-2008 *012

LEE, Michael Young. CB #7200 1148 UNC-H 27599 #016-11-1984 L1994 **PM CN** *020 †60

LEE, Peter Hong. ■ 27516 #005-06-1974 L1997 **FM** *030 †18

LEE, Sean Michael. ■ 27517 #008-01-2005 **GS** *012

LEE, Yeon Hee. ■ 27516 #583-01-1986 L2004 *100

LEE, Yueh Zenas. 101 MANNING DR, CB 7510 27514 #036-01-2006 **DR** *012

LEHM, Jan Peters. 7010 BURNETT WOMACK-ANES 27599 #297-03-1984 L1995 **AN** *020

LEIGH, Margaret Warren. 130 MASON FARM RD, CAMPUS BOX #7220 27599 #051-07-1976 L1982 **ID PD** *050 †55

LEIGHT, William Derek. 101 MANNING DR, CB7070 27514 #036-01-2004 **OTO** *012

LEMASTERS, John Jay. NC SCH OF MED ANATOMY 27514 #023-07-1975 L1975 **OS** *050

LENGOWSKI, Kristin Louise. 101 MANNING DR 27514 #030-06-1981 L1989 **P PTH** *020 †75

LENIEK, Karyn Lynn. ■ 27516 #016-11-2005 L2005 **GPM** *012

LENTZ, Aaron Claude. ■ 27516 #036-01-2006 **GS** *100

LESESNE, Henry Roby. 101 MANNING DR 27514 #047-05-1967 L1971 **GE IM** *020 †20

LEUCHTMANN, Peter L. 110 S ESTES DR 27514 #017-20-1999 L2005 **VIR R** *020 †80

LEVINE, Amy Allen. ■ 27514 #051-04-1987 L1994 **PD** *020 †70,55

LEVINE, Daniel Israel. 143 W FRANKLIN ST, STE 202 27516 #869-02-1934 L1937 **ON** *075

LEVINE, Melvin David. 1450 RALEIGH RD, STE 100 27517 #024-01-1966 L1985 **PD** *030 †55

LEVINSON, Sidney Leonard. 940 AIRPORT RD 27514 #035-20-1974 L1977 **GE IM** *020 †20

LEVY, Robert Isaac. ■ 27516 #035-19-1947 L1956 **P** *050 †75

LEVY, Stanley B. 891 WILLOW DR, STE 1 27514 #010-02-1971 L1974 **D** *020 †15

LEWIS, Carmen L. 5039 OLD CLINIC BLDG, CB 7110 UNIV OF NORTH CARO 27599 #048-12-1988 L1997 **GPM** *012

LEWIS, Eric Ward. ■ 27517 #025-01-1978 L1981 **ID IM** *050 †20

LEWIS, Kristi Anne. 101 MANNING DR, CB#7593 27514 #021-01-2005 **PD** *012

LEWIS, Matthew Craig. ■ 27516 #036-01-2008 *012

LIANG, Yinghua. ■ 27516 #243-32-1985 L2007 **IM** *020 †20

LICHTMAN, Steven Nathan. 200 MASON FARM RD, STE 7220 27514 #065-01-1978 L1985 **PD GE** *020 †15

LILES, Edmund Allen, Jr. CB# 7593 27599 #036-01-1996 L1997 **MPD** *020 †20,55

LIM, Moe. ■ 27516 #024-01-1999 L2005 **ORS** *100 †40

LIN, Rosalind Hweimei. 101 MANNING DR 27514 #047-05-2002 L2004 **P** *020 †55

LINDEN, Thomas Robt. ■ 27514 #005-02-1977 L1978 **CHP P** *020

LINDSEY, Byron Anthony. CB # 7160, MANNING DR, PSYCHIATRY DEPT/UNC-CH 27599 #036-08-1984 L1987 **P** *020 †75

LINDSEY, Julie Evelyn Nie. 101 CONNER DR, STE 402 27514 #036-01-2001 L2005 **FM** *020 †18

LINENGER, Jerry M. ■ 27514 #025-07-1981 L1987 **GPM AM** *050 †70

LINGLEY, Lauren Hoskins. 513 MANNING DR, CB 7595 27599 #036-01-1995 L1998 **FM** *020 †18

LININGER, Ruth Anne. BRINKHOUS-BULLETT CB #7525, DEPT PATHOLOGY & LAB MED 27599 #036-01-1990 L1994 **PTH PHP** *020 †50

LINTHAVONG, Kanhka. ■ 27517 #036-01-2008 *012

LIPPER, Steven. ■ 27517 #024-05-1972 L1973 **P PA** *071

LIPTZIN, Myron Bennett. ■ 27514 #035-45-1959 L1965 **P** *020 †75

LITALIEN, Anita Jo. CB 7594, GR FL NEUROS BLDG 27599 #003-01-2003 L2006 **EM** *100 †16

LIU, Guifen Gloria. 101 MANNING DR 27514 #243-64-1983 L1999 **PM** *020 †60

LIVASY, Chad Allen. ■ 27599 #018-03-1993 L1998 **PCP** *020 †50

LOCHOW, Steven Charles. ■ 27517 #055-02-2002 L2007 **ORS** *020

LODA, Frank A, Jr. UNC MEDICAL SCHOOL, DEPT PEDIATRICS 27514 #047-05-1960 L1964 **PD** *050

LOEHR, James Paul. UNIV OF N CAROLINA, CB #7220 27599 #028-02-1981 L1991 **PDC PD** *020 †55

LOH, Yenlin Judith. FAMILY RACTICE CENTER, CB 7586 27599 #041-14-2003 L2004 **FM** *100

LOHR, Jacob Andrew. 130 MASON FARM RD, UNIV NC CAMPUS BOX 7220 S 27599 #036-01-1967 L1967 **PD OS** *050 †55

LONG, Walker Anderson. 245 INDIAN TRAIL RD 27514 #036-01-1976 L1976 **PDC NPM** *050 †55

LONGNECKER, Matthew Paul. ■ 27516 #032-01-1981 L1982 **PHP NTR** *050 †20

LONGPHRE, Johnpaul Morgan. ■ 27516 #036-01-2003 L2006 **GPM** *020

LONGPHRE, Kaori Miyata. N2201 UNC HOSPITALS, DEPARTMENT OF ANESTHESIA, 27599 #572-58-2001 L2006 **APM** *020 †05

LOPEZ, Fernando Alonzo. ■ 27516 #023-01-2000 L2007 **EM** *100 †20,16

LOSKEN, H Wolfgang. CAMPUS BOX 7195, 7040 BURNETT-WOMACK BUILDI 27599 #836-02-1963 L2001 **PS** *020

LOTZ, Ruth Johanna. 507 HIGHGROVE DR 27516 #036-05-1999 L2002 **PD** *020 †55

LOVE, Pamela Denise. CB #7470, CAMPUS HLTH SERVICES 27599 #036-01-1988 L1989 **FM** *020 †18

LOWRY, Cheryl Jones. ■ 27517 #036-01-2005 L2008 **IM** *012

LUCAS, Dayna E Baerncopf. ■ 27514 #035-19-1972 L1975 **PD** *020 †55

LUCAS, Miha S. ■ 27514 #001-02-1999 L2002 **EM** *020 †16

LUCAS, Warner Jos. 101 MANNING DR, UNC HOSPITALS 27514 #011-03-1983 L1986 **AN** *020 †05

LUGO, Aida M. 130 MASON FARM RD 27599 #042-01-1984 L2007 **D** *020 †15 ‡

LUO-TSENG, Ingrid. 101 CONNER DR STE 200 27514 #033-06-1999 L2003 **PM** *100 †60 ‡

LURY, Kenneth Michael. CB #7510, 2000C OLD CLINIC 27599 #028-34-1979 L1993 **RNR** *020 †80

LUSKEY, Mary Jeanne. ■ 27516 #023-01-2002 L2002 **PD** *100

LUTZ, Melissa Mc Intire. ■ 27514 #036-01-1994 **PD** *100

LUYANDO, Yvonne. 109 CONNER DR, STE 1101 27514 #035-01-1984 L1990 **FM** *020 †18

LYKOPOULOU, Stella. 101 MANNING DR 27514 #418-02-1972 **PD PHP** *050

LYLES, Johnnie Deforrest. ■ 27514 #036-01-2007 **GS** *012

LYNCH, Andrew Keane. 101 MANNING DR, #7200 RM 1181 1ST FL MAIN 27514 #051-07-2002 L2006 **PM** *012

LYNN, Thomas Edward. ■ 27516 #010-02-1987 L1989 **FM** *020 †18

MACFARLAND, Joseph Alfred. 101 MANNING DR 27514 #035-01-1967 L1971 **IM GP** *020

MACKAY, Karin A. CB #7155, 7015D BURNETT-WOMACK BUILD 27599 #048-02-1999 L2002 **NEP** *020 †55

MACKLIN, Daniel Mark. CB# 7220 BIOINFORMATICS, DEPT. OF PEDIATRICS 27599 #017-20-1994 L1998 **GPM** *020 †55

MACKLIN, Michael Neal. 101 CLOISTER CT, STE C 27514 #023-01-1978 L1979 **P PYA** *020 †75

MADANICK, Ryan David. UNIV OF NORTH CAROLINA, CB 7080 BIOINFORMATIC 4142 27599 #011-02-1998 L2006 **GE** *030 †20

MADDEN, Margaret R Harte. ■ 27514 #035-09-1943 L1967 **P** *071

MADDEN, Thomas James. ■ 27514 #016-02-1944 L1952 **PTH** *071 †50

MADISON, Donald Lewis. ■ 27516 #005-12-1965 L1969 **FM GPM** *020

MALANGA, C J. ■ 27599 #055-01-1997 L2004 **CHN** *020

MALENBAUM, Joshua Hale. ■ 27514 #041-01-2006 L2006 **AN** *012

MALIK, Rajesh Kumar. ■ 27514 #917-10-1981 L1991 **PHO PD** *020 †55

MALKIN, Morton David. 940 MARTN LTHR KNG JR BLVD 27514 #016-42-1987 L2000 **IM** *020 †20

MALLOY, Erin Marie. 110 MANNING DR, DEPT OF PSYCHIATRY CB 7160 27599 #011-03-1993 L1998 **P CHP** *020 †20

MALOUF, Nadia Najla. 101 MANNING DR 27514 #605-01-1962 L1970 **PTH OS** *020 †50

MALTBIE, Allan Armstrong. 109 CONNER DR, BUILDING #3, STE 203 27514 #012-05-1969 L1973 **P PYA** *020 †75

MANDEL, Stanley Robert. ■ 27599 #051-01-1962 L1969 **GS TS** *030 †85,90

MANICKAM, Kandamurugu. ■ 27514 #539-06-2002 L2006 **MG** *012 †20

MANIK, Christopher Paul. 5039 OLD CLINIC BUILDING, CAMPUS BOX 7110 27599 #041-01-1989 L2006 **IM** *020 †20

MANIKUMAR, Arun. ■ 27517 #036-01-2003 L2005 **EM** *020 †16

MANN, Elizabeth Sprague. 101 MANNING DR, UNC HOSPITALS 27514 #035-20-1969 L1976 **AN PD** *030 †05

MANN, John Douglas. 751 BURNETT WOMACK BLVD, CB 7025 UNC CAMPUS 27599 #035-20-1969 L1976 **N** *050 †75

MANNING, James Elbert. CAMPUS BOX 7594, DEPT OF EMERG MED 27599 #036-01-1985 L1989 **EM** *050 †16

MARDER, Amanda Lauren. 101 MANNING DR, CAMPUS BOX 7600 27514 #011-02-2002 L2004 **OBG** *100

MARGOLIS, David Michael. CB #7435, 3302 MICHAEL HOOKER RESEAR 27599 #024-07-1985 L2005 **ID IM** *050 †20

MARGOLIS, Lewis Harvey. ■ 27517 #016-02-1974 L1979 **PD PHP** *050 †55

MARGOLIS, Peter Adam. 201 SILVER CEDAR CT 27514 #035-19-1980 L1987 **PD PHP** *050 †55

MARKEWICH, Stephen Dougla. 101 MANNING DR 27514 #661-02-2005 **AN** *012

MARKOWITZ, Samuel Nachman. 101 MANNING DR DEPT OPH 27514 #550-01-1973 L1984 **OPH** *020 †35

MARQUESS, Joel Stephen. ■ 27514 #036-01-2008 *012

MARSHALL, Allen Fletcher. ■ 27516 #036-01-2004 **OTO** *012

MARSHALL, Diane Duvall. CB #7596, 4TH FLOOR, DEPT OF PEDS/NEONATAL 27599 #036-05-1991 L1995 **NPM** *020 †55

MARSHALL, Francies. ■ 27517 #035-06-1946 L1973 **OS PD** *071 †55

MARSTON, William Arnold. UNIV OF NC DEPT VACCULAR S, 3024 BURNETT WOMACK BLDG 27599 #051-01-1988 L1993 **VS** *020 †85

MARTIN, Holly Renee. 1450 RALEIGH RD, STE 100 27517 #020-12-2001 L2004 **DBP** *012 †55

MARTIN, Victor N. 725 AIRPORT RD STE 300 27514 #913-06-1970 L1983 **DR** *020

■ = Address Information Privacy Protected

MARTIN, William Frederick. ■ 27514 #054-04-1986 L1988 **AN** *020 †85

MARTINELLI, Susan Marie. N2201 UNC HOSPITAL, CB 7010 27599 #056-05-2003 L2007 **ACA** *012

MASSING, Mark Wayne. ■ 27516 #036-07-1994 *100

MASZKIEWICZ, Amy C. 503 TINKERBELL RD 27517 #041-12-1997 L2003 **NM** *100 †80,28

MATHAN, Satish. 601 WESTMINSTER DR 27514 #056-06-1999 L2002 **VIR** *100 †80

MATHEIS, Patricia Ann. 101 MANNING DR, OGMEROOM 1107-A 27514 #007-02-2002 L2004 **D** *100

MATHEWS, Stephanie Peters. 101 MANNING DR 27514 #045-04-2005 L2007 **PTH** *012

MATHUR, Sameer. ■ 27517 #041-01-1999 L2005 **OSS** *020 †40

MATHYS, Kenneth Clifford. ■ 27517 #038-06-2004 L2008 **OPH** *012

MATTERN, William Douglas. 513 MANNING DR, CB# 7595 WLM B ACICK BLDG 27599 #035-01-1965 L1973 **NEP IM** *030 †20

MATTSON, Gerri Lynn. 402 STONEHILL RD, ABC PEDIATRICS OF DUNN PA 27516 #051-04-1993 L1999 **PD** *020 †55

MAURO, Matthew A. CB 7510, UNIV OF NORTH CAROLINA 27599 #035-20-1977 L1978 **VIR DR** *020 †80

MAXWELL, Jeffry Christoph. ■ 27514 #036-07-2008 *012

MAYER, David Crisler. 101 MANNING DR, UNC HOSPITALS 27514 #021-01-1986 L1991 **AN** *020 †05

MAYGARDEN, Susan Jane B. MANNING DRIVE 27514 #051-04-1983 L1987 **ATP PCP** *020 †50

MC CAFFREY, Martin John. ■ 27516 #035-03-1986 L2006 **NPM** *020 †55

MC CARTNEY, Cheryl D F. CB# 7000, 4068 BONDURANT HALL 27599 #016-06-1971 L1976 **P OBG** *040 †75

MC CARTNEY, William Hugh. 101 MANNING DR 27514 #016-06-1969 L1976 **NM DR** *020 †80,28

MC CLAFFERTY, Hilary H. 611 CHURCHILL DR 27517 #025-01-1986 L2005 **PD** *020 †55

MCCLUNE, Jason Roberts. ■ 27514 #012-01-2006 **IM** *012

MC CLURE, Robert Kevin. 7160 UNC DEPT OF PSYCHIATR 27599 #054-04-1993 L2007 **P** *020 †75

MC CLURE, Sara Courts. ■ 27517 #036-05-1951 L1951 **P GP** *071 †18

MC COY, Marshall Clarke. 101 MANNING DR, UNIV NC DEPT EM 27514 #036-08-1984 L1985 **EM** *020 †16

MC CUTCHAN, James Hutton. CB #7470 SHS BLDG, UNC STUDENT HLTH SERVICEA 27599 #023-07-1961 L1962 **IM** *071

MCDONALD, Morgan Fitz. 1838 MARTN LTHR KNG JR, STE B19 27514 #047-05-2003 L2007 **MPD** *100 †20,55

MC DONNELL, Wm Foskey, III. ■ 27514 #028-02-1977 L1978 **GPM PHP** *050

MC FADDEN, Cornell I. ■ 27514 #035-19-1943 **GYN** *071 †30

MC FARLANE, Claude. 101 MANNING DR, UNC HOSPITALS 27514 #036-01-1983 L1996 **AN** *020 †05

MC GANN, Kathleen Anne. ■ 27516 #041-01-1985 L2006 **PD** *050 †55

MC GEE, Janey Roxanna. ■ 27599 #036-01-2001 L2006 **AN** *100 †55

MC GUINNESS, Gail A G. 111 SILVER CEDAR CT, AMERICAN BOARD PEDIATRICS 27514 #024-07-1972 L1973 **NPM PD** *030 †55

MCGUIRE, Rachel Knight. ■ 27514 #021-01-1993 L2001 **PD** *020 †55

MC HUTCHISON, John Geo. ■ 27517 #143-02-1981 L2002 *020

MC ILWAIN, David Lee. 101 MANNING DR, DPT PHYS 27514 #028-02-1964 L1964 **OS** *050

MC INTYRE, Donald K. ■ 27514 #041-09-1943 L1972 **FM** *071

MC KAY, Cecilia Smith. 101 CONNER DR, STE 402 27514 #012-22-1987 L1997 **IM** *020 †20

MC KENZIE, Edward B, Jr. MANNING DR ANES 27514 #036-01-1985 L1986 **AN** *020 †05

MC LEAN, Samuel Allen. CAMPUS BOX 7594, DEPARMENT OF EMERGENCY MED 27599 #025-01-1995 L2007 **EM** *020 †20,16

MC LELLAND, Robert. CB 7510, UNC-RADIOLOGY 27599 #038-41-1948 L1972 **R** *040 †80

MC LENDON, Wm Woodard. 513 MANNING DR, CB# 7595 WLM B ACICK BLDG 27599 #036-01-1956 L1956 **CLP PTH** *071 †50

MC LEOD, Malcolm Noell. 901 WILLOW DR STE 3 27514 #036-01-1965 L1965 **PYA** *020

MC MILLAN, Campbell W. 101 MANNING DR 27514 #036-05-1952 L1952 **HEM ON** *071 †55

MC PHAIL, Lindsee Ellen. ■ 27516 #036-01-2003 **GS** *012

MCRACKAN, Daniel Ian. UNIV OF N CAROLINA DIV OF, 2140 BIOINFORMATICS BLDG C 27599 #045-01-2004 **GS** *100

MCWILLIAMS, Andrew David. ■ 27514 #036-01-2008 *012

MEARS, Gregory D. UNC DEPT OF EM CB #7594 27599 #028-46-1985 L1986 **EM** *020 †16

MEEKER, James Edwardweeks. UNIV OF N CAROLINA SCH OF, 3314 BIOINFORMATICS BUILDI 27599 #036-01-2005 **ORS** *012

MEHROTRA, Abhishek. NEUROSCIENCE HOSP CB #7594, DEPT OF EMGY MED 27599 #038-40-2000 L2003 **EM** *020 †16 ‡

MEHTA, Shyam Parsram. ■ 27517 #495-08-1961 L1973 **IM NEP** *071

MELENDEZ, Nydia Margarita. CB 7025, 3114 BIOINFORMATICS BLDG 27599 #042-01-1997 L2000 **N** *020 †75

MELIONES, Jon Nicholas. CB 7220, UNIVERSITY OF NORTH CAROLI 27599 #024-07-1984 L1992 **PDC PD** *020 †55

MELONE, George Anthony, Jr. 1800 E FRANKLIN ST STE 8 27514 #016-43-1986 L1988 **EM GS** *020

MELTON, M Stephen. ■ 27517 #016-43-2002 L2007 **AN** *100 †05

MELTZER, Eric Barrie. ■ 27516 #035-08-2000 L2007 **PCC** *100 †20

MELTZER-BRODY, Samantha E. CB#7160 UNC AT CHAPEL HILL, DEPARTMENT OF PSYCHIATRY 27599 #016-06-1996 L1997 **P** *020 †75

MELVILLE, Mary Lou. 123 KINGSTON DR STE 105 27514 #048-02-1971 L1981 **P** *075 †75

MENDELSOHN, Ronald Edward. ■ 27514 #023-01-1953 L1984 **AN** *072 †05

MENDES, Robert R. 210 BURNETT WOMACK, CB 7212 27599 #011-02-1996 L2001 **VS** *020 †85

MENDIVIL, Alberto. ■ 27514 #049-01-2003 L2005 **OBG** *100

MENG, Aaron Gavin. 101 MANNING DR, CB # 7160 27514 #033-06-2003 L2006 **CHP** *012

MENGE, Michael Scott. ■ 27514 #025-07-1960 L1961 **OTO** *071 †45

MENSH, Maurice. ■ 27517 #010-01-1939 L1940 **IM GE** *071 †20

MEREDITH, Travis Ashby. CB #7040, 617 BURNETT-WOMACK BUILDIN 27599 #023-07-1969 L2000 **OPH** *040 †35

MERRITT, Bradley Gene. 101 MANNING DR, OGMEROOM 1107-G 27514 #036-01-2005 L2007 **D** *012

MERRITT, Kathy Ann. 205 SAGE RD, CHAPEL HILL PEDIATRICS PA 27514 #036-07-1985 L1990 **PD** *020 †55

MESSENHEIMER, John A, Jr. 101 MANNING DR 27514 #023-07-1970 L1978 **N IM** *020 †75

MESSER, Hannah Imwold. ■ 27516 #045-01-2007 **PM** *012

MESSER, William Brogdon. ■ 27516 #036-01-2006 **IM** *012

MEYER, Anthony Andrew. CB 7050, UNC DEPT OF SURGERY 27599 #016-02-1977 L1985 **GS OS** *030 †85

MEYERS, Karen Veneri. ■ 27517 #036-05-1995 L2003 **AN** *05

MEYERS, Michael Owen. 3010 OLD CLINIC BLDG, CB 7213 27599 #036-05-1995 L2003 **GS** *020 †85

MIDDENDORF, Heidi Elise. 180 PROVIDENCE RD, STE 5 27514 #038-43-1988 L1990 **P CHP** *020 †75

MILANO, Peter M. 103 MASON FARM RD, CB #7052 27599 #035-03-2001 L2004 **GS** *012

MILES, Paul Vernon. 111 SILVER CEDAR CT 27514 #005-14-1972 L1975 **PD** *062 †55

MILL, Michael Robt. UNC-CH CB# 7065, 3040 BURNETT-WOMACK BLDG. 27599 #007-02-1980 L1988 **TS** *040 †85,90

MILLER, Aaron Joel. 1838 MARTN LTHR KNG JR, STE B-19 27514 #041-01-1996 L1997 **IM** *020 †20

MILLER, Ann Elizabeth. ■ 27517 #036-07-1987 L2007 **OBG** *020 †30

MILLER, Arlene Nichols. 101 CONNER DR STE 302, LUTHERAN FMLY SVCS ACT TM 27514 #036-01-1993 L1995 **P** *020

MILLER, Cecil Arden. ■ 27514 #008-01-1948 L1969 **PHP PD** *040

MILLER, Christopher Ryan. 920 BRINKHOUS-BULLITT, BOX 7525 27599 #001-02-2002 L2007 **NP** *100

MILLER, Paula Freeman. 940 MARTN LTHR KNG JR BLVD 27514 #036-01-1983 L1984 **CD IM** *020 †20

MILLER, Thomas M. CB 7110 5039 OLD CLINIC 27599 #036-01-1977 L1977 **IM IMG** *020,55

MILLER, William Clarence. UNC CHAPEL HILL, CB# 7435; 2105F MCGAVRAN 27599 #023-07-1985 L1994 **ID EP** *050 †20

MILLS, Kyle Charles. ■ 27516 #036-01-2008 *012

MIN, Sherene Shakib. CB #7030, UNC SCHL OF MED, 4TH FLOOR BIOINFORMATICS B 27599 #036-01-1997 L2000 **ID** *020 †20

MINOGUE, Michael Francis. ■ 27516 #036-07-1991 L1998 **IM EM** *020 †16,20

MINOZZI, Michael Francis. 301 KILDAIRE RD, STE 200 27516 #035-46-1999 L2002 **PD** *020 †55

MITTELSTAEDT, Carol Ann. CB 75101 MAC NIDER, UNC SCHOOL OF MEDICINE 27599 #004-01-1971 L1976 **R NM** *062 †80

MOHAN, Siva Bhatlapenumar. 130 MASON FARM RD, CB# 7075 27599 #654-01-2000 L2003 **IC** *020 †20

MOLINA, Paul Lee. UNIV OF NC SCH MED, CAMPUS BOX 7510 DEPT DR 27599 #036-01-1983 L1984 **DR** *020 †80

MOLL, Stephan. 101 MANNING DR 27514 #409-05-1986 L1999 **HO** *020 †20

MONAHAN, Elizabeth Gomba. 727 EASTOWNE DR STE 200A 27514 #051-01-1990 L1994 **OBG** *020 †30

MONAHAN, Paul Edward, II. PEDIATRICS, HEMATOLOGY/ONC, CB #7220, 418 MACNIDER BLD 27599 #051-01-1990 L1996 **PHO** *020 †55

MONGE, Maria Claire. ■ 27514 #016-06-2007 **MPD** *012

MONROE, John Thaddeus, Jr. 1100 FRANKLIN SQ 27514 #036-01-1955 L1955 **P PYA** *071 †75

MONROE, Rasheeda Taliah. 101 MANNING DR, CB #7593 27514 #036-08-2005 L2008 **PD** *012

MONTEITH, Charles Walton. 1765 DOBBINS DR 27514 #005-02-1997 L2000 **OBG** *020 †30

MOODY, Rex Jason. 194 FINLEY GOLF COURSE RD, STE 7 27517 #036-01-1987 L1988 **P** *020 †75

MOORE, Louis Patterson. 109 CONNER DR, BLDG 3 27514 #048-02-1966 L1969 **P CHP** *020

MORETZ, Rebecca Lee. ■ 27516 #036-01-2005 L2006 **P** *012

MORGAN, Charles Michael. ■ 27517 #036-01-2008 L2012 *012

MORGAN, Douglas Robt. CB 7080, 726 BURNETTE WOMACK BLDGIN 27599 #038-06-1991 L1996 **GE IM** *020 †20

MORGAN, Lynne R. 1838 MARTN LTHR KNG JR 27514 #038-06-1991 L1996 **PD** *020 †55

MORGAN, Stephanie Shannon. ■ 27517 #036-01-2008 *012

MORILLAS, Hilda Nizzet. 101 MANNING DR 27514 #011-03-2003 L2006 **PCC** *012 †20

MORRELL, Dean Scott. 130 MASON FARM RD 27599 #036-01-1997 L1998 **D** *020 †15

MORRIS, David Eric. 101 MANNING DRIVE, NC CLINICAL CANCER CENTER 27599 #010-02-1994 L1995 **RO** *020 †80

MORRIS, Margaret Reiner. 301 KILDAIRE RD, STE 200 27516 #036-01-1993 L1996 **PD** *020 †55

MORRIS, Shannon Renae. 3009 OLD CLINIC BLDG, CB# 7305 27599 #038-06-2002 L2005 **HO** *012 †20

MORRIS, Tammy Lynn. ■ 27516 #036-08-2004 L2007 **PD** *020 †05

MORROW, Jason David. ■ 27516 #048-02-2004 L2007 **IM** *020 †20

MORTON, Christopher W. 205 SAGE RD, CHAPEL HILL PEDIATRICS PA 27514 #016-45-1997 L2001 **PD** *020 †55

MOSHESH, Malana Keiko. 1765 DOBBINS DR, PLANNED PARENTHOOD 27514 #010-03-1997 L2001 **OBG** *020 †30

MOSS, Nancy Christina. UNIV OF N CAROLINA SCH OF, 182 WING D, CB #7228 27599 #010-01-2003 **GS** *012

MOUNCE, Genevieve Patman. ■ 27516 #048-13-2002 L2006 **PAN** *012 †05

MUELLER, Robert Arthur. 101 MANNING DR, DEPT ANES 27514 #026-04-1965 L1971 **AN CD** *020 †05

MUENZER, Joseph. 101 MANNING DR, UNC HOSPITALS 27514 #038-06-1979 L1993 **PDE** *020 †55,19

MUHLEBACH, Marianne. BIO INFORMATICS CB 7220, UNC CHAPEL HILL PEDS 27599 #154-07-1988 L1999 **PD PDP** *020 †55

MUKHERJI, Suresh Kumar. 101 MANNING DR, UNC HOSPITALS 27514 #010-02-1987 L1994 **DR** *020 †20

MULCRONE, Daniel Patrick. ■ 27516 #036-01-2008 L2008 *012

MULKERN, Anne M. 109 CONNER DR, # 111-106 27514 #010-01-1986 L1991 **P** *020

MULLIS, Neal Thos. ■ 27514 #012-01-1979 L1988 **IM** *020

MUNNIS, Holly Noel. ■ 27517 #045-01-2005 **AN** *012

MUNOZ, Maria Cristina. 4015 OLD CLINIC BUILDING, UNIV OF N.C. CB 7570 27599 #005-02-1988 L1994 **OBG D** *020 †30

MUNRO, Andrew David. ■ 27514 #036-07-2008 *012

MUNSAT, Karen Marie. 180 PROVIDENCE RD STE 5, CHAPEL HILL PSYCH PA 27514 #038-43-1990 L1993 **CHP P** *020 †75

MURAYAMA, Shigeo. 101 MANNING DR 27514 #572-03-1979 L1991 **NP** *020

MURDOCH, David Martin. 19 FRANCES ST 27517 #045-01-1999 L2003 **PCC** *100 †20

MURPHY, Myrlin Lee. 7470 UNIVERSITY OF NC, UNIVERSITY OF NC 27599 #036-01-1982 L1983 **P** *020 †75

MURPHY, Timothy Daniel. ■ 27516 #036-01-2008 *012

MURROW, Richard Wm. 3114 BIOINFORMATICS BLDG, NEUROLOGY DEPARTMENT 27599 #019-02-1985 L2003 **N IM** *020 †75 ‡

MYERSON, Andrew Abraham. 1829 E FRANKLIN ST, STE 1200D 27514 #005-19-1986 L1990 **P** *020 †75

NADEAU, Denise A. UNC SCHOOL OF MEDICINE, DEPT OF OB/GYN, 27599 #035-48-1976 L1996 **OBG** *020 †30

NAFTEL, Albert J, Jr. 101 MANNING DR, CAMPUS BOX 7160 27514 #001-02-1986 L1988 **P** *020 †75

NAFTEL, Herman Aronov. ■ 27516 #036-01-2008 *012

NAGASE, Daniel. 101 MANNING DR # 722, UNIVERSITY OF NORTH CAROLI 27514 #064-01-2004 **GS** *100

NANDA, Monika. UNIV NORTH CAROLINA HOSP, CB 7010 N2201 27599 #495-93-1999 L2006 **AN** *100 †05

NEBEL, William Arthur. 110 CONNER DR, STE 4 27514 #036-01-1962 L1962 **OBG** *020 †30

NEISH, Donald Dewitt. ■ 27517 #041-13-1958 L1974 **IM IMG** *071 †20

NELSON, Amanda E. UNC CAMPUS BOX #7280, 3300 THURSTON BLDG, MANNIN 27599 #047-05-2002 L2006 **RHU** *012 †20

NEURINGER, Isabel Penny. MANNING DRIVE, UNC HOSPITAL 101 27599 #010-01-1989 L1993 **PCC** *020 †20

NEWTON, Terel Spencer. 101 MANNING DR, DEPT OF ANESTHESIOLOGY 27514 #036-01-2006 **AN** *012

NEWTON, Warren Polk. UNIVERSITY OF N CAROLINA, CAMPUS BOX 7595 MANNING DR 27599 #016-06-1984 L1986 **FM** *030 †18

NG, Jakun Willard. ■ 27514 #036-01-2008 *012

NG-CASHIN, Judith F. 130 MASON FARM RD # 7030, UNIV OF NORTH CAROLINA 27599 #016-01-1994 L1998 **ID** *020 †20

NICHOLAS, Kremer Barr. UNIV OF N CAROLINA SCH OF, 520 OLD INFIRMARY/CB7510 27599 #004-01-2004 **DR** *012

NICHOLAS, Linda Meredith. 101 MANNING DR RM 10300, DEPT P CB #7160 NEURO SCI 27514 #036-01-1991 L1992 **P** *020 †75

NICHOLLS, John Capehart. 101 MANNING DR, DEPT OF PSY CB#7160 10625 27514 #036-01-2004 L2007 **CHP** *012

NICHOLS, Timothy Chas. 130 MASON FARM RD, CB# 7075 27599 #051-04-1978 L1981 **CD IM** *020 †20

NICKELEIT, Volker. ■ 27599 #409-12-1985 L2000 **PTH** *020 †50

NIEMAN, Lynn Marie. N2201 UNC HOSP, DEPT OF ANES 27599 #038-40-2001 L2006 **AN** *020 †05

NISHIKAWA, Brett Ryan. ■ 27514 #023-12-1999 L2000 **GPM** *012

NOAH, Terry Lee. 130 MASON FARM RD, CAMPUS BOX #7220 27599 #025-01-1985 L1989 **PDP** *050 †55

NOBLE, Paul Wesley. ■ 27517 #035-19-1984 L2006 **PUD IM** *020 †20

NOE, Frances Elsie. ■ 27514 #050-02-1954 L1956 **AN OS** *071

NONOY, Nathaniel Paul. 225 BLUEFIELD RD 27517 #005-12-2002 L2005 **PAN** *012 †05

NOONE, Peadar Gerard. 724 BURNETT WOMACK CB 7020, DIV OF PULMONARY DISEASES 27599 #539-05-1983 L1994 **PCC** *020 †20

NORFLEET, Edward Alvin. 101 MANNING DR, UNC HOSPITALS 27514 #036-01-1970 L1970 **AN** *020 †05

NOVIKOVA, Nadiya. 101 MANNING DR, UNIV OF NC HOSP 27514 #913-97-1994 **P** *012

NOVOTNY, Debra Budwit. ■ 27517 #036-01-1986 L1989 **PTH** *020 †50

NUSSBAUM, Abraham Michael. 101 MANNING DR, OGMEROOM 1107-G 27514 #036-01-2004 L2007 **P** *012

NUZUM, Claude Thos. DEPT. OF MEDICINE, CB#7185, SCHOOL OF MEDICINE 27599 #024-01-1964 L1975 **GE IM** *040 †20

O'BIEN, Jennifer Anne. UNIV OF N CAROLINA SCH OF, 3018 OLD CLINIC BLDG CB 76 27599 #054-04-2006 **IM** *012

O'CONNOR, Wendi Gayle. ■ 27516 #045-01-2006 L2006 **NM** *012

OH, John Namki. 101 MANNING DR, UNC HOSPITALS 27514 #041-13-1994 L2006 **PM** *020 †60

OH, Stacie Hayley. ■ 27514 #019-02-2006 **AN** *012

O'KEEFE, Edward John. UNIV NC AT CHAPEL HILL, STE 3100 CB 7287 27599 #008-01-1966 L1978 **D** *050 †15

OLCOTT, Christopher W. CB #7055, CB #7055 27599 #035-45-1991 L2001 **ORS** *020 †40

OLDACH, David Wm. ■ 27516 #023-01-1986 L1988 **ID IM** *020 †20

OLDHAM, H Newland. ■ 27517 #048-04-1961 L1966 **TS** *062 †85,90

OLLILA, David Wm. 3010 OLD CLINIC BLDG, DEPT OF SURG CB #7213 27599 #038-41-1990 L1998 **GS SO** *085

OLNEY, John M, Jr. ■ 27514 #024-01-1947 L1955 **GS** *020 †85

OLNEY, Mary Susan. ■ 27514 #005-14-1982 L1986 **PTH** *074 †50

OLSEN, Brian Stevens. 20160 WH CB 7221, 101 MANNING DRIVE 27599 #019-02-2002 L2007 **CCP** *012 †55

OLUSESI, Olusegun Olaleka. ■ 27510 #036-01-2008 *012

OMRAN, Abdel Rahim. 101 MANNING DR 27514 #330-02-1952 **PHP OS** *050

O'NEAL, Brian Vaughn. 101 MANNING DR, DEPT EM 27514 #033-06-2007 **EM** *012

ONTJES, David Ainsworth. UNIV OF NCAROLINA, 257 MACNIDER 27599 #024-01-1964 L1969 **IM END** *020 †20

ORDRONNEAU, Victoria Rink. ■ 27516 #036-01-1992 *075

ORLANDO, Roy. 103 MASON FARM RD # 70, RM 7312C 27599 #010-02-1968 L1971 **GE** *050 †20

ORLOWSKI, Marian. ■ 27517 #759-10-1952 **PA GP** *050

ORLOWSKI, Robert Zygmunt. MASON FARM RD LCCC 22-003, CB # 7295 27599 #008-01-1991 L1998 **ON IM** *020 †20

ORRINGER, Eugene Paul. DEANS OFFICE, SCH OF MED CB #7000 27599 #041-12-1969 L1971 **HEM IM** *030 †20

OSSI, Michael Jos. 101 MANNING DR, UNC HOSPITALS 27514 #023-01-1972 L1989 **PD** *020 †55

OVERBY, David Wayne. 4035 BURNETT WOMACK CB7081, UNC CHAPEL HILL DEPT SURG 27599 #036-08-2000 L2005 **GS** *020 †85

OWENS, Jenny Mcenery. 101 MANNING DR, UNL HOSPITALS 27514 #045-01-2001 L2003 **P** *020

OWENS, Thomas Darrell. 101 MANNING DR, CB #7525 27514 #036-01-1997 L2002 **PTH** *100 †50

PACT, Virginia Wilson. 101 CONNER DR, STE 200 27514 #858-01-1977 L1982 **N** *020 †75

PAGANO, Joseph Stephen. UNC SCHOOL OF MEDICINE 27599 #008-01-1957 L1965 **IM ID** *030

PAGE, Branson Halsted. ■ 27517 #036-01-2005 L2008 **EM** *012

PAGE, Cristen P. ■ 27514 #036-01-2002 L2005 **FM** *100

PAGLIEI, Jennifer Lee. ■ 27514 #036-01-2005 L2008 **IM** *012

PAHEL, Laurie J. 101 CLOISTER CT, STE D 27514 #036-01-1995 L1999 **P** *020

PALDINO, Michael. ■ 27517 #035-09-2003 **DR** *012

PALMER, Jeffress Gary. 101 MANNING DR 27514 #012-05-1944 L1952 **HEM IM** *071 †20

PALMER, Lena Brice. ■ 27516 #027-01-2004 L2007 **IM** *100 †20

PAMPLIN, Charles L, III. ■ 27514 #023-01-1973 L1973 **PA IM** *071 †20

PANCALDO, Ariana. 101 MANNING DR 27514 #035-20-1987 L1990 **FM** *020 †18

PAPANDRIA, Dominic Joseph. ■ 27517 #036-01-2008 *012

PAPEZ, Michael James. UNIV OF N CAROLINA SCH OF, 303 BRINKHOUS-BULLITT BLDG 27599 #036-01-2005 L2006 **PTH** *012

PAREKH, Selene Gunvant. CB #7055, 3135 BIOINFORMATICS BUILDI 27599 #024-05-1999 L2006 **ORS** *100

PARIKH, Anup H. ■ 27514 #036-01-2004 **DR** *012

PARK, Yara Audeh. ■ 27517 #001-02-2004 **BBK** *012 †50

PARKER, Kristen Michelle. 101 MANNING DR, RM 1107-A 27514 #048-16-2002 L2006 **GS** *012

PARSONS, Alden Maier. ■ 27517 #036-01-1999 L2006 **TS** *012 †85

PARSONS, Stephen F. ■ 27517 #036-01-1999 L2003 **NPM** *100 †55

PASCOE, David Earl. ■ 27517 #036-07-2004 L2005 **D** *012

PASSANNANTE, Anthony N. N2201, UNC HOSP 27599 #035-15-1985 L1987 **AN IM** *020 †20,05

PATEL, Depesh Kanaiyalal. CB# 7470, UNC-CH SHS 27599 #305-01-2001 L2005 **FM** *020 †18

PATEL, Dhavalkumar D. CAMPUS BOX #7280, 3330 THURSTON BLDG - MANNI 27599 #036-07-1989 L1994 **RHU AI** *050 †20,03

PATEL, Gaurang Manilal. 101 MANNING DR, UNIV OF NC HOSPS 27514 #012-01-2006 L2006 **N** *012

PATEL, Jignesh M. 101 MANNING DR, UNC HOSP RADIO DEPT 27514 #033-06-2002 L2006 **DR** *012

PATEL, Laura Elizabeth. UNIV OF N CAROLINA SCH OF, 3018 OLD CLINIC BLDG/CB760 27599 #026-04-2005 L2008 **IM** *012

PATEL, Mihir Ranchhod. 101 MANNING DRIVE, G0412 NEUROSCIENCE HOSPITA 27599 #036-01-2006 L2008 **OTO** *012

PATEL, Sachin Bhupendra. UNIV OF N CAROLINA SCH OF, 3018 OLD CLINIC BLDG/CB760 27599 #026-04-2005 L2008 **IM** *012

PATEL, Shipra. ■ 27517 #041-15-2002 L2005 **PDE** *012 †55

PATEL, Sima Sudhir. UNIV OF N CAROLINA SCH OF, 3018 OLD CLINIC BLDG CB 76 27599 #012-21-2006 **IM** *012

PATHMAN, Donald Earl. 513 MANNING DR, CB 7595 27599 #041-01-1981 L1987 **FM GPM** *050 †18

PATTERSON, Jerry Eugene. 501 EASTOWNE DR, STE 110 27514 #036-01-1975 L1975 **OS** *071

PATTERSON, Kristine Blair. 211A W CAMERON AVE, CB #7215 27516 #012-05-1996 L2000 **ID** *100 †20 ‡

PATTERSON, Winston C, Jr. 99 MANNING DR # 7075, UNC CHAPEL HILL 27514 #012-05-1989 L2001 **IM** *020 †20

PATTISHALL, Edward Nolan. 101 MANNING DR, UNC HOSPITALS 27514 #038-06-1980 L1983 **PDP PD** *071 †55

PAULK, Elizabeth Parran. ■ 27516 #011-03-2007 **PD** *012

PAVIC, Dag. 2033 OLD CLINIC BLDG, UNIV OF N CAROLINA 27599 #957-01-1990 L2001 **R** *020

PAYNE, Diane Elizabethse. ■ 27517 #019-02-2004 **ORS** *012

PEACOCK, Erle E, Jr. ■ 27514 #024-01-1949 L1953 **PS GS** *071 †85,65

PEARSON, Matthew Dean. ■ 27517 #036-01-2006 **GS** *012

PECK, Martha Gabriel. 101 MANNING DR, OGMEROOM 1107-G 27514 #036-01-2004 L2006 **FM** *020 †18

PEDEN, David Blaine. 104 MASON FARM RD, CMPS BX 7310 EPA HMN STUD 27599 #055-01-1984 L1992 **PD** *020 †03,55

PEDERSEN, Cort Andrew. UNC DEPT OF PSYCHIATRY, CB #7160 27599 #036-01-1979 L1984 **P** *050 †75

PELTZER, Sonia Rapaport. ■ 27517 #051-01-1991 L2005 **FM PD** *020 †18

PEMBERTON, Lily Kathryn. ■ 27514 #036-01-2008 *012

PENDERGRAFT, William Fran, III. ■ 27516 #036-01-2008 *012

PENDHARKAR, Sima Suhas. ■ 27516 #036-01-2008 *012

PENG, Tai-Chan. 1002 FLO BLDG 231H 27514 #869-04-1959 **END REN** *050

PEPPERCORN, Amanda Sue. 130 MASON FARM RD, CAMPUS BOX 7215 27599 #024-01-1998 L2005 **IM ID** *050 †20

PEPPERCORN, Jeffrey M. DIVISION HEMATOLOGY/ONCOLO, UNIVERSITY OF NORTH CAROLI 27599 #024-01-1998 L2005 **ON HO** *050 †20

PEPPLE, Philip Todd. 101 MANNING DR 27514 #665-01-2007 **GS** *012

PERAULT, Peter Zander. 101 CLOISTER CT STE A 27514 #305-02-1977 L1983 **P PYA** *020 †75

PEREZ, Gerardo Alejandro. UNC PHYSICIANS SERVICES 27514 #649-01-1976 L1978 **AN** *100

PEREZ-REYES, Mario. UNC CB 7175 MED RES A 27599 #649-01-1952 L1966 **PA P** *030

PERILSTEIN, Roger Donald. 100 EUROPA DR STE 260 27517 #041-13-1982 L1984 **P** *020 †75

PERIZZOLO, Karen Elaine. ■ 27516 #005-11-1987 L1988 **IM** *020 †20

PERKINS, Diana Otylia. CB 7160, UNIV OF NORTH CAROLINA 27599 #023-01-1984 L1987 **P** *020 †75

PERL, Edward R. 5109 NEUROSCIENCE RES BLDG, UNIVERSITY/NC, CB #7545 27599 #016-11-1949 L1971 **OS** *050

PERNIA, Marianna Helena. 32405 ARCHDALE 27517 #001-06-2001 L2004 **IM** *020

PERRIN, Eliana Miller. 130 MASON FARM RD, DEPT OF PEDS CB 7220 27599 #035-45-1997 L2000 **PD** *020 †55

PERRY, John Randolph, Jr. N C M H RADIOL DEPT 27514 #047-06-1967 L1976 **NM R** *020 †20,28

PERRY, Victor Lynn. 3012 BURNETT WOMACK, CB# 7060 27599 #008-01-1993 L2007 **NS CFS** *012

PETERSEN, Ruth. ■ 27516 #036-01-1989 L2006 **GPM** *100 †70 ‡

PETERSON, Gary. 659 EDWARDS RIDGE RD, SOUTHEAST INSTITUTE 27517 #011-04-1974 L1984 **P CHP** *020 †75

PETERSON, Herbert Bryson. ■ 27599 #041-12-1977 L1982 **OBG** *020 †70,30

PETERSON-CARMICHAEL, Stace. UNIV OF N CAROLINA SCH OF, CB7593 27599 #036-01-2001 L2004 **PDP** *012 †55

PHARR, Emily Elizabeth. ■ 27514 #036-05-2006 **N** *012

PHILLIPS, Adrienne Linton. 101 MANNING DR, UNIV OF NC HOSPS 27514 #021-05-2007 **AN** *012

PHILLIPS, Harry Tarley. ■ 27517 #836-02-1938 L1971 **PHP** *071 †70

PHILPOT, Edward Earl. 1289 N FORDHAM BLVD # A 27514 #034-01-1980 L2001 **A IM** *062 †20,03

PIGNONE, Michael Patrick. CB 7110, 5039 OLD CLINIC BLDG 27599 #005-02-1993 L1996 **IM** *050 †20

PILLSBURY, Harold C, III. 7070 UNIVERSITY OF NC, OTOLARYNGOLOGY HEAD & 27599 #010-01-1972 L1973 **OTO NO** *020 †45

PIPKIN, Clare Alexandra. ■ 27516 #028-02-2000 L2007 **D** *020 †15

PISANO, Etta Driscoll. 101 MANNING DR, UNC HOSPITALS 27514 #036-07-1983 L1989 **DR** *020 †80

PISCOYA, Jose Luis, Jr. ■ 27517 #036-01-2008 *012

PITA, Kristine Angela. ■ 27516 #036-01-2008 *012

PITTMAN, Jessica Erin. 101 MANNING DR, UNIV OF NC HOSPS 27514 #028-02-2004 L2007 **PDP** *012 †55

■ = Address Information Privacy Protected

PIVEN, Joseph. 7023 NEUROSCIENCES HOSP, CB # 3366 27599 #023-01-1981 L1999 **CHP P** *050 †75
PLEVY, Scott Eric. ■ 27516 #035-01-1988 L2006 **GE** *020 †20 ‡
POINTER, Ivy Peed. ■ 27517 #036-01-2006 **PD** *012
POLLARD, Nell Brock. ■ 27514 #036-01-2008 *012
POPE, Janey Lynn. 100 EUROPA DR STE 341 27517 #020-02-1972 L1979 **CHP P** *075 †55,75
PORTERFIELD, Deborah S. 5034 OLD CLINIC BLDG, UNC CHAPEL HILL CB 7105 27599 #005-02-1993 L1998 **IM** *050 †20,70
POSEY, Kimberly Dionne. ■ 27516 #025-07-2003 L2008 **MPD** *020
POTTS, Rebekah Grace. ■ 27514 #036-01-2008 *012
POWELL, Cynthia Marion. MED WING E, CB 7487 27599 #051-04-1987 L1993 **MG PD** *030 †55,19
POWELL, Gwendolyn Susan. ■ 27514 #011-02-1981 L1984 **OM IM** *030 †70
POWERS, William John. 3114 BIOINFORMATICS BLG, UNIV OF NC SCHOOL OF MED 27599 #035-20-1975 L2007 **N NM** *050 †20,75
PRABHAKARAN, Sujatha. ■ 27514 #038-43-2002 L2007 **OBG** *100
PRABHAKARAN, Viswanathan. ■ 27514 #495-04-1966 L1972 **FM GP** *071
PRAKKEN, Steven Dale. 100 EUROPA DR, STE 260 27517 #040-02-1982 L2002 **P** *020 †75
PRANGE, Arthur J, Jr. 513 MANNING DR, CB# 7595 WLM B ACICK BLDG 27599 #025-01-1950 L1954 **P** *071 †75
PRASAD, Ravindra Vikram. N 2201 UNC HOSPITAL, CB 7010 DEPT OF ANESTH 27599 #025-01-1993 L1997 **AN** *020 †05
PRASAD, Suman. 101 CONNER DR, STE 402 27514 #496-07-1985 L2003 **IM** *020 †20
PRAZMA, Jiri. 101 MANNING DR DEPT OTO 27514 #286-02-1960 **OTO** *050
PRESTON, Edwin T, Jr. ■ 27514 #036-07-1960 L1960 **ORS PM** *071 †40
PRICE, Carmelita Nicole. UNC DEPT OF FAM MED, CB 7595 27599 #045-01-2004 L2006 **FM** *020
PRICE, Julie Bridget. 7595 MANNING DR, CB# DEPT FAM MED 27599 #036-07-1982 L1983 **FM** *020 †18
PRICE, Wayne Alfred. UNIV OF N CAROLINA, 4TH FLOOR UNC HOSPITALS 27599 #045-01-1985 L1988 **NPM PD** *050 †55
PRIMACK, William Arthur. CB #7155, UNC SCHOOL OF MED 27599 #024-07-1970 L2004 **PN PD** *020 †55 ‡
PROSCIA, Nicole. ■ 27516 #035-09-2004 L2007 **DR** *012
PRUTHI, Raj Som. CB 7235, 2140 BIOINFORMATICS, 27599 #036-07-1992 L1998 **U** *020 †95
PRYSTOWSKY, Stephen David. ■ 27517 #023-07-1971 L1973 **D RHU** *020 †15 ‡
PURI, Mala. 3341 BIO MOLECULAR BLDG, DEPT OF PDE BOX 7039 27599 #039-01-2001 L2007 **PDE** *100 †55
PUTALIK, Kimberly A. ■ 27514 #043-01-1994 L2007 **PD** *020 †55
PYATI, Srinivas. 105 CABERNET DR 27516 #495-35-1988 L2004 *100
QUINLIVAN, Evelyn Byrd. 101 MANNING DR, CM 7030 UNC 27514 #036-07-1985 L1988 **ID IM** *020 †20
QUINN, Harold Jos, Jr. PO BOX 4883 27515 #021-01-1958 L1958 **OTO** *071 †45
QUINONES, Marlon Patricio. NEUROSCI HOSP, CB# 7160 10625 27599 #264-26-1999 **P** *012
RABA, Ernest Aloysius. 104 S ESTATE DR 27514 #048-13-1972 L1975 **ADM P** *071 †75
RABINOWITZ, Samuel J. ■ 27517 #352-10-1933 L1973 **GP** *071
RACINE, Christopher Willi. ■ 27516 #036-01-2008 *012
RADISCH, Deborah Lynn. 1001 BRINKHOUS BULLIC BLDG, CAMPUS BOX 7580 OCME 27599 #036-05-1980 L1981 **FOP GPM** *062 †50
RAFT, Elizabeth Vance. 414 CALDWELL EXT, NORTHSIDE CHILDREN FAM CNS 27516 #036-01-1960 L1960 **CHP P** *030
RAFTERY, Laura Lynn. ■ 27514 #036-01-2004 L2007 **HO** *012 †20
RAGUSA, Christine Ann. ■ 27517 #012-05-2004 **GPM** *100 †70
RAKLEY, Susan Merle. ■ 27516 #016-02-1983 L2001 **IM** *074 †20
RANDOLPH, Greg Dean. 725 AIRPORT RD, CB 7590 27514 #036-01-1990 L1993 **GPM** *020 †55
RANSOHOFF, David Franklin. DEPT OF MEDICINE, CB#7080 27599 #038-06-1972 L1991 **GE IM** *050 †20
RAO, Caroline Hebert. 2238 NELSON HWY, STE 100 27517 #038-40-1996 L2002 **D** *020 †15
RAO, Jayalakshmi Koppaka. 2202 KERR HALL, UNC SCHOOL OF PHARMACY, CB 27599 #011-03-1987 L2008 **RHU IM** *040 †20
RASQUIN-WEBER, Andree M. BURNETT WOMACK CB #7080 27514 #165-07-1965 L1994 **IM** *020
RATHMELL, Wendy Kimryn. ■ 27516 #005-11-1998 L2003 **HO** *020 †20
RAUPP, Mark Douglas. 120 CONNER DR, MEDICINE PA 27514 #033-05-1994 L2005 **FM** *020 †18
READY, Neal Edward. ■ 27514 #047-05-1986 L2006 **ON** *020 †20
REARDON, Whitman Lilley. 940 MARTN LTHR KNG JR BLVD 27514 #036-01-1990 L1992 **IM** *020 †20
REDDICK, Bonzo Kwesi. 590 MANNING DR - CB7595 27599 #012-21-2002 L2004 **FM** *100 †18
REDDING-LALLINGER, Rupa C. 418 MAC NIDER BLDG UNC-CH, DEPT PEDIATRICS CB 7220 27599 #035-20-1980 L1994 **PHO HEM** *020 †20,55
REEB, Kenneth Geo. ■ 27514 #056-05-1963 L1987 **FM PD** *071 †55,18
REED, Douglas Bruce. ■ 27514 #028-46-1978 L1979 **DR** *020 †80
REED, John Pearson. ■ 27514 #036-01-2008 *012
REED, Robin Marie. ■ 27516 #004-01-2007 **P** *012
REEDER, Katherine Elizabe. 5039 OLD CLINIC BUILDING, UNC HOSPITALS DEPT OF MEDI 27599 #001-02-2004 L2007 **IM** *100 †20
REEVES, Justin Gary. ■ 27514 #036-01-2007 **IM** *012
REHDER, Kyle Jason. 101 MANNING DR, CB# 7593 27514 #036-01-2003 L2006 **CCP** *012 †55
REID, Pamela Eve. 180 PROVIDENCE RD, STE 9 27514 #045-04-1989 L1994 **P** *020 †75
REILLY, Rachel Mary. UNIV OF N CAROLINA SCH OF, 3314 BIOINFORMATICS BUILDI 27599 #038-41-2005 **ORS** *012
REISMAN, David. 101 MANNING DR 27514 #048-02-1995 L1997 **IM** *020 †20
RENNER, Jordan Bayfield. 101 MANNING DR 27514 #051-01-1980 L1982 **DR** *020 †80
RENNICK, Barbara R. ■ 27514 #025-01-1950 **PA OS** *071
RETSCH-BOGART, George Z. 130 MASON FARM RD, DEPT OF PEDS CB 7220 27599 #038-41-1978 L1986 **PDP PD** *050 †55
REULAND, Daniel S. 1838 AIRPORT RD, STE B-19 27514 #023-07-1991 L1998 **IM** *020 †20
REYES, Mario Lim. 101 MANNING DR 27514 #748-02-1947 L1975 **IM GP** *020
REYNOLDS, Elizabeth Sewel. ■ 27514 #004-01-2008 *012
RICCIONI, Marcus Everest. 8807 GALAX CT 27516 #047-20-1990 L2005 **EM** *020 †18
RICH, Preston Berkeley. CB#7228, 4008 BURNETT WOMACK BLDG 27599 #051-04-1993 L2000 **GS** *020 †85
RICHARDS, Jennifer. 101 MANNING DR, OGMEROOM 1107-G 27514 #035-06-2005 L2006 **P** *012
RICHMOND, Isabelle L. ■ 27514 #036-07-1974 L1975 **NS** *071 †25
RIESENMAN, Kathryn P. 101 MANNING DR, CB 7510 UN OF NC HOSP RAD 27514 #028-34-2001 L2006 **DR** *020 †80
RINGEL, Yehuda. 101 MANNING DR, UNC HOSPITALS 27514 #550-03-1991 L2001 **GE** *020
RIVADENEIRA, Alfredo C. 100 MASON FARM RD 27599 #132-02-1990 L1996 **RHU** *020 †20
RIVERO, Hedrick Jay. UNC MED, DEPT RADIOLOGY CB#7510 27599 #042-01-1978 L2003 **DR PDR** *020 †55,80
RIZZIERI, Kellie E. 403 ENGLEWOOD DR 27514 #035-45-1991 L1998 **HO** *020 †20
RIZZOLO, Peter Jos. UNC PHYSICIANS SERVICES 27514 #030-06-1955 L1978 **FM** *071 †18
ROBERTS, Harold Ross. 416 BURNETT WOMACK CB 7035, UNIV OF NC 27514 #036-01-1955 L1955 **IM OS** *071
ROBINSON, Blair Vernon. CB7232, CHILDREN'S HEART CENTER 27599 #036-01-1993 L1999 **PDC** *020 †55
ROBINSON, Mamie Nelle. 101 MANNING DR CB760, UNC HOSPITALS 27514 #012-01-2007 **OBG** *012
ROGAN, Walter J. 5810 HIDEAWAY DR 27516 #005-02-1975 L1978 **GPM** *050 †70
ROGERS, Heather Ann. 927 SALUDA CT 27514 #051-07-1999 L2005 **CHP** *020 †75
ROPER, Maryann. ■ 27517 #041-14-1975 L1976 **PHO PD** *030 †55
ROPER, William Lee. 125 MACNIDER HALL, UNC SCHOOL OF MEDICINE 27599 #001-02-1974 L2003 **PHP PD** *030 †55,70
ROSE, Austin Samuel. 7070 UNIVERSITY OF NC, OTOLARYNGOLOGY HEAD & 27599 #036-01-1997 L1999 **OTO** *020
ROSENBERG, Beth Sharon. 940 AIRPORT RD, CHAPEL HILL INTERNAL MEDIC 27514 #041-07-1991 L1994 **CD IM** *020 †20
ROSENMAN, Julian G. 101 MANNING DR 27514 #048-12-1977 L1981 **RO** *020 †80
ROSENTHAL, Marjorie Sue. UNC SCH OF MED CB #7225, DEPT PEDS-DIV GEN PED/ADOL 27599 #008-01-1995 L2002 **PD** *050 †55
ROSS, Laura Leslie. AMERICA BUI, STE 306 BANK OF 27599 #036-05-1995 L1997 **IM** *020 †20
ROTH, Heidi Lynne. 3114 BIOINFORMATICS BLDG., UNC/NEUROLOGY 27599 #024-01-1993 L2002 **N** *020 †75
ROUBEY, Robert Arthur S. 100 MASON FARM RD 27599 #021-05-1981 L1988 **RHU IM** *050 †20
ROWELL, Candra Elita. ■ 27517 #036-01-2008 *012
ROYAL, Billy Williamson. ■ 27515 #036-05-1958 L1958 **PFP P** *072
RUBENSTEIN, David Scott. UNC-CHAPEL HILL, CB 7287 DEPT DERM 27599 #036-07-1993 L1994 **D** *020 †15
RUBERY, Bryon Evan. 130 MASON FARM RD, CB# 7075 27599 #001-02-1997 L2001 **ICE** *020 †20
RUBINOW, David Russell. CB 7160, 1051 NEUROSCIENCES HOSPITA 27599 #008-02-1975 L2006 **P** *020 †75 ‡
RUFF, Gregory L. 55 VILCOM CENTER DR # 310 27514 #025-01-1978 L1986 **PS GS** *020 †85,65
RUMA, Michael S. CB 7516 214 MACNIDER BLDG, DEPT OF OB/GYN-DIV OF MFM 27599 #030-06-2001 L2005 **OBG MFM** *020
RUNGE, Marschall Stevens. 125 MACNIDER HALL CB 7005, UNIVERSITY OF NC CHAPEL 27599 #023-07-1984 L2000 **IM** *020 †20
RUNGE, Susan Riggs. 3100 THURSTON 27599 #004-01-1980 L2003 **D** *020 †05,15
RUNKLE, Richard Daniel, III. 101 MANNING DR, UNIV OF NC HOSP 27514 #036-08-2007 **AN** *012
RUNYAN, Desmond Kimo. DEPT OF PEDIATRICS, UNIV OF NORTH CAROLINA MED 27599 #026-04-1976 L1979 **PD GPM** *040 †70,55
RUSSELL, Deborah Olive. ■ 27516 #036-01-1986 L1988 **P** *020 †75
RUSSO, Mark Wm. 101 MANNING DR 27514 #035-47-1992 L1995 **GE** *020 †20
RUVO, Andrew Thomas. 501 EASTOWNE DR, STE 110 27514 #036-01-2003 L2007 **GS** *100
SABA, Paul John. ■ 27514 #067-01-1980 L1992 **IM** *020 †20
SADIQ, Timothy Suleman. 101 MANNING DR, UNIV OF NORTHCAROLINA HOSP 27514 #019-02-1999 L2002 **CRS** *100
SAFRANSKY, Norma Frances. 109 CONNER DR 27514 #036-01-1988 L1990 **P** *071 †75
SAG, Alan Alper. ■ 27516 #036-01-2008 *012
SALIMI, Kayvon. 101 MANNING DR, CB 7160 UNC HOSPITALS 27514 #028-02-1999 L2006 **P** *020 †75
SAMPSON, Andrew Joseph. ■ 27516 #038-45-2006 **IM** *012
SAMS, Cassandra Marie. ■ 27514 #036-01-2008 *012
SAMUEL, Jonathan Charles. ■ 27514 #016-06-2004 L2007 **GS** *012
SANDERS, Charles Addison. 100 EUROPA DR STE 170 27517 #048-12-1955 L1955 **CD IM** *071 †20
SANDERS, Wm Eugene, Jr. 205 WEYER DR 27516 #036-01-1985 L1986 **CD IM** *020 †20
SANDLER, Robert Saml. UNIVERSITY OF N CAROLINA, CB#7555, 4157 BIOINFORMATI 27599 #008-01-1975 L1978 **GE IM** *050 †20
SANFORD, Garrett Brian. ■ 27517 #004-01-2003 L2008 **CD** *012 †55
SANOFF, Scott Leonard. UNIV OF N CAROLINA SCH OF, 7024 BURNETT-WOMACK BLDG 27599 #038-06-2002 L2007 **NEP** *100 †20
SAPP, Robert Frederick. ■ 27517 #036-01-2008 *012
SARTOR, Carolyn. 101 MANNING DR, DEPT OF RADIATION ONCOLOGY 27514 #025-01-1992 L1998 **RO** *020 †80
SARTOR, Ryan Balfour. 101 MANNING DR 27514 #048-04-1974 L1978 **GE IM** *050 †20
SASAKI, Deanna Mary. ■ 27514 #056-05-2003 **NS** *012
SATHER, Randall Kenneth. ■ 27514 #012-01-1969 L1973 **R** *030 †80
SAUNDERS, Barry Ferguson. 101 MANNING DR 27514 #023-01-1986 L1987 **IM** *020 †20
SAUTER, Suzanne V. ■ 27514 #036-01-1974 L1974 **RHU PM** *071 †20
SAVENDAHL, Lars S G. ■ 27516 #858-04-1986 **PDE** *100
SAYA, Justin Michael. ■ 27516 #036-01-2008 *012
SCARLETT, Yolanda Valjene. CB 7080, 724 BURNETT WOMACK, 27599 #036-01-1989 L1992 **GE** *020 †20
SCATLIFF, James H. 101 MANNING DR DEPT RAD 27514 #016-06-1952 L1966 **R** *040 †80
SCHAEFER, Frauke Christia. 1709 LEGION RD, STE 226 27517 #409-22-1984 L2005 **P** *020 †75
SCHARDT-SACCO, Debra M. ■ 27517 #036-01-1994 L1995 **GS** *020
SCHECHTMANN, Marcelo Andr. 101 MANNING DR, UNIV OF NC HOSP 27514 #132-01-1994 **GS** *012
SCHER, Richard Kempner. 130 MASON FARM RD 27599 #010-03-1955 L2006 **D** *020 †15 ‡
SCHLEGEL, Mary Elizabeth. JAMES A TAYLOR BLDG, CB #7470, CAMPUS HEALTH SE 27599 #035-47-1991 L2000 **OBG** *020 †30
SCHOFIELD, Kelly Allan. ■ 27517 #036-07-2001 *100
SCHOLER, Matthew Jon. NEUROSCIENCES HOSP, CB 759, UNC HOS- DEPT OF EMERG MED 27599 #035-09-2000 L2003 **EM** *020
SCHROECK, Hedwig. 101 MANNING DR 27514 #409-40-2004 **AN** *012
SCHROEDER-CHANEY, Kristin. UNIVERSITY OF N CAROLINA S, CB #7593 27599 #010-02-2007 **PD** *012
SCHULTZ, Sara Ann. ■ 27514 #038-06-2008 *012

■ = Address Information Privacy Protected

SCHWARZ, Emily Jean. 130 MASON FARM RD 27599 #021-01-2003 L2004 **D** *020 †15

SCOTCHIE, Jessica Graham. 101 MANNING DR, CAMPUS BOX 7570 UNC HOSP 27514 #011-03-2001 L2005 **OBG REN** *020 †30

SCOTT, Alan Fulton. 101 MANNING DR 27514 #041-01-1943 L1943 **GP** *071

SCOTT, Charles Corey. 101 MANNING DR, UNIV OF NC HOSP 27514 #048-04-2006 **EM** *012

SCOTT, Lincoln Bain. ■ 27517 #041-01-1958 L1971 **PD ADL** *071 †55

SCOTT, Peter Vincent. 101 MANNING DR DEPT ANES 27514 #917-30-1962 **AN** *100

SCROGGS, Mark Wade. 55 VILCOM CENTER DR, STE 140 27514 #036-07-1984 L1985 **OPH PTH** *020 †50,35

SEAL, Elston, Jr. MED RES BLDG C UNV OF NC 27514 #051-04-1972 L1977 **OS GP** *071

SEIBOLD, Anita Marie. ■ 27516 #016-11-2006 **IM** *012

SEIGEL, Jonathan Kevin. UNIVERSITY OF N CAROLINA S, CB #7593 27599 #028-03-2007 **PD** *012

SELZMAN, Craig H. 3040 BURNETT WOMACH, DIV CARDIOTHORACIC SRG-UNC 27599 #048-04-1993 L2003 **TS** *020 †85,90

SELZMAN, Kimberly Anne. 130 MASON FARM RD, 4TH FL 27599 #041-13-1996 L2003 **CD** *100 †20

SEMELKA, Richard Chas. 101 MANNING DR, UNC HOSPITALS 27514 #062-01-1983 L1993 **R** *020 †80

SEN, Souvik. NEUROLOGY DEPT, CB 7025 27599 #495-38-1990 L2002 **N CD** *050 †75

SENA-SOBERANO, Arlene C. 130 MASON FARM RD # 7030, UNIVERSITY OF NORTH CAROLI 27599 #036-01-1992 L1995 **ID** *020 †20

SENIOR, Brent Anthony. 7070 UNIVERSITY OF NC, OTOLARYNGOLOGY HEAD & 27599 #025-01-1990 L1999 **OTO** *020 †45

SERODY, Jonathan Stuart. ■ 27514 #051-01-1986 L1988 **ID IM** *020 †20

SESSIONS, John T, Jr. UNIV NC SCH OF MED, DEPT MED 27514 #012-05-1945 L1952 **GE IM** *020 †20

SHACKELFORD, Joseph Roy. 101 MANNING DR 27514 #047-05-1959 L1984 **FM** *071 †18

SHAH, Monty Suresh. 101 MANNING DR, 510 OLD INFIRMARY 27514 #048-16-2006 **DR** *012

SHAH, Rupali Navin. NEUROSCIENCES HOSPITAL, G0412 27599 #012-05-2007 **OTO** *012

SHAH, Sanjeev Pravin. UNIV OF N CAROLINA SCH OF, 3018 OLD CLINIC BLDG/CB700 27599 #045-01-2002 L2005 **CD** *012 †20

SHAH, Shilpa Ramesh. 618 EDISTO CT 27514 #496-38-1990 L2003 **PD FM** *030 †55

SHAH, Sidharth Anilkumar. 101 MANNING DR, UNIV OF N CAROLINA SCH OF 27514 #019-02-2004 L2007 **IM** *100 †20

SHAH, Usman. 101 MANNING DR 27514 #056-06-2003 L2006 **HO** *012 †20

SHAHEEN, Nicholas James. CB#7080, 101 MANNING STREET 27599 #016-02-1991 L1994 **GE** *020 †20

SHALOM, Rose. CB #7470 27599 #024-01-1978 L1980 **P IM** *020 †20,75

SHAPIRO, Glen Edward. UNIV OF N CAROLINA SCH OF, 182 WING D, CB #7228 27599 #054-04-2003 L2005 **GS** *100

SHAPIRO, Mark Louis. ■ 27516 #305-01-1997 L2006 **TRS CCS** *020 †85

SHARP, Michael Conant. UNIV OF NC CB 7340, OCME/FSN CHASE HALL 27599 #024-01-1974 L1977 **PD** *040 †55

SHARPLESS, Julie Lund. UNIV OF N CAROLINA, CB 7170 6111 THURSTON 27599 #008-01-1992 L2002 **END DIA** *050 †20

SHAVER, Joyce Carolyn. ■ 27517 #035-20-1957 L1975 **IM END** *020

SHAW, Eva Nicolenepr. ■ 27514 #036-01-2008 *012

SHEA, Katherine Marie. ■ 27514 #040-02-1978 L1981 **GPM** *020 †55

SHEA, Thomas Chas. CB 7305, HEMATOLOGY ONCOLOGY 27599 #036-01-1978 L1983 **HEM ON** *020 †20

SHEAFFER, Charles Isaac. 110 CONNER DR STE 4 27514 #051-01-1958 L1961 **PD** *050 †55

SHEAHAN, Richard Gerard. 130 MASON FARM RD, DIVISION OF CARDIOLOGY 27599 #539-02-1984 L2000 **CD** *020

SHEAR, Meyer R. ■ 27516 #023-01-1937 L1937 **IM** *071

SHEIKH, Arif. 101 MANNING DR, RM 2028 OLD CLINIC BLDG 27514 #025-07-1994 L2004 **NM IM** *020 †20,28

SHEIKH, Mohsin Siraj. 101 MANNING DR, UNC HOSPITAL 27514 #422-01-2002 L2008 **PMM** *012

SHELDON, George Frank. 4006 BURNETT-WOMACK BLDG, CB# 7050 27599 #019-02-1961 L1984 **GS TRS** *040 †85

SHEPPA, Charles Michael. ■ 27517 #038-06-1975 L1993 **EM IM** *020 †20,16

SHERIDAN, Brett Courtney. CB #7065, 3032 BURNETT-WOMAC BLDG 27599 #048-04-1992 L2002 **TS** *020 †85,90

SHERIDAN, Stacey Lynn. 5039 OLD CLINIC BLDG, CB 7110 UNC-CH/DIV GEN MED 27599 #041-14-1996 L1999 **IM GPM** *050 †20,70

SHERMAN, Paula Ann. ■ 27514 #036-01-2004 L2006 **P** *012

SHERRILL, Matthew A. 101 MANNING DR, DEPT OF SURGERY 27514 #048-16-1999 L2000 **GS** *012 ‡

SHETH, Samar Santosh. ■ 27514 #036-01-2008 *012

SHIEH, Richard Chen-Hai. ■ 27517 #385-03-1954 L1978 **R** *020 †80

SHILLITO, John, Jr. ■ 27517 #024-01-1952 L1953 **NS** *071 †25

SHILOH-MALAWSKY, Yael. 101 MANNING DR 27514 #550-02-1996 **N** *012

SHIMPI, Rahul Arun. ■ 27516 #036-01-2001 L2004 **GE** *100

SHIN, John Shangkyun. 1829 E FRANKLIN ST # 900B 27514 #018-03-1991 L2001 **CHP** *020 †75

SHLUGMAN, David. ■ 27514 #836-02-1974 **AN** *020

SHOCKLEY, Linda Jane. ■ 27517 #017-20-1976 L1989 **PD** *020 †55

SHOCKLEY, William Wilson. 7070 UNIVERSITY OF NC, OTOLARYNGOLOGY HEAD & 27599 #017-20-1976 L1989 **FPS HNS** *020 †45

SHORES, Carol Getker. 7070 UNIVERSITY OF NC, OTOLARYNGOLOGY HEAD & 27599 #036-01-1995 L1996 **OTO** *020 †45

SHORES, Nathan Joseph. 1605 VILLAGE CROSSING DR 27517 #045-01-2004 L2007 **GE** *012 †20

SHRESTHA, Roshan. 711 BURNETT WOMACK BLDG, UNC HOSP 27599 #160-03-1984 L1998 **GE** *020 †20

SHUMATE, Janelle Adenika. 101 MANNING DR, CB#7593 27514 #036-01-2006 **PD** *012

SHY, Carl Michael. 101 MANNING DR DEPT EPIDEM 27514 #056-06-1962 L1971 **PHP GPM** *050

SIDANA, Lalita Vijay. 32405 ARCHDALE 27517 #495-55-1992 L2005 **IM** *020 †20

SIEBENS, David Phillips. 1603 CLAYMORE RD 27516 #028-02-1983 L1986 **IM** *020 †20,70

SIGEL, Carlie Selbo. ■ 27599 #036-01-2003 L2005 **PTH** *012

SIGOUNAS, Dimitri. ■ 27514 #036-01-2008 *012

SIGOUNAS, Vaia Yioula. ■ 27514 #036-01-2008 *012

SIKICH, Linmarie. CB #7160, DEPT OF PSYCHIATRY 27599 #028-02-1987 L1995 **CHP P** *050 †75

SIKORA, Ewa Maria. 180 PROVIDENCE RD STE 5 27514 #759-08-1992 L2000 **P** *020 †75

SILVERMAN, Robert Arnold. ■ 27517 #041-01-1965 L2006 **IM END** *020 †20 ‡

SIMMONS, Michael Anthony. UNC CHAPEL HILL SCH MED, CB 7000 125 MACNIDER BLDG 27599 #024-01-1967 L1995 **PD NPM** *040 †55

SIMO, Kerri Ann. CB#7211, 4024 BURNETT-WOMACK BLDG 27599 #041-02-2002 L2007 **GS** *020

SIMON, Noelle Monika. 101 MANNING DR, CB 7594 27514 #036-01-2004 L2006 **EM** *020

SIMPSON, Ross J. 99 MANNING DRIVE CB 7075, 6TH FLOOR BURNETT WOMACK B 27599 #010-02-1973 L1977 **CD IM** *050 †20

SIMS, Christopher E. ■ 27514 #023-07-1984 L2007 **IM RHU** *050 †20

SINGER, Paul Richard. ■ 27517 #035-45-1973 L1974 **OPH OS** *071 †35

SINGERMAN, Jeffrey David. ■ 27517 #010-02-2005 **IM** *012

SINGH, Amrit Rabindar. 513 MANNING DR, CB 7595 27599 #055-01-1990 L1992 **FM FPG** *020 †18

SINGH, Bikramjit. 101 MANNING DR 27514 #495-96-2002 **ORS** *012

SINGH, Harbax Kaur. ■ 27517 #036-08-1997 L2001 **OPH** *020

SINGLETON, Jennifer Wales. 205 SAGE RD, CHAPEL HILL PEDIATRICS PA 27514 #048-04-2000 L2003 **PD** *100 †55 ‡

SLADEN, Arnold. ■ 27517 #917-19-1952 L1968 **CCA OS** *071 †05

SLATKOFF, Susan Faith. 513 MANNING DR, CB 7595 27599 #041-01-1978 L1981 **FM** *020 †18

SLECHTA, Ryan Matthew. ■ 27516 #036-01-2004 **ORS** *012

SLIFKIN, Merle June. ■ 27514 #036-01-1980 *100

SLOAN, Gerald Mark. 513 MANNING DR, CB# 7595 WLM B ACICK BLDG 27599 #024-01-1976 L1995 **PS** *071 †85,65

SLOANE, Philip David. 513 MANNING DR, CB 7595 27599 #038-43-1975 L1979 **FM IMG** *040 †18

SMARR, Erwin R. ■ 27517 #041-02-1949 L1995 **P** *071 †75

SMELZER, Timothy Harvey. 101 MANNING DR 27514 #035-01-1962 L1969 **IM PUD** *071 †20

SMITH, Charles Edward. ■ 27514 #010-01-1941 L1968 **P** *071

SMITH, David Albert. 101 CLOISTER CT STE B 27514 #001-02-1980 L1983 **CHP PYA** *020 †75

SMITH, Eugenia Britt. 502 RANSOM ST 27516 #036-01-1990 L1991 **EM** *020 †16

SMITH, Fred Geo, Jr. 101 MANNING DR 27514 #005-14-1955 L1989 **PD NEP** *030 †55

SMITH, Gregory Wayne. 101 MANNING DR 27514 #045-01-2003 L2006 **NEP** *012 †20

SMITH, Ira Q. 300 MEADOWMONT VILLAGE CIR, STE 311 27517 #036-05-1979 L1983 **OBG** *062 †30

SMITH, Jacqueline Nicole. ■ 27517 #036-01-2005 L2006 **P** *012

SMITH, Jeffrey Keith. UNIV NORTH CAROLINA, CB 7510 DEPT RADIO 27599 #021-06-1987 L1993 **DR RNR** *020 †80

SMITH, Kelly Marie. ■ 27516 #036-01-2008 *012

SMITH, Linnea Louise. ■ 27516 #036-01-1976 L1976 **P** *074

SMITH, Sidney Crawley, Jr. 99 MANNING DRIVE, BURNETT-WOMACK BLDG CB7075 27599 #008-01-1967 L1993 **CD IM** *040 †20

SMITHERMAN, Andrew B. ■ 27517 #036-08-2007 **MPD** *012

SNIDER, Barbara Geliebter. ■ 27517 #035-19-1979 L1999 **P CHP** *040 †75

SNIPES, Rose Gunter. ■ 27516 #036-01-1980 L1982 **NEP IM** *020 †20

SOARES, Jair C. CB 7160, 10612 NEUROSCIENCES HOSPIT 27599 #187-04-1990 L2007 **P** *020 †75

SOCINSKI, Mark Anthony. UNC-CHAPEL HILL, CB#7305 3009 OLD CLINIC BL 27599 #050-02-1984 L1995 **ON** *050 †20

SOCOLAR, Rebecca Sheline. UNC - CHAPEL HILL, CB #7225 WING MED SCHOOL 27599 #036-01-1984 L1992 **PD** *020 †55

SOHN, David H. ■ 27514 #005-18-2002 L2003 **OSM** *012

SOLANDER, Sten Yngve. 101 MANNING DR, UNC HOSPITALS 27514 #858-04-1988 L1999 *100

SOLLE, Michael Edward. 101 MANNING DR, DEPT OF RADIOLOGY 27514 #036-01-2004 **DR** *012

SOLTYS, John Jos. ■ 27514 #024-01-1959 L1975 **P CHP** *071 †75

SONIS, Jeffrey Hal. UNIV OF NC AT CHAPEL HILL, MANNING DRIVE 27599 #041-01-1980 L1981 **GPM** *020 †70,18

SOO, Liang Yee. ■ 27514 #036-05-1958 L1958 **NS** *071 †25

SOPER, John Tunnicliff. UNIV OF NC CHAPEL HILL, CB #7570 5017 OLD CLNC BLD 27599 #018-03-1978 L1982 **OBG GO** *020 †30

SORROW, John M, Jr. ■ 27515 #041-01-1946 L1946 **IM CD** *071 †20

SOUTH, Andrew Patrick. 101 MANNING DR 27514 #038-06-2000 L2003 **NPM** *100 †55

SOUTH, Mary Mcdonough. 101 MANNING DR, UNC HOSPITALS-DEPT OB/GYN 27514 #038-06-2001 L2004 **OBG** *020

SOVENYHAZY, Kristine Mari. UNIVERSITY OF N CAROLINA S, CB #7593 27599 #045-01-2007 **PD** *012

SOWA, Nathaniel Adam. ■ 27516 #036-01-2008 *012

SPAGNOLI, Anna. PEDIATRIC ENDOCRINOLOGY, 3341 MBRB, CB #7039 27599 #561-32-1988 L2007 **PDE** *020 †55

SPANOS, Alan. 1829 E FRANKLIN ST, STE 200A 27514 #917-09-1973 L1980 **OS FM** *020 †18

SPARLING, Philip F. 103 MASON FARM RD, 8341 MED BIOMOL RESEARCH B 27599 #024-01-1962 L1969 **ID IM** *030 †20

SPECTOR, Neil Lee. 101 MANNING DR 27514 #033-05-1982 L1999 **IM N** *020 †20

SPENCER, Donald Chas. 513 MANNING DR, CB 7595 27599 #005-14-1977 L1980 **FM** *040 †18

SPENCER, Roger Felix. CB 7160 DEPT OF PSY 27599 #024-01-1959 L1963 **P PYA** *020 †75

SPIELMAN, Fred John. 101 MANNING DR 27514 #012-01-1978 L1982 **AN** *020 †05

SPIRO, Philip Marget. 800 EASTOWNE DR STE 106 27514 #008-01-1983 L1984 **P** *020 †75

SPRUYT, Dirk Jacobus. ■ 27516 #035-45-1954 L1973 **PHP** *072 †70

STADIEM, Raymond Benjamin. ■ 27516 #036-01-2008 *012

STAEBLER, Andreas Manfred. ■ 27517 #036-01-2008 *012

STAFFORD, Renae Elizabeth. 180 MEDICAL SCHOOL BLDG D 27599 #012-05-1993 L2000 **CCS** *020 †85

STANDER, Sally Gowen. ■ 27514 #051-04-2008 *012

STAREK, Peter Josef Karl. 101 MANNING DR DEPT TS 27514 #038-40-1964 L1971 **TS GS** *071 †85,90

STARNES, Harrison Ben. 101 MANNING DR, UNIV OF NC HOSPS 27514 #004-01-2004 L2007 **CD** *012 †20

STARNES, Sheryl Ann. 1838 MARTN LTHR KNG JR 27514 #036-01-1996 L2001 **PD** *020 †55

STAVAS, Joseph Michael. CB7510, UNIVERSITY OF NC AT CHAPEL 27599 #030-06-1982 L2004 **DR** *020 †80

STAVE, Gregg Martin. ■ 27514 #036-07-1984 L1988 **IM OM** *062 †20,70

STEEGE, John Francis. UNIV OF NC AT CHAPEL HILL, DEPT OBG CB #7570 27599 #008-01-1972 L1977 **OBG** *020 †30

STEENLAND, Peter Richard. 101 MANNING DR, UNIV OF NC HOSP 27514 #036-01-2006 **NS** *012

STEIN, Leonard Donald. 130 MASON FARM RD # 7220, DEPT OF PEDIATRICS, UNIV O 27599 #012-01-1975 L1987 **PD** *050 †55

STEINER, Anne Zweifel. 4001 OLD CLINIC BUILDING, OBSTETRICS & GYNECOLOGY, C 27599 #012-05-1998 L2006 **OBG** *020 †30

STELLA, Michael Joseph. 101 MANNING DR, OGME 27514 #005-06-2001 L2003 **PAN** *100 †05

STEPHENS, George Vincent. 727 EASTOWNE DR STE 300B 27514 #036-01-1985 L1988 **P** *020 †75

STEPHENSON, Thomas Noel. 194 FINLEY GOLF COURSE RD 27517 #025-01-1972 L1975 **P CHP** *020

STERNSCHEIN, Irving. ■ 27517 #038-41-1942 L1944 **P PYA** *071 †75

STETSON, Margaret Ann. 110 TIMBERHILL PL 27514 #035-45-1977 L1978 **FM EM** *020 †18

STEVENSON, Bernadette Mie. 27516 #011-02-2006 **P** *012

STEWART, Elee Elijah. 101 MANNING DR, DEPT OF ANESTHESIOLOGY 27514 #036-01-2005 **AN** *012

STEWART, Jessica Jane. ■ 27517 #017-20-2006 **MPD** *012

STEWART, Robert Dennis. CB 7065, 3042 BURNETT WOMACK BLDG. 27599 #016-06-1993 L2007 **TS** *020 †85,90

STILES, Alan Davis. ■ 27516 #036-01-1977 L1980 **NPM** *020 †55

STOCKMAN, James A, III. 111 SILVER CEDAR CT 27514 #041-02-1969 L1992 **PD PHO** *030 †55

STOUFFER, George Andrew. UNIVERSITY OF N CAROLINA, CARDIOLOGY 27599 #023-01-1987 L2000 **IM CD** *020 †20

STRAUSS, Robert Allen. BC #7516 UNC, DEPT OF OB/GYN, 27599 #041-13-1992 L1996 **OBG** *020 †30

STRICKLER, John Howard. ■ 27517 #016-02-2005 L2005 **IM** *012

STROUP, Thomas Scott. UNIV OF NORTH CAROLINA, DEPT P CB 7160 27599 #036-01-1989 L1995 **P** *020 †75

STRUM, Julie Ryan. 101 MANNING DR, DEPT OF ANESTHESIOLOGY 27514 #036-01-2004 L2007 **AN** *012

STUART, Gretchen Sauer. 4012 OLD CLINIC, CB 7570 27599 #021-01-1994 L2006 **OBG** *020 †30

STUMPF, Walter Erich. U-NC SCH MED LAB REP BIO 27514 #407-30-1952 **OS N** *050

STYNER, Maya Shalev. UNC HOSPITAL, CB 7005 DEPT OF INT MED 27599 #036-01-2002 L2007 **END** *012 †20

SUBERMAN, Rick Ian. ■ 27517 #036-01-1970 L1970 **DR PDR** *020 †80

SUBRAMANIAN, Kiona Rae. 113 CHANNING LN 27516 #056-06-2001 L2004 **FM** *020 †18

SUCHINDRAN, Sujit. ■ 27516 #036-01-2008 *012

SUETA, Carla Ann. 99 MANNING DR, CB# 7075 27514 #036-01-1985 L1988 **CD IM** *040 †20

SUGIOKA, Mary T H. ■ 27517 #036-07-1967 L1967 **PD CHN** *020 †55

SUH, Paul Boksuk. 101 CONNER DR STE 200 27514 #036-01-1983 L1984 **OSS ORS** *020 †40

SULLIVAN, Patrick Francis. CB #7264, UNC-DEPT OF GENETICS 27599 #005-02-1988 L2003 **P** *020

SUMMER, George K. ■ 27514 #024-01-1951 L1952 **PD GPM** *072 †55

SUNG, Jade Jye. 101 MANNING DR, UNC HOSPITALS 27514 #004-01-2002 L2004 **EM** *020 †16

SUROWITZ, Joshua Benjamin. ■ 27517 #036-01-2007 **OTO** *012

SUSAC-PAVIC, Stela. ■ 27516 #957-01-1996 **FP** *012

SUTHERLAND, Denise Helena. ■ 27514 #010-03-1982 L2003 **FM** *020 †18

SUTHERLAND, Richard Wood. CAMPUS BOX 7235, CB 7235 UNIVERSITY OF N C 27599 #040-02-1989 L2001 **UP** *020 †95

SUTTON, Leslie Elizabeth. 32405 ARCHDALE, DOCTORS MAKING HOUSECALLS 27517 #036-08-2002 L2005 **IMG** *020 †20

SUZUKI, Kinuko I. 101 MANNING DR 27514 #572-16-1959 L1986 **NP ATP** *050 †50

SUZUKI, Kunihiko. UNIV NC SCH MED BSRC 7250 27599 #572-03-1959 L1963 **OS N** *050

SWAGER, Lauren Whitney. 101 MANNING DR. CB# 7160, UNC HOSPITALS, DEPT. OF PS 27599 #055-01-2003 L2007 **CHP** *012

SWITZER, Janie Jackson. ■ 27514 #036-01-1971 L1971 **PHP** *020 †70

SYAL, Rishi. ■ 27517 #036-01-2003 L2007 **DR** *012

SYED, Arjumand Bano. 1001 S HAMILTON RD, AVALON MEDICAL GROUP 27517 #704-06-1995 L2003 **IM** *100 †20

TAFT, Timothy Ned. 3153 BIOINFORMATICS BLDG, CB # 7055 27599 #028-03-1969 L1973 **ORS OSM** *020 †40

TAMADDON, Houman S. UNIV OF N CAROLINA SCH OF, 182 WING D, CB #7228 27599 #035-15-2002 **VS** *012

TAN, Walter Ang. CB 7075, BIOINFORMATICS BL, CARDIOLOGY, UNC HOSPITALS 27599 #748-02-1990 L2002 **CD IM** *020 †20

TANG, Julia Wai-Chi. 940 MARTN LTHR KNG JR BLVD 27514 #036-01-1999 L2001 **GE** *030 †20

TANNER, T Bradley. 1506 E FRANKLIN ST, STE 200 27514 #051-01-1988 L1998 **P** *020 †75

TATE, David Andrew. CB#7075, SCH OF MED 27599 #036-01-1982 L1985 **CD IM** *020 †20

TATUM, Gregory Howard. 200 MASON FARM RD, BIOINFORMATICS BLDG 5TH 27514 #026-08-1999 L2002 **PDC** *020 †20

TAYLOR, Catherine Anne. 101 MANNING DR, DEPT PSYCH 27514 #047-06-1957 L1963 **P CHP** *071 †55,75

TAYROSE, Gregory Abram. ■ 27514 #036-01-2008 *012

TENNANT, Joshua Neal. ■ 27514 #036-01-2007 **ORS** *012

TENNISON, Michael Byron. BOX 37025, UNC SCHOOL OF MEDICINE 27599 #024-01-1975 L1979 **CHN N** *020 †55,75

TEPLIN, Stuart Warren. ■ 27517 #041-01-1973 L1978 **PD PN** *071 †55

TEPPER, Joel Elliott. RAD-ONC UNC MED CB 7512 27599 #028-02-1972 L1987 **RO** *020 †80

TESCHE, Leora Jeanne. ■ 27517 #036-01-2005 **GS** *012

TESSER, Rachel Adelle. 110 CONNER DR STE 2 27514 #012-01-1998 L2003 **OPH** *020 †35

TEW, Franklin Truett. 130 MASON FARM RD, CB# 7075 27599 #036-01-1969 L1994 **CD** *020 †20

THANANOPAVARN, Paul. ■ 27514 #005-06-2003 L2008 **MPM PM** *012

THEODORE, Adrea. MED SCHOOL, DEPT OF PEDIATRICS CB #722 27599 #051-01-1994 L1997 **PD GPM** *020 †70,55

THEODORE, Dickens. 130 MASON FARM RD, 1140A BIOINFORMATICS BLDG 27599 #051-01-1994 L1997 **ID IM** *050 †20

THIWAN, Syed Ismail M. 130 MASON FARM RD, UNIVERSITY OF N CAROLINA 27599 #495-95-1990 L1997 **GE** *012 †20

THOMAS, Anna Laura. ■ 27516 #036-01-2004 L2007 **PD** *020 †55

THOMAS, Colin G, Jr. 4005 BURNETT WOMACK, CB 7228 27599 #016-02-1943 L1952 **GS** *072 †85

THOMAS, Jerome Mathew. 101 MANNING DR 27514 #012-21-2003 L2006 **CD** *012 †20

THOMAS, Lindsey Ann. ■ 27516 #036-01-2008 *012

THOMAS, Nancy Ellen. 130 MASON FARM RD 27599 #035-20-1987 L1992 **D** *020 †15

THOMAS, Naveen C. 101 MANNING DR, UNCH DEPT. OF PSYCHIATRY 27514 #012-05-2002 L2003 **P** *100

THOMPSON, Christopher Cha. UNIV OF N CAROLINA SCH OF, DEPT OF EMERGENCY MEDICINE 27599 #056-06-2004 L2006 **EM** *100

THOMPSON, Robert Leslie. ■ 27516 #027-01-1961 L1982 **FOP CLP** *071 †50

THOMPSON, Robin D. 891 WILLOW DR, STE 1 27514 #037-01-1998 L1999 **D** *020 †15

THORP, John Mercer, Jr. DEPT OBGYN CB #7516, UNC HOSPITAL 27599 #036-08-1983 L1986 **MFM OBS** *020 †30

TILLEY, Stephen Lloyd. UNIV OF N.C. CAPEL MILL, BIOINFORMATICS BLDG 27599 #036-01-1992 L1995 **PCC** *020 †20

TINKHAM, Nicholas Hayden. ■ 27517 #036-01-2008 *012

TINTINALLI, Judith Ellen. UNC SCHOOL OF MEDICINE, CAMPUS BOX 7594 27599 #025-07-1969 L1991 **EM IM** *030 †20,16

TOBIN, Christopher Gregg. 510 MEADOWMONT VILLAGE CIR 27517 #048-04-1996 L2001 **GP** *020

TOBIN, Rebecca Brown. 1717 LEGION RD, STE 103 27517 #036-01-1993 L1996 **FM** *020 †18

TOLLESON, Christopher Mah. 101 MANNING DR, UNIV OF NC HOSPS 27514 #012-01-2006 **N** *012

TOLLEY, Aubrey G. ■ 27514 #051-01-1952 L1956 **P** *072 †75

TOMLINSON, John Pitt, III. ■ 27515 #012-05-1961 L1996 **PHP OM** *071 †70

TOMSICK, Robert S. 130 MASON FARM RD 27599 #036-01-1976 L1977 **D** *020 †15

TOROK, Bradley Allan. 110 TIMBERHILL PL 27514 #025-01-1998 L2001 **FM** *020 †18

TRAMMELL, Aaron Wayne. ■ 27516 #036-01-2008 *012

TREVETT, Thomas Neil, Jr. CB #7516, 214 MACNIDER 27599 #035-06-1998 L2002 **OBG** *020 †30

TRIMBERGER, Mary Elizabet. ■ 27517 #036-01-2005 L2008 **PD** *012

TRUCKNER, Robert Thos. ■ 27517 #025-01-1987 L2005 **PD** *020 †55

TRUITT, Sherstin G. ■ 27517 #017-20-2002 L2006 **PCC** *012 †20

TUCKER, George Reginald. ■ 27517 #036-01-1955 L1955 **FM** *071 †18

TUCKER, Landrum S, Jr. 2005 N LAKESHORE DR 27514 #005-11-1966 L1971 **P PYA** *020 †75

TURAN, Naciye. ■ 27517 #011-04-2005 **DR** *012

TUTTLE, Gregory Howard. TAYLOR BLDG, CB 7470 JAMES A 27599 #036-01-1978 L1979 **FM EM** *020 †16,18

TYLER, Eileen Patricia. N C MEM HOSP 27514 #041-13-1979 L1980 **AN** *020 †05

UNDERWOOD, Edward Thos. ■ 27514 #035-09-1958 **PD** *071 †55

UNDERWOOD, Louis Edwin. BIDMOLECULAR BLDG, 3341 MEDICAL 27599 #047-05-1961 L1963 **END PD** *050 †55

UNGER, Joshua Mostkoff. ■ 27514 #036-07-2006 **GS** *012

URDA, Michael Martin. NEUROSCI HOSP, CB# 7160 10625 27599 #012-01-2007 **P** *012

URSANO, Amy Marie. 101 MANNING DR, DEPT PSYCH CB #7160 27514 #036-01-1997 L1998 **P** *020 †75

VALLEY, Robert David. 513 MANNING DR, CB# 7595 WLM B ACICK BLDG 27599 #051-01-1980 L1982 **AN PD** *040 †55,05

VAN AALST, John Ananda. 7040 BURNETT-WOMACK BLDG, CAMPUS BOX 7195 27599 #047-05-1993 L2004 **PS CFS** *020 †85,65

VAN DER HORST, Charles M. 547 BURNETT-WOMACK, UNC AT CHAPEL HILL CB# 703 27599 #024-01-1979 L1982 **ID IM** *050 †20

VANDER ZWAAG, Carol Jane. 800 EASTOWNE DR, STE 200 27514 #035-47-1986 L1991 **P CHP** *020 †75

VAN DEVENTER, Hendrick W. 3009 OLD CLINIC BLDG, CB # 7305 27599 #051-04-1993 L1997 **HO** *020 †20

VAN HORN, Sharon E. 205 SAGE RD, CHAPEL HILL PEDIATRICS PA 27514 #019-02-1987 L2006 **PD P** *020 †55

VAN LE, Linda Thuyhoa. CB #7570, UNIVERSITY OF NORTH CAROLI 27599 #005-02-1983 L1989 **GO GYN** *020 †30

VAN WYK, Judson J. 101 MANNING DR 27514 #023-07-1948 L1955 **END PD** *050 †55

VARIA, Mahesh Kumar A. 101 MANNING DRIVE, NC CLINI CENCER CTR CB #75 27599 #917-06-1967 L1976 **RO** *020 †80

VARNER, Catherine Elizabe. ■ 27517 #036-01-2008 *012

VAUGHN, Bradley Vance. CB 7025, UNIV OF NC 27599 #041-14-1986 L1990 **N SME** *020 †75

VAVALLE, John Paul. ■ 27517 #036-01-2004 L2007 **IM** *012 †20

VENERACION, Melissa Deleo. ■ 27517 #020-12-2007 **AN** *012

VENESS-MEEHAN, Kathleen A. UNIV OF NC HOSP, CAMPUS BOX 7596 27599 #035-45-1983 L1990 **NPM** *020 †55

VERMA, Lalit Mohan. ■ 27517 #023-01-1998 L2007 **IM** *020 †20

VERNAZZA, Pietro Luigi. ■ 27516 #869-07-1982 *100

VIERA, Anthony Joseph. 101 MANNING DR, DEPT FMLY MED CHAPEL HILL 27514 #045-01-1996 L2004 **FM** *020 †18

VIMMERSTEDT, Margaret B. UNC STU HLT SER CB 7470 27599 #038-06-1985 L1988 **IM DIA** *020 †20

VINES, Dain Edsel. 101 CONNER DR, STE 402 27514 #036-01-1996 L2000 **FM** *020 †18

VISCO, Anthony Gabriel. DEPT OF OB/GYN, CB7570 UNIVERSITY OF NC 27599 #035-15-1993 L1997 **OBG** *020 †30

VISH, Shannon Scholl. 101 MANNING DR, OGMEROOM 1107-G 27514 #036-01-2003 L2006 **GE** *012 †20

VOLK, Matthew John. ■ 27517 #048-04-2007 **IM** *012

VOLMAR, Keith Eberhard. 101 MANNING DR, WOMEN'S AND CHILDREN'S HOS 27514 #035-06-1998 L2002 **PCP** *020

VON ALLMEN, Daniel. UNC-CH, CB# 7223, 3010 OLD CLINIC 27599 #050-02-1986 L2003 **PDS** *020 †85

VON STIEGLITZ, Jutta F. ■ 27599 #409-21-1995 L2004 **PD** *100 †55

VOORHEES, Peter Michael. ■ 27516 #025-01-1997 L2001 **HO** *020 †20

VUKOSON, Matthew Bruce. U.N.C. STUDENT HEALTH SERV 27599 #055-01-1977 L1980 **FM** *020 †18

WACKER, Kristen Laura. 301 KILDAIRE RD, STE 200 27516 #048-13-1989 L1992 **PD** *020 †55

WAICUS, Kelly Marie. CB 7470, UNC CAMPUS HLTH SVCS 27599 #036-01-1995 L1998 **PD PSM** *020 †55

WALASIN, Robert Michael. ■ 27516 #036-01-1987 L1989 **EM** *020 †18

WALKER, Heather Whitt. CB #7200, UNC SCHOOL OF MEDICINE 27599 #020-12-2002 L2007 **SCI** *100 †60

WALKER, Richard Isley. MANNING DRIVE 27514 #024-01-1954 L1954 **HEM IM** *071

WALKER, Vester Wade, Jr. UNC CHAPEL HILL, CB# 7305 3009 OLD CLINIC B 27599 #036-01-2001 L2001 **HO** *020

WALKUP, Margaret Hosfield. ■ 27517 #048-13-2002 **GS** *012

WALLACE, John, II. 425 RIDGECREST DR 27514 #067-01-1995 L1998 **PFP** *020 †75

WALLACE, Wesley Marion. UNC SCHOOL OF MEDICINE, CAMPUS BOX 7594 27599 #048-04-1975 L1991 **EM FM** *020 †16

WALLAS, Charles Henry. ■ 27517 #028-02-1964 L1994 **BBK CLP** *062 †20,50

WALLEN, Eric Mark. 2134 BIOINFORMATICS BLDG, CB 7235 27599 #005-14-1994 L2003 **U** *020 †95

WALTERS, Ruth A F. ■ 27514 #036-01-2002 L2004 **DMP** *012 †50

WALTON, Leslie Augustus. UNIV OF N CAROLINA, CB#7570 MACNIDER BLDG 27599 #035-08-1964 L1972 **ON OBS** *020 †30

WANG, Nadia. 2238 NELSON HWY, STE 100 27517 #024-05-2002 L2003 **DMP** *012 †15

WARREN, Camille Marie. ■ 27517 #036-01-1980 L1982 **OM IM** *020 †20

WARREN, Sarah L. 101 MANNING DR 27514 #051-04-1949 L1949 **FM OM** *071

WARSHAUER, David Mitchell. 101 MANNING DR 27514 #036-01-1978 L1980 **DR D** *020 †80

WASHINGTON, Clarence Jos. 101 CONNER DR, STE 402 27514 #025-01-1974 L2006 **OBG** *075

WATKINS, Paul Brent. RM 3005 APCF, CAMPUS BOX 7600 27599 #035-20-1979 L1999 **IM GE** *050 †20

WATSON, Lea Corinne. ■ 27516 #051-04-1997 L1998 **PYG** *100 †75

WATSON, Robert Anthony. ■ 27516 #917-05-1993 L2003 **GS** *100 †85

WAUGH, Michael Stuart. ■ 27514 #036-07-2001 L2006 **PCP** *100 †50

WEAVER, Elizabeth Grace. UNIV OF N CAROLINA SCH OF, 3018 OLD CLINIC BLDG CB 76 27599 #036-01-2006 **IM** *012

WEBER, David Jay. 547 CLIN SCI BLDG 229 H 27514 #005-18-1947 L1987 **ID IM** *050 †20,70

WEEKS, Paul Martin. ■ 27516 #036-01-1958 L1958 **HS PS** *071 †85,65

WEIG, Spencer Greenwood. CB 7025, UNC SCHOOL OF MEDICINE 27599 #035-47-1973 L2004 **CHN CN** *020 †55,75 ‡

WEIGLE, Kristen Ann. ■ 27516 #041-12-1976 L1987 **PD ID** *050 †55

WEIL, Amy Brett. OLD CLINIC BLDG, 5TH FLOOR, OF GEN INT MED,CAMPUS BOX 27599 #035-45-1994 L1998 **IM** *020 †20

WEINBERG, Ethel Schwartz. ■ 27517 #041-09-1961 L1962 **AN** *030

WEINER, Frank. ■ 27517 #010-02-1962 L1999 **PD** *020 †55

WEISS, James Richard. 101 CLOISTER CT, STE C 27514 #021-05-1973 L1976 **P** *020 †75

WEISSLER, Mark Christian. 7070 UNIVERSITY OF NC, OTOLARYNGOLOGY HEAD & 27599 #024-05-1980 L1986 **OTO HNS** *040 †45

WEITZNER, Stanley Wallace. ■ 27516 #035-19-1953 L1977 **AN** *071 †05

WELBORN, April Eve. NEUROSCI HOSP, CB# 7160 10625 27599 #012-01-2007 **P** *012

WELLEN, Marcus Gregory. 101 MANNING DR, CB#7160 10625 NEUROSCIENCE 27514 #021-01-2004 L2007 **P** *012

WELLS, Ellen. UNIVERSITY OF N CAROLINA, CB 7570, MACNIDER BUILDIN 27599 #036-01-1984 L1987 **OBG** *040 †30

WELLS, Martin Carr. ■ 27514 #836-04-1982 **HS** *020

WENZEL, Donald J. 108 SAINT ANDREWS PL 27517 #010-02-1968 L1976 **R** *020 †80

WEST, Anne Elizabeth. ■ 27514 #021-44-1998 *100

WEST, Kelly Leigh. ■ 27517 #035-47-2008 *012

WESTON, Brent W. DEPT PEDIATRICS 7220 27599 #036-07-1985 L1986 **PHO PD** *020 †55

WHALEY, John Lambdin. ■ 27514 #051-04-1948 L1953 **IM** *071 †20

WHANG, Young E. UNC LINEBERGER CANCER CTR, CB 7295 27599 #016-02-1989 L1998 **HO IM** *050 †20

WHEELER, Sarah Ellen. ■ 27517 #048-04-2006 **P** *012

WHINNA, Herbert Charles. 101 MANNING DR, UNC HOSPITALS 27514 #036-01-1994 L1999 **PTH** *020 †50

WHITE, Andrea A. ■ 27517 #065-06-1999 L2006 *100

WHITE, Becky L. 130 MASON FARM RD, CB #7030 27599 #051-01-1992 L1996 **ID** *020 †20

WHITE, James Alexander. ■ 27517 #065-06-1999 **CD** *100

WHITE, Lynn Katherine. ■ 27514 #024-01-1984 L2005 **IM** *020 †20

WHITEHEAD, Clay Carlton. 215 MARILYN LN, ADVANCED PSYCHOTHERAPEUTIC 27514 #005-14-1968 L2000 **P PYA** *020 †75

WHITLEY, Brian Michael. ■ 27517 #001-02-2007 **GS** *012

WHITSEL, Eric Anders. 137 E FRANKLIN ST, PGM BOA CENTER, SUITE 306 27514 #036-01-1993 L2000 **IM** *020 †20

WILCOX, Benson Reid. 354 WING C CB #7065, UNC HOSPITALS 27599 #036-01-1957 L1957 **TS** *071 †85,90

WILCOX, Claire L Berteel. CB #7510 UNC, UNC DEPT OF RADIO 27599 #025-01-1973 L1975 **DR** *020 †80

WILEY, Jane. ■ 27517 #025-01-1970 L1971 **GP EM** *020

WILEY, John Kimmel. ■ 27517 #041-01-1967 L1968 **NS AM** *071 †25

WILHELMSEN, Kirk Child. UNC CHAPEL HILL, CB 7264 DEPT OG GENETICS 27599 #056-05-1986 L2004 **N** *020 †75

WILKES, Nancy Cecil. CB 7010, 223 BURNETT WOMACK 27599 #047-06-1987 L1991 **AN** *020 †05

WILLIAMS, Carmen Judson. ■ 27517 #036-07-1986 L1988 **OBG REN** *020 †30

WILLIAMS, Jennelle S. 2238 NELSON HWY, STE 500 27517 #051-01-1989 L1997 **D** *020 †15

WILLIAMS, Jonathan Martin. 11312 US HGHWY 15 501 N #3, CHATHAM CROSSING MEDICAL C 27517 #036-01-1999 L2003 **MPD** *020 †20,55

WILLIAMS, Kia Jeanell. 101 MANNING DR, UNIVERSITY OF NORTH CAROLI 27514 #012-21-2001 L2004 **FM** *020 †18

WILLIS, Park Weed, IV. 99 MANNING DR, CB# 7075 6TH FLOOR 27514 #025-01-1975 L1978 **CD IM** *020 †20

WILLIS, Tina Schade. 209 CHATEAU PL 27516 #030-05-1997 L2004 **PD** *020 †55

WILSON, Crystal Renee. ■ 27514 #036-01-2008 *012

WILSON, Frank Crane. 130 MASON FARM RD, CB7055 DEPT. OF ORTHOPEDIC 27599 #012-01-1954 L1964 **ORS** *071 †40

WILSON, Lindsay Ann. ■ 27516 #036-01-2008 *012

WILSON, Mitchell J. CAMPUS BOX 7110, 5039 OLD CLINIC BLDG. 27599 #048-02-1993 L2002 **IM** *020 †20

WILSON, Robert S. ■ 27517 #023-07-1944 L1945 **ORS** *071 †40

WINCHESTER, Mark Allan. 401 VILLAGE CROSSING DR 27517 #005-02-1974 L2008 **CD IM** *020 †20 ‡

WINDHAM, Laura Clark. 301 KILDAIRE RD, STE 200 27516 #036-01-1997 L2000 **PD** *020 †55

WINTERS, Scott Lee. 420 BURNETT-WOMACK CB7020, DEPT OF MEDICINE PULMONARY 27599 #016-11-1996 L1999 **PCC** *020 †20

WINZELBERG, Gary Springer. CB 7550, 141 MACNIDER BLDG 27599 #032-01-1996 L2002 **IM IMG** *020 †20

WITHROW, Glenn Ashley. 1728 FORDHAM BLVD, 151 RAMS PLZ 27514 #036-01-1982 L1984 **FM OS** *020 †18

WOHL, Darren. ■ 27514 #550-03-1994 L2006 **GE IM** *020 †20

WOHL, David Alain. 7215 UNIVERSITY OF NC 27599 #033-06-1991 L1994 **ID** *020 †20

WOLFE, Honor Morin. 214 MACNIDER, CB#7516, UNC OB/GYN DIV MATERNAL-FE 27599 #035-15-1981 L2000 **OBG** *040 †30

WONG, Wyman Kay. ■ 27517 #143-02-1948 L1971 **CD IM** *020

WOOD, John Howard. 110 CONNER DR, STE 2 27514 #036-01-1990 L1994 **OPH** *020 †35 ‡

WOOD, Karen Suzanne. 4TH FLOOR WUNC HOSPITALS, DEPT PEDIATRICS 27599 #036-01-1992 L1995 **NPM** *020 †55

WOOD, William Allen, Jr. ■ 27516 #036-07-2003 L2007 **HO** *012 †55

WOOD, William B. ■ 27516 #036-01-1956 L1956 **PUD IM** *071

WOODBURY, John W. ■ 27514 #024-01-1945 L1970 **IM** *071 †20

WOODYEAR, Wynne E. 1838 AIRPORT RD, STE B-19 27514 #055-01-1987 L1990 **IM** *020 †20

WOOSLEY, John Thos. CAMPUS BOX 7525, DEPT OF PATHLGY UNC 27599 #012-01-1984 L1986 **ATP DMP** *020 †50

WORSHAM, Kyle Austin. 1709 LEGION RD, STE 102 27517 #051-01-1993 L1994 **P** *020 †75

WRIGHT, John David, Jr. CB#7040, 5110 BIOINFORMATICS BLDG 27599 #008-01-1972 L2002 **OPH OS** *020 †35

WROTH, Shelley Wilson. 1512 E FRANKLIN ST, STE 100 27514 #035-01-1995 L1999 **OBG** *020 †30

WROTH, Thomas H. 101 MANNING DR, UNC FAMILY MED 27514 #035-01-1995 L1998 **GPM** *020 †18,70

WU, Diem Nguyen. 130 MASON FARM RD 27599 #051-01-2000 L2005 **D** *020 †15

WU, Jennifer Marie. ■ 27599 #005-02-1999 L2003 **OBG** *100

WURZELMANN, John Irving. ■ 27514 #035-46-1986 L1989 **GE** *020 †20

WYSOR, William G, Jr. ■ 27517 #051-01-1950 L1957 **IM GE** *071 †20

XIANG, Dong. ■ 27514 #243-08-1989 *012

YAMADA, Akira. 932 FACULTY LAB BLDG 231 H 27514 #572-12-1974 L1982 **RHU NEP** *020

YAMBOR, Mari Martha. 1829 E FRANKLIN ST, STE 101 27514 #055-01-1980 L1990 **P EM** *020 †75

YANKASKAS, James Robt. 7011 THURSTON BOWLES, CB 7248 27599 #008-02-1978 L1980 **PUD IM** *050 †20

YANOVITCH, Tammy Lyn. ■ 27517 #039-01-2002 L2006 **OPH** *100 †35

YANUCK, Cheryl Hoffman. 101 CLOISTER CT STE B 27514 #035-15-1988 L1992 **P** *020 †75

YAO, Zhenhai. 223 BURNETT WOMACK BLDG, UNIVERSITY OF NORTH CAROLI 27599 #243-21-1987 L2001 **AN** *020 †05

YEATES, Andrew Eccles. ■ 27517 #016-06-1977 L1983 **DR** *020 †80

YEH, Jen Jen. ■ 27599 #023-07-1996 L2005 **GS** *100 †85

YELIN, Karina Mabel. 101 MANNING DR, CTR FOR DEVELOPMENT & LEAR 27514 #132-01-1996 **DBP** *012

YOON, Sora Christina. ■ 27516 #035-19-2000 L2005 **DR** *100 †80

YOUNG, Simon Christopher. 101 MANNING DR DEPT END 27514 #671-02-1984 **END** *020

YOUNG, Steven Lawrence. CB#7570, DEPT OB/GYN, 4005 OLD CLIN 27599 #011-02-1991 L2004 **OBG** *020 †30

YOUNG, W P Wiltsee. ■ 27514 #051-04-1958 L1980 **ADL GP** *071 †55

YOUNT, William Jay. 100 MASON FARM RD 27599 #056-05-1960 L1970 **RHU A** *020 †03,20

YU, Hong. ■ 27514 #243-71-1984 L2006 **IMG** *020 †20

YU, Kathy Kakee. 55 VILCOM CENTER DR # 142 27514 #021-01-1998 L1999 **OTO** *020 †45

YUSCHOK, Theresa Anna. 101 CLOISTER CT, STE D 27514 #016-06-1986 L1990 **P** *020 †75

ZACK, Gwyneth Anne. 101 MANNING DR CB760, UNC HOSPITALS 27514 #016-01-2007 **OBG** *012

ZACKS, Steven Lawrence. CB7080, UNIV OF NC/CHAPEL HILL 27599 #065-01-1991 L1996 **HEP GE** *020 †20

ZANATION, Adam Mikial. ■ 27517 #036-01-2002 L2007 **OTO** *100

ZDANSKI, Carlton Jude. 7070 UNIVERSITY OF NC, OTOLARYNGOLOGY HEAD & 27599 #036-01-1994 L1996 **PDO GS** *020 †45

ZEDEK, Daniel Clayton. ■ 27517 #045-04-2004 L2006 **PTH** *012

ZEHL, Donald Nicholas. ■ 27517 #050-02-1957 L1990 **OPH** *071 †35

ZEISEL, Steven H. SCHOOL OF PUBLIC HEALTH, CAMPUS BOX #7461 27599 #024-01-1975 L1990 **NTR PD** *050

ZELASKO, Scott Matthew. ■ 27514 #041-15-2002 L2003 **DR** *012

ZINNER, Tanya Ellen. 101 MANNING DR, CB# 7200 27514 #035-15-1987 L2000 **PM** *020 †60

ZOLNOUN, Denniz Asad. CB 7570 OLD MCNIDER BLDG, DEPT OB/GYN U OF N CAROLNA 27599 #016-11-1995 L1999 **OBG** *020 †30

ZOLOTOR, Adam Jason. CB#7595 MANNING DR, UNC FAMILY PRACTICE CENTER 27599 #036-01-1998 L2001 **FM** *020 †18

ZURA, Marianne Gerard. 1450 RALEIGH RD, STE 200 27517 #051-01-1997 L2000 **PD** *020 †55

ZWEIG, Sherrie Elizabeth. ■ 27516 #036-01-1985 L1986 **IM** *020 †20

CHARLOTTE — MECKLENBURG

ABAQUETA, Alvin Y. 8401 MEDICAL PLAZA DR, STE 300 28262 #748-21-1992 L1998 **FM** *020 †18

ABBOTT, Kristi Deshannon. ■ 28277 #047-20-2006 **PD** *012

ABERNATHY, Elizabeth Ila. 1350 S KINGS DR 28207 #036-01-2001 L2004 **IM** *020

ABERNETHY, John Lloyd, Jr. 5431 EAGLE LAKE DR 28217 #036-07-1980 L1984 **PTH DMP** *020 †50

ABINANTI, Nicole. 3623 LATROBE DR, STE 216 28211 #035-47-1999 L2005 **DR OS** *020 †80

ABNER, Monique Lisa. 10030 PARK CEDAR DR, STE 101 28210 #041-14-1988 L1997 **PS** *020 †65

ABORN, Lyn Susan. PO BOX 32861, CAROLINAS MEDICAL CENTER 28232 #005-11-2002 L2005 **EM** *020 †16

ADAM, Sarah Noe. ■ 28209 #047-06-1993 *100

ADAMS, Bryan Charles. 101 E WT HARRIS BLVD, STE 1121 28262 #036-05-1994 L1997 **PD** *020 †55

ADAMS, George Leslie. 7845 COLONY RD, STE 4143 28226 #021-01-1967 L1970 **P PHP** *062 ‡

ADAMS, Gerald Leon. 1928 RANDOLPH RD, STE 208 28207 #036-01-1965 L1965 **GS** *020 †85

ADCOCK, Jimmie Warren. 100 N TRYON ST STE 75 28202 #036-01-1982 L1983 **IM** *020 †20

ADHIKARI, Sapana. 1100 BLYTHE BLVD 28203 #024-05-2002 L2006 **EM** *020 †16

ADKINS, Henry Thos. 3623 LATROBE DR STE 216, MECKLENBURG RADIOLOGY ASSO 28211 #012-01-1936 **R** *071

ADKINS, Henry Thos, Jr. 200 HAWTHORNE LN, INPATIENT MEDICINE 28204 #012-01-1965 L1972 **R** *020 †80

ADLAKHA, Harkiran. 101 E WT HARRIS BLVD, STE 1212 28262 #495-08-1980 L1998 **PTH** *020 †50

AFULUKWE, Ifediora F. 300 BILLINGSLEY RD, STE 102 28211 #690-04-1989 L1998 **PCC** *020 †20

AGARWAL, Aarti. ■ 28277 #036-01-2003 L2005 **IM** *100 †20

AGGARWAL, Puneet Kumar. 1100 BLYTHE BLVD, CAROLINAS REHABILITATION 28203 #051-04-2001 L2006 **PMM** *100 †60

AGHA, Maher Salah. 2115 E 7TH ST, STE 102 28204 #305-01-1993 L1996 **IM** *020

AGNER, David Marshal. 1100 BLYTHE BLVD, CAROLINA REHABILITATION 28203 #036-08-1994 L1998 **PM** *020 †60

AGUNOBI, Charles K. ■ 28216 #690-06-1986 L1994 **IM** *020 †20

AHMED, Amina. 1628 E MOREHEAD ST 28207 #036-01-1990 L1997 **PD PDI** *020 †55

AIKEN, Janet Karen. 10628 PARK RD, CMC-PINEVILLE 28210 #036-01-1976 L1979 **IM** *020 †20

AKANDE, Adewunmi Abiodun. 10504 PARK RD 28210 #690-06-1986 L1997 **AN** *020 †20,05

AL-AJLOUNI, Said Moh'D. ■ 28211 #418-02-1980 L1996 *020

ALBAINY, Bolivar. ■ 28278 #308-01-1960 L1966 **IM** *071

ALBANESE, Lisa Nicole. PO BOX 32861, CAROLINAS MED CTR 28232 #056-05-2006 **PM** *012

ALBERGOTTI, Julian S, Jr. 200 HAWTHORNE LN 28204 #036-01-1955 L1955 **OM FM** *071 †18

ALBRIGHT, Harold Dowe. 1701 ABBEY PL 28209 #036-08-1982 L1983 **IM** *020 †20

ALBRIGHT, Joseph L, Jr. 8810 BLAKENEY PROFESSNL DR, STE 100 28277 #036-01-1982 L1994 **IM** *020 †20 ‡

ALDERMAN, James Francis. 4501 CAMERON VALLEY PKWY, STE 100 28211 #045-01-1982 L1987 **PD** *020 †55

ALESSANDRINI, Edward S. 8918 BLAKENEY PROFESSNL DR, STE 130 28277 #020-02-2001 L2005 **OMF** *020

ALEXANDER, James C. 3030 RANDOLPH RD, MECKLENBURG MEDICAL GROUP 28211 #067-01-1997 L2000 **IM** *020 †20

ALEXANDER, James Frosst. 3030 RANDOLPH RD, MECKLENBURG MEDICAL GROUP 28211 #067-01-1963 L1964 **GE IM** *020 †20

ALEXANDER, James Robert. 10512 PARK RD, STE 101 28210 #036-01-2000 L2001 **PM** *020 †60

ALEXANDER, John Edward. 1718 E 4TH ST, STE 501 28204 #036-07-1980 L1991 **CD IM** *020 †20

ALEXANDER, John Eugene. 3535 RANDOLPH RD, MECKLENBURG MEDICAL GROUP 28211 #047-07-1965 L1973 **ORS** *020

ALEXANDER, Leon Geo, Jr. ■ 28278 #036-07-1973 L1973 **TS** *020 †85,90

ALEXANDER, Michael S. 3623 LATROBE DR, STE 216 28211 #035-09-1978 L1984 **NM DR** *020 †80,28

ALFIERI, Paul Justin. 101 E WT HARRIS BLVD, STE 1213 28262 #041-13-1996 L2002 **CD** *020 †20

ALLBERT, John R. 1718 E 4TH ST, STE 404 28204 #048-02-1986 L1988 **OBG MFM** *020 †30

ALLEN, Fred Huntley, Jr. 1001 BLYTHE BLVD, STE 601 MEDICAL CENTER PLA 28203 #035-01-1959 L1959 **N** *071 †75

ALLEN, Marcella Sue. 2915 COLTSGATE RD, STE 102 28211 #048-13-1999 L1999 **FM** *020 †18

ALLGOOD, Sara Elizabeth. 5717 ALBEMARLE RD 28212 #045-01-1974 L1984 **EM FM** *020 †16

ALLRED, Timothy Scott. 333 JEREMIAH BLVD 28262 #001-02-1993 L1998 **DR** *100

ALMQUIST, Perry Futral. 4501 CAMERON VALLEY PKWY, STE 100 28211 #051-01-1982 L1985 **PD** *020 †55

ALMQUIST, Robert Earl. 10000 PARK CEDAR DR 28210 #035-01-1982 L1984 **FM** *020 †18

ALTANY, Franklin E. ■ 28211 #036-07-1952 L1957 **PS** *071 †65

ALTER, George Jos. 6035 FAIRVIEW RD 28210 #021-01-1979 L1991 **OPH** *020 †35

ALTIZER, James Witten. 10502 PARK RD, STE 102 28210 #051-04-1985 L1999 **OS** *020 †20

ALUKO, Akinyele Olawale A. 1718 E 4TH ST, STE 501 28204 #690-01-1978 L1989 **CD IM** *020 †20

ALUKO, Gbenga. 1805 MILTON RD 28215 #690-08-1992 L2005 **IM** *020 †20

AMIDON, Geoffrey Richard. PO BOX 32861, CAROLINAS MED CTR 28232 #305-01-2000 **FM** *100

AMIN, Asim. 1000 BLYTHE BLVD, BLUMENTHAL CANCER CENTER 28203 #704-01-1985 L2005 **ON** *020 †20

AMIN, Ketan Bipinchandra. 330 BILLINGSLEY RD, STE 100 28210 #473-04-2000 L2004 **IM** *020

AMIRI, Michael Majid. 1900 RANDOLPH RD, STE 1010 28207 #902-07-1991 L2002 **CN** *020 †75

AMOR, Antonio R, Jr. 4525 CAMERON VALLEY PKWY 28211 #748-01-1973 L2001 **FM** *020 †20

ANDERSON, Christopher A. 3101 LATROBE DR, STE 100 28211 #041-09-1988 L1989 **EM** *020 †16

ANDERSON, Jack David. 7030 PINEVILLE MATTHEWS RD 28226 #016-06-1971 L1986 **PD** *020 †55

ANDERSON, James Dick. 1023 EDGEHILL RD S 28207 #011-03-1963 L1967 **OBG** *071 †30

ANDERSON, Keith Alan. ■ 28209 #039-01-2006 L2007 **FP** *012

ANDERSON, Richard Dawson. ■ 28211 #035-01-1960 L1972 **R NM** *072 †80,28

ANDERSON, Robert Bentley. 15825 JOHN J DELANEY DR, STE 100 28277 #056-06-1983 L1984 **ORS** *020 †40

ANDERSON, Roger F, Jr. 200 QUEENS RD, STE 400 28204 #036-07-1981 L1990 **RO** *020 †80

ANDREWS, David Scott. 1718 E 4TH ST, STE 701 28204 #038-40-1975 L1983 **TS** *020 †85,90

ANDRINOPOULOS, George C. 2028 RANDOLPH RD 28207 #418-01-1966 L1976 **OBG NPM** *020 †30 ‡

ANIKWUE, C C. 1928 RANDOLPH RD 28207 #919-05-1970 L2005 **OBG** *020 †30

ANTHONY, Nicholas Eisenho. ■ 28210 #011-05-2008 *012

ANTHONY-WILLIAMS, Adelle. 7221 PINEVILLE MATTHEWS RD, STE 200 28226 #035-19-1992 L1996 **AN PME** *020 †05

ANTOSZYK, Nicholas. ■ 28211 #035-09-1948 L1952 **AI IM** *071 †03

ARAD, Jonathan Kirsch. ■ 28202 #550-04-2004 **GS** *012

ARAIN, Shazia Akhtar. 9040 NATIONS FORD RD 28273 #704-25-1995 L2002 **IM** *020 †20

ARDIS, Mark Burkett. ■ 28210 #025-01-1955 L1998 **P** *072 †75

ARMSTRONG, Beverly Weller. ■ 28207 #035-15-1941 L1948 **OTO OS** *071 †45

ARONOFF, Gerald M. 1900 RANDOLPH RD STE 606 28207 #033-05-1972 L1994 **PMM P** *020 †75

ARORA, Mohanlal Virbhan. 927 EAST BLVD 28203 #495-33-1963 L1994 **AN CCM** *020

ARRONTE, Nora Marie. 1718 E 4TH ST, STE 907 28204 #035-20-2002 L2006 **OBG** *020

ARRU, Jason Michael. ■ 28205 #020-02-2005 **GS** *012

ARTHO, Melanie Renee. ■ 28270 #048-15-2008 *012

ASBEE, Shelly Marie. ■ 28216 #018-03-2004 L2008 **OBG** *012

ASHE, William Shecut, Jr. 411 BILLINGSLEY RD, STE 104 28211 #045-01-1988 L1991 **PDP** *020 †55

ASHER, Anthony Lawrence. 225 BALDWIN AVE, ASSOCIATES 28204 #025-07-1987 L1995 **NS GS** *020 †20

ASHKIN, Kenneth Todd. 1900 RANDOLPH RD, STE 1010 28207 #041-07-1987 L1994 **N SME** *020 †75

ASIMOS, Andrew Wm. 1000 BLYTHE BLVD 28203 #041-12-1990 L1994 **EM** *020 †16

ASKINS, Wm Francis, Jr. 1901 RANDOLPH RD 28207 #028-34-1982 L2002 **AN** *020 †05

ASRAEL, Gerson. ■ 28211 #023-01-1959 L1966 **U** *071 †95

ATKINSON, George Jay. 1000 BLYTHE BLVD, CHARLOTTE INSTITUTE OF REH 28203 #048-04-2001 L2005 **PM** *020 †60

ATTORRI, Robert Jos. 1900 RANDOLPH RD, STE 210 28207 #041-01-1984 L1994 **PDS** *040 †85 ‡

AUGUSTUS, Carl Trent. 8426 MEDICAL PLAZA DR, STE 400 28262 #045-01-1989 L2006 **IM** *020

AUSTIN, Jonathan Gregory. 1900 RANDOLPH RD 28207 #036-01-1994 L2005 **EM** *020 †16

AVERY, Nneka Tene. 1801 ROZZELLES FERRY RD 28208 #038-41-1997 L1998 **FM** *020 †18

AYERS, Lorri Yaroma. 4525 CAMERON VALLEY PKWY, STE 3100 28211 #038-40-1990 L1994 **IM** *020 †20

BABICH, John Franklyn. 10460 PARK RD, STE 100 28210 #008-01-1984 L1998 **RHU IM** *020 †20

BACH, Philip John. 10512 PARK RD STE 101 28210 #056-05-1966 L1967 **ORS** *020 †40

BADIKA, Ndofunsu. 2860 FREEDOM DR, FREEDOM MEDICAL CLINIC 28208 #422-01-1997 L2005 **IM** *020 †20

BAEUERLE, Jeffery Jay. 1901 RANDOLPH RD 28207 #048-14-1987 L1994 **AN PME** *020 †05

BAILEY, Clayton R. 10226 COULOAK DR 28216 #566-01-1981 L1996 **FM** *020 †18

BAILEY, John Russell. 1718 E 4TH ST STE 501 28204 #047-05-1989 L1992 **ICE CD** *020 †20

BAILEY, Luna Deshawn. 7006 SHANNON WILLOW RD, EAR, NOSE, THROAT & AUDIOL 28226 #035-06-1998 L2004 **OTO** *020 †20

BAIRD, Christopher W. 1001 BLYTHE BLVD, STE 300 28203 #036-01-1998 L2006 **TS** *100 †85,90

BAJAJ, Priya K. 15110 JOHN J DELANEY DR, STE 100 28277 #035-03-1994 L2000 **OBG** *020 †30

BAKER, John Woodward. 1000 BLYTHE BLVD, CAROLINAS MEDICAL CENTER 28203 #051-01-1971 L1975 **IM** *030 †16

BAKER, Marty Allen. 10348 PARK RD, STE 300 28210 #051-04-1998 L2000 **PD** *020 †55

BALE, Charles Stephen. 15110 JOHN J DELANEY DR, STE 100 28277 #020-02-1982 L1983 **OBG** *020 †30

BALL, Joy Kendrick. 2630 E 7TH ST, STE 101 28204 #047-20-2002 L2005 **PD** *020 †55

BALLARD-BARBASH, Rachel M. 1350 S KINGS DR 28207 #025-01-1980 L1986 **GPM NTR** *050 †20

BALLINGER, William Edward, Jr. 1000 BLYTHE BLVD, CHAROLINAS PATHOLOGY GROUP 28203 #011-03-1974 L1991 **ATP NP** *020 †50 ‡

BAMBINI, Daniel Andrew. 1900 RANDOLPH RD, STE 210 28207 #019-02-1991 L2001 **PDS** *020 †85

BANKS, Peter M. 101 E WT HARRIS BLVD, STE 1212 28262 #024-01-1971 L1996 **PTH IM** *020 †50

BANKS, Rachel Renee. 251 EASTWAY DR 28213 #019-02-2004 L2007 **FM** *020 †18

BARBERA-HELLNER, M. 10512 PARK RD, MECKLENBURG MEDICAL GROUP 28210 #021-01-1999 L2005 **HO** *020 †20

BARKENBUS, John Erol. 5208 PARK RD 28209 #017-20-2001 L2003 **P** *020 †75

BARKLEY, David Alexander. 15110 JOHN J DELANEY DR, STE 100 28277 #036-05-1988 L1990 **OBG** *020 †30

BARKLEY, John Eldridge. 1420 E SEVENTH ST 28204 #036-01-1990 L1996 **PCC** *020 †20

BARKLEY, Karl Lee, II. 10310 MALLARD CREEK RD, UNIVERSITY FAMILY PHYSICIN 28262 #036-05-1986 L1989 **FM** *020 †18

BARNARD, Anne Elizabeth. 200 S COLLEGE ST, MECKLENBURG MEDICAL GROUP 28202 #051-01-1995 L1998 **IM** *020 †20

BARNES, Ajiri Smith. ■ 28262 #017-20-2005 **FP** *012

BARNES, Sharrol Elizabeth. 5933 BLAKENEY PARK DR, GYNECOLOGY PA 28277 #011-03-1992 L1996 **OBG** *020 †30

BARR, Robert Marlowe. 3623 LATROBE DR, STE 216 28211 #005-02-1988 L1995 **RNR** *020 †80

BARR, Tara Nakayama. ■ 28211 #005-02-1991 L1995 **IM** *020 †20

BARRINGER, Thos Avery, III. 1350 S KINGS DR, CMC-MP 28207 #036-01-1979 L1980 **FM** *020 †18

BARRON, Jerry Lynn. 449 N WENDOVER RD, STE A 28211 #048-02-1984 L1985 **ORS OSM** *020 †40

BARRON, Lorraine Faye. 10628 PARK RD, MOD 400 28210 #045-04-1997 L2004 **IM** *020 †20

BARTEE-ALLEN, Sylvia Ann. 10310 MALLARD CREEK RD, UNIV OF FAMILY PHYSICIANS 28262 #027-01-1992 L1997 **FM** *020 †18

BARTHOLOMEW, Cynthia Lea. ■ 28209 #041-09-1982 L1985 **PD** *020 †55

BARTLES, Lewis Winston. 1043 E MOREHEAD ST, STE 107 28204 #045-01-1967 L1969 **PTH EM** *020 †50

BARTON, Forbes M, Jr. 2001 VAIL AVE 28207 #047-06-1963 L1970 **GS** *020

BASRAWALA, Zane Kevin. 201 QUEENS RD, CAROLINAS, PLLC 28204 #036-01-2000 L2006 **U** *100

BATRA, Kalindi Aimee. ■ 28278 #056-05-2003 L2008 **FM** *100 †18

BATTS, Jayne Johnson. 1000 BLYTHE BLVD, CAROLINAS MEDICAL CENTER 28203 #036-08-1990 L1997 **IM** *020 †20

BAUCOM, Mary Padgett. PO BOX 32861 28232 #036-01-1980 L1981 **IM** *040 †20

BAUM, Shari J. 2835 JEFF ADAMS DR, STE A 28206 #011-02-1993 L2002 **IM** *020 †20

BAUMBLATT, Glenn Jay. 1909 J N PEASE PL, UNIVERSITY RIDGE STE 201 28262 #056-05-1955 L1996 **IM** *020 †20 ‡

BEARD, John Nichols. 2711 RANDOLPH RD, STE 301 28207 #036-01-1964 L1965 **OM PD** *020 †55

BEASLEY, Michael Edward. 2215 RANDOLPH RD, CHARLOTTE PLASTIC SURGERY 28207 #036-01-1980 L1982 **PS GS** *020 †65

BEATTY, Michael Andrew. 2001 VAIL AVE, MEDICAL ASSOCIATES 28207 #016-06-1997 L1998 **EM** *020 †16

BEAVER, Clint Richard. ■ 28202 #036-05-2007 **FP** *012

BEAVER, Walter B, Jr. 1025 MOREHEAD MEDICAL DR, STE 300 28204 #036-01-1984 L1989 **ORS GS** *020 †40

BEDNAR, Edward Jos. 10620 PARK RD STE 108, MERCY MEDICAL PARK BLDG 40 28210 #025-07-1982 L1988 **PS** *020 †65 ‡

BELANGER, Theodore Andrew. 1025 MOREHEAD MEDICAL DR, STE 300 28204 #056-05-1997 L2003 **OSS ORS** *020 †40

BELGRAVE, Enrico O. 4525 CAMERON VALLEY PKWY, STE 3100 28211 #035-19-1989 L1999 **IM** *020 †20

BELK, Harold Dean. 6407 IDLEWILD RD 28212 #045-01-1960 L1966 **OM** *030 †70

BELL, Don Antonio. 3623 LATROBE DR, STE 216 28211 #036-01-1984 L1994 **RNR DR** *020 †20,80

BELL, Michael John. 1701 EAST BLVD, CHARLOTTE RADIOLOGY 28203 #026-04-1963 L1971 **R NM** *020 †80,28

BELLE, Beverly Ann. 200 HAWTHORNE LN 28204 #028-02-1993 L1998 **OBG** *020

BENEDUM, John Loyle. 3030 RANDOLPH RD STE 200, MECKLENBURG MEDICAL GROUP 28211 #055-01-1973 L1975 **IM** *020 †20

BENFIELD, Edward S. 501 BILLINGSLEY RD 28211 #008-02-1979 L1994 **P** *020 †75

BENJAMIN, Sanford Philip. 2001 VAIL AVE, CMC MERCY HOSP 28207 #025-07-1968 L1978 **PTH GP** *020 †50

BENNETT, William Tyson. 3626 LATROBE DR 28211 #021-01-1965 L1968 **CD IM** *020 †20

BENSON, Quintina Louise. ■ 28213 #036-01-2006 **FP** *012

BENSON, Terry Lee. 335 N CASWELL RD 28204 #033-05-1975 L1986 **FM** *020 †18

BENTON, Thomas Wyatt. 1901 RANDOLPH RD 28207 #036-01-1983 L1984 **AN** *020 †05

BERGMAN, Robert Lewis. 2225 TOWNSHIP RD 28273 #016-02-1962 L1963 **P** *020 †75

BERLING, Donald Paul. 2711 RANDOLPH RD, STE 400 28207 #038-45-1986 L1992 **IM** *020 †20

BERMAN, Larry F. 10620 PARK RD, STE 128 28210 #550-02-1987 L1990 **IM EM** *020 †20

BERNAL, Steven David. 14215 BALLANTYNE CORPRT PL 28277 #010-02-2001 L2008 **PD** *020 †55

BERNING, Lenora Wong. 1900 RANDOLPH RD 28207 #048-13-1990 L1991 **EM** *020 †16

BERNSTEIN, Daniel Jos. 4428 TAGGART CREEK RD, WORKWELL 28208 #025-12-1978 L1992 **GP OM** *075 ‡

BEUHLER, Michael C. 4400 GOLF ACRES DR, BLDG J 28208 #035-48-1997 L2002 **EM** *020 †16

BEURSKENS, Maureen Leonie. 1025 MOREHEAD MEDICAL DR, SUTIE 400 28204 #024-16-1981 L1992 **OBG** *020 †30

BEYER, Sara. 6708 ALBEMARLE RD, ALBEMARLE ROADFAMILY PRACT 28212 #036-01-1996 L1997 **FM** *020 †18

BHAGIA, Priti. 7903 PROVIDENCE RD, STE 100 28277 #495-20-1993 L2004 **IM** *020 †20 ‡

BHAGIA, Sarjoo Mohandas. 1025 MOREHEAD MEDICAL DR, STE 300 28204 #495-28-1989 L2003 **PM** *020 †60

BHASIN, Rohit Ike. 1918 RANDOLPH RD STE 130, CHARLOTTE SURGICAL GROUP 28207 #012-05-1999 L2005 **GS** *020 †85

BHAT, Sheela. 2001 VAIL AVE, MEDICAL ASSOCIATES 28207 #041-07-1982 L1987 **EM** *020 †16

BHATIA, Aashim. ■ 28269 #010-03-2008 *012

BHOJWANI, Jennifer Michel. 101 E WT HARRIS BLVD, STE 5301 28262 #055-02-2000 L2001 **OBG** *020

BHOJWANI, Navin Chandru. 10340 PARK RD 28210 #016-02-1998 L1999 **OBG** *020 †30

BIANCHI, Raymond F. 1000 BLYTHE BLVD 28203 #011-03-1973 L1975 **IM** *040 †20

BILSKA, Magdalena Alicja. ■ 28203 #036-01-2006 **FP** *012

BINNS, Pamela Michelle. 2610 W ARROWOOD RD, STEELE CREEK FAMILY PRACTI 28273 #045-01-2003 L2005 **FM** *020

BLACK, Edward Barnwell. 1701 EAST BLVD, ADMIN OFFICE 28203 #036-07-1970 L1978 **DR NM** *020 †20

BLACK, Hugh Ratchford, II. 8045 PROVIDENCE RD, STE 300 28277 #051-01-1990 L1997 **PDP** *020 †55

BLACK, James Hampton, Jr. 200 HAWTHORNE LN 28204 #036-05-1963 L1963 **IM NEP** *071 †20,03

BLACK, John Wm. 3623 LATROBE DR, STE 216 28211 #010-02-1990 L1996 **DR** *020 †80

BLACK, Laura Ann. 10344 PARK RD STE 300 28210 #012-01-1996 L1997 **FM** *020 †18

BLACKLEY, Donald Wayne. 927 EAST BLVD 28203 #012-01-1986 L1990 **AN** *020 †05

BLACKMON, Terri Elizabeth. 501 BILLINGSLEY RD 28211 #036-01-1994 L1997 **P** *020 †75

BLACKWELL, James Matthew. 1000 BLYTHE BLVD, DEPARTMENT OF INTERNAL MED 28203 #012-01-2003 L2006 **IM** *100 †20

BLACKWELL, Thomas Harold. 1000 BLYTHE BLVD 28203 #030-06-1988 L1992 **EM** *020 †16

BLAHA, Stephen Joseph. ■ 28277 #036-05-2008 *012

BLAND, Mark Leekley. 14215 BALLANTYNE CORPRT PL, STE 110 28277 #036-01-1997 L2001 **OBG** *020 †30

BLISS, Susan Alicia. 1025 MOREHEAD MEDICAL DR, STE 500 28204 #033-05-1994 L1999 **OBG** *020 †30

BLITSTEIN, Bryan Drew. 1918 RANDOLPH RD, STE 130 28207 #028-46-1992 L1997 **GS** *020 †85

BLOCK, Jared Gavin. 101 E WT HARRIS BLVD, BLVD 1212 28262 #016-11-1993 L1999 **HMP** *050 †50

BLUMENFELD, Julian. 200 HAWTHORNE LN 28204 #035-09-1983 L1991 **AI** *020

BLUMER, John Redmond. 6035 FAIRVIEW RD 28210 #026-04-1987 L1992 **OTO** *020 †45

BOATRIGHT, James Richard. 1025 MOREHEAD MEDICAL DR, STE 300 28204 #028-02-1966 L1967 **HS ORS** *020 †40

BOCKENEK, William Louis. 1100 BLYTHE BLVD 28203 #011-04-1986 L1987 **PM SCI** *030 †60

BODTKE, Susan K. 2801 RANDOLPH RD, STE 101 28211 #041-14-1985 L2001 **FM** *020 †18

BOEHM, O Robert. 2630 E 7TH ST, STE 100 28204 #019-02-1973 L1997 **AI IM** *020 †20,03

BOERTJE, Douglas Lee. 1000 BLYTHE BLVD, DEPARTMENT OF PEDIATRICS 28203 #020-02-1999 L2006 **PD** *020 †55 ‡

BOESEL, Richard Ralph. 5435 PROSPERITY CHURCH RD, STE 2200A 28269 #047-05-1983 L1987 **OBG** *020 †30

BOHMER, James Thomas. 14215 BALLANTYNE CORPRT PL, STE 110 28277 #019-02-1995 L1996 **OBG** *020 †30

BOHN, Jeffrey Andrew. 1918 RANDOLPH RD, STE 500 28207 #038-41-1980 L1988 **GS** *020 †85

BOLDEN, Jason Edward. 2001 VAIL AVE, MEDICAL ASSOCIATES 28207 #036-07-1998 L2006 **EM** *020

BOLEN, Christine Marie. ■ 28277 #051-04-2001 L2007 **PHO** *100 †55

BOLOURI, Mohammad Reza. 485 N WENDOVER RD, PRESBYTERIAN NEUROLOGY CEN 28211 #308-10-1990 L2004 **N** *020 †75

BOLZ, Everett Arthur. 6035 FAIRVIEW RD, THROAT ASSOCIATES, PA 28210 #038-40-1966 L1971 **OTO SME** *071 †45

BONKOVSKY, Herbert Lloyd. 1000 BLYTHE BLVD, CAROLINAS MEDICAL CENTER 28203 #038-06-1967 L2008 **GE IM** *020 †20 ‡

BONKOVSKY, Sarah Louise. ■ 28277 #024-16-2001 L2006 **IM** *020

BONNER, Steven Paul. 309 S SHARON AMITY RD, STE 100 28211 #004-01-1979 L1984 **FM** *020 †18

BONO, Erika Lee. 1001 BLYTHE BLVD, MEDICAL CENTER PLAZA, SUIT 28203 #047-05-2002 L2006 **IM** *100 †20

BOORTZ-MARX, Richard Levi. 1718 E 4TH ST, STE 300 28204 #025-07-1991 L2006 **AN PMM** *020 †05

BORHAN-MANESH, Shahrzad S. ■ 28269 #422-01-2002 L2007 **OBG** *020

BORRESEN, Thor Erik. 1900 RANDOLPH RD, STE 1010 28207 #033-05-1979 L1996 **N CN** *020 †75

BOSSE, Michael Jos. 1001 BLYTHE BLVD, STE 602 28203 #023-01-1978 L1993 **ORS** *020 †40

BOURGEOIS, John Elliott. 6035 FAIRVIEW RD, THROAT ASSOCIATES, PA 28210 #051-01-1979 L1982 **OPH** *020 †35

BOUSABA, George Yousef. ■ 28269 #781-06-1982 *100

BOWEN, Christina Michelle. ■ 28210 #036-08-2003 **FP** *012

BOWEN, Josie Barnes. ■ 28209 #036-01-2001 L2004 **EM** *020

BOWEN, Robert Calvin, III. 3030 RANDOLPH RD 28211 #036-01-1999 L2002 **IM** *020 †20

BOWLES, Anne Erskine. 1350 S KINGS DR, MYERS PARK CLINIC 28207 #023-07-2002 L2006 **IM** *020 †20

BOWLES, Claire. 150 PROVIDENCE RD, BRADFORD CLINIC PROVIDENCE 28207 #012-01-1997 L2001 **OBG** *020 †30

BOWMAN, Jerry Lee. 3101 LATROBE DR, PIEDMONT EMERGENCY MEDICIN 28211 #036-08-2004 L2007 **EM** *100

BOX, J Herron. 10460 PARK RD, STE 100 28210 #036-05-1973 L1974 **RHU** *020 †20

BOX, Patrick. 10460 PARK RD, CAROLINA BONE & JOINT 28210 #011-03-1973 L1974 **RHU** *020 †20

BOYD, James Francis. 2711 RANDOLPH RD, STE 100 28207 #036-07-1974 L1985 **ON HEM** *020 †20

BOYER, Patricia Kimberly. 6845 FAIRVIEW RD, SPECIALISTS, PA 28210 #045-01-1981 L1993 **P PYG** *020 †75

BOYES, James G, Jr. ■ 28212 #065-06-1953 L1958 **HS ORS** *071 †40

BRACEWELL, Gregory. 1000 BLYTHE BLVD 28203 #012-01-1980 L1987 **OBG** *020 †30

BRACKEN, Anthony W. 101 E WT HARRIS BLVD, STE 1213 28262 #041-13-1982 L1990 **CD IM** *020 †20

BRACKEN, Roberta Samelson. 1918 RANDOLPH RD STE 220, OSTEOPOROSIS CONSULTANTS 28207 #041-13-1983 L1992 **END IM** *020 †20

BRADBURY, Thomas Lane, Jr. 1915 RANDOLPH RD, ORTHOCAROLINA 28207 #012-01-2001 L2006 **ORS** *020

BRADFORD, Williamson, Jr. 150 PROVIDENCE RD 28207 #041-01-1957 L1957 **GYN OS** *020 †30

BRADNER, Richard Le Queux. 9720 S TRYON ST, ARROWOOD CLINIC 28273 #036-01-1979 L1985 **IM** *020 †16

BRADSHAW, Tamara Lynn. PO BOX 32861, DEPT OF OB/GYN 28232 #055-01-2005 **OBG** *012

BRADY, Jos Lawrence, Jr. 320 W 9TH ST 28202 #036-01-1982 L1985 **PD NPM** *020 †55

BRANCATO, Jason Anthony. 3030 RANDOLPH RD STE 2, MECKLENBURG MEDICAL GROUP 28211 #036-08-2005 L2008 **IM** *012

BRANDON, Rochelle Monique. 5435 PROSPERITY CHURCH RD, STE 2100/EASTOVER UNIV OB/ 28269 #036-01-1993 L1999 **OBG** *020 †30

BRANDWIJK, Marian J. ■ 28207 #016-42-1998 L2007 **PD** *020 †55

BRANN, Oscar Sven. 3030 RANDOLPH RD, MECKLENBURG MEDICAL GROUP 28211 #048-04-1984 L2004 **GE HEP** *040 †20

BRANNER, Christopher M. 1718 E 4TH ST, STE 208 28204 #036-05-2001 L2007 **PG** *020 †55

BRANNER, William Arthur. 4335 COLWICK RD 28211 #036-01-1986 L1988 **OPH** *020 †35

BRANNON, Ronald Hoffman. 1901 RANDOLPH RD 28207 #048-04-1991 L1995 **AN** *020 †05

BRANT, Thomas Alan. 1900 RANDOLPH RD 28207 #028-03-1994 L1998 **EM** *020 †16

BRANTLEY, David Allen. 4525 CAMERON VALLEY PKWY, STE 4100 28211 #036-05-1996 L2002 **END** *020 †20

BRAR, Preetinder Paul S. 8029 CORPORATE CENTER DR 28226 #496-14-1979 L1993 **CHP P** *020 †75

BRAUNING, Genevieve Noel. 5516 CENTRAL AVE 28212 #051-01-2003 L2005 **FM** *020 †18

BRAWLEY, Bob Watson. 1010 EDGEHILL RD N 28207 #036-01-1959 L1959 **NS** *071 †25

BRAY, Christopher Chase. PO BOX 32861, CAROLINAS MED CTR 28232 #045-01-2006 **ORS** *012

BREACH, Karen Ellen. 101 E WT HARRIS BLVD, STE 1121 28262 #010-01-1984 L1987 **PD** *020 †55

BREARLEY, William Dubose. ■ 28209 #045-01-2005 L2007 **IM** *012

BREAUX, Jennifer Ann. PO BOX 32861, DEPT OF OB/GYN 28232 #021-05-2005 **OBG** *012

BREEN, Michael Philip. 6324 FAIRVIEW RD, STE 120 28210 #041-12-1992 L2007 **DR** *020 †80

BREGIER, Charles A, Jr. 10514 PARK RD, PRESBYTERIAN URGENT CARE 28210 #025-07-1981 L1982 **EM** *020 †16

BREITENBACH, Lisa Maida. 501 BILLINGSLEY RD 28211 #012-01-1981 L1986 **P** *030 †75

BREWER, Robyn Betrice. ■ 28205 #045-01-2007 **FM** *012

BRICK, Wendy Gram. 1025 MOREHEAD MEDICAL DR, DRIVE #200 28204 #012-01-1995 L2002 **HO IM** *020 †20

BRIDGES, Lindsay Caldwell. ■ 28211 #036-01-1992 L1995 **FM** *020 †18

BRIDGES, Lloyd Leslie. 6708 ALBEMARLE RD, ASSOCIATES ALBEMARLE 28212 #011-02-1993 L1996 **FM** *020 †18

BRIGHAM, Craig Donald. 1025 MOREHEAD MEDICAL DR, STE 300 28204 #016-06-1982 L1988 **ORS** *020 †40

BRIGHAM, Joan S. 1801 E FIFTH ST, STE 108B 28204 #025-12-1976 L1989 **IM** *020 †20

BRIGHT, Robert Paul. 501 BILLINGSLEY RD 28211 #036-01-1991 L1996 **P** *040 †75

BROCK, Edson Geo, II. ■ 28277 #012-05-1987 L1999 **EM** *020 †16

BROCKMAN, Catalina Delgra. 11030 GOLF LINKS DR, STE 100 28277 #055-01-1993 L1996 **PD** *020 †55

BROCKMEIER, Stephen F. 2826 RANDOLPH RD 28211 #010-02-2001 L2007 **OSM** *020

BROGAN, Marlene Marie. 5208 PARK RD 28209 #047-20-1992 L1996 **P** *020

BROOKS, Douglas Paul. 5435 PROSPERITY CHURCH RD, STE 2200 28269 #055-01-1997 L2006 **FM** *020 †18

BROOKS, Wm Lester, Jr. ■ 28207 #036-07-1947 L1948 **IM RHU** *071 †20

BROWN, Charles Jacob. 2310 RANDOLPH RD # A 28207 #036-01-1987 L1992 **D** *020 †15

BROWN, Eric David. 2001 VAIL AVE, MEDICAL ASSOCIATES 28207 #005-14-1999 L2002 **EM** *020 †16

BROWN, Karl. ■ 28203 #005-02-1993 L2007 **ID IM** *020 †20 ‡

BROWN, Leah Chevon. ■ 28262 #038-40-2003 L2004 **ORS** *012 †55

BROWN, Rhett. 5516 CENTRAL AVE 28212 #045-01-1989 L1992 **FM** *020 †18

BROWN, Ronald Lauchlin. 150 PROVIDENCE RD 28207 #045-01-1974 L1978 **OBG** *020 †30

BROWN, Susan Bartow. 5435 PROSPERITY CHURCH RD, STE 2200A 28269 #050-02-1998 L2007 **OBG** *020 †30

BROWNE, Lauren. 2015 RANDOLPH RD, SUTIE 208 28204 #024-05-1994 L2000 **GE** *020 †20

BROWNE, Richard Everette. 1001 BLYTHE BLVD, STE 300 28203 #024-05-1993 L2000 **CD** *020 †20

BROWNING, David Judson. 6035 FAIRVIEW RD 28210 #036-07-1981 L1982 **OPH** *020 †35

BRUCE, Joel Edward. 8936 BLAKENEY PROFESSNL DR 28277 #051-01-1987 L1996 **NEP IM** *020 †20

BRUMIT, Marla Crow. 2425 PARK RD, AMERICAN RED CROSS BLOOD 28203 #047-20-1997 L2005 **BBK** *062 †50

BRUNTON, Stephen A. 12105 COPPER WAY, STE 202 28277 #143-08-1974 L2004 **FM FPG** *020 †18

BRYANT, Paulette Charese. 1712 E 4TH ST, PRESBYTERIAN BLUME PEDIATR 28204 #024-01-1985 L2005 **PD** *020 †55

BRYANT, William Franklin. 10348 PARK RD, STE 300 28210 #036-07-1958 L1958 **PD** *020 †55

BUCHANAN, Dale Conway. 1901 RANDOLPH RD 28207 #045-01-1982 L1988 **AN PD** *020 †55,05

BUCHANAN, Sonya Wynee. 1410 W MOREHEAD ST, STE 200 28208 #047-07-1995 L1999 **OM** *020

BUCHSBAUM, Michael Scott. 2001 VAIL AVE, MEDICAL ASSOCIATES 28207 #011-04-1996 L2001 **OS** *020 †20,16

BUCKLER, Michelle Ann. ■ 28210 #045-01-2005 **OBG** *012

BUCKNER, David Lee. 2001 VAIL AVE, CAROLINAS HEALTHCARE SYSTE 28207 #003-01-1998 L2007 **IM** *020 †20

BUEHRIG, Christopher K. 8936 BLAKENEY PROFESSNL DR 28277 #045-01-1996 L2003 NEP IM *020 †20

BUI, Hong Thi. ■ 28209 #045-04-2006 PD *012

BULLARD, Graham Wesley. 927 EAST BLVD 28203 #036-01-1981 L1982 AN PME *020 †05

BULLARD, Kenneth Penn. ■ 28211 #036-05-1966 L1966 PS *071 †65

BULLARD, Mark Jeffrey. 1000 BLYTHE BLVD, CARLOINAS MED CTR 28203 #038-41-2001 L2004 EM *020 †16

BULLOCK, William Robt. 100 N TRYON ST, PHYSICIANS 28202 #047-06-1968 L1969 IM ADM *020 †20

BURGESS, Jason Shade. 1416 E MOREHEAD ST, SPECIALISTS 28204 #036-01-1996 L2002 VS *020 †85

BURGESS, Shawn Theodore. PO BOX 30756, 1900 RANDOLPH ROAD SUITE 28230 #051-01-2000 L2007 EM *020

BURGESS, William Patrick. 2711 RANDOLPH RD, STE 400 28207 #011-02-1977 L1982 NEP LM *050 †20

BURKE, Henry Lawrence. 1420 E 7TH ST, CHARLOTTE REGION 28204 #010-02-1991 L1993 PUD *020 †20

BURKE, Jennifer Willis. 101 E WT HARRIS BLVD, STE 5002 28262 #036-08-1995 L1997 IM *020 †20

BURNS, Martin Alan. 3623 LATROBE DR, STE 216 28211 #047-05-1986 L1992 DR *020 †80

BURNSIDE, Patrick Russell. ■ 28207 #036-08-2007 *012

BURQUEST, Bret Owen. 1515 MOCKINGBIRD LN, STE 530 28209 #011-02-1961 L1985 P ADP *020 †75

BURSON, Jana Kaye. 145 REMOUNT RD, MCLEOD ADDICTIVE DISEASE C 28203 #038-40-1987 L2000 IM *020 †20

BUSHEY, Jennifer Louise. ■ 28214 #051-07-2001 L2007 PD *020 †55

BUTER, Thomas Henry. 10512 PARK RD STE 101, CHARLOTTE ORTHOPEDIC SPECL 28210 #025-01-1975 L1976 ORS *020 †40

BUTLER, Jennifer Ruth. PO BOX 32861, CAROLINAS HLTH CARE SYS 28232 #051-01-1997 L2005 OBG *020 †30

CALABRETTA, Arthur M. 1918 RANDOLPH RD, STE 850 28207 #041-14-1975 L1998 PS GS *020 †65

CALDWELL, William Mckamie. 1918 RANDOLPH RD, STE 310 28207 #036-08-1998 L2003 OTO A *020 †45

CALHOUN, Benjamin C. 1000 BLYTHE BLVD 28203 #012-01-1999 L2004 PTH *020 †50

CALLAHAN, Catherine B. 10512 PARK RD, MECKLENBURG MEDICAL GROUP 28210 #012-01-1999 L2001 IM *020 †20

CAMERON, Calvin Brian. 1901 RANDOLPH RD 28207 #062-01-1977 L2003 AN *020 †05 ‡

CAMILO, Osvaldo Arturo. 1718 E 4TH ST, STE 404 28204 #308-01-1986 L2004 CN *020

CAMP, John Frederick. 927 EAST BLVD 28203 #041-02-1978 L1985 AN PME *020 †05

CAMP, Steven Martin. ■ 28209 #048-15-2004 GS *012

CAMPBELL, Faye Sherwood. 1900 SELWYN AVE, HEALTH AND WELLNESS CENTER 28274 #041-12-1994 L2000 IM *020 †20

CAMPBELL, Grant Liles. 101 E WT HARRIS BLVD, STE 5301 28262 #036-01-1997 L1998 OBG *020 †30

CAMPBELL, James Archibald. 2801 RANDOLPH RD STE 200 28211 #036-01-1960 L1960 OBG *071 †30

CAMPBELL, James Kirk. 1001 BLYTHE BLVD, MED CTR PLAZA, SUITE 500 28203 #045-01-1993 L1996 GE IM *020 †20

CAMPBELL, Jessica Erin. ■ 28209 #036-01-2005 L2007 FP *012

CAMPBELL, Vivian Denise. 501 BILLINGSLEY RD, CAROLINAS MEDICAL CENTER- 28211 #038-41-1989 L1997 P *020 †75

CANTUARIA, Guilherme H. 200 HAWTHORNE LN 28204 #187-33-1992 L2004 OBG GO *020 †30

CAPIZZI, Michelle C. 1900 RANDOLPH RD 28207 #051-07-1989 L1998 PEM *074 †55

CAPO, Jason Alan. ■ 28205 #026-08-2007 ORS *012

CAPPLEMAN, William F, III. 330 BILLINGSLEY RD, STE 100 28211 #036-07-1979 L1981 IM *020 †20

CAPUANO, Melissa Margo. 1918 RANDOLPH RD STE 2 28207 #011-03-2002 L2007 END *020 †20

CARDWELL, Jeffrey Glen. 10310 MALLARD CREEK RD, UNIVERSITY FAMILY PHYSICIA 28262 #011-03-1988 L1990 FM *020 †18

CARLSON, Beth Lynn. 6708 ALBEMARLE RD 28212 #035-15-1996 L2005 FM *020 †18

CARLTON, Thomas Kern, III. 2610 E 7TH ST, THE REHAB CENTER INC 28204 #036-05-1989 L1993 PM *020 †60

CARMICHAEL, Dennis D. 2014 PARK DR 28204 #803-01-1950 L1957 CHP *071

CARNEY, Kelly Anne. ■ 28209 #036-01-2005 PD *012

CARR, Chpryelle. ■ 28211 #012-22-2007 PD *012

CARRUTH, Marc Ronald. 2615 E 7TH ST, CAROLINA SKIN SURGERY CTR 28204 #036-07-1993 L1997 DS D *020 †15

CARTER, Coleman Delynne. 1900 RANDOLPH RD, STE 500 28207 #036-01-1971 L2004 IM *020 †20

CARTER, Kenneth Olander. 501 BILLINGSLEY RD 28211 #033-05-1985 L2002 P *020 †75

CARTER, Kevin Sterling. 28210 #024-07-2007 PD *012

CASE, Caroline Margaret. 200 S COLLEGE ST, MECKLENBURG MEDICAL GROUP 28202 #045-01-1996 L2004 IM *020 †20

CASEY, Virginia Fishburne. 1025 MOREHEAD MEDICAL DR, STE 300 28204 #039-01-1999 L2005 OP *020 †40

CASINGAL, Vincent Philip. 1000 BLYTHE BLVD 28203 #051-07-1998 L2005 GS *100 †85

CASNER, Elizabeth Eden. 28210 #007-02-2005 L2008 EM *012

CASSANI, Lisa Suzanne. ■ 28226 #036-01-2008 *012

CASTILLO-TOHER, Miriam A. 8401 MEDICAL PLAZA DR, STE 250 28262 #016-42-1984 L1991 FM *020 †18

CASTRO, Dana Edward. 501 BILLINGSLEY RD 28211 #035-03-1982 L2001 P *020 †75

CATES, Casey A. 1616 SCOTT AVE, CMC ORTHOPAEDICS 28203 #048-13-2002 L2007 ORS *020

CATHEY, Reginald Lamont. ■ 28217 #036-08-2002 GS *012

CAUDLE, Suzette Surratt. 1000 BLYTHE BLVD, DEPARTMENT OF PEDIATRICS 28203 #045-04-1986 L1991 PD CCM *040 †55

CAUGHRAN, John H. 1901 RANDOLPH RD 28207 #017-20-1951 L1958 ORS *020 †40

CHACONAS, Aris Evan. 1918 RANDOLPH RD STE 400, PRESBYTERIAN NEOUROLOGY 28207 #010-02-1988 L1997 N *020 †75

CHAI, Janie Yun. 2711 RANDOLPH RD, RANDOLPH RD 28207 #012-01-1998 L2004 PD *020 †55

CHAMBERS, Kenneth Henley. 1718 E 4TH ST STE 202 28204 #047-07-1959 L1960 OBG *071 †30

CHAMBLEE, Donald Vance. 231 S SHARON AMITY RD 28211 #047-06-1956 L1956 GP A *071 †18

CHAN, Barry Bing-Kong. 1718 E 4TH ST, STE 701 28204 #016-06-1987 L1996 TS VS *020 †85,90

CHAN, Ruben C. 200 HAWTHORNE LN, PICS OFFICE 28204 #748-08-1988 L1996 IM *020 †20

CHANG, Sung Kyu. 927 EAST BLVD 28203 #036-01-2000 L2005 APM AN *020 †05

CHAPLIN, Charles H. ■ 28207 #041-02-1953 L1953 PS *071 †18

CHAPMAN, Geoffrey Sewall. 2711 RANDOLPH RD, STE 100 28207 #005-02-1975 L1985 ON HEM *020 †20

CHAPPELL, Dale Brian. ■ 28207 #032-01-1999 *100

CHATURVEDI, Indira. ■ 28269 #495-57-1994 PD *100 ‡

CHEIFETZ, Paul Adam. ■ 28207 #035-19-2002 L2007 NEP *020 †20

CHEN, Thomas Tong-Yong. 1901 RANDOLPH RD 28207 #244-01-1968 L1978 AN CCA *020 †05 ‡

CHENG, Iris Sugie. 1000 BLYTHE BLVD, P O BOX 32861 28203 #005-02-1989 L1996 IM *020 †20

CHERER, Allen John. 200 HAWTHORNE LN 28204 #012-01-1977 L1994 NPM PD *020 †55

CHILDERS, Jacob A. 7810 PROVIDENCE RD, STE 102 28226 #048-14-2002 L2005 FM *020 †18

CHILDERS, Melvin Davis. 4335 COLWICK RD 28211 #051-04-1958 L1962 OPH OS *071 †35

CHIN, James Y. 200 HAWTHORNE LN, SPECIALISTS, PRESBYTERIAN 28204 #033-05-1995 L1998 IM *020 †20

CHINTALAPATI, Sitarama R. 200 HAWTHORNE LN 28204 #495-11-1994 L2008 MPD *020 †20

CHITTENDEN, Tamara E. 200 S COLLEGE ST, MECKLENBURG MEDICAL GROUP 28202 #050-02-1998 L2001 IM *020 †20

CHIU, Michelle Karen. 1000 BLYTHE BLVD, 7TH FL 28203 #012-01-1993 L1999 NPM PD *020 †55

CHORNESKY, Samuel. ■ 28204 #024-07-1959 L1985 P *071

CHRISTENBURY, Jonathan D. 3621 RANDOLPH RD 28211 #036-07-1980 L1982 OPH PS *020 †35

CHRISTIAN, Eugene Paul. 309 S SHARON AMITY RD, STE 102 28211 #041-13-1981 L2005 ORS OSM *020 †40

CHRISTMAS, Ashley Bretton. 1000 BLYTHE BLVD, DEPART OF SURGERY, MEB 6TH 28203 #020-02-2000 L2006 GS *020 ‡

CHRISTOFFERSEN, Brett A. 11030 GOLF LINKS DR, STE 100 28277 #004-01-1995 L1998 IM *020 †20

CHRYSLER, Charles Otis. 3319 GRESHAM PL 28211 #038-40-1956 L1960 FM *071 †18

CHUANG, Peale. 2711 RANDOLPH RD, STE 400 28207 #007-02-2000 L2007 NEP *020 †20 ‡

CHUN, Erica Pamela. 2001 VAIL AVE, MEDICAL ASSOCIATES 28207 #051-01-1998 L2001 EM *020 †16

CITRON, David S. 1112 HARDING PL, BIOETHICS RESOURCE STE 200 28204 #028-02-1944 L1951 IM FM *072 †20,18

CLARK, David, Jr. ■ 28270 #010-03-1982 L1987 FM *020 †18

CLARK, John Blue, Jr. 1900 RANDOLPH RD 28207 #047-05-1973 L1979 EM IM *020 †20,16

CLARK, Kenosha Yarneisha. ■ 28262 #045-01-2006 OBG *012

CLARK, Talaya Blakey. 1801 ROZZELLES FERRY RD 28208 #041-15-2002 L2004 FM *020 †18

CLARK, William Mackey. 3623 LATROBE DR STE 216, MECKLENBURG RADIOLOGY ASSO 28211 #024-01-1971 L1972 R *020 †80

CLAVIO, Estrelita Nancy R. 10036 PARK CEDAR DR 28210 #748-01-1975 L1994 PUD IM *020 †20

CLAYPOOLE, Amy Ileen. ■ 28270 #038-40-1989 L1990 IM *020 †20

CLEEK, John Brooks. 2608 E 7TH ST, MECKLENBURG MEDICAL GROUP 28204 #012-01-1985 L1986 IM ON *020 †20

CLEGG, Herbert Wm, II. 2600 E 7TH ST, STE 100 28204 #036-07-1975 L1982 PD ID *020 †55

CLEMENT, Wesley Dobbs. 230 E WT HARRIS BLVD C-13, CAROLINAS EYE CENTER 28262 #047-07-1971 L1975 OPH *020

CLEMENTS, Thad Aaron. 8401 MEDICAL PLAZA DR, STE 300 28262 #019-02-1995 L1998 FM *020 †18

CLEMONS, Alison Ruwet. 1601 ABBEY PL, CAROLINAS HEALTHCARE URGEN 28209 #047-06-1999 L2006 EM *020 †16

CLEMONS, William Eric. 3541 RANDOLPH RD, STE 200 28211 #047-06-1999 L2006 P *100 †75

CLEVELAND, Jeffrey Allen. 10348 PARK RD, STE 300 28210 #036-05-1988 L1994 PD *020 †55

CLINARD, George Craig. 101 E WT HARRIS BLVD, STE 1213 28262 #036-05-1990 L1996 CD *020 †20

CLONTZ, Ted Hamilton. 200 HAWTHORNE LN, SPECIALISTS/PRESBYTERIAN H 28204 #036-05-1980 L1981 FM *020 †20

CLYNE, Stephen Bernard. 10352 PARK RD 28210 #036-05-1999 L2002 OTO *020 †45

COBB, Pamela Griffin. 251 EASTWAY DR, NORTHPARK, OB DEPT 28213 #041-01-1992 L2004 OBG *020 †30

COBEY, William G. ■ 28278 #036-07-1953 L1955 PD OS *071 †55

COCHRAN, Stephen George. 1000 BLYTHE BLVD, DEPT OF INTERNAL MEDICINE(28203 #017-20-1997 L1998 CCM *020 †20

COFIE, Abelard K. 8401 MEDICAL PLAZA DR, STE 200 28262 #654-01-1984 L1991 PD *020 †55

COGGINS, Kenneth Gerald. 1001 BLYTHE BLVD STE 403 28203 #012-01-1994 L1997 PCC *020 †20

COHEN, Arthur Robt. 200 HAWTHORNE LN 28204 #048-04-1977 L1986 PTH *062 †50

COHEN, Todd Douglas. 10520 PARK RD, STE 140 28210 #035-45-1989 L1995 U *020 †95

COLAVITA, Paul Gerard. 1001 BLYTHE BLVD, STE 300 28203 #036-05-1979 L1982 CD IM *020 †20

COLE, Alice W. 4525 CAMERON VALLEY PKWY, STE 3100 28211 #012-01-1995 L1996 IM *020 †20

COLE, Ian Oluremileku. ■ 28216 #025-01-2007 EM *012

COLES, Debra Lynn. 1001 BLYTHE BLVD, STE 500 28203 #036-01-1988 L1989 IM *020 †20

COLLAWN, Thomas Herbert. ■ 28211 #023-01-1956 L1959 AN *071 †05

COLLIN, Charles Frederick. 1918 RANDOLPH RD, STE 500 28207 #021-01-1975 L1987 GS SO *020 †85

COLLINS, Gregory Vincent. 330 BILLINGSLEY RD STE 100 28211 #039-01-1982 L1985 IM EM *020 †20

COLLINS, Kelly Marie. PO BOX 32861, CAROLINAS MED CTR 28232 #038-45-2007 IM *012

COLLINS, Richard E. 2630 E 7TH ST, STE 100 28204 #045-01-1988 L1994 AI *020 †55,03

COLLINS, Vasiliki S. 3621 RANDOLPH RD, STE 200 28211 #045-01-1988 L1994 AN *020 †05

COLUCCIELLO, Stephen A. 10628 PARK RD 28210 #023-01-1981 L1992 EM *020 †16

COMISKY, William Merrill. 10508 PARK RD, PINEVILLE 28210 #055-02-1986 L1989 PD *020 †55

COMPTON, David Alan. 2835 JEFF ADAMS DR, VIRGINIA DEPARTMENT OF HEA 28206 #051-04-1984 L1991 UCM OM *020 †70

COMPTON, Kenneth W. 6035 FAIRVIEW RD 28210 #045-04-1981 L1986 OTO *020 †45

CONARD, David Lloyd. 8401 MEDICAL PLAZA DR #200 28262 #035-45-1981 L1984 IM *020 †20

CONNOR, Patrick Michael. 1025 MOREHEAD MEDICAL DR, STE 300 28204 #039-01-1990 L1996 ORS *020 †40

CONSTANTINE, Jeffrey C. 200 S COLLEGE ST, MECKLENBURG MEDICAL GROUP 28202 #036-05-2000 L2003 IM *020 †20

COOK, Briggs Edward, Jr. 4335 COLWICK RD, FOR SIGHT 28211 #023-07-1995 L2001 OPH *020 †35

COOK, Charles Edward. 927 EAST BLVD 28203 #024-01-1982 L1996 AN *020 †05

COOK, Joseph Wm, Jr. 1001 BLYTHE BLVD STE 300 28203 #036-07-1968 L1968 TS *071 †85,90

COOK, Marcus Peter. 1918 RANDOLPH RD, STE 700 28207 #036-07-1997 L2005 OSM *020 †40

COOK, Tyson Willis. ■ 28209 #038-41-2006 EM *012

COOLEY, Gerald Earl. 10000 PARK RD, STE 100 28210 #036-01-1992 L1996 D *020 †15

COOLS, Kathleen Tricia. PO BOX 32861, DEPT OF OB/GYN 28232 #047-07-2007 OBG *012

COOPER, Tim Ervin. 330 BILLINGSLEY RD, STE 100 28211 #036-07-1959 L1959 IM PUD *071 †20

COPELAND, Donald Lee. 501 BILLINGSLEY RD 28211 #036-01-1963 L1963 FM *071 †18

COPLAND, Spencer Thomas. 5516 CENTRAL AVE, EASTLAND FAMILY PRACTICE 28212 #036-01-2005 L2007 FP *012

COPPAGE, Kevin Bernard. 200 HAWTHORNE LN 28204 #018-03-1992 L2001 NPM PD *020 †55

COPPAGE, Patricia Ashley. 1000 BLYTHE BLVD 28203 #036-01-2000 L2003 PD *020 †20

COPPEDGE, Thos Oliver, Jr. 200 HAWTHORNE LN 28204 #036-05-1947 L1947 R *071 †80

CORBIER, Michelle T. ■ 28262 #025-12-1994 L2007 PD *030 †55

CORDLE, Randolph Jay. 1000 BLYTHE BLVD, MEB 3RD FL DEPT OF EME MED 28203 #038-41-1992 L2005 PD *020 †55,16

CORIC, Domagoj. 225 BALDWIN AVE 28204 #036-05-1992 L1994 NS OS *020 †25

CORNWELL, Andrew Alfred. ■ 28241 #040-02-1999 L1999 FM *071 †18

CORNWELL, Michelle A. ■ 28241 #019-02-1999 L1999 FM *020

COSCULLUELA, Pedro E. 1001 BLYTHE BLVD, STE 200 28203 #042-02-2001 L2006 ORS *100

COUGHLIN, Kathryn Ann. 1001 BLYTHE BLVD, DEPT OF INTERNAL MEDICINE 28203 #020-12-1984 L1989 N *071 †20

COUNCIL, John C, Jr. 14214 BALLANTYNE LAKE RD, STE 300 28277 #036-01-1961 L1961 PD *020 †55

COURTLANDT, Cheryl Denise. 1000 BLYTHE BLVD, P O BOX 32861 28203 #033-06-1983 L1997 PD *020 †55

COUTTS, Clarence P. ■ 28202 #495-52-1982 L1993 IM *020

COVINGTON, Valenica Diane. 1918 RANDOLPH RD, STE 670 28207 #036-01-1983 L1984 FM *020 †18

COWAN, David Emerson. 10620 PARK RD STE 218, CAROLINA UROLOGY CTR 28210 #036-07-1955 L1955 U *071 †95

COWAN, Michael Andrew. 225 BALDWIN AVE, CAROLINA NEURO & SPINE 28204 #012-01-1993 L1999 NS *020 †25

COWELL, Brenda Kay. 1001 BLYTHE BLVD, STE 500 28203 #036-01-1989 L1992 IM *071 †20

COX, Jack Landon. 2320 CASCADE POINTE BLVD 28208 #027-01-1980 L2000 FM *040 †18

COX, Pamela G. ■ 28209 #038-44-1996 L1997 ID *100 †20

COYLE, Joseph Paul. 927 EAST BLVD, BOX 36351 28203 #041-09-1978 L1986 AN CCA *020 †05

CRAIG, Matthew Ramey. 720 E MOREHEAD ST, STE 301 28202 #028-46-2001 L2004 IM *020 †20

CRAIG, Sandra Anne. 1000 BLYTHE BLVD, CAROLINAS MEDICAL CENTER 28203 #051-04-1987 L1990 EM *020 †16

CRAIN, Jack Lee. 1524 E MOREHEAD ST 28207 #004-01-1966 L1984 REN GYN *020 †30

CRANDALL, Robert Gordon. ■ 28226 #064-01-1956 L1981 P *071 †75

CRANE, Monica Kim. 28203 #041-02-2001 L2006 FM FPG *020 †18

CRAVEN, Dallas Clifford, Jr. 2104 RANDOLPH RD 28207 #036-01-1975 L1980 GS *020 †85

CRAVEN, Jesse Clarence. 1701 ABBEY PL, CHARLOTTE INTERNAL MEDICIN 28209 #036-01-1962 L1962 IM *071 †20

CRAVEN, Murray B, III. 330 BILLINGSLEY RD STE 100, RANDOLPH INTERNAL MEDICINE 28211 #036-01-1985 L1988 IM *020 †20

CRAWFORD, John Thos. 9101 MONROE RD, STE 155 28270 #036-05-1987 L1988 FM *020 †18

CREMISI, Henry David. 2301 W MOREHEAD ST # 101, SOUTHEAST RENAL ASSOCIATES 28208 #024-07-1988 L1991 NEP *020 †20

CRISP, Catrina Carleen. 1900 SELWYN AVE 28274 #047-06-2005 L2005 OBG *012

CRISWELL, Bryan Keith. 15105 JOHN J DELANEY DR, STE E 28277 #034-01-1998 L2007 PS *020 †65

CROMWELL, William C. 125 BALDWIN AVE, STE 200 28204 #021-05-1987 L2002 FM OS *020 †18

CROSBY, Kim Leigh. 2131 AYRSLEY TOWN BLVD, STE 200 28273 #016-11-1991 L1998 GS OS *020 †85

CULP, Pamela Jean. 3623 LATROBE DR STE 216, MECKLENBURG RADIOLOGY ASSC 28211 #036-05-1982 L1984 DR R *020 †80

CULPEPPER, Fred C, III. 14214 BALLANTYNE LAKE RD, PROVIDENCE PEDIATRICS 28277 #021-05-1967 L1972 PD *020 †55

CUPID, Melissa Weatherspo. 1805 MILTON RD, AMERICARE HEALTH PC 28215 #038-45-1997 L2003 FM *020 †18

CYZNER, Ronnie. 10370 PARK RD, STE 102 28210 #035-09-1993 L1999 GE IM *020 †20

DAFTARY, Shoobha Shashi. ■ 28277 #011-03-1989 L1991 CCM IM *100

DAILY, Jeffrey Morris. 1100 KENILWORTH AVE, STE 202 28204 #016-01-1986 L1991 ORS *020 †40

DAIR, Marvin Paul. 1000 BLYTHE BLVD 28203 #021-01-2003 L2006 IM *020 †20

DALE-SHALL, Amanda Watson. ■ 28214 #038-43-2001 L2007 PN *100 †55

D'ALESSANDRO, Donald F. 1025 MOREHEAD MEDICAL DR, STE 300 28204 #010-02-1983 L1989 ORS *040 †40

DALRYMPLE, Brian Anderson. 1000 BLYTHE BLVD, ANNEX BUILDING 28203 #012-01-1995 L1996 IM *020 †20

DALSANIA, Mital Parag. 1718 E 4TH ST, STE 404 28204 #496-26-1994 L2006 N *020 †75

DAMANI, Manish Nalin. 1718 E 4TH ST, STE 807 28204 #038-44-1995 L2001 U *020 †95

DANIELS-MITCHELL, Karen E. 5801 EXECUTIVE CENTER DR, STE 100 28212 #033-06-1985 L1988 FM *020 †18 ‡

DANNER, Christopher John. 2801 RANDOLPH RD, STE 200 28211 #021-05-1997 L2001 OBG *020 †30

DANNER, Omar Karreim. 6000 FAIRVIEW RD, STE 1200 28210 #001-02-1995 L2004 GS CCS *020 †85

DARDEN, Bruce Vaiden, II. 2001 RANDOLPH RD 28207 #036-01-1982 L1983 ORS *020 †40

DARROW, George Lester. 2001 VAIL AVE, MEDICAL ASSOCIATES 28207 #036-08-1999 L2001 EM *020 †16

DASHER, George Albert. 10512 PARK RD, THE CAROLINAS PINEVILLE 28210 #012-01-1973 L1974 U *020 †30

DASHER, Meredith Leigh. 10348 PARK RD, STE 100 28210 #024-07-1999 L2005 D *020 †15

DAUGHERTY, Harry Karrick. 1001 BLYTHE BLVD, STE 300 28203 #020-02-1959 L1963 TS *071 †85,90

DAUGHERTY, Stephen A. 11010 DAVID TAYLOR DR 28262 #056-05-1991 L1996 OPH PO *020 †35

DAUL, Anne Marie. ■ 28203 #056-05-2006 EM *012

DAVIS, Daniel Thomas. 1350 S KINGS DR, CMC MYERS PARK ORTHOPAEDIC 28207 #021-01-1976 L1999 ORS *020 †40

DAVIS, George Kevin. 200 HAWTHORNE LN, SPECIALISTS/PRESBYTERIAN H 28204 #012-01-1986 L1989 IM *020 †16

DAVIS, Harriet Neely. 10000 PARK CEDAR DR 28210 #036-01-1999 L2002 FSM *020 †18

DAVIS, James Alexander. 1900 RANDOLPH RD 28207 #036-05-1988 L1990 EM *020 †16

DAVIS, Wiley Mason, Jr. 11030 GOLF LINKS DR STE 10 28277 #036-08-1986 L1988 FM *020 †18

DAWKINS, Rosamuel. 1406 BEATTIES FORD RD, NORTH WEST MEDICAL CENTER 28216 #036-05-1973 L1973 GE IM *020 †20

DAWSON, William Bowker. 2001 VAIL AVE 28207 #051-01-1989 L1997 N IM *020 †75

DAYAL, Usha. 12311 COPPER WAY, STE 230 28277 #495-27-1980 L1997 PD CHN *020 †75,55

DEAN, Donna Michelle. 3101 LATROBE DR, STE 100 28211 #020-12-1994 L1998 IM PD *020 †20

DEAN, Elizabeth Anne. 4525 CAMERON VALLEY PKWY, STE 3100 28211 #036-05-1984 L1987 IM *020 †20

DE BUYS, Holly Virginia. 4525 CAMERON VALLEY PKWY, STE 2100 28211 #001-02-1998 L2000 D *020 †15

DEE, Arthur L. 1000 BLYTHE BLVD 28203 #023-07-1951 L1971 ATP *020 †50

DE HOFF, Philip W. 1718 E 4TH ST, STE 907 28204 #011-04-1980 L1983 OBG *020 †30 ‡

DEHORITY, Dixon Remy. 9101 MONROE RD STE 155, CROWN POINT FAMILY PHYSICI 28270 #051-04-1989 L1991 FM *020 †18

DEHORITY, Elizabeth S. 1601 ABBEY PL 28209 #025-01-1991 L1995 FM *020 †18

DE LA TORRE, Ernesto E. ■ 28270 #036-05-1998 L2007 FM *020 †18

DEMCHAK, Susan Mcbrayer. 15110 JOHN J DELANEY DR, STE 100 28277 #045-01-1995 L2003 OBG *020 †30

DENNIS, Patrick M. 3621 RANDOLPH RD, CHRISTENBURY EYE CENTER 28211 #010-02-1976 L1980 OPH *020 †35

DENNIS, Ronald Green. 6035 FAIRVIEW RD, THROAT ASSOCIATES PA 28210 #036-05-1971 L1971 OTO *020 †45

DENNY, Roger Roswell. 1000 BLYTHE BLVD 28203 #035-47-1993 L2002 GS *020 †85

DESAI, Sujata R. ■ 28215 #495-97-1983 P *100

DE SANTIS, Andrea M. 251 EASTWAY DR, CMC-NORTHPARK 28213 #041-77-1995, ▲ L1999 FM *020 †18

DESENA, Curtis Wm. 10310 MALLARD CREEK RD, UNIVERSITY FAMILY PHYSICIA 28262 #011-03-1992 L1994 FM *020 †18 ‡

DESHMUKH, Vinay. 225 BALDWIN AVE 28204 #011-03-1997 L2003 NS *020 †25

DEVINE, Brian David. 10220 PROSPERITY PARK DR, STE 300 28269 #041-02-1997 L2004 FM *020 †18

DEWS, Marshall Andrew. 7800 PROVIDENCE RD, STE 203 ARBORETUM PEDIATIR 28226 #051-01-1996 L2003 PD *020 †55

DIAZ BUXO, Jose Antonio. 1001 MOREHEAD SQUARE DR, STE 470 28203 #042-01-1970 L2004 NEP IM *040 †20

DIAZ DE LA ROCHA, Lisette. ■ 28211 #305-01-2007 FP *012

DICKERSON, Ginger Ann. 101 E WT HARRIS BLVD, STE 5301 28262 #027-01-1994 L1998 OBG *020 †30

DICKERSON, Leon A, Jr. 2001 RANDOLPH RD, ORTHOCAROLINA 28207 #055-01-1970 L1974 ORS *020 †40

DICKINSON, Ada Barbara. 3535 RANDOLPH RD, STE 206 28211 #308-11-1985 L1993 PD *020

DICKSON, Flynn Keels. ■ 28211 #045-01-1967 L1974 OTO A *071 †45

DICKSON, Griggs Cameron. ■ 28209 #036-01-1955 L1955 PD *071 †55

DIEDRICH, Andrea Lynn. 3541 RANDOLPH RD, CAROLINA NEUROLOGICAL 28211 #012-05-1992 L1996 N *020 †20

DIEHL, Lance Earle. 1718 E 4TH ST, HAWTHORNE CARDIOTHORACIC & 28204 #041-13-1995 L2004 GS *020 †85

DIEMONT, Stephen T. 2001 VAIL AVE, MEDICAL ASSOCIATES 28207 #030-05-1990 L1993 EM *020 †16

DILLARD, Sam Booker. ■ 28210 #018-03-1946 L1946 D *071 †15

DINOME, Anthony Jos, Jr. 501 BILLINGSLEY RD 28211 #036-01-1987 L1991 P *020 †75

DITESHEIM, Jeffrey Alan. 9336 BLAKENEY HEATH RD, STE 130 28277 #035-19-1985 L1995 PS GS *020 †65

DIVISH, Margaret Mary. 7810 PROVIDENCE RD, STE 103 28226 #035-46-1991 L1996 IM *020 †20

DOCKERY, Michael Lee. 101 E WT HARRIS BLVD, STE 5001 28262 #011-03-1990 L1996 OSM ORS *020 †40

DOLCE, Charles James. ■ 28269 #422-01-2002 L2007 GS *100 †85

DOLLAR, James. 101 E WT HARRIS BLVD, STE 1212 28262 #028-03-1986 L1999 PTH NP *020 †50

DOMAN, Kathleen Anne. 2711 RANDOLPH RD, STE 400 28207 #036-07-1985 L1990 IM *020 †20

DOMNINA, Yuliya Anatoliev. 1001 BLYTHE BLVD STE 300, SANGER CLINIC 28203 #913-36-1996 L2007 CCP *100 †55

DON, Scott Anthony. 335 BILLINGSLEY RD, STE 103 28211 #003-01-1993 L1999 PS *020 †65

DOOLITTLE, Thomas P. 927 EAST BLVD 28203 #056-06-1990 L1998 AN *020 †20

DORE, Joseph Basil. 2001 VAIL AVE, MEDICAL ASSOCIATES 28207 #021-05-1995 L2000 EM *020 †20,16

DORNBLAZER, George Henry. 1332 HARDING PL 28204 #055-01-1977 L1985 P *020 †75

DORSETT, John D, Jr. 1701 ABBEY PL 28209 #028-02-1951 L1951 IM CD *020 †20

DORSEY, Steven Elliott, Jr. 7800 PROVIDENCE RD STE 203, ABRORETUM PEDS 28226 #055-02-2001 L2004 PD *020 †55

DOSS, Jerome Faulkner. ■ 28210 #018-03-1958 L1959 OBG *071 †30

DOTY, John Douglas, II. 1001 BLYTHE BLVD 28203 #047-06-1996 L2007 PCC *020 †20,55

DOUGHERTY, Richard Allen. 10450 PARK RD, STE 210 28210 #035-08-1987 L1993 IM *020 †20

DOWDY, David Andrew. 1718 E 4TH ST, STE 501 28204 #008-02-1976 L1981 CD IM *020 †20

DOWNING, Wilma Theodora. 14214 BALLANTYNE LAKE RD, PROVIDENCE PEDIATRICS 28277 #041-09-1993 L1996 PD *020 †55

DOYLE, James Michael. 3832 MONROE RD 28205 #010-02-1992 L1997 ANM PAN *020 †05

DRAGO, Paul Carl. 14835 JOHN J DELANEY DR, STE 210 28277 #038-40-1990 L1997 CS FPS *020 †45

DRIES, Andrew Michael. ■ 28210 #035-45-2001 L2007 GE *020

DUCEY, Joseph Paul. 1901 RANDOLPH RD 28207 #005-15-1981 L1993 AN *020 †20,05

DUDLEY, Allison Johnson. 1315 EAST BLVD, STE 280 28203 #036-01-1978 L1981 PD *020 †55

DUFFY, John Chas. 3621 RANDOLPH RD 28211 #035-09-1960 L1997 CHP PFP *030

DUGGINS, Christopher Jay. 1901 RANDOLPH RD 28207 #047-06-1992 L2000 AN *020 †05

DUKES, William Eugene, Jr. 526 S CHURCH ST 28202 #045-01-1980 L1985 OM FM *020 †18

DULIN, Michael F. 5516 CENTRAL AVE 28212 #048-14-1998 L1999 **FM** *020 †18
DULIN, Thomas Leroy. ■ 28211 #036-07-1957 L1997 FM *071 †18
DUNAWAY, Howard Yates, III. 1915 RANDOLPH RD 28207 #036-05-1977 L1979
    ORS OSM *020 †40
DUNBAR, Elizabeth C. 1900 RANDOLPH RD 28207 #028-46-1994 L1998 **EM** *020 †16
DUNBAR, Kenneth Ray. 2321 W MOREHEAD ST 28208 #055-01-1981 L1988 **NEP IM** *071
DUNMIRE, Carole Ruth. 501 BILLINGSLEY RD 28211 #016-01-1985 L1989 **CHP** *020 †75
DUNN, Kelli Coop. PO BOX 32861, 1000 BLYTHE BLVD 28232 #036-01-2000 L2003
    END IM *020 †20
DUPONT, Andrea Mikolajczy. 1900 RANDOLPH RD 28207 #010-01-1993 L2000 **EM** *020 †16
DU PUY, S Stuart, Jr. 301 HAWTHORNE LN 28204 #011-03-1969 L1972 **U** *020 †95
DUTTON, Carolyn Stacy. 2001 VAIL AVE, MEDICAL ASSOCIATES 28207 #422-01-2001 L2006
    OS *100 †20,16
DYAR, Stephen Howard, Jr. ■ 28270 #045-01-2006 IM *012
DYER, Emmet Hunter. 225 BALDWIN AVE 28204 #027-01-1988 L1994 **NS** *020 †25
EAKER, Kathryn Grace. 1000 BLYTHE BLVD 28203 #036-01-2004 L2007 **PD** *100 †55
EALY, George Thos. ■ 28210 #020-02-1987 MM OS *050
EASON, Renita Patryce. ■ 28277 #047-06-2006 L2007 **FP** *012
EAVES, Felmont F, III. 11220 ELM LN, CHARLOTTE PLASTIC SURGERY 28277
    #047-06-1987 L1997 **PS** *020 †85,65
EBBERS, M Brophy. 1718 E 4TH ST, STE 805 28204 #005-06-1998 L2006 **UP** *020
ECHTERLING, Susan C. 7108 PINEVILLE MATTHEWS RD, STE 102 28226 #032-01-1980 L1996
    EM GP *020 †16
EDELEN, Connie Ann. ■ 28211 #011-04-2006 L2006 **PM** *012
EDLIN, Jennifer Susan. 2001 VAIL AVE, MEDICAL ASSOCIATES 28207 #017-20-1998 L2001
    EM *020 †16
EDWARDS, Charles Hillman. 1718 E 4TH ST, STE 701 28204 #036-01-1973 L1973
    TS *020 †85,90
EDWARDS, Ellison Francis. 501 S SHARON AMITY RD, STE 300 28211 #036-01-1961 L1961
    FPS HNS *020 †45
EDWARDS, Irene Elizabeth. 4335 COLWICK RD, STE D 28211 #036-05-1976 L1979
    D IM *020,55,15
EDWARDS, Jonathan Arnold. 8401 MEDICAL PLAZA DR, STE 200 28262 #038-40-1991 L1994
    IM *020 †20
EDWARDS, Nathaniel C. 1001 BLYTHE BLVD, STE 300 28203 #051-01-1991 L1997
    CD IM *020 †20
EICHENBRENNER, Timothy J. 2630 E SEVENTH ST, STE 101 28204 #051-07-1979 L1982
    PD *020 †55
EIGBE EDOSOMWAN, Esther. ■ 28270 #665-01-2004 L2007 **IM** *020 †20
EKE-ALUKO, Ehimwema A. 3333 WILKINSON BLVD, P O BOX 668095 28208
    #690-02-1983 L1998 **PD** *020 †15
EKWONU, Tagbo John. 4444 THE PLZ STE D, EASTOWNE FAM PHY 28215 #690-04-1990 L1999
    FM *020 †18 ‡
EKWUEME-STURDIVANT, Nnemka. 1918 RANDOLPH RD, STE 220 28207 #690-04-1992 L2004
    END *100 †20
ELCHOUFI, Mayssoun. ■ 28210 #051-07-2002 L2007 IM *020 †20
EL HEMAILLY, Hala Ahmed T. ■ 28277 #915-02-1982 L1994 **PD** *020 †55
ELLER, Chad Raynard. 2001 VAIL AVE, MEDICAL ASSOCIATES 28207 #011-04-1994 L2003
    EM *020 †16
ELLIOTT, Alan Lee. 1918 RANDOLPH RD, STE 600 28207 #047-20-2000 L2003 **RHU** *020 †20
ELLIOTT, Joseph A, Jr. 1900 RANDOLPH RD STE 714 28207 #025-01-1944 L1944 **D** *071 †15
ELLIS, Clarence O'Neil. 7945 N TRYON ST, STE 112 28262 #036-01-1980 L1984 **IM** *020 †20
ELLIS, Dee Ann. 8500 ANDREW CARNEGIE BLVD 28262 #045-01-1988 L1993 **IM** *020 †20
ELLIS, Mark Chas. 501 BILLINGSLEY RD 28211 #016-45-1986 L2003 **P** *020 †75
ELLISON, Aaron Gregory. 3101 LATROBE DR, INTERNAL MEDICINE SPECIALI 28211
    #028-03-2002 L2004 **FM FSM** *020 †20
EMEZIE, Anthonia Ogechi. 3531 RANDOLPH RD, PEDIATRIC ASSOCIATES 28211
    #690-10-1990 L2003 **PD** *100 †55
EMKO, Sooky. ■ 28226 #583-03-1962 L1974 **AN** *071 †05
ENGEN, Allison Casey. 1000 BLYTHE BLVD, CAROLINAS MEDICAL CENTER 28203 .
    #045-01-2004 L2007 **PDS** *020 †55
ENGINEER, Madhu. 7820 BALLANTYNE COMNS PKWY, STE 108 28277 #496-38-1972 L1991
    CHP P *020 †75
ENSOR, Robert Dale. 101 E WT HARRIS BLVD, STE 5202 28262 #038-40-1961 L1964 **U** *071 †95
ENTWISTLE, Celia B. 1900 RANDOLPH RD 28207 #048-12-1982 L1992 **GP** *020 †16
EPPS, Earl Jos. 700 S TORRENCE ST, STE 210 28204 #047-07-1973 L1980 **FM** *020 †18
ERRINGTON, Glenn W. 2711 RANDOLPH RD, STE 400 28207 #025-07-1978 L1985
    AI IM *020 †20,03
ERSTON, Walter F. ■ 28209 #035-15-1970 L1995 DR *020 †80
ERUCHALU, Obinna N F. 1928 RANDOLPH RD, STE 312 28207 #690-01-1978 L1989
    GS VS *020 †85
ESHRAGHI, Shervin. 1000 BLYTHE BLVD, DEPARTMENT OF NEUROLOGY 28203
    #665-01-1998 L2005 **N CN** *020 †75
ESKIND, Lon Brian. 1000 BLYTHE BLVD 28203 #001-06-1991 L1998 **GS TTS** *020 †85
ESKRIDGE, Carolyn Davis. 1025 MOREHEAD MEDICAL DR 28204 #021-05-1992 L1999
    OBG *020 †30
ESTHER, Mary Susan. 6035 FAIRVIEW RD 28210 #028-03-1980 L1996 **SME P** *020 †75
ESTWANIK, Joseph John. 335 BILLINGSLEY RD 28211 #036-05-1973 L1973 **ORS** *020 †40
ETOMI, Michael E. 2711 RANDOLPH RD, STE 400 28207 #690-05-1979 L1992 **NEP** *020 †20
EUBANKS, William Malcolm. 200 HAWTHORNE LN 28204 #012-01-1954 L1960 **OBG** *071 †30
EUSTANCE, Nicole Carol. ■ 28209 #041-13-2007 IM *012
EVANGELIST, Felix Anthony. 3601 E INDEPENDENCE-204 28205 #010-02-1958 L1971
    TS *020 †85,90
EVANS, Adrienne Coker. 8420 UNIVERSITY EXC PRK DR, PARK DR. 28262 #012-21-1998 L2001
    IM *020 †20
EVANS, Akita C. ■ 28269 #043-01-2007 FP *012
EVANS, Ernest Craig. 10512 PARK RD, STE 111 28210 #045-01-1973 L1988 **GS** *020 †85
EVANS, John Willis, Jr. 6324 FAIRVIEW RD, STE 120 28210 #027-01-1975 L1998 **DR** *020 †80
EVANS, Lilian Qushair. 720 E MOREHEAD ST, STE 301 28202 #036-07-2001 L2005 **FM** *020 †20
EVANS, Susan Lynn. 1001 BLYTHE BLVD, STE 602 28203 #038-41-1999 L2006 **CCS** *100 †85
EVANS, Toni I. 1000 BLYTHE BLVD 28203 #038-45-1981 L1998 **RHU IM** *020 †20
EVERS, Sameena Hassan. 1315 EAST BLVD, STE 280 28203 #041-01-1998 L2004 **PD** *020 †55
EVIVIE, Patrick E. 3627 BEATTIES FORD RD 28216 #690-06-1985 L1996 **IM** *020 †20
FADIAL, John Murray. 28202 #041-03-1967 L1996 **FM** *071
FAGAN, James Arthur. 3623 LATROBE DR, STE 216 28211 #045-01-1966 L1969
    DR NM *020 †80,28

FAIR, Malika Akua. ■ 28203 #025-01-2006 **EM** *012
FALCON, Amalia S. 8401 MEDICAL PLAZA DR, STE 305 28262 #924-01-1973 L1990 **P** *020
FARAH, Naguib H. 200 HAWTHORNE LN 28204 #915-03-1987 L1994 **EM** *020 †18
FARAHANY, Hossein H. 3626 LATROBE DR 28205 #517-01-1968 L1973 **CD IM** *020 †20
FARMER, Charles Dudley. 2711 RANDOLPH RD, STE 400 28207 #017-20-1958 L1966
    NEP IM *020 †20
FARRELL, Bart. 411 BILLINGSLEY RD 28211 #021-05-2004 L2006 **GS** *100
FARRELL, Brian Beckman. 411 BILLINGSLEY RD, STE 105 28211 #021-05-2001 L2004 **GS** *020
FAVARO, Justin Peter. 2711 RANDOLPH RD, STE 100 28207 #045-01-2000 L2003 **HO** *020 †20
FEE, Bruce E. 3623 LATROBE DR, STE 216 28211 #030-06-1972 L1978 **R** *020 †80
FEEZOR, Charles Noel, Jr. 1900 RANDOLPH RD, STE 310 28207 #036-05-1962 L1962
    U *020 †95
FEHRING, Thomas Keith. 1000 BLYTHE BLVD 28203 #048-02-1980 L1986 **ORS** *020 †40
FELD, Leonard Gary. 1000 BLYTHE BLVD, DEPARTMENT OF PEDIATRICS 28203
    #035-06-1979 L2006 **PN PD** *020 †55 ‡
FELDMAN, Cary Scott. 6000 FAIRVIEW RD, STE 330 28210 #025-07-1981 L2007 **CS** *020 †18
FELKNER, Mary Martha B. 2600 E 7TH ST, STE 100 28204 #036-01-1992 L1995 **PD** *020 †55
FELKNER, Richard Sidney. 6035 FAIRVIEW RD, THROAT ASSOCIATES, PA 28210
    #028-02-1960 L1967 **OTO** *071 †45
FERNANDEZ-TATUM, Alejandro. ■ 28210 #036-01-2005 GS *012
FERNANDO, Jayaweerage G. 2711 RANDOLPH RD, STE 207 28207 #220-01-1986 L1999
    IM *020 †20
FERRARI, Herbert A. ■ 28226 #132-01-1954 L1966 **PTH** *071 †05
FERRARO, Roberto Fulvio. 101 E WT HARRIS BLVD, THE CAROLINAS PLLC 28262
    #016-01-1993 L1998 **U** *020 †95
FERREE, Carolyn R Black. 200 QUEENS RD, STE 400 28204 #036-05-1970 L1971 **RO** *020 †80
FERREE, Charles Elliot. 10512 PARK RD, MECKLENBURG MEDICAL GROUP 28210
    #036-01-1980 L1983 **IM** *020 †20
FERRELL, Kenneth E, Jr. 1701 ABBEY PL 28209 #036-01-1985 L1988 **IM** *020 †20
FERRIS, Christopher D. 3030 RANDOLPH RD, MECKLENBURG MEDICAL GROUP 28211
    #023-07-1993 L2004 **GE** *020 †20
FILIPPI, Robin Lee. 8401 MEDICAL PLAZA DR, STE 200 28262 #012-05-1999 L2005 **IM** *020 †20
FINE, Katie Snead. ■ 28226 #016-06-1994 L1998 **PD** *020 †55
FINGER, Frederick Eli, III. 225 BALDWIN AVE, CAROLINA NEUROSURGERY & SP 28204
    #047-05-1976 L1985 **NS** *020 †25
FINICAL, Stephan John. 2215 RANDOLPH RD, CHARLOTTE PLASTIC SURGERY 28207
    #010-21-1988 L2001 **PS HS** *020 †85,65
FINKLEA, Orion Townsend. 1333 ROMANY RD 28204 #045-01-1955 L1963 **U** *071 †95
FINLON, Michael Harold. 101 E WT HARRIS BLVD, STE 5301 28262 #036-05-1999 L2003
    OBG *020 †30
FISCHER, Joal. 1018 EAST BLVD 28203 #016-11-1974 L1977 **OS PD** *072
FISHER, David Geo. 8800 N TRYON ST 28262 #051-04-1983 L1988 **NPM PD** *020 †55
FISHER, Edward Carl. 1918 RANDOLPH RD, STE 350 28207 #036-05-2000 L2002 **NEP** *020 †20
FISHER, Edward Carl. 1025 MOREHEAD MEDICAL DR 28204 #047-06-1971 L1974
    OBG *020 †30
FISHER, Marshall Louis. 4417 OGLUKIAN RD 28226 #016-11-1935 L1995 **P** *072 †75
FISHER, Tara Beth. 101 E WT HARRIS BLVD, STE 1121 28262 #051-01-1995 L1955 **OTO** *020 †55
FITZGERALD, Randie Schact. 1718 E 4TH ST, STE 601 28204 #035-75-1999, ▲ L2005
    CHP *020 †75
FLEISCHLI, James Edward. 1025 MOREHEAD MEDICAL DR, STE 300 28204
    #048-04-1994 L2001 **ORS** *020 †40
FLEISHMAN, Lawrence Mark. 7030 PINEVILLE MATTHEWS RD, SOUTH CHARLOTTE PRIMARY
    CA 28226 #036-01-1982 L1985 **IM** *020 †20
FLETCHER, Amy Marie. 1718 E 4TH ST, STE 307 28204 #036-05-1996 L1997 **OBG** *020 †30
FLETCHER, Sidney Marc. 1900 RANDOLPH RD 28207 #048-12-1994 L1995 **EM** *020 †16
FLIPPO, Teresa Skidmore. 10512 PARK RD, STE 111 28210 #055-01-1986 L1989
    GS SO *020 †85
FLOBERG, Dane Robert. 10816 BLACK DOG LN, STE 160 28214 #036-07-1994 L2004
    FM *020 †18
FLOOD, Curtis Lee. 1900 RANDOLPH RD STE 1016 28207 #036-08-1984 L1989 **OBG** *020 †30
FOKIN, Alexander A. CAROLINAS MED CTR, C/O FRANCIS ROBICSEK 28232
    #913-69-1987 L1994 **PDS** *020
FOLLMER, Ronald L, Jr. 1010 EDGEHILL RD N, CAROLINAS MED CTR/NEUROSCI 28207
    #041-13-1966 L1976 **N** *020 †75
FOLSTAD, Steven G. 1900 RANDOLPH RD 28207 #048-04-1990 L1991 **EM** *020 †16
FONTANA, John Louis. 927 EAST BLVD, CONSULTANTS, PA 28203 #023-12-1987 L2002
    AN *020 †05
FORD, Marsha Dean. 1000 BLYTHE BLVD, EMERGENCY DEPT 28203 #045-01-1979 L1982
    EM ETX *040 †20,16
FORSTMANN, Charity Lynn. 10310 MALLARD CREEK RD, UNIVERSITY FAMILY PHYSICIA 28262
    #051-01-2002 L2004 **FM** *020 †18
FORT, Lynn, III. 200 HAWTHORNE LN 28204 #036-07-1960 L1960 **GS TS** *020 †85,90
FORTNER, Molly Rae. 3030 RANDOLPH RD, MECKLENBURG MEDICAL GROUP 28211
    #036-01-2003 L2006 **IM** *020 †20
FOSTER, James Edward. 1025 MOREHEAD MEDICAL DR, STE 300 28204 #051-01-1971 L1996
    ORS *020 †40
FOSTER, Michelle Lynette. 1000 BLYTHE BLVD, DEPT OF INTERNAL MED 28203
    #036-01-2001 L2003 IM *100
FOSTER, Telezee L. 335 BILLINGSLEY RD, STE 101 28211 #047-07-1960 L1966 **GS** *020 †85
FOTIADIS, Chris Neil. 2711 RANDOLPH RD, STE 400 28207 #016-06-1991 L1998 **NEP** *020 †20
FOUST, John Worth. 6035 FAIRVIEW RD 28210 #036-05-1980 L1986 **OTO HNS** *071 †45
FOX, J Thos, Jr. 200 HAWTHORNE LN 28204 #036-01-1960 L1960 **P** *071
FOX, Suzanna Jane. 101 E WT HARRIS BLVD, STE 5301 28262 #012-01-1991 L1995
    OBG *020 †30
FRAGULIDIS, Georgios P. PO BOX 32861 28232 #418-01-1985 *100
FRAMM, David Jonathan. 1900 BRUNSWICK AVE, MECKLENBURG MEDICAL GROUP 28207
    #010-01-1986 L1992 **CD** *020
FRANCIS, Robert Boyer. PO BOX 7900 28241 #041-13-1946 L1989 **IM ON** *071 †20
FRANK, Alisha Marie. ■ 28278 #036-01-2008 *012
FRANKLIN, Dennis Eugene. ■ 28210 #021-01-1977 L1977 **P N** *020 †75
FRASER, Donald Doyle. 1901 BRUNSWICK AVE STE 240 28207 #033-05-1980 L1981 **D** *020 †15
FRASER, Helen Roemer. 200 HAWTHORNE LN, INPATIENT MEDICINE 28204
    #038-06-1976 L1980 **PTH** *020 †50
FRAZIER, Arnold Ray. 1350 S KINGS DR, CMC MYERS PARK 28207 #020-12-1969 L1974
    PUD IM *040 †20
FREEMAN, Kevin Henry. 5435 PROSPERITY CHURCH RD, STE 1500 28269 #012-05-1979 L1984
    PD *020 †55

FREEMAN, M Sean. 11220 ELM LN, STE 101 28277 #056-05-1982 L1988 **FPS OS** *020 †45
FREEMAN, Tyler Ira. 1005 S KINGS DR 28207 #016-42-1959 L2007 **OM IM** *071 †20
FREEMAN-KWAKU, Mala A. 3125 SPRINGBANK LN, STE B 28226 #051-01-1998 L2002 **OBG** *020 †30
FRENETTE, Gary Patrick. 1100 S TRYON ST STE 400 28203 #025-01-1990 L1996 **HO** *020 †20
FREUND, Donald Robt. 200 HAWTHORNE LN 28204 #041-13-1954 L1987 **OBG** *071 †30
FRICK, Steven Lee. 1001 BLYTHE BLVD STE 602, DEPT OF ORTHOPAEDIC SURGER 28203 #045-01-1991 L1992 **OP** *020 †40
FRIEDLAND, Michael Brian. 1001 BLYTHE BLVD, STE 500 28203 #035-47-1992 L1995 **IM** *020 †20
FRONAPFEL, Paul Jacob. 1901 RANDOLPH RD 28207 #026-08-2002 L2006 **PAN** *020 †05
FRYE, Joseph Craig, Jr. ■ 28226 #036-01-1960 L1960 **R** *020 †80
FRYE, Michael Kermit. 2001 VAIL AVE, MEDICAL ASSOCIATES 28207 #017-20-1995 L1998 **EM** *020 †16
FULLER, Harold J, Jr. 501 BILLINGSLEY RD 28211 #012-01-1985 L2001 **P** *020 †75
FULLER, Peggy Anita. 2630 E 7TH ST, STE 200 28204 #024-07-1984 L1997 **D OS** *020 †15
FULLER, Rollin William. 1900 RANDOLPH RD 28207 #026-04-1994 L1999 **EM** *020 †16
FURNEY, Kym Orsetti. 10512 PARK RD, MECKLENBURG MEDICAL GROUP 28210 #035-45-1992 L2002 **IM** *020 †20
FURNEY, Scott Leo. 1000 BLYTHE BLVD 28203 #025-01-1992 L2002 **IM** *020 †20
FURST, Joseph A, Jr. 4221 TUCKASEEGEE RD 28208 #036-01-1985 L1986 **FM EM** *040 †18 ‡
GAGE, Jennifer Cerny. 927 EAST BLVD 28203 #036-07-1991 L1993 **AN** *020 †05
GAHAN, Kelly Elizabeth. PO BOX 32861, CAROLINAS MED CTR 28232 #007-02-2007 **EM** *012
GAJEWSKI, Timothy Andrew. 101 E WT HARRIS BLVD, THE CAROLINAS PLLC 28262 #047-06-1985 L1990 **U** *020 †95
GALASKA, P Norbert. 2001 VAIL AVE, MEDICAL ASSOCIATES 28207 #048-12-1991 L2002 **EM** *020 †16
GALEA, Lawrence J. 1900 CENTRAL AVE 28205 #038-41-1980 L2000 **NS** *075
GALITSIS, Krista Gaines. 4530 PARK RD STE 200, 2801 CRISMAN ST 28209 #001-06-1990 L2004 **PD** *020 †55
GALLIS, Harry Anthony. 1001 BLYTHE BLVD, STE 602 28203 #036-07-1967 L1967 **ID IM** *030 †20
GALUSHA, Bryant L. 1000 BLYTHE BLVD 28203 #038-06-1952 L1957 **PD** *071 †55
GANEM, Jacques Paul. 1718 E 4TH ST, STE 807 28204 #035-08-1993 L1998 **U** *020 †95
GANGULI, Chandana. 1001 BLYTHE BLVD STE 500 28203 #023-07-1994 L2003 **IM** *020 †20
GARCIA, Ted. 15110 JOHN J DELANEY DR, STE 100 28277 #011-04-1993 L1997 **OBG** *020 †30
GARD, Dwayne Thomas. ■ 28226 #012-01-2005 L2007 **IM** *012
GARDNER, Derek C. 1900 RANDOLPH RD STE 310, METROLINA UROLOGY CLNC 28207 #010-03-1979 L1984 **U** *020 †95
GARG, Anand G. ■ 28278 #495-12-1960 L1975 **NS** *071 ‡
GARMESTANI, Adrian Scott. 1900 RANDOLPH RD 28207 #055-02-2001 L2005 **EM** *020 †16
GARMESTANI, Amy Lynne. 7810 PROVIDENCE RD, STE 102 28226 #055-02-2001 L2005 **FM** *100 †18
GARMON-BROWN, Ophelia E. 1918 RANDOLPH RD, STE 175 28207 #036-01-1980 L1981 **FM** *020 †18
GARNER, Leon C, Jr. 15825 JOHN J DELANEY DR, BALLANTYNE MEDICAL GROUP 28277 #001-02-1988 L1989 **IM** *020 †20
GARRETT, Victoria E. ■ 28211 #045-01-1998 L2005 **FSM** *020 †16
GARTNER, Seth Hawkins. 2001 VAIL AVE, MEDICAL ASSOCIATES 28207 #036-05-1992 L1997 **EM** *020 †16
GARVEY, Joseph L, Jr. 1000 BLYTHE BLVD 28203 #038-41-1988 L1991 **EM** *020 †16
GASKIN, E Reed. 10724 PARK RD 28210 #012-05-1951 L2003 **OPH** *071 †35
GASKIN, Lewis Reed. 135 S SHARON AMITY RD, STE 100 28211 #012-05-1980 L1984 **OPH** *020 †35
GASPARI, Michael Marion. 10370 PARK RD, STE 102 28210 #041-09-1981 L1982 **GE IM** *020 †20
GASTON, Raymond Glenn. 1025 MOREHEAD MEDICAL DR, STE 300 28204 #047-06-2001 L2007 **HS** *020
GAUL, John Stuart, Jr. 1915 RANDOLPH RD 28207 #041-13-1946 L1946 **HS ORS** *071 †40
GAUL, John Stuart, III. 1915 RANDOLPH RD, ORTHOCAROLINA 28207 #036-01-1982 L1984 **ORS HS** *020 †40
GAVIGAN, Thomas Jos. 15830 JOHN J DELANEY DR, STE 175 28277 #010-02-1974 L1983 **GE IM** *020 †20
GEE, Jonathan Benjamin. ■ 28277 #045-01-2003 L2007 **MPD** *100 †20,55
GEHRING, Jennifer E. 2001 VAIL AVE, MEDICAL ASSOCIATES 28207 #017-20-2000 L2002 **EM** *020 †16 ‡
GEISSINGER, Wm Tuttle. 1918 RANDOLPH RD 28207 #051-01-1965 L1973 **GS** *020 †85
GELLAR, Richard. 3303 LATROBE DR 28211 #036-07-1969 L1985 **P** *020 †75
GELLER, Harley Steven. 927 EAST BLVD 28203 #026-04-1983 L1997 **AN** *020 †05 ‡
GENKINS, Steven Mark. 3623 LATROBE DR, STE 216 28211 #035-01-1980 L1986 **DR IM** *020 †20,80
GERGER, Zachariah. 927 EAST BLVD 28203 #048-78-1983, ▲ L1996 **AN PME** *020 †05
GERSIN, Keith Steven. 1000 BLYTHE BLVD, 6TH FL 28203 #010-02-1991 L2006 **GS** *020 †85
GESING, Bernard Francis. 1900 RANDOLPH RD 28207 #012-01-1979 L1980 **FM** *020 †18
GETZ, Stanley Branner, Jr. 900 EAST BLVD 28203 #051-01-1977 L1991 **PS HS** *020 †85,65
GEYER, Pleas Rogers. 501 BILLINGSLEY RD, MECKLENBURG MENTAL HEALTH 28211 #045-01-1976 L1990 **CHP** *020 †75
GHREBREMEDHIN, Aster. 2711 RANDOLPH RD, RANDOLPH RD 28207 #905-01-1984 L1993 **PD** *020 †55
GHUNEIM, Nizar Mohamed. 1900 RANDOLPH RD 28207 #051-01-1985 L1989 **EM** *020 †18
GIBLIN, Thomas Richard. 300 BILLINGSLEY RD STE 105 28211 #012-05-1955 L1963 **PS** *071 †65
GIBSON, Floyd Brian. 6035 FAIRVIEW RD, CHARLOTTE EYE EAR NOSE THR 28210 #036-05-1986 L1987 **OTO FPS** *020 †45
GIDDINGS, Allison Bowman. ■ 28209 #045-01-2007 **OBG** *012
GIEDRAITIS, Robert Basil. 7825 BALLANTYNE COMNS PKWY, STE 150 28277 #010-02-1987 L1996 **PM** *020 †60
GIFTOS, Peter Michael. 2600 E SEVENTH ST, STE 100 28204 #011-03-1999 L2001 **PD** *020 †55
GILBERT, Paul Pressly. 1915 RANDOLPH RD, CHARLOTTE ORTHOPEDIC SPECL 28207 #036-07-1977 L1983 **ORS** *020 †40
GILBERT, Richard Lee. 1000 BLYTHE BLVD, CAROLINAS MED CTR 28203 #005-02-1982 L1987 **AN IM** *020 †05
GILBERT, Shiloh Virginia. PO BOX 32861, CAROLINAS MED CTR 28232 #007-02-2007 **EM** *012
GILL, Jasleen. 501 BILLINGSLEY RD, CMC - RANDOLPH 28211 #495-43-1990 L2002 **P** *020 †75
GILL, Lowell Harley. 1918 RANDOLPH RD STE 700 28207 #036-07-1970 L1970 **ORS R** *020 †40
GILLESPIE, Richard Ramas. 3135 SPRINGBANK LN, THROAT PA 28226 #036-07-1994 L2001 **OTO HNS** *020 †45
GILLETTE, Michael Tiffany. 927 EAST BLVD 28203 #035-06-1977 L1981 **AN CCA** *020 †05
GILLETTE, Susan Kraus. ■ 28226 #035-06-1978 L1982 **P** *020 †75
GILLIAM, Misha Rhodes. ■ 28270 #020-12-2002 L2006 **IM** *020 †20
GINGRAS, Jeannine L. 1900 RANDOLPH RD, STE 112 28207 #050-02-1978 L1983 **NPM PD** *040 †55
GIVENS, Lauri Patrice. 1718 E 4TH ST, STE 201 28204 #036-08-2001 L2006 **OBG** *020 †30
GIVENS, Linda Moore. 3030 RANDOLPH RD, STE 102 28211 #036-01-1985 L1987 **PD** *020 †55
GLASS, Casey Mathew. 1000 BLYTHE BLVD, EMERGENCY MEDICINE 28203 #041-14-2004 L2006 **EM** *020
GLASS, Larry Thos. 7030 PINEVILLE MATTHEWS RD 28226 #010-02-1977 L1988 **PD EM** *020 †55
GLEDITSCH, Scott Duane. 501 BILLINGSLEY RD 28211 #041-09-1978 L2007 **P** *020 †75 ‡
GLENN, Maria Frances. ■ 28210 #011-02-2007 **EM** *012
GLENN, Stephanie Morrow. 1918 RANDOLPH RD 28207 #036-05-1981 L1982 **FM FPG** *020 †18
GLOVER, John Snow. 1718 E 4TH ST, STE 307 28204 #036-07-1959 L1959 **OBG** *071 †30
GODSEY, Raleigh K, Jr. 10340 PARK RD 28210 #027-01-1986 L1990 **OBG** *020 †30
GODWIN, Winston Y, Jr. 10512 PARK RD, STE 111 28210 #045-01-1978 L1985 **GS** *020 †85
GOINS, Natasha Ann Halmi. 6733 FAIRVIEW RD, STE A 28210 #048-13-1997 L2008 **PD** *074 †55
GOINS, Robert Alan. 1000 BLYTHE BLVD 28203 #047-05-1995 L2002 **PD** *020 †55
GOLD, Steven Ralph. 6035 FAIRVIEW RD, CHARLOTTE EYE,EAR,NOSE,AND 28210 #024-05-1982 L1993 **NO OTO** *020 †45
GOLDBERG, Trevor Ian. 5933 BLAKENEY PARK DR, STE 200 28277 #836-01-1975 L1981 **OTO** *020 †45
GOLDMAN, Steven Jay. 5933 BLAKENEY PARK DR, GYNECOLOGY PA 28277 #035-08-1985 L2006 **OBG** *020 †30
GOLEMBE, Barry L. 1000 BLYTHE BLVD, 7TH FL 28203 #051-04-1974 L1979 **PD** *020 †55
GOODMAN, Sarah Elizabeth. 10220 PROSPERITY PARK DR, STE 300 28269 #028-03-2002 L2004 **FM** *020 †18
GOPAL, Arun Kumar. ■ 28226 #036-01-2006 L2006 **P** *012
GOPALAKRISHNAN, Santosh K. 720 E MOREHEAD ST, STE 301 28202 #495-33-1994 L2002 **IMG** *020 †20
GOPALREDDY, Vani Vallore. ■ 28226 #496-39-1993 L2007 **PG** *071 †55
GORDON, Demetria Yvette. 1718 E 4TH ST, STE 907 28204 #045-01-2002 L2007 **OBG** *020
GORES, Paul Farrell. 1000 BLYTHE BLVD 28203 #036-07-1980 L1994 **GS VS** *020 †85
GORSKI, Sonya Dawn. 1000 BLYTHE BLVD 28203 #051-04-1995 L1998 **PM** *020 †60
GOSHORN, Erin B. 5933 BLAKENEY PARK DR, STE 200 28277 #038-43-1986 L1992 **PO** *020 †35
GOSLEN, Junius Blake. 1918 RANDOLPH RD, STE 550 28207 #036-01-1973 L1973 **D IM** *020 †20,15
GOTTLIEB, Jonathan R. 2001 RANDOLPH RD, 1611 NW 12 AVENUE 28207 #011-02-2002 L2007 **ORS** *020
GOURLEY, Blanton Craig. 1025 MOREHEAD MEDICAL DR, STE 400 28204 #036-01-1981 L1983 **OBG** *020 †30
GOUTOS, Ioannis Demetrius. ■ 28211 #418-01-1969 L1977 **CCM** *020
GRAFTON, Lori Marie. ■ 28277 #035-45-2003 L2005 **PM** *100
GRAHAM, Amanda Joy. ■ 28269 #038-43-2006 **FP** *012
GRAMMER-PACICCO, Elaine M. 7800 PROVIDENCE RD, STE 203 28226 #035-09-1985 L1995 **PD** *020 †55
GRANT, Heather Monique. 1801 ROZZELLES FERRY RD 28208 #038-40-2001 L2003 **FM** *020 †18
GRAPER, Robert Gordon. 2915 COLTSGATE RD, STE 103 28211 #038-41-1982 L1989 **PS** *020 †85,65
GRATTAN, Elizabeth Grambr. 15830 JOHN J DELANEY DR, STE 100 28277 #045-04-2003 L2007 **D** *020 †15
GRAY, Brian Thos. 1901 RANDOLPH RD 28207 #048-14-1986 L1992 **AN** *020 †05
GRAY, David Maxwell. ■ 28204 #055-01-1980 L2004 **EM OM** *020 †16
GRAY, Elizabeth Ann. PO BOX 32861, CAROLINAS MED CTR 28232 #045-01-2007 **EM** *012
GRAYSON, Galen. 817 E MOREHEAD ST, STE 200 28202 #024-01-1988 L1996 **OPH** *020 †35
GREEN, Edward Graham. ■ 28277 #047-06-1963 L1966 **PD ADL** *071
GREEN, Edward Morris. ■ 28210 #012-01-2006 **EM** *012
GREEN, Faison. 10310 MALLARD CREEK RD 28262 #011-03-1999 L2000 **FM** *020
GREEN, Karen Elizabeth. 5200 PARK RD, STE 108 28209 #036-05-2001 L2005 **P** *020 †75
GREEN, Shana Dale. 1718 E 4TH ST, STE 604 28204 #045-01-2002 L2004 **CHN** *020
GREEN, William Robt. 1901 RANDOLPH RD 28207 #016-06-1973 L1989 **AN** *020 †05
GREENBERG, David Neal. 200 HAWTHORNE LN, P O BOX 33549 28204 #051-04-1988 L1998 **NPM PD** *020 †55
GREENBERG, Richard Paul. 2910 SELWYN AVE, STE 327 28209 #561-01-1969 L1997 **NS** *030 †25
GREENE, Craig Alan. 1718 E 4TH ST, STE 202/302 28204 #045-01-1986 L1992 **PDC** *020 †55
GREENE, Frederick Leslie. 1000 BLYTHE BLVD, 7TH FL 28203 #051-01-1970 L1997 **GS SO** *040 †85
GREENE, Lynne Michelle. 11030 GOLF LINKS DR, STE 100 28277 #004-01-1995 L2008 **IM** *020 †20
GREENE, Ralph Leon, Jr. 4525 CAMERON VALLEY PKWY, STE 3100 28211 #055-01-1970 L1974 **IM** *020 †20
GREENFIELD, Russell H. 1408 EAST BLVD STE B, CAROLINAS INTEGRATIVE HEAL 28203 #016-42-1984 L1988 **EM** *020 †16
GREENHOOT, Jerry Harvey. ■ 28207 #005-14-1962 L1973 **NS** *071 †25
GREENHOOT, Kathryn W. 200 HAWTHORNE LN, INPATIENT MEDICINE 28204 #005-14-1962 L1973 **AN** *071 †05
GREENMAN, David Brian. 300 BILLINGSLEY RD, STE 109 28211 #036-01-1999 L2000 **OPH** *020 †35
GREENMAN, Herb Emanuel. 300 BILLINGSLEY RD, STE 109 28211 #036-07-1999 L2004 **OPH** *020 †35
GREENMAN, Maxwell. 300 BILLINGSLEY RD STE 109 28211 #035-19-1967 L1973 **OPH OS** *020 †35
GREENWOOD, James B, Jr. PO BOX 18248 28218 #041-01-1944 L1944 **FM** *071 †18
GREER, Stephen Edward. 1900 RANDOLPH RD 28207 #055-01-2000 L2002 **EM** *020 †16
GREIG, John Hamilton. 927 EAST BLVD, CONSULTANTS, PA 28203 #803-05-1956 L1973 **AN** *071 †05
GRIFFIN, Ezra Danl. 1822 BRUNSWICK AVE 28207 #036-01-1973 L1973 **OBG** *020 †30
GRIFFIN, Gail Michelle. 1718 E 4TH ST, STE 201 28204 #010-03-1996 L2004 **OBG** *020 †30
GRIFFIN, William Lewis. 1915 RANDOLPH RD, ORTHOCAROLINA 28207 #020-02-1982 L1983 **ORS** *020 †40
GRIFFITH, Todd Frederick. 2711 RANDOLPH RD, STE 400 28207 #036-01-1997 L2001 **NEP** *020 †20

■ = Address Information Privacy Protected

GRIGG, Claud Mc Neill. 1350 S KINGS DR DEPT INT 28207 #036-01-1961 L1961 **IM** *040 †20
GRIGGS, James Philip, Jr. 7810 PROVIDENCE RD, STE 102 28226 #036-08-1990 L1992 **FM** *020 †18
GRIGGS, Richard C. 1901 RANDOLPH RD 28207 #041-12-1999 L2000 **AN** *020 †05
GRIMES, John Alexander. 1000 BLYTHE BLVD 28203 #036-05-1994 L2000 **AN** *020 †05
GRITTER, Nancy Jo. 2711 RANDOLPH RD, STE 400 28207 #017-20-1992 L1998 **NEP IM** *020 †20
GRIVAS, Nicholas E. 1420 E SEVENTH ST 28204 #048-12-1965 L1974 **NS** *020 †25
GROOVER, Calton Douglas. PO BOX 32861 28232 #012-01-1962 L1967 **PTH** *020 †50
GROSE, Robert Brian. 1918 RANDOLPH RD STE 175, PRESBYTERIAN URGENT CARE 28207 #055-01-1997 L1998 **EM** *020 †16
GROSS, Kirsten Marie. 10514 PARK RD, PIEDMONT EMERGENCY MED ASS 28210 #036-01-1988 L1989 **EM** *020 †16
GROVER, Arun K. 10320 FELD FARM LN, STE 300 28210 #308-11-1990 L2003 **IM** *020 †20
GRUBB, Walter Lee, Jr. 1000 BLYTHE BLVD 28203 #051-04-1961 L1971 **DR** *071 †80
GUENTER, Jonathan M. ■ 28270 #049-01-2006 **EM** *012
GUFFIN, Shawn Thomas. 927 EAST BLVD, SE ANES CONSULTANTS PA 28203 #001-02-2001 L2007 **AN** *020 †05
GUICE, Stephen Lee, III. 1918 RANDOLPH RD, STE 210 28207 #021-05-1972 L1994 **U UP** *020 †95
GUISE, Barbara Matheny. 1900 RANDOLPH RD 28207 #012-05-1995 L1997 **EM** *020 †16
GULATI, Sanjeev Kumar. 1001 BLYTHE BLVD, STE 300 28203 #041-01-1994 L2002 **CD** *020 †20
GULLEDGE, Christopher J. ■ 28202 #045-01-1999 L2002 **PTH** *020
GUNDLACH, Timothy Erik. 927 EAST BLVD, CONSULTANTS, PA 28203 #056-05-1985 L2006 **AN PME** *020 †05 ‡
GUNTER, Andrew Wallace. 101 E WT HARRIS BLVD, STE 1121 28262 #045-01-1997 L2002 **PD** *020 †55
GUPTA, Kapil. ■ 28269 #422-01-1995 L2004 **DMP** *020 †50 ‡
GUPTE, Manjusha Arun. 8515 BROWNES POND LN, EVOLUTION AESTHICS MED SPA 28277 #028-03-1993 L2002 **IM** *020 †20
GUSMER, Peter Baxter. ■ 28277 #033-06-1989 L1995 **DR** *020 †80
GUTTIKONDA, Riteesha. ■ 28203 #043-01-2002 L2007 **RHU** *020 †20
GUYTON, Anna Jane. ■ 28262 #051-01-1991 L1994 **FM** *071 †18
HAGLER, Brian Neal. 1918 RANDOLPH RD, STE 175 28207 #036-08-2001 L2004 **FM** *020 †18
HAGLER, Rachel Hunt. 11030 GOLF LINKS DR, STE 100 28277 #036-08-2001 L2003 **FM** *020 †18
HAHN, David Michael. PO BOX 32861, CAROLINAS MEDICAL CENTER 28232 #917-01-1984 **OTR** *100
HALE, Floyd Bruce. 200 HAWTHORNE LN, C/O PRESBYTERIAN HEALTHCAR 28204 #030-05-1982 L1986 **IM** *020 †20
HALEY, Michael Wade. 1000 BLYTHE BLVD, INTERNAL MEDICINE DIVISION 28203 #045-04-1999 L2001 **CCM** *020 †20
HALL, George Danl. 3111 SPRINGBANK LN STE 6 28226 #036-08-1985 L1989 **ADM FM** *020 †18
HALL, James Bryan. 1000 BLYTHE BLVD, CAROLINAS MEDICAL CTR 28203 #045-01-1974 L1980 **GO GYN** *040 †30
HALL, Mary Nolan. 5516 CENTRAL AVE 28212 #035-20-1983 L1987 **FM** *040 †18
HALL, Timothy James. 2001 VAIL AVE, MEDICAL ASSOCIATES 28207 #036-01-1983 L1984 **EM OM** *020 †16
HALLMAN, Jott Christopher. PO BOX 32861, CAROLINAS MED CTR 28232 #011-75-2006, ▲ **OBG** *012
HALMI, Nicholas Stephen. ■ 28277 #473-01-1947 *050
HAMID, Mary Kim. 1918 RANDOLPH RD, PHYSICIANS RANDOLPH 28207 #001-02-2002 L2005 **IM** *020 †20
HAMID, Nady. ■ 28270 #001-02-2005 **ORS** *012
HAMILTON, Brian Hugh. 3623 LATROBE DR, STE 216 28211 #036-01-1991 L1997 **VIR** *020 †80
HAMILTON, Frank H, Jr. 200 HAWTHORNE LN 28204 #051-01-1951 L1951 **A IM** *075
HAMILTON, James Pressly. 2104 RANDOLPH RD 28207 #041-01-1958 L1958 **PDS** *071 †85
HAMMER, Donald Edwin. ■ 28203 #035-45-1966 L1973 **EM** *020
HAMMOND, Flora Mc Connell. 1100 BLYTHE BLVD, CHARLOTTE INSTITUTE OF REH 28203 #021-01-1990 L1995 **PM** *020 †60
HAMMONDS, William Mark. 6035 FAIRVIEW RD 28210 #012-01-2001 L2006 **OPH** *020 †35
HAMRICK, Ladd Watts, Jr. ■ 28207 #036-05-1946 L1946 **IM NM** *071 †28,20
HANGER, Barry John. 15110 JOHN J DELANEY DR, MECKLENBURG MEDICAL GROUP 28277 #836-02-1990 L2007 **IM** *020 †20
HANLEY, Edward N, Jr. 1000 BLYTHE BLVD 28203 #050-02-1975 L1989 **ORS** *020 †40 ‡
HANNA, Pamela Gayle. 10628 PARK RD 28210 #036-01-1986 L1990 **AN** *020 †05
HANNAH, Joanna Amorette. 1100 BLYTHE BLVD 28203 #036-01-2004 L2008 **PM** *012
HANRAHAN, Philip Anthony. 15825 JOHN J DELANEY DR, STE 200 28277 #035-09-1988 L1995 **IM** *020 †20
HANSEN, Todd Richard. 1900 RANDOLPH RD 28207 #026-08-1991 L1992 **EM** *020 †16
HANSON, John Stephen. 2015 RANDOLPH RD, CHARLOTTE 28207 #028-02-1979 L1984 **GE IM** *020 †20
HARBEN, Douglas James. 200 HAWTHORNE LN 28204 #035-15-1970 L1979 **D** *071 †15
HARBOLD, Norris Brown, Jr. 1001 BLYTHE BLVD, STE 300 28203 #010-01-1966 L1971 **CD IM** *020 †20
HARBURY, Stephanie Newby. 1000 BLYTHE BLVD 28203 #036-07-1985 L1991 **AN** *020 †05
HARDY, James Jos. 1718 E 4TH ST STE 707 28204 #036-01-1985 L1988 **OBG** *020 †30
HARDY, Stephen Carl. 5821 FAIRVIEW RD, STE 415 28209 #051-01-1985 L2006 **N** *020 ‡
HARLEY, Robert Edwin. 1918 RANDOLPH RD, STE 310 28207 #024-01-1989 L1996 **OTO FPS** *020 †45
HARMATY, Myron. 3500 MT HOLLY HUNTERSVL RD, MOUNTAIN ISLAND URGENT 28216 #409-16-1973 L1987 **EM IM** *020 †20,16
HARPER, Gerald B, Jr. 1901 RANDOLPH RD 28207 #036-01-1983 L1984 **AN** *020 †05
HARRELL, Jane Stubbs. 4525 CAMERON VALLEY PKWY, STE 3100 28211 #036-05-2000 L2002 **IM** *020 †20
HARRELL, Lonnie C. 150 PROVIDENCE RD 28207 #036-01-1972 L1972 **OBG** *020 †30
HARRINGTON, Amanda Leigh. ■ 28205 #011-02-2004 **PM** *012
HARRIS, Anderson P. ■ 28210 #023-07-1946 L1963 **U** *071 †95
HARRIS, Charles Walker. 1701 ABBEY PL 28209 #036-01-1960 L1960 **IM CD** *020 †20
HARRIS, Elizabeth Hackman. 4525 CAMERON VALLEY PKWY, UNC HOSPITALS 28211 #051-04-2001 L2006 **IM** *100 †20
HARRIS, Harvey L. 1900 RANDOLPH RD STE 1016 28207 #047-07-1981 L1989 **OBG** *020 †30
HARRIS, Heather-John. ■ 28205 #036-01-2003 L2005 **FM** *020 †18
HARRIS, Rachel Michelle. 10210 COULOAK DR STE E, MOUNTAIN ISLAND 28216 #027-01-1998 L2007 **FM** *020 †18
HARRIS, Stephen Davis. 200 HAWTHORNE LN, DEPT OF PATHOLOGY, PRESBYT 28204 #036-01-1984 L1991 **PTH PCP** *020 †50
HARRISON, Frank N H, Jr. 1000 BLYTHE BLVD, DEPT OF OB/GYN 28203 #012-01-1973 L1974 **OBG** *020 †30 ‡
HARRIS-OWENS, Marcia Anne. 1000 BLYTHE BLVD 28203 #012-01-1987 L1989 **OBG** *020 †30
HART, Carolyn Elizabeth. 1900 RANDOLPH RD, STE 1010 28207 #012-05-1987 L1992 **CHN N** *020 †75
HART, George Milburn. 2711 RANDOLPH RD, STE 400 28207 #036-05-1986 L1991 **NEP** *020 †20
HARTINGER, Brian Mark. 1000 BLYTHE BLVD, DEPT OF PEDIATRICS 28203 #030-05-1998 L2005 **PD** *020 †55
HARTMAN, Mark Bently. 2801 RANDOLPH RD, STE 100 28211 #036-05-1987 L1993 **ORS** *020 †40
HARTNAGEL, Wm Robt, Jr. 501 BILLINGSLEY RD 28211 #038-40-1980 L1997 **CHP P** *020 †75
HASHIMOTO, Laura Nickles. 1000 BLYTHE BLVD, DIVISION OF NEONATOLOGY 28203 #051-07-1997 L2003 **NPM** *020 †55 ‡
HASINOFF, Ian Keith. 1901 RANDOLPH RD 28207 #062-01-1981 L2005 **AN CCA** *020 †05 ‡
HATFIELD, Sara Jeanne. 1900 RANDOLPH RD 28207 #017-20-1990 L2000 **PD** *020 †55
HAUSCHKA, Jennie Jarvis. ■ 28211 #055-01-2006 **OBG** *012
HAWES, Cecil Jennings. 1333 ROMANY RD 28204 #047-05-1942 L1942 **U OS** *071 †95
HAWES, Saml Pinckney, III. 201 QUEENS RD 28204 #047-05-1967 L1971 **U** *071 †95
HAWES, Stephen James, Jr. 1900 RANDOLPH RD, STE 216 28207 #036-01-1976 L1982 **ID IM** *020 †20
HAWKINS, Eric Ray. ■ 28226 #036-01-2007 **EM** *012
HAYES, Chason Spencer. 10460 PARK RD, STE 100 28210 #011-02-1989 L1994 **ORS** *020 †40
HAYES, Daniel Harvey. 1000 BLYTHE BLVD, CAROLINAS MEDICAL CENTER 28203 #045-01-1981 L1993 **GS OS** *020 †85
HAYES, Harland Norman. ■ 28270 #049-01-2006 **EM** *012
HAYNES, Emily Nicole. ■ 28269 #051-04-2006 **FP** *012
HAYS, Edward Parker, Jr. 1000 BLYTHE BLVD 28203 #016-11-1991 L1992 **EM** *020 †16
HEAFNER, Michael Daniel. 225 BALDWIN AVE 28204 #036-05-1979 L1989 **NS** *020 †25
HECKAMAN, James David. 12311 COPPER WAY, CAROLINA NEUROLOGICAL 28277 #017-20-1971 L2006 **N** *020 †75
HEFFNER, Alan Christopher. 1000 BLYTHE BLVD, DEPARTMENT OF INTERNAL MED 28203 #051-04-1997 L2007 **EM** *020 †16
HEIL, Thomas Luke. 927 EAST BLVD 28203 #055-01-1992 L2000 **APM** *020 †05
HELFMAN, Todd Alan. 9335 BLAKENEY HEATH RD 28277 #028-34-1991 L1998 **D** *020 †15
HEMELT, Virginia A. 5008 MORROWICK RD 28226 #010-02-1976 L1992 **FM** *030 †18
HENDERSON, David Anthony. 200 HAWTHORNE LN, SPECIALISTS 28204 #036-05-1994 L1997 **IM** *020 †20
HENDRA, Jill Lynne. 501 BILLINGSLEY RD 28211 #025-76-1981, ▲ L1989 **P** *020 †75
HENDRIX, A Montgomery. 1900 RANDOLPH RD 28207 #012-01-1978 L1981 **EM GP** *020 †16
HENEGAR, Martin Mcmillan. 225 BALDWIN AVE, ASSOC, PA 28204 #036-01-1990 L1997 **NS** *020 †25
HENIFORD, Brant Todd. 1000 BLYTHE BLVD 28203 #045-01-1989 L1998 **GS** *020 †85
HENIFORD, Briana Wright. 900 EAST BLVD, SURGERY 28203 #020-02-1989 L1998 **OTO DS** *020 †45
HENNESSY, Robin Joan. 309 S SHARON AMITY RD, COTSWOLD PLAZA II, SUITE 3 28211 #396-02-1980 L1988 **PS GS** *071 †65
HENRY, Christopher Sterli. ■ 28215 #036-01-2004 L2008 **PD** *012
HENSON, Gala Cureton. 251 EASTWAY DR 28213 #036-01-1998 L2002 **FM** *020 †18 ‡
HEPPLER, James Scott. 1900 RANDOLPH RD, STE 216 28207 #007-02-1987 L2001 **PUD CCM** *020 †20
HERBERT, Allison C. 3030 RANDOLPH RD, MECKLENBURG MEDICAL GROUP 28211 #036-01-2003 L2006 **IM** *020 †20
HERNDON, Sarah Elizabeth. 501 BILLINGSLEY RD 28211 #036-01-2001 L2006 **P** *020
HERNDON, William Alfred. 1001 BLYTHE BLVD, STE 300 28203 #011-03-1972 L1975 **ORS** *020 †40
HERON-DAVIS, Ruthann A. 150 PROVIDENCE RD, BRADFORD CLINIC - CHARLOTT 28207 #011-02-1996 L2004 **OBG** *020 †30
HERRIN, Robert Alexander. 475 N WENDOVER RD 28211 #036-01-1979 L1980 *020
HERSHEY, Charles Dana, Jr. 927 EAST BLVD 28203 #041-01-1970 L1976 **AN** *020 †05
HERSHLINE, Roger Kenneth. 4428 TAGGART CREEK RD, STE 101 28208 #041-12-1991 L1999 **IM** *020
HESS, Philip Jos. 1001 BLYTHE BLVD STE 300 28203 #038-40-1968 L2005 **TS** *020 †85,90
HESTER, M Mark. 9101 MONROE RD, STE 155 28270 #012-01-1986 L1989 **FM** *020 †18 ‡
HESTER, Mark Anthony. 9101 MONROE RD, STE 155 28270 #036-07-1994 **NS** *100
HEYER, Robert Allan. 1001 BLYTHE BLVD, STE 507 28203 #048-12-1973 L1978 **PUD IM** *020 †20
HICKEY, Docia Elizabeth. 1000 BLYTHE BLVD 28203 #036-05-1975 L1975 **NPM** *020 †55
HICKMAN, Jennifer Martin. ■ 28277 #045-04-2004 L2008 **OBG** *012
HICKMAN, Kathy Jean. 5113 PIPER STATION DR, STE 207 28277 #051-07-1989 L1990 **P CHP** *020 †75
HICKS, Jeanne Ellen. ■ 28270 #047-06-1966 L1967 **RHU PM** *040 †60
HICKS, Jesse Robinson. 2001 RANDOLPH RD, CHARLOTTE SPINE CTR 28207 #051-01-1953 L1960 **ORS** *071 †40
HIGGINS, Robert Victor. 1000 BLYTHE BLVD 28203 #036-08-1982 L1983 **GO** *040 †30
HIGGINS, Shellee Teets. 101 E WT HARRIS BLVD, STE 1121 28262 #041-09-1990 L1993 **PD** *020 †55
HIGHLEY, Frank Shapley. 429 S SHARON AMITY RD, STE A 28211 #051-01-1979 L1980 **P** *020 †75
HIGHT, Nicole Bernice. ■ 28216 #012-05-2004 L2007 **PD** *100 †55
HILL, Bruce Shawn. 300 BILLINGSLEY RD, STE 204 28211 #001-02-1994 L2000 **RHU** *020 †20
HILL, Cynthia Rochelle. 1801 ROZZELLES FERRY RD, CMC BIDDLE POINT 28208 #051-04-1995 L1998 **FM** *020 †18
HILL, Richard D. 2301 KELLER AVE 28216 #010-03-1953 L1959 **OBG** *071 †30
HILLEN, George Philip, III. ■ 28270 #051-01-1967 L1972 **OPH** *071 †35
HILLIARD, Michele Yolanda. ■ 28216 #035-01-1991 L2004 **MG** *071
HILLMAN, Vincent. 4221 TUCKASEEGEE RD 28208 #422-01-1996 L2004 **FM** *020
HINES, Ryan James. 2001 VAIL AVE, MEDICAL ASSOCIATES 28207 #035-06-2002 L2005 **EM** *020 †16
HINNANT, Elizabeth Torren. ■ 28211 #051-07-2006 **FP** *012
HINSHAW, Howard Thos. 200 HAWTHORNE LN 28204 #036-01-1966 L1966 **DIA END** *071 †20
HINSON, Nicole Suzanne. 200 HAWTHORNE LN 28204 #036-05-1993 L1998 **IM** *020 †20
HINSON, Sharon Foster. 9201 UNIVERSITY CITY BLVD, BROCKER HEALTH CENTER UNCC 28223 #036-08-1990 L1991 **IM** *020

HIPP, Stephen Walker. 1718 E 4TH ST STE 607 28204 #036-01-1983 L1984 **NS** *020 †25

HIPPEN, Benjamin Erik. 2711 RANDOLPH RD STE 400, METROLINA NEPHROLOGY 28207 #048-04-1999 L2005 **NEP** *020 †20

HITCHO, Eileen Beth. ■ 28226 #012-01-2007 **EM** *012

HO, Victor W. 3623 LATROBE DR, STE 216 28211 #036-07-1987 L1993 **IM** *020 †80

HOAGLAND, Robert J. ■ 28210 #035-20-1933 L1958 **IM** *071 †20

HOANG, Bang Co. 2711 RANDOLPH RD 28207 #941-01-1966 L1984 **IM** *020 †20

HOBEN, Michael Skow. 200 GREENWICH RD 28211 #036-01-1998 L1999 **FM** *020 †18

HOBSON, Jack Brown. 200 HAWTHORNE LN 28204 #036-01-1957 L1957 **GPM ON** *071 †20

HODGES, Horace Hayden. 125 BALDWIN AVE 28204 #041-01-1940 1940 **IM** *071 †20

HODSDON, Edward E. ■ 28211 #024-07-1940 **OPH** *071

HOENIG, Michael Parker. ■ 28211 #012-05-2002 L2006 **ORS** *020

HOFFERBERT, Paul Wesley. 8800 N TRYON ST, CAROLINAS MEDICAL CENTER-U 28262 #036-01-1995 L1998 **IM** *040 †20

HOKE, Harold R. 4401 COLWICK RD STE 210 28211 #036-05-1952 L1952 **GYN OBG** *071

HOLLADAY, Glenn Clyde. 2711 RANDOLPH RD, STE 305 28207 #045-01-1980 L1983 **PD** *020 †55 ‡

HOLLAND, Walter Bowlin. 6035 FAIRVIEW RD 28210 #036-05-1975 L1976 **OPH** *020 †35

HOLLEMAN, Jeremiah H, Jr. 1001 BLYTHE BLVD, STE 300 28203 #021-01-1971 L1984 **GS VS** *020 †85

HOLLENBECK, John Ivor. 10512 PARK RD, STE 111 28210 #038-40-1968 L1976 **GS SO** *071 †85

HOLLENBERG, Bennett Roy. 3623 LATROBE DR STE 216, MECKLENBURG RADIOLOGY ASSO 28211 #017-20-1981 L1985 **DR** *020 †80

HOLLINGSWORTH, W Claude. 1718 E 4TH ST STE 307 28204 #036-05-1959 L1959 **OBG** *071 †30

HOLLOWAY, Edwin Thos. 1900 RANDOLPH RD 28207 #025-01-1976 L1982 **EM PD** *020 †55,16

HOLMES, Norman Albert. 1901 RANDOLPH RD 28207 #038-40-1984 L1989 **CCM OSM** *020 †05

HOLSHOUSER, John Warren. 1001 BLYTHE BLVD, STE 300 28203 #036-01-1996 L2000 **ICE CD** *020 †20

HOLTZMULLER, Kent C. 3030 RANDOLPH RD, MECKLENBURG MEDICAL GROUP 28211 #038-40-1982 L2004 **GE LM** *020 †20 ‡

HOLWAY, Brent Patrick. 927 EAST BLVD 28203 #036-07-1988 L1994 **AN PD** *020 †05,55

HOMESLEY, Howard David, Jr. 449 N WENDOVER RD STE A, SPECIALISTS 28211 #036-05-1997 L2003 **OAR** *020

HONDROS, Dimitrios P. 9101 MONROE RD, STE 155 28270 #036-05-2003 L2006 **FM** *020 †18

HONEYCUTT, Danny Morris. 7903 PROVIDENCE RD, STE 100 28277 #036-05-1979 L1980 **FPG** *020 †18

HOOD, Christopher Kennedy. 200 HAWTHORNE LN 28204 #041-02-1954 L1954 **GYN** *071 †30

HOOVER, Hunter Ashley. 6035 FAIRVIEW RD 28210 #036-01-1988 L1993 **OTO** *020 †45

HOPE, Harold Pagan, Jr. 14830 CHOATE CIR 28273 #045-01-1967 L1974 **GS** *071 †85

HOPE, William Witherspoon. 1000 BLYTHE BLVD, DEPT OF GENERAL SURGERY 28203 #045-01-2001 L2006 **GS** *020

HORACEK, Henry Jos, Jr. 10716 CARMEL COMMONS BLVD, STE 120 28226 #036-01-1979 L1980 **CHP** *075 †75

HORNER, Donald Stanley. 330 BILLINGSLEY RD, STE 201 28211 #023-01-1975 L1982 **OBS GYN** *020 †55,30

HORN-MC LEOD, Jonnie M. UNCC STATEION COLL HUM DEV 28223 #021-01-1949 L1998 **PD** *071

HORTON, James Marvin. 1350 S KINGS DR, MYERS PARK, DEPT OF MED 28207 #036-07-1977 L1984 **IM ID** *020 †20

HORTON, Raymond C. 2001 VAIL AVE, MEDICAL ASSOCIATES 28207 #045-04-1997 L2004 **EM** *020 †16

HOSSEINIAN, Mahmood. 10502 PARK RD, STE 150 28210 #517-01-1966 L1977 **AN** *020 †05

HOUCHIN, Lisa. 130 PROVIDENCE RD 28207 #005-11-1992 L1999 **PDE** *020 †55

HOUCK, William Stokes, III. 1718 E 4TH ST, STE 208 28204 #045-01-1991 L1997 **GE PG** *020 †55

HOUGH, Mac J. ■ 28209 #051-04-1945 L1997 **OPH** *071 †35

HOUSER, Stephen Andrew. 927 EAST BLVD 28203 #041-14-1995 L2003 **AN** *020 †05

HOUSTON, Shirley Ann. 6429 BANNINGTON RD, STE B 28226 #045-01-1982 L1989 **IM** *020 †20

HOWARD, Daniel Karl. 1001 BLYTHE BLVD STE 500, MEDICAL CENTER PLAZA 28203 #056-05-1987 L1995 **PUD CCM** *020 †20

HOWARD, Jerome. 6111 RUMPLE RD 28262 #035-15-1970 L1973 **FM** *020 †18

HOWARD, Matthew Kevin. PO BOX 32861, DEPT OF INTERNAL MEDICINE 28232 #012-01-2005 **IM** *012

HOWELL, N Neil. 6035 FAIRVIEW RD 28210 #036-01-1966 L1966 **OTO** *020 †45

HOWELL, Rogers Glenn, II. 200 HAWTHORNE LN 28204 #036-01-1982 L1984 **NPM PD** *020 †55

HSU, Kevin. 1718 E 4TH ST, STE 501 28204 #023-01-1997 L2004 **ICE** *020 †20

HUDSON, Albert Denning. 1001 BLYTHE BLVD STE 500 28203 #036-01-1986 L1988 **IM** *020 †20

HUDSON, Karla Genet. 200 S COLLEGE ST, MECKLENBURG MEDICAL GROUP 28202 #026-08-1998 L2006 **IM** *020 †20

HUDSON, Paul Jos. 14830 CHOATE CIR, SIM 28273 #023-07-1976 L2000 **PHP IM** *062 †20

HUFF, Janice Elizabeth. 5516 CENTRAL AVE, DEPT OF FAMILY MEDICINE 28212 #028-34-1985 L1987 **FM** *040 †18

HUGGINS, Mandy Jo. ■ 28211 #017-20-2006 **PM** *012

HUGHES, Bruce Wray. 10310 MALLARD CREEK RD, UNIV FAMILY PHYSICIANS 28262 #051-01-1988 L1991 **FM** *020 †20

HUGHES, Carl Ansel, III. 10512 PARK RD, MECKLENBURG MEDICAL GROUP 28210 #045-01-1996 L1997 **FM** *020 †20

HULL, Lauren Bennett. 10000 PARK CEDAR DR 28210 #036-08-2003 L2006 **FM** *020 †18

HUMPHREY, John Edward, Jr. 3303 LATROBE DR 28211 #036-07-1975 L1979 **P PYG** *020 †75

HUMPHRIES, Charles Thos. 8045 PROVIDENCE RD STE 300 28277 #047-05-1980 L1987 **A PDP** *020 †55

HUNDLEY, Jeanea Renee. 2115 E 7TH ST, STE 102 28204 #035-06-1995 L1999 **EM** *020 †16

HUNGNESS, Susan Irene. 2630 E 7TH ST STE 100, CAROLINA ASTHMA AND ALLERG 28204 #016-01-2002 L2007 **AI** *020 †20,03

HUNSTAD, Joseph Paul. 8605 CLIFF CAMERON DR, STE 100 28269 #025-12-1981 L1987 **PS OS** *020 †65

HUNT, Jody Christina. ■ 28210 #054-04-2006 **IM** *012

HUNT, Ronald D. 927 EAST BLVD 28203 #048-02-1987 L1991 **AN** *020 †05

HUNTER, James Clinton. PO BOX 32861, CAROLINAS MEDICAL CENTER 28232 #051-01-1983 L2006 **EM** *020 †16

HURST, Bradley Shawn. 1000 BLYTHE BLVD 28203 #048-14-1984 L1985 **REN OBG** *020 †30

HUSTEAD, Judy Diane. 135 S SHARON AMITY RD, STE 100 28211 #019-02-1984 L1989 **OPH** *020 †35 ‡

HUTCHESON, J Sterling. 2711 RANDOLPH RD, STE 400 28207 #023-07-1961 L1968 **A RHU** *071 †03

HUTCHINS, Kenneth Raymond. 200 HAWTHORNE LN 28204 #025-01-1963 L1972 **U** *071 †95

HUTCHINSON, Forney, III. 1025 MOREHEAD MEDICAL DR, STE 200 28204 #036-07-1968 L1968 **HS ORS** *071 †20

HUYNH, Phi Tan Nguyen. 4920 ALBEMARLE RD, NORTHCROSS MEDICAL CENTER, 28205 #409-24-1992 L2005 **FM** *020 †18

HUYNH, Toan Thiet. 1000 BLYTHE BLVD 28203 #054-04-1990 L1997 **CCS** *020 †85

HUYNH, Tuan Anh. 7940 WILLIAMS POND LN, STE 250 28277 #030-05-1995 L2003 **FM** *020 †18

HYLAND, Jeffrey David. 1000 BLYTHE BLVD, DEPT OF EMERGENCY MEDICINE 28203 #025-07-2001 L2004 **EM** *020 †16

IANNITTI, David Anthony. 1000 BLYTHE BLVD, MEB 6TH FLOOR 28203 #043-01-1991 L2006 **GS** *020 †20

IBE, M Elena G. 200 GREENWICH RD 28211 #065-01-1985 L1994 **FM** *020 †18

IDLIBI, Omar M. 1815 BACK CREEK DR, STE 100 28213 #875-02-1979 L1993 **PTH PCP** *030 †50

IGEL, Andrea Marie. 1000 BLYTHE BLVD 28203 #038-44-1987 L1996 **PD PEM** *020 †55

IGHADE, Andrew Eluonye. 2540 W ARROWOOD RD, MIDCAROLINA PEDIATRICS 28273 #690-06-1994 L2002 **PD** *020 †55

IMSEIS, Hytham Manuel. 1718 E 4TH ST, STE 404 28204 #021-05-1991 L1997 **MFM OBG** *020 †30

INSKO, Erik Kenton. 3623 LATROBE DR, STE 216 28211 #041-01-1996 L2003 **DR** *020

IPPOLITO, Mark Richard. 5821 FAIRVIEW RD, STE 409 28209 #035-06-1992 L2000 **CN N** *020 †75

IRBY, Pierce B, III. 1023 EDGEHILL RD S, MCKAY UROLOGY 28207 #023-12-1983 L1999 **U AM** *020 †95

IRWIN, Todd Andrew. 1001 BLYTHE BLVD, STE 200 28203 #025-07-2002 L2007 **ORS** *020

ISAACS, Steven Greer. 200 HAWTHORNE LN 28204 #020-02-1980 L1984 **EM** *020 †16

ISBELL, Marvin Daniel. PO BOX 32861, DEPT OF GENERAL SURGERY 28232 #039-01-2004 **GS** *012

ISENHOUR, Jennifer Lynn. 1000 BLYTHE BLVD 28203 #051-04-1996 L1997 **EM** *020 †16

ISIGUEN, Dennis Gandeza. 8401 MEDICAL PLAZA DR, STE 350 28262 #654-01-1983 L1998 **IM** *020

IWAOKA, Robert Steven. 1718 E 4TH ST, STE 501 28204 #016-11-1981 L1982 **CD EM** *020 †20

IYER, Sanjay Shyan. 1010 EDGEHILL RD N, DIVISION OF NEUROLOGY 28207 #012-01-2000 L2006 **N** *020 †75

JACKSON, Meghan Genelle. ■ 28213 #036-01-2006 **PD** *012

JACKSON, Yolanda Renee. 4530 PARK RD, STE 200 28209 #033-06-1993 L2005 **PD** *020 †55

JACOBS, David Geo. 1000 BLYTHE BLVD 28203 #035-20-1979 L1995 **GS TRS** *020 †85

JACOBS, Gordon Waldemar. 10724 PARK RD STE 204 28210 #018-03-1958 L1989 **GS** *071 †85

JACOBS, Lane Knox. 1350 S KINGS DR, DEPT INTERNAL MED 28207 #039-01-1988 L1997 **IM** *040 †20

JACOBS, William Edward. 2215 RANDOLPH RD, CHARLOTTE PLASTIC SURGERY 28207 #041-01-1969 L1977 **PS GS** *020 †85,65

JACOBSON, Charles Lyle. ■ 28277 #026-04-1965 L1966 **END IM** *062 †20

JAECKEL, Kerrith Lyn. 2711 RANDOLPH RD, STE 501 28207 #011-03-1994 L1997 **PD** *020 †55

JAIN, Astrid Genda. 1025 MOREHEAD MEDICAL DR 28204 #047-05-1993 L1997 **OBG** *020 †30

JAIN, Kamla Terese. 14214 BALLANTYNE LAKE RD, MEDICAL ASSOCIATES OF 28277 #036-05-1994 L2000 **FM** *020 †20

JAMES, Charles G. 700 E STONEWALL ST STE 130 28202 #047-01-1953 L1954 **IM** *071

JAMES, Kenesha Hilda. ■ 28216 #036-05-2006 **IM** *012

JAMES, Richard Jeremy. 4525 CAMERON VALLEY PKWY, STE 2500 28211 #016-42-2001 L2007 **OBG** *020 †30

JAMES-RODRIGUEZ, Felice A. 251 EASTWAY DR, CMC - NORTH PARK 28213 #036-07-2000 L2003 **FM** *100 †18

JASZEWSKI, Paul Kevin. 927 EAST BLVD 28203 #056-05-1985 L1989 **AN PME** *020 †05

JAWAD, Jay Ahmed. 501 BILLINGSLEY RD 28211 #041-02-1993 L1995 **CHP** *020 †75

JELLINEK, Lawrence Roger. 127 N TRYON ST UNIT 417 28202 #005-02-1974 L1998 **EM OM** *020 †16

JENKINS, Loni Elise. ■ 28209 #012-21-2007 **FP** *012

JERBY, Brian Leroy. 2015 RANDOLPH RD STE 201, CHARLOTTE COLON & RECTAL S 28207 #045-04-1992 L1999 **CRS** *020 †85,10

JERNIGAN, Peter Allen. 1901 RANDOLPH RD 28207 #048-04-1976 L1990 **AN** *020 †18,05

JERVIS, Lisa J. 7810 PROVIDENCE RD, STE 101 28226 #028-34-1991 L1999 **OBG** *020 †30

JESSE, Nathan Marc. 200 HAWTHORNE LN, PRESBYTERIAN HOSPITAL 28204 #055-02-2001 L2007 **NPM** *100 †55

JETT, Harriman Harding. 2104 RANDOLPH RD 28207 #045-01-1967 L1968 **GS** *020 †85

JEWELL, James Lee. 7903 PROVIDENCE RD, STE 100 28277 #038-45-1982 L1983 **FPG** *020 †18

JEWELL, Martie Lee. 15110 JOHN J DELANEY DR, MECKLENBURG MEDICAL 28277 #036-01-1999 L2000 **D** *020 †15

JOHNS, Jeffery Scott. 1100 BLYTHE BLVD, CAROLINAS REHABILITATION 28203 #036-07-1995 L2002 **PM SCI** *020 †60

JOHNSON, Adeyemi Sanyade. 1718 E 4TH ST, STE 501 28204 #690-02-1981 L1992 **CD** *020 †20

JOHNSON, Andrea D. 4501 CAMERON VALLEY PKWY, MECKLENBURG MEDICAL GROUP 28211 #041-09-1994 L2001 **ON** *020 †20

JOHNSON, Christine L. ■ 28270 #010-02-1998 L2007 **PD** *020 †55

JOHNSON, Jeremiah John. ■ 28270 #023-12-1998 L2007 **EM** *020 †16

JOHNSON, Michael Eugene. 1000 BLYTHE BLVD, ANNEX BUILDING - MMG 28203 #041-09-1995 L2001 **ID** *020 †20

JOHNSON, Walter Wallace. 1918 RANDOLPH RD, PHYSICIANS RANDOLPH 28207 #035-08-1983 L1997 **IM** *020 †20

JOHNSTON, Harvey W. ■ 28269 #010-01-1952 L1956 **U** *071 †95

JOHNSTON, John Gardner. 1000 BLYTHE BLVD 28203 #036-01-1969 L1969 **PD ADL** *071 †55

JONES, Alan Edward. 1000 BLYTHE BLVD, DEPT OF EMERGENCY MEDICINE 28203 #027-01-1999 L2000 **EM** *020 †16

JONES, Carroll Payne, III. 1001 BLYTHE BLVD, STE 200 28203 #012-01-1998 L2003 **OFA** *020 †40

JONES, James Buckner. 3541 RANDOLPH RD, MECKLENBURG MEDICAL GROUP 28211 #047-05-1979 L1984 **PUD IM** *020 †20

JONES, Jerry Anthony. 700 S TORRENCE ST STE 110 28204 #047-07-1974 L1979 **IM GE** *020 †20

JONES, Melissa Michele. ■ 28205 #028-78-2005, ▲ L2008 **FP** *012

JONES, Philip Brent. 2711 RANDOLPH RD STE 512, RANDOLPH OB/GYN ASSOC 28207 #036-08-1982 L1983 **OBG** *020 †30

■ = Address Information Privacy Protected

JONES, Robert Lee, Jr. 5516 CENTRAL AVE, CMC - EASTLAND FAMILY PRAC 28212 #038-41-1990 L1997 **FM** *020 †18

JONES, Tammy Rochelle. 1918 RANDOLPH RD, STE 275 28207 #004-01-1995 L1998 **FM** *020 †18

JORGENSON, Aric Stephen. ■ 28210 #007-02-2005 L2007 **EM** *100

JOSEPH, Gregory Justin. 3623 LATROBE DR, STE 216 28211 #010-02-1984 L1999 **DR OS** *020 †80

JOYCE, Donald Geo. 120 PROVIDENCE RD 28207 #065-09-1963 L1967 **ORS** *020 †40

JUSTIN, Rodney K. 2711 RANDOLPH RD, US HEALTHWORKS 28207 #025-12-1972 L1974 **FM EM** *020

JUSTIS, Peter Stinnett. 1001 BLYTHE BLVD, STE 500 28203 #036-08-1990 L1992 **IM** *020 †20

JUSTUS, Steven Geo. 3101 LATROBE DR 28211 #036-01-1982 L1985 **EM** *020 †16

JYOTHINAGARAM, S G. 10320 MALLARD CREEK RD, STE 180 28262 #495-37-1982 L1994 **END IM** *020 †20

KAISER, Jeffrey Anthony. ■ 28215 #008-02-1976 L1979 **P** *020

KAISER, Jessica Nicole. 10000 PARK CEDAR DR 28210 #051-07-2003 L2005 **FM** *020 †18

KALICH, Jennifer Ann. 1025 MOREHEAD MEDICAL DR 28204 #025-01-1996 L2000 **OBG** *020 †30

KALINA, Kent Michael. 501 BILLINGSLEY RD 28211 #036-01-1979 L1980 **P ADP** *071 †75

KALINSKI, Marta Maria. 3315 SPRINGBANK LN, STE 304 28226 #759-01-1984 L1993 **IM** *020

KAMERER, Donald B, Jr. 6035 FAIRVIEW RD 28210 #024-01-1982 L1987 **OTO HNS** *020 †45

KANE, Loren Scott. 2700 COLTSGATE RD, STE 101 28211 #035-06-1997 L2000 **IM** *020 †20 ‡

KANELOS, Sharon. 1100 BLYTHE BLVD, CHARLOTTE INSTITUTE/REHAB 28203 #038-41-1996 L2000 **PM** *020 †60

KANNAN, Tamilarasi. 8420 UNIVERSITY EXC PRK DR, DRIVE STE 850 28262 #495-04-1986 L1994 **IM** *020 †20

KANSUPADA, Kashyap B. 1000 BLYTHE BLVD 28203 #038-44-1991 L1996 **OPH** *020 †35

KAPADIA, Sheena. 1918 RANDOLPH RD 28207 #004-01-1995 L1997 **IM** *020 †20

KAPUSTIN, Andrew Jay. 3623 LATROBE DR, STE 216 28211 #024-01-1999 L2005 **DR** *020 †80

KARNER, Steven Franklin. 3541 RANDOLPH RD, CAROLINA NEUROLOGICAL 28211 #039-01-1990 L1997 **N** *020 †75

KARUNAKAR, Madhav Ayodhya. 1616 SCOTT AVE, CAROLINAS MEDICAL CENTER 28203 #048-04-1993 L2007 **OTR** *020 †40

KASHIF, Ahmad. 1918 RANDOLPH RD, STE 600 28207 #915-02-1982 L1993 **RHU** *020 †20

KASHIMAWO-AKANDE, Saidat. 501 BILLINGSLEY RD 28211 #035-06-1993 L1997 **P** *020 †75

KASTEN, Kevin R. ■ 28270 #048-02-2006 **GS** *012

KATIBAH, William Geo. 10320 MALLARD CREEK RD, STE 100 28262 #036-05-1984 L1987 **FM** *020 †18

KATIKITHALA, Sashivani. ■ 28270 #495-58-2000 L2007 **IM** *020 †20

KATZ, Crystal Duncan. 927 EAST BLVD 28203 #036-01-1991 L2001 **AN** *020 †20

KAUFMAN, Michael David. 1010 EDGEHILL RD N 28207 #036-07-1971 L1977 **N IM** *020 †75

KAUR, Suneet. 1000 BLYTHE BLVD 28203 #035-03-1999 L2003 **IM** *020 †20

KEENER, Stephen Robt. 249 BILLINGSLEY RD, MECKLENBURG COUNTY HEALTH 28211 #036-07-1980 L1984 **PHP FM** *030 †70,18

KEITH, Spurgeon C, III. 1620 SCOTT AVE 28203 #021-06-1983 L1991 **AN PME** *020 †05

KELEMEN, William A. ■ 28270 #038-40-1950 L1959 **IM** *071

KELLAM, James F. 1000 BLYTHE BLVD 28203 #065-01-1973 L1991 **OTR** *020 †40

KELLEY, Theodore Maxwell. ■ 28269 #047-06-2007 **FP** *012

KELLY-JONES, Alyse M. 2801 RANDOLPH RD, STE 200 28211 #011-03-1994 L1999 **OBG** *020 †30

KENDALL, Michael Wm. 3026 SPRINGBANK LN STE 1, CHARLOTTE MEDICAL CLINIC 28226 #036-01-1992 L1995 **IM** *020 †20

KENNELLY, Michael Jos. 1023 EDGEHILL RD S 28207 #038-41-1989 L1995 **U** *020 †95

KERCHER, Kent Williams. 1000 BLYTHE BLVD, CAROLINAS MEDICAL CENTER 28203 #036-01-1994 L2000 **GS** *020 †85

KERECMAN, Richard Arden. 7810 PROVIDENCE RD, ARBORETUM URGENT CARE 28226 #036-05-1970 L1970 **FM** *020 †18

KERNS, William Powell, II. 1000 BLYTHE BLVD, EMERGENCY DEPT 28203 #051-04-1985 L1988 **EM** *020 †16

KERSTEN, Brian Paul. 15110 JOHN J DELANEY DR, MECKLENBURG MEDICAL 28277 #038-43-2000 L2002 **IM** *020 †20

KESSLER, Chad Stephen. 6035 FAIRVIEW RD 28210 #021-05-2002 L2007 **OTO** *020

KETRON, John Otey. 11030 GOLF LINKS DR, STE 100 28277 #051-04-1982 L1986 **PD** *020 †55

KHALATBARI, Dara. ■ 28277 #036-07-2003 L2007 **OPH** *020

KHAN, Masood Nawaz. 320 LILLINGTON AVE, STE 201 28204 #495-21-1972 L1992 **IM CD** *020 †20

KHAN, Tooba. ■ 28277 #704-02-1995 L2006 **CN** *020 †75

KHANNA, Neera. 10410 PARK RD STE 100, SOUTH CHARLOTTE PEDIATRICS 28210 #496-07-1991 L2003 **PD** *020 †55

KIDD, Ralph Vincent, Jr. ■ 28209 #021-01-1947 L1953 **IM** *071

KILBANE, Sheila Ann. 5435 PROSPERITY CHURCH RD, STE 1500 28269 #038-40-2002 L2005 **PD** *020

KINZIE, Erik Lee. 1000 BLYTHE BLVD 28203 #040-02-2001 L2004 **P** *020 †75

KIPNIS, Robert Joel. 1918 RANDOLPH RD, STE 600 28207 #036-07-1985 L1990 **RHU IM** *020 †20

KIRK, Benjamin Alan. 1001 BLYTHE BLVD, CHARLOTTE MEDICAL CLINIC 28203 #055-01-1996 L1999 **IM** *020 †20

KIRKLAND, John Alvin, Jr. 201 QUEENS RD 28204 #036-01-1985 L1986 **U** *020 †95

KISH, Inga Hawfield. 2001 VAIL AVE, MEDICAL ASSOCIATES 28207 #045-01-1994 L1995 **EM** *020 †16

KLAPTHOR, Lauren Booth. 1901 RANDOLPH RD 28207 #045-01-1981 L1989 **AN** *020 †05

KLEIN, Deysy Martinez. 1901 RANDOLPH RD 28207 #847-04-1962 L1968 **AN** *071

KLEIN, Emanuel. ■ 28211 #020-02-1957 L1958 **FM D** *020 †18

KLEIN, Jeffrey Allen. 1900 RANDOLPH RD 28207 #036-01-1994 L2001 **EM** *020 †16

KLEINMANN, Richard Eckert. 1918 RANDOLPH RD STE 220, & OSTEOPOROSIS CONSULTANTS 28207 #041-01-1973 L1988 **END IM** *020 †20

KLIMAS, John T. 2630 E 7TH ST, STE 108 28204 #035-06-1973 L1976 **AI PD** *020 †55,03

KLINE, Jeffrey Allen. 1000 BLYTHE BLVD BOX 3286, CAROLINAS MEDICAL CENTER 28203 #051-04-1990 L1992 **EM** *020 †16

KLINE, Victoria Ann. ■ 28262 #008-02-2003 L2006 **FM** *020

KLOCHANY, Alan. 927 EAST BLVD, P O BOX 36351 28203 #028-34-1985 L2002 **AN** *020 †05

KLOTZ, Darrell Alexander. 6035 FAIRVIEW RD, ASSOCIATES, PA 28210 #035-45-1995 L2002 **OTO** *020 †45

KNEISL, Jeffrey S. 1001 BLYTHE BLVD, STE 602 28203 #016-06-1980 L1992 **ORS ON** *020 †40 ‡

KNUTSON, Heather Stout. 7810 PROVIDENCE RD, STE 102 28226 #038-40-1997 L2001 **PD** *020 †55

KOCMOND, Jonathan Howard. 1315 EAST BLVD, STE 280 28203 #016-11-1997 L2004 **PD** *020 †55

KOCONIS, Christ Alexatos. 1928 RANDOLPH RD, STE 106 28207 #038-40-1962 L1969 **OTO HNS** *071 †45

KODZWA, Dorothy Mandipari. ■ 28217 #036-05-2007 **IM** *012

KOKENES, Dennis D. 15830 JOHN J DELANEY DR, CHARLOTTE 28277 #036-01-1987 L1992 **GE** *020 †20

KOKLANARIS, Nikki. 1000 BLYTHE BLVD, CAROLINAS MED CTR 28203 #041-13-1999 L2006 **OBG** *020 †30

KONDOVSKI, Sterjo. ■ 28202 #957-02-1968 L1985 **GP** *071

KONEFAL, John Buckley. NORTHEAST RADIATION ONC SE, BATT CANCER CTR STE B10 28204 #050-02-1984 L1989 **RO** *020 †80

KONEN, Joseph Christopher. 5516 CENTRAL AVE 28212 #035-15-1979 L1987 **FM GPM** *030 †70,18

KOONCE, Elizabeth White. 2600 E 7TH ST, STE 100 28204 #036-01-1984 L1991 **PD** *020 †55

KOSAREK, Francis J. 3623 LATROBE DR, STE 216 28211 #035-01-1990 L1997 **DR** *020 †80

KOSOBUCKI, Brian R. 1718 E 4TH ST STE 908, CONSULTANTS, PA 28204 #036-05-1998 L2004 **OPH** *020 †35

KOSSOVE, Irene Levy. ■ 28211 #051-04-1939 L1940 **GYN IM** *071

KOTHADIA, Jamnadas M. 200 HAWTHORNE LN 28204 #495-48-1983 L1991 **NPM PD** *020 †55

KOURI, William Herbert. ■ 28210 #036-01-1961 L1961 **FM GP** *071 †18

KRAMER, Norman John. 4525 CAMERON VALLEY PKWY, STE 4100 28211 #041-02-1965 L1975 **END IM** *020 †20

KREISMAN, Steven. 7810 PROVIDENCE RD, STE 102 28226 #016-11-1979 L1982 **FM** *020 †16,18

KREMERS, Mark Stuart. 1718 E 4TH ST STE 501, MID CAROLINA CARDIOLOGY, P 28204 #017-20-1979 L1990 **ICE CD** *020 †20

KREMERS, Scott Alex. 1918 RANDOLPH RD, STE 450 28207 #017-20-1974 L1979 **PUD IM** *020 †20

KRESHON, Martin John, Sr. 3315 SPRINGBANK LN, STE 204 28226 #056-06-1954 L1957 **OPH** *071 †35

KRISHNA, Ashwin Subramani. ■ 28207 #047-06-2007 **PD** *012

KRUG, Joseph H, Jr. 135 S SHARON AMITY RD, STE 100 28211 #035-01-1982 L1990 **OPH** *020 †35

KRZYZANIAK, Raymond L. 1043 E MOREHEAD ST, STE 107 28204 #017-20-1979 L2007 **PTH HMP** *020 †20

KUESER, Thomas Jos. 1000 BLYTHE BLVD BX 32861, DEPT OF NEONATOLOGY 28203 #028-34-1980 L1989 **NPM PD** *020 †55

KUKREJA, Neeta. 10344 PARK RD, STE 100 28210 #495-45-1987 L1997 **PD** *020 †55

KUREMSKY, Marshall A. ■ 28203 #035-01-2003 L2007 **ORS** *012

KUTNER, William Alvin. 4601 PARK ROAD STE 300, MOORESVILLE, NC 28117 28290 #036-07-1970 L1986 **ORS** *020 †40

KUWADA, Timothy Shig. 1001 BLYTHE BLVD, STE 602 28203 #008-02-1998 L2004 **GS** *100 †85

KWAKU, Hans Manuel. 3627 BEATTIES FORD RD 28216 #412-01-1996 L2003 **IM** *020 †20

LACKEY, Philip Carlyle. 4539 HEDGEMORE DR, STE 100 28209 #036-01-1990 L1996 **ID** *020 †20

LACKEY, Victoria Donovan. 3030 RANDOLPH RD, MECKLENBURG MEDICAL GROUP 28211 #036-01-1992 L2005 **IM** *020 †20

LACOUTURE, John Edwin. 300 BILLINGSLEY RD STE 101, JOHN E. LACOUTURE, MD, PA 28211 #051-01-1975 L1978 **IM IMG** *020 †20

LAIRD, Amanda Michelle. 1918 RANDOLPH RD, STE 130 28207 #021-06-2000 L2002 **GS** *020 †85

LAIRD, William Kenneth. 10502 PARK RD, STE 100 28210 #065-01-1968 L1974 **PS** *020 †65

LAKIN, Christopher Morgan. 101 E WT HARRIS BLVD, STE 1121 28262 #036-01-1980 L1982 **PD OS** *020 †55 ‡

LALKA, Stephen Gary. 1001 BLYTHE BLVD, STE 300 28203 #035-45-1980 L2005 **VS** *020 †85

LAMOTHE, Traci Aurelia. 14215 BALLANTYNE CORP PL, STE 130 28277 #036-01-1998 L1999 **PD** *020 †55

LANDIS, Edward E, Jr. 200 HAWTHORNE LN 28204 #020-02-1962 L1969 **PUD IM** *071 †20

LANDIS, Eric Tyler. 10512 PARK RD, MECKLENBURG MEDICAL GROUP 28210 #036-01-1997 L2000 **IM** *020 †20

LANE, Jennifer Alice. 251 EASTWAY DR, NORTHPARK 28213 #035-48-1992 L1996 **OBG** *020 †30

LANE, Jerald Paul. 1900 RANDOLPH RD 28207 #028-03-1963 L1967 **P** *075 †75

LANE, John Henry. ■ 28207 #023-07-1958 L1964 **PTH** *040 †50

LANE, Sara Elizabeth. 28209 #051-04-2007 **OBG** *020

LANG, Joseph Paul. 4539 HEDGEMORE DR, STE 100 28209 #038-45-1988 L1995 **IM ID** *020 †20

LANTZ, Sarah Michelle. ■ 28205 #017-20-2008 *012

LAPP, Charles Warren. 10344 PARK RD STE 300 28210 #035-03-1974 L1975 **IM PD** *020 †20,55 ‡

LARDI, Rachel Nicole. ■ 28213 #056-06-2006 **IM** *012

LARK, Rebecca Long. 4539 HEDGEMORE DR, STE 100 28209 #047-05-1994 L2000 **ID** *020 †20

LARKIN, Glenn M. 4815 N SHARON AMITY RD 28205 #165-04-1966 L1968 **FOP LM** *074

LARSEN, William Gustav. 7920 MOORES CHAPEL RD, NORTHWEST FAMILY PHYSICIAN 28214 #036-08-1987 L1993 **FM** *020 †18

LARSON, Timothy Brad. ■ 28210 #038-40-2007 **ORS** *012

LARSON, Tracy Mann. 2711 RANDOLPH RD STE 512 28207 #051-04-1995 L1999 **OBG** *020 †30

LARUE, James Caldwell. ■ 28214 #051-04-2006 **IM** *012

LASSITER, Jennifer W. 2630 E 7TH ST, STE 101 28204 #001-02-1996 L2006 **PD** *020 †55

LASTER, Andrew Jay. 1918 RANDOLPH RD, STE 600 28207 #023-07-1979 L1982 **RHU IM** *020 †20

LATHAM, Ruth Christina. ■ 28210 #051-04-2002 L2007 **FM** *020

LAU, Charles Tseng. ■ 28203 #035-06-2000 L2007 **DR** *100 †80

LAVIS, Timothy D. 1100 BLYTHE BLVD, CAROLINAS REHABILITATION 28203 #048-12-2001 L2006 **PM** *100 †60

LAWRENCE, Patricia A. 1001 BLYTHE BLVD STE 402 28203 #051-01-1950 L1954 **GYN** *071 †30

LAXER, Eric Brian. 15825 JOHN J DELANEY DR, STE 100 28277 #067-01-1988 L1995 **ORS** *020 †40

LAYTON, Dennis Sheldon. 330 BILLINGSLEY RD STE 10 28211 #055-01-1976 L1979 **IM** *020 †20

LE, Mark Tuan. 4920 ALBEMARLE RD 28205 #045-04-1993 L1997 **IM EM** *020 †20

LEAKE, Jonathan Aaron. ■ 28203 #035-01-2005 L2007 **EM** *012

LEATH, Thomas Edward. 6125 TYVOLA CENTRE DR 28217 #045-01-1955 L1956 **GP** *071

LE-BLISS, Mary Tram. 4922 ALBEMARLE RD, NORTH CROSS MEDICAL CENTER 28205 #011-03-1994 L1997 **IM** *020 †20

LEE, James Edward. 7731 LITTLE AVE STE 100 28226 #036-07-1979 L1983 **CHP P** *050 †75

LEE, Soong Hyun. 1000 BLYTHE BLVD 28203 #583-02-1963 L1972 **P** *020 †75

LEE, Tong Hoon. ■ 28277 #583-02-1953 L1976 **FM** *071

LEE, Yen-Chich. 1901 RANDOLPH RD 28207 #244-05-1968 L1975 **AN** *020 †05

LEFAIVRE, Jean-Francois. 1000 BLYTHE BLVD 28203 #067-06-1988 L1995 **PS CFS** *020 †65

LEFKOWITZ, David, III. 2630 E 7TH ST, STE 100 28204 #021-01-1965 L1972 **AI PDA** *020 †55,03

LELIO, David Francis. 501 BILLINGSLEY RD 28211 #305-01-1989 L2003 **CHP P** *030 †75

LEMASTER, Kimberly Paige. 11030 GOLF LINKS DR, STE 100 28277 #036-08-1993 L1996 **PD** *020 †55

LEMERMAN, Amy Leigh. 1900 RANDOLPH RD, STE 900 28207 #036-05-2003 L2006 **EM** *020 †16

LENKER, Michael D. 1328 KENILWORTH AVE 28203 #048-14-1984 L1997 **R PTH** *020 †80

LENNOX, Peter Anthony. 2300 RANDOLPH RD, STE A 28207 #061-01-1991 L1998 **PS** *020 †65

LESSARIS, Karen J. 1000 BLYTHE BLVD 28203 #016-45-1993 L2000 **NPM** *020 †55

LESSER, Philip Steven. 1001 BLYTHE BLVD, STE 601 28203 #045-01-1967 L1977 **N** *020 †55,75

LETICA, Mark. 10320 MALLARD CREEK RD, CAROLINA NEUROLOGICAL 28262 #025-07-1987 L2000 **N** *020 †75

LETTMAN, Nadine Amorette. 2001 VAIL AVE, MEDICAL ASSOCIATES 28207 #035-20-2002 L2006 **EM** *020 †16

LEVINE, Elissa Rosenfeld. 7810 BALLANTYNE COMNS PKWY, STE 201 28277 #024-05-1998 L2004 **PD** *020 †55

LEVINE, Joshua David. 1918 RANDOLPH RD, STE 310 28207 #024-05-1997 L2003 **OTO** *020 †45

LEVY, Jay B. 3125 SPRINGBANK LN 28226 #048-12-1989 L1996 **UP** *020 †95

LEVY, Kathy Dodson. 1001 BLYTHE BLVD, STE 500 28203 #048-14-1987 L1996 **IM** *020 †20

LEWIN, Marc Robert. 10000 PARK CEDAR DR, CARMEL FAMILY PHYSICIANS, 28210 #065-06-1990 L1994 **FM** *020 †18

LEWIS, Andrew Jackson. 2801 RANDOLPH RD STE 200 28211 #001-02-1957 L1958 **GYN** *071 †30

LEWIS, Daniel Michael. 2630 E 7TH ST, STE 200 28204 #036-01-1980 L1981 **D** *020 †15

LIEBERMAN, Jesse Aaron. ■ 28211 #036-05-2004 L2006 **PM** *012

LIETZ, Timothy Edward. 1900 RANDOLPH RD 28207 #048-40-1990 L1994 **EM** *020 †16

LIMENTANI, Steven A. 1100 S TRYON ST, STE 400 28203 #024-07-1986 L1995 **ON HEM** *020 †20

LINDBLOM, Scott Shannon. 1001 BLYTHE BLVD, STE 500 28203 #056-06-1989 L1996 **PCC SME** *020 †20

LINDERMAN, James Alan. 1000 BLYTHE BLVD 28203 #017-20-1976 L1981 **PD** *020 †55

LINDNER, Leslie Hansen. 7810 PROVIDENCE RD, STE 101 28226 #041-01-1992 L1996 **OBG** *020 †30

LINDOW, Larry Gene. PO BOX 1047 28201 #016-11-1968 L1977 **OS IM** *030

LINDSAY, Maryanne. 2001 VAIL AVE, MEDICAL ASSOCIATES 28207 #045-04-1993 L1996 **EM** *020 †16

LINEBERGER, Adrian S, III. 927 EAST BLVD 28203 #036-05-1981 L2004 **AN** *020 †05 ‡

LINGO, Stephen Todd. 3025 SPRINGBANK LN, COMPLEX #100 28226 #038-40-1994 L2006 **IM** *020 †20

LINNEY, George Edward, Jr. ■ 28211 #012-01-1969 L1972 **PD** *030 †55

LIPFORD, Edward Holdman. 1000 BLYTHE BLVD 28203 #047-05-1977 L1986 **PTH** *020 †50

LIPTON, Jordan Douglas. 6115 PARK SOUTH DR, STE 100 28210 #067-01-1990 L1993 **GP EM** *020 †16

LISZKA, Thomas Geo. 14135 BALLANTYNE CORPRT PL, STE 150 28277 #041-12-1985 L1996 **PS HS** *020 †65

LITTLE, Donald Forrest. 1718 E 4TH ST, STE 601 28204 #001-02-1959 L1965 **OBG** *071 †30

LITTLE, Harry Marette. 1900 RANDOLPH RD 28207 #036-05-1980 L1981 **EM** *020 †18,16

LITTMANN, Laszlo. 1000 BLYTHE BLVD, CAROLINA MEDICAL CENTER 28203 #473-01-1970 L1993 **IM CD** *020 †20

LIVINGSTON, Michael B. 1100 S TRYON ST, STE 400 28203 #045-01-1984 L1989 **HEM ON** *020 †20

LOBDELL, Kevin Wallace. 1000 BLYTHE BLVD 28203 #025-07-1986 L2004 **CCS** *020 †85,90

LOCASCIO, David Frank. 1900 RANDOLPH RD 28207 #016-01-1995 L2000 **EM** *020 †16

LOCK, Richard Reynolds. 3320 EASTOVER RIDGE DR # B, CAROLINAS HOSPITALISTS GRO 28211 #024-05-1993 L2001 **IM** *020 †20

LOCKHART, Evelyn Louise. 2425 PARK RD 28203 #036-01-2001 L2008 **PTH BBK** *020

LOEFFLER, Bryan Jeffrey. ■ 28210 #023-01-2005 L2006 **ORS** *012

LOGAN, Keith. 1718 E 4TH ST, STE 801 28204 #010-01-1990 L1998 **P** *020 †75

LOGAN, William Sumner. 1928 RANDOLPH RD STE 316 28207 #036-07-1968 L1968 **D** *020 †15

LOHAVICHAN, Verachai. 8936 BLAKENEY PROFESSNL DR 28277 #036-01-1996 L2001 **NEP** *020 †20

LOMBARD, Robert Marion. 1000 BLYTHE BLVD, 5TH FLOOR MEDICAL EDUCATIO 28203 #041-14-1980 L2007 **PUD CCM** *020 †20

LOMBARDI, V Alan. 8320 UNIVERSITY EXC PRK DR, STE 104 28262 #041-12-1980 L1988 **P ADP** *020 †20

LONERGAN, Maryrose Turner. 1901 RANDOLPH RD 28207 #030-06-1982 L1994 **AN** *020 †05

LONG, Charles W, Jr. 1000 BLYTHE BLVD 28203 #012-01-1984 L1988 **AN** *020 †05

LONG, William Joseph, Jr. 8401 MEDICAL PLAZA DR, STE 300 28262 #012-01-1980 L1981 **FM** *020 †18

LONGEE, Darryl Chas. 1000 BLYTHE BLVD, PEDIATRIC HEMATOLOGY/ONCOL 28203 #004-01-1983 L2007 **PHO PD** *050 †55

LORCH, Frank Ernest, IV. 7825 BALLANTYNE COMNS PKWY, STE 150 28277 #038-40-1990 L2002 **PM** *020 †60

LORCH, Susan Lynn. ■ 28210 #020-12-2005 **PM** *012

LORD, Christopher E. 501 BILLINGSLEY RD 28211 #048-02-1999 L2002 **ADP** *020 †75

LORENZEN, Brent Christoph. ■ 28211 #047-05-2008 *012

LORENZO, Emily Estandian. 10210 COULOAK DR STE E, MT ISLAND 28216 #748-16-1997 L2006 **FM** *020

LORIMER, Susan Mary. ■ 28277 #062-01-1981 L1996 *020

LOVE, Dexter Wayne. PO BOX 32861, MEDICAL EDUCATION 28232 #023-07-2002 L2003 **ORS** *020

LOVELL, Roger Dwight. 1000 BLYTHE BLVD, DEPT INT MED STE 504 28203 #012-01-1986 L1998 **ID** *020 †20

LOWDER, Laura Hines. 15110 JOHN J DELANEY DR, STE 100 28277 #036-08-1997 L2001 **OBG** *020 †30

LUCAS, Jack Alan. 1025 MOREHEAD MEDICAL DR 28204 #036-01-1982 L1983 **OBG** *020 †30

LUCAS, Robt Theodore, Jr. 200 HAWTHORNE LN 28204 #021-01-1954 L1959 **PD** *071 †55

LUCCERINI, Silvia L. 3315 SPRINGBANK LN STE 302 28226 #132-01-1987 L2005 **CHP** *020 †75

LUCKTONG, Ekachai. 2001 VAIL AVE, MEDICAL ASSOCIATES 28207 #055-01-1997 L2000 **EM** *020 †16

LUMSDEN, Erika G. 1025 MOREHEAD MEDICAL DR, STE 300 28204 #024-01-1997 L2003 **HS** *020 †40

LUPO, Susan Elizabeth. 1400 LINDA LN 28211 #036-05-1979 L1981 **AN IM** *020 †20,05

LUPTON, Laura Lake. 309 S SHARON AMITY RD, STE 100 28211 #166-02-2001 L2004 **FM** *100 †18

LURIE, Scott N. 1132 GREENWOOD CLFS 28204 #036-07-1987 L1988 **P** *020 †75

LUTIN, Charles David. 7810 PROVIDENCE RD STE 102, CHS URGENT CARE-ARBORETUM 28226 #036-07-1977 L1979 **FM** *040 †16,18

LYDAY, William Davie. 225 HAWTHORNE LN 28204 #036-07-1953 L1954 **TS GS** *071 †85,90

LYKE, Allison C.. ■ 28209 #036-01-2007 IM *012

MABRY, David Bruce. 7030 PINEVILLE MATTHEWS RD 28226 #012-01-1995 L1997 **IM** *020 †20

MAC DONALD, Donald E. ■ 28210 #803-02-1948 L1953 **P** *071 †75

MAC DONALD, Paul Ryan. 2219 E 7TH ST 28204 #011-04-1998 L2003 **N** *020 †75

MAC DONALD, Wm Webster. 1025 MOREHEAD MEDICAL DR, STE 400 28204 #035-15-1968 L1978 **OBG** *071 †30

MAC INTYRE, James C. 501 BILLINGSLEY RD 28211 #035-03-1972 L2000 **CHP P** *020 †75

MACK, Peter Bowman. ■ 28209 #016-43-2007 **FP** *012

MACNEILL, Emily Champe. ■ 28211 #017-20-2002 L2007 **OS** *100 †55

MADDUX, Helen Ross. 200 QUEENS RD, STE 400 28204 #036-05-1980 L2002 **RO PD** *020 †55,80

MADJAROV, Jeko Metodiev. 1001 BLYTHE BLVD STE 300, THE SANGER CLINIC 28203 #198-01-1995 L2005 **VS** *100 †85

MADSEN, Christian Victor. 4600 HOLBROOK DR 28212 #038-40-1979 L1982 **FM OM** *020 †18

MAHDI, Nasser. ■ 28226 #797-02-1988 L1993 **CD IM** *020 †20

MAHONEY, John Francis. 1100 S TRYON ST, STE 400 28203 #041-12-1984 L1991 **ON HEM** *020 †20

MAIR, Eric Alan. 6035 FAIRVIEW RD, CEENTA, SOUTHPARK OFFICE 28210 #048-04-1986 L2006 **OTO** *020 †45 ‡

MAJORS, Roy Alan. 1915 RANDOLPH RD 28207 #012-01-1985 L1991 **ORS** *020 †40

MAKEMSON, Scott C. 1025 MOREHEAD MEDICAL DR, STE 400 28204 #038-41-1995 L1999 **OBG** *020 †30

MAKHULI, Mark Joseph. ■ 28277 #035-19-1995 L2001 **U** *020

MAKOWSKI, Sheryl Franklin. ■ 28226 #016-02-1983 L1985 **PD** *040 †55

MALAK, Darryl Evan. 1901 RANDOLPH RD 28207 #016-43-1992 L2005 **AN** *020 †05

MALLICO, Eric John. ■ 28209 #008-02-2003 **GS** *012

MALLONEE, Michael Steven. 6035 FAIRVIEW RD, THROAT 28210 #011-02-1973 L1980 **OTO** *020 †45

MALTA, Katherine M. 10816 BLACK DOG LN STE 160 28214 #038-40-1997 L1998 **FM** *020 †18

MALTON, Mark Leland. 135 S SHARON AMITY RD, STE 100 28211 #025-01-1982 L1987 **OPH** *020 †35

MAMMANO, Kimberly Anne. 5435 PROSPERITY CHURCH RD, STE 2200A 28269 #035-47-1999 L2004 **OBG** *020

MANCUSO, Erin Michelle. PO BOX 30756, 1900 RANDOLPH RD STE 900 28230 #041-14-2001 L2004 **EM** *020

MANILOFF, Gary Bruce. 1918 RANDOLPH RD, STE 600 28207 #550-02-1981 L1993 **RHU IM** *020 †20

MANN, Christopher Hayes. PO BOX 32861, DPET OF ORTHO SURGERY 28232 #036-08-2004 L2007 **ORS** *012

MANN, Laurene Carol. 841 BAXTER ST, STE 112 28202 #025-07-1982 L1988 **DR** *020 †80

MANNE, Prasad Purna. 1000 BLYTHE BLVD, ANNEX BUILDING 28203 #759-12-2000 L2005 **IM** *020

MANOS, Heather Michelle. ■ 28205 #036-01-2006 **FP** *012

MANOUSOS, George Anthony. 1000 BLYTHE BLVD, LEVINE CHILDREN'S HOSPITAL 28203 #036-07-2002 L2004 **PD** *100

MARASHI, Amir H. 10035 PARK CEDAR DR, STE 300 28210 #021-06-1999 L2002 **OMF** *020

MARCH, Holly Ann. 3108 EASTOVER RDG RD # 835 28211 #035-15-1990 L1997 **P** *020

MARCHICK, Michael Robert. ■ 28202 #041-12-2005 L2008 **EM** *012

MARIN, Rigoberto Lacayo, Jr. ■ 28217 #056-05-2006 L2008 **FM** *100

MARION, Dominique Estee. 1350 S KINGS DR, CMC MYERS PARK PEDIATRICS 28207 #025-12-2003 L2006 **PD** *020 †55

MARKO, Bruce Howard. 15830 JOHN J DELANEY DR, STE 250 28277 #030-05-1985 L1996 **OBG** *020 †30

MARLOWE, Thomas Stanley. 400 CLARICE AVE, STE 100 28204 #017-20-1999 L2005 **FM OS** *020 †18

MARSH, Eric Alan. 1000 BLYTHE BLVD, ANNEX BUILDING 28203 #012-01-2003 L2006 **IM** *020 †20

MARSHBURN, Paul Bartow. 1000 BLYTHE BLVD, DEPT OB 28203 #012-05-1984 L1985 **REN OBG** *020 †30

MARTIMBEAU, Pierre. 330 BILLINGSLEY RD, STE 202 28211 #067-02-1966 L1980 **GO GYN** *020 †30

MARTIN, Edward Stephens. 2600 E 7TH ST, STE 100 28204 #041-01-1969 L1969 **PD** *020 †55

MARTIN, Kimmery Dawn. 2001 VAIL AVE, MEDICAL ASSOCIATES 28207 #020-02-1998 L2001 **EM** *020 †16

MARTIN, Thomas Chas, Jr. 1000 BLYTHE BLVD 28203 #051-01-1992 L2001 **PTH** *020 †50

MARTINIE, John Bennett. 1000 BLYTHE BLVD, DEPT OF GENERAL SURGERY 28203 #041-14-1995 L2005 **GS** *020 †85

MARTORANO, Melissa Ann. ■ 28211 #020-12-2008 *012

MARX, John Andrew. 1000 BLYTHE BLVD 28203 #005-11-1977 L1991 **EM** *020 †16

MASON, David Pomeroy. 2001 VAIL AVE, MEDICAL ASSOCIATES 28207 #024-16-2001 L2004 **EM** *020 †16

MASON, J Bohannon. 1915 RANDOLPH RD, ATTN: JEAN DEHNER 28207 #045-01-1989 L1993 **ORS** *020 †40

MASON, Thomas Lee. 1900 RANDOLPH RD 28207 #036-01-1991 L1992 **EM** *020 †16

MASONIS, John Leander. 1025 MOREHEAD MEDICAL DR, STE 300 28204 #041-02-1996 L1997 **ORS** *020 †40

MASSENGILL, Susan Foster. 1628 E MOREHEAD ST 28207 #036-08-1987 L1988 **PN PD** *020 †55

MASSEY, Chas Caswell, Jr. 2015 RANDOLPH RD STE 201 28207 #036-07-1961 L1961 **CRS** *071 †20

MATHAPATI, Shakuntala. ■ 28277 #495-99-2000 L2006 **IM** *020 †20

MATHEWS, Emmett C, Jr. 1718 E 4TH ST STE 501, MID CAROLINA CARDIOLOGY 28204 #051-01-1968 L1988 **CD IM** *020 †20

MATKINS, Jerry Franklin. 1025 MOREHEAD MEDICAL DR 28204 #036-01-1992 L1996 **OBG** *020 †30

MATKINS, Preeti Patel. 1000 BLYTHE BLVD, DEPT OF PEDIATRICS 28203 #036-01-1992 L1995 **PD ADL** *020 †55

MATLEY, Ryan Christopher. ■ 28203 #038-41-2007 **EM** *012
MATTHEW, Deborah Faith. 15105 JOHN J DELANEY DR, SIGNATURE WELLNESS 28277 #062-01-1994 L1998 **PD** *020 †55
MATTHEWS, David Cary. 1719 SOUTH BLVD, # B 28203 #038-41-1974 L1982 **PS** *020 †85,65
MATTHEWS, Linda Johnson. 101 E WT HARRIS BLVD, STE 1212 28262 #036-01-1990 L1992 **PTH** *020 †50
MATTHEWS, Michelle L. 1000 BLYTHE BLVD, MAILING: P O BOX 32861 28203 #038-44-1992 L1998 **OBG REN** *020 †30 ‡
MAUERHAN, David Robt. 1000 BLYTHE BLVD 28203 #038-41-1978 L1983 **ORS** *020 †40 ‡
MAWJI, Zubina M. 15110 JOHN J DELANEY DR, MECKLENBURG MEDICAL 28277 #041-14-1996 L2005 **IM** *020 †20
MAY, Bryan Vincent. 927 EAST BLVD 28203 #045-04-2001 L2007 **AN** *100 †05
MAY, Harvey Craig. 2711 RANDOLPH RD STE 305 28207 #021-01-1942 L1950 **GYN** *071 †30
MAYER, Katherine Anne. ■ 28203 #019-02-2006 **EM** *012
MAYNARD, Jonathan Ray. ■ 28211 #020-12-2008 *012
MAZZELLA, William John. 1000 BLYTHE BLVD 28203 #036-01-1998 L2001 **IM** *020 †20
MBADINUJU, Adanma Ijeoma. 1918 RANDOLPH RD, STE 175 28207 #661-02-2002 L2005 **FM** *020 †18
MC ADAMS, Charles R, Jr. ■ 28226 #041-02-1945 L1945 **GS** *071
MC ADAMS, Stephen Alan. 1718 E 4TH ST, STE 501 28204 #017-20-1978 L2000 **CCM PUD** *030 †20 ‡
MC ALISTER, James A, Jr. 1901 RANDOLPH RD 28207 #036-05-1969 L1969 **PTH** *071 †50
MC BRIDE, Robert Bennis. 101 E WT HARRIS BLVD, STE 1110 28262 #055-01-1980 L1981 **ORS** *020 †40
MC BRYDE, John Peter. 1000 BLYTHE BLVD, DEPT OF EMERGENCY MEDICINE 28203 #045-01-1992 L1996 **EM ESM** *020 †16
MC CAIN, Glenn Alan. 300 BILLINGSLEY RD STE 102 28211 #065-01-1971 L1992 **RHU** *020 †20
MC CLELLAND, William A. 3135 SPRINGBANK LN, THROAT PA 28226 #051-01-1989 L1994 **OTO GS** *020 †45
MC CORD, Robert Gardner. ■ 28277 #056-05-1974 L1975 **PTH** *071 †50 ‡
MC COY, Thomas Hatton. 200 HAWTHORNE LN 28204 #036-01-1981 L1986 **ORS** *020 †40
MCCURDY, Eleanor Anne. 1000 BLYTHE BLVD 28203 #038-41-1997 L2003 **OBG** *020 †30
MC CURDY, Lewis Hall, III. 4539 HEDGEMORE DR 28209 #001-02-1996 L2003 **ID** *020 †20
MCCUTCHEON, Edward. 2001 VAIL AVE, MEDICAL ASSOCIATES 28207 #055-01-1999 L2002 **EM** *020 †16
MC DEAVITT, James Thos. 1000 BLYTHE BLVD, CAROLINAS HEALTHCARE SYSTE 28203 #036-05-1986 L1991 **PM** *020 †60
MC DERMOTT, James Emmett. 1001 BLYTHE BLVD 28203 #055-01-1987 L2000 **PTH** *020 †20,50
MC DERMOTT, Marie Muller. ■ 28226 #041-07-1957 L1982 **OS** *071
MCDONALD, Curtis Ray. PO BOX 32861, DEPT OF PATHOLOGY 303BBB 28232 #036-08-2006 **PD** *012
MC DONALD, Robert L. 200 HAWTHORNE LN 28204 #001-02-1985 L1986 **IM** *020 †20
MC DOUGAL, Jennifer Lea. ■ 28202 #012-05-2002 L2007 **VS** *012 †85
MCDOWELL, Amanda Lynn. ■ 28211 #038-45-2005 L2008 **PD** *012
MC ELGUNN, Patrick Shane. 5815 BLAKENEY PARK DR, STE 100 28277 #060-01-1977 L2006 **D** *020 †15 ‡
MC ELROY, Kimberly Anne. ■ 28277 #016-43-1988 L1998 **IM** *020 †20
MC ELWEE, Thomas Brenton. 1918 RANDOLPH RD, STE 130 28207 #021-01-1980 L1981 **GS** *020 †85
MC EWEN, Luther M, III. 1515 MOCKINGBIRD LN # 540 28209 #036-01-1971 L2000 **P ADM** *020
MC GEE, John Asbury. 1000 BLYTHE BLVD 28203 #036-01-1958 L1958 **GYN** *071 †30
MC GHEE, James Ernest, Jr. 2115 E SEVENTH ST, STE 102 28204 #012-05-1988 L1994 **FM** *020 †18
MC GINNIS, L Scott, III. 200 HAWTHORNE LN, PRESBYTERIAN HOSP 28204 #012-01-1989 L1993 **RO** *020 †80
MC GINNIS, Leeann M. 3030 LATROBE DR 28211 #025-01-1979 L1984 **AN PME** *020 †05
MC GUIRE, Jayne T. 1000 BLYTHE BLVD 28203 #033-05-1987 L1991 **AN PME** *020 †05
MC INTOSH, Margaret. 5540 DOVERSTONE CT 28208 #035-06-1981 L1992 **FM** *020 †18
MC INTYRE, Clarence A, Jr. ■ 28211 #007-02-1956 L1961 **PD** *071 †55
MC IVER, John Christensen. 1000 BLYTHE BLVD 28203 #010-02-1995 L2003 **IM** *020 †20
MC KAY, Clinton Hull. 1001 BLYTHE BLVD, STE 500 28203 #047-06-1939 L1947 **IM** *071 †20
MC KAY, Hamilton W, Jr. 2711 RANDOLPH RD, STE 400 28207 #023-07-1955 L1956 **A IG** *071
MC KOY, Teressa Yvette. 9908 COULOAK DR, STE 202 28216 #036-01-1993 L1996 **FM** *020 †18
MC LANAHAN, Charles Scott. 225 BALDWIN AVE, CAROLINA NEUROSURGERY & SP 28204 #035-01-1973 L1980 **NS NSP** *020 †25
MC LEAN, Jonathan Owens. 1718 E 4TH ST STE 501, MECKLENBURG CARDIOVASCULAR 28204 #036-01-1971 L1971 **CD** *020 †20
MC LEOD, Tonya Shonelle. 5815 BLAKENEY PARK DR, STE 100 28277 #036-01-2001 L2006 **D** *020 †15
MC LOUGHLIN, Jill H. 1524 E MOREHEAD ST 28207 #036-01-1983 L1986 **IM** *020 †20
MC MAHON, Daniel P. 1000 BLYTHE BLVD, 7TH FL 28203 #010-02-1978 L1996 **HEM PD** *020 †55
MCMILLAN, Edward Beman. 1718 E 4TH ST, STE 501 28204 #036-07-1990 L1996 **CD** *020 †20
MC MILLAN, Marshall P. 9101 MONROE RD, STE 155 28270 #045-01-1984 L1987 **FM** *020 †18
MC MILLAN, Thos Henry, Jr. ■ 28209 #012-05-1953 L1958 **IM** *071 †20
MCMINN, Melanie Truesdale. ■ 28226 #010-01-2008 *012
MC MURRAY, John Harvey. 3303 LATROBE DR 28211 #036-01-1976 L1977 **P** *020 †75
MC NAMARA, John F, II. 2711 RANDOLPH RD STE 5 28207 #038-40-1976 L1980 **OBG** *020 †30
MC NELIS, Michael John. 1901 RANDOLPH RD 28207 #051-07-1985 L1991 **AN** *020 †05
MC PHEE, Sherryl Ann. 7030 PINEVILLE MATTHEWS RD 28226 #038-40-1993 L1999 **IM** *020 †20
MC PHERSON, Vanessa Lee. 5516 CENTRAL AVE 28212 #036-01-1994 L1997 **FM** *020 †18
MEADOWS, Fred Canning. ■ 28270 #012-01-1943 L1950 **OTO** *071
MEALS, Joanna Elizabeth. 1000 BLYTHE BLVD, CAROLINAS HEALTHCARE SYSTE 28203 #054-04-2004 L2007 **PD** *020 †55
MEGREMIS, Tommy L. 5933 BLAKENEY PARK DR, STE 101 28277 #036-01-1984 L1987 **OBG** *020 †30
MEHTA, Alpa Arun. ■ 28207 #001-06-2004 L2006 **IM** *020 †20
MEHTA, Anita. 6608 E WT HARRIS BLVD # A 28215 #495-20-1988 L1996 **PD** *020
MEHTA, Praful Chandulal. 459 N WENDOVER RD 28211 #495-23-1972 L1979 **P** *020 †75
MEHTA, Raj Kumar. 927 EAST BLVD, P O BOX 36351 28203 #305-01-1999 L2003 **PAN** *100 †05
MEHTA, Shraddha Shrestha. ■ 28211 #004-01-1999 L2007 **OBG** *020 †30
MELVIN, Jean Allen. 3303 LATROBE DR, EASTOVER PSYCHO/PSYCHIATRI 28211 #036-01-1986 L1987 **P** *020 †75
MEMMEN, Andrea. 10512 PARK RD, MECKLENBURG MEDICAL GROUP 28210 #036-05-1997 L2000 **IM** *020 †20
MENDELSOHN, David Russell. 2610 W ARROWOOD RD 28273 #036-01-2002 L2005 **FM** *020 †18
MENDEZ, Kiru Korea. 8800 N TRYON ST, CMC UNIVERSITY 28262 #036-08-2004 L2007 **IM** *020 †20
MENDOZA, Stephen Victor. 1901 RANDOLPH RD 28207 #048-13-1994 L2002 **AN** *020 †05
MENK, Emil J. 1901 RANDOLPH RD 28207 #020-12-1981 L1991 **AN PME** *020 †05
MENSCER, Darlyne. 5516 CENTRAL AVE, EASTLAND FP 28212 #036-01-1979 L1980 **FM FPG** *040 †18
MERTEN, Gregory John. 2711 RANDOLPH RD, STE 400 28207 #026-04-2000 L2002 **NEP** *020 †20
MESSICK, Brent Hamilton. ■ 28202 #654-01-2005 **FP** *012
METCALF, Michael Richard. 3333 WILKINSON BLVD, METROLINA COMPREHENSIVE HE 28208 #010-03-1982 L1985 **IM** *020 †20
MILES, Benjamin Carl. ■ 28269 #017-20-2006 **OBG** *012
MILES, William Scherer. 1000 BLYTHE BLVD 28203 #051-07-1986 L1995 **CCS** *020 †85
MILLARD, Jonathan Kevin. 2001 VAIL AVE, MEDICAL ASSOCIATES 28207 #036-05-2000 L2003 **EM** *020
MILLER, Barbara Kathleen. 5933 BLAKENEY PARK DR, STE 200 28277 #051-01-1998 L2005 **OPH** *020 †35
MILLER, David Weldon. 1025 MOREHEAD MEDICAL DR, DRIVE #200 28204 #012-01-1990 L1996 **HO** *020 †20
MILLER, Edith Hamilton. 1000 BLYTHE BLVD, CAROLINAS MEDICAL CENTER 28203 #045-01-1975 L2004 **DIA END** *020 †20
MILLER, Joshua Seth. 1025 MOREHEAD MEDICAL DR, 2ND FL 28204 #045-01-1986 L1988 **PME AN** *020 †05 ‡
MILLER, Kathlynn D. ■ 28269 #041-07-1979 **PTH IG** *050
MILLER, Michael John. 1718 E 4TH ST STE 501, MID CAROLINA CARDIOLOGY 28204 #041-12-1985 L1987 **IC CD** *020 †20
MILLER, Richard Francis. 15110 JOHN J DELANEY DR, MECKLENBURG MEDICAL 28277 #041-14-1995 L2006 **CD** *020 †20
MILLER, Stuart Otto. 10310 MALLARD CREEK RD 28262 #038-43-1999 L2000 **FM** *020 †18
MILLS, Alyssa Ann. ■ 28209 #008-02-2000 L2004 **OBG** *020 †30
MILTON, Cecil Jerome. 2300 RANDOLPH RD STE B 28207 #036-05-1956 L1956 **ORS** *071 †40
MINOR, Cassandra R. 8401 MEDICAL PLAZA DR, STE 140 28262 #016-02-1992 L1997 **GE** *020 †20
MITCHELL, Alice Marina. 1000 BLYTHE BLVD BOX 32861, DEPT OF EMERGENCY MEDICINE 28203 #049-01-2001 L2004 **EM** *100 †16
MITCHELL, Stephanie C. ■ 28262 #035-06-1994 L1997 **IM** *020
MITLEHNER, Richard John. 101 E WT HARRIS BLVD, STE 5002 28262 #035-48-1992 L1996 **IM** *020 †20
MITRA, Avick Goran. 1000 BLYTHE BLVD 28203 #012-05-1984 L1987 **MFM OBG** *020 †30
MIZE, Edwin Sims. ■ 28210 #027-01-1963 L1964 **GP** *071
MODI, Ankita. ■ 28204 #038-44-2002 L2007 **PD** *100 †55
MODY, Natwar Jethalal. ■ 28277 #495-01-1959 L1973 **PTH IG** *020 †50
MOGHADAMIAN, Eric Scott. ■ 28205 #020-12-2002 L2007 **ORS** *100
MOGOLLON, Gustavo. 2425 PARK RD 28203 #264-01-1950 L1969 **PTH** *071 †50
MOGUL, Mark Jeffrey. 1712 E 4TH ST, BLUME CHILDREN'S CANCER CL 28204 #035-15-1987 L2003 **PHO PD** *020 †55
MOHANAN, Sveta. 1801 ROZZELLES FERRY RD 28208 #495-37-1998 L2003 **FM** *020 †18
MOHANTY, Kathy Garland. ■ 28209 #036-01-1998 L2001 **PD** *020 †55
MOKRIS, Jeffrey Geo. 1025 MOREHEAD MEDICAL DR, STE 300 28204 #038-41-1979 L1980 **OAR** *020 †40 ‡
MOLITIERNO, Joseph Albert. 3125 SPRINGBANK LN, STE E 28226 #036-01-2000 L2006 **U** *020
MOLL, Matthew Todd. 101 E WT HARRIS BLVD, STE 5002 28262 #041-09-1998 L2001 **IM** *020 †20
MONROE, Michael Hanson. 1000 BLYTHE BLVD, DEPT OF INTERNAL MEDICINE 28203 #011-03-1994 L1996 **IM** *020 †20
MONSON, Robert Chas, II. 1918 RANDOLPH RD STE 1 28207 #025-01-1973 L1978 **GS TRS** *020 †85
MONTZ, Nancy Collette. 646 WESTINGHOUSE BLVD 28273 #021-05-2000 L2004 **IM** *020 †20
MOORE, Brian Allen. 3101 LATROBE DR, STE 100 28211 #010-02-1994 L2000 **EM** *020 †16
MOORE, David Huddler. 5435 PROSPERITY CHURCH RD, STE 1500 28269 #017-20-1976 L1980 **PD PDI** *020 †55
MOORE, Elizabeth Fink. 1701 ABBEY PL 28209 #048-15-1992 L1995 **IM** *020 †20
MOORE, Kent Elliot. 1718 E 4TH ST, STE 804 28204 #051-04-1993 L1993 **OMF PS** *020
MOORE, Mc Kenzie P, Jr. ■ 28210 #045-01-1944 L1967 **PTH** *071 †50
MOORE, Stephen Chas. 10340 PARK RD 28210 #045-01-1990 L1994 **OBG** *020 †30
MOOREFIELD, William G, Jr. 10512 PARK RD, STE 101 28210 #036-07-1969 L1969 **ORS** *020 †40
MOOSE, D William, Jr. 10508 PARK RD, STE 104 28210 #036-05-1982 L1988 **GS HS** *020 †85
MORALES, Richard. 1901 RANDOLPH RD 28207 #008-01-1983 L1991 **AN** *040 †05
MORAN, Amanda Lynn. 4501 CAMERON VALLEY PKWY, STE 100 28211 #055-01-1998 L1999 **PD** *020 †55
MORAN, Elizabeth B. ■ 28209 #036-05-2004 L2008 **OBG** *012
MORGAN, Elizabeth Sarah. ■ 28278 #035-45-1994 L2008 **OBG** *020 †30
MORGAN, Hillary Stewart. 15110 JOHN J DELANEY DR, MECKLENBURG MEDICAL 28277 #012-01-2003 L2006 **IM** *020 †20
MORGAN, Robert Johnson. 1025 MOREHEAD MEDICAL DR, STE 300 28204 #045-01-2003 L2008 **ORS** *012
MORGAN, Stephen Duane. 1000 BLYTHE BLVD 28203 #012-01-2003 L2006 **IM** *020 †20
MORRIS, David Perry, Jr. 429 BILLINGSLEY RD 28211 #041-01-1948 L1981 **ADM FM** *072 †70
MORRIS, Krista S. 14215 BALLANTYNE CORPRT PL, STE 1 28277 #036-01-1997 L2001 **PD** *020 †55
MORRIS, Sarah N. 5933 BLAKENEY PARK DR, GYNECOLOGY PA 28277 #045-01-1999 L2003 **OBG** *100
MORRIS, Thomas C. 1718 E 4TH ST, STE 907 28204 #036-01-1997 L2001 **OBG** *020 †30
MORRISON, John Gordon. 2015 RANDOLPH RD, STE 201 28207 #036-07-1981 L1992 **CRS** *020 †10,85
MORTEL ANDERSEN, Malou C. ■ 28210 #748-18-1982 **P** *050
MORTON, Duncan, Jr. 1900 RANDOLPH RD STE 210 28207 #036-01-1966 L1966 **PDS** *020 †85 ‡
MOSS, David Scott. 10320 MALLARD CREEK RD, STE 120 28262 #036-05-1983 L1984 **IM** *020 †20
MOSTAFA, Gamal. 1000 BLYTHE BLVD 600, CAROLINAS MEDICAL CENTER 28203 #915-02-1983 L2000 **GS** *020 †85

■ = Address Information Privacy Protected

MOTUZ, Daniel John. 10512 PARK RD, STE 203 28210 #649-33-1981 L1987 **AN** *020 †05

MOZAYENI, Reza. 3025 SPRINGBANK LN STE 200 28226 #035-03-1991 L2000 **OPH** *020 †35

MUELLER, Andrew T. 11030 GOLF LINKS DR, STE 100 28277 #036-01-1996 L1998 **FM** *020 †18

MUELLER, Joseph Cole. 200 GREENWICH RD 28211 #036-01-1993 L2005 **FM** *020 †18

MULL, Courtney Dawn. 1000 BLYTHE BLVD, FAMILY MEDICINE 28203 #036-01-2004 L2007 **FM** *020 †18

MULLIS, William F. 2410 ROSWELL AVE, UNIT 301 28209 #041-01-1968 L2008 **PS GS** *071 †85,65

MUNAVALLI, Girish S. 1918 RANDOLPH RD, STE 550 28207 #012-21-1998 L2004 **D** *020 †15

MUNDLE, Linda Bick. 501 BILLINGSLEY RD 28211 #036-08-1985 L1989 **P** *020 †75

MUNDORF, Thomas Kent. 1718 E 4TH ST STE 703 28204 #036-05-1982 L1983 **OPH** *020

MURN, Alvin. 1900 RANDOLPH RD 28207 #041-12-1989 L2002 **EM** *020 †16

MURPHY, Daniel Raleigh. 1000 BLYTHE BLVD 28203 #012-01-1984 L1988 **AN** *020 †05

MURPHY, John B, Jr. 927 EAST BLVD, SOUTHEAST ANESTHESIOLOGY C 28203 #036-05-1982 L1983 **AN IM** *020 †05

MURPHY, Michael Francis. 927 EAST BLVD 28203 #064-01-1978 L2000 **EM** *020 †05,16

MURREY, Daniel Beasley. 1025 MOREHEAD MEDICAL DR, STE 300 28204 #024-01-1992 L1998 **ORS** *020 †40

MUTCH, Jason Allan. 1900 RANDOLPH RD 28207 #036-08-1997 L1998 **EM** *020 †16

MYERS, Brian G. 3500 MT HOLLY HUNTERSVL RD, STE 200 28216 #037-01-1992 L1999 **FM** *020 †18

MYERS, Erinn Michelle. PO BOX 32861, DEPT OF OB/GYN 28232 #047-06-2007 **OBG** *012

MYLES, Olubunmi A. 1805 MILTON RD, PLAZA MEDICAL CENTER 28215 #690-05-1992 L2005 **FM** *020 †18

NADERI, Mohamad Sirus. 58071 SHARON ROAD 28210 #517-01-1951 L1977 **AN GS** *071 †05

NADIMINTI, Uma. 2310 RANDOLPH RD, DERMATOLOGIC LASER CENTER 28207 #041-04-2001 L2007 **D** *020 †15 ‡

NADKARNI, Abhijeet Shripa. ■ 28277 #496-38-2000 L2004 **ID CCM** *020

NAHOURAII, Robert A. 1900 RANDOLPH RD, STE 1010 28207 #041-12-1989 L1992 **CHN PD** *020 †75,55

NAIK, Prexa Dolatrai. ■ 28210 #045-04-2007 **FP** *012

NAMI, Alireza. 332 LILLINGTON AVE, JOINT AND MUSCLE MEDICAL C 28204 #422-01-1994 L2004 **RHU** *020 †20

NAMI, Lilit M. 10628 PARK RD STE 112, CAROLINAS HOSP GRP PINEVL 28210 #913-38-1993 L2004 **IM** *020 †20

NANDURKAR, Sanjay. ■ 28277 #495-76-1983 L2006 **PM** *100 †60

NASH, Hoke Smith. 3800 SHAMROCK DR 28215 #047-05-1954 L1961 **OTO** *071 †45

NAUMANN, Robert Wendel. 1025 MOREHEAD MEDICAL DR, STE 60 28204 #001-02-1988 L1996 **OBG GO** *040 †30

NAZEMZADEH, Reza. 4501 CAMERON VALLEY PKWY, MECKLENBURG MEDICAL GROUP 28211 #048-14-2000 L2006 **HO** *020 †20

NEAL, Patricia Roseanne. DEPT OF PEDS 401 AHEC, CAROLINAS MED CTR 28232 #017-20-1980 L1989 **NPM** *012

NEALE, Wirt Thos. 1315 EAST BLVD, STE 280 28203 #047-06-1969 L1970 **PD** *020 †55

NEEL, Jill Lynn. 1918 RANDOLPH RD, STE 275 28207 #055-01-1995 L1999 **FM** *020 †18

NELSON, James E. 149 PROVIDENCE RD, PRESBYTERIAN PEDIATRIC NEU 28207 #016-11-1994 L2006 **CHN** *020 †55

NELSON, Maureen Rose. 1100 BLYTHE BLVD, CHARLOTTE INSTITUTE OF REH 28203 #016-11-1985 L2002 **PM** *020 †60

NELSON, Robert Darrell. 1900 RANDOLPH RD 28207 #036-05-2001 L2004 **EM** *020 †16

NELSON, Teresita Y. 12311 COPPER WAY, STE 200 28277 #036-02-1989 L1994 **CHN** *020 †75

NESBIT, William Michael S. 1350 S KINGS DR 28207 #051-01-1962 L1969 **N** *071 †75

NESS, Daniel Thos. 5815 BLAKENEY PARK DR, STE 100 28277 #028-34-1987 L1994 **PS GS** *020 †85,65

NEUSPIEL, Daniel Robt. 1000 BLYTHE BLVD, LEVINE CHILDREN'S HOSPITAL 28203 #033-05-1979 L2007 **PD ADM** *020 †55,70 ‡

NEWCOMB, Fredrick L, Jr. 927 EAST BLVD 28203 #036-07-1987 L1991 **AN** *020 †05

NEWCOMB, William Levin. 1000 BLYTHE BLVD, CAROLINAS MEDICAL CENTER 28203 #051-04-2000 L2006 **GS** *020 †20

NEWMAN, David Earl. 5435 PROSPERITY CHURCH RD, STE 2200A 28269 #011-03-1988 L1992 **OBG** *020 †30

NEWMAN, Edwin. 1701 EAST BLVD, ADMIN OFFICE 28203 #018-03-1961 L1967 **R** *020 †80

NGUYEN, Duong Huu. 1025 MOREHEAD MEDICAL DR, STE 300 28204 #004-01-1988 L1988 **P** *020 †75

NGUYEN, Phuong Hoang. ■ 28203 #011-05-2006 **GS** *100

NGUYEN, Thuanhanh Thi. 1433 EMERYWOOD DR, STE D 28210 #942-01-1989 L2001 **IM** *020 †20

NGUYEN, Tuong Dai. 6404 ALBEMARLE RD, STE J&K 28212 #041-13-1996 L2007 **IM** *020

NGUYEN, Vu Q C. 1100 BLYTHE BLVD 28203 #025-12-1993 L1998 **PM OS** *020 †60

NICHOLSON, Henry Hale, Jr. 635 MANNING DR 28209 #036-07-1947 L1949 **CRS GS** *020 †10,85

NICHOLSON, Myron Vernon. 1025 MOREHEAD MEDICAL DR 28204 #023-01-1980 L1984 **OBG** *020 †30

NICKISCH, Florian. 1001 BLYTHE BLVD, STE 200 28203 #409-16-1998 L2005 **ORS** *100

NIETERS, Gerald Francis. ■ 28216 #028-34-1966 L1969 **R** *020 †80

NIX, Jerry Dale. 1900 RANDOLPH RD 28207 #036-01-1991 L1994 **EM** *020 †16

NIXON, Deborah L. 15830 JOHN J DELANEY DR, STE 100 28277 #036-01-1992 L1998 **D** *020 †20,15

NIXON, John Randall. 3623 LATROBE DR, STE 216 28211 #048-12-1978 L1987 **DR** *020 †75,80

NOELL, John Stanford. ■ 28297 #036-01-1956 L1956 **GP OBG** *075

NOLL, Bruce K. 501 BILLINGSLEY RD, CAROLINAS MED CTR 28211 #041-13-1982 L1983 **P** *020 †75

NOONAN, Laura Kathrine. CAROLINAS MED CTR, DEPT PEDS 28232 #003-01-1987 L1990 **PD** *020 †55

NORMAN, Michael Edward. 1000 BLYTHE BLVD, CAROLINAS MED CTR DEPT PED 28203 #041-01-1965 L1994 **NEP PD** *030 †55

NORRIS, John Gray. 2630 E 7TH ST, STE 100 28204 #012-01-1993 L1995 **AI IM** *020 †20,03

NORROD, Holly Susan. PO BOX 32861 28232 #048-15-2005 **IM** *012

NORTHCUTT, Hugh Neal. 15110 JOHN J DELANEY DR, STE 100 28277 #045-04-1984 L1985 **OBG** *020 †30

NORTON, Catherine B. 7920 MOORES CHAPEL RD, NORTHWEST FAMILY PHYSICIAN 28214 #759-03-1985 L1997 **FM** *020 †18 ‡

NORTON, Mark Jay. 1900 RANDOLPH RD 28207 #036-05-1977 L1984 **AN** *020 †05

NOVICK, Thomas Leonard. 1918 RANDOLPH RD, STE 500 28207 #036-07-1978 L1981 **GS VS** *020 †85

NUNLEY, Wallace Clay, Jr. 1000 BLYTHE BLVD, CAROLINAS MEDICAL CENTER 28203 #051-01-1973 L1989 **OBG REN** *020 †30

NUSSBAUM, Rachel. 1315 EAST BLVD UNIT 718 28203 #035-20-2002 L2005 **D** *100 †15

NUSSBAUM, Tzvi. 1000 BLYTHE BLVD, 4TH FL 28203 #016-42-1997 L2005 **VS** *020 †85

NWAUCHE, Ugwuala. 6010 E WT HARRIS BLVD, MT ZION MED CLNC 28215 #690-12-1988 L2004 **IM** *020 †20

O'BAR, Paul Rupert. 200 HAWTHORNE LN 28204 #039-01-1957 L1970 **IM D** *071 †20

OBENG, Francis. 2540 W ARROWOOD RD, STE 110 28273 #412-02-1994 L2002 **IM** *020 †20

OBERER, Daniel Michiel. 225 BALDWIN AVE 28204 #023-07-2000 L2006 **NS** *020

OBERLE, Robert Joseph. ■ 28211 #048-12-2007 **IM** *012

O'BRIEN, James Patrick, Jr. ■ 28226 #011-04-2001 L2007 **DR** *020 †80

O'BRIEN, Paul S. ■ 28207 #038-40-1951 L1955 **R** *071 †80

O'CONNELL, Lisa Carol. 3101 LATROBE DR, INTERNAL MEDICINE SPECIALI 28211 #016-42-1989 L1996 **IM** *020 †20

O'CONNOR, Maeve Edel. 2630 E 7TH ST STE 100 28204 #045-04-1997 L2003 **AI IM** *020 †20,03

OESTERHELD, Javier E. 1000 BLYTHE BLVD, LEVINE CHILDRENS HOSPITAL 28203 #042-03-2001 L2007 **PHO** *020 †20

OGU, Donatus. ■ 28277 #308-03-1985 L1993 **IM** *020 †20

OHL, Matthew David. 101 E WT HARRIS BLVD, STE 1110 28262 #055-01-1984 L1989 **ORS** *020 †40

OHMSTEDE, Catherine Sauls. 1315 EAST BLVD, STE 280 28203 #011-03-2001 L2006 **PD** *020 †55

OHMSTEDE, David Picman. ■ 28211 #036-05-1996 L2006 **PD** *020 †55

OKE, Edward Jeffrey. 3623 LATROBE DR, STE 216 28211 #025-01-1980 L1984 **DR** *040 †80

O'KEEFE, Patrick Joseph. 3623 LATROBE DR, STE 213 28211 #011-04-2000 L2006 **DR MSR** *020 †80

OKWARA, Benedict Onwukwe. 2938 THE PLZ 28205 #422-01-1984 L1991 **IM** *020 †20

OLADIGBO, Makanjuola Iyio. ■ 28277 #690-05-1988 L2004 **IM** *020

OLIVER, Kenneth Leon. 2801 RANDOLPH RD, STE 200 28211 #036-05-1965 L1966 **OBG** *020 †30

OLOWOFOYEKU, Bamisegun V. 508 EASTWAY DR, STE A 28205 #010-03-1975 L1982 **GS** *020 †85

O'MALLEY, John Edward. 5821 FAIRVIEW RD, STE 218 28209 #025-01-1967 L2007 **CHP P** *020 †75 ‡

O'MALLEY, Patrick Martin. 1000 BLYTHE BLVD 28203 #036-08-2004 L2007 **EM** *020

OMURA, Akiko. PO BOX 38176, 10926 QUALITY DR 28278 #035-08-2000 L2004 **PM** *100 †60

O'NEILL, Michael Raymond. 1718 E 4TH ST STE 807 28204 #036-05-1976 L1981 **U** *020 †95

ONER, Vedat Omer. ■ 28210 #902-01-1947 L1959 **GP PHP** *020

ONWUKWE, Augustine N. 200 HAWTHORNE LN, PRESBYTERIAN INPATIENT CAR 28204 #690-02-1980 L1995 **FM EM** *020 †18

ORIAKU, Obinna Chika. 801 CLANTON RD, STE C-110 28217 #690-06-1990 L2000 **IM** *020 †20

ORLAND, Paul Jay. 1918 RANDOLPH RD, STE 500 28207 #035-45-1988 L1995 **VS GS** *020 †85

ORR, Samuel Lawrence. 1000 BLYTHE BLVD #045-01-1968 L1971 **ATP** *020 †50

ORVILLE, Stephen Wyatt. 1900 RANDOLPH RD 28207 #036-05-1991 L1997 **EM** *020 †16

OSAKO, Phaenarete Hisako. 8310 UNIVERSITY EXC PRK DR, STE 550 28262 #008-01-1993 L2005 **PD** *020 †55

OSIER, Lois Kathleen. 10512 PARK RD, STE 101 28210 #024-16-1989 L1994 **HS** *020 †40

O'SULLIVAN, Julie. 2001 VAIL AVE, MEDICAL ASSOCIATES 28207 #025-07-2003 L2006 **EM** *020 †16

OVERBEY, Warren Mcleod. 5435 PROSPERITY CHURCH RD, STE 2200A 28269 #036-05-1986 L1987 **OBG** *020 †30

OWEIDA, Samuel Joseph. 10520 PARK RD, STE 105 28210 #041-12-1979 L1985 **ORS** *050 †40

OWEN, Dale, Jr. 1900 BRUNSWICK AVE 28207 #036-05-1986 L1988 **CD** *020 †20

OWEN, Kenneth Eugene. ■ 28207 #038-41-1955 L1991 **AN** *020 †05

PACICCO, Thomas John. 1001 BLYTHE BLVD STE 500, MEDICAL CENTER PLAZA 28203 #035-09-1985 L1995 **GE** *020 †20

PACK, Leslie Anne. ■ 28204 #055-02-2006 **IM** *012

PACKMAN, Charles Henry. 1000 BLYTHE BLVD, DEPT OF INTERNAL MEDICINE 28203 #021-05-1967 L1998 **HEM IM** *040 †20

PADMA, Srikanth. ■ 28277 #495-21-1986 L2007 **GS TTS** *100

PAGE, George Dantzler. ■ 28210 #012-05-1942 L1949 **GS** *071 †85

PAIGE, Sophia Lorraine. 1000 BLYTHE BLVD 28203 #038-40-1992 L1996 **OBG** *020 †30

PAL, Sridhar Earni. 1100 S TRYON ST, STE 400 28203 #028-46-1998 L2000 **HO IM** *020 †20

PALASTI, Sandra. 6035 FAIRVIEW RD, THROAT ASSOCIATES PA 28210 #033-06-1988 L1994 **OTO** *020 †45

PALERMO, Nancy Anne. 1718 E 4TH ST, STE 307 28204 #011-04-1990 L1994 **OBG** *020 †30

PALMER, Melissa Camille. ■ 28204 #020-02-2004 L2007 **IM** *020

PALMERTREE, Katherine K. 8800 N TRYON ST, CAROLINAS HOSPITALIST GROU 28262 #036-05-1997 L2003 **IM** *020 †20

PAMINTUAN, Grace Cruz. 10616 METROMONT PKWY, STE 104 28269 #748-07-1985 L1997 **FM** *020 †18

PAPPAS, Alexander James. 1001 BLYTHE BLVD, STE 200 28203 #045-01-2002 L2006 **OFA** *020

PARDEE, A C. 1918 RANDOLPH RD, PHYSICIANS RANDOLPH 28207 #001-02-1981 L1985 **IM** *020 †20

PARIYADATH, Manoj. PO BOX 32861, CAROLINAS MEDICAL CENTER 28232 #045-01-2002 L2005 **EM** *100 †16

PARK, Richard In. 10502 PARK RD STE 150, CONSULTANTS, PA 28210 #016-02-1992 L1997 **APM** *020 †05

PARKE, James Clifton, Jr. ■ 28211 #036-01-1954 L1954 **PD OS** *071 †55

PARKER, Gregory Dean. 1718 E 4TH ST STE 707 28204 #036-01-1984 L1985 **OBG** *020 †30

PARKER, Jeremy Michael. ■ 28226 #045-01-2007 **IM** *012

PARKER, Mark Wm. 130 PROVIDENCE RD 28207 #038-40-1978 L1988 **END PD** *020 †55

PARKER, Thomas Eugene. 330 BILLINGSLEY RD, STE 107 28211 #038-40-1974 L1994 **IM** *020 †20

PARKERSON, Walter Tuck. ■ 28209 #036-07-1960 L1960 **OPH** *071 †35

PARKS, Boyd Lee. 101 E WT HARRIS BLVD, STE 5301 28262 #012-05-1983 L1990 **OBG** *020 †30

PARMLEY, Matthew Clay. ■ 28216 #039-01-2001 L2006 **TS** *012

PARSONS, Daniel Joseph. 1001 BLYTHE BLVD, STE 500 28203 #036-07-2001 L2003 **D** *020 †15

PARSONS, Robert Gregory. 1701 EAST BLVD 28203 #011-03-1969 L1975 **DR OS** *030

PARULKAR, Shantala Akhil. 3101 LATROBE DR 28211 #496-25-1996 L2004 **IM** *020

PASCAL, John Wm. 10516 PARK RD, PINEVILLE 28210 #012-05-1979 L1988 **FM** *020 †18

PASEK, David Jos. ■ 28215 #038-41-1981 L1982 **OM GP** *020

PASQUINI, John Aldo. 1718 E 4TH ST STE 501, MECKLENBURG CARDIOVASCULAR 28204 #008-02-1980 L1985 **CD IM** *020 †20

PATEFIELD, Arthur James. 1900 RANDOLPH RD STE 216 28207 #010-02-1980 L1992 **PUD IM** *020 †20

PATEL, Alka. ■ 28226 #917-18-1985 L1994 **AN** *020 †05
PATEL, Jay Arunkumar. ■ 28209 #045-04-2005 L2008 **PD** *012
PATEL, Meera Manhar. ■ 28211 #055-01-2007 **PD** *012
PATEL, Roopen. ■ 28204 #038-44-2002 L2007 **AI** *020 †20,03
PATEL, Roshni Arvind. 330 BILLINGSLEY RD, STE 101 28211 #051-01-2003 L2005 **FM** *020 †18
PATEL, Sanjay Ramanbhai. 101 E WT HARRIS BLVD, STE 1213 28262 #035-19-1995 L2002
    CD *020 †20
PATEL, Vasant B. 10732 OLD WAYSIDE RD, CAROLINA CARDIOLOGY ASSOCI 28277
    #048-14-1993 L2001 **CD** *020 †20
PATON, Beverley Lauren. ■ 28202 #038-41-2003 **GS** *012
PATT, Rhonda Pennington. 4501 CAMERON VALLEY PKWY, STE 100 28211 #055-01-2000 L2002
    PD *020 †55
PATTERSON, Anthony Curtis. 7301 CARMEL EXECUTV PRK DR, STE 200 28226
    #012-01-1985 L1991 **P IM** *075 †75
PATTERSON, Kenneth Thos. ■ 28277 #036-01-1986 L1989 **FM** *020 †18
PATWARDHAN, Vrushali N. 200 HAWTHORNE LN, SPECIALISTS 28204 #496-30-1992 L2005
    PD *020 †55
PAUL, Jonathan James. 10616 METROMONT PKWY, CHARLOTTE SPORTS MEDICINE 28269
    #041-12-1991 L1997 **ORS** *020 †40
PAYNE, Thomas Arthur. PO BOX 32861, CAROLINAS MEDICAL CENTER 28232
    #036-01-1989 L2001 **NPM PD** *020 †55
PEAKER, Brandy Lenet. ■ 28216 #023-01-2005 L2008 **FP** *012
PEARSON, David Andres. 1000 BLYTHE BLVD, DEPT OF EMERGENCY MEDICINE 28203
    #047-05-2002 L2006 **EM** *100 †16
PEARSON, James David. 1901 RANDOLPH RD 28207 #019-02-1980 L1990 **AN PMM** *020 †05
PECK, Jason Alexander. 3541 RANDOLPH RD, MECKLENBURG MEDICAL GROUP 28211
    #035-45-1997 L2003 **P** *100 †75
PEDERSON, Lee Carl. 1918 RANDOLPH RD, STE 130 28207 #039-01-1994 L2003 **GS** *020
PELEAUX, Ramon Dennis. 475 N WENDOVER RD 28211 #036-01-1991 L1993 **OS** *020
PELUCIO, Marcus Aldomiro. 3303 LATROBE DR 28211 #041-14-1991 L2006 **P** *020 †75
PELUCIO, Maria Tereza. 1000 BLYTHE BLVD, P O BOX 32861 28203 #024-05-1989 L1994
    EM *020 †16
PEPINE, Anne. ■ 28209 #011-03-1994 **IM** *100
PERETSMAN, Samuel Jay. 201 QUEENS RD 28204 #024-05-1983 L1995 **U SO** *020 †95
PEREZ, Luis Manuel. 1718 E 4TH ST STE 805 28204 #035-46-1988 L1990 **UP U** *020 †95
PERLIK, Paul Christopher. 1915 RANDOLPH RD, ORTHOCAROLINA, PA 28207
    #051-07-1978 L1989 **HS ORS** *020
PERRI, James Anthony. 3101 LATROBE DR 28211 #033-06-1998 L2004 **EM** *020 †16
PERRONE, Andrea Judith. PO BOX 32861, DEPT OF PHYS MED/REHAB 28232 #021-05-2004
    PM *012
PERRY, Elizabeth Marshall. 6115 PARK SOUTH DR, STE 100 28210 #051-04-1991 L1997
    EM *020 †16,20
PERRY, Glenn Bradford. 2826 RANDOLPH RD 28211 #041-13-1978 L1983 **ORS OSM** *020 †40
PERRY, M Elizabeth Bolter. 6115 PARK SOUTH DR, STE 100 28210 #011-02-1992 L1996
    AN *020 †05
PETERSON, David M, Jr. BUILDING 1A1, 1525 WEST W.T. HARRIS BOUL 28288
    #001-02-1972 L1977 **IM** *020 †20
PETOK, Tina. 8220 UNIVERSITY EXC PRK DR, STE 107 28262 #038-43-1984 L1988
    GYN *020 †30
PETRILLI, Robert. 1900 RANDOLPH RD 28207 #011-04-1982 L1983 **EM** *020 †16
PETROVSKI, Kristina Ann. ■ 28203 #045-04-2007 **OBG** *012
PETTIS, Karlton Shea. 7945 N TRYON ST, STE 112 28262 #036-01-1996 L2003 **IM** *020 †20
PETTRONE, Kristen Aimee. 3101 LATROBE DR, PIEDMONT EMERGENCY MED ASS 28211
    #021-01-2000 L2003 **EM** *020 †16
PETTY, Jerry Miller. 225 BALDWIN AVE 28204 #036-01-1960 L1960 **NS** *020 †25
PFEIFFER, Frederick E, II. 1900 RANDOLPH RD, STE 1010 28207 #047-05-1976 L1985
    N IM *020 †20,75
PFEIFFER, Roxane Javid. 1900 RANDOLPH RD STE 1010 28207 #035-45-1979 L1985
    P CHP *074 †75
PFISCHNER, Wm Carl E, Jr. ■ 28213 #041-12-1948 L1949 **PHP GPM** *071
PHAM, Hiep Thanh. 7903 PROVIDENCE RD 28277 #011-04-1987 L1996 **IMG** *020 †18
PHELPS, James S, Jr. 2815 CRISMAN ST 28208 #023-01-1952 L1952 **GP** *071
PHILLIPS, John Goudelock. 15110 JOHN J DELANEY DR, STE 100 28277 #045-01-1979 L1984
    OBG OBS *020 †30
PHILLIPS, Thomas Hogeman. 201 QUEENS RD 28204 #010-01-1984 L1993 **U GS** *020 †95
PHILPOTT, Christine Hidal. 200 HAWTHORNE LN 28204 #021-05-2001 L2006 **PD ADL** *020 †55
PIERCE, Katherine Jeanne. 1918 RANDOLPH RD 28207 #011-03-1982 L1993 **IM** *020 †20
PINCKNEY, Joseph Delacy, Jr. 251 EASTWAY DR 28213 #051-01-1996 L2001 **FM** *020 †18
PINEIRO, Victor Manuel. 1000 BLYTHE BLVD, LEVINE CHILDREN'S HOSPITAL 28203
    #042-01-1980 L2007 **PD** *020 †55
PIXLEY, Roland Laurens. 1025 MOREHEAD MEDICAL DR, STE 400 28204 #036-05-1983 L1987
    OBG *020 †30
PLAZA, Jose Luis. 2001 VAIL AVE, MEDICAL ASSOCIATES 28207 #036-01-1994 L1997
    EM *020 †16
PLONK, James Wendell. 1001 BLYTHE BLVD, STE 500 28203 #036-07-1968 L1968
    END IM *020 †20
PLUMMER, Janelle Renee. ■ 28270 #011-03-2004 L2007 **PD** *020 †55
POCHICK, Meredith Givens. 1000 BLYTHE BLVD 28203 #036-05-2003 L2006 **PD** *020 †55
POCIASK, Stephen Bryan. ■ 28277 #010-02-1997 L2004 **AN** *020 †05
POINDEXTER, Marisa Getter. 101 E WT HARRIS BLVD #5002, NORTH CHARLOTTE MED
    SPEC 28262 #026-04-2002 L2005 **IM** *020 †20
POINTON, Catherine Jeanne. 10348 PARK RD, STE 100 28210 #035-09-1990 L1997
    D *020 †20,15
POLK, Christopher Michael. 4539 HEDGEMORE DR, ID CONSULTANTS, PA 28209
    #048-02-2001 L2007 **ID** *020
POLLARD, John Alan. 927 EAST BLVD 28203 #352-08-1962 L1967 **AN** *020
POLLARD, Richard John. 927 EAST BLVD 28203 #036-01-1991 L1996 **AN** *020 †05 ‡
POMERANTZ, Richard W. 1900 RANDOLPH RD, STE 216 28207 #038-43-1993 L2008
    PCC SME *020 †20
PONTES, Mariette Angela. 2001 VAIL AVE, MEDICAL ASSOCIATES 28207 #035-06-1987 L1990
    EM *020 †16
PORTER, Charles Alexander. 2801 RANDOLPH RD, STE 200 28211 #041-02-1966 L1971
    OBG OS *020 †30
PORTER, Mark Alan. 10620 PARK RD, STE 230 28210 #016-06-1978 L2001 **N** *020 †75
PORTER, William Garrison. ■ 28207 #045-01-1963 L1970 **IM HEM** *071 †20
POSTON, Wm Karnes, Jr. 200 HAWTHORNE LN 28204 #055-01-1979 L1990 **PTH** *020 †50

POTINY, Suma. ■ 28269 #036-01-2005 **PD** *012
POWE, Charles Edwin. 8206 PROVIDENCE RD # 1200 28277 #045-01-1958 L1963
    GYN *071 †30
POWELL, Stephen Howard. 335 N CASWELL RD, PRESBYTERIAN SENIOR HEALTH 28204
    #041-01-1972 L1998 **IM IMG** *020 †20
PRATT, Broc Lane. 10620 PARK RD, STE 102 28210 #011-03-1997 L2005 **PS** *020
PRENDIVILLE, Simon S. 2015 RANDOLPH RD, CHARLOTTE 28207 #010-02-1997 L2003
    GE *020 †20
PRESSLY, Claude Lowry. 2300 RANDOLPH RD 28207 #041-01-1943 L1943 **GS TS** *071 †85,90
PRICE, David Evan. 5516 CENTRAL AVE 28212 #012-01-1999 L2000 **FSM** *020 †18
PRICE, Grady Edwin. 120 PROVIDENCE RD 28207 #036-07-1960 L1960 **ORS** *071 †40
PRIDE, Harold Sylvester. 1000 BLYTHE BLVD 28203 #047-07-1959 L1960 **FM PD** *071
PRIEST, David Harding. 4539 HEDGEMORE DR, STE 100 28209 #036-05-1999 L2005
    ID *020 †20
PRIMOS, Wm Angelo, Jr. 1915 RANDOLPH RD, ORTHOCAROLINA, PA 28207
    #027-01-1985 L1990 **FSM ADL** *020 †55
PRINCE, Robert Melvin. 1819 SARDIS RD N STE 360 28270 #045-01-1956 L1960 **P GP** *020 †75
PRITCHARD, William Lee. ■ 28211 #023-07-1956 L1963 **NS** *071 †25
PROKO, Erika Paige. ■ 28220 #036-01-2007 **IM** *012
PROSSER, Jodie. 4501 CAMERON VALLEY PKWY, STE 100 28211 #045-01-1996 L1999
    PD *020 †55
PRUITT, Wesley Blake. ■ 28210 #012-01-2005 **IM** *012
PRYOR, James Clifton. 501 BILLINGSLEY RD 28211 #045-01-1985 L1987 **P** *020 †75
PUGH, James Edwin, Jr. 1900 RANDOLPH RD, STE 1010 28207 #041-01-1967 L1983
    N *020 †75 ‡
PUGH, Lovetta. 101 E WT HARRIS BLVD, STE 3111 28262 #036-05-1979 L1984 **GS EM** *020 †85
PURDUM, Preston P, III. 300 BILLINGSLEY RD, STE 200 28211 #051-04-1984 L1995
    HEP GE *020 †20
PURDY, James Scott. 2100 REXFORD RD, STE 300 28211 #036-05-1990 L1993 **FM** *020 †18
PURI, Sajeev K. 5933 BLAKENEY PARK DR, STE 200 28277 #036-05-2000 L2005 **OTO** *020 †45
PURI, Sankalp. 1900 RANDOLPH RD 28207 #036-05-1999 L2002 **EM** *020 †16
PUSKARICH, Michael Alexan. ■ 28270 #056-05-2007 **EM** *012
PUTMAN, Steven Frederick. 12311 COPPER WAY, STE 200 28277 #016-06-1978 L1984
    N *020 †75
PUTTERMAN, Paul Stuart. 309 S SHARON AMITY RD, STE 310 28211 #051-01-1977 L1980
    PD *020 †55
QI, Ming. ■ 28209 #051-07-2005 L2008 **EM** *012
QUARLES, Robert Paul. 3623 LATROBE DR, STE 216 28211 #028-02-1989 L1993
    NM *020 †80,28
QUARLES, Susan Dru Thomas. 300 BILLINGSLEY RD, FIRST CHARLOTTE PHYS 28211
    #020-12-1990 L1993 **IM** *071 †20
QUEEN, Deborah Fryer. 10508 PARK RD, PINEVILLE 28210 #001-02-1995 L1998 **PD** *020 †55
QUILLIN, Shawn Paul. 3623 LATROBE DR, STE 216 28211 #028-02-1990 L1995 **DR** *020 †80
QURESHI, Aamer A. 2630 E 7TH ST STE 210 28204 #704-02-1989 L2002 **CD IC** *020 †20
QURESHI, Nosheen Tirmizi. 251 EASTWAY DR, CMC NORTHPARK 28213 #704-20-1997 L2005
    FM *020 †18
RAAD, George Louis. 2125 BERRYHILL RD 28208 #045-01-1982 L1983 **FM** *030 †18
RACHIMA, Richard Ron. 10516 PARK RD, PINEVILLE PRIMARY CARE 28210
    #045-01-1998 L2001 **FM** *020 †18
RAFFERTY, Maureen. 15110 JOHN J DELANEY DR, MECKLENBURG MEDICAL 28277
    #041-14-1995 L2006 **IM OS** *020 †20
RAGER, Kristin Michele. 251 EASTWAY DR, TEEN HEALTH CONNECTION 28213
    #020-02-1998 L2006 **ADL** *020 †55
RAINBOW, Catherine Rogers. ■ 28270 #051-07-2007 **FP** *012
RAJ, Vishwa Sharma. 1100 BLYTHE BLVD, DEPT PM&R 28203 #033-06-2003 L2007 **PM** *020
RAJA, Atif Yasin. ■ 28215 #036-01-2006 **AN** *012
RAMA, Ganapathy Pedamale. 200 HAWTHORNE LN, 7TH FL 28204 #495-09-1981 L2002
    PD NPM *020 †55
RAMKUMAR, Usha. 1350 S KINGS DR 28207 #495-04-1986 L1997 **PD** *020 †55
RAMSEY, Cecelia Bishop. 10514 PARK RD 28210 #036-01-1988 L1993 **EM** *020 †16
RANDALL, Samuel John, Jr. ■ 28277 #038-40-1942 L1986 **D** *072 †15
RANKIN, R Pinkney, Jr. 1718 E 4TH ST STE 307 28204 #041-01-1952 L1952 **GYN** *020 †30
RANSON, John Lester, Jr. 1900 RANDOLPH RD 28204 #041-02-1942 L1942 **IM OS** *071
RANSON, William Alexander. ■ 28210 #041-02-1948 L1948 **IM** *071
RAO, Prashanth Ramakrishn. 8401 MEDICAL PLAZA DR, STE 100 28262 #496-35-2003 L2005
    IM *012
RAO, Themanth P. 2219 E 7TH ST 28204 #495-04-1988 L1996 **N** *020 †75
RAPISARDO, Thomas Roy. 1000 BLYTHE BLVD 28203 #028-34-1978 L1986 **IM** *020 †20
RAPPAPORT, Daniel Shapiro. ■ 28270 #026-04-1987 L2001 **IM** *020 †20
RASHID, Daniel. 2001 VAIL AVE, MEDICAL ASSOCIATES 28207 #038-43-2002 L2008
    EM *020 †16
RATHBUN, Mary Anne. 1000 BLYTHE BLVD 28203 #035-03-1970 L1977 **NPM PD** *020 †55
RATTERREE, Jasper Calhoun. 1900 RANDOLPH RD 28207 #047-05-1988 L1989 **EM** *020 †16
RAVENET, Louis. ■ 28270 #275-01-1957 L1975 **P N** *071 †75
RAWLS, Benjamin Ellis. 1000 BLYTHE BLVD, ANNEX BLDG 28203 #045-04-1996 L2001
    IM *020 †20
RAYMOND, Kent Howard. 2711 RANDOLPH RD STE 400 28207 #028-02-1977 L1988
    NEP IM *020 †20
RAYMOND, Lawrence W. 5516 CENTRAL AVE 28212 #035-20-1964 L1989
    OM PUD *040 †20,70 ‡
RAYMORE, Sandra Hope. ■ 28270 #024-05-1983 L1986 **IM** *020 †20
REAMES, Mark Kevin. 1001 BLYTHE BLVD, STE 300 28203 #045-01-1985 L1993
    TS CD *020 †85,90
REAMES, Patrick Martin. 4201 TOTTENHAM RD 28226 #048-12-1958 L1966 **R** *071 †80
REARDON, Kathleen Marie. 5435 PROSPERITY CHURCH RD, STE 1500 28269
    #021-01-1977 L1984 **PD** *020 †55
REAVES, Charles Edwin. 435 N WENDOVER RD 28211 #027-01-1967 L1987 **D DMP** *020 †15
REDDICK, Bradley Harris. 3303 LATROBE DR 28211 #047-06-1996 L2002 **CHP** *020 †75
REDDY, Veerabhadra K. ■ 28203 #016-06-2002 L2007 **ORS** *100
REDVANLY, Richard David. 1001 BLYTHE BLVD, CAROLINAS MED CTR 28203
    #035-09-1987 L1999 **DR** *020 †80
REEN, Bernard Murty, III. 1718 E 4TH ST, STE 501 28204 #010-02-1980 L1989 **CD IM** *020 †20
REEVES, Curtis Coleman, Jr. 824 EASTWAY DR 28205 #047-07-1977 L1981 **OPH** *020 †35
REGER, Jill Elizabeth. 3541 RANDOLPH RD, MECKLENBURG MEDICAL GROUP 28211
    #045-01-2001 L2006 **RHU** *020
REGER, Lance Boyd. 501 BILLINGSLEY RD, CMC-RANDOLPH 28211 #045-01-1999 L2000
    P *020

REIF, Michael Steven. 1001 BLYTHE BLVD, STE 500 28203 #016-11-1994 L1996 **PCC** *020 †20

REILING, Richard Bernard. 200 HAWTHORNE LN, PRESBYTERIAN CANCER CENTER 28204 #024-01-1967 L2003 **GS SO** *030 †85 ‡

RENALDO, Donald Philip. 1718 E 4TH ST STE 908 28204 #041-13-1974 L1979 **OPH** *020 †35

RENNICK, John H, Jr. 6101 CARNEGIE BLVD, STE 500 28209 #036-01-1982 L1983 **FM** *020 †18

RENTZ, David Edward. 3101 LATROBE DR, PIEDMONT EMERGENCY MED ASS 28211 #021-01-2000 L2004 **EM** *020 †16

REPTA, Remus. 9201 UNIVERSITY CITY BLVD, # H 28223 #040-02-2002 L2007 **PS** *100

RESNIK, Alan. 3114 MONROE RD 28205 #649-14-1972 L1979 **IM AM** *020

RESTO, Wilma. 100 N TRYON ST, PHYSICIANS 28202 #035-20-1989 L1994 **IM** *020 †20

RESTREPO-GARTNER, C M. 1100 BLYTHE BLVD, AND REHABILITATION 28203 #036-05-1993 L1997 **PM** *020 †20

REYNOLDS, Christopher R. 1900 RANDOLPH RD 28207 #036-07-2003 L2006 **EM** *020 †16

REYNOLDS, Gregory Brian. ■ 28270 #001-02-2003 L2007 **OBG** *020

REYNOLDS, Kathryn Elaine. 1001 BLYTHE BLVD, STE 500 28203 #011-02-2001 L2007 **END** *020

REYNOLDS, Mark Stephen. 14215 BALLANTYNE CORPRT PL, STE 1 28277 #051-01-1995 L2003 **EM** *020

REYNOLDS, Sarah Helms. 1901 RANDOLPH RD 28207 #051-01-1996 L2003 **IM** *020 †20

RHODES, Marsha J. 1000 BLYTHE BLVD 28203 #001-02-1981 L1985 **PD** *040 †55

RHODES, Nathan Paul. PO BOX 30756, 1900 RANDOLPH RD STE 90 28230 #041-14-2005 L2008 **EM** *012

RHYNE, Alfred L, III. 2001 RANDOLPH RD, ORTHOCAROLINA PA 28207 #036-01-1984 L1985 **ORS** *020 †40

RICE, Andrea Simmons. 3333 WILKINSON BLVD 28208 #045-01-1992 L1994 **PD** *020

RICE, William Chas. 201 QUEENS RD 28207 #011-03-1969 L1974 **U** *020 †95

RICH, Charles B, Jr. 200 S COLLEGE ST, MECKLENBURG MEDICAL GROUP 28202 #036-05-1982 L1986 **IM** *020 †20

RICHARDSON, Bertha P. 2711 RANDOLPH RD, STE 120, P O BOX 37225 28207 #036-05-1977 L1977 **IM GE** *020 †20

RICHTER, Stephanie R. 10348 PARK RD, STE 300 28210 #048-04-1993 L2001 **PD** *020 †55

RICKEY, Colleen Molloy. 1000 BLYTHE BLVD, ANNEX BLDG., 1ST FLOOR 28203 #036-01-2002 L2005 **IM** *020 †20

RIDDLESBERGER, M M, Jr. 3623 LATROBE DR, STE 216 28211 #023-01-1968 L1995 **R** *020 †80

RIDLEY, Miriam E. 135 S SHARON AMITY RD, STE 100 28211 #065-01-1975 L1987 **OPH OS** *020 †35

RIEMANN, Lana Janelle. 1420 E 7TH ST, HOSPICE & PALLIATIVE CARE 28204 #036-01-1996 L1997 **FM** *020 †18

RILEY, Kathleen Ann. 14214 BALLANTYNE LAKE RD, PROVIDENCE PEDIATRICS 28277 #035-03-1990 L1992 **PD** *020 †55

RILEY, Kimberly. 14214 BALLANTYNE LAKE RD, STE 300 28277 #036-05-1994 L1995 **PD** *020 †55

RILEY, Scott Ivan. ■ 28273 #051-07-2005 L2008 **EM** *012

RINALDI, Michael Joseph. 1001 BLYTHE BLVD, STE 300 28203 #035-20-1994 L2002 **CD** *020 †20

RINGWOOD, John Wm. 200 HAWTHORNE LN 28204 #036-05-1977 L1990 **PEM PD** *020 †55

RIOPEL, Donald Aime. 1001 BLYTHE BLVD STE 300, THE SANGER CLINIC 28203 #011-03-1963 L1984 **PDC PD** *020 †55

RISH, Carlos Meyer. 1928 RANDOLPH RD STE 21, RANDOLPH MEDICAL CENTER 28207 #649-14-1982 L2003 **FM GS** *020 †18

RISSMILLER, Richard W, Jr. 1350 S KINGS DR 28207 #036-05-1998 L2000 **PCC** *020 †20

RISSMILLER, Scott Clifton. 1000 BLYTHE BLVD 28203 #012-01-1997 L2000 **IM** *020 †20

RITCH, Douglas Lamar. 2001 VAIL AVE 28207 #036-01-1963 L1963 **IM CD** *071

RIVERA, Epifanio. 4600 HOLBROOK DR 28212 #042-01-1976 L1999 **FM** *020 †18

RIVERA, Michelle Lorraine. 3623 LATROBE DR, STE 216 28211 #024-01-1992 L1997 **DR** *020 †80

ROBERTS, Eugene L, Jr. 501 BILLINGSLEY RD 28211 #027-01-1978 L1983 **P FM** *020 †18,75

ROBERTS, Richard S. 2630 E 7TH ST, STE 100 28204 #035-01-1978 L1980 **AI PD** *020 †55,03

ROBERTS, Thomas Adams, Jr. 2015 RANDOLPH RD, CHARLOTTE 28207 #036-01-1970 L1970 **GE IM** *020 †20

ROBERTS, Thomas Gerald, Jr. 227 W TRADE ST, STE 2140 28202 #024-01-1997 L2007 **HO** *020 †20

ROBERTS, William Henry. 6035 FAIRVIEW RD 28210 #012-01-1983 L1991 **OS OTO** *020 †45

ROBERTS, William Stanley. 1000 BLYTHE BLVD 28203 #051-01-1975 L1980 **CD IM** *020 †20

ROBERTSON, Cheryl Reis. 3541 RANDOLPH RD STE 300 28211 #020-12-1985 L1991 **RHU IM** *020 †20

ROBERTSON WHITE, Heather. 1718 E 4TH ST STE 707 28204 #036-01-2000 L2001 **OBG** *020

ROBICSEK, Francis. 1001 BLYTHE BLVD, STE 300 28203 #473-01-1950 L1958 **TS GS** *072 †85,90

ROBICSEK, Livia Kadar. ■ 28211 #473-01-1955 **PTH PD** *071

ROBINETTE, George D, II. 501 BILLINGSLEY RD 28211 #045-01-1992 L1993 **P** *020 †75

ROBINSON, Douglas Baird. 1001 BLYTHE BLVD, STE 500 28203 #041-12-1985 L1994 **IM END** *020 †20

ROBINSON, Elliot Payne. ■ 28207 #051-01-2008 **012**

ROBINSON, Lisa Jeannine. 5821 FAIRVIEW RD, STE 409 28209 #035-20-1991 L1999 **HMP** *020 †50

ROBINSON, Rachel Rochelle. PO BOX 32861, DEPT OF OB/GYN 28232 #048-13-2007 **OBG** *012

ROBINSON, Wesley Bradford. 927 EAST BLVD 28203 #012-05-1982 L1985 **AN** *020 †05

RODDEY, John Gardiner, Jr. 2015 RANDOLPH RD, CHARLOTTE 28207 #036-01-1990 L1996 **GE** *020 †20

RODDEY, Oliver Fennell. 2600 E 7TH ST, STE 100 28204 #036-01-1955 L1955 **PD** *071 †55

RODDEY, Patricia K. 3030 RANDOLPH RD STE 202 28211 #036-01-1990 L1992 **D** *020 †15

ROELS, Dorothy M. ■ 28277 #352-06-1949 L1977 **PHP** *020

ROEMER, Clifford Eric. 3623 LATROBE DR, STE 216 28211 #038-06-1976 L1980 **DR** *020 †80

ROGERS, Larry Arch. ■ 28226 #036-07-1965 L1965 **NS** *071 †25

ROGERS, Louise Cree. 2801 RANDOLPH RD, STE 200 28211 #010-02-1992 L1996 **OBG** *020 †30

ROGERS, Mary Kathryn. 1000 BLYTHE BLVD, DEPT OF PEDIATRIC 28203 #045-04-1988 L1992 **PD** *040 †55

ROHDE, Lisa Diane. 2001 VAIL AVE, PRESBYTERIAN INPATIENT CAR 28207 #036-01-1992 L1994 **IM** *020 †20

ROLBAND, Gary Chas. 3541 RANDOLPH RD, MECKLENBURG MEDICAL GROUP 28211 #050-02-1986 L1989 **IM END** *020 †20

ROMANOFF, Mark Elliott. 927 EAST BLVD 28203 #008-02-1983 L1993 **AN** *020 †05

RONCEVICH, Sharon Mary. 149 PROVIDENCE RD 28207 #045-01-1988 L1996 **PD** *020 †55

ROOCHVARG, Linda Berger. 2931 SIMMON TREE RD 28270 #035-45-1981 L1995 **PD ADL** *020 †55

ROPER, John Tracy. ■ 28207 #045-01-1955 L1955 **ORS** *071 †40

ROSE, Rachel Elizabeth. ■ 28205 #051-07-2008 *012

ROSEN, Douglas Michael. 2015 RANDOLPH RD STE 201 28207 #011-03-1997 L2003 **CRS** *020 †85,10

ROSEN, Gerald Bruce. 135 S SHARON AMITY RD, STE 100 28211 #035-08-1985 L2006 **OPH** *020 †20,35

ROSENFELD, Jeffrey. 1000 BLYTHE BLVD, CAROLINAS NEUROMUSCULAR 28203 #023-01-1990 L1998 **N NP** *020 †75

ROSS, Otho Bescent, Jr. 28210 #036-07-1943 L1943 **IM** *071 †20

ROSSER, George Thomas. ■ 28207 #047-06-1962 L1966 **DR** *071 †80

ROSTAN, Elizabeth F. 1918 RANDOLPH RD, STE 580 28207 #036-01-1995 L1997 **D DS** *020 †15

ROTBERG, Michael Howard. 1000 BLYTHE BLVD 28203 #036-07-1979 L1991 **OPH** *020 †35

ROUHIPOUR, Vargha. 1000 BLYTHE BLVD, MEB #503 28203 #048-13-2001 L2006 **ORS** *100

ROUSE, Kelley Howard. 9908 COULOAK DR, STE 201 28216 #012-05-2000 L2006 **OBG** *020

ROUSE, Strutha Charles, II. 11010 DAVID TAYLOR DR 28262 #012-05-2000 L2006 **OPH** *100 †35

ROUSH, Timothy Starling. 1001 BLYTHE BLVD, STE 300 28203 #023-12-1984 L2001 **GS VS** *020 †85

ROWE, Lorenz. ■ 28269 #033-05-1984 L1998 **GS** *020 †85

ROY, Perry James. 8401 MEDICAL PLAZA DR 28262 #020-02-1993 L1997 **IM PD** *020 †55,20

RUBIN, Ilya. 1901 RANDOLPH RD 28207 #913-32-1988 L2007 **AN** *020 †05

RUDISEL, Kevin Michael. 200 HAWTHORNE LN, SPECIALISTS/PRESBYTERIAN H 28204 #033-06-1983 L1991 **IM** *020 †20

RUNYON, Michael Scott. PO BOX 32861, CAROLINAS MEDICAL CENTER 28232 #011-03-2000 L2002 **EM** *020 †16

RUPAR, David Gerard. 1000 BLYTHE BLVD, CAROLINAS MED CTR DEPT PED 28203 #010-02-1979 L1988 **PD PDI** *040 †55

RUPE, Carol Anne. 3230 PROSPERITY CHURCH RD, STE 101 28269 #010-02-1984 L1993 **FM** *020 †18

RUPPENTHAL, Carl Robt, Jr. 1350 S KINGS DR 28207 #041-01-1960 L1968 **IM HEM** *071 †20

RUSS, Donald James. 4525 CAMERON VALLEY PKWY, STE 3100 28211 #023-01-1973 L1974 **IM** *020 †20

RUSSELL, Henry Edwin. 521 E MOREHEAD ST, STE 300 28202 #016-06-1972 L2001 **GS** *020 †85

RUSSO, Cheryl A. 1001 BLYTHE BLVD, STE 300 28203 #035-15-1998 L2001 **CD** *020 †20

RYAN, Amy Garrett. 2600 E 7TH ST, STE 100 28204 #051-01-1995 L1996 **PD** *020 †55

RYAN, Matthew Anthony. 200 HAWTHORNE LN, PRESBYTERIAN HOSPITAL 28204 #028-34-1988 L1992 **IM** *020 †20

RYAN, Ronald Garvin. 5435 PROSPERITY CHURCH RD, STE 1100 28269 #041-02-1995 L2005 **FM UCM** *020 †18

RYDER-COOK, Allan S. 10620 PARK RD STE 230 28210 #067-01-1979 L1996 **N** *020 †20,75

RYSKIEWICH, Paul Danl. 1901 RANDOLPH RD 28207 #036-05-1982 L1983 **AN** *020 †05

SAALWACHTER, Alison Roman. ■ 28226 #051-01-2001 L2001 **GS** *100

SACCO, Sara Elizabeth. 1900 RANDOLPH RD STE 1010 28207 #011-03-1983 L1989 **N** *020 †75

SACRA, Richard Amsden. ■ 28241 #024-16-1989 L1996 **FM** *020 †18

SADDY, Chanchal R. 1701 ABBEY PL 28209 #495-45-1990 L1996 **IM** *020 †20

SAGUNARTHY, Rabindra. ■ 28217 #496-34-2003 L2007 **IM** *100 †20

SAILER, Kaaren Sue. 601 E 5TH ST STE 140 28202 #024-04-1990 L1993 **FM** *020 †18

SAINZ, Alfonso E. ■ 28209 #847-04-1968 L1973 **OBG** *020 †30

SAIR, Farrukh Iqbal. 1901 RANDOLPH RD 28207 #036-01-2001 L2005 **APM** *020 †05

SAKALA, Rajesh D. 200 HAWTHORNE LN, PRESBYTERIAN INPATIENT CAR 28204 #495-33-1994 L1999 **IM** *020 †20

SALAMA, David John. 927 EAST BLVD 28203 #056-06-1989 L1999 **AN** *020 †05

SALAZAR, J Octavio. 501 BILLINGSLEY RD 28211 #264-05-1972 L2005 **CHP** *030 †75 ‡

SALE, Lori Anne. 1320 FILLMORE AVE UNIT 102 28203 #004-01-2002 L2005 **FM** *100 †18

SALLEY, Brunson M, Jr. 7300 SARDIS RD 28270 #012-01-1964 L1965 **FM** *020 †18

SALMON, John Stuart. 101 E WT HARRIS BLVD, STE 1214 28262 #047-05-1999 L2005 **HO** *020 †20

SALMON, Robert Bruce. PO BOX 36937 28236 #028-02-1961 L1967 **R** *071 †80

SALO, Jonathan Cyrus. 1025 MOREHEAD MEDICAL DR, DR #600 28204 #005-02-1985 L2002 **SO IG** *020 †85

SALVEMINI, Philomena Gius. PO BOX 32861, DEPT OF OB/GYN 28232 #038-45-2005 **OBG** *012

SALZMAN, Jessica. ■ 28217 #051-07-2008 *012

SAMAREL, Matthew David. 8169 ARDREY KELL RD, KIDS FIRST PEDIATRICS, P.A 28277 #024-07-1988 L2002 **PD** *020 †55

SAMUELS, Walter Ray. 150 PROVIDENCE RD 28207 #036-01-1961 L1961 **OBG** *071 †30

SANDBERG, James Wm. 8401 MEDICAL PLAZA DR 28262 #056-06-1987 L1993 **GE PD** *020 †55

SANDERS, Jason Browning. 6035 FAIRVIEW RD 28210 #045-01-1999 L2005 **OPH** *020 †35

SANDOVAL, John Joseph. 1901 RANDOLPH RD 28207 #007-02-2003 L2007 **AN** *020

SANFORD, Steven Byron. 2711 RANDOLPH RD, STE 305 28207 #025-07-1991 L1998 **GS HS** *020 †85

SANGMUAH, Eliza N. 200 HAWTHORNE LN, PRESBYTERIAN HOSPITAL 28204 #412-01-1996 L2005 **IM** *020 †20

SANGMUAH, Eugene Bowa. 200 HAWTHORNE LN 28204 #412-01-1993 L2001 **IM** *020 †20

SANTANDER, Samuel H. 3621 RANDOLPH RD # 100 28211 #024-05-1989 L1998 **OPH** *020

SAPPENFIELD, Daniel. 10000 PARK CEDAR DR, CARMEL FAMILY PHYSICIANS, 28210 #036-01-1987 L1989 **FM** *020 †18

SARETT, Joshua Danl. 1900 RANDOLPH RD 28207 #017-20-1985 L1988 **EM** *020 †16

SATTERFIELD, Jamison J. 7800 PROVIDENCE RD STE 204 28226 #012-01-1986 L1989 **PD** *020 †55

SAUDER, Russell Allen. 927 EAST BLVD 28203 #038-43-1980 L2005 **AN CCM** *020 †55,05 ‡

SAUNDERS, Timothy Gray. 6035 FAIRVIEW RD, CHARLOTTE EENT ASSOC 28210 #036-01-1981 L1982 **OPH PO** *020 †35 ‡

SAVITSKY, Ivan. 9332 S TRYON ST 28273 #025-07-1994 L1995 **FM** *020 †18

SAWYER, Norman M. 2024 RANDOLPH RD, STE A 28207 #010-01-1960 L1972 **OPH** *071 †35

SAXE, Jessica Schorr. 1801 ROZZELLES FERRY RD 28208 #024-07-1977 L1978 **FM** *020 †18

SAYSON, Samuel Calderon. 1901 RANDOLPH RD 28207 #023-12-1989 L2000 **AN PME** *020 †05

SCANGA, Daniel Raymond. 3623 LATROBE DR, STE 216 28211 #036-07-1999 L2005 **NM R** *020 †80,28

SCANNELL, Brian Patrick. PO BOX 32861, CAROLINAS MED CTR 28232 #036-01-2006 **ORS** *012

SCELZA, William Michael. 1100 BLYTHE BLVD, CAROLINAS REHABILITATION 28203 #038-06-1998 L2006 **SCI** *020 †60

SCHAEPER, Mark Matthew. 10310 MALLARD CREEK RD 28262 #038-41-1998 L1999 **FM** *020 †18

SCHAFERMEYER, Robert Wm. 1000 BLYTHE BLVD, CAROLINAS MEDICAL CTR 28203 #028-03-1973 L1981 **EM PEM** *040 †55,16 ‡

SCHAIBLE, Tiffany. PO BOX 32861, DEPT OF PEDS 28232 #035-15-2005 **PD** *012

SCHARF, Carl James. 1901 RANDOLPH RD 28207 #030-06-1978 L1985 **AN** *020 †05

SCHARSTEIN, Robert. 1701 EAST BLVD 28203 #045-01-1984 L1991 **DR NM** *020 †30

SCHERR, John Morris. 1000 BLYTHE BLVD, ANNEX 28203 #012-01-1979 L2002 **IM** *020 †20

SCHIFFERN, Lynnette Marie. 1000 BLYTHE BLVD, CAROLINAS MEDICAL CENTER 28203 #045-01-2000 L2006 **CCS** *100 †85

SCHLAUTMAN, Stacey Dawn. 5516 CENTRAL AVE, EASTLAND FAMILY PRACTICE 28212 #028-03-2002 L2005 **FM** *040 †18

SCHMALSTIEG, Walter Lee. 501 BILLINGSLEY RD 28211 #048-04-1974 L1996 **CHP P** *020 †75

SCHMIDT, Jeffrey Jay. 1918 RANDOLPH RD, STE 400 28207 #396-27-1981 L1985 **N** *020 †75

SCHMITZ, Robert Joseph. 15830 JOHN J DELANEY DR, CHARLOTTE 28277 #019-02-1995 L2001 **GE** *020 †20

SCHNEIDER, Peter John. 5435 PROSPERITY CHURCH RD, STE 2200A 28269 #051-01-1983 L1985 **OBG** *020 †30

SCHNEIDER, Robert Edward. 1000 BLYTHE BLVD 28203 #030-06-1970 L1985 **EM U** *020 †95,16

SCHNEIDER, Scott Matthew. 10340 PARK RD 28210 #010-01-1990 L1994 **OBG** *020 †30

SCHNIDER, Stuart Lee. 505 E 6TH ST, UNIT 1401 28202 #038-06-1983 L1987 **GYN MDM** *020

SCHOLZ, David Geo. 2015 RANDOLPH RD, CHARLOTTE 28207 #026-08-1983 L1989 **GE IM** *020 †20

SCHOTTHOEFER, Erin O'Mall. 6035 FAIRVIEW RD 28210 #025-07-2002 L2006 **OPH** *020 †35

SCHUG, John Butler. 1718 E 4TH ST STE 907 28204 #045-01-1957 L1961 **OBG** *071 †30

SCHULMAN, Andrew M. ■ 28226 #035-15-1998 L2007 **PDS** *020 †85

SCHULTZ, Michael Timothy. ■ 28209 #051-07-2005 **EM** *012

SCHUMACHER, Donald. 401 S SHARON AMITY RD, STE A 28211 #561-01-1970 L1975 **IM NTR** *020

SCHUPBACH, Curtis Wayne. 2620 E 7TH ST, EASTOVER MED PK 28204 #028-02-1969 L1974 **D** *020 †15

SCHWARTZ, Jared Naphtali. 200 HAWTHORNE LN 28204 #036-07-1973 L1974 **PTH** *020 †50

SCOBEY, Martin Wm. 1000 BLYTHE BLVD, 5TH FLOOR MEB, 505C 28203 #047-06-1980 L1984 **IM** *020 †20

SCOTT, David Allan. ■ 28209 #051-07-2005 L2005 **PM** *012

SCOTT, Marty Benard. 5425 SUMMER POND CT 28226 #020-02-1982 L1982 **CCP PD** *020 †55

SCOVILL, David Matthew. 3623 LATROBE DR, #216 MECKLENBURG RAD ASSOC 28211 #005-06-1990 L1996 **DR** *020 †80

SCULLY, Karen Elizabeth. 10933 FOXHAVEN DR 28277 #065-05-1979 L2007 **D** *062 ‡

SEARLES, Anthony David. 10400 HADLEIGH PL 28210 #010-03-1982 L1995 **P** *020

SEBOLD, Edwin James. 1915 RANDOLPH RD, ATTN:CREDENTIALING COORDIN 28207 #035-15-1986 L1993 **ORS OS** *020 †40

SEEHORN, Charles Lee, III. 1918 RANDOLPH RD, STE 600 28207 #047-06-1997 L2002 **RHU** *020 †20

SEGEBARTH, Paul Bradley. ■ 28210 #020-12-2002 L2007 **ORS** *100

SEILER, Beth A. 2630 E 7TH ST, STE 100 28204 #038-40-1991 L1996 **AI** *020 †55,03

SELLE, Jay Gregory. 1001 BLYTHE BLVD, SANGER CLINIC PA 28203 #025-07-1968 L1976 **TS** *071 †85,90

SEMEKO, Eric. 1718 E 4TH ST, STE 805A 28204 #913-84-1996 L2004 **P** *020 ‡

SEMPLE, Roxanne Denise. 9908 COULOAK DR, STE 103 28216 #012-21-1992 L2005 **PD** *020 †20

SENSENBRENNER, John W. 330 BILLINGSLEY RD STE 100 28211 #036-08-1984 L1987 **IM** *020 †20

SETHI, V Sagar. 7301 CARMEL EXECUTV PRK DR 28226 #649-33-1986 L1990 **P** *020

SEWARD, Daniel Peter. 7004 SMITH CORNERS BLVD, STE A 28269 #025-07-1987 L1990 **IM PD** *020,55

SEWARD, James Lemar. 15830 JOHN J DELANEY DR, STE 100 28277 #038-43-1999 L2003 **D** *020 †15 ‡

SEXTON, Filmon Mack, Jr. 101 E WT HARRIS BLVD, STE 1212 28262 #045-01-1979 L1992 **ATP DMP** *020 †50

SHAFFNER, Susan Casper. 4501 CAMERON VALLEY PKWY, STE 100 28211 #036-05-1984 L1986 **PD** *020 †55

SHAFRAN, Kerry Mark. 3006 BAUCOM RD STE 100 28269 #036-05-1986 L1991 **D** *020 †15

SHAH, Avinash. 2115 E 7TH ST STE 102 28204 #577-01-1978 L1986 **HO IM** *020

SHAH, Bijal Bharat. ■ 28203 #012-05-2006 **EM** *012

SHAH, Devendra C. 5208 PARK RD 28209 #495-22-1980 L1994 **P PYG** *020

SHAH, Jugalkishor K. 10724 PARK RD, BLDG 200 28210 #495-23-1973 L1983 **CD IM** *020 †20

SHAH, Mehul Hemant. ■ 28262 #496-38-1993 L1997 **IM HOS** *020 †20

SHAH, Nandlal C. 2001 VAIL AVE 28207 #495-22-1957 L1979 **PM** *071 †60

SHAH, Narendra K. 10035 PARK CEDAR DR, STE 100 28210 #495-49-1975 L1994 **FM** *072 †18

SHAH, Rina Kirit. ■ 28277 #036-05-2008 *012

SHAHAN, Cynthia Lee. 3132 LATROBE DR 28211 #036-08-1989 L1994 **CHP** *020 †75

SHANDERA, Kevin C. 10512 PARK RD, THE CAROLINAS PINEVILLE 28210 #048-04-1987 L1998 **U** *020 †95

SHANKS, Daniel Erle. 1000 BLYTHE BLVD, DEPARTMENT OF NEUROLOGY 28203 #051-01-1982 L2005 **CHN OS** *020 †55,75

SHANKS, David Edward. 1928 RANDOLPH RD STE 215 28207 #036-05-1966 L1998 **PUD IM** *075 †20

SHANNON, Mitsuko Perry. 501 BILLINGSLEY RD 28211 #055-02-1988 L1993 **CHP P** *020 †75

SHANNON, Patricia G Moyer. 1100 BLYTHE BLVD 28203 #038-45-1998 L1999 **PM** *020 †60

SHAPIRO, Marvin B. 1001 BLYTHE BLVD, STE 500 28203 #001-02-1966 L1973 **IM GE** *020 †20

SHARKEY, Kevin Cronin. 1718 E 4TH ST, STE 501 28204 #012-05-1994 L2002 **CD** *020 †20

SHARMA, Isha Puri. 10000 PARK CEDAR DR 28210 #017-20-1995 L2003 **FM** *020 †18

SHARMA, Ramesh M. 7800 PROVIDENCE RD, STE 209 28226 #495-09-1968 L1995 **TS VS** *020 †85,90

SHAUGER, Kenneth Leslie. 1000 BLYTHE BLVD #036-01-1993 L2001 **N** *020 †75

SHAVER, David Corydon. 1718 E 4TH ST, STE 404 28204 #004-01-1976 L1993 **MFM OBG** *020 †30

SHAVER, Edward F, Jr. 1718 E 4TH ST, STE 303 28204 #021-01-1959 L1964 **OTO** *071 †45

SHAVER, Samuel Lelus. ■ 28214 #004-01-1958 L1960 **GP** *071

SHEARER, James Neil. 2711 RANDOLPH RD STE 502 28207 #035-09-1975 L1982 **PS HS** *020 †85,65

SHELTON, Gary Ryan. 4525 CAMERON VLY PKWY, STE 3100 28211 #047-06-2004 L2007 **IM** *020 †20

SHEMTOV, Rachel Chaya. 1001 BLYTHE BLVD 28203 #008-01-2004 L2007 **IM** *100 †20

SHENOY, Vittal Balkunje. 1000 BLYTHE BLVD 28203 #495-35-1977 L1982 **ATP CLP** *050 †50 ‡

SHIVE, Robert Mac Gregor. 6050 HICKORY GROVE RD, 4927 MONROE RD 28215 #036-01-1961 L2003 **P** *071

SHOAF, Edwin Huss, Jr. 1918 RANDOLPH RD, PHYSICIANS RANDOLPH 28207 #036-05-1975 L1975 **IM** *020 ‡

SHOEMAKE, Joshua Kevin. 4501 CAMERON VALLEY PKWY, MECKLENBURG MEDICAL GROUP 28211 #012-01-2002 L2004 **IM** *020 †20

SHOOK, Paul Raymond. 1901 RANDOLPH RD 28207 #036-05-2000 L2004 **AN** *020 †05 ‡

SHULSTAD, Andrew Robert. 4501 CAMERON VALLEY PKWY, STE 100 28211 #012-01-1996 L1999 **PD** *020 †16

SIBOLD, Harry Eugene. 1900 RANDOLPH RD 28207 #047-20-1991 L1992 **EM** *020 †16

SICARD, Michael William. 6035 FAIRVIEW RD, THROAT ASSOCIATES PA 28210 #036-07-1993 L1999 **OTO** *020 †45

SIDDIQUI, Huma Jabeen. ■ 28269 #704-08-1993 L2004 **IM** *100

SIDES, Andrew Wesley. ■ 28210 #045-04-2006 **IM** *012

SIGMON, James Lewis, Jr. 9332 S TRYON ST 28273 #036-01-1966 L1966 **FM IM** *071 †18 ‡

SIGMON, Richard Lee, Jr. 1001 BLYTHE BLVD, STE403 28203 #036-01-1979 L1980 **GE PD** *020 †20,55

SILTON, Richard P. 2630 E 7TH ST STE 100, CAROLINA ASTHMA & ALLERGY 28204 #035-03-1982 L1994 **AI IM** *020 †20,03

SIMMONS, Sandra Jean. 725 PROVIDENCE RD, STE 301 28207 #021-05-1989 L1994 **P** *020

SIMON, Carla Jude. 200 HAWTHORNE LN, PRESBYTERIAN INPATIENT CAR 28204 #016-01-2000 L2004 **IM** *020 †20

SIMONTON, Chas Alison, III. 3520 BLACKHORSE LN, C/O THE SANGER CLINIC P.A. 28210 #024-01-1980 L1984 **CD IM** *020 †20

SIMS, Stephen Hubert. 1616 SCOTT AVE, DEPT. OF ORTHOPAEDICS 28203 #045-01-1983 L1989 **ORS** *020 †40

SINCLAIR, Ronald Meredith. 200 HAWTHORNE LN 28204 #041-09-1983 L2002 **HOS IM** *020 †20

SING, Jeanne M Voltaggio. 905 DOCTORS BLDG 28207 #021-01-1954 L1960 **P** *020

SING, Robert Lloyd. 3600 WOODPARK BLVD STE A 28206 #036-07-1954 L1954 **PTH** *030 †50

SINGER, Ronald Wayne. 15825 JOHN J DELANEY DR, STE 100 28277 #011-03-1990 L1995 **ORS** *020 †40

SINGH, Jaspal. 1000 BLYTHE BLVD, INTERNAL MEDICINE DEPARTME 28203 #016-11-1999 L2003 **PCC** *100 †20

SINGH, Pradeep. 10732 OLD WAYSIDE RD, CAROLINA CARDIOLOGY ASSOCI 28277 #496-04-1981 L1992 **CD IM** *020 †20

SINGHI, Sushil K. 10724 PARK RD BLDG 200, STE 201 28210 #495-20-1982 L1994 **CD IM** *020 †20

SINN, Michele Birch. 1801 ROZZELLES FERRY RD, CAROLINAS MEDICAL CENTER - 28208 #051-01-1998 L1999 **FM** *020 †18

SIPAVICIUS, Remigijus. ■ 28203 #913-49-1997 *100

SKIPPER, Eric R. 1001 BLYTHE BLVD, STE 300 28203 #036-05-1985 L1991 **TS VS** *020 †85,90

SLAUGHTER, Gary Byron. 2630 E SEVENTH ST, STE 200 28204 #047-07-1997 L2001 **D** *020 †15

SLIZ, Nicholas B, Jr. 1001 BLYTHE BLVD, STE 300 28203 #036-01-1994 L2005 **PDC PD** *020 †55

SLOAN, Jeffrey Clyde. 10732 OLD WAYSIDE RD, CAROLINA CAARDIOLOGY ASSOC 28277 #550-02-1982 L1992 **IM CD** *071 †20

SMALL, Stephen Andrew. 1900 RANDOLPH RD 28207 #012-05-1997 L2005 **EM** *020 †16

SMART, Carl Andre. 2711 RANDOLPH RD STE 208 28207 #041-13-1988 L1994 **PUD IM** *020 †20

SMITH, Alleyne Patricia. ■ 28262 #035-06-1990 L1995 **IM** *020

SMITH, Blake Andrew. ■ 28209 #056-05-2006 **EM** *012

SMITH, Daron James. 3135 SPRINGBANK LN, THROAT PA 28226 #001-02-1993 L1998 **OTO** *020 †45

SMITH, David Lawrence. 135 S SHARON AMITY RD, STE 100 28211 #012-05-1979 L1993 **OPH OS** *020 †35

SMITH, David Scott. 3535 RANDOLPH RD, WENDOVER BUILDING, SUITE 2 28211 #001-06-1998 L2004 **GE** *020 †20

SMITH, Douglas Ray. 1918 RANDOLPH RD STE 275 28207 #036-05-1963 L1963 **GP** *071 †18

SMITH, Henry Louis, II. 10348 PARK RD, STE 300 28210 #041-01-1966 L1966 **PD** *020 †55

SMITH, Holly Gwen. 8169 ARDREY KELL RD 28277 #024-01-1986 L2005 **PD** *020 †55

SMITH, James Anderson. 8401 MEDICAL PLAZA DR, STE 250 28262 #041-02-1986 L1987 **EM** *020 †16

SMITH, Kevin Lindsay. 2215 RANDOLPH RD, CHARLOTTE PLASTIC SURGERY 28207 #051-07-1979 L1987 **PS HS** *020 †85,65

SMITH, Kevin Scott. 101 E WT HARRIS BLVD, STE 1212 28262 #018-03-1993 L1998 **PTH** *020 †50

SMITH, Lane Mcneil. ■ 28277 #051-04-2003 L2006 **EM** *020 †16

SMITH, Mark David. 225 BALDWIN AVE, CAROLINA NEUROSURGERY & SP 28204 #012-01-1997 L2003 **NS** *020 †25

SMITH, Martha Gibson. 1132 GREENWOOD CLFS 28204 #045-01-1989 L1990 **P** *020 †75

SMITH, Ralph Jos. 1900 RANDOLPH RD 28207 #038-45-1983 L2004 **PD PEM** *020 †55

SMITH, Rebecca L. 10502 PARK RD, STE 100 28210 #048-04-1990 L1999 **D** *020 †15

SMITH, Richard Thos, Jr. 1001 BLYTHE BLVD, STE 300 28203 #011-03-1978 L1987 **PD** *020 †55

SMITH, Robert Michael. 1420 E 7TH ST, HOSPICE AT CHARLOTTE 28204 #041-12-1997 L1999 **FM** *020 †20

SMITH, Roger Enos. 1701 ABBEY PL 28209 #016-11-1964 L1972 **CD IM** *020 †20

SMITH, Scott Leander. 3030 RANDOLPH RD, MECKLENBURG MEDICAL GROUP 28211 #011-03-1994 L1999 **ORS** *020 †20

SMITH, Shelia Deloise. 2630 E 7TH ST, STE 101 28204 #036-01-1998 L2007 **PD** *020 †55

SMOAK, Charles Kelly. 4501 CAMERON VALLEY PKWY, STE 100 28211 #036-07-1998 L2005 **PD** *020 †55

SNITZ, Arnold Ira. 2620 E 7TH ST 28204 #051-01-1975 L1977 **PD** *020 †55

SNODGRASS, Brett Thomas. ■ 28203 #028-46-2007 **GS** *012

SNYDER, Christopher Alan. 1928 RANDOLPH RD, STE 316 28207 #047-20-1988 L1994 **D** *020 †20,15

SNYDER, John Michael. 200 HAWTHORNE LN, INPATIENT MEDICINE 28204 #060-01-1968 L1975 **AN OS** *071 †05

SNYDER, Thomas Jerome. 5815 BLAKENEY PARK DR, STE 200A 28277 #016-06-1985 L2003 **EM** *020 †55

SOKANY, Nancy Marie. 15110 JOHN J DELANEY DR, MECKLENBURG MEDICAL 28277 #038-40-1988 L1993 **IM** *020 †20

SOLOMON, Philip Jay. 5933 BLAKENEY PARK DR, STE 100 28277 #011-04-1988 L1992 **OBG** *020 †30

SOMERSTEIN, David Eugene. 1900 RANDOLPH RD STE 310 28207 #045-01-1966 L1967 **U** *095 †95
SOYODE-ETOMI, Olatokunbo. 7221 PINEVILLE MATTHEWS RD, TRAVEL MEDICINE #200 28226 #690-01-1981 L1993 **IM** *020 †20
SPANGENTHAL, Selwyn. 1918 RANDOLPH RD, STE 440 28207 #836-02-1974 L1982 **PUD IM** *020 †20
SPARKS, Edwin Wayne, Jr. 501 BILLINGSLEY RD, CMC - RANDOLPH 28211 #036-05-1993 L1994 **P** *020 †75
SPATARO, Joseph David. 6101 IDLEWILD RD STE 300, IDLEWILD MEDICAL CTR 28212 #035-03-1981 L2003 **FM** *020 ‡
SPEIGHT, Mark Oneal. 9101 MONROE RD, STE 155 28270 #036-08-1987 L1994 **FM** *020 †18
SPELL, Arthur Bennett. 4501 CAMERON VALLEY PKWY, STE 100 28211 #011-03-1991 L1994 **PD** *020 †55
SPENCE, John Edward. 1628 E MOREHEAD ST 28207 #051-01-1981 L1991 **MG PD** *020 †55,19
SPIERS, Latessa S. 1701 ABBEY PL 28209 #036-08-1992 L2002 **IM** *020 †20
SPITZ, Adam Frederick. 1918 RANDOLPH RD STE 220, PRESBYTERIAN ENDO & OSTEO 28207 #035-08-1988 L1995 **END MPD** *020 †20
SPOLNICKI, Wanda. 200 S COLLEGE ST, MECKLENBURG MEDICAL GROUP 28202 #051-04-1990 L1993 **IM** *020 †20
SPRINGER, Bryan Donald. 1915 RANDOLPH RD, ORTHOCAROLINA, PA 28207 #055-02-1999 L2005 **ORS** *020 †40
SPRINGER, Lisa Melanie. 200 HAWTHORNE LN, PRESBYTERIAN HOSPITAL 28204 #409-21-1998 L2002 **IM** *020 †20
SPROUL, Matthew Thomas. ■ 28209 #036-01-2005 L2007 **FP** *012
STAMOU, Sotiris. ■ 28211 #418-01-1993 L2001 **TS** *012 †85
STARKS, Lawanna Marie. 2315 W ARBORS DR, STE 115 28262 #026-04-1997 L2006 **PD** *020 †55
STARMAN, James Steven. ■ 28209 #041-12-2007 **ORS** *012
STEFANIDIS, Dimitrios. 1000 BLYTHE BLVD, MEB 601 28203 #418-02-1995 L2006 **GS** *020 †85
STEIN, Aviva Ruth. 7810 PROVIDENCE RD, STE 101 28226 #035-47-1997 L2004 **OBG** *020 †30
STEINMULLER, Warren Jay. 225 E KINGSTON AVE 28203 #028-02-1981 L1991 **CHP P** *020 †75
STEPHENS, Kathryn J. 431 N WENDOVER RD 28211 #036-01-1978 L1979 **OBG** *020 †30
STERN, Herbert Joel. 1001 BLYTHE BLVD STE 300 28203 #045-01-1984 L1990 **PDC** *020 †55
STERN, Jenny Kern. ■ 28226 #035-15-1983 L1987 **IM** *074 †20
STERN, Thomas Patrick. 1350 S KINGS DR 28207 #004-01-1997 L2004 **PCC** *020 †20,55
STEVENS, Holly Ann. 1718 E 4TH ST, STE 201 28204 #036-01-1993 L1997 **OBG** *020 †30
STEVENS, Robert Lewis. ■ 28269 #008-02-2005 **GS** *012
STEWARD, Emmett F. 200 HAWTHORNE LN 7B 28204 #036-01-1988 L1991 **IM** *020 †20
STEWART, Donald Houston. 8800 N TRYON ST 28262 #035-15-1990 L1995 **OPH** *020 †35
STEWART, Faith Ashley. ■ 28210 #045-04-2007 **IM** *012
ST FORT, Sherma. PO BOX 32861, DEPT OF OB/GYN 28232 #011-03-2004 **OBG** *012
STIEGEL, Robert Mark. 1001 BLYTHE BLVD, STE 300 28203 #036-01-1979 L1981 **TS** *020 †85,90
STORY, Ellen Shannon. ■ 28270 #027-01-1990 L1997 **END IM** *020 †20
STORY, John Scott. 1010 EDGEHILL RD N 28207 #027-01-1989 L1996 **N** *020 †75
STOWE, Barry Michael. 927 EAST BLVD, SE ANESTHESIOLOGY CONSULT 28203 #012-05-1998 L2002 **AN PAN** *020 †05
STOWE, Mary Wassell. 1025 MOREHEAD MEDICAL DR, STE 200 28204 #036-08-1983 L1994 **IM** *020 †20
STRAIT, Thomas Taylor. ■ 28209 #045-04-2006 **IM** *012
STRANICK, Francis Jos. 1901 RANDOLPH RD 28207 #030-06-1986 L1995 **AN PD** *020 †05,55
STRATTON, James David. 5100 SHARON RD, BOX 100 28210 #016-01-1937 L1946 **OPH** *071 †35
STRINGHAM, Lisa Wood. 1900 RANDOLPH RD 28207 #019-02-1999 L2002 **EM** *020 †16
STUBBS, Erin Hollingswort. ■ 28207 #036-05-2006 **PD** *012
STUBBS, Thomas Mangum. 1000 BLYTHE BLVD, DEPT OF OBGYN 28203 #036-07-1975 L1990 **OBG MFM** *020 †30
STURGESS, Susan Denise. 2001 VAIL AVE, MEDICAL ASSOCIATES 28207 #028-46-1996 L2000 **EM** *020 †16
STURNER, William Quentin. ■ 28277 #028-34-1959 L1992 **PFP LM** *062 †50 ‡
STUVER, David Byron. 8816 CHALLIS FARM RD 28226 #041-12-1985 L1986 **IM OM** *020
SUDY, Donald John. 4423 SHARON RD 28211 #054-04-1994 L2002 **EM** *020
SUFFREN, Samantha. ■ 28269 #036-08-2002 L2006 **P** *100
SUGAR, Oscar. ■ 28226 #010-01-1942 L1944 **NS N** *071 †25
SUGG, William Caswell, Jr. 720 E MOREHEAD ST, STE 101 28202 #012-05-1961 L1962 **IM PUD** *020 †20
SULLIVAN, David Matthew. 1000 BLYTHE BLVD, CAROLINAS MEDICAL CENTER 28203 #041-09-1996 L1997 **EM** *020 †16
SULLIVAN, Sharon Renee. 7800 PROVIDENCE RD STE 203 28226 #041-09-1996 L1997 **PD** *020 †55
SULLIVAN, Timothy Michael. 2001 VAIL AVE, MEDICAL ASSOCIATES 28207 #038-41-1996 L1999 **EM** *020 †16
SUNDARARAMAN, Michael Ana. ■ 28202 #143-03-2002 L2006 **EM** *100 †16
SUNDBERG, Thomas C. 4525 CAMERON VALLEY PKWY, STE 4100 28211 #409-20-1976 L1982 **RHU IM** *020 †20
SUNDERLAND, Brent. 1718 E 4TH ST, STE 601 28204 #048-14-1990 L2002 **CHP P** *020 †75
SUSI, Beth Elisa. 1350 S KINGS DR, DEPT OF MEDICINE 28207 #011-03-1994 L1997 **IM** *040 †20
SUTHERLAND, Amanda Jane. 501 BILLINGSLEY RD, BEHAVIORAL HEALTH CENTER- 28211 #065-01-1984 L1998 **P** *020 †75
SUTHERLAND, Frederick S. 6035 FAIRVIEW RD 28210 #036-07-1986 L1988 **OPH** *020 †35
SUTHERLAND, Steven M. 3303 LATROBE DR 28211 #047-20-1986 L1991 **P CHP** *020 †75
SUTTON, Elena Kay. 5435 PROSPERITY CHURCH RD, STE 2200A 28269 #018-03-1998 L1999 **FM** *020 †18
SUTTON, Richard Loring. 1900 RANDOLPH RD 28207 #038-40-1974 L1975 **EM** *020 †16
SVENDSEN, Thor Owen. 1718 E 4TH ST, STE 307 28204 #036-01-1992 L1996 **OBG** *020 †30
SWAIMOVA, Iveta. 1918 RANDOLPH RD, PHYSICIANS RANDOLPH 28207 #286-03-1992 L2003 **IM** *020
SWANEY, Michael James. 1718 E 4TH ST STE 801, PRESB HOSP MED TOWER 28204 #025-07-2001 L2006 **P CHP** *020 †75
SWANSON, Douglas Richard. 1000 BLYTHE BLVD, DEPT OF EMERGENCY MEDICINE 28203 #011-04-1992 L1995 **EM** *020 †16
SWANSON, Mark Robt. 1416 E MOREHEAD ST 28204 #025-01-1973 L1978 **GS** *020 †85
SWETENBURG, Raymond Lee. 2600 E 7TH ST, STE 100 28204 #036-07-1976 L1978 **PD** *020 †55
SYMANSKI, John David. 1001 BLYTHE BLVD STE 300, THE SANGER CLINIC PA 28203 #036-01-1988 L1989 **CD IM** *020 †20

SYPHARD, Susan. 7810 PROVIDENCE RD, STE 102 28226 #038-75-2000, ▲ L2001 **FM** *020 ‡
SYRACUSE, Royce Rosario. 135 S SHARON AMITY RD, STE 100 28211 #035-06-1995 L1999 **OPH** *020 †35
TA, Nang Van. 3007 CENTRAL AVE, CENTRAL CARE CLINIC 28205 #941-01-1972 L1989 **IM** *020
TA, Nguyen Viet. 1433 EMERYWOOD DR, STE D 28210 #305-01-1996 L1999 **PD UCM** *020 †55
TAIT, David Loren. 1000 BLYTHE BLVD, CAROLINAS MEDICAL CTR 28203 #047-06-1987 L1998 **GO OBG** *020 †30
TAIT, Mary Rebecca Moore. 251 EASTWAY DR 28213 #047-06-1987 L1998 **PD** *020 †55
TAKAHASHI, Rebecca Lynn. 5435 PROSPERITY CHURCH RD, STE 1500 28269 #030-06-1998 L2001 **PD** *020 †55
TAM, Kim Hung. 1918 RANDOLPH RD, STE 440 28207 #051-04-1984 L1987 **IM** *020 †20
TAN, Ehrlich Cu. 3541 RANDOLPH RD, MECKLENBURG MEDICAL GROUP 28211 #017-20-2000 L2005 **CN** *020 †75
TANNER, David Cleon. 4539 HEDGEMORE DR, STE 100 28209 #012-01-1986 L1992 **IM ID** *020 †20
TANNER, Kenneth S, Jr. ■ 28210 #024-01-1943 L1947 **GS** *071 †85
TARRY, Wallace Clements. 1718 E 4TH ST, STE 701 28204 #036-07-1989 L2002 **VS** *020 †85
TART, James Milton, Jr. 2801 RANDOLPH RD 28211 #041-13-1953 L1957 **OBG** *071 †30
TATE, George Whaley, Jr. 6035 FAIRVIEW RD, TLC LASER CENTER 28210 #048-12-1968 L1977 **OPH** *020 †35
TATE, Tiffany Green. 501 BILLINGSLEY RD 28211 #038-41-1996 L2005 **P** *020 †75
TAUB, Neal Stephen. 2001 VAIL AVE 28207 #048-04-1987 L1992 **PM IM** *020 †60
TAUTJO, Edward Gale. 200 HAWTHORNE LN 28204 #748-11-1992 L1997 **IM** *020 †20
TAYAL, Vivek Shanti. 1000 BLYTHE BLVD, P O BOX 32861 28203 #051-04-1986 L1987 **EM** *020 †16
TAYLOR, Anna Holton Ralei. 4501 CAMERON VALLEY PKWY, STE 100 28211 #036-05-2002 L2005 **PD** *020
TAYLOR, Harvey Grant. 2711 RANDOLPH RD STE 100, CHARLOTTE, PA 28207 #036-07-1972 L1997 **IM HO** *020 †20
TAYLOR, Jerry Jurgen. ■ 28262 #036-08-1989 L1996 **EM** *020 †16
TAYLOR, John Bruce. 1025 MOREHEAD MEDICAL DR 28204 #051-04-1978 L1980 **OBG** *020 †30
TAYLOR, Kyla Nichelle. ■ 28212 #025-12-2005 **PD** *012
TAYLOR, Latimer Anthony. 7945 N TRYON ST, STE 112 28262 #036-01-1995 L1998 **IM** *020 †20
TAYLOR, Laura Leigh. 2630 E 7TH ST, STE 101 28204 #012-22-1998 L2001 **PD** *020 †55
TAYLOR, Lori Mccain. 200 GREENWICH RD 28211 #051-04-1996 L1999 **FM** *020 †18
TAYLOR, William Farnham. 3101 LATROBE DR, STE 100 28211 #035-20-1973 L1990 **EM IM** *071 †20,16
TAYLOR-PARRIS, Jo Ann. 3333 WILKINSON BLVD, CENTER, P O BOX 668093 28208 #566-01-1987 L2005 **FM** *020 †18 ‡
TCHEREMISSINE, Oleg V. 501 BILLINGSLEY RD 28211 #913-69-1989 L2006 **P** *020
TEAFF, Nancy Lee. 1524 E MOREHEAD ST 28207 #036-01-1978 L1982 **REN** *020 †30
TEAGUE, Alice B. 1023 EDGEHILL RD S 28207 #045-01-1985 L1989 **OBG** *020 †30
TEAGUE, Carmen Icard. 200 S COLLEGE ST, MECKLENBURG MEDICAL GROUP 28202 #036-01-2001 L2002 **IM** *020
TEDLA, Kedist. 200 HAWTHORNE LN, SPECIALISTS 28204 #025-07-1998 L2004 **IM** *020 †20
TEIGLAND, Chris Michael. 1023 EDGEHILL RD S 28207 #036-07-1980 L1987 **U OS** *020 †95
TEIGLAND, Lillian M. 6324 FAIRVIEW RD STE 201, SOUTH PARK FAMILY PHYS 28210 #036-07-1980 L1987 **FM** *020 †18
TEMPLE, Ana-Maria M. 1000 BLYTHE BLVD, DEPARTMENT OF PEDIATRICS 28203 #036-01-1999 L2005 **PD** *020 †55
TEOTIA, Sumeet Sorel. 11220 ELM LN, CHARLOTTE PLASTIC SURGERY 28277 #051-01-1996 L2005 **PS** *510 †85
TERNES, John Phillip. 10512 PARK RD, STE 101 28210 #023-12-1982 L1994 **HS AM** *020 †40
TERRELL, Mwatabu Maekundu. 3101 LATROBE DR, PLEDMONT EMERGENCY MEDICIN 28211 #047-05-1998 L2001 **EM** *020 †16
THAKKAR, Vipul Vinod. 200 QUEENS RD, STE 400 28204 #011-03-2001 L2007 **RO** *020 ‡
THALINGER, Alan Robt. 4501 CAMERON VALLEY PKWY, STE 200 28211 #051-01-1972 L1979 **ON IM** *020 †20
THERTULIEN, Raymond. 2711 RANDOLPH RD, STE 140 28207 #035-45-1994 L2007 **HO IM** *050 †20
THOMAS, Jerona Alysse. ■ 28216 #036-05-2008 *012
THOMAS, Patricia J. 1000 BLYTHE BLVD 28203 #036-01-1983 L1985 **GS** *040 †85
THOMAS, Sandra Joanne. ■ 28211 #048-13-1985 L1989 **NEP IM** *020 †20
THOMASON, Michael Hale. 1000 BLYTHE BLVD 28203 #036-01-1978 L1979 **GS TRS** *020 †85
THOMLEY, Alan Miles. 1001 BLYTHE BLVD STE 300 28203 #011-02-1977 L1978 **CD IM** *020 †20
THOMPSON, Donovan Aaron. 2001 VAIL AVE, MEDICAL ASSOCIATES 28207 #025-07-1994 L1997 **EM** *020 †16
THOMPSON, John Albert, Jr. 2310 RANDOLPH RD 28207 #036-05-1967 L1967 **D** *020 †15
THOMPSON, Myrna Ruby. 1200 JULES CT 28226 #041-13-1975 L1998 **CHP P** *020
THOMPSON, Robert Bruce. ■ 28262 #011-02-1987 L2004 **N** *075
THOMPSON, Stephen Brian. ■ 28226 #036-01-2007 **IM** *012
THOMSPON, W Chandler, Jr. 3535 RANDOLPH RD STE 201W 28211 #035-20-1950 L1955 **GS** *020 †85
TIDWELL, John Wm, II. 15830 JOHN J DELANEY DR 28277 #025-01-1965 L1972 **OBG** *020 †30
TIERNEY, Daniel Joseph. 2711 RANDOLPH RD, STE 400 28207 #038-06-1995 L2000 **NEP** *020 †20
TILLERSON, Elbert Stinson. 10628 PARK RD 28210 #045-01-2001 L2007 **OS** *020 †20,75
TILLETT, Charles W. 200 HAWTHORNE LN 28204 #023-07-1946 L1946 **OPH** *071 †35
TIMMONS, Barney F. ■ 28210 #045-01-1945 L1945 **OPH OTO** *071
TIMMONS, Otwell Dudley. 1000 BLYTHE BLVD, CAROLINAS MEDICAL CENTER 28203 #004-01-1984 L1993 **CCP PD** *040 †55
TOATLEY, Donald U. 1918 RANDOLPH RD, STE 670 28207 #010-01-1982 L2002 **OBG** *071 †30
TOBBEN, Paul John. 3623 LATROBE DR, STE 216 28211 #047-05-1984 L1991 **R** *020 †80
TOEBBE, Laura Sieffert. 3025 SPRINGBANK LN, STE 100 28226 #047-06-1992 L2003 **IM** *020 †20
TOMASZEWSKI, Christian A. 1000 BLYTHE BLVD, DEPT OF EMERGENCY MEDICINE 28203 #041-14-1986 L1988 **EM UM** *040 †16
TOMBOC, Marlah T. 130 PROVIDENCE RD 28207 #748-19-1992 L2002 **PDE** *020 †55 ‡
TOMCHO, John J. 7810 BALLANTYNE COMNS PKWY, STE 106 28277 #041-77-1998, ▲ L2004 **FM** *020 †18
TOOTHMAN, Donald E. 3623 LATROBE DR, STE 216 28211 #036-01-1983 L1984 **R** *020 †80
TOPPIN, Jean Michelle. 3025 SPRINGBANK LN, STE 100 28226 #035-47-2000 L2007 **IM** *020 †20
TOUSSAINT, James L. 15830 JOHN J DELANEY DR, CHARLOTTE 28277 #037-01-1984 L1989 **GE IM** *020 †20

■ = Address Information Privacy Protected

TOWNES, Pia Nichol. PO BOX 668034 28266 #036-08-1993 **P** *100

TRAN, Duc Quang, Jr. ■ 28270 #045-04-2006 **IM** *012

TRAXLER, Maryann. 6429 BANNINGTON RD, STE B 28226 #035-48-1982 L1997 **IM** *020 †20

TRENHOLM, James Andrew. PO BOX 32861 28232 #064-01-1996 *100

TRENT, Lori Ann. 1350 S KINGS DR, MYERS PARK PEDIATRICS 28207 #051-01-1997 L2001 **PD** *020 †55

TRIVEDI, Amit Raj. 1000 BLYTHE BLVD, MEDICAL EDUCATION BUILDING 28203 #001-02-2001 L2005 **EM** *100 †16

TRIVETTE, Dayna Denise. 7030 PINEVILLE MATTHEWS RD 28226 #036-05-1985 L1988 **PD** *020 †55

TROLLIP, Dawn Stanford. PO BOX 32861, DEPT OF OB/GYN 28232 #036-01-2005 **OBG** *012

TSAHAKIS, Paul John. 7825 BALLANTYNE COMNS PKWY, STE 150 28277 #051-04-1984 L1991 **ORS** *020 †40

TSAI, George S C. 2001 VAIL AVE 28207 #244-05-1970 L1977 **GP** *020

TSAI, William Tekang. 1000 BLYTHE BLVD, MEDICAL EDUCATION BLDG, 3 28203 #025-12-1995 L2006 **CCP** *100 †55

TUCKER, Paul C, Jr. 1918 RANDOLPH RD 28207 #012-01-1965 L1973 **GE** *071

TUCKER, Peter Loren. 300 BILLINGSLEY RD STE 105 28211 #036-05-1981 L2005 **PS GS** *020 †65 ‡

TUCKER, W Stuart, Jr. 330 BILLINGSLEY RD, STE 100 28211 #051-01-1978 L1984 **END IM** *020 †20

TUCKER, Walter Robt. 335 N CASWELL RD 28204 #036-01-1974 L1974 **FM** *020 †18

TUMLIN, James Alan. 2301 W MOREHEAD ST, SOUTHEAST RENAL ASSOCIATES 28208 #011-04-1986 L2005 **NEP** *020 †20

TURK, Peter Smith. 2104 RANDOLPH RD 28207 #017-20-1985 L1993 **SO GS** *020 †85

TURNER, Murray Wells. 2411 HATHERLY RD 28209 #036-05-1980 L1981 **NEP IM** *020 †20

TURNER-LAWRENCE, Danielle. ■ 28203 #025-01-2005 L2008 **EM** *012

TYNAN, Macdara Gerard. 1000 BLYTHE BLVD, CAROLINAS MEDICAL CENTER 28203 #539-04-1986 L2006 *020 †55

UGLAND, David Nels. 135 S SHARON AMITY RD, STE 100 28211 #048-04-1980 L1985 **OPH** *020 †35

ULLER, Jeffrey Kiyoshi. 1900 RANDOLPH RD 28207 #005-02-1997 L2001 **EM** *020 †16

ULMER, Travis Charles. ■ 28207 #038-40-2004 L2007 **EM** *020

UNDERWOOD, Gregory Alan. 1001 BLYTHE BLVD, STE 500 28203 #036-01-1983 L1985 **PUD IM** *020 †20

URAIZEE, Ashfaq. 2825 RANDOLPH RD 28211 #036-07-1987 L2000 **AN** *020 †05

URI, Daniel Steven. 3623 LATROBE DR, STE 216 28211 #005-02-1989 L1996 **DR** *020 †80

UTOH, Jancy Chukwuemeka. ■ 28273 #690-04-1997 L2005 **PD** *020

UZOMBA, Godwin Obinna. 10512 PARK RD, STE 210 28210 #308-03-1995 L2000 **IM** *020 †20

VADEN, Tracela Cameron. 14214 BALLANTYNE LAKE RD, STE 100 28277 #012-22-1997 L2003 **IM** *020 †20

VADNAIS, Paul Alfred. 1901 RANDOLPH RD 28207 #036-01-1979 L1984 **AN** *020 †05

VALDER, Odette Cianchini. 2017 E 7TH ST 28204 #048-04-1990 L1995 **P** *020 †75

VALDER, Stephen John. 14214 BALLANTYNE LAKE RD, PROVIDENCE PEDIATRICS 28277 #048-04-1992 L1995 **PD** *020 †55

VALLAT, Val Pierre. 3006 BAUCOM RD, STE 100 28269 #033-06-1988 L1996 **D** *020 †15

VANDERNOORD, Ronald. 101 E WT HARRIS BLVD, STE 5001 28262 #012-01-1992 L2001 **PM** *020 †60

VANDER NOOT, Ross Martin. ■ 28270 #001-02-2005 **EM** *012

VAN DER VEER, Craig A. 225 BALDWIN AVE 28204 #016-42-1979 L1986 **NS** *020 †25

VANDERWEL, Mark Roger. 130 PROVIDENCE RD 28207 #025-12-1997 L2000 **PDE** *020 †55

VANDIVER, Thomas Jackson. 150 PROVIDENCE RD 28207 #012-05-1976 L1980 **GYN** *020 †30

VAN GURP, John Ronald. 3111 SPRINGBANK LN, STE J 28226 #005-14-1987 L1991 **D DS** *020 †15 ‡

VAN VOORHIS, Kerry Thomas. 1000 BLYTHE BLVD, P O BOX 32861 28203 #011-03-1998 L2003 **PD** *020 †55

VAUGHAN, John Watt. 7810 PROVIDENCE RD, STE 102 28226 #051-04-1971 L1989 **FM OS** *020 †18

VAUGHN, Robert Dee, Jr. 101 E WT HARRIS BLVD, SPECIALISTS 28262 #047-07-1976 L1981 **GS** *020 †85

VELARDO, Bernard. 927 EAST BLVD 28203 #025-07-1984 L2000 **AN CCA** *020 †05

VELLIGAN, Christopher E. 3101 LATROBE DR 28211 #017-20-1995 L1997 **EM** *020 †16

VERMEULEN, Fred Donald. 4500 NORAS PATH RD, DILWORTH SURGICAL SPECLSTS 28226 #038-06-1976 L1982 **CRS GS** *020 †10,85

VERNON, Michael Stephen. 15110 JOHN J DELANEY DR, STE 200 28277 #036-05-1979 L1984 **FM FPG** *040 †18

VERONEE, Charles Durant. 1000 BLYTHE BLVD 28203 #036-07-1985 L1990 **AN GS** *020 †05

VERRILL, Matthew Millikan. ■ 28270 #038-43-2007 **FP** *012

VERROSS, William Edward. 15830 JOHN J DELANEY DR, STE 275 28277 #012-01-1974 L1994 **OBG** *020 †30

VERVILLE, Thomas David. 4539 HEDGEMORE DR, STE 100 28209 #039-01-1988 L1993 **ID IM** *020 †20

VESA, Allin Cornelius. 2001 VAIL AVE, MEDICAL ASSOCIATES 28207 #017-20-2000 L2003 **EM** *020 ‡

VICK, Ralph Nelson. 101 E WT HARRIS BLVD, THE CAROLINAS PLLC 28262 #036-01-1997 L2001 **U** *020 †95

VICK, Tara Michelle. 1000 BLYTHE BLVD DEPT OB, CAROLINAS MEDICAL CENTER 28203 #054-04-1997 L2001 **OBG** *040 †30

VIDWAN, Parampreet Singh. ■ 28269 #036-01-2005 L2008 **IM** *012

VILLIER, James Anthony. 330 BILLINGSLEY RD, STE 100 28211 #020-12-1975 L1976 **IM** *020 †20

VINCENT, Andrew Brian. PO BOX 32861, CAROLINE MED CTR RM 605 28232 #671-01-1989 **OTR** *100

VINCENT, Mark Anthony. 10840 BALLNTYN CMNS PKWY P 28277 #051-04-1992 L1995 **FM** *020 †18

VISSER, Philip Albert. 1000 BLYTHE BLVD, MAILING: P O BOX 32861 28203 #018-03-1976 L1983 **GS** *040 †85

VOCI, Vincent Eugene. 2620 E 7TH ST, VOCI CENTER 28204 #020-02-1974 L1985 **PS HS** *020 †85,65

VOELLINGER, David Compton. 2300 RANDOLPH RD STE A 28207 #001-02-1994 L2002 **GS** *020 †85

VOGELHUT, Mark Michael. 1901 RANDOLPH RD 28207 #036-01-1974 L2003 **AN** *020 †05 ‡

VOSS, Bruce Vincent. 1000 BLYTHE BLVD 28203 #035-47-1985 L1991 **AN CCA** *020 †05

VULLO, John Frank. ■ 28210 #028-46-2002 L2007 **AN** *100 †05

WACHTER, Francis Wilfred. 200 HAWTHORNE LN, INPATIENT MEDICINE 28204 #041-02-1960 L1974 **PTH** *071 †50

WADE, Ronald Vaughn. 1000 BLYTHE BLVD 28203 #045-01-1970 L1988 **OBG** *071 †30 ‡

WADLINGER, Joseph Allen. ■ 28269 #025-07-1982 L1983 **FM** *075

WAGNER, Kristin Elizabeth. 1918 RANDOLPH RD, STE 130 28207 #041-13-1996 L2003 **GS** *020 †85

WAGONER, David Kirk. 2711 RANDOLPH RD STE 501 28207 #036-01-1971 1971 **PD** *020 †55

WAGSTAFF, Joseph Edward. 1628 E MOREHEAD ST 28207 #016-02-1986 L2004 **PD** *050 †19,55

WAIT, Dwight Wm, III. ■ 28207 #036-01-1971 L1971 **IM ADM** *020

WALDMAN, Gary David. 10042 PARK CEDAR DR STE B 28210 #016-01-1977 L1982 **D** *020 †15

WALDROP, Norman Erskine, III. ■ 28210 #001-02-2006 **ORS** *012

WALKER, Andrew Wm. 300 BILLINGSLEY RD, STE 105 28211 #047-05-1960 L1968 **PS HS** *071 †85,65

WALKER, Anne English. 149 PROVIDENCE RD, DILWORTH PEDIATRICS 28207 #036-01-1980 L1983 **PD ADL** *020 †55

WALKER, Cheryl Lynn. 1404 BEATTIES FORD RD, STE 103 28216 #036-07-1983 L2007 **AI IM** *020 †20,03

WALKER, Courtnye Allyson. ■ 28270 #045-01-2002 L2007 **TS** *012

WALKER, Gena Marie. 1000 BLYTHE BLVD, CAROLINAS HOSPITALIST GROU 28203 #055-01-2000 L2007 **MPD** *020

WALKER, L G. 1001 BLYTHE BLVD, STE 602 28203 #001-02-1956 L1969 **GS** *071 †85

WALKER, Phillip Jackson. 2711 RANDOLPH RD, STE 400 28207 #051-01-1964 L1977 **NEP IM** *020 †20

WALKER, William Alfred. 2015 RANDOLPH RD, STE 201 28207 #036-01-1978 L1985 **CRS GS** *020 †10,85 ‡

WALLACE, Eric Lee. 1918 RANDOLPH RD, CHARLOTTE SURG GRP STE 130 28207 #047-05-2001 L2006 **GS** *020

WALLACE, James Wm Scott. 3303 LATROBE DR 28211 #055-01-1983 L1987 **P** *020 †75

WALLACE, Lester B, Jr. 1000 BLYTHE BLVD 28203 #047-07-1973 L1977 **OBG** *020

WALLENHAUPT, Stephen Lee. 301 HAWTHORNE LN 28204 #036-05-1978 L1982 **TS VS** *020 †85,90

WALLER, Elizabeth Rachel. 10520 PARK RD 28210 #041-15-2002 L2007 **OPH** *020

WALSH, Joseph Michael. 1900 RANDOLPH RD, STE 1010 28207 #041-09-1982 L1993 **N** *020 †75

WALTERS, Kenneth Christia. ■ 28205 #045-01-2005 **GS** *012

WALTHALL, Julius B, Jr. 10000 PARK CEDAR DR 28210 #036-01-1978 L1982 **FM EM** *020 †16,18

WANG, Eric Anthony. 3816 LATROBE DR, CHARLOTTE RADIOLOGY 28211 #023-07-1999 L2005 **VIR** *020 †80

WARD, Simon Vivian. 14215 BALLANTYNE CORPRT PL, STE 110 28277 #021-05-1941 L1942 **OBG** *071 †30

WARD, Simon Vivian, III. 1718 E 4TH ST, STE 307 28204 #021-05-1981 L1987 **OBG GYN** *071 †30

WARD, William Alan. 1025 MOREHEAD MEDICAL DR, STE 300 28204 #041-12-1979 L1985 **ORS HS** *020 †40

WARES, Catherine Marie. ■ 28210 #036-01-2007 **EM** *012

WARNER, Charles Ernest. 4501 CAMERON VALLEY PKWY, STE 100 28211 #036-07-1958 L1958 **PD** *071 †55

WARREN, Casper Carl. 200 HAWTHORNE LN 28204 #036-01-1959 L1959 **AN** *071 †05

WARREN, Eric Thomas. 1000 BLYTHE BLVD, CMC-FAMILY MEDICINE 28203 #036-01-2003 L2005 **FSM** *020 †18

WASHBURN, Kurt Richard. 1900 RANDOLPH RD, STE 1010 28207 #016-43-1994 L2004 **N** *020 †75

WASHINGTON, Boyd Vindell. 2001 VAIL AVE, MEDICAL ASSOCIATES 28207 #051-01-1990 L1997 **EM** *020 †16

WASHINGTON, Hattina Denis. ■ 28214 #012-01-2006 **PD** *012

WATERHOUSE, Robert L, Jr. 10520 PARK RD, STE 140 28210 #016-06-1985 L1999 **U** *040 †95

WATKINS, Carlton Gunter. ■ 28209 #028-02-1943 L1943 **PD** *072 †55

WATKINS, Garth Stephen. ■ 28277 #036-01-2008 *012

WATKINS, James Allison. 10344 PARK RD, SPECIALISTS 28210 #047-07-1976 L1981 **GS VS** *020 †85

WATLING, Bradley A. 2001 VAIL AVE, MEDICAL ASSOCIATES 28207 #025-07-1996 L1999 **EM** *020 †16

WATSON, Daniel Lee. 201 QUEENS RD 28204 #023-07-1990 L1996 **U** *020 †95

WATSON, David Wm. 1900 RANDOLPH RD 28207 #035-15-1964 L1973 **U** *071 †95

WATSON, Pierce Eugene. 4458 ANTELOPE LN, P O BOX 480190 28269 #041-13-1967 L1968 **EM FM** *020 †18

WATTENBARGER, John M. 1025 MOREHEAD MEDICAL DR, STE 300 28204 #048-12-1988 L1994 **ORS** *020 †40

WATTERSON, Paul A. 2215 RANDOLPH RD, CHARLOTTE PLASTIC SURGERY 28207 #010-01-1982 L1984 **PS GS** *020 †85,65

WATTS, Hope Whyte. 8420 UNIVERSITY EXC PRK DR, DRIVE STE 850 28262 #041-07-1988 L1998 **FM** *020 †18

WATTS, Larry Thos. 1001 BLYTHE BLVD, STE 300 28203 #036-05-1987 L1997 **TS** *020 †85,90

WAXMAN, Dael Martin. 5516 CENTRAL AVE 28212 #019-02-1985 L1996 **FM** *040 †18

WEBSTER, Joel S. 309 S SHARON AMITY RD, STE 200 28211 #023-01-1953 L1973 **CD PDC** *071 †20

WEBSTER, Leslie Tillotson. 1918 RANDOLPH RD, STE 130 28207 #038-06-1994 L1999 **GS** *020 †85

WEEMS, Larry Byrum, II. 3101 LATROBE DR, PIEDMONT EMERGENCY MEDICIN 28211 #012-01-1990 L1993 **FM** *020 †18

WEIDA, Carol Jean. 1000 BLYTHE BLVD 28203 #041-14-1990 L1992 **PTH** *020 †50

WEIDMAN, Frederick H, III. 135 S SHARON AMITY RD, STE 100 28211 #055-01-1984 L1990 **OPH** *020 †35

WEIDNER, Gregory Robt. 15110 JOHN J DELANEY DR, MECKLENBURG MEDICAL 28277 #035-45-1991 L1995 **IM** *020 †20

WEIDNER, Julianne Falwell. 4525 CAMERON VALLEY PKWY, STE 3100 28211 #035-45-1992 L1995 **IM** *020 †20

WEILBACH, Heidi. 101 E WT HARRIS BLVD, SPECIALISTS 28262 #028-02-2000 L2005 **GS** *020 †85

WEINGARTEN, Norden Miles. 1726 E SEVENTH ST 28204 #023-01-1976 L1987 **ID IM** *071 †20

WEINRIB, David Allan. 1350 S KINGS DR 28207 #001-02-1989 L1995 **ID IM** *020 †20

WEISNER, Bradley Kent. 201 QUEENS RD 28204 #036-01-1985 L1994 **U** *020 †95

WELBORNE, Barry Mc Neil. 1001 BLYTHE BLVD, STE 500 28203 #036-01-1967 L1967 **CD IM** *020 †20

WELCH, Lillian Paulette. ■ 28269 #051-04-1992 L1996 **HO** *020 †20

WELSHOFER, John Arthur. 14135 BALLANTYNE CORP PL, CORPORATE PLACE 28277 #038-41-1990 L1994 **PM** *020 †60

WERNIKOFF, Stuart Yale. 2015 RANDOLPH RD STE 210 28207 #035-06-1983 L1984 **D** *020 †15
WERTH, Thomas Edward. 15830 JOHN J DELANEY DR, CHARLOTTE 28277 #019-02-1985 L1992 **GE IM** *020 †20
WESLEY, David Odell. 401 N TRYON ST, STE 700 28202 #005-18-1979 L1980 **IM** *020 †20
WESTFALL, Amanda J. PO BOX 32861, CAROLINAS MED CTR 28232 #048-12-2007 **EM** *012
WESTON, Steven Arthur. 2131 AYRSLEY TOWN BLVD, STE 200 28273 #016-45-1986 L1991 **GS VS** *020 †85
WEYERS, Cheryl Marie. 1001 BLYTHE BLVD STE 500, MEDICAL CENTER PLAZA 28203 #041-12-1999 L2007 **PCC** *020 †20
WHALEN, Joseph Benedict. 1000 BLYTHE BLVD 28203 #038-43-1986 L1998 **FM** *020 †18
WHEELER, Anthony H. 3711 LATROBE DR, STE 530 28211 #036-01-1977 L1985 **N** *020 †75
WHELAN, Frederick J. ■ 28210 #035-08-1950 **R** *071
WHELAN, Joseph Gibson, Jr. 3816 LATROBE DR, CHARLOTTE RADIOLOGY 28211 #020-02-1963 L1988 **DR GE** *020 †80
WHELAN, Joseph Gibson, III. 1524 E MOREHEAD ST 28207 #020-12-1990 L2004 **OBG** *020 †30
WHITE, Garrett Douglas. 2301 W MOREHEAD ST, STE B 28208 #019-02-1997 L2007 **NEP** *020 †20
WHITE, Lena Katherine. 5717 ALBEMARLE RD, 249 BILLINGSLEY ROAD 28212 #036-01-1981 L1982 **FM** *020 †18
WHITE, Mack Willis, III. 7030 PINEVILLE MATTHEWS RD, SOUTH CHARLOTTE PRIMARY CA 28210 #036-01-1979 L1980 **IM** *020 †20
WHITE, Patricia Schaffer. 5516 CENTRAL AVE 28212 #024-01-1986 L1991 **FM** *020 †18
WHITE, Richard L, Jr. 1000 BLYTHE BLVD 28203 #035-01-1986 L1995 **GS SO** *020 †85
WHITE, Thomas Hugh. 1718 E 4TH ST # 30 28204 #036-07-1959 L1959 **OBG** *020 †30
WHITE, William Elliott. ■ 28210 #036-05-1946 L1947 **PD** *071 †55
WHITESIDE, Daniela. 817 E MOREHEAD ST, STE 200 28202 #409-36-1996 L2005 **OPH** *020
WHITESIDE, Donald C. 5435 PROSPERITY CHURCH RD, STE 2200A 28269 #036-01-1980 L1984 **GYN** *020 †30 ‡
WHITESIDE, John Harvey. 150 PROVIDENCE RD 28207 #065-01-1957 L1973 **GYN** *071
WHITESIDES, Daniel Baxter. 1524 E MOREHEAD ST, REACH 28207 #036-07-1976 L1985 **OBG** *020 †30
WHITFIELD, John David. ■ 28205 #047-06-2007 **GS** *012
WHITTEN, Mary Kathryn. 1025 MOREHEAD MEDICAL DR 28204 #012-01-1993 L1997 **OBG** *020 †30
WICKER, Bobby Thos, Jr. 1025 MOREHEAD MEDICAL DR, STE 400 28204 #020-12-1991 L1995 **OBG** *020 †30
WILDER, Brian John. 927 EAST BLVD 28203 #051-01-1984 L1987 **AN PMM** *020 †05
WILKINSON, Henry A, III. ■ 28211 #012-01-1960 L1974 **PTH** *071 †50,28
WILLIAMS, Andrea M. 7006 SHANNON WILLOW RD 28226 #035-06-1994 L2001 **OTO A** *020 †45
WILLIAMS, Charles D, Jr. ■ 28270 #036-07-1950 L1954 **PUD IM** *071 †20
WILLIAMS, Jerome E, Jr. 1718 E 4TH ST STE 501, MID CAROLINA CADIOLOGY,P.A 28204 #035-19-1989 L1996 **CD** *020 †20
WILLIAMS, John Everett. 927 EAST BLVD 28203 #012-01-1984 L2004 **AN** *020 †05
WILLIAMS, Laramie Ann. 7800 PROVIDENCE RD, STE 203 28226 #011-03-1987 L1990 **PD** *020 †55
WILLIFORD, John K, Jr. 1901 RANDOLPH RD 28207 #036-05-1979 L1986 **AN** *020 †05
WILSON, Candace Iman. ■ 28277 #036-05-2008 *012
WILSON, Daniel Culp. ■ 28209 #036-05-2007 **IM** *012
WILSON, Diana Lorraine. ■ 28226 #019-02-2002 L2007 **OBG** *020
WILSON, Henry Van P, III. 3535 RANDOLPH RD 28211 #023-07-1961 L1964 **GS TS** *071 †85
WILSON, James Michael. 441 N WENDOVER RD 28211 #038-45-1985 L1995 **RHU IM** *020 †20
WILSON, Michael Brian. 1000 BLYTHE BLVD, DIVISION OF PEDIATRICS INT 28203 #045-04-1990 L2005 **CCP PD** *020 †55
WILSON, Michelle Janeen. ■ 28226 #038-40-2005 **IM** *012
WING, Richard Lee. 1524 E MOREHEAD ST 28207 #036-01-1976 L1976 **GYN** *020 †30
WINKLER, Cornelia Anne. 200 HAWTHORNE LN, PRESBYTERIAN INPATIENT PED 28204 #409-21-1986 L2003 **PN** *020 †55
WINTER, Ann Leigh. 100 N TRYON ST, PHYSICIANS 28202 #045-01-2000 L2003 **IM** *020 †20
WINTER, Eric Herbert. 1620 SCOTT AVE 28203 #035-01-1983 L2001 **AN** *020 †05
WISE, Christopher Lynn. ■ 28216 #028-34-2002 L2007 **ORS** *100
WISE, Daniel Edwin. 125 BALDWIN AVE, # 204 28204 #036-40-1969 L1972 **CD** *020 †20
WISE, Fred Eugene, Jr. 200 HAWTHORNE LN 28204 #051-04-1945 L1954 **R** *071 †80
WITCHER, Julie Rebecca. ■ 28204 #012-01-2005 **PD** *012
WITHROW, Jerry Wayne. 9332 S TRYON ST 28273 #036-01-1980 L1983 **FM** *020 †18
WITTLER, Mary A. 1000 BLYTHE BLVD, MEB 3RD FLOOR 28203 #048-13-2000 L2003 **EM ETX** *020 †16
WOLFSON, Kenneth Adam. 1701 EAST BLVD, CHARLOTTE RADIOLOGY 28203 #016-02-1994 L2000 **DR** *020 †80
WOLTZ, John H E. 150 PROVIDENCE RD 28207 #041-01-1942 L1942 **GYN** *071 †30
WONG, Allen. 1701 ABBEY PL, CHARLOTTE INTERNAL MEDICIN 28209 #023-12-1987 L1997 **LM** *020 †20
WOOD, Hobart Rowe. 618 N COLLEGE ST 28202 #056-06-1944 L1968 **FOP PTH** *062 †50
WOOD, James Edward, III. 8936 BLAKENEY PROFESSNL DR 28277 #004-01-1996 L1997 **NEP** *020 †20
WOOD, Paula Lee. 200 HAWTHORNE LN, C/O PICS TEAM 28204 #045-01-1987 L2001 **IM** *020 †20
WOOD, Stacey Allen, Jr. 1718 E 4TH ST STE 707 28204 #036-07-1983 L1987 **OBG** *020 †30
WOODARD, Warden Lewis, III. 101 E WT HARRIS BLVD, STE 1214 28262 #036-01-1981 L1983 **ON** *020 †20
WOODSON, James Vincent. 1000 BLYTHE BLVD 28203 #051-01-2003 L2006 **EM** *020 †16
WOODWARD, M Bryan, III. 6115 PARK SOUTH DR STE 100 28210 #045-04-1986 L1995 **EM FM** *020 †18
WOODY, Joe Harris. 4335 COLWICK RD 28211 #036-05-1958 L1958 **OPH** *020 †35
WOOLLEN, Thomas Hayes, Jr. 200 GREENWICH RD 28211 #036-05-1991 L1993 **FM** *020 †18
WORRELL, Alanna Jones. 1001 BLYTHE BLVD, MEDICAL CENTER PLAZA 28203 #001-02-1997 L1999 **IM** *020 †20
WORTMAN, Wm Jerome, Jr. 200 HAWTHORNE LN 28204 #036-05-1964 L1964 **GYN** *071 †30
WRENN, Richard Nickles. ■ 28210 #036-07-1947 L1955 **ORS** *071 †40
WRIGHT, Nioke Paula. 8800 N TRYON ST 28262 #024-07-2004 L2007 **IM** *100 †20
WRIGHT-ETTER, Pamela. 435 N WENDOVER RD 28211 #038-43-1982 L1988 **P PFP** *075 †20
WRINKLE, Geoffrey Thomas. 10000 PARK CEDAR DR 28210 #051-01-1993 L1996 **FM** *020 †18
WU, Jack. 3101 LATROBE DR, STE 100 28211 #019-15-1997 L2003 **EM** *020 †16
WYCKOFF, Robert Lewis. ■ 28215 #005-12-1958 L1959 **P LM** *040
WYMER, Kasey Elizabeth. ■ 28204 #036-01-2006 **PD** *012

WYNN, Michelle Hewlett. 1918 RANDOLPH RD STE 670, P O BOX 668093 28207 #036-01-1980 L1980 **PD** *020 †55
WYNN, Richard Thos. 1132 LINDA LN, STE 100 28211 #036-05-1992 L1995 **FM** *020 †18
WYRICK, Susan Davis. 4601 PARK RD, STE 100 28209 #021-05-1987 L1995 **PD** *020 †55
WYTTENBACH, Ann Garnett. 7810 PROVIDENCE RD, STE 102 28226 #019-02-1989 L1993 **FM** *020 †20
WYTTENBACH, Rebecca Jean. 1000 BLYTHE BLVD 28203 #019-02-1992 L1995 **PD** *020 †55
YANCEY, Joel Benton. ■ 28270 #036-05-2008 *012
YANG, Che-Ming. 1901 RANDOLPH RD 28207 #011-02-1986 L1989 **AN** *020 †05
YARBOROUGH, Jesse G, Jr. 927 EAST BLVD 28203 #036-01-1978 L1979 **AN** *020
YAVORSKI, Robert Thos. 1001 BLYTHE BLVD STE 500, MEDICAL CENTER PLAZA 28203 #021-01-1987 L1996 **GE** *020 †20
YAVORSKI, Sarah Schlater. 1718 E 4TH ST, STE 307 28204 #021-01-1983 L1996 **OBG** *020 †30
YEBOAH, Christiana. ■ 28210 #024-05-2003 **GS** *100
YEH, Stephen Mingjye. 2001 VAIL AVE, MEDICAL ASSOCIATES 28207 #024-07-2000 L2003 **EM** *020 †16
YEOMANS, Jay Anthony. 501 BILLINGSLEY RD 28211 #422-01-1987 L1991 **P N** *020 †75
YEVAK, Richard John, Jr. 927 EAST BLVD 28203 #041-13-1986 L1994 **AN** *020 †05
YOUNG, Edwin Samuels, Jr. 1000 BLYTHE BLVD, CAROLINAS MEDICAL CENTER 28203 #036-05-1985 L1987 **PD CCM** *020 †55
YOUNG, Frank Alfred. ■ 28210 #067-01-1956 L1987 **FM** *071 †85
YOUNG, John Adam. 3315 SPRINGBANK LN, STE 204 28226 #036-01-1960 L1960 **OPH** *071 †35
YOUNG, Kisha Rochelle. ■ 28270 #011-03-2006 L2007 **FP** *012
YOUNG, Timothy Paul. 1100 BLYTHE BLVD, CHARLOTTE INSTITUTE OF REH 28203 #021-01-2002 L2006 **PM** *100 †60
YOUNT, James Alvin. 1900 BRUNSWICK AVE, MECKLENBURG MEDICAL GROUP 28207 #036-01-1966 L1966 **IM CD** *020 †20
YUN, Mary Meiling. ■ 28226 #025-01-1992 L1996 **PD** *075
ZASTROW, Joseph Francis. 1437 SCOTT AVE 28203 #056-06-1987 L1988 **FM** *020 †18
ZBAN, Thomas Andrew. 1901 RANDOLPH RD, PRESBYTERIAN ORTHO HOSP 28207 #055-02-1996 L2001 **DR** *020 †80
ZBAN, William Matthew. 1900 RANDOLPH RD 28207 #055-02-1989 L1990 **EM** *020 †16
ZBINDEN, Louis H, III. 1416 E MOREHEAD ST, STE 1416 28204 #048-12-1990 L1993 **GS VS** *020 †85
ZENG, Guangbin. 1918 RANDOLPH RD, STE 670 28207 #243-52-1985 L2001 **FM** *020 †18 ‡
ZERKLE, Andrew Joseph. 150 PROVIDENCE RD 28207 #038-41-1993 L1997 **OBG** *072 †30
ZIMMER, Mary Jean. 10508 PARK RD, PINEVILLE 28210 #011-04-1985 L1988 **PD** *020 †55
ZIMMERMAN, Steven Elliot. 401 N TRYON ST, STE 800 28202 #035-20-1976 L1979 **ON IM** *071 †20
ZIMMERN, Samuel Hyams. 1001 BLYTHE BLVD, STE 300 28203 #023-07-1974 L1982 **ICE CD** *020 †20
ZINK, Irene Marie. 1801 ROZZELLES FERRY RD, CMC - BIDDLEPOINT 28208 #038-41-1996 L1997 **FM** *020 †18
ZIPKIN, Dietlinde Wohrer. 6725 FAIRVIEW RD STE A 28210 #154-07-1981 L1994 **IM** *020 †20
ZORET, Carol Lynne. 10030 PARK CEDAR DR, STE 100 28210 #051-04-1986 L1987 **IM** *020 †20
ZUGER, James H. 3816 LATROBE DR, CHARLOTTE RADIOLOGY 28211 #024-05-1973 L1977 **R** *020 †80
ZUKAITIS, Mark Guy. 2825 RANDOLPH RD 28211 #030-05-1975 L1975 **AN** *020 †05
ZWENG, Thomas Nelson. 200 HAWTHORNE LN, BOX 33549 28204 #005-14-1984 L1995 **GS** *020 †85

CHEROKEE – SWAIN

BULLOCK, Ann Kathleen. DHHS PHS IHS 28719 #054-04-1987 L1990 **FM** *020 †18
FARRELL, Mary Anne. HOSPITAL RD 28719 #041-01-1976 L1986 **ADM FM** *030 †18
FREE, Lisa Holbrook. 1194 NEWFOUND GAP HWY 28719 #040-06-2000 L2004 **FM** *020 †18
MILLER, Frank Black. 59 ECHOTA CHURCH RD 28719 #025-01-1974 L1975 **CHP P** *020 †75
ROSS, Robert Edward, Jr. CHEROKEE INDIAN HOSPITAL, 1 HOSPITAL RD 28719 #027-01-2000 L2001 **FM** *020 †18
TOEDT, Dominique M Gooby. CALLER BOX C-268, CHEROKEE INDIAN HOSPITAL 28719 #035-48-1993 L2000 **IM** *020 †20

CHERRY POINT – CRAVEN

KERTH, William J. PSC 8023, BLDG 4389, BEAUFORT RD 28533 #038-40-1953 L1953 **TS** *020 †85,90

CHERRYVILLE – GASTON

AGNER, Marshal E. ■ 28021 #036-07-1952 L1954 **GP** *071
WHITE, Thomas Rhyne. 112 OAK ST 28021 #036-07-1980 L1982 **FM** *020 †18
YOUNG, Charles Richard. 120 S MOUNTAIN ST, CAROMONT FAMILY MEDICINE 28021 #036-08-1989 L1990 **FM** *020 †18 ‡

CHINA GROVE – ROWAN

BURKE, Anthony L. ■ 28023 #055-01-1982 L1989 **GS VS** *020 †85
HORNSBY, Robert Anderson. 308 E CENTERVIEW ST 28023 #036-08-1992 L2004 **FM** *020 †18
TROYER, Eric Chas. 302 S MAIN ST 28023 #045-04-1988 L1995 **FM** *020 †18
WALKER, Orrin Abraham. 308 E CENTERVIEW ST, SOUTH ROWAN FAMILY PRACTIC 28023 #045-04-1997 L2000 **FM** *020 †18

CHINQUAPIN – DUPLIN

BOYETTE, Edward Lee. 2699 S. NC 41 & 50 28521 #036-05-1954 L1954 **FM FPG** *071 †18

CHOCOWINITY – BEAUFORT

BENTZEL, Carl Johan. ■ 27817 #001-02-1958 L1984 **NEP IM** *071 †20

■ = Address Information Privacy Protected

CHEN, Grace W. ■ 27817 #748-10-1984 L1995 **FM** *020 †18
CINOCCA, Ronald Joe. ■ 27817 #047-05-1975 L1976 **EM** *020 †20
FREEMAN, Melissa Allison. ■ 27817 #035-15-2006 **IM** *012
GALUSZKA, Albin A. ■ 27817 #024-07-1942 L1970 **U** *071 †95
GERRITSEN, Roy Wm. ■ 27817 #035-09-1960 L1961 **GS** *071 †85
RUCQUOI, Marc Guillaume. 740 BRAGAW LN, CHOCOWINITY FAMILY CARE 27817 #050-02-1998 L2005 **FM** *020 †18
TINGELSTAD, Jon Bunde. ■ 27817 #024-01-1960 L1976 **PD PDC** *071 †55

CLAREMONT – CATAWBA

HAWKINS, Mark Douglas. 3221 W MAIN ST, CIAREMONT FAMILY MEDICINE 28610 #001-06-1990 L1996 **FM** *020 †18
LARSON, Sean Mark. 2890 S LOOKOUT ST, CLAREMONT FAMILY PRACTICE 28610 #026-04-1999 L2006 **FM** *020 †18
RICHARDSON, Patrice Tracy. ■ 28610 #047-07-2006 **PD** *012
ROSS, James Miller. 3319 S LOOKOUT ST 28610 #047-06-1963 L1965 **FM** *020 †18

CLAYTON – JOHNSTON

ABDEL-KHALEK, Ihab A A. 11708 US HIGHWAY 70 W 27520 #915-08-1976 L1999 **PDE** *020
ABU-SALHA, Mohammad Y. 112 S ELLINGTON ST, JOHNSTON PSYCHIATRIC ASSOC 27520 #528-03-1983 L1998 **P** *020 †75
ANDERSON, Russell Dean. ■ 27527 #036-07-1984 L1998 **IM HEM** *020 †20
ARTMAN, Michael Scott. 555 MEDICAL PARK PL, PEDIATRICS 27520 #051-01-1993 L1996 **PD** *020 †55
ATKESON, Benjamin Granger. 555 MEDICAL PARK PL, STE 201 27520 #010-02-1996 L2004 **IM** *020 †20
BASS, Thomas Rector. 221 BARBOUR ST 27520 #047-06-1957 L1960 **GP OS** *071
BERGWALL, Anne Parker. 17 N ASHLYN DR 27527 #050-02-1991 L2001 **AN** *020 †05
BEST, Debra Lynn. 555 MEDICAL PARK PL, STE 208 27520 #016-06-2001 L2004 **PD** *020 †55
BRADSHAW, Preston H, Jr. 215 MUIRFIELD LN 27527 #048-07-1995 L1998 **FM** *071 †95
BURNETT-LEWIS, Tara Laver. 126 ALEAH CT 27520 #047-07-1995 L1998 **FM** *020 †18
BUTLER, Richard Carson. ■ 27527 #007-02-1994 L2001 **EM** *020 †16
CAPPS, Michael Thomas. 100 GUY RD 27520 #036-01-2000 L2004 **MPD** *020
CARTER, Eric Gordon. 8484 US HIGHWAY 70 W 27520 #011-02-1987 L1989 **IM NTR** *050 †20
DEGELE, Bridget Mc Namara. 555 MEDICAL PARK PL, PEDIATRICS 27520 #036-07-2000 L2003 **PD** *020 †55
FRIEDMAN, Kenneth Stan. 11618 US HIGHWAY 70 W #204 27520 #028-02-1979 L2001 **CD** *020
GRING, Christian N. 555 MEDICAL PARK PL, STE 201 27520 #051-01-1999 L2006 **CD** *100 †20
HARRIS, Brian Keith. 236 BUTTERNUT DR 27520 #036-05-1992 L2000 **FM** *020 †18
JACKSON-CLARK, Juliana S. 555 MEDICAL PARK PL, PEDIATRICS 27520 #036-01-2001 L2003 **PD** *020 †55
JANIS, Eric Thomas. 555 MEDICAL PARK PL, STE 208 27520 #023-07-1989 L1996 **CD** *020 †20
JONES, Eric Crayton. 555 MEDICAL PARK PL, STE 208 27520 #055-02-1999 L2002 **PD** *020 †55
JONES, Richard Mack. 555 MEDICAL PARK PL, STE 200 27520 #012-01-1989 L1997 **OTO** *020 †45
JONES, Sharmila M. 555 MEDICAL PARK PL, STE 208 27520 #055-02-1999 L2002 **PD** *020 †55
KREMER, Glenda Marie. 208 PARKRIDGE DR, FAMILY PRACTICE 27527 #038-41-2002 L2006 **FM** *020 †18
KRYN, Edward Thadde. 101 WINDING WOOD DR 27520 #065-06-1975 L1994 **FM** *020 †18 ‡
MANN, Larry Douglas. 555 MEDICAL PARK PL, PEDIATRICS 27520 #055-02-1983 L1987 **PD** *020 †55
MC DONAGH, Thomas Henry M. PO BOX 19 27528 #539-06-1976 L2000 **FM** *020 †18
MEEHAN, Joan Nemy. 100 GUY RD 27520 #038-75-1984, ▲ L1987 **FM** *020 †18
MELTON, Jameelah Ayesha. 555 MEDICAL PARK PL, PEDIATRICS 27520 #036-08-2004 L2007 **PD** *020 †55
OVERCASH, Harold Payne. 555 MEDICAL PARK PL, PEDIATRICS 27520 #036-01-1979 L1982 **PD** *020 †55
PATEL, Rakesh Amrutlal. ■ 27527 #495-22-1995 L2003 **IM** *020 †20
PHALEN, Elizabeth Ann. ■ 27520 #539-02-1990 L2001 **FM** *020 †18
ROSE, Virgil Lowell, Jr. 555 MEDICAL PARK PL, STE 207 27520 #039-01-1980 L1989 **ON HEM** *020 †20
TALERICO, Paul. 716 NEUSE RIDGE DR 27527 #035-15-1989 L1994 **FM** *020 †18
TORTORA, Frank. 555 MEDICAL PARK PL, STE 207 27520 #561-17-1940 L1943 **GP PHP** *071
VAIDYA, Bhavna P. 105 S ELLINGTON ST 27520 #495-37-1999 L2004 **FM** *020 †18
WEFALD, Franklin Chas. 555 MEDICAL PARK PL, STE 201 27520 #023-07-1985 L1987 **CD IM** *020 †20
WILLIAMS, Charles Edwards. 236 BUTTERNUT DR 27520 #036-05-1997 L2000 **FM** *020 †18

CLEMMONS – FORSYTH

AYOUB, Joseph Samy. ■ 27012 #048-16-2004 L2007 **DR** *100
BABCOCK, Michael John. ■ 27012 #036-05-2007 **IM** *012
BEEKMAN, Daniel Jerome. ■ 27012 #038-43-2004 L2006 **IM** *100 †20
BELLAMY, Henry M, Jr. 7604 PENLAND CT 27012 #051-04-1958 L2001 **RO END** *030 †20
BOYD, Michael Brian. ■ 27012 #036-05-2002 L2008 **PCC** *012 †20
BRAME, Robert William. 1033 PRESTWICK CT 27012 #036-01-1955 L1955 **OBG** *040 †30
BRAMMER, Glenn Michael. ■ 27012 #055-02-2004 L2004 **CD** *012 †20
BUJARD, Robert Saml. ■ 27012 #048-04-1958 L1986 **P** *030
CHILDS, David Dixon. ■ 27012 #036-05-2001 L2006 **DR** *020 †80
COBBETT, Ethel Marie. ■ 27012 #047-20-2007 **FP** *012
CRANDELL, Jason Malcolm. 2511 NEUDORF RD STE D, PSIMED, PA 27012 #036-05-1978 L1979 **P** *020
DELISIO, Kesah Lynn. ■ 27012 #036-08-2007 **EM** *012
DORT, Charles Webb. ■ 27012 #041-09-1984 L1988 **P** *020
DYAL-DOTTIN, Kamal. ■ 27012 #566-01-1979 L1992 **IM** *012
EDWARDS, Henry Douglas. ■ 27012 #012-22-2007 **PTH** *012
ELLIS, Ezra Daniel. ■ 27012 #036-05-2003 L2007 **HMP** *012 †50
FLOCH, Howard Fred. 4478 MORATOCK LN, SAMARITAN HOSPITAL 27012 #041-09-1972 L1996 **GS EM** *020 †85
FLORACK, Bridget B. ■ 27012 #048-14-1990 L1994 **AN** *074 †05

FLORACK, James A. ■ 27012 #048-14-1990 L1994 **AN** *020 †05
FORTNER, Michael Cameron. ■ 27012 #041-14-2006 **EM** *012
GEIER, Christine Elise. ■ 27012 #036-05-2008 **P** *020
GIROUARD, Michael Paul. 2554 LEWISLVILLE CLEMMNS RD, STE 109 27012 #021-06-1980 L2005 **GPM** *020
HARMON, Lisa. ■ 27012 #036-05-2008 *012
HORTON, Paul Edward. 3841 TANGLE OAK DR 27012 #048-02-1976 L1977 **EM** *020 †16
JAO, Geoffrey Te. ■ 27012 #748-01-2001 L2007 **IM** *020 †20
JOHNSON, Alex Charles. ■ 27012 #040-02-2003 L2007 **CD** *012 †20
KALALA, Jamal M. 6861 ROLLINGWOOD DR 27012 #915-04-1981 L1992 **NEP IM** *020 †20
KASELIS, Michael, Jr. ■ 27012 #038-45-1997 L1998 **DR** *020
KIRLEY, Stephen Walter. 2554 LEWISVILLE CLEMMNS RD, STE 310 27012 #036-05-1975 L1975 **P** *020 †75
LEWIS, John Meriwether. ■ 27012 #051-01-1976 L1982 **AN** *072 †05
LIU, Baogang. 6741 FAIRWOOD CT 27012 #243-46-1989 *100
MANTIN, Arie M. 2245 LEWISVILL CLMNS RD #C, CLEMMONS URGENT & PRI CARE 27012 #561-17-1980 L2000 **FM** *020 †18
MARLETTE, Marnie E. 2554 LEWISVILLE CLEMMNS RD, STE 109 27012 #036-05-1992 L1995 **FM** *020 †18
MARSHALL, William Jeffrey. 2255 LEWISVILL CLMNS RD #E 27012 #036-05-1983 L1984 **P** *020
MARTIN, Robert Shayn. ■ 27012 #036-05-2001 L2004 **GS** *020 †85
MC CAULEY, Roger Lee. 7600 LASATER RD, SALEM PSYCHIATRIC ASSO,P.A 27012 #055-01-1970 L1976 **P** *020 †75
MILLER, Lisa Lynn. 2554 LEWISVILLE CLEMMNS RD, STE 109 27012 #038-44-2000 L2003 **FM** *020 †18
MUELLER-HEUBACH, Eberhard. PO BOX 1335 27012 #407-22-1966 L1989 **OBG MFM** *071 †30
NACZKI, Lisa C. 2554 LEWISVILLE CLEMMNS RD, STE 109 27012 #016-43-1998 L1999 **FM** *020 †18
NEKL, Casey Guy. ■ 27012 #030-05-2005 **OTO** *012
NIFONG, Frank Miller. PO BOX 988 27012 #041-02-1943 L1943 **FM** *071
PASSERO, Nicholas John. 6301 STADIUM DR 27012 #055-02-1989 L1990 **FM** *020 †18
POLLOCK, Deborah Hinch. 6301 STADIUM DR 27012 #036-05-1994 L1996 **FM** *020 †18
PUBANTZ, David Jerret. ■ 27012 #036-01-2006 **PD** *012
PYLE, Jeremy William. ■ 27012 #016-11-2005 **PS** *012
PYLE, Meghan Kennelly. ■ 27012 #036-05-2007 **AN** *012
ROBBINS, Katherine Mae. ■ 27012 #016-45-2005 **PTH** *012
ROBBINS, Kevin Merritt. ■ 27012 #039-01-2003 L2005 **FM** *020 †18
ROBINSON, Eric Randy. ■ 27012 #003-01-2007 **FP** *012
SAAD, Mustafa. ■ 27012 #704-22-1989 L2006 **N** *100
SIMPSON, Jason Ferebee. ■ 27012 #036-05-2008 *012
STEFANESCU, Beatrice V. 6650 VALLEYOAK DR, 226 MEDICAL PLAZA LANE 27012 #781-04-1991 L2008 **NPM** *020 †55
STOVER, Jennifer Anne. ■ 27012 #055-02-2004 L2008 **FM** *020
STRIBLING, Jennifer Tillm. ■ 27012 #012-01-2005 L2008 **PD** *012
STRIBLING, Warren Kyle. ■ 27012 #012-01-2005 L2008 **IM** *012
WALL, Ralph Lane, Jr. 6960 HARPER VIEW CT 27012 #036-01-1978 L1983 **IM** *020 †20
WARNIMONT, Christopher J. 105 STADIUM OAKS DR 27012 #035-06-1990 L1995 **MPD PD** *020 †55,20
WESTALL, Holly Lynette. ■ 27012 #036-05-2003 **FM** *020 †18
WOBKER, Sara Elizabeth. ■ 27012 #036-01-2008 *012
WRAY, Walter Harrill, Jr. 6301 STADIUM DR, # 500 27012 #011-03-1974 L1975 **FM** *020 †18

CLEVELAND – ROWAN

BARR, John Findley. 11711 STATESVILLE BLVD, CLEVELAND CENTER 27013 #041-09-1980 L1982 **FM** *020 †18
FRANKLIN, Paula Dawn. 11709 STATESVILLE BLVD 27013 #025-01-1992 L1999 **PD** *020 †55

CLIMAX – RANDOLPH

LITTLE, James Conrad, Jr. 1008 NC HIGHWAY 62 E 27233 #036-01-1968 L1968 **FM** *020 †18 ‡

CLINTON – SAMPSON

BARR, Falvy Carl, Jr. 607 BEAMON ST 28328 #021-05-1972 L1979 **PTH FOP** *020
BRASTED, Edward David. 607 BEAMON ST 28328 #018-03-1972 L1994 **AN** *020 †05
BRYAN, Elizabeth D. 603 BEAMAN ST 28328 #036-05-2001 L2004 **FM** *020 †18
BUCHANAN, Wm Edward, Jr. 1740 SOUTHEAST BLVD 28328 #051-04-1981 L1993 **NEP IM** *020 †20
CALDWELL, Bruce Francis. ■ 28328 #036-01-1963 L1963 **EM GS** *020 †85
CARR, Henry James, Jr. 607 BEAMON ST 28328 #036-07-1954 L1954 **IM** *071
CARR, William Curtis. 403 FAIRVIEW ST 28328 #036-07-1984 L1985 **IM PD** *020 †55
CONWAY, Ada Marie. 403 FAIRVIEW ST, CLINTON MEDICAL CLINIC, IN 28328 #055-01-1994 L2005 **PD** *020 †55
COOK, Brian C. 215 BEAMAN ST 28328 #048-14-2001 L2006 **RO** *100 †20
COTTER, Jason. 603 BEAMAN ST, STE 200 28328 #041-09-1998 L2003 **GS** *020 †85
CUNNINGHAM, John David. 504 BALSEY ST 28328 #041-02-1979 L2001 **OTO HNS** *020 †45 ‡
DAMBECK, Allyn Benard. 607 BEAMON ST, SAMPSON CO MEM HOSP 28328 #050-02-1954 L1977 **FM** *071
DOUGHERTY, John Wallace. ■ 28328 #026-04-1944 L1944 **D DMP** *071 †15
ENRIQUEZ, Julita Carlos. ■ 28329 #748-07-1954 **OBG** *074
FAJARDO, Agapito Lacson. 906 N US 421 HWY 28328 #748-01-1971 L1976 **GP EM** *020
FAKHRI, Mouahed Iyad. 620 COLLEGE ST, INTERNAL MEDICINE CLINIC, 28328 #875-01-1996 L2003 **IM** *020 †20
GINTHNER, Terry Patrick. PO BOX 619, 409C COOPER DR 28329 #017-20-1978 L1988 **DR** *020 †80
GOBIEN, Rolf Peter. 607 BEAMAN ST, DEPT OF RADIOLOGY 28328 #050-02-1971 L1984 **DR** *020 †80
HERRING, Rufus M, Jr. 403 FAIRVIEW ST 28328 #036-05-1969 L1969 **PD** *020 †55
HO, Grace Weikong. 403 FAIRVIEW ST 28328 #035-09-1995 L1998 **FM** *020 †18
HUFF, William Alexander. 520 BEAMON ST 28328 #036-08-1992 L1998 **ORS** *020 †40

HYMAN, Henry T. 516 BEAMAN ST 28328 #028-79-1976, ▲ L1993 **OBG** *020 †30

JANSSEN, Shelley Lynne. 1004 BEAMAN ST, CLINTON URGENT CARE 28328 #036-08-1997 L1999 **FM** *020 †18

JOHNSON, Michael Donald. 504 BALSEY ST 28328 #036-01-1988 L1993 **OTO** *020 †45

LEAK, Frank Walter. 403 FAIRVIEW ST, CLINTON MEDICAL CLINIC, IN 28328 #036-01-1967 L1967 **FM** *071 †18

LU, Yuan. 1740 SOUTHEAST BLVD 28328 #243-16-1987 L1998 **NEP** *020 †20

MARSTON, Charles Thos. 516 BEAMAN ST 28328 #036-01-1978 L1979 **PD** *020 †55

MARTINEZ, Paul A. 607 BEAMON ST 28328 #308-11-1986 L1993 **FM** *020 †18

MC CONNELL, Ezra Lee, III. 1740 SOUTHEAST BLVD 28328 #047-20-1987 L1996 **NEP IM** *020 †20

MC DEVITT, Gordon Robts. 409C COOPER DR, CLINTON X-RAY ASSOCIATES 28328 #041-02-1986 L1994 **DR** *020 †80,28

MC PHAIL, John Finley. 603 BEAMON ST, WOODSIDE PROF BLDG STE 200 28328 #011-03-1973 L1990 **GS** *020 †85

MERRITT, John Cary. 306 BEAMAN ST 28328 #010-03-1970 L1972 **OPH PD** *040 †35

MORKOS, Eskander George. 607 BEAMAN ST, SAMPSON MEDICAL CENTER 28328 #915-03-1993 L2003 **APM** *020 †05 ‡

MOSS, Henry Lee. 603 BEAMAN ST, WOODSIDE PROFESSIONAL BUIL 28328 #024-01-1973 L1995 **ORS** *020 †40

NEWTON, John Thos. 403 FAIRVIEW ST, CLINTON MEDICAL CLINIC INC 28328 #036-01-1981 L1982 **FM** *020 †18

NUAMAH, Richmond Kwaku. 1740 SOUTHEAST BLVD 28328 #038-06-1995 L1999 **IM NEP** *020 †20

OAKES, Richard E, II. 417 VANCE ST, STE A 28328 #055-01-1995 L2005 **OBG** *020 †30

PEAK, Latham C. 403 FAIRVIEW ST 28328 #036-05-1951 L1951 **FM** *072 †18

RANDOLPH, Victor F. 607 BEAMON ST, SAMPSON REG MED CTR ER DEP 28328 #036-01-1993 L1995 **FM EM** *020 †18

ROBERTS, John Milton, Jr. 516 BEAMON ST 28328 #036-05-1974 L1974 **OBG** *020 †30

SESSOMS, Rodney Kevin. 500 BEAMAN ST 28328 #038-08-1989 L1991 **IM** *020

STRAIKO, Amy Kathryn. ■ 28328 #038-45-2002 L2005 **FM** *020 †18

SURRATT, John Peeler. 603 BEAMON ST 28328 #036-01-1971 L1971 **D** *020 †15

TATE, Kevin Douglas. 906 N US HIGHWAY 421, GOSHEN MEDICAL CENTER 28328 #051-04-2003 L2006 **FM** *020 †20

TAYLOR, Carolyn Rose. 411 VANCE ST 28328 #033-05-1976 L1981 **IM** *075

TSAO, Henry. 607 BEAMON ST 28328 #023-01-1986 L1992 **AN** *020 †05

VALENTI, Michael Arthur. 603 BEAMAN ST, STE 200 28328 #041-02-1993 L1998 **GS** *020 †85

VANCE, Tedman Luster. 205 DEER TRACK TRL 28328 #021-05-1994 L2001 **HS** *020 †40

VERRILLI, Albert A, III. 603 BEAMON ST 28328 #038-06-1984 L1985 **FM** *020 †18

VISER, Paul Edward. 603 BEAMAN ST, WOODSIDE PROFESSIONAL BLDG 28328 #036-01-1984 L1985 **IM** *020 †20

VOGELSANG, Glenn David. 516 BEAMAN ST, GOSHEN MEDICAL CENTER - RO 28328 #305-01-1996 L2000 **FM** *020 †18 ‡

WARREN, Larry E. ■ 28328 #036-01-1974 L1974 **IM EM** *020 †20

WATTS, Lawrence James. 607 BEAMON ST 28328 #005-12-1994 L1997 **FM** *020 †18

WEBB, Robert Kent. 1740 SOUTHEAST BLVD 28328 #055-01-1967 L1973 **NEP IM** *020 †20

WHITLEY, Daniel, Jr. 504 BALSEY ST 28328 #036-08-1983 L1984 **OTO SME** *020 †45

WOODS, Thomas Jefferson C. 603 BEAMON ST 28328 #027-01-1974 L1981 **OPH FM** *020 †35

ZUROWSKY, Philip Adam. 607 BEAMON ST 28328 #023-12-1985 L1988 **IM** *020 †20

CLYDE — HAYWOOD

ALBEA, Jeffrey Raymond. 262 LEROY GEORGE DR, STE M 28721 #021-05-1998 L2006 **NS** *020

BERNARD, Ronnell Paul. 262 LEROY GEORGE DR 28721 #021-05-1975 L1995 **AN** *020 †16,05

BREMER, Richard Alan. 90 HOSPITAL DR 28721 #049-01-1980 L1986 **AN** *020 †05

BRYSON, Aloha Emily. 262 LEROY GEORGE DR, PRIMEDOC OF HAYWOOD COUNTY 28721 #036-01-1998 L2000 **IMG PLM** *020 †20

BUNIO, Richard Allan. 262 LEROY GEORGE DR 28721 #062-01-1987 L1999 **FM** *020 †18

CAFFREY, Brian Beaumont. 6750 CAROLINA BLVD, 1409 28721 #036-01-1991 L1994 **FM** *020 †18

CALLAHAN, Richard Dale. 262 LEROY GEORGE DR 28721 #041-14-1977 L1993 **ON HEM** *075

CALVO, Jose Antonio. 262 LEROY GEORGE DR, PRIMEDOC OF HAYWOOD COUNTY 28721 #715-01-1997 L2004 **IM** *020 †20

CATTERSON, Christofer C. 600 HOSPITAL DR, STE 3 28721 #041-15-1999 L2005 **OSM** *100 †40

CHAIN, Jeffrey Robt. 600 HOSPITAL DR STE 3, ORTHOPAEDIC SPECIALISTS 28721 #041-02-1983 L1998 **ORS** *020 †40

COLON, Filiberto, Jr. 600 HOSPITAL DR, STE 9 28721 #048-14-1990 L1993 **GE IM** *020 †20

DANIELL, Rebecca S. 600 HOSPITAL DR, STE 9, LLP 28721 #035-45-1989 L1993 **IM** *020 †20

DANITSCHEK, Carl Norman. 262 LEROY GEORGE DR 28721 #019-02-1974 L1992 **AN** *071 †05

DELLA VECCHIA, Jason John. 262 LEROY GEORGE DR, PRIMEDOC OF HAYWOOD COUNTY 28721 #025-07-2001 L2004 **IM** *020 †20

DEWHURST, Donald Andrew, II. 262 LEROY GEORGE DR 28721 #036-05-1975 L1975 **EM** *020 †18

DINWIDDIE, William C, Jr. 262 LEROY GEORGE DR 28721 #047-05-1984 L2001 **FM** *020 †18

FEICHTER, Ralph Norbert. 600 HOSPITAL DR, STE 9 28721 #016-06-1956 L1964 **IM CD** *071 †20

FOX, Daniel Wade. 600 HOSPITAL DR, STE 9 28721 #001-02-1997 L2000 **IM** *020 †20

FREEMAN, Nancy Rouser. 6750 CAROLINA BLVD 28721 #036-01-1982 L1984 **FM** *020 †18

GHAUSSY, Najeeb Omar. 600 HOSPITAL DR STE 9 28721 #036-06-1998 L2004 **RHU** *020 †20

GRIMES, Jeffery Robert. 262 LEROY GEORGE DR 28721 #001-02-1987 L1990 **IM** *020 †20

GROSS, Charles M. 32 PHYSICIANS DR 28721 #008-01-1970 L2007 **CD** *020 †20 ‡

GROSSE, Jay Weston. 600 HOSPITAL DR, STE 9 28721 #038-40-1989 L2008 **IM** *020 †20

HARRIS, Glenn Allen, Jr. 32 PHYSICIANS DR 28721 #027-01-1992 L2000 **CD** *020 †20

HARSCH, Richard Henry. 6750 CAROLINA BLVD 28721 #012-05-1995 L1998 **FM** *020 †18

HARTZELL, Stephen Warren. 486 HOSPITAL DR 28721 #023-07-1995 L1999 **OPH** *020 †35

HELLER, Michael Steven. 600 HOSPITAL DR, STE 2 28721 #035-03-1975 L1990 **ON HEM** *020 †20

HOOLEY-GINGRICH, Joyce E. 15 FACILITY DR, HAYWOOD PEDS 28721 #055-01-1989 L1994 **PD** *020 †55

HUDERLY, Debera L. 262 LEROY GEORGE DR, STE X 28721 #026-04-1992 L1997 **DR** *020 †80

HUNTER, Shannon Elizabeth. 63 HAYWOOD PARK DR, THROAT SPECIALISTS 28721 #036-01-1998 L2001 **OTO** *020 †45

IACOVELLI, Benedetto, Jr. 262 LEROY GEORGE DR 28721 #010-01-1993 L1998 **FM EM** *020 †18

KELLY, Michael Elvin. ■ 28721 #021-01-1974 L1981 **VS GS** *020 †18,85

KEOGH, Michael James. 32 PHYSICIANS DR 28721 #033-06-1985 L1995 **CD IM** *020 †20

KING, Gerald W. 600 HOSPITAL DR STE 3 28721 #005-12-1977 L2007 **ORS** *020 †40 ‡

KONRAD, Patricia Noveck. 262 LEROY GEORGE DR 28721 #005-14-1966 L1997 **PTH PD** *020 †55,50

KUNZ, Kenneth R. 600 HOSPITAL DR, STE 2 28721 #062-01-1986 L2000 **ON** *020

LANE, Christopher H. 35 FACILITY DR, MAILING: P O BOX 279 28721 #047-06-1981 L1985 **OBG** *020 †30

LANG, Franklin R, Jr. 90 HOSPITAL DR, HAYWOOD COUNTY HOSPITAL 28721 #028-34-1979 L1992 **DR** *020 †80

LESESNE, Edward H, Jr. 6750 CAROLINA BLVD 28721 #036-01-1969 L1969 **FM** *071 †18

LINGER, Craig Harrison. 600 HOSPITAL DR, STE 9 28721 #047-05-1986 L1989 **IM** *020 †20

LIPHAM, Harry Glenn. 600 HOSPITAL DR STE 9, LLP 28721 #036-05-1976 L1981 **PUD IM** *020 †20

MARKOFF, David Dwight. 486 HOSPITAL DR 28721 #005-12-1986 L1990 **OPH** *020 †35

MASTERS, Michael Jason. 540 HOSPITAL DR 28721 #041-09-1975 L1982 **D** *020 †15

MATTHEWS, Robin Dempsey. 35 FACILITY DR, MAILING: P O BOX 279 28721 #001-02-1990 L1992 **OBG** *020 †30 ‡

MC CLURE, James Thos. 490 HOSPITAL DR 28721 #047-05-1988 L1996 **ORS OFA** *020 †40

MC KINNEY, Alexander S. 262 LEROY GEORGE DR 28721 #035-01-1959 L1985 **N** *071 †75

MC LELLAND, John Coite, III. 600 HOSPITAL DR, STE 9 28721 #036-05-1996 L1999 **IM** *020 †20

MCLELLAND, Karin Rainey. 15 FACILITY DR 28721 #036-05-1996 L2003 **PD** *020 †55

MC NEILL, Stephen Mark. 6750 CAROLINA BLVD 28721 #036-08-2002 L2004 **FM** *100 †18

MILLER, William Donald. 262 LEROY GEORGE DR, STE M 28721 #020-12-1996 L2002 **ORS** *020 †40

MINA, Alfred Albert. 40 BRETTWOOD TRCE 28721 #025-07-1997 L2003 **GS** *020 †85

MITTELMAN, Mark A. 262 LEROY GEORGE DR STE X 28721 #038-41-1989 L2003 **VIR DR** *020 †80

MORRIS, Mark David. 262 LEROY GEORGE DR, EMERG RM HAYWOOD REG MED 28721 #038-41-1977 L1983 **EM** *020 †16

MUNOZ, Luis Augusto. 262 LEROY GEORGE DR 28721 #011-03-1977 L1979 **PTH** *020 †50

NATHAN, Henry P. 600 HOSPITAL DR STE 9 28721 #035-46-1977 L1978 **GE IM** *020 †20

NERNEY, John Jos. 486 HOSPITAL DR 28721 #012-01-1970 L1976 **OPH** *071 †35

OSWALD, Michael Roy. 486 HOSPITAL DR 28721 #015-05-1995 L2001 **OPH** *020 †35

OWEN, William Boyd, Jr. 262 LEROY GEORGE DR 28721 #036-05-1971 L1971 **ORS** *020 †40

OWL-SMITH, Frances. 262 LEROY GEORGE DR 28721 #036-01-1987 L1989 **PTH** *020 †50

PALAY, Howard Wm. 600 HOSPITAL DR, STE 9 28721 #038-40-1981 L1994 **N CN** *020 †75

PERRY, Henry Baker, III. 50 WINDY HILL DR 28721 #023-07-1974 L1981 **GS** *020 †85

PETERSON, David Wm. 32 PHYSICIANS DR 28721 #026-04-1987 L1998 **CD** *020 †20

PHILLIPS, Benjamin R. 40 BRETTWOOD TRCE 28721 #033-05-1999 L2005 **GS** *020 †85

PHILLIPS, Ditte Gail. 600 HOSPITAL DR, STE 9 28721 #024-16-1989 L1996 **IM** *020 †20

QUEEN, Kathleen Taylor. 600 HOSPITAL DR, STE 9 28721 #036-01-1981 L1984 **RHU IM** *020 †20 ‡

REITZ, Eric David. 40 BRETTWOOD TRCE 28721 #019-02-1983 L1994 **GS** *020 †85

REY, Michael T. 262 LEROY GEORGE DR 28721 #035-06-1978 L1982 **EM** *020 †16

RICHARDS, Cynthia Gail. 6750 CAROLINA BLVD 28721 #051-01-1998 L2001 **FM** *020 †18

RIESTER, Clifford Rudi. 262 LEROY GEORGE DR, STE X 28721 #038-41-1993 L1998 **DR** *020 †80

ROGERS, John Bush, III. 576 LEROY GEORGE DR, PRIMEDOC OF HAYWOOD COUNTY 28721 #045-01-2001 L2002 **FM** *020 †18

SCHAEFER, John Albert. 262 LEROY GEORGE DR 28721 #038-41-1995 L2002 **IM** *020

SHARPTON, Bennie Reeves. 40 BRETTWOOD TRCE 28721 #012-01-1971 L1979 **GS** *020 †85

SINGLETON, Gina Rae. 540 HOSPITAL DR 28721 #047-20-1995 L1999 **D** *020 †15

STEELE, Richard Henry. 15 BRETTWOOD TRCE 28721 #021-01-1989 L1996 **FM** *020 †18

TANNEHILL, John Franklin. 414 HOSPITAL DR 28721 #021-01-1964 L1976 **OTO HNS** *020 †45

TEATER, Donald Robt. 262 LEROY GEORGE DR 28721 #038-40-1985 L1986 **FM** *020 †18

THOMAS, Charles Carroll, II. 600 HOSPITAL DR, STE 10 28721 #036-01-1970 L1970 **RO DR** *020 †80

THOMAS, Rufus Mc Afee. 540 HOSPITAL DR 28721 #021-01-1978 L1989 **D OS** *020 †15 ‡

TRENTHAM, Charles R, Jr. 262 LEROY GEORGE DR 28721 #047-06-1988 L2001 **AN PD** *020 †55,05

VERGES, Leonard Paul. 15 BRETTWOOD TRCE 28721 #021-01-1981 L1992 **U** *020 †95

WEAVER, James Paul. 600 HOSPITAL DR STE 9, MOUNTAIN MEDICAL GROUP LLP 28721 #036-05-1998 L2000 **IM** *020 †20

WEAVER, M Harrington. 262 LEROY GEORGE DR 28721 #036-05-1999 L2000 **PD** *020 †55

WELSH, Edmond Jos. 262 LEROY GEORGE DR 28721 #021-05-1990 L1992 **FM** *020 †18

WENZEL, Christopher Todd. 63 HAYWOOD PARK DR 28721 #036-07-1995 L1998 **OTO** *020 †45

WENZEL, Frederick Geo. 90 HOSPITAL DR 28721 #016-06-1959 L1966 **GS** *071 †85

WHITE, Jonathan Lance. 262 LEROY GEORGE DR, HAYWOOD REGIONAL 28721 #001-02-2000 L2003 **IM** *020 †20

WILBUR, Nila L. 262 LEROY GEORGE DR, STE X 28721 #016-45-1979 L1994 **R** *020 †80

ZACHER, Allan, III. 24 FALCON CREST LN, HAYWOOD PROFESSIONAL PARK 28721 #028-03-1983 L1986 **PME AN** *020 †05 ‡

COLFAX — GUILFORD

HUNT, William Jack. ■ 27235 #023-01-1943 L1943 **IM** *071

WELBORN, Julius W, Jr. 1953 HAYES SHORT LN 27235 #045-01-1951 L1952 **IM** *071

COLLETTSVILLE — CALDWELL

PAGE, Stephen Willis. 4329 COLLETTSVILLE RD, POST OFFICE DRAWER 9 28611 #047-07-1973 L1992 **GP** *020

COLUMBUS — POLK

AMBRUOSO, Victor Nicolas. 1451 HIGHWAY 108 W 28722 #132-01-1956 L1990 **TS GS** *020 †85,90

BERLINGER, Frederick Geo. ■ 28722 #016-42-1963 L1998 **END IM** *020 †20

BLANTON, John Earl, Jr. 101 HOSPITAL DR, ST. LUKE'S HOSPITAL - ER 28722 #045-01-1970 L2004 **FM** *020 †18

BLOMELEY, Charles Perry. 220 HOSPITAL DR 28722 #010-03-1965 L2007 **FM** *020 †18

BOLLING, Thomas Vance. 35 WALKER ST 28722 #005-12-1974 L1979 **GS** *020 †85

CAREY, Patrick Cairns. 101 HOSPITAL DR 28722 #038-40-1984 L2006 **IMG** *020 †20

CHANDLER, Wm Marcus, Jr. 28722 #012-01-1968 L1976 **GP** *020

DOERR, John C. ■ 28722 #020-02-1944 L1960 **AN** *071 †05

DURAN, Mary Katherine. 101 HOSPITAL DR, ST. LUKE'S HOSPITAL 28722 #045-04-1999 L2000 **FM** *020 †18

FIELD, Robert Clark. ■ 28722 #048-04-1957 L1986 **ORS** *071 †40

FISCHER, Martin Jos. 44 HOSPITAL DR, ST. LUKE'S PROFESSIONAL BL 28722 #028-02-1961 L1979 **GS TS** *071 †85,90

GRAZIANO, Dino August. 101 HOSPITAL DR, ST.LUKE'S HOSPITAL 28722 #010-02-1984 L1991 **EM FM** *020 †20

HARDING, Robert W. 52 HOSPITAL DR, STE 3A 28722 #035-06-1964 L1970 **IM** *071 †20

HOLLEMAN, James Bennett. 44 HOSPITAL DR, STE 1A 28722 #036-01-1992 L1998 **GS** *020 †85

KORNMAYER, John D. 45 E MILLS ST, P O BOX 608 28722 #018-75-1995, ▲ L1998 *020

LASSITER, Lonnie Wayne, II. 2881 NC 108 HWY E 28722 #036-08-1997 L2000 **FM** *020 †18

OWENSBY, C Norman. ■ 28722 #021-01-1958 L1963 **P** *071 †75

PALMER, Robert Marion. ST LUKES PROFESSIONAL BLDG 28722 #045-01-1955 L1956 **FM** *071 †18

PERRAUT, Thos Christopher. 192 HOSPITAL DR 28722 #020-02-1978 L1983 **OPH** *020 †35

REES, Matthew Mcguire. 52 HOSPITAL DR, RUTHERFORD INTERNAL 28722 #027-01-1988 L1996 **ON HEM** *020 †20

ROSENBERG, Brian Jay. 48 HOSPITAL DR, STE 2A 28722 #020-02-1999 L2004 **ORS** *020 †40

SALERNO, James Geo. 273 E MILLS ST, POB 457 28722 #033-05-1975 L1982 **GP** *020 †30

SCHAFER, Gary Robt. 52 HOSPITAL DR, RUTHERFORD INTERNAL 28722 #036-05-1986 L1992 **PUD IM** *020 †20

SLEE, Vergil N. ■ 28722 #028-02-1941 L1946 **OS** *072 †70

SNIPES, Garrett Ellis. 130 FOREST GLEN RD, HOSPICE OF THE CAROLINA FO 28722 #021-01-1975 L1996 **FM** *020 †18

SPANJER, Raymond F. ■ 28722 #035-19-1940 L1941 **IMG** *071

SPENCER, Wm Caldwell, III. 220 HOSPITAL DR 28722 #012-05-1966 L1990 **DR** *020 †80

SYN, Wai Yun. ■ 28722 #012-05-1959 L1963 **IM** *071

VESER, Belynda D. ■ 28722 #051-07-1995 L2006 **PYG** *020 †75

VIAR, Jeffrey K. 801 W MILLS ST, FOOTHILLS MEDICAL ASSOCIAT 28722 #028-78-1996, ▲ L1999 **FM** *020 †18

VIRTS, Earl Edward. ■ 28722 #051-04-1957 L1957 **PHP** *071 †70,18

WALTER, Cornelius T, Jr. 220 HOSPITAL DR, ST LUKE'S HOSPITAL 28722 #045-04-1993 L1996 **FM** *020 †18

WANLASS, Stanley A. ■ 28722 #035-09-1952 L1997 **GS** *071 †85

WHISKIN, Frederick Edward. 52 HOSPITAL DR 28722 #067-01-1948 L1986 **P** *071

CONCORD – CABARRUS

ADAMS, Lydia Heyel. 270 COPPERFIELD BLVD NE, STE 202 28025 #012-22-2005 L2006 **FP** *012

ALDOUS, Mark Daniel. 1070 VINEHAVEN DR, CABARRUS GASTROENTEROLOGY 28025 #036-07-1995 L1998 **GE** *020 †20

ALSABA, Khaled. ■ 28025 #875-01-1990 L1996 **IM** *020 †20

ANONICK, Patrick Kevin. 301 MEDICAL PARK DR, HEART GROUP OF CAROLINAS 28025 #051-01-1993 L1999 **CD** *020 †20

AREY, John Vincent. ■ 28025 #024-01-1946 L1946 **GYN** *071 †30

AVERETT, William Franklin. 845 CHURCH ST N, STE 310 28025 #036-05-2001 L2003 **IM** *020 †20

BAER, Claxton Allen. 201 LE PHILLIP CT NE 28025 #051-01-2000 L2004 **OPH** *020 †35

BAKER, James Laurence. 200 MEDICAL PARK DR, STE 330 28025 #045-04-1997 L2004 **RHU** *020 †20

BAKER, Kristin Dutrow. 200 MEDICAL PARK DR, STE 450 28025 #036-01-1989 L1991 **CHP** *020 †80

BAKER, Scott Mckinley. 212 LE PHILLIP CT NE, STE 201 28025 #036-01-1989 L1993 **DR** *020 †80

BAREFOOT, Thomas Kirby. 349 PENNY LN, COPPERFIELD OB/GYN, LLC 28025 #036-08-1986 L1994 **OBG** *020 †30

BARNES, Angela Denise. 920 CHURCH ST N, STE 300E 28025 #010-03-1995 L2000 **IM** *020 †20

BARONE, Barbara K. 920 CHURCH ST N 28025 #035-03-1993 L1996 **IM** *020 †20

BASTADJIAN, Sylvie. 1085 NE GATEWAY CT, STE 200 28025 #605-01-1990 L1994 **IM IMG** *020 †20

BAUMAN, Roc Winston. 1090 VINEHAVEN DR 28025 #036-01-1988 L1993 **GS VS** *020 †85

BEAL-LANDIS, Esther R. ■ 28025 #045-01-2000 L2007 **FM** *020 †18

BEAVER, Robert Howell. 354 COPPERFIELD BLVD NE 28025 #047-06-1973 L1974 **ORS** *020 †40

BELK, Cathy Christine. 70 LAKE CONCORD RD NE, STE 100 28025 #041-13-1980 L2008 **FM PME** *020

BENBOW, John Miller. 66 LAKE CONCORD RD NE 28025 #036-07-1973 L1975 **PD** *020 †55

BENGUR, Ahmet Resai. 100 MEDICAL PARK DR, STE 310 28025 #045-01-1982 L1992 **PDC PD** *020 †55

BERNARD, Joe David Jr. 200 MEDICAL PARK DR, STE 350 28025 #020-02-1994 L2000 **NS ESN** *020 †25

BLACK, Donald. ■ 28027 #035-15-1989 L1992 **CCP PD** *020 †55

BLACKMAN, Cameron Trent. 1084 VINEHAVEN DR, NORTHEAST UROLOGY 28025 #036-01-1988 L1994 **U UP** *020 †95

BLANKENBURG-BENTLEY, K. 1028 LEE ANN DR NE, STE 200 28025 #041-02-1991 L1998 **EM** *020 †16

BLEVINS, Julia Lynn. 1085 NE GATEWAY CT, STE 290 28025 #036-01-1989 L1992 **PD** *020 †55

BLUM, Jeffrey Clark. 212 LE PHILLIP CT NE, STE 201 28025 #023-01-1973 L1977 **DR IM** *020 †20,80

BOBBITT, James Danl. 33 LAKE CONCORD RD NE 28025 #055-01-1969 L1977 **OPH** *020 †35

BONGAARD, Bridget S. 301 MEDICAL PARK DR, STE 201 28025 #011-03-1983 L1984 **IM** *020 †20

BOOTH, Kellly Ann. 1054 BURRAGE RD NE, NORTHEAST OB-GYN ASSOCIATE 28025 #036-07-1993 L1997 **OBG** *020 †30

BRAUN, Mark Edward. 1085 NE GATEWAY CT, STE 200 28025 #041-15-2000 L2006 **IM** *020 †20

BRENS, Fatima Altagracia. 204 KINGSPORT DR NE 28025 #308-01-1996 L2006 **FM** *100 †18

BRESNAHAN, Linda Kay. 200 MEDICAL PARK DR, STE 430 28025 #017-20-1987 L1991 **OBG** *020 †30

BREZICKI, Paul Alexander. 888 CHURCH ST N 28025 #065-01-1979 L1985 **FM** *020 †18

BRIGHT, Dellyse Maxine. 270 COPPERFIELD BLVD NE, STE 102 28025 #023-01-1999 L2006 **FM** *020 †18

BRITTON, Leon Chas, Jr. 212 LE PHILLIP CT NE # 201, ASSOCIATES, P.A. 28025 #026-08-1989 L2005 **EM** *020 †16

BROWN, Ryan Anthony. 920 CHURCH ST N 28025 #036-01-1994 L2001 **IM** *020 †20

BROWN, Sandra Marie. 201 LE PHILLIP CT NE 28025 #016-06-1990 L2005 **OPH** *020 †35

BULLARD, Andrew Gray. 219 LE PHILLIP CT NE 28025 #036-01-1985 L1988 **PUD SME** *020 †20 ‡

BURCHFIELD, William John. 201 LE PHILLIP CT NE 28025 #025-01-1967 L1972 **OPH** *020 †35 ‡

BURGESS, Stephen Ben. 3020 WEDDINGTON RD, WEDDINGTON INT MED & PEDS 28027 #036-01-1995 L1999 **MPD** *020 †20,55

BURKE, David Jos. 354 COPPERFIELD BLVD NE 28025 #018-03-1967 L1974 **ORS** *020 †40

BURROUGHS, Kevin Emerson. 5641 POPLAR TENT RD, STE 102 28027 #036-01-1996 L1999 **FM FSM** *020 †18

BYRD, Vernon Dale. 212 LE PHILLIP CT NE, STE 201 28025 #036-08-1990 L1995 **RNR** *020 †80

CARROLL, Charles F, Jr. 920 CHURCH ST N 28025 #023-01-1953 L1956 **ATP** *071 †50

CASH, Sarah Harris. 335 PENNY LN 28025 #055-01-2000 L2001 **D** *020 †15

CENTERS, Scott Richard. 1028 LEE ANN DR NE, STE 200 28025 #011-02-2004 L2007 **EM** *020

CHALFANT, William Paxson. 56 LAKE CONCORD RD NE 28025 #010-01-1966 L1973 **GS** *071 †85

CHAPIN, Rebecca Burdette. 920 CHURCH ST N, STE 300E 28025 #026-04-1998 L2001 **IM** *020 †20

CHARANIA, Amin. 1000 COPPERFIELD BLVD, STE 124 28025 #704-02-1987 L1998 **IM** *020 †20

CHAUDHARY, Humaira K. 920 CHURCH ST N 28025 #704-25-1992 L2001 **NEP IM** *020 †20

CHEUNG, Catherine W. 920 CHURCH ST N, DEPT OF ANESTHESIA 28025 #041-09-1992 L1999 **AN** *020 †05

CHIEMPRABHA, Alan Wayne. 1070 VINEHAVEN DR, CABARRUS GASTROENTEROLOGY 28025 #027-01-1998 L2001 **GE** *020 †20

CHIKES, Peter George. 1085 NE GATEWAY CT, STE 100 28025 #036-01-1972 L1972 **OTO A** *020 †45

CHINIWALLA, Nirav Paresh. 1070 VINEHAVEN DR, CABARRUS GASTROENTEROLOGY 28025 #041-13-1999 L2006 **GE** *020 †20

CHIU, Patrick Yeechien. 920 CHURCH ST N, MSU/KCMS 28025 #025-12-2004 L2007 **IM** *020 †20

CHOW, Henry Yongheng. 200 MEDICAL PARK DR, STE 330 28025 #051-07-1991 L1996 **RHU IM** *020 †20

CHRISTOPHER, Thomas Jude. 100 MEDICAL PARK DR, STE 210 28025 #008-01-1990 L2000 **ICE** *020 †20

CHRISTOPHERSON, David Lee. 845 CHURCH ST N, STE 107 28025 #025-01-1974 L1991 **FM** *020 †18 ‡

CHRISTY, Ralph S, Jr. 200 MEDICAL PARK DR, STE 230 28025 #036-01-1983 L1986 **TS** *020 †85,90

CHRONISTER, Tara Lee. 920 CHURCH ST N, DEPT OF ANESTHESIA 28025 #004-01-1989 L1997 **AN** *020 †05

CHU, David Bao-Shan. ■ 28027 #048-04-1957 L1989 **CD IM** *071

CICCI, Christopher Kevin. 200 MEDICAL PARK DR, STE 230 28025 #035-08-1995 L2002 **VS** *020 †85,90

CICCI, Leigh Goodwin. 1085 NE GATEWAY CT, STE 200 28025 #036-01-1997 L2002 **IM** *020 †20

CLARK, Douglas Hendon. ■ 28025 #036-01-1975 L1975 **PD** *075

CLARKE, Noellee Tashina. 200 MEDICAL PARK DR, STE 430 28025 #011-03-2003 L2007 **OBG** *020

COALE, Melissa Marlowe. 335 PENNY LN 28025 #036-08-1994 L1998 **D** *020 †15

COLLINS, David Leonard. ■ 28025 #024-01-1954 L1954 **GS** *071 †85

CONDREY, Staci Faulkner. 3020 WEDDINGTON RD 28027 #036-08-1995 L1999 **MPD** *020 †20,55

COOKE, James Harbin, Jr. 920 CHURCH ST N, NORTHEAST IN PATIENT SERV 28025 #036-07-1976 L1979 **IM** *020 †20

CORBIER, Jeanronel. 990 LEE ANN DR NE, NORTHEAST PEDIATRIC NEUROL 28025 #025-12-1995 L2006 **CHN** *020 †75

CORRELL, Earl Eugene. 920 CHURCH ST N 28025 #047-06-1946 L1947 **GP** *071

COTTRELL, William Milnes. 920 CHURCH ST N, DEPARTMENT OF ANESTHESIA 28025 #012-05-1975 L1978 **AN** *020 †05

CROLEY, Granville G, II. 56 LAKE CONCORD RD NE 28025 #047-20-1987 L1992 **GS VS** *020 †85

CROOK, John Newman. 56 LAKE CONCORD RD NE 28025 #036-07-1966 L1966 **GS VS** *071 †85

CROSLAND, Cathryn L. 1054 BURRAGE RD NE, NORTHEAST OB-GYN ASSOCIATE 28025 #020-12-1985 L1987 **OBG** *020 †30

CULLEN, Christine Anne. 920 CHURCH ST N, DEPT OF ANESTHESIA 28025 #023-12-1989 L2002 **AN** *020 †05

CURLEE, Lewis E. ■ 28025 #036-05-1950 L1950 **ORS TRS** *071 †40

DALTON, Thomas Andrew. 1070 VINEHAVEN DR 28025 #023-01-1987 L1993 **GE IM** *020 †20

DAVIDSON, Larry Steve. 200 MEDICAL PARK DR, STE 350 28025 #036-08-1988 L2000 **NS** *020 †25

DAVY, Leigh Erin. 2693 WINGRAVE ST NW 28027 #011-04-2002 L2007 **CHP** *020

DEBORD, Joseph Michael. 1084 VINEHAVEN DR, NORTHEAST UROLOGY 28025 #055-01-1990 L2002 **U** *020 †95

DE JAK, Dorothy Ann. ■ 28025 #035-01-1975 L1986 **NM** *050 †20,28

DELANEY, Paul Andrew. 270 COPPERFIELD BLVD NE, STE 102 28025 #010-02-2001 L2004 **FM** *020

DHANDE, Vijay Govind. 920 CHURCH ST N, NORTHEAST MEDICAL CENTER 28025 #495-28-1976 L1983 **NPM PD** *020 †55

DOUGLASS, David Paul. 66 LAKE CONCORD RD NE, CABARRUS PEDIATRICS CLINIC 28025 #047-05-1996 L1999 **PD** *020 †55

DOVER, Cathy Nicholson. 920 COPPERFIELD BLVD NE, COPPERFIELD WELLNESS & WEI 28025 #036-08-1996 L1997 **EM OS** *020 †16

DUNN, Laura L. 380 COPPERFIELD BLVD NE 28025 #048-16-1992 L2002 **CHP** *020 †75

DZIADZIOLA, James Kenneth. 200 MEDICAL PARK DR, STE 200 28025 #025-07-1991 L1997 **OTO** *020 †45

EDWARDS, Bryan Todd. 354 COPPERFIELD BLVD NE 28025 #036-08-1998 L2006 **ORS** *020 †40

ELLIS, Mark Edward. 920 CHURCH ST N, DEPT OF ANESTHESIA 28025 #045-01-1989 L1993 **AN** *020 †05

ELLIS, Shannon Scott. 270 COPPERFIELD BLVD NE, STE 202 28025 #047-20-2005 L2007 **FM** *100

ENGSTROM, George Alfred. 66 LAKE CONCORD RD NE 28025 #036-07-1959 L1959 **PD** *071 †55

ERDIN, Robert Alexander. 354 COPPERFIELD BLVD NE 28025 #012-01-1999 L2004 **ORS** *020 †40

EVANS, William Andrew. 920 CHURCH ST N 28025 #036-05-1996 L1997 **PTH** *020 †50

FARRIS, Gerard Edward. 1028 LEE ANN DR NE STE 200 28025 #021-05-1993 L1999 **EM** *020 †16

FERRERAS, Herminia. 100 MEDICAL PARK DR, STE 310 28025 #748-10-1983 L2002 **N** *020 †75

FERRIS, Andrew Gillett. 319 PENNY LN, DBA PIEDMONT ORTHOPEDIC SP 28025 #041-77-2001, ▲ L2006 *020

FLOWE, Benjamin H. 920 CHURCH ST N 28025 #036-07-1949 L1950 **GS TS** *071 †85,90

FLOWERS, George Adam. 354 COPPERFIELD BLVD NE 28025 #016-06-1994 L2003 **OSM** *020 †16

FOUST, Kim Marie. 200 MEDICAL PARK DR, STE 300 28025 #038-43-1992 L1997 **IM** *020 †20

FOUST, Robert Thos. 1070 VINEHAVEN DR 28025 #047-06-1980 L1981 **GE** *020 †20

FOWLER, Fred Chas. 270 COPPERFIELD BLVD NE 28025 #036-05-1986 L1993 **GE HEP** *020 †20

FRANCESCO, Jeffrey A. 920 CHURCH ST N 28025 #035-03-1986 L1991 **IM** *020 †20

FREIDINGER, Brad Alan. ■ 28027 #036-07-2002 L2007 **ORS** *020

FROMKE, Jon Eric. 212 LE PHILLIP CT NE, STE 201 28025 #026-04-1996 L2001 **DR** *020 †80

FROMKE, Mark Kwen. 212 LE PHILLIP CT NE, STE 201 28025 #028-34-1994 L1999 **DR AR** *020 †80

FURR, Carl Augustus. 1054 BURRAGE RD NE 28025 #036-01-1958 L1958 **OBG** *071 †30

GABLE, Ronald Selman. 33 LAKE CONCORD RD NE 28025 #012-01-1965 L1979 **OPH** *020 †35

GADUDASU, Gouri. ■ 28027 #495-65-1997 L2000 **IM** *020

GAINES, Ashley Pendleton. 1085 NE GATEWAY CT, STE 200 28025 #045-04-1999 L2002 **IM** *020 †20

GALVIN, Jeffrey M. 552 CAMROSE CIR NE 28025 #035-15-1994 L2002 **EM** *020 †16

GARWOOD, Susan Renee. 920 CHURCH ST N, C/O NORTHEAST INFECTIOUS D 28025 #016-45-1985 L1988 **ID IM** *020 †20

GASKIN, Steve Michael. 1028 LEE ANN DR NE, STE 200 28025 #008-01-1987 L1994 **EM** *020 †16

GENTRY, Mary Katherine. ■ 28027 #036-08-2007 **FP** *012

GERDES, Joseph J. 212 LE PHILLIP CT NE, STE 201 28025 #010-02-1970 L1971 **DR** *020 †80

GERIG, John Stephen. 200 MEDICAL PARK DR, STE 320 28025 #010-02-1978 L1998 **NEP IM** *020 †20

GETTER, Michael Dennis. 354 COPPERFIELD BLVD NE 28025 #051-04-1981 L1992 **ORS** *020 †40

GILMORE, Ina Mae. 920 CHURCH ST N, NORTHEAST INFECTIOUS DIS 28025 #041-02-1981 L1999 **ID** *020 †20

GISMONDI EAGAN, Carmella. 200 MEDICAL PARK DR SU 28025 #041-12-1996 L2008 **IM** *020 †20

GOGLIN, William K, Jr. 920 CHURCH ST N, DEPT OF ANESTHESIA 28025 #010-01-1982 L1989 **AN** *040 †05

GOLLAPUDI, Anil K. ■ 28027 #495-50-1974 L1980 **IM CCM** *020 †20

GOLLAPUDI, Sobha Rani. 9681 WIDESPREAD AVE NW 28027 #495-50-1978 L1996 **IM** *020 †20

GOODRICH, Daniel Paul. ■ 28025 #012-01-2003 L2004 **FM** *020 †18

GOODWIN, Linda Sue. 1501 NEW GATE CT NW, CREATIVE RISK ANALYSIS INC 28027 #030-05-1984 L2002 **OS IMG** *062 †20

GREENE, Jeffrey Holden. 920 CHURCH ST N, CARE DEPT 28025 #041-02-1992 L1998 **PUD** *020 †20

GUPTA, Aradhana Patel. 200 MEDICAL PARK DR, STE 300 28025 #422-01-1995 L2002 **IM** *020 †20

HALL, John David. 380 COPPERFIELD BLVD NE, PSYCHOLOGICAL INSTITUTE 28025 #012-01-1997 L2005 **ADP P** *020 †75

HALSTENBERG, William K. 200 MEDICAL PARK DR, STE 320 28025 #038-43-1988 L1994 **IM** *020 †20

HAMMERS, Lynn M. ■ 28027 #018-03-1985 L1990 **GPM EM** *062

HAMMONDS, Robert Eugene. 113 COUNTRY CLUB DR NE 28025 #012-01-1958 L1961 **OTO** *071

HANCOCK, James E. 920 CHURCH ST N, DEPT OF ANESTHESIA 28025 #055-01-1986 L1999 **AN** *020 †05

HARPER, David Keith. 201 LE PHILLIP CT NE 28025 #036-01-1981 L1985 **OPH** *020 †35

HARRIS, Erin Fields. 1085 NE GATEWAY CT, STE 290 28025 #045-04-2004 L2007 **PD** *020 †55

HARRISON, Matthew Philip. 1028 LEE ANN DR NE, STE 100 28025 #051-04-1998 L2001 **FM** *020 †18

HARSCH, Alan David. 100 MEDICAL PARK DR, STE 310 28025 #012-05-1982 L2008 **PD** *020 †55

HAWES, Sara Kathleen. 1070 VINEHAVEN DR 28025 #305-01-2000 L2007 **GE** *020 †20

HENDRIX, James Grant. 354 COPPERFIELD BLVD NE 28025 #045-04-1987 L1992 **ORS** *020 †40

HENRY, Hector Himel, II. 5789 VILLAGE DR, CABARRUS UROLOGY CLINIC 28027 #021-01-1965 L1967 **U** *020 †95

HICKS, Anna Laurie. 66 LAKE CONCORD RD NE 28025 #012-01-1986 L1989 **PD** *020 †55

HICKS, Gloria W. 1065 VINEHAVEN DR 28025 #041-13-1979 L1981 **PD** *020 †55

HINSON, Tony Ray. 920 CHURCH ST N, CABARRUS INPATIENT MEDICIN 28025 #036-08-1989 L1991 **IM** *020 †20

HIPONA, Maria L. 1018 LEE ANN DR NE, INTERNAL MEDICINE ASSOCIAT 28025 #748-08-1988 L1995 **IM** *020 †20

HO, Albert Feng. 920 CHURCH ST N, SPECIALISTS, NORTHEAST MED 28025 #051-04-1990 L1999 **AN** *020 †05

HOFF, H Richard. ■ 28027 #035-19-1955 L1956 **IM CD** *071 †20

HOFFMAN, Jeffrey Dale. 270 COPPERFIELD BLVD NE, STE 102 28025 #036-01-1989 L1990 **FM** *020 †18

HOLLAND, Daniel Lee. 1028 LEE ANN DR NE, STE 100 28025 #036-08-1996 L1997 **FM** *020 †18

HOLT, James Anthony. 200 MEDICAL PARK DR, STE 460 28025 #051-04-1998 L2003 **END** *020 †20

HOOVER, John David. ■ 28025 #036-08-1995 L2005 **GS PDS** *020 †85

HOOVER, William David, Jr. 335 PENNY LN 28025 #036-01-1986 L1987 **D** *020 †15

HOPPER, Kelly Susan. ■ 28027 #036-05-2005 **FP** *012

HOUSTON, Michael Anthony. 56 LAKE CONCORD RD NE 28025 #036-01-2001 L2004 **GS** *100 †85

HUGHES, Lynn Allen. 200 MEDICAL PARK DR, STE 200 28025 #039-01-1968 L1972 **OTO A** *020 †45

HUMES, Ilona Spitsyna. 315 MEDICAL PARK DR, STE 202 28025 #913-47-1991 L2007 **IM** *020 †20

IGLEHART, James Nelson. 200 MEDICAL PARK DR, STE 400 28025 #020-02-1986 L1991 **GS** *020 †85

JARCHOW, Robert Clayton. 200 MEDICAL PARK DR, STE 500 28025 #028-03-1975 L1990 **OTO FPS** *020 †45

JASMINE, Mark Scott. 354 COPPERFIELD BLVD NE 28025 #024-01-1982 L1984 **ORS OSM** *020 †40

JENKINS, Timothy Owen. 212 LE PHILLIP CT NE, STE 201 28025 #036-01-1982 L1988 **VIR DR** *020 †80

JENKINS, Wanda. 211 LE PHILLIP CT NE 28025 #038-41-1979 L1983 **OBG** *020 †30

JOHNSON, Dan Earnhardt. ■ 28025 #036-01-1958 L1958 **PD** *071 †55

JOHNSON, Ernest Frank, III. 200 MEDICAL PARK DR, STE 320 28025 #051-01-1999 L2005 **NEP** *020 †20

JONES, Carla Deneen. 270 COPPERFIELD BLVD NE, STE 102 28025 #018-03-1993 L1996 **FM** *020 †18

JONES, Clayton J. 1452 HIGHWAY 29 N, CONCORD FAMILY PHYSICIANS 28025 #047-06-1952 L1958 **GYN** *071 †30

JONES, Michael Clayton. 349 PENNY LN, STE 349 28025 #036-05-1986 L1991 **OBG** *020 †30

JONES, Thomas Rodenbough. 212 LE PHILLIP CT NE, STE 201 28025 #001-02-1994 L1996 **DR** *020 †80

JORGE, Carlos Bernard. 964 COPPERFIELD BLVD NE, DBA: FARRINGTON FAMILY MED 28025 #308-02-1999 L2002 **FM** *020 †18

JOSEPHSON, Jill Patrice. 200 MEDICAL PARK DR, STE 430 28025 #011-03-1993 L1998 **OBG** *020 †30

KACZMAREK, Michael Kitson. 1028 LEE ANN DR NE, STE 200 28025 #045-04-2000 L2005 **EM** *020 †16

KALDY, Patricia Marie. 888 CHURCH ST N 28025 #036-05-1980 L1981 **UCM FM** *020 †18

KATAJA, Marylu B. 920 CHURCH ST N, NORTHEAST MEDICAL CENTER 28025 #008-02-1987 L1996 **EM** *020 †16

KEIPPER, Vincent Lee. 1085 NE GATEWAY CT, STE 200 28025 #047-05-1973 L1977 **IM IMG** *020 †20

KELLING, Douglas George. 200 MEDICAL PARK DR, STE 550 28025 #024-01-1972 L1974 **IM PUD** *020 †20

KELLY, Kristina Lysell. 900 BRANCHVIEW DR NE, STE 110 28025 #036-08-1998 L2002 **PD** *020 †55

KELLY, Patrick Thomas. 219 LE PHILLIP CT NE 28025 #021-05-1990 L1992 **PUD** *020 †20

KINNEY, Robert Bruce. 920 CHURCH ST N, DEPT OF PATHOLOGY 28025 #036-07-1981 L1985 **PTH** *020 †50

KLEIN, David Fremd. 398 COPPERFIELD BLVD NE 28025 #038-40-1986 L1993 **PS HS** *020 †85,65

KROLL, Christopher Robert. 100 MEDICAL PARK DR, STE 210 28025 #036-01-1995 L1998 **IC** *020 †20

KRUSE, Kevin Richard. 100 MEDICAL PARK DR, STE 210 28025 #038-40-1989 L1996 **IM CD** *020 †20

KRUSELL, Allan Robt. 920 CHURCH ST N, NORTH E MEDICAL CENTER 28025 #024-07-1986 L1995 **IM** *020 †20

KUNESH, Benjamin Paul. 390 COPPERFIELD BLVD NE 28025 #018-03-1991 L1994 **IM** *020 †20

LAM, Gordon Kawing. 200 MEDICAL PARK DR, STE 330 28025 #036-07-2001 L2007 **RHU** *100

LANE, William Henry. 7752 GATEWAY LN, STE 100 28027 #036-07-1992 L2002 **FM** *020 †18

LANGFORD, F P Johns. 1085 NE GATEWAY CT, STE 100 28025 #027-01-1989 L1995 **FPS OTO** *020 †45

LARK, Kurt Karl. 201 LE PHILLIP CT NE, CABARRUS EYE CENTER, PA 28025 #047-05-1994 L2000 **OPH** *020 †35

LARRABEE, Laura Jean. 66 LAKE CONCORD RD NE 28025 #036-05-1984 L1987 **PD** *020 †55

LECLAIR, James Donald. 212 LE PHILLIP CT NE, STE 201 28025 #041-09-1994 L2002 **DR RNR** *020 †80

LESHER, John Michael. 200 MEDICAL PARK DR, STE 350 28025 #021-01-2002 L2007 **PM PRS** *020 †60

LILES, George Welch. 920 CHURCH ST N 28025 #036-07-1944 L1944 **GS** *020

LIPSITZ, David Uri. 1084 VINEHAVEN DR, NORTHEAST UROLOGY 28025 #007-02-1990 L1995 **U** *020 †95

LOCKHART, David A. ■ 28025 #036-07-1951 L1952 **PD** *071 †55

LOFTUS, James Morgan. 354 COPPERFIELD BLVD NE 28025 #010-02-1974 L1979 **ORS** *020 †40

LONG, Frank Edward. 1054 BURRAGE RD NE 28025 #023-01-1975 L1976 **OBG** *020 †30

LONG, Thomas Theron, III. ■ 28027 #036-05-1966 L1966 **GE IM** *071 †20

LOUIE, Angela Kay. 380 COPPERFIELD BLVD NE 28025 #046-01-2002 L2007 **P** *020 †75

LUCAS, Steven Edward. 270 COPPERFIELD BLVD NE, STE 201 28025 #036-08-2002 L2004 **FM** *020 †18

MAH, Hans Sanghoon. 66 LAKE CONCORD RD NE 28025 #051-01-1999 L2001 **PD** *020 †55

MAHONEY, Laurie Kay. 1028 LEE ANN DR NE, CABARRUS EMERGENCY MEDICIN 28025 #035-08-2005 L2008 **EM** *012

MALONE, John Hugh, Jr. 1452 HIGHWAY 29 N, ARDSLEY MEDICAL GROUP PA 28025 #036-07-1960 L1960 **IM** *071 †20

MASIUS, William Glenn. 1028 LEE ANN DR NE, STE 200 28025 #036-08-1990 L1991 **EM** *020 †16

MASSEY, Dillard Thomas, Jr. ■ 28025 #036-08-2002 L2003 **PD** *100

MAY, Gayle Lynn. 920 CHURCH ST N, NOTHEAST INPATIENT SERVICE 28025 #048-04-2000 L2006 **IM** *020 †20

MC GRIFF, Buhilda. 992 COPPERFIELD BLVD NE, CAROLINA PEDIATRIC EYE SPE 28025 #011-02-1991 L1997 **OPH PO** *020 †35

MC KILLION, Patrick Chas. 920 CHURCH ST N STE 301E, NE MEDICAL ASSOCIATES 28025 #033-05-1987 L2004 **CCM PUD** *020 †20

MC KINSEY, Jonathan P. 380 COPPERFIELD BLVD NE, PSYCHOLOGICAL INSTITUTE 28025 #011-03-1997 L2004 **PYG PFP** *020 †75

MC MURRY, David Willis. 200 MEDICAL PARK DR, STE 300 28025 #036-01-1982 L1985 **IM** *020 †20 ‡

MC PHERSON, Milton L, Jr. 920 CHURCH ST N, NORTHEAST MEDICAL CENTER 28025 #051-07-1980 L1994 **IM CCM** *020 †20

MEIGHEN, Michael John. 354 COPPERFIELD BLVD NE 28025 #038-41-1995 L1997 **PM PRS** *020 †60

MILLER, David Clinton. 270 COPPERFIELD BLVD NE, STE 102 28025 #011-03-1971 L1996 **FM** *030 †18

MILLER, Douglas Arthur. 1028 LEE ANN DR NE, STE 200 28025 #010-02-1989 L1997 **EM** *020 †16

MOCK, Laura Jean. 66 LAKE CONCORD RD NE 28025 #041-14-1992 L1995 **PD** *020 †55

MOGABGAB, Edward Roddy. 940 LEE ANN DR NE 28025 #021-01-1980 L1995 **EM IM** *020 †20,16

MONROE, George Clarke. 390 COPPERFIELD BLVD NE 28025 #048-04-1975 L1979 **IM** *020 †20

MOON, James Patrick. 1054 BURRAGE RD NE 28025 #046-01-1979 L1987 **OBG** *020 †30

MOORE, Brian Thos. 200 MEDICAL PARK DR, STE 400 28025 #021-06-1984 L1989 **GS VS** *020 †85

MOORE, Christina Lynn. 212 LE PHILLIP CT NE, STE 201 28025 #051-01-1998 L2003 **EM** *020 †16

MORGAN, Amy Forsythe. 920 CHURCH ST N 28025 #041-02-1993 L1996 **PD** *020 †55

MULDOWNEY, Sean Michael. 1028 LEE ANN DR NE, STE 200 28025 #036-01-1991 L1995 **VIR DR** *020 †80

MULLIS, Garrick Brent. 1028 LEE ANN DR NE, STE 200 28025 #036-05-2001 L2004 **EM** *020 †16

MYERS, Earl Jos. 212 LE PHILLIP CT NE, CEMA 28025 #038-44-1983 L2000 **EM** *020 †16

NASIR, Ayesha. 270 COPPERFIELD BLVD NE 28025 #704-01-2001 **FP** *012

NELSON, Yvonne Sue. 354 COPPERFIELD BLVD NE 28025 #028-03-1982 L1984 **FM** *020 †18

NEULANDER, Matthew Jonah. 1028 LEE ANN DR NE, STE 200 28025 #033-06-2001 L2004 **EM** *020 †16

NIBLOCK, Franklin C. 120 LAKE CONCORD RD NE 28025 #036-07-1953 L1953 **PD** *071

NICHOLSON, Charles P, Jr. 9000 AVIATION BLVD 28027 #047-06-1958 L1960 **GS AM** *072 †85

NOBLE, Andrew Raymond. 354 COPPERFIELD BLVD NE 28025 #041-02-2006 L2006 **ORS** *020

NOFAL, Philip A, Jr. 188 UNION ST S 28025 #045-01-1992 L1994 **CHP** *020 †75

NORDAN, John Mc Lean. 1084 VINEHAVEN DR, NORTHEAST UROLOGY 28025 #036-05-1969 L1969 **U** *020 †20

NORTH, James Hugh, Jr. 200 MEDICAL PARK DR, STE 400 28025 #041-13-1986 L2006 **SO GS** *020

NOVITT, Cecilia Anne. 5641 POPLAR TENT RD, STE 101 28027 #040-02-1996 L2003 **FM** *020 †18 ‡

NYMBERG, Jerome H, III. 270 COPPERFIELD BLVD NE, STE 102 28025 #038-41-1982 L1995 **FM** *020 †18

O'BRIEN, Stephen Jos, III. 66 LAKE CONCORD RD NE, CABARRUS PEDIATRIC CLINIC 28025 #020-12-1991 L1995 **PD** *020 †55

OTTENI, Gerald Vincent. 212 LE PHILLIP CT NE, STE 201 28025 #051-01-1970 L1975 **DR** *020 †80

OZMENT, Richard Vince. 200 MEDICAL PARK DR, STE 400 28025 #012-05-1988 L1993 **GS** *020 †85

PANCOTTO, Frank Salvatore. 1070 VINEHAVEN DR 28025 #016-42-1975 L1980 **GE IM** *020 †20

PANNER, Eric John. 349 PENNY LN, COPPERFIELD OB/GYN 28025 #051-04-1991 L1995 **OBG** *020 †30

PARK, Ted Anthony. 920 CHURCH ST N, INPATIENT SERVICES 28025 #047-20-2002 L2004 *100

PATEL, Ashesh Hemant. 100 MEDICAL PARK DR, STE 210 28025 #051-01-2001 L2007 **CD** *020

PATEL, Yogesh K. 390 COPPERFIELD BLVD NE, COPPERFIELD INTERNAL MEDIC 28025 #025-07-1989 L1992 **IM** *020 †20

PERLMAN, Jason Matthew. 270 COPPERFIELD BLVD NE, CABARRUS FAMILY MEDICINE 28025 #654-01-2006 **FP** *012

PERRY, Jennifer Suzette. 304 WINECOFF SCHOOL RD 28027 #036-01-1994 L1997 **FM** *020 †18

PFEIFER, Thea Lindenman. 100 MEDICAL PARK DR, STE 310 28025 #019-02-1987 L1994 **PDE** *020 †55

PHILLIPS, Eslie Rolland. ■ 28025 #051-07-1984 L1987 **IM** *020 †16

PICOT, Francois Jacques. 319 PENNY LN 28025 #021-01-1989 L1999 **N** *020 †75

PILLER, Christine Frances. 920 CHURCH ST N 28025 #041-02-1992 L2001 **HMP** *020 †50

PIRRELLO, Jon Robert, Jr. 1090 VINEHAVEN DR, CAROLINA WEIGHT LOSS SURGE 28025 #035-09-2000 L2006 **GS** *100 †85

PLANER, Jonathan Alan. 920 CHURCH ST N, STE 255 28025 #036-01-2003 L2006 **NEP** *012 †20

POCHICK, Keith Allen. 1028 LEE ANN DR NE, STE 200 28025 #036-05-2003 L2006 **EM** *020 †16

POPE, Allison Chase. 5641 POPLAR TENT RD 28027 #041-02-2003 L2007 **FM** *020 †18

PRAKASH, Hemant. 1040 VINEHAVEN DR, CONCORD CHILDRENS CLINIC 28025 #495-08-1981 L1987 **NPM PD** *020 †55

PRESTA-CARNES, Marla M. 920 CHURCH ST N 28025 #016-02-1982 L1987 **OBG** *020 †30

PRICHARD, Elizabeth Hyde. 920 CHURCH ST N 28025 #045-04-1986 L1988 **PTH DMP** *020 †50

QUIGG, Gary Ray. 2308 KANNAPOLIS HWY, UNIVERSITY MEDICAL ASSOCIA 28027 #018-03-1978 L1979 **IM** *020 †20

QUINN, Robert Danl, Jr. 25 LAKE CONCORD RD NE 28025 #038-40-1980 L1986 **HNS OTO** *020 †45

RABARA, Hitesh P. 219 LILY GREEN CT NW 28027 #495-48-1992 L2002 **IM** *020 †20

RACKOFF, Geoffrey David. 200 MEDICAL PARK DR, STE 300 28025 #038-44-1994 L1997 **IM** *020 †20

RAFLO, Gary Todd. 201 LE PHILLIP CT NE 28025 #051-01-1974 L1992 **OS** *020 †35

RASMUSSEN, Jane Elliott. ■ 28027 #008-01-1990 L1991 **END NEP** *100 †20

REIFF, Mark. 5641 POPLAR TENT RD, STE 101 28025 #016-11-1996 L1997 **FM** *020 †18

RHEE, Harrison Kuhn. 1085 NE GATEWAY CT, THE CAROLINAS CONCORD 28025 #024-07-1999 L2005 **U** *020 †95

RHODES, David Franklin. 1070 VINEHAVEN DR 28025 #047-05-1985 L1990 **GE IM** *020 †20

RICHARDS, Tess Georgette. 270 COPPERFIELD BLVD NE, STE 202 28025 #654-01-2006 **FP** *012

RILEY, David Lindley. 212 LE PHILLIP CT NE, STE 201 28025 #051-04-1973 L1979 **DR** *020 †80

RIVELL, James Paul. 1018 LEE ANN DR NE 28025 #023-01-1990 L1995 **IM** *020 †20

RIZWAN, Shafeequr. 270 COPPERFIELD BLVD NE, STE 202 28025 #496-27-1997 L2007 **FSM** *012

ROBINSON, Mark David. 270 COPPERFIELD BLVD NE, STE 201 28025 #041-01-1983 L1989 **FM** *040 †18

ROCHE, Joseph James. 335 PENNY LN 28025 #010-01-1983 L1987 **D** *020 †15

ROSE, Brian Todd. 354 COPPERFIELD BLVD NE, NORTHEAST ORTHOPAEDICS, PA 28025 #031-01-1999 L2004 **ORS OSS** *020

ROSSITCH, John C. 212 LE PHILLIP CT NE, STE 201 28025 #036-07-1988 L1989 **DR NM** *020 †80,28

ROYCROFT, Robert David. 3020 WEDDINGTON RD, WEDDINGTON MED/PEDS 28027 #036-01-1995 L1999 **MPD** *020 †20,55

RUSSELL, Lori Danielle. 390 COPPERFIELD BLVD NE, COPPERFIELD INTERNAL MED 28025 #038-41-1994 L2006 **IM** *020 †20

SAAD, Daniel Frederick. 100 MEDICAL PARK DR, STE 310 28025 #045-01-1998 L2007 **PDS** *012

SAFI, Roozchehr None. 270 COPPERFIELD BLVD NE, STE 202 28025 #517-11-2002 **FP** *012

SAKACH, Valerie Adele. 920 CHURCH ST N 28025 #041-12-1980 L1994 **PD** *020 †55

SANDERS, Mark Savalas. 56 LAKE CONCORD RD NE 28025 #036-08-2000 L2005 **GS** *020 †85

SANDERS, Susan Culp. 335 PENNY LN 28025 #036-07-1988 L1991 **D** *020 †15

SCHAEFER, Michele Nicole. 380 COPPERFIELD BLVD NE, NORTHEAST PSYCHIATRIC & PS 28025 #030-05-2000 L2005 **P** *100 †75

SCHERER, Markus David. 100 MEDICAL PARK DR, STE 210 28025 #056-05-1994 L2000 **CD** *020 †20

SCHIFFERN, Shadley C. 354 COPPERFIELD BLVD NE 28025 #054-04-2000 L2006 **ORS** *020

SCHMIDT, Brian Joseph. 200 MEDICAL PARK DR, STE 400 28025 #038-43-2000 L2005 **GS** *020 †85

SCHMIDT, Jeffrey Scott. 200 MEDICAL PARK DR, STE 400 28025 #055-01-1989 L1994 **GS** *020 †85

SCHMIT, Donald Bernard. 920 CHURCH ST N, DEPT OF ANESTHESIA 28025 #051-01-1992 L1998 **AN** *072 †05

SCHWALBE, Frank Conrad. 920 CHURCH ST N, DEPT OF ANESTHESIA 28025 #011-03-1991 L1995 **AN** *020 †05

SCHWARTZ, Garry H. 100 MEDICAL PARK DR, STE 110 28025 #035-03-1994 L2005 **HO** *020 †20

SHEAFOR, Douglas Houston. 212 LE PHILLIP CT NE, STE 201 28025 #028-02-1992 L1996 **DR** *020 †80

SHEN, Qing. ■ 28027 #243-45-1990 L2003 **IM** *020 †20

SHERIDAN, David James. 212 LE PHILLIP CT NE, STE 201 28025 #036-01-1987 L1991 **DR** *020 †80

SIKES, Thomas Edward, Jr. 354 COPPERFIELD BLVD NE 28025 #012-01-1970 L1974 **ORS GP** *020 †40

SILVER, Robert Adam. 920 CHURCH ST N, PEDIATRIX MEDICAL GROUP OF 28025 #041-09-1990 L1996 **NPM PD** *020 †55

SIMPSON, Joseph Paul. 56 LAKE CONCORD RD NE 28025 #036-05-1991 L2000 **GS** *020 †85

SIROIS, John G. 212 LE PHILLIP CT NE, STE 201 28025 #035-03-1988 L1994 **EM** *020 †16

SKAHEN, James Raymond. 354 COPPERFIELD BLVD NE 28025 #035-15-1990 L1996 **HS** *020 †40

SMITH, Anthony George. 200 MEDICAL PARK DR, STE 400 28025 #038-45-1999 L2005 **GS** *020 †85

SMITH, Terri Sells. 920 CHURCH ST N 28025 #036-08-1995 L1999 **MPD** *020 †20,55

SNYDER, Christopher, III. 7752 GATEWAY LN STE 100, LAKESIDE PRIMARY CARE 28027 #051-04-1975 L1991 **FM** *020 †18

SPAIN, Blake Addison. 920 CHURCH ST N 28025 #017-20-1989 L2007 **PCC IM** *020 †20

SPENCER, Honnie Patricia. 298 LINCOLN ST SW, LOGAN FAMILY MEDICINE 28025 #038-06-1995 L1997 **FM** *020 †18

STACKHOUSE, Daniel Jay. 212 LE PHILLIP CT NE, STE 201 28025 #036-01-1988 L1994 **DR** *020 †80

ST CLAIR, Steven Howard. 707 MEMORIAL BLVD 28025 #035-01-1987 L1988 **OM** *062 †70

STEFFENS, Thomas Albert. 100 MEDICAL PARK DR, STE 110 28025 #024-07-1982 L1992 **ON IM** *020 †20

STEGMAN, Joseph Conradt. 990 LEE ANN DR NE, SUBURBAN PEDIATRIC CLINIC 28025 #017-20-1978 L1987 **PD ADL** *020 †55

STOUDMIRE, Jonathan Keith. 380 COPPERFIELD BLVD NE, PSYCHOLOGICAL INSTITUTE 28025 #038-44-2000 L2005 **PFP** *100

SUMICH, Andrew Ivan. 200 MEDICAL PARK DR, STE 350 28025 #041-05-2001 L2005 **PM** *020 †60

SUMNER, William Thomas. 335 PENNY LN 28025 #036-07-1996 L1997 **D** *020 †15 ‡

SURRATT, Robert Walter. 1085 NE GATEWAY CT, STE 200 28025 #036-07-1978 L1981 **IM** *020 †20

SWAN, Bill Joe. ■ 28025 #047-06-1954 L1960 **AN PUD** *071 †05

SWARNA, Anjani Devi. ■ 28027 #496-24-1992 L1999 **IM** *020 †20

TAKLA, Medhat William. 200 MEDICAL PARK DR, STE 230 28025 #036-07-1985 L1995 **TS** *020 †85,90

TALBOT, John Cyril. 920 CHURCH ST N, SPECIALISTS, NORTHEAST MED 28025 #047-20-1989 L1997 **AN** *020 †05

TALTON, Charles Chadwick. 270 COPPERFIELD BLVD NE, STE 202 28025 #036-05-2003 L2006 **FP** *012

TANKERSLEY, William S. 354 COPPERFIELD BLVD NE 28025 #005-12-1988 L1999 **ORS** *020 †40

TER POORTEN, Jon C. 335 PENNY LN, DERMATOLOGY GROUP OF THE 28025 #048-14-1995 L2000 **D** *020 †15

TER POORTEN, Maryanna C. 335 PENNY LN 28025 #045-01-1999 L2003 **D** *020 †15 ‡

THILL, Jennifer Kristin. ■ 28025 #048-02-1997 L1998 **FM** *020 †18

THOMAS, Amy Mc Ilveen. 920 CHURCH ST N, STE 301E 28025 #047-06-1992 L2005 **PUD CCM** *020 †20

THOMPSON, Kerriann Rochel. ■ 28025 #001-02-2005 L2008 **IM** *012

TIGNOR, David Cowden. 5641 POPLAR TENT RD, STE 101 28027 #051-04-1999 L2000 **FM** *020 †18

TOMLIN, Edwin Merrill. 102 LAKE CONCORD RD NE 28025 #047-06-1946 L1956 **U** *071 †95

TRAHEY, Thomas Francis. 301 MEDICAL PARK DR, HEART GROUP OF THE CAROLIN 28025 #036-05-1984 L1986 **CD IM** *020 †20

TRAMONTANA, Jane Maria. 219 LE PHILLIP CT NE 28025 #021-01-1987 L1996 **CCM IM** *020 †20

TROMBLEY, Michael John. 7752 GATEWAY LN, STE 100 28027 #035-45-1991 L1994 **FM** *020 †18

TROWBRIDGE, Thomston S. ■ 28027 #011-03-1994 L1997 **EM** *020 †16

TRUFANT, Scott Kenneth. 7752 GATEWAY LN STE 100, LAKESIDE PRIMARY CARE 28027 #036-01-1997 L1999 **FM** *020 †18

TSANG, Connie. 315 MEDICAL PARK DR, STE 202 28025 #067-01-1994 L2002 **N** *020 †75

TURNER, John David. 200 MEDICAL PARK DR, STE 250 28025 #012-05-1992 L2002 **HO** *020 †20

VAN RAVESTEYN, Jan August. 304 WINECOFF SCHOOL RD 28027 #016-42-1996 L1997 **FM** *020 †18

VARGA, John Todd. 200 MEDICAL PARK DR STE 43, CONCORD WOMEN SPECIALTY

VUONG, Trang Tuquynh. 7752 GATEWAY LN, STE 100 28027 #011-03-1996 L2006 **MPD** *020 †20,55

WAGNER, Jill Michelle. 200 MEDICAL PARK DR STE 43, CONCORD WOMEN SPECIALTY CT 28025 #051-07-1994 L1995 **OBG** *020 †30

WALDEN, Tony Lee. 200 MEDICAL PARK DR, STE 460 28025 #036-01-1981 L1985 **END IM** *020 †20

WALL, James Grier. 100 MEDICAL PARK DR, STE 110 28025 #036-01-1982 L1986 **HEM ON** *040 †20

WARD, Marc Edward. 319 PENNY LN, PIEDMONT ORTHOPEDIC SPECIA 28025 #020-02-1999 L2007 **ORS** *020 †40

WASSEL, John Jos. 920 CHURCH ST N 28025 #010-02-1974 L1981 **ORS UM** *020

WAX, Tim Davis. 212 LE PHILLIP CT NE, STE 201 28025 #027-01-1989 L1991 **PTH** *020 †50

WEHRUNG, David Earl. 212 LE PHILLIP CT NE, STE 201 28025 #038-41-1984 L1988 **DR** *020 †80

WELCH, Kenneth James. 1028 LEE ANN DR NE, STE 200 28025 #036-08-1988 L1990 **EM** *020 †16

WELSCH, Nelly Frances. 380 COPPERFIELD BLVD NE 28025 #045-01-2001 L2006 **P** *100

WENNING, Michael Theodore. ■ 28027 #011-04-2002 L2007 **P** *020

WESTON, David Chadwick. 5641 POPLAR TENT RD, STE 101 28027 #045-04-2000 L2001 **FM** *020 †18

WEVER, Aaron Sidscott. 335 PENNY LN 28025 #036-01-2002 L2004 **D** *020 †15

WHEATLEY, James W. 89 BRIDLEWOOD PL NE 28025 #023-01-1976 L1980 **OPH** *020 †35

WHEELER, James Arnold. 1054 BURRAGE RD NE 28025 #036-08-2002 L2006 **OBG** *020

WHELESS, James E, Jr. 130 LAKE CONCORD RD NE 28025 #045-04-1988 L1991 **IM** *072 †20

WHICKER, Winfry Evans. 3700 TAYLOR GLEN LN # 355C 28027 #036-05-1963 L1963 **FM** *071

WHITNER, Tanya Elizabeth. 920 CHURCH ST N, STE 3005 28025 #045-04-2002 L2003 **IM** *020 †20

WILLIAMS, Landirs Shaun. 920 CHURCH ST N, NORTHEAST ANESTH & PAIN 28025 #012-21-1993 L2004 **AN PME** *020 †16

YAP, Elsa Dumaug. ■ 28025 #748-11-1963 L1974 **PTH** *020 †50

YOUNG, Karlon K H. 920 CHURCH ST N 28025 #014-01-1978 L1987 **AN** *020 †05

ZAGAR, Christopher Alan. 7752 GATEWAY LN, STE 100 28027 #034-01-2000 L2002 **FM** *020 †18 ‡

ZOPP, Amanda Jane. 212 LE PHILLIP CT NE, STE 201 28025 #036-05-1996 L1997 **EM** *020 †16

CONOVER – CATAWBA

BRITTON, Mary. 1105 FAIRGROVE CHRCH RD SE, UNIFOUR URGENT CARE 28613 #038-44-1997 L2000 **FM** *020 †18

COFFEY, David G, III. 305 1ST ST E, PO DRAWER 1239 28613 #036-08-1994 L1997 **FM** *020 †18

COLE, Debra Wulfhorst. 3314 16TH AVE SE STE 12 28613 #036-05-1988 L1991 **PD** *020 †55

DOHENY, William R. 3511 GRAYSTONE PL SE, GRAYSTONE FAMILY HEALTHCAR 28613 #305-01-1989 L1993 **FM** *020 †18

FISHER, Michael Lawrence. 1105 FAIRGROVE CHRCH RD SE, UNIFOUR URGENT CARE 28613 #017-20-1995 L1998 **FM** *020 †18

FITZGERALD, Dwight Melvin. 3513 GREYSTONE PL 28613 #016-11-1969 L1976 **GS TS** *020 †85

GOLD, Steven A. 3511 GRAYSTONE PL SE, GRAYSTONE FAM HLTHCARE P.A 28613 #065-01-1977 L1994 **FM PHP** *020 †18

HARGROVE, Roderick Neil. 3521 GRAYSTONE PL SE 28613 #036-01-1998 L2007 **OPH** *020 †35

HIGHTSHUE, David Clayton. 3775 SARAZEN CT NE 28613 #017-20-1967 L1989 **OBG** *020 †30

LANEY, Thomas F, Jr. 3511 GRAYSTONE PL SE, GRAYSTONE FAMILY HEALTH 28613 #036-01-1999 L2001 **FM** *020 †18

LILLARD, Patrick Lynn. 3724 ROCK BRIDGE DR NE 28613 #038-41-1966 L1987 **PM GP** *020 †25,75

LONG, William E. 305 1ST ST E, PO DRAWER 1239 28613 #036-01-1972 L1972 **FM** *020 †18

LOWERY, Gayla Sue. 212 9TH ST NE 28613 #036-05-1978 L1979 **RO** *020 †80

MICHAEL, Douglas W. 305 1ST ST E, PO DRAWER 1239 28613 #041-02-1979 L1981 **FM** *020 †18

MIKUS, Kevin P. 305 1ST ST E, PO DRAWER 1239 28613 #025-07-1982 L1984 **FM** *020 †18

PATEL, Kant. ■ 28613 #409-02-1967 L1977 **FM GYN** *071

PILAND, John Henry. ■ 28613 #051-07-1985 L1990 **FM OM** *020 †16

PILAND, Kimberly Morgan. 4039 LEE CLINE RD, KIMBERLY PILAND, MD, PLLC 28613 #051-07-1985 L1991 **EM** *020 †16

SPEES, Lynn B. 3411 GREYSTONE PL 28613 #036-05-1975 L1975 **PD** *020 †55

THOMPSON, Aaron D, Jr. 3513 GRAYSTONE PL SE 28613 #051-01-1986 L1994 **GS** *020 †85

VIERLING, Brian Stephen. 305 1ST ST E, PO DRAWER 1239 28613 #028-34-1999 L2000 **FM FPG** *020 †18

CONWAY – NORTHAMPTON

TAYLOR, Francis Marvin. 111 E MAIN ST 27820 #036-08-1998 L1999 **FM** *020 †18

CORNELIUS – MECKLENBURG

ALEXANIAN, Amy Lowery. 19620 W CATABWA AVE 28031 #036-08-1999 L2000 **FM** *020 †18

ASTLE, Nancy J. 19900 W CATAWBA AVE STE B 28031 #060-01-1983 L1994 **D** *020 †15

ATRAK, Taisser Mostafa. ■ 28031 #306-01-1985 L2004 **NPM PD** *020 †55 ‡

BELL, Amelia Fort. 18920 N BEATTIES FORD RD 28031 #036-01-1984 L1997 **NPM PD** *020 †55

BIRD, Whitworth F, Jr. ■ 28031 #035-20-1958 L2007 **IM END** *020 ‡

CAMPBELL, John Floyd. ■ 28031 #038-06-1978 L1978 **IM** *020 †20

CAPPS, Richard Henry, Jr. 19620 W CATAWBA AVE, LAKESIDE FAMILY PHYSICIANS 28031 #036-08-1999 L2000 **FM** *020 †18

CHAPMAN, Todd Masters. ■ 28031 #036-05-1979 L1980 **OSS** *071 †40

COOK, David Martin. 19620 W CATAWBA AVE 28031 #036-01-1990 L1992 **FM** *020 †18 ‡

CULP, John Harry, Jr. 18515 STATESVILLE RD, STE C6 28031 #005-12-1961 L1964 **GYN** *020 †30

DEVINE, Stacey Etheridge. 19620 W CATAWBA AVE 28031 #045-01-1997 L2004 **FM** *020 †18

FALEWEE, Dominique A. 19620 W CATAWBA AVE, STE 204 28031 #396-02-1981 L1999 **CD** *020 †20

GALENTINE, Paul Guy. 19900 W CATAWBA AVE, FOUNTAIN PLAZA 28031 #036-07-1976 L1984 **OPH** *020 †35

GASKINS, Wendy Talley. 8311 MAGNOLIA ESTATES DR 28031 #036-08-1993 L1997 **PD** *020 †55

HARLEY, David Hardman. ■ 28031 #047-05-2000 L2007 **PS OTO** *020 †45

HARSTON, Phillip Reed. 18515 STATESVILLE RD, STE C6 28031 #020-02-1979 L1982 **OBG** *020 †30

HORD, Charles David. ■ 28031 #005-02-1982 L1995 **APM** *020 †05

JACOBS, Warren Allan. ■ 28031 #021-05-1958 L1973 **CD IM** *020 †20

LASSITER, Kenneth Robt L. ■ 28031 #036-07-1961 L1961 **NS** *071 †25

LAYMAN, Holly M. 17810 STATESVILLE RD, 3 OAKHURST PL STE 321 28031 #041-78-2001, ▲ L2004 *020

LEVINSKY, Matthew J. 19620 W CATAWBA AVE, STE 204 28031 #016-01-1996 L2005 **ICE** *020 †20

LINDQUIST, Lee Beth. 19620 W CATWBA AVE, LAKESIDE FAMILY PHYSICIANS 28031 #027-01-1987 L1992 **FM** *020 †18

LOWRY, R Tempest. ■ 28031 #038-06-1963 L1972 **EM GS** *071

MADRID, Gianna Demos. 20808 N MAIN ST, STE 103 28031 #011-02-1990 L2000 **PD** *020 †55

MARSHALL, Chas Foster, Jr. 19900 W CATAWBA AVE 28031 #045-01-1969 L1973 **PO** *020 †35 ‡

MATTHEWS, Andrew L. 19402 LAUREL GLEN AVE 28031 #048-04-1992 L2000 **EM** *020 †16

MC ALLISTER, David W. 18515 STATESVILLE RD, STE C6 28031 #036-05-1970 L1970 **OBG** *020 †30

NARA, Prasunamba Naga. ■ 28031 #495-50-1963 L1986 **AN** *020 †05

NARA, Sreeramulu N. ■ 28031 #495-62-1968 L1986 **U** *020 †95

NAUMANN, Janice S. 18515 STATESVILLE RD, STE C6 28031 #011-02-1988 L1996 **OBG** *020 †30

NICHOLS, Richard Truman. ■ 28031 #016-06-1969 L1970 **U** *071 †95

RASHET, Emanuel. ■ 28031 #028-34-1962 L1965 **PD** *071 †55

RIOU, Jeanpierre Alain. 19615 LIVERPOOL PKWY 28031 #035-19-1987 L1994 **PS** *020 †85,65

ROBERTS, Dayne K. ■ 28031 #038-43-1988 L2001 **DR** *020 †80

ROSE, Danielle Malbasa. 19607 W CATAWBA AVE 28031 #012-01-1990 L1992 **PD OS** *020 †55

SCHAUDER, Craig Stephen. 19900 W CATAWBA AVE, LAKESIDE COSMETIC SURGERY 28031 #025-01-1987 L1994 **D** *020 †15

SCHNEIDER, Lori Beth. 19615 LIVERPOOL PKWY STE A 28031 #035-19-1990 L1994 **N** *020 †75

SCHWALBE, Marcella Saylor. ■ 28031 #011-03-1993 L1996 **PD** *020 †55

SHULTZ, Kirkwood Tanner. 19900 W CATAWBA AVE STE C 28031 #036-07-1966 L1967 **IM END** *020

THOMAS, Michael Beman. 19620 W CATAWBA AVE 28031 #025-01-1979 L1981 **FM** *020 †18

TRIMARCHI, Albert Jos. ■ 28031 #561-17-1957 L1961 **AN FM** *071

WEEKS, Katherine Pratt. 19620 W CATAWBA AVE 28031 #036-08-1991 L1994 **FM** *020 †18

WINTER, John Arthur. ■ 28031 #035-06-1955 L1958 **RHU IM** *071 †20

WOLFF, Christian George. 19620 W CATAWBA AVE 28031 #001-02-1994 L1997 **FM** *020 †18

ZETLAU, Lori Sonja. ■ 28031 #056-06-1990 L1991 **IM** *075

COROLLA – CURRITUCK

THORP, James Horace M. ■ 27927 #036-01-1957 L1957 **GYN** *071 †30

CRAMERTON – GASTON

STORK, Richard James. ■ 28032 #051-04-1987 L2007 **APM** *020 †05

YUNG, Donald Jay. ■ 28032 #035-15-1960 L1964 **OPH** *071 †35

CREEDMOOR – GRANVILLE

AQUINO, John Michael. 2527 E LYON STATION RD 27522 #065-01-1991 L1995 **FM** *020 †18

BOSTELMAN, Catherina M. 2527 E LYON STATION RD 27522 #038-43-1998 L2000 **FM** *020 †18

DAVIS, Dereck Bernard. ■ 27522 #001-06-2001 L2007 **P** *020

ELLIOTT, James F, Sr. ■ 27522 #036-07-1954 L1954 **P** *071

GRANT, William Howard, Jr. 1614 NC HIGHWAY 56, COMMUNITY IMMEDIATE CARE C 27522 #001-02-1995 L2001 **FM** *020 †18

HOFFMEIER, Craig Alan. 2527 E LYON STATION RD 27522 #021-05-1986 L1987 **FM** *020 †18

JUER, Robert Craig. 2528 E LYON STATION RD 27522 #047-06-1979 L1985 **FM** *020 †18

LEE, Essie. 1614 NC HIGHWAY 56 27522 #005-12-1998 L2003 **FM** *020 †18

NELSON, Julia Kathryn. 2527 E LYON STATION RD 27522 #036-01-1997 L2000 **FM** *020 †18

SEN, Ananya Biswas. 2527 E LYON STATION RD 27522 #495-39-1989 L2006 **FM** *020 †18

SMITH, Allen Thos. 2527 E LYON STATION RD 27522 #023-12-1983 L2006 **FM** *020 †18

STALL, Tamra Hammond. 2527 E LYON STATION RD 27522 #038-06-1987 L1990 **FM** *020 †18

WILLIAMSON, Kwanna Vernit. ■ 27522 #036-01-2004 L2005 **P** *012

CROSSNORE – AVERY

BAKER, Charles Edwin. 1 CROSSNORE DR 28616 #036-01-1973 L1973 **FM PD** *020 †55,18

SMITH, Eustace H. GARRETT MEM HOSP 28616 #051-04-1950 L1951 **FM** *071

CRUMPLER – ASHE

BUTLER, Douglas John. RR 1 BOX 140A 28617 #038-40-1978 L1979 **FM EM** *020 †18

FREEMAN, Roy O. ■ 28617 #036-05-1953 L1953 **GP FM** *071

CULLOWHEE – JACKSON

ALLEN, Norma Royse. ■ 28723 #041-07-1956 L1973 **GP EM** *071

BOWLES, James Terrell. ■ 28723 #012-01-1970 L1971 **OTO** *071 †45

LOHMANN, Joni Marie. ■ 28723 #038-41-1989 L1994 **BBK** *020 †50

DALLAS – GASTON

AGOR, Longinus Olewuike. 107 N SUMMEY ST 28034 #690-02-1981 L2003 **IM** *020 †20

BERRY, Patricia Anne. 824 LOWER DALLAS HWY, DALLAS FAMILY MEDICINE 28034 #023-12-1995 L2005 **FM** *020 †18

CALOGERO, Thomas John. 824 LOWER DALLAS HWY, DALLAS FAMILY MEDICINE PA 28034 #035-15-2001 L2005 **FM** *020 †18

KAKRAKANDY, Arshad Nayamv. 107 N SUMMEY ST, FIRST FOUNDATION CLINIC 28034 #495-37-1998 L2005 **IM** *020 †20

RAFIQUE, Iram. 107 N SUMMEY ST, FIRST FOUNDATION CLINIC 28034 #704-21-1994 L2004 **IM** *020 †20

WEERAKOON, Ranjit. 701 W TRADE ST 28034 #220-02-1967 L1988 **IM PUD** *020 †20

WILL, Thomas A. ■ 28034 #036-05-1948 L1949 **GP** *071

DANA – HENDERSON

FOZZARD, Harry Allen. PO BOX 574, 16 GEORGIANNA LN 28724 #028-02-1956 L2001 **CD IM** *050

DANBURY – STOKES

MENDOZA, Dominador M, Jr. PO BOX 111 27016 #748-01-1968 L1977 **GS EM** *020 †85

DAVIDSON – MECKLENBURG

BEAMON, Ronnie Thurston. 705 GRIFFITH ST, STE 100 28036 #036-01-1982 L1983 **FM** *020 †18
BENSON, John Fisher. ■ 28036 #023-01-1947 L1955 **RHU IM** *071 †20
BRINGEWATT, Tamara Jean. ■ 28036 #036-01-1993 L1997 **OBG** *071
BROWN, Ernest Hyde. ■ 28036 #036-01-1957 L1957 **GYN** *071 †30
COMEAU, Sharyn Marie. 903 NORTHEAST DR, STE 102 28036 #305-01-1994 L2005 **CHP** P *020 †75
COREY, Charles Craig. ■ 28036 #010-01-1987 L1990 **EM** *020 †16
CREER, Raycinia Kimlayana. 705 GRIFFITH ST STE 100 28036 #028-34-2001 L2004 **FM** *020 †18
DAVIS, George Wm, Jr. ■ 28036 #019-02-1941 L1958 **P** *071 †75
ELLITHORPE, Chas Thurman. ■ 28036 #036-05-1970 L1970 **FM** *020 †18
FEIR, Terence Chas. ■ 28036 #060-01-1954 L1995 **P OS** *020 †75
FIGUEROA, Robert Lawrence. 705 GRIFFITH ST, STE 100 28036 #045-04-1996 L2001 **FM** *020 †18
FITZGERALD, Thomas M, Jr. ■ 28036 #050-02-1989 L1993 **P** *020 †75
FRANCIS, Susanne Elizabet. PO BOX 6088, DAVIDSON COLLEGE PO 28035 #048-13-2008 *012
GLASGOW, Douglas S M. ■ 28036 #067-01-1943 L1950 **IM** *071
HASKINS, Donald Miller. ■ 28036 #024-01-1947 L1967 **OS IM** *071 †20
HAY, Samuel Hutson. 400 AVINGER LN 28036 #024-01-1948 L1948 **IM** *071 †20
HESS, Carolyn Lorraine. 705 GRIFFITH ST STE 100 28036 #036-01-2000 L2001 **FM** *020 †18
HUMMEL, Craig Brewster. 18830 RIVER WIND LN 28036 #049-01-1978 L2004 **P** *030 †75 ‡
JAMES, Richard T, Jr. ■ 28036 #041-01-1943 L1954 **IM OM** *071 †20
KIM, Oksoon. ■ 28036 #583-03-1955 L1992 **IMG NM** *071 †28
KIMMEL, Donald L, Jr. PO BOX 1719 28036 #041-13-1960 *075
LAMBETH, John Phillip. PO BOX 6662, DAVIDSON COLLEGE 28035 #036-01-2006 **IM** *012
LODS, Stephen Christopher. 2101 SHILOH CHURCH RD, STE 101 28036 #017-20-1994 L1998 **PD** *020 †55
MABRY, Earl Winters. ■ 28036 #039-01-1971 L1975 **U** *020 †95
MACRIE, Jessica Webster. ■ 28036 #022-75-2006, ▲ L2008 **FP** *012
MANGE, Stephen Kennedy. 705 GRIFFITH ST, STE 100 28036 #001-06-1980 L1983 **PD** *020 †55
MYERS, Griffin Robert. PO BOX 6235 28035 #016-02-2007 *012
MYERS, Raymond Russell. 2101 SHILOH CHURCH RD, STE 101 28036 #422-01-1998 L2005 **PD** *020 †55
OLSON, Duane Chas. ■ 28036 #026-04-1965 L1966 **ORS** *074 †40
SHERRILL, Stephanie Bundy. 2101 SHILOH CHURCH RD, STE 101 28036 #036-08-1991 L1992 **PD** *020 †55
STEED, Amy H. 2101 SHILOH CHURCH RD, STE 201 28036 #045-01-1997 L2004 **IM** *020 †20
TARTE, Nancy B. 705 GRIFFITH ST, STE 100 28036 #048-14-1986 L1992 **PD** *020 †55
WHITE, Craig Justice. ■ 28036 #024-01-1986 L1990 **FM** *020 †18
WILLIAMS, William Thos. 209 DELBURG ST, STE 105 28036 #048-04-1973 L1977 **IM PD** *030 †55,20

DELCO – COLUMBUS

BUMGARDNER, Richard Catoe. 27443 ANDREW JACKSON HWY E, EAST COLUMBUS PRIMARY CARE 28436 #036-01-1997 L2000 **IM** *020 †20
HETER, Michael Allen. 25805 ANDREW JACKSON HWY E, DELCO URGENT CARE 28436 #035-08-1980 L1992 **FM** *020 †18

DENTON – DAVIDSON

BAKER, Clifton Ayres. 482 SURRATT RD 27239 #036-05-1983 L1984 **EM FM** *020 †18
BREWER, Thomas Edmund, Jr. 18539 S NC HIGHWAY 109, DENTON MEDICAL CENTER, PA 27239 #036-05-1983 L2005 **GP EM** *075

DENVER – LINCOLN

AHIGIAN, Gerald Thomas. 2266 N HIGHWAY 16 28037 #654-01-1982 L1989 **FM IM** *020 †18
BURKE, Timothy Alan. ■ 28037 #047-05-1985 L1993 **AN** *020 †05
CHANDLER, Joe Thurston. ■ 28037 #045-01-1963 L1971 **NEP IM** *071 †20
CHI, Hong-Yup. 6127 HIGHWAY 16 S 28037 #051-04-1966 L1970 **FM** *072
GREGORY, William Lyon. ■ 28037 #045-01-1955 L1957 **GP OS** *020
HABASHI, Maher Fahim. 2266 N HIGHWAY 16 28037 #330-02-1960 L1990 **HS** *020 †40
HABASHI-AHIGIAN, Susane. 2266 N HIGHWAY 16 28037 #654-01-1983 L1989 **FM** *020 †18
HILDEBRAND, Stephen Ward. 7482 WATERSIDE CROSNG BLVD, STE 202 28037 #036-01-1998 L2005 **OBG** *020 †30
JAROSZEWSKI, David Louis. 5732 HIGHWAY 150 E 28037 #056-06-1980 L1998 **FM** *020 †18 ‡
NADRA, Wissam Edward. 275 N HIGHWAY 16, STE 103 28037 #654-01-1989 L2000 **PD** *020
REDELSPERGER, Rodney Lane. 294 N HIGHWAY 16, STE A 28037 #665-01-1997 L2002 **IM** *020 ‡
STOFFEL, Elisabeth Anne. 7482 WATERSIDE CROSNG BLVD, STE 202 28037 #041-01-2006 L2006 **FM** *020 †18
SYKOLA, Raymond, Jr. ■ 28037 #036-05-2001 L2003 **AN** *020 †05
TOMOVICH, Vesna. 275 N HIGHWAY 16, STE 104 28037 #038-44-1998 L2004 **FM** *020 †18
WALRATH, David Langdon. ■ 28037 #033-05-1970 L2005 **GS GP** *020 †85 ‡

DILLSBORO – JACKSON

BRIUKS-CANNON, Velta F. 342 HILL STREET 28725 #594-01-1943 L1963 **PD** *071 †55

DOBSON – SURRY

BOLLING, Gwendolyn M. 118 HAMBY RD, & NUTRITION 27017 #023-01-1980 L2000 **IM** *020 †20

RAJECKA, Zuzana. ■ 27017 #286-12-1994 L1999 **IM** *020 †20

DUBLIN – BLADEN

JUDY, Lewis Martin. PO BOX 70, 567 PEGGYS COVE PL 28332 #055-01-1964 L1996 **EM FM** *040 †18,16
SUMMERLIN, Robert Lee. HIGWAY 410, DUBLIN CLINIC PA 28332 #036-01-1955 L1955 **FM** *071

DUNN – HARNETT

AGRAWAL, Neeraj R. 700 TILGHMAN DR, CAROLINA DUNN 28334 #495-28-1987 L1996 **HO** *020 †20
ALAHARI, Durga. 700 TILGHMAN DR, STE 704 28334 #496-24-1990 L2000 **PD** *020 †55
BARNES-DURITY, Monica D. 3331 EASY ST 28334 #566-01-1995 L2001 **FM** *020 †18 ‡
BETHEA, Barbara Lowe. 700 TILGHMAN DR STE 726 28334 #036-01-1982 L1983 **IM** *020 †20 ‡
BOK, Willem Eduard. 801 TILGHMAN DR, STE D 28334 #836-02-1963 L2000 **P N** *020 †75
BRINKMAN, Dennis Michael. 800 TILGHMAN DR, BETSY JOHNSON REGIONAL HOS 28334 #025-01-1971 L2001 **AN** *05
BROWN, Howard Richard. 805 TILGHMAN DR, STE C 28334 #005-15-1984 L2001 **OSM OAR** *020 †40 ‡
BRYANT, Michael Steven. 700 TILGHMAN DR, STE 710 28334 #020-02-1982 L1990 **GS** *020 †85
CAMPBELL, Elizabeth E. 700 TILGHMAN DR, CAROLINA DUNN 28334 #036-07-1982 L1984 **HEM ON** *020 †20
CHANG, Te-Ming Tommy. 700 TILGHMAN DR, VILLAGE SURGICAL ASSOCIATE 28334 #041-12-1997 L2002 **GS** *020 †85
CHIODO, Mary Ann. 104 TILGHMAN DR 28334 #055-01-1989 L1994 **PD** *020 †55
CHIODO, Vincent M. 104 TILGHMAN DR 28334 #055-01-1989 L1994 **PD** *020 †55
CHOI, Ji-Ho. 3331 EASY ST 28334 #583-03-1995 L2006 **FM** *100 †18
DUNCAN, Stacy Allen, Jr. 800 TILGHMAN DR 28334 #036-01-1956 L1956 **FM** *071 †18
ELLMERS, Brent Raymond. 700 TILGHMAN DR STE 718 28334 #017-20-1990 L1998 **GS** *020 †85
GIEBMANNS, Thomas. 805 TILGHMAN DR STE B 28334 #041-09-1998 L2002 **OBG** *020 †30
GOUBRAN, Michel. 801 TILGHMAN DR 28334 #915-04-1962 L2003 **IM OBG** *020 †30
GRAY, Patrick Hampton. 103 HUNT DR 28334 #036-05-1980 L1984 **OBG** *020 †30
HANCOCK, Richard Paul. 700 TILGHMAN DR 28334 #023-07-1961 L1965 **GS TS** *071 †85
JACKSON, Shari Scott. 104 TILGHMAN DR 28334 #048-13-1999 L2004 **PD** *020 †55
JAVED, Hanif. PO BOX 1389, C/O BRENT ADAMS LAWYERS 28335 #704-01-1960 L1985 **OPH** *071 †35
JOHNSON, Gale Denning. ■ 28334 #041-02-1944 L1944 **GS** *020 †85
LALLINGER, Gunther Jos. 800 TILGHMAN DR 28334 #409-16-1972 L1982 **EM IM** *020 †20
LEE, Eun Kyung. 3331 EASY ST 28334 #583-06-2001 L2007 **IM** *020 †20
LEE, Thomas C Y. 700 TILGHMAN DR 28334 #385-02-1958 L1977 **GS** *020 †85
LOPEZ, Manuel Emilio. 700 TILGHMAN DR, STE 720 28334 #005-06-1983 L1994 **IM** *020 †20
MANN, John Robt. 700 TILGHMAN DR, STE 716 28334 #045-01-1974 L1975 **GP** *020
MARIA, Josette. 800 TILGHMAN DR 28334 #041-09-1996 L2001 **IM IMG** *020 †20
MARQUARDT, Mark John. 800 TILGHMAN DR 28334 #026-04-1974 L1986 **FM** *040 †18
MC ELYNN, Kenneth Robert. 3331 EASY ST, TRI-COUNTY COMMUNITY HEALT 28334 #041-02-1999 L2004 **FM** *020 †18
MC KNIGHT, Martha Anne. 3331 EASY ST, CENTER 28334 #036-07-1981 L1998 **P CHP** *020 †75
MOHAMED, Adel W. 800 TILGHMAN DR 28334 #330-02-1965 L1975 **U** *020 †95
MOORE, Cassandra Nicole. 700 TILGHMAN DR, STE 706 28334 #034-01-1999 L2002 **HO** *020
PAI, Vinaya Balakrishna. 104 TILGHMAN DR, ABC PEDIATRICS OF DUNN, PA 28334 #004-01-2002 L2007 **PD** *100
PARIKH, Jay R. 700 TILGHMAN DR, STE 702 28334 #495-23-1979 L1995 **ORS** *020 †40
PATEL, Divya J. 805 TILGHMAN DR STE C, BROWN ORTHOPEDIC SURGERY 28334 #496-41-1997 L2004 **PM** *020 †60
PEREDA, Lourdes Amparo. 104 TILGHMAN DR 28334 #737-01-1993 L2004 **NPM PD** *020 †55
POE, Robert Wayne. 805 TILGHMAN DR STE A, HARNETT EAR,NOSE AND THROA 28334 #004-01-1982 L1987 **OTO FPS** *020 †45
PRASAD, Venkat L. 800 TILGHMAN DR 28334 #495-01-1983 L1998 **FM** *020 †18
RANA, Ahmad S. 800 TILGHMAN DR, BETSY JOHNSON REGIONAL HOS 28334 #704-01-1987 L1997 **IM** *020
REDDY, Indira Madulapalli. 861 TILGHMAN DR, STE 103 28334 #495-70-1995 L2004 **GE** *020 †20
ROBINSON, Linda M. 800 TILGHMAN DR 28334 #036-01-1976 L1976 **FM** *020 †18
SADAGOPAN, Radhika. 802 TILGHMAN DR 28334 #495-16-1988 L2006 **PD** *020 †55
SEDDON, Jennifer Lynn. 700 TILGHMAN DR STE 730 28334 #919-03-1968 L1985 **FM** *020 †18
SEDDON, John Michael. 700 TILGHMAN DR, STE 722 28334 #919-03-1967 L1977 **U** *020 †95
SEN, Shuvendu. ■ 28334 #495-46-1993 L2007 **NM** *012 †20
TAYLOR, Thomas L. 800 TILGHMAN DR 28334 #035-20-1953 L1972 **R** *020 †80
TREMONT, Stephen John. 700 TILGHMAN DR, STE 706 28334 #024-07-1974 L1979 **ON IM** *075 †20
VALDIVIA, Ricardo Luis. 3331 EASY ST 28334 #737-01-1992 L2006 **FM** *020
YOFFE, Mark. 700 TILGHMAN DR, CAROLINA DUNN 28334 #011-03-1977 L1982 **ON HEM** *020 †20
ZIA, Asif. 861 TILGHMAN DR, STE 105 28334 #690-03-1989 L1998 **IM** *020 †20
ZICH, Michael John. 608 TILGHMAN DR 28334 #016-11-1975 L1984 **OBG** *020 †30

DURHAM – DURHAM

ABBOTT, Gian Thomas. ■ 27713 #917-06-1984 L1994 *020
ABDELMALEK, Manal F. ■ 27712 #028-46-1992 L2006 **GE HEP** *040 †20
ABDELMONEM, Ashraf M. ■ 27707 #915-04-1989 L1999 **PHO** *020 †55
ABELLI, Gina Marie. ■ 27713 #035-03-2005 **PD** *012
ABERNATHY, William S. 2609 N DUKE ST 27704 #035-01-1969 L1980 **CD IM** *020 †20
ABERNETHY, Amy Pickar. 25177 MORRIS BLDG BOX 3436, DUKE UNVERSITY MEDICAL CEN 27710 #036-07-1994 L1996 **HO** *071 †20
ABRAHAM, Dennis Manaloor. ■ 27703 #041-02-2002 L2005 **CD** *012 †20
ABRAMSON, Murray A. 718 RUTHERFORD ST 27705 #036-07-1991 L1994 **ID** *071 †20
ACHARYA, Anjana N. 1301 FAYETTEVILLE ST, CENTER INC 27707 #495-76-1973 L1994 **IM** *020 †20

■ = Address Information Privacy Protected

ACHNECK, Hardean Eric. ■ 27705 #008-01-2005 **GS** *012
ADAMS, Dolph Oliver. 718 RUTHERFORD ST 27705 #012-01-1965 L1965 **PTH IG** *050 †50
ADAMS, George Liell. ■ 27705 #036-08-2000 L2003 **IC** *012 †20
ADAMS, Julie Lynn. ■ 27707 #005-12-2002 L2006 **P** *100 †75
ADAMS, Kelley Michelle. ■ 27713 #047-06-2004 L2006 **P** *012
ADAMS, Martha B. 3024 PICKETT RD 27705 #051-01-1976 L1978 **IM IMG** *020 †20
ADAMSON, David Cory. RESEARCH DR, DUMC MSRB 479 BOX 2624 27710 #023-07-1998 L2005 **NS** *020
ADAMSON, Megan Cason. ■ 27713 #024-05-2008 *012
ADDISON, W Allen. BOX 3296 DUKE UN MEDICAL C 27710 #036-07-1960 L1960 **GYN** *020 †30
ADELI, Mehdi Mohammad. ■ 27713 #875-01-1993 L2003 **AI** *012 †55
ADEROJU, Elizabeth O. 4220 N ROXBORO ST, PALMETTO FAMILY HEALTH 27704 #047-07-2001 L2006 **IM** *020
ADKINS, Deanna Wilson. DIV OF PEDIATRIC ENDOCRINO, DUMC 3080 27710 #012-01-1997 L2001 **PDE** *020 †55
ADLAND, Peter F. 21 W COLONY PL STE 230 27705 #010-02-1975 L1980 **P CHP** *020 †75
ADOMONIS, Henry John. 5400 S MIAMI BLVD 27703 #067-01-1977 L1994 **GP** *020
AFSHARI, Natalie Adel. BOX 3802 27710 #005-11-1995 L2001 **OPH** *020 †35
AGATUCCI, Frank Alan. 3643 N ROXBORO ST, DURHAM REGIONAL HOSPITAL 27704 #016-11-1992 L2001 **EM** *020 †16
AGRAWAL, Swati. 4101 N ROXBORO ST 27704 #011-02-1997 L2001 **IM** *020 †20
AKASHI, Marc Kenichiro. P. O. BOX 3127 27710 #032-01-2007 **PD** *012
AKINLI, Leyla Bozgoz. ■ 27712 #902-10-1965 L1979 **P** *020
AKWARI, Anne Micheaux. ■ 27707 #010-03-1976 L1978 **OM** *030
AKWARI, Onye Egesi. DEPT OF SURGERY DUKE UNIVE 27710 #005-06-1970 L1978 **AS OS** *020 †85
ALBALA, David Mois. BOX 3457, DEPT OF SURGERY/DIV OF URO 27710 #025-12-1983 L2001 **U EM** *020 †95
ALBERT, David Ernest. DUKE MEDICAL CENTER 27706 #036-07-1983 *100
ALBRIGHT, Carol Anne. ■ 27705 #036-01-2005 **IM** *012
ALDER, Brian Douglas. ■ 27705 #036-07-2008 *012
ALDOSARI, Mohammed Saeed. DUKE MEDICAL CTR, DUMC 3936 27710 #797-01-1993 L2002 **CHN** *020 †55,75
ALDRIDGE, Julian Mc Clees, III. DUMC, BOX 3293 27710 #036-05-1998 L2002 **HS** *020 †40
ALEHAN, Dursun. PO BOX 3090, DUKE UNIVERSITY MED CTR 27710 #902-10-1987 **PDC** *100
ALEXANDER, Barbara Dudley. DUKE UNIV MED CTR, BOX 3035 27710 #036-08-1993 L1999 **MM ID** *020 †20
ALEXANDER, John Hunter. DUKE MEDICAL CENTER, BOX 3300 27710 #041-01-1993 L1996 **CD** *020 †20
ALEXANDER, Karen Patton. ROOM 7068 NORTH PAVILION, 2400 PRATT STREET DCRI 27710 #036-07-1992 L1996 **CD** *020 †20
ALEXANDER, Kenneth Andrew. ■ 27710 #054-04-1989 L1992 **PDI** *050 †55
ALEXANDER, Ratan. 718 RUTHERFORD ST 27705 #917-07-1987 L1997 **AN** *100
AL-GHAMDI, Saleh Ali A. ■ 27705 #797-02-1989 **PCC** *100 †20
AL-HADDAD, Christiane Eli. 3807 ERWIN ROAD, DUKE EYE CENTER 27710 #605-01-2000 L2005 **IM** *100
ALHASANIAH, Saad Mohammed. BOX 31282, DUMC 27710 #797-04-1994 L2008 **IM** *100 †20
AL-HAYK, Kefah Adnan. RM 1255 1LDUKE CLINIC, DUKE UNIVERSITYEMG LABNEUR 27710 #575-02-1996 L2002 **CN** *020 †75
ALI, Robin Renee. ■ 27701 #036-01-2000 L2005 **IMG** *020 †18
ALIABADI, Hamidreza. ■ 27707 #051-04-2003 **NS** *012
ALI-OSMAN, Francis R. ■ 27705 #048-13-2004 **GS** *012
AL-KHATIB, Sana M. 2400 PRATT ST 27705 #605-01-1993 L1996 **ICE** *020 †20
ALLEMAN, Matthew Clayton. ■ 27713 #021-01-2007 **GS** *012
ALLEN, Charles Davis, III. ■ 27713 #036-08-2006 **IM** *012
ALLEN, Diane Mary. BOX 3384, DUMB 27710 #036-07-1995 L1998 **HS** *020 †40
ALLEN, Idi Nkubo. ■ 27703 #033-05-2004 L2008 **AN** *012
ALLEN, Nancy Bates. DUKE MEDICAL CENTER, CB 3440 27710 #024-07-1978 L1981 **RHU IM** *020 †20
ALLEN, Trina Bernadette. ■ 27704 #035-06-1995 **CHP** *100
ALLINGHAM, Robert Rand. BOX 3802, ERWIN RD 27710 #038-41-1979 L1993 **OPH** *050 †18,35
ALLISON, Sheila Gayle. 6216 FAYETTEVILLE RD, STE 105 27713 #047-07-1980 L1997 **OBG** *020 †30
ALLPRESS, Stephen Matthew. ■ 27707 #671-02-1985 **PTH** *100
ALMENOFF, June Sherie. ■ 27705 #035-47-1985 L1993 **IM U** *020 †20
ALMOND, Maria Luisaganan. ■ 27707 #024-01-2006 **P** *012
ALPERT, Hilary Marie. DUMC 3616 RM 5830 27710 #025-01-2007 **OBG** *012
ALSPAUGH, James A, II. 718 RUTHERFORD ST 27705 #036-07-1991 L1995 **ID** *020 †20
ALSUGAIR, Abdulaziz Saleh. 718 RUTHERFORD ST 27705 #575-01-1988 L1997 **NM** *020 †28
ALTENHOF, Brent Michael. ■ 27713 #038-43-2006 L2006 **AN** *012
ALTOMARE, Ivy Paige. 3100 TOWER BLVD STE 600, UNIVERSITY TOWER 27707 #033-05-2001 L2007 **HO** *020
ALTSHULLER, Lillis F. 4020 N ROXBORO ST 27704 #038-06-1954 L1970 **PD** *071 †55
ALVA, Juan J. 609 WILLIAM VICKERS AVE 27701 #028-34-1960 L1977 **IM GE** *020 †20 ‡
ALVAREZ, Matthew Francis. P.O. BOX 3616 ERWIN ROAD, DEPARTMENT OF OB/GYN 27710 #038-40-1998 L2002 **OBG** *020 †30
AMALDOSS, Nirmala Mathew. 1824 HILLANDALE RD, VA MEDICAL CENTER CLINIC 27705 #496-07-1984 L2003 **IMG** *020 †20
AMANI, Ahmad Hamed. ■ 27713 #654-01-2000 L2007 **CCS** *100 †85
AMATO, Mary Theresa. 3414 N DUKE ST 27704 #036-07-1991 L1994 **EM** *020 †16
AMOS, Dennis Bernard. DUKE MEDICAL CENTER 27706 #352-07-1951 **IG PTH** *050
AMRHEIN, Timothy James. DUKE UNIV MED CTR, DEPT OF RADIOLOGY 27710 #035-09-2006 **DR** *012
ANDERSON, Albert Munirl. DUKE UNIVERSITY MEDICAL CE, BOX 3824 27710 #036-01-2000 L2005 **ID** *100 †20
ANDERSON, Deverick John. DUMC BOX 3824, DUKE UNIVERSITY MEDICAL CE 27710 #036-07-2001 L2004 **ID** *020
ANDERSON, Edward E. DUKE UNIV MED CENTER, BOX 3124 #1 HOSPITAL DRIVE 27710 #018-03-1941 L1942 **OPH** *071 †35
ANDERSON, Edward Everett. 4101 N ROXBORO ST 27704 #036-07-1958 L1959 **U** *071 †95
ANDERSON, Kathleen Anna. ■ 27713 #011-03-2003 L2007 **AN** *100
ANDERSON, Kenton Lee. ■ 27713 #005-15-2006 **EM** *012
ANDERSON, Page Albert W. BOX 3218 DUKE MED CTR 27710 #036-07-1964 L1965 **PDC PD** *050 †55
ANDERSON, Robert Wm. P O BOX 2636, ROOM 431 MSRB, DUMC 27710 #016-06-1964 L1994 **TS** *020 †85,90
ANDERSON, Rosemarie. ■ 27701 #023-01-1999 L2006 **P** *074
ANDERSON, William Blair. BOX 3802, DUKE UNIVERSITY EYE CENTER 27710 #026-04-1948 L1963 **CHP P** *071 †55,75
ANDERSON, Wm Banks, Jr. BOX 3802 27710 #024-01-1956 L1956 **OPH** *020 †35
ANDOLSEK, Kathryn. BOX 3195 DUMC 27710 #016-06-1975 L1977 **FM FPG** *020 †18
ANDRAWES, Michael Nathan. ■ 27707 #036-01-2004 L2008 **AN** *012
ANDREWS, Paul Stephen. 5726 FAYETTEVILLE RD, DURHAM OBSTETRICS AND 27713 #036-01-1981 L1982 **OBG** *020 †30
ANDREWS, Peter Ian. PO BOX 51729 27717 #143-07-1979 L1994 **N** *100
ANDREWS, Robert William. 205 FRASIER ST 27704 #036-05-1980 L1985 **U** *020 †95
ANGLE, Marcia Ann. 221 DEER CHASE LN 27705 #036-07-1981 L1982 **FM GPM** *062 †70,18
ANIL, Potti. 101 SCIENCE DRIVE, BOX 3382 27708 #495-27-1995 L2006 **HO** *100
ANLAR, Banu Fatma. 2312 PRATT ST # 8 27705 #902-05-1978 **CHN** *100
ANLYAN, William G. DUKE SCHOOL OF MEDICINE 27710 #008-01-1949 L1951 **GS** *071 †85,90
ANSONG, Annette Kesewah. 1 DUKE MEDICAL CTR, DEPT OF PEDIATRICS 27710 #010-03-2002 **PDC** *012 †55
ANTONELLI, Jodi. DUKE UNIV MED CTR, PO BOX 2922 27710 #041-02-2006 **U** *012
APPEL, James Ziegler, III. ■ 27705 #041-02-2001 **GS** *012
ARCASOY, Murat Osman. DUMC BOX 3912, DUKE UNIV MED CTR 27710 #902-04-1987 L1999 **HEM HO** *020 †20 ‡
ARDOIN, Stacy Ann. T0909 CHC BUILDING, DUMC 3212 27710 #038-40-1997 L2006 **RHU** *100 †20,55
AREPALLY, Gowthami. RESEARCH DRIVE, RM 116, RESEARCH PARK I 27710 #047-05-1989 L2001 **HEM** *020 †20
ARGENTA, Anne Elizabeth. ■ 27713 #036-01-2008 *012
ARMITAGE, Beth Alison. PO BOX 2905, DUKE UNIV MED CTR 27710 #035-01-1997 L1999 **N** *020 †75
ARMSTRONG, Andrew John. 2424 ERWIN RD, STE 606 27705 #051-01-2000 L2006 **HO** *100 †20
ARMSTRONG, Brenda Estelle. DUMC, BOX 3195 27710 #028-34-1974 L1979 **PDC PD** *020 †55
ARMSTRONG, Michael B. 222 BELL BUILDING, BOX 2916 27710 #026-04-2001 L2007 **PHO** *050 †55
ARMSTRONG, Sarah Commisso. 4020 N ROXBORO ST, DUKE CHILDREN'S PRIMARY CA 27704 #051-01-2000 L2006 **PD** *020 †55 ‡
ARNAOUT, Rand Khaled. PO BOX 2898, DUKE UNIV MED CTR 27710 #575-01-1989 L1994 **AI** *100 †03,55
ARNOLD, Staci Denise. ■ 27705 #036-07-2006 **PD** *012
ARORA, Alisha. ■ 27705 #025-01-2001 L2005 **GS** *100
ARROWSMITH, Joseph E C. ERWIN RD-DUKE UMC DEPT AN, BOX 3904 27710 #352-07-1985 L1996 **AN** *020
ARTZ, Evelyn M. BOX 3080, DUKE UNIVERSITY MED CTR 27710 #021-05-1998 L2006 **PD PDE** *020 †55 ‡
ASBURY, Melanie Nicole. ■ 27713 #036-01-2006 *012
ASCHER, John Albert. ■ 27707 #036-01-1980 L1982 **P** *050 †75
ASH, Brian Gettinger. ■ 27705 #041-01-2006 **AN** *012
ASHBURN, Jean Hearst. ■ 27713 #036-05-2006 **GS** *012
ASHLEY, Patricia. DUKE UNIV MED CTR, BOX 3179 27710 #048-12-1991 L2002 **PD** *020 †55
ASNANI, Aarti. ■ 27704 #036-07-2008 *012
ATCHLEY, Allen Edgar. ERWIN ROAD, DUMC BOX 31037 27710 #047-06-2003 L2006 **CD** *012
ATHAVALE, Kamlesh Vasant. ■ 27713 #496-38-1994 L2006 **PD** *020 †55
ATHIRAKUL, Krairerk. 508 FULTON ST, DURHAM VA MEDICAL CENTER 27705 #891-07-1986 L1996 **NEP** *020 †20
ATTARIAN, David Edward. 3116 N DUKE ST, DUKE HEALTH CTR 27704 #036-07-1980 L1984 **ORS OAR** *020 †40
ATTARIAN, Edward. ■ 27712 #035-03-1955 L1975 **GE IM** *071 †20 ‡
ATWATER, Amber Reck. ■ 27707 #016-11-2002 L2008 **D** *012 †20
ATWATER, Brett David. ■ 27707 #016-02-2002 L2005 **CD** *012 †20
AUCUTT-WALTER, Natalie Ma. ■ 27713 #041-14-2004 L2008 **N** *012
AURAND, Lisa. 4024 STIRRUP CREEK DR, STE 700 27703 #033-05-2000 L2000 **END IM** *050 †20 ‡
AUSTIN, Paul Ethan. 3414 N DUKE ST, STE 400 27704 #036-01-1989 L1992 **EM** *020 †16
AUTEN, Richard L, Jr. RESEARCH DRIVE DUKE UNIVER, 366 SANDS BLDG DUMC BOX 33 27710 #036-01-1981 L1984 **PD** *020 †55
AWDEH, Richard Mahir. ■ 27705 #008-01-2004 **OPH** *012
AYENI, Tina Abisolaadey. ■ 27703 #026-08-2005 **OBG** *012
AZAM, Anita. 58 GRAPEVINE TRL 27707 #160-09-2001 L2007 **PDE** *012
AZBELL, Jennifer Michelle. 1 DUKE MEDICAL CTR, DEPT MEDICINE 27710 #012-01-2003 **PHO** *012 †55
AZIZ, Samina Abdul. ■ 27713 #704-25-1994 L2000 **CHP** *020 †75
AZONOBI, Ijeoma Chinweoke. ■ 27704 #012-21-2005 **OBG** *012
BABAOFF, Marcus Elijah. ■ 27713 #036-01-2008 *012
BABCOCK, Andrew Carl. ■ 27713 #036-01-2007 **FP** *012
BACON, David Scott. 3643 N ROXBORO ST 27704 #036-07-1990 L1991 **AN** *020 †05
BAE, Jonathan Gregory. ■ 27713 #051-04-2005 **MPD** *012
BAGLEY, Adrianne Williams. DUKE UNIV MED CTR, BOX 3179 DIV OF NEONATOLGY 27710 #023-07-2001 L2007 **PD** *020 †55
BAHNSON, Tristram Dan. P.O. BOX 2959, DUKE UNIVERSITY MED CENTER 27710 #005-02-1984 L1997 **ICE IM** *050 †20
BAILEY, Clarence Almon. 4022 FREEDOM LAKE DR 27704 #036-01-1958 L1963 **PD A** *071 †03,55
BAILEY, Michelle L. 6301 HERNDON RD 27713 #035-08-1995 L1998 **PD** *020 †55
BAINBRIDGE, Daniel Tom. 4101 N ROXBORO ST 27704 #068-01-1995 L2000 *100
BAKELAAR, Ryan Timothy. ■ 27712 #033-05-2003 L2007 **OBG** *020 ‡
BAKER, Arthur Maine. ■ 27703 #045-01-2004 L2008 **OBG** *012
BAKER, Cheryl Ann. BOX 3164, DUKE UNIVERSITY MEDICAL CE 27710 #035-03-1995 L1998 **IM** *020 †20
BAKER, Jay Alan. DEPARTMENT OF RADIOLOGY, DUKE UNIVERSITY MEDICAL CN 27710 #036-07-1992 L1996 **DR** *020 †80
BAKER, Jeffrey Paul. 6301 HERNDON RD, DUKE CHILDRENS PRIMARY CAR 27713 #036-07-1984 L1990 **PD** *020 †55
BAKER, John Terrill. 2609 N DUKE ST, STE 700 27704 #024-01-1971 L1974 **IM** *020 †20
BALASUBRAMANIAN, Malar. ■ 27708 #038-06-2001 **PD** *100
BALFANZ, James Gregory. ■ 27705 #048-14-2007 **AN** *012
BALIUS, Anastasia Marie. TRENT DR DAVIDSON BLDG, M148 27710 #036-07-2001 L2008 **VIR** *012 †80
BALSARA, Keki Rohinton. BX 3951 M148 DAV BLD 27710 #041-01-2003 **GS** *012

7252

■ = Address Information Privacy Protected

BALTHAZAR, Ursula. ■ 27707 #016-43-2004 L2008 **OBG** *012
BAND, Joanne Fern. 4020 N ROXBORO ST, BOX 3675 27704 #008-01-1998 L2002 **PD** *020 †55
BANDA, Harriet Nkhwanjiwa. ■ 27713 #036-01-2008 *012
BANEZ, Winston. 1611 UNIVERSITY DR RM 2C 27707 #748-02-1989 L1993 **PD** *100 †55
BANKS, Faye Theresa. 1301 FAYETTEVILLE ST 27707 #051-04-1982 L1985 **IM** *020 †20
BAPPANAD, Divya Kumar. ■ 27701 #010-01-2007 **IM** *012
BARADA, Franc Alexander. 4004 BEN FRANKLIN BLVD 27704 #051-01-1971 L1980
  RHU IM *020 †20
BARBAS, Andrew Serghios. DUKE UNIVERISTY MED CTR, DUMC BOX #3443 27710
  #036-07-2007 **GS** *012
BARBEITO, Atilio. BOX 3094, DUKE UNIVERSITY MEDICAL CE 27710 #132-07-1998 L2004
  AN *100 †05
BARBER, James Bernard. 1821 GREEN ST 27705 #036-01-1990 L1993 **IM** *020
BARBER, Leo T, III. 1301 FAYETTEVILLE ST 27707 #010-01-1982 L1985 **IM** *020 †20
BARBORIAK, Daniel Paul. BOX 3808, DUMC 27710 #024-01-1986 L1996 **R N** *020 †80
BARCLAY, Joshua Scott. 2301 ERWIN RD, DUKE UNIV HOSP 27710 #023-01-2002 L2006
  IM PLM *020 †20
BARCO, Daniel Harris. ■ 27713 #036-07-1972 L1974 **FM** *030 †18
BARFIELD, Michael Everett. ■ 27705 #036-07-2008 *012
BARKAUSKAS, Christina E. PO BOX 2634 DUMC 27710 #036-07-2004 **PCC** *012 †20
BARKER, Gregory Mark. ■ 27713 #048-12-2005 **MPD** *012
BARKER, Piers Christopher. DUKE UNIVERSITY MEDICAL CE, BOX 3090 27710
  #035-20-1995 L2004 **PDC** *020 †55
BARNETT, Jason Cory. ■ 27713 #020-02-2002 L2008 **OBG** *020 †30
BARR, Daniel Coke. ■ 27701 #036-07-2008 *012
BARRETT, Amanda Clarice. ■ 27707 #011-03-2004 L2006 **EM** *012
BARRETT, Justin Anton. ■ 27705 #010-01-2005 L2008 **EM** *012
BARRIE, Arthur Marion, III. DUMC, BOX 31030 27710 #038-41-2003 L2006 **GE** *020 †20
BARROILHET, Lisa Marie. ■ 27713 #026-04-2005 **OBG** *012
BARTELL, Holly L. ■ 27705 #048-14-2006 **IM** *012
BARTLETT, John Alexander. BOX 3238, DUKE UNIVERSITY MED CTR 27710
  #051-01-1981 L1982 **ID IM** *020 †20
BARTLETT, Kathleen W. ■ 27707 #036-07-2000 L2002 **PD** *020 †55
BARTZ, Brett Hamiltonhu. DUKE UNIV MED CTR, DEPT OF RADIOLOGY 27710 #025-01-2006
  DR *012
BASAMANIA, Carl John. 249 E NC HIGHWAY 54 27713 #010-01-1984 L1995 **ORS GS** *020 †40
BASHORE, Thomas Michael. DUKE UNIV MED CTR, BOX 3012 27710 #038-40-1972 L1973
  CD IM *020 †20
BASS, Beaty Lee, Jr. 4315 BEN FRANKLIN BLVD 27704 #036-01-1971 L1973 **IM** *020 †20
BASTIAN, Lori Anne. ■ 27707 #012-05-1987 L1990 **IM** *020 †20
BASURA, Gregory Joseph. ■ 27707 #054-04-2005 **OTO** *012
BAUCOM, Robert Leslie. ■ 27701 #036-01-1960 L1960 **P** *071
BEADLES, Christopher A. ■ 27713 #048-13-2004 **AN** *100
BEARELLY, Srilaxmi. BOX 3802 27710 #036-06-1999 L2003 **OPH** *020 †35
BECKER, Mary C. ■ 27705 #023-07-1950 L1951 **PHP** *071
BECKER, Matthew Charles. DUMC, BOX 31262 27710 #035-15-2002 L2005 **CD** *012
BECKER, Richard Clinton. ■ 27705 #038-41-1982 L2003 **CD HEM** *020 †20 ‡
BEDLACK, Richard Stanley. 932 MORREENE RD 27705 #008-02-1995 L2000 **N** *020 †75
BEDNARSKI, Brian Keith. ■ 27705 #025-01-2003 **GS** *012
BEDROSIAN, Camille Lucia. 718 RUTHERFORD ST 27705 #024-01-1983 L1987
  HEM ON *050 †20
BEHAR, Victor Saml. DUKE MEDICAL CENTER, BOX 3126 27710 #036-07-1961 L1961
  CD IM *020 †20
BEHERA, Millie Aliva. DUKE UNIV MEDICAL CENTER, BOX 3143 CLINIC 1K 27710
  #068-01-1999 L2004 **OBG** *020 †30
BELCHER, Vernee Nicole. 3643 N ROXBORO ST, DUKE DURHAM REGIONAL HOSPI 27704
  #008-01-2004 L2007 **IM** *020 †20
BELHORN, Linda Raines. 4004 BEN FRANKLIN BLVD 27704 #036-01-1987 L1999
  RHU IM *020 †20
BELITSKY, Catherine Ann. 2020 W MAIN ST 27705 #064-01-1988 L1997 **P** *020 †75
BELL, David Fowler, Jr. ■ 27705 #023-01-1945 L1948 **PTH** *071
BELLIL, Yanis. ■ 27713 #045-04-2004 L2007 **IM** *012 †20
BEN-DAVIES, Maureen Eyatu. ■ 27713 #036-07-2004 L2006 **D** *012
BENITEZ-GRAHAM, Anamaria. ■ 27705 #036-07-2004 L2006 **D** *012
BENJAMIN, Brian Jeffrey. 2609 N DUKE ST 27704 #035-45-1991 L1992 **FM** *020 †18
BENJAMIN, Daniel K, Jr. 2400 PRATT ST, RM 0311 27705 #051-01-1995 L2001 **PDI** *020 †55
BENJAMIN, Dinesh. ■ 27703 #495-27-2004 *100
BENJAMIN, Jennifer Ruth. ■ 27713 #041-02-2004 L2008 **NPM** *012 †55
BENJAMIN, Mignon Froom. 2609 N DUKE ST 27704 #035-45-1991 L1993 **FM** *020 †18
BENNER, Eric James. ■ 27713 #030-05-2006 **PD** *012
BENNETT, John Douglas. BOX 3808 DUMC 27710 #067-01-1983 *100
BENNETT, Kyla Megan. DUKE UNIV MED CTR, GENERAL SURGERY RES TRAINI 27710
  #036-07-2006 **GS** *012
BENNETT, Mark Jonathan. 4101 N ROXBORO ST 27704 #917-06-1990 L2001 *100
BENNETT, Mikal Nasir. ■ 27703 #033-05-2004 L2007 **EM** *100
BENNETT, Nadia Leanda. ■ 27705 #023-01-2007 **IM** *012
BENNETT GUERRERO, Elliott. BOX 3094, DUKE UNIV MED CT, DEPT OF
  ANESTHESIOLOGY 27710 #024-01-1991 L2003 **CCA** *020 †05
BENONIS, James George. DUKE UNIVERSITY MEDICAL CE, BOX 3094 27710
  #041-13-2002 L2006 **AN** *100 †05
BENTLEY, Alexandra D. ■ 27713 #023-01-2006 **PD** *012
BENTLEY, Rex Colle. 4101 N ROXBORO ST 27704 #024-01-1986 L1992 **PTH** *020 †50
BENTON, Catherine Luden. MEDICAL CENTER, DUKE UNIVERSITY 27710 #035-01-2003 L2007
  DR *012
BERCHUCK, Andrew. BOX 3079, DUKE UNIV MED CTR 27710 #038-06-1980 L1987
  GO *050 †30
BERDAHL, John Palmer. DUKE UNIV EYE CTR, BOX 3802 27710 #026-08-2004 L2008 **OPH** *012
BERGLUND, Laura Harman. 4315 BEN FRANKLIN BLVD 27704 #036-01-1989 L1990
  IM *020 †20
BERKOBEN, Michael Scott. BOX 3014, DUKE UNIVERSITY MEDICAL CE 27710
  #041-01-1986 L1993 **IM** *020 †20
BERLANGIERI, Salvatore U. BOX 3949 DIV NUC MED 27710 #143-08-1982 **NM** *020 †28
BERLIN, Melvin. DUMC PO BOX 2914 27710 #036-07-1953 L1979 **GP OS** *071
BERMAN, Wallace Frank. 120 BELL BUILDING, BOX 3009, DUKE UNIV MED CE 27710
  #026-04-1969 L2000 **PG PD** *030 †55

BERNARD, Thomas Norton. ■ 27712 #012-01-2008 *012
BERNSTEIN, Douglas Michae. DUKE UNIV MED CTR, GENERAL SURGERY RESIDENCY 27710
  #023-07-2007 **GS** *012
BERREY, Miriam Michelle. ■ 27707 #012-01-1993 L1995 **ID** *100 †20
BERRY, Mark Francis. ■ 27713 #041-01-1999 L2001 **TS** *012
BESTAWROS, Michael Thomas. ■ 27701 #012-05-2005 **IM** *012
BETHEL, Mary Angelyn. DUMC, BOX 3604 27710 #036-07-1999 L2004 **END** *050 †20
BEUMER, Halton Wolfgang. ■ 27705 #005-06-2007 **OTO** *012
BEYER, John Leslie. DUKE UNIV MEDICAL CENTER, BOX 3519 27710 #048-12-1989 L1997
  P PYG *050 †75
BHATI, Rajendra Sunao. ■ 27713 #021-06-2002 L2005 **GS** *012
BHATTI, Muhammad Tariq. 2351 ERWIN RD, DUMC BOX 3802 27710 #035-09-1993 L2006
  OPH N *020 †35
BHATT-MACKIN, Seamus Mich. ■ 27713 #016-06-2004 **P** *012
BIDEGAIN, Margarita. 104 BELL BLDG BOX 3179, DUKE UNIV MED CTR 27710
  #924-01-1984 L1999 **NPM PD** *020 †55
BIGNER, Darell Doty. RESEARCH DR DUKE UNIV MED, 177 MSRB BOX 3156 27710
  #036-07-1965 L1966 **NS OS** *050
BINDER, Jay Allen. BX 3951 M148 DAV BLD 27710 #038-06-1998 **DR** *100
BISSET, Geo Simpson, III. DUKE UNIVERSITY MEDICAL CE, DEPT OF RADIOLOGY 27710
  #011-04-1975 L1994 **PDR PDC** *020 †55,80
BISSONNETTE, Linda Marie. 3310 CROASDAILE DR, STE 400 27705 #550-02-1995 L1998
  FM *020 †18
BLACK, Kyle Emerson, Jr. 120 WILLIAM PENN PLZ 27704 #036-05-1978 L1986 **ORS** *020 †40
BLACK, Mitchell Collins. ■ 27713 #036-08-2007 **IM** *012
BLACKFORD, Susan P. 4220 N ROXBORO ST 27704 #036-07-1991 L2002 **IM** *020 †20
BLACKSHEAR, Perry Justin. D U M C BOX 3897, DUKE UNIVERSITY MED CTR 27710
  #024-01-1977 L2002 **END IM** *050 †20
BLACKWELL, Kimberly L. 4101 N ROXBORO ST 27704 #026-08-1994 L1995 **HO** *020 †20
BLAKE, Alecia Camille. ■ 27713 #012-21-2004 L2004 **AN** *100
BLAKE, Dahlia Ann. DUMC, BOX 2733 27710 #033-06-1996 L2004 **PCC** *020 †20
BLAND, Amy E. DUKE UNIV MED CTR, DUMC BOX 3079 27710 #030-06-2001 L2005
  OBG GO *020 †30
BLAZER, Dan German, II. BOX 3003, DUKE HOSPITAL SOUTH TRENT 27710
  #047-06-1969 L1975 **P IMG** *050 †75
BLAZING, Michael August. BOX 3126 DUKE NORTH 27710 #005-02-1987 L1995 **CD** *020 †20
BLENKARN, George Douglas. DUKE MEDICAL CENTER, BX 3094 27710 #065-01-1958 L1970
  AN *020 †05
BLEVINS, Douglas Dane. ■ 27713 #051-01-1976 L2007 **ID IM** *020 †20 ‡
BLOCH, Edmond Cecil. ■ 27705 #836-02-1946 L1977 **AN PD** *071
BLOOMFIELD, Gerald Samuel. DUMC, BOX 31372 27710 #023-07-2002 L2007 **CD** *012 †20
BLOTZER, Angela Marie. ■ 27713 #036-01-2007 **GS** *012
BOEHME, Larry Reinhardt. ■ 27713 #018-03-1973 L2000 **FM** *020 †18 ‡
BOIMAN, Erica Elaine. ■ 27707 #036-07-2003 L2007 **OBG** *100
BOLES, Jeremiah Chad. ■ 27713 #036-01-2005 L2008 **IM** *012
BOLING, Christy Linnette. ■ 27713 #023-07-2004 **MPD** *012
BOLLINGER, Ralph Randal. BOX 2910 DUKE HOSP 27710 #021-01-1970 L1974 **GS IG** *020 †85
BOLOGNESI, Michael Paul. ■ 27705 #036-07-1998 L2004 **ORS** *100 †40
BOMBERG, Robert Bryan. ■ 27705 #036-07-1964 L1972 **IM** *020 †20
BONAVITA, Lisa Rose. ■ 27713 #041-14-2006 **PD** *012
BONIN, Andrew A. 2100 ERWIN RD, DUKE UNIV MED CTR BOX 3886 27710 #036-07-1975 L1976
  FM FSM *030 †18
BONNER, Mack, Jr. ■ 27712 #041-13-1965 L1973 **IM PHP** *030 †20
BOOKER, Millicent Candene. DUKE UNIV MED CTR, DEPT OF PEDIATRICS 27710
  #036-01-2005 L2007 **PD** *020 †55
BOOKMAN, Laurel Beth. ■ 27713 #050-02-2003 L2007 **NPM** *012 †55
BORDADOR, Basilia B. DUKE MEDICAL CTR 27706 #748-07-1965 **CHP PD** *020
BOREL, Cecil O. BOX 3094, DEPT OF ANESTHESIOLOGY 27710 #041-09-1977 L1993
  IM *020 20,05
BORGES-NETO, Salvador. DEPT OF RADIOLOGY/NUCLEAR, DUKE UNIV MEDICAL
  CENTER 27710 #187-13-1984 L1994 **NM** *020 †28
BORTZ, Lanelle Henzler. ■ 27707 #036-01-2003 **AN** *100
BOSSEN, Edward Hecht. DUKE HOSPITAL, DUKE HOSPITAL BOX 3712 27710
  #036-07-1965 L1966 **PTH** *020 †50
BOSWELL, Elizabeth Louise. ■ 27713 #012-22-2007 **PTH** *012
BOSWELL, Kristen Elisabet. ■ 27713 #036-08-2005 L2008 **PD** *012
BOULKINA, Lioubov Semenov. 5316 HIGHGATE DR STE 12, UNC AT CHAPEL HILL 27713
  #913-15-1990 L2005 **END** *012 †20
BOURGEOIS-GAVARDIN, M. ■ 27707 #036-07-1955 L1961 **AN** *071 †05
BOUSSIOS, Helen. ■ 27715 #036-07-2005 **MPD** *012
BOUSTANY, Rose-Mary N. PED NEUROLOGY, DUKE UNIV MED CTR 27710 #605-01-1979 L1988
  CHN OS *071 †19,75
BOWEN, Laura Madeline. 6020 FAYETTEVILLE RD, TRIANGLE FAM PRACTICE 27713
  #012-01-2003 L2006 **FM** *100 †18
BOWERS, James Ronald. BOX 3000, DUMC 27710 #056-05-1999 L2005 **ORS** *020 †40
BOWIE, James Dwight. BOX 3808 27710 #039-01-1967 L1979 **R DR** *071 †80
BOWMAN, Mary Catherine. ■ 27713 #011-03-1999 L2005 **ID** *012
BOWMAN, Rachel Dawn. ■ 27713 #047-06-2006 **FP** *012
BOYCE, Matthew Scot. ■ 27703 #051-04-2005 **N** *012
BOYD, Brita Nieland. DUMC 3967, DEPT OB-GYN 27710 #041-07-1989 L2003
  OBG MFM *020 †30
BOYD, Malinda Rashan. ■ 27703 #036-07-2007 *012
BRABHAM, William Walter. 1000 MCQUEEN DR, # 12107 27705 #045-01-2005 **IM** *012
BRADFORD, Daniel William. 508 FULTON ST, MHSL (116A) 27705 #036-01-1998 L2001
  P *020 †75
BRADLEY, Don Wayne. PO BOX 2291, BC/BS OF NC 27702 #051-04-1976 L1980 **OS** *030 †18
BRADLEY, Sarah Lynn. ■ 27704 #018-03-2007 **OBG** *012
BRADY, Carla Wheaton. 508 FULTON ST BLDG 16, VAMC/HSR&D (152) 27705
  #051-01-1997 L2004 **GE** *020 †20
BRADY, Matthew Joseph. ■ 27707 #032-01-2002 L2005 **NR** *012 †80
BRADY, Peter Kales. 3643 N ROXBORO ST, EMERGENCY DEPT 27704 #027-01-1989 L1992
  EM *020 †16
BRAITHWAITE, Mary Fox. P. O. BOX 3127 27710 #036-01-2007 **PD** *012
BRAITHWAITE, Susan S. 5316 HIGHGATE DR, STE 221 27713 #016-02-1969 L2002
  END IM *040 †20 ‡

BRANAGAN, Natalie Mari. ■ 27707 #023-01-2005 L2008 **IM** *012
BRANCAZIO, Leo Richard. BOX 3967, DUMC, DEPT OB/GYN, 4010 HOSPITAL 27710 #055-01-1988 L2001 **OBG** *020 †30
BRANCH, Malcolm Stanley. TRENT DRIVE DUMC, P.O. BOX 3662 27710 #012-01-1984 L1988 **GE IM** *020 †20
BRANCH, Mark, III. ■ 27704 #036-01-1987 L1988 **PUD** *020 †20
BRAND, Rusty Christopher. DUKE S CLIINIC BOX 3269, DEPT OF ORTHOPEDIA SURG 27710 #025-01-1994 L1996 **OAR** *020 †40
BRANTLEY, Jeffrey G. MBSA DUMC BOX 3022 27710 #036-01-1977 L1977 **P** *040 †75
BRASE, Rainer. 3523 N ROXBORO ST 27704 #407-07-1987 L1995 *020
BRAZER, Scott Robt. 249 E NC HIGHWAY 54, STE 200 27713 #038-06-1981 L1982 **GE** *020 †20
BREDEHOEFT, Steven John. ERWIN ROAD, BOX 2928 27710 #019-02-1974 L1988 **PTH** *040 †50
BREEN, Patrick Jos. 3643 N ROXBORO ST 27704 #539-04-1959 L1967 **AN** *020
BREITFELD, Philip Paul. DUKE UNIV MEDICAL CENTER, BOX 2916 27710 #035-45-1979 L2000 **PHO PD** *050 †55
BRENCKMAN, Wayne D, Jr. 5518 COLE MILL RD, PARKLANDS 27705 #008-01-1963 L1975 **ON HEM** *050 †20
BRENYO, Andrew James. ■ 27712 #035-06-2006 **IM** *012
BRESLIN, Dara Stephen. ERWIN RD BOX 3094, DEPT OF ANES DUKE UNIV 27710 #539-04-1993 L2001 **AN** *020
BRESSLER, Garrett Schell. 1920 FRONT ST 27705 #036-07-1978 L1982 **D** *020 †15
BREWINGTON, Beatrice Y. ■ 27705 #047-20-1998 L2006 **OPH** *020 †35 ‡
BREZINA, Dawn Leslie. 3643 N ROXBORO ST 27704 #011-02-1975 L1981 **IM** *020 †20
BRIDGE, Kevin Alan. ■ 27713 #036-01-2008 L2008 *012
BRIDGES, Edward Karl. ■ 27707 #036-01-1978 L1979 **P** *020 †75
BRIERE, Elizabeth Ann. 2800 MERIDIAN PKWY, STE 100 27713 #035-46-1977 L2003 **PD** *020 †55
BRIGGS, Melissa Antoinett. ■ 27713 #041-01-2007 **MPD** *012
BRIGHT, Cedric Marc. 508 FULTON ST, VA MED CTR ACS 11C 27705 #036-01-1990 L1997 **IM** *020 †20
BRIGHT, David Keith. 4205 BEN FRANKLIN BLVD, ASSOCIATES PA 27704 #036-07-1993 L1996 **IM** *020 †20
BRIGMAN, Brian Eugene. DUKE UNIVERSITY MEDICAL CE, BOX 3312 27710 #036-01-1994 L2001 **ORS** *020 †40
BRILL, Seuli Moushumi. ■ 27707 #038-45-2006 **MPD** *012
BRITT, Robert Carl. 1011 LAMOND AVE 27701 #036-01-1961 L1961 **IM PUD** *020 †20
BRITZ, Gavin Wayne. DUKE UNIVERSITY, DIV OF NEURSURGERY 27710 #836-01-1987 L2007 **NS** *020 †25
BRIZEL, David Manfield. BOX 3085 27710 #016-06-1983 L1987 **RO** *020 †80
BRODIE, H Keith H. 3211 SHANNON RD, STE 603 27707 #035-01-1965 L1974 **P** *071 †75
BRONEC, Peter Robt. 3901 N ROXBORO ST, STE 101 27704 #036-07-1981 L1987 **NS** *020 †25
BRONNER, Leslie. 2213 ELBA ST 27705 #036-07-1999 L2004 **P** *020 †75
BROOKS, Chamaine Renee. ■ 27707 #036-01-2008 *012
BROOKS, Kelli Rachel. ■ 27710 #036-07-1999 L2003 **CCS** *012 †85
BROTHERS, George B, Jr. 1901 HILLANDALE RD, STE F 27705 #024-07-1976 L1979 **RHU** *020 †20
BROTHERS, Matthew Barclay. ■ 27707 #036-01-2008 *012
BROWDER, James P, III. 3 TRAFALGAR PL 27707 #036-01-1970 L1970 **OTO HNS** *020 †45
BROWN, Ann Julia. TRENT DR, BOX 3611 DUMC 27710 #005-11-1988 L1992 **END IM** *050 †20
BROWN, Carrie Louisa. ■ 27713 #036-07-2004 L2008 **P** *012
BROWN, Christopher Alan. DUKE UNIV MED CTR, ORTHOPAEDIC SURGERY 27710 #038-41-2006 **ORS** *012
BROWN, Christopher Robert. DUMC, BOX 3000 27710 #051-04-2000 L2001 **ORS** *020
BROWN, Haywood Laverne. BOX 3084 - MED CTR, GYNECOLOGY 27710 #036-05-1978 L2002 **OBG** *020 †30
BROWN, James Trig P. 4205 BEN FRANKLIN BLVD, DURHAM INTERNAL MEDICINE A 27704 #028-02-1977 L1981 **IM** *040 †20
BROWN, Kelan James. ■ 27713 #045-01-2005 L2007 **DR** *012
BROWN, Kevin Desean. ■ 27713 #010-03-2003 L2007 **IM** *100 †20
BROWN, Monte Dean. DUKE UNIVERSITY, MEDICAL CTR 3701 27710 #048-04-1986 L1987 **CD IM** *020 †20
BROWN, Shari Lynn. ■ 27713 #036-01-2008 *012
BROWN, Susan E. 3643 N ROXBORO ST 27704 #010-02-1976 L1978 **FM** *020 †18 ‡
BROWN, Suzette Natasha. P. O. BOX 3127 27710 #043-01-2007 **PD** *012
BROWN, Tanilla Louise. ■ 27707 #036-01-2008 *012
BROWNE, James Andrew. ■ 27713 #023-07-2004 **ORS** *012
BROYLES, William Kevin. 1901 HILLANDALE RD, PHYSICIANS, INC SUITE D 27705 #011-03-1986 L1987 **FM** *020 †18
BRUNNER, Michael David. DUKE UNIV MED CTR BOX 3094 27710 #917-07-1986 **AN** *020
BRUNNER, Mike Patrick. ■ 27713 #038-40-2007 **IM** *012
BRUSATO, Christine Ann. ■ 27713 #033-05-2004 L2006 **FM** *020 †18
BRYCE, Sarah R Slavitt. 1004 BROAD ST 27705 #036-07-1988 L1992 **P** *020 †75
BRYSON, Paul Craig. ■ 27713 #041-12-2004 **OTO** *012
BUCHANAN, Robert A, Jr. 2609 N DUKE ST 27704 #036-05-1969 L1969 **CD IM** *020 †20
BUCKLEY, Charles Edward. 3621 WESTOVER RD 27707 #036-07-1954 L1954 **AI IM** *050 †03,20
BUCKLEY, Edward G. DUKE MEDICAL CENTER, BOX 3802 27710 #036-07-1977 L1978 **OPH** *020 †35
BUCKLEY, Niall J. 205 FRASIER ST 27704 #539-04-1979 L1991 **U GS** *020 †95
BUCKLEY, Patrick Jos. BOX 3712, DUKE UNIVERSITY MEDICAL CE 27710 #028-02-1976 L1999 **PTH HMP** *020 †50
BUCKLEY, Rebecca Hatcher. BOX 2898 DUKE UNIV MED CTR 27710 #036-01-1958 L1958 **AI PD** *050 †55,03
BUCKNER, Tyler Wayne. ■ 27713 #036-01-2005 **MPD** *012
BUCKWALTER, John David. 3643 N ROXBORO ST 27704 #036-01-1982 L1985 **AN** *020 †05
BULA, Melania Liza. ■ 27713 #042-03-1996 L2006 **DR** *020 †80
BULLARD, Elizabeth Sofia. ■ 27713 #048-15-2003 L2007 **P** *100
BULLARD, Ty L. ■ 27713 #048-12-2002 L2007 **AN** *100 †05
BULLER, Christopher E H. ■ 27707 #065-06-1984 **CD** *100
BURBRIDGE, Rebecca Ann. ■ 27703 #055-01-2003 L2007 **GE** *012 †20
BURCH, Daniel Jos. ■ 27713 #047-05-1984 L1985 **ID IM** *020 †20
BURCH, Warner Miller, Jr. DUKE MEDICAL CENTER, BOX 3283 27710 #036-05-1971 L1971 **END IM** *020 †20
BURFEIND, William Richard. ■ 27710 #035-01-1994 L1996 **TS GS** *020 †85,90
BURGESS, Douglas Michael. ■ 27713 #028-34-2006 **P** *012

BURHANS, Rollin S, Jr. ■ 27705 #020-02-1963 L1968 **GS** *020 †85
BURK, Carol Danko. 2609 N DUKE ST, STE 1000 27704 #041-12-1983 L1993 **PD PHO** *020 †55
BURK, David Lawrence. 2713 WINTON RD 27707 #041-12-1981 L1993 **DR** *020 †80
BURKE, James Robt. DUKE UNIVERSITY MEDICAL CT, BOX 2900 27710 #035-08-1985 L1989 **N** *020 †75
BURKE, Julie Marie. ■ 27713 #028-34-2007 **P** *012
BURKE, Paul Francis. DUKE SOUTH HOSPITAL CLINIC, DUMC 3634 27710 #016-01-2000 L2004 **N** *100 †75
BURKHART, Rebecca Elizabe. ■ 27713 #036-01-2007 **IM** *012
BURKS, Arvil Wesley, Jr. BOX 3530, DEPT OF PEDIATRICS 27710 #004-01-1980 L1983 **A PD** *030 †55,03
BURRIDGE, Suzanne K. ■ 27710 #038-41-2003 L2007 **NEP** *012
BURSEY, Keisha Lynn. ■ 27713 #012-21-2003 L2007 **OBG MFM** *100
BURTON, Claude Shreve, III. D.U.M.C ERWIN ROAD, HOSPITAL SOUTHBOX 3511 27710 #036-07-1979 L1981 **D IM** *020 †20,15
BURTON, Henry Blakely. ■ 27704 #045-01-1961 L1990 **P** *020
BUSCHER, April L. 508 FULTON ST, 1ST FL 27705 #036-07-2004 L2007 **IM** *020
BUSE, John Bernard. 5316 HIGHGATE DR, STE 125 27713 #036-07-1986 L1994 **DIA END** *020 †20
BUSH, Andrew Panchenko. 5400 S MIAMI BLVD, CONCENTRAL MED CTR 27703 #033-05-1989 L1995 **ORS** *020 †40
BUSH, Errol Lovester. ■ 27704 #036-07-2003 **GS** *012
BUSHNELL, Cheryl Diane. RESEARCH DRIVE RM 227C DUM, BOX 2900 BRYAN RESEARCH BL 27710 #056-06-1995 L1996 **N** *020 †75
BUTLER, Mark Damon. ■ 27705 #007-02-1980 L1983 **OS** *050
BUTTERLY, David Wm. BOX 3014, DUKE UNIVERSITY MEDICAL CE 27710 #036-07-1987 L1990 **NEP IM** *020 †20
BYRNE, Susan I. BOX 3841, DUMC 27710 #539-02-1993 L2002 **HO** *020 †20
BYUN, Angela Youngmee. DUKE UNIV MED CTR, BOX 3212 27710 #036-08-2004 **PPR** *012 †55
CABUGWASON, Lucila Noval. 11011 PARK RD 27713 #748-11-1963 L1979 **GP** *020
CAHILL, Mark Terrence. BOX 3802, ERWIN ROAD, DUKE UNIVERSITY EYE CENTER 27710 #539-04-1991 L2001 **OPH** *020
CAIRNS, Charles Bennett. ERWIN ROAD, DUMC 3096, DUKE NORTH 27710 #036-01-1986 L2004 **EM** *020 †16
CALDWELL, David Stewart. P O BOX 2978, DUKE UNIV MED CENTER 27710 #036-05-1971 L1971 **RHU IM** *020 †20
CALIFF, Robert Mc Kinnon. ROOM 1117 DAVISON BLDG, 200 TRENT DRIVE 27710 #036-07-1978 L1982 **CD** *050 †20
CAMITTA, Michael G W. BOX 3090, DUKE UNIVERSITY MEDICAL CE 27710 #048-13-1996 L2004 **PDC** *020 †55
CAMPBELL, George Wesley. ■ 27705 #045-01-1958 L1958 **IM END** *020
CAMPBELL, Shannelle Ae. ■ 27713 #008-01-2004 **GS** *012
CANCEL, Quinton Victor. ■ 27703 #036-07-2002 L2008 **U** *012
CANLAS, Karen Rivera. ■ 27705 #020-02-2001 L2005 **GE** *100
CANNING, Mary Louise. BOX 3837, DUMC 27710 #036-01-1985 L1989 **P** *020
CANNON, Trinitia Yevette. ■ 27713 #035-45-2003 **OTO** *012
CANTOR, Warren J. BOX 3357, DUMC 27710 #065-06-1991 **CD** *100 †20
CANTRELL, Leigh Anne. ■ 27713 #036-01-2003 L2007 **OBG** *100
CANTU, Edward, III. ■ 27707 #035-01-2000 L2004 **TS** *012
CANZONERI, Bernard Joseph. ■ 27713 #021-06-2001 L2006 **OBG** *100
CAOILI, Elaine Marie. 718 RUTHERFORD ST 27705 #025-01-1993 L1998 **DR** *020 †80
CAPEHART, Bruce P. 508 FULTON ST, VAMC DURHAM PSYCHIATRY (11 27705 #048-12-1991 L1993 **P PYM** *020 †75
CAPRARELLA, Angelo Michae. ■ 27707 #035-06-2003 L2007 **PAN** *012
CARAM, Lauren Brett. ■ 27705 #039-01-2001 L2005 **ID** *100
CARBONI, Michael Paul. BOX 3090, DUMC 27710 #038-44-1990 L2004 **PDC** *020 †55
CARLSON, Alan Neil. BOX 3802 27710 #036-07-1981 L1987 **OPH OS** *050 †35
CAROTHERS, Brent Hamilton. ■ 27713 #051-01-2006 **PD** *012
CAROTHERS, Josh Tolbert. DUMC, BOX 3000 27710 #038-41-2002 L2007 **ORS** *020
CARPENTER, Frederick, Jr. 3643 N ROXBORO ST 27704 #056-05-1982 L1985 **AN** *020 †05
CARPENTER, Gene Ammon, II. BOX 3951 27710 #025-01-2000 L2003 **DR** *020 †80
CARR, Avis Michelle. ■ 27704 #036-08-2007 **OBG** *012
CARR, John Ferguson, II. 823 BROAD ST 27707 #047-06-1968 L1975 **D** *071 †15
CARRAWAY, Martha Sue. 718 RUTHERFORD ST 27705 #036-05-1988 L1989 **PUD** *020 †20
CARRIKER, Curtis Glen. ■ 27713 #048-15-2007 **EM** *012
CARROLL, Barbara Anne. ERWIN RD, DUMC 3808 27710 #005-11-1972 L1984 **DR** *040 †20
CARROLL, Bernard James. DUKE UNIV MED CTR, BOX 3950 27710 #143-02-1964 L1983 **P** *030
CARROLL, Victoria Louise. ■ 27713 #051-01-2005 **P** *012
CARSON-DE WITT, Roslyn S. ■ 27707 #025-12-1991 *100
CARTWRIGHT, Peter Scott. ■ 27705 #025-01-1977 L2002 **OBG** *020 †30
CARVER, Alissa Renee. ■ 27707 #001-02-2007 **OBG** *012
CASPARI, Rael. ■ 27713 #003-01-2004 **PD** *012
CASSARA, Joseph E. ■ 27713 #050-02-2001 L2004 **GE** *012 †20
CASTELLANO, Francis M. ■ 27713 #048-45-2002 L2004 **DR** *100 †80
CASTOR, John Matthew. ■ 27713 #038-06-2005 **IM** *012
CATES, Willard, Jr. 2224 E NC HIGHWAY 54 27713 #008-01-1971 L1995 **GPM ID** *030 †70
CATO, Allen. 200 WEST PARK CORP CTR, 4364 S ALSTON AVE 27713 #036-07-1969 L1969 **PD PA** *050
CAVENAR, Jesse Oscar, III. ■ 27707 #665-01-2003 L2007 **P** *100
CAVENDER, Matthew Aaron. ■ 27707 #001-02-2006 **IM** *012
CAVENEY, Brian James. DUKE HOSPITAL, RM 4290 27710 #055-01-2002 L2004 **OM** *020 †70
CAVENEY, Erica. DUKE UNIV MED CTR, DIV OF ENDO 27710 #055-01-1998 L2002 **END** *020 †20
CELAURO, Kathryn Pierce. ■ 27707 #047-05-2006 **OBG** *012
CEPPA, Eugene Pedro. ■ 27713 #023-07-2003 **GS** *012
CERNANEC, Julie Marie. ■ 27712 #036-07-2006 **PD** *012
CHAH, Jane Alice. BX 3951 M148 DAV BLD 27710 #023-01-2000 L2001 **GPM** *100
CHAI, Chanhthevy S. 1901 HILLANDALE RD, STE D 27705 #036-01-2000 L2003 **FM** *020 †18
CHAISSON, Neal Fruet. ■ 27707 #051-01-2006 **IM** *012
CHALABI, Jamal. 300 ALEXANDER AVE, BOX 2629 27705 #875-02-1983 L2007 *100
CHALLA, Pratap. BOX 3802 27710 #011-03-1993 L1998 **OPH** *020 †35
CHAMBERS, Jeffrey Roy. 3308 DURHAM CHAPEL HL BLVD, STE 131 27707 #025-01-1986 L1987 **P** *050 †75
CHAMPION, Lawrence Andrew. 2609 N DUKE ST, STE 306 27704 #056-05-1973 L1975 **P** *020
CHANCELLOR, Jennifer Ann. ■ 27713 #001-02-2004 L2008 **OBG** *012
CHANDLER, Adam Franklin. ■ 27705 #004-01-2007 **EM** *012

■ = Address Information Privacy Protected

CHANDLER, Justin William. ■ 27713 #041-12-2004 **ORS** *012
CHANDLER, Mark C. 3713 UNIVERSITY DR, STE B 27707 #056-05-1982 L1987 **P CHP** *020 †75
CHANDLER, Nicole Lynne. ■ 27713 #041-12-2004 L2007 **PD** *012 †55
CHANDRA, Abhinav. BOX 3096 27710 #038-40-1995 L2001 **IM EM** *020 †16
CHANEY, Erin Elizabeth. ■ 27713 #036-01-2007 **AN** *012
CHAO, Nelson Jen An. 2400 PRATT ST STE 9011 27705 #008-01-1981 L1996 **ON HEM** *050 †20
CHAPMAN, Alison Kristen. ■ 27713 #047-05-2005 L2008 **PD** *012
CHAPMAN, Robert Sedgwick. US ENIVONMENTAL PROTECTN, B-243-01 NCEA-RPT 27711 #024-01-1971 **PHP ID** *050
CHARGUIA, Nadia Elizabeth. ■ 27713 #036-01-2007 **P** *012
CHASTAIN, Cody Allan. ■ 27713 #005-12-2008 *012
CHATCHATEE, Pantipa. PO BOX 2898, DUKE UNIV MED CTR 27710 #891-01-1987 **AI** *100
CHATTERJEE, Arundhati. ■ 27713 #495-02-1976 L1988 **PTH** *020 †50
CHATTERJEE, Srobona Tublu. 718 RUTHERFORD ST 27705 #024-05-1990 L1994 **IM GPM** *040 †20
CHAUHAN, Vijay Singh. PO BOX 3374, DUKE UNIV MED CTR 27710 #065-09-1992 **CD** *100 †20
CHAVALA, Sai Hemath. 27705 #028-46-2001 L2007 **OPH** *100 †35
CHECK, Jennifer Faith. ■ 27713 #036-01-2006 **PD** *012
CHEEK, John Merritt, Jr. ■ 27705 #036-05-1945 L1945 **GS TS** *071 †85
CHEIFETZ, Ira Marc. DUKE UNIV MED CTR, BOX 3046 27710 #008-01-1989 L1992 **CCP PD** *020 †55
CHEN, Christine Wong. 3643 N ROXBORO ST 27704 #036-07-1997 L2001 **IM** *020 †20
CHEN, James T. ERWIN RD, RM 1418 27705 #385-03-1950 L1966 **DR OS** *040 †80
CHEN, Jerome Gene. ■ 27713 #036-01-2004 L2007 **CCP** *012 †50
CHEN, Juhsien. PO BOX 95006, DUKE UNIVERSITY 27708 #036-07-2007 **IM** *012
CHEN, Mingda. ■ 27713 #020-02-2005 **AN** *012
CHEN, Yuan-Tsong. BOX 3028 DUKE UNIV MED CTR 27710 #244-02-1973 L1983 **OS PD** *020 †19
CHENG, Allen Cheuk-Seng. PO BOX 3867, DUMC 27710 #143-02-1993 *100
CHEPKE, Craig Thomas. ■ 27701 #035-19-2005 **P** *012
CHERAN, Sylvia. DUKE MEDICAL CENTER, BOX 2914 27710 #495-04-1973 L1977 **P** *020 †75
CHERRY, Anne Dillard. ■ 27705 #036-07-2008 *012
CHIA, Jessica Yeuling. ■ 27703 #021-05-2003 L2007 **PCC** *012 †20
CHIANG, Ambrose An-Po. DUMC 2733, DUKE UNIV MED CTR 27710 #244-04-1981 L1995 **PUD CCM** *020 †20
CHIANG, Dian-Jung. BX 3951 M148 DAV BLD 27710 #244-02-2004 **IM** *012
CHILDS, John Michael. 27707 #038-06-2005 **PTH** *012
CHILUKURI, Mohan Murali. 2400 BROAD ST, DURHAM FAMILY PRACTICE 27704 #020-12-1982 L1993 **FM FPG** *020 †1
CHILUKURI, Vani Rao. 718 RUTHERFORD ST 27705 #495-11-1982 L1993 **N** *072 †18,75
CHIN, Brian Michael. ■ 27705 #047-05-2004 **DR** *012
CHIN, Jeanette Ruth. ■ 27705 #047-05-2004 **OBG** *012
CHIN, Yungping. P. O. BOX 3127 27710 #048-12-2007 **PD** *012
CHINN, Ivan Kingyue. BOX 3068, DUKE UNIVERSITY MEDICAL CT 27710 #048-12-2001 L2008 **PD AI** *100 †55,03
CHIREAU, Monique Vera. ■ 27713 #043-01-1991 L2000 **OBG** *020 †30
CHISSELL, Hugh Richard. ■ 27705 #017-07-1985 L1995 *020
CHIUMENTO, Andrea Beth. BX 3951 M148 DAV BLD 27710 #422-01-2005 **EM** *012
CHO, Alex Han. ■ 27705 #026-04-2001 L2005 **IM** *020
CHO, James C.. ■ 27704 #422-01-2004 L2003 **P IM** *012
CHOCK, Johanna Yhua. DUMC 3505, DUKE UNIVERSITY MEDICAL CE 27710 #016-02-1998 L2004 **HO** *020 †20
CHOI, Jonathan Dale. ■ 27705 #036-07-2008 *012
CHOI, Kelly Mi. DUMC, BOX 31133 27710 #016-06-1998 L2002 **CD** *020 †20
CHOI, Steve Sok. 595 LASALLE ST, STE 1073 BOX 3256 27710 #143-11-1999 L2005 **GE** *100
CHORLEY, Candice Sally. ■ 27713 #047-07-2008 L2012 *012
CHOU, Nancy Chihyu. PO BOX 2634 DUMC 27710 #019-02-2004 L2007 **PCC** *012 †20
CHOW, Jessica Heng. ■ 27705 #036-07-2006 **OPH** *012
CHRISMAN, Allan Krekeler. 718 RUTHERFORD ST 27705 #010-01-1971 L1991 **CHP P** *040 †75
CHRISTOPHER, Eric James. ■ 27710 #056-01-1996 L1998 **HOS P** *020 †20,75
CHU, Fey. ■ 2400 #038-06-1942 **GS GE** *071
CHU, Vivian H. BOX 3824, ERWIN ROAD, DUKE UNIVERSITY MEDICAL CE 27710 #035-01-2000 L2003 **IM ID** *050 †20
CHUDGAR, Saumil Mahendra. ■ 27713 #036-07-2005 L2008 **IM** *012
CHUNG, Aimee Byonghee. ■ 27712 #036-08-2005 **MPD** *012
CHUNG, Richard Joonoh. BOX 3127 DUMC, 5409 DUKE NORTH 27710 #008-01-2005 **MPD** *012
CHUTE, John Patrick. ■ 27710 #010-02-1990 L2004 **HO** *020 †20
CHYLINSKI, Stefan. DUKE MEDICAL CENTER 27710 #759-09-1967 **TS** *050
CIECKO, Shawn Christopher. ■ 27704 #035-06-2004 **OTO** *012
CINCLAIR, Robert Donald. ■ 27713 #048-02-2004 L2008 **AN** *012
CLAPP, James Robt. 4030 KING CHARLES 27707 27710 #036-01-1957 L1957 **IM NEP** *020 †20
CLARK, Charles Edward, III. 3643 N ROXBORO ST 27704 #025-01-1968 L1975 **OTO FPS** *071 †45
CLARK, Douglas Winston. 2609 N DUKE ST, STE 1000 27704 #036-01-1983 L1985 **PD** *020 †55
CLARK, Karen Harrell. 3643 N ROXBORO ST 27704 #001-02-1982 L1986 **OBG** *020 †30
CLARK, Lisa Anne. 3116 N DUKE ST 27704 #024-01-1994 L1996 **GS** *020 †85
CLARK, Richard V. 718 RUTHERFORD ST 27705 #054-04-1977 L1992 **END DIA** *050 †20
CLARK, Tameta Rosette. DEPT OF ANESTHESIOLOGY, DUMC 3094 27710 #036-01-2004 L2008 **AN** *012
CLARKE, Bridger Wesley. ■ 27713 #051-01-2006 **IM** *012
CLARKE, Scott Russell. 5726 FAYETTEVILLE RD, STE 102 27713 #036-07-1995 L2000 **OTO** *020 †45
CLARKE-PEARSON, Daniel L. BOX 3079, DUKE MEDICAL CENTER 27710 #038-06-1975 L1979 **GO** *020 †30
CLARY, Bryan Marshall. DUKE UNIVERSITY MED CTR, TRENT DR. 27710 #005-02-1991 L1997 **GS** *020 †85
CLAVIEN, Pierre Alain. 718 RUTHERFORD ST 27705 #869-04-1982 L1993 *020
CLAVIEN-BUCHS, Sylvie. ■ 27704 #869-04-1992 L1995 *020
CLAY, Alison Suzanne. 14 SCOTTISH LN 27707 #016-02-1998 L2003 **PCC** *100 †20
CLAYTON, Daniel Alexander. ■ 27704 #007-02-2003 **NS** *012
CLEMENTS, Dennis A. 3024 PICKETT RD 27705 #035-45-1973 L1974 **PD ID** *030 †55
CLEMENTS, Fiona Marshall. DUME BOX 3094, DEPT ANES 27710 #036-07-1975 L1976 **AN IM** *020 †20,05
CLEMENTS, Walter L. ■ 27707 #001-02-1981 L1994 **GPM** *020

CLINTON, Megan Ann. ■ 27713 #026-04-2006 **AN** *012
CLOUTIER, Charles Albert. 508 FULTON ST 27705 #025-07-1997 L1998 **P** *020 †75
CLOWSE, Martin Converse. 5832 FAYETTEVILLE RD, STE 113 27713 #036-07-1996 L2005 **IM** *020 †20
CLOWSE, Megan Elizabeth. DUKE UNIVERSITY MEDICAL CE, BOX 3544 27710 #047-05-1999 L2005 **RHU** *100 †20
COBB, Fred Ross. 508 FULTON ST 27705 #027-01-1964 L1966 **CD NR** *050 †20
COBLENTZ, Craig Llewellyn. ERWIN RD 27710 #065-10-1980 L1986 **DR PUD** *020
COCHRAN, Chad Elliott. ■ 27713 #054-04-2007 **EM** *012
COETZEE, Lance Johan. PO BOX 3704 27710 #836-03-1983 L1995 **U** *100
COFFMAN, Thomas Myron. 4101 N ROXBORO ST 27704 #038-40-1980 L1984 **NEP IM** *050 †20
COGHILL, James Marvin, Jr. 4220 N ROXBORO RD 27710 #051-04-2001 L2004 **HO** *100
COHEN, Adi. ■ 27710 #035-19-1997 L2003 **IM** *020 †20
COHEN, Harvey Jay. DUKE MEDICAL CENTER, BOX 3003 27710 #035-08-1965 L1971 **IMG IM** *030 †20
COHEN, Seth Morris. DUMC BOX 3805 27710 #036-01-2000 L2006 **OTO** *020 †45
COHEN, Shawn Lawrence. 4101 N ROXBORO ST 27704 #067-01-1994 L1999 **OPH** *020 †35
COLE, Marg Eva Morris. 5726 FAYETTEVILLE RD, DURHAM OBSTETRICS AND 27713 #024-01-1993 L1997 **OBG** *020 †30
COLEMAN, Arnett. 1901 HILLANDALE RD, STE F 27705 #036-07-1975 L1976 **IM** *020
COLEMAN, Kevin Maurice. ■ 27713 #048-04-2004 L2007 **IM** *020 †20
COLEMAN, Ralph Edward. PO BX 3949 27710 #028-02-1968 L1979 **NM IM** *020 †20,28
COLIN, Brian Joseph. DEPT OF ANESTHESIOLOGY, DUMC 3094 27710 #035-08-2007 **AN** *012
COLLEGE, Dennis Lawrence. 3643 N ROXBORO ST 27704 #036-05-1976 L2007 **IM HOS** *020 †20 ‡
COLLINS, Bradley Henry. 510 NANTAHALA DR 27713 #036-07-1989 L1996 **GS** *020 †85
COLLINS, Timothy Alan. 932 MORREENE RD 27705 #025-07-1988 L1996 **N** *020 †75
COLON-EMERIC, Cathleen S. BOX 3003 DUMC 27710 #023-07-1994 L1995 **IMG** *020 †20
COLVIN, Oliver Michael. DUMC 3814, 409 JONES BLDG 27710 #028-02-1961 L1995 **IM OS** *050
CONLON, Niamh Mary. P O BOX 3094, DEPT OF ANESTHESIOLOGY 27710 #539-02-2001 *100
CONLON, Peter Jos, Jr. 718 RUTHERFORD ST 27705 #539-06-1986 L1994 **NEP** *020
CONNELLY, Scott Vincent. P. O. BOX 3127 27710 #033-06-2007 **PD** *012
CONNER, Matthew J. ■ 27713 #048-12-2007 **P** *012
CONNOR, Kathryn Mc Cabe. BOX 3812, DUKE UNIV MEDICAL CTR 27710 #023-01-1993 L1996 **P** *050 †75
CONSTANTINESCU, Octav Cri. DEPT OF ANESTHESIOLOGY, DUMC 3094 27710 #005-14-2007 *012
CONTARINO, Michael Rene. ■ 27707 #036-01-2008 *012
CONVERY, Patricia Ann. ■ 27713 #036-07-2008 *012
COOK, Alan. 99 LAKESHORE DR 27713 #036-01-1998 L1999 **P** *020 †75
COOK, Christopher Mark. ■ 27713 #047-06-2003 L2008 **ORS** *012
COOK, Jonathan Lambert. DUKE UNIV MED CTR, DEPT DERM BOX 3915 27710 #045-01-1992 L1999 **D DS** *020 †15
COOK, Wesley Allen, Jr. 718 RUTHERFORD ST 27705 #040-02-1963 L1970 **NS** *071 †25
COONRAD, Evelyn Vail. 3643 N ROXBORO ST 27704 #036-07-1949 L1952 **ON HEM** *071
COONRAD, Ralph Woodward. ■ 27707 #036-07-1947 L1950 **ORS HS** *071 †40
COOPERMAN, Nathan Daniel. ■ 27705 #036-07-2008 *012
COPELAND, Joyce Ann. 2100 ERWIN ROAD, DUKE FAMILY MED CTR 27710 #036-01-1975 L1975 **FM** *020 †18
COPLAND, Susannah Daly. 5704 FAYETTEVILLE RD, DUKE FERTILITY CTR 27713 #026-08-1999 L2007 **OBG REN** *020
COPP, Michael Vivian. ■ 27715 #917-07-1983 L1993 **AN** *030
COPPRIDGE, Alton J. ■ 27705 #035-01-1953 L1953 **U** *071 †95
COREY, Gordon Ralph. DUKE MEDICAL CENTER 27710 #048-04-1973 L1979 **ID IM** *020 †20
CORLESS, Joseph Michael. 3123 CAMELOT CT 27705 #036-07-1972 L1973 **OPH N** *050
CORSINO NUNEZ, Leonor Ada. DUMC BOX 3951, OFFICE OF GME 27710 #308-04-1999 L2006 **END** *012 †20
COTHRAN, Roger Lee, Jr. ERWIN ROAD, DUMC 3808 27710 #036-07-1995 L2000 **DR** *020 †80
COTTEN, Charles Michael. 204 BELL BLDG DUMC, BOX 3179 DUMC 27710 #011-02-1986 L1996 **NPM** *020 †55
COTTER, Gad. 2400 PRATT ST, PO BOX 17969 27705 #550-01-1989 L2004 *100
COTTLE, Patrick Michael. ■ 27713 #038-06-2003 L2007 **IM** *020 †20
COUGHLIN, James I. ■ 27712 #035-06-1966 L1999 **IM** *030 †20
COUSINS, Kurt Laurence. ■ 27707 #036-01-2008 *012
COUSINS, Scott Wm. BOX 3802 27710 #038-06-1982 L2005 **OPH IG** *020 †35 ‡
COX, Brady Barton. ■ 27712 #049-01-2006 **EM** *012
COX, Christopher Ethan. PULMONARY/CCM MSRB 275, DUKE UNIVERSITY MED CTR 27710 #045-01-1997 L2000 **PCC** *050 †20
COX, Edwin Baggett. 4411 BEN FRANKLIN BLVD 27704 #036-07-1971 L1974 **ON HEM** *071 †20
COX, Gary Matthew. DUKE MEDICAL CENTER, BOX 3281 27710 #051-01-1989 L1995 **ID** *020 †20
COX, Mary Elizabeth. ■ 27713 #048-14-2004 L2006 **END** *012 †20
COYNE, Tamera Dynene. ■ 27707 #036-07-1991 L1993 **GPM PD** *020 †20,55
CRAIG, Michael John. ■ 27713 #021-01-2005 **MPD** *012
CRANE, George Wm, Jr. ■ 27707 #016-06-1946 L1949 **D** *071 †15
CRANE, Larry Martin. 5107 SOUTHPARK DR, STE 101 27713 #048-04-1968 L1972 **DR** *020 †20
CRAWFORD, Jeffrey. BOX 3476 DUMC 27710 #038-40-1974 L1980 **HEM ON** *030 †20
CRAWFORD, Jennifer J. ■ 27705 #026-07-1988 L2001 **PD** *020 †55
CRAWFORD, Lawrence Edward. 3000 ERWIN ROAD BOX 3126, DUKE UNIVERSITY MEDICAL CE 27710 #051-01-1987 L2001 **CD** *020 †20
CRAWLEY, Brianna Kathleen. PO BOX 97291, DUKE UNIVERSITY 27708 #005-18-2008 *012
CRISCIONE, Lisa Giorgina. BOX 3490 DUMC 27710 #036-07-1998 L2002 **RHU** *020 †20
CROSS, Cindy A. BOX 3192 DUMC, 19 CLOVER DRIVE 27710 #047-06-1991 L1998 **OBG** *020 †30
CROW, Jennifer H. ■ 27705 #033-05-2005 **PTH** *012
CROWDER, Terrence Tevon. ■ 27704 #004-01-2003 L2006 **ORS** *012
CROWLEY, Anna Lisa. DUMC, BOX 31092 27710 #038-40-1998 L2005 **CD** *020 †20
CROWLEY, Matthew Janik. 508 FULTON ST, DURHAM VA MEDICAL CENTER 27705 #032-01-2004 L2007 **IM** *020 †20
CROWLEY, Steven Daniel. DUKE UNIV MEDICAL CENTER, BOX 3014 27710 #036-07-1996 L1997 **NEP** *020 †20
CROZIER, Joseph Charles. ■ 27707 #036-07-2008 *012
CRUME, Lou Ann. 718 RUTHERFORD ST 27705 #020-12-1986 L1987 **P** *020 †75
CRUMP, John Andrew. BOX 3867, ERWIN ROAD, DUKE UNIVERSITY MEDICAL CE 27710 #671-01-1993 L2006 **MM** *100

CSAKY, Karl Geza. 2351 ERWIN RD, DUMC BOX 3802 27710 #020-02-1983 L1983
OPH IM *020 †35 ‡

CSORBA, Amy Ruth. 3001 ACADEMY RD, STE 200 27707 #036-07-1984 L1985 FM *020 †18 ‡

CUFFE, Michael Scott. 1131 S DUKE ST, GREEN ZONE 27710 #036-07-1991 L1993
CD IM *030 †20

CULLEN, Nicole Rose. ■ 27713 #041-12-2008 *012

CULTON, Yancey Goelet. 407 CRUTCHFIELD ST, CENTER FOR WOMEN 27704
#036-07-1956 L1956 GYN OBG *071 †30

CUMMINGS, De Lora B. 1821 HILLANDALE RD, HILLANDALE MEDICAL CENTER 27705
#035-03-1989 L1998 FM *020 †18

CUMMINGS, Keith Lamont. ■ 27707 #036-07-2008 *012

CUMMINGS, Thomas John. P O BOX 3712, DUKE UNIVERSITY MEDICAL CE 27710
#033-06-1991 L2000 PTH *020 †50

CUNNINGHAM, Coleen Green. BOX 3499, DUKE UNIVERSITY MEDICAL SC 27710
#035-15-1985 L2003 PD ID *012

CURRY, Bryan Heath. 2609 N DUKE ST 27704 #010-03-1995 L2002 CD *020 †20

CUTSON, Toni Michele. 4321 MEDICAL PARK DR, STE 101 27704 #051-04-1980 L1984
FM IMG *020 †18

CVEJIN, Snezana Zivojina. 3643 N ROXBORO ST 27704 #957-08-1980 L1990 P *020 †75

DACOSTA, Victor Manuel. ■ 27705 #005-15-2007 OTO *012

DALY, John T. 4425 BEN FRANKLIN BLVD 27704 #035-20-1968 L1969 PTH FOP *020 †50

D'AMICO, Thomas A. ERWIN ROAD/DUMC BOX 3496, DUKE UNIVERSITY MEDICAL CE 27710
#035-01-1987 L1993 TS *020 †85,90

DANCEL, Ria Drapete. ■ 27713 #036-01-2006 MPD *012

DANEKAS, Megan Mowery. ■ 27713 #047-06-2005 FP *012

DANEKAS, Michael Gene. ■ 27713 #047-06-2005 L2007 AN *012

DANESHMAND, Mani Ali. ■ 27713 #035-03-2004 GS *012

DANFORD, Jerry Lee. 3643 N ROXBORO ST 27704 #036-07-1967 L1967 GYN *071 †30

DANIEL, John Thos, Jr. 507 LINWOOD AVE 27701 #010-03-1964 L1969 GS GP *020 †85

DANIEL, Marcella Faye. ■ 27705 #036-07-2007 *012

DANIELS, Ernest Gilbert. 507 FULTON ST, VETERAN'S ADMINISTRATION 27705
#038-40-1983 L1993 IM OM *020 †20

DANKO, Melissa Ellen. ■ 27704 #041-12-2005 GS *012

DARWISH, Husam Hussain. PO BOX 2923 27710 #797-02-2000 L2008 ORS *100

DASGUPTA, Neela. ■ 27713 #023-07-2006 IM *012

DASH, Rajesh Chandra. 4101 N ROXBORO ST 27704 #016-11-1995 L1998 PCP *020 †50

DASHER, David Albert. 27707 #036-01-2004 L2005 D *012

DA SILVA, Barbara A. ■ 27713 #067-01-1992 L1997 IM *020 †20

DATTO, Michael Bradley. ■ 27710 #036-07-1999 L2001 PTH *020 †50

DAUGHTRIDGE, Sarah Ellen. ■ 27707 #036-01-1992 L2000 IM *020 †20

DAVIS, Angela Marie. 4101 N ROXBORO ST 27704 #045-01-1995 L2001 PCC AI *020 †20

DAVIS, Margaret Enneking. ■ 27707 #011-05-2007 IM *012

DAVIS, Robert D, Jr. DUKE UNIV MED CTR, BOX 3864 27710 #005-14-1984 L1992
TS *020 †90,85

DAVIS, Samuel Morgan. ■ 27713 #036-05-2005 ORS *012

DAVIS, Wendy Zaroff. DUKE UNIV MED CTR, BOX 3913 27710 #036-07-1989 L1991
GE IM *020 †20

DAWSON, Robert Edward. 512 SIMMONS ST 27701 #047-07-1943 L1946 OPH *071 †35

DAYMONT, Molly Jeanne. PO BOX 94366 27708 #051-04-2005 N *012

DEANS, Elizabeth Innes. ■ 27713 #036-01-2008 N *012

DEAR, Guy De Lisle. 1200 ERWIN RD 27710 #917-03-1979 L1987 AN *020

DE BELLIS, Michael D. BOX 3613, DUKE UNIVERSITY MEDICAL CE 27710 #035-08-1987 L2002
P CHP *050 †75

DE BRUIJN, Norbert Paulus. DUKE UNIV MEDICAL CTR, BOX 3094 27710 #660-02-1976 L1984
GP *020

DECAMP, Lisa Ross. ■ 27713 #036-07-2004 L2007 PD *012 †55

DE CASTRO, Carlos M, III. BOX 3872 DUMC 27710 #048-12-1985 L1991 HO IM *020 †20

DECASTRO, Laura M. 2212 ELBA ST, DUMC BOX #3939 27705 #308-01-1986 L1998
HO *020 †20

DE CASTRO COSTA, Sylvia F. ■ 27707 #847-13-1995 L2000 MM *100 †20

DECHOW, Denise. 6020 FAYETTEVILLE RD 27713 #051-04-1996 L1999 FM *020 †18

DECKER-PHILLIPS, Martha L. 6301 HERNDON RD 27713 #036-08-1985 L1991
OBG *020 †19,30

DECROOS, Francis Charindr. DUKE UNIV EYE CTR, BOX 3802 27710 #036-07-2006 L2006
OPH *012

DEEPMALA, None. P O BOX 3951, DUKE UNIV MED CTR 27710 #496-07-2006 P *012

DEHMER, Jeffrey Joseph. ■ 27713 #036-01-2006 GS *012

DEKONING, Elisha Paul. ■ 27707 #032-01-2005 L2008 EM *012

DELANEY, Jeffrey William. DUMC, DIV OF PED CARDIOLOGY-BOX 27710 #030-06-1994 L2004
PDC *100 †55

DELANY, David John. RR 1 BOX 201D 27705 #917-20-1963 DR *020 †80

DELATTE, Rachel Jeanne. ■ 27713 #021-06-2005 OBG *012

DELGAIZO, Daniel John. ■ 27713 #010-01-2004 ORS *012

DELL, Diana Lynn. DUMC BOX 3263, DUKE UNIV MED CTR 27710 #021-05-1982 L1993
P OBG *020

DELLIGATTI, Brian James. ■ 27707 #023-01-2006 EM *012

DELMONTE, Derek Wills. DUKE UNIV EYE CTR, BOX 3802 27710 #025-01-2006 L2006
OPH *012

DE LONG, George Robt. TRENT DRIVE, BOX 3936 27710 #024-01-1961 L1988 CHN *071 †75

DE MARIA, Eric J. 3643 N ROXBORO ST 27704 #024-05-1983 L2005 GS *020 †85

DEMKE, Joshua Charles. ■ 27707 #048-15-2003 OTO *012

DEPLATCHETT, Kathryn Midd. ■ 27713 #051-04-2008 *012

DERIAN, Thomas Craig. 3901 N ROXBORO ST, STE 301 27704 #027-01-1981 L1987
OSS *020 †40

DERY, Jean-Pierre. ■ 27713 #067-04-1995 IC CD *020 †20

DESIMONE, Noelle Annette. ■ 27707 #036-07-2006 AN *012

DESJARDINS, Annick. DUMC 3624, ROOM 047, BAKER HOUSE, TRE 27710
#067-06-1998 L2005 *100

DEV, Prakash Kumar. 27705 #672-01-1992 *100

DEWEESE, Gary Kenneth. 2609 N DUKE ST 27704 #036-07-1986 L1988 CD IM *020 †20

DE WITT, Toby Benj. 1200 BROAD ST 27705 #025-12-1988 L1991 CHP *020 †75

DHRUVA, Nirav Suresh. ■ 27713 #012-01-2004 L2007 HO *012 †20

DIAMANTOUROS, Pantelis. PO BOX 31070 27710 #065-05-1999 *100

DIBERNARDO, Louis Robt. DUMC, BOX 3712 27710 #036-07-1991 L1998 PTH *020

DIDOLKAR, Manjiri Mukund. ■ 27713 #051-04-2003 L2003 DR *012

DIEHL, Anna Mae Elizabeth. 595 LASALLE ST, SUITE 1073 27710 #010-02-1978 L2004
GE IM *020 †20 ‡

DIEHL, Louis F. TRENT DR RM 25153, DUKE UNIV MED CTR 27710 #010-02-1975 L2004
ON HEM *020 †20 ‡

DIESEN, Diana Leigh. ■ 27705 #051-01-2004 GS *012

DILISI, Jeffrey Peter. 3643 N ROXBORO ST 27704 #041-02-2003 L2006 IM *100

DIMITROULIAS, Apostolos. ■ 27710 #418-02-1998 L2008 OAR *012

DI NAPOLI, Raphael J, Jr. ■ 27705 #035-08-1959 L1979 PHP AM *030 †70

DIODATO, Luis Hector. ■ 27707 #132-01-1988 L2001 GS *100

DIXON, Natalia Eugenia. ■ 27710 #264-16-1994 L2007 PHO *100 †55

DIXON, Terry Carlyle. DUKE UNIV MED CTR, DEPT OF PEDIATRICS, RM 540 27710
#036-07-2002 L2004 PDI *012 †55

DOBSON, Sean Wayne. ■ 27713 #036-05-2005 AN *012

DODD, Leslie Gail. 718 RUTHERFORD ST 27705 #031-01-1987 L1993 PTH *020 †50

DODSON, Kelly Dawn. 3643 N ROXBORO ST, DURHAM REGIONAL HOSPITAL 27704
#048-12-2004 L2007 IM *020

DOKA, Najah Ibrahim. ■ 27705 #035-19-2005 L2008 IM *012

DOKUN, Ayotunde Oluropo. DUMC, BOX 31132 27710 #035-47-2003 L2007 END *012

DOLINSKY, Diana Kay. ■ 27713 #028-02-2006 PD *012

DOLOR, Rowena Joy. 2400 PRATT ST, DUKE CLINICAL RESEARCH INS 27705
#036-07-1991 L1993 IM *050 †20

DOMINGUEZ, Arturo. BX 3951 M148 DAV BLD, DEPT OF INT MED 27710 #048-12-2007 IM *012

DOMKOWSKI, Patrick Wilson. ■ 27710 #010-02-1997 L2001 GS *100 †85

DONAHUE, Katrina. 14 GREYSTONE CT 27713 #038-41-1996 L1999 FM OS *050 †70,18

DONAHUE, Mark Paul. BOX 31101, DUMC 27710 #038-41-1996 L1999 CD *020 †20

DONATUCCI, Craig Francis. BOX 3274, DUKE UNIV MED CTR 27710 #041-13-1979 L1993
U *020 †95

DONELL, Bridget B. ■ 27713 #041-13-2002 L2005 CCP *012 †55

DONNELLY, Meghan Ann. ■ 27707 #036-07-2006 OBG *012

DONOGHOE, Nicholas Jason. ■ 27701 #023-07-2007 *012

DOOLEY, Joshua Ryan. DEPT OF ANESTHESIOLOGY, DUMC 3094 27710 #041-12-2004 L2008
AN *012

DORAISWAMY, Pudugramam M. TRENT DR DUMC, DUMC BOX 3018 PSYCH DEPT 27710
#495-94-1987 L1994 P *012

DOSTER, Lashawnda Patrice. ■ 27704 #012-21-2005 L2008 PD *012

DOUGLAS, Pamela Susan. PO BOX 17969, DUKE CLINICAL RESEARCH 27715
#051-04-1978 L2004 CD IM *030 †20 ‡

DOWNING, Brian E. ■ 27713 #051-04-2005 L2007 EM *012

DOWNING, Tacy Elizabeth. ■ 27713 #036-07-2007 MPD *012

DRAFFIN, Richard Marion. 3643 N ROXBORO ST 27704 #036-07-1975 L1977 PTH *062 †50 ‡

DRESSER, Michael Edward. ■ 27701 #036-07-1985 *100

DRISCOLL, Timothy Alan. BOX 3350, PEDIATRIC STEM CELL/ONCOLO 27710
#038-40-1990 L1993 PHO *020 †55

DRUCKER, Joan Liversidge. 1106 W CORNWALLIS RD, STE 102 27705 #051-01-1980 L1983
ID IM *050 †20

DRUCKER, Robert Patrick. RM 5409 DUKE N ERWIN, BOX 3127 DUMC 27710
#036-07-1979 L1983 ID PD *040 †55

D'SILVA, Marisa Romilda. 508 FULTON ST 11C 27705 #036-01-1992 L1997 IM *020 †20

DU BOSE, John Mc Neely. 3200 CROASDAILE DR STE 201 27705 #023-07-1959 L1960
GS TS *020 †85,90

DUMBLETON, Siobhan Ann. 4101 N ROXBORO ST 27704 #539-04-1988 L2000
DR VIR *020 †80

DUNCAN, Elizabeth Anne. BOX 3712 DUKE HOSP SOUTH, DEPT OF PATH 27710
#048-12-2000 L2001 IM *012

DUNCAN, Jacqueline P. DUKE UNIV MED CTR, PO BOX 3834 27710 #566-01-1994
GPM *100 †20,70

DUNCAN, Richard Dean, III. 5726 FAYETTEVILLE RD, DURHAM OBSTETRICS AND 27713
#047-06-1994 L1998 OBG *020 †20

DUNCAN, Scott Meacham. DUKE UNIV MED CTR, DEPT OF RADIOLOGY 27710 #020-02-2005
DR *012

DUNK, Andrea Monroe. 5107 SOUTHPARK DR, CHAPEL HILL PEDIATRICS PA 27713
#036-07-1995 L1997 PD *020 †55

DUNLAP, Harold Earl. ■ 27705 #039-01-1955 L1955 GS OS *071 †85

DUNN, Lawrence Anthony. 3001 ACADEMY RD, STE 240 27707 #025-01-1984 L1986
P PMM *020 †75

DUNNIGAN, Erin Elizabeth. ■ 27705 #038-40-2006 IM *012

DUPONT, Allison Gail. ■ 27713 #017-20-2003 L2006 CD *012 †20

DUPONT WYANT, Danielle Ad. ■ 27713 #024-16-2005 PD *012

DURACK, David Tulloch. 1700 WOODSTOCK RD 27705 #143-06-1969 L1978 IM ID *030 †20

DWANE, Peter D. BOX 3094 ERWIN RD, DUMC DEPT OF ANESTH 27710 #067-01-1967 L1996
AN *020 †05

DYKES, James Russell. 112 SWIFT AVE 27705 #036-07-1980 L1981 FM *020 †18 ‡

DYSON, Matthew Dale. ■ 27713 #036-01-2004 L2007 DR *012

DZAU, Jacqueline Robyn. ■ 27705 #036-07-2008 *012

DZAU, Victor Jos. 106 DAVISON BLDG BOX 3701, DUKE UNIV MEDICAL CTR 27710
#067-01-1972 L2005 CD IM *050 †20 ‡

DZIRASA, Erikka Daniene. DUKE UNIV MED CTR, DEPT OF PSYCHIATRY 27710 #036-07-2006
P *012

EADS, Emily Dawn. ■ 27707 #036-07-2006 DR *012

EAPEN, Zubin John. ■ 27713 #036-07-2005 IM *012

EARL, Nancy Lorraine. FIVE MOORE DRIVE 27709 #036-01-1982 L1986 IM *020

EASLEY, Mark Erik. BOX 2950 3116 N DUKE ST, DUKE UNIVERSITY MED CTR 27710
#051-01-1992 L1999 ORS *020 †40

EASLEY, Ronald Byron. 6005 RUSSELL RD 27712 #039-01-1971 L1975 IM END *020 †20

EASTWOOD, James David. BOX 3808 ERWIN ROAD, DUKE UNIVERSITY MEDICAL CE 27710
#035-06-1992 L1998 RNR R *020 †80

EBERT, Charles Stephen, Jr. ■ 27713 #036-01-2002 OTO *012

EBLE, Joseph Martin. ■ 27707 #036-07-2008 *012

ECHOLS, Melvin Ray. RM 8254 DUKE NORTH, BOX 3182 DUMC 27710 #012-21-2002 L2006
CD *012 †20

ECK, John Bright. BOX 3094, 3413 DUKE HOSP NORTH 27710 #036-07-1992 L1995
AN *020 †05

ECK, Walter Edward. ■ 27705 #041-12-1955 L1956 FM EM *071

ECKEL, Jason James. 508 FULTON ST 27705 #038-40-2004 L2007 NEP *012 †20

EDAVETTAL, Mathew Mathew. DUKE UNIV MED CTR, BOX 3807 27710 #021-05-2001 GS *012

EDELMAN, David Edward. 508 FULTON ST, VA MED CTR/AMBL 27705 #048-04-1991 L1994
IM *020 †20

EDGHILL, Benjeil Z. DEPARTMENT OF OPHTHALMOLOG, DUKE UNIVERSITY MEDICAL CE 27710
#036-07-2002 L2006 OPH *100 †35

EDMOND, Sura Us. ■ 27704 #036-08-2006 OBG *012

EDMUNDS, John Stewart. ■ 27713 #045-01-2002 L2007 NR *012 †80

EDWARDS, Caroline Coor. ■ 27707 #036-07-2007 L2007 GS *012

EDWARDS, Eric. ■ 27713 #047-05-2005 MPD *012

EDWARDS, George Sadler, III. ■ 27713 #036-01-2008 *012

EEDES, Christopher Robert. BOX 3712, DUMC 27710 #836-02-1985 L2001 PCP *100 †50

EFFERT, Peter J. DUKE MEDICAL CENTER 27706 #409-39-1988 U *100

EGGER, Helen Link. STE 22, 905 W MAIN ST 27701 #048-01-1991 L2002 CHP *020

EGNACZYK, Gregory Francis. ■ 27713 #038-41-2003 L2006 CD *012 †20

EHLERS, Jesmin Potter. ■ 27713 #018-03-2008 *012

EICHELBERGER, Kacey Young. ■ 27701 #045-01-2006 OBG *012

EICHNER, Brian Howard. ■ 27704 #035-06-2006 PD *012

EILY, Kiara Simone. 3414 N DUKE ST, STE 400 27704 #036-05-1991 L1993 EM *020 †16

EISENSON, Howard J. 804 W TRINITY AVE, DUKE DIET AND FITNESS CENT 27701
#036-07-1979 L1980 FM *020 †18

ELBERT-AVILA, Katja Ingri. DUKE UNIV MED CTR, BOX 3003 27710 #025-01-1999 L2002
IMG *040 †20

EL-CHAMMAS, Khalil Ibrahi. BX 3951 M148 DAV BLD, DEPT OF PEDIATRICS 27710
#605-01-2003 PD *012

ELDAIF, Bassem Mounir. DUKE UNIV MED CTR, DEPT OF SURGERY BOX 3707 27710
#036-07-2002 L2008 U *012

EL DAIRI, Mays Antoine. ■ 27707 #605-01-2001 L2005 *100

EL HUSSEINI, Nada Kais. BX 3951 M148 DAV BLD 27710 #605-01-2004 N *012

ELIASON, Harold Wm. ■ 27705 #023-01-1927 L1927 PD *071

ELLESTAD, Sarah Catherine. ■ 27705 #035-15-1999 L2003 OBG *100

ELLINWOOD, Everett Hews. RESEARCH DR, DUMC BOX 3870 SANOS BLDG # 27710
#036-01-1959 L1959 OS P *050 †75

ELLIOTT, Rebecca Lynn. ■ 27707 #036-07-2006 IM *012

ELMALLAH, Mohammed Kamal. ■ 27703 #048-04-2002 L2006 OPH *100 †35

EL-SALEM, Khalid Issa. ■ 27705 #575-02-1996 L2001 CN *020 †75

EL- YAMAN, Raed Ahmad. PO BOX 3094, SUITE 3409B 27710 #902-05-2001 CCA *100

EMANI, Sitaram Manohar. ■ 27710 #024-01-1997 L2004 TS *100 †85

EMICK, Dawn Marie. ■ 27713 #023-07-2006 GS *012

ENDRIGKEIT, Uta Sabine. ■ 27705 #409-23-1989 *100

ENGLAND, Ruth Elizabeth. ■ 27707 #539-03-1985 *100

ENGLISH, Peter Calvin. BX 3951 M148 DAV BLD PED 27710 #036-07-1975 L1978 PD *071 †55

ENGSTROM, Bjorn Ingemar. ■ 27713 #032-01-2007 L2007 IM *012

ENNS, Robert A. DUKE UNIV MED CTR 3913 27713 #061-01-1988 L1997 IM *020 †20

ENTERLINE, David Scott. DUKE UNIVERSITY MED CTR, DEPT RAD BOX 3808 27710
#036-01-1982 L1984 RNR VIR *020 †80

ENYEDI, Laura Barlow. BOX 3802 27710 #036-01-1993 L1997 PO OPH *020 †35

EPLING, Carol Ann. DUKE HOSPITAL, RM 4290 27710 #051-01-1989 L1995 OM IM *020 †20,70

EPSTEIN, David L. BOX 3802, DEPT OF OPHTHALMOLOGY 27710 #023-07-1968 L1992
OPH *030 †35

ERAMI, Cauveh. ■ 27707 #036-01-2002 PDC *012

ERWIN, Charles Wm. DUKE UNIV MEDICAL CENTER, DEPT OF PSYCHIATRY 27710
#048-02-1960 L1963 N P *040 †75

ESCALONA, Patricio R. 3906 COLORADO AVE 27707 #231-01-1987 L1992 P *020 †75

ESCARAVAGE, George Kevin, Jr. ■ 27713 #036-01-2002 L2006 OPH *100 †35

ESCARAVAGE, Vaishali Gupt. ■ 27713 #036-01-2002 L2003 D *012

ESCLAMADO, Ramon Mitra. ■ 27712 #005-19-1983 L2006 OTO *020 †45 ‡

ESMAILI, Neda. ■ 27713 #056-05-2006 OPH *012

ESTES, E Harvey. ■ 27707 #012-05-1947 L1953 IM *071 †20

EU, Pang-Chieh Jerry. 4101 N ROXBORO ST 27704 #016-02-1992 L1999 PCC *020 †20

EVANS, Brian Randall. 205 FRASIER ST 27704 #038-43-2000 L2003 U *100

EVANS, Edward Anthony. BOX 3127 DUMC 27710 #033-05-1998 L2002 MPD *020 †20

EVANS, Harris Lane. 4101 N ROXBORO ST 27704 #036-01-1955 L1955 P *020

EVANS, John Alfred. ■ 27705 #047-06-1998 L2006 GE *100 †20

EVANS, Kimberley Jessica. BOX 3014, DUKE UNIVERSITY MEDICAL CE 27710
#033-05-1998 L2003 NEP *020 †20

EVANS, Sarah Elizabeth. ■ 27703 #036-07-2006 GS *012

EVERHART, Terry Lee. ■ 27703 #036-01-2008 *012

EWARD, William Curtis. ■ 27713 #050-02-2006 ORS *012

EXUM, Stephanie Roxanne. ■ 27712 #036-08-2000 L2000 P IM *100 †20,75

EYLER, Christine Elissa. ■ 27707 #036-07-2008 *012

FABER, Sara Bigelow. ■ 27713 #023-01-2007 MPD *012

FABIATO, Kristin. ■ 27713 #051-04-2004 L2004 END *012 †20

FADIREPO, Babarinde Olago. DUKE UNIV MED CTR, DEPT OF COMMUNITY AND FAMI 27710
#026-04-2005 FP *012

FAEHNRICH, Jana Alexandra. PO BOX 3904, DUKE UNIV MED CTR 27710 #869-07-1983 L1995
AN *020

FAHRNER, Jill Ann. ■ 27713 #036-01-2006 PD *012

FAHY, Cormac John. ■ 27710 #539-03-1993 L2003 AN *100

FAISON, Vanosia Shablee. ■ 27703 #025-07-2003 L2007 MPD *020

FALGOWSKI, Sarah Elizabet. ■ 27713 #010-02-2005 P *012

FALLETTA, John Matthew. DUKE UNIVERSITY MED CTR, BOX 2991 27710 #019-02-1966 L1976
PHO *030 †55

FALLS, Beverly Harrington. ■ 27705 #036-01-1987 L1989 OBG *020 †30

FARB, Joshua Benjamin. ■ 27705 #024-05-2002 L2002 RNR *012 †80

FARMER, Jennifer Burke. ■ 27705 #036-08-2005 CHP *012

FARMER, Jos Clarence, Jr. DUMC BOX 3805 27710 #036-07-1962 L1962 OTO NO *030 †45

FARRELL, Stephanie Aileen. ■ 27713 #048-04-2006 AN *012

FATUNASE, Oluwatoyosi Ade. ■ 27713 #036-07-2007 IM *012

FAULCON, Clarence Lee. 27701 #035-08-1983 L1986 IM *020

FAULCON, Sheritia Tijuana. ■ 27713 #036-01-2004 L2007 CHP *012

FEARRINGTON, Sandra J. 4113 CAPITOL ST, STE A 27804 #032-01-1991 L1996 PS *020 †65

FEBBO, Phillip George. DUMC BOX 3382, IGSP 27710 #005-02-1993 L2004 HO IM *020 †20

FEILER, Michael Justin. DUMC BOX 3662 27710 #033-05-1998 L2003 GE *020 †20

FEINGLOS, Mark N. ERWIN ROAD, BOX 3921 27710 #067-01-1973 L1974 DIA END *020 †20

FELDMAN, Jerome Myron. 500 FULTON ST, VA HOSPITAL 27705 #016-06-1961 L1967
END IM *050 †20

FELKER, Gary Michael. BOX 31185, DUMC 27710 #036-07-1993 L2002 CD *020 †20

FELS, Edward Craig. ■ 27705 #035-08-2001 L2001 RHU *012 †20

FERGUSON, Emily Carpenter. ■ 27705 #036-07-2008 *012

FERNANDEZ, Mark Michael. ■ 27713 #036-07-2007 IM *012

FERRANDINO, Aimee L. ■ 27713 #035-19-2001 L2007 OBG *100 †30

FERRANDINO, Michael. ■ 27713 #035-19-2001 L2007 U *100

FERRANTI, Jeffrey Michael. BX 3951 M148 DAV BLD 27710 #067-01-2000 L2003 NPM *100 †55

FERRARI, Lisa M Piglia. 2609 N DUKE ST, CENTRAL MED. PARK, STE 100 27704
#036-07-1994 L1996 PD *020 †55

FERRELL, Michael Shay. DUMC, BOX 3000 27710 #051-04-2002 L2007 ORS *020

FERRO, Richard Todd. 718 RUTHERFORD ST 27705 #033-06-1994 L1998 FM FSM *020 †18

FERRY, Scott Thomas. ■ 27713 #016-11-2002 L2008 ORS *012

FERTEL, Daniel Harold. DUKE UNIV MED CTR, BOX 3221 27710 #038-40-2002 L2006
PCC *012 †20

FETKO, Linda Louise. 5726 FAYETTEVILLE RD, DURHAM OBSTETRICS AND 27713
#036-07-1996 L1997 OBG *020 †30

FIEDOREK, Frederick T, Jr. 5316 HIGHGATE DR, STE 125 27713 #024-01-1981 L1992
END IM *050 †20

FIELDS, Timothy Allen. DUMC, BOX 3712 27710 #036-07-1996 L1999 PTH *020 †50

FILIP, Stanley John. BOX 3267, DUKE UNIVERSITY MEDICAL CE 27710 #035-47-1979 L1990
OBG *020 †30

FINCH, James N. 910 BROAD ST 27705 #011-04-1981 L1984 FM *020 †18

FINDLAY, Jean Marjorie H. 5315 HIGHGATE DR, STE 101 27713 #919-01-1970 L1975
PD *020 †55

FINEFROCK, Anne Elizabeth. ■ 27705 #036-01-2007 IM *012

FINEMAN, Lewis David. ■ 27709 #035-19-1963 L1964 IM *071 †20

FINLEY, Alan Christopher. ■ 27713 #045-01-2004 L2007 AN *012

FINN, Alexander Jankovic. ■ 27705 #036-07-2006 PTH *012

FINNEGAN, Brian J. BX 3951 M148 DAV BLD 27710 #305-01-2005 L2008 EM *012

FIRSZT, Rafael. ■ 27710 #067-01-2005 L2007 PD *012

FISCHER, Stephanie Silvia. ■ 27710 #836-01-1993 L2003 *020

FISCUS, Lynne Christine. ■ 27713 #036-01-2003 L2006 MPD *100 †20,55

FISHER, Deborah Anne. BOX 3913 DUMC 27710 #047-05-1996 L1999 GE *020 †20

FISHER, Elizabeth Anne. ■ 27713 #007-02-2006 IM *012

FISHER, Gregory Alan. 5315 HIGHGATE DR, STE 101 27713 #011-04-1976 L1978 PD *020 †55

FISHER, Jessica Megan. ■ 27713 #036-01-2008 *012

FISHER, Michael John. ■ 27713 #051-01-2002 L2005 DR *100 †80

FISHER, Samuel Rankin. DUKE MEDICAL CENTER, BOX 3805 SURG 27710 #036-07-1975 L1975
OTO HNS *020 †45

FISHMAN, Felicity Georgin. DUKE UNIV MED CTR, ORTHOPAEDIC SURGERY 27710
#035-09-2006 ORS *012

FITCH, Robert Douglas. DUKE MEDICAL CENTER, BOX 2911 27710 #036-07-1976 L1982
ORS *020 †40

FITZHUGH, David Jordan. ■ 27713 #051-04-2004 IM *012

FITZPATRICK, Clayton B. DUMC 3084, DEPARTMENT OF OB/GYN 27710 #020-02-2001 L2006
OBG *100

FITZPATRICK, Laura Leigh. DUMC, BOX 3924 27710 #036-01-2002 L2005 END *100 †20

FITZSIMMONS, Keri Ann. ■ 27713 #036-01-2003 L2006 PD *020 †55

FITZSIMONS, Nicholas John. DUKE UNIV MED CTR, PO BOX 2922 27710 #036-01-2003 U *012

FLANAGAN, Ellen Marie. 1 ERWIN ROAD, BOX 3094 DUMC 27710 #036-01-1999 L2003
AN *020 †05

FLEMING, Ron Delayne. 4220 N ROXBORO ST 27704 #047-05-1984 L1993 IM *020 †20

FLEURY, Tammie Monique. ■ 27707 #005-14-1993 P *100

FONG, John K. PO BOX 2291, BCBS OF NORTH CAROLINA 27702 #035-06-1984 L1985
OBG *020 †30 ‡

FONTENOT, Emily Marie. ■ 27713 #021-06-2007 GS *012

FOO, Wen-Chi. ■ 27704 #036-07-2008 *012

FOREMAN, John Wm. ERWIN ROAD, BOX 3959 DUMC 27710 #023-01-1973 L1993
PN IM *020 †55

FORMAN, Eric Jason. ■ 27713 #035-08-2006 OBG *012

FORMAN, Leslie Mitchell. BOX 3516, DUKE UNIV MEDICAL CENTER 27710 #024-07-1972 L1989
P *020 †75

FORSHA, Daniel Eric. ■ 27712 #007-02-2007 PD *012

FORTIN, Donald Frederick. 3905 COTTONWOOD DR 27705 #024-16-1984 L1991
CD IM *020 †20

FORTIN, Terry Ann. DUKE UNIVERSITY MEDICAL CE, BOX 31202 27710 #024-16-1999 L2006
CD *100 †20

FORTNER, Christopher Neil. MED CTR, BOX 3127, DUKE UNIV 27710 #038-41-2002
PDP *012 †55

FORTNEY, Jennifer Taylor. ■ 27710 #023-01-1978 L1980 AN *020 †05

FOSSE, Kristen Ann. ■ 27705 #012-01-2007 IM *012

FOSTER, Mary Helen. ERWIN RD, BOX 3014, DUKE UNIVERSITY MED CENTER 27710
#036-01-1982 L2000 NEP IM *020 †20

FOSTER, Wm Leicester, Jr. 508 FULTON ST # 114, DURHAM VA MED CTR 27705
#036-07-1974 L1976 DR *020 †80 ‡

FOWLER, Cynthia Lee. 100 RODOLPHE ST, BIO MERIEUX 27712 #048-12-1983 L1983
IM ID *050 †20

FOWLER, Natalie Logan. 2100 ERWIN ROAD 27710 #028-02-2000 L2005 FM *020 †18

FOWLER, Vance G, II. BOX 3281 DUKE UNIV MEDICAL, ROOM 34428 RED ZONE DUKE S 27710
#036-01-1993 L1995 ID *020 †20

FOWLER, Walter Earle. 4205 BEN FRANKLIN BLVD, ASSOCIATES PA 27704 #036-07-1986 L1987
IM HEM *020 †20

FOX, Elisabeth June. 718 RUTHERFORD ST 27705 #352-07-1955 L1961 AN *040 †05

FRANCES, Allen J. BOX 3950, DUKE UNIV MED CTR 27710 #035-08-1967 L1992
P PYA *020 †75

FRANCESCHINI, Nora. ■ 27707 #187-02-1986 L1998 NEP *020 †20

FRANCZAK, Mark S. 2609 N DUKE ST, STE 620 27704 #035-01-1988 L1990 N *020 †75

FRANK, Michael M. DUMC - BOX 2611, DEPARTMENT OF PEDIATRICS 27710
#024-01-1960 L1990 AI PDA *050 †03

FRANZ, Lauren. ■ 27713 #836-04-2002 P *012

FRANZCAK, Jenny. 6020 FAYETTEVILLE RD, TRIANGLE FAMILY PRACTICE 27713
#055-01-1988 L1990 FM IM *020 †18

FRAS, Anne Marie. DUMC, BOX 3094 DEPT OF ANESTH 27710 #025-01-1993 L1997
APM AN *020 †05

FRAS, I Michael. ■ 27703 #041-15-2002 L2007 NR *012 †80

FRAZIER, Camille Genise. DUKE UNIV MED CTR, BOX 31128 27710 #038-06-1999 L2000
ICE *012 †20

FREDERICK, Heather Jane. DUKE UNIV MEDICAL CENTER, BOX 3094 27710 #036-07-2002 L2004 **PAN** *020

FREEDLAND, Stephen Jay. DUKE UNIV MED CTR, DUMC 3850 27710 #005-19-1997 L2005 **U** *050 †95

FREEDMAN, Neil Jonathan. DUKE UNIV MED CTR, BOX 3187 27710 #024-01-1985 L1990 **CD IM** *020 †20

FREEDMAN, Sharon F. BOX 3802 27710 #024-01-1985 L1990 **OPH** *020 †35

FREEMARK, Michael Scott. DUKE MED CTR, BOX 3080 27710 #036-07-1976 L1979 **PD** *020 †55

FREUND, Dianne Michele. ■ 27705 #036-01-1990 L1994 **FM** *020 †18

FRIEDMAN, Allan Howard. BOX 3807, DUKE UNIVERSITY HOSPITAL 27710 #016-11-1974 L1980 **NS** *040 †25

FRIEDMAN, Henry S. TRENT DRIVE, BOX 3624 RM 047 BAKER HOUS 27710 #035-15-1977 L1983 **PD** *050 †55

FRIEDMAN, Nancy Eisenberg. BOX 3080, DUKE UNIVERSITY MED 27710 #051-04-1975 L1980 **PDE PD** *020 †55

FRIEDMAN, Stephen Wm. 1901 HILLANDALE RD 27705 #021-01-1972 L1973 **FM** *020 †18

FRITCHIE, Karen Joy. ■ 27713 #033-06-2005 L2007 **PTH** *012

FROTHINGHAM, Richard. DUMC BOX 103020, DUKE UNIV MED CTR 27710 #036-07-1981 L1990 **ID IM** *020,55 ‡

FROTHINGHAM, Thomas Eliot. ■ 27705 #024-01-1951 L1973 **PD ID** *072 †55

FRUSH, Donald Paul. BOX 3808 RADIOLOGY, DUKE MEDICAL CENTER 27710 #036-07-1985 L1987 **DR PD** *020 †80

FUCHS, Herbert Edgar. BOX 3272 DUMC 27710 #036-07-1984 L1990 **NS NSP** *020 †25

FUCHS, Kaspar. ■ 27705 #407-19-1948 L1988 **NS** *071 †25

FULKERSON, Conrad Carnes. 3001 ACADEMY RD STE 240 27707 #028-03-1969 L1974 **P IM** *020 †20,75

FULKERSON, William J, Jr. DUKE UNIV MED CTR, BOX 3708 27710 #036-01-1977 L1983 **PUD IM** *030 †20

FULLILOVE, Rowland E J. 27713 #023-01-1951 L1964 **OS P** *071

FUNK, Margo Christiane. ■ 27712 #028-02-2006 **P** *012

FYNN, Nicola Charis. ■ 27713 #038-40-2006 **FP** *012

GABBARD, Scott Lanier. ■ 27707 #038-06-2006 **IM** *012

GABRIELCZYK, Marek R. DUKE MEDICAL CENTER 27710 #917-07-1978 *100

GACA, Jeffrey Giles. DEPT OF SURGERY, DUKE UNIV MED CTR 27710 #035-01-1998 L2002 **TS** *012 †85

GADDE, Kishore Murali. 718 RUTHERFORD ST 27705 #495-50-1978 L1994 **P** *020 †75

GADKOWSKI, Lara Beth. ■ 27713 #041-02-2002 L2008 **ID** *012 †20

GAEDE, Jane C Taylor. DUKE UNIV MED CTR, BOX 3712 DEPT OF PATH 27710 #036-07-1966 L1966 **ATP PTH** *020 †50 ‡

GAGLIANO, Martha Ellen. 2609 N DUKE ST, STE 1000 27704 #036-07-1982 L1985 **PD** *020 †55

GAGLIARDI, Jane Patricia. BOX 3837, DUMC 27710 #036-07-1998 L2002 **OS** *020 †20,75

GAGNIER, R Paul. ■ 27713 #024-07-1987 L1989 **IM** *030

GAINOR, Lauren Harmon. ■ 27713 #036-01-2008 L2008 *012

GALANOS, Anthony Nick. BOX 3003, DUKE UNIV MED CENTER 27710 #001-06-1986 L1989 **IMG IM** *050 †20

GALBREATH, Andrew David. ■ 27713 #025-76-2004, ▲ L2007 **N** *012

GALLAGHER, David Michael. 3643 N ROXBORO ST, HOSPITALIST PROGRAM 27704 #010-01-1990 L2006 **IM** *020 †20

GALLEGO ATTIS, Maria Isab. ■ 27705 #011-02-2004 L2007 **PTH** *012

GALPIN, Lauren Elizabeth. ■ 27713 #028-02-2006 **MPD** *012

GAN, Tong-Joo. BOX 3094, DEPT OF ANESTHESIOLOGY 27710 #917-25-1986 L1997 **AN** *020 †05

GANAPATHY, Sugantha. ■ 27710 #495-53-1973 L2002 **AN** *020

GARANTZIOTIS, Stavros. BOX 2629, RESEARCH DRIVE, DUKE UNIVERSITY MEDICAL CE 27710 #409-05-1995 L2000 **PCC** *020 †20

GARBUTT, John Tener. 718 RUTHERFORD ST 27705 #041-13-1962 L1969 **GE IM** *071 †20

GARCIA RODRIGUEZ, Charles. DUKE UNIV 27710 #352-24-1989 L1998 *100

GARD, Allison Kay. 1901 HILLANDALE RD, STE B 27705 #016-11-1990 L2000 **FM** *020 †18

GARGES, Harmony Phillips. DEPT. OF PEDIATRICS, DUMC BOX 3499 27710 #036-07-1998 L2001 **PDI** *050 †55

GARMAN, Katherine S. ■ 27705 #036-07-2002 L2006 **GE** *012 †20

GARRETT, William Elwood, Jr. BOX 3338 DUKE UNIVERSITY M 27710 #036-07-1976 L1982 **ORS OSM** *020 †40

GARST, Jennifer Lynn. ERWIN RD/TRENT DRIVE, BOX 3198 27710 #012-01-1990 L1996 **HO** *050 †20

GARTNER, Gary Steven. 3708 MAYFAIR ST STE 206, MEDSTAFF 27707 #036-01-1990 L1995 **PD** *020 †55

GARVER, Dennis Wayne. 3643 N ROXBORO ST, DURHAM REGIONAL HOSPITAL 27704 #023-01-1996 L1999 **IM** *020 †20

GASKILL, Trevor Ryan. ■ 27713 #019-02-2005 **ORS** *012

GASKINS, Nicole Dehaven. ■ 27707 #036-01-2008 *012

GASPARETTO, Cristina. 4101 N ROXBORO ST 27704 #561-17-1986 L1997 **HO** *020 †20

GAUGER, Joerg. ■ 27710 #409-25-1991 L2005 *100

GAUTHIER, Alain. PO BOX 3094, DEPARTMENT OF ANESTHESIA 27710 #067-01-1997 L2002 *100

GAVRILOVA-JORDAN, Larisa. 5704 FAYETTEVILLE RD, DUKE UNIVERSITY FERTILITY 27713 #913-22-1998 L2006 **OBG** *100 †30

GAWECKI, Tomasz. 4419 BEN FRANKLIN BLVD 27704 #759-12-1993 L2003 **NEP** *020 †20

GAZZOLA, Maria Marta De O. DUKE UNIV MEDICAL CENTER, DEPT OF PSYCHIATRY 27710 #187-06-1983 L2003 **CHP** *020 †55

GBADEGESIN, Rasheed Adeba. ■ 27707 #690-01-1987 L2007 **PN** *100 †55

GEARY, Leon Wallace. 3916 BEN FRANKLIN BLVD, DURHAM REGIONAL HOSPITALIS 27704 #048-15-1975 L1979 **PUD A** *071 †20

GEBEL, Peter Paul. ■ 27705 #024-01-1958 L1965 **CD IM** *071 †20

GEBER, Sharron Ruth. ■ 27705 #012-01-1981 L1982 **P** *020 †75

GEHRIG, Thomas Richard. ERWIN ROAD, DUKE NORTH, ROOM 7624 27710 #011-03-1994 L2002 **CD** *020 †20

GELLAD, Ziad Fouad. ■ 27713 #023-07-2003 L2006 **GE** *012 †20

GENTRY, John Richard. 6 CORIANDER CT 27713 #045-01-2001 L2008 **CHP** *012

GEOGHEHAN, Justin Gerald. ■ 27707 #539-04-1982 **GS** *020

GEORGE, Daniel James. 2400 PRATT ST, DUKE CLINICAL RESEARCH INS 27705 #036-07-1992 L2003 **ON** *020 †20

GEORGE, Jonathan Roulette. ■ 27713 #036-07-2008 *012

GEORGIADE, Gregory S. PO BX 3960 27710 #036-07-1974 PS **TRS** *020 †65,85

GERARDO, Charles John. ERWIN ROAD, BOX 3096 DUMC 27710 #005-19-1994 L2000 **EM** *020 †16

GERMANA, Sarah Piecuch. ■ 27713 #024-01-2004 L2007 **PD** *100

GERSING, Kenneth Ronald. BOX 3018, DUKE UNIVERSITY MEDICAL CT 27710 #054-04-1993 L1997 **P** *020 †75

GEST, Kathleen Louise. 1301 FAYETTEVILLE ST 27707 #036-07-1989 L1992 **PD PHP** *020 †55

GESTY-PALMER, Diane. BOX 3924 DUMC 27710 #036-07-1997 L2003 **END** *020 †20

GETTES, Edith Madeline. 3713 UNIVERSITY DR, STE A 27707 #036-01-2003 L2007 **P** *012

GEYER, Mark Russell. ■ 27713 #048-04-2006 **ORS** *012

GHATE, Sujata Vijay. ■ 27710 #036-01-1994 L1997 **DR** *020 †80

GHERT, Michelle Aileen. BOX 3000, DUMC 27710 #047-05-1996 L2001 **ORS** *020

GHOSH, Nirmalya Kumar. 5211 TAHOE DR 27713 #495-32-1959 L1990 **IM** *020 †20

GIANNETTO, Lisa Ann. 3475 ERWIN RD, WALLACE CLINIC STE 204 27705 #016-43-1986 L1988 **IM** *020 †20

GIANNOPOULOS, Athanasios. 1515 W NC HIGHWAY 54, STE 130 27707 #418-01-1966 **PS** *100

GIANNOPOULOU, Athina A. 1515 W NC HIGHWAY 54 # 130, FACES PLASTIC SURGERY 27707 #418-02-1987 L1999 **PS** *020 †65

GIANTURCO, Daniel T. 2925 FRIENDSHIP RD 27705 #035-06-1960 L1966 **P** *020 †75

GIBBS, Carol Minnette. 5306 NC HIGHWAY 55, STE 105 27713 #036-01-1995 L1996 **P** *040 †75

GIBSON, William G H. DUKE MEDICAL CENTER, BOX 2752 27710 #036-07-1977 L1979 **PTH** *100

GIFFORD, Cameron Douglas. 4205 BEN FRANKLIN BLVD, ASSOCIATES PA 27704 #039-05-1988 L2001 **IM** *020 †20

GILBERT, Brett Jason. ■ 27703 #036-07-2003 **ORS** *012

GILES, Brenda-Louise. ■ 27710 #065-06-1991 L1998 **PDP** *100 †55

GINSBERG, Brian. DUKE UNIV MEDICAL CTR, DEPT OF ANES BOX3094 27710 #836-01-1975 L1986 **AN PME** *020 †05

GIRAGOS, John Garabed. 20 W COLONY PL STE 260 27705 #605-01-1963 L1970 **P PYA** *020 ‡

GLASGOW, Robert Ronald Ma. DUMC 3704, DUKE UNIVERSITY MEDICAL CE 27710 #060-02-1996 L2002 **ORS** *100

GLOTZBACH, Jason Paul. ■ 27707 #021-01-2005 **GS** *012

GLOWER, Donald Duane, Jr. PO BX 3851 27710 #023-07-1980 L1989 **TS** *020 †85,90

GOCKERMAN, Jon Paul. 508 FULTON ST 27705 #016-02-1967 L1983 **ON HEM** *020 †20

GOETZ, Lisa Marie. ■ 27705 #047-05-2000 **IM** *100

GOLANDER, Avraham. DUKE MEDICAL CENTER, BOX 3080 27710 #550-01-1970 L1977 **END** *020

GOLBY, Mary Blue. ■ 27704 #010-01-1953 L1954 **IM** *071

GOLBY, Robert Louis. ■ 27704 #036-01-1955 L1955 **CLP** *071

GOLDBERG, Joel Steven. 508 FULTON ST 27705 #036-07-1977 L1981 **PME** *020 †05

GOLDBERG, Kenneth Charles. 718 RUTHERFORD ST 27705 #056-06-1994 L1995 **IM** *020 †20

GOLDBERG, Ronald Norman. 4101 N ROXBORO ST 27704 #005-14-1972 L1996 **PD NPM** *050 †55

GOLDFLAM, Martha Jane. ■ 27705 #035-08-1997 L2000 **FM** *020 †18

GOLDNER, Richard Douglas. DUKE UNIVERSITY MEDICAL CE, DEPARTMENT OF OTHOPAEDIC S 27710 #036-07-1974 L1974 **ORS HS** *020 †40

GOLDSTEIN, Larry Bruce. DUKE UNIV MED CTR, BOX 3651 27710 #035-47-1981 L1985 **N** *050 †75

GOLDSTEIN, Ricki F. BOX 3179 DUKE U MED CTR, DIVISION OF PERINATAL MED 27710 #035-20-1981 L1985 **NPM PD** *020 †55

GOLDSTEIN, Solomon I. ■ 27713 #869-02-1936 L1937 **CD IM** *071

GOLI, Veeraindar. 932 MORREENE RD, # 258 27705 #495-21-1978 L1985 **P PME** *020 †75

GONG, Zuying J. 4101 N ROXBORO ST 27704 #243-16-1986 L1999 **PTH** *020 †50

GONZALES, Jeffrey Joseph. ■ 27710 #016-11-2002 L2006 **AN** *100 †05

GONZALEZ DE LA FUENTE, Seb. ■ 27713 #132-07-1998 **GS** *012

GOODMAN, Philip Cary. BOX 3808, DUKE UNIV MEDICAL CENTER 27710 #005-14-1970 L1991 **R IM** *020 †80

GOODMON, Anna Brame. ■ 27707 #036-01-2004 L2007 **PD** *020 †55

GOPWANI, Priya Raj. ■ 27713 #025-01-2007 **MPD** *012

GORDON, David Charles. DUMC 3096, DUKE UNIVERSITY HEALTH SYS 27710 #024-01-2001 L2005 **EM** *100 †16

GOREE, John Ashley. ■ 27707 #036-07-1955 L1955 **DR** *071 †80

GOSPE, Sidney Maloch, III. ■ 27705 #036-07-2008 *012

GOTTFREDSSON, Magnus. PO BOX 3824, DUKE UNIV MED CTR DEPT MED 27710 #484-01-1990 L1996 **ID** *100 †20

GOTTFRIED, Marcia Ruth. DUKE UNIV MED CTR, BOX 3712 27710 #016-06-1978 L1984 **ATP** *050 †50

GOUDAR, Ranjit Kumar. ■ 27713 #036-07-2004 **HO** *012 †20

GOVERT, Joseph Alan. ■ 27705 #005-15-1989 L1991 **PUD** *020 †20

GOYAL, Vinita. ■ 27713 #054-04-2003 L2007 **OBG** *100

GRABER, Andrew Robert. ■ 27705 #051-04-2006 **N** *012

GRACE, Eugene Vernon. 911 BROAD ST 27705 #025-01-1956 L1956 **OPH** *071 †35

GRACES, Patricio Borromeo. DUKE HOSP N ERWIN RD 27710 #060-02-1990 L1995 *020

GRADISON, Margaret. DUKE FAMILY MEDICINE CENTE, 2100 ERWIN ROAD 27710 #038-41-1981 L1994 **FM** *020 †18

GRADY, Allen Thomas. ■ 27707 #036-01-2008 *012

GRAFFAGNINO, Carmelo. DUKE UNIV MEDICAL CENTRE, BOX 2946 27710 #065-06-1985 L1992 **N** *020 †20

GRAFSTEIN, Neil H. DIVISION OF UROLOGY, BOX 3, DUKE UNIVERSITYMEDICAL CEN 27710 #035-08-2000 L2006 **U** *020

GRAHAM, Aubrey Jolly. ■ 27713 #011-03-2006 **IM** *012

GRANILLO, Olivia Marie. ■ 27713 #036-07-2008 *012

GRANT, Augustus O, Jr. BOX 3504, DUKE UNIV MED CTR 27710 #919-03-1971 L1980 **CD IM** *050 †20

GRANT, Gerald Arthur. ■ 27705 #005-11-1994 L2006 **NS** *020 †25

GRANT, James Applewhite. ■ 27705 #036-07-2008 *012

GRANT, John Palmer. 3116 N DUKE ST STE 209 27704 #016-02-1969 L1978 **GS** *020 †85

GRANT, Stuart Alan. BOX 3094, DEPT OF ANESTHESIA 27710 #919-05-1989 L1999 **AN** *100

GRAY, Alice Lee. ■ 27701 #025-01-2004 **PCC** *012 †20

GRAY, Beverly Allen. ■ 27701 #036-01-2007 **OBG** *012

GRAY, Darrell Mason. ■ 27704 #010-03-2007 **IM** *012

GRAY, Lindsay Carter. OB-GYN DEPT:DUMC, ROOM 246 BAKER HOUSE BOX 3 27710 #036-05-1999 L2003 **OBG** *020 †30

GRAYBILL, Megan Marie. ■ 27713 #041-13-2007 **AN** *012

GREANEY, Kathleen M. DUKE UNIV MED CTR, DEPT OF PEDIATRICS 27710 #033-06-2001 L2004 **PD** *020 †55

GREBE, John Harry. ■ 27713 #030-05-2004 L2007 **NPM** *012 †55

GREEN, Jennifer Brigitte. ROOM 280 BAKER HOUSE, DUMC BOX 3222 27710 #051-01-1993 L1996 **END** *020 †20

GREEN, Patrick Daniel. ■ 27713 #036-01-2008 *012

GREENBERG, Arthur. ■ 27710 #028-02-1975 L1997 **NEP IM** *020 †20

GREENBERG, Charles Steven. BOX 2603, RESEARCH DRIVE 27710 #041-09-1976 L1983 **ON HEM** *050 †20

GREENBLATT, Lawrence H. 4220 N ROXBORO ST, DUKE OUTPATIENT CLINIC 27704 #016-06-1990 L1994 **IM** *020 †20

GREENE, Jeffrey David. 2609 N DUKE ST, STE 1000 27704 #036-07-1997 L2000 **PD** *020 †55

GREENE, Vanessa Lee. BX 3951 M148 DAV BLD 27710 #422-01-2005 L2008 **EM** *012

GREENFIELD, Joseph C. DUKE UNIV MED CENTER BOX 3 27710 #012-05-1956 L1957 **CD** *071 †20

GREENFIELD, Ruth Ann. 4101 N ROXBORO ST 27704 #036-07-1985 L1990 **CD IM** *020 †20

GREGORY, Julie Marie. ■ 27713 #041-02-2005 L2008 **FP** *012

GREINER, Daniela. ■ 27705 #409-23-1991 **D** *100

GREMILLION, David Henry. 3804 SHAFTSBURY ST 27704 #021-05-1972 L1988 **IM ID** *040 †20

GRICHNIK, James Michael. BOX 3135, DUKE UNIVERSITY MEDICAL CE 27710 #024-01-1990 L1994 **D ON** *020 †15

GRICHNIK, Katherine P. DUKE UNIVERSITY MEDICAL CE, DEPT OF ANESTHESIA 27710 #024-07-1987 L1991 **AN** *020 †05

GRIFFIN COREY, Elizabeth. ■ 27705 #054-04-2006 **OBG** *012

GRIFFITH, Barbara Duff. 3414 N DUKE ST, STE 400 27704 #036-01-1999 L2002 **EM** *020 †16

GRIFFITH, Brian Carey. ■ 27705 #036-07-2008 *012

GRIFFITHS, Ryan Scott. ■ 27707 #040-02-2005 L2008 **IM** *012

GRILLEY, Juneko Elaine. ■ 27713 #056-05-2003 L2003 **HO** *012 †20

GROCOTT, Hilary P Thomas. 718 RUTHERFORD ST 27705 #068-01-1990 L1996 **AN** *020

GROSSI, Peter Michael. ■ 27712 #036-07-2002 **NS** *012

GROSSMAN, Herman Lewis. ■ 27705 #035-01-1953 L1971 **PDR** *020 †55

GROTEGUT, Chad Aaron. ■ 27710 #041-13-1999 L2000 **OBG** *020 †30

GRUNINGER, Robert Park. 718 RUTHERFORD ST 27705 #035-09-1957 L1993 **CLP ID** *030 †20

GUAJARDO, Cesar. 20 W COLONY PL ■ WEST-160 27705 #649-02-1961 L1966 **CHP P** *040 †75

GUERRA, Daniel Rene. MAILBOX # 31065, DUKE UNIVERSITY MEDICAL CE 27710 #024-01-2001 L2004 **CD** *012

GUEVARA, Carlos Javier. ■ 27705 #036-07-2006 L2006 **ORS** *100

GUICE, Karen S. BOX 3123, DEPT OF SURGERY 27710 #034-01-1977 L1991 **PDS GS** *050 †85

GULERIA, Sher Singh. 109 ASHWORTH DR 27707 #495-03-1960 L2003 **IM IMG** *020 †20 ‡

GUMP, William Corbly. ■ 27710 #020-02-2001 L2004 **NS** *012

GUNN, Laura Ann. 300 CRUTCHFIELD ST, PLASTIC SURGERY CENTER 27704 #047-06-1991 L2000 **PS** *020 †85,65

GUNN, Michael Dee. DUKE UNIV MEDICAL CENTER, ERWIN RD BOX 3547 27710 #048-12-1983 L1999 **IM** *020 †20

GUPTA, Anil Kumar. ■ 27705 #035-03-2007 **ORS** *012

GUPTA, Deepak Kumar. ■ 27713 #038-40-2005 **IM** *012

GUPTA, Preeya Kshettry. ■ 27705 #016-06-2006 L2006 **OPH** *012

GUPTILL, Jeffrey Talbot. DUKE UNIV MED CTR, BOX 2905 27710 #051-04-2005 L2005 **N** *012

GURLEY, Susan B. DUMC 103015 27710 #028-02-1998 L2005 **NEP** *050 †20

GURURANGAN, Sridharan. 4101 N ROXBORO ST 27704 #495-16-1981 L1999 **PD PHO** *020 †55

GUTMAN, Laura E Thurston. 718 RUTHERFORD ST 27705 #005-11-1962 L1973 **ID PD** *050 †50

GUTMAN, Robert Allan. 4419 BEN FRANKLIN BLVD 27704 #011-03-1962 L1973 **IM NEP** *020 †20

GUTTER, Guido Peter. 4113 CAPITOL ST STE B 27704 #869-07-1977 L1987 **PS HS** *020 †65

GUY, Cynthia Dianne. DUKE UNIV MED CTR, DEPT OF PATH BOX 3712 27710 #045-01-1993 L1999 **PCP** *020 †20

GUYTON, John Richard. DUKE UMC DEPT MED, BOX 3510 27710 #024-01-1973 L1992 **IM END** *020 †20

HAAG, Jason Christopher. ■ 27713 #051-07-2006 **IM** *012

HABERLE, Sinisa. ■ 27713 #036-01-2008 *012

HABIB, Ashraf Samir. BOX 3094, DEPT OF ANESTHESIA 27710 #915-04-1987 L2000 **AN** *020

HAFEEZ KHAN, Muhammad Fai. ■ 27710 #704-01-2000 L2006 **SME** *012

HAGLUND, Michael Martin. 718 RUTHERFORD ST 27705 #054-04-1987 L1995 **NS** *020 †25

HAHN, Carol Anne. DUMC DEPT RAD ONC, BOX 3085 27710 #010-02-1990 L1995 **RO** *020 †80

HAITHCOCK, Daniel B. 5407 RUSSELL RD 27712 #038-06-2000 L2004 **ICE** *012 †20 ‡

HALBROOKS, Ronald F. 5832 FAYETTEVILLE RD, STE 113 27713 #048-02-1983 L1989 **IM** *020 †20

HALE, Laura Pope. BOX 3712, DUKE UNIV MC 2608 27710 #036-07-1991 L1995 **PTH** *050 †50

HALEY, Nancy Rebecca. 2810 MERIDIAN PKWY, STE 148 27713 #051-07-1984 L1991 **BBK HM** *062 †20

HALISCHUK, Grant F. 1910 SEDWICK RD, STE 300B 27713 #067-01-1983 L1986 **P** *030 †75

HALL, Austin Barrett. 433 W MAIN ST 27701 #019-02-2000 L2004 **P** *020 †75

HALL, Kenneth Daland. BOX 3068 DUKE UNIV MED CTR 27710 #036-07-1953 L1955 **AN** *020 †05

HALL, Ranota Thomas. 5001 S MIAMI BLVD, VALUEOPTIONS 27703 #047-20-1987 L1988 **CHP** *020 †75

HALL, Reginald Lawrence. 120 WILLIAM PENN PLZ, TRIANGLE ORTHOPAEDIC ASSOC 27704 #036-07-1983 L1986 **ORS** *040 †40

HALL, Russell P, III. DUKE MEDICAL CENTER, BOX 3135 27710 #028-03-1975 L1984 **D IM** *050 †15

HALL, William Brooks. 8010 SUNDANCE CIR 27713 #036-01-2004 L2007 **IM** *100 †20

HALSTATER, Brian Hugh. DUMC 3886 27710 #033-06-1995 L2004 **FM** *020 †18 ‡

HAMILTON, Carol Dukes. DUKE MEDICAL CENTER, BOX 3306 27710 #049-01-1985 L1988 **ID IM** *020 †20

HAMILTON, Elizabeth H. 2609 N DUKE ST STE 403, DURHAM DERMO ASSOC 27704 #036-01-1988 L1992 **D** *020 †15

HAMILTON, Jean Ann. 918 9TH ST 27705 #048-13-1977 L1992 **P PA** *050

HAMILTON, John David. VET ADMIN HOSP 27705 #007-02-1964 L1968 **ID IM** *050 †20

HAMILTON, Michael Amin. 804 W TRINITY AVE, DUKE DIET FITNESS CTR 27701 #035-45-1964 L1971 **IM FM** *071 †20,18

HAMMOND, Chas Bessellieu. 718 RUTHERFORD ST 27705 #036-07-1961 L1961 **OBG END** *040 †30

HAMPTON, Daniel Doran. BX 3951 M148 DAV BLD, DEPT OF GASTRO- DUMC 3913 27710 #038-40-2004 **GE** *012 †20

HANDELSMAN, Leonard. ■ 27705 #035-46-1980 L1998 **P** *050 †75

HANEY, John Carroll. ■ 27705 #036-07-2004 **GS** *012

HANISH, Steven Ira. DEPT OF SURGERY, DUKE UNIVERSITY MEDICAL CE 27710 #017-20-2000 L2003 **GS** *020 †85

HANKINS, Kelly Jo. ■ 27713 #036-01-2008 *012

HANKS, Brent Allen. ■ 27713 #048-04-2006 **IM** *012

HANSELL, Harriet Ng. DUEK FAMILY MED, DUMC 3886 27710 #036-01-2003 L2004 **FM** *020 †18

HANSON, Michael Ward. ERWIN ROAD P.O. BOX 3949, DUKE UNIVERSITY MEDICAL CE 27710 #055-01-1974 L1987 **CD IM** *020 †20,28

HANSON, Neil Ali. ■ 27707 #036-07-2006 **AN** *012

HAPONIK, Stacy Gannaway. ■ 27713 #036-01-2005 **IM** *012

HAQQ, Andrea Maria. BOX 3080, 306FA BELL BUILDING 27710 #060-02-1994 L2002 **PDE** *020 †55

HARDAKER, William Thos. DUKE MEDICAL CTR, BOX 3956 27710 #036-07-1973 L1979 **ORS** *020 †40

HARDMAN, H David. DUKE UNIMERSITY MED CTR, DEPT OF ANESTHESLOLOGY 27710 #026-04-1981 L1983 **AN** *020 †05

HARE, Roy Allen. 2609 N DUKE ST STE 205 27704 #036-05-1945 L1945 **IM** *071

HAREGEWOIN, Abebe. ■ 27713 #366-01-1976 L1994 **RO** *020

HARGETT, Charles William. BOX 31166, DUKE UNIVERSITY MEDICAL CE 27710 #051-01-1999 L2006 **PCC** *012

HARMAN, Harriet Maxwell. ■ 27705 #047-05-1962 L1963 **P GP** *071

HARMEL, Merel Hilber. ERWIN RD 27710 #023-07-1943 L1971 **AN** *072 †05

HARMON, Barbara Jean. ■ 27713 #033-05-1976 L1977 **IM** *100 †20

HARMON, Paula Janelle. ■ 27713 #012-21-2006 **OTO** *012

HARPOLE, David H, Jr. 2424 ERWIN RD, STE 403 27705 #051-01-1984 L1985 **TS** *020 †85,90

HARPOLE, Linda Heskestad. 3024 PICKETT RD, DUKE UNIVERSITY MEDICAL CE 27705 #036-07-1992 L1996 **IM** *020 †20

HARRAH, John Dae, Jr. 27701 #055-02-2001 L2001 **EM** *020 †16

HARRELL, Robert A, III. 4004 BEN FRANKLIN BLVD 27704 #023-07-1980 L1982 **RHU IM** *020 †20

HARRELL, Russell. 507 LINWOOD AVE 27701 #036-01-1980 L1984 **FM** *020 †18

HARRELL, Sampson Emanuel. ■ 27707 #036-01-1972 L1972 **FM** *020 †18

HARRELSON, John Miles, III. DUKE MED CTR, BOX 3023 27710 #036-07-1965 L1965 **ORS PTH** *020 †50,40

HARRINGTON, Lynn Marie. ■ 27713 #051-04-2005 **PD** *012

HARRINGTON, Robert Arthur. 2400 PRATT ST 27705 #024-07-1986 L1993 **CD** *050 †20

HARRIS, Jason Randall. DUKE UNIV MED CTR, DEPT OF RADIOLOGY 27710 #024-01-2002 L2007 **VIR** *012 †80

HARRIS, Stephen Lamont. ■ 27713 #017-20-2005 **RO** *012

HARRISON, Jan Clark. 105 NEWSOM ST, STE 106 27704 #035-19-1985 L1988 **IM** *020 †20

HARRISON, Jeremy Don. ■ 27713 #012-05-2006 **MP** *012

HARRISON, John Kevin. DUKE UNIV MED CTR, BOX 3331 27710 #035-19-1984 L1988 **CD IM** *020 †20

HARRISON, Myleme Ojinga. BOX 3837, DUMC 27710 #047-06-1997 L2001 **OS** *020 †75

HARRISON, Robert William. ■ 27707 #023-01-2005 L2008 **IM** *012

HART, Sarah Rachel. P. O. BOX 3127 27710 #036-07-2007 **PD** *012

HART-BROTHERS, Elaine M. 1901 HILLANDALE RD, STE F 27705 #024-07-1976 L1979 **IM OS** *020 †20

HARTMAN, Mary Elizabeth. ■ 27710 #035-45-1999 L2006 **CCP** *100 †55

HARTWIG, Matthew Galen. ■ 27707 #036-07-2001 **GS** *012

HARVEY, Nicholas James. ■ 27710 #917-05-1989 L2002 *020

HASS, Emily Elizabeth. 6301 HERNDON RD, BOX 3228 27713 #041-14-1994 L2002 **CD** *012 †20

HASSETT, Margaret Alycia. 2609 N DUKE ST 27704 #036-07-1978 L1984 **CD IM** *020 †20

HASTINGS, Susan Nicole. BOX 3003, DUMC, ROOM 3502, DUKE SOUTH 27710 #036-01-1998 L2004 **IMG** *100 †20 ‡

HASWELL, Chevon Monique. PO BOX 97571, DUKE UNIVERSITY 27708 #024-01-2007 **IM** *012

HATA, Jonathan Andrew. ■ 27713 #036-07-2000 L2007 **GS** *100

HATEF, Dan Amir. ■ 27705 #023-01-2004 **GS** *100

HAVENS, Andrea Kathryn. ■ 27707 #036-07-2007 **IM** *012

HAVRILESKY, Laura Jean. ■ 27705 #036-07-1995 L1998 **OBG** *020 †30

HAWES, Jodi Jane. ■ 27705 #035-03-2005 **N** *012

HAWKINS, Ashley Davis. DUKE UNIV MED CTR, DEPT OF RADIOLOGY 27710 #036-05-2004 **DR** *012

HAWKINS, Hilary Norman. ■ 27713 #036-01-2003 L2005 **FM** *020 †18

HAYASHI, Madoka. ■ 27704 #572-20-2007 **PD** *012

HAYASHI, Masanori. ■ 27704 #572-20-2005 **PD** *012

HAYAT, Sumera. 6301 HERNDON RD, DUKE FAMILY MEDICINE 27713 #041-02-1995 L2003 **FM** *020 †18

HAYES, Christine Marie. ■ 27710 #023-01-2004 L2006 **PD** *020

HAYES, Melissa Allyson. ■ 27701 #021-01-2006 **DR** *012

HAYNES, Barton Ford. BOX 3258 DUKE MED CTR 27710 #048-04-1973 L1980 **ID AI** *050 †20,03

HAYNES, Caroline Peterson. 3923 WENTWORTH DR, DURHAM 27707 #036-07-1983 L1988 **P** *040 †75

HAZEL, Letitia Marie. PO BOX 19491, NC CENTRAL UNIV 27707 #036-05-1998 L2001 **FM** *020 †18

HEACOCK, Michael Neil. ■ 27713 #038-40-2007 **IM** *012

HEAD, James Ernest. ■ 27703 #036-07-2008 *012

HEATH, John Franklin. 3643 N ROXBORO ST 27704 #039-01-1987 L1999 **AN** *020 †05

HECKMAN, Daniel Scott. ■ 27713 #041-12-2005 **ORS** *012

HEDGPETH, Edward M, Jr. 3643 N ROXBORO ST 27704 #036-01-1962 L1962 **OPH** *020 †35 ‡

HEFLIN, Mitchell Tod. DUMC, 2511 BLUE ZONE DUKE SOUTH 27710 #051-01-1994 L1996 **IMG** *020 †20

HEGARTY, Veronica M. PO BOX 3003, DUKE UNIV MED CTR 27710 #539-03-1984 L1996 *020

HEGLAND, Donald Dale. BOX 31187, DUMC 27710 #011-03-1999 L2000 **ICE** *100 †20

HEIM, Kathryn Anne. ■ 27707 #020-02-2007 *012

HEINE, Mark Dieter. 4125 BEN FRANKLIN BLVD, STE 160 27704 #038-06-1985 L1989 **P** *020 †75

HEINE, Robert Phillips. BOX 3967, DUKE MEDICAL CENTER SOUTH 27710 #048-15-1986 L2000 **OBG MFM** *020 †30

HEINZ, Edward Ralph. DUKE UNIV MED CENTER 27710 #041-01-1955 L1978 **DR** *071 †80

HEITMAN, Joseph Barry. ■ 27705 #035-20-1992 *050

HELMS, Clyde Arthur. BOX 3808 ERWIN ROAD, DEPARTMENT OF RADIOLOGY 27710 #048-13-1972 L1996 **DR** *040 †80

HEMBREE, Walter Chad. ■ 27705 #036-07-2006 **ORS** *012

HENDERSON, Phillippa Jane. 227 BAKER HOUSE, BCC3824 27710 #036-07-1997 L2003 **END** *020 †20

HENDRICKS, Anne Lowrey. ■ 27705 #025-12-1979 L2003 **P** *020 †75 ‡

HENDRICKS, Melissa Anne. BX 3951 M148 DAV BLD 27710 #035-48-2006 **PD** *012

HENDRY, Paul Jonathan. DUKE MEDICAL CENTER 27706 #065-09-1981 **TS** *020 †85

HENEGHAN, Joan Patricia. ERWIN ROAD, DEPT OF RADIOLOGY 27710 #539-04-1988 L1997 *020

HENEGHAN, Michael Anthony. 4101 N ROXBORO ST 27704 #539-04-1992 L1999 *100

HENKE, Elizabeth. 2609 N DUKE ST 27704 #917-18-1974 L1979 **CD IM** *020 †20,19

HERBEL, Bryon L. 718 RUTHERFORD ST 27705 #037-01-1986 L1990 **P CHP** *020 †75

HERBERT, James Taylor. ■ 27705 #036-07-2008 *012

HERMAN, Daniel Curtis. ■ 27713 #036-01-2008 *012

HERMANN, Richard Paul. MD #58A, AGENCY 27711 #028-34-1992 L2005 **PTH** *020 †50,60

HERNANDEZ, Adrian Felipe. 2400 PRATT ST 27705 #048-12-1997 L2001 **CD** *020 †20

HERNANDEZ, Eduardo. ■ 27705 #649-01-1965 L1974 **IM NEP** *071

HERNANDEZ, Michelle L. ■ 27713 #036-01-2002 L2007 **AI** *100 †55,03

HERNDON, Leon Walker, Jr. BOX 3802 27710 #036-01-1991 L1995 **OPH** *020 †35

HEROD, Jerrell Waika. ■ 27713 #023-07-2007 **IM** *012

HEROLD, Christina I. ■ 27701 #024-01-2002 L2002 **HO** *012 †20

HERSHFIELD, Michael S. PO BX 3049 27710 #041-01-1967 L1976 **RHU IM** *050

HERTZBERG, Barbara S. BOX 3808 DUKE MED CTR, DEPT OF RADIOLOGY 27710 #036-07-1980 L1983 **DR** *020 †80

HERTZBERG, Michael Andrew. 508 FULTON ST, DEPT OF PSYCHIATRY 27705 #036-01-1985 L1988 **P** *020 †75

HESTER, Willie Edward, Jr. ■ 27704 #036-08-2001 L2007 **NEP** *012 †20

HETHERINGTON, Seth V. 4222 EMPEROR BLVD, STE 335 27703 #036-01-1978 L1995 **PD ID** *050 †55

HEWITT, John David. PO BOX 3951, HOUSE STAFF OFFICE 27710 #036-07-1999 L2000 **ORS** *020 †40

HEYDA, Ratha Dasi. ■ 27707 #036-07-2008 *012

HEYDEN, Siegfried H. DUKE MEDICAL CENTER 27710 #407-30-1951 **R** *050

HEYMAN, Albert. ERWIN RD, DUMC 3203 27705 #023-01-1940 L1954 **N** *050 †20,75

HEYNEMAN, Laura Elizabeth. DUKE UNIV MEDICAL CENTER, DEPT OF RADIOLOGY BOX 3808 27710 #036-01-1992 L1997 **DR** *020 †80

HEYWARD, Neysa Y. 1301 FAYETTEVILLE ST 27707 #038-45-1981 L1984 **PD** *020 †55

HICK, Ryan Walter. ■ 27713 #036-07-2004 **D** *012

HICKEY, Jason David. 3D RIVER BIRCH RD 27705 #036-07-1999 *100

HICKMAN, Meridythe Ashley. ■ 27713 #048-12-2003 L2007 **OBG** *100

HICKS, Charles Byron. 718 RUTHERFORD ST 27705 #010-01-1979 L1993 **ID IM** *050 †20

HIDA, Tetsuo. DUKE MEDICAL CENTER 27710 #572-20-1973 **OS** *100

HIGGINBOTHAM, Eric Alan. 2307 WILSON ST 27705 #048-14-1996 L1999 **EM** *020 †20,55,16

HIGGINS, Kristin Ann. DUKE UNIV MED CTR, BOX 3805 27710 #021-01-2006 **RO** *012

HIJAZI, Mohammed Hassan. DUMC BOX 3221 27710 #797-02-1991 **PCC** *012

HIJMANS, Jacinta Cato. BOX 3916, DUKE UNIV MED CENTER 27710 #660-03-1949 L1956 **GE IM** *072

HILL, Adam Charles. ■ 27707 #917-07-1983 *020

HILL, Lindsay. ■ 27713 #041-14-2005 **AN** *012

HILL, Steven Ellis. ERWIN ROAD (BOX 3094), DUKE UNIVERSITY MEDICAL CE 27710 #047-05-1986 L1995 **AN CCM** *020 †20,05

HILTON, Andrew Kent. 4101 N ROXBORO ST 27704 #143-07-1983 L1994 *020

HINES, Marcono Raymond, Jr. ■ 27712 #036-08-2007 **IM** *012

HO, Alex. ■ 27713 #011-05-2005 L2007 **EM** *012

HO, Jonathan Ngoc. ■ 27713 #056-06-2006 **EM** *012

HO, Lisa Meiling. 1300 ERWIN ROAD, BOX 3808, DUMC 27710 #023-01-1992 L1997 **DR** *020 †80

HO, Sammy. DUMC BOX 3913, DIVISION OF GASTROENTEROLO 27710 #035-48-1998 L2000 **GE** *020 †20

HO, Vicki Cathy. 3643 N ROXBORO ST 27704 #036-01-2001 L2004 **IM** *020

HOBART, Seth G, Jr. 3643 N ROXBORO ST 27704 #051-01-1950 L1955 **OTO HNS** *071 †45

HOBBS, Juliann Cotter. ■ 27707 #036-01-2006 **AN** *012

HOBBS, Richard Preston, III. ■ 27707 #036-01-2006 **MPD** *012

HOBSON-WEBB, Lisa Deneen. DUMC 3403, DUKE UNIVERSITY MEDICAL CE 27710 #020-12-2001 L2004 **N** *020 †75

HOCHREUTENER, Helen Agnes. DUKE MEDICAL CENTER 27710 #869-07-1982 **AI** *012

HOCKER, Michael Brian. 986 IVY MEADOW LN, DUMC #3096 27710 #007-02-1993 L2002 **EM** *020 †16

HODGINS, Lewis Roger. 718 RUTHERFORD ST 27705 #035-08-1985 L1987 **AN CCM** *020 †05

HODRICK, Jeffrey Thomas. DUMC, BOX 3000 27710 #041-14-2002 L2007 **ORS** *100

HOENIG, Helen Marie. 508 FULTON ST, PM&RS (117) DURHAM VAMC 27705 #003-01-1985 L1993 **IMG** *020 †20

HOFFA, Mary Hannah. ■ 27705 #010-02-2006 **MP** *012

HOFFMAN, Jonathan Robert. ■ 27713 #035-19-2007 **IM** *012

HOFFMAN, Maureane. 508 FULTON ST, VA MED CTR LAB SERV # 113 27705 #018-03-1982 L1983 **BBK HMP** *050 †50

HOFFMAN, Ruth Sterling. 27705 #021-01-1958 L1977 **IM** *071

HOJMAN, Horacio M. ■ 27707 #132-07-1984 L2007 **CCS** *020 †85

HOLCOMBE, Faith Hollowell. DUMC, MEDICINE 27710 #028-02-1980 L1992 **IM** *020 †20

HOLLAND, David Preston. BOX 3824 MEDICAL CENTER 27710 #012-05-1995 L2006 **ID** *012 †20

HOLLENBECK, Scott Thomas. ■ 27710 #038-40-2000 L2007 **PS** *012 †85

HOLLINGSWORTH, Caroline L. 4101 N ROXBORO ST 27704 #048-02-1996 L2001 **PDR** *020 †80

HOLLINGSWORTH, John W, II. BOX 3136, DUKE UNIVERSITY MEDICAL CE 27710 #048-02-1996 L2004 **PCC** *020 †20 ‡

HOLLOWAY, Sarah Kay. ■ 27705 #025-01-2005 **PD** *012

HOLLOWELL, Robert Perry, III. ■ 27705 #036-07-2008 *012

HOLMER, Shelley Anne. BOX 3950, 4584 WHITE ZONE DUKE SOUTH 27710 #047-06-2002 L2006 **P** *020 †75

HOLMUHAMEDOVA, Madina Ekh. ■ 27710 #016-42-2008 *012

HOLSINGER, Tracey Beth. 508 FULTON ST, MAIL STATION 116A 27705 #051-01-1992 L1993 **P PYG** *075 †75

HOLTON, Jennifer Elizabet. ■ 27713 #041-01-2007 **P** *012

HOMI, Hercilia Mayumi. P O BOX 3094, DUKE UNIV MEDICAL CTR 27710 #187-53-1986 L2004 **AN** *100

HOMMEL, Erin Pinkerton. ■ 27712 #048-12-2005 **IM** *012

HONG, Beatrice Doi-Yee. BOX 31159, DUMC 27710 #023-07-2002 L2005 **END** *012 †20

HOOVER, Sean Christopher. ■ 27705 #011-02-2006 L2008 **AN** *012

HORNE, Amilda Knox. 1316 MARTIN LUTHR KNG PKWY 27707 #017-20-1983 L1990 **P PYG** *020 †75

HORNE, Kristopher Cornell. ■ 27707 #047-06-2002 L2007 **DR** *100 †80

HORNE, Lillian Rae. ■ 27713 #041-12-1984 L1985 **FM** *020 †18

HORNIK, Christoph Paul Vi. BX 3951 M148 DAV BLD 27710 #409-05-2005 **PD** *012

HORRIGAN, Joseph Patrick. 2006 SUNSET AVE 27705 #035-45-1988 L1990 **CHP P** *050 †75

HORST, Frank. DUKE UNIV MED CTR, ORTHOPAEDICS DUMC 2912 27710 #409-02-1988 **ORS OFA** *020

HORWITZ, Mitchell Eric. DUMC BOX 3961, TRANSPLANT PROGRAM 27710 #016-01-1992 L2003 **HEM ON** *020 †20

HOSEIN, Fareeda. 3643 N ROXBORO ST, DURHAM REGIONAL HOSPITAL 27704 #038-40-1996 L2005 **IM** *012

HOSFORD, David Akers. 508 FULTON ST, BLDG 16 27705 #012-05-1983 L1987 **N** *050 †75

HOSTLER, David Christian. ■ 27704 #036-07-2008 *012

HOVIS, Christopher Lee. 2508 SEVIER ST 27705 #047-06-2001 L2006 **DR** *020 †80

HOWELL, David Noble. ■ 27705 #036-07-1984 L1987 **PTH** *020 †50

HOWELL, Druhan Lowry. ■ 27713 #001-06-2003 L2005 **AI** *012 †20

HOWELL, James T. ■ 27705 #038-41-1944 L1945 **OS** *071 †20

HOWELL, Paul Edwind, Jr. ■ 27713 #041-01-2003 L2007 **PM** *012

HRANITZKY, Patrick M. DUMC, BOX 31070 27710 #048-12-1996 L2001 **ICE** *020 †20

HSIAO, Leal Kang. DUKE UNIV MED CTR, DEPT OF COMMUNITY AND FAMI 27710 #005-11-2006 L2007 **FP** *012

HSU, Chung-Ping. DUKE UNIV MED CTR-SURG 27710 #244-03-1980 **GS** *100

HSU, Jerry Yungchi. DUMC, BOX 31084 27710 #005-11-2004 L2006 **IM** *100 †20

HSU, Shiaowen David. ■ 27713 #036-01-2001 L2005 **HO** *100

HUANG, Andrew Ta-Fu. BUILDING 320 RESEARCH DRIV, DUKE UNIV MEDICAL CNTRSAND 27710 #385-02-1964 L1971 **HEM IM** *020

HUANG, Erich Senin. ■ 27701 #036-07-2003 **GS** *012

HUANG, Melissa. ■ 27704 #036-01-2004 **CD** *012 †20

HUANG, Samuel Fongyin. 205 FRASIER ST 27704 #005-18-1994 L2002 **U** *020 †95

HUANG, Steven Yizen. ■ 27713 #041-01-2005 L2003 **DR** *012

HUANG, Yuh-Chin. ERWIN RD 27710 #244-02-1983 L1989 **PUD IM** *020

HUDSON, Edward Valentine. 3901 N ROXBORO ST # 15249 27704 #036-05-1962 L1962 **OTO** *071 †45

HUDSON, William R. BOX 3805, DUKE UNIVERSITY MEDICAL CE 27710 #036-05-1951 L1951 **OTO** *071 †45

HUENING, Michael Andrew. ■ 27712 #033-05-2003 L2004 **PCP** *012 †50

HUFFMAN, Kim Marie. BOX 3327 DUMC 27710 #045-01-2000 L2003 **RHU** *050 †20

HUGHES, Betsy Deanina. ■ 27713 #012-01-2007 **GS** *012

HUGHES, George Charles, IV. DUKE UNIVERSITY MEDICAL CE, BOX 31224 27710 #036-07-1995 L2002 **TS** *100 †85,90 ‡

HUH, Billy Keon. 932 MORREENE RD 27705 #001-02-1993 L1997 **AN PME** *020 †05

HUMPHREYS, Margaret. 3024 PICKETT RD 27705 #024-01-1987 L1993 **IM** *020 †20

HUNDLEY, Julie Elizabeth. 5414 WHISPERWOOD DR 27705 #048-12-1998 L2002 **IM** *020 †20

HUNNICUTT, Addie Stark. ■ 27713 #045-04-2002 L2003 **CHN** *012 †55

HUNT, Susan Elizabeth. DUMC 3127, 5409 DUKE HOSPITAL NORTH 27710 #025-01-2004 L2008 **MPD** *012

HUNT, Tyehimba Afrika. ■ 27713 #036-01-1999 L2000 **CHP** *020 †75

HURST, Jason Michael. ■ 27713 #010-02-2003 L2008 **ORS** *012

HURWITZ, Barrie James. DUKE UNIV MED CTR, BOX 3184 27710 #836-01-1968 L1978 **N IM** *020 †20

HURWITZ, Herbert Ira. 718 RUTHERFORD ST 27705 #041-02-1988 L1996 **ON** *020 †20

HUSAIN, Aatif Mairaj. DUKE UNIVERSITY MEDICAL CE, 202 BELL BUILDING 27710 #704-20-1989 L1996 **N CN** *020 †20

HUSSAIN, Hammad. ■ 27707 #704-25-2001 L2004 **IMG** *012

HUTCHINGS, Yalonda Lanora. ■ 27707 #036-07-2008 *012

HUTCHINSON, Charles Blake. ■ 27703 #001-02-2006 **PTH** *012

HUTTEMEIER, Peter C. BOX 3094 DUMC 27710 #297-01-1977 L1990 **AN** *020

IAROVICI, Doris Monica. 1004 BROAD ST 27705 #008-01-1992 L1993 **P** *072 †75

IDRISS, Salim Farouk. BOX 3090 DUMC 27710 #036-07-1996 L1999 **PDC** *020 †55

INDRIASON, Olafur S. 718 RUTHERFORD ST 27705 #484-01-1987 L1995 **NEP** *020 †20

ING, Richard John. P O BOX 3094, D U M C DEPT ANES 27710 #836-01-1988 L2000 **AN** *020

INRIG, Jula Leigh. FULTON ST, BOX 3104 27710 #005-12-2000 L2003 **NEP** *100

IRVINE, Lena Elizabeth. ■ 27713 #011-04-2006 **P** *012

ISAACS, Robert Eric. DUKE NEUROSURG, DUMC BOX 3807 27710 #048-04-1995 L2005 **NS** *020 †25

ISARIYAWONGSE, Brandon Ka. ■ 27707 #036-07-2008 *012

ISBEY, Susan Foster. 4205 BEN FRANKLIN BLVD, ASSOCIATES PA 27704 #036-01-1987 L1990 **ID** *020 †20

ISELIN-CHAVES, Irene Anne. 718 RUTHERFORD ST 27705 #869-04-1985 L1997 *020

ITSKOVICH, Andrea Cynthia. ■ 27704 #005-06-2004 L2004 **N** *100

IUGA, Aurel Ovidiu. ■ 27705 #781-01-1999 L2001 *100

IZATT, Susan Flynn. BOX 3179, HOSPITAL DRIVE, 204 BELL BUILDING 27710 #024-07-1987 L2001 **NPM** *020 †55

IZLAR, Henry Le Roy, Jr. ■ 27704 #036-07-1948 L1953 **IM CD** *020 †20

JACK, Megan Christine. ■ 27713 #010-02-2004 L2007 **GS** *012

JACKSON, George William. DUKE UNIV MED CTR, BOX 3148 27710 #038-06-1968 L1982 **OM FM** *030 †70

JACKSON, James Wm, Jr. ■ 27709 #021-05-1988 L1995 **NEP** *020 †20

JACKSON, Joseph Augustus. 6301 HERNDON RD, DUKE CHILDREN'S PRIMARY CA 27713 #051-01-2004 L2007 **PD** *020

JACKSON, Kevin Patrick. BOX 31021, DUKE UNIVERSITY MEDICAL CE 27710 #035-01-2000 L2003 **ICE** *100 †20

JACKSON, Larry Roanald. ■ 27713 #011-03-2007 **IM** *012

JACKSON, Lisa Amaya. 3613 DUKE UNIV MEDICAL CEN 27710 #036-01-1986 L1987 **CHP** *050 †75

JACOBI, Peter De Greeff. 2400 BROAD ST 27704 #038-06-1979 L1980 **FM** *020 †18

JACOBS, Danny Odell. P.O. BOX 3704, DEPARTMENT OF SURGERY 27710 #038-02-1979 L2003 **GS OS** *020 †85

JACOBS, Ramon Eduardoacos. ■ 27713 #036-01-2002 L2006 **MPD** *100 †20,55

JACOBS, Steven Jay. WELLCOM RESEARCH LAB 27709 #024-05-1968 L1979 **END IM** *050 †20

JACOKES, Dennis Neill. 4309 EMPEROR BLVD STE 125, IMPERIAL CENTER FAMILY MED 27703 #036-01-1987 L1992 **FM** *020 †20

JAFFE, Glenn Jay. BOX 3802 27710 #005-02-1983 L1989 **OPH** *020 †35

JAFFE, Tracy Anne. BOX 3808, DUKE UNIVERSITY MEDICAL CE 27710 #048-12-1996 L1999 **DR** *020 †20

JAGADESAN, Raghuram. BOX 3221, DUMC 27710 #539-03-1990 **PCC** *100

JAGGERS, James. DUKE UNIV MEDICAL CENTER, BOX 3474 27710 #030-05-1988 L1996 **TS** *020 †85,90

JAIN, Nina. ■ 27713 #011-03-2002 L2005 **PDE** *012 †55

JAMES, Andra Hohler. 4302 DULA ST 27705 #051-01-1993 L1995 **OBG MFM** *040 †30

JAMES, Michael Lucas. DUKE UNIVERSITY MEDICAL CE, DUMC BOX 3094 27710 #021-05-1999 L2000 **AN** *100 †75,05

JAROSZ, Jennifer Ann. ■ 27703 #035-15-2008 *012

JARRAH, Rima Joy. 1 DUKE MEDICAL CTR, DEPT OF PEDIATRICS 27710 #036-01-2002 L2005 **CCP PD** *012

JARVIS, Wingrove Theophil. BOX 3077, DUKE UNIV MED CTR 27710 #566-01-1993 L2006 **OSS** *100

JAY, Gary Wayne. ■ 27707 #016-06-1976 L1977 **N PMN** *062 ‡

JAZWINSKI, Alison Beth. ■ 27705 #041-02-2006 **IM** *012

JECK, Lida Morawetz. 1502 W NC HIGHWAY 54, STE 302 27707 #036-07-1977 L1981 **PYA P** *020 †75

JELESOFF, Nicole Elise. 3116 N DUKE ST 27704 #010-02-1991 L1997 **END** *020 †20

JELIC, Jeffrey S. 5501 FORTUNES RIDGE DR, STE G 27713 #051-04-1996 L1999 **OMF CS** *020

JENKINS, Casey D. ■ 27707 #025-07-2002 L2008 **HSO** *012

JENNINGS, Jonathan Lamar. ■ 27704 #036-01-2008 *012

JENNINGS, Robert B. BOX 3712 DUKE UNIV MED CEN 27710 #016-06-1950 L1975 **PTH CD** *050 †50

JENTZER, Jacob Colin. ■ 27713 #035-45-2008 *012

JERGE, Kari Fitzgerald. ■ 27713 #016-02-2006 **GS** *012

JEWELL, Elizabeth Lin. ■ 27710 #032-01-2002 L2007 **OBG** *100

JEWELL, Sisi Njia. ■ 27707 #038-40-2005 **IM** *012

JIANG, Wei. DUKE UNIV MED CTR, BOX 3366 27710 #243-13-1982 L2001 **IM P** *050 †20

JO, Jennifer Miree. 1901 HILLANDALE RD, STE B 27705 #016-06-2000 L2003 **FM** *020 †18 ‡

JOHNSON, Benjamin Frankli. ■ 27704 #036-07-2008 *012

JOHNSON, Caryn Jeanine. ■ 27707 #035-06-2004 **OBG** *012

JOHNSON, Christopher Patr. ■ 27713 #051-04-2005 **EM** *012

JOHNSON, Clarissa Estell. ■ 27704 #038-06-2003 L2006 **PHO** *012 †55

JOHNSON, Cynthia Lynn. BOX 3127 DUMC 27710 #035-45-1999 L2003 **MPD** *020 †20,55

JOHNSON, David Neil. DUMC 3403, TRENT DR CLINIC 1L RM 1255 27710 #055-01-2003 **N** *100

JOHNSON, Deborah Beverley. 1301 FAYETTEVILLE ST 27707 #010-03-1997 L2005 **IM** *020 †20

JOHNSON, Edward Alex. ■ 27705 #036-08-2006 **PD** *012

JOHNSON, Eric Stalin M E. PO BOX 122233 27709 #917-04-1970 **PHP** *050

JOHNSON, Jason Nathaniel. ■ 27713 #021-05-2006 **PD** *012

JOHNSON, Kimberly Sherell. DUKE UNIV MEDICAL CTR, DIV GERIATRICS DUMC3003 27710 #023-07-1997 L1998 **IMG** *020 †20

JOHNSON, Kwame. ■ 27704 #036-07-2008 *012

JOHNSON, Kyle Edwin. ■ 27713 #004-01-2006 L2008 **P** *012

JOHNSON, Lareisha Melai. BX 3951 M148 DAV BLD 27710 #010-03-1997 **FM** *100

JOHNSON, Lauren Patricia. DEPT OF COMM & FAM MED, DUMC BOX 2899 27710 #036-01-1993 L2001 **FM** *020 †18

JOHNSON, Libre Evan. 5317 HIGHGATE DR, STE 117 27713 #041-12-2000 L2003 **FM** *020 †18

JOHNSON, Sally Rebecca. 5317 HIGHGATE DR, STE 117 27713 #025-07-1999 L2001 **FM** *020 †18

JOHNSON, Tonica Vinetta. 4102 N ROXBORO ST 27704 #012-05-1999 L2006 **OPH** *100 †35

JOHNSON, Victoria K. BOX 3886 DUMC, 2100 ERWIN RD 27710 #005-14-1985 L1986 **EM RO** *020 †18

JOHNSTON, Jeffrey Monroe. 3030 CORN WALLACE RD 27709 #036-07-1977 L1989 **CCM DIA** *030 †20

JOHNSTON, Suzanne Carol. ■ 27705 #045-01-2003 L2007 **IM** *012

JOHNSTON, William Webb. ERWIN RD 27710 #036-07-1959 L1959 **PTH OS** *071 †50

JOLLIS, James Gerard. 1 DUKE MEDICAL CTR, DUMC BOX 3254 27710 #038-40-1986 L1992 **CD IM** *020 †20

JOLLY, Puneet Singh. DUKE UNIV MED CNTR, BOX 3085 27710 #010-02-2006 L2006 **RO** *012

JONES, Cheryl Ann. DEPARTMENT OF ANESTHESIOLO, DUKE UNIVERSITY MEDICAL CE 27710 #008-02-2002 L2006 **AN** *100 †05

JONES, Claudia Kay. DUKE UNIVERSITY MEDICAL CE, BOX 3712 27710 #036-07-1985 L1998 **PTH PCP** *020 †50

JONES, Everett R, Jr. ■ 27705 #035-15-1981 L2005 **PYG P** *030 †75 ‡

JONES, Kim Richard. 2609 N DUKE ST 801 27704 #036-01-1986 L1988 **OTO** *020 †45

JONES, Lindsay Dianne. ■ 27704 #036-07-2008 *012

JONES, Marsha Rene. 3030 CORNWALLIS RD 27709 #051-04-1982 L1984 **HEM ON** *050

JONES, Morris Alexander. 2609 N DUKE ST, STE 303 27704 #036-01-1959 L1959 **R** *071 †80

JONES, Patricia Denise. ■ 27713 #035-03-2007 **MPD** *012

JONES, Robert Howard. 4101 N ROXBORO ST 27704 #023-07-1965 L1972 **TS** *020 †85,90

JONES, William Schuyler. DUKE UNIVERSITY MEDICAL CE, BOX 31152 27710 #004-01-2001 L2004 **CD** *012

JOSEPH, Akaninyene Sunday. 121 BASSET HALL DR, DURHAM 27713 #690-02-1992 L2004 **IM** *020 †20

JOSHI, Anand Bhagwan. ■ 27707 #038-44-2003 L2003 **PM** *012

JOSHI, Sangeeta Prabhakar. ■ 27705 #495-28-1993 L2005 **PCC** *012 †20

JOVANOVIC, Vuk. ■ 27707 #409-20-2003 L2007 **OBG** *020

JOWELL, Paul Simon. BOX 3662, DUKE UNI 27710 #836-02-1983 L1989 **GE IM** *020 †20

JOY, Scott Victor. 3024 PICKETT RD 27705 #041-12-1992 L1995 **IM** *020 †20

JOYCE, Maria Josephine. DURHAM VA MEDICAL CENTER, SERVICE 113, RMF-3167 27710 #024-05-1996 L1997 **ID** *020 †20

JOYNER, Benny Levander, Jr. ■ 27707 #036-01-2002 L2006 **CCP** *012 †55

JOYNER, Patrick Wakefield. ■ 27707 #025-01-2004 **ORS** *012

JOYNER, Raymond Edward. 205 FRASIER ST 27704 #036-05-1968 L1968 **U UP** *020 †95

JUEL, Vern C. DUKE UNIVERSITY MED CTR, BOX 3403 27710 #016-11-1989 L2004 **N CN** *020 †75

KAHN, Lauren Alexandra. ■ 27705 #036-07-2008 *012

KALLAS, Taylor James. BX 3951 M148 DAV BLD 27710 #422-01-2005 L2007 **EM** *012

KALLIANOS, John Andrew. 4309 MEDICAL PARK DR, STE 100 27704 #036-07-1986 L1987 **IM PD** *020 †20,55

KAMAL, Adil Saddiq Ahmed. PO BOX 3094, DUKE UNIV MED CTR DEPT AN 27710 #797-02-1992 L2001 **AN** *100 †05

KAMINETZKY, Catherine P. 508 FULTON ST, AMB CARE (11C) DVAMC 27705 #036-07-1998 L2001 **IM** *040 †20

KAMINSKI, David Wilburn. 5212 MCCORMICK RD 27713 #036-05-2000 L2003 **EM** *020 †16

KAMINSKI, Suzanne Bukrey. ■ 27713 #025-01-2004 **OBG** *012

KANAFANI, Zeina Adnan. BX 3951 M148 DAV BLD 27710 #605-01-1999 **ID** *100

KANALY, Charles William. ■ 27705 #047-05-2005 **NS** *012

KANALY, Travis Edward. ■ 27713 #039-01-2005 L2005 **N** *012

KANE, William Harrison. DUKE UNIV MED CTR, DIV OF HEMATOLOTY/ONCOLOGY 27710 #028-02-1982 L1988 **HEM IM** *020 †20

KANJ, Souha Sami. 718 RUTHERFORD ST 27705 #605-02-1987 L1991 **ID** *020 †20

KANN, Joel. 5716 FAYETTEVILLE RD, DUKE URGENT CARE SOUTH 27713 #051-07-1989 L1990 **FM** *020 †18

KANTER, Ronald Jay. BOX 3090, ERWIN RD RM 7502, DUKE UNIVERSITY MEDICAL CE 27710 #047-05-1979 L1987 **PDC PD** *020 †55

KAPILA, Atul. DUKE UMC BOX 3094 27704 #917-07-1984 **AN** *100

KAPPELMANN, Rick Bernard. 4102 N ROXBORO ST 27704 #028-03-1983 L1984 **OTO** *020 †45

KARIKARI, Isaac Obiri. DUKE UNIV MED CTR, DUMC BOX #3443 27710 #036-07-2006 **GS** *012

KARIMAN, Khalil. 1901 HILLANDALE RD, DURHAM MEDICAL CENTER 27705 #517-04-1969 L1976 **PUD IM** *020 †20

KARIS, Joannes G H. ERWIN RD 27710 #660-04-1952 L1975 **AN** *071 †05

KAROL, David Edward. ■ 27713 #038-06-2007 **MP** *012

KASSEM-MOUSSA, Hassan A. ■ 27710 #605-01-1995 L2000 **N** *100 †75

KASUGANTI, Shilpa Rao. ■ 27713 #016-06-2004 L2008 **PM** *012

KATAKAM, Lakshmi Iswarya. DUKE UNIV MED CTR, BOX 3179 27710 #011-03-2003 **NPM** *012 †55

KATZ, Daniel Herbert. ■ 27710 #033-05-1997 L2006 **ICE** *020 †20

KATZ, Jason Neil. ■ 27703 #036-01-2000 L2006 **CD** *012

KATZ, Michael Geoffrey. ■ 27707 #035-45-2007 **IM** *012

KATZ, Samuel L. BOX 2925, DUKE UNIV MED CENTER 27710 #024-01-1952 L1968 **iD PD** *050 †55

KAUFMAN, Adam Mccall. MEDICAL CENTER, DUKE UNIVERSITY 27710 #024-01-2007 **ORS** *012

KAUFMAN, Andrew Russell. ■ 27713 #045-01-2004 **P** *012

KAUFMAN, Russel Eugene. 3900 HOPE VALLEY RD 27707 #038-40-1973 L1977 **HEM ON** *050 †20

KAUL, Mala Shaykher. 3643 N ROXBORO ST, DURHAM REGIONAL HOSPITAL 27704 #011-02-2003 L2006 **RHU** *012 †20

KAUL, Prashant. ■ 27713 #917-03-1998 L2006 **CD** *012 †20

KAVANAUGH, Patrick E. 6020 FAYETTEVILLE RD 27713 #036-08-1995 L1998 **FM** *020 †18

KAYE, Keith Steven. DUMC BOX 3152 27710 #041-01-1994 L2000 **IM ID** *020 †20

KAZAN, Rania Youssef. DUMC BOX NB 3430 27710 #605-01-1998 L2005 **IM** *020 †20

KEALEY, Susan Maria. OFFICE OF GRADUATE MED EDU, BOX 3951 27710 #539-04-1995 L2003 **RNR** *020

KEENAN, Alison Carroll. ■ 27713 #036-01-2008 *012

KELLEY, Michael John. 508 FULTON ST, DURHAM VA HOSPITAL 27705 #025-01-1985 L1988 **ON IM** *050 †20

KELLEY, Scott Streater. 3609 WATKINS RD 27707 #018-03-1982 L1992 **ORS OAR** *020 †40

KELLEY, Wayne. ■ 27713 #045-01-2005 **ORS** *012

KELLY, James Reginald. 3643 N ROXBORO ST 27704 #036-07-1970 L1976 **IM MDM** *020 †20 ‡

KELSEY, Christopher Ryan. ■ 27710 #007-02-2002 L2007 **RO** *100

KELTON, John Greenhow. DUKE MEDICAL CENTER 27710 #065-06-1973 **HEM IM** *050

KEMPER, Alex Randall. 2400 PRATT ST, ROOM 0311 TERRACE LEVEL 27705 #036-07-1993 L1996 **PD GPM** *050 †55

KENAN, Daniel J. ■ 27710 #036-07-1995 L1997 **PTH** *020

KENDALL, Stephan Disean. BOX 3841, DUKE UNIVERISITY MEDICAL C 27710 #035-03-1999 L2002 **HO** *100 †20

KENDALL, William F, Jr. ■ 27713 #025-12-1995 L2005 **GS** *100

KENNEDY, Richard C, Jr. 5716 FAYETTEVILLE RD 27713 #016-11-1985 L1988 **FM** *020 †18

KENNEDY, Stacy Denise. ■ 27705 #041-13-2004 **RHU** *012 †20

KERN, Frank Howard. DUKE UNIV MC, BOX 3046 27710 #041-01-1982 L1988 **AN PD** *020 †55,05

KERNODLE, Carey Elizabeth. DUKE UNIV MED CTR, DIVISION OF HEMATOLOGY/ONC 27710 #036-08-2002 L2008 **HO** *012 †20

KEVILL, Katharine Anne. ■ 27705 #036-07-1994 L2005 **PDP** *100 †55

KHAROD, Bhairavi V. ■ 27707 #012-01-2002 L2006 **OPH** *100

KHERANI, Aftab Razak. ■ 27707 #036-07-1999 L2000 **GS** *100

KHURI, Nadeem Emile. ■ 27713 #051-01-2004 **GS** *012

KHWAJA, Radhika. 508 FULTON ST, C7001 VAMC 27705 #495-45-1993 L2002 **HO** *020 †20

KIEFER, Todd Lee. ■ 27713 #021-05-2004 L2005 **CD** *012

KIHLSTROM, Bruce Lee. 2309 SPARGER RD 27705 #036-01-1972 L1973 **NS** *020 †25

KIHM, John Turner. 3811 N ROXBORO ST, STE B 27704 #025-07-1984 L1987 **IM** *020 †20

KILANI, Ramsey Khair. ■ 27713 #003-01-2002 L2005 **RNR** *012 †80

KILEFF, Moyra Eleanor. 3643 N ROXBORO ST 27704 #075-01-1973 L1977 **AN** *020 †05

KILLAM, Allen Page. BOX 3122 DUKE UNIV MED CTR 27710 #048-02-1960 L1981 **OBG MFM** *050 †30

KILLENBERG, Paul Gustav. #1 HOSPITAL DRIVE BOX 3946 27710 #041-01-1963 L1972 **IM HEP** *040 †20

KIM, Connie Eunjung. ■ 27710 #041-12-2001 L2006 **DR** *020 †80

KIM, Dong Won. ■ 27713 #005-12-2003 **RO** *012

KIM, Edwin Hyungkeun. ■ 27713 #033-06-2005 L2008 **PD** *012

KIM, Jay Han. 205 FRASIER ST, TRIANGLE UROLOGY ASSOCIATE 27704 #024-05-1989 L1993 **U** *020 †95

KIM, Kyung Mee. ■ 27713 #051-04-2007 **IM** *012

KIM, Raymond Jinsuk. BOX 3934, DUKE UNIV MED CTR 27710 #035-01-1990 L2002 **CD** *020 †20

KIM, Terry. 2351 ERWIN RD BOX 3802 27710 #036-07-1992 L1997 **OPH** *020 †35

KIM, Yang Kon. ■ 27712 #583-01-1961 L2003 **PTH CLP** *071 †50 ‡

KIMBROUGH, Dorlan Jamal. ■ 27705 #047-05-2007 **IM** *012

KIMMICK, Gretchen G. BOX 3204, SUITE 3800, DUKE SOUTH 27710 #036-05-1989 L1992 **ON IM** *020 †20

KIMPLE, Randall Joel. ■ 27713 #036-01-2005 **RO** *012

KINDER, Allison Lee. DUKE UNIV MED CTR, DEPT OF ANESTHESIOLOGY 27710 #055-02-1988 L1992 **PD** *020 †05

KING, Aliceson Yvette. ■ 27713 #036-07-1999 L2003 **PD** *020

KING, Kara Olisa. DUMC 3616, RM 5830 27710 #036-07-2006 **OBG** *012

KINGHORN, Warren Anderson. ■ 27705 #024-01-2003 L2007 **P** *012

KINNEY, Thomas Roberts. 3120 DEVON RD, BOX 3462 27707 #036-07-1970 L1970 **PHO PD** *020 †55

KINSINGER, Linda Sue. 3022 CROASDAILE DR STE 200 27705 #018-03-1979 L1987 **IM GPM** *030 †20,70

KIRCHMANN, Eric Lee. DUKE UNIVERSITY MEDICINE C, DUMC BOX 3837 27710 #028-02-1995 L2000 **IM** *020 †75

KIRSCH, Susan Sugarman. 5322 HIGHGATE DR, STE 144 27713 #012-01-1998 L2007 **PD** *020 †55

KISHWANI, Priya Sunil. 237 BELL BLDG, TRENT DR, DIV OF MEDICAL GENETICS 27710 #495-17-1990 L1995 **PD** *020 †55,19

KISSLO, Joseph Andrew, Jr. P.O. BOX 3818, ERWIN ROAD DUKE SOUTH 27710 #041-09-1967 L1974 **CD IM** *020

KISTLER, Henry Evans, Jr. ■ 27705 #036-07-1961 L1961 **P** *071 †30

KITKO, Carrie Lynn. DEPARTMENT OF PEDIATRICS, DUKE UNIVERSITY MEDICAL CE 27710 #038-40-1999 L2002 **PHO** *100 †55

KLASSEN, Preston Scott. 4101 N ROXBORO ST 27704 #030-05-1994 L1997 **NEP** *020 †20

KLEIN, Brita Renee. ■ 27712 #035-45-2006 **P** *012

KLEIN, Stephen M. BOX 3094, DEPT OF ANESTHESIOLOGY 27710 #033-05-1992 L1996 **AN** *020 †05

KLEM, Igor. P O BOX 3951, DUKE UNIV MED CTR 27710 #154-07-1997 *100

KLEM, Peter Anton. ■ 27705 #035-15-1962 L1963 **P** *071 †75

KLEVEN, Daniel Thomas. ■ 27710 #036-01-2004 **PTH** *012

KLINK, Joseph Clair. ■ 27707 #017-20-2005 **U** *012

KLINKNER, Michael Wayne. 1901 HILLANDALE RD, DUKE URGENT CARE 27705 #025-01-1998 L1991 **FM EM** *020 †18

KLINTWORTH, Gordon K. BOX 3802 27710 #836-01-1957 L1963 **PTH NP** *050 †50

KNAACK, William R. 508 FULTON ST 27705 #056-06-2000 L2004 **IM** *020 †20

KNIGHT, Jennifer Marcelle. ERWIN RD 27710 #566-01-1988 **PDP** *100 †55

KNUDSEN, Nancy Wolters. DUMC BOX 3094 ROOM 2262DN, DUKE UNIV MED CENTER 27710 #028-46-1991 L1995 **CCA** *020 †05

KNUTSON, Tamra Marie. ■ 27703 #026-04-2005 **DR** *012

KOCINA, Sandra. ■ 27707 #409-04-2003 **PD** *012

KOCIOL, Robb D. ■ 27713 #024-03-2004 L2007 **CD** *012 †20

KOEBERL, Dwight Dudley. TRENT DRIVE, BOX 3528, BELL BLDG237 27710 #026-08-1990 L1999 **PD** *020 †55,19

KOENEN, Mark Allen. ■ 27705 #035-19-2000 L2005 **PFP** *100 †55

KOENIG, Harold Geo. 2213 ELBA STREET, BOX 3400, DEPT OF PSYCHIATRY 27710 #005-02-1982 L1988 **P FM** *020 †18,75

KOEPKE, John Arthur. ■ 27705 #035-05-1956 L1980 **BBK HEM** *071 †50

KOLLS, Bradley Jason. DUKE UNIV MED CTR, BOX 2905 27710 #005-15-2001 L2005 **N** *020 †75

KOMADA, Michael Rudolph. 2609 N DUKE ST 27704 #036-05-1993 L1996 **IC** *020 †20

KONG, David Franklin. CARDIOVASCULAR DIV BOX 385, DUKE UNIV MEDICAL CTR 27710 #023-07-1993 L1994 **IC** *020 †20

KONG, Garheng Albert. ■ 27705 #036-07-2001 *100

KONG, Waitak. PO BOX 3385, DUKE UNIV MED CTR 27710 #065-01-1992 **CD** *100 †20

KONG, Yihong. DUKE MEDICAL CENTER 27710 #385-03-1958 L1967 **CD IM** *100 †55

KONTOS, Christopher Dale. 718 RUTHERFORD ST 27705 #051-04-1989 L1993 **CD** *020 †20

KOONTZ, Bridget Fey. ■ 27707 #024-01-2002 L2007 **RO** *100

KOONTZ, Jason Ian. DUMC, BOX 31275 27710 #024-01-2002 **CD** *012 †20

KOREISHI, Aaleya Faruk. DUKE EYE CTR, DUMC BOX 3802 27710 #025-01-2000 L2006 **OPH** *020 †35

KORI, Shashidar H. BOX 2964 ERWIN RD, DUKE UNIV MEDICAL CENTER 27710 #495-37-1971 L1999 **N ON** *050 †75

KOSANIN, Radoslav. 300 CRUTCHFIELD ST 27704 #957-02-1965 L1978 **AN** *020 †05

KOTCHMAR, Dennis John. US EPA HERL MD 54 27711 #045-01-1978 **PHP** *030

KOUKOUBIS, Theodosios D. DUKE UNIV MED CTR, DEPT HAND SURG 27710 #418-04-1983 **HS** *020

KOURANY, Wissam Mohammad. DUMC 3014, DUKE UNIVERSITY MEDICAL CE 27710 #605-01-1998 L2005 **NEP** *100 †20

KOVACH, Stephen John, III. 5204 KEMMONT DR 27713 #010-01-1997 L2004 **PS** *020 †85

KOVALIK, Jean Paul. ■ 27705 #047-05-2002 **END** *012 †20

KOWEEK, Lynne Michelle. BOX 3951, DUMC 27710 #036-07-1997 L2002 **DR** *020 †80

KOZLOWSKA, Elzbieta. 4419 BEN FRANKLIN BLVD 27704 #759-03-1985 L2005 **NEP OS** *020 †20

KRAKOW, Elizabeth Florenc. DUKE UNIV MED CTR, BOX 31054 27710 #067-01-2003 **IM** *100 †20

KRAMER, Judith M. 4101 N ROXBORO ST 27704 #036-01-1977 L1980 **IM** *050 †20

KRANSDORF, Evan Paul. ■ 27704 #024-01-2006 **IM** *012

KRANZ, Peter George. DUKE UNIV MED CTR, DEPT OF RADIOLOGY 27710 #036-01-2003 **DR** *012

KRASCHNEWSKI, Jennifer Ly. DUMC, BOX 31100 27710 #056-05-2004 L2007 **IM** *020 †20

KRASINSKI, Kevin Leo. ■ 27713 #024-07-2002 L2002 **OSM** *012

KRAUS, Virginia Byers. BOX 3416, DUKE UNIVERSITY 27710 #036-07-1982 L1985 **RHU IM** *050 †20

KRAUS, William E. 4101 N ROXBORO ST 27704 #036-07-1982 L1985 **CD IM** *020 †20

KRAVITZ, Richard Mark. DIV OF PED PULMONARY DISEA, DUMC 2994 27710 #041-13-1984 L1998 **PDP PD** *020 †20

KREDICH, Nicholas Michael. 57 KIMBERLY DR 27707 #025-01-1962 L1963 **IM RHU** *050 †20

KREISSMAN, Susan Gail. BOX 2916, DUKE MEDICAL CENTER 27710 #035-47-1985 L2000 **PHO** *050 †55

KRIEKARD, Peter John. ■ 27713 #007-02-2007 **IM** *012

KRISHNAN, Ranga R. BOX 3950, DEPARTMENT OF PSYCHIATRY 27710 #495-04-1980 L1982 **P** *050 †75

KRISHNARAJ, Arun. ■ 27713 #024-01-2008 **DR** *012

KRUCOFF, Mitchell Wolfe. 508 FULTON ST, RM A3006 27705 #010-01-1980 L1988 **CD CCM** *020 †20

KRUG, David Kenneth. ■ 27713 #005-14-2004 **DR** *012

KRYSTAL, Andrew Darrell. BOX #3309, DUKE UNIVERSITY MEDICAL CT 27710 #036-07-1987 L1989 **P** *050 †75

KUBAL, Timothy Edward. ■ 27707 #011-05-2007 **IM** *012

KUBER, Sanjay Bhikhubhai. 5303 US HIGHWAY 70 W 27705 #654-01-1997 L2005 **APM** *020

KUBIT, Christiane Lynn. ■ 27713 #038-43-2006 **P** *012

KUDERER, Nicole. PO BOX 3645, DUKE UNIV 27710 #035-03-2002 L2007 **HO** *012

KUDESIA, Rashmi. ■ 27701 #036-07-2008 *012

KUDLER, Harold Stephen. 508 FULTON ST 27705 #035-08-1979 L1984 **P** *040 †74

KUEBER, Garril Louis, Jr. 2609 N DUKE ST, STE 301 27704 #021-05-1997 L1999 **GPM** *100 †20

KUESTER, Steven Donald. ■ 27713 #038-41-2005 **AN** *012

KULWICHIT, Wanla. ■ 27707 #891-01-1987 **ID** *100

KUO, Anthony Nanlin. DUMC BOX 3802, DUKE UNIVERSITY EYE CENTER 27710 #047-05-2002 L2006 **OPH** *100 †35

KUO, Paul C. DUKE UNIV MEDICAL CENTER, 110 BELL BUILDING 27710 #023-07-1985 L2000 **GS** *020 †85

KURITZKY, Jack Joseph. ■ 27713 #035-45-2008 **IM** *012

KURLANDER, Roger Jay. 718 RUTHERFORD ST 27705 #016-02-1971 L1976 **HEM ON** *050 †20

KURTZBERG, Joanne. BOX 3350, 2400 PRATT STREET 27710 #035-09-1976 L1983 **PHO** *020 †55

KURUP, Vinod Viswanath. 3643 N ROXBORO ST, HOSPITAL MEDICINE 27704 #056-05-1996 L2007 **IM** *020 †20

KUSHINS, Stephen Isaac. ■ 27713 #033-05-2004 L2008 **AN** *012

KUSSIN, Peter Saml. ■ 27710 #035-47-1985 L1989 **PUD IM** *020 †20

KWAN, William Allen, Jr. ■ 27713 #051-01-2007 **MPD** *012

LACHIEWICZ, Ave Maria. 402 TRENT DR, DUKE UNIVERSITY CE 27705 #026-04-1980 L1984 **PD** *100 †55

LACSINA, Joshua Rene. ■ 27707 #036-07-2008 *012

LADEWSKI, Lisa Ann. ■ 27707 #025-01-2007 **PD** *012

LAGER, Joanne Jenkins. DUMC BOX 2916, TRENT DRIVE, BELL BLDG, RM 27710 #036-07-1998 L2000 **PHO PHM** *050 †55

LAGOO, Anand Shreeram. DUMC BOX 3712, DEPARTMENT OF PATHOLOGY 27710 #495-28-1981 L2000 **HMP PTH** *020 †50

LAGOO-DEENADAYALAN, S A. BOX 3110, ROOM 3456 ERWIN, DEPT. OF SURGERY, DUMC 27710 #495-28-1982 L2000 **GS** *020 †85

LAHOUD, Rony Nehme. ■ 27713 #036-01-2008 *012

LAKEY, James Randall. ■ 27713 #001-06-2002 L2004 **PCC** *012 †20

LAKEY, Wanda Cook. ■ 27713 #001-06-2002 L2005 **END** *100 †20

LALANI, Tahaniyat. BOX 31015, DUMC 27710 #704-25-2000 L2008 **ID** *012 †20

LALLIER, Charles Wesley. 5315 HIGHGATE DR, STE 101 27713 #051-01-1981 L1984 **PD** *020 †55

LAM, Gregory Kawah. DUMC 31278, DUKE UNIVERSITY MEDICAL CE 27710 #035-45-2002 L2005 **CD** *012 †20

LAMANTIA, Michael Andrew. ■ 27713 #035-46-2005 L2008 **IMG** *012

LAMBETH, William Rick. 2609 N DUKE ST 204 27704 #036-05-1974 L1974 **OBG** *071 †30

LAMPSON, Benjamin Logan. ■ 27713 #036-07-2008 *012

LANASA, Mark Christian. ■ 27713 #041-12-2002 L2005 **HO** *012 †20

LANDOLFO, Elizabeth Anne. BOX #3675, GENERAL PEDIATRICS 27710 #062-01-1985 L1993 **PD** *020 †55

LANIER, Verne Clifton, Jr. 300 CRUTCHFIELD ST 27704 #047-05-1966 L1966 **PS HS** *020 †85,65

LANZINGER, Marcella J. DEPARTMENT OF ANESTHESIOLO, DUKE UNIVERSITY MEDICAL CE 27710 #409-40-1995 L2001 **AN** *020 †05

LAPP, Kathleen G. BOX 3837, DUMC 27710 #045-01-1998 L2000 **CHP** *020 †75

LARGENT, Carrie Ann. ■ 27707 #036-07-2008 *012

LARK, Amy Langdon. ■ 27713 #036-01-2001 L2007 **PTH** *100 †50

LARK, Robert Kamiel. DUKE UNIV MED CTR, DIV OF ORTHO SURG 27710 #036-01-2004 **ORS** *012

LAROSE, Connor Raymond. DUKE UNIV MED CTR, DIV OF ORTHO SURG 27710 #038-41-2005 **ORS** *012

LARRIER, Deidre Roseanne. ■ 27705 #024-01-2001 L2001 **GS** *020

LARRIER, Nicole Alison. BOX 3085, DEPT. OF RADIATION ONCOLOG 27710 #023-07-1999 L2004 **RO** *100 †80

LASCOLA, Christopher D. BOX 3951, DUMC 27710 #016-02-1998 L2003 **RNR** *020 †80

LASKEY, Robin Anne. ■ 27712 #051-04-2007 **OBG** *012

LASKOWITZ, Daniel Todd. 2900 ERWIN RD, DUMC 27705 #036-07-1991 L1997 **N** *040 †75

LASSITER, Tally Edward. 508 FULTON ST, RM A5004 27705 #024-01-1982 L1983 **OSM** *020 †40

LAUBACH, Anjolie Elizabet. ■ 27705 #036-01-2004 **AN** *012

LAUBACH, Jacob Peter. DUKE UNIV MED CTR, BOX 3841 27710 #036-07-1999 L2001 **HO** *012 †20

LAUBACH, Justin Edward. ■ 27713 #035-09-2006 **IM** *012

LAUBACH, Susan Stefanac. ■ 27713 #005-02-2002 L2003 **AI** *012

LAUSIER, Evangeline Rita. 3024 PICKETT RD, DUKE PRIMARY CARE 27705 #050-02-1979 L1991 **IM** *020 †20

LAVIN, Gordon Kyle. ■ 27707 #038-06-1978 L1981 **P** *020 †75

LAVIN, Peter Joseph. ■ 27705 #539-06-1998 **IM NEP** *100

LAWRANCE, Jeremy Andrew L. ■ 27707 #836-02-1985 L1994 *020

LAWRENCE, Laura Brooke. 5322 HIGHGATE DR STE 144, UNIV PEDIATRICS 27713 #036-07-2001 L2004 **PD** *020 †55

LAWSON, Jeffrey Harold. DUKE UNIVERSITY MEDICAL CE, RM 481 MSRB BOX 2622 RESEA 27710 #050-02-1991 L1999 **GS** *020 †85

LAWSON, Jennifer Mah. 4020 N ROXBORO ST, DUKE CHILDREN'S PRIMARY CA 27704 #050-02-1990 L1993 **PD** *020 †55

LE, Thu Huy. 4101 N ROXBORO ST 27704 #010-01-1993 L1995 **NEP** *020 †20

LEASE, Erika Diane. ■ 27707 #054-04-2004 L2008 **MPD** *012

LECHNER, Logan Leo. ■ 27707 #019-02-2007 **OBG** *012

LEDER, Richard Adam. DUKE UNIV MED CTR, BOX 3808 DEPT OF RADIO 27710 #024-05-1984 L1988 **DR** *020 †80

LEDERER, David Elliott. ■ 27707 #024-07-2002 L2007 **OPH** *100

LEE, Annie Chiasan. ■ 27705 #028-02-2004 L2008 **OPH** *012

LEE, Christine Euisung. 6104 FAYETTEVILLE RD, STE 108 27713 #025-01-1989 L1994 **OPH** *020 †35

LEE, Chung-Suk Charles. ■ 27713 #038-44-1990 L1993 **IM** *020 †20

LEE, Elaina L. 6216 FAYETTEVILLE RD, STE 103 27713 #038-45-1991 L1994 **FM** *020 †18

LEE, Ellie R. BOX 3951, DUMC 27710 #012-05-1996 L2001 **DR** *100 †80

LEE, Eric Abraham. ■ 27701 #036-07-2008 *012

LEE, Erica Young. ■ 27705 #035-20-2006 L2006 **DR** *012

LEE, Jeanne. ■ 27705 #036-07-2006 **IM** *012

LEE, Jonathan Chuangyien. ■ 27713 #051-01-2005 **MP** *012

LEE, Noel Mijean. ■ 27713 #051-01-2005 L2008 **IM** *012

LEE, Paul Pue-Jung. ERWIN RD, BOX 3802 DUKE EYE CTR 27710 #025-01-1986 L1997 **OPH PHP** *050 †35

LEE, Paula Sowon. DUMC 3084, DUKE UNIVERSITY MEDICAL CE 27710 #021-01-2000 L2001 **OBG** *020 †30

LEE, Richard Hsangyang. ■ 27713 #012-05-2005 **IM** *012

LEE, Sabina Mikyong. 3024 PICKETT RD 27705 #001-02-1989 L1993 **ID** *020 †20

LEE, Sheila Seto. ■ 27713 #034-01-2002 **DR** *012

LEE, Steve C. ■ 27713 #005-12-2003 L2008 **OTO** *012

LEFKOWITZ, Robert Jos. DUKE MEDICAL CENTER, BOX 3821 27710 #035-01-1966 L1973 **IM CD** *050 †20

LEHR, Janet Elaine. 3001 ACADEMY RD, STE 200 27707 #011-03-1982 L1989 **FM** *020 †18

LEHRICH, Ruediger Wilhelm. BX 3951 M148 DAV BLD 27710 #409-33-1995 L2004 **NEP** *100

■ = Address Information Privacy Protected

LEIGH, Fawn Aymee. ■ 27705 #016-02-1999 L2005 **N CHN** *100
LEIGH-FLEMING, Jan A. 5832 FAYETTEVILLE RD, STE 113 27713 #010-02-1986 L1995
   IM *020 †20
LEIGHT, George Staples. BOX 3513, EDWIN ROAD 27710 #036-07-1972 L1979 **GS SO** *071 †85
LEINBACH, Jonathan Eaton. 2020 W MAIN ST, MAIN ST CLCL ASSOC 27705
   #021-05-1998 L1999 **P** *020
LEINEWEBER, Stephen B. ■ 27710 #016-01-1995 L2001 **CCP** *020
LEITHE, Linda. BOX 3808, ERWIN ROAD, DUKE UNIVERSITY MEDICAL CE 27710
   #038-40-1982 L1987 **R N** *080
LEMONS, Jason Aaron. ■ 27704 #012-01-2004 **AN** *012
LEMUTH, Danielle Katharin. ■ 27701 #048-14-2004 **DR** *012
LENFESTEY, Robert William. DUKE UNIV MED CTR, BOX 3179 27710 #036-01-2002 L2007
   NPM *012
LENGEN, Sarah Kristen. ■ 27713 #038-40-2004 **OBG** *012
LEONARDI, Robert Anthony. ■ 27713 #045-01-2006 **IM** *012
LEPPERT, Phyllis Carolyn. 630 BAKE HORSE/100 TRENT D, DUKE DEPT OF OB/GYN 27710
   #036-07-1973 L1976 **OBG PD** *030 †30
LESSNE, Mark Lewis. ■ 27713 #024-05-2005 L2005 **DR** *012
LEVESQUE, Marc C. 3112 DEERCHASE WYND 27712 #008-01-1989 L1995 **RHU** *050 †20
LEVIN, L Scott. DUKE UNIV MED CTR, BOX 3945 27710 #041-13-1982 L1983
   PS ORS *020 †65,40
LEWIN, Marc Roy. DUKE UNIV MED CTR, BOX 3712 27710 #027-01-2003 L2006 **DMP** *012 †50
LEWIS, Darrell V, Jr. 1 HOSPITAL DRIVE, BOX 3430 DEPT OF PEDIATRIC 27710
   #026-04-1969 L1975 **CHN** *050 †75
LEWIS, Heather Katherine. ■ 27703 #008-02-2004 L2007 **EM** *100
LEWIS, Katherine Alter. ■ 27713 #005-19-2006 **EM** *012
LEWIS, Kristina Henderson. ■ 27705 #021-01-2007 L2007 *012
LEWIS, Rachel Eva. ■ 27705 #035-09-2007 **PD** *012
LI, Jennifer Shiunroh. BOX 3090, ERWIN RD 27710 #036-07-1987 L1989 **PDC** *020 †55
LIDDLE, Rodger Alan. ■ 27707 #047-05-1978 L1988 **GE IM** *020 †20
LIDOR, Cobi. ■ 27707 #550-03-1983 **ORS** *100
LIEDTKE, Wolfgang B. DUMC, BOX 2900 27710 #409-22-1989 L2004 **N** *100
LIEN, Lillian Frances. DUKE UNIVERSITY MED CTR, BOX 2956 27710 #036-07-1999 L2000
   END *100 †20
LIGHTFOOT, Harrell Oba. ■ 27713 #036-01-2008 *012
LIKES, Creighton Edward. ■ 27713 #045-01-2003 L2007 **OBG** *020
LIM, Ing Haan. BX 3951 M148 DAV BLD, DUKE UNIV MED CTR 27710 #825-01-1995 **IC** *100
LIMA, Brian. DUKE UNIV MED CTR, DEPT OF SURGERY 27710 #036-07-2002 **GS** *012
LIMKAKENG, Alexander Tan. BOX 3096, DUKE UNIVERSITY MEDICAL CE 27710
   #041-01-2001 L2006 **EM** *020 †16
LIN, Erica Peiyeh. ■ 27713 #048-14-2004 **AN** *012
LIN, Shu S. ■ 27705 #036-07-1992 L1994 **TS** *020 †85,90
LINARDIC, Corinne M. BOX 2916 DUMC, DIV PEDS HEME-ONC 27710 #036-07-1995 L2001
   PHO *050 †55
LINDSAY, Beth Hays. DUMC BOX 3085 27710 #012-01-1987 L1992 **RO** *020 †80
LINDSAY, David Richard. DEPT OF ANESTHESIOLOGY, BOX 3094 DUMC 27710
   #023-01-1994 L1997 **APM** *020 †05
LINEBERGER, Catherine K. BOX 3094, DUKE UNIV MEDICAL CTR 27710 #036-01-1987 L1991
   AN IM *020 †05
LINEBERGER, Robert Propst. 3643 N ROXBORO ST 27704 #036-01-1984 L1991 **IM** *020 †20
LINEFSKY, Jason Phillip. ■ 27713 #051-07-2004 L2007 **IM** *020 †20
LINFORS, Eugene Wm. 4205 BEN FRANKLIN BLVD, ASSOCIATES PA 27704 #036-07-1971 L1977
   IM *020 †20
LING, Julia Kuo-Fang. ■ 27705 #035-01-1950 **CHP PD** *071 †55,75
LITHMAN, Jerry Richard. 1515 W NC HIGHWAY 54 # 210 27707 #011-03-1974 L1988
   P N *020 †75 ‡
LITINSKI, Mikhail Borisov. ■ 27710 #913-06-1997 L2005 **PCC** *100 †20
LIU, Qingyang. 4315 BEN FRANKLIN BLVD, CENTRAL INTERNAL MED PA 27704
   #243-21-1995 L2000 **IM** *020 †20
LIVENGOOD, Chas Harris, III. P O BOX 3291, DUKE HOSP 27710 #036-07-1976 L1978
   OBG ID *030
LIVINGSTON, Elizabeth G. DUKE MEDICAL CTR, BOX 3967 27710 #036-07-1984 L1988
   MFM OBG *020 †30 ‡
LIVINGSTON, Nancy Tribley. 1502 W NC HIGHWAY 54, STE 302 27707 #036-07-1972 L1973
   P PYA *020 †75
LOBACH, David Franklin. ■ 27705 #036-07-1987 L1990 **END** *062 †20
LOBACH, Mary Lee Howell. DUKE UNIV MED CTR 27710 #047-05-1984 L1986 **OBG** *020 †30
LOBATO, Robert Lee. DEPT OF ANESTHESIOLOGY, DUMC 3094 27710 #005-11-2004 **AN** *012
LOCHNER, Heather Virginia. ■ 27705 #024-05-2002 L2002 **HSO** *012
LOCKHART, Walter S, Jr. ■ 27707 #036-05-1944 L1944 **NS** *071 †25
LODGE, Andrew James. BOX 3340, DUKE UNIV MED CTR 27710 #036-07-1993 L1998
   TS GS *020 †85,90
LOEHR, Walter Jos. 4301 BEN FRANKLIN BLVD, REGIONAL SURG ASSOC 27704
   #035-20-1963 L1971 **GS TS** *071 †85
LOMMATZSCH, Steven E. ■ 27707 #038-43-2002 L2007 **PCC** *012 †20
LONBARD, Frederick Wilhel. ERWIN ROAD, DUMC; BOX 3094 27710 #836-04-1992 L2001
   AN *020
LONDON, Stephanie. PO BOX 12233, NIEHS MD A3-05 27709 #024-01-1983 L1990
   IM OM *050 †20,70
LONDON, William Lord. 2609 N DUKE ST STE 1000 27704 #036-01-1955 L1955
   PD PHO *020 †20
LONG, Robert James. 3323 PARK OVERLOOK DR 27712 #014-01-1995 L2001 **FM** *020 †18
LOONEY, Christopher Boyd. ■ 27707 #036-01-2006 L2006 **DR** *012
LOPEZ MARTI, Maria Guadal. ■ 27713 #132-01-2002 L2004 **PDI** *012 †55
LORIMER, William Van. 4315 BEN FRANKLIN BLVD 27704 #035-47-1972 L1991
   IM OM *020 †70,20
LOU, Junyang. ■ 27712 #028-02-2006 **IM** *012
LOW, Vincent Hock Seng. DUMC BOX 3808 27710 #143-06-1983 L1994 *020
LOWE, James Edward. DUKE UNIVERSITY MEDICAL CE, P.O. BOX 3954 27710
   #005-14-1973 L1975 **TS** *020 †85,90
LOWE, James Edward, Jr. 4101 N ROXBORO ST 27704 #047-07-1975 L2000 **PS** *075 †65 ‡
LU, Kim Haan. ■ 27707 #024-07-2007 **PD** *012
LUM, Helen. ■ 27705 #047-06-2002 L2006 **IMG** *100
LUMB, George Dennett. ■ 27707 #352-07-1939 L1939 **PTH** *020
LUNDBERG, Dab B A. BOX 3801 DUMC 27710 #858-03-1967 *100
LUNSFORD, Keri Elizabeth. ■ 27713 #038-40-2007 **GS** *012

LUTZ, Robert Paul. ■ 27704 #036-01-1982 L2001 **FM EM** *075 †18
LUU, Kieu Xuan. ■ 27704 #041-14-2005 **AN** *012
LYE, James Stephen. ■ 27707 #036-01-2007 **PD** *012
LYERLY, Anne D. DUMC BOX 3618, DUKE UNIVERSITY MEDIAL CEN 27710 #036-07-1995 L2001
   OBG †30
LYERLY, Herbert Kim. 2424 ERWIN RD STE 601, BOX 2714 27710 #005-14-1983 L1990
   GS *020 †85
LYLES, Kenneth Ward. 508 FULTON ST, MEDICAL CENTER 27705 #051-04-1974 L1979
   IMG END *050 †20
LYMAN, Gary Herbert. ■ 27705 #035-06-1972 L2007 **ON HEM** *020 †20 ‡
LYNN, William S. 4364 S ALSTON AVE 27713 #035-01-1946 L1950 **PUD OM** *050
MA, Alice Deling. ■ 27713 #025-01-1989 L1998 **HO** *020 †20
MAAR, Rosina H. 2520 MERIDIAN PKWY, STE 400 27713 #012-21-1988 L1993 **IM** *020 †20
MACAULAY, John C. ■ 27705 #035-03-1952 L1993 **PD** *071 †55
MACHALICKY, Jason Scott. ■ 27713 #005-12-2002 L2006 **CHP** *020
MACHEMER, Christine Anna. 3325 CHAPEL HILL BLVD 27707 #409-25-1959 L1978 **P** *071 †75
MACHEMER, Robert. DUMC, BOX 3802 27710 #407-05-1959 L1978 **OPH** *071 †35
MAC INTYRE, Neil Ross, Jr. BOX 3911 DUKE UNIV MED CTR 27710 #035-20-1972 L1981
   PUD IM *050 †20
MACK, Brigid Eagan. ■ 27713 #035-06-2005 **FP** *012
MAC LAURIN, Nancy Ann. 5726 FAYETTEVILLE RD, DURHAM OBSTETRICS AND 27713
   #008-02-1998 L2002 **OBG** *020 †30
MACLEOD, David Brett. 718 RUTHERFORD ST 27705 #917-29-1987 L1998 *020
MADAN, Raman. 4101 N ROXBORO ST 27704 #495-45-1977 L1998 *100
MADDEN, John Francis. DUKE UNIV MED CTR, ROOM 3105 SOUTH HOSPITAL 27710
   #036-07-1989 L1993 **PTH MM** *020 †50
MAGE, Bernard Marie P. ■ 27707 #396-32-1977 L1982 **RHU** *020
MAHAFFEY, Kenneth Wm. 2400 PRATT ST, INST, ROOM 0311 TERRACE LE 27705
   #054-04-1989 L1996 **CD** *020 †20
MAHAR, Annabelle Mary. ■ 27710 #143-01-1993 L2002 *020
MAIMON, Arthur Currie. ■ 27717 #016-11-1948 L1949 **GP PD** *074 †55
MAITRE, Nathalie Linda. 1 DUKE MEDICAL CTR, DEPT OF PEDIATRICS 27710 #045-01-2002
   NPM *012 †55
MAJOR, Nancy Marie. ERWIN RD, BOX 3808 DEPT RADIOLOGY 27710 #024-07-1988 L1996
   DR *062 †80
MAJURE, Joseph Marc. ROOM 5409 DN, DUMC 3127 27710 #027-01-1981 L1987 **PD** *020 †55
MAKAR, Vivian Onsy. 5315 HIGHGATE DR, STE 101 27713 #051-04-1999 L2002 **PD** *020 †55
MALAKAUSKAS, Sandra Marie. ■ 27713 #005-02-2002 L2007 **NEP** *012 †20
MALCOLM, William Ferris. DUMC BOX 3127, DUKE UNIVERSITY MEDICAL CE 27710
   #026-04-1998 L2001 **PD** *020 †55
MALENBAUM, Bruce Terry. 2609 N DUKE ST, STE 801 27704 #041-01-1977 L1980
   OTO HNS *020 †45
MALINZAK, Elizabeth B. ■ 27705 #036-07-2008 *012
MALLETTE, Quinterol J. ■ 27708 #036-07-2001 *100
MALMQUIST, Herbert E. ■ 27705 #374-01-1954 L1965 **GP** *071
MALONE, Alfred Lashawn. ■ 27703 #038-06-2004 L2006 **DR** *012
MALONEY, Kelly E. ■ 27710 #064-01-1989 L2005 **U** *020 †95
MALVEHY, Mario Albert. 3643 N ROXBORO ST, EMGY DEPT 27704 #011-02-2000 L2003
   EM *020
MANASCO, Penelope K. 5 MOORE DR # MAIC3662, GLAXO WELLCOME INC 27701
   #021-01-1984 L1989 **END PD** *020 †55
MANCHESTER, Amy Kantipong. ■ 27713 #048-13-2006 **AN** *012
MANGARELLI, Caren. 6301 HERNDON RD 27713 #016-11-1996 L2003 **PD** *020 †55
MANGEL, Allen Wayne. 718 RUTHERFORD ST 27705 #010-02-1988 L1990 **GE IM** *050
MANGRUM, Wells Isaac. ■ 27712 #026-08-2005 L2005 **DR** *012
MANNING, Stuart Hall. 2609 N DUKE ST STE 301 27704 #036-07-1976 L1979 **IM** *020 †20
MANTYH, Christopher R. DEPT. OF SURGERY BOX 3117, DUKE UNIVERSITY MEDICAL CE 27710
   #056-05-1991 L1998 **CRS** *020 †85,10
MANZON, Anthony. 3643 N ROXBORO ST, DURHAM REG HOSP 27704 #561-17-1993 L2004
   IM *020
MARBURGER, Tessa Leone. ■ 27705 #025-01-2006 L2006 **N** *012
MARCH, John Steven. 718 RUTHERFORD 27710 #005-14-1978 L1990 **CHP P** *020 †18,75
MARCHAND, Mark David. BOX 3808, ERWIN ROAD 27710 #048-04-2002 L2007 **RNR** *012 †80
MARCOM, Paul K. DEPT OF INTERN MED, DUKE HOSP, BRE ONCOL PROG 27710
   #048-04-1989 L1991 **ON** *050 †20
MARCOZZI, David Edward. 6507 DRAEBURY LN 27713 #422-01-1998 L2002 **EM** *020 †16
MARCUS, Jeffrey Robert. DUMC 3974, DUKE UNIVERSITY MEDICAL CE 27710
   #025-01-1994 L2002 **GS PS** *020 †85
MARGOLIS, Judith O. DUKE EYE CENTER, DUKE UNIVERSITY MEDICAL CE 27710
   #007-02-1984 L1990 **AN** *020 †05
MARK, Daniel. 4101 N ROXBORO ST 27704 #024-07-1978 L1982 **CD IM** *020 †20
MARK, Jonathan B. BOX 3094, DEPT OF ANESTHESIOLOGY 27710 #005-11-1978 L1992
   AN *020 †05
MARK, Stephen Dwight. ■ 27707 #671-01-1983 **U** *100
MARKERT, Mary Louise. RESEARCH DRIVE, ROOM 109B, RESEARCH PARK 4 27710
   #036-07-1982 L1984 **IG PDA** *050 †55,03
MARKS, David M. BOX 3950, DUKE UNIVERSITY MEDICAL CE 27710 #048-02-1995 L2006
   P *020 †75
MARKS, Sarah Lee. ■ 27713 #051-01-2005 **PD** *012
MARKS, Victor John. ■ 27713 #051-01-2005 **D** *012
MAROOF, Mohammed. DUKE MEDICAL CENTER, BX 3083 27710 #704-08-1964 L1978 **AN** *020
MARROQUIN, Carlos Ernesto. ROOM 110 BELL BUILDING, BOX 3512 27710
   #005-14-1994 L2002 **GS** *020
MARSHALL, Harvey Edwin. MEDICAL CENTER, BOX 2612 DUKE UNIVERSITY 27710
   #036-05-1991 L1995 **PUD** *020 †20
MARSHALL, Julie Marie. ■ 27713 #028-03-2004 L2008 **AN** *012
MARSICANO, Thomas Hobbs. 4020 N ROXBORO ST # N-100 27704 #038-40-1973 L1986
   TS *020 †85,90
MARSIL, Gigi Milou. ■ 27713 #036-01-2007 **IM** *012
MARSLAND, Thomas Wilson. 5317 HIGHGATE DR, STE 117 27713 #051-04-1999 L2002
   FM *020
MARTIN, Cade Michael. ■ 27704 #024-01-2003 L2006 **DR** *012
MARTIN, David Patrick. DEPT OF ANESTHESIOLOGY, DUMC 3094 27710 #038-06-2006 **AN** *012
MARTIN, Ian Bebvon Kuwait. DUMC, BOX 3096 27710 #041-15-2000 L2005 **EM** *100 †20,16
MARTIN, Joy Colleen. ■ 27705 #025-07-2000 L2004 **EM** *100 †16
MARTIN, Paul Langlie. DUKE UNIV MED CENTER, BOX 3350 27710 #028-02-1987 L1992
   PHO *020 †55

MARTIN, Suzanna Elizabeth. ■ 27713 #048-14-2005 L2008 PD *012
MARTINEZ, Loren Lynn. ■ 27707 #038-40-2007 IM *012
MARTINEZ, Salutario J R. DUKE UNIV 27710 #275-01-1960 L1975 R *040 †80
MARTINEZ-BIANCHI, Viviana. DUMC 3886 27710 #132-04-1990 L2006 FM *020 †18
MARTINEZ JIMENEZ, Santiago. P.O. BOX 3808, DEPT OF RADIOLOGY 27710 #264-10-1996 L2006 *020
MARTINU, Tereza. DUMC, BOX 31312 27710 #067-01-2002 L2005 PCC *012 †20
MARUM, Tiffany. 3612 SHANNON RD STE 105 27707 #011-03-1998 L2003 FM *020 †18
MARX, Christine Elizabeth. 508 FULTON ST 27705 #036-07-1992 L1998 P *020 †75
MARZETTE, Lionel Anthony. ■ 27713 #001-02-2006 L2007 IM *100
MASK, William Kenneth. 5921 BEECH BLUFF LN 27705 #036-07-1988 L2004 DR *020 †80
MASSENBURG, Althea Elaine. 4003 N ROXBORO ST, LAKEWOOD PEDIATRICS & 27704 #025-01-1996 L1999 MPD *020 †20
MASSEY, Edward Wayne. NEUROLOGY DUKE UNIVERSITY 27710 #048-02-1970 L1979 N *020 †75
MASSEY, Janice May. RM 1255, BOX 3403, DUKE SOUTH CLINI 27710 #010-02-1978 L1981 N CN *020 †75
MATA, Brian Albert. ■ 27713 #036-07-2007 ORS *012
MATAR, Luke Daniel. 718 RUTHERFORD ST 27705 #143-02-1988 L1998 *100
MATCHAR, David Bruce. 508 FULTON ST 27705 #023-01-1980 L1983 IM *050 †20
MATHER, Richard Charles. ■ 27712 #036-07-2005 ORS *012
MATHEW, Dana Richards. ■ 27713 #035-09-2006 EM *012
MATHEW, Joseph P. BOX 3094, DUMC 27710 #048-12-1986 L1998 AN *020 †05
MATHIAS, Matthew David. 6020 FAYETTEVILLE RD 27713 #041-02-1996 L2005 FM *020 †18
MATTAS, Anne Toohey. 4004 BEN FRANKLIN BLVD, DR. TOHHEY'S OFFICE 27704 #030-05-1977 L1986 RHU IM *020 †20
MATTIOLI, Mark Anthony. 3508 UNIVERSITY DR STE A 27707 #561-17-1985 L1995 CHP P *020
MATTOX, Daniel Lee. 3643 N ROXBORO ST, PRACTICE 27704 #036-01-1978 L1979 IM P *030 †20
MAURO, Patricia Marchase. 2609 N DUKE ST, STE 204 27704 #035-20-1977 L1978 D *020 †15
MAVROS, Sharon Ann. ■ 27705 #036-07-1989 L2006 DR *020 †80 ‡
MAXFIELD, Charles M. ■ 27705 #032-01-1988 L2006 DR *020 †80 ‡
MAXWELL, George Larry, Jr. 4101 N ROXBORO ST 27704 #036-01-1991 L1996 OBG *020 †30
MAY, Christopher Heath. ■ 27705 #048-12-2007 IM *012
MAYHOOD, Meghan Kristine. ■ 27703 #036-07-2008 *012
MAYS, Rhett Churchill. DUMC BOX 3127 27710 #004-01-2006 MPD *012
MAYTAN, Margaret. BOX 3950, DUKE UNIVERSITY MEDICAL CE 27710 #858-04-1996 L2006 P *100
MAZIARZ, Eileen Katherine. ■ 27705 #030-05-2007 IM *012
MAZUGI, Ali. ■ 27705 #517-01-1958 L1977 PD *071 †55
MC ADAMS, Holman Page. DUKE UNIV MED CTR, DEPT OF RADIOLOGY 27710 #036-07-1986 L1987 DR *020 †80
MC ANDREW, Philip Thomas. DUKE UNIV MEDICAL CTR, DPT OF RADIOLOGY 27710 #919-03-1984 L1995 *100
MC BRIDE, William Thomas. DUKE UNIV MED CTR BOX 3094 27710 #539-01-1987 L1995 *020
MCCABE, Daniel Burton. BX 3951 M148 DAV BLD 27710 #021-01-2005 L2008 P *012
MC CALLUM, Rex Monroe. BOX 2954, DUKE UNIV SCH OF MED 27710 #047-05-1980 L1983 RHU IM *030 †20
MC CANN, Richard Lucas. DUKE MEDICAL CENTER, BOX 2990 27710 #035-20-1974 L1983 VS GS *020 †85
MCCARTHY, Grace Chungyee. ■ 27705 #051-01-2006 AN *012
MCCARTY, Jennifer Susan. ■ 27713 #038-06-2007 AN *012
MCCLAIN, Micah Thomas. ■ 27707 #039-01-2004 IM *100
MC COLLUM, Donald E. 508 FULTON ST, SURGICAL SERVICE (112) 27705 #036-05-1953 L1953 ORS *071 †40
MC COMBS, Steven Kelly. 2655 MERIDIAN PKWY 27713 #036-01-1980 L1981 FM IM *062
MCCOY, Keith Hunter. ■ 27707 #036-01-2006 L2007 P *012
MC COY, Ralph C, III. 3400 WAKE FOREST RD, DUKE HEALTH RALEIGH HOSP 27703 #012-05-1967 L1973 ATP PTH *020 †50
MC CRACKEN, Joseph Stuart. 2609 N DUKE ST STE 620 27704 #036-07-1975 L1977 OPH *020 †35
MC CRARY, Marion. 4205 BEN FRANKLIN BLVD, ASSOCIATES PA 27704 #036-01-1999 L2000 IM *020 †20
MC CRORY, Douglas Chas. 2200 W MAIN ST, STE 220 27705 #011-02-1986 L1989 IM *050 †20
MC CUEN, Brooks Walton. BOX 3802 27710 #035-01-1974 L1979 OPH *020 †35
MCCULLOCH, Scott Vandervo. ■ 27713 #036-01-2007 AN *012
MC DERMOTT, Vincent G M. BOX 3808 DUMC 27710 #539-05-1982 L1993 DR *100 †80
MC DONAGH, David Lawrence. DUMC BOX 3094, DEPARTMENT OF ANESTHESIOLO 27710 #010-02-1998 L2001 AN CCA *020 †75,05
MC DONALD, Betty Stewart. 1301 FAYETTEVILLE ST 27707 #028-02-1990 L1997 PD *020 †55
MCDONALD, Marie. 3000 ERWIN RD 27705 #539-03-1985 L1998 PD *020 †19
MC DONNELL, Jean Ellen. ■ 27713 #018-03-1968 L1969 PD *020
MC DOWELL, Roddy David, Jr. ■ 27704 #020-02-2002 L2005 PDC *012 †55
MC EWAN, Angus I. BOX 3094 DUMC 27710 #775-01-1983 L1993 *100
MC EWAN, Mary Margaret P. DUKE MEDICAL CENTER 27706 #065-01-1972 IM CD *050 †20
MC EWEN, Sara Banks. ■ 27705 #021-01-1983 L1984 PTH *020
MCFARLIN, Jessica Mai. ■ 27705 #020-12-2006 N *012
MC GEE, Shaun Gerard. DUMC BOX 3808 27710 #917-07-1985 *020
MCGOLDRICK, Suzanne Marga. BX 3951 M148 DAV BLD 27710 #409-05-2005 PD *012
MC GONEGLE, Shane James. ■ 27713 #038-41-2003 L2006 DR *012
MC GOOGAN, Katherine Eile. ■ 27713 #011-02-2005 L2008 PD *012
MC GUIRE, Heather Lynn. DUKE UNIV MED CTR, BOX 3014 27710 #028-02-1998 L1999 NEP *100 †20
MCGUIRE, Stephanie Rosema. ■ 27713 #025-01-2006 AN *012
MC HUTCHISON, Lynda L B. 3839 REGENT RD 27707 #021-06-1987 L2003 PHL *020 †30
MCILWAIN-DUNIVAN, Gena. ■ 27713 #034-01-2003 L2007 OBG *100
MC INTOSH-VICK, Oveta B. 1301 FAYETTEVILLE ST 27707 #036-01-1983 L1985 PD *020 †55
MCIVER, Nancie Jo. ■ 27713 #026-08-2003 PDE *012 †55
MC KEOWN, Janet Claire. 1901 HILLANDALE RD STE D 27705 #065-01-1990 L1998 FM *020 †18
MC KEOWN, Martin James. BOX 2900, DUKE UNIVERSITY MEDICAL CE 27710 #065-01-1990 L1998 N *050 †75
MCKIE, Janay Elizabeth. ■ 27705 #036-07-2008 *012
MCKIERNAN, Kristy Lynn. DUKE UNIV MED CTR, PO BOX 2922 27710 #035-03-2003 U *012
MC KINNEY, Ross Erwin, Jr. DUKE UNIV MED CTR, BOX 3461 27710 #035-45-1979 L1984 PD ID *030 †55
MCKINNON, Stuart James. BOX 3802 ERWIN ROAD, DUKE UNIVERSITY EYE CENTER 27710 #021-05-1990 L2005 OPH *020 †35
MC LEAN, Heather Seabury. BOX 2801 DUKE UNIV MED CTR, PED HOSP & EMERG MED DIV 27710 #025-01-1996 L2007 PD *020 †55
MC LEAR, Ronald Kent. 3643 N ROXBORO ST 27704 #038-40-1975 L1977 EM *020 †16
MC LENDON, Roger Edwin. 3643 N ROXBORO ST 27704 #012-01-1982 L1984 NP ATP *020 †50
MCLENDON, Terry Bowman. 2400 PRATT ST, 7TH FLOOR - RM 0311 TERRAC 27705 #033-06-1999 L2004 IM *020 †20
MC LEOD, Andrew Alasdair. ■ 27704 #917-30-1974 L1982 CD *020
MC LEOD, Michael Eugene. ■ 27710 #036-07-1960 L1961 IM GE *020 †20
MC MAHON, Timothy Jos. 4101 N ROXBORO ST 27704 #021-01-1993 L1995 PCC *020 †20
MC MANUS, Thomas Jos. ERWIN RD 27710 #024-05-1955 HEM IM *071
MCNAMARA, Erin Rebekah. ■ 27701 #010-02-2006 U *012
MC NAMARA, James O. 4101 N ROXBORO ST 27704 #025-01-1968 L1973 N *050 †75
MC NEILL, Diana Bures. DUMC, BOX 3158 27710 #036-07-1982 L1987 IM *020 †20
MC PHERSON, Harry Thurman. BOX 3006 DUKE HOSPITAL 27710 #036-07-1948 L1950 END IM *020 †20
MC QUEEN, Dianne Frances. 1502 W NC HIGHWAY 54, STE 103 27707 #036-01-1983 L1987 P *020
MCQUEEN, Lauren Alexandra. ■ 27707 #039-01-2008 *012
MC SHANE, James Abram. 6 POINTE VIEW CT, CENTER FOR EMERGENCY MEDIC 27713 #036-01-2003 L2007 EM *020 †16
MCSWAIN, Steven David. ■ 27713 #036-01-2002 L2004 CCP *012 †20,55
MEADOR, Keith Glenn. 508 FULTON ST 27705 #020-02-1982 L1983 P IMG *020 †75
MEDAIYESE, Ayorinde Adeba. ■ 27713 #690-08-1992 L2004 PCC *012 †20 ‡
MEDLEY, John Harley. ■ 27713 #028-03-2004 AN *012
MEDURI, Christopher Umber. ■ 27713 #047-06-2006 IM *012
MEHTA, Madhu Kaur. ■ 27713 #001-02-2005 PM *012
MELGIRI, Ryan Dhruvaraj. ■ 27713 #036-07-2003 *100
MELNICK, Abigail H. BX 3951 M148 DAV BLD 27710 #035-47-2000 L2001 AN *020 †05
MELTON, Cathleen Marie. 1301 FAYETTEVILLE ST 27707 #016-06-1990 L1994 IM *020 †20
MENDIRATTA, Prateek. ■ 27710 #051-04-2002 L2005 HO *012 †20
MENTOCK, Sabrina Marie. 6216 FAYETTEVILLE RD, STE 103 27713 #007-02-1988 L1989 GP *020
MERCK, Lisa Helene. ■ 27713 #016-42-2002 L2007 EM *012
MEREDITH, Michael William. 6301 HERNDON RD 27710 #036-01-1994 L1997 IM *020 †20
MERKLE, Elmar Max. ERWIN RD RM 1917 DUKE NO, BOX 3808 DEPT OF RADIO 27710 #409-41-1991 L2003 R *100
MESIS, Rachel Gabrielle. RESIDENCY PROG, GENERAL SURGERY 27710 #036-07-2007 GS *012
METJIAN, Ara D. ■ 27713 #041-15-2001 L2004 HO *012 †20
METTU, Priyathamsai. ■ 27707 #036-07-2005 OPH *012
METZ, Alan. GLAXO SMITH KLINE, 5 MOORE DRIVE 27709 #836-01-1978 L1992 P OS *050 †75
METZ, Gregory Martin. ■ 27713 #039-01-2004 AI *012 †20
MEYER, Andrew Frederic. BOX 3083 DUKE MED CTR 27710 #035-08-1969 L1977 AN *020 †95,05
MEYER, Angela Marlo. ■ 27713 #003-01-2002 L2005 GE *012 †20
MEYER, Jeffrey John. ■ 27705 #016-02-2003 RO *012
MEYER, Jennifer L. ■ 27710 #024-16-2006 EM *012
MEYER, Laura Tamiko. ■ 27712 #036-07-2003 L2003 DR *012
MEZA, Elizabeth Rose. ■ 27713 #025-01-2008 *012
MHOON, Justin Thomas. DUKE UNIV MED CTR, BOX 2905 27710 #011-04-2006 N *012
MICHELSON, Peter Howard. ■ 27705 #041-02-1983 L2006 PDP *020 †55
MICHENER, James Lloyd. 319 HANES HOUSE, DUKE MEDICAL CENTER 27710 #024-01-1978 L1979 FM MDM *030 †18
MIDDLETON, John Paul. BOX 3014, DUKE UNIVERSITY MEDICAL CE 27710 #051-04-1983 L1986 NEP IM *020 †20
MILAN, Kristina Elisabeth. ■ 27707 #035-45-2005 OBG *012
MILANO, Carmelo Alessio. DUMC BOX 3043 27710 #016-02-1990 L1992 TS *020 †90,85
MILES, Jodie D. ■ 27713 #010-02-2006 ORS *012
MILES, Karen Denise. ■ 27713 #011-05-2005 P *012
MILLEN, Cori Kristen. ■ 27713 #025-76-2004, ▲ L2008 N *012
MILLER, Becky Bartley. ■ 27713 #056-06-2005 IM *012
MILLER, Carlton David. 4205 BEN FRANKLIN BLVD, ASSOCIATES PA 27704 #036-01-1987 L1989 IM *020 †20
MILLER, Chad Michael. BX 3951 M148 DAV BLD 27710 #036-07-1999 L2002 DR *020
MILLER, David Edmond. ■ 27707 #036-07-1956 L1956 CD IM *071 †20
MILLER, Jason Thomas. ■ 27713 #012-01-2006 NS *012
MILLER, Javier, Jr. ■ 27713 #011-05-2005 GS *100
MILLER, Kibbe Marie. ■ 27707 #039-01-2005 L2008 PD *012
MILLER, Lauren Shenk. DUKE UNIV MED CTR, DEPT OF RADIOLOGY 27710 #038-40-2006 L2006 DR *012
MILLER, Michael Joseph, Jr. DUKE UNIV MED CTR MS3008, DUKE NORTH HOSP RM 1502 27710 #041-09-1994 L2003 VIR *020 †80
MILLER, Warren Ray. ■ 27713 #048-14-2006 AN *012
MILLS, James Steven. BOX 31286, DUKE UNIVERSITY MEDICAL CE 27710 #011-03-2000 L2003 IC *012 †20
MILLS, Lisa Renee. ■ 27713 #045-01-2006 PD *012
MILO COTTER, Olga. 2400 PRATT ST, DCRI RM 8061 27710 #913-19-1993 L2005 IM CD *100
MINCHEW, Joe Tommy. 3609 WATKINS RD 27707 #023-07-1988 L1994 ORS OSS *020 †40
MINER, Dean Scott. 4020 N ROXBORO ST, DUKE HEALTH CENTER 27704 #011-03-1993 L2005 MPD PD *040 †20,55
MING, David Yung. ■ 27705 #048-02-2006 MPD *012
MIRALLES, Gines Diego. P.O. BOX 3284, DUKE UNIVERSITY MEDICAL CE 27710 #132-01-1986 L2008 ID *020 †20
MISTRY, Kshitij Pankaj. ■ 27710 #036-05-1997 L2004 CCP *100 †55
MITCHELL, Calvin Harrison. BOX 3802 DUKE EYE CLINIC 27710 #036-07-1958 L1958 OPH *020 †35
MITCHELL, Davin Gerrard. ■ 27703 #025-07-2004 L2004 AN *012
MITCHELL, Duane Anthony. ■ 27713 #036-07-2001 PTH *100
MITCHELL, Kelly Westbrook. ■ 27707 #036-01-2004 IM *012
MITCHELL, Robert G. ERWIN RD BOX 31315, DUKE UNIVERSITY MEDICAL CE 27710 #005-02-1999 L2006 CD *100 †20
MITCHELL, Robert Michael. ■ 27710 #918-01-1992 L2002 *020

■ = Address Information Privacy Protected

MITITELU, Mihai. 74 JUSTIN CT 27705 #036-05-2008 *012

MOBLEY, Victoria Ln. ■ 27705 #036-07-2004 L2007 IM *100 †20

MODELL, Jack Gary. 5 MOORE DR 27709 #007-02-1982 L1985 PHM P *062 †75

MOHANTY, Bibhu Datta. ■ 27705 #036-07-2008 *012

MOLDENHAUER, Julie S. ■ 27707 #025-07-1997 L2007 MG *020 †19,30

MONK, Terri Gay Luedtke. BOX 3094, ANESTHESIOLOGY 27710 #030-05-1977 L2004 AN *020 †05

MONROE, Yvonne Lee. 1502 W NC HIGHWAY 54, CAROLINA PARTNERS IN 27707 #036-01-1986 L1987 P PMM *020 †75

MONSON, Donald Malvin. ■ 27712 #056-05-1955 L1962 R *071 †80

MONTANA, Gustavo S. DUKE UNIV MEDICAL CTR, RAD/ONC DEPT BOX 3085 27710 #264-01-1960 L2007 RO *071 †80

MOOBERRY, Micah Joe. ■ 27713 #004-01-2004 L2008 MPD *012

MOODY, Michael Anthony. BXO 3499 DUMC PEDS INF DIS 27710 #036-07-1999 L2003 PD *020 †55

MOON, Richard E. DUKE MEDICAL CENTER, BOX 3094 27710 #067-01-1973 L1983 AN PCC *020 †20,05

MOON, Samuel David. DUKE HOSPITAL, RM 4290 27710 #051-04-1975 L1989 OM *020 †70

MOON, Thomas Joseph. ■ 27713 #048-13-2005 PD *012

MOORE, Joseph Odell. BOX 3872, DUKE HOSPITAL 27710 #023-07-1970 L1977 ON IM *020 †20

MOORE, Lawrence White, Jr. 4102 N ROXBORO ST 27704 #036-07-1963 L1963 OPH *020 †35 ‡

MOORE, Pierce Jones, III. 2828 CROASDAILE DR 27705 #005-12-1975 L2001 FM *020 †18 ‡

MOORE, Scott Danl. DUKE UNIVERSITY MEDICAL CE, BOX 3309 27710 #051-01-1986 L1992 P *020 †75

MOORE, Scott Matthew. ■ 27707 #036-01-2007 GS *012

MOORMAN, Claude T, III. BOX 3639 DUMC 27710 #038-41-1987 L2001 ORS OSM *020 †40

MOREFIELD, Steven Quentin. ■ 27709 #036-07-1991 *040

MORETTI, Eugene William. ERWIN RD., DEPT OF ANESTHES. #3094 27710 #041-13-1993 L1997 AN CCA *020 †05

MOREY, Rajendra Annasaheb. BOX 3918, DURHAM VA MEDICAL CENTER 27710 #041-09-1997 L2002 P *020 †75

MORGAN, Brooke Asheley. ■ 27710 #036-01-2008 †012

MORGAN-DEWITT, Esi M. ■ 27712 #028-02-1999 L2005 PPR *050 †55

MORGENLANDER, Joel C. BOX 3394, DUKE UNIVERSITY MEDICAL CE 27710 #041-12-1986 L1991 N *020 †20

MORRIS, Arthur James. BOX 3879 27710 #671-01-1983 L1992 *100

MORRIS, Beatriz Blanco. 4020 N ROXBORO ST 27704 #042-01-1988 L1995 PD *020 †55

MORRIS, Dexter L. FIVE MOORE DRIVE, GLAXOSMITHKLINE 27709 #048-04-1984 L1985 EM PHP *020 †20,16

MORRIS, Geo Thos Arnold. ■ 27705 #036-05-1959 L1959 IM *071 †20

MORRIS, James Jos. 4101 N ROXBORO ST 27704 #038-05-1959 L1966 CD IM *071 †20

MORRIS, John Louis. 5716 FAYETTEVILLE RD 27713 #038-40-1986 L1989 EM FM *020 †18

MORRIS, Kenneth Gregory. 508 FULTON ST, VA MEDICAL CENTER 27705 #038-40-1972 L1985 CD IM *020 †20

MORRIS, Mary Ann. DUKE MEDICAL CENTER, MSC 3080 27710 #004-01-1972 L1973 END PD *020 †55

MORRIS, Mary Lide. ■ 27705 #036-05-1957 L1957 R NM *071 †80,28

MORRISON, Jennifer Anne. ■ 27713 #036-01-2006 IM *012

MORRISON, Lake Daniel. ■ 27701 #041-01-1998 L2006 PCC *100 †20

MORSE, Michael Aaron. 4101 N ROXBORO ST 27704 #008-01-1990 L1996 HO *020 †20

MOSES, John W, Jr. 4020 N ROXBORO ST, DUKE PEDIATRIC CLINIC 27704 #045-01-1983 L1986 PD *020 †55

MOSS, Larry Gene. ■ 27710 #048-04-1980 L2005 END IM *050 †20 ‡

MOTT, Ryan Thomas. DUKE UNIV MED CTR, BOX 3712 27710 #011-04-2002 L2006 PTH *100 †50

MOUL, Judd Wendell. 508 FULTON ST 27705 #041-02-1982 L1988 U ON *020 †95 ‡

MOUSALLEM, Talal Imad. ■ 27705 #041-01-2003 PD *012

MOWERY, Yvonne Marie. ■ 27713 #036-07-2012 *012

MOYA, Martin Pedro. BOX 3179, DUMC 27710 #132-09-1992 L2000 NPM *100

MOYER, Kurtis Eugene. ■ 27710 #046-01-2007 PS *012 †85

MOYLAN, Cynthia Ann. ■ 27707 #011-02-2002 L2006 GE *012 †20

MOYLAN, Joseph Anthony. 7 PILTON PL 27705 #024-05-1964 L1975 TRS GS *020 †85

MRUTHYUNJAYA, Prithvi. BOX 3802 27710 #035-03-1996 L2000 OPH *020 †35

MUDRICK, Daniel S. ■ 27710 #023-07-2003 L2007 CD *012 †20

MUIR, Andrew Joseph. RM 0307, 1 TRENT DR BOX 3913 27710 #036-07-1993 L1995 GE *020 †20

MUIR, Holly Ann. ERWIN RD, BOX 3094, DEPT OF ANESTHESIOLOGY 27710 #064-01-1983 L1998 AN *020

MUIR, Kelly W. DUKE UNIV EYE CENTER, BOX 3802 27710 #036-07-2001 L2004 OPH *020 †35

MUKERJI, Nirvan. 219 IVY MEADOW LN 27707 #035-48-2002 L2006 NEP *100 †20

MUKUNDAN, Srinivasan. DUMC BOX 3808 27710 #012-05-1996 L2002 RNR *020 †80

MULHEARN, Thomas James. ■ 27707 #021-05-2004 L2007 CD *012 †20

MULLIGAN, Stephanie Maria. ■ 27701 #051-07-2007 P *012

MUNRO, Brian Eric. ■ 27713 #051-01-2005 L2005 DR *012

MUNRO, Rebecca Lynn. ■ 27713 #051-01-2006 OBG *012

MURDOCH, David Roger. PO BOX 3824, DUKE UNIV MED CTR 27710 #671-01-1985 MM ID *100

MUREEBE, Leila. ■ 27710 #041-07-1992 L2007 VS *020 †85

MURPHY, Chas Edmond, Jr. 3901 N ROXBORO ST, STE 101 27704 #036-07-1982 L1991 TS GS *020 †90,85

MURPHY, Thomas Miles. 302A BELL SERVICE ROAD, BOX 2994 27710 #035-45-1973 L1993 PUD PD *020 †20,55

MURRAY, Jane Hospodar. 5501 FORTUNES RIDGE DR # A 27713 #036-01-1984 L1986 FM *020 †18

MURRAY, John Carroll. TRENT DR, BOX 2907 DIV DERM-DUMC 27710 #036-07-1977 L1982 D *020 †15

MURRAY, Maxine Lorraine. 5315 HIGHGATE DR, STE 101 27713 #041-12-1984 L1994 PD *020 †55

MURTHA, Amy Patricia. BOX 3967, OB/GYN, MATERNAL FETAL MED 27710 #041-07-1992 L1996 OBG *020 †30

MURTY, Lakshmi Chandrika. ■ 27713 #036-01-2007 IM *012

MUSSER, Robert Clayton. DUKE UNIVERSITY MEDICAL CE 27710 #039-01-2000 L2003 IM OS *030 †20

MUSTAFA, Mahmond M. ■ 27710 #575-01-1980 L2001 PD *020 †55

MUTAFYAN, Gevorg Arutyuno. DUKE UNIVERSITY MEDICAL CE, DEPARTMENT OF ENDOSURGERY 27710 #913-01-1995 L2006 GS *100 †85

MYATT JONES, Javar Burrel. ■ 27707 #025-07-2008 *012

MYERS, Barry S. ■ 27701 #036-07-1991 *100

MYERS, Evan Robt. DUKE MEDICAL CENTER 27710 #041-01-1988 L1990 OBG *020 †30

MYERS, Laurie Anne. DUKE UNIVERSITY MEDICAL CE, BOX 3559 27710 #038-40-1992 L1995 AI *020 †55,03

MYERS, Sarah Ann. 1300 MORREENE RD 27705 #036-07-1989 L1991 D *020 †15

MYTHEN, Michael Gerard. 718 RUTHERFORD ST 27705 #917-07-1984 L1995 *040

NADLER, Elisabeth Barrett. 6020 FAYETTEVILLE RD, TRIANGLE FAMILY PRACTICE 27713 #035-19-1985 L1989 FM FSM *020 †18

NAFTOLOWITZ, David Fred. 112 SWIFT AVE 27705 #035-03-1986 L1991 P ADP *020 †75

NAGGIE, Susanna. BOX 31317, DUMC 27710 #023-07-2002 L2005 ID *012 †20

NAIR, Lekshmi Thankam. ■ 27710 #038-40-2003 L2006 END *012 †20

NAIR, Raj Gopal. ■ 27713 #001-06-2002 L2007 RHU *012 †20

NAKAYAMA, John Mitsuo. DUMC 3616, RM 5830 27710 #014-01-2007 OBG *012

NANDA, Kavita. 508 FULTON ST, DURHAM VA MEDICAL CENTER 27705 #035-03-1990 L1996 OBG *020 †30

NANTON, Andrew Geoffrey. 508 FULTON ST, DUKE UNIV MED CTR 27710 #021-01-2004 L2006 CHP *012

NARAYAN, Aditee Pradhan. BOX 3127, DUMC 27710 #036-07-2000 L2003 PD *020 †55

NASHOLD, James R B. ■ 27701 #036-08-1989 NS *020

NEAL, Charles Bodine. 5322 HIGHGATE DR STE 144 27713 #036-07-1955 L1955 PD *071 †55

NEELON, Francis A. 3543 ROSE OF SHARON RD 27712 #024-01-1962 L1970 IM END *020 †20

NEELY, Mark Howard. ■ 27713 #036-07-2006 DR *012

NEIGHBORS, Jenni Rasnake. ■ 27713 #047-06-2004 L2007 AN *012

NELIUS, Sigrid Johanna. 26 OLD OAK CT 27705 #407-16-1949 L1961 IM GPM *020

NELSON, Jennifer Elizabet. ■ 27713 #036-01-2005 GS *012

NELSON, Kelly Carter. ■ 27713 #036-01-2004 L2005 D *012

NELSON, Leann. 4101 N ROXBORO ST 27704 #048-14-1986 L1987 P *020 †75

NELSON, Rendon Clive. BOX 3808, DEPT OF RADIOLOGY 27710 #005-12-1980 L1994 DR *020 †80

NENE, Ruta Ravindra. 65 LAKE VILLAGE DR 27713 #038-06-2002 L2007 P *100

NEUBAUER, Nikki Lynn. ■ 27707 #038-06-2005 OBG *012

NEVILLE, Amy Marie. ■ 27705 #025-07-2002 L2007 DR *100 †80

NEWBERN, Dorothee Kim Dan. ■ 27713 #036-05-2005 PD *012

NEWBORG, Barbara C. ■ 27705 #023-07-1949 L1949 IM *071

NEWBY, L Kristin. ERWIN RD, BOX 3213 27710 #017-20-1987 L1993 CD *020 †20

NEWCOMB, Thomas F. 1824 HILLANDALE RD 27705 #041-12-1951 L1986 IM ON *071 †20

NEWMAN, Glenn Edwin. DUKE UNIV MEDICAL CENTER, DEPARTMENT OF RADIOLOGY 27710 #036-07-1973 L1983 DR *020 †80

NEWMAN, Mark Franklin. DUKE N 3412, DUMC 3094 27710 #020-02-1985 L1992 AN *040 †05

NEWTON, Sandra Jo. 1965 IVY CREEK BLVD, NORTH CAROLINA 27707 #025-07-1984 L1985 FM *020 †18

NG, Amy Hoi-Mei. ■ 27704 #036-01-2008 *012

NG, Khye Weng. 3643 N ROXBORO ST 27704 #825-01-1956 L1972 N IM *071 †75

NGUYEN, Can M. BOX 31117 27710 #067-01-1994 IM *100 †20

NGUYEN, Kari Huong. 3643 N ROXBORO ST, DEPT OF HOSPITAL MEDICINE 27704 #041-14-2001 L2005 IM *020

NGUYEN, Lisa Thao. DUMC BOX 3127 27710 #036-07-2006 MPD *012

NGUYEN, Thanh Bin. ■ 27705 #067-01-1990 DR *020 †80

NICHOLAS, Suzanne Judith. ■ 27713 #004-01-2004 CHP *012

NICHOLLS, Peter Jeffrey. ■ 27701 #035-01-2002 OS *100

NICHOLS, William Garrett. ■ 27707 #036-07-1995 L1997 ID *050 †20

NIELSEN, Karen Cristina. PO BOX 3094 #4 27710 #187-08-1995 L1999 AN *020

NIENABER, Jeffrey John. ■ 27707 #030-05-2003 GS *012

NIEVES, Angel. BX 3951 M148 DAV BLD 27710 #033-05-2001 L2005 OBG *100 †30

NILSSON, Kent Ronald, Jr. ■ 27713 #023-07-2002 L2005 CD *012 †20

NIMJEE, Shahid Mehdi. ■ 27705 #036-07-2006 NS *012

NIMMANNIT, Akarin. ■ 27707 #891-02-1999 IM *100

NOLAN, Robert Louis. 718 RUTHERFORD ST 27705 #064-01-1974 L1997 DR *020 †80

NORCROSS, William P. 3643 N ROXBORO ST 27704 #041-14-1998 L2002 AN *020

NORRIS, Regina Derstine. DUKE UNIV MED CTR, DEPT OF SURGERY 27710 #036-07-2002 U *012

NOVAK, James Edmund. ■ 27713 #025-01-2002 L2006 NEP IM *050 †20

NOVOSAD, David Cheney. ■ 27713 #001-02-2007 P *012

NOWELL, Lisa Anne. ■ 27705 #036-07-2008 *012

NUNLEY, James Albert. DUKE UNIV MED CTR, BOX 2923 27710 #021-01-1973 L1979 ORS OFA *020 †40

NYE, Mary Jane Love. ■ 27707 #036-07-1961 L1961 PD *071

OATES, Carolyn Taylor. 508 FULTON LN 27705 #047-05-1999 L2002 P *020 †75

OBANDO, Jorge V. DUKE UNIV MED CTR, DUMC BOX 3662 27710 #737-06-1992 L2005 GE *020 †20

OBIE, Kanecia Lashea. DUMC BOX 3127 27710 #036-07-2007 MPD *012

OBOHO, Ikwo Kitefre. ■ 27713 #047-05-2007 IM *012

O'BRIEN, Cara Louise. ■ 27705 #028-02-2004 L2008 IM *012

O'BRIEN, Megan E. 4207 COBSCOOK DR 27707 #023-01-1998 L2005 P *020 †55

OCHELLO, Charles Thomas, Jr. ■ 27705 #021-05-2007 EM *012

O'CONNELL, Martin Joseph. ■ 27710 #539-04-1994 L2002 NR *100

O'CONNELL, Thomas L, Jr. 5316 HIGHGATE DR, STE 125 27713 #036-01-1995 L1998 END IM *020 †20

O'CONNOR, Christopher M. RM 7401, ERWIN ROAD, BOX 3356, DUKE HOSP NORTH 27710 #023-01-1983 L1987 CD IM *020 †20

O'CONNOR, John F. BOX 3662, DUKE UNIV MEDICAL CENTER 27710 #539-02-1983 L1998 GE *020 †18,20

ODDONE, Eugene Zaverio. 508 FULTON ST 27705 #007-02-1985 L1987 IM GPM *020 †20

ODERE, Fred Gordon. 2 KIMBERLY DR 27707 #010-01-1970 L1974 PTH *020 †50

O'DONNELL, Timothy. 1901 HILLANDALE RD, STE B 27705 #038-43-1993 L1994 FM *020 †18

OGUNNAIKE, Damilola. ■ 27713 #035-20-2004 L2007 PD *020 †55

OHMAN, Erik Magnus. DUKE UNIV MED CTR, BOX 3126 27710 #539-06-1981 L1991 CD CCM *020

OKEKE, Nwora Lance. BX 3951 M148 DAV BLD 27710 #005-11-2007 IM *012

OLDHAM, Emily Elizabeth. ■ 27713 #051-01-2007 IM *012

OLENIACZ, Joseph Paul. 5107 SOUTHPARK DR, CHAPEL HILL PEDIATRICS PA 27713 #051-04-1981 L1990 PD *020 †55

OLIMPO, Julita S Castillo. 1811 COLE MILL RD, 1811 COLE MILL RD 27712 #748-01-1954 L1977 **CHP P** *020

OLIVER, Thomas K, Jr. ■ 27707 #024-01-1949 L1987 **PD** *071 †55

OLSEN, Elise Arline. PO BOX 3294, DUKE MED CTR 27710 #048-04-1978 L1980 **D ON** *020 †15

OLSEN, Katie Jo. ■ 27704 #011-03-2005 **IM** *012

OLSON, John Ackerman. BOX 2945, DUKE UNIVERSITY MEDCIAL CE 27710 #011-03-1992 L2000 **GS** *020 †85

OLSON, Ronald Paul. BOX 3094, DEPT OF ANESTHESIOLOGY 27710 #060-02-1986 L1998 **FM FSM** *020 †18

OLSON, Steven A. DUKE UNIV MED CENTER, BOX 3389 27710 #028-03-1986 L2000 **ORS OTR** *072 †40

OLUFOLABI, Adeyemi John. 4101 N ROXBORO ST 27704 #690-01-1986 L1997 **AN** *020

O'NEILL, Erica Lynn. ■ 27713 #041-12-2007 **OBG** *012

O'NEILL, Thomas Joseph, IV. ■ 27713 #051-01-2007 **IM** *012

ONG, Yee Siang. ■ 27705 #917-03-1996 *100

ONKEN, Jane Elizabeth. BOX 3902, DUKE UNIVERSITY MEDICAL CE 27710 #010-01-1987 L1993 **GE IM** *020 †20

ONUOHA, Maximus E. 1801 FAYETTEVILLE ST 27707 #690-04-1980 L1994 **IM EM** *020

ONWUBALILI, Ndidiamaka Ch. 2301 ERWIN RD, RM 5830 27710 #032-01-2004 L2008 **OBG** *012

ONYIAH, Joseph C. ■ 27713 #036-07-2007 **IM** *012

OOI, Richard Gek Beng. DUKE UNIV MED CTR, BOX 3094 27710 #917-02-1984 L1993 *100

O'RIORDAN, Eugene Francis. PO BOX 13588 27709 #539-02-1951 L1960 **AN PUD** *030 †05

ORLANDO, Lori Ann. 2200 W MAIN ST STE 220 27705 #021-01-1998 L2002 **IM** *020 †20

OROZCO, Ian James. 5316 HIGHGATE DR, STE 125 27713 #038-06-2002 L2005 **END IM** *100 †20

ORTEL, Thomas L. BOX 3422 DUMC 27710 #017-20-1985 L1989 **HEM IM** *050 †20

OSBORNE, Dennis Richard S. DUKE MEDICAL CENTER 27706 #671-01-1961 L1979 **R** *020

OSENBACH, Richard Kenneth. BOX 3807, DUKE UNIV MED CTR 27710 #041-02-1983 L2001 **NS PMM** *025

O'SHEA, John C. BOX 31207, DUMC 27710 #539-02-1989 L1999 **CD** *020 †20

OSHRAIN, Mindy. 1004 BROAD ST 27705 #036-07-1983 L1987 **P** *020 †75

OSTEEN, Kristie Dawn. ■ 27705 #012-22-2003 L2007 **AN** *100

OSTERHOUT, Shirley E K. DUKE MEDICAL CENTER 27710 #036-07-1957 L1957 **PD OS** *071 †55

OSTERHOUT, Suydam. ■ 27705 #036-07-1950 L1954 **OS ID** *071 †20

OSTRANDER, Matthew James. ■ 27713 #026-04-2005 L2005 **N** *012

OSTROVSKY, Daniel Allen. BOX 3675, 4020 NORTH ROXBORO ROAD 27710 #024-16-1999 L2004 **MPD** *020 †55,20

OSTROWSKI, Carole. ■ 27707 #016-43-1985 L1989 **PD** *074 †55

OTI, Christopher Nnanna. DUMC 3228, DEPT MED DUKE UNIV MED CTR 27710 #913-05-1982 L2002 **IM** *020 †20

OTTOLENGHI, Athos B. DUKE MEDICAL CENTER 27706 #561-14-1946 **OS** *050

OTUBU, Oritsetsema Grace. ■ 27713 #036-01-2008 *012

OWEN, Wendy Gail. 508 FULTON ST, AMBULATORY CARE 11C 27705 #036-01-2000 L2001 **IM** *020 †20

OWEN, William Franklin, Jr. ■ 27715 #024-07-1980 L1999 **NEP IM** *030 †20

OWENS, Susan Elizabeth. 4020 N ROXBORO ST, DUKE CHILDREN'S PRIMARY CA 27704 #035-06-1995 L1998 **PD** *020 †55

OWENS, Thomas Andrew. 4020 N ROXBORO ST 27704 #035-06-1995 L1998 **MPD PD** *020 †20,55

OWUSUASIEDU, Georgina. ■ 27713 #051-04-2007 **PD** *012

OZMENT, Caroline Pinson. ■ 27705 #001-06-2003 L2003 **CCP** *012 †55

PADDISON, George Marion. 3643 N ROXBORO ST, DURHAM GENERAL HOSPITAL 27704 #036-01-1966 L1966 **R** *071 †80

PADHA, Vivek Pratap. 2100 ERWIN RD, PICKEN'S CLINIC 27705 #496-17-1995 L2002 **DR** *012 †18

PADUSSIS, James Constanti. 1337 TRAIL VIEW LN 27713 #024-05-2005 **GS** *012

PAGE, Bernadette H Ryan. 2500 SHENANDOAH AVE 27704 #016-43-1970 L1988 **EM** *020 †16

PAGE, John Ralph. 901 CLARENDON ST 27705 #016-43-1970 L1988 **EM MDM** *020 †16

PAGE, Neil Edmund. 3211 SHANNON RD, STE 300 27707 #023-12-1995 L2000 **FM** *020 †18

PAL, Jay Deep. ■ 27705 #016-42-2001 L2003 **TS** *012

PALMER, Scott Michael, Jr. RM 128, BELL BLDG ERWIN RD 27710 #036-07-1993 L1994 **PCC** *020 †20

PALTA, Manisha. ■ 27713 #011-03-2007 **IM** *012

PANDYA, Yagnik Krishnakan. ■ 27705 #495-06-2003 L2006 **GS** *012

PAPE, Jennifer M. ■ 27712 #048-14-2006 **MPD** *012

PAPPAS, Theodore Nick. BOX 3479, DUKE UNIV MED CTR 27710 #038-40-1981 L1988 **GS** *020 †85

PARIKH, Dipen Subhash. ■ 27713 #048-14-2003 L2007 **NEP** *012 †20

PARIKH, Palak S. ■ 27707 #048-16-2006 **IM** *012

PARIKH, Suhag Hasmukhrai. BOX 3350, DUKE UNIV MED CTR 27710 #495-19-1988 L2003 **PHO PD** *020 †55

PARK, Robert Sang Hoon. DUKE MEDICAL CENTER, DUMC 3096-DIV EMERG MED 27710 #036-01-1998 L2003 **EM** *100 †16

PARKER, Joseph B, Jr. ■ 27705 #047-06-1941 L1948 **P** *071 †75

PARKER, Rodney Douglas. ■ 27713 #036-07-2002 **P** *020

PARKER, Sarah Cates. 906 BROAD ST, WHOLE HEALTH PSYCHIATRY 27705 #016-06-2003 L2002 **P** *020 ‡

PARKER, Stephen Ray. ■ 27712 #017-20-2005 **NS** *012

PARKERSON, Geo Robt, Jr. 3643 N ROXBORO ST 27704 #036-07-1953 L1974 **FM** *030 †18

PARRETT, Timothy James. ■ 27705 #025-01-1996 L2000 **PTH** *020 †50

PARRILLO, Stephen J. BOX 3094 DUKE UNIV MED CTR, DEPT OF ANESTHESIA 27710 #561-01-1980 L1987 **AN IM** *020 †05

PARTRIDGE, James A. 4003 N ROXBORO ST, LAKEWOOD PEDIATRICS & 27704 #422-01-1995 L2000 **MPD** *020 †20 ‡

PARVATA, Reddy C P. 3643 N ROXBORO ST 27704 #495-62-1961 L1979 **AN** *020 †05

PASCARELLA, Luigi. ■ 27713 #561-05-2001 **GS** *100

PASTULA, Daniel Michael. ■ 27704 #036-07-2008 *012

PATEL, Bhaskar R. ■ 27712 #495-23-1978 L1987 **FM** *100

PATEL, Chetan Bharat. ■ 27713 #048-12-2002 L2006 **CD** *012 †20

PATEL, Mahesh Jagubhai. ■ 27703 #021-01-2003 L2007 **CD** *012 †20

PATEL, Manesh Raman. DUMC, BOX 31349 27710 #012-05-1997 L2001 **IC** *100 †20

PATEL, Mayur Bipin. ■ 27707 #047-05-2002 **GS** *012

PATEL, Uptal Dinesh. DUMC 3646, DUKE CLINICAL RESEARCH INS 27710 #005-02-1997 L2005 **NEP PN** *050 †20,55

PATERSON, Anne. PO BOX 3808, DUKE UNIV MED CTR 27710 #917-20-1990 **PDR** *100

PATERSON, Robt Worcester. 6301 HERNDON RD 27713 #036-07-1979 L1981 **IM** *040 †20

PATIL, Neil Aneel. ■ 27713 #011-04-2002 L2007 **DR** *100 †80

PATKAR, Ashwin Anand. 4323 BEN FRANKLIN BLVD 27704 #496-38-1988 L2004 **P** *020 †75 ‡

PATZ, Edward F, Jr. DEPT OF RADIOLOGY BOX 3808, DUKE MEDICAL CENTER 27710 #023-01-1985 L1991 **DR** *020 †80

PAULSEN, Grant Chris. ■ 27707 #007-02-2005 **MPD** *012

PAULSON, Erik K. DEPT OF RAD, DUKE UNIV MED CTR 27705 #036-07-1985 L1990 **DR IM** *020 †80

PAWLOSKI, John Robert. ■ 27710 #028-34-1994 L1995 **HO** *020 †20

PAYATAKES, Alexander Harr. BX 3951 M148 DAV BLD 27710 #418-03-1994 L2006 **HS** *020

PAYNE, Asha Soyini. DUKE UNIV MED CTR, DEPT OF PEDIATRICS ROOM 54 27710 #036-07-2005 L2008 **PD** *012

PAYNE, Deborah Ann. 725 BROAD ST, CAROLINA BEHAVIORAL CARE, 27705 #038-45-1998 L2000 **CHP P** *020

PAYNE, Richard. DUKE ICEOL, 2 CHAPEL DR 27708 #024-01-1977 L2008 **N PLM** *062 †75

PAYNE, Victoria Mitchell. 508 FULTON ST, DURHAM VA MEDICAL CENTER 27705 #036-05-1999 L2003 **P** *020

PAYYAPILLI, Rose J. ■ 27713 #036-07-2005 **GS** *100

PEAKMAN, Lindsay Anne. ■ 27707 #028-02-2004 L2007 **PD** *020 †55

PEERY, Charles Andrew. ■ 27705 #036-07-2005 **AN** *012

PEETE, Charles Henry, Jr. 2609 N DUKE ST STE 204 27704 #024-01-1947 L1947 **GYN** *071 †30

PELLOM, Gary Lee. 3643 N ROXBORO ST 27704 #036-01-1988 L1992 **AN** *020 †05

PENNELL, Angela Michelle. ■ 27713 #007-02-2004 L2006 **AN** *012

PENNELL, Heather Nicole. ■ 27707 #036-01-2005 **GS** *012

PENNINGTON, Robert Clay. 4309 MEDICAL PARK DR 27704 #036-01-1986 L1987 **IM** *020 †55,20

PENNY, Peggy Jean. ■ 27713 #021-05-2003 L2007 **PAN** *012

PEPPER, Matthew Daniel. PO BOX 96046, DUKE UNIVERSITY 27708 #025-01-2007 **PD** *012

PERANGELO, Linda H. ■ 27713 #036-07-1978 L2005 **AI PDA** *020 †55,03 ‡

PERDUE, Jedidiah James. ■ 27713 #039-01-2004 L2008 **P** *012

PEREA, Elena. ■ 27713 #036-01-2006 L2007 **P** *012

PEREZ, Phillip Carlos. DUKE UNIV MED CTR, DEPT OF PSYCHIATRY 27710 #038-06-1997 L2000 **P** *100

PERFECT, John Robt. DUKE MEDICAL CENTER 27706 #038-43-1974 L1980 **ID** *050 †20

PERHAC, John Stephen, II. ■ 27713 #036-01-2008 *012

PERKINS, Mark D. BOX 3867, DUKE UNIVERSITY MEDICAL CE 27710 #048-12-1984 L1993 **MM PD** *020

PERRY, Dwight Dean. 4102 N ROXBORO ST 27704 #036-01-1980 L1984 **OPH** *020 †35

PERRY, Stephanie L. ERWIN/TRENT DRIVE, ROOM 0563 STEAD BLDG. 27710 #036-05-1996 L2004 **HO** *020 †20

PERSON, Ameen Fareed. ■ 27713 #025-07-2004 L2007 **CD** *012 †20

PERSON, Anna Kristine. ■ 27701 #010-01-2005 **IM** *012

PESTANA, Ivo Alexander. BX 3951 M148 DAV BLD 27710 #011-02-2000 L2007 **PS** *012 †85

PESTER, Lucy Amelia. BOX 3951 27710 #917-28-1995 *062

PETERS, William P. 4620 CREEKSTONE DR, STE 200 27703 #035-01-1978 L1985 **ON IM** *020 †20

PETERSEN, John Louis. DUMC, BOX 31228 27710 #054-04-1995 L1998 **IC** *020 †20

PETERSEN, Beth Eileen. 3713 UNIVERSITY DR STE B, LAKEWOOD SOUTH FAMILY PRAC 27707 #010-01-1990 L1999 **FM** *020 †18

PETERSON, Eric David. 2400 PRATT ST RM 7009, DUKE CLINICAL RESEARCH INS 27705 #041-12-1988 L1993 **CD** *050 †20

PETERSON-LAYNE, C L. DUKE UNIV MED CTR, CB 3094 DEPT ANES 27710 #036-07-1998 L2000 **AN** *020 †05

PETRELLA, Jeffrey R. ERWIN RD, BOX 3808 DUMC 27710 #033-06-1987 L1997 **RNR R** *020 †80

PEYSER, Bruce Theodore. 3024 PICKETT RD 27710 #035-20-1983 L2005 **IM** *020 †20 ‡

PFEIFFER, Christopher Dan. ■ 27713 #038-40-2003 L2004 **ID** *012 †20

PHAM, Duykhanh Thi. ■ 27701 #036-07-2001 **GS** *012

PHAM, Nam-Kha Nguyen. DEPT OF ANESTHESIOLOGY, DUMC 3094 27710 #011-03-2007 **AN** *012

PHAM, Thi Lang Chau. 1912 ALEXANDER DR 27709 #396-34-1984 *020 †19

PHELPS, Anne Frances. 3024 PICKETT RD, DUKE GENERAL INTERNAL MED 27705 #025-01-1998 L2001 **IM** *020 †20

PHILCOX, Stephen. TRENT DR OFF ERWIN RD, DUKE UMC DIV GASTRO 27706 #143-03-2001 L2008 *100

PHILLIP, Derick Edwin. ■ 27710 #041-09-1985 L1986 **IM** *020 †20

PHILLIPS, Anne Sarah. DUMC BOX 3094 27710 #918-01-1984 **AN** *040

PHILLIPS, Harry R, III. ERWIN ROAD, DUMC 3126 27710 #036-07-1975 L1980 **CD** *020 †20

PHILLIPS, Trevor Grant. ■ 27713 #008-01-2005 L2007 **EM** *012

PHUA, Ghee Chee. ■ 27707 #825-01-1997 L2006 *100

PIACENTINO, Valentino, III. BX 3951 DAV BLD, DUKE UNIV MED CTR 27710 #041-13-2006 **GS** *012

PIANTADOSI, Claude A. BOX 3315, DUKE UNIVERSITY MEDICAL CE 27710 #023-07-1975 L1981 **PUD IM** *050 †20

PICCINI, Jonathan Paul. BOX #31115, DUKE UNIVERSITY MEDICAL CE 27710 #016-06-2002 L2005 **CD** *012 †20

PICKENS, Edward Munyan. 5322 HIGHGATE DR, STE 144 27713 #036-01-1993 L1996 **PHO** *020 †55

PIERCE, Meredith Jane. ■ 27701 #054-04-2004 **D** *012

PILKINGTON, Thomas Michae. ■ 27713 #023-07-2004 **OTO** *012

PINEO, Caleb Evans. ■ 27701 #036-01-2008 *012

PINNELL, Sheldon Richard. ERWIN RD, DUKE HOSP S RM 4044 27710 #008-01-1963 L1973 **D** *071 †15

PIPER, Lauren. ■ 27713 #038-06-2004 **CCP** *012

PISCITELLI, Joanne T. BX 3951 M148 DAV BLD 3456 27710 #036-07-1980 L1983 **OBG AN** *020 †30

PISETSKY, David Stephen. VET ADMIN HOSP, DEPT MED 27705 #035-46-1973 L1978 **IM RHU** *050 †20

PISETSKY, Ingrid C B. ■ 27707 #035-46-1971 L1978 **P PYA** *020 †75

PISHARODY, Anita M. 6020 FAYETTEVILLE RD 27713 #495-32-1991 L1999 **FM** *020 †18

PITT, Geoffrey Stuart. ■ 27710 #023-07-1993 L2007 **CD IM** *050 †20

PITTS, Theodore Marius. 400 CRUTCHFIELD ST, STE B 27704 #008-01-1977 L1982 **OSS** *020 †40

PIZZO, Salvatore Vincent. DUKE MEDICAL CTR, BOX 3712 27710 #036-07-1973 L1973 **PTH** *050 †50

PLANTE, Beth Jennifer. ■ 27713 #024-16-2002 L2006 **REN OBG** *020 †30

PLANTE, Troilus Anthony. ■ 27713 #024-16-2002 L2006 **EM** *100 †16
PODGER, Kenneth A. ■ 27705 #036-07-1940 L1947 **OBG** *071 †30
PODGOREANU, Mihai Victor. DEPT OF ANESTH BOX 3094, DUKE UNIV MED CTR 27710 #781-01-1993 L2000 **AN CCA** *050 †05
POINDEXTER, Gabriele Beer. ■ 27701 #012-05-2005 L2006 **D** *012
POLASCIK, Thomas James. 3116 N DUKE ST, DUKE HEALTH CTR 27704 #016-02-1991 L1998 **U** *020 †95
POLESKI, Martin. DUKE UNIV MEDICAL, BOX 3662 27710 #067-01-1973 L2003 **IM GE** *020 †20 ‡
POLLOCK, Laurie. 3802 ERWIN RD, DUKE EYE CENTER 27705 #023-07-1986 L1992 **OPH** *020 †35
POPISH, Paul Wm. 115 MARKET ST STE 201, CDSA 27701 #035-08-1966 L1994 **PD** *071 †55
PORTENIER, Dana Dale. 3116 N DUKE ST STE 209, WEIGHT LOSS SURGERY CENTER 27704 #045-01-1999 L2005 **GS** *020 †85
PORTER, Isaac William. ■ 27713 #020-12-2005 **OPH** *012
POSTEL, Eric Attila. BOX 3802, 2351 ERWIN ROAD 27710 #041-02-1991 L1996 **OPH** *020 †35
POTTER, Joan Garska. 5400 S MIAMI BLVD, STE 112 27703 #055-01-1980 L1982 **FM** *020 †18
POURTAHERI, Neema. ■ 27713 #021-01-2007 *012
POVSIC, Thomas Joseph. BOX 3437, DUMC 27710 #024-01-1995 L1997 **IC** *020 †20
POWELL, Alexandra Newlin. 2020 W MAIN ST STE 20 27705 #041-02-1998 L1999 **P** *020 †75
POWELL, Natasha Nicole. ■ 27703 #038-06-2005 **EM** *012
POWERS, Benjamin Jared. BOX 31323, DUMC 27710 #005-18-2002 L2005 **IM** *100 †20
POWERS, Ciaran James. BX 3951 M148 DAV BLD 27710 #010-02-2003 **NS** *012
POWERS, Mark Anthony. 2609 N DUKE ST STE 504 27704 #032-01-1977 L1979 **PUD CCM** *020 †20
POZA JUNCAL, Esther. 105 NEWSOM ST, STE 106 27704 #003-01-1984 L1987 **IM** *020 †20
PRADHAN, Shan M. ■ 27713 #005-06-2002 L2007 **HO** *012 †20
PRASAD, Vinod Kumar. DUKE UNIVERSITY MEDICAL CE 27710 #495-45-1983 L2003 **PHO** *020 †55
PREMINGER, Glenn Michael. PO BOX 3167 DEPT UROLOGY, DUKE UNIVERSITY MED CTR 27710 #035-09-1977 L1978 **U END** *020 †95
PRENTICE, Robert Derek. 1965 IVY CREEK BLVD, P O BOX 2291 27707 #919-03-1970 L1979 **OS FM** *072
PRESAR, Ashley Rebekah. ■ 27706 #036-07-2008 *012
PRESSLEY, Crystal Michael. ■ 27707 #036-01-2008 L2008 *012
PRESTON, John F, Jr. ■ 27713 #036-07-1935 L1941 **AM OM** *071
PRESTON, Robert James. BX 3951 M148 DAV BLD 27710 #539-04-2005 **EM** *012
PREUD'HOMME, Xavier Alpho. ■ 27705 #165-01-1993 L2006 **OS** *100 †20
PRICE, Cecil Dwight. 22 PARK PL BOX 12833 27712 #036-05-1982 L1986 **FM EM** *020 †18
PRICE, David Talmadge. ■ 27710 #045-04-1982 L2006 **PD** *020 †55
PRICE, Kenneth Owen. 3901 N ROXBORO ST STE 101 27704 #036-05-1997 L2000 **NS** *020
PRICE, Nicole. 2609 N DUKE ST 27704 #036-07-1998 **AN** *100
PRICE, Robert Edwin, Jr. ■ 27707 #036-01-1964 L1964 **NS** *071
PRICE, Thomas Michael. 5704 FAYETTEVILLE RD, DUKE FERTILITY CLNC 27713 #036-01-1984 L2002 **REN OBG** *020 †30 ‡
PRICE, William Armistead. 810 IREDELL ST 27705 #036-01-1985 L1987 **P** *020 †70,75
PRIMIS, Sydney Partin. ■ 27710 #036-01-2001 L2007 **CCP** *020 †55
PRINCE, Rebecca Ann. DUKE UNIV MED CTR, DEPT OF SURGERY 27710 #040-02-2002 **GS** *012
PRITCHARD, Edward Lewis C. 1821 HILLANDALE RD STE 1B, PMB 333 27705 #038-40-1971 L1975 **CD** *050 †20
PROCTOR, Leslie Kay. ■ 27713 #007-02-2006 **IM** *012
PROIA, Alan David. DUKE UNIV MED CTR, BOX 3712 27710 #035-20-1980 L1982 **ATP** *020 †50
PROSE, Neil Stuart. BOX 3252, DUKE UNIVERSITY MED CTR 27710 #035-19-1975 L1977 **D PD** *020 †15,55
PROSNITZ, Leonard Richard. DUKE UNIV MED CTR, BOX 3085 27710 #035-08-1961 L1983 **RO** *020 †80
PROTOPSALTIS, Themistocli. DUKE UNIV MED CTR, DIVISION OF ORTHOPAEDIC SU 27710 #035-01-2001 L2005 **HSO** *012
PROVENZALE, Dawn T. 508 FULTON ST, VA MEDICAL CTR 27705 #035-03-1984 L1992 **GE IM** *020 †20
PROVENZALE, James M. BOX 3808, DUKE UNIV MEDICAL CENTER 27710 #035-03-1983 L1992 **RNR** *020 †75,80
PRUITT, Scott Knowles. BOX 3966, DUKE UNIVERSITY MEDICAL CE 27710 #035-01-1987 L1997 **GS SO** *020 †85
PRYOR, Aurora Dawn. DEPT OF SURGERY, DUKE UNIV MED CTR 27710 #036-07-1995 L1996 **GS** *020 †85
PULNIK, Jason William. ■ 27713 #048-02-2002 L2005 **DR** *100 †80
PUN, Patrick Hank. BOX 3014 DUMC 27710 #047-05-2001 L2004 **NEP IM** *050
PUNNAHITANANDA, Santi. ■ 27713 #891-01-1988 **NPM** *100
PURDY, Teresa. 508 FULTON ST, DURHAM VAMC 27705 #045-04-1998 L1999 **P** *020 †75
PURDY, William Kimball. BOX 2899, DUKE CLINIC TRENT DRIVE 27710 #038-06-1977 L1998 **PD** *020 †55
PURVES, Dale. ■ 27710 #024-01-1964 L1968 **OS** *050
PUSCAS, Liana. BOX 3805, DUKE SOUTH 27710 #011-02-1996 L2004 **OTO** *020 †45
PUTMAN, Charles Edgar. 718 RUTHERFORD ST 27705 #048-02-1967 L1977 **R IM** *030 †20,80
PUVVADA, Soham Dinesh. ■ 27713 #011-04-2006 **IM** *012
QUARFORDT, Dawn Kersten. ■ 27705 #036-01-1997 **IM** *100
QUE, Loretta Georgina. 718 RUTHERFORD ST 27705 #016-02-1989 L1996 **PUD** *020 †20
QUIGLEY, Peter Jos. ■ 27707 #539-05-1976 L1989 **CD IM** *020
QUINN, Jennifer Ann. DUMC 3624, 47 BAKER HOUSE, TRENT DRIV 27710 #036-08-1994 L1999 **N** *020 †75
QUINN, Michele Terese. ■ 27701 #036-07-2001 **OBG** *012
QUINONES, Anamaria. BOX 3951, DUMC 27710 #024-07-1997 L2000 **PDR** *020 †80
QUINONES MAYMI, Desiree M. ■ 27713 #042-01-1996 L2001 **DR** *020 †80
QUIRKE, Dale Patrick. ■ 27713 #038-41-2007 **EM** *012
QURESHI, Javeria Shaheen. ■ 27713 #036-07-2002 L2006 **GS** *012
QURESHI, Jawad Ahmad. BOX 3802, DUKE UNIVERSITY EYE CENTER 27710 #036-07-2002 L2006 **OPH** *100 †35
RAASCH, Eric Warren. ■ 27704 #039-01-2004 L2006 **NEP** *012 †20
RABINOVICH, Diana C. 2401 ERWIN ROAD, BOX 3212 27710 #016-45-1985 L2001 **PPR PD** *050 †55
RABOSTO, Pablo Martin. 3643 N ROXBORO ST 27704 #726-01-1996 L2003 **IMG** *100
RADTKE, Rodney Allan. BELL DRIVE, DUMC-3678 ROOM 2026 BELL B 27710 #016-06-1980 L1984 **N** *020 †75

RAHMAN, Ziaur. DEPT OF ANESTHESIOLOGY, DUKE UNIVERSITY MEDICAL CE 27710 #495-15-1969 L1980 **AN** *020
RAHN, Karyn W. ■ 27704 #036-07-1999 L2005 **GPM** *020
RAI, Rachna. ■ 27707 #048-12-2008 **PD** *012
RAILEY, Kenyon Michael. ■ 27707 #028-34-2005 L2007 **FP** *012
RAINEY, Dennis Carl. ■ 27713 #010-03-1988 L1990 **EM** *020 †16
RAJAGOPAL, Kumbakonam K. ■ 27712 #016-02-2002 **GS** *012
RAJAGOPAL, Shilpa. BX 3951 M148 DAV BLD 27710 #462-01-1999 L2006 **PD** *100 †55
RAJAGOPAL, Sudarshan K. ■ 27712 #016-02-2006 **IM** *012
RALL, David P. PO BOX 12233 27709 #016-06-1951 **IM** *030
RAMAMURTHY, Meera. ■ 27707 #041-12-2005 L2008 **IM** *012
RAMAN, Yeshesvini. 508 FULTON ST 116A, (VA MEDICAL CENTER) 27705 #495-49-1994 L2004 **OBG** *020 †75,20
RAMCHANDRAN, Rajeev S. P.O. BOX 3802, DUKE EYE CENTER 27710 #035-45-2003 L2007 **OPH** *100
RAMIAH, Veshana Sinthal. ■ 27712 #836-01-1990 L2007 **HO** *020 †20
RAMSEY, Colleen Patricia. 4220 N ROXBORO ST 27704 #033-05-1992 L1995 **IM** *020 †20
RAMSEY, Shelileah Nicole. ■ 27713 #011-03-2003 L2004 **RO** *012
RANA, Asim Khurshid. ■ 27703 #704-15-1994 L2000 **CHP** *100 †75
RAND, Stephanie Slater. 5315 HIGHGATE DR, STE 101 27713 #036-08-1987 L1990 **PD** *040 †55
RANDOLPH, Byron Richard. 1301 FAYETTEVILLE ST 27707 #047-07-1985 L1995 **IM** *020 †20
RANKIN, Julie Catharine. ■ 27707 #048-12-2007 **IM** *012
RAO, Arati Vasant. ERWIN ROAD, DUKE UNIVERSITY MEDICAL CE 27710 #495-28-1996 L2003 **IMG** *020 †20
RAO, Sabina. ■ 27703 #496-39-1999 L2006 **P** *100
RAO, Sunil Vadlakonda. BOX 31231, DUMC 27710 #038-40-1996 L1999 **IC** *020 †20
RASSI, Andrew N.. ■ 27707 #038-06-2006 **IM** *012
RAVANBAKHT, Jason Ali. CARE CL, DUKE PAIN & PALLIATIVE 27710 #036-01-2003 L2008 **PMM** *012
RAVIN, Carl Eric. BOX 3808, DUKE MEDICAL CENTER 27710 #035-20-1968 L1978 **DR** *030 †80
RAWLINGS, Ron Howard. ■ 27704 #030-05-2006 **AN** *012
RAY, Gregory Thomas. ■ 27713 #036-07-2003 L2004 **MGP** *012
RAY, Veronica Josephine. 1301 FAYETTEVILLE ST 27707 #036-01-1979 L1981 **IM** *020 †20
RAYBURG, Melissa Sue. 2400 PRATT ST STE 1400, DUKE UNIV MEDICAL CENTER 27705 #025-12-2002 L2005 **PHO** *012 †55
REAGAN, Robert William, Jr. 205 FRASIER ST 27704 #036-01-1998 L2003 **U** *020 †95
REARDON, David Allen. DUMC BOX 3624, THE BRAIN TUMOR CENTER 27710 #024-07-1986 L2000 **PHO** *050 †55
RECKHOW, Alan Harding. ■ 27705 #035-06-1946 **PD** *071 †55
RECKLESS, John Brian. ■ 27705 #352-01-1954 L1960 **P OS** *072 †75
REDDAN, Donal Noel. 2400 PRATT ST, BOX 3646 27705 #539-04-1992 L1999 **NEP** *020 †20
REDDY, Elizabeth A. ■ 27701 #035-45-2002 L2004 **ID** *012 †55
REDDY, Madhavi Gade. 815 BROAD ST, PRIORITY CARE 27705 #496-23-2002 L2008 **FM** *020
REDDY, Srinevas K. ■ 27713 #056-05-2003 **GS** *012
REDDY, Suraj A. ■ 27713 #048-04-2002 L2007 **DR** *100 †80
REDDY, Vinay Chintala. ■ 27713 #012-21-2004 L2007 **FM** *100 †18
REDICK, Lloyd Franklin. ■ 27705 #036-07-1985 L1974 **AN** *071 †05
REDMAN, Richard Clark. ■ 27713 #054-04-2003 L2006 **PCC** *012 †20
REEBYE, Uday Nitin. 5318 NC HIGHWAY 55, STE 106 27713 #036-01-2004 L2007 **OMF** *020
REED, Katherine Bruya. ■ 27712 #054-04-2004 L2004 **P** *012
REED, Melissa Rebecca. ■ 27703 #040-02-2003 L2003 **FP** *012
REEDY, Michael Kay. ERWIN RD, 458 SANDS BLDG 27710 #054-04-1962 **OS** *040
REEVES, Gordon Reginald. ■ 27713 #036-01-2004 L2007 **IM** *020 †20
REEVES, Travis Daniel. ■ 27705 #036-07-2008 *012
REGAN, Conor Matthew. ■ 27713 #015-01-2007 **ORS** *012
REGAN, Robert Ward, Jr. 205 FRASIER ST 27704 #024-07-1948 L1954 **OM IM** *020 †20
REID, Carl Claymon. ■ 27713 #165-01-1960 L2006 **OS AN** *071
REID, Carl Claymon, III. ■ 27705 #035-09-2000 L2003 **IM** *012
REID, India Fredrica. 508 FULTON ST, DURHAM VA MEDICAL CENTER 27705 #033-06-1999 L2003 **IMG** *020
REIMAN, Robert Ellis, Jr. 718 RUTHERFORD ST 27705 #038-06-1987 L1994 **EM** *020 †28
REIN, Matthew Gordon. ■ 27705 #035-08-2008 *012
REISNER, Colin. PO BOX 13398 27709 #836-01-1987 L2000 **AI IM** *050 †20,03
RELLER, Lyman Barth. BOX 3938 DUKE UNIV MED CTR 27710 #051-01-1966 L1988 **ID IM** *030 †20
RENUART, A W. ■ 27712 #036-07-1956 L1958 **CHN PD** *071 †55
RESTEL, Bradley H. ■ 27713 #048-13-2005 **DR** *012
REYNOLDS, Mark Steven. 923 BROAD ST 27705 #021-01-1983 L1988 **P** *020 †75
REYNOLDS, Renee Monique. DUKE UNIV MED CTR, DIVISION OF NEUROSURGERY 27710 #035-15-2006 **NS** *012
RHEE, Eleanor Hoon Joo. DEPT OF OB/GYN, DUKE UNIV MED CTR 27710 #008-01-1998 L2002 **OBG** *020
RHO, Silvia Yunghee. ■ 27705 #036-07-2007 **PD** *012
RHODES, John Flint, Jr. DUKE UNIV MEDICAL CTR 3090, ROOM 7506B 27710 #036-08-1993 L2003 **PDC** *055
RHYNE, Randall Trenton. ■ 27713 #036-01-2008 *012
RHYNER, John David. ■ 27704 #036-07-2008 *012
RICE, Amy Marie. DUMC 3094, DUKE UNIVERSITY MEDICAL CE 27710 #065-01-1990 L2005 **AN** *020 ‡
RICE, Tara Michelle. ■ 27713 #036-01-1999 **PD** *012
RICH, Jeremy Naftali. BOX 2900 RESEARCH DRIVE, DUKE UNIV MEDICAL CENTER 27710 #036-07-1993 L1998 **N** *020 †75
RICH, Melissa M. 2609 N DUKE ST, STE 503 27704 #041-02-1993 L2000 **GE** *020 †20
RICH, Rebecca S. 3414 N DUKE ST, STE 400 27704 #043-01-1983 L1992 **EM** *020 †20,16
RICHARD, Marc Joseph. ■ 27705 #050-02-2001 L2007 **HS** *100
RICHARD, Michael Jason. 3807 ERWIN ROAD, DUKE EYE CENTER, P.O. BOX 27710 #024-05-2001 L2005 **OPH** *100 †35
RICHARDS, Michael Henry. 1301 FAYETTEVILLE ST 27707 #010-03-1997 L2001 **IM** *020 †20
RICHARDSON, David L. DUMC BOX 3192, DEPT OF OB/GYN 27710 #045-01-1973 L1990 **GYN** *040 †30
RICHARDSON, Taryn R. ■ 27713 #010-03-2003 L2005 **AI** *012
RICHARDSON, William James. ORTHOPAEDIC SURGERY, DUKE U MED CTR 27710 #051-07-1977 L1987 **ORS** *012 †20
RICHEY, Sarah Marie. ■ 27707 #028-34-2004 L2008 **P** *012
RICHTER, Kimberly Anne. 4419 BEN FRANKLIN BLVD 27704 #036-05-1995 L1996 **NEP IM** *020 †20

RIDDLE, Eric Dwight. ■ 27713 #030-05-2004 L2008 **MPD** *012

RIEDEL, Richard Francis. DUKE SOUTH, DUMC, BOX 3841, 3RD FLOOR, RED Z 27710 #041-02-2000 L2001 **HO** *100 †20

RIEFKOHL, Ronald Edward. 110 E CARVER ST 27704 #021-01-1972 L1979 **PS** *020 †85,65

RIESENMAN, Paul Joseph. ■ 27713 #056-06-2003 L2007 **GS** *012

RIVELLI, Sarah Kerry. BOX 3369, DUKE UNIVERSITY MEDICAL CE 27710 #165-01-2001 L2006 **OS** *100 †20

RIZZIERI, David Alan. 718 RUTHERFORD ST 27705 #035-45-1991 L1997 **HO** *020 †20

RO, Richard Youshin. ■ 27712 #036-07-2005 **DR** *012

RO, Sarah Jean. 2100 ERWIN RD 27705 #005-12-1991 L1998 **FM** *020 †18

ROBBINS, Jack Guyes. ■ 27707 #036-07-1948 L1950 **D** *071 †15

ROBBOY, Stanley J. DUMC-3712 27710 #025-01-1965 L1992 **PTH** *020 †50

ROBERT, Sara Page. 4020 N ROXBORO ST, DEPT OF PEDIATRICS 27704 #016-43-1999 L2000 **PD** *020 †55

ROBERT, Scott Matthew. BOX 3367, DUKE UNIVERSITY MEDICAL CE 27710 #041-01-1999 L2003 **IM** *020 †20,55

ROBERTS, Jeffrey Benningt. ■ 27707 #051-04-2004 L2007 **FSM** *012 †18

ROBERTS, Joseph Linton. 4101 N ROXBORO ST 27704 #012-05-1981 L1996 **AI PD** *020 †55,03

ROBERTSON, Cary Nobles. DUMC, BOX 3833 27710 #021-01-1977 L1978 **U** *020 †95

ROBERTSON, J David. ■ 27710 #024-01-1945 L1975 **OS** *050

ROBERTSON, Katina Denise. ■ 27707 #036-07-2008 *012

ROBERTSON, Kerri Margret. BOX 3094 DEPT OF ANES, DUKE UNIV MED CTR 27710 #061-01-1980 L1993 **AN** *020 †20

ROBERTSON, Piers William. 718 RUTHERFORD ST 27705 #143-01-1986 L1997 **AN** *100

ROBINSON, Lisa Annette. 4101 N ROXBORO ST 27704 #065-01-1991 L1995 **PN** *020 †55

ROBINSON, Timothy John. ■ 27705 #036-07-2008 *012

ROCA, Luis Enrique. PO BOX 99174 27708 #051-04-2005 **OBG** *012

ROCHA, Ana Thereza C. BX 3951 M148 DAV BLD 27710 #187-01-1995 **PCC** *100 †20

ROCHA, Paulo Novis. ■ 27710 #187-01-1995 L2000 **NEP** *020 †20

ROCHE, Anthony Michael. ■ 27710 #836-04-1993 L2003 *020

ROCHE, David Henry. 6D RIVER BIRCH RD 27705 #671-02-1987 **PTH** *020

ROCHE, Joseph Paul. ■ 27713 #056-06-2007 **OTO** *012

ROCKMAN, Howard Allan. DUKE UNIVERSITY MEDICAL CE, DUMC 3104 27710 #067-01-1983 L1997 **CD IM** *020 †20

ROCKWELL, William James K. ■ 27707 #036-07-1961 L1961 **P** *071 †75

ROE, Matthew Todd. 2400 PRATT ST RM 7037 27705 #036-07-1993 L1995 **CD** *020 †20

ROELANDS, Jennifer Jane. ■ 27713 #055-18-2004 L2008 **OBG** *012

ROGERS, Holly Blaine. 718 RUTHERFORD ST 27705 #048-12-1990 L1994 **P** *020 †75

ROGERS, Jennifer Lee. ■ 27713 #017-20-2005 L2008 **IM** *012

ROGERS, Lesco Lloyd. 932 MORREENE RD 27705 #032-01-1990 L1996 **AN** *020 †05

ROGERS, Todd Allen. 3414 N DUKE ST, STE 400 27704 #036-01-1991 L1992 **EM** *020 †16

ROGG, Luise E. ■ 27713 #048-12-2005 **PD** *012

ROGGLI, Victor Louis. BOX 3712 DUKE UNIV MED CTR 27710 #048-04-1976 L1980 **PTH** *062 †50

ROHRER, Sally Cathleen. ■ 27713 #001-02-2005 **MPD** *012

ROLLER, Josh E. ■ 27710 #039-01-2001 L2006 **GS** *020

ROMA, Domenick Joseph. ■ 27713 #035-45-2008 *012

ROMAN, Nancy Lynn. 1502 W NC HIGHWAY 54, STE 302 27707 #023-01-1992 L1996 **P** *020

ROMETO, David Andrew. ■ 27710 #038-06-2006 **IM** *012

RONAN, Shawn Michael. ■ 27710 #026-04-2003 L2007 *100

ROSA, Matthew Henry. ■ 27710 #024-01-2003 L2005 **P** *100

ROSATI, Robert Anthony. 3543 ROSE OF SHARON RD 27712 #036-07-1967 L1967 **CD IM** *020 †20

ROSE, Anelia Presson. 6011 FAYETTEVILLE RD, STE 104A 27713 #036-05-1998 L2000 **FM** *020 †18

ROSE, Daniel Todd. BOX 3000, DUMC 27710 #036-07-2000 L2002 **ORS** *020 †40

ROSE, Erin Christine. ■ 27713 #030-05-2004 L2008 **AN** *012

ROSENBERG, Michael Jos. 2510 MERIDIAN PKWY 27713 #005-19-1975 L1983 **SO EM** *050 †20,70

ROSENBERG, Paul. 209 RESEARCH DR, DUMC MSRB 27710 #033-05-1992 L2002 **CD** *020 †20

ROSENBLITT, Daphne B A. 3721 UNIVERSITY DR STE C 27707 #036-07-1974 L1975 **PYA P** *020

ROSENBLITT, Donald Lewis. 3721 UNIVERSITY DR STE C 27707 #036-07-1973 L1975 **PYA CHP** *020

ROSENTHAL, Amy Jo. 3643 N ROXBORO ST 27704 #051-04-1987 L1998 **IM IMG** *020 †20

ROSES, Allen David. ONE SCIENCE DR, DUKE UNIVERSITY / RDT CTR 27708 #041-01-1967 L1970 **N** *050 †75

ROSOFF, Philip Martin. BOX 2916, 217A BELL BUILDING 27710 #038-06-1978 L1995 **PD HEM** *050 †55

ROSS, James Grooms. 2609 N DUKE ST, STE 801 27704 #036-01-1986 L1992 **OTO** *020 †45

ROSS, Paden Danielle. ■ 27704 #036-07-2006 **MPD** *012

ROSSE, Wendell Franklyn. ERWIN RD, DUKE SOUTH RM 0563 27710 #016-02-1958 L1966 **HEM IM** *050 †04

ROTH, Christopher John. ■ 27707 #025-01-2004 L2008 **DR** *012

ROTH, Michael Edward. ■ 27713 #038-44-2003 L2005 **PTH** *100

ROTHSCHILD, Andrew C. ■ 27701 #041-01-1996 L2000 **IM** *020 †20

ROTHSCHILD, Barbra B. ■ 27701 #036-01-1995 L2000 **IM OBG** *020 †20

ROURK, Malcolm H, Jr. ERWIN ROAD, DUKE S, DUKE UNIV MED CTR 27710 #041-01-1963 L1963 **GE PD** *050 †55,03

ROUSE, James Bristol. 2609 N DUKE ST, CENTRAL MEDICAL PARK, STE 27704 #036-07-1965 L1965 **PD** *020 †55

ROWAN, Peter Robert. PO BOX 3000, DUKE UNIV MED CTR-ORTH SUR 27710 #143-05-1989 **HS** *012

ROWE, Keisha Lashan. ■ 27713 #036-01-2002 L2004 **PN** *012

ROWELL, Jennifer Voigt. BOX 3924 DUMC, DUKE UNIV MED CTR 27710 #045-01-2004 L2006 **END** *012 †20

ROY, Lipi. ■ 27707 #021-01-2008 *012

ROYAL, Vernice. 6301 HERNDON RD 27713 #036-07-1992 L1995 **IM** *020 †20

ROZEAR, Marvin Price. DUKE S TRENT DRIVE, BAKER HOUSE, ROOM 122 27710 #036-07-1966 L1966 **N** *020 †75

RUBIN, Jessie. ■ 27705 #869-05-1941 L1942 **D** *071 †15

RUBINO, Margaret Mary. ■ 27713 #010-02-2004 L2007 **PD** *100 †55

RUFF, Sarah Christine. ■ 27713 #025-12-2005 L2008 **FP** *012

RUSSELL, Michael Linn. 4101 N ROXBORO ST 27704 #036-01-1985 L1990 **PUD IM** *020 †20

RYAN, Andrew Francis. ■ 27703 #056-06-2006 **DR** *012

RYAN, David Hallmark. ■ 27713 #051-01-2007 **OBG** *012

RYAN, James Patrick, V. ■ 27713 #036-01-2008 L2008 *012

RYAN, John Mark. DIV OF INTER'L RADIOLOGY, DEPT OF RADIOLOGY, ROOM 15 27710 #539-03-1988 L1998 **VIR R** *040

RYAN, Shaida Khajenasir. PO BOX 52666 27717 #036-01-2001 L2005 **AN** *020

SAAB, Raya Hamad. BX 3951 M148 DAV BLD 27710 #605-01-1999 **PHO** *100 †55

SABESAN, Vani Janaki. ■ 27713 #017-20-2004 L2007 **ORS** *012

SABISTON, David Coston, Jr. 718 RUTHERFORD ST 27705 #023-07-1947 L1964 **TS GS** *071 †85,90

SALAHUDDIN, Fawzia K. ■ 27704 #704-02-1994 L2003 **PCC** *100 †20

SALDIN, Kamaldeen Rizvie. DUMC BOX 2906 27710 #473-02-1998 **N NRN** *012

SALDIVAR, Laura Escoto. 4020 N ROXBORO ST 27704 #005-11-1991 L2007 **PD** *020 †55

SALICRU, Adriano N. ■ 27713 #048-14-2007 **IM** *012

SALTZMAN, Herbert A. BOX 3838, PULMONARY DEPARTMENT 27710 #041-02-1952 L1959 **PUD IM** *071 †20

SAMAD, Zainab. BX 3951 M148 DAV BLD, DUKE UNIV MED CTR 27710 #704-25-2000 **CD** *012 †20

SAMALA, Sujana. ■ 27713 #654-01-1997 L2004 **PCP** *020 †50

SAMBUR, Marnie Renee. ■ 27713 #041-02-2004 *100

SAMPATHKUMAR, Sophiya. ■ 27703 #495-27-2003 **P** *012

SAMPSON, John Howard. ERWIN ROAD, DUKE UNIV MED CTR 27710 #062-01-1990 L1996 **NS** *020 †25

SAMUHEL, Kristen Ann. ■ 27712 #036-01-2006 **FP** *012

SANCHEZ, Katya Maria. ■ 27713 #726-01-1996 L2002 **DMP** *020 †50

SANDER, Margie Catherine. ■ 27713 #038-43-2006 **FP** *012

SANDERS, Donald Benj. TRENT DRIVE, RM 1255 CLINIC 1L DUKE CLI 27710 #024-01-1964 L1980 **N CN** *040 †75

SANDERS, Edward Garner. 3643 N ROXBORO ST, REGIONAL ANESTHESIA 27704 #036-01-1985 L1990 **AN PD** *020 †05

SANDERS, Jeffrey Benjamin. ■ 27705 #007-02-2008 *012

SANDERSON, Iain Colin. 2424 ERWIN RD STE 10000, DUMC BOX 2718 27705 #917-09-1985 L1993 **AN** *020 †05

SANDHU, Amandeep Kaur. ■ 27713 #036-05-1994 L1996 **IM** *020

SANDHU, Navreet. DUKE UNIV MED CTR, BOX 2634 27710 #305-01-2001 L2008 **PCC** *012 †20

SANFORD, Nadia Sheree. ■ 27713 #012-01-2003 L2008 **GE** *012 †20

SANFORD, Ryan Bobbitt. ■ 27713 #036-01-2007 **IM** *012

SANGVAI, Devdutta G. BOX 2899 DUMC, DUKE UNIVERSITY MEDICAL CE 27710 #038-43-1998 L2001 **FM** *030 †18

SAPPENFIELD, David Luther. 4102 N ROXBORO ST 27704 #036-01-1984 L1985 **OPH** *020 †35 ‡

SARASWAT, Akhil. ■ 27707 #056-06-2006 **EM** *012

SARPONG, Ayesha Adjei. ■ 27704 #036-07-2008 *012

SARRAF-YAZDI, Shiva. ■ 27710 #036-07-1999 L2004 **GS** *100 ‡

SATHY, Shailaja Janaki. ■ 27707 #028-02-2005 **IM** *012

SAWCHUK, Corey William T. 718 RUTHERFORD ST 27705 #062-01-1987 L1996 **AN** *020

SCALES, Charles. ■ 27705 #036-07-2004 **U** *012

SCALES, Jeffrey W. 6216 FAYETTEVILLE RD, STE 102 27713 #041-01-1987 L1994 **D** *020 †55

SCALLION, Ralph Michael. 3815 WAKE FOREST RD 27703 #038-06-1975 L1979 **IM** *020 †05

SCANGA, Lori Renee. 3643 N ROXBORO ST, HOSPITALIST PROGRAM DURHAM 27704 #036-07-1999 L2002 **PTH** *012 †20

SCARBOROUGH, John Emerson. P.O. BOX 3443, DUKE UNIVERSITY MEDICAL CE 27710 #036-07-1998 L2005 **CCS** *100 †85

SCARGLE, Michelle Ross. ■ 27710 #011-02-2000 L2003 **PFP** *020 †75

SCHANBERG, Laura Eve. 4101 N ROXBORO ST 27704 #036-07-1984 L1987 **PPR** *050 †55

SCHANBERG, Saul Murray. BOX 3813 DUKE UNIV MED CTR 27710 #008-01-1964 L1968 **PA PD** *050

SCHAUBERGER, James Scott. ■ 27713 #001-02-2006 **DR** *012

SCHER, Richard Lyle. DUKE UNIV MED CTR, BOX 3805 OTO 27710 #038-41-1985 L1992 **HNS OTO** *020 †45

SCHMECHEL, Donald Everett. DUKE MEDICAL CENTER, BOX 3951 NEUROLOGY 27710 #024-01-1974 L1982 **N** *050 †55

SCHMIDT, Evelyn D. 1301 FAYETTEVILLE ST 27707 #036-07-1951 L1971 **OS PD** *030 †55

SCHMITZ, Robert Lowell. ■ 27707 #028-02-1978 L1979 **FM EM** *020 †18

SCHNEIDER, Brian J. 508 FULTON ST, DURHAM VA MEDICAL CENTER 27705 #048-12-2004 L2007 **IM** *020 †20

SCHOLER, Andrea Marie. 7 CASABELLE CT 27713 #035-09-2000 L2002 **PD** *020 †55

SCHONFELD, Daniel G. PO BOX 12525 27709 #041-09-1950 L1973 **AN** *071 †05

SCHREINER, Virginia J. 5322 HIGHGATE DR, STE 144 27713 #036-01-1992 L1995 **PD** *020 †55

SCHRODER, Jacob Niall. ■ 27712 #010-02-2001 **GS** *012

SCHROECK, Florian Rudolf. BX 3951 M148 DAV BLD 27710 #409-40-2004 **U** *012

SCHROEDER, Emily Bartlett. ■ 27705 #036-07-2006 **IM** *012

SCHROEDER, Rebecca Ann. DUKE UNIVERSITY MEDICAL CE, BOX 3094 27710 #051-01-1989 L2001 **GS** *020 †05

SCHULER, Kevin Michael. ■ 27713 #020-12-2006 **OBG** *012

SCHULMAN, Kevin Alan. PO BOX 90120 27708 #035-19-1988 L1999 **IM** *050 †20

SCHULMAN, Scott R. P.O. BOX 3094, DUKE UNIV MEDICAL CENTER 27710 #010-01-1982 L1991 **AN** *020 †55,05

SCHULTZ, John Robt. DUMC 3094, DUKE UNIVERSITY MEDICAL CE 27710 #005-12-1991 L1999 **AN** *020 †05

SCHULZ, David Ian. DUMC3808 27710 #025-12-2003 L2006 **DR** *012

SCHUMACHER, Kurt Robert. ■ 27713 #025-01-2005 L2008 **PD** *012

SCHWARTZ, John Meese. ■ 27705 #041-12-1939 L1950 **GP** *071

SCHWARZ, Karl W. ■ 27713 #065-06-1997 L2004 **PS** *020 ‡

SCHWEITZER, Georgia Marie. ■ 27705 #036-07-2008 *012

SCOTT, Aaron Titus. ■ 27713 #027-01-2002 L2007 **ORS** *020

SCOTT, Adrienne Williams. ■ 27713 #041-15-2002 L2006 **OPH** *100 †35

SCOTT, Burton Lasater. 932 MORREENE RD, BOX 3333 27705 #011-02-1990 L1994 **N** *050 †75

SCOTT-HARRIS, Dianne L. 1300 MORREENE ROAD, DUMC 3094 27710 #036-01-1978 L1980 **AN** *020 †05

SCRUGGS, Justin Richard. ■ 27713 #045-01-2007 **PM** *012

SEBASTIAN, Mark Wm. DUKE MEDICAL CENTER, DUKE BOX 3533 27710 #016-01-1987 L1994 **VS** *020 †85

SECORD, Angeles Alvarez. BOX 3079, DUKE UNIVERSITY MEDICAL CE 27710 #054-04-1994 L1999 **OBG** *020 †30

SEED, Patrick Casey. PO BOX 103100, PEDIATRICSPEDIATRIC INFECT 27710 #035-45-1998 L2006 **PDI** *100 †55

■ = Address Information Privacy Protected

SEGER, Lesta Dell. ■ 27707 #046-01-2007 **PD** *012
SEIGLER, Hilliard Foster. DUKES S TRENT DR BLUE ZONE, BOX 3966 ROOM 3537 27710 #036-01-1960 L1960 **GS** *020 †85
SELLERS, Matthew Blair. ■ 27713 #045-01-2007 **IM** *012
SELLERS, Randy Phillip. 2020 W MAIN ST, MAINSTREET CLINICAL ASSOCS 27705 #036-01-1992 L1994 **P** *020 †75
SELLIN, Angela Katherine. ■ 27713 #048-12-2007 **P** *012
SERAFIN, Donald. 824 ANDERSON ST, SERAFIN PLASTIC SURGERY PL 27705 #036-07-1964 L1964 **PS GS** *020 †85,65
SERLO, Adam David. ■ 27713 #036-01-2004 L2007 **GS** *100
SERRA, Richard Kenneth. 27705 #025-01-1977 L1980 **EM FM** *020 †18,16
SESHADRI, Chetan. DUKE UNIV MED CTR, DEPT OF MED 27710 #033-05-2001 L2004 **ID** *012
SESSOMS, Stuart Mc Guire. PO BOX 2291, B CROSS B SHIELD 27702 #051-04-1946 L1968 **OS IM** *071 †20
SETJI, Noppon Pooh. ■ 27712 #051-01-1998 L2003 **IM** *020 †20
SEVERANCE, Harry W, Jr. BOX 3096, ERWIN ROAD 27710 #036-07-1981 L1983 **EM IM** *020 †16
SEXTON, Daniel John. DUKE UNIVERSITY MEDICAL CE 27710 #016-06-1971 L1974 **ID IM** *040 †20
SHA, Ronald Steven. 804 W TRINITY AVE, DUKE DIET AND FITNESS CENT 27701 #026-04-1972 L1993 **FM** *020 †18
SHADDUCK, Phillip P. 4301 BEN FRANKLIN BLVD 27704 #005-14-1986 L1993 **GS** *020 †85
SHADFAR, Scott. ■ 27707 #039-01-2008 *012
SHAFER, Aaron. ■ 27713 #041-12-2002 L2006 **OBG** *100
SHAH, Anish Anilkumar. ■ 27713 #051-04-2006 **OBG** *012
SHAH, Bijal Dinesh. ■ 27713 #011-04-2004 **MPD** *012
SHAH, Bimal Ramesh. DUMC 31199, DUKE UNIVERSITY MEDICAL CE 27710 #036-07-2002 L2005 **CD** *012 †20
SHAH, Krupal Rohit. ■ 27707 #036-07-2008 *012
SHAH, Poorvi Jagdish. 4003 N ROXBORO ST, LAKEWOOD PEDIATRICS & 27704 #036-01-1998 L2002 **IM PD** *020 †20,55
SHAH, Radhika. 3643 N ROXBORO ST, DEPT OF HOSPITAL MEDICINE 27704 #654-01-2000 L2005 **IM** *100
SHAH, Shetal Indravadan. BOX 3127, DUMC 27710 #035-20-2000 L2003 **NPM** *100 †55
SHAH, Svati Hasmukh. BOX 31105, DUMC 27710 #054-04-1998 L2003 **CD** *020 †20
SHAH, Tilak Upendra. ■ 27713 #036-01-2006 **IM** *012
SHAHEEN, Amy Wiegner. 6301 HERNDON RD 27713 #016-02-1993 L1996 **IM** *020 †20
SHAIKEWITZ, Samuel T. ■ 27707 #028-02-1988 L1998 **NEP** *020 †20
SHAMMA, Amal Mohammed R. ■ 27707 #605-01-1968 L1973 **OS PD** *050 †55
SHANG, Allan Bruce. DUMC BOX 3094, DUKE UNIV MED CENTER 27710 #050-02-1993 L1998 **AN** *020 †05
SHANNON, Roger Hall. 508 FULTON ST 27705 #010-01-1956 L1991 **R** *020 †80
SHAPIRO, Adam Joshua. ■ 27707 #067-01-2004 L2007 **PD** *012 †55
SHAPIRO, Judith R. 823 BROAD ST 27705 #035-46-1964 L2001 **D** *020 †15
SHAPIRO, Leonid. PO BOX 2723, DUMC 27710 #036-07-1997 *012
SHARARAH, Ala Ihsan. 718 RUTHERFORD ST 27705 #605-01-1987 L1990 **GE IM** *020 †20
SHARMA, Hemant Prashad. DUKE UNIV MED CENTER, BOX 31139 27710 #035-01-2001 L2004 **AI** *012 †55
SHARMA, Pooja. ■ 27707 #041-15-2008 *012
SHARMA, Poonam. ■ 27713 #051-01-2007 **IM** *012
SHARP, Scott Ronald. ■ 27705 #048-14-2006 **OTO** *012
SHAW, Genora Lassiter. ■ 27705 #047-07-1960 L1961 **GP** *071
SHAW, Heather Stuart. DUKE UNIVERSITY MEDICAL CE, BOX 3381 ERWIN ROAD 27710 #036-07-1993 L1998 **HO** *020 †20
SHAW, Maren Golding. ■ 27713 #036-01-2006 L2007 **D** *012
SHEEHAN, Ramon Edward. 508 FULTON ST, DEPARTMENT OF RADIOLOGY 27705 #671-01-1990 L2002 *020
SHELHORSE, Mark Edwin. 300 W MORGAN ST STE 1402 27701 #012-01-1981 L1982 **P** *030 †75
SHELINE, Barbara L. 2100 ERWIN RD 27710 #036-01-1984 L1990 **OS FM** *020 †18
SHELINE, Jonathan Lee. 3001 ACADEMY RD, STE 200 27707 #036-01-1984 L1985 **FM EP** *020 †18
SHENOY, Chetan Nagendra. ■ 27705 #495-65-2002 L2007 **IM** *100 †20
SHEPARD, Taylor Hill. ■ 27707 #048-12-2007 **OTO** *012
SHETTY, Anup Shashindra. PO BOX 94867 27708 #048-12-2007 L2007 **IM** *012
SHILL-NOVAK, Jessica Eve. DUMC 3924 27710 #025-07-2001 L2005 **END IM** *100
SHIMM, Cynia Brown. ■ 27705 #008-01-1950 L1998 **P PYA** *071 †75
SHIPLEY, Michael Burgess. 4220 ROXBORO RD 27710 #036-07-1974 L1975 **IM GE** *020 †20
SHIREY, Kristen Grace. ■ 27713 #038-40-2005 **MP** *012
SHIRLEY, Hoke Harold. 3104 CROASDAILE DR 27705 #021-01-1958 L1998 **IM EM** *071 †20,16
SHOFER, Scott Leigh. 413 LOBLOLLY DR 27712 #024-05-2001 L2004 **PCC** *100
SHORTELL, Cynthia E K. ■ 27713 #035-20-1984 L2005 **VS** *020 †85
SHULER, Jimmie Lou Blake. 1301 FAYETTEVILLE ST 27707 #047-07-1978 L1982 **PD** *074
SHUMANN, Elizabeth Mary. ■ 27713 #051-04-2006 **P** *012
SICKEL, Micah Jeremy. ■ 27713 #023-01-2003 L2008 **CHP** *012
SICKENGER, Karen E. ■ 27712 #051-07-1993 L2005 **AN** *020 †05
SIDDIQI, Zaeem Azfer. BOX 3403, DEPT OF NEURO.DUKE UNIV 27710 #704-22-1987 L2001 **CN** *100 †75
SIDDLE, Jennifer Duckett. ■ 27713 #036-01-2004 L2005 **CHP** *012
SIDHU-MALIK, Navjeet Kaur. 4037 PURPLE ZONE, DIVISION OF DERMATOLOGY 27710 #036-07-1986 L1988 **D** *012 †15
SIEKER, Herbert Otto. PO BOX 3822 27710 #028-02-1948 L1950 **AI PUD** *071 †20
SILBERMAN, Harold Reiter. ■ 27705 #028-02-1956 L1957 **IM IMG** *071 †20
SILBERMAN, Michael Keith. ■ 27705 #038-07-1984 L1987 **DR** *075 †80
SILVER, Frankie-Lynn. 2351 ERWIN RD, DUKE UNIVERSITY EYE CENTER 27705 #035-48-2001 L2005 **OPH** *100
SIMEL, David Lee. 508 FULTON ST, DURHAM VETERANS AFFAIRS CT 27705 #036-07-1980 L1983 **IM** *020 †20
SIMKIN, Ruth Joy. ■ 27701 #060-02-1973 L1987 *020
SIMONDS, Wickham Bryant. 6905 FAYETTEVILLE RD, STE 201 27713 #036-08-1997 L2000 **EM** *020 †16
SINDRAM, David. ■ 27713 #660-03-2002 **GS** *012
SINDRAM-TRUJILLO, Aliana. DEPT OF ANESTHESIOLOGY, DUMC 3094 27710 #036-01-2005 **AN** *012
SINGH, Anoop Kumar. ■ 27713 #539-03-2001 L2002 **PDC** *100 †55
SINGLETARY, Robert Lysand. ■ 27710 #036-07-2005 L2007 **EM** *012

SINGLETARY, William Vance, Jr. 4205 BEN FRANKLIN BLVD, ASSOCIATES PA 27704 #036-07-1975 L1978 **GE IM** *020 †20
SINGLETON, Samuel Winston. 3030 CORNWALLIS RD 27709 #352-08-1952 L1970 **PA PD** *071 †55
SINN, Leslye M. 2609 N DUKE ST, STE 400 27704 #036-01-1996 L1997 **P** *020
SIVAK, Christopher Geo. 2828 CROASDAILE DR 27705 #041-09-1989 L1991 **EM IM** *020 †20
SKAINS, Mark Charles. ■ 27713 #021-01-2002 L2005 **CD** *012 †20
SKEEN, Mark Brian. ■ 27712 #011-02-1982 L2002 **N** *020 †20,75
SKELTON, Matthew Rama. ■ 27713 #041-02-2001 L2005 **HO** *012 †20
SKETCH, Michael H, Jr. BOX #3157, DUKE UNIV MEDICAL CENTER 27710 #030-06-1984 L1990 **CD IM** *012 †20
SLADE, David J. ■ 27703 #035-15-2000 **PDP** *012
SLAVIK, Tomas. ■ 27707 #836-03-1989 **PTH** *100
SLEDGE, Taineisha Cellel. ■ 27704 #036-01-2008 *012
SLIFER, Michael A. BOX 3837, DUMC 27710 #048-13-1999 **PYG** *100
SLOWIK, May Kuo. BOX 3127, DUKE UNIVERSITY MEDICAL CE 27710 #005-02-2003 L2006 **PD** *100 †55
SLUBICKI, Monica Nora. DUKE UNIV MED CTR, DEPT OF PSYCHIATRY 27710 #036-01-2006 **P** *012
SMALL, Maria Jacqueline. ■ 27713 #036-08-1994 L2007 **OBG** *020 †30
SMARZ, Thomas Richard, Jr. DUKE UNIVERSITY MEDICAL CE, BOX 3014 27710 #010-02-1998 L2001 **NEP** *100 †20
SMITH, Alastair Douglas. RM 04245, RED ZONE DEK SOUTH HOSP 27710 #919-01-1988 L1998 *020
SMITH, Almaz Aster. P.O. BOX 3886, DUMC DEPT OF FAMILY MEDICI 27710 #048-13-1992 L1994 **FM** *020 †18
SMITH, Ana Carla Perez. ■ 27713 #011-02-2003 **CHP** *012
SMITH, Benjamin Barnes. ■ 27710 #018-03-2002 L2004 **VIR** *012 †80
SMITH, Edward Clinton. ■ 27713 #027-01-2002 L2007 **NMN** *012
SMITH, Fred Oliver. PO BOX 13979 27709 #011-03-1964 L1973 **FM GPM** *071 †18
SMITH, Jennifer Elizabeth. ■ 27713 #036-05-2007 **P** *012
SMITH, Jessica Lynn. ■ 27713 #041-12-2005 **IM** *012
SMITH, Joshua Robert. ■ 27707 #036-01-2008 *012
SMITH, Kelly Frances. ■ 27707 #023-01-1991 L1994 **IM** *100 †20
SMITH, Leah Shutt. ■ 27713 #045-01-2003 L2006 **PD** *100 †55
SMITH, Peter Kent. TRENT DR, 4532 BLUE ZONE DUKE SOUTH 27710 #036-07-1977 L1983 **TS GS** *020 †85,90
SMITH, Phillip Brian. DUKE UNIV MED CTR, DEPT OF PEDIATRICS 27710 #012-22-2001 L2007 **NPM** *020 †55
SMITH, Roberts H. 5716 FAYETTEVILLE RD 27713 #048-14-1990 L1994 **IM PD** *020 †55,20
SMITH, Spencer Crawford. ■ 27704 #023-01-2008 *012
SMITH, Stephen Richard. DUKE UNIV M C, BOX 3014 27710 #036-07-1985 L1988 **NEP IM** *020 †20
SMITH, Tony Preston. BOX 3808, DUKE UNIVERSITY MEDICAL CE 27710 #036-08-1981 L1985 **DR** *020 †80
SMITH, Vynedra Amille. 3643 N ROXBORO ST, DUKE UNIV HEALTH SYS, DEPT 27704 #016-42-2001 L2005 **IM** *020 †20
SMITH-BANKS, Albertina D. 3822 HOPE VALLEY RD, SUNSHINE PEDIATRICS & ADOL 27707 #036-01-1990 L1993 **PD** *020 †55
SNODGRESS, Sean Joseph. ■ 27713 #005-15-2002 L2005 **RNR** *012 †80
SNYDER, Jonathan Reich. ■ 27713 #036-05-2004 **ORS** *012
SNYDER, Laurie Dee. DUMC 3221 27710 #036-07-2000 L2006 **PCC** *100 †20
SNYDER, Martha Ashley. 3024 PICKETT RD 27705 #051-04-1999 L2001 **PD** *020 †55
SNYDER, Matthew James. BOX 31275 DUMC 27710 #051-04-1999 L2001 **HMP** *020 †50
SNYDERMAN, Ralph. 2424 ERWIN RD, BOX 3059 27705 #035-08-1965 L1972 **IM RHU** *030 †20,03
SO, Anthony Deh-Cheun. PO BOX 90314, 201 SCIENCE DR 27708 #025-01-1987 L1988 **IM** *020 †20
SOBOLEWSKI, Craig Jos. BOX 3192, DUKE UNIVERSITY MEDICAL CE 27710 #038-40-1992 L2003 **OBG** *020 †30
SODA, Elizabeth Anne. ■ 27713 #007-02-2006 **IM** *012
SODERBERG, John Milton. ■ 27703 #008-01-2004 **D** *012
SOKAL, David Chas. ■ 27709 #035-06-1976 L1977 **PHP FM** *050 †70
SOLIC, John Michael. ■ 27713 #041-12-2005 **ORS** *012
SOLIK, Steven Craig. 2609 N DUKE ST, STE 503 27704 #025-12-1988 L1993 **GE IM** *020 †20
SOMAYAJULA, Suvarchala. ■ 27713 #051-04-2006 **N** *012
SOMJEN, George Gustav. ERWIN RD, DUKE BLDG 314 NANALINE H 27705 #660-01-1956 **OS** *050
SOMMA, Jacques. ERWINN ROAD, 3425 DUKE NORTH HOSPITAL 27710 #067-02-1991 L1998 **AN** *050
SOMMER, Courtney. ■ 27707 #036-01-2006 **GS** *012
SOMMER, David B. ■ 27713 #036-07-2008 *012
SOMMER, Joachim Rainer W. DEPT OF PATHOLOGY, DUKE UNIV MED CTR 27710 #407-16-1951 L1960 **PTH** *050 †50
SOMMERVILLE, Kenneth Wm. PO BOX 110167 27709 #041-02-1976 L2004 **N PA** *050 †75 ‡
SONNIER, Harold Lloyd. ■ 27713 #021-06-2002 L2007 **RNR** *012 †80
SONNYCALB, Meredith Rebec. ■ 27713 #038-45-2005 **AN** *012
SONYIKA, Chionesu Kwesi. ■ 27713 #012-21-2004 L2007 **AN** *100
SOO, Mary Scott. BOX 3808, 2ND FL S HOSP, DUKE UNIVERSITY MEDICAL CE 27710 #036-05-1987 L1991 **DR** *020 †80
SOO, Michael Landron. 2609 N DUKE ST 27704 #036-05-1987 L1991 **N CN** *020 †75
SOPPITT, Andrew James. 718 RUTHERFORD ST 27705 #917-01-1988 L1998 *020
SORENSEN, Richard F. ■ 27705 #056-06-1953 L1954 **FM** *071
SORIANO, Catherine. ■ 27710 #038-40-2001 L2004 **P** *100 †75
SOTOLONGO, Hugo Fortunato. ■ 27713 #275-01-1948 L1973 **GP OBG** *071
SOULIER, Matthew Frost. 4214 BRENMAR LN 27713 #049-01-2002 L2005 **PFP** *012 †75
SOUTHERLAND, Lauren Talan. ■ 27707 #036-07-2008 *012
SPACH, Madison Stockton. 718 RUTHERFORD ST 27705 #036-07-1954 1954 **PDC PD** *050 †55
SPANARKEL, Marybeth. 2609 N DUKE ST, STE 503 27704 #036-07-1979 L1987 **IM GE** *020 †20
SPARKS, Matthew Aaron. ■ 27707 #004-01-2003 L2007 **NEP** *012 †20
SPAULDING, Jean Gaillard. 2 GREEN MILL LN, STE 1500 27707 #036-07-1973 L1973 **CHP P** *030 †75
SPECK, Karen Elizabeth. ■ 27707 #047-06-2005 **GS** *012
SPECTOR, Nicole Cafazzo. PO BOX 3951 # M148 DAV BLD, DUKE UNIV MED CTR 27710 #047-05-1998 **FM** *100

SPEIER, Susanne Edith. ■ 27705 #409-21-1989 **CHN** *100
SPENCER, Joshua Andrew. ■ 27713 #047-06-2005 L2008 **IM** *012
SPESSOT, Alexandra Lynn. DUKE UNIV MED CTR, DEPT OF PSYCHIATRY 27705 #035-01-2005 **P** *012
SPIELMANN, Audrey Lynn. 4101 N ROXBORO ST 27704 #061-01-1992 L1999 *020 †80
SPOCK, Alexander. DUKE UNIV MED CTR, DEPT OF PEDS 27710 #023-01-1955 L1960 **PDA PD** *075 †55,03
SPORN, Thomas Arthur. 718 RUTHERFORD ST 27705 #010-02-1986 L1993 **PTH** *020 †20,50
SPRATT, Susan Elizabeth. ERWIN DR DUKE MEDICAL CTR, 3311 DUMC DIV ENDOCRINOLGY 27710 #024-01-1995 L2001 **END** *020 †20
SPRITZER, Charles Edward. ERWIN RD, DUKE UNIV MED CTR 27710 #041-12-1981 L1986 **DR** *020 †20
SPURNEY, Robert Frank. 508 FULTON ST, B3002 DURHAM VA HOSPITAL 27705 #038-40-1983 L1989 **NEP IM** *020 †20
SQUIRE, Deborah Louise. DUKE MEDICAL CENTER, BOX 3675 27710 #016-06-1978 L1984 **PD FSM** *020 †55
SREBRO, Sharon Handy. ■ 27713 #036-07-1994 L1996 **DR** *020
SRYGLEY, Fletcher Douglas. ■ 27705 #048-12-2004 L2008 **GE** *012 †20
STACK, Andrew Phillip. ■ 27713 #055-02-2008 *012
STACK, Richard Sean. 3908 PATRIOT DR, STE 170 27703 #025-07-1976 L1982 **CD** *020 †20
STACKHOUSE, Danielle Andr. ■ 27713 #021-01-2006 **U** *012
STACY, Mark Allen. 932 MORREENE RD, BOX 3333 27705 #028-03-1986 L2003 **N** *020 †75 ‡
STADLER, Michael Edward. ■ 27713 #056-05-2006 **OTO** *012
STAFFORD, Harry Cozene, Jr. DUKE UNIV MED CTR, DEPT OF FAMILY PRACTICE 27710 #036-01-2002 L2005 **FSM** *100 †18
STAFFORD-SMITH, Mark. 718 RUTHERFORD ST 27705 #067-01-1983 L1994 **AN** *020 †05
STAHL, Rhonda Harris. BOX 3951, DUKE UNIVERSITY MEDICAL CE 27710 #011-03-2002 L2004 **PYG** *020 †75
STAHMER, Sarah Anne. ■ 27712 #035-20-1984 L2007 **CD IM** *020 †20,16
STAMLER, Jonathan Solomon. DUKE UNIV MED CTR, BOX 2612 27710 #035-47-1985 L1994 **CD PUD** *020 †20
STANFIELD, Amy Brame. 105 NEWSOM ST, STE 101 27704 #036-01-1998 L2000 **OBG** *020 †30
STANGER, Ryan Patrick. ■ 27713 #012-01-2006 **AN** *012
STANKUS, Paul Victor. 3643 N ROXBORO ST 27704 #036-01-1976 L1976 **AN** *020 †05
STANLEY, Samuel David. 3116 N DUKE ST, DUKE HEALTH CENTER 27704 #036-07-1993 L1997 **ORS** *020 †40
STANSFIELD, William Ellio. ■ 27713 #067-01-2002 L2007 **GS** *100
STAPLES, Betty. 4020 N ROXBORO ST 27704 #023-01-1998 L2000 **PD** *020 †55
STARK, Aleksandra Catheri. ■ 27713 #035-09-2007 **IM** *012
STARK, Valerie Lynn. ■ 27713 #011-04-2007 **PD** *012
STASHENKO, Gregg Joseph. ■ 27713 #047-05-2004 L2007 **PCC** *012 †20
ST CLAIR, Eugene Wm. BOX 3874 27710 #055-01-1981 L1982 **IM RHU** *050 †20
ST CLAIR, Shannon Mitchel. ■ 27713 #055-01-2006 **IM** *012
ST CLAIRE, Karen Sue. CTR BOX 3675, DUKE UNIV MED CTR 27710 #048-02-1982 L1987 **PD** *020 †55
STEELE, Mark Patrick. 148 BELL BLDG, BOX 3171, DUMC 27710 #016-11-1982 L1990 **PUD** *020 †20
STEELE, Susan Marie. DUK UNIV MED CTR, DEPT OF ANES, BX 309 27710 #016-11-1983 L1990 **AN** *040 †05
STEFANIAK, Heather Marie. ■ 27713 #056-06-2003 L2007 **GS** *100
STEFFENS, David Carl. 932 MORREENE RD 27705 #048-14-1988 L1990 **P PYG** *050 †75
STEIN, Amy. 2609 N DUKE ST, STE 204 27704 #035-08-1999 L2001 **D** *020 †15
STEIN, Jeannette. 508 FULTON ST 11C 27705 #036-01-1981 L1982 **IM** *020 †20
STEIN, Roy Mendel. 508 FULTON ST, DURHAM VA MEDICAL CTR (116 27705 #036-07-1980 L1985 **P** *020 †75
STEINBACH, William Joseph. ■ 27705 #036-01-1998 L2001 **PDI** *020 †55
STEINOUR, Nicholas Paul. ■ 27705 #011-02-2007 **EM** *012
STENGELE, Brigita T. 718 RUTHERFORD ST 27705 #409-21-1989 L1995 **FM** *020 †18
STEPHANY, Alyssa Marie. ■ 27705 #035-15-2004 L2008 **MPD** *012
STEPHENS, Rasheeda Kamil. ■ 27713 #047-05-2006 **IM** *012
STERN, Adam Baker. ■ 27713 #035-09-2006 **IM** *012
STETS, Joan Marie. 2609 N DUKE ST, STE 612 CENTRAL MEDICAL PA 27704 #038-40-1977 L1982 **PS GS** *020 †85,65
STEVENSON, Karl Wm. 4125 BEN FRANKLIN BLVD 27704 #036-05-1966 L1966 **CHP P** *020 †75
STEVENSON, Marvaretta Mie. ■ 27713 #045-01-2004 **HO** *012 †20
STEWART, Laura Evelyn. ■ 27707 #036-07-2003 L2007 **PTH** *012
STEWART, Robert Douglas. 305 BROOK CHASE LN, DURHAM PHYSICIANS, PA 27705 #055-01-1974 L1976 **IM** *020 †20
ST GEME, Joseph W, III. DUKE UNIV MEDICAL CENTER, BOX 3352 27710 #024-01-1984 L2005 **PD PDI** *020 †55
STIBER, Jonathan Andrew. BOX 3176, DUKE UNIVERSITY MEDICAL CT 27710 #035-19-1997 L2000 **CD** *020 †20
STICKEL, Delford Le Few. ERWIN RD 27710 #036-07-1953 L1958 **GS** *071 †85,90
STIEHL, Barbara Jill. ■ 27705 #036-01-1981 L1992 **CCM AN** *075 †20,05
STIFLER, Robert Bailey. 4022 FREEDOM LAKE DR, REGIONAL PEDIATRIC ASSOCIA 27704 #023-01-1973 L1985 **PD** *050 †55
STOCKBRIDGE, Norman L. ■ 27710 #036-07-1978 *100
STOKES, Thomas Angier, Jr. 2609 N DUKE ST 27704 #036-07-1955 L1955 **GYN** *071 †30
STOLP, Bryant Walter. DEPT OF ANESTHESIOLOGY, DUKE UNIV MED CTR 27710 #036-01-1988 L1990 **AN** *020 †05
STONE, Lorraine Marie. 2424 ERWIN RD STE 1105, BOX 2720 27705 #036-01-2002 L2004 **IMG** *020 †18
STOPFORD, Woodhall. 2200 W MAIN ST, STE 400 27705 #024-01-1969 L1970 **OM OS** *020 †20,70
STORY, David James. ■ 27705 #021-05-2006 **EM** *012
STOUT, Jason Eric. BOX 3306 DUMC 27710 #035-15-1996 L1997 **ID IM** *020 †20
STRAHL, Nathan Robt. 3308 DURHAM CHAPEL HL BLVD, STE 100 27707 #036-01-1983 L1984 **P** *020 †75
STRAITON, Timothy Peter. DUKE UNIVERSITY, DEPT PATH 27710 #067-01-1992 **PTH** *100
STRATTON, I Janice Deas. 414 E MAIN ST 27701 #021-01-1961 L1970 **PHP PD** *020
STRITTMATTER, Warren J. 725 BROAD ST, DUKE UNIV MED CTR 27705 #036-07-1973 L1977 **N** *050 †75
STROHKIRCH, Jeremy Richar. ■ 27713 #025-07-2007 **EM** *012
STROUD, Steven Dean. ■ 27713 #004-01-2007 **MPD** *012
STRYJEWSKI, Martin Estani. TRENT DR BLUE ZONE DUKE S, RM 1558 27710 #132-01-1994 **ID** *100

STUBBS, Allston Julius, IV. ALLSTON JULIUS STUBBS IV, BOX 3000 ORTHO DIV 27710 #036-07-1999 L2002 **OSM** *100
STYRON, Andrea Susan. ■ 27713 #016-11-2005 **AN** *012
STYRON, James. ■ 27713 #016-11-2005 **P** *012
SU, Hansen. BOX 3837, DUKE UNIVERSITY MEDICAL CE 27710 #033-06-2000 L2003 **P** *020
SUBER, Robert Lee. ■ 27705 #036-07-2005 L2005 **DR** *012
SUDA, Kenji. PO BOX 3179 27715 #572-77-1985 **NPM** *100
SUGIOKA, Kenneth. BOX 3094, DEPT OF ANESTHESIOLOGY/DUM 27710 #028-02-1949 L1954 **AN** *071 †05
SUHOCKI, Paul Vincent. 4101 N ROXBORO ST 27704 #010-02-1985 L1990 **DR** *020 †80
SULLIVAN, Daniel Carl. 2424 ERWIN RD, STE 602 27705 #050-02-1970 L1978 **DR NR** *020 †80,75
SULLIVAN, Keith Michael. 2400 PRATT ST STE 1100, BOX 3961 27710 #017-20-1971 L1999 **ON HEM** *050 †20
SULLIVAN, Robert Jos, Jr. DUKE UNIV MEDICAL CENTER, BOX 3003 27710 #035-20-1966 L1971 **IM IMG** *020 †70,18 ‡
SUM-PING, Sam Thio. DVMC 3094, DEPARTMENT OF ANESTHESIA 27710 #917-08-1978 L1998 **CCA AN** *020 †05
SUN, Albert Y. ■ 27713 #033-05-2003 L2007 **CD** *012 †20
SUN, Jessica. 1 DUKE MEDICAL CTR, DEPT OF PEDIATRICS 27710 #033-05-2003 L2006 **PHO** *012 †55
SUNDAY, Mary Elizabeth. DUMC, BOX 3712 27710 #024-01-1982 L2006 **ATP** *020 †50 ‡
SUNDY, John Sargent. BOX 3278, ROOM 014 BAKER H, DUKE UNIVERSITY CENTER 27710 #041-09-1991 L1994 **RHU AI** *050 †03,20
SUNER, Ivan Jose. ■ 27710 #008-01-1992 L2005 **OPH** *020 †35
SUSCO, David Michael. 1911 HILLANDALE RD STE 104 27705 #041-14-1983 L1987 **P** *020 †75
SUTHERLAND, Suzanne Marie. ■ 27717 #025-12-1988 L1991 **P** *050 †75
SUTTON, Linda Marie. 3100 TOWER BLVD, STE 600 UNIV TOWER 27707 #024-16-1987 L1994 **ON HEM** *020 †20
SUWANAWIBOON, Bundarika. MEDICAL CENTER, DUKE UNIVERSITY 27710 #891-02-1998 **HO** *100 †20
SVETKEY, Laura Pat. BOX 3075, DEPT OF MEDICINE DIV NEPHR 27710 #024-01-1979 L1982 **IM** *050 †20
SWAMINATHAN, Madhav. DUMC BOX 3094 27706 #496-09-1990 L2000 *100
SWAMY, Geeta Krishna. BOX 3967, DUKE UNIVERSITY MEDICAL CE 27710 #036-01-1997 L2001 **OBG** *020 †30
SWANSON, Jennifer Louise. 5400 S MIAMI BLVD, STE 112 27703 #051-01-1988 L1991 **EM** *020 †16
SWARTZ, Marvin Stanley. BOX 3173 27710 #024-07-1980 L1982 **P** *020 †75
SWEENEY, Alison Evelyn. ■ 27705 #036-07-2007 **PD** *012
SWENSON, Aaron Wendell. ■ 27713 #018-03-2005 L2008 **PD** *012
SWICK, Matthew Jay. 120 WILLIAM PENN PLZ, TRIANGLE ORTHOPAEDIC ASSOC 27704 #011-04-2002 L2007 **ORS** *012
SYBERT, Cathleen Mary. ■ 27713 #023-01-2006 **GS** *012
SZABOLCS, Pal. 2400 PRATT ST, BOX 3350 27705 #473-01-1985 L1998 **PHO** *020 †55
SZCZECH, Lynda Anne. BOX 3646 ERWIN ROAD, DUKE UNIVERSITY MEDICAL CT 27710 #041-02-1991 L1993 **NEP** *020 †20
TABER, Brooks William. ■ 27713 #045-01-2004 L2007 **DR** *012
TABRIZI, Katayoun. 3906 SOMERSET DR 27707 #517-01-1984 L1991 **P PFP** *062 †75
TAEKMAN, Jeffrey Marc. DUMC 3094, DEPT OF ANESTHESIA 27710 #036-05-1991 L1999 **AN** *020 †05
TAFOLLA, Elizabeth Marie. ■ 27712 #036-07-2008 *012
TALATI, Naasha J.. BX 3951 M148 DAV BLD, DUKE UNIV MED CTR 27710 #704-25-2000 **ID** *012 †20
TALBOT, Leonard Anthony. ■ 27704 #036-07-2007 **AN** *012
TALNER, Norman S. 718 RUTHERFORD ST 27705 #025-01-1949 L1992 **PDC** *040 †55
TALTON, Ingeborg H. ■ 27705 #407-06-1952 L1966 **AN** *071 †05
TANAKA, David Timothy. BOX 3179 27710 #023-07-1979 L1987 **PD PUD** *020 †55
TANNER, Michael Crandall. ■ 27713 #036-01-2004 L2007 **OPH** *012
TANTIBHEDHYANGKUL, Julieru. ■ 27707 #891-02-1998 L2005 **OBG** *100
TAPSON, Victor Fallis. 351 BELL BLDG, BOX 31175 27710 #041-09-1982 L1989 **PUD CCM** *020 †75
TARDIFF, Barbara E. 718 RUTHERFORD ST 27705 #008-01-1983 L1995 **AN** *020 †55,05
TARRANT, Teresa Kathleen. DUMC, 31277 27710 #011-03-1999 L2000 **RHU** *100 †20,03
TASHJIAN, Jessica A. ■ 27707 #036-07-2008 *012
TATHAM, Nerine Eslorna. 1318 BROAD ST, NERINETATHAM, MD 27705 #010-03-1992 L1998 **P** *020 †75
TAUB, Harry Evan. 4407 SUN VALLEY DR 27707 #032-01-2001 L2006 **CHP** *020
TAWNEY, Paul Wimer. 3609 WATKINS RD 27707 #034-01-1989 L1995 **IM** *020 †60
TAYLOR, Bruce Jackson, Jr. ■ 27707 #012-22-1993 L1999 **PS** *012 †85
TAYLOR, Jack Arthur. 111 T W ALEXANDER DR, NIH NAT'L INST OF ENVIRON 27705 #056-05-1984 L1986 **GPM** *020 †70
TAYLOR, Jennifer Lynn. BOX 3127 DUMC 27710 #036-07-1998 L2002 **PCC** *020 †55,20
TAYLOR, Paul Andrew. DUKE MEDICAL CENTER 27710 #917-20-1974 L1980 **NEP IM** *020
TAYLOR, Robert E. 4210 N ROXBORO ST, STE 140 27704 #001-02-1976 L1991 **OTO A** *020 †45
TAYLOR, Steve Myer. ■ 27705 #036-07-2004 **ID** *012
TAYLOR, Warren Douglas. DUKE SOUTH BLDG ZONE RM 35, DUMC BOX 3903 27710 #011-04-1996 L1997 **PYG** *020 †75
TAYLOR, William Christoph. ■ 27713 #036-08-2004 L2007 **HO** *012
TAYLOR, William Murrell. ■ 27701 #051-04-1959 L1960 **P IMG** *072 †75
TCHENG, James Enlou. 2424 ERWIN RD STE 403 27705 #023-07-1982 L1988 **CD IM** *020 †20
TEABERRY, Vanessa Suzanne. ■ 27707 #036-07-2006 **GS** *012
TEBBIT, Christopher Lee. ■ 27713 #036-07-2001 L2001 **OTO** *012
TEETER, Miriah Michael. ■ 27701 #036-01-2002 L2005 **OPH** *012
TEITELMAN, Melissa. DUKE UNIVERSITY MEDICAL CE, GASTROENTEROLOGY DIVISION 27710 #041-13-1999 L2000 **GE** *100 †20
TEJADA SOLARES, Victor M. ■ 27707 #429-01-1968 L1985 **CHP P** *071
TELEN, Marilyn J. DUKE UNIV MED CTR, BOX 2615 27710 #035-19-1977 L1983 **HEM BBK** *050 †20
TEMPELHOF, Michael Willia. ■ 27713 #016-43-2006 **IM** *012
TENCLAY, Shanna Claire. ■ 27707 #016-06-2003 L2005 **ACA** *012
TENDLER, David Andrew. 3643 N ROXBORO ST 27704 #008-01-1993 L1999 **GE IM** *020 †20
TESSON, Alan Ray, Jr. ■ 27713 #011-03-2006 **IM** *012
THAKUR, Mugdha Ekanath. DUMC BOX 3386 27710 #496-38-1994 L2003 **PYG** *020 †75
THARWANI, Haresh M. ELBA ST, DUMC 3516 27710 #704-16-1990 L2000 **P** *020 †75

■ = Address Information Privacy Protected

THIELMAN, Nathan Maclyn. TRENT DRIVE - BOX 3281, DUKE UNIVERSITY MEDICAL CT 27710 #036-07-1990 L2000 **ID** *020 †20
THOMAS, Cathy Wall. 3643 N ROXBORO ST 27704 #036-01-1984 L1986 **AN** *020 †05
THOMAS, Daniel Stephen. ■ 27705 #012-01-2005 **AN** *012
THOMAS, Donald Anton. 3217 DEERCHASE WYND 27712 #036-01-1966 L1966 **PD** *071
THOMAS, John. DEPT OF RADIOLOGY, DUMC-38, DUKE UNIVERSITY MEDICAL CE 27710 #495-31-1987 L2000 **DR** *020 †80
THOMAS, Kevin Lindsey. 4705 DUTCHESS LN 27707 #036-01-1999 L2000 **ICE** *100 †20
THOMAS, Michael Peter. ■ 27707 #041-12-2005 **IM** *012
THOMPSON, Caroline Way. ■ 27710 #020-01-1991 L2004 **PDR** *020 †80
THOMPSON, Corey Adam. ■ 27713 #026-04-2004 **ORS** *012
THOMPSON, David A. 3609 WATKINS RD, CLINIC 27707 #036-01-1996 L1997 **HS** *020 †40
THOMPSON, Nancy Elaine. ■ 27705 #017-20-1969 L1996 **PD** *020 †55
THOMPSON, William Moreau. IRWIN ROAD, BOX 3808 27710 #041-01-1969 L1972 **R** *020 †80
THORMAHLEN, Ross N. ■ 27705 #048-12-2004 L2007 **AN** *012
THORNBURG, Courtney Dawn. TRENT DR, DUMC BOX 2916 27710 #036-07-1998 L2005 **PHO** *020 †55
THORNE, Leigh Boyette. ■ 27707 #045-01-1995 L2003 **PTH** *020 †50
THORNTON, Victoria L. DUMC BOX 3096, EMERGENCY DEPT. 27710 #010-02-1980 L2000 **EM** *020 †16
THRALL, Grace Coddington. CIVITAN BLDG ROOM 272B, 2213 ELBA STREET 27710 #008-02-1991 L1997 **P** *020 †75
THUNBERG, Christopher A. ■ 27713 #041-12-2003 L2007 **ACA** *012
THYAGARAJAN, Ananth. ■ 27713 #038-44-2004 **AI** *012 †55
TIGHE, Robert Matthew. ■ 27712 #047-06-2002 L2006 **PCC** *012 †20
TIGHE DE SOTO, Jennifer L. ■ 27703 #030-06-2006 **EM** *012
TIMOSZYK, Katherine Wanda. BX 3951 M148 DAV BLD, DUKE UNIV MED CTR 27710 #035-06-1999 L1999 **N** *100
TINCH, Brian Terry. ■ 27713 #012-22-2004 L2007 **PD** *100 †55
TOCHACKOVA, Marta. ■ 27713 #286-05-1962 L1989 **GYN** *071
TODD, Jamie Lynn. ■ 27713 #007-02-2005 **IM** *012
TOHER, Raymond Jos, Jr. 4220 N ROXBORO ST, DURHAM MEDICAL CENTER P.A 27704 #036-07-1975 L1978 **IM** *020 †20
TOLLEFSON, Denise Diane. 1910 SEDWICK RD, STE 400B 27713 #019-02-1991 L1993 **FM** *020 †18
TOLOZA, Eric Miguel. DUMC BOX 3048 27710 #005-14-1991 L2000 **TS GS** *020 †85,90
TONG, Betty Caroline. ■ 27713 #036-07-1999 L2005 **TS** *012 †85
TONSTAD, Per Sigve K. 104 PRESCOTT DR 27712 #005-12-1979 L1987 **IM** *020 †20
TOOMAYAN, Glen Alan. ■ 27713 #036-07-2003 L2005 **DR** *012
TORREY, Richard Kendrick. 4309 EMPEROR BLVD STE 125 27703 #021-05-1980 L1983 **FM** *020 †18
TOTH, Alison Patricia. 317 FINCH YEAGER BLDG, DUMC BOX3970 DUKE SPRT MED 27710 #036-07-1994 L2001 **ORS OSM** *020 †40
TOTH, Cynthia Ann. ERWIN RD, DUKE UNIVERSITY EYE CENTER 27710 #041-07-1983 L1993 **OPH** *020 †35
TOURIAN, Ara Yervant. HOSPITAL DR, BAKER HOUSE RM 122 CB 3066 27710 #018-03-1958 L1969 **N PMM** *071 †75
TRANI, Jose Luis, Jr. DUKE UNIV MED CTR, DEPT OF SURGERY 27710 #041-01-2001 **GS** *012
TREECE, Amy Elaine. ■ 27713 #051-04-2004 L2006 **PCC** *012 †20
TREMBATH, Dimitri George. ■ 27712 #018-03-2001 L2007 **PTH** *100 †50
TRICOCI, Pierluigi. 2400 PRATT ST, DUKE CLINICAL RESEARCH 27705 #561-01-1998 L2008 **CD** *050
TRIMBLE, Kimberly Sharae. 6301 HERNDON RD, DUKE UNIVERSITY INTERNAL M 27713 #039-01-2001 L2004 **IM** *100
TRINH, Jane Vy. 3643 N ROXBORO ST 27704 #036-07-2002 L2006 **MPD** *100 †20,55
TRIPLETT, Gayle K. ■ 27707 #001-06-1979 L1985 **P** *071 †75
TRIVEDI, Bhavya. DUKE UNIV MED CTR, DEPT OF PEDIATRICS 27710 #011-02-2001 **PDC** *012 †55
TROBBIANI, Dina Marie. ■ 27712 #051-07-2001 **FOP** *100
TROPEA, Kristen Alison. ■ 27705 #012-06-2004 **PD** *012
TROST, Melanie Eileen. ■ 27707 #036-01-2001 L2004 **FM** *100 †18
TROST, William Thomas. 1418 N DUKE ST 27701 #056-06-2000 L2003 **P** *020 †75
TROY, Jeffrey Alan. ■ 27713 #051-04-2003 L2006 **DR** *012
TROY, Rachel Ammons. ■ 27713 #051-04-2003 L2007 **NPM** *012 †55
TSAI, Stella Yu-Chen. ■ 27707 #244-02-1990 **RO** *100
TSALIK, Ephraim Lee. ■ 27704 #035-01-2005 L2008 **IM** *012
TSCHANNEN MORAN, Bryn Mar. ■ 27705 #012-05-2007 **MPD** *012
TSENG, Henry C. ■ 27707 #041-01-2002 L2006 **OPH** *100 †35
TSENG, Timothy Yuting. ■ 27713 #036-07-2003 **GS** *012
TUCCI, Debara Lyn. BOX 3805 DEPT SURG, DUKE UMC DIV OTO 27710 #051-01-1985 L1992 **OTO NO** *020 †45
TUCHMAN, Sascha Alexander. DUMC 31378 27710 #010-02-2003 L2006 **HO** *012 †20
TUCKER, Marcy Schwartz. DUMC 3094 27710 #016-02-1997 L2002 **AN** *020
TUCKER, Stephanie. ■ 27713 #041-02-2004 L2006 **IM** *100
TUDOR-WILLIAMS, Gareth. BOX 2951 27710 #917-21-1977 **IMG** *100
TULSKY, James Aaron. 2424 ERWIN RD STE 1105, HOCK PLAZA 27705 #016-11-1987 L1993 **IM PLM** *050 †20
TUREK, Joseph. DUKE UNIV MED CTR, DEPT OF SURGERY 27710 #016-11-2002 **TS** *012
TURER, Aslan Teyfik. DUEK UNIV MED CTR 27710 #005-02-2001 L2004 **CD** *012
TURI, Jennifer Ann. ERWIN ROAD, BOX 3046 27710 #024-16-1995 L2000 **CCP** *020 †55
TURLEY, Richard. OTOLARYNGOLOGY-HNS, DUMC BOX 3805 27710 #025-01-2006 **OTO** *012
TURLEY, Ryan Scott. ■ 27712 #036-07-2007 **GS** *012
TURLINGTON, Katherine W. 1301 FAYETTEVILLE ST, LINCOLN COMM HLTH CTR 27707 #011-04-1984 L1988 **PD** *020 †55
TURNER, Anne Mc Naughton. 3114 CROASDAILE DR 27705 #043-01-1985 L1988 **PHO PD** *020 †55
TURNER, Dennis Alan. BX 3807 DUKE UNV MED CTR 27710 #017-20-1975 L1989 **NS** *020 †25
TUTTLE, Janet Elizabeth. 718 RUTHERFORD ST 27705 #036-05-1988 L1995 **CCS** *020 †85
TWEED, John Lindsey. 718 RUTHERFORD ST 27705 #036-07-1987 L1992 **CHP** *020 †75
TWERSKY, Jack Issac. 504 FULTON ST, MAILCODE 182 27705 #041-09-1982 L1996 **IMG IM** *020 †20
TYLER, Douglas Scott. BOX 3118, DEPT OF SURGERY 27710 #032-01-1985 L1991 **GS SO** *020 †85
UDAYAKUMAR, Krishnakumar. ■ 27713 #036-07-2004 L2007 **IM** *020 †20
UDOJI, Mercy Adaobi. DEPT OF ANESTHESIOLOGY, DUMC 3094 27710 #047-05-2007 **AN** *012

UDOM, Imaobong. ■ 27704 #024-05-2008 *012
ULSHEN, Martin Howard. GI & NUTRITIONBOX 3009, DIVISION OF PEDIATRIC 27710 #035-45-1969 L1999 **GE PD** *050 †55
UM, John Y. ■ 27705 #043-01-1999 L2007 **TS** *100 †85
UNDERKOFFLER, Danielle Ma. ■ 27705 #036-07-2007 **IM** *012
UNO, Marili. ■ 27707 #051-04-2004 **OBG** *012
UNROE, Mark Alexander. ■ 27713 #038-40-2005 **IM** *012
UNTCH, Brian Roy. ■ 27712 #016-43-2004 **GS** *012
URBAN, Bruno J. ERWIN RD, RM 102 27710 #407-22-1960 L1972 **AN PME** *071 †05
URBANIAK, James Randolph. DUKE UNIV MED CTR, BOX 2912 27710 #036-07-1962 L1962 **ORS HS** *020 †40
URONIS, Hope Elizabeth. DUMC 3841, 3829 DUKE SOUTH, RED ZONE 27710 #035-06-2000 L2004 **HO** *100 †20
UTHE, William Frederick. 5832 FAYETTEVILLE RD, STE 113 27713 #038-43-1974 L1977 **IM** *020 †20
VALEA, Fidel Arthur. 203 BAKER HOUSE, BOX 3084 27710 #035-48-1985 L1987 **GO OBG** *020 †30
VAN BRUGGEN, June P. ■ 27707 #036-07-1970 L1970 **P** *075
VAN DAM, Cornelius N. ■ 27713 #056-06-2002 L2005 **ID** *012 †20
VANDEMARK, Robert. DUMC, DEPT OF RADIOLOGY 27710 #035-15-1980 L1982 **DR EM** *020 †80,16
VANDEVEN, Thomas John. ■ 27701 #036-07-2006 L2006 **AN** *012
VAN HAASTEREN, Loretta. 7010 NC HIGHWAY 751, PROMPT MED AT SOUTH POINT 27707 #024-05-1977 L1998 **IM** *020 †20
VAN LANDINGHAM, Kevan E. BELL SERVICE DR, DUMC 3678 202F BELL BLDG 27710 #051-01-1985 L1992 **N CN** *020 †75
VAN MATRE, Reed Matthew. BOX 3094, DUKE UNIVERSITY MEDICAL CE 27710 #016-06-2002 L2003 **AN** *100 †05
VAN METER, Susan Ann. 718 RUTHERFORD ST 27705 #039-01-1991 L1995 **P** *020 †75
VANN, Dorothea Deimel. ■ 27707 #035-20-1937 L1940 **PD** *071 †55
VANN, Robin Raul. 3802 ERWIN RD, WADSWORTH BLDG DUKE EYE CT 27710 #036-05-1994 L1998 **OPH** *020 †35
VANSCOYOC, Erin Elizabeth. BOX 3127 DUMC, 5409 DUKE NORTH 27710 #036-07-2005 **MPD** *012
VANTERPOOL, Stephanie Gra. ■ 27713 #036-07-2005 **AN** *012
VARIA, Indira Mahesh. 718 RUTHERFORD ST 27705 #495-48-1968 L1976 **P** *020 †75
VARKEY, Jay Basil. ■ 27713 #056-06-2002 L2005 **ID** *012 †20
VARSHNEY, Pooja. ■ 27713 #048-04-2004 **AI** *012 †55
VAS, Steven Tedford. DUKE UNIV MED CTR, DEPT OF PSYCHIATRY 27710 #041-12-2005 **P** *012
VASLEF, Steven Nicholas. DUKE UNIV MED CTR, BOX 102345 27710 #051-01-1984 L1994 **GS CCS** *020 †85
VASQUEZ, Brandi Lynn. ■ 27705 #040-02-2004 **OBG** *012
VAVOULIS, George Andrew. ■ 27707 #026-04-1977 **NS** *100
VELAZQUEZ, Eric Jose. 2400 PRATT ST 27705 #035-46-1994 L1996 **CD IM** *050 †20
VENKATESAN, Priya. ■ 27705 #036-07-2005 **D** *012
VEREEN, Ronald Lloyd. 3200 CROASDAILE DR 27705 #036-07-1981 L1989 **P** *020 †75
VIENS, Nicholas Adam. ■ 27713 #036-07-2007 **ORS** *012
VIGLIANTI, Benjamin Logan. ■ 27712 #036-07-2006 **DR** *012
VILLAMIZAR ORTIZ, Nestor. 508 FULTON ST, M148 DAV BLDG 27705 #264-04-2001 **GS** *012
VILLANI, John Joseph. 3523 COURTLAND DR 27707 #036-07-2002 L2004 **EM** *100 †16
VINSON, Emily Nicole. DEPT. OF RADIOLOGY, BOX 38, DUKE UNIVERSITY, ERWIN ROA 27710 #036-07-1999 L2002 **DR** *020 †80
VINSON, Rachel Elizabeth. ■ 27713 #051-04-2007 **PD** *012
VISCARDI, Lenora C. 2609 N DUKE ST 27704 #020-02-1989 L1995 **MPD PD** *020 †55,20
VISSAGE, Claudia Kristine. ■ 27713 #045-01-2007 **IM** *012
VLAHOVIC, Gordana. 3841, DUKE UNIVERSITY MEDICAL CE 27710 #957-01-1987 L2001 **HO** *020 †20
VOGEL, Francis Stephen. ■ 27705 #038-06-1944 L1961 **PTH NP** *030 †50
VOLIN, Jill Catherine. ■ 27707 #012-05-2004 L2006 **P** *012
VOLLMER, Robin T. 508 FULTON ST, DEPT 27705 #036-07-1967 L1967 **PTH D** *020 †50
VOLZ, Elizabeth Michelle. ■ 27703 #035-06-2005 L2008 **IM** *012
VOSS, Miranda. DUKE UNIVERSITY MEDICAL CE, DEPARTMENT OF SURGERY 27710 #919-01-1987 *100
VOTE, David Anthony. F 6 MALL CTE 3823 27710 #143-02-1990 **IM** *100
VREDENBURGH, James Jos. DUKE UNIV MEDICAL CENTER, BOX 3624 27710 #050-02-1983 L1990 **HEM ON** *020 †20
VUJASKOVIC, Zeljko. DUKE UNIV MEDICAL CENTER, RADIATION ONCOLOGY BOX3455 27710 #957-01-1985 L2003 *020
WACHTER, Adam Connell. ■ 27708 #003-01-2006 **IM** *012
WAGNER, Anja. BX 3951 M148 DAV BLD, DUKE UNIV MED CTR 27710 #409-33-1997 L2008 **IM** *100
WAGNER, Galen Strohm. 2400 PRATT ST, TERRACE LEVEL, RM 0306 27705 #036-07-1965 L1971 **CD IM** *020 †20
WAHIDI, Momen M. ERWIN RD, BOX 3683 DUMC 27710 #875-01-1992 L1999 **PCC** *020 †20
WAITE, Kathleen Ann. DUKE UNIV MED CTR, BOX 3228 27710 #036-07-1990 L1992 **IM** *020 †20
WAKAKURI, Hiromi. BX 3951 M148 DAV BLD ANES 27710 #572-32-1971 **AN** *100
WAKELING, Howard G. DUKE UNIV BOX 3094-ANES 27704 #917-07-1988 L1996 *100
WALD, Marla Frances. 3622 LYCKAN PKWY, WESTGATE II, STE 6006 27707 #396-24-1988 L2006 **CHP** *020 †75 ‡
WALDAU, Ben. DUKE UNIV MED CTR, BOX 3807 27710 #409-10-2002 **NS** *012
WALKER, Latoya Nicole. ■ 27713 #036-01-2008 L2008 **P** *012
WALKER, Victoria Ann. ■ 27705 #048-14-2002 L2007 **IMG** *100 †20
WALL, Brian Patrick. 2609 N DUKE ST, STE 306 27704 #036-01-1997 L1998 **P** *020
WALLACE, Amy Hooks. ■ 27705 #036-05-2007 **OBG** *012
WALLACE, Dana Jack. ■ 27713 #036-07-2005 **OPH** *012
WALLACE, David Keith. BOX 3802 27710 #017-20-1990 L1995 **OPH** *020 †35
WALLACE, Michelle Christi. DUMC, BOX 3090 27710 #012-21-2008 **PDC** *012 †55
WALLACE, Thomas W. ■ 27707 #012-05-2006 L2006 **CD** *012 †20
WALLEN, Katharine Elizabe. ■ 27707 #010-02-2006 **PD** *012
WALLS, Bertram Emmanuel. 2828 CROASDAILE DR 27705 #036-07-1976 L1976 **OBG** *020 †30
WALMER, David Keith. 5704 FAYETTEVILLE RD, DUKE FERTILITY CENTER 27713 #036-01-1983 L1987 **REN OBG** *020 †30
WALSH, Mark Devlin, Jr. ■ 27705 #024-05-2000 L2008 **PS** *012 †85
WALSH, Molly Mc Carthy. ERWIN ROAD, BOX 3802, DUKE EYE CENTER 27710 #021-01-2000 L2004 **OPH** *020 †35

WALSH, Ruth. DUKE UNIV MED CTR, BOX 3808 27710 #039-01-1987 L1993 **DR** *040 †80

WALTER, Emmanuel Benjamin. 3024 PICKETT RD 27705 #023-01-1983 L1987 **PD ID** *020 †55

WALTER, Melanie Rebecca. ■ 27704 #003-01-2005 **D** *012

WALTERS, Christopher R. ■ 27713 #036-05-2001 L2007 **IC** *012

WALTERS, Robert William. ■ 27705 #018-03-2003 L2007 **D** *100 †15

WALTHER, Philip John. 1587 HOSP S BOX 3314 27710 #036-07-1975 L1982 **U SO** *020 †95

WANG, Andrew. 718 RUTHERFORD ST 27705 #036-07-1990 L1995 **CD** *020 †20

WANG, Caroline. ■ 27705 #036-07-2003 L2006 **IM** *100 †20

WANG, Chunsheng. 508 FULTON ST, BLDG 16 27705 #243-03-1987 L2007 **P** *100

WANG, Clark John. 905 CLARION DR 27705 #036-07-1988 L1989 **P** *020

WANG, Endi. ■ 27705 #243-72-1982 L2007 **HMP PTH** *020 †50

WANG, Hsioh-Shan. ERWIN RD 27710 #385-02-1953 L1964 **P** *071 †75

WANG, Kyne Martin. 4022 FREEDOM LAKE DR, REGIONAL PEDIATRIC ASSOC P 27704 #016-06-1996 L1999 **PD** *020 †55

WANG, Mei. 1901 HILLANDALE RD, STE F 27705 #036-01-1998 L2001 **IM** *020 †20

WANG, Tracy Yuping. 2400 PRATT ST RM 7068, CTR/DUKE CLINICA 27705 #024-01-2001 L2004 **CD** *100 †20

WANNER, Erin Colleen. ■ 27713 #005-18-2005 L2007 **PD** *012

WARBURTON, Samuel W, Jr. DUKE UNIV MEDICAL CE, BOX 3886 27710 #041-01-1969 L1979 **FM** *040 †18

WARD, Cary Cecile. ■ 27707 #051-01-1999 L2007 **CD** *100 †20

WARD, David Patrick. 4221 PLEASANT GREEN RD 27705 #038-06-1973 L1975 **IM** *050 †20 ‡

WARD, Emad. 508 FULTON ST, DURHAM VA MEDICAL CENTER 27705 #306-01-1988 L2003 **IM** *020 †20

WARDEN, Kendall Carnes. 718 RUTHERFORD ST 27705 #028-03-1992 L1993 **CHP** *020 †75

WARNER, David Saml. DUMC, BOX 3094 27710 #056-05-1980 L1994 **AN** *050 †05

WARRINGTON, Jill Scott. BX 3951 M148 DAV BLD 27710 #024-07-2004 **PTH** *012

WARTINBEE, Daniel Anthony. MEDICAL CENTER, DUKE UNIVERSITY 27710 #056-06-2007 **ORS** *012

WASHO, Michael Jung. ■ 27713 #041-12-2001 L2006 **P** *100

WASKIN, Hetty Anne. PO BOX 51035 27717 #025-01-1978 L1988 **ID IM** *030 †20

WATERMAN, Diedrich C. ■ 27705 #011-03-1980 L1982 **EM IM** *020 †20

WATERS, Kevin Barry. 3475 ERWIN RD, STE 204 27705 #034-01-1984 L1999 **IM** *020 †20

WATSON, Stephanie Anne. ■ 27705 #048-13-2008 *012

WATT, Kevin Michael. ■ 27701 #036-01-2006 **PD** *012

WATTS, John Alexander. ■ 27703 #035-15-2006 **DR** *012

WATTS, Lashonda Denise. ■ 27707 #036-07-2008 *012

WAUGH, Robert Andrew. BOX 3032, ERWIN ROAD, DUKE MEDICAL CENTER 27710 #041-01-1966 L1972 **CD** *050 †20

WEBER, Thomas Jos. BAKER HOUSE, STE 07, RM 08, P O BOX 3470 27710 #035-09-1954 L1955 **FM** *071

WEBSTER, George David. DUKE MEDICAL CENTER, BOX 3146 DEPT OF SURG 27710 #917-01-1968 L1978 **U** *020 †95

WECHSLER, Daniel Steven. 211 BEIL BLDG DUMC 2916, DUKE UNIV PED HEMO-ONCOGY 27710 #067-01-1987 L2006 **PHO PD** *050 †55

WECHSLER, Stephanie Burns. DUMC 3090, DUKE UNIV MED CTR 27710 #048-14-1987 L2006 **MG PDC** *020 †55,19

WEIDNER, Alison Catherine. BOX 3192 DUMC 27710 #036-07-1992 L1996 **OBG** *020 †30

WEIGLE, Nancy Jean. ■ 27705 #010-01-2000 L2003 **FM** *020 †18

WEINBERG, Joe Brice. VET ADMIN HOSP HEMA 27705 #004-01-1969 L1979 **HEM ON** *050 †20 ‡

WEINER, Jonathan J. 508 FULTON ST # 116A 27705 #036-01-1987 L1988 **P PFP** *020 †75

WEINER, Richard David. BOX 3309, DUKE UNIVERSITY MEDICAL CE 27710 #036-07-1974 L1974 **P CN** *030 †75

WEINERTH, John Louis. 6 WHITE ASH DR 27712 #024-01-1967 L1971 **U GS** *020 †95

WEINRICH, Elise. 2609 N DUKE ST, STE 204 27704 #045-01-1978 L1982 **D** *020 †15

WELDON, Bruce Craig. P O BOX 3094, DUKE UNIVERSITY MEDICAL CE 27710 #028-34-1978 L2004 **AN CCM** *020 †55,05

WELLMAN, David Kenton. 17 ALTMONT CT 27705 #036-07-1972 L1972 **EM** *020 †85

WELLS, Gregory E. 6216 FAYETTEVILLE RD, STE 105 27713 #047-07-1981 L1982 **AN IM** *020 †05 ‡

WELLS, Michael B. ■ 27713 #048-04-2004 L2007 **OPH** *012

WELLS, Samuel Alonzo, Jr. 2400 PRATT ST STE 0311, AMERICAN COLL OF SURG 27705 #012-05-1961 L1972 **GS** *030 †85

WELSBY, Ian James. ERWIN ROAD BOX 3094, DUKE UNIVERSITY MEDICAL CE 27710 #917-07-1990 L2000 **CD** *020

WELTY-WOLF, Karen E. ERWIN RD, DUKE UNIVERSITY MEDICAL CE 27710 #036-07-1986 L1987 **PUD ID** *050 †20

WENGER, Thomas Lee. 1313 N GREGSON ST 27701 #024-05-1971 L1981 **IM CD** *030 †20

WENZLIK, Adam Clark. 4003 N ROXBORO ST, LAKEWOOD PEDIATRICS & 27704 #038-40-1997 L2003 **FM** *020 †18

WEST, Dava Susanne. ■ 27713 #020-02-2007 **PTH** *012

WESTMAN, Eric Chas. 4020 N ROXBORO ST 27704 #056-05-1986 L1990 **IM** *050 †20

WHALEN, Robert Emmet. ■ 27707 #035-20-1956 L1959 **CD IM** *071 †20

WHANGER, Alan Duane. ■ 27705 #036-07-1956 L1968 **P IMG** *071 †75

WHELAN, John Wm, Jr. 4220 ROXBORO RD 27710 #041-02-1990 L1996 **IM** *020 †20

WHITAKER, Harry A. ■ 27705 #036-07-1956 L1956 **A PD** *071 †03

WHITE, David Cloid. DEPT OF SURGERY, DUKE UNIV MED CTR 27710 #051-01-1996 L2000 **TS** *100 †85,90

WHITE, Heidi Brainard. BOX 3003, TRENT DRIVE 27710 #028-02-1989 L1994 **IMG** *020 †20

WHITE, Rebekah Ruth. ■ 27710 #036-07-1997 L2000 **GS** *020 †85

WHITEHURST, Arthur W. 205 FRASIER ST 27704 #051-01-1968 L1972 **U** *020 †95

WHITESIDE, Michael Brooks. ■ 27705 #035-06-2002 L2007 **DR** *100 †80

WHITING, Eric Douglas. ■ 27710 #032-01-2001 L2002 **DR** *100 †80

WHITLATCH, Lyman William. ■ 27707 #024-05-2003 L2003 **NS** *012

WHITSON, Heather E. BX 3951 M148 DAV BLD 27710 #035-20-2000 L2003 **IMG** *020 †20

WICKE, Susan Holly. 112 SWIFT AVE 27705 #038-40-1989 L1993 **P** *020 †75

WIDMANN, Frances King. VET ADMIN HOSP, DEPT LAB 27705 #038-06-1960 L1961 **PTH** *071 †50

WIECH, Carolyn Anne. ■ 27713 #035-06-2007 **EM** *012

WIEGAND, Paul Harris. 3414 N DUKE ST, STE 400 27704 #036-05-1982 L1983 **EM** *020 †20,16

WIENER, Dana Nowicki. BOX 3094, DUKE UNIVERSITY MEDICAL CT 27710 #036-07-1989 L1993 **AN** *020 †05

WIENER, John Saml. DUMC BOX 3831, DUKE UNIVERSITY MEDICAL CE 27710 #021-01-1988 L1991 **UP U** *020 †95

WIGFALL, Delbert Raye. DUKE UNIVERSITY MEDICAL CE, P.O.BOX 3959, 27710 #012-05-1979 L1987 **PN PD** *050 †55

WILBANKS, George Dewey. ■ 27705 #036-07-1956 L1956 **GO GYN** *071 †30

WILCOX, Allen James. NATL INST ENVIRONMNTL HLTH 27709 #025-01-1973 L1975 **GPM** *050 †70

WILDER, Christine Marie. DUKE UNI MEDICAL CENTER, BOX 3857 DEPT OF PHYSCTRY 27710 #051-01-2002 L2007 **P** *100

WILFERT, Catherine M M. BOX 2951, DUKE UNIV MED CTR 27710 #024-01-1962 L1969 **ID PD** *030 †55

WILKE, Lee Gravatt. 3116 N DUKE ST 27704 #036-07-1993 L2000 **GS** *020 †85

WILKES, Trevor Watland. ■ 27713 #020-12-2003 L2008 **ORS** *012

WILKINS, Robert Henry. BOX 3807 DUKE HOSP 27710 #041-12-1959 L1959 **NS** *071 †25

WILKINS, Sarah Lyn. ■ 27713 #036-07-2008 *012

WILKINSON, Jeffrey Paul. DUKE UNIVERSITY MEDICAL CE, P O BOX 3192 27710 #023-07-1993 L1997 **OBG** *020 †30

WILKINSON, Robert Holden. ■ 27705 #028-02-1958 L1967 **NM R** *071 †80,28

WILLETT, Christopher Geo. ■ 27705 #024-07-1981 L2004 **RO** *020 †80 ‡

WILLIAMS, Alton Leroy. BEHAVIORAL SCS, BOX 3950, DEPT OF PSYCHIATRY & THE 27710 #008-01-1996 L2004 **P** *100 †75

WILLIAMS, Brandon Martin. ■ 27707 #051-07-2007 **IM** *012

WILLIAMS, Christine Anne. ■ 27713 #007-02-2006 **MPD** *012

WILLIAMS, Edward S. 3643 N ROXBORO ST 27704 #036-01-1954 L1954 **IM CD** *071 †20

WILLIAMS, Eric Sean. 3573 SUGAR TREE PL 27713 #024-01-2004 L2008 **IM** *012 †20

WILLIAMS, John W, Jr. 2424 ERWIN RD STE 1105, HOCK PLAZA 27705 #036-01-1984 L1988 **IM** *020 †20

WILLIAMS, Larry Wayne. DUKE MEDICAL CENTER, BOX 3559 27710 #036-07-1977 L1980 **AI PD** *050 †55,03

WILLIAMS, Laura. ■ 27713 #048-02-2005 **IM** *012

WILLIAMS, Redford B, Jr. 2212 ELDER ST, DUKE UNIVERSITY MEDICAL CE 27710 #008-01-1967 L1972 **P** *050 †20

WILLIAMS, Robert Ernest. DUKE UNIV MED CTR, BOX 3324 27710 #036-08-1998 L2003 **PYG** *020

WILLIAMS, Robert Sanders. BOX 2927, DUKE UNIV SCHL OF MED 27710 #036-07-1974 L1979 **CD IM** *030 †20

WILLIAMS, Zinaria Yvonne. 2351 ERWIN ROAD, DUKE UNIVERSITY EYE CENTER 27710 #033-06-2002 L2006 **OPH** *020 †35

WILLIAMSON, Edwin Dargan. 1 DUKE MEDICAL CTR, DEPT OF PEDIATRICS 27710 #035-01-2003 L2006 **PD** *100

WILLIAMSON, Roston M. 306 S GREGSON ST 27701 #012-01-1951 L1961 **OBG** *020 †30

WILLIFORD, Margaret E. BOX 3808 ERWIN ROAD, DEPT OF RADIOLOGY DUMC 27710 #036-07-1976 L1979 **DR** *020 †80

WILLIMON, Samuel Clifton. ■ 27707 #012-05-2005 **ORS** *012

WILSON, James S, Jr. 4301 BEN FRANKLIN BLVD 27704 #036-01-1975 L1982 **GS** *020 †85

WILSON, Joanne A Peebles. PO BX 3858 27710 #036-07-1973 L1986 **GE IM** *020 †20

WILSON, Kenneth Heaton. 508 FULTON ST, VA MEDICAL CENTER 27705 #036-01-1974 L1986 **ID IM** *050 †20

WILSON, Sylvia Helen. ■ 27713 #011-03-2005 **AN** *012

WINCHESTER, John B. ■ 27713 #051-01-2003 L2007 **AN** *100

WINCHESTER, Sara Mc Crone. ■ 27713 #051-01-2003 L2006 **CHN** *012 †55

WINN, Michelle Parthenia. BOX 2903 ERWIN ROAD, DUKE UNIV MEDICAL CENTER 27710 #036-08-1992 L1996 **NEP IM** *050 †20

WINSLOW, Bristol R. 4205 BEN FRANKLIN BLVD, ASSOCIATES PA 27704 #036-01-1994 L1996 **IM** *020 †20

WINSTON, James Richard. ■ 27712 #041-01-1975 L2007 **IM N** *020 †20

WINTERS, Steven Craig. 120 WILLIAM PENN PLZ, TRIANGLE ORTHOPAEDIC ASSOC 27704 #033-05-1987 L2003 **ORS** *020 †40

WINTON, Robert Emmett. 21 W COLONY PL STE 230 27705 #047-05-1972 L1978 **P** *020 †75

WISER, Jessica Lyon. ■ 27707 #036-07-2008 *012

WITHERS, Charles Albert, II. ■ 27705 #036-07-2008 *012

WITSELL, David Latham. 3805 TRENT DRIVE 27710 #007-02-1990 L1994 **OTO** *020 †45

WITT, Scott Allan. ■ 27712 #049-01-2003 L2008 **NPM** *012

WITTELS, Benjamin. ERWIN RD 27710 #026-04-1953 L1970 **PTH** *071 †50

WIYGUL, Jeremy Buchanan. DUKE UNIV MED CTR, PO BOX 2922 27710 #048-15-2001 L2007 **U** *020

WOFFORD, Taylor Stevens. ■ 27713 #027-01-2007 **IM** *012

WOKHLU, Nancy. 220 W NC HIGHWAY 54, STE 101 27713 #495-51-1968 L1982 **IM** *020

WOLF, Andrew Ira. BOX 3951, DEPT OF INTERNAL MEDICINE 27710 #041-02-2003 **GE** *012 †20

WOLF, Julius. ■ 27712 #024-05-1943 L1944 **IM GE** *071 †20

WOLF, Matthew Joseph. DUKE UNIVERSITY MEDICAL CE 27710 #028-02-2000 L2004 **CD** *100 †20

WOLFE, Ann Fierro. ■ 27705 #041-13-1961 L1965 **PD GP** *071

WOLFE, Cameron Robert. ■ 27705 #143-02-2000 **ID** *012

WOLFE, Valerie Marie. ■ 27705 #036-07-2007 *012

WOLFE, Walter Geo. DUKE UNIV MED CENTER, BOX 3507 27710 #041-13-1963 L1964 **TS GS** *020 †85,90

WONG, Terence Zekon. DUKE UNIVERSITY MEDICAL CE, DEPT OF RADIOLOGY BOX 3949 27710 #032-01-1990 L1998 **NR R** *020 †80

WOODRUM, Robert Scot. 5107 S PARK DR, STE 201 27713 #033-06-1989 L1992 **PD** *020 †55

WOODS, Christopher W. 508 FULTON ST, DURHAM VAMC 27705 #036-07-1994 L1995 **ID** *020 †20

WOODS, Edward Louis. ■ 27707 #036-01-1978 L1986 **IM** *075

WOODS, Suzanne K. 1002 LAMOND AVE 27701 #038-43-1994 L1996 **MPD PD** *020 †20,55

WOODWARD, Julie A. BOX 3802 27710 #048-14-1993 L2000 **OPH** *020 †35

WORLEY, Gordon. BOX 3120, DUKE UNIVERSITY MEDICAL CE 27710 #024-01-1973 L1979 **PD** *020 †55

WORSHAM, Anthony James. ■ 27704 #007-02-2006 **IM** *012

WRAY, Walter Harrill, III. ■ 27713 #036-05-2007 **ORS** *012

WRIGHT, David Robert. DUKE UNIV MED CENTER, BOX 3094 27710 #917-14-1990 L1999 *020

WRIGHT, Paul Harlan. 4125 BEN FRANKLIN BLVD, STE 140 27704 #036-05-1974 L1974 **ORS** *020 †40

WRIGHT, Tarra Marie. ■ 27707 #036-07-2003 L2007 **OPH** *100

WRIGHT, Virginia Frederic. ■ 27703 #010-03-2003 L2007 **IMG** *012

WU, Lawrence Reginald. BOX 3886, DUKE UNIVERSITY MEDICAL CE 27710 #036-07-1982 L1985 **FM** *020 †18

WU, Samuel Saint. ■ 27713 #038-43-2001 L2004 **CD** *012 †20

WU, Wang-Kuen. ■ 27705 #385-02-1956 L1971 **PTH** *071 †50

WYLIE, John David. ■ 27707 #028-02-2006 **DR** *012
WYMORE, Lucas R. ■ 27707 #048-16-2008 *012
WYNGAARDEN, James Barnes. ■ 27710 #025-01-1948 L1956 **IM** *030 †20
WYNN, James O, Jr. 3901 N ROXBORO ST 27704 #035-20-1951 L1958 **IM OS** *020 †20
XU, Fang. 521 EDINBOROUGH DR 27703 #243-48-1995 *012
YAMAGUCHI, Yasuo. DUKE MEDICAL CTR, BX 31184 27710 #572-07-1977 **GS** *100
YANCY, William Samuel. 2609 N DUKE ST, CENTRAL MEDICAL PARK, STE 27704 #036-07-1965 L1965 **PD ADL** *071 †55
YANCY, William Samuel, Jr. 508 FULTON ST, VAMC (152) HSR&D 27705 #036-08-1995 L2000 **IM** *050 †20
YANG, Benjamin Kattle. DUKE UNIV MED CTR, PO BOX 2922 27710 #005-11-2001 L2007 **U** *020
YANG, Charlie Ching. 120 WILLIAM PENN PLZ 27704 #036-05-2001 L2007 **ORS** *020
YANG, Yiping. DUKE UNIV MED CTR, DIV OF MEDICAL ONCOLOGY 27710 #243-43-1985 L2002 **ON** *020 †20
YARGER, William Ellsworth. ■ 27705 #048-04-1963 L1971 **NEP** *030 †20
YARLEY, Dewey Hobson. 4315 BEN FRANKLIN BLVD 27704 #036-01-1956 L1956 **IM** *071 †20
YARNALL, Kimberly Sue. BOX 3886 DUMC, 2100 ERWIN ROAD 27710 #011-03-1985 L1986 **FM** *030 †18
YEE, Linton Lopaka. ■ 27710 #014-01-1988 L2007 **PD** *020 †55
YELIN, Gershon. ■ 27707 #550-01-1960 L1967 **P** *071
YOO, David Sunghyun. DUKE UNIV MED CTR, BOX 3805 27710 #036-07-2004 **RO** *012
YOO, Jin Soo. DUKE UNIV MED CTR, DEPT OF SURGERY 27710 #051-01-2002 **GS** *012
YORK, Sally Jane. DUMC 3813, C318 LSRC 27710 #028-02-1996 L1997 **HO** *020 †20
YOUENS, Kenneth Emory. ■ 27713 #048-12-2005 **PTH** *012
YOUNES, Maher Nabil. ■ 27707 #605-01-2001 **OTO** *012
YOUNG, Alveth Joyce. ■ 27703 #305-01-1995 **PYG** *100
YOUNG, Brett Madison. ■ 27705 #026-08-2006 L2006 **DR** *012
YOUNG, Christopher Carlo. BOX 3094, DUMC, DEPT OF ANESTHESIOLOGY 27710 #035-09-1987 L1992 **CCA** *020 †05
YOUNG, James Robert. ■ 27707 #036-01-2008 L2008 *012
YOUNG, Lindsay Michelle. ■ 27707 #036-01-2008 L2008 *012
YOUNG, Stephen Lowe. 508 FULTON ST 27705 #005-02-1968 L1971 **PUD IM** *040 †20
YOUNG, Terri Lois. DUKE UNIV EYE CTR, BOX 3802 27710 #024-01-1986 L2005 **OPH PO** *020 †35 ‡
YOUNG, Timothy Noel. 4102 N ROXBORO ST, NORTH CAROLINA EYE & EAR C 27704 #036-07-1996 L2000 **OPH** *020 †35
YOWELL, Robert Kluttz. 5726 FAYETTEVILLE RD, STE 101 27713 #036-07-1961 L1961 **OBG** *071 †30
YUKL, Steven Alexander. BX 3951 M148 DAV BLD 27710 #025-01-2000 L2004 **ID** *012 †20,55
YUNG, Sunny Chung. ■ 27710 #001-02-2004 L2007 **ID** *012 †20
ZAAS, Aimee K. DUKE UNIVERSITY MEDICAL CE, BOX 3355 27710 #016-06-1998 L2001 **ID** *100 †20
ZAAS, David William. DUMC 3501 27710 #016-06-1998 L2001 **PCC** *050 †20
ZAFAR, Syed Yousuf. ■ 27701 #038-43-2002 L2008 **HO** *012 †20
ZAKARIA, Hassan. ■ 27701 #012-01-2003 L2003 **GPM** *012
ZANGA, Joseph Robert. ■ 27713 #036-01-2004 **MP** *012
ZARZAR, Theodore Rudolf. ■ 27713 #036-01-2006 L2008 **P** *012
ZELDIN, Darryl Craig. LPP MD D2-01, 111 T W ALEXANDER DRIVE 27705 #017-20-1986 L1994 **PUD CCM** *050 †20
ZELKO, Russell Rudolph. 120 WILLIAM PENN PLZ 27704 #035-20-1967 L2007 **ORS** *020 †40
ZENN, Michael Robert. 136 BAKER HOUSE-TRENTDRIVE, #3358 27710 #035-20-1988 L1995 **PS FPS** *020 †85,65
ZHANG, Liqun. PO BOX 3951, M148 DAV BLDG 27710 #243-69-1991 L2005 **N** *012
ZHANG, Wei. 4082 HOSPITAL SOUTH, BOX 3812 27710 #243-16-1990 L2002 **P** *020 †75
ZIA, Shams. ■ 27710 #704-02-2000 L2007 **NEP** *012 †20
ZIDAR, David Alexander. BOX 31176, DUMC 27710 #036-07-1998 L2002 **CD** *012 †20
ZIEL, Patricia Ann. DUMC BOX 3253 27710 #025-01-1968 L1980 **P** *012 †20
ZINK, Stephen Iver. 3514 SHERIDAN DR 27707 #008-02-2002 L2007 **DR** *020 †80
ZIPKIN, Daniella Ann. 4220 N ROXBORO ST, DUKE OUTPATIENT CLINIC 27704 #005-02-1999 L2007 **IM** *020 †20
ZOMORODI, Ali Reza. DUKE UNIV MED CTR 27710 #036-07-2000 L2006 **NS** *100
ZULA, Jean Elizabeth. 27712 #036-01-1988 L1992 **P** *020 †75
ZURA, Robert Douglas. DUMC BOX 3389, DIV OF ORTHOPAEDIC SURGERY 27710 #023-07-1994 L2004 **OTR** *020 †20
ZURICK, Andrew Oliver, III. ■ 27705 #038-41-2003 L2006 **CD** *012 †20
ZUSSMAN, Matthew Eric. ■ 27713 #056-05-2005 **PD** *012

EAST BEND – YADKIN

ARIAS, Roque Manuel. 112 E MAIN ST, CAROLINA GENERAL & INTEGRA 27018 #001-02-1982 L1988 **GP OS** *020
RIDGWAY, Alton H. ■ 27018 #017-20-1942 L1983 **FM AN** *071 †18
ROSE, Richard Phillip. ■ 27018 #036-05-1964 L1964 **ORS** *071 †40

EAST FLAT ROCK – HENDERSON

WATSON, Jason Lee. ■ 28726 #038-43-2002 L2004 **FM** *020 †18

EDEN – ROCKINGHAM

ABRUZZI, Gina M. 117 E KINGS HWY 27288 #035-15-1998 L2001 **EM** *020 †16
ANWAR, Mohammad Saeed. 701 S VAN BUREN RD, STE A 27288 #704-08-1968 L1979 **IM** *020 †20
AUSTIN, James Craig. 405 THOMPSON ST 27288 #025-07-1978 L1982 **IM** *075 †20
BARLOW, Linda Namutebi. 520 S VAN BUREN RD, EDEN PEDIATRICS 27288 #010-03-1996 L2001 **PD** *020 †55
BEAVERS, Clarence Henry. 247B W KINGS HWY 27288 #055-01-1985 L1990 **FM** *020 †18 ‡
BLUTH, Kirk Daniel. 515 THOMPSON ST, STE 2 27288 #051-07-1997 L2007 **FM** *020 †18
BUCY, Mark Christopher. 520 S VAN BUREN RD, MEDICAL OFFICE BLDG 2 27288 #055-01-1998 L2001 **PD** *020 †55
BUIST, Nigel A. 522 S VAN BUREN RD 27288 #065-10-1976 L1992 **OBG** *020
BURKE, Anne. 518 S VAN BUREN RD STE 5 27288 #539-04-1988 L2006 **GE** *100 †20

CALL, David L. 117 E KINGS HWY 27288 #036-01-1977 L1977 **DR** *020 †80
CAPLE, Karen Sheree. ■ 27288 #036-01-1980 L1982 **RO** *020
CARTER, Charletta R. 520 S VAN BUREN RD, BLDG 2 27288 #016-42-2001 L2004 **PD** *020
DANIEL, Terry Glen. 250 W KINGS HWY, DAYSPG FAM MED ASSOC 27288 #055-01-1988 L1989 **FM** *020 †18
DAWSON, Shelton Phelps. 705 S VAN BUREN RD BLDG 3 27288 #010-01-1955 L1971 **PD** *020 †55
DE MASON, Marc. 515 THOMPSON ST STE B, PIEDMONT SURGICAL ASSOCIAT 27288 #025-01-1978 L1983 **GS** *020 †85 ‡
DESAI, Chetan Hasmukhbhai. 405 THOMPSON ST, EDEN INTERNAL MEDICINE, PL 27288 #495-48-1994 L2007 **IM** *020 †20
DOONQUAH, Kofi Adeleke. 608 S LINDEN DR, STE E 27288 #047-07-1993 L2000 **N** *020 †75
DORMAN, Jon Dudley. 608 S LINDEN DR, STE E 27288 #008-01-1961 L1967 **N** *020 †75
FLEISHMAN, Henry Arnold. 515 THOMPSON ST, STE B 27288 #012-05-1974 L1979 **GS CRS** *020 †85 ‡
GILES, Karen Levette. 117 E KINGS HWY, MOREHEAD MEMORIAL HOSPITAL 27288 #051-04-1996 L2006 **DR** *020 †80
HAINES, Carroll Fogg, Jr. 515 THOMPSON ST STE A 27288 #041-09-1978 L1982 **OPH** *020 †35
HASANAJ, Xaje Adem. 701 S VAN BUREN RD, STE A 27288 #957-09-1984 L1994 **IM** *020 †20
HENDERSON, William Walker. 518 S VAN BUREN RD 27288 #025-01-1938 L1939 **IM** *072
HOWARD, Kevin Price. 250 W KINGS HWY 27288 #025-07-1982 L1985 **IM** *020 †18
HUNG, Estelle Cline. 439 W KINGS HWY, THE CENTER FOR COUNSELING, 27288 #036-05-2000 L2004 **P** *020 †75 ‡
HUNTER, James Arthur. 608 S LINDEN DR STE G 27288 #005-18-1988 L1994 **DR** *020 †80
JAVAID, Mohammad Iqbal. 515 THOMPSON ST STE C 27288 #704-01-1968 L1977 **U** *020 †95
JORDAN, Mark Saunders. ■ 27289 #051-01-1991 L1995 **PTH** *020 †50
KARB, Kenneth Saml. 516 S VAN BUREN RD 27288 #051-01-1972 L1978 **ON HEM** *020 †20
KENNY, Karen Sue. 522 S VAN BUREN RD 27288 #051-04-2000 L2004 **OBG** *020
KEYS, Roy Robt. 117 E KINGS HWY, MOREHEAD MEMORIAL HOSPITAL 27288 #039-01-1990 L2006 **EM** *020 †16
KING, Anne Bryson. 520 S VAN BUREN RD, STE 2 27288 #036-01-1980 L1982 **PD** *020 †55
KRISHNAN, Sethu. 515 THOMPSON ST STE C 27288 #495-53-1973 L1987 **U FM** *020 †95
LAW, Inger Marasha. 520 S VAN BUREN RD 27288 #001-06-1993 L1996 **PD** *020
MACRI, Anthony John. ■ 27288 #041-02-1962 L1973 **PTH** *071 †50
MAGRINAT, Gustav Chas. 522 S VAN BUREN RD 27288 #036-01-1987 L1990 **ON HEM** *020 †20
MC DOWELL, Samuel. 518 S VAN BUREN RD 27288 #045-01-1996 L1998 **GE** *020 †20
MC FALLS, Frederick D. 150 PARK RD 27288 #036-07-1959 L1980 **P GP** *071
MC GINLEY, Scott Michael. 520 S VAN BUREN RD, STE 1 27288 #033-05-1988 L2003 **OSM** *020 †40
MC GUIRE, Paul Frederick. 117 E KINGS HWY, MOREHEAD MEMORIAL HOSPITAL 27288 #051-07-1994 L1998 **EM** *100
MC KAY, James Coley. 518 S VAN BUREN RD, STE 9 27288 #010-02-1978 L1988 **NEP IM** *020 †20
MCKAY, Jeremy Larvadain. ■ 27288 #024-01-2008 *012
MC LEOD, William J. 522 S VAN BUREN RD 27288 #065-06-1978 L1992 **OBG** *020
MERRITT, Thomas Rodman. 520 S VAN BUREN RD, STE 1 27288 #065-05-1975 L1980 **ORS** *020 †40
NOETZEL, Harry Albert. 515 THOMPSON ST STE D 27288 #067-01-1983 L1994 *020
PARSONS, James Baker. 117 E KINGS HWY 27288 #011-03-1972 L1977 **IM** *020 †20
PIGGOTT, Dionne Michelle. 522 S VAN BUREN RD 27288 #036-01-2003 L2007 **OBG** *020
PLOMARITIS, Titus, Jr. 110 S PARK TER 27288 #024-05-1981 L1987 **ORS** *020
POLLINA, Christopher John. 117 E KINGS HWY, MOREHEAD MEMORIAL HOSPITAL 27288 #041-12-2000 L2003 **EM** *020
ROBERTSON, Amanda Jo. ■ 27288 #036-08-2008 *012
SACRINTY, Nicholas W. 608 S LINDEN DR STE E 27288 #036-05-1952 L1952 **IM CD** *071
SASSER, Paul Wm. 250 W KINGS HWY 27288 #036-01-1984 L1985 **FM EM** *020 †18
SHAH, Ashish Champaklal. 405 THOMPSON ST, MEDICINE ASSOC 27288 #495-23-1992 L1998 **IM** *020 †20
SMITH, Richard Francis. 518 S VAN BUREN RD, RICHARD FRANCIS SMITH PA 27288 #020-12-1974 L2003 **OTO** *020 †45 ‡
SNYDER, Frank Chipman. 608 S LINDEN DR 27288 #051-04-1986 L1994 **DR** *020 †80
TAPPER, David Brian. 515 THOMPSON ST STE D 27288 #023-01-1979 L1982 **FM OS** *020 †18
VYAS, Dhruv B. 405 THOMPSON ST, EDEN INTERNAL MEDICINE ASS 27288 #495-76-1989 L1996 **IM** *020 †20
YUAN, Jason Shihning. 117 E KINGS HWY 27288 #051-04-1992 L2006 **EM** *020 †16

EDENTON – CHOWAN

ALI, Ahmad Jafar. 314 W QUEEN ST 27932 #036-01-1993 L1996 **FM** *020 †18
BAKER, Marvin I. 102 E KING ST, EDENTON RADIOLOGY LTD 27932 #011-03-1960 L1981 **R NM** *071 †80,28
BLAKEMORE, Wm Stephen. 101 MARK DR 27932 #539-06-1979 L1980 **OPH** *020 †35 ‡
BOEHLING, Peter Francis. 309 N BROAD ST, WOMEN'S HEALTH OF EDENTON 27932 #051-04-1988 L1995 **OBG** *020 †30
CHUA, Arlene Ng. 211 VIRGINIA RD 27932 #036-08-1995 L2001 **FM EM** *020 †18
COLODNEY, Ellen Jennifer. ■ 27932 #033-06-1983 L1996 **PM** *020 †60
DAVIS, Robert Alden, Jr. 201 VIRGINIA RD 27932 #036-05-1981 L1986 **GS GP** *020 †85
DE VINE, Leibert E. 314 W QUEEN ST, BOX 298 27932 #038-40-1975 L1979 **FM** *020 †18
DICKIE, Jamie Kirk. 211 VIRGINIA RD 27932 #051-04-1980 L1981 **EM** *020 †16
DIMARTINO, Thomas Calvin. 201 VIRGINIA RD 27932 #047-07-1990 L1994 **FM** *020 †18
DOBRANSKY, Roman Steven. 222 VIRGINIA RD, CHOWAN HEART CENTER 27932 #396-05-1983 L2005 **IM IMG** *020 †20
DURUMAN, Bora Abdullah. ■ 27932 #051-04-1994 L1998 **OBG** *020 †30 ‡
FRANCIS, John Arlie. 309 N BROAD ST 27932 #055-01-1971 L1979 **OBG** *020 †30
GAVIGAN, Karen Dalquist. 105 MARK DR, CHOWAN PEDIATRICS 27932 #036-08-1999 L2002 **PD** *020 †55
HASKETT, Joseph Ray, Jr. 104 MARK DR 27932 #036-01-1976 L1976 **IM** *020 †20
HUDSON, Gregory Lee. 211 VIRGINIA RD 27932 #036-07-1981 L1985 **P** *020
LA BARBERA, Frank Raymond. PO BOX 346 27932 #035-19-1982 L2007 **OBG** *020 †30 ‡
LEWIS, Luanne Kem. 211 VIRGINIA RD 27932 #036-05-1983 L1986 **IM** *020
MC CARTHY, Francis M. 701 LUKE ST STE C, ORTHOPEDICS, PA 27932 #011-02-1983 L1990 **ORS** *020 †40
MC LEES, Byron D. 213 QUEEN ANNE DR 27932 #036-07-1967 L1967 **CD OS** *050 †20
O'LEARY, James Francis. 201 VIRGINIA RD 27932 #539-02-1968 L1979 **GS FM** *020 †85

■ = Address Information Privacy Protected

PERRY, John Christopher. 701 LUKE ST 27932 #011-03-1979 L1982 **FM** *020 †18
REIHELD, Robert Gale. ■ 27932 #038-40-1969 L2002 **FM AN** *020 †18
RESTA, Bartholomew Jos. 203 EARNHARDT DR, CHOWAN PEDIATRICS 27932 #038-40-1981 L2008 **PD** *020 †55 ‡
REYNOLDS, Joel Crist. 210 N BROAD ST 27932 #017-20-1986 L1999 **U GS** *020 †95 ‡
SAFILLE, Eduardo Felix. 222 VIRGINIA RD 27932 #011-02-1982 L2006 **CD IM** *020 †20
SHEFLIN, Scott Mitchell. 211 VIRGINIA RD 27932 #041-09-1990 L1992 **FM FSM** *020 †18
SHIELDS, Claire Sikoryak. 211 VIRGINIA RD 27932 #036-08-1995 L1998 **FM** *020 †18
SULLIVAN, Matthew Patrick. 211 VIRGINIA RD 27932 #005-14-1995 L2001 **EM** *020 †16
TAYLOR, Stafford J. 211 VIRGINIA RD 27932 #045-04-1993 L1996 **IM** *020
THAUNG, Mehm Thein. 211 VIRGINIA RD 27932 #209-01-1971 L2002 **GS** *020 †85
TRIPP, Joseph Elliott. 428 OLD HERTFORD RD, JOSEPH E TRIPP MD 27932 #036-08-2000 L2003 **EM** *020
VOIGT, Ward Landis. 211 VIRGINIA RD 27932 #036-01-1963 L1963 **GS** *071 †85
WRIGHT, David Orlo. 211 VIRGINIA RD 27932 #036-05-1958 L1958 **PD FM** *071 †18

EFLAND – ORANGE

EPPARD, Gregory Grayston. ■ 27243 #036-01-2008 *012
LEVITT, Stephen Robt. ■ 27243 #038-06-1976 L1977 **P** *020
RIZZONE, Katherine Helen. ■ 27243 #036-01-2008 *012
ROBERTS, Jesse Earle. ■ 27243 #021-05-1961 L1965 **RHU** *071 †20

ELIZABETH CITY – PASQUOTANK

AJUMOBI, Omezie Samuel. ■ 27909 #035-47-1999 L2002 **FM** *100 †18
ALLEN, Kevin Paul. 504 E ELIZABETH ST, STE 4 27909 #035-01-1986 L2003 **PD** *020 †35
ALVAREZ, Joseph Michael. 400 S ROAD ST, STE D1 27909 #008-02-1984 L1992 **U** *020 †95
ASIKA, Kimkya Chinwe. 107 MEDICAL DR 27909 #010-03-1980 L1987 **FM** *020 †18
ATIENZA, Daniel Mosquera. 1503B N ROAD ST 27909 #748-10-1983 L1997 **HO IM** *020 †20
BALLENGER, Cynthia Ann. 1144 N ROAD ST, ONCOLOGY CENTER 27909 #036-01-1995 L1996 **RO** *020 †80
BAWTINHIMER, Gary Geo. 305 MAIN STREET EXT 27909 #023-01-1979 L1980 **P** *020 †75
BIGGERS, William Alan, Jr. 1144 N ROAD ST 27909 #045-04-1992 L1998 **EM** *020 †16
BLUMBERG, Andrey Imants. 1134 N ROAD ST STE 3 27909 #041-13-1975 L1995 **OTO GS** *020 †45
BOUNOUS, Judith Frances. ■ 27909 #036-05-1970 L1970 **PD** *020 †55
BRANDSPIGEL, Karl. 206 HASTINGS LN 27909 #005-02-1975 L1978 **NEP IM** *020 †20
BRENTJENS, Mathijs Henri. 504 E ELIZABETH ST, STE 7 27909 #035-06-2000 L2005 **D** *020 †15
BRENTJENS, Veronica A. 504 E ELIZABETH ST, STE 7 27909 #660-03-1964 L1996 **D** *020
BROWN, Jennifer Sue. 1851 W EHRINGHAUS ST, BOX 155 27909 #020-12-1978 L1980 **PD** *075 †55
CARTER, Barbara. 1141 N ROAD ST STE I 27909 #041-02-1993 L1997 **OBG** *020 †30
CARTER, David Lance. 1138 N ROAD ST 27909 #041-02-1992 L1997 **GS** *020 †85
CARTER, Imhotep Kevin A. 119 BIRDIE LN, P O BOX 2532 27909 #016-11-1989 L2004 **UCM PUD** *020
CARTER, Stephen Lindsay. 105 MEDICAL DR 27909 #041-02-1990 L2000 **GS** *020 †85
CERVENY, Kimberly Carter. 102 MEDICAL DR, TARHEEL INTERNAL MEDICINE 27909 #051-04-1996 L2001 **RHU IM** *020 †20 ‡
CHANDI, Tejwant Singh. 1507 N ROAD ST, STE 3 27909 #495-03-1988 L1997 **IM** *020 †20
COHEN, Stuart Evan. 1144 N ROAD ST, DEPT OF ANESTHESIA 27909 #033-05-1993 L1998 **AN** *020 †05
COLEMAN, Nita Rose. 1141 N ROAD ST STE M, COASTAL PEDIATRICS 27909 #048-13-1979 L1981 **PD** *020 †70
CRAWFORD, John Custis. HLTH DEPT CEDAR/HARNEY STS 27909 #051-01-1937 L1955 **OBG** *071 †30
DAVIS, David M. 1144 N ROAD ST 27909 #038-45-1985 L1986 **EM** *020 †18
DAY, Chester La Vern. 305 E MAIN ST 27909 #019-02-1973 L2002 **P** *020 †75
DEANGELIS, Kiernan Thomas. ■ 27909 #036-08-2004 L2006 **EM** *020
DE NUNZIO, Neil Louis. 1144 N ROAD ST 27909 #041-02-1982 L1985 **IM** *020 †20
DOLESHAL, Barbara. 305 E MAIN ST, ALBEMARLE MENTAL HEALTH CE 27909 #048-13-1990 L2006 **P** *020 †75
DONOHOE, Margaret Rose. 1134 N ROAD ST, STE 3 27909 #041-13-1985 L1998 **IM AI** *020 †20,03
DRISKILL, Brent Ray. ■ 27909 #023-12-2005 L2005 *100
DROSNES, Dean Leonard. 1134 N ROAD ST, STE 3 27909 #041-13-1985 L1998 **OTO** *020 †45
EADIE, Edward B, Jr. 1134 N ROAD ST, STE 5 27909 #051-01-1967 L1973 **U** *020 †95
ENGLISH, Kristi Lynne. 112 MEDICAL DR 27909 #036-08-1997 L2001 **OBG** *020 †30
EVANS, Pamela Sue Whiting. 100 MEDICAL DR, STE 5 27909 #016-11-1995 L1999 **N** *020 †75
FABER, Steven Mark. 405 HASTINGS LN 27909 #561-20-1983 L1992 **GE IM** *020 †20
FULLER-HINES, Jessica Lee. 110 MEDICAL DR STE 5 27909 #041-02-2003 L2007 **PM** *020
GALLANT, Roger Donald. 1144 N ROAD ST, ALBEMARLE HOSPITAL 27909 #005-12-1994 L2003 **EM** *020
GARMAN, Steve Michael. 1507 N ROAD ST SU 27909 #422-01-1992 L1996 **IM** *020 †20
GILBERT, Michael T. 1144 N ROAD ST 27909 #035-09-1967 L1973 **OPH** *071 †35
GOODSTEIN, Richard S. 1507 N ROAD ST, STE 1 27909 #028-78-1976, ▲ L2008 **PUD** *020
GRAHAM, John Calhoun, Jr. 303 E MAIN ST, ALBEMARLE RADIOLOGY LTD 27909 #036-01-1961 L1961 **DR NM** *072 †80
HAND, Le Roy C, Jr. 1144 N ROAD ST 27909 #036-05-1950 L1950 **EM** *071
HARESCH, John Watts. 1134 N ROAD ST, STE 9 27909 #036-01-2000 L2001 **FM** *020 †18 ‡
HARRELL, Wm Fletcher, Jr. 1142 N ROAD ST 27909 #051-01-1943 L1947 **PD** *071
HEYDER, Albrecht Mark. 111 MEDICAL DR STE A 27909 #051-07-1985 L1990 **PUD IM** *020 †20
HOIDAL, Charles R. 615 S HUGHES BLVD, 615 S HUGHES BLVD 27909 #041-02-1982 L1991 **EM ESM** *020 †16
HOLT, Robert Owen. 112 MEDICAL DR, COASTAL WOMEN'S CLINIC 27909 #017-20-1993 L1996 **OBG** *020 †30
HUBBARD, Karl Winsor. 1140 N ROAD ST 27909 #020-02-1982 L1995 **ORS** *075 †40
HUNSBERGER, Kurt Lee. 102 MEDICAL DR # B 27909 #016-06-1969 L1975 **IM** *071 †20
IKE, Christopher O. 1144 N ROAD ST 27909 #048-02-2001 L2005 **CD** *100 †20
JACKSON, Anthony W. 1121 N ROAD ST, STE A 27909 #047-06-1982 L2007 **OTO** *020 †45 ‡
JACKSON, Celia M. 1144 N ROAD ST 27909 #047-06-1995 L1998 **EM** *020 †16
JENKINS, Samuel Gatlin. 105 MEDICAL DR 27909 #036-01-1955 L1955 **GS** *071 †85 ‡
KINARIWALA, Jayesh J. 1141 N ROAD ST, COASTAL PEDIATRICS 27909 #495-89-1984 L1996 **PD** *020 †55
KINARIWALA, Smruti Jayesh. 1141 N ROAD ST STE M, COASTAL PEDIATRICS, PA 27909 #495-89-1986 L1996 **PD** *020 †55
KING, Kathryn Jones. 711 ROANOKE AVE 27909 #045-01-1985 L1987 **PD** *020 †55
KIZEN, Paul Andrew. 112 MEDICAL DR 27909 #056-05-1977 L1980 **OBG** *020 †30
LAMM, Kenneth Rand. 1144 N ROAD ST 27909 #036-01-1991 L1995 **PTH** *020 †50
LORD, Archibald L, Jr. ■ 27909 #010-01-2001 L2008 **IM** *020
LOVELLE-ALLEN, Susan E. 1134 N ROAD ST STE 2 27909 #035-01-1988 L2002 **PS OS** *020 †85,65
MANNING, Stewart Cleaves. 111 MEDICAL DR STE B 27909 #051-04-1986 L1989 **NEP IM** *020 †20
MANULI, Steven Philip. 100 MEDICAL DR 27909 #036-01-1995 L1996 **IM** *020 †20
MARKER, Douglas E. 1144 N ROAD ST 27909 #020-02-1969 L1990 **ORS** *020 †40
MARTINEZ, Octavio Nestor. ■ 27906 #048-04-1997 L2006 **P** *020 †55,75
MARTZ, Michael Roy. 1144 N ROAD ST 27909 #055-01-1979 L1980 **FM** *020 †18
MC DONALD, Janice A. 1134 N ROAD ST, STE 2 27909 #024-01-1987 L2001 **D** *020 †15
MERRITT, Karen Whitney. 100 MEDICAL DR 27909 #025-07-1988 L2007 **IMG IM** *020 †20
MODROW, Peter Albert. 1144 N ROAD ST 27909 #036-01-1965 L1965 **AN P** *020 †05
MONCLA, Alfred Marie, Jr. 1144 N ROAD ST 27909 #021-05-1964 L2002 **OBG** *020 †30
MONCLA, Paul Richard. 1141 N ROAD ST, STE I 27909 #036-08-1998 L1999 **OBG** *020 †30
MONDS, Alvah Price. 615 S HUGHES BLVD, FIRST CHOICE URGENT CARE, 27909 #036-01-1978 L1980 **EM** *020 †16
MOORE, Daniel Hood. 504 E ELIZABETH ST, STE 5 27909 #036-01-1994 L2001 **OBG** *020 †30
MORROW, Melody Ann. 1503 N ROAD ST 27909 #041-07-1976 L1987 **OPH** *020 †35
MOSS, Kenneth Wayne. 100 MEDICAL DR, NEUROLOGY SERVICES OF ALBE 27909 #020-02-1959 L1960 **PD** *071 †55
NASH, Thomas Palmer, III. ■ 27909 #047-06-1945 L1953 **GS** *071 †85
PARANJAPE, Suvinay B. 100 MEDICAL DR 27909 #038-06-1995 L2004 **END** *020 †20
PETERS, Brandon Moseley. 206 S ROAD ST 27909 #036-07-1989 L1990 **FM** *020 †18
PHARR, Maria P. 1141 N ROAD ST, STE G 27909 #041-02-1992 L2001 **FM** *020 †18
POWELL, Robert Narraway. 102 MEDICAL DR 27909 #036-05-1970 L1970 **IM** *020 †20
RAMSAMOOJ, Ravi. 206 HASTINGS LN 27909 #056-06-1999 L2004 **NEP** *020 †20
RAO, Annapurna C. 1144 N ROAD ST, DEPT. OF RADIOLOGY 27909 #495-70-1975 L2003 **DR** *020 †80
REDDING, Marshall Simms. ■ 27909 #036-07-1966 L1966 **OPH** *071 †35
REICHENBACH, Daniel James. 1138 N ROAD ST, CAROLINA SURGICAL CARE 27909 #038-40-1999 L2008 **GS** *020 †85
ROBERTSON, Carroll B, III. 902B ROANOKE AVE 27909 #036-08-1992 L1993 **FM** *020 †18
ROBERTSON, Joseph L. 1144 N ROAD ST, ALBEMARLE HOSPITAL 27909 #048-04-1975 L1977 **PTH** *020 †50
RODRIGUEZ, James. 1851 W EHRINGHAUS ST, COASTAL PEDIATRICS 27909 #422-01-1989 L2004 **PD** *020 †55
RUIZ, Antonio Jose. 1138 N ROAD ST 27909 #051-07-1985 L1991 **GS** *020 †85
SAMAN, Shaker George. 1503B N ROAD ST 27909 #875-01-1994 L2005 **HO** *020 †20
SAMPSON, Marian Antonette. ■ 27906 #047-07-2005 **OBG** *012
SAWYER, Barbara Ann. 410 E MAIN ST STE 202 27909 #036-08-1991 L1995 **P CHP** *020
SELIG, Julian Wood, Jr. ■ 27909 #036-01-1959 L1959 **P** *071
SHERIFF-CARTER, Katrina D. 1141 N ROAD ST, STE M 27909 #016-11-2001 L2005 **PD** *020
SINGH, Jasvinder Pal. 1507 N ROAD ST, STE 1 27909 #495-03-1983 L1991 **IM PCC** *020 †20
SMITH, Bryan Dorsey. 305 E MAIN ST 27909 #012-05-1990 L2002 **CHP** *020 †75
SONNINO, Victor Guy. 100 MEDICAL DR, NORTHEAST NEUROSCIENCE, IN 27909 #561-11-1973 L2000 **NS** *020 †25
SOUTHWORTH, Alvin Judson. 1134 N ROAD ST 27909 #051-04-1957 L1978 **OBG** *071 †30
SPRUILL, Joseph Milton. 107 MEDICAL DR 27909 #036-05-1974 L1974 **FM** *020 †18
STEVENSON, Paul Lindsay. 112 MEDICAL DR 27909 #036-08-1991 L1995 **OBG** *020 †30
SUE, Michael. 1134 N ROAD ST STE 8 27909 #566-01-1987 L1996 **GE IM** *020 †20
SURFACE, Luther Brooks. ■ 27906 #036-08-1994 **PTH** *100
SUTTON, Sidney Michael. 1141 N ROAD ST STE G 27909 #051-07-1982 L1985 **FM** *020 †18
SWARUP, Jitendra. 1503 N ROAD ST 27909 #010-03-1991 L1995 **OPH** *020 †35
TERRYBERRY, Daniel Scott. 1141 N ROAD ST, STE I 27909 #035-06-1988 L1992 **OBG** *020 †30
THAI, Quoc-Anh. 105 N ROAD ST, QA THAI NEUROSURGERY CENTE 27909 #023-07-1999 L2006 **NS** *020 ‡
THOMPSON, Alfred Hunter. 305 E MAIN ST 27909 #023-01-1982 L2002 **P** *020 †75
THORP, Adam T, IV. 1134 N ROAD ST, STE 7 27909 #010-01-1983 L2006 **ORS** *020 †40
TINSLEY, James Whitfield. ■ 27909 #051-04-1957 L1957 **OPH** *071
TOLSON, Roger John. 1207 FAIRFAX AVE 27909 #917-29-1957 L1974 **IM** *020
TOLSON, Timothy A. 615 S HUGHES BLVD, STE C 27909 #036-08-1991 L1994 **AI IM** *020
VERDI, Vincent James. 109 JORDON PLZ, COASTAL EYE CENTER 27909 #041-13-1998 L2003 **OPH** *020 †35 ‡
WASSINK, William Klein. ■ 27909 #660-03-1948 L1954 **GP** *020 †18
WATSON, James Morris. ■ 27909 #025-01-1967 L1974 **ORS** *020 †40
WATTS, Daron Alan. ■ 27909 #038-40-1998 L1999 **IM** *020 †20 ‡
WHITE, Lindsey Lee. 1134 N ROAD ST, STE 9 27909 #036-05-1984 L1985 **CD IM** *020 †20
WITWER, Timothy Slayton. 1207 N ROAD ST 27909 #024-05-1971 L1980 **IM FM** *020 ‡
WOOD, Angela Kay. 1141 N ROAD ST, STE M 27909 #041-14-1986 L1990 **PD** *020 †55
WOOD, John Brianthomas. 1141 N ROAD ST STE K 27909 #041-14-1985 L1990 **OTO** *020 †45

ELIZABETHTOWN – BLADEN

AYCOCK, Susan Elizabeth. 300A MCKAY ST 28337 #036-08-1987 L1988 **FM OBS** *020 †18
BARNHILL, Otha Allen. ■ 28337 #051-01-1953 L1953 **GP** *071 †18
BINDER, George Arthur. 501 S POPLAR ST 28337 #016-11-1973 L1977 **DR** *020 †80
BRIDGERS, Stephen Burney. 300A MCKAY ST, BLADEN MEDICAL ASSOCIATES 28337 #036-08-1985 L1986 **FM** *020 †18
CLARY, Anthony Ray. 300 MCKAY ST, STE F 28337 #012-01-1989 L2003 **OBG** *020 †30
COTTLE, Ronald Wade. 501 S POPLAR ST 28337 #036-01-1983 L1986 **FM** *020 †18
CREED, Don Wendell. PO BOX 1477 28337 #045-01-1974 L1976 **GP** *020
DEL DO, Shari Ann. 501 S POPLAR ST, BLADEN CTY HOSP EMER DEPT 28337 #051-04-1981 L1987 **FM EM** *020 †18 ‡
DUERR, Karl Michael. 501 S POPLAR ST 28337 #409-16-1990 L1993 **IM PD** *020 †20,55
ELDER, Kerren Harry. 501 S POPLAR ST 28337 #010-03-1988 L2000 **HEM** *020 †20
ENOJADO, Silverio Castro. 501 S POPLAR ST 28337 #748-01-1961 L1975 **GP** *020
FALTER, Richard Thos, Jr. 501 S POPLAR ST 28337 #019-02-1992 L1998 **DR RNR** *020 †80
FRANKLIN, David Chas. 299 WESTWOOD CIR 28337 #001-02-1974 L1996 **GS** *020 †85
GEMMA, Frank Eugene. 501 S POPLAR ST 28337 #051-04-1960 L1969 **GS** *071 †85 ‡

■ = Address Information Privacy Protected

GRAHAM-HOSKINS, Pearly. 300A MCKOY ST, BLADEN MEDICAL ASSOCS 28337 #036-01-1977 L1978 **IM** *020 †20

HUNT, Shirlene. PO BOX 517, 300A MCKAY ST 28337 #036-08-1984 L1999 **IM** *020 †20

KIM, Jong Whan. 501 S POPLAR ST 28337 #056-05-1995 L2001 **IM IMG** *020 †20

KOTZAN, Jeffrey Michael. DEPT OF RADIOLOGY, BLADEN COUNTY HOSPITAL 28337 #036-08-1994 L1998 **DR** *020 †80

LANIER, Vicki Marie. PO BOX 447, 1100 CROMARTIE RD 28337 #036-08-1994 L1995 **EM** *020 †16

MARTIN, Harold Lynn. 501 S POPLAR ST, BLADEN COUNTY HOSPITAL 28337 #010-03-1973 L2006 **GS EM** *020 †85 ‡

PHILLIPS, Bruce Alton, Jr. 507 DOCTORS DR 28337 #036-01-1967 L1967 **IM GE** *020 †20

RICH, Robert L, Jr. PO BOX 517, 300 A EAST MCKAY ST 28337 #036-05-1984 L1985 **FM** *020 †18

WOLEBEN, Martyn Dean. 300 MCKAY ST, STE F 28337 #027-01-1988 L2003 **OBG** *020 †30

ELK PARK – AVERY

SANTANA SANTIAGO, Hector. ■ 28622 #308-01-1973 L1975 **EM** *071

ELKIN – SURRY

APOLTAN, Ioana Mihaela. 640 PARKWOOD MEDICAL PARK 28621 #781-01-1992 L2000 **IM** *020 †20

BARRON, Timothy D. 680 PARKWOOD MEDICAL PARK 28621 #047-06-1994 L2005 **GS** *020 †85

BRIDGES, Michael Howard. 250 JOHNSON RIDG MDCL PARK 28621 #038-45-1992 L2002 **MPD** *020 †55,20

CAMPBELL, Robert Coulter. 177 PARKWOOD DR, PARKWOOD EYE CENTER 28621 #041-13-1971 L2000 **OPH** *020 †35

CANUPP, Tony Wayne. 500 CHATHAM MEDICAL PARK 28621 #036-05-1973 L1973 **EM IM** *020

CHINN, Mark Hanna, IV. 189 SAMARITANS RIDGE RD 28621 #051-01-2001 L2005 **P** *020

CHRISTENSEN, Wayne Nels. 180 PARKWOOD DR 28621 #056-06-1983 L1990 **PTH** *020 †50

DREW, William Edward. 340 PARKWOOD MEDICAL PARK 28621 #010-02-1984 L2007 **N AM** *020 †75

ERLANDSON, Stephen Eric. 600 CHATHAM MEDICAL PARK, PA 28621 #036-01-1975 L1975 **FM** *020 †18

EVANS, Charlotte Ann. 600 CHATHAM MEDICAL PARK, PA 28621 #045-04-1985 L1986 **FM PLM** *020 †18

FAULK, Woodruff Word. 500 CHATHAM MEDICAL PARK 28621 #048-04-1973 L1976 **FM** *020

FIETS, Gregory Lee. 180 PARKWOOD DR, REGIONAL CANCER CENTER 28621 #016-11-1987 L2006 **RO** *020 †80 ‡

FRANCE, James Edward. 180 PARKWOOD DR, EMERGENCY RM 28621 #041-12-1987 L2004 **EM FM** *020 †18

GAMBILL, John Milton. ■ 28621 #038-06-1951 L1951 **P GP** *020

GARRISON, Paul L, Jr. 500 CHATHAM MEDICAL PARK 28621 #036-05-1985 L1988 **IM** *020 †20

GOLASZEWSKI, Glenn David. 124 SAMARITANS RIDGE RD 28621 #011-02-1992 L2001 **FM** *020 †18

GULLEY, Paul Hudson. 500 CHATHAM MEDICAL PARK 28621 #036-05-1978 L1981 **IM END** *020 †20

HEINER, Mark David. 201A ELDON PARKS DR 28621 #049-01-1990 L2007 **OBG** *020 †30

HOLDEN, Deborah Lynn. 180 PARKWOOD DR 28621 #010-02-1984 L1990 **AN** *020 †05

KINGMAN, Gilson John. 150 CHATHAM MEDICAL PARK 28621 #051-01-1987 L2001 **PS** *020 †65

KODEJS, Libuse. 640 PARKWOOD MEDICAL PARK, INTERNAL MEDICINE 28621 #286-11-1977 L2000 **IM** *020 †20

LEWE, Robert Hyuck. 200 JOHNSON RIDG MDCL PARK 28621 #048-14-1994 L1999 **U** *020

MARROUM, Marie-Claire. 180 PARKWOOD DR 28621 #605-02-1968 L1976 **ATP** *020 †50

MC ILVEEN, Peter Francis. 690 PARKWOOD MEDICAL PARK 28621 #008-02-1999 L2003 **OBG** *020 †30

MERLO, Richard Bartlett. ■ 28621 #036-07-1961 L1961 **R NM** *071 †80,28

MINOTTI, Americo M, Jr. 250 JOHNSON RIDG MDCL PARK 28621 #048-14-1991 L1996 **OTO** *020 †45

NABORS, Lawrence Howard. 201 W MAIN ST 28621 #036-05-1977 L1978 **FM GS** *020 †85

NEUMARK, Andras. 380 PARKWOOD MEDICAL PARK, INTERNAL MEDICINE 28621 #473-01-1985 L1997 **IM** *020 †20

NICHOLSON, John Anthony. 177 PARKWOOD DR 28621 #028-34-1974 L1997 **OPH** *071 †35

OLIVER, John Gladson. 180 PARKWOOD DR 28621 #011-02-1975 L1980 **OPH** *020 †35

PALERMO, James Anthony. 300 JOHNSON RIDGE RD, MEDICAL PARK 28621 #036-01-1997 L2002 **RO** *020 †80

PEACOCK, Kevin Howard. 300 JOHNSON RIDG MDCL PARK 28621 #051-04-2001 L2004 **HO** *100

PETERSON, Robert Goodloe. 680 PARKWOOD MEDICAL PARK 28621 #036-05-1977 L1978 **TS GS** *020 †90,85

PIERSON, Steven Scott. 189 SAMARITANS RIDGE RD, NEW RIVER BHC 28621 #036-05-1972 L1972 **P** *020 †75

RHYNE, Darryl Bruce. 660 PARKWOOD MEDICAL PARK 28621 #001-06-1993 L1996 **FM** *020 †18

SHUCK, Linda M. 100 JOHNSON RIDGE RD, MEDICAL PARK 28621 #055-75-1994, ▲ L2005 **CD IM** *020 †20

SOOS, Tamas. 380 PARKWOOD MEDICAL PARK, INTERNAL MEDICINE PA 28621 #473-01-1994 L2000 **IM** *020 †20

SORESCU, Mugurel Lucian. 640 PARKWOOD MEDICAL PARK 28621 #781-01-1992 L2001 **IM** *020 †20

STEINER, Drew John. 100 CHATHAM MEDICAL PARK, ELKIN FAMILY PRACTICE 28621 #010-02-1989 L1999 **FM EM** *020 †18

STEWART, Wells, Jr. 177 PARKWOOD DR 28621 #048-04-1986 L1991 **OPH** *020 †35

STUART, Hal Martin. ■ 28621 #036-05-1956 L1956 **FM** *071 †18

TAYLOR, Vernon W, Jr. 180X PARKWOOD DR, FOOTHILLS FAMILY MEDICINE 28621 #041-02-1938 L1938 **GP** *071

THOMAS, Christopher Reid. 505 SAMARITANS RIDGE CT 28621 #012-01-2001 L2001 **HO** *020

VYBIRAL, Tomas. 640 PARKWOOD MEDICAL PARK 28621 #869-01-1982 L1993 **CD IM** *020 †20

WALKER, Stephen Thos. 124 SAMARITANS RIDGE RD 28621 #051-04-1989 L1993 **IM PD** *020 †55,20

ELLENBORO – RUTHERFORD

KELLER, Jeffrey Blake. 221 DYCUS RD, STE C-2 28040 #036-05-1982 L1984 **GE IM** *020 †20

SMITH, Melanie Rowe. 143 HENRIETTA ST 28040 #036-08-1994 L1995 **UCM** *071

ELLERBE – RICHMOND

KOPYNEC, Bohdan Wm. 112 E BALLARD ST, FIRSTHEALTH FAMILY CARE CT 28338 #035-01-1978 L1999 **FM OM** *020 †18 ‡

RANKIN, Pressley R, Jr. 261 2ND ST 28338 #036-05-1947 L1948 **FM** *071

ELM CITY – WILSON

CABRAL, Gonzalo. 8282 S NC HIGHWAY 58 27822 #132-02-1990 L1997 **IM** *020 †20

RICHARDS, Robert Day. ■ 27822 #051-04-1954 L1957 **FM AM** *020 †18

ROGERS, William E. 3892 RIVIERA DR 27822 #012-05-1977 L1981 **DR PDR** *020 †80 ‡

ELON – ALAMANCE

DONDIEGO, Richard M. 812 W HAGGARD AVE, ALAMANCE FAMILY PRACTICE 27244 #042-03-1981 L2004 **IM BBK** *020 †20

HEDRICK, James Fletcher. 908 S WILLIAMSON AVE 27244 #036-08-1998 L1999 **FM** *020 †18

HUDSON, William P, II. ■ 27244 #036-05-1993 L1994 **AN** *020

KING, Wm Lyon Mac Kenzie. ■ 27244 #064-01-1960 L1971 **P** *071

NIEMEYER, Meindert Albert. 812 W HAGGARD AVE 27244 #660-04-1981 L2006 **FM** *075 †18

PRINGLE, Joseph Ross, Jr. 908 S WILLIAMSON AVE 27244 #036-01-1975 L1977 **PD** *020 †55

SATOR-NOGO, Jasna. 908 S WILLIAMSON AVE 27244 #957-08-1978 L2001 **PD** *020 †55

ELON COLLEGE – ALAMANCE

HAWKINS, James Hubert. ■ 27244 #041-02-1946 L1946 **GP** *075

WATSON, Robert A. ■ 27244 #035-45-1953 L1953 **FM FPG** *071 †18

EMERALD ISLE – CARTERET

BROADWELL, Richard O, III. ■ 28594 #036-05-1978 L1979 **GP GS** *020 ‡

CANIPE, Tommie Lee. 7901 EMERALD DR, STE 7 28594 #036-05-1959 L1959 **GS TS** *020 †90,85

CHITTUM, Susan Lynne. ■ 28594 #051-07-1983 L1986 **OBG** *030 †30

FORD, Charles Phillip, Jr. ■ 28594 #041-04-1943 L1961 **OS OM** *071

GRADY, John Carl. ■ 28594 #036-08-2005 L2007 **FP** *012

HARRIS, James Merrimon. 7901 EMERALD DR, EMERALD ISLE PRIMARY CARE, 28594 #023-12-1995 L1998 **FM** *020 †18

HECKERT, Reed Mitchell. ■ 28594 #023-12-2005 L2006 *020

KLIMASKI, David John. ■ 28594 #041-15-2006 L2007 **GS** *020

KUHN, Michael Alan. ■ 28594 #041-15-1997 L2000 **OSM** *020 †40

PIVER, James D. 2515 OCEAN DR 28594 #041-01-1943 L1944 **FM** *071 †85

PUGLIESE, Douglas J. ■ 28594 #041-15-2003 L2003 **IM** *020

WARD, Virginia Wooten. 7901 EMERALD DR, STE 7 28594 #036-08-1994 L1996 **FM** *020 †18

WRIGHT, Joseph Dewitt. ■ 28594 #055-01-1973 L1986 **OBG** *020 †30

ENFIELD – HALIFAX

CRAIG, William Kenneth M. 114 MARKET ST, MEDICAL CLINIC OF ENFIELD 27823 #036-05-1946 L1947 **GP** *030

MANN, William Marion, Jr. PO BOX 715 27823 #036-05-1957 L1957 **P IM** *071

WOOD, Sherrod N. ■ 27823 #041-02-1950 L1950 **GP** *071

ENGELHARD – HYDE

LIVERMAN, Henry J. PO BOX 218 27824 #020-02-1950 L1950 **FM AM** *071

ERWIN – HARNETT

ADAIR, William Edward, Jr. 410 DENIM DR 28339 #041-13-1938 L1938 **GP GS** *072

JUBERG, Richard Gerald. 901 DENIM DR 28339 #036-08-1982 L1986 **FM OBG** *020 †18

RAMASWAMY, Mamatha. 518 E H ST 28339 #496-39-1990 L2000 **IM** *020 †20

RAO, Lakshman. 518 E H ST B 28339 #649-33-1983 L1988 **IM** *020 †20

ROSADO, Marcos Gilberto. 410 DENIM DR, GOOD HOPE HOSPITAL 28339 #042-02-1990 L1995 **AN GP** *020

SANKA, Venkata Sai Shanka. 901 DENIM DR 28339 #496-31-1997 L2003 **IM** *020 ‡

SCHARLE, Diane M. 410 DENIM DR 28339 #051-04-1978 L1982 **GP IM** *075

SINGH, Vinod. 410 DENIM DR 28339 #495-41-1978 L1990 **IM FM** *020 †20

STEWART, Christopher Wade. 410 DENIM DR 28339 #036-08-1998 L2002 **IM** *020 †20

ETOWAH – HENDERSON

BOSHOLM, Carol Christine. PO BOX 2107, 167 ETOWAH CTR DR 28729 #033-05-1989 L1996 **IM** *075 †20

DYSART, George Barton. ■ 28729 #045-01-1955 L1960 **FM** *020

FAIRMONT – ROBESON

GRIMM, Paul Jeffrey. 101 N WALNUT ST, FAIRMONT MEDICAL CLINIC 28340 #045-01-1992 L2000 **FM FSM** *020

HOWIE, Eugenia Brooks. 101 N WALNUT ST 28340 #036-01-1978 L1979 **FM** *020

■ = Address Information Privacy Protected

VERRETT, Charlotte Inez. 1212 S WALNUT ST 28340 #005-12-1983 L1994 **GP** *020 ‡
ZELIKOVSKY, Shirley Sharo. 101 N WALNUT, SRMC CLINIC 28340 #550-03-2003 L2007 **FM** *020

FAIRVIEW – BUNCOMBE

BASCH, Ladislaus P. ■ 28730 #154-07-1946 L1951 **FM** *071 †18
BOESHORE, Eric Russell. ■ 28730 #041-13-1992 L1995 **IM** *020 †20
BREED, Floyd Maurice. RR 7 BOX 1290 28730 #067-01-1940 L1971 **OM** *071
FLOREN, Roger C. PO BOX 1160 28730 #005-12-1939 L1965 **P** *071
GRAF, George P. ■ 28730 #056-05-1950 L1981 **EM** *075
ISRAEL, John Robert. ■ 28730 #041-12-1962 L1971 **PS** *071 †65
MADAY, Gary J. ■ 28730 #028-34-1980 L1982 **PTH** *075 †50
MULLINS, Amanda Catherine. ■ 28730 #041-15-2006 **PTH** *012
POWELL, Geraldine M. 40 EMMETT HOLLAR 28730 #539-04-1970 L1985 **P** *020 †50,75
REDDY, Ajita Kota. ■ 28730 #048-12-2000 L2005 **DR** *100 †80
SLOAN, Ira Harry. ■ 28730 #016-11-1967 L1998 **P** *030 †75
STEWART, Betty Greene. ■ 28730 #036-07-1965 L1970 **P N** *020 †75
TURPIN, James Wesley. ■ 28730 #012-05-1955 L1974 **OM EM** *020
VASEY, Janet Kersten. ■ 28730 #017-20-1983 L1986 **IM** *020 †20
ZIMMERMAN, Brian Scott. ■ 28730 #041-15-1999 L2002 **IM** *020 †20

FAISON – SAMPSON

DELGADO CABEZA, Jose A. 444 SW CENTER ST 28341 #935-07-1996 L2002 **IM** *020 †20
GONCHER, John Stephen, Jr. 444 SW CENTER ST, GOSHEN MEDICAL CLINIC 28341 #016-43-1965 L2004 **OBG** *020 †30
JACOBS, Kenneth Lee. 444 SW CENTER ST, GOSHEN MEDICAL CENTER 28341 #036-01-1992 L2001 **OBG** *075
TRAGLER, Ancilla Theresa. 444 SW CENTER ST, GOSHEN MEDICAL CENTER 28341 #495-01-1969 L2002 **PD** *020 †55

FARMVILLE – PITT

ASTIN, Matthew Raymond. ■ 27828 #012-22-2006 **MEM** *012
BARROW, Roy Douglas. 3681 N MAIN ST, STE 114 27828 #036-08-1990 L1991 **IM** *020 †20
BRAMLEY, Michael Laird. 3444 S CONTENTNEA ST 27828 #008-01-1973 L1975 **PD GP** *020 †55
BRINN, Nathan Andrew. ■ 27828 #047-06-2001 L2005 **MPD** *100 †20,55
COKER, Rebecca Sue. 3444 S CONTENTNEA ST 27828 #016-01-1983 L1996 **PD** *020 †55
EHRLICH, Susan. 3411 S CONTENTNEA ST 27828 #024-07-1985 L1986 **P** *020 †75
FITZGERALD, Charles E, Jr. ■ 27828 #036-01-1960 L1960 **IM OM** *020 †20
HAMSTEAD, Steven Lynn. 3681 N MAIN ST, STE 114 27828 #036-05-1985 L1986 **IM** *020 †20
HINSON, Patricia. 3681 NORTH MAIN ST, STE 114 27828 #020-02-1998 L2001 **IM** *020 †20
MARANA, Enrique Villa. 3485 N MAIN ST, FARMVILLE INTERNAL MEDICIN 27828 #748-20-1989 L2000 **IM** *020 †20
OGLE, John Marshall, Jr. 3444 S CONTENTNEA ST 27828 #036-08-1999 L2002 **PD** *020 †55
PIPPIN, Richard Lee. 3681 N MAIN ST, STE 114 27828 #036-08-1983 L1984 **IM** *020 †20
PREVATTE, Steven Harold. 3444 S CONTENTNEA ST 27828 #036-08-1986 L1987 **PD** *020
RHYNE, J David. 3444 S CONTENTNEA ST 27828 #036-08-2002 L2005 **PD** *020 †55
SHELTON, Pheston Gray. ■ 27828 #036-08-2005 **OS** *100
SUTTON, Ernest O, III. 3444 S CONTENTNEA ST 27828 #036-05-1995 L1998 **PD** *020 †55
TYLER, Brian Carey. 3444 S CONTENTNEA ST 27828 #045-01-1994 L2000 **PD** *020 †55

FAYETTEVILLE – CUMBERLAND

ABBASINEJAD, Meisha Kama. 3650 CAPE CENTER DR, STE 200 28304 #010-03-1998 L2003 **PM** *020 †60
ABOAGYE-KUMI, Moses Yaw. 557 SANDHURST DR, CAROLINA KIDNEY CARE 28304 #412-02-1990 L2006 **NEP** *020 †20
ABRAHAMS, Lawrence M. ■ 28311 #047-05-1961 L1961 **P IM** *071 †75
ACHUKO, Maureen Ngozi. 557 SANDHURST DR, FAYETTEVILLE NEPHROLOGY AS 28304 #690-05-1989 L2002 **NEP** *020 †20
ADHOLLA, Paul O. 1520 OWEN PARK LN, OWEN PARK PEDIATRICS, PA 28304 #577-01-1987 L1995 **PD** *020 †55
AGYENIM-BOATENG, Aboagye. 3601 CAPE CENTER DR, BIRTH AND WOMEN'S CARE, PA 28304 #412-02-1996 L2006 **OBG** *100
AHMAD, Wahaj-Ud-Din. 2300 RAMSEY ST, C/O VAMC 28301 #704-01-1957 L1973 **N IM** *071 †75
AHMED, Shahzad. 2300 RAMSEY ST, E R DEPARTMENT 28301 #704-02-1985 L2004 **IM** *020 †20
AINOLHAYAT, Cecilia. 2112 SKIBO RD 28314 #319-01-1988 L1996 **FM** *020 †18
ALCOVER, Brenda Judith. ■ 28314 #022-01-1981 L1985 **GS** *030 †85
ALEXANDER, Joe M. 2911 BREEZEWOOD AVE, STE 201 28304 #045-01-1973 L1989 **FM** *020 †18
ALLEN, Gail Atkins. 1638 OWEN DR, P O BOX 2000 28304 #036-08-1986 L1995 **PEM PD** *040 †55
ALLEYNE, Grant L. ■ 28303 #566-01-1970 L1976 **OBG** *071
ALLISON, David J. 1301 MEDICAL DR, CAROLINA REGIONAL RADIOLOG 28304 #055-01-1982 L1986 **DR NM** *020 †80
ANDERSON, Philip Allen. 200 FORSYTHE ST, P O BOX 87448 28303 #025-01-1972 L1975 **FM** *050 †34
ANDERSON, Scott G. 1638 OWEN DR 28304 #048-12-2001 L2005 **OBG** *020 †30
ANDREWS, Elena Nicolayevn. 3412 RAMSEY ST 28311 #913-80-1989 L2006 **FM** *100 †18
ANNAMANENI, Ravinder K. 4140 FERNCREEK, STE 601 28314 #495-65-1988 L2005 **GS CRS** *100 †85
APPEL, Barbara Lynn. 2035 VALLEYGATE DR, STE 101 28304 #051-01-1981 L1990 **PD** *020 †55
APPEL, Robert Albert. 1786 METROMEDICAL DR 28304 #051-01-1981 L1990 **U** *020 †95
ARAGHI, Sasan Saedi. 6387 RAMSEY ST UNIT 210, HEALTH PAVILION NORTH OF C 28311 #305-01-2000 L2004 **FM** *020 †18
ARLE, Steven Wayne. ■ 28311 #409-16-1981 L1991 **RNR** *020

ARMSTEAD, Phyllis. 2000 FORT BRAGG RD 28303 #041-09-1992 L2001 **P** *020 †75
AROCA, Estuardo E. 6387 RAMSEY ST, UNIT 210 28311 #035-75-1997, ▲ L2002 *020
ARORA, Aman. 1638 OWEN DR, CAPE FEAR VALLEY MEDICAL A 28304 #495-45-2002 L2007 **IM HOS** *020 †20
ASARE, Frederick Kwesi. ■ 28314 #412-02-2000 L2006 **IM** *100 †20
ASEMOTA, Ogienwonyi E. 507 SANDHURST DR 28304 #690-06-1982 L1997 **PD** *020 †55
ASKINS, James Holloway. 3308 MELROSE RD 28304 #047-06-1964 L1971 **ORS** *071 †40
ATASSI, Inad Badreddin. 2018 FORT BRAGG RD, STE 126B 28303 #875-01-1972 L1980 **NS** *020 †25 ‡
AUDU, Raymond Oche. ■ 28306 #690-07-1989 L2007 **IM** *020 †20
AUL, Christopher Taylor. 6387 RAMSEY ST, HEALTH PAVILION NORTH EXP 28311 #028-02-1977 L1980 **FM UCM** *030 †18
AUNG, Thidar. 2300 RAMSEY ST, MEDICAL CENTER 28301 #209-01-1985 L2001 **IM** *020 †20
AZAD, A K. ■ 28314 #160-02-1982 L2002 **IM** *020 †20
BACON, Martin Eldridge. 150 ROBESON ST 28301 #047-05-1980 L1990 **CD IM** *020 †20
BAKDOUD, Zuhair. ■ 28311 #409-05-1969 L2002 **PD NPM** *020 †55
BAKRI, Amit Kamal. ■ 28303 #005-11-2007 *012
BAKRI, Kamal Manubhai. 6387 RAMSEY ST, FAYETTEVILLE 28311 #495-23-1972 L1982 **ON IM** *020 †20 ‡
BALL, Chuck Leroy. 1601 OWEN DR 28304 #047-07-2004 **FM** *100
BANKES, Anthony Shawn. ■ 28306 #023-12-2000 L2001 **FM** *020 †20
BANZON, Roberto Palacio. 1638 OWEN DR, VALLEY MEDICAL ASSOCIATES 28304 #748-01-1990 L1998 **IM** *020 †20
BAREFOOT, Arnold B, Jr. 2950 VILLAGE DR, STE 100 28304 #036-01-1982 L1983 **OBG** *020 †20
BARNES, Christopher John. 3308 MELROSE RD, FAYETTEVILLE ORTHOPEDIC 28304 #038-40-1997 L2000 **OSM** *020
BAROODY, Brent Joseph. ■ 28306 #045-04-1999 L2006 **OBG** *020 †30
BARRY, William. ■ 28303 #036-01-1956 L1956 **FM EM** *071 †18
BASH, Dennis Philip. 1638 OWEN DR, CAPE FEAR VALLEY HEART & S 28304 #038-43-1990 L2006 **PD** *020 †55
BEAL, Evelyn N. 2125 VALLEYGATE DR, STE 201 28304 #038-41-1995 L2000 **OBG** *020 †30
BELL, Ronald Lee, Jr. 4534 RAEFORD RD, FIRST MED 28304 #055-01-1976 L1994 **FM** *020 †18
BELLIAN, Kenneth Thomas. 1839 QUIET CV 28304 #051-01-1993 L1998 **OTO** *020 †45
BELTZ, Charles Robert, III. ■ 28311 #036-01-1994 L1996 **P** *075
BERKOFF, Molly C. 1601 OWEN DR, SOUTHERN REGIONAL AHEC 28304 #035-01-2000 L2003 **PD** *100 †55
BEYER, Alfred James, Jr. 2857 SKYE DR 28303 #038-06-1967 L1982 **GS** *020 †85
BEYER, Catherine M H H. 1213 WALTER REED RD 28304 #038-06-1967 L1972 **PD** *071 †55
BHATT, Dushyant Nanubhai. 2300 RAMSEY ST 28301 #495-23-1971 L1985 **IM** *020 †20
BLAIR, Timothy Pierce. 3634 CAPE CENTER DR, CAPE FEAR CARDIO ASSOC 28304 #051-01-1974 L1990 **CD IM** *020 †20
BOLAND, Edward Hall. 4305 HUNTSFIELD RD 28314 #045-01-1994 L2001 **GPM FM** *062 †70,18
BONEY, Mark Avery. 1638 OWEN DR, CAPE FEAR VALLEY MEDICAL C 28304 #041-07-1990 L1998 **EM** *020 †16
BONGU, Ram Mohan Rao V. 101 ROBESON ST STE 202, CAPE FEAR VALLEY HEALTH SY 28301 #495-65-1990 L2003 **IMG** *020 †18
BOOTH, Christine Dennett. ■ 28306 #011-02-2001 L2002 **OBG** *020
BOWLES, Robert Bradford. 1905 SKIBO RD 28314 #051-01-1993 L1995 *020
BOWSHER, Barbara Lynne. ■ 28311 #055-01-1995 L1997 **ADL** *020 †55
BRAR, Navpreet Singh. 1830 OWEN DR, RM 200 28304 #495-45-2000 L2007 **CHP** *020 †75
BRIGGS, John Glenn, Jr. 1774 METROMEDICAL DR, FAYETTEVILLE PLASTIC SURGE 28304 #036-01-1969 L1969 **PS** *020 †65
BRIGHT, Crystal Deon. 1601 OWEN DR, MED P 28304 #047-07-2006 L2006 **FP** *012
BRIONES, Lorenzo C. ■ 28304 #748-10-1965 L1971 **IM IMG** *020 †20
BROOKS-FERNANDEZ, Connie. 1220 WALTER REED RD, STE 100 28304 #036-08-1993 L1997 **FM** *020 †20
BROUSSARD, Bradley. 4140 FERNCREEK, STE 801 28314 #048-13-1991 L1996 **ORS** *020 †40
BROWN, Heather S. 1601 OWEN DR, SOUTHERN REGIONAL AHEC FAM 28304 #011-75-2006, ▲ **FP** *012
BROWN, Stephanie Delores. 2950 VILLAGE DR, WOMEN'S WELLNESS CENTER 28304 #036-01-1995 L2000 **IM** *020
BRYAN, John Hugh. 6387 RAMSEY ST 28311 #036-01-1969 L1969 **RO PD** *020 †55,80
BRYAN, Leslie Jane. 2300 RAMSEY ST, VAMC FAYETTEVILLE 28301 #035-48-2000 L2008 **IM IMG** *020
BUENAVENTURA, Jason Bened. ■ 28314 #041-77-2006, ▲ L2008 **FP** *012
BUFF, Judith Ann. 1307 AVON ST 28304 #055-01-1972 L1976 **D** *020
BURRI, Radha Chandana. ■ 28311 #495-21-2001 L2008 **PD** *020
BUTLER, Brad Everette. 1601 OWEN DR 28304 #036-08-2003 L2006 **FM** *020 †18
BYAKIKA, Richard Luboga. ■ 28303 #905-01-2001 L2007 **IM** *020 †20
BYRNES, David Albert. ■ 28312 #045-04-2007 L2007 **P** *012
CABRERA, Jorge Luis. ■ 28303 #011-02-2004 L2007 **FM** *020 †18
CAMERON, Hugh Scott, II. 1638 OWEN DR 28304 #036-01-1999 L2005 **NPM** *020 †55
CAMPBELL, Todd C. ■ 28314 #041-14-1997 L2003 **GS** *020 †85
CARLSON, Robert Eric. 4140 FERNCREEK DR STE 8 28314 #005-14-1991 L1997 **ORS** *020 †40
CARR, Sandra M. 1601 OWEN DR 28304 #048-02-1996 L1997 **FM** *020 †18
CARTER, Jan Marie. PO BOX 2000, 1638 OWEN DR 28302 #051-07-1982 L1992 **NPM PD** *020 †55
CARTER, Paul Maurice. 101 ROBESON ST STE 2 28301 #010-03-1969 L1976 **GS VS** *020 †85
CAZAN, Gianina. ■ 28304 #057-27-1998 L2000 **OBG** *020
CHANA, Avtar Singh. 1601 OWEN DR, FAHEC 28304 #305-01-2005 **FP** *012
CHANDLER, Mark Steven. 109 BRADFORD AVE, METAL HEATH CENTER 28301 #036-08-1986 L1991 **P IM** *020 †75
CHANDRA, Dinesh N. 1218 WALTER REED RD 28304 #495-52-1976 L1994 **NEP IM** *020 †20
CHANG, Kisook. 109 BRADFORD AVE, CUMBERLAND COUNTY MENTAL H 28301 #583-03-1961 L1974 **P** *020 ‡
CHARYA, Sampath V. 4140 FERNCREEK DR, STE 501 28314 #495-57-1982 L1997 **N** *020 †75
CHATTERJEE, Kanan. 2300 RAMSEY ST RM 190, VA MED CTR 28301 #495-39-1976 L1985 **FM** *020 †18
CHAUDHURI, Debi Prasad. 1617 OWEN DR 28304 #495-32-1962 L1975 **GS** *020 †85
CHAUDHURI, Surajit. 1205 CAPE CT STE B 28304 #495-32-1982 L1994 **ON HEM** *020
CHENGAPPA, Kambayanda L. 2300 RAMSEY ST, VETERANS MEDICAL CENTER 28301 #495-33-1971 L1975 **IM** *020 †20
CHIMA, Chukwuemeka O. 1601 OWEN DR 28304 #690-10-1991 L2003 **ID** *020 †20
CHIPMAN, Martin. 1638 OWEN DR 28304 #048-04-1960 L1983 **N OS** *020 †75

CHOI, Young Sammy. 5117 CLIFFDALE RD, MANNA CHURCH 28314 #039-01-1985 L1990 **IM PD** *020 †20,55
CHOWDHURY, Shabbir Ahmed. 1830 OWEN DR, RM 200 28304 #160-06-1984 L2004 **P** *020 †75
CHUNG, Christian Youngmin. 1880 QUIET CV 28304 #010-03-1984 L1989 **GE IM** *020 †20
CHUNG, Peter Karl. 2300 RAMSEY ST 28301 #566-01-1983 L1997 **IM** *020 †20
CISZEK, Thomas Arthur. 1638 OWEN DR 28304 #028-34-1977 L1985 **NPM PD** *020 †55
CLARK, Franklin St Clair. 1945 FORDHAM DR 28304 #036-01-1973 L1973 **GS** *020 †85
CLARK, Lorinda Mc Gildery. ■ 28306 #036-08-1996 **P** *100
CLARK, Louis Phillip, Jr. 4140 FERNCREEK DR, STE 801 28314 #047-07-1970 L1984 **HS** *020 †40
CLASSEN, James Anthony. 1841 QUIET CV 28304 #045-01-1980 L1988 **GS** *020 †85
CLAY, Keia K. 1601 OWEN DR, SOUTHERN REGIONAL AHEC 28304 #016-11-1999 L2006 **FM** *020 †18
COHEN, Joseph. 3656 CAPE CENTER DR, CAROLINA CARDIOLOGY 28304 #035-09-1982 L2005 **CD IM** *020 †20
COLLINS, Jason Garret. 1638 OWEN DR, CAPE FEAR VALLEY EMERGENCY 28304 #011-04-1998 L2007 **EM** *020 †16
COOLEY, Cornell Thos. ■ 28303 #025-01-1977 L1979 **FM** *020
COOPER, George Leonard. 2139 VALLEYGATE DR, STE 101A 28304 #035-03-1991 L1996 **OPH** *020 †35
COOPER, Sharon W. 510 WATERVIEW CT 28301 #047-07-1976 L1996 **ADL PD** *020 †55
COPELAND, Gary Benj. 1726 METROMEDICAL DR 28304 #036-05-1960 L1960 **OPH** *020 †35
CRAIB, Carole M Fetzer. 150 ROBESON ST 28301 #021-01-1990 L1996 **AN** *020 †05
CROSS, Bill. ■ 28312 #011-75-2004, ▲ L2005 **EM** *020
CURSEEN, Albert F, Jr. 1756 METROMEDICAL DR, LAFAYETTE CLINIC, PA 28304 #051-04-1981 L1993 **PUD IM** *020 †20
CUSI, Antonio. 3035 BOONE TRAIL EXT, STE H 28304 #748-01-1974 L1989 **P** *020 †75
DAKA, Matthew Amiebi. 3649 CAPE CENTER DR, FAYETTEVILLE HEART CENTER 28304 #690-12-1990 L2007 **IC CD** *100 †20
DALVI, Sanjiv S. 2911 BREEZEWOOD AVE, STE 100 28303 #495-78-1985 L1998 **IM** *020 †20
DALVI, Sumedha Sanjiv. 2911 BREEZEWOOD AVE, STE 100 28303 #495-01-1992 L1998 **IM** *020 †20
DALY, Liam Noel. 210 FAIRWAY DR 28305 #539-06-1960 L1967 **P OS** *030 †75
DANCEL, Jose Cabauatan. 217 GLENSFORD DR 28314 #748-10-1978 L1995 **FM** *020 †18
DANFORTH, Wendell Calvin. 2047 VALLEYGATE DR 28304 #035-20-1990 L2008 **OPH OS** *020 †35
DANIEL, Crowell T, Jr. 1638 OWEN DR 28304 #051-04-1948 L1948 **OBG** *071 †30
DANIELS, Anthony Maurice. 2041 VALLEYGATE DR 28304 #023-12-1993 L2000 **GE** *020 †20
DANTZLER, Leon Entea, Jr. 1262 OLIVER ST, # A 28304 #036-01-1987 L1990 **IM** *020 †20
DAVE, Jayesh Bhalushanker. 1201 WALTER REED RD 28304 #495-23-1977 L1984 **IM** *020 †20
DAVIDSON, Leo W. 1841 QUIET CV 28304 #048-12-1987 L1992 **GS** *020 †85
DAVIES, John Aloysius. ■ 28314 #690-01-1978 L2002 **EM IM** *020 †16
DAVIS, Alan Shay. 2029 VALLEYGATE DR, FAYETTEVILLE WOMENS CARE 28304 #036-01-1994 L1998 **OBG** *020 †30
DAVIS, Alan Wayne. ■ 28304 #023-12-1996 L1998 **FM** *020 †18
DAVIS, Andrea P. 1601 OWEN DR 28304 #041-78-2005, ▲ L2008 **FP** *012
DAVIS-SANDERS, Beverly A. 1301 MEDICAL DR 28304 #010-03-1971 L1976 **DR OS** *020 †28,80
DE BOER, John Lawrence. 3415 MELROSE RD B, JOHN L DEBOER, MD, FACS 28304 #050-02-1971 L1988 **GS** *020 †85
DE OCAMPO-SCHILLING, Anna. 1540 PURDUE DR STE 101, RAINBOW PEDIATRICS OF FAYE 28303 #035-19-1993 L2001 **PD PEM** *020 †55
DESAI, Nilay Vipinbhai. ■ 28311 #495-23-1997 L2007 **END** *020 †20
DESAI, Nitin Dahyabhai. 1309 MEDICAL DR 28304 #495-23-1984 L1996 **IM** *020 †20
DESAI, Viren. 150 ROBESON ST 28301 #495-89-1990 L2001 **AN** *020 †05
DESVERREAUX, Robert W. 217 ST THOMAS RD 28311 #010-02-1993 L2004 **GP** *020
DEV, Gautam. 1205 CAPE CT, STE A 28304 #495-38-1984 L1995 **PCC SME** *020 †20
DEVASTHALI, Shirish. 2125 VALLEYGATE DR, STE 101 28304 #913-06-1980 L1990 **HO IM** *020 †20
DHANDHA, Medhavini H. 1638 OWEN DR 28304 #495-28-1976 L1994 **PD** *020 †55
DICKERSON, Andrea Blythe. 2029 VALLEYGATE DR, STE 101 28304 #036-01-1995 L2000 **OBG** *020 †30
DICKERSON, Edward Ernest. 2053 VALLEYGATE DR, STE 101 28304 #012-21-1992 L1994 **FPS** *020 †45
DISTELL, Bruce Michael. 1301 MEDICAL DR, CAROLINA REGIONAL RADIOLOG 28304 #041-01-1986 L1989 **DR** *020 †80
DOBSON, Casey William. ■ 28314 #036-01-2002 **FM** *100
DOBYNS, Perrin Thomas. ■ 28311 #047-06-1995 L2007 **FM** *020 †18
DONESON, Ira Nathaniel. 2300 RAMSEY ST, FAYETTEVILLE VAMC 28301 #019-02-1966 L1967 **P IM** *020 †75
DRAGER, Sandra L. 1601 OWEN DR, MED P 28304 #048-13-2002 L2004 **FP** *012
DRAKE, David E. 907 HAY ST, STE 101 28305 #036-07-1951 L1993 **GP** *071
DRAPKIN, Brock. 1638 OWEN DR, CAPE FEAR VALLEY HOSPITAL 28304 #035-46-1988 L2007 **IM** *020 †20 ‡
DUNCAN, John David. ■ 28311 #048-02-1968 L2004 **R** *075 †80
DURHAM, Susan Watson. 1638 OWEN DR 28304 #047-06-1986 L1990 **AN** *020 †05
DURODOYE, Oluyemisi Modin. 101 ROBESON ST STE 405, REG DIAB & ENDO CTR 28301 #690-01-1994 L2005 **END** *020 †20
DURR, Thomas Edward. ■ 28312 #023-07-1977 L1980 **PD** *020
DWIVEDI, Ghanshyam P. 1778 METROMEDICAL DR 28304 #496-38-1978 L1988 **IM** *020 †20
EARLA, Janaki Ram Prasad. ■ 28314 #495-11-1986 L2007 **IM** *100 †20
EJEH, Sylvester Uchenna. 909 S MCPHERSON CHURCH RD, WEST GA HEART & VASCULAR C 28303 #690-07-1989 L2006 **CD** *020 †20
EJINDU, Uwadiogbu Odinaka. ■ 28311 #690-15-1997 L2007 **PD** *020
ELGENDY, Issa Mostafa. 1262B OLIVER ST, MELROSE PEDIATRIC CARE 28304 #915-03-1978 L2000 **PD NPM** *020 †55
ELLIS, Charles Robt. ■ 28312 #036-05-1982 L1984 **FM OM** *020 †70,18
ELLISON, Gerald Lynn. 1638 OWEN DR 28304 #010-01-1965 L1972 **R** *071 †80
ELLISON, Richard Wesley. ■ 28311 #012-01-1992 L2004 **PS** *020 †85
ESENSOY, Taner. 1540 PURDUE DR, STE 101 28303 #902-03-1985 L1996 **PD** *020 †55 ‡
ESTES, Allison E. 514 OWEN DR, HARTNESS CONVENIENT CARE 28304 #048-15-2003 L2006 **PD** *100
FAILLACE, Deon Frances. 2041 VALLEYGATE DR, STE 202A 28304 #025-01-1976 L1987 **GS** *020 †85
FARMER, Donald Wm. 1301 MEDICAL DR, MAILING: P O BOX 87488 28304 #016-45-1979 L1993 **R** *020 †80
FAYKUS, Max H, Jr. 1301 MEDICAL DR, CAROLINA REGIONAL RADIOLOG 28304 #048-14-1987 L1993 **DR** *020 †80
FERRATO, Kenneth Paul. 1931 DANTE LN UNIT 104 28314 #038-44-1998 L2006 **EM** *020 †16
FIGUEROA, Jocelyn. ■ 28306 #033-05-2003 L2005 **FM** *020 †18
FIGUEROA, Lenardo E. 1463 PAMALEE DR 28303 #748-08-1992 L1999 **FM** *020 †18
FISHER, David R. 1301 MEDICAL DR 28304 #034-01-1979 L1983 **DR** *020 †80
FLANAGAN, James Patrick. 4140 FERNCREEK DR, STE 801 28314 #048-13-1992 L1997 **ORS** *020 †40
FLEISHMAN, Malcolm. ■ 28303 #036-01-1954 L1954 **IM OM** *071
FLEISHMAN, Samuel Alan. 1213 WALTER REED RD 28304 #036-08-1990 L1995 **P** *020 †75
FLEISHMAN, Stephen Baer. 1830 OWEN DR, BHVRL MEDCN CTR CUMBERLAND 28304 #023-01-1974 L1976 **CHP P** *071
FLEMING, Brian Keith. 1307 AVON ST 28304 #051-04-1984 L1987 **FM** *020 †18
FLOM, Jonathan Andrew. 1830 OWEN DR, RM 200 28304 #037-01-1998 L2004 **P** *020 †75
FLOWERS, Sylvania V. ■ 28301 #036-08-1996 L1996 **IM** *100
FONDINKA, Godfrey S. 6770 SURREY RD 28306 #217-01-1986 L2003 **FM EM** *020 †18 ‡
FRANCO, Jorge Luis. 2500 VILLAGE DR, STE 100 28304 #036-01-1986 L1988 **FM** *020 †18
FRANZONI, Garrett. 1537 OWEN PARK LN, CAPE FEAR REG UROL CLNC 28304 #010-02-1989 L1994 **U** *020 †95
FRIEDRICHS, Robt Richard. 1839 QUIET CV 28304 #028-34-1970 L1992 **OTO** *020 †45
FRIEND, Charles Wain. 1211 IRELAND DR A, DEVELOPMENTAL EVAL. CTR 28304 #012-05-1970 L1981 **PD PHP** *071 †55
FRY, Vincent Todd. ■ 28314 #038-41-2005 L2007 **FP** *012
GADIPUDI, Venu. 2500 VILLAGE DR STE 102, CAROLINA NEUROLOGY ASSOCAT 28304 #495-50-1990 L2004 **N** *020
GAITHER, Ronald Spencer. ■ 28303 #047-07-1969 L1974 **OBG** *020
GALI, Shobha Rani. 1248 FORT BRAGG RD 28305 #495-62-1999 L2005 **FM** *020 †18
GALLAHER, Keith James. 1638 OWEN DR, POST OFFICE BOX 2000 28304 #041-14-1982 L1990 **NPM PD** *020 †55
GARBER, Edgar Clyde, Jr. 1638 OWEN DR 28304 #051-04-1944 L1947 **GYN** *071 †30
GARDNER, Francis S, Jr. ■ 28314 #023-01-1951 L1951 **GYN** *071 †30
GARG, Kusum. 2414 HOPE MILLS RD 28304 #495-05-1987 L1999 **IM** *020 †20
GARG, Sanjay. ■ 28314 #495-73-1995 L2007 **RHU** *012 †20
GARISON, Gary Brown. 1638 OWEN DR 28304 #041-13-1962 L1970 **IM** *020
GASKINS, Raymond A, Jr. 405 OWEN DR 28304 #036-01-1975 L1975 **FM OM** *020 †18
GASTON, Johnny Eugene. 2312B MURCHISON RD 28301 #038-43-1974 L1977 **PD** *020 †55
GATES, Daniel George. ■ 28311 #023-12-1996 L1998 **CD** *020 †20
GEIGER, James Michael. 810 ELM ST 28303 #021-06-1973 L1976 **OPH** *020 †35
GESZLER, Gerianne. 2950 VILLAGE DR, STE 100 28304 #036-07-1985 L1986 **OBG** *020 †30
GHASSEMIAN, Jafar Nosrat. 2300 RAMSEY ST 28301 #517-01-1971 L1996 **IM END** *020 †20
GILBERT, David Branson. 3649 CAPE CENTER DR 28304 #007-02-1965 L1971 **CD IM** *020 †20
GILBERT, Stanley Keith, Jr. 4140 FERNCREEK DR, STE 801 28314 #051-01-1975 L1981 **ORS** *020 †40
GIMESH, John Sigmund. 3415 MELROSE RD STE C 28304 #473-01-1954 L1981 **PD** *071 †55
GINN, Stephen Mabry. 3634 CAPE CENTER DR, CAPE FEAR CARDIO ASSOC 28304 #038-43-1985 L1992 **CD** *020 †20
GLASER, Mark Stuart. 524 BEAUMONT RD, CAPE FEAR VALLEY EXPRESS C 28304 #010-02-1977 L1978 **EM GP** *020 †16
GLATZ, Guy Gregory. 1638 OWEN DR DEPT EMG, CAPE FEAR VALLEY MED CTR 28304 #041-14-1987 L1993 **EM FM** *020 †18
GLATZ, Lauren Marie. ■ 28314 #041-02-1985 L1994 **FM** *020 †18
GLUCK, Honi Lee. 1830 OWEN DR, RM 200 28304 #035-45-1987 L1993 **P** *020 †75
GODWIN, Harold Lacy. ■ 28305 #024-01-1947 L1947 **OS** *071
GOODING, Stephen Council. 1320 MEDICAL DR 28304 #036-05-1965 L1965 **OBG** *020 †30
GOODMAN, David Andrew. 4140 FERNCREEK DR STE 601, FERNCREEK GENERAL SURGERY, 28314 #917-21-1984 L1999 **GS** *020 †85
GOOTMAN, Aaron Harvey. 1840 OWEN DR STE 103, P O BOX 40107 28304 #045-01-1978 L2002 **AN PD** *020 †55,05
GORDON, Daniel Solomon. 3628 CAPE CENTER DR 28304 #023-12-1991 L1997 **DR** *020 †80 ‡
GORDON, David Michael. ■ 28306 #056-06-2005 L2006 **FP** *012
GORDON, Lakshmi. 2029 VALLEYGATE DR, STE 101 28304 #035-09-1993 L2000 **OBG** *020 †30
GOSWAMI, Promilla. 2300 RAMSEY ST, VETERANS AFFAIRS MEDICAL C 28301 #496-38-1964 L1999 **IM** *020 †20
GRAFENBERG, Matthew Ryan. ■ 28306 #023-12-2002 L2008 **OTO** *020
GRAFF, Louis G. ■ 28304 #041-02-1952 L1975 **AN** *071
GRAHAM, Ernesto Jf. 2915 RAEFORD RD STE 203, OB GYN 28303 #041-12-1992 L1996 **OBG** *020 †30
GRAHAM, Mark Alan. 3425 MELROSE RD, BEHAVIORAL HEALTH CARE 28304 #051-04-1988 L1998 **P** *020 †75
GRAY, Donna Elizabeth. 1219 WALTER REED RD, HIGHLAND VALLEY PEDIATRIC 28304 #010-03-1995 L2002 **PD** *020 †55
GREENE, Walter Blair. 4140 FERNCREEK DR, STE 801 28314 #036-01-1972 L1972 **OP OFA** *020 †40
GUNTER, Rita Louise. 227 FOUNTAINHEAD LN 28301 #036-01-1976 L1976 **PD** *020 †55
GUPTA, Chander K. 4140 FERNCREEK DR, STE 202 28314 #496-04-1978 L1996 **PD** *020 †55
GUPTA, Rakesh. 1880 QUIET CV, CAPE FEAR CENTER FOR DIGES 28304 #495-98-1980 L1990 **GE IM** *020 †20
HAAS-WESTON, Carlos F. 1638 OWEN DR 28304 #649-03-1959 L1985 **IM** *071 †20
HAIGLER, Lori Annette. 1601 OWEN DR, SOUTHERN REGIONAL AHEC 28304 #036-01-2002 L2004 **FM** *100 †18
HAIR, Glenn Edgar. 3314 MELROSE RD STE 100 28304 #036-01-1959 L1959 **OTO** *071 †45
HAITHCOCK, William Dana. 2029 VALLEYGATE DR, STE 101 28304 #045-01-1973 L1977 **GYN** *071 †30
HALL, Andre Felton. 3601 CAPE CENTER DR 28304 #038-41-1992 L1996 **OBG** *020 †30
HALL, James Saml. 1219 WALTER REED RD 28304 #036-07-1957 L1957 **PD** *071 †55
HAMMOND, Monique N. 1601 OWEN DR, MED P 28304 #005-77-2007, ▲ **FP** *012
HANNAN, Mohammed A. 2149 VALLEYGATE DR, STE 102 28304 #160-02-1985 L1999 **IM** *020 †20
HAQ, Muhammad Wasi. 227 FOUNTAINHEAD LN, E NEWTON SMITH PUBLIC HLTH 28301 #704-04-1979 L1997 **FM** *020 †18
HARANATH, Bogolu S. 3677 GLENBARRY CIR 28314 #495-50-1973 L1983 **DR** *020 †80
HARDISON, Joe Wm. 1320 MEDICAL DR 28304 #036-01-1965 L1965 **OBG** *071 †30
HARDISON, Lewis B. ■ 28303 #036-05-1952 L1952 **FM** *071 †18
HARRIS, Larry Coleman. 1271 OLIVER ST BOX 40405 28304 #036-07-1977 L1979 **PD** *020 †55
HARRISON, Richard James, Jr. ■ 28314 #048-04-2001 L2006 **ORS HS** *020

■ = Address Information Privacy Protected

HARTNESS, Christopher Bri. 328 COLINWOOD DR 28303 #051-04-2008 *012

HATCHER, Walter Benj. 3628 CAPE CENTER DR #036-08-1986 L1995 **DR NR** *020 †80

HAYES, Bennett Allen. 150 ROBESON ST 28301 #036-01-1957 L1957 **GYN** *071 †30

HAYES, Gerry Stetson. 2300 RAMSEY ST, USVA MED CTR 28301 #051-04-1971 L1974 **OPH PHP** *030 †35

HECKEL, Charles Gordon. ■ 28304 #051-01-1970 L1971 **LM AN** *062 †05

HENDERSON, Melvin Lee. 3601 CAPE CENTER DR, BIRTH & WOMENS CARE 28304 #036-07-1977 L2001 **OBG** *020 †30

HENDERSON-HINES, Nancy. 3412 RAMSEY ST, CFVMC 28311 #020-12-1990 L1993 **FM** *020 †18

HENLEY, John T, Jr. 1839 QUIET CV 28304 #036-01-1972 L1972 **OTO** *020 †45

HERRING, Stephen Mitchell. 516 BEAUMONT RD 28304 #036-05-1984 L1992 **PS** *020 †65

HESSENTHALER, Mark Eric. 711 EXECUTIVE PL, CHILD, ADOLESCENT AND ADUL 28305 #166-01-2001 L2007 **CHP** *020

HILES, Jason Michael. 28306 #023-12-1999 L2001 **GS** *020 †85

HILL, David Ashley. 1262 OLIVER ST, STE A 28304 #036-08-1997 L2001 **IM** *020 †20

HILL, Taneka Marie. 1601 OWEN DR 28304 #036-08-2004 L2006 **FM** *020 †18

HINES, Michele La Rue. ■ 28314 #046-01-1979 L1980 **R** *071

HINES, Robert Lee. 3637 CAPE CENTER DR 28304 #036-01-1978 L1980 **U** *020

HODGES, Ana Ceide. 2035 VALLEYGATE DR, STE 101 28304 #011-02-1992 L2000 **PD** *020 †55

HODGES, Michael Carson. 3634 CAPE CENTER DR 28304 #011-02-1998 L1998 **CD** *020 †20

HOROWITZ, Joel. 1841 QUIET CV, VILLAGE SURGICAL ASSOC 28304 #041-12-1988 L1995 **SO GS** *020 †85

HOSSAIN, Mir Mohd. Moshar. ■ 28314 #160-05-1995 L2007 **IM** *020 †20

HOWARD, James Starkey, III. 350 WAGONER DR, STE 103 28303 #036-01-1968 L1968 **GS** *071

HOWILER, Wm Edward, Jr. 1738 METROMEDICAL DR 28304 #045-01-1970 L1977 **GE IM** *071 †20

HTUN, Pyi Thet. 2149 VALLEYGATE DR 28304 #209-01-1980 L1998 **IM** *020 †20

HUGHES, John Robert. ■ 28311 #023-12-2002 L2008 **EM** *020 †16

HUGHES, Linda Kathryn. 200 FORSYTHE ST 28303 #011-02-1988 L1989 **FM** *020 †18

HUSAIN, Ali Khalid. 2153 VALLEYGATE DR, STE 101 28304 #496-38-1983 L2000 **TS** *020 †90,85

IGWILO, Obinna Chukwudi. 1220 WALTER REED DR, STE 102 28304 #690-04-1986 L2001 **GS AS** *020 †85

ISKANDER, Niveen Youssef. 1638 OWEN DR 28304 #036-08-1992 L1996 **PD** *020 †55

ISLAM, S.M. Jafrul. 2300 RAMSEY ST, VA MED CTR ANES SVC 28301 #160-02-1982 L2004 **AN** *020

IZURIETA, Henry. 514 BEAUMONT RD 28304 #847-04-1961 L1971 **IM OM** *020 ‡

JACKSON, Linda S. ■ 28314 #051-04-1997 L1999 **PD** *020 †55

JAHANGIR, Tahmida. 709 HAY ST 28301 #160-02-1982 L1994 **PD** *020 †55

JAIN, Manoj Kumar. 2300 RAMSEY ST, DEPT OF RAD VA MED CTR 28301 #495-45-1990 L2003 **R NR** *020 †80,28

JAUFMANN, Bruce Paul. 3650 CAPE CENTER DR 28304 #035-03-1984 L1993 **NS** *020 †25

JEAN JOSEPH, Yves M. 1601 OWEN DR 28304 #649-14-2004 **FM** *100

JESSUP, Pamela Hendrick. 1702 OWEN DR, US HEALTHWORKS 28304 #036-05-1977 L1978 **FM OM** *020 †18

JEWELL, John Nathan. 1638 OWEN DR 28304 #038-45-2001 L2006 **EM** *020 †16

JOHNSEN, Madalyn Linnetta. ■ 28312 #056-05-1943 L1948 **IM** *071

JOHNSON, Delores Lorraine. 3601 CAPE CENTER DR, BIRTH & WOMENS CARE, PA 28304 #010-03-1999 L2004 **OBG** *100

JOHNSON, James Erwin. 3308 MELROSE RD, FAYETTEVILLE ORTHOPEDIC 28304 #026-04-1969 L1978 **ORS** *020 †40

JOHNSON, Sabena Adepeju. 1638 OWEN DR 28304 #690-12-1989 L2003 **IM** *100 †20

JOHNSON, Samuel Vercile. 227 FOUNTAINHEAD LN 28301 #010-03-1957 L1975 **GP** *020

JONES, John Richard. 2041 VALLEYGATE DR 28304 #647-14-1978 L1987 **GE** *020 †20

JONES, John Wesley. 1638 OWEN DR 28304 #036-07-1976 L1981 **GE IM** *020 †20

JONES, Johnnie E. 1261 OLIVER ST 28304 #047-07-1976 L1980 **OBG** *020 †30

JONES, Karen V. 4140 FERNCREEK DR, STE 801 28314 #041-13-1988 L1995 **ORS** *020 †40

JONES, Michael Reesal. 1261 OLIVER ST 28304 #036-07-2000 L2004 **OBG** *020 †30

JONES, Tara M R. 2590 EDMONTON RD, 2590 EDMONTON RD 28304 #047-07-1976 L1980 **FM** *020 †18

JONES, Wendy Pilar. 2950 VILLAGE DR, STE 100 28304 #036-08-2000 L2004 **OBG** *020

JORDAN, Sheryl Gillikin. 1301 MEDICAL DR, CAROLINA REGIONAL RADIOLOG 28304 #036-01-1985 L1988 **DR** *020 †80

JORDAN, Stuart Harrington. 2950 VILLAGE DR, STE 100 28304 #036-01-1985 L1987 **OBG** *020

JORDAN, Weldon Huske. 114 BROADFOOT AVE 28305 #024-01-1947 L1947 **IM** *071 †20

JORDAN, William Rand. 2014 LITHO PL 28304 #036-01-1970 L1970 **U** *020 †95

KAMINENI, Neelima. ■ 28311 #495-37-2001 L2007 **IM** *020

KANG, Hwa Ing. 2300 RAMSEY ST 28301 #506-02-1965 L1976 **P** *020 †75 ‡

KANSORA, Mary Beth. 2139 VALLEYGATE DR, STE 101A 28304 #035-03-1996 L2000 **OPH** *020 †35

KANTESARIA, Atul N. 1724 ROXIE AVE, MENTAL HEALTH CENTER 28304 #495-22-1982 L1994 **P** *020 †75

KARIYIL, Joseph T. 1778 METROMEDICAL DR 28304 #495-80-1986 L1999 **NEP** *020 †20

KASARI, Mark Aarne. 557 SANDHURST DR 28304 #665-01-1997 L2002 **NEP IM** *020 †20

KASSEL, Burton Anton. ■ 28311 #038-40-1956 L1988 **FM** *071 †18

KASTNER, Robert John. 3634 CAPE CENTER DR, CAPE FEAR CARD ASSOC 28304 #023-01-1987 L1998 **CD IM** *020 †20

KAUR, Narinder. 1601 OWEN DR, MED P 28304 #305-01-2006 **FP** *012

KEALY, Ryan M. 1601 OWEN DR, DEPT FM 28304 #048-14-2007 **FP** *012

KECKICH, Walter A. 2300 RAMSEY ST, VA MEDICAL CENTER OF FAYET 28301 #017-20-1971 L2004 **P PYG** *020 †75

KELLY, Catherine Margaret. 413 OWEN DR, STE 201 28304 #038-43-1990 L1991 **FM** *020 †18

KELLY, William Huske. 1606 MORGANTON RD, BOX 53127 28305 #036-01-1989 L1992 **PD** *020 †55

KERANEN, Victor Jos. 3314 MELROSE RD, STE 104 28304 #036-07-1964 L1964 **NS** *071 †25

KERNS, Joshua Simon. ■ 28314 #047-07-2003 **PD** *100

KETHEESWARAN, Markandu. 1209 CAPE CT 28304 #422-01-1990 L1997 **ON IM** *020 †20

KHAN, Abdul Talib. ■ 28303 #704-02-1985 L2003 **IM** *020 †20

KHASRU, Muhammed Amir. 1309 MEDICAL DR, STE 101 28304 #160-02-1982 L2001 **N** *020 †75

KHIATANI, Vishal. ■ 28303 #051-04-2007 **GS** *012

KHINE, Kyaw. 2300 RAMSEY ST, VA MEDICAL CENTER 28301 #209-01-1980 L2004 **IM** *020 †20

KHODAPARAST, Hamid. 2300 RAMSEY ST, VA MEDICAL CENTER 28301 #517-01-1966 L1992 **PUD IM** *071 †20

KHURANA, Rajesh Kumar. 1307 AVON ST 28304 #065-01-1993 L1995 **FM** *020 †18

KILGORE, Larry Chas. 1220 WALTER REED RD 28304 #004-01-1981 L2001 **FM** *075 †18

KILLAM, Arthur Robt. ■ 28303 #024-05-1944 L1973 **GS** *071 †85

KIM, Sarah. 1317 MEDICAL DR 28304 #005-12-1950 L1980 **AI** *071 †03 ‡

KIM, William No Chun. 1317 MEDICAL DR 28304 #005-12-1952 L1980 **OBG A** *071

KLANG, Thor. 3634 CAPE CENTER DR, CAPE FEAR CARDIOLOGY ASS 28304 #035-09-1988 L1995 **CD** *020 †20

KODALI, Usha. 3649 CAPE CENTER DR, FAYETTERVILLE HEART CENTER 28304 #495-50-1986 L1991 **CD** *020 †20

KODALI, Valli P. 2041 VALLEYGATE DR 28304 #495-11-1984 L1992 **GE IM** *020 †20

KOHTZ, Scott Allen. ■ 28311 #030-05-1994 L1994 **IM** *020 †20

KOMANDUR, Revati. 1262A OLIVER ST, CAPE FEAR VALLEY INTERNAL 28304 #495-05-1987 L1996 **IM** *020 †20

KOMES, Sermsook. ■ 28303 #891-01-1958 L1968 **CLP PTH** *020 †50

KOMMU, Chandrasekh. 6387 RAMSEY ST, UNIT 210 28311 #048-12-1993 L1996 **FM** *020 †18

KOO, Kim-Eng. 3650 CAPE CENTER DR 28304 #004-13-1982 L2000 **NS** *020 †25

KOSKINEN, Kenneth Ralph. 3322 MELROSE RD 28304 #023-01-1966 L2003 **AM EM** *020 †55

KOTZEN, Rene Marlon. 266 COURTYARD LN 28303 #550-02-1988 L2002 **NS** *020 ‡

KOUBA, Stephen Howard. 4140 FERNCREEK DR, STE 801 28314 #010-02-1980 L1985 **ORS** *020 †40

KRAKOVER, Brian Alan. ■ 28303 #051-04-2001 L2003 **EM** *020 †16

KREBS, Christopher Michae. ■ 28311 #023-12-2005 L2007 **FP** *012

KRISHNA, Kalpana. 1218 WALTER REED RD, INTERNAL MEDICINE, PA 28304 #495-37-1986 L1995 **IM** *020 †20

KUBIT, Victor Francis. 2525 RAEFORD RD, STE B 28305 #041-12-1994 L2001 **AN** *020 †05

KULKARNI, Abhijit Anil. ■ 28304 #010-02-1997 L2001 **N IM** *020

KULKARNI, Sayali Abhijit. ■ 28304 #496-38-2000 L2005 **P** *100 †75

KUMAR, Arvind. 2041 VALLEYGATE DR 28304 #495-54-1992 L2000 **GE IMG** *020 †20

KUNDURU, Chandrasekhar R. 2300 RAMSEY ST, FUAMC EMER ROOM 28301 #495-62-1987 L2002 **IM** *020 †20

LAL, Jagdish. 6958 NEXUS CT, STE 101 28304 #495-03-1981 L1999 **IM** *020 †20

LAY, Jennifer Lynn. ■ 28311 #020-12-2000 L2003 **FM** *020 †20

LEKE, Michael A. 1251 OLIVER ST, CAROLINA VASCULAR INSTITUT 28304 #217-01-1990 L2007 **VS GS** *020 †85

LE MASTER, Pierre C. 1291 OLIVER ST 28304 #011-03-1971 L1975 **PD** *020 †55

LESICA, John Jos. 1830 OWEN DR, RM 200 28304 #010-02-1983 L1987 **CHP P** *020 †55,75

LESPES, Eric J. ■ 28314 #440-01-1978 L2007 **P** *100

LEWIS, Anessa Janine. 2950 VILLAGE DR, WOMEN'S WELLNESS CENTER PA 28304 #036-08-1999 L2003 **OBG** *020 †30

LIDONNICI, Kenneth Robt. 559 EXECUTIVE PL, STE 202 28305 #028-02-1989 L1994 **PTH** *020 †50

LITTLE, Julia Elizabeth. ■ 28312 #024-01-1987 L1993 **GS** *020 †85

LIVINGSTON, James L. 1463 PAMALEE DR, WESTSIDE MEDICAL CARE 28303 #036-08-1985 L1988 **FM OBS** *020 †18

LOCKLEAR, Irlene. 1201 WALTER REED RD 28304 #039-01-1993 L1999 **PCC** *020 †20

LOGEL, Robert John. 3308 MELROSE RD, FAYETTEVILLE ORTHOPEDIC 28304 #028-03-1972 L1976 **ORS** *072 †40

LOGUE, Stephen Stuart. 1843 QUIET CV 28304 #036-01-1979 L1982 **IM** *020 †20

LOHAVICHAN, Virat. ■ 28305 #891-02-1963 L1973 **IM** *071

LOMIS, Nick Nikolaost T. 3628 CAPE CENTER DR, CAROLINA IMAGING CENTER 28304 #023-12-1990 L2002 **DR** *020 †40

LONG, Horace Robt. 1606 MORGANTON RD, FAYETTEVILLE CHILDRENS CLI 28305 #036-08-1986 L1989 **NPM** *020 †55

LOUGHLIN, Howard Hopkins. 1601 OWEN DR 28304 #041-01-1970 L1975 **PD** *030 †55

MACK, Barbara. 1638 OWEN DR 28304 #024-05-1986 L1991 **GP** *071

MAHER, Fayez Anis. ■ 28305 #330-03-1954 L1981 **CD IM** *020 †20

MALICK, Sajjad A. 6387 RAMSEY ST, FAYETTEVILLE 28311 #704-02-1988 L1999 **HO IM** *020 †20

MALISH, Richard Glade. 3656 CAPE CENTER DR, CAROLINA CARDIOLOGY PA 28304 #023-12-1996 L2007 **CD** *020 †20

MANI, Aleyamma Jiji. 2300 RAMSEY ST, FAYETTEVILLE VA 28301 #495-63-1991 L1998 **IM** *020 †20

MANNING, Kenneth Russell. 6387 RAMSEY ST 28311 #051-04-1987 L1988 **ON** *020 †20

MANSFIELD, Eric Lemoine. 2053 VALLEYGATE DR, STE 101 28304 #012-21-1991 L1998 **OTO** *020 †45

MARTINEZ, Anthony. ■ 28306 #048-02-2002 **FM** *100

MASOOD, Habib Abul. 2300 RAMSEY ST, VA MEDICAL CENTER 28301 #160-02-1982 L2004 **IM** *020 †20

MATHEW, K Thomas. ■ 28305 #495-27-1980 L1998 **OBG** *020

MATLACK, Robert Kepler, Jr. 2587 RAVENHILL 28303 #036-08-1996 L2002 **P** *020 †75

MATTHEW-THOMPSON, Laura. 2151 SKIBO RD, STE 100 28314 #010-03-1980 L2001 **FM** *020 †18

MAUGHAN, Robert Emmett. 3650 CAPE CENTER DR 28304 #035-08-1988 L1998 **TS** *020 †85,90

MC ALISTER, Linda Theresa. 511 OWEN DR 28304 #005-02-1978 L1984 **OBG** *020 †30

MC CONNELL, Jane Morehead. ■ 28314 #024-07-1987 L1996 **EM** *020 †18,16

MC CUTCHEN, Thomas M, Jr. 1219 WALTER REED 28304 #047-05-1963 L1968 **PD** *020 †55

MC DANIEL, Jack Paschal. 2125 VALLEYGATE DR, STE 201 28304 #036-01-1956 L1956 **GYN** *071 †30

MC FADDEN, Donald Douglas. 2300 RAMSEY ST 28301 #065-06-1975 L1981 **GS** *020 †85 ‡

MC FADYEN, Oscar L, Jr. ■ 28304 #005-07-1940 L1941 **IM** *071

MC FARLANE, Douglas S. 4140 FERNCREEK DR, STE 801 28314 #919-03-1969 L1992 **ORS** *100 †40

MCGRAW, Scott Thos. 726 RAMSEY ST STE 7 28301 #056-06-1989 L1994 **DR** *020 †80

MC GUIRE, Arthur M. 2300 RAMSEY ST, DEPT OF SURGERY VA HOSP 28301 #026-04-1957 L1957 **GS AM** *020 †85

MC ILWAIN, Anjanette L. 1271 OLIVER ST 28304 #010-03-1996 L2002 **PD** *020 †55

MC ILWAIN, Thos Pinckney. 1638 OWEN DR 28304 #045-01-1975 L1987 **P** *020 †75

MC LEAN, James Wilton. ■ 28305 #035-19-1943 L1947 **IM** *071

MC LESTER, William Dumas. 1635A OWEN DR 28304 #036-01-1965 L1965 **OPH PTH** *071 †50,35

MC MAHON, Connette Pearl. 4723 FLINTCASTLE RD 28314 #036-07-2000 L2004 **OBG** *020 †30

MEAKEM, Thomas James, III. 1301 MEDICAL DR 28304 #010-01-1987 L1994 **DR** *020 †80

MEEK, Joe Bernard. ■ 28304 #045-01-1964 L1973 **ORS** *020 †40

MEEKS, Robert Earl, Jr. 2950 VILLAGE DR, STE 100 28304 #012-22-1989 L1993 **OBG** *020 †30

MEEKS, Toni A Davis. 1843 QUIET CV 28304 #012-22-1989 L1993 **IM** *020 †20
MEHTA, Hasumati V. 518 SANDHURST DR 28304 #496-38-1969 L1975 **GYN GP** *020 †18
MEHTA, Vijaykumar. 518 SANDHURST DR, MEHTA MEDICAL SERVICES 28304 #495-23-1957 L1974 **HEM IM** *020 †20
MELTON, Gwenesta Barnum. 1756 METROMEDICAL DR, LAFAYETTE CLINIC PA 28304 #021-01-1979 L1989 **RHU IM** *020 †20
MELTON, Kenneth. 557 SANDHURST DR, CAROLINA KIDNEY CARE PA 28304 #021-01-1978 L1989 **NEP IM** *020 †20
MENDES, Celia Maria. 1905 SKIBO RD 28314 #043-01-1991 L1995 **OBG** *020 †30
MERGY, James Arthur. 1601 OWEN DR 28304 #005-02-1987 L1993 **FM** *020 †18
MERZ, Miriam Sloan. ■ 28311 #032-01-2002 L2002 **FP** *012 †18
MESSNER, Keith Harold. ■ 28314 #041-13-2003 L2006 **EM** *020 †16
MEYER, Graham Scott. ■ 28314 #065-06-1986 L1998 **EM PEM** *020 †16
MEYER, Hans Peter. 2300 RAMSEY ST 28301 #005-14-1964 L1994 **ORS** *071 †40
MEYER, Jeffrey Scot. ■ 28304 #010-01-2002 L2004 **P** *020 †75
MILLER, Dudley Conley. 150 ROBESON ST 28301 #028-03-1959 L1969 **OBG** *072 †30
MILLER, Ernesto Armentia. 1516 OWEN DR 28304 #748-09-1967 L1984 **GP** *071
MILLER, Horace Wm, IV. 1774 METROMEDICAL DR 28304 #036-01-1982 L1983 **PS HS** *020
MILLER, Stephen Gary. 3427 MELROSE RD 28304 #041-14-1998 L2005 **PDC** *020 †55
MILLER, William Carey. ■ 28304 #045-01-1958 L1967 **R** *071 †80
MINER, David D. 2029 VALLEYGATE DR, STE 101 28304 #048-04-2003 L2007 **OBG** *020
MITCHELL, James Alistair. 1601 OWEN DR, PRACTICE 28304 #040-02-1999 L2004 **FM** *020 †18
MITCHELL, Sharon Sonia. 1307 AVON ST 28304 #010-03-1986 L1989 **FM** *020 †18
MITHANI, Hasmukhlal A. ■ 28314 #915-03-1965 L1978 **OPH GP** *071 †35
MITTAL, Sanjay. 557 SANDHURST DR, CAROLINA KIDNEY CARE 28304 #496-09-1989 L2003 **NEP IM** *020 †20
MOORE, Gordon Sampson. 1601 OWEN DR # B 28304 #047-07-1972 **FM** *020
MOORE, Michael Radford. ■ 28306 #023-12-2005 L2007 **FP** *012
MORFESIS, Florias Andreas. 513 OWEN DR 28304 #041-14-1979 L1997 **GS SO** *020 †85
MORRIS, Deborah Lynn. 420 OWEN DR 28304 #036-01-1992 L1993 **UCM FM** *020
MORRISON, Robert H. 1638 OWEN DR 28304 #051-01-1944 L1955 **OBG** *071 †30
MOULTRIE, Johnnie Lewis. 1601 OWEN DR, AHEC FAMILY 28304 #036-08-2003 L2006 **FM** *020 †18
MU, Thornton S. ■ 28311 #048-15-2003 L2005 **PD** *020 †55
MUENZNER, Paul Scott. ■ 28311 #020-12-1973 L1997 **ORS** *020 †40
MULLEN, Patrick Dennis. 2300 RAMSEY ST 28301 #030-05-1974 L1995 **GS HS** *020 †85
MUNUGOTI, Srinivas. 3634 CAPE CENTER DR, CAPE FEAR CARDIOLOGY ASSOC 28304 #495-21-1992 L2002 **CD** *020 †20
MURPHY, Bryant Armond. 150 ROBESON ST 28301 #036-05-1997 L2000 **AN** *020 †05
MURRAY, Valerie Ann. 823 ELM ST, STE 205 28303 #035-19-1981 L1991 **P CHP** *020 †75
MYERS, Danny Allen. 2014 LITHO PL 28304 #036-01-1975 L1977 **U GS** *071 †95
MYERS, Susan Gail. 501 EXECUTIVE PL STE A 28305 #038-44-1987 L1995 **P PYG** *020 †75
MYNENI, Prasanthi. 2300 RAMSEY ST, VA MEDICAL CENTER 28301 #495-58-1980 L1997 **P ADP** *020 †75
MYNENI, Venkata N. 2300 RAMSEY ST, VA MEDICAL CENTER 28301 #495-50-1976 L1997 **FM** *020 †18
NAIK, Ajit Nagarji. 2944 BREEZEWOOD AVE STE 10, MAILING: P O BOX 87022 28303 #495-48-1974 L1991 **IM** *020 †20
NASIRI, Mohammad Sabur. 508 SANDHURST DR 28304 #160-03-1982 L1992 **PD** *020 †55
NATARAJA, H. 2300 RAMSEY ST, VA MEDICAL CTR 28301 #495-09-1972 L1977 **P PYG** *020 †75
NATARAJAN, Sheila. ■ 28306 #036-01-2007 **IM** *012
NAZIR, Tariq. 2125 VALLEYGATE DR, STE 101 28304 #704-16-1990 L2004 **IM HO** *020 †20
NETTLES, George Stueard. ■ 28311 #045-01-1963 L2005 **IM** *020
NEWMAN, Edwin Carraway, III. 4140 FERNCREEK DR, STE 801 28314 #036-08-2002 L2006 **ORS** *020
NEWMAN, William Harold. ■ 28305 #036-05-1956 L1956 **GS TS** *071 †85,90
NGUYEN, Don Khiem. 5149 BRAGG BLVD, ALPHA THERAPEUTIC CORPORAT 28303 #941-01-1966 L1984 **GP** *071
NINAN, Champil Abraham. VET CENTER 28301 #495-27-1957 L1989 **U** *020
NIX, Tandeka Moneak. 1638 OWEN DR 28304 #001-02-1999 L2000 **FM** *020 †18
NOLAN, James Francis. 1786 METROMEDICAL DR 28304 #041-12-1984 L1994 **U** *020 †95
NORDNESS, Paul Jorgen. 1841 QUIET CV 28304 #047-05-1995 L2004 **VS** *020 †85
NOREM, Julia. 405 OWEN DR 28304 #036-01-1994 L1995 **FM** *020 †18
NORRIS, Cynthia Mae. 413 OWEN DR, STE 202 28304 #004-01-1987 L1995 **FM** *020 †18
NWAMARA-AKA, Emmanuel Oke. 1638 OWEN DR, VALLEY MEDICAL ASSOCIATES 28304 #690-06-1983 L2006 **IM HOS** *020 †20
NWOSU, Agodichi U. 909 S MCPHERSON CHURCH RD 28303 #690-08-1983 L2000 **CD** *020 †20
OBI-GWACHAM, Nwaobiara O. 1638 OWEN DR, CAPE FEAR VLY HLTH SYS VMA 28304 #690-02-1983 L2003 **IM** *020 †20
OGUNWO, Susannah Ibironke. 1638 OWEN DR, CAPE FEAR VALLEY HEALTH SY 28304 #690-05-1989 L2006 **FPG** *020 †18
OHADUGHA, Godfrey E. 6387 RAMSEY ST 28311 #649-14-1980 L1985 **FM** *020 †18
OJO, Babatunde Abiodun. 1815 FORT BRAGG RD 28303 #690-05-1986 L1999 **IM** *020 †20
OKONKWO, Ifeyinwa Juliana. 101 ROBESON ST, STE 202 28301 #690-04-1991 L2007 **IMG** *100 †20
OKOYE, Obiefuna Perry. 101 ROBESON ST, STE 405 28301 #690-04-1996 L2006 **ID IM** *020
OLSON, David Reese. ■ 28305 #028-03-1993 L1996 **PD GP** *020 †55 ‡
OLSON, Elis Yngve. 521 BEAUMONT RD, PEDIATRIC ADMINISTRATION 28304 #012-05-1986 L1999 **PD** *020 †55
ORTIZ, Fernando L. ■ 28314 #042-03-1985 L1989 **FM** *030 †18
OWENS, Bennett G, Jr. ■ 28311 #012-05-1964 L1996 **FM AM** *071 †70,18
PACK, Elliot Roy. 1919 GILLESPIE ST 28306 #010-02-1974 L1976 **GYN PHP** *020
PANG, Clarito Mendoza. 1262 OLIVER ST, MELROSE PEDIATRIC CARE 28304 #748-02-1967 L1987 **PD GP** *020 †55
PANTELAKOS, Constantine G. 1839 QUIET CV 28304 #036-07-1957 L1957 **OTO** *020
PANTELAKOS, George C. 1248 FORT BRAGG RD, HAYMOUNT PRIMARY CARE CENT 28305 #036-08-1987 L1998 **FM** *020 †18
PANTELAKOS, Steven Thos. 1839 QUIET CV 28304 #036-08-1988 L1991 **OTO** *020 †45
PARACHA, Muhammad A. 3656 CAPE CENTER DR, CAROLINA CARDIOLOGY 28304 #704-02-1986 L2001 **CD** *020 †20
PARENTE, Lynn Tavares. 439 WESTWOOD SHOPPING CTR 28314 #041-15-2002 L2004 **OBG** *020 †30
PARFITT, Henry Edward, Jr. 1786 METROMEDICAL DR 28304 #036-01-1975 L1982 **U** *020 †95
PARIKH, Rakesh A. 1638 OWEN DR 28304 #495-76-1980 L1996 **PM** *020 †60
PARIKH, Roshan P. 2944 BREEZEWOOD AVE, STE 101 28303 #495-76-1984 L1997 **IM** *020 †20
PARKER, David Ray. ■ 28304 #036-08-1999 L2003 **FM** *020 †18
PATAKI, Istvan Steven. 6387 RAMSEY ST 28311 #065-01-1994 L2005 **RO** *020 †80
PATEL, Arvindkumar K. 2300 RAMSEY ST 28301 #495-22-1982 L1994 **IM** *020 †20
PATEL, Divyang Rambhai. 3649 CAPE CENTER DR 28304 #495-76-1986 L1995 **CD** *020 †20
PATEL, Hemangini K. 4140 FERNCREEK DR STE 501, CAPE FEAR NEUROLOGY ASSOC 28314 #495-23-1979 L1996 **N CN** *020 †75
PATEL, Jirpesh. 2300 RAMSEY ST, VA MEDICAL CENTER 28301 #495-22-1993 L2001 **CHP P** *020
PATEL, Kalpesh Sureshbhai. 1638 OWEN DR, CAPE FEAR VALLEY HEALTH SY 28304 #495-23-1999 L2005 **IM** *100 †20
PATEL, Kamlesh P. 1301 MEDICAL DR, STE B 28304 #495-23-1979 L1996 **IM** *020 †20
PATEL, Pravinkumar K. 3653 CAPE CENTER DR 28304 #690-01-1985 L1995 **IM** *020 †20
PATEL, Rameshchandra V. 1220 WALTER REED RD RU 28304 #495-22-1982 L1994 **IM** *020 †20
PATEL, Sandip S. 3653 CAPE CENTER DR, MAILING: P O BOX 41806 28304 #495-22-1988 L1995 **IM** *020 †20
PATEL, Shashikant J. 3514 VILLAGE DR, SOUTHERN INTERNAL MEDICINE 28304 #495-89-1984 L1999 **IM** *020 †20
PATEL, Sheel. 1726 METROMEDICAL DR, CAPE FEAR EYE ASSOCIATES, 28304 #038-44-2001 L2006 **OPH** *020 †35
PAYNE, Frederick B, Jr. 1781 METROMEDICAL DR, FAYETTEVILLE ANESTHESIA PA 28304 #036-01-1985 L1988 **AN** *020 †05
PENNINK, Menno. 235 OLD ST, # 101 28301 #660-01-1965 L1974 **NS** *071
PENROSE, John F. 743 MAGELLAN CT 28311 #028-46-1984 L2004 **AI RHU** *020 †20,55
PERRITT, Terezinha M. 2300 RAMSEY ST 28301 #187-02-1978 L1984 **IM** *020 †20
PHILLIPS, Thirston Savoy, Jr. 597 OLIVER ST 28304 #055-75-2000, ▲ L2004 **PM** *020 †60
PINNELL, Charles W, III. ■ 28311 #051-04-1979 L1998 **OBG** *020 †30
POGLINCO, John Anthony. ■ 28303 #008-01-1959 L1998 **FM OBG** *020 †30
POLLARD, John Christopher. 1219 WALTER REED RD 28304 #051-01-1968 L1974 **PD** *020 †55 ‡
POMERANS, Mark. 1766 METROMEDICAL DR 28304 #924-01-1964 L1979 **GP** *071
PONDER, Jerome Vincent. 1617 OWEN DR 28304 #036-05-1997 L1999 **OBG** *020 †30 ‡
POPIO, Kenneth Angelo. 1638 OWEN DR 28304 #035-01-1966 L2001 **CD IM** *071 †20
POULOS, John Emanuel. 2041 VALLEYGATE DR 28304 #036-08-1991 L1998 **GE** *020 †20
POWELL, William C. 1606 MORGANTON RD 28305 #036-05-1952 L1997 **PD** *071 †55
QIAN, Xiao Yan. ■ 28314 #243-16-1987 L2000 **IM** *020 †20
QUASHIE, Dawn Valaire. 2135 VALLEYGATE DR, STE 101 28304 #036-05-1995 L1998 **FM** *020 †18
QUICK, Clifton M. ■ 28301 #010-03-1949 L1949 **OPH OS** *071
QUINLAN, Kevin John. 5085 MORGANTON RD, RAPHA PRIMARY CARE CENTER 28314 #008-02-1984 L2000 **IM EM** *020 †20
QUINONES, Deogracia. 1537 OWEN PARK LN 28304 #042-01-1982 L1992 **U** *020 †95 ‡
QURESHI, Fahim U. 109 BRADFORD AVE, 109 BRADFORD AVE 28301 #704-16-1984 L2000 **CHP** *020
RAHMAN, Md. Shafiqur. ■ 28303 #160-07-1997 L2007 **IM** *020 †20
RAHMAN, Mizanur. 2300 RAMSEY ST, VA MEDICAL CENTER 28301 #160-02-1985 L2005 **PYG** *020 †75
RAMACHANDRAN, Rangasamy. 1766 METROMEDICAL DR, FAYETTEVILLE NEUROLOGY ASS 28304 #495-99-1978 L1997 **N** *020 †75
RAY, John Make, Jr. 3625 CAPE CENTER DR 28304 #047-07-1999 L2000 **FM** *020 †18
REAVES, Leonard E, III. 334 NORTHVIEW DR, VANSTORY HILLS 28303 #036-01-1961 L1961 **GE IM** *020 †20
REED, John Joseph, Jr. 1638 OWEN DR, CAPE FEAR VALLEY MEDICAL C 28304 #010-02-1985 L1988 **EM** *020 †16
REESAL, Michael R. 3415 MELROSE RD C 28304 #918-01-1955 L1996 **OM GP** *020 †50,70
RICHTER, Brad Arthur. 1781 METROMEDICAL DR, FAYETTEVILLE ANESTHESIA, P 28304 #056-06-1991 L2000 **AN** *020 †05
RICHTER, Holly Mallett. 3616B CAPE CENTER DR 28304 #036-01-1994 L1995 **PD** *020 †55
RIESBERG, Jamie C. ■ 28314 #023-12-2003 L2005 **FM** *020 †18
RIGGINS, Jimmie Wayne. 1726 METROMEDICAL DR 28304 #023-12-1988 L1998 **OPH** *020 †35
RITCHEY, John Phillip. 810 ELM ST 28303 #040-02-1965 L1973 **OPH** *071 †35
RIVERS, Rueben N. 1314 MEDICAL DR STE 102 28304 #036-07-1978 L1982 **IM** *020 †20
RIZVI, Syed Asif Raza. 105 ROXIE AVE 28304 #704-20-1984 L1994 **END IM** *020 †20
ROBERSON, Elizabeth S. 2587 RAVENHILL DR 28303 #055-02-1995 L2008 **PYG P** *020 †75
ROBERTS, Leroy, Jr. 2015 VALLEYGATE DR, STE 101 28304 #041-13-1976 L1987 **RNR DR** *020 †80
ROBINSON, Gary James. 1 HAMILTON ST 2539, FORT BRAGG VHC 28307 #010-03-1991 L1994 **FM** *020 †18
ROBISON, Joseph Evans. 3308 MELROSE RD, FAYETTEVILLE ORTHOPAEDICS 28304 #011-03-2001 L2007 **HS** *020
ROCHMAN, Stephen Chas. 1537 OWEN PARK LN 28304 #047-07-1970 L1977 **U** *020 †95
ROMEO, Joseph. 1706 CEDAR CREEK RD 28312 #422-01-1987 L1996 **PD AN** *020 †55
ROMYN, Antonie Martinus. ■ 28311 #016-11-1974 L1996 **NM PTH** *020 †50,28
ROSEMOND, John H, Jr. 811 STAMPER RD, BRAGG FAM PRAC CLINIC 28303 #038-40-1979 L1989 **FM** *020 †18 ‡
ROTHSTEIN, Manfred S. 1308 MEDICAL DR, FAYETTEVILLE DERMATOLOGY 28304 #036-07-1974 L1975 **D** *020 †15 ‡
ROULHAC, Maurice Raynard. 1251 OLIVER ST, CAROLINA VASCULAR INSTITUT 28304 #011-04-1987 L1993 **VS** *020 †85
ROUX, Richard Eugene. 1301 MEDICAL DR 28304 #010-02-1988 L1993 **DR** *020 †80
RUCKER, Tinsley White. 1307 AVON ST 28304 #012-05-1976 L1984 **FM** *020 †18
RUIZ-COPHER, Marie Prisci. 1219 WALTER REED RD, HIGHLAND VALLEY PEDS CARE 28304 #748-02-1987 L2001 **PD** *020 †55
RYNNE, Michael V. 2300 RAMSEY ST, FAYETTEVILLE NC VA 28301 #065-01-1971 L2004 **OPH** *020 †35 ‡
SADAT, Abdul Qayom. 1638 OWEN DR 28304 #118-01-1978 L1991 **EM P** *020 †18
SAINI, Hari Parshad. 3656 CAPE CENTER DR, CAROLINA CARDIOLOGY 28304 #038-45-1992 L2003 **CD** *020 †20
SALAHUDDIN, Abu N. 2149 VALLEYGATE DR 28304 #160-02-1981 L1997 **IM EM** *020 †20
SALIBA, Constantin. 1638 OWEN DR 28304 #605-02-1950 L1969 **GS TRS** *020
SALZBERG, Lenard D. 1601 OWEN DR 28304 #035-03-1988 L1989 **FM** *020 †18
SAMPSON, Carolyn Marie. 1307 AVON ST 28304 #036-01-1986 L1988 **FM NS** *020 †18
SANCHEZ-RIVERA, Efrain A. 3322 MELROSE RD 28304 #042-03-1991 L2006 **CCP** *020 †55
SAND, Vijaichand S. PO BOX 9404, MEDICAL CENTER 28311 #495-20-1963 L1971 **U EM** *071 †95 ‡

■ = Address Information Privacy Protected

SANDERS, Michael S. ■ 28304 #010-03-1971 L1976 IM *071 †20
SANDERSON, William Earl. 2409 MURCHISON RD, MURCHISON MEDICAL CARE 28301 #036-01-1984 L1985 FM *020 †18
SANGAVARAM, Sirisha. 1601 OWEN DR, MED P 28304 #422-01-2007 FP *012
SANTANGELO, Amy Chen. 1905 SKIBO RD 28314 #010-02-1992 L1999 IM *020 †20
SANTIAGO-MALDONADO, Ida. ■ 28312 #042-01-1995 L1998 NM IM *020 †20,28
SANTZ, Jos I. Rosario. 1601 OWEN DR 28304 #305-01-2002 L2005 IM *020 †18
SAPPENFIELD, Luther Cook. 2139 VALLEYGATE DR, STE 101A 28304 #036-07-1957 L1957 OPH *020 †35
SASHIDHAR, Sreelekha. 2109 VALLEYGATE DR, STE 101 28304 #495-80-1990 L1996 PD *020 †55
SCHAEFER, William Dickson. 3308 MELROSE RD, FAYETTEVILLE ORTHOPEDIC 28304 #036-05-1996 L1997 ORS *020 †40
SCHAIDER, Elisabeth A. 2525 RAEFORD RD STE B, CUMBERLAND ANESTHESIA ASSO 28305 #039-01-1990 L2001 AN *020 †05
SCHAUER, Jeanne A Semones. 1638 OWEN DR 28304 #036-01-1981 L1985 P *020
SCHELL, Scott Thos. 3616 CAPE CENTER DR, CAPE CENTER PSYCHIATRY 28304 #038-40-1967 L1985 P *030 †75
SCHUSTER, Jennifer Ann. 1638 OWEN DR 28304 #038-45-2001 L2006 EM *020 †16
SCHUTZER, David Alan. 911 HAY ST, HIGHLAND OBG 28305 #033-06-1993 L1997 OBG *020 †30
SENGSTAKEN, Elizabeth Ann. 2300 RAMSEY ST, VA MEDICAL CTR 28301 #050-02-1989 L1995 FM *020 †18
SERANO, Richard Doro. 3645 CAPE CENTER DR, BOX 44035 28304 #051-01-1973 L1975 N *020 †75
SETLIK, Andrea Maria. ■ 28314 #048-13-2003 L2007 PD *020 †55 ‡
SETSER, Bradley Scott. 1638 OWEN DR, EMERGENCY DEPARTMENT 28304 #024-05-1996 L2007 EM *020 †16
SEWANYANA, Steven S. 5617 RAMSEY ST 28311 #905-01-1991 L2005 PDI *020 †55
SHAH, Sanjay. 1218 WALTER REED RD, SANDHILLS NEPH & IM PA 28304 #495-45-1990 L1998 NEP IM *020 †20
SHAH, Sanjay Bachubhai. 2525 RAEFORD RD STE B 28305 #495-22-1987 L2001 AN *020 †05
SHAH, Syed Salman A. 3419A MELROSE RD, SANDHILLS HEART SURGERY, P 28304 #704-01-1996 L2005 TS *100 †85,90
SHAKFEH-ELGENDY, Samar. 6387 RAMSEY ST, EXPRESS CARE 28311 #875-01-1987 L2006 FM *020 †18
SHARIFUZZAMAN, Abu Asad M. 2300 RAMSEY ST, VA MEDICAL CENTER 28301 #160-02-1983 L2005 IM *020 †20
SHAW, Frank Stedman. 202 DEVANE ST 28305 #041-01-1959 L1959 PD PDA *071 †55
SHEKHAR, Shobha. 1540 PURDUE DR, STE 101 28303 #495-09-1996 L2006 PD *020 †55
SHELBURNE, John Danl. 2300 RAMSEY ST 28304 #036-07-1972 L1972 ATP *030 †50 ‡
SHELTON, Stuart David. 2109 VALLEYGATE DR 28304 #051-07-1989 L1996 OBG MFM *020 †30
SHEREFF, Richard Henry. 139 HUNTER CIR 28304 #047-06-1970 L1977 D *020 †15
SHUH, Monson. 957 OLD MCPHERSON CHRCH RD, CHURCH ROAD 28303 #047-06-1993 L2003 AN *020 †05
SHWE, Kyi Kyi. ■ 28314 #209-01-1991 L1997 IM *020 †20
SIEWERS, Christian F. 405 FORSYTHE ST, # 130 28303 #051-04-1944 L1950 PM ORS *071 †40
SILES, Fernando J. 559 EXECUTIVE PL, STE 202 28305 #847-13-1980 L1999 PTH *020 †50
SINGH, Avtar. 109 BRADFORD AVE, METAL HEATH CENTER 28301 #036-05-1988 L2003 P *020
SINGH, Gurpreet. 1830 OWEN DR RM 200, OF CAPE FEAR VALLEY HLTH S 28304 #036-01-1992 L1997 P *020 †75
SINGH, Kulwant. 1601 OWEN DR 28304 #495-05-1949 L1987 GP EM *020
SIY-HIAN, Bienvenido C. 508A OWEN DR 28304 #748-10-1971 L1977 IM IMG *020 †20
SLEHRIA, Sanjeev S K. 1880 QUIET CV 28304 #495-48-1988 L2004 GE *020 †20
SMITH, Billy Ray. 2109 VALLEYGATE DR, STE 201 28304 #036-08-2000 L2002 PM *020 †60
SMITH, Rudolph Verdi. 414 OWEN DR 28304 #047-07-1970 L1988 OPH *020
SNEAD, James Walter. 3308 MELROSE RD, FAYETTEVILLE ORTHOPEDIC 28304 #017-20-1999 L2005 OSM *100 †40
SODHI, Neena. 1317 MEDICAL DR 28304 #051-04-1981 L1990 A IM *020 †20,03
SODHI, Vimal Kumar. ■ 28314 #495-45-1976 L1978 NM *020 †18,28
SOLIMAN, Safi Sobhy. 2300 RAMSEY ST, FAYETTEVILLE VA HOSPITAL 28301 #915-04-1981 L1993 IM *020 †20
SPEARMAN, Darren Christop. 570 CASTLE RISING RD, # 2G 28314 #023-12-2004 L2005 IM *020 †20
SPIVEY, Beverly Jean. 1314 MEDICAL DR, STE 102 28304 #036-07-1978 L1982 FM *020 †18
SQUIRES, Stuart Morris. PO BOX 53844 28305 #036-08-1995 L2000 AN PAN *020 †05
STANG, Christopher M. 2927 BOLLA DR 28306 #028-78-2007, ▲ FP *012
STANSBERRY, Howard Arthur. 3318 MELROSE RD 28305 #055-01-1979 L1982 EM IM *020 †20,16
STAPLETON, Sydney Scott. 1726 METROMEDICAL DR 28304 #036-01-1980 L1981 OPH *020 †35
STEFFES, Bruce Carl. 1638 OWEN DR 28304 #025-01-1976 L1982 GS *071 †85
STEPHENSON, Shelby A. 1404 OWEN DR # 64363 28304 #047-07-1975 L1981 OPH *020
STEWART, Albert, Jr. 114 BROADFOOT AVE 28305 #028-02-1944 L1948 IM *071 †20
STEWART, David Dubose. 114 BROADFOOT AVE 28305 #045-01-1982 L1985 IM *020 †20
STOWE, Fred Reece, Jr. 169 FOCH ST 28306 #036-01-1958 L1958 N AM *020 †55,75
STRAUTHER, Gregory Ross. 4140 FERNCREEK DR, STE 601 28314 #012-05-1995 L2005 CCS *020
STRICKLAND, Myron Scott. 2029 VALLEYGATE DR, FAYETTEVILLE WOMENS CARE 28304 #036-08-1984 L1985 OBG *020 †30
SUTTON, William Wade. 2300 RAMSEY ST, FAYETTEVILLE VETERANS HOSP 28301 #047-05-1978 L1981 GE IM *020 †20 ‡
SWEENEY, Charles Whitcomb. 1638 OWEN DR, EMERGENCY DEPARTMENT 28304 #011-04-1988 L2000 GPM *020 †16
SY, Angelito C. 1219 WALTER REED RD 28304 #748-10-1989 L1995 PD *020 †55
SZWEJBKA, Paul Eric. 4140 FERNCREEK DR, STE 401 28304 #045-04-2000 L2004 N *020 †75
TAIWO, Adebukola Aina. 1638 OWEN DR, CAPE FEAR VALLEY HEALTH SY 28304 #690-02-2000 L2005 IMG *020
TATUM-KODZAI, Zavette M. 1638 OWEN DR 28304 #012-21-1996 L2000 AN *020
TAWFIK, Youssef Shoukry. 1641 OWEN DR 28304 #915-04-1983 L1996 IM *020 †20
TAYAO, Manuel Soco. ■ 28311 #748-02-1954 L1990 VS TS *020 †85,90
TAYLOR, Randolph Wilkerson. ■ 28306 #026-24-2006 L2008 FP *012
TEER, David Allen. 150 ROBESON ST, DAVID TEER MD 28301 #036-08-1988 L1991 FM *020 †18
THOM, Arleen Kaye. 1301 MEDICAL DR 28304 #023-07-1983 L1993 GS SO *020 †85
THOMAS, James Mc Neil. 1841 QUIET CV 28304 #011-03-1967 L1988 GS *020 †85
THORPE, Bryant D. 1301 MEDICAL DR 28304 #035-45-1998 L2004 VIR *020 †80

TOBIN, H Wayne. 109 BRADFORD AVE, METAL HEATH CENTER 28301 #005-11-1965 L2000 P *020 †75
TODD, Timothy Andrew. 217 GLENSFORD DR, NEXTCARE URGENT CARE CENTR 28314 #047-06-1984 L1990 GP *020
TONOG, Jose Tan. 524 BEAUMONT RD, VALLEY EXPRESS CARE 28304 #748-01-1975 L1995 IM *020 †16
TOOMEY, Kathleen Elinor. 1211A IRELAND DR, SERVICE AGENCY 28304 #041-07-1973 L2000 PD LM *062 †19,55
TORRES, Maria Aurora R. ■ 28305 #748-10-1989 L1998 NM *020
TRAN-PHU, Lan P. 227 FOUNTAINHEAD LN, CUMBERLAND COUNTY HLTH DEP 28301 #396-36-1986 L1997 PD *020 †55
TREZAK, Brian Thomas. ■ 28305 #035-15-1996 L2007 IM *020 †20
UBA, Daniel Chidi. 1905 SKIBO RD STE 100, RAPHA HEALTH SYSTEMS, INC 28314 #690-04-1988 L2001 IM *020 †20
USLICK, Bryan David. 1880 QUIET CV 28304 #038-40-1991 L1995 GE *020 †20
VAIKUNTH, Aparna. 1601 OWEN DR, AHEC FAMILY 28304 #036-08-2005 L2008 FP *012
VALLECILLO, Reinaldo. ■ 28314 #275-01-1950 L1970 AN GP *071
VAN TRAN, Lucas. 101 ROBESON ST STE 304 28301 #941-01-1976 L1983 N *020 ‡
VASSER, Elizabeth Catheri. 1601 OWEN DR, MED P 28304 #048-15-2006 FP *012
VENTURA-BRASWELL, Ada M. 1320 MEDICAL DR, DUKE OB-GYN CAPE FEAR VLY 28304 #011-02-1995 L1999 OBG *020 †30
VICK, William Woodrow. 1638 OWEN DR 28304 #036-07-1987 L1990 PTH *020 †50
VIETA, Paul Anthony. ■ 28303 #033-05-1966 L1975 OBG *071 †30
VILLAROMAN, Ruben R. 2300 RAMSEY ST, VETERANS AFFAIR MEDICAL CE 28301 #748-01-1969 L1973 IM *020 †20
VILLENA, Maria Joanna S. 200 FORSYTHE ST 28303 #305-01-2002 L2005 FM *020 †18
VINODHKUMAR, Juanda Key. ■ 28314 #038-40-2004 L2004 FP *012
VOGEL, Hans Peter. 1638 OWEN DR 28304 #036-07-1980 L1984 PTH *020 †50
VORDER BRUEGGE, Colin F. ■ 28303 #047-06-1939 L1939 PTH *071 †50
VORDER BRUEGGE, William F. 2041 VALLEYGATE DR 28304 #051-01-1981 L1993 GE *020 †20
WADON, Carol Marie. 3650 CAPE CENTER DR # 100 28304 #035-03-1983 L1989 NS *020 †25
WAHBEH, Camille J. 3609 CAPE CENTER DR 28304 #605-01-1977 L1983 OBG MFM *020 †30
WALDEN, Thomas Lorenzo, Jr. 6387 RAMSEY ST 28311 #010-02-1993 L1998 RO *020 †80
WALEK, Walter Bondi. 559 HAY ST, FAYETTEVILLE ASSOC LAB MED 28305 #035-06-2000 L2006 PTH PCP *100 †50
WALLACE, Charles Dixon. 2300 RAMSEY ST 28301 #036-01-1958 L1958 P *071
WALLIN, Rolf Bolin. 1781 METROMEDICAL DR, FAYETTEVILLE ANESTHESIA PA 28304 #036-01-1984 L1985 AN *020 †05
WALSH, Zane Thomas, Jr. 2930 VILLAGE DR 28304 #036-08-1986 L1990 PM P *020 †60
WALSH RENE, Kathleen. 2300 RAMSEY ST, VAMC 28301 #035-48-1991 L2001 IM *020 †20
WANG, Jingchuan. 1638 OWEN DR 28304 #243-58-1984 L2002 PCP *020 †50
WARFEL, Claudine Yinchi. 1638 OWEN DR 28304 #036-08-2007 FP *012
WATSON, Maria Jeanette. 1756 METROMEDICAL DR 28304 #041-02-1990 L1999 RHU *020 †20
WEAVER, Roy Albert. CAPE FEAR VALLEY HOSPITAL, DEPT OF PATHOLOGY 28302 #036-01-1963 L1963 PTH *020 †50
WEBSTER, Jos Carlton, Jr. ■ 28311 #001-02-1974 L1991 OBG *071 †30
WEDLAKE, Tiffany M. ■ 28311 #012-01-2004 L2007 PD GP *020
WEED, Tonja Ielene Palaur. ■ 28305 #051-04-1998 L1998 PS *100
WEINRAUCH, Martin Howard. ■ 28314 #056-06-1989 L1997 P *020 †75
WELLS, Charles Lewis. 1638 OWEN DR 28304 #041-12-1959 L1963 PTH *071 †50
WELLS, Matthew Kent. 1638 OWEN DR, P O BOX 2000 28304 #039-01-2002 L2006 EM *020
WENDORFF, Hermann J. 2300 RAMSEY ST, FAYETTEVILLE VAMC 28301 #737-06-1972 L1980 END IM *020 †20
WHETSELL, Douglas Wayne. 1746 METROMEDICAL DR, ANNEX & SLEEP LABORATORY 28304 #045-01-1968 L1984 PUD IM *020 †20
WHITAKER, Miles Warren. 1726 METROMEDICAL DR, CAPE FEAR EYE ASSOCIATES, 28304 #005-12-1985 L1993 OPH *020 †35
WIGGS, William James, Jr. 1839 QUIET CV 28304 #036-08-1990 L1995 OTO *020 †45
WILBURN, Clinton Dennis. 907 HAY ST 28305 #010-03-1975 L1982 PD *020
WILLIAMS, Bobbili Victor. ■ 28314 #495-21-1983 L2007 IM *020 †20
WILLIAMS, Jesse Franklin. ■ 28301 #010-03-1970 L1975 PHP FM *030
WILLIAMS, Noralean. 705A CUMBERLAND ST 28301 #010-03-1970 L1975 IM *020 †20
WILLIAMS, Roger Scott. ■ 28311 #012-01-2007 FP *012
WILLIS, William Allen. 2850 VILLAGE DR, STE 103 28304 #045-01-1972 L1978 P *020 †75
WILSON, Barbara Jane. 2300 RAMSEY ST, DEPT OF SURGERY VA MED CTR 28301 #038-41-1984 L2004 GS HS *020 †85
WISE, Barbara Virginia. 1830 OWEN DR, RM 200 28304 #051-04-2002 L2006 P *100 †75
WITHERS, L Dale. 957 OLD MCPHERSON CHRCH RD 28303 #012-05-1977 L1980 AN *020
WOLFORD, Jerald Franklin. 1638 OWEN DR 28304 #030-05-1983 L1988 PTH HMP *020 †50
WOOD, Brandt T. 2029 VALLEYGATE DR, FAYETTEVILLE WOMENS CARE 28304 #018-75-1997, ▲ L2004 OBG *020 †30
WOODCOCK, Michael Geo. 2047 VALLEYGATE DR 28304 #047-07-1980 L1981 OPH OS *020 †35
WRATNEY, Angela T. 524 BEAUMONT RD 28304 #012-05-1998 L2003 CCP *100 †55
WRIGHT, Eugene Edward. 1638 OWEN DR 28304 #036-07-1978 L1979 IM *030 †20
WURAPA, Eyako Kofi. PO BOX 2000, 1638 OWEN DR 28302 #041-14-1995 L2002 GPM *020 †18,70
YAMAMOTO, Joni. 1601 OWEN DR, SOUTHERN REGIONAL AHEC 28304 #005-12-2001 L2003 FM *020
YANG, Frank. 2300 RAMSEY ST, SURGICAL SERVICE 28301 #016-02-1983 L1985 GS *020 †85
YOEDIONO, Ruly. ■ 28311 #506-05-1971 L1977 PTH OS *020 †50
YOUNG, Carol Ray, Jr. 1638 OWEN DR, CAPE FEAR VALLEY MEDICAL C 28304 #010-02-1992 L1998 PUD *071 †20
YU, Zhong. 1638 OWEN DR 28304 #243-46-1982 L2004 IM *020 †20 ‡
ZAFIROV, Dimiter Hristov. 2041 VALLEYGATE DR 28304 #198-03-1971 L2000 IM *020 †20
ZALAZNIK, Mark Stephen. 1301 MEDICAL DR 28304 #055-02-1993 L1998 DR *020 †80
ZIMMERMAN, Johnny Edward. ■ 28311 #036-08-2005 *100

FEARRINGTON – CHATHAM

GLOWACKI, Raymond Martin. ■ 27312 #025-01-1960 L1985 D *071 †15
JAENIKE, John Robt. ■ 27312 #035-45-1948 L1953 IM *030 †20
LEVY, Richard Warren. ■ 27312 #021-01-1947 L1947 NS *071 †25
MAZZOCCO, Victor Eugene. ■ 27312 #051-04-1961 L1962 IM *071 †20

MC CUTCHEON, Sue Ann. ■ 27312 #035-06-1956 L1958 **IM HEM** *071 †20
MC NULTY, John R. ■ 27312 #067-01-1953 L1960 **GS** *071 †85
MOSS, Rebecca Kristin A. ■ 27312 #047-06-1966 L1988 **PTH** *071
RESTIVO, Marion C. ■ 27312 #023-01-1957 L1965 **DR** *071 †80

FLAT ROCK – HENDERSON

BULL, Janet Hunter. 571 S ALLEN RD 28731 #048-12-1981 L1998 **OBG** *020 †30
FARRELL, Francis Jos. 412 LEDGEMONT CT 28731 #010-02-1960 L1996 **AI PD** *071 †55,03 ‡
GARCIA-ARIZ, Manuel C. ■ 28731 #847-05-1974 L2004 **OP ORS** *020 †40 ‡
HILL, Paul Edward. ■ 28731 #036-07-1954 L1954 **IM** *071 †20
HOVENDON, Jennifer L. 581 S ALLEN RD, FOUR SEASONS HOSPICE 28731
    #023-07-1994 L1995 **FM** *020 †18
HUNTLEY, Mark Ronnial. 228 ESTATE DRIVE 28731 #036-05-1991 L1992 **FM** *020 †18
HYLER, James Elmer. 571 S ALLEN RD, 4 SEASONS HOSPICE CARE 28731
    #001-02-1974 L2005 **FM** *020 †18
JEGGE, Gerard Francis. ■ 28731 #035-01-1948 L1959 **GS** *071 †85
LAMB, Leta Carlson. FOUR SEASONS HOSPICE, 571 S ALLEN RD 28731 #012-01-1981 L1997
    RO *020 †80 ‡
LA TOURETTE, Kenneth A. 436 RUTLEDGE DRIVE 28731 #035-19-1939 L1954 **PTH** *071 †50
OLDHAM, Richard Randolph. ■ 28731 #047-05-1971 L1971 **PTH** *020 †50
SHETTERLY, Roger Davis. ■ 28731 #038-41-1967 L1974 **OPH** *071 †35
SNIDER, A Rebecca. ■ 28731 #045-01-1974 L1992 **PD CD** *020 †55
WEIL, Dane Alan. VA MEDICAL CENTER, 1100 TUNNEL RD 28731 #039-01-1992 L1993
    U *020 †95
WEILL, Hans. ■ 28731 #021-01-1958 L1958 **PUD IM** *050 †20

FLEETWOOD – ASHE

COX, George Elton. ■ 28626 #016-11-1956 **PTH** *071
STEINMETZ, Rodney Dunlap. ■ 28626 #016-06-1952 L1953 **OPH** *071 †35

FLETCHER – HENDERSON

AHMAD, Sameera. ■ 28732 #704-21-1995 L2006 **IM** *100 †20
BLIEVERNICHT, Stephen W. 242 OLD CONCORD RD, PAIN CARE & INTEGRATIVE ME 28732
    #012-05-1969 L1980 **GS** *020 †85
BONNEY, Stephen Ronald. 115 N AMBLE LN 28732 #005-12-1993 L1997 **AN** *020 †05
BOSWORTH, Michele Catheri. 1542 CANE CREEK RD 28732 #055-01-2003 L2005 **FM** *020 †18
BUTCHER, Dewayne F. MAPLES ROAD, PARK RIDGE HOSPITAL 28732 #005-12-1968 L1989
    EM FM *020 †18
CHEN, Eric Hong-Wen. ■ 28732 #036-01-2007 **FP** *012
DURANT, William C. NAPLES RD 28732 #033-05-1980 L1988 **IM** *020
FEY, Geoffrey Lyman. ■ 28732 #422-01-2001 L2006 **DR** *020 †28,80
HANSCOM, Alfred C. ■ 28732 #005-12-1953 L1981 **PDA EM** *071 †05,16,18
INGRAM, Denise Gumbinger. 57 HOWARD GAP RD, PARK RIDGE MED ASSOC. 28732
    #036-01-1998 L1999 **FM** *020 †18
KIM, Paul S. 3159 HENDERSONVILLE RD, P O BOX 38 28732 #038-40-1993 L2000 **HO** *020 †20
LANG, John Michael. 125 VANCE HILL DR, PARK RIDGE MEDICAL ASSOCIA 28732
    #051-04-1998 L1999 **FM** *020 †18
LARSON, John Merton. ■ 28732 #016-11-1959 L1960 **AN** *071 †05
LOKEN, Kenneth Odell. 80 DOVE HOLLOW RD 28732 #056-05-1961 L1984 **PTH** *071 †50
MAY, William Edward. NAPLES RD 28732 #027-01-1970 L2002 **IM** *020 †20 ‡
REGUYAL, Chona Soria. 12B CANE CREEK RD, WESTERN CAROLINA MEDICAL A 28732
    #748-16-1991 L2003 **FM** *020 †18
SHEPARD, Harley G. ■ 28732 #050-02-1951 L1952 **OM GPM** *071 †70
SMITH, Robert Lewis. 127 VANCE HILL DR 28732 #051-07-1995 L1998 **FM** *020 †18
STEINER, Harry Emile. NAPLES RD 28732 #035-03-1973 L1977 **EM** *020 †85
TAUB, Julie Allison. ■ 28732 #032-01-2001 L2004 **IM** *020
TAYLOR, Joan Murphy. 95 N AMBLE LN 28732 #005-12-1978 L1979 **AN PME** *020 †05
WEINER, Eric David. 100 HOSPITAL DR 28732 #051-01-1985 L2006 **IM** *020 †20 ‡
WILCHER, Jonathan Michael. ■ 28732 #051-04-2004 L2006 **EM** *020

FOREST CITY – RUTHERFORD

ARCHER, Willis Arthur. 1178 OLD CAROLEEN RD 28043 #036-01-1966 L1966 **PD** *020 †55
BEASLEY, Lawrence Burton. 1178 OLD CAROLEEN RD, COUNSELING SERVICES. DOC B 28043
    #045-01-1987 L1990 **P** *020 †75
BELL, Brian Wayne. 374 HUDLOW RD, HOSPICE OF RUTHERFORD 28043 #004-01-1995 L2003
    FM *020 †18
BENNETT, John Mark. 281 E MAIN ST, FOREST CITY FAMILY MEDICIN 28043
    #036-01-1987 L1988 **FM** *020 †18
BETOR, Catherine Canada. 640 OAK ST 28043 #036-01-1993 L1998 **PO** *020 †35
BONFIELD, Kenneth Robt. 640 OAK ST 28043 #035-08-1988 L1994 **OPH** *020 †35
DAVIS, Andrew Calvin. 640 OAK ST 28043 #045-01-1979 L1983 **OPH** *020 †35
DELAGARZA, Jerald A. 1178 OLD CAROLEEN RD 28043 #048-14-1998 L2002 **PD** *020 †55
DICKSON, Loretta Anne. 281 E MAIN ST, FOREST CITY FAMILY MEDICIN 28043
    #045-01-1997 L2000 **FM** *020 †18
ENGLAND, Bobby Flay. 124 GROCE ST 28043 #045-01-1962 L1963 **GP** *020
GODFREY, Joe Brannon. 124 GROCE ST 28043 #045-01-1962 L1965 **FM** *020 †18
GOODE, Gregory Blake. 1178 OLD CAROLEEN RD 28043 #045-04-1989 L1992 **PD** *020 †55
GREEN, Thomas John. 334 WHISPERING PINES CIR 28043 #025-12-1998 L2001 **IM** *020 †20
GREENLEE, Cynthia Renee. 1178 OLD CAROLEEN RD, STE 100 28043 #036-01-2001 L2004
    PD *020 †55
LOWRY, Jonathan C. 640 OAK ST 28043 #041-02-1989 L1995 **OPH PS** *020 †35
MERCER, Michele L. 124 GROCE ST, PRACTICE, 124 GROCE ST 28043 #011-02-2000 L2003
    FM *020 †18
ORRISON, William Gresham. 640 OAK ST 28043 #048-02-1969 L1970 **OPH** *020 †35
PATEL, Sangnya R. 181 DANIEL RD, EAST CAROLINA UNIVERSITY 28043 #495-23-1990 L1995
    IM *020 †20
POWELL, Anita Hill. 1178 OLD CAROLEEN RD 28043 #047-06-1983 L1989 **PD** *020 †55

RAYNOR, Leighton A. 640 OAK ST 28043 #036-01-1977 L1980 **OPH** *020 †35
REED, Robert Leslie. ■ 28043 #041-13-1963 L1964 **AN** *071 †05
ROBERTS, Jeffrey Scott. 171 DANIEL RD 28043 #051-07-1985 L1999 **DR** *020 †80
SALISBURY, James Arthur. 640 OAK ST 28043 #021-01-1977 L1979 **OPH** *020 †35
SCOTT, Stephen Sherrod. 640 OAK ST 28043 #045-04-1997 L2003 **OPH OS** *020 †35
SELSOR, Linda Carol. 651 WITHROW RD, RUTHERFORD DERMATOLOGY PA 28043
    #036-01-1982 L1983 **D** *020 †15 ‡
SHAPIRO, William Hartman. 181 DANIEL RD, BOX 1560 28043 #038-40-1961 L1968
    IM CD *071 †20
THIBODEAU, Denis Laurent. 124 GROCE ST, ENGLAND & GODFREY FAMILY P 28043
    #063-01-1995 L1998 *020
WALTON, William Harold, II. 640 OAK ST 28043 #033-05-1995 L2004 **OPH** *020 †35
WITMAN, Barry Hugh. 124 GROCE ST, ENGLAND & GODFREY FAM PRAC 28043
    #056-05-1980 L1999 **FM** *020 †18
ZIOMEK, Paul Henry. 181 DANIEL RD 28043 #308-11-1987 L1992 **IM** *020 †20

FORT BRAGG – CUMBERLAND

ALLEN, Rodney H. REILLY RD, BOX 93, BODG 4-2817 28310 #036-01-1988 L1991
    OBG *020 †30
ALLEN, Theodore Lee. MCXC-COD, ATTN: CREDENTIAL OFFICE 28310 #047-07-1975 L1986
    OM AM *030
BAILEY, Edward Hutchins. WOMACK ARMY MED CTR, MCXC-COD 28310 #023-12-1997 L1999
    FM *020 †18
BAL, George Kalwant. WOMACK ARMY MED CTR 28310 #023-12-1991 L1999 **ORS** *020 †40
BALDEN, Erin Louise. REILLY RD, BOX 93, BODG 4-2817 28310 #023-12-1996 L2000
    IM *020 †20
BARNES, Scott Danl. WOMACK ARMY MEDICAL CENTER, FORT BRAGG NC 28310
    #016-06-1991 L1993 **OPH** *020 †35
BELPREZ, Megan Melissa. WOMACK ARMY MED CTR, FAMILY MED RESIDENCY PROGR 28310
    #025-12-2006 L2008 **FP** *012
BLEASE, Robert Ernest. 2817 REILLY RD, ATTN: CREDENTIAL OFFICE 28310
    #023-12-2000 L2008 **ORS** *020
BONGU, Deepika. WOMACK ARMY MEDICAL CTR, ROBINSON HEALTH CLINIC 28310
    #496-27-1992 L2003 **FM** *020 †18
BRANCH, James Brookes. REILLY RD BLDG 4-2817, WOMACK ARMY MEDICAL CENTER 28310
    #033-05-1998 L2000 **PTH** *020 †50
BREZINA, Edward S. MCXC-COD, WOMACK ARMY MEDICAL CENTER 28310
    #005-06-1948 L1949 **FM CLP** *020 †50,18
BRIDE, John Paul. MCXC-COD, WOMACK ARMY MEDICAL CENTER 28310 #010-01-1993 L2008
    IM *020 †20
BURLINGAME, Brian Scott. REILLY RD, BOX 93, BODG 4-2817 28310 #024-05-1994 L1997
    GS *020 †85
BURR, Jean Ellen. 2817 REILLY RD, WAMC STOP A 28310 #023-12-2000 L2000 **PD** *020 †55
CANNON, Marjory Elaine. 2817 REILLY RD, MEDICAL HOLDOVER DEPT 28310
    #056-05-1996 L2002 **FM** *020 †18
CARLTON, Darrel Keith. ■ 28310 #023-12-1998 L1999 **OPH** *020 †35
CARROLL, Robert Bruce. 2817 REILLY RD, WOMACK ARMY MED CTR, STOP 28310
    #021-06-1998 L2007 **OPH** *020 †35
CARUSO, Fred Anthony. BLDG 4-2817 REILLY ROAD, MCXC-QSD-CRED BOX 93 28310
    #033-05-1987 L1995 **PDR** *020 †80
CAVICCHIA, Melinda Ann. 2817 REILLY RD, WOMACK AMC, STOP A 28310 #038-40-1991 L1993
    FM *020 †70,18
CHAMBERS, Matthew Scott. 2817 REILLY RD, WOMACK AMC, STOP A 28310
    #023-12-2004 L2006 **FM** *100
CHESNEY, Ursula Yvette. 2817 RALEIGH RD, WOMACK ARMY MED CTR 28310
    #023-12-1990 L1994 **PD** *020 †55
CHIMIDZA, Lekgobo. 2817 REILLY RD, DPC DP 28310 #010-03-1987 L1994 **PD** *020 †55
CHRISTOPHER, Frank L. 82ND AIRBORNE DIV, OFF OF DIVISION SURGEON 28310
    #024-05-1995 L1997 **EM AM** *020 †16
CLARK, Jeffrey Brothers. BLDG 4-2817 REILLY ROAD, MCXC-QSD-CRED BOX 93 28310
    #036-08-1984 L1987 **PHP** *020 †70,18
CLARK, Kendall Robt. ■ 28310 #001-02-1992 L2002 **DR** *012 †18
COLO, Andrea Jean. 2817 REILLY RD, WOMACK ARMY MEDICAL CENTER 28310
    #024-05-1992 L2005 **EM** *020 †16
COOPER, Ellis Oneal, III. ■ 28310 #021-01-1995 L2004 **ORS** *020 †40
CRUM, William Paul. WOMACK AMC, ATTN: CREDENTIAL OFFICE 28310 #023-12-1996 L1998
    FM *020 †18
CURRY, Thomas Kieran. BLDG4-2817 REILLY ROAD, MCXC-QSD-CRED BOX 93 28310
    #028-34-1991 L1993 **VS** *100 †85
CZARNIK, James Edward. 2817 REILLY RD STOP A, WOMACK ARMY MEDICAL CENTER 28310
    #023-12-1993 L1995 **EM** *020 †16
CZARNIK, Katherine Anne. WAMC 28310 #023-12-1993 L2004 **D** *020 †15
DEVEAUX, Peter Gerard. WOMACK ARMY MEDICAL CENTER, FORT BRAGG NC 28310
    #016-42-1994 L1994 **CRS GS** *020 †85,10 ‡
DOOLITTLE, Andrew Maurice. WOMACK ARMY MEDICAL CENTER, FORT BRAGG NC 28310
    #024-05-1999 L2007 **OTO** *020 †45 ‡
DRAGOVICH, Anthony Louis. 2817 REILLY RD, WOMACK ARMY MEDICAL CENTER 28310
    #028-34-2000 L2007 **AN** *020 †05
DUNN, Kathleen Anne. JSOMTC, SWCS 28310 #036-08-1984 L1988 **GPM PD** *062 †70,55
EARWOOD, Maryellen R. OFFICE, ATTN: MCXC - COD CREDENTIA 28310 #023-12-1995 L1996
    PM *020 †60
EASTY, David Mark. BLDG 4-2817 REILLY RD, MCXC-QSD-CRED BOX 93 28310
    #023-12-1997 L1999 **EM** *020 †16
EDGAR, Erin Paul. 2817 REILLY RD, WOMACK AMC, STOP A 28310 #023-12-1992 L1994
    FM *020 †18
ERTESCHIK, Nathan. 0 NORMANDY DR DEPT MED, WOMACK ARMY MED CTR 28307
    #010-01-1979 L2005 **IM** *030 †20
ESPINOSA, Randall Alan. 2817 REILLY RD, MCXC-COD CREDENTIALS 28310
    #007-02-1987 L1988 **ORS** *020 †40
GABEL, Robert Michael. BLDG 4-2817 REILLY ROAD, MCXC-COD CREDENTIALS OFFIC 28310
    #030-06-1971 L1972 **GPM** *070 ‡
GABRIEL, Mary E. 2817 REILLY RD, PES/MEB WAMC STOP A 28310 #032-01-1981 L2001
    GPM AM *020 †70

GANTT, Chas Bernard, Jr. 2817 REILLY RD, WOMACK ARMY MED CTR 28310 #001-02-1966 L1975 **R NM** *020 †80

GARDNER, Camille Mercedes. ST EXT., BLDG 5-4257, BASTOGNE 28310 #041-15-1999 L2007 **FM** *020 †18

GAUER, Robert Leroy. DEPT. OF FAMILY PRACTICE, WOMACK ARMY MEDICAL CENTER 28310 #036-05-1995 L2001 **FM** *020 †18

GERASIMON, Gregg Gordon. WOMACK AMC, ATTN: CREDENTIAL OFFICE 28310 #010-02-1999 L2007 **IM ISM** *020

GHADYALI, Saira Moiez. WOMACK ARMY MED CTR, ATTN: CREDENTIAL OFFICE 28310 #023-12-1993 L1997 **PS** *020 †85,65

GOBALEZA, Dominador Geli. BLDG 4-2817, RILEY RD, WOMACK ARMY MED CTR 28310 #023-12-1994 L2008 **CHP PFP** *020 †75

GOODEN, Charles Michael. CREDENTIALS OFFICE, MCXC-COD 28310 #004-01-1995 L1997 **GS** *020 †85

GORMAN, Alfred Carl. CEN (W2L6AA), WOMACK ARMY MED 28310 #012-21-1991 L2007 **CD** *020 †20

GOULD, Darin Edward. ■ 28307 #005-12-1999 L2000 **CHP** *020 †75

GRADY, James Dominic. MCXC-COD, ATTN: CREDENTIAL OFFICE 28310 #023-12-1995 L1997 **FM UM** *020 †18

GRIEF, William Joshua. WOMACK ARMY MED CTR, ATTN: CREDENTIAL OFFICE 28310 #023-12-2000 L2002 **FM** *020 †18 ‡

GRIGGS, Kenneth Alan. BLDG 4-2817 REILLY ROAD, ATTN: MCXC-QSD-CRED BOX 93 28310 #023-12-1994 L2000 **DR** *020 †80

GUIDRY, Bret Allen. BLDG. 4-2187 REILLY ROAD, WOMACK AMC 28310 #021-05-1997 L1999 **OBG** *020 †75

GUPTA, Vinita. WOMACK HOSP DEPT PEDS 28307 #495-77-1978 L1991 **PD IM** *020 †55

HALEY, Chad Allen. WOMACK HOSPITAL 28310 #010-02-1998 L1999 **ORS** *020 †40

HENRY, Michael David. 2817 REILLY RD, WOMACK ARMY MEDICAL CENTER 28310 #010-03-1998 L1999 **FM** *100

HESTER, Deirdre Flynn. BASTOGNE EXTENSION DRIVE, BLDG 5-4257 28310 #041-12-1998 L2005 **PD** *020 †55

HIRSCH, Jo Ellen. BUILDING 5-6247 BASTOGNE E, CLARK CLINIC 28310 #038-06-1996 L2001 **IM** *020 †20

HOMMER, Dean Harry. BLDG 4-2817, RILEY RD, WOMACK ARMY MED CTR 28310 #023-12-1999 L2008 **PM** *100 †60

HUSSAIN, Faheem. 2817 REILLY RD, STOP A 28310 #024-05-1995 L2002 **DR** *020 †80

INGRAM, Alisa Dawn. BLDG 5-4257 BASTOGNE, CLARK HEALTH CLINIC 28310 #036-08-2000 L2005 **FM** *020 †18 ‡

INOUYE, Dean Akira. BLDG 4-2817 REILY RD, DPT OF BEH HLTH WOMACK 28310 #014-01-1986 L1987 **CHP PFP** *020 †75

IRIZARRY, Daniel Jason. BLDG 4-2817 REILY ROAD, MCXC-QSD-CRED BOX 93 28310 #023-12-1997 L1999 **FM** *020 †18

JOHNSON, Jeffrey John. REILLY RD, BOX 93, BODG 4-2817 28310 #007-02-1991 L1993 **FM** *020 †18

JOHNSON, Joseph Patrick. 1422 TAGAYTAY ST, BLDG C RM 212 28310 #011-02-1999 L2001 **FM** *020 †18

JOHNSON, Scott Jerry. BUILDING 4-2817, PULMONARY CLINIC 28310 #023-12-1993 L2003 **PCC IM** *020 †20

KANE, Shawn Francis. 2817 REILLY RD, ATTN:MCXC-COD. 28310 #023-12-1995 L1996 **FSM** *020 †18

KIMES, Howard Michael. LOGISTICS AVE BLDG M, JOEL HLTH CLNC 28310 #038-40-1977 L1983 **FM FPG** *020 †18

KINGSBURY, Jeffrey Lane. MCXC-COD, ATTN: CREDENTIAL OFFICE 28310 #023-12-1989 L1992 **GPM** *020 †18,70

KOMANDUR, Shyamsunder. BASTOGNE EXT, BLDG 5-4257 28310 #495-05-1980 L1996 **PD** *020 †55

LANDERS, Andrews Lowell. WOMACK ARMY MED CTR, ATTN:CREDENTIAL OFFICE 28310 #021-01-1996 L1998 **FM** *020 †18

LATZKA, Michael Thomas. WOMACK ARMY MED CTR, ATTN:CREDENTIAL OFFICE 28310 #023-12-1994 L1995 **FM** *020 †18

LAURENCE, William Richard. 2817 REILLY RD, WAMC STOP A 28310 #041-02-1982 L1996 **FM** *030 †18

LAY, John Preston, Jr. MCXC-COD, WOMACK ARMY MEDICAL CENTER 28310 #023-12-2000 L2003 **FM** *020 †18

LEDFORD, Cheryl Lynn. WOMACK ARMY MED CTR, MAJ CHERYL LEDFORD SEBESTA 28310 #048-13-1996 L1997 **ORS** *020 †40

LEE, Charlotte Marie. DEPT OF PEDIATRICS, WOMACK AMC STOP A 28310 #023-12-1998 L2008 **PD** *020 †18

LEE, Sean Kealiiokama. ■ 28310 #023-12-1994 L1996 **FM** *020 †18

LEONARD, Lucas Randall. 4817 REILLY RD., WOMACK ARMY MEDICAL 28310 #016-11-2003 L2006 **IM** *020 †20

LEUSINK, William Douglas. MCXC-COD, ATTN: CREDENTIAL OFFICE 28310 #023-12-1997 L2008 **CHP** *020 †75

LITTRELL, Anthony Charles. 2817 REILLY RD, ATTN: CREDENTIAL OFFICE, M 28310 #023-12-1995 L1998 **GPM** *050 †70

LOWE, Jason B. 2817 REILLY RD, WOMACK AMC/DEPT. OF ORTHOP 28310 #016-43-2002 L2007 **ORS** *020

LUTZ, Robert H. 2817 REILLY RD STOP A, WOMACK AMC 28310 #023-12-1993 L1997 **EM** *030 †16

LYNCH, Steven Andrew. 2817 REILLY RD, WOMACK AMC 28310 #036-08-2004 L2006 **FM** *020 †18

MARTINS, Albert J. BLDG 4-2817, RILEY RD, WOMACK ARMY MED CTR 28310 #023-12-1986 L1988 **N** *020 †75

MC CLENATHAN, Bruce M. BLDG. 4-2817 REILLY ROAD, ATTN: CREDENTIAL OFFICE 28310 #001-06-1999 L1999 **AI** *100 †20,03

MC DONALD, Kelly Colleen. WOMACK ARMY MED CTR, ATTN: CREDENTIAL OFFIFE 28310 #048-04-2000 L2001 **FM** *020 †18

MC DONALD, Neil Aiken. 2817 REILLY RD, WOMACK ARMY MED CTR 28310 #024-05-2002 L2007 **AN** *020 †05

MEANS, Gary Edward, Jr. 2-82D AVN BN AEROMED FCLTY, 82D ABN DIV 28310 #023-12-2002 L2003 **FM** *020 †18

MEKO, Christian James. 2817 REILLY RD, WAMC STOP A 28310 #032-01-2002 L2002 **FM** *020 †18

MELVIN, Shirley S. 4257 BASTOGNE EXT #5-4257, WOMACK ARMY MC CLARK HLTH 28310 #011-03-1977 L1977 **IM** *020

MILLER, Anna. 2817 REILLY RD, WOMACK ARMY MED CTR-STOP A 28310 #025-07-1988 L2005 **RNR** *020 †80

MIRANDA, Jose Jamil. 2817 REILLY RD, WOMACK AMC 28310 #008-01-2002 L2007 **ORS** *020

MOON, Christopher H. BLDG 4-2817 REILLY RD, WOMACK ARMY MED CTR 28310 #023-12-1999 L2001 **GS** *020

MORGAN, Andrew Richard. 2817 REILLY RD, ATTN: CREDENTIAL OFFICE 28310 #023-12-2002 L2006 **EM** *020 †16

MURCIN, Scott James. 2817 REILLY RD, WOMACK AMC, STOP A 28310 #023-12-2003 L2005 **PD** *020 †55

NEVIN, Remington Lee. 2500 NORMANDY DR, USA MEDDAC 28307 #023-12-2002 L2003 **GPM** *020 †70

NOEL, Derek Thomas. WOMACK ARMY MED CTR, FAMILY MEDICINE RES PROGRA 28310 #023-01-2006 L2008 **FP** *012

NOLLER, Mark Wescott. WAMC, STOP A, MCXC COD, WOMACK ARMY MED CTR 28310 #028-34-1998 L1999 **U** *020 †95

NUNEZ, Timothy Charles. REILLY RD, BLDG 4-2817, ATTN: CREDENTIAL OFFICE 28310 #041-13-1994 L1995 **CCS** *012 †85

OAKS, Howard Grady. 2817 REILLY RD, WAMC STOP A, MCXC-COD 28310 #023-12-1988 L2002 **AI** *020 †55,03

OLSON, Kathleen Lucille. BLDG 4-2817, BOX 281, DEPARTMENT OF PEDIATRICS 28310 #026-04-1996 L1997 **PD** *020 †55

PALMQUIST, Frederick V. BLDG 4-2817 REILLY ROAD, MCXC-QSD-CRED BOX 93 28310 #010-02-1988 L2002 **AN** *020 †05

PAPPAS, Chris George. MCXC-COD, BODG 4-2817, WOMACK AMC 28310 #023-12-1996 L1997 **FM** *020 †18

PAQUETTE, Edmond L. WOMACK ARMY MEDICAL CENTER, ATTN: CREDENTIAL OFFICE 28310 #043-01-1994 L1996 **U** *020 †95

PAYNE, Mercedes Valencia. 2539 HAMILTON ST, BLDG 1 28311 #051-04-1997 L1998 **FM** *020 †18

PREVOST, Leo David, Jr. INTERNAL MEDICINE DEPT, WOMACK ARMY MEDICAL CTR 28310 #047-07-1980 L1983 **IM** *020

RAVE, Michael Anthony. WOMACK ARMY MED CTR., DEPUTY DIR CLINICAL SRVCS 28310 #023-12-1989 L1995 **CD** *020 †20

REARDON, Joseph William. 2817 REILLY RD, WAMC STOP A, MCXC-COD 28310 #004-01-1998 L2000 **FM** *020 †18

REARDON, Ruth Ann. WOMACK ARMY MED CTR, ATTN: CREDENTIAL OFFICE 28310 #004-01-1998 L2006 **PTH** *020

RODRIGUEZ, Norberto A, Jr. WOMACK ARMY MEDICAL CENTER, FAMILY PRACTICE RESIDENCY 28310 #048-02-2004 L2006 **FM** *020

RODRIGUEZ, Wilfredo. WOMACK ARMY MED CTR, ATTN: CREDENTIAL OFFICE 28310 #042-02-1997 L2004 **OBG** *020 †30

ROY, Marc Noel. REILLY RD, ATTN EMERG DEPT, WOMACK ARMY MEDICAL CENTER 28310 #050-02-1999 L2002 **EM** *020 †16

SACHAR, David Scott. WOMACK ARMY MEDICAL CENTER, FORT BRAGG NCMCXC-COD 28310 #023-12-1997 L2008 **GE** *100 †20

SANTANGELO, James Richard. WOMACK ARMY HOSPITAL, DEPT OF ORTHOPAEDICS 28310 #023-12-1990 L2004 **OFA** *020 †40

SCOTT-LOWE, Janine Anita. BLDG C-1722 TAGAYTAY ST, ROBINSON HEALTH CLINIC 28310 #008-02-1996 L1997 **FM** *020 †18

SIMON, Clayton D. MCXC-COD, ATTN: CREDENTIAL OFFICE 28310 #048-04-1995 L1998 **BBK** *020 †50

SMITH, David Sanford. 2817 REILLY RD, MCXC-ANESTHESIOLOGY 28310 #040-02-1977 L1978 **AN** *020 †05

SUMEY, Keith Douglas. MCXC-COD, CREDENTIALS, WOMACK ARMY MEDICAL CENTER 28310 #023-12-1997 L1998 **EM** *020 †16

TAYLOR, Charles L. MED CTR, MCXC-COD, WOMACK ARMY 28310 #001-06-1995 L1996 **EM** *020 †16

TAYLOR, Jonathan Craig. 2817 REILLY RD, WAMC STOP A / MCXC-COD 28310 #051-01-1999 L2001 **FM** *020 †18 ‡

TAYLOR, Shawn Frank. DEPT OF EMERGY MED, WOMACK ARMY MED CTR 28310 #023-12-1998 L2006 **EM AM** *020 †16

THOMAS, Sean Francis. 2817 REILLY RD, ATTN: CREDENTIAL OFFICE,MC 28310 #023-12-1997 L2006 **FM** *020 †18

TURNER, Clesson Edwin. MCXC-COD ATTN: CREDENTIALS, WOMACK ARMY MEDICAL CENTER 28310 #050-02-1999 L2001 **MG** *012 †55

VREELAND, Matthew John. 2817 REILLY ST, WOMACK AMC 28310 #023-12-1997 L2003 **EM** *020 †16

WALLACE, Gary Rhett. MCXC-COD CREDENTIALS, WAMC STOP A 2817 RD 28310 #048-14-1994 L1995 **FM** *020 †18

WALTERS, Terry Jane. ■ 28307 #023-12-1984 L1987 **IM** *020 †20

WARREN, Harry L. ■ 28307 #048-16-1982 L1983 **ORS** *020 †40

WAYNE, James Allen, Jr. 2817 REILLY RD, FORT BRAGG NC 28310 #021-01-2000 **PD** *020 †55

WEBER, Thomas Jos. MCXC-COD, WOMACK AMC 28310 #016-02-1989 L1994 **END** *020 †20

WEED, Albert Charles, III. MCXC-COD, WOMACK AMC 28310 #051-01-1998 L1999 **GS** *020 †85

WHITE, Daniel Wayne. MCXC-COD ATTN: (CREDENTIAL, WOMACK ARMY MEDICAL CENTER 28310 #023-12-1994 L1996 **OSM** *020 †40

WILLIAMS, Michael Burton. WOMACK ARMY MED CTR 28310 #011-02-1999 **EM** *020

WILSON, Ramey Luther. 2817 REILLY RD, WAMC STOP A 28310 #023-12-2002 L2004 **IM** *020 †20

WOHLRAB, Kurt Patrick. ■ 28310 #016-42-2002 L2007 **ORS** *020

YAMAMOTO, Christopher J. MCXC-COD, WOMACK ARMY MEDICAL CENTER 28310 #005-12-2001 L2003 **FM** *020

FOUR OAKS – JOHNSTON

ARCE, Felipe Jesus. ■ 27524 #041-15-2000 L2007 **PD** *020

FRANKLIN – MACON

ADAN, Victor. 120 RIVERVIEW ST 28734 #012-01-1993 L2000 **EM FM** *020 †18 ‡

ARCHER, Thomas Patrick. 121 RIVERVIEW ST, STE A 28734 #023-01-1981 L1995 **OBG** *020

ARUWANI, Versi Mal. 55 MEDICAL PARK DR, STE 116 28734 #704-16-1990 L2000 **IM HOS** *020 †20

BAKER, J Scott. 190 RIVERVIEW ST, SMOKEY MOUNTAIN HEALTHCARE 28734 #048-16-1991 L1995 **FM** *020 †18

BALDWIN, Boyce David, Jr. 120 RIVERVIEW ST 28734 #036-08-1987 L1989 **EM** *020 †16

BATTLE, Ben Haskew, Jr. 190 RIVERVIEW ST 28734 #036-01-1981 L1982 **FM** *020 †18 ‡

BELL, Joseph Oscar, III. 2648 GEORGIA RD, WESTERN CAROLINA DIGESTIVE 28734 #036-01-1966 L1966 **AN** *020 †05

BERGER, Frederick Allen. 55 MEDICAL PARK DR, STE 114 28734 #028-34-1972 L1975 **PD** *020 †55

BORUSZAK, Allan N. 121 RIVERVIEW ST 28734 #016-11-1979 L2004 **OBG** *075 †30

BRIDGES, William Zachery. 166 HOLLY SPRINGS PARK DR 28734 #012-05-1991 L1999 **OPH** *020 †35

BURRELL, Adam Walter. 161 IOTLA ST 28734 #036-05-1995 L1999 **FM OBS** *020 †18

CHOI, San Ho. 56 MEDICAL PARK DR, STE 202 28734 #583-01-1963 L1972 **GS** *020

COLTON, Sharon Ann. 120 RIVERVIEW ST 28734 #040-02-1970 L1982 **EM IM** *020 †20,16

DAVIS, N Park, II. 120 RIVERVIEW ST, EMERGENCY DEPARTMENT 28734 #036-01-1966 L1966 **EM** *020 †85

DAVIS, Todd Driscoll. 55 HOLLY SPRINGS PARK DR 28734 #033-05-1983 L1986 **FM IMG** *020 †18

DAVIS, William T. RIVERVIEW & WHITE OAK STS 28734 #051-01-1951 L1974 **P PHP** *071

EGGE, Shana. 278 RIVERVIEW ST 28734 #041-15-1999 L2004 **PD** *020 †55

EGGE, Steven Douglas. 278 RIVERVIEW ST 28734 #046-01-1998 L2002 **PD** *020 †55

ESTERWOOD, Anthony James. 55 HOLLY SPRINGS PARK DR 28734 #038-41-1987 L1989 **FM** *020 †18 ‡

FARLEY, David Lee. 55 MEDICAL PARK DR STE 114 28734 #012-01-1981 L1986 **IM** *020 †20

FRANKS, David Alan. 120 RIVERVIEW ST 28734 #020-12-1985 L1987 **IM** *020

GRAVELLE-CAMELO, Sheryl L. 55 HOLLY SPRINGS PARK DR 28734 #036-08-1991 L1994 **PD** *020 †55

HANDLEY, William Judson. 55 HOLLY SPRINGS PARK DR 28734 #012-01-1983 L1985 **ORS** *020 †40

HELM, Kit Christopher. 56 MEDICAL PARK DR 28734 #017-20-1997 L2000 **FM** *020 †18

HINSHAW, Wm Banks, Jr. 55 HOLLY SPRINGS PARK DR 28734 #035-03-1978 L1982 **OBG** *020 †30

HYMAN, Miles Donald. 1018 E MAIN ST 28734 #048-12-1963 L1999 **AN** *020

IMAHARA, John Kay. ■ 28734 #021-05-1964 L1990 **P** *071

JAILWALA, Jeegar A. 459 E PALMER ST 28734 #495-23-1991 L2002 **GE** *020 †20

JOHNSON, Trent Andrew. 248 RIVERVIEW ST 28734 #045-06-1996 L1971 **R NM** *020 †80

KEELY, Paul Chambers. 100 THOMAS HEIGHTS RD, SMOKY MOUNTAIN AREA MENTAL 28734 #036-05-1978 L1979 **P ADL** *020

KEGAN, Michael John. 55 MEDICAL PARK DR, STE 108 28734 #396-08-1985 L2003 **CD IM** *020 †20

KESSLER, James Patrick. 56 MEDICAL PARK DR, STE 302 28734 #038-40-1978 L1986 **ORS HS** *020 †40

KING, Garland Coffield. 56 MEDICAL PARK DR 28734 #036-01-1981 L1982 **FM** *020 †18

LAPKOFF, James Hillel. 120 RIVERVIEW ST 28734 #308-02-1984 L2005 **EM HEM** *020 ‡

LONG, Cathy L Romine. ■ 28734 #055-01-1981 L1988 **AN** *020 †05

LONG, Jim Thos, Jr. 120 RIVERVIEW ST 28734 #045-01-1979 L1988 **AN** *020 †05

MARKLE, Robin Elaine. 55 HOLLY SPRINGS PARK DR 28734 #035-03-1978 L1982 **OBG** *020 †30

MASSEY, R M. 190 RIVERVIEW ST, SMOKEY MOUNTAIN HEALTCARE 28734 #047-05-1972 L1996 **GPM PHP** *030 †70

MC CANN, William Allen. 55 MEDICAL PARK DR, STE 112 28734 #010-02-1994 L1996 **AI** *020 †03,55

MC LEAN, Walter C, Jr. 166 HOLLY SPRINGS PARK DR 28734 #051-01-1975 L1981 **OPH** *020 †35

MC MILLIN, Philip Wayne. ■ 28734 #035-06-1961 L1962 **AN** *071 †05

MILLER, Henry Herman. ■ 28734 #019-02-1963 L1964 **GP** *071

MORRIS, Edwin Lee. 1214 E MAIN ST 28734 #036-01-1974 L1978 **FM** *020 †18

NOHRIA, Virinder. ■ 28734 #917-03-1985 L1994 **P** *020 †75

PETTY, Scott Miller. 248 RIVERVIEW ST, NANTAHALA RADIOLOGY ASSOC 28734 #036-01-1988 L1990 **DR** *020 †80

ROBLES, Gilberto. 56 MEDICAL PARK DR, STE 303 28734 #649-14-1980 L1993 **GS** *020 †85

ROHLFING, Michael Bruce. 120 RIVERVIEW ST 28734 #016-11-1977 L1978 **PTH OS** *020 †50

ROSENFELD, Lona S. ■ 28734 #005-02-1960 L1961 **GYN GP** *075 †30

RUSSELL, Donald Wayne. 55 MEDICAL PARK DR, STE 112 28734 #012-05-1984 L1990 **AI IG** *020 †20,03

SHALLER, Charles Alva. 36 WESTGATE PLZ 28734 #005-06-1986 L1994 **OPH** *020 †35

SMITH, David Matthew. 161 IOTLA ST 28734 #005-12-2001 L2004 **FM** *020 †18

STRIBLING, Michael Dean. 120 RIVERVIEW ST 28734 #045-01-1984 L1989 **U** *020 †95

SUSFAL, Ewa Anna. 55 MEDICAL PARK DR 28734 #759-06-1978 L2004 **IM** *020 †20

TAYLOR, Adela Virginia. 55 MEDICAL PARK DR 28734 #759-03-1992 L1999 **AI** *020 †03,55

VARGAS, Carlos A. 35 MEDICAL PARK DR, STE 116 28734 #036-01-1996 L1999 **FM** *020 †18

WALKER, Michael Lee. ■ 28734 #023-01-1972 L1980 **N** *071 †75

WELLS, Sarah Elizabeth. ■ 28734 #036-01-2005 L2007 **P** *012

WILDE, Gustav Crede. 55 MEDICAL PARK DR, STE 104 28734 #038-06-1987 L1988 **FM** *020 †18

WILLIAMS, Robert Donald. 56 MEDICAL PARK DR STE 201 28734 #011-02-1976 L2003 **IM OS** *020 †20

WILSON, Thomas Clinton. 55 HOLLY SPRINGS PARK DR 28734 #017-20-1969 L1999 **FM** *020 †18

WOLF, Sondra Kaye. 56 MEDICAL PARK DR 28734 #017-20-1997 L2000 **FM** *020 †18

FRANKLINTON – FRANKLIN

BURDETTE, Fred M, Jr. ■ 27525 #045-01-1942 L1947 **GP** *071

PARKER, Earl Wingate. ■ 27525 #035-01-1957 L1957 **OBG** *074 †30

PETRICK, Thomas J. ■ 27525 #035-01-1948 L1987 **OS OBG** *062 †30

REPASS, James Caldwell. ■ 27525 #051-04-1961 L1963 **CHP P** *020

WOODBURN, Donald Wayne. 3386 US 1 HWY 27525 #010-03-1982 L2000 **IM EM** *020

FUQUAY VARINA – WAKE

BARNETT, Ley Imboden. 1006 PROCURE DR, STE 100 27526 #036-08-1991 L1995 **FM** *020 †18

BHAVARAJU, Ratna Kiran. ■ 27526 #495-11-1999 L2007 **N** *100

CURRIN, Joe Badgett, Jr. 500 N ENNIS ST 27526 #036-05-1961 L1961 **IM** *020

DARRELL, Thomas Cook. 431 N JUDD PKWY NE, FUQUAY VARINA FAMILY PRACT 27526 #036-01-1983 L1986 **FM** *020 †18 ‡

DE VENTE, Jason Edward. 431 N JUDD PKWY NE, FUQUAY VARINA FAM PRACT 27526 #036-01-1998 L1999 **PD** *020 †18

DOUGLAS, Shelley Ryan. ■ 27526 #036-01-2007 **PD** *012

DUPUY, Gary Paul. 1000 N MAIN ST 27526 #021-01-1996 L2006 **PD** *020 †55

DURAND-SMITH, Jennifer Al. 1000 N MAIN ST 27526 #048-04-2004 L2007 **PD** *020 †55

FLEISCHHAUER, Thos Frazee. 409 WAKE CHAPEL RD 415 27526 #051-01-1979 L2005 **NEP IM** *020 †20

GALLAGHER, Kathleen Ann. 1000 N MAIN ST 27526 #036-05-1994 L1997 **PD** *020 †55

HEFFNER, Cathy Marie. 130 N JUDD PKWY NE, SOUTHERN WAKE FAMILY MEDIC 27526 #038-41-2003 L2006 **FM** *100 †18

IBN MAHFOUDH, Ahmed M. 409 WAKE CHAPEL RD 27526 #496-31-1995 L2001 **IM** *020

JOHNKUTTY, Soma Susan. 130 N JUDD PKWY NE, SOUTHERN WAKE FAMILY MEDIC 27526 #035-48-1999 L2006 **PD** *020 †55

JONES, William Osborne. 1000 N MAIN ST, STE 103 27526 #036-01-1957 L1957 **PD** *071

KIM, Dong Irl. ■ 27526 #583-04-1969 L1976 **AN** *075

MINOR, Walter Nathan. 400 W RANSOM ST 27526 #025-01-1973 L1975 **GP** *020

NOBLE, Ellenetta Beachley. ■ 27526 #041-01-1938 L1939 **GP** *071

PARK, David Daegeun. 119 S FUQUAY AVE 27526 #583-02-1960 L1976 **FM** *071

POWELL, Hugh Murray, Jr. 1000 N MAIN ST 27526 #051-07-1980 L1983 **PD** *020 †55

ROACH, Kenneth William. 1000 N MAIN ST, STE 204 27526 #041-07-1998 L2003 **OPH** *020 †35

ROBINSON, Amy Lynn. 1000 N MAIN ST 27526 #041-12-1997 L2000 **PD** *020 †55,30

SHEELEY, Enid N Quintero. 301 LYNWOOD LN 27526 #024-01-1989 L1999 **P** *020 †75

SHOFFNER, Jonathan Daniel. 1000 N MAIN ST 27526 #036-01-1998 L2001 **PD** *020 †55

SHUMAN, Alison Weems. ■ 27526 #033-05-2003 L2005 **CCP** *012 †55

SIMPSON, Mark Watkins. 1000 N MAIN ST 27526 #036-05-1980 L1981 **PD** *020 †55

UGOCHUKWU, Kingsley Chuks. 130 N JUDD PKWY NE, SOUTHERN WAKE FAMILY MEDIC 27526 #690-06-1982 L2004 **FM** *020 †18

VERNON, Kurt Gerard. 1004 PROCURE DR 27526 #010-03-1990 L1995 **GE** *020 †20

ZANONE, Justin William. ■ 27526 #010-02-2004 L2007 **EM** *020

GARNER – WAKE

ALBRIGHT, Daniel James. 109 FOREST HILLS DR 27529 #021-05-1987 L1993 **ORS** *020 †40

ALLEN, Charles Upton. ■ 27529 #036-05-1995 L1997 **GS** *020

ALLEN, Jill Burmeister. 912 7TH AVE 27529 #025-01-1993 L1996 **FM** *020 †18 ‡

ANDERSEN, William K. 1005 VANDORA SPRINGS RD, SPORTS MEDICINE 27529 #035-19-1991 L1996 **ORS** *020 †40

BAGWELL, Johnny Wayne. 801 POOLE DR 27529 #036-05-1976 L1979 **FM** *020 †18

BERNSTEIN, Jerry Chas. 800 BENSON RD, ASSOCIATES PA 27529 #036-01-1970 L1971 **PD PDA** *020 †55

BLISS, Pennie Sue. 222 MAST DR, KIDS CARE PEDIATRICS 27529 #030-05-1994 L1997 **PD** *020 †55

BOWEN, Janet Wilder. 22 SHIPWASH DR 27529 #047-06-1985 L1988 **FM** *020 †18 ‡

BRAMMER, Thomas Dalton. 801 POOLE DR 27529 #051-04-1983 L1986 **FM** *020 †18

BREINER, Jeffrey Hugh. 200 HEALTH PARK DR, STE 100 27529 #041-07-1995 L1997 **IM** *020 †20

BRITT, James Woodrow. 800 BENSON RD, ASSOCIATES PA 27529 #036-07-1994 L1997 **PD** *020 †55

BROWN, Wallace David. 800 BENSON RD, GARNER PEDIATRICS 27529 #035-45-1968 L1973 **PD IM** *020 †55

CLAYTON, Robert E. 811 US HIGHWAY 70 W 27529 #047-07-1985 L1986 **FM** *020 †18

COURTNEY, Tracy Lamar. ■ 27529 #036-01-2008 *012

CRUMPLER, Randall Scott. 801 POOLE DR 27529 #036-05-1980 L1983 **FM** *020 †18

CURZAN, Mark Anthony. 1005 VANDORA SPRINGS RD, SPORTS MEDICINE 27529 #005-14-1994 L1998 **OSM** *020 †40

EATON-JONES, Suzanne E. 801 POOLE DR 27529 #036-07-1996 L1997 **FM** *020 †18

ESKANDER, Hoda Selim. ■ 27529 #915-02-1977 L1990 **P** *020

FERNANDEZ, Gonzalo Andres. 112 DONMOOR CT 27529 #012-01-1998 L2001 **FM** *020 †18

FOSTER, Sharon M. 800 BENSON RD, ASSOCIATES PA 27529 #036-01-1979 L1983 **PD IM** *020 †20,55

GALLUP, Steven Brian. 801 POOLE DR 27529 #036-07-1991 L1995 **FM** *020 †18

GODFREY, Wanda Lee. 5156 NC HIGHWAY 42 W, WAKE URGENT CARE & FAMILY 27529 #024-16-1989 L1993 **FM** *020 †18

GOLLEHON, Douglas Lee. 1005 VANDORA SPRINGS RD, SPORTS MEDICINE 27529 #051-07-1978 L1985 **ORS OSM** *020 †40

GRAY, Edwin Ronald. 811 US HIGHWAY 70 W 27529 #001-02-1967 L2000 **EM FM** *020 †18

HEDGEPETH, James Randy. 800 BENSON RD, ASSOCIATES PA 27529 #036-01-1983 L1985 **PD** *020 †55

HELMS, Robert Cobb. 800 BENSON RD, ASSOCIATES PA 27529 #047-06-1980 L1996 **PD OS** *020 †55

HEWETT, Frederick Allen. 800 BENSON RD, ASSOCIATES PA 27529 #036-08-1999 L2002 **PD** *020 †55

HUNT, Sarah Ogrosky. 800 BENSON RD, ASSOCIATES PA 27529 #051-01-1998 L2001 **PD** *020 †55

JOHNSON, Jeffrey Craig. 800 BENSON RD, ASSOCIATES PA 27529 #036-01-1994 L1996 **PD** *020 †55

JONES, Jason Daniel. 801 POOLE DR 27529 #036-05-1997 L1998 **FM** *020 †18

KARTHEISER, Karen Ann. 800 BENSON RD, ASSOCIATES PA 27529 #026-04-1986 L1989 **PD** *020 †55

KATZIN, David Simon. ■ 27529 #011-02-1959 L1988 **IM ID** *071 †20

KETCHAM, William Stewart. 958 VANDORA SPRINGS RD 27529 #055-01-1984 L1985 **D** *020 †20,15

KOSCIELNIAK, Walter Tony. 800 BENSON RD, ASSOCIATES PA 27529 #051-01-1992 L1995 **PD** *020 †55

KRAKAUER, Joel David. 109 FOREST HILLS DR 27529 #005-18-1989 L1995 **HS** *020 †40

KRULL, Ronald David. 811 US HIGHWAY 70 W 27529 #048-13-2000 L2004 **FM** *020 †18

LOS, Silvia Giselle. ■ 27529 #132-01-1998 L2006 **FM** *020 †18

MANNE, Murthy G K. 934 VANDORA SPRINGS RD 27529 #495-50-1969 L1977 **PD** *020 †55 ‡

MARTINI, Douglas John. 1005 VANDORA SPRINGS RD, SPORTS MEDICINE 27529 #051-01-1987 L1993 **OSM** *020 †40

MAYER, Karen Elizabeth. 200 HEALTH PARK DR, STE 100 27529 #051-01-1992 L1995 **IM** *020 †20

MC DANIEL, Wm Jason, Jr. 109 FOREST HILLS DR, STE 10 & 20 27529 #036-01-1967 L1967 **ORS** *071 †40 ‡

MONTGOMERY, Stephen Paul. 109 FOREST HILLS DR, STE 10 & 20 27529 #016-01-1974 L1980 ORS *071 †40

NELSON, Leonard D, Jr. 109 FOREST HILLS DR, STE 10 & 20 27529 #036-05-1984 L1990 ORS *020 †40

PARIKH, Harivadan K. 801 US HIGHWAY 70 W, DOCTOR'S URGENT CARE CENTE 27529 #495-22-1964 L1973 FM *071 †18

PARKER, Lisa M L. 222 MAST DR 27529 #038-41-1992 L1999 PD *020

PARKERSON, Nicole Fisher. 800 BENSON RD, ASSOCIATES PA 27529 #051-01-1997 L2000 PD *020 †55

PATTERSON, Dwayne Edward. 109 FOREST HILLS DR 27529 #051-01-1989 L1997 PM *020 †60

PLEASANTS, Gregory Todd. 801 POOLE DR 27529 #036-08-1996 L1999 FM *020 †18

PRICE, Harvey Craig. 800 BENSON RD, STE 10 27529 #036-01-1978 L1983 OTO *020 †45

REED, Marjorie Eleanor. 2664 TIMBER DR 27529 #010-03-1996 L1999 FM *020 †18

REINKE, Derek Lawrence. 1005 VANDORA SPRINGS RD, SPORTS MEDICINE 27529 #038-43-1993 L1999 OSM *020 †40

ROBINSON, Lindwood. 141 BAYLEIGH CT 27529 #036-01-1997 L2008 EM *020

RUSHER, John Wallis. 800 BENSON RD, ASSOCIATES PA 27529 #036-01-1994 L1996 PD *020 †55

SAAD, Maged Hanna. 893 US HIGHWAY 70 W STE 20 27529 #915-02-1961 L1975 P D *020 †75 ‡

SHAIKH, Ghulam. 171 MAST DR 27529 #704-16-1987 L1995 IM *020 †20

SKILLEN, Richard Don. 902 RICHARDSON RD, WESTERN ROAD 27529 #050-01-1971 L1973 GP GPM *071

SPIVEY, David Eugene, Jr. 801 POOLE DR 27529 #036-05-1987 L1989 FM *020 †18

SUBEDI, Rajesh. ■ 27529 #672-02-2000 L2007 FM *020 †18

SZURA, Brian Thos. 1005 VANDORA SPRINGS RD, SPORTS MEDICINE 27529 #038-06-1985 L1992 ORS *020 †40

TAYLOR, Melinda Catherine. 800 BENSON RD, ASSOCIATES PA 27529 #036-01-1993 L1995 PD *020 †55

TETREAULT, Debra Jeanette. 222 MAST DR, KIDS CARE PEDIATRICS 27529 #001-02-1990 L1998 PD *040 †55

THOMAS, Cherisse Jamala. ■ 27529 #036-08-2006 MPD *012

TURNER, Steven Howard. 200 HEALTH PARK DR, STE 100 27529 #016-11-1985 L1995 IM *020 †20

WARSHAUER, Kristy. 220 US HIGHWAY 70 W 27529 #003-01-1984 L1989 IM *020

WINKEL, Jodi M. 801 POOLE DR 27529 #036-01-1995 L1997 FM *020 †18

WYKER, Robert Terlinck. 109 FOREST HILLS DR 27529 #051-01-1982 L1987 ORS *020 †40

GASTONIA – GASTON

ABERNETHY, William Borden, Jr. 610 DEERWOOD DR, MD 28054 #036-01-1960 L1960 PD *071 †55

ACOSTA, Albis. 815 COX RD 28054 #011-03-1992 L1996 N *020 †75

ADCOCK, George Edward, III. 991 W HUDSON BLVD 28052 #036-08-1997 L2001 OBG *020 †30

AIKEN, Warwick, III. 1867 REMOUNT RD, CAROMONT INTERNAL 28054 #036-01-1976 L1979 IM *020 †20

AJAO, Olufolarin A. 2664 COURT DR, STE A 28054 #690-08-1987 L1995 IM *020 †20

AKERS, Richard Edwin. 2555 COURT DR STE 150 28054 #045-01-1970 L1974 OPH *020 †35 ‡

AKHIMIEN, Azemobo Charles. 839 MAJESTIC CT, STE 3 28054 #690-02-1980 L2000 IM *020 †20

ALLAN, James Thomas, Jr. 620 SUMMIT CROSSING PL, GASTON RADIOLOGY 28054 #041-01-1970 L1976 R *020 †80

ALLF, Bryan Ewing. 2555 COURT DR, STE 150 28054 #036-07-1987 L1988 OPH *020 †35

ANDREOU, Costa. 2555 COURT DR, STE 300 28054 #836-01-1990 L1999 CD IC *020 †20

ANTHONY, Luther L. 1896 REMOUNT RD 28054 #041-02-1953 L1953 IM CD *071 †20

ANTHONY, William Edward. 311 W 3RD AVE 28052 #036-08-1990 L1992 FM *020 †18

ARCHIBALD, Ian D. 2525 COURT DR 28054 #671-02-1978 L2004 ORS *020 †40 ‡

ARN, Anthony Raymond. 2555 COURT DR, STE 250 28054 #038-40-1984 L2002 CD IM *020 †20

ARNEY, Gerald Wayne. 620 SUMMIT CROSSING PL, STE 106 28054 #047-06-1974 L1979 DR *020 †80 ‡

ARTER, James Lee. 2555 COURT DR, STE 300 28054 #012-01-1998 L2005 CD *020 †20

AUSTIN, Demetria Yvette. 2240 REMOUNT RD, CAROMONT INPATIENT 28054 #051-07-2000 L2003 IM *020 †20

AVIOLI, Richard Chas. 934 COX RD, . 28054 #045-01-1985 L1992 ORS GS *020 †40

AYCOCK, Perry Wm, Jr. 660 SUMMIT CROSSING PL, STE 301 28054 #045-01-1968 L1973 IM GE *020 †20

BAAGIL, Hasan Mohamad. 1315 E GARRISON BLVD 28054 #506-02-1961 L1978 FM *071 †18

BABB, Jeffrey Dean. 2525 COURT DR 28054 #010-31-1993 L1995 AN *020 †05

BAJWA, Ajay S. 2555 COURT DR, CAROLINA HEART 28054 #035-09-1996 L2002 IM *020 †20

BAKER, David Stanford, II. 706 SUMMIT CROSSING PL 28054 #004-01-1976 L1977 HS ORS *020 †20

BANERJEE, Anup. ■ 28054 #495-79-1994 L2006 PCC *020 †20

BARRINGER, Robt Phillips. 660 SUMMIT CROSSING PL, STE 201 28054 #036-01-1966 L1966 IM *071 †20

BATLEY, Jason J. 934 COX RD 28054 #035-45-1996 L2006 ORS *020 †40

BAUER, Daniel R. 2240 REMOUNT RD, CAROMONT INPATIENT 28054 #035-15-2001 L2006 IM *020 †20

BEDINGFIELD, Jacqueline V. 2544 COURT DR, STE C 28054 #045-01-1993 L1996 PD *020 †55

BELL, George A. ■ 28054 #024-01-1951 L1952 IM OS *020 †85

BELL, George Christopher. 2240 REMOUNT RD, CAROMONT INPATIENT 28054 #016-11-1988 L2007 IM *020 †20

BHALLA, Harpreet. 2555 COURT DR, CAROLINA HEART 28054 #035-19-1991 L2000 IC CD *020 †20

BIZUNEH, Amsalu Moges. 2240 REMOUNT RD, CAROMONT INPATIENT 28054 #012-05-2003 L2006 IM *020 †20

BLAKE, Robert Adams. 902 COX RD 28054 #045-01-1965 L1969 ORS *020 †40

BOLIN, Lewis B, Jr. 603 COX RD, MERCY MEDICAL GROUP 28054 #036-05-1982 L1983 FM *020 †18

BONNIN, Irvin Raymond, Jr. 991 W HUDSON BLVD 28052 #021-05-1964 L1974 GYN *020 †30

BOOHENE, Paulina A Essah. 991 W HUDSON BLVD 28052 #412-02-1992 L2004 NPM *020 †55

BOYLAN, Verena Marianna. 2555 COURT DR, STE 120 28054 #429-01-1985 L1997 OBG *020 †30

BRANDON, Daniel Ray. 705 SUMMIT CROSSING PL, STE 150 28054 #036-05-1965 L1965 GP *071

BROWN, Aaron Daniel. 3050 RIVERWOOD PKWY, CAROMONT FAMILY MEDICINE 28056 #028-34-2000 L2003 FM *020 †18 ‡

BROWN, Malgorzata Anna. 3050 RIVERWOOD PKWY, STE B 28056 #036-01-1998 L2001 FM *020 †18

BROWN, Martin Todd. 2325 ABERDEEN BLVD STE A, GASTON EYE ASSOCIATES 28054 #036-01-1986 L1990 OPH *020 †35

BRYANT, Acquinonett N. 2680 ABERDEEN BLVD, STE A 28054 #011-03-2001 L2005 OBG *020

BUNGCAYAO, Kimberly Mae. 2544 COURT DR STE F 28054 #035-20-2000 L2005 NEP *020 †20

BURGESS, Kenneth David. 3845 S NEW HOPE RD 28056 #036-01-1984 L1988 FM *020 †18

BUZZEO, Brian Derek. 631 COX RD, GASTON UROLOGICAL ASSOCS, 28054 #047-05-1992 L1997 U *020 †95

BYRUM, Christopher E. 2544 COURT DR STE A 28054 #051-01-1988 L1998 P *075 †75

CADDICK, William James. 1040 X RAY DR STE B 28054 #011-03-1986 L1991 GE IM *020 †20

CAKIR, Beril. 2240 REMOUNT RD, CAROMONT INPATIENT 28054 #902-05-1991 L2002 IM *020 †20 ‡

CALABRIA, Rafael A. 238 WILMOT DR, PILLAI NEUROPSYCHIARIC CTR 28054 #042-01-1964 L1996 CHP P *030 †75

CALLICUTT, Christopher S. 2544 COURT DR, ASSOCIATES PA 28054 #036-08-1997 L2003 GS VS *020 †85

CAULFIELD, Kathryn Ann. 2391 COURT DR STE 120, OF THE CAROLINAS 28054 #041-12-1988 L1996 HS *020 †40

CAULFIELD, Walter H, III. 2391 COURT DR, STE 120 28054 #041-12-1988 L1996 PS *020 †85,65

CHAMBERS, Robert E. 1839 E GARRISON BLVD 28054 #036-07-1952 L1956 PD *071 †55

CHANDER, Ernest Romesh. 1552 UNION RD STE C, CAROLINAS PSYCHIATRIC ASSO 28054 #495-08-1965 L1994 P *020 †75

CHANDER, Pushpa. 1552 UNION RD STE C 28054 #495-08-1966 L1994 IM *020

CHUNG, Dawn Anne. 2240 REMOUNT RD, CAROMONT INPATIENT 28054 #033-05-2001 L2004 IM *100

CLARK, Alan Boyd. 2240 REMOUNT RD, CAROMONT INPATIENT 28054 #036-05-1988 L1991 IM *020 †20

CLARK, Chad Michael. 620 SUMMIT CROSSING PL, STE 106 28054 #028-02-1998 L2004 DR *020 †80

CLEVELAND, Brett S. 2525 COURT DR 28054 #012-01-1991 L1995 AN PME *020 †05

CLONINGER, Karen Lynn. 2544 COURT DR, STE C 28054 #036-05-1987 L1990 PD *020 †55

COLLIER, Annamarie Reddin. 620 SUMMIT CROSSING PL, STE 106 28054 #036-01-1984 L1992 DR *020 †80

CONNER, Joel Dewitt. 2525 COURT DR 28054 #036-01-1957 L1958 GYN *071 †30

COSTNER, James Mitchell. 3715 UNION RD, RIVERWOOD MEDICAL ASSOCS, 28056 #036-08-1991 L1994 FM *020 †18

COTTER, Daniel Timothy. 2525 COURT DR 28054 #020-12-1983 L1986 AN *020 †05

COUTURE, Mark Moscoe. 2544 COURT DR, STE G 28054 #067-01-1974 L1979 GS VS *071 †85

COX, Russell Jackson. 2544 COURT DR 28054 #048-13-1979 L1982 PD *020 †55

CRAMP, Diana Lyn. ■ 28054 #035-46-2004 L2007 EM *020

CRAWFORD, Jane Hall. 2290 REMOUNT RD 28054 #045-01-1993 L1996 FM *020 †18

D'AMORE, Kirsten Gross. 2525 COURT DR 28054 #016-06-1995 L1999 PM *020 †60

D'AMORE, Martin James. 620 SUMMIT CROSSING PL, STE 106 28054 #016-01-1994 L1999 VIR *020 †80

DASHIELL, John James. 2544 COURT DR, STE F 28054 #051-07-1998 L2005 NEP *020 †20

DAVIS, Ellen S. 2711 X RAY DR, CAROMONT PEDIATRIC 28054 #051-04-1993 L1998 PD *020 †55

DAVIS, Todd Richard. 2525 COURT DR 28054 #051-04-1993 L1998 CCA *020 †05

DEAS, David John. 1006 UNION RD STE B 28054 #036-07-1961 L1961 P *020

DEWEESE, Renee M. 620 SUMMIT CROSSING PL, GASTON RADIOLOGY 28054 #035-05-1995 L2000 RNR *020 †80

DIBERT, Kanchan Puranik. 111 E 3RD AVE 28052 #047-06-1990 L1993 IM *020 †20

DIBERT, Steven Wesley. 2555 COURT DR STE 400 28054 #038-40-1990 L1991 N RNR *020 †75

DICKSON, Brice T, Jr. ■ 28054 #041-02-1944 L1944 IM *071

DIFINI, John Anthony. 815 COX RD 28054 #010-02-1982 L1992 N OS *020 †75

DIGBY, Ronald Wyman. 660 SUMMIT CROSSING PL, STE 201 28054 #012-01-1971 L1977 CD IM *020 †20

DOVER, Stanley Frank. 2525 COURT DR 28054 #036-01-1999 L2000 AN *020 †05

DRAKE, Samuel Thos. 2550 COURT DR STE 201 28054 #045-01-1973 L1979 GE IM *020 †20

DRAUGHN, David Gardner. 2555 COURT DR, STE 440 28054 #027-01-1987 L1993 GS *020 †85

DUARTE, Anthony Clement. 2525 COURT DR, GASTON MEMORIAL HOSPITAL 28054 #060-01-1988 L2002 EM *020

DUL, Kevin. 620 SUMMIT CROSSING PL, STE 106 28054 #048-14-1987 L2002 DR RNR *020 †80

DYKE, Cornelius Mckown. 2555 COURT DR, CAROLINA HEART 28054 #036-07-1987 L1998 TS *020 †85,90

EDGE, Mark Thomas. 2525 COURT DR 28054 #001-02-1994 L2002 R RNR *020 †80

ERUCHALU, Ifeanyichukwu M. 900 COX RD, STE B 28054 #690-04-1989 L1995 IM *020 †20

EVANOFF, Allison Marie. 2290 REMOUNT RD 28054 #036-07-1996 L1997 FM *020 †18

EVANS, Ronald Lyn. 2525 COURT DR 28054 #045-01-1981 L1987 AN EM *020 †05

EZE, Augustine Richard. 227 WILMOT DR STE A, SPECIALISTS, PA 28054 #010-02-1987 L1996 VS *020 †85

FARR, Arman Khaksar. 2311 ABERDEEN BLVD, STE B2 28054 #036-07-1994 L2002 OPH *020 †35

FEINBERG, Eric Brian. 2680 ABERDEEN BLVD STE A 28054 #041-09-1991 L1999 OBG *020 †30

FISHER, Carl Ellis. 2544 COURT DR, STE C 28054 #036-01-1969 L1969 PD *020 †55 ‡

FOLKS, Jacqueline Denise. 1867 REMOUNT RD STE D, CAROMONT INTERNAL MEDICINE 28054 #045-04-1995 L2002 IM *020 †20 ‡

FORBES, Neville W. 2525 COURT DR 28054 #566-01-1982 L1996 GE IM *020 †20

FRICKER, Richard Alan. 2240 REMOUNT RD, CAROMONT CRITICAL CARE 28054 #038-45-1988 L2006 CCM *020 †20

GAINES, Jill Andrea. 2680 ABERDEEN BLVD, STE A 28054 #030-05-1999 L2003 OBG *020 †30

GAMBOA, Andres Eduardo. 414 S YORK ST 28052 #264-01-1954 L1969 FM PD *071 †18

GAMMON, Gary Glenn. 2240 REMOUNT RD, CAROMONT INPATIENT 28054 #050-02-1982 L1991 HOS IM *020 †20

GARRETT, John Bostian. 631 COX RD 28054 #045-01-1973 L1981 U *020 †95 ‡

GASLIN, Michael T. 2520 ABERDEEN BLVD 28054 #035-15-2002 L2007 OTO *020 †20

GIBBS, Stuart Wynn. ■ 28054 #036-05-1944 L1944 R *071 †80

GIHWALA, Ramesh. 825 MAJESTIC CT, STE A 28054 #305-01-1985 L1993 P *020

GIRMAY, Aregai A. 991 W HUDSON BLVD 28052 #016-11-1992 L1997 FM *020 †18

GODBOLE, Sulabha S. 2240 REMOUNT RD, CAROMONT INPATIENT 28054 #047-20-2003 L2006 IM *020 †20

GORE, Herman Clark. 900 COX RD, STE A 28054 #041-09-1994 L1999 PM PMM *020 †60

GORE, Shawnya Ayers. 1867 REMOUNT RD, STE D 28054 #045-04-1996 L1999 **IM** *020 †20
GROSSMAN, Sarah Rona. 1839 E GARRISON BLVD 28054 #036-05-1990 L1993 **PD** *020 †55
GUDEMAN, Steven Kent. 2555 COURT DR 28054 #038-41-1976 L1992 **NS** *020 †25
HAMMOND, Wm Howard, Jr. ■ 28054 #047-07-1963 L1964 **GP** *071
HANSEN, Todd Stewart. 2525 COURT DR 28054 #001-02-1996 L1997 **FM** *020 †18
HARLEY, William Ben, II. 2711 X RAY DR, NFECTIOUS DISEASE 28054 #045-04-1989 L1994 **IM ID** *020 †20
HARRIS, Kelvin Crews. 2680 ABERDEEN BLVD, STE A 28054 #036-01-1986 L1990 **OBG** *020 †30
HATSIOS, George John. 620 SUMMIT CROSSING PL, STE 106 28054 #035-06-1994 L2000 **NM DR** *020 †28,80
HAYES, Wm Clayton, Jr. 825 MAJESTIC CT STE B 28054 #036-01-1974 L1976 **PD** *020 †55
HECKEL, Mark Campbell. 2555 COURT DR, CAROLINA HEART 28054 #041-13-1999 L2005 **CD IM** *020 †20
HEMBREE, Eugene E, Jr. 991 W HUDSON BLVD 28052 #045-01-1966 L1971 **OBG** *020 †30
HIGH, James Richard. 2711 X RAY DR, CAROMONT PEDIATRIC 28054 #036-05-1996 L2001 **PD** *020 †55
HOFFMAN, Catherine Ann. 640 SUMMIT CROSSING PL, STE 204 28054 #038-41-1994 L1998 **MPD PD** *020 †20,55
HOLTZMAN, Ronald Bennett. 2525 COURT DR, GASTON MEMORIAL HOSP 28054 #016-01-1983 L2005 **NPM** *020 †55
HONEYCUTT, Sammy Carol. 2525 COURT DR 28054 #036-01-1974 L1976 **EM FM** *062
HOVIS, Scott Marion. 2544 COURT DR STE G, GASTONIA SURGICAL ASSOCIAT 28054 #036-08-2001 L2006 **VS** *020 †85
HUBBARD, James L. 991 W HUDSON BLVD 28052 #041-77-1994, ▲ L2006 **OBG** *020
HUMPHRIES, Renee Annette. 2525 COURT DR, MEDICAL STAFF OFFICE 28054 #038-41-2000 L2003 **EM** *100 †16
HUNTER, William Dean. 2555 COURT DR STE 400 28054 #010-02-1990 L2000 **NS** *020 †25
HURST, Lawrence Bradford. 2544 COURT DR, STE C 28054 #036-01-1994 L1998 **PD** *020 †55
HUTCHINS, Charles Hubert. 750 COX RD 28054 #012-01-1966 L1970 **OTO FPS** *020 †45
IBRAHIM, Radwan A. 211 S CHESTNUT ST 28054 #915-04-1985 L1997 **IM** *020 †20
JAMES, John Clay. PO BOX 6099, 3680 ROBINWOOD RD 28056 #036-05-1957 L1957 **GP** *071 †18
JAMES, Shana Danette. 991 W HUDSON BLVD, PRESBYTERIAN URGENT CARE 28052 #010-03-1995 L1996 **FM** *020 †18
JARMAN, William Henry, Jr. 620 SUMMIT CROSSING PL, STE 108 28054 #036-01-1967 L1967 **ORS** *071 †40
JARRATT, Mikell Jenkins. 1021 X RAY DR 28054 #027-01-1987 L1994 **PUD CCM** *020 †20
JARVIS, James Luther. ■ 28054 #036-05-1946 L1946 **R** *071 †80,28
JOHNSON, David Michael. 660 SUMMIT CROSSING PL, STE 301 28054 #005-12-1993 L2000 **IM** *020 †20
JOHNSON, Erik Charles. 2525 COURT DR 28054 #035-47-1998 L2004 **ORS OSM** *020 †40
JONES, John Fletcher. 2525 COURT DR 28054 #036-08-1983 L1985 **AN IM** *020 †05
JORDAN, Richard M. 620 SUMMIT CROSSING PL, STE 106 28054 #036-05-1983 L1987 **DR** *020 †80
JUSTICE, Jason Robert. 2240 REMOUNT RD, CAROMONT CRITICAL CARE 28054 #038-43-2001 L2005 **CCM** *100
KACMAR, Jennifer E. 991 W HUDSON BLVD 28052 #041-02-1996 L2006 **OBG** *020 †30
KAHN, Robert Howard. 1072 X RAY DR, STE A 28054 #035-19-1972 L1976 **D** *020 †15
KALEAB, Birhane G. 1343 E GARRISON BLVD, CAROLINA MEDICAL CLINIC 28054 #366-01-1982 L2004 **FM** *020 †18
KALIA, Anoop Kumar. 252 WILMOT DR 28054 #495-03-1990 L2002 **CHP** *020 †75
KANSUPADA, Ameesha K. 2240 REMOUNT RD, CAROMONT INPATIENT PHYSICI 28054 #036-01-1993 L1996 **IM** *020 †20
KEATHLEY, Franklin Burr. 2525 COURT DR 28054 #047-06-1946 L1950 **D A** *020
KELLY, Daniel Lee. 603 COX RD 28054 #051-04-1983 L1989 **FM EM** *020 †18
KERBOW, Michele Marie. 2555 COURT DR, STE 250 28054 #045-04-2002 L2006 **P** *020
KING, Glendall Lee. 902 COX RD, GASTON ORTHOPAEDIC CLINIC 28054 #028-02-1955 L1965 **ORS** *071 †40
KLASING, Donald Rollin. 2240 REMOUNT RD, CAROMONT PSYCHIATRIC 28054 #001-02-1996 L2006 **P** *020 †75
KLEIN, Alan David. 959 COX RD 28054 #038-06-1982 L2001 **D** *020 †15
LADD, Robert Julius. 640 SUMMIT CROSSING PL, STE 208 28054 #010-03-1964 L1971 **OM GP** *062 †85
LAHSER, Charles Irving. ■ 28054 #036-05-1946 L1946 **PD** *071 †55
LANCASTER, David Steven. 2525 COURT DR, GASTON MEMORIAL HOSPITAL 28054 #045-04-2003 L2006 **EM** *020
LATHAM, Robert Q, Jr. 3715 UNION RD 28056 #045-04-1990 L2000 **FM** *020 †18
LAYNE, David Andrew. 3715 UNION RD, RIVERWOOD MEDICAL ASSOC 28056 #012-05-1987 L1993 **FM EM** *020 †18
LEE, Barry Russell. 631 COX RD 28054 #021-01-1987 L1993 **U** *020 †95
LEEPER, Wm Edward, Jr. ■ 28054 #036-07-1943 L1944 **IM** *071 †20
LEFLER, Rodger Wendell. 1038 X RAY DR 28054 #016-11-1977 L2000 **IM** *020 †20
LEONE, Cheryl H Levine. 2525 COURT DR 28054 #021-01-1969 L1978 **CLP ATP** *020 †50
LEONE, Philip Geo. 2525 COURT DR 28054 #021-01-1968 L1978 **PTH CLP** *020 †50
LESTER, Robert Hilton. 991 W HUDSON BLVD 28052 #036-01-1975 L1979 **OBG** *020 †30
LETTS, Dustin Patrick. 2555 COURT DR, STE 300 28054 #012-22-1999 L2007 **IC** *020 †20
LIGHT, Andrew Ira. 1089 X RAY DR 28054 #021-01-1983 L1988 **GS VS** *020 †85
LIGHT, Vicki Weiss. 2555 COURT DR, STE 120 28054 #021-01-1983 L1990 **OBG** *020 †30
LONGBINE, Timothy Wayne. 2525 COURT DR 28054 #055-02-1995 L1996 **AN** *020 †05
LOSTETTER, Stephen John. 620 SUMMIT CROSSING PL, STE 106 28054 #055-01-1995 L2000 **DR** *020 †80
LUBEGA, Margaret. 1032 X RAY DR 28054 #905-01-1984 L2002 **PD** *020
LUND, Michael James. 2325 ABERDEEN BLVD STE A, GASTON EYE ASSOCIATES 28054 #017-20-1991 L1995 **OPH** *020 †35
LUPSE, Raymond Morris. 603 COX RD 28054 #038-06-1977 L1988 **GYN** *020
LUVIS, Luhubanduwaduge D. 2682 COURT DR STE B 28054 #220-01-1971 L1977 **IM** *020 †20
LYNSHUE, Kecha Annmarie. 991 W HUDSON BLVD 28052 #036-01-2000 L2001 **PD** *100 †55
MAC LAUGHLIN, Jayne Marie. 2525 COURT DR, GASTON MEMORIAL HOSPITAL 28054 #017-20-2002 L2006 **EM** *100
MAHMOOD, Shakeer. 2525 COURT DR 28054 #495-33-1989 L1999 **IM** *020 †20
MAIER, George Wm. 2555 COURT DR, CAROLINA HEART 28054 #036-07-1982 L1991 **TS VS** *020 †85
MAITRA, Ranjan Simon. 706 SUMMIT CROSSING PL 28054 #025-01-1993 L2000 **OSM ORS** *020 †40
MAJOR, David Albert. 2555 COURT DR STE 200, CAROLINA HEART SPECIALISTS 28054 #036-05-2001 L2007 **CD** *020

MALONE, Mary Winefride. ■ 28052 #352-06-1950 **GP** *074
MALONEY, Eugene Douglas. 1437 E FRANKLIN BLVD 28054 #036-07-1962 L1963 **P EM** *020
MANCINI, Sheri Ann. 2525 COURT DR 28054 #041-12-1996 L2006 **GS** *020 †85
MANTOOTH, Gregory Allen. 959 COX RD 28054 #047-06-1993 L2001 **PS** *020 †85,65
MARISIDDAIAH, Harish. 2711 X RAY DR, NFECTIOUS DISEASE 28054 #495-33-1987 L1995 **ID IM** *020 †20
MARLOWE, Edgar Earl, Jr. 1613 W GARRISON BLVD 28052 #047-06-1962 L1965 **GP CD** *071
MARQUAND, Wesley Lee. 2711 X RAY DR 28054 #023-12-1989 L1991 **FM** *020 †18
MATTHEW, Matthew T. 2525 COURT DR 28054 #062-01-1994 L1998 **AN PME** *020 †05
MC CLELLAN, Daniel Lee. 2544 COURT DR, ASSOCIATES PA 28054 #011-03-1985 L1990 **GS** *020 †85
MC CULLEN, Bobby Kenneth. 2325 ABERDEEN BLVD STE A 28054 #036-01-1988 L1989 **OPH** *020 †35
MC HALE, Patricia Lynn. 706 SUMMIT CROSSING PL 28054 #048-04-1997 L2003 **OSM** *020 †40
MC NIFF, Thos Edward, III. 2525 COURT DR 28054 #051-04-1992 L1999 **CCA** *020 †05
MEHTA, Malti Praful. 1040 X RAY DR STE C, PIEDMONT PSYCHIATRIC ASSOC 28054 #495-22-1970 L1980 **P** *020 †75
MEHTA, Sunil. 815 COX RD, GASTON NEUROLOGICAL 28054 #305-01-2003 L2007 **N** *020
MEMOLO, Mark William. 620 SUMMIT CROSSING PL, STE 106 28054 #041-02-1987 L1988 **VIR IM** *020 †80
MIJUMBI, Olivia Bridget. 813 S OAKLAND ST STE A, CAROLINA PEDIATRIC CENTER 28054 #905-01-1991 L1997 **PD** *020 †55
MILES, John Ralph. 825 MAJESTIC CT, STE F 28054 #051-01-1973 L1974 **VS GS** *020 †85
MILLER, Andrew Cleveland. 311 W 3RD AVE 28052 #036-01-1955 L1955 **GP** *071 †18
MILLER, Charles Valentine. ■ 28054 #035-45-1942 L1954 **PHP NM** *071 †50
MILLER, George Rolfe. 902 COX RD, GASTON ORTHOPAEDIC CLINIC 28054 #035-45-1943 L1950 **ORS** *071 †40
MILLER, Robert William. 620 SUMMIT CROSSING PL, STE 106 28054 #041-09-1988 L2001 **DR** *020 †80
MILROY, Gregory Todd. 2711 X RAY DR, CAROMONT PEDIATRIC 28054 #045-01-1992 L1998 **PD** *020 †55
MOORE, Regina Frances. ■ 28056 #038-43-1998 *100
MOORE-TAYLOR, Michelle J. 825 MAJESTIC CT STE B, PEDIATRIC & ADOLESCENT MED 28054 #036-01-1994 L1997 **PD** *020 †55
MOSKOWITZ, Mark S. 1089 X RAY DR 28054 #024-05-1974 L1980 **GS VS** *020 †85
MURPHY, Thomas Lynch. 1021 X RAY DR 28054 #024-01-1973 L1981 **PUD IM** *020 †20
NEAL, James Earl. 1072 X RAY DR 28054 #047-07-1968 L1974 **IM RHU** *020 †20
NEEDELL, James Edward. 1021 X RAY DR 28054 #041-09-1995 L2000 **IM** *020 †20
NESKY, Mark Allen. 2711 X RAY DR, NFECTIOUS DISEASE 28054 #038-43-1995 L1997 **ID** *020 †20
NGUYEN, Chris Brian. ■ 28052 #045-04-2000 L2006 **PTH** *020 †50
NIEMEYER, Charles John. 620 SUMMIT CROSSING PL, STE 108 28054 #036-07-1966 L1966 **ORS** *020 †40
NIGBOR, Douglas Alan. 2544 COURT DR, STE F 28054 #017-20-1998 L2004 **NEP** *020 †20
NIJHER, Harpreet K. 2525 COURT DR 28054 #035-45-1998 L2002 **AN** *020
NORCROSS, Frederick C. 1839 E GARRISON BLVD 28054 #010-01-1964 L1969 **PD** *071 †55
NUTT, Suzanne Hamilton. 2555 COURT DR STE 400 28054 #036-08-1989 L1993 **N** *020 †75
OCLOO, Shirley Daikie. 991 W HUDSON BLVD 28052 #021-05-1993 L1995 **FM** *020 †18
O'CONNOR, Kevin Michael. 2525 COURT DR, GASTON COUNTY, PLLC 28054 #025-07-1989 L2006 **EM** *020 †16 ‡
OGDEN, Robert Harvey. 1501 HEATHERLOCH DR 28054 #012-01-1963 L1969 **GYN** *071 †30
O'LEARY, Gregory James. 527 S NEW HOPE RD, WHITESTONE FAMILY MEDICINE 28054 #041-02-1994 L2001 **FM** *020 †18
OSEMEKA, Austin A. 2682 COURT DR, STE A 28054 #690-01-1986 L1997 **IM** *020 †20
OWENSBY, Charlton Norman. 2525 COURT DR 28054 #036-05-1984 L1985 **OM LM** *020
OWUSU-ADDO, Yaw A. 640 SUMMIT CROSSNG PL #204 28054 #412-01-1985 L1995 **IM PD** *020 †55,20
PAI, Suhas. 2555 COURT DR 28054 #045-01-2000 L2007 **NS** *020
PARLIER, Reggie David. 2544 COURT DR STE D, NEW HOPE FAMILY MEDICINE 28054 #036-07-1987 L1994 **FM OBS** *020 †18 ‡
PATE, Jay S.. 3532 ARAGLIN DR 28056 #654-01-2001 L2004 **IM** *100 †20
PATEL, Manish Prafulla. 924 COX RD, PIEDMONT UROLOGY 28054 #038-45-1997 L2002 **U** *020 †95
PATEL, Manu Hira. 2711 X RAY DR, CAROMONT FAMILY MEDICINE 28054 #495-96-1972 L1995 **FM** *020 †18
PATEL, Natu Vallavbhai. 635 COX RD, STE E 28054 #495-76-1973 L1983 **IM EM** *020 †20
PATEL, Subhash P. 432 E LONG AVE, STE 1 28054 #495-23-1975 L1997 **P** *020 †75
PATEL, Vipul Manilal. ■ 28056 #305-01-2000 L2007 **HO** *100
PEACE, Nyota Afi. 991 W HUDSON BLVD 28052 #045-01-2001 L2005 **OBG** *100
PEARSON, Darryl H. 991 W HUDSON BLVD, DEPARTMENT 28052 #047-07-1983 L1987 **OBG** *020 †30
PICKFORD, Heather Ann. 620 SUMMIT CROSSING PL, STE 106 28054 #025-12-1993 L1998 **DR** *020 †80
PILLAI, Ashokkumar P. 238 WILMOT DR 28054 #495-66-1986 L1994 **N** *020 †75 ‡
PILLAI, Jeyakumar P. 238 WILMOT DR 28054 #496-01-1978 L1985 **P** *020 †75
POLEN, Christopher Lynn. 2240 REMOUNT RD, CAROMONT CRITICAL CARE SPE 28054 #055-01-1995 L2007 **CCM PD** *020 †20
POWELL, Monica J. 991 W HUDSON BLVD 28052 #010-03-2001 L2005 **PD** *020 †55
POWERS, Tonya Kim. 2525 COURT DR 28054 #045-04-1995 L1998 **APM** *020 †05
PRAKASH, Angela. 1867 REMOUNT RD, CAROMONT INTERNAL 28054 #012-01-2003 L2006 **IM** *020 †20
QUAID, Gina Ann. 2544 COURT DR, ASSOCIATES PA 28054 #054-04-1995 L2006 **GS** *020 †85
RADFORD, Maurice Gene, Jr. 2544 COURT DR, STE F 28054 #036-01-1990 L1996 **NEP** *020 †20
REYNOLDS, Eugene, II. 991 W HUDSON BLVD, GASTON FAMILY HEALTH SERVI 28052 #047-07-1995 L1996 **FM** *020 †18
RICHMOND, Robt Southwick. 2525 COURT DR 28054 #028-02-1964 L1981 **PTH BBK** *020 †50
ROACH, Annette Patricia. 2555 COURT DR, STE 120 28054 #035-47-1996 L2004 **OBG** *020 †30
ROBINSON, Robert Carl, III. 2240 REMOUNT RD, CAROMONT INPATIENT 28054 #016-11-2002 L2005 **IM** *020 †20
RODENBERGER, Paul M. 631 COX RD, GASTON UROLOGICAL ASSOCIAT 28054 #041-13-1999 L2007 **U** *020 †95
RUSSO, Patrick Jos, Jr. 2555 COURT DR, STE 300 28054 #030-06-1992 L2003 **CD** *020 †20
SALES, Eileen Frances. 2555 COURT DR STE 120 28054 #035-48-1990 L1994 **OBG** *020 †30
SALTMARSH, Christopher Wm. 620 SUMMIT CROSSING PL, STE 106 28054 #011-02-1981 L1996 **DR** *020 †80

■ = Address Information Privacy Protected

SANCHEZ, Alexander F, Jr. 705 SUMMIT CROSSING PL, OCCUPATIONAL MEDICINE 28054 #011-03-1975 L1976 **OM FM** *030 †18,70

SANDERS, James Allen. 512 E FRANKLIN BLVD 28054 #036-05-1963 L1963 **ORS** *071 †40

SANDIFER, Honora Manning. 2240 REMOUNT RD, CAROMONT PSYCHIATRIC 28054 #045-04-1999 L2003 **P** *020 †75 ‡

SCHANG, Angela K. 3481 FIELDSTONE DR 28056 #011-03-1997 L2003 **U** *020 †95

SCHEITLER, John Lawrence. 640 SUMMIT CROSSING PL, STE 204 28054 #036-08-1996 L1998 **MPD** *020 †20,55

SCHENK, Gary Scott. 1381 E GARRISON BLVD 28054 #012-01-1988 L1991 **FM** *020 †18

SCHULS, Erik Lawrence. 2240 REMOUNT RD, CAROMONT INPATIENT 28054 #035-15-1996 L2003 **IM** *020 †20

SCHULTZ, Sandra Beth. 1089 X RAY DR, CAROLINA SURGERY 28054 #056-05-1989 L1995 **GS** *020 †85

SEEAR, Torben. ■ 28054 #297-01-1941 L1954 **OBG** *071 †30

SHAH, Ketan Dhan. 603 COX RD 28054 #036-07-1995 L2000 **IM** *020 †20

SHANNON, Wm Bartholomew. 1061 X RAY DR 28054 #012-05-1976 L1981 **OPH** *020 †35

SHASTRY, S Chandra S. 660 SUMMIT CROSSING PL, STE 103 28054 #495-72-1970 L1980 **IM DIA** *020 †20

SHEW, Katherine Denise. 959 COX RD 28054 #051-04-2003 L2007 **D** *020 †15

SHUKLA, Nilima Vikram. 839 MAJESTIC CT STE 1 28054 #495-23-1980 L1988 **P** *020 †75

SHUKLA, Vikram Rasiklal. 839 MAJESTIC CT STE 8 28054 #495-22-1978 L1988 **P CHP** *020 †75

SICILIA, Carlos Alejandro. 2544 COURT DR, ASSOCIATES PA 28054 #132-06-1982 L1989 **GS VS** *020 †85

SIDO, Obukohwo Francis. 224 S NEW HOPE RD, STE C 28054 #690-02-1981 L1994 **IM** *020 †20

SILKSTONE, William Lee. 1839 E GARRISON BLVD 28054 #025-07-1971 L1979 **PD** *020 †55

SILVOY, Edward John. 1010 X RAY DR, STE A 28054 #035-09-1971 L1978 **OTO PS** *020 †45

SIMONSEN, Jeremy Wendell. 2525 COURT DR, EMERGENCY DEPARTMENT 28054 #021-01-1999 L2002 **EM** *020 †16

SINAI, Laura. 825 MAJESTIC CT STE B 28054 #033-06-1990 L2004 **PD** *020 †55

SINGER, Rody Ben. 2240 REMOUNT RD 28054 #033-06-1998 L2003 **MPD** *020 †20,55

SINGH, Harcharan. ■ 28056 #495-03-1962 L2007 **OPH** *020 †35

SINGH, Inderjeet. 635 COX RD STE G 28054 #036-06-1992 L1998 **GS** *020 †85

SIVA, Sivalingam. 900 COX RD 28054 #825-01-1965 L1975 **NS** *020

SLOAND, Timothy Peter. 620 SUMMIT CROSSING PL, STE108 28054 #035-45-1988 L2003 **ORS** *020 †40

SMITH, Michael Alson. 2525 COURT DR 28054 #036-07-1986 L1989 **FM** *020 †18

SMITH, Michael Joseph. 2240 REMOUNT RD, CAROMONT INPATIENT PHYSICI 28054 #422-01-2001 L2007 **IM** *020

SMITH, Ramada Sherice. 2555 COURT DR, GASTON PERINATAL CENTER 28054 #025-07-1987 L2004 **MFM** *020 †30

SMITH, Rodney Wilson. 2525 COURT DR 28054 #021-01-1989 L1995 **U** *020 †95

SNYDER, Timothy Calvin. 660 SUMMIT CROSSING PL, STE 303 28054 #005-12-1992 L1999 **OMF PSH** *020

STONE, Jenny Lee. 959 COX RD 28054 #024-01-1982 L2007 **D** *020 †15 ‡

SUTTON, Laddeus Leon. 2555 COURT DR, STE 300 28054 #036-08-1987 L1993 **CD IM** *020 †20

TAMBERELLA, Michael R, III. 2555 COURT DR, CAROLINA HEART 28054 #021-05-1996 L2004 **IC** *020 †20

TAORMINA, Velma Villalon. 991 W HUDSON BLVD 28052 #048-15-1990 L1996 **GYN** *020 †30

TARASKA, Gregory John. 2525 COURT DR 28054 #041-02-1990 L1992 **EM** *020 †16

TAYLOR, James Edward. 631 COX RD 28054 #012-01-1977 L1982 **U** *071 †95

THOMAS, David Timothy. 660 SUMMIT CROSSING PL, STE 301 28054 #036-01-1988 L1991 **IM** *020 †20

THOMAS, Henry Fuller, Jr. 902 COX RD, PARK 28054 #036-01-1966 L1966 **AS CD** *071 †85

THOMASON, Henry C, Jr. 1021 X RAY DR 28054 #036-01-1967 L1967 **CD IM** *020 †20

THOMASON, Henry C, III. 620 SUMMIT CROSSING PL, STE 108 28054 #036-01-1995 L2000 **ORS** *020 †40

THOMPSON, Jill Ellen. 2555 COURT DR STE 400 28054 #036-01-1991 L1993 **RNR** *020 †80

THOMPSON, Mark Allen. 2555 COURT DR, CAROLINA HEART 28054 #041-12-1985 L2000 **CD** *020 †20

THRELKELD, Melinda Sue. 2525 COURT DR 28054 #038-06-2004 L2007 **EM** *020

TIMMONS, Benson E, IV. 649 N NEW HOPE RD, SOUTHEASTERN PLASTIC SURGE 28054 #036-08-1985 L1990 **PS HS** *020 †85,65

TRACY, Steven Lynn. 2525 COURT DR 28054 #018-03-1980 L1981 **PTH** *020 †50

TYNER, Hugh Edward. 2525 COURT DR 28054 #036-05-1946 L1946 **GS** *071 †85

VALEDON, Francisco A. 1867 REMOUNT RD, STE 2 28054 #042-01-1989 L2002 **IM** *020 †20

VANDERMEER, Christopher J. 620 SUMMIT CROSSING PL, STE 106 28054 #051-04-1998 L2001 **RNR** *020 †80

VAN METER, Richard A. 3715 UNION RD, RIVERWOOD MEDICAL ASSOCIAT 28056 #041-02-1994 L2001 **IM** *020 †18

VARGAS, Carlos A. 1381 E GARRISON BLVD, GASTON RADIOLOGY PA 28054 #176-01-1963 L1976 **DR** *071 †80

VILLARREAL, Jaime. 1038 X RAY DR 28054 #016-11-1991 L1998 **IM** *020 †20

WALKER, Constance Elaine. 1839 E GARRISON BLVD 28054 #048-02-2002 L2005 **PD** *020 †55

WALLACE, Robert Bruce. 1548 UNION RD STE D, CAROLINA PHYSICAL MEDICINE 28054 #064-01-1976 L1979 **FM** *020 ‡

WARLICK, John Thos, III. 631 COX RD 28054 #045-01-1966 L1971 **U** *071 †95

WATKINS, William Spencer. 2450 ABERDEEN BLVD STE A, GASTON GASTROENTEROLOGY 28054 #010-02-1986 L1988 **GE IM** *020 †20

WATTS, John C, III. 1839 E GARRISON BLVD 28054 #021-01-1984 L1989 **PD** *020 †55

WEBSTER, Hala J. 660 SUMMIT CROSSING PL, STE 301 28054 #038-06-1994 L1999 **IM** *020 †20

WEISS, Juli Stone. ■ 28056 #021-01-1984 L1991 **AN** *020 †05

WHALEN, Mark Jeffrey. 2525 COURT DR, GASTON MEMORIAL HOSPITAL 28054 #041-12-1990 L1995 **PTH** *020 †50

WHALEN, Sean Patrick. 620 SUMMIT CROSSING PL, STE 106 28054 #005-15-2002 L2007 **DR** *020

WHITAKER, Albert, Jr. 224 S NEW HOPE RD, POST OFFICE 4015 28054 #047-07-1977 L1979 **FM** *020 †18

WHITESIDES, Edward S. 630 SUMMIT CROSSING PL, CAROLINA ORTHOPAEDICS 28054 #036-07-1951 L1952 **ORS** *071 †40

WILKINSON, John J. 2525 COURT DR, EMERGENCY DEPT 28054 #041-12-1994 L1997 **EM** *020 †16

WILKINSON, Michelle E. 2290 REMOUNT RD 28054 #041-12-1994 L1997 **FM** *020 †18

WILLIAMS, Cassandra. ■ 28056 #035-06-2005 L2008 **IM** *012

WILLIAMS, Ernest C. ■ 28056 #021-01-1951 L1956 **GS TS** *071

WILLIAMS, Harry Kenneth. 1089 X RAY DR 28054 #051-01-1987 L2006 **GS** *020 †85

WITTENBERG, Peter H. 2525 COURT DR 28054 #007-02-1964 L1978 **PTH** *020 †50

WOODIN, Kathleen Anne. 825 MAJESTIC CT, STE B 28054 #033-05-1981 L2000 **PD ID** *020 †55

WU, Maryanne E. 2240 REMOUNT RD, CAROMONT INPATIENT 28054 #035-15-1997 L2003 **IM** *020 †20

WYCKOFF, Elita Nichelle. 2555 COURT DR, STE 120 28054 #045-01-2001 L2005 **OBG** *020 †30

YANEZ, Miguel Angel. 959 COX RD 28054 #042-01-1986 L2008 **PS** *020 †65 ‡

YORK, David A. 603 COX RD 28054 #065-01-1981 L2004 **FM EM** *020 †18

ZOUZOULAS, Stephen S. 2555 COURT DR, CAROLINA HEART 28054 #048-02-1999 L2006 **CD** *020 †20

GATES — GATES

JONES, Marcus Rodriquez. ■ 27937 #051-07-1996 L1996 *100

GATESVILLE — GATES

JONES, Rayette Pollard. 501 MAIN ST 27938 #051-07-1996 L2001 **IM** *020 †20

GERMANTON — STOKES

HOLLINGSWORTH, Harry W. ■ 27019 #047-06-1935 L1968 **OM** *071

MOLINA, German. ■ 27019 #308-03-1985 L1995 **P** *020 †75

GERTON — HENDERSON

EARNHARDT, James F. ■ 28735 #036-01-1964 L1964 **PD** *020 †55

STEPP, Hestley Danard. ■ 28735 #036-05-1959 L1959 **PD** *071 †55

GIBSONVILLE — GUILFORD

PHILLIPS, Charles Woodrow. 108 E MINNEOLA ST 27249 #036-01-1958 L1958 **GP AM** *020

SCHUMPERT, Millie Hancock. ■ 27249 #023-07-1962 L1965 **AI PD** *071 †55

GLEN ALPINE — BURKE

NAGY, Barbara Ann. PO BOX 837, 301 LINVILLE ST 28628 #012-05-1982 L1992 **IM PD** *020 †20,55 ‡

GLENVILLE — JACKSON

COATES, Michael Robt. ■ 28736 #011-03-1972 L1973 **PS GS** *020 †65

KNIGHT, Edward Washburn. PO BOX 58 28736 #035-15-1956 L1995 **ON IM** *071

STONE, Harry Harlan. ■ 28736 #012-05-1955 L1955 **GS TRS** *071 †85

WILLIAMS, Jonathan R, Jr. ■ 28736 #021-01-1965 L1994 **PLM** *071 †20

GLOUCESTER — CARTERET

PACE, Karl Busbee, Jr. ■ 28528 #041-02-1947 L1947 **OS D** *075 †15

GOLDSBORO — WAYNE

AHMED, Maqsood. 2902 CENTRAL HEIGHTS RD #A 27534 #704-21-1985 L1997 **PM** *020

AKHTAR, Waheed. 2400 WAYNE MEMORIAL DR 27534 #704-01-1982 L1995 **CD** *020 †20

ALEXANDER, Ansha Rhea Ear. 2609 MEDICAL OFFICE PL, EASTERN MED ASSOC 27534 #422-01-1999 L2004 **MPD** *100 †20,55

AMAEFULE, Celestine I. 1104 GRACIE PL 27534 #016-43-1986 L1993 **IM** *020 †20

AMSELLEM, David. 201 STEVENS MILL RD 27530 #396-04-1973 L1976 **P** *020

ANJANADEVI, Tripuraneni. 400 OLD SMITHFIELD RD 27530 #495-50-1961 L1978 **GP** *020 †85

ARTIS, Karlus Cornelius. 1600 WAYNE MEMORIAL DR # C 27534 #036-08-1990 L1991 **GP FM** *020

BATEMAN, Wallace Bryson, Jr. 2700 WAYNE MEMORIAL DR 27534 #036-01-1976 L1976 **EM** *020 †16

BAUER, Gregory Scott. 2808 MCLAMB PL 27534 #028-02-1995 L2001 **ORS** *020 †40

BENNETT, Paul Clifford. 2607 MEDICAL OFFICE PL 27534 #036-07-1955 L1955 **FM** *071

BERKELEY, Scott Bruce, Jr. 2700 WAYNE MEMORIAL DR 27534 #023-01-1953 L1953 **GS IMG** *071

BHATTI, Muhammad A. 2807 MCLAMB PL, WAYNE FAMILY MEDICAL CTR 27534 #308-05-1986 L1993 **FM** *020 ‡

BLAND, Ralph Wingate. ■ 27534 #036-05-1952 L1952 **GS TS** *071 †85,90

BOMBATEPE, Vamik. 2607 MEDICAL OFFICE PL, STE B 27534 #902-03-1951 L1962 **FM IMG** *071 †18

BORCHARDT, Christopher J. 1050 JABARRAH AVE, SEYMOUR JOHNSON AFB 27531 #005-12-1996 L1997 **AM** *020 †70

BOWEN, Marta Renee. 201 STEVENS MILL RD, DHHS-CHERRY HOSPITAL 27530 #045-04-1997 L2003 **OS** *020

BRENTON, Bradley Clark. 2700 WAYNE MEMORIAL DR 27534 #018-03-1979 L1980 **DR** *020 †80

BRUBECK, Ellen. 400 OLD SMITHFIELD RD, O'BERRY CTR 27530 #038-40-1975 L1976 **FM FPG** *020 †18

BUNCH, Michael Eugene. 400 OLD SMITHFIELD RD, O'BERRY CENTER 27530 #036-08-1993 L1997 **GS** *020

CALOIA, Lori Anne. 1050 JABARRAH AVE, 4TH MDG/SGHC 27531 #025-12-2004 L2005 *100

CAMPBELL, Robert Richard. 2700 MEDICAL OFFICE PL 27534 #051-04-1966 L1971 **R** *020 †80

CAMPBELL, Walker Hawes. 102 HANDLEY PARK CT 27534 #051-04-1963 L1973 **GYN** *071 †30

■ = Address Information Privacy Protected

CARMACK, K Kilauea. 2609 MEDICAL OFFICE PL 27534 #014-01-1983 L1997 **FM** *075
CECIL, Stephen G. 2700 WAYNE MEMORIAL DR 27534 #020-12-1981 L1984 **AN** *020 †05
CHAUDHRY, Usman-Ul-Haq. ■ 27530 #704-20-2000 L2007 **FM** *100 †18
CHEATHAM, Alvin Everett. 212 N SPENCE AVE, DOCTOR'S URGENT CARE CENTR 27534 #011-03-1980 L2001 **IM FM** *020 †20
CHENGAPPA, Kuliakanda M. 201 STEVENS MILL RD 27530 #495-37-1973 L1977 **P** *020
CHENGAPPA, Nalini K. PO BOX 59, CHERRY HOSP 27533 #495-33-1979 *075
CHITTILLA, Venkata R. 201 STEVENS MILL RD, CHERRY HOSPITAL 27530 #495-11-1988 L1996 **P** *020
CHOUDARY, Motaparthy V S. 2705 MEDICAL OFFICE PL 27534 #495-98-1974 L1981 **GE IM** *020
CHOWDHURY, Paritosh Roy. ■ 27534 #160-02-1984 L2007 **P PYG** *100
CIPRIANI COLEMAN, Wendy. 2609 MEDICAL OFFICE PL, EASTERN MEDICAL ASSOCIATES 27534 #038-45-2000 L2003 **FM** *020
CLARKE, Donald Keith. 2607 MEDICAL OFFICE PL, GOLDSBORO FAMILY PHYSICIAN 27534 #036-08-1989 L1990 **FM** *020 †18
COOK, Marilue Moser. 2706 MEDICAL OFFICE PL, GOLDSBORO PEDIATRICS, PA 27534 #041-12-1987 L1990 **PD** *020 †55
CREGAN, Kevin Michael. 2700 WAYNE MEMORIAL DR 27534 #041-12-1991 L2005 **DR** *020 †80 ‡
CRIDER, James Allen. 1050 JABARRAH AVE, 4TH MEDICAL GROUP 27531 #020-02-1999 L2000 **FM** *020 †18
CROWGEY, James Lawrence. 2700 WAYNE MEMORIAL DR 27534 #051-04-1985 L1991 **AN** *020 †05
DANIELS, Charles Andrew. 2700 WAYNE MEMORIAL DR 27534 #047-05-1966 L1970 **PTH ID** *020 †50
DE ARAUJO, William. 2808 MCLAMB PL 27534 #036-01-1990 L1991 **ORS TRS** *020 †40
DE VARONA, Angela Ruiz. ■ 27530 #275-01-1951 L1975 **P GP** *071
DE VARONA, Jose Miguel. 201 STEVENS MILL RD 27530 #275-01-1951 L1971 **GP P** *072
DOLAN, Erin Marie. 1050 JABARRAH AVE, 4TH MDG/SGHC 27531 #011-04-2002 L2002 **P** *020
DOVE, Dalton Edward. 2609 MEDICAL OFFICE PL 27534 #036-08-1990 L1996 **PCC CCM** *020 †20
DROTTS, Daniel Lowell. 2604 MEDICAL OFFICE PL 27534 #024-05-1992 L2001 **EM** *020 †16
DUGOM, Muin M. 2400 WAYNE MEMORIAL DR, STE J 27534 #913-32-1985 L1996 **IM** *020 †20
DUNMIRE, Robert B, III. 2809 MCLAMB PL 27534 #011-02-1984 L1986 **NPM PD** *020 †20,55
EDWARDS, Vance Holden. 2700 WAYNE MEMORIAL DR 27534 #036-05-1993 L1998 **NM** *020 †80,28
ETHERINGTON, John L. 2700 WAYNE MEMORIAL DR 27534 #065-05-1936 L1946 **OPH OTO** *071 †45,35
EVANS, Michael Allen. 106 DOBBS PL 27534 #024-01-1998 L2004 **EM** *020 †16
EWY, Marvin Franklin. 2811 MCLAMB PL, TUCSON HEART SUREONS 27534 #038-40-1987 L2007 **TS VS** *020 †90,85
FISHER, John A. 2400 WAYNE MEMORIAL DR, STE E 27534 #041-09-1952 L1984 **ADM** *071 †55
FORREST, Terry Lee. 103 COX BLVD # BOX10907 27534 #036-01-1982 L1984 **OPH** *020 †35
FREDERICK, Laurence Davis. 2808 MCLAMB PL 27534 #045-01-1984 L1990 **ORS** *020 †40
FULBRIGHT, Deborah Kay. 2700 WAYNE MEMORIAL DR, WAYNE MEMORIAL HOSPITAL 27534 #004-01-1979 L1983 **PTH** *020 †50
FULLINGTON, Douglas A. 2400 WAYNE MEMORIAL DR 27534 #012-05-1994 L2000 **IM** *020 †20
GAGLIANO, Louis Anthony. 400 N WILLIAM ST 27530 #165-04-1971 L1972 **P PYG** *020 †75 ‡
GAITHER, Anthony Clark. 2607 MEDICAL OFFICE PL, GOLDSBORO FAM PHYS 27534 #036-08-1989 L1991 **FM** *020 †18
GALLUCCI, Richard Pat. ■ 27534 #025-07-1964 L1991 **AN FM** *071 †18
GARCIA, Gilbert Jos, Jr. 2811 MCLAMB PL 27534 #048-13-1978 L1984 **GS VS** *020 †85
GEBREMESKEL, Tesfa-Alem. 201 STEVENS MILL RD, HLTH & HUMAN SRVES 27530 #366-01-1987 L2003 *020 †75
GEER-BRENTON, Linda Lou. 2700 MEDICAL OFFICE PL 27534 #038-40-1981 L1982 **DR** *071 †80
GICANA-VOCALAN, Chuchi. 203 STRATFORD RD 27534 #748-01-1967 L1980 **CHP P** *020
GOODEN, Michael Dean. 102 HANDLEY PARK CT 27534 #036-01-1973 L1974 **OBG** *020 †30
GRANT, Terry Alan. 2604 MEDICAL OFFICE PL, IMMEDIATE CARE 27534 #036-08-1989 L1990 **EM** *020 †16
GREGG, Charles Eli. 1727 W NEW HOPE RD, WAYNE CO ANESTHESIA 27530 #036-05-1974 L1974 **AN** *020 †05
GRIFFIN, Ashton Thos. 2400 WAYNE MEMORIAL DR 27534 #036-07-1958 L1958 **FM PD** *020 †18
GUPTA, Gool Kapadia. 2704 MEDICAL OFFICE PL 27534 #495-45-1966 L1975 **PUD IM** *020
GUPTA, Jagmohan Dass. 2704 MEDICAL OFFICE PL 27534 #495-29-1966 L1974 **CD IM** *020 †20
HARDIN, William E. ■ 27534 #039-01-1976 L1980 **FM** *020 †18
HARVIN, Allan Brabham. ■ 27530 #036-05-1968 L1968 **ORS** *075 †40
HASSELKUS, Herman E.. ■ 27534 #649-13-1996 L2006 **FPG** *020
HAVERKAMP, John. 2700 WAYNE MEMORIAL DR 27534 #660-06-1971 L1980 **D** *020 †15
HAWKINS, Sherman Melvin. 1112 GRACIE PL, ASSOCIATES 27534 #010-02-1987 L2006 **U** *020 †95
HAYES, Lonnie M. 501 W PINE ST 27530 #010-03-1958 L1963 **GS GP** *071 †85
HENDRICKS, David Martin. ■ 27530 #045-01-1988 L2000 **AN** *020 †05
HIGGINS, Stephen Wayne. ■ 27534 #023-12-1989 L1991 **FM AM** *030 †18
HOEPER, Edwin Wm. 2706 MEDICAL OFFICE PL 27534 #016-06-1965 L1988 **P N** *020 †75
HOOK, William Charles. 1050 JABARRAH AVE, 4 MDG/SGHC 27531 #025-01-1999 L2000 **FM** *020 †18
HORTON, Teague Lon. 2706 MEDICAL OFFICE PL 27534 #035-06-1999 L2003 **PD** *020 †55
HOUGH, Dorcas Mae. 400 OLD SMITHFIELD RD 27530 #021-05-1980 L1983 **IM PHP** *030
HOUSE, Richard James. 1008 E ASH ST 27530 #017-20-1971 L1984 **OS** *020
HUSSAIN, Khwaja. 201 STEVENS MILL RD 27530 #160-01-1978 L1997 **FM** *020 †18
HUSSEY, Felicia Duff. 327 N SPENCE AVE 27534 #036-08-1996 L1997 **FM** *020 †18
ILUNGA, Christine Kabanga. 2400 WAYNE MEMORIAL DR, STE D 27534 #165-03-1987 L1998 **NEP** *020 †20
IRVIN, Stephen Brian. 1050 JABARRAH AVE, SEYMOUR JOHNSON AFB 27531 #036-01-1984 L2000 **FM** *020 †18
JABBOUR, Hassan. 201 STEVENS MILL RD, CHERRY HOSPITAL 27530 #875-02-1988 L2001 **P** *020
JAMIESON, Anna. 400 N WILLIAM ST, WAYNE PSYCHIATRIC ASSCS PA 27530 #048-04-2000 L2006 **P** *020
JENNINGS, John Lee, Jr. 2613 HOSPITAL RD, GOLDSBORO SKIN CENTER PA 27534 #051-07-1978 L1983 **D** *020 †15
JOHNSON, Kimberly Ann. 201 STEVENS MILL RD 27530 #038-40-1997 L1998 **P** *020 †75
JOHNSON, Lorin Elaine. 1050 JABARRAH AVE, SJAFB 27531 #005-14-1997 L2005 **IM** *020 †20
JONES, Gilbert Kirkhart. 2604 MEDICAL OFFICE PL 27534 #036-08-1995 L1996 **EM** *020 †16
JORDAN, Jamie Ryan. ■ 27530 #036-05-2003 L2003 **IM** *020 †20
KARIKKINETH, Ajoy Chandap. 2704 MEDICAL OFFICE PL 27534 #495-31-2001 L2005 **IM** *020 †20
KASPAR, John Victor. 1112 GRACIE PL, ASSOCIATES 27534 #036-05-1991 L1997 **U** *020 †95
KATZ, Barry I. 625 COUNTRY DAY RD 27530 #016-06-1993 L1999 **NS** *020 †25
KEMP, Robert David. 1704 WAYNE MEMORIAL DR, # A 27534 #654-01-1988 L1994 **NEP** *020 †20
KERLIN, Kevin J. 2802 MCLAMB PL 27534 #033-05-1988 L1992 **RO** *020 †80
KNUTSON, Thomas Marvin. 2604 MEDICAL OFFICE PL 27534 #026-04-1979 L1981 **EM FM** *020 †18,16
KOHLI, Asha Kiran. 2300 US HIGHWAY 70 W 27530 #495-41-1972 L1982 **P CHP** *020
KOKIKO, George Victor. CALLER BOX 8001 27533 #036-05-1956 L1956 **PTH** *020 †50
KOLLURU, Mangaraju. 201 STEVENS MILL RD, CHERRY HOSPITAL 27530 #495-11-1970 L1982 **GP PD** *020 †55
KRISHNAPRASAD, H N. 2811 MCLAMB PL 27534 #495-22-1970 L1979 **GS** *020 †85
KRISHNARAJ, Muthaiya P. 2307 NORWOOD AVE, STE D 27534 #495-53-1968 L1979 **P** *020
LACIN, Robert. 2700 WAYNE MEMORIAL DR 27534 #869-05-1986 L1995 **NS** *020 †25
LAFAVE, Mark Steven. 1112 GRACIE PL, ASSOCIATES 27534 #036-05-1988 L2005 **U** *020 †95
LARSON, Robert Eric. 2700 WAYNE MEMORIAL DR 27534 #036-01-1992 L1997 **DR** *020 †80
LE, Solange Trinh. 1707 WAYNE MEMORIAL DR, MEDSTAT CENTRE 27534 #036-08-1994 L1995 **FM** *020 †18
LE, Tin Trong. 1707 WAYNE MEMORIAL DR, MEDSTAT CENTRE 27534 #941-01-1965 L1981 **GP** *071
LIES, Stephen Craig. 102 HANDLEY PARK CT 27534 #036-07-1976 L1979 **OBG** *020 †30
LOGAN, Brent Justin. 2706 MEDICAL OFFICE PL, GOLDSBORO PEDIATRICS 27534 #051-01-2004 L2007 **PD** *020 †55
LONG, Ronald Morgan. 1208 PARKWAY DR STE C 27534 #047-06-1981 L1984 **AN** *071 †05
MACATANGAY, Nelson M. 201 STEVENS MILL RD, CHERRY HOSPITAL 27530 #748-07-1965 L1976 **P** *050
MAIER, Rudolph Jos. 201 W ASH ST STE 1 27530 #016-43-1963 L1985 **N PMM** *020 †75
MALEKPOUR, Bahman. 2805 MCLAMB PL 27534 #409-21-1964 L1976 **P** *020 †75
MANGUM, Vernon Pressley. ■ 27530 #036-07-1956 L1956 **GP** *071
MARGOLIS, Jeffrey Alan. 2701 MEDICAL OFFICE PL 27534 #036-01-1978 L1979 **IM** *020 †20
MASSEY, Clinton Edward. 625 COUNTRY DAY RD, GOLDSBORO NEUROLOGICAL SUR 27530 #012-01-1978 L2002 **NS** *020 †25 ‡
MATTEGUNTA, Suneetha. 201 STEVENS MILL RD, CHERRY HOSPITAL 27530 #023-01-1995 L2002 **CHP** *020 †75
MAYO, Philip Douglas. 2609 MEDICAL OFFICE PL 27534 #033-06-1987 L1993 **PUD CCM** *020 †20
MC CONNAUGHEY, John Scott. 422 DOGWOOD TRL 27534 #017-20-1979 L1980 **FM** *020 †18
MC LAMB, Joseph Timothy. 2700 WAYNE MEMORIAL DR 27534 #036-01-1967 L1967 **ORS** *071 †40
MC LAMB, Saml Baggett, Jr. 201 COX BLVD 27534 #036-05-1975 L1977 **IM** *020
METCALF, Gregory Stuart. 2400 WAYNE MEMORIAL DR 27534 #020-02-1993 L1996 **IM** *020 †20
MEYER, Robert Swenson. 208 N HERMAN ST 27530 #041-13-1974 L1977 **FM FPG** *020 †18
MOYE, Phillip Walker. 2609 MEDICAL OFFICE PL 27534 #665-01-2004 L2007 **FM** *020
MOYE, Steven Boyd. 2604 MEDICAL OFFICE PL 27534 #036-08-2000 L2002 **EM** *020 †16
MURTHY, Smitha. ■ 27534 #496-35-2003 **P** *012
MYERS, Steven Alexander. 212 N SPENCE AVE 27534 #028-46-1975 L2001 **FM OS** *020 †18
NATHANIEL, Davis. 201 STEVENS MILL RD 27530 #495-47-1968 L1981 **IM** *020
NAZIR, Tabinda. 2609 MEDICAL OFFICE PL, EASTERN MEDICAL ASSOCIATES 27534 #704-20-1985 L2005 **ID IM** *020 †20 ‡
NEUMANN, Tomas Andres. 2809 MCLAMB PL 27534 #132-01-1972 L2002 **NEP IM** *020 †20
NEWELL, Howard W, Jr. 2400 WAYNE MEMORIAL DR 27534 #036-01-1984 L1985 **IM** *020 †20
NOWACHEK, Glen A. 2608 HOSPITAL RD 27534 #016-43-1986 L1990 **OBG** *020 †30
OBENOUR, Linda Ruth Clark. 1002 N SPENCE AVE, OBENOUR LINDA, MD 27534 #036-07-1966 L1966 **OPH** *020
OTTAVIANI, Robert A. 2808 MCLAMB PL 27534 #025-07-1999 L2005 **ORS** *020
OWENS, Robert Carl. U-2 BUILDING,LOOP DRIVE, CHERRY HOSPITAL 27533 #048-02-1979 L1991 **IM** *075 †20
PARKER, Talbot F, Jr. 102 HANDLEY PARK CT 27534 #041-02-1951 L1951 **OBG** *020 †30
PATE, Chris Anthony. 2280 US HIGHWAY 70 W 27530 #036-08-1985 L1988 **FM** *020 †18
PATEL, Jaimita Vipulkumar. 2701 MEDICAL OFFICE PL, GOSHEN MEDICAL CENTER 27534 #495-23-1992 L2006 **FM** *020 †18
PAULINO, Jorge Martin. 2700 WAYNE MEMORIAL DR, WAYNE MEMORIAL HOSPITAL 27534 #308-01-1989 L2002 **IM IMG** *020 †20
PEDRAZA, Hector Manuel. 2808 MCLAMB PL 27534 #036-05-1982 L1988 **ORS** *020 †40
PERUMALLU, Tripuraneni L. ■ 27530 #495-11-1962 L1978 **P GP** *020
PIECH, Tara N. 1050 JABARRAH AVE, SEYMOUR JOHNSON AFB 27531 #023-12-2000 L2004 **FM** *020 †18
PITTARD, Gina Horan. 201 STEVENS MILL RD, CHERRY HOSPITAL 27530 #001-06-1994 L1998 **FM** *020 †18
POINDEXTER, Todd Windle. ■ 27534 #051-04-1993 L1995 **FM** *020 †18
POOLE, Daniel Thomas. 2609 MEDICAL OFFICE PL 27534 #036-08-1994 L1998 **IM** *020 †75
POTTS, Frederick Latham. 2604 MEDICAL OFFICE PL 27534 #036-08-1984 L1985 **EM** *020 †16
PRICE, Amy Vann. 2700 WAYNE MEMORIAL DR 27534 #036-05-1985 L1986 **FM** *020 †18 ‡
RAGHU, Vijayalakshmi. 2701 MEDICAL OFFICE PL, GOSHEN MEDICAL CENTER 27534 #495-99-1995 L2007 **FM** *020 †18
RALPH, James Walker. ■ 27534 #036-07-1962 L1966 **OTO A** *071
RAUF, Zahid. 201 STEVENS MILL RD, CHERRY HOSP U4 BLDG 27530 #704-21-1983 L2003 **CHP P** *020
ROCKWELL, David Allen. 2808 MCLAMB PL, GOLDSBORO ORTHOPAEDIC ASSO 27534 #036-01-1974 L1979 **ORS** *020 †40
ROETHLING, Hans Peter. 102 HANDLEY PARK CT 27534 #036-01-1992 L1996 **OBG** *020 †30
RUSSELL, Douglas M. 2700 WAYNE MEMORIAL DR 27534 #036-01-1967 L1967 **GS** *020 †85
SABANAYAGAM, M K. 2307 NORWOOD AVE STE D, E CAROLINA PSYCH CONSULTS 27534 #220-01-1966 L1987 **P** *020 †75
SAEED, Azeem. 2807 MCLAMB PL 27534 #704-01-1998 L2004 **IM** *020
SANFORD, Virginia Oates. 1506 WAYNE MEMORIAL DR # D 27534 #036-07-1956 L1956 **GP PD** *020
SASSER, Patrick Henry. ■ 27534 #036-05-1955 L1955 **GP** *071
SHREENATH, Ajay Iyengar. 1704A WAYNE MEMORIAL DR, CAROLINA NEPHROLOGY, PA 27534 #422-01-2000 L2005 **NEP** *020 †20

■ = Address Information Privacy Protected

7287

SMITH, Lloyd Hamlin. 2604 MEDICAL OFFICE PL, SPECIALISTS, INC, P O DRAW 27534 #051-04-1975 L1981 **EM** *020 †16

SOLTIS, Craig Allan. 2604 MEDICAL OFFICE PL 27534 #038-43-1987 L2001 **EM** *020 †16

SRIRAMAN, Vellore R. ■ 27534 #495-04-1957 L1978 **P** *020

STACKHOUSE, William James. 201 COX BLVD 27534 #012-05-1976 L1980 **IM IMG** *020 †20

STATUTO, Donald Thos. ■ 27534 #561-01-1978 L2005 **OM** *020 †20

STOCKDALE, Wayne Harrop. WAYNE MEM HOSP 27533 #020-02-1945 L2003 **EM GS** *071

STOCKTON, Leon Eugene. 2811 MCLAMB PL 27534 #422-01-1997 L2003 **GS** *020

SWANTON, Joseph Everett. 400 OLD SMITHFIELD RD, O'BERRY CENTER 27530 #036-01-1960 L1960 **OBG OS** *075

SWEDENBURG, Mark Gregory. 400 OLD SMITHFIELD RD, NC DHHS O'BERRY CENTER 27530 #025-07-1978 L2002 **FM GPM** *020 †70

TABE, Wilson Egbe. 1314 WAYNE MEMORIAL DR # C 27534 #561-11-1994 L2001 **FM IM** *020 †18

TEASLEY, Barry Hoyle. 103 COX BLVD 27534 #036-01-1978 L1982 **OPH** *020 †35

THOMPSON, Charlotte Ann. 2700 WAYNE MEMORIAL DR 27534 #036-07-1974 L1974 **IMG PUD** *020

TURNER, William Bomar, III. 1112 GRACIE PL, ASSOCIATES 27534 #045-01-1980 L1985 **U GS** *020 †95

TYNDALL, Hubert Durwood. ■ 27534 #036-01-1954 L1954 **GP** *020

UNGER, Richard Hans. 214 CREEKSIDE DR 27534 #033-05-1963 L1996 **GS** *071 †85

UPPAL, Alok. 201 STEVENS MILL RD, CHERRY HOSPITAL 27530 #495-90-1976 L1991 **P** *020

UPPAL, Karuna. 201 STEVENS MILL RD 27530 #495-90-1976 L1996 **P** *020

VARNEY, David Allen. 1112 GRACIE PL, ASSOCIATES 27534 #010-02-1968 L1976 **U GS** *020 †95

VAWTER, Kenneth Wayne. 1050 JABARRAH AVE, SEYMOUR JOHNSON AFB 27531 #023-12-2004 L2005 **GS** *020

VITOLS, Edite. 201 STEVENS MILL RD 27530 #036-07-1955 L1955 **P** *071

WAIEN, Saiqua Akbar. 2809 MCLAMB PL 27534 #422-01-1997 L2005 **NEP IM** *020

WALLACE, Lawrence. ■ 27530 #036-08-1997 L2000 **ORS** *020

WELSH, John Saml, Jr. 102 HANDLEY PARK CT 27534 #045-01-1989 L1993 **OBG** *020 †30

WEST, Thaddeus C, III. 2400 WAYNE MEMORIAL DR 27534 #036-08-1993 L1996 **IM** *020 †20

WHITMIRE, Lelan Franklin. 2700 WAYNE MEMORIAL DR 27534 #012-05-1985 L1990 **DR** *020 †80

WILKINS, Kenneth Worth. ■ 27530 #023-01-1944 L1945 **OBG** *071

WILSON, Arthur Ross, Jr. 2707 MEDICAL OFFICE PL 27534 #041-13-1974 L1978 **OTO** *071 †45

YOUNG, Jordan Terrell. 2700 WAYNE MEMORIAL DR 27534 #661-02-2003 L2007 **IM** *100 †20

YOUNGS, Franklin Jay. 201 STEVENS MILL RD 27530 #035-15-1945 L1959 **R** *071

ZARA, Leonardo Montuya. 2607 MEDICAL OFFICE PL, PLACE STE 27534 #748-01-1981 L2001 **IM** *020 †20

ZBARCEA, Gratiela Elena. 205 MOURNING DOVE LN 27534 #781-04-1995 L2006 **P** *020 †75

ZWERLING, Charles Saml. 2709 MEDICAL OFFICE PL 27534 #561-01-1977 L1981 **OPH** *020 †35

GRAHAM – ALAMANCE

ALDRIDGE, Barbara Darnell. 236 RIVERBEND RD 27253 #036-08-1999 L2001 **FM** *020 †18

BAIRD, James Hamilton. 133 AUTO PARK DR STE A, THE BARIATRIC CLINIC, PA 27253 #051-04-1963 L1968 **OBG** *071 †30

CLINE, John Wm. ■ 27253 #051-04-1958 L1963 **OPH** *071 †35 ‡

CRADDOCK, John Goodwin. 5041 E GREENSBR CHPL HL RD, RD 27253 #036-07-1954 L1954 **IM ID** *020

CRISSMAN, Mark Anders. 214 E ELM ST 27253 #041-13-1980 L1981 **FM** *020 †18

DARCEY, Dennis John. 5466 THREE WATERS RD 27253 #036-01-1986 L1987 **OM IM** *020 †70

HAWKINS, James Hubert, Jr. 316 1/2 S MAIN ST 27253 #036-01-1978 L1979 **FM** *020 †18 ‡

LEININGER, James Parkin. ■ 27253 #036-01-2006 **FP** *012

LIN, Sheeng Wu. ■ 27253 #385-01-1965 L1973 **OBG** *020

MOORE, Justin Broyce. ■ 27253 #019-02-2003 L2006 **END** *012 †20

PIERSON, Lee Moschler. ■ 27253 #036-01-2008 *012

POLANCO, Leonard F. 217 E ELM ST 27253 #048-12-1984 L1990 **EM** *020 †85

STRICKLAND, James Donald. 109 S MAPLE ST, ALAMANCE COUNTY JAIL 27253 #021-01-1978 L1979 **EM OM** *020 †16

TATE, Denny Cook. 316 1/2 S MAIN ST 27253 #036-01-1984 L1985 **IM** *020 †20

WILSON, William Preston. 323 W HARDEN ST 27253 #036-07-1947 L1958 **P N** *072 †75

WOLF, Jack Haywood. 236 RIVERBEND RD 27253 #036-01-1986 L1987 **FM** *020 †18

GRANDY – CURRITUCK

CLAGNAZ, Peter John. PO BOX 855, 6644 CARATOKE HWY 27939 #035-45-1977 L2007 **P IM** *020 †20,75 ‡

GRANITE FALLS – CALDWELL

CORPENING, William Nye. PO BOX 200 28630 #023-01-1943 L1943 **FM** *071

CURTIS, Richard Franklin. 147 WINWOOD CIR 28630 #045-01-1967 L1982 **DR NM** *020 †80

GUTTLER, Sanford Dennis. 1 TRADE ST 28630 #041-13-1978 L1994 **FM** *020 †18

KERR, Kirsten Suzanne. 1 TRADE ST 28630 #004-01-1998 L2001 **FM** *020 †18

MASTERS, David Lee. 4355 HICKORY BLVD LOWR LE 28630 #036-08-1995 L2003 **PD** *020 †55

OXFORD, Robert Glenn. 28630 CAMPGROUND RD 28630 #036-08-2004 L2006 **NS** *012

SHARMA, Govind S. 27 N MAIN ST 28630 #495-37-1956 L1995 **EM IM** *020 †16

WAECHTER, Deborah Hauser. 4355 HICKORY BLVD, THE FALLS MEDICAL PARK 28630 #036-08-1999 L2001 **FM** *020 †18

GREEN MOUNTAIN – YANCEY

GARRIQUES, Ian Lloyd, Jr. ■ 28740 #035-09-1969 L2006 **IM ID** *020 †20 ‡

GREENSBORO – GUILFORD

ABDEL HADI, Zaidoon Moh'D. 706 GREEN VALLEY RD, STE 212 27408 #875-03-2001 **IM** *100

ABIDE, Mary Theresa. ■ 27408 #051-01-1986 L1995 **NM** *020 †28

ABRAHAMS, Stuart Joel. 6 SAINT REGIS CT 27408 #023-01-1957 L1964 **OBG GYN** *020 †30

ADAMS, Douglas Harvey. ■ 27408 #041-07-1986 L1989 **OM FM** *020 †18,70

ADELMAN, James U. 1414 YANCEYVILLE ST 27405 #016-06-1967 L1973 **N** *020 †75

ADKINS, Gretchen Lea. 1507 WESTOVER TER, STE C 27408 #020-12-2002 L2006 **OBG** *020

AGNEW, Elizabeth Bagby. ■ 27405 #041-77-2006, ▲ **IM** *012

AKINTEMI, Olakunle B. ■ 27410 #690-01-1977 L1985 **PD** *040 †55

ALBERTINI, John Gerald. 3107 BRASSFIELD RD, SKIN SURGERY CENTER 27410 #016-02-1993 L1997 **DS D** *020 †15

ALBON, Dana Petronela. 1200 N ELM ST 27401 #781-03-2001 **IM** *012

ALEJANDRO, Luis. 5817 HIGH POINT RD, FARM 27407 #051-01-1999 L2002 **FM** *020 †18

ALEXANDER, Mary B. 510 N ELAM AVE, STE 202 27403 #033-05-1979 L1982 **PD** *020 †55

AL-HEGELAN, Mashael Saleh. PO BOX 1382, DUKE MED CTR 27402 #797-01-2000 **IM** *012

ALLEN, Anthony Terrance. 501 N ELAM AVE 27403 #038-40-1995 L1998 **EM** *020 †16

ALLEN, Pamela Gutbier. ■ 27403 #036-01-2003 L2008 **ORS** *012

ALNAQUIB, Nawar Mohammed. 700 WALTER REED DR, MOSES CONE BEHAVIOR HEALTH 27403 #528-01-1968 L1999 **CHP** *012

ALTHEIMER, Michael David. 1002 N CHURCH ST 27401 #018-03-1981 L1986 **END IM** *020 †20

ALUISIO, Frank Victor. 3200 NORTHLINE AVE, STE 200 27408 #012-05-1991 L1995 **ORS** *020 †40

AMOS, Jack Edwin. 409 PARKWAY STE B 27401 #036-05-1975 L1975 **PD** *020 †55

ANDERSON, Theodore S, Jr. 122 N ELM ST, STE 400 27401 #036-05-1975 L1975 **PD** *020 †55

ANDREE, Ernest Ashmore. 1200 N ELM ST, MOSES H CONE MEM HOSPITAL 27401 #220-01-1979 L1991 **PTH** *020 †50

ANDRINGA, Richard Cornell. 3402 BATTLEGROUND AVE, BATTLEGROUND URGENT CARE 27410 #056-05-1974 L1975 **AN PD** *020 †55,05

ANDY, Camille Lee. 1125 N CHURCH ST, MOSES CONE FAMILY MED 27401 #025-01-1995 L1997 **FM** *040 †18

APLINGTON, James Page. 1401 BENJAMIN PKWY 27408 #023-07-1966 L1967 **ORS GP** *020 †40

ARCEO, Dina Lucille. 1002 N CHURCH ST, STE 401 27401 #055-01-1995 L1999 **DR** *020 †80

ARFEEN, Syed Taj-Ul. 700 WALTER REED DR, MOSES CONE BEHAVIORAL HEAL 27403 #704-02-1990 L2005 **PYG** *020

ARKIN, Roy Marc. 200 E NORTHWOOD ST STE 300 27401 #035-09-1969 L1976 **GS** *020 †85

ARON, Talia Miller. ■ 27408 #036-08-2007 **FP** *012

ARONSON, Elizabeth Adcock. ■ 27410 #036-05-1986 L1990 **OBG** *020

ARONSON, Richard Adler. 2703 HENRY ST, GUILFORD MEDICAL ASSOCIATE 27405 #036-05-1986 L1990 **IM** *020 †20

ARRINGTON, John Hodge, III. 501 N ELAM AVE 27403 #021-01-1967 L1977 **DMP PTH** *071 †50

AVBUERE, Edwin Aziegbe. 3231 YANCEYVILLE ST, ALPHA CLINICS, PA 27405 #690-02-1990 L2001 **IM** *020 †20

AVVA, Ravi R. 2703 HENRY ST, GUILFORD MEDICAL ASSOC PA 27405 #036-07-1995 L1997 **IM** *020 †20

BADAWI, Raouf Fahmy. 2311 W CONE BLVD STE 245 27408 #915-02-1963 L1973 **P IM** *020 †75

BAGWELL, Melissa Lee. ■ 27410 #027-01-2006 **FP** *012

BAIRD, Haynes Wallace. 706 GREEN VALLEY RD, STE 104 27408 #036-01-1969 L1969 **PTH** *030 †50

BAKARE, Mobolaji Babatope. 1200 N ELM ST, MOSES CONE MEMORIAL HOSPIT 27401 #690-05-1990 L2005 **IM HOS** *020

BALAN, Bindubal K. 3824 N ELM ST 27455 #495-33-1993 L2003 **END IM** *020 †20

BALL, Russell Allen. 706 GREEN VALLEY RD # 104 27408 #055-01-1989 L1999 **PTH** *020 †50

BALLEN, Patrick Laselve. 1002 N CHURCH ST, CENTRAL CAROLINA SURGERY 27401 #035-20-1975 L1979 **GS** *020

BARBER, William Byron, II. 1591 YANCEYVILLE ST # 100 27405 #045-01-1979 L1991 **PS GS** *020 †85,65

BARDELAS, Jose Antonio. 104 E NORTHWOOD ST, OF NORTH CAROLINA 27401 #023-07-1973 L1977 **PDA PD** *020 †55,03

BARKLEY, Karl Lee. 1200 N ELM ST 27401 #036-01-1962 L1962 **OBG** *020 †30

BARNES, Kenneth Patrick. ■ 27455 #539-04-2003 L2007 **FSM** *012 †20

BARRY, Paul Douglas. 1002 N CHURCH ST, STE 401 27401 #036-01-1976 L1976 **DR NM** *020 †80

BARTKO, Albert Kenneth. 1915 LENDEW ST STE 300 27408 #038-40-1988 L1992 **PM OM** *020 †60

BARTLE, Bryan Kurt. 2704 HENRY ST, OFGREENSBORO PA 27405 #023-01-1986 L1994 **TS** *020 †85,90

BARTLETT, John W. 201 N EUGENE ST, GREENSBORO MNTL HLTH 27401 #036-01-1983 L1984 **P** *020 †75

BAXLEY, Mary John. 403 PARKWAY STE B, INTERNAL MEDICINE - PEDIAT 27401 #036-01-1982 L1983 **IM PD** *020 †55,20

BEAN, Cecil Wesley. 522 N ELAM AVE, STE 202 27403 #036-05-1986 L1989 **GS** *020 †85,65

BEANE, Jeffrey Carlton. 1401 BENJAMIN PKWY, GREENSBORO ORTHOPAEDIC CEN 27408 #024-05-1988 L1993 **ORS** *020 †40

BEATON, Robert L, Jr. 501 N ELAM AVE 27403 #004-01-1982 L2002 **EM** *020 †16

BEAVERS, William Olive. ■ 27403 #016-06-1944 L1944 **OS GP** *071

BEDNARZ, Nancy Mc Bryde. 501 N ELAM AVE 27403 #048-02-1997 L2002 **RO** *020 †80

BEDNARZ, Paul Anthony. 1401 BENJAMIN PKWY, GREENSBORO ORTHOPAEDICS 27408 #033-05-1994 L2002 **ORS** *020 †40

BENNETT, Hugh H, Jr. ■ 27401 #041-01-1945 L1947 **OS R** *071 †80

BENSIMHON, Daniel Robert. 1126 N CHURCH ST 27401 #041-12-1998 L2001 **CD** *020 †20

BENSIMHON, Pamela. ■ 27408 #041-12-1998 L1999 **PHO** *020 †55

BERGIN, Donald John. 1002 N CHURCH ST STE 200 27401 #036-07-1975 L1979 **OPH FPS** *020 †35 ‡

BERLINER, Steven Harvey. 801 GREEN VALLEY RD, THE WOMEN'S HOSPITAL OF GR 27408 #035-08-1978 L1997 **OBG** *020 †30

BERNARD, George E. ■ 27410 #016-06-1970 **OS** *062

BERNSTEIN, Jonna Lynn. 1200 N ELM ST 27401 #035-46-1976 L1979 **IM** *020 †20

BERRY, Francis X. 3560 WILDFLOWER DR, # 317 27410 #010-02-1942 L1953 **OBG U** *071 †30

BERTRAND, Margaret E L. 1126 N CHURCH ST 27401 #048-04-1974 L1975 **R** *020 †80

BERTRAND, Scott Alan. 1211 VIRGINIA ST 27401 #048-04-1973 L1975 **AN** *105

BEST, David Chas. 600 PASTEUR DR 27403 #036-05-1977 L1980 **PS** *020 †65

BEVIS, Timothy H. 1002 N CHURCH ST, STE 200 27401 #011-02-2002 L2006 **OPH** *020 †35

BHUSAL, Yogesh. ■ 27401 #672-01-2001 **IM** *012

BIGGERSTAFF, Teresa Gehre. 2516 OAKCREST AVE, STE B 27408 #021-05-2004 L2007 **GS** *100

BLACK, Erin Elizabeth. 603 DOLLEY MADISON RD, STE A 27410 #011-75-2004, ▲ L2007 **FM** *012

BLACKMAN, Christopher Y. 300 W NORTHWOOD ST 27401 #036-05-2000 L2005 **ORS** *020 †40

■ = Address Information Privacy Protected

BLAND, Veita Joyce. 1317 N ELM ST STE 7 27401 #041-13-1978 L1982 **FM OS** *020 †18
BLIETZ, Melinda Ann. 1317 N ELM ST, STE 1B 27401 #018-03-1999 L2002 **DR** *020 †80
BLOMGREN, Peter Frederick. 317 W WENDOVER AVE 27408 #017-20-1974 L1977 **FM** *020 †18
BLOMQUIST, Gustav A, Jr. 1021 E WENDOVER AVE, STE 103 27405 #047-05-1973 L1974 **NS PS** *071
BLOUNT, Alvin Vincent, Jr. 1106 E MARKET ST 27401 #010-03-1947 L1948 **GP GS** *072
BODNER, Wm Raymond, Jr. 515 COLLEGE RD, STE 18 27410 #028-34-1963 L1972 **P** *020
BOETTE, Richard Walters. 515 COLLEGE RD, STE 11 27410 #045-01-1966 L1983 **PD** *020
BOGAVELLI, Vijayalaxmi. 201 N EUGENE ST, THE GUILFORD CENTER 27401 #495-21-1972 L1995 **CHP P** *020 †75
BOLES, Mark Alan. 1002 N CHURCH ST, STE 401 27401 #038-44-1987 L1997 **DR NM** *020 †28,80
BOOK, Roy D. PO BOX 13890 27415 #012-22-1996 L1997 **P ADM** *020
BOTERO, Ernesto. 1130 N CHURCH ST, STE 200 27401 #264-02-1973 L1984 **NS** *020 †25
BOUSKA, David Edward. 5710 HIGH POINT RD STE I, REGIONAL PHYSICIANS PRIMAR 27407 #030-05-1990 L1991 **FM** *020 †18
BOVARD, Jody Lynn. 510 N ELAM AVE, STE 101 27403 #041-12-2002 L2007 **OBG** *020
BOWERS, David Mc Donald. 1126 N CHURCH ST, STE 101 27401 #036-05-1980 L1991 **PS GS** *020 †85,65
BOWIE, Walter Scott, III. 719 GREEN VALLEY RD 27408 #055-01-1964 L1968 **GYN** *020 †30
BOWMAN, Wm Edmund, Jr. 1200 N ELM ST STE 1049, MOSES CONE HEALTH SYSTEM 27401 #036-01-1974 L1981 **GS VS** *030 †85
BOYER, Jay Alan. ■ 27407 #024-07-1966 L1976 **DR OS** *020 †80
BRACKBILL, Thomas Andrew. 1002 N CHURCH ST, STE 103 27401 #035-01-1968 L1975 **CD IM** *020 †20
BRADLEY, Harold John, Jr. 509 N ELAM AVE, FL 2 27403 #036-01-1957 L1957 **U** *020 †95
BRASSFIELD, Mark Mossman. 1307 W WENDOVER AVE 27408 #016-06-1982 L1985 **PD** *020 †55
BRATTON, Teresa S. 501 N ELAM AVE 27403 #047-05-1974 L1982 **PDA A** *020 †55,03
BRENNAN, Michael J. 301 E WENDOVER AVE, STE 311 27401 #024-16-1978 L1999 **END PD** *071 †20,55
BRETT, Charles Burden. 1307 W WENDOVER AVE 27408 #036-01-1971 L1971 **PD** *020 †55
BREWER, James Chester, Jr. ■ 27410 #036-07-1959 L1959 **FM PD** *071
BREWINGTON, Thomas E, Jr. 807 SUMMIT AVE 27405 #047-07-1969 L1971 **OPH** *020 †35
BRODIE, Bruce Rogers. 1126 N CHURCH ST 27401 #028-02-1970 L1973 **CD IM** *020 †20
BRODIE, Dora M. 520 N ELAM AVE 27403 #036-07-1975 L1975 **GE** *020 †20
BROOKS, Dahari Durwin. 1401 BENJAMIN PKWY, UMASS MEMORIAL HEALTHCARE 27408 #035-20-1996 L2008 **OSS** *020 †40
BROOKS, Olga Yevseyevna. 1921 NEW GARDEN RD, APT B303 27410 #913-65-1981 L2007 **IM** *020 †20
BROWN, Margaret Denny. 1002 N CHURCH ST, STE 401 27401 #036-01-1991 L1996 **DR** *020 †80
BRUCE, James C. 603 SUMMIT AVE, STE 103 27405 #010-01-1951 L1955 **CD IM** *072 †20
BRUMBACK, George Franklin. 8 N POINTE CT 27408 #047-06-1959 L1964 **OPH** *071 †35
BRYAN, Edwin Lancaster. ■ 27410 #041-01-1961 L1961 **IM CD** *071 †20
BUCCINI, Robert Vincent. 1002 N CHURCH ST, STE 2 27401 #016-02-1981 L1986 **GE IM** *020 †20
BYERS, John Maxwell. 321 W WENDOVER AVE 27408 #048-14-1989 L1994 **OTO** *020 †45
BYRUM, Robert Stuart. 520 N ELAM AVE, LEBAUER HEALTHCARE 27403 #036-01-2000 L2006 **IM** *020 †20
CABBELL, Kyle Lawrence. 1130 N CHURCH ST, # 200 27401 #005-14-1991 L1998 **GS NS** *072 †25
CABEZA, Yuri Milton. ■ 27455 #231-01-1987 **IM** *012
CAFFREY, William Danl. 300 W NORTHWOOD ST 27401 #036-07-1982 L1989 **ORS** *020 †40
CALHOUN, Anne Hord. 1414 YANCEYVILLE ST 27405 #047-06-1979 L2001 **IM N** *020 †20
CAMPBELL, John Franklin. 1200 N ELM ST, MOSES CONE HEALTH SYSTEM 27401 #012-05-1981 L1988 **ID IM** *020 †20
CANFIELD, Tanya Jayne. ■ 27407 #028-03-2000 L2002 **FM** *020 †18 ‡
CARANDANG, Napoleon Veluz. ■ 27410 #748-02-1962 L1977 **OM GE** *075
CARDENOSA, Gilda. 1317 N ELM ST, STE 1B 27401 #035-01-1984 L2000 **DR** *020 †80
CARLOS, Rita Q. 801 GREEN VALLEY RD 27408 #748-08-1982 L1989 **NPM PD** *020 †55
CARTER, Arthur Francis. 1200 E MARKET ST 27401 #010-03-1976 L1981 **ORS** *020
CARTER, Philips John, Jr. 1401 BENJAMIN PKWY 27408 #021-01-1962 L1969 **ORS** *071 †40
CASSIANO, Coley James. 301 E WENDOVER AVE, STE 215 27401 #035-06-1975 L1976 **FM** *020 †18
CASSUTO, Jerry. ■ 27407 #035-08-1956 L1975 **OM FM** *072 †70
CHAMBLISS, Marshall Lee. 1125 N CHURCH ST 27401 #051-01-1986 L1996 **FM** *020 †18
CHAMPEY, Daniel Ryan. 1126 N CHURCH ST, STE 200 27401 #665-01-2001 L2005 **N** *020 †75
CHAPMAN, Elma E S. 1200 N ELM ST 27401 #001-02-1970 L1975 **PHP EM** *074
CHARRON, Mariane. ■ 27410 #067-06-2007 **IM** *012
CHASE, Robert Eugene. 3625 N ELM ST STE 11 27455 #056-06-1967 L1973 **AN** *071 †05
CHILDRESS, Cynthia Holmes. 1317 N ELM ST, STE A 27401 #036-01-1993 L1997 **IM** *020
CHRISTIAN, Bernie J. PO BOX 21688 27420 #036-05-1951 L1951 **GP OM** *071
CILOGLU, Figen. 301 E WENDOVER AVE STE 200 27401 #036-01-1987 L1988 **IM** *020 †20
CLANCE, Keith Montgomery. 520 N ELAM AVE 27403 #011-04-1986 L1992 **PUD** *020 †20
CLARK, David Charles, Jr. 1002 N CHURCH ST, STE 401 27401 #019-02-1986 L1990 **DR RNR** *020 †80
CLARK, Preston S, Jr. 1511 WESTOVER TER STE 101 27408 #035-19-1973 L1976 **END IM** *020 †20
CLARK, William Douglas. 510 N ELAM AVE, STE 202 27403 #036-08-1992 L1995 **PD** *020 †55
CLINKSCALES, Norman Bull. 3801 W MARKET ST, SOUTHEASTERN RADIOLOGY, PA 27407 #045-01-1981 L2000 **DR** *020 †80
CLONINGER, Kenneth L, Jr. ■ 27455 #023-01-1961 L2000 **NS** *020 †25
CLOWARD, Davis L. 3833 HIGH POINT RD 27407 #045-04-1990 L1996 **IM** *020 †20
CLUTTS, George Robt. ■ 27407 #016-06-1948 L1948 **GS** *071 †85 ‡
COBB, Jennifer Christine. 1123 N CHURCH ST, MOSES CONE URGENT CARE 27401 #005-02-1996 L2006 **EM** *020 †16
COHEN, Jonathan Bart. ■ 27455 #035-08-2007 **IM** *012
COHEN, Max William. 1002 N CHURCH ST, STE 301 27401 #051-04-1996 L2002 **OSS** *020 †40
COLADONATO, Joseph A. 309 NEW ST 27405 #041-02-1995 L2002 **NEP** *020 †20
COLE, Tara Janelle. 301 E WENDOVER AVE, STE 300 27401 #036-08-2002 L2006 **OBG** *020
COLEY, Harrill Christophe. 3518 N ELM ST 27455 #654-01-2001 L2008 **GS HS** *020 †85
COLL, Paolo. ■ 27455 #275-04-1993 L2005 **FM** *020 †18
COLLINS, Daniel Leo. 510 N ELAM AVE, STE 302 27403 #016-42-1991 L1995 **PM** *020 †60
COLLINS, Diana Burke. 301 E WENDOVER AVE, STE 300 27401 #036-05-1987 L1991 **GYN** *020 †30
COLLINS, Robert Andrew. 1401 BENJAMIN PKWY, GREENSBORO ORTHOPAEDIC CTR 27408 #036-05-1985 L1987 **ORS** *020 †40
CONTOGIANNIS, Mary Ann. 211 STATE ST 27408 #036-08-1987 L1988 **PS** *020 †65
COOPER, Alan Wilson. 2835 HORSE PEN CREEK RD, STE 101 27410 #036-01-2001 L2003 **PD** *020 †55
COOPER, Michael David. 1126 N CHURCH ST, STE 300 27401 #055-02-2000 L2007 **IC** *020 †20
CORNETT, Thomas Anthony. 1002 N CHURCH ST, CENTRAL CAROLINA SURGERY 27401 #038-41-1996 L1998 **GS** *020 †85
CORTES, Octavio Manuel. ■ 27410 #847-04-1957 L1963 **R RNR** *071 †80
COTTLE, Carey Gordon, Jr. 600 GREEN VALLEY RD, STE 204 27408 #036-01-1987 L1990 **P** *020 †75
COURTS, Andrew Johnson. ■ 27408 #036-01-1958 L1958 **CHP P** *071
COUSINS, Sheronette Ann. 1908 LENDEW ST 27408 #043-01-1987 L1998 **OBG** *020 †30 ‡
COX, Craig Harness. 501 HICKORY BRANCH DR 27409 #012-01-1990 L1997 **FM** *020 †18
CRAM, Gary Paul, Jr. 301 E WENDOVER AVE, STE 211 27401 #036-05-1994 L2001 **NS** *020 †25
CRAVEN, Nicole Jean. 1416 YANCEYVILLE ST, STE 1 27405 #021-01-2001 L2004 **PD** *020 †55
CRAWFORD, Marshall K. 1200 N ELM ST, INTERNAL MEDICINE OFFICE 27401 #036-05-2003 L2006 **IM** *100 †20
CRENSHAW, Brian Sanders. 1126 N CHURCH ST 27401 #047-06-1990 L1992 **CD** *020 †20
CREWS, David Allen. 3625 N ELM ST, STE 110A 27455 #036-01-1981 L1982 **AN PMM** *020 †05
CROSBY, Faith Bernadette. 719 GREEN VALLEY RD, STE 209 27408 #045-01-1977 L1979 **PD** *020 †55
CROSS, Alred C, Jr. ■ 27410 #004-01-1953 L1968 **OM GP** *071
CROSSLEY, James John. 100 E NORTHWOOD ST 27401 #035-20-1967 L1975 **OTO HNS** *020 †45 ‡
CUNNINGHAM, Scott Lance. 600 GREEN VALLEY RD, STE 204 27408 #036-07-1981 L1984 **P ADP** *020 †75
CURNES, John Taylor. 1002 N CHURCH ST, STE 401 27401 #021-01-1978 L1980 **DR OS** *020 †80
CYKERT, Samuel. 1200 N ELM ST, INTERNAL MEDICINE PROGRAM 27401 #017-20-1983 L1984 **IM CCM** *040 †20
DALESSIO, Thomas Louis. 1313 CAROLINA ST 27401 #012-01-1998 L1999 **MSR** *020 †80
DALLDORF, Peter Gilbert. 1915 LENDEW ST, GUILFORD ORTHOPAEDIC/SPORT 27408 #036-01-1988 L1994 **ORS** *020 †40
DALTON-BETHEA, Shawn M. 1130 N CHURCH ST, STE 200 27401 #036-08-2001 L2007 **PM** *020 †60
DAMBRO, Timothy J. ■ 27455 #654-01-1986 L2007 **DR OS** *062 ‡
DASANAYAKA, Gayani Yahamp. 1309 N ELM ST 27401 #025-07-2000 L2001 **IM** *020 †20
DAUB, Steve Alan. 104 POMONA DR 27407 #020-12-1976 L1978 **FM** *020 †18
DAVANZO, Christie. 801 GREEN VALLEY RD 27408 #036-01-1981 L1999 **NPM** *020 †55
DAVIDSON, Alan, III. 501 N ELAM AVE 27403 #036-01-1968 L1968 **EM FM** *020 †16,18
DAVIS, Jerome Irvin. 3402 BATTLEGROUND AVE 27410 #036-05-1973 L1992 **GP IMG** *020 ‡
DAVIS, Robert Nicholas. 600 WALTER REED DR 27403 #036-07-1962 L1962 **D** *020 †15
DAVIS, Timothy Eugene. 1002 N CHURCH ST, CENTRAL CAROLINA SURGERY 27401 #004-01-1971 L1978 **GS CRS** *020 †85
DAVIS, Wesley Boyd. 1908 LENDEW ST, WENDOVER OB/GYN & INFERTIL 27408 #036-01-1997 L1998 **OBG** *020 †30
DAVIS, William Bradley. 1307 W WENDOVER AVE 27408 #045-04-1996 L1999 **PD** *020 †55
DAY, Thomas Gordon. 1125 N CHURCH ST 27401 #020-02-2004 L2007 **FSM** *012 †18
DEAN, Eric Lynn. 2710 HENRY ST, STE 100B 27405 #036-01-1979 L1981 **IM** *020
DEAN, Gregory Scott. 300 W NORTHWOOD ST, PIEDMONT ORTHOPEDICS 27401 #036-07-1993 L1997 **ORS** *020 †40
DEATON, Philip Carl. 200 E NORTHWOOD ST STE 504 27401 #036-01-1966 L1966 **NS** *071 †25
DE CARVALHO E SILVA, Jose. ■ 27455 #187-49-1976 **OBG** *012
DEES, Janet Lee. 2835 HORSE PEN CREEK RD, STE 101 27410 #036-08-1992 L1995 **PD** *020 †55
DE GENT, Guy Elisa C. 1126 N CHURCH ST 27401 #165-08-1987 L1994 **CD** *020 †20
DELCAMBRE, Charles A. 301 E WENDOVER AVE, STE 300 27401 #048-04-1988 L2004 **OBG** *020 †30
DENENNY, Bruce John. 501 N ELAM AVE 27403 #026-04-1991 L2000 **AN** *020 †05
DENNARD, Turner H. ■ 27420 #010-03-1950 L1950 **PD** *020
DEPCIK, Natalie Dale. 706 GREEN VALLEY RD, STE 104 27408 #047-05-1998 L2002 **DMP** *020 †50
DE STEFANO, Neil Michael. 5515 RIDINGATE CT 27455 #035-09-1956 L1963 **GS GYN** *020
DETERDING, James Le Roy. 309 NEW ST 27405 #030-05-1979 L1982 **NEP IM** *020 †20
DEVESHWAR, Sanjeev. 1317 N ELM ST 27401 #917-06-1979 L2000 **RNR** *020 †75,80
DEVESHWAR, Shaili. 300 W NORTHWOOD ST 27401 #496-04-1987 L2000 **RHU IM** *020 †20,55
DEWEY, Elizabeth Rae. 501 HICKORY BRANCH DR 27409 #016-11-2001 L2003 **FM** *020 †18
DICKSTEIN, Sherry Anne. 1908 LENDEW ST 27408 #050-02-1978 L1982 **OBG** *020 †30
DILDA, Kimberlee Anne. ■ 27455 #036-01-2007 **FP** *012
DILLARD, Naima A. 301 E WENDOVER AVE, STE 400 27401 #010-01-1998 L2002 **OBG** *020 †30
DILWORTH, John Herbert. 300 W NORTHWOOD ST 27401 #051-01-1958 L1969 **ORS** *071 †40
DIMAGUILA, Mary Ann. 801 GREEN VALLEY RD 27408 #748-01-1985 L1996 **NPM** *020 †55
DOHMEIER, Carmen. 1126 N CHURCH ST, STE 200 27401 #409-21-1995 L2003 **CN SME** *020 †75
DOOLITTLE, Robert P. 104 POMONA DR 27407 #001-02-1974 L1976 **GP AMI** *020
DOUGH, Robert L, Jr. 520 N ELAM AVE 27403 #036-05-1982 L1983 **FM** *020 †18
DOVER, Caron B. 1002 N CHURCH ST, STE 401 27401 #048-12-1996 L1999 **DR** *020 †80
DOVER, Kevin Glenn. 1002 N CHURCH ST, STE 401 27401 #012-01-1996 L1997 **VIR** *020 †80
DOWNEY, William Edward. 1126 N CHURCH ST 27401 #036-07-1996 L2003 **IM VM** *020 †20
DOYLE, Owen Wm. ■ 27408 #008-01-1947 L1954 **R OS** *072 †80 ‡
DUDA, Marcus Valentine. 300 W NORTHWOOD ST 27401 #036-05-1991 L1993 **ORS** *020 †40
DUDLEY, Laura Shannon. 1046 E WENDOVER AVE 27405 #012-05-1991 L1995 **PD** *020 †55
DUGUAY, Veronique. ■ 27408 #067-06-2006 **IM** *012
DUNCAN, Graham Shaw. ■ 27408 #036-01-2005 **FP** *012
DUNN, Presley Zachary, Jr. ■ 27410 #036-01-1955 L1955 **PD** *071 †55
DYE, David Goddard. 809 GREEN VALLEY RD 27408 #012-01-1968 L1979 **ORS** *071 †40
EAGLE, Elizabeth Anne. 1002 N CHURCH ST, STE 401 27401 #036-01-1979 L1982 **DR** *020 †80
EARLS, Marian Frances. 1046 E WENDOVER AVE, GUILFORD CHILD HEALTH, INC 27405 #024-16-1984 L1985 **PD** *030 †55 ‡
EDMUNDS, John Howard. 301 E WENDOVER AVE, STE 310 27401 #023-12-1981 L1995 **CD IM** *020 †20
EDWARDS, Charlene. 1200 N ELM ST 27401 #023-01-1989 L1993 **APM** *020 †05
EDWARDS, Ephraim Zeno. ■ 27410 #010-03-1952 L1952 **AN PUD** *020 †05
EDWARDS, James Leon, Jr. 1002 N CHURCH ST, STE 2 27401 #045-01-1981 L1982 **GE IM** *020 †20

■ = Address Information Privacy Protected

EDWARDS, Zenia Colette. ■ 27410 #041-01-1985 L1986 **GE IM** *020 †20
EGGLESTON-CLARK, Valenica. ■ 27408 #036-08-2005 L2008 **FP** *012
EHINGER, Robert Richard. 301 E WENDOVER AVE, STE 215 27401 #036-01-1990 L1991 **FM** *020 †18
ELKINS, Robert Wm. 7 YARDARM CT 27455 #041-02-1965 L1983 **ORS** *020 †40
ELKINS, Wilson Oliver. 1200 N ELM ST 27401 #036-05-1970 L1970 **FM** *020 †18
ELLISON, Sean Alfred. 520 N ELAM AVE, LE BAUER HEALTHCARE 27403 #036-01-1983 L1995 **IM END** *020 †20
ELMAHDY, Wagdy Abdel-M. 1309 LEES CHAPEL RD 27455 #915-03-1985 L1999 **FM** *020 †18
ELNOUR, Elwaleed Mohamed. 1200 N ELM ST 27401 #848-05-1997 L2007 **IM** *020 †20
ELSNER, Henry Jos. 1130 N CHURCH ST, # 200 27401 #033-06-1983 L1989 **NS OSS** *020 †25
EMERICK, John Paul. 302 FALLING LEAF LN 27410 #033-05-1975 L1995 **P** *020 †75
END, Christopher Alexande. ■ 27410 #036-01-2007 **IM** *012
ENNEVER, Peter Robt. 501 N ELAM AVE, CONE REGIONAL CANCER CTR 27403 #010-01-1988 L1995 **ON** *020 †20
EUBANKS, Amy Harvey. 1416 YANCEYVILLE ST, STE 1 27405 #001-06-1995 L1998 **PD** *020 †55
EVANS, George Harrison. ■ 27420 #047-07-1933 L1934 **GP GS** *071
EWELL, Charles L, Jr. 501 N ELAM AVE 27403 #036-01-1984 L1987 **AN** *020 †05
FARLEY, Robert Hugh. 1103 N ELM ST 27401 #028-34-1956 L1964 **GS** *071 †85
FARMER, Susan Abigail. ■ 27409 #036-05-2007 **PD** *012
FARRELL, Susan Elizabeth. 2000 PISGAH CHURCH RD #100 27455 #019-02-1971 L1972 **OS PD** *020 †55 ‡
FEATHERSTON, Mark Wm. 1130 NEW GARDEN RD, STE 125 27410 #036-07-1989 L1990 **FM** *020 †18
FEINSTEIN, Daniel Jay. 520 N ELAM AVE, LEBAUER HEALTHCARE 27403 #654-01-1998 L2008 **CCM** *020 †20
FELDMANN, John Emerson. 501 N ELAM AVE, REGIONAL CANCER CENTER 27403 #035-20-1968 L2003 **ON HEM** *030 †20
FELIZ ORTIZ, Abraham. ■ 27410 #308-02-2005 **IM** *012
FERGUSON, Kermit E. ■ 27405 #010-03-1986 *100
FERNANDEZ, Eldaliz A. PO BOX 26170, STUDENT HLTH SRVS/GOV BLDG 27402 #042-03-1981 L1989 **IM** *020
FERNANDEZ, Juan H. 719 GREEN VALLEY RD # 305 27408 #042-03-1983 L1988 **OBG** *020 †30 ‡
FIELDS, Karl Bertrand. 1125 N CHURCH ST, FAMILY PRACTICE CENTER 27401 #020-12-1976 L1977 **FM FSM** *040 †18
FIELDS, Mark Lewis. 614 PASTEUR DR 27403 #036-01-1981 L1985 **FM** *020
FILLIPO, Brian Harvey. 1200 N ELM ST 27401 #041-09-1983 L2005 **IM** *030 †20 ‡
FISCHER, Gary Jay. 1002 N CHURCH ST, STE 401 27401 #028-03-1972 L1974 **DR** *020 †80 ‡
FISHER, Denise. 1200 N ELM ST, INCOMPASS HOSPITALISTS 27401 #036-08-1998 L1999 **IM** *020 †20
FISHER, Otis Norwood. ■ 27408 #036-01-1959 L1959 **R** *071 †80
FITZGERALD, William E, Jr. 2903 HAMDEN DR 27405 #021-05-2000 L2001 **AN** *020 †05
FOLLO, Paige Bill. 1209 MAGNOLIA ST 27401 #024-01-1947 L1954 **PD** *071 †55
FONTAINE, Timothy P. 719 GREEN VALLEY RD 27408 #041-12-1981 L1989 **OBG** *020 †30
FORBES, Redwell Kay. ■ 27410 #023-01-1961 L1965 **OBG** *071
FORD, Elizabeth S Linson. ■ 27408 #041-01-1943 L1951 **PD** *071 †55
FORE, Steven Ronald. 1103 N ELM ST STE 302 27401 #036-05-1968 L1968 **GYN** *020 †30
FOREMAN, Robert Hugh. 603 DOLLEY MADISON RD, STE A 27410 #038-41-1973 L1976 **FM** *020 †18
FORHAN, Sara Ellen. 5603 W FRIENDLY AVE, STE B # 245 27410 #005-02-1983 L1987 **OBG** *020 †30
FORREST, William Womble. ■ 27402 #024-01-1948 L1948 **PTH** *062 †50
FORTUNE, Alexander F. 501 N ELAM AVE 27403 #036-08-1985 L1989 **AN** *020 †05
FORTUNE, Benj Fletcher. ■ 27408 #041-02-1941 L1941 **AN** *071
FOSTER, Michael Alan. 3625 N ELM ST, STE 110A 27455 #748-16-1987 L1993 **AN IM** *020 †20,05
FRAZIER, Charles Earl. 200 E NORTHWOOD ST, STE 206 27401 #047-07-1968 L1973 **NEP IM** *071
FREDERICK, Charles Eugene. 1200 N ELM ST 27401 #018-03-1981 L1982 **AN** *020 †05
FREEMAN, Marshall Craig. 1414 YANCEYVILLE ST 27405 #025-07-1995 L2002 **CN N** *020 †75
FROELICH, Mary Elizabeth. 201 N EUGENE ST, GUILFORD CTR 27401 #036-01-1988 L1993 **CHP** *020 †55,75
FRY, John Rudolph. 3312 BATTLEGROUND AVE 27410 #056-05-1959 L1965 **OPH** *071 †35
FRY, Stephen Ashley. 1200 N ELM ST 27401 #051-01-1990 L2000 **FM** *020 †18
FUCHS, Katherine Elizabet. 1200 N ELM ST, FAMILY MEDICINE RES PROG 27401 #041-13-2006 **FP** *012
FULLER, David Lee. 612 PASTEUR DR STE 200 27403 #028-02-1973 L1975 **PYA P** *020 †55
GABLE, Elizabeth Kaye. 1200 N ELM ST 27401 #036-05-1983 L1986 **PD** *020 †55
GALLERANI, Peter Mark. 1002 N CHURCH ST, STE 401 27401 #036-05-1991 L1992 **DR** *020 †80
GARBA, Mohammad Lawal. 1200 N ELM ST, INCOMPASS HEALTH INC 27401 #690-03-1990 L2005 **IM** *020 †20
GARBER, Ronald Lewis. 309 NEW ST 27405 #045-01-1967 L1973 **NEP IM** *020 †20
GARDNER, Robert W. 3800 ROBERT PORCHER WAY 27410 #036-05-2000 L2002 **FM** *020 †18
GARFINKEL, Daniel. 102 POMONA DR 27407 #036-05-1955 L1955 **FM** *071 †18
GARRETT, Norman H, Jr. 1200 N ELM ST 27401 #036-07-1950 L1952 **IM END** *071 †20
GARVEY, Alfred Hamilton. ■ 27408 #036-05-1954 L1954 **U** *071 †95
GATES, Donna Ruth. 3800 ROBERT PORCHER WAY, STE 200 27410 #055-02-1984 L1986 **FM** *020 †18
GATES, Robert Nevill. 301 E WENDOVER AVE STE 200, TANNEBAUM 27401 #036-01-1983 L1994 **IM** *020 †20
GAY, April Lavelle. 5817 HIGH POINT RD, EAGLE PHYSICIANS ADAMS F 27407 #036-05-2004 L2007 **PD** *020
GAY, Robert Milton. 2407 DEER TRACK LN 27455 #021-01-1963 L1971 **PTH MM** *020 †50
GEGICK, Charles Geo. 1002 N CHURCH ST 27401 #016-43-1969 L1973 **END IM** *020 †20
GEGICK, Stephen John. ■ 27410 #036-05-2008 *012
GERKIN, Todd Michael. 1002 N CHURCH ST, CENTRAL CAROLINA SURGERY 27401 #051-01-1987 L1993 **GS CCS** *020 †85 ‡
GERTZ, Dale Sussman. 1046 E WENDOVER AVE 27405 #012-01-1992 L1996 **PD** *020 †55
GESSNER, Carl Edward. 520 N ELAM AVE 27403 #023-01-1990 L1992 **GE IM** *020 †20
GHERGHE, Cristina. 1200 N ELM ST, MOSES CONE HOSP 27401 #781-01-2001 **IM** *012
GILBERTI, Lynne Marie. ■ 27406 #036-05-1992 L1995 **FM** *020 †18
GILBERTI, Michael V. ■ 27406 #016-43-1945 L1946 **GS OS** *071 †85
GILMORE, Brooks Webster. 501 N ELAM AVE 27403 #041-01-1956 L1956 **IM** *071
GIOFFRE, Ronald Anthony. 1401 BENJAMIN PKWY, GREENSBORO ORTHOPAEDIC CTR 27408 #056-06-1965 L1979 **ORS** *020 †40
GO, Cristina Yip. ■ 27406 #748-01-1994 L2000 **CN** *020 †75
GOLLEHON, Steven Greg. 301 E WENDOVER AVE, STE 111 27401 #021-05-1998 L2000 **GS** *020
GONZALEZ LAWLESS, Carmen. 520 N ELAM AVE 27403 #051-07-1984 L2000 **PUD** *020 †20
GOODCHILD, Nigel Thos. 501 N ELAM AVE 27403 #917-20-1969 L1987 **RO** *020 †80
GOODRICH, Robert Gerard. 510 DAYBREAK SQ S 27455 #036-01-1999 L2000 **D** *020 †15
GOSRANI, Nimish C. 104 W NORTHWOOD ST, STE A 27401 #917-20-1988 L1997 **IM** *020 †20
GOSRANI, Shilpa Nimish. 409 PARKWAY, # G 27401 #045-04-1995 L1998 **PD** *020 †55
GOTTSEGEN, Daniel Leo. 719 GREEN VALLEY RD 27408 #024-07-1969 L1973 **GYN** *020 †30
GOULD, Karen Podlipsky. 510 N ELAM AVE, STE 303 27403 #038-40-1998 L2002 **D** *020 †15
GOULD, Sigmund S. 405 PARKWAY STE B 27401 #035-06-1971 L1977 **OPH EM** *020 †35 ‡
GRAMIG, William M, III. 1401 BENJAMIN PKWY 27408 #047-06-1993 L1999 **HS** *020 †40
GRANA, Lisa Marguerite. 1517 N CHURCH ST 27405 #036-01-1992 L1996 **OBG** *020 †30 ‡
GRANDIS, Arnold Stephen. 801 GREEN VALLEY RD 27408 #036-07-1974 L1978 **MFM OBS** *020 †30
GRANFORTUNA, James M. 501 N ELAM AVE, MOSES CONE REGIONAL CANTER 27403 #035-47-1980 L1990 **HO ON** *020 †20 ‡
GRAVELY, Barbara Jean. ■ 27405 #047-07-1964 L1968 **IM** *071
GRAVES, John Lee. 1915 LENDEW ST 27408 #051-01-1988 L1995 **ORS** *020 †40
GREEN, Arthur Gerrish, III. 1309 N ELM ST 27401 #021-01-1973 L1976 **IMG IM** *020 †20
GREEN, Edwin Jay. 1317 N ELM ST STE 2 27401 #047-06-1974 L1975 **IM EM** *020 †20
GREEN, Gretchen Elizabeth. 1317 N ELM ST, STE 1B 27401 #043-01-2000 L2006 **DR** *100 †80
GREEN, Robert David. 31 KINGLET CIR, 31 KINGLET CIRCLE 27455 #035-09-1961 L1993 **OPH** *020 †35 ‡
GREENE, Jeffrey Richard. 104 POMONA DR 27407 #011-04-2002 L2006 **FSM** *020 †18
GREWAL, Michelle Lynette. 1507 WESTOVER TER 27408 #036-01-1995 L1999 **OBG** *020 †30
GRIFFIN, Elaine Collins. 301 E WENDOVER AVE, STE 215 27401 #048-04-1989 L1996 **FM** *020 †18
GRIFFIN, John Jos, Jr. 301 E WENDOVER AVE, STE 200 27401 #048-04-1989 L1996 **IM** *020 †20
GROAT, Robert Lanier. 1317 N ELM ST STE 4 27401 #024-01-1970 L1974 **OPH** *020 †35
GROSS, Ned Jay. 806 GREEN VALLEY RD # 208 27408 #023-12-1988 L2000 **D** *020 †15 ‡
GROSS, Steven Cummins. ■ 27410 #051-07-1996 L1998 **GS** *020 †85
GROVE, David Dwight. 1511 WESTOVER TER, STE 201 27408 #016-02-1970 L1980 **CD IM** *020 †20
GRUBER, Hope M. 510 N ELAM AVE, STE 303 27403 #041-13-1982 L1987 **D** *020 †15
GUERRINI, James Gary. 3833 HIGH POINT RD 27407 #024-05-1992 L2004 **FM** *020 †18 ‡
GUEST, Chris Warren. 102 POMONA DR, URGENT MEDICAL & FAMILY CA 27407 #039-01-1974 L1977 **IM FM** *020 †20
GUICE, Richard Eric. 1507 WESTOVER TER 27408 #012-01-1989 L1991 **OBG** *071 †30
GYARTENG-DAKWA, Kwadwo. 2100 W CORNWALLIS DR, STE N 27408 #913-84-1990 L2005 **CCA** *020
HAGEN, Christine Louise. ■ 27455 #012-01-2003 L2008 **CN** *012
HALE, Wayne Andrew. 1125 N CHURCH ST, FAMILY PRACTICE CENTER 27401 #041-12-1974 L1986 **FM FPG** *040 †18
HALL, John Howland. 1305 W WENDOVER AVE 27408 #036-07-1964 L1964 **D** *071 †15
HALL, John Howland, Jr. 1305 W WENDOVER AVE STE D 27408 #036-05-1988 L1992 **D** *020 †15
HALL, Neil King. 2500 SUMMIT AVE, HOSPICE AND PALLIATIVE CAR 27405 #035-15-1975 L2006 **IMG** *020 †18
HALL, Sylvia Ann. 415 PISGAH CHURCH RD 27455 #047-06-1967 L1968 **P** *071
HANDY, Michael Harvey. 3515 W MARKET ST, STE 110 27403 #036-07-1999 L2005 **ORS OTR** *020 †40
HARDCASTLE, Kristen Renee. 1002 N CHURCH ST, CENTRAL CAROLINA SURGERY 27401 #038-40-1991 L1996 **GS** *020 †85
HARKINS, Paul Duane. 1505 WESTOVER TER, PIEDMONT ORTHOPEDICS 27408 #041-12-1962 L1973 **ORS RO** *071 †40
HARPER, Charles Augustus. 706 GREEN VALLEY RD, STE 506 27408 #036-01-1985 L1989 **OBG** *020 †30
HARPER, Paul Stanton. 201 TOPWATER LN 27455 #048-12-1977 L1978 **DR NM** *020 †80
HARRIS, Carlton Mc Kenzie. ■ 27408 #036-05-1947 L1948 **IM** *071
HARRIS, Donald Philip. ■ 27408 #036-01-1961 L2000 **IM** *075
HARRIS, William Randall. 3511 W MARKET ST, STE A 27403 #036-01-1989 L1992 **FM** *020 †18
HARSHAW, Charles Wm, Jr. 1010 N ELM ST 27401 #036-01-1971 L1973 **IM** *020 †20
HARTMAN, Jessica Elizabet. 1200 N ELM ST, DEPT FM 27401 #036-01-2007 **FP** *012
HARWANI, Mohan Nenumal. 200 E NORTHWOOD ST, STE 504 27401 #495-19-1982 L1996 **CD** *020 †20
HASSELL, Charles Matthews. ■ 27408 #041-01-1958 L1958 **PTH DMP** *071 †50
HASSELL, Dayne D, III. 1002 N CHURCH ST, STE 401 27401 #016-02-1993 L1998 **VIR** *020 †80
HATCHER, Jeffrey Charles. 1200 N ELM ST, MOSES CONE HEALTH SYSTEM 27401 #020-02-1994 L2001 **ID** *020 †20
HATCHER, Martin A, Jr. 1305 W WENDOVER AVE 27408 #036-07-1962 L1962 **N** *075 †75
HATCHETT, John Franklin. 3625 N ELM ST STE 110A 27455 #036-01-1987 L1991 **AN** *020 †05
HAYES, John Chas. 1002 N CHURCH ST, STE 2 27401 #036-05-1986 L1991 **GE IM** *020 †20
HAYGOOD, Vanessa Pearline. 301 E WENDOVER AVE, STE 400 27401 #024-01-1978 L1981 **GYN** *020 †30
HECKER, Kathryn J. 1511 WESTOVER TER, STE 107 27408 #048-12-1991 L1997 **OPH** *020 †35
HEJAZI, Masoud Seyed. 620 S ELM ST STE 312, TRIAD BEHAVIORAL RESOURCES 27406 #517-08-1977 L1988 **P CHP** *020 †75
HELLER, Joel Harvey. 603 DOLLEY MADISON RD, STE A 27410 #010-01-1973 L1976 **FM** *020 †18
HENDERSON, Cathy Lynn. 1046 E WENDOVER AVE, GUILFORD CHILD HLTH INC 27405 #036-08-1991 L1995 **PD** *020
HENDERSON, David James. 104 W NORTHWOOD ST, STE E 27401 #036-01-1979 L1982 **PD** *020 †55
HENLEY, Thomas Franklin. 801 GREEN VALLEY RD 27408 #036-07-1968 L1968 **OBG** *020 †30
HENN, Adam Ryan. 1317 N ELM ST, STE 1B 27401 #018-03-1999 L2002 **VIR** *020 †80
HENSEL, William Arthur. 1125 N CHURCH ST 27401 #038-40-1978 L1984 **FM** *040 †18
HENSON, Joseph Bascom, Jr. 1107 W FRIENDLY AVE 27401 #041-13-1945 L1946 **IM AM** *020
HERNANDEZ ACOSTA, Estela. ■ 27410 #308-02-2004 **IM** *012
HERRICK, Robert Henry. 201 N EUGENE ST, THE GUILFORD CENTER 27401 #035-01-1956 L1996 **CHP P** *040 †75
HERTLE, Xaver Franz. 5318 W FRIENDLY AVE 27410 #407-16-1950 L1958 **P** *071
HERTWECK, Donald Edward. 1593 YANCEYVILLE ST, STE 200 27405 #035-15-1997 L1998 **IM** *020 †20

HESSLING, Janice J. ■ 27401 #036-07-1989 L1990 **PTH ALI** *062 †50

HICKLING, William Henry. 1126 N CHURCH ST STE 200, GUILFORD NEUROLOGICAL ASSO 27401 #035-20-1978 L1981 **CHN N** *020 †55,75

HICKS, Roselyn Marie. 104 E NORTHWOOD ST 27401 #036-08-1997 L2002 **AI** *020 †55,03

HILL, Gerald Kenneth. 1317 N ELM ST STE 7, ROCKINGHAM MED & SURG ASSO 27401 #036-08-1984 L1987 **FM** *020 †18

HILTS, Michael John. 201 E WENDOVER AVE 27401 #049-01-1995 L1996 **FSM** *020 †18

HIPP, Larry Lee. ■ 27455 #038-40-1962 L1978 **OM** *071 †70

HIRSCH, James Ronald. 1130 N CHURCH ST, # 200 27401 #056-06-1992 L1998 **NS** *020 †25

HO, James Juiming. 7360 W FRIENDLY AVE, STE 102 27410 #305-01-1996 L2005 **IM UCM** *020

HOBBS, Jennifer Elise. ■ 27410 #036-01-2007 **FP** *012

HOFFMAN, Carl Maurice. 201 POMONA DR STE E 27407 #011-02-1967 L1973 **GYN** *020 †80

HOLDERNESS, Howard, Jr. 1200 N ELM ST 27401 #036-01-1965 L1965 **PS GS** *020 †85,65

HOLLAND, Richard Mark. 1507 WESTOVER TER 27408 #020-12-1980 L1982 **OBG** *020 †30

HOLLANDER, Edward M. 8 N POINTE CT 27408 #056-05-1962 L1971 **OPH** *020 †35

HOLLIDAY, Joseph Lambert. 301 N EUGENE ST BOX 3508 27401 #047-05-1973 L1974 **PHP** *030 †70

HOLMBERG, Ricky David. 1200 N ELM ST 27401 #060-02-1975 L1984 **N** *020

HONGALGI, Anand. ■ 27410 #495-37-1994 L2007 **IM** *020 †20

HOPPER, David Hershey. 104 POMONA DR 27407 #036-01-1976 L1976 **FM** *020 †18

HOSS, Arthur. 1002 N CHURCH ST, STE 401 27401 #036-05-1995 L1996 **VIR** *020 †80

HOUSTON, Frank Matt. 2704 SAINT JUDE ST, GREENSBORO DERM ASSOCIATES 27405 #021-05-1964 L1970 **D** *020 †15

HOWELL, Tamieka. ■ 27410 #035-09-2005 L2007 **FP** *012

HOXWORTH, Benjamin Tappan. 1002 N CHURCH ST, CENTRAL CAROLINA SURGERY 27401 #038-41-1980 L1987 **GS** *020 †85

HU, Jeffrey Tzuliang. 1002 N CHURCH ST, STE 401 27401 #021-06-1994 L1998 **DR** *020 †80

HUDNALL, Shane Robert. ■ 27410 #017-20-2007 **FP** *012

HUFFMAN, Diane Louise. 515 COLLEGE RD 27410 #036-05-1976 L1977 **FM ADL** *071 †18

HULSEMANN, Susan Jane A. 3824 N ELM ST 27455 #064-01-1992 L2007 **FM** *040 †18

HUNG, Patrick Deantzo. 1593 YANCEYVILLE ST, STE 100 27405 #051-04-1999 L2005 **GE** *020 †20

HUNT, Kendra Eileen. ■ 27410 #036-01-2003 L2007 **OBG** *020

HUNT, Mary Ruth. 1125 N CHURCH ST 27401 #036-08-1995 L2002 **GPM** *020 †20,70

HUNTER, John Gray. 501 N ELAM AVE 27403 #041-01-1943 L1943 **GS** *071 †85

HUSAIN, Karrar. 301 E WENDOVER AVE, STE 200 27401 #023-01-1995 L2001 **IM** *020 †20

IBARRA, Maria Azucena. 5710 HIGH POINT RD STE I, ADAMS FARM SHOPPING CENTER 27407 #715-01-1981 L1994 **FM** *020 †18

IMBUS, Harold Roger. ■ 27455 #038-41-1954 L1970 **OM** *071 †70 ‡

INGRAM, Haywood Melton. 1002 N CHURCH ST, CENTRAL CAROLINA SURGERY 27401 #036-05-1978 L1984 **GS TRS** *020 †85

JACKLIN, Harold Norman. 1200 N ELM ST 27401 #035-15-1960 L1968 **OPH** *020 †35 ‡

JACKSON, Eleanor Carswell. 3625 N ELM ST, GREENSBORO ANESTHESIA PHYS 27455 #036-05-1988 L1990 **AN** *020 †05

JACKSON, Freeman Randolph. 1317 N ELM ST 27401 #012-01-1977 L1978 **DR** *020 †80

JACKSON, Jonathan Clayton. ■ 27401 #023-12-2002 L2004 **FM** *020 †18

JACKSON, Kyle Edward. 801 GREEN VALLEY RD 27408 #028-34-1986 L1990 **AN** *020 †05

JACKSON, Lisa Anne. 706 GREEN VALLEY RD, STE 506 27408 #035-19-1993 L1997 **OBG** *020 †30

JACKSON, Mishi Kavon. 603A DOLLEY MADISON RD 27410 #027-01-1997 L2006 **FM** *020 †18

JACOB, Sera Leigh. 321 W WENDOVER AVE 27408 #019-02-1994 L1996 **OTO** *020 †45

JACOBS, Daniel Patrick. 520 N ELAM AVE 27403 #016-06-1998 L2006 **GE** *020 †20

JACUBOWITZ, Sam. 501 N ELAM AVE 27403 #041-13-1987 L1993 **EM** *020 †16

JAROSAK, Peter James. 1307 W WENDOVER AVE 27408 #026-04-1972 L1976 **PD** *020 †55

JARRELL, Maureen Adele. 1908 LENDEW ST 27408 #011-03-1979 L1993 **OBG ON** *020 †30 ‡

JARRETT, Novlet Clair. 301 E WENDOVER AVE, STE 200 27401 #051-04-2002 L2006 **IM** *020 †20

JEFFRIES, Jasper B. 2401 S SIDE BLVD 27406 #010-03-1972 L1975 **GP** *020

JENKINS, Harvette C. 500 BANNER AVE 27401 #036-01-1995 L1999 **IM** *020 †20

JENKINS, Jeffrey David. 1130 N CHURCH ST, STE 200 27401 #041-13-1991 L1994 **NS** *020 †25

JENKINS, John Edward. 3803 ROBERT PORCHER WAY 27410 #045-01-1988 L1991 **IM** *020 †20

JENNINGS, Glenn Earl. 700 WALTER REED DR, BEHAVIORAL HLTH CTR 27403 #047-06-1977 L2004 **CHP P** *020 †18,75

JOHN, James Wm. 520 N ELAM AVE, LE BAUER & ASSOC. 27403 #017-20-1990 L1996 **IM** *020 †20

JOHNSON, Andrew Myron. ■ 27410 #047-05-1959 L1970 **PD IG** *072 †55

JOHNSON, Martin Kay, III. 1002 N CHURCH ST, STE 2 27401 #001-02-1974 L1977 **GE IM** *020 †20

JOINES, Jerry Dale. 1200 N ELM ST, MOSES H CONE HOSP 27401 #036-01-1988 L1991 **IM** *020 †20

JONES, Daniel Brian. 2704 SAINT JUDE ST, GREENSBORO DERMATOLOGY ASS 27405 #041-14-1989 L1993 **D** *020 †15

JONES, David Scott. 301 E WENDOVER AVE STE 211, WENDOVER MED CTR 27401 #036-05-1995 L1996 **NS** *020 †25

JONES, Drew Alexander. 2704 SAINT JUDE ST, ASSOCIATES 27405 #036-01-1991 L1993 **D** *020 †15

JONES, Enrico Guy. 5409 W FRIENDLY AVE, FRIENDLY URGENT CARE 27410 #017-20-1995 L1997 **FM** *020 †18

JONES, Lauren Natasha. 1200 N ELM ST, MOSES CONE HEALTH SYSTEM 27401 #024-05-2004 L2007 **FM** *020

JONES, Leigh H. ■ 27408 #036-01-1990 L1995 **OBG** *020 †30

JONES, Mary Catherine. ■ 27408 #051-04-2007 **FP** *012

JONES, Percy Elwood. 2401 S SIDE BLVD 27406 #047-07-1968 L1975 **PTH** *020 †50 ‡

JONNALAGADDA, Janardhana. 301 E WASHINGTON ST, STE 301 27401 #495-70-1992 L2005 **CHP** *075

JORDAN, Amy Young. 2704 SAINT JUDE ST, ASSOCIATES 27405 #036-05-1998 L2002 **D** *020 †15

JORDAN, Kenneth Wayne. 1046 E WENDOVER AVE, GUILFORD CHILD HEALTH, INC 27405 #016-45-1986 L2001 **PD** *040 †55

JORDAN, Peter Manning. 1002 N CHURCH ST STE 103, PROFFESIONAL MEDICAL CENTE 27401 #036-01-1985 L1986 **CD IM** *020 †20

JOSLIN, David Coker. 3625 N ELM ST, STE 110A 27455 #036-01-1985 L1992 **AN CCA** *020 †05,20

JOYE, David Brent. 3817 LAWNDALE DR, STE A2 27455 #036-05-1998 L1999 **P** *020 †75

JOYNER, Ronald Freeman. 27455 #036-01-1968 L1968 **FM EM** *020

KADAKIA, Ajay Shantilal. 108 E NORTHWOOD ST 27401 #495-01-1979 L1995 **CD IM** *020 †20

KAPLAN, David Mann. ■ 27410 #051-04-1971 L1976 **FM** *020 †18

KAPLAN, Robert David. 520 N ELAM AVE, LEBAUER HEALTHCARE 27403 #035-20-1979 L1994 **GE IM** *020 †20

KASIK, Lee. 1200 N ELM ST 27401 #018-03-1980 L1981 **AN** *020 †05

KATZ, Jeffrey David. 1126 N CHURCH ST 27401 #041-01-1976 L1977 **CD IM** *020 †20

KAUR, Rupinder. 706 GREEN VALLEY RD, STE 100 27408 #495-03-1982 L1995 **P** *020 †75

KAVANAUGH, Alison Scott. 433 W MEADOWVIEW RD 27406 #036-01-2003 L2006 **PD** *020 †55

KEIFFER, Rebecca E. 1307 W WENDOVER AVE 27408 #035-15-1998 L2000 **PD** *020 †55

KELLER, David Chas. 317 W WENDOVER AVE 27408 #028-02-1974 L1977 **FM** *020 †18

KENDALL, Adam Scott. 3200 NORTHLINE AVE, STE 200 27408 #036-01-2003 L2006 **FSM** *020 †18

KENNEDY, Rebecca Smith. 1002 N CHURCH ST, STE 401 27401 #036-01-1986 L1989 **R** *020 †80

KERSEY, Terry Wayne, Jr. 1002 N CHURCH ST, STE 103 27401 #036-08-1999 L2001 **CD IM** *020 †20

KILPATRICK, George R, Jr. 601 E MARKET ST 27401 #047-07-1968 L1973 **PUD IM** *020 †20

KIM, James D. 1511 WESTOVER TER, STE 201 27408 #024-07-2003 L2003 **AN** *100

KIM, James Youngchull. 1511 WESTOVER TER 27408 #038-43-1999 L2008 **IM** *020 †20

KINARD, James Donald. 501 N ELAM AVE 27403 #036-08-1988 L1993 **RO** *020 †80

KINDL, James Douglas. 719 GREEN VALLEY RD, STE 301 27408 #050-02-1978 L1979 **FM IM** *020 †18

KINGSLEY, Thomas Edward. 603A DOLLEY MADISON RD 27410 #023-12-1988 L1997 **FM** *020 †18

KIRCHMAYER, D M. 510 N ELAM AVE STE 302, THE CTR FOR PAIN & REHAB 27403 #056-06-1987 L1991 **PM** *020 †60

KIRK, Katherine Anne. ■ 27405 #047-20-2004 L2007 **IM** *100

KIRSTEINS, Andrew Edward. 510 N ELAM AVE, STE 302 27403 #016-11-1987 L1991 **PM** *020 †60

KISER, Jefferson B, Jr. ■ 27410 #051-04-1971 L1976 **N** *071 †75 ‡

KITCHENS, Thomas Russell. 1507 WESTOVER TER STE A, CAROLINA COSMETIC SURGERY 27408 #012-01-1969 L1976 **PS** *020 †65

KLEIN, Steven Cochran. 1126 N CHURCH ST 27401 #024-01-1983 L1987 **ICE CD** *020 †20,55

KNAPP, Eve Applebaum. 3824 N ELM ST 27455 #051-01-1995 L2001 **FM** *020 †18

KNAPP, Jon Robert. 1200 N ELM ST, EMERGENCY DEPT 27401 #010-01-1995 L2003 **EM** *020 †16

KNISELY, Samuel Scott. ■ 27410 #010-02-1987 L1993 **N** *075

KOEHLER, Robert Nicholas. 3800 ROBERT PORCHER WAY, STE 200 27410 #033-06-1981 L1982 **FM** *020 †18

KOHUT, Walter Dennis. 1511 WESTOVER TER, STE 201 27408 #038-41-1973 L1982 **IM END** *020 †20

KOZLOW, Eric Jon. 104 E NORTHWOOD ST, OF NORTH CAROLINA 27401 #012-05-1985 L1995 **AI IM** *020 †20,03

KPEGLO, Maurice Kobla. 2025 MARTIN LTHR KNG JR DR, KING DR 27406 #036-01-1983 L2008 **GP PD** *020

KRAMER, James Scott. 1130 N CHURCH ST, SPORTS MEDICINE CENTER 27401 #025-07-1989 L1990 **FM** *020 †18

KRAUS, Eric Marshall. 1126 N CHURCH ST, PA 27401 #041-12-1977 L1983 **OTO** *020 †45

KREGE, John Wilson. 300 W NORTHWOOD ST 27401 #012-05-1966 L1976 **ORS** *020 †40

KRINER, Arthur F, Jr. 1002 N CHURCH ST, STE 401 27401 #041-09-1969 L1973 **DR R** *071 †80 ‡

KRISHNAN, Sendil Kumar. 1200 N ELM ST 27401 #055-01-2001 L2004 **IM** *020 †20

KRISHNAN KUTTY NAIR, Prem. ■ 27455 #495-31-2001 L2007 **IM** *020 †20

KRISHNARAJ, Ramesh L. 3824 N ELM ST, JEANETTE 27455 #036-01-1997 L1999 **GPM** *020 †20

KRITZER, Randy Owen. 301 E WENDOVER AVE, STE 211 27401 #036-01-1983 L1990 **NS GS** *020 †25

KRUEGER, Andrew Carl. 4900 KOGER BLVD 27407 #056-06-1988 L1989 **IM** *040 †20

KRUSCH, Michael P. 1130 NEW GARDEN RD 27410 #016-42-1994 L1995 **IM PHL** *020 †20

KUHN, Thomas Howard. 2000 PISGAH CHURCH RD, DEVELOPMENTAL & PSYCH CTR 27455 #038-40-1977 L1988 **PD DBP** *020 †55

KUMAR, Ajay. 1002 N CHURCH ST 27401 #495-36-1976 L1986 **IM END** *020 †20

KUZMA, Gary Robt. 2718 HENRY ST 27405 #035-15-1975 L1981 **HS ORS** *020 †40 ‡

KWIATKOWSKI, Peter Frank. 520 N ELAM AVE 27403 #012-01-1976 L1982 **IM** *020 †20

LA LONDE, John Chas. 1581 YANCEYVILLE ST 27405 #038-40-1975 L1975 **FM** *020 †18

LANE, Timothy Walter. 1200 N ELM ST, MOSES H CONE MEMORIAL HOSP 27401 #035-20-1971 L1978 **ID IM** *020 †20

LANGLEY, Kim. 1046 E WENDOVER AVE, GUILFORD CHILD HEALTH 27405 #024-01-1972 L2006 **PD** *020 †55 ‡

LANTOS, Paul Michael. ■ 27455 #008-02-2000 L2007 **PDI** *100

LASHLEY, Curtis Ray. ■ 27410 #036-01-1959 L1959 **OS** *030

LAUENSTEIN, Kurt. 1123 N CHURCH ST, CARE CENTER 27401 #050-02-1977 L1982 **FM** *020 †18

LAVENDER, Dick Redmond. 300 W NORTHWOOD ST 27401 #036-05-1961 L1961 **ORS** *071 †40

LAVOIE, Marie-Lyne. 1908 LENDEW ST, WENDOVER OB-GYN &INFERTILI 27408 #067-01-1991 L1998 **OBG** *020 †30

LAWRENCE, Robt Livingston. 100 E NORTHWOOD ST 27401 #047-05-1963 L1972 **OTO** *071 †45

LAWRENCE, Thomas Earl. 1002 N CHURCH ST, STE 401 27401 #036-01-1987 L1988 **DR VIR** *020 †80

LAYSON, Rita Torres. 1200 N ELM ST 27401 #036-01-1984 L1986 **IM** *040 †20

LAZA, Sorin Christian. 1200 N ELM ST 27401 #781-03-2000 L2006 **IM** *020 †20 ‡

LE BAUER, Edmund Jos. 1126 N CHURCH ST 27401 #036-07-1960 L1960 **CD IM** *020 †20

LEBAUER, Eugene Shaner. 3201 BRASSFIELD RD STE 400 27410 #036-07-1965 L1965 **PUD A** *020

LE BAUER, Samuel M. 1200 N ELM ST 27401 #051-01-1967 L1974 **GE IM** *020

LEE, Chon. 1200 N ELM ST 27401 #035-46-1987 L1989 **CHN** *012 †55

LEE, James Mobley. ■ 27410 #036-07-1958 L1958 **TS** *071 †85,90

LEGGETT, Kelly Harris. 801 GREEN VALLEY RD, DEPT OB-GYN 27408 #036-05-2000 L2004 **OBG** *020

LEINER, Deborah. 719 GREEN VALLEY RD, PIEDMONT PEDIATRICS 27408 #020-12-1976 L1979 **PD** *020 †55

LEMLY, Regina G. 3803 N ELM ST, CONSUMER DEC SUP & ADVOC 27455 #036-05-1983 L2003 **IM** *030 †20 ‡

LENTZ, Robert Preston. 5817 HIGH POINT RD, STE 101 27407 #036-01-1982 L1985 **PD** *020 †55

LEONARD, Donald Dean. 1031 SUMMIT AVE 27405 #038-06-1956 L1963 **PTH DMP** *071 †50
LEONE, Michael Ralph. 1002 N CHURCH ST, CENTRAL CAROLINA SURGERY 27401 #041-02-1967 L1974 **GS** *020 †85
LESCHBER, Valerie Ann. 1200 N ELM ST, MOSES CONE HOSPITAL 27401 #048-14-2000 L2001 **IM** *020 †20
LESHIN, Barry. 3107 BRASSFIELD RD, SKIN SURGERY CENTER 27410 #048-14-1981 L1986 **DS PRD** *020 †15
LEVITIN, Peter Mark. 301 E WENDOVER AVE, STE 200 27401 #041-01-1969 L1975 **RHU IM** *020 †20 ‡
LEWIS, Jody Parks. ■ 27408 #036-05-2008 *012
LEWIT, Eliot J. 2721 HORSE PEN CREEK RD, STE 104 27410 #016-01-1982 L2000 **N** *020 †75
LIEBKEMANN, Walter D. 1002 N CHURCH ST, STE 401 27401 #021-01-1996 L1997 **DR** *020 †80
LINDER, Donald E. PO BOX 29343 27429 #036-05-1974 L1974 **AN** *020 †05
LINDSEY, Anita. 1002 N CHURCH ST STE 3, CENTRAL CAROLINA SURGERY,P 27401 #027-01-1986 L1991 **GS** *075 †85
LINGAO, Julio M. ■ 27410 #748-07-1953 L1968 **IM** *071
LIPOVAN, Mircea. ■ 27409 #781-04-1962 L1981 **R GP** *020 †80
LIPSEY, John Crawford. 5140 DUNSTAN RD 27405 #021-01-1956 L1956 **OS EM** *072 †55
LIPTON, Dennis Jay. 1200 N ELM ST 27401 #048-14-1997 L1998 **IM** *020 †20
LITTLE, Alfred Boyd. 1331 N ELM ST 27401 #036-01-1978 L1979 **CD IM** *020 †20
LITTLE, Edgar Watson. 1307 W WENDOVER AVE 27408 #036-01-1971 L1971 **PD** *020 †55
LITTLE, Kevin Lorne. 603 DOLLEY MADISON RD A, GUILFORD COLLEGE 27410 #010-01-1984 L1986 **FM** *020 †18
LITZ, Mariel Melissa S. 201 N EUGENE ST, ALAMANCE-CASWELL MH/DD/SAA 27401 #055-01-1987 L1999 **P CHP** *020 †75
LIVESAY, Lennis Pearcy. 501 N ELAM AVE 27403 #045-04-1985 L1988 **ON HEM** *020 †20
LOACH, Kenneth Wm. ■ 27410 #352-04-1951 L1960 **P** *071
LOMAX, Charles Weston. 311 W WENDOVER AVE 27408 #036-05-1968 L1969 **OBG** *020 †30
LOMAX, Laura Lea. 2704 SAINT JUDE ST, ASSOCIATES 27405 #036-01-1985 L1987 **D** *020 †15
LONG, Kyle Yan. 3511 W MARKET ST, STE 100 27403 #422-01-2000 L2004 **P** *020 †75
LONG, Paul De Mars. 501 N ELAM AVE 27403 #025-01-1962 L1971 **ORS OSM** *020 †40 ‡
LONON, Robert Warren, Jr. 3625 N ELM ST STE 110A 27455 #036-07-1969 L1973 **AN** *020 †05
LOTT, Tamika Jo. 1125 N CHURCH ST, MOSES CONE FAMILY PRACTICE 27401 #033-06-2002 L2004 **FM** *020 †18
LOVE, James Mc Lean. 1910 N CHURCH ST, INC. 27405 #036-07-1972 L1972 **N** *020 †75
LOWE, David C. 1507 WESTOVER TER 27408 #028-03-1991 L1993 **OBG** *020 †30
LOWE, Melissa Vaughn. 1307 W WENDOVER AVE, WENDOVER PEDIATRICS 27408 #045-01-1991 L1994 **PD** *020 †55
LOWNES, Charles Edward. 1601 E MARKET ST, N CAROLINA A&T STATE UNIV 27411 #036-01-1979 L1980 **FM EM** *020 †16,18
LUCAS, Deborah Maria. 3801 W MARKET ST 27407 #038-43-1987 L1991 **DR** *020 †80
LUCAS, Kathleen Ellen. 1416 YANCEYVILLE ST STE 1 27405 #055-02-1984 L1987 **PD** *020 †55
LUCEY, Stephen Davis. 300 W NORTHWOOD ST 27401 #045-01-1994 L1996 **ORS** *020 †40
LUGO, Irving A. 700 WALTER REED DR, MOSES CONE BEHAVIORAL HLTH 27403 #042-01-1980 L1986 **P** *020 †75
LUPTON, Emmett S. ■ 27455 #035-19-1938 L1938 **D PD** *071 †15
LUPTON, Frederick Arthur. 1587 YANCEYVILLE ST 27405 #036-05-1986 L1989 **D** *020 †15
LUSK, John Alexander, III. 2500 SUMMIT AVE, HOSPICE GREENSBORO 27405 #001-02-1951 L1958 **PLM IM** *071 †20
LYLES, Graham Warner. ■ 27401 #036-01-2007 **IM** *012
LYNAGH, William Aloysius. 2605 SOUTHWICK DR 27455 #023-01-1985 L1997 **FM MDM** *030 †18
MABRY, Edward Bloxton. 5817 HIGH POINT RD STE 202 27407 #036-07-1953 L1957 **GYN** *071 †30
MAC ARTHUR, Robert D. 301 E WENDOVER AVE, STE 200 27401 #036-05-1994 L1995 **IM** *020 †20
MAC LEOD, Wendy Ellen. 3803 N ELM ST, UNITED HEALTHCARE 27455 #001-02-1977 L1996 **PD MDM** *030 †55
MACPALM, Frederick Yao. ■ 27407 #036-08-2008 *012
MAGOD, Marc Emanuel. 1002 N CHURCH ST, STE 2 27401 #012-05-1986 L1992 **GE IM** *020 †20
MAHAFFEY, Danielle Lee. 3800 ROBERT PORCHER WAY 27410 #017-20-1996 L1997 **FSM** *020 †18 ‡
MANN, Jyothi Nat. 1593 YANCEYVILLE ST, BLDG A 27405 #495-10-1985 L1993 **GE** *020 †20
MANNING, James E, IV. 500 PARKMONT DR 27408 #051-04-1992 L2002 **P** *020 †75
MANNING, James Sloan. 501 HICKORY BRANCH DR 27409 #027-01-1984 L2001 **FM** *020 †18
MANNING, Matthew A. 501 N ELAM AVE, RADIATION ONCOLOGY 27403 #051-04-1996 L2001 **RO** *020 †80
MANSELL, Eric Arthur. 301 E WENDOVER AVE, STE 100 27401 #011-03-1997 L1998 **DR** *020 †80
MANZOOR, Shazli. ■ 27408 #704-20-1989 L1996 **PUD** *020 †20
MARKS, Edgar Seymour. ■ 27405 #036-05-1945 L1948 **IM OM** *072
MARSHALL, Bernard Anthony. 802 GREEN VALLEY RD, STE 108 27408 #010-03-1972 L1976 **OBG** *020 †30
MARTIN, Charles F. ■ 27405 #020-02-1951 L1967 **OM** *072 †70
MARTIN, Matthew Brunson. 1002 N CHURCH ST, CENTRAL CAROLINA SURGERY 27401 #048-12-1979 L1980 **AS TRS** *020 †85
MARTIN, Melanie Joy. 3824 N ELM ST 27455 #005-11-1992 L1998 **IM** *020 †20
MARTIN, Tanya Denise. 5500 W FRIENDLY AVE, STE 201 27410 #041-13-1998 L2001 **FM** *020 †18
MASSAGEE, James Terrill. 3625 N ELM ST STE 110A 27455 #036-01-1982 L1983 **AN CD** *020 †05
MASSEY, David Barnett. 3800 ROBERT PORCHER WAY, STE 200 27410 #041-02-1982 L1983 **FM EM** *020 †18
MATTERN, Christopher W. 1313 CAROLINA ST 27401 #026-08-1999 L2002 **RNR** *020 †80
MATTHEWS, James Austin. 719 GREEN VALLEY RD, STE 101 27408 #036-05-1981 L1985 **OBG** *020 †30
MATTHEWS, John Dail. ■ 27408 #045-01-1979 L1984 **OPH** *020 †35 ‡
MAXWELL, James Heath. 1002 N CHURCH ST, STE 401 27401 #020-12-1978 L1982 **DR** *020 †80
MAYER, Kenneth Richard. 3511 W MARKET ST, STE A 27403 #035-15-1992 L2006 **FM** *020 †18
MAYER, Norman Michael. 501 N ELAM AVE 27403 #036-05-1975 L1975 **EM** *020 †16
MAYNARD, David Russell. 1211 VIRGINIA ST 27401 #036-07-1965 L1965 **AN** *071 †05
MAZZOCCHI, Annmarie. 1581 YANCEYVILLE ST 27405 #035-01-1982 L1983 **FM** *020 †18
MC CLUNG, Jeffrey Thomas. 3560 WILDFLOWER DR, PIEDMONT SENIOR CARE 27410 #012-01-1998 L1999 **IM** *020 †20
MC COMB, John Sanford. 1507 WESTOVER TER 27408 #036-05-1980 L1983 **OBG** *020 †30
MC CONVILLE, Parker S. 4807 FOREST OAKS DR 27406 #036-08-2003 L2005 **FM** *020 †18
MC CORMICK, Hilary. 1046 E WENDOVER AVE, GUILFORD CHILD HEALTH, INC 27405 #048-04-1989 L2004 **PD** *020 †55
MC COY, Bruce P. 526 N ELAM AVE, STE 201 27403 #038-40-1971 L1980 **D DMP** *020 ‡
MCCUEN, Christine Lee. 8 N POINTE CT 27408 #041-12-2002 L2006 **OPH** *020 †35
MC DIARMID, Todd Durant. 1125 N CHURCH ST 27401 #036-01-1991 L1993 **FM** *020 †18
MC DOWELL, Frank, Jr. ■ 27406 #047-07-1959 L1960 **P GP** *071
MC GEE, Robert S Jr. ■ 27407 #036-05-1994 L1995 **PTH** *020 †50
MC KENZIE, Wayland Wilson. 1500 E MARKET ST STE H 27401 #036-01-1974 L2005 **FM** *020
MC KENZIE, William M, Jr. 501 HICKORY BRANCH DR 27409 #036-05-1975 L1975 **PHP FM** *020 †18
MC KEOWN, William David. 1511 WESTOVER TER, STE 103 27408 #036-05-1976 L1976 **IM** *020 †20
MC KIE, James. 802 GREEN VALLEY RD, STE 106 27408 #033-05-1977 L1982 **GE IM** *020
MC KINLEY, Dominic Wayne. 1915 LENDEW ST 27408 #038-45-1997 L1998 **FSM** *020 †18
MC KINNEY, Parish Ann. 3817 LAWNDALE DR STE D 27455 #036-08-1993 L1997 **P** *020 †75
MC NEILL, Wendy Kay. 603 DOLLEY MADISON RD A, EAGLE FAMILY MEDICINE GU 27410 #036-01-1993 L1996 **FM OBS** *020 †18
MC PHAIL, Schubert Dean. 719 GREEN VALLEY RD, STE 103 27408 #045-01-1963 L1971 **OBG** *020 †30
MC PHERSON, Barbara B. 1002 S EUGENE ST 27406 #036-01-1983 L1986 **FM** *020 †18
MC RAE, Marvin E. ■ 27410 #051-04-1938 L1949 **D** *071 †15
MEDOFF, Alan Sherwood. ■ 27408 #035-09-1948 L1950 **IM** *071 †20
MEDOFF, Jeffrey Roy. 7 CORPORATE CENTER CT, STE C 27408 #035-09-1977 L1980 **GE IM** *020 †20 ‡
MEISINGER, Todd Douglas. 510 N ELAM AVE, STE 101 27403 #028-34-1993 L1997 **OBG** *020 †30
MENZER, Frieda Margarite. 1200 N ELM ST, EAGLE PHYSICIANS 27401 #047-06-1996 L1997 **IM** *020 †20
MEYERDIERKS, Elizabeth M. 300 W NORTHWOOD ST 27401 #021-01-1981 L1987 **HS ORS** *020 †40
MEZER, Howard Cabitt. 1103 N ELM ST, STE 302 27401 #024-07-1977 L1983 **GYN REN** *020 †30
MILLER, Robert C. 510 N ELAM AVE, STE 202 27403 #036-01-1998 L2001 **PD** *020 †55
MILLER, Stephen Maurice. 1309 N ELM ST, PIEDMONT SENIOR CARE, PLLC 27401 #036-01-1974 L1976 **EM FM** *020 †18
MILLS, Wardell Hardee. ■ 27410 #036-07-1940 L1940 **OPH OTO** *071 †45
MITCHELL, Lewis Dean. 301 E WENDOVER AVE, STE 215 27401 #011-04-1982 L1984 **FM** *020 †18
MOHAMED, Mohamed Kamel. 501 N ELAM AVE 27403 #915-04-1984 L2005 **HO IM** *020 †20
MOLPUS, John Lane. 1200 N ELM ST 27401 #011-04-1998 L1999 **EM** *020 †16
MONGUILOD, Juan-Carlos. 2500 SUMMIT AVE 27405 #847-06-1991 L1998 **IM PLM** *020 †20
MOORE, Ann Lee Sudholt. ■ 27402 #028-03-1972 L1974 **FM** *020
MOORE, John Andrew. ■ 27408 #051-04-1948 L1954 **IM RHU** *071 †20
MORCOS, Victor Hanna. 236 S ELM ST, STE E 27401 #915-04-1964 L1973 **P GP** *020 †75
MOREIRA, Roy. 411 PARKWAY, STE F 27401 #495-31-1975 L1994 **IM** *020 †20
MORENO-COLL, Adlih. ■ 27455 #275-01-1997 **FP** *012
MORONO PONCE, Idaylis. 1200 N ELM ST 27401 #275-01-1994 **FP** *012
MORTENSON, Rodney Allen. 300 W NORTHWOOD ST 27401 #005-06-1967 L1969 **ORS** *020 †40
MOSER, Edgar Strock, Jr. 3511 DOGWOOD DR 27403 #051-04-1984 L1990 **DR** *071 †80
MULBERRY, Elizabeth M. 1439 E CONE BLVD 27405 #016-11-1990 L2000 **IM PD** *020 †55,20
MULVANEY, Gerald Garfield. 1517 N CHURCH ST 27405 #024-05-1978 L1982 **OBG** *020 †30
MUNDY, John Christian. 1126 N CHURCH ST, PA 27401 #051-01-1975 L1990 **OTO** *020 †45
MURINSON, Donald Scott. 501 N ELAM AVE, CANCER CENTER 27403 #050-02-1972 L1986 **ON HEM** *020 †20
MURPHY, Daniel Francis. 1130 N CHURCH ST STE 100, SPORTS MEDICINE CENTER 27401 #041-13-1981 L1986 **ORS OSM** *020 †40
MURRAY, Alexander Vance. 3511 W MARKET ST, STE A 27403 #051-01-1983 L1985 **FM** *020 †18
MURRAY, Robert Jos, Jr. 501 N ELAM AVE 27403 #051-01-1980 L1986 **RO** *020 †80
NADEL, Scott Martin. 520 N ELAM AVE 27403 #011-02-1975 L1980 **PUD IM** *020 †20
NAGAPPAN, Suresh. 1200 N ELM ST 27401 #025-12-1999 L2004 **PD** *020 †55
NAHSER, Philip Jos, Jr. 1002 N CHURCH ST STE 103 27401 #036-01-1988 L1994 **CD** *020 †20
NEAL, William Ronald. 1507 WESTOVER TER 27408 #036-01-1974 L1974 **OBG** *020 †30
NEWMAN, Christopher E. 100 E NORTHWOOD ST 27401 #036-05-1984 L1987 **OTO** *020 †45
NEWMAN, David Harold. 1002 N CHURCH ST, CENTRAL CAROLINA SURGERY 27401 #036-05-1980 L1985 **GS** *020 †85
NICHOLS, Harold Alfonzo. 509 N ELAM AVE, 3RD FLOOR, SUITE D 27403 #036-01-1976 L1977 **TS** *020 †85
NICOLA, Andraos N. 201 N EUGENE ST, GUILFORD CENTER 27401 #605-01-1953 L1973 **P** *071
NISHAN, Peter Chas. 1126 N CHURCH ST 27401 #024-16-1987 L1994 **CD IM** *020 †20
NITKA, James Edward. 300 W NORTHWOOD ST, PIEDMONT ORTHOPEDIC ASSOC 27401 #003-01-1983 L1989 **OSS ORS** *020 †40
NOLAN, Clyde, Jr. 1317 N ELM ST STE 9 27401 #036-01-1974 L2003 **D IM** *020 †15
NORINS, Michael Elliott. 520 N ELAM AVE, LEBAUER HEALTHCARE 27403 #036-01-1986 L1987 **IM** *020 †20
NORRIS, Steven Roland. 1401 BENJAMIN PKWY 27408 #047-05-1993 L2002 **ORS** *020 †40
NUDELMAN, Robert Wayne. 1130 N CHURCH ST, STE 200 27401 #024-05-1982 L1988 **NS** *020 †25
ODDONO, E J, Jr. 801 GREEN VALLEY RD 27408 #561-16-1988 L1994 **APM AN** *020 †05
ODOGWU, Ifeoma Lauretta. 501 N ELAM AVE 27403 #539-06-1989 L2003 **ON** *020 †20
O'KELLEY, Brian Scott. 510 N ELAM AVE STE 202, GREENSBORO PEDIATRICS INC 27403 #036-01-1997 L2000 **PD** *020 †55
OKOCHA, Chiedu. ■ 27455 #690-06-1988 L2004 **IM** *020 †20
OLIN, Matthew David. 3200 NORTHLINE AVE, STE 200 27408 #036-05-1998 L2001 **ORS** *020 †40
OLSON, Steven R. 1002 N CHURCH ST, STE 401 27401 #036-01-1986 L1993 **RNR DR** *020 †80
ORR, George Michael. 1511 WESTOVER TER, MERRITT MEDICAL PLAZA 27408 #041-12-1975 L1994 **GE IM** *020 †20
ORTMANN, Fred William, IV. 1401 BENJAMIN PKWY, PALMETTO RICHLAND 27408 #034-01-2001 L2007 **HS** *020
OSBORNE, James Chas. 301 E WENDOVER AVE STE 200, EAGLE INTERNAL MEDICINE 27401 #036-01-1983 L1984 **IM** *020 †20 ‡
OSEI-BONSU, George. 324 W WENDOVER AVE STE 20, MAILING: P O BOX 14520 27408 #412-02-1994 L2002 **IM** *020 †20

■ = Address Information Privacy Protected

OSSEY, Kevin David. 1200 N ELM ST 27401 #836-02-1981 L1984 **AN IM** *020 †05

OWEN, Clarence Hays. 2704 HENRY ST, CVTS OF GREENSBORO 27405 #036-07-1989 L1991 **TS** *020 †85,90

OWSLEY, Todd Gene. 2516 OAKCREST AVE, STE B 27408 #036-01-1990 L1994 **OS FPS** *020

PADULA, Joseph Peter. 2401 SOUTHSIDE BLVD, VENCOR HOSPITAL 27406 #035-01-1971 L1996 **PUD IM** *020 †20

PAEZ, Daniel F. ■ 27410 #264-01-1956 L1972 **IM GP** *020

PANG, Richard Y.. 1511 WESTOVER TER, STE 201 27408 #422-01-2000 L2003 **IM** *020 †20

PANOSH, Wanda E. 3803 ROBERT PORCHER WAY, LEBAUER HEALTHCARE, PA 27410 #041-12-1978 L1982 **MPD PD** *020 †20,55

PARKER, Herman R, Jr. 1200 N ELM ST 27401 #036-01-1967 L1968 **IM** *071

PARKER, Michael Dean. 501 N ELAM AVE, WESLEY LONG HOSPITAL 27403 #036-07-1968 L1969 **DR RHU** *075 †20,80

PARNELL, Lisa Stigler. 1200 N ELM ST, STE 1049 27401 #048-16-2003 L2006 **PD** *100 †55

PASHAYAN, Annette G. 1211 VIRGINIA ST, GATE CITY ANESTHESIA, INC 27401 #036-05-1978 L1996 **AN** *040 †05

PATEL, Jay Krishnavadan. 1200 N ELM ST, DEPT INTERNAL MEDICINE 27401 #577-02-2001 L2007 **IM** *020

PATEL, Sejal Shashin. ■ 27407 #495-23-1998 **IM** *012

PATERSON, Daniel Geo. 2703 HENRY ST 27405 #010-01-1988 L1998 **IM** *020 †20

PATRICK, John David. 501 N ELAM AVE 27403 #045-04-1987 L1989 **PTH PCP** *020 †50

PATSEAVOURAS, Louie Lee. 1200 N ELM ST 27401 #036-01-1961 L1961 **FPS OTO** *020 †45

PATTERSON, David Read. 1200 N ELM ST 27401 #036-01-1973 L1973 **GE IM** *020 †20

PATTERSON, Furnifold M S. ■ 27410 #041-01-1939 L1939 **CD** *071 †85

PATTERSON, Peter Hay. ANNA GOVE STUDENT HLTH CTR, U N C G 27402 #024-07-1957 L1997 **ADL PD** *020 †55 ‡

PAUL, Melinda C. 433 W MEADOWVIEW RD 27406 #036-01-1977 L1977 **PD** *020 †55

PAUL, Vincent Edgar. 1915 LENDEW ST 27408 #036-01-1976 L1976 **ORS** *020 †40

PAYNE, Christopher R. ■ 27408 #035-01-1996 L2004 **DR** *020 †80

PEELE, Mark Edward. 1331 N ELM ST 27401 #036-01-1984 L1988 **CD IM** *020 †20

PELLIGRA, Salvatore John. 2718 HENRY ST 27405 #035-03-1981 L1984 **PM PRS** *020 †60

PENDSE, Prabhakar Damodar. 301 E WENDOVER AVE, STE 311 27401 #495-01-1959 L1972 **PDS** *020 †85

PEREZ-FIERY, Denise. ■ 27408 #024-05-1976 L1997 **PD** *020 †55

PERINI, Mark Andrew. 2703 HENRY ST 27405 #036-05-1998 L1999 **IM** *020 †20

PERRY, John Nicholas, Jr. 520 N ELAM AVE 27403 #041-12-1988 L1994 **GE** *020 †20

PHARR, Walter Davidson. 1511 WESTOVER TER, STE 201 27408 #036-07-1985 L1986 **IM** *020 †20

PHIFER, Nancy Welcome. 1200 N ELM ST, MOSES CONE MEMORIAL HOSPIT 27401 #036-01-1987 L1989 **IM** *020 †20

PHILLIPS, Mark Lucas. 522 N ELAM AVE, STE 203 27403 #036-05-1980 L1981 **AN** *020 †20,05

PHILLIPS, Mary Linley. 2705 HENRY ST, TRIAD IMAGING 27405 #056-05-1985 L1991 **DR** *020 †80

PHILLIPS, Minta Elizabeth. 1002 N CHURCH ST, STE 401 27401 #024-01-1981 L1991 **DR** *020 †80

PICKARD, Warren Thomas, II. ■ 27410 #036-01-2005 L2008 **FP** *012

PIERSON, George Herman. 1200 N ELM ST DEPT RAD 27401 #036-07-1954 L1954 **DR** *071 †80

PITTMAN, Pamela Martin. 3511 W MARKET ST, STE 100 27403 #036-05-1979 L1980 **P** *020 †75

PLOTNIKOV, Alex V. 520 N ELAM AVE, LE BAUER HEALTH CARE 27403 #913-15-1988 L1996 **IM** *020 †20

PLOVSKY, Gerald Irving. 3511 W MARKET ST, STE 100 27403 #051-04-1984 L1991 **IM P** *020 †75,20

PLUMMER, Charles Wayne. 920 CHERRY ST 27401 #036-07-1978 L1993 **AN** *020 †05

PODGORNY, George. 1200 N ELM ST 27401 #036-05-1962 L1969 **EM GS** *071 †85 ‡

POLITE, Ronald Dewitt. 1200 N ELM ST 27401 #010-03-1997 L2002 **IM** *020 †20

POOL, Henry Andrae. 301 E WENDOVER AVE, STE 211 27401 #028-03-1991 L1997 **NS** *020 †25

POOL, Leigh Ann S. 510 N ELAM AVE, STE 202 27403 #028-03-1992 L1998 **PD** *020 †55

POTTER, Patricia Lynn. 1211 VIRGINIA ST 27401 #036-05-1976 L1976 **AN** *020 †05

POWELL, Alvin Caldwell. 309 NEW ST 27405 #024-07-1982 L1990 **IM NEP** *020 †20

PRATT, Tanya Suzanne. 801 GREEN VALLEY RD, 801 GREEN VALLEY RD 27408 #036-01-1998 L2003 **OBG FM** *020 †18,30

PRESSON, Thomas Lemuel. 1401 BENJAMIN PKWY 27408 #036-01-1965 L1965 **ORS** *071 †40

PRESTON, Helen Music. 301 E WENDOVER AVE STE 310, EAGLE CARDIOLOGY 27401 #020-12-1993 L2000 **CD** *020 †20

PRICE, Thomas Baker. ■ 27408 #036-07-1964 L1964 **GS** *071 †85

PROSE, Claudia Chanlett. 1046 E WENDOVER AVE, GUILFORD CHILD HEALTH 27405 #036-01-1994 L1997 **PD** *020 †55

PUCHAKAYALA, Thanuja Kuma. ■ 27409 #495-62-1999 L2006 **IM** *020 †20

PUDLO, Ronald Jeffery. 510 N ELAM AVE, STE 202 27403 #016-06-1982 L1983 **PD** *020 †55

PULITZER, Donald Richard. 1200 N ELM ST, MOSES H CONE MEM HOSPITAL 27401 #021-05-1977 L1996 **ATP DMP** *020 †50

PURRINGTON, Jacinda Isley. 1309 N ELM ST 27401 #036-01-1995 L1998 **IM** *020

PUZIO, Lawrence Stanley. 510 N ELAM AVE, STE 202 27403 #047-05-1991 L1994 **PD** *020 †55

PYE, Joseph Patrick. ■ 27407 #422-01-2005 **FP** *012

QUINLAN, Aveline F. 3824 N ELM ST, EAGLE PHYS 27455 #010-03-1996 L2000 **PD** *020 †55

RABOLD, Leonard James. ■ 27410 #047-05-1941 L1948 **IM** *071 †20

RAMA, Christina Phyllis. ■ 27455 #036-05-2002 L2004 **IM** *020 †20

RAMACHANDRAN, Ajith. 1511 WESTOVER TER, STE 201 27408 #495-31-1991 L2003 **IM** *020 †20

RAMASUBRAMANIAM, Hamsakum. ■ 27410 #033-05-1996 L2005 **MPD** *020 †20,55

RAMOS, Richard Darren. 1401 BENJAMIN PKWY, GREENSBORO ORTHO 27408 #038-41-1996 L1998 **PM PMM** *020 †60

RANKIN, Gary A. 1204 MAPLE ST 27405 #048-04-1986 L1992 **OPH** *020 †35

RANKINS, Victoria Rogers. 1439 E CONE BLVD 27405 #036-01-1994 L1998 **FM** *020 †18

RANSOM, Carla Elizabeth. ■ 27410 #036-01-2005 **OBG** *012

RANSOM, James Laurence. 801 GREEN VALLEY RD 27408 #036-05-1973 L1973 **NPM PHO** *020 †55

RAY, Danielle Sue. 501 N ELAM AVE 27403 #045-01-1993 L1996 **EM** *020 †16

RAY, Larry Dale. 201 N EUGENE ST 27401 #019-02-1987 L1998 **P** *020 †75

READE, Robert A, Jr. 3511 W MARKET ST, STE A 27403 #051-07-1979 L1985 **FM** *020 †18

READLING, Randy Darene. 2711 PINEDALE RD STE D, GUILFORD DIAG TRTMNT CTR 27408 #036-08-1992 L1993 **P** *020 †75

REDDY, Keshavpal. 3511 W MARKET ST, STE 100 27403 #495-21-1982 L1989 **P CHP** *020 †75

REED, Makeecha Tenale. ■ 27410 #036-05-2006 **FP** *012

REESE, Betti Dejarnette. 5500 W FRIENDLY AVE, STE 201 27410 #038-45-1997 L2001 **FM** *020 †18

REID, Maria Graham. 510 N ELAM AVE, STE 202 27403 #036-01-1997 L1999 **PD** *020 †55

REID, Steven Hunter. 1002 N CHURCH ST, STE 401 27401 #036-07-1985 L1988 **DR** *020 †80

REITNAUER, Pamela Jean. 1200 N ELM ST, PEDIATRIC TEACHING PROGRAM 27401 #036-01-1990 L1992 **PD CG** *020 †19,55

RENDALL, John Lloyd. 300 W NORTHWOOD ST 27401 #036-07-1973 L1973 **ORS** *020 †40

REUTTER, Jason Charles. 706 GREEN VALLEY RD, STE 104 27408 #018-03-1999 L2002 **DMP** *100 †50

REYNOLDS, Michael Leroy. 1126 N CHURCH ST STE 200 27401 #048-02-1996 L2001 **N** *020 †75

REZAI, Reza M. 3824 N ELM ST 27455 #305-01-2004 L2007 **SME FM** *100 †18

RHOADS, Edward John. 522 N ELAM AVE, STE 101 27403 #036-07-1975 L1978 **P PYA** *020 †75

RICHARDSON, Carol Warner. 522 N ELAM AVE, STE 101 27403 #036-08-1982 L1984 **P** *020 †75

RICHARDSON, Kathy Wray. 510 N ELAM AVE, STE 101 27403 #036-01-1996 L2000 **OBG** *020 †30

RICHTER, Karen Lynne. 104 POMONA DR 27407 #036-08-1993 L1995 **FM** *020 †18

RIGGS, Robert J. 2708 HENRY ST 27405 #021-05-1995 L1998 **GS** *020

RITTER, Joseph Geo. 2014 NEW GARDEN RD STE C 27410 #041-12-1956 L1988 **AN GP** *071 ‡

RIVARD, Sandra. 301 E WENDOVER AVE STE 400 27401 #067-06-1989 L1999 **OBG** *020 ‡

ROBERTS, Angela. 301 E WENDOVER AVE, STE 400 27401 #036-01-1999 L2003 **OBG** *020

ROBERTS, Kenneth Barry. 1200 N ELM ST, MOSES CONE MEM HOSP 27401 #023-07-1969 L1997 **PD ID** *040 †55

ROBERTS, Ronald W. 1002 N CHURCH ST, STE 101 27401 #036-01-1977 L1977 **IM** *020 †20

ROBERTSON, Noelle Celine. 1125 N CHURCH ST 27401 #036-01-2002 L2004 **FSM** *020 †18

ROBINSON, Edward N, Jr. 1200 N ELM ST 27401 #036-05-1979 L1988 **ID** *020 †20

ROBINSON, Orlando F. 1200 N ELM ST 27401 #016-42-2001 L2005 **IM** *100

ROBINSON, Stephen Cary. 1200 N ELM ST 27401 #036-07-1967 L1967 **NS** *071 †25

ROBSON, Michael Gavin. 1309 N ELM ST 27401 #067-01-1984 L1993 **IM IMG** *020 †20

ROCHELLE, Young, Jr. ■ 27401 #036-01-1987 *071

ROGERS, Charles Stewart. 1200 N ELM ST, MOSES CONE HOSP 27401 #036-01-1973 L1973 **IM** *040 †20

ROLLINS, Hal Judd, Jr. 8 N POINTE CT 27408 #036-07-1958 L1958 **OPH** *020 †35 ‡

ROMAINE, Cynthia P. 802 GREEN VALLEY RD, STE 200 27408 #036-05-1982 L1986 **OBG** *020 †30

ROMM, Fredric Jay. 2500 SUMMIT AVE 27405 #024-01-1970 L1981 **FM PHP** *040 †70,18

ROSE, George Stevenson, II. 501 N ELAM AVE 27403 #036-05-1998 L2002 **AN** *020 †05

ROSE, Philip David. 801 GREEN VALLEY RD, WOMANS HOSPITAL OF GREENSB 27408 #869-05-1964 L2003 **OBG** *020 †30 ‡

ROSEN, Richard James. 1032 PROFESSIONAL VLG 27401 #010-01-1955 L1965 **IM HO** *071 †20

ROSENBERG, Stanley J. 3625 N ELM ST, STE 110A 27455 #025-01-1968 L1975 **AN** *071 †05

ROSENBLOOM, Alan Abraham. 1910 N CHURCH ST, STE 4 27405 #035-19-1969 L1998 **END IM** *020 †20

ROSENBOWER, Todd James. 1002 N CHURCH ST, CENTRAL CAROLINA SURGERY 27401 #017-20-1991 L1997 **GS** *020 †85

ROSS, Charles Alan. 603 DOLLEY MADISON RD, STE A 27410 #036-01-1987 L1988 **FM** *020 †18

ROSS, Charles Vasil. ■ 27455 #025-07-1953 L1955 **OBG** *071 †30

ROSS, Paula Virginia. 1126 N CHURCH ST 27401 #025-01-1989 L1999 **CD** *020 †20

ROTHBART, Robert Mitchell. 1126 N CHURCH ST 27401 #008-01-1978 L1992 **CD IM** *050 †20

ROWAN, Frank Jos, III. 1915 LENDEW ST, GUILFORD ORTHO & SPORTS ME 27408 #011-03-1981 L1993 **ORS** *020 †40

ROWAND, Mark Baker. ■ 27410 #041-14-2006 L2008 **FP** *012

ROWE, William Thomas. 1511 WESTOVER TER, STE 201 27408 #036-01-1969 L1969 **RHU IM** *020 †20

ROY, Mark Wm. 1130 N CHURCH ST, STE 200 27401 #020-12-1987 L1993 **NS** *020 †25

RUBIN, David Martin. 1124 N CHURCH ST STE 400 27401 #036-01-1968 L1968 **PD** *020 †55

RUBIN, Peter. 501 N ELAM AVE, CENTER 27403 #060-02-1988 L1993 **ON IM** *020 †20

RUIZ, Cesar A. ■ 27410 #737-01-1962 L2005 **GE** *020 †20

RUSKIN, Jerome. 301 E WENDOVER AVE STE 200 27401 #035-46-1960 L1965 **IM CD** *071 †20

RUSSELL, Eugene F, III. 510 N ELAM AVE STE 101 27403 #051-01-1965 L1974 **OBG** *071 †30

RUSSO, John M. 2703 HENRY ST, GUILFORD MEDICAL ASSOCIATE 27405 #035-15-1998 L1999 **IM** *020 †20

SAMSON, Eric Salazar. 1200 N ELM ST 27401 #055-75-2000, ▲ L2004 **IM** *020

SANCHEZ-LUGO, Lizette. ■ 27455 #036-01-1993 **IMG** *100

SANDERS, Robyn Nicholle. 1593 YANCEYVILLE ST, STE 200 27405 #010-03-1997 L2000 **IM** *020 †20

SANDERS, Stephen Brian. 201 N EUGENE ST, GUILFORD CENTER 27401 #036-05-1981 L1985 **P** *020

SASTRY, Sangeeta R. ■ 27405 #496-22-2005 **IM** *012

SCHAAL, Jennifer Carol. ■ 27410 #036-01-1982 L1986 **GYN** *071 †30 ‡

SCHERTZ, Robert Darryl. 309 NEW ST 27405 #016-11-1988 L1990 **NEP IM** *020 †20

SCHILLER, Ernest Lee. 2504 SUMMIT AVE 27405 #047-05-1974 L1977 **PD** *020 †55

SCHOOLER, Vincent Cyril. 1002 N CHURCH ST, STE 2 27401 #036-01-2000 L2003 **GE** *020 †20

SCHUSTER, Stephen Barber. 501 N ELAM AVE 27403 #038-40-1980 L1982 **AN** *020 †05

SCOTT, John Layne. ■ 27455 #036-05-1967 L1967 **DR OS** *071 †28,80

SEGAL, Jeffrey Jonathan. ■ 27410 #048-04-1984 L2000 **NS GS** *071 †25

SENA, Carol Little. 201 N EUGENE ST 27401 #036-01-1981 L1984 **P** *075 †75

SETHI, Pramodkumar. 1126 N CHURCH ST STE 200, MAILING: P O BOX 29568 27401 #495-28-1989 L2004 **N** *020 †75

SETHI, Shashi K. 719 GREEN VALLEY RD, STE 105 27408 #496-07-1965 **OPH OS** *020

SETHI, Shashi Kumar. 719 GREEN VALLEY RD, STE 105 27408 #495-45-1967 L1986 **OPH** *020 †35

SEVIER, Robert English. 2703 HENRY ST, GUILFORD MEDICAL ASSOCIATE 27405 #036-01-1966 L1966 **END IM** *020 †20

SHADAD, Firas N. ■ 27410 #038-43-2000 L2006 **HO** *020 †20

SHAFER, Donald Thornton. 801 GREEN VALLEY RD 27408 #036-05-1974 L1975 **AN** *020 †05

SHARPLESS, Edward Arthur. BOX X3 WESLEY LONG HSP 27402 #036-01-1961 L1961 **PTH** *071 †50

SHARPLESS, Martha K K. ■ 27408 #036-01-1959 L1959 **PD OS** *071 †55

SHAW, Jo Ann. 1200 N ELM ST, MOSES H CONE MEM HOSPITAL 27401 #055-01-1986 L1988 **PTH PCP** *020

SHAW, William Douglas, Jr. 2703 HENRY ST 27405 #036-05-2001 L2003 **IM** *100

SHEA, Michael Patrick. 104 POMONA DR 27407 #016-43-1999 L2000 **FM** *020 †18

SHELBURNE, Palmer Friend. ■ 27408 #036-01-1955 L1955 **CD IM** *071 †20

SHELTON, Kimberly Reenee. 1593 YANCEYVILLE ST, STE 200 27405 #036-01-1994 L1995 **IM** *020 †20

NORTH CAROLINA
GREENSBORO

SHEPHERD, Robert Edward. 1002 N CHURCH ST, STE 401 27401 #036-05-1979 L1980 DR *020 †80

SHERRILL, Gary Bradley. 501 N ELAM AVE, CENTER 27403 #036-01-1989 L1993 HO *020 †20

SHEVITZ, David Mark. 4900 KOGER BLVD, STE 125 27407 #051-04-1987 L2007 EM *020 †16

SHICK, Michael Trevor. 1317 N ELM ST, STE 1B 27401 #045-01-1996 L1998 DR *020 †80

SHIELDS, Thomas Weadock. ■ 27403 #035-20-1996 L1999 EM *020 †16

SHOGRY, Mark Edward. 1002 N CHURCH ST, STE 401 27401 #047-05-1985 L1990 DR RNR *020 †80

SIERADZAN, Aaron Yambor. ■ 27406 #055-01-2007 IM *012

SILLMON, David Wilde. 1511 WESTOVER TER 27408 #036-01-1963 L1963 IM *071

SILWAL, Adwait. ■ 27401 #672-01-2002 *100

SIMEL, Paul Jos. ■ 27410 #024-05-1955 L1961 OPH *071 †35

SIMMONS, Jason Davis. ■ 27408 #036-01-2008 *012

SIMONDS, David Bruce. 520 N ELAM AVE, LEBAUER HEALTHCARE, PA 27403 #036-05-1990 L1997 CCM PUD *020 †20

SINGER, James Danl. 1200 N ELM ST 27401 #036-01-1989 L1990 AN *020 †05

SINGER, James Willard. 1209 MAGNOLIA ST 27401 #038-40-1961 L1966 PD *071 †55

SINGER, Patricia G. 603A DOLLEY MADISON RD 27410 #036-01-1989 L1991 IM *020 †20

SMIR, Bassam N. 1200 N ELM ST, MOSES H CONE MEM HOSPITAL 27401 #575-01-1987 L1999 HMP *020 †50

SMITH, Barbara Ellen. 700 WALTER REED DR 27403 #036-01-1983 L1985 CHP *020 †75

SMITH, Bryan Wesley. 4512 WEYBRIDGE LN, ATLANTIC COAST CONFERENCE 27407 #036-07-1988 L1990 PSM GP *020 †55

SMITH, Candace Thiele. 3511 W MARKET ST, STE A 27403 #020-12-1987 L1988 FM *020 †18

SMITH, Dallas Aaron, Jr. 3801 W MARKET ST 27407 #036-05-1976 L1976 R *020 †80

SMITH, Donald Dewey. 104 E NORTHWOOD ST 27401 #036-07-1960 L1961 PD *071 †55

SMITH, Gregory Edward. 1200 N ELM ST 27401 #056-05-1979 L1981 AN *020 †05

SMITH, Henry W B. 301 E WENDOVER AVE, STE 310 27401 #024-01-1978 L1987 CD *020 †20

SMITH, John Randolph. 301 S ELM ST STE 305-6 27401 #036-08-1995 L1998 P *020

SMITH, Kristi Ann. 104 POMONA DR 27407 #012-22-2002 L2005 FM *020 †18

SMITH, Lynn Kebel. 802 GREEN VALLEY RD, STE 200 27408 #018-03-1984 L1988 GYN *020 †30

SMITH, Mark H. ■ 27410 #011-03-1988 IMG *020

SMITH, Mc Crae Sidney. 801 GREEN VALLEY RD 27408 #036-01-1985 L1987 PD *020 †55

SMITH, Wm Siegfried, Jr. 311 W WENDOVER AVE 27408 #036-07-1961 L1961 GYN *071 †30

SOMMER, Simone S. 1200 N ELM ST 27401 #010-01-1983 L2001 FM *050 †18

SOOD, Vineet. 520 N ELAM AVE 27403 #665-01-1998 L2005 PCC *020 †20

SOOSAIMANICKAM, Seraphine. 1309 N ELM ST, PIEDMONT SENIOR CARE, PLLC 27401 #495-42-2000 L2006 IMG *020 †20

SOUTH, Stephen Alan. 2703 HENRY ST, GUILFORD MEDICAL ASSOCIATE 27405 #036-05-1987 L1992 END IM *020 †20

SPANGLER, Ernest B, Jr. ■ 27410 #041-01-1952 L1959 R *071 †80

SPAULDING, Rebecca Lyn. 300 W NORTHWOOD ST 27401 #020-12-1999 L2001 FM *020 †18

SPENCER, Michael Antonio. 719 GREEN VALLEY RD, STE 303 27408 #010-03-1988 L2001 OPH PO *020 †35

SPIVAK, Kitty. 411 PARKWAY STE J 27401 #869-07-1966 L1975 PM OBG *020

SPLIT, James Frederick. ■ 27455 #025-01-1979 L2006 AN EM *020 †16,05 ‡

SPRUILL, Jerome O. 1307 N ELM ST 27401 #047-07-1979 L1984 CD IM *020

SRODON, Monica. 1200 N ELM ST 27401 #023-01-1999 L2005 PCP *020 †50

STAFFORD, Willie R, Jr. 3803 ROBERT PORCHER WAY 27410 #036-01-1956 L1956 FM OM *020

STAHL, John Allen. 1002 N CHURCH ST, STE 401 27401 #036-07-1991 L1992 DR AR *020 †80

STAHR, Benjamin Jos. 801 GREEN VALLEY RD 27408 #020-12-1981 L1993 DMP PTH *020 †50

STANLEY, Angela Jolene. 1200 N ELM ST, MOSES H CONE MEMORIAL HOSP 27401 #036-01-1986 L1988 PD *020 †55

STARK, Malcolm T, Jr. 520 N ELAM AVE 27403 #035-19-1985 L1992 GE IM *020 †20

STARR, Henry Frank, Jr. ■ 27407 #041-02-1948 L1948 OS GP *071

STEINER, Jane L. 2307 W CONE BLVD, STE 100 27408 #035-48-1978 L1987 P CHP *020 †75

STEINL, Kevin Edward. 501 N ELAM AVE 27403 #025-07-1994 L1998 EM *020 †16

STERN, Joseph David. 1130 N CHURCH ST, # 200 27401 #025-01-1989 L1996 NS *020 †25

STEUTERMAN, Mary C. 706 GREEN VALLEY RD, STE 104 27408 #028-34-1978 L1980 PTH *020 †50

STEVENS, Elliott W, Jr. 1018 N ELM ST 27401 #036-01-1966 L1966 A PUD *071 †03,20 ‡

STIEFEL, Joseph Walter. 1910 N CHURCH ST 27405 #047-06-1958 L1960 N *071 †75

STILES, Dana Dee. 3817 LAWNDALE DR, STE A2 27455 #047-20-1995 L1997 P *020 †75

STINSON, Helen Marie. 1200 N ELM ST 27401 #047-06-1966 L1972 PS *071

STONE, Jennifer Lynn. 1125 N CHURCH ST 27401 #047-20-2004 L2007 FM *020 †18

STONEBURNER, Sara Ellen. 8 N POINTE CT 27408 #036-07-1983 L1991 OPH PD *020 †35

STONECIPHER, Karl Gene. 3312 BATTLEGROUND AVE 27410 #039-01-1986 L1991 OPH *020 †35

STONEKING, Hal Thos. 301 E WENDOVER AVE, STE 200 27401 #012-02-1983 L1984 IMG IM *020 †20

STOREY, Amanda Lara. 1125 N CHURCH ST 27401 #011-04-2002 L2004 FM *100 †18

STRAND, Terry Stanin. 501 N ELAM AVE 27403 #036-01-1994 L1995 IM *020

STRECK, Christian John. 1002 N CHURCH ST, CENTRAL CAROLINA SURGERY 27401 #011-03-1971 L1978 GS *020 †85

STRINGER, Arthur Vernon. 301 E WENDOVER AVE, STE 400 27401 #036-07-1982 L1984 OBG *020 †30

STRINGFIELD, Barry Dean. 204 MANCHESTER PL 27410 #025-12-1975 L1995 IM FM *020 †20

STRONG, John Arthur. 1002 N CHURCH ST, STE 401 27401 #025-12-1988 L1993 DR *020 †80

STROTHER, Eric Furman. 1211 VIRGINIA ST 27401 #048-12-1994 L1999 AN *020 †05

STROUD, Taylor Hamer. 1313 CAROLINA ST 27401 #036-01-2000 L2005 NM *020 †80,28

STUCKEY, Thomas David. 1200 N ELM ST 27401 #038-40-1979 L1981 CD IM *020 †20

SULLIVAN, Corinna Lee. 1200 N ELM ST 27401 #051-07-1997 L2004 IM *020 †20

SULLIVAN, Raymond C, Jr. 1511 WESTOVER TER STE 201, MERRITT MEDICAL PLZ 27408 #011-03-1969 L1974 IM AM *020 †20

SUMMER, Jennifer. 2835 HORSE PEN CREEK RD, STE 101 27401 #035-15-1999 L2000 PD *020 †55

SUMNER, Brian Andrew. 1307 W WENDOVER AVE 27408 #036-05-1998 L2000 PD *020 †55

SUN, Vyvyan Yelin. 3511 W MARKET ST, STE A 27403 #036-01-2001 L2004 FM *020 †18

SUPPLE, Kevin Mark. 1401 BENJAMIN PKWY, GREENSBORO ORTHOPAEDIC CEN 27408 #005-06-1988 L1993 ORS *020 †40

SWARTZ, Zachary Theodore. 510 N ELAM AVE, STE 302 27403 #051-04-1996 L2000 PM *020 †60

SWAYNE, David William. 3511 W MARKET ST, STE A 27403 #036-05-2000 L2001 FM *020 †18

SWORDS, Bruce Henry. 3803 ROBERT PORCHER WAY 27410 #001-02-1992 L1996 IM *020 †20

SYPHER, Robt Van Cleve, Jr. 2718 HENRY ST, THE HAND CENTER OF GREENSB 27405 #035-15-1977 L1983 HS OS *020 †40

SZYPULSKI, Jacek J. 522 N ELAM AVE STE 203 27403 #759-03-1975 L1995 P *071 †75

TAAVON, Richard Jos. 1908 LENDEW ST, WENDOVER OB/GYN & INFERTIL 27408 #023-01-1988 L1996 OBG REN *020 †30

TAFEEN, Stuart Orrin. 1900 ASHWOOD CT 27455 #035-15-1974 L1975 D *020 †15

TALBOT, David Campbell. 1002 S EUGENE ST 27406 #041-01-1989 L1991 IM *020 †20

TALBOT, Kyle Darren. 1317 N ELM ST, STE 1B 27401 #018-03-1999 L2006 DR *020 †80

TALLY, William J. ■ 27410 #021-01-1944 L1996 PUD IM *071 †20

TANG, Yui-Lin Ellen. 501 N ELAM AVE 27403 #244-02-1983 L1990 NPM PD *020 †55

TARASIDIS, Kyriakos. 19 WINDROCK WAY 27455 #012-05-1996 L2001 AN *020

TAYLOR, Gerald Dale. 700 WALTER REED DR 27403 #045-01-1970 L1987 CHP P *020 †75

TAYLOR, Gregg Wm. 1126 N CHURCH ST 27401 #020-01-1991 L1999 CD IM *020 †20

TAYLOR, Jean Gregory. ■ 27408 #036-01-1984 L1985 IM ADL *062 †20

TAYLOR, Melissa Lynn. 2500 SUMMIT AVE, 324 W WENDOVER AVENUE 27405 #422-01-1998 L2004 IM *020 †20 ‡

TENNANT, Stanley Neal. 1002 N CHURCH ST, STE 103 27401 #036-05-1978 L1983 CD IM *020 †20

TEOH, Su Wooi. 1126 N CHURCH ST, PA 27401 #048-12-2000 L2006 OTO *020

TESFAYE, Daniel. ■ 27455 #913-17-1988 L1999 N *020 †75

TESSMANN, Don Steven. 612 PASTEUR DR 27401 #056-05-1976 L1980 P *071

THACKER, Robert Keller. 603 DOLLEY MADISON RD, STE A 27410 #011-03-1973 L1976 FM *020 †18

THIMMAPPA, Sandya. 1317 N ELM ST, STE 4 27401 #051-04-1997 L2002 OPH *020

THOMPSON, Burke E. 1200 N ELM ST 27401 #011-04-1996 L2003 TRS CCS *020 †85

THORNTON, Sharon Longshor. 3107 BRASSFIELD RD, SKIN SURGERY CENTER 27410 #038-40-1999 L2005 D *020 †15

TILLEY, William Spencer, Jr. 1002 N CHURCH ST, STE 202 27401 #036-05-1979 L1985 CD IM *020 †20

TISOVEC, Richard Warren. 2703 HENRY ST 27405 #016-11-1999 L2002 IM *020 †20

TODD, Jeffrey Allen. 3803 ROBERT PORCHER WAY, 3803 ROBERT PORCHER WAY 27410 #038-40-1973 L1974 FM *020 †18

TOMA, Sameh Kamal. 1517 N CHURCH ST 27405 #036-01-1988 L1991 OBG *020 †30

TOMBLIN, James Edward. 1507 WESTOVER TER 27408 #036-01-1986 L1990 OBG *020 †30

TOOKE, Michael T. 1915 LENDEW ST, GUILFORD ORTHOP & SPORTS M 27408 #065-05-1972 L2005 OSS *020 †40 ‡

TOTH, Paul Stephen, III. 1002 N CHURCH ST, CENTRAL CAROLINA SURGERY 27401 #036-05-1996 L2000 GS *020 †85

TOWNSEND, Murphy F, Jr. ■ 27408 #036-05-1961 L1962 IM *071

TRICHE, Jessica Lee. ■ 27410 #036-08-2007 FP *012

TRUESDALE, Gerald Lynn. 2716 HENRY ST 27405 #016-02-1975 L1982 PS HS *020

TRUSLOW, William Worth. 409 PARKWAY, STE A 27401 #036-08-1988 L1991 RHU IM *020 †20

TSUEI, Matthew Kai. 1002 N CHURCH ST, CENTRAL CAROLINA SURGERY 27401 #036-05-1995 L1997 GS *020 †85 ‡

TULLO, Teresa Louise. 1200 N ELM ST, MOSES CONE MEM HOSP 27401 #036-01-2001 L2002 IM *020

TURNER, Traci Rhoderick. 301 E WENDOVER AVE, STE 310 27401 #041-14-1992 L1995 ICE CD *020

TURNER, Wm Harrison, III. 2704 SAINT JUDE ST 27405 #051-04-1968 L1973 D *020 †15

TWISELTON, Louise Ann. 510 N ELAM AVE STE 202, GREENSBORO PEDIATRICIANS, 27403 #036-08-1991 L1995 PD *020 †55

TYSINGER, John Reed. 1511 WESTOVER TER, STE 201 27408 #045-01-1970 L1972 CD IM *020

TYSON, Samuel Lester. 3810 N ELM ST, STE 209 27455 #024-07-1985 L1989 OPH *020 †35

UHL, Mark Winslow. 1200 N ELM ST, MOSES CONE HEALTH SYSTEM 27401 #011-03-1985 L1993 CCP *020 †20

VALCOUR, Rebecca Rugg. 510 N ELAM AVE STE 202, GREENSBORO PEDIATRICIANS I 27403 #050-02-1989 L1996 PD *071 †55

VANSTORY, Madeleine Bell. ■ 27401 #036-08-2005 L2008 FP *012

VAN TRIGT, Peter, III. 2704 HENRY ST, OF GREENSBORO 27405 #021-01-1977 L1980 TS TRS *020 †85,90

VANWINKLE, Robert C. 1307 W WENDOVER AVE 27408 #047-05-2000 L2003 PD *020 †55

VAPNE, Ekaterina. 2835 HORSE PEN CREEK RD, STE 101 27410 #913-15-1991 L2004 PD *020 †55

VARANASI, Jay Srinivas. 301 E WENDOVER AVE, STE 310 27401 #035-06-1999 L2001 IC *020 †20

VAUGHAN, Edwin Warner. ■ 27403 #051-01-1937 L1940 IM *071

VEAZEY, William Burt. 1200 N ELM ST, DEPT RADIOLOGY 27401 #023-07-1990 L1993 R MSR *020 †80 ‡

VERNON, Cheryl Ann. 603 DOLLEY MADISON RD A, GUILFORD CLG WALK IN CLNC 27410 #036-05-1987 L1988 FM *020 †18

VIGLIONE, Cheryl Anne. 3801 W MARKET ST 27407 #041-14-1979 L1982 DR *020 †80

VIYUOH, Adeline Chia. 1200 N ELM ST 27401 #001-02-1996 L2005 IM *020 †20

VOLLMER, Kelly Lynn. 1002 S EUGENE ST 27406 #016-01-1986 L2002 IM *020 †20

VONFANGE, Timothy James. 1126 N CHURCH ST 27401 #017-20-2004 L2006 FSM *012 †18

VOYTEK, Anna. 300 W NORTHWOOD 27401 #035-45-1983 L1984 ORS *020 †40

VULGAROPULOS, Spyro Peter. 1517 N CHURCH ST 27405 #036-01-1988 L1991 OBG *020 †30

WAGNER, Suzanne. 1046 E WENDOVER AVE, GUILDFORD CHILD HEALTH 27405 #040-02-1983 L1986 PD *020 †55

WAINER, Robert Alan. 1130 N CHURCH ST STE 100, SPORTS MEDICINE CENTER 27401 #036-01-1984 L1985 ORS *020 †40

WALD-SCOTT, Coridalia. 1100 REVOLUTION MILL DR 27405 #715-01-1970 L1977 PTH PCP *020 †50

WALL, Thomas Craven. 1126 N CHURCH ST 27401 #036-05-1982 L1984 CD IM *020 †20

WANEK, Elizabeth Ann. 6 N POINTE CT 27408 #030-06-1982 L1989 PDS GS *020 †18

WANG, Hao. 1915 LENDEW ST, STE 200 27408 #243-47-1984 L2003 PM PME *020 †60 ‡

WANGELIN, Robert Lester. 2804 ASBURY TER 27408 #055-01-1972 L2001 P *075 †75

WARD, David Townsend. 1124 N CHURCH ST, CAROLINA BONE & JOINT 27401 #055-01-1986 L2004 ORS *020

WARNER, Pamela Grey. 719 GREEN VALLEY RD, STE 209 27408 #036-08-1996 L1998 PD *020 †55

WATERMAN, Angela Jennings. 301 E WENDOVER AVE STE 200 27401 #036-05-1990 L2001 IM *020 †20

WEATHERLY, Carl H. 510 N ELAM AVE, STE 202 27403 #036-07-1949 L1956 PD OS *020 †55

WEATHERLY, William Jesse. 1002 N CHURCH ST, CENTRAL CAROLINA SURGERY 27401 #036-01-1970 L1970 GS *020 †85

WEBB, Amy Elizabeth. ■ 27403 #036-01-2004 L2007 FM *020 †18

WEINGARTEN, Jerry. ■ 27407 #051-04-1971 L1978 **PTH** *020 †50

WEINGOLD, Matthew Adam. 2718 HENRY ST 27405 #010-01-1989 L1999 **HS** *020 †40

WEINTRAUB, Richard A. 1331 N ELM ST 27401 #010-02-1970 L1976 **CD IM** *020 †20 ‡

WEISS, Joseph Walton. 522 N ELAM AVE STE 2, GUILFORD PSYCHIATRIC ASSOC 27403 #038-43-1977 L1978 **P** *020 †75

WEISSMAN, James Michael. 301 E WENDOVER AVE, STE 200 27401 #016-11-1970 L1977 **GE IM** *020 †20

WELLS, Rheudolph James. 501 N ELAM AVE 27403 #051-04-1956 L1962 **OTO** *071 †45

WENTZ, Elliott Lee. 501 N ELAM AVE 27403 #025-12-1988 L1989 **FM** *020 †18

WERT, Michael Bruce. 520 N ELAM AVE, LEBAUER HEALTHCARE 27403 #047-05-1982 L1988 **PUD IM** *020 †20

WESTERMANN, Carola Jo. 3800 ROBERT PORCHER WAY, STE 200 27410 #008-02-1987 L1996 **FM** *020 †18

WEYMANN, Catherine Ann. 1126 N CHURCH ST, STE 200 27401 #003-01-1986 L1991 **N RNR** *020 †75

WHELAN, Meg Anne. 3201 BRASSFIELD RD STE 200 27410 #035-48-2000 L2005 **AI PD** *020 †55,03

WHITE, Cynthia S. 3511 W MARKET ST, STE A 27403 #025-01-1995 L1996 **FM** *020 †18

WHITE, Wain Luther. 1200 N ELM ST, MOSES H CONE MEM HOSPITAL 27401 #045-01-1972 L1987 **PTH** *020 †50

WHITENER, Robert W. 1024 PROFESSIONAL VLG 27401 #016-06-1954 L1954 **P** *071

WHITFIELD, Bryan Justin. ■ 27408 #010-01-2008 *012

WHITFIELD, Peter White. 300 W NORTHWOOD ST 27401 #010-01-1974 L1980 **ORS** *020 †40

WILLIAMS, Celeste Elena. ■ 27455 #035-20-1990 L1994 **OBG** *020 †30

WILLIAMS, John D, Jr. ■ 27403 #041-13-1930 L1931 **GYN** *071

WILLIAMS, Julie Anne. ■ 27401 #036-05-1994 L1996 **IM** *020 †20

WILLIAMS, Tracy Leigh. 801 GREEN VALLEY RD, WOMEN'S HOSPITAL 27408 #019-02-2003 L2006 **FM** *100 †18

WILLIFORD, James Scott. 1200 N ELM ST, DEPT OF PSYCHIATRY 27401 #036-01-1989 L1990 **P** *020 †75

WILLIS, Charles Keith. 1126 N CHURCH ST, STE 200 27401 #051-01-1984 L1989 **N EM** *020 †75

WILSON, Charles Harrison. 1200 N ELM ST # 1113 27401 #051-04-1973 L1977 **TS VS** *071 †85,90

WILSON, Stanley Clayton. 409 PARKWAY 27401 #038-04-1973 L1974 **FM** *071 †18

WIMMER, John Easter. 801 GREEN VALLEY RD, WOMEN'S HOSPITAL OF GREENS 27408 #051-04-1971 L1981 **NPM** *020 †55

WINTER, Kenneth Howe. 1317 N ELM ST, STE 1B 27401 #036-01-1975 L1976 **DR** *020 †80

WOLFF, George T. 1200 N ELM ST 27401 #041-02-1952 L1952 **FM** *071 †18

WOLTERS, Sharon. 3800 ROBERT PORCHER WAY, EAGLE FAMILY MED 27410 #748-16-1994 L2002 **FM** *020 †18

WOODS, Wayne G. 719 GREEN VALLEY RD, STE 203 27408 #036-01-1977 L1977 **D** *020 †15

WOODY, Rosanna C. 1305 W WENDOVER AVE STE D 27408 #036-05-1998 L1999 **D** *020 ‡

WORLAND, David Eric. 16 OAK BRANCH DR, STE D 27407 #017-20-1974 L1977 **AN** *020

WRENN, Earle L, Jr. ■ 27410 #023-07-1947 L1955 **PDS** *071 †85

WRIGHT, Patrick E, Jr. 520 N ELAM AVE 27403 #047-05-1982 L1995 **PUD CCM** *020 †20

WU, Justin Ja-Li. 501 N ELAM AVE 27403 #036-07-1990 L1995 **RO PD** *020 †80

WYATT, James O, III. 1002 N CHURCH ST, CENTRAL CAROLINA SURGERY 27401 #005-11-1985 L2000 **CRS VS** *020 †85

YAMAGATA, Glenn Takeshi. 1002 N CHURCH ST, STE 401 27401 #035-45-1993 L1998 **VIR DR** *020 †80

YATES, Mark Chas. 300 W NORTHWOOD ST 27401 #028-46-1982 L1988 **ORS** *020 †40

YERRABAPU, Sailaja. ■ 27408 #495-62-2001 **IM** *012

YOUNG, Clinton Driver. 520 N ELAM AVE 27403 #051-01-1974 L1979 **PUD SME** *020 †20 ‡

YOUNG, Jeremy Nathan. 1200 N ELM ST 27401 #665-01-2007 **IM** *012

YOUNG, Kyle Allen. 1317 N ELM ST, STE 1B 27401 #036-05-1969 L1969 **DR** *020 †80,28

YOUNG, Peter Russell. 1002 N CHURCH ST, CENTRAL CAROLINA SURGERY 27401 #012-05-1961 L1962 **GS** *020 †85

YOUNG, Rondall Atlee. 719 GREEN VALLEY RD 27408 #396-06-1983 L1987 **PD** *020 †55

YOUNG, William Oliver. 1305 W WENDOVER AVE STE C 27408 #045-01-1989 L2005 **PO OPH** *020 †35

ZAMMIT, Joseph Luke. 501 N ELAM AVE 27403 #036-05-1986 L1987 **FM EM** *020 †18

ZIEGLER, Brent Christian. ■ 27401 #038-45-2002 L2002 **GS** *012

ZIEMINSKI, John Joseph. 1511 WESTOVER TER, STE 201 27408 #010-01-1971 L1997 **PLI** *020 †20

GREENVILLE – PITT

ABBOTT, Susan Brinkman. 2 DOCTORS PARK, THE BRODY SCHOOL OF MEDICI 27834 #038-40-2002 L2005 **MPD** *100 †20,55

ABDALLAH, Jorge Maria. 855 JOHNS HOPKINS DR, EASTERN ONCOLOGY & HEMATOL 27834 #132-06-1982 L1996 **HEM ON** *020 †20

ABDEL-RAHMAN, Rania. 600 MOYE BLVD, PCMH TA-347 27834 #036-08-2004 L2005 **IM** *100 †20

ABROKWAH, James. ■ 27858 #412-01-1978 L2006 **GS** *100

ACOSTA, Daniel. 600A COUNTRY CLUB DR, SERVICES, PLLC 27834 #028-03-1996 L2001 **P** *020 †75 ‡

ADAM, Amimi Sandra. 2100 STANTONSBURG RD, FAMILY PRACTICE CENTER 27834 #690-02-2001 **FP** *012

ADAMS, Harry Glenn. 600 MOYE BLVD, DEPT OF MED 27834 #048-04-1968 L1984 **ID IM** *040 †20

AGLE, Steven C. ■ 27834 #048-14-2006 **GS** *012

AHMED, Adnan. 2100 STANTONSBURG RD 27834 #704-02-2002 **FP** *012

AHMED, Sagir. 1800 W 5TH ST, STE 2 27834 #160-02-1982 L1996 **CD** *020 †20

ALBERNAZ, Jose Geraldo. ■ 27858 #187-06-1947 L1971 **N NS** *071 †25

ALBERNAZ, Marcus Sailer. 850 JOHNS HOPKINS DR 27834 #038-44-1984 L1989 **OTO FPS** *020 †45

ALEXANDER, Annetta Cheryl. 2100 STANTONSBURG RD 27834 #308-03-2005 **MPD** *012

ALLISON, Ron Russell. 600 MOYE BLVD 27834 #035-08-1987 L2001 **RO** *020 †80

ALLOWAY, Jeff Alexander. 1850 W ARLINGTON BLVD, PHYSICIAN'S EAST, P.A. 27834 #038-41-1985 L1987 **IM** *020 †20

ALMASRI, Ghiath Mohamad. 600 MOYE BLVD 27834 #875-01-1993 L2002 **IM** *020 †20

ALSENTZER, Ulrich Karl. 2100 STANTONSBURG RD 27834 #409-19-1978 L1985 **PM SCI** *071 †60

AMBROSE, Jason Richard. 600 MOYE BLVD, BRODY SCHOOL OF MEDICINE 27834 #036-08-1996 L2003 **FM** *020 †18

AMES, David Anthony. 501 PALADIN DR 27834 #067-01-1968 L1977 **P** *020 †75

ANDERSON, Curtis Austin. ■ 27834 #036-05-1995 L2003 **TS** *100 †85

ANDERSON, Elizabeth S. 2978 NC HIGHWAY 43 N, STE 101 27834 #036-05-1997 L2007 **PD** *020 †55

ANDERSON, Linda C. 600 MOYE BLVD, BRODY BLDG 3E149 27834 #035-03-1989 L1999 **CCM PCC** *020 †20

ANDISH, Kevan Kheyr. 2100 STANTONSBURG RD 27834 #654-01-2007 *012

ANEJA, Arun. ■ 27858 #036-01-2007 *012

ANEJA, Bela Laroia. ■ 27858 #496-07-1982 L1987 **IM** *020 †20

ANTONACCI, Diana Jo. 905 JOHNS HOPKINS DR, DEPT OF PSYCHIATRIC MEDICI 27834 #016-45-1982 L1983 **CHP P** *020 †75

APPERT, Gregory Cameron. 600 MOYE BLVD, BRODY S OF M AT E CAROLINA 27834 #036-08-2006 L2006 **IM** *012

ARANYOS, Judit. 2100 STANTONSBURG RD 27834 #473-03-1998 **PD** *012

ARASTU, Hyder Husain. 600 MOYE BLVD, ECU/BRODY SCHOOL OF MEDICI 27834 #704-02-1977 L1979 **RO** *020

ARCARA, Lynn Kristen. 1850 W ARLINGTON BLVD 27834 #011-02-1995 L1999 **MSR** *020 †80

ARCOT, Anuradha N. 600 MOYE BLVD, DEPT OF PATHOLOGY 27834 #495-65-1988 L2004 **PCP** *100 †50

ARCOT, Narender D. 600 MOYE BLVD, 4N-72 BSOM 27834 #495-65-1986 L2001 **FPG** *012 †18

ARTIS, Isaac Amos, Jr. 80 HOWELL ST 27834 #047-07-1972 L1976 **IM CD** *020

ARUMUGHAM, Pradeep Subram. 1850 W ARLINGTON BLVD 27834 #495-31-1999 L2003 **IM** *020 †20

ASCH, Adam Steven. 600 MOYE BLVD, DIV OF HEAMTOLOGY - ONCOLO 27834 #041-02-1979 L2006 **HEM IM** *020 †20 ‡

ATKINSON, Saml Marvin, Jr. 600 MOYE BLVD, EAST CAROLINA UNIV 27834 #036-07-1961 L1961 **GYN** *040 †30

ATORUDIBO, Yvonne Ibifuro. ■ 27834 #036-08-2008 *012

ATTIAH, Nadir Monir. 2100 STANTONSBURG RD, DOCTORS PARK 1-A 27834 #915-04-2008 **P** *012

AUSTIN, Laura Mclemore. ■ 27834 #036-08-2008 *012

AUSTIN, Trevor Clark. ■ 27834 #036-08-2008 *012

AVERY, Scott Robt. 101 BETHESDA DR, DIV OF PHYSICIANS EAST, P. 27834 #039-01-1990 L1994 **OBG** *020 †30

AWAN, Obaid Ur Rehman. 2100 STANTONSBURG RD 27834 #704-01-2005 **FP** *012

AYALA BUSTAMANTE, Everick. 2100 STANTONSBURG RD, PITT CO MEM HOSP 27834 #737-06-2001 **IM** *100

BABB, Joseph Dolby. 2100 STANTONSBURG RD 27834 #023-07-1966 L1995 **IC CD** *040 †20

BAINES, Torrey. 1850 W ARLINGTON BLVD 27834 #011-02-2001 L2005 **CCP** *012 †20,55

BAKAJ, Gentiana. 2100 STANTONSBURG RD 27834 #422-01-2007 **IM** *012

BALDREE, Louanne. ■ 27834 #036-08-1985 L1986 **PN** *020 †55

BALDWIN, Joy Angela. 261 BELVOIR HWY, COMMUNITY HLTH CTR 27834 #050-02-2004 L2007 **FM** *020 †18

BALLANCE, William A, Jr. 600 MOYE BLVD 27834 #036-08-1984 L1987 **PTH PCP** *020 †50

BANE, Susan Marie. 101 BETHESDA DR 27834 #016-11-1997 L2001 **OBG** *020 †30

BARCHMAN, Mary Jane. 2355 W ARLINGTON BLVD, ECU PHYS & NEPH & HYPER 27834 #038-44-1985 L1995 **NEP IM** *020 †20

BARD, Michael Richard. 600 MOYE BLVD, BRODY SCHOOL OF MEDICINE 27834 #041-02-1995 L2001 **CCS** *020 †20

BARKER, Cynthia D Peebles. 2160 HERBERT CT, ECU WOMENS PHYSICIANS 27834 #036-05-1986 L1990 **OBG** *020 †30

BARONDES, Michael J. 301 BOWMAN GRAY DR 27834 #024-05-1983 L1996 **OPH** *020 †35

BARRIER, Charles Harold. 1850 W ARLINGTON BLVD, PHYSICIANS E PA 27834 #036-01-1979 L1980 **GE** *020 †20

BARSANTI, Christopher M. 810 WH SMITH BLVD 27834 #051-01-1985 L1991 **ORS** *020 †40

BARTLETT, Edwin Clary. 810 WH SMITH BLVD 27834 #036-01-1978 L1981 **ORS OSM** *020 †40

BARTLETT, Stephen R. ■ 27858 #036-07-1943 L1950 **GS** *071

BASILI, Richard Louis, Jr. 2080 W ARLINGTON BLVD # B, ASSOCIATESPA 27834 #036-08-1993 L2007 **AN** *020 †05

BASNIGHT, Lynda Lorraine. 600 MOYE BLVD, BRODY SCHOOL OF MEDICINE 27834 #031-01-1990 L1995 **PD** *020 †55

BASS, Andora Lynn. 600 MOYE BLVD, BRODY SCHOOL OF MEDICINE 27834 #036-08-1999 L2006 **CCP** *100 †20,55

BAUER, Robert. 301 BOWMAN GRAY DR 27834 #016-11-1998 L2006 **OPH** *020 †35

BELLIN, Lisa Sheri. 600 MOYE BLVD, BRODY 4S-22 27834 #041-02-1993 L2005 **GS SO** *020 †85

BENNETT, Jennifer Millice. ■ 27858 #036-08-2006 **IM** *012

BENNETT, Jeremy Jon. ■ 27834 #019-02-2005 L2007 **EM** *012

BENSON, Nicholas Herod. 600 MOYE BLVD, BRODY SCHOOL OF MEDICINE 27834 #046-01-1980 L1983 **EM** *030 †16

BERNARD, Bradley Charles. ■ 27858 #016-45-2006 **EM** *012

BERRY, Todd Matthew. ■ 27834 #036-08-2008 *012

BEST, Andrew A. 2100 STANTONSBURG RD 27834 #047-07-1951 L1953 **FM** *071

BIDGOLI, Arash. ■ 27834 #048-78-2016, ▲ L2008 **PM** *012

BIGGERSTAFF, Michael A. 2430 EMERALD PL STE 201, EAST CAROLINA ANESTHESIA A 27834 #045-01-1983 L1990 **AN** *020 †05

BIJELAC, Marica. ■ 27858 #957-08-1987 **P** *012

BLACKHAM, Jason Lee. ■ 27858 #049-01-2003 L2003 **FSM** *100 †20

BLACKMON, Floriece M G. 1850 W ARLINGTON BLVD 27834 #036-01-1982 L1986 **DR** *020 †80

BLANCH, Tanya Malka. 2100 STANTONSBURG RD 27834 #654-01-2006 **IM** *012

BLUMENTHAL, Amy Lee. 2251 STANTONSBURG RD 27834 #036-08-2000 L2004 **OBG** *020 ‡

BODEA, Marioara. 2100 STANTONSBURG RD 27834 #781-05-1995 L2006 **PM** *020

BOGEY, William M, Jr. 600 MOYE BLVD 27834 #036-08-1984 L1988 **VS** *040 †85

BOGHOSSIAN, Van. ■ 27858 #875-02-1995 L2007 **OS** *100

BOLIN, Paul, Jr. 600 MOYE BLVD 27834 #036-01-1984 L1989 **NEP IM** *020 †20

BONOMO, Steven Robert. 1850 W ARLINGTON BLVD 27834 #035-46-1994 L2007 **GS** *020 †85

BOSWELL, Elizabeth Kathle. 2100 STANTONSBURG RD 27834 #305-01-2005 **OBG** *012

BOURNE, Christina Lynn. DEPT EMERGENCY MEDICINE, BRODY SCHOOL AT EDU 27834 #041-12-1996 L2001 **EM** *020 †16

BOUTILIER, Susan B. 2100 STANTONSBURG RD 27834 #005-19-1993 L1997 **CHN** *020 †75,55

BOWER, Curtis Edward. 600 MOYE BLVD, ECU DEPT OF SURGERY 27834 #041-02-2000 L2003 **GS** *020 †85

BOWYER, Allen Frank. ■ 27858 #005-12-1959 L1978 **CD OS** *071

BOYETTE, Deanna Marie. 810 WH SMITH BLVD 27834 #036-08-1988 L1994 **ORS** *020 †40

BRAY, Emily L Schrock. 1705 W 6TH ST, QUAD C 27834 #016-11-1974 L1997 **FM FPG** *040 †18
BRECHTELSBAUER, Paul B. 850 JOHNS HOPKINS DR 27834 #036-01-1991 L1992 **OTO** *020 †45
BREMER, Chas Christopher. 600 MOYE BLVD 27834 #036-07-1964 L1964 **FM** *071 †18
BRESCIA, Donald Michael. 2100 STANTONSBURG RD 27834 #033-06-1996 L1999 **PCC** *012 †20
BRESTEL, Eric Paul. 1150 E ARLINGTON BLVD 27858 #011-03-1972 L1987 **A RHU** *020 †20,03
BREUER, Anthony Carl. 2280 HEMBY LN 27834 #024-01-1970 L1997 **N IM** *020 †20,75
BREZINA, Paul Robert. ■ 27834 #036-08-2004 L2005 **OBG** *012
BRIGHT, Don Clark. 2430 EMERALD PL, # 201 27834 #036-01-1971 L1971 **AN** *020 †05
BRILEY, Laura Dennison. ■ 27858 #036-08-2005 L2005 **D** *012
BRILLANT, Patrick T. 1850 W ARLINGTON BLVD 27834 #011-02-1988 L2003 **CRS** *020 †85,10
BRINN, Melissa Chardos. 600 MOYE BLVD 27834 #047-06-2001 L2004 **PD** *020 †55
BRITT, Keith Anthony. 908 BREMERTON DR 27858 #036-08-1986 L1996 **FM** *020 †18
BRODISH, Brian Nathaniel. 8 DOCTORS PARK, THROAT, HEAD & NECK SURGER 27834 #036-05-1994 L2000 **OTO HNS** *020 †45
BROOKS, Clyde L, Jr. 690 MEDICAL DR 27834 #036-01-1985 L1988 **IM** *030 †20
BROOKS, John Howard. ■ 27858 #036-08-2002 L2007 **CD** *012
BROWN, Charles Kevin. 600 MOYE BLVD, BRODY SCHOOL OF MEDICINE 27834 #051-04-1981 L1982 **EM** *040 †16
BROWN, Edward Charles, III. 810 WH SMITH BLVD 27834 #036-01-1993 L1998 **OAR** *020 †40
BROWN, William Edward. 1850 W ARLINGTON BLVD 27834 #036-08-1981 L1982 **OBG FM** *075 †18,30
BRYANT, Dwayne Gregory. 2577 W 5TH ST, WALTER B JONES TREATMENT C 27834 #047-07-1992 L1998 **IM P** *020
BUCKMAN, Francis Evans. 600 MOYE BLVD, ECU SCHOOL OF MEDICINE 27834 #412-01-1994 L2005 **FM** *100 †18
BUCKNER, Kori Lynn. ■ 27834 #036-08-2008 *012
BUCKWALD, Sharon. 600 MOYE BLVD 27834 #035-19-1974 L2003 **NPM PD** *050 †55
BULLARD, Crystal Rose. ■ 27834 #036-08-2008 *012
BUNN, Barry Duke. 600 MOYE BLVD 27834 #036-08-1995 L1996 **EM** *020 †16
BURGESS, Russell Earle. 600 MOYE BLVD 27834 #036-05-1974 L1974 **ON HEM** *020 †20
BURKE, Lillian Patricia. 600 MOYE BLVD, LEO JENKINS CANCER CTR 27834 #026-04-1979 L2002 **IM HO** *020 †20
BURKE, William Allen. 600 MOYE BLVD, E 117. 27834 #036-08-1982 L1983 **D** *020 †15
BURLINGHAM, Byron Thos. 2100 STANTONSBURG RD, DEPT MICROBIOLOGY 27834 #018-03-1966 **ID MM** *040
BUSHER, Janice Therese. 2210 HEMBY LN, STE 101 27834 #033-05-1979 L1986 **IM** *040 †20
BUTLER, Dorothy Wolf. 600 MOYE BLVD 27834 #048-14-1990 L1991 **GYN OBG** *040 †18,30 ‡
BYRD, James Christopher. ■ 27834 #026-04-1978 L1995 **IM** *040 †20
BYRUM, Graham Vance, Jr. 511 PALADIN DR, EASTERN NEPHROLOGY ASSOCIA 27834 #036-05-1980 L1985 **NEP IM** *020 †20
CABARRUS, Brian Ray. ■ 27834 #036-08-2001 L2006 **IC** *012 †20
CABINUM-FOELLER, Elaine. 600 MOYE BLVD, ECU BRODY SCHOOL OF MEDICI 27834 #036-08-1995 L2000 **PD** *040 †55
CAIN, Kressida Tirea. ■ 27834 #001-06-2002 L2007 **PTH** *100
CALHOUN, Rebecca Anne. 600 MOYE BLVD, DEPT OF EMERGENCY MEDICINE 27834 #036-08-2003 L2007 **EM** *020
CAMNITZ, Paul Samuel. 850 JOHNS HOPKINS DR, POB # 5007 27834 #036-01-1974 L1974, OTO FPS *020 †45
CAMPBELL, Diane J. 704 WH SMITH BLVD, STE B 27834 #047-07-1977 L1985 **OBG** *020 †30
CANIPE, Michelle Leigh. ■ 27834 #036-08-2008 *012
CAO, Qing. ■ 27858 #243-65-1991 **FP** *012
CAPSAVAGE, John Adam, Jr. 2355 W ARLINGTON BLVD, ECU SCHOOL OF MEDICINE 27834 #035-03-1966 L1996 **NEP IM** *071 †20
CARDEN, Andres Scott. 2100 STANTONSBURG RD, PITT COUNTY MEMORIAL HOSP 27834 #305-01-2002 L2005 **HO** *012 †20
CARLSON, Eric Barnett. 2090 W ARLINGTON BLVD # A, EASTERN CARDIOLOGY PA 27834 #041-09-1980 L1983 **CD IM** *020 †20
CARPENTER, Robin Claire. ■ 27834 #027-01-2003 L2003 **GS** *012
CARRAWAY, Holly Alisha. ■ 27858 #036-08-2007 *012
CARRILERO, Luis Pablo. ■ 27834 #132-01-1990 **PM** *100
CARRION, Monica Jeanett. 600 MOYE BLVD, DEPT OF PM & R 27834 #715-01-1995 L2005 **PM** *020 †60 ‡
CARRIZO, Laura Elda. 2100 STANTONSBURG RD, DEPT MED 27834 #132-02-1989 **IM** *012
CARTER, James Walter. 605 MILL RUN RD 27834 #023-07-1964 L1972 **GS TS** *030 †85,90
CARTER, Kelly Anne. ■ 27834 #056-05-2005 L2007 **EM** *012
CASCIO, Wayne Eugene. 2100 STANTONSBURG RD 27834 #023-01-1980 L1982 **CD IM** *030 †20
CATROU, Paul Gregoire. 600 MOYE BLVD, BRODY SCH MED AT ECU 27834 #021-01-1974 L1990 **CLP PCH** *020 †50
CEDARS, Joan Adelia. ■ 27858 #036-08-1991 L1996 **PTH** *020 †50
CERVI, Mark Richard. 2460 EMERALD PL 27834 #422-01-1988 L1991 **IM** *020
CHANGAPPA, Sunny B. 2100 STANTONSBURG RD, DEPT OF INTERNAL MEDICINE 27834 #036-08-2005 **IM** *012
CHAPLINSKI, Thomas Jos. 1850 W ARLINGTON BLVD 27834 #016-02-1977 L1981 **ON HEM** *020 †20
CHAPMAN, William H H, III. 600 MOYE BLVD, ECU DEPT OF SURGERY 27834 #032-01-1987 L1994 **GS** *020 †85
CHIA, Prudence Ngoin. 2100 STANTONSBURG RD, DIV OF GENERAL IM 27834 #047-06-2004 **MPD** *012
CHILDS, Carter J. 600 MOYE BLVD, ECU BSOM 27834 #036-05-1994 L1996 **CCM** *020 †20
CHITWOOD, Walter R, Jr. 600 MOYE BLVD, PCMH TA 277 27834 #051-01-1974 L1983 **TS GS** *040 †85,90
CHIU, Stephen Kun. ■ 27858 #051-04-2006 **IM** *012
CHOWDHARY, Rasheel Akbar. 2100 STANTONSBURG RD, DEPT MED 27834 #704-30-2001 **IM** *012
CHRISTIANO, Anthony J, Jr. 850 WH SMITH BLVD 27834 #036-05-1987 L1994 **CD** *020 †20
CHRISTIANO, Cynthia Rae. 600 MOYE BLVD 27834 #036-08-1997 L1998 **NEP** *020 †20
CHRISTIE, John Doyle. 600 MOYE BLVD 27834 #048-02-1982 L1989 **PTH** *020 †50
CHU, Fan. 600 MOYE BLVD - LSB248, THE BRODY SCHOOL OF MEDICI 27834 #067-01-1995 L2001 *100
CHUNG, Arlene Eunhee. ■ 27834 #036-08-2005 **MPD** *012
CICHON, Martin Peter. ■ 27858 #759-18-2003 L2007 **FM** *100 †18
CLARK, Adam Nathaniel. 850 WH SMITH BLVD 27834 #035-46-1997 L2007 **ICE** *020 †20
CLARK, Brian Mullin. 600 MOYE BLVD, ECU BRODY SCHOOL OF MEDICI 27834 #050-02-1994 L2001 **OBG** *020 †30

CLAY, Thomas Howard. 600 MOYE BLVD 27834 #036-01-1979 L1985 **CHP P** *072
CLAYDON, Crisanta Sage. 600 MOYE BLVD, PCMH TA-164 27834 #051-04-1997 L2004 **OBG** *020
CLEMENT, James Edwin. ■ 27858 #036-07-1954 L1955 **GYN** *020 †30
CLEMENT, Phillip Arthur. 600 MOYE BLVD 27834 #036-05-1992 L1998 **EM** *020 †16
COLLIER, David Nash. 600 MOYE BLVD 27834 #036-08-2001 L2004 **PD** *020 †55
COOK, Fiona Jackson. 600 MOYE BLVD, BRODY SCHOOL OF MEDICINE 27834 #036-07-1984 L1988 **END** *020 †20
COOK, Paul Peniston. 600 MOYE BLVD, BRODY 3E-113 27834 #012-01-1982 L1984 **ID IM** *040 †20
COOK, Richard Chung-Sop. 600 MOYE BLVD, EAST CAROLINA UNIVERSITY 27834 #060-01-1992 L2004 *020
COOK-NOBLE, Cathleen Mari. 600 MOYE BLVD, # 3E139 27834 #041-14-2007 **PD** *012
COOPER, James Bryan. 2280 HEMBY LN 27834 #036-08-2000 L2004 **N** *020 †75
COSTA, Christopher Charle. 3422 WESTGATE DR 27834 #308-13-1998 L2004 **IM** *020
COSTA, Nadiesda Almanzar. 600 MOYE BLVD RM 340 27834 #308-01-1998 L2005 **NEP** *012 †20
COULTER, Norman A. ■ 27858 #024-01-1950 **OS** *071
COURTNEY, Christine A. ■ 27834 #035-15-2003 L2006 **EM** *100 †16
COWAN, Lisa Renee. ■ 27834 #036-08-2007 **EM** *012
COX, Robert Wayne. 1913 E FIRE TOWER RD, STE E 27858 #064-01-1987 L1996 **FM** *012
COYLE, Michael Patrick. 1204 E FIRE TOWER RD, FIRETOWER MEDICAL OFFICE 27858 #038-45-1984 L1995 **PD IM** *020 †55,20 ‡
CRISP, Sellers Luther. 622 MEDICAL DR 27834 #036-01-1960 L1960 **ORS** *071 †40
CROSKERY, Richard Wm. 1850 W ARLINGTON BLVD 27834 #038-40-1981 L1983 **IM** *020 †20
CROWDER, Cherrie Mae. ■ 27834 #036-08-2008 *012
CUELLAR, Jacob Gonzales. ■ 27834 #036-08-2008 *012
CULBERTSON, Amy Lyn. 2100 STANTONSBURG RD 27834 #305-01-2004 L2008 **PM** *012
CUMMINGS, James John. 600 MOYE BLVD, DEPARTMENT OF PEDIATRICS 27834 #035-15-1982 L1998 **NPM PD** *020 †55
CUMMINGS, Kris Baker. ■ 27858 #036-08-2004 L2006 **IM** *020
CUMMINGS, Matthew Shea. ■ 27834 #036-08-2004 L2007 **IM** *100 †20
DAESCHNER, Charles Wm, III. 600 MOYE BLVD 27834 #048-02-1976 L1990 **PD** *020 †55
DALY, Claudia Hauck. 600 MOYE BLVD 27834 #036-08-2001 L2002 **FM** *020 †18
DALZELL, William A, IV. 600 MOYE BLVD, PCMH TA-260 27834 #055-01-1984 L2004 **PDI** *020 †55
DANIEL, Myriam Mariejude. 1006C WH SMITH BLVD, CENTER 27834 #035-06-1989 L1994 **IM** *020 †20
DASH, Aruna. ■ 27858 #496-05-1991 **PTH** *012
DASNADI MBBS, Shaeequa Pa. 2100 STANTONSBURG RD, DIV OF PEDIATRICS 27834 #495-99-2003 **PD** *012
DAUGHERTY, Janice Elaine. 600 MOYE BLVD, BRODY 4N-78 FAM MED 27834 #036-05-1978 L1981 **FM FMG** *020 †20
DAVID, Giovanni Paolo Gos. ■ 27834 #748-10-2002 **GS** *100
DAVIS, Donald Fales. ■ 27858 #036-05-1955 L1955 **P** *072
DAVIS, Drew Edward. ■ 27834 #036-08-2008 *012
DAVIS, George Edward. 600 MOYE BLVD 27834 #047-06-1970 L1975 **PD** *020 †55
DAVIS, Gregory Brant. 2430 EMERALD PL, STE 201 27834 #012-05-1998 L2002 **AN** *020 †05 ‡
DAVIS, John Brently. ■ 27858 #051-07-2005 **PTH** *012
DAWKINS, Howard G, Jr. 2577 STANTONSBURG RD 27834 #036-05-1968 L1968 **CS PS** *020 †65 ‡
DAWSON, William Sidney. 1701 E 14TH ST 27858 #051-04-1961 L1962 **GP** *020 †18 ‡
DE BECK, Thomas Wade. 2280 HEMBY LN 27834 #023-01-1964 L1979 **SME N** *020 †75
DEFREITAS, Dorian Joseph. 2593 THACKERY RD 27834 #539-05-2001 L2005 **IM** *012
DE GROOT, Christopher M. 1001 E 4TH ST DEPT PSYCH, BRODY MED SCI BLDG # 4E-67 27858 #038-40-1987 L1997 **P** *020 †75 ‡
DELBRIDGE, Theodore R. 600 MOYE BLVD, DEPT OF EMGY MED 3ED-313 27834 #051-07-1989 L2006 **EM** *020 †16
DELLASEGA, Mark. 1850 W ARLINGTON BLVD 27834 #019-02-1975 L1981 **GE IM** *020 †20
DELUCA, Christina Joanne. ■ 27834 #036-08-2006 **OBG** *012
DENNISON, Whitney Jo. ■ 27834 #055-02-2004 **CHP** *012
DEVENTE, James Edward. 2160 HERBERT CT 27834 #036-08-2001 L2005 **OBG** *100 †30
DEWOLFE, Melissa Ann. ■ 27858 #041-77-2007, ▲ **GS** *012
DEYTON, Robert Guy, Jr. 101 BETHESDA DR 27834 #036-07-1955 L1955 **GYN** *071 †30
DIAMOND, John M. 600 MOYE BLVD, BRODY SCHOOL OF MED AT ECU 27834 #010-03-1979 L1984 **CHP P** *040 †75 ‡
DIAMOND, Michael Simpson. ■ 27834 #036-08-2008 *012
DICK, Jewel Stoneman. ■ 27858 #047-07-1983 **P** *071
DIETRICH, Robert Anthony. 1850 W ARLINGTON BLVD 27834 #010-01-1980 L1991 **PUD** *020 †20
DILL, Heather Renee. 2100 STANTONSBURG RD, DEPT OF PEDIATRICS 27834 #036-08-2005 L2008 **PD** *012
DOBBS, Larry Joe, Jr. 600 MOYE BLVD 27834 #019-02-1989 L1998 **PTH** *020 †50
DOHERTY, Lisa Leonhardt. 600 MOYE BLVD, ECU FAMILY PRACTICE 27834 #036-08-2004 L2005 **FM** *100 †18
DOMBROSKI, Raymond A. 600 MOYE BLVD 27834 #051-01-1978 L1982 **OBG** *020 †30
DOMBY, Brian Christopher. ■ 27834 #036-08-2008 *012
DORMAN, Deidre Rose. 1001 W 5TH ST, EAST CAROLINA UNIVERSITY 27834 #017-20-2002 L2006 **FM** *020 †18
DOUGLAS, Edgar Smith, Jr. 204 HAMPTON CIR, BROOKVALLEY SUBD 27858 #051-04-1961 L1964 **OBG** *071 †30
DOWLING, Marie Ann. ■ 27834 #017-20-2007 **EM** *012
DRAKE, Almond J, III. 600 MOYE BLVD, ENDOCRINOLOGY DIVISION 27834 #036-07-1983 L1984 **IM END** *020 †20
DRAUGHON, Johnson Puett, Jr. 208 S ELM ST 27858 #036-08-1996 L1998 **FM** *020 †18
DUBOSE, Jon D. 1850 W ARLINGTON BLVD, PHYSICIANS EAST, PA 27834 #045-04-1999 L2001 **MPD** *020 †20,55
DUKE, Josiah William. 810 WH SMITH BLVD 27834 #051-04-1994 L2002 **ORS** *020 †40
DUNCAN, Robert Auldon. 2430 EMERALD PL, STE 201 27834 #012-05-1992 L2000 **AN** *020 †05
DUNHAM, Charles Kendrick. ■ 27834 #036-08-2003 L2005 **MP** *012
DUNHAM, Mayisha White. ■ 27834 #036-08-2004 L2008 **PM** *012
EARLY, Jacquelyn Ann. 2100 STANTONSBURG RD 27834 #038-44-2004 L2007 **EM** *020
EASTERBROOK, James S. 402 BOWMAN GRAY DR 27834 #048-04-1973 L1990 **DR** *020 †80
EDRALIN, Lenard Joseph. 2100 STANTONSBURG RD 27834 #654-01-2005 **PD** *012
EHINGER, Robert Frederick. ■ 27858 #035-45-1947 L1978 **PHP PD** *071 †70

■ = Address Information Privacy Protected

EILEN, Dana Joel. ■ 27858 #820-02-2006 IM *012
EJAZ, Sohail. ■ 27834 #704-01-1994 L2005 NEP *020 †20
ELBEERY, Joseph Raymond. 600 MOYE BLVD, BRODY SCHOOL OF MEDICINE 27834 #010-02-1985 L1992 TS CD *020 †85,90
ELLIS, Thomas Jos. 1204 E FIRE TOWER RD 27858 #036-08-1992 L1994 FM *020 †18
ELMERGAWI, Mohammed. 600 MOYE BLVD 27834 #915-04-2006 GS *012
ENGELKE, Stephen Carl. 600 MOYE BLVD 27834 #023-07-1974 L1979 NPM PD *020 †55
ENGSTROM, Elana Lusk. ■ 27858 #036-08-2008 *012
ESHELMAN, Curtis James. 600 MOYE BLVD 27834 #025-01-1971 L1975 FM *020 †18
EVANS, Amos Ray. 1705 W 6TH ST, STE H 27834 #036-01-1962 L1962 P *071
FADEYI, Emmanuel Adegoke. 600 MOYE BLVD 7S-10, BRODY SCHOOL OF MEDICINE D 27834 #305-01-1999 L2007 BBK *012
FADIA, Toral Madanmohan. 2215 LOCKSLEY WOODS DR 27858 #422-01-2000 L2005 CHP *100 †75
FAGUNDUS, Duncan Mcleod. 1850 W ARLINGTON BLVD 27834 #036-08-1988 L1990 RHU MPD *020 †20,55
FAIRBROTHER, David Lovell. 2 DOCTORS PARK, ECU PEDIATRIC CARDIOLOGY 27834 #036-08-1997 L1998 PDC PD *020 †55
FALGE, Robert Newton. 800 MOYE BLVD STE 200, CLINIC 27834 #017-20-1984 L2000 FM *020 †18
FARRAR, Robert Allen, Jr. ■ 27858 #051-01-2003 L2007 PTH *100
FAULK, Clinton Edwin. 600 MOYE BLVD, EAST CAROLINA UNIVERSITY B 27834 #665-02-2001 L2004 PM *100 †60
FEARRINGTON, Eric Lindsay. 2 MEDICAL PAVILION, W 5TH ST 27834 #036-01-1957 L1957 CD IM *071 †20
FERGUSON, Alfred Lea. 1031 E ROCK SPRING RD, PITT INTRNL & RENAL MED AS 27858 #047-06-1961 L1966 NEP IM *071
FERGUSON, Jeffrey Dean. ■ 27858 #051-01-2002 L2007 EM *020 †16
FERGUSON, Jennifer. 2450 EMERALD PL, CAROLINA WOMEN'S PHYSICIAN 27834 #048-15-1992 L1997 OBG *020 †30
FERGUSON, T Bruce, Jr. 27834 #028-02-1979 L1987 TS *020 †85,90
FERGUSON, Thomas B. 600 MOYE BLVD, ECU BRODY SCHOOL OF MEDICI 27834 #036-07-1947 L1950 CD TS *020 †85,90
FIGUEROA, Elizabeth. BRODY 3E 139E 27858 #035-09-1982 L2001 PD *020 †55
FINESTONE, Douglas Howard. 1705 W 6TH ST STE H 27834 #051-04-1979 L1981 P PYA *020 †75 ‡
FINLEY, James Leo. 600 MOYE BLVD, ECU BRODY SCHOOL OF MEDICI 27834 #041-07-1978 L1983 PTH PCP *020 †50
FIORDALISI, Irma. 600 MOYE BLVD 27834 #035-08-1978 L1991 PD CCM *040 †55
FIRNHABER, Jonathon Mark. 600 MOYE BLVD, FAMILY MEDICINE CENTER 27834 #007-02-1990 L1996 FM *040 †18
FISH, Laura Renee. 600 MOYE BLVD 27834 #036-08-2006 L2007 EM *012
FISH, Robert Ray. ■ 27858 #036-08-2008 *012
FISHER, Harriett Paige. 2251 STANTONSBURG RD, PHYSICIANS EAST, P.A. 27834 #036-08-1995 L1997 OBG *020 †30
FISHER, Maxwell Ellis. 511 PALADIN DR 27834 #036-01-1998 L2004 NEP *020 †20
FLEMING, Duard F, Jr. 402 BOWMAN GRAY DR 27834 #036-05-1972 L1973 N IM *020 †20
FLYNN, Jessica Weeks. ■ 27834 #036-08-2008 *012
FLYNN, Ruth Caynap. 600 MOYE BLVD 27834 #748-10-1996 L2003 P *020
FOGARTY, John. 1850 W ARLINGTON BLVD 27834 #422-01-1987 L1994 PUD CCM *020 †20
FOLEY, William Sudduth, III. 600 MOYE BLVD 27834 #020-12-1998 L2002 MPD *020 †20
FONTANA, Umberto Gaetano. 850 WH SMITH BLVD 27834 #051-04-1987 L1994 CD *020 †20
FOREMAN, Susan Downer. 925 CONFERENCE DR, SOUTH CHARLES PROFESSIONAL 27858 #036-01-1978 L1979 PD *020 †55
FOUNTAIN, Raetta Bevan. 2465 EMERALD PL, ATLANTIC GASTROENTEROLOGY 27834 #001-02-1992 L2006 GE IM *020 †20
FRANCKE, Eric Ivars. ■ 27834 #036-01-2000 L2007 OSS *100
FRANK, Anthony Jon, Jr. 2100 STANTONSBURG RD 27834 #051-07-1994 L1997 EM *020 †16
FRANKLIN, Joseph Andrew. 400 SPRING FOREST RD 27834 #036-08-1997 L2003 PS *020 †85
FRAZIER, David Worth. 2340 HEMBY LN, STE 100 27834 #036-07-1988 L1989 ICE CD *020 †20
FREDERICK, Andre Dean. 600 MOYE BLVD, PCMH-TA RM 340 27834 #036-08-2005 L2007 IM *012
FRELIX, Gloria Dolores. 600 MOYE BLVD, LEO W. JENKINS CANCER CENT 27834 #047-07-1976 L1980 RO *020
FRERE, Robert Carroll. 2280 HEMBY LN 27834 #038-40-1984 L2000 N CN *020 †75
FREUND, William Lee, Jr. ■ 27834 #019-02-2002 GS *012
FRY, Elizabeth Powell. 1850 W ARLINGTON BLVD 27834 #048-04-1996 L2007 FP *012
GAGNON, Gregory Arthur. 600 MOYE BLVD 27834 #021-05-1982 L1989 PTH *020 †50
GAMMON, Walter Ray. 420 SPRING FOREST RD 27834 #036-01-1971 L1971 D IM *020 †20,15
GARRISON, Herbert Gaston. 600 MOYE BLVD 27834 #036-01-1986 L1988 EM GPM *020 †16
GARRISON, Judie Lynn. 400 SPRING FOREST RD, GREENVILLE PLASTIC SURGERY 27834 #036-01-1986 L1995 PS *020 †85,65
GARRY, Joseph Patrick. 600 MOYE BLVD, MEDICINE, DEPT OF FAMILY M 27834 #026-04-1991 L1997 FM FSM *020 †18
GAVIGAN, James Richard. 275 BETHESDA DR, EASTERN UROLOGICAL ASSCS, 27834 #020-12-1967 L1971 U *020 †95
GAY, Frank Lipscomb, Jr. 101 BETHESDA DR 27834 #012-05-1986 L1994 OBG *020 †30
GAY, Hiram Alberto. 600 MOYE BLVD, DEPT OF RADIATION/ONCO 27834 #042-01-2000 L2005 RO *020 †80
GAY, Wilton Carlyle, Jr. 503 BOWMAN GRAY DR STE B 27834 #036-08-1982 L1983 FM *020 †18
GEMELLI, Peter. 2100 STANTONSBURG RD 27834 #305-01-2004 L2007 PM *012
GERARDO, James Anthony. ■ 27858 #036-08-2002 L2007 CD *012 †20
GERKIN, Susan Renee. 600 MOYE BLVD 27834 #422-01-1998 L2001 NEP *020 †20
GERSH, Benjamin Cohen. ■ 27834 #036-08-2006 FP *012
GHASSEMIAN, Andrew Jafar. ■ 27834 #036-08-2005 D *012
GHOBRIAL, Mona Mounir. 2100 STANTONSBURG RD 27834 #915-04-1994 FP *012
GIBBS, John W, III. 2280 HEMBY LN 27834 #051-04-1998 L2003 CN *020 †55
GILBERT, Charles Franklin. 600 MOYE BLVD 27834 #036-01-1959 L1959 PTH *072 †50
GILLIKIN, Marcus Ward. PO BOX 30696 27833 #036-05-2000 *030
GILLILAND, M G F. 600 MOYE BLVD, BRODY SOM AT ECU 27834 #016-43-1969 L1989 FOP ATP *020 †50
GLASER, Fred Bernard. 2577 W 5TH ST, DRUG ABUSE TREATMENT CENTE 27834 #024-01-1993 L1994 P *050
GLOMB, Nicolaus Walterspi. ■ 27858 #036-08-2008 *012
GOETTLER, Claudia Ellen. 600 MOYE BLVD, DIV OF TRAUMA / S.C.C 27834 #010-01-1995 L2002 CCS *020 †85

GOOD, Celeste Margarita. 707 WH SMITH BLVD 27834 #308-08-1984 L1988 P *020 †75
GOOD, Kevin Straight. 707 WH SMITH BLVD 27834 #308-03-1981 L1987 N GP *020 †75
GOODMAN, Peggy Ellen. 600 MOYE BLVD 27834 #001-06-1986 L1992 EM *040 †16
GORRIN-RIVAS, Manuel Jose. 2430 EMERALD PL STE 201 27834 #935-01-1992 L2006 AN *105
GOTH, Karen Mary. ■ 27834 #035-06-2005 L2008 PD *012
GOUGH, John Edward. 600 MOYE BLVD, 3 ED 300 27834 #036-01-1990 L1992 EM *040 †16
GRAHAM, David Earl. ■ 27834 #036-08-1993 GS *100
GRAHAM, Toney, III. ■ 27834 #047-07-2006 IM *012
GREEN, David Emanuel. ■ 27858 #270-02-1999 L2007 IM *020
GREEN, Stephen Clark. 600 MOYE BLVD 27834 #021-01-1966 L1989 OBG *020 †30
GRUBB, Christopher Thomas. 2430 EMERALD PL, STE 201 27834 #036-08-2000 L2002 AN *020 †05
GUIDONI, Marcia. 600 MOYE BLVD 27834 #396-06-1979 L1982 EM FM *020 †16
GWALTNEY, Michael Lawrenc. ■ 27858 #036-08-2008 *012
HABAL, Nizar. 2223 HEMBY LN, SURGERY 27834 #035-09-1993 L2000 SO GS *020 †85
HABIB, Asma Shahid. 2100 STANTONSBURG RD, DEPT IM 27834 #051-04-2006 MPD *012
HACK, Jason Benjamin. 600 MOYE BLVD, PCMH, 3ED-309 27834 #035-08-1993 L1999 EM *020 †16
HADI, Hamid A. 600 MOYE BLVD 27834 #118-01-1964 L1987 MFM OBS *040 †30
HAFIZ, Razia Sultana. ■ 27858 #160-02-1998 FP *012
HAISCH, Carl Eugene. 600 MOYE BLVD RM 4, BRODY SCHOOL OF MEDICINE 27834 #054-04-1973 L1980 GS TTS *020 †85
HALE, John Chas. 905 JOHNS HOPKINS DR, PHYSICIANS EAST, PA 27834 #025-07-1970 L1976 GS *020 †85
HALLIDAY, Bradford E. 2100 STANTONSBURG RD 27834 #003-01-1990 L1995 PTH *020 †50
HALLOCK, J Douglas. ■ 27858 #035-20-1952 L1967 GS EM *071 †85
HAMILTON, Gene Thos. 419 LEE ST 27858 #016-06-1967 L1973 ORS *020 †40
HAMRA, Badri Jos. 203 GOVERNMENT CIR, PITT CO MENTAL HLTH CTR 27834 #605-01-1978 L1984 P *020 †75
HAMRICK, Irene. 600 MOYE BLVD, CAROLINA UNIVERSITY, SCHOO 27834 #036-08-1995 L1996 FPG FM *040 †18
HAMRICK, Timmons Hicks. 600 MOYE BLVD, BRODY BLDG, 4E59 27834 #036-08-1993 L1996 CHP *020
HANNON, David W. ■ 27834 #011-04-1977 L1992 PD PDC *020 †55
HANRAHAN, Leo Robt. 7E-128 BRODY BLDG DEPT PTH, ECU BRODY SOM 27834 #035-15-1972 L1977 OS *040 †10
HAQUE, Mahfuzul. 600 MOYE BLVD 27834 #160-02-1982 L2007 *020
HARDING, David Wayne. 2100 STANTONSBURG RD, DEPT CD 27834 #036-01-2004 L2007 CD *012 †20
HARDY, Ira May, II. 2390 HEMBY LN 27834 #036-01-1963 L1963 NS *020 †25
HARDY, John Gregg. 2280 HEMBY LN 27834 #036-05-1973 L1973 N *020 †75
HARMON, Betty. 2355 HEMBY LN 27834 #036-08-1995 L2000 RHU *020 †20
HARMON, Helen Easter. 2355 HEMBY LN 27834 #036-01-1984 L1985 RHU IM *020 †20
HARNER, Kyle Charles. 2355 HEMBY LN 27834 #051-04-1997 L2005 RHU IM *020 †20
HARRINGTON, Daphne Melvin. ■ 27858 #036-08-2008 *012
HARRIS, Beverly Moore. 2251 STANTONSBURG RD, PHYSICIANS EAST, PA 27834 #036-08-1990 L1994 OBG *020 †30
HARRIS, Chrystal Bernice. ■ 27834 #036-08-2008 *012
HARRIS, Glenn David. 600 MOYE BLVD 27834 #035-08-1988 L1991 PD *020 †55
HARSSEMA, Martin J. 3535 S MEMORIAL DR, # C 27834 #048-14-2000 L2001 AM FM *020
HART, Jennifer Lane. ■ 27858 #048-14-2007 FP *012
HARVELL, James C, Jr. 810 WH SMITH BLVD 27834 #036-08-1983 L1988 ORS OSS *020
HASAN, Saman. 2100 STANTONSBURG RD, DOCTOR PARK 1-A 27834 #495-77-1997 L2007 P *012
HASSAN, Syed Ansar Ul. ■ 27834 #067-01-1998 L2007 TS CD *040
HASTINGS, Barry Russell. 990 JOHNS HOPKINS DR, GREENVILLE SURGICAL 27834 #038-45-1991 L1998 GS *020 †85
HASTY, Christopher Clay. 810 WH SMITH BLVD 27834 #036-07-1994 L1999 ORS *020 †40
HAVEN, Andrew Eddy. 2251 STANTONSBURG RD, PHYSICIAN EAST, PA 27834 #036-01-1978 L1980 OBG *020 †30
HAYSLIP, Clifford C, Jr. 600 MOYE BLVD, ECU BRODY SCHOOL OF MEDICI 27834 #012-05-1976 L1992 REN OBG *020 †30
HAYSLIP, Virginia M. ■ 27834 #051-04-1980 L1987 PM *074 †60
HE, Weixiong. 2100 STANTONSBURG RD, PCMH 340 27834 #243-21-1995 L2007 IM *020 †20
HERNANDEZ GONZALEZ, Andrea. 2100 STANTONSBURG RD 27834 #270-02-2002 P *012
HERRING, Richard Charles. ■ 27834 #036-08-2004 L2008 MPD *012
HEWAN-LOWE, Karlene Opal. 600 MOYE BLVD, BRODY SCHOOL OF MED ECU 75 27834 #566-01-1972 L2001 PTH *020 †50
HILLENBRAND, Karin Marie. 600 MOYE BLVD, BRODY SCHOOL OF MED PEDS 27834 #051-04-1989 L1995 PD *020 †55
HINES, Benjamin Gerald, Jr. 275 BETHESDA DR 27834 #036-01-1982 L1983 U *020 †95
HO, Jason Griffith. ■ 27834 #036-08-2005 L2008 PD *012
HODGIN, Thomas Whitson, Jr. 1850 W ARLINGTON BLVD 27834 #036-01-1997 L1999 IM *020 †20
HOGGARD, Jeffrey Gordon. 600 MOYE BLVD 27834 #036-01-1982 L1992 NEP IM *020 †20
HOLBROOK, Carter Tate, III. 1628 W ARLINGTON BLVD 27834 #036-01-1975 L1975 PD PHO *020 †55
HOLLOWELL, Kerry Lynn. ■ 27858 #036-08-2006 GS *012
HOLTER, John Frederick. 2577 W 5TH ST 27834 #041-14-1979 L1984 PUD *050 †20
HOMESLEY, Howard David. 600 MOYE BLVD 27834 #036-01-1967 L1969 GO ON *071 †30
HONG, Heng. 600 MOYE BLVD RM 7S-10, DEPARTMENT OF PATHOLOGY/ B 27834 #243-16-1982 L2005 PCP *100 †50
HOOD, Opal Jean. 105 WINDEMERE CT 27858 #027-01-1976 L1990 CG PD *040 †55,19
HOOD, Richard T, Jr. ■ 27858 #036-05-1948 L1949 AI *071
HOOKER, James Benjamin. BRODY SCHOOL OF MED 27834 #036-01-2005 PD *012
HOUBI, Yasin. ■ 27834 #286-01-1995 FP *012
HOWARD, Shirley Martin. ■ 27858 #051-04-1943 L1943 GYN *071 †30
HOWELL, Amy Wood. ■ 27834 #036-08-2006 PD *012
HOWELL, Eric Richard. ■ 27834 #036-08-2004 D *012
HOYER, Robert Christian. 600 MOYE BLVD 27834 #026-04-1975 L1998 PD *020 †55
HUBBARD, Jeremy Slade. 275 BETHESDA DR, EASTERN UROLOGICAL ASSOCIA 27834 #023-07-2003 L2007 U *012
HUDSON, David Wesley. ■ 27834 #036-08-2004 GS *012
HUGHES, James Lewis. PITT O MEM HOSP 288 2W 27835 #023-01-1955 L1980 PD *071 †55

HUMBERT, James Ronald W. 2100 STANTONSBURG RD, ECU PEDIATRICS 288 27834 #869-04-1964 L2001 **PHO PD** *030 †55

HUNTER, Thomas Titus. 2100 STANTONSBURG RD 27834 #036-01-1983 L1984 **GS EM** *020

HURWITZ, Jennie Rachel. ■ 27834 #051-07-2007 **PD** *012

HUTCHINSON, David Knox. 1913 E FIRE TOWER RD, STE E 27858 #036-01-1995 L1996 **EM** *020 †16

HUTCHINSON, Mary Allen. 420 SPRING FOREST RD 27834 #036-08-1997 L2000 **D** *020 †15

IMHOFF, Anna Lorraine. 1803 BLOOMSBURY RD 27858 #021-01-1998 L2002 **OBG** *020 †30

IMRAN, Mustafa. 2100 STANTONSBURG RD, DEPT OF FAMILY PRACTICE 27834 #704-02-2002 **FP** *012

IRONS, Cary Frederick, III. ■ 27858 #051-04-1941 L1946 **FM** *071

IRONS, Malene G. ■ 27858 #051-04-1941 L1946 **PD** *071

IRONS, Thomas Grant. 525 MOYE BLVD 27834 #036-01-1972 L1972 **PD** *030 †55

ISLER, Christy Michelle. 600 MOYE BLVD 27834 #020-02-1994 L1996 **MFM OBS** *020 †30

JACOB, Jose. 2315 EXECUTIVE CIR STE A, CAROLINA EAST CARDIOLOGY 27834 #495-52-1983 L2002 **CD** *020 ‡

JACOBS, Tracy C. ■ 27858 #001-06-2008 *012

JAHRSDORFER, Charles Edwa. 3282 CHARLES BLVD 27858 #422-01-2000 L2004 *020 ‡

JAMES, James Franklin. 600B COUNTRY CLUB DR 27834 #047-06-1963 L1967 **P PHP** *020 †75

JAZBEH, Basel. 2100 STANTONSBURG RD, DEPT FM 27834 #875-02-2003 **FP** *012

JOHNS, Ann Greene. ■ 27858 #036-08-1994 L2003 **FM** *020

JOHNSON, Ashleigh Tennill. ■ 27858 #036-08-2008 *012

JOHNSON, Ashton Fox. 600 MOYE BLVD, EAST CAROLINA FAMILY MEDIC 27834 #036-08-2002 L2004 **FM** *040 †18

JOHNSON, Kim Marcel. 2100 STANTONSBURG RD, DEPT FAM PR 27834 #051-04-1994 **FM** *100

JOHNSON, Lynn Roy. 2010 W ARLINGTON BLVD 27834 #041-12-1984 L1997 **AN IM** *020 †05

JOHNSON, William Eugene, IV. 1850 W ARLINGTON BLVD 27834 #036-08-2003 L2006 **IM** *020

JOHNSRUDE, Irwin Stanley. 1711 W 6TH ST 27834 #062-01-1956 L1966 **DR** *071 †80

JONES, Billy Ernest. 600 MOYE BLVD # DERM, ECU SCHOOL OF MEDICINE 27834 #036-07-1958 L1958 **D** *020 †15

JONES, D E Darnell. 308 QUEEN ANNES RD 27858 #036-07-1968 L1968 **OBG** *030 †30

JONES, Gary Christopher. 3282 CHARLES BLVD, CAROLINA EAST FAMILY MED 27858 #036-01-1983 L1985 **FM** *020 †18

JONES, Indie Fay. ■ 27858 #035-06-2005 **IM** *012

JONES, Perrin Wayne. 2430 EMERALD PL, STE 201 27834 #036-05-1999 L2003 **AN** *020 †05

JORDAN, Joseph C. 1913 E FIRE TOWER RD, STE E 27858 #036-08-1992 L1995 **FM** *020

JUSTIS, Christopher M. 2100 STANTONSBURG RD 27834 #036-08-1985 L1990 **AN** *020

KABA, Suela. ■ 27834 #120-01-1991 **FP** *012

KAHWAGI, Maya Antoine. 2100 STANTONSBURG RD, PITT COUNTY MEM HOSP 27834 #605-02-2002 **FP** *012

KALEKA, Ravneet Kaur. 2100 STANTONSBURG RD 27834 #496-68-2003 **IM** *012

KANSAGRA, Sujay Mansukhla. ■ 27834 #036-07-2006 **PD** *012

KAOUD, Hany Aziz. 2100 STANTONSBURG RD, DOCTORS PARK 1-A 27834 #665-01-2003 **P** *012

KARDYS, Clark Michael. ■ 27834 #048-02-2004 **GS** *012

KATARIA, Sudesh. 600 MOYE BLVD 27834 #496-07-1965 L1979 **PD OS** *020 †55

KATARIA, Yash Pal. 600 MOYE BLVD 27834 #495-03-1959 L1978 **PUD IG** *020

KATWA, Geeta. 600 MOYE BLVD, DEPT OF MEDICINE BRODY BLD 27834 #495-21-1979 L2000 **RHU** *020 †20

KAVURU, Mani Subrahmanya. 600 MOYE BLVD, EAST CAROLINA UNIV, BRODY 27834 #038-44-1984 L2005 **PUD IM** *020 †20

KEENE, Darlene Jacqueline. 600 MOYE BLVD 27834 #036-08-1989 L1992 **NPM PD** *020 †55

KELLEY, Colin Thos. ■ 27858 #023-12-1988 L1990 **CHP PYG** *020 †75

KENDRICK, William Thomas. 511 PALADIN DR, EASTERN NEPHLGY ASSIC 27834 #036-08-1997 L2003 **NEP** *020 †20

KENNY, James Michael. ■ 27858 #030-06-1963 L1963 **PUD IM** *071

KENNY, Jean Felty. ■ 27858 #023-07-1957 L1981 **PD ID** *071 †55

KHAN, Saadia Irem. ■ 27834 #305-01-2005 **PD** *012

KIEFER, Jeffrey Scott. 1501 MUIRFIELD DR 27858 #034-01-1991 L1992 **EM** *020 †16

KIKER, Zachary Philip. ■ 27834 #036-08-2008 *012

KINNEY, Karen Anne. 600 MOYE BLVD 27834 #001-02-1990 L1991 **EM** *020 †16

KITTEN, Suzanna Frances. 1A DOCTORS PARK, ECU PSYCHIATRY 27834 #016-11-2005 L2008 **P** *012

KNAPP, Gregory William. 600 MOYE BLVD, EASTERN CAROLINA FAM PRACT 27834 #036-08-2000 L2001 **FM** *020 †18

KNOTT, Rufus Henry. 2100 STANTONSBURG RD 27834 #036-01-1964 L1964 **OTO PUD** *020 †45

KNUCKLES, Gwendolyn. 2317 EXECUTIVE CIR STE A, WOMEN'S HEALTH CENTER OF G 27834 #021-01-1984 L1995 **OBG** *020 †30

KNUPP, Charles Leonard. 600 MOYE BLVD 27834 #023-01-1976 L1980 **IM HEM** *020 †20

KOCHER, Thomas Zachary. 2100 STANTONSBURG RD 27834 #024-07-2004 **PTH** *012

KOEHLER, Kevin Scott. ■ 27834 #036-08-2008 *012

KOEHNE, Catherine Ann. ■ 27834 #561-06-1982 **P** *100

KOLANGADEN, Zubin Paulson. 2100 STANTONSBURG RD, DEPT IM 27834 #665-01-2006 **IM** *012

KOLTIS, Gordon Gary. 801 WH SMITH BLVD, CAROLINA RADIATION MEDICIN 27834 #056-05-1981 L1989 **RO** *020 †80

KONDURU, Chandana. ■ 27834 #495-70-1997 L2005 **IM** *100 †20

KOONCE, Thomas Fredrick. 600 MOYE BLVD 27834 #036-01-1999 L2002 **FM** *020

KOPELMAN, Arthur E. 600 MOYE BLVD, DEPT OF PEDIATRICS 27834 #035-45-1963 L1978 **PD** *020 †55

KORNEGAY, Christopher Cha. ■ 27834 #036-08-2005 L2008 **MPD** *012

KORNEGAY, Jeffrey Todd. ■ 27834 #036-08-2006 **IM** *012

KORNEGAY, Jonathan Harget. ■ 27834 #036-08-2008 *012

KOUTLAS, Theodore C. 600 MOYE BLVD 27834 #054-04-1987 L1993 **PCS** *020 †85,90

KOWALSKI, Maria. ■ 27858 #759-03-1950 L1974 **PD EM** *071 †55,16 ‡

KRAEMER, Thomas Gerard. 2160 HERBERT CT, ECU WOMEN'S PHYSICIANS 27834 #038-41-1992 L1997 **OBG** *020 †30

KRAGEL, Peter J. 2100 STANTONSBURG RD, PITT COUNTRY MEM HOSP 27834 #010-02-1981 L1998 **PTH** *030 †50

KRAMER, Thomas F. 101 BETHESDA DR 27834 #021-01-1953 L1953 **OBG** *071 †30

KREEGER, Richard Wayne. 600 MOYE BLVD, 378 PCMH TEACHING ANNEX 27834 #036-01-1981 L2003 **ICE CD** *012 ‡

KROL, Amber. ■ 27834 #038-75-2005, ▲ **OBG** *012

KUDITHIPUDI, Vijayasree. 2100 STANTONSBURG RD, DEPT CD 27834 #495-50-1998 L2005 **CD** *012 †20

KUMAR, Manika. ■ 27834 #036-08-2007 **IM** *012

KUSHNICK, Theodore. 600 MOYE BLVD, ECU SCHOOL OF MEDICINE 27834 #024-01-1951 L1979 **PD OS** *071 †19,55

KYPSON, Alan Patrick. 600 MOYE BLVD, ECU BRODY SCHOOL OF MEDICI 27834 #035-01-1993 L1997 **TS GS** *020 †85,90

LA CROIX, Christopher E. 1850 W ARLINGTON BLVD 27834 #026-04-2000 L2005 **IM** *020 †20

LAM, Hung Du. 2100 STANTONSBURG RD 27834 #305-01-2007 **PD** *012

LAMM, Kevin Michael. ■ 27834 #036-08-2008 *012

LAND, Eurgia Chas. 3110 S EVANS ST 27834 #010-03-1975 L1977 **IM** *020 †20

LANDUCCI, Dante. 600 MOYE BLVD, RM AD-52 27834 #041-12-1982 L1999 **PUD** *020 †20

LANE, Winston Earl, III. 1705 W SIXTH ST, STE H 27834 #036-08-1985 L1987 **P** *020 †75

LANG, Joanne. ■ 27858 #036-07-1981 L1983 **OBG** *071 †30

LANG, Michael Christopher. 600 MOYE BLVD, PITT COUNTY MEMORIAL HOSPI 27834 #036-08-2002 L2004 **IM P** *040 †20

LARKIN, Ernest W, III. 600 MOYE BLVD 27834 #051-04-1970 L1975 **PTH ATP** *020 †50

LARSEN, Lars Christian. 600 MOYE BLVD, DEPT OF FAMILY MEDICINE 27834 #035-15-1973 L1983 **FM** *030 †18 ‡

LARSON, Richard Martin. 905 JOHNS HOPKINS DR, PHYSICIANS EAST, PA 27834 #036-07-1974 L1976 **GS** *020

LASHLEY, Graham Garrison. 2430 EMERALD PL, STE 201 27834 #049-01-1997 L1998 **AN** *020 †05

LAURORA, Rosanne Vivian. 2160 HERBERT CT, ECU WOMEN'S PHYSICIANS 27834 #033-06-1995 L2005 **OBG** *020 †30

LAUT, Jennifer Marie. ■ 27834 #036-08-2008 *012

LAW, Yiik. 2100 STANTONSBURG RD, PITT CO MEM HOSP 27834 #539-05-2001 **GS** *012

LAWRENCE, Michael A. 3205 E BAYWOOD LN 27834 #275-03-1987 L2002 **FPG** *020 †18

LEACOCK, Rodney Owen. 2280 HEMBY LN, EAST CAROLINA NEUROLOGY, I 27834 #010-03-1992 L2003 **N** *020 †75

LEE, Daniel. 2280 HEMBY LN 27834 #020-12-1988 L1992 **N SME** *020 †75

LEE, Jesse Thomas. 1850 W ARLINGTON BLVD 27834 #036-07-1981 L1982 **ON HEM** *020 †20

LEE, Kenneth Piljae. ■ 27834 #665-02-2003 **P** *012

LEE, Mark Hong. 600 MOYE BLVD, ECU BRODY SCHOOL OF MEDICI 27834 #583-01-1982 L2004 **HEM** *100 †20

LEE, Tae Joon. 600 MOYE BLVD, BRODY 4N-64 27834 #036-01-2001 L2005 **FPG** *020 †18

LEONARD, John Richard, III. 2325 STANTONSBURG RD 27834 #036-01-1970 L1970 **NS** *020 †25

LEONG, Khye Sheng. 2465 EMERALD PL 27834 #010-01-1994 L1998 **IM GE** *020 †20

LEONHARDT, Gary Gene. 2577 W FIFTH ST 27834 #036-08-1989 L1990 **P IM** *030 †20,75

LEPERA, Pamela Ann. 600 MOYE BLVD, 3E-127 BRODY SCIENCE BUILD 27834 #041-77-1988, ▲ L1996 **ON HEM** *020 †20

LEVINE, Gary Ira. 600 MOYE BLVD 27834 #025-07-1976 L1996 **FM** *040 †18

LEWIS, Michael Justin. 600 MOYE BLVD, HEALTH SCIENCES 27834 #055-01-1974 L2003 **FM** *030 †18 ‡

LEWIS, Richard Stewart. 420 SPRING FOREST RD 27834 #036-08-1997 L1998 **D DS** *020 †15 ‡

LILES, Darla Kaye. 600 MOYE BLVD 27834 #028-46-1986 L1990 **HEM** *020 †20

LIN, Hui. 2100 STANTONSBURG RD, DEPT MED 27834 #243-21-1995 **IM** *012

LIN, Wei. 600 MOYE BLVD, BRODY MEDICAL SCIENCE BUIL 27834 #243-16-1985 L2004 **IM** *020 †20

LINDBECK, Eric Orr. 850 JOHNS HOPKINS DR 27834 #023-01-1988 L1994 **OTO** *020 †45

LINDQUIST, Leo A. ■ 27858 #025-01-1953 L1973 **GS** *071 †85

LITCHFORD, David Williams. ■ 27858 #047-06-2004 **P** *012

LOCHMULLER, Christopher M. ■ 27834 #036-08-2003 **PTH** *012

LOCKLEAR, Charlene Reshel. ■ 27834 #036-08-2008 *012

LODESERTO, Frank Joseph. 2100 STANTONSBURG RD 27834 #422-01-2007 **MPD** *012

LONG, Mareen Ann. ■ 27834 #036-08-1995 L2003 **FP** *012

LONG, Michael August. ■ 27834 #036-08-2008 *012

LONGEST, Sonya Blanchard. 600 MOYE BLVD, DEPT OF PSYCHIATRY 27834 #036-08-2002 L2006 **CHP** *100

LOPEZ, Andre Luis. 600 MOYE BLVD, FAMILY PRACTICE CENTER 27834 #035-06-1997 L1998 **FM** *020 †18

LOPEZ, Cynthia L Robinson. 845 JOHNS HOPKINS DR STE A, EASTERN NEUROLOGY & NEURO 27834 #038-45-1986 L1990 **N IM** *020 †75

LOVE, Katie Marie. ■ 27858 #035-06-2006 **GS** *012

LOWERY, Patricia Vaughan. 600 MOYE BLVD 27834 #036-08-1985 L2002 **NPM** *012 †55

LUPIA, Raul Humberto. 600 MOYE BLVD 27834 #132-07-1984 L1994 **EM CD** *020

LURITO, Karen Furlonge. 600 MOYE BLVD 27834 #023-01-1996 L2002 **PD PDC** *020 †55

LYALL, John Gregory. ■ 27834 #036-08-2004 L2007 **IM** *020 †20

LYNCH, Cynthia Anne. ■ 27858 #041-15-2001 L2002 **HO** *012

LYNCH, Stephen Francis. 800 MOYE BLVD, GREENVILLE VA CLINIC 27834 #041-09-1998 L2005 **FM** *020 †18

MABRY, Frederick Harrison, III. ■ 27834 #036-08-2008 *012

MAC DONALD, Kenneth G. 2455 EMERALD PL, SOUTHERN SURGICAL ASSOC 27834 #055-01-1981 L1983 **GS AS** *020 †85

MAC DONALD, Robert Gene. 804 JOHNS HOPKINS DR 27834 #065-06-1959 L1966 **IMG IM** *071

MACGILVRAY, Scott Steven. 600 MOYE BLVD 27834 #016-43-1987 L2004 **NPM** *020 †55

MADANI, Navid. 704 WH SMITH BLVD, UCLA DIVISION OF DIGESTIVE 27834 #409-04-1990 L2007 **GE** *020 †20

MAGEAU, Ronald Paul. ■ 27858 #023-01-2001 **PTH** *012

MAJSTORAVICH, Sarah Jo. ■ 27834 #036-08-2008 *012

MALIK, Kashif Nadeem. 1A DOCTORS PARK, DEPT OF PSYCHIATRY 27834 #704-22-1999 **P** *012

MALLETTE, Julius Quintin. 600 MOYE BLVD, 1 SOUTH 10 27834 #036-08-1982 L1984 **OBG** *040 †20

MANALO, Erwin Marc. 600 MOYE BLVD 27834 #005-12-1999 L2003 **PM** *020 †60

MANDAPAKA, Sangeeta. ■ 27834 #495-37-1999 L2005 **CD** *012 †20 ‡

MANGAN, Sharon Ann. 600 MOYE BLVD, BRODY BLDG—3E-139 27834 #035-19-1990 L1996 **PD ADL** *020 †55

MANGUM, Sarah Rose. OF PEDS, ECU SCHOOL OF MED, DEPT 27858 #036-08-1991 L1993 **PD IM** *020

MANN, Christian. 2455 EMERALD PL 27834 #409-10-1990 L1998 **GS** *020 †85

MANN, Richard Harvey. 1850 W ARLINGTON BLVD 27834 #036-01-1982 L1984 **PUD IM** *020 †20

MANNING, Steven Mark. ■ 27834 #036-08-2008 *012

MANUEL, Crystal April. 1A DOCTORS PARK, ECU PSYCHIATRY 27834 #036-08-2001 L2006 OS *100

MANWARING, Mark Louis. 2100 STANTONSBURG RD 27834 #035-06-2004 L2006 GS *012

MARCH, Juan Alberto. 600 MOYE BLVD 27834 #035-15-1989 L1992 EM *040 †16

MARCUARD, Stefano M Paolo. 800 MOYE BLVD 27834 #869-07-1977 L1983 GE *020 †20

MARKELLO, James Ross. ■ 27858 #035-06-1961 L1977 PD *071 †55

MARTENSEN, Robt Lawrence. 600 MOYE BLVD, BRODY 2S 17E 27834 #032-01-1974 L1975 EM OS *040 †16

MATHAI, Angie Elizabeth. 2100 STANTONSBURG RD 27834 #305-01-2005 MPD *012

MATHIS, James L. 2100 STANTONSBURG RD, DEPT PSYCH 27834 #028-34-1949 L1976 P *071 †75

MATHUR, Vinita. 2515 BOWMAN GRAY DR, GREENVILLE PATHOLOGY 27834 #495-37-1996 L2005 PTH ATP *100

MATTHEWS, Joanne Maria. 1850 W ARLINGTON BLVD 27834 #035-08-1999 L2006 GE *100 †20

MAXWELL, Stephen Royce. 600 MOYE BLVD, PCMHTA 340 27834 #305-01-2005 IM *012

MAYO, Kathy Diane. 707 WH SMITH BLVD 27834 #036-08-1990 L1991 P *020 †75

MAZER, Mark Allen. ■ 27834 #165-03-1980 L2006 CCM IM *012

MC CONNELL, Robert Wm. 9 DOCTORS PARK 27834 #051-04-1959 L1965 R NM *071 †80,28

MC DONALD, Kimberly Kay. 201 GOVERNMENT CIR 27834 #051-07-1995 L2005 GPM *020 †70

MC ELLIGOTT, Jacinta. 600 MOYE BLVD 27834 #539-06-1978 L1988 PM *020 †60

MC GILL, Shevonda Trisha. ■ 27834 #020-02-2002 L2006 OBG *100 †30

MC GILLICUDDY, Denis M. 810 WH SMITH BLVD 27834 #025-01-1975 L1980 ORS *020 †40

MC GINTY, Kaye L. 600 MOYE BLVD, ECU DEPT OF PSYCHIATRY 27834 #042-02-1989 L1994 CHP *020 †75

MC KENNEY, Donna K. 600 MOYE BLVD 27834 #012-01-1988 L1995 IM *040 †20

MCKINNEY, Joshua Daniel. ■ 27834 #036-08-2008 *012

MC KNIGHT, Kevin Michael. 1850 W ARLINGTON BLVD, CRYSTAL COAST ARTHRITIS CE 27834 #030-06-1986 L1989 RHU IM *012

MCNALLY, Michael Morgan. ■ 27834 #048-14-2006 GS *012

MC NEILL, Elizabeth L. 600 MOYE BLVD 27834 #036-08-1998 L1999 IM *020 †20

MEBANE, Angela. 1204 E FIRE TOWER RD, ECU PHYSICIANS 27858 #036-01-1997 L1998 FM *020 †18

MEETZE, William Howard. 600 MOYE BLVD, ECU SCHOOL OF MEDICINE 27834 #045-01-1979 L1992 NPM PD *020 †55

MEGA, Benjamin T. ■ 27858 #043-01-2007 GS *012

MEGA, Lesly V Tamarin. 600 MOYE BLVD # 4E98B 27834 #024-05-1968 L1982 CHP P *040 †75

MEGGS, William Joel. 600 MOYE BLVD, RM 3ED311 27834 #011-02-1979 L1988 EM ETX *020 †20,03,16

MEHLHOP, Paul David. 2395 HEMBY LN, THE ALLERGY CENTER, PA 27834 #035-01-1991 L1998 AI PD *020 †55,03

MEHTA, Hiren Harshadray. 2100 STANTONSBURG RD, PITT CO MEM HOSP 27834 #305-01-2006 MPD *012

MELVIN, Winslow Britt. 2430 EMERALD PL, # 201 27834 #036-08-1985 L1989 AN *020 †05

MENDOZA, Ricardo Manalo. ■ 27858 #051-07-2003 GS *100

MEREDITH, John Thos. 600 MOYE BLVD 27834 #048-02-1987 L1995 EM *020 †16

MERRILL, Richard Hosmer. 990 JOHNS HOPKINS DR, THE KIDNEY CENTER PA 27834 #024-05-1966 L1979 NEP IM *020 †20

METCALF, Mignon. ■ 27834 #036-08-2008 *012

MEWBORN, Quentin A, Jr. 2210 HEMBY LN STE 105 27834 #036-01-1969 L1969 FM *020 †18

MEYER, Claudine Gahamanyi. ■ 27834 #036-08-2005 L2008 IM *012

MICHAEL, David Ferguson. 1850 W ARLINGTON BLVD 27834 #038-40-1994 L1996 IM *020 †20

MILLAN, Raymundo D. 600 MOYE BLVD, BRODY SCHOOL OF MEDICINE 27834 #748-02-1992 L1999 SCI PME *020 †60

MILLER, Brian Douglas. ■ 27858 #036-01-2006 EM *012

MILLER, Ellis A. 304 E COLLEGE ST 27834 #308-11-1987 P *100

MIN, Christopher Justus. ■ 27834 #036-08-2007 IM *012

MINARD, Raymond Bruce. 2010 W ARLINGTON BLVD 27834 #036-08-1981 L1984 AN PMM *020 †05

MITIKU, Belachew. EAST CAROLINA UNIV-SURG 27858 #165-03-1970 L1996 *020

MODI, Seema Chhotalal. 600 MOYE BLVD, ECU SCHL OF MED, BRODY 4N- 27834 #048-04-1996 L2000 FPG *020 †18

MOLINARO, Jason Rocco. ■ 27834 #012-01-2005 GS *100

MONROE, Edwin W. ■ 27858 #041-01-1951 L1951 IM *071 †20

MOODY, Marsa Genann. ■ 27834 #036-08-2008 *012

MOORE, Daniel Paul. 600 MOYE BLVD, DEPT OF PHYSICAL MED & REH 27834 #041-02-1990 L1995 PM *020 †60

MOORE, Laura Verde De For. 2100 STANTONSBURG RD, PITT CO MEM HOSP 27834 #187-47-1997 L2007 IM *100 †20

MOORE, Veda. 301 BOWMAN GRAY DR 27834 #041-02-1990 L1995 OPH *020 †35

MORALES, Sergio Eli. ■ 27858 #025-01-2004 MEM *012

MORAN, Andrew Gregory. 2100 STANTONSBURG RD 27834 #049-01-1999 L2002 NM *020 †80

MORAN, Jon Frederick. 600 MOYE BLVD, BRODY SCHOOL OF MEDICINE 27834 #028-02-1973 L1995 TS *020 †85,90

MORGAN, Caroline Leggett. ■ 27834 #036-08-2006 PD *012

MORROW, John Howard. 201 GOVERNMENT CIR 27834 #036-08-1985 L1988 FM PHP *030 †18

MOTEN, Simon Christopher. 600 MOYE BLVD, DEPT OF SUGERY 27834 #143-01-1991 L2004 *030

MOVAHED, Assad. 2100 STANTONSBURG RD, DEPT CARD 27834 #517-07-1975 L1986 CD OS *020 †20

MUFTI, Shayasta Shaheen. ■ 27834 #704-20-2003 IM *012

MULLICK, Monalisa. 2100 STANTONSBURG RD 27834 #028-46-1997 L1999 MPD *020 †20,55

MULLINS-HODGIN, Rita Joyc. 2100 STANTONSBURG RD, PITT COUNTY MEMORIAL HOSPI 27834 #020-12-1997 L1999 MPD *020 †20,55

MULLIS, Sylvia Jones. 1913 E FIRE TOWER RD, STE E 27858 #036-08-1988 L1990 FM *020 †18

MUNGAL, Vishal. 2100 STANTONSBURG RD 27834 #305-01-2007 MPD *012

MURAD, Joseph Louis. 1730 W 5TH ST 27834 #036-01-1957 L1957 OBG *020 †30

MURPHREE, Allison Leigh. ■ 27834 #036-08-2008 *012

MURPHY, Gregory Francis. 275 BETHESDA DR, ESTERN UROLOGICAL ASSOCIAT 27834 #036-01-1989 L1993 U *020 †95

MURPHY, Richard James. 420 SPRING FOREST RD, EASTERN DERMATOLOGY &PATHO 27834 #035-19-1958 L1959 CD IM *020 †20

MURPHY, Richard James. 420 SPRING FOREST RD, EASTERN DERMATOLOGY 27834 #036-08-1995 L1999 D *020 †15

MURTHY, Kumbaiah N. 600 MOYE BLVD, DEPARTMENT OF PSYCHIATRY 27834 #495-09-1974 L1985 P N *040 †75

NADKARNI, Vaishali Rahul. ■ 27834 #496-15-1999 FP *012

NARASIMHAN, Lakshmi. 600 MOYE BLVD 27834 #495-09-1979 L1995 CD IM *020 †20

NASIR, Summiyah. ■ 27834 #704-15-2002 FP *012

NAZIRI, Wahid. 2455 EMERALD PL 27834 #051-01-1988 L1997 GS *020 †85

NDILI, Ogugua Nnamaka. 2100 STANTONSBURG RD 27834 #690-01-1998 L2006 IM *020 †20

NEFF, Richard A. 8 DOCTORS PARK, INTERVENTIONAL RADIOLOGY 27834 #016-11-1977 L2008 VIR *020 †80 ‡

NEHUS, Nathan Robert. 600 MOYE BLVD, DEPT OF EMERGENCY MED 27834 #305-01-2005 EM *012

NEKKANTI, Rajasekhar. 2100 STANTONSBURG RD 27834 #496-24-1993 L2002 CD *100 †20

NELSON, Keith Hunter. 600 MOYE BLVD, ECU BRODY SCHOOL OF MEDICI 27834 #036-05-1997 L2001 OBG *020 †30

NELSON, Todd Brandon. ■ 27834 #036-08-2007 IM *012

NEWELL, Mark A. 602 MOYE BLVD, DEPT OF SURGERY 27834 #048-12-1992 L2003 GS *020 †85

NEWMAN, Robert Jos. ■ 27858 #051-01-1979 L2001 FM FPG *020 †18

NEWTON, Dale Alan. 600 MOYE BLVD, ECU BRODY SCHOOL OF MEDICI 27834 #036-01-1973 L1974 PD *030 †20,55

NEWTON, Douglas F. 1850 W ARLINGTON BLVD 27834 #035-15-1968 L1975 GE IM *020 †20

NEWTON, Edward Robson. 600 MOYE BLVD 27834 #016-43-1977 L1998 MFM OBG *030 †30

NGUYEN, Khanh Phuong. 600 MOYE BLVD, ECU BRODY SCHOOL MEDICINE 27834 #051-07-1996 L2002 CCP *020 †55

NIFONG, Leslie Wiley. 600 MOYE BLVD 27834 #036-08-1990 L1998 TS GS *020 †85,90

NOVICK, Lloyd Folston. 600 MOYE BLVD, HARDY BLDG 27834 #035-19-1965 L1967 PHP PD *030 †70 ‡

NOVOTNY, William Edward. 600 MOYE BLVD 27834 #038-43-1981 L1993 PD *020 †55

NUNEZ, Ann Caroline. 600 MOYE BLVD 27834 #935-01-1995 L2003 PM *020 †60

OAKLEY, Stanley P, Jr. 600 MOYE BLVD 27834 #036-08-1982 L1983 P PYG *040 †75

OBI, Reginald Ifeanyi. ■ 27858 #690-04-1992 L2004 IM *020 †20

ODEKE, Sylvester. 600 MOYE BLVD 27834 #905-01-1986 L2002 END *020 †20

OEHLER, Elizabeth C. 2100 STANTONSBURG RD, DEPT EM 27834 #048-14-2005 L2007 EM *012

OLSSON, John Mark. 600 MOYE BLVD 27834 #041-14-1979 L1998 PD *040 †55

OROGBEMI, Babatunde Odebu. 600 MOYE BLVD 27834 #033-05-2004 L2008 MEM *012

O'ROURKE, Peter John, III. 2430 EMERALD PL, STE 201 27834 #008-02-1990 L1996 AN PME *020 †05

ORR, Lynn Huie, Jr. 1800 W 5TH ST, STE 2 27834 #036-05-1974 L1974 CD IM *020 †20

OSEROFF, Allen Lewis. 2090 W ARLINGTON BLVD, STE B 27834 #010-01-1980 L1989 CD IM *020 †20

OVE, Roger. ■ 27834 #016-11-1995 L2005 IM *020 †80

OZIMEK, Christopher Louis. 1826 W ARLINGTON BLVD, CHILDREN'S HEALTH SERVICES 27834 #036-08-2002 L2005 PD *020 †55

PACE, Charles T. 1707 W 6TH ST 27834 #041-02-1949 L1949 OPH *020

PACIS, Jamie Jill. ■ 27834 #654-01-2005 P *012

PADGETT, Adam O'Neal. ■ 27858 #036-08-2008 *012

PANCOAST, Thomson Cable. 600 MOYE BLVD 3E-149, DEPT. OF MEDICINE/PULMONAR 27834 #010-01-1992 L2007 PCC IM *020 †20

PANEA, Oana Raluca. 600 MOYE BLVD 27834 #781-01-1999 L2006 FSM *012 †18

PARK, Hee Kim. 420 SPRING FOREST RD, EASTERN DERMATOLOGY& PATHO 27834 #583-08-1969 L1975 DMP ATP *020 †50

PARKER, Alison Anne. ■ 27834 #036-08-2008 *012

PATEL, Amit Ajitkumar. 600 MOYE BLVD, PCMH TA 340 27834 #665-01-2005 IM *012

PATEL, Chirag Arvind. 600 MOYE BLVD, BRODY SCHOOL OF MEDICINE 27834 #038-44-2005 PM *012

PATEL, Chirag Harikrishna. 600 MOYE BLVD 27834 #308-13-2001 L2004 PCC *012 †20

PATEL, Jayesh Kanchanlal. 850 WH SMITH BLVD 27834 #036-08-1988 L1990 CD *020 †20

PATEL, Jignasa J. 705 WH SMITH BLVD, PITT INTERNAL MED 27834 #495-23-1984 L1993 IM *020 †20

PATEL, Kanchanlal B. 2710 S MEMORIAL DR 27834 #495-23-1961 L1974 PHP FM *071

PATEL, Kirtida. 1913 E FIRE TOWER RD, STE E 27858 #305-01-2002 L2007 PRS FM *020 †18

PATEL, Roy Sureshkant. 2100 STANTONSBURG RD 27834 #305-01-2007 IM *012

PATEL, Shirley Harish. 1913 E FIRE TOWER RD, STE E 27858 #495-99-2000 L2007 FM *100

PATEL, Sonya. ■ 27834 #010-03-2007 MEM *012 †75

PATEL, Tarak Harikrishna. 2100 STANTONSBURG RD, PCMH 340 27834 #308-13-2001 DR *012

PATTERSON, Leigh A. 600 MOYE BLVD, DEPARTMENT OF EMERGENCY ME 27834 #001-02-1999 L2005 EM *020 †16

PATTON, Denzil Dean. 600 MOYE BLVD, BRODY SCHOOL OF MEDICINE 27834 #055-01-1972 L1986 FM *020 †18

PEARSALL, David W, Jr. 600 MOYE BLVD 27834 #036-01-1969 L1973 GS *020 †85

PEARSALL, Miller Bowen. ■ 27858 #036-08-2008 *012

PEART, Brian John. ■ 27858 #048-14-2007 EM *012

PEDEN, James Gwyn, Jr. 600 MOYE BLVD 27834 #036-01-1979 L1980 P IM *030 †20,75

PENCE, Jeffrey Carl. 600 MOYE BLVD, ECU PHYSICIANS 27834 #035-09-1986 L1995 PDS *020 †85

PENDER, John Robert, IV. 2100 STANTONSBURG RD 27834 #041-02-1999 L2003 GS *020 †85

PERDUE, Philip Sutherland. 810 WH SMITH BLVD 27834 #051-01-1988 L1995 OSM *020 †40

PERKIN, Ronald Murray. 600 MOYE BLVD, ECU BRODY SCHOOL OF MEDICI 27834 #011-04-1976 L2000 CCP SME *030 †55 ‡

PETERSON, Noel. PCMH TA RM 340, ECU SCHOOL OF MEDICINE 27858 #665-01-2002 L2006 CD *012 †20

PHILIPS, Ateiat Z. 1970 W ARLINGTON BLVD, CAROLINA PSYCHIATRY 27834 #915-04-1981 L1996 P *020 †75

PHILLIPS, Charles Mc Gloh. 600 MOYE BLVD, BRODY 3E-117 27834 #048-13-1983 L1986 D *020 †20,15

PHILLIPS, Stephen Lamar. 925C CONFERENCE DR, EASTERN PEDIATRICS, PA 27858 #045-01-1994 L1997 PD *020 †55

PHILPOT, Kelly W. 1204 E FIRE TOWER RD 27858 #028-46-1997 L1998 FM *020 †18

PHILPOT, Kirk Andrew. 1850 W ARLINGTON BLVD, PHYSICIANS E PA 27834 #028-46-1997 L1999 OS *020 †20

PIERCE, Jeffrey Norman. 600 MOYE BLVD, BRODY SCH OF MED 27834 #047-05-1991 L2002 PM *020 †60

PILATO, Marc Anthony. 2430 EMERALD PL 27834 #033-06-1984 L1991 AN *020 †05

PILLAY, Midesha. 1913 E FIRE TOWER RD, STE E 27858 #836-01-1995 L2005 FPG *020 †18

PINN, Melva Evette. 2100 STANTONSBURG RD 27834 #036-08-2007 L2007 IM *012

PLUCINSKI, Teresa Mary. ■ 27858 #051-01-1989 L1993 PM *040 †60

POFAHL, Walter E, II. 600 MOYE BLVD, BRODY SCHOOL OF MEDICINE 27834 #055-01-1988 L2000 GS AS *020 †85

PORIES, Walter Julius. 600 MOYE BLVD 27834 #035-45-1955 L1977 **GS TS** *050 †85,90 ‡
PORTER, Joshua Graham. ■ 27858 #036-08-2008 *012
PORTERFIELD, Christopher. ■ 27834 #665-01-2006 **IM** *012
POTTER, Ornella Judith. ■ 27834 #308-05-2002 **P** *012
POWELL, Charles Steven. 600 MOYE BLVD #020-12-1978 L1987 **VS GS** *020 †85
PREVILL, James Marshall. 600 MOYE BLVD, TA-389 PCMH 27834 #055-01-1970 L1998 **ON IM** *020 †20
PREVILL, Kathleen Vincent. 600 MOYE BLVD, ECV BRODY SCHOOL OF MEDICI 27834 #055-01-1970 L1998 **PD ADL** *030 †55
PRICE, Donald Lowell, Jr. 2280 HEMBY LN, EAST CAROLINA NEUROLOBY, I 27834 #035-20-1990 L1998 **NP** *020 †75
PRICE, Elaine Carole. 2425 HEMBY LN 27834 #035-03-1984 L1991 **OPH** *071 †35
PRICE, William L. 600 MOYE BLVD 27834 #035-03-1994 L1998 **EM** *020 †20
PRIVETTE, Douglas Craig. 850 WH SMITH BLVD 27834 #036-01-1976 L1976 **CD** *020 †20
PUHR, Dianna Dawn. ■ 27834 #036-08-2006 **MPD** *012
PUHR, Joshua Stephen. 600 MOYE BLVD, 3ED-320 27834 #047-20-2004 L2006 **MEM** *012
PYRTLE, Jay Malone. 600 MOYE BLVD, BRODY S OF M AT E CAROLINA 27834 #036-08-2006 **IM** *012
QURESHI, Atif S. 600 MOYE BLVD, 3E-149 BRODY BLDG 27834 #704-21-1997 L2006 **PUD CCM** *100 †20
RAAB, Mary Jerista. 600 MOYE BLVD 27834 #041-07-1968 L1977 **IM** *020
RAMIREZ, Maria Eugenia. 2100 STANTONSBURG RD, PCMH 340 27834 #935-01-1994 L2006 **IM** *100
RAMSDELL, Charles Michael. 1850 W ARLINGTON BLVD, PHYSICIANS EAST, PA 27834 #021-05-1965 L1971 **RHU IM** *071 †20
RANA, Madhvi. 2100 STANTONSBURG RD 27834 #422-01-2002 L2008 **ID** *012 †20
RAND, Cecil Holmes, Jr. 1800 W 5TH ST 27834 #036-01-1961 L1961 **PUD IG** *071 †20
RANKIN, Corwin Jawayne. 2100 STANTONSBURG RD, DEPT IM 27834 #036-08-2007 **MPD** *012
RAWL, Richard Preston. 600 MOYE BLVD 27834 #036-05-1978 L1980 **FM** *020 †18
REECE, Amanda Jane. 2100 STANTONSBURG RD, PITT CO MEM HOSP 27834 #654-01-2006 **PD** *012
REED, John David. 511 PALADIN DR, EASTERN NEPHROLOGY ASSOCIA 27834 #036-01-1986 L1991 **NEP IM** *020 †20
REEDER, Timothy John. 600 MOYE BLVD, ECU BRODY SCHOOL OF MEDICI 27834 #038-40-1995 L1998 **EM** *020 †16
REEG, Scott Eric. 2390 HEMBY LN, CENTER FOR SCOLIOSIS & SPI 27834 #016-11-1989 L1993 **OSS** *020 †40
REEVES, Hugh Mallory, Jr. 275 BETHESDA DR 27834 #001-02-2001 L2006 **U** *020
REICHEL, Michael Eugene. 600 MOYE BLVD, BSOM 27834 #023-01-1974 L2002 **PD OS** *020 †55
REIN-WARREN, Norma Kemper. ■ 27858 #036-08-1994 *100
RENFROW, Stephen Ford, Jr. ■ 27834 #036-08-2008 *012
REYNOLDS, Kim Aurora. 622 S MEMORIAL DR 27834 #036-08-1998 L2003 **CHP** *020
REYNOLDS, Melissa C. ■ 27834 #055-75-2007, ▲ *012
REZAIE, Salim Reza. 2100 STANTONSBURG RD, P O BOX 6028 27834 #048-16-2005 L2008 **MEM** *012
RICE, John Lanier. 1705 W SIXTH ST, 1705 W 6TH ST 27834 #036-05-1992 L1996 **P** *020 †75 ‡
RICHARDSON, Maurice Devon. 2100 STANTONSBURG RD, PO BOX 6028 27834 #047-07-2004 L2007 **PTH** *012
RIMKIENE, Ruta. 2100 STANTONSBURG RD, FAMILY PRACTICE CENTER 27834 #913-49-1996 **FP** *012
RIZZUTI, Richard Philip. 400 SPRING FOREST RD, GREENVILLE PLASTIC SURGERY 27834 #036-08-1983 L1985 **PS GS** *020 †85,65
ROBB, Jeffrey Wallace. 2430 EMERALD PL, # 201 27834 #025-07-1980 L1981 **AN** *020 †05
ROBERTSON, Howard D. 1850 W ARLINGTON BLVD 27834 #020-02-1974 L1988 **CRS GS** *020 †85,10
ROBEY, Claude. 1850 W ARLINGTON BLVD 27834 #396-01-1979 L1994 **END DIA** *020 †20
ROBEY, Walter Chas, III. 600 MOYE BLVD, ECU SCHOOL OF MEDICINE 27834 #396-01-1980 L1994 **EM** *040 †16
ROBINSON, Ketarah Cherese. ■ 27834 #036-08-2008 *012
ROBINSON, Sharon Massey. 1850 W ARLINGTON BLVD 27834 #036-08-1999 L2002 **IM** *020
RODRIGUEZ, Evelio. 600 MOYE BLVD, RM 257 27834 #035-03-1995 L2004 **TS** *100 †85,90
RODRIGUEZ, Luis Ernesto. 600 MOYE BLVD 27834 #270-02-1994 L2000 **EM** *100 †20,16
ROMANO, Noemi Gabriela. 2100 STANTONSBURG RD 27834 #023-01-1999 L2002 **IM** *020 †20
ROSE, John David. 1800 W 5TH ST 27834 #041-01-1972 L1975 **CD IM** *020 †20
ROSS, Meredith Richmond. 105 WHITE OAK DR 27858 #027-01-1979 L2001 **FPG** *020 †18
ROTONDO, Michael F. 600 MOYE BLVD 27834 #010-02-1984 L1999 **GS CCS** *020 †85
RUCKER, William Lee. 600 MOYE BLVD, EAST CAROLINA UNIVERSITY P 27834 #045-01-1980 L1983 **GS VS** *040 †85
RUGNATH, Dinesh. ■ 27834 #495-37-1997 **PTH** *012
RUMLEY, Richard Lee. 503 BOWMAN GRAY DR, STE A 27834 #036-01-1978 L1979 **ID IM** *020 †20
RUSSELL, Laura Ann. ■ 27834 #025-07-2006 **EM** *012
RUSSO, Suzanne Mary. ■ 27834 #036-01-1995 L1997 **RO** *020 †80
RYAN, Caroline Dorothea. 275 BETHESDA DR 27834 #036-08-1998 L2007 **U** *020 †95
RYAN, Jason. 2080 W ARLINGTON BLVD # B, EAST CAROLINA ANESTHESIA A 27834 #016-11-1998 L2002 **AN** *020
SADLER, Aerica. ■ 27858 #036-08-2008 *012
SAEED, S Atezaz. 600 MOYE BLVD STE 4E-102, BRODY SCHL OF MED, ECU 27834 #704-02-1982 L2004 **P MDM** *030 †75 ‡
SAGRAVES, Scott Gary. 600 MOYE BLVD, DEPT OF SURGERY 27834 #016-42-1993 L2000 **CCS** *020 †85
SAID ALI, Mohamed Abdelmo. 600 MOYE BLVD, DEPT OF MEDICINE, PCMH, TA 27834 #915-04-1988 L2006 **IMG** *020
SAJEEVAN, Sujatha. ■ 27834 #495-04-1994 **FP** *012
SANDOVAL, Alexius Enrique. 600 MOYE BLVD 27834 #748-02-1998 **PM** *020
SANG, Charlie Jos, Jr. 2150 HERBERT CT, DIV OF PEDIATRICS CARDIOLO 27834 #021-01-1983 L1989 **PDC PD** *020 †55
SASTRY, Tejaswi R.. ■ 27834 #496-22-2001 L2006 **HO** *012 †20
SAUL, Robert Franklin. 2280 HEMBY LN, EAST CAROLINA NEUROLOGY, I 27834 #051-04-1976 L2005 **N** *020 †75 ‡
SAVAGE, Roytesa M. 600 MOYE BLVD 27834 #036-08-1999 L2002 **PD** *020 †55
SAYERS, Ronald Merle. 9 DOCTORS PARK, EASTERN RADIOLOGISTS 27834 #038-40-1999 L2004 **RNR** *020 †80
SCARBORO, Steven Chad. ■ 27834 #036-05-2007 **EM** *012
SCHENARTS, Paul Jos. 600 MOYE BLVD 27834 #008-02-1992 L2001 **CCS** *020 †85

SCHEUER, Alfred Quinn. 2001 WOODWIND DR, EASTERN PSYCHIATRIC & BEHA 27858 #008-01-1968 L2006 **PD** *020 †55 ‡
SCHLITZKUS, Lisa Lynn. ■ 27858 #048-14-2006 **GS** *012
SCHMIDT, Jeffrey Eugene. 600 MOYE BLVD, BRODY SCHOOL OF MEDICINE 27834 #004-01-1990 L2007 **CCP** *020 †55
SCHMIDT, Susan Ann. 600 MOYE BLVD, EASTERN CAROLINA UNIVERSIT 27834 #036-08-2002 L2004 **FM** *020 †18
SCHOSSER, Robert Hill. 600 MOYE BLVD, BRODY 3E-117 27834 #020-02-1970 L2004 **D DMP** *020 †15 ‡
SCHWARTZ, Joshua David. 2430 EMERALD PL, STE 201 27834 #050-02-1983 L1991 **AN IM** *020 †20,05
SCOGGINS-AMBROSE, Heather. 1850 W ARLINGTON BLVD 27834 #036-08-1998 L2003 **HO** *020 †20
SCOTT-KRAEMER, Mary S. 600 MOYE BLVD 27834 #038-45-1993 L1997 **IM** *020 †20
SEIBEL, Kathleen Marie. 600 MOYE BLVD, DEPT OF PSYCHIATRY, BRODY 27834 #026-04-1985 L1986 **P** *040 †75
SEKHON, Navdeep Singh. ■ 27834 #005-18-2007 **EM** *012
SEMBRANO, Roderick Nubla. 600 MOYE BLVD 27834 #748-02-2004 **PM** *012
SEMER, Diane Alane. 1850 W ARLINGTON BLVD 27834 #036-08-1985 L1992 **OBG** *020 †30
SEPICH, Christopher Micha. ■ 27858 #036-08-2008 *012
SESSOMS, Cory John. ■ 27834 #036-08-2008 *012
SEWELL, Kia Renece. 600 MOYE BLVD, MEMORIAL HOSPITAL 27834 #010-02-2006 **IM** *012
SHACKELFORD, Donald Paul. 2251 STANTONSBURG RD, WOMENS CLINIC 27834 #036-05-1991 L1995 **OBG** *020 †30
SHAFFER, Holly Candice. ■ 27858 #036-01-2005 **D** *012
SHAH, Nirmish. 1850 W ARLINGTON BLVD 27834 #654-01-2000 L2005 **PHO** *012 †20
SHAHID, Aamina. 2100 STANTONSBURG RD 27834 #704-01-2005 **FP** *012
SHAIKH, Azra Perveen. ■ 27834 #308-13-2001 L2007 **FM** *100 †18
SHAMMAS, Rony Labib. 850 WH SMITH BLVD 27834 #605-01-1987 L1991 **CD IM** *020 †20
SHANMUGAM, Kalpana. 2100 STANTONSBURG RD 27834 #495-59-1996 **P** *012
SHAPPLEY, Ben Gordon. 300 BETHESDA DR 27834 #051-01-1966 L1971 **PD** *020 †55
SHAW, Robert Arnett. 1850 W ARLINGTON BLVD, PHYSICIANS EAST, PA 27834 #036-07-1976 L1981 **PUD** *020 †20
SHERROW, Nicholas Charles. ■ 27858 #020-02-2002 L2008 **NPM** *012 †55
SHORE, Brad Leon. ■ 27834 #036-08-2008 *012
SHULTZABERGER, Richard Z. 1850 W ARLINGTON BLVD, PHYSICIANS EAST, PA 27834 #041-09-1981 L1985 **IM** *020 †20
SIEBEL, Stephan. 2100 STANTONSBURG RD 27834 #409-25-2006 **PD** *012
SIEGEL, John Edward. STUDENT HEALTH SERVICE 27834 #036-05-1966 L1966 **FM FSM** *020 †18
SILVI, Evan Christopher. ■ 27834 #030-06-2004 **IM** *100
SIMPSON, Jerry Allen. 850 WH SMITH BLVD 27834 #036-08-1994 L1996 **CD** *020 †20
SIMPSON, Marshall Craig. 503 BOWMAN GRAY DR, STE B 27834 #036-08-1987 L1990 **FM** *020 †18
SINAR, Dennis Robt. 600 MOYE BLVD 27834 #038-40-1973 L1981 **GE IM** *020 †20
SINGH, Harmeet. 2355 W ARLINGTON BLVD 27834 #495-03-1997 L2003 **NEP** *040 †20 ‡
SINGH, Harsharan Kaur. 600 MOYE BLVD 27834 #036-08-1985 L1989 **PTH AN** *020 †50
SIRAJ, Dawd Said. 600 MOYE BLVD 27834 #366-03-1992 L2002 **ID** *020 †20
SLAUGHTER, Van, Jr. 2100 STANTONSBURG RD 27834 #654-01-2006 **IM** *012
SLOOP, Catherine Marie. 2425 HEMBY LN, GREENVILLE EYE CLINIC 27834 #036-05-1993 L1997 **OPH** *020 †35
SMALLWOOD, Brandon Lee. 3689 IVY RD 27858 #020-12-2003 L2005 **EM** *020 †16
SMITH, Anthony Crozat. 600 MOYE BLVD 27834 #001-02-1998 L2001 **IM** *020 †20
SMITH, Brian Thomas. 2206 SADDLE RIDGE PL, EASTERN CAROLINA PSYCHIATR 27858 #036-08-1995 L2009 **P** *020 †20
SMITH, Cameron Langley. 420 SPRING FOREST RD 27834 #036-01-1971 L1971 **D** *020 †15 ‡
SMITH, Esther Pauline. 2100 STANTONSBURG RD, PITT CO MEM HOSP 27834 #665-02-2006 **PD** *012
SMITH, Kitila A. ■ 27834 #036-08-2008 *012
SMITH, Michael Earl. 925 CONFERENCE DR 27858 #036-08-1988 L1992 **CHP** *020 †75
SMITH, Michael Kevin. 850 WH SMITH BLVD 27834 #051-04-1998 L2005 **CD IM** *020 †20
SMITH, Nancy Lane. 600 MOYE BLVD 27834 #051-04-1991 L1996 **PTH** *020 †50
SMITH, Teresa Annette. 1688 E ARLINGTON BLVD, MED-CENTER 1 27858 #036-08-1988 L1990 **IM OM** *020 †20
SNYDER, Danal Sue. ■ 27858 #036-08-2004 L2007 **FM** *020
SNYDER, David Keith. 1850 W ARLINGTON BLVD, PHYSICIANS EAST 27834 #038-43-1981 L1985 **END IM** *020 †20
SONG, Juliet Kim. 2080 W ARLINGTON BLVD # B 27834 #583-08-1965 L1971 **AN** *071
SPRINGS, De Shonta L. ■ 27834 #036-08-2003 **OBG** *012
STANLEY, Karl Harvey. 2100 STANTONSBURG RD 27834 #010-03-1976 L1977 **P GP** *020 †75
STANSFIELD, Karrie Ann. ■ 27834 #036-08-2005 L2008 **PD** *012
STARR, Shane Randal. ■ 27858 #011-04-2004 **PTH** *012
STEED, Robert Dennis. 503 CARNOUSTIE DR 27858 #012-01-1981 L1987 **PDC PD** *040 †55
STEEL, Marilyn Leonard. 620 S MEMORIAL DR, BULDING B 27834 #036-08-1989 L1991 **IM** *071 †20
STEIN, Peter Michael. 1850 W ARLINGTON BLVD, PHYSICIANS EAST, PA 27834 #023-07-1984 L1993 **GE HEP** *020 †20
STEINBERG, Steven Andrew. 301 BOWMAN GRAY DR 27834 #035-08-1986 L1991 **OPH** *020 †35
STEINER, Manfred. ■ 27858 #154-07-1955 L1994 **HEM IM** *050
STEINHORST, Bernward. 600 MOYE BLVD 27834 #409-25-1990 L2001 **GS** *020 †85
STEINWEG, Kenneth Keller. 600 MOYE BLVD, ECU BRODY SCHOOL OF MEDICI 27834 #036-01-1975 L1978 **FM FPG** *020 †18
STEPANIAN, Assia A.. 600 MOYE BLVD, ECU SCHL OF MED 27834 #913-06-1992 L2004 **OBG** *100
STEPHENSON, Hale Hampton. 101 BETHESDA DR, C/O PHYSICIANS EAST, PA 27834 #036-08-1988 L1991 **OBG** *020 †30
STEVENS, Jennifer Calfee. 2251 STANTONSBURG RD 27834 #036-08-2000 L2002 **OBG** *020
STONE, Roger William. ■ 27858 #036-08-2008 *012
STONER, Michael Clinton. 600 MOYE BLVD, RM TA237 27834 #035-06-1996 L2005 **VS** *100 †85
STRAUSBAUCH, Paul H. 600 MOYE BLVD 27834 #011-02-1974 L1978 **PTH** *040 †50
STRAYHORN, Shakonda Lasha. 2100 STANTONSBURG RD, DEPT OF OB/GYN 27834 #038-41-2006 **OBG** *012
STRICKLAND, Julie Ann. 1941 TARA CT, APT 101 27858 #036-08-2004 L2007 **PD** *100 †55
STRICKLAND, Shelly Ronita. ■ 27834 #036-08-2008 *012

■ = Address Information Privacy Protected

STROPE, Gerald Leland. 600 MOYE BLVD 27834 #035-45-1974 L1975 **PDP PD** *020 †55

STURGIS, Thomas Michael. 2465 EMERALD PL 27834 #033-06-1986 L1992 **GE HEP** *020 †20

SURLES, Lara Kester. 600 MOYE BLVD 27834 #036-08-1999 L2001 **FPG** *020 †18

SUTTON, Carole Ann. ■ 27834 #036-05-1995 L1997 **PTH** *020 †50

SWANSON, Erin Marie. ■ 27834 #036-08-2008 *012

SWINKER, Marian Lea. 600 MOYE BLVD, ECU BRODY SCHOOL OF MEDICI 27834 #041-14-1978 L1994 **OM FM** *030 †70,18

SWITZER, Bruce Dale. 600 MOYE BLVD 27834 #045-01-1997 L1998 **IM** *020 †20

SYMONS, Nicole Leigh. 600 MOYE BLVD, ECU FAMILY PRCTICE CTR 27834 #035-06-1997 L1998 **FM** *020 †18

SZALKOWSKI, Maciej. 800 MOYE BLVD, VA MEDICAL CENTER 27834 #759-11-1997 L2006 **FM** *100 †18

TABRIZI, Elnaz Nassehzade. 600 MOYE BLVD 27834 #036-08-2006 **IM** *012

TAFT, Richard Chesson. 101 BETHESDA DR 27834 #036-01-1972 L1972 **OBG** *020 †30

TAFT, William Holston, III. 101 BETHESDA DR 27834 #036-08-2000 L2004 **OBG** *020 †30

TAHA, Sherif Hosny M. 2100 STANTONSBURG RD 27834 #915-03-1981 L2002 **AI PD** *020 †03,55

TALANTOV, Andrei Vsevolod. 2100 STANTONSBURG RD 27834 #913-03-1993 L2007 **IM** *100 *012

TALENTE, Gregg Michael. 600 MOYE BLVD 27834 #036-01-1995 L2001 **MPD** *020 †20,55

TALENTO, Romualdo V. ■ 27858 #051-07-2006 **PTH** *012

TALLEY, Jessica Dawn. 600 MOYE BLVD, BRODY SCHOOL OF MEDICINE 27834 #055-01-2002 L2007 **CHP** *012

TANENBERG, Robert Jay. 600 MOYE BLVD, 3E-129 DEPT ENDOCRINOLOGY 27834 #016-11-1971 L1998 **DIA END** *020 †20

TANGREDI, Christine M. 2280 HEMBY LN 27834 #031-01-1997 L2002 **N** *020 †75

TAYLOR, Allen. 9 DOCTORS PARK 27834 #036-07-1947 L1952 **R** *071 †80

TAYLOR, Jonathan Harris. 275 BETHESDA DR 27834 #036-08-2002 L2007 **U** *020

TAYLOR, Mandrill Raemone. ■ 27834 #036-08-2008 *012

TAYLOR, Marshall Carney. 511 PALADIN DR 27834 #051-01-1970 L1978 **DR** *020 †20

TAYLOR, Marshall Carney, Jr. 511 PALADIN DR 27834 #036-08-1996 L2001 **NEP** *020 †20

TAZKARJI, M. Bachir. 500 MOYE BLVD, FAMILY PRACTICE CLINIC 27834 #875-02-1998 L2006 **FM** *100 †18

TERRELL, Thomas Roland. 600 MOYE BLVD, BRODY SCHL OF MED EVU 27834 #012-05-1991 L1993 **FM FSM** *020 †18

TEWARI, Anand. 2080 W ARLINGTON BLVD # B, PITT COUNTY ANESTH ASSOC 27834 #062-01-1984 L2001 **AN** *020 †05

THIELE, Ronald Lewis. ■ 27858 #025-07-1948 L1972 **OS PHP** *071 †55

THOMAS, Roger Edmund. 705 WH SMITH BLVD 27834 #065-10-1977 L1983 **FM** *040

THOMPSON, Douglas John. ■ 27858 #012-01-1993 L2007 **HO** *012 †20

THOMPSON, Reva Marcia L. 1850 W ARLINGTON BLVD 27834 #023-01-1978 L2005 **DR** *020 †80

TIRUPATTUR, Prakash. ECU SCHOOL OF MEDICINE 27858 #495-73-1984 L1992 **CD** *020 †20

TITONE, Charles Wm. 1840 W ARLINGTON BLVD 27834 #010-03-1984 L2003 **OPH** *020 †35

TOSCHLOG, Eric Andrew. 600 MOYE BLVD, DEPT OF SURGERY 600 MOYE B 27834 #038-41-1993 L2000 **CCS** *020 †85

TRAN, Boi Phuong. ■ 27834 #047-20-2008 **EM** *012

TREADWELL, Edward Louis. 600 MOYE BLVD, DEPT OF MED/RHEUMLGY 27834 #036-07-1975 L1976 **RHU IM** *020 †20

TRENT, Lee Royal, III. 608 E 10TH ST 27858 #051-04-1977 L1978 **FM** *075 †18

TREVATHAN, Gordon E, Jr. ■ 27834 #007-02-1951 L1954 **PD CHN** *071 †55

TRINH, Hai Hong. 2100 STANTONSBURG RD, DEPARTMENT OF EMERGENCY ME 27834 #012-01-2002 L2003 **EM** *020 †16

TRISTRAM, Debra Ann. 600 MOYE BLVD, ECU BSOM 600 MOYE BLVD 27834 #035-03-1982 L1998 **PD ID** *050 †55

TUCCI, Keith A. 2100 STANTONSBURG RD 27834 #011-02-1985 L1993 **NS** *020 †25

TUCKER, Donald Hugh. ■ 27858 #036-07-1958 L2002 **CD IM** *020 †20

TURFBOER, Robert. ■ 27858 #660-02-1942 L1961 **P** *071

TURLAPATI, Lakshmi Anupam. 2100 STANTONSBURG RD, PCMH 340 27834 #495-21-2002 L2007 **IM** *020 †20

TUTTLE, Bryan Tremayne. ■ 27834 #036-08-2008 *012

TYLER, Shannon A. 600 MOYE BLVD 27834 #036-08-1997 L1999 **P** *020 †75

TYSON, George Hart, III. ■ 27834 #048-13-2003 **GS** *012

UGOJI, Amanze Olufemi Ofo. 2100 STANTONSBURG RD, PITT COUNTY MEMORIAL HOSPI 27834 #690-07-1996 L2007 **FM** *020 †18

USALA, Anton-Lewis. 1800 N GREENE ST STE B, CTMG, INC. 27834 #041-02-1983 L1990 **PDE** *020

VANDERFORD, Joel Leonard. 2100 STANTONSBURG RD 27834 #305-01-2007 **PD** *012

VAN EYK, Jason Joseph. 600 MOYE BLVD, DEPT OF MEDICINE, PEDIATRI 27834 #036-08-2003 L2005 **MPD** *020

VAN HOUTEN, Peter Arthur. 2501 STANTONSBURG RD STE A 27834 #011-02-1982 L1988 **OPH** *020 †35

VANNORSDALL, Mark. 511 PALADIN DR 27834 #043-01-1996 L2000 **NEP** *020 †20

VARGHESE, Shona Susan Pau. 600 MOYE BLVD 27834 #496-40-1995 L2004 **IM** *020

VARJU, Gabor Tibor. 1850 W ARLINGTON BLVD 27834 #473-03-1995 L2005 **PCC IM** *020 †20

VARNER, Dwan Quennel. ■ 27858 #036-08-2005 L2008 **IM** *012

VENKATARAMAN, Srimathi. 1A DOCTORS PARK, PITT CO MEM HOSP 27834 #495-59-1988 L2008 **P** *012

VERASTEGUI, Juan Gualbert. 2100 STANTONSBURG RD 27834 #737-01-1996 **IM** *012

VERMUND, Halvor. 600 MOYE BLVD # RAD, ECU SCHOOL OF MEDICINE 27834 #693-01-1943 L1989 **RO R** *071 †80

VICK, J Bernard. 905 JOHNS HOPKINS DR 27834 #036-05-1957 L1997 **GS TS** *071 †85,90

VICKERS, Raymond. ■ 27858 #917-20-1950 L1993 **FPG PYG** *062 †18

VIEAGES, Ananda Leah. ■ 27858 #036-08-2008 *012

VILLAROSA, Leonardo Leopa. 600 MOYE BLVD 27834 #748-01-2002 **PM** *012

VINOGRADOV, Mikhail. 600 MOYE BLVD, LEOGENSON CANCER CENTER 27834 #913-37-1986 L2004 **HO** *012

VISCARDI, Jeffrey Joseph. 301 BOWMAN GRAY DR 27834 #035-08-1985 L1990 **OPH** *020 †35

VOGEL, Nancy Louise. 925 CONFERENCE DR, BHAVIORAL SPECIALISTS 27858 #038-41-1982 L1993 **P PD** *020 †55,75

VOLKMAN, Alvin. 2100 STANTONSBURG RD, EAST CAROLINA UNIVERSITY 27834 #035-06-1951 L1977 **PTH** *040 †50

VOOS, Kurt. 2390 HEMBY LN 27834 #020-02-1993 L2001 **OSS ORS** *020 †40

WADDELL, Andrea Garcia. 600 MOYE BLVD, BRODY SCH OF MED 27834 #012-22-2004 L2008 **D** *012

WAHLEN, John Edward. 9 DOCTORS PARK, RADIOLOGY 27834 #005-12-1996 L2007 **DR** *100 †80

WAIBEL, Brett Harden. 600 MOYE BLVD 27834 #047-06-2000 L2005 **GS** *020 †85

WAIVERS, Leo Edward. 2210 HEMBY LN, STE 101 27834 #033-05-1980 L1986 **IM FM** *020 †20

WALKER, Paul Raymond. 600 MOYE BLVD, DIV OF HEM & ONCOLOGY/ BRO 27834 #017-20-1979 L2006 **ON IM** *040 †20

WALKER, Ray Carter. 600 MOYE BLVD 27834 #008-01-1971 L1972 **P** *071

WALKER, William Ray. 3408 DUNHAVEN DR 27834 #051-04-1968 L2002 **P** *040 †75

WALLER, Carrie Elizabeth. 1826 W ARLINGTON BLVD 27834 #036-07-1998 L2004 **PD** *020 †55

WARD, Demetrice Louise. ■ 27834 #036-08-1997 L2007 **PM** *100

WARREN, Mark Lowe. 1850 W ARLINGTON BLVD 27834 #036-01-1984 L1989 **END IM** *020 †20

WATSON, Ricky Lee. 600 MOYE BLVD, BRODY SCH OF MED AT ECU 27834 #036-08-1990 L1991 **FM** *020 †20

WAUGH, William Howard. ■ 27858 #024-07-1948 L1971 **OS NEP** *071

WEATHERS, Vivian J. 6 DOCTORS PARK, DEPT OF PSYCHIATRIC MEDICI 27834 #654-01-1987 L1997 **P** *012

WEED, Matthew Thomas. 2100 STANTONSBURG RD, PITT CO MEM HOSP 27834 #422-01-2006 **IM** *012

WEISMILLER, David Glenn. 600 MOYE BLVD 27834 #041-02-1991 L1996 **FM** *020 †18

WEISS, Richard. 2100 STANTONSBURG RD, DEPARTMENT OF PMR 27834 #422-01-2004 **PM** *012

WELCH, Jack H. 2080 W ARLINGTON BLVD # B 27834 #036-01-1963 L1963 **AN** *071 †05

WEST, Robert Lee. 1800 W 5TH ST, STE 2 27834 #036-01-1959 L1959 **PTH** *020 †50

WHITE, Randal Earl. 1850 W ARLINGTON BLVD 27834 #055-01-1980 L1983 **RHU IM** *020 †20

WHITTED, Thurman, Jr. 600 MOYE BLVD 27834 #047-20-1995 L1996 **PM** *020 †60

WILHELMSEN, Bruce Douglas. 810 WH SMITH BLVD 27834 #036-07-1979 L1984 **ORS** *020 †40

WILK, Leonard Mark. 600 MOYE BLVD 27834 #759-18-2003 L2007 **FM** *100 †18

WILLIAMS, Frances E. 800 MOYE BLVD, VA OUTPATIENT CENTER 27834 #024-05-1996 L2000 **IM** *020 †20

WILLIAMS, John Mark. 600 MOYE BLVD, RM 277 27834 #036-07-1976 L1985 **TS** *020 †85,90

WILLIAMS, Lawrence Albert. 2100 STANTONSBURG RD 27834 #305-01-2007 **PTH** *012

WILLIAMS, Randolph Meade. 810 WH SMITH BLVD 27834 #051-01-1971 L1978 **ORS** *020 †40

WILLIAMS, Rhoderick T, Jr. 905 JOHNS HOPKINS DR 27834 #036-01-1967 L1967 **DR R** *020 †80

WILLIAMS, Richard F, Jr. 600 MOYE BLVD, BRODY SCHOOL OF MEDICINE 27834 #036-07-1986 L1989 **GS** *020 †85

WILLIAMS, Sarah Allison. ■ 27834 #036-08-2007 **GS** *012

WILLIAMS, Sharon Letitia. ■ 27858 #036-01-2003 **GS** *012

WILLIAMSON, Shirley T. ■ 27835 #036-05-1980 L1982 **FM** *020 †18

WILLIS, Stephen Edgar. 2000 VENTURE TOWER DR, STE 210 27834 #051-01-1981 L1984 **FM** *020 †18

WILLSON, Chas Frederick. 600 MOYE BLVD 27834 #051-01-1974 L1976 **PD GP** *020 †55

WIMBERLY, John A. PO BOX 7007 27835 #020-02-1952 L1977 **GP** *020

WINSTEAD, J Lindsay, Jr. ■ 27858 #036-01-1958 L1958 **GS** *020 †85

WOELK, Joshua Lane. ■ 27858 #019-02-2005 **OBG** *012

WOOD, William Chadwick. 2100 STANTONSBURG RD 27834 #047-06-1969 L2001 **CD IM** *040 †20

WOODALL, Anna Marie. ■ 27834 #036-08-2008 *012

WOOTEN, Harriet L Husted. ■ 27858 #023-01-1950 L1955 **FM PHP** *071 †18

WOOTEN, Stephen Lamont. 810 WH SMITH BLVD 27834 #036-07-1981 L1986 **ORS HS** *020 †40

WORKMAN, Jonathan Robert. 850 JOHNS HOPKINS DR 27834 #038-41-1993 L1998 **OTO GS** *020 †45

WORSLEY, Stephen Cole. 1696 E ARLINGTON BLVD 27858 #036-07-1979 L1980 **PD** *100

YAN, Yun. 2100 STANTONSBURG RD 27834 #243-38-1982 **PD** *012

YANG, Chao-Yung. 2100 STANTONSBURG RD 27834 #244-01-1969 L2001 **AN** *020 †05

YILDIRIM, Yilmaz. 2100 STANTONSBURG RD 27834 #902-05-1994 **PD** *012

YONGUE, Judith Salle. 107 COMMERCE ST STE D 27858 #036-01-1962 L1962 **P GP** *020 †18,75

YOSHIDA, Shunsuke. ■ 27834 #038-41-2007 **GS** *012

YOUMANS, Tonia Marcia. 600 MOYE BLVD, PITT COUNTY MEMORIAL HOSP 27834 #665-01-2006 **IM** *012

ZAKI, Zohreh. PO BOX 6028, PITT CO MEMORIAL HOSPITAL 27835 #517-01-1991 L2001 **PCP** *020 †50

ZANGA, Joseph Robt. 600 MOYE BLVD, RVU BRODY SCHOOL OF MEDICI 27834 #016-43-1971 L2003 **PD PEM** *040 †55 ‡

ZAPIACH, Mauricio. 600 MOYE BLVD # 30, ECU-GASTRO DIVISION 27834 #033-05-1997 L2003 **IM** *020 †20

ZERI, Richard Stephen. 600 MEDICAL DR, PLASTIC SURGERY CTR 27834 #010-02-1989 L1991 **PS HS** *020 †65,85

ZHANG, Junhong. 600 MOYE BLVD, ECU PHYSICIANS PCMH TA389 27834 #243-29-1985 L2005 **IM** *020 †20

ZHU, Gening. 2577 W FIFTH ST, WBJ-ADATC 27834 #243-29-1985 L2003 **P** *020

ZOUEV, Alexandr. 1 DOCTORS PARK, # A 27834 #913-66-1989 L2004 **P** *100

ZOUEVA, Svetlana. 2100 STANTONSBURG RD 27834 #913-66-1991 **P** *012

GRIFTON – PITT

BARNES, M Russell, Jr. HWY 11 S, GRIFTON MEDICAL CARE 28530 #036-05-1948 L1949 **OBG GS** *072

CARSON, Jack Oliver. MCCRAE ST 28530 #023-01-1952 L1952 **FM** *071 †18

SHAPIRO, Solomon. ■ 28530 #051-01-1980 L1985 **FM** *020 †18

TROUTMAN, Belk Connor. ■ 28530 #023-01-1952 L1952 **GP** *020

GRIMESLAND – PITT

PARKER, Joseph Clinton. ■ 27837 #036-08-2003 L2007 **NEP** *012 †20

REITER, Todd Michael. ■ 27837 #748-10-2004 L2007 **PM** *012

GROVER – CLEVELAND

SALUKE, Julia Kathryn. 217 N MAIN ST, GROVER FAMILY PRACTICE 28073 #038-45-1992 L1995 **FM** *020 †18

■ = Address Information Privacy Protected

HAMLET – RICHMOND

AKHTAR, Afaque. 104 JEFFERSON ST 28345 #704-02-1989 L2004 **IM** *020 †20
ANSARI, Soukath. 102 ENDO LN 28345 #495-95-1972 L1984 **GE IM** *020 †20
ATWATER, Terresa Loretta. 1000 W HAMLET AVE 28345 #036-01-1981 L1983 **P** *020
BAYAZID, Saeb. 105 W MAIN ST, P O BOX 1227 28345 #875-01-1981 L1995 **GS VS** *020 †85
BOWMAN, Melva Richardson. 224 W MAIN ST, P O BOX 1209 28345 #036-01-1989 L1992 **FM** *020 †18
COTTRELL, Alesia Dawn. 1000 W HAMLET AVE 28345 #036-01-1997 L2002 **FM** *020
COULSON, Alan Stewart. 108 ENDO LN, STE 1 28345 #917-07-1969 L2000 **TS** *020 †85,90
GUEVARA, Jason Edward. 1000 W HAMLET AVE 28345 #005-02-1988 L1999 **ORS OAR** *020 †40
HUFFMAN, Elaine W. 1021 W HAMLET AVE STE 5, P O BOX 1227 28345 #036-01-1977 L1977 **FM** *020 †18
MANGRUM, Charlita Rose. ■ 28345 #025-07-1988 L2004 **FM** *020 †18
MC QUEEN, Fred Douglas. 104 RICE ST 28345 #010-03-1973 L1974 **FM** *020 †18
NASCIMENTO, Luiz. ■ 28345 #187-03-1970 L1988 **IM** *075
QUEEN, Hugh Oscar. 317 CHARLOTTE ST 28345 #012-01-1952 L1954 **FM** *071
SHILEN, Thomas Sevier. 100 JEFFERSON ST, P O BOX 1147 28345 #041-02-1959 L1991 **AN** *020 †05
THAKKAR, Bharatkumar. 106 JEFFERSON ST 28345 #495-22-1973 L1995 **IM** *020 †20
TUTEN, Harry Lane, Jr. 108 ENDO LN, STE 1 28345 #045-01-1979 L2006 **GS** *020 †85
VEASY, George D. 1021 W HAMLET AVE, STE 4 28345 #049-01-1976 L1999 **ORS HS** *020 †40
WAGNITZ, John Gabriel. 1000 W HAMLET AVE 28345 #038-40-1967 L1984 **P OS** *030 †75 ‡

HAMPSTEAD – PENDER

ABAN, Kenric Turingan. ■ 28443 #023-12-2005 L2006 *020
BEIRNE, Martin C. ■ 28443 #539-01-1972 L1980 **FM OS** *020
BLOUNT, Marsha Wells. 14905 US HIGHWAY 17 N 28443 #036-01-1997 L2005 **FM** *020 †18
BONK, Johan Pieter. ■ 28443 #660-04-1952 L1963 **R OS** *071 †80
DASHOW, Larry Joel. ■ 28443 #041-02-1985 L2003 **GS GE** *020 †85
DOMBROWSKI, Edwin Henry. 18676 US HIGHWAY 17 N 28443 #035-15-1961 L1995 **A IM** *071
FISCHER, Joseph Wm. 301 WIDGEON DR 28443 #047-06-1967 L1988 **R** *020 †80
GARG, Shyam L. 14980 US HIGHWAY 17 N 28443 #495-69-1976 L1982 **IM IMG** *020 †20
HAINES, Richard L. 15360 US HIGHWAY 17 N 28443 #051-01-1947 L1997 **IM** *071 †20
KIRK, Charles Dayton. ■ 28443 #036-01-1969 L1969 **AN CCA** *020 †05
MATTOX, William Jos. 16150 US HWY 17 N, STE C 28443 #004-01-1959 L1972 **FM** *020
MOULTON, David Lynwood. 15444 US HWY 17 N, STE 210 28443 #023-12-2000 L2004 **P** *100 †75
PATEL, Aneel N. ■ 28443 #496-38-1958 L1994 **P N** *020 †75 ‡
SEWARD, Kathy Ellen. 135 DOGWOOD LN, KATHY E SEWARD 28443 #041-13-1997 L2001 **IM** *020 †20
SLOAN, Randy Mark. 14905 US HWY 17 N, FAMILY MEDICINE PA 28443 #010-03-1989 L1995 **FM** *020 †18
ULISNIK, Wayne Richard. ■ 28443 #035-20-1959 L1987 **OBG IM** *071 †30

HARBINGER – CURRITUCK

DAHM, Norman Richard. ■ 27941 #051-01-1961 L1996 **OBG PHP** *071 †30

HARRELLSVILLE – HERTFORD

BANASZAK, Renee Marie. 135 APACHE RD, 103 E. MAIN STREET 27942 #036-08-2005 L2006 **FP** *012
LASSITER, Gaddy Matheson. ■ 27942 #036-08-1998 L1999 **FM** *020 †18

HARRISBURG – CABARRUS

ALOTTA, Michele. 8924 SAINT GEORGES CT 28075 #041-01-1979 L2004 **OBG** *020 †30
BEAVER, Brittian Wood. 4315 PHYSICIANS BLVD, STE 201 28075 #036-05-1997 L1998 **OBG** *020 †30
BLANKS, Esther Lavenia. 5427 HIGHWAY 49 S 28075 #036-05-2004 L2006 **IM** *020 †20
BRANDNER, Michael Dean. 4315 PHYSICIANS BLVD, STE 201 28075 #016-06-1987 L1995 **OBG** *020 †30
BRAY, Kirsten Nicole. 8386 BURGUNDY RIDGE DR 28075 #010-03-1995 L2001 **GPM** *100
CROOK, Janet Uhlan. 4315 PHYSICIANS BLVD, STE 101 28075 #051-01-1986 L1989 **FM** *020 †18
DELANEY, Rebecca Anne. 4315 PHYSICIANS BLVD, STE 101 28075 #036-08-2001 L2004 **FM** *020
FAIRCLOTH, Jackie Rex, Jr. 12170 UNIVERSITY CITY BLVD, PHYSICIANS 28075 #051-07-1999 L2001 **FM** *020 †18
FYLER, Dawn Jackson. 5427 HIGHWAY 49 S, NORTHEAST PSYCHIATRIC SERV 28075 #025-01-1993 L2007 **P** *020 †75
GOLI, Shailaja. 7811 WOODMERE DR 28075 #495-37-1999 L2007 **IM** *100 †20
HA, Victor Linkhian. 4315 PHYSICIANS BLVD, STE 101 28075 #036-08-1998 L1999 **FM** *020 †18
LEVIN, Hal Warren. 5427 HIGHWAY 49 S 28075 #041-13-1991 L1994 **PD** *020 †55
MARTIN, Stacey Windham. 4315 PHYSICIANS BLVD, STE 101 28075 #045-01-1998 L1999 **FM** *020 †18
MATL, Leona. 5427 HIGHWAY 49 S 28075 #048-14-1997 L2004 **PD** *020 †55
MC MILLAN, Jennifer Lee. 12170 UNIVERSITY CITY BLVD, PHYSICIANS 28075 #020-02-1984 L1986 **FM** *020 †18
NUSE, Patricia Lyn. 5427 HIGHWAY 49 S, PIEDMONT PEDIATRICS 28075 #055-01-1994 L1998 **MPD** *020 †20,55
PITTMAN, Susan Renay. 12170 UNIVERSITY CITY BLVD, PHYSICIANS 28075 #036-08-1998 L2001 **FM** *020 †18
POLLACK, Ronald A. 4315 PHYSICIANS BLVD, STE 101 28075 #051-04-1986 L1987 **FM** *020 †18
PORTWOOD, Glen Loy. 4315 PHYSICIANS BLVD 28075 #012-01-1989 L1993 **GE** *020 †20
REN, Jane. 12170 UNIVERSITY CITY BLVD, PHYSICIANS 28075 #048-13-2001 L2004 **FM** *071 †18

SPELLS, Rosalind Ann. 5427 HIGHWAY 49 S, NORTHEAST PSYCHIATRIC SERV 28075 #048-02-2002 L2007 **CHP** *020 †75
STATIS, Jennifer L. 5427 HIGHWAY 49 S, PIEDMONT PEDIATRIC CLINIC 28075 #016-42-2003 L2006 **PD** *020 †55
SUGGS, Theodore Franklin. 12170 UNIVERSITY CITY BLVD, PHYSICIANS 28075 #036-01-1982 L1983 **FM** *020 †18
WALKER, Katherine M. 4315 PHYSICIANS BLVD, STE 101 28075 #035-15-2001 L2004 **FSM** *020 †18
WHITE, Gloria J. 12170 UNIVERSITY CITY BLVD, PHYSICIANS 28075 #048-14-1998 L2002 **FM** *020 †18
WOOSLEY, Kirk Lyle. 12170 UNIVERSITY CITY BLVD, PHYSICIANS 28075 #036-01-1993 L1995 **FM** *020 †18

HATTERAS – DARE

BLAIR, James Seaborn, III. PO BOX 340 27943 #036-08-1987 L1988 **FM** *020 †18
BURROUGHS, Franklin D. PO BOX 83, 57115 KOHLER DR 27943 #036-01-1963 L1963 **FM** *071 †18
CRABTREE, Thomas Bentley. PO BOX 340, HATTERAS 27943 #051-07-1996 L2000 **FM** *020 †18
HODGES, Joseph Al, Jr. ■ 27943 #036-08-1989 L1991 **FM** *020 †18

HAVELOCK – CRAVEN

BARDEN, Graham A, Jr. 218 STONEBRIDGE SQ 28532 #036-07-1948 L1950 **PD** *020
BARDEN, Graham A, III. 218 STONEBRIDGE SQ 28532 #036-07-1982 L1985 **PD** *020 †55
COPELAND, Benjamin Judson. 218 STONEBRIDGE SQ 28532 #036-08-2001 L2004 **PD** *020 †55
CRAWFORD, Charles Marston. 218 STONEBRIDGE SQ 28532 #016-01-1998 L2001 **MPD** *020 †20,55
ELLIOT, Jonathan Neil. ■ 28532 #036-08-2004 L2006 **FM** *020 †18
GINTAUTIENE, Kristina. 532 WEBB BLVD 28532 #649-33-1986 L1991 **IM** *020 †20
GUNSTEN, Gregory G. 218 STONEBRIDGE SQ 28532 #033-06-1987 L1994 **PD** *020 †55
HEALY, Paul J. 532 WEBB BLVD 28532 #010-02-1985 L1993 **IM EM** *020 †20
JOYNER, Ronnie Stephen. 200 STONEBRIDGE SQ 28532 #036-01-1976 L1976 **OBG** *020 †30
KAFER, Lisa Michele. 218 STONEBRIDGE SQ 28532 #036-05-1999 L2003 **PD** *020 †55
LINS, Jo Ellyn Wishart. ■ 28532 #028-03-1964 L1964 **PTH** *75 †50
MARTIN, Dennis Keith. 200 STONEBRIDGE SQ 28532 #036-01-1978 L1979 **OBG** *020 †30
MICHELSON, Jeffrey Alan. 200 STONEBRIDGE SQ 28532 #011-04-1984 L1999 **OBG** *020 †30
MICHELSON, Melinda B. 200 STONEBRIDGE SQ 28532 #036-08-1983 L1984 **OBG** *020 †30 ‡
MOELLER, Garland Radford. 532 WEBB BLVD 28532 #036-07-1977 L1980 **RHU IM** *020 †20
MORGAN, Chris Elizabeth. 200 STONEBRIDGE SQ 28532 #036-08-1989 L1992 **OBG** *071 †30
PARKER, Charles Lawrence. 200 STONEBRIDGE SQ 28532 #017-20-1973 L1976 **OBG REN** *020 †30 ‡
PATTERSON, Rolvix H, Jr. 200 STONEBRIDGE SQ 28532 #036-08-1988 L1991 **OBG** *020 †30
PAUL, Daniel Eugene. 532 WEBB BLVD 28532 #035-01-1994 L1999 **IM** *020 †20
PEREZ-MONTES, Marcelo R. 925 E MAIN ST, STE 18 28532 #306-01-1986 L2005 **GP OM** *020 ‡
SEMPLE, George J. ■ 28532 #041-77-1996, ▲ L1997 **FM** *030 †18
SKLADAN, Lee Ann. 218 STONEBRIDGE SQ 28532 #001-02-1998 L2002 **PD** *020 †55
STONE, Valerie Jean. ■ 28532 #025-01-1997 *100
TAYLOR, Charles Anthony. 104 SEA BISQUIT DR 28532 #010-02-1990 L1994 **FM** *020 †18
TINGA, John Hinnes. 200 STONEBRIDGE SQ 28532 #036-05-1915 L1975 **OBG** *020 †30
TRULUCK, Thomas Brian. 200 STONEBRIDGE SQ 28532 #045-01-1975 L1979 **OBG** *020 †30
WARREN, Calvin Glenn, Jr. 218 STONEBRIDGE SQ 28532 #036-01-1986 L1987 **PD** *020 †55
WEBSTER, Kedric Edward. PO BOX 2127 28532 #023-12-1999 L2001 **OBG** *020 †30
WECHGELAER, Peter. ■ 28532 #023-12-1995 L1996 **OS** *020 †70
WEST, Janet Marie. ■ 28532 #026-04-2005 L2006 **FM** *020
WITHERSPOON, Linda Sue. ■ 28532 #020-02-1982 **P** *074

HAYESVILLE – CLAY

APPLETON, B Gray. 423 LAKESHORE DR, EMERGENCY MEDICAL GROUP 28904 #004-01-1970 L1998 **EM** *020
ETHRIDGE, Julian Herman. ■ 28904 #004-01-1971 L1976 **EM** *020 †16
SMITH, James Franklin. RR 2 28904 #036-01-1962 L1962 **OBG** *075 †30

HAYS – WILKES

ALBERT, Susan Layne. PO BOX 82, 5229 ROCK CREEK RD 28635 #021-01-1994 L1997 **FM** *020 †18
LADA, Melinda Peterson. PO BOX 82, 5229 ROCK CREEK RD 28635 #036-05-1999 L2003 **FM** *020 †18

HAZELWOOD – HAYWOOD

MOORE, John Phillips. PO BOX 86 28738 #047-06-1939 L1939 **R** *071 †80
STRINGFIELD, James K. ■ 28786 #041-02-1951 L1951 **FM** *071 †18

HENDERSON – VANCE

ALLIGOOD, David Blair. 120 CHARLES D ROLLINS RD 27536 #036-05-1990 L1991 **FM** *020 †18
ANIEKWENSI, Francis Chukw. ■ 27537 #690-04-1994 L2006 **FM** *020 †18
BERNSTEIN, Daniel. 451 RUIN CREEK RD, STE 204 27536 #025-07-1968 L1975 **OPH** *020 †35 ‡
BLOSSER, Anita Louise. 480 RUIN CREEK RD 27536 #020-12-1991 L1994 **FM** *020 †18
BURWELL, Walter Brodie. ■ 27536 #021-01-1941 L1945 **IM OM** *071 †20
CALLAHAN, Joseph Brodhead. ■ 27537 #041-12-1968 L1975 **OBG** *071 †30
CATES, Daphne Joan. 381 RUIN CREEK RD 27536 #011-02-2000 L2001 **FM** *020 †18 ‡
CATHCART, Cornelius F. 451 RUIN CREEK RD, STE 101 27536 #036-01-1976 L1976 **PD** *020 †55
CHARLTON, Glenn Baker. 566 RUIN CREEK RD 27536 #041-02-1976 L2007 **EM FM** *020 †18,16

■ = Address Information Privacy Protected

CHUDASAMA, Laxmikant H. 568 RUIN CREEK RD, STE 102 27536 #495-23-1977 L1992 IM *020

COLLINS-OGLE, Michelle D. 511 RUIN CREEK RD STE 104A 27536 #025-07-1986 L2000 PD ID *020 †55

CURFMAN, Leslie. ■ 27537 #041-01-1979 END IM *020

DEAL, Martin Tyler. 568 RUIN CREEK RD, STE 2 27536 #039-01-1994 L2004 IM PLM *020 †20 ‡

DENNIS, William Austin. 568 RUIN CREEK RD 27536 #036-08-1999 L2002 FM *020 †18

DOOKHAN, Dianne Beverly. 568 RUIN CREEK RD, STE 5 27536 #654-01-1989 L2000 BBK PCP *020 †50

DOSHI, Veena Himatlal. 568 RUIN CREEK RD, STE 5 27536 #495-96-1974 L1994 PTH *020 †50

DUBINSKI, Mark A. 120 CHARLES D ROLLINS RD, STE 201 27536 #033-06-1986 L1992 GE *020 †20

FAWCETT, Thomas A. 566 RUIN CREEK RD, STE 105B 27536 #036-07-1986 L1987 AN *020 †05

FRANKS, Lydia A Johnson. 566 RUIN CREEK RD 27536 #036-01-1984 L1988 PTH *075 †50

GEORGE, Cosmos N. 451 RUIN CREEK RD STE 202 27536 #010-03-1977 L1983 OBG *020 †30

GOODWIN, James Oscar. 566 RUIN CREEK RD, BOX 59 27536 #036-01-1970 L1970 OBG *071 †30

GOODWIN, Joel Sexton, II. 120 CHARLES D ROLLINS RD, STE 206 27536 #036-01-1990 L1999 CCS *012 †85

GREEN, James Preston. 176 BECKFORD DR 27536 #047-07-1955 L1959 GP *072

GREENE, John Robt, III. 946 W ANDREWS AVE STE X, SPECIALISTS, P.C. 27536 #010-03-1978 L1992 EM *020 †16

GRUCHACZ, Mark John. 568 RUIN CREEK RD, STE 002 CAROLINA ADULT MED 27536 #041-13-1994 L1997 IM *020 †20

HAGAN, Paul, Jr. 120 CHARLES D ROLLINS RD, STE 201 27536 #036-01-1987 L1992 IM IMG *020 †20

HALL-WILSON, Hope. 480 RUIN CREEK RD 27536 #010-03-1990 L2005 FM *020 †18

HAMPTON, Cynthia A. 451 RUIN CREEK RD, STE 204 27536 #048-14-1985 L1989 OPH *020 †35

HAMPTON, James Weldon. 511 RUIN CREEK RD, STE 101 27536 #048-14-1981 L1986 OBG *020 †30

HENRY, Camille. ■ 27536 #010-02-1984 L2005 GPM *020

JONES, Harvey Michael. 957 MEADOW LN 27536 #028-02-1966 L1974 PTH *071 †50

KENNEY, James Eugene. 176 BECKFORD DR 27536 #001-02-1976 L1979 FM *020 †18

KO, Young-Hwan. 568 RUIN CREEK RD, STE 105 27536 #583-06-1968 L1979 AN *020

KWIATKOWSKI, Timothy Carl. 566 RUIN CREEK RD 27536 #051-01-1994 L1997 FM EM *020 †18

LAPINSKES, Zane Ian. 566 RUIN CREEK RD 27536 #036-01-2000 L2003 FM *020 †18

LATEEF, Mohammad F Danish. 125 CHARLES D ROLLINS RD, VANCE CLINIC 27536 #704-21-1986 L2003 P *020 †75

MATTESON, Rhonda Jean. 480 RUIN CREEK RD 27536 #038-41-1988 L1989 FM *020 †20

MAYO, Joseph D, Jr. ■ 27536 #041-01-1949 L1949 FM *071 †18

MC CASKILL, Samuel Gault. 511 RUIN CREEK RD STE 101 27536 #048-04-1973 L1984 OBG *020 †85

MEADOR, Philip Dale, Jr. 568 RUIN CREEK RD, STE 120 27536 #036-01-1971 L1971 D *020 †15

MILLS, John Franklin. 480 RUIN CREEK RD 27536 #036-05-1982 L1984 FM *020 †18

MILLS, Randolph D. ■ 27536 #036-05-1951 L1951 FM *071

MITCHELL, Ricky Devon. 451 RUIN CREEK RD STE 101, HENDERSON PEDIATRIC CENTER 27536 #023-07-1996 L1999 PD *020 †55

MULCAHY, Joseph Wm. 120 CHARLES ROLLINS RD, STE 206 27536 #028-34-1984 L1993 GS *020 †85

NEGRON, Rafael M. 120 CHARLES ROLLINS RD, STE 205 27536 #042-01-1982 L2008 ORS *020 †40

NOEL, Robert F, Jr. 120 CHARLES ROLLINS RD, STE 206 27536 #036-01-1989 L1999 GS *020 †95

OGLE, Adrian Mahendra. 511 RUIN CREEK RD, STE 104B 27536 #036-05-1991 L2000 U *020 †96

PALMER, Catherine L. 568 RUIN CREEK RD, STE 5 27536 #010-01-1995 L2003 PTH *020 †50

PARHAM, Sumner Malone. ■ 27536 #023-01-1945 L1945 OBG *071 †30

PRUITT, Enas Lee. 480 RUIN CREEK RD, HENDERSON FAMILY HEALTH CL 27536 #018-03-1997 L2000 FM *020 †18

RAPCHIK, Joel. 568 RUIN CREEK RD 27536 #036-07-1971 L1992 IM A *020 †20

REDDY, Putlur Ramachandra. 511 RUIN CREEK RD, STE 105 27536 #495-21-1962 L1977 IM ON *020

REDDY, Saraladevi B S. 511 RUIN CREEK RD, STE 105 27536 #495-62-1966 L1977 PTH *020 †50

ROBINSON, Cynthia. 120 CHARLES ROLLINS RD, STE 206 27536 #036-05-1984 L1989 GS *020 †85

SCHWARTZBERG, Stuart G. ■ 27536 #064-01-1965 L1993 GS VS *071 †85

SESSIONS, Fadrienne H. 451 RUIN CREEK RD STE 1 27536 #024-07-1985 L1992 PD *020 †55

SESSIONS, Willie James. 568 RUIN CREEK RD, STE 122 27536 #024-07-1985 L1992 CD IM *020

SINGH, Ashish. 568 RUIN CREEK RD, STE 127 27536 #495-53-1993 L2003 PCC *020 †20

SMITH, Carl Lynwood. 568 RUIN CREEK RD STE 128, ELECTROMYOGRAPHYSPORTS MED 27536 #041-12-1988 L2001 PM *020 †60

SMITH, Gary Anthony. ■ 27537 #305-01-2004 L2008 FP *012

SOUKKAR, Mouhammad Farouk. 566 RUIN CREEK RD 27536 #875-01-1969 L1975 GE *020 †20

SUNDAR, Valarmathi. 511 RUIN CREEK RD, STE 105 27536 #495-66-1987 L2001 FM *020 †18

SUNDAR, Veerappan. 511 RUIN CREEK RD STE 105, ASSOCIATES, PA 27536 #495-59-1985 L1999 IM *020 †20

TABET, Munther Salim. 120 CHARLES D ROLLINS RD, STE 101 27536 #605-01-1987 L1998 N *020

TIMMONS, Martha Chrystie. 511 RUIN CREEK RD, STE 101 27536 #036-01-1975 L1975 GYN *020 †30

TRIVEDI, Kirit. 568 RUIN CREEK RD, STE 1 27536 #495-23-1966 L1976 GP GS *020 †85

TUCKER, Wm Beverly, III. 568 RUIN CREEK RD 27536 #036-01-1966 L1966 FM *071 †18

VIJAYA, Linga. 568 RUIN CREEK RD STE 121 27536 #495-11-1961 L1975 U *020 †95

VU, Khanh Tuan. 381 RUIN CREEK RD 27536 #019-02-1985 L1993 FM OBG *020 †18

WELSH, Mark Allen. 2000 COLEMAN PL, DEPT. OF ANESTHESIA 27536 #051-04-1981 L1992 AN *020 †05

HENDERSONVILLE – HENDERSON

ABUMOUSSA, Lateef I. 741 6TH AVE W 28739 #915-02-1979 L1994 IM *020 †20

ALBERS, Charles Allen. 835 FLEMING ST 28791 #048-04-1976 L1981 GS *020 †85

ALEXANDER, William M. ■ 28793 #045-01-1945 L1949 IM PUD *071

ARCARA, Victoria Marie. ■ 28792 #021-01-1992 L1996 OBG *020 †30

BAILEY, Royce Kandan. 50 HOSPITAL DR, STE 3B 28792 #005-12-1980 L1987 CD IM *020 ‡

BAKER, Brent Thomas. 600 BEVERLY HANKS CTR 28792 #045-01-1998 L2001 PD *020 †55

BAKER, Edgar David. 510 FLEMING ST STE A 28739 #047-06-1962 L1966 FM *020 †18

BARRY, Joseph Aloysius. ■ 28739 #020-02-1955 L1956 IM IMG *071 †20

BELL, John Davis. 715 FLEMING ST 28791 #036-01-1972 L1972 AN *020 †05

BENTSON, Edward Keith. 715 FLEMING ST 28791 #132-01-1981 L1988 IM *020 †20

BINDEWALD, Eric Stewart. 50 HOSPITAL DR, STE 2D 28792 #011-04-1979 L1998 IM IMG *020 †20

BLACK, Martin Larry. 800 N JUSTICE ST, MARGARET R PARDEE HOSP 28791 #050-02-1980 L1987 DR *020 †80

BLAKELY, Gene Thornton. 800 FLEMING ST 2 28791 #021-01-1954 L1970 EM GS *020

BOELKE, Donald Richard. ■ 28739 #010-01-1958 L1962 ORS *071 †40

BOLEMAN, Robert Chas. 800 N JUSTICE ST 28791 #047-20-1982 L1995 EM IM *020 †20

BRABHAM, Felicia Browne. 401 6TH AVE W 28739 #045-01-1984 L1987 IM *020 †20

BROADWELL, Freeman Edward. 1027 FLEMING ST 28791 #036-05-1987 L1993 PM *020 †60

BROCK, Richard Ronald. ■ 28739 #041-02-1958 L1959 R *071 †80

BROOKS, Werner Commodore. 712 FLEMING ST 28791 #036-07-1990 L1997 ORS *020 †40

BROWN, Frank Mac. 1027 FLEMING ST 28791 #005-12-1963 L1974 ORS GP *020 †40

BROWN, Mark Edward. ■ 28792 #020-02-1980 L1991 AN *020 †05

BRYAN, Clayton H. 1701 OLD VILLAGE RD, CAROLINA OPHTHALMOLOGY 28791 #036-01-1991 L1992 OPH *020 †20

BYRD, Eric Wayne. 735 6TH AVE W 28739 #028-03-1997 L2001 IM *020 †20

BYRD, Lelan Clinton. 512 6TH AVE W 28739 #012-01-1986 L2007 U *075 †95 ‡

CALDEMEYER, John E. 800 N JUSTICE ST, MARGARET R PARDEE HOSP 28791 #017-20-1978 L1979 DR *020 †80

CANON, John Chambless. 800 N JUSTICE ST, PARDEE HOSPITAL-EMERGENCY 28791 #047-06-1982 L1983 FM *020 †18

CASERIO, James J, Jr. 547 N JUSTICE ST 28739 #041-12-1978 L1982 IM *020 †20

CHRISTIANSON, Dana John. 215 THOMPSON ST 28792 #047-05-1981 L1985 OPH *020 †35

CLARK, Christopher Todd. 741 6TH AVE W, HFHC 28739 #036-07-1993 L2003 IM *020 †20

CLARY, Lois Gail. 617 6TH AVE W 28739 #051-04-1985 L1991 PUD CCM *020 †20

CORNELIUS, Mark William. 741 6TH AVE W 28739 #012-05-2005 L2006 FP *012

COSGROVE, Kenneth E. 705 6TH AVE W 28739 #035-19-1946 L1953 IM CD *071 †20

CRANE, Steven Douglas. 741 6TH AVE W, HENDERSONVILLE FAMILY HLTH 28739 #038-06-1983 L1986 FM *020 †18

CRAWFORD, John L, III. 1701 OLD VILLAGE RD 28791 #036-05-1974 L1974 OPH *071 †35

CRITIKOS, John P, II. 691 BLYTHE STREET CT 28739 #045-01-1988 L1994 CD IM *020 †20

CULVER, Donald Lee. 132 HOMESTEAD FARM CIR 28792 #005-12-1968 L1999 IMG IM *020 †20

CURRAN, Diana. 1200 SPARTANBURG HWY, STE 100 28792 #025-01-1993 L1994 FM *020 †18 ‡

DAS, Amal K, Jr. 1027 FLEMING ST, HENDERSONVILLE ORTHO 28791 #017-20-1982 L1988 ORS OAR *020 †40

DAS, Anita Krishna. 27 DOCTORS DR 28792 #017-20-1985 L2003 OBG *020 †30

DECKER, Douglass A, Jr. ■ 28739 #041-01-1965 L1971 N *071 †75

DEMOCKER, Sharon Kay. 907 GOLDEN GATE DR, FAMILY MEDICINE 28739 #045-01-1999 L2003 FM OS *020 †55

DENNIS, Kenneth Michael. 110 CHADWICK SQUARE CT # A 28739 #011-03-1974 L1977 PD *020 †55

DENNISON, H Eugene. 630 5TH AVE W 28739 #025-01-1961 L1968 OBG *071 †30

DONALDSON, David Scott. 512 6TH AVE W 28739 #036-08-1992 L1999 U GS *020 †95

DUNN, Jack Newton. 512 6TH AVE W 28739 #045-01-1960 L1970 U *071 †75

DURHAM, Cecil Tracy, Jr. 511 6TH AVE W 28739 #045-01-1966 L1973 N *071 †75

DYER, Robert K. ■ 28739 #051-01-1953 L1964 PHP U *071 †95

EATON, Robert Farrell. 1027 FLEMING ST 28791 #021-05-1966 L1975 ORS *071 †40

EDWARDS, Elizabeth Ann. ■ 28739 #012-01-1993 L1996 PD *020 †55

EISENHAUER, Thomas L. 80 DOCTORS DR, STE 1 28792 #045-04-1987 L1992 GS *020 †85

ELLIS, David Anderson. 727 OAKLAND ST 28791 #021-01-1983 L1987 OBG *020 †30

ESTES, Ralph C. 1027 FLEMING ST 28791 #048-13-1982 L1991 ORS *020 †40

EVANS, Richard Warren. 840 FLEMING ST 3 28791 #051-07-1976 L1986 RHU IM *020 †20

FALVO, Samuel C. 715 FLEMING ST 28791 #010-02-1952 L1959 CRS GS *071 †85

FANN, Benjamin Bradley. 2920 HAYWOOD RD 28791 #007-02-1979 L1988 OBG *020 †20

FLECHAS, Jorge David. 80 DOCTORS DR STE 3 28792 #005-12-1977 L1980 FM *020 †18

FORD, Albert S, Jr. 132 HOMESTEAD FARM CIR 28792 #047-07-1981 L1994 ID *020 †20

FORTH, Paul Taber, Jr. 741 6TH AVE W 28739 #005-07-1970 L1970 IM END *020 †20

FOWLER, Wesley Caswell. 511 6TH AVE W 28739 #036-05-1995 L1998 NS *020 †25

FRANCIS, Robert Dean. 2920 HAYWOOD RD, WESTERN CAROLINA ORTHOPEDI 28791 #036-07-1977 L1977 ORS *020 †40

GARLAND, Donald Merrill. 159 STONE HOUSE RD 28739 #035-45-1961 L2002 OM *020 †70

GASKILL, William Marvin. 741 6TH AVE W, FAMILY PRACTICE 28739 #005-12-2002 L2005 GS *020 †18

GERLING, William L. 50 DOCTORS DR STE 1 28792 #005-12-1976 L1992 FM FPG *020 †18

GILPIN, Allen Bruce. 518 6TH AVE W 28739 #051-07-1991 L1991 FP *020 †18

GLASSMAN, Stuart Lewis. 840 FLEMING ST, STE 1 28791 #011-02-1973 L1986 GS CD *020 †85

GLEATON, Hugh Elbert, Jr. 404 S MAIN ST 28792 #012-01-1965 L1971 OPH *071 †35

GLENN, David Locke, Jr. 561 FLEMING ST 28739 #045-01-1976 L1980 GS EM *020 †85

GODEHN, Donald John, Jr. 506 PARK HILL CT STE 1 28739 #036-05-1972 L1977 D *020 †15

GOODFIELD, Peter. 691 BLYTHE STREET CT 28739 #035-19-1979 L1985 CD IM *020 †20 ‡

GOODWIN, Linda Sipress. 600 BEVERLY HANKS CTR 28792 #041-14-1981 L1985 PD ADL *020 †55

GRIGGS, James Young. ■ 28792 #036-05-1944 L1944 GS OS *071 †85

GUPTA, Aneeta Jain. 50 HOSPITAL DR, STE 1 28792 #495-20-1982 L2001 N *020 †75

HAAK, Rudy. ■ 28792 #005-12-1949 L1949 AN *071 †05

HANSEL, Kevan Richard. 510 BALSAM RD 28792 #055-02-2000 L2003 FM *020 †18 ‡

HARLEY, John Crittenden. 715 FLEMING ST 28791 #036-01-1973 L1973 GP OS *020 †16

HAWK, Rodney James. 512 PARK HILL CT 28739 #041-12-1970 L1977 OTO *020 †45

HELPPIE, Joanne Elizabeth. 724 5TH AVE W 28739 #020-05-1983 L1987 IM IMG *020 †20

HENINGER, Wendelin Marie. 513 N JUSTICE ST 28739 #001-06-1988 L1997 CHP *020 †75

HENRICHS, Charles. 800 N JUSTICE ST, MARGARET PARDEE HOSP 28791 #005-12-1974 L1984 EM IM *020 †16,18

HERBERT, Teresa Mary. 50 HOSPITAL DR, STE 5D 28792 #917-12-1984 L1999 PD *020 †55

HERMANN, Elmer Raymond. ■ 28791 #056-05-1959 L1960 OM AM *072 †70

HERMANN, Patricia Dolan. ■ 28791 #056-06-1958 L1985 GPM *020

HILL, John Kimbrough. 1824 PISGAH DR 28791 #001-06-1997 L2002 HO *020 †20

HOLT, Robert Flewelling. ■ 28792 #005-12-1971 L1976 **EM GPM** *020

HOOPER, Virgil Roy. ■ 28792 #023-01-1956 L1959 **AN** *071

HOROWITZ, Alfred L. 807 N JUSTICE ST, MARGARET R PARDEE HOSP 28791 #035-20-1968 L2002 **DR** *020 †80

HORWITZ, James Lawrence. 110 CHADWICK SQUARE CT # A 28739 #025-07-1988 L1989 **PD** *020 †55

HUDSPETH, Richard William. 741 6TH AVE W, HENDERSONVILLE FAM HEALTH 28739 #036-01-1997 L2005 **FM** *020 †18

HUFFMAN, Allan Day. 80 DOCTORS DR, STE 1 28792 #001-02-1983 L1989 **GS VS** *020 †85

HUNTLEY, Douglas Brett. 1027 FLEMING ST, STE B 28791 #036-01-1989 L1995 **GS** *020 †85

HUSTED, David Shakespeare. 50 HOSPITAL DR, STE 5A 28792 #011-03-2001 L2007 **P** *020 †75

IACONO, Paul Ernest. 513 N JUSTICE ST, MOUNTAIN LAUREL COMMUNITY 28739 #045-04-1993 L1996 **PD** *020 †55

IOSUE, Albert Michael. 515 FLEMING ST 28739 #038-06-1966 L1979 **DR NM** *072 †80,28

IRVING, Richard C. CAROLINA VILLAGE 28739 #036-07-1941 L1957 **AN GP** *071

JACOBIUS, Francis Michael. ■ 28791 #869-01-1964 L1966 **EM PHP** *030 †16

JAY, Victor V. ■ 28739 #407-19-1948 L1952 **OS GP** *071 †18

JENKINS, Carlton A. 800 N JUSTICE ST, MARGARET R PARDEE HOSP 28791 #036-01-1983 L1984 **DR** *020 †80

JERNIGAN, James A. ■ 28791 #028-02-1949 L1981 **IM IMG** *071 †20

JIMENEZ, Edgar John. 80 DOCTORS DR, STE 2 28792 #011-04-1981 L1987 **OBG** *071 †30

JIMENEZ, Ronald Jay. 80 DOCTORS DR STE 2, PARK RIDGE WOMEN'S CENTER 28792 #005-12-1989 L2001 **OBG** *020 †30

JOHNSON, Clifford Paul. 50 HOSPITAL DR STE 2A, MOUNTAIN VIEW UROLOGICAL P 28792 #026-04-1985 L1995 **U** *020 †95

JOHNSON, Michele E. 136 HOMESTEAD FARM CIR 28792 #021-01-1981 L1997 **ADP P** *020 †55,75

JOHNSON, Travis Duane. 741 6TH AVE W 28739 #045-01-2004 L2006 **FM** *020 †18

JONES, Geoffrey Lee. 741 6TH AVE W, HENDERSONVILLE FAMILY HEAL 28739 #035-20-1996 L2005 **FM** *020 †18

JONES, Michael Chas. 835 FLEMING ST 28791 #036-01-1972 L1972 **GS** *020 †85

JOSEPH, Mark Allen. 1701 OLD VILLAGE RD 28791 #055-01-1998 L2006 **OPH** *020 †35

KAUFMAN, Carol Hope. 1200 SPARTANBURG HWY, STE 100 28792 #048-14-1979 L1981 **PHP FM** *020 †18

KELLY, Timothy Joseph. ■ 28791 #036-01-2005 **FP** *012

KEPPLER, C Burton. ■ 28792 #005-12-1965 L1985 **AN FM** *071 †18

KEPPLER, Eileen. 50 HOSPITAL DR, STE 2B 28792 #005-12-1995 L1999 **OBG** *020 †30

KHAN, Tariq Rafiq. ■ 28792 #704-01-1982 L1990 **PD** *020 †55

KILFOIL, Mary Martha. 705 6TH AVE W, STE A 28739 #649-14-1987 L1994 **IM** *020 †20

KIM, Clara Eunhe. 741 6TH AVE W 28739 #035-06-1996 L2002 **IM** *071 †20

KING, Bridget Demor. ■ 28791 #018-03-1987 L2007 **FM** *020 †18

KIRKLEY, Margaret Anne. 518 6TH AVE W 28739 #803-03-1968 L1976 **FM** *020

KIRKLEY, Sidney Eugene. 518 6TH AVE W 28739 #045-01-1966 L1976 **IM** *030 ‡

KLYM, Robert P. 800 N JUSTICE ST, MARGARET R PARDEE HOSP 28791 #033-06-1988 L1997 **RNR R** *020 †80

KONST-SKWIOT, Kelli Jo. ■ 28791 #104-01-2005 **FP** *012

KRAEBBER, David Mc Kenzie. 512 6TH AVE W, WESTERN CAROLINA URO. ASSO 28739 #012-01-1981 L1988 **U** *020 †95

KRING, Susan Jane. 2579 CHIMNEY ROCK RD 28792 #041-07-1986 L2004 **FM** *020 †18

KRISHINGNER, Gene Lavere. RR 8 BOX 81A 28791 #005-12-1965 L1975 **GS VS** *020 †85

KRUEGER, Andrew Howard. 50 HOSPITAL DR STE 2A 28792 #038-43-1995 L2001 **U** *020 †95

KRUEGER, Hilary M. 50 HOSPITAL DR STE 2A 28792 #038-43-1995 L2001 **D** *020 †15

KRUM, Ronald Eugene. 111 FALLING WATERS RD 28792 #005-12-1960 L1970 **FM FPG** *071 †18

LABORDE, Robert Paul. 709 5TH AVE W 28739 #021-05-1986 L1991 **OPH** *020 †35

LACKEY, Steven Kenneth. 165 COOLRIDGE ST 28792 #028-03-1986 L1987 **FM** *020 †18

LACY, Thomas Harrison. 715 FLEMING ST, PARDEE HOSP 28791 #041-12-1996 L2002 **EM** *020 †16

LAMBERT, Kathleen Cooney. ■ 28739 #024-07-1995 L1998 **IM** *020 †20

LAMPLEY, William Askew. 116 BRIDGEWOOD LANE 28791 #023-01-1944 L1945 **OS GS** *071

LANGE, John. 511 6TH AVE W, HEALTH CENTER 28739 #035-20-1955 L1993 **IM OM** *030

LARTEY, Philip Larko. 50 HOSPITAL DR, STE 5A 28792 #913-15-1995 L2004 **P** *020 †75 ‡

LEVENE, Jan Louise. 691 BLYTHE STREET CT 28739 #030-05-1981 L1994 **IM CD** *020 †20

LIBERT, Cynthia Jane. 2579 CHIMNEY ROCK RD 28792 #016-43-2002 L2003 **FM** *020 †18

LILLY, Edward Guerrant. 712 FLEMING ST, BLUE RIDGE BONE & JOINT 28791 #036-07-1993 L2000 **ORS** *020 †40

LOOMIS, Ralph Chas. 511 6TH AVE W 28739 #017-20-1976 L1982 **NS GS** *020 †25 ‡

LOVE, David Eugene. 513 JUSTUS STREET 28739 #005-12-1965 L1971 **GYN** *020 †30

LOVE, Jennifer Lin. 741 6TH AVE W, WEST CAROLINA MED ASSOC 28739 #036-08-2000 L2003 **IM** *020 †20

LOWE, Charmaine Pamela A. 110 WILLIAMS ST 28792 #917-01-1976 L1989 **P CHP** *020

LUGUS, Thomas Rein. 207 LINDA VISTA DR, FOUR SEASONS FAMILY CARE 28792 #012-01-1985 L1988 **FM** *020 †18

LUTZ, James Dwight. ■ 28739 #036-07-1945 L1948 **AN GP** *071

MACKEL, David Frederick. 1027 FLEMING ST 28791 #017-20-1974 L1982 **ORS** *020 †40

MAIZITE, Visvaldis. ■ 28792 #154-02-1947 **GP** *071

MALATY, Wail. 741 6TH AVE W, STE B 28739 #048-04-1986 L1995 **FM** *020 †18

MANDELBAUM, Mark A. 709 N JUSTICE ST, STE D 28791 #039-01-1979 L2006 **N** *020 †75 ‡

MANLY, David Tupper. 50 HOSPITAL DR, STE 5QA 28792 #036-01-1986 L1987 **IM P** *020 †75

MARKS, Jeffry Lee. ■ 28791 #055-01-1970 L1971 **PD** *075 †55

MARTIN, Dennis Lee. 511 6TH AVE W 28739 #051-01-1965 L1974 **N** *071 †75

MARTIN, William Chas. ■ 28791 #005-19-1983 L1986 **DR** *020 †80

MATHEWS, Jennifer Lee. 510 BALSAM RD 28792 #047-06-1991 L1993 **FM** *020 †18

MC CONNACHIE, Charles C P. 1027 FLEMING ST 28791 #917-30-1961 L1972 **ORS** *071 †40

MC GEE, Donna Brock. 50 HOSPITAL DR STE 5B 28792 #036-01-1997 L2000 **FM** *020 †18

MC GRADY, Kathleen Reilly. ■ 28791 #023-01-1951 L1970 **PD** *071 †55

MC LEAN, Walter C. 840 FLEMING ST, STE 6 28791 #051-01-1946 L1946 **OTO** *071 †45

MEDINA, William Douglas. 1824 PISGAH DR 28791 #020-12-1976 L1995 **ON HEM** *020 †20

MEEHAN-DE LA CRUZ, K. PO BOX 5151, CORNER HOWARD GAP & 64E 28793 #023-07-1996 L1999 **FM** *020 †18

MERRELL, Betsy Salsbury. 611 5TH AVE W 28739 #036-05-2003 L2005 **FM** *020 †18

MOFFITT, William Ronald. 643 5TH AVE W 28739 #036-01-1978 L1979 **FM FSM** *020 †18

MOORE, Maria G. 50 HOSPITAL DR, STE 4B 28792 #011-02-1981 L1982 **ON HEM** *020 †20

MOORE, Michael Norman. 735 6TH AVE W 28739 #011-02-1981 L1982 **ESM EM** *020 †16

MOORE, Richard Benj. ■ 28739 #047-05-1955 L1955 **U** *071 †95

MOORE, Ruchi Patel. 80 DOCTORS DR, STE 2 28792 #012-01-2002 L2004 **OBG** *100

MORRIS, John Steven. 617 6TH AVE W 28739 #001-02-1983 L1985 **PUD CCM** *020 †20

MORROW, Robert Allen. 835 FLEMING ST 28791 #038-41-1995 L2001 **GS** *020 †85

MOSS, Derek William. 600 BEVERLY HANKS CTR 28792 #012-01-1997 L2001 **PD** *020 †55

MURPHY, George Robt, Jr. 741 6TH AVE W 28739 #021-01-1976 L1997 **IM** *020 †20

NAPOLI, David Chas. 712 FLEMING ST, BLUE RIDGE BONE & JOINT 28791 #035-08-1991 L2006 **HS ORS** *020 †40

NAVON, Samuel Edward. 1701 OLD VILLAGE RD, CAROLINA OPHTHALMOLOGY 28791 #035-45-1989 L2000 **OPH** *020 †35 ‡

NEWELL, Frank D. ■ 28791 #065-05-1946 L1952 **OBG** *071 †30

NIGRINY, James Jacob. ■ 28739 #035-03-1965 L1970 **OBG** *020 †30

NOVAK, Timothy David. 800 N JUSTICE ST 28791 #035-48-1999 L2006 **EM** *020 †16

OVERSTREET, William L, III. 420 5TH AVE W, STE 300 28739 #045-01-1989 L1996 **PS** *020 †65

PANDIT, Ivy Chand. 132 HOMESTEAD FARM CIR 28792 #495-27-1978 L2001 **IM IMG** *020 †20

PANDIT, Subodh Kumar. ■ 28791 #495-27-1975 L2000 **IM** *020 †20

PARK, Robert Inyeung. 1701 OLD VILLAGE RD 28791 #035-03-1996 L2007 **OPH** *020 †35

PARKER, Paul Edwin. 828 FLEMING ST STE A, PIEDMONT HENDERSONVILLE AN 28791 #051-07-1986 L1989 **AN** *020

PATRICK, Kevin Michael. 828 FLEMING ST STE A 28791 #048-12-1993 L1994 **CCA** *020 †05

PATTEN, Kathryn Furr. 27 DOCTORS DR 28792 #036-08-1995 L1999 **OBG** *020 †30

PERNIE, Keith Howard. 715 FLEMING ST, MARGARET R PARDEE MEMORIAL 28791 #025-07-1990 L1997 **AN** *020 †05 ‡

PETERSEN, Walter Robt. ■ 28792 #035-06-1943 L1947 **ORS** *071 †40

PLYLER, William Lanson. 735 6TH AVE W 28739 #036-01-1994 L1997 **IM** *020 †20

POSSINGER, Clive F, Jr. 50 HOSPITAL DR STE 2D 28792 #005-12-1965 L1973 **IM** *020

PRECHTER, Gary Chas. 50 HOSPITAL DR STE 1C, CHEST CONSULTANTS, P.A. 28792 #021-01-1977 L1996 **PUD IM** *020 †20

PRICE, David Charles. 561 FLEMING ST 28739 #001-02-2000 L2005 **GS** *020 †85

PYLES, Jerald Dennis. 705 6TH AVE W, STE A 28739 #036-07-1974 L1977 **IM** *020 †20

RADFORD, James E, Jr. 1824 PISGAH DR 28791 #025-01-1983 L1994 **ON** *020 †20

RAMSAK, Amy Karen. 715 FLEMING ST 28791 #047-20-1995 L2007 **IM** *020 †20

REINHART, John B. ■ 28791 #036-05-1943 L1943 **CHP PD** *072 †55,75

REVEL, Kathleen. ■ 28792 #005-15-1964 L1965 **IM GP** *071

RHOTON, Eric Loren. 511 6TH AVE W 28739 #011-03-1985 L1992 **NS** *020 †25

RICCO, Ralph N. 807 N JUSTICE ST, HENDERSONVLE RADIOLGCL CNS 28791 #048-02-1993 L1999 **DR** *020 †80 ‡

ROBERTS, James Allen. ■ 28792 #016-02-1959 L1960 **U** *071 †95

ROBERTS, Thos Luther, III. 735 6TH AVE W 28739 #035-01-1971 L1983 **PS HS** *020 †65

ROSKOSKI, Robert, Jr. 221 HAYWOOD KNOLLS DR 28791 #016-02-1964 L1970 **IM** *050

ROSNER, Michael John. 80 DOCTORS DR, STE 4 28792 #051-04-1972 L2008 **NS** *020 ‡

ROSS, John Marion. 27 DOCTORS DR 28792 #045-01-1955 L1963 **GYN** *071 †30

ROWELL, John Putnam. RR 9 BOX 487 28792 #038-41-1937 L1973 **IM** *071 †20

RUSSELL, Larry Joe. 800 N JUSTICE ST 28791 #020-12-1986 L1999 **FM EM** *071 †18

SANDBORN, William Deal. 117 TANAGER LN, PARK RIDGE PSYCHIATRY 28792 #005-12-1965 L1971 **P** *020 †85,75

SCHEUNEMAN, Allen Fred. ■ 28739 #030-05-1954 L1954 **FM** *071 †18

SCHORR, Sandra. 100 HOSPITAL DR, PARK RIDGE HOSP 28792 #016-06-1976 L2004 **PD** *020 †55

SECOSAN, Craig John. 215 THOMPSON ST 28792 #028-02-1981 L1985 **OPH** *020 †35

SELLERS, Phillip Alan. 705 6TH AVE W, STE A 28739 #036-05-1957 L1957 **IM** *071 †20

SETTI, Lara. 741 6TH AVE W, HENDERSON FAMILY HEALTH CE 28739 #036-01-1999 L2003 **FM** *020 †18

SHAKER, Hayam Kamal. 741 6TH AVE W 28739 #915-02-1980 L2000 **FM** *020 †18

SHELINE, Alan Eugene. ■ 28739 #017-20-1958 L1959 **CD IM** *071

SHELTON, Richard K. 800 N JUSTICE ST, MARGARET R PARDEE HOSP 28791 #051-01-1979 L1987 **R** *020 †80

SILVER, Jon M. 511 6TH AVE W 28739 #036-07-1986 L1991 **NS** *020 †25

SIMONS, William John. 50 HOSPITAL DR STE 5A 28792 #036-01-1972 L1972 **P IM** *020 †20,75

SKWIOT, Matthew Kenneth. ■ 28791 #104-01-2005 **FP** *012

SLAWEK, David Francis. 510 FLEMING ST 28739 #051-01-1969 L1972 **IM IMG** *020 †20

SMITH, Anne B. 600 BEVERLY HANKS CTR 28792 #045-01-1996 L2000 **PD** *020 †55

SMITH, Thomas Charles. ■ 28792 #016-06-1962 L1963 **PA GP** *030

SNELLMAN, Pentti Otto R. ■ 28791 #374-01-1962 L1973 **GP** *071

SPENGLER, John R. ■ 28739 #028-34-1953 L1965 **R OS** *072 †80

STALFORD, Michael Dee. 81 DOCTORS DR 28792 #051-01-1993 L2005 **OTO** *020 †45

STEINHARDT, Allen Simon. ■ 28791 #035-19-1954 L1997 **PD** *071 †55

STELTER, Gerald Paul. ■ 28791 #056-05-1959 L1990 **IM** *071

STEWART, James Luther. ■ 28739 #045-01-1958 L1958 **PD PHO** *072 †55

STOKER, Gerald Lee. ■ 28791 #017-20-1963 L1967 **D** *071 †15

STONE, Cameron Mclure. 840 FLEMING ST, STE 6 28791 #051-04-1995 L2001 **OPH** *020 †35

STONE, Elwood Eugene, Jr. ■ 28739 #036-01-1981 L1982 **VIR DR** *020 †80 ‡

STRICKLAND, Wm Herman. 741 6TH AVE W 28739 #036-05-1954 L1954 **FM** *020 †18

TALLMAN, Jacob Michael. ■ 28791 #035-06-2006 **FP** *012

THOMAS, Colin Edward. 512 6TH AVE W # W-2 28739 #021-05-1967 L1974 **U** *020 †95

THOMAS, David Carl. 110 CHADWICK SQUARE CT # A, RAINBOW PEDIATRICS 28739 #036-05-1997 L2000 **PD** *020 †55

TOMSKI, Steven Michael. 617 6TH AVE W 28739 #056-06-1986 L2006 **PCC SME** *020 †20

TRACE, Ian Ernest. 558 FLEMING ST 28739 #010-03-1970 L1974 **R** *020 †80

TRANI, Paul Eugene. 2579 CHIMNEY ROCK RD 28792 #051-04-2001 L2004 **PD** *020 †55

TRIMBLE, Stewart Alan. 800 N JUSTICE ST, PARDEE HOSPITAL 28791 #012-22-2003 L2006 **IM** *020

URITIS, Mary Anne K. 50 HOSPITAL DR, STE 5D 28792 #038-41-1983 L1997 **PD** *020 †55

VAN DER WERF, Jos Nelson. 212A THOMPSON ST 28792 #010-01-1973 L1974 **EM** *020 †18

VEAZEY, Daniel Burt. 611 5TH AVE W, STE A 28739 #036-01-1981 L1982 **FM** *020 †18

VERM, Alan Murray. 215 THOMPSON ST 28792 #048-04-1997 L2002 **OPH** *020 †35

VOLK, James Victor. 50 HOSPITAL DR, STE 5D 28792 #036-05-1972 L1975 **PD** *020 †55

WALKER, Mcarthur, Jr. 828 FLEMING ST STE A 28791 #045-04-1990 L1994 **AN** *020 †05

WALKER, Paul Creasy, III. 705 6TH AVE W STE D 28739 #036-05-1981 L1983 **FM** *020 †18

WARD, Robert Wm. 617 6TH AVE W 28739 #001-02-1988 L1998 **PUD** *020 †20

WATTERS, John Lomnet. 643 5TH AVE W, QUALITY HEALTHCARE ASSOCIA 28739 #028-78-2001, ▲ L2002 **FM** *020 †18

WELLS, Andrew H. 800 N JUSTICE ST, DEPT OF RADIOLOGY 28791 #036-05-1988 L1994 **DR VIR** *020 †80

WELTER, Sylvia L. ■ 28739 #407-16-1944 L1961 **OPH** *074

WEST, Jeanette F. 80 DOCTORS DR, STE 2 28792 #011-03-2002 L2006 **OBG** *020

■ = Address Information Privacy Protected

WHITAKER, Gary Randall. 212 THOMPSON ST STE A 28792 #021-01-1968 L1976 **EM** *030 †16
WILHELM, Jennifer W. 741 6TH AVE W 28739 #047-06-1999 L2002 **IM** *020 †20
WILLIAMS, John Howard. ■ 28791 #048-04-1964 L1968 **R** *071 †80
WYSOKINSKI, Mark L. 705 6TH AVE W 28739 #041-13-1992 L2000 **IM** *020 †20 ‡
YODER, Daniel Mark. 215 THOMPSON ST 28792 #036-07-1998 L2003 **OPH** *100 †35
YOST, Basil Otto, III. 691 BLYTHE STREET CT 28739 #051-04-1980 L1989 **CD IM** *020 †20
ZAHN, Roland Manfred. 828 FLEMING ST, STE A 28791 #038-41-1993 L1997 **AN** *020 †05
ZINN, W Berkeley. ■ 28739 #038-41-1934 L1976 **R** *071 †80

HENRICO – NORTHAMPTON

CALDWELL, Marilyn L Bell. PO BOX 88 27842 #036-05-1977 L1977 **EM IM** *020 †20,16

HERTFORD – PERQUIMANS

LANE, Robert Earl. 600 S CHURCH ST, COASTAL CAROLINA FAMILY 27944 #021-01-1967 L1973 **FM EM** *020 †18
MOSS, Kenneth Wayne. ■ 27944 #010-02-1979 L1993 **N** *020 †75
THORNE, Norman Alan. 27944 #036-07-1958 L1958 **P NM** *071 †80,28,75

HICKORY – CATAWBA

ABERNETHY, Henry Walter. 1806 12TH AVE NE 28601 #036-01-1955 L1955 **FM IM** *071 †18
ADAIR, Brian C. 858 2ND ST NE 28601 #035-01-1997 L2001 **OPH** *020 †35
AL-KOUTAMI, Ghassan. 810 FAIRGROVE CHURCH RD 28602 #875-01-1987 L1993 **CD** *020 †20
ALLPORT, Simon J. 415 N CENTER ST STE 300 28601 #017-07-1992 L1999 **GE** *020 †20
ANDERSON, Daniel Edward. 1771 TATE BLVD SE, STE 103 28602 #035-06-1986 L1995 **PUD CCM** *020 †20
ANDERSON, Mark Jerome. 1202 N CENTER ST, VIEWMONT UROLOGY CLINIC, P 28601 #048-04-1986 L1992 **U GS** *020 †95
ATKINS, Mark Russell. 1899 TATE BLVD SE, STE 1105 28602 #036-05-1989 L1992 **PTH** *020 †50 ‡
AUTEN, Grace Mc Call. 1985 TATE BLVD SE, STE 720 28602 #036-07-1982 L1983 **ID IM** *020 †20
BARBER, Anthony Rodman. 311 9TH AVENUE DR NE 28601 #020-02-1985 L1999 **END** *020 †20
BARKER, James Thomas. 24 2ND AVE NE, STE 201 28601 #055-02-1999 L2004 **P IM** *020 †75
BARNETTE, Daniel Craig. 810 FAIRGROVE CHURCH RD 28602 #036-08-1988 L1993 **AN** *020 †05
BARTLEY, C Murray. 810 FAIRGROVE CHURCH RD 28602 #038-45-1987 L1991 **AN** *020
BATES, Paul Kenneth. 240 18TH STREET CIR SE, CATAWBA PEDIATRIC ASSOCIAT 28602 #020-02-1969 L1974 **PD** *020 †55
BAUER, John Montgomery. 1899 TATE BLVD SE, STE 1105 28602 #021-05-1976 L1976 **PTH** *020 †50
BERGAMO, Bethany Michele. 304 10TH AVE NE, STE 101 28601 #036-08-1997 L2004 **D** *020 †15
BERRY, Bruce Ellis. 2850 TATE BLVD SE, HART INDUSTRIAL CLINIC 28602 #004-01-1977 L1985 **EM DR** *020
BERRY, David Don. 352 2ND ST NW, STE 205 28601 #048-02-1978 L2004 **PD** *020 †55
BILHORN, Denise Holloman. 915 TATE BLVD SE, STE 170 28602 #036-01-1981 L2006 **OBG** *074 †30
BISHOPRIC, Frances Alice. 1205 N CENTER ST 28601 #045-01-1978 L1979 **OBG** *020 †30
BLANCHAT, Timothy Jos. 335 4TH ST NW 28601 #055-01-1974 L1977 **IM CD** *020 †20
BOLICK, Debra Anderson. 255 18TH STREET CIR SE 28602 #007-02-1989 L1990 **P PYG** *020 †50
BOOKER, John Parks, Jr. 18 13TH AVE NE 28601 #045-01-1967 L1973 **DR** *020 †80
BOOLS, John Christopher. 18 13TH AVE NE 28601 #038-43-1980 L1981 **VIR DR** *020 †80
BOWEN, Samuel T. 1470 9TH AVENUE DR NE 28601 #048-14-1984 L1987 **IM OM** *020 †20
BOYD, Robert Douglas. 1205 N CENTER ST 28601 #027-01-1983 L1987 **OBG** *020 †30
BOYLES, Larry Wayne. 415 N CENTER ST STE 202 28601 #036-01-1970 L1970 **N IM** *020 †75
BOYLES, Wayne F. ■ 28601 #028-02-1952 L1952 **FM** *071 †18
BRADSHAW, Peter Holbrook. 415 N CENTER ST, STE 102 28601 #036-01-1982 L1987 **GS VS** *020 †85
BRAUNSTEINER, Aaron J. 415 N CENTER ST 28601 #025-07-1995 L2000 **EM** *020 †16
BRAUNSTEINER, Melissa M. 212 29TH AVE NE STE 1, NORTH HICKORY FAMILY PRACT 28601 #025-07-1996 L2000 **FM** *020 †18 ‡
BRIGGS, Daniel Ross. 415 N CENTER ST, STE 201 28601 #036-01-1999 L2006 **AN** *020 †20,05
BRIGGS, Stacy Wood. ■ 28601 #036-01-1997 L2003 **PDP** *020 †55
BROOKS, Gregory Todd. 2820 16TH ST NE 28601 #055-01-1996 L1999 **FM** *020 †18
BROOKS, Thomas Wm, III. ■ 28601 #012-01-1962 L1969 **DR NM** *071 †80,28
BROSELOW, James Barry. 810 FAIRGROVE CHURCH RD 28602 #033-05-1969 L1979 **FM** *020 †18,16
BROWN, Donald Hugh, II. 420 N CENTER ST 28601 #045-01-1992 L1996 **AN** *020 †05
BROWN, Michelle Marie. 415 N CENTER ST STE 201 28601 #011-03-1991 L2001 **AN PME** *020 †05
BROWN, Paul Eugene. 214 18TH ST SE, P O BOX 20500 28602 #036-01-1969 L1969 **ORS** *071 †40
BURTON, Michael Paul. 24 2ND AVE NE 28601 #051-04-1990 L1997 **FM** *020 †18
BYERLY, W Grimes, Jr. ■ 28601 #024-01-1952 L1952 **GS** *071 †85
CADET, Melinda Maria. 28601 #033-05-1988 L1994 **P** *020 †75
CAIN, Felicia Kay. 415 N CENTER ST STE 201 28601 #055-01-1987 L1991 **AN** *020 †05
CALDWELL, Ronald David. 230 18TH STREET CIR SE, PIEDMONT RHEUMATOLOGY, PA 28602 #051-01-2001 L2006 **RHU** *020
CAPOROSSI, Lisa Lynn. 212 29TH AVE NE 28601 #036-05-2000 L2001 **FM** *020 †18
CAPOROSSI, Paul Vincent. ■ 28601 #033-05-1965 L1974 **OBG** *071 †30
CARLTON, Richard Alan. 420 N CENTER ST 28601 #024-16-1981 L1989 **TS** *020 †85,90
CARROLL, Alicia Marie. 2660 TATE BLVD SE, STE 200 28602 #033-06-1995 L2001 **OPH** *020
CARTER, Lawrence Stroud. 21 18TH AVE NW, ADULT INTERNAL MEDICINE 28601 #036-05-1993 L1996 **IM EM** *040 †20
CHAMBERS, Dana. 810 FAIRGROVE CHURCH RD 28602 #036-08-1995 L1998 **FM** *020 †18
CHATHAM, Scott Thomas. 1501 TATE BLVD SE 28602 #036-01-1997 L1998 **OBG** *020 †30
CHESSON, Andrew Long, III. ■ 28602 #021-05-2000 L2003 **FM** *100 †18
CHIRA, Ebele Chidum. 311 9TH AVENUE DR NE 28601 #690-02-1991 L2007 **END** *020

CHRISTENSEN, Harvey Earl. 810 FAIRGROVE CHURCH RD 28602 #005-11-1960 L1971 **GS TS** *071 †85
CHUANG, Meiyu. 810 FAIRGROVE CHURCH RD 28602 #021-05-1989 L2001 **CD** *020 †20
CLARK, Henry Vondell. 810 FAIRGROVE CHURCH RD 28602 #036-08-1993 L1998 **FM** *020 †18
COATES-WYNN, Geoffrey S. ■ 28601 #036-05-1999 L2005 **PM** *020 †60
COCHRANE, Josh. 415 N CENTER ST 28601 #007-02-1997 L2000 **EM** *020 †16
COFFEY, Jason Allen. 415 N CENTER ST 28601 #047-20-1998 L2000 **EM** *020 †16
COLE, Roger Dale. 304 10TH AVE NE 28601 #036-05-1988 L1994 **OTO OM** *020 †45
COLEMAN, Lester L, Jr. ■ 28601 #036-05-1950 L1950 **GP** *071
CONRAD, Ryan Scott. 1985 TATE BLVD SE, STE 600 28602 #017-20-1999 L2005 **N** *020 †75
COOK, Leland James. 415 N CENTER ST, STE 102 28601 #020-12-1979 L1984 **GS OS** *020 †85
CORDER, John Steven. 2359 SPRINGS RD NE 28601 #055-01-1988 L1991 **FM** *020 †18
COTTON, Michael Alan. 335 4TH ST NW 28601 #048-15-1998 L2000 **IM** *020 †20
COX, Montgomery H. 415 N CENTER ST, STE 102 28601 #045-01-1997 L2003 **GS** *020 †85
CRAIN, Bernard James, III. 810 FAIRGROVE CHURCH RD 28602 #035-15-1970 L1975 **EM GP** *020 †16
CROCKER, Kelly Bisceglia. 420 N CENTER ST 28601 #036-05-1992 L1995 **PD** *020 †55
DAHLSTEN, John Andrew. 415 N CENTER ST STE 103 28601 #018-03-1982 L1983 **GPM** *020 †05
DAVIS, Charles Barton. 1120 FAIRGROVE CHURCH RD, STE 12 28602 #036-01-1993 L1995 **P** *020 †75
DAVIS, John Woodrow. ■ 28601 #041-02-1946 L1947 **FM** *071 †18
DEATON, Hugo L. 415 N CENTER ST, STE 102 28601 #031-01-1957 L1958 **GS TS** *071 †85,90
DE LA GARZA, Carlos A. 24 2ND AVE NE 28601 #007-02-1976 L1984 **FM PM** *020 †18
DEL CHARCO, John Oscar. 810 FAIRGROVE CHURCH RD 28602 #011-04-1993 L1997 **RO** *020 †80
DE LEARY, Geoffrey Donald. 1202 N CENTER ST, VIEWMONT UROLOGY CLINIC P. 28601 #025-01-1989 L1995 **U** *020 †95
DE LOS SANTOS, Manuel T. 810 FAIRGROVE CHURCH RD 28602 #001-02-1962 L1971 **OBG** *071 †30
DE SANTIS, Michael C. 52 12TH AVE NE, HICKORY FAMILY PRACTICE AS 28601 #038-40-1992 L1998 **FM** *020 †18
DEW, John Albert, Jr. 335 4TH ST NW, HICKORY ACUTE CARE SPECIAL 28601 #036-08-1983 L1991 **PUD CCM** *020 †20
DIAMONTI, Gregory. 415 N CENTER ST, STE 300 28601 #035-08-1996 L2002 **GE** *020 †20
DICKEY, Richard Allen. ■ 28601 #035-01-1963 L2001 **END** *071 †20
DICKINSON, Michael Wright. 415 N CENTER ST, STE 102 28601 #051-01-1975 L1975 **GS VS** *020 †85
DILLON, Daniel Christian. 1045 25TH AVENUE DR NW 28601 #017-20-1968 L1974 **GE IM** *020 †20 ‡
DONEPUDI, Venkatarama S. 311 9TH AVENUE DR NE 28601 #654-01-1995 L2003 **END** *020 †20
DUFOUR, Harold C, Jr. 1501 TATE BLVD SE 28602 #021-05-1991 L1995 **OBG** *020 †30
DURALIA, David Robert. 1985 STARTOWN RD 28602 #045-01-1999 L2002 **FM** *020 †18
DY, Johnny Reyes. 810 FAIRGROVE CHURCH RD 28602 #748-20-1988 L2001 **IC CD** *020 †20
EARL, John Keith. 31 1ST AVE SE 28602 #039-01-1972 L1976 **FM** *020 †18
EDERMA, Arvo Bruno. ■ 28601 #036-05-1957 L1957 **GPM OM** *071 †70
EINFALT, Eric Stephen. 810 FAIRGROVE CHURCH RD 28602 #041-12-1989 L1992 **EM** *020 †16
EINSTEIN, Norman Zelig. 810 FAIRGROVE CHURCH RD, CATAWBA MEMORIAL HOSPITAL 28602 #024-07-1973 L1983 **EM IM** *020 †20,16
ELLER, Douglas Alan. 1202 N CENTER ST, VIEWMONT UROLOGY CLINIC 28601 #017-20-1992 L1998 **U** *020 †95
ELLISON, Matthew David. 1781 TATE BLVD SE, STE 201 28602 #056-06-1994 L2007 **OTO FPS** *020 †45
ENNIS, George Elliott. 420 N CENTER ST 28601 #036-01-1958 L1958 **IM** *020 †20
ESPEY, Dan, Jr. ■ 28602 #020-02-1947 L1951 **FM PUD** *071 †18
ESPIRITU, Maria Carmen E. 3246 6TH AVE SE 28602 #748-07-1988 L2003 **PM PME** *020 †60
EUSTICE, Isabelle Hamori. 810 FAIRGROVE CHURCH RD 28602 #021-01-1997 L2002 **PYG** *020 †75
FAHL, James Cox. 810 FAIRGROVE CHURCH RD 28602 #024-01-1948 L1972 **GS** *071 †85
FARKAS, Kimberly Worrell. 915 TATE BLVD SE, STE 170 28602 #045-01-1991 L1995 **OBG** *020 †30
FARRIS, Katherine Ann. ■ 28601 #016-06-2000 L2002 **FM** *020 †18
FARRIS, Stephen Louis. 18 13TH AVE NE 28601 #016-06-2001 L2007 **DR** *020 †80
FARUQUE, Laura M. 915 TATE BLVD SE, STE 170, WESTOVER PARK 28602 #038-44-1985 L1989 **OBG** *020 †30
FARUQUE, Mark Ahmed. 1232 SHILOH CHURCH RD, POST OFFICE BOX 6306 28601 #038-44-1985 L1989 **FM** *020 †18
FEAR, Olan De Witt, Jr. ■ 28601 #165-04-1960 L1984 **IM** *071
FEWELL, Jos Euranus, Jr. 50 13TH AVE NE STE 2B 28601 #045-01-1974 L1984 **PS** *020 †18
FISHER, George Burch, Jr. 1870 N CENTER ST 28601 #051-01-1976 L2001 **D IM** *020 †20,15
FITZ, Thomas E. 420 N CENTER ST 28601 #036-07-1950 L1952 **IM CD** *071 †20
FOSTER, John Thomas. ■ 28601 #036-07-1962 L1962 **OPH** *071 †35
FRANKEL, Nicholas. 18 13TH AVE NE 28601 #051-04-1975 L1979 **DR RNR** *020 †80 ‡
FRIERSON, Angela Marie. 1375 4TH STREET DR NW, THE CHILDHEALTH CENTER, PA 28601 #035-45-1996 L1999 **PD** *020 †55
FROEDGE, Jerry K. 240 18TH STREET CIR SE, UNIFOUR MEDICAL COMMONS 28602 #020-02-1969 L1974 **PD EM** *020 †55
GACHET, Fred Smith, Jr. 3131 9TH STREET DR NE, UNIT 41 28601 #023-07-1957 L1965 **GYN OS** *071 †30
GAITHER, James Comer. 1771 TATE BLVD SE, STE 103 28602 #028-02-1961 L1962 **IM** *020 †20
GARDNER, William Ronald. 420 N CENTER ST 28601 #011-02-1963 L1972 **GS VS** *071 †85
GEISSELE, Alfred Earl. 420 N CENTER ST 28601 #041-09-1984 L1995 **OSS ORS** *020 †40
GERRARD, Edward Rolland. 1202 N CENTER ST 28601 #048-04-1967 L1974 **U** *020 †95
GERRARD, Edward Rolland, Jr. 1202 N CENTER ST 28601 #036-08-1999 L2004 **U** *020 †95
GILDERSLEEVE, Ronald C. 810 FAIRGROVE CHURCH RD, WESTERN PIEDMONT 28602 #040-02-1993 L1998 **AN** *020 †05
GILL, Daniel Newell. 2336 1ST AVE SW 28602 #011-02-1992 L1998 **FM** *020 †18
GIOMETTI, Jon Allen. 810 FAIRGROVE CHURCH RD 28602 #047-06-1994 L2002 **EM** *020 †16
GLENN, Robert Frederick. 24 2ND AVE NE, MEDICAL ARTS CLINIC CENTER 28601 #047-05-1985 L1993 **FM** *020 †18
GOFORTH, James Walter. 2972 N CENTER ST 28601 #045-01-1983 L1986 **EM IM** *020 †20
GOODIN, Thos Elliott, III. 810 FAIRGROVE CHURCH RD, WESTERN PIEDMONT 28602 #047-06-1966 L1967 **AN** *071
GOODMAN, Benjamin W. 24 2ND AVE NE 28601 #047-06-1951 L1954 **GP OM** *072
GOODMAN, Benjamin Warren. 2820 16TH ST NE 28601 #036-01-1972 L1972 **FM** *020 †18 ‡

GOODSON, Bruce Michael. 1251 16TH ST NE, BOX 11223 28601 #654-01-1985 L1989 FM *020 †18

GRAY, Clare Lawrence. 335 4TH ST NW, HICKORY ACUTE CARE SPECIAL 28601 #026-04-1995 L2000 IM *020 †20

GRAY, Lee Virdis, III. 1344 N CENTER ST, STE A 28601 #036-01-2001 L2004 NEP *100 †20

GREER, Gary Wayne. 810 FAIRGROVE CHURCH RD 28602 #024-01-1979 L1996 EM *020 †16

GRIESEN, Dawn E. 304 10TH AVE NE 28601 #048-04-1998 L2003 OTO *020 †45

GUARINO, Clinton Toms. 1321 N CENTER ST 28601 #036-05-1996 L1999 IM *020

GUARINO, Guy Jos. ■ 28601 #021-05-1957 L1967 PTH *071 †50

HANSON, Eric W. 415 N CENTER ST, STE 201 28601 #011-03-1993 L1998 AN *020 †05

HARBISON, Warren Grant. 1120 FAIRGROVE CHURCH RD, STE 12 28602 #054-04-2000 L2005 P *020 †75 ‡

HARDAWAY, David Madison. 1202 N CENTER ST 28601 #036-05-1983 L1989 U *020 †95

HARLAN, Steven Dane. 18 13TH AVE NE 28601 #028-03-1976 L1977 DR VIR *020 †80

HARPER, Keith William. 18 13TH AVE NE 28601 #024-05-1998 L2003 DR *020 †80

HARRAGHY, Claire Holland. 915 TATE BLVD, STE 170 28602 #036-01-1999 L2003 OBG *020 †30

HARRILL, Willard Cardwell. 304 10TH AVE NE 28601 #051-04-1992 L1996 OTO *020 †45

HARRIS, James Woodrow, Jr. 858 2ND ST NE 28601 #038-40-1990 L1997 OPH *020 †35

HART, Robert Eric. 221 13TH AVENUE PL NW, STE 202 28601 #036-01-1989 L1990 FM *020 †18

HART, Robert Wm, III. 2850 TATE BLVD SE, HART INDUSTRIAL CLINIC 28602 #045-01-1965 L1966 FM OM *071 †18

HARVEY, David Leslie. 1899 TATE BLVD SE 28602 #020-12-1983 L1988 NEP IM *020 †20

HEARON, Brian Paul. 1771 TATE BLVD SE STE 2 28602 #027-01-1977 L1981 CD IM *020 †20

HENNINGTON, Mark Henry. 810 FAIRGROVE CHURCH RD 28602 #027-01-1986 L1991 TS VS *020 †85,90

HERFURTH, Thomas. 415 N CENTER ST, STE 201 28601 #036-05-1992 L1994 AN *020 †05

HIGERD, Michele Lynn. 1899 TATE BLVD SE 28602 #045-01-1995 L2000 NEP *020 †20

HIGHLAND, Kelly Edwards. 1899 TATE BLVD SE, STE 1105 28602 #036-05-1986 L1990 PTH *074 †50

HIGHLAND, Robert Alan. 1501 TATE BLVD SE 28602 #050-02-1990 L1994 OBG *020 †30

HILL, Thomas Robts. 810 FAIRGROVE CHURCH RD, WESTERN PIEDMONT 28602 #036-05-1988 L1992 AN PME *020 †05 ‡

HIRSCH, Michael Mark. 11 13TH AVE NE 28601 #051-04-1993 L1999 IM *020 †20

HODGES, James Robinson. 52 12TH AVE NE, HICKORY FAMILY PRACTICE AS 28601 #025-01-1972 L1977 FM IM *020 †18

HOFFMAN, Scott David. 1 3RD AVE SW 28602 #056-06-1986 L1989 FM *100 †18

HOLTZMAN, Adrian Wei. ■ 28601 #012-01-2001 L2006 DR *020 †80

HOLTZMAN, Allison Leigh. ■ 28601 #012-01-2001 L2004 FM *100 †18

HOOVER, Don Leo. 1940 BRIARWOOD DR, P O BOX 10094 28602 #021-06-1984 L1987 FM *020 †18

HUFFMAN, Allen Wm, Jr. 1205 N CENTER ST 28601 #036-01-1967 L1967 OBG *020 †30

HUGGINS, Henry L, Jr. 810 FAIRGROVE CHURCH RD 28602 #036-08-1984 L1985 EM *020 †16

HUGHES, Garland Lynn. 810 FAIRGROVE CHURCH RD 28602 #017-20-1990 L1996 IM *020 †20

HUNT, Christopher Loren. 415 N CENTER ST STE 201 28601 #030-05-1990 L1994 AN *020 †05

HUNT, Dori Lee. 1771 TATE BLVD SE, STE 202 28602 #030-05-1997 L1998 D *020 †15

IGDAL, Henry. 50 13TH AVE NE, STE 2A 28601 #422-01-1986 L1992 IM CRS *050 †20

INGLEFIELD, Joseph T, III. 220 18TH STREET CIR SE 28602 #051-04-1982 L1987 AI PDA *020 †55,03

ISENHOWER, Joseph Andrew. 24 2ND AVE NE 28601 #036-05-1954 L1954 FM *071 †18

ISSERMAN, Steven Michael. 810 FAIRGROVE CHURCH RD 28602 #011-02-1996 L2005 CD *020 †20

JACOBS, Michael Todd. 18 13TH AVE NE, CATAWBA RADIOLOGICAL 28601 #036-07-1996 L2001 DR *020 †80

JARRETT, William Andrew. 1781 TATE BLVD SE, STE 201 28602 #036-08-1996 L2001 OTO *020 †45

JENNINGS, Clark Wm. 420 N CENTER ST 28601 #021-01-1954 L1961 ORS *071 †40

JOHNSON, Charles Stewart. 1771 TATE BLVD SE, STE 202 28602 #038-43-1997 L2001 D *020 †15

JOHNSON, Jeremy Clyde. 214 18TH ST SE 28602 #021-01-1998 L1999 OSM *020 †40

JONES, David Marshall. 1899 TATE BLVD SE, STE 2108 28602 #051-01-1983 L1989 NS *020 †25

JONES, Pamela Kramish. ■ 28601 #051-01-1983 L1989 PD *020 †55

JONES, Wm Brewster, III. 420 N CENTER ST 28601 #005-19-1977 L1978 EM *020 †16

JOSLYN, Ann Kathryn. 858 2ND ST NE 28601 #036-07-1983 L1986 OPH *020 †35

KAHILL, Ailisa Hipp. ■ 28601 #036-05-2005 L2008 FP *012

KAUTH, Brian Gerard. 2386 SPRINGS RD NE, NORTHEAST FAMILY PRACTICE 28601 #035-03-1997 L2005 FM *020 †18

KESSEL, John Woodruff. 1985 STARTOWN RD, FAIRBROOK CLINIC 28602 #055-02-1990 L1992 FM *020 †18

KHEIREDDINE, Glencora Hel. ■ 28601 #036-01-2006 IM *012

KIELL, Charles Steven. 415 N CENTER ST, STE 102 28601 #033-05-1985 L1992 GS VS *020 †85

KIKEL, Stephen Phillip. ■ 28601 #016-42-1983 L1989 EM *020

KIM, Tong-Su. 24 2ND AVE NE 28601 #583-02-1951 L1967 P *071

KING, Walter Lee. 415 N CENTER ST 28601 #051-01-1967 L1971 OPH *020 †35

KOEHLER, Jan Olson. 415 N CENTER ST 28601 #041-14-1973 L2000 EM IM *020 †16

KOSCHESKI, Caroll Dean. 415 N CENTER ST 28601 #021-05-1986 L1991 GE *020 †20

KOSTUCHENKO, Paul John. 1771 TATE BLVD SE STE 202 28602 #051-04-1999 L2004 D DMP *020 †15

KUCH, Jeffrey Hamilton. 1914 PLAZA DR 28602 #024-01-1974 L2001 FM FPG *020 †20,18

KURAD, J Ward. 1202 N CENTER ST 28601 #023-01-1960 L1967 U *071 †95

LAFAVORE, Paul Richard. 415 N CENTER ST, STE 201 28601 #050-02-1992 L1996 AN PME *020 †05

LAFFERTY, John W. ■ 28601 #021-01-1946 L1951 PD *071 †55

LARISCY, Christopher L. 420 N CENTER ST 28601 #045-01-1990 L2001 AN *020 †05

LARSON, Seth Edward. 1985 TATE BLVD SE 28602 #026-04-1999 L2006 N *020 †75

LEFLER, Wade Hampton, Jr. 420 N CENTER ST 28601 #036-05-1963 L1963 OPH *071 †35

LEONARD, Baxter C J. 24 2ND AVE NE 28601 #036-01-1972 L1972 FM *020 †18

LEUZ, Christopher A, III. 447-01-1964 L1965 PS GS *075 †65

LOCKE, Ronald Newton. 1501 TATE BLVD SE STE 202 28602 #012-05-1984 L1995 GS EM *020 †85

LOMBOY, Carl Trinidad. 1771 TATE BLVD SE #051-01-1986 L1993 CD *020 †20

LOVIN, Vickie West. 915 TATE BLVD SE, STE 170 28602 #036-05-1981 L1985 GYN *020 †30

LOWRY, Brian Patrick. ■ 28601 #036-08-1994 L1994 EM *020 †16

LOWRY, Joy Sigmon. 240 18TH STREET CIR SE 28602 #036-08-1994 L1996 PD *020 †55

LUCKADOO, Laura J. 1455 25TH AVE NE 28601 #016-01-1992 L1996 PD *020 †55

LUNEY, Derek Johnedward. 810 FAIRGROVE CHURCH RD 28602 #012-01-1988 L1996 CD IM *020 †20

LUPTON, Bruce Barry. ■ 28601 #035-09-1959 L1960 IM CD *071 †20

LUPTON, Richard Greg. 925 10TH AVENUE DR NW 28601 #035-09-1981 L2006 OS CCM *020 †20

LYNN, Arthur Simonton, Jr. 1771 TATE BLVD SE, STE 103 28602 #036-01-1962 L1962 IM CD *020 †20

MARCHESE, Mark Jos. 1899 TATE BLVD SE STE 2108 28602 #035-45-1983 L1989 NS *020 †25

MASSENGILL, Alan David. 18 13TH AVE NE 28601 #028-34-1988 L1997 DR *020 †80

MASSENGILL, Judy Brakovec. 415 N CENTER ST, STE 201 28601 #028-34-1988 L1997 AN *020 †05

MAULDIN, Frank Wm. 420 N CENTER ST 28601 #027-01-1985 L1993 OTO *020 †45

MC CLOSKEY, Scott Michael. 420 N CENTER ST 28601 #023-01-1975 L1980 NS *020 †20

MC CLUER, Bryan Andrew. 1501 TATE BLVD SE STE 202, CAROLINA SURGERY & CANCER 28602 #001-06-1999 L2004 GS *020 †85

MC CRACKEN, Howard F, Jr. 964 18TH AVENUE CIR NW 28601 #649-14-1975 L1985 FM *020

MC DONALD, Ralph Norman. 1771 TATE BLVD SE STE 201 28602 #055-01-1982 L1988 IM CD *020 †20

MC DONELL, Charles F, Jr. 210 13TH AVENUE PL NW 28601 #021-01-1968 L1974 OBG *020 †30

MC DOUGAL, Emory Gary. 1899 TATE BLVD SE, STE 2106 28602 #001-06-1977 L1982 VS GS *020 †85

MC GINNIS, Mark R. 810 FAIRGROVE CHURCH RD 28602 #055-01-1984 L1992 HS ORS *020 †40

MC INTYRE, Stephen Ross. 1940 BRIARWOOD DR, MT VIEW FAMILY PRACTICE 28602 #045-01-1984 L1993 FM *020 †18

MC KARAHER, Anne Schreck. ■ 28601 #036-05-1987 L1990 PD *020 †55

MC KARAHER, Chas Wesley. 2972 N CENTER ST 28601 #036-08-1987 L1988 EM FM *020 †18

MC KEAN, Thomas Kevin. 24 2ND AVE NE, MEDICAL ARTS BUILDING 28601 #021-05-1993 L1997 P *020 †75

MC KENNEY, Todd Whitney. 810 FAIRGROVE CHURCH RD, WESTERN PIEDMONT 28602 #048-14-1986 L2003 AN *020 †05 ‡

MC NABB, Mc Kendree E. 24 2ND AVE NE, STE 210 28601 #004-01-1962 L1988 PUD IM *020 †20

MEIER, John Harvey. 415 N CENTER ST, STE 300 28601 #012-01-1985 L1994 GE IM *020 †20

MENARD, Dale Anthony, Jr. 1985 TATE BLVD SE, STE 600 28602 #012-05-1987 L1994 N *020 †75

MERTA, Steven Richard. 1205 N CENTER ST 28601 #035-09-1989 L1997 OBG *020 †30

MILLER, Douglas Parker. 810 FAIRGROVE CHURCH RD 28602 #028-02-1973 L1974 IM *020 †20

MILLER, Joel Byron. 1501 TATE BLVD SE 28602 #036-05-1974 L1974 GYN *020 †30

MILLER, Peter Danl. 915 TATE BLVD SE, STE 120 28602 #045-01-1987 L1995 NS GS *020 †25

MONTES, Anita Claire. 1052 13TH ST SE 28602 #005-18-1981 L1990 OBG *020 †30 ‡

MOORE, Reginald Graham. 2972 N CENTER ST 28601 #036-07-1975 L1978 OS FM *020 †18

MOORE, Thomas Robt. 415 N CENTER ST, STE 201 28601 #036-01-1992 L1998 AN *020 †05

MOREWITZ, Nancy Doralie. 915 TATE BLVD SE, STE 162 28602 #051-07-1981 L1986 N *020 †75

MORGANTE, Patrick. 52 12TH AVE NE 28601 #028-79-1997, ▲ L1998 FM *020 †18 ‡

MORRISON, John Andrew. 810 FAIRGROVE CHURCH RD 28602 #036-01-1996 L2001 IC *020 †20

MOSS, Paul. 3189 SHORT RD 28602 #036-05-1954 L1954 GP *020

MUNOZ, Rigardy P. 255 18TH ST SE 28602 #748-01-1983 L1997 CHP ADP *020 †75

MYLES, Sidney Lopez. 1771 TATE BLVD SE, STE 103 28602 #036-08-2000 L2005 OS *020 ‡

NELSON, John Douglas. 2359 SPRINGS RD NE 28601 #021-06-1983 L1987 FM FPG *020 †18

NEUWIRTH, Bryan Richard. 261 18TH STREET CIR SE, UNIFOUR MEDICAL COMMONS 28602 #036-01-1991 L1992 OMF CS *020

NICKS, Carl Michael. 214 18TH ST SE 28602 #036-01-1983 L1988 ORS *020 †40

NICKS, Sally Agner. ■ 28601 #036-01-1983 L1988 RHU IM *020 †20

NIELAND, Robert Bruce. ■ 28602 #018-03-1969 L1974 FM *071 †18

NORMAN, Elizabeth S. 1899 TATE BLVD SE, STE 1105 28602 #012-05-1999 L2001 PTH *020 †50

OBERLIN, Deloy Chas. 415 N CENTER ST, STE 201 28601 #005-11-1976 L1978 AN *020 †05

O'CONNOR, Robert Darrell. FAIRGROVE CHURCH RD 28603 #051-04-1960 L1967 OTO *071 †45

OLYMPIO, Georgia K. 1899 TATE BLVD SE, STE 1105 28602 #011-03-1982 L1984 PTH *020 †50

ORLOWSKI, Richard. 225 18TH ST SE, HEMATOLOGY, P O BOX 3710 28602 #028-02-1978 L1982 ON HEM *020 †20

OSBAHR, Albert J, III. 810 FAIRGROVE CHURCH RD, OCCUPATIONAL HEALTH 28602 #036-01-1985 L1990 OM FM *020 †70,18 ‡

OURSLER, Ralph Everett. 858 2ND ST NE 28601 #036-05-1995 L1999 OPH *020 †35

OWENS, Frederick Thos. 810 FAIRGROVE CHURCH RD 28602 #012-01-1970 L1976 PCC IM *020 †20

PABST, Susan Janis. 1501 TATE BLVD SE 28602 #036-08-1990 L1996 GS *020 †85

PAIGE, Glenn Barton. 415 N CENTER ST, STE 201 28601 #021-05-1990 L2001 AN *020 †05

PARISH, Kenneth Leroy. 415 N CENTER ST, STE 102 28601 #023-07-1985 L1999 GS *020 †85

PARKER, James Lee. 1899 TATE BLVD SE, STE 1105 28602 #036-01-1963 L1963 PTH *020 †50

PARROTT, James Hunter. 1985 TATE BLVD SE, STE 600 28602 #045-04-1992 L1997 CHN *020 †75

PASPA, Philip Alexander. 810 FAIRGROVE CHURCH RD 28602 #035-08-1984 L1989 CD *020 †20

PATEL, Ashish Dahya. ■ 28602 #496-01-2000 L2005 IM *020 †20

PATEL, Sanjay. 810 FAIRGROVE CHURCH RD 28602 #017-20-1994 L2001 CD *020 †20

PATRONE, Vincent Jos. 810 FAIRGROVE CHURCH RD 28602 #035-15-1982 L1998 CD IC *020 †20

PAUL, Richard Vincent. 1899 TATE BLVD SE, STE 2101 28602 #024-16-1981 L2001 NEP IM *020 †20

PAYNE, Dayton Dennis, Jr. 230 18TH STREET CIR SE, PIEDMONT RHEUMATOLOGY, PA 28602 #055-01-1987 L1992 RHU IM *020 †20

PEAK, E Louis. 36 14TH AVE NE 28601 #012-05-1997 L2002 ORS *020 †40

PEARCE, Richard Edward. 18 13TH AVE NE 28601 #036-08-1988 L1993 R *020 †80

PETERS, Sarah. 24 2ND AVE NE 28601 #704-06-1964 L1989 P *020 †75

PETERSON, Robert Lind. 1501 TATE BLVD SE 28602 #054-04-1971 L1977 OBG *020 †30

PIERCE, Robert James, Jr. 1202 N CENTER ST 28601 #036-01-1964 L1964 U *071 †95

PISEL, Gregory Allen. 1344 N CENTER ST, STE A 28601 #016-45-1990 L1999 NEP *020 †20

POLLOCK, Joseph Jordan. 415 N CENTER ST, STE 204 28601 #010-01-1958 L1986 PUD IM *071 †20

POLSTER, Scott David. 24 2ND AVE NE 28601 #041-09-1992 L1997 **FM** *020 †18 ‡

PRASHER, Sanjay. 810 FAIRGROVE CHURCH RD 28602 #495-39-1984 L2003 **CD IM** *020 †20

PRICE, Billy Lee, Jr. 1771 TATE BLVD SE, STE 103 28602 #036-08-1990 L1993 **IM** *020 †20

PRUITT, Jerry L. 245 11TH AVE NE 28601 #036-05-1971 L1971 **D** *020 †15

PUESCHEL, Jeanette Karen. 1985 TATE BLVD SE, STE 600 28602 #032-01-1997 L2007 **N** *020 †75

PURUT, Cemil Mehmet. 420 N CENTER ST 28601 #036-07-1987 L1989 **TS VS** *020 †90,85

PYREDDY, Pavan. ■ 28602 #495-62-1997 L2007 **IM** *100 †20

RAUTIOLA, Eric Clifton. 18 13TH AVE NE 28601 #025-12-1987 L1992 **NR** *020 †80,28

RAYMOND, Keith Allen. 731 5TH ST SW 28602 #041-02-1992 L1998 **FM** *020 †18

REECE, Neil Scott. 858 2ND ST NE, STE 303 28601 #036-05-1994 L1997 **FM** *020 †18

REED, Charles Nathan. 1870 N CENTER ST 28601 #036-01-1979 L1980 **D IM** *020 †15

REICHLING, Robert Joseph. 50 13TH AVE NE 28601 #038-41-1998 L2001 **IM** *020 †20

RERKPATTANAPIPAT, Pairoj. 810 FAIRGROVE CHURCH RD 28602 #891-01-1993 L2006 **CD** *020 †20

RICHARDSON, Ryan Nelson. 210 13TH AVENUE PL NW 28601 #033-06-1996 L2000 **OBG** *020 †30

ROBERTS, Bennie Dwayne. 415 N CENTER ST, STE 201 28601 #036-01-1987 L1988 **AN PME** *020 †05

ROBERTSON, Kent Alan. 415 N CENTER ST, STE 201 28601 #021-05-1976 L1985 **AN IM** *020 †20,05

ROSENFELD, Allan Gregory. 1899 TATE BLVD SE, STE 2108 28602 #023-01-1985 L1991 **NS** *020 †20

ROSS, Andrew Michael Hume. 810 FAIRGROVE CHURCH RD 28602 #917-23-1971 L2001 **CD IM** *020 †20

RUDISILL, Elbert A, Jr. 731 5TH ST SW 28602 #036-05-1977 L1997 **FM** *020 †18

RUSS, Donald Barnard. 3050 11TH AVENUE DR SE 28602 #036-01-1976 L1976 **P** *020 ‡

SALOMON, Richard Jay. 1985 TATE BLVD SE, HICKORY DERMATOLOGY 28602 #025-01-1982 L1983 **D** *020 †15 ‡

SANDERSON, Steven Lee. 221 13TH AVENUE PL NW, STE 101 28601 #038-41-1997 L1999 **FM** *020 †18

SANTOSO, Rudy. 1019 LENOIR RHYNE BLVD SE 28602 #506-05-1971 L1982 **P N** *020

SARANTOU, Terry. 415 N CENTER ST STE 102 28601 #016-11-1989 L1997 **GS SO** *020 †85

SCHEIL, Charles David. 18 13TH AVE NE, CATAWBA RADIOLOGIC ASSOC 28601 #036-01-1988 L1992 **R NM** *020 †80

SCHMITT, Raymond Francis. ■ 28601 #021-05-1959 L1969 **CHP** *071 †75

SCHNEIDER, Inaam Jamil. 415 N CENTER ST STE 1 28601 #025-07-1977 L1988 **IM** *020

SCHNEIDER, Richard Jos. 415 N CENTER ST STE 1, INTERNAL MEDICINE GROUP PA 28601 #025-07-1976 L1988 **IM** *020 †20

SCHULTZ, Richard Darryl. 810 FAIRGROVE CHURCH RD 28602 #035-09-1988 L1996 **CD IM** *020 †20

SCULLOCK, Michelle Denise. 915 TATE BLVD SE, STE 170 28602 #047-06-1993 L2001 **IM** *020 †20

SESHUL, Merritt John. 304 10TH AVE NE, HEAD & NECK SURGERY CENTER 28601 #001-02-1994 L2001 **OTO** *020 †45

SESHUL, Michael B, Sr. 810 FAIRGROVE CHURCH RD 28602 #021-05-1969 L2002 **DR NM** *020 †80 ‡

SESHUL, Raymond. ■ 28601 #021-05-1942 **IM** *071 †20

SHAW, Andrew Blair. 1120 FAIRGROVE CHURCH RD, STE 28 28602 #038-41-1990 L1999 **CHP** *020 †75

SHENOY, Nitin Purushotham. 1771 TATE BLVD SE, STE 103 28602 #036-01-1994 L1994 **IM** *020 †20

SHUE, Grady Van, Jr. ■ 28601 #036-08-1997 L2005 **DR** *020 †80

SICILIANO, Steven Andrew. 50 13TH AVE NE STE 2B 28601 #045-01-1986 L1993 **PS** *020 †85,45

SIGMON, William Reginald. 810 FAIRGROVE CHURCH RD 28602 #036-01-1987 L1988 **RO IM** *020 †80

SIMS, William Leonard. 1985 TATE BLVD SE 28602 #020-12-1979 L1985 **NS** *020 †25

SINCLAIR, Carter A. ■ 28601 #051-01-1952 L1954 **EM** *071 †18

SLEDGE, Scott Charles. 335 4TH ST NW 28601 #012-01-1996 L1997 **IM** *020 †20

SMEEKS, Frank Chase, III. 420 N CENTER ST 28601 #047-07-1995 L1998 **EM** *020 †16

SMITH, Allen Orlin. 415 N CENTER ST, STE 202 28601 #016-11-1969 L1988 **N CN** *020 †75

SMITH, William Thomas. 50 CLONINGER MILL RD NE, PREMIER INTERNAL MEDICINE, 28601 #036-08-1993 L1997 **IM** *020 †20

SRAN, Sarbjeet Kaur. 912 2ND ST NE 28601 #027-01-1983 L1987 **AI** *020 †55,03

STEARNS, Brent Ashley. 6018 POWDER POINT DR, STEARNS LLC 28601 #016-11-1987 L1992 **DR** *062 †80

STEG, Brian David. 810 FAIRGROVE CHURCH RD 28602 #038-06-1978 L1979 **IM** *020 †20

STERLING, Robert Todd. 1899 TATE BLVD SE, STE 1105 28602 #051-07-1981 L1983 **PTH** *020 †50

STEVENS, Robert Bruce. 415 N CENTER ST STE 103 28602 #038-41-1978 L1985 **AN** *020 †05

STUMPE, William Mann. 420 N CENTER ST 28601 #035-08-1948 L1952 **OM IM** *071 †28,20

STYER, Stephen Philip. 415 N CENTER ST 28601 #038-44-1998 L2002 **EM** *020 †16

SUMMER, Kenneth Virgil. 1375 4TH STREET DR NW, THE CHILDHEALTH CENTER 28601 #045-04-1985 L1988 **P** *020 †20

SUMMERS, Shane Orndorff. 221 13TH AVENUE PL NW, STE 202 28601 #038-40-1991 L1994 **FM** *020 †18

SWANK, Gregory Michael. 1771 TATE BLVD SE, STE 202 28602 #033-05-1991 L1997 **PS** *020 †85,65

SYNN, Jay. 24 2ND AVE NE 28601 #021-01-1992 L2000 **P** *020 †75

TART, David E. 304 10TH AVE NE, STE 101 28601 #036-01-1974 L1974 **D IM** *020 †20,15

TATE, Michael Noah. 225 18TH ST SE, NW CAROLINA ONCOLOGY 28602 #036-01-1982 L1983 **ON IM** *020 †20

THORWARTH, Wm Thos, Jr. 18 13TH AVE NE 28601 #032-01-1975 L1977 **DR NM** *020 †80

TIFFANY, Mark Alan. 2165 MEDICAL PARK DR 28602 #005-18-2000 L2004 **AN** *020 †05

TOMLINSON, Shannon K. 810 FAIRGROVE CHURCH RD 28602 #038-43-1998 L1999 **RO** *020 †80

TOY, Nancy Joan. 1501 TATE BLVD SE 28602 #038-45-1991 L1995 **OBG** *020 †30

TRADO, Charles Elmendorf. 24 2ND AVE NE 28601 #036-01-1959 L1959 **P GP** *071 †75

TRENT, Douglas Ernest. ■ 28601 #041-12-1964 L1990 **OBS GYN** *020 †30

VAN NOY, Joanna Watson. 1899 TATE BLVD SE, PIEDMONT PATHOLOGY ASSOCIA 28602 #027-01-1991 L1997 **PTH** *020 †50

VILLACORTE, Lizette Santo. 1120 FAIRGROVE CHURCH RD, STE 12 28602 #748-01-1990 L2003 **P** *100

VOGEL, Joseph Vincent. 1899 TATE BLVD SE, STE 1105 28602 #036-07-1977 L1982 **PTH** *020 †50

WALKER, Jason Alexander. 1501 TATE BLVD SE 28602 #036-05-1997 L2001 **OBG** *020 †30

WALSH, Alicia Ann. 915 TATE BLVD SE, STE 170 28602 #033-05-1995 L2006 **OBG** *020 †30

WARREN, Thomas Larry. 1985 TATE BLVD SE, FIRST PLAZA BLDG STE 763 28602 #001-02-1963 L1970 **GYN** *020 †30

WEISGERBER, David Wm. 307 10TH AVE NE 28601 #038-43-1981 L1989 **IM** *020 †20

WELCH, Carl Lester. 221 13TH AVENUE PL NW 28602 #012-01-1965 L1968 **FM** *020 †18

WELLMAN, Samuel Davis. 352 2ND ST NW, STE 205 28601 #055-02-1983 L1994 **NPM PD** *020 †55

WESSELMAN, David Michael. 810 FAIRGROVE CHURCH RD 28602 #034-01-1978 L2005 **EM** *020 †20,16

WHIDDON, Scott Morrison. ■ 28601 #011-02-1978 L1986 **DR** *020 †80

WHITE, James Clarence. ■ 28601 #038-06-1940 L1973 **IM CD** *020

WHITTON, Allison Curtis. 1501 TATE BLVD SE 28602 #038-34-1999 L2000 **OBG** *020 †30

WILEY, Thomas M. 810 FAIRGROVE CHURCH RD 28602 #023-12-1986 L2005 **CD** *020 †20

WILKINSON, John Douglas. 2386 SPRINGS RD NE 28601 #054-04-1971 L1992 **FM** *020 †18

WILLIAMS, Larry Thos. 1018 10TH STREET LN NW 28601 #036-01-1979 L1985 **AN** *020 †05

WILLIAMS, Randal James. 858 2ND ST NE, GRAYSTONE EYE EAR NOSE/THR 28601 #036-07-1969 L1969 **OPH OS** *020 †35

WILLIAMS, Robert Cyrus. 1781 TATE BLVD SE STE 201 28602 #045-01-1971 L1978 **OTO** *020 †45

WILLIAMS, Thomas Reginald. 858 2ND ST NE 28601 #016-11-1989 L1995 **OPH** *020 †35

WILLIAMS, Wheaton John. 810 FAIRGROVE CHURCH RD, HICKORY ID CONSULTANTS 28602 #012-01-1985 L2001 **ID IM** *020 †20

WILLIAMSON, Steven Grover. 810 FAIRGROVE CHURCH RD 28602 #016-11-1986 L1987 **EM** *020 †16

WILSON, Kathy Tingle. 1771 TATE BLVD SE, STE 103 28602 #027-01-2001 L2007 **PCC** *020

WILSON, Wayne Vincent. 1232 SHILOH CHURCH RD 28601 #045-01-1986 L1989 **FM** *020 †18

WINFIELD, Heber Grey, III. 214 18TH ST SE 28602 #036-01-1970 L1970 **ORS** *020 †40

WISE, John Edney. 11 13TH AVE NE, STE 103 28601 #036-01-1960 L1960 **IM GPM** *020

WOLD, James Palmer. 420 N CENTER ST 28601 #018-03-1989 L1993 **AN** *020 †05

WOLD, Karen Trygg. 1985 TATE BLVD SE, HICKORY DERMATOLOGY 28602 #033-05-1984 L1993 **D IM** *020 †20,15

WOTRING, James William, Jr. 1501 TATE BLVD SE 28602 #051-04-1961 L1967 **GYN** *020 †30

WRIGHT, Frank David. 415 N CENTER ST, STE 300 28601 #047-06-1992 L1998 **GE** *020 †20

YAPUNDICH, Robert. 1985 TATE BLVD SE, STE 600 28602 #055-01-1991 L1996 **N** *020 †75

YODER, Suzanne Russ. 24 2ND AVE NE 28601 #020-02-1993 L2001 **P** *020 †75

YOUNG, William Lee, III. 52 12TH AVE NE 28601 #051-01-1974 L1977 **FM** *020 †18

HIGH POINT – GUILFORD

AGBEMABIESE, Martin Kwaku. 624 QUAKER LN, STE D101 27262 #008-02-2003 L2006 **IM** *030 †20

AGUIAR, Rafaela Maria. 4590 PREMIER DR, DEEP RIVER FAMILY MEDICINE 27265 #008-02-1994 L1996 **FM** *020 †18

AL-KHORI, Fareed Farah. 721 N ELM ST, STE 101 27262 #875-01-1985 L1999 **CD IM** *020 †20

ANDERSON, James C, IV. 624 QUAKER LN, STE 100E 27262 #048-04-1993 L1997 **PD** *020 †55

APPEL, Richard Gary. 404 WESTWOOD AVE, STE 105 27262 #036-05-1976 L1978 **NEP IM** *020 †20

ARAVIND, Moogali Manjappa. 3604 PETERS CT, BETHANY MEDICAL CENTER 27265 #495-98-1986 L1997 **IM** *020

ARNOLD, Gordon Bruce. 404 WESTWOOD AVE, STE 203 27262 #016-01-1962 L1969 **IM** *020 †20

ARTHUR, Robert K. ■ 27265 #023-01-1951 L1957 **OBG** *071 †30

ARUS, Ariel David. 645 N MAIN ST 27260 #042-01-1980 L1997 **OBG GS** *020 †30

AUMAN, Edwin Lewis. 624 QUAKER LN, STE 200E 27262 #036-05-1955 L1955 **IM** *020 †20

AVERETT, Leland Stanley. 319 WESTWOOD AVE 27262 #036-01-1954 L1954 **FM GP** *071

BALSLEY, Robert E. ■ 27262 #051-01-1944 L1949 **EM PD** *071 †55

BARBEE, Lewis Elisha. ■ 27260 #010-03-1963 L1965 **GP EM** *071

BARNETT, Tasha Denee. ■ 27265 #001-06-2004 L2007 **PD** *020

BASHORE, Christopher J. 611 N LINDSAY ST, STE 200 27262 #025-01-1991 L1993 **ORS OMO** *020 †40

BEAUFORD, Wayne. 507 N LINDSAY ST 27262 #047-07-1984 L1992 **PUD IM** *020 †20

BELL, Ira E, III. 624 QUAKER LN, STE 101A 27262 #036-01-1982 L1983 **DR** *020 †80

BELL, Ira Eugene. 624 QUAKER LN, STE 117B 27262 #012-01-1945 L1950 **RO DR** *071 †28,80

BENNETT, Herron K. 601 N ELM ST 27262 #036-05-1952 L1956 **OBG** *071 †70,30

BERNTHAL, Theodore G, Jr. 217 GATEWOOD AVE 27262 #045-01-1973 L1976 **PD** *020 †55

BHATTI, Jamila Shaheen. 624 QUAKER LN, STE D101 27262 #704-21-1984 L2002 **IM** *020 †20

BICKLEY, Samuel Taylor. 3604 PETERS CT 27265 #036-05-1961 L1961 **GP** *020 †18

BIESECKER, Gary Leroy. 611 N LINDSAY ST 27262 #030-05-1968 L1976 **GS** *020 †85

BLAKE, John Paul. 211 S CENTENNIAL ST, HIGH POINT CENTER 27260 #036-05-1960 L1960 **P** *020

BLAZEK, F Douglas. 611 N LINDSAY ST 27262 #041-02-1983 L1988 **GS CRS** *020 †85

BRATH, Peter Christian. 607 IDOL ST, CORNERSTONE CRITICAL CARE 27262 #048-14-1994 L1997 **CCA AN** *040 †05

BRIGMAN, Paul Hamer. 231 PLAZA ST 27263 #036-01-1954 L1954 **EM GP** *020

BROOKS, Ralph Elbert, Jr. 624 QUAKER LN STE 100E 27262 #036-01-1955 L1955 **U** *071 †95

BRUMFIELD, Christopher S. 611 N LINDSAY ST, STE 200 27262 #036-05-1994 L2000 **ORS** *020 †20

BRUTON, Amy Marie. 645 N MAIN ST 27260 #051-07-2002 L2004 **OBG** *020

BUNEMANN, Lee Martin. 217 GATEWOOD AVE 27262 #025-07-1988 L1990 **PD** *020 †55

BURAPAVONG, T David. 416 GATEWOOD AVE 27262 #891-03-1969 L1974 **PS** *020 †85,65

BURCH, Larry Thos. ■ 27265 #025-01-1964 L1976 **P** *072

BURNEY, Donald Patrick. 306 WESTWOOD AVE, STE 505 27262 #028-02-1970 L1979 **TS** *020 †85,90

BURNS, Kevin Lee. 810 N LINDSAY ST 27262 #036-01-1994 L2001 **IM** *020 †20

BUSBY, Julian Goode. 712 N ELM ST, CAROLINA WOMANCARE,PA 27262 #036-01-1970 L1975 **OBG** *020 †30

CHALFA, Nicolai. 1720 WESTCHESTER DR 27262 #011-03-1976 L1977 **OM FM** *020 †18

CHALLA, Surya Kantam. 507 N LINDSAY ST 2ND FL, BETHANY MEDICAL CENTER 27262 #495-21-1971 L1981 **P** *020

CHALLA, Venkata Ramana. 507 N LINDSAY ST, 2ND FL 27262 #495-70-1969 L1978 **NP PTH** *050 †50

CHEEK, Herman Barrett. 306 WESTWOOD AVE, STE 401 27262 #036-05-1983 L1989 **CD** *020 †20

CHEN, Eric. 624 QUAKER LN STE D101 27262 #038-75-1999, ▲ L2004 **MPD** *020 †20,55
CHINNASAMI, Bernard Ravi. 302 WESTWOOD AVE 27262 #495-04-1988 L1992 **ON** *020 †20
CHIU, Jenyung Andy. 300 GATEWOOD AVE 27262 #422-01-1995 L2007 **CD IC** *020 †20
CHUNG, Zun Sub. 2926 S MAIN ST 27263 #583-03-1965 L1976 **FM** *020
CLARK, Michael Scott. 211 S CENTENNIAL ST, GUILFORD CENTER 27260 #048-16-1989 L1992 **CHP** *020 †75
CLOUTIER, Michael Gene. 624 QUAKER LN STE 117B, HIGH POINT RADIOLOGICAL SE 27262 #020-02-1973 L1983 **DR** *020 †20,80
COPE, Darrell Anthony. 400 N ELM ST, HIGH POINT OB/GYN ASSOC 27262 #036-07-1990 L1994 **OBG** *020 †30
CORNELL, David Wade. 1720 WESTCHESTER DR, MED CENTRAL/MEDVENTURES 27262 #056-06-1992 L1995 **FM** *020 †18
CORRINGTON, Kip Alan. 1720 WESTCHESTER DR 27262 #048-16-1999 L2000 **FM** *020 †18
COSGROVE, Robert Jos. PO BOX 16364 27261 #011-02-1985 L1989 **AN** *020 †05
COUGHLIN, Paul William F. 607 IDOL ST 27262 #036-01-1978 L1980 **U** *020 †95
COX, Ronnie Lewis. 624 QUAKER LN STE 205A 27262 #036-07-1961 L1961 **GP IM** *071 †20
CRAWFORD, Robert Cecil. 712 N ELM ST 27262 #036-07-1965 L1965 **OBG** *020 †30
CROWELL, Charles Carlos. 624 QUAKER LN STE D-20 27262 #036-05-1972 L1972 **CD** *020
CRUZ, Nestor, Jr. 611 N LINDSAY ST 27262 #048-12-1989 L1998 **VS** *020 †85
DAKORIYA, Swati Satya. 211 S CENTENNIAL ST 27260 #047-20-2000 L2005 **P** *020
DANSIE, Kim D. 1836 EASTCHESTER DR STE 1 27265 #036-05-1987 L1989 **P CHP** *020 †75
DASHER, James. 611 N LINDSAY ST 27262 #041-01-1993 L1998 **GS** *020 †85
DAVANZO, Robert John. 307 LINDSAY ST, CORNERSTONE EYE CARE 27262 #036-01-1981 L1998 **OPH** *020 †35 ‡
DAVIS, John Franklin. 1105 N LINDSAY ST 27262 #036-05-1990 L1991 **FM** *020 †18
DEATON, Jeffrey Lynn. 2783 NC HIGHWAY 68 S, STE 104 27265 #047-05-1983 L1990 **OBG REN** *020 †30
DESALVO, Gary John. 901 N LINDSAY ST 27262 #041-07-1991 L1994 **HNS** *020
DEXTER, Stephen Eugene. ■ 27265 #422-01-2006 **IM** *012
DICKSON, Christopher S. 306 WESTWOOD AVE, STE 505 27262 #024-16-1987 L1996 **VS** *020 †85
DIGBY, Donald Joe. 1105 N LINDSAY ST 27262 #012-01-1976 L1984 **OPH** *020 †35
DILLARD, Thomas Wayne. ■ 27262 #036-01-2004 L2007 **PD** *020 †55
DORN, Henry Hartzog, III. 401 WESTWOOD AVE 27262 #045-01-1996 L2000 **OBG** *020 †30
DOUGLASS, Donald P. ■ 27262 #036-05-1953 L1953 **GS TS** *071 †85
DRAELOS, Michael Thos. 624 QUAKER LN, STE 105 27262 #003-01-1982 L1987 **GE** *020 †20
DRAELOS, Zoe Diana. 2444 N MAIN ST 27262 #003-01-1983 L1987 **D DS** *020 †15 ‡
DUCKETT, Ralph Howard. 607 IDOL ST 27262 #036-05-1986 L1987 **U** *020 †95
EARLY, Todd Franklin. 306 WESTWOOD AVE, STE 505 27262 #051-07-1985 L1991 **VS** *020 †85
ECKELBERG, Todd Michael. ■ 27265 #035-09-1999 **IM** *012
EISENBERG, Joshua Aaron. 611 N LINDSAY ST 27262 #041-02-1999 L2006 **VS** *020 †85
ELENDU, Sebastine Izu. 601 N ELM ST, HIGHPOINT REGIONAL HEALTH 27262 #690-02-1999 L2004 **PCC** *020 †20
ELLIS, Gregory Carl. 624 QUAKER LN, STE 100E 27262 #045-01-1985 L1992 **PD** *020 †55
ENGELMANN, John A, Jr. 2125 CROSSING WAY CT APT H 27262 #023-12-1984 L1997 **AN** *020
EPES, Charles Richard. 1429 JOHNSON ST 27262 #051-01-1968 L1971 **OPH** *020 †35
ERDIN, Robt Alexander, Jr. 306 WESTWOOD AVE, STE 401 27262 #012-01-1973 L1978 **CD IM** *020 †20
ERRICO, James Melton. 307 LINDSAY ST, CORNERSTONE EYE CARE 27262 #023-07-1964 L1971 **OPH** *020 †35
ESKEW, Lawrence Andrew. 607 IDOL ST 27262 #036-05-1993 L1994 **U** *020 †95
FARABOW, William Sidney. ■ 27262 #012-05-1963 L1967 **GYN** *071 †30
FARAH, Brian Andrew. 320 BOULEVARD ST, REGIONAL PSYCHIATRIC ASSOC 27262 #045-01-1990 L1991 **P** *020 †75
FARRINGTON, John Kirby. 307 LINDSAY ST 27262 #036-01-1957 L1957 **OBG** *071 †30
FERARU, Elaine Rose. 624 QUAKER LN, STE 100C 27262 #010-01-1981 L1997 **N GP** *020 †75
FIELDS, Charles Edward. 306 WESTWOOD AVE, STE 505 27262 #051-04-1995 L2004 **VS** *020 †85
FISHER, David Michael. 601 N ELM ST 27262 #036-05-1996 L1999 **EM** *020 †16
FLETCHER, Richard Van, Jr. 721 N ELM ST, STE 102 27262 #047-05-1974 L1978 **OBG** *020 †30
FORD, Charles Stephen. 624 QUAKER LN, STE 100C 27262 #045-01-1979 L1982 **N** *020 †75
FORD, Stephen Mitchell. 624 QUAKER LN STE 206C 27262 #047-20-1984 L2001 **P** *075 †75
FORTNEY, Austin Powell. 833 MONTLIEU AVE 27262 #012-05-1946 L1951 **IM IMG** *071
FREEMAN, Chara Chinyere. ■ 27265 #055-01-2008 *012
FREUND, Victor Thomas. 404 WESTWOOD AVE, STE 201 27262 #036-08-1994 L2007 **NS** *020 †25
FULLERTON, Heather D. 404 WESTWOOD AVE STE 207, PAIN ASSOCIATES 27262 #021-06-1996 L2003 **PM PRS** *020 †60
FULTON, James Walker. 400 N ELM ST 27262 #036-07-1957 L1957 **GYN** *071 †30
GALLAGHER, Theresa Ciardi. 601 N ELM ST, COGENT HOSPITALIST PHYSICI 27262 #041-07-1992 L2002 **IM** *020 †20
GALLEMORE, Warren Gholson. 810 N LINDSAY ST, CORNERSTONE MEDICAL SPEC 27262 #012-01-1975 L1978 **IM** *020 †20
GAY, Robert Milton, Jr. 810 N LINDSAY ST 27262 #036-01-1990 L1996 **RHU** *020 †20
GEHRIS, John M. 319 WESTWOOD AVE, HIGH POINT PRIMARY CARE 27262 #041-09-1981 L1997 **IM** *020 †20
GENIEC, Paul. 624 QUAKER LN, STE 201C 27262 #049-01-1964 L1966 **OTO PS** *020 †45
GERHARDT, Edward Burton. 601 N ELM ST 27262 #051-01-1981 L1989 **TS** *020 †85,90
GIBSON, Mitchell Earl. ■ 27265 #036-01-1985 L1987 **P** *020 †75
GOLDSTON, Thomas David. 601 N ELM ST 27262 #036-01-1980 L1983 **PD** *020 †55
GREENE, Eleanor E W. 4510 PREMIER DR, TRIAD WOMEN'S CENTER 27265 #036-01-1981 L1986 **OBG** *020 †30
GUMPRECHT, Ernest Chas. 306 WESTWOOD AVE, STE 401 27262 #054-04-1981 L2004 **CD IM** *020 †20 ‡
HAIMES, David Michael. 905 PHILLIPS AVE, HIGH PT FAM PRAC ASSOC PA 27262 #011-03-1979 L1984 **FM** *020 †18 ‡
HALL, Marshall Craig. 218 GATEWOOD AVE 27262 #020-02-1987 L1998 **U** *020 †95
HARISH, Vallathucherry C. 302 WESTWOOD AVE 27262 #495-59-1991 L2003 **HO** *020 †20
HARRIOTT, John Thomas. 1429 JOHNSON ST 27262 #035-46-1983 L1993 **OPH IM** *020 †20,35
HARRISS, William Fred. 1500 CRESTLIN DR 27262 #036-05-1966 L1966 **R** *020 †80
HAWKS, Al N. 607 IDOL ST 27262 #036-05-1979 L1982 **FM** *020 †18 ‡
HAWORTH, Chester Carl, Jr. 624 QUAKER LN, STE 100C 27262 #036-07-1963 L1963 **N IM** *020 †20,75
HAYES, Paul Gregory. 306 WESTWOOD AVE, STE 505 27262 #065-10-1982 L1991 **VS CCS** *020 †85
HENDRICKSON, Steven Craig. 306 WESTWOOD AVE, STE 505 27262 #036-07-1989 L1995 **TS** *020 †85,90
HERZBERG, Tara Raquel. 1208 EASTCHESTER DR, STE 200 27265 #041-02-2001 L2006 **DR** *020
HIATT, Paul Kevin. 1208 EASTCHESTER DR, STE 200 27265 #036-01-1986 L1989 **DR** *020 †80
HICKS, Kristin Denise. 404 WESTWOOD AVE STE 203 27262 #047-07-2001 L2004 **IM** *020 †20
HIGGINS, Lloyd Malcolm. 601 N ELM ST 27262 #021-05-1955 L1965 **PTH** *071 †50
HOLLAR, Carlin Bullard. 404 WESTWOOD AVE, STE 107 27262 #036-05-1999 L2002 **D** *020 †15
HONEYCUTT, Boyd Knetsar. 4135 MENDENHALL OAKS PKWY 27265 #047-06-1969 L1992 **MDM IM** *030 †20
HOPKINS, Marbry Benj, III. 601 N ELM ST 27262 #051-01-1977 L1981 **PTH BBK** *020 †50
HURRELBRINK, Lester E, III. 624 QUAKER LN, STE 105 27262 #021-05-1981 L1987 **GE IM** *020 †20
HUSSEY, Michael Brush. 606 N ELM ST 27262 #051-01-1961 L1971 **NS** *020 †25
HUSSIENO, Muhammad Ammar. 624 QUAKER LN, STE 100D 27262 #875-01-1994 L2006 **PUD IM** *020 †20
HUTTON, William Eugene. 1105 N LINDSAY ST 27262 #036-05-1972 L1972 **OPH** *020 †35
IGWEMEZIE, Benjamin M. 635 N MAIN ST, BMI NEPHROLOGY SYSTEMS, IN 27260 #690-04-1987 L1994 **NEP IM** *020 †20
INGRAM, Charles Hal. ■ 27260 #023-01-1943 L1943 **GS** *071 †85
IRVING, Steven P. 901 N LINDSAY ST 27262 #001-02-1978 L1980 **PS** *020
JACKSON, Barney R. ■ 27265 #010-03-1980 L1983 **FM** *020 †18,16
JACOBS, James Curtis. 306 WESTWOOD AVE, STE 501 27262 #036-01-1986 L1989 **OBG** *020 †30
JARRELL, Renaldo Andrew. 601 N ELM ST, HIGH POINT REGIONAL HOSPIT 27262 #016-45-1990 L2005 **IM** *020 ‡
JARRETT, Thomas Edward. 507 N LINDSAY ST 27262 #045-01-1978 L1982 **IM** *020 †20 ‡
JEDLICA, Michele T. 601 N ELM ST 27262 #036-05-1997 L1999 **PD** *020 †55
JENKINS, Sharrah Ericka. 2401 HICKSWOOD RD B, REGIONAL PHYSICIANS 27265 #012-21-1999 L2002 **IM** *020
JOHNSON, Robert C. 606 N ELM ST 27262 #005-12-1949 L1954 **ORS** *071 †40
JONES, Charles Bradley. 624 QUAKER LN, STE 100D 27262 #036-08-2000 L2002 **IC** *012 †20
JONES, Perry Eugene. 401 FERNDALE BLVD 27262 #023-12-1989 L2002 **AN** *020 †18,05
JOYCE, George Wm. 624 QUAKER LN 27262 #036-05-1960 L2003 **IM NEP** *071 †20
KALIL, Darryl Alfred. 300 GATEWOOD AVE 27262 #836-02-1974 L1997 **IM CD** *020 †20
KALISH, Michael John. 4590 PREMIER DR, DEEP RIVER FAMILY MEDICINE 27265 #048-14-1985 L1987 **FM** *020 †18
KAY, James David. 624 QUAKER LN, STE 100D 27262 #041-02-2001 L2005 **CD** *012
KEEVER, Richard Alan. ■ 27262 #036-01-1969 L2005 **OTO** *075 †45
KELLY, Samuel Steven. 4590 PREMIER DR 27265 #016-45-1993 L2000 **FM** *020 †18
KIRBY, Deborah Lynette. 624 QUAKER LN STE 206C, HIGH POINT NEUROLOGICAL AS 27262 #004-01-2003 L2007 **CN** *012
KIRBY, Samuel Craig. 404 WESTWOOD AVE, STE 107 27262 #036-08-1982 L1986 **D** *020 †15
KOCHEKIAN, Karen Lorraine. ■ 27265 #036-08-1982 L1984 **PD** *020
KONTOS, Jimmy Larry. 624 QUAKER LN, STE 100D 27262 #036-01-2001 L2005 **IC** *012 †20
KREMER, William Alfred. 231 PLAZA LN, MED CENTRAL SOUTH 27263 #036-08-1991 L1992 **FM OM** *020 †18
LARGEN, Kevin Neal. 601 N ELM ST 27262 #051-04-1998 L2001 **EM** *020 †16
LAUER, Tommie Fantine. 624 QUAKER LN 27262 #036-01-1977 L1979 **P** *071 †75
LAWSON, James Douglas. 306 WESTWOOD AVE, STE 505 27262 #047-06-1974 L1981 **VS** *020 †85
LEAGUE-SOBON, Jennifer A. 1720 WESTCHESTER DR, MEDCENTRAL 27262 #011-04-1996 L1998 **FM** *020 †18
LEINBACH, Robert Frederic. 624 QUAKER LN, STE 208C 27262 #036-05-1999 L2005 **OTO** *020 †45
LENNON, Kenneth Charles. 611 N LINDSAY ST, STE 200 27262 #036-01-1994 L2000 **ORS** *020 †40
LEUNG, Yatwah. 218 GATEWOOD AVE, PIEDMONT PROSTRATE CTR 27262 #043-01-1991 L2000 **RO** *020 †80
LIM, Alexander Junghwan. 401 FERNDALE BLVD 27262 #041-12-1994 L2002 **AN** *020 †05
LIN, Weichen. 1208 EASTCHESTER DR, STE 200 27265 #035-19-1995 L2000 **DR** *020 †80
LOKE, Monica Weifunn. 710 N ELM ST 27262 #016-02-1988 L2004 **NS** *020 †25
LOUK, Douglas Keith. 400 N ELM ST, HIGH POINT OB/GYN ASSOC 27262 #051-07-1984 L1988 **OBG** *020 †30
LUCAS, Michael John. 611 N LINDSAY ST STE 200 27262 #036-01-1991 L1997 **ORS** *020 †40
LUKENS, Mark Leroy. 1208 EASTCHESTER DR, STE 200 27265 #038-43-1989 L1998 **DR VIR** *020 †80
MANNING, Patsy Ruth. ■ 27265 #047-06-1984 L1986 **GE IM** *020 †20
MARKHAM, Robert Wade. 601 N ELM ST 27262 #036-07-1963 L1963 **D** *020 †15
MARLOWE, James Manning. 624 QUAKER LN # 200 27262 #036-01-1960 L1960 **ORS** *020 †40
MARTIN, Wells, III. HIGH POINT MEM HOSP 27260 #038-41-1976 L1980 **DR** *020 †80
MATTERN, Shannon T. 400 N ELM ST, HIGH POINT OB/GYN ASSOC 27262 #026-08-1999 L2003 **OBG** *020 †30
MC FADDEN, John C. 905 PHILLIPS AVE, HIGH POINT FAMILY PRACTICE 27262 #041-13-1986 L1992 **FM** *020 †18
MC FALLS, Vernon Wendell. 624 QUAKER LN, STE 211B 27262 #036-01-1958 L1958 **PD** *020 †55
MC NAMARA, Michael Thos. 645 N MAIN ST 27260 #050-02-1977 L1988 **OBG** *020 †30
MICHAEL, Jay Benj. 401 FERNDALE BLVD 27262 #036-01-1989 L1999 **AN** *020 †05
MICHAL, Wm Norwood, Jr. 624 QUAKER LN 27262 #036-01-1960 L1960 **PD** *071 †55
MIGLIARDI, Robert Tad. 404 WESTWOOD AVE, STE 107 27262 #045-01-1992 L1997 **ATP D** *050 †15
MILLER, Joseph Keith. 606 N ELM ST 27262 #035-06-1983 L1988 **N CN** *020 †75
MILLS, Stephen Alan. 306 WESTWOOD AVE, STE 505 27262 #067-01-1971 L1980 **TS** *020 †90,85
MOORE, David Ferguson, Jr. 624 QUAKER LN, STE 208C 27262 #047-06-1988 L1994 **OTO** *020 †45
MOSER, Eric Todd. 624 QUAKER LN, STE 100C 27262 #036-05-1993 L1998 **CN PME** *020 †75
MULLINS, Timothy Leon. 607 IDOL ST 27262 #055-01-1982 L1988 **U** *020 †95
MURDOCK, Kirk Albert. 1429 JOHNSON ST 27262 #021-01-1988 L1996 **OPH** *020 †35 ‡
MYERS, Alexander Gordon. 131 W PARRIS AVE STE 6 27262 #036-05-1986 L1988 **P** *020 †75
MYERS, Marybeth Conway. 404 WESTWOOD AVE, STE 103 27262 #036-05-1986 L1989 **PD** *020 †55
NEAVE, Victoria C D. 404 WESTWOOD AVE, STE 201 27262 #051-04-1980 L1986 **NS** *020 †25
NELSON, Kristine Anne. 1801 WESTCHESTER DR 27262 #308-07-1982 L1995 **PLM** *020
NOAH, Hugh Bryan. 611 N LINDSAY ST, STE 200 27262 #036-05-1966 L1966 **ORS** *020 †40

■ = Address Information Privacy Protected

OAKS, Ann Burkhalter. 601 N ELM ST 27262 #001-02-1991 L1992 **PTH** *020 †50
O'KEEFFE, Michael Edward. 306 WESTWOOD AVE, STE 501 27262 #036-05-1997 L2001 **OBG** *020 †30
ORR, Richard Lowman, Jr. 624 QUAKER LN, STE 200E 27262 #045-01-1980 L1983 **IM** *020 †20
OSKARSSON, Helgi Julius. 300 GATEWOOD AVE 27262 #484-01-1983 L1998 **CD** *020 †20
OWINGS, William Richard. 401 FERNDALE BLVD 27262 #020-12-1980 L1983 **AN CCM** *020 †05
PANJABI, Rajesh Ramesh. 2304 GORDON RD 27265 #036-01-2008 *012
PARKS, Seigle Wilson. ■ 27262 #023-01-1939 L1940 **OM** *071
PATEL, Kalpen N. 400 N ELM ST, HIGH POINT OB/GYN ASSOC 27262 #048-02-1994 L1995 **OBG** *020 †30
PAYNE, George Harold, Jr. ■ 27262 #030-05-1981 L1982 **EM** *020 †16
PERRY, Angela Lynn Doss. 905 PHILLIPS AVE 27262 #055-01-1994 L2002 **IM** *020 †20
PETERS, Lenin Joseph. 507 N LINDSAY ST 27262 #495-31-1974 L1985 **GE** *020 †20
PHIPPS, Carl David. 624 QUAKER LN, STE 208C 27262 #036-05-1993 L1998 **OTO** *020 †45
PICKLESIMER, Fred Leon. ■ 27262 #036-05-1966 L1966 **OTO GP** *071 †45
PLOWDEN, James Francis. 302 WESTWOOD AVE 27262 #045-01-1973 L1978 **ON IM** *020
POLLOCK, Nelson Earl. 810 N LINDSAY ST 27262 #012-01-1975 L1978 **IM** *020 †20
PORTNER, Bruce S. 624 QUAKER LN, STE 200E 27262 #305-01-1982 L1995 **IM PD** *020
POSTON, Mary Allison. 624 QUAKER LN, STE 100E 27262 #036-01-1995 L2000 **PD** *020 †55
POWELL, Jerry Lamon. 905 PHILLIPS AVE 27262 #036-08-1995 L1999 **MPD** *020
PUSCHINSKY, Richard W. 624 QUAKER LN STE 103C 27262 #048-04-1989 L1995 **U** *020 †95
RADIONCHENKO, Yulia Vladi. 307 LINDSAY ST, CORNERSTONE EYE CARE 27262
 #913-08-1988 L2007 **GS** *100
RAVENEL, Samuel Du Bose. 624 QUAKER LN, STE 100E 27262 #036-07-1964 L1964
 ID *020 †55
RAVENEL, Samuel F, II. 624 QUAKER LN, STE 100E 27262 #045-01-2001 L2004 **PD** *020
REEDER, Alton Alfred. 624 QUAKER LN STE C105 27262 #036-01-1962 L1962 **GE IM** *020 †20
RHOTON, Albert John. 624 QUAKER LN, STE 105 27262 #011-03-1987 L1988 **GE IM** *020 †20
RICE, Kathleen Mary. 905 PHILLIPS AVE, HIGH POINT FAMILY PRACTICE 27262
 #051-07-1996 L1997 **FM** *020 †18
RIERSON-SMITH, Leslie. 624 QUAKER LN, STE 100E 27262 #036-08-1993 L1997 **PD** *020 †55
ROBINSON, James Thos. ■ 27262 #051-04-1955 L1957 **FM** *071 †18
RODENBERG, Denny Mikel. 1011 N LINDSAY ST, STE 200 27262 #039-05-1990 L1997
 GS *020 †85
ROHRBECK, Steven Craig. 306 WESTWOOD AVE, STE 401 27262 #041-01-1985 L1992
 IM *020 †20
ROSES, Timothy Glenn. 4224 ROCK BRIDGE RD 27262 #004-01-1993 L1997 **DR** *020 †80
ROSS, David Bruce. 404 WESTWOOD AVE, STE 205 27262 #047-05-1980 L1986 **ORS** *020 †40
ROSTAND, Robert Alton. 624 QUAKER LN, STE 200E 27262 #024-07-1972 L1978
 IM PUD *020 †20
ROWE, Charles Eugene, Jr. 1221 STURBRIDGE AVE 27262 #051-01-1965 L1971 **U** *020 †95
ROWLEY, Mark Andrew. 404 WESTWOOD AVE, STE 205 27262 #051-04-1990 L1992
 ORS *020 †40
RUBNER, Raymond Charles. 624 QUAKER LN STE 117B, P O BOX 5007 27262
 #041-12-1996 L2000 **DR** *020 †80
RUEHLE, Stephen Saml. 624 QUAKER LN, STE 201C 27262 #038-40-1976 L1979
 IM OS *020 †20
SANDERS, George Herbert S. 302 WESTWOOD AVE 27262 #036-01-1988 L1991
 HO IM *020 †20
SANSING, Mary Tinsley. 400 N ELM ST, HIGH POINT OB/GYN ASSOC 27262
 #021-05-1981 L1987 **OBG** *020 †30
SARMIENTO, Pete M. 3604 PETERS CT 27265 #748-08-1990 L1997 **IM** *020 †20
SATER, Richard Arnold. 624 QUAKER LN, STE 100C 27262 #036-07-1991 L1998 **N CN** *020 †75
SCHOENHOFF, Deborah D. 601 N ELM ST 27262 #038-41-1990 L1994 **IM** *020 †20
SCHOOFF, Kenneth Geo. ■ 27262 #025-01-1960 L1997 **P** *020 †75
SCHULZ, Thomas J. ■ 27260 #016-06-1964 L1972 **ORS TRS** *071 †40
SCHWIETZ, Leigh Anne. 100 WESTWOOD AVE, OF NORTH CAROLINA P 27262
 #051-04-1981 L2003 **AI IM** *020 †20,03
SHEARIN, Mary Denise. 624 QUAKER LN, STE 105 27262 #036-01-1989 L1991 **GE** *020 †20
SHULL, Kenneth Castles. 611 N LINDSAY ST 27262 #045-01-1973 L1979 **VS AS** *020 †85
SKAROTE, Samuel Jos, Jr. 3607 INNWOOD ST 27265 #038-44-1987 L1998 **PCC** *020 †20
SMITH, Edward Shiang-Lin. 404 WESTWOOD AVE, STE 107 27262 #036-05-1998 L2001
 D DMP *020 †15
SMITH, Lafayette Lyle. 624 QUAKER LN STE 200D, CORNERSTONE INTERNAL MEDIC 27262
 #045-01-1972 L1977 **IM** *020 †20
SMITH, Roger Enos, Jr. 810 N LINDSAY ST 27262 #036-05-1999 L2001 **END** *020 †20
SPEIGHT, Kevin Lewis. 401 FERNDALE BLVD, CAROLINA ANESTHESIOLOGY, P 27262
 #045-01-1985 L1986 **AN PME** *020 †05
SPILLANE, William Francis. 606 N ELM ST 27262 #033-05-1984 L1992 **N** *020 †05,75
STAGG, Paul Lynwood, III. 1208 EASTCHESTER DR, STE 200 27265 #036-05-1996 L2000
 R *020 †80
STAMBAUGH, Elisabeth M. 306 WESTWOOD AVE, STE 501 27262 #051-01-1994 L1998
 OBG *020 †30
STEWART, Shawn Scott. 779 N MAIN ST 27262 #038-40-1979 L1988 **IM N** *071 †75
STONE, Grady Mitchell. 624 QUAKER LN, STE 200D 27262 #036-01-1975 L1979 **IM** *020 †20
STONEKING, Bradley Jon. 607 IDOL ST 27262 #047-05-1993 L2003 **U** *020 †95
STOVALL, Vicki Mizue. 404 WESTWOOD AVE, STE 105 27262 #036-05-1987 L1990
 NEP *020 †20
STRAUSS, Brian Scott. 404 WESTWOOD AVE, STE 107 27262 #036-01-1987 L1990 **D** *020 †15
SWING, Donald C, Jr. PO BOX 6415 27262 #036-08-1989 L1993 **PTH** *012 †30
SZYPKO, Paula Elizabeth. 101 NEAL PL, STE 103 27262 #036-05-1981 L1983
 ATP CLP *062 †20,50
TAHA, Samina Habib. 400 E COMMERCE AVE 27260 #005-11-1999 L2002 **PD** *020 †55
TARTER, David Michael. 624 QUAKER LN, STE D101 27262 #020-12-1998 L2000
 MPD *020 †20,55
TAYLOR, Gregory Wayne. 601 N ELM ST, HP - 5 27262 #036-05-1979 L1993 **FM** *030 †18,16
TAYLOR, Linda Morris. 601 N ELM ST 27262 #010-03-1989 L1995 **EM** *020 †16
TAYLOR, Phyliss Nicole. 601 N ELM ST 27262 #047-07-2001 L2003 **P** *020 †75
TEPEDINO, Michael Emile. 307 LINDSAY ST, CORNERSTONE EYE CARE 27262
 #035-09-1989 L1993 **OPH** *020 †35
TERRELL, Grace Emerson. 624 QUAKER LN, STE 200E 27262 #036-07-1989 L1990
 IM MDM *020 †20
TERRELL, Sara Eldora H. ■ 27262 #036-07-1953 L1953 **IM** *071
TERRELL, Thomas Eugene. ■ 27262 #036-07-1953 L1953 **IM GPM** *071
TESTER, Richard Dean. 1211 WESTMINSTER DR 27262 #051-04-1958 L1961
 DR NM *020 †80,28

TILLMAN, Otis Edward. ■ 27260 #010-03-1957 L1958 **FM GP** *072
TILLMAN, Otis Edward, Jr. ■ 27260 #036-05-1990 L1991 **IM** *020 †20
TOLEDO, Teodoro Keith. 624 QUAKER LN, STE 105 27262 #020-02-1995 L2005 **GE** *020 †20
TONUZI, Lirim. 624 QUAKER LN, STE 100C 27262 #035-06-2000 L2005 **N CN** *020 †75
TONUZI, Racquel Marie. 624 QUAKER LN, STE 200E 27262 #035-06-1999 L2005 **MPD** *020
TORELLI, Julius N. 3610 PETERS CT, # 100 27265 #011-04-1986 L1992 **CD** *020 †20
TRIPLETT, Patricia Fowler. 624 QUAKER LN, STE D101 27262 #036-01-1991 L1993 **ID** *020 †20
TUCKER, William York, Jr. 306 WESTWOOD AVE, STE 505 27262 #036-05-1968 L1968
 TS *020 †85,90
VANCE, John Hale. 401 FERNDALE BLVD 27262 #036-05-1982 L1989 **AN** *020 †05
VAZIRI, Boyd Kavan. 1105 N LINDSAY ST 27262 #016-43-2001 L2005 **OPH** *020 †35
VELAZQUEZ, Gretchen Y. 624 QUAKER LN, STE 200D 27262 #048-13-2001 L2003 **IM** *020
WAGNER, David H. ■ 27262 #010-03-1980 L1982 **FM** *020 †16,18
WALKER, John Jos. 624 QUAKER LN, STE 105 27262 #035-15-1987 L2002 **GE IM** *020 †20
WALLACE, Hugh T. 1016 OLD CREEK CROSSING LN 27265 #036-05-1960 L1962 **GP** *020
WALLMEYER, Kenneth. 306 WESTWOOD AVE, STE 401 27262 #056-06-1978 L2006
 CD NM *020 †20 ‡
WALSH, Thomas Raymond. 611 N LINDSAY ST 27262 #036-05-1984 L1991 **GS VS** *020 †85
WAMSLEY, James Kevin. 4170 MENDENHALL OAKS PKWY, STE 110 27265
 #035-09-1998 L1999 **FM** *050
WARBURTON, Mark Jos. 611 N LINDSAY ST STE 200 27262 #036-05-1976 L1976 **ORS** *020 †40
WARD, Robert Jeffrey. 507 N LINDSAY ST 27262 #020-02-1982 L1988 **IM** *020 †20
WEAVER, John Wayne. 905 PHILLIPS AVE, HIGH POINT FAMILY PRACTICE 27262
 #036-05-1984 L1987 **FM IM** *020 †18 ‡
WEBSTER, Laurence Seaton. 3605 PETERS CT 27265 #030-05-1970 L1995 **ORS EM** *020 †16
WELLER, Edward Brooks. 611 N LINDSAY ST STE 200 27262 #020-02-1979 L1984
 ORS *020 †40
WHITE, James Thos. 601 N ELM ST 27262 #021-01-1972 L1977 **PTH** *020 †50
WHITE, Ronda Snow. 601 N ELM ST 27262 #036-05-1983 L1987 **OBG** *020 †30
WIDNER, Larry Allen. 624 QUAKER LN, STE 117B 27262 #045-01-1973 L1984 **R** *020 †80
WIGGINS, David S. ■ 27265 #035-09-1988 L1997 **EM** *020 †16
WILLARD, Virgil V, II. 1011 N LINDSAY ST, STE 202 27262 #036-05-1981 L1982 **PS GS** *020 †65
WILLIAMS, Elliott Fennell. 401 FERNDALE BLVD 27262 #036-01-1988 L1991 **AN** *020 †05
WILLIAMS, Evelyn Benita. ■ 27260 #036-08-2002 L2006 **OBG** *100
WILLIAMS, Lawrence Dale. 611 N LINDSAY ST 27262 #036-05-1982 L1983 **GS VS** *020 †85
WILLIFORD, Susan Kidwell. 624 QUAKER LN, STE 105 27262 #036-05-1984 L1995 **ON IM** *020 †20
WOODRUFF, William Walter. 1208 EASTCHESTER DR, STE 200 27265 #036-07-1982 L1983
 DR *020 †80
WOODS, Samuel T. 624 QUAKER LN, STE 200D 27262 #847-02-1981 L2007 **NEP IM** *020 †20
ZANARD, Robyn Kim. 1838 EASTCHESTER DR, STE 100 27265 #036-01-1998 L1999
 FM *020 †18
ZANONE, Dana Brooke. 2401 HICKSWOOD RD, STE 104 27265 #041-14-1998 L1999
 FM *020 †18
ZARITZKY, David Ron. 1208 EASTCHESTER DR, STE 200 27265 #011-03-1974 L1976
 DR *071 †80
ZEKAN, Jeanne Marie. 404 WESTWOOD AVE, HIGH POINT NEPHROLOGY ASSO 27262
 #055-02-1987 L1989 **NEP** *020 †20
ZIOLKOWSKA, Aldona. 2209 EASTCHESTER DR, STE 103 27265 #759-08-1990 L1999
 RHU *020 †20

HIGHLANDS – MACON

BARRY, Carey Neilson. ■ 28741 #036-07-1949 L1973 **U** *071 †95
BAUKNIGHT, Charles Wm. ■ 28741 #012-05-1961 L1963 **OBG** *071 †30
BAUMRUCKER, John F. 171 HOSPITAL DR, STE 700 28741 #038-41-1970 L1971 **FM** *020 †18
BLACK, Paul Wm. 224 KNOB HL, C/O BLACKWOOD 28741 #020-02-1960 L1961 **PS** *071 †85,65
BRYANT, Henry H, III. ■ 28741 #012-05-1944 L1986 **GS** *071 †85
BUCHANAN, Robert Taylor. 209 HOSPITAL DR, STE 202 28741 #012-01-1969 L1972
 PS HS *020 †85,65 ‡
CABIRAN, Paul Squire. 209 HOSPITAL DR, STE 302 28741 #021-05-1991 L2004 **D** *020 †15
CURTIS, Earnest M. ■ 28741 #035-20-1953 L2001 **GYN** *071 †30 ‡
ESTES, James Wm. ■ 28741 #012-01-1963 L1963 **VS** *071 †85
HAIR, Judson Elam. ■ 28741 #045-01-1952 L1952 **FM OM** *071 †18
HAWKINS, Jack Milton. ■ 28741 #012-05-1964 L1964 **PYA P** *020
HELLER, David Bernhardt. 306 FALLS CT 28741 #041-02-1947 L1949 **ORS GS** *071 †40
HODNETTE, Frank B. ■ 28741 #021-01-1942 L1978 **GYN** *071 †30
MARTORELL, Richard A. PO BOX 866 28741 #047-06-1948 L1977 **FM** *030 †18
MIXSON, William Tunno, Jr. ■ 28741 #041-13-1948 L1994 **OBG GYN** *071 †30
MULLEN, Donald Collins. ■ 28741 #036-07-1961 L1961 **TS** *071 †85,90
OLSON, Paul Richard. 209 HOSPITAL DR, STE 301 28741 #050-02-1968 L1977 **FM** *030 †18
PLAUCHE, Herbert Kay. 171 HOSPITAL DR, STE 400 28741 #012-05-1963 L1997 **ORS** *020 †40
REGISTER, Saml David, III. 1532 CULLASAJA CLUB DR 28741 #012-01-1981 L2001
 AN *020 †05
REYNAUD, Louis F. ■ 28741 #023-01-1950 L1950 **PD** *071
SAPOLSKY, Jack Louis. ■ 28741 #047-06-1964 L1964 **U** *020 †95
SCHOENFELD, Lawrence V. ■ 28741 #010-01-1967 L1968 **U** *071 †95
SHERRER, Carl Willis. 209 HOSPITAL DR STE 104 28741 #012-05-1968 L1999
 OBG PTH *020 †30
STINNETT, Rodney Gay. ■ 28741 #051-04-1974 L1986 **DR NM** *020 †80
VIHLEN, Frederick E. ■ 28741 #041-13-1951 L1973 **OS GP** *020
WAGNER, Debra Ann. 209 HOSPITAL DR, STE 203 28741 #011-03-1985 L2005
 GYN IM *020 †20 ‡
WAGNER, Mark Stephen. 209 HOSPITAL DR, STE 203 28741 #011-03-1984 L2004
 IM *020 †20 ‡
WHEELER, David Marvin. 190 HOSPITAL DR 28741 #047-05-1985 L1986 **FM** *020 †18
WHEELER, Patti Beard. 1029 HICKS RD 28741 #036-01-1985 L1986 **FM** *020 †18
WHITEHEAD, C Mark, Jr. ■ 28741 #021-01-1966 L1972 **U** *071 †95
WILLIAMS, Louis A. ■ 28741 #012-01-1953 L1968 **GP** *071
WILSON, Neille Alford. 189 HIDDEN VILLAGE TRL 28741 #045-01-1973 L2000
 DR FM *020 †18,80

HILDEBRAN – BURKE

CONSING, Jesse Rey N. 517 MAIN AVE W 28637 #748-14-1990 L1998 **FM** *020 †18

SWISHER, Aaron Mark. ■ 28637 #038-44-1994 L1997 **FM** *020 †18

HILLSBOROUGH – ORANGE

AXELBANK, Arthur. 210 S CAMERON ST, ORANGE FAMILY MEDICAL GROU 27278 #035-46-1978 L1980 **FM** *020 †18
BAUM, Stephan Fredrick. ■ 27278 #018-03-1991 L1997 **CHP P** *020 †75
BOND, Virginia Kathryn. ■ 27278 #036-01-2008 *012
BRADFORD, Susan E. ■ 27278 #024-05-1967 L2007 **PTH**,**FM** *020 †50 ‡
BRITTINGHAM, L A, Jr. ■ 27278 #051-04-1964 L1974 **DR** *020 †80
BRUCH, Suzanne Margarete. 4018 SUMMER LN 27278 #036-07-2000 L2002 **P** *020 †75 ‡
CAO, Wenhong. ■ 27278 #243-76-1983 *100
CRUMMETT, Daniel David. 405 MEADOWLAND DR, HILLSBOROUGH FAMILY PRACTI 27278 #025-07-1982 L1983 **FM** *020 †18
DEAR, Janet Kidd. 210 S CAMERON ST 27278 #036-01-2001 L2004 **FM** *020 †18
DENT, Sara Jamison. PO BOX 100 27278 #045-01-1945 L1953 **AN** *071 †05
DOBBINS, Robert Lester. ■ 27278 #047-05-1993 L1996 **END** *020 †20
FERA, Dennis Wm. 1000 CORPORATE DR, STE 209 27278 #035-15-1983 L1988 **PM GP** *020
GREASON, Frances C. ■ 27278 #036-08-1991 L1993 **CHP** *020
HANWAY, James Wm. ■ 27278 #035-01-1954 **IM** *071 †20
HARMON, Perry Monroe. ■ 27278 #036-01-1974 L1981 **GYN** *071 †30 ‡
HIGGS, Philip Edward. ■ 27278 #011-03-1974 L2004 **HS PS** *020 †65
HOFFMAN, Theodore F, Jr. 819 ORANGE HIGH SCHOOL RD 27278 #036-01-1978 L1981 **AN** *020
HULETTE, Christine Marie. 1804 US70E 27278 #020-02-1983 L1987 **NP PTH** *050 †50
JOHNSON, Victoria Gwynn. 210 S CAMERON ST 27278 #036-08-2001 L2004 **FM** *020 †18
JOSEPH, Michael Carver. ■ 27278 #005-02-1976 L1986 **PD** *020 †70
KAPELUK, Sharon Theresa. ■ 27278 #036-01-1991 L1992 **AN** *020 †05
KENT, Theresa Rae. ■ 27278 #055-02-2006 **PM** *012
KLEIN, Jonathan Edan. 210 S CAMERON ST 27278 #035-15-1984 L1985 **FM** *020 †18
LANDRY, Kerry Lee. ■ 27278 #050-02-2003 L2008 **CHP** *100
LITTLETON, Amanda Carol. ■ 27278 #008-02-2008 *012
MEADE, Kristin Elinor. ■ 27278 #005-11-2006 **MPD** *012
MILES, Edward Francis. 1605 FOREMAN ST, RADIATION ONCOLOGY 27278 #023-12-2000 L2001 **RO** *012
MILLET, Robert Anthony. 105 W CORBIN ST STE 104 27278 #021-05-1991 L1993 **P** *020 †75
MOURO, Cameron Michael. ■ 27278 #025-01-2003 L2007 **OBG** *100
MURPHY, Barbara Anne. 2700 NEW SHARON CHURCH RD 27278 #041-07-1975 L1978 **EM** *062 †16
NACHMAN, Ginette Sandra. ■ 27278 #041-07-1985 **P** *020
NIX, Jeffrey Wells. ■ 27278 #020-12-2006 **GS** *012
OLMEDO, Mario Ernesto. ■ 27278 #036-01-2005 L2007 **FP** *012
PAGE, Coin Tuman. 405 MEADOWLAND DR 27278 #036-01-1983 L1984 **FM** *020 †18
PENASKOVIC, Kenan Miles. ■ 27278 #036-01-2002 L2005 **P** *012
PETER, Robert Hatton. 118 W TRYON ST 27278 #036-07-1961 L1961 **CD** *020 †20
POWELL, Ronald Jones. ■ 27278 #041-12-1982 L1986 **IM** *020
RAO, Jyothi Poovandur. ■ 27278 #496-59-1997 L2000 **END** *020 †20
RINGEL, Sarah Cornwell. 101 E CORBIN ST 27278 #036-07-1985 L1986 **FM** *020 †18
SATTER, Jane. 405 MEADOWLAND DR 27278 #005-02-1983 L1984 **FM** *020 †18
SCHMADER, Kenneth Edwin. ■ 27278 #036-05-1980 L1983 **IMG IM** *020 †20
SHAPLEY-QUINN, Todd W. 405 MEADOWLAND DR 27278 #025-07-1984 L1987 **FM** *020 †18
SHATTUCK, Trisha Miller. ■ 27278 #008-02-2006 **PTH** *012
SINGER, F Philip G. 101 E CORBIN ST 27278 #036-07-1975 L1976 **FM** *020 †18
SMITH, Caroline Clements. 2125 OLD FOREST DR 27278 #004-01-2000 L2003 **PD** *020 †55
SOMERS, William Alan. 3634 SPARROW HAWK CRST, BUSH-SOMERS, PA 27278 #036-07-1972 L1972 **ORS** *020 †40
SPARKS, Louise Harrison. ■ 27278 #050-02-1980 L1986 **ID IM** *020 †20
SPENCER, Michele Joy. ■ 27278 #024-16-2004 **MG** *012
STINCHCOMBE, Thomas E. 1818 VALLEY CREEK DR, UNIVERSITY OF NC MEDICAL S 27278 #051-01-1995 L1998 **HO** *020 †20
SYKES, Richard Scott. ■ 27278 #036-01-1983 L1984 **P** *050
TAN, Cheem Huay. ■ 27278 #825-01-1987 **CD** *100
WELLS, James Shelton, Jr. 5024 BOULDER RUN 27278 #036-01-1977 L1978 **P PYG** *020 †75
WESSON, Lynn Elise. 301 W MARGARET LN, P O BOX 23 27278 #036-01-1978 L1983 **P U** *020 †75
YOUNG, Janet Simmons. 1607 DUNN PL 27278 #036-08-1997 L2001 **EM** *020 †16

HOBBSVILLE – GATES

JONES, Mary M Schwab. ■ 27946 #041-07-1947 L1978 **FM** *075

HOLLY RIDGE – ONSLOW

LANGNER, Juliette P. 206 N DYSON ST, PENSLOW MEDICAL CENTER 28445 #036-08-1994 L1995 **FM** *020 †18
SOLAN, Gwen. 308 US HIGHWAY 17 N, FAMILYCARE OF HOLLYRIDGE 28445 #010-01-1985 L1994 **GP FM** *075
WHATLEY, Joseph Wm, Jr. ■ 28445 #036-07-1959 L1959 **PD A** *071

HOLLY SPRINGS – WAKE

CARAVALHO, Joseph, Jr. ■ 27540 #023-12-1983 L2003 **CD IM** *020 †28,20
CZECH, Julie Ann. 190 ROSEWOOD CENTRE DR, STE 100 27540 #025-07-1991 L2000 **IM** *020 †20
DANNEY, Christopher Marc. ■ 27540 #048-14-2003 L2008 **ORS** *012
DAR, Mohammed Mujtaba. ■ 27540 #036-07-1995 L1998 **HO** *020 †20
DUNCAN, Douglas David. ■ 27540 #001-02-1996 L1998 **ORS** *020
GEORGITIS, John Wilson. 1140 HOLLY SPRINGS RD, LAFAYETTE CLINIC PA 27540 #050-02-1976 L1984 **AI PD** *020 †55,03
KHARA, Parminder G. 500 HOLLY SPRINGS RD, STE 100 27540 #610-01-1994 L2006 **FM EM** *020 †20

LINCOLN, Clinton Robt. ■ 27540 #051-04-1960 L1963 **ORS RHU** *071 †40
MADAN, Ragini Tandon. 500 HOLLY SPRINGS RD, ROAD SUITE100 27540 #496-07-1978 L1998 **FM** *020 †18
NILOVA, Olga. 500 HOLLY SPRINGS RD 27540 #913-69-1997 L2006 **PD** *020 †55
SEBAS, Patricia Alice. 500 HOLLY SPRINGS RD, HOLLY SPRINGS MEDICAL CENT 27540 #055-02-1986 L1993 **PD** *020 †55
SRAMKA, Jan. ■ 27540 #286-02-1962 L1973 **PTH** *075 †50
THAMOTHARAMPILLA, Sivaraj. 500 HOLLY SPRINGS RD, STE 100 27540 #422-01-1991 L1999 **IM** *020 †20
YEARWOOD, Beverly Ann. 500 HOLLY SPRINGS RD 27540 #012-21-1998 L2007 **PD** *020 †55
ZIMMERMAN, Laura Ida. ■ 27540 #036-01-2007 **EM** *012

HOOKERTON – GREENE

RIBEIRO, Donald Alan. 516 S WILLIAM HOOKER DR 28538 #036-08-1986 L1987 **FM** *020 †18

HOPE MILLS – CUMBERLAND

ALVARADO, Melitza. ■ 28348 #042-01-1995 L2004 **P** *020
BUENASEDA, Jose Ornum. 3436 N MAIN ST 28348 #748-01-1998 L2006 **PD** *020
BUENASEDA, Leamor De Leon. 3436 N MAIN ST 28348 #748-01-2000 L2006 **PD** *020 †55
BUFALINI, Mark E. ■ 28348 #008-02-2003 L2007 *100
CHAO, Albert Chung-Kuang. 4092 PROFESSIONAL DR 28348 #036-07-1990 L1996 **FM** *020 †18
ELBINIAS-TAN, Shirley P. 4092 PROFESSIONAL DR, HOPE MILLS FAMILY CARE 28348 #748-02-1986 L2002 **FM FPG** *020 †18
FERGUSON, Robert Lee, Jr. 3622 N MAIN ST 28348 #561-17-1980 L1991 **IM FM** *020
FIGUEROA, Deborah A. 4092 PROFESSIONAL DR, HOPE MILLS FAMILY CARE 28348 #748-08-1991 L1999 **FM** *020 †18
JAIN, Ashokkumar C. 3436 N MAIN ST 28348 #495-37-1993 L2001 **PD** *020 †55
KUZMA, Micaiah Matthew. ■ 28348 #005-12-2003 L2005 **FM** *020 †18
MC CUTCHAN, Wenda E. 3441 N MAIN ST, STE D 28348 #048-15-1995 L2003 **FM** *020 †18
MOORE, Jacqueline Diana. ■ 28348 #023-12-2007 *100
OKONS, Toby. 3758 S MAIN ST, HOPE MILLS URGENT CARE MED 28348 #308-11-1987 L1996 **IM** *020 †20
WORDEN, Neil A. 209 LAKEVIEW RD 28348 #020-02-1951 L1954 **FM** *072 †18

HOT SPRINGS – MADISON

FINK, Burton M. ■ 28743 #035-09-1971 L2006 **U** *071 †95 ‡

HUBERT – ONSLOW

ADAMS, Shana Patrice. ■ 28539 #001-02-2001 L2004 **OBG** *020
GILLE, Theresa Mary. ■ 28539 #051-07-2005 L2005 *100
LEDFORD, Alin Vaunpono. ■ 28539 #014-01-2004 **FM** *100
MAC GILVRAY, Marcel Alain. ■ 28539 #045-01-2002 L2007 **DR** *100 †80
MARTIN, Electra C. ■ 28539 #035-06-1997 L2007 **EM** *020 †16
SCHINDELAR, H Oscar. ■ 28539 #010-03-1958 L1976 **IM END** *020

HUDSON – CALDWELL

GOINS, James Robt. 270 PINE MOUNTAIN RD 28638 #036-01-1977 L1978 **OBG** *020 †30
KNAPP, Jeffrey Andrew. 270 PINE MOUNTAIN RD 28638 #051-07-1988 L1997 **ORS** *020 †40
MCBURNEY, Richard O. 270 PINE MOUNTAIN RD, STE 1 28638 #055-01-1985 L1991 **FM IMG** *020 †18
MC MENEMY, John William. 589 MAIN ST, MAIN STREET MEDICAL PARK 28638 #038-45-1993 L1996 **FM** *020 †18
PEKMAN, William Martin. 270 PINE MOUNTAIN RD 28638 #016-02-1978 L1985 **HS ORS** *020 †40
REESE, Benjamin Wayne. 270 PINE MOUNTAIN RD, STE 5 28638 #023-01-1987 L1998 **FM** *020 †18

HUNTERSVILLE – MECKLENBURG

AGNELLO, Victor Alexander. 16627 BIRKDALE CMNS PKWY, STE 210 28078 #010-01-1997 L2005 **IM AI** *020 †20,03
ALEXANIAN, Aram. 10030 GILEAD RD, STE 140 28078 #036-08-2000 L2002 **FM** *020 †18
ANYAOGU, Chinyere N. 10235 HICKORYWOOD HILL AVE, THE WOMEN'S CARE CENTER, P 28078 #690-04-1991 L2002 **OBG** *020 †20,30
ARCHER, Beth Alyson. 10030 GILEAD RD STE 200, UNIV MED DR HUNTERSVILLE 28078 #028-46-1989 L1995 **IM** *020 †20
BAKER, Brian Dale. 16525 HOLLY CREST LN, STE 150 28078 #036-01-1998 L1999 **FM** *020 †18
BARRINGER, Loveleen Kaur. 16525 HOLLY CREST LN, STE 150 28078 #025-07-1997 L2004 **FM** *020 †18
BARROCAS, Joseph. 16630 NORTHCROSS DR, INTERNAL MEDICINE 28078 #035-06-1991 L2005 **MPD** *020 †55,20
BATCHELOR, Thomas Allen. 16455 STATESVILLE RD, STE 360 28078 #051-01-1994 L1998 **IM** *020 †20 ‡
BERGER, Jeffrey Allen. 16525 HOLLY CREST LN 28078 #020-12-1995 L1996 **FM** *072 †18
BESSENT, Yvette Elaine. 16455 STATESVILLE RD, STE 400 NORTHCROSS MED PAR 28078 #036-01-1991 L1997 **OBG** *020 †20
BEUTEL, William D. 16627 BIRKDALE CMNS PKWY, STE 100 28078 #016-11-1979 L1986 **GS** *020 †85
BOCHACKI, Zofia. 10225 HICKORYWOOD HILL AVE 28078 #759-07-1979 L2000 **P** *020 †75
BOCK, William Clifford. 10300 GILEAD RD, STE 344B 28078 #045-01-1985 L1986 **ICE CD** *020 †20
BODNER, Russ Adam. 16623 BIRKDALE CMNS PKWY, STE 110 28078 #041-07-1990 L1997 **N** *020 †75
BROTZE, Scott A. 16525 HOLLY CREST LN, CHARLOTTE 28078 #048-14-1997 L2002 **GE** *020 †20

■ = Address Information Privacy Protected

BROWN, Angela Janine. 16455 STATESVILLE RD, STE 360 28078 #023-01-1993 L2005
IM *020 †20

BUMGARNER, Laurie S. 9815 SAM FURR RD # J # 112 28078 #036-05-1988 L1989 FM *020 †18

BURCAL, John Hall. 16455 STATESVILLE RD 28078 #025-07-1980 L1993 PD *020 †55

BUTLER, Ronald Dean. 10030 GILEAD RD, STE 290 28078 #036-01-1986 L1998 ON *020 †20

CAPIZZI, Peter Jos. 8712 LINDHOLM DR, STE 308 28078 #051-07-1990 L1997 PS *020 †65,85

CARPENTER, Kent Dee. 10030 GILEAD RD 28078 #012-01-1984 L1987 IM *020 †20

CARR, John Daniels. 103 COMMERCE CTR DR, STE 103 28078 #011-02-1987 L1998
IM *020 †20

CASTILLO, Vincent Palanca. ■ 28078 #748-08-1991 L2000 FPG *020 †18

CHAI, Seungjean. 10030 GILEAD RD 28078 #012-01-1998 L2004 HO *020 †20

CHASNIS, Alexander Walter. 10030 GILEAD RD, STE 160 28078 #025-07-1999 L2003
PM PMM *020 †60

CIEZA, Octavio. 14330 OAK HILL PARK LN, STE 202 28078 #737-01-1990 L2006 IM ID *020 †20

CLARK, David Ronald. 10030 GILEAD RD, STE 350 28078 #025-12-1993 L2004
IM PCC *020 †20

CLEMENTS, John Carl. 16633 BIRKDALE CMNS PKWY 28078 #038-43-1992 L1997
GE *072 †20 ‡

CLEMONS, Justina Maria. 16455 STATESVILLE RD 28078 #010-03-1993 L1996 PD *020 †55

CONNELLY, Christopher S. 16623 BIRKDALE CMNS PKWY, STE 110 28078 #036-05-1993 L1997
N *020 †75

CRUICKSHANK, Frederick. 103 COMMERCE CENTRE DR, STE 103 28078 #422-01-1995 L2006
ID *020

CULTON, Julian Clark. 16455 STATESVILLE RD, STE 280 28078 #036-07-1956 L1956
OPH *071 †35

DALTO, Carmine. 10030 GILEAD RD, STE 350 28078 #035-19-1976 L1980 PUD CCM *020 †20

DAVIS, William Hodges. 10030 GILEAD RD, STE 160 28078 #021-01-1985 L1992 ORS *020 †40

DAY, Temple Vashti. 16455 STATESVILLE RD, STE 360 28078 #036-08-1998 L2001 IM *020 †20

DELANEY, Devon Briggs. 16455 STATESVILLE RD, STE 400 28078 #035-47-1993 L1997
OBG *020 †30

DELAY, Brian Scott. 10030 GILEAD RD, STE 160 28078 #038-40-1995 L2001 OSM *020 †40

DONATELLI, Francis J, Jr. PO BOX 668 28070 #041-13-1965 L1973 EM *020 †18,16

DUNDER, Steven Gary. 10030 GILEAD RD 28078 #030-05-1999 L2006 HO *020 †20

EDWARDS, Allen Richard. 16525 HOLLY CREST LN, STE 120 28078 #036-01-1979 L1980
OM FM *020 †70,18

ENGLISH, Martin Everett. 16455 STATESVILLE RD, STE 360 28078 #023-01-1993 L1996
IM *020 †20

FARNHAM, Robert, III. 10030 GILEAD RD 28078 #041-01-1974 L1975 PTH *020 †50

FERDINANDS, Lillian S. 16630 NORTHCROSS DR, & INTERNAL MEDICINE 28078
#035-09-1993 L1997 PD *020 †55

FICENEC, Michael C. 16455 STATESVILLE RD 28078 #051-01-1998 L2005 PD *020 †55

FISHER, Jonathan E. 10030 GILEAD RD, STE 201 28078 #035-47-1998 L2008 CD *020 †20

FLANNERY, William Kevin. 16630 NORTHCROSS DR, DBA HUNTERSVILLE PEDS & IN 28078
#035-09-1993 L1997 IM PD *020 †55,20

FORSYTH, Bradley Keith. ■ 28078 #021-05-2004 OBG *012

GAMBINO, John Peter. ■ 28078 #035-09-1993 L2004 IM *020 †20

GARBER, Daniel Thos. 16623 BIRKDALE CMNS PKWY, STE 110 28078 #051-04-1992 L1997
N SME *020 †75

GARCIA, Joseph Anthony. 10030 GILEAD RD, STE 140 28078 #018-03-1994 L2004
FM FSM *020 †18

GARWACKI, Christopher. 10030 GILEAD RD 28078 #016-11-1996 L2000 PCP *020 †50

GAZAK, John Michael. 16525 HOLLY CREST LN, STE 230 28078 #041-01-1974 L1981
UP PD *020 †95

GIBSON, John Mc Neill. 16455 STATESVILLE RD, MECKLENBURG MEDICAL GROUP 28078
#036-01-1972 L1972 IM *020 †20

GORSUCH, Lisa Ann. 10030 GILEAD RD, STE 350 28078 #036-05-1992 L1996 OBG *020 †30

HABASHI, Nader M. 9816 SAM FURR RD, STE 101 28078 #654-01-1984 L1989 IM PUD *020 †20

HARVEY, Beth Alaina. ■ 28078 #021-05-2006 OBG *012

HAUCH, Thomas Wray. 10030 GILEAD RD 28078 #016-06-1972 L1977 ON HEM *020 †20

HENDLER, Jay Mark. 10030 GILEAD RD, STE 350 28078 #035-19-1985 L1991
PUD CCM *020 †20

HIGGS, Vetta B. 16455 STATESVILLE RD, MECKLENBURG MEDICAL GROUP 28078
#001-06-1996 L1997 HO *020 †20

HINES, Mark Christopher. 8712 LINDHOLM DR STE 302, CENTER 28078 #041-14-1994 L2002
IM *020 †20

HODGES, Timothy Wm. 9726 SAM FURR RD, STE 2200 28078 #016-42-1984 L2006
FM *020 †18

HOFFMAN, Stanley David. 9604 HOLLY POINT DR 28078 #035-19-1974 L2000 D IM *020 †15

HOLT, John Burnett. 10030 GILEAD RD 28078 #018-03-1999 L2004 HMP *100 †50

HUBER, Kenneth R. ■ 28078 #036-05-2006 IM *012

HUDSON, Tonya Marie. 9726 SAM FURR RD, NORTHCROSS FAM PHYSICIANS 28078
#024-05-1992 L1994 FM *020 †18

INGLE, Jenifer Weatherly. ■ 28078 #036-01-2008 *012

IRONS, George Vernon, Jr. 10030 GILEAD RD, STE 201 28078 #001-02-1956 L1964
CD IM *020 †20

JAYNE, Beth Ann. 16630 NORTHCROSS DR 28078 #035-15-1999 L2003 MPD PD *020 †20,55

JENIKE, Thomas Edward. 16525 HOLLY CREST LN 28078 #038-40-1995 L1996 FM *020 †18

JERVIS, Oliver W, Jr. 10030 GILEAD RD, STE 350 28078 #016-11-1990 L1994 CCM *020 †20

JOHNS, Shari Schneider. 16525 HOLLY CREST LN, STE 150 28078 #025-01-1997 L1999
FM *020 †18

JOSEPHSON, Steven Arthur. 16525 HOLLY CREST LN, CHARLOTTE 28078 #035-09-1990 L1998
GE *020 †20

JUTRAS, Mark Livingston. 9800 KINCEY AVE, STE 160 28078 #048-02-1982 L2006
REN GYN *020 †30

KOIS, Jean Marie. 9800 KINCEY AVE 28078 #041-14-1989 L2004 D IM *020 †20,15

KOMPANIK, Heather Carroll. ■ 28078 #036-08-2007 FP *012

LAKE, Josephine Hooten. 16630 NORTHCROSS DR, INTERNAL MEDICINE 28078
#024-07-1994 L1998 MPD PD *020 †20,55

LAWSIN, Stella Reyes. 16455 STATESVILLE RD 28078 #748-10-1989 L2001 PD *020 †55

LE, Cuong Peter. 13220 ROSEDALE HILL AVE, PROGRESSIVE MEDICAL ASSOCS 28078
#045-04-1988 L2002 IM *020 †20

LE, Stacy Comfort. 13220 ROSEDALE HILL AVE, PROGRESSIVE MEDICAL ASSOCI 28078
#045-04-1988 L2004 IM *020 †20 ‡

LESSARIS, Thomas Peter. 10030 GILEAD RD, PHYSICIAN PLZ STE 360 28078
#016-45-1991 L2000 IM PD *020 †55,20

LEVINE, Jonathan Keith. 10030 GILEAD RD 28078 #036-01-1986 L1992 IM HO *020 †20

LICAUSE, Gina Garrett. 10030 GILEAD RD, STE 140 28078 #038-41-1989 L1992 FM *020 †18

LITTLE, Charles Andrew. ■ 28078 #036-08-2002 L2006 PD *100 †55

LITTLE, Jennifer Long. 10030 GILEAD RD STE 350, HUNTERSVILLE OBSTETRICS & 28078
#036-08-2002 L2006 OBG *012

LIU, Bing. 16623 BIRKDALE CMNS PKWY, STE 110 28078 #243-45-1990 L2003 N *020 †75

LOVEJOY, Hugh Munro, Jr. 16455 STATESVILLE RD, STE 280 28078 #045-01-1988 L1989
OTO *020 †45

MC CLURE, Stephen Paul. 10030 GILEAD RD 28078 #038-40-1976 L2004 PTH HMP *020 †50 ‡

MC CULLOUGH, Timothy John. ■ 28078 #035-06-1980 L1982 AS GS *020 †85

MEYER, Barbara Ellen. 10030 GILEAD RD # 140, LAKESIDE FAMILY PHYSICIANS 28078
#051-07-1990 L1993 FM *020 †18

MILAM, Robert Alden, IV. 10030 GILEAD RD, STE 160 28078 #047-05-1997 L2003 ORS *020 †40

MILES, Erik John. 13620 REESE BLVD E, STE 110 28078 #048-15-2000 L2007 PS *020 †85

MILTICH, Michael Fiegel. 16455 STATESVILLE RD, STE 280 28078 #025-07-1978 L1983
OTO PDO *020 †45

MITCHELL, Robert David. 16623 BIRKDALE CMNS PKWY, STE 110 28078 #025-01-1982 L1988
N IM *020 †20,75

MITCHELL, William Robt. 10030 GILEAD RD, STE 290 28078 #020-02-1990 L1991 ON *020 †20

MONZAVIFAR, Javad. 10030 GILEAD RD, PRESBYTERIAN HOSPITAL HUNT 28078
#409-20-1993 L2003 IM *020 †20

MOORE, John H, III. 16525 HOLLY CREST LN, CHARLOTTE 28078 #012-05-1977 L1982
GE IM *020 †20

MUKKAMALA, Sasirekha. 16455 STATESVILLE RD, STE 104 28078 #495-04-1988 L1995
PD *020 †55

NIKROOZ, Pouneh M. 16633 BIRKDALE CMNS PKWY 28078 #036-08-1998 L2004 GE *020 †20

NOWICKY, David John. 403 GILEAD RD STE B, NORTH MECKLENBURG PLASTIC 28078
#038-44-1990 L2002 PS *020 †65

PEACOCK, Mark Douglas. 16623 BIRKDALE CMNS PKWY, STE 130 28078 #036-01-1982 L1986
OBG *020 †30

PENA, Jose Raul. 9800 KINCEY AVE, STE 150 28078 #045-04-1987 L2005 D DMP *020 †50,15

PERSAUD, Dennis Seetall. 407 GILEAD RD 28078 #913-92-1987 L2003 FM *100 †18

PHILLIPS, Stan Dale. 9710 SAM FURR RD, UNIT D 28078 #036-08-1991 L1997 OTO *020 †45

POWDERLY, John Dwyer, II. 9801 KINCEY AVE STE 145 28078 #010-02-1995 L2000
HO *020 †20,55

PRECHTEL, Leslie Andrew. ■ 28078 #016-01-2000 L2007 EM *020

PREIK, Curtis Reinhold. ■ 28078 #654-01-2005 FP *012

PRYOR, Evelyn Baranco. 16455 STATESVILLE RD, MECKLENBURG MEDICAL GROUP 28078
#012-01-2000 L2006 IM *020

QUINN, Jane Ann. 10030 GILEAD RD, # 200 28078 #056-06-1983 L2007 IM *071 †20

REULBACH, Todd Russell. 16455 STATESVILLE RD, STE 280 28078 #036-05-1995 L1997
OTO *020 †45

REVIS, Sheley Rene. 10030 GILEAD RD, STE 200 28078 #036-01-1992 L1995 IM *020 †20

RIBAKOVE, Everett Craig. 10030 GILEAD RD 28078 #035-03-1994 L2001 HO IM *020 †20

ROSENBERG, Dan Larson. 10030 GILEAD RD, CABARRUS FAMILY MEDICINE 28078
#305-01-2003 L2006 FM *020 †18

RUSSO, Kristin Mahri. ■ 28078 #036-05-2006 OBG *012

SANDERS, Foster J, Jr. 10030 GILEAD RD 28078 #047-05-1970 L1988 PTH *020 †50

SCHNEIDER, Barry Randall. 16455 STATESVILLE RD, STE 114 28078 #036-01-1980 L1987
IM GE *020 †20

SCHOLL, Geo Kenneth, Jr. 16455 STATESVILLE RD, STE 420 28078 #047-06-1967 L1973
U *020 †95

SCOTT, Deborah Annette. 16455 STATESVILLE RD, STE 104 28078 #036-01-1978 L1980
PD *020 †20

SHARAWY, Ehab Mohamed. 10030 GILEAD RD, STE 350 28078 #012-01-1994 L2000
OBG *020 †30

SHERRILL, Thomas Michael. 16525 HOLLY CREST LN, STE 150 28078 #036-08-1990 L1991
FM *020 †18

SHERRILL, Wm Chas, Jr. 13815 PROFESSIONAL CNTR DR, # 100 28078 #011-03-1979 L1980
IM PUD *020 †20

SILVERMAN, Marshall Avery. 10030 GILEAD RD, STE 200 28078 #021-01-1992 L1998
IM *020 †20

SITTLER, Stephanie Cate. 9726 SAM FURR RD, NORTHCROSS FAMILY PHYSICIA 28078
#038-41-1996 L1999 FM *020 †18

SMITH, James Patrick. 10030 GILEAD RD, STE 350 28078 #021-05-1996 L2005
PCC SME *020 †20

SPIERS, Jason Blaine. 10030 GILEAD RD, STE 350 28078 #047-06-1991 L2002 PCC *020 †20

STONE, Robin Leigh. 13123 ROSEDALE HILL AVE 28078 #028-03-2001 L2006 P *020

STRAWTHER, Philip Arledge. 16627 BIRKDALE CMNS PKWY 28078 #048-12-1983 L1990
PS *020 †65

SUPROCK, Mark Douglas. 10030 GILEAD RD, STE 160 28078 #041-09-1981 L2006
ORS OSM *020 †18,40

SUTTON, Julian T. ■ 28078 #023-01-1951 L1951 GS GP *071 †18

TAGLE, Laura Koeppel. ■ 28078 #011-02-2005 L2008 IM *012

THESTRUP, Lars. ■ 28078 #051-04-2004 L2007 EM *020

THOMPSON, Ricky Alan. 10030 GILEAD RD 28078 #047-20-1990 L1993 PTH *020 †50

USZENSKI, Ronald T. 10030 GILEAD RD STE 201 28078 #422-01-1986 L2006 CD IM *020 †20

VESANO, Jack L. 10030 GILEAD RD, STE 160 28078 #055-01-1968 L1969 ORS *020 †40

VUONG, Dao Quynh. 10030 GILEAD RD, STE 350 28078 #011-04-1994 L1998 OBG *020 †30

WALLS, Jeffrey Glen. 10030 GILEAD RD, STE 350 28078 #016-02-1993 L2003 PUD *020 †20

WEEKS, Kenneth Durham. 10030 GILEAD RD STE 201 28078 #036-07-1974 L1978
CD IM *020 †20

WEIGEL, Mark Turner. 16455 STATESVILLE RD # 280 28078 #038-44-1983 L1984
OTO FPS *020 †45

WHITESIDE, Brandon C. 16600 BIRKDALE CMNS PKWY, STE E 28078 #045-04-1995 L2004
OPH *020 †35

WINEGARDNER, Linda Still. 9718 SAM FURR RD UNIT A 28078 #045-01-1992 L1998
FM *020 †18

WITKIN, Michael. 16455 STATESVILLE RD, STE 200 28078 #041-01-1964 L2005
IM END *020 †20

ZUHOSKY, Joseph Patrick. 9611 SHERRILL ESTATES RD, STE B 28078 #038-40-1993 L1998
PM PRS *020 †60

ZURAWICK, Jennifer Jean. ■ 28078 #047-06-2003 L2007 MPD *020 †20

HURDLE MILLS – PERSON

CARRASCO, Vincent N. ■ 27541 #035-03-1984 L1986 OTO NO *020 †45

■ = Address Information Privacy Protected

DALTON, Bruce Atwood, Jr. ■ 27541 #036-01-1969 L1969 **OM PHP** *030 †55,70

INDIAN TRAIL – UNION

ADAMS-DENNY, Natasha Ann. 6030 W HIGHWAY 74, UNION OBSTETRICIAN & 28079 #035-08-1995 L2002 **OBG** *020 †30

AGOCS, Eva. 6030 W HIGHWAY 74, STE D 28079 #473-01-1992 L1997 **IM** *020 †20

BARRON, Angela H. 6030 W HIGHWAY 74, STE D 28079 #045-01-1998 L2000 **IM** *020 ‡

CAMP, Michael Scott. 6030 W HIGHWAY 74, STE D 28079 #001-06-1991 L1994 **IM** *020 †20

CHALAVADI, Lakshmi. 6030 W HIGHWAY 74 STE D, DOVE INTERNAL MEDICINE 28079 #495-58-1995 L2002 **FPG** *020 †20

CHEN, Douglas Sou. 6208 CREFT CIR, STE 222 28079 #010-02-1997 L1998 **FM** *020 †18 ‡

CHILDS, Thomas Ray. 6030 W HIGHWAY 74, STE A 28079 #027-01-1992 L2005 **FM UCM** *020 †18

COOK, Donald Eugene, Jr. 4503 OLD MONROE RD, INDIAN TRAIL FAMILY MEDICI 28079 #036-05-1981 L1983 **FM** *020 †18

DICHOSO-WOOD, Maria G. 4503 OLD MONROE RD, INDIAN TRAIL FAM MEDICINE 28079 #038-43-1993 L1996 **FM** *020 †18 ‡

FRIEDMAN, Steven J. ■ 28079 #035-46-1968 L1972 **PS** *020 †85,65

FUNDERBURK, Cullie F. ■ 28079 #028-34-1975 L1977 **PUD** *071

GANZON, Rodolfo Bautista. 6030 W HIGHWAY 74, STE D 28079 #748-10-1988 L2001 **NEP** *020 †20

HOCKEY, David Michael. 1480 WESLEY CHAPEL RD, SUN VALLEY FAMILY PHYSICIA 28079 #036-05-2000 L2001 **FM** *020 †18

JONES, Donald Carter. 6030 W HIGHWAY 74, UNION OBSTETRICIAN & 28079 #038-44-1992 L1998 **OBG** *020 †30

KENDRICK, Alfred Eugene. 6030 W HIGHWAY 74, STE A 28079 #016-11-1975 L2005 **PD** *020 †55 ‡

KRESHON, Martin John, Jr. 6030 W HIGHWAY 74, STE E 28079 #047-20-1986 L1991 **CD IM** *020 †20

LAGUERRE, Jacques P. ■ 28079 #036-05-2003 L2006 **FM** *020

LINDSAY-BARBER, Mary L. 6030 W HIGHWAY 74, STE F 28079 #024-01-1990 L1993 **PD** *020 †55

MATAS, Nicholas Stephen. 6030 W HIGHWAY 74, STE E 28079 #024-16-1990 L1997 **CD** *020 †20

PIERCE, Mart T. ■ 28079 #047-07-1953 L1954 **FM OBG** *071

PURI, Reema. 6030 W HIGHWAY 74 STE F 28079 #001-02-2002 L2005 **PD** *020 †55

RAO, Innanje Ravindranath. 6030 W HIGHWAY 74, STE E 28079 #495-16-1965 L1975 **CD** *020

SOBEL, Barry Adam. 6030 W HIGHWAY 74, UNION OBSTETRICIAN & 28079 #041-09-1992 L2000 **OBG** *020 †30

SULLIVAN, James Michael. ■ 28079 #041-09-1981 L1985 **FOP** *020 †50

SUNDERLAND, Theresa Kay. ■ 28079 #048-14-1987 L2003 **PD CCP** *020 †55

THOMPSON, John Mckee. 6030 W HIGHWAY 74, UNION OBSTETRICIAN & 28079 #035-15-1988 L2006 **OBG** *020 †30

VELASCO, Luis David. 6030 W HIGHWAY 74, STE D 28079 #016-11-1984 L1987 **IM** *020 †20

WEGENER, Adam Danl. 6030 W HIGHWAY 74, STE D 28079 #017-20-1985 L1996 **CD IM** *020 †20

IRON STATION – LINCOLN

MA, Yih Huei. RR 1 BOX 487 28080 #244-02-1951 *100

JACKSON – NORTHAMPTON

DE LOATCH, Raven Lionel. 9425 NC HIGHWAY 305, RURAL HEALTH GROUP JACKSON 27845 #036-08-1984 L1987 **IM** *020 †20

JACKSON SPRINGS – MOORE

CHANDLER, Mark Harvey. RR 1 BOX 221 27281 #012-01-1983 *020

JACKSONVILLE – ONSLOW

ADAMS, Larry Lee. 317 WESTERN BLVD 28546 #036-01-1972 L1972 **R** *020 †80

ALBERT, Zachary Ira. ■ 28546 #028-79-2005, ▲ L2006 **GP** *020

ALMEIDA, John Leonard, Jr. 317 WESTERN BLVD, LAB ONSLOW MEM HOSP 28546 #045-01-1976 L1985 **PTH** *030 †50

AWOMOLO, Adesola. 221 MEMORIAL DR 28546 #690-01-1988 L2001 **HEM** *020 †20

BARNES, Victor Russell. 1703 COUNTRY CLUB RD, STE 204 28546 #036-08-1989 L1993 **P** *020 †75

BATCHELLER, Edgar H, Jr. 255 MEMORIAL DR 28546 #051-01-1964 L1970 **GS** *020 ‡

BENDERMAN, Anthony Wayne. ■ 28540 #047-07-2002 L2003 **PTH** *100

BIANCHI, Edgardo Hugo. 1703 COUNTRY CLUB RD, STE 202 28546 #132-04-1969 L1978 **CD IM** *020

BIDSTRUP, Kathryn Lauren. ■ 28540 #051-01-2004 L2006 **FM** *020 †18

BINDEWALD, Matthew G. ■ 28546 #014-01-2002 L2004 **GS** *020

BJORNSSON, Gottskalk T. ■ 28546 #484-01-1964 L1998 **PUD** *020

BLACKWELL, Francis M. 317 WESTERN BLVD, EAGLE HOSPITALISTS ONSLOW 28546 #045-01-1984 L1992 **FM** *020 †85,18

BLOSS, Katy Lynn. ■ 28540 #025-01-1997 L2006 **EM** *020

BORAWSKI, Joseph Brian. ■ 28546 #035-03-2004 L2004 *100

BRUMBACK, Frank Edgar. ■ 28540 #024-01-1947 L1969 **GP** *071

BUZOLICH, Shari Lynn. ■ 28546 #028-46-2004 L2005 **NS** *012

CAILING, Milagros Palad. 3652 HENDERSON DR, ONSLOW MEDICAL SPECIALTY C 28546 #748-02-1993 L2005 **NEP IM** *020

CHEKAN, George, Jr. ■ 28546 #023-01-1980 L1989 **AN** *020 †05

CHUNG, Hong-Yill. 317 WESTERN BLVD 28546 #583-03-1969 L1978 **GP EM** *020 ‡

COLLIGAN, Joseph Francis. 825 GUM BRANCH RD STE 109 28540 #016-43-1958 L1984 **CHP P** *072 †75 ‡

COLLINS, Natalear Rolline. 325 WESTERN BLVD, ONSLOW DOCTORS CARE, INC. 28546 #036-08-1981 L2000 **EM GP** *075

COOPER, Erica Victoria. ■ 28546 #036-05-2002 L2003 **GS** *020 †85

CRIST, Takey. 250 MEMORIAL DR 28546 #036-01-1965 L1965 **OBG GP** *020 †30 ‡

D'ANGELO, Elizabeth G. 317 WESTERN BLVD 28546 #051-01-1991 L1997 **DR RNR** *020 †80

DAVIS, Leon Douglas. 245 MEMORIAL DR 28546 #036-01-1975 L1976 **OBG** *020 †30

DAY, Cyrus M, Jr. ■ 28546 #020-02-1966 L1976 **AN** *071

DE GREGORIO, Peter A. 1021 HARGETT ST, VA CBOC 28540 #035-01-1969 L1990 **IM P** *020

DESUYO, Eusebio Chiong. 3652 HENDERSON DR 28546 #748-11-1987 L2005 **PCC SME** *020 †30

DEYTON, John Wesley, Jr. 124 MEMORIAL DR 28546 #036-01-1956 L1956 **GYN GP** *020 †30

DIAZ, Denis Manuel. ■ 28546 #011-04-2002 L2004 **PD** *020 †55

DI FIORE, Ralph Jos. 200 DOCTORS DR, STE J 28546 #012-01-1968 L2003 **ORS** *020 †40

DILL, Franklin Geo. 124 MEMORIAL DR 28546 #035-20-1963 L1967 **GYN** *020 †30

EDWARDS, Timothy Freeman. 245 MEMORIAL DR 28546 #036-05-1978 L1979 **OBG** *020 †30

EGLI, Graciela F. 120 SIDNEY LN 28540 #748-02-1989 L2003 **PD** *020 †55

EHRHART, Troy Justin. 317 WESTERN BLVD 28546 #041-13-1995 L2002 **FM** *020 †18

EHRMANN, John Clarence, III. ■ 28546 #023-12-2005 L2007 *020

ELLIOTT, Adrian Nmn. ■ 28546 #036-01-2005 L2006 *020

ENDERLIN, Harry T. 510 COLLEGE ST 28540 #024-05-2001 L2006 **CHP** *100

EWEJE, Peter A. 4 OFFICE PARK DR 28546 #690-01-1986 L1997 **GE IM** *020 †20

FAN, Sik Man. ■ 28546 #462-01-1970 L1996 **GS** *020 †85

FEOLE, John Benedict. 3606 HENDERSON DR, COASTAL DIAGNOSTIC IMAGING 28546 #030-06-1988 L2001 **DR NM** *020 †80

FERNANDEZ, Dominick R. ■ 28546 #048-13-2004 L2006 **P** *100

FLAGG, Seth Yawki. ■ 28540 #024-07-2006 L2007 **FM** *020

FOSTER, Michael Patrick. ■ 28546 #047-06-2003 L2004 *020

FOX, Raymond Morris, Jr. ■ 28540 #047-05-1964 L1973 **OBG** *020 †30

FRINK, Marshall Brantley. 317 WESTERN BLVD 28546 #036-05-1981 L1982 **GP** *030

GALLAGHER, Edgar Givens. 255 MEMORIAL DR 28546 #036-01-1965 L1965 **GS TS** *020 †85,90

GANT, James Curtis. 51 OFFICE PARK DR 28546 #048-02-1983 L1988 **PD** *020 †55

GARCIA, Dynela Louise. ■ 28546 #035-09-2005 L2007 **FM** *100

GARRETT, Charles L, Jr. 132 DOCKSIDE DR 28546 #045-01-1966 L1976 **PTH FOP** *030 †50

GARRETT, James Ellis. 317 WESTERN BLVD, ONSLOW MEMORIAL HOSPITAL 28546 #045-01-1973 L1974 **EM GP** *020 †16

GARRUTO, Bryan David. 6 OFFICE PARK DR 28546 #033-05-2001 L2006 **OPH** *020 †35

GEROCK, Henry Walter, Jr. 317 WESTERN BLVD 28546 #036-01-1963 L1963 **FM** *020 †18

GOPICHAND, Ishwar Hakumal. 120 MEMORIAL DR, JACKSONVILLE CHILDREN'S CL 28546 #748-02-1990 L1996 **PD** *020 †55

GORDON, Jason Andrew. ■ 28546 #023-12-2008 *012

GORDON, Wendy Taylor. ■ 28546 #023-12-2008 *012

GREGORY, Hugh Stanley. ■ 28546 #036-01-1964 L1964 **OTO UM** *071 †45

GRIJALVA, Steven Dionisio. ■ 28540 #023-12-2005 L2006 *020

GROSS, Jeffrey Louis. 124 MEMORIAL DR 28546 #038-40-1972 L1980 **ORS** *020 †40

GUDGER, John Chas. 317 WESTERN BLVD 28546 #036-01-1980 L1983 **EM IM** *020

GURGANUS, Elisabeth J M. ■ 28540 #023-01-1948 L1952 **PD** *071

GUYER, Eva Ruth Ward. 217 STATION ST 28546 #036-05-1983 L1987 **FM** *020 †18

HAMBIDGE, William Raymond. BREWSTER RD 28547 #025-07-1970 L1971 **OBG GP** *075

HAMBRIGHT, Wesley Francis. 291 HUFF DR 28546 #036-07-1982 L1986 **OBG** *020 †30

HAMMOCK, Ronald Mack. 200 DOCTORS DR 28546 #025-01-1977 L1982 **U** *020 †95

HAN, Timothy Mark. 3050 HENDERSON DR 28546 #045-01-2003 L2004 **DR** *100

HARRISON, Lucius Ashton. ■ 28541 #051-04-1956 L1970 **DR OS** *020

HAY, Susan Ann. 1021 HARGETT ST, VA CBOC 28540 #020-12-1993 L1997 **P** *020 †75

HAYE, Henry Solomon. 291 HUFF DR 28546 #566-01-1979 L1984 **OBG** *020 †30

HEBREO, Joseph Darryl. ■ 28546 #035-46-2004 L2005 *100 †20

HENNESSY, Mark Edward. 29 OFFICE PARK DR, SOUTHERN WINDS INTERNAL ME 28546 #539-06-1991 L1995 **IM** *020 †20

HENRIE, Edwin John. BREWSTER RD 28547 #041-09-1962 L1975 **OSM GS** *071 †85

HESTER, Joseph Mc Murray. BREWSTER RD 28547 #036-05-1944 L1947 **IM PUD** *074

HIBBARD, Dana Marie. ■ 28546 #023-12-2005 L2006 **FM** *020

HILL, Tammy Nicole. ■ 28540 #048-16-2001 L2001 **EM** *100

HOAG, Stephen Day. ■ 28546 #023-12-1998 L1999 **FM** *020 †18

HODGSON, Wesley Raymond. ■ 28546 #051-04-2003 L2004 **OBG** *020

HOLLIS, James Robert. ■ 28546 #028-34-2004 L2006 **IM** *012

HOWARD, George A, III. 299 DOCTORS DR 28546 #036-08-1982 L1986 **DR** *020 †80

HSU, Sean Shaiofong. 215 STATION ST, NEUROSURGERY CONSULTANTS, 28546 #025-01-1986 L1998 **NS** *020 †25

HUEBNER, Michelle Linn. ■ 28546 #023-12-2005 **FM** *020

ISSA, Mahmoud Abou. 224 MEMORIAL DR, STE A 28546 #875-01-1971 L1978 **GE IM** *020 †20

JACKSON, Donald Charles. 317 WESTERN BLVD 28546 #917-10-1954 L1973 **DR** *020 †80

JARVIS, Lorraine Noreen. 120 MEMORIAL DR, JACKSONVILLE CHILDS CLC 28546 #035-03-1993 L1994 **PD** *020 †55

JAYARAJ, Tuluri Saml. ■ 28546 #495-50-1968 L2005 **PD** *020 †55

JOHNSON, Earl Thos, Jr. 1250 WESTERN BLVD, STE L2 28546 #036-05-1986 L1987 **IM** *020

JOHNSON, Janet. ■ 28540 #041-12-1986 L1991 **GE IM** *062 †20

JOHNSTON, Carol Ann. 6 OFFICE PARK DR 28546 #035-45-1986 L1990 **OPH** *020 †35

JOHNSTON, Scott Richard. 12 OFFICE PARK DR 28546 #035-45-1986 L1992 **APM** *020 †05

JONNALAGADDA, Murali Rao. 192 VILLAGE DR 28546 #495-50-1964 L1975 **P PHP** *020 †75 ‡

JONNALAGADDA, Venkata R. ■ 28546 #306-01-2001 *100

JOSILEVICH, Michael. 1701 COUNTRY CLUB RD 28546 #561-17-1984 L1995 **IM** *020 †20

KALE, Milton Paul. 51 OFFICE PARK DR 28546 #041-02-1971 L1994 **PD** *020 †55

KAYYE, Paul T. 215 MEMORIAL DR, ONSL-CARTR BEHAVIOR HLTH S 28546 #011-02-1962 L1967 **CHP P** *020 †75

KELL, Robert Edward. 247 MEMORIAL DR 28546 #025-07-1972 L1996 **OBG GP** *020 †30

KELLY, William Ferris, Jr. 317 WESTERN BLVD 28546 #004-01-1986 L1991 **PTH** *020 †50

KEWISH, Steven Alan. ■ 28546 #038-40-1993 L1994 **FM** *040 †18

KEYES, Booker T, Jr. 247 MEMORIAL DR 28546 #017-20-1976 L1988 **U** *020 †95

KRAUSE, Robert A. 11 OFFICE PARK DR 28546 #036-07-1978 L1981 **FM** *020 †18

LARSON, Kelly Suzanne. ■ 28546 #046-01-2006 **FP** *012

LASATER, John David. 445 WESTERN BLVD 28546 #039-01-1978 L1987 **U** *020 †95

LAYLE, Stacey Lynn. 11A MEMORIAL DR 28546 #025-07-1995 L2002 **FM** *020 †18

LE, Quang Phong. ■ 28540 #024-07-2002 L2006 **EM** *020

LEE, Meng Martin. ■ 28540 #035-19-2001 L2006 **GS** *020 †85

LEUNG, Richard Kin-Fook. 29 OFFICE PARK DR 28546 #462-01-1967 L1992 **CD IM** *020 †20

LEWIS, Eric Van. ■ 28540 #047-07-1999 L2008 **HS** *020

LORENTZEN, James Clifford. 317 WESTERN BLVD 28546 #048-04-1983 L1997 **R IM** *020 †20,80 ‡

■ = Address Information Privacy Protected

LYNCH, Michelle Muma. ■ 28546 #023-12-2007 FP *012
MARTIN, Chas Richardson. 2 DEWITT ST STE 2, CENTER 28540 #036-07-1963 L1963 PD *020 †55
MC CLINTICK, Marcia L. ■ 28540 #023-12-2004 L2005 PD *100
MC CLURG, Joel Charles. 237 WHITE ST, COASTAL CAROLINA ORTHO SUR 28546 #038-43-1995 L2003 ORS *020 †40
MEARNS, Thomas Jefferson. 325 WESTERN BLVD, ONSLOW DOCTORS CARE 28546 #055-01-1965 L1968 GP *020
MELANSON, Julia. 250 MEMORIAL DR, TAKEY CRIST, MD PA 28546 #022-75-1995, ▲L2003 OBG *020
MESSEC, Harry S, Jr. 308 DOLPHIN DR 28546 #048-13-1992 L1998 FM *020 †18
MIKHAIL, Ashraf Gad. 510 COLLEGE ST 28540 #915-03-1988 L2002 CHP P *020 †75
MIKHAIL, Fayez Fawzy. ■ 28546 #915-04-1981 L2001 FM *020 †18
MILEWSKI, Francis Jos. 317 WESTERN BLVD 28546 #041-02-1991 L1996 OTO A *020 †45
MILLER, John Scott, Jr. 317 WESTERN BLVD 28546 #036-05-1960 L1960 EM IM *020
MITTAL, Madhur. 120 MEMORIAL DR 28546 #495-36-1988 L1997 NPM PD *020 †55
MOORE, Thomas Phillip. ■ 28540 #036-01-1955 L1955 R *071 †80
MURFIN, Wesley Warren. 1 MATTHEW CT 28546 #022-02-1974 L1981 IM *020 †20
OJEBUOBOH, Ibikunle A. 22 OFFICE PARK DR, OMNI CLINIC, PA 28546 #690-01-1986 L1999 IM *020 †20
OLEGARIO, Arnold Camacho. 51 OFFICE PARK DR 28546 #748-11-1989 L2006 PD *020 †55
OLSEN, Kenneth Geo. 166 MEMORIAL CT, SURGI CARE OF JACKSONVILLE 28546 #007-02-1967 L1972 AN *071 †05
OSUNKOYA, Abayomi W. 25 OFFICE PARK DR, EAST CAROLINA MED ASSOCS 28546 #690-01-1987 L2001 IM IMG *020 †20
PATEL, Swetang M. 2587 HENDERSON DR 28546 #495-23-1992 L2006 FM *020 †18
PATLAK, Erwin M. 215 MEMORIAL DR, CARE SERVICES 28546 #016-11-1952 L1985 P FM *071
PATSELAS, Timothy N. 255 MEMORIAL DR 28546 #051-07-1988 L1989 GS *020 †85
PIERCE, Brandon Keefe. ■ 28546 #041-02-2005 L2006 FM *020
PRICE, Clyde Kent. 264 MEMORIAL DR 28546 #038-44-1987 L1991 OPH OS *020 †35
PYLES, Tameka Jeannine. ■ 28546 #023-01-2006 L2007 *012
REICHLING, Pirkko Esteri. 165 CENTER ST 28546 #374-03-1970 L1984 GP *071
RICHARDS, Browyn Patrice. ■ 28546 #023-01-1997 L1998 FP *012
ROGERS, Garrett Lee. 162 ALDERSGATE RD 28546 #048-14-1973 L1976 CD *020 †20
ROGERS, Noel Bruce. 128 MEMORIAL DR 28546 #010-02-1967 L1972 ORS *020 †40 ‡
ROJY, Thomas Jos, Jr. 43 OFFICE PARK DR 28546 #033-05-1986 L1994 PS HS *020 †85,65 ‡
ROS, Jose Ignacio L. 3245 HENDERSON DR 28546 #748-19-1989 L2002 IM *020 †20
SALCEDO, Gina Marie Gayle. ■ 28546 #014-01-2003 L2006 FM *100
SCHOEN, Martin William. NAVAL BRANCH MED CLNC, PSC BOX 21034 28545 #024-01-2006 L2007 *012
SHETH, Hemant Natverlal. 317 WESTERN BLVD 28546 #495-17-1978 L1990 AN *020 †05
SHIRLEY, Douglas Pierce. 215B STATION ST, JACKSONVILLE DERMATOLOGY 28546 #027-01-1971 L1998 D GP *020 †15
SHUSKO, Michael Patrick. ■ 28540 #036-05-2002 L2003 FM *020 †18
SMITH, Damain Anthony. 245 MEMORIAL DR 28546 #038-40-1992 L2007 OBG *020 †30
SPARKS, Chad Stephendoct. ■ 28546 #014-01-2004 L2005 *100 †20
STELMACH, Suzanne T E. ■ 28540 #024-05-1975 L1980 PD *020 †55
STEWART, John Ernest. ■ 28540 #308-13-2001 L2006 IM *020
STOHRER, Thomas Walter. 317 WESTERN BLVD 28546 #016-11-1987 L1991 DR *020 †80
STREETER, Gregory Dean. 200 DOCTORS DR STE H 28546 #036-01-1980 L1981 FM DIA *020 †18
SUHR, Christopher. 255 MEMORIAL DR 28546 #036-07-1991 L2005 GS *020 †85
SWAMY, Chaya. ■ 28546 #495-33-1980 L1981 IM *020 †20
SWAMY, Kumar N. 144 MEMORIAL CT 28546 #495-09-1972 L2007 PD AI *020 †55,03 ‡
TAJELDIN, Adnan. 200 DOCTORS DR STE 1 28546 #875-01-1972 L1977 IM AI *020
TARVER, James Kennedy. 317 WESTERN BLVD 28546 #023-12-1993 L1995 *020 †80
THOMAS, Koithara Varkey G. 200 DOCTORS DR, STE L 28546 #495-63-1984 L2003 IM *020 †20
THOMAS, Ricky Allan. 2587 HENDERSON DR 28546 #016-01-1980 L1992 FM EM *020 †18
THORNTON, Donnyel Tarvara. ■ 28546 #047-06-2005 L2006 GP *020
TOMESCU, Elvira Marica. ■ 28546 #781-01-1970 L1986 PTH BBK *020 †50
TOMEU, Enrique Jose. 250 MEMORIAL DR 28546 #036-01-1980 L1998 OBG *020 †30
TOWNSEND, James W, Jr. 3280 HENDERSON DR, # C 28546 #041-02-1969 L1997 PD OS *071 †55
TSE, Alex Yu Chow. 114C MEMORIAL DR 28546 #462-01-1971 L1975 PD A *020 †55
TSE, Andre Kon-Sang. 158 MEMORIAL CT 28546 #462-01-1971 L1976 CD NC *020 †20
TURLINGTON, Wade Robt. 200 DOCTORS DR STE M 28546 #036-01-1969 L1969 FM *020 †18
VERBRUGGEN, Hugo C J. BREWSTER RD 28547 #165-01-1956 L1994 ORS *071 †40
WALSH, Patrick James. 445 WESTERN BLVD 28546 #036-08-1993 L1994 U *020 †95
WARREN, Rufus Hawkins. 317 WESTERN BLVD 28546 #051-04-1961 L1978 GP *020
WATKINS, Marc Robert. ■ 28540 #047-07-2002 L2003 GPM *012
WEBB, Charles Marshall. 317 WESTERN BLVD 28546 #045-01-1981 L2004 OBG *020 †30
WESTBROOK, John Andrew. 255 MEMORIAL DR 28546 #021-05-1972 L1992 CRS GS *020 †10,85
WHITLOCK, Gary Thos, III. 215 MEMORIAL DR 28546 #036-01-1978 L2008 EM *020 †16
WILLIAMS, Gregory A. 237 WHITE ST 28546 #010-03-1975 L1984 OBG *020 †30
WILLIAMS, Johnny Lee. 247 MEMORIAL DR 28546 #010-03-1975 L1975 OBG *020 †30
WILLIAMS, Lennox George. 255 MEMORIAL DR 28546 #566-01-1979 L1992 VS GS *020 †85
WILLIAMS, Paul F. 250 MEMORIAL DR 28546 #036-01-1965 L1994 OBG *020 †30
WILSHIRE, Larry Brent. 6 OFFICE PARK DR 28546 #055-01-1974 L1984 OPH AS *020 †35
WOLANSKI, Terrence Philip. 117 KING RICHARD CT, MAILING: P O BOX 12276 28546 #051-01-1971 L1982 PUD IM *020
WOOLFREY, Michael R. 200 DOCTORS DR, STE J 28546 #063-01-1991 L1998 ORS *020
WRIGHT, Jeffrey W. 411 WESTERN BLVD STE C, ATLANTIC FETAL MEDICINE 28546 #048-13-1984 L1985 MFM OBG *020 †30
YOUNG, Garret Pinkney. 317 WESTERN BLVD 28546 #036-08-1989 L1990 NM *020 †80

JAMESTOWN — GUILFORD

AMEEN, William Otis. 700 W MAIN ST 27282 #036-05-1973 L1973 FM EM *020 †16,18
DOERR, Monica Elizabeth. 604 W MAIN ST 27282 #011-02-1988 L1994 IM END *050 †20
ELSAID, Hind Izzeldin. ■ 27282 #848-04-1997 L2007 IM *020 †20
HOPPER, William Falcon. 4810 W WENDOVER AVE 27282 #055-01-1972 L1972 IM PUD *020 †20 ‡

HORN, Helen Amelia. ■ 27282 #023-01-1944 L1997 PTH *071 †50
HUFFMAN, Josephine Kather. ■ 27282 #048-13-2007 OBG *012
JOBE, Daniel Brian. 604 W MAIN ST, CORNERSTONE INTERNAL MED 27282 #036-05-1993 L1994 IM *020 †20
KAVANAGH, Weatherly T. ■ 27282 #051-04-1949 L1949 PD PHP *071
LOWNE, Yvonne R. 4810 W WENDOVER AVE 27282 #041-77-1995, ▲L1999 FM *020 †18
MILES, Linda Michele. 700 W MAIN ST 27282 #036-05-1993 L1996 FM *020 †18
PAZ, Jose Ernesto. 4810 W WENDOVER AVE 27282 #737-01-1992 L2003 IM GP *020 †20
POWELL, Cordi Rumph. ■ 27282 #036-08-1997 PM *100
RUBENS, Jonathan Saml. 2 STONE RIDGE CT 27282 #036-05-1987 L1995 EM *020 †16
STALLINGS, Shiela Clark. ■ 27282 #036-08-1999 L2002 FM *020 †18
THOMAS, Saramaiz Afsani. ■ 27282 #035-06-2005 L2005 IM *012
WOODY, Jonathan Harris. ■ 27282 #036-05-1998 L1999 *020 †16

JARVISBURG — CURRITUCK

OWENS, James Lee. HIGHWAY 158 27947 #036-08-1988 L1989 FM *020 †18

JEFFERSON — ASHE

BADGER, Michael Channing. 200 HOSPITAL AVE, STE 3 28640 #036-08-1998 L1999 FM *020 †18
BRADLEY, Elizabeth Leigh. 200 HOSPITAL AVE, # 7 28640 #036-01-1991 L1992 FM *020 †18
BREEDEN, Patricia Cleary. ■ 28640 #027-01-1991 L1991 EM *020 †16
BURNETT, John Eric, Jr. ■ 28640 #025-01-1943 L1975 OBG *071 †30
CALHOUN, Richard Keith. 200 HOSPITAL AVE 28640 #036-01-1982 L1986 FM EM *020 †18
CAMPBELL, Christopher D. 200 HOSPITAL AVE STE 7 28640 #036-05-1988 L1989 FM *020 †18
CHAMBERLAIN, Staci A. 200 HOSPITAL AVE, ASHE MEMORIAL HOSPITAL 28640 #011-03-1997 L2003 EM *020 †18
DARTER, Danielle Judith. 200 HOSPITAL AVE STE 3, P O BOX 369 28640 #051-04-2000 L2005 FM *020 †18
FACTOR, David Lee. 200 HOSPITAL AVE 28640 #016-01-1989 L1996 DR *020 †80
GROENKE, Melinda Donelle. 200 HOSPITAL AVE, MT JEFFERSON FAMILY MEDICI 28640 #038-45-2000 L2004 FM *020 †18
HAMBY, James Lawrence. 200 HOSPITAL AVE 28640 #023-01-1967 L1972 U *020 †95
HERSHNER, Gregory Scott. PO BOX 765 28640 #038-41-1987 L1988 FM *020 †18
INGLEDUE, Vickie Fowler. 200 HOSPITAL AVE STE 6, MOUNT JEFFERSON FAMILY MED 28640 #036-07-1995 L1997 FM *020 †18 ‡
JONES, Charles Wade. 200 HOSPITAL AVE STE 5, P O BOX 1509 28640 #036-05-1992 L1997 GS VS *020 †85
JONES, Dean Cicero, Jr. 200 HOSPITAL AVE 28640 #036-01-1956 L1956 GS *020 †85
KURTZ, Elam Stoltzfus. 200 HOSPITAL AVE STE 7, HIGH CTY FAMILY MEDICINE 28640 #038-06-1955 L1956 FM *071 †18
KURTZ, Kevin John. 200 HOSPITAL AVE STE 7, HIGH CTY FAMILY MEDICINE 28640 #036-08-1990 L1991 FM *020 †18
MARINAKIS, Christopher A. 200 HOSPITAL AVE 28640 #036-08-1999 L2004 U *020 †95
MILLER, Charles Griffith. 200 HOSPITAL AVE 28640 #036-01-1986 L1987 U *020 †95
MILLER, Edward James. 200 HOSPITAL AVE STE 3 28640 #036-01-1962 L1962 GP *020
PITTS, Gary Wayne. 200 HOSPITAL AVE 28640 #047-06-1974 L1976 U GP *020 †95
SANTOS, Chauncey Beltran. 200 HOSPITAL AVE, STE 2 28640 #748-11-1973 L1986 ORS *020
SUNDIN, John Alvar. 200 HOSPITAL AVE, STE 5 28640 #051-04-1987 L2006 GS *020 †85 ‡
YOUNT, Philip Clair, Jr. 151 MEDICAL PARK DR 28640 #036-08-1986 L1987 FM *020 †18
ZAWODNIAK, Mark J. 200 HOSPITAL AVE 28640 #016-11-1980 L2004 IM *020 †20

JONAS RIDGE — BURKE

HEMMINGS, Hugh Carroll. GENERAL DELIVERY 28641 #036-01-1954 L1954 PD *071

JONESVILLE — YADKIN

BALLARD, Evan Adolphus. 4000 S SWAIM STREET EXT 28642 #036-07-1976 L1977 FM *020 †18
BALLARD, William Evan. 4000 S SWAIM STREET EXT, JONESVILLE FAM MED CTR 28642 #036-01-2005 L2008 FP *012
GRIFFIN, Eugene W, III. 4000 S SWAIM STREET EXT 28642 #036-07-1977 L1979 FM FPG *020
GRONER, Christopher W. 112 N SWAIM ST 28642 #019-02-1976 L1979 FM EM *020 †18
SHELBURNE, Thomas Maynard. 4000 S SWAIM STREET EXT 28642 #036-07-1977 L1979 FM FSM *020 †18

KANNAPOLIS — CABARRUS

ALLEN, Andrea Ross. 5003 HOSPICE LN 28081 #010-01-1984 L2007 FM FPG *020 †18
AUSTEN, Michael John. ■ 28081 #665-02-2007 FP *012
BAKER, Linny Marshall. 1307 S CANNON BLVD, CABARRUS HEALTH ALLIANCE 28083 #036-07-1960 L1960 PD A *020 †55
BIANCHI, Kerry Rotondi. 559 JACKSON PARK RD 28083 #036-05-2001 L2002 IM *020
BOWEN, Meredith Davis. ■ 28081 #036-08-2007 FP *012
BURCHETT, Stephanie Ann. 559 JACKSON PARK RD 28083 #047-06-1997 L2000 IM *020
CHEEK, Karol Cross. 1307 S CANNON BLVD, CABARRUS HLTH ALLIANCE 28083 #045-01-1987 L1994 FM *020
CONROY, Rosolena Visco. 1307 S CANNON BLVD, CABARRUS HEALTH ALLIANCE 28083 #035-15-1988 L1997 PD *020 †55
DAVID, Rachal Alice. ■ 28083 #021-05-2004 L2005 FM *020 †18
DE PAULIS, Anna Ingeborg. ■ 28081 #297-01-2003 L2007 IM *020 †20
ERDIN, Jennifer Ann. 3396 CLOVERLEAF PKWY, SUBURBAN PEDIATRICS 28083 #012-01-1999 L2004 PD *020 †55
GAINES, Tara Goodlett. 543 JACKSON PARK RD 28083 #045-04-1999 L2002 PD *020 †55
GREEN, Heidi Louise. 1305 S CANNON BLVD, DAYMARK RECOVERY SERVICES 28083 #021-01-1999 L2003 P *020 †75
HA, Anupama Singh. 220 DALE EARNHARDT BLVD 28081 #036-08-1998 L1999 FM *020 †18

HERMOSISIMA, Eddie R. 707 S MAIN ST 28081 #748-11-1966 L1978 **GP** *020

HOUSTON, Shelley Adkins. 3396 CLOVERLEAF PKWY 28083 #036-01-2001 L2004 **PD** *020 †55

LESSANE, Beverly Joyce. 521B N CANNON BLVD, LESSANE & AUGUSTUS INTERNA 28083 #036-01-1988 L1990 **IM** *020 †20

LEVY, Robert Michael. 220 DALE EARNHARDT BLVD 28081 #036-08-2005 L2007 **FP** *012

MCMURRAY, Roger Jacob. ■ 28081 #036-08-2008 *012

MORGANN, Robert G. 3396 CLOVERLEAF PKWY 28083 #048-13-1987 L1988 **PD** *020 †55

MORRIS, Brigid Ann. 559 JACKSON PARK RD, KANNAPOLIS INTERNAL MEDICI 28083 #045-04-1990 L2000 **IM** *020 †20

MOSER, Robert Gerard. 559 JACKSON PARK RD 28083 #020-12-1989 L1994 **IM** *020 †20

NG, Chun-Ho Patrick. ■ 28083 #012-01-1985 L2007 **FM EM** *020 †18

OLEKSY, Gregory John. 220 DALE EARNHARDT BLVD 28083 #056-06-2002 L2004 **FM** *020 †18

PARK, Yoo Sun. 5983 ROLLING RIDGE DR 28081 #583-03-1963 L1982 **IMG PM** *020

PECKINPAUGH, James M. 2402 S CANNON BLVD, SOUTH CANNON MEDICAL, P.A. 28083 #038-41-1987 L1990 **FM** *020 †18

PHILLIP, Wayne Billy. 559 JACKSON PARK RD 28083 #036-05/1992 L1995 **IM** *020 †20

PRESSLY, Mary Earle. 3396 CLOVERLEAF PKWY, SUBURBAN PEDIATRIC CLINIC 28083 #045-01-2002 L2005 **PD** *020 †20

SARTIANO, George Philip. ■ 28081 #035-19-1960 L1990 **ON HEM** *040

SELDEN, Kymberly Floyd. 3396 CLOVERLEAF PKWY 28083 #036-01-1999 L2002 **PD** *020 †55

SHEPHERD, James Harrison. 220 DALE EARNHARDT BLVD 28081 #036-05-1994 L1997 **FM** *020 †18

SOUCIE, Carol. 543 JACKSON PARK RD 28083 #028-34-1988 L1993 **PD** *020 †55

STEINBACHER, Erika Anu. 220 DALE EARNHARDT BLVD 28081 #036-01-1992 L1995 **FM** *020 †18

STEWART, Laclaire William. 3396 CLOVERLEAF PKWY 28083 #036-01-1999 L2004 **PD** *020 †55

THOMAS, Harold David, III. 559 JACKSON PARK RD, KANNAPOLIS INTERNAL MEDICI 28083 #041-12-1980 L1994 **IM CD** *020 †20

TOKUNBOH, J I Kehinde. 1961 DALE EARNHARDT BLVD 28083 #690-06-1979 L1998 **IM** *020 †55,20

TRANTHAM, Erin June. 220 DALE EARNHARDT BLVD 28081 #036-01-2003 L2005 **FM** *020 †18

TUTTLE, John Cloyd. 117 S MAIN ST 28081 #036-05-1983 L1984 **FM** *020 †18

VARGAS, Victor Manuel. 220 DALE EARNHARDT BLVD, CABARRUS FAMILY MEDICINE 28081 #654-01-2006 **FP** *012

KENANSVILLE — DUPLIN

AMMAR, Mohamed Ibrahim. 401 N MAIN ST AND HWY 11 28349 #330-04-1965 **OBG** *071

CRAWFORD, Gary Stephen. 401 N MAIN ST AND HWY 11 28349 #539-06-1984 L1994 **FM** *020 †18

GHEBREMEDHIN, Selamwit. 308 WILLIAMSON ST 28349 #422-01-1999 L2002 **PD** *020 †55

GRIGSBY, Kimberly Denise. 401 N MAIN ST AND HWY 11 28349 #036-01-1989 L1991 **IM** *020

LYONS, James Vincent. PO BOX 278, N MAIN STREET 28349 #539-05-1966 L1978 **DR** *040

MILLER, Dyrek E. PO BOX 490, 417 N MAIN ST STE B 28349 #566-01-1989 L2003 **GS** *020 †85

NGO, Corazon Ke. 214 DUPLIN ST 28349 #748-01-1965 L1973 **IM** *020 ‡

PHILLIPS, Jasper Louis. 401 N MAIN ST AND HWY 11 28349 #036-01-1964 L1964 **GS** *071 †85

QADIR, Misbah. 226 MAGNOLIA EXT 28349 #704-01-1997 L2005 **HEM** *020 †20

WATSON, Peter Robins. 226 MAGNOLIA EXT 28349 #036-01-1983 L1984 **IM ON** *020 †20

KENLY — JOHNSTON

WOODBRIDGE, Michael V. 400 N ENGLEWOOD DR 27542 #010-02-1993 L1999 **IM** *020 †20

KERNERSVILLE — FORSYTH

ALSUP, Robert Martin. 280 BROAD ST STE C 27284 #036-01-1974 L1977 **OTO** *020 †45

ANDERSON, Mark Edward. 1617 NC HIGHWAY 66 S 27284 #028-03-1986 L2004 **OBG** *020 †30

AUSTIN, William Elliott. 280 BROAD ST, STE A 27284 #051-04-1975 L1976 **GE IM** *020 †20

BALL, Rebecca Ann. 815 OLD WINSTON RD 27284 #036-07-1990 L1993 **PD** *020 †55

BASILE, Vito. 280 BROAD ST STE F 27284 #036-01-1991 L2001 **DR** *020 †80

BENFIELD, Jacob Lloyd. ■ 27284 #036-05-2008 *012

BESS, Wyndee Leigh. ■ 27284 #036-08-2002 L2004 **AN** *100 †05

BLACKARD, William G. 280 BROAD ST, STE A 27284 #051-04-1990 L1997 **GE** *020 †20

BOALS, Aaron Michael. 291 BROAD ST 27284 #018-03-1996 L2001 **FM** *020 †18 ‡

BORDEN, Lester Stuart, Jr. 500 PINEVIEW DR 27284 #038-40-2000 L2004 **U** *020 †95

BOYD-KRANIS, Robin Lynn. 280 BROAD ST STE F 27284 #041-13-1991 L2001 **DR** *020 †80

BROWN, Michael Osborne. ■ 27284 #047-07-1979 L1985 **OBG** *020

CLEMENS, Dennis Mark. 280 BROAD ST STE F 27284 #045-01-1987 L1989 **R** *020 †80

CONTENTO, Joseph Chas. 280 BROAD ST STE F 27284 #011-03-1983 L1984 **DR** *020 †80

CROWDER, Sakeitha Ltia. ■ 27284 #036-05-2005 **IM** *012

CURLING, Otis D, Jr. 149 N CHERRY ST 27284 #051-01-1984 L1986 **NS PMM** *020

DAHLSTEDT, Stephen M. 500 PINEVIEW DR 27284 #051-04-1986 L1992 **U GS** *020 †95 ‡

DAVIS, Ronald Lee, III. 500 PINEVIEW DR 27284 #021-05-1981 L1987 **U** *020 †95

EVANS, Robert James. 500 PINEVIEW DR 27284 #041-02-1982 L1990 **U** *020 †95

FARIS, John Chas. 280 BROAD ST STE F 27284 #036-01-1967 L1967 **DR OS** *020 †80

FARRELL, Frank Wilson, Jr. 280 BROAD ST STE F 27284 #036-05-1962 L1962 **RNR R** *020 †80

GIBBS, James Saml. 280 BROAD ST, STE A 27284 #051-04-1967 L1973 **GE IM** *020 †20

GOLWYN, Daniel Howard, Jr. 280 BROAD ST STE F 27284 #011-04-1991 L2000 **R** *020 †80

GRAPEY, David Stanley. 280 BROAD ST STE F 27284 #023-07-1988 L1994 **U** *020 †95

HAMILTON, Robert Wm. 1487 OLD COACH RD 27284 #035-06-1963 L1974 **NEP IM** *071 †20

HOPKINS, Judith Owen. 445 PINEVIEW DR, STE 200 27284 #051-01-1977 L1979 **ON HO** *020 †20

HORVATH, Michelle A. 1617 NC HIGHWAY 66 S 27284 #051-01-1995 L2003 **OBG** *020 †30

HROMADKA, Michael Vincent, Jr. ■ 27284 #036-01-2008 *012

HUMPHRIES, Raleigh Green. 500 PINEVIEW DR 27284 #051-01-1983 L1988 **U** *020 †95

HUNT, Thomas Holmes. 280 BROAD ST STE F 27284 #036-05-1971 L1971 **DR NM** *020 †80

JANEWAY, David Vanzandt. 280 BROAD ST STE B 27284 #051-01-1985 L1986 **ORS** *020 †40

JUDGE, Cathy Mae. 280 BROAD ST STE B 27284 #055-02-1993 L1995 **FM** *020 †18

KAPLAN, Richard David. 1617 NC HIGHWAY 66 S 27284 #041-01-1975 L1979 **OBG** *020 †30

KELLY, William Sherwood. 420 W MOUNTAIN ST 27284 #020-02-1981 L1982 **FM FPG** *020 †18

KIMBROUGH, Houston M. 500 PINEVIEW DR 27284 #051-01-1972 L1978 **U** *020 †95 ‡

LAUFFENBURGER, Michael D. 280 BROAD ST, STE B 27284 #036-01-1995 L2001 **ORS** *020 †40

MAC DIARMID, Scott Avard. 500 PINEVIEW DR 27284 #064-01-1985 L2003 **U** *020 †95

MALINDA, Paul Francis. 9495 DURANGO DR 27284 #023-01-1987 L1996 **EM FM** *020 †18 ‡

MANAVI, Cyrus K. ■ 27284 #036-08-2006 L2007 **PTH** *012

MARSH, Robert Anthony. ■ 27284 #038-43-2005 **NS** *012

MAYANS, David Ryan. ■ 27284 #019-02-2008 *012

MC CULLOUGH, David L. 500 PINEVIEW DR, ALLIANCE UROLOGY SPEC 27284 #036-05-1964 L1964 **U** *020 †95

MCDOWELL, John Newton. ■ 27284 #036-01-2004 L2006 **AN** *012

MC GLASSON, Linda Mc Fall. ■ 27284 #047-06-1986 L1987 **P** *020 †20,75

MCNAIR, Jenifer Gibson. ■ 27284 #048-13-2004 L2007 **IM** *012

MCNICHOL, Tj. ■ 27284 #654-01-2005 L2007 **GS** *100

MESCHAN, Rachel Farrer. ■ 27284 #036-05-1957 L1957 **OBG OS** *071

METHENEY, Catherine D. 1635 NC HIGHWAY 66 S, STE 210 27284 #036-05-2003 L2005 **FM** *100 †18

MICHAELIS, Charles E. ■ 27284 #005-12-1953 L1954 **AN** *071

MILNER, Thos Hamilton, III. 280 BROAD ST STE F 27284 #012-01-1968 L1969 **DR** *020 †80

MINER, Brendan Maney. 280 BROAD ST STE F 27284 #035-06-1995 L2002 **DR** *020 †80

MIXON, Henry Terrell. 280 BROAD ST, STE A 27284 #021-01-1986 L1991 **GE** *020 †20

NAYLOR, Lee Ann Allen. 280 BROAD ST STE F 27284 #045-01-1983 L1985 **DR** *020 †80

NEAL, Sara L. ■ 27284 #036-05-1994 L1996 **FM** *020 †18

NESI, Marc H. 500 PINEVIEW DR 27284 #440-01-1971 L1982 **U** *020 †95 ‡

NNADI, Victoria O. 445 PINEVIEW DR, STE 240 27284 #023-01-1996 L2006 **IM** *020 †20

OBEID, Issam Saleem. ■ 27284 #473-02-1995 L2006 **IMG** *100 †18

OPALSKI, Deborah. ■ 27284 #041-78-2002, ▲ L2007 **FP** *012

OTTELIN, Mark Conrad. 500 PINEVIEW DR 27284 #045-01-1987 L1992 **U UP** *020 †95

PASCHOLD, Eugene H. 445 PINEVIEW DR, STE 200 27284 #036-05-1978 L1979 **ON IM** *020 †20

PETERSON, Lloyd John. 500 PINEVIEW DR 27284 #016-06-1969 L1973 **U** *020 †95 ‡

POWELL, Tasha Renee. ■ 27284 #036-05-2008 *012

RADIONTCHENKO, Alexei. 291 BROAD ST, KERNERSVILLE FAMILY PRACTI 27284 #913-08-1988 L1998 **FM** *020 †18

RECORD, Charles Leo. 291 BROAD ST 27284 #036-05-1986 L1989 **FM** *020 †18

RECORD, S Leo, Jr. 220 COKESBURY ST 27284 #036-05-1964 L1964 **FM** *020 †18

RICHARDS, Kyle Adam. ■ 27284 #056-06-2007 **GS** *012

RIESER, Geoffrey Davis. 280 BROAD ST STE F 27284 #045-01-1985 L1987 **DR** *020 †80

RODRIGUEZ, Fabian Donovan. ■ 27284 #047-20-2002 L2006 **IM** *012

ROSS, Allan. 1617 NC HIGHWAY 66 S 27284 #041-01-1975 L1979 **OBG** *020 †30 ‡

RUBIN, Michael Hotelling. 280 BROAD ST, STE A 27284 #045-01-1970 L1977 **GE IM** *020 †20

RYTER-BROWN, Sherry M. 291 BROAD ST 27284 #036-05-2001 L2002 **FM** *020 †18

SHEARER, Heather Hill. 445 PINEVIEW DR, STE 200 27284 #012-05-1999 L2002 **HO** *020 †20

SILVA, Brook Amundson. 1617 NC HIGHWAY 66 S 27284 #026-04-1992 L2000 **OBG** *020 †30

SKINNER, Elizabeth N. 445 PINEVIEW DR, STE 200 27284 #012-05-1999 L2003 **OBG** *020 †30

SNIDER, Alison Townsend. 900 OLD WINSTON RD, STE 222 27284 #036-05-2001 L2003 **FM** *020 †18

STACKS, Warren Dean. 815 OLD WINSTON RD 27284 #004-01-1987 L1994 **FM** *020 †18

STAGG, Lura W. 110 HARMON LN STE A, FSLR PEDS 27284 #036-05-1968 L1968 **PD ADL** *020 †55

STALLWORTH, Mark Jung. 280 BROAD ST STE F 27284 #021-01-1988 L1994 **VIR DR** *020 †80

STANCIL, Jennifer Marie. ■ 27284 #036-01-2004 L2007 **PD** *100 †55

STAUB, Christine E. 7737 PEARMAN QUARRY RD 27284 #035-45-1984 L1986 **FM** *020 †18

SULLIVAN, Elizabeth Ann. ■ 27284 #004-01-2008 *012

SURAL, Ronald Frank. 500 PINEVIEW DR 27284 #025-01-1967 L1974 **U GS** *020 †95

SWEENEY, John Thayer. 280 BROAD ST, STE A 27284 #038-40-1961 L1961 **GS GP** *071 †85

TABOR, Aaron Thomas. 1031 E MOUNTAIN ST, BLDG 302 27284 #023-07-1997 *020

TANNENBAUM, Sigmund Ian. 500 PINEVIEW DR 27284 #036-07-1975 L1976 **U** *020 †95

THOMPSON, Daniel Vladinir. ■ 27284 #036-05-2004 **IM** *012

VICK, Jennifer Grimes. ■ 27284 #051-04-2004 L2007 **PD** *012

WASHBURN, Scott Alan. 445 PINEVIEW DR 27284 #004-01-1986 L1990 **GYN OBS** *040 †30

WEBER, Michelle Hickman. ■ 27284 #036-05-2006 **PTH** *012

WEIN, Robert Michael. 1617 NC HIGHWAY 66 S 27284 #051-01-1972 L1978 **OBG** *020 †30

WIGGINS, Thomas Barnes. 280 BROAD ST STE F 27284 #036-05-1983 L1985 **DR** *020 †80

WOLFMAN, Neil Turner. 280 BROAD ST STE F 27284 #035-03-1971 L1978 **DR AS** *020 †80

WOOD, David Richard. 280 BROAD ST, STE A 27284 #038-40-1975 L1976 **GE IM** *020 †20

KILL DEVIL HILLS — DARE

NICHOLAS, Theodore W. 3210 N CROATAN HWY, STE 3 27948 #654-01-1997 L2002 **PM PME** *020 †60 ‡

PICKREL, Jerry Cline. 1237C S VIRGINIA DARE TRL, TRAIL 27948 #021-01-1958 L1959 **PTH** *071 †50

SLEDGE, John Burton, Jr. ■ 27948 #036-07-1955 L1955 **PHP** *071

STEINER, Michael Lee. 2400 N CROATAN HWY STE C 27948 #055-01-1967 L1975 **OPH** *020 †35

SULLIVAN, James J. ■ 27948 #025-07-1951 L1952 **DR R** *071

KING — STOKES

BAGINSKI, Scott Garret. ■ 27021 #038-41-2004 L2004 **DR** *012

BEAVERS, Carl Michael. 216 MOORE RD 27021 #036-05-1978 L1994 **FM** *020 †18

BELL, Carl Ellis. PO BOX 2170, 577 S MAIN ST 27021 #047-01-1945 L1965 **GP OS** *075

GRAHAM, William A, IV. 216 MOORE RD, MOUNTAINVIEW MEDICAL ASSOC 27021 #036-05-1997 L1998 **FM** *020 †18

JUNG, Peter W. 216 MOORE RD, MOUNTAIN VIEW MEDICAL 27021 #035-45-1978 L1994 **FM** *020 †18

MC MILLIAN, Traci D. 216 MOORE RD 27021 #036-05-1998 L1999 **FM** *020 †18

MORA, Edgar Rodolfo. ■ 27021 #429-02-2002 L2006 **IM** *100 †20

NEWSOME, Samuel Carl. 304 MOUNTAIN VIEW RD 27021 #036-05-1975 L1975 **FM FPG** *020 †18

NICHOLS, Michelle L. 167 MOORE RD, PILOT MEDICAL ASSOCIATES 27021 #027-01-1990 L1993 **FM** *020 †18

NICHOLS, Michelle Rogers. 167 MOORE RD, UPPR LEVEL 27021 #036-08-1996 L1998 **FM** *020 †18

POLLOCK, David Carl. 216 MOORE RD 27021 #036-05-1992 L1993 **ORS** *020 †40

POLLOCK, Frank Edward, Jr. 216 MOORE RD 27021 #036-05-1983 L1984 **ORS** *020 †40

VOGLER, Scott Lindsey. 216 MOORE RD 27021 #036-05-1998 L1999 **FM** *020 †18 ‡

WORTMAN, Paul Douglass. 216 MOORE RD STE 200, MOUNTAINVIEW SKIN CARE PC 27021 #033-05-1986 L1992 **D** *020 †20,15

KINGS MOUNTAIN – CLEVELAND

ADELEKUN, Temidayo A. 502 W KING ST # 20, SOUTHERN CLINICS AND URGEN 28086 #690-01-1983 L2000 **IM UCM** *020 †20

ANDERSON, Christian G. 502 W KING ST STE 100, CHRISTIAN ANDERSON MD BX39 28086 #412-01-1985 L1995 **IM EM** *020 †20

ASHRI, Neeraj. 827 E KING ST, MEDICAL ASSOCIATES OF KING 28086 #495-45-1996 L2004 **END** *100 †20

BINION, Gerald Ray. 821 W KING ST 28086 #048-12-1962 L1973 **OBG** *071 †30

CHEN, Keh-Fang. 706 W KING ST 28086 #385-02-1968 L1974 **OBG** *020 †30

DAWSON, John Charles S. 706 W KING ST 28086 #065-06-1977 L1995 **FM** *020 †18 ‡

DAY, Philip Mark. 706 W KING ST 28086 #025-12-1982 L1984 **GP** *075

DELANEY, Ronald K. 608 W KING ST 28086 #063-01-1975 L1995 *020

DURHAM, Thomas Garrison. 812 W KING ST 28086 #045-01-1958 L1959 **GP** *071

FLOWE, Kenneth Michael. 706 W KING ST 28086 #036-05-1987 L1993 **EM** *020 †85

GANGOO, Abdul Rashid. 810 W KING ST 28086 #495-51-1968 L1978 **IM ID** *020 †20

GARDNER, Richard Dennis. 103 S WATTERSON ST 28086 #047-06-1975 L1992 **ORS ADL** *020 †55,40

GELOT, Deepak Ramchandra. 707 W KING ST 28086 #036-01-1991 L1993 **FM** *020 †18

GENTRY, John Billy. 706 W KING ST, KINGS MOUNTAIN HOSP 28086 #036-01-1959 L1959 **ATP CLP** *020 †50

LAMPLEY, Charles Gordon. 706 W KING ST 28086 #036-01-1989 L1990 **OBG** *020 †30

MAYSE, Ray Scott. 510 W KING ST 28086 #036-05-1976 L1979 **IM** *020 †20

MC GILL, John C. ■ 28086 #047-05-1946 L1950 **GP** *071

OESTERLE, John Robt. 706 W KING ST 28086 #025-07-1991 L1999 **AN** *020 †05 ‡

PLONK, George Webb. ■ 28086 #041-02-1944 L1944 **GS** *071 †85

POINT, Robert Beverly. ■ 28086 #051-01-1955 L1988 **D** *071 †15

ROBERSON, Lewis H, II. 812 W KING ST 28086 #036-08-1992 L1995 **FM** *020 †18

ROBINSON, Sam Leslie. 706 W KING ST 28086 #047-06-1953 L1965 **GS TS** *071 †85,90

SINCOX, Francis John. 819 SUNNYSID SHDY RST RD R, FAMILY PRACTICE 28086 #012-05-1958 L1963 **FM AM** *020

SMITH, Jeffrey Galt. 214 CLEVELAND AVE, CAROMONT FAMILY MEDICINE 28086 #047-07-1990 L1996 **FM** *020 †18

STALLINGS, Martin Wade. 108 EDGEMONT DR 28086 #001-02-1969 L1974 **PD** *020 †55

THOMBS, Everette Bernard. 711 W MOUNTAIN ST 28086 #010-03-1978 L1981 **IM CD** *020

TOFFOLO, R Ronald. ■ 28086 #035-06-1957 L1984 **R** *020 †80

WILSON, Lisa Michelle. 214 CLEVELAND AVE, CAROMONT FAMILY MEDICINE 28086 #038-43-2000 L2002 **FM** *020 †18

KINSTON – LENOIR

ADAMS, Richard J. KINSTON CLINIC 28501 #038-40-1960 L1989 **OS GS** *030 †85

ADKINS, Mark Allen. 701 DOCTORS DR, STE M 28501 #011-03-1982 L1989 **DR** *020 †80

AGSTEN, Joseph Edward. 107 AIRPORT RD 28501 #036-01-1973 L1973 **FM** *020 †18

ANAND, Rakesh Tarlok Nath. 1905 ESSEX ST 28504 #577-01-1979 L1987 **AN** *020 †05

ANTONOWICH, Fred. ■ 28501 #035-19-1956 L1984 **EM GS** *071 †85

ATASSI, Nawaf G. 608 AIRPORT RD, EASTERN NEPHROLOGY ASSOCIA 28504 #875-01-1983 L1992 **IM NEP** *020 †20

ATILLA, Mehmet A. 744 AIRPORT RD, EASTERN CAROLINA PHYSICIAN 28504 #902-07-1986 L1997 **MPD** *020 †20,55

BAIRD, David Bruce. 100 AIRPORT RD, KINSTON PA 28501 #036-01-1987 L1989 **PTH PCP** *020 †50

BAKER, Joan Margo. 701 DOCTORS DR STE F 28501 #036-01-1979 L2002 **OBG** *020

BAKER, Michael Sean. 701 DOCTORS DR, STE E 28501 #036-08-1997 L2001 **OBG** *020 †30

BERRY, John, Jr. 701 DOCTORS DR 28501 #024-01-1980 L1984 **GS** *020 †85

BHOTIWIHOK, Preecha. 100 AIRPORT RD #143-01-1971 L1977 **AN GP** *071

BOUZIGARD, Raymond Jos. 701 DOCTORS DR 28501 #021-05-1966 L1974 **R RO** *071 †80

BOYD, Gwendolyn M. ■ 28504 #036-01-1977 L1977 **OBG** *075 †30

BRAYTON, Michelle. ■ 28504 #035-06-1992 L2003 **AN** *020

BREEN, Francis A, Jr. 100 AIRPORT RD 28501 #041-02-1963 L2002 **ON HEM** *020 †20 ‡

BROOKS, Charles Michael. 701 DOCTORS DR, STE E 28501 #036-05-1981 L1984 **OBG** *020 †30

CABUNGCAL, Catherine Roy. 744 AIRPORT RD, EASTERN CAROLINA PHYSICIAN 28504 #041-09-1996 L2006 **IM** *020 †20

CARRASCO, Leonor C. 905 N QUEEN ST 28501 #748-01-1963 L1987 **A PD** *020

CLASSEN, Charles H, Jr. 701 DOCTORS DR STE G, KINSTON CLINIC NORTH 28501 #023-01-1966 L1975 **ORS EM** *020 †40

COLLINS-SNYDER, Lori Jean. 107 AIRPORT RD, LENOIR FAMILY MEDICINE 28501 #665-01-2004 L2007 **FM** *020

CONSTANCE, Christian M. 608 AIRPORT RD 28504 #067-02-1988 **IM** *020 †20

COOPER, Edwin Branan, Jr. 701 DOCTORS DR 28501 #036-07-1966 L1966 **ORS PM** *071 †40

COTTEN, Aaron Rodney. 100 AIRPORT RD, DEPT OF EMERGENCY MED 28501 #036-08-1992 L1995 **EM** *020

COX, Ralph Lee. 100 AIRPORT RD 28501 #020-02-1987 L1994 **U** *020 †95

CRAIG, Isaac Alan. 100 AIRPORT RD, DEPT PATH 28501 #036-01-1968 L1968 **PTH** *020 †50

CRISP, Laddie Conway, Jr. 107 AIRPORT RD 28501 #036-08-1987 L1988 **FM** *020 †20

CROMER, William Browning. 2415 W VERNON AVE, CASWELL CTR 28504 #036-05-1956 L2002 **GP** *075

CUMMINGS, Richard Edward. 5080 US HIGHWAY 70 W 28504 #011-02-1977 L1984 **PS** *020 †65

CZUBA, Michael Terrence. 1402 GREENBRIAR RD 28501 #038-40-1974 L1998 **DR FM** *020 †18,80

DALE, Frederick Payne. ■ 28503 #041-13-1946 L1947 **GS OS** *071 †85

DEAN, Robert James. ■ 28504 #035-06-1947 L1978 **AN** *074

DEEPE, Robert Moses. 701 DOCTORS DR, STE A 28504 #038-41-1979 L1980 **GS** *020 †85

DICKSON, Robert Trulock. 701 DOCTORS DR STE N, KINSTON CLINIC NORTH 28501 #012-01-1979 L1985 **GE IM** *020

DOEPKER, Kimberly Ann. 100 AIRPORT RD, DEPT OF EMERGENCY MED 28501 #038-41-2003 L2006 **EM** *020 †16

DRIVER, Robert Edward. 100 AIRPORT RD, DEPT OF EMERGENCY MED 28501 #041-15-2000 L2005 **EM** *020 †16

ELLIS, Rickie Wade. 2901 N HERRITAGE ST, EASTPOINTE-KINSTON 28501 #036-08-1995 L2001 **P** *020

ELMORE, William Glenn. 701 DOCTORS DR, STE M 28501 #036-07-1968 L1968 **DR** *071 †80

FEASEL, Michael John. 100 AIRPORT RD, LENOIR MEMORIAL HOSPITAL 28501 #038-41-1981 L1988 **EM** *020 †16

FINIZIO, Tobin Andrew. 100 AIRPORT RD 28501 #010-02-1993 L2003 **DR** *020 †80

FLORES-TEJANO, Adelinda M. ■ 28504 #748-02-1963 L1972 **AN OS** *071 †05

FLOURNOY, John Eppes. 701 DOCTORS DR 28501 #051-04-1966 L1971 **R** *020 †20

FOGLEMAN, Ross Lee, Jr. ■ 28504 #036-07-1953 L1955 **FM** *071 †18

GALLAHER, Robert Thos. 706 ROSEANNE DR 28504 #052-02-1984 L1989 **PCC IM** *020 †20

GAYEN, Tapan Kumar. ■ 28504 #160-02-1983 L2005 **IM** *020 †20

GILMORE, Samuel Joseph. 701 DOCTORS DR, KINSTON CLNC NORTH STE E 28501 #017-20-1968 L1974 **OBG** *020 †30

GOFORTH, John Parker. 100 AIRPORT RD 28501 #036-08-1986 L1989 **IM** *020 †20

HADDAD, Michel Geo. 100 AIRPORT RD, KINSTON PA 28501 #036-05-1989 L1992 **PTH** *020 †50

HENDERSON, John P, Jr. ■ 28504 #036-05-1951 L1951 **U** *071

HENSHAW, Dan Maxson. KINSTON DERMATOL CLN N, STE F 28501 #016-06-1957 L1995 **D** *020 †15

HERLONG, John Osborne. 701 DOCTORS DR STE M, EASTERN RADIOLOGISTS, INC. 28501 #045-01-1994 L1998 **DR** *020 †80

HERRING, Charles Leonidas. ■ 28501 #036-01-1955 L1955 **IM** *071

HNATOV, Alex. 703 DOCTORS DR 28501 #068-01-2000 L2005 **RO** *100

HNATOV, Andrej. 703 DOCTORS DR 28501 #068-01-1998 L2003 **RO** *020 †80

HOSEA, Robert Haywood. 701 DOCTORS DR STE K, KINSTON CLNC N 28501 #021-01-1973 L1978 **OTO** *020 †45

HOUSE, Joseph Bernard. 100 AIRPORT RD, DEPT OF EMERGENCY MED 28501 #025-07-2005 L2007 **EM** *012

HUBERMAN, Richard Allen. 100 AIRPORT RD 28501 #035-19-1972 L1973 **ORS** *020 †40

IBEGBU, Ikechukwu Eric. 905 N QUEEN ST, STE A 28501 #690-04-1995 L2004 **GE** *020 †20

IQBAL, Mohammad Omer. 701 DOCTORS DR, STE N 28501 #704-05-1997 L2007 **IM** *020 †20

JARMAN, Wayne Thos. 703 ROSEANNE DR, # D 28504 #036-05-1974 L1974 **GS** *020 †85

JILCOTT, Rupert W, III. 701 DOCTORS DR STE H 28501 #012-05-1974 L1976 **IM** *020 †20 ‡

JOHN, John Kunnuthara. 744 AIRPORT RD 28504 #495-37-1995 L2000 **IM** *020 †20

JOHN, Rekha E. 608A AIRPORT RD 28504 #495-45-1994 L2000 **NEP IM** *020 †20

JOHNSON, Kenneth Lee, II. 701 DOCTORS DR STE N 28501 #036-08-1997 L1998 **IM** *020 †20

KASSELT, Max Rolf. 2104 N HERRITAGE ST, KASSELT BONE JOINT CTR 28501 #836-02-1976 L1992 **ORS HS** *030 †40

KATZ, Joseph. ■ 28501 #012-01-1954 L1956 **GP IM** *071

KING, Michael Brian. 701 DOCTORS DR STE N, KINSTON CLINIC NORTH 28501 #036-01-1971 L1971 **CD IM** *020 †20

KIROLLOS, Alan Nageeb. 2503 N QUEEN ST, KINSTON CARDIOLOGY ASSOCIA 28501 #915-05-1981 L1993 **CD IM** *020 †20

KIROLLOS, Hanan Shaker. 905 N QUEEN ST, SEABOARD ALLERGY & ASTHMA 28501 #915-05-1989 L1996 **AI IM** *020 †03,20

KLETZING, Karl Herbert. 100 AIRPORT RD, DEPT OF EMERGENCY MED 28501 #011-02-2005 L2007 **EM** *012

KOZEL, William Lee. 100 AIRPORT RD 28501 #036-01-1996 L1997 **DR** *020 †80

KROEGER, Richard James. 1100 HARDEE RD STE 103, KINSTON DIGESTIVE DISEASES 28504 #035-15-1978 L1984 **GE IM** *020 †20

KUNSTLING, Carl R. ■ 28501 #018-03-1941 L1975 **EM GS** *071 †85

LAIT, Marci. 701 DOCTORS DR STE K, FALLON CLINIC WORCESTER 28501 #016-11-1996 L2007 **OTO** *020 †45

LANGLEY, John Thos. 701 DOCTORS DR 28501 #036-07-1955 L1955 **ORS** *071

LA PRADE, Bennett W. 2440 DOGWOOD LN 28504 #051-01-1956 L1963 **OBG** *071 †30

LAVARREDA, Carlos Alfonso. 2908 N HERRITAGE ST 28501 #429-01-1961 L1992 **GS TS** *030 †20

LAWSON, Luan. 100 AIRPORT RD, DEPT OF EMERGENCY MED 28501 #036-08-1998 L1999 **EM** *020 †16

MC CARRON, Ann. 2415 W VERNON AVE, CASWELL CENTER 28504 #004-01-1981 L1996 **PD** *020 †55

MINTZ, Rudolph Ivey, Jr. 400 GLENWOOD AVE, KINSTON CLINIC STE 11 28501 #036-01-1967 L1967 **GYN** *020 †30

MITRA, Shyamal Kishore. 701 DOCTORS DR, STE N 28501 #495-41-1977 L1992 **CD** *020 †20 ‡

MURRAY, James O S, Jr. ■ 28501 #024-05-1952 L1954 **GS GP** *071 †85

NUNNERY, William Ernest. ■ 28501 #019-02-1942 L1946 **U** *074 †95

NYE, Sylvanus Wm. 100 AIRPORT RD 28501 #035-45-1957 L1958 **PTH** *071 †50

OKONKWO, Ambrose Sunday. 2502 N HERRITAGE ST STE A, HOPE PHYSICIANS 28501 #051-04-1994 L1999 **FM** *020 †18

PARKER, Samuel Lester, Jr. ■ 28501 #010-01-1942 L1942 **GYN OS** *071 †30

PATE, Eugene Wesley, Jr. 701 DOCTORS DR 28501 #036-01-1963 L1963 **ORS** *071 †40

PATRICK, Simmons I. ■ 28504 #036-07-1950 L1951 **R** *071 †80

PERRY, Ely Jackson. ■ 28501 #036-01-1954 L1954 **OS** *075

PIERCE, Hubert Gaines. 100 AIRPORT RD 28501 #036-05-1958 L1958 **IM** *020

PULLY, Rose. ■ 28501 #041-01-1951 L1951 **FM** *071 †18

RAJU, Yeddu Babu R P. 2415 W VERNON AVE, CASWELL CENTER 28504 #495-50-1958 L1976 **IM IMG** *020

RANDOLPH, Teigha Jan. 701 DOCTORS DR, STE N 28501 #055-02-1989 L1992 **IM** *020 †20

RASPBERRY, Carolyn Denise. ■ 28501 #036-08-1997 **P** *100

REYNOLDS, Leslie Denise. 1100 HARDEE RD, STE 104 28504 #036-07-1991 L1996 **N** *020 †75

RISK, Gregory Conway. 100 AIRPORT RD, DEPT OF EMERGENCY MED 28501 #017-20-1993 L1999 **EM MDM** *020 †16

RIZWAN, Muhammad Zahid. 701 DOCTORS DR, STE N 28501 #704-21-1997 L2004 **IM** *020

ROMNEY, Sharon Denise. PO BOX 2429, ALBEMARLE PEDIATRICS 28502 #010-03-1993 L1996 **PD** *020

ROYALS, Hoover M, Jr. 2415 W VERNON AVE, CASWELL CENTER 28504 #036-05-1985 L1986 **FM** *020 †18

ROY CHOWDHURY, Kishore. ■ 28504 #160-02-1984 L2007 **IM** *100 †20

SABISTON, Frank, Jr. 701 DOCTORS DR, STE A 28504 #036-01-1964 L1964 **GS GP** *020 †85

SAPASETTY, Ram A. 608 AIRPORT RD, SOUTHEASTERN NEPHROLOGY AS 28504 #495-21-1984 L1997 **IM NEP** *020 †20

SARACINO, Joseph A. 2602 N HERRITAGE ST 28501 #033-06-1987 L1992 **GE IM** *020 †20

SHELDON, Charles Bryan. 100 AIRPORT RD, DEPT OF EMERGENCY MED 28501 #045-04-2004 L2006 **EM** *020

■ = Address Information Privacy Protected

SPADER, Bryan Dale. 2901 N HERRITAGE ST 28501 #030-05-1967 L1997 **P** *020 †75
SPIGNER, Prescott B, Jr. ■ 28501 #045-01-1953 L1958 **ORS** *071 †40
STEFFEE, Craig Harold. 100 AIRPORT RD #036-05-1993 L1996 **PTH PCP** *020 †50
STEGBAUER, Scott Allen. 518 PLAZA BLVD, STE 2 28501 #056-06-1984 L2007 **ORS** *020 †40
SUTTON, Frank Morrison, Jr. 1005 WEST RD, LENOIR MEMORIAL HOSPITAL 28501
   #036-05-1997 L2005 **AN** *020
TANNER, Maurice B. ■ 28501 #051-04-1960 L1960 **DR RO** *071 †80
TEJANO, Felipe Mazon. 701 DOCTORS DR 28501 #748-02-1963 L1972 **U** *071
THRELKELD, Billie Jo. 100 AIRPORT RD, DEPT OF EMERGENCY MED 28501
   #020-02-2000 L2003 **EM** *020
TRINH, Elizabeth Buice. 100 AIRPORT RD 28501 #012-01-2001 L2003 **EM** *020 †16
TROTTER, Melora Jeanne. 100 AIRPORT RD, EMERGENCY DEPARTMENT 28501
   #045-04-2001 L2005 **EM** *020 †16
UPPIN, Ashokkumar S. 2415 W VERNON AVE, CASWELL CENTER 28504 #495-23-1961 L1972
   GS *020 †85
WATFORD, Douglas E. 400 GLENWOOD AVE, STE 3 28501 #047-07-1985 L1992 **FM** *020
WEATHERDON, Derek Scott. 107 AIRPORT RD, LENOIR FAMILY MED 28501
   #065-06-1995 L2000 **FM** *020 †18
WEST, George Harper. 111 AIRPORT RD 28501 #036-05-1967 L1967 **IM CD** *020 †20
WHITLARK, Joseph David. 2714 WESTBROOKE DR 28504 #045-04-1985 L2001 **GS** *020 †85,90
WILLIAMS, Jonathan Edward. 100 AIRPORT RD, DEPT OF EMERGENCY MED 28501
   #036-08-2004 L2006 **EM** *020
WILTCHER, Christopher A. 324 N QUEEN ST 28501 #047-20-1991 L2005 **OBG** *020 †30
WOLICKI, Joanna. 2901 N HERRITAGE ST STE C, EAST COVE PSYCHIATRIC SERV 28501
   #036-08-1996 L2000 **P** *020
WOOTEN, Cecil Wm, Jr. ■ 28503 #024-01-1945 L1945 **GP** *071
WRIGHT, Walter Lee. 701 DOCTORS DR 28501 #036-01-1980 L1981 **OPH** *020 †35

KITTY HAWK – DARE

ADAMI, John Louis. 5136 N CROATAN HWY, DARE HEART CENTER 27949 #561-07-1983 L1993
   CD CCM *020 †20
BALLESTEROS-BERNARDO, G D. 5200 N CROATAN HWY, STE 11 27949 #748-16-1982 L1998
   PD *075 †55
BURCHETT, Troy Lincoln. ■ 27949 #020-12-1964 L2005 **U NEP** *071 †95 ‡
CHASE, Jeffrey M. 4820 N CROATAN HWY 27949 #041-02-1986 L1998 **ORS** *020 †40
CRUTCHFIELD, Wm Monroe. 5200 N CROATAN HWY, ASTHMA & ALLERGY 27949
   #036-01-1966 L1966 **OTO A** *020 †45
DENARO, Frank, Jr. ■ 27949 #010-01-1963 L1965 **OBG** *071 †30
DE VORE, Jay Saml. 5200 N CROATAN HWY 27949 #016-02-1966 L2001 **AN PMM** *020 †05 ‡
HUDSON, Sarah Tilton. 5200 N CROATAN HWY, STE 11 27949 #036-01-1982 L1985
   PD *020 †55
HURLEY, Daniel Jos, Jr. 5200 N CROATAN HWY 27949 #051-07-1980 L1981 **GP EM** *020
JENKINS, Joseph Thomas. 5200 N CROATAN HWY 27949 #036-01-1998 L2000 **GS** *020 †85
MC CAIN-JOHNSON, Lisa E. 5200 N CROATAN HWY, STE 11 27949 #047-07-1998 L2002 *020
MC KENNA, Matthew John. 4820 N CROATAN HWY 27949 #010-02-2000 L2005 **ORS** *020 †40
PEAT, Kenneth Wm. 5200 N CROATAN HWY, REGIONAL MEDICAL CENTER 27949
   #020-12-1977 L2005 **DR** *020 †80 ‡
PHARR, Tarkten Alexander. 5200 N CROATAN HWY 27949 #041-02-1992 L2001 **VS** *020 †85
POPE, Thomas Bryant. ■ 27949 #051-04-1934 L1934 **OS** *072
POWELL, Jeffrey Peter. 5565 N CROATAN HWY, T/A CHESAPEAKE ENT ASSOC P 27949
   #035-06-1975 L1980 **OTO AI** *020 †45
SAWIN, Shannon Mullis. 4112 N CROATAN HWY 27949 #036-01-2001 L2003 **FM** *020 †18
SJOERDSMA, Albert. ■ 27949 #016-02-1949 L1989 **OS CD** *050 †20
SUMNERS, Ann Cara. 5200 N CROATAN HWY 27949 #036-08-2001 L2004 **FM** *020 †18
THORNTON, Jack Walker. 5200 N CROATAN HWY, ASTHMA & ALLERGY 27949
   #027-01-1964 L1969 **HNS OTO** *020 †45
WALKER, Dana M Sherrick. 5200 N CROATAN HWY 27949 #036-05-1984 L1987 **FM** *020 †18
WATERS, Edward Gilmay, Jr. ■ 27949 #035-09-1955 L1956 **EM** *020
WILKINSON, James S, Jr. 5200 N CROATAN HWY 27949 #036-08-1984 L1985 **GP IM** *020

KNIGHTDALE – WAKE

ADAMS, Robert Stark, Jr. 7124 KNIGHTDALE BLVD, KNIGHTDALE PRIMARY CARE 27545
   #036-05-1991 L1994 **FM** *020 †18
BERDIA, Vijay Chand. PO BOX 428 27545 #495-83-1960 L1977 **FM** *071
BUTLER, Linda Hipp. 742 MCKNIGHT DR, ADOLESCENT CENTER 27545 #036-01-1991 L1995
   PD *020 †55
COMBS, Jason Todd. ■ 27545 #051-07-2000 L2007 **IM** *020 †20
FOWLER, Amy B. 742 MCKNIGHT DR, ADOLESCENT CENTER 27545 #036-01-1994 L1997
   GPM *020 †70,55
FRANKLIN, Earl Ruffin. 742 MCKNIGHT DR, ADOLESCENT CENTER 27545 #036-01-1973 L1975
   PD *020 †55
KUBICKI, Steven Paul. 742 MCKNIGHT DR, ADOLESCENT CENTER 27545 #010-01-1984 L1990
   PD *020 †55
NIGALYE, Rajendra L. 111 N 1ST AVE 27545 #495-34-1982 L1989 **IM IMG** *020 †20
PHADKE, Madhav Vishnu. 111 S 1ST AVE, KNIGHTDALE MEDICAL CENTER 27545
   #495-20-1962 L1992 **GS ON** *020 †85
PHADKE, Usha Madhav. 111 S 1ST AVE, KNIGHTDALE MEDICAL CENTER 27545
   #495-34-1965 L1992 **FM** *020
PICCINI, Megan Cornwall. 742 MCKNIGHT DR, ADOLESCENT CENTER 27545
   #036-06-2002 L2005 **PD ADP** *071 †75
PITA, James L, Jr. 1032 TARFORD PL 27545 #025-07-1983 L1987 **EM** *020 †16
RULE, Carolee Ann. 742 MCKNIGHT DR, ADOLESCENT CENTER 27545 #016-06-1994 L1999
   PD *020 †55
RYAN, Jeffrey Charles. 742 MCKNIGHT DR, ADOLESCENT CENTER 27545 #038-43-1994 L1997
   PD *020 †55

KURE BEACH – NEW HANOVER

DIPERSIO, Deborah Ann. PO BOX 763 28449 #036-05-1990 L1994 **RNR DR** *020 †80
MARGOLIS, Ethel Brown. ■ 28449 #024-05-1963 L1964 **PD** *071 †55

WIEBE, Richard Herbert. ■ 28449 #068-01-1962 L1982 **OBG REN** *030 †30

LA GRANGE – LENOIR

BEAN, Cory Duane. 114 E RAILROAD ST 28551 #001-02-2000 L2002 **PD** *020 †55
GRIFFIN, Christopher P. 114 E RAILROAD ST 28551 #010-03-1996 L1998 **PD** *020 †55
HAYNES, Carl Lewis, Jr. 101 S CAREY ST 28551 #036-01-1980 L1981 **EM** *020 †18
LARSON, Michele Cherry. 114 E RAILROAD ST 28551 #036-01-1991 L1993 **PD** *020 †55
MAC DONALD, Katherine T. 114 E RAILROAD ST 28551 #036-08-2002 L2006 **PD** *020 †55
NICKENS, Larry Cobb. 114 E RAILROAD ST 28551 #036-01-1981 L1984 **PD** *020 †55
PONZI, Joseph Wm. 114 E RAILROAD ST 28551 #035-08-1973 L1979 **PD** *020 †55
SCHOSSER, Erika Marie. 114 E RAILROAD ST 28551 #020-12-2000 L2005 **PD** *020 †55
TAYLOE, David Thos, Jr. 114 E RAILROAD ST 28551 #036-01-1974 L1976 **PD** *020 †55
YEH, Siegfried Changrong. 114 E RAILROAD ST 28551 #020-12-1994 L1997 **PD** *020 †55
ZIEMER, Carey Michael. 114 E RAILROAD ST 28551 #012-05-1983 L1984 **PD FM** *020 †55,18

LAKE LURE – RUTHERFORD

BURCH, William H. 2556 MEMORIAL HWY 28746 #038-06-1950 L1953 **FM GP** *020
PITTMAN, Hugh Donald. ■ 28746 #038-40-1957 L1957 **OBG** *071 †30

LAKE TOXAWAY – TRANSYLVANIA

BROWN, John Pitts, Jr. ■ 28747 #045-01-1962 L1966 **IM** *071
BUEHLER, James Raymond. 16825 ROSMAN HWY, TOXAWAY HEALTH CENTER 28747
   #038-43-1978 L2002 **FM FPG** *020 †18
DOYLE, Richard Stewart. ■ 28747 #047-06-1954 L1954 **GS TS** *071 †85,90
NORAN, William Harold. ■ 28747 #026-04-1968 L1991 **N** *071 †75

LAKE WACCAMAW – COLUMBUS

BLANKS, Deidra Arelene. ■ 28450 #036-08-2004 L2006 **OTO** *012

LANSING – ASHE

CLAY, Henry Tucker, Jr. 138 N FORK NEW RIVER RD 28643 #012-01-1987 L1990 **FM** *020
HAUPT, Ronald Anthony. ■ 28643 #005-12-1962 L1981 **EM** *071 †18
KNAPP, Stanley Charles. 500 ROOSTER RIDGE RD 28643 #005-12-1962 L1963
   GPM OM *071 †70
PATTERSON, Joseph F, Jr. ■ 28643 #024-01-1942 L1942 **AN GS** *071 †85,05
WALLACE, Kelley, Jr. ■ 28643 #036-01-1963 L1963 **PS GS** *071 †85,65

LAUREL HILL – SCOTLAND

FUCHS, Paul Daniel. 9241 MORGAN ST, LAUREL HILL FAMILY MED 28351 #045-01-1977 L1997
   FM FPG *020 †18 ‡

LAUREL SPRINGS – ALLEGHANY

DU SOLD, Jacqueline K. ■ 28644 #016-43-1959 L1977 **GP PD** *071
DU SOLD, William David. ■ 28644 #016-43-1959 L1977 **GS** *071 †85
GASKIN, Lewis James. ■ 28644 #012-05-1958 L1961 **AN** *071

LAURINBURG – SCOTLAND

AZEEM, Amir. 422 S KING ST, SCOTLAND MED CENTER 28352 #704-02-2000 L2006
   IM *100 †20
BALL, Frank Jervey, Jr. 601 E LAUCHWOOD DR 28352 #045-01-1976 L1981 **IM** *020 †20
BETHEL, Bradley Hutch. 601 E LAUCHWOOD DR 28352 #649-14-1981 L1989 **IM** *020
BLOCK, Matthew. 1601B MEDICAL DR 28352 #035-19-1990 L2001 **CD** *020 †20
BOTWRIGHT, Gene Robt, Jr. 500 E LAUCHWOOD DR, BOX 800 28352 #036-08-1990 L1996
   FM *020 †18
BROOKS, Michael Lee. 500 E LAUCHWOOD DR, BOX 800 28352 #036-05-1979 L1985
   IM EM *020
BURKE, Joseph A. 500 E LAUCHWOOD DR BOX 800 28352 #010-02-1964 L1982
   R NM *062 †55
BYRD, Jeffrey Keith. 418 S KING ST 28352 #036-08-2002 L2005 **PD** *020 †55
CARTER, Ralph Edward, III. 500 E LAUCHWOOD DR BOX 800 28352 #036-05-1980 L1982
   ORS *020 †40
COLLINS, Amie Noelle. 500 E LAUCHWOOD DR, CABELL EMERGENCY PHYSICIAN 28352
   #011-02-2000 L2007 **EM** *020
CURRIN, James Mitchell, Jr. 515 E LAUCHWOOD DR 28352 #036-05-1977 L1977 **FM** *020 †18
DIER, Gary Lawrence. 500 E LAUCHWOOD DR, RADIOLOGY DEPARTMENT 28352
   #023-01-1981 L2003 **DR IM** *020 †20,80 ‡
DILLINGHAM, Wm Stephen. 1224 BIGGS ST, CENTER 28352 #036-07-1966 L1966
   P ADP *071 †75
DOCKERY, Martina Lynett. 500 E LAUCHWOOD DR, WAGRAM FAMILY PRACTICE 28352
   #041-09-1997 L1998 **FM** *020 †18
FAKADEJ, Anna Frances. 514 S MAIN ST 28352 #055-01-1991 L1997 **OPH** *020 †35
FAULKENBERRY, Bradford K. 1707 BERWICK DR STE A 28352 #045-01-1981 L1988
   FM *020 †18
FISHER, Aikya Somea. 500 E LAUCHWOOD DR, SCOTLAND MEMORIAL HOSPITAL 28352
   #011-02-1996 L2000 **AN** *020
FISHER, George Walton, Jr. 2200 ELM AVE 28352 #036-05-1943 L1943 **OPH** *071 †35
FOLLETT, Joseph Vincent. 500 E LAUCHWOOD DR, LAFAYETTE CLINIC PA 28352
   #060-01-1981 L2001 **AI IM** *020 †20,03
FRENCH, Thomas Nash. ■ 28352 #036-01-1966 L1966 **U** *020 †95

GASPER, Jonathan Leekapua. 500 E LAUCHWOOD DR, SCOTLAND MEMORIAL HOSPITAL 28352 #014-01-1995 L1996 **FM** *020 †18

GREIMEL, Deborah White. 1708 US HIGHWAY 401 S 28352 #051-07-1996 L1997 **IM** *020 †20

GYVES, John Wm. 503 E LAUCHWOOD DR, LAURINBURG CANCER CENTER, 28352 #056-06-1977 L1993 **HO** *020 †20

HARRIS, Glenn Ray. 1707 BERWICK DR STE B 28352 #036-01-1990 L1993 **FM** *020 †18

HARRIS-HICKS, Janet Eliza. 105 MCALPINE LN 28352 #036-01-2000 L2004 **OBG** *020

HELMS, Ernest Little, III. 500 E LAUCHWOOD DR, SCOTLAND CANCER TRTMNT CTR 28352 #045-01-1986 L2003 **RO** *020 †80

HENLEY, Thomas Franklin. ■ 28352 #024-01-1938 L1947 **P** *071 †55,75

HOWARD, Tharon Currin. 418 S KING ST 28352 #036-08-1991 L1994 **PD** *020 †55

HOWELL, David Alexander. 500 E LAUCHWOOD DR, BOX 800 28352 #045-01-1982 L1983 **FM** *020 †18

IFTIKHAR, Shaukat. ■ 28352 #704-02-1989 L2000 **GE IM** *020 †20

IQBAL, Muhammad Jawad. 422 S KING ST, SCOTLAND MEDICAL CENTER 28352 #704-01-1995 L2003 **CCM** *020 †20

KARAMALEGOS, Antonios Z. 103B MCALPINE LN 28352 #025-12-1983 L1988 **U** *095

KOHN, Harvey David. 505 E LAUCHWOOD DR 28352 #065-01-1972 L1993 **OBG** *020

LAKE, Michael Thomas. 500 E LAUCHWOOD DR 28352 #036-08-1998 L2006 **GS** *020 †85

LANUTI, Stephen L. 1600 MEDICAL DR 28352 #654-01-1989 L1996 **GS GE** *020 †85

LAVIGNE, Mark Kino. 1705 BERWICK DR STE B 28352 #036-08-1990 L1994 **OTO** *020 †45

LAWAL, Olujide Gbolahan. 1705 BERWICK DR STE A 28352 #690-02-1987 L2000 **CD IM** *020 †20

LEE, Esther Joo. 1709 BERWICK DR STE A, SCOTLAND DERMATOLOGY, PA 28352 #036-01-1991 L1992 **D IM** *020 †15

LESLIE-BROWN, Heather F. 105 MCALPINE LN, CAROLINAS WOMEN'S CENTER, 28352 #041-13-1995 L2005 **OBG** *020 †30

LIAO, Fu-Che. 500 E LAUCHWOOD DR BOX 800 28352 #385-02-1960 L1974 **OTO** *020 †45

LOCKLEAR, Jennifer Picken. 700A PROGRESS PL 28352 #036-08-2004 L2005 **FM** *020 †18

MABRY, Frederick H, Jr. 418 S KING ST 28352 #036-01-1977 L1977 **PD** *020 †55

MAHON, John Karl. 704A PROGRESS PL 28352 #041-14-1972 L2002 **N** *020 †75 ‡

MASILELA, Aubrey Monde. 500 E LAUCHWOOD DR, BOX 800 28352 #577-01-1976 L1991 **EM IM** *020 †20,16

MC ARN, Hugh M. 422 S KING ST 28352 #036-07-1953 L1953 **FM** *071 †18

MC CASKILL, Lloyd Curtis. 500 E LAUCHWOOD DR, BOX 800 28352 #036-01-1955 L1955 **GP** *020

MC CUTCHEN, William, III. 500 E LAUCHWOOD DR, SCOTLAND MEMORIAL HOSPITAL 28352 #028-78-2000, ▲ L2005 **AN APM** *020

MC GUIRT, Wyman Thomas. 1705 BERWICK DR STE B 28352 #036-05-1996 L2002 **OTO** *020 †45

MC QUEEN, James Aubrey. 418 S KING ST, THE PURCELL CLINIC, P.A. 28352 #036-01-1970 L1970 **PD** *020 †55

MITCHELL-FRYE, Linda Kay. 105 MCALPINE LN 28352 #036-01-1989 L1990 **OBG** *020 †30

MOORE, Jeffrey Alan. 601 E LAUCHWOOD DR # 1889 28352 #055-01-1982 L1987 **IM PUD** *020 †20

MOSES, Timothy Alan. 521 E LAUCHWOOD DR 28352 #028-34-1986 L1995 **U** *095

NAVAID, Musharraf. 422 S KING ST 28352 #704-02-1991 L1998 **ON** *020 †20

NEAL, John Wm. 500 E LAUCHWOOD DR, BOX 800 28352 #036-07-1956 L1956 **GP OS** *020

NEAL, John Wm, IV. 519 E LAUCHWOOD DR 28352 #036-07-1976 L1977 **FM EM** *020 †18

NEDEROSTEK, Douglas Frank. ■ 28352 #042-02-1996 L1999 **EM** *020 †16

NISBETT, Donald A. 616 ATKINSON ST 28352 #035-46-1979 L1982 **FM** *020 †18

O'DONNELL, Michael P. 418 S KING ST 28352 #045-01-1997 L2000 **PD** *020 †55

PURCELL, William Robt. 418 S KING ST 28352 #036-01-1956 L1956 **PD** *020 †55

RAHMATHULLA NOORMOHIDEEN, ■ 28352 #495-95-1995 L2002 **IM** *020 †20

RAYBON, Kelvin Blaine. 500 E LAUCHWOOD DR, SCOTLAND CANCER TREATMENT 28352 #021-01-1989 L2007 **HO IM** *020 †20

REESE, Martha Katherine. ■ 28352 #023-07-1935 L1947 **CHP P** *071 †55

RICHARDSON, Donna M. 500 E LAUCHWOOD DR, SCOTLAND MEMORIAL HOSP 28352 #020-02-1978 L1983 **PTH** *020 †50

RUSH, Paul Fletcher. 1604 MEDICAL DR 28352 #045-04-1982 L1983 **ORS** *071 †40

RUSSELL, A Yvonne Hillier. ■ 28352 #016-02-1958 L1960 **PD ADL** *071 †55

SHEARER, James Eugene. 500 E LAUCHWOOD DR, BOX 800 28352 #045-01-1984 L1989 **DR** *030 †80

SMID, John Andre. 1604 MEDICAL DR, SCOTLAND ORTHOPEDICS, PA 28352 #016-11-1991 L1996 **ORS** *020 †40

SMITHWICK, James David. 418 S KING ST 28352 #036-01-1970 L1970 **PD** *020 †55

STATEN, James Richard. 500 E LAUCHWOOD DR, SCOTLAND MEMORIAL HOSPITAL 28352 #048-12-1985 L2004 **OM** *020 †70

TATUM, Ben Sullivan. ■ 28352 #045-01-1959 L1960 **GYN** *071 †30

WILLIAMS, David Armon. ■ 28352 #036-01-1957 L1957 **FM** *020 †18

WOMBLE, Edwin Cornelius. ■ 28352 #045-01-1942 L1942 **GP OS** *071

LAWNDALE – CLEVELAND

CASH, Ted Freemon. 5009 FALLSTON RD, CENTER 28090 #036-08-1985 L1988 **FM EM** *020 †18

CLONINGER, Kenneth Kyle. 5009 FALLSTON RD, CENTER 28090 #036-08-1984 L1995 **FM** *020 †18

LEICESTER – BUNCOMBE

DVORETZ, David Abraham. ■ 28748 #869-05-1937 **GP** *071

HILL, Katherine Terrell. ■ 28748 #055-75-2007, ▲ *012

ROBERTS, Virginia S. ■ 28748 #020-02-1966 L1976 **ADM GP** *020

LELAND – BRUNSWICK

ALATAR, Kira M. 110A VILLAGE RD NE 28451 #012-22-1994 L1998 **FM** *020 †18 ‡

AUSTRIA, Maria Lourdes C. 509 OLDE WATERFORD WAY, STE 203 28451 #748-10-1988 L2001 **PD** *020 †55

BATISH, Sanjay. 101 BALDWIN DR 28451 #038-44-1994 L1998 **FM** *020 †18

MORGAN, Alan Lee. 509 OLDE WATERFORD WAY, STE 201 28451 #036-01-1996 L1999 **IM** *020 †20

MOUGH, Rhonda Bloom. ■ 28451 #041-12-2001 L2007 *020 †20

POLE, Samuel Boyce, III. ■ 28451 #010-01-1943 L1977 **OPH** *071 †35

RICKMAN, Christopher Edwa. ■ 28451 #047-06-2007 **OBG** *012

RIPPY, William D. ■ 28451 #036-07-1950 L1951 **GP** *071

SIUTA, Jonathan R. 117H VILLAGE RD NE, WILMINGTON HEALTH ASSOCIAT 28451 #035-06-2002 L2004 **MPD** *020 †55

TOLER, Richard Lee. ■ 28451 #055-75-2006, ▲ **OBG** *012

UPCHURCH, Tania Fitzgeral. ■ 28451 #036-01-2003 *100

VREELAND, Gloria Ruth S. 117H VILLAGE RD NE 28451 #005-15-1979 L2004 **FM OBG** *020 †18

LENOIR – CALDWELL

ABERNETHY, David Lee. 308 MULBERRY ST SW 28645 #036-05-1976 L1976 **FM OS** *020

BAST, Randal Paul. 401 MULBERRY ST SW, CALDWELL SURGICAL ASSOCS 28645 #036-01-1993 L1998 **GS** *020 †85

BAUER, Michael Brian. 322 MULBERRY ST SW, STE B 28645 #020-02-1990 L1999 **U** *020 †95

BELK, Robert Saml. 322 MULBERRY ST SW, THOMPSON MEDICAL SPEC PA 28645 #045-01-1969 L1973 **CD IM** *075 †20

BENITEZ, Gary Tagniam. 1766 CONNELLY SPRINGS RD, CALDWELL FAMILY PHYSICIANS 28645 #748-01-1979 L1995 **FM** *020 †18

BONET, Mayra Ivonne. 321 MULBERRY ST SW, CALDWELL MEMORIAL HOSP 28645 #042-03-1994 L1996 **AN** *020

BOWEN, John Henry. 321 MULBERRY ST SW 28645 #036-01-1980 L1982 **FM** *020 †18

BRAILEY, Ellores E. 3110 WINTER HAWK LN 28645 #010-03-1980 L1983 **OBG** *020

BRANT, Andrew Robertson. 321 MULBERRY ST SW 28645 #036-05-1997 L1999 **PTH** *020 †50

BURBRIDGE, Geoffrey Ralph. 322 MULBERRY ST SW, STE A 28645 #041-02-1977 L2001 **IM** *020 †20

CARPENTER, Kenneth C. ■ 28645 #036-05-1947 L1948 **FM** *071

CARSWELL, Jane Triplett. 401 MULBERRY ST SW BX 960 28645 #051-04-1958 L1961 **FM** *071 †18

CLAPP, Christopher R. 3431 MORGANTON BLVD SW 28645 #036-05-1994 L1996 **PD** *020 †55

CRUTCHER, Kenneth Lloyd. 321 MULBERRY ST SW 28645 #036-07-1984 L1985 **FM EM** *020 †18

DACUS, Robert Mabry, IV. 348 HARPER AVE NW, WOMENS CARE SPECIALISTS 28645 #036-01-1991 L1995 **OBG** *020 †30

DARSIE, James Leigh. 401 MULBERRY ST SW, # 11 28645 #048-04-1966 L1968 **OTO** *020 †45

DILL, David Lee. 321 MULBERRY ST SW 28645 #012-01-1972 L1976 **DR NM** *020 †80

DODDS, Terry C. 401 MULBERRY ST SW, STE 202 28645 #011-04-1980 L1987 **PD** *020 †55

DRAVLAND, Jonas Eric. 401 MULBERRY ST SW, MULBERRY PEDIATRICS 28645 #060-02-1986 L1993 **PD** *020 †55

DUBOW, Ronald H. 2651 MORGANTON BLVD SW 28645 #033-05-1978 L2006 **MPD IMG** *020 †20,55 ‡

EVANS, David James. 222 MORGANTON BLVD SW 28645 #010-01-1988 L2005 **OBG** *020 †30

FENG, Changjian. 321 MULBERRY ST SW, DEPT ANESTH CALDWELL HOSP 28645 #243-52-1980 L2004 **AN PME** *100

FORNASIER, Frank Peter. 2651 MORGANTON BLVD SW, A DIV OF CALDWELL MED HOSP 28645 #065-09-1989 L1990 **FM GP** *020

GABRIEL, Zizette Moheb. 321 MULBERRY ST SW, CALDWELL MEMORIAL HOSPITAL 28645 #915-03-1989 L2004 **AN PME** *05

GOLLMAN, Daniel Bernard. 429 HIGHLAND AVE SW 28645 #016-42-1978 L1988 **AN** *020 †05

GOUDAS, Leonidas A. 401 MULBERRY ST SW STE 101 28645 #032-01-1997 L2003 **GS** *020 †85

GOULD, George. 1901 CONNELLY SPRINGS RD 28645 #561-01-1978 L1999 **FM** *020 †18

GRIFFIN, Joseph Laird. 233 MAIN ST SW 28645 #012-01-1972 L1978 **OBG ID** *020 †30

GRIFFIN, Richard Madison. 2060 HICKORY BLVD SW 28645 #012-05-1959 L1960 **OPH** *071 †35

GUERRA, Marc Francis. 321 MULBERRY ST SW 28645 #036-06-1980 L1983 **FM** *020 †18

HAGGERTY, Phillip John, II. 1085 CEDAR HILLS CT SE 28645 #001-02-1996 L2000 **AN** *020

HAIRFIELD, Theo Vincent. 321 MULBERRY ST SW 28645 #036-05-1954 L1954 **GP** *071

HAMILTON-BRANDON, L. 2651 MORGANTON BLVD SW, WESTPOINTE MEDICAL PRACTIC 28645 #036-08-1994 L1996 **FM** *020 †18

HARRIS, William Rix. 2060 HICKORY BLVD SW 28645 #036-01-1956 L1956 **OPH** *071 †35

HAYNES, Gregory Delano. 401 MULBERRY ST SW, STE 206 28645 #026-04-1981 L2008 **GE IM** *020 †20

HERMAN, Dennice Hickman. 1731 CONNELLY SPRINGS RD 28645 #036-08-1986 L1988 **EM FM** *020 †18

HO, Peter Chun-Kit. 322 MULBERRY ST SW, STE B 28645 #035-19-1976 L1994 **U** *020 †95

HUGHES, Jack David. 322 MULBERRY ST SW 28645 #038-41-1965 L1990 **PUD IM** *020 †20

KEVERLINE, Jeffrey Paul. 1041 MORGANTON BLVD SW, STE 200 28645 #041-13-1995 L2000 **ORS** *020 †40

KUNKLE, Andra Godsoe. 401 MULBERRY ST SW 28645 #048-02-1989 L1993 **PD** *020 †55

KUZMYK, Susan M. 1766 CONNELLY SPRINGS RD 28645 #065-10-1988 L1995 **FM** *020

LEWIS, Newman M, Jr. 212 MULBERRY ST SW 28645 #036-08-1984 L1987 **FM** *020 †18

LILJEBERG, Robert Louis. 1041 MORGANTON BLVD SW, STE 200 28645 #021-05-1988 L1994 **ORS OSM** *020 †40

LONGAS, Philip Lee. 321 MULBERRY ST SW 28645 #047-20-1995 L2006 **IM** *020 †20

LOWRY, David Alan. 321 MULBERRY ST SW 28645 #047-05-1988 L1996 **IM CCM** *020 †20

MAC GUIRE, Osborne Rainer. 321 MULBERRY ST SW 28645 #021-01-1974 L1977 **EM FM** *020 †16,70

MAGGIORE, John Richard. 212 MULBERRY ST SW 28645 #030-05-1969 L1999 **FM** *020 †18

MATHIS, William F. 321 MULBERRY ST SW 28645 #047-06-1977 L1987 **FM OS** *020 †18 ‡

MC CLINTON, Diana C. 321 MULBERRY ST SW, CALDWELL MEMORIAL HOSPITAL 28645 #023-01-1995 L2000 **EM PEM** *020 †55,16

MC CORMICK, John Thomas. 1041 MORGANTON BLVD SW, STE 200 28645 #012-05-1974 L1975 **ORS** *020 †40

MC NEILL, Donald D, Jr. 321 MULBERRY ST SW, CALDWELL MEMORIAL HOSPITAL 28645 #036-01-1965 L1965 **PTH FOP** *020 †50

METZGER, George Andrew. 321 MULBERRY ST SW 28645 #023-01-1972 L1977 **IM NEP** *020 †20

MORGAN, Nancy Elaine. 321 MULBERRY ST SW 28645 #038-40-1979 L1981 **FM** *020 †18

NICHOLS, George L, Jr. 321 MULBERRY ST SW 28645 #036-05-1993 L1994 **PTH** *020 †50

PEZZI, Thomas Andrew. 401 MULBERRY ST SW, STE 200 28645 #041-13-1991 L2000 **GS** *020 †85

PICTON, John Mark. 1966 MORGANTON BLVD SW # B, CALDWELL CO. HEALTH DEPART 28645 #036-08-1987 L1990 **OBG** *020 †30

POWELL, John David. 1731 CONNELLY SPRINGS RD 28645 #012-01-1993 L1996 **FM** *020 †18

■ = Address Information Privacy Protected

PURCELL, Valerie Doggett. ■ 28645 #036-08-1988 L1997 **FM** *071 †18
RAY, Thomas More. 902 KIRKWOOD AVE NW 28645 #051-04-1991 L1995 **PM** *020 †60
ROACH, Robert B. 401 MULBERRY ST SW 28645 #041-13-1943 L1943 **GS** *071
ROGERS, Robert Lee, Jr. 308 MULBERRY ST SW, GRIFFIN J LAIRD MD 28645
#012-01-1957 L1963 **OBG** *071
ROSARIO, Jorge E. 321 MULBERRY ST SW 28645 #042-02-1999 L2002 **IM** *020
SCHEIL, Charles Philip. 401 MULBERRY ST SW, STE 206 28645 #036-07-1958 L1958
FM *071 †18
SCHMIDT, Jay John. 2310 HICKORY BLVD SW, STE B 28645 #020-02-1980 L1993 **IM** *020 †20
SCOTT, Stephen Carlisle. ■ 28645 #051-04-1982 L1985 **PUD CCM** *062 †20
SCROGGIN, John B. 115 PRESTWOOD DR SE 28645 #048-02-1960 L1961 **GP A** *071
SHULL, Lonnie Newell, Jr. 401 MULBERRY ST SW STE 101, POST OFFICE BOX 1648 28645
#045-01-1969 L1974 **GS OS** *020 †85
SOWELL, James Richard. 321 MULBERRY ST SW, CALDWELL MEMORIAL HOSPITAL 28645
#045-04-1981 L1997 **EM** *020
STALHEIM, Rodney Martin. 322 MULBERRY ST SW 28645 #045-01-1971 L1979 **CD IM** *020 †20
STANISLAW, James Edward. 1041 MORGANTON BLVD SW 28645 #008-01-1991 L1996
ORS *020 †40
STRAWN, Marjorie Oakes. ■ 28645 #041-07-1952 L1955 **PHP** *071
THOMPSON, James Roy. 212 MULBERRY ST SW 28645 #045-01-1977 L1992 **FM** *020 †18
TILLEY, Paul Donald. 1501 NORWOOD ST SW STE C 28645 #036-05-1959 L1959 **GP** *071
TYE, John Garold. 2060 HICKORY BLVD SW 28645 #038-41-1979 L1980 **OPH** *020 †35
VONGKOVIT, Piyapong. 401 MULBERRY ST SW, STE 210 28645 #891-04-1987 L1993
HO *020 †20
VU, Jenette Thu. 1731 CONNELLY SPRINGS RD 28645 #038-44-1994 L1997 **IM** *020 †20
WALTON, Carey James. ■ 28645 #036-05-1955 L1955 **IM** *072
YAEGER, Theodore E, Jr. 321 MULBERRY ST SW 28645 #041-09-1981 L2006 **RO NR** *020 †80 ‡

LEWISTON — BERTIE

ALEXANDER, James C, Jr. 3539 GOVERNORS RD, PERDUE FARMS WELLNESS CENT 27849
#023-12-1980 L1981 **FM OM** *020 †70,18

LEWISVILLE — FORSYTH

ANGELL, Daune D. 1020 HAUSER RD 27023 #020-12-1984 L1985 **EM** *020 †16
BAIRD, Kelly Wallace. ■ 27023 #036-05-2005 **AN** *012
BARHAM, Kelly Lynne. ■ 27023 #036-05-2003 L2007 **D** *020 †15
BEERMAN, Paul Jay. 5011 HIDDEN LAKE TRL 27023 #023-07-1975 L1975 **R** *020 †80
BUTLER, Radford N. ■ 27023 #036-05-1950 L1950 **IM** *071
CRAIG, Margaret Louise. SONATA DR 27023 #036-01-1965 L1965 **P CHP** *020
DANIEL, Rebecca Woods. ■ 27023 #036-05-2002 **AN** *012
GARLAND, Wesley Scott. ■ 27023 #024-05-1955 L1960 **OM** *071
GETZ, Lawrence G, Jr. ■ 27023 #021-01-1967 L1969 **TRS GS** *071 †85
HAMPTON, James H, Jr. 6750 SHALLOWFORD RD 27023 #036-05-1952 L1952 **FM GP** *071 †18
HANES, Holly Crain. ■ 27023 #036-05-2005 **PD** *012
HESS, Terry Douglas. 1225 LEWISVILLE CLEMMNS RD, FAMILY MEDICAL ASSOCS 27023
#051-01-1987 L1991 **FM** *020 †18
HUNSINGER, Edward Neal. ■ 27023 #011-03-1976 L1995 **FM MDM** *020 †18
KANE, Peter V. ■ 27023 #025-07-1950 L1951 **GP GS** *071 †85
KNOVICH, Mary Ann. 365 FOX RIDGE CIR 27023 #041-14-1996 L1998 **HEM IM** *020 †20 ‡
LEE, David Ethan. 1225 LEWISVILLE CLEMMNS RD 27023 #036-05-2003 L2006 **FM** *020 †18
LIS, Kimberly Jean. 1225 LEWISVILLE CLEMMNS RD, FAMILY MEDICAL ASSOC 27023
#051-01-2002 L2005 **FM** *020 †18
MOLERO, Mariela Minerva. ■ 27023 #935-03-1990 L2004 **IM** *020 †20
MOORE, Franklin Robert. ■ 27023 #025-07-2001 **PTH** *012
PAULEY, Alicia Denise. 1225 LEWISVILLE CLEMMNS RD 27023 #055-02-1994 L1995
FM *020 †18
REID, Stephanie Theros. ■ 27023 #036-05-1982 L1984 **AN** *040 †05
SCHWARTZ, Joshua Zachary. ■ 27023 #036-05-2003 **FM** *100
SCHWARTZ, Melanie D. ■ 27023 #036-05-2004 **OBG** *012
SUMMER, Garry Michael. 6614 SHALLOWFORD RD, LEWISVILLE FAMILY PHYSICIA 27023
#036-08-1995 L2002 **FM** *020 †18
TALEVI, Carolina Ogm. ■ 27023 #836-01-1989 **FM** *100
TAYLOR, Richard Calvert. ■ 27023 #036-07-2001 **PTH** *012
WILLIAMS, William Cameron. 1225 LEWISVILLE CLEMMNS RD 27023 #016-06-1984 L1985
FM *020 †18
YANG, Qing. ■ 27023 #243-94-1983 L2006 **NPM** *100 †55
YEBOAH, Joseph. ■ 27023 #412-01-1999 L2005 **CCM** *012 †20

LEXINGTON — DAVIDSON

ADAMS, Donald Glenn. 101 W MEDICAL PARK DR 27292 #036-05-1980 L2005 **FM** *020 †18
ALLEN, Martin A. 250 HOSPITAL DR 27292 #020-12-1986 L1993 **OBG** *020 †30
APPLEGATE, Michael Dale. 100 HOSPITAL DR 27292 #036-01-1995 L1997 **N** *020 †75
ARNOLD, Terry Vincent. 901 E CENTER ST, MAILING: P O BOX 1946 27292 #038-40-1973 L1978
IM FM *020 †20
AZAR, George Anis. 510 EMERGENCY DR 27292 #024-16-2002 L2006 **ORS** *020
BARDOU, Mark Wm. 250 HOSPITAL DR 27292 #036-05-1976 L1984 **EM FM** *020 †18,16
BAZEL, Sohail. 105 HOSPITAL DR 27292 #704-01-1983 L1996 **IM** *020 †20
BLACK, James Franklin. 106 W MEDICAL PARK DR # B 27292 #036-01-1975 L1976
OBG *020 †30
BLACKERBY, Wm Carroll. ■ 27295 #036-05-1975 L1975 **EM FM** *020 †18 ‡
BOLSTAD, Karl Edward. 510 EMERGENCY DR 27292 #025-01-1972 L1979 **ORS** *020 †40
BOYLE, Daniel P. 208 W CENTER ST, STE B 27292 #043-01-1993 L2001 **DR** *020 †80
BRIGGS, Gerald Paul. ■ 27292 #065-05-1968 L1968 **GP** *071
BROWN, Melanie Anne. 2827 SHORELINE DR 27292 #012-01-2000 L2002 **AN** *100
BURKE, James Otis, Jr. 8 MEDICAL PARK DR 27292 #036-01-1965 L1965 **PD** *020 †55
CABRAL, Deborah Barbara. 250 HOSPITAL DR 27292 #035-06-1980 L2003 **FM** *020 †18
CARROLL, Tiffeny Annette. 250 HOSPITAL DR 27292 #012-01-2000 L2004 **OBG** *020
COLLINS, Timothy Scott. 1370 PIEDMONT DR, STE 202 27295 #023-07-1994 L1997
HO *020 †20

COOPER, Debra Lyn. 250 HOSPITAL DR, LEXINGTON MEM HOSP EMER DP 27292
#017-20-2002 L2004 **EM** *020
CRUMP, Carolyn Faydene. ■ 27292 #010-01-1976 L2007 **DR FM** *020
CULLOM, Joseph Wm. 10 MEDICAL PARK DR, STE 4 27292 #045-01-1973 L1984
GS VS *020 †85
DE SANTIS, Donald. 10 MEDICAL PARK DR, STE 4 27292 #035-09-1962 L2002 **GS OS** *020 †85
DIXON, Dirk Stancill. ■ 27292 #036-05-1965 L1965 **DR** *072 †80
FLYNN, Charles Lanier. 429 ASHMOOR LN 27295 #036-05-1985 L1992 **IM** *020 †20
GARVIN, Tarsha Valencia. 250 HOSPITAL DR 27292 #036-08-1997 L2005 **APM** *020
GREEN, James Judd, Jr. 208 W CENTER ST, STE B 27292 #036-01-1993 L1998 **DR** *020 †80
HAMPTON, Curtis Tonyray. ■ 27292 #020-12-2003 L2006 **NPM** *012 †55
HARRIS, Samuel Ranchor. 7 MEDICAL PARK DR 27292 #036-01-1968 L1968 **OBG** *020 †30
HAWKINS, Thomas Ashley. 2 HOSPITAL DR 27292 #045-01-1995 L2002 **OPH** *020 †35
HILL, Keith Daniel. ■ 27295 #036-05-1985 *012
HINSON, Jonathan Cordell. 110 W MEDICAL PARK DR 27292 #036-05-1990 L1993 **FM** *020 †18
HSIEH, Stephen Szuheng. 104 W MEDICAL PARK DR, HIGH ROCK INTERNAL MEDICIN 27292
#036-05-1995 L1997 **IM** *020 †20
HUGGINS, Michael Bradford. 10 MEDICAL PARK DR, STE 4 27292 #036-01-1981 L1986
GS VS *020 †85
HUGHES, Thomas Patrick. 250 HOSPITAL DR 27292 #021-01-1979 L1984 **GE IM** *020 †20
JOINER, Jancinta. 58 US HIGHWAY 64 W STE C, URGENT CARE 27295 #020-12-1996 L2005
FM *020 †18
KAMMIRE, Gordon Chas. 510 EMERGENCY DR 27292 #036-05-1983 L1985 **ORS** *020 †40
LEWIS, Arch Ritchie. 58 US HIGHWAY 64 W STE C, URGENT CARE 27295 #036-05-1965 L1965
OM PUD *030
LI, Michael Ting. ■ 27292 #243-72-1990 L2006 **IM** *100 †20
LODA, Margaret Amanda. 8 MEDICAL PARK DR, LEXINGTON PEDIATRIC CLINIC 27292
#036-05-2001 L2004 **PD** *100
LOHR, Lloyd Dermot. 7 MEDICAL PARK DR 27292 #036-01-1961 L1961 **OBG** *020 †30
LONG, James Randall. 114 W MEDICAL PARK DR 27292 #036-01-1986 L2004 **IM** *020 †20
LUPRECHT, Geri Lyn. 220 E 1ST AVENUE EXT, DAYMARK RECOVERY SERVICES 27292
#056-06-1982 L1993 **P** *020
MARINO, Baptiste Steven. 250 HOSPITAL DR, LEXINGTON MEMORIAL HOSPITA 27292
#038-43-1986 L1991 **AN** *020 †05
MARKS, Phillip Glenn. 106 W MEDICAL PK DR STE A 27292 #016-42-1983 L1990 **U** *020 †95
MEEKS, Leigh Milam. 8 MEDICAL PARK DR, LEXINGTON PEDIATRICS 27292
#055-02-1995 L2005 **PD** *020 †55
MEYER, Paul F. 102 W MEDICAL PARK DR 27292 #030-05-1978 L1990 **FM** *020 †18
MOCK, David Carlton. 250 HOSPITAL DR 27292 #036-05-1946 L1946 **GP** *071
MOORE, William Henry S. ■ 27295 #010-03-1967 L1968 **GP** *071
MUNGALPARA, Vinod Nagji. 250 HOSPITAL DR, LEXINGTON PAIN CTR 27292
#495-01-1989 L2004 **AN PME** *020
ORMOND, David E. 208 W CENTER ST, STE B 27292 #048-15-1987 L2000 **DR** *020 †80
PETERSEN, Kenneth Michael. 5 MEDICAL PARK DR 27292 #035-08-1974 L1980 **GS** *020 †85
PHILLIPS, Michael Jerome. 106 W MEDICAL PK DR 27292 #021-06-1984 L1989
OTO A *020 †45
REID, James E, Jr. 1266 RUFF LEONARD RD 27295 #036-08-1982 L1987 **AN IM** *020
RESTREPO-ISAZA, Guillermo. 250 HOSPITAL DR 27292 #264-01-1954 L1985 **PTH** *020 †50
RIGGAN, Jasper Simmons. 510 EMERGENCY DR 27292 #036-05-1989 L1991 **ORS** *020 †40
ROWLAND, John Christopher. 8 MEDICAL PARK DR 27292 #019-02-1979 L1995 **PD** *020 †55
ROY, Sudip Kumar. 101 W MEDICAL PARK DR 27292 #028-46-1998 L2002 **FM** *020 †18
ROZANOV, Cheryl Valerie. 220 E 1ST AVE, STE 10 27292 #160-01-1989 L2006 **CHP P** *020 †75
SADLER, Malin Abraham. 101 W MEDICAL PARK DR 27292 #007-02-1992 L2002 **FM** *020 †18
SCARFF, John Edwin, Jr. ■ 27293 #036-05-1963 L1963 **U GS** *020 †85,95
SHAFFER, John Sheridan. 4 MEDICAL PARK DR 27292 #038-06-1974 L1980 **U** *071
SHAH, Deepti Umesh. 1631 COTTON GROVE RD 27292 #036-01-2006 *012
SLYMAN, James Francis. 2 HOSPITAL DR 27292 #036-05-1977 L1981 **OPH EM** *020 †35 ‡
SNIDER, Bobby E. 206 W CENTER ST STE B 27292 #036-05-1953 L1953 **FM OBS** *071
STRADER, Eugene Ray. 250 HOSPITAL DR 27292 #036-05-1956 L1956 **FM** *020 †18
STRADER, Hunter Gordon. 2 CHERRY ST 27292 #036-07-1958 L1958 **FM** *071 †18
SUN, Yun. 105 HOSPITAL DR 27292 #243-38-1988 L1995 **IM** *020 †20
SUNDARARAJAN, S. 102 W MEDICAL PARK DR, LEXINGTN FAM PHYSICIANS PA 27292
#495-04-1986 L1996 **FM** *020 †18
TEAM, Robert Alston. 101 W MEDICAL PARK DR 27292 #036-05-1952 L1952 **GP OS** *020
THOMAS-SLADE, Venezela E. 101 W MEDICAL PARK DR 27292 #036-05-1999 L2002
FM *020 †18
TIMBERLAKE, Robert Edgar. 8 MEDICAL PARK DR 27292 #051-01-1987 L1989 **PD** *020 †55
UHLIN, Stephen Richard. 6 MEDICAL PARK DR 27292 #038-40-1970 L1978 **D IM** *020 †20,15
VAUGHAN, Elizabeth Rankin. 250 HOSPITAL DR 27292 #051-01-1979 L1984 **EM IM** *020 †20,16
WEISER, Mark Robt. 110 W MEDICAL PARK DR 27292 #055-01-1983 L1989 **FM** *020 †18
WELBORN, James T. ■ 27292 #023-01-1948 L1948 **GP** *071
WORTH, Kellye Nichelle. 250 HOSPITAL DR 27292 #036-08-2004 L2007 **EM** *020

LIBERTY — RANDOLPH

GLASCO, Thomas Robt. PO BOX 159 27298 #051-01-1958 L1967 **GP** *071
HAMRICK, Maura Lynn. PO BOX 99, 504 N GREENSBORO ST 27298 #036-01-1997 L1998
FM *020 †18
JAMES, Robert Mitchell. 10046 OLD LIBERTY RD, KARAM FAMILY PRACTICE 27298
#036-08-1987 L1988 **FM** *020 †18
KARAM, Philip Jerome. 10046 OLD LIBERTY RD 27298 #021-05-1979 L1980 **FM EM** *020 †18

LILLINGTON — HARNETT

CASTRO, Maria Cristina. 100 S 10TH ST 27546 #264-19-1996 L2006 **PD** *020 †55
DAVE, Nailesh Dilipkumar. 350 PINE STATE ST 27546 #495-22-1990 L1999 **N** *020 †75
GALBRAITH, Jack. ■ 27546 #065-06-1984 L1990 **GP** *020
KHOUDARY, Kevin Paul. 100 S 10TH ST 27546 #033-06-1991 L1999 **U** *020 †95
MC QUADE, James Stanley. ■ 27546 #918-01-1969 L1973 **AN** *075
REYES, Rodolfo C. 100 S 10TH ST 27546 #748-10-1981 L1996 **FM** *020 †20
REYES, Rodolfo L. 100 S 10TH ST 27546 #748-01-1952 L1990 **PM** *020 †60
SLOAN, Jessica Marie. ■ 27546 #036-01-2008 *012
TORTORA, Frank L. 100 S 10TH ST 27546 #012-05-1977 L1979 **U** *020 †95

UNGER, Henry Alan. 100 S 10TH ST 27546 #047-05-1972 L1976 **U** *020 †95
WAYCASTER, Ronald Lance. 150 PINE STATE ST 27546 #027-01-1993 L1997 **P CHP** *020 †75
WILLIFORD, John K. 900 S 9TH ST 27546 #036-05-1946 L1946 **FM** *072 †18

LINCOLNTON – LINCOLN

ANTLEY, Ray Mills. 200 N GROVE ST 28092 #012-05-1962 L1966 **DR PD** *020 †19,80 ‡
ANTLEY, Ray Mills, Jr. 200 N GROVE ST 28092 #017-20-1988 L1998 **DR** *020 †80
ASWAD, Margo Andrea. 1047 GASTON ST, MAILING: P O BOX 127 28092 #035-09-1989 L1997 **GS VS** *020
BATHULA, Sailatha. 308 S ACADEMY ST 28092 #495-21-1999 L2005 **IM** *020 †20
BENTON, Cammy Renae. 200 GAMBLE DR 28092 #036-08-2000 L2003 **FM** *020 †18
BIAS, Donald Forest, Jr. 1470 E GASTON ST, STE 300 28092 #055-01-1986 L1997 **FM** *020 †18
BUCKLEN, Keith Robert. 206 GAMBLE DR STE C, LINCOLN MEDICAL ARTS BLDG 28092 #041-14-1976 L2005 **GS GE** *020 †85 ‡
CABINUM, Domingo E, Jr. ■ 28092 #748-02-1961 L1981 **ORS** *020
CANADAY, Maurice Lewis. 200 GAMBLE DR 28092 #036-01-1958 L1958 **FM CD** *020 †18
CARLTON, Adam Danl. 747 S LAUREL ST 28092 #005-14-1989 L2004 **OBG** *020 †30
CHANG, John Shyueyi. 112 DOCTORS PARK 28092 #244-01-1971 L1978 **OBG** *020
CHANG, Richard Inki. 900 DONITA DR 28092 #036-05-1997 L2002 **OPH** *020 †35
CLONINGER, Karen Gail. 908 DONITA DR 28092 #036-05-1979 L2000 **CD IM** *020 †20
COVINGTON, Melony K. 853 S LAUREL ST, THE SANGER CLINIC 28092 #045-01-1998 L2004 **CD** *020 †20
CROWELL, Gordon Cameron. ■ 28092 #036-01-1957 L1957 **IM** *071 †20
CRUMLEY, Charles Edwin. 751 S LAUREL ST 28092 #036-01-1970 L1970 **IM** *020 †20
CUCINIELLO, Jodi Noel. 612 CENTER DR 28092 #011-03-2003 L2006 **FM** *020 †18
DIXON, Robert Ross. 108 DOCTORS PARK 28092 #036-05-1968 L1968 **PD** *020 †55
EZIRI, Emeka U Michael. 206 GAMBLE DR STE D 28092 #690-10-1988 L2001 **PCC** *020 †20
FALLS, Claude Thos. 501 N ASPEN ST 28092 #045-01-1979 L1981 **PS** *020 †65,85
FITZGERALD, John H, Jr. 626 CLARK DR 28092 #051-01-1938 L1940 **FM PD** *071
FOTINOS, Peter Nick. 113 DOCTORS PARK 28092 #036-01-2002 L2006 **FM** *020 †18
GAMBLE, John Reeves, Jr. 200 GAMBLE DR 28092 #023-01-1946 L1946 **GP GS** *020
HABASHI, Neveen Maher. 501 N ASPEN ST 28092 #654-01-1983 L1988 **CCM IM** *020 †20
HARRILL, Kiran Cummings. 108 DOCTORS PARK 28092 #051-04-1994 L1994 **PD** *020 †55
HERMANN, James Howard. 2705 QUEENS DR, CONSULTANTS 28092 #005-12-1972 L1973 **EM** *020 †18,16
HINKLE, Robert Linville. ■ 28092 #036-01-1970 L1970 **GPM** *020 †55
HURLEY, Peter Tanner. 1470 E GASTON ST 28092 #038-45-1988 L1992 **OSM** *020 †40
HUSSAIN, Ghulam. 1446 E GASTON ST, LINCOLN MED PARK STE 101 28092 #704-09-1988 L1999 **PD** *020 †55
ISRAEL, Rabindran. 1756 HICKORY SPRINGS LN 28092 #495-16-1964 L1993 **PD ADM** *020 †55
KIEFER, Mark Lewis. 1470 E GASTON ST, LINCOLN COUNTY PLLC 28092 #051-04-1994 L2001 **FM** *020 †18
KLETT, Carrie Christine. 644 CLARK DR, LAKEVIEW OBSTETRICS & GYNE 28092 #051-04-1993 L2005 **OBG** *020 †30
KOCH, Daniel Gregory. 1470 E GASTON ST, STE 600 28092 #007-02-1993 L2004 **FM** *020 †18
LAWING, Daniel Philmon. 200 GAMBLE DR 28092 #036-01-1962 L1962 **GP** *020
LAWING, Karl L. ■ 28092 #021-01-1953 L1953 **GP GS** *075
MC GREGOR, Judith Craig. 200 N GROVE ST 28092 #012-05-1985 L1990 **DR** *020 †80
MIEDEMA, Edward Bruce. 206 GAMBLE DR STE C, 206 GAMBLE DRIVE 28092 #025-01-1975 L2003 **U** *020 †95
MILLSAPS, David Mc Iver. 108 DOCTORS PARK 28092 #036-07-1977 L1979 **PD** *020 †55
MIRANDA, Rafael Angel. 308 S ACADEMY ST, LINCOLN INTERNAL MEDICINE, 28092 #042-01-2002 L2006 **IM** *020
NORCROSS, Jason Patrick. 1470 E GASTON ST 28092 #036-01-2001 L2005 **ORS** *020
OKAFOR, Ifeanyichukwu O. PO BOX 1967 28093 #690-01-1987 L2002 **IM** *020 †20
PERRY, Deborah. 107 N CEDAR ST 28092 #016-11-1996 L1999 **PLM** *020 †18
RADUT, Toma. 308 S ACADEMY ST 28092 #781-06-1976 L1997 **IM** *020 †20
REDMOND, Berniece E. 1460 E GASTON ST 28092 #036-08-1993 L1994 **OBG GPM** *020 †30
REID, R Leary. 614 CENTER DR 28092 #036-05-1954 L1954 **FM** *071 †18
REID, Robert Leary, Jr. 614 CENTER DR 28092 #036-05-1979 L1981 **FM** *020 †18
RIVES, Karenmarie Barbara. 701 S LAUREL ST 28092 #048-04-1984 L1996 **ORS** *020 †40
SABOORTINAT, Mofrad. 113 DOCTORS PARK 28092 #517-01-1966 L1976 **PD** *020 †55
SCHER, Stephen Barry. 105 DAVE WARLICK DR 28092 #025-01-1965 L1992 **FM AI** *075 †18
SCHWANZ, Joan Irene Downe. 614 CENTER DR, LINCOLN FAMILY PRACTICE 28092 #065-06-1976 L1997 **FM MDM** *020 †18
SMITH, Thomas W. 151 SIGMON RD 28092 #035-06-1964 L1976 **IM PUD** *020
SYKES, Paul Wilson. 612 CENTER DR 28092 #012-01-1990 L1993 **FM** *020 †18
TRAN, Raymond. 614 CENTER DR 28092 #017-20-1997 L1999 **FM** *020 †18
UDECHUKWU, Maurice Uchenn. 630 CLARK DR 28092 #690-01-1987 L2004 **IM** *100 †20
VEST, Susan Conger. 1470 E GASTON ST, STE 300 28092 #020-02-1993 L1997 **MPD PD** *020 †55,20
WESTRA, Donald Freeman. 112 DOCTORS PARK, LINCOLN OBSTETRICS & GYNEC 28092 #038-40-1978 L1979 **OBS GYN** *020 †30
WISE, Charlotte Marie. 112 DOCTORS PARK 28092 #016-11-1986 L1991 **OBG** *020 †30

LINDEN – CUMBERLAND

JOHNSON, Niel Anthony. ■ 28356 #023-12-1992 L2006 **FM EM** *030 †18

LINVILLE – AVERY

DAVNE, Albert. ■ 28646 #035-06-1950 L1951 **PS** *071 †65
GOETTMAN, William Ivan. PO BOX 785 28646 #028-02-1958 L1966 **GS** *071 †85
MC GOWAN, Ronald Lee. PO BOX 357, 884 GRASSY CREEK RD 28646 #041-13-1958 L1993 **CD IM** *071 †20 ‡
SPORN, Max. ■ 28646 #016-42-1954 L1972 **IM CD** *071
STHAY, Michael A. ■ 28646 #040-02-1983 L2006 **FM EM** *020 †18
WEEMS, Wade Scott. PO BOX 785 28646 #036-07-1962 L1962 **U** *020 †95
YALE, Jerry David, Jr. 436 HOSPITAL DRIVE, STE 230 28646 #036-01-2004 L2007 **FM** *020

LITTLE SWITZERLAND – MCDOWELL

KING, Stephen Hall. ■ 28749 #012-05-1961 L1968 **PHP IM** *071 †70

LITTLETON – HALIFAX

ANDERSON, John T. ■ 27850 #017-20-1952 L1952 **OS** *050
BURTON, Ashby J, III. 108 MOSBY AVE 27850 #051-07-1982 L1985 **FM** *020 †18
GROSS, Richard Henry. 108 MOSBY AVE, RURAL HEALTH GROUP, INC. 27850 #041-09-1961 L1991 **GP GS** *020 †85 ‡
RUIZ DE VILLA, Amada. 121 RIVERBLUFF RD 27850 #020-12-1979 L1983 **OPH** *020
WEISHAAR, Leo G, Jr. ■ 27850 #035-19-1943 **GP** *071

LOCUST – STANLY

BILLINGSLEY, Andrew Trent. 1010 MAIN ST W 28097 #035-09-1993 L1998 **OPH** *020 †35
VARGAS, Ricardo. 236 MARKET ST, STE 103 28097 #033-05-1996 L1997 **FM** *020 †18

LOUISBURG – FRANKLIN

ALINSONORIN, Cesar F, Jr. 205 SANDALWOOD AVE 27549 #748-02-1995 L2003 **PCC** *100 †20
AL SABBAGH, Ghassan. 626 N BICKETT BLVD 27549 #875-01-1983 L2000 **GE** *020 †20
BLACKBURN, Warren Allen. 205 SANDALWOOD AVE STE C, FRANKLIN FAMILY MEDICINE 27549 #023-12-1982 L1992 **FM** *020 †18
BURGGRAAFF, Barbara Ann. 1501 N BICKETT BLVD, STE C 27549 #018-03-1991 L2005 **OTO** *020 †20
CALDWELL, Chad Dewey. 1501 N BICKETT BLVD, STE A 27549 #041-07-1996 L2007 **GS VS** *020 †85
COLLINS, Nicole Annette. 205 SANDALWOOD AVE, BOX 589 27549 #041-14-1996 L1998 **IM IMG** *020 †20
GALLAND, Mark William. 1501 N BICKETT BLVD, STE E 27549 #021-01-1994 L2003 **ORS** *020 †40
GOLDBACH, Norman Jos. 1501 N BICKETT BLVD, STE G 27549 #041-02-1984 L2007 **U GS** *020 †95
HILBERT, Tammy. 1501 N BICKETT BLVD, STE D 27549 #038-41-1999 L2006 **OBG** *020 †30
KILE, Paul Edward. 502 KENAN RD 27549 #024-07-1982 L1985 **IM** *020 †20
KING, David James. 948 N MAIN ST, LOUISBURG INT MED 27549 #033-06-1982 L1989 **IM** *020 †20
KRONENBERG, Andrew Clark. 500 REDWOOD LN 27549 #001-02-1996 L2006 **CD IC** *020 †20
MARTINEZ, Jose Gabriel. 100 HOSPITAL DR 27549 #429-01-1982 L1995 **IM** *020 †20
MEDDERS, James Doyle. 100 HOSPITAL DR 27549 #036-01-1956 L1956 **GP IM** *071
ORTEGA, Agnes Lynett. 1501 N BICKETT BLVD STE D 27549 #038-41-1995 L2007 **OBG** *020 †30
PERDUE, Jasper Burt, Jr. ■ 27549 #036-05-1964 L1964 **GS** *071 †85
REYES, Lavinia T. 205 SANDALWOOD AVE 27549 #748-01-1991 L1997 **IM** *020 †20
SAYLES, William Alexander. 601 N BICKETT BLVD 27549 #011-03-1982 L1989 **FM EM** *020 †18
SEVILLA, Sharon C. 205 SANDALWOOD AVE, FRANKLIN PEDIATRIC CARE 27549 #748-01-1991 L1997 **PD** *020 †55
SHAH, Abid Ali. 100 HOSPITAL DR, FRANKLIN REGIONAL MEDICAL 27549 #422-01-1995 L2005 **IM** *020 †20
SHAHRIER, Mamun. 626 N BICKETT BLVD, CONSULTANTS 27549 #160-02-1984 L2003 **GE HEP** *020 †20
SHAUT, Christopher A. 928 N MAIN ST 27549 #035-03-1976 L1990 **GS** *020 †85
STOVER, Phillip Earl. 205 SANDALWOOD AVE, STE E 27549 #051-07-1980 L1981 **FM EM** *020 †18
THOMPSON, Tim Brian. 205 SANDALWOOD AVE 27549 #028-03-1990 L2003 **IM** *020 †20
TIDMORE, Hollis D. 1501 N BICKETT BLVD STE A, CAPITAL SURG SPECLTS PA 27549 #027-01-1980 L1990 **GS VS** *062 †85
TRINH, Thuhuong Le. 107 INDUSTRIAL DR, STE C 27549 #045-01-1994 L1997 **FM** *020 †18
WAKEFIELD, Philip Earl. 1015 LAKE ROYALE 27549 #051-01-1984 L2005 **D** *020 †15
WHEELESS, Clifford R. 1501 N BICKETT BLVD, STE E 27549 #036-01-1992 L1998 **ORS** *020 †40
WHELESS, Thomas Omega. 100 HOSPITAL DR 27549 #036-05-1943 L1943 **FM OBG** *020

LOWELL – GASTON

LOWERY, Charles Donald. 205 W 1ST ST 28098 #036-05-1958 L1958 **FM OS** *020 †18

LUMBERTON – ROBESON

ALLEN, David Roger, Jr. 404 HATFIELD CT 28358 #025-07-1993 L1998 **ORS** *020 †40
ANDREWS, Bob B. 300 W 27TH ST 28358 #019-02-1951 L1957 **PTH** *071 †50
AUGUSTINE, Santhosh. 101 W 27TH ST 28358 #495-31-1985 L1996 **GE** *020 †20
AZIZ, Saqib. 300 W 27TH ST, SRMC, MEDICAL STAFF OFFICE 28358 #704-20-1999 L2006 **IM** *020 †20
BAILEY, John Richard. 205 W 29TH ST 28358 #045-01-1962 L1969 **OPH** *071
BAKER, Edwin L, III. 800 OAKRIDGE BLVD 28358 #051-01-1984 L1989 **OBG** *020 †30
BAKER, Horace M, Jr. ■ 28358 #036-07-1944 L1944 **GS** *071
BAROWSKY, Robert Thos. 4311 LUDGATE ST, # C 28358 #056-05-1980 L2001 **OPH** *020 †35
BEASLEY, Charles Ronald. 395 W 27TH ST 28358 #036-07-1980 L1985 **PUD IM** *020 †20
BEKIC, George Paul. 300 W 27TH ST 28358 #011-75-1997, ▲ L2004 **CD** *020 †20
BRITT, Samuel Emerson, II. 3001 N ELM ST 28358 #036-05-1980 L1982 **GS** *020 †85
BULLARD, Teresa. 450 COUNTRY CLUB RD, HLTH CENTER 28360 #036-08-1992 L1999 **CHP** *020
BULLARD, Tracy Elizabeth. 325 ROSLYN DR 28358 #036-01-2001 L2002 **FM** *020 †18
BURKE, Les G K Q. ■ 28358 #007-02-2002 L2007 **PCP** *100 †50
BURLESON, William Rowell. 815 OAKRIDGE BLVD 28358 #036-01-1964 L1964 **U** *020 †95
CAMPBELL, Jeffrey P. 730 OAKRIDGE BLVD, STE C 28358 #036-01-1988 L2004 **OTO FPS** *020 †45
CARBALLO, Frank Edward. 395 W 27TH ST 28358 #011-04-1989 L2003 **IM** *020 †20
CHANDER, Archana Vijaya. 400 LIBERTY HILL RD, LUMBERTON CHILDREN'S CLINI 28358 #422-01-2004 L2007 **PD** *020 †55

CHERICHELLA, Robert John. 300 W 27TH ST 28358 #033-05-1995 L2000 **DR** *020 †80
CLAYTON, Tawanda Bowden. 800 OAKRIDGE BLVD 28358 #036-01-1986 L1989 **OBG** *020 †30
COLEY, Elwood B. 400 LIBERTY HILL RD 28358 #041-01-1952 L1952 **PD** *030 †55
COX, Dakota Demetri. 400 LIBERTY HILL RD 28358 #036-05-1999 L2002 **PD** *020
CUMMINGS, Samuel Mac. 800 OAKRIDGE BLVD, WOMENS LIFE CTR LUMBERTON 28358 #036-01-1985 L1986 **OBG** *020 †30
DE LA SERNA, F Alberto. 403 W 27TH ST 28358 #132-05-1983 L2004 **CD IC** *100
DEVINE, Gerard Michael. 395 W 27TH ST 28358 #035-08-1973 L1976 **IM** *020 †20
DOUGLAS, A Eugene. 300 W 27TH ST 28358 #036-01-1959 L1959 **P** *071
DUNLAP, Jack E. ■ 28358 #047-06-1952 L1961 **ORS** *071 †40
DUNN, Shepard N. 401 W 27TH ST 28358 #023-07-1952 L1976 **OPH** *071 †35
EARNEST, Robert Rhea. 460 COUNTRY CLUB RD 28360 #012-05-1968 L1970 **PD ADL** *020 †55
ERMINI, Edward Benedict. 4303 LUDGATE ST 28358 #001-06-1990 L1999 **OTO A** *020 †45
FELSING, Nancy Ellen. ■ 28358 #031-01-1987 L1989 **PD CCP** *020 †55
FLORIAN, Thomas Francis. 4308 LUDGATE ST 28358 #051-01-1988 L1999 **PM** *020 †60
FRANZONI, Dora Elvia. 102 W 27TH ST 28358 #010-02-1989 L1994 **AN PME** *020 †05
GASQUE, Boyd B, Jr. 300 W 27TH ST 28358 #036-01-1977 L1977 **DR** *020 †80
GATIWALA, Indravadan S. 785 OAKRIDGE BLVD 28358 #495-89-1981 L1996 **N SME** *020 †75
GERALD, Laura Iris. 400 LIBERTY HILL RD 28358 #023-07-1995 L1998 **PD** *020 †55
GERBER, Dixon Wm. 500 W 27TH ST 28358 #038-41-1974 L1991 **ORS** *020
GORDON, Paul Anthony N. 725 OAKRIDGE BLVD, STE A1 28358 #422-01-1995 L1999 **FM** *020 †18 ‡
GUHA, Subrata. 300 W 27TH ST 28358 #024-05-1986 L1989 **EM** *020
HARDIN, Christina. 400 LIBERTY HILL RD, LUMBERTON CHILDREN'S CLINI 28358 #036-01-1999 L2001 **PD** *020 †55
HARDIN, James B. 2901 N ELM ST 28358 #036-01-1977 L1977 **FM** *071 †18
HAWORTH, Charles S. 2905 N ELM ST 28358 #036-07-1982 L1996 **NS** *020 †25
HEARNE, Larry A. 800 OAKRIDGE BLVD 28358 #047-07-1985 L1991 **OBG** *020
HEGDE, Sadananda Belinje. 4384 FAYETTEVILLE RD 28358 #495-37-1973 L1981 **IM CD** *020 †20 ‡
HENDRICKS, Andrew Adam. 4390 FAYETTEVILLE RD, SOUTHEASTERN DERMATOLOGY 28358 #051-01-1974 L1980 **D CS** *020 †15 ‡
HEPLER, John Davis. 300 W 27TH ST 28358 #051-01-1969 L1978 **OBG** *020 †30
JACKSON, Anita Louise. 4315 LUDGATE ST 28358 #016-11-1990 L1997 **OTO AI** *020 †45
JACKSON, Staley Thos. 4380 FAYETTEVILLE RD 28358 #038-40-1979 L1989 **ORS** *020
JAYASWAL, Ankesh. ■ 28358 #495-54-1993 L2004 **IM** *020
JESSIE, Timothy Antonio. 730 OAKRIDGE BLVD, STE A 28358 #036-08-1999 L2005 **GS** *020 †85
JOHNSON, Richard Dewitt. 300 W 27TH ST 28358 #495-01-1992 L1993 **PTH** *020 †50 ‡
JONES, Connie Locklear. 300 W 27TH ST, SOUTHEASTERN REGIONAL MEDI 28358 #036-08-1993 L1995 **FM** *020 †18
KHAN, Jamshed Khalid. 395 W 27TH ST 28358 #704-01-1996 L2003 **IM IMG** *020 †20
KIDD, Michael Gene. 102 W 27TH ST, P O BOX 2370 28358 #001-02-1984 L1988 **AN** *020 †05
LANE, Mary Boggs. 295 W 27TH ST 28358 #047-06-1984 L1988 **GYN** *020 †30
LEE, Henry Neill. 395 W 27TH ST, LUMBERTON MEDICAL CLINIC P 28358 #036-01-1956 L1956 **IM GE** *071 †20
LEGET, Gail A. 300 W 27TH ST 28358 #396-24-1991 L1998 **HO** *020 †20
LOCH, Walter Eric. 4303 LUDGATE ST 28358 #539-06-1982 L2003 **OTO PS** *020 †45
LOCKLEAR, Ferriss Yarnell. 4320 FAYETTEVILLE RD 28358 #036-01-1984 L1985 **GP** *020
LOCKLEAR, Gregory. 202 W 27TH ST 28358 #036-01-1984 L1986 **IM** *020 †20
LOHAVICHAN, Choomsang. 720 WESLEY PINES RD 28358 #891-02-1965 L1973 **NEP IM** *071
LOWERY, Jason Eric. ■ 28358 #036-08-2008 *012
LOWRY, Rhonda S. 402 N PINE ST 28358 #036-08-1994 L1996 **FM** *020 †18
LOWRY, Tulula Locklear. 4320A FAYETTEVILLE RD 28358 #036-08-1991 L1992 **FM** *020 †18
MAHMOOD, Ahmad Ali Omar. 1200 PINE RUN DR, GIBSON CANCER CENTER 28358 #528-02-1973 L2004 **ON IM** *020 †20 ‡
MAYNOR, Jayne Patrice. 102 W 27TH ST 28358 #036-01-1987 L1991 **AN** *020 †05
MAZUMDER, Sudipta. 300 W 27TH ST, P O BOX 1408 28358 #495-38-2000 L2006 **IM** *100 †20
MC ALLISTER, John D, Jr. 2601 N ELM ST, STE A 28358 #036-01-1985 L1996 **IM** *075
MC CLAIN, Mack Ira. 209 W 27TH ST 28358 #039-01-1962 L1989 **R RO** *020 †80
MC CORMICK, Carolyn Brumm. 300 W 27TH ST 28358 #018-03-1972 L1975 **FM** *071 †18
MC JILTON, Roy Alan. 300 W 27TH ST 28358 #028-34-1964 L1984 **OTO** *071 †45
MC LEOD, James Donald. 300 W 27TH ST, SOUTHEASTERN REGIONAL MEDI 28358 #036-05-2003 L2006 **FM** *020 †18
MERCHANT, Audrea Kay. 207 W 29TH ST, SOUTHEASTERN REGIONAL MENT 28358 #036-07-1998 L2003 **OS** *100
MILLER, Eric Wesley. 102 W 27TH ST, LUMBERTON ANESTHESIA CONSU 28358 #036-01-1986 L1987 **AN** *020 †05
MONTILUS, Macadolf. 202 W 27TH ST 28358 #422-01-1994 L1997 **IM** *020
MONTILUS, Sandhya Anne. 725 OAKRIDGE BLVD, STE B1 28358 #422-01-1994 L1997 **IM** *020
MOUSER, Timothy Scott. 205 W 29TH ST, SOUTHEASTERN EYE CARE, PA 28358 #047-20-1998 L2004 **OPH** *020
MOZINGO, George Wm, III. 815 OAKRIDGE BLVD 28358 #045-01-1976 L1985 **U** *020 †95
MUSCOREIL, Steven. 3001 N ELM ST 28358 #038-44-1992 L2000 **GS** *020 †85
NAIK, Somnath. 4384 FAYETTEVILLE RD, MEDICAL SPEC CLINIC PA 28358 #496-38-1975 L1982 **IM PUD** *020 †20
NEAL, Walter Ernest, Jr. 300 W 27TH ST 28358 #051-04-1966 L1972 **OBG** *020 †30
O'DONNELL, Robert Wm. 207 W 29TH ST, HEALTH CENTER 28358 #023-01-1974 L2001 **P CHP** *020
ONIME, Godfrey Dele. 4348A FAYETTEVILLE RD, SOUTHEASTERN MEDICAL PRACT 28358 #035-19-1996 L2002 **GE** *020 †20
OSEKI, Collins Osaze. 401 W 27TH ST 28358 #690-13-1988 L2005 **IM** *020 †20
PARKER, James Edwin Stone. 209 W 27TH ST, PO DRAWER 1527 28358 #020-02-1989 L1995 **DR** *020 †80
PATEL, Hiren R. 3009 N ELM ST 28358 #495-22-1988 L1994 **IM** *020 †20
PINEDA, Michole C M. 400 LIBERTY HILL RD 28358 #748-01-1991 L2006 **PD** *020 †55
PITTMAN, Alfred R, Jr. ■ 28358 #036-07-1945 L1945 **IM** *071 †20
PITTS, Venus Idette. 725 OAKRIDGE BLVD STE A2 28358 #024-01-1996 L1999 **IM** *020 †20
POJOL, Ricardo O. 400 LIBERTY HILL RD, LUMBERTON CHILDREN'S CLINI 28358 #748-10-1989 L1995 **PD** *020 †55
PRASAD, Alka. 300 W 27TH ST, SOUTHEASTERN REGIONAL MEDI 28358 #496-38-1991 L2005 **IM** *020 †20
PRATHER, Trina Lenita. 300 W 27TH ST 28358 #035-03-1995 L2006 **MPD** *020 †20
PROVOSTY, George Hurst. 300 W 27TH ST 28358 #021-05-1966 L1972 **DR NM** *020 †28
PURDY, Randall Lee, Jr. 450 COUNTRY CLUB RD 28360 #039-01-1993 L1998 **P CHP** *020
RAHMAN, Khawaja Yassir. 220 WINTERGREEN DR STE A 28358 #704-01-1997 L2004 **IM** *100

RICE, John Russell. 395 W 27TH ST 28358 #011-02-1968 L1969 **RHU IM** *020 †20
RICHARDSON, David Lee. 395 W 27TH ST 28358 #036-07-1974 L1977 **IM** *020 †20
ROBERTS, Joseph Earl, Jr. 3005 N ELM ST 28358 #036-01-1987 L1988 **FM** *020 †18
ROBINSON, Arthur J. 1000 WESLEY PINES RD # 108 28358 #010-03-1950 L1950 **GP** *020
ROBINSON, Karen Margaret. 400 LIBERTY HILL RD, LUMBERTON CHILDREN'S CLINI 28358 #068-01-1993 L1995 **FM** *020 †18
ROBINSON, Karen Yvonne. 400 LIBERTY HILL RD 28358 #041-01-1977 L1999 **PD** *020 †55
ROYAL, Stephen Harold. 2610 N ELM ST, SOUTHEASTERN CARDIOLOGY, P 28358 #422-01-1981 L1991 **CD IM** *020 †20
ROZIER, John Chas, Jr. 295 W 27TH ST 28358 #036-05-1967 L1967 **GYN AM** *020 †30
SAMALA, Venkata Lakshmi. ■ 28358 #495-62-1991 L2004 **CHP** *100 †75
SCHLESSELMAN, Leroy R. 300 W 27TH ST, SOUTHWESTERN REGIONAL MED 28358 #018-03-1984 L1999 **EM FM** *020 †18,16
SHARMA, Anup Kumar. ■ 28358 #748-21-1999 L2007 **IM** *020 †18,20
SHARMA, Sunil. 300 W 27TH ST, SE REG MED CTR 28358 #041-09-1987 L1991 **IM EM** *020 †20
SHETTY, Amita Sadashiv. 4384 FAYETTEVILLE RD 28358 #495-17-1987 L1997 **IM** *020 †20
SHORT, Sydney Glen. 403 W 27TH ST 28358 #055-01-1983 L2004 **CD** *020 †20
SIMAYS, Andrew Edward. 209 W 27TH ST, LUMBERTON RADIOLOGICAL ASS 28358 #021-06-1991 L2006 **R** *020 †80
STEWART, Thomas Sandner. 815 OAKRIDGE BLVD 28358 #038-40-1990 L1996 **U** *020 †95
STUART, Dennis O'Garey. 800 MARTIN LUTHR KNG JR DR 28358 #051-04-1982 L1986 **FM** *020 †18
SURYADEVARA, Raveendra. 207 W 29TH ST, HEALTH 28358 #495-50-1969 L1999 **P** *020 †75
TALIP, Frederick Andoy. 4300 FAYETTEVILLE RD 28358 #748-11-1992 L2004 **RHU IM** *020 †20
TAYLOR, Edward Frederic. 4348 FAYETTEVILLE RD 28358 #041-09-1982 L1991 **IM** *020 †20
TAYLOR, Robin Yolanda. 402 N PINE ST, STE C 28358 #036-08-1995 L1996 **FM** *020 †18
THAKUR, Veda Nand. 500 KENSINGTON ST 28358 #495-24-1963 L1973 **ORS TRS** *020
THOMPSON, Marvin Whitaker. ■ 28360 #036-05-1962 L1962 **PTH** *020 †50 ‡
TORRES, Analyn Medina. 4300 FAYETTEVILLE RD 28358 #748-01-1993 L2004 **END** *020 †20
VAZQUEZ, Angel L. 450 COUNTRY CLUB RD 28360 #308-03-1985 L1997 **P** *020
VEERAGANDHAM, Ajay Kumar. 450 COUNTRY CLUB RD, SOUTHEASTERN REGIONAL MENT 28360 #496-24-1990 L2003 **P** *100
VIAS, Pinakin P. 4384 FAYETTEVILLE RD 28358 #495-01-1989 L1996 **IM** *020 †20
VILLANI, Peter Louis. 3001 N ELM ST 28358 #055-01-1972 L1978 **GS VS** *020 †85
WARD, Doctor Ernest, Jr. 300 W 27TH ST 28358 #036-05-1945 L1945 **GS TRS** *071 †85
WARREN, Roger Danl. 2601 N ELM ST, STE A 28358 #004-01-1982 L1983 **FM** *020 †18
WHALEY, Donald Ralph. 760 OAKRIDGE BLVD 28358 #012-01-1989 L1993 **OPH** *020 †35
WHITMAN, Bruce Steven. 315 LONDONDERRY DR 28358 #018-75-1983, ▲ L1999 **EM** *020
WILLIAMSON, Barry Eugene. 300 W 27TH ST 28358 #036-05-1993 L1995 **GS** *020 †85
WILLIAMSON, Warren Ligon. 3001 N ELM ST, LUMBERTON SURGICAL ASSOCIA 28358 #021-05-1966 L1973 **GS** *020 †85
YOUNG, Robt Lassiter, Jr. 103 W 27TH ST, LUMBERTON CHILDREN'S CLINI 28358 #036-07-1961 L1961 **PD** *030
ZENG, Jianfeng. 4850 FAYETTEVILLE RD STE E 28358 #243-45-1982 L2001 **N** *020 †75

MACCLESFIELD – WILSON

DREW, John Edwin. PO BOX 337 27852 #036-05-1960 L1960 **FM GP** *071 †18

MACON – WARREN

DIECKMANN, Merwin Richard. ■ 27551 #018-03-1954 L1982 **FM** *071 †18

MADISON – ROCKINGHAM

DAY, Robert Glynn. 401 W DECATUR ST, STE A 27025 #047-06-1999 L2005 **FM** *020 †18
HOCHREIN, James. 401 W DECATUR ST, STE B 27025 #038-40-1990 L1994 **CD** *020 †20
NYLAND, Leonard R. 723 AYERSVILLE RD 27025 #035-03-1989 L1991 **FM** *020 †18
SLOTNICK, Lawrence S. 401 W DECATUR ST, STE A 27025 #035-08-1970 L1977 **PUD A** *020 †20 ‡
SUE, Samuel Arthur. 401 W DECATUR ST 27025 #036-05-1956 L1956 **ORS** *071 †40
WRENN, John Jeffries. 401 W DECATUR ST, STE B 27025 #047-06-1985 L1988 **U** *020 †95

MAGGIE VALLEY – HAYWOOD

ARNOLD, Laurence Ian. 98 CREEKSIDE DR 28751 #016-43-1983 L2005 **PS HS** *020 †65
BOONE, Paul David. ■ 28751 #045-01-1955 L1960 **PTH** *020 †50
SORAK, Katica. PO BOX 969, 18 COUNTRY CLUB DR 28751 #957-02-1958 L1974 **DR NM** *071

MAGNOLIA – DUPLIN

RICHARDS, Randall George. ■ 28453 #038-41-2002 L2005 **MPD** *020

MAIDEN – CATAWBA

HALL, Mauverine Jo. 510 ISLAND FORD RD 28650 #020-12-1985 L1994 **FM** *020 †18
LINEBERGER, Adrian S, Jr. ■ 28650 #036-01-1955 L1955 **PTH NM** *071 †50,28
NAPIER, Lowell Gregory. 510 ISLAND FORD RD 28650 #020-12-1985 L1994 **FM** *020 †18
PEELER, Forrest E. 137 ISLAND FORD RD 28650 #051-04-1950 L1951 **FM FPG** *071
SCHULTZ, Curtis Donald. 137 ISLAND FORD RD, MAIDEN FAMILY PRACTICE 28650 #011-02-1983 L1999 **FM** *020 †18

MANSON – VANCE

HAGER, Angela Alicia. PO BOX 425, 1 OPPORTUNITY DR 27553 #036-08-1996 L1998 **FM** *020 †18

MANTEO – DARE

FARROW, Johnny Lee. ■ 27954 #036-08-1993 L1994 **FM** *020

■ = Address Information Privacy Protected

GLOVER, Renee Adams. ■ 27954 #036-07-1984 L1991 **D DMP** *020 †15
HOLTON, Walter Leggett. N MAIN HWY, DARE MEDICAL ASSOCIATES PA 27954 #036-07-1973 L1974 **FM** *020 †18
JUNG, Robert Marc. ■ 27954 #024-07-1962 L1964 **ORS** *020 †40
ROCK, Pauline Lothrop T. ■ 27954 #041-07-1966 L1971 **PTH** *071 †50

MAPLE HILL – PENDER

JONES, James Grady. 4811 NC HIGHWAY 50, MAPLE HILL MEDICAL CENTER 28454 #036-05-1959 L1959 **FM** *071 †18

MARION – MCDOWELL

ACREE, Jeffrey S. 83 W MEDICAL CT, STE B 28752 #035-03-1992 L1998 **FM** *020 †18
ACUFF, Calvin Clifford. 430 RANKIN DR 28752 #005-12-1956 L1956 **EM** *071 †18
ALBRITTON, Mark Walden. ■ 28752 #012-01-1990 L2003 **FM** *020 †18
ALEXANDER, James Ray. 136 CREEKVIEW CT 28752 #047-06-1980 L1988 **GE IM** *020 †20
ALI, Shamshad. 31 E MEDICAL CT, # 1 28752 #495-15-1960 L1974 **PD NPM** *020 †55 ‡
ALLEN, John O H. 430 RANKIN DR 28752 #036-05-1951 L1951 **FM** *071
BARNHARDT, Luther Ernest. 900 MEDICAL CT, MCDOWELL RADIOLOGY 28752 #036-07-1958 L1958 **R NM** *071 †80,28
BARTELS, Pamela Kay. 1860 SUGAR HILL RD, MC DOWELL MED ASSOC 28752 #016-11-1987 L1988 **FM** *020 †18
BOND, Thomas Madison. 136 CREEKVIEW CT 28752 #036-01-1980 L1984 **GE IM** *020 †20
BRYAN, Angela J. 472 RANKIN DR, HEALTH PLUS 28752 #016-45-1998 L2007 **FM** *020 †18
BURTON, Mark Wesley. 100 SPAULDING RD, STE 1 28752 #047-06-1986 L1989 **IM** *020 †20
CHUNG, Joseph Y. 430 RANKIN DR 28752 #583-02-1966 L1972 **GS GP** *020 †85
DEHOLL, John David, Jr. 20 MEDICAL PARK DR 28752 #051-01-1991 L1997 **U** *020 †95
DENUNA, Vicente B, Jr. 146 N LOGAN ST 28752 #748-01-1964 L1974 **AS GS** *020
ENDE, Amy Smith. 1860 SUGAR HILL RD, 1860 SUGAR HILL RD 28752 #036-01-1990 L1996 **PD** *020 †55
FOWLER, William Varn. 1860 SUGAR HILL RD, MCDOWELL MEDICAL ASSOCIATE 28752 #036-01-1978 L1979 **FM** *020 †18
GREEN, George Cameron. 60 S MEDICAL CT 28752 #021-01-1981 L2004 **ORS** *020 †40
HAND, Joshua Peter. 1860 SUGAR HILL RD 28752 #027-01-1999 L2002 **FM** *020 †18
HANOWELL, Robert Goddin. 486 SPAULDING RD, CATAWBA VALLEY BEHAVIORAL 28752 #016-43-1989 L2004 **FM** *020
HARLAN, William Robt. 136 CREEKVIEW CT 28752 #036-07-1991 L1993 **GE IM** *020 †20
KATH, Philip Douglas. 40 E MEDICAL CT 28752 #026-08-1976 L1981 **OPH** *020 †35
MAY, David Thomas. 136 CREEKVIEW CT 28752 #036-01-1993 L1995 **GE** *020 †20
MC ENTIRE, Jerrill Lee. 430 RANKIN DR, THE MCDOWELL HOSPITAL 28752 #036-01-1971 L1973 **FM GS** *020 †18
MC INTOSH, Archibald N. 219 S MAIN ST 28752 #036-07-1944 L1948 **GP** *071
MELVIN, Frank Michael. 20 MEDICAL PARK DR, STE 2 28752 #027-01-1985 L1999 **OTO** *020 †45
MONTEZ, Xiaokun. 63 S MEDICAL CT, STE B 28752 #243-39-1985 L2005 **PD** *020 †55
MOODY, Mark Lawrence. 63 S MEDICAL CT 28752 #010-02-1987 L1992 **ORS OSS** *020 †40
NEWCOMER, Michael Kermit. 136 CREEKVIEW CT 28752 #038-06-1988 L2000 **GE** *020 †20
PATEL, Narendra Ashabbai. 6 E MEDICAL CT, # 2 28752 #495-89-1975 L1984 **U** *020 †95
PATEL, Nisha Jayantilal. 6 E MEDICAL CT STE 1 28752 #495-89-1974 L1984 **GYN** *020 †30
PEREZ, Rodney Alexander. 136 CREEKVIEW CT 28752 #047-20-1994 L2000 **GE** *020 †20
PRICE, Andrew Richard. ■ 28752 #036-07-1965 L1965 **IM NEP** *030 †20
PULIZZI, John Sebastian. 146 N LOGAN ST 28752 #041-09-1991 L1996 **GS** *020 †85
RAGAZ, Florian J B. 231 E COURT ST 28752 #056-05-1949 L1953 **CD GP** *020
RHENEY, Theodore Branch. 20 MEDICAL PARK DR, STE 2 28752 #012-01-1993 L1995 **OTO** *020 †45
SALSMAN, Richard. 20 S MEDICAL CT 28752 #048-13-1987 L1991 **OBG** *020 †30
SEAL, Stephen Randall. 20 MEDICAL PARK DR, STE 2 28752 #021-06-1983 L1989 **HNS OTO** *020 †45
SECH, Scott Michael. 20 W MEDICAL CT, STE 1 28752 #048-12-1993 L1999 **U** *020 †95
SIMOLKE, Gregory A. 20 S MEDICAL CT 28752 #048-04-1987 L1992 **OBG** *020 †30
SMITH, Richard Lloyd. 136 CREEKVIEW CT 28752 #021-01-1972 L1975 **GE IM** *020 †20
ST BERNARD, Edward Lyle. 100 SPAULDING RD, STE 1 28752 #422-01-1989 L1994 **PUD** *020 †20
WILLIS, Larry Franklin. 40 E MEDICAL CT 28752 #012-01-1968 L1974 **OPH** *020 †35

MARS HILL – MADISON

BARNHARDT, Virginia J. 119 MOUNTAIN VIEW RD, PROGRAM 28754 #036-01-1989 L1990 **FM** *020 †18
BRADLEY, Teresa K. 119 MOUNTAIN VIEW RD, PROGRAM 28754 #036-08-1994 L1995 **FM** *020 †18
FIREMAN, Richard Lee. ■ 28754 #041-02-1969 L1974 **EM** *020
HARRIS, Lawrence Stanley. ■ 28754 #038-06-1962 L1977 **FOP NP** *071 †50
JONES, Frielden Bertie. 119 MOUNTAIN VIEW RD, PROGRAM 28754 #036-01-1976 L1976 **FM** *020 †18
LAWRANCE, Orren. ■ 28754 #028-79-1950, ▲ L1950 *071
NICHOLS, Kimberly R. 119 MOUNTAIN VIEW RD, PROGRAM 28754 #035-45-1990 L1993 **FM** *020 †18
POORBAUGH, David Mark. 1642 WALKER BRANCH RD 28754 #034-01-1982 L1985 **IM EM** *020 †20,16
POWELL, William E, Jr. ■ 28754 #041-02-1950 L1950 **GP** *072
RICHARDSON, Judith Mae. ■ 28754 #020-02-1977 L1988 **IM** *020 †20
SCHLEDER, Kristi Jo. 119 MOUNTAIN VIEW RD, PROGRAM 28754 #016-45-1986 L1988 **FM** *020 †18
STRAIT, Colleen Elizabeth. ■ 28754 #035-15-2007 **FP** *012
WHITE, Annette Marie. 119 MOUNTAIN VIEW RD, PROGRAM 28754 #003-01-1982 L1983 **IM** *020 †20

MARSHALL – MADISON

COOK, David Cleo. 125 SERENITY ON THE IVY LN 28753 #047-06-1972 L1992 **P CHP** *020

COVERDALE, Janice Noel. 590 MEDICAL PARK DR, PROGRAM 28753 #020-02-1976 L1982 **PD** *020
DALY, Marianna Tepaske. 590 MEDICAL PARK DR, PROGRAM 28753 #036-08-1985 L1986 **FM PHP** *020 †18
HUDSON, Page. ■ 28753 #051-04-1956 L1968 **FOP PTH** *071 †50
OGG, Nicole. 590 MEDICAL PARK DR, PROGRAM 28753 #048-14-1998 L1999 **FM** *020 †18
SCHROEDER, Louis Allan. 590 MEDICAL PARK DR, PROGRAM 28753 #020-02-1975 L1982 **IM** *020

MARSHVILLE – UNION

GREENE, Joseph E. 303 OLD HIGHWAY 74 28103 #012-01-1949 L1961 **GP** *072
HENRY, Gary Wayne. 520 W MAIN ST 28103 #036-08-1987 L1988 **FM** *020 †18

MATTHEWS – MECKLENBURG

ALEXANDER, Henry C, Jr. ■ 28105 #036-07-1949 L1953 **IM PUD** *071 †20
AQUINO, Daniel Anthony. 332 SAM NEWELL RD, STE 2000 28105 #035-48-1993 L1998 **IM** *020 †20 ‡
ATLAS, Walter Gerard. 1401 MATTHEWS TOWNSHP PKWY, STE 101 28105 #035-09-1983 L1992 **OPH** *020 †35
BARATTA, Pasquale D. 2435 PLANTATION CENTER DR, STE 110 28105 #035-06-1981 L1993 **FM** *020 †18
BERKOWITZ, Gerald Phillip. 1500 MATTHEWS TOWNSHP PKWY 28105 #047-06-1974 L1983 **PD NPM** *020 †55
BICKET, William John, II. 1450 MATTHEWS TOWNSHP PKWY, PARKWAY, STE 270 28105 #036-01-1983 L1990 **PS** *020 †65,85
BLANTON, Chas Mc Anally. 1401 MATTHEWS TOWNSHP PKWY, STE 100 28105 #036-08-1992 L1995 **PD** *020 †55
BLOUNT, Charles Whitner. 1450 MATTHEWS TOWNSHP PKWY, STE 450 28105 #012-01-1973 L1975 **FM** *020 †18
BRADFORD, Edward Ayers. 332 SAM NEWELL RD, STE 2000 28105 #011-03-1976 L1980 **IM** *020 †20
BRYSON, Betty Lee. ■ 28105 #020-12-1974 L1988 **GS EM** *071 †85
BURGESS, William C, Jr. 1401 MATTHEWS TOWNSHP PKWY, PHYSICIANS #048-13-1987 L1991 **IM** *020 †20
CARR, Thomas Anthony. 1450 MATTHEWS TOWNSHP PKWY, CHARLOTTE 28105 #028-46-1982 L1987 **GE IM** *040 †20
CASTELLION, Deena Manon. 1450 MATTHEWS TOWNSHP PKWY, STE 200 28105 #036-05-1993 L1997 **OBG** *020 †30
CAUDILL, Fred Welden, III. 130 MATTHEWS STATION ST 28105 #020-02-1987 L1991 **P** *020 †75
CHANEY, Robert Dale. ■ 28105 #017-20-1963 L1963 **AN** *071 †05
CHHEDA, Monica Eve. 2407 PLANTATION CENTER DR, PROVIDENCE PEDIATRICS 28105 #036-08-2003 L2006 **PD** *020 †55
COHEN, Bruce Elliot. 1450 MATTHEWS TOWNSHP PKWY, STE 150 28105 #012-01-1991 L2001 **ORS** *020 †40
CONNER, William Jordan. 211 W MATTHEWS ST, STE 102 28105 #036-01-1996 L1997 **FM** *020 †18
COPSIS, Peter Nicholas. 332 SAM NEWELL RD, STE 2000 28105 #036-01-1989 L1990 **IM** *020 †20
CRADDOCK, Larry Wayne. 1450 MATTHEWS TOWNSHP PKWY, STE 300 28105 #001-02-1972 L1992 **OBG** *075 †30
CRAIG, Michael Wilson. 1401 MATTHEWS TOWNSHP PKWY, STE 100, P.O. BOX 338 28105 #036-08-1983 L1985 **PD** *020 †55
CROSBY, Betty Jean Hall. 1401 MATTHEWS TOWNSHP PKWY, STE 100 28105 #036-01-1978 L1979 **PD** *020 †55
CROSS, Analisa. 1401 MATTHEWS TOWNSHP PKWY, PHYSICIANS 28105 #010-03-1983 L1991 **IM** *020 †20
CROWDER, Mary Thelma. 113 N AMES ST, MATTHEWS HEALTH CLINIC 28105 #051-01-1986 L1990 **GYN** *020 †30 ‡
CUTRONE, Martin Bernard. 1450 MATTHEWS TOWNSHP PKWY, STE 380 28105 #035-45-1986 L2003 **CD** *020 †20
DAVENPORT, John Emmett. 332 SAM NEWELL RD, STE 2000 28105 #034-01-1974 L1980 **IM** *020 †20
DEAL, Stephen Edgar. 1450 MATTHEWS TOWNSHP PKWY 28105 #036-01-1986 L1987 **GE IM** *020 †20
DICKENS, Jennifer Clark. 1450 MATTHEWS TOWNSHP PKWY 28105 #001-02-2000 L2004 **FM** *020 †18
DOWNS, Posey Edgar, Jr. ■ 28105 #036-05-1952 L1952 **OBG** *071 †30
DUNN, Marisa. 1500 MATTHEWS TOWNSHP PKWY 28105 #017-20-1999 L2003 **IM** *020
DU PUY, David Norris. 1450 MATTHEWS TOWNSHP PKWY, STE 150 28105 #011-02-1970 L1971 **ORS** *020 †40
ELGAMAL, Hazem Mohamed. 101 E MATTHEWS ST, STE 800 28105 #026-04-1998 L2005 **D** *020 †15
ENGSTROM, Paul Chas. ■ 28105 #036-05-1983 L1992 **PD NPM** *020 †55
EZZO, Stephen James. 1401 MATTHEWS TOWNSHP PKWY, STE 100 28105 #028-34-1985 L1987 **PD** *020 †55
FERRARI, Victor Steven. 1401 MATTHEWS TOWNSHP PKWY, STE 212 28105 #036-01-1987 L1999 **PS GS** *020 †85,65 ‡
FISHBURNE, Cary N, Jr. 1450 MATTHEWS TOWNSHP PKWY, STE 200 28105 #051-01-1994 L1996 **OBG** *020 †30
FISHBURNE, Cary Nelson. 1450 MATTHEWS TOWNSHP PKWY, STE 200 28105 #051-01-1974 L1974 **IM CD** *020 †20
FLIPPO, Jack L, Jr. 4105 MATTHEWS MINT HILL RD 28105 #001-02-1982 L1984 **PD** *020 †55
FLORES, Robert Andrew. 1401 MATTHEWS TOWNSHP PKWY, STE 101 28105 #024-01-1986 L1993 **OPH** *020 †35 ‡
FOULKE, Richard Stevens. 3036 SENNA DR 28105 #033-06-1983 L1993 **HEM ON** *020 †20
FOWLER, Wyatt Charles. 1450 MATTHEWS TOWNSHP PKWY, STE 320 28105 #036-05-1985 L1990 **SO GS** *020 †85
FULP, Sam Russell. 1450 MATTHEWS TOWNSHP PKWY, CHARLOTTE 28105 #036-05-1983 L1988 **GE IM** *020 †20
GABRIELS, Joseph Ross. ■ 28105 #035-03-1955 L1961 **OBG** *072 †30
GARDELLA, John Eugene. 1500 MATTHEWS TOWNSHP PKWY, PRESBYTERIAN HOSPITAL 28105 #035-19-1974 L1979 **IM** *020 †20

GARNER, Stuart Jos. 1450 MATTHEWS TOWNSHP PKWY 28105 #012-05-1980 L1986 PCC PUD *020 †20

GARUBA, Abdul Karim. 3030 SENNA DR, POLYCLINIC MEDICAL CENTER, 28105 #187-04-1985 L2000 CCM *020 †20

GIFFORD, Jonathan Harston. ■ 28105 #031-01-2006 GS *012

GODWIN, Herman Allen, Jr. 1450 MATTHEWS TOWNSHP PKWY, STE 360 28105 #036-05-1963 L1963 ON HEM *020 †20

GOODMAN, Donald Bruce. 1450 MATTHEWS TOWNSHP PKWY 28105 #036-01-1973 L1976 PD *020 †18

GOSS, Laurie Ottaway. 1401 MATTHEWS TOWNSHP PKWY, STE 100 28105 #051-01-2002 L2004 PD *020 †55

GRIFFIN, Keith Evans. 1700 MATTHEWS TOWNSHP PKWY, PRESBYTERIAN URGENT CARE L 28105 #036-01-1990 L1991 IM *020 †20

GULLICKSON, Matthew Alan. 1450 MATTHEWS TOWNSHP PKWY, STE 150 28105 #016-43-2000 L2006 ORS *020

HAIGLER YOUNCE, Laura L. 1450 MATTHEWS TOWNSHP PKWY, STE 380 28105 #036-05-1990 L1991 CD *020 †20

HALL, David Hartman. 1450 MATTHEWS TOWNSHP PKWY 28105 #036-07-1984 L1987 FM *020 †18

HAROUNY, Victor Robt. 1450 MATTHEWS TOWNSHP PKWY, STE 200 28105 #036-06-1983 L1987 OBG *020 †30

HELTON, Jennifer Leigh. 101 E MATTHEWS ST, STE 600 28105 #036-01-1989 L1994 D *020 †15

HOLEVAS, John George. 3330 SISKEY PKWY, STE 200 28105 #036-05-1985 L1987 IM *020 †20

HOUGH, Terrance Lee. ■ 28105 #036-05-1974 L1974 AN *074

JACKSON, Mashira Denisha. ■ 28105 #012-21-2007 FP *012

JOHNSON, Pamela Ann. 1340 MATTHEWS TOWNSHP PKWY, STE 301 28105 #051-07-1990 L1992 PD *020 †55

KARRIKER, Charlotte K. 1401 MATTHEWS TOWNSHP PKWY, PHYSICIANS 28105 #036-08-1994 L1995 IM *020 †20

KISELLA, John David. 1208 MANN DR STE 100, MAILING: P O BOX 749 28105 #021-06-1995 L2004 CS *020

KLOTZ, Jennifer Lynn. ■ 28105 #036-01-2005 L2008 PD *012

KNISH, Edward J, Jr. 201 E MATTHEWS ST 28105 #047-05-1983 L1986 IM *020 †20

KOPCZYNSKI, Todd Michael. 1450 MATTHEWS TOWNSHP PKWY, STE 300 28105 #036-01-1992 L1996 OBG *020 †30

KREMPEC, Jeffrey Aaron. ■ 28105 #025-01-2005 ORS *012

LADOGANA, Michael. 1500 MATTHEWS TOWNSHP PKWY, PICS 28105 #048-14-1998 L2002 IM *020 †20

LADWIG, Jason Ronald. 1450 MATTHEWS TOWNSHP PKWY 28105 #025-12-2000 L2007 PCC *020

LAND, Michael Roy. 1450 MATTHEWS TOWNSHP PKWY, STE 200 28105 #017-20-1980 L1983 OBG *020 †30

LASSITER, Lance King. 3036 SENNA DR, PIEDMONT ONCO SPECIALIST 28105 #001-02-1996 L2004 ON *020 †20

LAVONAS, Krista Michelle. 1401 MATTHEWS TOWNSHP PKWY, STE 100 28105 #017-20-1999 L2002 PD *020 †55

LOVE, Mary Bunch. ■ 28105 #036-05-1951 L1951 OS PUD *071

LOWE, Carl Jarrett, Jr. 1450 MATTHEWS TOWNSHP PKWY, STE 320 28105 #012-05-1997 L2002 GS *020 †85

MAHARAJH, Garnet D. 1340 MATTHEWS TOWNSHP PKWY, STE 301 28105 #036-05-1985 L1987 PD *020 †55

MALONE, David Paul. 1401 MATTHEWS TOWNSHP PKWY, PHYSICIANS 28105 #055-01-1990 L1999 IM *020 †20

MARTIN, Michael Jay. 1401 MATTHEWS TOWNSHP PKWY, PHYSICIANS 28105 #051-01-1988 L1991 IM *020 †20

MAUGEL, Larry Edwin. 1450 MATTHEWS TOWNSHP PKWY 28105 #038-43-1975 L1992 FM *020 †18

MAXWELL, Charliese. ■ 28105 #036-01-1981 L1985 PD *071

MC ADAMS, Lou Ann. 113 N AMES ST 28105 #017-20-1987 L1999 FM *020 †18

MC CREA, Kimberly Ann. 1450 MATTHEWS TOWNSHP PKWY 28105 #045-01-1987 L1994 PCC IM *020 †20

MEADE, Kyle Patrick. 1450 MATTHEWS TOWNSHP PKWY 28105 #018-03-2000 L2003 PCC *020 †20

MEEK, James Michael. 1450 MATTHEWS TOWNSHP PKWY, STE 300 28105 #056-05-1996 L1997 OBG *020 †30

MEEK, Kelly E. 1450 MATTHEWS TOWNSHP PKWY 28105 #045-01-1996 L1997 OBG *020 †30

MELKONIAN, Michael George. 1450 MATTHEWS TOWNSHP PKWY, STE 320 28105 #056-06-1995 L2001 GS *020 †85

MINDER, Joseph Kamel. 103 CHAPHYN LN 28105 #605-01-1978 L1990 U *020 †95

MODY, Sachin Surendra. 2407 PLANTATION CENTER DR, STE 102 28105 #422-01-1997 L2006 FM *020 †18

MOHANTY, Sanjib Prasad. 1450 MATTHEWS TOWNSHP PKWY, CHARLOTTE 28105 #036-01-1999 L2002 GE *020 †20

MUSA, Gregory David. 1401 MATTHEWS TOWNSHP PKWY, PHYSICIANS 28105 #048-12-1991 L1996 IM *020 †20 ‡

NEWMAN, Alfred Jackson, III. 3036 SENNA DR, ASSOCIATES 28105 #001-02-1999 L2004 HO *020 †20

NIESS, Gary Stewart. 1450 MATTHEWS TOWNSHP PKWY, STE 380 28105 #036-01-1973 L1973 CD *020 †20

NORRIS, Clarence Eugene. 148 E CHARLES ST STE B 28105 #649-14-1977 L1994 FPG PM *020 †18

OTEY, Asim Salih. ■ 28105 #033-06-2004 L2008 PM *012

OWENS-JARRELL, Susan L. 1401 MATTHEWS TOWNSHP PKWY, PHYSICIANS 28105 #036-08-1994 L1995 IM *020 †20

PARISH, Michele Kathareen. 1401 MATTHEWS TOWNSHP PKWY, STE 100 28105 #036-08-1987 L1988 PD *020 †20

PARSONS, Marshal Ray. 1450 MATTHEWS TOWNSHP PKWY, STE 320 28105 #034-01-1977 L1986 GS *020 †85

PLONK, John Butler, Jr. 2407 PLANTATION CENTER DR, PROVIDENCE PEDIATRICS 28105 #036-01-1981 L1988 PD *020 †55

PRESSLY, James Allen. 1450 MATTHEWS TOWNSHP PKWY, STE 250 28105 #036-01-1966 L1966 ORS *020 †40

PRICE, Gregory Michael. 4105 MATTHEWS MINT HILL RD 28105 #036-01-2002 L2005 FM *020 †18

PRICE, Robert Warren. 1450 MATTHEWS TOWNSHP PKWY, STE 380 28105 #023-12-1988 L2001 CD IM *020 †20

RAKKHIT, Tina. ■ 28105 #012-05-2006 TY *012

REID, John Heyward. 1401 MATTHEWS TOWNSHP PKWY, STE 220 28105 #045-01-1973 L1979 D FM *020 †15

ROBERSON, George Donald. 101 E MATTHEWS ST, STE 600 28105 #051-04-1958 L1964 OTO *071 †45

ROE, David Wilson. 1450 MATTHEWS TOWNSHP PKWY 28105 #016-45-1996 L2003 PCC *020 †20,55

ROGERS, Jim A. 101 E MATTHEWS ST STE 600 28105 #048-14-1985 L1987 D *020 †15

ROMAIN, Rolande Charles. 3030 SENNA DR, POLYCLINIC MED CTR 28105 #440-01-1971 L1981 PD *020 †55 ‡

RONDEAU, Sheila S. 1500 MATTHEWS TOWNSHP PKWY, PRESBYTERIAN INPATIENT CAR 28105 #048-14-1988 L1992 IM *020 †20

RUDISEL, Nettie Y Beverly. 1401 MATTHEWS TOWNSHP PKWY, PHYSICIANS 28105 #051-04-1984 L1991 IM *020 †20

SHEPHERD, Jack Paul, III. 1700 MATTHEWS TOWNSHP PKWY, PRESBYTERIAN URGENT CARE 28105 #036-08-1995 L2002 FM *020 †18

SHROFF, Mona Mansukh. ■ 28105 #016-11-1993 L1993 DR *020 †80

SILVER, John Robt. 1401 MATTHEWS TOWNSHP PKWY, STE 101 28105 #036-01-1988 L1994 OTO *020 †45

SMITH, Michael Warren. 332 SAM NEWELL RD, STE 2000 28105 #045-01-2000 L2003 IM *020 †20

SMITH, Stanton James. ■ 28105 #047-07-1980 L2005 P *020 †75

SMOLEN, Paul Mathieu. 2407 PLANTATION CENTER DR, PROVIDENCE PEDIATRICS 28105 #033-06-1978 L1979 PD *020 †55

SPIES, Robert Scott. 1401 MATTHEWS TOWNSHP PKWY, STE 100 28105 #036-01-1995 L1997 PD *020 †55

SPITZHOFF, Frederick M. ■ 28105 #035-09-1948 L1949 AN *071 †05

STEWART, Kathleen H. 167L S TRADE ST 28105 #035-15-1991 L1995 PD *020 †55

STOCKWELL, Henry P. 4105 MATTHEWS MINT HILL RD 28105 #067-01-1961 L1967 PD *071 †55

STUNTZ, Richard C, Jr. 726 FREDRICKSBURG RD, EMP 28105 #036-01-1984 L1985 EM OM *020 †16

SVECHARNIK, Marina. ■ 28105 #036-01-2004 L2007 FM *020 †18

SWEENEY, Michael Francis. 1450 MATTHEWS TOWNSHP PKWY, STE 200 28105 #035-06-1993 L1997 OBG *020 †30

TEMPLE, John David. 1450 MATTHEWS TOWNSHP PKWY, STE 150 28105 #036-01-1999 L2005 OSM *020 †40

THOMAS, Walter E, Jr. 1401 MATTHEWS TOWNSHP PKWY, STE 100 28105 #036-05-1984 L1986 PD *020 †55

THOMPSON, Eric Bennett. 1450 MATTHEWS TOWNSHP PKWY 28105 #001-02-1987 L1996 IM *020 †20

TOUSSI, Azita-Azar. 2651 CIRCA DR 28105 #869-04-1987 L1996 EM *020 †16

WIESE, Rachel Lynn. 1401 MATTHEWS TOWNSHP PKWY, STE 100, P.O. BOX 338 28105 #051-01-1994 L1997 PD *020 †55

WILLIAMSON, Joyce M. 101 E MATTHEWS ST, CHARLOTTE DERMATOLOGY PA 28105 #803-03-1958 L1966 D *020 †20

WOLFHOPE, Barbara Lee. 1450 MATHWS TWNSHP #450, MATTHEWS FAMILY PHYSICIANS 28105 #041-09-1976 L1986 FM *020 †18

WUNDERLICH, Colleen Ann. ■ 28105 #422-01-2000 L2007 PM *020 †60

YARBROUGH, Lucy Moore. 1401 MATTHEWS TOWNSHP PKWY, STE 101 28105 #045-01-2001 L2005 OPH *020

YOUNG, Pamela Burkholder. 1401 MATTHEWS TOWNSHP PKWY, STE 100 28105 #051-04-1989 L1994 PD *020 †55

MATTHEWS – UNION

BOS, John F. ■ 28104 #051-04-1951 L1955 PTH CLP *071 †50

BREWSTER, Vann Allen. ■ 28104 #012-01-1960 L1975 OM *071

HERMAN, Andrew C. ■ 28104 #028-34-1998 L2004 NPM *020 †55

JAGDON, Wilfredo M. ■ 28104 #748-07-1961 L1982 EM *071

PERROTTA, Richard John. ■ 28104 #028-34-1972 L1973 OTO *020 †45

RENNYSON, Stephen Louis. ■ 28104 #051-07-2006 GS *100

RICH, Lindsey Michelle. ■ 28104 #051-07-2007 FP *012

STOUT, James Stevens. ■ 28104 #012-01-1957 L1975 OM EM *071

MAXTON – ROBESON

CAMPBELL, Arthur Leslie. 22401 ANDREW JACKSON HWY, LUMBER RIVER HEALTH CARE C 28364 #023-12-1997 L1998 FM *020 †18

DEESE, Joseph Earl. 110 PRESTON RD, RT 3 BOX 130C 28364 #036-01-1978 L1979 EM *020 †16

MANUSOV, Eron Grant. ■ 28364 #023-12-1984 L1998 FSM *020 †18

ROBERSON, Jennifer. 610 E MARTN LTHR KNG JR DR, ROBESON HEALTH CARE CORPOR 28364 #036-01-2001 L2004 FM *100 †18

ROWSON, Jonathan David. 1010 W. SANDERS ST, MAXTON FAM PRAC CTR 28364 #035-15-1995 L1998 FM *020 †18

UGAH, Nwannadiya Glory. 610 E MARTN LTHR KNG JR DR 28364 #690-12-1988 L1998 FM *020 †18

MAYODAN – ROCKINGHAM

QURESHI, Ayyaz M. 505 N 3RD AVE 27027 #704-02-1975 L1984 IM ON *020

MC LEANSVILLE – GUILFORD

HENRY-SMITH, Carol Ann-Ma. ■ 27301 #649-19-2001 L2005 IMG *020 †18

NNAEMEKA-OKOYEH, Rita Obi. ■ 27301 #690-01-1984 L2005 PD *020 †55

MCCUTCHEON FIELD – ONSLOW

MC NIFF, Katherine B. BUIDING AS 100 28545 #051-04-2003 L2007 GP *020

■ = Address Information Privacy Protected

MEBANE – ALAMANCE

AVATO, Cosmo P. ■ 27302 #041-09-1949 L1953 **PTH** *020 †50
BECK, J Montgomery. ■ 27302 #038-06-1944 L1952 **GP OS** *071 †95
BLISS, Laura Katherine. 100 E DOGWOOD DR, BROOKHOLLOW FAMILY MEDICAL 27302 #036-01-1989 L1995 **FM** *020 †18
DEW, Rachel Elizabeth. 300 PEBBLE BEACH DR 27302 #055-01-2000 L2002 **P** *020
DUFFY, Diane Marie. 943 S 5TH ST 27302 #011-04-1989 L1992 **PD** *020 †55
ELY, Ralph Lawrence, III. 102 MEDICAL PARK DR, STE A 27302 #036-07-1977 L1987 **GS VS** *020 †85
FU, Jessica Amy. ■ 27302 #036-05-2002 L2005 **PHO** *012 †55
GRANDIS, Heidi Marie. ■ 27302 #036-01-2006 **FP** *012
HARDIE-HOOD, Robin L. 1107 S FIFTH ST 27302 #041-13-1998 L2004 **HO IM** *020 †20
HATHORN, James Walker. 1107 S FIFTH ST 27302 #036-07-1979 L1987 **ON ID** *020 †20
JONES, Deanna Craven. 1242 S FIFTH ST C 27302 #036-07-1979 L1987 **FM** *020 †20
JUENGEL, Paul Henry, III. 102 MEDICAL PARK DR, STE B 27302 #025-07-1981 L1986 **OTO HNS** *020 †45
LANGLEY, Ricky Lee. 1506 MILES CHAPEL RD, KERNODLE CLINIC 27302 #036-05-1983 L1985 **IM OM** *020 †20,70
MC GRATH, Timothy John. 101 MEDICAL PARK DR 27302 #012-01-2000 L2002 **FM** *020 †18
MEBANE, Giles Yancey. ■ 27302 #036-07-1954 L1954 **UM FM** *071 †18
ORENDORFF, Rebecca Lynn. 100 E DOGWOOD DR 27302 #035-15-2002 L2006 **FM** *020 †18
POLLOCK, Stephen Chaim. 3005 TIMBERLYNE CT 27302 #016-11-1981 L1987 **OPH** *030 †35
SHEIKH, Shehzad Zafar. ■ 27302 #704-01-2002 L2007 **IM** *100 †20
STEIN, David Alan. 101 MEDICAL PARK DR 27302 #023-12-1989 L1999 **FM** *020 †18
STEWART, Suzanne Biehn. ■ 27302 #036-01-2007 **GS** *012
THIES, David Newcomb. 101 MEDICAL PARK DR, KERNODLE CLINIC 27302 #012-05-1993 L1997 **MPD** *020 †20,55
VELDHOUSE, Thomas James. ■ 27302 #016-01-2007 **EM** *012
WILLETT, Glenn Roger. 101 MEDICAL PARK DR, KERNODLE CLINIC MEBANE 27302 #026-04-1988 L1995 **FM** *020 †18
WORAWATTANAKUL, Mingmuang. ■ 27302 #748-11-1988 L1994 **MPD PG** *100 †55
YORK, Serena Famatta. ■ 27302 #610-01-1987 L2000 **IM** *020 †20

MIDLAND – CABARRUS

CLOUD, E Elaine. 12925 HIGHWAY 601, MIDLAND FAMILY MEDICINE 28107 #036-08-1997 L1999 **FM** *020 †18
DY, Marc Kenneth. 12925 HIGHWAY 601, STE 300 28107 #041-09-1993 L1996 **FM** *020 †18
TOGLIA, Joseph Umbert. ■ 28107 #561-17-1951 L1960 **N** *071 †75

MIDWAY PARK – ONSLOW

SHAN, Tanveer H. 241 FREEDOM WAY, STE B 28544 #308-11-1986 L1994 **P ADP** *040

MILL SPRING – POLK

BLOMELEY, Heather Ilene. ■ 28756 #005-12-1991 L1992 **PAN AN** *020 †05
HOPKINS, Richard Glenn. 1400 HIGHWAY 9 N 28756 #025-01-1955 L1976 **GP** *071
LOVE, Harry Morrow Pierce. ■ 28756 #041-02-1966 L1990 **ORS** *071 †40

MILLS RIVER – HENDERSON

NORTON, Howard B. 4184 HAYWOOD RD, IN MILLS RIVER VALLEY 28759 #045-01-1953 L1957 **GP** *071
ROBINSON, Rebekah Ann. 9 CROSSROADS DR 28759 #045-04-1994 L1995 **FM** *020 †18
STEIN, Louis Philip. 344 S MILLS RIVER RD 28759 #036-05-1970 L1970 **CHP** *020 †75
WEBB, Bob L. 9 CROSSROADS DR, MILLS RIVER FAMILY HLTH CT 28759 #017-20-1984 L1992 **FM** *020 †18

MINNEAPOLIS – AVERY

HUDSON, Richard Carl. ■ 28652 #038-40-1959 L1992 **OBG** *071 †30

MINT HILL – MECKLENBURG

BERGER, Erica Lynn. 10545 BLAIR RD 28227 #056-05-2001 L2007 **PD** *020 †55
BIASINI, Benedict A. ■ 28227 #056-06-1943 L1944 **FM** *071
CHEN, Jenny Lee. 11307 HAWTHORNE DR, MINT HILL FAMILY PRACTICE 28227 #010-01-1999 L2006 **FM OBS** *020 †18
GROSS, Pushpa Lall. 7110 LAWYERS RD 28227 #050-02-1984 L1986 **FM** *020 †18
HARVEY, Marc Christopher. 11307 HAWTHORNE DR, MINT HILL FAMILY PRACTICE 28227 #051-01-2000 L2002 **FM** *020 †18 ‡
HEITBRINK, Mark John. 11307 HAWTHORNE DR 28227 #038-40-1980 L1994 **FM** *020 †18
LAWSON, Mary Lou. 7110 LAWYERS RD 28227 #036-01-1984 L1998 **FM** *020 †18
LESTER, Susan Michelle. 11307 HAWTHORNE DR, PRESBYTERIAN REGIONAL HEAL 28227 #051-01-1997 L2000 **FM** *020 †18
MC KOY, Kelvin Leon. ■ 28227 #036-01-2000 *100
MORCOS, Kenneth Andrew. 11304 HAWTHORNE DR, MINT HILL PRACTICE 28227 #038-41-2000 L2001 **FM** *020 †18
MUNHYANG, Lee. ■ 28227 #583-08-1979 L1990 **PD** *020 †55
PATEL, Hiten Kaushik. 7110 LAWYERS RD 28227 #036-01-1995 L1997 **FM** *020 †18
RICHARDSON, Michael S. 10545 BLAIR RD, STE 2100 28227 #036-01-1986 L1990 **IM** *020 †20
SCHWILM, Arlen Lee. ■ 28227 #051-04-1967 L1973 **D** *071 †15
SHARMA, Madhu. ■ 28227 #024-07-1986 L2007 **RO** *080 †80 ‡
SIMON, Stephanie Young. 10545 BLAIR RD, STE 2100 28227 #011-02-2004 L2007 **IM** *020 †20
SPEARS, Mark Alan. 10545 BLAIR RD, STE 2100 28227 #036-01-1991 L2007 **IM** *020 †20

MOCKSVILLE – DAVIE

CAPRIOLA, Michael John. 223 HOSPITAL ST, P O BOX 1209 27028 #007-02-1996 L2004 **FM** *020 †18
CHAMPE-SEAGLE, Melissa R. 375 HOSPITAL ST, STE 200 27028 #036-05-1995 L1997 **IM** *020 †20
DAUBERT, Harlan Beaver. 223 HOSPITAL ST 27028 #041-13-1986 L1992 **ORS** *020 †40
EDWARDS, Joel Lynn. 485 VALLEY RD 27028 #036-05-1976 L1976 **FPG** *020 †18
EVANS, James Harvey. 101 WILKESBORO ST STE 2, 101 WILKESBORO STREET STE 27028 #036-08-1990 L1993 **FM** *020 †18
GONZALEZ, Jesus. 100 RIDGEVIEW DR 27028 #016-11-1987 L1992 **IM** *020 †20
HARRISON, William Henry, III. 485 VALLEY RD, MEDICAL ASSOCIATES OF DAVI 27028 #021-05-1979 L1981 **FM** *020 †18
HEATON, Samuel Arthur, Jr. ■ 27028 #012-01-1946 L1946 **PHP** *071
KIMBERLY, George Douglas. ■ 27028 #036-05-1958 L1958 **FM** *020 †18
KNIGHT, Charlene Presley. ■ 27028 #036-01-2002 L2005 **IM** *020 †20
LUTHER, Annette Marie. ■ 27028 #048-12-1978 L1986 **OBG** *071 †30
NGUYEN, Phuong Minh. 485 VALLEY RD 27028 #011-04-1997 L2005 **FM** *020 †18
PEARCE, Larry Allen. 217 DAYSPRING WAY, DAYSPRING MEDICAL CTR 27028 #036-05-1961 L1961 **N PA** *020 †75
RENFROE, Melanie S. 222 HOSPITAL ST 27028 #027-01-1986 L1989 **FM** *074 †18
RENFROE, William O'Brien. 485 VALLEY RD 27028 #027-01-1986 L1989 **FM** *020 †18
SLATE, Francis Wesley. ■ 27028 #836-02-1947 L1957 **GS** *071 †85
TONIDANDEL, Ashley Maner. ■ 27028 #048-04-2003 L2004 **AN** *100

MONCURE – CHATHAM

BISHOP, Melissa Elizabeth. 7228 MONCURE PITTSBORO RD 27559 #048-14-1993 L1997 **FM** *020 †18
DELGADO, Katharine Cioffi. 7228 MONCURE PITTSBORO RD 27559 #035-01-1998 L2001 **PD GPM** *020 †55,70 ‡
GILMER, Melissa Danielle. 7228 MONCURE PITTSBORO RD 27559 #055-01-2000 L2003 **FM** *020
HOLLINGSWORTH, Jane Dixon. 7228 MONCURE PITTSBORO RD 27559 #036-01-1981 L1984 **IM** *020
LIN, Doris. ■ 27559 #005-02-2001 L2006 **OTO** *020 †45
PITTS, Susan Sajeski. 7228 MONCURE PITTSBORO RD 27559 #041-07-1982 L1984 **PD PHP** *020 †55
TEMPEST, David Lawrence. 7228 MONCURE PITTSBORO RD 27559 #005-14-1986 L1988 **FM** *020 †18
WATSON, Michael C, Jr. 7228 MONCURE PITTSBORO RD 27559 #045-01-1984 L1990 **GS FM** *020 †18
WEEKS, Cynthia Burns. 7228 MONCURE PITTSBORO RD 27559 #008-02-1992 L1996 **FM** *020 †18

MONROE – UNION

ABDA, Sandra Marie. 701 E ROOSEVELT BLVD, STE 600 28112 #041-07-1973 L1978 **ORS OS** *020 †40
ABRAMSON, Daniel J. ■ 28110 #023-01-1938 L1948 **GS** *071 †85
ADEKANMBI, Adebola K. 404 S SUTHERLAND AVE 28112 #690-01-1991 L1999 **IM** *020 †20
ALLISON, David Campbell. 1420 E FRANKLIN ST, MONROE FAMILY MED CTR 28112 #051-04-1992 L1998 **FM** *020 †18
ANDERSON, Evelyn K. 1301 DOVE ST 28112 #008-01-1993 L1994 **FM** *020 †18
AUSTIN, Robert Gray, Jr. ■ 28112 #036-05-1970 L1970 **OPH** *071 †35
BARTLEY, Karen Marcella. 1106 REYNOLDS ST 28112 #001-06-1995 L2000 **FM** *020 †18
BILLETT, Jeanette Marie. 1420 ELLEN ST 28112 #038-45-1986 L2000 **CD** *020 †20
BIZZELL, Nancy Evelyn. 3016 OLD CHARLOTTE HWY # C, CAROLINA OCCMED, PLLC 28110 #012-05-1981 L1984 **IM** *020 †20
BLANK, Roy Crary. 1640 E ROOSEVELT BLVD 28112 #023-01-1972 L1986 **NTR IM** *020 †20
BLOOS, Werner Michael. 1423 E FRANKLIN ST, STE B 28112 #041-12-1985 L1996 **CD IM** *020 †20
BOBBILI, Krishna Kanth. 600 HOSPITAL DR 28112 #496-01-1996 L2005 **IM** *020
BOWER, Edward Birch. 900 E SUNSET DR # A 28112 #041-02-1970 L1977 **GS VS** *020 †85
BROUSE, Gregory Michael. 1650 FAULK ST, STE A 28112 #023-01-1993 L1999 **HO** *020 †20
BROWN, Justin Chamberlin. 701 E ROOSEVELT BLVD 28112 #036-01-1999 L2006 **OPH** *020 †35
CAMPO, Daniel. 1106 REYNOLDS ST, STE 100 28112 #048-02-1982 L2002 **FM** *020 †18
CATTIE, John Vincent. 1315 E SUNSET DR, STE 100 28112 #041-02-1974 L1979 **GS OS** *020 †85
COLVIN, Anthony David. 1338 E SUNSET DR 28112 #047-06-1992 L1994 **GE** *020 †20
COOK, James William. 1315 E SUNSET DR, STE 100 28112 #048-04-1997 L2005 **GS** *020 †85
DAVID, Glen James. 701 E ROOSEVELT BLVD, STE 600 28112 #422-01-2002 L2007 **PM** *100 †60
DAYAL, Ashrito Kumar. 701 E ROOSEVELT BLVD, STE 600 28112 #495-27-1977 L1995 **IM** *020 †20
DESAI, Tanvi Naresh. 1328 PATTERSON ST, UNION PEDIATRICS 28112 #038-45-2004 L2007 **PD** *100 †55
DOOHAN, Thomas James. 600 HOSPITAL DR, CAROLINAS MEDICAL CENTER U 28112 #539-06-2001 L2006 **EM** *020 †16
DUNCAN-BUTLER, Susan Oliv. 1328 PATTERSON ST, UNION PEDIATRICS 28112 #566-01-1995 L2001 **PD** *020 †55
ERCKMAN, Paul Neff. 1307 E FRANKLIN ST E B, BOX 629 28112 #012-01-1963 L1993 **PD** *020 †55
EUSEBIO, Jose Emmanuel S. 1420 ELLEN ST 28112 #748-02-1982 L1997 **CD IM** *020 †20
EVANS, David Arnold. 1408 FRANKLIN ST 28110 #036-01-1967 L1967 **GYN** *071 †30
FAROOQ, Ahmed Omer. 613 E ROOSEVELT BLVD 28112 #704-02-1990 L2005 **ID** *020 †20
FINCK-ROTHMAN, Denise R. 613 E ROOSEVELT BLVD 28110 #035-03-1975 L1999 **FM** *020 †18
FORESTIER DIAZ, Pablo. 407 W ROOSEVELT BLVD 28110 #042-01-1972 L1995 **IM** *020
FREIMAN, Sarise. 1423 E FRANKLIN ST, STE A 28112 #035-09-1976 L1995 **N** *020 †75
GOLDBERGER, Neal Michael. 701 E ROOSEVELT BLVD, STE 200A 28112 #024-07-1982 L2001 **AN PMM** *020 †05
GREENBERG, William Roger. 503 E WINDSOR ST B 28112 #048-02-1971 L1982 **AN RO** *020 †05

■ = Address Information Privacy Protected

HAGLER, Dan N. 600 HOSPITAL DR, CMC - UNION HOSPITAL 28112 #051-01-1982 L1987 ID MDM *030 †20 ‡

HAIGLER, Stuart Steven. 1640 CAMPUS PARK DR, STE C 28112 #036-05-1985 L1987 IM *020 †20

HALL, Theresa Stelling. ROOSEVELT BLVD, UNION CTY HEALTH DEPT 28112 #035-48-1992 L1995 FM *020 †18

HARTNESS, John F, Jr. 600 HOSPITAL DR, CMC UNION 28112 #036-01-1970 L1970 EM IM *020 †20,16

HAWKINS, Kay Lawhon. ■ 28112 #036-05-1983 L1987 OBG *020 †30

HELMUTH, Willard Vernon. 1224 W ROOSEVELT BLVD, UNION COUNTY HEALTH DEPT. 28110 #038-06-1967 L2000 NPM *020 †55

HOLLER, Jody Dale. 602 S SUTHERLAND AVE, ROCKY RIVER FAMILY PHYSICI 28112 #305-01-1999 L2002 FM *020 †18

HOLLIER, Chandra Smith. 1408 E FRANKLIN ST, ORMAND CENTER FOR WOMEN 28112 #036-01-1994 L2001 OBG *020 †30

HOOVER, Charles Henry, III. 1303 DOVE ST, 1303 DOVE STREET 28112 #036-01-1977 L1977 IM *020 †20

HOPPER, Clyde G, Jr. PO BOX 1429 28111 #045-01-1950 L1961 R *071 †80

HOWARD, Chad Daniel. 600 HOSPITAL DR, CAROLINAS MEDICAL CENTER U 28112 #036-05-1995 L2002 IM *020 †20

HUTCHINGS, Jeffrey Charle. ■ 28110 #019-02-2005 L2008 FP *012

IBRAHIM, Nadia Makram. 404 S SUTHERLAND AVE 28112 #915-03-1967 L1996 PD *020 †55

IGBINADOLOR, Awawu E. 600 HOSPITAL DR 28112 #690-06-1988 L2000 IM *020 †20

IPAPO, Virgilio S. 1315 E SUNSET DR, STE 100 28112 #748-01-1971 L1986 GS VS *020

IULIANO, Philip James. 1420 ELLEN ST 28112 #024-16-1989 L1991 CD *020 †20

JEWELL, Gary Welch. 6 E FRANKLIN ST, UNION OBSTETRICIAN & 28112 #020-02-1971 L1974 OBG *020 †30 ‡

JOHNSON, Paul Einar. ■ 28110 #026-04-1955 L1992 R *071 †80

JOHNSON, Tiv Ashanti. 1315 E SUNSET DR, STE 100 28112 #041-01-1998 L2005 GS *100 †85

KADIJEVIC, Robert John. 1328 PATTERSON ST, UNION PEDIATRICS 28112 #021-01-2001 L2004 PD *020

KING, Joseph John. 701 E ROOSEVELT BLVD, STE 600 28112 #041-02-1973 L1978 ORS *071 †40

KITCHIN, Alvin Paul, Jr. 1420 E FRANKLIN ST, MONROE FAMILY MEDICAL CENT 28112 #036-05-1962 L1962 FM D *020 †18

KOWALCHUK, Glen John. 1420 ELLEN ST 28112 #033-06-1982 L1989 CD IM *050 †20

LAMARQUE, Donna Lynn. ■ 28110 #051-07-2006 FP *012

LANE, Millicent A Francis. 1424 E FRANKLIN ST 28112 #011-03-1987 L1987 OBG *020

LEITNER, Thomas Courtenay. 1428 ELLEN ST STE A 28112 #045-01-1979 L1986 U *020 †95

LESTER, William Mckinley. 1106 REYNOLDS ST, STE 102 28112 #051-01-1997 L1998 FM *020 †18

LOPER, Peter Louis. 1428 ELLEN ST, STE B 28112 #038-06-1976 L1981 PUD *020 †20

MAC, Ivan. 1410 E FRANKLIN ST 28112 #036-05-2000 L2004 OPH *020 †35

MC CULLOCH, Harlan Arthur. 600 HOSPITAL DR 28112 #038-43-1984 L1985 AN GP *020 †05

MC DONALD, Camille A. 1640 E ROOSEVELT BLVD, SOUTHERN PIEDMONT PRIMARY 28112 #035-09-1999 L2006 FM *020 †18

MEADE, John Bernard. 808 CIRCLE DR, ORTHOCAROLINA 28112 #021-01-1986 L1991 ORS *020 †40

MENENDEZ, Carolyn Sue. 1315 E SUNSET DR, UNION SURGICAL ASSOCIATES 28112 #051-07-1998 L2008 GS *020 †85

MILLER, Harold Milton. 600 HOSPITAL DR, UNION REGIONAL MEDICAL CTR 28112 #005-15-1972 L1985 EM FM *020 †18,16

NAGEL, William Frank. 412 E FRANKLIN ST 28112 #016-11-1985 L1993 FM *020 †18

NELSON, Donald Carl. 600 HOSPITAL DR 28112 #041-03-1970 L1974 FM *071 †16

OGBATA, Sylvester Izuchuk. 404 S SUTHERLAND AVE, FIRST CARE MEDICAL CLINIC 28112 #690-12-1994 L2004 IM *020 †20

OKOLI, Alphonsus. 404 S SUTHERLAND AVE, GRIFFIN INTERNAL MEDICINE 28112 #690-04-1984 L1996 IM *020 †20

ORMAND, Thoman Lane. 1408 E FRANKLIN ST 28112 #036-01-1958 L1958 OBG *071 †30

OUTEN, Ronnie Brian. 600 HOSPITAL DR 28112 #036-01-1998 L1999 FM *020 †18

PAK, Chinho. 1190 W ROOSEVELT BLVD 28110 #045-04-1999 L2003 P *020 †75

PATEL, Latika Dushyant. 1424 E FRANKLIN ST, CAROLINA OB/GYN 28112 #495-19-1975 L1989 OBG *040 †20

PATIL, Chandrashek Yadao. 1106 REYNOLDS ST, STE 100 28112 #036-07-1998 L2002 FM *020 †18

PERERA, Srimathie Indira. 412 E FRANKLIN ST, CLINIC 28112 #220-01-1976 L1995 IM *020 †20

PERKINS, Gwendolyn Myrtis. 600 HOSPITAL DR 28112 #041-13-1977 L1980 FM *020 †18

RICHARDS, Michael Douglas. 613 E ROOSEVELT BLVD 28112 #025-07-1987 L2004 FM *020 †18

SEEN, Nelson Der. 1420 ELLEN ST 28112 #036-05-1988 L1995 CD *020 †20

SINK, David Walker. ■ 28112 #036-05-1996 L1999 NPM *012 †55

SNYDER, Alexander Benj. 1420 E FRANKLIN ST, MONROE FAMILY MEDICAL CENT 28112 #035-03-1965 L1973 IM *020

SOWDEN, Richard Guy, Jr. 1503 E FRANKLIN ST 28112 #041-02-1970 L1978 U *020 †95 ‡

SPECTOR, Leo Reuben. 808 CIRCLE DR 28112 #024-16-2001 L2006 ORS *020

SPRINGS, Boyd Williams. 806 CIRCLE DR 28112 #045-01-1960 L1965 GP OBS *020

STACK, Robert Kevin. 1423 E FRANKLIN ST, STE B 28112 #025-07-1981 L1983 CD IM *020 †20

STAMATAKOS, Theodoros S. 1428 ELLEN ST STE A 28112 #035-09-1988 L2000 U *020 †95

STEPHENSON, Stephen. 1338 E SUNSET DR 28112 #422-01-1997 L2004 GE *020 †20

STEWART, H Lee. ■ 28110 #036-07-1965 L1965 OPH *020 †35

STRANGE, Kristin Kirk. 3816 SARDIS CHURCH RD, CTR FOR CHILD & ADOL MED 28110 #045-04-1994 L1995 PD *020 †55

SURESH, R. 1428 ELLEN ST, STE B 28112 #495-09-1986 L2006 PCC IM *020 †20

TAN, James Michael Aruj. 600 HOSPITAL DR, UNION REGIONAL MEDICAL CTR 28112 #748-11-1980 L1991 FM *020 †18

TAYLOR, Jimmy Lynn. ■ 28112 #036-05-1962 L1962 FM *071 †18

TAYLOR, Richard Allen. ■ 28112 #036-05-1969 L1969 PD *075 †55

TELLIS, Valencia. 1106 REYNOLDS ST, STE 100 28112 #025-12-2000 L2003 FM *020 †18

THEVAOS, George Philip. 3816 SARDIS CHURCH RD, STE 108 28110 #012-01-1995 L1999 PD *020 †55

TSERING, Chock. 1414 ELLEN ST 28112 #495-52-1977 L2001 N PME *020 †75

TWERDI, Christine D. 3816 SARDIS CHURCH RD, STE 108 28110 #036-01-2002 L2005 *020 †55

VICK, John C. 1106 REYNOLDS ST, STE 100 28112 #036-01-1977 L1977 FM *020 †18

WALK, Philip. 600 HOSPITAL DR 28112 #038-43-1982 L1987 AN PME *020 †05

WETTER, James M. 820 BRIDGEWATER DR 28112 #035-06-1974 L1978 FM IM *040 †18

WHINNA, James David. 1744 WILLIAMS RD 28110 #036-01-1981 L1982 GS VS *020 †85

WISE, Jaime Christine. 1106 REYNOLDS ST, UNION FAMILY PRACTICE 28112 #011-02-2004 L2008 FP *012

YUDELL, Robert Benj. 701 E ROOSEVELT BLVD, LAUREL EYE ASSOCIATES 28112 #036-07-1954 L1957 OPH *071 †35

MONTREAT — BUNCOMBE

ALVIS, Joel Lawrence. ■ 28757 #047-06-1953 L1954 U *071 †95

CLARK, Newton Thos, Jr. PO BOX 370 28757 #045-01-1966 L1966 ORS GP *071 †40

NEALE, Henry Whitehead. ■ 28757 #051-04-1964 L1994 PS GS *071 †85,65

TOPPLE, Stanley Craig. ■ 28757 #012-05-1957 L1981 ORS *020 †40

VERNER, Hugh David. 132 KANAWHA DR 28757 #023-07-1943 L1947 IM *071 †20

MOORESBORO — RUTHERFORD

JAMES, Charles Newton. 605 NC 120 HWY 28114 #051-04-1967 L1968 GP GPM *071

RALPH, Robert Allan. 605 NC 120 HWY, RUTHERFORD EAST MEDICAL SV 28114 #025-07-1979 L1994 FM *020 †18

MOORESVILLE — IREDELL

ADAMS, Todd J. 146 MEDICAL PARK RD # 206, LAKESHORE WOMENS SPCLSTS 28117 #036-01-1997 L2003 OBG *020 †30

AJJAN, Mahdi. 171 FAIRVIEW RD, LAKE NORMAN REGIONAL HOSPI 28117 #875-03-1995 L2007 IM *020 †20

ALHUSSAINI, James Talat. 131 MEDICAL PARK RD, STE 303 28117 #036-01-1991 L2001 OBG *020 †30

AL-KHALDI, Aous Salim. 106 JADE SPRING CT, 106 JADE SPRING CT. 28117 #875-01-1971 L1977 R *020 †80

ALLAN, John Jos. 359 WILLIAMSON RD 28117 #019-02-1991 L1997 CD *020 †20

ALLEN, James Browden, III. 157 PROFESSIONAL PARK DR, STE A 28117 #036-01-1998 L2001 IM *020 †20

APPLETON, Rebecca Jane. 478 WILLIAMSON RD, STE B 28117 #023-01-1996 L1999 FM *020 †18

BARKER, Timothy Andrew. 357 WILLIAMSON RD, PIEDMONT HEALTHCARE, PA 28117 #036-05-1997 FSM *020 †18

BARTELL, Christi Nacole. 142 PROFESSIONAL PARK DR, STE 300 28117 #045-04-2002 L2006 PD *100

BARTON, Dewey Lockwood. ■ 28117 #036-07-1956 L1956 R *071 †80

BEACH, Laurie Jeanne. 131 MEDICAL PARK RD, STE 308 28117 #047-06-1984 L1989 AN *020 †05

BENSON, James A. 171 FAIRVIEW RD, P O BOX 3250 28117 #024-05-1974 L2000 IM *020 †20

BERTSCH, Michelle Marie. 123 PROFESSIONAL PARK DR, SUITE200 28117 #038-43-1993 L2002 GS *020 †85

BIEHLER, Darren Foster. 131 MEDICAL PARK RD, STE 308 28117 #036-01-1988 L1994 AN *020 †05

BLACKBURN, Brian Bruce. 118 GATEWAY BLVD, STE A 28117 #045-01-1984 L1985 IM *020 †20

BLUE, Martin Luther. ■ 28115 #036-08-1995 L2005 PS *020

BRADLEY, Steven Howell. 131 MEDICAL PARK RD, STE 201 28117 #021-05-1988 L1990 AN PME *020 †05

BRADS, Mackenzie Marie. ■ 28117 #036-08-2007 FP *012

BUNDY, Robert Francis, Jr. 130 PLANTATION RIDGE DR 28117 #036-08-1993 L1994 FM *020 †18

CALHOUN, Aubrey Danl. 171 FAIRVIEW RD 28117 #036-01-1983 L1986 IM *020 †20

CAMPBELL, Edward Stephen. 357 WILLIAMSON RD 28117 #036-05-1981 L1984 FM *020 †18

CAMPBELL, Francis Michael. 123 PROFESSIONAL PARK DR, STE 200 28117 #045-01-1979 L1981 GS *020 †85

CASTIGLIA, Anthony J. 570 WILLIAMSON RD, STE C 28117 #010-02-1957 L1995 FM *020 †18

CASTILLO, Alissandro R. 478 WILLIAMSON RD, STE B 28117 #036-05-1992 L1999 FM *020 †18

CHANEY, Arthur William. 170 MEDICAL PARK RD 28117 #051-01-1995 L2000 RO *020 †80

COHEN, Donald L. 132 GATEWAY BLVD 28117 #035-06-1980 L1988 OPH *020 †35

CRAM, Michael Raymond. 137 PROFESSIONAL PARK DR, STE D 28117 #018-03-1993 L1999 U *020 †95

CROWE-CHINUNTDET, Tonya. 131 MEDICAL PARK RD 28117 #036-05-1992 L1996 OBG *071 †30

DAVIS, Peyton Wayne. 123 PROFESSIONAL PARK DR, STE 200 28117 #012-01-1998 L1999 GS *020 †85

DEAN, Susan Jane. 122 GATEWAY BLVD, STE D 28117 #038-43-1985 L1996 PS *020 †65

DEDDENS, Alan Eugene. 359 WILLIAMSON RD 28117 #020-02-1987 L1994 OTO A *020 †45

DITELLA, Philip John. ■ 28117 #016-43-1972 L1973 NEP IM *071 †20

DORAZIO, Edmund, Jr. 171 FAIRVIEW RD 28117 #035-15-1975 L2004 EM FM *020 †18,16

DOSHI, Avani Mahendra. 656 CARPENTER AVE 28115 #038-41-2000 L2004 PD *020 †55

DUBOIS, Craig Danl. 124 PROFESSIONAL PARK DR, STE A 28117 #038-40-1990 L1994 N *020 †75

DUMOND, Sara O. 142 PROFESSIONAL PARK DR, STE 300 28117 #055-01-2000 L2002 PD *020 †55

DUNAWAY, Byron Edward. 359 WILLIAMSON RD 28117 #012-05-1989 L1989 ORS *020 †40

DUNLOP, Richard Wm. 118 GATEWAY BLVD, STE E 28117 #011-02-1980 L2007 DR R *020 †80 ‡

EAGLE, David Anthony. 170 MEDICAL PARK RD, STE 101 28117 #051-01-1993 L2000 HO *020 †20

EAGLE, Khanh Le. 656 CARPENTER AVE 28115 #051-01-1993 L2000 PD *020 †55

EDMISTON, William J, Jr. 131 MEDICAL PARK RD, STE 308 28117 #305-01-1991 L2000 APM *020

ELKINS, Stephanie Banasza. 130 PLANTATION RIDGE DR, LAKESIDE FAMILY PHYSICIANS 28117 #016-11-2002 L2003 FM *020 †18

ENYEART, Peter Jay. ■ 28117 #038-41-1967 L2006 PUD CCM *071 †20

FAHEY, Sean Michael. 157 PROFESSIONAL PARK DR, STE A 28117 #036-05-1998 L2002 RHU *020 †20

FERGUSON, Amy Poteat. 656 CARPENTER AVE, LAKE NORMAN PEDIATRICS 28115 #036-05-1984 L1987 PD *020 †55

FERGUSON, Stephen Dexter. 137 PROFESSIONAL PARK DR, STE A 28117 #036-05-1984 L1987 IM *020 †20

FRY, Patrick Louis. ■ 28117 #036-01-1993 L1996 IM *020 †20

GATLIN, John Chas. 548 WILLIAMSON RD, STE 6 28117 #045-01-1989 L1998 IM *020 †20

GATLIN, Lu Vaughan. 548 WILLIAMSON RD, STE 6 28117 #045-01-1990 L1999 IM *020 †20

GAUNT, George Loren, Jr. PO BOX 3460 28117 #008-01-1982 L1983 GP *020

GILLIS, John Francis. 185 JOE KNOX AVE 28117 #023-12-1984 L1995 OPH *020 †35

GISH, David Lawrence. 123 PROFESSIONAL PARK DR, STE 200 28117 #019-02-1993 L1998 GS *020 †85

GOODSON, Mark A. 114 WELTON WAY, STE A 28117 #654-01-1991 L1997 PM PMM *020 †60

GRAJEWSKI, Robert Sigmund. 131 MEDICAL PARK RD, STE 305 28117 #035-47-1978 L1987 U *020 †95

GRIGSBY, Hardin Bland. ■ 28117 #017-20-1955 L1965 GYN REN *071 †30

GROSS, Thomas Emil. 417 E STATESVILLE AVE 28115 #008-02-1974 L1989 FM FPG *020 †18

HAAHS, Michael M. 134 MEDICAL PARK RD # 100 28117 #583-03-1988 L1994 IM GE *020 †20

HALL, Gregory B. 150 FAIRVIEW RD, STE 300 28117 #048-14-1990 L1996 GS *020 †85

HANCOCK, Nancy Lucille. ■ 28117 #036-01-2008 *012

HARDEE, Michael Wayne. 444 WILLIAMSON RD, STE E 28117 #036-07-1996 L2000 FM *020 †18

HARTLE, Edgar Owen. 171 FAIRVIEW RD, DEPT OF PATH LK NORMAN REG 28117 #041-14-1981 L1983 PTH EM *020 †50,16

HEAFNER, Bob Oliver. ■ 28117 #036-05-1958 L1958 GP OS *071

HEIDER, Timothy Ryan. 123 PROFESSIONAL PARK DR, STE 200 28117 #036-01-1999 L2000 GS *020 †85

HENDERSON, Andrew M, Jr. ■ 28115 #036-05-1950 L1950 FM *071

HILLSGROVE, David Curtis. 124 WELTON WAY 28117 #036-01-1988 L1994 ORS OSM *020 †40

HOLMES, Gilbert Larry. 417 E STATESVILLE AVE, PRIMARY CARE ASSOCIATES 28115 #012-01-2003 L2006 FM *020 †18

HOWE, Harold Ragan, Jr. 131 MEDICAL PARK RD, STE 202 28117 #036-05-1980 L1982 TS VS *020 †85,90

HUFFMAN, Ronald Chas. 798 OAK RIDGE FARM HWY, STE A 28115 #036-01-1979 L1980 FM *020 †18

JACKSON, William Thos. 131 MEDICAL PARK RD, STE 208 28117 #019-02-1964 L2002 ORS HS *020 †40

JAMES, Mary Margaret. 142 PROFESSIONAL PARK DR, STE 300 28117 #051-04-1997 L2000 PD *020 †55

JESSUP, Ryan Lea. 311 WILLIAMSON RD, STE 100 28117 #036-01-1999 L2002 PD *020 †55

JOHNSON, John Anthony. 858 BRAWLEY SCHOOL RD, STE C 28117 #020-02-1997 L2000 *020

JOHNSON, Matthew J. 131 MEDICAL PARK RD, STE 206 28117 #011-02-1996 L1999 GS *020

JUNG, Ki Soo. 157 PROFESSIONAL PARK DR 28117 #036-05-1999 L2004 CN N *020 †75

KILBY, Michael W. 359 WILLIAMSON RD 28117 #654-01-1990 L1998 FM *020 †18

KIM, Shawn S. 930 W WILSON AVE 28117 #025-07-1997 L2004 IM *020 †20

KLANDUCH, Frank Anthony. ■ 28117 #005-12-1997 L2005 EM *020 †16

KOEHLER, Daniel N. 134 MEDICAL PARK RD, STE 111 28117 #041-77-1989, ▲ L1996 CD IM *020

KONSTANDT, David Benjamin. 137 PROFESSIONAL PARK DR, STE D 28117 #025-07-1999 L2005 U *020 †95

KRUMDIECK, Richard. 156 CENTRE CHURCH RD STE 2, ONCOLOGY SPECIALISTS 28117 #001-02-1986 L1997 HEM *020 †20

KUO, Timothy. 170 MEDICAL PARK RD, STE 101 28117 #047-05-2000 L2005 HO *100 †20

LATZ, John Edward, Jr. 116 S MAIN ST, STE 205 28115 #036-05-1991 L1992 P *020 †75

LATZ, Tracy Thompson. 116 S MAIN ST STE 302 28115 #036-05-1990 L1991 P *020 †75

LIEU, Chong-Hieun. 930 W WILSON AVE 28117 #583-02-1970 L1977 GP PD *020 †55

LOSINSKI, Tiana Noelle. 150 FAIRVIEW RD, STE 210 28117 #011-04-2004 L2007 FM *020 †18

LOUGHRIDGE, Carole Jean. 930 W WILSON AVE 28117 #048-15-1989 L1993 IM *020

MARAMRAJ, Kishan Rao. 125 DAYS INN DR 28117 #021-05-1997 L2004 FM *020 †18

MARSHALL, Lisa Gayle. 311 WILLIAMSON RD, STE 100 28117 #045-01-1983 L2001 PD *020 †55

MATHER, Bruce Scott. 130 PLANTATION RIDGE DR, LAKESIDE FAMILY PHYSICIANS 28117 #045-01-1994 L2001 FM *020 †18

MATHEW, Thomas Basil. 652 CARPENTER AVE 28115 #055-02-1994 L1997 IM *020 †20

MATTHEWS, Roland Dellwood. 140 CARRIAGE CLUB DR 28117 #023-01-1948 L1948 FM OM *071 †18

MC DONALD, James Patrick. 124 WELTON WAY 28117 #025-01-1987 L1993 ORS *020 †40

MC MULLEN, Jonathan N. 340 RIVERWOOD RD, AESTHETIC ANESTHESIA, PA 28117 #021-01-1992 L2005 AN *020 †05

MC NABB, James Wm. 455 E STATESVILLE AVE 28115 #011-04-1982 L1985 FM *020 †18

MECHAEL, Shawky Fahmy M. ■ 28117 #915-03-1954 L1996 OBG *071 †30

MEETZE, Keith Adam. 131 MEDICAL PARK RD STE 30, LAKE NORMAN EARS NOSE & TH 28117 #045-01-1999 L2004 OTO *100 †45

MELVIN, Teresa Bowen. 131 MEDICAL PARK RD, STE 303 28117 #036-01-1987 L1989 OBG *020 †30

MILLER, Michael Grant, Jr. 131 MEDICAL PARK RD, STE 303 28117 #036-05-1999 L2003 OBG *020 †30

MILLER, Robert B. 151 KEEL CT 28117 #065-01-1977 L1982 OTO HNS *071 †45

MONTGOMERY, Emmett F. 191A W PLAZA DR, ADVANCED HEALTHCARE 28117 #036-08-1989 L1992 FM *020 †18

MONTGOMERY, Rebecca Piles. 191A W PLAZA DR 28117 #020-12-1989 L1996 FM *020 †18

MURPHY, John Fletcher. ■ 28117 #010-02-1967 L1969 IM ID *071 †20

NABORS, Emily Marie. 396 WILLIAMSON RD, PRIMARY CARE ASSOCIATES 28115 #045-04-1999 L2002 FM *020 †18 ‡

NANCE, Alisa Carrigan. 150 FAIRVIEW RD, STE 210 28117 #036-05-1996 L1999 FM *020 †18 ‡

NAVARRO-MCGUINESS, Cheryl. ■ 28115 #028-79-2003, ▲ L2006 FM *020

NIELSEN, Jeffrey Winther. 170 MEDICAL PARK RD, STE 140 28117 #011-03-1987 L2000 NEP IM *020 †20

OBI, Augustine. 930 W WILSON AVE, TRINITY HEALTH CARE 28117 #690-02-1981 L1994 IM END *020 †20

O'DONNELL, Laura. 656 CARPENTER AVE 28115 #422-01-1999 L2003 PD *020

O'LENIC, Timothy David. 131 MEDICAL PARK RD, STE 308 28117 #011-04-1987 L1999 AN *020 †05

PANUSKI, Rebecca M. 130 PLANTATION RIDGE DR, STE 100 28117 #012-01-1995 L1998 FM *020 †18

PATEL, Manish Govind. 157 PROFESSIONAL PARK DR, PARK DRIVE 28117 #012-01-1998 L2000 IM *020 †20

PATEL, Rajal Mahesh. 396 WILLIAMSON RD, PRIMARY CARE ASSOCIATES 28117 #025-01-1992 L1999 FM *020 †18

PATEL, Tushar R. 132 GATEWAY BLVD 28117 #035-06-1995 L2004 OPH *020 †35

POLSKY, Stewart Michael. 137 PROFESSIONAL PARK DR, STE D 28117 #041-09-1995 L2002 U *020 †95

POOR, Christopher Sutton. 170 MEDICAL PARK RD, STE 103 28117 #012-01-1995 L2004 PCC *020 †20

POTH, Robert Alexander. 311 WILLIAMSON RD, STE 100 28117 #041-13-1996 L2006 PD *020 ‡

RAVIN, Adam Gates. 146 MEDICAL PARK RD, STE 106 28117 #036-07-2000 L2003 PS *020

RAY, Robin Costner. 656 CARPENTER AVE, LAKE NORMAN PEDIATRICS ASS 28115 #036-05-1984 L1987 PD *020

RENICH, Michaela Elaine. 417 E STATESVILLE AVE 28115 #035-09-1995 L1998 FM *020 †18

RINKER, Shelley Husband. 311 WILLIAMSON RD STE 100 28117 #045-04-1989 L1992 PD *020 †55

ROBLES, Emma Enid. ■ 28117 #041-13-1958 L1960 GP PD *071

ROQUE, Susan Lovejoy. 131 MEDICAL PARK RD, STE 304 28117 #036-07-1991 L1995 OBG *020 †30

RYAN, Michael Whiting. ■ 28117 #025-07-2000 L2007 GE *020

SALLAH, Joumana Hassani. 412 E CENTER AVE, TELECARE MENTAL HLTH SVS 28115 #875-02-1989 L2004 P *020 ‡

SCHERCZINGER, Richard. 134 MEDICAL PARK RD, STE 111 28117 #036-01-1994 L2000 CD *020 †20

SCHIMEL, Lawrence Fay. 131 MEDICAL PARK RD 28117 #034-01-1970 L1989 OBG *020 †30

SHERRILL, Scott Anderson. 131 MEDICAL PARK RD, STE 204 28117 #045-01-1984 L1989 ORS *020

SIEGEL, Margaret Payne. 142 PROFESSIONAL PARK DR, STE 300 28117 #012-01-1997 L2000 PD *020 †55

SKEEN, William Waldo. 417 E STATESVILLE AVE 28115 #010-01-1960 L1960 GP OBG *071

STANLEY, Rodney Jay. 124 WELTON WAY 28117 #019-02-2000 L2006 ORS *020

STOWE, Stephen Paul. 170 MEDICAL PARK RD, STE 140 28117 #038-06-1964 L1992 GE IM *020 †20

STOWE-ONG, Michelle M. 134 MEDICAL PARK RD, STE 108 28117 #012-05-1992 L1998 IM *020 †20

SUGARMAN, Daniel Israel. 134 MEDICAL PARK RD, STE 111 28117 #016-11-1976 L1994 CD *020 †20

SUGARMAN, Joel Harold. 150 FAIRVIEW RD, STE 110 28117 #036-05-2000 L2005 D *020 †15

SURDULESCU, Sever Catalin. 170 MEDICAL PARK RD, STE 103 28117 #781-01-1992 L2000 PCC *020 †20

THOMAS, Lisa Schroepfer. 136 GATEWAY BLVD STE A, ADOLESCENT MEDICINE, PA 28117 #011-03-1992 L1994 PD *020 †55

THORNER, Kim Marie. ■ 28117 #035-08-1995 L2006 PTH *012 †50

TILT, Elizabeth Ellen. 136 GATEWAY BLVD, STE A 28117 #051-07-1992 L1995 PD *020 †55

VALLET, Herbert Lawrence. ■ 28117 #064-01-1965 L1965 PD END *071 †55

VANNESS, William Charles. 128 E PLAZA DR, THE PAIN & REHAB INSTITUTE 28115 #017-20-1996 L2000 PM PME *020 †60

VORWALD, Frederick Urban. 357 WILLIAMSON RD 28117 #056-06-1983 L1995 FM *020 †18

WARREN, Deborah Parry. 131 MEDICAL PARK RD, STE 303 28117 #036-05-1996 L2000 OBG *020 †30

WARREN, Thomas Brent. 131 MEDICAL PARK RD # 302, THROAT 28117 #036-05-1994 L2000 OTO *020 †45

WASHINGTON, Marcus Ashton. 125 DAYS INN DR 28117 #038-45-1999 L2005 FM *020 †18

WATTS, Greta Yvonne. 104 PIER 33 DR, UNIT 316 28117 #036-07-1993 L1997 OBG *020 †30

WETTREICH, Herb Lee. 131 MEDICAL PARK RD, STE 302 28117 #033-05-1984 L1990 OTO GS *020 †45

WEVER, Marcus Lynn. 400 E STATESVILLE AVE, STE 200 28115 #016-45-1987 L1989 GS *020 †85

WILKINS, Dieter Harry. ■ 28117 #035-09-1964 L1972 GP GPM *020

WILLIAMS, Randy Paul. 131 MEDICAL PARK RD, STE 201 28117 #039-05-1989 L1990 AN PME *020

WILSON, James David. 171 FAIRVIEW RD 28117 #038-40-1988 L1991 OBG FM *020 †30,18

WILSON, Thomas Scott. 149 YEAGER RD 28117 #041-02-1981 L1984 EM *020 †16

WILSON, Virgil Archibald. 131 MEDICAL PARK RD, STE 201 28117 #036-01-1954 L1954 AN *071 †05

WOLFE, Steven Frederick. 114 GATEWAY BLVD, STE D 28117 #005-02-1992 L1996 D *020 †15

YATES, Christopher John. 131 MEDICAL PARK RD, LAKE NORMAN ANESTHESIA 28117 #012-01-2001 L2005 AN *020 †05

ZOLZER, James G. 146 MEDICAL PARK RD # 206 28117 #010-02-1985 L1988 OBG *020 †30

MORAVIAN FALLS – WILKES

BENNETT, John Northwood. ■ 28654 #067-01-1947 L1951 R NM *071 †80

MOREHEAD CITY – CARTERET

AQUADRO, Charles Frasure. 3500 ARENDELL ST 28557 #047-06-1952 L1969 GP OM *071

BATES, Thomas Edward. 3714 GUARDIAN AVE, STE W 28557 #041-13-1992 L2004 ORS *020 †40

BELL, Jennifer Leigh. ■ 28557 #038-43-1987 L1989 EM *020 †16

BELL, Michael Anthony. 3714 GUARDIAN AVE, STE W 28557 #036-08-1985 L1989 GS *020 †85

BEYER, Alfred J, III. 3500 ARENDELL ST 28557 #036-01-1993 L2001 DR *020 †80

BLOOMFIELD, Richard Alan. 3500 ARENDELL ST 28557 #023-01-1970 L1978 FM AM *020 †18

BORDEN, Richard W. 3714 GUARDIAN AVE, STE W 28557 #036-07-1953 L1955 GP OBG *071

BREEDEN, Thomas Eugene. 1205 ARENDELL ST STE C 28557 #045-01-1960 L1963 GYN *071 †30

BROCKMAN, Robert James. 3714 GUARDIAN AVE, STE W 28557 #045-01-1988 L1995 VS GS *020 †85

BUSTEED, Timothy Alan. 4725 COUNTRY CLUB RD 28557 #017-20-1994 L1999 IM *020 †20

CADER, Cas. 505 N 35TH ST 28557 #041-07-1985 L1992 FM *020 †18

CARBONELL, Antonio Miguel. 215 N 35TH ST 28557 #010-02-1969 L1984 PS *020 †65 ‡

CHANCE, James Kenneth. 3504 BRIDGES ST, COASTAL EYE CLINIC PA 28557 #036-05-1976 L1976 OPH *020 †35

CHARLESWORTH, Amy Sue. 3500 ARENDELL ST 28557 #051-04-1999 L2004 FPG *020 †18

COLES, Robert Emmet. 3714 GUARDIAN AVE, STE W 28557 #036-07-1993 L1999 ORS *020 †40

CONRAD, Katrina. 312 COMMERCE AVE, STE A 28557 #034-01-1994 L2002 OBG *020 †30

COTTON, Leonard Bryan, Jr. 5420 HWY 70 W 28557 #023-07-1964 L2003 **IM PUD** *020 †20
D'ANDREA, Nicole Maria. 3511 JOHN PLATT DR, CARTERET OB-GYN ASSOCIATES 28557 #036-01-1996 L2001 **OBG** *020 †30
DAVIS, Alonzo James, IV. 3332 BRIDGES ST, STE D 28557 #036-08-1993 L1994 **IM** *020 †20
DRURY, Bradford David. 3714 GUARDIAN AVE, STE W 28557 #024-16-1985 L1994 **GS** *020 †85
DUDA, John Robt. 3500 ARENDELL ST, CARTERET GENERAL HOSPITAL 28557 #041-12-1982 L2001 **EM** *020 †16
EVERETT, Catherine Joyce. 3500 ARENDELL ST 28557 #036-01-1976 L1976 **R** *020 †80
FALLS, Darryl Lee. 1508 ARENDELL ST 28557 #036-01-1980 L1981 **OBG** *020 †30
GAINEY, John White. ■ 28557 #036-01-1955 L1955 **GP** *071
GARRETT, Lee Scott. 5420 HIGHWAY 70 W, VA OUTPATIENT CLNC 28557 #067-01-1976 L1979 **FM** *020 †18
GARRISON, Robert Walter. 221B PROFESSIONAL CIR, CARTERET SURGICAL ASSOCIAT 28557 #038-06-1976 L1981 **U** *020 †95
GOODMAN, Terrence Lynn. 306 MEDICAL PARK CT 28557 #035-20-1974 L1978 **IM PD** *020 †20,55
GOULD, John Jay. 3332 BRIDGES ST, STE 3B 28557 #016-42-1989 L2000 **CD IM** *020 †20
GRAHAM, Gloria F. 306 MEDICAL PARK CT 28557 #036-05-1961 L1961 **D** *020 †15 ‡
GRAY, Michael A. 3104 ARENDELL ST, CARTERET URGENT & FAMILY 28557 #048-14-1983 L1984 **GP IM** *020
GREER, Steven Patrick. 221A PROFESSIONAL CIR 28557 #051-07-2001 L2005 **IM** *020
GROSS, Earl Geo. 3500 ARENDELL ST 28557 #041-13-1971 L1999 **D DMP** *020 †15
GUIRGUES, Ashraf Faaek. 3714 GUARDIAN AVE, STE E 28557 #041-12-1997 L2002 **ORS** *020 †40
HALL, William James, Jr. 208 N 6TH ST 28557 #020-02-1977 L1980 **OTO FPS** *071 †45
HARKER, Margaret Nelsen. 3608 MEDICAL PARK CT 28557 #010-01-1968 L1974 **GP ON** *020
HOLLAND, Roger Evan. 3500 ARENDELL ST, COLEMAN RADIATION ONCOLOGY 28557 #014-01-1995 L2000 **RO** *020 †80
HUNSINGER, Drew Chas. 3820 BRIDGES ST STE B, ONSLOW CARTERET BEH HLTH 28557 #036-01-1964 L1964 **PD FM** *020 †55
JOHNSON, John T, Jr. 3714 GUARDIAN AVE, STE W 28557 #036-05-1994 L2003 **GS** *020 †85
JOHNSON, Theresa Suzanne. 3511 JOHN PLATT DR 28557 #036-08-2001 L2003 **OBG** *020
KANICH, Robert Emil. 3500 ARENDELL ST 28557 #051-04-1962 L1972 **CLP PTH** *071 †50
KILUK, Andrew Kenneth. 3604 MEDICAL PARK CT 28557 #051-01-1992 L2006 **PD** *020 †55
KLINE, Michael Scott. 3500 ARENDELL ST, DEPARTMENT OF ANESTHESIOLO 28557 #045-01-1984 L1992 **AN** *020 †05
KLOSE, Arthur Gordon. 3714 GUARDIAN AVE 28557 #047-05-1983 L1985 **U AM** *020 †95
KNELSON, John Henry. 3510 JOHN PLATT DR 28557 #016-06-1960 L1969 **PD NPM** *020 †55
KUNKEL, Cooper Dave. 3504 BRIDGES ST 28557 #051-01-1956 L1962 **OPH** *071 †35
LAWRENCE, Larry Douglas. 306 MEDICAL PARK CT 28557 #020-02-2004 L2007 **IM** *020 †20
LAWRENCE, Mary Katherine. 306 MEDICAL PARK CT 28557 #010-01-1983 L1986 **IM END** *020 †20
LEE, Chong-Kwan. 3500 ARENDELL ST 28557 #583-01-1956 L1986 **AN** *020 †05
LEWIS, Barton Lee. 400 COMMERCE AVE, STE A 28557 #047-06-1987 L2002 **P** *020 †75
LOWRY, Michael Hunter. 3500 ARENDELL ST 28557 #036-01-1996 L1997 **EM** *020 †16
LUCAS, Kathryn Jean. 611 N 35TH ST 28557 #036-01-1980 L1981 **END IM** *020 †20
MAJSTORAVICH, Joseph, Jr. 300 MEDICAL PARK CT BLDG 1 28557 #036-01-1974 L1974 **OPH** *020 †35 ‡
MARSON, Dean Randall. 3714 GUARDIAN AVE STE E, CARTERET SURGICAL ASSOC 28557 #035-46-1992 L2001 **GS** *020 †85
MCCALLUM, Jeffrey Borden. 5420 HWY 70 W, VA PRIMARY CARE CLINIC 28557 #036-08-2002 L2005 **IM** *020 †20
MCCALLUM, Olivia Jasvant. 3511 JOHN PLATT DR 28557 #036-08-2002 L2006 **OBG** *020
MC GEE, James E, Jr. ■ 28557 #051-04-1943 L1943 **GP GS** *071 †85
MEEKINS, Bettina Bass. 3504 BRIDGES ST 28557 #011-02-1982 L1983 **OPH OS** *020 †35
MERRICK, Homer C, III. 3715 GUARDIAN AVE, P O BOX 914 28557 #051-07-1980 L1999 **IM** *020 †20
MOORE, Jeffrey Kevin. 3714 GUARDIAN AVE, STE W 28557 #023-01-1983 L1988 **ORS** *020 †40
MOOREHEAD, Katharine S. 3510 JOHN PLATT DR 28557 #035-47-1997 L2007 **PD** *020
MORRISON, Leon M, Sr. 3511 JOHN PLATT DR 28557 #011-03-1975 L1976 **OBG** *020 †30
MOYNIHAN, Jennifer Kim. ■ 28557 #023-01-2003 L2006 **PD** *020 †55
NUTZ, Joseph Frank, Jr. 3004 BRIDGES ST, BRIDGE MILL PROFESSIONAL P 28557 #041-02-1992 L1995 **FM** *020 †18
OLIVER, George Motley, Jr. 302 PENNY LN 28557 #036-01-1970 L1971 **OBG** *020 †30 ‡
OUANO, Dean Palanca. 3504 BRIDGES ST 28557 #043-01-1990 L1994 **OPH** *020 †35
PATRICK, James Timothy. 3402 MANDY LN 28557 #017-20-1986 L1991 **N RNR** *020
PROVATAS, Anastas. 3500 ARENDELL ST 28557 #008-02-1985 L1995 **IM ON** *020 †20
PURUSHOTHAMAN, Chandroth. 212 PENNY LN 28557 #495-44-1965 L1982 **CD IM** *020 †20
RANDALL, Eugene Henry. 5420 HIGHWAY 70 W, VA CLINIC 28557 #051-04-1970 L1997 **P GP** *020 †75
RAWLS, William Cleaton. 3511 JOHN PLATT DR 28557 #036-01-1966 L1966 **OBG** *071 †30
RAWLS, Wm Cleaton, Jr. 3511 JOHN PLATT DR, CARTERET OBG ASSOC PA 28557 #036-05-1985 L1987 **OBG** *020 †30
REECE, Donald Brooks, II. 208 PENNY LN, STE 2 28557 #054-04-1971 L1973 **FM GPM** *020 †18
RICE, Philip Scott. 500 N 35TH ST 28557 #014-01-1985 L1987 **GP** *020
RICHARDS, Charles Patrick. 3504 BRIDGES ST, COASTAL EYE CLINIC 28557 #035-01-1997 L1998 **OPH** *020 †35
RICHARDSON, Steven Todd. 3500 ARENDELL ST 28557 #055-01-1990 L1994 **AN** *020 †05
ROCCI, Charles. 3500 ARENDELL ST, CARTERET GENERAL HOSPITAL 28557 #035-06-1994 L2004 **EM** *020 †16
ROSANIA, Richard Alan. 4915 ARENDELL ST # 211 28557 #016-11-1993 L1997 **AN** *020 †05
RULE, William Stanley. 3604 MEDICAL PARK CT 28557 #036-01-1973 L1973 **PD A** *020 †55
SUN, Nancy N. 3500 ARENDELL ST, CARTERET GENERAL HOSPITAL 28557 #010-01-2000 L2004 **EM** *020 †16
TOKARSKY, Gregory Paul. 3500 ARENDELL ST 28557 #041-02-2003 L2006 **EM** *020 †16
VRADELIS, Thomas Theodore. 3511 JOHN PLATT DR 28557 #038-41-1994 L1998 **OBG** *020 †30
WALKER, William Thos, Jr. 306 MEDICAL PARK CT 28557 #023-07-1979 L1982 **IM** *020 †20 ‡
WARDELL, Walter John. 3500 ARENDELL ST 28557 #033-06-1989 L1993 **IM** *020 †20
WAY, Brady Cole. 210 PENNY LN 28557 #036-05-1976 L1976 **GS** *020
WAY, John Edward. 3 MEDICAL PARK 28557 #023-01-1938 L1938 **GS ORS** *071
WENTZ, Irl J. 3500 ARENDELL ST 28557 #023-01-1946 L1954 **ORS EM** *071 †40
WHITAKER, Donald Nash, Jr. 300 PENNY LN, CAROLINA HEART 28557 #036-05-1975 L1975 **CD IM** *020 †20
WOOLFREY, Karen G H. 3500 ARENDELL ST, EMERGENCY DEPT 28557 #063-01-1991 L1998 **EM** *020 †16
WORTHEN, Mark S. 115 TAYLOR LN 28557 #308-03-1982 L1987 **FM** *020 †18
WRAY, Richard Henry, III. 3714 GUARDIAN AVE 28557 #036-01-1968 L1968 **GS TS** *071 †85,90
WRIGHT, Darren Scott. 3511 JOHN PLATT DR 28557 #055-01-1996 L2000 **OBG** *020 †30
YURKO, John Evans. 3714 GUARDIAN AVE, CARTERET SURGICAL ASSOCIAT 28557 #051-04-1963 L1969 **GS** *020 †85
ZETTL, Matthew Lee. 3714 GUARDIAN AVE, STE E 28557 #021-01-1975 L1975 **ORS** *020 †40

MORGANTON – BURKE

ABERNATHY, David Smith. 341 E PARKER RD 28655 #036-07-1980 L1983 **IM** *020 †20 ‡
ABRAHAM, Kurian Chiramel. 207 QUEEN ST, MEMORY CLINIC 28655 #496-01-1983 L2001 **P** *020
AHSANUDDIN, Khaja M. 2203 S STERLING ST, GRACE HOSPITAL PROFESSIONA 28655 #495-21-1961 L1985 **P CHP** *020 †75
AHSANUDDIN, Rasheda N. 113 FOOTHILLS DR, STE B 28655 #495-21-1962 L1985 **P FM** *020 †75
ALAM, Sitara J. 1000 S STERLING ST 28655 #160-01-1984 L1996 **IM ID** *020 †20
ANDERSON, Larry Glenn. 503 E PARKER RD 28655 #016-11-1967 L1975 **ORS** *020 †40
AZBELL, Raymond Allen, II. 2201 S STERLING ST, EMERGENCY DEPT 28655 #001-06-1981 L1988 **EM** *020 †16
BADEN, T James. 111 FOOTHILLS DR, WESTERN PIEDMONT DERM 28655 #012-05-1977 L1978 **D IM** *020 †20,15 ‡
BAIG, Mirza Moin. 1000 S STERLING ST 28655 #495-21-1949 L1975 **IM** *071
BAKER, Scott Wm. 402 S STERLING ST 28655 #035-45-1983 L1991 **AN PME** *020 †05
BARBER, Kent Kerwin. ■ 28655 #654-01-1996 **AN** *100
BARRON, John I. 411 S KING ST 28655 #047-06-1950 L1951 **GP OBG** *071
BATTS, Mark Burrel. 2201 S STERLING ST, DEPT OF ER 28655 #036-08-1988 L1990 **EM** *020 †16
BOONE, Sharon Kate. 2209 S STERLING ST STE 300, FAMILY MEDICAL ASSOC 28655 #047-20-1986 L1990 **FM** *071 †18
BOWEN, J Hartley, III. 2201 S STERLING ST 28655 #041-02-1977 L1979 **PTH** *020 †50
BOYER, George Norman. 1000 S STERLING ST 28655 #036-05-1946 L1946 **P** *071
BRAZINSKI, Mark Steven. 503 E PARKER RD 28655 #010-02-1989 L1998 **ORS** *020 †40
BREITER, Eric Todd. 1000 S STERLING ST, BROUGHTON HOSP 28655 #001-02-1995 L1997 **P CHP** *020 †75
BREITER, Katherine Lay. ■ 28655 #045-01-1994 L2007 **P CHP** *020 †75
BROOKS, Amy S. 320 S GREEN ST 28655 #021-05-1996 L1999 **OS** *020
BROUSSARD-SMITH, Susan. 503 E PARKER RD, CAROLINA ORTHOPAEDICS PA 28655 #021-06-1990 L1995 **AN** *020 †05
BUKHARI, Mushtaq Ahmad. 107B MICA AVE 28655 #495-51-1968 L1978 **GE IM** *020 †20
CARRION, Ivan. 100 MEDICAL HEIGHTS DR 28655 #042-01-1980 L1986 **PD** *020 †55
CHIMIAK, James Michael. 2201 S STERLING ST 28655 #036-01-1986 L1994 **AN OS** *071 †05 ‡
CHUNG, Hae Jin. 105 COAL CHUTE RD 28655 #583-04-1966 L1989 **P** *020 †75
CLARY, Greg Lawson. 111 FOOTHILLS DR STE B, MEDICAL ALLIANCE CLINIC 28655 #048-14-1992 L1994 **P IM** *020 †20,75
CLONTZ, Luther Hall. 2201 S STERLING ST 28655 #036-01-1957 L1957 **GP PM** *020
CLOUD, William Graydon. 117 FOOTHILLS DR, MAILING: P O BOX 1807 28655 #051-01-1977 L1983 **GS** *020 †85
COLLETT, Ellen Calhoun. 103 MEDICAL HEIGHTS DR 28655 #036-01-1999 L2002 **IM** *020 †20
COLLETT, James Rountree. ■ 28655 #024-01-1944 L1944 **IM** *071 †20
COX, James Roger, II. ■ 28655 #055-01-2003 L2007 **AN** *100
CROFT, James Morris. 352 E PARKER RD STE A 28655 #012-01-1964 L1965 **FM FPG** *020 †18
CROOM, Dorwyn Wayne, II. 2201 S STERLING ST 28655 #028-02-1976 L1979 **PTH** *020 †50
CRUZ, Corazon S. 300 ENOLA RD 28655 #748-08-1961 L1980 **FM DR** *071
DAVIS, Deborah Hogan. 103 MEDICAL HEIGHTS DR, BURKE PRIMARY CARE, LLC 28655 #036-01-1981 L1997 **FM** *020 †18
DEEKENS, Stewart A, Jr. 115 FOOTHILLS DR 28655 #051-04-1978 L1981 **FM** *020 †18
DEMBSKI, John Eric. 350 E PARKER RD 28655 #039-01-1991 L1998 **FM** *020 †18
DIOQUINO, Renato Mercado. 300 ENOLA RD, WESTERN CAROLINA CENTER 28655 #748-01-1964 L1974 **IM PUD** *020
DOYLE, Larry Nelson. 1000 S STERLING ST BOX 137 28655 #040-02-1958 L1964 **P** *075 †75
DUDLEY, Robert Edward. 1000 S STERLING ST 28655 #038-06-1968 L1975 **P** *020 †75
ELLERTSON, David Garth. 117 FOOTHILLS DR 28655 #016-42-1998 L2005 **TS** *020 †85
ELLISON, Carroll Wendell. 500 E PARKER RD 28655 #012-01-1968 L1975 **OBG** *020 †30
EVANS, Sr, III. 500 E PARKER RD 28655 #047-05-2001 L2005 **OBG** *020
FINE, James Randolph. 2201 S STERLING ST 28655 #422-01-1987 L2002 **AN** *020 †05
FORGY, Byron Keith. ■ 28655 #011-02-1972 L1978 **GS** *071 †85
FRASCA, Anthony Adolph. 1000 S STERLING ST, BROUGHTON HOSPITAL 28655 #045-04-1997 L1999 **P** *020 †75
GAWOROWSKA, Joanna Maria. 1000 S STERLING ST 28655 #759-03-1967 L1990 **P IM** *020 †75
GESSNER, Martin Thomas. 103 MEDICAL HEIGHTS DR 28655 #036-05-1997 L1998 **IM** *020 †20
GILES, John Henry. ■ 28655 #036-05-1959 L1959 **GS** *071 †85
GONZALEZ, Anne Ricardo. 103 MEDICAL HEIGHTS DR 28655 #051-07-1999 L2003 **IMG** *020 †18
HALL, Walter Howard. 352 E PARKER RD STE B 28655 #036-01-1994 L1998 **OBG** *020 †30
HAMEL, John D. 2201 S STERLING ST, DEPT OF ER 28655 #048-13-1992 L1993 **EM** *020 †16
HAMER, Alfred Wilson, Jr. 215 W PARK DR 28655 #036-01-1958 L1958 **OBG** *020 †30
HAMRICK, Clinton Wade. 2201 S STERLING ST, DEPT OF ER 28655 #036-08-1996 L2001 **EM** *020 †16
HART, Elzie Franklin, Jr. 350 E PARKER RD 28655 #036-01-1967 L1967 **OTO A** *020 †45
HAWKINS, Seth Christopher. 2201 S STERLING ST, DEPT OF ER 28655 #036-01-2000 L2003 **EM** *020 †16
HAYS, Natasha T. 517 E FLEMING DR, DEVELOPOMENTAL EVALUATION 28655 #026-04-1981 L1984 **PD** *020 †55
HEETH, William L. 300 ENOLA RD 28655 #048-14-1986 L1997 **IM** *020
HERINGTON, David Stickel. 505 W FLEMING DR 28655 #023-01-1983 L1985 **FM** *020 †18
HILL, Roger Rush. 103 MEDICAL HEIGHTS DR 28655 #005-12-1989 L1992 **FM** *020 †18
HOLLER, Edwin Hobbs. 500 E PARKER RD 28655 #045-01-1985 L1993 **GS** *020 †85
HOWARD, Clifford, Jr. 2201 S STERLING ST, GRACE HOSP RADIOLOGY 28655 #036-08-2002 L2004 **DR** *100 †80
HOWERTON, Philip Thos. ■ 28655 #036-07-1958 L1958 **R** *071 †80

7326

■ = Address Information Privacy Protected

HUFFMAN, Robert Edward. 1000 S STERLING ST, BROUGHTON HOSPITAL 28655 #047-06-1963 L1971 **P** *075 †75

HUSSEIN, Diaa Eldin A M. 2201 S STERLING ST 28655 #915-02-1978 L2000 **FM** *020 †18

IQBAL, Javed. 1000 S STERLING ST 28655 #704-16-1987 L1999 **P CHP** *020 †75

JAMES, Kurisummootil S. 1000 S STERLING ST, BROUGHTON HOSP 28655 #495-63-1975 L1997 **P** *020

JARRAH, Azmi Shafiq. 100 MEDICAL HEIGHTS DR 28655 #605-01-1961 L1972 **PD NEP** *071 †55

JARRAH, Maha Bachour. WESTERN CAROLINA CENTER 28655 #605-02-1966 L1973 **PD P** *071

JENSEN, Roger David. 300 ENOLA RD, J IVERSON RIDDLE DEVELOPME 28655 #030-05-1975 L1986 **FM** *020 †18

JONES, Gregory Lee. 2201 S STERLING ST 28655 #012-01-1984 L1991 **RO PLM** *020 †80

KAARIAINEN, Ismo Mikael. 2201 S STERLING ST 28655 #017-20-1995 L2001 **NEP IM** *020 †20

KILBRIDE, Emer Mary. ■ 28680 #539-04-1994 *100

KILBRIDE, Kevin Anthony. 1000 S STERLING ST 28655 #539-04-1961 L1977 **P** *020 †75

KIRCHOFF, Patrice Marie. 300 S STERLING ST 28655 #028-34-1986 L1992 **AI PD** *020 †20,03,55

KIRK, David William, Jr. 607 E PARKER RD 28655 #024-05-1994 L1998 **OBG** *020 †30

KREBS, George Henry, Jr. 1000 S STERLING ST # 79, BROUGHTON HOSP 28655 #047-06-1981 L1982 **P FM** *030 †75,18

KUMAR, Amit. 2201 S STERLING ST, GRACE HOSPITAL 28655 #495-36-2001 L2005 **IM** *020

LEE, Choo Hyung. ■ 28655 #583-01-1948 L1972 **IM HEM** *071 †20

LEO, Robert Anthony. 2201 S STERLING ST 28655 #011-02-1977 L1983 **EM GP** *020 †16

LIM, Roger B. 2201 S STERLING ST, DEPT OF ER 28655 #056-05-2000 L2003 **EM** *020 †16

LOWE, William D. 503 E PARKER RD 28655 #048-14-1986 L2007 **ORS** *020 †40

MACNICHOL, Glenn Edward. 402 S STERLING ST 28655 #041-14-1987 L1991 **AN PMM** *020 †05

MADISON, James Thos. ■ 28655 #045-01-1978 L1981 **PD** *071 †55

MAHORNEY, Steven Louis. 300 ENOLA RD, J. IVERSON RIDDLE DEVELOP. 28655 #021-05-1973 L1976 **P** *020 †75

MALIK, Syed. 117B FOOTHILLS DR, CAROLINA PULMONARY AND COM 28655 #704-02-1988 L2005 **PUD** *020 †20

MANGUM, Addison Goodloe. 2201 S STERLING ST 28655 #036-01-1958 L1958 **R** *071 †80

MANHIANI, Rajwinder Singh. 2201 S STERLING ST, GRACE HOSPITAL, MSS DEPT 28655 #495-03-1998 L2005 **IM** *020 †20

MARELLA, Punnaiah Chowdar. 2201 S STERLING ST, GRACE HOSPITAL 28655 #495-21-1999 L2006 **IM** *020 †20

MARTIN, Margaret Michele. 300 N GREEN ST, STE 210 28655 #051-01-1996 L2000 **PD** *020 †55

MARTIN-GEORGESON, M I. 1000 S STERLING ST 28655 #005-12-1994 L2007 **P** *075

MAUNEY, Nolan Rudolph. 300 ENOLA RD, J IVERSON RIDDLE DEV CTR 28655 #051-04-1972 L1975 **FM** *020 †18

MAXY, Ralph J. 503 E PARKER RD 28655 #035-19-1994 L2000 **ORS** *020 †40

MC CUEN, Suzannah King. 1000 S STERLING ST, BROUGHTON HOSPITAL 28655 #045-04-1989 L2001 **PYG P** *020 †75

MC MANUS, Mark Warren. 304 S GREEN ST 28655 #038-45-1987 L1988 **FM** *020 †18 ‡

MEDINA, Rudy Tom. 100 MEDICAL HEIGHTS DR 28655 #005-02-1988 L1997 **PD** *050 †55

MELTON, James Durant. 350 E PARKER RD 28655 #036-01-1970 L1970 **FM** *020 †18

MILLER, Ryan Vern. 2209 S STERLING ST, STE 600 28655 #038-43-1990 L1996 **CD** *020 †20

MOHAMMED, Suneel. 107B MICA AVE, GASTROENTEROLOGY SPECIALIS 28655 #495-44-1986 L1997 **GE IM** *020 †20

MOHIUDDIN, Masood. 1000 S STERLING ST, BROUGHTON HOSPITAL 28655 #306-01-1985 L1990 **P FM** *020

MOIR, Ronald Jeffrey. 2201 S STERLING ST 28655 #036-08-1984 L2005 **AN** *075 †05

NATHANI, Shujaat Ali. 1000 S STERLING ST, BROUGHTON HOSPITAL 28655 #704-02-1985 L2001 **P** *020 †75 ‡

NORTHAM, Linda Lee. 1000 S STERLING ST, BROUGHTON HOSP 28655 #047-06-1998 L2003 **CHP** *020 †75

OGRODOWCZYK, Todd Eric. 2201 S STERLING ST 28655 #047-06-1999 L2005 **PTH** *020 †50

OLSON, Jennifer Jean. 2201 S STERLING ST 28655 #038-45-1999 L2002 **FM** *020 †18

OMER, Syed. 1000 S STERLING ST 28655 #495-21-1951 L1972 **N IM** *071

OWEN, Charles Malcolm. ■ 28655 #040-02-1970 L1973 **D** *020 †15

PASCALE, James Anthony. 2201 S STERLING ST, BLUE RIDGE HEALTHCARE 28655 #036-05-1972 L1972 **NPM PD** *020 †55

PATEL, Jayendrakumar I. 2201 S STERLING ST 28655 #496-38-1969 L1979 **AS GS** *020 †85

PATEL, Mahendrabhai N. 2201 S STERLING ST, BLUE RIDGE HEALTH CARE 28655 #917-08-1974 L2006 **IM** *020 ‡

PLYLER, Edward Thurman. 103 MEDICAL HEIGHTS DR 28655 #036-01-1981 L1984 **FM** *020 †18

POOLE, Shannon Simpson. 607 E PARKER RD 28655 #051-01-1989 L2004 **OBG** *020 †30

POPE, Thomas David. 607 E PARKER RD 28655 #048-04-1972 L1979 **OBG AM** *020 †30

POTOCKI, Jason John. 113A FOOTHILLS DR, SPINE INSTITUTE 28655 #051-04-2001 L2007 **ORS** *100

RAMIA, Carlos Gustavo. 2201 S STERLING ST 28655 #319-03-1981 L2002 **AN** *020

REDDY, Vijaya Kumar Konda. 2201 S STERLING ST, GRACE HOSPITAL 28655 #495-62-1981 L2003 **NPM PD** *020 †55

REUBENS, M Lawrence. 28655 #035-19-1958 L1965 **CD IM** *071 †20

RICHARDSON, Clay Wm. 103 MEDICAL HEIGHTS DR 28655 #036-01-1982 L1983 **FM** *020 †18

RIDDLE, Joseph Iverson. ENOLA RD 28655 #036-01-1956 L1956 **P CHP** *030

ROBINSON, Laurie Cox. 103 MEDICAL HEIGHTS DR 28655 #012-01-1998 L2001 **FM** *020 †18 ‡

ROBINSON, Timothy Michael. 103 MEDICAL HEIGHTS DR 28655 #012-01-1998 L2001 **FM** *020 †18 ‡

ROLLER, Jeffery Earl. 2201 S STERLING ST, DEPT OF ER 28655 #036-01-1988 L1990 **EM** *020 †16

ROSS, Mary Kay. 120 POWE ST 28655 #020-02-1996 L2003 **EM** *020 †16

SATHIRAJU, Sarveshwara R. 1000 S STERLING ST, BROUGHTON HOSPITAL 28655 #495-21-1973 L1999 **IM** *020 †20

SCHEROCK, Deanna Lynn. 103 MEDICAL HEIGHTS DR 28655 #011-02-1994 L1995 **FM** *020 †18

SCHWARTZ, Matthew Charles. 2201 S STERLING ST, DEPT OF ER 28655 #023-07-2003 L2007 **MPD** *100 †20

SCHWARZ, Matthew Knox. 2201 S STERLING ST, GRACE HOSPITAL 28655 #033-05-1999 L2002 **EM** *020 †16

SCOGGINS, Scott C. 103 MEDICAL HEIGHTS DR 28655 #011-02-1994 L1995 **FM** *020 †18

SCOTT, Don Joe. 2201 S STERLING ST, ER DEPARTMENT 28655 #016-11-1977 L1979 **EM** *020 †16

SEAGLE, Roger Lee. 505 E PARKER RD 28655 #036-05-1979 L1980 **CD IM** *020 †20

SEMIDEI, Rafael George. 1000 S STERLING ST 28655 #016-02-1991 L2001 **P PYG** *020

SHAH-KHAN, Sardar Mahmood. 303 S COLLEGE ST 28655 #495-21-1961 L1970 **IM** *020 †20

SHAMBLIN, William Jos, Jr. 5150 WESTERN AVE, FOOTHILLS CORRECTIONS INST 28655 #001-02-1971 L1975 **CHP P** *020 †75

SHANNON, Thomas M. ■ 28655 #539-01-1939 L1953 **GP P** *071

SHANNON, Walter Danl, Jr. ■ 28655 #005-14-1992 L2003 **P** *020

SHAPIRO, Daniel Allen. 2201 S STERLING ST 28655 #036-01-1978 L1979 **AN** *020

SINGH SRAN, Manjinder. ■ 28655 #495-10-1996 L2006 **IM** *020 †20

SMITH, Stephen Keith. 103 MEDICAL HEIGHTS DR 28655 #045-01-1986 L1988 **FM** *020 †18

SPIGGLE, John Alexander. 500 E PARKER RD 28655 #047-06-1969 L1976 **U** *020 †95

STUTESMAN, Michael Steven. 341 E PARKER RD, MORGANTON INTERNAL MED 28655 #048-04-1979 L1981 **IM EM** *020 †20

SUH, Sang Hyon. 1000 S STERLING ST 28655 #583-01-1956 L1972 **GS** *071

SUH, Young Soo. 1000 S STERLING ST 28655 #583-01-1956 L1977 **GP** *071

SYMINGTON, Richard Chas. 2201 S STERLING ST 28655 #027-01-1969 L1990 **AN** *020 †05

VARELAS, Dimitrios I. 1000 S STERLING ST, DIMITRIOS IOANNOU VARELAS 28655 #418-01-1970 L1996 **P** *075

WALKER, Earl William. 503 E PARKER RD 28655 #047-06-2000 L2006 **ORS** *100

WALSH, James John. 1000 S STERLING ST, BROUGHTON HOSP 28655 #036-01-1989 L1990 **P ADP** *020 †75

WHALLEY, John Frederick. 100 MEDICAL HEIGHTS DR 28655 #036-05-1973 L1973 **PD** *020 †55

WHEELER, Carroll Ray. 1000 S STERLING ST, BROUGHTON HOSPITAL 28655 #028-02-1976 L1999 **P** *020 †75

WHYTE, Thomas Russell. 2201 S STERLING ST 28655 #010-01-1962 L1990 **DR** *020 †80

YOUNG, Jamie Stapp. ■ 28655 #020-02-2001 L2006 **IM** *020

YOUSUFF, Sarah S. ■ 28655 #048-02-1988 L2002 **PME AN** *020 †05

MORRISVILLE – WAKE

ABBOTT, Maxwell Bret. ■ 27560 #038-41-2002 L2007 **DR** *100 †80

ADEYINA, Feyisayo Iyabode. 6402 MCCRIMMON PKWY, STE 100 27560 #473-04-1996 L2007 **FM** *020 †18 ‡

AGBETUNSIN, Caroline O. ■ 27560 #690-07-1988 L1993 **PD** *020 †55

BALDRIDGE, Kathleen G. ■ 27560 #035-20-1988 L2003 **OPH** *020 †35

BLOOMFIELD, Richard Alan, Jr. ■ 27560 #036-08-2008 *012

BLUM, David Elias. ■ 27560 #005-18-1985 L1986 **N CN** *020 †75

BRILEY, Libbie Parker. 5927 S MIAMI BLVD, QUINTILES 27560 #036-07-1999 L2002 **NEP** *050 †20

CABELL, Christopher H. 5927 S MIAMI BLVD, QUINTILES INC 27560 #036-07-1994 L1995 **CD** *050 †20

CADIGAN, Patrick Jos. ■ 27560 #030-06-1986 L1989 **IM** *020 †20

CAMPBELL, Douglas S. 2101 GATEWAY CENTRE BLVD, STE 200 27560 #014-01-1977 L1983 **OM EM** *062 †20,70

CARMEL, Harold. 1 COPLEY PKWY STE 534, COMPREHENSIDE NEURO SCIENC 27560 #035-47-1974 L1998 **P** *030 †75

CHAUDHARY, Sanjay. ■ 27560 #495-37-1996 L2004 **RHU** *100 †20

CHELLAPPA, Christanand. ■ 27560 #495-27-1968 L1995 **PD NPM** *020 †55

DEV, Sandesh. ■ 27560 #038-40-1998 L2008 **CD** *020 †20

DI LIBERTI, John Henry. 5927 S MIAMI BLVD, QUINTILES MEDICAL SVCS 27560 #038-41-1970 L2001 **GPM PD** *050 †55,19,70

ELKO, Lucinda Marie. 1800 PERIMETER PARK DR, STE 275 27560 #028-34-1999 L2005 **ID** *100 †20

FAULKNER, John Jay. 133 KEYBRIDGE DR, STE C 27560 #065-09-1980 L1998 *020 ‡

FIROZVI, Asra S. ■ 27560 #048-15-2002 L2008 **OPH** *020

HOLT, Jayne Elizabeth. 170 SOUTHPORT DR, MEDSTAFF 27560 #036-08-1983 L1993 **PD** *020 †55

HUGHES, Claude L, Jr. 5927 S MIAMI BLVD, QUINTILES 27560 #036-07-1980 L1983 **REN OBG** *050 †30

KELLY, Edward Allen. 3900 PARAMOUNT PKWY, PHARMACEUTICAL PRODUCT DEV 27560 #035-01-1971 L1972 **FM** *020

LAAST, John Luke. ■ 27560 #036-08-1994 **PM PHP** *020

LAGADAPATI, Bhavani. ■ 27560 #495-70-1990 L2007 **IM** *020 †20 ‡

LIONE, Kristin Kay. ■ 27560 #056-05-2000 **OBG** *100

LIU, Liherng. ■ 27560 #036-05-2007 **GS** *012

LOZEVSKI, Jonathan Leonid. ■ 27560 #003-01-2003 L2006 **DR** *012

MAC PEEK, David Martin. ■ 27560 #561-17-1981 L2007 **RHU PMM** *020 ‡

MASAND, Prakash S. 1130 W HILLS CT 27560 #495-17-1982 L2001 **P** *040 †75

MC KEE, Kelly Tilson, Jr. 5927 S MIAMI BLVD, QUINTILES INC 27560 #051-01-1976 L1992 **ID PD** *050 †55

MENOFF, Anne Leslie. 5927 S MIAMI BLVD, QUINTILES INC 27560 #045-01-1985 L1991 **IM** *100

NANDA, Charu. ■ 27560 #496-02-1998 **IM** *012

NEWSAM, Gabrielle Denize. 133 KEYBRIDGE DR, STE C 27560 #033-05-1999 L2005 **PD** *020

O'CONNELL, Gabriela. 133 KEYBRIDGE DR, STE E 27560 #561-02-1984 L1998 **P** *020 †75

PAREKH, Hasmukh Ratilal. ■ 27560 #495-22-1962 L1974 **GS** *020 †85

PAREKH, Ranjan H. ■ 27560 #495-01-1968 L1977 **PTH EM** *020 †50

PROCTOR, Spencer James. ■ 27560 #038-40-2006 **EM** *012

RAO, Pejawar Muralidhar. 309 MILLET DR 27560 #495-04-1962 L2002 **GS** *020 †85

SAWHNEY, Sangeeta. 1800 PERIMETER PARK DR, PPD 27560 #011-02-1999 L2002 **IM** *020 †20

SCHNEIDER, Frank. ■ 27560 #409-40-2003 **PTH** *012

SCURLOCK, David Ross. ■ 27560 #004-01-1990 L1991 **FM** *020 †18

SIDDIQI, Shabana Qaiser. ■ 27560 #704-02-1992 *100

SMILEY, Margaret Lynn. 3500 PARAMOUNT PKWY 27560 #036-07-1978 L2007 **ID IM** *050 †20

TAN, Bich Ngoc. ■ 27560 #036-01-2004 L2007 **IM** *020 †20

TEEL, Gregory Tyrone. 170 SOUTHPORT DR, MEDSTAFF 27560 #036-01-1984 L1986 **FM GPM** *020 †18

THINY, Michelle Terese. 5927 S MIAMI BLVD, THE UNIV OF NO CAROLINA-CH 27560 #025-01-1997 L2001 **GE** *100 †20

WEATHERS, Rinson Aldo. ■ 27560 #036-08-1987 L1988 **IM** *020

WEGNER, Lynn Mowbray. 3500 GATEWAY CENTRE BLVD, STE 140 27560 #039-01-1984 L1989 **PD** *020 †55

WEGNER, Steven Edward. 3500 GATEWAY CTR BLVD, STE 130 27560 #039-01-1980 L1989 **PD** *030 †55

ZAIDAT, Osama Othman M. 306 TROLLEY CAR WAY 27560 #575-01-1993 L2003 **N** *020 †75

■ = Address Information Privacy Protected

MOUNT AIRY – SURRY

ANDERSON, Travis Lamar. 351 RIVERSIDE DR, TELECARE INC 27030 #036-08-1992 L1999 P *020

APPLER, Mark Lee. 830 ROCKFORD ST 27030 #036-05-1980 L1985 **GE IM** *020 †20

ARNOLD, James Gordon. 510 S SOUTH ST 27030 #051-04-1987 L2003 **OBG** *020 †30

ATHAR, Mohammed Abdulahad. ■ 27030 #036-01-2007 **IM** *012

ATHAR, Mohammed Azhar. 826 MARSHALL ST 27030 #495-21-1965 L1977 **FM EM** *020

BAGINSKI, Stephanie L. 910 WORTH ST, FOOTHILLS PRIMARY CARE 27030 #038-41-2004 L2007 **FM** *020 †18

BALAJI, Talluri. 708 S SOUTH ST 27030 #495-21-1972 L1986 **U** *020 †95

BALOGH, Tamas. 905 ROCKFORD ST 27030 #473-01-1988 L1996 **CD** *020 †20

BARRETT, Rolland John, II. 865 W LAKE DR 27030 #025-01-1979 L1985 **GO** *020 †30

BOKESCH, Charles Richard. 708 S SOUTH ST 27030 #012-05-1973 L1974 **IM CD** *020 †20

BURCIU, Catalin Gh I. 905 ROCKFORD ST 27030 #781-01-1989 L1999 **IM** *020 †20

CARPENTER, Myra Lynne. 510 S SOUTH ST 27030 #055-01-1993 L1997 **OBG** *020 †30

CHAPMAN, Jennifer Hancock. 905 ROCKFORD ST 27030 #036-08-1997 L1999 **FM** *020 †18

CHEEMA, Asad Imtiaz. ■ 27030 #704-21-1998 **IM** *100

CHEEMA, Yasir Imtiaz. ■ 27030 #704-21-1998 L2007 **PUD** *020

CHRYSSON, Nick Geo, Jr. 865 W LAKE DR 27030 #036-07-1987 L1988 **HO IM** *020 †20

CORBIN, Robert Scott. 708 S SOUTH ST 27030 #004-01-1992 L1997 **GS** *020 †85

DANIELS, Mae Angeli. 423 S SOUTH ST 27030 #748-10-1989 L1995 **PD** *020 †55

DARLING WILLIAMS, Melinda. 423 S SOUTH ST STE 101 27030 #017-20-1992 L1997 **PD** *020 †55

DEVORE, Amy Elizabeth. 304 E INDEPENDENCE BLVD, STE 201 27030 #011-03-2003 L2006 **D** *100 †15

DEVORE, Druery Reed. 510 S SOUTH ST 27030 #011-03-2000 L2004 **OBG** *020

DIXON, David Rodolph. 910 WORTH ST 27030 #036-01-2000 L2002 **FM** *020 †18

ELLSWOOD, William H. ■ 27030 #024-07-1949 L1952 **R** *071 †90

EVERHART, Carlton Dhu. 911 WORTH ST 27030 #036-05-1958 L1958 **FM GP** *071 †18

GARDNER, Donald Nelson. 280 N POINTE BLVD 27030 #036-08-1983 L1986 **FM** *020 †18

GITT, Kenneth Daryl. 510 S SOUTH ST 27030 #030-05-1980 L1984 **OBG** *020 †30

GIZDARSKI, Veselin Stoyan. ■ 27030 #198-01-1987 L2007 **IM** *020 †20

GRIFFIN, Adrian Mark. 351 RIVERSIDE DR 27030 #036-05-1977 L1977 **P PYG** *020

GRYMES, W Lloyd. 731 WORTH ST 27030 #047-06-1957 L1964 **GP OS** *071

GUIDETTI, Richard Raymond. 830 ROCKFORD ST 27030 #036-05-1972 L1972 **AN** *020 †05

HAKANSON, Robyn Joan. 414 W LEBANON ST 27030 #036-07-1995 L1996 **ORS** *020 †40

HALL, J Grayson. 3637 OLD HIGHWAY 601 27030 #036-01-1957 L1957 **FM** *072 †18

HENNIS, Hugh Linwood, III. 1008 OLD ROCKFORD ST 27030 #045-01-1986 L1992 **OPH** *020 †35

HINES, Susan Jean. 865 W LAKE DR 27030 #038-41-1987 L2000 **ON HEM** *020 †20

HOOKS, William Borden, Jr. 865 W LAKE DR 27030 #036-01-1970 L1970 **FM** *020 †18

ILYASOV, Andrey Alexandro. ■ 27030 #913-15-1987 L2005 *100 †20

JACKSON, David Dewitt. PO BOX 191, 705 S SOUTH ST 27030 #036-05-1973 L1973 **GS** *020 †85

JACKSON, Joseph Andrew. 865 W LAKE DR 27030 #036-01-1972 L1972 **FM** *020 †18

JACKSON, Richard De Witt. ■ 27030 #041-13-1945 L1945 **GS** *071 †85

JACOBS, Bradley Edgar. 933 OLD ROCKFORD ST 27030 #001-02-1997 L1998 **OBG** *020 †30

JARRELL, W Eric. ■ 27030 #051-01-1954 L1956 **GP** *071

KEITH, Theodore Allen. 847 W LAKE DR 27030 #036-05-1967 L1967 **CD IM** *020 †20

KERLEY, Roger Kenny. 865 W LAKE DR 27030 #036-01-1979 L1980 **IM** *020 †20

KRISKA, Jan. 905 ROCKFORD ST, INT MED 27030 #286-03-1991 L1997 **IM** *020 †20

LAWRENCE, Benj Jones, Jr. 813 ROCKFORD ST 27030 #041-02-1947 L1947 **GS OS** *071 †85

LOGAN, Jennifer Coleman. 280 N POINTE BLVD 27030 #023-01-1998 L2007 **GS** *020 †18

MAJURE, David Andrew. 2007 N MAIN ST, MAJURE SKIN CARE & WELLNES 27030 #036-05-1998 L2001 **FM** *020 †18

MALONE, John Green. 830 ROCKFORD ST 27030 #036-05-1989 L1994 **N CN** *020 †75

MANAK, Marianthe. 910 WORTH ST 27030 #038-43-2003 **FM** *020

MC CLANAHAN, Lori E. 423 S SOUTH ST 27030 #012-01-2001 L2005 **PD** *020 †55

MIDDLETON, Roy Bruce. 708 S SOUTH ST, SURRY SURGICAL ASSOCIATES 27030 #021-06-1978 L1979 **GS VS** *020 †85

MILLER, Vincent Vivian. 830 ROCKFORD ST 27030 #836-02-1974 L1990 **FM EM** *020 †18

MINTON, Challie Alvis. ■ 27030 #305-01-2006 **FP** *012

NOWAK, Ilka Vanessa. 830 ROCKFORD ST 27030 #429-02-2001 L2006 **IM** *100 †20

NYIGU, Kurwa N. 860 ROCKFORD ST, HOSPITALISTS OF MOUNT AIRY 27030 #035-15-2001 L2006 **IM** *020 †20

PARKER, Robert L, Jr. 933 OLD ROCKFORD ST 27030 #036-05-1982 L1984 **OBG REN** *020 †30

PARRISH, Thomas E, Jr. 865 W LAKE DR, MEDICAL ASSOCIATES OF SURR 27030 #045-04-1982 L2006 **FM** *020 †18

PECK, Joseph C. ■ 27030 #041-13-1953 L1954 **GP** *071

PETRI, Lisa Anne. 910 WORTH ST, FOOTHILLS PRIMARY CARE 27030 #051-07-1993 L2004 **FM** *020 †18

PRESKE, Richard Jos. 1015 WORTH ST 27030 #017-20-1980 L1985 **OPH** *020 †35

REFVEM, William Eric. 708 S SOUTH ST, SPORTS MEDICINE 27030 #010-02-1982 L1996 **ORS GS** *020 †40

REYNOLDS, Stacee E. 933 OLD ROCKFORD ST 27030 #048-14-1998 L2000 **OBG** *020 †30

ROBERTSON, Amy Denise. 830 ROCKFORD ST, NORTHERN HOSPITAL OF SURRY 27030 #025-12-1999 L2002 **IM** *020 †20

ROBERTSON, James Wallace. ■ 27030 #025-12-1995 L1998 **PD** *020 †55

ROBINSON, Lasean Bost. 830 ROCKFORD ST, COUNTY 27030 #038-08-2003 L2006 **IM** *100

SCANNELL, Elizabeth Rose. 2007 N MAIN ST, PIEDMONT 27030 #305-01-1998 L2002 **AI** *020 †20,03

SEID, Melvin Hank. 933 OLD ROCKFORD ST 27030 #027-01-1995 L1997 **OBG PHM** *020 †30

SMITH, Robert Lee. 830 ROCKFORD ST, NORTHERN HOSP OF SURRY COU 27030 #051-01-1964 L1965 **PTH** *071 †50

THOPPIL, Cecil K. 865 W LAKE DR, MEDICAL ASSOCIATES OF SURR 27030 #495-31-1987 L1992 **PD PHP** *020 †55 ‡

TRINH, Thai Quoc. 910 WORTH ST, AEGIS FAMILY HEALTH CENTER 27030 #045-04-1994 L2005 **FM** *020 †18

TURMAN, William Clayton. 1218 STATE ST, STE 500 27030 #011-03-1992 L1994 **EM** *020 †16

URMOS, Lajos. 805 MERITA ST 27030 #062-01-1978 L1987 *020

VAUGHN, Tom Jimison, Jr. 510 S SOUTH ST 27030 #051-01-1975 L2002 **OBG** *075 †30

WALKER, Lawrence C, Jr. 933 OLD ROCKFORD ST 27030 #036-07-1960 L1960 **OBG OS** *071 †30

WHITMAN, Courtenay S, IV. 414 W LEBANON ST 27030 #033-06-1981 L1988 **ORS OSM** *020 †40

WILLIAMSON, Robert Van. 708 S SOUTH ST, BLUE RIDGE ORTHOPAEDICS 27030 #036-05-1993 L2005 **ORS** *020 †40

MOUNT GILEAD – RICHMOND

GARLAND, Thomas F, III. 202 N MAIN ST 27306 #056-05-1980 L2007 **FM** *020 †18

MOUNT HOLLY – GASTON

BEATTY, Lee Alexander. 215 S MAIN ST, RIVERBENND FAMILY PRACTICE 28120 #036-05-1978 L1980 **FM** *020 †18

BOWER, James Charles. 215 S MAIN ST, THE SANGER CLINIC 28120 #041-14-1994 L2000 **CD** *020 †20

COMAR, Kevin Munish. 547 HIGHLAND ST 28120 #038-44-2002 L2008 **GE** *012 †20

GALLAGHER, Bryan James. ■ 28120 #010-02-1988 L1991 **IM** *020 †20

LINSTER, John M, Jr. 112 WOODLAWN RD, CAROMONT FAMILY MEDICINE 28120 #016-11-1982 L1998 **FM FPG** *020 †18

REAVES, John Earl, Jr. 215 S MAIN ST 28120 #001-02-1987 L1990 **FM** *020 †18

RUSNAK, Renee None. ■ 28120 #038-43-2002 L2005 **IM** *020 †20

TOOSI, Soraya A. 215 S MAIN ST, RIVER BEND FAMILY PRACTICE 28120 #048-14-1989 L1993 **FM** *020 †18

MOUNT OLIVE – WAYNE

CAMP, Gregory Burnham. ■ 28365 #038-06-1965 L1992 **P OS** *020

DRAUGHON, Thomas Scott. 201 N BREAZEALE AVE, MT OLIVE FAMILY MEDICINE C 28365 #036-08-2001 L2002 **FM** *020

JENKINS, Alma Faye. 201 N BREAZEALE AVE 28365 #047-07-1979 L1996 **IM** *020 †20

KADIR, Md. Humayun. 201 N BREAZEALE AVE 28365 #160-02-1984 L2005 **FPG** *020 †18

KORNEGAY, Hervy Basil. 201 N BREAZEALE AVE 28365 #036-05-1957 L1957 **FM FPG** *020 †18

KORNEGAY, Hervy Basil, Jr. 201 N BREAZEALE AVE 28365 #036-08-1994 L1996 **EM** *020 †16

LAMBERT, James Royall. 130 NE CENTER ST 28365 #036-05-1978 L1979 **FM** *020 †18 ‡

ROBINSON, Alex Ray. ■ 28365 #036-08-2000 *100

SHACKELFORD, Robert H. 201 N BREAZEALE AVE 28365 #036-05-1947 L1948 **FM** *071 †18

SIDDIQUE, Sufia. 201 N BREAZEALE AVE, MOUNT OLIVE FAMILY MEDICIN 28365 #160-02-1989 L2006 **FM** *020 †18

TALTON, Robert Kevin. 201 N BREAZEALE AVE 28365 #036-08-1997 L1998 **FM** *020 †18

MOUNT PLEASANT – CABARRUS

ANDERSEN, Susan Ruth. 8560 COOK ST, CABARRUS FAMILY MEDICINE P 28124 #011-04-1992 L1995 **FM** *020 †18

BARRINGER, Archie Lipe. ■ 28124 #041-13-1936 L1936 **GP** *071

CROSLAND, David Bailey. 3350 HAHN BLVD 28124 #036-01-1958 L1958 **OBG** *071 †30

DOBSON, Lolo Allen, Jr. 8560 COOK ST 28124 #036-05-1980 L1981 **FM** *020 †18

KELLY, Darren Brent. 8560 COOK ST, MT. PLEASANT 28124 #045-01-1993 L1997 **FM** *020 †18

LEE, Soojung. 8560 COOK ST 28124 #038-45-2003 L2004 **FM** *020 †18

LUOMA, David Carl. 8560 COOK ST 28124 #036-01-2002 L2003 **FM** *020 †18

RHODES, Charles W W. 8560 COOK ST, MT PLEASANT 28124 #036-05-1980 L1981 **FM** *020 †18

SEXTON, Cheryl L. 8560 COOK ST 28124 #024-05-1996 L1997 **FM** *020 †18

MOUNT ULLA – ROWAN

RANKIN, Richard B, Jr. ■ 28125 #036-07-1953 L1953 **OPH** *071 †35

MOYOCK – CURRITUCK

BROWN, Charles Calvin. ■ 27958 #035-08-1984 L1987 **AN** *020

MURFREESBORO – HERTFORD

ALSTON, Michael Curtis. 305 BEECHWOOD BLVD, MURFREESBORO PRIMARY CARE 27855 #036-01-1978 L1979 **FM** *020 †18

ANTHONY, Meredith R, Jr. 501 N 4TH ST 27855 #010-02-1985 L1992 **FM** *020 †18

BISHOP, Charles Kellye. ■ 27855 #047-07-1968 L1971 **IM** *020

CANIPE, Hilary. 305 BEECHWOOD BLVD 27855 #036-05-1996 L2004 **FM** *020 †18

MC LEAN, Augustus A, Jr. ■ 27855 #051-04-1945 L1945 **GP** *071

PATEL, Kaushik Kantilal. 504 E MAIN ST 27855 #495-22-1996 *100

REVELLE, Bonnie C. PO BOX 448 27855 #036-08-1981 L1983 **PD ADL** *074 †55

MURPHY – CHEROKEE

ARMSTRONG, Emily Tatum. PO BOX 949, 7730 HWY 294 28906 #036-07-1984 L2007 **FM** *020 †18

BOLAND, Pamela Gray. 125 MEDICAL PARK LN, STE H 28906 #012-01-1978 L1980 **PD** *020 †55

BURISHKIN, Daniel Chapman. 4130 US HWY 64 E, MURPHY MED CTR 28906 #005-12-1977 L1982 **EM** *020 †18

CLARKSON, Jenkins Lucas. 75 MEDICAL PARK LN, STE D 28906 #045-01-1994 L1998 **OBG** *020 †30

DAVIS, Brent Alan. 145 MEDICAL PARK LN, STE I 28906 #028-34-1994 L2006 **ORS** *071 †40

DIXSON, George Randall. 4733 HIGHWAY 64 E, STE C 28906 #036-07-1976 L1977 **DR** *020 †80

DOAN, Terrence Babbit. 145 MEDICAL PARK LN, STE L 28906 #048-12-1973 L1988 **GS** *020 †85

EICHENBAUM, Daniel M. 1321 W US HIGHWAY 64 28906 #008-01-1969 L1985 **OPH** *020 †35

FAKADEJ, Alexander Victor. 176 WHISPERWOOD LN 28906 #051-01-1961 L1961 **N CHN** *020 †55,75

FREDRIKSEN, Susan. 281 VALLEY RIVER AVE, MURPHY COUNCILING CTR 28906 #016-42-1976 L2002 **P GP** *020 †75

■ = Address Information Privacy Protected

GARRETT, Valerie Dee. STE 5, MURPITY MED LANE, VALLEY RIVER MED GRP., INC 28906 #027-01-1993 L1997 **IM** *020 †20

HEAVNER, Teresa Ann. 125 MEDICAL PARK LN, STE F 28906 #036-05-1987 L1990 **FM** *020 †18

HOLDER, Larry Benson. 75 MEDICAL PARK LN STE A 28906 #011-03-1965 L1984 **OBG** *020 †30

JORDAN, Barbara Moore. ■ 28906 #036-01-1954 L1954 **P** *071 †75

KHAN, Rashid H. 4130 US HWY 64 E 28906 #308-11-1983 L1997 **IM** *020 †20

KORDUS, Michael James. 4130 US 64 E, MURPHY MEDICAL CENTER 28906 #011-03-1995 L1998 **FM** *020 †18

LAMBOY, Eugenio Antonio. 3905 HIGHWAY 64 E, STE 7 28906 #649-14-1976 L1991 **IM** *020 †20

LARSON, Jeffery Dee. 4188 HIGHWAY 64 E, STE 1 28906 #001-02-1983 L1986 **IM IMG** *020 †20

LAUFER, Frederick James. 4130 E US HIGHWAY 64 28906 #035-08-1984 L1997 **DR** *020 †20,80

LEE, Michael Dearman. 4130 US HWY 64 E, 105-B 28906 #048-04-1995 L2005 **AN** *020 †05

MANNING, Michael Scott. 4130 HIGHWAY 64 E, MURPHY MEDICAL CENTER 28906 #001-02-1985 L1988 **IM** *020

MARKOV, Peter I. ■ 28906 #198-01-1956 L1980 **R** *020

MARTIN, Jeffrey Hugh. 145 MEDICAL PARK LN, STE 1 28906 #036-08-1996 L2005 **U** *020 †95

MEINECKE, Henry Milton. 4188 US 64 E, STE 8 28906 #004-01-1967 L1989 **GS** *020 †85

MELSON, Michelle Renee. 4733 E US HIGHWAY 64, STE B 28906 #028-46-1990 L1997 **P** *020

MITCHELL, Brian Patrick. ■ 28906 #041-12-1974 L1976 **IM** *020 †20

MOCK, David John. 3905 HIGHWAY 64 E, PEACHTREE PLACE STE 9 28906 #016-11-1987 L1995 **CCM** *020 †20

MOCK, Robert James. 4733 E US HIGHWAY 64, STE A 28906 #016-11-1992 L1997 **GE IM** *020 †20

MORELAND, Robert Eric. 75 MEDICAL PARK LN, STE C 28906 #041-12-1978 L1995 **FM** *020 †18

MUGHARBIL, Ziyad Hasan. 4188 E US HIGHWAY 64, STE 6 28906 #605-01-1980 L1987 **U** *020

O'NEILL, Damien. 4130 HIGHWAY 64 W, EMERGENCY DEPT 28906 #036-08-1992 L1993 **EM GP** *020

OPOLINER, Larry H. 145 MEDICAL PARK LN, STE J 28906 #024-05-1975 L2004 **GS** *020 †85

RAO, Shiva D. 4188 HIGHWAY 64 E STE 2 28906 #495-42-1963 L1978 **GS** *021 †85

RICE, Edmond Lee, Jr. 4130 HIGHWAY 64 E, MURPHY MEDICAL CENTER 28906 #012-05-1973 L1997 **ORS GS** *020

SCHWAB, Donald Francis. 4130 E US HIGHWAY 64 28906 #056-05-1961 L1982 **GP AN** *020

SO, Laurence Siason. 4130 E US HIGHWAY 64 28906 #748-02-1995 L2001 **IM** *020 †20

SOLOMON, Robert Erik. 125 MEDICAL PARK LN, STE H 28906 #041-09-1991 L1994 **PD** *020 †55

SPENCER, John Raymond. ■ 28906 #005-12-1953 L1957 **FM** *075

STROUP, Daniel Foster. 125 MEDICAL PARK LN, STE F 28906 #036-05-1979 L1982 **FM** *020 †18

WALTERS, William Mark. 4130 US HWY 64 E 28906 #012-01-1983 L1989 **FM** *020 †18

WATRAS, Charles Stephen. 64 PEACHTREE ST, STE 7 28906 #027-01-1975 L1989 **FM** *020 †18

WEISENBURGER, Richard T. 4130 HIGHWAY 64 E STE J 28906 #028-79-1982, ▲ L2007 **OTO HNS** *020 ‡

WELLS, David A. RR 4 BOX 216 28906 #012-01-1949 L1949 **FM** *071 †18

WELLS, Helen Lewis. ■ 28906 #036-05-1946 L1947 **FM** *071

ZIMMER, Stephen. 4188 US 64 E, STE 12 28906 #065-05-1983 L1998 **FM** *020 †18

NAGS HEAD – DARE

ACOSTAMADIEDO, Jose M. 4800 S CROATAN HWY 27959 #264-12-1990 L1998 **HO** *020 †20

AUSTIN, Amanda Caldwell. PO BOX 1628, 2522 S CROATAN HWY 27959 #036-08-1995 L1996 **FM** *020 †18

AUSTIN, Maria Nicole. ■ 27959 #036-01-2004 L2007 **EM** *020

BAILEY, Claude Fletcher. ■ 27959 #023-01-1945 L1945 **OBG** *071 †30

BAXTER, Brian Donnan. 4800 S CROATAN HWY, EMERGENCY DEPARTMENT 27959 #051-07-1991 L2000 **EM** *020 †16

CROW, Harold Eugene. 2604 S BRIDGE LN 27959 #028-03-1963 L1996 **FM** *071 †18

DAVIDSON, Charles Stephen. 2808 S CROATAN HWY C-1, OUTER BANKS MEDICAL CENTER 27959 #020-12-1974 L1977 **EM FM** *020 †16,18

DWYER, Daniel Patrick. 4810 S CROATAN HWY, STE 250 27959 #035-09-1990 L1994 **OBG** *020 †30

FRY, Robert Waverly. ■ 27959 #051-04-1958 L1959 **GP** *072

GEARY, Candice Ann. 4917 S CROATAN HWY 27959 #051-07-1994 L1999 **OBG** *020 †30

GRAY, Derwin Pearson. 4917 S CROATAN HWY 27959 #021-01-1984 L1993 **OBG** *020 †30

HALLORAN, Jennifer. 4810 S CROATAN HWY, HEALTH EAST FAMILY CARE 27959 #055-01-1999 L2003 **MPD** *020 †20,55

HAMMER, Jeffery Chas. 4917 S CROATAN HWY 27959 #051-07-1985 L1990 **OBG** *020 †30

KEENAN, Joseph Gerard. ■ 27959 #025-12-1985 L1997 **MPD PD** 27959

KNAPP, Paul. 4800 S CROATAN HWY, THE OUTER BANKS HOSPITAL 27959 #038-40-1999 L2005 **FM** *020 †18

LEVER, Roger Guy. 4800 S CROATAN HWY, OUTER BANKS HOSPITAL 27959 #007-02-1999 L2004 **FM** *020 †18

LIGE, Christian Thor. 100 E DUNE ST, HEALTHEAST - FAMILY CARE 27959 #422-01-1999 L2002 **PD** *020 †55

MATHISON-EZIEME, Linda J. 4917 S CROATAN HWY 27959 #035-45-1998 L2006 **OBG** *020 †30

MC PHERSON, Scott R. 4800 S CROATAN HWY, THE OUTERBANKS HOSP-EMERG 27959 #035-15-2001 L2005 **EM** *020

METCALF, Vern Arthur. 4810 S CROATAN HWY, STE 100 27959 #422-01-1996 L1999 **IM** *020 †20

MORWAY, Linda Frances. 4800 S CROATAN HWY, THE OUTER BANKS HOSPITAL 27959 #038-06-1996 L2001 **EM** *020 †16

POULIS, Demetri Tony. 4810 S CROATAN HWY, STE 120 27959 #035-19-1983 L2003 **GS CRS** *020 †85 ‡

RUSSELL, Michael Wesley. 4800 S CROATAN HWY, THE OUTER BANKS HOSPITAL 27959 #051-04-1981 L2002 **AN CCA** *020 †05

SEIBERT, Jennifer Louise. 4800 S CROATAN HWY, THE OUTER BANKS HOSPITAL 27959 #038-40-1999 L2006 **FM** *020 †18

SKLAR, Marshall Dore. 4125 S CROATAN HWY, OUTER BANKS CANCER CENTER 27959 #024-01-1971 L1979 **RO IM** *020 †80

SMITH, Michael Lantry. 4810 S CROATAN HWY STE 120 27959 #056-06-1972 L2003 **GS ON** *020 †85

SUPAN-MC PHERSON, Karen A. 4800 S CROATAN HWY, THE OUTERBANKS HOSP-EMERG 27959 #035-15-2001 L2005 **EM** *020

THOMPSON, David Stuart. 4810 S CROATAN HWY, STE 100 27959 #036-08-1996 L1998 **MPD** *020 †20,55

WESSEL, Richard Fredrick. 4923 S CROATAN HWY 27959 #051-07-1990 L2008 **CD** *075 †20

WINFREE, Benjamin M. 4810 S CROATAN HWY, STE 250 27959 #038-43-2002 L2006 **OBG** *020

NASHVILLE – NASH

BELLO, Broderick Cande. 111 W CHURCH ST, BOICE-WILLIS CLINIC 27856 #051-01-1994 L2001 **FM** *020 †18

BONDY, Paul Villere. 111 W CHURCH ST, BOICE-WILLIS CLINIC 27856 #021-06-1990 L1991 **FM** *020 †18

BROWN-KING, Monique Y. ■ 27856 #051-04-2001 L2007 **CHP** *100

EMANUEL, Shandal Shanee. 155 NASHVILLE COMMONS DR 27856 #036-08-2001 L2005 **MPD** *020 †55,20

FULLER, David Henry, Jr. 225 W WASHINGTON ST 27856 #036-05-1952 L1952 **P** *071 †75

HEATER, Yasmin. 102 INDUSTRIAL DR, MAILING: P O BOX 1171 27856 #012-01-1993 L2000 **IM** *020

LIVERMAN, Joseph T. 111 W CHURCH ST, BOICE-WILLIS CLINIC NASHVI 27856 #036-05-1953 L1954 **FM** *020

PHIPPS, Ervin Lamar. 155 NASHVILLE COMMONS DR 27856 #036-08-1990 L1992 **FM** *020 †18

SINHA, Sujata. ■ 27856 #025-07-1989 L1994 **EM** *020

NEBO – MCDOWELL

ATKINSON, Thomas Temple. 5920 US HIGHWAY 70 E, MCDOWELL MEDICAL ASSOCIATE 28761 #036-05-1977 L1977 **FM** *020 †18

GRIFFIN, Teresa Beverly. 1800 FONTA FLORA DR 28761 #038-06-1993 L2003 **FM** *020 †18

MC CALL, Michael A. ■ 28761 #036-07-1952 L1953 **FPG** *071 †18

ORANGE, Melanie Markham. 5920 US HIGHWAY 70 E, MCDOWELL MEDICAL ASSOCIATE 28761 #001-02-1991 L1993 **FM** *020 †18

WELLS, Philip Hunt. ■ 28761 #011-03-1969 L2006 **AN AM** *020 †18,05 ‡

NEW BERN – CRAVEN

AHLBERG, David Joseph. 415 BROAD ST 28560 #005-12-2002 L2005 **P** *020

APOSTOLOU, Michael P. 1425 S GLENBURNIE RD, STE 2 28562 #051-07-1992 L1997 **N** *020

ARROWOOD, John Patterson. 3110 WELLONS BLVD, ASSOCIATES, PLLC 28562 #036-05-1990 L1998 **OTO** *020 †45

ARROWOOD, Kyle Binning. 3252 WELLONS BLVD 28562 #036-05-1990 L1998 **PDR** *020 †80

ARTHUR, Barton Stevenson. 738 NEWMAN RD, NEW BERN ORTHOPAEDIC ASSOC 28562 #036-08-1993 L1998 **ORS** *020 †40

ASHFORD, Charles Hall, Jr. ■ 28560 #023-07-1962 L1963 **TS VS** *071 †85,90

AYERS, John Clifford. 2604 DR M L KING JR BLVD 28562 #036-07-1954 L1954 **FM IM** *071 †18

BAGGETT, John Robt. 702 NEWMAN RD 28562 #036-01-1956 L1956 **IM** *071 †20

BALLARD, Harry Hampton. 701 NEWMAN RD 28562 #055-01-1971 L1976 **GS** *020 †85

BALLENGER, Clarence E, III. 729 PROFESSIONAL DR 28560 #045-01-1978 L1981 **N EM** *020 †75 ‡

BANKER, Lisa Marie. 200 CASTLE RIDGE RD, IDEAL HEALTH CARE, PLLC 28562 #038-43-1990 L1993 **IM** *020 †20

BANKER, Millard Fillmore. 2000 NEUSE BLVD 28560 #038-43-1990 L1993 **FM** *020 †18

BAREFOOT, Verna Young. ■ 28560 #010-01-1950 L1951 **PHP** *071

BARNWELL, Sydney Fitz C. 2818 NEUSE BLVD 28562 #010-03-1955 L1965 **OS GS** *020 †85

BATTERSBY, Brian John, Jr. 612 MCCARTHY BLVD, COASTAL ORTHOPEDICS 28562 #045-01-1985 L1991 **ORS** *020 †40

BECKWITH, George Hughes. 702 NEWMAN RD, MCCARTHY SQUARE 28562 #036-01-1971 L1976 **CD IM** *020 †20

BELL, Edwin Lillington. 702 NEWMAN RD 28562 #036-07-1982 L1986 **PUD CCM** *020 †20

BELL, Wm Harrison, III. 2203 NEUSE BLVD 28560 #036-07-1980 L1988 **VS CD** *020 †85

BENDER, Neil Carmichael. 2000 NEUSE BLVD 28560 #036-01-1963 L1963 **IM** *020 †20

BENNERT, Keith Wilkinson. 2129 S GLENBURNIE RD 28562 #038-06-1988 L1993 **PTH PCP** *020 †50

BENSON, Jane Ellen. ■ 28560 #011-02-2005 L2007 **FM** *020

BLACK, David Lloyd. ■ 28562 #041-15-2005 L2006 **FM** *020

BLACKERBY, James Nicholas. 2000 NEUSE BLVD 28560 #020-02-1956 L1963 **GS** *020 †85

BLAIR, Richard Daniel. 970 NEWMAN RD 28562 #024-01-1994 L2000 **NEP** *020

BLAIR, Robt Gillespie, Jr. 738 NEWMAN RD 28562 #036-01-1970 L1970 **ORS** *020 †40

BOBBETT, Gordon H, II. 800 HOSPITAL DR, STE 2 28560 #045-01-1995 L2001 **EM** *020 †18,16

BOBBITT, Wm Haywood, III. 975 NEWMAN RD 28562 #036-07-1977 L1982 **IM CCM** *020 †20

BOUNOUS, Christine Graham. 730 NEWMAN RD 28562 #036-07-1982 L1984 **IM** *020 †20

BOUNOUS, Edwin P, Jr. 730 NEWMAN RD 28562 #036-07-1980 L1984 **IM EM** *020 †20

BRADLEY, Raymond Jordon. 738 NEWMAN RD, CAROLINA ORTHOPAEDIC AND S 28562 #045-01-1997 L2003 **ORS** *020 †40

BRIGHT, Donald Stanleigh. 738 NEWMAN RD 28562 #023-01-1967 L1968 **ORS HS** *020 †40

BUFF, Samuel Joseph. 720 NEWMAN RD 28562 #036-07-1977 L1979 **DR** *062 †80

BULL, Thomas Albert. 2807 NEUSE BLVD 28560 #011-03-1964 L2003 **P CHP** *020 ‡

BURKART, Thomas Elma. 970 NEWMAN RD 28562 #045-01-1973 L1978 **NEP IM** *020 †20

BURNETT, John Wesley, Jr. 2000 NEUSE BLVD 28560 #051-04-1971 L1976 **FM** *020 †18

BYRD, David Evan. 975 NEWMAN RD, CCHC ENDOSCOPY CENTER, INC 28562 #001-02-1989 L1997 **GE** *020 †20

CAMERON, Harold H. 802 MCCARTHY BLVD, COASTAL EYE CLINIC P.A. 28562 #036-01-1970 L1970 **OPH** *020 †35

CARPEROS, Stephanie D. 810 KENNEDY AVE, NEW BERN FAMILY PRACTICE 28560 #012-05-1986 L2001 **IM** *020 †20

CARRIS, Leigh Ann. 2604 DR M L KING JR BLVD 28562 #036-01-1993 L1998 **PD** *020 †55

CHO, John. 1915 TRENT BLVD 28560 #041-12-1987 L2002 **ON IM** *020 †20

CLARK, Joel Arnold, Jr. 2000 NEUSE BLVD 28560 #051-01-1956 L1964 **U** *071 †95

CLARK, William Sidney. 2719 NEUSE BLVD, STE B 28562 #051-01-1987 L1991 **AN** *020 †05

COLE, Elizabeth Gail. ■ 28562 #036-08-2006 **OBG** *012

COOPER, Lyle Ray. 2000 NEUSE BLVD 28560 #036-01-1980 L1981 **IM** *020 †20

DALRYMPLE, Stephen J. ■ 28560 #010-01-1988 L1995 **NS** *020 †25

DANIEL, Louis Broaddus. ■ 28562 #036-05-1956 L1956 ORS *071 †40
DAVIDSON, Andrew. 3515 TRENT RD 28562 #036-01-1969 L1969 OPH *020 †35
DAVIS, Junius W, Jr. ■ 28560 #045-01-1946 L1946 PHP PD *071 †55
DAVIS, Michael Edwin. 2000 NEUSE BLVD 28560 #036-05-1991 L1995 IM *020 †20
DAVIS, Michael Lee. 670 CARDINAL RD 28562 #055-01-1974 L1979 IM *020 †20 ‡
DE GRAW, Martin Crawford. 1040 MEDICAL PARK AVE 28562 #036-05-1981 L1984 FM *020 †18
DELANEY, Christopher Sean. 2000 NEUSE BLVD, COASTAL REHABILITATION CTR 28560 #033-06-1990 L1994 PM *020 †60
DOUGHERTY, Douglas Andrew. ■ 28560 #035-48-2001 L2007 RNR *100 †80
DOYLE, George Mark. 705 NEWMAN RD, NEW BERN UROLOGY CLINIC, I 28562 #023-07-1985 L1987 U *020 †95
DUFFY, John Sparrow. 2604 MARTIN LUTHER KING J 28562 #305-01-2000 L2003 FM *020 †18 ‡
ECKBERG, David Edward. N B ANES ASSOC PA PBO 5007 28561 #036-05-1969 L1973 AN *020 †05
ENGBER, Peter Bruce. 941 NEWMAN RD 28562 #561-17-1971 L2003 D *071 †15 ‡
ENGEL, Steven Mark. 1700 NEUSE BLVD 28560 #041-02-1973 L1976 PD *020 †55
EVERETT, Roy Nathan. 2000 NEUSE BLVD 28560 #051-07-1979 L1984 PUD *020 †20
FAIDAS, Anna. 3322 WELLONS BLVD, COASTAL ONC & HEM 28562 #418-02-1982 L1996 ON HEM *020 †20
FARINA, Nicholas. 1917 TRENT BLVD, EASTERN CAROLINA INTER MED 28560 #035-46-1995 L1998 IM *020 †20
FISHER, Robert John. 2000 NEUSE BLVD 28560 #041-13-1995 L1998 EM *020 †16
FRASER, David Donald. 1406 NEUSE BLVD 28560 #036-08-1986 L1987 RHU IM *020 †20
FUJIMAGARI, Michael M. 670 CARDINAL RD, COASTAL INT MED & CARDIO 28562 #041-14-1993 L2001 IM *020 †20
FUJIMAGARI, Tak. ■ 28562 #067-01-1956 L1964 DR OS *020
FUTCH, William S, Jr. 3100 WELLONS BLVD 28562 #051-07-1990 L1996 GE *020 †20
GARMISE, David Bruce. ■ 28562 #036-01-1960 L1960 OTO *072 †45
GARRETT, Tolly Williams. 703 NEWMAN RD 28562 #001-02-1994 L1996 PD *020 †55
GEER, Kevin Chas. 242 SHORELINE DR 28562 #051-07-1986 L2003 EM *020 †16
GOODWIN, Bonnie Jeanne. 2000 NEUSE BLVD 28560 #032-01-1977 L1983 ON HEM *020 †20
GORDIN, Kristi Dawn. 2604 DR M L KING JR BLVD 28562 #012-21-2000 L2002 PD *020 †55
GORMAN, Richard Forbes, Jr. 1915 TRENT BLVD 28560 #036-05-1997 L1999 HO *020 †20
GRADY, Richard Dwight. 3110 WELLONS BLVD, ASSOCIATES, PA 28562 #036-01-1977 L1977 OTO *020 †45
GRAY, John Lawrence. 2203 NEUSE BLVD 28560 #036-07-1985 L1995 VS GS *020 †85
GRECO, Peter Paul. 1425 S GLENBURNIE RD, STE 3 28562 #033-05-1967 L1973 D *020
GREEN, Philip David. 1040 MEDICAL PARK AVE 28562 #023-01-1970 L1979 FM EM *020 †16
GREWAL, Satpal Kaur. 1425 S GLENBURNIE RD 28562 #495-03-1963 L1978 RO *071 †80
GRICE, Ormond Drew. 701 NEWMAN RD 28562 #036-01-1967 L1967 GS *020 †85
GROVER, William Howell. 680 GOOSE CREEK RD, MEMORIAL HOSPITAL OF GULFP 28562 #051-01-1978 L1979 ID *050 †16
GUNN, Patricia G. ■ 28563 #917-06-1954 L1982 AN *071
HALLIGAN, Michael Edward. 2000 NEUSE BLVD, HEART CTR CARDIAC SURG 28560 #041-12-1985 L1997 TS GS *020 †85,90
HANKERSON, Robert G. ■ 28560 #030-05-1932 L1933 GP *071
HARMON, Steven Kent. 2000 NEUSE BLVD 28560 #028-03-1982 L1983 EM FM *020 †18
HARPE, Keith Gray. 2300 NEUSE BLVD, EMERGENCY DEPARTMENT 28560 #036-08-1986 L1989 EM *020 †16
HARSHMAN, David Leonard. 701 NEWMAN RD 28562 #047-05-1985 L1992 GS *020 †85
HARUM, Kirk Edward. 2111 NEUSE BLVD STE J 28560 #011-02-1987 L1992 AN *020 †05
HARVEY, Bertha B. 1405 TATUM DR 28560 #045-01-1982 L2002 P *075 †75
HEAD, Charles Moreland. ■ 28562 #001-02-1957 L1988 OBG *071 †30
HELD, Mark Chas. ■ 28562 #010-02-1988 L1995 NS *020 †25
HENRY, Jason Lemarr. ■ 28562 #047-20-2004 L2005 *100
HENSLEY, Terry Glenn. 227 TICINO CT 28562 #020-02-1997 L2004 EM *020 †16
HESTER, Thomas Oma. 3110 WELLONS BLVD, COASTAL EAR, NOSE & THROAT 28562 #036-08-1991 L1998 OTO *020 †45
HILLER, Carl Julien. 1413 TATUM DR 28560 #045-01-1962 L1968 ORS *071 †40
HINES, Marcono Raymond. 1813 S GLENBURNIE RD 28562 #036-01-1975 L1978 FM *020
HODGES, Marcus Arendell. 810 KENNEDY AVE 28560 #036-08-1996 L2000 FM *020 †18
HOFFMAN, Annette M. ■ 28560 #836-03-1965 L1972 PS OTO *075 †45
HOLMES, Robert Peel. 702 NEWMAN RD 28562 #036-01-1956 L1956 IM *071 †20
HUFFMAN-ZECHMAN, Ellen R. 2417 NEUSE BLVD 28562 #036-08-1994 L1996 OBG *020
HUNT, William B, Jr. 19 BATTS HILL RD 28562 #036-05-1953 L1953 PUD *071 †03,20
JREISAT, Khaled Farid I. 729 PROFESSIONAL DR, COASTAL NEUROLOGICAL ASSOC 28560 #473-03-1978 L1983 PD CHN *020 †55,75
KERKERING, Kathryn W. 2842 NEUSE BLVD, CHILDREN'S DEV. SERVICES A 28562 #051-04-1974 L2002 NPM *020 †55
KING, Kathryn P. 1822 S GLENBURNIE RD #6 #3 28562 #036-01-1988 L1989 AN *020 †05
KIRBY, Alex Ray. 1001 NEWMAN RD, THE HEART CENTER OF EASTER 28562 #036-08-1996 L2003 IC CD *020 †20
KIRBY, Mary Banaszak. 1040 MEDICAL PARK AVE, NEW BERN FAMILY PRACTICE 28562 #036-08-1996 L2003 FM *020 †18
KLEIN, Kenneth Leroy. 600 MCCARTHY BLVD 28562 #038-45-1983 L1989 D DS *020 †15
KOONTZ, Stanley Eugene. ■ 28562 #422-01-2003 L2006 EM *020 †16
KRUKOWSKI, James Andrew. 2719 NEUSE BLVD, STE B 28562 #035-15-1991 L1995 AN *020 †05
KUHN, Robert Anthony. 312 PLANTATION DR 28562 #005-11-1944 L1998 FM NS *071 †25
KUMAR, Sanjay. 1319 S GLENBURNIE RD, STE D 28562 #495-29-1988 L2002 PM *020 †60
LARNICK, Mark Randall. 670 CARDINAL RD, COASTAL INTER MED & CARDIO 28562 #041-14-1994 L2000 IM *020 †18,20
LATHER, Ronald Michael. 1917 TRENT BLVD 28560 #035-03-1990 L1992 IM *020 †20
LAURORA, Nicholas Stephen. ■ 28562 #033-05-1963 L1969 OBG *020 †30
LAVINE, Gary Harold. 2000 NEUSE BLVD, CRAVEN REGIONAL MEDICAL CE 28560 #001-06-1994 L2006 EM *020 †16
LEACH, Pamela Sue. ■ 28560 #004-01-2003 L2004 GS *020
LEWISON, John Frederick. 2000 NEUSE BLVD 28560 #023-01-1993 L1998 IM *020 †20
LITTLEJOHN, Lanny F, Jr. ■ 28560 #045-04-1999 L2004 EM *012
LITWAK, Joseph Martin. 2000 NEUSE BLVD 28560 #016-42-1993 L1997 IM *020 †20
LONG, John J. ■ 28562 #028-79-2003, ▲ L2007 AN *020
LOPEZ, Osvaldo Adrian. 102 MONTREUX LN 28562 #005-18-1995 L2008 IM *020 †20
LORIO, William Paul. 1917 TRENT BLVD 28560 #036-01-1992 L1994 IM *020 †20
LUCAS, Kent Vincent. 702 NEWMAN RD, NEW BERN INTERNAL MEDICINE 28562 #055-02-1996 L1999 IM *020 †20
LYNCH, Richard Oneal. 4705 KIROLINA PL, NAVAL HOSPITAL 28560 #036-08-2000 L2002 FM *020 †18
MAC DONALD, Henry John. 3110 WELLONS BLVD, ASSOCIATES, PA 28562 #036-01-1969 L1969 OTO *020 †45
MAHANEY, John Philip, Jr. 1040 MEDICAL PARK AVE 28562 #051-04-1971 L1974 FM *020 †18
MANGUN, Jennie Craig. PO BOX 13187, 2604 DR MARTIN LUTHER KING 28561 #020-02-1993 L2006 PD *020 †55
MANLEY, James Jos. 800 HOSPITAL DR, STE 3 28560 #033-05-1978 L1981 FM EM *020 †18
MARTIN, Gary Leonard. 2117 S GLENBURNIE RD, SUITES 9 & 10 28562 #023-12-1997 L2007 FM *020 †18 ‡
MAY, Ronald Bruce. 2000 NEUSE BLVD, CRAVEN REGIONAL MEDICAL CE 28560 #041-01-1973 L1974 PD PHO *030 †55
MAYBEE, David Brian. 702 NEWMAN RD 28562 #010-02-1995 L2004 PCC *020 †20
MC NABB, Gregory Scott. 2117 S GLENBURNIE RD, EASTERN CAROLINA INTERNAL 28562 #023-12-2001 L2002 OTO *020
MC NEILL, Mary R Davis. ■ 28560 #021-05-1956 L1959 GP PD *071
MC QUADE, John Francis. 670 CARDINAL RD 28562 #008-01-1973 L1975 CD IM *020 †20
MIAO, Kai. 2000 NEUSE BLVD 28560 #243-29-1983 L2001 IM *020 †20
MILLER, Donald Glen. ■ 28560 #041-02-1955 L1955 EM GP *071
MIZELLE, Christopher B. 941 NEWMAN RD 28562 #036-01-2000 L2001 D *020 †15
MOELLER, Mark Bolton. 2000 NEUSE BLVD 28560 #032-01-1977 L1981 IM ID *020 †20
MOELLER, Wendy. 2604 MARTN LTHR KNG JR 28562 #036-07-1977 L1982 GE IM *020 †20
MONTEIRO, Robert Wm. 2000 NEUSE BLVD 28560 #010-01-1992 L1995 IM *020 †20
MONTERO, Manuel. 970 NEWMAN RD 28562 #308-03-1988 L1998 NEP *020 †20
MOORE, Leann Ruth Deal. 3252 WELLONS BLVD 28562 #051-04-1983 L1990 FM *020 †18
MOORE, Ronald Alvin. 702 NEWMAN RD 28562 #036-01-1972 L1972 IM GE *020 †20
MOORE, Staley Cook. 3252 WELLONS BLVD 28562 #036-01-1982 L1990 PUD *020 †18
MORGAN, Richard Earl. 701 NEWMAN RD 28562 #036-05-1973 L1973 GS *020 †85
MOSTELLAR, Henry Curtis. 701 NEWMAN RD 28562 #001-06-1983 L1985 GS SO *020 †85
MURPHY, Michael Durant. ■ 28562 #036-05-1990 L1994 IM *020
MURPHY, Sean James. 1403 MCCARTHY BLVD 28562 #041-77-1996, ▲ L2005 D DS *020 †15
MURRAY, Warren Edward, Jr. 702 NEWMAN RD 28562 #041-02-2000 L2001 IM *020 †20
MUTHER, Ellis F. 1315 S GLENBURNIE RD STE C 28562 #021-01-1960 L1969 N P *020 †75
NEWELL, Robert B, Jr. 2129 S GLENBURNIE RD 28562 #016-06-1970 L1986 PTH CLP *020 †50
NEWMAN, Walter Jos. 970 NEWMAN RD 28562 #036-07-1975 L1978 IM NEP *020 †20
NORRIS, Louis Jerome. ■ 28562 #035-19-1954 L1955 GS OS *071
NUNN, Michael K. 750 MCCARTHY BLVD, COMMUNITY WELLNESS CENTER 28562 #055-75-1991, ▲ L1992 P OMM *020 †75
NUR, Waeil Ali. 2000 NEUSE BLVD 28560 #041-14-2001 L2004 PD *020 †55
NYARKO, Stanley J. 722 NEWMAN RD 28562 #024-01-1999 L2007 RNR *012 †80
OLIVER, David Clark. 702 NEWMAN RD 28562 #036-05-1974 L1974 IM CD *020 †20
OVERBY, Joseph Randal, Jr. ■ 28562 #036-05-1971 L1971 FM *020 †18
PAHLM-WEBB, Ulrika Sofia. 730 NEWMAN RD 28562 #858-01-1999 L2004 IM *020 †20
PANZA, William Sebastian. 2719 NEUSE BLVD, STE B 28562 #036-07-1988 L2000 AN *020 †05
PARHAM, Allan Mathis. ■ 28562 #030-05-1971 L1978 AN CCM *020 †05
PARK, Angela Miwoo. 1001 NEWMAN RD 28562 #038-06-1995 L2006 ICE *020 †20
PARK, Gregory P. ■ 28560 #583-01-1964 L1994 GPM EM *071
PAUL, Caroline. 701 NEWMAN RD 28562 #035-01-1994 L1999 GS *020 †85
PEARSON, Stephen Hilding. ■ 28560 #023-12-2005 L2006 GS *020
PELLETIER, Gerald, Jr. 800 HOSPITAL DR STE 7 28560 #036-01-1967 L1967 ORS *071 †40
PETERSON, Vivian Marie. 2000 NEUSE BLVD 28560 #038-43-1995 L2004 IM *020 †20
PETROV, Nickolas. PO BOX 2157, DEPT AN 28561 #286-04-1951 L1963 AN *100
PHILIPPART, Christopher A. 2000 NEUSE BLVD, CRAVEN REGIONAL MEDICAL CE 28560 #036-05-1994 L1995 RO EM *020 †80
POLO, Cynthia Keane. 1403 MCCARTHY BLVD 28562 #023-12-1990 L2000 PD *020 †55
POLO, James Michael. 1403 MCCARTHY BLVD 28562 #023-12-1990 L1999 D *020 †15
PRESTON, Ronald Allyn. 2000 NEUSE BLVD 28560 #051-04-1970 L1971 IM OS *020 †20
REARDON, Michael Lanese. 2000 NEUSE BLVD 28560 #038-40-1994 L1998 IM *020 †20
REDDING, Ralph Arnold. 2000 NEUSE BLVD 28560 #060-01-1960 L1994 IM PUD *020
REDEKER, Chas Conrad, Jr. 2117 S GLENBURNIE RD 28562 #054-04-1976 L1993 FM EM *020 †16
REIDA, Ronald Jack. 2000 NEUSE BLVD 28560 #019-02-1967 L1983 EM PD *071
RHODES, James Slade, Jr. ■ 28562 #051-04-1941 L1941 GP *071
ROBERTSON, John Patrick. 2719 NEUSE BLVD, STE B 28562 #051-01-1992 L1996 AN *020 †05
ROQUE ROMERO, Leopoldina. ■ 28562 #275-01-1943 L1976 P PD *020
ROWE, Kristina D. 2000 NEUSE BLVD, CRAVEN REG MED CTR 28560 #008-02-1987 L2001 IM *020 †20
ROWLETT, Jos Peterson, III. 2117 S GLENBURNIE RD, ECIM URGENT MEDICAL CARE 28562 #036-05-1975 L1975 EM GP *020
SALINAS, Ruben R. 3282 WELLONS BLVD, NEW BERN PROF HLTH SVCS 28562 #649-30-1980 L2002 P *020 †75
SCHUETTE, Patrick John. ■ 28562 #023-12-2000 L2007 AN *020
SHIELDS, Wright Davis. 702 NEWMAN RD 28562 #051-01-1984 L1991 IM *020 †20
SIDES, Stephen Nelson, II. 722 NEWMAN RD 28562 #036-08-1991 L1993 DR VIR *020 †80
SINNING, Mark Alan. 2203 NEUSE BLVD 28560 #019-02-1978 L1986 TS VS *020 †85,90
SKWERER, Robert Gordon. 403 GEORGE ST 28560 #035-08-1982 L2002 P *020 †75
SLOAN, Timothy Council. 720 NEWMAN RD 28562 #036-05-1997 L1998 DR *020 †80
SMITH, James Phillip. ■ 28562 #035-15-1999 L2001 OBG *020
SMITH, John Matthew. 1917 TRENT BLVD 28560 #036-05-1992 L1994 IM *020 †20
SNYDER, John Andrew. 722 NEWMAN RD, COASTAL RADIOLOGY 28562 #051-04-1995 L2002 DR *020 †80
SORROW, Kristen Melinda. ■ 28560 #012-22-2007 PD *012
STEEL, John G. 3515 TRENT RD, VILLAGE SQUARE STE 10 28562 #036-01-1977 L1984 N *020 †75 ‡
STIMSON, Alan Christopher. 114 MANDY LN 28562 #001-02-1992 L1995 EM *020 †16
STONE, Harry Benj, III. ■ 28560 #036-07-1965 L1965 OTO A *071 †45
STROUD, Larry Ashley. 1001 NEWMAN RD 28562 #036-05-1990 L1993 CD *020 †20
SWITZER, Paul Edward. ■ 28560 #016-06-1966 L1991 FM *020 †18
TAYLOE, John Cotten, Jr. PO BOX 2604 28561 #036-01-1960 L1960 ORS *071
TAYLOR, Jeffrey Scott. 3515 TRENT RD 28562 #016-11-1977 L1983 OPH EM *020 †35
TAYLOR, Michael Martin. 2000 NEUSE BLVD 28560 #055-01-1992 L1998 IM *020 †20
TELLIS, Angelo Anthony. 2111 NEUSE BLVD STE J, CRYSTAL COAST PAIN MANAGEM 28560 #045-01-1995 L1999 PM *020 †60
TOURIGNY, Paul Rene. 2604 DR M L KING JR BLVD 28562 #041-09-1984 L1994 GE IM *020 †20
TRACEY, Robert William. ■ 28560 #041-01-2005 L2005 *020

■ = Address Information Privacy Protected

TRAN, Huy Tan. ■ 28562 #050-02-2004 L2005 **GS** *020

UNDERHILL, Thurlow Reed. 705 NEWMAN RD, NEW BERN UROLOGY CLINIC, I 28562 #036-01-1970 L1970 **U** *020 †95

VANDERSEA, Harold M. 738 NEWMAN RD 28562 #035-06-1970 L1977 **ORS** *020 †40

VILLAVICENCIO, Carlos E. 112 WALDEN RD 28562 #016-06-1998 L1998 **PD** *020 †55

WARD, Richard Mayhew. 2129 S GLENBURNIE RD 28562 #036-07-1980 L1983 **PTH** *020 †50

WARREN, James O'Tuel. 2000 NEUSE BLVD 28560 #045-01-1988 L1993 **GE** *020 †20

WERTMAN, Mark Graham. 738 NEWMAN RD 28562 #055-01-1980 L1985 **ORS GS** *020 †40

WHALEY, Marcus Craig. PO BOX 13187, 2604 DR MARTIN LUTHER KING 28561 #036-08-2000 L2003 **PD PSM** *020 †55

WHEATLEY, William B. 738 NEWMAN RD 28562 #051-04-1990 L1994 **OSM** *020 †40

WHETSTONE, David Rodwell. ■ 28562 #036-08-2004 L2007 **EM** *020

WHITMORE, Robert Burton. 705 NEWMAN RD 28562 #051-07-1982 L1992 **U** *020 †95

WILKINS, Kenneth W, Jr. 975 NEWMAN RD 28562 #036-01-1980 L1981 **IM** *020 †20

WILLIAMS, John A, III. 1001 NEWMAN RD 28562 #010-02-1984 L1993 **CD IM** *020 †20

WIN, Andrew A. 702 NEWMAN RD 28562 #033-06-1997 L2003 **CD** *020 †20

WINTERS, Richard R W. 1425 S GLENBURNIE RD 28562 #028-34-1970 L1985 **PS** *020 †65

YEREX, Joyce A. ■ 28563 #803-02-1955 L1988 **R** *071 †80

ZAVELO, Craig Mathew. 670 CARDINAL RD, COASTAL INTER MED & CARDIO 28562 #035-15-1982 L1991 **PUD IM** *020 †20

ZECHMAN, James Michael. 2000 NEUSE BLVD 28560 #011-02-1989 L1992 **AI** *020 †20,03

NEWELL — MECKLENBURG

LEWCHALERMWONG, Jacquelyn. ■ 28126 #036-08-2006 *012

NEWLAND — AVERY

BARKER, Joseph David. 177 NEW VALE RD, MOUNTAIN LAUREL INTERNAL M 28657 #047-06-1985 L1993 **IM AN** *020 †20

CLARK, Robert Dale. 448 CRANBERRY ST 28657 #048-13-1997 L1998 **FM** *020 †18

ESTES, Marion M. 28657 #012-01-1943 L1951 **P** *071 †75

RHEA, William Gardner, Jr. 3329 LAND HBR, 109 STONY CREEK LOOP 28657 #047-05-1958 L2005 **GS TS** *071 †85,90 ‡

NEWPORT — CARTERET

DANA, Maurice Francis. PO BOX 1689 28570 #036-01-1983 L1986 **D** *020 †18

HILDEBRANDT, Richard John. ■ 28570 #036-07-1959 L1959 **MFM OBS** *071 †30

JONES, Jeffrey David. 135 GULL HARBOR DR 28570 #035-45-1971 L1973 **GE IM** *020 †20

NEWTON — CATAWBA

BARNES, James Allan, Jr. 105 N MAIN AVE, NEWTON WOMEN'S CARE 28658 #055-02-1987 L1994 **OBG** *075 †30

CALDWELL, Lawrence M, II. 24 S BRADY AVE 28658 #036-01-1971 L1971 **IM GE** *020

CAMPBELL, Donald A. 829 W 25TH ST 28658 #041-12-1981 L1989 **ORS** *020 †40

DE PERCZEL, John Leslie. 829 W 25TH ST 28658 #016-43-1972 L1979 **ORS** *020 †40

DUANY, Virginia C. ■ 28658 #011-75-2004, ▲ L2007 **FM** *100

FORSHEY, Alan Gray. 767 W 1ST ST, NEWTON FAMILY PHYSICIANS P 28658 #038-40-1978 L1982 **FM EM** *020 †18

KIRKLAND, Timothy H. 829 W 25TH ST 28658 #048-15-1991 L1997 **HS ORS** *020 †40

LONDON, Deborah Louise. 2180 NORTHWEST BLVD, CATAWBA VALLEY PRIMARY CAR 28658 #036-08-1991 L1993 **FM** *020 †18

LOPINA, Bartholomew J. 767 W 1ST ST 28658 #036-01-2000 L2001 **FM** *020 †18 ‡

MEASE, Willis Eugene. ■ 28658 #030-05-1945 L1948 **FM** *072

PARKER, Bill Jack. 3121 PLATEAU RD, CROSSROADS FAM MED CARE 28658 #020-12-1986 L1989 **FM** *020 †18

PELTZER, David Eric. 767 W 1ST ST 28658 #051-01-1991 L1994 **FM PD** *020 †18

SANDERS, Kenton Lee. 3975 ROBINSON RD 28658 #019-02-1986 L2004 **PLM IM** *030 †20

SCHULTEN, Herbert John. 829 W 25TH ST 28658 #023-01-1970 L1977 **ORS** *071 †40

SHERFEY, Shannon Marie. 767 W 1ST ST, NEWTON FAMILY PHYSICIANS, 28658 #036-05-2000 L2001 **FM** *020 †18

STORY, Alan Wade. 767 W 1ST ST 28658 #036-01-1996 L1999 **FM** *020 †18

THOMPSON, William C, III. 3975 ROBINSON RD, PALLIATIVE CARE CENTER AND 28658 #055-01-1978 L1981 **FM** *020 †18

TUKEL, Suleyman Resat. 2180 NORTHWEST BLVD 28658 #902-01-1953 L1971 **FM** *071 †18

WOFFORD, Benjamin. 105 N MAIN AVE 28658 #047-06-1966 L1971 **GP** *072

YAUSSY, Kenneth Arden. 767 W 1ST ST 28658 #038-40-1982 L1984 **FM** *020 †18

NEWTON GROVE — SAMPSON

APOLINARIO, Arthur E. 301 MAIN ST, NEWTON GROVE FAMILY MEDICI 28366 #021-01-1996 L1999 **FM** *020 †18

BAUMAN, Ted Albert. 301 MAIN ST 28366 #036-01-1998 L2001 **FM** *020 †18

PALMER, Gilbert Field V. 301 MAIN ST 28366 #036-08-1998 L1999 **FM** *020 †18

ROUSE, John Lawrence. 301 MAIN ST 28366 #036-05-1973 L1973 **FM** *020 †18

SMITH, John Braswell, Jr. 301 MAIN ST 28366 #036-01-1977 L1977 **FM** *020 †18

YANG, Ken Tung. 301 MAIN ST 28366 #035-09-1995 L1998 **FM** *020 †18

NORLINA — WARREN

COFFMAN, Donald Ralph. 1173 US HIGHWAY 1 N 27563 #016-11-1968 L1969 **GP** *020

PERRY, James Howard. ■ 27563 #010-03-1976 L1978 **GP** *020

NORTH TOPSAIL BEACH — ONSLOW

BEEBE, Christian Andrew. ■ 28460 #023-12-2003 L2005 **FM** *100

ROSS, Elliot Mitchell. ■ 28460 #023-12-2005 L2006 **FM** *020

NORTH WILKESBORO — WILKES

APGAR, Robert Geo. 1370 W D ST 28659 #033-06-1980 L1998 **GS** *020 †85

ARNOLDUS, Christina L. 1900 W PARK DR, VALLEY RADIOLOGY 28659 #025-01-1995 L2007 **DR** *020 †80

BAUGHAM, Leonard Andrew. 408 8TH ST 28659 #012-01-1975 L1976 **GS** *020 †85

BENNETT, Craig Randall. 1914 W PARK DR 28659 #036-01-1981 L1985 **ORS** *020 †40

BLACKWELL, Michael A. 1915 W PARK DR, STE 108 28659 #036-08-1990 L1995 **OBG** *020 †30

BOWMAN, James Thos. 702 13TH ST 28659 #036-05-1977 L1977 **FM** *020 †55

BOWMAN, Karolen Church. 702 13TH ST 28659 #036-05-1977 L1977 **IM PD** *020 †55

BRANYON, David Watterson. 1430 WILLOW LN, PO DRAWER 1287 28659 #001-02-1975 L1978 **P CHP** *020 †75

BRYAN, Thomas Rhudy. 1917 W PARK DR 28659 #036-05-1954 L1954 **PD OBG** *071

CAVE, John Sevier. 1370 W D ST 28659 #649-33-1987 L2001 **EM IM** *020 †20

CHANDRA WANDERMAN, M. 1919 W PARK DR 28659 #035-46-1992 L2004 **CD** *020 †20

CICHON, Zbigniew. 110 JEFFERSON ST, STE 103 28659 #759-10-1980 L1996 **IM** *020 †20

CLASSEN, Adrienne Charles. 1925 W PARK DR 28659 #036-01-1993 L2004 **PD** *020 †55

CLEVENGER, Jeffrey Cabot. 1919 W PARK DR 28659 #045-04-1991 L2000 **CD** *020 †20

CURL, Kenneth Frank. 1404 WILLOW LN, P O BOX 1303 28659 #012-05-1983 L1987 **IM PD** *020 †20,55

DAWSON, Jack Alexander. 1370 W D ST 28659 #036-05-1961 L1961 **IM PUD** *071

DERICK, Jeffrey Michael. 1919 W PARK DR 28659 #010-02-1980 L1981 **FM** *020 †18

DRUCKER, Michael Neil. 1919 W PARK DR 28659 #035-19-1992 L1999 **CD** *020 †20

EMERY, Henry Ronald, Jr. 1919 W PARK DR 28659 #045-04-2000 L2003 **FM** *020 †18

ESSEX, Charles Phillip. 702 13TH ST, 'PO BOX 1348 28659 #056-06-1979 L1997 **FM** *020 †18

FESPERMAN, Joseph C, Jr. 1534 W D ST, WILKES FAMILY HEALTH CENTE 28659 #036-01-1977 L1977 **FM** *020 †18

FISHER, William Gregory. 1370 W D ST 28659 #035-15-1991 L1994 **EM FM** *020 †18

FITZPATRICK, Hugh. 1370 W D ST 28659 #051-04-1950 L1951 **EM PHP** *071

GILLILAND, Kerry Jay. 1919 W PARK DR 28659 #036-05-1976 L1976 **CD IM** *020 †20

GROTE, Thomas Howard. 1370 W D ST 28659 #036-07-1981 L1987 **ON IM** *020 †20

GULDEN, Kirk Douglas. 1534 W D ST 28659 #035-20-1977 L1980 **FM** *020 †18

HEFNER, Kenny Dewayne. 1919 W PARK DR 28659 #036-01-1993 L1997 **MPD PD** *020 †55,20

HENRICK, William Robt. ■ 28659 #041-02-1971 L1975 **AN CCM** *071 †05

HOFFMAN, Carl White. 1012 E ST 28659 #036-05-1967 L1967 **R** *071 †80

HORTON, Benion Samuel. 1902 W PARK DR, NW CAROLINA WOMENS CTR 28659 #012-22-1996 L2005 **OBG** *020 †20

JEWELL, James Edward. 1919 W PARK DR 28659 #047-06-1994 L1998 **MPD** *020 †20,55

KEYS, Alan Clinton. 8TH DOCTORS BLDG 28659 #036-08-1985 L1990 **GS** *020 †85

KILBY, Larry Shelton. ■ 28659 #036-05-1968 L1968 **GP OS** *020

KIMBLETON, Dennis Paul. 1370 W D ST 28659 #010-01-1975 L1979 **EM** *020 †18,16

LANDON, Henry Clayton, III. 1370 W D ST 28659 #051-01-1947 L1948 **FM IM** *071

MAHAN, Charles Scott. 1912 W PARK DR 28659 #011-04-1993 L1999 **ID** *100 †20

MANNAVA, Venkata Siva Nag. 1404 WILLOW LN, GREENWAY HEALTHCARE 28659 #495-58-1995 L2005 **IM** *020 †20

MC NEIL, Stephen Lynn. 1430 WILLOW LN, NEW RIVER BEHAVIORAL HLTH 28659 #036-08-1985 L1986 **CHP P** *020 †75

NEAL, De Mar Austin, III. 1404 WILLOW LN STE B, DEMAR NEAL, MD, FACS 28659 #038-40-1978 L1983 **GS VS** *020 †85

PATTERSON, Harold C. PO BOX 607 28659 #036-05-1945 L1945 **OPH** *071 †35

PATTERSON, John Byron. 1919 W PARK DR 28659 #036-01-1994 L1996 **CD** *020 †20

PENNINGTON, Robert Carl. 110 JEFFERSON ST STE 107 28659 #055-02-1990 L1997 **ORS** *020 †40

PETERSON, Donald Douglas. 408 8TH ST 28659 #016-02-1970 L1977 **U** *020 †95

PINKERTON, Jerry Lyle, Jr. 1915 W PARK DR, STE 103 28659 #039-05-1989 L1993 **IM PD** *020 †20,55

PONTZER, John Tuckerhaywa. 1925 W PARK DR 28659 #051-01-1997 L2000 **PD** *020 †55

POWERS, John Charles. 1919 W PARK DR 28659 #036-05-1998 L1998 **FM** *020 †18

RATHMELL, Dariel Lorraine. 1916 W PARK DR 28659 #033-05-1984 L1988 **IM** *020 †20

REBAND, Pamela Brenkert. 384 ARMORY RD 28659 #027-01-1982 L1997 **AN PME** *020 †05

REID, Carol Denise Rogers. 301 9TH ST 28659 #036-01-1981 L1984 **AN** *020 †05

RENALDO, Gary Jos. 1919 W PARK DR 28659 #055-01-1983 L1989 **IM CD** *020 †20

ROUGEOU, Glendon Paul. 1534 W D ST 28659 #021-06-2004 L2007 **FM** *020 †18

SINGH, Sunita. 1902 W PARK DR 28659 #495-15-1991 L2002 **IM** *020 †20

SMITH, Duane Howard. 112 BOONE TRL 28659 #038-41-1958 L1974 **OBG OBS** *020 †30

SPENCER, Francesca D. 240 JEFFERSON ST 28659 #038-40-1987 L1993 **CD** *020 †20

SWOFFORD, Joel Howard. 1919 W PARK DR, MED ASSOC OF WILKES 28659 #036-05-1987 L1990 **FM** *020 †18

TEMPLETON, Bradley Davis. 1370 W D ST 28659 #036-05-1977 L1980 **IM** *020 †20

TSAI, Jen-Lo. 1917 W PARK DR 28659 #244-04-1970 L1978 **PD** *020 †20

TUCKER, Wm Arnold, Jr. GENERAL DELIVERY 28659 #035-15-1961 **P OS** *075 †75

VAN NOY, Timothy Quinn. 1925 W PARK DR 28659 #027-01-1994 L1997 **PD** *020 †55

WALLACE, Hugh James. 1370 W D ST 28659 #051-04-1989 L1997 **HO IM** *020 †20

WATKINS, William L. 1916 W PARK DR 28659 #041-09-1996 L1998 **IM** *020 †20

NORWOOD — STANLY

BENSON, Christopher C. ■ 28128 #035-08-1992 L1999 **GE** *020 †20

OAK ISLAND — BRUNSWICK

ALMIRALL, Peter D. 8715 E OAK ISLAND DR, OAK ISLAND MED CTR 28465 #065-01-1978 L1982 **FM OM** *020 †18

ARVIDSON, J Morgan. 4700 E OAK ISLAND DR STE F 28465 #045-01-2005 L2007 **FM** *020 †18

CARLSON, Richard Jos. ■ 28465 #041-09-1971 L1982 **P** *020 †75

FORTNEY, Sidney Ray. 8715 E OAK ISLAND DR 28465 #036-07-1963 L1963 **IM END** *020 †20

LUTZ, Charles Larry. ■ 28465 #021-01-1970 L1971 **IM GE** *071 †20

MAZIE, Armand S. ■ 28465 #561-01-1938 L1944 **PD** *071

OAK RIDGE — GUILFORD

ALBRIGHT, Michael Edward. 2205 OAK RIDGE RD, STE BB 27310 #048-14-1999 L2001 **PD** *020 †55

EARLY, Terrence Stephen. 2205 OAK RIDGE RD, STE K 27310 #036-07-1982 L1986 **P** *020 †75
FIELDS, Valerie Jeanette. ■ 27310 #019-02-1991 L1997 **PTH PCP** *020 †50
FRIED, Robert Leslie. 1510 NC HIGHWAY 68 N 27310 #035-03-1980 L1982 **FM** *020 †18
HUA, Claire Phung. ■ 27310 #032-01-2002 *100
MAC DONALD, Laurie P. 2205 OAK RIDGE RD, STE BB 27310 #036-05-1999 L2001 **PD** *020 †55
MEYERS, Stephen Clinton. 1510 NC HIGHWAY 68 N, EAGLE FAMILY MED OAK RIDGE 27310 #020-02-1996 L1997 **FM** *020 †18
SCHMANDT, Susanne M. ■ 27310 #409-23-1993 **CHN** *100
SOLDATO COUTURE, Cathy M. 2205 OAK RIDGE RD, STE BB 27310 #036-01-1994 L1998 **PD** *020 †55
WALKER, George Kirk. 2205 OAK RIDGE RD, STE BB 27310 #036-05-1985 L1986 **PD** *020 †55

OAKBORO – STANLY

ROYER, Harrell Clark, Jr. 112 E 1ST ST 28129 #012-22-1996 L1998 **FM** *020 †18

OCEAN ISLE BEACH – BRUNSWICK

HARRIS, Herbert Witt, Jr. ■ 28469 #051-04-1961 L1961 **D A** *071 †15
LUKASIK, John. ■ 28469 #016-11-1954 L1986 **OBG** *071 †30
PHILLIPS, Robert Derrick. 1767 HARBORAGE DR SW APT 3 28469 #041-01-1952 L1952 **P** *020 †85,75
RHOADS, John Mc Farlane. ■ 28469 #041-13-1943 L1956 **P PYA** *071 †75
ROSS, Gary Dean. 25 UNION SCHOOL RD NW 28469 #055-02-1988 L1989 **IM** *020 †20
SUH, Kendall H. 50 MOORE ST, P O BOX 5189 28469 #039-05-1985 L1986 **EM** *020 †18
SUMMERLIN, Rebecca Clare. 120 CAUSEWAY DR, STE 3 28469 #036-08-1995 L1996 **FM** *020 †18
WALKER, William Pinkney. 6818 BEACH DR SW 28469 #036-08-1992 L1995 **IM** *020 †20

OCRACOKE – HYDE

WESTERVELT, F B, Jr. 27960 #051-01-1955 L1955 **NEP IM** *071 †20

OLD FORT – MCDOWELL

ELLIS, George Greene. PO BOX 1000, 1725 BAT CAVE RD 28762 #020-02-1962 L1965 **FM** *071 †18
MOOMAW, William Charles. PO BOX 789, 102 THOMAS RD 28762 #038-43-1995 L1999 **FM** *020 †18
TURNBULL, Joseph Taylor. 102 THOMAS RD, SERVICE, INC 28762 #041-12-1970 L1974 **FM** *020 †18

ORIENTAL – PAMLICO

STALLINGS, Tolbert Lacy. PO BOX 828 28571 #036-07-1954 L1954 **GS** *071 †85
SULLIVAN, James Geo. ■ 28571 #010-02-1948 L1950 **PS** *071 †65
WILLI, Marc Anthony. 901 BROAD ST, PAMLICO MEDICAL CENTER P 28571 #038-45-1983 L1989 **FM** *020 †18

OXFORD – GRANVILLE

ANDERSON, John B, Jr. 101 PROFESSIONAL PARK, STE A 27565 #038-41-1980 L1983 **FM** *020 †18
BARKER, Carolyn Culbreth. ■ 27565 #036-01-1958 L1958 **P** *071
BENTLEY, Steven Edmunds. 1010 COLLEGE ST, GRANVILLE HOSPITAL 27565 #012-01-1978 L2000 **EM** *020 †16
BLUM, Fredric. 203 E INDUSTRY DR 27565 #035-19-1985 L1987 **D** *020 †15
BYRD, Jesse Randall. 1010 COLLEGE ST, GRANVILLE MEDICAL CENTER 27565 #047-07-1982 L1988 **EM IM** *020
CHAVIS, La Rhoda Francine. 1032 COLLEGE ST 27565 #408-30-1982 L1995 **IM** *020
DANIEL, Louie Saml. 196 PINE CONE DR 27565 #023-01-1940 L1940 **GP** *071
DAY, Eugene Davis, Jr. 1010 COLLEGE ST 27565 #036-08-1981 L1982 **FM** *020 †18
DOUGHERTY, Diane E. ■ 27565 #041-14-1991 L2002 **FM** *071 †18
DRAKE, Wilton Rodwell, Jr. PO BOX 367, GRANVILLE-VANCE DIST HLTH 27565 #036-01-1972 L1972 **PHP FM** *030 †18
ERTISCHEK, Stephen. 1032 COLLEGE ST 27565 #561-01-1974 L1978 **IM** *020 †20 ‡
ETTER, Lawrence. 203 E INDUSTRY DR 27565 #008-01-1999 L2003 **D** *020 †15
EYSTER, James Melvin. 4124 BLUE MOUNTAIN RD 27565 #017-20-1980 L1982 **DR** *020 †80
FINCH, Charlie Bryan. ■ 27565 #036-07-1954 L1992 **FM** *071
FRUTH, Joanne Marie. 101 PROFESSIONAL PARK # A, PARK DRIVE 27565 #038-43-1987 L1994 **FM** *020 †18
FULLER, Virginia Sahr. 1010 COLLEGE ST 27565 #041-07-1972 L2001 **AN** *030 †05 ‡
JINDAL, Vinod Kumar. 1001 COLLEGE ST, P O BOX 914 27565 #495-29-1984 L2000 **OPH** *035
KINDMAN, L Allen. 102 PROFESSIONAL PARK 27565 #035-47-1983 L1993 **CD IM** *020 †20
KOINIS, Thomas Frank. 1010 COLLEGE ST 27565 #038-06-1980 L1983 **FM** *020 †18
KUMAR, Balvinder. 1010 COLLEGE ST, GRANVILLE HEALTH SYSTEM 27565 #495-36-1992 L2007 **IM** *020 †20
LEWIS, Stacy B, Jr. 101 PROFESSIONAL PARK # B 27565 #012-22-1986 L1987 **OBG** *020
MACK, Latonja Euniece. 101 PROFESSIONAL PARK, STE A 27565 #036-01-1996 L2004 **FM** *020 †18
MC CARTHY, James Andrew. 1018 COLLEGE ST 27565 #012-05-1980 L2000 **OBG** *020 †30
MONICAL, Cheryl Joyce. 101 PROFESSIONAL PARK # A, PARK DRIVE 27565 #026-04-1990 L2001 **FM** *020 †18
NAJI, Yousef M. 1010 COLLEGE ST 27565 #875-01-1976 L1997 **IM** *020 †20
PERREN, Richard Stephen. ■ 27565 #025-07-1984 L1988 **EM** *020 †16
PETWAY, Joseph Keill, Jr. ■ 27565 #010-03-1974 **PD D** *062
REEDER, Paul A, Jr. ■ 27565 #023-01-1961 L1979 **GS** *071 †85
REGAN, Joanna Janette. ■ 27565 #036-01-2004 L2008 **PD** *012
SPIVEY, Netasha Danyale. 1018 COLLEGE ST 27565 #036-08-1998 L2002 **OBG** *020 †30

TAYLOR, Richard Lewis. 101 PROFESSIONAL PARK # A, OXFORD FAMILY PHYSICIANS 27565 #036-01-1962 L1962 **FM** *071 †18
WATSON, John W. ■ 27565 #051-04-1953 L1955 **FM** *071 †18
WEGENER, Michael Edward. 103 PROFESSIONAL PARK # B, PARK DRIVE 27565 #033-06-1989 L2005 **GS GE** *020 †85
WILLIAMS, James D. ■ 27565 #035-46-1990 L2003 **FPS OTO** *020 †45

PARKTON – ROBESON

KIRBY, Stephanie Lynn. ■ 28371 #055-01-2002 L2003 **FM** *020 †18

PEMBROKE – ROBESON

BELL, Joseph Tyron. 812 CANDY PARK RD 28372 #036-01-1986 L1989 **PD** *020 †55
BRAYBOY, Jacob Ryan. ■ 28372 #036-08-2005 **FP** *012
BROOKS, Martin Luther. 7729 NC HWY 711 28372 #025-01-1957 L1958 **GP OS** *071
BURKE, Annette Blackmon. 812 CANDY PARK RD 28372 #036-05-1978 L1982 **PD** *071 †55
COLLINS, Paul Dwayne. 923 W 3RD ST, WEST PRIMARY CARE 28372 #036-05-2001 L2007 **FM** *020 †18
LOCKLEAR, J C. ■ 28372 #036-07-1984 L1987 **IM** *020
LOCKLEAR, Sarah Ransom. PO BOX 1240, 149 CYPRESS LN 28372 #036-01-2006 **PD** *012
LOWRY, Jadene. ■ 28372 #036-01-2007 **FP** *012
LOWRY, Katie. 812 CANDY PARK RD, PEMBROKE PEDIATRICS 28372 #036-08-2000 L2003 **PD** *020 †55 ‡
LOWRY, Terry Stephen. ■ 28372 #036-01-1996 L2005 **TS** *020 †85,90
MAYNOR, Thomas Eddison, II. ■ 28372 #036-08-1997 L2000 **FM** *020
PERMASHWAR, Balichand. 307 E WARDELL DR 28372 #566-01-1995 L2005 **FPG** *020 †18
RYAN, William Scott. 812 CANDY PARK RD 28372 #019-02-1973 L1985 **PD** *020 †55 ‡
WATSON, Linwood Worth. 410D S JONES ST 28372 #036-08-2001 L2004 **FM** *020 †18
WEST, Danny Lee. 102 LIVERMORE DR 28372 #036-08-1998 L1999 **FM** *020 †18
WEST, James Earl. ■ 28372 #036-01-1998 L1999 **IM** *020 †20
WORIAX, Frank. 3609 W 3RD ST, PEMBROKE MED CTR 28372 #036-07-1976 L1976 **FM** *075 †18

PENLAND – MITCHELL

O'BANION, Laura Schulman. PO BOX 41, 83 GRACERUTH RD 28765 #016-11-1987 L1998 **PD EM** *071 †55
RENICK, John Terry. PO BOX 42 28765 #012-05-1966 L1971 **P** *020 †75

PENROSE – TRANSYLVANIA

BROWNING, Theresa Rita. PO BOX 517 28766 #020-12-1981 L1981 **PD** *020 †55

PFAFFTOWN – FORSYTH

CAMPBELL, James Stewart. 3705 SAPONA TRL, MEDESIGN 27040 #035-03-1970 L1975 **GP OS** *062
GAILLARD, John Palmer. ■ 27040 #045-01-2005 L2006 **EM** *012
GLEN, Dulaney. ■ 27040 #035-01-1967 L1979 **IM** *071 †20
HERBER, Richard R. 4690 YADKINVILLE RD, STE B 27040 #048-04-1988 L1990 **FM** *020 †18
MARX, Samuel Benno. ■ 27040 #067-01-1948 L1966 **GPM PHP** *071 †18
ROCAMORA, Lee R. 412 LAUREL PARK RD 27040 #036-01-1977 L1977 **IM GE** *020 †20
TAUSSIG, Jacob Stewart. ■ 27040 #019-02-2005 L2006 **DR** *012
WARD, Amy Elizabeth. ■ 27040 #036-05-1995 L1996 **PD AI** *020 †55,03
ZHU, Xiaoying. ■ 27040 #243-76-1992 **AN** *012

PIKEVILLE – WAYNE

BLACKMAN, Jesse Aycock. 5413 US HIGHWAY 117 N 27863 #036-01-1973 L1973 **GP** *020

PILOT MOUNTAIN – SURRY

KEITH, Randall Scott. COOK SCHOOL ROAD 27041 #036-05-1981 L1990 **FM** *020 †18
LANKFORD, C Wayne. 883 COOK SCHOOL RD 27041 #051-04-1981 L1984 **FM** *020 †18
MATTHEWS, Marjorie Fisher. 529 W MAIN ST 27041 #036-05-1961 L1961 **FM** *030 †18

PINE KNOLL SHORES – CARTERET

GOLDBERG, Corinne Leilani. ■ 28512 #045-01-2002 L2002 **PTH** *100 †50
GRAHAM, James H. ■ 28512 #001-02-1949 L1989 **DMP D** *071 †15

PINEBLUFF – MOORE

RICHARDSON, Lucille W. ■ 28373 #051-04-1943 L1956 **IM PUD** *071 †20

PINEHURST – MOORE

ACKER, Jeffrey Chas. PO BOX 3000, DEPT RADATION ONCOLOGY 28374 #036-07-1989 L1992 **RO** *020 †80
ALBRECHT, Robert Joseph, Jr. 5 FIRST VLG 28374 #021-05-1996 L2002 **VS GS** *020 †85
ALLEN, David Geoffrey. 220 PAGE RD, PINEHURST MEDICAL CLINIC 28374 #036-07-1967 L1967 **ON IM** *020 †20
ALLEN, William Walker. ■ 28374 #047-06-1953 L1960 **OBG** *071
AMBATI, Mehar Srivani R. 205 PAGE RD, PINEHURST MEDICAL CLINIC 28374 #496-24-1994 L2004 **CD** *020 †20

ANDREWS, Ellen. 110 PAGE RD 28374 #050-02-1975 L1980 **N P** *020 †75
ANTIL, Michael Alan. 205 PAGE RD, C/O PINEHURST MEDICAL CLIN 28374 #012-05-2002 L2005 **IM** *020 †20
ATIENZA, Romeo B. 165 PAGE RD, MOORE CARE BOX 5 28374 #748-02-1963 L1973 **EM GS** *071 †16
ATKINSON, Clinton Kesler. 5 FIRST VLG 28374 #036-01-1996 L2002 **VS GS** *020 †85
AVERBOOK, Allen Wayne. 210 FRYE RD 28374 #012-05-1986 L1998 **VS GS** *062 †85
BAHNER, Don Robt, Jr. 155 MEMORIAL DR 28374 #038-45-1987 L1992 **EM OM** *020 †16
BEEBLE, John. ■ 28370 #035-03-1948 L1951 **CD** *071
BINNEY, Jeffrey Noel. 90 MEMORIAL DR, PINEHURST MEDICAL CLINIC 28374 #041-14-1977 L2003 **IM** *020 †20 ‡
BLAKELY, Greg Michael. 205 PAGE RD, PINEHURST MEDICAL CLINIC 28374 #016-11-2002 L2005 **IM** *020 †20
BOOKMYER, Robert M. ■ 28374 #025-07-1950 L1951 **PD PDA** *071 †55
BOYCE, Ker. 205 PAGE RD, PINEHURST MEDICAL CLINIC 28374 #012-05-1983 L1999 **ICE CD** *020 †20
BRENNER, Mark Earl. 5 FIRST VLG 28374 #035-06-1979 L1988 **ORS** *020 †40
BRIDGMAN, John Alfred. 300 PAGE RD 28374 #023-01-1992 L1996 **EM** *020 †16
BRUNO, Jenifir Josephine. 155 MEMORIAL DR, BOX 3000 28374 #030-06-1996 L2002 **MPD** *020 †20,55
BUSSEY, George Davis. 155 MEMORIAL DR, FIRSTHEALTH OF THE CAROLIN 28374 #051-07-1977 L2001 **P PFP** *030 †75
CADDELL, Tillie Horkey. PINEHURST MEDICAL CLINIC 28374 #012-01-1951 L1953 **GP** *071
CAREY, Edward Daniel. 55 JUNIPER CREEK BLVD 28374 #041-02-1961 L1994 **GP** *071
CASEY, David Joseph. 5 FIRST VLG 28374 #024-05-1996 L2001 **OAR** *020 †40
CASSIDY, James Jos. ■ 28374 #035-03-1955 L1987 **OBG** *075 †30
CAVROS, Nick George. 7 REGIONAL CIR 28374 #418-01-1986 L2003 **CD** *020 †20
CHAMBERLAIN, Robert J, Jr. 5 FIRST VLG 28374 #010-02-1992 L1994 **U** *020 †95
CHINTALAPUDI, Giridhar. 295 OLMSTED BLVD, MELLON BLDG, STE 12 28374 #495-62-1984 L2000 **N P** *020 †75
CLEARY, Jimmie Ray. 1600 MORGANTON RD LOT J- 28374 #036-05-1960 L1960 **EM IM** *020 †16
CLINTON, Robert A, Jr. 6 REGIONAL DR, STE C 28374 #016-11-1998 L2005 **FM** *020 †18
COBOS, Fernando Andres. 35 MEMORIAL DR, P O BOX 3000 28374 #264-04-1991 L2004 **P** *020 †75
COLLINS, Francis F. 205 PAGE RD, PINEHURST MEDICAL CLINIC 28374 #050-02-1972 L1976 **PUD IM** *020 †20
CONTI, Neil Allen. 5 FIRST VLG 28374 #036-01-1992 L1998 **ORS** *020 †40
CORRIGAN, Francis Chas. PO BOX 1911, 10 AVIEMORE DR 28370 #041-01-1984 L1991 **AN IM** *020 †05
COWHERD, David Mc Lellan. 205 PAGE RD, PINEHURST MEDICAL CLINIC I 28374 #036-01-1981 L1982 **CD IM** *020 †20
COX, Stanley Cullen. 5 FIRST VLG, PINEHURST SURGICAL CLNC 28374 #007-02-1968 L1969 **OTO** *020 †45
CUMMINGS, Robin Gary. 35 MEMORIAL DR 28374 #036-07-1983 L1991 **CD GS** *062 †85,90
DALES, Richard Lemont. 5 FIRST VLG, PINEHURST SURGICAL 28374 #045-01-1976 L1987 **GS** *020 †85
DALEY, Michael Bernard. 90 MEMORIAL DR, PINEHURST MEDICAL CLINIC I 28374 #045-01-1978 L1981 **IM** *020 †20
DAVIS, Keith Edward. 205 PAGE RD 28374 #036-01-1987 L1997 **CD IM** *020 †20
DAYMUDE, Marc Laurence. ■ 28374 #023-12-1990 L1996 **EM** *020 †16
DIFRISCHIA, Daniel S, Jr. ■ 28374 #041-14-1993 L1998 **IM** *020 †20
DOOLEY, Robert Thos. 811 STAMPER RD, BRAGG FAM PRAC CLNC 28374 #039-01-1958 L1995 **PD** *071 †55
DUFFY, Peter Louis. 7 REGIONAL CIR, PINEHURST CARDIOLOGY CONSU 28374 #035-09-1980 L1995 **CD IM** *020 †20
EATON, Kathleen Marie. 5 FIRST VLG 28374 #035-08-1988 L2006 **PM** *020 †60
EDWARDS, Michael Donald. 5 TOWHEE RUN 28374 #016-06-1997 L2002 **DR** *020 †80
ELLIS, John Nelson. 1600 MORGANTON RD LOT E1 28374 #019-02-1966 L1973 **ORS** *071 †40
FEDDER, David Peter. 5 FIRST VLG 28374 #016-11-1986 L1992 **ORS** *020 †40
FERRERI, Eugene Albert. ■ 28374 #038-06-1937 L1980 **GP OM** *071
FESSENDEN, John Michael. 5 FIRST VLG 28374 #030-06-1997 L2003 **GS OS** *020 †85
FLEISCHER, Gary Daniel. ■ 28374 #024-07-1993 L2006 **ORS** *020 †40
FORSBERG, Roy T. ■ 28370 #041-01-1945 L1946 **SO** *071
FOSTER, Toby Eugene. ■ 28374 #012-22-2003 L2004 **PTH** *020 †50
GIBBONS, Jeffrey Roger. 120 APPLECROSS RD 28374 #039-01-1990 L1998 **EM** *020 †16
GIBSON, Jackson Vaughan. 90 MEMORIAL DR, PINEHURST MEDICAL CLINIC 28374 #036-01-1980 L1983 **IM** *020 †20
GRAHAM, Ted Alan. 135 LAKESIDE CT 28374 #048-16-1997 L2000 **EM** *020 †16
GREENWOOD, William Ralph. 155 MEMORIAL DR 28374 #034-01-1982 L1986 **EM** *020 †16
GRIEWE, Greg Lewis. 5 FIRST VLG 28374 #010-01-1991 L2003 **U** *020 †95
GRINE, Reynold Carter. 185 PAGE RD STE A, PINEHURST DERMATOLOGY 28374 #045-01-1993 L1997 **D** *020 †15
GUALTEROS, Oscar M. ■ 28374 #847-11-1991 L2005 **IM** *020
HAKAS, Joseph Francis, Jr. 205 PAGE RD, PINEHURST MEDICAL CLINIC 28374 #041-09-1987 L2002 **CD NC** *020 †20
HALL, Roberta Jean. ■ 28374 #051-04-1945 L1983 **PHP GP** *071
HARMODY, Matthew Richard. 155 MEMORIAL DR 28374 #038-06-1997 L1998 **EM** *020 †16
HASBROUCK, Walter Hughson. ■ 28374 #035-09-1955 L1957 **IM CD** *040 †20 ‡
HEIM, Lori J. 293 OLMSTED BLVD, MCCORMICK BLDG STE 1 28374 #023-12-1986 L2006 **FM** *020 †18
HIPP, David Eric. 90 MEMORIAL DR, PINEHURST MEDICAL CLINIC 28374 #016-06-1991 L1999 **IM** *020 †20
HOLLER, Matthew Brady. 155 MEMORIAL DR, PINEHURST MEDICAL CLINIC 28374 #047-20-2000 L2006 **IM** *020 †20
HOLLINGSWORTH, D V. ■ 28374 #038-41-1963 L1998 **EM FM** *071 †18
HOLTZMAN, Mollie. 205 PAGE RD 28374 #016-06-1991 L1999 **PM** *020 †60
HOSTETLER, Herbert James. 165 PAGE RD, BOX 19 28374 #016-11-1959 L1983 **AN GP** *071 †05
HOY, John Franklin. 1600 MORGANTON RD LOT Y96 28374 #043-01-1993 L2001 **VIR** *020 †80
HUCKS-FOLLISS, Anthony G. 289 OLMSTED BLVD STE 5, SANDHILLS NEUROSURGERY 28374 #051-01-1969 L1975 **NS** *020
HUEY, Jerry Paul. ■ 28374 #422-01-1982 L1992 **PTH** *020 †50
JACOBSON, Severt Harold. PO BOX 3070, 40 MCDONALD RD W 28374 #026-04-1965 L1977 **NS CCS** *020
JACQUES, Robert S. 110 PAGE RD 28374 #005-12-1953 L1954 **EM GP** *071 †18

JAMESON, John Webster, III. 10 AVIEMORE DR, CENTER PA 28374 #038-41-1986 L2002 **FM** *020 †18
JAWANDA, Jaspaul Singh. 155 MEMORIAL DR 28374 #025-01-1999 L2002 **ID** *020 †20
JINGLE, Linda Hoover. 155 MEMORIAL DR 28374 #038-44-1989 L1992 **EM** *020 †16
JOHNSTONE, William Miller, Jr. 5 FIRST VLG, PINEHURST SURG CLN 28374 #036-08-1989 L1990 **OBG** *020 †30
KAMP, William Taylor. ■ 28374 #028-34-1956 L1989 **GS TRS** *071 †85
KARAN, Steven Michael. 10 FIRST VLG, PINEHURST, PA 28374 #041-13-1985 L1997 **AN PME** *020 †05
KENT, Steven Michael. 205 PAGE RD, PINEHURST MEDICAL CLINIC 28374 #036-07-1995 L2006 **CD** *020 †20
KEPICH, Margaret Susan. 205 PAGE RD, PINEHURST MEDICAL CENTER, 28374 #025-07-1991 L1996 **IM** *020 †20
KHAN, Kamal Ahmed. 205 TALL TREES DR 28374 #306-01-1985 L1999 **PD** *020
KILPATRICK, Jefferson K. 5 FIRST VLG, PINEHURST SURGICAL CLNC 28374 #036-05-1994 L2000 **OTO** *020 †45
KILPATRICK, W Kirby. ■ 28374 #036-01-1964 L1964 **OBG** *071 †30
KING, Candace Williamson. 289 OLMSTED BLVD, STE 5 28374 #036-01-1988 L1990 **D** *020 †15 ‡
KING, Stephen Curtis. 155 MEMORIAL DR 28374 #036-01-1988 L1989 **RO** *020 †80
KISER, Andy Christopher. 5 FIRST VLG 28374 #036-01-1992 L1997 **TS** *020 †90,85
KLENZAK, Jennifer S. 293 OLMSTED BLVD STE 7 28374 #036-01-1997 L1999 **NEP** *020 †20
KLUMPAR, David Ivan. 125 FOX HOLW, # 210 28374 #035-01-1985 L1991 **D FM** *020
KOCHENDERFER, Joann Marie. 205 PAGE RD, PINEHURST MEDICAL CLINIC, 28374 #038-43-2002 L2007 **END** *020 †20
KOCHENDERFER, Mark David. 220 PAGE RD, PINEHURST MEDICAL CLINIC 28374 #055-01-1999 L2002 **HO** *100 †20
KRAHNERT, John Frederick. 155 MEMORIAL DR 28374 #036-05-1983 L1990 **TS** *020 †85,90
KRISHNA, Cynthia Elner W. 165 PAGE RD STE 5, COMPANY HEALTH/MOORE CARE 28374 #041-13-1980 L1982 **GP** *020 †20
KRUSE, Richard S. 30 MEMORIAL DR 28374 #010-02-1971 L1972 **DR NM** *071 †80 ‡
KUZMA, Paul J. 300 PAGE RD, MOORE REG HOSPITAL 28374 #035-03-1991 L2000 **AN PME** *020 †05
LAM, Douglas Edward. 10 AVIEMORE DR 28374 #025-07-1976 L1977 **FM** *020 †18
LANDERS, Mark Douglas. 7 REGIONAL CIR 28374 #051-07-1990 L2003 **CD ICE** *020 †20
LARSEN, Eric. 35 MEMORIAL DR, P O BOX 2000 28374 #038-06-1965 L1972 **GS CD** *020 †85
LEBER, Christopher. ■ 28374 #035-19-1982 L1983 **ORS** *020 †40
LENAHAN, Charles Rodney. 5 FIRST VLG 28374 #020-02-1982 L1987 **U** *020 †95
LETIZIA, Kathleen Ann. 205 PAGE RD 28374 #041-07-1996 L1999 **IM** *020 †20
LIFFRIG, James Richard. ■ 28374 #023-12-1993 L1994 **FM** *020 †18
LISTROM, Chad David. 155 MEMORIAL DR 28374 #038-06-2001 L2005 **EM** *020 †16
LOVIER, John Arthur, Jr. 5 FIRST VLG 28374 #035-45-2000 L2002 **OBG** *020 †30
LUCAS, Wayne Burton. 205 PAGE RD, PINEHURST MEDICAL CLINIC, 28374 #051-04-1992 L1998 **IM** *020 †20
LUPKAS, Raymond R, Jr. ■ 28374 #041-09-1985 L1994 **AN** *020 †05
LYNN, Donald Mc Cord. 110 PAGE RD 28374 #038-41-1954 L1989 **OS PD** *072 †55
LYNN, Nicholas Jay. 155 MEMORIAL DR, P O BOX 3000 28374 #038-40-1984 L1999 **NPM** *020 †55 ‡
MANDELL, Mary Thomas. 35 MEMORIAL DR, P O BOX 3000 28374 #012-05-1996 L1997 **P** *020 †75
MARROW, Henry Gregory. 110 PAGE RD 28374 #036-07-1978 L1980 **PTH** *062 †50
MARTIN, David Farra. 205 PAGE RD, PINEHURST MEDICAL CLINIC 28374 #036-05-1980 L1983 **GE IM** *020 †20
MARTIN, Lawrence Wm, II. 30 MEMORIAL DR 28374 #048-12-1990 L1996 **VIR** *020 †80
MAYNOR, Bobby R, Jr. 205 PAGE RD, PINEHURST MEDICAL CLINIC, 28374 #036-07-1988 L1989 **IM** *020 †20
MAYS, Brooks Bellamy. 205 PAGE RD, PINEHURST MEDICAL CLINIC 28374 #045-04-2002 L2006 **END** *020 †20
MC ALLISTER, R G, Jr. ■ 28374 #051-04-1967 L1986 **CD PA** *071 †20
MC CORMICK, Rufus P. ■ 28374 #038-06-1940 L1940 **GS** *071 †85
MC DEARMON, William Dyson. 110 PAGE RD 28374 #051-04-1988 L1990 **PTH** *020 †50
MC DEVITT, Noel Bruce. 20 MEMORIAL DR 28374 #036-01-1964 L1964 **PS FPS** *020 †85,65 ‡
MC FADDEN, James Stuart. 110 PAGE RD 28374 #036-01-1971 L1971 **AN** *020 †05
MC GEE, Bonnie Lynn. ■ 28374 #035-46-1998 L2004 **EM** *020 †16
MEDFORD, Mark Fredric. PO BOX 3000, 155 MEMORIAL DR 28374 #036-08-1995 L1999 **MPD PD** *020 †20
MEINDL, George Thos. ■ 28374 #041-12-1960 L1963 **DR RO** *071 †80 ‡
MERCIER, Randall Robt. 5 REGIONAL CIR STE B 28374 #021-01-1980 L2007 **IM** *020 ‡
MILLER, Mary Suzanne. 35 MEMORIAL DR 28374 #036-05-2000 L2002 **OBG** *020
MISCHINSKI, Matthew M. ■ 28374 #041-13-1950 L1988 **EM** *071 †40,16
MITCHELL, Charles K, Jr. 5 FIRST VLG 28374 #036-08-1990 L1996 **GS** *020 †85
MONDI, Philip Gerard. 205 PAGE RD, PINEHURST MEDICAL CLINIC 28374 #035-15-1993 L1996 **IM** *020 †20
MONROE, John Lauchlin. 155 MEMORIAL DR 28374 #036-01-1962 L1962 **OTO HNS** *071 †45
MOORE, John Roger, IV. 5 FIRST VLG 28374 #027-01-1995 L2001 **OAR** *020 †40
MORRIS, John Robt. ■ 28374 #045-01-1961 L1973 **VS TS** *071 †85,90
MORRIS, Walter Smith, III. 205 PAGE RD, PINEHURST MEDICAL CLINIC, 28374 #036-01-1992 L1993 **IM** *020 †20
MORROW, Jerry Fleming. 205 PAGE RD 28374 #039-01-1963 L1988 **P PYG** *020 †75
MORROW, Roy Andrew. ■ 28374 #064-01-1945 L1951 **GS** *071 †85
MURPHY, Leslie Catherine. 205 PAGE RD, PINEHURST MEDICAL CLINIC 28374 #012-01-1995 L2000 **IM** *020 †20
NELSON, James Roger. ■ 28374 #054-04-1959 L2007 **N** *020 †75
NEVILLE, Cecil H, Jr. ■ 28374 #036-01-1960 L1960 **ORS** *020 †40
OAKLEY, Ward Sayre, Jr. 5 FIRST VLG 28374 #047-06-1975 L1983 **ORS** *020 †40
OLDROYD, Matthew L. 155 MEMORIAL DR 28374 #016-42-1997 L2001 **AN PME** *020 †05
OLDROYD, Robert G. PO BOX 3000, DEPT OF ANES, MOORE REG HO 28374 #016-42-1992 L1999 **AN** *020 †05
PARISH, Havner Hurd, Jr. ■ 28374 #028-02-1956 L1957 **U** *072 †95
PARRISH, Joseph Lester. 205 PAGE RD, PINEHURST MEDICAL CLINIC 28374 #047-06-1980 L1988 **CD CCM** *020 †20
PATRICK, William Ward. 155 MEMORIAL DR 28374 #010-02-1974 L1977 **EM FM** *020 †70,18
PATTERSON, Furnifold, Jr. 205 PAGE RD, PINEHURST MEDICAL CLINIC I 28374 #041-01-1971 L1971 **CD IM** *020 †20
PETERSON-SURI, Mary. 35 MEMORIAL DR, MOORE REGIONAL HOSPITAL 28374 #048-14-1995 L1999 **EM** *020 †16

PIERRE-LOUIS, Renan. 26 RIVIERA DR 28374 #440-01-1959 L1997 **FM PTH** *020 †50,18
PLACE, Lawrence Burt. MOORE REGIONAL HOSPITAL, DEPT OF ANESTHESIOLOGY 28374 #045-01-1983 L1992 **AN** *020 †05
PLACE, Robert Arthur. ■ 28374 #041-02-1971 L1978 **TS** *071 †85,90
POHLMEYER, Robert Austin. 220 PAGE RD, PINEHURST MEDICAL CLINIC 28374 #038-45-2000 L2002 **HO** *020 †20
PRESCOTT, Joseph A. ■ 28374 #035-09-1952 L1953 **FM PUD** *020
PRINCE, Gus Donald. 10 AVIEMORE DR, PINEHURST FAMILY CARE CENT 28374 #065-01-1973 L1993 **FM** *020 †18 ‡
PULEO, Ellen Anne. 70 MEMORIAL DR, PINEHURST WOMEN'S CLINIC, 28374 #036-07-1979 L1982 **OBG** *020 †30
PULEO, Joel Greg. 70 MEMORIAL DR 28374 #036-07-1979 L1996 **OBG** *020 †30
RANK, William Benj. ■ 28374 #038-41-1956 L1956 **U** *020 †95
REEVES, John Albert. ■ 28374 #023-01-1961 L2000 **OPH** *071 †35
REINHARDT, Clare E. 10 AVIEMORE DR, CENTER PA 28374 #041-02-2000 L2004 **FM** *100 †18
REINHARDT, Matthew F. ■ 28374 #041-02-2000 L2003 **EM** *020
REVILLE, Jacland Frank, Jr. ■ 28374 #036-05-2001 L2003 **AN** *020 †05
RICHMAN, Jonathan Miller. PO BOX 1749, 1 PAGE RD 28370 #048-04-1989 L1997 **N IM** *020 †75
ROBERSON, Michelle G. 30 MEMORIAL DR, PINEHURST RADIOLOGY 28374 #036-01-1992 L1999 **DR** *020 †80
ROMIG, Ronald Stanley. ■ 28374 #035-20-1955 L1996 **CRS GS** *071 †85
ROSTAN, Stephen Edwin. 185 PAGE RD STE A, PINEHURST DERMATOLOGY P.A 28374 #047-05-1970 L1971 **D DMP** *020 †15
ROWLAND, Michael C. 5 FIRST VLG 28374 #035-06-1975 L1979 **GS GE** *071 †85 ‡
RUDNICK, Seth Allen. ■ 28374 #051-01-1974 L1978 **OS** *030 †20
SALVADOR, Saul Arturo G. 155 MEMORIAL DR 28374 #748-01-1992 L2004 **IM** *020 †20
SCHABER, John David. ■ 28374 #023-12-2000 L2005 **PTH** *020 †50
SCHIRMER, Charles Carr. 110 PAGE RD 28374 #004-01-1987 L2003 **PTH** *020 †50 ‡
SCHNEIDER, Harold. ■ 28374 #035-09-1965 L1968 **OPH** *071 †35 ‡
SCHNEIDERMAN, Roy. 1600 MORGANTON RD LOT Q5, PARADIGMHEALTH 28374 #550-02-1986 L1995 **NPM PD** *062 †55
SCHULTE, Donald Raymond. 155 MEMORIAL DR 28374 #020-02-1957 L1964 **P CHP** *020
SCHWARTZ, Harvey R. 325 PAGE RD BLDG 3, DBA PINEHURST ALLERGY & AS 28374 #165-01-1976 L1989 **AI PD** *020 †55,03
SHEPHERD, John David. 293 OLMSTED BLVD, STE 7 28374 #030-06-1996 L2002 **IM** *020 †20
SHULER, Robert Keith, Jr. ■ 28374 #012-05-1968 L2005 **OPH** *100 †18
SHUPECK, Malcolm. 5 FIRST VLG 28374 #051-04-1981 L1989 **NS** *020 †25
SIMPSON, Patrick Joseph. 205 PAGE RD, PINEHURST MEDICAL CLNC 28374 #036-01-1993 L1994 **CD** *020 †20
SINCLAIR, Misty L. 1 PAGE RD 28374 #048-15-2001 L2005 **N** *020 †75
SLEMMONS, Barton Kent. ■ 28374 #016-11-1954 L1955 **ORS** *071 †40
SMITH, Jerry Edward. 2 MEMORIAL DR 28374 #036-01-1961 L1961 **OBG** *071 †30
SNYDER, Robert Dean. 1 PAGE RD, PINRHURST NEUROLOGY 28374 #055-01-1990 L1997 **N** *020 †75
SOBOEIRO, Michael Francis. 205 PAGE RD, PINEHURST MEDICAL CLINIC 28374 #036-01-1991 L1994 **IM** *020 †20
SOMERVILLE, Donald L. ■ 28374 #024-01-1945 L1950 **IM** *071
STANFIELD, Bernard M. 5 FIRST VLG, PINEHURST SURGICAL CNLN 28374 #028-03-1972 L1988 **U** *095
STAUB, Ernest Wilson. ■ 28374 #016-06-1957 L1965 **TS VS** *071 †85,90
STEINER, Robert Clayton. 5 FIRST VLG, PINEHURST SURGICAL 28374 #010-01-1990 L1996 **CCS** *020 †85
STORCH, Samuel Jay. 46 MEMORIAL DR, MID CAROLINA UROL 28374 #010-02-1980 L1986 **U** *095
STROBEL, Steven Paul. PAGE ROAD, MOORE REGIONAL HOSPITAL 28374 #038-40-1987 L1995 **EM** *020 †16
SUBIN, Diane Cusumano. 40 AVIEMORE DR 28374 #035-47-1982 L1986 **D** *020 †15
SUBIN, Glen D. 40 AVIEMORE DR 28374 #035-08-1982 L1986 **ORS HS** *020 †40
SURMONTE, John Anthony. ■ 28374 #041-02-1947 L1986 **GS** *071 †85
SWANTKOWSKI, Thos Marian. 205 PAGE RD, PINEHURST MEDICAL CLINIC 28374 #041-13-1978 L1979 **GE IM** *020 †20
TAYLOR, James Edward, II. 200 MEYER FARM DR, C/C 33 ELKTON DRIVE 28374 #036-01-1994 L2001 **AN** *020 †75
TELLEZ, Henry. 295 OLMSTED BLVD, MELLON BUILDING, STE 12 28374 #264-05-1988 L1995 **N** *020 †75
THOMPSON, Loren Levalle. ■ 28374 #056-06-1946 L1948 **DR** *071 †80
THORNTON, David C. 205 PAGE RD, PINEHURST MEDICAL CLINIC 28374 #010-02-1992 L2002 **PCC** *071 †20
THWAITES, Brian Keith. MOORE REGIONAL HOSPITAL, DEPT OF ANESTHESIOLOGY 28374 #016-06-1988 L1996 **AN** *020 †05
TRUESDELL, Alexander G. ■ 28374 #005-06-1998 L1999 **IM** *020 †20
TUZIO-WASHINGTON, Tonianne. 5 FIRST VLG 28374 #051-04-1995 L2001 **AN** *020 †05,55
UNG, Padiwath C. 90 MEMORIAL DR, PINEHURST MEDICAL CLINIC 28374 #035-45-1996 L1999 **IM** *020 †20
VARANASI, Ravikant V. 205 PAGE RD, PINEHURST MEDICAL CLINIC 28374 #041-07-1993 L2002 **GE** *020 †20
VERCHICK, Julie Gale. 155 MEMORIAL DR, FIRST HEALTH REGL HSOP 28374 #036-01-1997 L1998 **EM** *020 †16
VON HARDENBERG, Hanna. 293 OLMSTED BLVD, STE 7 28374 #759-07-1994 L2003 **NEP** *020 †20
WADDELL, Roger Dale. 110 PAGE RD 28374 #007-02-1981 L2007 **FPS** *075 ‡
WAHL, Michele Kalman. ■ 28374 #047-20-1988 L1989 **P** *020 †75
WAHL, Samuel Isaac. ■ 28374 #047-20-1988 L2006 **DR VIR** *020 †80
WALTERS, Ronald Dean. 293 OLMSTED BLVD, MCCORMICK BLDG, SUITE #1 28374 #041-13-1978 L2001 **IM** *020 †20
WASHINGTON, Raymond Gross. 5 FIRST VLG 28374 #051-04-1995 L2001 **GS** *020 †85
WEIDAW, Harold Richard. PO BOX 1835 28374 #041-02-1954 L1971 **AI IM** *020
WEISS, Susan Michelle. ■ 28374 #038-43-2006 **PTH** *012
WETMORE, Robert J. 1600 MORGANTON RD, LOT H3 28374 #036-07-1944 L1947 **PYA PS** *071
WHITE, Geoffrey Gunby. 5 FIRST VLG 28374 #021-01-1986 L1992 **U** *020 †95
WICKER, Joseph Beaman. PAGE ROAD, MOORE REGIONAL HOSPITAL 28374 #047-06-1978 L1982 **AN** *020 †05
WILLARD, Ellen Marie. 220 PAGE RD, PINEHURST MEDICAL CLINIC 28374 #036-05-1985 L1991 **HO IM** *020 †20
WILLIAMS, Diane Metzler. 205 PAGE RD, PINEHURST MEDICAL CLINIC I 28374 #026-04-1987 L1990 **GE HEP** *020 †20

WILLIAMSON, Cile Harding. 5 FIRST VLG 28374 #036-01-1994 L1998 **OBG** *020 †30
WILSON, Suzanne Lee. 155 MEMORIAL DR, PINEHURST MEDICAL CLINIC 28374 #017-20-1994 L2006 **MPD** *020 †20
WINTER, James Andrew. 110 PAGE RD 28374 #038-40-1991 L1995 **PTH DMP** *020 †50
WISNIEWSKI, Wlodzimierz M. 155 MEMORIAL DR, NICU 28374 #759-04-1991 L2006 **NPM PD** *020 †55
WLODARSKI, Gregory H. 289 OLMSTED BLVD, PINETREE CLINIC STE 7 28374 #759-03-1986 L1995 **FM** *020 †18
YOUNT, Loren Jos. ■ 28374 #038-40-1959 L1959 **MDM** *030
ZOELLNER, Steven M. 20 MEMORIAL DR 28374 #025-07-1982 L1989 **GS** *020 †85,65 ‡

PINEVILLE — MECKLENBURG

FU, Hung-Jen. ■ 28134 #385-01-1961 L1972 **GS TS** *071 †90,85
GEIGER, Douglas Farrell. 321 S POLK ST, STE 2A 28134 #038-43-1987 L1992 **ORS OSS** *020 †40
HENNEMAN, Dorothy Hughes. ■ 28134 #023-07-1949 L1953 **OS** *050
KUITEMS, Fredrick Henry. ■ 28134 #010-01-1954 L1985 **GS GP** *071 †85
PLAZA, Michael Jonathan. ■ 28134 #036-05-2008 *012

PINK HILL — DUPLIN

LITTLE, Edwin P. 103 S CENTRAL AVE 28572 #041-02-1980 L1983 **FM** *020 †18

PINNACLE — STOKES

CAUDLE, Crystal Lynn. ■ 27043 #036-01-1992 **AN** *100
WHEELER, Richard Lee. 392 JIM MCKINNEY RD 27043 #007-02-1982 L1989 **FM** *020 †18

PISGAH FOREST — TRANSYLVANIA

ELLIS, Ruth M. ■ 28768 #024-05-1952 L1953 **OBG GP** *072 †30
HALLETT, Erwin B. GENERAL DELIVERY 28768 #035-45-1946 L1954 **GS VS** *072 †85
KEMPE, Ludwig G. ■ 28768 #869-02-1942 L1949 **NS N** *071 †25
LOZANO, Joseph John. 5848 OLD HENDERSONVILL HWY 28768 #665-01-1997 L2001 **IM PD** *020
MCCARTY, Gregory Scott. 313 KNOB RD 28768 #036-08-1991 L1993 **EM** *020 †16
MILNER, Paul F A. ■ 28768 #539-04-1954 L1978 **HEM PCP** *071
PINEIRO, Minerva. 2134 CAMPBELL DR, BREVARD FAMILY PRACTICE 28768 #654-01-1997 L2002 **FM** *020 †18
STRATTON, Albert Fite, Jr. ■ 28768 #021-01-1952 L1984 **FM** *071 †18
TRIPP, Elizabeth Louise. 313 KNOB RD 28768 #036-08-1993 L1996 **EM** *020 †16
UPDIKE, Edwin H. ■ 28768 #035-01-1949 L1953 **GS** *071 †85

PITTSBORO — CHATHAM

ANGERS, John W. ■ 27312 #067-01-1953 L1961 **IG ON** *071
ARKY, Albert Milton. ■ 27312 #039-01-1955 L1958 **PD** *072 †55
BARCLAY, Margaret J F. ■ 27312 #060-01-1945 L1953 **AN** *071
BARRETT, Judith P Nevyas. ■ 27312 #028-02-1963 L1964 **FM** *071 †18
BERL, Soll. ■ 27312 #038-06-1950 L1950 **OS P** *071
BOSWELL, John Iverson. 250 FEARRINGTON POST 27312 #051-01-1957 L1958 **PYA P** *071 †75
BURGERT, Woody. 855 EAST ST, PITTSBORO FAMILY MEDICINE 27312 #011-03-1999 L2002 **FM** *020 †18
CARPENTER, Wm Hawkins. ■ 27312 #045-01-1965 L1965 **OBG** *020 †30
CLARK, Patricia Ellen. ■ 27312 #051-04-1985 L1986 **P** *020 †75
COLLINS, Myra Lou. ■ 27312 #028-02-1976 L1981 **BBK** *030 †50
CUTLER, Leonard. ■ 27312 #869-02-1955 L1959 **R** *071 †80
FRASER, Jenny Elise. ■ 27312 #056-05-1997 L1999 **MPD** *020 †20,55
GARLICK, Wm Lynnewood. 200 E SALISBURY ST 27312 #010-01-1979 L1980 **FM** *020 †18
GERBER, Arthur M. ■ 27312 #035-20-1969 L2002 **NS N** *071 †25
GROSS, Samuel. 1085 FEARRINGTON POST, 40 MCDOWELL STREET 27312 #035-45-1955 L1998 **HEM PD** *040 †25
GULATI, Ajay Sujan. ■ 27312 #048-04-2000 L2007 **PG** *100 †55
HOLT, James Beatty. 75 OLD GRAHAM RD 27312 #036-01-1977 L1977 **FM** *020 †18
KESSEL, Elton. ■ 27312 #016-42-1953 L1983 **PHP** *071 †70
KEY-SOLLE, Mikelle L. ■ 27312 #036-01-2002 L2005 **PD** *100 †55
KIBBE, David Chase. ■ 27312 #038-06-1979 L1991 **FM MDM** *020 †18
KITAY, Julian I. ■ 27312 #024-01-1954 L1955 **END** *071
KUTSCH, Richard Michel. ■ 27312 #012-05-1975 L1990 **FM** *020
LEWIS, Philip H. ■ 27312 #041-77-1954, ▲ L1954 **ORS** *072
MAC DONALD, Carolyn. PO BOX 1686 27310 #051-07-1980 L1995 **PM ID** *050 †60
MAC FARLANE, Dorothy K. ■ 27312 #023-01-1976 L1977 **PHP** *071
MCBEE-PIERCE, Kristin Amb. ■ 27312 #001-02-2006 **PTH** *012
MCGREGOR, Julie Anne Gibs. ■ 27312 #036-05-2004 L2007 **NEP** *012 †20
MULLER, Peter Ray. ■ 27312 #036-01-1987 L1990 **OBG** *020 †30
NIGAM, Gunjan. 75 OLD GRAHAM RD 27312 #495-74-1999 L2006 **FM** *020 †18
PETERSON, Ralph Edward. ■ 27312 #035-01-1946 L1952 **END OS** *050
REDMAN, Rebecca Ann. 2702 JAY SHAMBLEY RD 27312 #056-05-2003 L2006 **HO** *012 †20
REES, Roberts Moss. ■ 27312 #041-13-1945 L1950 **PA IM** *071
SCHACHNER, Carol Schrenk. ■ 27312 #038-08-1964 L1973 **GPM** *020
SPERDUTO, Robert Danl. ■ 27312 #041-01-1964 L1966 **OPH** *071 †35
STAUB, Robert David. ■ 27312 #041-13-1964 L1967 **EM FM** *020 †18,16
TYLER, Michael Jos. 75 OLD GRAHAM RD 27312 #041-13-1979 L1981 **FM ADM** *020 †18
UMPHREY, Lisa Gail. ■ 27312 #005-12-2004 L2007 **CD** *012 †20
VENTO, Rebecca Amber. ■ 27312 #035-09-2005 **MPD** *012
VOLODKA, Karina Maria. ■ 27312 #016-45-1998 L2005 **NPM** *012 †55
WILFERT, Rachel Ann. ■ 27312 #036-07-2001 **IM** *100

■ = Address Information Privacy Protected

PLEASANT GARDEN – GUILFORD

PARSONS, Andrea Jo. ■ 27313 #036-01-2005 L2006 **AN** *012
RIDDLE, William Mark. ■ 27313 #036-08-1985 L2002 **FM EM** *075 †18

PLYMOUTH – WASHINGTON

JEON, Myung-Kil. 1 MEDICAL PLZ 27962 #583-02-1970 L1975 **GP** *020
MOORMAN, Claude T, II. 539 WASHINGTON ST, MAILING: P O BOX 386 27962 #036-07-1966 L1966 **LM AN** *030 ‡
OAK, Chang Yoon. 1 MEDICAL PLZ 27962 #583-01-1970 L1983 **IM GP** *020
PARE, Jean-Louis. 1006 US HIGHWAY 64 E, PLYMOUTH PRIMARY CARE 27962 #067-04-1984 L2004 **FM** *020
STANTON, Allie Mc Leod. 209 OLD ROPER RD 27962 #047-06-1943 L1951 **GS EM** *071
VENABLE, Robert Lee. HWY 64 E, ROANOKE MEDICAL CENTER 27962 #007-02-1976 L1977 **GP** *020
WATSON, Larry Irving. ■ 27962 #036-01-2006 **GS** *012
WESTBERG, Milton Delin. ■ 27962 #005-12-1963 L1984 **FM** *072 †18

POINT HARBOR – CURRITUCK

GAHAGAN, Robert Barrett. ■ 27964 #051-01-1946 L1981 **IM END** *071 †20
LEA, Joseph Davis. ALBETUCK FARM 27964 #021-05-1940 L1969 **IM** *071 †20

POLLOCKSVILLE – JONES

BENSON, Elizabeth Ann. HWY 17 SOUTH, ECIM 28573 #038-06-1988 L1993 **IM** *020 †20
DRAKE, James Edwin. PO BOX 10 28573 #036-01-1968 L1968 **DR** *020 †80
TOWARNICKY, Michael Robt. PO BOX 68, 137 MEDICAL LN 28573 #038-40-1983 L1987 **IM** *020 †20

POPE AIR FORCE BASE – CUMBERLAND

BAXTER, Felicia Marie. 383 MAYNARD ST, ATTN: CREDENTIAL OFFICE 28308 #011-03-1997 L2000 **PD** *020 †55
BOHNSACK, Kevin John. 383 MAYNARD ST, 43 MEDICAL GROUP/SGQ 28308 #016-06-1998 L1999 **FM** *020 †18
BRYANT, Cyrus Litchford. 383 MAYNARD ST, ATTN: CREDENTIAL OFFICE 28308 #024-16-1998 L2005 **FM** *020 †18
GIDDINS, Danielle L. 383 MAYNARD ST, 43 MDG 28308 #041-02-2002 L2006 **FM** *100 †18
KEHREN, Jessica Ann. 383 MAYNARD ST, 43 MDG/CREDENTIALS OFFICE 28308 #023-12-2004 L2005 *100
PASTORE, Joyce B. 383 MAYNARD ST, 43D MEDICAL GROUP 28308 #016-42-1992 L1993 **IM AM** *020 †20
SCHWARTZ, Gerald Richard. 383 MAYNARD ST, 43 MDGGSGHC 28308 #035-08-1972 L1973 **EM** *020 †16
SLYTER, Thomas Michael. 383 MAYNARD ST BLDG 307A, 43D MEDICAL GROUP/ADOS CC 28308 #054-04-1986 L1988 **AM OM** *030 †70
WILSON, Robert Allen. 383 MAYNARD ST, 43 MDGGSGHC 28308 #010-02-1985 L1988 **DR EM** *020 †16
WRIGHT, Jessica Margaret. 383 MAYNARD ST, ATTN CREDENTIAL OFFICE 28308 #021-01-2001 L2003 **FM** *020 †18

POWELLS POINT – CURRITUCK

HEYDER, Dietrich W. SR 1119 27966 #407-23-1954 L1979 **P** *062 †75

PRINCETON – JOHNSTON

CAPPS, Donna Michelle. 213 BARDEN ST, HORIZON FAMILY MEDICINE, P 27569 #036-01-2000 L2001 **FM** *020 †18
SHAFTNER, Kim K. 213 BARDEN ST 27569 #038-40-1980 L2003 **FM GP** *075 ‡
VURLICER, Kira L. 213 BARDEN ST, HORIZON FAMILY MEDICINE 27569 #048-13-2000 L2004 **FM** *020 †18

PROSPECT HILL – CASWELL

MEYERS, Tracy E. 140 MAIN ST 27314 #035-19-1986 L2000 **FM** *020 †18
PICKARD, Carl Glenn, Jr. 140 MAIN ST 27314 #036-01-1962 L1962 **IM** *020 †20
SELVIDGE, Wm Mayhew, Jr. PO BOX 4, 140 MAIN ST 27314 #027-01-1986 L1989 **FM** *020 †18

PROVIDENCE – CASWELL

KIAT, Peter Q. ■ 27315 #748-01-1960 L2004 **EM** *071 †16
MOORE, Frederick Ernest. ■ 27315 #055-01-1983 L1986 **FM** *072 †18

RAEFORD – HOKE

ABREU, Sue H. 613 SADDLEBRED LN 28376 #023-12-1982 L1994 **NM DR** *030 †28
ALMONY, Jeffrey Stewart. 102 W SOUTHERN AVE 28376 #048-14-1999 L2004 **HNS** *020 ‡
BUCHELE, Barry Kevin. 313 TEAL DR, STOP 1 28376 #048-13-1975 L1979 **OBG** *020 †30
BULLIS, William John, II. 313 TEAL DR, STOP 1 28376 #010-02-1991 L1999 **OBG** *020 †30
BYRON, John Walter. 313 TEAL DR, STOP 1 28376 #023-12-1985 L1996 **OBG** *020 †30
CAVALLARO, Julia Michelle. ■ 28376 #017-20-2006 L2007 **FP** *012
CHAMBERS, Doris Elizabeth. ■ 28376 #023-07-1945 L1951 **ORS** *071 †40
CHU, H Willy. 313 TEAL DR, STOP 1 28376 #036-07-1983 L1990 **GS** *020 †85
COHEN, Alan Brent. ■ 28376 #051-04-1965 L2004 **GS** *020 †85 ‡

ELSAID, Sameh Fouad. 855 OLD NC 211 HWY, MC CAIN HOSPITAL 28376 #915-03-1994 L2003 **ID IM** *020 †20
FARMER, Cheryl Belinda. 159 MERCY DR 28376 #036-01-1998 **FM GPM** *020
FASOLAK, Walter S. 313 TEAL DR, STOP 1 28376 #028-78-1984, ▲ L1990 **OBG** *020 †30
FERNANDEZ, Gabriel I. 405 S MAIN ST, HOKE FAMILY MEDICAL CTR 28376 #042-03-1990 L1999 **FM** *020 †18
GHOLSTON, Lisa Regina. 855 OLD NC 211 HWY 28376 #036-01-1993 L1993 **IM** *020 †20
GRUMBO, Robert Jesse. ■ 28376 #023-12-2008 *012
HASSON, Jonathan Edward. 313 TEAL DR STOP 1 28376 #035-03-1977 L1991 **VS GS** *020 †85
HENDERSON, George P, Jr. 313 TEAL DR STOP 1 28376 #036-01-1964 L1964 **OTO FPS** *071 †45
KANTOROWSKI, Pamela G. 313 TEAL DR, STOP 1 28376 #036-07-1990 L1994 **OBG** *020 †30
KHAN, Iqbal Mohammad. 855 OLD NC 211 HWY 28376 #704-01-1966 L1996 **IM HEM** *020 †20
LEE, Kyu Yong. 855 OLD NC 211 HWY 28376 #583-10-1968 L1980 **GP** *020
LONG, Clifford James. 313 TEAL DR STOP 1 28376 #025-07-1977 L1981 **OBG** *020 †30
LOWRY, Garnett Marcus. 313 TEAL DR 28376 #036-01-1999 L2001 **FM** *020 †18
MANESS, Michael James. 313 TEAL DR STOP 1 28376 #036-01-1975 L1977 **OBG** *020 †30
MC ALLISTER, Vincent B. ■ 28376 #036-08-1993 L1996 **P** *100
OLVEY, Kendall Reid. 313 TEAL DR, STOP 1 28376 #001-02-1998 L2005 **OBG** *020 †30
PHILLIPS, Charles A Speas. 313 TEAL DR STOP 1, FIRSTHEALTH FAM CARE CTR 28376 #016-06-1947 L1949 **GP** *071 †85
SMITH, Arletty Del Pilar. 405 S MAIN ST, HOKE FAMILY MEDICAL CENTER 28376 #715-01-1990 L2001 **FM** *020 †18
SMITH, Karen Linnear. 929 W PROSPECT RD 28376 #041-09-1989 L1991 **FM** *020 †18 ‡
STREITMAN, John E. 313 TEAL DR STOP 1 28376 #048-13-1999 L2006 **TS** *020 †85,90
TOWNSEND, Robt Glenn, Jr. 405 S MAIN ST 28376 #020-02-1961 L1964 **FM** *071 †18
ZOTA, Ramnik. ■ 28376 #495-23-1971 L1974 **FM PUD** *020 †18

RALEIGH – WAKE

AARONS, Alan Lawrence. 4301 LAKE BOONE TRL, STE 309 27607 #023-01-1988 L1993 **IM** *020 †20,03
AARONS, Maureen Leahy. 3225 BLUE RIDGE RD, STE 101 27612 #023-01-1988 L1990 **D** *020 †20,15
ABDOU, Francis John. PO BOX 18139 27619 #035-15-1988 L1999 **AN PME** *020 †05
ABEDI, Kheyrolah. ■ 27613 #517-01-1970 L1987 **GS** *071
ABERNETHY, M Lisa. 3225 BLUE RIDGE RD, STE 101 BLUE RDG DERMATOLO 27612 #036-01-1987 L1994 **D** *020 †15
ABO-KAMIL, Tariq. ■ 27604 #154-01-1997 L2005 **IM** *100 †20
ABRAMS, Jeffrey Edward. 3024 NEW BERN AVE STE C, WAKEMED FACULTY PHYSICIANS 27610 #036-01-1995 L1999 **CCS** *020 †85
ADAM, Amer. 3024 NEW BERN AVE, STE 301 27610 #036-01-1995 L1999 **IM** *020 †20
ADAMSON, William Talbot. 3948 BROWNING PL, SURGEONS 27609 #036-07-1990 L2004 **PDS** *020 †85
ADELMAN, Richard D. 7320 SIX FORKS RD STE 260 27615 #016-06-1975 L1986 **FM FSM** *020 †18
ADEWUNMI, Obafemi Adegbem. ■ 27603 #690-01-1997 L2004 **IM** *020
AFEWORKI, Hanna Gebretati. ■ 27615 #366-01-1987 L2007 **PD** *020 †55
AGAYOFF, John Danl, Jr. 3400 EXECUTIVE DR, STE 101 27609 #035-08-1965 L1987 **GE IM** *020 †20
AHMAD, Sarwat W. ■ 27606 #704-06-1965 L1976 **P** *020 †75
AHMED, Iftequar U. 3225 BLUE RIDGE RD STE 113 27612 #495-65-1981 L1997 **IM IMG** *020 †20
AHUJA, Anant Vijay. ■ 27615 #035-09-2005 L2007 **IM** *012
AKKALADEVI, Shailaja. ■ 27606 #495-57-1996 L2007 **IM** *100 †20
ALDERMAN, Allison M, Jr. 4420 LAKE BOONE TRL 27607 #036-05-1946 L1947 **FM** *071
ALEXANDER, Benjamin S. 3024 NEW BERN AVE STE 307, WAKEMED FACULTY PHYSICIANS 27610 #036-01-1995 L1998 **PD** *020 †55
ALEXANDER, Maria Premilla. 2406 BLUE RIDGE RD, STE 100 27607 #011-03-2004 L2007 **PD** *100
ALLAN, Gordon Wm. ■ 27607 #065-01-1952 L1965 **GS** *020
ALLEN, James Richard. ■ 27617 #037-01-1970 L1971 **PHP PD** *030 †55
ALLEN, Le Roy. ■ 27607 #036-05-1946 L1947 **NS** *071 †25
ALLEN, Louis David. 3124 BLUE RIDGE RD 27612 #012-01-1978 L1981 **PD** *020 †55
ALLEN, Robert Lee. 5838 SIX FORKS RD, STE 100 27609 #036-05-1979 L1982 **NS** *020 †25
ALLEY, John Granville, Jr. 4420 LAKE BOONE TRL 27607 #036-01-1998 L1999 **RNR** *020 †80
ALPHIN, Robert Stancil. 3100 SPRING FOREST RD, MAILING: P O BOX 18139 27616 #036-05-1990 L1995 **AN** *020 †05
ALSPAUGH, Carrie Deener. 3225 BLUE RIDGE RD, STE 101 27612 #036-01-1991 L1995 **D** *020 †15
AMMAR, Mohamed Ibrahim. ■ 27613 #915-04-1965 L1981 **OBG** *071
AMOS, Keith Dave. ■ 27614 #024-01-1997 L2007 **GS** *020 †85
ANDEREGG, Mark Robert. ■ 27608 #010-02-1994 L2008 **AN** *020 †05
ANDERSON, Donna Grey. 4414 LAKE BOONE TRL 27607 #036-07-1982 L1985 **PD** *020 †55
ANDERSON, Troy Fletcher. 701 EXPOSITION PL, STE 218 27615 #005-12-1990 L1994 **IM** *020 †20
ANDES, Willard Abe. ■ 27608 #021-01-1968 L2005 **HEM ON** *071 †20 ‡
ANDREW, Wallace F, Jr. 3515 GLENWOOD AVE, RALEIGH ORTHO CLINIC 27612 #051-01-1975 L1981 **HS OSM** *020 †40
ANDREWS, Jennifer Carol. 3000 NEW BERN AVE, WAKE MED HOSPITALS 27610 #011-04-2004 L2007 **PD** *100 †55
ANDRUS, Thomas Ross, Jr. 3809 COMPUTER DR, STE 200 27609 #036-01-1978 L1982 **D** *020 †15
ANNAMRAJU, Venkata Siddha. 820 S BOYLAN AVE, MCBRYDE BLDG, 5-E 27603 #495-53-1998 L2004 **IM** *020 †20 ‡
ARCHIE, Jos Patrick, Jr. 3000 NEW BERN AVE, STE 1100 27610 #036-01-1968 L1968 **VS GS** *071 †85
ARMSTRONG, Jose Luis. 4601 LAKE BOONE TRL, S-2E 27607 #042-02-1986 L1991 **IM PMM** *020
ASHBURN, Philip Eugene. 3100 BLUE RIDGE RD, STE 300 27612 #036-05-1974 L1974 **GE IM** *020 †20
ASKAR, Abdallah Onsy. 820 S BOYLAN AVE, DOROTHEA DIX HOSPITAL 27603 #915-06-1970 L1984 **P FM** *020 †75
ASKEW, Anne Preston. 4420 LAKE BOONE TRL 27607 #036-07-1956 L1956 **PD GE** *071 †55

■ = Address Information Privacy Protected

ATASOY, Erhan Cemil. 2800 BLUE RIDGE RD, STE 306 27607 #020-02-1995 L2000 **AN** *020 †05
ATKINSON, Alvan William. 3000 NEW BERN AVE 27610 #041-02-1971 L1979 **TS** *020 †85,90
ATREE, Behnaz S. ■ 27614 #041-09-1996 L2000 **IM** *020
ATREE, Susheel Vaidya. 10000 FALLS OF NEUSE RD, STE 201 27614 #041-09-1996 L2000
   IM *020 †20
AUMAN, George Louis. 4414 LAKE BOONE TRL 27607 #036-05-1968 L1968 **PD** *020 †55
AVERY, Kirsten Hill. 2605 BLUE RIDGE RD STE 300, BLUE RIDGE FAMILY PRACTICE 27607
   #035-20-1996 L1999 **FM** *020 †18 ‡
AYCOCK, Jean Elizabeth. 867 WASHINGTON ST 27605 #036-01-1982 L1986 **P** *020 †75
AYOUBI, Nasib A. ■ 27606 #875-01-1983 L1995 **RHU IM** *020 †20
AYSCUE, Grace Thompson. 3126 BLUE RIDGE RD, STE G-100 27612 #036-01-1994 L1996
   FM *020 †18
AZIKIWE, Ndidi Nelly. 3024 NEW BERN AVE, STE 304 27610 #041-15-1999 L2005 **GS** *020 †85
AZRAK, Michael James. 4420 LAKE BOONE TRL, RALEIGH EMERGENCY 27607
   #036-05-1998 L1999 **EM** *020 †16
AZZI, Anthony Francesco. 10224 DURANT RD, STE 109 27614 #012-01-1984 L1989
   END IM *020 †20
BAE, Jinsun Christine. ■ 27614 #045-04-1997 L2003 **FM** *020
BAHADORI, Reza. 3012 FALSTAFF RD 27610 #517-03-1961 L1988 **OBG REN** *071
BAHNA, Mohsen S. ■ 27613 #649-14-1986 L1998 **IM** *020 †20
BAJZAK, Kristina Ilona. 10941 RAVEN RIDGE RD, STE 109 27614 #063-01-1993 L2004
   GYN *020 †30
BAKER, Carissa Marrie. ■ 27617 #041-01-2003 **PDC** *012 †55
BAKER, Dana Danielle. ■ 27616 #036-01-2008 *012
BALLA, Joseph. 3000 FALSTAFF RD 27610 #016-11-1988 L1990 **P PYG** *020 †75
BALOCH, Mohammad Haroon. 3126 BLUE RIDGE RD 27612 #704-01-1970 L1981
   FM GP *020 †18 ‡
BAPAT, Vijaya Vijay. DOT/DMV, 1100 NEWBERN AVENUE 27699 #495-20-1960 L1995
   PHP PD *030 †55
BARAKAT, Ahmad B. 5816 CREEDMOOR RD STE 105 27612 #875-02-1988 L1997 **AI** *020 †20 ‡
BARBORIAK, Peter N. 820 S BOYLAN AVE, DOROTHEA DIX HOSPITAL 27699
   #036-07-1989 L1991 **CHP** *020 †75
BARDINI, John Andrew. 3400 WAKE FOREST RD 27609 #033-05-1996 L2002 **DR** *020 †80
BARISH, Charles Franklin. 3100 BLUE RIDGE RD STE 300 27612 #011-03-1980 L1981
   GE IM *020 †20
BARLOW, Tanneisha S. 4414 LAKE BOONE TRL, STE 205 27607 #025-12-2001 L2005
   OBG *020 †30
BARNES, Larry. 2920 LEGGING LN 27615 #036-07-1974 L1982 **OPH GP** *050
BARNETT, Stewart Doak. 4700 FALLS OF NEUSE RD, STE 400 27609 #036-08-1991 L1995
   P PHM *050
BARRIE, Kimberly Ann. 8300 HEALTH PARK, STE 109 27615 #024-07-1995 L2001
   HS ORS *020 †40
BARRINGER, Thaddeus J, Jr. 3900 BROWNING PL STE 20 27609 #021-01-1978 L1982
   P *020 †75
BARTZ, Raquel Rae. 3024 NEW BERN AVE STE 30, WAKEMED FACULTY PHYSICIANS 27610
   #054-04-1998 L2001 **AN** *012 †20
BASH, Karen Louise. 3024 NEW BERN AVE, STE 306 WAKE AHEC OB/GYN 27610
   #041-12-1988 L1992 **OBG** *040 †30
BASS, Brian Edmond. 3805 COMPUTER DR 27609 #011-03-1989 L1993 **OBG** *020 †30
BASSALY TADROS, Guirguis. ■ 27613 #915-02-1979 **MPD** *071
BASTEK, Tara Kopp. 3000 NEW BERN AVE, NEONATOLOGY - THIRD FLOOR 27610
   #051-07-1996 L2004 **NPM** *020 †55
BATAWI, Alain. ■ 27614 #869-04-1984 L2000 **IM** *020 †20
BATCH, Deirdre Anne V. 187 WIND CHIME CT STE 202, PREVENTIVE HLTH CARE ASSOC 27615
   #047-07-1976 L1982 **GYN PHP** *020
BATTAGLINO, Michael Paul. 2601 LAKE DR, STE 201 27607 #035-09-1994 L1998 **GE** *020 †20
BATTLE, Constance Yvonne. 1611 E MILLBROOK RD 27609 #011-02-1982 L1985 **OBG** *020 †30
BATTS-MURRAY, Doris J. ■ 27604 #036-01-1979 L1981 **FM** *020 †18
BAUER, Maureen S. 3400 WAKE FOREST RD 27609 #048-14-1997 L2002 **PCP** *020
BAUM, Michael. ■ 27615 #041-01-1978 L1981 **EM IM** *020 †20,16
BEAN, Gary Owen. 4414 LAKE BOONE TRL, STE 502 27607 #036-05-1976 L1980 **FM** *020 †18
BEATTY, Zoe Ann. 2417 ATRIUM DR, STE 200 27607 #036-01-2001 L2005 **OBG** *020 †30
BEAUCHAMP, Charles. 23 SUNNYBROOK RD STE 107, RALEIGH VA OUTPATIENT CLIN 27610
   #036-07-1975 L1975 **IM** *020 †20
BECHERER, Paul Robt. 2304 WESVILL CT STE 240 27607 #016-11-1983 L1985 **IM** *050 †20
BECKER, Denis I. 3410 EXECUTIVE DR STE 205 27609 #020-12-1972 L1974 **END IM** *020 †20
BEEBER, Alan Roger. 4420 LAKE BOONE TRL, REX HEALTHCARE 27607 #051-04-1971 L2001
   P GP *040 †75
BELCEA, Octavian Mircea. 2810 WAKEFIELD PINES DR, STE 115 27614 #041-15-2000 L2002
   FM *020 †18 ‡
BELLAMY, Wm Edward, Jr. ■ 27617 #036-05-1947 L1948 **IM PUD** *071 †20
BELLARD, James Ernest. 3900 BROWNING PL, STE 201 27609 #012-05-1981 L1984
   P PFP *020 †75
BENAVIDES, Lorena. 3809 COMPUTER DR, STE 201 27609 #035-01-2001 L2006 **OBG** *020
BENEVIDES, Marc David. 2800 BLUE RIDGE RD, STE 405 27607 #036-01-1995 L2001
   U *020 †95
BENGTSON, Mary K Witges. STUDENT HEALTH SERVICES, NC STATE UNIVERSITY 27695
   #016-45-1976 L1983 **FM FSM** *020 †18
BENNER, Alisha Beth. 3024 NEW BERN AVE, WAKEMED FACULTY PHYSICIANS 27610
   #030-05-2002 L2006 **IM** *020 †20
BENNETT, Brian Chas. 2800 BLUE RIDGE RD, STE 405 27607 #047-05-1989 L1995 **U** *020 †95
BENNETT, Stacy Kaija. 3024 NEW BERN AVE, STE 302 27610 #038-40-2002 L2007 **GS** *100 †85
BENNETT, Ward Emerson. 6801 PLEASANT PINES DR, STE 105 27613 #036-08-1992 L1993
   FM EM *020
BENSON, John Dewitt. 4420 LAKE BOONE TRL, REX HEALTH PATH DEPT 27607
   #036-01-1978 L1979 **PTH** *050 †50
BENTLEY, John Gregory. 3480 WAKE FOREST RD, STE 208 27609 #422-01-1998 L2002
   PM *020 †60
BERGER, Bruce R. ■ 27613 #026-04-1977 L1982 **PFP CHP** *020 †75 ‡
BERLIN, Corey. 3410 EXECUTIVE DR, STE 205 27609 #041-09-1992 L1996 **END** *020 †20
BERNARDINI, Marcus Q. ■ 27617 #065-06-1999 **OBG** *100
BERRY, Brendan Charles. 3000 NEW BERN AVE, WAKE MEDICAL CENTER 27610
   #023-01-1998 L2001 **EM** *020 †16
BERRY, William Rosser. 4101 MACON POND RD, CAROLINA 27607 #036-07-1974 L1978
   ON HEM *020 †20
BERTICS, Gregory Michael. 10880 DURANT RD, STE 200 27614 #036-07-1982 L1987
   N *020 †75

BETTS, Wilmer Conrad. 400 NEWTON RD 27615 #036-07-1948 L1997 **P ADP** *071 †75
BHATTI, Kausar Amjad. ■ 27606 #704-06-1972 L1975 **P** *020
BHIWANDIWALLA, Pouruchis. 3100 DURALEIGH RD, STE 204 27612 #495-01-1968 L1988
   OBG PHP *020 †30 ‡
BIANCHI, Gregory David. ■ 27607 #016-01-1994 L2006 **U** *020 †95
BIERMAN, David Ralph. 4601 LAKE BOONE TRL STE 2D 27607 #016-45-1985 L1986
   CHP P *020 †75
BILBRO, Robert Hodges. 3521 HAWORTH DR 27609 #036-01-1966 L1966 **IM CD** *020 †20
BIRMINGHAM, Lorraine F. 3400 EXECUTIVE DR, STE 201 27609 #036-07-1981 L1984
   FM *020 †18
BISWAS, Sukanto. 3024 NEW BERN AVE, STE 304 27610 #495-45-1986 L2003
   GS CCS *020 †85
BLACK, Tracy Marie. 3410 EXECUTIVE DR, STE 205 27609 #010-03-1988 L1994
   END IM *020 †20
BLACKLEY, Roy J. 325 N SALISBURY ST RM 628 27603 #067-01-1953 L1953 **P** *030
BLAIR, Ellen Kay. 8724 COMPASS LN 27615 #041-02-1988 L2008 **IM** *020 †20
BLAKELEY, Dean Dewayne. 1001 ROCK QUARRY RD 27610 #028-03-1988 L1992 **IM** *020 †20
BLANK, Jonathan Wm. 3400 WAKE FOREST RD, AT DUKE HEALTH RALEIGH 27609
   #035-20-1985 L1988 **AN PME** *020 †05
BOARD, Robert Jeffrey. 3320 EXECUTIVE DR, STE 111 27609 #036-07-1974 L1978
   OPH *020 †35
BODENSTINE, Thomas Robert. 1321 OBERLIN RD STE A, OBERLIN ROAD PEDIATRICS, P 27608
   #051-07-1997 L2000 **PD** *020 †55
BOERNER, David Franklin. 2304 WESVILL CT, STE 210 27607 #041-14-1976 L1980
   IM PCC *020 †20
BOLDING, William Robt. 3100 SPRING FOREST RD, STE 130 27616 #036-01-1981 L1984
   AN *020 †20
BOLIEK, Bruce Stephen. 3320 EXECUTIVE DR, STE 111 27609 #036-01-1987 L1995
   OPH *020 †35
BOMMAREDDI, Anu Radha. 2417 ATRIUM DR, PA 27607 #038-43-1997 L1999 **FM** *020 †18
BOOK, Wendy Lynn Taylor. 10831 FOREST PINES DR, STE 11 27614 #036-07-1999 L2002
   PD *020 †55
BOOKERT, Lisa M. 3000 NEW BERN AVE 27610 #010-03-1979 L1986 **FM** *020 †18
BOONE, David Warner. 14341 NEW FALLS OF NEUSE 27614 #036-01-1987 L1994
   ORS OFA *020 †40
BOONE, Stephen C. ■ 27609 #036-07-1965 L1965 **NS** *071 †25
BOOTH, Frank Matthew, Jr. ■ 27615 #051-04-1945 L1946 **FM IM** *020
BORTOFF, Gregory A. 4020 WESTCHASE BLVD, STE 390 27607 #035-15-1994 L1995
   DR *020 †80
BOTSTEIN GLICK, Sandra M. 4420 LAKE BOONE TRL 27607 #035-08-1987 L1989
   PD ADL *020 †55
BOWMAN, Michael Higgins. 1540 SUNDAY DR 27607 #038-40-1976 L1977 **N EM** *020 †75
BOYCE, Stephen Eugene. 10208 CERNY ST, STE 300 27617 #011-03-1982 L1988 **OTO** *020 †45
BOYD, Jessamy Anne. ■ 27613 #048-16-2003 L2004 **RO** *012
BOYSE, Margaret Brown. 4201 LAKE BOONE TRL, STE 200 27607 #048-14-1995 L2003
   D *020 †15
BOYSE, Tedric Dale. 114 WIND CHIME CT 27615 #047-05-1998 L2004 **DR** *020 †80
BRAASCH, Ernest Russell. 3726 CAMLEY AVE 27612 #035-08-1970 L1973 **P PYA** *020 †75
BRAITHWAITE, Heather. ■ 27613 #035-09-2001 L2004 **EM** *020 †16
BRAMSON, Brian Thomas. 2620 NEW BERN AVE, WAKE HEALTH SERVICES, INC 27610
   #024-01-1999 L2003 **ID** *100 ‡
BRATZKE, Edward Chas. 3100 SPRING FOREST RD, STE 130 27616 #011-04-1991 L1996
   CCA *020 †05
BRAYBOY, Terrence Dean. 3000 NEW BERN AVE 27610 #036-01-1994 L2001 **EM** *020 †16
BRENNEMAN, Terry Richard. 5816 CREEDMOOR RD STE 104 27612 #035-19-1976 L1983
   PD *020 †55
BRIDGEFORD, Edward P. 3024 NEW BERN AVE 27610 #011-04-1999 L2004 **HOS IM** *020 †20
BRODY, Seth Chas. 3024 NEW BERN AVE STE 306, AHEC OB/GYN DEPT 27610
   #024-07-1992 L1996 **OBG** *020 †30
BROOMHALL, Patricia. ■ 27612 #917-05-1950 L1974 **FM ADL** *071 †18
BROUGHTON, Arthur Calvin. ■ 27608 #051-04-1937 L1937 **IM** *071
BROWN, Daniel Elmer. 3124 BLUE RIDGE RD 27612 #036-01-1965 L1965 **PD** *071 †55
BROWN, Edwin Alan. 2304 WESVILL CT STE 240 27607 #001-02-1983 L1986 **ID IM** *020 †20
BROWN, Josephine Rebecca. 800 SAINT MARYS ST, STE 100 27605 #033-05-1986 L1995
   FM *020 †18
BROWN, Laura Devereux. 10208 CERNY ST, STE 300 27617 #011-03-1997 L2002 **OTO** *020 †45
BROWN, Richard Everit. ■ 27604 #566-01-1997 L2007 **IM** *100
BROWNE, Jeffrey. ■ 27613 #008-02-2002 L2005 **DR** *100 †80
BROWNSTEIN, Michelle R. 2301 REXWOODS DR, STE 116 27607 #005-14-1991 L1996
   GS *020 †85
BROWNSTEIN, Robert Andrew. 4420 LAKE BOONE TRL, RALEIGH EMERGENCY 27607
   #005-14-1991 L1994 **EM IM** *020 †20,16
BRUCH, Richard Franklin. 8300 HEALTH PARK, STE 109 27615 #016-11-1972 L1977
   ORS *020 †40
BRUEGGEMANN, Daniel. ■ 27617 #051-04-2008 *012
BRUNDLE, Scott Harding. 2406 BLUE RIDGE RD, STE 170 27607 #025-01-1997 L2000
   FM *020 †18
BRUSINO, F Gregory. 3100 SPRING FOREST RD, CRITICAL HEALTH SYSTEMS 27616
   #035-06-1983 L1985 **AN** *050 †05
BRYANT, Joshua Andrew. ■ 27617 #005-14-2004 **DR** *012
BUCHHEIT, Thomas Edward. 2800 BLUE RIDGE RD, STE 306 27607 #012-05-1994 L1998
   APM IM *100 †05
BUCKLEY, Michael Francis. 4414 LAKE BOONE TRL, STE 308 27607 #036-08-1994 L1996
   OBG *020 †30
BUGAJ, Gregory Michael. 7021 HARPS MILL RD, STE 100 27615 #035-06-1994 L2003
   IMG *020 †20
BUKOWSKI, Timothy. 2406 BLUE RIDGE RD, STE 190 27607 #035-06-1987 L1995
   UP U *020 †20
BULLARD, Dennis E. 1540 SUNDAY DR STE 214 27607 #028-34-1975 L1982 **NS** *020 †25
BURKARD, John L, Jr. 2417 ATRIUM DR, PA 27607 #055-01-1994 L1996 **FM** *020 †18
BURKE-HAYNES, Karen A. 10941 RAVEN RIDGE RD, STE 105 27614 #035-45-1985 L1993
   PD *030 †55
BURKHEAD, Margaret Kelly. ■ 27608 #034-01-1997 L2007 **FM** *100 †18
BURROUGHS, Frederick D. 4551 NEW BERN AVE, STE 160 27610 #047-07-1966 L1969 **PD** *020
BURROUGHS, Paul L, Jr. 3410 EXECUTIVE DR 27609 #036-01-1966 L1966 **ORS** *071 †40
BURROUGHS, Paul L, III. 3410 EXECUTIVE DR 27609 #036-01-1994 L1999 **ORS** *020 †40

BURT, Mark Anthony. 8300 HEALTH PARK, STE 109 27615 #025-07-1995 L2000 **ORS** *020 †40

BURTON, Earl Edward, Jr. 3900 BROWNING PL STE 202 27609 #051-04-1968 L1970 **D IM** *020 †20,15

BUTTAR, Daljit S. 4201 LAKE BOONE TRL, STE 103 27607 #495-29-1979 L1987 **PMM N** *020 †75

BUZAN, Andrew William. 3000 NEW BERN AVE, WAKEMED 27610 #654-01-2002 L2007 **IM** *100 †20

BYNUM, Debra Lynn. 3024 NEW BERN AVE, STE 301 27610 #036-01-1994 L1996 **IMG** *020 †20

CALDWELL, James Paul. ■ 27615 #050-02-1968 L1974 **IM** *020 †20

CALLAWAY, George Hadley. 3515 GLENWOOD AVE, RALEIGH ORTHOPAEDIC CLINIC 27612 #024-01-1988 L1994 **OSM ORS** *020 †40

CAMP, Brian Hunter. 8301 BANDFORD WAY 27615 #048-14-1995 L1997 **IM** *020

CAMP, Thomas Francis, Jr. ■ 27609 #012-05-1962 L1969 **IM CD** *071 †20

CAMPAIOLA, Jean Mary. ■ 27615 #024-16-1988 L1996 **P** *020 †75

CAMPBELL, Donald Barnes. 3100 BLUE RIDGE RD, STE 300 27612 #001-02-1971 L1976 **IM** *020 †20

CAMPBELL, Joseph D. 3404 WAKE FOREST RD, STE 100 27609 #041-12-1988 L1992 **OBG** *020 †30

CAMPBELL, Kevin Ray. 3000 NEW BERN AVE, STE G100 27610 #036-05-1996 L1999 **ICE** *020 †20

CANALE, Sean Thos. 4414 LAKE BOONE TRL, STE 211 27607 #021-05-1991 L2001 **GS AS** *020 †85

CANNON, Gregory James. 3000 NEW BERN AVE, WAKE MEDICAL CENTER 27610 #047-05-1994 L2002 **EM** *020 †16

CANNON, Helen Christy. ■ 27615 #041-07-1967 L1977 **PD** *020 †55

CANNON, Woodward. 2800 BLUE RIDGE RD 27607 #024-01-1970 L1977 **GS AM** *020 †85 ‡

CAPPS, Mary Traylor. 4551 NEW BERN AVE, STE 160 27610 #011-03-2001 L2004 **PD** *020 †55

CARBONE, John Stephen. 4277 MAIL SERVICE CTR, 341 W. MORGAN ST, RANDALL 27699 #051-01-1988 L2003 **P** *020 †75

CARDUCCI, Bryan. 5129 CARTER ST 27612 #041-07-1981 L1996 **EM** *020 †16

CARLETON, Christine A. ■ 27601 #051-04-2002 L2006 **PD** *100

CARLINO, Richard Edward. 3633 HARDEN RD, SURGERY PA 27607 #033-06-1984 L1989 **PS GS** *020 †85,65

CARLSON, Curtis Bradley. 3100 BLUE RIDGE RD, STE 300 27612 #028-02-1991 L1994 **IM** *020 †20

CARLSON, Timothy Don. 3716 NATIONAL DR, STE 224 27612 #038-06-1980 L1983 **P** *020 †75

CARNES, Kenneth Michael. 1540 SUNDAY DR 27607 #028-02-1992 L1997 **N** *020 †75

CARONE, Patrick Patteson. 3000 NEW BERN AVE, CAROLINA REHAB ASSOCIATION 27610 #051-01-1994 L1998 **PM** *020 †60

CARR, James Stewart. 3404 WAKE FOREST RD, STE 200 27609 #065-05-1987 L1992 **GYN** *020 †30

CARR, Josiah M, II. 3400 EXECUTIVE DR STE 205, PIEDMONT MEDICAL ASSOCIATE 27609 #045-01-1989 L1992 **FM** *020 †18

CARR, Marjorie Barnwell. 2800 BLUE RIDGE RD, STE 401 27607 #036-01-1976 L1976 **PD** *020 †55

CARTER, Alan Bruce. ■ 27604 #036-07-1962 L1962 **CHP P** *072 †55,75

CARTER, Jean Whitmore. 4414 LAKE BOONE TRL, STE 210 27607 #036-01-1978 L1986 **OBG** *020 †30

CARTER, Steven Ricker. 4020 WESTCHASE BLVD # 390, RALEIGH RADIOLOGY ASSOCS. 27607 #051-04-1999 L2005 **DR** *020 †80

CARTER, Timothy Robert. 4420 LAKE BOONE TRL 27607 #051-01-1984 L1989 **PTH** *020 †50

CARUSO, Carole. ■ 27614 #041-12-1980 L1990 **AN** *020 †05

CASANI, Julie Ann Paula. 10402 PUMPKIN LN 27614 #035-19-1980 L2006 **EM** *020 †20,16

CASEY, Mary Colleen. 4420 LAKE BOONE TRL, RALEIGH EMERGENCY 27607 #038-45-1996 L1999 **EM** *020 †16

CASEY, Michael Joseph. 3604 BUSH ST, WAKE NEPHROLOGY ASSOCIATES 27609 #036-01-1996 L1998 **NEP** *020 †20

CASEY, Michele Roberts. 3100 DURALEIGH RD STE 200 27612 #036-01-1995 L1996 **FM** *020 †18 ‡

CASTELLOE, Thomas Edison. 4420 LAKE BOONE TRL 27607 #036-01-1956 L1956 **ORS** *071 †40

CASTILLER, Francis Adan. 3480 WAKE FOREST RD, STE 414 27609 #748-01-1999 L2007 **PCC** *020 †20

CAUDLE, Robert Jos. 3633 HARDEN RD STE 102 27607 #036-05-1981 L1988 **ORS PD** *020 †40

CAULWAY, Kimberly Ann. 14501 NEW FALLS OF NEUSE R, WAKE FOREST NEIGHBORHOOD M 27614 #041-13-1998 L2005 **FM** *020 †18

CAVINESS, Perry Alonzo. 3301 TERMINAL DR 27604 #036-01-1991 L1992 **FM** *020 †18 ‡

CEFALU, Salvador J. ■ 27612 #021-05-1960 L1962 **P IMG** *071 †75

CELLA, John Robt. PO BOX 19509 27619 #036-01-1964 L1964 **R** *071

CHAKSUPA, Dan. 2304 WESVILL CT, STE 210 27607 #055-01-2002 L2005 **IM** *020 †20

CHALLGREN, Eric Daniel. 4201 LAKE BOONE TRL, STE 200 27607 #038-43-1998 L2002 **D** *020 †15

CHAMBLEE, H Royster, Jr. 20 ENTERPRISE ST 27607 #036-07-1960 L1960 **OPH** *020 †35

CHANDER, Rajat. 6080 SIX FORKS RD STE C 27609 #036-07-1991 L1994 **GE** *020 †20

CHANG, Felicia. 1034 BRAGG ST, NCCIW 27610 #038-06-1996 L2000 **IM** *020 †20

CHARLES, Kirk Lesly. 3000 NEW BERN AVE, WAKEMED MEDICAL CENTER 27610 #036-07-1999 L2006 **VS** *020

CHARLTON, Philippa Ann. 2408 PERENIAL ST 27603 #036-01-1987 L1991 **PDE** *020 †19,55

CHASE, George O. ■ 27613 #036-07-1951 L1952 **PTH FOP** *071 †50

CHASE, Sheldon. 859 WASHINGTON ST, PSYCHIATRIC ASSOCIATES OF 27605 #025-01-1970 L1974 **P** *020 †75

CHATTERJEE, Benu. 6090 SIX FORKS RD # A 27609 #495-09-1980 L1984 **IM** *020 †20

CHAUDHRY, Abdul Ghafoor. 3214 CHARLES B ROOT WYND, STE 203 27612 #704-01-1970 L1982 **GS TS** *020 †85,90

CHAUDHRY, Nivedita. 10117 SPORTING CLUB DR, DURHAM VA MEDICAL CENTER 27617 #496-07-1988 L2004 **P** *020 †75 ‡

CHAWLA, Cynamon K. 4020 WAKE FOREST RD # 201 27609 #041-13-1999 L2006 **OBG** *020 †30

CHAWLA, Sameer Naren. 3000 NEW BERN AVE 27610 #041-13-1999 L2006 **U** *020 †95

CHEEK, John Christopher. ■ 27609 #036-01-1984 L2002 **N** *075 †75

CHEELY, George Rayburn. 3000 NEW BERN AVE, STE 1200 27610 #041-01-1974 L1977 **CD IM** *020 †20

CHEELY, George Rayburn, Jr. ■ 27613 #041-01-2008 *012

CHEEVERS-WOODS, Tanya R. 820 S BOYLAN AVE, DOROTHEA DIX HOSPITAL 27603 #047-07-1978 L1999 **ADP PD** *020 †18,75

CHEN, Hsiupei. 2800 BLUE RIDGE RD, STE 306 27607 #036-07-1999 L2003 **APM** *020 †05

CHEVY, Cherry. 3900 BROWNING PL, STE 201 27609 #055-01-1997 L1999 **CHP** *020 †75

CHHABRA, Ajaib Singh. ■ 27614 #495-34-1955 L1974 **PS** *020 †65

CHHABRA, Rajinder K. ■ 27614 #495-03-1957 L1979 **OBG** *020

CHIAVETTA, John Bryan. 14341 NEW FALLS OF NEUSE 27614 #036-01-1999 L2004 **ORS** *020 †40

CHIAVETTA, Stephen V. 4420 LAKE BOONE TRL 27607 #056-06-1969 L1976 **PTH HMP** *020 †50

CHILES, John Timothy. ■ 27612 #016-02-1969 L1973 **VIR R** *071 †80

CHILMAN, John Howard. ■ 27615 #917-29-1958 L1995 **P** *020 †75

CHIU, Jackson. 2815 CATES AVE OB 7312, STUDENT HLTH 2ND FL 27695 #004-01-1983 L1989 **P** *020

CHIULLI, Richard Allen. 2800 BLUE RIDGE RD, STE 503 27607 #024-05-1977 L1982 **GS OS** *020 †85

CHIUTEN, Delia Fungshe. 820 S BOYLAN AVE 27603 #748-02-1971 L1989 **IM ON** *020

CHMELEWSKI, Walter L. 2418 BLUE RIDGE RD STE 105 27607 #041-12-1986 L1987 **RHU A** *020 †20

CHO, Dong Lim. ■ 27613 #583-02-1956 L1984 **PTH** *030

CHOUDRY, Shehzad Hafiz. 2800 BLUE RIDGE RD, STE 306 27607 #045-04-2000 L2005 **APM** *100 †75 ‡

CHOW, Arthur Yichia. 3000 NEW BERN AVE, STE G100 27610 #005-02-1999 L2005 **CD** *020 †20

CHURCH, C Franklin. 3400 WAKE FOREST RD 27609 #036-07-1963 L1963 **FM D** *071 †18

CINOMAN, Michael Ira. 3024 NEW BERN AVE, WAKE MEDICAL CENTER 27610 #023-01-1987 L1994 **CCP** *020 †55

CITRON, Michael Owen. ■ 27612 #038-41-1984 L1995 **EM GP** *020 †16

CLAPACS, John Terry, II. 5530 MUNFORD RD, STE 119 27612 #036-07-1992 L1993 **P** *020 †75

CLARK, Erika Louise. 4414 LAKE BOONE TRL, STE 205 27607 #041-12-1993 L1997 **OBG** *020 †30

CLARK, George T, III. 2800 BLUE RIDGE RD 27607 #036-01-1985 L1987 **GS** *020 †85

CLARKSON, Mark William. 10208 CERNY ST, STE 300 27617 #051-01-1991 L1996 **OTO** *020 †45

CLELAND-ROBERTS, Elizabeth. 2620 NEW BERN AVE 27610 #036-08-2003 L2006 **PD** *020 †55

CLEPPER-FAITH, Melissa R. 2406 BLUE RIDGE RD, PEDIATRICS 27607 #011-04-1990 L1994 **PD** *020 †55

CLIFFORD, Philip Earle. 8300 HEALTH PARK, STE 109 27615 #011-03-1993 L1997 **ORS** *020 †40

CLINE, Steven Geo. 1931 MAIL SERVICE CTR, NC DIVISION OF PUBLIC HLTH 27699 #035-06-1947 L1949 **R** *072

CLINE, William Tucker. 8300 HEALTH PARK, STE 211 27615 #036-07-1978 L1983 **GS** *020 †85

CLOUGH, Alissa Marie. ■ 27610 #030-05-2001 L2004 **MPD** *100 †20,55

COCHRANE, Sandra Victoria. 567 E HARGETT ST, WAKE COUNTY HUMAN SERVICES 27601 #041-09-1984 L1993 **P** *020

COFFER, Bertram Watts. 3100 SPRING FOREST RD, STE 130 27616 #036-01-1969 L1969 **AN CCM** *020 †05

COLE, James Simpson. 3320 WAKE FOREST RD 27609 #018-03-1963 L1991 **IM CD** *050 †20

COLEMAN, Ruth Marie. 4414 LAKE BOONE TRL, STE 300 27607 #051-04-2002 L2006 **OBG** *020

COLEMAN, Stephen Ray. 3100 DURALEIGH RD, STE 380 27612 #011-03-1980 L1998 **PD** *020 †55

COLLAWN, James Belknap. 3100 SPRING FOREST RD, STE 130 27616 #036-01-1987 L1989 **AN** *020 †05

COLLAZO, Linda I. 4551 NEW BERN AVE, STE 160 27610 #042-02-2000 L2006 **PD** *020 †55

COLLINS, Ann Sharpe. 4414 LAKE BOONE TRL 27607 #036-07-1991 L1995 **OBG** *020 †30

COLLMAN, Mitchell Scott. 4301 LAKE BOONE TRL, STE 309 27607 #035-03-1979 L1982 **CD EM** *020 †20

COLSON, Lacy A. 123 SUNNYBROOK RD, STE 120 27610 #010-03-1972 L1973 **IM** *020 †20

COLVARD, David Fred. 3725 NATIONAL DR STE 228 27612 #036-07-1978 L1980 **P UM** *020 †75

COLVIN, Larry Gregg. 3024 NEW BERN AVE, STE 301 27610 #036-07-1997 L2003 **IM** *020 †20

COMBS, Diana Lynn. ■ 27606 #036-05-2007 **PD** *012

COMER, Wilson Sidney, Jr. 867 WASHINGTON ST 27605 #036-01-1977 L1977 **P** *020 †75

COMSTOCK, Michael Chester. 3410 EXECUTIVE DR 27609 #010-01-1986 L1993 **ORS OSM** *020 †40

CONGDON, Mark Henderson. ■ 27615 #051-01-1957 L1983 **P** *071

CONGER, Lawrence Kendall. 8010 ARCO CORPORATE DR, STE 100 27617 #036-08-1997 L2006 **EM** *020 †16

CONLEY, Mary G. 3414 SIX FORKS RD 27609 #422-01-1994 L2000 **FM** *020 †18

CONNELL, April A. 10 SUNNYBROOK RD 27610 #011-04-1980 L1993 **PD** *050 †55

CONRAD, Douglas Michael. 4505 FAIR MEADOWS LN, STE 208 27607 #045-01-1974 L1975 **CHP P** *020

COOK, Charles Alvin. 3414 SIX FORKS RD 27609 #024-07-1975 L1980 **NEP IM** *020 †20

COOK, Kenton Rollin. 4420 LAKE BOONE TRL 27607 #048-14-1997 L2000 **HOS** *020 †20

COOK, Kristin Michelle. ■ 27617 #010-01-2007 *012

COOK, Raymond D. 3024 NEW BERN AVE, OTOLARYNGOLOGY HEAD & 27610 #036-01-1997 L1999 **OTO FPS** *020

COOK, Robyn Margaret. ■ 27613 #026-08-1989 L1989 **OBG** *020 †30

COOKE, John Arthur, Jr. 806 SPRINGMOOR DR 27615 #035-08-1940 L1940 **GS** *071

COOPER, Claire. 6512 SIX FORKS RD 27615 #036-07-1978 L1979 **P** *075 †75

COOPER, Randolph Arend. 3000 NEW BERN AVE, STE G100 27610 #036-07-1987 L1989 **CD** *020 †20

COPELAND, Dana Derward. 3000 NEW BERN AVE 27610 #036-07-1972 L1974 **PTH NP** *020 †50

CORBIN, George Wesley, Jr. ■ 27613 #041-01-1943 L1943 **GP** *071

CORCORAN, Gavin R. ■ 27614 #836-01-1987 L1992 **ID IM** *020 †20

CORKEY, Paula Lucile. ■ 27607 #036-07-1999 L2000 **P** *100

CORKEY, William Barnette. 3100 SPRING FOREST RD, STE 130 27616 #036-07-1999 L2002 **AN** *020 †05

CORRIGAN, Mark Hn. ■ 27605 #051-01-1984 L1988 **P** *020 †75

CORSON, Pamela Kay. 3000 NEW BERN AVE, EMERGENCY ROOM 27610 #017-20-1986 L1994 **EM** *020 †16

CORVIN, George Patrick. 5530 MUNFORD RD STE 119 27612 #001-02-1992 L1997 **P PFP** *020 †75

CORVIN, Karen W. 2605 BLUE RIDGE RD, STE 150 27607 #001-02-1992 L1996 **OBG** *020 †30

COUCHMAN, Grace Marie. 2601 LAKE DR, STE 301 27607 #007-02-1985 L1987 **OBG** *020 †30

COURIE, Maurice Nickola. ■ 27609 #036-07-1959 L1959 **GYN** *071 †30

COVINGTON, Connell. 3350 SIX FORKS RD 27609 #036-01-1976 L1978 **PD** *020

COVINGTON, Donald Scott. 1101 DRESSER CT, WAKE SURGICAL CENTER 27609 #036-01-1989 L1995 **GS** *020 †85

COVINGTON, Suzanne Steele. 2406 BLUE RIDGE RD, STE 100 27607 #036-05-2005 L2006 **PD** *012

■ = Address Information Privacy Protected

COXE, James Sherwood, III. 4420 LAKE BOONE TRL 27607 #036-01-1971 L1971 END IM *020 †20

COYLE, Helene Victoria. ■ 27617 #539-06-2003 L2004 NPM PD *012 †55

CRACKER, Andrew John. 3000 NEW BERN AVE 27610 #045-01-1988 L1992 OBG *020 †30 ‡

CRANE, Jeffrey Major. 4420 LAKE BOONE TRL, REX CANCER CENTER 27607 #011-03-1977 L1989 HO HEM *020 †20

CRATER, Christina H. 3100 BLUE RIDGE RD, STE 300 27612 #047-06-1995 L2005 IM *020 †20

CROMARTIE, Henry L, III. 4101 MACON POND RD, CAROLINA 27607 #036-01-1979 L1981 ON IM *020 †20

CROSBY, Kenneth Lee, Jr. 2315 MYRON DR, EASTER SEALS-UCP/ASAP INC. 27607 #036-01-1999 L2001 P *020 †75

CROSS, Nancy Virginia. 2304 WESVILL CT, STE 210 27607 #045-01-1994 L2000 IM *020 †20

CROWLEY, Nancy Jean. 2301 REXWOODS DR, STE 116 27607 #036-07-1985 L1988 GS *020 †85

CROWTHER, James David. 3410 EXECUTIVE DR STE 103 27609 #041-14-1996 L2001 ORS *020 †40 ‡

CRUMPLER, Earl H, Jr. 3100 SPRING FOREST RD, STE 130 27616 #036-08-1985 L1986 AN GS *020 †05

CUADRA, Michael R. ■ 27614 #748-01-1958 L1965 PTH PCP *071 †50

CUMMINGS, James Lee, II. 3100 SPRING FOREST RD 27616 #055-01-1990 L1994 AN *020 †05

CUNNINGHAM, Calhoun Dove. ■ 27608 #045-01-1996 L2004 OTO *020 †45

CURRIN, Robert Graves. ■ 27612 #045-01-1945 L1948 PD OBS *071

CURTIS, Clifford A N. ■ 27619 #047-07-1976 L1989 IM *020 †20

CUSHMAN, Marjorie. ■ 27607 #035-45-1956 L1991 PHP PD *030 †70

CUTCHIN, Lawrence M. 222 N PERSON ST, C/O NORTH CAROLINA MED SOC 27601 #036-01-1962 L1962 IM PD *030 †20

CVETKOVSKI, Boris. 2011 FALLS VALLEY DR, STE 106 27615 #035-19-1991 L2005 GE *020 †20

CZITO, Toni Michelle. 3000 NEW BERN AVE 27610 #012-01-1996 L2001 EM *020 †16

DAHRINGER, Vincent P. 4700 FALLS OF NEUSE RD, NORTH TOWER SUITE 180 27609 #012-01-1990 L1995 OPH *020 †35

D'ALONZO, Richard Concezi. 908 VANCE ST 27608 #028-34-2003 L2004 ACA *012

DAMSKER, David Colin. 10 SUNNYBROOK RD STE 307, WAKE COUNTY HUMAN SERVICES 27610 #041-15-2000 L2003 GPM *020 †70

DANIEL, Thomas Brantley. ■ 27612 #036-05-1943 L1943 U *071 †95

DANIEL, Walter Eugene, III. 3100 SPRING FOREST RD, STE 130 27616 #036-01-1979 L1981 AN *020 †05

DANIELS, Patsy Foster. 809 SPRING FOREST RD, STE 100 27609 #036-01-1982 L1983 FM *020 †18

DARKES, Leroy Scott. 512 E DAVIE ST 27601 #033-06-1982 L1989 IM *020 †20

DASCOMB, Harry Emerson. 3000 NEW BERN AVE, WAKE CO MED CTR C/O WAK 27610 #035-45-1943 L1973 IM ID *071 †20

DAUD, Mian Bashir. STUDENT HEALTH SERVICE, NC STATE UNIVERSITY 27695 #704-01-1971 L1989 PD FM *020 †18

DAUMEN, J Rebecca. 4414 LAKE BOONE TRL 27607 #056-05-1995 L1997 PD *020 †55

D'AVANZO, Nicholas Joseph. 3124 BLUE RIDGE RD, STE 102 27612 #035-06-1986 L1990 PD *020 †55 ‡

DAVE, Shilpa Jagdishchand. ■ 27604 #495-22-1993 L2008 PD *012

DAVIDIAN, Vartan A, Jr. 1112 DRESSER CT 27609 #036-01-1967 L1967 PS *071 †85,65

DAVIES, Megan Maria. 4416 WINGATE DR 27609 #036-01-1991 L1992 FM *020 †18

DAVIS, Arthur Bryan. 4278 MSC, 831 W MORGAN ST 27699 #041-09-1991 L2002 GS *020

DAVIS, Arthur E, Jr. ■ 27608 #026-04-1953 L1962 PTH OS *071 †50

DAVIS, Cara Lee. 2431 SPRING FOREST RD, STE 111 27615 #051-01-1985 L1993 IM OM *020 †20

DAVIS, Dwight Groome. 3000 NEW BERN AVE 27610 #041-02-1954 L1961 GS TS *071 †85

DAVIS, Glenn Miller. 2304 WESVILL CT STE 360 27607 #045-01-1974 L1987 PS *020 †85,65

DAVIS, Whitney Kent. 4020 WESTCHASE BLVD, STE 350 27607 #036-01-1984 L1985 DR *020 †80

DAW, Jeffrey Richard. 4325 LAKE BOONE TRL, STE 315 27607 #036-01-1990 L1996 CD *020 †20

DAWOD, Dawod Abd Elmagid. 1924 QUAIL RIDGE RD 27609 #915-04-1980 L2005 FM *020 †18

DEBNAM, George C. 524 S BLOUNT ST 27601 #047-07-1951 L1951 FM OBG *071

DEBNAM, Marie Georgette. 1615 E DAVIE ST 27610 #047-07-1991 L1995 IM *020

DEBNAM, Marjorie L. 524 S BLOUNT ST 27601 #047-07-1991 L1995 IM *020

DEFLORA, Ellen. 4420 LAKE BOONE TRL 27607 #048-02-1988 L1991 PD *020 †55

DEGESYS, Gintaras Eduard. 4020 WESTCHASE BLVD, STE 390 27607 #038-41-1979 L1983 DR *050 †80

DEJARNETTE, Lisa Faye. 4420 LAKE BOONE TRL, REX HEALTHCARE HOSP 27607 #036-01-1986 L1989 IM *020 †20 ‡

DE LEON, Arturo De Jesus. 1109 DRESSER CT 27609 #748-08-1961 L1971 FM IM *020 †18

DELLAERO, David Thos. 8300 HEALTH PARK, STE 109 27615 #048-04-1990 L1993 ORS OSM *020 †40

DENTON, Robert James. 4420 LAKE BOONE TRL, RALEIGH EMERGENCY 27607 #055-01-1991 L1992 EM *020 †16

DESTEFANO, Amy Ann. 4420 LAKE BOONE TRL, RALEIGH EMERGENCY 27607 #036-01-1991 L1992 EM *020 †16

DETWEILER, Donald Gene. 4020 WESTCHASE BLVD, STE 390 27607 #012-05-1978 L1980 DR *020 †80

DEUTSCH, Margaret Ann. 10010 FALLS OF NEUSE RD, CAROLINA NORTH RALEIGH 27614 #056-06-1984 L1987 ON IM *020 †20

DEVALAPALLI, Vandana P. 3024 NEW BERN AVE STE 301 27610 #495-65-1983 L1992 IM *020 †20

DEVEAU, Jane Mcnab. 227 SUNNYBROOK RD, RALEIGH VA CBOC 27610 #036-01-1996 L1997 PYG *100 †75

DE WITT, Michael Edward. 211 E SIX FORKS RD, STE 101 27609 #023-01-1981 L1989 CHP P *020 †75

DE WITT, Sarah Elizabeth. 600 N PERSON ST 27604 #048-01-1994 L2000 ORS OFA *020 †40

DHILLON, Tej Pal Singh. ■ 27613 #495-03-1963 L1975 ORS *071 †40

DICKENS, Mahlon Alan. 2709 BLUE RIDGE RD STE 100 27607 #036-05-1991 L1995 OPH *020 †35

DICKERSON, Jill Burnett. 4551 NEW BERN AVE, STE 160 27604 #047-06-1996 L1997 PD *020 †55

DIEHL, Cynthia Lyn. 5212 CARTER ST 27612 #036-01-1996 L1997 PS *012 †85

DIEHL, Lee Harold. 1108 DRESSER CT 27609 #007-02-1992 L1994 OSM *020 †40

DILALLA, Gayle Ackerman. 8300 HEALTH PARK, STE 211 27615 #028-46-1987 L2003 GS *020 †85 ‡

DI LORENZO, Robert Alan. 4420 LAKE BOONE TRL, RALEIGH EMERGENCY 27607 #016-11-1983 L1992 EM NS *020 †16

DIMMIG, Thomas Alva. 8300 HEALTH PARK, STE 109 27615 #036-07-1976 L1978 ORS *020 †40

DINGMAN, Catherine Hobbs. 1100 DRESSER CT STE 200 27609 #036-01-1984 L1988 GYN *020 †30

DINGMAN, Stephen Michael. ■ 27613 #036-01-1999 NS *062

DJANG, William T. 3949 BROWNING PL, WAKE RADIOLOGY CONSULTANTS 27609 #023-07-1977 L1984 DR RNR *020 †80

DONOHUE, Christian Daniel. 3305 SUNGATE BLVD, STE 100 27610 #024-07-1997 L2003 IM *020 †20

DONOHUE, Hugh. 701 CORPORATE CENTER DR, CIGNA HEALTHCARE 27607 #036-07-1975 L2000 GS VS *030 †85

DORFMAN, Brett Edward. 3024 NEW BERN AVE, OTOLARYNGOLOGY HEAD & 27610 #012-05-1996 L1998 OTO *020 †45

DORFMAN, Margaret J. 5711 SIX FORKS RD, ASSOC 27609 #024-07-1977 L1981 P *020 †75

DOSHI, Gunvantray K. 3400 WAKE FOREST RD 27609 #495-17-1955 L1988 PM OTO *020 †60

DOSHI, Hirendra N. 2600 ATLANTIC AVE, TRIANGLE GASTROENTEROLOGY 27604 #496-38-1981 L1987 GE IM *020 †20

DOSHI, Usha V. ■ 27614 #496-38-1971 L1986 NPM PD *074 †55

DOSHI, Vasant N. 6901 BUCKHEAD DR 27615 #495-22-1970 L1985 N *020

DOUGHERTY, Kevin Edward. 3100 BLUE RIDGE RD STE 300 27612 #023-01-1985 L1988 IM *020 †20

DOYLE, Kevin Michael. 10208 CERNY ST, STE 300 27617 #036-07-1991 L1994 OTO FPS *020 †45

DRABICK, Andrew Jos. 3500 BUSH ST, STE 103 27609 #041-13-1985 L1994 FM *020 †18

DRAGELIN, Joel Bruce. 1101 DRESSER CT 27609 #041-02-1987 L1994 GS *020 †85

DUBAL, Nirali Manish. 7205 STONEHENGE DR 27613 #495-23-1994 L2003 PD *020 †55

DUBOW, David Alan. 3000 NEW BERN AVE DEPT EM 27610 #036-05-1988 L1991 EM *020 †16

DUCKETT, Olly Christopher. 3000 NEW BERN AVE, MEDICAL OFFICE BUILDING 27610 #051-04-1995 L2000 OS EM *020 †16,55

DUNATOV, Christopher Jos. 3024 NEW BERN AVE, WAKEMED FACULTY PHYSICIANS 27610 #054-04-1992 L1996 CCM IM *020 †20

DUNCAN, Irenee May. 8300 HEALTH PARK, STE 229 27615 #045-01-1998 L2004 GS OTO *020

DUNLAP, William Marshall. 3521 HAWORTH DR 27609 #036-07-1965 L1965 ON HEM *020

DUNN, Karen Diane. 4420 LAKE BOONE TRL 27607 #035-09-1976 L1988 PD AI *020 †55,03

DUNN, Laurie Louise. 3000 NEW BERN AVE, DEPT NEONATOLOGY 27610 #036-07-1981 L1987 NPM PD *020 †55

DUNSTON, Armayne G. 1034 BRAGG STREETMSC4287, NC CORRECTIONAL INST FOR W 27699 #047-07-1971 L1976 IM *030

DURFEE, Michael Fulk. ■ 27607 #051-01-1963 L1964 ADL PD *071 †55

DURLAND, William F, Jr. 3010 ANDERSON DR 27609 #036-01-1998 L2003 OTO *020 †45

DYKES, Joseph Hubbard. ■ 27603 #011-03-1976 L1978 GPM *050 †20

EARNHARDT, J William. 2800 BLUE RIDGE RD, STE 403 27607 #045-04-1982 L1983 CD IM *020 †20

EASTER, Harley Clifton, Jr. 3400 WAKE FOREST RD, RAEIGH COMMUNITY HOSPITAL 27609 #051-01-1977 L1981 EM FM *020 †18,16

EATON, Bernard Thos. 3801 LAKE BOONE TRL 27607 #036-01-1985 L1994 P *020

ECHT, Audrey Faye. 10931 RAVEN RIDGE RD, STE 101 27614 #017-20-1990 L2000 D IM *020 †15

EDDLEMAN, David Beauchamp. 2800 BLUE RIDGE RD 27607 #012-05-2000 L2005 GS *020 †85

EDER, Susan Louise. 4020 WESTCHASE BLVD, STE 130 27607 #035-46-1983 L1991 CHP P *020 †75

EDMONDSON, Donald Ausbon. 3100 SPRING FOREST RD, STE 130 27616 #036-01-1985 L1989 AN *020 †05

EDMUNDSON, Henry Garland. ■ 27613 #036-08-2003 L2007 P *100

EDMUNDSON, Warner Wells. 3521 HAWORTH DR 27609 #036-01-1980 L1981 IM *020 †20

EDRINGTON, Richard David. 2800 BLUE RIDGE RD, STE 500 27607 #020-02-1977 L1979 GS VS *020 †85

EDWARDS, Donna Helen. ■ 27608 #047-20-1999 L2007 IM *020 †20

EDWARDS, Elmo Stephen. 2800 BLUE RIDGE RD STE 501 27607 #036-07-1963 L1963 PD *071 †55

EDWARDS, Geo Sadler, Jr. 3404 WAKE FOREST RD 27609 #036-01-1978 L1984 HS ORS *020 †40

EDWARDS, George Sadler. 3404 WAKE FOREST RD, STE 303 27609 #036-01-1957 L1957 ORS *020 †40

EDWARDS, James Ronald. 3000 NEW BERN AVE 27610 #036-01-1958 L1958 PTH CLP *020 †50

EFIRD, Randy Clyde. 3100 SPRING FOREST RD, STE 130 27616 #036-05-1986 L1986 AN *020 †05

EHLERT, Kurt Jonathan. 3633 HARDEN RD STE 102 27604 #056-06-1987 L1999 ORS *020 †40

EISINGER, Dina Beth. 8300 HEALTH PARK, STE 109 27615 #008-01-1989 L2003 PM *020 †60

ELLINGTON, Kenneth Scott. 3400 WAKE FOREST RD 27609 #036-01-1990 L1995 PTH *020 †50

ELLISON, Maxlyn La Vie. 2920 HIGHWOODS BLVD STE 1, ELLISON & ASSOC. OF RALEIG 27604 #036-08-1993 L1998 CHP P *020 †75

EMERY, Daryl Chas. 4414 LAKE BOONE TRL, STE 409 27607 #036-05-1981 L1986 CD *020 †20

EMERY, John Bloom, Jr. 512 E DAVIE ST 27601 #036-07-1963 L1966 IM LM *020 †20

EMLER, Katrin Elizabeth. 3521 HAWORTH DR 27605 #051-04-2001 L2001 OBG *020 †30

ENDER, Bulent. 2417 ATRIUM DR, STE 101 27607 #051-04-1987 L1993 GE IM *020 †20

ENGEL, Jeffrey Phillip. 1902 MAIL SERVICE CTR, EPIDEMIOLOGY 27699 #023-07-1981 L1988 ID *030 †20

ENGEMANN, John Joseph. 2304 WESVILL CT, STE 240 27607 #025-07-1996 L1999 ID *020 †20

ENGLEHARDT, John Mark. 8300 HEALTH PARK, STE 327 27615 #036-05-1985 L1991 ICE CD *020 †20

ERICSON, Douglas Paul. 13132 ASHFORD PARK DR 27613 #017-20-1986 L2000 DR *020 †80

ESPINO-DE LEON, Rosemary. 2903 ADRIAN CT 27604 #748-08-1961 L1977 AN *072

ESPOSITO, Robert M. 5620 SIX FORKS RD, STE 104 27609 #035-01-1981 L1995 ORS OSM *062 †40

ETIENNE, Stefanie L. 1001 ROCK QUARRY RD, ROCK QUARRY ROAD FAMILY ME 27610 #048-02-2002 L2003 FM *020 †18

EURE, Charles Allan. 3521 HAWORTH DR 27609 #036-01-1967 L1967 IM *020 †20

EVERETT, Vivian Denise. 3024 NEW BERN AVE, STE 307 27610 #045-04-1984 L1986 PD *030 †55

FAISON, Genevieve Sanatra. 2620 NEW BERN AVE, WAKE HEALTH SERVIES INC 27610 #045-01-1997 L2000 PD *020 †55

FAJGENBAUM, David Moniek. 3410 EXECUTIVE DR 27609 #021-01-1975 L1980 ORS *020 †40

FAJGENBAUM, Michael C. 3410 EXECUTIVE DR, STE 103 27609 #021-01-1982 L1988 ORS *020 †40

FALSONE, Joseph Michael. 3320 WAKE FOREST RD, STE 204 27609 #035-06-1994 L2002 **CD** *020 †20

FAN, Jack J. 3000 NEW BERN AVE 27610 #244-05-1968 L1975 **FM PD** *020 †18

FAN, William Li-Goon. 3604 BUSH ST 27609 #036-01-1999 L2002 **NEP IM** *020 †20

FARAG, Ahmed Abdelkader. 4420 LAKE BOONE TRL 27607 #915-02-1987 L1999 **IM** *020 †20

FARLEY, William Winfree. 4420 LAKE BOONE TRL 27607 #051-04-1943 L1947 **PD OS** *071 †55

FAUST, Kirk Berry. 1101 DRESSER CT 27609 #001-02-1982 L1983 **GS** *020 †85

FEARNOT, Robert Francis. 2430 GARDEN HILL DR # 108 27614 #047-07-1980 L1983 **P** *020 †75

FEINSON, Theodore Sloane. 3000 NEW BERN AVE, WAKEMED INTENSIVIST MEDICI 27610 #035-09-1978 L2001 **CCM PCC** *020 †20

FELDMAN, Kristen Cone. 4414 LAKE BOONE TRL, STE 405 27607 #012-05-2000 L2004 **OBG** *020 †30

FENNELL, Patrick Stanley. 3909 SUNSET RIDGE RD, STE 103 27607 #023-01-1984 L1994 **PD** *020 †55

FERDON, Benjamin Bethea. 3100 BLUE RIDGE RD, STE 200 27612 #021-01-1962 L1968 **IM** *071 †20

FERGUSON, Michael Owen. 3024 NEW BERN AVE, OTOLARYNGOLOGY HEAD & 27610 #036-01-1997 L1999 **OTO** *020 †45

FERRALL, Isabel Maria. 10 SUNNYBROOK RD, WAKE COUNTY HUMAN SERVICES 27610 #036-05-1988 L1995 **PD** *020 †55

FERRELL, William Gregory. 1540 SUNDAY DR 27607 #036-05-1985 L1987 **N** *020 †75

FIGUEROA, Lisa Maria. 4100 WAKE FOREST RD 27609 #036-01-1991 L2005 **EM** *020

FIGUEROA, Yvette. 10405 LESLIE DR 27615 #041-01-1991 L2003 **CHP** *020 †75

FINEBERG, David Aaron. ■ 27615 #550-02-1988 L1990 **PS** *075

FINKEL, Marc Alan. 114 WIND CHIME CT, CAPITAL RADIOLOGY 27615 #035-46-1983 L1985 **RNR DR** *020 †80

FISHER, Lara. 4414 LAKE BOONE TRL, STE 405 27607 #041-13-1994 L2001 **OBG** *020 †30

FLANAGAN, Angelia L Moore. 2600 ATLANTIC AVE, MAILING: P O BOX 17266 27604 #036-01-1991 L1993 **OBG** *020 †18

FLANAGAN, Phelicia A. 4414 LAKE BOONE TRL # 210 27607 #036-08-2001 L2005 **OBG** *020 †30

FLANNELLY, Christina G. 7205 STONEHENGE DR 27613 #036-07-1988 L1991 **PD** *020 †55

FLEMING, Robert Henry. 2800 BLUE RIDGE RD STE 501 27607 #036-05-1960 L1960 **PD** *020 †55

FLEMING, Terence John. 2500 BLUE RIDGE RD, STE 417 27607 #010-02-1999 L2001 **EM** *020 †16

FLESCHER, Jonathan. 3100 BLUE RIDGE RD, STE 300 27612 #035-46-1983 L1991 **IM PUD** *020 †20

FLETCHER, Robert Geo. 4100 WAKE FOREST RD, NEXTCARE DOCTOR'S URGENT C 27609 #038-40-1963 L1982 **OM GP** *020 †70

FLICK, Conrad Lloyd. 3500 BUSH ST, STE 103 27609 #036-07-1989 L1990 **FM** *020 †18

FLOREA, Sorin Marcel. 3024 NEW BERN AVE, STE 301 27610 #781-03-1995 L2005 **IM** *020 †20 ‡

FLYNN, Matthew Kent. 5603 DURALEIGH RD, STE 111 27612 #036-07-1996 L2002 **D** *020 †15

FLYNN, Theresa Marie. 10 SUNNYBROOK RD, CHILD HEALTH CLINIC 27610 #036-07-1996 L2002 **IM** *012 †55

FOGARTIE, James E, Jr. 2800 BLUE RIDGE RD 27607 #045-01-1982 L1997 **VS** *020 †85

FOGEL, Lisa Ellen. 2605 BLUE RIDGE RD, STE 220 27607 #036-01-1997 L2006 *020 †35

FOOR, Robert Edward. 2605 BLUE RIDGE RD, STE 240 27607 #422-01-1981 L1987 **PD** *020 †55

FORBES, Mary Joan. 3900 BROWNING PL, STE 101 27609 #036-01-1992 L1995 **IM** *020 †20

FORD, Russell Philip. 3100 SPRING FOREST RD, STE 130 27616 #051-01-1998 L2001 **AN** *020 †05

FOREMAN, Brett Hugh. 8300 HEALTH PARK, STE 107 27615 #036-08-2000 L2002 **FSM** *020 †18

FORSYTH, Richard James. 3320 EXECUTIVE DR STE 214 27609 #064-01-1975 L1981 **FM** *020

FORTIER, Kenneth Jos. 2301 REXWOODS DR, STE 114 27607 #032-01-1976 L1979 **OBG** *020 †30,50

FOSTER, James Robt. 3000 NEW BERN AVE, STE G100 27610 #035-20-1969 L1975 **CD IM** *020 †20

FOSTER, William Wade. 3320 EXECUTIVE DR, STE 111 27609 #036-05-1972 L1972 **OPH** *071 †35

FOWLKES, William M, Jr. ■ 27612 #036-05-1944 L1944 **P** *071

FOX, Powell Graham, Jr. 3400 WAKE FOREST RD 27609 #051-04-1952 L1959 **U MDM** *072 †95

FRANK, James Lawrence. 8300 HEALTH PARK, STE 109 27615 #036-07-1965 L1965 **ORS** *020 †40

FRATER, Craig Ryan. 3000 NEW BERN AVE, WAKE EMERGENCY PHYSICIAN P 27610 #038-41-1999 L2002 **EM** *020 †16

FREEDMAN, Steven Mitchell. 1540 SUNDAY DR, RALEIGH NEUROLOGY ASSOCS, 27607 #041-01-1972 L1976 **N** *020 †75

FREEMAN, Douglas G, Jr. 3831 MERTON DR 27609 #036-07-1968 L1968 **RHU AI** *020 †20,03

FRERICHS, R Everett. 7205 STONEHENGE DR 27613 #047-05-1986 L1988 **PD** *020 †55

FREY, Sascha. 3000 NEW BERN AVE, WAKEMED 27610 #011-02-1998 L2002 **MPD** *020 †20,55

FRIEDLAND, Beth Rena. 3000 NEW BERN AVE 27610 #011-03-1979 L1984 **OPH PA** *020 †35

FUKUSHIMA, Takanori. 4030 WAKE FOREST RD, STE 115 27609 #572-40-1968 L1998 **NS** *020

FULGHUM, Mary Susan Kirk. 3809 COMPUTER DR, STE 201 27609 #036-01-1971 L1971 **GYN** *071 †30

FULLER, Sally Sanders. 3000 NEW BERN AVE 27610 #045-01-1982 L1983 **EM** *020 †16

GABR, Rhonda Winstead. 1540 SUNDAY DR, RALEIGH NEUROLOGY ASSOCS, 27607 #055-01-1998 L2001 **N** *020

GACENGECI, David Mbugua. 3019 FALSTAFF RD, HOLLY HILL HOSPITAL 27610 #577-01-1976 L2001 **P** *020 †75

GADA, Preston Herbert. 4420 LAKE BOONE TRL 27607 #051-04-1963 L1968 **GS CD** *071 †85

GADDY, Robert Edwin. 3900 BROWNING PL, STE 101 27609 #036-07-1959 L1959 **IM CD** *071 †20

GAGE, Giuliana. 5300 SIX FORKS RD STE 205 27609 #561-01-1966 L1975 **P CHP** *071 †75

GAINES, Ira Lewis. 2605 BLUE RIDGE RD, STE 150 27607 #036-05-1986 L1990 **OBG** *020 †30

GAINES, Roy Eugene. 4201 LAKE BOONE TRL 27607 #038-41-1993 L1994 **GS** *020

GAMBLIN, George Thos. 3410 EXECUTIVE DR STE 205 27609 #027-01-1977 L1987 **END IM** *020

GAMMON, Charles Michael. 3725 NATIONAL DR, STE 227 27612 #036-01-1993 L1995 **P** *020 †75

GANTT, Angela Brawley. 3024 NEW BERN AVE, STE 306 27610 #036-01-1998 L2002 **OBG** *020 †30

GARDNER, Jerome B. 2709 BLUE RIDGE RD, STE 300 27607 #036-08-1983 L1984 **OBG** *020 †30

GARDNER, Robert Edward. ■ 27609 #051-01-1964 L1968 **FM GS** *020

GARNER, Timothy Bryan. 1100 DRESSER CT, STE 100 27609 #036-05-1983 L1988 **NS** *020 †25

GARRABRANT, Edgar C, III. 3100 SPRING FOREST RD, STE 130 27616 #045-01-1993 L1997 **AN** *020 †05

GARRETT, Carolyn Marie. P.O. BOX 7304, 2815 CATES AVENUE 27695 #051-04-1995 L1998 **FM** *020 †18

GARRETT, Leland Earl, Jr. 3604 BUSH ST, WAKE NEPHROLGY ASSO PA 27609 #045-01-1976 L1979 **NEP IM** *020 †20

GARRIGA, Joshua E. 3320 WAKE FOREST RD, STE 310 27609 #048-02-1997 L2005 **IM** *020 †20

GARRIGA, Quay Mc Lean. ■ 27606 #048-02-1997 L2001 **MPD** *020,55

GARRISON, Scott Keenan. 3100 SPRING FOREST RD 27616 #036-01-1992 L1997 **AN** *020 †05

GAUSMANN, Amanda Langenba. 4414 LAKE BOONE TRL, STE 308 27607 #036-01-2002 L2006 **OBG** *020 †30

GAVAZOV, Miroslav I. 3100 DURALEIGH RD, STE 304 27612 #198-01-1982 L1997 **FM GYN** *020

GENTRY, James Henry. ■ 27615 #007-02-1955 L2003 **OPH** *071 †35 ‡

GERBER, Matthew Joseph. 10208 CERNY ST, STE 300 27617 #023-01-1997 L2002 **OTO HNS** *020 †45

GERMAN, Benjamin T. 3000 NEW BERN AVE, WAKE EMERGENCY PHYSICIANS 27610 #030-06-2001 L2003 **EM** *020 †16

GERSH, Scott W. 3400 WAKE FOREST RD, RALEIGH COMMUNITY HOSPITAL 27609 #005-06-1981 L1986 **IM** *020 †20

GESSNER, Richard R. 2800 BLUE RIDGE RD STE 4 27607 #036-01-1995 L1997 **PD** *020 †55

GHATE, Jayashri Vijay. 3225 BLUE RIDGE RD, STE 101 27612 #036-01-1996 L1997 **D** *020 †15

GILKEY, Margueritte. 3024 NEW BERN AVE, STE 306 27610 #011-03-1982 L1984 **OBG** *020 †30

GILLESPIE, Michael Joseph. 3100 BLUE RIDGE RD 27612 #041-15-2001 L2004 **CD** *012

GILL-MURDOCH, Carrie. 3100 SPRING FOREST RD, STE 130 27616 #001-06-1991 L1999 **CCA** *020 †05

GILMER, Benjamin Paul. ■ 27609 #036-08-2006 **FP** *012

GILMER, Peter Winston. 8300 HEALTH PARK, STE 109 27615 #051-01-1980 L1984 **ORS** *020 †40

GINN, Fred Le Gray. ■ 27606 #036-07-1962 L1966 **PTH** *020 †50

GINN, William M. 2800 BLUE RIDGE RD STE 205 27607 #036-01-1959 L1959 **CD IM** *071 †20

GIZZIE, Paula Elisa. 3400 WAKE FOREST RD 27609 #036-05-1984 L1988 **OBG** *020 †30

GLENN, Susan Annette. 1540 SUNDAY DR 27607 #039-01-1993 L1998 **N** *020 †75

GLOVER, Anne Katherine. 10441 MONCREIFFE RD, STE 101 27617 #055-01-1997 L2001 **MPD** *020 †20,55

GO, Brian Mingtao. 3000 NEW BERN AVE, STE 1200 27610 #041-09-1992 L1995 **CD** *020 †20

GOEL, Atul Kumar. 3301 TERMINAL DR, ATTN: UNIT 26, DR. GOEL 27604 #035-15-1986 L1989 **FM** *020 †18

GOEL, Radha. 3480 WAKE FOREST RD, STE 410 27609 #048-04-1999 L2005 **CD** *020 †20

GOETZL, Ugo. 1540 SUNDAY DR, MILLENNIUM NEUROLOGY ASSOC 27607 #035-09-1968 L1977 **N P** *020 †75

GOFF, David Albert. 2620 NEW BERN AVE, WAKE HEALTH SERV INC 27610 #036-01-1981 L1983 **IM PD** *020 †20,55

GOLD, Michael. ■ 27614 #011-02-1988 L1993 **N** *050 †75

GOLDMAN, Alan Lawrence. 2800 BLUE RIDGE RD, STE 401 27607 #028-02-1963 L1971 **PD** *071 †55

GOLDMAN, Brian Herbert. 3521 HAWORTH DR 27609 #036-05-1990 L2001 **IM** *020 †20

GOLDSTON, William Robt. 4420 LAKE BOONE TRL, STE 303 27607 #036-07-1963 L1963 **OBG** *071 †30

GOLWALA, Ajey Babubhai. 2500 BLUE RIDGE RD, STE 327 27607 #495-89-1983 L1992 **IM** *020 †20

GOMBAS, Otto F. ■ 27609 #473-03-1952 L1962 **PTH OS** *071 †50

GONZALEZ-CLANTON, John F. ■ 27616 #649-01-1971 L1979 **PD** *020

GOODSON, John Phillip. 2800 BLUE RIDGE RD STE 503 27607 #036-01-1963 L1963 **GS** *071 †85

GORE, Ronald Gene. 3100 SPRING FOREST RD, STE 130 27616 #024-01-1979 L1982 **AN PD** *020 †55,05

GOTTOVI, Daniel. 4731 SHANNONHOUSE DR, APT102 27612 #035-45-1965 L1969 **IM PUD** *071 †20

GRANADOS, Juan L. 3024 NEW BERN AVE STE 306, WAKEAHEC DEPT OB GYN 27610 #847-04-1966 L1987 **MFM OBG** *020 †30

GRANT, George Redd, Jr. 2625 APPLIANCE CT, MEPS 27604 #036-07-1963 L1963 **IM NEP** *020 †20

GRANT, Hugh Judd, Jr. 4414 LAKE BOONE TRL, STE 210 27607 #036-01-1969 L1969 **GYN** *020 †30

GRAY, Christa Lynn. 4420 LAKE BOONE TRL, MAILING ADDRESS: P.O. BOX 27607 #005-15-2001 L2006 **AN** *020 †05

GREEN, Jonathan Scott. 4420 LAKE BOONE TRL, REX HEALTHCARE 27607 #036-07-1998 L2001 **IM** *020 †20

GREEN, Julius Alpheus. ■ 27615 #036-01-1957 L1957 **DR** *071 †80

GREENBERG, Gary Norman. 1390 CAPITAL BLVD, URBAN MINISTRIES OF WAKE C 27603 #016-06-1978 L1982 **IM OM** *020 †20,70

GREENWALD, Kim Zisholz. 3400 WAKE FOREST RD 27609 #025-07-1988 L1993 **AN** *020 †05

GREER, Thomas Bywater. 4420 LAKE BOONE TRL 27607 #036-05-1954 L1954 **GYN** *020 †30

GRIFFIN, Newton Bramblett. 4420 LAKE BOONE TRL 27607 #047-05-1957 L1968 **OBG** *071 †30 ‡

GRIFFITH, Corinne. 2417 ATRIUM DR, PA 27607 #051-01-1994 L1995 **FM** *020 †18

GRIFFITH, John Keven. 3000 NEW BERN AVE 27610 #038-06-1985 L1991 **PUD CCM** *020 †20

GRIFFITHS, Frances H. ■ 27616 #067-01-1969 L1986 **FM** *071 †18

GRIFFITHS, William Owen. 3024 NEW BERN AVE, STE 301 27610 #017-20-1995 L1998 **IM** *020 †20

GRIGG, Wendell R, Jr. 859 WASHINGTON ST, PSYCHIATRIC ASSOCIATES OF 27605 #036-01-1971 L1971 **P PYA** *020 †75

GRIMES, David Alan. 3901 COMPUTER DR 27609 #036-01-1973 L1974 **OBG PHP** *050 †70,30

GRIPPO, Allen Edward. ■ 27609 #041-13-1962 L1963 **GP P** *020 †75

GROCE, James Gray. 820 S BOYLAN AVE, DOROTHEA DIX HOSPITAL 27603 #036-01-1971 L1971 **P** *020 †75

GROFF, Amy Diane. 4420 LAKE BOONE TRL # 303 27607 #036-07-1995 L1996 **OBG** *020

GROSS, Scott Kim. 3024 NEW BERN AVE STE 301, HOSPITAL MEDICINE SERVICE 27610 #038-44-1995 L1998 **IM** *020 †20

GUESS, Tiona Deson. ■ 27617 #036-07-2008 *012

GULLEDGE, Sidney Loy, III. 4301 LAKE BOONE TRL # 200 27607 #036-05-1976 L1976 **OPH** *020 †30

GUNNELLS, James Caulie. 3604 BUSH ST, WAKE NEPHROLOGY ASSOCIATES 27609 #045-01-1956 L1958 **NEP IM** *071 †20

GUNTER, Arilus Dawan. 2605 BLUE RIDGE RD, STE 150 27607 #025-12-1994 L1998 OBG *020 †30

GUPTA, Manu B. 3400 WAKE FOREST RD 27609 #025-01-1993 L1998 AN *020 †05

GUPTILL, Alison Prestia. 14501 NEW FALLS OF NEUSE R 27614 #035-06-2003 L2006 FM *020 †18

GUPTON, Stephen Thos. ■ 27607 #036-01-1957 L1957 N *071

GURKIN, Brett Alexander. 6812 JUSTICE DR 27615 #036-01-2001 L2005 P *020

GURVICH, Mark Israel. ■ 27612 #913-01-1961 L1994 IM *020

HAAKENSON, Gary A. 2417 ATRIUM DR, STE 200 27607 #048-04-1972 L1978 OBG *020 †30

HAGE, William Dirk. 8300 HEALTH PARK STE 109 27615 #036-07-1996 L2002 ORS *020 †40

HAIZLIP, Thomas Matthews. 5201 REMBERT DR 27612 #036-01-1958 L1958 CHP P *040 †75

HALL, Helen E. ■ 27615 #051-04-1950 L1953 OS *071

HALL, Robert M. ■ 27609 #024-01-1943 L1947 PHP GPM *071 †70

HALL, Warner Leander. 2709 BLUE RIDGE RD STE 300 27607 #036-07-1961 L1961 OBG *071 †30

HALME, Jouko Kalervo. 2500 BLUE RIDGE RD, STE 300 27607 #374-01-1968 L1980 REN GYN *071 †30 ‡

HAMILTON, Penny Jo. 3000 NEW BERN AVE 27610 #036-07-1996 L1997 EM *020 †16

HAMMER, Douglas Ira. 2605 BLUE RIDGE RD, STE 300 27607 #024-07-1962 L1970 FM OM *020 †70,16,18 ‡

HAMMOND, Mary E Granade. 2500 BLUE RIDGE RD 27607 #011-03-1974 L1977 REN GYN *071 †30

HAMP, Dirk. 4551 NEW BERN AVE, STE 160 27610 #047-05-1991 L2003 PD *020 †55

HAMRICK, Alger Vason. 3400 WAKE FOREST RD 27609 #036-01-1972 L1972 FM *020 †18

HAMRICK, George Lee, Jr. 8300 HEALTH PARK, STE 327 27615 #036-01-1987 L1991 IM CD *020 †20

HANSEN, Jonathan James. 820 S BOYLAN AVE, INTERNAL MEDICINE 27603 #017-20-2003 L2004 GE *012 †20

HARDEN, Paul, Jr. 2011 FALLS VALLEY DR 27615 #041-13-1979 L1982 OBG *020 †30

HARDENBERGH, Joan Marasco. ■ 27615 #008-01-1956 L1958 PD *071

HARDISON, Cynthia Stoltze. ■ 27608 #016-06-1954 L1963 IM HEM *071

HARDISON, Joseph Hammond. ■ 27608 #036-07-1956 L1956 IM GE *020 †20

HARDISON, Mitchell Dale. 3900 BROWNING PL, STE 101 27609 #036-01-1980 L1982 IM *020 †20

HARPER, Robt Norment, Jr. 2011 FALLS VALLEY DR, STE 106 27615 #036-05-1977 L1977 GE IM *020 †20

HARPER, Wayne Lee. 3100 BLUE RIDGE RD, STE 300 27612 #036-07-1978 L1980 IM FM *020 †20

HARRIS, James Todd. 2800 BLUE RIDGE RD, STE 501 27607 #036-08-1993 L1996 PD *020 †55

HARRIS, Robert Thos. 3521 HAWORTH DR 27609 #012-05-1978 L1981 IM OS *071 †20

HARRIS, Tina Griffin. 3521 HAWORTH DR, RALEIGH MEDICAL GROUP 27609 #036-01-1999 L2001 IM *020 †20

HARRISON, Dionne Dillon. 8360 SIX FORKS RD, STE 202 27615 #035-06-2003 L2005 P *020

HART, Fiona Kay. ■ 27612 #026-04-2005 L2005 AN *012

HART, Timothy Bertrand. 23 SUNNYBROOK RD STE 113 27610 #051-04-1979 L1984 PUD IM *020 †20

HARTWELL, Erin Kathleen. ■ 27615 #036-01-2005 OBG *012

HARTYE, James Kilcoyne. 102 N TARBORO RD 27610 #047-05-1977 L1978 FM *020 †18

HARWOOD, Timothy Neil. 3100 SPRING FOREST RD, STE 130 27616 #028-03-1984 L1989 AN *020 †05

HASHEMEE, Sayed Abdul R. 217 COOKE ST, MAILING: P O BOX 90817 27601 #118-01-1981 L1994 FM *020 †18

HAUGAN, Charul G. 4420 LAKE BOONE TRL, RALEIGH EMERGENCY 27607 #026-04-1998 L1999 EM *020 †16

HAUSER, Michael Winn. 1539 IREDELL DR 27608 #036-01-1994 L1996 AN *020 †55,05

HAYES, D Allen. 3480 WAKE FOREST RD, STE 414 27609 #051-01-1972 L1977 PUD IM *020 †20

HAYES, Richard Ivan. 4414 LAKE BOONE TRL, STE 405 27607 #038-40-1966 L1973 GYN *071 †30

HAYNES, Lawrence Bowman. 6131 FALLS OF NEUSE RD, STE 200 27609 #047-06-1961 L1967 AN *071 †05

HAYWOOD, Bertron Don. 4420 LAKE BOONE TRL 27607 #047-07-1970 L1974 GYN *020 †30

HAYWOOD, Hubert B. 2304 WESVILL CT STE 240 27607 #036-01-1972 L1972 ID *020 †20

HEATON, Frederick C. 3809 COMPUTER DR 27609 #036-01-1972 L1972 GYN *020 †30

HEDRICK, William Weston. 1805 N NEW HOPE RD 27604 #036-05-1957 L1957 FM P *072 †18

HEFFRON, Timothy James. 10010 FALLS OF NEUSE RD, STE 12 27614 #041-02-1976 L2000 OTO PS *020 †45

HELTON, Laura Elaine. ■ 27609 #012-05-2000 L2005 PHP *020

HELTON, Todd Edward. 3900 BROWNING PL, STE 101 27609 #036-08-1998 L2000 IM *020 †20

HELTON, William Charles. 3000 NEW BERN AVE 27610 #011-02-1969 L1978 TS *020 †85,90

HENDERSON, David Yeardley. 2417 ATRIUM DR, STE 200 27607 #051-04-1981 L1984 OBG *020 †30 ‡

HENDERSON, Paul Manning. 3320 EXECUTIVE DR, STE 214 27609 #036-01-1998 L1999 FM *020 †16

HENNESSY, Georgia Ann. 4551 NEW BERN AVE, STE 160 27610 #020-02-2002 L2005 PD *020 †55

HENRY, Christy Louise. 3024 NEW BERN AVE, STE 301 27610 #054-04-1998 L2001 IM *020 †20

HENSLEY, Michele. ■ 27608 #036-07-1982 L1995 FM *020 †18

HERRERA, Gloria Patricia. 2501 ATRIUM DR, STE 310 27607 #264-04-1990 L1999 IM *020 †20

HEY, Lloyd Albert. 3404 WAKE FOREST RD, STE 203 27609 #024-01-1988 L1995 ORS *020 †40

HICKS, Charles Henry. 3400 EXECUTIVE DR STE 201 27609 #036-01-1976 L1981 CD IM *071 †20

HIGH, Rhett Chas. 1112 DRESSER CT 27609 #023-07-1989 L1994 PS *020 †85,65

HILL-GARRETT, Karen. 7021 HARPS MILL RD, STE 100 27615 #048-14-1995 L2000 MPD PD *020 †55,20

HILLSMAN, Philip Lee. 3900 BROWNING PL, STE 201 27609 #047-06-1987 L1988 P ADM *020 †75

HINCHEY, Paul Robert. 3000 NEW BERN AVE 27610 #035-06-2002 L2005 EM *020 †16

HINN, Gregory Colin. 4020 WESTCHASE BLVD, STE 390 27607 #036-05-1989 L1995 DR *020 †80

HIRASAKI, Ken K. ■ 27616 #048-14-2002 L2004 VIR *012 †80

HO, Janice Wanda. ■ 27603 #023-01-2000 L2000 *062

HOCKING, Leslie Beth. 220 SWINBURNE RD, WAKE COUNTY HUMAN SERVICES 27610 #024-07-1983 L1991 P PYG *020 †75

HODGES, Charles Michael. 3400 WAKE FOREST RD, R C H INPATIENT MED SRVC 27609 #011-02-1984 L2001 IM *020 †20

HODGES, Sarah Holste. 10010 FALLS OF NEUSE RD, STE 12 27614 #056-05-1999 L2004 OTO *020 †45

HOELLERICH, Vincent L. 3100 SPRING FOREST RD, STE 130 27616 #030-05-1983 L1987 AN CCA *020 †05

HOGAN, Lisa. ■ 27615 #036-01-1986 L2007 CS OM *020 †85

HOLLAND, Thomas Lawrence. ■ 27605 #036-05-2005 IM *012

HOLLAND O'CONNELL, Tracey. 4020 WESTCHASE BLVD, STE 350 27607 #036-01-1996 L1997 DR *020 †80

HOLLY, John Durward, IV. 3024 NEW BERN AVE STE 301 27610 #051-04-2002 L2005 IM *100 †20

HOLMES, Douglas Kent. 3909 SUNSET RIDGE RD # 201 27607 #036-01-1980 L1993 OTO PDO *020 †45

HOLMES, Valerie Frances. 700 SPRING FOREST RD STE 1 27609 #020-02-1980 L1983 P PYG *020 †75

HOLT, Elizabeth Hope. 3410 EXECUTIVE DR STE 205 27609 #036-05-1986 L1988 IM END *020 †20

HOLT, Fred Frisch. 4928 MISTY OAK DR 27613 #055-01-1968 L1999 OTO *071 †45

HOLT, John Plummer, Jr. 2600 ATLANTIC AVE, STE 100 27604 #036-08-1986 L1987 GE IM *020 †20

HOLT, Kenneth Albert. 3320 EXECUTIVE DR, STE 222 27609 #010-02-1995 L1999 IM *020 †20

HOLT, Windsor Austin. 3404 WAKE FOREST RD, STE 100 27609 #038-06-1964 L1965 OBG *071 †30

HOLTKAMP, John H. 4505 FAIR MEADOWS LN, BLUE RIDGE PLAZA SUITE 204 27607 #035-19-1980 L2000 CHN *075 †55

HOLTON, Alan Leon. 2301 REXWOODS DR STE 11, LOCATION: 2709 BLUE RIDGE 27607 #050-02-1985 L1992 FM *020 †20

HOMEISTER, Michelle M. 2605 BLUE RIDGE RD, STE 150 27607 #025-12-1996 L2005 OBG *020 †30

HONEYCUTT, Lattie F, Jr. 2000 AURORA DR 27615 #036-01-1967 L1967 DR *020 †80

HONEYCUTT, Travis Clarke. 3024 NEW BERN AVE STE 307, WAKEMED FACULTY PRACTICE 27610 #036-01-1998 L1999 CCP *100 †55

HONG, Janice Radoslovich. 10000 FALLS OF NEUSE RD, STE 303 27614 #041-02-1994 L2003 VS *020 †85

HOOK, Carol Kikkawa. ■ 27612 #047-05-1997 L2007 PD *020 †55

HOOK, Matthew Alan. 3000 NEW BERN AVE, STE G100 27610 #047-05-1997 L2006 IC *020 †20

HORGAN, Laura Earle. 3601 MSC CENTER 27699 #051-01-1995 L1997 CHP *020 †75

HORSLEY, Thomas Martin. ■ 27615 #023-07-1945 L1951 IM *071

HORTON, Robert Marshall. 3124 BLUE RIDGE RD STE 1 27612 #051-04-1972 L1974 FM *020 †18

HOSSAIN, Mohammad D. 3214 CHARLES B ROOT WYND, STE 213 27612 #160-02-1982 L1997 IM PD *020 †20

HOWELL, Jennifer Occhipin. 4414 LAKE BOONE TRL, STE 205 27607 #024-16-1996 L1999 OBG *020 †30

HOYTE, Sandra M. 1617 RONALD DR 27609 #917-28-1979 L1996 IM *020 †20

HSU, Diana. ■ 27612 #036-01-2007 L2007 AN *012

HU, Edward Paihsiang. 4420 LAKE BOONE TRL, REX HOSPITALIST TEAM 27607 #028-02-1999 L2002 IM *020 †20

HUANG, Jeffrey Allen. 2605 BLUE RIDGE RD, STE 300 27607 #036-05-2000 L2007 FM *020 †18

HUBBARD, William Colvin. 3000 NEW BERN AVE 27610 #036-01-1966 L1966 PD *071 †55

HUDSON-FRALEY, Anita M. 7019 HARPS MILL RD, ANITA M. HUDSON-FRALEY 27615 #036-08-1992 L1996 OBG *020 †30

HUGGINS, Clarence Pope. 3100 SPRING FOREST RD, STE 130 27616 #045-01-1990 L1994 AN *020 †05

HUGHES, Sarah Plowman. 3100 BLUE RIDGE RD, STE 300 27612 #048-14-2002 L2006 MPD *020 †20,55

HULL, Christian Manning. 7913 VANDEMERE CT 27615 #025-01-1997 L1999 IM *020 †20

HULL, Keith Lowell, Jr. 1540 SUNDAY DR, RALEIGH NEUROLOGY ASSOCS, 27607 #036-07-1975 L1979 N IM *020 †75

HUMAYUN, Dabiruddin. 3214 CHARLES B ROOT WYND, STE 213 27612 #160-02-1977 L2004 MPD PD *020 †20,55 ‡

HUNT, Christopher L. 3000 NEW BERN AVE 27610 #047-07-1944 L1946 GP GS *071

HUNT, Karen. 4420 LAKE BOONE TRL, RALEIGH EMERGENCY 27607 #016-06-1998 L2001 EM *020 †16

HUNT, Kerry Edmund. ■ 27613 #025-07-1986 L2007 OPH PTH *020 †35

HUNT, Susan Diane. ■ 27612 #036-01-1985 L1989 IM PTH *075

HUNTER, Robert Merrill. 3000 NEW BERN AVE 27610 #036-05-1978 L1985 TS *020 †85,90

HUTZENBUHLER, Angela Noel. 8300 HEALTH PARK, STE 209 27615 #019-02-1989 L1992 GE *020 †20

IBACH, Anne Leigh. 2800 BLUE RIDGE RD, INTERNAL MEDICINE 27607 #041-07-1988 L1991 IM *020 †20

IBRAHIM, Sherine Adnan. 4016 BARRETT DR, STE 101 27609 #036-01-1981 L1983 PD *020 †55 ‡

IGBOEKWE, Vincent C. 1300 WESTERN BLVD, NC DEPT OF CORRECTION 27699 #690-01-1984 L1998 IM *020 †20

INGE, Jack Ransom, II. 4414 LAKE BOONE TRL, STE 300 27607 #036-08-1993 L1997 OBG *020 †30

INGRAM, Christopher Wm. 2304 WESVILL CT STE 240 27607 #036-05-1983 L1988 ID IM *020 †20

INGRAM, David Lane. 3000 NEW BERN AVE 27610 #008-01-1967 L1974 ID PD *040 †55

IRWIN, Traci Elizabeth. 1540 SUNDAY DR, RALEIGH NEURO ASSOC PA 27607 #036-01-1998 L2003 CHN *020 ‡

ISBELL, W Marty. 14341 NEW FALLS OF NEUSE 27614 #047-20-1998 L2004 OSM *020 †40

ISMAIL, Samina. 3126 BLUE RIDGE RD, CAPITAL PHYSICIANS GROUP 27612 #704-16-1996 L2004 FM *100 †18

ISRAEL, Rodger David. 3100 BLUE RIDGE RD, STE 300 27612 #011-04-1986 L1991 IM IMG *020 †20

ITO, Kristin E. 505 OBERLIN RD STE 204, WAKE TEEN MEDICAL SERVICES 27605 #024-01-1999 L2000 MPD *020 †20,55

JACOBS, William R. 3521 HAWORTH DR, RALEIGH MEDICAL GROUP 27609 #048-02-1986 L1990 IM ISM *020 †55,20

JACOBSON, Robert Carl. 3400 WAKE FOREST RD, AT DUKE HEALTH RALEIGH 27609 #010-02-1979 L1985 AN CCA *020 †05

JACOKES, Allison Lewis. 4020 WAKE FOREST RD, HEALTHCARE 27609 #036-01-1988 L1992 OBG *020 †30

JAGADEESAN, Singaravelu. 4201 LAKE BOONE TRL, STE 1 27607 #495-66-1989 L2004 N *020 †75

JAGLA-SCHUDEL, Danuta. 1300 WESTERN BLVD, CENTRAL PRISON 27606 #759-01-1988 L1997 P *020 †75

JAIN, Rekha. 2411 E MILLBROOK RD # 111 27604 #495-20-1976 L1980 **IM** *020
JALKUT, Mark William. 4301 LAKE BOONE TRL 27607 #005-11-1998 L2004 **U** *020 †95
JAMES, Selina L. 3200 BLUE RIDGE RD, STE 210 27612 #035-15-1989 L1996 **IM** *020 †20
JANIS, Martin. 3921 SUNSET RIDGE RD, STE 101 27607 #035-19-1963 L1999 **IM IMG** *020 †20
JANSON, Bruce Harold. 3100 SPRING FOREST RD, STE 130 27616 #016-42-1984 L1988 **AN IM** *05
JARIWALA, Arvind N. 3100 BLUE RIDGE RD, STE 300 27612 #495-76-1976 L1983 **IM IMG** *020 †20
JAVANGULA, Himabindu. ■ 27614 #495-50-1996 L2007 **CHP** *100
JEFFERS, Robert Gordon. 2406 BLUE RIDGE RD, STE 100 27607 #021-01-1974 L1982 **PD** *020 †55
JEFFRIES, Thomas Lee. 8331 BANDFORD WAY, STE 101 27615 #036-01-1989 L1992 **FM** *020 †18
JENKINS, Albert M, Jr. 3821 MERTON DR 27609 #038-41-1947 L1953 **R OS** *071 †80
JENKINS, Tammy Hall. 6829 FALLS OF NEUSE RD, STE 105 27615 #036-01-1989 L2001 **OBG** *020
JERNIGAN, Nancy Elizabeth. 6040 SIX FORKS RD, # A 27609 #036-01-1965 L1965 **P PYA** *020
JERRETT, Justine G. 3801 LAKE BOONE TRL, STE 320 27607 #038-43-1993 L2006 **P** *020 †75
JOBE, Robert Lee. 3000 NEW BERN AVE, STE G100 27610 #036-01-1987 L1993 **CD** *020 †20
JOHNSON, Albin Willard. ■ 27612 #036-07-1958 L1964 **OPH** *071 †35
JOHNSON, David Wesley. 4109 WAKE FOREST RD, STE 100 27609 #051-04-1981 L1982 **FM** *020
JOHNSON, Holly Pugh. 3320 EXECUTIVE DR, STE 111 27609 #041-02-1986 L1988 **OPH** *020 †30
JOHNSON, Jana G. 3024 NEW BERN AVE, WAKEMED FACULTY PHYSICIANS 27610 #048-14-1991 L1994 **GPM** *020 †70,20
JOHNSON, Jennifer Ann. ■ 27613 #024-07-2005 **AN** *012
JOHNSON, Peter C. ■ 27614 #035-15-1980 L1982 **PS** *030 †85,65
JOHNSON, Philip Byron. 4012 BOULDERS VIEW DR 27609 #036-02-1991 L2000 **EM** *020 †16
JOHNSON, Sally A C. ■ 27615 #041-02-1976 L1977 **PFP P** *062 †75
JONES, David Herman. ■ 27609 #036-01-1959 L1959 **OPH** *071 †35
JONES, David Turner. 3410 EXECUTIVE DR 27609 #004-01-1993 L2006 **ORS** *020 †40
JONES, Ellen Louise. 3320 WAKE FOREST RD, STE 130 27609 #032-01-1992 L1998 **RO** *020 †80
JONES, Jonathan Laird. 2725 COOLEEMEE DR 27608 #036-01-1988 L1990 **EM** *020 †16
JONES, Larry Thos. ■ 27604 #047-07-1980 L1992 **PD** *020
JONES, Mary Elizabeth. 3200 BLUE RIDGE RD STE 210, RALEIGH ADULT MEDICINE, P. 27612 #036-01-1996 L2000 **IM** *020 †20
JORDAN, Ernest Dwight. ■ 27614 #018-03-1955 L1956 **GP IM** *071
JORDAN, Horace Mendall. ■ 27607 #036-05-1968 L1972 **D** *020
JORDAN, Timothy Dwight. 2709 BLUE RIDGE RD, STE 100 27607 #048-04-1993 L1998 **OPH** *020 †35
JOSEPHS, Scott Tracy. 701 CORPORATE CENTER DR 27607 #041-01-1987 L2000 **IM** *020 †20
JOYNER, Sheryl Scott. 2610 NEW BERN AVE, ALLIANCE MEDICAL MINISTRY 27610 #011-02-1988 L1990 **IM PD** *020 †55,20
JOYNER, Susan Jane. 3400 WAKE FOREST RD 27609 #036-01-1984 L1985 **OPH** *071 †35
JOYNER, Walton K, Jr. 3900 BROWNING PL STE 200 27609 #036-01-1986 L1990 **OPH** *020 †35
KABIR, Fathima N. 14460 NEW FALLS OF NEUSE, STE 149 27614 #495-04-1989 L1996 **IM** *020 †20
KAGAN, Steven Anthony. 2800 BLUE RIDGE RD, STE 500 27607 #024-16-1990 L2003 **VS** *020 †85
KAHLON, Kanwaljit Singh. ■ 27614 #495-03-1999 L2006 **IM** *020 †20
KAMDAR, Mukesh Nautam. 3100 DURALEIGH RD 27612 #495-92-1979 L1989 **P** *020 †75
KAMM, Rick Rande. 2011 FALLS VALLEY DR 27615 #018-03-1970 L1976 **OBG** *020 †30
KANE, Richard Douglas. 4301 LAKE BOONE TRL, STE 300 27607 #016-06-1971 L1973 **U OS** *095
KANOF, Abram. ■ 27609 #035-08-1928 L1971 **PD** *071 †55
KANOF, Elizabeth Pascher. ■ 27615 #036-07-1960 L1965 **D** *071 †15
KAPLAN, Daniel Max. 3024 NEW BERN AVE STE 301 27610 #036-01-1989 L1996 **IM** *020 †20
KAPLAN, David Chas. ■ 27614 #016-11-1991 L1998 **IM EM** *020 †20
KAPLAN, Seth A. 3100 BLUE RIDGE RD, STE 300 27612 #041-02-1989 L1990 **GE IM** *020 †20
KAPPELMAN, Michael David. ■ 27609 #028-02-2001 L2007 **PG** *100 †55
KARAM, Michael Qustandi. 4024 BARRETT DR STE 104 27609 #915-02-1967 L1976 **IM** *020
KASTL, Stephen Carlton. ■ 27613 #020-15-1976 L1976 **OBG** *062 †30
KATZ, Andrew Lee. 3000 NEW BERN AVE 27610 #036-01-1997 L2000 **AN PD** *012 †55
KAVDE, Uday Shashikant. 4900 WAKE FOREST RD 27609 #010-03-1990 L1995 **GS** *020 †85
KAWASAKI, David Masao. ■ 27617 #038-40-1956 L2004 **OBG** *071 †30 ‡
KEENER, Joseph Keith. 3604 BUSH ST 27609 #028-34-1975 L1979 **NEP IM** *020 †20
KEENEY, Ronald Eric. 4700 FALLS OF NEUSE RD, INC RESEARCH 27609 #028-03-1968 L1977 **PD PHM** *062 †55
KEIRAN, Donna Lynn. 4420 LAKE BOONE TRL 27607 #001-06-1981 L1984 **PD** *020 †55
KELLER, Laurence Harvey. ■ 27615 #010-01-1992 L1995 **PDC** *012
KELLEY, John Simpson. 8300 HEALTH PARK, STE 327 27615 #036-05-1974 L1974 **IM** *020 †20
KELLY, Laura Herring. 4414 LAKE BOONE TRL, STE 103 27607 #036-08-1996 L1997 **PD** *020 †55
KELLY, Michael Walker. 10321 LUMLEY RD, # 200 27617 #048-12-1983 L1989 **OPH** *020 †35
KELLY, Richard Alexander. ■ 27609 #036-07-1954 L1956 **NR** *071
KELSCH, John Martin, Sr. 3400 WAKE FOREST RD 27609 #020-02-1976 L1979 **EM** *020 †16
KENAN, Le Roy Fulton. ■ 27609 #036-05-1956 L1956 **GP** *072
KENNEDY, Andrew Scott. 3821 MERTON DR 27609 #005-12-1991 L1995 **RO** *020 †80
KENNEDY, Willard Lee. 8300 HEALTH PARK, STE 327 27615 #036-05-1975 L1975 **IM CD** *020 †20
KERR, Kristi Ann. 2709 BLUE RIDGE RD, STE 290 27607 #047-05-1996 L2001 **OBG** *020 †30
KESSLER-HUDAK, Deborah F. 8311 BANDFORD WAY, STE 101&103 27615 #038-41-1988 L1998 **OPH** *020 †35
KHAN, Nazim Uddin Azam. 2406 BLUE RIDGE RD, STE 150 27607 #704-09-1985 L1999 **IC** *100 †20
KHOSLA-GUPTA, Bobbie A. 2709 BLUE RIDGE RD 27607 #036-01-1997 L2002 **OPH** *020 †35
KHOURY, Joseph M. 4201 LAKE BOONE TRL, STE 205 27607 #010-02-1981 L1994 **U** *020 †95
KHUSAYEM, Mazen. 3000 NEW BERN AVE 27610 #875-02-1987 L1999 **IM** *020 †20
KICKLIGHTER, Stephen D. 3000 NEW BERN AVE 27610 #012-01-1993 L1999 **NPM** *020 †55
KILEY, James Wm. 3320 EXECUTIVE DR, STE 111 27609 #038-41-1976 L1980 **OPH** *020 †35
KILLINGER, William Allen. 3000 NEW BERN AVE 27610 #051-01-1985 L1996 **TS** *020 †85,90
KIM, Charles Yoon. ■ 27617 #035-01-2001 L2004 **DR** *012

KIM, Young Cue. ■ 27615 #583-03-1968 L1976 **IM** *020
KIMBRELL, Odell C, Jr. ■ 27615 #041-01-1951 L1951 **IM OM** *071 †20
KIMMEL, Sandy Jean. 3400 EXECUTIVE DR, STE 203 27609 #003-75-2000, ▲ L2004 **N** *020 †75
KING, J Le Roy. 6131 FALLS OF NEUSE RD, STE 200 27609 #036-05-1958 L1958 **AN** *071
KING, Jerome Stovall. 4420 LAKE BOONE TRL 27607 #010-01-1963 L1974 **NS** *020 †25
KIRBY, Matthew Walker. ■ 27616 #048-12-2003 L2006 **DR** *012
KIRK, David. 3000 NEW BERN AVE, WAKEMED HOSPITALS 27610 #027-01-2000 L2004 **PCC** *020 †20
KIRKPATRICK, James Wm. 300 N MCDOWELL ST, EPIDEMI.SEC.OF OF PUB HLTH 27603 #048-12-1972 L2002 **PHP** *020 †70
KIRSCHBAUM, Jan Ellen. ■ 27612 #016-11-1982 L1995 **P** *020 †75 ‡
KITTELBERGER, Keith Paul. 2800 BLUE RIDGE RD, STE 306 27607 #047-07-1988 L1993 **AN PME** *05
KNELSON, Mark Henry. 4020 WESTCHASE BLVD, STE 390 27607 #036-01-1985 L1990 **VIR DR** *020 †80
KNOOP, John Douglas. ■ 27614 #020-12-1974 L1975 **OTO** *071 †45
KNUDSEN, Michael W. 4551 NEW BERN AVE, STE 160 27610 #028-46-1989 L1992 **PD** *020 †55
KO, Hee Won. ■ 27615 #583-06-1971 L1979 **P** *071
KOBS, Jeffrey Kent. 3515 GLENWOOD AVE, 3515 GLENWOOD AVE 27612 #056-06-1987 L1993 **ORS** *020 †40 ‡
KOCSIS, Paul Mark. 859 WASHINGTON ST, PSYCHIATRIC ASSOCIATES OF 27605 #036-05-1990 L1994 **P** *020 †75
KOEBLE, Carol June. 3024 NEW BERN AVE STE 306, DEPT OB/GYN 27610 #023-12-1988 L2005 **OBG** *020 †30
KOELEVELD, Robin F. 3700 BARRETT DR 27609 #035-01-1985 L1992 **NS GS** *020 †25
KOENIG, Daniel William. 23 SUNNYBROOK RD 27610 #036-07-1986 L1988 **NEP IM** *020 †20
KOHAGEN, Kenneth Richard. 8300 HEALTH PARK, STE 209 27615 #038-06-1988 L1994 **GE HEP** *020 †20
KOLARZ-JOZEWICZ, Laura K. 3404 WAKE FOREST RD, STE 101 27609 #759-08-1979 L1991 **N** *020 †75
KOLKIN, Jon. 3404 WAKE FOREST RD 27609 #012-05-1977 L1980 **ORS** *020 †40
KONANC, David Aslan. 1540 SUNDAY DR, RALEIGH NEUROLOGY ASSOCS, 27607 #036-01-1992 L1997 **N CN** *020 †75
KONIDENA, Snehalatha. ■ 27607 #495-58-2000 L2006 **IM** *100 †20
KOPP, Elliot J. 1631 MIDTOWN PL, STE 101 27609 #035-15-1973 L1982 **RHU A** *020 †20,03
KOURY, Jill Barbara. 1701 KNOX RD, KOURY EYE CLINIC, LLC 27608 #021-01-1981 L1997 **OPH** *020 †35
KRATZ, Robert Kevin. 3400 WAKE FOREST RD 27609 #020-12-1973 L1977 **EM IM** *020 †20,16
KRAUS, Emily Joy. 505 OBERLIN RD, PHYSICIAN, WAKE TEEN 27605 #041-12-2005 L2008 **PD** *012
KRISHNAN, Vinod M. 3480 WAKE FOREST RD, STE 502 27609 #038-44-2002 L2007 **CN** *100
KRITZ, Alan Daniel. 4101 MACON POND RD, CAROLINA 27609 #028-02-1985 L1996 **HEM ON** *020 †20
KRUPSKI, Tracey Lynn. 3480 WAKE FOREST RD, STE 506 27609 #051-04-1996 L2005 **U** *020 †95
KULLER, Jeffrey Adam. 2406 BLUE RIDGE RD, STE 200 27607 #038-41-1984 L1992 **OBG MFM** *020 †19,30
KUMAR, Venkatasubramanian. 3301 TERMINAL DR, DDS 27604 #495-04-1975 L1994 *020
KUNSTLING, Ted Richard. 3480 WAKE FOREST RD, STE 414 27609 #036-07-1968 L1968 **PUD IM** *020 †20
KURZMANN, Richard Walter. 4414 LAKE BOONE TRL, STE 308 27607 #051-01-1969 L1972 **OBG** *020 †30
KUSUMI, Yoshi-Taro. 4505 FAIR MEADOWS LN, STE 203 27607 #572-28-1961 L1971 **P N** *071
KYEREMATEN, Gabriel A. 1300 WESTERN BOULEVARD 428, NC DEPT OF CORRECTION 27699 #041-07-1994 L1998 **IM** *020
LADAPO, Jumoke Mary. ■ 27610 #041-12-2004 L2008 **FP** *012
LA FORCE, Craig Fred. 4301 LAKE BOONE TRL # 309 27607 #041-02-1975 L1980 **A** *020 †55,03
LAGARDE, William Henry. 3024 NEW BERN AVE, STE 307 27610 #021-01-1998 L2001 **PDE** *020 †55
LAHOUD, Chawki Assaad. ■ 27615 #605-03-1989 L1995 **AI MPD** *020 †20
LAMBERT, Kathleen Elizabe. 4420 LAKE BOONE TRL, REX HOSPITAL 27607 #051-04-2002 L2005 **HO** *012 †20
LAMBETH, Wm Arnold, III. 1112 DRESSER CT 27609 #036-01-1971 L1971 **PS** *020 †85,65
LANCASTER, Michael S. 1100 NAVAHO DR STE 105 27609 #021-01-1975 L1978 **CHP P** *020 †75
LANDOLF, Michael Jos. 4909 GREEN RD, CONCENTRA MEDICAL CTRS-RAL 27616 #035-15-1986 L1996 **IM** *020 †20
LANDVATER, Lance Eric. 3000 NEW BERN AVE 27610 #036-05-1977 L1987 **TS** *020 †85,90
LANE, John Aiden. 2301 REXWOODS DR, STE 114 27609 #055-01-1983 L2005 **OBG** *020 †30
LANE, William Norman. 3024 NEW BERN AVE, WAKE MED FACLTY PHYSICIANS 27610 #036-07-1978 L2001 **IM** *020 †20
LANG, John Albert, III. 3521 HAWORTH DR 27609 #036-01-1974 L1982 **IM** *020 †20
LANGE, Patricia Adele. 3948 BROWNING PL, SURGEONS 27609 #051-04-1996 L2003 **GS** *020 †85
LARA, Patricio Pasler. ■ 27615 #231-03-1963 L1972 **P PFP** *062
LARCADE, Lee Alan. 1500 SUNDAY DR, STE 200 27607 #039-01-1985 L1988 **P** *020 †75
LARIMER, Mark Robert. 4414 LAKE BOONE TRL, STE 502 27607 #041-14-1984 L1996 **FM** *020 †18
LARSON, Thomas Carl. 3601 MSC CENTER, DOROTHEA DIX HOSPITAL 27699 #012-05-1995 L1997 **CHP** *020 †75
LATIMER, Ann D. 6512 SIX FORKS RD STE 103 27615 #036-01-1977 L1977 **D** *020 †15
LAW, Michael Morris. 10941 RAVEN RIDGE RD, STE 103 27614 #012-05-1988 L2000 **PS HS** *020 †65
LAWRENCE, William Wesley. 2501 MAIL SERVICE CTR, NV DIV MEDICAL ASSISTANCE 27699 #036-05-1993 L1997 **PD** *030 †55
LE, Hung Ngoc. 3803B COMPUTER DR, STE 201 27609 #396-08-1992 L1997 **IM** *020 †20
LEACOCK, Benjamin William. ■ 27615 #028-34-2007 **EM** *012
LEATHERMAN, Hugh K, Jr. 2800 BLUE RIDGE RD, STE 405 27607 #045-01-1981 L1983 **U** *020 †95
LEB, Stephen Marc. 3336 SIX FORKS RD 27609 #011-02-1975 L1986 **GS** *020 †85
LEBENSON, Bernard S. 4420 LAKE BOONE TRL 27607 #051-04-1977 L1979 **U** *020 †95
LECHNER, Shiley Ann. 3000 NEW BERN AVE 27610 #041-12-1998 L2000 **EM** *020 †16
LEE, Peter Hogyun. 3024 NEW BERN AVE STE 30, WAKEMED FACULTY PHYSICIANS 27610 #036-01-1994 L1997 **IM** *020 †20
LEE, William David, Jr. 2607 BLUE RIDGE RD, STE 300 27607 #036-01-1974 L1974 **FM** *020 †18

LEET, Douglas Chas. 2800 BLUE RIDGE RD, STE 405 27607 #016-02-1975 L1977 **U** *020 †95
LE GRAND, Gordon Buck. ■ 27608 #036-01-1965 L1965 **PTH** *062 †50
LEHAN, Leigh Steele. 2800 BLUE RIDGE RD, STE 401 27607 #036-01-1981 L1984 **PD** *020 †55
LEHRMAN, Arthur. ■ 27617 #035-03-1958 L1959 **PS** *071 †65
LEIDY, Lu Ann. 820 S BOYLAN AVE 27603 #036-07-1982 L1986 **CHP P** *020 †75
LEITHE, Mark Earl. 3000 NEW BERN AVE, STE 1200 27610 #038-40-1983 L1989 **CD IM** *020 †20
LEKAN, Carol Catherine. 3404 WAKE FOREST RD, RALEIGH INTERNAL MEDICINE 27609 #038-40-1987 L2001 **D** *020 †15
LE LIEVER, William Chas. 1311 SAINT MARYS ST 27605 #065-05-1974 L1987 **OTO FPS** *020 †45
LEONE, Peter A. 10 SUNNYBROOK RD, DEPT HLTH CLN 27610 #038-44-1982 L1988 **ID IM** *020 †20
LERCH, Victor. ■ 27615 #024-05-1985 L1986 **FM** *020 †18
LESTINI, William F. 3320 WAKE FOREST RD # 430, TRNGL SPINE BACK CARE CTR 27609 #010-02-1983 L1992 **OSS** *020 †40
LEV, Ian Michael. 5540 CENTERVIEW DR STE 423 27606 #041-02-1968 L1976 **P** *020
LEVIN, Raphael A. ■ 27612 #041-02-1939 L1940 **GP** *071
LEVIN, Stephen W. 319 CHAPANOKE RD 27603 #047-06-1976 L1979 **PD** *020 †55
LEVIN, Stuart Jeffrey. 3100 BLUE RIDGE RD STE 100 27612 #036-01-1988 L1994 **IM** *020 †20
LEVINE, Ronald Howard. ■ 27609 #035-08-1959 L1965 **PHP PD** *071 †55,70
LEVY, Susan Rae. 3019 FALSTAFF RD 27610 #035-45-1979 L1983 **P** *020 †75
LEWIS, Deborah L. 700 EXPOSITION PL, STE 111 27615 #038-40-1981 L1990 **FM** *020 †18
LIAO, Lawrence. 3320 WAKE FOREST RD, STE 202 27609 #036-07-1996 L2000 **CD** *020 †20
LIEBELT, Ralph Arthur. 8300 HEALTH PARK, STE 109 27615 #038-06-1982 L1989 **ORS** *020 †40
LIEBOWITZ, Steven Marc. 3850 ED DR, STE 100 27612 #035-19-1982 L1988 **IM** *020 †20
LIGHTSEY, Joseph M. 831 W MORGAN ST, HEALTH SERVICES-DOC 27603 #035-06-1976 L1979 **IM** *020
LILLEY, Lori Brown. 3024 NEW BERN AVE, STE 304 27610 #036-01-1990 L1996 **GS** *020 †85
LIN, Alice A. ■ 27613 #025-01-2003 L2007 **M** *100
LIN, Christopher. ■ 27613 #038-43-2002 L2007 **PM** *100 †60
LIN, Pyng Jing. ■ 27613 #244-02-1980 **TS** *020
LIND, Heide Maria. 3400 WAKE FOREST RD 27609 #018-03-1979 L1993 **PTH** *020 †50
LINSTER, Dorothy Mae. 3000 NEW BERN AVE 27610 #036-01-1978 L1980 **OBG** *020 †30
LINTHICUM, Karin Siri. 3900 BROWNING PL, STE 202 27609 #010-02-1990 L1992 **D** *020 †20,15
LISH, Michael Clarke. 3100 SPRING FOREST RD, STE 130 27616 #005-18-1982 L1990 **AN CCM** *020,05
LITTLETON, Robert Elton. 2709 BLUE RIDGE RD, STE 300 27607 #036-01-1981 L1982 **OBG** *020 †30
LIVINGSTON, Kim. 5838 SIX FORKS RD, STE 100 27609 #045-01-1985 L1993 **NS** *020 †25
LOCKLEAR, Jimmy. 4325 LAKE BOONE TRL, STE 315 27607 #036-01-1980 L1985 **CD IM** *020 †20
LOGEL, Kevin John. 3515 GLENWOOD AVE, RALEIGH ORTHOPAEDIC CLINIC 27612 #036-01-1999 L2005 **ORS** *100 †40
LOIBISSIO, Joseph Charles. 2406 BLUE RIDGE RD, STE 100 27607 #035-09-2003 L2006 **PD** *020 †55
LONG, Fred Jos. 3410 SIX FORKS RD 27609 #047-07-1972 L1978 **GS** *020 †85
LONGMUIR, Ian Stewart. N C STATE UNIV BIOCHEM 27695 #352-03-1948 **OS** *050
LONGO, Christopher Robert. 2800 BLUE RIDGE RD, DIAGNOSTICS 27607 #024-07-1996 L2006 **VS** *020 †85
LOPEZ-CLAROS, Marcelo E. 220 SWINBURNE RD 27610 #231-01-1984 L1989 **P** *020 †75
LOURDURAJ, Leena Thomas. ■ 27614 #495-52-1994 L2006 **DMP** *100 †50
LOVDAL, Jamie Alpern. 3396 SIX FORKS RD, UNIVERSAL FAMILY MEDICINE 27609 #036-07-1998 L1999 **FM** *020 †18
LOWNES, Holly E. 3709 CATHEDRAL BELL DR 27614 #047-07-1983 L1984 **FM FPG** *020 †18
LOWNES, Robert Lefonia. 3400 WAKE FOREST RD, DUKE HEALTH RALEIGH HOSP 27609 #047-07-1973 L1975 **IM EM** *020 †20,16
LOWRY, Roy Frank, Jr. 1422 E MILLBROOK RD 27609 #036-01-1968 L1968 **OPH** *020 †35
LOWY, Ralph Edward. 3019 FALSTAFF RD 27610 #165-04-1970 L1971 **GP** *020
LUCEY, Donald Truesdell. 8025 CREEDMOOR RD 27613 #036-07-1963 L1963 **U** *071 †95
LUCKING, Robert Geo, Jr. 27613 #025-07-1977 L1978 **P PFP** *020 †75
LUE, John Francis, Jr. 3850 ED DR, STE 100 27612 #021-01-1994 L1998 **IM** *020 †20
LUKES, Andrea Steele. 2500 BLUE RIDGE RD, STE 300 27607 #036-07-1994 L1998 **OBG** *020 †30
LUNSFORD, Julia Ogden. ■ 27605 #036-01-1987 L1988 **P** *020 †75
LUTZ, Andrew Gardner. 3100 SPRING FOREST RD, CRITICAL HEALTH SYSTEMS 27616 #041-14-2002 L2006 **AN** *100 †05
LUTZ, Rodney Sean. 3400 WAKE FOREST RD 27609 #038-43-1995 L2001 **GS** *020 †85
LYLE, William Glenn. 1112 DRESSER CT, RALEIGH PLASTIC SURGERY CE 27609 #025-07-1986 L2000 **PS** *020 †85,65
LYNN, Clabe Webster, Jr. ■ 27613 #051-04-1958 L1960 **P** *071 †75
MACCIOLI, Gerald Anthony. 3100 SPRING FOREST RD, MAILING: P O BOX 18139 27616 #031-01-1984 L1985 **AN CCA** *020 †05
MAC CORMACK, John Newton. PO BOX 29601 27626 #036-01-1962 L1962 **PHP OS** *030 †70
MAC DONALD, Phyllis M B. ■ 27615 #041-13-1943 L1961 **PM** *071
MAC PHEE, Keelee Joy. 4414 LAKE BOONE TRL, STE 407 27607 #024-16-1997 L2003 **PS** *100
MADDEN, Cynthia. 2406 BLUE RIDGE RD STE 190, ACCENT URGENT CARE 27607 #020-12-1989 L1993 **EM** *020 †16
MADDISON, Sarah Daniel. 4414 LAKE BOONE TRL, STE 300 27607 #036-08-1998 L2002 **OBG** *020 †30
MADDOX, Thomas Wilbur. 2800 BLUE RIDGE RD, STE 503 27607 #001-02-1979 L1985 **GS** *020 †85
MADRY, Herbert R, Jr. 3821 MERTON DR 27609 #036-05-1956 L1956 **DR** *071 †80
MAGOLAN, Jerome J, Jr. 3000 NEW BERN AVE 27610 #056-06-1981 L1985 **OPH OS** *020 †35
MAILLARD, Jean-Marie. 1902 MAIL SERVICE CTR, NC DHHS 27699 #396-34-1983 L1997 **GPM** *020 †70
MAJORS, Robert Powell, Jr. 3000 NEW BERN AVE 27610 #010-01-1961 L1961 **OTO HNS** *071 †45
MALIN, Jonathan Adam. 3000 NEW BERN AVE, DEPT OF EMERGENCY MEDICINE 27610 #051-07-1993 L2000 **EM** *020 †16
MALLON, William James. 8300 HEALTH PARK, STE 109 27615 #036-07-1984 L1990 **ORS OSM** *020 †40
MANGANO, Charles Angelo, Jr. 3000 NEW BERN AVE STE 1, RALEIGH CARDIOLOGY ASSOCIA 27610 #035-45-1974 L1975 **CD IM** *020 †20
MANGANO, Joseph Anthony. 3000 NEW BERN AVE 27610 #035-09-1954 L1974 **IMG IM** *020

MANIKTALA, Anita. 2406 BLUE RIDGE RD, STE 190 27607 #032-01-1995 L1997 **PD** *020 †55
MANITIUS, Eva Maria. 10831 FOREST PINES DR, STE 110 27614 #759-03-1983 L1994 **IM** *020 †20
MANKIN, Keith Pinkney. 3515 GLENWOOD AVE, RALEIGH ORTHOPAEDIC CLINIC 27612 #041-12-1988 L2000 **OP ORS** *020 †40
MANLY, Isaac Vaughn. 2800 BLUE RIDGE RD, STE 503 27607 #024-01-1946 L1946 **GS TS** *020 †85,90
MANN, Courtney Hopkins. ■ 27614 #047-05-1994 L2001 **EM** *020 †16
MANN, James Tift, III. 3000 NEW BERN AVE, STE G100 27610 #036-01-1969 L1969 **CD IM** *020 †20
MANN, Scott Geoffrey. 820 S BOYLAN AVE 27603 #036-05-1997 L2001 **IM** *020 †20
MANRING, Erik Alexander. 3100 BIRNAMWOOD RD, EMERGENCY DEPARTMENT 27607 #036-08-1994 L1995 **EM** *020 †16
MARCH, Michael Ross. 4414 LAKE BOONE TRL, STE 311 27607 #038-40-1991 L1995 **OBG** *020 †30
MARGRAF, Russell Reid. 5838 SIX FORKS RD, STE 100 27609 #035-03-1996 L2001 **NS** *020 †25
MARKS, John Jacob. 700 EXPOSITION PL, STE 161 27615 #036-01-1979 L1985 **GYN** *020 †30
MAROOF, Shaheda Fatima. 4041 ED DR # 102 27612 #495-65-1979 L1984 **P** *020 †75
MARSH, Stephen Saunders. 3117 POPLARWOOD CT, STE 114 27604 #036-05-1986 L1995 **FM** *020 †18 ‡
MARSHALL, Leslie Patricia. 2500 BLUE RIDGE RD, STE 417 27607 #051-04-1988 L1991 **IM** *020 †20
MARSHALL, Robert Nelson. 3000 NEW BERN AVE 27610 #036-01-2001 L2005 **AN** *020 †05
MARSHBANKS, Mary Alice. 3024 NEW BERN AVE 27610 #036-01-1989 L1992 **IM** *020 †20
MARSTON, Laurie May. 3809 COMPUTER DR, STE 201 27609 #050-02-1989 L1992 **OBG** *020 †30
MARTIN, A Michele. 4414 LAKE BOONE TRL, STE 210 27607 #036-08-1993 L1997 **OBG** *020 †30
MARTIN, Allison Eileen. ■ 27606 #010-02-1998 **IM** *100
MARTIN, Jeffrey Dean. 3301 TERMINAL DR, DISABILITY DETERMINATION 27604 #047-06-1983 L1994 **PM** *062 †18
MARTIN, Meri King. 8101 BROWNLEIGH DR 27617 #001-02-2001 L2002 **FOP FOP** *012
MARTIN, Philip Lee. 2801 BLUE RIDGE RD STE 200 27607 #036-01-1973 L1973 **OPH** *020 †35
MARUCHECK, John Thomas. 3320 WAKE FOREST RD, STE 310 27609 #039-01-1978 L1981 **IM** *020 †20
MASK, Allen Greene, Jr. 2610 NEW BERN AVE 27610 #036-01-1978 L1982 **AN IM** *075
MASON, Eric W. 3100 SPRING FOREST RD, STE 130 27616 #011-02-1980 L1985 **AN CCM** *020 †05
MASOOD, Naseem Jehan. 3214 CHARLES B ROOT WYND, STE 211 27612 #495-21-1982 L1996 **PUD IM** *020 †20
MASOOD, Syed Ahmed. 3214 CHARLES B ROOT WYND, STE 211 27612 #495-57-1980 L1996 **IM ID** *020 †20
MATHEIS, Edward John. 3024 NEW BERN AVE, STE 301 27610 #048-02-1988 L1989 **CCM** *020 †20
MATHEWS, William B, Jr. 3000 NEW BERN AVE 27610 #021-01-1962 L1974 **FM** *071 †18
MATTHEWS, Charles Jos. 2501 ATRIUM DR, 4TH FLOOR, SUITE 400 27607 #051-01-1978 L2005 **N** *075 †75
MATTHEWS, Elena M. 3601 MSC, DOROTHEA DIX HOSPITAL 27699 #561-01-1987 L1998 **P** *020 †20,75
MATTHEWS, John Lyle. 3725 NATIONAL DR, STE 227 27612 #036-01-1994 L1995 **CHP** *020 †75
MATTHEWS, Robert Dean. 3024 NEW BERN AVE, STE 300 27610 #047-05-1986 L2003 **U** *020 †95
MAUNEY, J David, III. 859 WASHINGTON ST 27605 #036-01-1983 L1985 **P** *020
MAYO, James Perry, Jr. DOROTHEA DIX HOSPITAL, CHERRY BLDG 27699 #036-01-1979 L1983 **P** *020 †75
MAZZAGLIA, Joseph Ronald. 3019 FALSTAFF RD, HOLLY HILL HOSPIAL 27610 #035-09-1971 L1972 **P GP** *020 †75
MAZZOCCHI, Leo Frank. 3614 HAWORTH DR 27609 #051-04-1964 L1968 **R** *020 †80
MC AFEE, Gary Owen. ■ 27615 #018-03-1996 L1996 **DR** *100
MC ALLISTER, J Gray, III. 1055 DRESSER CT, CAROLINA PARTNERS IN 27609 #036-01-1960 L1960 **P CHP** *020
MC BRIDE, Jack Marvin, Jr. ■ 27615 #036-07-1982 L1986 **FM OM** *030 †18
MC CASKILL, Rodney Lee. 3000 NEW BERN AVE 27610 #036-08-1995 L1997 **EM** *020 †16
MC CLURE, Mark Warren. 3200 BLUE RIDGE RD, STE 118 27612 #017-20-1976 L1989 **U** *020 †95 ‡
MC CORMICK, Keith Lyndon. 2011 FALLS VALLEY DR, STE 100 27615 #036-01-1994 L1995 **OPH** *020 †35
MC CUNE, Bryan Kurtis. ■ 27608 #030-05-1983 L1995 **PTH HMP** *020 †50
MC DONALD, Cary Crane. 3000 NEW BERN AVE, DEPT. OF EMERGENCY SERVICE 27610 #036-01-1987 L1991 **EM** *020 †16
MC DONALD, Thaddeus L, III. 3000 NEW BERN AVE, WAKE AHEC DEPTOF OB/GYN 27610 #036-01-1987 L1992 **OBG** *020 †30
MC ELVEEN, John Thos, Jr. 3100 DURALEIGH RD STE 300, CLINIC 27612 #036-01-1978 L1986 **OTO** *020 †45
MC EWEN, John Duncan. 3000 FALSTAFF RD 27610 #021-01-1982 L1984 **P** *020 †75
MC GRORY, Edward Jos, Jr. 2709 BLUE RIDGE RD, STE 100 27607 #045-01-1974 L1979 **OPH** *020 †35
MCHUGH, Damian Francis. 4420 LAKE BOONE TRL, RALEIGH EMERGENCY 27607 #917-08-1990 L1999 **EM** *020 †16
MCIVER, Mandisa Anjail. ■ 27614 #005-12-2003 L2007 **PD** *020 †55
MC KAY, Michael Dixon. 8300 HEALTH PARK, STE 209 27615 #012-01-1982 L1987 **GE IM** *020 †20
MC KENZIE, Sheppard A, III. 2011 FALLS VALLEY DR 27615 #036-01-1974 L1974 **OBG IM** *020 †20,30
MC KINLEY, Steven Hang. 2709 BLUE RIDGE RD, STE 100 27607 #025-01-2002 L2007 **OPH** *020 †35
MC KINNEY, Leslie Cheryl. 2406 BLUE RIDGE RD, STE 190 27607 #036-01-1986 L1988 **EM** *020 †16
MC LAURIN, Anne Norris. 1001 ROCK QUARRY RD 27610 #038-41-1974 L1978 **FM** *020 †18
MC LAURIN, Robt Love, Jr. 1528 IREDELL DR 27608 #038-41-1981 L1989 **RO** *020 †80
MC MAHON, Steven John. 10208 CERNY ST, STE 300 27617 #012-05-1996 L2007 **OTO** *020
MC MANN, Amy Elizabeth. ■ 27613 #036-07-1996 **071**
MCMILLAN, Michele Halby. 7205 STONEHENGE DR 27613 #036-08-1994 L1997 **PD** *020 †55
MCNEAL-TRICE, Kenya A. 3024 NEW BERN AVE, STE 307 27610 #025-07-2002 L2005 **PD** *100 †55

MCNEILL, Sabra A. 4020 WESTCHASE BLVD, STE 350 27607 #036-01-1976 L1976 **DR** *020 †80
MC REE, Christine J Ellis. DOROTHEA DIX HOSP, CHILD PSYCHIATRY DEPT 27603 #021-01-1946 L1956 **CHP** *072
MEARES, Ben Miller. PO BOX 19366 27619 #045-01-1964 L1965 **R** *020 †80
MEARES, Ben Miller, Jr. 2800 BLUE RIDGE RD, STE 401 27607 #036-01-1999 L2002 **PD** *020 †55
MEDERO-ENG, Miriam. 3801 COMPUTER DR, STE 200 27609 #035-47-1998 L2007 **PD** *020 †55
MEHANY, Albert Edward. 3324 SIX FORKS RD, KAISER PERMENANTE 27609 #005-14-1999 L2007 **CD** *020 †20
MEIER, John Jacob. 3024 NEW BERN AVE 27610 #016-02-2004 L2008 **MPD** *012
MELE, Paul Francis. 4420 LAKE BOONE TRL, RALEIGH EMERGENCY 27607 #021-01-1982 L1988 **EM OM** *020 †16
MELVIN, Al Leodus. 3100 SPRING FOREST RD, STE 130 27616 #036-01-1986 L2002 **AN** *020 †05
MEREDITH, Scott Davis. 10010 FALLS OF NEUSE RD, STE 203 27614 #051-01-1987 L1994 **OTO** *020 †45
MEROD, Marjorie Eleanor. 2800 BLUE RIDGE RD, STE 210 27607 #035-46-1984 L1988 **OBG** *020 †30
MERRICK, Howard Arthur. 3900 MERTON DR, STE 150 27609 #011-02-1964 L1968 **P** *020
MERRITT, Ashley Grant. 4020 WESTCHASE BLVD, STE 390 27607 #001-02-1998 L2002 **DR** *020 †80
MERRITT, James Mitchell. 3000 NEW BERN AVE, WAKE MEDICAL CENTER 27610 #036-01-1987 L1989 **EM** *020 †16
MERTZ, Deborah Kay. ■ 27615 #038-43-1992 L1995 **AN** *020 †05
MERTZ, John Thos. ■ 27615 #038-40-1991 L2003 **AN** *020 †05
MERWARTH, Charles Richard. 4420 LAKE BOONE TRL 27607 #036-07-1955 L1955 **IM A** *020 †20
MESSER, Rosa Yueh. 10000 FALLS OF NEUSE, STE 201 27614 #016-06-1996 L2001 **IM** *020 †20
MESSER, Terry Michael. 3404 WAKE FOREST RD 27609 #016-06-1995 L2001 **HS ORS** *020 †40
MESSERLY, David Robert. 4420 LAKE BOONE TRL, RALEIGH EMERGENCY 27607 #038-40-2002 L2005 **EM** *020 †16
METIKO, Olushola Jones. 1300 WESTERN BLVD 27606 #690-03-1979 L1998 **IM** *020 †20
MEYER, William Robt. 2601 LAKE DR, STE 301 27607 #051-01-1983 L1993 **REN OBG** *020 †30
MEYERHOFFER, Lori Abel. 512 E DAVIE ST 27601 #011-04-1994 L1998 **IM** *020 †20
MEYMANDI, Assad. 3320 EXECUTIVE DR, STE 216 27609 #010-01-1962 L1966 **P N** *020 ‡
MIAH, Rohima Davi. 1055 DRESSER CT, CAROLINA PARTNERS IN 27609 #038-40-1996 L1997 **P** *020 †20
MICHAEL, Patricia Ann. ■ 27613 #036-01-1985 *100
MICHAU, Kenneth Joe, II. 4420 LAKE BOONE TRL, RALEIGH EMERGENCY 27607 #038-40-1996 L1999 **EM** *020 †16
MIDDLETON, Gordon Kennedy. 1321 OBERLIN RD, OBERLIN ROAD PEDIATRICS 27608 #036-05-1955 L1955 **PD OS** *071 †55
MIHALOVICH, Timothy J. 3949 BROWNING PL, WAKE RADIOLOGY CONSULTANTS 27609 #019-02-2001 L2004 **DR** *100 †80
MIKLES, Mark Raymond. 14341 NEW FALLS OF NEUSE 27614 #041-02-1998 L2004 **ORS** *020 †40
MILAZZO, Angelo Stephen. 3713 BENSON DR STE 202 27609 #035-48-1996 L1997 **PDC** *020 †55
MILLER, David Edward. 3000 NEW BERN AVE, WAKE AHEC OBG 27610 #036-07-1973 L1976 **P** *020 †30
MILLER, Elizabeth. 2815 CATES AVE., NCSU HEALTH SERVICES 27695 #024-01-1994 L1995 **MPD** *020 †20,55
MILLER, Jody W. 3000 FALSTAFF RD, ATTN: J'METRIA 27610 #051-07-2001 L2003 **PYG** *020 †75
MILLER, Karen Elizabeth. 2304 WESVILL CT, STE 210 27607 #036-07-1982 L2005 **IM** *020 †20
MILLER, Orlando Phil. 3575 GLENWOOD AVE 27612 #035-01-1959 L1968 **ORS** *071 †40
MILLER, Philip R, Jr. 3100 BLUE RIDGE RD STE 300 27612 #036-05-1967 L1967 **CD IM** *020 †20
MILLER, Shelly Ann. 4100 WAKE FOREST RD, DOCTORS URGENT CARE CTR 27609 #008-02-1991 L1995 **FM** *020 †18
MILLER, William Stacy. 4201 LAKE BOONE TRL, STE 200 27607 #036-01-1961 L1961 **D** *071 †15
MILLWARD, David Kent. 3000 NEW BERN AVE 27610 #010-01-1965 L1969 **CD IM** *020 †20
MILOWIC, Kristi Lynn. 1540 SUNDAY DR 27607 #048-12-1988 L1994 **PD** *020 †55
MIRANDA, Harvey Rustia. 10441 MONCREIFFE RD, STE 101 27617 #036-01-2002 L2004 **FM** *020 †18
MIRZA, Raeesa Wajahat. ■ 27612 #704-21-2004 **IM** *012
MISCHEN, Blaine Thomas. ■ 27617 #036-07-2008 *012
MISTROT, Jean Jacques. 3020 NEW BERN AVE # 560 27610 #048-04-1968 L1982 **TS** *071 †85,90
MITCHELL, Joshua Brannon. 4420 LAKE BOONE TRL 27607 #047-06-2001 L2007 **DR** *100 †80
MOGHAZI, Sammy A. 3604 BUSH ST, WAKE NEPHROLOGY ASSOCIATES 27609 #036-01-1996 L2001 **NEP** *020 †20
MOHAMED, M Hisham. 3214 CHARLES B ROOT WYND, STE 217 27612 #915-07-1977 L1995 **IM** *020
MOHAN, Meena K. 4420 LAKE BOONE TRL 27607 #496-21-1990 L1999 **IM** *020 †20
MOHIUDDIN, Ishtiaque H. 2406 BLUE RIDGE RD, STE 150 27607 #160-02-1982 L2004 **CD** *100 †20
MOHR, Linda Chappell. 4020 WAKE FOREST RD STE 2, HEALTHCARE, PA 27609 #036-01-1980 L1984 **OBG** *020 †20,30
MOHS, Gregory John. 3024 NEW BERN AVE STE 306, WAKE MED FAC PHYS 27610 #026-04-1991 L1998 **OBG** *040 †30
MOLLIN, Daniel Joseph, Jr. 3100 BLUE RIDGE RD, STE 300 27612 #035-06-1993 L1996 **IM** *020 †20
MONACO, Thomas Jos, Jr. 3100 SPRING FOREST RD, STE 130 27616 #036-01-1991 L1993 **AN** *020 †05
MONAHAN, Michael. 3604 BUSH ST 27609 #012-05-1984 L1991 **NEP IM** *020 †20
MONDOU, Elsa Beth. ■ 27616 #035-06-1982 L1992 **PTH** *020 †50
MONG, James Arthur. 4414 LAKE BOONE TRL, STE 210 27607 #038-41-1980 L1983 **OBG** *020 †30
MONTANA, Leslie. 220 SWINBURNE RD 27610 #036-01-1996 L2002 **P** *020 †75
MOODY, Mary Frances. 4420 LAKE BOONE TRL 27607 #036-01-1989 L1993 **OBG** *020 †30
MOONEY, Alfonso John, III. 1251 GOODE ST, HEALING PLACE WAKE CTY 27603 #025-01-1974 L1977 **FM OS** *020 †18
MOORE, Glenndale. 2949 NEW BERN AVE STE 112A 27610 #036-01-1979 L1980 **CD IM** *020

MOORE, Stephen Irwin, III. 3500 BUSH ST STE 103 27609 #036-01-1981 L1982 **FM** *020 †18
MOORE, Susan Gibbs. 4420 LAKE BOONE TRL, STE 200 27607 #036-01-2000 L2006 **HO** *020 †20
MORAN, Joseph Conrad. 2801 BLUE RIDGE RD STE 101, ADVANCED LAPAROSCOPIC ASSO 27607 #305-01-1997 L2004 **GS** *020 †85
MOREA, Christopher Jos. ■ 27615 #010-02-1988 L1994 **PS** *020 †65
MOREADITH, Randall Wade. 8311 BRIER CREEK PKWY, STE 105-162 27617 #036-07-1984 L1986 **IM** *020 †20
MORGAN, Anthony Dean. 3400 WAKE FOREST RD, DUKE RALEIGH HOSPITAL 27609 #036-07-1975 L1977 **IM HOS** *020 †20
MORGAN, Roger Eliot. ■ 27615 #016-11-1983 L1998 **GS TRS** *075 †85
MORGENLANDER, Marcia A. 2406 BLUE RIDGE RD, STE 190 27607 #041-12-1988 L1991 **PD** *075 †55
MORRIS, Peter Jos. 220 SWINBURNE RD, PO46833 27610 #036-01-1978 L1981 **PD PHP** *030 †55,70
MORRIS, Thomas. NC DPH/VPH, MSC 1912 27699 #041-09-1987 L2000 **ID IM** *062 †20
MORRIS, Vicki Morgan. 2304 WESVILL CT STE 240 27607 #051-01-1987 L1992 **ID** *020 †20
MORRISON, Marion E. 3320 WAKE FOREST RD, STE 310 27609 #033-06-1987 L1994 **IM** *020 †20
MORROW, Melanie Brooke. 3100 SPRING FOREST RD, CRITICAL HEALTH SYSTEMS OF 27616 #038-44-2000 L2002 **AN** *020
MORROW, Sarah A Taylor. 4905 WATERS EDGE DR, ELECTRONIC DATA SYSTEMS AD 27606 #023-01-1944 L1945 **PHP PD** *071 †70
MORSE, Eric Dalton. 8300 HEALTH PARK, STE 201 27615 #016-06-1998 L2005 **P ADP** *020
MOSELEY, Robert Galloway. ■ 27614 #036-07-1957 L1957 **PD** *071 †55
MOSER, Wade Hauser, Jr. 1120 WAGON RIDGE RD 27614 #036-01-1974 L1974 **DR** *020 †80
MOSTELLER, Gregory James. 4420 LAKE BOONE TRL, RALEIGH EMERGENCY 27607 #038-40-1996 L2006 **EM** *020 †16
MOTT, Delora Fowler. ■ 27609 #010-01-1947 L1949 **N** *071
MOTT, Howard O. ■ 27614 #010-01-1944 L1947 **IM CD** *071 †20
MOURAD, Wael Fouad. ■ 27606 #915-04-1998 **PD** *100
MUNN, Albert Rogers, III. 720 W JONES ST 27603 #036-01-1985 L1986 **OPH** *020 †35
MUNT, Robert L, Jr. 4414 LAKE BOONE TRL 27607 #036-01-1977 L1977 **PD** *020 †55
MURNANE, Mary Beth. 3909 SUNSET RIDGE RD, STE 103 27607 #021-05-1981 L1989 **PD** *020 †55
MURPHY, William Alton. ■ 27615 #036-01-1974 L1978 **EM** *020
MURRAY, Jeffrey Aaron. 8300 HEALTH PARK, STE 109 27615 #051-01-1992 L1999 **OSM** *020 †40
MUSANTE, David Benjamin. 8300 HEALTH PARK, STE 109 27615 #051-01-1996 L2002 **ORS** *020 †40
MYATT, Jennifer Hedgepeth. 3200 BLUE RIDGE RD STE 210 27612 #036-05-1986 L1995 **IM IMG** *020 †20
MYERS, Jonathan Brent. 331 S MCDOWELL ST 27601 #036-05-1998 L1999 **EM** *020 †16
MYERS, Richard Stanton. 2800 BLUE RIDGE RD, STE 503 27607 #028-02-1965 L1972 **GS** *071 †85,90
NACOUZI, Michele. 6729 FALLS OF NEUSE RD, STE 110 27615 #035-09-1991 L1995 **FM** *020 †18
NACOUZI, Vincent. 6733 FALLS OF NEUSE RD, NORTH RALEIGH MEDICAL CENT 27615 #035-09-1990 L1994 **EM** *020 †16
NADEAU, Meghan Hennessey. ■ 27615 #020-12-2008 *012
NAGARAJ, Lavanya Vaidya. 3225 BLUE RIDGE RD STE 101 27612 #036-01-2002 L2003 **D** *020 †15
NAGLE, H Troy, Jr. ■ 27650 #011-02-1981 **OS** *050
NANCE, Keith Vanallen. 4420 LAKE BOONE TRL, REX HOSPITAL/DEPT.OF PATHO 27607 #036-08-1985 L1987 **PTH PCP** *020 †50
NARAHARI, Naveen. 8300 HEALTH PARK, STE 209 27615 #038-40-1998 L2005 **GE** *100 †20
NARAYAN, Roger Jagdish. ■ 27612 #036-05-2001 *100
NARAYANASWAMY, Sanjay A. 3400 WAKE FOREST RD, DUKE RALEIGH HOSPITAL 27609 #495-09-1992 L2001 **IM** *020 †20
NASH, Scott David. 10208 CERNY ST 27617 #036-01-2000 L2006 **AI** *020 †55
NASHOLD, Blaine S, Jr. 4420 LAKE BOONE TRL 27607 #020-02-1949 L1955 **NS** *071 †25
NASIM, Ali Khalid. 27617 #016-11-2004 L2007 **DR** *012
NASIR, Adnan M. 4414 LAKE BOONE TRL, STE 408 27607 #035-45-1995 L1996 **D** *020 †15
NASLUND, Patricia Keogh. 1540 SUNDAY DR, RALEIGH NEUROLOGY ASSOCS, 27607 #036-07-1994 L1999 **N** *020 †75
NASR, Viviane. 3200 BLUE RIDGE RD STE 210, RALEIGH ADULT MEDICINE 27612 #605-02-1986 L1999 **IM** *020 †20
NASRUDDIN, Shaheda. ■ 27606 #496-27-1994 L2007 **IM** *020 †20
NECHYBA, Christian A. 2605 BLUE RIDGE RD, STE 100 27607 #011-03-1997 L2002 **PD** *020 †55
NEEL, Elizabeth. NCSU CAMPUS BOX 7304 27695 #036-08-1997 L2000 **PD** *020 †55
NEELY, Constance Sue. ■ 27614 #051-01-1974 L1996 **IM** *020 †05
NEFF, Karen Elaine. 3024 NEW BERN AVE STE 300, WAKEMED FACULTY PHYSICIANS 27610 #041-14-2001 L2004 **PD** *020 †55
NEIGHBORS, Joseph D. 4301 LAKE BOONE TRL 27607 #051-04-1990 L1997 **U** *020 †95
NELSON, Christopher G. 4420 LAKE BOONE TRL, REX HOSPITAL 27607 #028-34-1998 L2001 **IM** *020 †20
NESBIT, Frederick. ■ 27612 #869-04-1953 L1974 **P** *071
NEVILLE, Michael James. 3000 NEW BERN AVE 27610 #036-05-1995 L1996 **AN** *020 †05
NEWELL, Josephine E. ■ 27612 #023-01-1949 L1949 **OS GP** *071
NEWELL, Lanny Richard. 4201 LAKE BOONE TRL, STE 5 27607 #036-01-1975 L1977 **GE IM** *020 †20
NEWHALL, Philip Mayes. 4301 LAKE BOONE TRL 27607 #024-01-1994 L1998 **U** *020 †95
NEWLIN, Jackie Ann. 2709 BLUE RIDGE RD, STE 300 27607 #036-01-1983 L1984 **OBG** *074 †30
NEWMAN, Andrea W. 10 SUNNYBROOK RD, WAKE COUNTY DEPARTMENT OF 27610 #035-46-1987 L1994 **PD** *020 †20
NEWMAN, Jack N, Jr. 10010 FALLS OF NEUSE RD, STE 307 27614 #010-01-1989 L1999 **CD** *020 †20
NEWMAN, Ralph Howard. ■ 27612 #016-01-1986 L1996 **P** *020 †75
NEWMAN, Rosemarie C. 10000 FALLS OF NEUSE RD 27614 #035-09-1980 L1998 **GYN** *020 †30
NEWMAN, Tina M. 3000 NEW BERN AVE, WAKE EMERG PHYS PA 27610 #035-15-2000 L2003 **EM** *020 †16 ‡
NEWMAN, William Neal. 3000 NEW BERN AVE, STE G100 27610 #036-07-1977 L1982 **CD ICE** *020 †20
NG, Godofredo T. 1101 DRESSER CT 27609 #748-02-1962 L1969 **GS TS** *071 †85
NG, Peter Conrad. 1101 DRESSER CT 27609 #036-08-1996 L2002 **GS** *020 †85

NG, Wing Kee. 3000 NEW BERN AVE, CAROLINA REHAB & SURGICAL 27610 #048-04-1995 L2005 **PM** *020 †60

NGUYEN, Quynhanh Thi. 4420 LAKE BOONE TRL, REX HOSPITAL 27607 #026-04-1999 L2002 **IM** *020 †20

NICHOLS, Mark Lovel. 1300 SAINT MARYS ST 4TH FL 27605 #051-04-1971 L1980 **IM EM** *071 †20,16

NICHOLSON, Charles H, III. 3100 SPRING FOREST RD, STE 130 27616 #035-06-1982 L1986 **AN PME** *020 †05

NOAH, Van Batchelor. 2709 BLUE RIDGE RD 27607 #036-05-1966 L2005 **OPH** *071 †35

NOBLE, Richard Claiborne. 3320 WAKE FOREST RD, STE 310 27609 #036-01-1984 L1986 **IM** *020 †20

NONEMAN, Jack W, Jr. 8300 HEALTH PARK, STE 327 27615 #036-01-1977 L1977 **CD IM** *020 †20

NORTON, Deborah Ruth. 3000 NEW BERN AVE 27610 #016-11-1984 L1988 **FM** *020 †70,18

NOVEK, Steven Jai. ■ 27615 #036-01-1989 L1992 **PD** *020 †55

NUNNERY, Elizabeth Marie. ■ 27612 #045-01-2006 **PTH** *012

NUTT, James Edward. 8300 HEALTH PARK, STE 327 27615 #012-01-1974 L1980 **CD IM** *020 †20

O'BRIEN, Patrick James. 3000 NEW BERN AVE 27610 #035-09-1981 L1991 **PM** *020 †60

O'CONNELL, Denis. ■ 27606 #561-02-1983 L1998 **PD** *020 †55

O'CONNELL, Patrick Austin. 2304 WESVILL CT, STE 210 27607 #036-01-2000 L2006 **IM** *020 †20

OEI, Monica. 3100 DURALEIGH RD, STE 100 27612 #016-11-1997 L2007 **FM** *020 †18

OJEDA, Tomas. 4420 LAKE BOONE TRL, REX HEALTHCARE,HOSPITALIST 27607 #649-02-1970 L1988 **IM NEP** *020 †20

OLAJIDE, Oludamilola A. 4420 LAKE BOONE TRL, REX CANCER CENTER, SUITE 2 27607 #690-01-2000 L2006 **HO** *020 †20

OLARTE, John Paul. 5530 MUNFORD RD, STE 119 27612 #047-05-2003 L2005 **P** *020

OLLER, Dale Wm. 3024 NEW BERN AVE, STE 304 27610 #010-01-1968 L1987 **GP TRS** *020 †85

O'NEIL, Bert Howard. 3000 NEW BERN AVE 27610 #005-14-1994 L2001 **HO** *020 †20

OPOKU-AGYEMANG, Patrick D. ■ 27613 #409-04-1980 **NM** *100

ORDONEZ, Esperanza Maria. 4822 SIX FORKS RD STE 104, CAROLINA IMMEDIATE CARE202 27609 #024-05-1978 L1980 **EM** *020

ORELLANA, Juan. 3141 JOHN HUMPHRIES WYND 27612 #035-47-1978 L1998 **OPH** *020 †35

ORENSTEIN, Raphael Simha. 8300 HEALTH PARK, STE 109 27615 #012-05-1992 L1997 **PM** *020 †60

O'ROURKE, James Ralph, Jr. 7021 HARPS MILL RD, HARPS MILL INTERNAL MEDICI 27615 #020-12-1966 L1972 **IM A** *020

O'ROURKE, Katherine M. 3225 BLUE RIDGE RD, STE 101 27612 #038-43-1993 L1997 **D** *020 †15

OSCHWALD, Donald L A, Jr. 3633 HARDEN RD STE 200 27607 #034-01-1978 L1986 **PS** *020 †65

OSE, Dennis Eugene. 3000 NEW BERN AVE, PATHOLOGY LAB 27610 #036-07-1979 L1980 **PTH** *020 †50

OSSMAN, Paul Douglas. ■ 27608 #036-01-2006 **IM** *012

OSTROW, Barry Seymour. 3900 BROWNING PL, STE 201 27609 #025-01-1966 L1973 **P PYG** *020 †75

OWENS, Thomas Dew. 820 S BOYLAN AVE, 3601 MAIL SERV CTR 27699 #021-06-1985 L1987 **P PFP** *020 †75

OYLER, Rebekah Marie. 3809 COMPUTER DR, STE 200 27609 #041-14-1994 L1995 **D** *020 †15

PAAR, John Arthur. 3000 NEW BERN AVE, STE G100 27610 #041-12-1960 L1961 **CD IM** *020 †20

PAGE, Ernest B, Jr. ■ 27607 #036-07-1949 L1953 **CD IM** *071 †20

PAGE, Nina Musselman. ■ 27607 #036-07-1949 L1951 **OS** *071

PAI, Poulomi Jeevan. ■ 27617 #496-36-1996 L2005 **PHO** *012

PANDIRI, Mohini. 203 SACRED WOODS WAY 27607 #495-58-2000 L2006 **IM** *020 †20

PAPALAS, John Anthony, III. ■ 27612 #036-08-2006 **PTH** *012

PARADOWSKI, Linda Joann. 4420 LAKE BOONE TRL 27607 #035-06-1980 L1990 **PUD IM** *020 †20

PAREKH, Komal Hasmukh. 3124 BLUE RIDGE RD 27612 #055-01-1997 L2001 **PD** *020 †55

PAREKH, Murtaza. 2417 ATRIUM DR, STE 150 27607 #048-12-1999 L2007 **GE** *100 †20

PARIKH, Pankaj N. 3406 SIX FORKS RD 27609 #495-23-1979 L1994 **CD IM** *020 †20

PARIKH, Rajiv S. ■ 27617 #048-12-1992 L2005 **EM FM** *020 †18 ‡

PARKER, Leonard Alden, Jr. 2600 NEW BERN AVE 27610 #036-01-1980 L1981 **DR** *020 †80

PARNELL, Jerome Patrick. 2800 BLUE RIDGE RD, STE 405 27607 #035-08-1974 L1981 **U** *020 †95

PARRISH, Margaret Lucille. ■ 27615 #036-05-1974 L1983 **N NP** *020 †20,75

PARSONS, James Sheridan. 704 W JONES ST 27603 #036-01-1976 L1976 **IM IMG** *020 †20

PARSONS, William Jonathan. 8300 HEALTH PARK, STE 327 27615 #032-01-1980 L1985 **CD** *020 †20

PASCHAL, George W. 2800 BLUE RIDGE RD 27607 #036-05-1973 L1973 **GS** *020 †85

PASI, Deepak. 8300 HEALTH PARK, STE 327 27615 #495-36-1974 L1983 **CD IM** *020 †20

PASI, Mohit. 8300 HEALTH PARK, STE 327 27615 #496-09-1988 L2001 **CD IM** *020 †20

PASI, Sonia. 3948 BROWNING PL, PLACE,STE 109 27609 #496-17-1991 L2002 **APM** *100 †75

PATE, Dewey Harris. 3000 NEW BERN AVE 27610 #036-01-1958 L1958 **PTH CLP** *071 †50

PATE, Susan. 4420 LAKE BOONE TRL 27607 #036-01-1979 L1981 **N** *020

PATEL, Kamini A. 10010 FALLS OF NEUSE RD, STE 100 27614 #654-01-1988 L1997 **PD** *020 †55

PATEL, Rig S. 8300 HEALTH PARK, STE 209 27615 #917-25-1989 L2001 **GE IM** *030 †20

PATEL, Swapnesh M. 3000 NEW BERN AVE, DEPT. OF EMERGENCY MEDICIN 27610 #005-12-1999 L2002 **EM** *020 †16

PATEL, Vijay Manu. 3801 COMPUTER DR, STE 104 27609 #036-01-1994 L1995 **FM** *020 †18

PATTERSON, Bernard L. ■ 27604 #051-04-1952 L1953 **FM AN** *071 †18

PATTERSON, Hubert Clifton. 10208 CERNY ST, STE 300 27617 #036-01-1974 L1983 **OTO** *020 †45

PATTERSON, Sheila Lynn. 4701 CREEDMOOR RD, STE 101 27612 #025-01-1982 L1996 **OS** *020

PAULI, Jon Warren. 2304 WESVILL CT, STE 210 27607 #036-01-1994 L1987 **IM** *020 †20

PAYNE, Cynthia Susan. 4020 WESTCHASE BLVD, STE 390 27607 #038-43-1980 L1984 **DR** *020 †75,80

PEARCE, Patricia. 181 WIND CHIME CT STE 101 27615 #020-12-1979 L1986 **P** *020 †75

PEDIADITAKIS, Nicholas. ■ 27612 #418-02-1954 L1961 **P PHP** *020 †75

PELLEGRINI, Deborah Quint. 3000 NEW BERN AVE 27610 #038-41-1994 L2004 **AN** *020 †05

PENDERGAST, Warren Josef. 200 HORIZON DR # 218 27615 #026-04-1986 L1987 **P ADP** *020 †75

PERCIACCANTE, James V. 3000 NEW BERN AVE, WAKE MEDICAL CENTER 27610 #035-15-1995 L2001 **NPM** *020 †55

PERKINS, A Thos, IV. 1540 SUNDAY DR, RALEIGH NEUROLOGY 27607 #038-44-1991 L1995 **SME N** *020 †75

PERKINS, Christopher Mark. 7021 HARPS MILL RD 27615 #036-07-1985 L1988 **IM** *030 †20

PERKINS, Henry Thos. ■ 27613 #036-07-1957 L1957 **IM** *071

PERLMUTT, Louis M. 3821 MERTON DR 27609 #036-01-1977 L1977 **DR R** *020 †80

PERNICIARO, Jessica Lynn. 415 WEATHERGREEN DR 27615 #023-07-2008 *012

PERRIN, Jeffrey Braxton. 4551 NEW BERN AVE, STE 160 27610 #001-02-1997 L2000 **PD** *020 †55

PERRY, John Ethwell R, III. 3024 NEW BERN AVE, STE 301 27610 #036-01-1988 L1994 **IM** *020 †20

PETE, Karl Lyndell. 3024 NEW BERN AVE 27610 #036-07-1992 L2003 **U** *020 †95

PETERS, Douglas Ahern. 701 CORPORATE CENTER DR 27607 #005-06-1977 L2006 **IM** *030 †20

PETERSEN, Kristi. ■ 27612 #018-03-1984 L1990 **IM OM** *030 †20

PETERSON, Bret Charles. ■ 27617 #007-02-2007 **ORS** *012

PETERSON, James W. 3320 WAKE FOREST RD, STE 202 27609 #035-45-1988 L2004 **CD IM** *020 †20

PETERSON, Paul C. 3480 WAKE FOREST RD # 502, DUKE NEURO OF RALEIGH 27609 #048-02-1995 L2003 **N** *020 †16,75 ‡

PEYTON, Robert B. 3000 NEW BERN AVE 27610 #035-19-1977 L1985 **TS** *020 †85,90

PFLUGRATH, Ann M. ■ 27608 #048-12-1987 L1991 **AN** *020 †05

PHICHITH, Alounthith. ■ 27615 #012-21-2004 L2007 **IM** *100

PHILLIPS, J Duncan. 3948 BROWNING PL, SURGEONS 27609 #005-02-1986 L1999 **PDS** *020 †55

PIEHL, Mark Donald. 3000 NEW BERN AVE, WAKE MED, PEDIATRICS DEPT 27610 #036-01-1995 L1997 **CCP** *100 †20,55

PIERCE, Edwin L. 3400 WAKE FOREST RD 27609 #036-05-1952 L1952 **IM** *071

PIERSON, Willard C, Jr. 2417 ATRIUM DR STE 150, DIGESTIVE HEALTHCARE PA 27607 #036-07-1966 L1966 **GE IM** *071 †20

PILATI, David Michael. 3410 SIX FORKS RD 27609 #035-06-1997 L1999 **GS** *020 †85

PINE, Krista Miranda. 3721 BENSON DR, KRISTA M. PINE, MD 27609 #005-06-2000 L2006 **P** *020 †20

PIQUERAS, Eduardo Antonio. 3000 NEW BERN AVE, WAKE EMERGENCY PHYSICIANS, 27610 #036-08-2000 L2003 **EM** *020 †16

PITTMAN, Jerry Michael. 8312 CREEDMOOR RD, TREMONT MED CTR 27613 #001-06-1979 L1982 **GP EM** *071

PITTMAN, John C. 4505 FAIR MEADOWS LN, STE 111 27607 #012-22-1986 L2002 **NTR** *020

PITTMAN, William Gibbs. 3024 NEW BERN AVE, STE G03 27610 #036-01-1998 L2001 **IM** *020 †20

PIZZINO, Joanne Louise. 2431 SPRING FOREST RD, STE 111 27615 #038-40-1982 L1993 **OM FM** *030 †70,18

PLACIDE, Jon Saurel. 2605 BLUE RIDGE RD, STE 150 27607 #047-07-2001 L2005 **OBG** *020

PLESCIA, Marcus G. 1915 MAIL SERVICE CTR, DIVISION OF PUBLIC HEALTH 27699 #036-01-1990 L1995 **FM** *020 †18

PLETCHER, Cynthia Ann. 2620 NEW BERN AVE 27610 #025-01-1985 L1988 **FM** *020 †18

PLETCHER, David W, III. 4420 LAKE BOONE TRL 27607 #025-01-1985 L1987 **FM** *020 †18

PODNOS, Yale David. 1101 DRESSER CT 27609 #005-15-1998 L2006 **GS** *020 †85

POLAVARAPU, Naveena. 3301 WALNUT CREEK PKWY 27606 #496-24-1997 L2003 **IMG** *020 †20

POLLOCK, Morris Arthur. 2417 ATRIUM DR STE 150, DIGESTIVE HEALTHCARE PA 27607 #041-02-1969 L1976 **GE** *020 †20

POOLE, Alison Jean. ■ 27615 #010-01-2006 **EM** *012

POOLE, James Morrison. 4551 NEW BERN AVE, STE 160 27610 #045-01-1976 L1979 **PD PDA** *020 †20

POOLE, Robert F, Jr. 4551 NEW BERN AVE, STE 160 27610 #036-07-1947 L1955 **PD** *020

POPOVICH, Karen Stacy. 3320 EXECUTIVE DR, THE RALEIGH EYE CENTER PA 27609 #036-01-1990 L1995 **OPH** *071 †35

POST, James Richard. 3404 WAKE FOREST RD 27609 #038-43-1992 L1998 **HS** *020 †40

POWELL, David Clifton. 1101 DRESSER CT 27609 #036-01-1978 L1979 **GS EM** *020 †85

POWELL, Erin Katherine. ■ 27606 #036-01-2007 **FP** *012

POWELL-TILLMAN, Levonne. 3601 MAIL SERVICE CTR, 820 SOUTH BOYLAN AVENUE 27699 #036-01-1999 L2002 **IM** *020 †20

POWER, Abhijit Bhaskar. 3024 NEW BERN AVE, STE 301 27610 #036-01-1994 L1998 **IM GP** *020 †20

POWER, Bhaskar Dayaram. ■ 27603 #495-01-1957 L1984 **OTO AI** *020 ‡

PRATT, Laura Winstead. 2815 CATES AVE CMP BX 7304, N C S U STUDENT HLTH SVCS 27695 #036-05-1972 L1972 **FM** *020 †18 ‡

PRESSON, Thomas Lemuel, Jr. 3949 BROWNING PL, WAKE RADIOLOGY CONSULTANTS 27609 #036-05-1995 L1996 **VIR** *020 †80

PRICE, Nerissa Marge. 16 N BOYLAN AVE, STE 301 27603 #036-01-2000 L2006 **CHP** *020 †75

PRITCHETT, Newton Geo. ■ 27608 #064-01-1942 L1953 **IM** *071 †20

PRITCHETT, Rildia Jones. 4414 LAKE BOONE TRL, STE 308 27607 #036-01-1982 L1985 **OBG** *020 †30

PROCTER, William Ivan. 3900 BROWNING PL STE 101 27609 #036-07-1957 L1957 **IM** *071 †20

PUCILOWSKA, Jolanta B. 820 SOUTH BOYLAN AVENUE 27699 #759-03-1977 L2008 **P** *020

PUCILOWSKI, Olgierd A. 2304 WESVILL CT, STE 280 27607 #759-03-1977 L2000 **P** *020 †75

PUENTE, Fernando Rene. 4420 LAKE BOONE TRL 27607 #036-08-1981 L1991 **D** *020 †18,15

PUGH, Magda El-Raheb. 10010 FALLS OF NEUSE RD, STE 12 27614 #915-02-1978 L1989 **OTO** *020 †45

PUGH, Vernon W, Jr. 1321 OBERLIN RD 27608 #041-02-1953 L1953 **PD** *071

PUGH, Vernon W, III. 3400 WAKE FOREST RD 27609 #041-02-1986 L1989 **DR** *020 †80

PURUSHOTHAMAN, Shiny. 3024 NEW BERN AVE STE 301, WAKEMED FACULTY PHYSICIANS 27610 #036-08-2001 L2005 **IM** *100

PYLE, Robert Noble, Jr. ■ 27615 #023-01-1976 L1980 **ORS** *075

QUEEN, Laurinda Lee. 3921 SUNSET RIDGE RD # 202 27607 #003-01-1981 L1982 **D** *071

QUIGLEY, Brian Steven. 4420 LAKE BOONE TRL, RALEIGH EMERGENCY 27607 #035-15-1993 L1994 **EM** *020 †18

RADFORD, Wanda Lee. 4420 LAKE BOONE TRL, STE 308 27607 #036-01-1975 L1975 **GYN** *020 †30

RAINES, Lawrence M, III. 859 WASHINGTON ST 27605 #036-01-1993 L1994 **P ADP** *020 †75

RAJAN, Mythili. 3024 NEW BERN AVE, STE 200 27610 #495-04-1972 L1978 **PD** *040 †55

RALEY, Jennifer Lynn. 3000 NEW BERN AVE, DEPT OF EMERGENCY MEDICINE 27610 #028-34-1998 L1999 **EM** *020 †16

RAMOS, Ralph Saml. 3100 SPRING FOREST RD, CRITICAL HEALTH SYSTEMS 27616 #012-01-1989 L1998 **AN** *020 †05

RAMQUIST, Neil Albert. 1212 CEDARHURST DR 27609 #005-19-1977 L1978 **DR EM** *020 †80

■ = Address Information Privacy Protected

RAMSEY, Roscoe Wm, Jr. ■ 27609 #047-07-1979 L1979 **FM** *020 †18
RANDALL, Gordon Raver. 3821 MERTON DR, WAKE RADIOLOGY CONSULTANTS 27609 #047-06-1978 L1997 **DR OS** *020 †80
RANSOM, Earl Stacy, Jr. 2912 RYTON CT 27613 #036-05-1986 L1987 **AN** *020 †05
RANSON, Matthew Thomas. ■ 27613 #055-01-2003 L2007 **PMM** *012
RAPPAPORT, Eric. 3404 WAKE FOREST RD, STE 100 27609 #011-02-1982 L1986 **OBG** *020 †30
RASHID, Inam. 3100 DURALEIGH RD 27612 #704-01-1987 L1995 **FM** *020 †18
RATHKE, Kevin M. 1540 SUNDAY DR, RALEIGH NEUROLOGY ASSCS, P 27607 #012-22-1996 L2002 **CN** *020 †75
RAVAL, Jay Suman. ■ 27614 #036-01-2006 L2006 **PTH** *012
RAWAL, Kapil. ■ 27607 #495-73-1979 L1983 **N** *020 †75
RAYMOND, Elizabeth Gray. 100 S BOYLAN AVE 27603 #035-01-1984 L2006 **OBG** *020 †30
READING, Jeremy K. ■ 27612 #048-13-2001 L2006 **AN** *100 †05
REDDY, B Amarendra. 3000 NEW BERN AVE, STE 1200 27610 #495-65-1968 L1975 **CD** *020 †20
REES, Michael Stevens. 3200 BLUE RIDGE RD STE 210, RALEIGH ADULT MEDICINE, PA 27612 #047-05-1976 L1979 **IM** *020 †20
REES, Terry Taylor. ■ 27612 #021-01-1955 L1987 **GS TS** *071 †85,90
REIBEL, Donald Baumann. ■ 27613 #017-20-1957 L1964 **ORS** *071 †40
REID, David Marshall. 2418 BLUE RIDGE RD, STE 201 27607 #036-01-1975 L1977 **P CHP** *020 †75
REIGEL, Haidee. ■ 27615 #035-48-1974 L1986 **IM** *075 †20
REILLY, John Francis, Jr. 4101 MACON POND RD, CAROLINA 27607 #036-05-1990 L1994 **RO** *020 †80
REKUC, Gregory Matthew. 3200 BLUE RIDGE RD, STE 210 27612 #011-03-1981 L1984 **IM** *020 †20
RENDLEMAN, David Atwell. 3410 EXECUTIVE DR 27609 #036-01-1970 L1970 **ORS** *020 †40
REYNOLDS, John Bennie, Jr. 2604 IMAN DR 27615 #036-01-2001 **PHM** *030
RHODES, James Kent. ■ 27613 #036-05-1947 L1948 **GS TS** *020 †85
RHODES, John Flint. ■ 27612 #036-01-1962 L1962 **U** *071 †95
RHYNE, Jimmie Lee. ■ 27612 #023-01-1948 L1948 **PHP PD** *071 †55
RICE, Henry Elliot. 3404 WAKE FOREST RD, STE 302 27609 #008-01-1988 L1998 **PDS** *020 †85
RICH, Cadmus Collins. 2901 MOUNTAIN ASH CT, 4102 N ROXBORD ROAD 27614 #036-01-1995 L1996 **OPH** *020 †35
RICH, Kenneth John. 1100 DRESSER CT, STE 100 27609 #035-06-1978 L1984 **NS** *020 †25
RICHARDSON, Christin Neal. 4414 LAKE BOONE TRL, STE 308 27607 #036-01-2001 L2005 **OBG** *020 †30
RICHMAN, Allison. ■ 27612 #010-01-2001 L2004 **IM** *020
RICKARD, Kathleen Ann. ■ 27613 #041-09-1983 L1994 **PUD CCM** *020 †20
RIDGWAY, Beth A. 1300 WESTERN BLVD, CENTRAL PRISON MENTAL HLTH 27606 #038-40-1989 L1991 **P PYG** *020 †75
RIEKER, Robert Paul, Jr. 3400 WAKE FOREST RD 27609 #036-05-1997 L1998 **AN** *020 †05
RISKE, Paul Scott. 2709 BLUE RIDGE RD, STE 100 27607 #016-43-1998 L2002 **OPH** *020 †35
ROBACZEWSKI, David Lee. 3000 NEW BERN AVE 27610 #036-05-1990 L1991 **GS** *020 †85,90
ROBBINS, Brian Vernon. 3000 FALSTAFF RD, CRISIS AND ASSESSMENT SERV 27610 #045-04-2003 L2005 **P** *020
ROBERTS, Lee Ann Rhudy. 5816 CREEDMOOR RD STE 209 27612 #028-02-1980 L1985 **GYN** *020 †30
ROBERTS, Lisa Marie. 10941 RAVEN RIDGE RD, STE 109 27614 #036-01-1996 L1997 **GYN** *020 †30 ‡
ROBERTS, Surry Parker. ■ 27605 #036-01-1966 L1966 **RHU** *071
ROBINSON, Chas Hall, Jr. 2709 BLUE RIDGE RD, STE 100 27607 #036-07-1975 L1976 **OPH** *020 †35
ROBINSON, Leslie B. 3100 DURALEIGH RD 27612 #036-01-1995 L1996 **FM** *020 †18
ROBINSON, Stephen Eric. 3320 WAKE FOREST RD, STE 202 27609 #036-05-1999 L2005 **CD** *020 ‡
ROCHE, Andrea Decsi. 4420 LAKE BOONE TRL, STE 302 27607 #036-01-1997 L2001 **OBG** *020 †30
RODMAN, Michael David. 3024 NEW BERN AVE 27610 #024-16-1982 L1989 **IM** *020 †20
ROEDE, Elizabeth Cate. 10941 RAVEN RIDGE RD, STE 109 27614 #036-01-1999 L2004 **GYN U** *020
ROGERS, Stephen R. 3400 WAKE FOREST RD 27609 #001-06-1994 L1996 **APM** *020 †05
ROLLINS, Robert Le Roy. 820 S BOYLAN AVE 27603 #036-07-1956 L1956 **P PFP** *020 †75
ROOKER, Sara Lynn. 4905 GREEN RD STE 100 27616 #036-08-1999 L2001 **FM** *020 †18
ROOKWOOD, Jacqueline L. ■ 27614 #035-09-1993 L2005 **IM** *020 †20
ROSE, Grace Willett. 701 EXPOSITION PL, STE 218 27615 #036-07-1983 L1989 **IM** *020 †20
ROSE, Gregory Chas. 4325 LAKE BOONE TRL, STE 315 27607 #028-34-1980 L1987 **CD IM** *020 †20
ROSEN, Alan Lee. 3400 WAKE FOREST RD 27609 #035-45-1979 L1983 **DR** *020 †80
ROSENBAUM, David Henri. ■ 27608 #051-01-2002 L2007 **EM** *020 †16
ROSENBLUM, Shepherd F. 3633 HARDEN RD STE 102 27607 #035-19-1988 L1998 **OSM** *020 †40
ROSS, Ana Silvia. 2418 BLUE RIDGE RD, STE 105 27607 #187-08-1985 L1991 **RHU** *020 †20
ROTH, Todd Jason. 4020 WESTCHASE BLVD, STE 350 27607 #048-13-1997 L2000 **DR** *020 †80
ROY, Brandon P. 3024 NEW BERN AVE 27610 #026-04-1999 L2005 **GS** *020 †85
RUBIN, David Bernard. ■ 27613 #016-01-1975 L1977 **IM PUD** *020 †20 ‡
RUBINO, John. 3521 HAWORTH DR, RALEIGH MEDICAL GROUP 27609 #008-02-1983 L1984 **IM A** *020 †20
RUIZ, Fernando Rey. 4096 BARRETT DR 27609 #231-01-1965 L1976 **P IMG** *062 †75
RUSH, Elizabeth Anne. 3949 BROWNING PL, WAKE RADIOLOGY 27610 #004-01-1990 L1995 **DR** *020 †80
RUSINEK, Christopher S. 10321 LUMLEY RD, STE 200 27617 #025-07-2000 L2006 **OPH** *020 †35
RUSSELL, Roger Bivins. 3633 HARDEN RD, SURGERY PA 27607 #036-05-1976 L1983 **PS HS** *020 †85,65
RUTHERFORD, Edmund James. 3024 NEW BERN AVE, STE 304 27610 #041-12-1984 L1997 **GS CCS** *020 †85
RYAN, Kevin John. ■ 27614 #005-19-1982 L1991 **OBG** *020
SAACKS, Cynthia Brewer. 2011 FALLS VALLEY DR 27615 #048-12-1991 L1995 **OBG** *020 †30
SAAD, Samy Rizkallah. 3000 NEW BERN AVE, EMERGENCY PHYSICIAN 27610 #915-07-1984 L2000 **PD PE** *020 †55
SACHDEVA, Alka Vaishali. 8300 HEALTH PARK STE 309, REX HEALTHCARE 27615 #038-44-1996 L1999 **IM** *020 †20
SACHDEVA, Neeraj Kumar. 2601 LAKE DR STE 201 27607 #035-09-1995 L1999 **GE** *020 †20
SAIK, Denise Susan. 3601 MSC CENTER 27699 #021-05-1982 L1984 **IM AMI** *030 †20
SALEEBY, Richard Geo. 3814 BROWNING PL STE 100 27609 #041-02-1946 L1947 **OS** *071

SALEEBY, Richard Gibran. 3814 BROWNING PL STE 100 27609 #036-01-1984 L1985 **CRS GS** *020 †85,10
SALLEH, Judith. 3601 MSC CENTER, DOROTHEA DIX STATE HOSPITA 27699 #035-48-1981 L2006 **FM** *020 †18
SAMARGYA, Katherine Diane. 2418 BLUE RIDGE RD STE 10, ADOLESCENT MEDICINE 27607 #011-04-1990 L1997 **PD** *020 †55
SAMIA, M A. 2731B CAPITAL BLVD 27604 #036-08-1990 L1991 **FM** *020 †18
SANCHEZ, Clare Jeanne. 4909 GREEN RD, CONCENTRA MED CTR 27616 #007-02-1975 L1984 **IMG** *020
SANDERS, Ernest Lenwood, Jr. 2949 NEW BERN AVE STE 108 27610 #038-40-1976 L1985 **FM** *020 †18
SANDERS, Stephen Pruett. 3404 WAKE FOREST RD, STE 302 27609 #020-02-1975 L1996 **PDC PD** *020 †55
SANDHU, Ritu Raj. 3024 NEW BERN AVE STE 306 27610 #036-01-1995 L1999 **OBG** *040 †30
SARGEANT, Angus G, Jr. ■ 27615 #036-05-1953 L1953 **OS IM** *071
SARTSCHEV, Caroline Ann. 1921 FALLS VALLEY DR, ASSOCIATES 27615 #041-02-1987 L2006 **PD** *020 †15
SATTERFIELD, Benton Sapp. 2801 BLUE RIDGE RD STE G50 27607 #036-07-1962 L1962 **GYN** *020 †30
SATYAPRIYA, Ajay Simha. 820 S BOYLAN AVE 27603 #038-41-2003 L2008 **ACA** *012
SAWICKI, Carole Caldwell. ■ 27612 #036-01-1992 L1995 **FM** *050 †18
SCARANTINO, Chas Walter. 4420 LAKE BOONE TRL, REX CANCER CENTER 27607 #036-05-1973 L1974 **RO** *020 †80
SCARBOROUGH, Dawson E, Jr. 3000 NEW BERN AVE, DEPT PATH 27610 #036-01-1962 L1962 **PTH** *020 †50
SCARBOROUGH, Walter A, Jr. 1004 DRESSER CT STE 101 27609 #036-07-1967 L1967 **P** *030 ‡
SCHECTER, Nancy. 1631 MIDTOWN PL, STE 102 27609 #036-07-1979 L1983 **N** *020 †75
SCHINDZIELORZ, Andrew H. ■ 27606 #055-02-1985 L1993 **IM** *020 †20
SCHNEIDER, Joel Evan. 4325 LAKE BOONE TRL, STE 315 27607 #036-01-1985 L1993 **CD IM** *020 †20
SCHOTZINGER, Robert Jos. ■ 27612 #038-06-1992 **IM** *100 †20
SCHRICKER, Paul Oskar. 3404 WAKE FOREST RD 27609 #038-06-1989 L1996 **ORS** *020 †40
SCHULTE, Barbara Mary. ■ 27609 #010-02-1967 L1978 **PD** *071 †55
SCHULZ-BUTULIS, Beth. 5603 DURALEIGH RD, STE 111 27612 #038-75-1998, ▲ L2006 **D** *020 †15
SCHWAM, Steven. ■ 27614 #011-02-1979 L2000 **AN** *020 †05
SCHWARZ, Christopher John. 2601 LAKE DR STE 201, RALEIGH MEDICAL GROUP, PA 27607 #025-07-1990 L1998 **IM** *020 †20
SCHWARZ, Ronald Paul. 3521 HAWORTH DR 27609 #035-20-1977 L1979 **GE IM** *020 †20
SCONTSAS, George John. 220 HORIZON DR, STE 218 27615 #051-01-1977 L2001 **N** *075
SCOTT, Harry White. ■ 27605 #036-01-1962 L1962 **D** *020 †15
SCOVIL, James A, Jr. 23 SUNNYBROOK RD STE 109 27610 #036-01-1971 L1971 **CD** *020 †20
SEGAL, Alan Bruce. 4414 LAKE BOONE TRL, STE 405 27607 #035-48-1994 L1998 **OBG** *020 †30
SEGAL, Herbert Erwin. ■ 27614 #036-07-1967 L1969 **MDM GPM** *030 †70
SELLERS, Bobby Eugene. 3900 BROWNING PL 27609 #047-06-1963 L1966 **P** *071
SENA, Thomas John. 2800 BLUE RIDGE RD, STE 401 27607 #036-03-1983 L1984 **PD** *020 †55
SENTER, William Jeffress. 704 W JONES ST 27603 #023-01-1942 L1942 **IM** *071
SEVILLA, Milton Jesus C. 14341 NEW FALLS OF NEUSE, STE 122 27614 #748-01-1990 L2001 **PD** *020 †55
SEWARD, Paul North. ■ 27603 #024-01-1968 L2007 **PD EM** *020 †55,16
SEYMOUR, Robt Edward, III. 3100 SPRING FOREST RD, MAILING: P O BOX 18139 27616 #036-08-1986 L1987 **AN** *020 †05
SHABAN, Stephen Francis. 2800 BLUE RIDGE RD, STE 405 27607 #035-47-1982 L1988 **U REN** *020 †95
SHAH, Nirupama B. 820 S BOYLAN AVE 27603 #495-22-1970 L1980 **IM** *020
SHAH, Syed Majid Ali. 2500 BLUE RIDGE RD, STE 321 27607 #704-01-1983 L1990 **IM** *020 †20
SHAH, Vinod Kantilal. ■ 27615 #495-48-1974 L1998 **IM** *020
SHAW, Mary Cassie. 1321 OBERLIN RD, STE A 27608 #036-08-1996 L2000 **MPD** *020 †20,55
SHAW, Richard Marius. ■ 27615 #759-02-1941 L1953 **IM** *071
SHEPARD, Robert Chas. ■ 27617 #036-07-1978 L2007 **HO ON** *020 †20 ‡
SHERMAN, Steven Vincent. 3100 SPRING FOREST RD, STE 130 27616 #038-06-1995 L1997 **AN** *020 †05
SHETTY, Rupa Ravindra. 3019 FALSTAFF RD, HOLLY HILL HOSPITAL 27610 #496-01-1993 L2006 **CHP** *020
SHICK, Jafar Mo. 3100 SPRING FOREST RD, STE 130 27616 #517-01-1961 L1969 **AN** *020 †05
SHOKOR, Nada Abdulkhaliq. ■ 27615 #528-01-1995 L2007 **DMP** *100
SHORT, Douglas Brian. 3521 HAWORTH DR 27609 #036-08-2002 L2005 **IM** *020 †20
SHROFF, Rushad Darius. 3100 DURALEIGH RD, STE 202 27612 #495-17-1996 L2001 **IMG** *020 †20
SHUKLA, Ajay Kumar. ■ 27604 #495-45-1991 L2006 **N** *100
SIBRACK, Gerald Bruce. 1100 NAVAHO DR STE 105 27609 #025-12-1975 L1980 **P CHP** *020
SICHEL, Lawrence Mark. 7021 HARPS MILL RD 27615 #025-01-1987 L1999 **IM** *020 †20
SICKING, Dan Thos. 14341 NEW FALLS OF NEUSE, STE 100 27614 #038-40-1981 L1993 **IM** *020 †20
SIDDIQUI, Nouman. 3320 EXECUTIVE DR, STE 111 27609 #036-07-1999 L2003 **OPH** *020 †35
SIDES, Evin Henderson, III. 4420 LAKE BOONE TRL 27607 #036-01-1965 L1965 **IM ID** *050
SIDHU, Balwinder S. 3200 FAIRHILL DR, STE 106 27612 #495-03-1978 L1993 **IM** *020 †20
SIDHU, Kulbir Kolby. 4101 MACON POND RD, CAROLINA 27607 #065-10-1995 L2005 **RO** *020 †80
SILVER, Marc Todd. 3000 NEW BERN AVE, STE 1200 27610 #024-01-1989 L1995 **CD IM** *020 †20
SILVER, William Paige. 8300 HEALTH PARK, STE 109 27615 #036-05-1997 L2005 **OSM ORS** *020 †40
SIMEONSSON, Kristina L. 1902 MAIL SERVICE CTR 27699 #036-01-1996 L1997 **PD** *020 †55
SINCLAIR, Sherry Lynn. 2418 BLUE RIDGE RD STE 105 27607 #036-08-1993 L1998 **RHU** *020 †20
SINDEN, John Rankin. 3000 NEW BERN AVE # 1200 27610 #036-05-1985 L1992 **CD IM** *020 †20
SINDEN, Susan Grambow. ■ 27608 #036-05-1985 L1992 **PD** *075 †55
SINGH, Hardayal. 3404 WAKE FOREST RD, STE 201 27609 #495-29-1994 L2004 **ORS** *020 †40
SINGH, Rawinder Jit. 1034 BRAGG ST, NC CORRECTIONAL INST WOMEN 27610 #495-29-1983 L2002 **PYG PFP** *020
SINGLETARY, Kimberly R. 3000 NEW BERN AVE, EMERGENCY MEDICINE DEPT 27610 #036-01-1998 L2002 **EM** *020 †16
SMITH, Amaziah P. ■ 27606 #023-07-1945 L1948 **FM IM** *071

SMITH, Boylston D, Jr. ■ 27608 #023-01-1952 L1981 **P** *071

SMITH, Carrie Dow. 3024 NEW BERN AVE 27610 #036-01-1997 L2002 **PD** *020 †55

SMITH, Charles Gregory. 225 N MC DONALD ST, NC DHHS/EPIDEMICLGY 27699 #036-01-1977 L1977 **PHP** *062

SMITH, David Arthur. 2800 BLUE RIDGE RD 27607 #024-05-2000 L2006 **GS** *020 †85

SMITH, James Almer. 1055 DRESSER CT, CAROLINA PARTNERS IN 27609 #010-03-1976 L1980 **P ADP** *020 †75

SMITH, Jane Swan. 7019 HARPS MILL RD, STE 100 27615 #038-41-1981 L1983 **IM** *020 †20

SMITH, Jean Charlotte. 10 SUNNYBROOK RD 27610 #010-03-1975 L1984 **PD** *040 †55

SMITH, John Robt, Jr. 3024 NEW BERN AVE, STE 301 27610 #036-08-1986 L1987 **FM** *020 †18

SMITH, Katherine Mary. 3909 SUNSET RIDGE RD, STE 103 27607 #010-01-1987 L1994 **PD** *020 †55

SMITH, Lyman S W. 3515 GLENWOOD AVE, 3515 GLENWOOD AVE 27612 #036-07-1984 L1991 **ORS OSM** *020 †40

SMITH, Matthew Brian. ■ 27609 #036-01-2008 *012

SMITH, Michael David. 2011 FALLS VALLEY DR 27615 #036-05-1986 L1990 **OBG** *020 †30

SMITH, Patricia Walsh. 2406 BLUE RIDGE RD, STE 280 27607 #021-01-1981 L1991 **OPH** *020 †35

SMITH, Paula Yvonne. 4278 MSC, 831 WEST MORGAN STREET 27699 #036-01-1983 L1985 **FM** *030 †18

SMITH, Scott Victor. 4420 LAKE BOONE TRL, COMPREHENSIVE LAB SERVICES 27607 #036-01-1992 L1995 **PTH** *020 †50

SMITH, Stephen Wayne. 4420 LAKE BOONE TRL, REX HEALTHCARE 27607 #036-01-1973 L1973 **IM CD** *020 †20

SMITH, Vincent Charles. 4420 LAKE BOONE TRL, DEPT OF PATHOLOGY 27607 #036-01-1997 L2002 **PTH** *020 †50

SMITHSON, Anne Johnson. 3800 HILLSBOROUGH ST, MEREDITH CLG CARROLL HLTH 27607 #051-01-1986 L1995 **FM** *020 †18

SMITHSON, Robert Hamilton. 3900 BROWNING PL, STE 101 27609 #051-01-1986 L1992 *020 †20

SNOW, Jeffrey Louis. 5530 MUNFORD RD STE 119 27612 #023-01-1987 L1988 **CHP P** *020 †75

SNOW, Leo Beman. ■ 27609 #041-13-1947 L1955 **R** *071 †80

SNYDER, Edward Sutton. ■ 27615 #010-02-1965 L1972 **DR** *071

SNYDER, Graham Edwin. 3000 NEW BERN AVE, DEPT OF EMERGENCY MEDICINE 27610 #036-01-1999 L2002 **EM** *020 †16

SOKOLEV, Valentyna. 3301 TERMINAL DR 27604 #011-04-1980 L2005 **FM PHP** *030 †18

SOLDIN, James Vincent. 3200 BLUE RIDGE RD STE 210, RALEIGH ADULT MEDICINE, PA 27612 #026-04-1978 L1991 **IM** *020 †20

SONI, Anant Bhupatlal. 3124 BLUE RIDGE RD, STE 103 27612 #495-23-1973 L1990 **IM GE** *020 †20

SONI, Chandrakanta A. 800 SAINT MARYS ST STE 100 27605 #495-20-1976 L1990 **IM EM** *075

SORGE, John Phillip. 4420 LAKE BOONE TRL 27607 #035-45-1982 L1983 **PTH** *020 †50

SPARROW, Nathaniel Louis. 3010 ANDERSON DR 27609 #036-01-1957 L1957 **OTO** *071 †45

SPEER, Kevin Paul. 3404 WAKE FOREST RD, STE 201 27609 #023-07-1985 L1990 **GS** *020 †40

SPRUILL, Thomas Rayford. 3900 BROWNING PL, STE 201 27609 #021-05-1983 L1985 **P** *020 †75

STAFFORD, Steven James. 2800 BLUE RIDGE RD, STE 405 27607 #016-02-1976 L1982 **U EM** *020 †95

STARKENBURG, Robert Jos. 2800 BLUE RIDGE RD, STE 300 27607 #021-05-1979 L1987 **IM** *020 †20

ST CLAIR, Samuel Keith. ■ 27607 #051-04-1981 L1990 **NS GS** *020 †25

STEFFENS, Rebecca Rowland. 2605 BLUE RIDGE RD, STE 300 27607 #036-08-1997 L2000 **FM** *020 †18

STEFFENS, Robert Mark. 3000 NEW BERN AVE 27610 #036-08-1997 L2000 **EM** *020 †16

STEPHENS, John Ruan. 3024 NEW BERN AVE, STE G03 27610 #036-01-1997 L2001 **MPD** *020 †20,55

STEPHENS, Tammi Lenee. 4414 LAKE BOONE TRL, STE 300 27607 #051-01-1988 L1992 **OBG** *020 †30

STEPHENSON, Anne E. DOROTHEA DIX HOSPITAL, 3601 MSC CENTER 27699 #036-05-1989 L1993 **IM** *020 †20

STEVENS, James Romer. 8300 HEALTH PARK, STE 107 27615 #036-08-1987 L1990 **FM FSM** *020 †18

STEWART, Antoinette Marie. 3321 BOULDER CT 27607 #036-01-1996 L2005 **CHP** *020

STEWART, Tina B. 1321 OBERLIN RD, STE A 27608 #036-08-1998 L2002 **PD** *020 †55

STILL, J Gordon. 700 SPRING FOREST RD 27609 #036-05-1978 L1981 **PD** *050 †55

STIRMAN, Jerry Archibald. 1101 DRESSER CT 27609 #048-02-1974 L1979 **GS** *020 †85

STOCKS, Lewis Henry, III. 4414 LAKE BOONE TRL, STE 309 27607 #056-06-1971 L1973 **GS PTH** *020 †85

STRADER, Kyle Woodrow. 3831 MERTON DR 27609 #055-01-1981 L1984 **RHU A** *020 †20 ‡

STRATAS, Nicholas Emanuel. 3900 BROWNING PL, STE 201 27609 #065-01-1957 L1960 **P PFP** *071 †75

STROZIER-MOSELY, V N. ■ 27614 #012-01-1957 L1962 **PD END** *071

STURDIVANT, Mark Cooper. 8300 HEALTH PARK, STE 211 27615 #036-01-1988 L1990 **GS** *020 †85

SUBRAMANIAM, Geeta. 3000 NEW BERN AVE, WAKE MEDICAL CENTER 27610 #043-01-2002 L2004 **IM** *020 †16

SULLIVAN, William Gregory. 3024 NEW BERN AVE STE 304 27610 #016-43-1960 L1971 **GS TRS** *020 †85 ‡

SUMPTER, Edwin Allen. ■ 27604 #051-01-1956 L1981 **PD** *071 †55

SUNDARAM, Senthil Nayagan. 3000 NEW BERN AVE, STE 1200 27610 #495-42-1990 L2003 **CD** *020 †20

SVARA, Claudia Jeffrey. 4030 WAKE FOREST RD, STE 202 27609 #036-01-1983 L1984 **RHU IM** *020 †20

SVED, Margery Sue. 629 OBERLIN RD 27605 #036-01-1979 L1980 **P** *020 †75

SWANN, Edwin Russell. 23 SUNNYBROOK RD, STE 199 27610 #036-01-1975 L1977 **OPH IM** *050 †35

SWEENEY, C A. 2815 CATES AVE CB 7304, NC STATE UNIV STUD HLTH SV 27695 #036-08-1983 L1987 **GYN** *020 †30

SWEENEY, C Leslie. ■ 27609 #036-07-1957 L2007 **FM** *075 †18

SWIERSZ, Angelica Lynn. 1321 OBERLIN RD 27608 #016-11-1995 L2001 **PD** *020 †55

SWIERSZ, Paul Joseph. 3000 NEW BERN AVE, DEPT OF EMERGENCY MEDICINE 27610 #016-11-1995 L2001 **EM** *020 †16

SYKES, Kassell Eugene, Jr. 3100 SPRING FOREST RD, STE 130 27616 #036-01-1988 L1990 **AN** *020 †05

TAAVONI, Shohreh. 3320 EXECUTIVE DR, CAPITAL FAMILY MEDICINE 27609 #422-01-1986 L1989 **IM** *020 †20 ‡

TABER, Julia Kreagar. 4420 LAKE BOONE TRL, REX HEALTHCARE DEPT RAD 27607 #036-07-1987 L1991 **R** *020 †80

TACKMAN, Anthony John. 3000 NEW BERN AVE, 3RD FLOOR-NEONATOLOGY 27610 #025-12-1993 L1999 **NPM** *020 †55

TAJELDIN, Samer. ■ 27604 #036-01-2000 L2006 **IM** *100 †20

TALLEY, David Robt. 401 E WHITAKER MILL RD, WAKE COUNTY HUMAN SERVICES 27608 #005-18-1980 L1984 **P** *020 †20

TANAKA, Jeffrey Jay. 2605 BLUE RIDGE RD STE 100, CENTER 27607 #005-14-1986 L1990 **PD** *020 †20

TANAS, Khalil Saliba. 212 SWINBURNE RD, WAKE COUNTY HUMAN SVCS 27610 #605-01-1972 L1974 **P** *020 †75

TANNER, John Peoples. 1001 ROCK QUARRY RD 27610 #036-08-2004 L2007 **FM** *020 †18

TAPP, Karen. 3024 NEW BERN AVE, STE 306 27610 #011-03-2000 L2002 **OBG** *020

TATARCHUK, Anna L. 2605 BLUE RIDGE RD, STE 150 27607 #011-03-2001 L2005 **OBG** *020

TAYLOR, Geraldine Rita. 14460 NEW FALLS OF NEUSE, STE 149-308 27614 #007-02-1978 L1988 **GYN REN** *020 †30

TAYLOR, Lesli Ann. 3948 BROWNING PL, SURGEONS 27609 #023-07-1981 L1990 **PDS GS** *020 †85

TAYLOR, Sharon Louise. 3404 WAKE FOREST RD, STE 202 27609 #035-19-1982 L1989 **ON HEM** *020 †20

TEASLEY, Myra Lynn. 4414 LAKE BOONE TRL, STE 300 27607 #047-06-1985 L1988 **OBG** *020 †30

TEHRANI, Shahram Taei. 4420 LAKE BOONE TRL, REX HOSPITAL 27607 #010-01-1995 L1999 **IM** *020 †20

TEREZIS, Teresa Nicole. 2610 NEW BERN AVE, ALLIANCE MEDICAL MINISTRY 27610 #038-41-1992 L2002 **IM** *020 †20

TESSIEN-READING, F C. 4420 LAKE BOONE TRL, REX PATHOLOGY ASSOCIATES 27607 #048-13-2000 L2006 **PTH** *100 †50

TEW, Melanie Lynn. 859 WASHINGTON ST, PSYCHIATRIC ASSOCIATES OF 27605 #036-01-2000 L2004 **P** *020 †75

THAMRONG, Ben. 3613 HAWORTH DR 27609 #891-02-1968 L1972 **OBG** *075 †30

THANANART, Sandra. 3100 BLUE RIDGE RD, STE 300 27612 #041-12-1999 L2002 **IM** *020 †20

THARRINGTON, Christopher. 1300 WESTERN BLVD, CP-ACH 27699 #036-07-1992 L1994 **DR** *020

THEKKEKANDAM, Janine Loui. ■ 27613 #036-01-2008 *012

THOMAS, Ben David. ■ 27615 #045-01-1944 L1946 **GP OS** *071

THOMAS, Dori Jean. 4551 NEW BERN AVE, STE 160 27610 #028-34-1996 L1999 **PD** *020 †55

THOMAS, Grace. ■ 27613 #036-05-1998 L2001 **EM** *020 †16

THOMAS, John Evans. ■ 27603 #036-02-1958 L1982 **PM AN** *030

THOMAS, Laura Oliver. 4020 WESTCHASE BLVD, STE 390 27607 #036-07-1990 L1993 **DR** *020 †80

THOMAS, Michael J. 2605 BLUE RIDGE RD, STE 190 27607 #055-01-1989 L1998 **END IM** *020 †20

THOMPSON, Lisa Horn. 3000 NEW BERN AVE, WAKE MEDICAL CENTER 27610 #016-11-1983 L1990 **EM** *020 †16

TILSON, Elizabeth C. 10 SUNNYBROOK RD, WAKE COUNTY HUMAN SERVICES 27610 #023-07-1993 L1996 **GPM PD** *020 †70,55

TILSON, Hugh Hanna. 1612 OBERLIN RD, APT 5 27608 #028-02-1964 L1979 **PHP GPM** *071 †70

TIM, Richard Walter. 1540 SUNDAY DR 27607 #005-18-1986 L1987 **N** *020 †75

TIMMONS, Phillip Zachary. 3604 BUSH ST, WAKE NEPHROLOGY ASSOCIATES 27609 #036-08-1990 L1995 **NEP** *020 †20

TOLIN, Kellie. 859 WASHINGTON ST, PSYCHIATRIC ASSOCIATES OF 27605 #004-01-1998 L2006 **P** *020 †75

TOLNITCH, Lisa Anne. 2301 REXWOODS DR STE 116 27607 #020-02-1983 L1988 **GS** *020 †85

TOPE, John Jeffrey. 8312 CREEDMOOR RD, TREMONT MEDICAL CENTER PA 27613 #045-01-1977 L1991 **EM** *075 †16

TORJESEN, Kristine Anne. 505 OBERLIN RD STE 204 27605 #026-04-1994 L2000 **PD** *020 †55

TORRES, Rafael Guillermo. 2500 BLUE RIDGE RD STE 401, TORRES QUALITY HEALTH CARE 27607 #264-04-1992 L1999 **FM** *020 †18

TORSONE, Andrea Lee. 2601 LAKE DR 27607 #035-06-1997 L2001 **OBG** *020 †30

TOSKY, George Michael. 4414 LAKE BOONE TRL, STE 308 27607 #036-05-1981 L1985 **OBG** *020 †30

TOWNSEND, Lloyd. ■ 27613 #038-06-1977 L1979 **PA IM** *050

TRAN, Luan Van. 3909 SUNSET RIDGE RD, STE 202 27607 #028-46-1993 L2003 **PHL** *020 †16

TRAVERS, Lori Ann. 3126 BLUE RIDGE RD, STE 100 27612 #010-02-1996 L2002 **OPH** *020 †35

TREADWAY, Robert Morris. 4414 LAKE BOONE TRL 27607 #035-05-1994 L1995 **AN** *020 †05

TROCINSKI, Douglas Robt. 3000 NEW BERN AVE, WAKE EMERGENCY PHYSICIANS, 27610 #028-02-1991 L2001 **EM** *020 †16

TROIANO, Jason Joseph. ■ 27695 #051-01-1999 L2006 **FM** *020 †18

TSIKTSIRIS, Louie E. 3831 MERTON DR, NORTH CAROLINA ARTHRITIS 27609 #065-09-1993 L2001 **RHU** *020 †20

TSOMIDES, Theodore. 3024 NEW BERN AVE, STE G03 27610 #024-01-1996 L2000 **IM** *020 †20

TUCCERO, Donna Marie. 2610 NEW BERN AVE, ALLIANCE MEDICAL MINISTRY 27610 #025-07-1989 L1990 **FM** *020 †18

TUMBAPURA, Anil Prakash. 2600 ATLANTIC AVE, STE 100 27604 #496-22-1991 L2002 **GE** *020 †20

TURNER, Shafonya Machelle. ■ 27610 #036-01-2005 **AN** *012

TUTTLE, Harrison Gray. 3515 GLENWOOD AVE 27612 #036-01-1999 L2005 **HS** *020 †40

TUVESON, Anne Terese. 4414 LAKE BOONE TRL, STE 408 27607 #010-02-2000 L2003 **D** *020 †15

TWEEDY, Damon Scott. ■ 27616 #036-07-2000 L2007 **P** *100

TWOMLEY, Katie Marie. 4420 LAKE BOONE TRL, HOSPITALIST MEDICINE DEPT 27607 #036-07-2003 L2006 **CD** *012 †20

TYREE, Larry Allen. ■ 27614 #036-05-1962 L1962 **FM** *071 †18

TYREY, Scott James. 3100 SPRING FOREST RD, STE 130 27616 #036-07-1988 L2002 **APM** *020 †05

TYSON, Treva Watkins. 3100 BLUE RIDGE RD, STE 300 27612 #036-01-1988 L1990 **IM** *020 †20

UDEKWU, Pascal Osita. 3000 NEW BERN AVE 27610 #690-01-1980 L1991 **GS TRS** *020 †55,85

UMESI, Obinnaya Chiegeiro. ■ 27614 #036-01-1987 L1988 **CD** *020 †20

UTECHT, Michael Jonathan. WAKE MED HOSP SYSTEMS, WAKE EMER PHYSICIANS, PA 27620 #025-07-1988 L1992 **EM** *020 †16

UTHMAN, Elmonttasir Mahgo. ■ 27611 #848-01-1995 L2000 **IM** *020 †20

VACCARO, Gina Maria. 3404 WAKE FOREST RD, STE 202 27609 #021-05-1998 L2004 **HO** *020 †20

VALONE, James Austin. 2800 BLUE RIDGE RD 27607 #035-06-1936 L1947 **PS** *071 †85

■ = Address Information Privacy Protected

VAN ARTHOS, William James. 3949 BROWNING PL, WAKE RADIOLOGY CONSULTANTS 27609 #035-09-1988 L1992 **R** *020 †80

VANCE, Charles Rainey. 3601 MAIL SERVICE CTR, FORENSIC DIVISION 27699 #036-07-1993 L1994 **P PFP** *020 †75

VANDERBERRY, Robert C, Jr. ■ 27616 #036-01-1968 L1968 **ADM PD** *030 †55

VAN DYCK, Peter B. 4601 LAKE BOONE TRL 27607 #050-02-1981 L1983 **P** *020 †75

VAN PALA, Henry Jos. 908 CAPITAL BLVD 27603 #025-12-1980 L1984 **GE IM** *020 †20

VAN VICKLE, Jennifer Sue. 4020 WESTCHASE BLVD, STE 350 27607 #036-07-1986 L1990 **DR** *020 †80

VASSEY, John Walter. ■ 27615 #036-01-1956 L1956 **R** *071 †80

VAUGHAN, Ross Leroy, Jr. 3000 NEW BERN AVE 27610 #036-01-1970 L1970 **NPM PD** *020 †55

VAUGHN, Bradley Kent. 3515 GLENWOOD AVE, RALEIGH ORTHOPEDIC CLINIC 27612 #016-11-1979 L1991 **ORS** *020 †40

VAUGHN, Donald Eugene. 331 S MCDOWELL ST 27601 #047-06-1957 L1961 **EM FM** *071 †16,18

VELOSA, Juan Fernando. 5530 MUNFORD RD, STE 119 27612 #264-05-1984 L2006 **CHP P** *020 †75

VENTERS, George Cole. 3410 EXECUTIVE DR 27609 #036-01-1971 L1971 **ORS** *020 †40

VERDINO, Nina Jaime. 4551 NEW BERN AVE, STE 160 27610 #654-01-2002 L2005 **PD** *020

VERGHESE, Kumari Daniel. 820 S BOYLAN AVE 27603 #495-37-1974 L1980 **P CHP** *020

VERSOLA, Manuel B. ■ 27612 #748-01-1966 L1974 **FM P** *020

VEST, Howard Ryland, Jr. 2308 WESVILL CT 27607 #051-01-1971 L1972 **AN** *020 †05

VICKERS, Marie Michele. 3000 NEW BERN AVE, 3RD FL NEONATOLOGY 27610 #055-01-1993 L1996 **NPM PD** *020 †55

VIG, Daniel Robt. 2800 BLUE RIDGE RD, STE 503 27607 #056-05-1992 L1999 **GS** *020 †85

VIJAY, Deepa. 3124 BLUE RIDGE RD 27612 #496-39-1993 L1999 **PD** *020 †55

VINSANT, Mary Louise. 3301 TERMINAL DR, NC DDS 27604 #011-02-1980 L1992 **PHP** *062

VIRGILI, Frank Loges, Jr. ■ 27612 #051-04-1976 L1979 **FM** *020 †18

VOGLER, Robert Cheatham. 3400 WAKE FOREST RD 27609 #036-01-1991 L1992 **RNR** *020 †80

VOLOW, Michael Robt. 8360 SIX FORKS RD 27615 #033-05-1964 L1969 **P PYG** *071 †75

VORA, Varsha S. 3019 FALSTAFF RD 27610 #495-89-1984 L1995 **CHP P** *074 †75

WADLEY, Robert Dale. 7780 BRIER CREEK PKWY, STE 200 27617 #045-01-1984 L2006 **APM** *020 †05

WAGNER, Joanne Estelle. 4551 NEW BERN AVE, STE 160 27610 #036-08-1997 L2003 **PD** *020 †55

WAGNER, Scott David. 10831 FOREST PINES DR, STE 104 27614 #041-12-1997 L2006 **FM** *020 †18

WAINER, James Adams. 867 WASHINGTON ST 27605 #036-01-1985 L1987 **P** *020 †75

WALDENBERG, Leopold Mark. 8300 HEALTH PARK, STE 211 27615 #024-07-1965 L1971 **GS CRS** *020 †85

WALKER, Melanie Paul. 2800 BLUE RIDGE RD STE 401, RALEIGH CHILDREN ADOL MED 27607 #036-01-1997 L2000 **PD** *020 †55

WALTERS, Bradford Blair. 920 MAIN CAMPUS DR, STE 400 27606 #024-01-1979 L1985 **NS** *050 †25

WANG, Cathay Chachy. 3400 WAKE FOREST RD 27609 #048-12-2003 L2006 **EM** *020 †16

WARDROP, Richard M, III. 3024 NEW BERN AVE, STE 301 27610 #038-40-2002 L2004 **MPD** *100 †20,55

WARREN-ULANCH, Julia G. 2605 BLUE RIDGE RD, STE 190 27607 #048-16-1998 L2006 **END** *020 †75

WASSERMAN, Bradley Jared. 1321 OBERLIN RD, STE A 27608 #023-01-2000 L2003 **PD** *020 †55

WASSERMAN, Martha C. 4420 LAKE BOONE TRL, REX HOSPITAL 27607 #027-01-1999 L2004 **DR** *100 †80

WASUDEV, Niku Pramod. 3949 BROWNING PL, NEUROSKELETAL IMAGING OF O 27609 #041-01-1994 L2007 **DR** *020 †80

WATSON, Eloise Bolyn. 4414 LAKE BOONE TRL, STE 300 27607 #036-01-1998 L2004 **OBG** *020

WATSON, Jerry Lynn, Jr. 4020 WESTCHASE BLVD, STE 350 27607 #048-12-1990 L1994 **DR** *020 †80

WATSON, Polly J. 2601 LAKE DR, STE 103 27607 #012-01-2000 L2005 **GYN** *020 ‡

WATTERS, Christopher Roy. 1212 CEDARHURST DR, STE 102 27609 #025-01-1983 L1991 **GS TS** *020 †85

WAY, William Greene, Jr. 3949 BROWNING PL, WAKE RADIOLOGY CONSULTANTS 27609 #051-01-1986 L1992 **DR** *020 †80

WEATHERLY, Cathi Elaine. 10 SUNNYBROOK RD, PRENATAL CLINIC 27610 #017-20-1985 L1995 **OBG** *020

WEAVER, Susan Tucker. 2610 NEW BERN AVE, ALLIANCE MEDICAL MINISTRY 27610 #036-07-1987 L1999 **IM** *020 †20

WEBER, Andrew Bernard. 4020 WESTCHASE BLVD, STE 390 27607 #041-13-1987 L1991 **DR** *020 †80

WEDEGAERTNER, Mary Loftus. 3000 NEW BERN AVE 27610 #047-06-1989 L1993 **PD** *020 †55

WEED, Barry Christopher. 27604 #036-08-1998 L2007 **P** *020

WEHBIE, Charles Sam. 8300 HEALTH PARK, STE 309 27615 #036-05-1982 L1985 **IM** *020 †20

WEHBIE, Robert Sam. 10010 FALLS OF NEUSE RD, CAROLINA NORTH RALEIGH 27614 #056-05-1988 L1989 **HO IM** *020

WEIGAND, Amy Marie. 3000 NEW BERN AVE, WAKE EMERGENCY PHYSICIANS 27610 #038-45-2000 L2005 **PE** *100 †16

WEINER, Timothy Mowll. 3948 BROWNING PL, SURGEONS 27609 #010-02-1989 L1997 **PDS** *020 †85

WEINREB, Seth Marshall. 2800 BLUE RIDGE RD 27607 #024-01-1996 L2001 **GS** *020 †85

WEINSTEIN, Michael H. 3000 NEW BERN AVE 27610 #016-06-1983 L2002 **PTH** *020 †50

WEIR, Samuel Gamble, III. 4020 WESTCHASE BLVD, STE 100 27607 #036-07-1982 L1984 **FM PHP** *020 †20

WEIR, Shawnee Dee. 3410 EXECUTIVE DR 27609 #026-04-1980 L1983 **END IM** *020 †20

WEISLER, Richard Harry. 700 SPRING FOREST RD, STE 125 27609 #036-01-1976 L1976 **P** *020 †75

WEISS, Brian D. 4420 LAKE BOONE TRL, RALEIGH EMERGENCY 27607 #051-04-1984 L1992 **EM** *020 †16

WELCH, Kurt Michael. 6040A SIX FORKS RD # 377 27609 #033-06-1995 **IM** *100

WELLS, Steven Ray. 2406 BLUE RIDGE RD, STE 200 27607 #036-05-1985 L1989 **OBG** *020 †30

WESLEY, Robert Benj. 3000 NEW BERN AVE, STE G100 27610 #012-05-1992 L1997 **CD** *020 †20

WESSELS, Frank Joseph. 3814 BROWNING PL, STE 100 27609 #035-03-1996 L2006 **CRS PRO** *020 †85,10

WESTON, Lynda Rigsbee. 220 SWINBURNE RD, WAKE COUNTY HUMAN SERVICES 27610 #036-05-1977 L1978 **P** *020 †75

WHELISS, John A. 4301 LAKE BOONE TRL STE 2 27607 #035-01-1952 L1954 **OPH** *071 †35

WHITE, Michael Jay. 2011 FALLS VALLEY DR 27615 #007-02-2001 L2005 **OBG** *020

WHITMER, Gilbert G, Jr. 1501 NINE IRON WAY, APT 304 27603 #023-07-1987 L2008 **ORS HS** *020

WHITNEY, Pamela Joyce. 10000 OLD WARDEN RD 27615 #039-01-1980 L1984 **N** *020 †75 ‡

WIATER, Joseph Gerard. 3000 NEW BERN AVE, DEPT OF EMERGENCY MEDICINE 27610 #025-01-1998 L2001 **EM** *020 †16

WICKHAM, Michael Quinn. ■ 27609 #036-07-2003 L2006 **ORS** *100

WIEGAND, Frederick G F. ■ 27608 #041-09-1946 L1969 **OBG** *071 †30

WIEGAND, Steven. 4420 LAKE BOONE TRL, RALEIGH EMERGENCY 27607 #041-09-1977 L1978 **EM FM** *020 †18,16

WILES, Steven Thos. 4325 LAKE BOONE TRL, STE 351 27607 #017-20-1990 L1993 **PD** *020 †55

WILEY, Jerry Wm. ■ 27604 #036-07-1974 L1977 **PD** *020

WILEY, Peter Vaneerde. 5711 SIX FORKS RD, ASSOC 27609 #010-02-1994 L1998 **P** *020 †75

WILKES, Karry Ruedebusch. 4420 LAKE BOONE TRL 27607 #020-12-2003 L2006 **PD** *020 †55

WILKINS, Ezra Brooks. 3100 DURALEIGH RD, STE 200 27612 #036-01-1975 L1975 **FM** *020 †18

WILLETT, Robert Walter. 4420 LAKE BOONE TRL 27607 #036-07-1948 L1953 **IM N** *020 †20

WILLEY, Juliana. 3000 NEW BERN AVE 27610 #036-08-1995 L2002 **GE IM** *020 †20

WILLEY, Leanna Bruen. 2605 BLUE RIDGE RD, STE 100 27607 #035-45-1994 L1998 **PD** *020 †55

WILLIAMS, Eric Rashad. 3904 IVERSON ST 27604 #036-05-2000 L2005 **CHP** *020 †75 ‡

WILLIAMS, John Howard. 4420 LAKE BOONE TRL, RALEIGH EMERGENCY 27607 #036-01-1983 L1989 **EM** *020 †20

WILLIAMS, Judson Blount, Jr. ■ 27609 #047-05-2007 **GS** *012

WILLIAMS, Randall Watts. 3809 COMPUTER DR, STE 201 27609 #036-01-1984 L1988 **OBG** *020 †30

WILLIAMS-TOONE, Deitra L. 2800 BLUE RIDGE RD 27607 #036-01-2000 L2005 **AN APM** *020 †05

WILMOTH, Gregory J. 4201 LAKE BOONE TRL, STE 200 27607 #036-05-1991 L1999 **D DS** *020 †15

WILSON, Christopher N. 7205 STONEHENGE DR 27613 #036-05-2002 L2004 **PD** *100 †55

WILSON, Jon Jay. 3480 WAKE FOREST RD, STE 208 27609 #038-75-1994, ▲ L2002 **PM PME** *020 †60

WILSON, Robert John, III. 8300 HEALTH PARK, STE 109 27615 #047-06-1986 L1994 **PM** *020 †60

WILSON, Sharmell Octavia. 4551 NEW BERN AVE, STE 160 27610 #036-08-1998 L2002 **PD** *020 †55

WINSLOW, Francis E, Jr. ■ 27608 #036-07-1953 L1953 **PD** *071 †55

WINTER, Edith Fang. 309 W MILLBROOK RD, STE 171 27609 #010-01-1982 L1995 **D GP** *020 †15

WIRTH, Lynne Susan. 3000 NEW BERN AVE 27610 #056-06-1985 L1989 **PD** *020 †55

WITMAN, Elizabeth Ann G. 3024 NEW BERN AVE, WAKE MED FACLTY PHYS 27610 #036-05-1985 L1988 **PD** *040 †55

WITT, Peter Nikolaus. ■ 27607 #407-01-1944 **OS** *050

WOJDYNSKA, Magdalena M. 2304 WESVILL CT, STE 280 27607 #759-03-1977 L1996 **P** *020

WOLFE, Nicole Francoise. 820 S BOYLAN AVE 27603 #021-06-1990 L1992 **P LM** *020 †75

WOOD, Mark Lyndon. 3009 NEW BERN AVE 27610 #036-01-1999 L2000 **ORS** *040

WOODARD, Paul Richard. 3100 SPRING FOREST RD, STE 130 27616 #036-01-1979 L1980 **AN** *020 †05

WOODRUFF, Leon Festus, Jr. 4420 LAKE BOONE TRL, STE 303 27607 #036-05-1972 L1972 **OBG** *020 †30

WOODS, Kristi Elena. 4551 NEW BERN AVE, STE 160 27610 #036-01-1998 L2001 **PD** *020 †55

WOOFTER, Aaron Lee. 3480 WAKE FOREST RD 27609 #038-40-2000 L2007 **GE** *020

WOOTEN, Jane Herring. ■ 27608 #036-07-1942 L1944 **PD** *071

WOOTEN, John D, III. 1540 SUNDAY DR 27607 #036-05-1984 L1986 **CHN PD** *020 †55,75

WORF, Bruce Douglas. 820 S BOYLAN AVE, DOROTHEA DIX HOSP 27603 #036-01-1980 L1984 **P** *020

WORRINGHAM, Steven B. 5613 DURALEIGH RD STE 101 27612 #051-07-2001 L2006 **P FM** *100

WRIGHT, Jill Catherine. 2620 NEW BERN AVE, NEW BERN RIDGE PEDIATRICS 27610 #036-01-1994 L1997 **PD** *020 †55

WU, Katherine Gutmann. 4201 LAKE BOONE TRL, STE 201 27607 #036-07-1982 L1990 **P** *020 †75

WU, Sandra S. ■ 27615 #028-02-1983 L1993 **AN** *071 †05

WYNIA, Virgil Howard. 3000 NEW BERN AVE # 1200 27610 #024-01-1972 L1974 **CD IM** *020 †20

YAMADI, Asghar. 3400 WAKE FOREST RD, DUKE RALEIGH HOSPITAL 27609 #422-01-1990 L1997 **IM PD** *020 †55,20

YARBOROUGH, Michael F. 3102 ETON RD 27608 #036-01-1972 L1972 **GS SO** *071 †85

YEAGER, Anne Kathryn. 4420 LAKE BOONE TRL 27607 #035-48-1995 L1997 **IM** *020 †20

YEAKEY, Anne Morton. 9413 KOUPELA DR 27615 #036-08-1986 L1994 **CCP PD** *040 †55

YELLIG, Edward Booth. ■ 27609 #042-10-1969 L1977 **IM P** *071 †20

YERRAMSETTY, Pavan K. 1540 SUNDAY DR 27607 #495-65-1990 L2000 **N PME** *020 †75

YOUNG, Joyce Marie. ■ 27612 #035-20-1981 L1989 **PHP** *030 †70

YOUNG, Thomas Edward. 3000 NEW BERN AVE 27610 #038-43-1979 L1981 **NPM** *040 †55

YOUSSEF, Amal Youssef A. 3400 WAKE FOREST RD, JOHNSTON MEMORIAL HOSPITAL 27609 #915-02-1986 L1995 **IM** *020 †20

ZAATARI, Ahmad Mustafa. ■ 27613 #605-01-1989 **PS** *020

ZARZAR, David Paul. 5711 SIX FORKS RD, ASSOC 27609 #036-01-1993 L1994 **P** *020 †75 ‡

ZARZAR, Michael Nakhleh. 5711 SIX FORKS RD, ASSOC 27609 #036-01-1984 L1985 **P** *020 †75

ZARZAR, Nakhleh Pacifico. 3108 ESSEX CIR 27608 #605-01-1956 L1963 **P** *071 †75

ZARZAR, Nicholas Saleh. 5711 SIX FORKS RD, ASSOC 27609 #036-01-1986 L1988 **P** *020 †75

ZEE, Wendell Jan. 3100 SPRING FOREST RD, STE 130 27616 #019-02-1985 L1989 **AN** *020 †05

ZEITLER, Kenneth Dale. 4420 LAKE BOONE TRL, STE 200 27607 #035-01-1975 L1978 **ON HEM** *020 †20

ZELLINGER, Michael Jay. 3000 NEW BERN AVE 52, SUITE G100 27610 #036-07-1973 L1980 **CD** *020 †20

ZENICK, Robin. 505 OBERLIN RD, STE 204 27605 #035-45-2001 L2003 **PD** *020 †55

ZEOK, John Victor. 3000 NEW BERN AVE 27610 #041-02-1967 L1991 **TS** *020 †85,90

ZEOK, Suzanne Springer. ■ 27615 #041-02-1969 L1981 **AN** *071

ZHAO, Jin. ■ 27604 #243-71-1982 L2006 **PTH** *062 †50

ZIDAR, James Patrick. 3480 WAKE FOREST RD, STE 410 27609 #016-43-1985 L1990 **CD IM** *020 †20

ZIKO, Barbara Clark. 2815 CATES AVE 27695 #036-07-1980 L1981 **EM OS** *020 †16

ZIMMERMAN, Eugenia Fay. 8300 HEALTH PARK STE 109 27615 #051-04-1998 L2006 **PM** *020 †60

ZIMMERMAN, Mark Woodrow. 2417 ATRIUM DR, STE 200 27607 #036-01-1990 L1994
OBG *020 †30
ZINN, Matthias Manfred. 1540 SUNDAY DR, RALEIGH NEUROLOGY 27607 #024-16-2002 L2007
CHN *020
ZIVALICH, Donna Marie. ■ 27615 #021-01-1978 L1996 PD *062 †55
ZORN, Suzanne Jennifer. 5711 SIX FORKS RD STE 207 27609 #041-14-1988 L1993
RHU *020 †20

RAMSEUR – RANDOLPH

SPRY, Heather Marie. 106 WEATHERLY SQ 27316 #036-08-2000 L2002 FM *020 †18 ‡

RANDLEMAN – RANDOLPH

BRADLEY, Betty B. 608 W ACADEMY ST, WHITE OAK URGENT CARE - RA 27317
#036-07-1979 L1980 FM OBS *020 †18
GRIFFIN, Charles C. 27317 #018-03-1946 L1966 GP *072 †85
HOOPER, Jeffrey Curtis. 702 S MAIN ST, RANDLEMAN MEDICAL CENTER 27317
#047-05-1995 L2005 FM *020 †18
KOSSOVER, Stuart Allan. 702 S MAIN ST 27317 #035-09-1990 L1993 IM *020 †20
SMITH, Ronald Dennis. 702 S MAIN ST, RANDLEMAN MEDICAL CENTER 27317
#016-06-1957 L1994 IM NEP *050 †20
WILSON, Amelia Pugh. 670 W ACADEMY ST, ASSOCIATES 27317 #025-12-1991 L2007
FM *020 †18

RED SPRINGS – ROBESON

CHAVIS, Herman. 1002C E 4TH AVE 28377 #036-01-1979 L1980 FM *020 †18
HA, Khie Sem. 229 S MAIN ST 28377 #244-02-1968 L1976 FM *020 †18
JOHNSON, Charles T, Jr. ■ 28377 #041-02-1953 L1953 GP *071
LOCKLEAR, Kenneth Edward. 1002C E 4TH AVE 28377 #036-01-1979 L1980 FM *020 †18
MOORE, Angelita Michelle. ■ 28377 #023-12-2001 FM *020 †18

REIDSVILLE – ROCKINGHAM

BATES, Dwight David. 1107 S MAIN ST 27320 #036-05-2001 L2005 OTO *020 †45
BEFEKADU, Belayenh S. 1352 W HARRISON ST 27320 #035-06-1988 L1995 NEP IM *020 †20
BRADFORD, William Dalton. 617 S MAIN ST 27320 #038-06-1958 L1965 PTH PD *050 †55,50 ‡
BRADFORD, William Strong. 617 S MAIN ST 27320 #308-01-1980 L1985 GS *020
BRADSHER, Ann Torian. 1816 RICHARDSON DR 27320 #056-05-1996 L2002 CD IM *020 †20
CAMPBELL, Leopold George. 618 S MAIN ST 27320 #566-01-1981 L2004 IM *020 †20
CAPOROSSI, Jeffrey Paul. 618 S MAIN ST 27320 #036-05-1991 L2002 EM *020 †16
CARLSON, Donald Patrick. 1818 RICHARDSON DR 27320 #056-05-1987 L1991 OBG *020 †30
COOK, Brian. 618 S MAIN ST 27320 #036-08-1989 L1990 EM FM *020 †18
CRESENZO, Mark Stephen. 1818 RICHARDSON DR, STE A 27320 #036-05-1981 L1987
*020 †20
CRESENZO, Victor M. ■ 27320 #036-05-1943 L1943 CD IM *071 †20
CROSBY, Lewis P. 506 SPRINKLE ST 27320 #020-02-1952 L1953 FM *071
EURE, Luther Haywood, Jr. 520 MAPLE AVE, STE C 27320 #036-05-1989 L2004 OBG *020 †30
FAGAN, Roy Otho, III. 618 S MAIN ST 27320 #045-01-1986 L1989 IM *020 †20
FANTA, Tesfaye Demissie. 910 W HARRISON ST, BOX 2837 27320 #366-01-1985 L1997
IM *020 †20
FERGUSON, John Vaughn. 520 MAPLE AVE STE C, FAMILY TREE OB GYN 27320
#036-01-1979 L1980 OBG EM *020 †30
FITZGERALD, Elizabeth R. 618 S MAIN ST 27320 #036-01-2000 L2006 PD *100
FREEMAN, John Campbell. 618 S MAIN ST 27320 #047-06-1968 L1993 EM IM *020 †20,16
FUSCO, Lawrence John. 1818 RICHARDSON DR, STE A 27320 #008-02-1982 L1997
EM *020 †20,16
GERMAN, Jereliss A N P. 1203 1/2 NORTHUP ST 27320 #047-07-1966 L1970 PD *071
GHIM, Michael Youngshik. 618 S MAIN ST 27320 #012-01-2002 L2005 EM *020 †16
GLICK, David. 618 S MAIN ST 27320 #041-02-1979 L2006 EM OM *020 †20,16
GOLDING, John Cabot, Jr. 1818 RICHARDSON DR, STE A 27320 #036-01-1996 L1999
FM *020 †18
GONZALEZ-CUNI, Luis G. 618 S MAIN ST 27320 #011-02-1983 L1987 AN *020
GUARINO, Joseph Anthony. 217 TURNER DR STE A 27320 #056-04-1986 L1994
OM GPM *020 †70
HALL, John Zachariah, II. 1123 S MAIN ST 27320 #036-01-2003 L2006 IM *020
HARRISON, Stanley Eugene. 27320 #033-05-1991 L1997 ORS OSM *020 †40
HAWKINS, Edward Lee. 406 PIEDMONT ST 27320 #001-02-1977 L1985 IM PUD *020 †20
HIXSON, Pauline Frances. 618 S MAIN ST 27320 #017-20-1975 L1995 EM *020 †18,16
JENKINS, Mark Alan. 1818 RICHARDSON DR STE E 27320 #038-06-1988 L1994 GS *020 †85
KEELING, John Wayne. 601 S MAIN ST 27320 #051-04-1975 L1976 ORS *020 †40
KNAPP, Iva Louise. 618 S MAIN ST 27320 #038-40-1980 L1992 EM *020 †20,16
KNOWLTON, Stephen Dana. 601 W HARRISON ST 27320 #024-07-1978 L1981 FM *020 †18
KOWALSKI, Paul Victor. 516 S MAIN ST 27320 #055-02-1984 L2003 OPH *020 †35
KRISHNAN, Gokul. 618 S MAIN ST, ANNIE PENN HOSPITAL 27320 #495-73-1999 L2006
IM *020 †20
LAWAND, Frank. 618 S MAIN ST 27320 #605-02-1949 L1978 TS GS *020 †05
LEE, James Gary. 1107 S MAIN ST 27320 #018-03-1967 L1975 OTO HNS *071 †45
LUKING, Scott Alfred. 520 MAPLE AVE, STE B 27320 #038-40-1988 L1991 FM *020 †18
LUKING, William Stephen. 520 MAPLE AVE 27320 #038-41-1984 L1990 FM *020 †18
MABE, Paul Alexander, Jr. 618 S MAIN ST 27320 #036-07-1953 L1954 GP *071
MC GOUGH, Wm Marion, Jr. 1818 RICHARDSON DR, STE A 27320 #027-01-1981 L1982
FM EM *020
MC GOWEN, Philip Hanks. 217 TURNER DR STE F, TRIAD MEDICINE & PEDIATRIC 27320
#004-01-2001 L2002 FM *020 †18 ‡
MC INNIS, Angus Guy. 1123 S MAIN ST 27320 #036-07-1957 L1957 FM *020 †18
METZ, Christine Mary. 621 S MAIN ST, STE 201 27320 #035-08-1994 L2006 IM *020 †20
NEIJSTROM, Eric Sherwood. 618 S MAIN ST 27320 #051-01-1976 L1979 ON HEM *020 †20
NEUSTADT, Philip Marc. 618 S MAIN ST, EMERGENCY DEPARTMENT 27320
#023-07-1981 L1999 EM *020

PAYNE, Clifton Gadberry. PO BOX 1857 27323 #036-01-1956 L1956 GP *020 †18
REHMAN, Najeeb Ur. 527 MAPLE AVE, R MICHAEL ROURK MD 27320 #704-04-1978 L1986
GE IM *020 †20
RICHARDSON, George Irvin. 1305 COACH RD BOX 1857 27320 #036-01-1955 L1955 GP *071
ROSEN, Jefry H. 1107 S MAIN ST 27320 #035-47-1992 L1997 OTO *020 †45
ROURK, Robert Michael. ■ 27323 #036-08-1985 L1987 GE IM *020 †20
SENGUPTA, Shari Leann. 730 S SCALES ST STE B 27320 #057-07-2000 L2003 P *020 †75
SHOEMAKER, David Link. 1107 S MAIN ST 27320 #036-07-1990 L1991 OTO *020 †45
SIMPSON, Margaret E. 618 S MAIN ST 27320 #566-01-1987 L1997 FM *020 †18
TRUSLOW, Roy Earl. 27320 #036-05-1945 L1945 R *071 †20
WHITLEY, Robert Riley. 618 S MAIN ST 27320 #036-01-1968 L1968 GP IM *020
WOLICKI, Karol Thaddeus. 1107 S MAIN ST 27320 #051-01-1981 L1986 OTO *020 †45
WOODWARD, Robert Warren. ■ 27320 #016-02-1961 L1982 OBG *071 †30
ZACKOWSKI, Scott Wm. 618 S MAIN ST 27320 #051-07-1984 L2006 EM GP *020 †16

RESEARCH TRIANGLE PARK – DURHAM

BEACH, Kathleen Jo. PO BOX 13398, 5 MOORE DR 27709 #024-16-1989 L1992
EP PHM *062 †20
BEELEN, Andrew Paul. ■ 27709 #035-15-1997 L2003 IM *020 †20
CICALE, Michael Jon. 5 MOORE DR, 17.1330A P.O. BOX 13398 27709 #010-02-1979 L2003
PUD IM *050 †20
IRIZARRY, Michael Carl. 5 MOORE DR, # 17-2123 27709 #010-02-1990 L2006 N IM *020 †75

RICH SQUARE – NORTHAMPTON

NAVARRO, Gilberto Pabalan. 265 S. MAIN STREET, RICH SQUARE MEDICAL CENTER 27869
#748-20-1988 L1996 IM *020 †20

RICHFIELD – ROWAN

PONS, Lara Junine. 137 HIGHWAY 49 N 28137 #036-05-1999 L2000 FM *020 †18

RICHLANDS – ONSLOW

BUGLISI, Lucille Ann. 154 BEULAVILLE HWY, SUN COAST MED 28574 #033-05-1994 L2005
FM *020 †18
DABNEY, Lisa Gene. 8210 RICHLANDS HWY 28574 #051-07-1985 L1996 FM *020 †18
SMITH, Stephanie Marie. ■ 28574 #023-01-2007 FP *012

ROANOKE RAPIDS – HALIFAX

ALFONSO, Gilberto Jorge. 802 CAMBRIDGE CT 27870 #055-01-1987 L1994 AN PME *020 †05
ANDOLE, Vijayalakshmi. PO BOX 1326, RURAL HEALTH GROUP 27870 #495-21-1989 L2005
FM *020
ANTONY, Jose Kandanatt. 306 BECKER DR 27870 #561-17-1978 L1985 IM CD *020 †20
BAKER, Dole Parker, Sr. 115 LONG CIR 27870 #041-02-1965 L2004 OTO *020 †45 ‡
BALLA, Somasekhara Raju. 270 SMITH CHURCH RD 27870 #495-11-1971 L2000
IM CD *020 †20
BALLOU, Karen Rene. 220 SMITH CHURCH RD 27870 #051-04-1983 L1988 CHP P *020 †75
BERNARDO, Danilo Reyes. 937 GREGORY DR 27870 #748-08-1978 L1988 NEP IM *020 †20
BERNARDO, Imelda B. ■ 27870 #748-08-1981 L1985 *075
BISSRAM, Ganesh. 130 CARDINAL DR 27870 #566-01-1972 L1981 ORS *020 †40
BONE, Leslie Ann. ■ 27870 #010-01-2008 *012
BOONE, John W, Jr. 120 PROFESSIONAL DR 27870 #036-05-1951 L1951 GPM OTO *071 †18
BROWN, Darrell James, Jr. 63 OFFICE PARK DR, SMITH CHURCH OBSTETRICS & 27870
#422-01-1988 L2007 OBG *020 †30
BUTCHER, Elizabeth Anne. ■ 27870 #055-01-1999 L2004 IM *020
BYRD, William Eugene. 1724 E 10TH ST 27870 #036-01-1970 L1970 RHU IM *020 †20
CACERES, Marco Antonio. 1108 DRAKE ST 27870 #451-01-1963 L1974 GS TS *020 †85
CHAPARRO, Abrahan. 1385 MEDICAL CENTER DR, ROANOKE CLINIC 27870
#264-01-1993 L2006 FM *020 †18 ‡
CHAUDHRY, Hashmat Ali. 608 JACKSON ST 27870 #704-04-1969 L1983 OPH GP *020 †35
CHETTY, Wilbert L. 244 SMITH CHURCH RD STE D 27870 #010-03-1984 L1987 IM *020 †20
COATH, Gwennaye Cherie. ■ 27870 #045-01-2004 L2007 FM *020 †18
COOPER, William C, Jr. 1261 JULIAN R ALLSBROK HWY, PRIMECARE MEDICAL CENTER 27870
#036-07-1960 L1960 PD *055
DAVIS, Frank Elbert. ■ 27870 #036-01-1973 L1973 GS TS *071 †85
DONTHI, Badriprasad. 915 PARK AVE, ROANOKE VALLEY PEDS 27870 #495-99-1991 L1998
PD *020 †55
EDWARDS, Carl Leon. ■ 27870 #422-01-1984 L1989 CD IM *020
FIORILLI, Mario G. 270 SMITH CHURCH RD 27870 #561-23-1971 L1975 IM ID *075 †20 ‡
FLEMING, George Edward. 250 SMITH CHURCH RD 27870 #041-02-1964 L1971 AN *020 †05
GELOO, Nadim Ahmad. 250 SMITH CHURCH RD, P O BOX 1089 27870 #051-04-1994 L1998
CD *020 †20
GLYNN, Edward Ivan. 1835 MEDICAL CENTER DRIVE 27870 #051-07-1999 L2002 FM *020 †18
GREGORY, Miles Cunningham. ■ 27870 #036-07-1959 L1959 PD *071
GUPTA, Kamlesh. 250 SMITH CHURCH RD, HALIFAX REGIONAL MEDICAL C 27870
#495-08-1967 L1982 GP PTH *020 †50
HENDRIX, Robert Andrew. 215 SMITH CHURCH RD 27870 #020-12-1978 L1992
OTO HNS *020 †45
HIMELSTEIN, Samuel Carl. 204 BECKER DR, 2 27870 #035-08-1965 L1991 OPH *020 †35
HOLM, Richard Philip. 244 SMITH CHURCH RD STE C 27870 #054-04-1979 L2004
ORS *020 †40
INGRAM, Paulette Keith. 529 BECKER DR 27870 #036-01-1982 L1984 PD ADL *020 †55
JACK, Jonathan Juturu. 270 SMITH CHURCH RD 27870 #495-70-1980 L1997 IM *020 †20
KETOFF, James Arnold. 97 NC HIGHWAY 125 27870 #018-03-1991 L2006 GS *020 †85
KIDIYOOR, Soumya Krishnam. ■ 27870 #495-98-2003 L2006 IM *012
MAMEDI, Ravinder. 321 NC HIGHWAY 125 27870 #495-21-1989 L1998 P PYG *020
MANICKAM, Natarajan. 270 SMITH CHURCH RD 27870 #495-42-1976 L1988 CD IM *020 †20

MARADIAGA, Gerardo M. 270 SMITH CHURCH RD 27870 #451-01-1982 L1995 **IM** *020 †20
MC CALEB, Jane Harvey. 250 SMITH CHURCH RD 27870 #028-03-1976 L1979 **FM** *020 †18
MC DONALD, Thomas Joseph. 1381 MEDICAL CENTER DR 27870 #047-20-1993 L1995 **OBG** *020 †30
MILLER, Isaac Henry. 270 SMITH CHURCH RD 27870, HALIFAX MEDICAL SPECIALIST 27870 #047-07-1983 L1988 **IM** *020
MINIELLY, Richard Wesley. 63 OFFICE PARK DR 27870 #065-06-1974 L1992 **OBS GYN** *020 †30
MOSS, John Simpson. 244 SMITH CHURCH RD STE C, NORTHERN CAROLINA ORTHOPED 27870 #051-04-1979 L2007 **ORS OSM** *020 †40
MYERS, John Jay. 120 PROFESSIONAL DR 27870 #041-13-1997 L2000 **FM** *020 †18 ‡
PANDARINATH, Gupta S. 270 SMITH CHURCH RD 27870 #495-33-1972 L1978 **GE IM** *020 †20 ‡
PATEL, Mahendra. 270 SMITH CHURCH RD, SPECIALISTS, PA 27870 #495-23-1976 L1983 **HO IM** *020 †20
PATEL, Nilpesh Mahesh. ■ 27870 #036-01-2004 **ORS** *012
PIGGOTT, Bert Cody, Jr. 19 E 11TH ST 27870 #036-01-1985 L1986 **DR** *020 †80
PINE, Harold Scott. 215 SMITH CHURCH RD 27870 #016-01-1995 L2001 **OTO** *020 †45
PRASAD, Degala Ramamohana. 105 W BECKER DR 27870 #495-50-1969 L1986 **P** *020 †75
PUTHENVEETIL, John Varkey. 306 BECKER DR, TWIN CITY INTERNAL MED & C 27870 #495-33-1963 L1971 **CD IM** *020 †20
RAJAN, Natarajan. 117 PROFESSIONAL DR, SAI UROLOGY, PA 27870 #495-42-1987 L1998 **U** *020 †95
RAO, Shiva Kumar. 40 ANNA LOUISE LN 27870 #495-35-1972 L1994 **GS GP** *020 †85
ROBERT, Kenneth Mark. 1385 MEDICAL CENTER DR 27870 #041-15-2000 L2003 **FM** *020 †18
ROBERTS, Tisa Ochelle. 1385 MEDICAL CENTER DR 27870 #007-02-2003 L2006 **FM** *100 †18
SAMPAT, Smita N. 270 SMITH CHURCH RD 27870 #495-65-1983 L2007 **IM IMG** *020 †20 ‡
SANTARINA, Lorenzo B, III. 937 GREGORY DR 27870 #748-01-1988 L2001 **IM NEP** *020 †20
SEKARAN, Meena. 270 SMITH CHURCH RD, HALISAX MEDICAL SPECIALIST 27870 #495-50-1980 L1989 **FPG** *020 †20
SEKARAN, Narayanachar C. 270 SMITH CHURCH RD 27870 #495-42-1975 L1989 **PUD** *020 †20
SHAKIR, Mohamad A.. ■ 27870 #528-02-1986 L2007 **FP** *012
SHEA, Richard Paul, Jr. 1381 MEDICAL CENTER DR 27870 #036-01-1991 L2006 **OBG** *020 †30
SINGER, Lawrence David. 1381 MEDICAL CENTER DR 27870 #038-06-2001 L2005 **OBG** *020
THANNIKKARY, Chanchamma A. 250 SMITH CHURCH RD 27870 #495-70-1972 L1987 **RO** *020 †80
THOMAS, Joey P. 250 SMITH CHURCH RD 27870 #495-44-1982 L1995 **AN** *020 †20,05
TIWARI, Sandeep Kumar. 2066 NC HIGHWAY 125 27870 #495-47-1995 L2003 **PD** *020 †55
VALLIANI, Maqsood Akbar A. ■ 27870 #704-16-1990 L2001 **PD AI** *020
WESTOVER, Edward Wm. 250 SMITH CHURCH RD, HALIFAX REGIONAL MEDICAL C 27870 #060-01-1983 L1991 **EM** *020 †20
WHITE, Matthew Stedman. ■ 27870 #036-05-2008 *012
WIER, Fred Eugene. 244 SMITH CHURCH RD, STE B 27870 #005-12-1974 L1979 **GS** *020
WILLIAMS, Dwight Morrison. 250 SMITH CHURCH RD 27870 #036-01-1982 L2008 **OBG** *075
WILLIAMSON, Charles E, Jr. 250 SMITH CHURCH RD, HALIFAX REGIONAL MEDICAL C 27870 #051-04-1983 L1990 **ORS** *020 †20
WILSON, Lauralee. ■ 27870 #041-14-1997 L2000 **FM** *020 †18 ‡
YERRA, Nagarjuna. 1007 GREGORY DR 27870 #495-65-1982 L1997 **GE MPD** *020 †20

ROARING GAP – ALLEGHANY

GRIFFIN, Wm Russell, Jr. ■ 28668 #036-05-1964 L1964 **ORS** *071 †40

ROBBINS – MOORE

BELL, William Lee. 300 S MIDDLETON ST 27325 #036-01-1978 L1979 **FM** *020 †18

ROBBINSVILLE – GRAHAM

CUSHMAN, Robert Gale. ■ 28771 #036-05-1946 L1947 **IM** *071 †20
JOHNSON, Patricia June. 409 TALLULAH RD, TALLULAH HEATLH CTR 28771 #001-02-1975 L1977 **GP** *020
KINDLEY, Robert Thos. 496 HOLLOWAY RD 28771 #036-01-1965 L1965 **PDA PD** *020 †55,03
LYNCH, Kathryn Jo. 409 TALLULAH RD 28771 #036-07-1995 L1996 **FM** *020 †18
QUENG, Joan Aimee. 409 TALLULAH RD 28771 #048-14-1996 L1997 **FM** *020
STEPHENS, James Edward. ■ 28771 #051-04-1960 L1961 **GP** *071

ROBERSONVILLE – PITT

GENNOSA, Thomas Joseph. 504 N MAIN ST, ROBERSONVILLE PHYSICIANS, 27871 #035-06-1996 L1999 **FM** *020 †18

ROCKINGHAM – RICHMOND

AARONS, Mark Gold. 115 MALLARD LN 28379 #048-04-1984 L2007 **NEP IM** *062 †20
ADDY, Douglas Michael. 110 MEDICAL CIR 28379 #045-01-1998 L2002 **OBG** *020 †30
AHDIEH, Masoud. 925 S LONG DR 28379 #517-03-1972 L1980 **PD OS** *020 ‡
ARENAS, Gilbert Domingo. 119 MEDICAL CIR 28379 #748-01-1978 L1992 **FM** *020
ASKARY, Nasser A. 921 S LONG DR, STE 104 28379 #517-07-1966 L1973 **OBG** *020 †30
BERK, Carl Warren. 109 PHYSICIANS PARK DR 28379 #003-01-1989 L1994 **OTO** *020 †45
CAMARGO-MIRANDA, Johnny E. 115 MALLARD LN 28379 #176-01-1980 L1991 **IM** *020 †20
CLONINGER, Giles Lathern. 925 S LONG DR 28379 #036-05-1954 L1954 **FM** *071
COVINGTON, Alpheus M. 303 LEAK ST 28379 #036-07-1950 L1952 **GS** *071
DANIEL, James Keith. 921 S LONG DR STE 101, MEDICINE 28379 #047-07-2001 L2006 **FM** *020 †20
ECHOLS, Everett R, Jr. ■ 28379 #047-07-1981 L1995 **P EM** *075
EGBE, Patrick Eyaye. 1219 ROCKINGHAM RD, STE 7 28379 #690-06-1991 L2006 **PD** *020 †55
EL-DROUBI, Hazem M K H. 111 MALLARD LN 28379 #915-04-1969 L2006 **U** *020 †95
FLANNERY, John Edward, Jr. 115 MALLARD LN 28379 #048-02-1980 L1983 **IM GP** *020 †20
FLEURY, Robert Andre. 109 MEDICAL CIR 28379 #036-05-1977 L1982 **P FM** *020 †75
FRANCIS, Sabina Petra. 921 S LONG DR, STE 203 28379 #005-06-1997 L2007 **OTO** *020 †45

HADLEY, Lanny Carroll. 921 S LONG DR, STE 207 28379 #005-12-1977 L2003 **OBG** *020 †30
HAJI SHEIKH, Moosa. ■ 28379 #517-01-1959 L1973 **IM CD** *071
HALL, Daniel Crawford. 104 PHYSICIANS PARK DR 28379 #036-05-1976 1976 **FM** *020 †18
HARVEY, Henry L, Jr. 110 S HANCOCK ST STE 200, SANDHILLS CHILDRENS DEVEL 28379 #036-05-1982 L1984 **PD** *020 †55
HASENMUELLER, Kirk Robt. 308 S LAWRENCE ST 28379 #038-43-1992 L1996 **FM** *020 †18
JOHNSON, Howard Mason, Jr. 921 S LONG DR, STE 101 28379 #001-02-1986 L1995 **FM** *020 †18
KHAN, Shamsul A. 1219 ROCKINGHAM RD STE 3 28379 #160-02-1981 L1996 **PD** *020
KHOSHNEVIS, Parviz. 921 S LONG DR, STE 202 28379 #517-05-1966 L1984 **OBG** *072
KURDI, Mostafa. 125 BILTMORE DR, STE 1 28379 #875-01-1993 L2006 **CCM** *020 †20 ‡
MIDDLETON, Patricia L. 921 S LONG DR, STE 207 28379 #517-08-1981 L1985 **OBG** *020 †30
MOHAMED, Mohamed Hassan M. 711 S LONG DR 28379 #848-01-1987 L2005 **PD** *020 †20
MOHAMMED, Amir M. 125 BILTMORE DR, STE 2 28379 #528-01-1982 L1995 **IM** *020 †20
PARRIS, Robert C. 106 PHYSICIANS PARK DR, SANDHILLS CARDIOLOGY, PC 28379 #566-01-1985 L2004 **CD** *020 †20
PATEL, Shilpesh Pramod. 115 MALLARD LN 28379 #495-33-1986 L1997 **IM** *020 †20
ROBES, Cecile Theresa. 921 S LONG DR STE 101, MEDICINE 28379 #025-76-1992, ▲ L2003 **FM** *020
RUCK, David Carl. 109 MEDICAL CIR 28379 #036-07-1979 L1994 **CHP P** *020 †75
SCOTT, Legrand T, Jr. ■ 28379 #045-01-1963 L1967 **GP** *071
SIDDIQUI, Adeel Mohammad. 115 MALLARD LN 28379 #024-05-1994 L2000 **IM** *020 †20
SNYDER, Mark P. 109 MEDICAL CIR 28379 #016-11-1998 L1999 **P** *020 †75
STROM, David Edward. 109 PHYSICIANS PARK DR 28379 #025-07-1983 L2002 **ORS** *020 †40
SWANSON, Charlie Lebron. 109 MEDICAL CIR 28379 #017-20-1991 L1993 **P** *020 †75
TAMAKLOE, Gilbert Tetteh. 109 MEDICAL CIR 28379 #275-01-1988 L2003 **P** *020 †75
VETTER, John Stanley. 921 S LONG DR STE 101 28379 #036-07-1954 L1956 **FM** *020 †18
WELLS, David Morelle. 129 FAIRWAY DR 28379 #027-01-1967 L1977 **DR** *020 †80
WELLS, Wendell D A, Jr. 921 E BROAD AVE 28379 #036-01-1979 L1982 **FM** *020 ‡
ZEIDAN, Zeidan Fadel. 921 S LONG DR, STE 206 28379 #915-08-1972 L1995 **GS** *050 †85

ROCKWELL – ROWAN

CERVIN, James R. ■ 28138 #048-02-1988 L1993 **PCP** *020 †50
CHOTINER, Bradley Scott. 316 E MAIN ST 28138 #031-01-1998 L2001 **FM** *020 †18
LAMM, Leroy Barden. ■ 28138 #036-05-1946 L1946 **P ADM** *071 †75
OLIVER, Joseph Andrew, III. 307 E MAIN ST, BOX 1060 28138 #422-01-1987 L1995 **FM** *020 †18
SMITH, Douglas Graham. ■ 28138 #036-01-1988 L1992 **P** *020 †75

ROCKY MOUNT – EDGECOMBE

NICHOLSON-WILSON, M. 111 S FAIRVIEW RD, ROCKY MOUNT OIC FAMILY MED 27801 #038-43-1991 L1994 **FM** *020 †18
RASSEKH, Ezzatollah. EDGECOMBE NASH, MH/DD/SA SERVICES 27801 #517-01-1942 L1969 **P** *071
WILSON, Theodore Edward. 111 S FAIRVIEW RD, ROCKY MOUNT OIC FAMILY MED 27801 #038-43-1991 L1994 **FM** *020 †18

ROCKY MOUNT – NASH

ABEL, Mark Steven. 804 ENGLISH RD, STE 100 27804 #017-20-1980 L1994 **FM** *020 †18
ADAMS, Kenneth R. 901 N WINSTEAD AVE, BOICE-WILLIS CLINIC 27804 #048-13-1994 L1997 **IM** *020 †20
ADKINS, Neal Ashley. 132 FOY DR, ROCKY MOUNT GYNECOLOGY 27804 #036-01-1972 L1972 **OBG EM** *020 †30
ANDERSON, Mark W. 901 N WINSTEAD AVE 27804 #048-12-1990 L2004 **GE** *020 †20
ANDRACCHIO, Vincent Chas. 3709 WESTRIDGE CIRCLE DR 27804 #041-02-1956 L1964 **AN** *071 †05
ATTIA, Raafat Ismail R. 804 ENGLISH RD, STE 100 27804 #915-04-1984 L2004 **IM** *020 †20
AVENT, John Thos. 1041 NOELL LN, STE 102 27804 #047-07-1968 L1975 **OBG** *071 †30
BAGGETT, Henry Clifford. 804 ENGLISH RD, STE 200 27804 #036-01-1970 L1970 **OTO** *071 †45
BAILEY, George Tillman, III. ■ 27804 #036-01-1981 L1982 **DR** *020 †80
BAILEY, Harold Albert. 100 NASH MEDICAL ARTS MALL 27804 #047-07-1979 L1982 **PD** *020 †55
BAILEY, Lloyd W. 3044 SUNSET AVE 27804 #041-02-1953 L1953 **OPH** *071
BALES, Donald W, Jr. 1051 COUNTRY CLUB DR 27804 #047-06-1982 L1985 **IM** *020 †20
BALIGA, Vasanth Bantwal. 100 NASH MEDICAL ARTS MALL 27804 #495-37-1981 L2001 **PD** *020 †55
BANKS-JACKSON, Roslyn C. 804 ENGLISH RD, STE 210 27804 #005-19-1998 L2005 **OBG** *020 †30
BASSETT-SHAFTOE, Linda A. 901 N WINSTEAD AVE 27804 #043-01-1988 L1995 **IM** *020 †20
BAULE, Raymond Michael. 4056 CAPITAL DR 27804 #035-47-1992 L2004 **NS** *100
BELLOFIORE-PLONSKI, Lisa. 901 N WINSTEAD AVE, BOX 7200 27804 #050-02-2004 L2007 **PD** *020 †55
BERNAT, Mark Andrew. PO BOX 8589 27804 #017-20-1986 L1994 **EM FM** *020 †18
BLOEM, Josephus Th. 3101 ZEBULON RD 27804 #660-03-1974 L1980 **ORS LM** *020
BOWEN, James Wm. 2460 CURTIS ELLIS DR 27804 #036-05-1986 L1990 **AN** *020 †05
BOWMAN, Jenee Lee. 1041 NOELL LN, STE 105 27804 #038-40-1992 L2002 **PUD** *020 †20
BOYETTE, Douglas Dewitt. 200 NASH MEDICAL ARTS MALL 27804 #036-08-1983 L1984 **OBG** *020 †30
BRANTLEY, David Spencer. 100 NASH MEDICAL ARTS MALL 27804 #023-12-1986 L1988 **PD UM** *020 †55
BRANTLEY, Julian C, Jr. ■ 27804 #041-02-1944 L1944 **GYN** *071 †30
BRANTLEY, Julian C, III. 132 FOY DR, ROCKY MOUNT GYNECOLOGY 27804 #036-01-1975 L1977 **OBG** *020 †30
BROWDER, David Allen. 600 NASH MEDICAL ARTS MALL, BOICE WILLIS CLINIC P.A. 27804 #036-01-1993 L1996 **FM** *020
BROWDER, Lesley Burkhead. 2460 CURTIS ELLIS DR 27804 #036-01-1993 L1996 **EM** *020 †16
BULLARD, Ingrid Michelle. 200 NASH MEDICAL ARTS MALL 27804 #036-08-2000 L2004 **OBG** *020 ‡
BUNTING, Douglas L, Jr. 901 N WINSTEAD AVE, BOICE WILLIS CLINIC 27804 #036-08-1994 L1995 **NEP IM** *020 †20

■ = Address Information Privacy Protected

BURKE, Tamara Francisco. ■ 27803 #016-11-1991 L1995 **EM** *100 †16
CAPPS, Gerald Wayne. 1031 NOELL LN 27804 #051-04-1992 L1999 **DR** *020 †80
CARROLL, William W. ■ 27804 #038-06-1953 L1974 **OPH** *071 †35
CASTILLOS, Francisco A. 1041 NOELL LN, STE 105 27804 #016-42-1995 L2004 **HO** *020 †20
CHAMBERLAIN, Matthew Paul. 600 NASH MEDICAL ARTS MALL, BOICE WILLIS CLINIC, PA 27804 #036-08-1990 L1992 **IM** *020 †20
CHESNUTT, Martha Johnston. 600 NASH MEDICAL ARTS MALL 27804 #036-08-2000 L2003 **IM** *020 †20 ‡
CHURCH, Susan Lynne. 100 NASH MEDICAL ARTS MALL 27804 #067-01-1982 L1985 **NPM** *050 †55
COCKRELL, Renee T. 141 STORAGE RD 27804 #056-05-1989 L1992 **PD** *030 †55
COLLINS, Matthew Till. 200 NASH MEDICAL ARTS MALL 27804 #036-01-1998 L2002 **OBG** *020 †30
COVINGTON, Alfred J, Jr. 124 FOY DR, SPECIALTY GROUP PA 27804 #023-07-1986 L1995 **AI IM** *020 †20,03
CRAWFORD, Michael Dillon. 2460 CURTIS ELLIS DR 27804 #055-01-1981 L1987 **OTO HNS** *020 †45
CRESTETTO, John Max. 901 N WINSTEAD AVE, STE 130 27804 #048-12-1994 L1997 **OS** *020
CROCKER, Daniel Lind. 1041 NOELL LN, STE 105 27804 #036-01-1970 L1970 **IM ON** *020 †20
DANAHY, Mark Steven. 2460 CURTIS ELLIS DR 27804 #026-04-2003 L2006 **EM** *020 †16
DAUDA, Mohamed Sheku. 1041 NOELL LN, STE 105 27804 #823-01-1998 L2007 **FM** *020 †18
DEANS, William Ronald. 901 N WINSTEAD AVE 27804 #048-02-1977 L1981 **N** *020 †75
DENGLER, William C, Jr. 800 TIFFANY BLVD, STE 211 27804 #051-04-1983 L1988 **GS** *020 †85
DERBYSHIRE, John Stuart. 1051 COUNTRY CLUB DR 27804 #038-40-1971 L1976 **IM** *020 †20
DONER, Mark. 901 N WINSTEAD AVE, BOICE-WILLIS CLINIC 27804 #024-05-1984 L1993 **IM PCC** *020 †20
ECKERT, David Wm. 2460 CURTIS ELLIS DR 27804 #025-01-1972 L2000 **PTH** *020 †50
ELLWANGER, Frederick, III. 109 SOUTHWICK CT 27804 #036-07-1968 L1973 **RO PD** *020 †55,80
ENGSTROM, Lincoln Loring. 2460 CURTIS ELLIS DR, NASH GENERAL HOSPITAL 27804 #036-05-1961 L1961 **R** *020 †80 ‡
FEDOR, Lubica. 500 NASH MEDICAL ARTS MALL, EDGECOMBE NASH MENTAL HLTH 27804 #286-03-1965 L1991 **P** *020
FRITZ, Richard Thos. 1031 NOELL LN 27804 #036-01-1976 L1980 **DR** *020 †80
FROHBOSE, Frederick A. 180 FOY DR 27804 #036-01-1989 L1994 **U** *020 †95
FROHBOSE, William Jos. ■ 27803 #051-04-1943 L1953 **U OS** *071 †95
FRYAR, Mel Webster. 132 FOY DR, ROCK MOUNT OB/GYN ASSOCIAT 27804 #036-05-1981 L1984 **OBG** *020 †30
GERLACH, Stephan Oscar. 106 NASH MEDICAL ARTS MALL, 3747 KIMBERLY JO DRIVE 27804 #016-01-1984 L1998 **EM** *020 †16
GIBSON, Leonard H, Jr. 901 N WINSTEAD AVE, IMAGING DEPARTMENT 27804 #036-08-1993 L1998 **DR** *020 †80
GLICKMAN, Seth William. 106 NASH MEDICAL ARTS MALL, SEACS 27804 #041-01-2000 L2003 **EM** *020
GLYNNE, Rose Kindy. 804 ENGLISH RD, STE 210 27804 #024-07-1988 L1993 **OBG** *020 †30
GOLD, Benjamin Miller. ■ 27804 #023-01-1947 L1947 **OBG** *071 †30
GONZALEZ, Manuel Alejandr. ■ 27803 #275-03-1995 L2006 **CD** *012 †20
GORBY, David R. 2460 CURTIS ELLIS DR, NASH GENERAL HOSPITAL 27804 #033-06-1981 L1997 **FM MDM** *030 †18
GRANT, Henry Boone. 416 HICKORY ST 27804 #036-07-1940 L1945 **PD** *072 †55
GRANT, James Wm. 100 NASH MEDICAL ARTS MALL 27804 #036-07-1979 L1983 **PDC** *020 †55
GREENE, Jama Bland. 901 N WINSTEAD AVE, BOICE-WILLIS CLINIC 27804 #036-01-1987 L1991 **IM** *071 †20
GUARINO, Rosario. 2460 CURTIS ELLIS DR, MEDICAL AFFAIRS OFFICE 27804 #033-06-1981 L1990 **N** *020 †75
GUILFOYLE, William M, Jr. 551 N WINSTEAD AVE, POST OFFICE BIX 421 27804 #010-02-1974 L1997 **EM** *020
HARDEN, William Boyd. 2460 CURTIS ELLIS DR, NASH HOSP EAGLE HOSPLTST 27804 #036-01-1976 L1976 **IM** *020 †20
HAREWOOD, Adrian Lashone. ■ 27804 #036-08-2005 **GS** *100
HARRIS, Tommy Ray. 140 N ENGLEWOOD DR, BOX 7695 27804 #036-01-1982 L1989 **OBG** *020
HARRISON, Walter Douglas. 901 N WINSTEAD AVE, P O BOX 7200 27804 #001-02-1985 L1991 **GS VS** *020 †85
HART, Jennifer Meade. 804 ENGLISH RD, STE 100 27804 #051-04-2000 L2004 **FM** *020 †18
HART, John Joseph. 804 ENGLISH RD, STE 100 27804 #010-02-2000 L2003 **FM** *020 †18 ‡
HAWES, M Linda. 901 N WINSTEAD AVE 27804 #036-01-1980 L1982 **NEP IM** *020 †20
HIGH, Larry Allison. 132 FOY DR, ROCKY MOUNT GYNECOLOGY 27804 #036-01-1972 L1972 **OBG** *020 †30
HOLLAND, Michael Day. 901 N WINSTEAD AVE, ROCKY MOUNT MEDICAL PARK 27804 #036-01-1978 L1979 **IM NEP** *020 †20
HOOD, James Martin. 600 NASH MEDICAL ARTS MALL 27804 #036-01-1986 L1987 **IM** *020 †20
HUFFMAN, John Christian. 901 N WINSTEAD AVE 27804 #036-01-1985 L1990 **IM ON** *020 †20
HUGHES, Ronald Eugene. 2460 CURTIS ELLIS DR 27804 #036-01-1978 L1981 **FM OM** *020 †18
INTINI, Ronald Saml. 2305 CREEKRIDGE DR 27804 #308-07-1983 L2001 **FM** *020 †18
JARVIS, Bennie Lea. 804 ENGLISH RD, STE 200 27804 #036-01-1985 L1990 **OTO GS** *020 †45
JENKINS, Stanleigh E, Jr. 804 ENGLISH RD, STE 100 27804 #036-01-1966 L1966 **GP** *020 †18
JOHNSON, Allen Mckenzie. 1031 NOELL LN 27804 #036-05-1989 L1999 **DR VIR** *020 †80
JOHNSON, Clanford Lyonel. 921 N WINSTEAD AVE 27804 #001-06-2001 L2004 **FM** *020 †18
JOHNSON, Kim Edward. 2460 CURTIS ELLIS DR 27804 #020-12-1984 L1987 **AN** *020 †05
JONES, William Robt. 900 SUNSET AVE 27804 #036-05-1947 L1948 **GP** *071
KEEN, Susan Kelly. 2460 CURTIS ELLIS DR 27804 #036-08-2003 L2005 **FM** *020 †18
KINNAIRD, Paul Mckee, Jr. 100 NASH MEDICAL ARTS MALL 27804 #020-02-1976 L1981 **PD** *020 †55
KORNEGAY, Lemuel W, Jr. ■ 27803 #036-07-1943 L1943 **GP** *020
KORNEGAY, Raymond D. 1041 NOELL LN 27804 #036-05-1945 L1945 **TS OS** *071 †85,90
KRONCKE, Frederick G, Jr. 200 NASH MEDICAL ARTS MALL 27804 #036-01-1970 L1970 **OBG** *020 †30
KUMAR, Kamlesh. 108 N ENGLEWOOD DR 27804 #495-41-1963 L1972 **PUD IM** *020
KUMAR, Satish Kumar. 108 N ENGLEWOOD DR 27804 #495-36-1962 L1972 **IM PUD** *020
LADWIG, Stephen Harold. 1031 NOELL LN 27804 #016-06-1972 L1978 **DR** *020 †80
LAING, Valerie. 6124 HAYWOOD DR 27803 #011-03-1988 L1990 **DS D** *020 †15
LASZEWSKI, Marzena Teresa. 1051 COUNTRY CLUB DR 27804 #024-05-1987 L1996 **IM EM** *020 †20
LAWRENCE-RAWLS, Stacey Mi. 2301 MEDPARK DR 27804 #036-01-2002 L2006 **P** *020
LOBAO, Celso Benedito. 2301 MEDPARK DR 27804 #025-12-1986 L1992 **P** *020 †75
MAAS, Sabine Mathilde. ■ 27804 #036-08-1996 L1997 **FM** *020 †18
MACAULAY, Robert Jos, Jr. 2460 CURTIS ELLIS DR 27804 #010-01-1956 L1960 **U** *071 †95
MACEDO, Nelson T L De. 2416 PROFESSIONAL DR 27804 #187-14-1973 L1987 **NS** *075 †25
MAH'MOUD, Mohammed A. 901 N WINSTEAD AVE, BOICE-WILLIS CLINIC 27804 #690-01-1989 L1997 **GE** *020 †20
MANLY, Julie Elder. 2460 CURTIS ELLIS DR 27804 #020-02-1999 L2006 **EM** *020
MARSIGLI, Adolfo Hector. 110 NASH MEDICAL ARTS MALL 27804 #132-01-1968 L1973 **ORS HS** *020 †40
MARSIGLI, Eduardo Oscar. 3068 SUNSET AVE 27804 #132-01-1968 L1974 **ORS** *020 †40
MARTIN, Willis Elwood. 3136 SUNSET AVE 27804 #036-01-1974 L1974 **D IM** *020 †15
MARTINEZ, Lucas. PO BOX 7546 27804 #847-04-1968 L1980 **NS** *020 †25
MARTING, Richard Edwin. 141 STORAGE RD, CDSA 27804 #020-12-1974 L1996 **PD OS** *020 †55
MASSAQUOI, Alfred Lamin. ■ 27803 #010-03-1979 L1984 **OBG EM** *020 †30
MATHES, Gordon L, Jr. 180 FOY DR 27804 #047-06-1976 L1983 **U** *020 †95
MC AULIFFE, John Edward. 2460 CURTIS ELLIS DR 27804 #005-19-1979 L1980 **AN** *020
MC AVOY, Greig Vincent. 220 NASH MEDICAL ARTS MALL 27804 #060-02-1989 L1995 **ORS** *020 †40 ‡
MCLEAN, Jennifer. ■ 27803 #010-01-2002 L2005 **FM** *020 †18
META, David Louis. 901 N WINSTEAD AVE 27804 #041-12-1993 L2007 **HO IM** *020 †20
MICHAL, Richard Glenn. 804 ENGLISH RD, STE 100 27804 #036-07-1980 L1983 **FM** *020 †18
MOHINDROO, Krishan Kumar. 2460 CURTIS ELLIS DR 27804 #308-13-2001 L2006 **FM** *020 †18
MOORE, Kenneth Earl. 2460 CURTIS ELLIS DR 27804 #028-02-1983 L1998 **IM PD** *020 †20,55
MORGAN, Benjamin Edward. 200 NASH MEDICAL ARTS MALL, NASH OB-GYN ASSOCIATES PA 27804 #036-05-1947 L1948 **GYN** *071 †30
MULLER, Peter. 901 N WINSTEAD AVE, P O BOX 7200 27804 #041-01-1980 L1990 **GS** *020 †85
MUSULIN, Matthew Michael. 901 N WINSTEAD AVE 27804 #020-12-2002 L2007 **CN** *020 †75
NELSON, James Gregory. 220 NASH MEDICAL ARTS MALL 27804 #036-08-1986 L1991 **ORS** *020 †40
NELSON-ROBINSON, Lisa C. 901 N WINSTEAD AVE 27804 #008-01-1985 L1993 **GS VS** *020 †85
NICHOLSON, James E, III. 2460 CURTIS ELLIS DR 27804 #036-01-1978 L1979 **EM FM** *020 †18
ORR, Jennifer Wells. 200 NASH MEDICAL ARTS MALL, NASH OB/GYN 27804 #051-04-1993 L1997 **OBG** *020 †30
OVERTON, Dolphin H. 132 FOY DR 27804 #036-07-1953 L1961 **OBG** *020 †30
OVERTON, Dolphin H, III. 2460 CURTIS ELLIS DR 27804 #036-08-1984 L1990 **CD IM** *020 †20
PAJEAU, Aurora Keith. 901 N WINSTEAD AVE 27804 #048-15-1986 L2002 **N IM** *020 †75
PARK, Frederick Kim. 4008 CAPITAL DR 27804 #016-11-1987 L1993 **PS** *020 †65
PARKER, Holly Howard. 804 ENGLISH RD, STE 100 27804 #036-08-1999 L2003 **FM** *020 †18
PARKER, John Ashley. 804 ENGLISH RD, STE 100 27804 #036-08-2000 L2003 **FM** *020 †18
PATE, Robert Mark. 1041 NOELL LN STE 103 27804 #048-12-1976 L1996 **GS GE** *020 †85
PATRONE, Nicholas A. 901 N WINSTEAD AVE 27804 #016-43-1976 L1977 **RHU IM** *020 †20 ‡
PAYNE, Fred W, Jr. 100 NASH MEDICAL ARTS MALL 27804 #047-05-1953 L1961 **GS** *071 †85
PEACOCK, Ivan Yopp. 1031 NOELL LN 27804 #023-12-1981 L1984 **DR GP** *020 †80
PERRY, Samuel Jos. 804 ENGLISH RD STE 100 27804 #036-05-1988 L1993 **FM** *020 †18
PETRUS, Christopher David. 180 FOY DR, ROCKY MOUNT UROLOGY 27804 #021-06-1996 L2001 **U** *020 †95
PITTMAN, William Bryan. 901 N WINSTEAD AVE 27804 #036-01-1971 L1976 **GE IM** *020 †20
PRASADA, Sudhir. 901 N WINSTEAD AVE, ROCKY MOUNT MEDICAL PARK 27804 #496-06-1980 L1993 **IM CD** *020 †20
PROCTOR, Camilla Allyn. 3009 ZEBULON RD 27804 #036-01-1968 L1968 **IM PUD** *020 †20
PUTMAN, Shawn Christopher. 3044 SUNSET AVE 27804 #036-06-1992 L1996 **OPH** *020 †35
RABIL, Donald Michael. 901 N WINSTEAD AVE 27804 #036-08-1983 L1984 **PUD IM** *020 †20
RAMSEY, Edward Allison. 100 NASH MEDICAL ARTS MALL 27804 #036-05-1975 L1975 **PD** *020 †55
RATCHFORD, George Rufus. 2460 CURTIS ELLIS DR 27804 #036-07-1956 L1956 **IM** *071 †20
RISER, Mark R. 2460 CURTIS ELLIS DR, NASH HEALTH CARE SYSTEMS 27804 #028-78-1995, ▲ L1999 **EM** *020 †18
ROBERTS, Joseph Edward. 2460 CURTIS ELLIS DR 27804 #036-05-1990 L1999 **AN PME** *020 †05
ROBERTSON, Leon W. ■ 27804 #036-05-1945 L1945 **FM** *071 †18
SCHELLENBERG, Robert Karl. 901 N WINSTEAD AVE 27804 #051-07-1985 L1987 **GE IM** *040 †20
SEAMAN, David Saml. 1041 NOELL LN, STE 105 27804 #008-02-1984 L2003 **GS TRS** *020 †85
SEIGMAN, Edwin L. ■ 27804 #023-01-1941 L1952 **DR** *071
SHADE, Charnette Huggins. 100 NASH MEDICAL ARTS MALL 27804 #036-01-1996 L2004 **PD** *020 †55
SHAW, Nancy A. 901 N WINSTEAD AVE 27804 #043-01-1983 L1991 **IM** *020 †20
SHERIDAN, Robert John. 600 NASH MEDICAL ARTS MALL, ROCKY MOUNT NASH PEDIATRIC 27804 #036-07-1948 L1953 **PD** *071 †55
SHIVER, Gerrie Michelle. 1051 COUNTRY CLUB DR 27804 #036-01-1987 L1996 **IM** *020 †20
SIGMON, Wilmont Luther. 2460 CURTIS ELLIS DR 27804 #045-01-1988 L1998 **AN** *020 †05
SIRISENA, Omatta Mahasen. PO BOX 7366 27804 #220-01-1964 L1974 **IM** *020 †20
SKINNER, Nadine Beach. 10589 E NC HIGHWAY 97 27803 #036-08-2002 L2004 **FM** *020 †18
SLATER, Cathy Allen. 901 N WINSTEAD AVE, BOICE-WILLIAS CLINIC, PA 27804 #036-07-1985 L1994 **D** *020 †15
SLATER, Douglas Kenneth. 901 N WINSTEAD AVE 27804 #036-07-1985 L1989 **EM IM** *020 †20 ‡
SMITH, Timothy Carl. 1051 COUNTRY CLUB DR 27804 #038-40-1971 L1974 **IM** *020 †20
SOLOVIEFF, Gregory V. 2460 CURTIS ELLIS DR 27804 #036-07-1973 L1974 **EM** *020 †18,16
SOWERWINE, Margaret Eva. 1061 RAPER RD 27804 #050-02-1982 L1985 **IM OM** *020 †20
STEWART, Martha Gilliland. ■ 27804 #020-02-1941 L1945 **OBG** *071 †30
SUCHNIAK, Jeffrey M. 901 N WINSTEAD AVE, BOICE - WILLIS CLINIC 27804 #048-04-1996 L2000 **D** *020 †15
TANANIS, Leonard J, Jr. 132 FOY DR 27804 #041-02-1989 L1995 **PM** *020 †60 ‡
TASCONE, Arthur Ugo. 2460 CURTIS ELLIS DR 27804 #035-48-1987 L1992 **EM** *020 †16
THAKKAR, Madhvi M. 600 NASH MEDICAL ARTS MALL 27804 #495-23-1987 L1998 **IM** *020 †20
THAKKAR, Maitreya B. 901 N WINSTEAD AVE, BOICE-WILLIS CLININC 27804 #495-23-1989 L1998 **CD** *020 †20
TODD, Stuart Kittredge. 901 N WINSTEAD AVE, ROCKY MOUNT MEDICAL PARK 27804 #047-06-1973 L1974 **GS** *071 †85
TREPANIER, Sara. 2460 CURTIS ELLIS DR 27804 #041-02-1994 L2004 **EM** *020 †16
VAN ZANT, Dennis Jack. 200 NASH MEDICAL ARTS MALL, NASH OB/GYN ASSOCIATES, PA 27804 #023-01-1990 L1998 **OBG** *020 †30
VARMA, Shalendra Kumar. 901 N WINSTEAD AVE, ROCKY MOUNT MEDICAL PARK 27804 #023-01-1982 L1989 **CD IM** *020 †20

■ = Address Information Privacy Protected

VIRE, Robert Winston. 901 N WINSTEAD AVE 27804 #025-01-1998 L2005 **GS** *020 †85
WAGNER, Paul Dean. 2460 CURTIS ELLIS DR 27804 #025-01-1994 L2004 **IM** *020 †20
WARREN, Julian M. 2460 CURTIS ELLIS DR 27804 #051-01-1956 L1957 **FM** *020
WATSON, Susan Austin. 400 NASH MEDICAL ARTS MALL 27804 #038-41-1981 L1986 **OPH** *020 †35
WEATHERS, Andrea Campbell. 901 N WINSTEAD AVE 27804 #036-08-1987 L1990 **PD** *020 †55
WESONGA, Sam. 921 N WINSTEAD AVE 27804 #017-20-1986 L1993 **FM** *020 †18
WHISNANT, Jos Durwood, Jr. 180 FOY DR, UROLOGY ASSOCIATES 27804 #036-05-1971 L1971 **U UP** *020 †95
WILLIS, Linda Lee. 2460 CURTIS ELLIS DR 27804 #036-08-1991 L1992 **DR** *020 †80
WILSON, Edwina Christine. 1041 NOELL LN, STE 105 27804 #051-07-1989 L1992 **FM** *020
WILSON, Moses Ellued, Jr. 140 N ENGLEWOOD DR, ENGLEWOOD OB-GYN ASSOCIATE 27804 #036-01-1976 L1976 **OBG** *020
WINTER, De Benj. 1808 WILLOW GLYNN RD 27804 #036-01-1980 L1983 **FM** *020 †16
WOODBURN, Scott Matthew. 2460 CURTIS ELLIS DR 27804 #041-07-1998 L2003 **IM** *020
YENNEY, Matthew Frederick. ■ 27803 #041-02-1954 L1961 **R OS** *072 †80
ZIMMERMAN, Tara Mills. 921 N WINSTEAD AVE 27804 #036-07-2000 L2003 **FM** *020 †18
ZIPF, Robert Eugene, Jr. 2460 CURTIS ELLIS DR 27804 #038-40-1966 L1967 **PTH FOP** *071 †50

ROCKY POINT — PENDER

AKIWUMI, Benjamin Olufemi. 27 COMMERCE DR 28457 #412-01-1982 L1999 **IM** *020 †20
BAKER, Constance Leigh. 7910 US HWY 117 S UNIT 100, BLACK RIVER HEALTH SERVICE 28457 #038-40-1999 L2003 **FM** *020 †18
HANINGER, Michael Kevin. ■ 28457 #038-40-1973 L1974 **OBG** *020 †30
ZINICOLA, Daniel Francis. 27 COMMERCE DR 28457 #305-01-1983 L1988 **GP PM** *020 ‡

ROLESVILLE — WAKE

BRADFORD-MORRIS, Mashelle. 310 S MAIN ST 27571 #025-76-1993, ▲ L1997 **FM** *020
CHELTENHAM, Mark Philip. ■ 27571 #010-03-2012 L2007 **P** *100
INGRAM, Robert Gregory. ■ 27571 #051-01-1981 L1983 **IM** *020 †20
TAYLOR, Robert Pelham. 102 SOUTHTOWN CIR 27571 #011-02-1983 L2001 **FM** *020 †18

ROSE HILL — DUPLIN

MASQUIL, Filipe Dom. 360 E CHARITY RD, PLAINVIEW HEALTH SERVICES 28458 #409-05-1983 L2001 **IM** *020 †20 ‡
MATTHEWS, George P. ■ 28458 #041-13-1943 L1943 **GP** *072

ROSEBORO — SAMPSON

HOWERTON, Shawn Michael. 304 W NC HIGHWAY 24 28382 #038-45-2002 L2005 **FM** *020 †18
POWELL, Eddie Nelson. 201 W CLINTON ST 28382 #041-09-1978 L1979 **GP** *020

ROSMAN — TRANSYLVANIA

HERMANNY, Gretchen K. 9526 ROSMAN HWY 28772 #033-05-1973 L1983 **IM PD** *020 †20 ‡

ROUGEMONT — ORANGE

BRANSCOM, Deanna Kay. 101 POLO PL 27572 #051-01-1994 L1999 **MPD** *020 †20,55
ORNING, Jennifer Lynn. ■ 27572 #005-06-2007 **GS** *012

ROWLAND — ROBESON

LEE, Pope Matthews. PO BOX 248 28383 #036-07-1956 L1956 **GP** *071

ROXBORO — PERSON

ADAMS, Beverly J S. 911 RIDGE RD, NORTH CAROLINA EYE & EAR 27573 #036-07-1976 L1997 **OTO FPS** *075 †45
AITKEN, George Stephen. 601 RIDGE RD 27573 #038-06-1982 L1995 **ORS** *020 †40
ALLEN, James Lathan. 911 RIDGE RD, STE A 27573 #012-05-1965 L1973 **OBG** *071 †30
ANTALIK, Thomas John. 511 RIDGE RD 27573 #038-40-1973 L1989 **GS** *020 †85
BELL, Dorothy Mc Farland. 911 RIDGE RD, STE A 27573 #016-02-1975 L1976 **OPH** *020 †35 ‡
BENNETT, Cynthia Cowan. 911 RIDGE RD 27573 #036-01-1993 L1997 **OBG** *020 †30
BIRD, Ann B. 911 RIDGE RD, STE A 27573 #036-01-1996 L2000 **OBG** *020 †30
BOWEN, Margaret P. 615 RIDGE RD 27573 #035-15-2002 L2006 **EM** *020
BRADSHER, J Donald. PO BOX 168 27573 #036-05-1945 L1945 **GP** *071
BROWN, Melinda Lee. 615 RIDGE RD, PERSON COUNTY MEMORIAL HOS 27573 #045-01-1988 L1997 **P** *020 †75
CATES, Terri Bridges. 796 DOCTORS CT, P O BOX 1236 27573 #036-01-2002 L2005 **PD** *020 †55
DE VILLIER, James Russell. 296 DENADA PATH 27574 #019-02-1977 L1995 **PTH EM** *020 †50
DHOOPATI, Vijay Rama Raju. 799 DOCTORS CT 27573 #495-21-1980 L1998 **FM** *020 †18
FOSTER, Robt Middleton, Jr. 503 RIDGE RD, RIDGE ROAD MEDICAL GROUP 27573 #051-04-1976 L1983 **FM** *020 †18
FRENDUTO, Frank Alan. 911 RIDGE RD, STE A 27573 #036-01-1994 L1998 **OBG** *020 †30
GENTRY, George Wesley, Jr. 503 RIDGE RD 27573 #036-01-1959 L1959 **GP** *071
GEORGE, Mathew. 783 DOCTORS CT STE B 27573 #495-63-1988 L2002 **GS** *020 †85
GODWIN, Patrick Lee, Jr. 609 PROFESSIONAL DR, NORTH STATE MED CTR 27573 #036-01-1992 L1995 **MPD PD** *020 †20,55
GRANGER, Ronald Eugene. 911 RIDGE RD, STE A 27573 #005-15-1977 L1981 **OBS OS** *020 †30
GUNTER, William Barrett. 911 RIDGE RD, STE A 27573 #012-05-1982 L1986 **OBG** *020 †30
HALL, William Lee. 615 RIDGE RD, DEPT. OF RADIOLOGY 27573 #036-07-1995 L2000 **DR** *020 †80

HEIDER, Angela Lowe. 911 RIDGE RD, STE A 27573 #036-01-1999 L2003 **OBG** *020
HEINLY, Craig Stephen. 921 RIDGE RD 27573 #036-07-1999 L2003 **D** *020 †15
JACKSON, Nathan Oscar. 355 S MADISON BLVD STE C 27573 #025-07-1976 L1991 **P** *020 †20
KAFER, Jeffrey Charles. 783 DOCTORS CT, STE B 27573 #036-08-1994 L1995 **IM** *020 †20
KAMARAJU, Sreemaha L. 615 RIDGE RD, OUTPATIENT PSYCHIATRY 27573 #495-11-1976 L1990 **P OS** *020 †75
KOVALIK, Eugene C. 611 RIDGE RD, GAMBRO HEALTHCARE-ROXBORO 27573 #067-01-1987 L1990 **NEP** *020
LANDEN, William Thos, Jr. 619 RIDGE RD, RADLGY PERSON MEM HOSP 27573 #036-05-1978 L1979 **DR** *020 †80
LEWIS, Henry, III. 615 RIDGE RD, STE 627 27573 #010-03-1981 L1987 **OBG** *020 †30
LONG, Stephen Nelson. 783 DOCTORS CT, STE B 27573 #036-05-1984 L1986 **IM D** *020 †20
LONG, Thomas Drumwright. 783 DOCTORS CT, STE B 27573 #036-05-1952 L1952 **IM** *071
LONG, Thomas Drumwright. 783 DOCTORS CT, STE B 27573 #036-08-1994 L1997 **IM** *020 †20
MANGUM, Richard Arnold. ■ 27573 #036-01-1964 L1964 **FM FPG** *071
MARROQUIN, Bridget Murphy. 911 RIDGE RD STE 2 27573 #035-15-1998 L2002 **AN** *012 †30
MCDANIELS, Christopher N. 609 PROFESSIONAL DR 27573 #001-02-1997 L2001 **MPD** *020 †20,55
MEIJER, Mark Erik. 702 N MAIN ST 27573 #041-13-1984 L1987 **FM** *020 †18
OLDS, William Bellamy. 757 CARVER DR 27573 #036-01-1981 L1982 **FM** *020 †18
OLSON, Denise Marie. 911 RIDGE RD 27573 #025-12-1988 L1993 **OBG** *020 †30
PEARCE, Philip Henderson. 911 RIDGE RD, STE A 27573 #036-07-1960 L1960 **GYN** *071 †30 ‡
POWELL, Marcy Stephens. 911 RIDGE RD, STE A 27573 #036-08-2002 L2006 **OBG** *020
RYAN, Patrick J M. ■ 27573 #539-03-1964 L1970 **IM** *075
RYAN, Sheila Ellen. 783 DOCTORS CT, STE C 27573 #050-02-1989 L1997 **OTO** *020 †45
SHORT, James Winn. 796 DOCTORS CT, BOX 1236 27573 #048-14-1989 L1991 **PD IM** *020 †55,20
WINSLOW, James Elbert, Jr. 609 PROFESSIONAL DR, J E WINSLOW JR MD PA 27573 #036-01-1970 L1970 **FM** *071 †18
YARBOROUGH, Kimberly M. 615 RIDGE RD 27573 #036-08-1992 L1994 **EM** *020 †16
ZILLES, Michael Mc Laren. 601 RIDGE RD, COUNTY 27573 #010-01-1994 L2001 **ORS** *020 †40

RURAL HALL — FORSYTH

COE, Lori Oakley. 290 W WALL ST 27045 #036-05-1994 L1995 **FM** *020 †18
STALLINGS, Davey Bingham. 100 E WALL ST 27045 #036-05-1957 L1957 **GP** *072
STONE, Ryan Alton. ■ 27045 #055-02-2004 L2007 **OBG** *012
ZIGLAR, Susan Kimberly. 6538 UNIVERSITY PKWY 27045 #036-05-1995 L1998 **FM** *020 †18

RUTHERFORD COLLEGE — BURKE

ARENSMAN, Todd Allen. ■ 28671 #036-08-1992 L1994 **FM** *020 †18
JACKS, Alan Fowler. 720 MALCOLM BLVD 28671 #021-05-1991 L1996 **GS** *020 †85
JOSHI, Hemen I. 560 MALCOLM BLVD, WESTERN PIEDMONT CLINIC 28671 #495-76-1975 L1980 **IM EM** *020 †20
LAFFERTY, John Morrison. PO BOX 597, 721D MALCOLM BLVD 28671 #036-01-1979 L1980 **OBG** *020 †30 ‡
REDDY, Sreenivas Madduri. 560 MALCOLM BLVD 28671 #495-21-1975 L1985 **IM HO** *020 †20
SATHIRAJU, Gowri Devi. ■ 28671 #495-62-1977 L1999 **FM** *020 †18
SHERRILL, John Holloway. PO BOX 815, 560 MALCOLM BLVD 28671 #036-05-1977 L1978 **IM** *020 †20

RUTHERFORDTON — RUTHERFORD

ALBALA, Natalie L. 288 S RIDGECREST AVE, RUTHERFORD INTERNAL 28139 #917-20-1986 L2004 **IM IMG** *040 †20
ALBALA, Todd Steven. 288 S RIDGECREST AVE, RUTHERFORD INTERNAL 28139 #654-01-1988 L2004 **IM** *020 †20
ALLINE, Kristin Mary. 288 S RIDGECREST AVE 28139 #021-01-1989 L2001 **IMG IM** *075 †20
BAKER, Bonner Lee. 288 S RIDGECREST AVE, RUTHERFORD HOSPITAL INC 28139 #012-01-1976 L2000 **IM** *030 †20
BOND, Charles Dana. 139 DOCTOR HENRY NORRIS DR 28139 #038-40-1988 L1990 **ORS** *020 †40
CASP, William Jos. 668 POORS FORD RD, CASP INTERNAL MEDICINE 28139 #041-12-1980 L1984 **IM** *020 †20
CROMWELL, Christopher R. 330 NC 108 HWY, SPECIALISTS IN PLASTIC SUR 28139 #041-13-1996 L2004 **PS** *020
CRUMMIE, Robert Gwinn. 236 CHARLOTTE RD 28139 #036-07-1965 L1965 **P PYG** *020
DAVIS, John Edward. 123 PARK LANE DR STE 100 28139 #035-01-1968 L1975 **ORS** *020 †40
DRABEK, Gregg Allen. 330 NC 108 HWY, REGIONAL MEDICAL CLINIC 28139 #046-01-1987 L2007 **GS VS** *020 †85
FADEM, Carmen Lauda. ■ 28139 #011-03-1984 L2001 **FM** *020 †18
FERGUSON, Patric Wesley. 288 S RIDGECREST AVE 28139 #021-06-1986 L1992 **OTO** *020 †45
FINCH, George Carlton, Jr. 288 S RIDGECREST AVE, RUTHERFORD HOSPITAL 28139 #036-01-1982 L1984 **FM** *020 †18
GODFREY, James Henry. 446 NC 108 HWY 28139 #051-01-1984 L1990 **OBG GS** *020 †30
GRISHAW, Edward Kenneth. 131 W 2ND ST 28139 #048-13-1992 L1994 **DR** *020 †80,28
HADEN, William Chalmers, Jr. 330 NC 108 HWY, PO BOX 510 28139 #036-01-1979 L1980 **GS** *020 †85
HENDRICK, Harry Vance. ■ 28139 #023-07-1943 L1947 **GS** *071
HOSKI, James Jos. 139 DOCTOR HENRY NORRIS DR 28139 #025-01-1985 L1991 **ORS OSS** *020 †40
HUGHES, Joe Don. 308 S RIDGECREST AVE 28139 #048-02-1959 L1964 **OBG** *071 †30
JACKSON, Anne Margeret. 141 LAUREL HILL DR STE 3 28139 #016-42-1991 L1998 **N** *020
JASKI, Thomas John. 288 S RIDGECREST AVE, RUTHERFORD INTERNAL 28139 #028-34-1967 L1973 **GE IM** *020 †20
JOSEPH, Mathukutty. 288 S RIDGECREST AVE, RUTHERFORD HOSPITAL, INC 28139 #409-04-1990 L2005 **ADP** *020
KALLENBACH, Kenneth Glen. 182 W COURT ST, WOODRIDGE PSYCHOLOGICAL AS 28139 #028-03-1986 L1998 **P** *020 †75
KEEVER, Rachel D. 290 N MAIN ST 28139 #036-01-1996 L1998 **CD** *020 †20
KIRKPATRICK, James Leroy. 1126 MOUNTAIN CREEK RD 28139 #012-01-1984 L1987 **AN** *020 †05

KIRKPATRICK, Jane Denman. 288 S RIDGECREST AVE, RUTHERFORD INTERNAL 28139 #012-01-1992 L1995 **IM** *020 †20

KIRKPATRICK, William S. ■ 28139 #012-01-1991 L1995 **AN** *020 †05

LANE, Harold Compton. 308 S RIDGECREST AVE 28139 #036-07-1953 L1954 **PD** *071 †55

LANE, L Ann Buchanan. ■ 28139 #004-01-1954 L1956 **PD** *071

LAWRENCE, Robert Scott. 288 S RIDGECREST AVE 28139 #045-01-1975 L1980 **FM** *020 †18

LESHER, Donald T. 288 S RIDGECREST AVE 28139 #047-06-1976 L1980 **DR NM** *020 †80

MC GRIFF, Gregory Duane. 288 S RIDGECREST AVE, RUTHERFORD INTERNAL 28139 #036-05-1994 L2002 **IM** *020 †20

MELSON, Stephen Jos. 288 S RIDGECREST AVE, RUTHERFORD INTERNAL 28139 #035-08-1991 L1997 **GE** *020 †20

MOORE, Craig Cowan. 288 S RIDGECREST AVE 28139 #561-17-1980 L1993 **PUD IM** *020 †20

MOORING, Franklin James. 288 S RIDGECREST AVE 28139 #036-08-1984 L1987 **DR** *020 †80

NEVILS, Ruth Ann. 288 S RIDGECREST AVE, RUTHERFORD INTERNAL 28139 #036-05-1986 L2001 **ON IM** *020 †20

PANOWICZ, Cynthia Ann. 141 TRYON RD STE A 28139 #041-12-1993 L1996 **PD** *020 †55

PENDLETON, Robin L. 446 NC 108 HWY 28139 #021-05-1989 L1993 **OBG** *020 †30

PERSON, Luther Gill. 308 S RIDGECREST AVE 28139 #025-01-1997 L2006 **DR** *020 †80

POWELL, William Stewart. 141 TRYON RD STE B 28139 #027-01-1978 L1989 **U** *020 †95

REILLY, Seema Nasreen. 288 S RIDGECREST AVE, RUTHERFORD INTERNAL 28139 #051-04-2001 L2001 **IM** *020 †20

ROGERS, Hobart Ray. ■ 28139 #036-05-1963 L1963 *071 †40

ROMZICK, Teresa Mary. 288 S RIDGECREST AVE 28139 #025-01-1979 L1994 **FM** *020 †18

RUDOLPH, Harry P, IV. 139 DOCTOR HENRY NORRIS DR 28139 #045-01-1989 L1994 **ORS** *020 †40

SABOLOVIC, Jeffrey C. 446 NC 108 HWY, RUTHERFORD OB-GYN ASSOCIAT 28139 #048-14-1994 L2003 **OBG** *020 †30

SCRUGGS, Michael Coleman. 288 S RIDGECREST AVE 28139 #036-05-1975 L1975 **DR OTO** *020 †45,80

SHEETS, Douglas Dean. 446 NC 108 HWY 28139 #017-20-1974 L1977 **GYN OBS** *020 †30

SKUDLARICK, John Lewis. 308 S RIDGECREST AVE 28139 #025-01-1973 L1978 **GS** *020 †85

STALLINGS, Robert Geo. 288 S RIDGECREST AVE, RUTHERFORD HOSP LAB 28139 #051-01-1981 L1985 **PTH** *020 †50

STEGEMOLLER, Ralph Warren. 134 PATTON CIR 28139 #011-02-1979 L1997 **EM** *020 †16

SUTTER, Sharren Esther A. 330 NC 108 HWY, RUTHERFORD SURGICAL ASSOCI 28139 #005-12-1973 L2006 **GS PD** *020 †85

TOLHURST, John Thos. 288 S RIDGECREST AVE 28139 #045-01-1988 L1989 **EM FM** *020 †18

TORREY, Kevin Rex. 288 S RIDGECREST AVE, RUTHERFORD INTERNAL 28139 #030-06-1992 L2001 **IM** *020 †20

VAN JURA, Jim. PO BOX 1407 28139 #038-40-1979 L1980 **FM** *020 †18

VAUGHN, John. 236 CHARLOTTE RD, THE RAINTREE CLINIC 28139 #803-05-1944 L1963 **HEM CLP** *020 †50

WHITWORTH, Claude Phillip. 288 S RIDGECREST AVE, RUTHERFORD INTERNAL 28139 #036-01-1979 L1981 **IM** *020 †20

WILTSE, Celeste G. 446 NC 108 HWY, RUTHERFORD OB/GYN 28139 #045-04-1995 L1999 **OBG** *020 †30

WINKER, Joel Edward. ■ 28139 #035-20-1963 L1971 **GYN** *071 †30

WRIGHT, Edward Thorburn. 141 TRYON RD STE B, FOOTHILLS UROLOGY 28139 #045-01-1990 L1996 **U** *020 †95

YELTON, Ernest Hugh. ■ 28139 #035-20-1943 L1943 **GP** *071

SAINT PAULS – ROBESON

BRADFORD, Arthur Louis. 635 N WILKINSON DR 28384 #010-03-1974 L1993 **EM FM** *020 †18

OSMAN, Mohamed Buwe Sidi. 125 E BROAD ST, PRIMARY CARE OF ST PAULS, 28384 #913-65-1979 L2002 **FM** *020 †18

SALISBURY – ROWAN

ABDALAH, Marvin Rene. 612 MOCKSVILLE AVE 28144 #010-03-1999 L2005 **DR** *020 †80

ABELLA, Erlinda Bathan. 118 N ELLIS ST 28144 #748-11-1971 L1979 **IM** *020 †20

ABELLA, Jose Bacalso. 118 N ELLIS ST 28144 #748-09-1962 L1972 **PD PDC** *075 †55

ABHAYAWARDHANE, Yamuna K. 1601 BRENNER AVE, CENTER 28144 #045-04-2001 L2005 *020

ABRAMS, Cyril. 911 W HENDERSON ST, STE 230 28144 #041-13-1979 L2003 **CD IM** *020 †20

AGNER, R Christopher. 611 MOCKSVILLE AVE, ROWAN DIAGNOSTIC CLNC PA 28144 #036-07-1975 L1977 **IM CD** *020 †20

ALLISON, Trevor Robert. 401 MOCKSVILLE AVE, STE 200 28144 #047-07-1998 L2001 **FM** *020 †18

AMARASINGE, Amara S. 1601 BRENNER AVE, W.G. BILL HEFNER MEDICALCE 28144 #220-02-1986 L1997 **IM** *020 †20

ANDERSON, Lynn Bivins. 400 MOCKSVILLE AVE, STE C 28144 #020-12-1986 L1990 **OBG** *020 †30

ANUKWUEM, Obioma Ikechukw. 1904 JAKE ALEXANDER BLVD W, STE 301 28147 #690-04-1994 L2006 **MPD** *020

ARMADA, Josefino G. 1601 BRENNER AVE, VA MEDICAL CTR 28144 #748-02-1971 L1988 **GP IM** *020

ARMOUR, Ross Blackmon. 1401 BRENNER AVE, VA MEDICAL CENTER 28144 #011-02-1975 L1995 **IM FM** *020 †20,18

AVERILL, Mary Carlisle. ■ 28147 #024-01-1977 L1981 **IM IMG** *020 †20

BACHL, Frederick Joseph. 129 WOODSON ST 28144 #024-07-1964 L1973 **PD** *071 †55

BAILEY, Hilda Hart. ■ 28144 #041-01-1945 L1946 **PD** *071

BAILEY, Ronald Wesley. 1601 BRENNER AVE, VETERANS AFFAIRS MED CTR 28144 #047-07-1982 L2000 **DR** *020

BALAZS, Rodica. 1601 BRENNER AVE, W.G. HEFNER VAMC 28144 #781-03-1973 L1994 **AN** *020 †05

BALE, Renuka Pathikonda. 1601 BRENNER AVE, W G HEFNER VA MEDICAL CENT 28144 #495-70-1973 L1994 **IM** *020 †20

BARRIER, Ronnie Jay. 650 JULIAN RD 28147 #036-01-1990 L1991 **FM** *020 †18

BEARSS, David Jonathan. 401 MOCKSVILLE AVE, SALISBURY-ROWAN MEDICAL CE 28144 #038-43-1992 L1996 **MPD** *020 †20,55

BELL, Heidi Grissom. ■ 28147 #036-08-2002 L2006 **OBG** *100

BERGSMA, Donald Roy, Jr. 800 W CEMETARY ST 28144 #021-05-1993 L1998 **OPH** *072 †35 ‡

BERTELS, Norman Hurst, III. 612 MOCKSVILLE AVE 28144 #051-04-1977 L1988 **AN** *020 †05

BERTRAM, Robert Alvin. 911 W HENDERSON ST, STE 110 28144 #020-12-1980 L1983 **U** *020 †95

BIRMINGHAM, William J. 911 W HENDERSON ST, STE 410 28144 #023-01-1987 L1994 **GS** *020 †85

BLACK, William Reid. 825 W HENDERSON ST, HEMATOLOGY/ONCOLOGY 28144 #036-05-1974 L1978 **ON IM** *020 †20

BLACK, Winsel O'Neal. 601 MOCKSVILLE AVE 28144 #010-03-1961 L1962 **GP** *071

BLUMENTHAL, Jessica Ellen. 911 W HENDERSON ST 28144 #051-01-1996 L2000 **OBG** *020 †30 ‡

BOZORGNIA, Noorollah. ■ 28146 #517-01-1953 L1970 **IM** *071

BRAZIS, Robert Carl. 1601 BRENNER AVE, SALISBURY VA HOSP 28144 #038-45-1983 L1984 **IM** *020 †20

BRINKLEY, William Mc Call. 825 W HENDERSON ST, HEMATOLOGY/ONCOLOGY 28144 #036-05-1993 L1995 **HO ON** *020 †20

BROWN, Lester George. 401 MOCKSVILLE AVE, STE 200 28144 #047-07-1998 L2001 **FM** *020 †18

BUMGARNER, John Henry. 612 MOCKSVILLE AVE 28144 #051-04-1966 L1967 **AN PUD** *071

BURTON, David Scott. 129 WOODSON ST 28144 #036-01-1998 L2000 **PD** *020 †55

BUSBY, Merle Rudy. 901 W HENDERSON ST 28144 #036-07-1970 L1970 **GS VS** *020 †85 ‡

CABAGNOT, Jesusa Reyes. ■ 28144 #748-09-1960 L1976 **FM RHU** *020 †18

CALLAWAY, Cliff. 628 W INNES ST 28144 #039-01-1970 L1977 **EM OM** *030

CALVERT, Samuel James. ■ 28144 #036-05-1947 L1948 **IM** *071

CAPITO, Paul Ray. 401 MOCKSVILLE AVE 28144 #055-01-1990 L2002 **DR VIR** *020 †80

CARLTON, Thomas Kern, Jr. 129 WOODSON ST 28144 #036-07-1963 L1963 **PD** *020 †55

CEKADA, Emil James. 911 W HENDERSON ST, STE 410 28144 #036-08-1991 L1997 **GS** *020 †85

CERALDI, Attilio Antonio. VA MEDICAL CTR, DEPT SURG 28144 #561-17-1951 L1980 **GS GP** *071 †85

CHAMBERLAIN, Scott M. 612 MOCKSVILLE AVE, ROWAN REGIONAL HOSPITAL 28144 #055-01-1988 L1995 **EM** *020 †20,16

CHAPMAN, James Emory, Jr. 1601 BRENNER AVE, DEPT SURG # 112 28144 #012-01-1979 L1998 **ORS OSM** *020 †40 ‡

CHILDRESS, Donna Reefe. 611 MOCKSVILLE AVE 28144 #036-01-2000 L2003 **IM** *020 †20

CHINIWALLA, Rupal N. 1601 BRENNER AVE, MAIL STOP 112E 28144 #035-06-1999 L2006 **OPH** *020 †35

CHRISTENBURY, Mary M. 1601 BRENNER AVE, W.G.(BILL) HEFNER VAMC 28144 #045-01-1980 L1983 **P** *020 †75

CLINE, Wayne Allen. 612 MOCKSVILLE AVE 28144 #036-05-1946 L1947 **U** *020 †95

CLINE, Wayne Allen, Jr. 911 W HENDERSON ST, STE 110 28144 #036-05-1976 L1982 **U** *020 †95

COCHRAN, W Gerald. 410 MOCKSVILLE AVE 28144 #041-13-1967 L1986 **PS OS** *020 †65 ‡

CODY, Edmund Joseph. 129 WOODSON ST 28144 #036-08-1993 L1996 **PD** *020 †55

COLLIAS, Constantine Paul. 1601 BRENNER AVE, DEPT OF VETERANS AFFAIRS M 28144 #045-04-1996 L1998 **P** *020 †75

COLWELL, Steven James. 612 MOCKSVILLE AVE 28144 #035-15-1995 L2000 **AN** *020 †05

COMADOLL, James Lyle. 1035 LINCOLNTON RD 28144 #026-04-1987 L1992 **ORS GS** *020 †40

CONNELLY, Jason Robert. 650 JULIAN RD 28147 #036-05-1997 L2000 **FM** *020 †18

CORLEY, Charles Austin. ■ 28146 #036-01-1993 L1999 **PD** *020 †55

CORPENING, Joseph D. 129 WOODSON ST 28144 #036-07-1952 L1953 **PD** *071 †55

CRAIGHEAD, Benjamin H. 129 WOODSON ST, SALISBURY PEDIATRIC ASSOCI 28144 #036-05-1999 L2003 **PD** *020 †55

CRAWFORD, John Robt, III. 310 N MAIN ST 28144 #036-01-1966 L1966 **OPH** *020 †35 ‡

DAGENHART, Timothy Lee. 1035 LINCOLNTON RD, ROMEDICAL CARE 28144 #036-08-1988 L1989 **EM FM** *020 †18

DASARI, Balasundaram. 1601 BRENNER AVE, VA MEDICAL CENTER 28144 #495-11-1958 L1982 **CHP P** *020

DASARI, Jalaja Ramaiah. ■ 28147 #495-50-1966 L1993 **P** *020

DEBRODER, Leslie Rupard. 1601 BRENNER AVE, VA MED CTR DEPT OF PATH 28144 #036-05-1992 L1994 **PTH** *020 †50

DE RIVERS, Mercedes M. 1601 BRENNER AVE, VA MEDICAL CTR 28144 #649-01-1960 L1977 **P PTH** *072 †50

DETRICK, Kenneth John. 205 E COUNCIL ST STE B 28144 #041-02-1975 L1995 **P NTR** *020 †75

DEURDULIAN, Corinne. 1601 BRENNER AVE, DEPARTMENT OF IMAGING 28144 #048-14-1999 L2004 **DR** *100 †80

DILORETO, David Danl. 650 JULIAN RD 28147 #023-01-1985 L1989 **FM** *020 †18

D'MELLO, Justino C. 1601 BRENNER AVE 28144 #704-02-1978 L2004 **PYG** *020 †75

DULA, Frederick Mast. 401 MOCKSVILLE AVE, STE 100 28144 #036-01-1981 L1982 **DR** *020 †80

EKNOYAN, Donald Peter. 1601 BRENNER AVE 28144 #048-04-2001 L2005 **P** *100 †75

ELLISON, Thomas Scott. 1035 LINCOLNTON RD, ROMEDICAL CENTER, INC 28144 #036-05-1987 L1997 **ORS** *020 †40

EVERHART, George Raymond, II. 650 JULIAN RD 28147 #036-05-1977 L1978 **FM** *071 †18

FARRINGTON, Cecil Murray. 401 MOCKSVILLE AVE 28144 #036-01-1972 L1972 **FM** *020

FAZIA, Robert Brian. 911 W HENDERSON ST STE 230 28144 #036-05-1989 L1995 **CD** *020 †20

FINCH, John R. 612 MOCKSVILLE AVE, ROWAN MEDICAL PRACTICES 28144 #048-43-2000 L2006 **MPD** *020

FINK, Gary Lee. 612 MOCKSVILLE AVE 28144 #036-01-1983 L1984 **IM** *020 †20

FISHER, Ada Markita. 1601 BRENNER AVE, VAMC 28144 #056-05-1975 L1978 **OM FM** *020 †18

FORT, Samuel Laurens, Jr. 203 MOCKSVILLE AVE, STE A 28144 #048-04-1967 L1995 **D EM** *020 †15

FRUCHTMAN, Marc Sol. 1406 W INNES ST A 28144 #045-01-1994 L1997 **FM** *020 †18

FRUCHTMAN, Parinda K. 1406 W INNES ST # A 28144 #045-01-1994 L1997 **FM** *020 †18

FURR, William Stephen. 400 MOCKSVILLE AVE, STE A 28144 #036-07-1986 L1989 **ORS OSM** *020 †40

GAWLAS, Dorota. 1601 BRENNER AVE, VA MEDICAL CENTER 28144 #913-13-1991 L2007 **P** *020 †75

GINN, Thomas Adam. 1035 LINCOLNTON RD, CORP, DBA ROMEDICAL CARE 28144 #036-05-2000 L2002 **HS** *020

GINN, Thomas Moss. 319 MOCKSVILLE AVE 28144 #036-05-1975 L1975 **IM** *020 †20

GISH, Larry Morgan. ■ 28144 #036-05-1964 L1964 **IM** *071 †20

GOODMAN, Myron Arthur. 601 MOCKSVILLE AVE 28144 #036-01-1965 L1965 **IM** *020 †20

GOODNER, James Vance. ■ 28145 #021-01-1972 L1980 **IM** *020 †20

GOODWIN, Joel Sexton. 911 W HENDERSON ST, STE 300 28144 #036-01-1959 L1959 **OBG** *071 †30

GOSS, Frederick Uhl. 611 MOCKSVILLE AVE 28144 #036-01-1980 L1981 **IM** *020 †20
GRAHAM, Chas Pattison, Jr. 1601 BRENNER AVE 112, VAMC SALISBURY 28144 #036-01-1965 L1965 **GS** *030 †85
GREGOIRE, James David. ■ 28147 #041-14-1991 L2004 **EM** *072 †16
GRIBETZ, Michael David. 2143 STATESVILLE BLVD, PMB 254 28147 #165-01-1976 L1977 **PFP PYG** *020 †75 ‡
GULYN, Anna Bauhofer. ■ 28144 #154-02-1957 L1974 **GP** *071
GUNDAVARAPU, Jyothirmayi. 1601 BRENNER AVE, WG BILL HEFFNER VA MEDICAL 28144 #495-65-1995 L2001 **IM** *020 †20
HALDEA, Asha. 310 MOCKSVILLE AVE 28144 #495-30-1976 L2002 **N** *020 †75
HALDEA, Daulat Singh. 310 MOCKSVILLE AVE 28144 #495-30-1976 L2001 **GE IM** *072 †20,55
HALL, Bahnson David. 911 W HENDERSON ST, STE 300 28144 #036-05-1974 L1974 **OBG** *020 †30
HALL, Joseph Cullen. ■ 28144 #047-05-1942 L1942 **OBG** *071 †30
HANSEN, Hans Christian. 1035 LINCOLNTON RD, RO MEDICAL CARE 28144 #007-02-1986 L1990 **AN** *020 †05
HARDIN, James Ronald. 800 W CEMETARY ST 28144 #047-07-1990 L2000 **OPH** *020 †35
HAYES, Hugh H, Jr. 1601 BRENNER AVE 28144 #047-06-1949 L1960 **R** *071 †80
HIGBEE, Jane Nash. ■ 28144 #048-02-1942 L1958 **GP P** *072
HIGHTOWER, Ann Lynette. ■ 28145 #016-06-1985 L2008 **IMG** *020 †20
HILL, Dennis Le Roy. 911 W HENDERSON ST, STE L30 28144 #005-06-1966 L1972 **N SME** *020 †75
HINSON, James Noah. 102 MOCKSVILLE AVE STE 204 28144 #036-05-1960 L1960 **CD IM** *020
HOLMES, Joseph Nathan. 221 JAKE ALEXANDER BLVD S 28147 #048-15-1986 L1989 **IM** *020 †20
HOLNESS, Kenworth F. 1601 BRENNER AVE 28144 #016-43-1993 L2000 **FM** *020 †18
HUDSON, Jennifer Garraty. 129 WOODSON ST 28144 #012-01-1996 L1999 **PD** *020 †55
HUMBLE, Robert Samuel. 605 GROVE ST, SALISBURY ORTHOPAEDIC ASSO 28144 #020-02-1989 L1994 **ORS OAR** *020 †40
HUMBLE, Scott David. ■ 28144 #036-05-1998 L2007 **PTH** *020
HUNTER, Marcia Rea. 1601 BRENNER AVE, VA MEDICAL CTR 28144 #422-01-1982 L1990 **IM** *030 †20
HURLEY, Robin Annette. 1601 BRENNER AVE, VAMC MAILCODE 11M 28144 #045-01-1990 L2004 **P** *030 †75
HYLL, Marsha Karin. ■ 28144 #035-01-1984 L1986 **IM** *020 †20
JAGARLAMUDI, Kiran Kumar. 611 MOCKSVILLE AVE 28144 #495-37-1998 L2007 **GE** *020 †20
JAIN, Prachee. 911 W HENDERSON ST, STE 120 28144 #422-01-2000 L2007 **IM** *020 †20
JAKSCH, Mary Gloria. VET ADMIN HOSP, DEPT PSYCH 28144 #041-09-1945 L1946 **P** *100
JAMISON, Laci Anne. ■ 28147 #036-01-2008 *012
JENSEN, Susan. 1600 BRENNER AVE BLDG 7, WE (BILL) HEFNER VAMC 28144 #035-15-1983 L1986 **PM** *020 †60
JOHNSON, Atlee Rollins, III. 911 W HENDERSON ST, STE 110 28144 #036-05-1987 L1988 **U** *020 †95
JOHNSON, Desiree Batrice. 201 WOODSON ST STE A, SALISBURY MEDICAL CLINIC 28144 #021-05-1995 L1998 **FM** *020 †18
JOHNSON, James Clifton. 401 MOCKSVILLE AVE, STE 100 28144 #036-05-1986 L1991 **DR RNR** *020 †80
JORDAN, Richard Dorn. ■ 28144 #036-01-1961 L1961 **R** *071 †80
KANDL, Louis Chas. ■ 28144 #041-09-1972 L1980 **IM ID** *020 †20
KAUFMANN, James Gregory. 410 MOCKSVILLE AVE 28144 #036-01-1987 L1989 **OPH** *020 †35
KHOR, Cameron Thiamhock. 332 VALENTINE CT 28147 #033-05-1997 L2006 **IM** *020 †20
KIRTLEY, Thomas Lloyd, Jr. 135 MOCKSVILLE AVE 28144 #051-04-1978 L1985 **FM** *020 †18
KNORR, Eric John. 612 MOCKSVILLE AVE, SALISBURY ANESTHESIA AND P 28144 #041-07-1995 L2001 **AN** *020 †05
KOONTZ, Wayne Carson. 129 WOODSON ST 28144 #036-05-1964 L1964 **PD** *020 †55
KRAMER, Barry Alan. 327 MOCKSVILLE AVE, THE SANGER CLINIC 28144 #041-09-1974 L1975 **P PYG** *020 †75 ‡
KRAMER, Barry Loren. ■ 28147 #038-40-1973 L2007 **CD** *020 †20 ‡
KRIBBS, John Benton. 650 JULIAN RD 28147 #041-02-1976 L1994 **EM FM** *020 †18
LATIMER, Harrison A. 1035 LINCOLNTON RD, ROMEDICAL CARE 28144 #036-01-1990 L1995 **OSM** *020 †40
LEE, Shih Ching. 1601 BRENNER AVE 28144 #244-03-1964 L1982 **IM END** *020
LINN, Joseph Ralph, Jr. 211 CONFEDERATE AVE 28144 #021-01-1974 L1975 **EM OBG** *071 †18
LINS, Mark David. 129 WOODSON ST, SALISBURY PEDIATRIC ASSCS, 28144 #036-05-1990 L1992 **PD** *020 †55
LOCKERT, Charles R L. ■ 28144 #047-05-1962 L1968 **ORS** *071 †40
LOMAX, Donald H. 1710 W INNES ST 28144 #036-05-1951 L2002 **FM** *071 †18
LOMBARD, Elizabeth. 612 MOCKSVILLE AVE 28144 #005-12-1953 L1954 **FM** *072
LOVE, Carolyn A. 1601 BRENNER AVE, VET ADMIN OF SALISBURY 28144 #025-12-1974 L2001 **IM** *020
MAGRYTA, Christopher J. 129 WOODSON ST 28144 #012-05-1996 L1999 **PD** *020 †55
MAHAN, Robert G. 114 STRATFORD RD 28146 #041-02-1967 L1988 **EM FM** *020 †18,16
MALONE, Helen Jean. 1601 BRENNER AVE, VETERANS ADMIN MEDICAL CTR 28144 #051-01-1996 L2000 **OBG** *020 †30
MALONE, Sean Ian. 611 MOCKSVILLE AVE 28144 #051-01-1996 L2000 **IM** *020 †20
MALONEY, Sean Robt. 1601 BRENNER AVE BLDG 7, VAMC REHAB MED SVC 28144 #012-05-1980 L1984 **PM OS** *020 †60
MARSHALL, Melanie Kristen. 550 N MAIN ST 28144 #020-02-2001 L2004 *020
MARTIN, Richard Wilson. 327 MOCKSVILLE AVE 28144 #035-20-1957 L1966 **GS GE** *071 †85
MASON, William Terry. 400 MOCKSVILLE AVE, STE A 28144 #023-01-1966 L1975 **ORS** *020 †40
MASSEY, Arletta Juliet. ■ 28147 #010-03-1965 L1973 **AN GP** *020 †05
MAYRAND, M Elizabeth. ■ 28144 #016-11-1945 L1968 **PTH CLP** *071 †50
MC BRINE, Wm John, Jr. ■ 28144 #033-05-1964 L1979 **R NM** *020 †80,28
MC CANTS, Deidra Dayoka. 1904 JAKE ALEXANDER BLVD W, STE 301 28147 #036-08-2003 L2006 **FM** *020 †18
MC ILTROT, Christopher E. 135 MOCKSVILLE AVE, STE 202 28144 #038-40-1994 L1999 **GS** *020 †85
MC NEILL, Robert Eric. 401 MOCKSVILLE AVE, STE 200 28144 #036-07-1984 L1987 **IM** *020 †20
MEDDA, Chitra. 1601 BRENNER AVE, W G HEFNER VA MEDICAL CENT 28144 #495-02-1983 L1997 **IM PHP** *020 †20
MERHOFF, Vance Fredrick. 911 W HENDERSON ST, STE 110 28144 #047-06-1996 L2002 **U** *020 †95
MIAN, Khalid Altaf. 1601 BRENNER AVE, VA MED CTR DEPT MED 28144 #704-02-1965 L1997 **CD IM** *020 †20
MILLS, Michael Kenneth. 400 MOCKSVILLE AVE, STE C 28144 #036-05-1982 L1984 **OBG** *020 †30
MORROW, Calvin F, Jr. 1601 BRENNER AVE, DEPARTMENT OF VETERANS AFF 28144 #036-01-1977 L1977 **PUD CCM** *020 †20
MORTON, Terrence D, Jr. 612 MOCKSVILLE AVE 28144 #036-01-1985 L1988 **EM** *020 †16
MURPHY, James A, Jr. 911 W HENDERSON ST 28144 #051-07-1992 L1996 **OBG** *020 †30
MURPHY, Thomas Lynch. 612 MOCKSVILLE AVE 28144 #024-01-1943 L1943 **GE IM** *071 †20
MUTHU, Amruthavalli. ■ 28146 #495-33-1970 L1997 **P** *020 †75
MYERS, Kim Morgan. 650 JULIAN RD 28147 #036-01-1983 L1985 **FM** *075 †18
NAGY, Christopher Keith. 605 GROVE ST, SALISBURY ORTHOPAEDIC ASSO 28144 #038-45-1990 L1996 **ORS OFA** *020 †40
NASH, Carl William. 1601 BRENNER AVE 28144 #004-01-1962 L1973 **R** *020 †80
NELSON, Eva O'Neal. 612 MOCKSVILLE AVE 28144 #036-08-1990 L1994 **AN** *020 †05
NELSON, Vaughn Paul. 612 MOCKSVILLE AVE 28144 #036-08-1990 L1994 **AN** *020 †05
NETI, Sastry Vishwanatha. 1601 BRENNER AVE, VAMC 11M-1 28144 #495-53-1971 L1989 **P** *020 †75
NEWMAN, Leon Bryant. 911 W HENDERSON ST, STE 410 28144 #001-02-1984 L1989 **GS** *020 †85
NINER, Joseph Anthony, Jr. 1107 STATESVILLE BLVD 28144 #023-01-1986 L1996 **OBG** *020 †30
NORDBERG, Kris O'Dell. 1601 BRENNER AVE 28144 #654-01-1987 L1993 **IM** *020 †20
OTT, Benjamin Thomas. 650 JULIAN RD 28147 #041-12-2001 L2004 **FM** *020 †18
PARADA, Malcolm Perry. ■ 28144 #038-41-1964 L1971 **OBG** *071 †30
PARROTT, Frank Strong. 612 MOCKSVILLE AVE 28144 #023-01-1943 L1943 **GS** *071 †85
PATEL, Falguni Dinesh. 1601 BRENNER AVE, VA MEDICAL CENTER 28144 #495-23-1996 L2006 **FM** *020 †18
PATEL, Jyoti M. ■ 28144 #495-23-1971 L1975 **FM FPG** *020 †50,18
PATEL, Nakul Ratilal. 1601 BRENNER AVE 28144 #495-47-1980 L1999 **IM** *020 †20
PATEL, Nilesh Vithalbhai. 611 MOCKSVILLE AVE 28144 #036-01-1992 L1998 **PCC** *020 †20
PATEL, Ramesh D. 1601 BRENNER AVE, MEDICAL CENTER 28144 #495-89-1982 L1992 **IM** *020 †20
PAUDEL, Padam Prasad. 229 MOCKSVILLE AVE, SALISBURY CANCER CENTER 28144 #209-01-1965 L1994 **RO** *071 †80
PERRY, Byron Leigh. 1601 BRENNER AVE, SURGERY DEPT 28144 #012-05-1971 L1976 **OTO HNS** *020 †45
PITSON, Lynn Christine. 400 MOCKSVILLE AVE, STE C 28144 #065-01-1985 L1990 **OBG** *020 †30
PLITMAN, Jonathan David. 1601 BRENNER AVE, HEFNER VA MEDICAL CENTER (28144 #047-06-1984 L1995 **PUD IM** *020 †20
POTTS, Ronald Sargent. ■ 28144 #067-01-1954 L1980 **PTH** *071 †50
PROCTOR, Stephen Duane. 421 STATESVILLE BLVD 28144 #036-05-1984 L1988 **PUD CCM** *020 †20
RALSTON, Jeffrey J. 401 MOCKSVILLE AVE, STE 100 28144 #055-75-1999, ▲ L2004 **DR** *020 †80 ‡
RELANGI, Rajani. 1601 BRENNER AVE, WG BILLHEFNER VAMC 28144 #495-21-1988 L2002 **RHU** *020 †20
RESTAR, Hernane Coloso. 1601 BRENNER AVE 28144 #748-08-1964 L1976 **IMG P** *020 ‡
REYNOLDS, James W, Jr. 612 MOCKSVILLE AVE 28144 #036-01-1964 L1964 **OTO A** *071 †45
REYNOLDS, John Ozment, Jr. 410 MOCKSVILLE AVE 28144 #036-01-1971 L1971 **OPH** *020 †35
RICH, Ryan Kevin. 612 MOCKSVILLE AVE, DEPT OF ANES-ROWAN REGAN M 28144 #036-05-2001 L2002 **AN** *020 †05
ROBAR, Carey Ann. 611 MOCKSVILLE AVE 28144 #016-06-1992 L2001 **END** *020 †20
ROBERTS, Thomas J. 612 MOCKSVILLE AVE 28144 #038-41-1952 L1952 **EM** *071
ROBERTSON, Lloyd H, Jr. 911 W HENDERSON ST 28144 #036-07-1960 L1960 **U** *071 †95
ROSADO, Victor Manuel. 650 STATESVILLE BLVD STE 1 28144 #042-01-1981 L1992 **P** *020 †75
ROSS, Rachel Hereford. 612 MOCKSVILLE AVE, DEPT PATH 28144 #001-02-1981 L1983 **PTH** *020 †50
ROY, Ranjan Shanti. 330 JAKE ALEXANDER BLVD W, STE 104 28147 #021-01-1987 L1995 **NS** *020 †25
ROY, Samuel Jonathan. 302 KINGSBRIDGE RD 28144 #035-45-2000 L2006 **PS** *100 †65
RUBIO, Ramon Mario. 1601 BRENNER AVE, ATTN: MENTAL HEALTH 28144 #231-01-1966 L1969 **P** *020 †75 ‡
RUSSELL, David Norman. 628 W INNES ST 28144 #036-01-1980 L1981 **GP EM** *020
RUSSO, Kathleen. 129 WOODSON ST, SALISBURY PEDIATRIC ASSCS, 28144 #041-07-1994 L1997 **PD** *020 †55
SALEHEEN, Qamar -Us-. ■ 28144 #704-20-1999 L2005 **IM** *100 †20
SALMAN, Sinasi. 310 STATESVILLE BLVD STE 2, NORTHLAKE NEPHROLOGY, PLLC 28144 #902-04-1981 L2002 **NEP IM** *020 †20
SCOTT, Gregory Earl. ■ 28147 #036-05-1992 L1994 **N** *020 †75
SEIFERT, Brent Williams. 611 MOCKSVILLE AVE 28144 #036-05-1992 L1996 **IM** *020 †20
SEIFFERT, Ingeborg. 1601 BRENNER AVE 28144 #407-05-1952 L1965 **IM IMG** *071
SENTER, R Gordon. 611 MOCKSVILLE AVE, ROWAN DIAGNOSTIC CLINIC 28144 #023-07-1966 L1972 **RHU** *020 †20
SHAFER, Frank T. 104 CIRCLE DR 28144 #036-05-1951 L1951 **IM** *071
SHAFER, Irving E, Jr. PO BOX 2449 28145 #051-04-1949 L1949 **R** *071 †80
SHAH, Binoy Jagdish. 1601 BRENNER AVE, MAILCODE: 11-M 28144 #305-01-2002 L2006 **P** *020
SHANNON, Gordon James. ■ 28144 #011-02-1961 L1990 **GS TS** *030 †85
SHANNON, William Gary. 1035 LINCOLNTON RD 28144 #036-05-1972 L1972 **PMM AN** *020 †05
SHELLHORN, Douglas Bert. 611 MOCKSVILLE AVE 28144 #036-05-1991 L1994 **IM** *020 †20
SIDDIQUI, Muhammad Yousuf. 1601 BRENNER AVE, VA MED CTR MED SVC 11G 28144 #704-02-1969 L1997 **PUD IM** *020 †20 ‡
SIERRA-RENTEN, Leslie. 612 MOCKSVILLE AVE 28144 #036-07-1985 L1991 **PTH** *020 †50
SINGLETON-YATAWARA, G. 911 W HENDERSON ST 28144 #051-07-1994 L1998 **OBG** *020 †30
SLOOP, Norman Ray. ■ 28144 #036-05-1959 L1959 **GP** *071
SMALLS-STOKES, Sheila Mar. 611 MOCKSVILLE AVE, RUTHERFORD INTERNAL MEDICA 28144 #041-09-1989 L1995 **N SME** *020 †75
SMITH, David Nimmons. 612 MOCKSVILLE AVE 28144 #036-05-1966 L1966 **IM** *030 †20
SOMMER, Martha Anne. 1601 BRENNER AVE, VA HOSP 28144 #016-45-1984 L1990 **IM** *020 †20
SOUTH, Bethany July. 650 JULIAN RD 28147 #048-12-2003 L2004 **FM** *020 †18
SPARGO, John Prichard. 612 MOCKSVILLE AVE 28144 #036-05-1955 L1955 **FM** *071 †18
SPELLS, Lori Briana Epps. 1601 BRENNER AVE, WG HEFNER VA MEDICAL CENTE 28144 #036-05-1998 L2002 **P** *020 †75
SPENCER, Frederick B, Jr. ■ 28144 #051-04-1945 L1945 **IM** *072
STAHLE, Scott Douglas. 911 W HENDERSON ST 28144 #038-45-1993 L1997 **OBG** *020 †30
STALLWORTH, Acquawon Jean. 1904 JAKE ALEXANDER BLVD W, STE 301 28147 #012-01-1998 L2001 **FM** *020 †18

■ = Address Information Privacy Protected

STEELE, Robert Gibson. 605 GROVE ST 28144 #012-05-1973 L1977 **ORS** *020 †40
STEIMEL, Herbert Anton. ■ 28144 #035-15-1960 L1982 **GS** *071 †85
STEINBERG, Sidney Raymond. 1601 BRENNER AVE, # 11G 28144 #020-12-1965 L1966 **GS VS** *040 †85
STOESSEL, Carole Jean. ■ 28144 #036-05-1963 L1963 **MM CLP** *074
SUBRAMANIAN, Thoppe V R. 1601 BRENNER AVE 28144 #495-66-1967 L1982 **P** *020
SUKKASEM, Yuthapong. 310 STATESVILLE BLVD 28144 #055-01-1990 L1993 **FM** *020 †18
SWANSON, Sandra L. 612 MOCKSVILLE AVE 28144 #030-05-1985 L1988 **D PD** *020 †55,15
TAJLILI, Morteza. 1601 BRENNER AVE 28144 #517-01-1969 L1991 **PTH** *020 †50
TANNEHILL, Robert Bruce. 129 WOODSON ST 28144 #012-01-1959 L1962 **PD** *071 †55
TEMPLETON, David Wesley. 612 MOCKSVILLE AVE, ROWAN REGIONAL MEDICAL CEN 28144 #028-46-1991 L1994 **EM** *020 †16
THEARD, Pierre-Richard D. 1601 BRENNER AVE, W G "BILL" HEFNER MEDICAL 28144 #440-01-1985 L2005 **PM SCI** *020 †60
THOMAS, Barbara Lowry. 427 W INNES ST 28144 #045-01-1985 L1988 **P** *020 †75
THOMPSON, Willard C, III. 721 GROVE ST 28144 #036-05-1981 L1988 **IM CD** *020 †20
THOMPSON, Willard Ray, Jr. 4 NORTH RD, 315 MOCKSVILLE AVE 28144 #051-04-1969 L1972 **OTO HNS** *020 †45
THRIVENI, Nice Pius. 1601 BRENNER AVE, HEFNER VAMC 28144 #495-63-1986 L2003 **P** *020 †75
THURM, Joel Alan. 1601 BRENNER AVE, STE 112 28144 #035-19-1967 L1998 **U** *020 †95
THURSTON, Thomas G, III. 911 W HENDERSON ST, STE 300 28144 #036-07-1968 L1968 **GYN** *071 †30
TOLSON, Carville Jos. 1315 S MAIN ST 28144 #005-12-1980 L1982 **GP GS** *020
TOWNS, Erron J. 129 WOODSON ST 28144 #030-06-2001 L2004 **PD** *020 †55
TUNA, Ishik Ceylan. 1601 BRENNER AVE, CENTER, SALISBURY VAMC 28144 #026-04-1980 L1983 **TS GS** *020 †85,90
UNTERREINER, Naomi. 1601 BRENNER AVE, WG HEFNER VAMC 28144 #836-03-1989 L2005 **DR** *020 †80
VOLKMER, Donald Durham. 1601 BRENNER AVE, VA MED CTR 28144 #016-06-1972 L1979 **IMG IM** *020 †20
WARD, Demming Morton. 612 MOCKSVILLE AVE 28144 #036-05-1974 L1974 **IM** *020 †20
WATFORD-VARGO, Becky A. ■ 28144 #035-06-1988 **IM** *020
WATSON, Kevin Whittington. 911 W HENDERSON ST, STE 410 28144 #036-01-1996 L2000 **GS** *020 †85
WATTS, Hugh Boyd. 1035 LINCOLNTON RD 28144 #047-06-1962 L1969 **ORS** *020 †40
WEBB, Wm Whitaker, Jr. 203 MOCKSVILLE AVE, STE A 28144 #036-01-1971 L1971 **D** *072 †15 ‡
WEBER, Joel Michael. 612 MOCKSVILLE AVE 28144 #036-01-1979 L1981 **PTH** *062 †50
WHITAKER, Robert Norton. 330 JAKE ALEXANDER BLVD W, STE 101 28147 #036-05-1990 L1995 **OTO A** *020 †45
WHITE, Diane Carol. 2143 STATESVILLE BLVD #C #3 28147 #010-03-1987 L2006 **IM** *020 †20
WILSON, Amy Elizabeth. 611 MOCKSVILLE AVE 28144 #041-12-2001 L2004 **IM** *020 †20
WILSON, Dennis Norman F. 911 W HENDERSON ST, STE 230 28144 #023-12-1986 L1998 **CD IM** *020 †20
WILSON, Robert B, II. 1809 BRENNER AVE, STE 205 28144 #039-01-1995 L1996 **APM AN** *100 †05
WIMMER, Mark Thomas. 825 W HENDERSON ST, HEMATOLOGY/ONCOLOGY 28144 #051-01-1994 L1995 **ON IM** *020 †20
WITHERS, Abner Carr. ■ 28147 #036-01-1962 L1962 **FM** *071 †18
WOOLWINE, Nathan Ashley. 611 MOCKSVILLE AVE, STE 202 28144 #047-06-1999 L2004 **NEP** *020 †20
WOOTEN, Wayne Brown. 401 MOCKSVILLE AVE STE 100 28144 #036-05-1974 L1974 **DR** *071 †80

SALUDA – POLK

ALLRED, David Price. 86 GREENVILLE ST 28773 #048-04-1966 L1994 **IM** *020 †20
ANDRUS, Charles Andrew. 178 TABLEROCK DR 28773 #045-01-1966 L1991 **GP OM** *020
BIGGERS, David Waring. 28773 #027-01-1988 L1992 **IM** *020 †16
HERRING, John Stephen, Jr. PO BOX 549 28773 #021-01-1963 L1995 **OBG** *020 †30
PFISTER, Robert Hans. 2727 MOUNTAIN PAGE RD 28773 #045-01-1995 L1998 **PD** *020 †55
WEST, Robert Bernard. ■ 28773 #035-01-1973 L1978 **ORS** *020 †40

SANFORD – LEE

ADKINS, Paula Clark. 1135 CARTHAGE ST, ATTN: DR. FRANK HARGETT 27330 #055-02-1996 L2006 **EM** *020 †16
AGONCILLO, Jose R, Jr. 2609 S HORNER BLVD, RAPID CARE URGENT CARE 27332 #748-01-1959 L1999 **FM** *020 †18 ‡
AINSLEY, Thellie R, Jr. 1007 CARTHAGE ST 27330 #036-01-1978 L1981 **IM IMG** *020 †20
ALEXANDER, Lawrence M. 515 CARTHAGE ST 27330 #036-07-1952 L1954 **FM** *072 †18
ASGHARIAN, Behnam. 110 DENNIS DR 27330 #035-06-1993 L2003 **GE** *020 †20 ‡
ATIEH, Mahmoud K. 110 FIELDS DR, PINEHURST MEDICAL CLINIC 27330 #575-01-1991 L1996 **IM IC** *020 †20
AYOADE, Folusakin O. 1135 CARTHAGE ST, ATTN: HOSPTALIST OFFICE 27330 #690-05-1997 L2005 **IM** *020 †20
BARNWELL, Valerie Jeanne. 1688 S HORNER BLVD 27330 #010-03-1985 L1992 **FM OM** *020 †18
BARSTOW, Craig Hamilton. ■ 27332 #023-12-2006 L2008 **FP** *012
BEEMER, Charles Theodore. 1816 DOCTORS DR, BOX 1169 27330 #045-01-1974 L1985 **ORS** *020 †40
BELL, Elizabeth Anne. 1135 CARTHAGE ST, CENTRAL CAROLINA HOSPITAL 27330 #036-01-1990 L1992 **AN** *020 †18
BIRCHARD, Teresa Thos. 1832 DOCTORS DR 27330 #010-01-1991 L2004 **OBG** *020 †30
BRIGGS, John Leslie. 1135 CARTHAGE ST 27330 #007-02-1981 L1984 **FM** *020 †18
BROWN, Anne Whitney. ■ 27330 #012-05-2003 L2006 **PCC** *012 †20
BUNAO, Alfred Sidney B. 1125 CARTHAGE ST 27330 #748-20-1986 L2003 **FM** *020 †18
CASWELL, Richard B, Jr. 1135 CARTHAGE ST, CENTRAL CAROLINA HOSPITAL 27330 #048-13-1994 L2003 **PDR** *020 †18
CHEESBOROUGH, John D. 827 S HORNER BLVD 27330 #036-07-1975 L1977 **D DMP** *020 †15 ‡
CILIBERTO, Samuel David. 101 S VANCE ST 27330 #035-08-1967 L1975 **ORS** *020 †40
CLINE, Robert Seitz. ■ 27330 #036-01-1957 L1957 **OM FM** *072 †18

COGGIN, James Michael. 1139 CARTHAGE ST, STE 107 27330 #036-01-1991 L1993 **GP PMM** *020
COHEN, Mauricio Gabriel. 1301 CENTRAL DR, CLINIC 27330 #132-05-1991 L2003 **CD IC** *040
COX, Stephen H. 1125 CARTHAGE ST 27330 #051-04-1977 L1984 **FM** *050 †18
DACKO, Douglas Mitchell. 1135 CARTHAGE ST 27330 #041-12-1971 L1988 **R** *020 †80
DEOCHAND, Mohan Charran. 114 S GULF ST 27330 #275-01-1983 L1999 **N SME** *020 †75
DHAWAN, Surinder. 611 WICKER ST 27330 #495-03-1989 L1997 **IM** *020 †20
DOUGLASS, Eric Jensenius. 1135 CARTHAGE ST, MEDICAL ARTS BLDG 101 27330 #028-03-1982 L1993 **AN** *020 †20
DUMMIT, Eldon Steven, Jr. 1135 CARTHAGE ST, MEDICAL ARTS BLDG 101 27330 #047-05-1959 L1972 **PTH CLP** *071 †50
EBKEN, Richard Keppler. 1816 DOCTORS DR 27330 #041-12-1968 L1982 **GS** *075 †85
ESPORAS, D C. 1816 DOCTORS DR 27330 #748-11-1968 L1974 **U** *020 †95
ESTES, Rebecca. 1135 CARTHAGE ST, CENTRAL CAROLINA HOSPITAL 27330 #017-20-1987 L1991 **AN** *020 †05
ESTEVEZ, Deborah. 1301 CENTRAL DR, UNC SANFORD SPECIALTY CLIN 27330 #032-01-2000 L2003 **IM** *020 †20
FULLER, Edwin Rudolph, III. 1301 CENTRAL DR, CLINIC 27330 #023-01-2000 L2005 **NEP** *020 †20
GARDNER, William Grant. ■ 27332 #038-41-1969 L2006 **ID IM** *020 †20 ‡
GARRETT, Dana Leann. 1125 CARTHAGE ST 27330 #045-04-1994 L1997 **FM** *020 †18
GORDON, Michael A. 709 WICKER ST, STE B 27330 #024-07-1976 L1987 **GS VS** *020 †85
GREGORY, Jennifer Barger. 555 CARTHAGE ST 27330 #036-08-1997 L1999 **MPD** *020 †20,55
GRIDER, Glenna Lea. 555 CARTHAGE ST 27330 #002-02-2001 L2005 **MPD** *020 †20,55
GROSS, William Henry. 27332 #041-02-1947 L1947 **AN** *071
GUEST, Pamela Jennymarie. 827 S HORNER BLVD, SANFORD DERMATOLOGY 27330 #048-02-1983 L1989 **D** *020 †20,15
HALL, William Ernest. 1911 K M WICKER DR 27330 #016-11-1973 L1984 **FM** *020 †18
HARGETT, Franklin. 1135 CARTHAGE ST 27330 #036-01-1983 L1984 **EM** *020 †18
HEIMBECKER, Paul Mark. 127 N STEELE ST, PAUL M HEIMBECKER MD PA 27330 #028-34-1990 L1994 **OBG** *020 †30
HOWARD, Paul Osmon. 1135 CARTHAGE ST 27330 #051-01-1955 L1957 **FM** *071 †18
HUSS, Andrew Michael. 1801 DOCTORS DR 27330 #039-01-2000 L2003 **PD** *020 †55
HUSS, Tara Mosley. 1801 DOCTORS DR 27330 #047-20-2000 L2003 **PD** *020 †55
JACKSON, Robert Bruce, II. ■ 27330 #036-01-1979 L1981 **OBG** *020 †30
JANTAC, Lukas. 110 FIELDS DR, PINEHURST MEDICAL CLINIC 27330 #023-01-2001 L2004 **CD** *020
JONES, Lisa Llewellyn. 1140 CARTHAGE ST 27330 #021-06-1988 L1993 **OBG** *020 †30
JORDAN, Robert Calhoun. ■ 27330 #036-01-1955 L1955 **DR NM** *071 †80
JURISICH, Steven Michael. 1818 DOCTORS DR, SANFORD SURGICAL CLINIC 27330 #021-05-1988 L1993 **GS** *020 †85
KEIFER, Cary Rebecca. 1801 DOCTORS DR 27330 #036-01-2004 L2007 **PD** *020 †55
KESLER, Archie Dean, Jr. ■ 27330 #051-04-1966 L1972 **OBG** *071 †30 ‡
KIM, Ipbi. ■ 27332 #005-12-1953 L1994 **OTO AI** *071 †45
KIRBY, Suzanne Lee. 1013 CARTHAGE ST 27330 #036-01-1988 L1991 **HEM** *020 †20
KIROL, Philip Michael. ■ 27332 #023-07-1960 L1962 **OBG** *071 †30
KREAM, Steven Jonathan. 1301 CENTRAL DR, UNC SANFORD SPECIALTY CLIN 27330 #028-02-1976 L2002 **PUD IM** *020 †20
LAMBERT, Jill Jimison. 1503 ELM ST, STE E 27330 #036-08-2001 L2002 **FM** *020 †18
LANGDON, Lori Moore. 1801 DOCTORS DR, SANFORD PEDIATRICS 27330 #036-07-1995 L1998 **PD** *020 †55
LARBI-SIAW, Kwame. ■ 27332 #412-01-1999 L2007 **IM** *100 †20
LITTLE, Douglas Jonathan. 136 CARBONTON RD STE A 27330 #036-01-1971 L1971 **IM CD** *075
LUTTERLOH, Isaac H, Jr. ■ 27330 #041-02-1952 L1952 **IM CD** *071
MAJERSKE, Cynthia Wilson. ■ 27332 #050-02-2001 L2006 **PM** *020 †60
MANGUM, John Rowland. 555 CARTHAGE ST 27330 #036-01-1981 L1982 **FM** *020 †18
MC CALL, Robt Donnell, Jr. 110 DENNIS DR 27330 #012-05-1985 L1989 **GE IM** *020 †20
MC CONVILLE, Robert H, Jr. 1125 CARTHAGE ST 27330 #017-20-1972 L1975 **FM FPG** *020 †18 ‡
MCCORD, Jennifer Elizabet. 1801 DOCTORS DR 27330 #047-20-2004 L2007 **PD** *020 †55
MENSE, Richard Hubert. ■ 27332 #028-34-1954 L1954 **GP** *071
MERRITT, Benjamin Keith. 127 N STEELE ST 27330 #036-01-1992 L1994 **OBG** *020 †18,30
METTS, Julius Franklin. 555 CARTHAGE ST, . 27330 #036-08-1982 L2006 **FM** *020 †18 ‡
MOTTL, Amy Katherine. 1301 CENTRAL DR, CLINIC 27330 #035-46-1999 L2002 **NEP** *020 †20
MULCAHY, Edward Richard. 101 S VANCE ST 27330 #050-02-1963 L1995 **ORS OS** *020 †40
NACHMAN, Patrick Henry. 1301 CENTRAL DR, CLINIC 27330 #024-05-1989 L1991 **NEP** *020 †20
NASSERI, Parinaz Baradara. 1139 CARTHAGE ST STE 105 27330 #517-08-1995 L2004 **IM** *020 †20
NAVE, Lester David, Jr. 555 CARTHAGE ST 27330 #036-05-1981 L1983 **FM** *020 †18
O'DONNELL, Gerard Jos. 1139 CARTHAGE ST, STE 110 27330 #561-06-1986 L1991 **IM** *020 †20
PATE, Marion Butler, III. 110 DENNIS DR 27330 #036-05-1981 L1986 **GE IM** *020 †20
PATTERSON, Robert Wm. 1503 ELM ST, STE E 27330 #036-01-1978 L1979 **FM NTR** *020 †18 ‡
PETERSON, John Linker. 1013 CARTHAGE ST 27330 #056-05-1983 L1989 **IM** *020 †20
PHILLIPS, Thomas Caldwell. 1139 CARTHAGE ST 27330 #012-05-1982 L1988 **NEP IM** *020 †20
PLEASANT, Henry N, Jr. 1140 CARTHAGE ST 27330 #036-08-1992 L1994 **OBG** *020 †30
PLUNKETT, William Gordon. 1139 CARTHAGE ST, STE 110 27330 #051-07-1983 L2006 **IM** *020 †20 ‡
PULKINGHAM, Nathan Carr. 1135 CARTHAGE ST, CENTRAL CAROLINA HOSP-PATH 27330 #036-08-1988 L1991 **PTH** *062 †50
PURVIS, William Henry. 1816 DOCTORS DR 27330 #036-01-1973 L1973 **U** *020 †95
REESE, Mitchell C. 1801 DOCTORS DR 27330 #051-04-1977 L1978 **PD** *020 †55
REISNER, Debra Marilyn. 1135 CARTHAGE ST 27330 #068-01-1981 L1983 **EM** *020
SAWYER, Thomas Rarick. 1223 CARTHAGE ST, CAROLINA EYE ASSOCIATES 27330 #025-01-1955 L1986 **OPH** *071 †35
SCHROEDER, Terry Milton. ■ 27330 #036-07-1973 L1978 **GS AS** *062 †85
SMITH, Erastus. 136 CARBONTON RD STE C 27330 #041-13-1973 L1976 **IM PHP** *020
SNYDER, B Stewart. 310 COURT SQ 27330 #045-04-1983 L1988 **FM OM** *020
STANTON, Edward Spires. 508 CARTHAGE ST 27330 #036-07-1979 L1984 **GS VS** *020 †85
SZABO, Stephen Anthony. 709 WICKER ST 27330 #033-05-1991 L1998 **OBG** *020 †30
TAYLOR, Robert Floyd. ■ 27332 #025-01-1944 L1945 **U** *071 †95
TERRY, William Vereen. 709 WICKER ST 27330 #036-05-1988 L1992 **OBG** *020 †30
TIRONA, Francisco P. 1135 CARTHAGE ST, 24 ON PHYSICIAN 27330 #748-01-1991 L1998 **IM** *020

■ = Address Information Privacy Protected

TORGERSON, Brian Charles. 1301B CARTHAGE ST 27330 #026-04-1978 L1988 **IM EM** *020 †20
TOZZI, Joseph Anthony. 2412 WILKINS DR, & OBSTETRICS PA 27330 #561-17-1986 L1998 **IM** *020
VERECZKEY-PORTER, Kinga. 1301 CENTRAL DR 27330 #473-02-1988 L2002 **RHU** *020 †20
WESTMORELAND, James P. 1135 CARTHAGE ST 27330 #041-01-1951 L1951 **IM OS** *075
WHITE, William Henry, Jr. 1140 CARTHAGE ST 27330 #036-01-1961 L1961 **GYN** *020 †30
WILLIAMS, Kenan Banks. ■ 27330 #041-02-1944 L1944 **PD** *071 †55
WILLIAMS, Lance Richard. 439 CROWN PT 27332 #041-12-1991 L1998 **RNR** *020 †80 ‡
WILSON, Thomas Alexander. 115 CARBONTON RD 27330 #036-01-1974 L1974 **P** *020
WITTENBORN, John William. 1135 CARTHAGE ST 27330 #422-01-1996 L2003 **DR** *020 †80
YOO, Sung Eun. 1301 CENTRAL DR, CLINIC 27330 #583-02-1994 L2004 **END** *100 †20
YOW, Kevin Brewer. 1125 CARTHAGE ST, SANDHILLS FAMILY PRACTICE, 27330 #036-01-1997 L1998 **EM** *020 †18
ZERR, Melissa Taunia. ■ 27332 #041-14-2005 L2005 **FP** *012

SAPPHIRE — JACKSON

FINNEY, Charles Eugene. ■ 28774 #012-05-1959 L1959 **GPM OPH** *072
HOLIMON, James Louis. 1600 US HWY 64 W 28774 #051-04-1969 L1969 **PTH GP** *071 †50
JONES, Frederic Gordon. ■ 28774 #012-01-1958 L1994 **CD IM** *071 †20

SCALY MOUNTAIN — MACON

CICHOSZ, Kenneth John. ■ 28775 #056-06-1960 L1961 **AN** *020 †05
SILLER, Everard Jos. ■ 28775 #012-01-1963 L1963 **N IM** *071

SCOTLAND NECK — HALIFAX

BYRUM, G Vance. 919 JR HIGH SCHOOL RD 27874 #036-05-1952 L1952 **FM FPG** *071 †18

SEAGROVE — RANDOLPH

ACHREJA, Manjeet Kaur B. 614 N BROAD ST, SEAGROVE MEDICAL CLINIC 27341 #496-03-1976 L1985 **FM** *020
GAGE, John F. 514 N BROAD ST, ASSOCIATES 27341 #011-02-1986 L1995 **FM** *020 †18

SEALEVEL — CARTERET

KINDELL, John Robt. HWY 70, SEA LEVEL CLINIC 28577 #051-01-1955 L1964 **GP PD** *071 †55

SELMA — JOHNSTON

WYMAN, Robert West. ■ 27576 #025-01-1967 L1972 **FM** *071

SEVEN LAKES — MOORE

KERR, John Mcclure, III. ■ 27376 #020-12-1999 L2006 **MPD** *020 †20,55

SEYMOUR JOHNSON AIR FORCE BASE — WAYNE

AGUILAR, Federico. 1050 JABARRAH AVE, 4TH MDG 27531 #042-03-1980 L1983 **PD PG** *020 †55
CAIN, Wilbert. 1050 JABARRAH AVE, ATTN: CREDENTIAL OFFICE 27531 #047-07-1986 L1988 **FM** *020 †18
MAYNARD, Dean Lane. 1050 JABARRAH AVE 27531 #030-06-1997 L2002 **FM** *020 †18

SHALLOTTE — BRUNSWICK

CRARY, Ely Jay. ■ 28470 #030-05-1963 L1986 **OPH** *050 †35
FAIRCLOTH, William Joseph. 460 HOLDEN BEACH RD 28470 #036-08-1993 L1995 **IM** *020
GRIMMETT, Matthew H. ■ 28468 #036-07-1943 L1949 **PD R** *071 †55,80
JOSEPH, David Alan. 4647 MAIN ST, STE 5 28470 #016-42-1973 L2006 **P** *020 ‡
LANGSTON, Bernard L. 341 WHITEVILLE RD NW 28470 #045-01-1972 L2003 **FM GP** *020
PRESSLEY, Rhonda D. 161 WILD RAVEN ST 28470 #036-05-1985 L1992 **FM** *020 †18
SAVARESE, Charles J, Jr. RESORT PLZ 28459 #010-01-1950 L1977 **FM CD** *071 †18
WARD, Bennie Brooks. 4748 MAIN ST 28470 #036-01-1959 L1959 **GP** *071

SHELBY — CLEVELAND

AHMED, Najla. 1019 N LAFAYETTE ST, STE 2 28150 #704-06-1980 L1994 **PD** *020 †55
AHMED, Syed Jawed. 1019 N LAFAYETTE ST, STE 1 28150 #704-02-1978 L1994 **NEP IM** *020 †20
ALAM, Muhammad Shah. 1019 N LAFAYETTE ST 28150 #160-02-1988 L2004 **NEP** *020 †20
ALDINGER, Kyle Anthony. 711 N DEKALB ST, SHELBY MEDICAL ASSOCIATES 28150 #010-02-1995 L2004 **IM** *020 †20
AYRONS, Keith Alan. 201 E GROVER ST 28150 #025-07-1989 L1995 **IM** *020 †20
BAILEY, Thomas Danl. 201 E GROVER ST 28150 #010-02-1978 L1982 **OPH OS** *020 †35
BALENTINE, Kerry Layne. 201 E GROVER ST, OUTPT BEHAVIORIAL HEALTH C 28150 #039-01-2001 L2005 **P** *020 †75
BARKER, David Bert. 951 WENDOVER HEIGHT DR 28150 #047-06-1971 L1980 **PLM EM** *030 †95
BARRINGER, Michael Lynn. 200 W GROVER ST, SHELBY SURGICAL ASSOCIATES 28150 #036-01-1976 L1976 **GS** *020 †85
BENFIELD, Brian Parick. 709 N DEKALB ST, ET 28150 #036-01-1996 L1997 **PD** *020 †55
BESSON, Gideon. 711 N DEKALB ST 28150 #035-46-1990 L1997 **PUD** *020 †20

BINION, Mark Lee. 709 N DEKALB ST 28150 #036-08-1989 L1992 **PD** *020 †55
BLACKBURN, Thomas Reid. 125 HILLSIDE DR, BOX 1179 28150 #036-05-1965 L1965 **DR** *020 †80
BLACKLEY, Shem K, III. 201 E GROVER ST 28150 #036-05-1983 L1988 **U** *020 †95
BLACKMAN, Douglas Allan. 200 W GROVER ST, SHELBY SURGICAL ASSOCIATES 28150 #036-01-1995 L1999 **GS** *020 †85
BOGAN, Stephen Jay. ■ 28150 #025-07-1984 L1993 **OPH IM** *020 †35
BOMBENGER, James John. 201 E GROVER ST, CLEVELAND REGIONAL MEDICAL 28150 #016-11-1973 L1983 **EM IM** *020 †20,16
BOUDREAU, Yves Pierre. 807 SCHENCK ST, STE 2 28150 #065-09-1989 L1996 **ORS** *020 †40
BOWLES, Richard M. 908 ELIZABETH RD 28150 #036-07-1952 L1953 **PD** *071
BOWLING, Richard F. 200 W GROVER ST, SHELBY SURGICAL ASSOCIATES 28150 #036-05-1953 L1953 **GS TS** *071 †85
BOYETTE, Douglas Ray. 111 W GROVER ST 28150 #036-05-1975 L1975 **CD IM** *020 †20
BRAME, Michael Eugene. 1001 N WASHINGTON ST 28150 #036-01-1994 L2000 **U GS** *020 †95
BROCKMAN, Steven Kenneth. 1112 YANCEY ST 28150 #038-06-1985 L1988 **PME AN** *020 †05
BROWNLEE, Jonathan I. 709 N DEKALB ST 28150 #045-01-1999 L2001 **PD** *020 †55
BURRUS, James Henry. 1203 E MARION ST 28150 #036-01-1957 L1957 **GYN** *071 †30
CAMPBELL, William Egbert. 222 N LAFAYETTE ST STE 1, SHELBY RADIOLOGICAL ASSOCS 28150 #036-05-1982 L1987 **VIR DR** *020 †80
CARTER, Numa R, Jr. 201 GROVER ST 28150 #036-05-1950 L1950 **FM** *071 †18
CAUNT, Calvin Leslie. 711 N DEKALB ST, SHELBY MEDICAL ASSOCIATES, 28150 #060-01-1990 L1997 **IM** *020 †20
CERJAN, Christopher M. 709 N DEKALB ST 28150 #012-01-1995 L1998 **PD** *020 †55
CHAMBERLAIN, Steven A. 355 W COLLEGE AVE A 28152 #045-01-1983 L1984 **OBG** *020 †30
CHARLES, William Jude. 201 E GROVER ST 28150 #305-01-1998 L2006 **HO** *020 †05
CHEANEY, Russell Alan. 1106 N WASHINGTON ST 28150 #020-02-1982 L1986 **AN** *020 †05
CHEN, Rita Elaine. 709 N DEKALB ST, MEDICAL UNIVERSITY OF SC-P 28150 #012-05-2005 L2008 **PD** *012
CLIFTON, Barbara Van Hoy. 711 N DEKALB ST, SHELBY MEDICAL ASSOCIATES, 28150 #036-05-1993 L1995 **IM** *020 †20
CLIFTON, Bobby Glenn, II. 1106 N WASHINGTON ST 28150 #047-06-1992 L1993 **AN** *020 †05
CLINE, Nancy Ellen. ■ 28150 #011-04-1994 L1998 **OPH** *020 †35
COALSON, Barry Edward. 711 N DEKALB ST, SHELBY MEDICAL ASSOCIATES, 28150 #012-01-1986 L1999 **CCM PUD** *020 †20
COLLIER, John Reginald, Jr. 1180 WYKE RD, CAROLINA EAR NOSE & 28150 #036-01-1977 L1977 **OTO** *020 †45
COLLINS, Ingeborg C. 110 W GROVER ST 28150 #036-05-1994 L1998 **OBG** *020 †30
COLLINS, Warren James. 315 GROVER STREET, MEDICAL DIRECTOR 28150 #036-07-1948 L1957 **GYN RO** *071 †30
COX, Bruce A, Jr. 807 SCHENCK ST STE 2, SHELBY BONE & JOINT CLINIC 28150 #016-42-1995 L2003 **ORS** *020 †40
CROW, John B. 201 E GROVER ST 28150 #036-05-1948 L1949 **FM** *020 †18
CROWLEY, Richard Vick. 205 LEE ST, CROWLEY GENERAL PRACTICE 28150 #012-05-1965 L1968 **GP** *071
CUMMINS, Larry Edward. 215 S WASHINGTON ST, STE 106 28150 #017-20-1961 L1985 **P CHP** *020
DAVIS, Daniel Edwin. 711 N DEKALB ST 28150 #036-05-1993 L2004 **IM** *020 †20
DAVIS, Thomas Rowland. 355 W COLLEGE AVE A 28152 #036-05-1986 L1987 **GYN** *020 †30
DEARMENT, Michael Clayton. 1198 WYKE RD, COMPREHENSIVE SLEEP CENTER 28150 #055-02-1998 L2004 **PCC SME** *020 †20 ‡
DE LA VEGA, Raul S, III. 222 N LAFAYETTE ST STE 1, SHELBY RADIOLOGICAL ASSOC 28150 #016-45-1979 L1980 **DR** *020 †80
DENNING, Christopher M. 201 E GROVER ST 28150 #012-01-1986 L1987 **FM** *020 †18
ELLIS, Michael Sydney. 1180 WYKE RD, CAROLINA EAR NOSE & 28150 #021-05-1966 L2005 **OTO FPS** *020 †45 ‡
EMERSON, Eric Tomson. 201 E GROVER ST 28150 #047-05-1990 L1997 **PS HS** *020 †65
FERRELL, Paul Brent. 711 N DEKALB ST 28150 #036-01-1975 L1975 **RHU IM** *020 †20
FIORE, Louis. 101 DELTA PARK DR 28150 #035-01-2005 L2005 **PM** *020
FORINASH, Robert Alan. 618 N MORGAN ST, FOOTHILLS CONSULTING ASSOC 28150 #045-04-1996 L2002 *020
FORTKORT, Peter T. 201 E GROVER ST, REGIONAL HEALTH SERVICES 28150 #012-01-1991 L2006 **IM** *020 †20
FRANKLIN, Richard Clifton. 1106 N WASHINGTON ST 28150 #036-05-1991 L1996 **AN** *020 †05
FRIEDMAN, Jacob. 807 SCHENCK ST, STE 2 28150 #035-46-1997 L2002 **ORS** *020 †40
GEBEL, Emile Louis. ■ 28150 #036-07-1962 L1962 **OPH** *071 †35
GEORGE, Garth Otto. 808 N WASHINGTON ST 28150 #422-01-1986 L2001 **GE** *020 †20
GILL, Brent Richard. 101 E GROVER ST 28150 #063-01-1990 L1998 **FM** *020 †18
GILLIATT, Cecil Lee, Jr. ■ 28150 #024-01-1962 L1963 **PD** *071 †55
GIRARD, Charles John, II. 222 N LAFAYETTE ST, STE 1 28150 #041-02-2002 L2007 **MSR** *012 †80
GOSSETT, Robert Peter. 1001 N WASHINGTON ST 28150 #048-13-1977 L1980 **U EM** *020 †95
GRINTON, Stephen Folger. 1198 WYKE RD, COMPREHENSIVE SLEEP CENTER 28150 #016-11-1981 L2004 **PD** *020 †20 ‡
HAMRICK, John C, Jr. 809 N LAFAYETTE ST STE A, CLEVELAND ORTHOPEDS ASSOC 28150 #036-05-1967 L1967 **ORS OSM** *071 †40
HANNAH, Frank Thos. 1622 E MARION ST, MORGANTON EYE PHYSICIANS 28150 #036-07-1964 L1964 **OPH** *020 †35
HANSMAN, Mark Anthony. 1106 N WASHINGTON ST 28150 #030-06-1989 L1999 **AN** *020 †05
HARDEMAN, Richard Austin. 315 E GROVER ST 28150 #012-05-1960 L1975 **FM** *020 †18
HAYEK, Charles Sigman. 709 N DEKALB ST 28150 #036-01-1985 L1988 **PD** *020 †55
HAYES, Patrick Robt. 101 DELTA PARK DR 28150 #010-02-1989 L1993 **ORS** *020 †40
HOBSON, Harry Douglas. 200 W GROVER ST 28150 #036-40-1988 L1993 **GS** *020 †85
HUGHLETT, Richard K. 201 E GROVER ST, DEPT OF ER 28150 #048-12-1994 L1997 **EM** *020 †16
INJEJIKIAN, Jirair I A. 709 E GROVER ST 28150 #605-01-1961 L1969 **GS TS** *075 †85,90
IQBAL, Aamir. 1019 N LAFAYETTE ST, STE 1 28150 #704-01-1986 L2002 **NEP** *020 †20
JAMES, Kevin Todd. 101 DELTA PARK DR, ORTHOCAROLINA 28150 #010-03-1985 L1996 **ORS AM** *020 †40
JONES, Mary Mckeel. 421 W MARION ST, CLEVELAND FAMILY PRACTICE 28150 #036-08-1986 L1987 **FM** *020 †18
JONES, Robert Spurgeon. 113 E GROVER ST 28150 #036-01-1954 L1954 **FM** *072 †18
JONES, Robert Spurgeon, Jr. 421 W MARION ST, CLEVELAND FMLY PRCTCE 28150 #036-08-1981 L1982 **FM** *020 †18
JONES, Stephen Watson. 113 E GROVER ST 28150 #036-08-1986 L1987 **FM** *020 †18
JUBANE, Alan Velez. 808 SCHENCK ST, CLECO MEDICAL CENTER OF SH 28150 #748-27-1987 L1997 **FM** *020 †18

KEELEY, Michael Murray. 355 W COLLEGE AVE A 28152 #036-01-1989 L1991 **OBG** *020 †30

KLEIN, Kevin Mart. 222 N LAFAYETTE ST 28150 #041-12-1980 L1994 **N** *020 †75

KODER, Brett Alison. 1180 WYKE RD, CAROLINA EAR NOSE & 28150 #021-05-1983 L1996 **OTO** *020 †45

LA CHANCE, Lynda. 807 SCHENCK ST STE 3, COUNTY 28150 #065-09-1989 L1996 **FM** *020 †18

LAMPLEY, Charles G, III. 110 W GROVER ST 28150 #036-05-1962 L1962 **OBG** *075 †30

LANEY, Robert Gaffney, III. 200 W GROVER ST 28150 #036-01-1981 L1986 **GS VS** *020 †85

LANGLEY, Chas Pitman, III. 711 N DEKALB ST, SHELBY MEDICAL ASSOC 28150 #036-01-1975 L1976 **IM** *020 †20 ‡

LEVY, Frederic Evan. 1180 WYKE RD, CAROLINA EAR NOSE & 28150 #016-01-1987 L1994 **OTO HNS** *020 †45

LOVE, Rebecca Jean. 113 E GROVER ST 28150 #036-05-1997 L2000 **FM** *020 †18

LOWRY, James Watkins. 201 E GROVER ST, DEPT OF ER 28150 #051-04-1994 L1998 **EM** *020 †16

MADISON, Christopher E. 808 SCHENCK ST, SHELBY FAMILY PRACTICE 28150 #036-08-1985 L1986 **FM** *020 †18

MANGUM, Gary Lionell. 201 E GROVER ST 28150 #036-05-1967 L1967 **ORS** *071 †40

MARTIN, Christian Eduardo. 113 E GROVER ST, JONES FAMILY PRACTICE 28150 #018-03-1998 L2001 **FM** *020 †18

MARTIN, Jerry Clinton. 1180 WYKE RD STE B, CLEVELAND NEUROLOGIC CLNC 28150 #016-43-1999 L2004 **N IM** *020 †20,75

MARTIN-HERRING, Dawn Lea. 355 W COLLEGE AVE A 28152 #039-01-1995 L2003 **OBG** *020 †30

MATULIS, Melissa Dawne. 201 E GROVER ST 28150 #055-01-1997 L1998 **HO** *020 †20

MAYFIELD, Kelli Burgin. 419 EARL RD, SHELBY WALK-IN MEDICAL CEN 28150 #047-20-1993 L2002 **FM** *020 †18

MC GRATH, James Gerard. 201 E GROVER ST 28150 #001-02-1995 L2005 **HO** *020 †20

MC MURRAY, Clarence M. ■ 28150 #036-05-1946 L1947 **IM** *071 †20

MC MURRAY, Dorothy E Gore. ■ 28150 #039-01-1945 L1948 **GP** *071

MC MURRY, Avery Willis. 201 GROVER ST 28150 #041-02-1945 L1945 **GS FPG** *071 †85

MELTON-SMITH, Renee B. 711 N DEKALB ST, SHELBY MEDICAL ASSOCIATES, 28150 #036-01-1992 L1996 **IM** *020 †20

MILLER, Donald S. 201 E GROVER ST 28150 #024-01-1962 L1967 **IM HO** *020

MILLER, Robert Michael. 808 SCHENCK ST 28150 #047-06-1967 L1975 **FM** *020 †18

MINUS, Joseph Sheppard. 201 GROVER ST 28150 #036-07-1965 L1965 **PD** *071 †55

MOOSE, Nancy Elizabeth. 709 N DEKALB ST, SHELBY CHILDREN'S CLINIC 28150 #036-08-1993 L1997 **PD** *020 †55

MULLEN, Joseph Patrick. 201 E GROVER ST 28150 #041-02-1973 L1993 **EM AM** *020 †16

MUNOZ, Paul. 201 E GROVER ST 28150 #024-01-1998 L2004 **EM** *020 †16

NAMAN, Carl Hawkins. 201 E GROVER ST 28150 #012-01-1967 L1974 **GS VS** *020 †85

NIBLACK, Brett Clayton. 355 W COLLEGE AVE A 28152 #036-05-1999 L2003 **OBG** *020 †30

NICHOLSON, Charles Alfred. 201 E GROVER ST, LABORATORY 28150 #039-01-1998 L2006 **PTH** *020

NORMAN, David Alan. 709 N DEKALB ST 28150 #001-02-1986 L1989 **PD** *020 †55

NORMAN, Katherine Leiter. 137 S POST RD 28152 #001-02-1986 L1989 **IM** *020 †20

O'DELL, Kevin Bruce. 201 E GROVER ST, DEPT OF ER 28150 #030-05-1983 L1990 **EM** *020 †16

OGGU, Bharani. 201 E GROVER ST 28150 #495-11-1996 L2006 **IM** *020 †20

PATEL, Sanjay Chandrakant. 111 W GROVER ST, THE SANGER CLINIC 28150 #473-03-1991 L1998 **CD** *020 †20

PEARSON, Lawrence H. 700 N LAFAYETTE ST 28150 #036-01-1979 L1980 **D IM** *020 †15 ‡

PEINDL, Paul Michael. 201 E GROVER ST, DEPT OF ER 28150 #041-09-1975 L1995 **EM** *020 †16

PERKINS, Petya Lee. 201 E GROVER ST, CLEVELAND MEM HOSP 28150 #036-01-1976 L1978 **RO** *071 †80

PERKINS, Robert Sanborn. 101 E GROVER ST, NETWORK 28150 #024-07-1960 L1983 **GS TS** *071 †85,90

PITCHER, Patricia. 709 N DEKALB ST, SHELBY CHILDREN'S CLINIC 28150 #035-15-1996 L1999 **PD** *020 †55

POTTS, James Martin. 200 W GROVER ST 28150 #012-01-1973 L1975 **GS** *020 †85

POWELL, Jess Averette. 222 N LAFAYETTE ST SU 28150 #047-06-1973 L1977 **DR** *020 †80

RABINDRAN, Evelyn A. 711 N DEKALB ST 28150 #037-01-1995 L1998 **IM** *020 †20

REIBER, Mark Edwin. 1180 WYKE RD, CAROLINA EAR NOSE & 28150 #038-41-1989 L2006 **OTO** *020 †45

REYNOLDS, John L. 1106 N WASHINGTON ST 28150 #649-14-1980 L1986 **AN GP** *020 †05

RIBADENEYRA, Michael G. 711 N DEKALB ST, SHELBY MEDICAL ASSOC PA 28150 #045-04-1996 L1999 **IM** *020 †20

RICHARDSON, Leslie Ann. 709 N DEKALB ST 28150 #050-02-1985 L1995 **OS** *020 †55

ROE, Rodney Allen. ■ 28150 #004-01-1968 L1988 **PTH** *071 †50

RYBNICEK, Karel F. 808 N WASHINGTON ST 28150 #286-04-1978 L1989 **GE IM** *020 †20

SANCHEZ, Ivan Orlando. 201 E GROVER ST, DEPT OF ER 28150 #025-01-1995 L1998 **EM** *020 †16

SARAZEN, Paul Mark, Jr. 201 E GROVER ST 28150 #036-07-1948 L1950 **PD** *071 †55

SECREST, Alvin Jackson. 1001 N WASHINGTON ST 28150 #036-05-1963 L1963 **U** *071 †95

SEEN, Teresa Guettler. ■ 28150 #036-05-1988 L1995 **PD** *074 †55

SELF, Jerry L. 3662 ARTEE RD 28150 #036-01-1977 L1977 **DR** *071 †80

SENNEWALD, Karen. 222 N LAFAYETTE ST STE 1, SHELBY RADIOLOGICAL ASSOCI 28150 #036-05-1985 L1993 **R NM** *020 †28,80,55

SETH, Brahmi Haritmai. 201 E GROVER ST 28150 #496-49-2001 L2007 **IM HOS** *020 †20

SHIPLEY, William Robert. 201 E GROVER ST, DEPT PATHOLOGY 28150 #045-04-1994 L1999 **PTH** *020 †50

SHOAF, Rebecca Williams. 709 N DEKALB ST 28150 #036-08-2001 L2003 **PD** *020 †55

SIDDIQUI, Mohammad Tahir. 1016 N LAFAYETTE ST 28150 #704-16-1990 L2000 **NEP** *020 †20

SIDHU, Surendrapal Singh. 114 LEE ST 28150 #495-05-1979 L1994 **FM FSM** *020 †18

SMITH, Brian David. 808 N WASHINGTON ST 28150 #036-01-1991 L1996 **GE IM** *020 †20

SMITH, Larry Edward. 808 SCHENCK ST 28150 #038-40-1977 L1994 **FM** *020 †18

SPINA, Lia M. 201 E GROVER ST 28150 #035-15-2001 L2007 **HO** *020

SPRAGINS, Joel Fred. 28151 #004-01-1964 L1971 **GE IM** *071 †20

STAMP, Ian Patrick. 1405A N LAFAYETTE ST, INTERNAL MED OF SHELBY 28150 #035-08-1990 L1998 **IM** *020

STEVENS, James Ashley, Jr. 201 E GROVER ST 28150 #010-01-1987 L1997 **DR** *020 †80

STORY, William Augustus. 805 N MORGAN ST, SHELBY RAD ASSOC 28150 #012-05-1958 L1966 **R** *071 †80

STOUNE, Amy Annelle. 808 SCHENCK ST, SHELBY FAMILY PRACTICE 28150 #028-78-2004, ▲ L2007 **FM** *100

STUCKY, William Vincent. 101 DELTA PARK DR 28150 #025-01-1985 L1990 **ORS** *020 †40

SURRATT, Wilson Farris. 1106 N WASHINGTON ST, SHELBY ANESTHESIOLOGISTS A 28150 #012-01-1983 L1986 **AN** *020 †05

TALLEY, Joseph Harold. 201 GROVER ST 28150 #051-01-1963 L1966 **FM** *075 †18

TAYLOR, Andrew John. 200 W GROVER ST 28150 #036-01-1998 L2002 **GS** *020 †85

TELLE, Lewis Donald. ■ 28150 #016-11-1943 L1948 **IM GS** *020 †85 ‡

THOMPSON, Forrest Leigh. 201 E GROVER ST 28150 #045-01-1993 L1986 **ON HEM** *020 †20

TOSCANO, Darlene K. 201 E GROVER ST 28150 #021-01-1999 L2004 **EM** *020 †16

TUBBS, Charles Otis. 201 E GROVER ST 28150 #039-01-1985 L1998 **DR** *020 †80

VAN FLEET, William Vernon. 416 N LAFAYETTE ST 28150 #010-01-1961 L1967 **P CHP** *020 †75

VINCENT, Dorothy Vaughn. 1429 E MARION ST, STE 5 28150 #012-01-1984 L2001 **PD** *020 †55

WEHMUELLER, Michael D. 222 N LAFAYETTE ST STE 1, SHELBY RADIOLOGICAL ASSOCI 28150 #025-01-1990 L1995 **DR** *020 †80

WILLIAMS, Irving. 917 N LAFAYETTE ST 28150 #308-07-1982 L1994 **IM** *020

WILLIAMS, Jack Dean. ■ 28150 #036-07-1965 L1965 **OTO** *071 †45

WOYCIECHOWSKA, J. 846 W WARREN ST, A-4 28150 #759-03-1963 L1996 **N** *020 †75

YATES, Steven Wayne. 201 E GROVER ST, CLEVELAND HEMATOLOGY & ONC 28150 #051-04-1987 L1993 **ON** *020 †20

YEN, Kenneth Tsu-Ching. 1198 WYKE RD 28150 #033-05-1997 L2006 **PUD CCM** *020 †20

YOUNG, Douglas Bryan. 200 W GROVER ST 28150 #036-01-1974 L1980 **GS TS** *020 †90,85

ZELLER, Frederick A. 1198 WYKE RD 28150 #055-01-1984 L1996 **PUD IM** *020 †20

ZUNIGA, Victor. 201 E GROVER ST 28150 #048-14-1999 L2007 **EM** *020 †16

SHERRILLS FORD – CATAWBA

ADAMS, Randy Steven. 8149 RIDGEWOOD RD, # 236 28673 #036-01-1980 L1981 **FM** *020 †18

CUTCHIN, Joseph Henry, Jr. ■ 28673 #036-07-1942 L1946 **GP IM** *071

SHILOH – CAMDEN

HOLLOWELL, Victor B. ■ 27974 #024-01-1946 L1953 **GS TS** *071 †85

SILER CITY – CHATHAM

BENEDETTO, Joseph Charles. 806 W 4TH ST, STE A 27344 #033-75-1984, ▲ L1993 **GS** *020

BUEBEL, Michael Scott. 311 N FIR AVE 27344 #045-01-1996 L2005 **FM** *020 †18

DAVIS, James Wayne. 311 N FIR AVE 27344 #036-05-1998 L2000 **FM** *020 †18

DEVRIES, Abigail Greiner. 224 S 10TH ST, SILER CITY COMM HLTH CNTR 27344 #036-01-2002 L2007 **FM** *020 †18

DYKERS, John Reginald, Jr. 401 N IVEY AVE STE A 27344 #036-01-1960 L1960 **FM** *020 †18

GIBSON, David Ellis. 311 N FIR AVE, CHATHAM PRIMARY CARE 27344 #012-01-2002 L2004 **FM** *020 †18

JORDAN, Sarah Turner. 224 S 10TH ST 27344 #036-01-1999 L2004 **FM** *020 †18

JOSHI, Jatin Harshad. 1002 N 2ND AVE 27344 #036-01-2006 L2007 **IM** *012

KNISLEY, Matthew Stephen. ■ 27344 #036-01-2008 *012

KOTHAPALLI, Nagasayana R. 315 E 3RD ST 27344 #495-11-1959 L1980 **GS GP** *020 †85

MC MANUS, Keith Eric. 801 W 3RD ST 27344 #036-01-1984 L1988 **FM FSM** *020 †18

SCHWANKL, James Edmund. 1002 W 3RD ST 27344 #026-04-1969 L1972 **PD** *020

SIMON, Robert Currie. ■ 27344 #028-02-1961 L1988 **GS VS** *062 †85

TORONTOW, Christopher J. 224 S 10TH AVE 27344 #036-01-1999 L2002 **FM** *020 †18

WHITT, Donna Jo. 311 N FIR AVE 27344 #036-01-2004 L2007 **FM** *100

ZERINGUE, Mark J. 421 N HOLLY AVE 27344 #012-05-1977 L1981 **FM** *020 †20

SKYLAND – BUNCOMBE

LORENZO, Luisa Almedia. PO BOX 1158, 1812 HENDERSONVILLE 28776 #036-01-1978 L1979 **PTH EM** *071 †16,50

PEREZ, Joselyn Mercedes. PO BOX 1768 28776 #042-01-1974 L1987 **FM** *020 †18

SMITHFIELD – JOHNSTON

AGRAWAL, Neeta Neeraj. 509 N BRIGHTLEAF BLVD, JOHNSTON MEMORIAL HOSP 27577 #495-22-1989 L2004 **HMP** *020 †50

ALIOTO, Richard J. 507 N BRIGHTLEAF BLVD, STE 100 27577 #035-45-1988 L1997 **ORS** *020 †40

ATHUS, Romain. 517 N BRIGHTLEAF BLVD 27577 #649-30-1995 L2005 **FM** *020 †18

ATSTUPENAS, Eliot Anthony. 509 N BRIGHTLEAF BLVD 27577 #036-01-1989 L1993 **EM** *020 †16

AVERY, Frank Walton. 509 N BRIGHTLEAF BLVD 27577 #036-01-1967 L1967 **PTH FOP** *020 †50

BATTEN, Woodrow. 601 N 8TH ST STE B 27577 #036-05-1944 L1945 **IM OS** *020

BIRD, Richard Edward. 507 N BRIGHTLEAF BLVD 27577 #036-05-1965 L1965 **DR** *020 †80

BLAKELY, Pamela Faye. 509 N BRIGHTLEAF BLVD 27577 #036-01-1993 L1996 **FM** *020 †18

BOWLING, Mark Gregory. 509 N BRIGHTLEAF BLVD 27577 #020-02-2000 L2003 **FM** *020 †18

BURGE, Holly Jean. 507 N BRIGHTLEAF BLVD 27577 #038-40-1985 L1987 **DR** *020 †80

BURKE, Eithne T. 507 N BRIGHTLEAF BLVD 27577 #539-05-1982 L1997 **DR** *020 †80

BYLCIW, Stanley Robt. 530 NORTH ST 27577 #561-17-1975 L1982 **ORS GS** *020 †40

CARLSON, Marie A. 507 N BRIGHTLEAF BLVD, STE 100 27577 #036-07-2000 L2003 **IM** *020 †20

CARPENTER, Sally Lawson. 11 BERKSHIRE PL 27577 #036-01-1983 L1985 **PD** *020 †55

CARTER, Craig Steven. 712 WILKINS ST, STE E 27577 #041-13-1981 L2005 **TS VS** *020 †85,90 ‡

CASKEY, Cynthia Irene. 507 N BRIGHTLEAF BLVD 27577 #045-01-1979 L1991 **R PD** *040 †80

CERWIN, Robert A. 507 N BRIGHTLEAF BLVD 27577 #035-20-1970 L1976 **R NM** *020 †28,80

CHANDLER, Kerry Eileen. 507 N BRIGHTLEAF BLVD 27577 #033-06-1988 L1996 **DR** *020 †80

CHAZLI, Firas. 509 N BRIGHTLEAF BLVD 27577 #781-01-1989 L1995 **IM PD** *020 †20

COATES, George Glenn. 507 N BRIGHTLEAF BLVD 27577 #005-15-1990 L1996 **DR** *020 †80

COATES, Karen Ann. 507 N BRIGHTLEAF BLVD 27577 #036-01-1988 L1990 **DR** *020 †80

COLLINS, James Bernard. 131 E MARKET ST 27577 #051-01-1990 L2000 **GS** *020 †85

CONN, Frank Wm. 509 N BRIGHTLEAF BLVD, JOHNSTON MEMORIAL HOSPITAL 27577 #041-07-1975 L2002 **GS** *020 †85 ‡

COOPER, Trella Shevonne. 517 N BRIGHTLEAF BLVD 27577 #036-01-1991 L2001 **PD** *020 †55

CORNETT, Joseph Buran. 507 N BRIGHTLEAF BLVD 27577 #051-01-1988 L1995 **RNR** *020 †80

■ = Address Information Privacy Protected

COURT, Charles Jos. 509 N BRIGHTLEAF BLVD, CAROLINA BONE & JOINT 27577 #045-01-1991 L2005 **APM** *020 †05
DAVIS, Rhonda Hardee. 410 CANTERBURY RD 27577 #036-01-1985 L1987 **FM** *020 †18
DOUGLAS, Margaret Rankin. 507 N BRIGHTLEAF BLVD 27577 #051-01-1983 L2000 **PDR PD** *020 †80,55
DOUGLAS, Martin Rans. 507 N BRIGHTLEAF BLVD 27577 #051-01-1989 L2000 **DR** *020 †80
EVANS, Regina Boggs. 300 S 3RD ST, STE C 27577 #017-20-1996 L2003 **OBG** *020 †30
FAKADEJ, Maria Margaret. 507 N BRIGHTLEAF BLVD, STE 100 27577 #055-01-1996 L2000 **IM** *020 †20
FAULKNER-ROYAL, Dina K. 509 N BRIGHTLEAF BLVD 27577 #028-02-1995 L2007 **PD** *020 †55
FEIN, Alan Bruce. 507 N BRIGHTLEAF BLVD 27577 #035-01-1978 L1981 **DR IM** *020 †20,80
FOSTER, Tanya Denise. 520 NORTH ST 27577 #033-06-2002 L2007 **OBG** *020
FOX, Kimberly Dawne. 507 N BRIGHTLEAF BLVD 27577 #422-01-1998 L2001 **MPD** *020 †55
GAAL, Imre, Jr. 507 N BRIGHTLEAF BLVD 27577 #032-01-1991 L1995 **DR** *020 †80
GUDURU, Usha Sudheer. 517 N BRIGHTLEAF BLVD, JOHNSTON COUNTY HEALTH DEP 27577 #495-57-1992 L2004 **FM** *020 †18
GULLOTTO, Carmelo. 507 N BRIGHTLEAF BLVD 27577 #036-07-1998 L2001 **DR** *020 †80
HARTMAN, Edwin Lonzo. 215 W TURLINGTON ST, POST OOFICE BOX 408 27577 #561-01-1975 L1978 **IM** *020
HAUGAN, Paul Andrew. 507 N BRIGHTLEAF BLVD 27577 #026-04-1998 L1999 **DR** *020 †80
HOFFMAN, Leroy Geo. 7 BERKSHIRE RD 27577 #036-05-1975 L1975 **RO PD** *020 †55,80
HUME, Douglas Peter. 509 N BRIGHTLEAF BLVD 27577 #041-02-1980 L1988 **EM** *020 †16
JOHNSON, Thomas Milton. 509 N BRIGHTLEAF BLVD 27577 #036-01-1957 L1957 **FM** *071
JORDAN, Christopher Page. 415 N 7TH ST STE C 27577 #036-08-1995 L2000 **GE** *020 †20
JORDAN, Laurie O. 509 N BRIGHTLEAF BLVD 27577 #036-01-1991 L1993 **AN** *020 †05
JORDAN, Lyndon Kirkman. 415 N 7TH ST, P O BOX 760 27577 #036-07-1961 L1961 **FM** *071 †18
JORDAN, Lyndon Kirkman. 507 N BRIGHTLEAF BLVD 27577 #036-07-1993 L1995 **DR** *020 †80
KATURU, Raghu Ramaiah. 601 N 8TH ST STE B, SMITHFIELD FAMILY PRACTICE 27577 #495-70-1991 L2004 **FM** *020 †18
KENNEDY, Susan Lucille. 507 N BRIGHTLEAF BLVD 27577 #041-02-1990 L1996 **DR** *020 †80
KENT, Carrie Sheek. PO BOX 1376, JOHNSTON MEMORIAL HOSPITAL 27577 #036-01-1994 L1999 **FM** *020 †18
KOFFER, Dennis Shelly. 131 E MARKET ST 27577 #056-06-1972 L1993 **GS** *020 †85
KREMER, Timothy Michael. 300 S 3RD ST, STE C 27577 #038-41-2002 L2006 **OBG** *020
KWONG, Michael D. 507 N BRIGHTLEAF BLVD 27577 #048-13-1997 L2003 **DR VIR** *020 †80
LAL, Madan. 925 N BRIGHTLEAF BLVD 27577 #495-03-1967 L1983 **OPH** *020 †35
LANDAU, Steven Edward. 707 WILKINS ST 27577 #041-13-1975 L1987 **FM** *020 †18
LEE, Catherine G. 7 BERKSHIRE RD 27577 #011-04-1988 L1993 **RO** *020 †80
LEE, Richard Sommerville. 709 NORTH ST, NEUSE GASTROENTEROLOGY PA 27577 #036-08-1983 L1984 **GE IM** *020 †20
LING, David. 507 N BRIGHTLEAF BLVD 27577 #036-07-1977 L1982 **DR** *020 †80
LIPPITT, Robert Gardner. 507 N BRIGHTLEAF BLVD 27577 #010-02-1985 L1990 **U** *020 †95
LIPTON, Melissa. 507 N BRIGHTLEAF BLVD 27577 #048-14-1997 L2000 **DR** *020 †80
LIVERMAN, Joseph Thos, Jr. 410 CANTERBURY RD 27577 #036-05-1980 L1981 **FM** *020 †18
LOW, William Y L. 509 N BRIGHTLEAF BLVD 27577 #065-01-1980 L2001 **FM EM** *020 †18
MARTIN, Philip Joseph. 509 N BRIGHTLEAF BLVD, JOHNSTON MEMORIAL HOSPITAL 27577 #654-01-2000 L2006 **AN** *020
MATZKO, John. 507 N BRIGHTLEAF BLVD 27577 #041-14-1990 L1996 **DR** *020 †80
MAX, Richard Jay. 507 N BRIGHTLEAF BLVD 27577 #033-06-1977 L1978 **DR** *020 †80
MELAMED, Joseph Wm. 507 N BRIGHTLEAF BLVD 27577 #008-01-1990 L1995 **DR** *020 †80
MERTEN, David Fischer. 507 N BRIGHTLEAF BLVD 27577 #038-41-1956 L1977 **PDR PD** *020 †55,80
MILLS, Steven Robt. 507 N BRIGHTLEAF BLVD 27577 #036-01-1972 L1972 **DR** *020 †80
MINTZ, Robert David. 507 N BRIGHTLEAF BLVD 27577 #035-48-1985 L1990 **DR RNR** *020 †80
O'DONNELL, Dennis Martin. 507 N BRIGHTLEAF BLVD 27577 #051-01-1974 L1992 **DR PUD** *020 †20,80
OH, Richard W. 509 N BRIGHTLEAF BLVD 27577 #041-12-1996 L1998 **FM** *020 †18
ORNITZ, Robert David. 7 BERKSHIRE RD 27577 #039-01-1971 L1975 **RO** *020 †80
OVERTON, Carroll C. 507 N BRIGHTLEAF BLVD 27577 #036-01-1991 L1992 **DR VIR** *020 †80
PARMAR, Madhu. 520 NORTH ST 27577 #305-01-1998 L2003 **OBG** *020 †30
PEARSON, Marilyn Roseann. 517 N BRIGHTLEAF BLVD, HEALTH DEPT. 27577 #036-01-1995 L1996 **FM** *020 †18
PEREZ, Efrain. 520 NORTH ST 27577 #042-03-1980 L1994 **OBG** *020 †30 ‡
PEREZ-SELDEN, Alice R. 712 WILKINS ST STE B 27577 #041-13-1979 L1986 **GS** *020
PETERS, Bryan Maclin. 507 N BRIGHTLEAF BLVD 27577 #036-07-1981 L1985 **DR** *020 †80
PITTARD, Jesse Calvin. 410 CANTERBURY RD 27577 #036-01-1977 L1977 **FM** *020 †18
POLLARD, Dulon Devon. PO BOX 411 27577 #036-07-1963 L1963 **P** *071 †75
POPE, Charles Vance. 507 N BRIGHTLEAF BLVD 27577 #036-01-1976 L1976 **DR EM** *020 †80
POSILLICO, Louis F. 507 N BRIGHTLEAF BLVD 27577 #010-02-1991 L1997 **DR NM** *020 †80,28
POWELL, Thomas Wm. 131 E MARKET ST 27577 #036-01-1974 L1974 **GS VS** *020 †85
POYET, Claire Marie. 507 N BRIGHTLEAF BLVD 27577 #036-07-1981 L1986 **DR** *020 †80
PRETTER, Philip C. 507 N BRIGHTLEAF BLVD 27577 #041-12-1992 L2000 **R VIR** *020 †80
RANGAR, Jitinder S. 601B BERKSHIRE RD 27577 #495-03-1964 L1982 **DR NM** *020 †80
ROSS, Michael Leonard. 507 N BRIGHTLEAF BLVD 27577 #016-06-1979 L1982 **DR** *020 †80
ROUGIERCHAPMAN, Duncan P. 507 N BRIGHTLEAF BLVD 27577 #036-07-1998 L2000 **DR** *020 †80
RYAN, Regina M. 410 CANTERBURY RD, HORIZON FAMILY MEDICINE 27577 #036-07-1984 L1991 **FM** *020 †18
SABA, Philip Robt. 507 N BRIGHTLEAF BLVD 27577 #041-12-1991 L2001 **RNR** *020 †80
SAILER, Scott Lee. 507 N BRIGHTLEAF BLVD 27577 #024-01-1984 L1988 **RO** *020 †80
SCHAAF, Robert Edmund. 507 N BRIGHTLEAF BLVD 27577 #024-07-1976 L1977 **DR NM** *030 †80 ‡
SECRIST, Randy Dean. 507 N BRIGHTLEAF BLVD 27577 #017-20-1980 L1988 **DR OS** *020 †80
SHAHIDA, Shubi. 712 WILKINS ST STE A, SHUBI SHAHIDA, MD, INC 27577 #495-31-1999 L2005 **IM** *020 †20
SHEIKH, Rashid Ahmed. 509 N BRIGHTLEAF BLVD, JOHNSTON MEMORIAL HOSPITAL 27577 #704-08-1989 L2000 **PPR PD** *020 †20,55
SHIROLKAR, Shailesh C. 509 N BRIGHTLEAF BLVD, CAPE FEAR VALLEY HEALTH SY 27577 #495-28-1991 L1999 **IM** *020 †20
SIERRA, John. 507 N BRIGHTLEAF BLVD 27577 #035-20-1983 L1990 **DR R** *020 †80
SINGH, Manmohan. 509 N BRIGHTLEAF BLVD 27577 #495-03-1960 L1972 **GS** *020
SPARGO, John Mark. 507 N BRIGHTLEAF BLVD 27577 #036-05-1982 L1989 **DR** *020 †80
STEVENS, Marc Sheldon. 540 NORTH ST 27577 #030-06-2000 L2007 **ORS** *020 †40 ‡
TAYLOR, Leslie L, III. 509 N BRIGHTLEAF BLVD 27577 #036-01-1980 L1981 **PTH HEM** *020
TURLINGTON, William Troy. 300 S 3RD ST, STE C 27577 #036-01-1991 L1992 **OBG** *020 †30
UDWADIA, Jamie. 509 N BRIGHTLEAF BLVD 27577 #305-01-1999 L2004 **PM OS** *020 †60 ‡
VARADARAJAN, Rupashree. 509 N BRIGHTLEAF BLVD 27577 #496-39-1996 L2004 **IM** *020
WATSON, Gwendolyn Renee. 713 WILKINS ST 27577 #036-08-1991 L1996 **FM** *020
WATSON, Stanley Rudolph. 410 CANTERBURY RD 27577 #036-01-1988 L1989 **FM** *020 †18
WEEKS-SHULKA, Susan Marie. 507 N BRIGHTLEAF BLVD 27577 #036-01-1991 L1996 **DR** *020 †80
WILSON, Russell Chapman. 507 N BRIGHTLEAF BLVD 27577 #036-07-1998 L2004 **DR** *020 †80
WOODALL, Leonard Schmick. 517 N BRIGHTLEAF BLVD 27577 #036-01-1956 L1956 **GYN** *071 †30
WU, Andrew Christopher. 507 N BRIGHTLEAF BLVD 27577 #028-02-1983 L1992 **VIR DR** *020 †80

SNEADS FERRY – ONSLOW

BRADFORD, Chad. ■ 28460 #048-13-1996 L1999 **P** *020 †75
CHRISTMAN, Emily Munro. ■ 28460 #010-02-2004 L2004 **GS** *100
GUNNETT, Sylvia Roberta. ■ 28460 #041-09-1969 L2003 **PTH** *071 †50
KAVANAUGH, Michael Joseph. ■ 28460 #016-43-2005 L2005 *020
KOSTECKI, Zbigniew M. ■ 28460 #759-08-1980 L1995 **FM** *020 †18
LEVINE, Charlotte Clark. ■ 28460 #023-07-1949 L1988 **FM GPM** *071 †18
MOYER, Louis Jeffrey. ■ 28460 #023-12-2004 L2005 *100
ORAM, Christian William. ■ 28460 #041-77-2006, ▲ L2007 *012
SIZEMORE, Daniel Chadwick. ■ 28460 #055-01-2003 L2004 *020
STANTON, James Earl. ■ 28460 #017-20-2006 L2007 *012
STERLING, Todd Henry. ■ 28460 #005-12-2004 L2005 **GS** *020
ZIMMER, Gregory James. ■ 28460 #023-12-1999 L2001 **EM** *020
ZIMMER, Sara B. ■ 28460 #023-12-1999 L2000 **PTH** *100 †50

SNOW HILL – GREENE

ALSTON, Nimia. 102 PARKWOOD DR, PARKWOOD MEDICAL CENTER 28580 #715-01-1987 L1997 **FM** *020 †18
OSTA, Elie Michel. 302 N GREENE ST 28580 #605-02-1991 L1995 **IM** *020 †20
ROBERTSON, Alexander, III. KATE B REYNOLDS PED CTR, 205 MLK PARKWAY 28580 #051-01-1957 L1989 **PD** *071 †55
SCOTT, Ann Mohney. 205 MARTIN L KING JR PKWY, KATE B REYNOLDS MEDICAL CE 28580 #036-08-1999 L2002 **FM OBG** *020 †18
WITT, Cynthia Jo. 302 N GREENE ST, P O BOX 658 28580 #036-05-1992 L2006 **FM** *020 †18

SOUTHERN PINES – MOORE

AMARESH, Amar Muniyappa. 355 S BENNETT ST 28387 #495-72-1990 L2006 **VIR** *020 †80
AUSTIN, Henry Vann. 681 S BENNETT ST, PINEHURST RHEUMATOLOGY CLI 28387 #036-07-1967 L1967 **RHU** *020 †20
BIRK, Wilbur Robt. ■ 28387 #025-01-1945 L1987 **AN** *071 †05
BOALS, Joseph C. 195 W ILLINOIS AVE, SANDHILLS PEDIATRICS 28387 #047-06-1993 L1996 **PD** *020 †55
BOLDEN, Richard Owen, Jr. ■ 28387 #023-01-1981 L2005 **DR** *020 †80 ‡
BONE, Samuel Nicholas, III. 355 S BENNETT ST 28387 #036-07-1987 L2002 **DR** *020 †80
BROWER, Jonathan Edward. 126 JAMES CREEK RD 28387 #005-14-2001 L2004 **EM** *020 †16
BROWN, Teresa Grace. 355 S BENNETT ST 28387 #036-01-1982 L1986 **DR** *020 †80
BRUTON, H David. 195 W ILLINOIS AVE 28387 #036-01-1961 L1961 **PD** *071 †55
BURNHAM, Steven James. 355 S BENNETT ST 28387 #047-05-1972 L1978 **VS GS** *020 †85
CARLTON, Wendi Mehler. 195 W ILLINOIS AVE 28387 #036-01-1994 L1999 **PD** *020 †55
CARTER, Steven Raymond. 2170 MIDLAND RD 28387 #036-05-1978 L1980 **AN** *020 †05
CEPEDA, Christopher M. 355 S BENNETT ST 28387 #011-02-2001 L2007 **RNR** *020 †80
CHOI, Andrew Inwon. 355 S BENNETT ST 28387 #016-06-1990 L1998 **DR** *020 †80
CRUELL, Randy Anthony. 355 S BENNETT ST 28387 #005-14-1993 L2002 **RNR** *020 †80
DEL MONACO, Brian Lee. ■ 28387 #023-12-1998 L2007 **EM** *020 †16
DELOSSANTOS ONGJOCO, R. 180 PERRY DR 28387 #035-08-1985 L1995 **P PYG** *020 †75
DEUCHER, Robert Leonard. 102 GOSSMAN RD, PINEHURST MEDICAL CLINIC 28387 #036-07-1992 L1994 **IM** *020 †20
DIASIO, Christoph Robert. 195 W ILLINOIS AVE 28387 #001-02-1998 L2001 **PD** *020 †55
DIETRICHSON, Wm Seward. PO BOX 2001 28388 #056-05-1948 L1980 **OBG** *071 †30
GOODRICH, Albert. ■ 28387 #017-20-1941 L1950 **EM GS** *071 †85
GRIFFIN, Neil Bostrom. 2170 MIDLAND RD 28387 #001-02-1984 L1994 **OPH** *020 †35
HARTSELL, Charles Jacob. 395 FAIRWAY DR # P 28387 #036-07-1958 L1958 **AN** *071 †05
HASERICK, John R. ■ 28387 #026-04-1941 L1970 **D DMP** *071 †15
HIDALGO, Hector Jesus. 355 S BENNETT ST 28387 #010-01-1976 L1980 **R** *020 †80
HOEHN-SARIC, Edward W L. 209 WINDSTAR PL, SOUTHERN PINES DIALYSIS CE 28387 #023-07-1989 L1997 **NEP** *020 †20
HUTCHINSON, Michael Irvin. 170 W HEDGELAWN WAY, MICHAEL I HUTCHINSON, MD 28387 #028-34-1976 L2004 **FM** *020 †18
JOHNSON, Keith Emery. 1852 US HIGHWAY 1 S, CAROLINA HEALTH QUEST 28387 #018-03-1982 L1986 **GP FM** *020
KENT, Karin Yount. 195 W ILLINOIS AVE 28387 #036-05-1995 L2006 **PD** *020 †55
KIZER, William Steel. ■ 28387 #048-13-2001 L2003 **U** *020
KOON, Crawford Bryan, Jr. 355 S BENNETT ST 28387 #036-01-1970 L1970 **DR** *020 †80
LESTER, James William, Jr. 355 S BENNETT ST 28387 #036-05-1983 L1990 **DR** *020 †80
LINA, John Raymond. ■ 28387 #033-05-1973 L1974 **DR** *020 †80
LOEHR, Stephen Peter. 355 S BENNETT ST 28387 #036-05-1995 L1997 **VIR** *020 †80
MARTIN, Kara. 681 S BENNETT ST 28387 #048-12-1990 L1996 **IMG RHU** *020 †20
MARTIN, Robert Gale. 2170 MIDLAND RD 28387 #036-01-1968 L1968 **OPH GP** *020 †35
MASON, Nora Catherine. 195 W ILLINOIS AVE, SANDHILLS PEDS 28387 #036-05-1995 L1998 **PD** *020
MC CRORY, Michael Elliott. 355 S BENNETT ST 28387 #024-07-1973 L1977 **DR** *020 †80 ‡
MESSNER, Daniel Kent. 2100 MIDLAND RD, CAROLINA EYE ASSOC 28387 #017-20-1981 L1986 **OPH** *020 †35
MILEWSKI, Ronald James. ■ 28387 #038-40-1979 L1980 **EM** *030 †16
MINCEY, Gregory J. 2170 MIDLAND RD 28387 #012-05-1977 L1983 **OPH** *020 †35
MORRISON, H Maxwell, Jr. ■ 28387 #036-01-1957 L1957 **OPH** *071 †35

■ = Address Information Privacy Protected

NEWTON, Leonard Jos. ■ 28387 #035-46-1977 L2005 **OTO A** *020 †45 ‡
NEWTON, Walter Monroe. ■ 28387 #045-01-1961 L1969 **PS GS** *020 †85,65
PATHAK, Hemang Jayendra. 355 S BENNETT ST 28387 #495-76-1990 L2002 **MSR** *020 †80
PENICK, George Dial. ■ 28388 #024-01-1946 L1946 **DMP ATP** *071 †50
PENNARDT, Andre Maria. 120 HILLWOOD CT 28387 #035-15-1991 L1999 **EM** *020 †16
REISIG, Michael Anthony. 135 TURNER ST, PREMIER PEDIATRICS, P.A. 28387
  #046-01-2001 L2007 **PD** *020 †55
RICE, James Edwin. ■ 28388 #038-40-1979 L1985 **ORS** *020 †40
ROBERSON, Jill Renae. 135 TURNER ST 28387 #021-01-1986 L1989 **PD** *020 †55
SAFRIT, Hal Dean. 355 S BENNETT ST 28387 #036-01-1982 L1983 **DR** *020 †80
SHERRINGTON, Brian Thomas. 195 W ILLINOIS AVE, SANDHILLS PEDIATRICS 28387
  #011-03-1973 L1976 **PD** *020 †55
SIMPSON, Dale Mc Clure. 180 PERRY DR 28387 #023-07-1976 L1979 **P ADP** *020 †75
SKEEN, James Thos. 205 HIGHLAND RD 28387 #045-01-1981 L1998 **AN** *020 †05
SODHI, Harbans Singh. ■ 28387 #495-03-1950 L1993 **PTH** *020 †50
STEWART, William Lee. 195 W ILLINOIS AVE 28387 #036-01-1979 L1980 **PD** *020 †55
STOLL, Michael Patrick. 355 S BENNETT ST 28387 #035-48-1990 L2005 **DR** *020 †80
SUMMERS, Andrew. 630 S BENNETT ST 28387 #055-01-1976 L1989 **EM** *020 †16
SUTTENFIELD, Virginia. PO BOX 2001 28388 #012-01-1944 L1944 **CHP P** *071
TART, James Alvin. ■ 28387 #036-05-1966 L1966 **CD IM** *071 †20
THOMPSON, Harry Glenn. ■ 28387 #041-13-1943 L1944 **OBG** *071 †30
THOMPSON, John Paul. 355 S BENNETT ST 28387 #036-07-1984 L1988 **DR** *020 †80
VARANASI, Sangeeta. 102 GOSSMAN RD, PINEHURST MEDICAL CLINIC 28387
  #036-01-1998 L2005 **IMG** *020 †20
VOORHEES, Diana Ruth. 355 S BENNETT ST 28387 #041-14-1981 L1985 **DR** *020 †80
WALLACE, Donald Kai. 102 GOSSMAN RD, NEESE FAMILY HEALTH CLINIC 28387
  #036-07-1959 L1959 **IM IMG** *020 †20
WEAVER, James Phillip. 355 S BENNETT ST 28387 #041-01-1969 L1983 **VS TS** *020 †85,90
WHITE, Charles Allen. ■ 28387 #038-06-1943 L1990 **CD IM** *071 †20
WHITE, Jeffrey Jason. 2170 MIDLAND RD, CAROLINA EYE ASSOCIATES, P 28387
  #056-05-2000 L2002 **OPH** *020 †35
WIENER, M David. 355 S BENNETT ST 28387 #035-19-1984 L1987 **DR RNR** *020 †80
WILLIAMS, David Leon. 400 NW BROAD ST 28387 #017-20-1968 L1970 **IM ON** *020 †20 ‡
WILLIAMS, Susan Catherine. ■ 28387 #036-08-2005 **NS** *012
WOLF, Harvey Hugh. 10935 S US HWY 15 501 28387 #041-13-1986 L1990 **IM** *020 †20
YANKES, Joseph Robt, Jr. 355 S BENNETT ST 28387 #041-12-1982 L1983 **DR** *020 †80

SOUTHPORT — BRUNSWICK

ADAMS, James Bruce. 1029 N HOWE ST, STE 100A 28461 #020-12-1979 L1981 **IM** *020 †20
ALDRICH, Juan Luis. 11 E 9TH ST 28461 #847-10-1973 L1996 **CD IM** *020 †20
ALLEN, Joanne Bell. 902 N HOWE ST, ORTHOPAEDIC SPECIALISTS 28461 #036-05-1989 L2001
  PM OM *020 †60
AZZATO, John Anthony. 902 N HOWE ST 28461 #041-02-1970 L1976 **ORS** *020 †40
BECKETT, Thomas Johnson. 1456 N HOWE ST, STE 202 28461 #036-08-1994 L1995
  IM *020 †20
BROWN, Rebecca Heil. 3599 GEORGE II HWY, BOILING SPRING LAKES FAMIL 28461
  #045-01-1997 L2006 **FM** *020 †18 ‡
BRUCE, William Henry, Jr. ■ 28461 #047-07-1943 L1952 **GYN** *071
COLE, Tollie Boyce. 719 N HOWE ST 28461 #036-01-1962 L1962 **OTO** *020 †45
CURTIN, Michael James. ■ 28461 #016-43-1964 L1999 **AN** *071 †05
DI MICELI, Ettore. ■ 28461 #056-06-1956 L1957 **AN** *072 †05
DREW, David Arthur. ■ 28461 #025-01-1961 L1962 **AN** *071 †05
DUNN, Clarence Alvin, Jr. ■ 28461 #036-01-1963 L1963 **ORS** *071
EASON, George Wm. 924 N HOWE ST 28461 #001-02-1974 L1975 **DR** *062 †80
FLOWERS, Jefferson M. ■ 28461 #045-01-1957 L2000 **EM** *020 †16
FORSTNER, James Robt. 4654 LONG BEACH RD SE 28461 #036-01-1973 L1977
  FM OBG *020 †18
HASHEMI, Ziaollah. 924 N HOWE ST, DOSHER MEMORIAL HOSPITAL 28461
  #036-05-1989 L1990 **EM** *020
HATCHFIELD, Harvey J. ■ 28461 #035-09-1945 L1946 **AN** *071 †05
HATEM, Joseph Patrick. 924 N HOWE ST, J ARTHUR DOSHER HOSPITAL 28461
  #036-01-1982 L1985 **IM** *020
HAWKINS, Richard D. 4831 PORT LOOP RD SE 28461 #036-07-1997 L2001 **OPH** *020 †35
HILAMAN, Brad Lee. 823 N ATLANTIC AVE 28461 #041-02-1976 L1995 **OBG LM** *020 †30
HILTZ, Douglas. 1456 N HOWE ST 28461 #035-03-1986 L1989 **IM CD** *020 †20
HOCKER, Shawn Brooke. 821 N ATLANTIC AVE 28461 #036-01-2000 L2006 **ORS** *020
HOLLAND, G Thomas. 924 N HOWE ST 28461 #036-01-1989 L1990 **FM OBG** *020 †18
IKALOWYCH, Sherry Zilbert. 905 N HOWE ST 28461 #033-05-2002 L2005 **IM** *020 †20
KAHAI, Jugta. 4734 LONG BEACH RD SE 28461 #496-21-1991 L1999 **CCP PD** *020 †55
LEONE, Kathleen Canning. 4831 PORT LOOP RD SE 28461 #010-02-1990 L1998 **OPH** *020 †35
LEVIN, Kenneth J. ■ 28461 #050-02-1961 L1972 **AN** *040 †05
MAC CALLUM, Daniel Bruce. 924 N HOWE ST, DOSHER MEMORIAL HOSPITAL 28461
  #055-01-1972 L2002 **IM** *020 †20
MARUSHACK, Michael Mark. 902 N HOWE ST 28461 #049-01-1986 L1999 **OSM ORS** *020 †40
MINOR, Andre Lemeac. 819 N ATLANTIC AVE, P O BOX 11027 28461 #036-08-1987 L1988
  IM *020 †20
MULFINGER, William Bruce. ■ 28461 #035-15-1969 L1974 **IM GE** *071 †20
MUSTER, William Jesse, Jr. ■ 28461 #035-05-1969 L1973 **PD** *071 †55
PIEPER, Terry Lee. 905 N HOWE ST 28461 #026-04-1999 L2000 **IM** *020 †20
RESCHLY, Keith Christian. 821 N ATLANTIC AVE 28461 #018-03-1987 L1988 **FM** *020 †18
SAVIDGE, Thomas Oliver. 905 N HOWE ST 28461 #041-09-1960 L1978 **IM CD** *020 †20 ‡
SEYMOUR, John Christopher. ■ 28461 #010-01-1965 L2008 **IM** *071 †20 ‡
SUCHECKI, Slade A. 3960 EXECUTIVE PARK BLVD, STE 600 28461 #020-75-2003, ▲ L2004
  FM *020 †18
TIMMONS, Robert Lansing. ■ 28461 #024-01-1953 L1958 **NS** *071 †25
WEINGARTEN, James Keller. 924 N HOWE ST, DOSHER MEMORIAL HOSPITAL 28461
  #045-01-1986 L1987 **IM** *020
WEISNER, Larry Felix. 621B N FODALE AVE, SOUTHPORT SURGICAL ASSOCS, 28461
  #561-01-1988 L1994 **GS VS** *020 †85
WOOD, Karen Elizabeth. 3599 GEORGE II HWY 28461 #041-02-1994 L2001 **FM** *020 †18
YAMUSAH, Nadine Anne. 924 N HOWE ST, J. ARTHUR DOSHER MEMORIAL 28461
  #759-04-2003 L2007 **IM** *100 †20
ZUKOSKI, Robert Michael. 904 N HOWE ST 28461 #041-02-1977 L1982 **GS** *020 †85

SPARTA — ALLEGHANY

ABSHER, Elsie Denise. 233 DOCTORS ST 28675 #036-01-1998 L2001 **FM** *020 †18
ASHLEY, Gale Jackson. 617 DOCTORS ST 28675 #036-01-1956 L1956 **GP** *071 †18
AYCOCK, James Bernice. ■ 28675 #036-05-1944 L1944 **DR** *071 †80
BANKS, Stacy Elizabeth. ■ 28675 #036-01-2007 **P** *012
BERES, Mary-Emma H. 233 DOCTORS ST, P O BOX 9 28675 #036-01-1994 L1998 **FM** *020 †18
CAHN, Jack Richard. 214 DOCTORS ST, ALLEGHANY FAMILY PRACTICE 28675
  #041-14-1972 L1975 **FM** *020 †18
CRAVEN, Nicholas Scott. ■ 28675 #036-07-1962 L1962 **FM P** *071 †75
DIGEL, Mary Carol. 214 DOCTORS ST, ALLEGHANY FAMILY PRACTICE 28675
  #036-07-1987 L1988 **FM** *020 †18
DRISCOLL, William Barry. 233 DOCTORS ST 28675 #010-02-1965 L2002 **GS TRS** *020 †85
GIVENS, Julian Lee. ■ 28675 #051-04-1957 L1961 **FM** *071 †18
HERAVI, Cyrus. 12 WILLIS ST 28675 #517-01-1962 L1971 **GS** *071 †85
HOWELL, Harry Slade, Jr. 233 DOCTORS ST 28675 #036-05-1968 L1968 **GS VS** *020 †85
JOHNSON, Harry Lester, Jr. 214 DOCTORS ST 28675 #036-01-1957 L1957 **EM P** *071
KOVACICH, John Jos. 248 DOCTORS ST, STE A 28675 #012-05-1976 L1979 **IM** *020 †20
LATHAM, Georgia Sue. 393 N MAIN ST, SHARE CLINIC 28675 #036-01-1986 L1993 **FM** *020 †18
LEE, Joseph David. 233 DOCTORS ST, P.O. BOX 9 28675 #041-13-1968 L1976 **R** *020 †80
LYON-SMITH, Mary E. 157 HEALTH SERVICES RD, ALLEGHANY HEALTH DEPARTMEN 28675
  #036-05-1977 L1979 **FM** *020 †18
MURPHY, Maureen Elise. 214 DOCTORS ST, ALLEGHANY FAMILY PRACTICE 28675
  #019-02-1985 L1986 **FM** *020 †18
RAY, Jeffrey Allen. 12 WILLIS ST STE C, NEW RIVER FAMILY MEDICINE 28675
  #036-08-1994 L1995 **FM** *020 †18
RUBIN, Herbert B. 233 DOCTORS ST 28675 #067-01-1968 L1996 **GS** *020 †85
SUBBIAH, Muruganathan P.. 665 S MAIN ST, BLUE RIDGE CARDIOLOGY & IN 28675
  #495-61-1994 L2004 **IM** *020 †20
TAYLOR, Kevin Lee. ■ 28675 #036-05-2006 **EM** *020
THORE, Tammy Lynn. 12 WILLIS ST, STE B 28675 #036-08-1986 L1992 **GS** *020

SPENCER — ROWAN

EDDINGER, Chas Frederick. ■ 28159 #036-01-1955 L1955 **GP** *072
KISER, Glenn Augustus. ■ 28159 #036-07-1941 L1946 **PD FM** *071
NICKERSON, Lloyd Emery. 300 N SALISBURY AVE, DBA FAMILY MEDICAL CARE 28159
  #039-05-1986 L1989 **FM OM** *020 †18

SPINDALE — RUTHERFORD

GUNN, R Bruce. 206 RESERVATION DR 28160 #036-01-1986 L1988 **FM EM** *020 †18
KNOELKE, Michael Walter. 271 CALLAHAN KOON RD, AREA MH/MR/SA 28160
  #011-02-1974 L1977 **P** *020
O'NEIL, Dennis Patrick. 206 RESERVATION DR 28160 #021-06-1995 L1998 **IM** *020 †18
PATTERSON, Patricia Gayle. ■ 28160 #048-02-1973 L1994 **NEP** *020 †20
WASHBURN, Harrill G, Jr. 206 RESERVATION DR 28160 #036-05-1994 L1997 **FM** *020
WASHBURN, Harrill Gene. 206 RESERVATION DR 28160 #036-05-1958 L1959 **GP** *071 †18
WINKER, Guyton Joel. 206 RESERVATION DR 28160 #036-05-1984 L1985 **FM** *020 †18
WINKER, Nancy Newcomb. 206 RESERVATION DR 28160 #036-05-1986 L1987 **FM** *020 †18

SPRING HOPE — NASH

BECKHAM, Michelle Lee. 100 DODD ST, BOICE-WILLIS CLINIC 27882 #036-01-1998 L1999
  FM *020 †18
LOWRY, Otis Megel. BRANCH ST 27882 #036-01-1956 L1956 **FM** *020
MAY, Alfred Thos, III. 100 DODD ST, BOICE-WILLIS CLINIC 27882 #036-08-1990 L1993
  FM *020 †18

SPRING LAKE — HARNETT

AZIZ, Khalid. 224 N MAIN ST 28390 #704-01-1983 L1997 **IM** *020 †20
HARDIN, Ronald David, Jr. ■ 28390 #004-01-2000 L2005 **GS** *020 †85
LEE, Maximilian Samuel. ■ 28390 #023-12-1998 L1999 **EM** *020 †16
LEWIS, Marvin. 6750 OVERHILLS RD 28390 #012-01-1986 L1989 **FM** *020 †18
LOPEZROCAFERNAND, A. ■ 28390 #042-01-2002 L2004 **P** *020 †75
RIEFKOHL, Waldemar Luis. ■ 28390 #041-13-2003 L2003 **OTO GS** *012
RIGAUD, Gardy J. ■ 28390 #649-39-1984 L2004 **P** *100
SUKHERA, Naveed A. 224 N MAIN ST, PO BOX 438 28390 #704-06-1984 L1997 **IM** *020 †20

SPRUCE PINE — MITCHELL

ALDRIDGE, Heidi. 342 OAK AVE 28777 #036-05-1993 L1996 **FM** *020 †18
ATWATER, John Spencer, Jr. 125 HOSPITAL DR 28777 #012-01-1970 L1977
  AI PDA *020 †55,03 ‡
BARRON, Bruce. 125 HOSPITAL DR 28777 #065-09-1969 L1977 **GS** *020 †85
BENNETT, George Ernest. ■ 28777 #011-03-1961 L1989 **GYN** *020 †30
BOBBE, Dorothy Jeanne D. PO BOX 9, SPRUCE PINE COMMUNITY HOSP 28777
  #041-01-1988 L1992 **FM** *074 †18
BROOKS, Rebecca Mater. ■ 28777 #036-08-1996 L1997 **FM** *020 †18
CADE, Jerry David. 125 HOSPITAL DR 28777 #005-18-1972 L1975 **FM PD** *020 †18
CARROLL, James Bruce. 125 HOSPITAL DR 28777 #035-15-1986 L1987 **FM** *020 †18
CASSANEGO, A Sergio. 7968 HIGHWAY 19 E 28777 #187-23-1978 L1997 **IM** *020 †20
CENDER, Craig Joseph. 125 HOSPITAL DR 28777 #011-03-1995 L1999 **GE PG** *020 †20,55
CIRELLI, Stephen R. 125 HOSPITAL DR, SPRUCE PINE COMM HOSP 28777
  #561-01-1986 L2004 **IM** *020 †20
CORT, Carolyn Le Nora Ray. 7968 HIGHWAY 19 E 28777 #036-05-1970 L1970 **PD** *020 †55
ERVINE, Harry F, Jr. 178 HOSPITAL DR, BLUE RIDGE WOMEN'S CARE 28777
  #748-08-1977 L2001 **OBG** *040
FLINT, Russell Austin. 78 BROAD ST 28777 #012-05-1987 L1993 **ORS** *020 †40

GARRETT, John William. 125 HOSPITAL DR 28777 #035-20-1983 L1985 GE IM *020 †20
HAAGA, James Arthur. 125 HOSPITAL DR 28777 #047-06-1980 L1983 IM *020 †20
HALL, Brent Dwayne. 125 HOSPITAL DR 28777 #036-08-1988 L1991 FOP *020 †50
HANCOCK, Wm Franklin, Jr. 125 HOSPITAL DR 28777 #036-01-1968 L1968 PTH CLP *020 †50
HILL, Steven Chas. 88 HOSPITAL DR 28777 #005-18-1972 L1975 FM *020 †18
HOEPPNER, David Lawrence. 125 HOSPITAL DR 28777 #062-01-1965 L1975 IM *020 †20
JOHNSON, Curtis C. RR 1 BOX 480 28777 #035-06-1953 L1977 GS *071 †85
JOHNSON, David Holloway. 7948 HIGHWAY 19 E 28777 #021-01-1967 L1974 PDC PD *020 †55
KING, Barbara Anne. 125 HOSPITAL DR 28777 #036-01-1982 L1984 FM *020 †18
KUHNE, Albert K. 125 HOSPITAL DR 28777 #036-01-1977 L1977 EM FM *020 †18
LARSON, David Wilbur. 496 ALTAPASS HWY 28777 #016-02-1967 L1973 IM IMG *020 †20
LARSON, Jennifer Ellen. PO BOX 9, 125 HOSPITAL DR 28777 #036-01-2000 L2006 IMG *100 †20
MAC LEAN, Susan Simmons. 7968 HIGHWAY 19 E 28777 #021-05-1980 L2000 PD *020 †55
MARSH, J Suzanne. 125 HOSPITAL DR 28777 #041-09-1968 L1979 EM GP *020
MC KAY, Martha King. 125 HOSPITAL DR 28777 #012-05-1986 L1990 IM *020 †20
NORTH, Stephen William. ■ 28777 #036-01-2000 L2006 ADL *020 †18
REED, Bert Thos. PO BOX 9 28777 #039-01-1963 L1972 PDA PD *074 †55
RHEINBOLT, Richard Merwin. 7968 HIGHWAY 19 E 28777 #004-01-1969 L2006 PHP *020 †55,70 ‡
ROBINSON, David B. 8017 HIGHWAY 19 E 28777 #039-05-1985 L1996 GS TRS *020 †85
SMOKER, Chad Eric. 88 HOSPITAL DR 28777 #017-20-2000 L2003 FM *100 †18
SNIDER, Susan Tripp. 36 HOSPITAL DR 28777 #036-01-1978 L1979 FM *020 †18
STEELE, Samuel M, Jr. 125 HOSPITAL DR, SPRUCE PINE COMMUNITY HOSP 28777 #019-02-1968 L1993 U *020 †95 ‡
THISSE, Joyce Bernice. 7968 HIGHWAY 19 E 28777 #047-05-1975 L1978 FM EM *020 †18
WILL, Melissa Anne. 7968 HIGHWAY 19 E 28777 #036-01-1982 L1998 PD *020 †55
WOOD, Matthew Wm. 125 HOSPITAL DR 28777 #028-03-1989 L1999 GE *020 †20
WOODARD, Arch. 125 HOSPITAL DR 28777 #005-06-1974 L1977 FM EM *020 †18

STANLEY – GASTON

CASE, Michael Stephen. 159 E DALLAS RD, SOUTH POINT FAMILY 28164 #021-05-1986 L1987 FM *020 †18
EDEL, Kenneth Patrick. 159 E DALLAS RD 28164 #018-03-1995 L1998 FM *020 †18
EMERSON, Russell Ian. 700 N MAIN ST, CAROMONT FAMILY MEDICINE 28164 #065-10-1972 L1992 FM *020 †18
FORRESTER, James Summers. 510 S HIGHWAY 27 28164 #036-05-1962 L1962 FM PHP *020 †70,18
GLASS, Gregory Lee. 159 E DALLAS RD 28164 #055-02-1991 L1994 FM *020 †18
LARSEN, Per Lykke. 700 N MAIN ST, CAROMONT FAMILY MEDICINE 28164 #065-10-1974 L1994 FM *020 †18
SIVARAMAN, Priya. 700 N MAIN ST, CAROMONT FAMILY MEDICINE 28164 #495-16-1998 L2005 FM *020 †18
TARKINGTON, Beth S. 510 S HIGHWAY 27 28164 #041-07-1981 L1984 FM *020 †18

STAR – MONTGOMERY

SCARBOROUGH, Chas F, Jr. PO BOX 309 27356 #041-02-1946 L1947 GP *071

STATESVILLE – IREDELL

ABELL, James Curtis. 925 THOMAS ST 28677 #036-01-1966 L1966 PD *020 †55
ADAMS, J A. 218 OLD MOCKSVILLE RD 28625 #051-01-1989 L2001 AN *020 †05
ADAMS, Richard Wesley. 770 HARTNESS RD, PIEDMONT HEALTH CARE 28677 #036-05-1962 L1963 ORS *020 †40
ALFORD, Peter Tyler. 728 HARTNESS RD 28677 #027-01-1979 L1983 PUD CCM *020 †20
ANTOSZYK, Andrew Nicholas. 646 HARTNESS RD 28677 #035-09-1983 L1984 OPH *020 †35
ANTOSZYK, James Howard. 646 HARTNESS RD 28677 #035-09-1979 L1996 OPH PO *020 †35
ARYEETEY, Robert Adjamah. 276 OLD MOCKSVILLE RD, STE 1100 28625 #412-02-1992 L2005 ID IM *020 †20
BARKER, Roger Wm. 218 OLD MOCKSVILLE RD 28625 #047-06-1967 L1973 OTO *071 †45
BARTELT, Perry Lester. 276 OLD MOCKSVILLE RD, STE 400 28625 #036-05-1984 L1987 FM *020 †18
BELLINGHAM, Daniel D. 705 GAITHER RD 28625 #049-01-1990 L1996 FM FSM *020 †18
BENFIELD, Ronald Wm. 702 HARTNESS RD 28677 #010-01-1981 L1986 ORS *020 †40
BENSON, Susan Rene. 129 SHERLOCK DR, PIEDMONT HEALTHCARE PEDS 28625 #055-01-1999 L2002 PD *020
BENTLEY, Ralph Luther. 557 BROOKDALE DR 28677 #036-01-1960 L1960 PD *020 †55
BLACKLEY, William Jackson. 619 SULLIVAN RD 28677 #036-01-1975 L1975 FM *020 †18
BORJA, Michael G. 1669 NORWOOD RD, NORTHLAKE PED CARE 28677 #748-01-1989 L1996 PD *020 †55
BOUHUSSEIN, Naim Ezzat. 738 BRYANT ST, STE A 28677 #051-07-1989 L1996 CD *020 †20
BOWEN, Benjamin Cureton. 218 OLD MOCKSVILLE RD 28625 #045-01-1963 L1968 FM *071 †18
BOWMAN, Geoffrey K. 1503 E BROAD ST 28625 #064-01-1982 L1995 OBG *020
BRADFORD, James Hedrick. 738 BRYANT ST, STE A 28677 #036-05-1975 L1975 CD IM *020 †20
BRANDON, Scott Craig. 774 HARTNESS RD 28677 #036-05-1997 L2007 HS *020 †40
BRECKWOLDT, Reid Douglas. 548 BROOKDALE DR 28677 #045-04-1993 L1998 DR *020 †80
BREMNOR, Judy Debra. ■ 28625 #566-01-1995 L2002 FM *020 †18
BRODKIN, Richard Alan. 276 OLD MOCKSVILLE RD, STE 800 28625 #036-05-1974 L1975 ON HEM *020 †20
BROWN, Robert Calvin. ■ 28625 #036-01-1959 L1959 PTH CLP *071 †50
CARRICO, Victoria Lee. 218 OLD MOCKSVILLE RD 28625 #038-41-1984 L1997 AN *020 †05
CASH, David Wayne. 310 DAVIE AVE 28677 #036-01-1982 L1983 FM *020 †18
CAUSEY, Andrew Jackson. ■ 28677 #047-05-1943 L1946 OPH OTO *071
CHERRY, William Hill. 218 OLD MOCKSVILLE RD 28625 #012-01-1956 L1965 OBG *071 †30
CHEWNING, Samuel J, Jr. 523 BROOKDALE DR 28677 #020-12-1979 L1980 OSS *020 †40
COARSEY, Stephen Mc Neil. 564 BROOKDALE DR 28677 #012-01-1982 L1984 OBG *020 †30
CORYELL, Carolyn Margaret. 557 BROOKDALE DR 28677 #012-05-1976 L1995 U *020 †95
DOAN, Bernice Hoanglan. 557 BROOKDALE DR, IREDELL MEMORIAL HOSPITAL 28677 #012-01-2003 L2006 IM *100
DOAN, Cuong Tan. 557 BROOKDALE DR 28677 #012-01-2003 L2006 FM *020
DULIN, Nancy Larson. 218 OLD MOCKSVILLE RD 28625 #001-02-1991 L2002 AN *020 †05
DUNLAP, Benjamin Emerson. 925 THOMAS ST STE C 28677 #036-01-1963 L1963 FM *020 †18
ELNAGGAR, Ahmed Sharaf I. 208 OLD MOCKSVILLE RD 28625 #915-04-1981 L1995 PCC OSM *020 †20
ENRIQUE, Ronel Rocha. 556 KITCHINGS DR 28677 #038-40-1987 L1993 OTO *020 †45
FAIR, Lisa Alverson. 1804 DAVIE AVE 28677 #036-01-1989 L1991 OBG *020 †30
FOREMAN, Frank Le Roy. 550 BROOKDALE DR 28677 #045-01-1971 L1978 D *020 †15
FOULKS, Carl Alvin, Jr. 208 OLD MOCKSVILLE RD 28625 #010-03-1997 L2003 GE *020 †20
FOUSHEE, James Sidney. 1804 DAVIE AVE 28677 #036-05-1982 L1985 IM *020 †20
FULGHUM, Edwin Morton, Jr. 208 OLD MOCKSVILLE RD 28625 #036-01-1974 L1974 OBG *020 †30
GARCHA, Trishwant Singh. 750 HARTNESS RD, STE E 28677 #010-03-1991 L2000 CN N *020 †75
GASTON, Thomas. 548 BROOKDALE DR 28677 #035-08-1994 L2005 DR *020 †80
GATLIN, Keith A, Jr. 218 OLD MOCKSVILLE RD 28625 #045-01-1979 L1984 CD IM *020 †20
GEORGESON, Ray Irwin. 766 HARTNESS RD 28677 #005-12-1989 L1996 CD *020 †20
GESSLER, Walter Curtis. 129 SHERLOCK DR 28625 #020-12-1995 L1998 PD *020 †55
GOOCH, Hubert L, Jr. 523 BROOKDALE DR 28677 #051-01-1988 L2001 ORS *020 †40
GOODSON, Phillip Richard. 1669 DAVIE AVE 28677 #036-05-1976 L1976 GYN *020 †30
GRIMM, Ruby Ann. 738 BRYANT ST 28677 #055-01-1975 L1977 ON HEM *020 †20
HALL, Christopher S. 704 HARTNESS RD 28677 #036-05-1994 L1998 AN *020 †05
HAMILTON, Buford L, Jr. 218 OLD MOCKSVILLE RD 28625 #041-01-1961 L1968 FM IM *071
HARBERTS, Arthur Stanley. 218 OLD MOCKSVILLE RD 28625 #869-07-1957 L1973 OBG *020 †30
HARDAWAY, John Steger. ■ 28677 #036-05-1952 L1952 FM PD *071 †18
HARR, Debra M. 557 BROOKDALE DR 28677 #036-05-1984 L1986 RO *020 †80
HARRIS, Bruce C. 208 OLD MOCKSVILLE RD 28625 #028-03-1981 L1986 GS AS *020 †85
HATHARASINGHE, Roger Amal. 138 SHERLOCK DR 28625 #422-01-1990 L1994 IM *020 †20
HENNINGER, Joseph Baylor. ■ 28677 #016-06-1946 L1946 IM *071
HICKS, Harlan Meguiel. 208 OLD MOCKSVILLE RD 28625 #051-01-1997 L2001 IM *020 †20
HILL, Patricia Kaye. 515 BROOKDALE DR 28677 #036-01-1979 L1980 P *020 †75
HUTCHINSON, Jon Ryan. 129 SHERLOCK DR 28625 #654-01-2001 L2007 PDC *020
HYPPOLITE, Jean-Claude. 2603 DAVIE AVE 28625 #440-01-1980 L1995 NEP IM *020 †20
ISFAN, Daniela. 708 HARTNESS RD 28677 #067-04-1986 L1996 FM *030 †18
JAROSZ, Todd S. 523 BROOKDALE DR 28677 #033-06-1993 L2006 ORS *020 †40
JETER, Natashia Ann. 1804 DAVIE AVE 28677 #045-01-2001 L2005 OBG *020 †30
JOHNSON, Tink A, III. 208 OLD MOCKSVILLE RD 28625 #047-06-1982 L1983 U *020 †95
KARNAP, Kristin Marie. ■ 28677 #036-05-2008 *012
KASWINKEL, Daryl Danl. 646 HARTNESS RD 28677 #047-06-1992 L1999 OPH *020 †35
KEARNEY, Bobby Paxton. 536 SIGNAL HILL DRIVE EXT 28625 #031-01-1985 L2001 AN PME *020 †05
KEPLEY, Michael Avery. 527 BROOKDALE DR 28677 #036-01-1980 L1984 OBG *020 †30
KIMBALL, Robert Roy. 619 SULLIVAN RD 28677 #064-01-1976 L1996 UCM FM *020 †18
KOGUT, David Gene. ■ 28625 #041-09-1975 L1979 IM GE *020 †20
KUHLMAN, Jeffrey Reme. 774 HARTNESS RD 28677 #024-01-1988 L1994 ORS *020 †40
KUTTEH, Hanna C. 564 BROOKDALE DR 28677 #605-01-1947 L1998 OBG *071
LAI, Chi-Kwong. 208 OLD MOCKSVILLE RD 28625 #244-03-1972 L1979 CD IM *020 †20
LANDAU, Steven Jay. 707 BRYANT ST, PIEDMONT HEALTHCARE PA 28677 #011-03-1993 L1995 OTO *020 †45
LAY, William Randall, III. 318 TURNERSBURG HWY, TELECARE INC 28625 #011-02-1985 L1987 P *020 †75
LELEUX-FAULK, Kellie A. 349 BROOKDALE DR 28677 #021-01-1991 L1996 END DIA *020 †20
LEWIS, Newman Maxville. 208 OLD MOCKSVILLE RD 28625 #036-05-1957 L1957 IM *071
LLOYD, Clarence Earl, Jr. 557 BROOKDALE DR 28677 #036-01-1974 L1974 DR OS *020 †80 ‡
LOHRMANN, Wolfgang Erich. 2603 DAVIE AVE 28625 #023-01-1988 L1996 NEP IM *020 †20
MADAN, Seema. 208 OLD MOCKSVILLE RD 28625 #010-01-1996 L2001 IM *020 †20
MARKS, Fred. 1804 DAVIE AVE 28677 #035-08-1976 L1979 IM *020 †20
MASTOR, Jason Elia. 276 OLD MOCKSVILLE RD 28625 #041-09-1996 L2004 P *020
MC CALL, Ben Waring. ■ 28625 #036-07-1955 L1961 CD *020 †20
MCCALL, Duncan Alexander. 766 HARTNESS RD 28677 #036-05-1989 L1994 RHU *020 †20
MC KAY, Ralph James. 704 HARTNESS RD, IREDELL ANESTHESIA ASSOC 28677 #018-03-1978 L1989 AN *020 †05
MC KENZIE, Edward B. ■ 28625 #035-45-1951 L1951 GS *071 †85
MC KINNON, Steve Malone. 1835 DAVIE AVE, STE 413 28677 #036-01-1979 L1984 OPH *020
MC LAURIN, Amy Elizabeth. 208 OLD MOCKSVILLE RD 28625 #004-01-1995 L2004 END *020 †20
MEADORS, Walter V, Jr. 1669 DAVIE AVE 28677 #036-01-1979 L1985 OBG *020 †30
MELUCH, Anthony Matthew. 704 HARTNESS RD 28677 #017-20-1986 L1989 AN PME *020 †05
MESSENGER, Mark Douglas. 124 SUNSET HILL DR 28625 #065-06-1993 L1997 PD *020 †55
MILLER, Michael Ray. 513 BROOKDALE DR 28677 #036-01-1986 L1987 FM *020 †18
MILLS, Warren Glenn. 704 HARTNESS RD 28677 #012-01-1990 L1996 AN *020 †20,05
MORAN, Joseph Edward. 138 SHERLOCK DR 28625 #033-06-1993 L1996 IM *020 †20
MULLIS, Ellyn Bain P. 405 BAYMOUNT DR 28625 #051-01-1986 L1989 PD *020 †55
MUTHU, Prem K. 215B W BROAD ST 28677 #496-39-1970 L1995 CHP *072
NICHOLSON, John Harvey. 470 CRAWFORD RD, ASMO OF N CAROLINA INC. 28625 #051-04-1945 L1945 IM *071 †20
PARKIN, Charles Evan. 125 SUPREME CT 28677 #047-06-1963 L1967 AN PUD *071 †05
PAVELOCK, Richard Michael. ■ 28625 #759-01-1986 L1990 IM *020 †20
PENCE, Carla Raffety. 1804 DAVIE AVE 28677 #036-05-1985 L1986 IM *020 †20
PETROZZA, Joseph Anthony. 707 BRYANT ST 28677 #041-02-1978 L1983 GE IM *020 †20
PIPPITT, Charles H, Jr. 276 OLD MOCKSVILLE RD, STE 800 28625 #036-05-1979 L1982 GO OBG *020 †30
PITTMAN, Eric Williams. 557 BROOKDALE DR 28677 #036-05-1966 L1966 PTH *020 †50
PRENDERGAST, Mark L. 707 BRYANT ST, UNITED MEDICAL GROUP, PA 28677 #048-04-1980 L1987 OTO FPS *020 †45
PRITCHARD, Douglas Dussel. 610 SIGNAL HILL DRIVE EXT, STE 100 28625 #036-05-1972 L1972 PME AN *020 †05
PUTRAKUL, Kobkit. ■ 28625 #891-02-1991 L2007 FM EM *020 ‡
RADER, Dale Kantrice. 340 SIGNAL HILL DR, STE A 28625 #010-03-1998 L2007 OSM *020 †40
RASHLEY, Elizabeth F. 129 SHERLOCK DR 28625 #045-04-1998 L2001 PD *020 †55
REINDOLLAR, Robert Wm. 555 KITCHINGS DR, STE D 28677 #023-01-1975 L1980 GE HEP *020 †20
RHYNE, James Moody. 757 BRYANT ST 28677 #036-01-1968 L1968 IM N *020 †20
ROARK, Roger Lee. 555 KITCHINGS DR STE C 28677 #036-05-1975 L1975 GS *020 †85

■ = Address Information Privacy Protected

ROBERTSON, Elisabeth M. 2341 SIMONTON RD, GORDON HOSPICE HOUSE 28625 #025-01-1981 L1991 **AN EM** *020 †16,05

ROLIH, Catherine A. 349 BROOKDALE DR 28677 #048-14-1989 L1992 **END IM** *020 †20

ROSSER, Stephen Parker. 750 HARTNESS RD STE G 28677 #036-05-1980 L1992 **GS** *020 †85

RUNHEIM, Andreas David. 1714 DAVIE AVE 28677 #036-05-2001 L2004 **N** *020 †75

SALTZMAN, Robert Ira. 770 HARTNESS RD, PIEDMONT HLTH CARE 28677 #035-09-1970 L1994 **ORS AM** *020 †40

SARGE, Terence J. ■ 28677 #056-06-1983 L1984 **OBG** *020 †30

SCHEIBNER, Stephen B. 208 OLD MOCKSVILLE RD, DEPT OF DEMATOLOGY, PO BX 28625 #004-01-1984 L1985 **D IM** *020 †20,15 ‡

SCHERER, Irvin Geo. 218 OLD MOCKSVILLE RD 28625 #019-02-1954 L1957 **FM** *071 ‡

SCHLESINGER, Michael H. 774 HARTNESS RD 28677 #035-09-1990 L1995 **U GS** *020 †95

SCHOPPS, Julie Hope. 129 SHERLOCK DR 28625 #048-04-1991 L1994 **PD** *020 †55

SELF, Craig Stephen. 646 HARTNESS RD 28677 #036-08-1994 L2006 **OPH** *020 †35

SERWINT, Michael Stanley. 365 BROOKDALE DR, HEMATOLOGY ONCOLOGY 28677 #016-02-1975 L2002 **ON HEM** *020 †20

SHAH, Nimesh Bhupendra. 3206 TAYLORSVILLE HWY 28625 #036-01-2000 L2004 **P** *071 †75

SHAPIRO, Scott Brian. 1703 DAVIE AVE 28677 #048-15-1986 L1996 **OBG** *020 †30

SHOLAR, Pam Westmoreland. 365 BROOKDALE DR, HEMATOLOGY ONCOLOGY 28677 #036-07-1981 L1986 **ON HEM** *020 †20

SINGH, Roshnara. 1804 DAVIE AVE 28677 #051-04-1989 L1993 **OBG** *020 †30

SLIWINSKI, Stanley F, Jr. 208 OLD MOCKSVILLE RD 28625 #023-07-1966 L1977 **OPH OS** *020 †35

SMITH, James Alan. 925 THOMAS ST, STE B 28677 #036-08-1986 L1988 **PD** *020 †55

SMITH, John Baldwin, III. 760 HARTNESS RD 28677 #051-04-1969 L1974 **N SME** *020 †55,75

SPENCE, Frank Jesse, Jr. 619 SULLIVAN RD 28677 #036-07-1981 L1982 **FM** *020 †18

STEVENSON, Robert M. 609B SULLIVAN RD 28677 #036-01-1959 L1959 **R** *020 †80

STOUT, Elmer Hancock, III. 138 SHERLOCK DR 28625 #011-02-1976 L1979 **IM A** *020

SWANEY, Paul Eugene. 555 KITCHINGS DR, STE A 28677 #038-40-1978 L1983 **GS VS** *020 †85

TEMPLETON, Thomas Brevard. ■ 28677 #042-01-1955 L1955 **IM** *071 †20

TONDO, Lewis J. 124 SUNSET HILL DR, CAROLINA SPECIALTY CARE 28625 #561-02-1988 L1993 **IM** *020 †20

TRITICO, Rocco Jos. 548 BROOKDALE DR 28677 #048-14-1976 L1979 **DR** *020 †80

VANCE, Teddy Bryan. 704 HARTNESS RD 28677 #055-02-1985 L1990 **AN** *020 †05

VIZEL, Elliott Jonathan. 708 HARTNESS RD 28677 #067-03-1986 L1996 **FM** *020 †18 ‡

VOULGAROPOULOS, Menelaos. 1503 E BROAD ST, CAROLINA FAMILY MEDICINE & 28625 #418-02-1985 L1991 **IM** *020 †20

WALKER, Harry Gordon. 310 DAVIE AVE 28677 #051-01-1949 L1949 **FM** *071

WALTERS, Henry Cephas, Jr. 1217 DAVIE AVE 28677 #045-01-1976 L1978 **IM** *020 †20

WARREN, Brent Blair. 646 HARTNESS RD 28677 #023-12-1993 L2003 **OPH** *020 †35

WASHINGTON, Rhonda E. 1804 DAVIE AVE 28677 #038-45-1999 L2005 **OBG** *020

WATSON, Jerome Thomas. 124 SUNSET HILL RD 28625 #051-01-1994 L1998 **PM** *020 †60

WHITAKER, Willie Roscoe. 706 HARTNESS RD 28677 #036-07-1976 L2003 **NEP IM** *020 †20

WHITE, William Andrew. 520 BROOKDALE DR 28677 #036-05-1984 L1987 **IM** *020

WILLHIDE, Margaret Jane. 127 COLUMBINE ST 28625 #051-04-1962 L1963 **PD PDA** *020 †55

WILLIAMS, Trevor Geo. 515 BROOKDALE DR 28677 #012-01-1948 L1950 **P** *030

WILLIAMSON, Mark Bascom. 218 OLD MOCKSVILLE RD 28625 #047-06-1982 L1997 **ORS OSS** *020 †40

WODECKI, Bob. 124 SUNSET HILL RD, CAROLINA SPECIALTY CARE PA 28625 #759-01-1986 L1993 **RHU** *020 †20

WODECKI, Debra Anne. 124 SUNSET HILL RD 28625 #759-01-1987 L1993 **IM** *020 †20

WOOD, Kenneth Ervin. 523 BROOKDALE DR 28677 #011-03-1970 L1978 **OSS** *020 †40

WRIGHT, Elizabeth Ann. 276 OLD MOCKSVILLE RD, STE 500 28625 #020-12-1967 L1968 **N CN** *020 †75

YOUNG, Leo Kwanlok. 509 BROOKDALE DR 28677 #014-01-1993 L1996 **FM** *020 †18

ZAPATA, Mario Guillermo. 276 OLD MOCKSVILLE RD, STE 100 28625 #132-02-1988 L2002 **P** *020 †75

STEDMAN — CUMBERLAND

FULP, Cammie Jo. 114 FORTE RD 28391 #036-05-1996 L1999 **FM** *020 †18 ‡

TUCKER, Jessica Maria. 114 FORTE RD, STEDMAN MEDICAL CARE 28391 #036-08-1999 L2002 **FM** *020 †18

SUGAR GROVE — WATAUGA

KAY, Lawrence L. 369 BURL HARMON RD, RR 1 BOX 106 28679 #039-01-1969 L1992 **DR** *020 †80

SUGAR MOUNTAIN — WATAUGA

NESBITT, James, III. ■ 28604 #001-02-1947 L1979 **R** *075 †80

SUMMERFIELD — GUILFORD

BURCHETTE, Bruce Wilson. 4431 US HIGHWAY 220 N 27358 #036-08-1989 L1990 **FM** *020 †18

BURNETT, Brent Alan. 4431 US HIGHWAY 220 N 27358 #017-20-1984 L1985 **FM** *020 †18

HUANG, William Weiting. ■ 27358 #036-01-2007 **IM** *012

JACKSON, Freeman Randolph. ■ 27358 #036-01-2005 **AN** *012

MATTHIEU, Donald E. ■ 27358 #036-05-1972 L1972 **PTH** *062 †50

NAJM, Elias George. ■ 27358 #605-01-1949 L1981 **GP** *071

PARKS, Lauren Denice. ■ 27358 #036-07-2006 **DR** *012

PULASKI, James Paul. 4301 HEPATICA CT 27358 #035-15-1971 L2007 **OPH** *020 †35 ‡

SPEAR, Tammy Rose. 1007-G HWY 150 WEST 27358 #024-01-1993 L1994 **FM** *020 †18

TURNBULL, Jennifer Ruth. 4431 US HIGHWAY 220 N, MOSES CONE FAMILY PRACTICE 27358 #036-08-2004 L2007 **FM** *020 †18

WILSON, Fred Henry. 4431 US HIGHWAY 220 N 27358 #036-01-1982 L1986 **FM** *020 †18

SUNSET BEACH — BRUNSWICK

BRANDT, Robert John. ■ 28468 #036-07-1958 L1958 **OM** *071 †70

CHURCH, Lori Ann. 710 SUNSET BLVD N STE B, OCEANSIDE FAMILY MEDICINE 28468 #665-01-1999 L2007 **FM** *020 †18 ‡

FLAHERTY, Thomas F. ■ 28468 #010-02-1963 L1967 **OBG OS** *020

KNERR, Richard Aaron. ■ 28468 #041-09-1955 L1956 **GP FM** *071

MCGANN, Robt Farquharson. ■ 28468 #917-29-1958 L1966 **FM FPG** *030 †18

YATES-BRITT, Rae Lynn. 710 SUNSET BLVD N, STE B 28468 #036-08-1997 L1998 **FM** *020 †18 ‡

YOUNG, Richard Lane. 710 S SUNSET BLVD # C 28468 #045-01-1979 L2002 **ORS** *075 †40

SUPPLY — BRUNSWICK

BOSTON, James E. 18 DOCTORS CIR, STE 2 28462 #305-01-1999 L2005 **IM** *020 †20

BRANN, Christopher A. 1 MEDICAL CENTER DR, SOUTHERN INDIANA ANESTHESI 28462 #024-05-1983 L2008 **AN PME** *020 †05 ‡

BROWN, Keith Eric. 1 MEDICAL CENTER DR 28462 #047-20-1999 L2003 **EM** *020 ‡

CARLEY, Richard Scott. 1 MEDICAL CENTER DR 28462 #025-07-1996 L1999 **EM** *020 †16

CRANE, Richard Denton. 16 MEDICAL CENTER DR, ATLANTIC INTERNAL MEDICINE 28462 #041-12-1994 L1997 **IM** *020 †20

GALLOWAY, Harry Lee. COLUMBIA BRUNSWICK HOSP 28462 #036-05-1962 L1962 **EM** *020 †18

HALL, Charles Daniel. 1 MEDICAL CENTER DR 28462 #036-07-1990 L1994 **N** *020 †75

HASSLER, Robert Emiel. 14 DOCTORS CIR STE 5 28462 #035-09-1960 L1984 **OBG** *020 †30

HAYES, Edward Elem. 12 MEDICAL CENTER DR 28462 #045-01-1978 L2002 **U** *020 †95 ‡

HOLT, Frank Loving, Jr. 3 MEDICAL CENTER DR 28462 #051-04-1980 L1999 **GE IM** *020 †20

ISENHOUR, Christopher B. 10 DOCTORS CIR 28462 #036-01-2002 L2003 **FM** *020 †18

KHAN, Mushtaq H. 690 OCEAN HWY W 28462 #495-57-1967 L1993 **GS GP** *020

KUBLEY, James Danl. 1 MEDICAL CENTER DR 28462 #017-20-1973 L1998 **FM ADM** *020 †18

LIZAK, Mark Anthony. 14 MEDICAL CENTER DR 28462 #041-12-1986 L1992 **OTO** *020 †45

MACK, Emili R. 14 DOCTORS CIR, STE 3 28462 #036-01-2002 L2005 **PD** *020 †55

MORGART, Douglas Raymond. 1 MEDICAL CENTER DR 28462 #041-14-1978 L1997 **EM** *020 †16 ‡

NEELEY, Christina Kay. 14 DOCTORS CIR, STE 3 SHORE FUN PED PA 28462 #045-01-1997 L1998 **PD** *020 †55

O'QUINN, Aglaia Nikides. ■ 28462 #036-07-1965 L1965 **CHP PD** *020 †55,75

PECK, Joanne Yonkondy. 14 DOCTORS CIR STE 3, SHORE FUN PEDIATRICS 28462 #024-01-1975 L2001 **PD** *020 †55

PERRY, Everett Lavern. 1 MEDICAL CENTER DR 28462 #036-05-1994 L1996 **AN** *020

PRICE, Mary E. 20 MEDICAL CAMPUS DR, STE 202 28462 #010-02-1986 L2004 **OPH OS** *020 †20,35

RAVINDRAN, Babysarojah. 20 MEDICAL CAMPUS DR, STE 106B 28462 #220-02-1976 L1995 **PUD IM** *020 †20

RILEY, Shawn Francis. 15 MEDICAL CENTER DR, CAROLINAS, P.C. 28462 #016-01-1988 L1993 **OPH** *020 †35

ROBERTS, Thomas Janney. PO BOX 139 28462 #051-01-1960 L1971 **EM GS** *075

SCALLION, Richard Ralph. 6 DOCTORS CIR STE 1, DBA BRUNSWICK SURGICAL ASS 28462 #012-01-1992 L2007 **GS** *020 †85

SEDER, Jeffrey David. 1 MEDICAL CENTER DR 28462 #308-07-1982 L1992 **CD IM** *020

SHERROD, William Maxwell. 1 MEDICAL CENTER DR 28462 #036-01-1998 L2001 **EM** *020 †16

SWAIM, Lindian Jos. 14 DOCTORS CIR, STE 5 28462 #036-01-1973 L1973 **OBG** *020 †30

THOMPSON, Angela Renee. 1 MEDICAL CENTER DR 28462 #025-07-1997 L2000 **FM** *020 †18

TILLOTSON, Mark. 6 DOCTORS CIR, STE 1 28462 #048-13-1988 L1993 **GS** *020 †85

WILLEFORD, Kenneth Lee. 10 DOCTORS CIR STE 2, COASTAL CAROLINAS INTEGRAT 28462 #010-01-1988 L1993 **APM** *020 †05

WILLIAMS, Jeffrey Chas. 1 MEDICAL CENTER DR 28462 #017-20-1984 L1994 **AN** *020 †05

WILSON, Larry Lee. 14 DOCTORS CIR, STE 5 28462 #020-12-1989 L2006 **OBG** *020 †30

WILSON, Susan. 14 DOCTORS CIR, STE 5 28462 #045-01-1991 L2006 **OBG** *020 †30

WU, Grace Yuen Man. ■ 28462 #917-02-1992 **IM** *100

YOUNKIN, Scott Wiley. 1 MEDICAL CENTER DR, BRUNSWICK COMMUNITY HOSPIT 28462 #028-02-1977 L2001 **ID IM** *020 †20

SURF CITY — ONSLOW

MACKEY, William Frederick. ■ 28445 #047-06-1940 L1941 **GYN** *071 †30

QUICK, Joshua David. ■ 28445 #035-09-2006 L2007 *012

YOUNG, William N, Jr. ■ 28445 #023-07-1949 L1975 **GP** *071

SWANNANOA — BUNCOMBE

FORBAT, Andrew Feodore. ■ 28778 #917-30-1946 L1988 **AN** *072 †05

GUTIERREZ, Hector P. ■ 28778 #275-01-1946 L1976 **U GS** *071 †95

KELLY, John Jay. 2296 US HIGHWAY 70 28778 #035-03-1979 L1980 **FM** *020 †18

MC CALL, Terry Wayne. ■ 28778 #305-01-2001 L2005 **IM** *020 †20

RODERICK, Marilyn Ann. 2296 US HIGHWAY 70 28778 #005-11-1983 L2004 **GP GYN** *020 ‡

SCHWARTZ, Michael J. ■ 28778 #034-01-1972 L1973 **GP ADL** *071 †55

SWANSBORO — CARTERET

CHAVEZ, Alexander C. 785A W CORBETT AVE, SWANSBORO CHILDREN'S & FAM 28584 #025-01-1988 L1988 **PD** *071 †55

HANLON, Thos Michael, Jr. ■ 28584 #050-02-1963 L1963 **PD** *071 †55

KLORIG, William Joseph. ■ 28584 #011-03-1999 L2001 **FM** *020 †18

SYLVA — JACKSON

ADAMS, Robert John. 68 HOSPITAL RD 28779 #038-06-1973 L1975 **IM** *020

AIELLO, Joseph Ralph. 655 ASHEVILLE HWY 28779 #010-02-1992 L1995 **NEP** *020 †20

ALDIS, William Leggett. ■ 28779 #024-01-1977 L1977 **IM** *020 †20

ANDERSON, Martha Frances. 81 MEDICAL PARK LOOP #203B, CAROLINA WEST RADIOLOGY 28779 #036-01-1981 L1982 **DR** *020 †80

BAILEY, Beth Ann. 186 MEDICAL PARK LOOP, STE 503 28779 #036-01-1980 L1989 **FM** *020 †18

■ = Address Information Privacy Protected

BALTA, Ofelia Cezarina. 63 HEALTHCARE DR, WNC INTERNAL MEDICINE 28779 #781-02-1991 L2003 **MPD** *020 †20,55

BEAUCHEMIN, Richard, Jr. 70 WESTCARE DR STE 403 28779 #023-01-1983 L1989 **OPH** *020 †35

BELSKY, Corinne Judith. 98A COPE CREEK RD, MERIDIAN BEHAVIORAL HEALTH 28779 #665-01-2000 L2005 **P PFP** *020 †75 ‡

BLACK, Steven Ray. 63 HEALTHCARE DR 28779 #305-01-1999 L2005 **IM P** *020 ‡

BOATRIGHT, Karl Craig. 80 HEALTHCARE DR, STE 101 28779 #024-01-1994 L2000 **ORS** *020 †40

BRANNING, Pamela Kaye. 186 MEDICAL PARK LOOP 28779 #027-01-1980 L1996 **OBG** *020 †30

BREWSTER, Penny Jean. ■ 28779 #023-01-1995 L2003 **IM** *020 †20

BUCKNER, Donald Thos, Jr. 154 MEDICAL PARK LOOP 28779 #036-01-1991 L1992 **CHP** *020 †75

BUENTING, John Ernst. 40 MITCHELL RD, ASSOCIATES, PA 28779 #021-01-1991 L1994 **OTO** *020 †45

CARRERAS, Jorge Luis. 68 HOSPITAL RD 28779 #042-01-1974 L1986 **FM EM** *020 †18,16

CHOI-CHUNG, Moon Soog. 74 EASTGATE DR 28779 #583-08-1966 L1983 **PM** *020

CHUNG, Il Whan. 74 EASTGATE DR, SYLVA UROLOGICAL PA 28779 #583-02-1963 L1973 **U** *071 †95

CROSS, Sarita Kumar. 655 ASHEVILLE HWY 28779 #036-01-1997 L2003 **NEP** *020 †20

DAVIS, Jeffrey Earl. 68 HOSPITAL RD 28779 #041-09-1982 L1985 **GP IM** *020

DAVIS, John Samuel. 68 HOSPITAL RD, HARRIS REGIONAL HOSP 28779 #012-01-1988 L2001 **PTH** *020 †50

DILL, Thomas Edward. 186 MEDICAL PARK LOOP, STE 501 28779 #012-01-1967 L1972 **PD** *071 †55

DIXON, Elizabeth Ellen. 68 HOSPITAL RD 28779 #051-01-1988 L1992 **IM PD** *020 †55,20

DOUGLAS, Benjamin. 40 MITCHELL RD, MOUNTAIN ENT ASSOCIATES 28779 #036-01-1975 L1983 **OTO** *020 †45

DURHAM, William Tracy. 655 ASHEVILLE HWY 28779 #036-01-2000 L2005 **IM** *020 †20

DURR, Walter Jacob. ■ 28779 #035-08-1937 L1951 **GS** *071

EL-BAYADI, Nagui Rizk. ■ 28779 #330-04-1957 L1969 **GS PS** *071 †85

ELMORE, Miles. 655 ASHEVILLE HWY 28779 #045-01-1971 L1976 **NEP IM** *020 †20

ENGLAND, Brian Kent. 655 ASHEVILLE HWY 28779 #020-02-1983 L1996 **NEP IM** *020 †20

FAULL, Clifford Edward. 80 HEALTHCARE DR STE 203 28779 #035-15-1974 L1975 **ORS** *071 †40

FREYFOGLE, Kathryn Rose. 655 ASHEVILLE HWY 28779 #012-05-1987 L1997 **NEP IM** *020 †20

GALLINGER, Roy Paul. 34 FISHER CREEK RD 28779 #036-05-1984 L1986 **FM** *020 †18

GEHRING, Paul Stanley. 293 HOSPITAL RD, SYLVA MEDICAL CENTER 28779 #038-41-1984 L1989 **FM** *020 †18

GRANING, George. ■ 28779 #041-01-1976 L1988 **FM** *020 †18

GRANING, Rolf Edward. ■ 28779 #023-12-2007 *012

GREEN, Teresa Duarte. 186 MEDICAL PARK LOOP, STE 503 28779 #051-04-1991 L2003 **PCC** *020 †20

GREEN, Waverly Sydnor, III. 186 MEDICAL PARK LOOP, STE 503 28779 #051-04-1987 L2003 **PUD SME** *020 †20

HADDOCK, Amos Earl. 80 HEALTHCARE DR, STE 201 28779 #036-01-1984 L1985 **CD IM** *020

HAN, Gwang Soo. 111 CENTRAL ST, SYLVA WOMEN'S CLINIC, P.A. 28779 #583-02-1963 L1974 **OBG** *020 †30

HARR, David Lee. 59 HOSPITAL RD 28779 #011-02-1976 L1989 **DR** *020 †80

HIGHTOWER, Michael Dean. 26 WESTCARE DR, STE 302 28779 #045-01-1986 L2007 **OBG** *020 †30

HURT, Joe Paul. 68 HOSPITAL RD 28779 #036-01-1965 L1965 **PTH** *071 †50 ‡

JACKSON, Beverly J Neely. ■ 28779 #036-07-1951 L1953 **PD** *071

KEEVER, Janine Lisa. 64 EASTGATE DR, SMOKY MTN OBG ASSOC PA 28779 #036-08-2000 L2004 **OBG** *020

LAWRENCE, Mark Erwin. 154 MEDICAL PARK LOOP 28779 #054-04-1980 L1984 **P** *020

MACKEY, Daniel John. 68 HOSPITAL RD, WESTCARE HEALTH SYSTEM 28779 #036-01-1996 L2007 **CCP** *020 †20,55

MAHAR, Matthew Alan. 137 MEDICAL PARK LOOP 28779 #030-05-1997 L2000 **FM** *020 †18

MANGUM, Michele. 73 EASTGATE DR 28779 #045-01-1983 L2001 **N** *020 †75

MANLEY, John Alan. 655 ASHEVILLE HWY 28779 #039-01-1995 L2000 **NEP** *020 †20

MATHEWS, Hurschell F. ■ 28779 #036-05-1960 L1977 **FM** *071 †18

MAULDIN, Gary Eugene. 68 HOSPITAL RD, WESTCARE HEALTH SYSTEM 28779 #012-01-1983 L1989 **AN** *020 †05

MC CORMICK, Michele Marie. ■ 28779 #045-01-1994 L1996 **PD** *020 †55

METTS, Robert Ernest. 80 HEALTHCARE DR, STE 203 28779 #008-02-1989 L2006 **ORS** *020 †40

MODUGNO, Robert. 64 EASTGATE DR 28779 #836-01-1971 L2006 **OBG** *020 †30

NASH, Will Light. 430 FISHER CREEK RD 28779 #048-12-1958 L1967 **FM** *020 †18

NESLEN, George Quayle, Jr. 80 HEALTHCARE DR, STE 203 28779 #010-01-1974 L1980 **ORS** *020 †40

NEWSOM, Georgia L. 101 ASHEVILLE HWY 28779 #154-02-1978 L1984 **GP IM** *020 †20

NIXON, Russell Scot. 293 HOSPITAL RD, SYLVA MEDICAL CENTER PA 28779 #027-01-1990 L1993 **IM** *020 †20

NOELL, William J, Jr. 37 MEDICAL PARK LOOP 28779 #004-01-1982 L1989 **GS TS** *020 †85

OLMEDA, Maria Martha. ■ 28779 #042-01-1969 L2004 **GE** *020

O'NEAL, Donald Patrick. ■ 28779 #045-01-1969 L1974 **GP** *020

PFLUEGER, Paul Christian. 80 HEALTHCARE DR, STE 203 28779 #021-01-1988 L1993 **ORS** *020 †40

POTTER, Graeme Maria. 69 EASTGATE DR 28779 #041-14-2000 L2007 **OBG** *020

PROVOST, Randall P. PO BOX 1045 28779 #012-01-1980 L1988 **IM** *020 †20

QUEEN, Steven Wesley. 293 HOSPITAL RD 28779 #036-08-1984 L1991 **IM** *020

QURESHI, Altamash Izhar. 68 HOSPITAL RD, OLDER ADULT HEALTH CTR 28779 #704-02-1992 L2005 **IMG** *100 †20

RAMSEY, David Madison, III. ■ 28779 #011-03-1976 L1982 **FM** *020 †18

ROBINSON, Gilbert Chase. 68 HOSPITAL RD, SYLVA ANESTHESIOLOGY 28779 #048-13-1990 L2001 **AN** *020 †05

RODDEN, Jimmy Lee. 68 HOSPITAL RD, HARRIS REGIONAL HOSP 28779 #036-01-1976 L1977 **EM** *020 †16

RUTH, Wayne Kimberly. 186 MEDICAL PARK LOOP, STE 503 28779 #036-07-1978 L1981 **PUD A** *020 †20

SAELI, Amadeo Benj. ■ 28779 #028-34-1943 L1949 **OBG** *071 †30

SAVELL, Randall Lester. 26 WESTCARE DR, STE 304 28779 #027-01-1982 L1991 **GE IM** *020 †20

SCHROEDER, Gerard R. 68 HOSPITAL RD, HARRIS REGIONAL HOSPITAL 28779 #035-48-1986 L1999 **AN** *020 †05

SEAGO, Judith Jones. 186 MEDICAL PARK LOOP, STE 501 28779 #020-02-1985 L1988 **PD** *020 †55

SELBY, William Lawrence. 68 HOSPITAL RD, HARRIS REG HOSP LAB 28779 #045-01-1986 L1990 **PTH PCP** *020 †50

SERVOSS, Ronald Lee. 68 HOSPITAL RD 28779 #005-12-1970 L1975 **AN** *020

SHAINBERG, Jodi Anne. 68 HOSPITAL RD, EMERGENCY DEPARTMENT 28779 #047-20-1991 L1995 **EM** *020 †16

SIMS, William L. 37 MEDICAL PARK LOOP 28779 #048-15-1989 L1998 **GS** *020 †85

STACK, Philip Edward. 26 WESTCARE DR, STE 304 28779 #039-05-1989 L1994 **GE** *020 †20

STANDRIDGE, Matthew Thoma. 81 MEDICAL PARK LOOP, STE 202 28779 #047-20-2004 L2007 **FM** *020 †18

STENHAMMAR, Ulrika Anna. 293 HOSPITAL RD 28779 #036-01-1996 L1998 **FM** *020 †18

SUPIK, Lawrence Francis. 80 HEALTHCARE DR, STE 203 28779 #036-08-1989 L2001 **ORS** *020 †40

THOMAS, David Shepard. 14 MEDICAL PARK LOOP 28779 #012-05-1978 L1996 **RO ON** *020 †20,80

VAN DUUREN, Anton. 81 MEDICAL PARK LOOP, STE 202 28779 #836-02-1975 L1999 **OBG** *020 †30

VO, Nam Dai. 655 ASHEVILLE HWY 28779 #036-01-2001 L2004 **NEP** *020

WHITT, John Alan. 635 MILL ST 28779 #036-08-1985 L2001 **P CHP** *075

WOLF, Thomas Jason. 63 HEALTHCARE DR 28779 #422-01-1998 L2002 **IM** *020 †20

WORD-SIMS, Winfield S. 655 ASHEVILLE HWY 28779 #016-06-1985 L1987 **NEP IM** *020 †20

TABOR CITY – COLUMBUS

KARL, John Yunho. 909 PIREWAY RD 28463 #583-15-1987 L1999 **FM** *020 †18

PERDUE, Christy T. 14508 JAMES B WHITE HWY S, SOUTH COLUMBUS MED CTR 28463 #036-08-2001 L2004 **FM** *020 †18

STOUT, William Allen. 909 PIREWAY RD 28463 #036-05-1961 L1961 **FM** *020

TAR HEEL – BLADEN

HEDGEPETH, Charles Dwight. 16526 NC HIGHWAY 87 W, SMITHFIELD FAMILY MEDICAL 28392 #036-01-1972 L1972 **FM EM** *020 †18

TARBORO – EDGECOMBE

ABULATIFA, Khalil T K. 111 HOSPITAL DR, HERITAGE HOSPITAL 27886 #575-01-2001 L2007 **IM** *020 †20

AL HOSAINI, Hassan. 101 CLINIC DR, TARBORO CLINIC, PA 27886 #875-03-1996 L2001 **IM** *020 †20

ALLEN-ALVA, Tonya L. 111 HOSPITAL DR, ATTN EMERGENCY DEPT 27886 #017-20-1993 L1998 **PTH** *020

ALLIGOOD, Gilbert Ray, Jr. 101 CLINIC DR, TARBORO CLINIC, PA 27886 #036-08-1986 L1987 **IM PD** *020 †20,55

BALLIN, Robert Hans Arthu. 5000 MCKENDREE CHURCH RD 27886 #858-02-1965 L1976 **AN PME** *071

BARBE, Robert Francis. 111 S FAIRVIEW CIR 27886 #051-04-1953 L1968 **OPH** *071 †35

BLYTH, Stacey Anne. 101 CLINIC DR 27886 #035-06-2001 L2004 **FM** *020 †18

BROOKS, John Irving. 101 CLINIC DR, TARBORO CLINIC PA 27886 #036-01-1958 L1958 **IM** *072 †20

CASTILLO, Emma Everlyn T. 2704 N MAIN ST STE A, TARBORO INTERNAL MED 27886 #748-01-1993 L2001 **ID** *020 †20

COCKRELL, Wiley Thurman. 101 CLINIC DR, TARBORO CLINIC, PA/IMMEDIA 27886 #036-08-1987 L1990 **FM** *020 †18

COWARD, Karen Denise. 101 CLINIC DR 27886 #036-08-1989 L1992 **FM** *020 †18

CRAWFORD, Robert Orr. 101 CLINIC DR 27886 #036-05-1954 L1954 **OPH** *071 †35

CRUMPLER, Hans Lucas. 101 CLINIC DR 27886 #036-05-1996 L2008 **FM** *020 †18

D'EMPAIRE, Alberto Jose. 2906 N MAIN ST 27886 #935-03-1967 L1991 **ORS** *020

GHANEM, Firas. 101 CLINIC DR 27886 #875-03-1995 L2001 **IM** *020 †20

HEMINGWAY, Geo Capers, Jr. 101 CLINIC DR 27886 #036-01-1963 L1963 **IM PD** *071

HOLLAND, James Eugene. 101 CLINIC DR 27886 #028-03-1975 L1979 **OPH** *020 †35

JORDAN, Betty Gelvez. ■ 27886 #264-13-1996 **FP** *012

KENDALL, James Eugene, Jr. 2704 N MAIN ST 27886 #036-08-1991 L1995 **OBG** *020 †30

LEE, David Wayne. 2704 N MAIN ST 27886 #036-01-1982 L1983 **OBG** *020 †30

LELAND, William Joseph. 101 CLINIC DR 27886 #036-01-1987 L1995 **IM** *020 †20

LOCASCIO, Elizabeth S. 111 HOSPITAL DR 27886 #036-08-2003 L2007 **MPD** *020 †20

LOVETTE, Kenneth Maurice. 2704 N MAIN ST, TARBORO WOMEN'S CENTER PA 27886 #036-01-1979 L2004 **OBG** *075 †30

MARROW, L Jane Gregory. ■ 27886 #036-07-1943 L1945 **GYN** *071

MIDDLETON, Charles Jos. 101 CLINIC DR 27886 #035-08-1964 L2004 **GS** *020 †85 ‡

MILLER, David Charles. 2906 N MAIN ST 27886 #041-09-1980 L1985 **ORS OS** *020 †40

MORGAN, John Garland. 101 CLINIC DR 27886 #036-07-1962 L1962 **GS VS** *020 †85

PATEL, Sujan Kirit. 111 HOSPITAL DR 27886 #036-08-2000 L2003 **IM** *020 ‡

PEELE, Lori Diane. 162 NC HIGHWAY 33 E 27886 #036-01-2001 L2005 **FM** *100 †18

PETERS, Robert Brookes, IV. 101 CLINIC DR 27886 #036-01-1980 L1981 **FM** *020 †18

PETRUZZIELLO, Mark John. 101 CLINIC DR 27886 #035-48-1992 L2000 **GS** *020 †85

PLOTKIN, Charles Neal. 100 HOSPITAL DR 27886 #010-01-1983 L1990 **AN** *020 †05

ROBERTSON, Thomas Jackson. 111 HOSPITAL DR 27886 #051-01-1988 L1998 **OPH** *020 †35 ‡

SIDHU, Rajinder Singh. ■ 27886 #308-13-1999 L2006 **FPG** *020 †20

SILVER, Jeffrey Alan. 101 CLINIC DR 27886 #035-09-1984 L1995 **PUD CCM** *020 †20

SMITH, Danielle Marie. 202 W BATTLE AVE 27886 #056-06-2000 L2004 **MPD** *020 †55,20 ‡

SPRUILL, Steven Carl. 2704 N MAIN ST 27886 #036-01-2001 L2003 **OBG** *020

SURLES, John William. 111 HOSPITAL DR 27886 #036-01-1995 L1996 **EM** *020 †16

TEMPLE, Peter Livermore. 101 CLINIC DR, TARBORO CLINIC PA 27886 #012-05-1963 L1968 **FM** *071 †18

THOMPSON, Kenneth C, Jr. ■ 27886 #038-41-1961 L1965 **P** *071 †75

VICK, Henry Vernell. 111 HOSPITAL DR 27886 #036-05-1955 L1955 **FM** *071 †18

WILLIAMS-WOOTEN, Ada F. 101 CLINIC DR 27886 #024-07-1983 L1990 **PD** *020 †55

WINSLOW, James Weeks. 101 CLINIC DR 27886 #036-01-1975 L1975 **FM** *071 †18

■ = Address Information Privacy Protected

TAYLORSVILLE – ALEXANDER

BOWMAN, Robley Kivette. ■ 28681 #036-01-1964 L1964 **P** *072
CHOONG, Han Pyo. 232 NORTHWOOD CIR, 232NORTHWOOD CIR 28681 #583-03-1961 L1972 **GP CRS** *020
CRAIG, Trevor John. 1668 NC HIGHWAY 16 S 28681 #038-40-1977 L1981 **FM** *020 †18
DE VRIES, Jill M. 1668 NC HIGHWAY 16 S, FAMILY CARE CENTER 28681 #056-06-1996 L1999 **FM** *020 †18
DE VRIES, Mark Joseph. 1668 NC HIGHWAY 16 S 28681 #036-08-1994 L1999 **FM** *020 †18
FAULKENBERRY, Russell W. 1668 NC HIGHWAY 16 S 28681 #036-05-1974 L1974 **FM** *020 †18
FOXWORTHY, James C, IV. 1668 NC HIGHWAY 16 S 28681 #054-04-1989 L1995 **GS** *020 †85
GEIDEMAN, William Michael. 1668 NC HIGHWAY 16 S 28681 #028-02-1993 L2000 **ORS** *020 †40
INMAN, Amy Caroline. 1668 NC HIGHWAY 16 S, FAMILY CARE CENTER 28681 #045-04-1994 L1997 **FM** *020 †18
INMAN, Joel Ray. 1668 NC HIGHWAY 16 S 28681 #036-08-1992 L1997 **FM** *020 †18
KASSMAN, Neil Matthew. 1668 NC HIGHWAY 16 S 28681 #041-12-1983 L1988 **GE IM** *020 †20
MERRILL, Steven Carlson. 50 MACEDONIA CHURCH RD, P O BOX 489 28681 #038-40-1977 L1980 **FM** *020 †18 ‡
MILLER, Hersey Eugene. 1668 NC HIGHWAY 16 S 28681 #036-05-1970 L1970 **OTO** *071 †45
NEWMAN, Robert Henry. 226 NC HIGHWAY 16 S 28681 #017-20-1976 L1980 **DR** *020 †80 ‡
PARDO, Sandra Kay. 50 MACEDONIA CHURCH RD, FAMILY MEDICAL ASSOCIATES 28681 #036-08-1998 L2003 **FM** *100 †18
ROBINSON, Gary Thos. 1668 NC HIGHWAY 16 S 28681 #035-46-1980 L1987 **GS** *020 †85
SELMAN, Richard David. 633 OLD LANDFILL RD, P O BOX 909 28681 #012-05-1972 L1975 **P ADP** *020 †75
SLADICKA, Stephen Joseph. 50 MACEDONIA CHURCH RD 28681 #041-13-1989 L1998 **ORS** *020 †40

TEACHEY – DUPLIN

BRYANT, Edward O. ■ 28464 #047-07-1984 L1987 **IM** *020

TERRELL – CATAWBA

VARGAS, Ramon Eduardo. ■ 28682 #035-46-1996 L2006 **FM** *020 †18 ‡

THOMASVILLE – DAVIDSON

ADERHOLDT, Marcus L, Jr. ■ 27360 #023-01-1943 L1943 **PD** *071
ALEXANDER, H Anthony. 1300 LEXINGTON AVE, ALEXANDER INTERNAL MED 27360 #036-05-1985 L1987 **IM** *020 †20 ‡
ASRES, Alehegn. 309 PINEYWOOD RD, THOMASVILLE 27360 #473-01-1982 L2004 **FM** *020 †18
BLACKWELL, Oscar M, III. 309 PINEYWOOD RD 27360 #012-05-1974 L1977 **IM** *020 †20
BLUE, Brian Alan. 211 OLD LEXINGTON RD 27360 #024-01-1987 L1999 **ORS OSS** *020 †40
BOSKEN, Donald Wm. 903 RANDOLPH ST, CHAIR CITY FAMILY PRACTICE 27360 #019-02-1974 L1977 **FM** *020 †18
BRAY, William Chas. 207 OLD LEXINGTON RD 27360 #041-09-1986 L1991 **GE IM** *020 †20
BRODER, Michael Sylvan. 207 OLD LEXINGTON RD, RADIOLOGY-THOMASVILLE MC 27360 #035-46-1969 L1976 **DR NM** *071 †80
BRYSON, Jonathan Scott. 1302 LEXINGTON AVE, THOMASVILLE OB/GYN ASSOC 27360 #036-08-1994 L1995 **OBG** *020 †30
BURCHEL, Harold Curtis. ■ 27361 #035-15-1967 L1973 **FM** *020 †18
BURTON, Frank. 1213 LEXINGTON AVE 27360 #038-44-1987 L1994 **OTO GS** *020 †45
BUSBY, William Jarvis. 1219 LEXINGTON AVE 27360 #036-01-1970 L1972 **ORS** *020 †40
BYRNES, Thomas H, Jr. 309 PINEYWOOD RD 27360 #036-07-1963 L1963 **IM** *071 †20
CARTER, Monica S. 309 PINEYWOOD RD, THOMASVILLE MEDICAL ASSOCI 27360 #041-77-2003, ▲ L2006 **IM** *020
CITRIN, Kerry Alan. 207 OLD LEXINGTON RD 27360 #041-09-1970 L1977 **GS** *071 †85
CLARK, Katherine Jean. 309 PINEYWOOD RD, THOMASVILLE MED ASSOC 27360 #035-09-1992 L1995 **IM** *020 †20
COOPER, Heather Lynn. 200 ARTHUR DR, THOMASVILLE/ARCHDALE PEDIA 27360 #048-13-1996 L1998 **PD** *020 †55
DALLIS, James. 1219 LEXINGTON AVE, REGIONAL PHYSICIANS ORTHOP 27360 #035-48-1992 L1997 **ORS** *020 †40
DEAN, Louis Alan. 903 RANDOLPH ST, STE 1 27360 #017-20-1980 L1983 **FM** *020 †18
DEANG, Cedric Rodriguez. 1219 LEXINGTON AVE, ASSOCIATES INC 27360 #748-08-1963 L1976 **GS GYN** *020 †85
DELLINGER, Robert C, Jr. 201 W HOLLY HILL RD, THOMASVILLE FAMILY PRACTIC 27360 #036-01-1982 L1992 **FM** *020 †18
DI MICHELE, Andrea Teresa. 1302 LEXINGTON AVE 27360 #016-43-2000 L2006 **OBG FM** *020 †18 ‡
DORTON, Phillip Kevin. 1302 LEXINGTON AVE 27360 #036-01-1980 L1981 **OBG** *020 †30
ELLIS, William Dewitt. 1302 LEXINGTON AVE 27360 #001-02-1982 L1994 **OBG** *020 †30
ENTWISTLE, Daniel Mark. 200 ARTHUR DR 27360 #001-02-1992 L1995 **PD** *020 †55
FURR, Sara Marcella. 711 NATIONAL HWY, STE 500 27360 #036-08-1990 L1993 **IM** *020 †20
FUTRELL, Thomas Milton. 201 W HOLLY HILL RD 27360 #041-13-1980 L1983 **FM** *020 †18
GENTRY, Daniel Earl. 201 W HOLLY HILL RD 27360 #017-20-1976 L1979 **FM** *020 †18
GRAEUB, Charles Max, Jr. 6285 OLD GREENSBORO RD 27360 #012-01-1981 L1986 **EM** *020 †16
HARDY, Stephen P. 200 ARTHUR DR, THOMASVILLE PEDIATRICS 27360 #065-01-1984 L1995 **PD** *020 †55
HAYES, Anthony Rodriguez. 903 RANDOLPH ST, THOMASVILLE 27360 #036-08-2003 L2005 **FM** *020 †18
HEDGPETH, Joseph Rowland. 1302 LEXINGTON AVE 27360 #036-05-1966 L1966 **OBG** *071 †30
HERRICK, Wayne Crosby. ■ 27360 #041-02-1981 L1995 **ORS** *071 †40
HIGHSMITH, George Perry. 309 PINEYWOOD RD 27360 #036-05-1946 L1946 **IM** *072 †20
HOCHMAN, Howard Gordon. 207 OLD LEXINGTON RD, THOMASVILLE MEDICAL CENTER 27360 #011-02-1984 L1986 **AN** *020 †05
HOUSER, Adam Dean. ■ 27360 #036-08-2008 *012
HURST, David Maurice. 1003 PINE NEEDLE LN 27360 #047-06-1962 L1968 **R NM** *020 †80,28

IMAM, Abul Foiz M. 903 RANDOLPH ST STE 1 27360 #160-02-1977 L1995 **FM EM** *020 †55,20
JOHNS, Terrance Percell. 309 PINEYWOOD RD, THOMASVILLE MEDICAL ASSOCI 27360 #051-01-1989 L1994 **IM** *020 †20
JONES, Edward Lenoir. 205 OLD LEXINGTON RD, DAVIDSON COUNTY MENTAL HEA 27360 #036-07-1955 L1956 **GP OS** *071
KANDT, Raymond Stephen. 1213 LEXINGTON AVE 27360 #051-01-1976 L1984 **CHN PD** *050 †55,75
KEATES, William Alden. 207 OLD LEXINGTON RD 27360 #039-01-2004 L2007 **IM** *020 †20
KELLER, Mark Robt. 207 OLD LEXINGTON RD 27360 #036-05-1985 L1986 **FM** *020 †18
KHAWAJA, Usman A. 211 OLD LEXINGTON RD 27360 #704-01-1989 L2001 **CD** *020 †20
KIRSCH, Carl Richard. 1302 LEXINGTON AVE 27360 #001-02-1984 L1988 **OBG** *020 †30
KRUGER, Karolyn Sue. 309 PINEYWOOD RD 27360 #036-05-1984 L1985 **IM** *020 †20
LANCE, Eric D. 1219 LEXINGTON AVE, ASSOCIATES INC 27360 #048-13-1998 L2004 **GS** *020 †85
LATHAM, William Carson. ■ 27360 #036-01-1962 L1962 **PTH** *020 †50
LEWIS, Brian Christopher. 1219 LEXINGTON AVE, ASSOCIATES INC 27360 #001-06-1997 L2002 **GS** *020 †85
MANGUNDAYAO, Felizardo. 207 OLD LEXINGTON RD 27360 #748-01-1967 L1977 **GP** *020
MANGUNDAYAO, Florita C. 207 OLD LEXINGTON RD 27360 #748-10-1970 L1977 **GP PD** *020
MC COOL, James Alvis. 207 OLD LEXINGTON RD 27360 #036-05-1964 L1964 **PTH** *020 †50
MCCUNE, Bruce Robert. 207 OLD LEXINGTON RD 27360 #011-03-1973 L1975 **GE IM** *020 †20
MC MURCHY, Charles R. 207 OLD LEXINGTON RD 27360 #027-01-1974 L1979 **GE IM** *020 †20
MIEDEN, Gregory Dean. 1213 LEXINGTON AVE 27360 #023-01-1989 L1993 **N** *020 †75
O'BRIEN, Linda Susan. 207 OLD LEXINGTON RD, INPATIENT PHYSICIANS OF DA 27360 #048-13-1985 L2001 **IM** *020 †20
PHILLIPS, Marvin Worth. ■ 27360 #051-04-1945 L1945 **FM** *071 †18
POLEYNARD, Gary D. 207 OLD LEXINGTON RD 27360 #021-05-1971 L1995 **GE** *020 †20
PRENDERGAST, Peter Gerard. 207 OLD LEXINGTON RD, INPATIENT PHYSICIANS OF DA 27360 #035-15-1984 L2007 **IM** *020 †20 ‡
RAMOS, Arlene Gacutan. 903 RANDOLPH ST 27360 #748-01-1987 L1999 **FM** *020 †18
RIGGAN, Cathy Snyder. 200 ARTHUR DR, THOMASVILLE ARCHDALE PEDIA 27360 #036-05-1989 L1992 **PD** *020 †55
ROSEN, David Aaron. 211 OLD LEXINGTON RD, THOMASVILLE MEDICAL CENTER 27360 #021-01-2002 L2005 **IM** *020 †20
SCHLANGER, Laurence W. 207 OLD LEXINGTON RD, THOMASVILLE MEDICAL CENTER 27360 #033-05-1983 L1993 **EM IMG** *020 †20
SEARS, Victor Wilson, Jr. 207 OLD LEXINGTON RD 27360 #036-05-1990 L1992 **GE** *020 †20
SMITH, David C. ■ 27360 #036-05-1943 L1944 **IM GP** *071
SMITH, Mark Douglas, II. 1219 LEXINGTON AVE, ASSOCIATES INC 27360 #048-15-1993 L1997 **GS** *020 †85
SOJKA, Peter Jacob. 207 OLD LEXINGTON RD, THOMASVILLE 27360 #016-11-1992 L1998 **AN** *020 †05
STANFIELD, Leslie C Cohen. 200 ARTHUR DR, THOMASVILLE-ARCHDALE PEDIA 27360 #036-01-1991 L2004 **PD** *020 †55
TOLLIVER, Jim Bert. 903 RANDOLPH ST, STE 1 27360 #020-02-1960 L1975 **GP** *071 †18
WAHID, A T M. 211 OLD LEXINGTON RD, DAVIDSON CARDIOLOGY 27360 #160-01-1989 L2006 **CD** *100 †20
WEAVIL, Patricia Dockery. 200 ARTHUR DR, THOMASVILLE/ARCHDALE PEDS 27360 #036-01-1981 L1982 **PD** *030 †55
WILLETT, Ralph Pope. 524 TURNER ST 27360 #036-07-1985 L1989 **IM** *020 †20
WILLIAMS, David Robt. 200 ARTHUR DR, THOMASVILLE PEDIATRICS 27360 #036-01-1963 L1963 **PD** *020 †55 ‡
YELTON, Blane Wesley, Jr. 211 OLD LEXINGTON RD 27360 #036-01-1971 L1971 **CD** *020 †20
YORK, Shelley C, Jr. 1300 LEXINGTON AVE 27360 #023-01-1951 L1952 **GS TS** *071 †85

TIMBERLAKE – PERSON

CRAFT, Patrick Phelps. ■ 27583 #036-08-1993 L1994 **EM FM** *020 †18

TODD – ASHE

BORCHERT, Lynn Gordon. ■ 28684 #025-01-1968 L1969 **GYN** *020 †30

TRENT WOODS – CRAVEN

ABHYANKAR, Vivek Vishwas. ■ 28562 #035-03-1998 L2005 **HO** *020 †20
BURTON, Ted Fuqua. ■ 28562 #051-04-1957 L1963 **OBG** *071 †30
BUSTARD, Victor Wm. 601 CHELSEA RD, STE 2 28562 #064-01-1959 L1976 **OBG PHP** *071 †30
GODWIN, Charles Donald. 2800 VILLAGE WAY 28562 #012-05-1978 L1989 **P** *020 †75
GREENE, Lindsey Allison. 155 TRENT SHORES DR 28562 #035-06-2008 *012
HARMATUK, Frances Agnes. ■ 28562 #035-15-1941 L1977 **P CHP** *071 †05,75
HEALY, Anne V Oppold. ■ 28562 #047-06-1985 L1986 **FM** *020 †20
KNAZEK, Richard Allan. ■ 28562 #038-40-1969 L1979 **END IM** *071 †20
LIPPITT, Devereux H, II. ■ 28562 #024-01-1947 L1960 **PTH** *071 †50
NASHICK, George Henry. ■ 28562 #008-02-1975 L1975 **GP** *071

TRENTON – JONES

CARAWAY, Treva Shanell. ■ 28585 #036-08-2005 **PD** *100
DUMAS, Mark Neal. 104 E LAKEVIEW DR 28585 #001-02-1981 L1986 **IM** *020 †20
INGRAM, Mario Deaundra. ■ 28585 #036-08-2005 **IM** *012
VIRK, Zia Ullah. 104 E LAKEVIEW DR 28585 #704-01-1988 L2000 **IM RHU** *020 †20

TRINITY – RANDOLPH

DAISY-MOSTAQUE, Selina. ■ 27370 #160-03-1980 L1988 **CHN** *020 †55

TROUTMAN – IREDELL

PATEL, Amrish Chimanlal. 154 S MAIN ST 28166 #917-25-1984 L1997 **FM D** *020 †18 ‡

PELLEGRINO, Yvette-Marie. 285 N MAIN ST, STE D 28166 #033-05-1999 L2005 **FM** *020 †18

TROY – MONTGOMERY

AVERBOOK, Emily Lance. 520 ALLEN ST 27371 #012-05-1988 L1999 **DR** *020 †80
BLAIR, Joseph R. ■ 27371 #041-02-1945 L1945 **OM** *030 †30
CLARK, Daniel Eason. 520 ALLEN ST 27371 #036-01-1961 L1961 **R** *071 †80
CLAUDIUS, Elizabeth R. ■ 27371 #495-27-1971 L1995 **IM** *020 †20
DEVEREUX, Dennis Franklin. 522 ALLEN ST, STE 202 27371 #005-19-1974 L2006 **GS SO** *020 †85
DU BOIS, David Neil. 520 ALLEN ST 27371 #010-02-1983 L1990 **EM UM** *020 †16
ELLER, Chrystal Faye. 522 ALLEN ST, STE 101 27371 #041-15-2004 L2007 **FM** *020 †18
ELLIOTT, William Gavin. 198 SUGAR LOAF DR 27371 #036-01-1987 L1991 **AN MDM** *020 †05
FURIE, David Martin. 520 ALLEN ST 27371 #035-47-1987 L1992 **DR RNR** *020 †80
GLENN, John Capers, Jr. ■ 27371 #036-07-1943 L1947 **R NM** *071 †80
GRIFFIN, Soledad Ceballos. 520 ALLEN ST 27371 #001-02-1984 L1994 **DR** *020 †80
HUDGINS, William Bradford. 520 ALLEN ST 27371 #048-12-1982 L1999 **DR** *020 †20,80
LETT, Pauline A.. ■ 27371 #422-01-2001 L2007 **ID** *020 †20
MAYNOR, Carolyn Chang. 520 ALLEN ST 27371 #036-07-1989 L1990 **DR** *020 †80
MC LEOD, Michael Scott. 835 ALBEMARLE RD, 835 ALBEMARLE RD 27371 #038-40-1995 L1998 **FM** *020 †18
MULLEN, Jana R. 835 ALBEMARLE RD, P O BOX 805 27371 #018-03-1991 L1996 **PD** *020 †55
ROBERSON, John Porter. 520 ALLEN ST 27371 #051-01-1989 L1999 **DR RNR** *020 †80 ‡
ROBERTSON, Michelle Willi. 520 ALLEN ST 27371 #043-01-1998 L2001 **OM** *020 †18
VANG, Touber. 522 ALLEN ST STE 203, P O BOX 575 27371 #025-07-1999 L2002 **FM** *020 †18
WOODYEAR, John M, Jr. 507 N MAIN ST, FAMILY CARE ASSOC, P.A. 27371 #422-01-1985 L1995 **FM** *020 †18

TRYON – POLK

AUSUM, John David. 10 THOUSAND PINES LN 28782 #025-01-1954 L1984 **D** *071 †15
BALDWIN, William Edwin, Jr. ■ 28782 #036-07-1942 L1946 **OM** *071
BOALS, Jos Calloway, III. ■ 28782 #047-06-1962 L1962 **ORS** *020 †40
BOSIEN, Marian M Kreider. ■ 28782 #041-01-1948 L1954 **AN OS** *071
CAREY, Brian E. 3919 LYNN RD, TRYON URGENT CARE 28782 #048-02-1987 L1999 **EM** *020 †16
COMSTOCK, Betsy S. 605 WILDBERRY LN 28782 #048-04-1958 L1987 **P PYA** *071 †75
CONRAD, Robert Nelson. ■ 28782 #019-02-1960 L1963 **PS** *071 †65
CROUNSE, Robert Griffith. ■ 28782 #008-01-1955 L1978 **D OS** *071 †15
FROEMMING, William E. ■ 28782 #016-02-1943 L1949 **OM** *071 †70
HARTMAN, George Edward. 25 SHIELDS DR UNIT 1 28782 #025-07-1974 L1978 **IM** *020
KIM, George Gi-Min. 2536 LYNN RD, STE B 28782 #005-12-1994 L1997 **IM** *020 †20
LESOWITZ, Robert Irwin. ■ 28782 #038-40-1965 L2001 **P CHP** *071 †75
MC CORMACK, Sandra Lee. 2819 LYNN RD 28782 #016-11-1979 L1982 **FM** *020 †18
MC SHERRY, Robert T. 118 DEVILS RIDGE LN 28782 #048-01-1950 L1991 **AN** *071 †05
MELLIES, Margot Jean. ■ 28782 #028-34-1967 L1967 **PD OS** *071 †55
PAGTER, Amos Townsend, Jr. 37 WILDERNESS RD 28782 #036-07-1955 L1961 **IM** *020 †20
RATCLIFFE, Robert Richard. ■ 28782 #051-01-1965 L1991 **P** *075 †75

UNION MILLS – RUTHERFORD

PURGER, John Clayton. ■ 28167 #011-02-1956 L1989 **OBG** *071 †30

VALDESE – BURKE

BETANCOURT, John C. ■ 28690 #654-01-1990 L1998 **FM** *020 †18
BOYD, Tammy Lamonica. 2659 US HIGHWAY 70 E, DREXEL MEDICAL PRACTICE 28690 #036-08-2001 L2005 **FM** *020 †18
BUJOLD, Edward James. 1001 MALCOLM BLVD 28690 #025-07-1977 L1986 **FM** *020 †18
BYRD, Kerry Wendell. 721 MALCOLM BLVD 28690 #036-05-1989 L1991 **FM** *020 †18
CHUNG, Keven Robt. VALDESE GENERAL HOSPITAL, EMERGENCY ROOM DEPT 28690 #005-12-1976 L1977 **EM** *020 †16
DALEY, Christopher Thomas. 720 MALCOLM BLVD, STE 102 28690 #063-01-1992 L2000 **ORS** *020 †40
DEATON, Pleasant Paul. 1001 MALCOLM BLVD 28690 #051-04-1953 L1960 **GS** *071 †85
DESAI, Urvi Gautam. 313 CRESCENT ST NE 28690 #495-23-1988 L1999 **N** *020 †75
FERRUCCI, William S, Jr. 720 MALCOLM BLVD, VALDESE GENERAL HOSPITAL 28690 #025-07-1978 L1996 **EM** *020 †16
GARROU, Benjamin. PO BOX 520, 808 GARDIOL AVE NE 28690 #036-01-1961 L1961 **IM** *020 †20
GENANT, Jackson Ross. ■ 28690 #046-01-1990 L1998 **FM** *020 †18
GLUGOVER, Donald Benjamin. 1001 MALCOLM BLVD 28690 #016-42-1962 L1985 **ORS** *071 †40
GONZALEZ, Michael Bryan. 720 MALCOLM BLVD, STE 200 28690 #051-07-2000 L2003 **PD** *020 †55 ‡
JACUMIN, Walter Joe. 1001 MALCOLM BLVD 28690 #051-04-1966 L1967 **R NM** *071 †80,28
JOHANSON, William Thos. 2659 US HIGHWAY 70 E 28690 #047-05-1979 L1994 **FM** *020 †18
JONES, Edward Bruce. 1001 MALCOLM BLVD 28690 #055-01-1984 L1993 **OTO GS** *020 †45
LANE, Edgar W, Jr. ■ 28690 #036-05-1944 L1944 **U** *020
MC DONALD, Christopher R. 720 MALCOLM BLVD, P O BOX 700 28690 #021-05-1972 L2002 **ON HEM** *020 †20
MOHIUDDIN, Mohammed M. ■ 28690 #495-21-1974 L1981 **OBG** *020 †30
NEALE, Richard C, Jr. MALCOLM BLVD, VALDESE GENERAL HOSP 28690 #051-04-1959 L1965 **PTH CLP** *071 †50
NEALE, Spottswood Pryor. ■ 28690 #051-04-1962 L1969 **PTH** *071 †50
POWELL, Kenneth Alton. 1001 MALCOLM BLVD 28690 #036-05-1960 L1960 **FM** *020 †18
RICE, Edward Ambler, Jr. 720 MALCOLM BLVD 28690 #045-01-1975 L1978 **EM** *020
SKOLOCHENKO, Michael. 1001 MALCOLM BLVD 28690 #051-04-1970 L1975 **FM** *020 †18 ‡
STEELE, Walter Franklin. 1001 MALCOLM BLVD 28690 #036-01-1966 L1966 **GS VS** *020 †85
THOMAS, James Jos. 1001 MALCOLM BLVD 28690 #016-11-1956 L1963 **PD** *071 †55
WHITE, Emmett Royce. 305 REFOUR ST NE 28690 #036-05-1954 L1954 **RO R** *020 †80

VALLE CRUCIS – WATAUGA

MC LAURIN, Lambert P. ■ 28691 #011-03-1967 L1968 **CD IM** *071 †20

VANCEBORO – CRAVEN

BABB, Tamara Cheatham. 620 FARM LIFE AVE 28586 #045-01-1981 L2002 **FM** *020 †18
ENGLEMAN, James D, Jr. 600 ALLIGATOR RD 28586 #020-02-1985 L2000 **FM** *075 †18
SANDHU, Gurinder Paul S. 260 NC HIGHWAY 43, VANCEBORO INTERNAL MED 28586 #495-29-1982 L1996 **IM** *020 †20

VASS – MOORE

FOWLER, Todd Robert. 164 CRANES CV 28394 #041-13-2000 L2005 **EM** *020 †16
KLEINSCHMIDT, Paul E. ■ 28394 #048-02-1993 L2000 **EM** *020 †16
LAW, Arthur G. ■ 28394 #010-01-1949 L1954 **P PYA** *071 †75
MARCHETTI, Louis Jos. 872 CASTLEBERRY CT, SANDHILLS UROLOGY, P.A. 28394 #033-05-1964 L1971 **U** *020 †95
ST JEAN, Michael Raymond. ■ 28394 #023-12-1990 L1992 **GS** *020 †85
WEBB, Joel Clark. ■ 28394 #034-01-1992 L2006 **OBG GO** *020 †30

VILAS – WATAUGA

SINNO, Anwar Ahmad. ■ 28692 #605-01-1963 L1976 **GP CHN** *071

WADE – CUMBERLAND

MAXWELL, James Henry. 7118 MAIN ST, WADE FMC 28395 #065-06-1979 L1993 **GP** *020 †18
REESE, Perry, III. HWY 301, WADE FAMILY MEDICAL CENTER 28395 #025-07-1990 L2000 **FM** *075 †18

WADESBORO – ANSON

BLUE, John Frederick. 500 MORVEN RD, ANSON COMMUNITY HOSPITAL 28170 #010-01-1978 L1979 **FM** *020 †18
BRACEY, Lisa Elaine. 212 S RUTHERFORD ST, WADESBORO PRIMARY CARE 28170 #010-03-1993 L1996 **FM** *020 †18
BURNEY, Fredric Arlen. 500 MORVEN RD 28170 #036-01-1962 L1962 **FM** *020 †18
DAVIS, Daniel Whitaker. 402 MORVEN RD 28170 #036-01-1959 L1959 **FM** *071 †18
DEEN, Floyd, Jr. 402 MORVEN RD 28170 #012-01-1969 L1969 **GP** *071
ELLIOTT, Sarah Powell. 904 MORVEN RD 28170 #010-01-1993 L1996 **PD** *020
ERTUGRUL, Gultekin. 500 MORVEN RD 28170 #902-10-1954 L1971 **GS CD** *071 †85,90
FORGIONE, Lisa Marie. 500 MORVEN RD, ANSON COMMUNITY HOSPITAL 28170 #035-15-1990 L2006 **FM** *020 †18
FRANCIS-BROWNE, Michell I. PO BOX 192, 203 SALISBURY ST 28170 #035-46-1996 L1998 **FM** *020 †18 ‡
HAHNER, Matthew. PO BOX 477, 407 S GREENE ST 28170 #308-03-1980 L1986 **GS** *071 †85
HAIDER, Syed Noman. 402 MORVEN RD, FLOYD DEEN MD,PA 28170 #704-02-1993 L1997 **IM** *020 †20
HERNANDEZ, Lynn Joanne. 110 E ASHE ST, ANSON COUNTY HEALTH DEPT 28170 #033-05-2002 L2005 **FM** *020 †18
HOBGOOD, Lacy Chadwick. 212 S RUTHERFORD ST, WADESBORO FAMILY MED 28170 #036-01-2003 L2007 **MPD** *100 †20
MALIK, Asim. 402 MORVEN RD 28170 #704-02-1994 L2003 **ID** *020 †20
MILLS, George T. 110 E ASHE ST, ANSON COUNTY HEALTH DEPT 28170 #005-12-1949 L1992 **GP PHP** *020 †18
MISHRA, Shashank. PO BOX 192, 203 SALISBURY ST 28170 #917-18-1997 L2003 **FM** *020
NIILEND, Olav. 500 MORVEN RD 28170 #067-01-1968 L1973 **EM PA** *020 †16
ONAFOWOKAN, Joel Adedoyin. 608 SALISBURY ST, AMERICARE HEALTH, PC 28170 #690-06-1998 L2004 **IM** *020
ROMMEL, Victoria. 510 MORVEN RD 28170 #041-07-1989 L1992 **FM** *020 †18
SAI, Abdolhakim Niazi. 208 HALL ST 28170 #517-01-1966 L1975 **IM** *020 †20 ‡
YASIN, Syed Muhammad Ali. ■ 28170 #704-21-2000 L2006 **IM** *100 †20

WAGRAM – SCOTLAND

HOLDEN, Ruth Ellen. ■ 28396 #007-02-1976 L1979 **GS** *100
MODI, Bhupendra. 16041 CADDIE CT, DEERCROFT SUBDIVISION 28396 #495-37-1991 L1997 **AN** *020 †05 ‡

WAKE FOREST – WAKE

ADETUNJI, Yemisi A. 1655 WAKE DR, STE 101 27587 #690-01-1987 L2001 **GPM** *020 †55
AKTARUZZAMAN, Mohammad. 1906 S MAIN ST, STE 216 27587 #160-06-1980 L1992 **AI** *020,03
BRANDES, Barbara Anne. 1655 WAKE DR, STE 101 27587 #033-06-1995 L2005 **PD** *020 †55
BROWN, Mark Steven. 835 WAKE FOREST BUSNS PARK, STE A 27587 #023-07-1986 L1992 **OTO GS** *020 †45
BRUCE-MENSAH, Kofi. 851 DURHAM RD, STE D 27587 #412-01-1986 L2001 **IM** *020 †20
BUNGART, Kimberly Jayne. 835 WAKE FORST BSNS PARK P 27587 #021-01-1991 L1994 **PD** *020 †55
BURTON, Philip Douglas. 123 CAPCOM AVE, STE ONE 27587 #036-08-1981 L1985 **FM** *020 †18
CEFALU, Joseph Anthony. 3213 ROGERS RD, VILLAGE FAMILY CARE OF WAK 27587 #036-08-2001 L2005 **FM** *020 †18
CHIMENTO, James John. ■ 27587 #007-02-1969 L1974 **ORS** *071 †40 ‡
CLARK, David Allan. 835 WAKE FOREST BUSNS PARK, STE A 27587 #051-01-1982 L1992 **OTO FPS** *020 †45
CLARK, William G. 2115 S MAIN ST STE A, WAKE FOREST URGENT CARE 27587 #036-01-1978 L1980 **EM** *020 †18

DENNIS, Steven Henry. 835 WAKE FOREST BUSNS PARK, STE A 27587 #036-01-1981 L1982 OTO *020 †45

ERCOLINO, Peter Salvatore. 835 WAKE FORST BSNS PARK P 27587 #035-06-1997 L1999 PD *020 †55

FUDGE, Elizabeth Brown. 11130 CAPITAL BLVD 27587 #012-01-2002 L2005 PDE *012 †55

GOSHA, Tonya Lashon. ■ 27587 #012-21-1989 L2005 GPM *020

HERRIOTT, Victoria M. 110 CAPCOM AVE, PEDIATRICS 27587 #036-01-1999 L2002 PD *020 †55

HOOD, Alton Lee. ■ 27587 #047-06-1959 L2006 EM GS *071

HUMMEL, Joseph Jacob. 1009 BINKLEY CHAPEL CT, TRAVELING PHYSICIAN 27587 #036-01-2002 L2005 FM *020 †18

JENKINS, Grant Wm. 1002 DURHAM RD, STE 800 27587 #016-11-1990 L1992 IM *020 †20

KHAN, Mohammad A K. 1751 S MAIN 27587 #160-01-1979 L1995 IM *020 †20

KOCIS, Edith. 11130 CAPITAL BLVD, GROWING CHILD PEDIATRICS, 27587 #035-19-1993 L2000 GPM *020 †55

KONOPKA, Scott Edward. 1964 S MAIN ST, HERITAGE FAMILY CARE 27587 #036-08-2001 L2008 FM *020 †18

KWARK, Soon A. 11635 CAPITAL BLVD, STE 200 27587 #021-05-1984 L1989 FM *020 †18

LAZORICK, Suzanne. 11130 CAPITAL BLVD, GROWING CHILD PEDIATRICS, 27587 #036-01-1995 L1998 GPM *100 †20,55

LINZAU, Jean Arthur. 1733 PASTURE WALK DR, 6323 GEORGIA AVE NW 27587 #010-03-1966 L2006 IM PHP *020 ‡

MAY, Stephen Christopher. ■ 27587 #409-16-1983 L1993 PD *020

MEDDERS, Russell Glen. 835 WAKE FOREST BUSNS PARK, STE A 27587 #036-01-1984 L1985 OTO HNS *020 †45

MINIOR, Daniel Christian. 7204 PANTONBURY PL 27587 #024-07-2000 L2004 EM *020 †16

MOORE, George Horace, Jr. 11635 CAPITAL BLVD, STE 200 27587 #036-08-1981 L1982 FM *020 †18

MULLEN, Matthew Paul. 2115 S MAIN ST STE A, WAKE FOREST URGENT CARE 27587 #041-13-1981 L1996 UCM GP *020

NAGUIB, Sherif Geo. 6217 TIFFIELD WAY, MAILING ADDRESS: P O BOX 27587 #915-02-1983 L2003 FM *020 †18

PACOS, Andrew Michael. 170 SCOTTS PINE CIR 27587 #035-06-1987 L2002 IM *020 †20

ROUNDS, John Carson. 3213 ROGERS RD 27587 #036-08-1988 L1991 FM *020 †18

SOLIMAN, Mona M. 11635 CAPITAL BLVD, STE 200 27587 #016-42-1997 L2002 FM PD *020 †18

SUGARMAN, Edward David. ■ 27587 #035-15-1963 L1964 ORS *071 †40

TANG, Grace. 11635 CAPITAL BLVD, STE 200 27587 #041-14-1998 L2004 FM *020 †18

TRELLA, Jennifer M. ■ 27587 #041-14-1993 L2006 PD *020 †55

TROUTMAN, James Michael. 11130 CAPITAL BLVD, GROWING CHILD PEDIATRICS 27587 #038-40-1994 L2002 PD EM *020 †55

VEGA, Henry. 8652 BARRETT RIDGE RD 27587 #011-03-1986 L1992 AN FM *020 †05

VISTA, Reynaldo Bueta. ■ 27587 #748-08-1963 L1971 PTH FOP *071 †50

WALSH, Amy J. 11635 CAPITAL BLVD, STE 200 27587 #010-02-1994 L1997 FM *020 †18

WEBER, Thomas Nelson. 1964 S MAIN ST, WAKE FOREST PA 27587 #051-04-1986 L1987 FM *020 †18

WEINSTEIN, Naomi D. 835 WAKE FORST BSNS PARK P 27587 #035-06-1996 L1999 PD *020 †55

WHITE, Carrington Wells. 1655 WAKE DR, STE 101 27587 #051-01-1997 L1998 PD *020 †55

WILKINS, Stanley A, Jr. 835 WAKE FOREST BUSNS PARK, STE A 27587 #036-01-1982 L1983 OTO HNS *020 †45

YEDDANAPUDI, Vasantha K. ■ 27587 #495-21-1966 L1977 PD *020 †55

WALKERTOWN — FORSYTH

BAIRD, Frances Gabbard. 5845 SULLIVANTOWN RD 27051 #036-05-1971 L1971 PTH *071 †50

CROSBY, Bradley J. ■ 27051 #036-05-2007 EM *012

SCHAEFFER, Stanley Dean. 2800 DARROW RD 27051 #055-01-1990 L1993 FM *020 †18

THOMPSON, Emily Ann. ■ 27051 #036-01-2007 PD *012

WALLACE — DUPLIN

BLAIR, Mott Parks, IV. 404 E MAIN ST 28466 #036-08-1987 L1989 FM *020 †18

FRANKOS, Mary A. 112 MEDICAL VILLAGE DR, WALLACE URGENT CARE 28466 #649-14-1981 L1987 IM *020

IACOVINO, John Ralph. ■ 28466 #024-07-1967 L2004 IM PUD *071 †20 ‡

MEYER, Mitchell Dean. 112 MEDICAL VILLAGE DR, WALLACE URGENT CARE 28466 #068-01-1981 L1997 FM *020 †18

REID, Rolyan Arokas. ■ 28466 #005-06-2003 L2007 MPD *020 †20

RICCI, Daniel Michael. 207 E MURPHY ST, BOX 968 28466 #041-09-1983 L1986 IM *020 †20

TRIBIE, Khadijia Delene. 251 SLOAN ST 28466 #012-21-2002 L2006 PD *020 †55

WELLS, Roxie Cannon. 112 MEDICAL VILLAGE DR, STE F 28466 #036-08-1999 L2002 FM *020 †18

WALNUT COVE — STOKES

ALECCE, Paul M. ■ 27052 #010-02-1953 L1973 OPH *020 †35

COLETTA, Harry Mario. PO BOX 678, 106 E 8TH ST 27052 #036-05-1977 L1980 FM *020 †18

ZARATE, Renato M. 1072 N MAIN ST 27052 #748-08-1969 L1974 IM *020 †20

WARRENTON — WARREN

DOUGLAS-LEWIS, Yvette. 518 W RIDGEWAY ST, WARRENTON FAMILY PRACTICE 27589 #036-01-1993 L1996 FM *020 †18

HOLT, Thomas. 209 FAIRVIEW ST 27589 #051-04-1938 L1938 OPH OTO *071 †45

WARSAW — DUPLIN

DAYS, Jacques Rodney. 121 W PLANK RD 28398 #012-01-1994 L1997 FM *020 †18

DRAUGHN, Roland C, Jr. 603 E COLLEGE ST 28398 #041-09-1983 L1989 OBG *020

GODWIN, Meredith Owen. ■ 28398 #036-08-2004 MP *012

JENNINGS, Winston, Jr. 121 W PLANK RD, BOX 821 28398 #035-08-1983 L1990 P *020

RAY, Horace Truman, Jr. ■ 28398 #023-01-1963 L1965 GP OS *020

WASHINGTON – BEAUFORT

ADLER, Ira Neil. 630 E 11TH ST 27889 #011-03-1995 L2000 DR *020 †80

AILSTOCK, Lysle Kennedy. 630 E 11TH ST 27889 #051-04-1991 L1996 DR *020 †80

AINSWORTH, Deborah L. 1206 BROWN ST 27889 #051-07-1987 L1990 PD *020 †55

AINSWORTH, Stephen R. 1207 HIGHLAND DR 27889 #024-16-1985 L1990 ORS *020 †40

ALBERNAZ, Vanessa Sailer. 630 E 11TH ST 27889 #038-41-1994 L1995 VIR *020 †80

ALLIGOOD, Toby Ray. 601 E 11TH ST 27889 #036-05-1976 L1976 D IM *020 †20,15

AUSTIN, Frederick D, III. 1380 COWELL FARM RD 27889 #036-01-1967 L1967 IM ID *020 †20

BALTIMORE, Charles L. 639 W 15TH ST, WASHINGTON EYE CLINIC 27889 #051-01-1969 L1972 OPH *020 †80

BARNES, Susan Joan. 630 E 11TH ST 27889 #033-05-1981 L2005 DR *020 †80 ‡

BEARDEN, Emmett Kimsey. 630 E 11TH ST 27889 #045-01-1955 L1994 R *071 †80

BEGELMAN, Keith Garrett. 630 E 11TH ST 27889 #033-06-2000 L2006 DR *100 †80

BERETICH, Melissa Anne. 628 E 12TH ST 27889 #036-08-2002 L2005 IM *020 †20

BERTSCH, Mary Jo. 619 E 12TH ST 27889 #045-07-1983 L1998 CD IM *020 †20

BIRDSONG, Debra Stein. 1206 BROWN ST 27889 #055-01-1989 L1995 PD *020 †55

BIRDSONG, Edward Lee. 1207 HIGHLAND DR 27889 #055-01-1989 L1995 HS *020 †40

BLOUNT, John Gray. ■ 27889 #036-01-1960 L1960 IM *071

BURROWS, John Howard. 628 E 12TH ST, ONCOLOGY CLINIC 27889 #025-01-1959 L2004 ON IM *020 ‡

CHIANG, Karl Sycherng. 630 E 11TH ST 27889 #012-01-1986 L1993 DR *020 †80

CLARK, Timothy Jos. 630 E 11TH ST 27889 #036-07-1981 L1985 DR *020 †80

COAN, Michael Robert. 630 E 11TH ST 27889 #016-06-1999 L2005 DR *100 †80

COATS, Ericka Deana. 630 E 11TH ST 27889 #010-03-1997 L2002 DR *020 †80

COLEMAN, James Barr. ■ 27889 #036-01-1973 L1973 GS *020 †85

CONWAY, Mary M. 212 STEWART PKWY 27889 #045-14-1985 L1995 IM *020

COOK, Elisabeth Stanger. 628 E 12TH ST, BEAUFORT COUNTY HOSPITAL 27889 #036-05-1977 L1977 EM *020 †16

COOK, Russell Clifford. 1206 BROWN ST 27889 #036-05-1976 L1979 PD *020 †55

COSENZA, David Antonio. ■ 27889 #023-01-1997 L2004 FM *020 †18

CRAWFORD, Michael Brett. 1202 BROWN ST 27889 #039-01-1984 L1989 U *020 †95

CREWS, Jennie Robertson. 1209 BROWN ST, MARION L SHEPARD CANCER CE 27889 #036-07-1990 L1992 ON *020 †20

DESROCHERS, David Alan. 630 E 11TH ST 27889 #035-20-1976 L1983 DR *020 †80

DUNCAN, Melissa Bruley. 630 E 11TH ST 27889 #012-05-1991 L2000 DR *020 †80

EASLEY, Henry A. 628 E 12TH ST 27889 #036-01-1982 L1983 OBG *020 †30

EDWARDS, Charles D. 418 E 12TH ST 27889 #036-05-1950 L1959 GS *071 †85

EGBERT, James Michael, Jr. 615 E 12TH ST, GENERAL SURGEON/SEABOARD S 27889 #036-08-1996 L2007 GS *020 †85

FARLEY, David Jefferson. 630 E 11TH ST 27889 #051-04-1978 L2001 R *020 †80

FINICAL, Eric James. 630 E 11TH ST 27889 #048-12-1988 L1990 DR *020 †80

HERBERT, Philip S, Jr. 1308 HIGHLAND DR 27889 #035-20-1951 L1977 P *072 †75

HILL, Edward Feldin. 501 W 15TH ST 27889 #028-02-1973 L1984 FM *020 †18

HINDSLEY, John Pack, Jr. 628 E 12TH ST 27889 #051-01-1970 L1978 U *071 †95

HOPE, William Cameron, IV. 630 E 11TH ST 27889 #036-01-1998 L2002 DR *020 †80

INZERILLO, John Joseph. 1209 BROWN ST, MARION L SHEPARD CANCER CE 27889 #308-08-1986 L1993 ON HEM *020 †20

JOHNS, Thomas Chet. 628 E 12TH ST 27889 #045-04-1996 L2003 FM *020 †18

JOHNSON, Dennis Ray. 630 E 11TH ST 27889 #036-08-1982 L1985 DR IM *020 †20,80

JOHNSON, Donald Carl. 628 E 12TH ST 27889 #036-05-1958 L1958 OPH *071 †35

JONES, Albert M. 760 MIMOSA SHORES RD 27889 #051-01-1951 L1960 OBG *071 †30

KARPINSKI, Mark Allan. 1206 BROWN ST 27889 #036-05-1987 L1995 PD *020 †55

KNOTT, Tara Marie. 1380 COWELL FARM RD 27889 #012-05-1992 L1998 IM *020 †20

KOLAPPA, Kalavathi. 1308 HIGHLAND DR, TIDELAND MENTAL HEALTH CEN 27889 #495-42-1977 L1986 P *020 †75

KOWALSKI, Henryk Mariusz. 630 E 11TH ST 27889 #024-07-1981 L1988 RNR DR *040 †80

KUSZYK, Brian Scott. 630 E 11TH ST 27889 #023-07-1994 L2000 DR *020 †80

LEWIS, David Dubrutz. 501 W 15TH ST 27889 #051-01-1991 L1992 FM *020 †18

LEWIS, Gregory Kenneth. 630 E 11TH ST 27889 #010-02-1989 L1995 RNR *020 †80

LIEDERBACH, Stephen James. 608 E 12TH ST 27889 #038-40-1985 L2006 IM *020 †20 ‡

LOBOS, Michael Jerome. 1202 BROWN ST, WASHINGTON UROLOGICAL ASSC 27889 #028-34-1986 L1992 U GS *020 †95

LURITO, Joseph Thos. 630 E 11TH ST 27889 #023-07-1992 L2002 RNR *020 †80

MANNING, James Roy, III. ■ 27889 #036-01-2002 L2005 IM *020 †20

MARTIN, Eric Meyer. 630 E 11TH ST 27889 #036-05-1994 L1998 RNR *020 †80

MC GUIRE, Timothy William. 615 E 12TH ST 27889 #025-07-1998 L2002 GS *020 †85

MC LAUGHLIN, Michael G. 630 E 11TH ST 27889 #033-05-1985 L1990 DR *020 †80

MEGA, Richard Stanley. 628 E 12TH ST 27889 #024-05-1968 L1982 OTO *071 †45

MEWBORNE, Jeffrey D. 630 E 11TH ST 27889 #048-12-1992 L1996 RNR *020 †80

MOORE, Paul Milton. 619 E 12TH ST 27889 #036-01-1959 L1959 GP *020 †18

MORSE, Nina Higgins. 628 E 12TH ST 27889 #041-07-1971 L1994 IM GP *020

NALL, Kenny Chas. ■ 27889 #012-01-1985 L1999 IM PCC *020 †20

NELSON, Lisa Carraway. ■ 27889 #036-08-2004 L2007 EM *020

NG, Victor Wang Ta. ■ 27889 #036-05-1959 L1960 FM *071 †18

NICHOLSON, Thomas Westray. 1380 COWELL FARM RD 27889 #036-01-1970 L1970 IM CD *020 †20

OETERS, Rhonda C. 628 E 12TH ST 27889 #048-02-1989 L1990 EM *020 †16

OLIVER, Andrew Blaine, Jr. 628 E 12TH ST 27889 #036-01-1981 L1984 OBG *020 †30

PARTRICK, Cornelius T. ■ 27889 #036-01-1954 L1954 IM *071 †20

PEACOCK, Brenda Smith. 1204 BROWN ST 27889 #045-01-1984 L1988 GYN *020 †30

PENDERS, Thomas M. 628 E 12TH ST 27889 #041-09-1973 L2004 P GPM *020 †75

PERKINS, Phillip Kerry. 1314 HIGHLAND DR 27889 #027-01-1987 L1991 EM *020 †16

PICTON, Douglas Wm. 630 E 11TH ST 27889 #036-08-1989 L1992 DR *020 †80

POTTER, Jeffrey Michael. 630 E 11TH ST 27889 #021-01-1998 L1999 RNR *020 †80

POWERS, Barry. 630 E 11TH ST 27889 #035-09-1975 L1977 DR *020 †80

PUGH, Raeford Theodore. ■ 27889 #036-01-1957 L1957 GP OS *071 †18

REEDY, Myles Lawson. 630 E 11TH ST 27889 #012-05-1998 L1999 RNR *020 †80

RESPESS, Rachel Harris. 628 E 12TH ST 27889 #036-08-1997 L2001 OBG *020 †30

RILEY, Judith A. 413 E MAIN ST 27889 #654-01-1986 L2004 IM ID *020 †20

RILEY, Patrick Michael. 424 WHARTON STATION RD, RT 1 27889 #025-12-1979 L1983 AN *020 †05

RISH, Berkley Lamont. ■ 27889 #036-05-1958 L1958 NS *071 †25

RITCHIE, David Jos. ■ 27889 #041-01-1956 L1995 R NM *072 †80,28

ROBBINS, Philip S. 1308 HIGHLAND DR 27889 #035-20-1954 L1976 P *071 †75

ROBINETTE, Joseph Judge. 630 E 11TH ST 27889 #038-06-2000 L2006 **DR** *100 †80
RUFFOLO, Thomas Anthony. 615 E 12TH ST 27889 #038-40-1985 L1991 **IM GE** *020 †20
SANDY, Robert E. ■ 27889 #041-12-1953 L1959 **R** *071 †80
SCHROEDER, Bruce F. 630 E 11TH ST 27889 #035-19-1990 L1996 **R** *020 †80
SEYMOUR, Heather Marie. 630 E 11TH ST 27889 #051-04-1999 L2005 **DR** *020 †80
SHELDON, Frank Chadwick. 1314 HIGHLAND DR 27889 #010-01-1962 L1973 **EM GP** *020 †85
SHUSTERMAN, Douglas J. 630 E 11TH ST 27889 #010-02-1993 L1996 **DR** *020 †80
SILVERTHORNE, Ray G. ■ 27889 #036-05-1951 L1951 **GYN** *071
SMITH, Allan R, III. 628 E 12TH ST 27889 #016-11-1994 L1997 **PTH** *020 †50
SPEROS, Thomas Lee. 628 E 12TH ST 27889 #036-01-1976 L2005 **FM** *020 †18
STAGE, Anson Hutchinson. ■ 27889 #010-01-1952 L1977 **OBG** *040 †20
STEPHENSON, Henry Louis. 615 E 12TH ST 27889 #036-01-1955 L1955 **CD IM** *072 †20
SWAMINATHAN, Viswanathan. 1308 HIGHLAND DR 27889 #495-66-1971 L1978 **P GP** *020 †75
SWARNER, David Reynolds. 1201 CAROLINA AVE 27889 #023-07-1961 L1994 **IM GE** *020
TAYLOE, David T. 608 E 12TH ST 27889 #041-01-1950 L1950 **PD** *071 †20
TAYLOE, Joshua. ■ 27889 #036-01-1961 L1961 **OBG** *071 †30
TAYLOR, William Martin. ■ 27889 #012-05-1953 L1953 **DR** *071 †80
TEIXEIRA, Fredrick A. 1380 COWELL FARM RD, ASSOCIATES 27889 #012-05-1992 L1998
    IM *020 †20
THAXTON, Anthony Grant. 630 E 11TH ST 27889 #012-05-2000 L2001 **DR** *100 †80
THOMAS, Christopher Crim. 630 E 11TH ST 27889 #036-05-1990 L1992 **VIR R** *020 †80
THOMAS, Karen Alligood. 1204 BROWN ST 27889 #036-08-1987 L1989 **FM** *020 †18
THOMPSON, Jacqueline Sue. 1204 BROWN ST 27889 #051-04-1989 L1996 **GYN** *020 †30
TIPTON, William Wakefield. 615 E 12TH ST 27889 #047-05-1982 L1988 **GS VS** *020 †85
TRIPP, Michael David. 630 E 11TH ST 27889 #036-08-1981 L1982 **DR VIR** *020 †80
TULLOH, Rosemary Helen. 630 E 11TH ST 27889 #024-05-1993 L2005 **DR** *020 †80
VAINRIGHT, Julian Robt. 630 E 11TH ST 27889 #041-01-1983 L1987 **DR** *020 †80
VITHALANI, Roger. 630 E 11TH ST 27889 #036-08-1992 L2001 **NM** *020 †80,28
WALTERS, Bobby Clifton, Jr. 630 E 11TH ST 27889 #036-08-1999 L2001 **RNR** *100 †80
WATERS, Zack James, Jr. 601 E 11TH ST 27889 #023-01-1961 L1968 **GS** *020 †85
WEAVER, Michael David. 630 E 11TH ST 27889 #047-06-1971 L1973 **DR** *020 †80
WHITMORE, J Stewart. ■ 27889 #028-02-1949 L1987 **R OS** *071 †80
WINEGARDNER, Stephen D. PO BOX 2786 27889 #036-08-1985 L1986 **FM** *020 †18
YOUNG, Richard Martin. 1380 COWELL FARM RD 27889 #039-01-1979 L1981
    EM IM *020 †20,16

WAXHAW – UNION

AHRENS, William Albert. ■ 28173 #035-48-1999 L2007 **SP** *100 †50
BELL, Ralph Monroe. ■ 28173 #041-02-1941 L1941 **IM** *071
BELLAVIA, Irm R. ■ 28173 #035-06-1995 L2002 **P** *020 †75
BERENFELD, Sharon Ann. ■ 28173 #011-03-1987 L1988 **IM** *020 †20
BORUN, Alexander Gregory. ■ 28173 #847-13-2005 **FP** *012
BRODERSEN, Allan. ■ 28173 #039-01-1985 L1998 **IM** *020 †20
COLLINS, Jonathan Mark. 1150 N BROOME ST, WAXHAW FAMILY PHYSICIANS 28173
    #036-08-1999 L2000 **FM** *020 †18
DALSANIA, Parag Shantilal. ■ 28173 #422-01-1997 L2000 **IM IMG** *020 †20
DOSS, Helen Sells. PO BOX 248, 6705 WYCLIFFE AVE 28173 #051-01-1979 L1985
    GP PD *020 †55
ENOHMBI, Emmanuel Tambi. ■ 28173 #690-06-1997 L2006 **IM** *020 †20
EVANS, Raeburn Maurice. ■ 28173 #038-41-1973 L1973 **FM** *071 †18
FOTE, Bertrand Pokam. ■ 28173 #010-03-2001 L2004 **EM** *020 †16
GAGE, Lucius Gaston, Jr. ■ 28173 #036-07-1948 L1952 **A RHU** *071
GARDNER, Todd Eric. ■ 28173 #041-09-1990 L2006 **EM** *020 †16
GILLESPIE, Neil Charles. ■ 28173 #045-01-1996 L2005 **AN** *020 †05
GUTHMANN, Howard M, II. 205 W SOUTH MAIN ST, WAXHAW FAMILY PHYSICIANS 28173
    #047-06-1981 L1989 **FM** *020 †18 ‡
IYER, Jennifer Carbaugh. 805 WANDERING WAY 28173 #012-01-1998 L2006 **CN** *020 †75
LYNIP, Stephen Arthur. ■ 28173 #035-15-1969 L1991 **PHP FM** *030
MARTIN, William G. 205 W SOUTH MAIN ST, WAXHAW FAMILY PHYSICIANS 28173
    #010-02-1981 L1993 **FM** *020 †18
MOGUL, Robin Jean. ■ 28173 #035-15-1990 L2006 **P** *020
NIECHNIEDOWICZ, Frank E. ■ 28173 #010-01-1975 L1978 **AN** *071
OSINLOYE, Adediji. 104 TOWTON CT 28173 #690-02-1989 L2004 **IM** *020 †20
SHENOUDA, Hany Shokry. ■ 28173 #915-02-1976 L2005 **END IM** *020 †20
TOMCHO, Paige Bua. 524 N BROOME ST, CAROLINAS HEALTHCARE SYSTE 28173
    #041-77-1998, ▲ L2004 **FM** *020 †18
YOCHEM, August S, Jr. ■ 28173 #020-02-1946 L1947 **P** *071 †75

WAYNESVILLE – HAYWOOD

ABBATE, Brazie Guy. 116 BALSAM DR 28786 #869-05-1960 L1971 **U** *071
ALLSBROOK, William Calvin. ■ 28786 #036-01-1970 L1970 **PTH** *040 †50
ARCENEAUX, Michelle Jean. ■ 28786 #021-05-1978 L1996 **N** *020 †71
BECK, Jere Le May. PO BOX 1050 28786 #001-02-1969 L1970 **OBG** *071 †30
BELL, Keturah Chesbrough. 1272 EAST ST 28786 #036-01-1997 L2000 **FM** *020 †18
BRASWELL, William Kelley. 40 GINGKO LN, DR BRASWELL MD 28786 #011-02-1977 L1978
    GS *020 †85
BROWN, George Wallace. 1088 BROWN AVE 28786 #036-01-1954 L1954 **FM** *071 †18
BROWN, Michael Ashley. 1088 BROWN AVE, HAZELWOOD FAMILY MED PLLC 28786
    #036-08-1988 L1992 **FM EM** *020 †18
BROWN, Roy W. ■ 28785 #016-43-1945 L1946 **GP OS** *071
BUSS, Russell Edward. ■ 28785 #005-02-1970 L1995 **EM** *020 †16
COLEMAN, Van Steenburgh. ■ 28785 #012-05-1971 L1972 **DR** *071 †80
DEWEES, Steven Philip. 220 SILVERBELL LN 28786 #036-01-1971 L1971 **IM** *020 †20
DICKERSON, A Jackson. ■ 28786 #036-05-1948 L1949 **GS TS** *071 †85
DUBIEL, Barbara Theresa. 289 ACCESS RD 28786 #047-05-1984 L2001 **IM OM** *020 †20
EGLINTON, Daniel Thomas. 35 VALLEY VIEW TER 28786 #034-01-1978 L1983 **ORS** *020 †40
FELDMAN, David Michael. ■ 28785 #016-06-1968 L1969 **R** *071 †80
FREEMAN, George Wells. ■ 28785 #036-05-1965 L1965 **FM** *071 †18
GILLIGAN, Kendall Allen. ■ 28786 #005-14-1977 L1979 **FM** *020 †18,16
HABAS, Jo Ellen. ■ 28786 #041-07-1981 L2007 **END IM** *020 †20 ‡
HOLMES, Matthew Elton. ■ 28786 #038-06-2000 L2002 **P** *020 †75 ‡

JABEN, Mark Jeffrey. 78 BOARDWALK LN 28786 #011-02-1981 L1985 **EM** *020 †16
JONES, Richard Brian. 35 VALLEY VIEW TER 28786 #036-08-1996 L2001 **ORS** *020 †40
KIRBY, Charles Gentry. 72 BALSAM DR, 72 BALSAM DR 28786 #047-06-1960 L1996
    OPH *071 †35
LARSON, Kelly Michelle. 556 HAZELWOOD AVE, URGENT CARE WEST 28786
    #016-42-1997 L2004 **FM** *020 †18
LENAR, Robert James. ■ 28785 #041-01-1962 L1973 **IM CD** *071
LOPEZ-STRATTON, Anna E. 1272 EAST ST 28786 #048-12-1995 L1997 **FM** *020 †18
LOVE, David Wm. 1088 BROWN AVE 28786 #011-03-1984 L2001 **FM** *075
MAXWELL, Keith Melvin. 35 VALLEY VIEW TER 28786 #039-05-1982 L1984 **ORS** *020 †40
MC CASTLAIN, Morris S, Jr. ■ 28786 #047-06-1965 L1965 **GS** *020 †85
MC CORD, Symm Hawes. ■ 28785 #012-01-1965 L1968 **FM** *074 ‡
MC NAUGHTON, Robert Avery. ■ 28786 #024-01-1945 L1948 **GE IM** *020 †20
MESSER, Virgil Marvin. ■ 28786 #036-05-1967 L1967 **IM** *071 †20
MILLER, Joseph. ■ 28786 #025-01-1967 L2006 **GS CRS** *071 †85 ‡
MILLING, James Reaves. ■ 28786 #045-01-1955 L1956 **GP OS** *071
MOSKOS, Frank. ■ 28786 #038-40-2004 L2008 **FM** *020 †18
MOTLEY, Gregory Stephen. 35 VALLEY VIEW TER 28786 #020-12-1991 L1995 **ORS** *020 †40
MULHOLLAND, David Grant. 1170 CRABTREE RD 28785 #041-02-1993 L1994 **FM** *020 †18
MYERS, Charles Jeffrey. ■ 28786 #017-20-1997 L2007 **OBG** *020
PASS, Michael Wayne. 1272 EAST ST, PRACTICE CENTER P.A. 28786 #021-06-1979 L1982
    FM *020 †18
RUDINS, Andrew. 35 VALLEY VIEW TER 28786 #051-04-1988 L1997 **PM PRS** *020 †60
SMITH, Albert H, Jr. 1426 N MAIN ST, OWEN-SMITH CLINIC PA 28786 #036-05-1951 L1951
    GP *071
SMITH, James Jos. ■ 28786 #023-01-1971 L1971 **P** *020 †75
STRINGFIELD, John William. 1272 EAST ST 28786 #036-07-1980 L1983 **FM** *020 †18
STRINGFIELD, Judith S. 1272 EAST ST, WAYNESVILLE FAMILY PRACTIC 28786
    #041-07-1980 L1983 **FM** *020 †18
TANNER, John Robt. ■ 28786 #038-40-1955 L1955 **IM** *075 †20
TWIDDY, Shannon Keith. ■ 28786 #038-44-1995 L1996 **FM** *020 †18
WARD, Thomas Sanders, Jr. 1272 EAST ST 28786 #051-07-1994 L1997 **FM** *020 †18
YUAN, Shang-Hsien. 720 CAMP BRANCH RD 28786 #917-04-1957 L1976 **PD** *040
ZASLOW, Ely David. 1088 BROWN AVE, HAYWOOD FAMILY MEDICINE, P 28786
    #036-01-1985 L1986 **FM** *020 †18

WEAVERVILLE – BUNCOMBE

ABERNATHY, Robert A, Jr. ■ 28787 #051-04-1950 L2004 **IM** *071 †20
ALSTOTT, David Frederick. ■ 28787 #017-20-1963 L1963 **PTH CLP** *062 †50
CAMPBELL, William Keith. 63 MONTICELLO RD 28787 #036-07-1975 L1976 **FM** *020 †18
CLAXTON, Calvin P, Jr. ■ 28787 #051-01-1962 TS *071 †85,90
COOK, Robert Adam. 63 MONTICELLO RD 28787 #045-01-1979 L1982 **FM** *020 †18
FEILER, Alan Howard. 63 MONTICELLO RD 28787 #035-15-1999 L2000 **FM** *020 †18
HRUSKA, Nathan Jon. 63 MONTICELLO RD, ASSOCIATES 28787 #018-03-1998 L2001
    FM *020 †18
JOHNSTON, Neil Van. ■ 28787 #067-01-1961 L1961 **OPH** *071 †35
LENTZ, Linda Marie. ■ 28787 #012-01-1988 L1991 **IM** *020 †20
LUCEY, John Denis. ■ 28787 #041-09-1970 L1978 **ORS** *071 †40
MC DADE, Henry Cooper, III. 201 FLAT CREEK VILLAGE DR, NORTH BUNCOMBE FAMILY
    MEDI 28787 #036-07-2003 L2005 **FM** *020 †18
MC QUISTON, Christina. 40 LOST COVE RD 28787 #919-05-1977 L1986 **IM** *020 †20
MOORE, Robert Brian. 201 FLAT CREEK VILLAGE DR, NORTH BUNCOMBE FAMILY MEDI 28787
    #012-01-2002 L2003 **FM** *020 †18
MOYANO, Maria J. ■ 28787 #847-04-1962 L1971 **P GP** *071
PARKER, Martha Elizabeth. ■ 28787 #036-01-1970 L1970 **IM** *071 †20
REAVIS, Richard Allen. ■ 28787 #036-01-1981 L1982 **GP** *020
WYCKOFF, Donald Roy. ■ 28787 #016-11-1980 L1981 **DR** *020 †80

WEBSTER – JACKSON

BROWN, Harry James. PO BOX 448 28788 #048-02-1985 L1993 **EM** *020 †18
CHEVILLE, Richard Arthur. PO BOX 315 28788 #018-03-1961 L1962 **PTH OS** *071
NITSCH, Karen Gayle. ■ 28788 #048-02-1982 L1983 **PDE** *020 †55
STEWART, Jimmie V. ■ 28788 #048-02-1968 L1988 **FM** *020 †18

WEDDINGTON – UNION

ANDERSSON, Nelsa Jean. 1928 WEDDINGTON RD, WEDDINGTON PRIMARY CARE 28104
    #041-07-1987 L1995 **FM** *020 †18
KANELOS, Dino Peter. 1932 WEDDINGTON RD, CAROLINA FAMILY HEALTHCARE 28104
    #038-41-1997 L1998 **FM** *020 †18
LADD, Susan Elise. 1928 WEDDINGTON RD 28104 #038-40-1999 L2002 **FM** *020 †18
LINCOLN, Michael Scott. 1928 WEDDINGTON RD, WEDDINGTON FAMILY MEDICINE 28104
    #036-01-1998 L2001 **FM** *020 †18
SHARMA, Anuj. 1928 WEDDINGTON RD, WEDDINGTON FAMILY MEDICINE 28104
    #036-01-1992 L1993 **FM** *020 †18

WELDON – HALIFAX

COCHRAN, Salter Josiah. 311 W 2ND ST, BOX 632 27890 #010-03-1948 L1950 **FM** *071
JARMAN, F Graham, Jr. ■ 27890 #051-04-1943 L1952 **GS** *071 †85
PHADE, Sachin Vijaykumar. ■ 27890 #055-01-2003 **GS** *012

WENDELL – WAKE

BRASHEAR, Ralph Guy. 217 COOK ST 27591 #038-40-1960 L1961 **FM** *020 †18
PETERSEN, Dustin Jay. ■ 27591 #024-05-2007 *012
STALLINGS, Stephen D, Jr. ■ 27591 #036-05-1946 L1947 **GP** *071

■ = Address Information Privacy Protected

WEST END – MOORE

BOYLES, Paul Weldon. 4196 SEVEN LAKES W, SEVEN LAKES VILLAGE 27376 #035-19-1953 L1972 **CD HEM** *071 †18
KADER, Ronald William. ■ 27376 #011-04-2004 L2006 **EM** *020
KENNEY, William Greer. ■ 27376 #038-06-1957 L1957 **PD** *030 †55
LEWIS, James Owen. 3310 SEVEN LAKES W 27376 #056-06-1986 L1997 **EM** *020 †16
MACAULAY, James Gillis. 116 SHERWOOD RD, 2133 SEVEN LAKES S. 27376 #038-06-1943 L1977 **GP** *071
PETER, Premkumar. ■ 27376 #495-20-1964 L2006 **P** *071 †75
PICACHE, Reginaldo Santos. ■ 27376 #748-02-1962 L1973 **GS** *030 †85
PIERONI, Daniel Wm. ■ 27376 #017-20-1965 L1990 **OPH** *071 †35
SHERWOOD, Zalmon Omar. ■ 27376 #038-06-1946 L1980 **GS** *071 †85
SIMPKINS, Darrell Gordon. 3004 SEVEN LAKES W 27376 #045-01-1982 L1986 **EM ESM** *020 †16
SQUIRE, Edward Noonan, Jr. ■ 27376 #020-12-1974 L1998 **AI PD** *071 †55,03 ‡
TICZON, Renato Angsico. ■ 27376 #748-01-1967 L1973 **IM PUD** *075

WEST JEFFERSON – ASHE

BENNETT, Bradford S. ■ 28694 #051-04-1941 L1985 **ORS** *071 †40
GROVES, Robert Blaine. 428 BLUFF RIDGE RD 28694 #020-02-1964 L1971 **R OS** *020 †80
KAUTZ, Lawrence Gordon. ■ 28694 #038-41-1962 L1988 **PD** *071
KEYS, Carson M. ■ 28694 #051-04-1952 L1953 **IM** *071
MILLER, Cameron Eugene. ■ 28694 #036-05-1946 L1947 **FM** *072

WHISPERING PINES – MOORE

GILMORE, William Edmund. ■ 28327 #056-05-1943 L1944 **GS TS** *071 †85
HEINE, Earle Rodman. ■ 28327 #024-01-1955 L1956 **EM AM** *071 †70
HENDERSON, Miller L. ■ 28327 #016-43-1949 L1979 **IM PUD** *071
LOOMIS, Frank J. ■ 28327 #025-01-1949 L1974 **FM** *071
RUOFF, Frederick August. ■ 28327 #041-09-1934 L1973 **R** *071 †80
TREBB, David Alan. ■ 28327 #035-06-2001 L2003 **PD** *020 †55

WHITEVILLE – COLUMBUS

AUSLEY, Mett Bagley. 500 JEFFERSON ST 28472 #036-01-1984 L1997 **PTH** *075 †50
BARBER, Christopher C. 800 JEFFERSON ST, STE 102 28472 #011-03-1987 L1988 **CD** *020 †20
BARNHILL, Peggy Sue. 619 JEFFERSON ST, SOUTHEAST INTERNAL 28472 #036-08-1997 L2002 **FM** *020
BASTUG, Demir Erol. 500 JEFFERSON ST, DEPARTMENT OF RADIOLOGY 28472 #055-01-1991 L1997 **DR** *020 †80
BERRY, Richard Garth. 500 JEFFERSON ST 28472 #005-15-1989 L1993 **IM IMG** *020 †20
BUCHANAN, William Preston. 800 JEFFERSON ST, STE 102 28472 #045-01-1986 L1987 **CD IM** *020 †20
BUNN, David Glenn. ■ 28472 #023-01-1947 L1988 **GP** *071
CADOGAN, Robert F. 209 W VIRGIL ST 28472 #010-03-1994 L2002 **FM GS** *020 †18
CAHN, Michael Louis. 611 N MADISON ST 28472 #033-05-1995 L2000 **GS** *020 †85
CHANGAPPA, Baduvanda U. 329 JEFFERSON ST 28472 #495-09-1973 L1983 **GS** *020 †85
COLLINS, Lauren Noelle. ■ 28472 #036-01-2007 **OBG** *012
DANIEL, Hugh Rollins. 220 JEFFERSON ST, WALTER SURGICAL ASSOCIATES 28472 #036-08-1985 L1991 **GS** *020 †85
DERCOLE, Francine Jo. 500 JEFFERSON ST 28472 #041-07-1989 L1993 **AN** *020 †05
DIMITRIOUS, Robin Zaki. 500 JEFFERSON ST 28472 #915-04-1966 L1979 **AN** *020
DONAYRE, Luis Ernesto. 711 N FRANKLIN ST 28472 #737-01-1959 L1967 **GS TS** *071 †85
FARIAS, Rose. 329 JEFFERSON ST, ROSE FARIAS MD 28472 #495-04-1962 L1977 **CD IM** *020 †20
FARIAS, Shobha Maria. 329 JEFFERSON ST 28472 #495-09-1973 L1983 **IM** *020
FERNZ, Miriam M. 626 JEFFERSON ST 28472 #495-33-1989 L1996 **IM** *020 †20
FLEMING, Richard C. 619 JEFFERSON ST, SOUTHEAST INTERNAL 28472 #035-03-1987 L1992 **IM** *020 †20
FORRESTER, James Summers, Jr. 800 JEFFERSON ST, STE 102 28472 #036-05-1996 L1997 **ICE** *020 †20
GLINSKI, Ronald Peter. 720 JEFFERSON ST, RT 2 BOX 32H 28472 #025-01-1975 L1980 **U** *020 †95
GORMAN, Francis Patterson. 1409 PINCKNEY ST, EVERGREEN BEHAVIORAL MANAG 28472 #305-01-2000 L2004 **CHP** *020
GRECO, David Lawrence. 220 JEFFERSON ST, WALTERS SURGICAL ASSOC 28472 #016-43-1991 L2000 **GS** *020 †85
HAMBY, Debra Annette. PO BOX 425 28472 #045-01-1980 L2000 **OPH** *020 †35
HASH, Volney Wade, Jr. 508 JEFFERSON ST 28472 #055-01-1963 L1994 **CD IM** *020 †20
HOBART, Frank Adams. 800 JEFFERSON ST, STE 102 28472 #036-08-1992 L1999 **CD** *020 †20
HODGSON, John David. 619 JEFFERSON ST, SOUTHEAST INTERNAL 28472 #010-02-1982 L1983 **IM** *020 †20 ‡
HUTCHINSON, Andrew J. 611 N MADISON ST 28472 #041-77-1996, ▲ L2002 **GS** *020
KINDSCHUH, Peter Michael. 627 JEFFERSON ST 28472 #016-43-1980 L1984 **OBG** *020 †30
KIRBY, Cynthia Kaye. 619 JEFFERSON ST, SOUTHEAST INTERNAL 28472 #036-01-1996 L1997 **IM** *020
MARTIN, David Anson, Jr. 619 JEFFERSON ST, SOUTHEAST INTERNAL 28472 #036-01-1994 L1995 **IM** *020
MATTHEWS, Coy Randolph. 800 JEFFERSON ST STE 116, 800 JEFFERSON ST SUITE 116 28472 #036-05-1988 L1993 **PD** *020 †55
MUNROE, John Francis. 619 JEFFERSON ST, SOUTHEAST INTERNAL 28472 #036-01-1960 L2008 **IM** *020
NOBLES, Rossie Dawn. ■ 28472 #036-08-1996 L1998 **OPH** *020
OBRECHT, William F. 500 JEFFERSON ST 28472 #023-01-1979 L1982 **AN IM** *020 †20,05
PHILLIPS, David Allen. 520 JEFFERSON ST, COLUMBUS COUNTY HOSP 28472 #025-07-1996 L2003 **EM** *020 †16
QUINONES, Jaime. 500 JEFFERSON ST 28472 #042-03-1983 L1992 **EM** *020 †16
SCHUETT, William Marvin. 604 N MADISON ST 28472 #051-01-1986 L1995 **ORS** *020
SMITH, William Thomas, IV. 800 JEFFERSON ST, STE 102 28472 #036-01-1996 L1999 **ICE** *020 †20

SOLOMON, Donald Jeffrey. 506 JEFFERSON ST 28472 #005-11-1981 L1984 **N** *020
STARK, Gregory Jay. 800 JEFFERSON ST STE 102, CARE 28472 #047-06-1991 L2000 **PD** *020 †55
THIGPEN, Fronis Ray. 823 JEFFERSON ST, WHITEVILLE MEDICAL ASSOC 28472 #036-01-1976 L1976 **FM FPG** *020 †18
TRAYLOR, Henry William, Jr. 823 JEFFERSON ST, WHITEVILLE MEDICAL ASSOC 28472 #010-02-1977 L1980 **IM EM** *020 †20
VAN DYCK, Timothy Kurt. 1409 PINCKNEY ST 28472 #016-06-1987 L2007 **P PYG** *020 †75 ‡
WALDMAN, Richard Alan. 823 JEFFERSON ST, WHITEVILLE MEDICAL ASSOC 28472 #035-19-1968 L1990 **PD OS** *020 †55
WALTERS, Hezekiah G, Jr. 711 N THOMPSON ST 28472 #023-01-1948 L1948 **GS** *020
WALTERS, Ronald Martin. 220 JEFFERSON ST 28472 #036-01-1981 L1986 **GS VS** *020 †85
WHEATLEY, Sam Nally. PO BOX 1408 28472 #020-12-1975 L1978 **OBG** *020 †30
WINSLOW, Timothy Merrill. 800 JEFFERSON ST, STE 102 28472 #024-07-1986 L1995 **IM** *020 †20

WHITSETT – GUILFORD

COYNE, Mark D. ■ 27377 #016-42-1983 L2006 **FM EM** *020 ‡
KHAN, Kalsoom Kausar. 945 GOLF HOUSE RD W 27377 #704-06-1989 L2004 **HO IM** *020 †20
LETVAK, Richard Ira. 940 GOLF HOUSE CT E 27377 #035-08-1985 L1997 **IM PD** *020 †20,55
SCHALLER, Robert Neal. 940 GOLF HOUSE CT E 27377 #010-02-1986 L1993 **FM** *020 †18
TOWER, Marne. 940 GOLF HOUSE CT E 27377 #025-07-1996 L1999 **FM** *020 †18

WHITTIER – JACKSON

ABRAM, Robert Michael. 263 WHITTIER CEMETARY ROAD 28789 #017-20-1973 L1989 **GP** *020
BOLTON, Barbara. PO BOX 950 28789 #055-02-1987 L1992 **EM OM** *020
SEALS, Daniel Hilton. E DICKS CREEK RD 28789 #041-13-1953 L1956 **IM GP** *071
TOEDT, Michael Edgar. ■ 28789 #023-12-1995 L1999 **FM** *020 †18
TRIGG, David Campbell. ■ 28789 #001-02-1974 L1982 **FM** *020 †18,16

WILKESBORO – WILKES

ABRAMS, Julie K. ■ 28697 #048-12-1997 L2001 **ADL** *020 †55
ALFORD, Glen Ernest. 146 HOLLOWVIEW DR 28697 #048-15-1991 L2002 **FM** *020 †18
BOND, John Lawrence, Jr. 1201 SCHOOL ST, WILKES GENERAL CLINIC BLDG 28697 #047-06-1954 L1960 **GS ORS** *020
CHURCH, Mary L Parker. 1707 INDUSTRIAL DR 28697 #036-01-1989 L1990 **FM** *020 †18
MC LARNEY, John Kenny. ■ 28697 #051-01-1989 L1997 **DR** *020 †80
MC MAHAN, Thomas Keith. 1710 PARKWOOD DR 28697 #028-02-1970 L1973 **IM** *020 †20
RANDALL, Wendell Lewis. 100 N BRIDGE ST, STE A 28697 #016-45-1985 L1992 **PTH** *062 †50
REDMAN, Michelle Lisa. 1710 PARKWOOD DR 28697 #051-01-1997 L2000 **IM** *020 †20
ROBERSON, Virgil O, III. 260 IVY LN 28697 #041-01-1971 **AN** *020 †05
SEALES, David Martin. 1520 MEADOWVIEW DR 28697 #021-05-1986 L1992 **N** *020 †75
THAKKAR, Pradip C. 1201 SCHOOL ST, STE F 28697 #495-22-1983 L1993 **NEP IM** *020 †20

WILLIAMSTON – MARTIN

AGEE, Robert Nelson. 102A MEDICAL DR 27892 #038-40-1966 L1985 **GS** *020 †85
AUTON, Robert G, Jr. 304 S MCCASKEY RD, NORTHEASTERN PRIMARY CARE 27892 #036-08-1988 L1991 **NPM PD** *020
BATHIA, Anil Laxmidas. 310 S MCCASKEY RD, MARTIN GEN HOSP 27892 #495-17-1973 L1993 **R** *020 †80
BISHOP, John Mason, Jr. ■ 27892 #051-04-1957 L1961 **GYN** *071 †30
CHUNG, Wan Soo. 307 S MCCASKEY RD 27892 #583-03-1971 L1977 **FM** *020
DOVER, Carl Thos, Jr. 312 S MCCASKEY RD 27892 #036-05-1977 L1978 **PD** *020 †55
JACOB, Gregorio Z, Jr. 310 S MCCASKEY RD, MARTIN GENERAL HOSPITAL 27892 #748-11-1989 L1995 **IM** *020 †20
LESTER, Stephen Ira. 220 GREEN ST 27892 #055-01-1973 L1977 **ORS** *020 †40 ‡
LEWIS, Beverly Ann. 310 S MCCASKEY RD 27892 #004-01-1979 L1982 **IM** *020
MC NEESE, Katherine Ann. 108 TRADE ST, MAILING: P O BOX 1659 27892 #036-08-1984 L1991 **IM PD** *020 †55,20
MILLER, George John, Jr. 220 GREEN ST 27892 #035-45-1967 L1979 **ORS** *020 †40
MOGHAZI, Abdel Monem A. 312 S MCCASKEY RD, ROANAKE WOMEN'S HEALTH CTR 27892 #330-02-1958 L1973 **OBG** *071
MORTON, Leslie Bryant. 310 S MCCASKEY RD 27892 #036-05-1952 L1952 **FM** *020
NEILSEN, Jennifer Ann. 104 MEDICAL DR 27892 #025-01-1993 L2002 **OBG** *020 †18
NEWMAN, David Grant. 310 S MCCASKEY RD, GENERAL HOSPITAL 27892 #422-01-1986 L1989 **AN PMM** *020 †05
OCAMB, Harold Dietsch. 1170 RIDGE ST 27892 #007-02-1955 L1976 **GS** *071 †85
O'NEAL, Melissa Gold. 104 MEDICAL DR, ROANOKE WOMEN'S HEALTHCARE 27892 #036-08-1999 L2003 **OBG** *020 †30
OPIELA, Jaroslaw Piotr. 316 S MCCASKEY RD 27892 #759-04-1990 L2006 **IM** *020 †20
RICCIO, Lin Mcpherson. ■ 27892 #036-08-2008 *012
RODRIGUEZ-CUE, Domingo. 105 S SMITHWICK ST 27892 #308-03-1985 L1995 **FM** *020 †18
SKAHILL, Steven Earl. 104 MEDICAL DR, ROANOKE MEDICAL ASSOCIATES 27892 #018-03-1986 L2002 **IM** *020 †20
SURKIN, Lee Alan. 310 S MCCASKEY RD, P O BOX 1128 27892 #041-09-1991 L1997 **CD IM** *020 †20
TANNER, Todd Fitzgerald. 310 S MCCASKEY RD, TARHEEL SURGICAL SPEC, LLC 27892 #036-01-1991 L1998 **GS** *020
TASKA, Ronald Joe. 102 MEDICAL DR 27892 #048-04-1973 L1975 **P PYA** *040 †75
UM, Ki-Bong. 310 S MCCASKEY RD 27892 #583-03-1971 L1981 **GP** *020 ‡

WILLOW SPRING – WAKE

HITCHNER, James C. ■ 27592 #041-02-1951 L1952 **FM OS** *071
VALVO, Barbara-Ann. ■ 27592 #041-14-1975 L1977 **GS** *020 †85

■ = Address Information Privacy Protected

WILMINGTON – NEW HANOVER

ABRAHAM, Victor E, III. 1606 PHYSICIANS DR, STE 101 28401 #041-13-1988 L1997 **U** *020 †95

ABRONS, S Albert. 1911 S 17TH ST, STE 130A 28401 #051-04-1976 L1997 **FM** *020 †18

ADAMS, Robert M, IV. 2301 DELANEY RD, CHILD, ADOLESCENT & ADULT 28403 #045-04-1999 L2007 **CHP** *020 †75

ADAMS, Sarah P. 1628 DOCTORS CIR 28401 #023-01-1988 L1990 **PD** *020 †55

ADGENT, James Kevin. 2131 S 17TH ST 28401 #654-01-2001 L2004 **IM** *020

ADLER, Svetlana A.. 2304 DELANEY RD, KNOX CLINIC PEDIATRICS, PL 28403 #913-95-1994 L2006 **PD** *020 †55 ‡

ADLER, Vladlen V. 2304 DELANEY RD, KNOX CLINIC PEDIATRICS, PL 28403 #913-95-1994 L2005 **PD** *020 †55

AFRIDI, Saifullah K. 2131 S 17TH ST, NEW HANOVER REGIONAL MEDIC 28401 #704-25-1990 L1995 **IM** *020 †20

ALBA, Maria Mercedes. 2304 DELANEY RD, KNOX CLINIC PEDIATRICS 28403 #748-02-1982 L1997 **PD** *020 †55

ALLEN, Molly Virginia. 2520 TROY DR 28401 #048-13-1980 L1982 **OPH** *020 †35

ALLEN, William Giles. 1090 MEDICAL CENTER DR 28403 #036-05-1976 L1981 **PUD IM** *020 †20

ALMEDOM, Mussie Haile. ■ 28412 #366-02-1985 L2006 **IM** *020 †20

ALMKUIST, Ralph D, II. 1302 MEDICAL CENTER DR 28401 #036-05-1971 L1971 **IM NEP** *071 *020

ALMOND, Charles Malcolm. 1960 S 16TH ST 28401 #036-01-1970 L1970 **FM** *020 †18

ALPER, Stephen Howard. 1606 PHYSICIANS DR, STE 104 28401 #035-08-1973 L1975 **P** *020 †75

AMERICO, Amy Ann. 1202 MEDICAL CENTER DR 28401 #051-04-1992 L2003 **IM** *020 †20

AMIN, Raaj Romesh. 1920 S 16TH ST, D/B/A THE CHILDREN'S CLINI 28401 #041-13-1998 L2002 **PD** *020 †55

AMOS, Barry Dean. 5301 WRIGHTSVILLE AVE 28403 #051-01-1978 L1992 **AN IM** *020 †05

ANAGNOST, John Wm. 1520 PHYSICIANS DR 28401 #041-02-1978 L1986 **ON HEM** *020 †20

ANDRACCHI, Susan. 1801 NEW HANVR MDCL PRK DR, PK 28403 #035-46-1991 L1997 **OPH** *020 †35

ANDREWS, Robert J. 2131 S 17TH ST 28401 #047-06-1946 L1948 **IM FM** *071 †18

ANTONELLI, Nadine Marie. 5502 CAPTAINS LN 28409 #036-01-1995 L1997 **OBG** *020 †30

ANTONIADES, Nicholas H. ■ 28403 #001-06-1982 L2007 **AN CS** *020 †05 ‡

ARB, Birgit. 1520 PHYSICIANS DR 28401 #041-14-1991 L1994 **ON IM** *020 †20

ARCE, Luisalberto Isaac. ■ 28409 #033-05-2004 L2005 **IM** *100

ARCHER, Noah Robt, Jr. 2421 SILVER STREAM LN 28401 #021-05-1989 L1992 **PD** *020 †55

ARMANI, Annemarie M. ■ 28405 #024-16-2001 M *012

ARMISTEAD, Howard L, Jr. ■ 28411 #051-01-1966 L1967 **FM OM** *020 †18

ARMITAGE, Mark Thomas. 5429 WRIGHTSVILLE AVE, PELICAN FAMILY MEDICINE 28403 #654-01-1996 L2001 **FM** *020

ARORA, Sunil Kumar. 2513 DELANEY RD, CENTER FOR PAIN MANAGEMENT 28403 #495-03-1981 L1995 **AN** *020 †05

ATLURI, Tej Kumar. ■ 28401 #496-24-2002 **IM** *012

AYLESWORTH, Susannah Cary. 1920 S 16TH ST, THE CHILDREN'S CLINIC 28401 #036-08-1999 L2002 **PD** *020 †55

AZIZI, Ghobad. 1717 SHIPYARD BLVD, STE 220 28403 #409-21-1993 L2000 **END** *020 †20

BACHMAN, David Stanley. 1202 MEDICAL CENTER DR 28401 #023-07-1969 L1984 **N CHN** *020 †55,75

BAHNER, Richard Scott. 8115 MARKET ST, STE 108 28411 #038-41-1988 L1997 **ORS HS** *020 †20

BAIJNATH, Nalini. 2131 S 17TH ST, NEW HANOVER REG MED CTR 28401 #661-02-2003 L2006 **FM** *100 †18

BAKER, Brenda Gibbs. 3807 PEACHTREE AVE 28403 #036-08-1998 L2001 **IM** *020 †20

BALLARD, Gajarah Baseemah. ■ 28403 #036-01-2006 *012

BARRI, Michael John, Jr. 3151 S 17TH ST 28412 #036-05-1981 L1982 **IM** *020 †20

BARTON, Andrew Chas. 5301 WRIGHTSVILLE AVE 28403 #016-11-1992 L1994 **AN** *020 †05

BASEGODA, Mario Baldomero. 5301 WRIGHTSVILLE AVE 28403 #429-01-1986 L2000 **IM** *020 †20

BEAM, Anne Young. 5058 WRIGHTSVILLE AVE 28403 #036-08-2002 L2005 **FM** *100 †18

BEAN, Virgil Edward. 5301 WRIGHTSVILLE AVE 28403 #036-05-1983 L1986 **AN** *020 †05

BEARD, Larry Neal, Jr. 1025 MEDICAL CENTER DR, DELANEY RADIOLOGISTS 28401 #051-01-1997 L2000 **DR** *020 †80

BEATY, Stephen. 925 N 4TH ST 28401 #038-75-1999, ▲ L2002 **FM** *020 †18

BEBB, Gregory Gerard. 1414 MEDICAL CENTER DR, ASSOCIATES 28401 #041-02-1987 L1997 **GS** *020 †85

BEBB, Kimberly Rouse. 2523 DELANEY RD, COASTAL FAM MED CTR 28403 #036-01-2000 L2001 **FM** *020 †18 ‡

BEITTEL, Timothy Michael. 311 JUDGES RD STE 4E 28405 #035-45-1996 L1999 **FM** *020 †18 ‡

BENJAMIN, Ronald Paul. 1104 MEDICAL CENTER DR 28401 #023-07-1964 L1995 **D** *020 †15

BENNETT, Robert Todd. 2512 DELANEY RD 28403 #016-42-1991 L1997 **UP U** *020 †95

BENTSEN, B Steven. 1911 S 17TH ST, STE 100 28401 #038-41-1983 L1984 **P ADP** *020 †75

BENTSEN, Isabella D. 2131 S 17TH ST 28401 #198-01-1990 L2001 **IM** *020 †20

BESTE, Janalynn Fish. 2523 DELANEY RD, COASTAL FAMILY MEDICINE 28403 #026-04-1995 L1996 **FM** *040 †18

BESTE, Todd Michael. 2131 S 17TH ST, COASTAL AHEC 28401 #026-04-1995 L1996 **OBG** *020 †30

BETTENDORF, Anna Peacock. 2208 S 17TH ST, SECOND FLOOR 28401 #036-01-1990 L1994 **PM** *020 †60

BEVIN, Avery A. 1904 TRADD CT 28401 #023-12-1998 L2005 **D DS** *020 †15

BHAN, Renuka. 2131 S 17TH ST 28401 #913-07-1996 **IM** *012

BHAT, Raja G. 5106 WRIGHTSVILLE AVE 28403 #495-27-1972 L1983 **IM** *020 †20

BHAT, Suma. ■ 28409 #036-01-2006 **PD** *012

BIRDSONG, Jeanne Lorraine. 3205 RANDALL PKWY, STE 203 28403 #041-02-1996 L2004 **PYG** *075

BISHOP, Andrew Hayward. 1202 MEDICAL CENTER DR, CARDIOLOGY 28401 #051-01-1997 L2005 **IC** *020 †20

BLACK, John Alexander. 1025 MEDICAL CENTER DR 28401 #036-05-1981 L1984 **DR** *020 †80

BLACKSTONE, Thomas Lee. 3505 CONVERSE DR STE 200 28403 #038-40-1969 L1971 **PD** *020 †55

BLAIR, Dwight Inghram. 145 CHIMNEY LN 28409 #055-01-1999 L2005 **IM** *020 †20

BLUE, Tony Oliver. 925 N 4TH ST, CENTER 28401 #036-01-1993 L1999 **MPD** *020 †20,55

BOBITT, John Ronald. 2131 S 17TH ST, NEW HANOVER MEMORIAL HOSPI 28401 #016-11-1964 L1986 **OBG MFM** *040 †20

BOEKER, Thomas. 3973B MARKET ST, BLDG D 28403 #043-01-1995 L1996 **P** *020 †75

BOHINC, Brittany Noel. ■ 28403 #038-44-2007 **IM** *012

BOLDIZAR, John David. 7420 MARKET ST 28411 #033-06-1996 L2003 **FM** *020 †18

BORING, Todd Allan. 3710 SHIPYARD BLVD, ECEP II, PA 28403 #422-01-2004 L2007 **EM** *020

BOSWELL, Robert Brooks. 3787 SHIPYARD BLVD 28403 #004-01-1995 L2001 **ORS OSM** *020 †40

BOTROS, Sherif Botros. 1625 DOCTORS CIR 28401 #036-01-1975 L1979 **OTO** *020

BOWERS-LEE, Cynthia Lee. 2131 S 17TH ST 28401 #038-43-1998 L2002 **EM** *020 †16 ‡

BOWLING, Jack Wayne, Jr. 2716 ASHTON DR 28412 #036-05-1994 L1996 **ORS** *020 †40

BOYD, Dale Woods. ■ 28405 #041-09-1961 L1989 **DR** *071

BOYD, Dale Woods. 5710 OLEANDER DR STE 108 28403 #041-09-1985 L1992 **ORS GS** *020 †40

BOYLAN, Patrick Thomas. 2716 ASHTON DR, WILMINGTON ORTH GROUP 28412 #038-44-1995 L2003 **PM** *020 †60

BRENNAN, Kevin. 1202 MEDICAL CENTER DR, WILMINGTON HEALTH ASSOCIAT 28401 #041-02-1991 L1996 **IM** *020 †20

BREWBAKER, Stephen Lewis. 1726 NEW HANVR MDCL PRK DR 28403 #036-05-1981 L1982 **OBG** *020 †30

BREZINSKI, Damian A. 1202 MEDICAL CENTER DR, WILMINGTON HEALTH ASSOCIAT 28401 #023-07-1989 L1992 **CD** *020 †20

BRIDGER, Dewey Herbert. 1960 S 16TH ST 28401 #036-05-1987 L1990 **FM** *020 †18

BRILEY, Clinton A, Jr. ■ 28405 #036-01-1976 L1993 **DR** *071 †80

BRINSON, George Moore. 8068 MARKET ST 28411 #036-01-1998 L2002 **OTO** *020 †45

BRITTON, Albert B. 4200 CHAPRA DR 28412 #038-41-1976 L2005 **PD** *020 ‡

BROADBENT, Bryan Jackson. 7420 MARKET ST 28411 #036-05-1990 L1992 **FM** *020 †18

BRODWATER, Brian Keith. 1025 MEDICAL CENTER DR 28401 #032-01-1993 L1995 **VIR** *020 †80

BROUGHTON, Justin J. 8 S 7TH ST 28401 #036-01-1993 L2000 **OTO** *020 †45

BROUHARD, David Michael. 5301 WRIGHTSVILLE AVE 28403 #005-12-2000 L2004 **AN** *020 †05

BROWN, Adam Pullan. 2800 ASHTON DR, STE 200 28412 #024-07-1987 L1995 **NS** *020 †25

BROWN, Alan Wesley. 1717 SHIPYARD BLVD, STE 140 28403 #051-04-1982 L1991 **OPH FM** *020 †18,35

BROWN, Ellen Eighan. 3720 SHIPYARD BLVD 28403 #038-45-1991 L1997 **OBG** *020 †30

BROWN, Noel Truitt. 2425 S 17TH ST 28401 #045-01-1972 L1978 **D** *020 †15

BROWN, Philip M, Jr. 1202 MEDICAL CENTER DR, . 28401 #036-08-1995 L1998 **VS GS** *020 †85

BROWN, Sonja Shanley. 1501 DOCK ST 28401 #011-02-1994 L1997 **FM** *020 †18 ‡

BROWN, Vikki Darlene. 1802 S 17TH ST, CAROLINA OB-GYN 28401 #036-08-1995 L1999 **OBG** *020 †30

BROWNLOW, Robert Lee, Jr. 1915 S 17TH ST STE 101 28401 #036-05-1985 L2005 **OPH OS** *020 †35 ‡

BULLARD, Lubin F, Jr. 5301 WRIGHTSVILLE AVE 28403 #036-07-1953 L1953 **OPH** *071

BUMBALO, Thomas Saml. 1202 MEDICAL CENTER DR 28401 #035-06-1992 L1998 **PCC** *020 †20

BUNN, David Glenn. 5919 OLEANDER DR, STE 109 28403 #036-01-1975 L1976 **OBG** *020 †30

BUONGIORNO, Paul A, Jr. 1402 S 17TH ST 28401 #010-02-1980 L1995 **P PFP** *020 †75 ‡

BURKETT, Jessica J. 1202 MEDICAL CENTER DR 28401 #036-01-1999 L2001 **FM** *020 †18

BUTLER, Frederick C, Jr. 3748 RESTON CT 28403 #036-07-1961 L1961 **OPH** *071 †35

BUTLER, Martin Joseph. 2131 S 17TH ST 28401 #036-01-2003 L2006 **IM** *020 †20

BYERLY, Claude Henry. ■ 28403 #041-13-1943 L1943 **FM** *072

BYRNE, Michael Francis. 1302 MEDICAL CENTER DR 28401 #917-06-1992 L2001 *071

CALHOUN, Linda P. 1725 NEW HANVR MDCL PRK DR 28403 #010-02-1985 L1986 **CD IM** *020 †20

CALLAWAY, S Clayton, Jr. 2311 DELANEY RD 28403 #012-05-1963 L1972 **OTO** *071 †45

CALLAWAY, Thomas Howard. ■ 28403 #047-05-1986 L1986 *075

CAMPBELL, Jack Swope. ■ 28403 #041-09-1946 L1968 **OTO PUD** *071 †45

CANNON, Jessica Hesford. 8064 MARKET ST 28411 #051-01-1997 L2001 **OBG** *071

CANNON, Kevin Dougherty. 1202 MEDICAL CENTER DR, WILMINGTON HEALTH ASSOCIAT 28401 #051-04-1997 L2001 **MPD** *020 †20

CAPEL, Gail Marie. 2208 S 17TH ST 28401 #036-01-1979 L2001 **DR** *020 †80

CAPOFERI, Nancy Carol. 1202 MEDICAL CENTER DR 28401 #025-01-1981 L1984 **CD IM** *071 †20

CARROLL, Sheri Lynn. 2131 S 17TH ST, COASTAL AHEC NEONATOLOGY 28401 #036-01-1997 L2002 **NPM** *020 †55

CARTER, Mary Allen. 1628 DOCTORS CIR 28401 #036-01-1986 L1988 **PD** *020 †55

CARTER, Michael Delane. 5302 OLEANDER DR, STE A 28403 #036-01-1986 L1988 **OSM** *020 †40

CASHMAN, John. 2512 DELANEY RD 28403 #041-02-1965 L1972 **U** *071 †95

CAUGHEY, Dale Wells, Jr. 5305 WRIGHTSVILLE AVE # A 28403 #036-07-1970 L1970 **FM IM** *020 †18

CAVENESS, Michael Bryan. 2131 S 17TH ST 28401 #036-01-1987 L1989 **IM** *020

CHASE, Timothy Lee. 1809 GLEN MEADE RD 28403 #036-05-1991 L1993 **OBG** *020 †30

CHEN, Chih Cheng. 1608 WELLINGTON AVE 28401 #244-04-1969 L1981 **N** *020

CHESSON, Arthur Saunders. ■ 28411 #036-05-1954 L1954 **PD OS** *071

CHIAVETTA, Stephen Victor. 8068 MARKET ST 28411 #036-01-1997 L2001 **OPH** *020 †35

CHIPLEY, Paul Simpson. 5301 WRIGHTSVILLE AVE 28403 #045-01-1990 L1995 **PME** *020 †05

CHOUDRY, Ahmad Bilal. 2131 S 17TH ST, INTERNAL MEDICINE DEPT 28401 #305-01-2002 L2006 **IM** *100

CHOUDRY, Shazia Amber. ■ 28401 #704-21-1999 *100

CHURCH, Jeffrey Scott. 2305 CANTERWOOD DR 28401 #055-01-1989 L1996 **PS** *020 †85,65

CLANCY, Michele Moran. 1406 PHYSICIANS DR 28401 #748-10-1978 L1988 **IM** *062 †20

CLANCY, Thomas Vincent. 2131 S 17TH ST, NEW HANOVER MEMORIAL HOSP 28401 #748-10-1979 L1987 **TRS GS** *020 †85

COIN, James Thaddeus. 1601 DOCTORS CIR 28401 #036-07-1984 L1985 **N** *020 †75

COLEMAN, Elizabeth Anne. 313 WALNUT ST STE 104, DOWNTOWN EXECUTIVE CENTER 28401 #036-01-1983 L1985 **P** *020 ‡

COLEMAN, Gordon Donald. 4316 HENSON DR, CHILDREN'S CLINIC/NORTHCHA 28405 #045-01-1975 L1978 **PD NPM** *020 †55

COLLINS, Samuel Brown. 3710 SHIPYARD BLVD, EASTERN CAROLINA EMERGENCY 28403 #036-08-1992 L1994 **EM** *020 †16

COLLINS, Sara Heath. 1437 MILITARY CUTOFF RD, STE 206 28403 #036-01-1988 L1992 **OBG** *020 †30

COLLINS, Stephen F. 2131 S 17TH ST 28401 #020-02-1962 L1969 **GP EM** *071

COMBS, John Gilbert, Jr. ■ 28403 #046-06-1966 L1972 **R** *071 †80 ‡

CONLEY, Martin James, Jr. 1515 DOCTORS CIR, HANOVER MED SPECIALIST PA 28401 #036-07-1973 L1981 **CD IM** *020 †20

COOPER, Joseph Litton. PO BOX 9025 28402 #021-01-1996 L1997 **OBG** *020

COOPER, William Henry, IV. 1500 MEDICAL CENTER DR 28401 #011-03-1981 L1985 GYN REN *020 †30

CORBETT, John Richard. 1960 S 16TH ST 28401 #036-05-1957 L1957 R RO *075 †80

CORBETT, Richard James. 1960 S 16TH ST 28401 #033-05-1963 L1967 FM ADM *071 †18

CORDERO, James Habbart. ■ 28412 #748-07-1960 OPH *071

CORTINA, Robert Michael. 1414 MEDICAL CENTER DR 28401 #035-09-1992 L2001 TS *020 †85,90

COSGROVE, Billie Forehand. 1104 MEDICAL CENTER DR 28401 #036-01-1992 L1993 D *020 †15

COSGROVE, Christopher C. 4114 SHIPYARD BLVD 28403 #036-01-1992 L1997 IM *020 †20

COURREGE, Marylou. 3904 OLEANDER DR STE 102 28403 #021-05-1982 L1987 D *020 †15

COVINGTON, Paul Steven. 929 N FRONT ST 28401 #001-02-1982 L1991 IM PHM *050 †20

CRACKER, Andrew Robert. 1809 GLEN MEADE RD 28403 #045-01-1962 L1967 GYN *020 †30

CRAFFORD, Wm Ashton, Jr. 1515 DOCTORS CIR, HANOVER MEDICAL SPECIALIST 28401 #023-07-1976 L1993 CD IM *020 †20

CRAVEN, Robert Brent. ■ 28409 #023-01-1970 L1971 ID IM *020 †20

CRAWFORD, Steven Todd. 1025 MEDICAL CENTER DR, DELANEY RADIOLOGISTS 28401 #017-20-1996 L1999 DR *020 †80

CREDLE, William Frontis. 1202 MEDICAL CENTER DR 28401 #051-04-1967 L1974 PUD *020 †20

CREIGHTON, Robt Kilgo, Jr. ■ 28409 #036-01-1961 L1961 OBG *030 †30

CROMER, John Willard, Jr. 4815 OLEANDER DR 28403 #030-05-1972 L1978 OM *020 †70

CROWDER, Mary Snyder. 3505 CONVERSE DR, STE 200 28403 #036-01-1998 L2000 PD *020 †55

CROWDER, Scott Geo. 2311 CANTERWOOD DR 28401 #041-01-1992 L1994 CHP *020 †75

CROWL, Frank David. 1801 S 17TH ST, STE 137 28401 #019-02-1985 L1994 AN *020 †05

CUMMINGS, Joseph Emile, II. ■ 28401 #047-07-1998 L2001 *020

CUNILL, Erica Sandra. ■ 28409 #055-01-2003 L2007 OBG *020

CUNNINGHAM, Nancy Marie. 1904 TRADD CT 28401 #010-02-1993 L2003 D *020 †15

DAILY, Celine Alisse. 1814 NEW HANVR MDCL PRK DR 28403 #020-12-1990 L1992 OBG *030 †30

DALEY, John Gilbert. 2131 S 17TH ST 28401 #008-01-1955 L1977 OBG END *040 †30

DALTON, Thomas Maxwell. 5301 WRIGHTSVILLE AVE 28403 #036-07-1992 L1997 AN *020 †05

DANIEL, Christian Page. 5145 S COLLEGE RD 28412 #036-05-1992 L1994 FM *020 †18

DARROW, Mark David. 2131 S 17TH ST, COASTAL AHEC 28401 #035-48-1983 L1993 IM IMG *040 †20

DAUM, Catherine Anne. 1202 MEDICAL CENTER DR 28401 #023-01-1986 L1988 GP *020 †20

DAVID, Ivan. 1912 TRADD CT, COASTAL THORACIC SURGICAL 28401 #561-11-1974 L1989 TS *020 †85,90

DAVIDSON, Dwight Douglas. 5301 WRIGHTSVILLE AVE 28403 #051-04-1980 L1994 IM AN *020 †20,05

DAYBELL, Dena Karen. 1202 MEDICAL CENTER DR 28401 #051-07-1995 L2000 ID PD *020 †20,55

DE BECK, Christian Thomas. ■ 28412 #055-01-2000 L2006 GS *020

DE MARIA, Alfred A, Jr. 1202 MEDICAL CENTER DR 28401 #038-40-1976 L1977 N SME *020 †75

DEMAS, Ronald Chas. 608 DAWSON ST STE 101, DAWSON ST URGENT CARE 28401 #017-20-1965 L1966 UCM N *020 †75

DENNIS, Steven Richard. 1602 PHYSICIANS DR, STE 101 28401 #035-03-1968 L1998 DR *020 †80

DESJARDINS, Richard F. ■ 28411 #024-07-1952 L1987 ADL OM *071

DICKERSON, Janice F. 7420 MARKET ST, NEW HANOVER MEDICAL GROUP 28411 #016-11-1995 L1996 FM *020 †18

DIETRICK, Ronald B. ■ 28405 #041-01-1953 L1983 GS OS *071 †85

DIETZGEN, Walter Anthony. PO BOX 4147 28406 #035-01-1971 L1989 P *020 †75

DINEEN, James Robt. 1222 MEDICAL CENTER DR 28401 #035-45-1945 L1958 OFA *071 †40

DIXON, Douglas Michael. 720 MARKET ST 28401 #665-01-1998 L2001 IM *020

DONAHUE, Michael Joseph. 1904 TRADD CT 28401 #030-06-1967 L1973 D *020 †15

DOSS, Roderick H. COASTAL A H E C 28402 #055-75-2003, ▲ L2008 OBG *012

DRAKE, Gregory Lee. 2202 MEDICAL CENTER DR, WHA MEDICAL CLINIC, PLLC 28401 #036-01-1978 L1979 U *020 †95

DRESSLER, Frederick A. 125 S 4TH ST 28401 #654-01-1982 L2003 IM *020 †20

DUNN, Thaddeus Leland. 1090 MEDICAL CENTER DR 28401 #036-07-1977 L1987 PUD CCM *020 †20

DURHAM, Stephen Bryan. 3710 SHIPYARD BLVD, ECEP II, PA 28403 #036-01-1995 L1998 EM *020 †16

DUROCHER, Kevin Howard. 2311 CANTERWOOD DR 28401 #056-05-1981 L1985 P *020 †75

DYE, Jenifer Mishael. 2131 S 17TH ST, DEPT OBG 28401 #012-01-2007 OBG *012

DYER, Guy David. 806 ROLLING HILLS CV 28409 #020-12-1977 L1978 IM *020

EAKINS, Darrin Franklin. 3787 SHIPYARD BLVD 28403 #036-05-1992 L1998 ORS *020 †40

EAKINS, J William. 1960 S 16TH ST 28401 #036-05-1970 L1970 ID IM *020 †20

EATON, Hubert Arthur, Jr. 411 N 7TH ST 28401 #047-07-1969 L2006 IM *020

EDWARDS, Kimberly R. 1904 TRADD CT 28401 #036-08-1999 L2003 D *020 †15

EDWARDS, Patrick Scott. 1914 GLEN MEADE RD, THE PEDIATRIC CENTER 28403 #036-08-1999 L2003 PD *020 †55

EILERT, John B. ■ 28411 #016-06-1966 L1968 OM GS *020 †85

EJINKONYE-AGBAFE, Dorothy. ■ 28412 #306-01-2005 FP *012

ELLIS, Patrick C. ■ 28405 #036-08-2001 L2007 CD *020

ESKEW, Thomas David, Jr. 1414 MEDICAL CENTER DR, ASSOCIATES 28401 #012-01-1994 L2000 GS *020 †85

ESPOSITO, David Anthony. 1717 SHIPYARD BLVD, STE 350 28403 #008-02-1984 L1989 OSM *020 †40

EVANS, Evan David. 1025 MEDICAL CENTER DR 28401 #036-01-1992 L2001 DR *020 †80

EVANS, Ha Ngoc. 1025 MEDICAL CENTER DR, DELANEY RADIOLOGISTS 28401 #017-20-1996 L2000 DR *020 †80

EVANS, Judson Holt. 5301 WRIGHTSVILLE AVE 28403 #036-08-1987 L1991 AN *020 †05

EVERHART, Robert Geo. 1202 MEDICAL CENTER DR 28401 #041-09-1981 L1987 CD IC *020 †20 ‡

EWING, John Alexander. ■ 28403 #803-03-1946 L1952 P ADP *071

EXPOSITO, Andres Joseph. 3710 SHIPYARD BLVD, MEDAC HEALTH SERVICES, PA 28403 #036-01-1995 L1998 EM *020 †16

FARRELL, Edwin G. 211 RIVER GATE LN, EDWIN G FARRELL MD 28412 #036-01-1971 L2007 PD ADL *072

FEHR, Adrienne D. 2523 DELANEY RD DEPT FP 28403 #038-75-2007, ▲ FP *012

FENSTER, Michael. ■ 28405 #035-08-1963 L1964 D *071 †15

FERNANDO, Wewalage Lionel. 2023 S 17TH ST, SOUTHEASTERN CENTER 28401 #220-01-1970 L1982 P *020

FERRY, Darwin John, Jr. ■ 28401 #056-05-1961 L1965 NS *071 †25

FICKLEN, Conway Hamilton. ■ 28403 #051-01-1954 L1959 OBG *071 †30

FIELDS, Jason Baker. 4320 HENSON DR 28405 #047-20-1996 L2007 PD *020 †55

FINK, Kenneth Irwin. 2131 S 17TH ST, NHRMC 28401 #051-07-1982 L2005 HO *020 †20

FISSCHER, Rolf Hendrik. 2023 S 17TH ST 28401 #660-03-1955 L1962 OS *071 †75

FOILES, Andrea Christine. 1809 GLEN MEADE RD 28403 #025-12-1998 L2002 OBG *020 †30

FOREHAND, Mary Leigh. 1628 DOCTORS CIR 28401 #036-01-1983 L1984 PD *020 †55

FOSTER, Mark Dupree. 2716 ASHTON DR 28412 #045-01-1983 L1989 ORS *020 †40

FRANKEL, Lawrence S. ■ 28411 #035-06-1970 L1971 PHO PD *020 †55

FREDERICK, Mary Gena. 1025 MEDICAL CENTER DR 28401 #020-02-1989 L1993 DR *020 †80

FRETWELL, Marsha Duke. 714 CHAMP DAVIS RD 28411 #035-20-1974 L1994 IMG IM *020 †20

FRUEH, Walter William. 3787 SHIPYARD BLVD 28403 #041-02-1999 L2005 OAR *020 †40

FULK, Robert Vernon, Jr. 2311 DELANEY RD 28403 #036-01-1965 L1965 OTO *071 †45

FUTCH, William A. ■ 28411 #035-09-1953 L1953 FM *071

GAJEWSKI, Walter Henry. 2131 S 17TH ST 28401 #045-01-1982 L2004 GO OBG *020 †30

GARIEPY, John Arthur. ■ 28411 #008-01-1954 L1994 GS GYN *071 †85

GARM, Kenneth Scott. 3710 SHIPYARD BLVD 28403 #051-04-1982 L1986 EM *020 †16

GAYLORD, Kevin Michael. 1515 DOCTORS CIR BLDG A 28401 #036-08-1998 L2005 GE IM *020 †20

GEBRAIL, Ayman. 2600 NEW VILLAGE WAY 28405 #875-01-1996 L2001 IM *020 †20

GEORGIEV, Boyan A. 1908 MEETING CT, CAROLINA PRIME INTERNAL ME 28401 #198-01-1985 L1998 IM *020 †20

GERRY, Russell Hal. 4000 SHIPYARD BLVD, STE 100 28403 #008-02-1985 L1999 IM *020 †20

GETZ, Donald David. 1104 MEDICAL CENTER DR 28401 #041-02-1966 L1974 ORS *071 †40

GIBSON, John Eugene. ■ 28405 #025-01-1964 L1965 D *071 †15

GILMORE, Brian Jan. 1090 MEDICAL CENTER DR, COASTAL PULM MED PA 28401 #041-01-1988 L1995 PUD *020 †20

GOELL, Robert S. ■ 28404 #028-02-1960 L1960 OBG *071 †30

GOLDSHOLL, Stacy Walton. ■ 28411 #036-01-1992 L2000 IM *020 †20

GOLDWASSER, Michael S. 2131 S 17TH ST, NEW HANOVER REGIONAL MEDIC 28401 #016-06-1984 L1990 OS IM *020

GONZALEZ, Jorge J M. 2131 S 17TH ST 28401 #231-01-1971 L1975 IM END *020 †20

GORDON, John Everett. ■ 28404 #038-41-1981 L1981 AN *071 †05

GOTTSCHALK, Bernard J, III. 2520 TROY DR, WILMINGTON TREATMENT CENTE 28401 #041-12-1981 L2006 HEM ON *075 †20

GOUDARZI, Hormoze Abbas. 1721 NEW HANVR MDCL PRK DR 28403 #917-23-1972 L1982 GS *020 †85

GOUDARZI, Kamran. 1721 NEW HANVR MDCL PRK DR 28403 #917-28-1978 L1981 GS *020 †85

GRAMLEY, Grace Ninan. 1912 MEETING CT, HANOVER INTERNAL MEDICINE 28401 #495-37-1988 L1998 IM *020 †20

GRAMLEY, William Andrew. 1515 DOCTORS CIR, BLDG C 28401 #036-01-1992 L1993 GE *020 †20

GREGOIRE, Ronald Paul. ■ 28409 #035-09-1974 L1994 NPM PD *020 †55

GREGORY, Dixon Elijah. 5145 S COLLEGE RD 28412 #036-08-1998 L2001 MPD *020 †20,55

GRIEB, Mark Christian. 1801 S 17TH ST, STE 137 28401 #047-05-1993 L2000 AN PMM *020 †05

GRIFFIN, Elizabeth Jane. 2131 S 17TH ST 28401 #027-01-1988 L1991 PD *020 †55

GRINE, William Bark. ■ 28403 #051-01-1960 L1964 U *071 †95

GRINER, Devan. 2131 S 17TH ST, PO BOX 9025 28401 #049-01-2006 GS *012

GUSE, Steven Todd. 2800 ASHTON DR STE 1 28412 #046-01-1998 L2007 PM *020 †40

GUTSIN, Richard Adam. 1615 DOCTORS CIR 28401 #035-75-1990, ▲ L1995 FM *020 †18 ‡

HAGE, Marvin Lewis. 5622 MARSH BAY DR 28409 #025-01-1967 L1984 MFM OBG *030 †30

HAHN, Charles Michael. 5301 WRIGHTSVILLE AVE 28403 #016-06-1987 L1992 AN PME *020 †05

HALL, Andrew Justin. 1025 MEDICAL CENTER DR 28401 #051-04-1996 L2000 VIR *020 †80

HALL, Gregory Grayson. 5301 WRIGHTSVILLE AVE 28403 #036-07-1983 L2004 AN *020 †05

HALL, Sandra L. 1802 S 17TH ST, CAROLINA OB GYN 28401 #051-04-1997 L2003 OBG *020 †30

HALL, Tana Louise. ■ 28409 #036-08-2006 OBG *012

HAMERSKI, Douglas Andrew. 1302 MEDICAL CENTER DR 28401 #026-04-1993 L2000 NEP *020 †20

HANNUM, Scott Quincy. 2716 ASHTON DR 28412 #038-43-1993 L1999 OAR *020 †40

HARDY, Stuart Mcdowell. 8068 MARKET ST 28411 #036-01-2001 L2006 OTO *020 †45

HARPER, James R, Jr. 1915 GLEN MEADE RD 28403 #036-01-1984 L1987 IM CD *020 †20

HARRIS, Clyde Louis. 3807 PEACHTREE AVE 28403 #036-01-1983 L1984 IM *020 †20

HARRIS, James Alan. 1411 PHYSICIANS DR 28401 #025-01-1989 L2001 GS *020 †85

HARRIS, Laura L. 1717 SHIPYARD BLVD, STE 140 28403 #036-08-1993 L1998 OPH *020 †35

HARRIS, Mark Danl. 1710 S 17TH ST, 1710 SOUTH 17TH ST 28401 #024-07-1992 L2001 RHU *020 †20

HARRIS, Toni. 1902 TRADD CT 28401 #024-07-1988 L1992 APM *020 †05

HARSHBARGER, John Lynn. 1710 S 17TH ST 28401 #041-13-1980 L1983 RHU IM *020 †20

HARUM, Karen S. 1960 S 17TH ST, STE 203 28401 #011-02-1987 L1991 PD *020 †55

HAWTHORNE, Henry C. 1920 S 16TH ST, THE CHILDREN'S CLINIC 28401 #051-01-1967 L1973 PD *020 †55

HAYASHI, Hiromichi. ■ 28409 #572-20-1951 L1984 GP GS *071 †85

HENDERSON, Gregory S. 1915 S 17TH ST, STE 100 28401 #047-05-1994 L1998 PTH *020 †50

HENDERSON, Heather Marie. 3141 KIRBY SMITH DR 28409 #036-01-1997 L2001 MPD *020 †20,55

HENIHAN, Robert Derek. 5115 OLEANDER DR 28403 #539-03-1990 L1998 GE IM *020 †20

HENTZ, Suzanne Kathleen. 4815 OLEANDER DR STE 202 28403 #036-08-1984 L1985 GYN *020 †30

HERION, John Murdoch. 1302 MEDICAL CENTER DR 28401 #036-01-1983 L1984 NEP IM *020 †20

HERION, Robin Wynne. 3710 SHIPYARD BLVD 28403 #045-01-1983 L1988 IM *020 †20

HERNANDEZ, Rick Jacob. 2131 S 17TH ST 28401 #665-02-2005 FP *012

HERRING, Charles Barry. 2131 S 17TH ST 28401 #025-01-1983 L1984 IM *020 †20

HESSION, Willard G. 1025 MEDICAL CENTER DR 28401 #016-06-1993 L2003 MSR *020 †80

HESTER, Darrell Ernest. 1915 GLEN MEADE RD 28403 #036-01-1987 L1991 OPH *020 †35

HICKEY, Derrick Gerard. 5305 WRIGHTSVILLE AVE, STE G 28403 #005-02-1996 L2002 ORS HS *020 †40

HICKS, Charles Montgomery. 1914 GLEN MEADE RD 28403 #036-01-1962 L1962 PD *071 †55

HILL, David Lloyd. 3505 CONVERSE DR, STE 200 28403 #048-14-1994 L1995 MPD PD *020 †20,55

HILL, Kelly Anne. 2131 S 17TH ST 28401 #055-01-2000 L2003 OBG *020 †30

HILL, Margaret. 2512 DELANEY RD, CONSULTS IN HYPERTENSION 28403 #036-01-1996 L1997 NEP *020 †20

HIMMERICH, Judy Unchong. ■ 28401 #011-02-2000 VIR *100

HINES, Jonathan S. 1202 MEDICAL CENTER DR 28401 #048-04-1992 L1994 IM *020 †20

HIRSCH, Steven Harold. 2215 CANTERWOOD DR, WILMINGTON INTERNAL MEDICI 28401 #012-01-1985 L1986 IM *020

HISLEY, John Chas. 2131 S 17TH ST 28401 #023-01-1965 L1974 OBG *071 †30

HOLDEN, Eugene M. ■ 28411 #024-07-1937 L1981 IM *072

HOLDSWORTH, Jeremy Paul. 4141 SHIPYARD BLVD, WILMINGTON FAM PHYS 28403 #051-01-1998 L2005 FM *020 †18

HOLT, William R, Jr. 1515 DOCTORS CIR, BLDG C 28401 #051-04-1977 L1980 CD IM *020 †20

HOOKER, Robert Walter. ■ 28411 #051-01-1966 L1967 IM *071

HOOKS, William Borden, III. ■ 28409 #036-01-2005 GS *012

HOOPER, Joseph Ward, Jr. 2131 S 17TH ST 28401 #024-01-1946 L1946 U *071 †95

HORGER, Edgar Olin, IV. 1606 WELLINGTON AVE 28401 #045-01-1989 L1992 PD *020 †55

HORNICK, Lisa June. 929 N FRONT ST 28401 #030-05-1991 L1994 IM *020 †20

HOWARD, Kirk Anderson. 5301 WRIGHTSVILLE AVE 28403 #041-01-1985 L1989 AN *020 †05

HUBBARD, Frank Alan. 1202 MEDICAL CENTER DR 28401 #054-01-1982 L1994 VS GS *020 †85

HUEHOLT, Therese Marie. 3963 MARKET ST, SOUTHEASTERN CENTER 28403 #005-06-1987 L1992 CHP *020 †75

HUFFMON, George Vanburen. 5301 WRIGHTSVILLE AVE 28403 #036-08-1992 L1998 NS *020 †25

HUNDLEY, James Davenport. 2716 ASHTON DR 28412 #036-01-1967 L1967 ORS *020 †40

HUNT, Oliver R, Jr. ■ 28412 #020-02-1951 L1969 TS *071 †85,90

HUNTER, Charles Edward. 1912 TRADD CT 28401 #001-02-1975 L1987 TS *020 †85,90

HUPPMANN, Joseph F. 1717 SHIPYARD BLVD, STE 100 28403 #021-06-1979 L1995 D *020

HUSSEY, Howard S, Jr. ■ 28411 #041-02-1942 L1942 GP *071 †18

HUTCHINS, Robert Harold. 1915 S 16TH ST 28401 #036-01-1976 L1976 IM *020 †20

HYDE, Austin T, Jr. 2321 DELANEY RD 28403 #051-01-1951 L1954 A IM *071

IRVIN, John David. 7110 WRIGHTSVILLE AVE, STE B4 28403 #038-06-1979 L1994 FM *020 †18

JACKSON, Eric Michael. 1914 GLEN MEADE RD, BJH COMPREHENSIVE HLTH SVC 28403 #045-01-2003 L2007 PD *020 †55

JACKSON, Grace Elizabeth. 1213 CULBRETH DR, STE 139 28405 #007-02-1996 L2002 FM P *100 †74

JAFFURS, Wm James, Jr. 5301 WRIGHTSVILLE AVE 28403 #010-01-1979 L1984 EM *020 †16

JAMES, Joseph Mc Craw. ■ 28403 #036-07-1955 L1955 DR NM *020 †80

JANOSKO, Edward O, II. 1606 PHYSICIANS DR, STE 102 28401 #008-01-1974 L1979 U *020 †95

JENSEN, Regina Marie. 4536 TECHNOLOGY DR, STE 3 28405 #048-15-1990 L1993 PTH *020 †20

JEWELL, Kathleen Theresa. 4005 OLEANDER DR, WILMINGTON HLTH ACESS-TEEN 28403 #041-02-1979 L1986 GPM PHP *020 †20

JIMENEZ, Hernan John. 2800 ASHTON DR, STE 100 28412 #035-48-1986 L2007 PM PME *020 †60 ‡

JOACHIM, Charles Louis. 1602 PHYSICIANS DR, STE 103 28401 #021-06-1993 L2003 AN *020 †05

JOHNSON, Betty Nell Hull. 2131 S 17TH ST 28401 #055-01-1974 L1983 AN *020 †05

JOHNSON, Burt Powers. 2023 S 17TH ST, SOUTHEASTERN CENTER 28401 #024-01-1967 L1975 P *020 †75

JOHNSON, David Alan. 1729 NEW HANVR MDCL PRK DR, EYE ASSOC OF WILMINGTON 28403 #028-02-1986 L2005 OPH PO *020 †35

JOHNSON, Donald Gene. 2212 DELANEY RD 28403 #055-01-1974 L1981 R NR *071 †80

JOHNSON, Gregory James. 1120 MEDICAL CENTER DR 28401 #038-43-2001 L2005 OPH *020 †35

JOHNSON, Kevin Earl. 2523 DELANEY RD, COASTAL FAMILY MEDICINE CE 28403 #039-01-1997 L1998 FM OS *020 †18 ‡

JOHNSON, Robert Ray, Jr. 4141 SHIPYARD BLVD, WILMINGTON FAMILY PHYSICIA 28403 #036-01-1992 L1994 FM ADL *020 †18

JOHNSON, Walter Taylor. ■ 28405 #036-07-1961 L1961 D DMP *071 †15

JONES, Jason Matthew. ■ 28412 #039-01-2003 GS *012

JONES, Michelle Fleeman. 8108B MARKET ST 28411 #036-08-1996 L1997 FM *020 †18

JONES, Neil Duane. ■ 28412 #030-05-2003 L2007 GS *012

JONES, Rachel Zloczover. 1809 GLEN MEADE RD 28403 #011-03-1998 L2002 OBG *020 †30

JONES, Robert Boyd. 2311 DELANEY RD 28403 #051-01-1964 L1972 OTO HNS *020 †45

JONES, William Hunter. 1414 S 39TH ST, WRIGHTSVILLE FAM PRAC 28403 #036-01-1994 L1997 FM *020 †18

JORDAN, Henry Davidson. ■ 28411 #012-05-1966 L1974 PTH *071 †50

JOSEPH, David Brian. 1802 S 17TH ST, D/B/A CAROLINA OB-GYN 28401 #011-03-1992 L1996 OBG *020 †30

JOSLIN, Richard Grant. 4815 OLEANDER DR 28403 #051-04-1974 L1977 FM *020

JOYNER, William Lawrence. 119 CHESTNUT ST, THE DOWNTOWN MED CENTER 28401 #041-02-1992 L1995 FM *020 †18

KAHN, Scott Michael. ■ 28409 #422-01-2004 FP *012

KAMITSUKA, Paul Finley. 1202 MEDICAL CENTER DR, WILMINGTON HEALTH ASSOCIAT 28401 #024-01-1982 L1994 ID IM *020 †20

KANE, Peter Neal. 1914 MEETING CT 28411 #035-09-1998 L2004 TS *020 †85

KANG, Cynthia Enhah. ■ 28409 #051-07-2002 L2006 OBG *100

KARRAS, Dean Harry. 1960 S 16TH ST 28401 #036-01-1993 L1994 IM *020 †20

KASH, Stephen Lee. 8068 MARKET ST 28411 #028-02-1968 L1975 OPH *071 †35

KASHGARIAN, Mark. 2002 EASTWOOD RD, STE 305 28403 #869-01-1954 L1956 P GPM *072

KASSENS, Catherine M H. 1984 S 16TH ST STE 1 28401 #028-02-1973 L1977 D *020 †15

KASSENS, Wm Diedrich, Jr. 1984 S 16TH ST STE 2 28401 #036-01-1971 L1971 IM GE *020 †20

KASTNER, Robert Jeffrey. 5245 S COLLEGE RD 28412 #051-07-1981 L1983 EM FM *020 †16,18

KAYS, Charles Richard. 2305 CANTERWOOD DR 28401 #045-01-1989 L1994 PS *020 †65

KEBEDE, Sosena. 2131 S 17TH ST, DEPT OF INT MED 28401 #036-01-2000 L2003 IM *020 †20

KEETON, Lisa Gwyn. 3807 PEACHTREE AVE 28403 #041-02-1997 L2000 IM *020 †20

KELLER, James Michael. 2606 IRON GATE DR STE 201 28412 #034-01-1991 L2005 PTH DMP *020 †50

KELLY, Timothy Gerald. 1915 TRADD CT 28401 #001-02-1984 L1988 OPH *020 †35

KESLER, James L. 8068 MARKET ST 28411 #028-02-1975 L1979 OPH *020 †35 ‡

KETCHAM, Ray Newton. ■ 28403 #055-01-1976 L1977 P *020 †75

KHAKEE, Abdulaziz G. 531 MCEACHERN DR 28412 #495-01-1955 L1987 P *071 †75

KHAN, Nawazish Ali. 3151 S 17TH ST 28412 #704-05-1998 IM *012

KHOSHNAW, Tara Aziz. 2131 S 17TH ST, NEW HANOVER REG MED CTR 28401 #528-06-1996 IM *012

KIM, Ian. 2008 GRAYWALSH DR 28405 #005-12-1992 L1994 GP EM *020

KING, Doris K. 1628 DOCTORS CIR, CAROLINA PEDIATRICS PA 28401 #036-01-1996 L1999 PD *020 †55

KING, Lunsford Richardson. 7741 MARKET ST, STE F 28411 #036-01-1996 L2001 P *020 †75

KING, William Walter. 5115 OLEANDER DR 28403 #036-01-1987 L1993 GE HEP *020 †20

KINNEBREW, Michael Clark. 1122 MEDICAL CENTER DR 28401 #048-14-1979 L1996 HNS FPS *072

KITTINGER, Joseph Wm, III. 5115 OLEANDER DR 28403 #004-01-1980 L1983 GE IM *020

KLEIN, Steven Douglas. 5115 OLEANDER DR 28403 #035-09-1998 L2005 GE *020 †20

KLINKER, Kelly Elizabeth. PO BOX 9025, MEDICAL C 28402 #017-20-2003 L2008 GS *012

KNAB, John Hunter. 2513 DELANEY RD, CENTER FOR PAIN MANAGEMENT 28403 #050-02-1993 L2000 AN *020 †05

KNEECE, Samuel Martin. 3307 PINNACLE PL 28411 #047-05-1985 L1989 P RO *020 †80,75

KNOTT, Jason Ralph. 2131 S 17TH ST 28401 #028-79-2004, ▲ L2008 OBG *012

KNOTT, Lawrence H. 1411 PHYSICIANS DR 28401 #036-05-1972 L1972 GS *020 †85

KNOX, Angelina Edralin. 2304 DELANEY RD 28403 #748-01-1959 L1968 PD CHP *020

KOEHLER, Melissa D. ■ 28406 #048-78-2004, ▲ L2008 OBG *012

KOFF, William Edward. 2131 S 17TH ST 28401 #036-05-1979 L1984 P N *020 †75

KOLLURU, Sarath Chandra. ■ 28412 #665-02-2006 IM *012

KOSERUBA, George Michael. 2304 DELANEY RD, KNOX PEDIATRIC CLINIC 28403 #005-12-1940 L1942 PD *071

KOTWALL, Cyrus Aspi. 2131 S 17TH ST, NEW HANOVER REGIONAL MED C 28401 #068-01-1978 L1993 GS SO *020 †20

KOTZ, Kenneth Wm. 1520 PHYSICIANS DR 28401 #023-01-1988 L2001 ON HEM *020 †20

KREPS, Matthew Michael. ■ 28405 #759-18-2004 IM *012

KROHN, John Ramon. 2305 CANTERWOOD DR 28403 #026-04-1966 L1975 PS *071 †85,65

KUCHAREWICZ, Jacek M. ■ 28412 #759-18-2004 L2005 IM *100

LACIVITA, Robert Joseph C. ■ 28411 #024-05-2005 L2007 IM *100

LAMAR, Heston Channing. 3710 SHIPYARD BLVD, ECEP 28403 #036-05-2002 L2004 EM *016

LANZI, Joseph Gabriel. ■ 28405 #023-01-1956 L1993 FM *071 †18

LARSON, Michael Jos. 28405 #748-01-1979 L2008 P *012

LATEEF, Kamran Naeem. ■ 28412 #654-01-2006 IM *012

LATEEF, Munsoor Naeem. ■ 28412 #820-02-2003 IM *100 †20

LAUGHLIN, Walter Price. 3710 SHIPYARD BLVD 28403 #016-01-1989 L2001 FM *020 †18

LEE, Mitchell Douglas. 1202 MEDICAL CENTER DR 28401 #036-08-1991 L1998 PCC *020 †20

LEE, Myoung Woon. ■ 28409 #583-09-1960 L1978 OBG *071

LEE, Thomas G. 3807 PEACHTREE AVE STE 101 28403 #051-07-1995 L1999 IM *020 †20

LEGERE, Brian Michael. 1090 MEDICAL CENTER DR 28401 #024-16-1994 L2000 PCC *020 †20

LENSCH, David Paul. 1801 S 17TH ST, STE 137 28401 #016-11-1987 L1988 AN PME *020 †05

LEONARD, Andre John. 4114 SHIPYARD BLVD, INTRA COASTAL INTERNAL MED 28403 #036-01-1995 L1998 IM *020 †20

LEWIS, Clifford Thomas, Jr. 1960 S 16TH ST 28401 #036-01-1967 L1967 IM *020 †20

LEWIS, William Lance. 1725 NH MEDICAL PARK DR, WILMINGTON CARDIOLOGY, PLL 28403 #011-02-1997 L1999 CD *020 †20

LEWISON, Kathleen E. 1717 SHIPYARD BLVD, STE 200 28403 #023-01-1993 L1997 OBG *020 †30

LEY, Stuart Bryson. 1501 MEDICAL CENTER DR 28401 #035-20-1974 L1994 END IM *020 †20

LIGUORI, John Carl. 2800 ASHTON DR, STE 100 28412 #010-02-1984 L1990 PM *020 †60

LINETT, Lawrence Max. 1717 SHIPYARD BLVD 28403 #003-02-1984 L1985 EM FM *020 †16

LIPPE, Craig Nathan. 1717 SHIPYARD BLVD, ORTHOPAEDIC SPECIALISTS PA 28403 #041-02-2000 L2006 ORS *020

LIU, Katharine. 5301 WRIGHTSVILLE AVE 28403 #036-01-1991 L2005 PCP HMP *020 †50

LJUNG, Martha Lee. 2902 HYDRANGEA PL 28403 #036-08-1990 L1993 EM *020 †16

LJUNG, Tor Martin. 1604 PHYSICIANS DR, STE 103 28401 #036-08-1990 L2000 PS *020 †65

LLOYD, Christian B. 1090 MEDICAL CENTER DR 28401 #011-04-1996 L2002 PCC *020 †20

LOCKLEAR, Maurice Kent. 8108B MARKET ST, WILMINGTON HEALTH ASSOC. 28411 #051-01-1988 L1996 FM *020 †18

LOESCH, Heather A. ■ 28403 #028-46-1994 L2000 D *020 †15

LOFGREN, Laif B. 2131 S 17TH ST 28401 #036-05-1983 L1986 OBG *020 †30

LOGAN, John Wells, III. 2131 S 17TH ST, DIVISION OF NEONATOLOGY, P 28401 #045-01-1995 L1998 NPM *100 †55

LOPEZ, Daniel Candelario. 2131 S 17TH ST, DEPT MED 28401 #665-02-2006 FP *012

LOSCHNER, Anthony Lukas. ■ 28405 #286-13-2005 IM *012

LOVETT, John W. 1905 GLEN MEADE RD 28403 #020-12-1982 L1987 U *030 †95

LUBANSKI, Robt Eugene, Jr. 5301 WRIGHTSVILLE AVE 28403 #035-15-1987 L1991 AN PME *020 †05

LUCAS, Sean Richard. 2321 DELANEY RD 28403 #036-08-2001 L2007 AI *020 †55,03 ‡

LYM, Laura Gale. ■ 28409 #539-06-1992 L2001 MPD *020

LYNN, Allison Badger. 1202 MEDICAL CENTER DR 28401 #010-01-1997 L2002 GS *020 †85

LYSNE, Dawn Elaine. ■ 28411 #026-04-1983 L1988 FM *020 †18

MACKEY, Wm Frederick, Jr. ■ 28412 #047-06-1969 L1975 CHP P,YA *075 †75

MAC QUEEN, Donald Miles. 2321 DELANEY RD, ASSOCIATES 28403 #036-01-1969 L1969 A PD *020

MAGLIONE, Anthony. 1725 NEW HANVR MDCL PRK DR, PARK DR 28403 #561-18-1980 L1996 CD IM *020 †20

MAGUIRE, Patrick David. 1988 S 16TH ST, ONCOLOGY 28401 #041-14-1995 L1998 RO *020 †80

MALOY, Thomas Howard. 5301 WRIGHTSVILLE AVE 28403 #001-02-1971 L1978 OPH *020 †35

MALYK, Bohdan. ■ 28405 #041-02-1968 L2001 GYN *071 †30

MANCUSI-UNGARO, Peter C. 2131 S 17TH ST, ZIMMER CANCER CTR 28401 #011-02-1968 L1975 ON HEM *020 †20

MANDEL, Daniel Carl. ■ 28412 #055-01-2007 OBG *012

MANION, Kernan Thos. 3415 WRIGHTSVILLE AVE 28403 #021-05-1978 L2002 P *020 †20

MARBURG, Kenneth Charles. 3710 SHIPYARD BLVD 28403 #023-01-1970 L1984 EM *020 †18,16

MARKS, Howard Fisher, Jr. 1912 TRADD CT, COASTAL THORACIS SURG 28401 #051-01-1981 L1988 TS CD *020 †85

MARKWORTH, James Warren. 3787 SHIPYARD BLVD 28403 #024-01-1969 L1978 ORS OS *071 †40

MARR, Albert Woodall. 2716 ASHTON DR 28412 #036-05-1993 L1995 ORS *020 †40

MARSHBURN, E Thomas, Jr. ■ 28412 #036-05-1947 L1948 IM OS *071

MARTIN, Christopher R. ■ 28412 #038-40-1973 L1981 FM *040 †18

MARTIN, Lois Beard. 7110 WRIGHTSVILLE AVE, STE B9 28403 #038-75-1991, ▲ L1996 D *020

MARTIN, Patrick David. 1201 MEDICAL CENTER DR 28401 #020-02-1975 L1993 P N *020 †75

MARTIN, Shona F. 5145 S COLLEGE RD 28412 #036-07-1995 L1996 **IM** *020 †20
MARTINKO, Thomas Michael. ■ 28411 #023-12-1983 L2006 **ADL PD** *020 †55
MASON, David Pendleton. 1809 GLEN MEADE RD 28403 #036-01-1975 L1976 **OBG** *020 †30
MASON, Lockert B. 2131 S 17TH ST 28401 #051-04-1945 L1945 **GS** *071 †85
MASTRANGELO, Michael R. 1515 DOCTORS CIR, BLDG B 28401 #020-12-1978 L1985 **GE IM** *020 †20
MATHEW, Anne Irene. ■ 28409 #024-16-1990 L1996 **P** *075 ‡
MATHEW, Rano Thos. 1907 S 17TH ST STE 1 28401 #024-16-1990 L1996 **P ADM** *020 †75
MAULTSBY, James Alexander. 1990 S 16TH ST, WILMINGTON PRIMARY CARE 28401 #036-05-1957 L1957 **ORS** *020 †40
MAXWELL, John Gary. 2131 S 17TH ST, AHEC SURGERY 28401 #049-01-1958 L1985 **GS TRS** *071 †85
MAY, Jeannine Meece. 1628 DOCTORS CIR, CAROLINA PEDIATRICS 28401 #011-04-1981 L1985 **PD** *020 †55
MC CABE, James Carden. 1302 MEDICAL CENTER DR 28401 #055-02-1988 L1989 **NEP IM** *020 †20
MC CALL, Catherine West. 330 MILITARY CUTOFF RD, ARBOR COURT STE B-4 28405 #012-05-1987 L1992 **P CHP** *020 †75
MC CALL, Wilmer C. ■ 28409 #041-12-1953 L1972 **R NM** *071 †80
MC CALLUM, James Henry. ■ 28409 #036-05-1954 L1954 **ADL OS** *071
MC CLAIN, Linda. 1717 SHIPYARD BLVD, STE 200 28403 #036-08-1986 L1993 **OBG** *020 †30
MC CLURG, Michelle Marie. 2131 S 17TH ST 28401 #038-43-1993 L2003 **P** *020 †75
MC CREA, William B. 5301 WRIGHTSVILLE AVE 28403 #048-14-1987 L2000 **AN GS** *020 †05
MC CRILLIS, Lee Ellen. ■ 28403 #038-45-1989 L1999 **OS** *020 †55
MC CULLOUGH, Michael D. 1025 MEDICAL CENTER DR, DELANEY RADIOLOGISTS 28401 #039-01-1982 L1986 **DR** *020 †80
MC CUSKEY, William Hanes. 1025 MEDICAL CENTER DR 28401 #055-01-1987 L1991 **DR** *020 †80
MC DONALD, Barbara Ellen. 2800 ASHTON DR, COASTAL REHABILITATION MED 28412 #047-20-1989 L1995 **PM** *020 †60
MC ENTIRE, Patrick Cary. 305 S 3RD ST, MURCHISON BLDG 28401 #045-01-1977 L1981 **EM OS** *020 †16
MC GARRITY, Michael Scott. 1515 DOCTORS CIR, BLDG C 28401 #035-15-1988 L1994 **END IM** *020 †20
MC KAIN, Laura Kay. 2131 S 17TH ST 28401 #010-02-1991 L1995 **OBG** *020 †30
MC KINNEY, Christopher D. 1915 S 17TH ST, STE 100 28401 #036-01-1989 L2003 **PTH** *020 †50
MC LAMB, Donald Lee, Jr. 3710 SHIPYARD BLVD, ECEP II, PA 28403 #036-01-2000 L2003 **EM** *100
MC LAREN, Matthew Douglas. 1602 PHYSICIANS DR, STE 104 28401 #422-01-1999 L2004 **AN** *100 †05
MC MANUS, Shea Eamonn. 3600 S COLLEGE RD, STE E 28412 #021-01-1994 L2008 **IM** *020 †20
MC MILLAN, Wm Owen, Jr. 2131 S 17TH ST 28401 #036-07-1963 L1963 **GE IM** *071 †20
MC MURRY, John Eugene, Jr. 2131 S 17TH ST 28401 #036-01-1980 L1982 **OTO** *020 †45
MC MURRY, Warren Winslow. 1411 PHYSICIANS DR 28401 #036-01-1981 L1987 **GS VS** *020 †85
MC NULTY, William, Jr. 1520 PHYSICIANS DR 28401 #045-04-1982 L1984 **HO** *020 †20
MC PHERSON, Belinda A. 8108B MARKET ST 28411 #036-08-1993 L1996 **FM** *020 †18
MC WILLIAMS, Michael Jay. ■ 28409 #010-02-1999 L2007 **ICE** *020 †20
MEDLEY, Mark Frederick. 1414 MEDICAL CENTER DR, ASSOCIATES 28401 #001-02-1989 L1995 **GS** *020 †85
MEISEL, Dean R. 8108B MARKET ST 28411 #011-03-1986 L1988 **IM PD** *020 †20,55
MELIN, Thomas Eric. 2800 ASHTON DR, STE 200 28412 #020-12-1984 L1987 **NS GS** *020 †25
MERTESDORF, James Michael. 1515 DOCTORS CIR, BLDG C 28401 #016-43-1978 L1984 **GE** *020 †20
MESSIER, Amy Eileen. ■ 28411 #051-04-2000 L2007 **FM** *020 †18
MESSIER, Matthew Roland. 7420 MARKET ST, NEW HANOVER MEDICAL GROUP 28411 #051-04-1999 L2007 **IM** *020 †20
MESSINA, Douglas Frank. 2520 TROY DR 28401 #011-03-1991 L1997 **ORS** *020 †40
METZ, Philip Steven. ■ 28411 #030-05-1969 L2002 **PS HS** *071 †85,65
MEYER, Albert Augustine. 2523 DELANEY RD 28403 #035-08-1975 L1977 **FM** *040 †18
MEYER, Clinton Louis. 5115 OLEANDER DR 28403 #063-01-1978 L1983 **GE IM** *020 †20
MEYER, Peter Karl. 601 S COLLEGE RD, HEALTH CENTER 28403 #038-40-1978 L1979 **EM** *020 †16
MEYERSON, Martin Benj. 1988 S 16TH ST, ONCOLOGY 28401 #016-11-1968 L1977 **RO** *020 †80
MICKLOS, D Vaughn. ■ 28411 #041-09-1966 L2005 **OM** *071 ‡
MILAM, Thomas Richerson. 1717 SHIPYARD BLVD STE 210 28403 #051-01-1998 L2002 **P** *020
MILES, David Ralph. 1717 SHIPYARD BLVD STE 300, MILES SURGICAL PLLC 28403 #025-01-1985 L1990 **GS VS** *020 †85
MILLER, Jon Kimberly. ■ 28403 #017-20-1983 L1989 **ORS OSS** *020 †40
MILLER, Justin Gregory. 5018 GORHAM AVE 28409 #047-06-2000 L2007 **IM** *020 †20
MINOR, Monique Renee. 3710 SHIPYARD BLVD, EAST CAROLINA EMERGENCY PH 28403 #051-01-1975 L1982 **EM** *020 †20,16
MINOR, Stanley Gill. 3710 SHIPYARD BLVD 28403 #036-01-1975 L1984 **FM** *020 †18
MLOT, Matthew John. 2131 S 17TH ST 28401 #025-07-1978 L2003 **GE** *020 †20 ‡
MOBLEY, Thomas B, III. 1905 GLEN MEADE RD 28403 #012-01-1972 L1977 **U** *030 †95
MOELLER, Michael John. 1515 DOCTORS CIR, HANOVER MEDICAL SPECIALIST 28401 #035-15-1978 L1988 **CD IM** *020 †20
MOORE, Barry Allen. 311 JUDGES RD STE 4E 28405 #019-02-1970 L1974 **P** *075 †75
MOORE, Horace G, Jr. 2131 S 17TH ST 28401 #023-07-1945 L1953 **GS TS** *071 †85
MOORE, Ralph B, Jr. 1920 S 16TH ST 28401 #035-20-1952 L1956 **PD** *071 †55
MOORE, Richard Sulter, Jr. 2716 ASHTON DR 28412 #036-01-1991 L1996 **ORS** *020 †40
MOORE, Robert Alexander. 1302 MEDICAL CENTER DR 28401 #036-05-1984 L1985 **NEP IM** *020 †20
MOORE, Robert Morgan. 1508 MEDICAL CENTER DR, MOORE ORTHOPAEDICS, PA 28401 #047-05-1975 L1981 **ORS** *020 †40
MORALES, Renee Christine. ■ 28403 #001-02-2007 **OBG** *012
MORAN, Harriet Jane. ■ 28403 #045-01-1984 L2005 **IM** *020 †20
MORGAN, Herman G, Jr. 2421 SILVER STREAM LN 28401 #036-01-1977 L1983 **PD** *020 †55 ‡
MORGAN, Mark Wayne. 2305 CANTERWOOD DR 28401 #036-05-1997 L2004 **HS** *020 †65
MORGAN, Nicholas Andrew. ■ 28401 #036-01-2007 **GS** *012
MORRIS, Kenny Jordan. ■ 28409 #036-01-1962 L1962 **R** *071 †80
MORTER, Gregory Alan. ■ 28412 #041-12-1986 L1993 **PD** *075 †55
MOULTON, Michael Paul. 3710 SHIPYARD BLVD, 3710 SHIPYARD BLVD 28403 #048-13-1991 L1994 **EM** *020 †16
MOYA, Fernando Rodrigo. 2131 S 17TH ST, COASTAL AHEC 28401 #231-03-1978 L2005 **NPM PD** *050 †55 ‡
MURAKATA, Linda Ann. 1915 S 17TH ST, STE 100 28401 #033-05-1985 L2005 **PTH IM** *020 †50 ‡
MURPHY, Kathryn Marie. 119 CHESTNUT ST, THE DOWNTOWN CLINIC 28401 #010-02-1984 L1997 **IM** *020 †20
MURPHY, Mark Timothy. 1725 NEW HANVR MDCL PRK DR 28403 #539-02-1990 L2000 **CD IM** *020 †20
MUSSELWHITE, Neill H, III. 5145 S COLLEGE RD 28412 #036-05-1975 L1975 **FM** *020
MYERS, Christopher Robert. 8788 TILBURY DR, MUSC - GRADUATE MEDICAL ED 28411 #011-03-2002 L2004 **PFP** *020 †75
MYERS, Kenneth William. 2321 DELANEY RD 28403 #051-04-1990 L2000 **AI IM** *020 †03,20
MYNATT, Richard Joseph. 1606 PHYSICIANS DR, STE 102 28401 #047-06-1977 L1980 **U** *020 †95
NACE, Mindy Lee. ■ 28412 #041-14-2007 **GS** *012
NANCE, Charles Lee, Jr. 5302 OLEANDER DR 28403 #036-07-1959 L1959 **ORS** *071 †40
NAPPER, Clay Hughes. ■ 28405 #036-05-1956 L1956 **IM** *071
NASCA, Richard Jos. ■ 28405 #010-02-1964 L1990 **ORS OSS** *071 †40
NASH, Marie Jaquelin. ■ 28409 #036-01-2000 L2002 **D** *020 †15
NEAL, Charles Rogers. 1988 S 16TH ST, ONCOLOGY 28401 #012-01-1983 L1992 **RO** *020 †80
NELSON, Jean Marie. 5301 WRIGHTSVILLE AVE 28403 #041-02-1988 L1992 **AN** *020 †05
NICHOLS, Li. 2131 S 17TH ST 28401 #243-69-1992 L2006 **IM** *020 †20
NICHOLS, Robert Vance. 1905 GLEN MEADE RD 28403 #036-01-1985 L1986 **U** *020 †95
NICKS, Dennis Bart. 2305 CANTERWOOD DR 28401 #028-03-1977 L1982 **PS HS** *020 †65
NOBLES, Michael Allen. ■ 28409 #047-06-2005 **OBG** *012
NOLAN, Jerome T, Jr. 1112 TWO MILE CIR W 28405 #035-45-1952 L1977 **GP** *072
NOVOSEL, Pamela Renee. 2131 S 17TH ST, COASTAL AHEC-OB/GYN 28401 #036-08-2005 **OBG** *012
OCHSNER, Katherine Isabel. 1729 NEW HANVR MDCL PRK DR 28403 #021-06-1987 L2000 **OPH** *020 †35 ‡
OLATIDOYE, Babatunde A. 1915 S 17TH ST, STE 100 28401 #036-01-1990 L1993 **PCP** *020 †50
O MALLEY, John Scott. 2716 ASHTON DR 28412 #035-15-1987 L1993 **ORS** *020 †40
ONEESE, Justin. ■ 28403 #025-12-2004 L2006 **AN** *100
O'NEIL, Kevin Michael. 1202 MEDICAL CENTER DR, PULMONARY CLINIC WHA 28401 #041-02-1983 L2003 **PUD CCM** *020 †20
OPPER, Frederick H. 1515 DOCTORS CIR, HANOVER MEDICAL SPECIALIST 28401 #016-42-1983 L1984 **GE NTR** *020 †20
ORMAND, John Wm, Jr. 1809 GLEN MEADE RD 28403 #036-01-1956 L1956 **OBG** *071 †30
OTT, Daniel David. 1920 S 16TH ST 28401 #036-01-2003 L2006 **PD** *020 †55
PACE, John Sanderson. 5301 WRIGHTSVILLE AVE 28403 #011-02-1971 L1973 **AN** *020 †05
PALEGA, Gregory. 7420 MARKET ST, OGDEN OFFICE 28411 #035-20-1994 L1995 **IM** *020 †20
PALLIN, Diana. ■ 28403 #781-03-2003 **IM** *012
PAPAGIKOS, Michael Alex. 3607 SAINT FRANCIS DR, NEW HANOVER RADIATION ONC 28409 #036-05-2001 L2004 **RO** *020
PARKER, John Charles. 1515 DOCTORS CIR, BLDG C 28401 #036-01-1997 L2001 **END IM** *020 †20 ‡
PARKER, Michael Young. 1111 MILITARY CUTOFF RD, STE 191 28405 #036-01-1978 L1980 **OTO HNS** *020 †45
PARKINSON, John. 2311 CANTERWOOD DR 28401 #045-01-1975 L1977 **P** *020 †75
PASQUARETTE, Mark Michael. 2131 S 17TH ST 28401 #041-02-1988 L1994 **OBG REN** *020 †30
PASQUARIELLO, John P, Jr. 1202 MEDICAL CENTER DR 28401 #010-02-1983 L1986 **IM** *020 †20 ‡
PATEL, Ami Sandip. 4000 SHIPYARD BLVD 28403 #495-23-1995 L2001 **IM** *020 †20
PATEL, Ekta Vinod. ■ 28409 #496-30-1999 L2007 **IM** *100
PATEL, Hemantkumar M. 1725 NEW HANVR MDCL PRK DR 28403 #041-14-1992 L2000 **CD** *020 †20
PATEL, Mitesh Kirit. ■ 28412 #033-06-2001 L2006 **GS** *020
PATEL, Praful Naranjibhai. 1725 NEW HANVR MDCL PRK DR, PARK DR 28403 #917-01-1978 L1990 **CD** *020 †20
PATEL, Sandip Jayantibhai. 1025 MEDICAL CENTER DR, DELANEY RADIOLOGIST GROUP 28401 #041-14-1994 L1999 **DR** *020 †80
PATEL, Shreyang Hemonsuro. 2131 S 17TH ST 28401 #305-01-2001 L2004 **IM** *100
PATHAK, Aman Jitendra. 2310 DELANEY RD 28403 #654-01-2000 L2006 **ID** *020
PATTERSON, Daniel Young. 1213 CULBRETH DR 28405 #020-12-1966 L1990 **P** *071 †75 ‡
PAWLOWSKI, James Thos. 2311 CANTERWOOD DR 28401 #010-02-1989 L1993 **P** *020 †75
PAYNE, Joseph M. 1202 MEDICAL CENTER DR 28401 #036-01-1984 L1985 **CRS GS** *020 †85,10
PAYNE, Paul Andrew. 1202 MEDICAL CENTER DR, WHA MEDICAL CLINIC, PLLC 28401 #036-07-1987 L2002 **CD** *020 †20
PECORARO, Francis S. 3787 SHIPYARD BLVD 28403 #305-01-1996 L2005 **PM** *020 †60
PEELER, Ronald Hubert. ■ 28409 #036-05-1981 L1982 **MDM EM** *030 †16
PELTSVERGER, Maya Yakovle. ■ 28412 #913-55-2001 **IM** *012
PENCE, James Jerome, Jr. 3014 WINGPOINTE PL 28409 #036-07-1959 L1959 **FM** *020
PENG, Yen-Lin. 8108B MARKET ST, WILMINGTON HLTH ASSOC 28411 #036-01-1996 L2000 **MPD** *020 †20,55
PENN, Robert Allan, Jr. ■ 28412 #017-20-1985 L2006 **IM** *020 †20 ‡
PERRITT, John O, Jr. ■ 28412 #041-01-1952 L1952 **R** *100 †80
PERRY, Robert Francis. 1017 ASHES DR STE 100 28405 #050-02-1993 L1994 **UCM** *020
PERSAUD, Kavita S. 5919 OLEANDER DR, STE 109 28403 #918-01-1989 L2001 **IMG IM** *020 †20
PETERSON, Cobern Van, Jr. 5301 WRIGHTSVILLE AVE 28403 #011-03-1985 L1990 **AN** *020 †05
PETRY, L Jeannine. ■ 28409 #038-43-1978 L1982 **FM** *071 †18
PHIFER, Jenifer Benjamina. ■ 28412 #104-01-2005 **FP** *012
PIERSON, Margaret Wooten. 7420 MARKET ST 28411 #036-08-2000 L2003 **FM** *020 †18
PIERSON, Noah Ross. 7420 MARKET ST 28411 #051-04-1992 L1993 **FM** *020 †18 ‡
PINO, Joseph Anthony. 2131 S 17TH ST, COASTAL AHEC 28401 #033-06-1996 L2001 **MPD** *020 †20,55
PISTONE, Daniel. ■ 28409 #132-04-1984 L1998 **P** *020 †75
PLAYER, Jennifer E. 1914 GLEN MEADE RD, THE PEDIATRIC CTR 28403 #012-22-2000 L2006 **PD** *020 †55
PLAYER, John Gregory. 5145 S COLLEGE RD 28412 #012-22-2001 L2006 **FM** *020 †18
POINT, Stuart Watkins. 1025 MEDICAL CENTER DR 28401 #055-01-1983 L1990 **R DR** *020 †80
POINTS, Gerald Lee, II. 5305 WRIGHTSVILLE AVE 28403 #020-12-1965 L1966 **IM FM** *071 †18
POLLOCK, Hoke Dickinson. 1625 DOCTORS CIR 28401 #036-01-1975 L1975 **OTO** *020 †45
POLLOCK, Hoke Ward. 3505 CONVERSE DR STE 200 28403 #036-01-2002 L2004 **PD** *020 †55

POLLOCK, Maria Gonzalez. ■ 28409 #036-07-2001 **PD** *100
POOL, Robert Smithwick. ■ 28405 #036-05-1955 L1955 **PTH** *071 †50
POOLE, Ernest Tilghman. 2131 S 17TH ST 28401 #036-07-1961 L1961 **OPH P** *071 †35
POTTLE, Thomas Galbraith. 5305 WRIGHTSVILLE AVE # K 28403 #051-04-1982 L1984 **PS** *020 †85,65
POTTS, Kevin Eugene. 3710 SHIPYARD BLVD, PHYSICIANS, PA 28403 #036-07-1995 L1996 **EM** *020 †16
POWELL, John Livingston. 2131 S 17TH ST 28401 #036-01-1968 L1968 **GO** *020 †30
PRICE, James Louis, III. 1612 DOCTORS CIR, SOUTHEASTERN OB-GYN ASSOC 28401 #036-01-1975 L1975 **OBG GYN** *020 †30
PRIDGEN, James Henry. 1925A OLEANDER DR 28403 #036-05-1984 L1985 **IM** *020
PRINCE, George Edward. ■ 28411 #036-07-1944 L1947 **PHP PD** *071 †55
PUETT, David Wilson. 1710 S 17TH ST 28401 #047-05-1988 L1993 **RHU** *020 †20
PURCELL, Peter Nelson. 1202 MEDICAL CENTER DR, WILMINGTON HLTH ASSOCS 28401 #036-08-1988 L1997 **VS** *020 †85
PUTCHA, Radha. 2222 S 17TH ST, COASTAL HOSPITALISTS 28401 #495-21-1981 L2006 **IM** *020 †20
RADACK, Matthew Chet. 3710 SHIPYARD BLVD, E CAROLINA EMER PHYSICANS, 28403 #035-45-1990 L1997 **EM** *020 †16
RAFALOWSKI, Alicja. 108 N KERR AVE STE E1 28405 #759-04-1979 L1997 **IM** *020 †20
RAGOZZINO, Mark Wm. 1025 MEDICAL CENTER DR 28401 #026-08-1982 L1987 **DR** *020 †80
RAJABI HANJANI, Mitra. ■ 28412 #517-11-1998 **IM** *012
RAMSAY, Jamie Alex. 5301 WRIGHTSVILLE AVE 28403 #025-01-1997 L2005 **AN** *020 †05
RANDIVE, Vijay Ramchandra. 6932 MARKET ST STE J, FAMILY PRACTICE 28411 #654-01-1989 L1993 **PTH** *020 †18
REESE, Kevin John. 2131 S 17TH ST, EMERGENCY DEPT 28401 #016-42-1993 L1997 **EM** *020 †16
REICHOW, Karen Mylenek. 2222 S 17TH ST 28401 #025-07-1993 L2003 **IM** *020 †20
REID, Thomas Beauregard. 615 SHIPYARD BLVD, COASTAL HORIZONS INC. 28412 #036-01-1980 L1981 **ADM IM** *020 †20
REMINGTON, John Lauren. 1025 MEDICAL CENTER DR 28401 #011-04-1979 L1983 **DR** *030 †80
RENGO, Rena B. ■ 28409 #025-01-1978 L2008 **PTH** *020 †50 ‡
RENTON, Patrick Joseph. ■ 28409 #051-04-2005 L2008 **PD** *012
REYNOLDS, Frank R. ■ 28403 #041-01-1944 L1944 **PD** *071 †55
RHODES, Herman Kyle. 1809 GLEN MEADE RD, GLEN MEADE OB-GYN, PA 28403 #036-01-1988 L1991 **OBG** *020 †30
RHYNE, Janelle Arolyn. 2029 S 17TH ST, NEW HANOVER COUNTY HEALTH 28401 #036-05-1983 L1984 **ID IM** *020 †20
RICCIARDELLI, Edward J. 1717 SHIPYARD BLVD STE 100 28403 #051-01-1985 L1996 **PS OTO** *020 †45,65 ‡
RICHARDS, Adrienne Laura. 1725 NEW HANVR MDCL PRK DR 28403 #023-07-1991 L1994 **CD IM** *020 †20
RIGGINS, Bruce W, Jr. 2023 S 17TH ST, SOUTHEASTERN CENTER FOR MH 28401 #012-01-1992 L1998 **CHP** *020 †75
ROBERSON, William Earl. 5305 WRIGHTSVILLE AVE, STE L 28403 #036-01-1966 L1966 **OBG** *020 †30
ROBERTS, Gregory John. 1202 MEDICAL CENTER DR 28401 #004-01-2001 L2007 **CD** *020
ROBERTS, Gretchen May. ■ 28411 #004-01-2001 L2003 **PD** *020 †55
ROBERTS, Lloyd Eugene. ■ 28411 #007-02-1969 L1978 **OBG** *071 †30
ROBINSON, Derrick L. 1302 MEDICAL CENTER DR, SOUTHEASTERN NEPHROLOGY AS 28401 #036-01-1992 L1994 **NEP** *020 †20
ROBINSON, James Hendry. 2505 S 17TH ST 28401 #036-01-1961 L1961 **AN** *071
ROBINSON, Norman Jeffrey. 2131 S 17TH ST 28401 #036-07-1963 L1963 **CD IM** *071 †20
ROBINSON, William Patrick. ■ 28409 #016-45-2000 L2004 **VS** *012
ROBISON, G Daniel, IV. 1809 GLEN MEADE RD, GLEN MEADE OB GYN, P.A. 28403 #036-05-1995 L1999 **OBG** *020 †30
ROBISON, William P. ■ 28403 #012-01-1951 L1975 **P** *071 †75
RODGER, Robert Mark. 3787 SHIPYARD BLVD 28403 #064-01-1982 L1991 **ORS OSS** *020 †40
ROSE, Junius Harris, III. PO BOX 4147 28406 #036-01-1993 L1995 **P** *020 †75
ROSE, Mara Frances. ■ 28411 #036-08-2005 L2005 **FM** *100
ROSENBERG, Eric Ronald. 1025 MEDICAL CENTER DR 28401 #035-09-1975 L1977 **DR** *020 †80
ROSENTHAL, Kim S. ■ 28412 #048-14-2000 L2006 **P** *100 †75
ROSS, Deborah Rosalie. 2250 SHIPYARD BLVD STE 3 28403 #026-04-1987 L1988 **CHP P** *020 †75
ROWLAND, Edmund Burrill. 3787 SHIPYARD BLVD, ATLANTIC ORTHOPEDICS, PA 28403 #041-13-1986 L2005 **HS ORS** *020 †40
ROYAL, Margit E. ■ 28403 #030-05-1983 L1989 **N** *071 †20,75
RUDYK, Mary Kathryn. 1709 S 16TH ST STE A, SENIOR HEALTH CENTER 28401 #065-10-1978 L1994 **IMG** *020
RUPPE, John P, Jr. 3904 OLEANDER DR, STE 102 28403 #035-19-1949 L1994 **D** *071 †15
RUSSELL, Anthony Otis. 1222 MEDICAL CENTER DR, CAROLINA ANESTHESIOLOGY 28401 #035-19-1987 L2007 **AN** *020 †05
RUSSELL, William Alton. 1905 GLEN MEADE RD 28403 #036-07-1987 L1989 **U** *020 †95
RUST, George K, Jr. 2131 S 17TH ST 28401 #036-05-1968 L1968 **GE IM** *030
SAID, Areen Turki. 1202 MEDICAL CENTER DR, WHA MEDICAL CLINIC, PLLC 28401 #575-01-1996 L2002 **N** *020 †20
SALYER, Beth Allison. ■ 28411 #023-12-2005 L2006 **OBG** *012
SAMPSON, Jos Luther, Jr. 5305 WRIGHTSVILLE AVE, STE K 28403 #051-04-1961 L1968 **PS HS** *071 †85,65
SANDERS, John Wesley, III. 2310 DELANEY RD 28403 #036-01-1981 L1982 **ID IM** *020 †20
SAN MIGUEL, Eduardo. 3710 SHIPYARD BLVD 28403 #036-08-1994 L1999 **EM** *020 †16
SARAN, Jeetpaul Singh. 28401 #495-43-2005 L2006 **IM** *012
SAWYER, David Thos. 1515 DOCTORS CIR, HANOVER MEDICAL SPECIALIST 28401 #041-02-1989 L1995 **CD** *020 †20
SAWYER, John W. ■ 28405 #038-06-1952 L1952 **IM** *071
SCHIMIZZI, Gregory Frank. 1710 S 17TH ST 28401 #025-07-1976 L1987 **RHU IG** *020 †20
SCHLEUPNER, Charles John. 2131 S 17TH ST, DEPT MEDICINE COASTAL AHEC 28401 #023-01-1972 L1998 **IM ID** *040 †20 ‡
SCHULTZ, David Martin. 1202 MEDICAL CENTER DR 28401 #035-45-1993 L2000 **IM** *020 †20
SCHUMAN, Paula Claire. 2131 S 17TH ST, SEAHEC 28401 #010-01-1976 L2008 **IM** *020 †20 ‡
SCIALABBA, Annette C. ■ 28409 #036-07-1987 L1994 **PD** *020 †55
SCIALABBA, Fred Anthony. 1025 MEDICAL CENTER DR 28401 #036-07-1987 L1994 **DR** *020 †80
SCOTT, Charles Matthew. 1202 MEDICAL CENTER DR 28401 #038-41-1975 L1983 **GS VS** *020 †85

SCULLY, Kevin Slean. 8115 MARKET ST, STE 108 28411 #051-01-1978 L1984 **ORS OSM** *020 †40
SEIDEL, Murray Kaye. 3787 SHIPYARD BLVD 28403 #041-01-1965 L1971 **ORS** *020 †40
SEMMEL, Brady James. 1122 MEDICAL CENTER DR 28401 #041-12-2000 L2001 **CS OMF** *020
SHAH, Jyotsna Jagmohandas. 2131 S 17TH ST 28401 #495-01-1964 L1974 **AN** *071
SHAH, Ramesh Manharlal. ■ 28412 #495-23-1964 L1973 **OBG** *071 †30
SHAH, Syed H. 2131 S 17TH ST 28401 #654-01-2006 **FP** *012
SHAKAR, Robert Michael, Jr. 5301 WRIGHTSVILLE AVE 28403 #011-03-1993 L1998 **AN** *020 †05
SHANAHAN, Joseph Charles. 1710 S 17TH ST 28401 #033-06-1997 L1998 **RHU** *020 †20
SHARAF, Mohamed. 2131 S 17TH ST, NEONATAL INTENSIVE CARE 28401 #915-07-1975 L2000 **NPM** *020 †55
SHEARIN, Wilbur Thaddeus. 1905 GLEN MEADE RD 28403 #036-05-1954 L1954 **U OS** *071 †95
SHEERIN, James Hall. 1202 MEDICAL CENTER DR 28401 #030-06-1970 L2004 **CD** *020 †20 ‡
SHIRO, Brian Chas. 1915 S 17TH ST, STE 100 28401 #050-02-1985 L1986 **PTH** *020 †50
SHUFORD, Wm Ferrell, Jr. 1202 MEDICAL CENTER DR 28401 #036-01-1961 L1961 **GE IM** *071 †20
SIMMONS, Roger Lee, Jr. ■ 28403 #020-12-1966 L1967 **IM** *030
SIMMS, Kristi Barger. 1202 MEDICAL CENTER DR, WILMINGTON HEALTH ASSOCIAT 28401 #047-20-2002 L2005 **IM** *020 †20
SIMPSON, Andrew Warren. 5302 OLEANDER DR STE A, MEDICINE, PLLC 28403 #036-08-2001 L2005 **ORS** *020
SINCLAIR, Robey Thos, Jr. 5303 WRIGHTSVILLE AVE 28403 #010-02-1938 L1938 **R GS** *071
SINGLETARY, Henry Pate. 2131 S 17TH ST, WILMINGTON PATHOLOGY ASSOC 28401 #016-06-1953 L1960 **PTH** *020 †18
SINGLETON, Adrienne Lynne. ■ 28411 #048-13-2001 L2006 **PAN** *020
SINGLETON, Brian Anthony. ■ 28411 #055-02-1999 L2007 **GS** *020 †80
SIPPLE, Edward M. ■ 28412 #023-01-1951 L1961 **R** *071 †80
SLOAN, David Bryan, Jr. 1915 GLEN MEADE RD 28403 #036-01-1963 L1963 **OPH** *071 †35
SLOAN, James Boykin. 1729 NEW HANVR MDCL PRK DR 28403 #036-01-1970 L1970 **OPH** *071 †35
SMITH, Lloyd A Warren. ■ 28412 #018-03-1944 L1992 **P** *071
SMITH, Philip Palmer. 5301 WRIGHTSVILLE AVE 28403 #016-11-1962 L1970 **IM OM** *071 †20,70
SMITH, Stanton Thomas. ■ 28403 #008-02-2005 L2006 **GS** *012
SMITH, Stephen Brian. 5301 WRIGHTSVILLE AVE 28403 #039-01-1984 L1987 **AN** *020 †05
SNIPE, Joel Janeen. ■ 28411 #045-01-2004 **OBG** *012
SNOW, David Howey. 1710 S 17TH ST 28401 #038-43-1990 L1998 **RHU** *020 †20
SNYDER, Frank Alan. 2215 CANTERWOOD DR 28401 #051-04-1986 L1987 **IM** *020
SNYDER, James Wm. 1515 DOCTORS CIR, BLDG C 28401 #036-01-1969 L1969 **CD IM** *020 †20
SNYDER, John Eaton, Jr. 2131 S 17TH ST, COASTAL AHEC INT. MEDICINE 28401 #024-16-2000 L2005 **IM** *020
SOLANKI, Rajesh B. 3505 CONVERSE DR, STE 200 28403 #036-08-2000 L2002 **PD** *020 †55 ‡
SOLOMON, Robert Douglas. ■ 28411 #023-07-1942 L1980 **PTH** *075 †50
SOTIR, Catherine Lee. 1202 MEDICAL CENTER DR, WHA MEDICAL CLINIC, PLLC 28401 #034-01-1994 L1995 **FM** *040 †18
SOUFFRONT VELEZ, Wilfredo. 311 JUDGES RD STE 4E, ACT MEDICAL GROUP 28405 #042-01-1963 L1996 **GPM OS** *020
SPICER, Samuel Sherman. 2131 S 17TH ST 28401 #045-01-1976 L1981 **MDM FM** *030 †16,18
SPRUILL, James Henry, Jr. ■ 28405 #036-01-1967 L1967 **N** *020 †75
STANFIELD, Elwin E. ■ 28405 #023-01-1949 L1974 **GP** *071
STANLEY, John Herbert, Jr. 1025 MEDICAL CENTER DR 28401 #036-01-1977 L1977 **DR** *020 †80
STARLING, Paul Britt. 5301 WRIGHTSVILLE AVE 28403 #036-05-1989 L1993 **AN** *020 †05
STAUB, Jonathan Simon. 1202 MEDICAL CENTER DR, MEDICAL CLINIC PLLC 28401 #056-06-1983 L1994 **IM** *020 †20
STEINKRAUS, Robert Ernest. ■ 28411 #035-45-1956 L1990 **IM** *071 †20
STELMACH, Hans. ■ 28401 #035-06-1998 L1999 **PFP** *020 †20
STENGEL, Deborah Ann. 1960 S 16TH ST 28401 #036-01-2001 L2003 **FM** *020 †18
STEVENS, Frank Wilson, Jr. 3205 RANDALL PKWY, STE 122 28403 #047-05-1972 L1996 **P CHP** *020 †75
STEWART, Donald Kent. PO BOX 9025, COASTAL AHACC DEPT SURG 28402 #035-09-2004 **GS** *012
STEWART, George Terry. 1802 S 17TH ST 28401 #036-01-1971 L1971 **OBG** *020 †30
STRATAS, Byron Aristotle. 1729 NEW HANVR MDCL PRK DR 28403 #036-08-1986 L1988 **OPH EM** *020 †35
SULLIVAN, Michael Durgin. 1814 GLEN MEADE RD 28403 #036-07-2000 L2001 **D** *020 †15
SUMMERS, Rachel. ■ 28412 #055-75-2004, ▲ **OBG** *012
SUTHERLAND, Mark Joseph. 1602 PHYSICIANS DR STE 104, WILMINGTON ANESTHESIOLOGIS 28401 #051-04-2001 L2006 **AN** *020
SUTTON, William Roger. 2716 ASHTON DR 28412 #036-01-1987 L1992 **ORS** *020 †40
SUVILLAGA, Victor I. 1230 MEDICAL CENTER DR 28401 #341-01-1977 L1997 **IM** *075
SWAN, Robert Wm. 2131 S 17TH ST, UNIVERSITY OB/GYN 28401 #016-06-1965 L1966 **GO GYN** *030 †30
SYLVESTRI, George Mark. 1202 MEDICAL CENTER DR 28403 #010-02-1984 L2000 **IM** *020 †20
SZABO, Laszlo Jozsef. ■ 28412 #473-04-1990 L1994 **P** *020 †75
TACKETT, Amos Darrell. 1411 PHYSICIANS DR 28401 #047-05-1969 L1978 **GS TS** *020 †85
TAMADON, Afshin. 3916 OLEANDER DR, P O BOX 7217 28403 #030-06-1993 L1998 **PM** *020 †60
TAMISIEA, J Richard. ■ 28409 #030-06-1964 L1970 **CD IM** *071
TANNER, Laura S. 2425 S 17TH ST 28401 #016-01-1987 L1991 **D** *020 †15
TANTA, Feras. ■ 28401 #875-01-2000 L2006 **IM** *020 †20
TATE, Thomas Dale. 1442 MILITARY CUTOFF RD 28403 #017-20-1966 L1985 **GP** *020
TAWAKOL, Hesham Shawki. 2131 S 17TH ST, NEW HANOVER REGIONAL MED. 28401 #915-04-1989 L2001 **NPM** *020 †55
TAYLOR, Britton Edgar. 1802 S 17TH ST 28401 #051-04-1963 L1973 **OBG** *020 †30
TAYLOR, Sherri Virginia. 3807 PEACHTREE AVE STE 101 28403 #036-01-1995 L1998 **IM** *020 †20
TEMPLE, Rufus Henry. 1606 PHYSICIANS DR, STE 102 28403 #036-01-1976 L1976 **GYN OBG** *020 †30
TERZIAN, Andrew. 3710 SHIPYARD BLVD, PHYSICIANS 28403 #041-15-2001 L2004 **EM** *100 †16
THACKER, Anmona Sudhir. 2304 DELANEY RD, KNOX CLINIC PEDIATRICS 28403 #495-76-1989 L2006 **PD** *020 †55
THOMAS, Alan Efird. 637 S KERR AVE 28403 #012-01-1974 L1975 **IM** *020
THOMPSON, Thomas Terry. ■ 28409 #051-04-1964 L1965 **DR** *020 †80

TIDLER, James. ■ 28412 #051-04-1944 L1949 **IM** *071 †20

TINSLEY, Ellis A, Sr. 1414 MEDICAL CENTER DR, WILMINGTON SURGICAL ASSOCI 28401 #047-05-1959 L2006 **GS VS** *071 †85,90

TINSLEY, Ellis Allan, Jr. 1414 MEDICAL CENTER DR, ASSOCIATES 28401 #036-01-1987 L1992 **VS** *020 †85

TOBIAS-BALDWIN, Rachel. 2029 S 17TH ST, NEW HANOVER COUNTY HEALTH 28401 #005-18-1999 L2005 *020 †70

TOLLEFSEN, Eva. 1717 SHIPYARD BLVD 28403 #030-05-1992 L1996 **OBG** *020 †30

TOPPERCER, Adam. ■ 28411 #759-03-1967 L1991 **U** *020 †20

TORRES, Sandra Susan. 1117 MEDICAL CENTER DR, COASTAL NEUROLOGY PLLC 28401 #187-58-1985 L1991 **N** *020 †75

TRIMPEY, Amanda Claire. 4815 OLEANDER DR 28403 #041-12-1994 L1997 **GPM** *020 †70

TSENG, John Tsung-Long. 5301 WRIGHTSVILLE AVE, EMERGENCY DEPT 28403 #049-01-1994 L1999 **EM** *020 †16

TURNBULL, David Milo. 3710 SHIPYARD BLVD 28403 #041-12-1970 L1972 **EM** *020 †20

TURNER, John Franklin, Jr. 1915 S 17TH ST, STE 100 28401 #012-01-1989 L2003 **HMP** *020 †50

TURNER, Lynda B. ■ 28409 #051-01-1991 L1993 **PD** *020 †55

UPPAL, Priyanka. ■ 28405 #495-03-2002 **IM** *012

VAN DER WOUDE, Rients. 20 S 16TH ST 28401 #660-01-1951 L1993 **ADM TS** *020 †85,90

VAN NYNATTEN, Fred H. 1990 S 16TH ST 28401 #165-01-1974 L1974 **IM** *020 †20

VAN RENS, Gerard Henderik. 1801 NEW HANVR MDCL PRK DR 28403 #660-01-1979 L1997 **OPH** *020 †35

VAN VELSOR, Harry. 2131 S 17TH ST 28401 #035-03-1947 L1954 **D** *071 †15

VARNEY, Michael John. 1442 MILITARY CUTOFF RD 28403 #038-45-1987 L1988 **EM IM** *020 †20

VERNON, Charles R. 7230 WRIGHTSVILLE AVE 28403 #038-06-1952 L1952 **P** *020 †75

VERNOOY, Robert Alan, Jr. 1202 MEDICAL CENTER DR, WILMINGTON HEALTH ASSOCIAT 28401 #035-45-1998 L2005 **ICE** *020 †20

VINCENT, Benjamin Garrett. 1703 POPE CT 28405 #036-01-2008 *012

VISSER, Melodye E. 1908 MEETING CT 28401 #051-01-1986 L1987 **FM** *020 †18

VISSER, Scott Wm. 4141 SHIPYARD BLVD 28403 #051-01-1986 L1987 **FM** *020 †18

VOGEL, Joshua Ian. 2131 S 17TH ST 28401 #045-01-1996 L1997 **OBG** *020 †30

VONBIBERSTEIN, Sarah E. 8068 MARKET ST 28411 #036-08-1991 L1992 **OTO** *020 †45

WALL, Benjamin Evans. 2800 ASHTON DR STE 100, COASTAL REHABILITATION MED 28412 #036-05-1993 L1997 **PM PMM** *020 †60

WALSTON, Abe, II. ■ 28405 #036-07-1963 L1963 **IM CD** *071 †20

WARD, Michael M. 5301 WRIGHTSVILLE AVE, CAPE FEAR HOSP EMERG DEPT 28403 #036-01-1977 L1980 **EM** *020 †16

WARHAFTIG, Jeffrey L. 1960 S 16TH ST 28401 #041-12-1994 L1997 **IM** *020 †20

WARING, Eveline Adams. 2710 PARK AVE 28403 #045-01-1996 L2001 **END** *020 †20

WARREN, Lewis Patrick, Jr. 2131 S 17TH ST 28401 #036-01-1976 L1976 **DR AN** *020 †20,80

WARSHAUER, Leo Victor. 1403 AUDUBON BLVD, # A-1 28403 #036-05-1986 L1989 **IM IMG** *020

WARSHAUER, Samuel Edward. 2131 S 17TH ST 28401 #051-04-1936 L1936 **IM CD** *071 †20

WATKINS, Pearlie Bradford, III. ■ 28405 #036-08-2008 *012

WEATHERFORD, David Allen. 1411 PHYSICIANS DR 28401 #045-01-1989 L1997 **VS** *020 †85

WEAVER, David Ellis. 1725 NEW HANVR MDCL PRK DR 28403 #048-12-1984 L2003 **CD** *020 †20

WEBSTER, Brian Richard. 2402 MEDICAL CENTER DR 28401 #036-01-1993 L1996 **IM** *020 †20

WEHNER, Joseph James. 1025 MEDICAL CENTER DR, DELANEY RADIOLOGISTS 28401 #041-14-1988 L1998 **RNR** *020 †80

WEINBERG, Elizabeth S. 1411 PHYSICIANS DR 28401 #036-01-1998 L2003 **GS** *100 †85

WEINEL, William Harvey. 2131 S 17TH ST 28401 #036-01-1954 L1954 **GYN OBS** *071 †30

WEINSTEIN, Robert Harvey. 2595 S 17TH ST 28401 #028-03-1967 L1974 **P** *020 †75

WEIS, Walter Francis, Jr. 401 CHESTNUT ST, STE A 28401 #041-02-1966 L1973 **ORS OS** *020 †40

WELLIVER, Gary Evan. 105 N 15TH ST 28401 #047-06-1966 L1983 **ORS** *072

WERK, Emile Eugene, Jr. NEW HANOVER MEM HOSP 28401 #038-41-1946 L1953 **IM END** *040 †20

WERTHEIMER, Thomas Albert. 1960 S 16TH ST 28401 #035-15-1996 L1999 **IM** *020 †20

WESTBROOK, Andrew Gocke. 2131 S 17TH ST 28401 #047-05-1993 L2003 **FM** *020 †18

WESTBROOK, Annick D. 2131 S 17TH ST, COASTAL AHEC 28401 #047-05-1993 L2003 **OBG** *020 †30

WESTRA, Igor. 1801 NEW HANVR MDCL PRK DR 28403 #032-01-1987 L1993 **OPH** *020 †35

WEYHER, John Edwin, Jr. ■ 28409 #041-02-1948 L1948 **U** *071 †95

WHITE, Kenneth Saml. 2305 CANTERWOOD DR 28403 #036-05-1983 L1984 **PS GS** *020 †85,65

WHITE, Warren Carlton. 2606 IRON GATE DR STE 201 28412 #045-01-1985 L1992 **PTH** *020 †50

WHITEHURST, Lee Albert. ■ 28405 #036-01-1972 L1972 **OSS** *020 †40

WHITEHURST, Walter C, Jr. 1025 MEDICAL CENTER DR, DELANEY RADIOLOGISTS 28401 #036-01-1968 L1968 **DR** *020 †18 ‡

WHITESIDES, Edward W. 1905 GLEN MEADE RD, UROLOGICAL ASSOC 28403 #036-01-1988 L1993 **U UP** *020 †95

WHITESIDES, Paul C, Jr. 1514 DOCTORS CIR, BLDG E 28401 #045-01-1977 L1982 **END** *020 †20

WHITTEN, Christopher John. 1602 PHYSICIANS DR 28401 #055-02-1984 L1989 **AN PME** *020 †05

WIEGMAN, Peter Jos. 1515 DOCTORS CIR, HANOVER MEDICAL SPECIALIST 28401 #045-01-1990 L2002 **CD** *020 †20

WILFONG, Robt Farrington. 2208 S 17TH ST, STE 201 28401 #036-07-1967 L1967 **NS** *020 †25

WILKINS, Lucien Sanders. 2131 S 17TH ST 28401 #051-04-1967 L1973 **GE IM** *071 †20

WILKINSON, Charles Albert. 2131 S 17TH ST 28401 #036-07-1956 L1956 **GS VS** *071 †85

WILLARD, Randall Norman. 3710 SHIPYARD BLVD, MEDAC/EASTERN CAROLINA EME 28403 #051-07-2001 L2004 **EM** *020 †16

WILLIAMS, Barton Gee. 2131 S 17TH ST 28401 #036-01-1989 L1990 **FM EM** *020 †18

WILLIAMS, Frank T. ■ 28409 #024-15-1947 L1949 **GP** *071

WILLIAMS, Matthew Michal. 8108B MARKET ST, WHA MEDICAL CLINIC, PLLC 28411 #023-01-1998 L2001 **FM** *020 †20

WILLIAMS, R Bertram, Jr. ■ 28403 #047-05-1943 L1949 **GS VS** *071 †85

WILLIAMS, Ross E. 1501 DOCK ST, DEVELOPMENTAL EVALUATION C 28401 #041-12-1972 L1998 **PD** *020 †55

WILLIAMSON, Joseph Edward. 3710 SHIPYARD BLVD, BCSP II, PA 28403 #036-01-1973 L1973 **FM** *020 †18,16

WILSON, Clarence L, II. 1809 GLEN MEADE RD 28403 #020-02-1974 L1977 **OBG** *020 †30

WILSON, Ewain P. 1202 MEDICAL CENTER DR 28401 #836-01-1982 L1998 **OTO** *020 †45

WILSON, Jack Kennedy, Jr. 637 S KERR AVE 28403 #027-01-1966 L1970 **IM OS** *020

WILSON, Robert Wayne. 2250 SHIPYARD BLVD STE 3, EVERGREEN BEHAVIORAL MGMT 28403 #036-08-1986 L1987 **P** *030 †75

WILSON, Steven Douglas. ■ 28405 #047-06-1986 L1987 **EM FM** *020 †18

WINNEBERGER, Ted Robison. 3710 SHIPYARD BLVD, PHYSICIANS, P.A. 28403 #039-01-1982 L1983 **EM** *020 †16

WITHERS, Sydnor T, Jr. 5058 WRIGHTSVILLE AVE 28403 #051-04-1973 L1976 **IM FM** *020 †18

WOLINS, Donald Morton. ■ 28412 #396-06-1964 L1966 **OBG** *071 †30

WOODS, Jonathan Bradley. ■ 28409 #036-01-2000 L2001 **NEP** *020 †20

WOODWORTH, Alfred Herman. 3710 SHIPYARD BLVD 28403 #035-03-1968 L1971 **EM FM** *020 †18

WORRIAX, James Doyle. ■ 28412 #047-07-2004 L2008 **FM** *100

WORTMAN, James Edward. 1902 MEETING CT 28401 #016-06-1974 L1978 **IM** *020 †20

WRIGHT, Brent Dean. 2131 S 17TH ST 28401 #028-03-1983 L2003 **OBG EM** *020 †30

WRIGHT, Lydia North. 2212 DELANEY RD 28403 #036-01-1989 L1992 **OBG MFM** *020 †30

WYNNEMER, Judith Ann. 119 CHESTNUT ST 28401 #056-05-1967 L1971 **IM** *075

XI, Fan. 2800 ASHTON DR STE 10 28412 #041-02-2001 L2005 **IM** *020

YATES, Jennifer Elaine. 2523 DELANEY RD, COASTAL FAM MED MHRMC 28403 #036-01-2002 L2003 **FM** *040 †18

YEARGAN, Sherman Austin, III. 2716 ASHTON DR, WILMINGTON ORTHOPAEDIC GRO 28412 #036-08-1997 L2006 **OSM OAR** *020 †20

YIP, Alex G. 2321 DELANEY RD, ALLERGY PARTNERS OF COASTA 28403 #024-05-1989 L1995 **AI PDA** *020 †55,03

YOFFE, Elizabeth Harrer. ■ 28403 #011-03-1977 L1982 **ON HEM** *020 †20

YOUNG, Stephen Lewis. 2222 WAVERLY DR 28403 #036-05-1983 L1995 **CCM IM** *020 †20

YUE, Byong Hak. ■ 28403 #583-06-1959 L1971 **GS PHP** *071

ZACK, Peter Geo. ■ 28403 #004-01-1960 L1970 **PD** *020 †20

ZAMORA, Ezequiel. ■ 28412 #270-02-2003 **IM** *012

ZAWADZKI, Cezary. ■ 28412 #759-18-2004 **IM** *012

ZEMAN, Peter Anton. 1905 GLEN MEADE RD 28403 #036-01-2000 L2005 **U** *020 †95

WILSON – WILSON

AL-HAIDARY, Anwar Darwish. 2503 WOOTEN BLVD SW 27893 #539-06-1981 L1993 **NEP IM** *020 †20

ALLEN, Rachel Diane. ■ 27893 #005-12-2005 L2008 **EM** *012

ANDERSEN, Susan Hollar. 1702 MEDICAL PARK DR W 27893 #036-08-1986 L1988 **PD** *020 †55

ANDERSON, Alton Ray. 4761 WARD BLVD 27893 #036-01-1977 L1980 **FM** *020 †18

ANDERSON, Dudley Buist. 1705 TARBORO ST SW 27893 #051-01-1964 L1971 **ON HEM** *020 †20

ANDERSON, Kent Thomas. 110 BRENTWOOD CENTER LN N 27896 #036-08-1982 L1983 **IM** *020 ‡

APPERT, Robert Albert. 1803 FOREST HILLS RD W 27893 #035-03-1971 L1976 **ORS** *020 †40

ASHRAF, Farasat Iqbal. 1705 TARBORO ST SW, WILSON MEDICAL CENTER 27893 #704-02-1990 L2000 **IMG** *020

ATKINS, James Norman. 2624 ORTHO DR W 27893 #036-05-1976 L1977 **ON IM** *020 †20

BAIO, Charles James. 200 GLENDALE DR W 27893 #011-02-1983 L1986 **IM** *020 †20

BARTON, Christine Ann. 200 GLENDALE DR W 27893 #031-01-1995 L1998 **IM** *020 †20

BATTAILE, Melinda June. 1705 TARBORO ST SW 27893 #023-01-1995 L2000 **IM** *020 †20

BOWEN, Michael Lynn. 2605 FOREST HILLS RD SW 27893 #017-20-1977 L1980 **FM EM** *020 †18

BOYD, Deborah D. 130 GLENDALE DR W 27893 #036-01-1977 L1977 **GS VS** *020 †85

BREWER, Douglas Carl. 1704 GLENDALE DR SW STE B 27893 #036-01-1974 L1974 **IM** *020 †20

BREZINA, Edward Sharp, Jr. 2500 HORTON BLVD SW 27893 #011-02-1975 L1981 **OBG** *020 †30

BRNA, Theodore Geo, Jr. 1705 TARBORO ST SW 27893 #051-04-1983 L1990 **FM** *020 †18

BUCK, John Hyunsoo. 1702 MEDICAL PARK DR W 27893 #035-03-1998 L2001 **PD** *020 †55

BULLARD, Hoke V, Jr. 2202 SULGRAVE DR NW 27896 #024-01-1951 L1951 **IM** *020 †20

BURDICK, Richard Lawrence. 200 GLENDALE DR W 27893 #051-01-1975 L1985 **IM** *020 †20 ‡

BURNETTE, J P. 2130 FOREST HILLS RD W, INTERNAL MEDICINE, LTD 27893 #036-05-1975 L1975 **IM** *020 †20 ‡

BUSCH, James Rowdon. 1702 MEDICAL PARK DR W 27893 #051-04-1972 L1984 **PD FM** *020 †55

BYNUM, Robert Wm, IV. 1704 GLENDALE DR SW STE H, WILL BYNUM MD, PA 27893 #036-01-1979 L1984 **NEP IM** *020 †20

CARTER, Kenneth Chas. 1705 TARBORO ST SW 27893 #036-05-1975 L1975 **EM** *020 †16

CASH, James Butler. 1705 TARBORO ST SW, WILSON MEMORIAL HOSPITAL 27893 #020-12-1977 L1983 **PTH PCP** *020 †50

CASSELL, Hershell Elmore. 1705 TARBORO ST SW, WILSON MEMORIAL HOSP ED 27893 #036-08-1993 L1995 **EM** *020 †20

CHANG, I-Wen. 2624 ORTHO DR W 27893 #036-05-2001 L2003 **HO** *020

CHHABRA, Ajinder Singh. 1709 MEDICAL PARK DR W, HEALTH SOUTH SURGECENTER 27893 #025-07-1987 L1994 **AN** *020 †05

CHRISTMANN, Linda M. 1705 TARBORO ST SW 27893 #048-14-1978 L2007 **PO OPH** *030 †35

CLARK, Edward Joseph, III. 1705 TARBORO ST SW 27893 #050-02-1995 L2001 **DR** *020 †80

CLARK, Lee Andrew. 1705 TARBORO ST SW 27893 #036-01-1956 L1956 **OPH** *071 †35

CRAVEN, William James. 2402 CAMDEN SW, STE 100 27893 #035-09-1988 L1990 **N** *020 †75

D'ANGELO, Paul Charles. 4908 PEBBLE BEACH CIR N 27896 #051-07-1995 L2001 **DR** *020 †80

DE GUEHERY, Lindsey E. 1812 GLENDALE DR SW, STE A 27893 #011-04-1979 L1984 **PUD SME** *020 †20

DEWALD, Jonathon Glen. 2605 FOREST HILLS RD SW 27893 #012-01-1980 L2007 **IM** *020 †20

DOYLE, Natalie Ann. 2806 WOOTEN BLVD SW 27893 #020-02-1995 L1998 **IM** *020 †20

EDMUNDSON, Marsha Overman. 4761 WARD BLVD 27893 #036-07-1978 L1979 **FM** *020 †18

FEKRAT, Sharon. 1707 MEDICAL PARK DR W 27893 #016-02-1991 L1998 **OPH** *020 †35

FIALLO, Amparito I. 303 GREEN ST E 27893 #016-42-1997 L2007 **FM** *020 †18 ‡

FITCH, Duane Douglas. 2402 CAMDEN SW STE 300, WILSON DIGEST DIS CTR PA 27893 #025-01-1979 L1982 **GE IM** *020 †20

FRANCIS, Richard Paul. 4761 WARD BLVD 27893 #008-02-1974 L1988 **GS GP** *020 †20

GHATE, Vijaykumar R. 2907 STEEPLE CHASE RD N 27896 #495-28-1960 L1971 **P GP** *020 †75

GLOVER, James Bunyan. 2506 NASH ST N, KIRKLAND & GLOVER GYNCLGY 27896 #036-01-1957 L1957 **GYN** *072 †30

GLOVER, Michael Griffin. 806 TARBORO ST W, P O BOX 7238 27893 #036-07-1983 L1990 **ORS** *020 †40

GREENLAW, Paul Reginald. 1803 FOREST HILLS RD W 27893 #024-07-1997 L2002 **ORS** *020

GRIFFIN, Stephanie Deal. 2546 WARD BLVD 27893 #036-08-1990 L1991 **FM** *020 †18

GRIFFIN, Thos La Fayette. ■ 27893 #012-01-1959 L1965 **U** *071 †95

GUAY, Paul Fernand. 1705 TARBORO ST SW, RADIOLOGY DEPT 27893 #035-09-1978 L1988 **DR GP** *020 †80 ‡

HAAS, David Robt. 1707 MEDICAL PARK DR W 27893 #041-02-1986 L1994 **OPH** *020 †35

HANSON, Arthur Henning. 2500 HORTON BLVD SW 27893 #010-01-1989 L1993 **OBG** *020 †30

HENCHEL, Kelly L. 1702 MEDICAL PARK DR W 27893 #025-07-1994 L1997 **PD** *020 †55

HERON, Kerrie-Anne A. 2402 CAMDEN ST SW, STE 800 27893 #036-07-1999 L2003 **IM** *020 †20

HOOPER, Thomas Eugene. 2130B FOREST HILLS RD W, MEDICINE, LTD 27893 #036-01-1973 L1973 **IM** *020 †20

ISAACS, George Coupland. 130 GLENDALE DR W 27893 #001-02-2002 L2005 **GS** *020 †85

JENNETTE, A T. 1803 FOREST HILLS RD W 27893 #036-01-1959 L1959 **ORS** *071 †40

JONES, Franklin Douglas. 1703 MEDICAL PARK DR W 27893 #051-07-1977 L1981 **NS EM** *020 †25

JONES, Jeffrey Emerson. 1705 TARBORO ST SW 27893 #055-02-1988 L1998 **DR** *020 †80

KAIROUZ, Jeanne Marie. 2605 FOREST HILLS RD SW, STE D 27893 #024-07-1997 L2007 **CD** *020 †20

KAIROUZ, Sebastien S. 2624 ORTHO DR W, SMOC 27893 #605-02-1995 L2007 **HO** *020 †20

KAVURU, Bush. 1705 TARBORO ST SW 27893 #495-11-1987 L1997 **P PYG** *020 †75

KRABILL, Lawrence David. 1725 TARBORO ST SW, WILSON IMMEDIATE CARE PA 27893 #038-40-1971 L1974 **IM EM** *020 †20

KUSHNER, Michael J. 1803 FOREST HILLS RD W 27893 #035-19-1977 L1990 **N PMM** *020 †75

LADWIG, Harold Allen. ■ 27893 #018-03-1947 L1978 **N** *071 †75

LAKSHMAN, Venkatesh. 2605 FOREST HILLS RD SW, WILSON GASTROENTEROLOGY 27893 #917-24-1990 L2005 **GE IM** *020 †20

LAWRENCE, Leesa Greer. 1702 MEDICAL PARK DR W 27893 #045-04-1990 L1993 **PD** *020 †55

LAZIO, Barbara Eileen. 1703 MEDICAL PARK DR W 27893 #038-41-1995 L2001 **NS** *020 †25

LEE, Kenneth Stuart. 1705 TARBORO ST SW 27893 #036-08-1981 L1983 **NS** *020 †25

LEMAIRE, Pierre-Arnaud. 130 GLENDALE DR W, WILSON SURGICAL ASSOCS 27893 #033-06-1985 L2004 **GS VS** *075 †85

LERRO, Keith Andrew. 2402 CAMDEN ST SW, STE 200 27893 #035-46-1997 L2003 **ON** *020 †20

LEWIS, Willis Edward. 1705 TARBORO ST SW, WILSON MEMORIAL HOSPITAL 27893 #036-05-1986 L1991 **PTH PCP** *020 †50

LI, Anson Sheungwai. 130 GLENDALE DR W, WILSON SURGICAL CENTER 27893 #036-07-1993 L1997 **GS** *020

LITTLE, Tonya Dee. 1704 GLENDALE DR SW, STE C 27893 #036-08-1996 L1997 **FM** *020 †18

LIU, Yu. 1705 TARBORO ST SW, WILSON MEDICAL CENTER 27893 #243-48-1992 L2006 **IM** *020 †20

LUND, John Jefferson. 2605 FOREST HILLS RD SW, WILSON CARDIOLOGY ASSOCIAT 27893 #051-01-1957 L1964 **CD IM** *020 †20

MABINE, Rita Kay. 2000 NASH ST N STE E 27893 #036-08-1998 L2003 **P** *020

MARSHALL, Manly Ernest. 2624 ORTHO DR W 27893 #051-01-1975 L1996 **ON HEM** *020 †20

MARTIN, Lewis Paul. 1803 FOREST HILLS RD W 27893 #051-04-1997 L2005 **ORS** *020 †40

MATACALE, Vaughn Mitchell. 1705 TARBORO ST SW, WILSON MEDICAL CENTER 27893 #041-15-2000 L2003 **IM** *020 †20

MATTOX, Huitt Everett. 1705 TARBORO ST SW 27893 #036-07-1954 L1954 **OBG** *071 †30

METTS, Jobe Coy, III. 2509 WOOTEN BLVD SW, WILSON UROLOGY 27893 #036-01-1991 L1993 **U** *020 †95

METTS, Margaret C. 1703 MEDICAL PARK DR W 27893 #047-05-1997 L2004 **RO** *020 †80

MICHALAK, Daniel Peter. 2500 HORTON BLVD SW 27893 #041-09-1980 L1984 **OBG** *020 †30

MUTYALA, Ramesh. ■ 27896 #495-65-1992 L2006 **IM** *020 †20

NELMS, Wallace Royce, Jr. 2546 WARD BLVD 27893 #012-01-1975 L1976 **FM** *020 †18

NEWSOME, George Edward. 1704 MEDICAL PARK DR W 27893 #036-01-1969 L1969 **OTO GS** *020 †45

PEREZ-NAVARRO, Paul A. 2605 FOREST HILLS RD SW 27893 #036-08-1991 L2001 **CD** *020 †20

PUGH, Christopher Brent. 2402 CAMDEN ST SW, STE 700 27893 #036-01-1997 L2001 **PCC** *020 †20

RAND, Tom Slade. 1705 TARBORO ST SW 27893 #036-01-1963 L1963 **ORS OS** *071 †40

RHODES, Cecil David. 2605 FOREST HILLS RD SW 27893 #036-05-1956 L1956 **IM** *071 †20

ROUNDER, James, Jr. 2509 WOOTEN BLVD SW, WILSON URO PA BOX 3329 27893 #004-01-1980 L1990 **U** *020 †95

RUSSELL, Joseph Dwight. 2503 WOOTEN BLVD SW 27893 #036-01-1969 L1969 **NEP IM** *020 †20

RYBURN, Samuel Benj. ■ 27896 #051-04-1954 L1957 **PD** *071

SAINT LOUIS, Immacula. 303 GREEN ST E, CAROLINA FAMILY HEALTH CEN 27893 #024-07-1993 L2005 **PD** *020 †55 ‡

SATTERFIELD, Robert N. 1705 TARBORO ST SW 27893 #051-04-1995 L2000 **ORS OSM** *020 †40

SATTERLY, R Alan. 2303 WELLINGTON DR SW # C 27893 #010-02-1972 L1977 **OTO** *020 †45

SEGLETES, Lori Ann. 1705 TARBORO ST SW 27893 #023-01-1995 L1996 **PTH** *020 †50

SEN, Bhupendra Lal. ■ 27896 #495-38-1952 L1963 **PUD IM** *071

SIDAROS, Medhat F. 110 BRENTWOOD CENTER LN N, WILSON MEDICAL ASSOCIATES, 27896 #915-05-1979 L2000 **ID** *020 †20

SIGMON, James Gregg. 4008 NC HIGHWAY 42 W 27893 #036-05-1985 L1987 **FM** *020 †18

SLOOP, Robert Felts, Jr. 1707 MEDICAL PARK DR W 27893 #036-01-1960 L1961 **OPH** *071

SMITH, Bradley Todd. 1803 FOREST HILLS RD W 27893 #036-05-1998 L2000 **OSM** *020 †40

SMITH, Jenny Grace. 2261 NASH ST NW 27896 #051-07-1998 L2000 **P** *020 †75

STARKEY, Suzanne. 2500 HORTON BLVD SW 27893 #038-40-1992 L1997 **OBG** *020 †30

STONE, Robert Thos. 2303 WELLINGTON DR SW # C 27893 #051-01-1965 L1972 **OTO** *020 †45

STOVER, John Oliver, Jr. 1705 TARBORO ST SW 27893 #051-04-1968 L1974 **DR NM** *020 †80

STREETER, Charles T. ■ 27896 #030-05-1945 L1955 **FM** *071

SUNDERMAN, Michael Robt. 1901 TARBORO ST SW 27893 #017-20-1977 L1980 **FM** *020 †18 ‡

TAYLOR, James Van, III. 1705 TARBORO ST SW 27893 #036-01-1980 L1981 **FM** *020 †18

THORNE, Darlene Cheryl. 1705 TARBORO ST SW, WILSON MEMORIAL HOSPITAL 27893 #036-01-1974 L1974 **PTH CLP** *020 †50

THURMAN, Roger Zalon. 1705 TARBORO ST SW 27893 #051-04-1965 L1972 **GS OM** *020 †85

TICKLE, Dewey Reid. ■ 27896 #036-07-1954 L1954 **R** *071 †80

TITUS, Anthony F. 1705 TARBORO ST SW, WILSON MEDICAL CENTER 27893 #038-45-1985 L2001 **FM** *020 †18

VAN BREE, Mark Preston. 2509 WOOTEN BLVD SW, WILSON UROLOGY PA 27893 #010-01-1989 L1995 **U** *075 †95

VANDEN BOSCH, Gerald C. 1803 FOREST HILLS RD W 27893 #025-07-1977 L1985 **ORS** *020 †40

VERMA, Krishna M. 1810 WESTWOOD AVE W 27893 #495-55-1970 L1990 **P** *020 †75 ‡

WESTER, Melissa King. 1700 TARBORO ST W, STE 102 27893 #036-08-2001 L2004 **FM** *020 †18

WESTER, Trent Wesley. 1700 TARBORO ST W, STE 102 27893 #036-08-2001 L2004 **FM** *020 †18

WHITAKER, James Allen, III. 2605 FOREST HILLS RD SW 27893 #036-01-1968 L1968 **CD IM** *020 †20

WILLIAMS, Martin Keith. 4761 WARD BLVD, NC SPECIAL CARE CENTER 27893 #036-08-1989 L1990 **P** *030 †75

WOODALL, Hal Breen. 1705 TARBORO ST SW 27893 #036-05-1975 L2006 **IM** *020 †20

WOODARD, Jerry Cleon. 2605 FOREST HILLS RD SW, WILSON GASTROENTEROLOGY PA 27893 #036-01-1968 L1968 **GE IM** *020 †20

WINDSOR – BERTIE

BROOKS, Ricky Lorenzo. 306 WINSTON LN 27983 #051-04-1982 L1987 **OBG** *020

DUNCAN, Hazel Vanessa. 104 RHODES AVE 27983 #275-01-1996 L2004 **FM** *020 †18 ‡

HARRIS, Phillip Gordon. 1403 S KING ST 27983 #036-08-1990 L1992 **FM** *020 †18

MADIGAN, Timothy Charles. 1403 S KING ST 27983 #305-01-2001 L2005 **FM** *020

SASEK, Milan. 401 STERLINGWORTH ST 27983 #286-11-1975 L1996 **IMG IM** *020 †20

YORK, Elizabeth Lane. 401 STERLINGWORTH ST 27983 #051-04-1982 L1985 **FM** *020 †18

WINNABOW – BRUNSWICK

THOMPSON, George R C. ■ 28479 #045-01-1939 L1942 **FM** *071

WINSTON-SALEM – FORSYTH

ABBOTT, Thomas Dean. 12208 N NC HIGHWAY 150 27127 #051-01-1983 L1984 **FM** *020 †18

ABDEL-RAOUF, Ahmed M. ■ 27101 #915-02-1986 **P** *012

ABERNETHY, Mary Katherine. ■ 27103 #036-05-2008 *012

ABRAMSON, Jon S. MEDICAL CENTER BLVD, WAKE FOREST UNIV, SCH OF M 27157 #036-05-1976 L1977 **ID PD** *050 †55

ADAIR, Norman Eugene. MED CTR BLVD 27157 #028-03-1973 L1981 **PUD CCM** *020 †20

ADAMS, Melanie. 186 KIMEL PARK DR 27103 #036-05-1989 L1993 **PD** *020 †55

ADAMS, Patricia Lee. MED CTR BLVD, DEPT OF MED/NEPH WFV SCHL 27157 #036-05-1974 L1974 **NEP** *020 †20

ADAMS, Wesley Harl. ■ 27103 #049-01-2004 L2008 **OPH** *012

ADCOCK, Eugene Wesley, III. MEDICAL CENTER BOULDEVARD, BOWMAN GRAY SCHOOL OF MEDI 27157 #036-05-1966 L1966 **NPM PD** *071 †55

ADDISON, Kevin Chancellor. WFUBMC, MEDICAL CENTER BLVD. 27157 #028-34-2000 L2006 **NPM** *055

ADKISSON, Victor T. 3333 SILAS CREEK PKWY 27103 #048-13-1987 L1994 **IM** *020 †20

ADLER, Michael L. MEDICAL CENTER BLVD 27157 #016-11-1973 L1990 **FM** *040 †18

AGARWAL, Mamta. WFUSM MEDICAL CENTER BLVD, DEPT OF NEPHROLOGY 27157 #495-41-1989 L2001 **NEP** *050

AGBORBESONG, Patience E. MED CTR BLVD 27157 #026-04-1997 L2000 **IM** *020 †20

AGGARWAL, Rahul. ■ 27127 #011-03-2001 L2006 **OD** *012

AHMAD, Bilal. ■ 27106 #495-51-1993 L2007 **IMG** *020 †20 ‡

AHMED, Rizwan. ■ 27157 #051-07-2003 L2007 **GE** *012 †20

AIKEN, Christopher Bruns. 632 HOLLY AVE 27101 #008-01-1999 L2001 **P** *020 †75

AJIBOYE, Norman A. OF MED, WAKE FOREST UNIV SCH 27157 #016-01-2005 **NS** *012

AJIZIAN, Samuel John. DEPT. OF ANESTHESIOLOGY, WAKE FOREST UNIV. HEALTH S 27157 #005-06-1989 L2001 **CCP** *020 †55

AKHTAR, Nadeem. 725 HIGHLAND AVE, DAYMARK RECOVERY SERVICES, 27101 #704-20-1989 L2002 **P** *020 †75

AKHTAR, Taha. ■ 27157 #704-25-2001 L2006 **IM** *100 †20

AKINOLA, Olayink Daniel. 3333 SILAS CREEK PKWY 27103 #690-01-1989 L2002 **IM** *020 †20

AKLILU, Mebea. MEDICAL CENTER BLVD, WAKE FOREST UNIV SCH OF MD 27157 #056-05-1998 L2004 **HO** *020 †20

AKMAN, Steven Alan. MED CTR BLVD 27157 #035-46-1975 L1995 **ON** *050 †20

ALBERTINI, Laurie Wng. MEDICAL CENTER BLVD 27157 #016-02-1993 L2002 **PD** *020 †55

ALBERTSON, David Allen. OF MEDICINE, WAKE FOREST UNIVERSITY SCH 27157 #051-01-1972 L1973 **GS OS** *020 †85

ALBERTSON, Elizabeth Ann. 140 KIMEL PARK DR 27103 #051-01-1991 L1992 **U** *020 †95

ALLEN, David Henry. ■ 27104 #028-02-1964 L1968 **CHP P** *071

ALLEN, Elizabeth Cobey. 3325 SILAS CREEK PKWY, DEPT OF PEDIATRICS 27103 #036-01-1985 L1987 **PD DBP** *040 †55

ALLEN, Elms Leach. 3333 SILAS CREEK PKWY, OFFICE OF MEDICAL AFFAIRS 27103 #036-05-1966 L1966 **ON HO** *050 †20

ALLEN, H Hamilton. 491 N CLEVELAND AVE 27101 #047-07-1957 L1965 **GS** *020 †85

ALLEN, Harvey H, Jr. 1959 PEACE HAVEN RD 27106 #036-05-1988 L1993 **IM GE** *020 †20

ALLEN, Stewart Glenn. ■ 27127 #036-05-2001 L2006 **OD** *012

ALMENGUAL, Terrence P. 3333 SILAS CREEK PKWY 27103 #011-03-1988 L1990 **AN** *020 †05

ALSON, Roy Lee. 121 POLO RD, NC-1 DMAT / NDMS / HHS 27105 #036-05-1985 L1988 **EM** *040 †16

ALSTON, Pamela Kaye. MEDICAL CENTER BLD 27157 #036-01-2001 L2005 **OBG** *020 †30

ALSUP, William Byrn. ■ 27106 #012-01-1940 L1947 **OTO** *071 †45

ALTASS, Jennifer Sylvia. 500 SHEPHERD ST STE 200, WFU PHYSICIANS OB/GYN 27103 #308-13-2001 L2006 **OBG** *020

AMIN, Aman Virendra. MED CTR BLVD, WAKE FOREST BAPT MED 27157 #012-22-2005 **IM** *012

AMITIE, Daniel Dean. MEDICAL CENTER BLVD, WFU SOM ANESTHSIOLOGY 27157 #017-20-2001 L2005 **CCA** *012 †05

AMPONSAH, Nana Kwame. ■ 27127 #016-06-2006 **NS** *012

ANDERSON, Anthony Shane. MEDICAL CENTER BLVD, WAKE FOREST SOM SECTION ON 27157 #045-01-2003 L2005 **RHU** *012 †20

ANDERSON, David Scott. 200 ROBINHOOD RD, MEDICAL PLAZA 27106 #020-02-2002 L2004 **PD** *020 †55

ANDERSON, Martha Torrey. MEDICAL CENTER BLVD 27157 #041-09-1989 L1992 **AN** *020 †05

ANDERSON, Robert Louis. 2830 MAPLEWOOD AVE STE B 27103 #030-06-1968 L1978 **OBG AM** *020

ANDERSON, Stephen G. 2927 LYNDHURST AVE 27103 #012-05-1963 L1964 **OBG** *020 †30

ANDREW, Raymond Hall. 250 CHARLOIS BLVD 27103 #016-11-1970 L1983 **P** *020 †75

ANDREWS, Danny Floyd. 250 CHARLOIS BLVD, WINSTON-SALEM HEALTH CARE 27103 #036-07-1983 L2005 **IM** *020 †20 ‡

ANDREWS, Mark Douglas. MED CTR BLVD 27157 #023-01-1977 L1982 **FM** *020 †18

ANGOBALDO TORRES, Jeff O. ■ 27127 #025-01-2002 L2008 **PS** *012

ANKNEY, Dana Elizabeth. ■ 27103 #036-05-2005 L2008 **PD** *012

ANTHONY, Evelyn Young. MED CTR BLVD 27157 #036-07-1996 L1998 **PDR** *020 †80

ANZ, Adam William. ■ 27127 #001-06-2006 **ORS** *012

ANZ, Bertrand Marquess. ■ 27127 #001-06-2004 L2006 **HO** *012 †20

APEL, Peter James. ■ 27103 #016-43-2006 **ORS** *012

APPLEGATE, Robert Jos. 1 MEDICAL CENTER DRIVE, OF MEDICINE, SEC OF CARDIO 27157 #051-01-1980 L1987 **CD IM** *020 †20

APPLEGATE, William Brown. MEDICAL CENTER BLVD, OFFICE OF THE DEAN WFUSM 27157 #020-02-1972 L1975 **IMG IM** *050 †20

ARCHER, Brent Joseph. ■ 27127 #001-02-2006 L2007 **IM** *012

ARGENTA, Louis Chas. MEDICAL CENTER BLVD, WAKE FOREST UNIV 27157 #025-01-1969 L1988 **PS** *020 †85,65

ARIAS, Lorraine Marie. MED CTR BLVD 27157 #051-04-1983 L1991 **AN** *020 †05

ARIZA, Fernando E. MEDICAL CENTER BOULEVARD, WAKE FOREST UNIVERSITY HEA 27157 #308-05-1990 L2001 **IM HOS** *020 †20

ARKFELD, Nichole Marie. ■ 27127 #038-41-2004 **IMG** *012 †20

ARMENTROUT, Mary E. 1900 S HAWTHORNE RD, PEDIATRICS 27103 #036-05-1998 L2002 **PD** *020 †55

ARMSTRONG, Deborah Austin. ■ 27103 #051-04-2002 L2002 **FP** *012

ARNAUD, Catherine H. 3333 BROOKVIEW HILLS BLVD, STE 105 27103 #048-16-1996 L2000 **OBG** *020 †30

ASHBURN, Joseph Charles. MED CTR BLVD 27157 #422-01-2007 **N** *012

ASSIMOS, Dean Geo. 140 CHARLOIS BLVD 27103 #016-43-1977 L1983 **U** *020 †95

ATALA, Anthony. 140 CHARLOIS BLVD 27103 #020-02-1985 L2004 **UP U** *020 †95

ATKINSON, Hal Huntley. MEDICAL CTR BLVD, STICHT CTR ON AGING 27157 #045-01-1998 L2000 **IM IMG** *020 †20

ATLURI, Kavitha Mummuneni. 250 CHARLOIS BLVD, WINSTON-SALEM HEALTH CARE 27103 #913-15-1997 L2006 **IM** *012

AUFFINGER, Susan. 3880 VEST MILL RD STE 100 27103 #035-15-1989 L1997 **FM** *020 †18

AUGOUSTIDES, Alexander T. 1411 PLAZA WEST DR 27103 #836-02-1985 L1992 **FM** *020 †18

AURINGER, Sam Thos. 3155 MAPLEWOOD AVE, TRIAD RADIOLOGY ASSOCIATES 27103 #035-15-1984 L1986 **PDR** *020 †80

AUSTIN, Clio Hamilton. 1930 PEACE HAVEN RD 27106 #041-13-1995 L2006 **PD** *020 †55

BADLANI, Charulata Gopal. WAKE FOREST UNIV MED CTR, DEPT OF NEURO REHAB DIV 27157 #495-17-1971 L2007 **PM** *020 †60 ‡

BADLANI, Gopal Hariram. 140 CHARLOIS BLVD 27103 #495-17-1973 L2007 **U** *020 †95 ‡

BAHRANI, Khosrow. 3111 MAPLEWOOD AVE STE 101 27103 #517-01-1962 L1973 **P PYG** *020 †75 ‡

BAILEY, Asha Lenora. ■ 27127 #041-77-2007 ▲ **IM** *012

BAILEY, Eugene Orell. BOWMAN GRAY S MED AFFL HOS 27103 #036-05-1983 **P** *100

BAILEY, Sara Lynn. ■ 27105 #036-05-1957 L1957 **GP** *020

BAILLIE, John. MEDICAL CENTER BOULEVARD, WAKE FOREST UNIV SCH 27157 #919-05-1977 L1988 **GE IM** *020

BAIN, Richard Morgan. MEDICAL CENTER BLVD, WAKE FOREST UNIV SCH MED 27157 #051-04-1998 L2005 **IMG PLM** *020 †20

BAINES, Patricia Ann. MEDICAL CENTER BOULEVARD, DEPT OF EMERGENCY MEDICINE 27157 #010-03-1993 L1996 **EM** *020 †16

BAKER, Alfred L. 3155 MAPLEWOOD AVE, FORSYTH RADIOLOGICAL ASSOC 27103 #036-05-1979 L1986 **DR** *020 †20,80

BAKER, Michael Dean. MED CTR BLVD 27157 #020-12-1994 L2000 **RNR** *020 †80

BALAMUCKI, Chris John. ■ 27103 #036-05-2007 **IM** *012

BALCH, Patty Joyce. 2828B MAPLEWOOD AVE 27103 #027-01-1985 L1986 **IM** *020

BALL, James Dale. MED CTR BLVD 27157 #016-06-1969 L1975 **NM R** *020 †80,28

BALLENGER, Claude Newton. ■ 27106 #051-01-1954 L1959 **PD CHP** *020 †55

BARBOUR, Meredith Faye. ■ 27103 #036-08-2005 L2008 **FP** *012

BARBOUR, Sarah Danialle. ■ 27103 #036-05-2007 **IM** *012

BARBOUR, Sarah Jane. ■ 27103 #048-14-2006 **AN** *012

BARNES, Craig Edwin. MEDICAL CENTER BLVD, DEPT OF RADIOLOGY, WFUSM 27157 #051-04-1987 L2001 **DR PDR** *040 †80

BARNETT, Heather Carpente. ■ 27103 #047-06-2005 L2006 **EM** *012

BARNETT, Ted Marcus. ■ 27127 #051-01-2004 **ORS** *012

BARNHART, Amanda. ■ 27103 #036-05-2004 L2008 **PD** *012

BARRETT, Heather H. ■ 27127 #016-11-2006 **OBG** *012

BARRY, David Werth. ■ 27103 #036-05-2008 *012

BARRY, Paul D. 1399 WESTGATE CENTER DR 27103 #035-06-1971 L1981 **OS** *030 †70

BARUCH, Amy Roseanne. 3333 SILAS CREEK PKWY, INPATIENT PHYSICIANS OF FO 27103 #036-05-1999 L2002 **IM** *020 †20

BASHER, Sharmin. ■ 27103 #045-01-2008 *012

BASRAI, Khaishoon N. 250 CHARLOIS BLVD 27103 #495-37-1991 L2004 **IM** *020 †20

BASS, David Alden. 300 S HAWTHORNE RD 27103 #023-07-1968 L1976 **ID** *050 †20

BATES, Shayne Ethan. ■ 27127 #055-02-2006 **PD** *012

BATHORY, Tamas Pa'L. 3333 SILAS CREEK PKWY 27103 #473-01-1986 L2001 **IM** *020 †20

BAUMAN, Loren Alec. MED CTR BLVD 27157 #030-05-1976 L1986 **CCM AN** *020 †55,05

BEARD, Eldon Severin. 1365 WESTGATE CENTER DR, STE C1 27103 #036-05-1982 L1983 **FM** *020 †18

BEASON, Edward Stewart. 1732 S HAWTHORNE RD 27103 #001-02-1963 L1964 **PS** *020 †85,65

BEATY, Laura M. 3RD FLOOR WATLINGTON, MEDICAL CENTER BOULEVARD 27157 #020-02-2002 L2004 **HO** *012 †20

BEATY, Michael Wesley. MED CTR BLVD 27157 #025-12-1994 L2000 **PTH** *020 †50

BECHER, Robert David. ■ 27101 #043-01-2006 **GS** *012

BECHTOLD, Robert Edmond. WAKE FOREST UNIV SCHL ME, DEPT OF RADIO 27157 #028-02-1979 L1983 **AR DR** *020 †80

BECK, Eric Wayne. 250 CHARLOIS BLVD 27103 #036-05-2000 L2004 **FM UCM** *020 †18

BECKMAN, Jennifer Kay. ■ 27103 #011-04-2007 **P** *012

BEEKMAN, James Frederic. ■ 27103 #038-43-2005 L2007 **IM** *012

BEISSWANGER, Amy Helen. ■ 27127 #036-05-2006 L2007 **PD** *020 †55

BELFORD, Peter Matthew. MEDICAL CENTER BLVD, WFUSM DEPT. INTERNAL MEDIC 27157 #036-05-2004 L2006 **IM** *100 †20

BELL, Alfred Dudley. 200 ROBINHOOD MEDICAL PLZ, FORSYTH PEDS AT ROBINHOOD 27106 #036-05-1993 L1995 **PD** *020 †55 ‡

BELL, William Lynn. DEPT OF NEURO, MEDICAL CENTER BOULEVARD 27157 #036-05-1977 L1978 **N CN** *020 †20,75

BELL, William O. 2810 MAPLEWOOD AVE, NEURO ASSOC CAROLINAS PA 27103 #041-09-1977 L1985 **NS** *020 †20

BELLE, John Stephen. ■ 27106 #036-08-2004 L2007 **HO** *012 †20

BELLINGER, Christina R. ■ 27157 #012-22-2006 L2007 **IM** *012

BENCHERIF, Badreddine. 1321 CROWNE PARK DR 27106 #125-01-1977 L2002 **NM** *020 †28

BENGTSON, Hans Carl. ■ 27103 #056-06-2007 **GS** *012

BENN, Dwight R. MEDICAL CENTER BLVD 27157 #035-15-2002 L2004 **NEP** *020 †20

BENNETT, Bernard Leroy. 3880 VEST MILL RD, STE 100 27103 #047-07-1980 L1993 **IM** *020 †20

BENNETT, Jerry Lee. 2808 MAPLEWOOD AVE 27103 #036-05-1967 L1967 **PD** *020 †55

BENSON, Paul Wesley. MED C, WAKE FOREST UNIV BAPTIST 27157 #045-04-2007 **IM** *012

BERGER, Valerie C. ■ 27106 #001-02-1999 L2000 **IM** *020 †20

BERGER, William Scott. 3333 SILAS CREEK PKWY 27103 #001-02-1999 L2004 **GS** *020 †85

BERGMAN, Simon. MED CTR BLVD 27157 #041-09-1992 L1999 **PCP** *050 †50

BERMAN, Jeffrey Michael. MEDICAL CENTER BLVD, DEPT ANES 27157 #847-01-1977 L1987 **AN CCM** *020 †20

BERRY, Michael Brandon. MEDICAL CENTER BOULEVARD, WAKE FOREST UNIVERSITY SCH 27157 #048-12-2001 L2005 **DR** *100 †80

BERTONI, Alain Gerald. MED CTR BLVD 27157 #023-07-1995 L2001 **IM EP** *050 †20

BERTRAM, Michael John. 170 KIMEL PARK DR, ORTHOPAEDIC SPECIALISTS OF 27103 #038-40-1999 L2007 **PM** *020 †60

BETTMANN, Michael Alfred. MEDICAL CENTER BOULEVARD, WFU SCHOOL OF MEDICINE-RAD 27157 #035-46-1969 L2005 **DR VIR** *020 †80

BEUTTEL, Stephen Chas. 190 KIMEL PARK DR, WINSTON-SALEM 27103 #036-07-1971 L1974 **END IM** *020 †20

BEY, Richard Doud. 1492 RYMCO DR 27103 #008-01-1979 L1983 **N CN** *020 †75

BHAMA, Anuradha Rani. ■ MED CTR BLVD 27157 #048-40-2007 **GS** *012

BHARTI, Gaurav. ■ 27104 #047-20-2006 **PS** *012

BIENENFELD, Maurice. 1400 WESTGATE CENTER DR, STE 200 27103 #041-09-1983 L1996 **IM** *020 †05

BIGGERSTAFF, Daniel Scott. 170 KIMEL PARK DR 27103 #012-01-2001 L2007 **OFA** *020

BILLINGS, Jack Smith. 1950 S HAWTHORNE RD 27103 #036-05-1958 L1959 **FM** *020 †18

BIRKEDAL, John Peter. MED CTR BLVD 27157 #030-06-1996 L2001 **ORS** *020 †40

BISSETTE, Stephen Glenn. 100 ROBINHOOD RD, MEDICAL PLAZA 27106 #036-05-1995 L1996 **FM** *020 †18

BITZAN, Martin. MED CTR BLVD 27157 #409-02-1980 L1998 **PD NEP** *020

BLACKBURN, Jeffrey Robert. ■ 27103 #045-04-2006 **IM** *012

BLACKHAM, Aaron Udell. ■ 27127 #038-41-2007 **GS** *012

BLACKSTOCK, Arthur W, Jr. MED CTR BLVD 27157 #036-08-1989 L1994 **RO** *020 †80

BLAIR, Russell Allen. MEDICAL CENTER BOUVELARD 27157 #038-43-2003 L2006 **PCC** *012 †20

BLAND, Deirdre Robinson. 201 EXECUTIVE PARK BLVD, BLUE RIDGE MEDICAL ASSOCIA 27103 #018-03-1987 L1993 **OBG** *020 †20

BLEECKER, Eugene R. NRC BLDG G53, MEDICAL CENTER BLVD 27157 #035-08-1968 L2001 **PUD IM** *050 †20

BLEVINS, Ashley Nicholl. ■ 27127 #047-20-2007 **AN** *012

BLEYER, Anthony John. MED CTR BLVD 27157 #048-04-1987 L1992 **NEP IM** *020 †20

BLOCK, Steven Martin. MEDICAL CENTER BLVD 27157 #836-01-1973 L1983 **NPM PD** *030 †55

BLOOMFELD, Richard Seth. MEDICAL CENTER BLVD 27157 #028-02-1994 L1996 **GE** *020 †20

BLOOMFIELD, Robert Lee. 1365 WESTGATE CENTER DR, G-1 27103 #036-07-1977 L1979 **IM** *020 †20

BLOUNT, Frederick A. ■ 27106 #041-01-1943 L1943 **PD CHP** *071 †55

BLUMSTEIN, Howard Andrew. MEDICAL CENTER BLVD, DEPT OF EMERGENCY MEDICINE 27157 #041-13-1990 L1999 **EM** *020 †16

BOGARD, Terrence Dale. 3333 SILAS CREEK PKWY, OB-ANESTHESIA/FORSYTH MED 27103 #056-06-1975 L1979 **AN OBG** *020 †05 ‡

BOGGS, Jane Gilbert. MEDICAL CENTER BLVD 27157 #051-04-1987 L2007 **N CN** *020 †75

BOHLE, David J. 186 KIMEL PARK DR, WINSTON-SALEM CARDIOLOGY 27103 #048-13-1989 L1992 **CD IC** *020 †20

BOHRER, Stanley Paul. MED CTR BLVD 27157 #024-01-1958 L1981 **DR PHP** *071 †80

BOKO, Tandeka S. ■ 27106 #018-03-1996 *100

BOLES, Carol Ann Hudak. MED CTR BLVD 27157 #038-44-1987 L1997 **DR OS** *020 †80

BOLIN, Elijah Holbrook. PO BOX 9431, WAKE FOREST UNIVERSITY 27109 #036-05-2007 **PD** *012

BOLINGER, Matthew Alan. ■ 27127 #038-40-2002 L2002 **OTO** *012

BOLLIG, Reagan William. ■ 27104 #001-06-2007 **GS** *012

BOLLING, Bruce Richard. 3001 MAPLEWOOD AVE, ARDMORE MEDICAL BUILDING 27103 #023-01-1981 L2000 **GS** *020 †85

BOND, Jeffrey Brent. MED CTR BLVD 27157 #047-05-1987 L1999 **OPH** *020 †35

BONFILI, Hubert Francis. 3801 N LIBERTY ST STE 210, SMITH REYNOLDS AIRPORT TER 27105 #028-34-1969 L1993 **OM AM** *071 †70,18 ‡

BONKOWSKE, Jeremy James. ■ 27127 #038-03-2006 **OPH** *012

BORCHELT, Bret David. 2827 LYNDHURST AVE 27103 #051-04-1991 L2000 **TS VS** *020 †85,90

BOURNE, Rae Lindsay. 1233 BRAEHILL TERRACE DR 27104 #010-03-1999 L2006 **RHU** *012 †20

BOWDEN, Amy Lynn. MED C, WAKE FOREST UNIV BAPTIST 27157 #045-01-2007 **IM** *012

BOWEN, Edwyn Taylor. 3746 VEST MILL RD 27103 #012-05-1955 L1961 **PD** *071 †55

BOWER, Stephen Lee. 185 KIMEL PARK DR, STE 100 27103 #055-01-1979 L1980 **DR RNR** *020 †80

BOWERS, Brandon Michael. ■ 27127 #019-02-2007 **IM** *012

BOWLING, Mark Rollin. ■ 27104 #036-08-2001 L2003 **PCC** *012 †20

BOWMAN, Kevin Michael. ■ 27103 #036-05-2008 *012

BOWTON, David Lowell. MEDICAL CENTER BLVD, ANESTHESIOLOGY/CRITICAL CR 27157 #016-11-1975 L1976 **PUD CCM** *020 †20

BOYCE, William H. MEDICINE, BOWMAN GRAY SCHOOL OF 27103 #041-01-1953 L1954 **U** *071 †75

BOYETTE, Gray Thos. ■ 27104 #036-05-1960 L1960 **IM GE** *071 †20

BOZEMAN, Elizabeth. ■ 27106 #045-04-1991 L2005 **FM GPM** *020 †70,18

BOZEMAN, William Pyle. MED CTR BLVD 27157 #045-01-1992 L2003 **EM** *020 †16

BRADBURY, David P. ■ 27103 #036-05-2008 *012

BRADEN, Gregory Alan. 200 ROBINHOOD MEDICAL PLZ 27106 #036-05-1982 L2004 **CD IM** *020 †20

BRADEN, Timothy Kevin. ■ 27127 #047-06-2005 **N** *012

BRADFORD, Barbara F. MED CTR BLVD 27157 #041-07-1972 L1990 **DR R** *050 †55,80

BRADFORD-KENNEDY, Djenaba. WFUBMC, HOUSE STAFF OFFICE 27157 #041-01-2000 L2002 DR *100 †80

BRADY, William Alex. 250 EXECUTIVE PARK BLVD 27103 #036-05-1970 L1970 N *020 †75

BRAITHWAITE, Adam Charles. 423 IVY GLEN DR 27127 #035-09-2002 L2003 DR *100 †80

BRANCH, Charles Leon, Jr. MEDICAL CENTER BLVD, BGSM MEDICAL CENTER 27157 #048-12-1981 L1983 NS *040 †25

BRANCH, James David. 224 TOWN RUN LN 27101 #010-03-1973 L1977 OPH *020

BRANHAM, H Ezell. 3333 BROOKVIEW HILLS BLVD, STE 109 27103 #045-01-1957 L1976 P CHP *020

BRAQUET, Ray M. ■ 27127 #021-06-2004 L2008 OBG *012

BRASHEAR, Allison. MEDICAL CENTER BLVD, WFUSM NEUROLOGY 27157 #017-20-1987 L2005 N *020 †75 ‡

BRASHER, Bruce. 250 CHARLOIS BLVD 27103 #036-07-1981 L1984 IM *020 †20

BRASWELL, Sherrill D, Jr. 105 VEST MILL CIR 27103 #036-05-1977 L1978 FM *020 †18

BRAVO, Julio R. 755 HIGHLAND OAKS DR, STE 101 27103 #042-01-1989 L2007 RHU IM *020 †20

BREGMAN, Benjamin Joseph. ■ 27101 #038-43-2006 IM *012

BRETT, Laura Kyle. ■ 27103 #036-05-2008 *012

BREWER, Jeffrey James. ■ 27127 #035-06-2005 L2006 GS *012

BRICE, Robert Saml, Jr. ■ 27106 #036-07-1960 L1960 GE IM *071 †20

BRITT, John Calvin. 110 CHARLOIS BLVD, ASSOCIATES, PA 27103 #036-07-1994 L1999 OTO *020 †45

BROCK, Margaret Funch. MED CTR BLVD 27157 #036-05-1994 L1995 AN *020 †05

BRODY, Jeffrey Arnold. 431 STAFFORDSHIRE RD 27104 #036-05-1989 L1990 DR *020 †80

BROWN, Kevin Nathaniel. 2025 FRONTIS PLAZA BLVD, STE 120 27103 #018-75-2002, ▲ L2007 CN *020

BROWN, Laurel A. ■ 27127 #048-16-2007 IM *012

BROWN, Malcolm Mc Dougal. 1900 S HAWTHORNE RD, STE 512A 27103 #035-01-1973 L1976 IM RHU *020 †20

BROWN, Thomas Lawrence. 2830 MAPLEWOOD AVE STE C 27103 #036-05-1977 L1982 OBG *020 †30

BROWN, Thomas Walter. MED CTR BLVD 27157 #038-06-1978 L1992 ADP PFP *075 †75

BROWN, Wm Ray, Jr. 3318 HEALY DR 27103 #036-05-1970 L1970 NS GS *020 †25

BROWNE, James Dale. MEDICAL CENTER BLVD, DEPT OF OTOLARYNGOLOGY WFU 27157 #012-01-1982 L1983 OTO NO *020 †45

BROWNING, Douglas Guy. 1903 S HAWTHORNE RD, SPORTS MEDICINE ASSOCIATES 27103 #036-05-1989 L1991 FSM FM *020 †20

BRUGGEN, Joel Thos. MED CTR BLVD 27157 #019-02-1983 L1998 IM *020 †20

BRUMM, Matthew Vincent. ■ 27103 #023-07-2007 IM *012

BRUNSTETTER, Richard W. 300 S HAWTHORNE RD 27103 #035-01-1955 L1988 CHP P *020 †75

BRYANT, Alton E, III. 2025 FRONTIS PLAZA BLVD, STE 120 27103 #051-04-1989 L2005 N *020 †75

BUCHANAN, Catherine Keys. MEDICAL CENTER BLVD, MEDICAL CENTER, STICHT CEN 27157 #036-05-1999 L2003 IM *020 †20

BUCKALEW, Vardaman Moore. MEDICAL CENTER BOULEVARD, WAKE FOREST UNIVERSITY HEA 27157 #041-01-1958 L1973 NEP IM *020 †20

BUHR, Gwendolen Toni. 3880 VEST MILL RD, STE 100 27103 #048-13-1998 L1999 IMG *020 †20

BURDEN, Susan Katharine. 27104 #025-01-2001 L2005 OPH *100 †35

BURDETTE, Jonathan Hill. MED CTR BLVD 27157 #047-06-1993 L1997 RNR *020 †80

BURGESS, Theresa C. 3821 FORRESTGATE DR 27103 #051-07-1980 L1985 P FM *020 †75

BURKART, John Mark. MEDICAL CENTER BLVD., WAKE FOREST UNIV. SCH. OF 27157 #016-01-1979 L1980 NEP IM *020 †20

BURKE, Gregory Leo. MED CTR BLVD 27157 #018-03-1981 CLP *050

BURNETT, Henry Warren. 110 OAKWOOD DR, STE 380 27103 #023-01-1989 L1996 OPH *020 †35

BURNS, Cynthia Anne. MEDICAL CENTER BLVD, WFUBMC-DEPT OF ENDOCRINOLO 27157 #036-05-2000 L2003 END *100

BUROW, Bethanie Kristin. MEDICAL CENTER BOULEVARD., WAKE FOREST SCHOOL OF MEDI 27157 #026-08-2003 L2006 AN *100

BURROW, James Scott. MEDICAL CENTER BLVD, DEPT. OF EMERGENCY MEDICIN 27157 #001-06-2005 L2007 EM *012

BUSLER, Jacob Forrest. ■ 27103 #047-05-2006 PTH *012

BUSS, David Humphrey. MEDICAL CENTER BLVD, WAKE FOREST UNIV 27157 #036-05-1966 L1966 PTH *020 †50 ‡

BUSS, Ryan Dean. ■ 27103 #017-20-2003 L2006 DR *012

BUTLER, Jerome Mack, Jr. ■ 27103 #036-05-2003 L2006 RO *012

BUTLER, Marcella M. 3155 MAPLEWOOD AVE, ATTN: ROXANNA LEONARD 27103 #047-07-1993 L2004 DR IM *020 †80

BYRUM, James Edwin, Jr. ■ 27106 #036-05-1968 L1968 EM *071

BYUN, Peggy Ann. 2808 MAPLEWOOD AVE, WINSTON-SALEM PEDIATRICS 27103 #036-01-1999 L2000 PD *020 †55

CABRERA, Maria Linda Tumb. ■ 27104 #748-02-1990 L2007 FM *100 †18

CAICEDO, Jennifer Laiacon. ■ 27103 #011-03-2002 L2005 AI *012 †55

CAICEDO, Ricardo Andres. ■ 27103 #011-03-2000 L2006 PG *100 †55

CALICOTT, Randy Wayne. MED CTR BLVD 27157 #047-06-1992 L2004 AN *020 †05

CALLES-ESCANDON, Jorge. MED CTR BLVD 27157 #649-01-1976 L2002 DIA *040 †20

CAMPBELL, Chas Bruce, III. 2827 LYNDHURST AVE, STE 204 27103 #051-01-1976 L1978 OPH PS *020 †35

CAMPBELL, Justin Doyle. ■ 27127 #001-06-2007 IM *012

CAMPOS, Claudia Lucia. 170 KIMEL PARK DR 27103 #264-04-1995 L2005 IM *020 †20,60

CAMPOS, Kevin Michael. ■ 27105 #036-05-2006 EM *012

CANN, Thomas Woodward, III. 3333 SILAS CREEK PKWY 27103 #036-05-1971 L1971 IM IMG *020 †20

CANNON, Karen Saville. 1900 S HAWTHORNE RD, PEDIATRICS 27103 #055-01-1990 L1995 PD *020 †55

CANNON, Michael Louis. MED CTR BLVD 27157 #036-08-1992 L1995 CCP *020 †55

CANNON, Thomas Bernard. 100 ROBINHOOD MEDICAL PLZ 27106 #036-01-1973 L1973 FM *020 †18

CANTLEY, Larry Keith. MEDICAL CENTER BLVD, WAKE FOREST UNIV SCH MED 27157 #055-01-1977 L1980 END *020 †20

CAPIZZANI, Tony Richard. MEDICAL CENTER BLVD, WFUBMC 27157 #047-06-2003 L2007 GS *012

CAPPELLARI, James Oliver. MED CTR BLVD 27157 #051-04-1985 L1989 PTH *020 †50

CARBONE, Dominick John. MEDICAL CENTER BLVD 27157 #025-01-1990 L2007 U *020 †95

CARD, John Patrick. 250 CHARLOIS BLVD 27103 #016-43-1994 L1997 IM *020 †20

CARESS, James Bayard. MEDICAL CENTER BLVD, DEPT OF NEUROLOGY 27157 #010-01-1990 L1996 N *020 †75

CARLSON, Kenneth Paul. 2932 LYNDHURST AVE 27103 #012-05-1955 L1965 U *072 †95

CARLTON, Will Yarborough. 2200 SILAS CREEK PKWY, STE 1A 27103 #036-05-1980 L1982 P FM *020 †75

CARNES, Jason Anthony. ■ 27103 #045-04-2008 *012

CARPISASSI, Melinda Dubos. ■ 27101 #036-08-2006 DR *012

CARR, David Ruddle. 3333 SILAS CREEK PKWY 27103 #036-07-1986 L1991 GS *020 †85

CARR, John Jeffrey. 2000 W 1ST ST STE 618 27157 #047-06-1989 L1991 DR PHP *050 †80

CARROLL, Mark Blanchard. 1311 WESTBROOK PLAZA DR 27103 #047-06-1991 L1997 CHP P *020 †75

CARTER, Aaron Michael. ■ 27107 #036-05-2005 L2006 AN *012

CARTER, Iverson Brooks. DEPARTMENT OF PSYCHIATRY, MEDICAL CENTER BOULEVARD 27157 #036-08-2004 L2005 CHP *012

CARTER, Jeffrey Eric. ■ 27106 #047-20-2005 GS *012

CARTER, Margaret F. ■ 27104 #036-05-1975 L1975 AN *071 †05

CARTWRIGHT, Michael S. OF MED, WAKE FOREST UNIV SCH 27157 #036-05-2002 L2006 N *020 †75

CARTWRIGHT, Sarah Lieber. MEDICAL CENTER BOULEVARD, WFUBMC 27157 #036-05-2002 L2004 FM *100 †18

CASE, Kimberly A. 101 HOSPICE LN 27103 #048-15-2004 L2007 FM *020 †18

CASERTA, Melanie Pockey. ■ 27127 #011-03-2003 L2006 R *100

CASHWELL, Leon F. MED CTR BLVD 27157 #036-01-1972 L1972 OPH *035

CASIMIR, Fitzgerald J. ■ 27127 #024-07-2000 L2008 GS *012

CASTELLANO, Vincent Paul. 3333 SILAS CREEK PKWY 27103 #035-06-1991 L1994 AN *020 †05

CASTELLINO, Sharon M. MEDICAL CENTER BOULEVARD, HEALTH SCIENCES BUILDING-D 27157 #036-07-1992 L1994 PHO *012

CASTILLO-NIEVES, Aida L. 725 HIGHLAND AVE, 2ND FL 27101 #042-02-1991 L2005 P *020 †75

CATH, Anne. 755 HIGHLAND OAKS, STE 102 27103 #038-06-1986 L2005 IM *020 †20 ‡

CAUTHEN, Natalie Causby. 1381 WESTGATE CENTER DR 27103 #045-04-1999 L2006 ID *020 †20

CAWOOD, Walter L. ■ 27104 #020-02-1946 L1993 R *071 †80

CAYWOOD, Devin Traer. ■ 27103 #048-04-2007 IM *012

CELESTINO, Frank Saml, Jr. 3RD FL PIEDMONT PLZ 1, MEDICAL CENTER BLVD 27157 #035-45-1978 L1984 FM FPG *040 †18

CHAMOVITZ, Allen H. 3880 VEST MILL RD, STE 100 27103 #020-02-1978 L2007 FM *020 †18

CHAN, Brandie Carmen. ■ 27103 #020-02-2007 PD *012

CHANDLER, Edgar Ted. MED CTR BLVD 27157 #036-01-1955 L1955 IM *020 †20

CHANDOS, Brandon James. 2025 FRONTIS PLAZA BLVD, STE 120 27103 #048-15-1992 L2005 CN *020 †75

CHANG, Michael Chiming. MED CTR BLVD 27157 #001-02-1987 L1994 CCS *020 †85

CHAO, Simon Wenwei. ■ 27157 #036-05-2003 L2004 AN *100

CHAPMAN, David Brandon. ■ 27107 #036-08-2006 OTO *012

CHASE, Chere Monique. 3333 SILAS CREEK PKWY, BOX 100 27103 #023-01-1997 L2003 N *020

CHATTERJEE, Arjun Bijoy. MEDICAL CENTER BLVD, CARE MEDICINE 27157 #038-41-1994 L2000 PCC OM *050 †20

CHAUVIN, Nancy A. ■ 27127 #035-15-2001 L2006 DR *012 †55

CHEE, Edwin Hawkman. 1381 WESTGATE CENTER DR 27103 #036-05-1992 L1994 IM *020 †20

CHEN, Michael Y M. BOWMAN GRAY SCH OF MED/RAD 27103 #243-16-1964 DR *050

CHEN, Peter Chang. ■ 27101 #036-05-2008 *012

CHEWNING, John Thomas. 160 CHARLOIS BLVD 27103 #011-03-1997 L2002 N *020 †75

CHILES, Caroline. MED CTR BLVD 27157 #036-07-1979 L1984 DR *020 †80

CHIN, Robert, Jr. MEDICAL CENTER BLVD, DEPT OF PULMONARY 27157 #010-01-1978 L1988 PUD IM *020 †20

CHIPMAN, Joseph Nathan. ■ 27103 #305-01-2004 L2008 N *012

CHOU, Carolyn Chiafen. MEDICAL CENTER BLVD, DEPT OF PEDIATRICS 27157 #026-04-1996 L2000 PD *020 †55

CHOWDHURY, Sharif M. 1901 S HAWTHORNE RD, STE 310 27103 #160-02-1989 L2004 GE *020 †20

CHRISTAKOS, Chris N. 105 VEST MILL CIR 27103 #036-05-1990 L1993 FM FSM *020 †18

CHRISTIAANSE, Mary E. MED CTR BLVD 27157 #038-40-1983 L1986 PD OS *062 †55

CHRISTIE, Jason Wayne. ■ 27127 #036-02-2006 GS *012

CHUNG, Edward. 3333 SILAS CREEK PKWY, CAROMONT INTERNAL MEDICINE 27103 #001-06-1999 L2001 IM *020 †20

CLARK, Clarence F, Jr. 190 KIMEL PARK DR, DEPT OF VA AFFAIRS 27103 #036-05-1948 L1949 GP PD *020 †55

CLARK, Hollins Peel. MED CTR BLVD 27157 #045-01-1994 L2000 DR *020 †80

CLARK, Jerry Randall, Jr. MED CTR BLVD 27157 #041-13-1997 L2001 AN *020 †05

CLARK, Margaret Anne. ■ 27104 #038-06-1979 L1982 IM *071 †20

CLARK, Paige Bennett. MED CTR BLVD 27157 #045-01-1999 L2000 NM *020 †28

CLARKE, Susan Oonagh. 1834 WAKE FOREST DR 27109 #539-04-2002 FSM *100

CLARKE, Thomas Lawrence. 501 N CLEVELAND AVE 27101 #047-07-1959 L1960 OBG *071 †30

CLAY, Kimberly Denise. ■ 27104 #036-01-2004 L2005 END *012 †20

CLEAVER, William Paul. 301 S HAWTHORNE RD, WAKE FOREST UNIV SCH OF ME 27103 #036-05-2006 IM *012

CLIFFORD, Barbara Ann. 200 ROBINHOOD MEDICAL PLZ, PLAZA DR 27106 #038-41-1983 L1990 PD *020 †55

CLINCH, Joanne Marie. ■ 27106 #033-06-1989 L2001 FM *020 †18

CLINE, David Martin. MED CTR BLVD 27157 #025-07-1982 L1985 EM *020 †16

CLINE, Lisa Senter. ■ 27104 #036-08-1993 *074

CLINGAN, Mary Jennings. ■ 27103 #036-05-2006 DR *012

CLOUSE, Jolene Renee. MED CTR BLVD, WAKE FOREST U 27157 #017-20-2003 L2006 FOP *012 †50

CLYNE, Brittany Bergin. MED CTR BLVD 27157 #036-05-2000 L2003 AN *100 †05

COATES, Michael Lee. MEDICAL CENTER BLVD, WAKE FOREST UNIV SCHOOL OF 27157 #051-04-1974 L1982 FM AMF *040 †18,16

COFIELD, Kattron Rhodes. ■ 27106 #036-05-2005 IM *012

COHEN, Gail Michelle. MED CTR BLVD 27157 #024-01-1995 L2003 PD *040 †55 ⸿

COHEN, Samuel David. ■ 27127 #036-05-2004 L2007 OTO *012

COLE, Jeffrey Randall. ■ 27101 #001-02-2004 GS *012

COLE, Paul Donald. 250 CHARLOIS BLVD 27103 #016-11-1980 L2002 DR *020 †20,80

COLEMAN, Jacob Charles. ■ 27127 #018-03-2006 **IM** *012

COLLIER, Keva Wontoria. ■ 27127 #036-05-2008 *012

COLLINS, David Dutrow. 3333 BROOKVIEW HILLS BLVD, STE 207 27103 #036-07-1975 L1983 **PUD CCM** *020 †20

COLLINS, John Kerry, Jr. 4410 PROVIDENCE LN, STE I 27106 #036-08-1997 L1998 **EM** *020 †16

COLLINS, Steven Wayne. 3333 SILAS CREEK PKWY 27103 #055-01-1983 L1984 **EM** *020 †16

COLLINS, William Stuart. ■ 27104 #036-07-1960 L1960 **P** *020 †75

COLLINSON, E Frank. ■ 27104 #919-05-1963 L2001 **DR NM** *072 †80

COLONNA, David Mayo. 3333 SILAS CREEK PKWY 27103 #051-04-1982 L1992 **GS** *020 †05

COMER, Robert Wallace. MED C, WAKE FOREST UNIV-BAPTIST 27157 #047-06-2003 L2007 **ID** *012 †20

COMERFORD, Aurora Jean. ■ 27103 #051-04-2004 **DR** *012

CONDON, Erik James. ■ 27127 #036-05-2005 L2006 **AN** *012

CONNOLLEY, Christopher D. 1901 S HAWTHORNE RD, STE 310 27103 #001-06-1999 L2005 **GE** *020 †20

CONNOR, Rebecca Fischer. ■ 27157 #035-03-2001 L2004 **HO** *100

CONNORS, Ngina. MEDICAL CENTER BLVD, WAKE FOREST UNIVERSITY 27157 #041-01-1997 L2002 **OBG** *020

CONRAD, Elizabeth. ■ 27104 #023-07-1943 L1946 **PD** *071 †55

CONTAG, Stephen Arthur. WAKE FOREST UNIVERSITY SC, OBSTETRICS AND GYNECOLOGY 27157 #319-01-1984 L2006 **OBG** *100

CONWAY, Jason David. ■ 27157 #036-01-1999 L2002 **GE** *100 †20

COOK, David Owen. 140 KIMEL PARK DR 27103 #036-05-1984 L1985 **U** *020 †95

COOK, Steven Lee. 114 CHARLOIS BLVD 27103 #023-01-1986 L1987 **OBG** *020 †30

COOPER, Jack Marshall. ■ 27127 #001-06-2007 **GS** *012

COOPER, Miles Robert. 300 S HAWTHORNE RD 27103 #036-05-1962 L1962 **ON HEM** *071 †20

COOPER, Stewart. 7990 N POINT BLVD, STE 100 27106 #067-01-1978 L1998 **FM** *020 †18

COPELAND, G Brent. 101 HOSPICE LN, HOSPICE & PALLIATIVE CARE 27103 #036-05-1988 L1995 **IM** *020 †20

COPELAND, Maike Naumann. ■ 27104 #033-06-1988 L1995 **IM PD** *020 †55,20

COPELAND, Stephen Jeffrey. MED CTR BLVD 27157 #038-40-1984 L1985 **AN** *020 †05

CORDELL, Alfred Robt. MEDICAL CENTER BLVD, DEPT CARDIOTHORACIC SURG 27157 #023-07-1947 L1950 **TS** *071 †85,90

CORRIERE, Matthew Abraham. ■ 27103 #012-22-1999 L2006 **VS** *012

COTOMAN, Dan Nicolae. ■ 27103 #781-05-1998 **P** *012

COUTURE, Daniel Edward. MEDICAL CENTER BLVD, DEPT NEUROSURGERY 27157 #051-01-2000 L2007 **NS** *100

COVITZ, Wesley. MEDICAL CENTER DRIVE, BOWMAN GRAY SCHOOL OF MEDI 27157 #038-41-1970 L1989 **PDC PD** *020 †55

COWAN, Robert Jenkins. ■ 27106 #036-01-1963 L1963 **NM NR** *071 †80,28

CRAIG, William Lewis, III. 170 KIMEL PARK DR 27103 #036-01-1993 L1998 **ORS** *020 †40

CRAVEN, Brandon Lee. ■ 27127 #036-05-2008 *012

CREECH, Elizabeth Ann. MEDICAL CENTER BLVD 27157 #036-01-1995 L1996 **NEP** *020 †20

CREGAN, Gregg Edward. 170 KIMEL PARK DR 27103 #041-02-1978 L1981 **ORS HS** *020 †40

CREQUE, Halimena M. 3000 BETHESDA PL, STE 801 27103 #036-05-1984 L1986 **P** *020 †75

CREWS, James C. UNIVERSITY SCHOOL, WAKE FOREST 27157 #021-06-1984 L1997 **AN** *020 †05

CROOK, Jerry Jackson, II. ■ 27127 #047-05-2003 L2006 **CD** *012 †20

CROSS, Karen Lynn. 101 HOSPICE LN, HOSPICE & PALLIATIVE CARE 27103 #031-01-1984 L2006 **IM** *020 †20 ‡

CROUSE, John Robt. MEDICAL CENTER BLVD, WAKE FOREST UNIV SCHOOL OF 27157 #035-08-1969 L1981 **IM** *050 †20

CROWE, John Albert, Jr. 190 KIMEL PARK DR, VA OUTPATIENT CLINIC 27103 #012-01-1967 L1974 **GS** *020 †85

CROWELL, Giles Franklin. 175 KIMEL PARK DR, STE 125 27103 #036-05-1979 L1980 **N** *020

CROWLEY, Mckay Bensen. ■ 27106 #045-01-2007 **IM** *012

CROZIER, James Eeds. 3073 TRENWEST DR 27103 #048-14-1981 L1999 **CD IM** *020 †20

CRUTCHLEY, Teresa Ann. ■ 27103 #031-01-2001 L2006 **VS** *012

CUDA, Jeremy Francis. OF MED, WAKE FOREST UNIV SCH 27157 #055-02-2006 **DR** *012

CULLEN, Peter Patrick. 250 CHARLOIS BLVD 27103 #035-15-1972 L1978 **IM** *020 †20

CULLER, Christopher Patri. ■ 27127 #051-01-2008 *012

CUNNINGHAM, Amanda Ring. 2017 WILLIAMSBURG MANOR CT 27103 #027-01-2003 L2008 **END** *012 †20

CUNNINGHAM, Jeffrey J. ■ 27103 #027-01-2003 L2008 **OTO** *012

CURL, Walton Wright. MEDICAL CENTER BLVD 27157 #036-07-1974 L1987 **ORS EM** *020 †40

CURRIE, Donald Patrick. 140 KIMEL PARK DR 27103 #036-07-1966 L1966 **U** *020 †95

CUTRI, Joseph John. 1868 RUNNYMEDE RD 27104 #010-02-1953 L1954 **P** *020 †75

DAEIHAGH, Pirouz. MEDICAL CENTER BLVD, WFUBMC - NEPHROLOGY 27157 #017-20-1993 L1999 **NEP** *020 †20

DALE, Andrew M. 3155 MAPLEWOOD AVE, FORSYTH RADIOLOGICAL ASSOC 27103 #048-02-1995 L1996 **FM** *020 †18

DALE, Andrew Mc Lean. 3155 MAPLEWOOD AVE 27103 #047-05-1981 L1990 **DR** *020 †80

DALTON, Timothy John. 1995 BETHABARA RD 27106 #047-20-1991 L1995 **IM PD** *020 †55,20

DAM, Quyen. 301 S HAWTHORNE RD, WAKE FOREST UNIV SCH OF ME 27103 #036-05-2007 **PD** *012

D'ANGELO, Robert. 3333 SILAS CREEK PKWY, OB ANES FORSYTH MED CTR 27103 #055-01-1987 L1991 **AN** *030 †05

DANZIGER, Sanford Emanuel. 3983 HSA CIR 27101 #048-04-1965 L1965 **P GPM** *020

DASHER, Lance Geoffrey. MEDICAL CENTER BLVD, WAKE FOREST UNIVERSITY BAP 27157 #012-01-2004 L2007 **DR** *012

DAVID, Lisa Renee. MEDICAL CENTER BLVD, DEPT OF PLASTIC SURG 27157 #017-20-1991 L1994 **PS** *020 †85,65

DAVIS, Asha Sherald. ■ 27127 #048-02-2006 **P** *012

DAVIS, Courtland H, Jr. MEDICAL CENTER BLVD 27157 #051-01-1944 L1952 **NS OS** *071 †25

DAVIS, Florence Elizabeth. 1373 WESTGATE CENTER DR, STE 210 27103 #036-05-1981 L1983 **P** *074 †75

DAVIS, James M, III. 3155 MAPLEWOOD AVE 27103 #036-01-1973 L1992 **R** *020 †80

DAVIS, John Blevins. 3333 SILAS CREEK PKWY 27103 #036-05-1980 L1985 **U** *020 †95

DAVIS, Jonathan Michael. MEDICAL CENTER BOULEVARD 27157 #021-06-2000 L2004 **IC** *012

DAVIS, Paul Lawson, III. ■ 27104 #036-05-2006 **OTO** *012

DAVIS, Ross Parker. ■ 27103 #001-02-2003 **GS** *012

DAVIS, Wayne E. PO BOX 24369 27114 #036-07-1949 L1954 **U** *071 †95

DAY, James Wm. 1381 WESTGATE CENTER DR 27103 #047-06-1975 L1981 **IM** *020 †20

DAY, Jennifer Beth. 1381 WESTGATE CENTER DR 27103 #055-02-1991 L1994 **PCC** *020 †20

DEAL, Dylan Nicole. 131 MILLER ST 27103 #045-01-2000 L2007 **ORS** *100

DEAN, J Christine. 1311 WESTBROOK PLAZA DR 27103 #308-07-1982 L1987 **N** *020

DEAN, Richard Henry. MEDICAL CENTER BLVD, WAKE FOREST UNIV SCHOOL OF 27157 #051-04-1968 L1987 **VS GS** *030 †85

DE COMARMOND, Charles A. MEDICAL CENTER BOULEVARD, WFU SCHOOL OF MEDICINE 27157 #286-03-1996 L2004 **ID** *020 †20

DE COMARMOND, Martina. ■ 27104 #286-03-1996 L2007 **PTH** *012

DECOOK, Charles Adam. MEDICAL CENTER BLVD, DEPT ORTHOPAEDICS 27157 #016-01-2002 L2003 **ORS** *012 †18

DEEN, Jason Brant. MEDICAL CENTER BOULEVARD 27157 #036-08-2002 L2007 **RNR** *012 †80

DEFEO, David. 3333 SILAS CREEK PKWY 27103 #041-15-2001 L2004 **PCC** *020

DE FRANZO, Anthony John. MEDICAL CENTER BLVD, DEPT OF PLASTIC SURG 27157 #010-01-1973 L1981 **PS HS** *020 †85,65

DEIBLER, Andrew Robert. 2636 BELWICK VILLAGE DR 27106 #045-01-2003 L2006 **DR** *012

DEKLE, Larry Carlton. 250 CHARLOIS BLVD 27103 #012-05-1968 L1977 **P** *020 †55,75

DE LA TORRE, Ernesto E. 2135 NEW WALKERTOWN RD, COMMUNITY CARE CTR 27101 #275-01-1952 L2006 **NS** *071 †25

DELIARGYRIS, Efthymios N. MEDICAL CENTER BOULEVARD, CARDIOLOGY 27151 #418-01-1991 L1997 **IC** *020 †20

DE MAESENEER, Michel. MEDICAL CENTER BOULEVARD, DEPARTMENT OF RADIOLOGY 27157 #165-06-1990 L2005 **R** *040

DEMONS SHEGOG, Jamehl L. MEDICAL CENTER BOULEVARD, J. PAUL STICHT CENTER 27157 #012-05-1994 L1996 **IM IMG** *020 †20

DENHAM, John Wm. 3333 SILAS CREEK PKWY 27103 #036-05-1966 L1966 **IM** *071 †18,20

DENISON, Adam Benj, Jr. ■ 27103 #038-06-1945 **GS** *071

DENIZARD, Nancy M. MEDICAL CENTER BOULEVARD, GENERAL INTERNAL MEDICINE 27157 #036-05-2002 L2006 **IM** *100 †20

DENSON, Rebecca Louise. MEDICAL CENTER BLVD 27157 #036-01-1994 L1999 **CCA** *020 †05

DEONANAN, Joel Krishna. ■ 27103 #036-05-2004 **GS** *012

DE TOLEDO, Joao Carlos. MEDICAL CENTER BLVD., DEPT OF NEUROLOGY 27157 #187-81-1981 L2007 **N** *020 †75

DEW, Jason Scott. MED CTR BLVD 27157 #055-01-2000 L2006 **VS** *100 †85

DEWAN, David Michael. 3333 SILAS CREEK PKWY, FORSYTH MEMORIAL HOSP 27103 #036-05-1971 L1971 **AN** *071 †05

DIBARI, Mauro. WAKE FOREST UNIVERSITY BMC, STIEGHT CENTER AGING 27157 #561-06-1983 L2000 **IMG CD** *020

DICKINSON, Paul Jos. MED CTR BLVD 27157 #048-04-1992 L2000 **OPH** *020 †35

DIERISSEAU, Patricia. WAKE FOREST U BAPTIST MED, DEPT OF INTERNAL MED 27157 #036-05-2004 L2007 **IM** *020 †20

DILLARD, Robert Guerard. DEPT OF PEDIATRICS, WAKE FOREST UNIV SCHOOL OF 27157 #008-01-1968 L1974 **NPM PD** *020 †55

DILLEY, James Richard. 730 HIGHLAND OAKS DR, STE 103 27103 #055-01-1974 L1982 **NEP IM** *020 †20

DI SANTIS, David J. MEDICAL CENTER BOULEVARD, DEPT OF RADIOLOGY 27157 #041-01-1979 L2006 **DR** *020 †80 ‡

DISON, Daniel Irwin. ■ 27127 #036-05-2008 *012

DITTMAR, Amy Michelle. OF MED, WAKE FOREST UNIV SCH 27157 #036-01-2004 **PTH** *012

DOANE, John Horton, Jr. ■ 27106 #041-01-1944 L1976 **IM** *071

DOCKERY-HOWARD, Pamela S. 2295 E 14TH ST 27105 #036-01-1983 L1985 **PD** *020 †55

DOLBARE, Emily Larae. ■ 27127 #001-02-2003 L2005 **NEP** *012 †20

DONGRE, Shrikumar Shripad. 3333 SILAS CREEK PKWY 27103 #496-38-1970 L1976 **AN** *020 †05

DORF, Erik Robert. ■ 27106 #007-02-2002 L2002 **HSO** *012

DOUTHIT, Jeffrey Jerome. ■ 27103 #036-05-1988 **FM** *100

DOWNEY, Lucy B. 1930 PEACE HAVEN RD 27106 #055-01-1984 L1985 **PD** *020 †55

DOYLE, Gregory Wm. MEDICAL CENTER BLVD 27157 #649-13-1981 L1987 **DR** *020

DRAFTS, Brandon Christian. ■ 27104 #045-04-2008 *012

DREVLAND, Synnoeve Saeter. MED CTR BLVD 27157 #693-04-2005 **IM** *012

D'SOUZA, J Vincent. MED CTR BLVD 27157 #495-33-1971 L1978 **R CD** *020 †80

DU BOSE, Thos Durward, Jr. 3RD FLOOR, WATLINGTON HALL, DEPT OF INTERNAL MEDICINE 27157 #001-02-1970 L2002 **NEP IM** *050 †20

DUCKETT, Charles Howard. ■ 27104 #036-05-1957 L1957 **FM** *071 †18

DUDLEY, Joseph Boyles. 3333 SILAS CREEK PKWY, FORSYTH MEM HOSP 27103 #041-01-1957 L1961 **PTH BBK** *071 †50

DUDLEY, Michael Eric. DEPT OF ANESTHESIOLOGY, MEDICAL CENTER BLVD. 27157 #041-15-2004 L2008 **AN** *012

DUNCAN, Brian Matthew. 3333 SILAS CREEK PKWY 27103 #036-08-2001 L2005 **EM** *020 †16

DUNCAN, David Allen. 2827 LYNDHURST AVE 27103 #011-03-1984 L1992 **TS** *020 †90,85

DUNDEE, David Thos. 3880 VEST MILL RD STE 100, PHYSICIANS ELDERCARE PA 27103 #041-13-1990 L2002 **FPG GP** *020

DUONG, Hai-Lang. MEDICAL CENTER BOULEVARD, DEPT OF OB/GYN 27157 #018-03-2001 L2006 **OBG** *020

DYER, Christopher Cornell. 190 KIMEL PARK DR, VA OUTPATIENT CLINIC 27103 #036-05-1989 L1992 **IM EM** *020 †20

DYER, Raymond Bruce. CENTER BLVD, UNIVERSITY MEDICAL 27157 #051-01-1977 L1983 **R AR** *040 †80 ‡

DYER, Raymond Douglas. ■ 27104 #051-04-1956 L1956 **FM EM** *071

EAKIN, Sarah Marie. ■ 27127 #041-15-2007 **PTH** *012

EARLY, I Gordon. 3333 SILAS CREEK PKWY 27103 #036-05-1950 L1950 **IM** *071 †20

EBERLE, Robert Adam. MEDICAL CENTER BLVD 27157 #036-05-1982 L1984 **IM** *020 †20

EDMONDS, John Henry. MED CTR BLVD, BOWMAN GRAY SCHOOL OF MED 27157 #036-05-1956 L1956 **CD IM** *071 †20

EDMUNDS, Suzanne Marie. MED CTR BLVD 27157 #005-06-1989 L2004 **CCP** *020 †55

EDSALL, Jason William. 3125 CREIGHTON LN 27127 #036-05-2000 L2001 **EM** *020

EDWARDS, Angela Fariss. MED CTR BLVD 27157 #036-05-1999 L2000 **AN** *020 †05

EDWARDS, Matthew Stevens. MED CTR BLVD 27157 #051-01-1995 L1996 **VS** *020 †85

EDWARDS, Palmer. 2990 BETHESDA PL STE 604A 27103 #036-05-1979 L1985 **CHP P** *071 †75

EGGERS, Gerald Wood. 3333 SILAS CREEK PKWY, DEPT OF PATH 27103 #001-06-1978 L1989 **PTH FOP** *020 †50 ‡

EGNATZ, Dennis Grant. 1520B MARTIN ST STE 206, OCCUP MED SOLUTIONS 27103 #008-01-1967 L1995 **OM FM** *020 †70,18

EICHINGER, Brian Michael. ■ 27103 #036-05-2008 *012

EICHMAN, Dave Steven. ■ 27106 #036-05-2005 L2007 **AN** *012

EICKMAN, John Patrick. ■ 27103 #037-01-2004 **NS** *012

EISENACH, James Conrad. 3333 SILAS CREEK PKWY, FORSYTH MEM HOSP 27103 #005-02-1982 L1986 **AN** *050 †05

ELESHA, William. 3333 SILAS CREEK PKWY 27103 #605-01-1945 L1953 **GS** *071 †85

■ = Address Information Privacy Protected

ELLIOTT, Harold Walker. WFU BMC MED CTR BLVD, DEPT OF PSYCHIATRY 27157 #045-01-1989 L1992 **P** *020 †75

ELLIS, Leslie Renee. MEDICAL CENTER BOULEVARD, COMPREHENSIVE CANCER CENTE 27157 #036-01-2000 L2006 **HO** *020

ELLIS, Thomas Leon. MED CTR BLVD 27157 #036-01-1993 L2000 **NS** *020 †25

ELSEY, Richard Lloyd, II. 3880 VEST MILL RD, STE 100 27103 #039-01-2001 L2004 **IMG** *020 †18

ELSTER, Allen De Vaney. MEDICAL CENTER BLVD, WFUBMC 27157 #048-04-1980 L1986 **DR** *030 †80

EMERSON, Kara Victoria. WFUBMC, DEPT OF PHYSICHIATRY 27157 #047-06-2005 **P** *012

EMERY, Terrylynne Adele. ■ 27103 #036-05-1989 L1993 **OBG** *020 †30

EMORY, Cynthia L. ■ 27127 #012-01-2004 **ORS** *012

ENGLISH, Betsy Maurice. 250 CHARLOIS BLVD 27103 #036-01-1989 L1991 **IM** *020 †20

ENNISS, Toby Merrill. ■ 27127 #049-01-2003 L2008 **GS** *012

ENRICH, Steven Daniel. ■ 27127 #035-03-2004 **OTO** *012

ENTRIKIN, Daniel William. MEDICAL CENTER BOULEVARD, WAKE FOREST UNIVERSITY SOM 27157 #005-18-2001 L2004 **DR** *020 †80

ERICKSON, Carrie Joy. 1900 S HAWTHORNE RD, PEDIATRICS 27103 #056-05-2004 L2007 **PD** *020 †55

ERNEST, Jos Mc Donald, III. DEPT STUDENT AFFAIRS, BOWMAN GRAY SCHOOL OF MED 27157 #027-01-1978 L1981 **MFM OBG** *020 †30

ERVIN, Sean Edward. MEDICAL CENTER BOULEVARD, GENERAL INTERNAL MEDICINE 27157 #665-01-1999 L2005 **MPD** *020

ESHAM, William Elwood. ■ 27104 #038-40-2003 L2007 **AN** *100

EVANS, Andrew Bennett. ■ 27103 #012-01-2006 **N** *012

EVANS, Aubrey Jackson. 140 KIMEL PARK DR 27103 #036-01-2002 L2007 **U** *020

EVANS, Charles B. 2830 MAPLEWOOD AVE STE B 27103 #011-04-1984 L1988 **GYN** *020 †30

EVANS, Lisa Smith. 3333 SILAS CREEK PKWY 27103 #011-04-1984 L1989 **RO** *020 †80

EVERETT, R Scott. ■ 27104 #027-01-2005 L2007 **EM** *012

EZEIGBO, Walter Azubuike. 7990 N POINT BLVD, STE 100 27106 #051-07-1992 L1996 **FM FSM** *020 †18

FAGG, John Anderson. 2901 MAPLEWOOD AVE 27103 #036-05-1971 L1971 **PS** *020 †65

FALLER, Nancy Irene. 160 KIMEL FOREST DR, STE 100 27103 #028-78-1984, ▲ L1994 **AN** *020 †05

FARLAND, Sandra Faye. ■ 27106 #051-04-2006 L2008 **FP** *012

FARMER, Tracie Christine. 730 HIGHLAND OAKS DR, STE 202 27103 #011-03-2002 L2007 **END** *020 †20

FARNEY, Alan Christopher. DEPT OF GEN SURGERY WAT-5, MEDICAL CENTER BOULEVARD 27157 #035-45-1987 L2003 **GS** *020 †85

FARRAH, Jason Paul. ■ 27114 #011-05-2006 L2008 **GS** *012

FARRELL, Melanie Tirronen. ■ 27106 #036-05-2007 **IM** *012

FARRELL, Patricia Carolyn. 1365 WESTGATE CENTER DR, STE M1 27103 #036-05-1987 L1988 **P** *020 †75

FAYNBOYM, Natalya B. G FLOOR, MEDICAL CENTER BLVD, STICH 27157 #036-05-2001 L2007 **PM** *020 †60

FEELY, Theodore Stevens. MEDICAL CENTER BOULEVARD, DEPARTMENT OF NEPHROLOGY 27157 #036-05-2003 L2005 **NEP** *012 †20

FEIEREISEL, Kirsten Brant. MEDICAL CENTER BLVD, WFUHS 27157 #023-01-2001 L2004 **IM** *100 †20

FEIG, Kevin Paul. 799 HIGHLAND AVE, HEALTH 27101 #035-09-1988 L2006 **AN** *020 †70

FELDMAN, Steven Richard. MEDICAL CENTER BLVD, WAKE FOREST SCHOOL OF MEDI 27157 #036-07-1985 L1987 **D DMP** *020 †15 ‡

FENNIMORE, Blair Preston. 301 S HAWTHORNE RD, WAKE FOREST UNIV SCH OF ME 27103 #036-05-2006 L2006 **IM** *012

FERGUSON, Robert Donald G. 3155 MAPLEWOOD AVE 27103 #065-09-1981 L2001 *020

FERGUSON, William Clay. 3333 SILAS CREEK PKWY 27103 #036-01-1960 L1960 **GS OS** *020 †85

FERNANDEZ, Adolfo Z, Jr. MEDICAL CENTER BLVD, DEPT OF SURGERY 27157 #036-07-1997 L2003 **GS** *020 †85

FERNANDEZ, Andrea S. 4 MEDICAL CENTER BLVD, WATLINGTON HALL 27157 #051-04-1999 L2003 **OBG** *020 †30

FERNANDEZ, Peter Mark. 145 KIMEL PARK DR, STE 330 27103 #045-01-2003 L2007 **PMM** *012

FIERY, Hubert Leroy. 250 CHARLOIS BLVD, NOVANT HEALTH 27103 #023-01-1976 L1997 **FM** *020 †18

FILER, Anne Catherine. ■ 27127 #036-05-2007 *012

FINA, Michael Francis. 1901 S HAWTHORNE RD # 310, PIEDMONT GASTRLGY SPECLTS 27103 #035-09-1975 L1980 **GE IM** *020 †20

FINCH, Robert Edwin, Jr. MEDICAL CENTER BLVD, WFUBMC DEPT PSYCH 27157 #036-01-1979 L1981 **P EM** *020 †20

FINK, James Thos. 600 HIGHLAND OAKS DR, PRIMECARE/NOVANT 27103 #035-06-1984 L1985 **EM FM** *020 †18

FINKLEA, Lee Kilpatrick. 1351 WESTGATE CENTER DR, FORSYTH PEDIATRICS PA 27103 #045-01-1979 L1983 **PD** *020 †55

FINN, Richard Connell. 250 CHARLOIS BLVD 27103 #021-01-1963 L1977 **OBG** *071 †30

FISCHER, Robert Michael. ■ 27103 #036-05-2008 *012

FISHER, Christen Julia. ■ 27103 #036-05-2003 L2006 **EM** *100

FISHER, David. ■ 27103 #036-05-2004 **PS** *012

FISHER, David Andrew. MEDICAL CENTER BLVD, WAKE FOREST UNIVERSITY BAP 27157 #016-01-2001 L2002 **IMG** *020 †18

FISHER, William Sloan, III. 110 CHARLOIS BLVD, PIEDMONT EAR, NOSE, AND TH 27103 #036-07-1974 L1974 **OTO** *071 †45

FITCH, Michael Thomas. MEDICAL CENTER BLVD., WAKE FOREST UNI HEALTH SCI 27157 #038-06-2001 L2002 **EM** *020 †16

FITZGERALD, David Michael. MED CTR BLVD 27157 #021-05-1980 L1989 **CD IM** *020 †20

FITZGERALD, Vera Ellen. 190 KIMEL PARK DR, DEPT OF VA AFFAIRS - OUTPA 27103 #748-10-1982 L1991 **IM** *020 †20

FLEISCHER, Alan B, Jr. MEDICAL CENTER BLVD, DEPT OF DERMADOLOGY-WFUSM 27157 #028-03-1987 L1988 **D** *020 †15

FLEMING, Charlene Jaquett. ■ 27127 #036-05-2006 **PD** *012

FLEMING, Shawn Howard. ■ 27127 #036-05-2004 **GS** *012

FLETCHER, Sarah Violet. MED C, WAKE FOREST UNIV BAPTIST 27157 #047-20-2007 **IM** *012

FLEZZANI, Paolo. 3333 SILAS CREEK PKWY 27103 #561-01-1977 L1982 **AN** *020 †05

FLOYD, Herbert Mynatt. MED CTR BLVD 27157 #036-05-1971 L1973 **AN** *020 †05 ‡

FOLDS, William Franklin. 2801 LYNDHURST AVE 27103 #036-05-1962 L1962 **FM PD** *020 †18

FOLEY, Joseph Dayton. MEDICAL CENTER BLVD, WAKE FOREST UNIV 27157 #005-12-2004 L2006 **CD** *012 †20

FONTANA-PENN, Mary E. INTERNAL MED - PULMONARY, MEDICAL CENTER BLVD 27157 #305-01-1986 L2003 **AI PD** *020 †20,55,03

FONTRIER, Toinette Helen. DEPT OF ANESTHESIA, BOWMAN GRAY SCHOOL OF MED 27157 #035-03-1978 L1983 **AN GS** *075 †05

FORD, Robert Virgil, Jr. 1900 S HAWTHORNE RD, PEDIATRICS 27103 #036-05-1971 1971 **PD** *020 †55

FOREMAN, Arthur S, Jr. MED CTR BLVD 27157 #036-05-1981 L1985 **AN** *020 †05

FOREST, Daniel Jordan. MED CTR BLVD 27157 #305-01-2005 **AN** *012

FORMANEK, Augustine. 300 S HAWTHORNE RD, DEPT OF RADIOLOGY 27103 #286-03-1947 L1980 **DR PD** *020 †80

FORSBERG, Clay Garrett. ■ 27103 #035-45-2006 **PS** *012

FORSBERG, Thomas Martin. MEDICAL CENTER BOULEVARD, DEPARTMENT OF EMERGENCY ME 27157 #035-06-2006 L2007 **EM** *012

FORTUNATO, John E, Jr. MEDICAL CENTER BOULEVARD, DEPARTMENT OF PEDIATRICS 27157 #024-07-1995 L2006 **PG** *100 †55

FOSTER, Bobby Maxwell. 3880 VEST MILL RD, STE 100 27103 #036-05-1957 L1957 **FPG** *071 †18

FOSTER, John Brian. WAKE FOREST UNIV EYE CTR, MED CTR BLVD 27157 #012-05-2006 **OPH** *012

FOSTER, Laura Culp. 140 KIMEL PARK DR 27103 #036-01-1996 L1997 **U** *020 †95

FOWLER, Reginald Jaye. 3333 SILAS CREEK PKWY 27103 #045-01-1996 L2003 **PCC** *020 †20

FOX, William Rhodes. 3333 BROOKVIEW HILLS BLVD, STE 109 27103 #036-05-1996 L1998 **P** *020 †75

FOY, Eleanor J Meschan. MEDICAL CTR BLVD, WAKE FOREST UNIV SCH OF MD 27157 #036-01-1971 L1971 **PD** *040 †55

FRANCK, George Henry. MEDICAL CENTER BLVD (DEPT, WAKE FOREST UNIVERSITY 27157 #017-20-1955 L1993 **OM GPM** *030 †70

FRANK, Harrison Gabriel. ■ 27104 #041-02-2007 **GS** *012

FRANKLIN, Walter Wayne. 250 CHARLOIS BLVD 27103 #036-01-1973 L1973 **PD CHP** *020 †55

FRAZIER, William David. ■ 27127 #011-02-2004 **OTO** *012

FREDERICK, Justin Allen. ■ 27106 #051-01-2004 L2007 **DR** *012

FREEDMAN, Barry Ira. MED CTR BLVD 27157 #035-08-1984 L1987 **NEP IM** *020 †20

FREIMANIS, Atis K. ■ 27113 #407-21-1951 L1956 **DR** *071 †80

FREIMANIS, Rita Irene. MEDICAL CENTER BLVD, DEPT OF RADIOLOGY WFUBMC 27157 #036-05-1985 L1987 **DR** *020 †80

FRENCH, Whitney James. 3333 SILAS CREEK PKWY 27103 #036-07-1982 L1988 **IM** *020 †20

FRIEDLAND, Carl Kampton. WINFIELD RIDGE DRIVE 27103 #041-01-1939 L1980 **IM** *071 †20

FRIEDMAN, Roland Morris. 140 KIMEL PARK DR 27103 #051-04-1988 L1992 **U** *020 †95

FRIESEN, Carrie Gabrielle. ■ 27104 #036-05-2005 L2007 **PD** *012

FRINO, John. MEDICAL CENTER BLVD, DEPT OF ORTHOPAEDICS 27157 #036-05-2000 L2006 **OP** *020

FRIZZELL, Bart Alan. MEDICAL CENTER BLVD 27157 #047-06-1996 L2001 **RO** *020 †80

FROMENT, Amand Marie. MEDICAL CENTER BLVD, NCBH DEPT OF ANESTH 27157 #017-20-2003 L2004 **AN** *020

FROMSON, Gerald A. 250 CHARLOIS BLVD, WINSTON SALEM HEALTH CARE 27103 #036-01-1977 L1980 **IM** *020 †20

FROMSON, Jean Veasey. 250 CHARLOIS BLVD 27103 #036-01-1977 L1980 **IM** *074 †20

FULLER, Lance Robert. MEDICAL CENTER BLVD, DEPT OF PSYCHIATRY WFUBMC 27157 #036-05-2003 L2007 **P** *012

FULLER, Stanley Brian. 3333 SILAS CREEK PKWY 27103 #036-05-1990 L1991 **CRS** *020 †10,85

FULORIA, Mamta. MEDICAL CENTER BLVD, DEPT OF PEDIATRICS 27157 #495-05-1992 L1998 **NPM** *020 †55

FUNDERBURK, Amon Lex. 250 EXECUTIVE PARK BLVD, PARK CENTER 27103 #036-05-1966 L1966 **END IM** *020 †20

FURBERG, Curt. BOWMAN GRAY SCH OF MED 27104 #858-03-1963 **IM** *040

FURLONG, Heather Marie. ■ 27127 #020-02-2000 L2006 **NPM** *100 †55

FURROW, Anne Paige Clifto. ■ 27107 #051-01-2004 L2007 **GS** *012

FUSSELL, Kevin Michael. 3001 LYNDHURST AVE, SALEM CHEST SPECIALSTS 27103 #012-01-1997 L2004 **PCC** *020 †20

GABY, Nancy Sue. 3000 BETHESDA PL STE 101 27103 #036-05-1978 L1980 **P** *020 †75

GADI, Rajyalakshmi. ■ 27127 #495-65-2002 L2007 **IM** *100 †20

GADI VENKATA VIZAYA, Bhask. ■ 27127 #495-11-2000 L2007 **IM** *020 †20

GAINOR, Charles Jos. 3333 SILAS CREEK PKWY 27103 #036-05-1984 L1985 **FM** *020 †18

GALBREATH, John Wallace. 1381 WESTGATE CENTER DR 27103 #045-01-1993 L2006 **IM** *020 †20

GALLAHAN, William Colin. ■ 27127 #051-01-2004 **GE** *012 †20

GALLUP, Kenneth R. 3333 SILAS CREEK PKWY 27103 #036-05-1973 L1973 **PUD IM** *020 †20

GAMBLE, Elizabeth Rhodes. ■ 27104 #036-01-1977 L1980 **IM** *040 †20

GANDHI, Lauren B Adams. 3333 BROOKVIEW HILLS BLVD, STE 204 27103 #045-01-1992 L1996 **D** *020 †15

GANDHI, Parag Dinesh. 2025 FRONTIS PLAZA BLVD, WINSTON SALEM 27103 #035-47-2000 L2006 **OPH** *020 †35

GANDHI, Sanjay Kumar. MED CTR BLVD 27157 #047-05-1992 L1996 **CD** *020 †20

GANSS, William Eugene. ■ 27103 #035-19-1948 L1950 **CHP** *071

GARDNER, Alison Rachel. MEDICAL CENTER BLVD 27157 #017-20-2001 L2004 **PD** *100 †55

GARDNER, James Douglas. 1351 WESTGATE CENTER DR 27103 #051-01-1987 L1996 **PD** *020 †20,55

GARDNER, Jeffrey C. ■ 27103 #036-05-2005 L2007 **AN** *012

GARRETT, Jeffrey Paul. ■ 27104 #036-08-2004 **ORS** *100

GARRISON, Michael Stephen. 1381 WESTGATE CENTER DR 27103 #036-01-1979 L1980 **IM** *020 †20 ‡

GARVIN, Abbott Julian. MED CTR BLVD 27157 #045-01-1972 L1997 **PTH** *030 †50

GARZA, Gabriel Rudolph. ■ 27103 #048-02-2007 **P** *012

GASSER, Tyler George. ■ 27103 #036-05-2008 *012

GEARY, Randolph Lee. MED CTR BLVD 27157 #054-04-1986 L1994 **VS GS** *020 †85

GEE, Christopher Jordon. WAKE FOREST UNIV EYE CTR, MED CTR BLVD 27157 #038-06-2006 **OPH** *012

GEER, Carol P. OF MED, WAKE FOREST UNIV SCH 27157 #023-07-1993 L2008 **RNR** *012 †80

GEISINGER, Kim R. MEDICAL CENTER BLVD, WAKE FOREST UNIV SCHOOL OF 27157 #041-07-1976 L1982 **ATP CLP** *020 †50

GELFAND, David Wm. DOWMAN GRAY MED SCH RAD 27103 #008-01-1962 L1975 **DR** *020 †80

GENDRACHI, Thomas. 3333 SILAS CREEK PKWY 27103 #654-01-1997 L2007 **AN** *020 †05

GERANCHER, John Chas. MEDICAL CENTER BLVD, WAKE FOREST UNIVERSITY BAP 27157 #041-01-1990 L1995 **AN** *020 †05

GERANCHER, Karen R. MED CTR BLVD 27157 #011-03-1993 L1999 **AN** *020 †30

GIANINI, Angela Mcclellan. ■ 27103 #011-03-2003 L2007 **PD** *100 †55

GIANINI, John William. ■ 27103 #011-03-2002 L2007 **R** *100 †80

GIBBONS, Jacquelyn Elaine. 3333 SILAS CREEK PKWY 27103 #045-01-1989 L1999 **AN** *020 †05

GIBSON, John Heyl. ■ 27107 #036-05-2002 L2006 **N** *020 †75

GIBSON, Kathleen. MEDICAL CENTER BLVD 27157 #036-01-1990 L1996 **PTH** *020 †50

GIBSON, Mary Campagna. ■ 27127 #016-45-2004 **N** *012

GIBSON, Robert L. ■ 27106 #051-04-1952 L1971 **AN** *020 †05

GIBSON, Robert Wylie, Jr. 3333 SILAS CREEK PKWY 27103 #036-05-1968 L1968 **P** *071 †75

GIEGENGACK, Matthew. ■ 27101 #035-01-2002 L2007 **OPH** *100

GILBERT, Henry Tucker. ■ 27106 #012-01-1969 L1976 **DR** *071 †80 ‡

GILBERT, Kemery Linay. ■ 27157 #036-05-2003 L2007 **PCP** *012 †50

GILBERT, Ryan Max. ■ 27157 #049-01-2004 **OTO** *012

GILLESPIE, Sarah E. MEDICAL CENTER BLVD, DEPT OF ANESTHESIA 27157 #047-06-1995 L2003 **AN GS** *020 †05

GILLIAM, John Hugh, III. 1129 W 4TH ST 27101 #051-04-1970 L1978 **GE IM** *020 †20

GILLIAM, Ryan Dwain. MEDICAL CENTER BOULEVARD, WAKE FOREST UNIVERSITY SCH 27157 #422-01-2006 **FP** *012

GILLILAND, Charles Andrew. ■ 27127 #055-02-2007 **FP** *012

GILLIS, Marcum Glenn. ■ 27101 #036-05-2008 *012

GILMORE, Christopher A. 145 KIMEL PARK DR, STE 330 27103 #047-06-2002 L2006 **APM** *020 †05

GIVENS, Davidson Howard. 3333 SILAS CREEK PKWY 27103 #036-05-1976 L1976 **CD** *020 †20

GIVNER, Laurence Bruce. MED CTR BLVD 27157 #023-01-1978 L1985 **ID PD** *020 †55

GLASS, Frederick W. BOWMAN GRAY AFFIL HOSPS 27103 #036-05-1950 L1950 **EM OS** *071 †85

GLAZIER, Steven Steuer. MED CTR BLVD 27157 #010-02-1987 L1993 **NS** *020 †25

GLENN, Richard Reece. ■ 27104 #036-05-1946 L1947 **PD** *071 †55

GLOCK, Michael Seth. MEDICAL CENTER BLVD, DEPT OF PEDIATRICS 27157 #051-04-1985 L1992 **PG** *020 †55

GLOVER, William Bryan. ■ 27103 #047-06-2004 L2007 **EM** *020

GODAT, Laura Nadine. ■ 27103 #036-05-2007 **GS** *012

GOENAGADIAZ, Eduardo Javi. ■ 27127 #036-05-2007 **AN** *012

GOFF, David Calvin, Jr. MEDICAL CENTER BLVD, DEPARTMENT OF EPIDEMIOLOGY 27157 #036-01-1986 L1996 **IM** *020 †20

GOGCU, Semsa. ■ 27157 #902-07-1996 **NPM** *012

GOINS, Jeanne Leigh. ■ 27103 #036-05-2008 *012

GOLDMAN, Neal David. MEDICAL CENTER BLVD 27157 #035-45-1992 L1999 **OTO** *020 †45

GONZALEZ, Antonia Rosario. 2928 MAPLEWOOD AVE 27103 #132-02-1968 L1975 **FM IM** *020

GOODE, David John. 3333 SILAS CREEK PKWY 27103 #036-05-1966 L1966 **P** *020 †75

GOODPASTURE, Meggan Lee. ■ 27103 #036-05-2005 L2008 **PD** *012

GORDON, Karyn Bayyinah. 2295 E 14TH ST STE 100, WAKE FOREST UNIVERSITY BAP 27105 #005-15-1995 L1998 **PD** *020 †55

GOTTLIEB, Louis Nathan. 631 COLISEUM DR 27106 #036-05-1962 L1962 **OPH** *020 †35

GRAHAM, Donald Dean, Jr. 3333 SILAS CREEK PKWY 27103 #030-05-1988 L1994 **PUD IM** *020 †20

GRAHAM, Stacy Harold. MEDICAL CENTER BLVD, WFUBMC 27157 #045-04-2003 L2006 **CD** *012 †20

GRANGER, Marilyn. 725 HIGHLAND AVE 27101 #041-02-1983 L1987 **P** *020 †75

GRANT, Willis Jackson. 250 CHARLOIS BLVD 27103 #036-01-1954 L1954 **P** *072 †75

GRANTHAM, David Wayne. MEDICAL CENTER BLVD, DEPARTMENT OF GENERAL SURG 27157 #036-01-2002 L2007 **GS** *100 †85

GRAY, John Henry, III. 2240 CLOVERDALE AVE, STE 193 27103 #036-05-1961 L1961 **IM** *071 †20

GRAY, Kala Cheryl. STUDENT BOX BGSM 27103 #036-05-1999 **P** *100

GREEN, Abby Margaret. ■ 27106 #035-19-2007 L2007 **PD** *012

GREEN, Nancy L Hansbrough. 251 N MAIN ST, REGIONAL OFFICE 27155 #020-02-1964 L1970 **R** *062 †80

GREEN, Robert Lorenza. ■ 27106 #036-01-1959 L1959 **R** *071 †80

GREENE-CHANDOS, Diana L. 2025 FRONTIS PLAZA BLVD, STE 120 27103 #003-01-1997 L2005 **N CCM** *020 †75

GREENWOOD, Gregory Todd. ■ 27106 #036-05-1999 L2000 **NEP** *020 †20

GREFE, Annette Elissa. MEDICAL CENTER BOULEVARD, WAKE FOREST UNIV HEALTH SC 27157 #001-02-1992 L2006 **CHN** *020 †75

GREINER, Mary Vaden. ■ 27127 #051-04-2005 L2007 **PD** *012

GREISS, Frank C, Jr. ■ 27104 #041-01-1953 L1960 **OBG** *071 †30

GREVEN, Craig Michael. MEDICAL CENTER BLDV 27157 #036-05-1983 L1984 **OPH** *020 †35

GREVEN, Kathryn M. MEDICAL CENTER BOULEVARD, BOWMAN GRAY SCHOOL OF MED 27157 #036-05-1983 L1985 **RO** *020 †80

GRIER, David Douglas. ■ 27106 #045-01-2001 L2006 **HMP** *100 †50

GRIESSEL, Chanda. 150 KIMEL PARK DR, STE 200 27103 #018-03-1997 L2003 **OPH FM** *012 †18

GRIFFIN, Albert Oscar. 1381 WESTGATE CENTER DR, FORSYTH INTERNAL MEDICINE 27103 #036-05-1961 L1961 **IM** *071

GRIFFIN, Andrew Steven. 180 KIMEL PARK DR, STE 110 27103 #036-05-1983 L1984 **U** *020 †95

GRIFFITH, Mary Ann. 1351 WESTGATE CENTER DR 27103 #055-02-1989 L1992 **PD** *020 †55

GROBAN, Leanne. MEDICAL CENTER BLVD, WAKE FOREST UN SCH OF MEDI 27157 #056-06-1992 L1996 **AN** *020 †05

GROSS, Kathy Lynn. ■ 27104 #035-45-1982 L1983 **PD** *075 †55

GRUEBEL, Timothy Lynn. ■ 27103 #036-05-2005 L2008 **AN** *012

GRUPKA, Nichon. 3333 SILAS CREEK PKWY 27103 #422-01-2000 L2006 **HMP OS** *020 †50

GUFFEY, Neal Hamilton, Jr. 3333 BROOKVIEW HILLS BLVD, STE 107 27103 #045-04-1992 L1995 **IM** *075

GULLEY, Marcus M. MED CTR BLVD 27157 #036-05-1951 L1955 **P** *071

GUNN, Charles Groshon, Jr. ■ 27106 #036-07-1948 L1952 **OM** *071 †70

GUO, Hongtao. MEDICAL CENTER BLVD, DEPARTMENT OF NEUROLOGY 27157 #020-12-2001 L2006 **APM** *100

GUPTA, Karn. ■ 27103 #496-43-2002 L2006 **IM** *100 †20

GUPTA, Prag. MEDICAL CENTER BOULEVARD, WAKE FOREST UNIV. HEALTH S 27157 #495-69-1999 L2004 **CCM** *012

GUPTA, Sumeer Kumar. MEDICAL CENTER BLVD., DEPARTMENT OTOLARYNGOLOGY 27157 #033-03-2001 L2004 **OTO** *100 †45

GURIEN, Andrew Michael. 3333 SILAS CREEK PKWY, FORSYTH MEDICAL CENTER 27103 #026-04-1993 L1998 **IM** *020 †20

GUSDON, Johnny Phillip. 107 CEDAR TRAILS CT 27104 #051-01-1984 L1985 **EM** *020 †18

GWYN, Paul Perkins, Jr. 2901 MAPLEWOOD AVE 27103 #035-01-1961 L1961 **PS** *071 †85,65

HABER, Michele A. MED CTR BLVD 27157 #048-15-1989 L1999 **IMG OS** *020 †20

HACKER, Brian David. ■ 27127 #051-04-2004 L2004 **AN** *012

HADLEY, Alexander Cox. 730 HIGHLAND OAKS DR, STE 101 27103 #036-05-1999 L2001 **NEP** *020 †20

HADLEY, Mary M. 1180 LAMONT DR 27103 #036-05-2001 L2002 **PD** *020 †55

HAGGERSON, George Wm. 3318 HEALY DR 27103 #025-07-1976 L1987 **GS** *020 †85

HAHN, Andrew Louis. ■ 27106 #042-07-1947 L1951 **IM NTR** *012

HAINES, Scott Robert. OF MED, WAKE FOREST UNIV SCH 27157 #023-01-2006 **N** *012

HAIRSTON, Kristen Gill. MEDICAL CENTER BOULEVARD, MAYA ANGELOU RESEARCH CENT 27157 #036-01-2001 L2006 **END** *020 †20

HAIRSTON, Oscar Grogan. ■ 27105 #047-07-1958 L1959 **FM OBG** *071

HAISTY, Wesley K, Jr. MEDICAL CENTER DRIVE, WFUMC 27157 #016-06-1966 L1977 **ICE IM** *071 †20

HALE, Lynn Mixon. 799 HIGHLAND AVE, P O BOX 686 27101 #036-05-1969 L1969 **PHP** *020

HALL, John David. ■ 27103 #010-02-2015 **AN** *012

HALL, Samuel Elijah. 250 CHARLOIS BLVD 27103 #036-07-1984 L1997 **GYN** *020 †30

HALVORSON, Jason Jeffrey. ■ 27103 #047-05-2007 **ORS** *012

HAM, D Wayne. ■ 27101 #035-03-1990 L1991 **IMG** *020 †18

HAMILTON, Adam John. ■ 27127 #038-43-2008 *012

HAMILTON, Kelly Marie. ■ 27127 #038-43-2007 **OBG** *012

HAMMON, Dudley Elliott. ■ 27103 #036-05-2005 **PD** *012

HAMMON, John Wm, Jr. MEDICAL CENTER BLVD 27157 #021-01-1968 L1969 **TS CD** *020 †85,90

HANEEF, Saadia. ■ 27103 #011-75-2004, ▲ **CHP** *012

HANSEN, Jason Paul. 125 SUNNYNOLL CT, STE 100 27106 #049-01-2003 L2007 **PRD** *012 †15

HANSEN, Kimberley J. WFU SCHOOL OF MEDICINE, SECT ON VASC & ENDOVASC 27157 #001-02-1980 L1981 **VS GS** *020 †85

HANSEN, Roger Gustav. 250 CHARLOIS BLVD 27103 #051-07-1983 L1993 **FM AM** *020 †18

HAPONIK, Edward Francis. MEDICAL CENTER BLVD., PULMONARY & CRITICAL CARE 27157 #036-05-1974 L1974 **PUD IM** *020 †20 ‡

HARDIE, Gregory Steven. 3333 SILAS CREEK PKWY 27103 #036-05-1980 L1983 **AN** *020 †05

HARKINS, Paul Channing. ■ 27104 #049-01-2003 L2007 **AN** *012

HARLE, Thomas Stanley. MED CTR BLVD 27157 #016-06-1957 L1997 **DR** *040 †80 ‡

HARPER, Amy Denise. MEDICAL CENTER BOULEVARD, SCIENCES 27157 #654-01-1998 L2007 **PD** *020 †55

HARPER, Katherine Meadows. 1900 S HAWTHORNE RD, STE 480A 27103 #036-01-1995 L1997 **PD** *020 †55

HARPER, Margaret Ann. 3333 SILAS CREEK PKWY 27103 #036-01-1974 L1974 **MFM OBG** *020 †30

HARPER, Scott Anderson. OF MED, WAKE FOREST UNIV SCHOOL 27157 #051-01-2006 **FP** *012

HARPER, Stephen Andrew. 110 CHARLOIS BLVD, PIEDMONT EAR, NOSE, AND TH 27103 #036-01-1995 L1998 **OTO** *020 †45

HARRELD, Kevin Lee. ■ 27104 #020-02-2005 **ORS** *012

HARRINGTON, Robert Noel. ■ 27106 #036-05-2003 L2004 **AN** *100

HARRIS, Brenda Fagan. DEPT OF PSYCHIATRY, WAKE FOREST UNIV SCH OF ME 27157 #011-03-1984 **P** *012

HARRIS, Charles Walker, Jr. 150 CHARLOIS BLVD 27103 #036-08-1993 L1996 **CD** *020 †20

HARRIS, Jimmie Lee. 3333 SILAS CREEK PKWY 27103 #051-04-1954 L1964 **GP** *020

HARRIS, Milton Dean. 3073 TRENWEST DR 27103 #048-12-1968 L1976 **CD** *020 †20

HARRIS, Sean Michael. 1901 S HAWTHORNE RD, STE 310 27103 #036-05-1996 L2002 **GE** *020 †20

HARRIS, William Lawrence. ■ 27127 #036-01-2006 L2008 **IM** *012

HARRISON, Frank Late, Jr. ■ 27106 #036-07-1968 L1968 **GP** *074

HARRISON, Lloyd Herritage. BOWMAN GRAY M C, DEPT U 27103 #036-05-1962 L1962 **U** *071 †95

HART, Oliver J, III. 140 KIMEL PARK DR, STE 110 27103 #036-05-1984 L1989 **U** *020 †95

HART, Oliver James, Jr. 140 KIMEL PARK DR 27103 #036-01-1959 L1959 **U** *020 †95

HARTLEY, Katherine Adair. ■ 27101 #047-06-2003 L2007 **DR** *012

HARTMAN, Joel Michael. MEDICAL CENTER BLVD., MUSC - GRADUATE MEDICAL ED 27157 #036-05-2002 L2005 **CD** *100 †20

HARTMANN, Erica Lyn. MEDICAL CENTER BLVD 27157 #028-46-1995 L2003 **NEP** *020 †20

HARTNESS, William Rufus. 4712 COUNTRY CLUB RD STE C 27104 #020-02-1938 L1938 **GP OTO** *071

HARTZ, John William. MED CTR BLVD, DEPT PATHOLOGY 27157 #024-01-1962 L1974 **ATP OS** *020 †50

HATA, Ryan Gene. ■ 27127 #056-06-2006 **EM** *012

HATCH, David Matthews. OF MED, WAKE FOREST UNIV SCH 27157 #017-20-2007 **AN** *012

HATZIS, Christopher Edwar. MEDICAL CENTER BOULEVARD 27157 #036-05-2004 L2006 **IM** *020 †20

HAVERSTOCK, Christina Lee. ■ 27127 #035-06-2004 L2008 **D** *012

HAWES, Diane Fuller. 3333 SILAS CREEK PKWY 27103 #051-01-1979 L1982 **FM** *020 †18

HAWFIELD, Amret Thompson. MEDICAL CENTER BOULEVARD, WAKE FOREST UNIV SCHOOL OF 27157 #036-05-2002 L2007 **NEP** *100 †20

HAWFIELD, Wesley Raymond. ■ 27104 #036-01-2003 L2007 **D** *020 †15

HAYDEN, Jennifer Lynn. ■ 27103 #048-02-2006 **IM** *012

HAYES, Kevin Randall. ■ 27127 #004-01-2007 **IM** *012

HAYS, John Lawrence. ■ 27127 #048-02-2005 L2008 **IM** *012

HEADLEY, Robert Nelson. BOWMAN GRAY SCH, DEPT MED 27103 #023-01-1956 L1963 **CD IM** *071 †20

HEALY, Joseph Stephen. DEPT. OF GASTROENTEROLOGY, WFUBMC 27157 #012-01-2002 L2005 **GE** *012 †20

HEALY, Patrick Kevin. 1381 WESTGATE CENTER DR 27103 #010-02-1980 L2005 **IM** *020 †20

HEATHERLY, Steven Joel. ■ 27106 #051-07-2007 **IM** *012

HEBERT, Stephen Wm. 2990 BETHESDA PL STE 602A 27103 #036-05-1972 L1972 **P N** *020 †75

HECK, Donald Vincent. 3155 MAPLEWOOD AVE, FORSYTH RADIOLOGICAL ASSOC 27103 #036-07-1993 L2002 **VIR** *020 †80

HEDRICK, Richard E, Jr. 2932 LYNDHURST AVE 27103 #036-05-1979 L1983 **OBG** *020 †30

HEINRICH, Marcela Isabel. MEDICAL CENTER BLVD 27157 #036-05-1996 L1998 **PD** *020 †55

HEITZ, Corey Regan. ■ 27104 #051-07-2005 L2007 **EM** *012

HELDERMAN, Jennifer B. MEDICAL CENTER BLVD, WAKE FOREST UNIV BAPTIST 27157 #036-08-2000 L2001 **PD NPM** *100 †55 ‡

HELLEBY, Leticia Estela. 2295 E 14TH ST 27105 #035-08-2004 L2007 **PD** *020

HELLER, Cherrie Dawn. MEDICAL CENTER BLVD 27157 #051-01-1997 L2000 **PD NPM** *050 †55

HELMAN, Melissa Ann. 114 CHARLOIS BLVD, WINSTON-SALEM WOMANCARE, P 27103 #038-41-1991 L1996 **OBG** *020 †30

HELMAN, Steven Edward. 3333 BROOKVIEW BLVD, STE 204 27103 #038-41-1992 L1994 IM *020 †20

HELMS, Jefferson B, Jr. 1381 WESTGATE CENTER DR 27103 #036-05-1962 L1962 IM *071

HEMAL, Ashok Kumar. 140 CHARLOIS BLVD 27103 #495-34-1981 L2007 *100

HEMKES, Nicole Tennille. ■ 27103 #011-04-2006 FP *012

HENRICHS, W Dean. 250 CHARLOIS BLVD, WINSTON-SALEM HEALTH CARE 27103 #019-02-1965 L1984 D DMP *015 ‡

HENSHAW, Daryl Steven. 301 S HAWTHORNE RD, WAKE FOREST UNIV SCH OF ME 27103 #036-05-2006 L2008 AN *012

HERMAN, Christopher M. 3880 VEST MILL RD, STE 100 27103 #012-01-1993 L1995 IM *020 †20

HERMAN, Mary P Seckman. ■ 27104 #012-01-1993 L1995 PTH *020 †50

HERRINGTON, David Mc Leod. MEDICAL CENTER BLVD, WAKE FOREST UNIV SCH MED 27157 #036-01-1983 L1990 CD IM *050 †20

HERRINGTON, Deirdre A. MEDICAL CTR BLVD, NC BAPTIST HOSP DIV ID 27157 #035-03-1978 L1982 ID IM *020 †20

HERTZ, George Erik. 3333 SILAS CREEK PKWY 27103 #041-12-1987 L1991 AN *020 †05

HESS, Mark Roland. MEDICAL CENTER BLVD, WFUBMC 27157 #036-08-1985 L1988 EM *020 †16

HEYMANN, Robert C. 3333 SILAS CREEK PKWY 27103 #036-05-1960 L1961 D *071

HIGH, Kevin Paul. INFECTIOUS DISEASE SECTION, SCHOOL OF MEDICINE 27157 #051-01-1986 L1993 ID IM *020 †20

HILL, Charles Arthur, III. ■ 27106 #036-05-2007 GS *012

HILL, Edward Gray, Jr. 3333 BROOKVIEW HILLS BLVD, STE 104 27103 #036-05-1980 L1982 N *020

HILL, Garick David. ■ 27103 #036-05-2007 PD *012

HILL, Ivor Dennis. MEDICAL CENTER BOULEVARD, WAKE FOREST UNIV. SCH. OF 27157 #836-02-1972 L1995 PG *020 †55

HILTON, Suzanne Elizabeth. 3333 BROOKVIEW HILLS BLVD, STE 107 27103 #036-08-1989 L1995 FM *020 †18

HINCKLEY, Michael Richard. ■ 27127 #049-01-2005 L2007 D *012

HINES, Anne Creech. 401 NORTHGATE PARK DR 27106 #051-07-1986 L1991 FM *020 †18

HINES, Michael Herbert. MED CTR BLVD 27157 #036-05-1986 L1987 PCS TS *020 †85,90

HINSON, Thomas Riley. 3333 SILAS CREEK PKWY 27103 #036-01-1979 L1980 PUD CCM *020 †20

HIOTT, Ann Elizabeth. MED CTR BLVD 27157 #036-01-1996 L1997 FM *020 †18

HIPP, Jennifer Anne. ■ 27103 #036-05-2008 *012

HIRATA, Takashi. ■ 27127 #036-05-2004 L2006 FM *020 †18

HITCHCOCK, Michael Geo. 3333 SILAS CREEK PKWY 27103 #671-02-1983 L1993 DMP ATP *020 †50

HITE, Robert Duncan, Jr. MEDICAL CENTER BLVD, PULMONARY/CRITICAL CARE 27157 #048-14-1986 L1994 PUD CCM *050 †20

HODGE, Ernest Benj. ■ 27101 #047-07-1956 L1964 AN *071 †05

HODGES, David Stewart. MEDICAL CENTER BOULEVARD, DEPARTMENT OF RADIOLOGY 27157 #036-05-2003 L2004 DR *020

HODGES, Steve James. 140 CHARLOIS BLVD 27103 #036-05-1998 L1999 UP *020 †95

HODSON, Darryl Shaw. 125 SUNNYNOLL CT, STE 100 27106 #036-05-1996 L2008 D *020 †15

HOEKSTRA, James Wm. MED CTR BLVD 27157 #025-01-1984 L2002 EM *040 †16

HOFFMANN, Ingrid M. 1364 WESTGATE CENTER DR, PIEDMONT 27103 #038-41-1996 L1999 AI *020 †55,03

HOGSETTE, Gerald Byron, Jr. 3333 SILAS CREEK PKWY 27103 #012-01-1975 L1995 IM *020 †20

HOLDER, David Michael. ■ 27106 #038-40-2008 *012

HOLLAND, James Patrick. 3073 TRENWEST DR 27103 #036-01-1980 L1986 CD *020 †20

HOLLAR, Larry Array, Jr. 105 VEST MILL CIR, CARTERET MEDICAL ASSOCIATE 27103 #036-05-1997 L1998 FM *020 †18

HOLLENBECK, Zoe P. MEDICAL CENTER BLVD, WAKE FOREST UNIVERSITY SCH 27157 #017-20-2006 L2007 OBG *100

HOLLIFIELD, William Wayne. ■ 27106 #036-01-1981 L1983 NS GS *020 †25

HOLMES, James Hill, IV. MEDICAL CENTER BOULEVARD, DEPARTMENT OF GENERAL SURG 27157 #048-12-1996 L2005 GS *020 †85

HOLMES, Robert J. 1901 S HAWTHORNE RD STE 31 27103 #048-12-1990 L1996 GE HEP *020 †20

HOLT, Rachel Williams. ■ 27127 #048-14-2005 L2007 IM *012

HOLT, Shea Ryan. ■ 27127 #048-02-2008 L2008 IM *012

HOLTHUSEN, Gregory Grant. 170 KIMEL PARK DR 27103 #056-05-1965 L1972 ORS *020

HOLTZMAN, Douglas Keith. MED CTR BLVD 27157 #045-04-1988 L2002 PD *020 †55

HOMER, Stephen Hubert. 3775 VEST MILL RD STE A 27103 #041-01-1961 L1967 ORS *020 †40

HOOD, David Dean. MED CTR BLVD 27157 #019-02-1979 L1983 AN *020 †20

HOOPES, Matthew Wade. ■ 27127 #036-05-2004 L2006 AN *012

HOOVER, Kim Gloria. 1702 S HAWTHORNE RD, TRI-CARE, P.A. 27103 #008-02-1983 L1984 CHP *075

HOPKINS, Lawrence David. 2001 TODAYS WOMAN AVE 27105 #036-05-1977 L1983 OBG GP *020 †30

HOPMEIER, Robin Rene. ■ 27103 #040-02-2004 AN *012 †55

HORNEY, Candace Wayne. ■ 27103 #048-14-2007 PTH *012

HORTON, Janet Knight. MEDICAL CENTER BOULEVARD, DEPT. OF RADIATION ONCOLOG 27157 #036-05-2001 L2002 RO *100 †80

HOTH, James Jason. MED CTR BLVD 27157 #021-06-1996 L2003 CCS *020 †85

HOUGH, Matthew G. MEDICAL CENTER BLVD, DEPT OF PYS WAKE FOREST 27157 #018-75-1998, ▲ L2003 CHP P *020

HOUGH, William Amos. 250 CHARLOIS BLVD 27103 #036-05-1973 L1973 IM *020 †20

HOWE, Cristin Parker. 3333 SILAS CREEK PKWY 27103 #036-05-2000 L2005 IM *020 †20

HOWE, David Jefferson. 170 KIMEL PARK DR 27103 #036-05-1998 L2005 ORS *020 †40

HOWELL, Amoreena Ranck. ■ 27127 #051-01-2005 FP *012

HOWELL, Charles M, Jr. ■ 27104 #041-01-1937 L1937 D A *071 †15

HOWELL, Frederick L. 140 KIMEL PARK RD 27103 #051-01-1968 L1977 U *020 †95

HOWELL, Hampton Alexander. 1345 WESTGATE CENTER DR #A, SALEM PLASTIC SURGERY 27103 #036-05-2000 L2006 PS *020 †65

HOWELL, Julius A. ■ 27104 #041-01-1943 L1943 PS *071 †45,65

HOWELL, Leigh Ellis. 600 HIGHLAND OAKS DR 27103 #036-08-2003 L2006 FM *020 †18

HOWELL, Travis Worth. 105 VEST MILL CIR 27103 #036-08-2003 L2006 FM *020 †18

HOWERTON, Russell Mars. MEDICAL CENTER BOULEVARD, WAKE FOREST UNIVERSITY 27157 #047-05-1983 L1992 GS *020 †85

HOYLE, John Russell. MED CTR BLVD 27157 #036-08-1995 L1996 CD *020 †20

HOYLE, Margarete Smith. 1900 S HAWTHORNE RD, STE 480A 27103 #036-05-1997 L1998 PD *020 †55

HUBBARD, Laura Ann. MED CTR BLVD 27157 #036-05-1991 L1995 FM *020 †18

HUBBARD, Stephen Adrian. 3333 SILAS CREEK PKWY 27103 #036-05-1988 L1990 EM *020 †16

HUCKS, George Edward, Jr. ■ 27127 #045-04-2006 PD *012

HUDSON, Cressent Marjorie. 100 ROBINHOOD MEDICAL PLZ 27106 #036-05-2001 L2003 FM *020 †18

HUDSON, Jon Edward. ■ 27157 #036-05-2004 U *012

HUDSON, Sarah Elizabeth. ■ 27127 #025-12-2006 PD *012

HUDSPETH, Allen S. DEPT CT SURGERY, MEDICAL CENTER BLVD 27157 #036-05-1953 L1953 TS *071 †85,90

HUEY, Charles. ■ 27103 #165-04-1966 L1972 N IM *050 †75

HUGHES, Carolyn Esther. 190 KIMEL PARK DR, VA CLINIC 27103 #026-04-1979 L2007 IM ID *020 †20 ‡

HUGHES, Doreen Louise. 331 HIGH ST STE 103, DOREEN L. HUGHES, MD 27101 #036-05-1990 L1993 P *020 †75

HUMPHREYS, Kathleen Maril. ■ 27127 #005-12-2005 IM *012

HUNDLEY, William Gregory. MED CTR BLVD 27157 #051-04-1988 L1996 CD *020 †20

HURD, David Duane. MED CTR BLVD, SECTION OF HEMATOLOGY/ONCO 27157 #016-11-1974 L1989 ON IM *020 †20

HURST, Daniel Johnson. 250 CHARLOIS BLVD 27103 #016-02-1967 L1983 IM PUD *020 †20

HUX, Stephen Marshall. 800 W CLEMMONSVILLE RD 27127 #036-01-1982 L1983 FM *020 †18

HYNES, Michael Loren. 3155 MAPLEWOOD AVE 27103 #025-01-2002 L2007 DR *020 †80

IANNUZZI, Nicholas P, III. 3010 MAPLEWOOD AVE, STE 122 27103 #036-05-1978 L1981 EM *020 †16

IBOAYA, Ehimemen O. OF MED, WAKE FOREST UNIV SCH 27157 #028-46-2004 L2006 AN *012 †20

IGBINIGIE, Theodore O. 3333 SILAS CREEK PKWY 27103 #690-06-1991 L2001 IM *020 †20

IKWECHEGH, Obinna Ogbonna. MEDICAL CENTER BLVD 27157 #690-16-1998 P *012

INMAN, Joseph Lucas. ■ 27106 #036-05-2002 L2007 OTO *100

IQBAL, Mohammed. DEPT OF PSYCHIATRY, WAKE FOREST UNIV SCH OF ME 27157 #306-01-2000 P *012

IRION, James Carney. 421 WIND HAVEN LN, AEGIS FAMILY HEALTH CENTER 27104 #036-01-1988 L1989 FM *020 †18

IRUELA, Maria Eugenia. 4020 HUNTSCROFT LN 27106 #036-07-1984 L1985 FM IMG *020 †18

ISKANDAR, Samy Samuel. DEPT OF PATHALOGY, WAKE FOREST UNIV SCHL 27157 #915-03-1971 L1983 ATP CLP *020 †50

ISRAEL, James Ray. ■ 27103 #036-05-1963 L1963 P FM *071 †75

IYER, Shridhar Narayan. ■ 27104 #665-01-2003 L2007 IM *100

JACKSON, David Stone, Jr. MEDICAL CENTER BLVD 27157 #036-05-1973 L1973 FM *020 †18

JACKSON, James Benjamin, III. ■ 27103 #036-05-2008 *012

JACKSON, Leron Celeste. 301 S HAWTHORNE RD, WAKE FOREST UNIV SCH OF ME 27103 #036-05-2007 L2007 GS *012

JACKSON, Richard Thos. MEDICAL CENTER BLVD, SCIENCES/DEPT OF NEUROLOGY 27157 #035-03-1974 L2005 N PMM *020 †75 ‡

JACKSON, Travis Harold. 175 KIMEL PARK DR, STE 125 27103 #048-04-1975 L1975 N *020 †75

JACOBS, David Jonathan. ■ 27157 #045-04-2005 L2007 OPH *012

JAIN, Rajay Kumar. MEDICAL CENTER BLVD, SECTION OF ANESTHESIA 27157 #496-18-1987 L2004 CCM *100 †20

JAMES, David T, III. ■ 27106 #028-03-2006 IM *012

JAMES, Francis Marshall. MEDICAL CENTER BLVD, BOWMAN GRAY SCH MED DEPT A 27157 #041-09-1961 L1968 AN *071 †05

JANEWAY, Richard. MEDICAL CENTER BLVD, MEDICINE 27157 #041-01-1958 L1963 N *071 †75

JANOSKI, Alfonso Hubert. 1232 BRAEHILL TERRACE DR 27104 #035-01-1961 L2000 END IM *030 †20,28

JARRAHI, Ali. 2830 MAPLEWOOD AVE STE A 27103 #517-01-1962 L1970 P PHP *020 †75 ‡

JARRETT, David Bailey. 1365 WESTGATE CENTER DR, STE L1 27103 #143-01-1969 L1997 P *020

JASON, Donald Richard. MED CTR BLVD 27157 #035-19-1970 L1992 FOP *040 †50

JEEVANANTHAM, Vinodh. ■ 27104 #496-23-2000 L2007 IM *020 †20

JEFFERY, Douglas R. MEDICAL CENTER BOULEVARD, WAKE FOREST UNIV MED CTRBL 27157 #035-06-1987 L1994 N *020 †75

JENNELL, Jamie Lynn. ■ 27106 #051-04-2006 OBG *012

JENNINGS, Jerome Edwin. 1900 S HAWTHORNE RD # 410 27103 #012-01-1969 L1970 ORS *020 †40

JENNINGS, W Bryan. 1900 S HAWTHORNE RD, STE 410 27103 #018-75-1998, ▲ L2004 OSM ORS *020

JENSEN, Courtney Ann. ■ 27106 #056-05-2005 RO *012

JEWETT, Tamison. MEDICAL CENTER BLVD, DEPARTMENT OF PEDIATRICS 27157 #003-01-1984 L1991 MG PD *020 †9,55

JINNAH, Riyaz Hassanali. MEDICAL CENTER BLVD, DEPARTMENT OF ORTHOPAEDICS 27157 #917-03-1977 L2006 ORS *040 †40

JOHARJI, Ghazi Mansour. ■ 27103 #797-01-1984 OTO *020

JOHN, Jarod K. ■ 27103 #041-13-2006 *012

JOHN, Jerry Mathew. 428 WIND HAVEN LN 27104 #025-12-2001 L2005 CD *012

JOHNSON, Annette Jean. MEDICAL CENTER BLVD, RADIOLOGY 27157 #051-04-1992 L2007 RNR *020 †80

JOHNSON, Christine Anna. WALSH FOREST SCHL OF MED, DEPT PEDS 27157 #024-07-1964 L1975 PD *020 †15,55

JOHNSON, Henry Parker. ■ 27127 #027-01-2005 IM *012

JOHNSON, Henry Wesley. ■ 27106 #036-05-1956 L1956 PD *071 †55

JOHNSON, Melanie Jeannine. ■ 27103 #036-05-2007 L2007 P *012

JOHNSON, Ryan Christopher. ■ 27103 #036-05-2008 *012

JOHNSRUDE, Curtis Brent. 145 KIMEL PARK DR STE 300, PIEDMONT TRIAD ANES 27103 #036-05-1983 L1987 AN *020 †05

JOLLY, Thomas Lynn. 600 HIGHLAND OAKS DR 27103 #036-05-1985 L1986 OM FM *020 †20

JONES, Allen Gafford. 3333 SILAS CREEK PKWY 27103 #027-01-1984 L1985 IM *020 †20

JONES, Beverly Nicholas. 3111 MAPLEWOOD AVE STE 105 27103 #036-01-1982 L1993 P PYG *020 †65

JONES, Champ M, Jr. 100 ROBINHOOD MEDICAL PLZ 27106 #045-01-1974 L1985 FM *020 †18

JONES, Edward Claude. MEDICAL CENTER BLVD 27157 #036-01-1980 L1988 P *020

JONES, James Marshall. ■ 27104 #047-01-1954 L1955 IM OS *071

JONES, Michael Eugene, Jr. MEDICAL CENTER BOULEVARD 27157 #051-07-2002 L2005 AN *020 †05

JONES, Preston Allen, Jr. ■ 27103 #045-04-2006 IM *012

JORDAN, Caitlin Stetson. ■ 27103 #051-07-2005 L2008 FP *012

JORIZZO, Johanna Regina. MED CTR BLVD 27157 #035-45-1981 L1996 DR *020 †80

JORIZZO, Joseph L. MEDICAL CENTER BLVD 27157 #024-05-1975 L1976 **D** *030 †15

JOSEPHSON, Sarah Kristina. PO BOX 9045 27109 #020-02-2007 **IM** *012

JOSIAH, Darnell Twain. ■ 27103 #036-05-2008 *012

JOY, Saju Daniel. MEDICAL CENTER BLVD, DEPARTMENT OF OB/GYN 27157 #036-01-1999 L2006 **OBG** *100 †30

KADER, Andrew K A. 140 CHARLOIS BLVD 27103 #061-01-2000 L2007 *100

KAHL, Frederic Ross. SCHOOL OF MEDICINE, WAKE FOREST UNIVERSITY 27157 #016-02-1967 L1975 **CD IM** *020 †20

KALAKISH, Samer Rida. MED CTR BLVD, WAKE FOREST U BAPTIST MED 27157 #605-01-2001 **U** *020 †20

KALATHOOR, Suneetha R. 1381 WESTGATE CENTER DR 27103 #012-01-1991 L1995 **ID** *020 †20

KALSY, Sapna. ■ 27103 #041-15-2005 L2008 **OBG** *012

KAMMIRE, Leslie Danese. BLVD, SCHOOL OF MED MEDICAL CENT 27157 #036-05-1986 L1988 **GYN** *020 †30

KANTOR, Oksana. ■ 27106 #913-97-1999 **AN** *012

KAPLAN, Sandra Davis. ■ 27127 #047-06-2004 **GS** *012

KAPOOR, Sakshi. ■ 27103 #496-20-1999 L2007 **N** *100 †75

KARALIS, Christos. MEDICAL CENTER BLVD, WAKE FOREST UNIV BMC 27157 #781-01-1990 L1998 **GE** *020 †20

KARCH, Joelle Elyse. ■ 27103 #035-06-2006 **OBG** *012

KARCHMER, Tobi Beth. MED CTR BLVD 27157 #024-01-1992 L2000 **ID IM** *030 †20

KARLSON, Karl Henrik. MEDICAL CENTER BLVD, WAKE FOREST UNIV MED SCHOO 27157 #021-01-1972 L2004 **PUD PD** *020 †55

KATOPES, Charles Peter. 2025 FRONTIS PLAZA BLVD, STE 200 27103 #035-08-2000 L2007 **GE** *020 †20 ‡

KAUFMAN, Elizabeth Doroth. ■ 27103 #051-01-2007 L2007 **IM** *012

KAVANAGH, Peter Vincent. MED CTR BLVD 27157 #539-03-1987 L1998 **DR** *020

KEELING, William Mc Clure. ■ 27104 #047-06-1946 L1978 **GS GP** *062 †85

KELLAM, Lori Goco. 760 HIGHLAND OAKS DR, STE 200 27103 #036-05-1991 L1996 **GS** *020 †85

KELLEY, Arthur Evans. 293 STAFFORDSHIRE RD, WOODLAKE PSYCHOLOGICAL & 27104 #055-01-1974 L1991 **CHP P** *020 †75

KELLING, Elisabeth Porter. ■ 27103 #036-08-2004 L2006 **PD** *100 †55

KELLY, David Alexander. ■ 27106 #049-01-2008 *012

KELLY, David Lee. MEDICAL CENTER BLVD, WAKE FOREST UNIV MED CTR 27157 #036-01-1959 L1959 **NS** *020 †25

KELLY, Elizabeth Whitaker. 2511 WOODBINE RD 27104 #036-05-2004 L2007 **EM** *100

KELLY, Jeffrey Scott. 4049 HUNTSCROFT LN 27106 #038-43-1981 L1982 **AN CCA** *020 †16,05

KELLY, Johnson Hall. 180 KIMEL PARK RD 27103 #036-05-1978 L1979 **U** *020 †95

KELLY, Robert Geo. 100 ROBINHOOD MEDICAL PLZ 27106 #045-01-1974 L1979 **FM** *020 †18

KEMPER, Kathi. PEDIATRICS MEDICAL CENTER 27157 #036-01-1982 L2001 **PD PDE** *020 †55

KENNEDY, Burton Lee. ■ 27127 #021-05-2005 **N** *012

KENNEDY, Charlie Lee. 2295 E 14TH ST, STE 100 27105 #047-07-1963 L1964 **PD** *020 †55

KENNEDY, Daniel Jos. 3333 SILAS CREEK PKWY 27103 #020-02-1987 L1989 **AN CCA** *020 †05,20

KERCHER, Katherine Rau. ■ 27103 #028-03-2005 **D** *012

KERNER, Theodore Chas. 3155 MAPLEWOOD AVE, TRIAD RADIOLOGY 27103 #036-01-1985 L1989 **DR RNR** *020 †80

KERR, Robert Morton. BOWMAN GRAY SCH MED GASTRO 27103 #035-20-1961 L1966 **GE** *040 †20

KERRIGAN, James Richard. WAKE FOREST UNIVERSITY HEA, DEPT OF PEDIATRICSHO85 27157 #041-14-1984 L2004 **PDE PD** *020 †55

KETHAVATH, Rameshwarna. ■ 27157 #005-12-2000 L2004 **AN** *100 †05

KEUNG, Yi-Kong. MED CTR BLVD 27157 #462-01-1985 L1999 **HO HEM** *020

KEYES, John Wesley, Jr. BOWMAN GRAY SCHOOL OF MEDI, P.E.T. CENTER 27157 #025-01-1965 L1991 **NM DR** *071 †28,80

KHAGHANY, Kamran John. ■ 27103 #025-12-2005 L2008 **DR** *012

KHATTAK, Afshan Hussain. ■ 27103 #704-25-1992 L1999 **NPM** *100 †55

KHOT, Prakash Nilkanth. 5041 UNIVERSITY PKWY 27106 #495-19-1967 L2000 **EM FM** *020 †16

KHOURY, Maroon Boulos. 185 KIMEL PARK DR, STE 100 27103 #605-01-1979 L1996 **DR** *020 †80

KHOURY, Sean. WFUBMC, HOUSE STAFF OFFICE 27157 #836-01-1992 L1999 **MSR** *020 †80

KIANI, Bahram. ■ 27103 #038-40-2005 L2005 **DR** *012

KIDDER, James Michael. ■ 27127 #024-07-2006 **PD** *012

KIELBASA, Johanna Marie. ■ 27103 #036-05-2007 *012

KIKERKOV, Angelce D. 3333 SILAS CREEK PKWY 27103 #957-04-1993 L2002 **IM** *020 †20

KILGUS, Douglas Jarnigan. CENTER BLVD, OF MEDICINE MED 27157 #035-03-1980 L1997 **ORS OTR** *020 †40

KILPATRICK, Josh Charles. ■ 27127 #048-16-2007 **FP** *012

KILPATRICK, Scott Ethan. 3333 SILAS CREEK PKWY 27103 #012-01-1990 L1993 **PTH** *020 †50

KIM, Jung-Yeol. MEDICAL CENTER BLVD, NEUROLOGY 27157 #583-04-1990 L2005 **N VN** *020

KIMBALL, James Norman. MED CTR BLVD 27157 #033-06-1998 L1999 **P PYM** *020 †75 ‡

KIMBERLY, James Robert, Jr. MED CTR BLVD 27157 #012-01-1995 L1997 **GE** *012 †20

KIMREY, Sabrina Lindsay. ■ 27104 #036-05-2008 *012

KIM-SHAPIRO, Jung Wha. ■ 27103 #036-05-2003 L2007 **PTH** *100 †50

KINCAID, Edward Hal. MED CTR BLVD 27157 #036-05-1994 L1996 **TS** *020 †85,90

KINCAID, Shiva. 1930 PEACE HAVEN RD, PEACE HAVEN 27106 #036-05-1995 L1996 **IM** *020 †20

KINDLE, Kesi Tabia. 3333 SILAS CREEK PKWY, HMP OF FORSYTH 27103 #010-03-1999 L2002 **IMG** *020 †20

KING, Kelly Lynn. ■ 27127 #055-75-2007, ▲ **IM** *012

KING, Marie Elizabeth. ■ 27127 #036-01-1997 L2003 **P** *062

KING, Michael E. 170 KIMEL PARK DR 27103 #036-01-1977 L1977 **ORS** *020 †40

KIRKLAND, Lea Harrell. 2990 BETHESDA PL STE 601A 27103 #045-01-1987 L1988 **CHP** *020 †20,75

KIRKLAND, Stephen M. 3073 TRENWEST DR 27103 #045-01-1983 L1986 **CD** *020 †20

KIRKMAN, Paul Madison. OF MEDICINE, BOWMAN GRAY SCHOOL 27157 #036-05-1965 L1966 **CD IM** *020 †20

KIRMAN, Christian Nathan. MEDICAL CENTER BOULEVARD 27157 #003-01-2005 L2008 **PS** *012

KIRSCH, M Lee. 3333 BROOKVIEW HILLS BLVD, STE 205 27103 #036-01-1974 L1974 **PS** *020 †65

KISS, Andrea T. 3333 SILAS CREEK PKWY 27103 #473-01-1991 L2001 **IM** *020 †20

KISTNER, Lisa Marie. 1930 PEACE HAVEN RD 27106 #035-45-1987 L2004 **IM** *020 †20

KITZMAN, Dalane Wm. MEDICAL CENTER BLVD, WAKE FOREST UNIV HEALTH 27157 #023-07-1984 L1987 **CD IM** *050 †20

KLATT, Laura Ann. OF MED, WAKE FOREST UNIV SCHOOL 27157 #036-01-2005 **FP** *012

KLAUSS, Gunnar. MED CTR BLVD 27157 #408-08-1998 **AN** *012

KLEIN, Steven Russell. 3333 BROOKVIEW HILLS BLVD 27103 #021-01-1974 L1977 **IM IMG** *020 †20

KLEPIN, Heidi Diana. MEDICAL CENTER BLVD, WAKE FOREST U SCH OF MED 27157 #045-01-1998 L2000 **HO** *100 †20

KLINEPETER, Kurt L. 3325 SILAS CREEK PKWY, DEPT OF PEDIATRICS 27103 #011-04-1980 L1985 **PD** *020 †55

KMAN, Nicholas Edward. MED CTR BLVD, WAKE FOREST UNIV 27157 #038-40-2004 L2006 **EM** *100

KNUDSON, Mark Paul. MEDICAL CENTER BLVD. 27157 #051-01-1982 L1987 **FM** *040 †18

KOBAYASHI, Daisuke. MED CTR BLVD 27157 #572-76-2001 **PD** *012

KOCH, Kenneth Louis, Jr. MED CTR BLVD 27157 #018-03-1975 L2002 **GE IM** *020 †20

KOHUT, Robert Irwin. MEDICAL CENTER BLVD, BOWMAN GRAY SCH MED 27157 #016-02-1960 L1979 **HNS OTO** *071 †45

KOK, Lai Chow. 186 KIMEL PARK DR 27103 #825-01-1990 L2004 **ICE CD** *020 †20

KOLASKI, Kat. MEDICAL CENTER BOULEVARD, DEPARTMENT OF ORTHOPEDICS 27157 #041-14-1988 L2001 **PM PD** *020 †60

KOLDER, Laurie Ann. OF MED, WAKE FOREST UNIV SCH 27157 #021-05-2006 **AN** *012

KOMAN, L Andrew. MEDICAL CENTER BLVD, WFU SCHOOL OF MEDICINE 27157 #036-07-1974 L1975 **ORS HS** *020 †40

KON, Neal David. MEDICAL CENTER BLVD, DEPT CARDIOTHORACIC SURGER 27157 #011-03-1979 L1980 **GS TS** *020 †85,90

KOONTZ, Frederick Alan. 3333 SILAS CREEK PKWY 27103 #036-05-1976 L1976 **AN** *020 †05

KOONTZ, Thomas Jeffrey. 3333 SILAS CREEK PKWY 27103 #036-01-1966 L1966 **GS** *020 †85

KOOY-SMITH, Gwyn Ellen. 1900 S HAWTHORNE RD, PEDIATRICS 27103 #036-05-1983 L1985 **PD** *020 †55

KORNEGAY, Alonzo D, Jr. 170 KIMEL PARK DR 27103 #045-01-1974 L1979 **ORS** *020 †40

KORTESIS, Bill Gus. ■ 27103 #036-05-2003 L2008 **PS** *012

KOSTERMAN, Allyson June. ■ 27103 #036-05-2008 *012

KOUBA, Erik Joseph. ■ 27106 #036-01-2007 *012

KOURI, Brian Edward. ■ 27103 #036-01-2002 L2006 **DR** *100 †80

KOURI, Vanessa Kristen. 5025 MEREWORTH CT 27104 #036-01-2002 L2006 **PD** *100 †55

KPODO, Anita Emefa. 301 S HAWTHORNE RD, WAKE FOREST UNIV SCH OF ME 27103 #036-05-2006 **PD** *012

KRAFT, Howard Andrew. 3333 BROOKVIEW HILLS BLVD, STE 104 27103 #012-01-2000 L2005 **N** *020 †75

KRAMER, Stephen I. MEDICAL CENTER BOULEVARD, WAKE FOREST UNIV HEALTH SC 27157 #041-02-1978 L1983 **P PFP** *020 †75

KREITER, Shelley Rae. 3746 VEST MILL RD 27103 #036-05-1992 L1995 **PD** *040 †55

KRETZSCHMAR, Deborah A. MEDICAL CENTER BOULEVARD, DEPT OF GASTROENTEROLOGY 27157 #023-12-1982 L2006 **GE IM** *020 †20 ‡

KRIBBS, Scott Bendon. 3333 SILAS CREEK PKWY 27103 #045-01-1999 L2000 **EM** *020 †16

KROOVAND, Roy Lawrence. 300 S HAWTHORNE RD 27103 #038-41-1968 L1984 **U PD** *040 †95

KROWCHUK, Daniel Peter. MEDICAL CENTER BLVD., WAKE FOREST UNIVERSITY 27157 #036-05-1977 L1990 **PD ADL** *040 †55

KUCERA, Kristin Ann. ■ 27106 #048-02-2007 **OTO** *012

KULITS, John Albert. 2821 MAPLEWOOD AVE, OPHTHALMOLOGIST 27103 #046-01-2001 L2007 **OPH** *020

KUMAR, Rahul. ■ 27103 #016-06-2002 L2006 **IM** *100 †20

KUMAR, Sandhya Rani. MEDICAL CENTER BLVD 27157 #495-95-1991 L2001 **N** *020 †75

KUMMER, Anthony Jos. 250 CHARLOIS BLVD 27103 #019-02-1987 L1994 **IM** *020 †20

KUNDU, Sarba. ■ 27103 #495-37-2000 L2005 **IM** *020 †20

KUNKLE, David Arthur. 140 KIMEL PARK DR 27103 #051-01-2002 L2008 **U** *012

KURUP, Shreekumar. MEDICAL CENTER BOULEVARD, WAKE FOREST UNIVERSITY EYE 27157 #495-44-1993 L2007 **OPH IM** *020 †20,35

KUTCHER, Michael A. MEDICAL CENTER BLVD, WAKE FOREST UNIV. SCH. MED 27157 #041-02-1974 L1981 **CD IM** *020 †20

LABER, Diane Melinda. ■ 27103 #038-41-2003 L2006 **AI** *012 †20

LABER, Patrick William. WAKE FOREST EYE CENTER, 1 MEDICAL CENTER BLVD. 27157 #038-41-2003 L2007 **OPH** *100

LACKEY, Vanessa Blair. ■ 27103 #027-01-2005 **IM** *012

LAGRIMAS, Dolores G. ■ 27103 #748-22-1989 **PTH** *100

LAGUERRE, Patrick Jacques. ■ 27101 #036-05-2005 **AN** *012

LAKOSKI, Susan Gilchrist. MEDICAL CENTER BLVD, INTERNAL MEDICINE/CARDIOLO 27157 #048-13-2000 L2003 **CD** *012 †20

LAMBETH, Wm Arnold, Jr. 3333 SILAS CREEK PKWY 27103 #036-07-1947 L1950 **OS CD** *071 †20

LAMKE, Geoffrey Todd. MEDICAL CENTER BOULEVARD, WFUBMC RADIOLOGY 27157 #026-08-2002 L2004 **MSR** *012 †80

LANAVA, Thomas S. 5640 UNIVERSITY PKWY 27105 #010-02-1970 L2001 **GP PTH** *020 †50

LANDIS, Darryl Lynn. 121 S STRATFORD RD 27104 #041-01-1989 L1995 **FM MDM** *020 †18

LANG, Jason Edward. MEDICAL CENTER BOULEVARD, DEPT ORTHOPAEDIC SURGERY 27157 #036-07-1999 L2007 **ORS** *020

LANGENBRUNNER, Adam David. ■ 27103 #047-20-2007 **EM** *012

LANKTON, Barbara H Ballow. 665 W 4TH ST 27101 #041-01-1971 L1977 **P** *020

LANKTON, James Wm. 3333 SILAS CREEK PKWY, DEPT ANES 27103 #041-01-1971 L1977 **AN** *020 †05

LANTELME, Bruce Edward. 7990 N POINT BLVD, STE 100 27106 #036-05-1983 L1996 **FM** *020 †18

LANTZ, Patrick Eugene. MED CTR BLVD 27157 #016-45-1983 L1990 **PTH** *020 †50

LARSON, Kip Leroy. 3155 MAPLEWOOD AVE 27103 #051-07-1978 L1982 **EM** *020 †16

LATA, Adrian Lucian. ■ 27104 #781-05-1996 L2008 **TS** *012 †85

LATHAM-SADLER, Brenda A. WFU FAMILY & COMMUNITY MED, MEDICAL CTR BLVD 3RD FLR P 27157 #036-05-1982 L1985 **FM** *020 †18

LATTA, Harold Frank, III. 200 ROBINHOOD MEDICAL PLZ, PLAZA DR 27106 #036-08-1987 L1989 **PD** *020 †55

LAUDADIO, Jennifer. ■ 27103 #012-01-2002 L2007 **MGP** *100 †50

LAURIENTI, Janna Denise. 1163 W END BLVD 27101 #048-02-1999 L2001 **NEP IM** *020 †20

LAURIENTI, Paul J. MEDICAL CENTER BLVD, DEPT OF RADIOLOGY 27157 #048-02-1999 **R NRN** *050

LAUVE, Lucie Marie. 1492 RYMCO DR 27103 #021-05-1991 L1995 **N** *020 †75

LAW, Jennifer Rachel. ■ 27127 #055-01-2006 **PD** *012

LAWING, William Lander. 3333 SILAS CREEK PKWY 27103 #036-01-1989 L1993 NEP IM *020 †20

LAWLESS, Michael Rhodes. OF MED, WAKE FOREST UNIV SCH 27157 #048-02-1968 L1974 PD *040 †55

LAXTON, Melissa A. MEDICAL CENTER BLVD 27157 #036-05-1998 L2001 AN *020 †05

LAY, Jessica A. 725 HIGHLAND AVE 27101 #001-02-1992 L1993 P *020 †75

LE, Katherine Yenkhang. ■ 27103 #036-05-2008 *012

LEDERER, James Weil, Jr. 2085 FRONTIS PLAZA BLVD, NOVANT HEALTH CLINICAL 1MP 27103 #036-01-1985 L1986 ID PDI *030 †20,55

LEE, Andrew Dongjun. MEDICAL CENTER BLVD 27157 #014-01-2006 L2006 D *012

LEE, Cassandra Alda. ■ 27103 #024-05-2001 L2008 ORS *012

LEE, Sherman Christopher. MEDICAL CENTER BLVD, WFU SCHOOL OF MED-ANESTHES 27157 #036-05-1999 L2004 AN *105

LEE, W Robert. MED CTR BLVD 27157 #051-01-1989 L1996 RO *020 †80

LEFEBVRE, Cedric William. MEDICAL CENTER BLVD, DEPT OF EMERGENCY MED 27157 #041-02-2003 L2005 EM *100 †16

LEFKOWITZ, David Solomon. MEDICAL CENTER BOULEVARD, OF MEDICINE 27157 #036-05-1978 L1982 N *020 †75

LEGGETT, Derrell Levohn. OF MED, WAKE FOREST UNIV SCH 27157 #001-02-2006 AN *012

LEIGHTON, Stephen Lesher. 1430 HSA LN 27101 #035-09-1976 L1979 FM PME *020 †18

LEKWAUWA, Uren N. 4045 UNIVERSITY PKWY, CENTERPOINT HUMAN SERVICES 27106 #690-03-1980 L1989 P ADM *030 †75

LEMLEY, Douglas Edwin. 250 CHARLOIS BLVD, WINSTON-SALEM HEALTHCARE 27103 #055-01-1982 L1987 DR IM *020 †20,80 ‡

LENCHIK, Leon. MEDICAL CENTER BOULEVARD, DEPARTMENT OF RADIOLOGY 27157 #016-06-1990 L1996 DR *020 †80

LENDLE, Donald Lawrence. 1995 BETHABARA RD, NORTH POINT MEDICAL ASSOCI 27106 #005-02-1974 L1980 FM *020 †18

LENTZ, Samuel Smith. MEDICAL CENTER BLVD, WAKE FOREST U SCH OF MED 27157 #036-05-1978 L1979 OBG GO *020 †30

LENZ, Carolyn. DEPT. OF INTERNAL MEDICINE, WFUBMC-MEDICAL CENTER BLVD 27157 #038-45-2003 L2005 IM *020 †20

LENZ, Peter Hoyt. DEPT. OF INTERNAL MEDICINE, WFUBMC-MEDICAL CENTER BLVD 27157 #038-45-2003 L2006 PCC *012 †20

LEONARD, Ralph Beaumont. 300 S HAWTHORNE RD 27157 #045-01-1977 L1978 EM *040 †16

LESKO, Nadine Maryanne. MED CTR 27157 #035-45-1981 L1982 DR *020 †80

LESSER, Glenn Jay. MED CTR BLVD 27157 #041-14-1987 L1995 ON OS *020 †20

LEVINE, Edward Allen. MEDICAL CENTER BLVD, DEPARTMENT OF SURGERY 27157 #016-42-1985 L1998 SO GS *020 †85

LEVITAN, Denise Angelique. MEDICAL CENTER BLVD 27157 #016-02-1998 L2004 HO *020 †20

LEVY, Pavel Jacob. CTR BLVD, OF MEDICINE MEDICAL 27157 #550-01-1979 L1997 VM OS *020

LEWIS, Andrew Jon. 245 CHARLOIS BLVD, VALAORAS & LEWIS OBSTETRIC 27103 #036-05-1998 L1999 OBG *020 †30

LEWIS, James Angus. ■ 27104 #011-03-1962 L1994 N PMM *020 †75

LEWIS, Zachary Thompson. MEDICAL CENTER BLVD, DEPT OF PATHOLOGY 27157 #012-22-2001 L2003 PTH *100 †50

LEYENDECKER, John Richard. MED CTR BLVD 27157 #041-01-1988 L2004 AR VIR *020 †80 ‡

LI, Gertrude Yingyu. ■ 27127 #036-05-2005 ORS *012

LI, Hong. ■ 27106 #243-16-1992 L2007 PTH *100

LI, Jing. ■ 27104 #243-36-1996 IM *012

LI, Zhongyu John. WAKE FORREST UNIV SCHOOL, DEPT OF ORTHOPAEDICS 27157 #243-43-1987 L2004 HS *100 †40

LICHSTEIN, Peter Riback. MEDICAL CENTER BLVD, WAKE FOREST UNIVERSITY SOM 27157 #025-01-1976 L1978 IM P *020 †20

LIE-NIELSEN, Erik Oistein. ■ 27103 #036-08-2002 L2005 IMG *020 †18

LIE-NIELSEN, Susan Turner. ■ 27103 #036-08-2001 L2005 DR *100 †80

LIGHTFOOT, James Christop. ■ 27127 #019-02-2006 IM *012

LIKASITWATTANAKUL, S. MEDICAL CENTER BLVD, BAPTIST MED CTR 27157 #891-03-1991 CHN *100

LIKITTANASOMBUT, Pornpatr. 341 VILLAGE CROSSING LN, APT D 27104 #891-02-1995 CN *100

LI-MASTERS, Tong. ■ 27127 #012-01-2005 L2006 IM *012

LIN, Jen-Jar. MEDICAL CENTER BLVD, WATLINGTON HALL 27157 #244-04-1980 L1994 PN PD *020 †55

LIN, Shaushau. OF MED, WAKE FOREST UNIV SCH 27157 #036-05-2006 AN *012

LINDEL, William Michael. 2927 LYNDHURST AVE, LYNHURST GYNECOLOGIC ASSOC 27103 #051-01-1984 L1987 OBG *020 †30

LINEBERRY, Jeffrey Todd. 301 S HAWTHORNE RD, WAKE FOREST UNIV SCH OF ME 27103 #036-05-2007 IM *012

LINGLE, Kevin Christian. MEDICAL CENTER BLVD., WAKE FOREST UNIVERSITY BAP 27157 #036-01-2006 L2007 IM *012

LINK, Arthur Stanley. 1381 WESTGATE CENTER DR 27103 #035-01-1972 L1976 ID IM *020 †20

LINK, Kerry Michael. MED CTR BLVD 27157 #035-45-1982 L1983 DR VIR *020 †80

LIPSCOMB, Lewis Dubard, Jr. 114 CHARLOIS BLVD 27103 #027-01-1999 L2000 OBG *020 †30

LISCHKE, Aimee Joy. 3333 BROOKVIEW HILLS BLVD, STE 107 27103 #041-02-1996 L1997 FM *020 †18

LITTLE, William Campbell. MEDICAL CENTER BOULEVARD, BOWMAN GRAY SCHOOL OF MEDI 27157 #038-40-1975 L1986 CD IM *020 †20

LITTLEJOHN, Thomas W, III. 1901 S HAWTHORNE RD, STE 306 27103 #036-01-1973 L1973 FM *050 †18

LIU, Debra Chih-Fen. 725 HIGHLAND OAKS DR, STE 106 27103 #054-04-1981 L1984 D *020 †20,15

LIVELY, Cyndy Ann. 2909 MAPLEWOOD AVE, PEDIATRICS 27103 #012-05-1977 L1983 PD *020 †55

LIZARDO, Diana Esther. 755 HIGHLAND OAKS DR, STE 202 27103 #042-02-1992 L2002 FM *020 †18

LLEWELLYN, Samara Mitchel. 3333 SILAS CREEK PKWY 27103 #036-08-2003 L2004 IM *020 †20

LLIBRE, Giovanni. 755 HIGHLAND OAKS DR, STE 202 27103 #308-05-1993 L1999 IM *020 †20

LOCKE, Adair Quaalebaum. ■ 27127 #045-04-2006 AN *012

LOESER, Richard F, Jr. MEDICAL CENTER BLVD, WAKE FOREST UNIV MED SCH 27157 #055-01-1984 L1985 IM *020 †20

LOGANATHAN, Amritraj Gane. ■ 27103 #038-40-2007 GS *012

LOKESH, Anitha. 250 CHARLOIS BLVD 27103 #495-98-1997 L2003 FM *020 †18

LONG, James Blakeley. ■ 27104 #045-04-2005 L2007 IM *012

LONG, John Damian. MEDICAL CENTER BOULEVARD, WAKE FOREST UNIVERSITY BAP 27157 #051-07-1989 L2006 GE IM *020 †20

LOOYSEN, Kara Denae. ■ 27103 #037-01-2004 N *012

LORD, Richard William, Jr. MED CTR BLVD 27157 #036-05-1988 L1999 FM *020 †18

LORENTZ, Wm Beall, Jr. MEDICINE, WAKE FOREST UNIV. SCHOOLE 27157 #041-02-1963 L1969 PN PD *030 †55

LOUDEN, Barrett Asher. ■ 27127 #055-01-2004 L2008 D *012

LOVORN, Megan Beth. MEDICAL CENTER BLVD. 27157 #051-07-2003 L2007 PM *100

LOWDER, Stephen Carlton. ■ 27103 #051-01-1966 L1999 END IM *071 †20

LOWDERMIK, Tad Williams. 3333 SILAS CREEK PKWY 27103 #011-02-1974 L1975 EM *020 †20

LOWE, Stephan Bechtler. 170 KIMEL PARK DR, CAROLINAS 27103 #036-01-1976 L1976 GS *020 †40

LOYD, Aaron Matthew. ■ 27103 #039-01-2005 L2005 D *012

LUBASH, Glenn David. 730 HIGHLAND OAKS DR, STE 103 27103 #035-08-1954 L2003 NEP IM *071 †20

LUCKETT, Jeremy. ■ 27103 #020-12-2008 *012

LUE, Alvin Joseph. WAKE FOREST, BOWMAN GRAY S, MEDICAL CENTER BLVD. 27157 #566-01-1981 L1995 FM FSM *020 †18

LUGOGO, Njira Lucia. WFUBMC MEDICAL CENTER BLVD, INTERNAL MEDICINE DEPT 27157 #051-04-2001 L2002 PCC *100

LUTHER, Vera Parkhurst. MED CTR BLVD 27157 #028-46-2001 L2002 ID *100

LYDERS, Eric Matthew. ■ 27103 #051-04-2003 L2006 DR *012

LYERLY, Mark Andrew. 145 KIMEL PARK DR, STE 220 27103 #036-07-1988 L1992 NS *020 †25

LYLES, Mary Fennell. MEDICAL CENTER BLVD, DEPT OF MEDICINE 27157 #027-01-1975 L1978 IMG IM *020 †20

MA, Jianjun. ■ 27104 #243-02-1989 ORS *012

MACDOWELL, Ana Luiza. MEDICAL CENTER BOULEVARD, WAKE FOREST UNIVERSITY SCH 27157 #187-13-1992 L2005 AI PD *020 †55,03

MAC GREGOR, Drew Alan. MED CTR BLVD 27157 #049-01-1986 L1990 CCM IM *020 †20

MAC MAHON, Marcus Thos. ■ 27106 #917-29-1960 L1979 GE IM *020

MACOSKO, Cecilie. ■ 27106 #036-05-2006 FP *012

MADDEN, Christopher A. 2000 FRONTIS PLZ BLVD #200, NOVANT MEDICAL GROUP 27103 #011-03-1991 L2006 IM *020 †20

MADDEN, Christopher R. 3333 SILAS CREEK PKWY, FORSYTH MEDICAL CENTER 27103 #012-01-1998 L1999 PCP *020 †50

MAGILNER, David Ira. MEDICAL CENTER BLVD, SCIENCES 27157 #024-01-1993 L2003 PD *020 †55

MAIER, Mark Powers, Jr. 12208 N NC HIGHWAY 150 27127 #045-01-1976 L1977 FM *020 †18

MALDJIAN, Joseph Antoine. MED CTR BLVD 27157 #033-05-1988 L2000 RNR R *020 †80

MALINOWSKI, Beata Larysa. ■ 27104 #759-04-2001 L2007 CCM *012 †20

MA'LUF, Tony Joseph. ■ 27106 #605-01-1966 L1999 OBG *020 †30

MANLEY, Ariana Citabria. ■ 27127 #012-01-2007 PTH *012

MANN, John Foster. 3333 SILAS CREEK PKWY 27103 #036-05-1993 L1995 GS *020 †85

MANNY, Theodore Bergen, Jr. ■ 27103 #048-12-2007 GS *012

MANTHEY, David Edwin. MEDICAL CENTER BLVD, WAKE FOREST SCH MED EMERGY 27157 #051-01-1991 L1999 EM *020 †16

MANUS, Sandi Lazette. MEDICAL CENTER BLVD., WAKE FOREST UNIVERSITY 27157 #055-01-1994 L1995 GE *020 †20

MARBLE, Robert Martin. ■ 27104 #027-01-2005 L2007 EM *012

MARKS, Malcolm Wernick. MEDICAL CENTER BLVD, WAKE FOREST SCHOOL OF MEDI 27157 #021-05-1975 L1988 PS GS *020 †85,65

MARKWALTER, Patrick S. 3155 MAPLEWOOD AVE 27103 #051-04-1994 L2001 DR *020 †80

MARLOWE-ROGERS, Heidi C. WFUBMC, HOUSE STAFF OFFICE 27157 #036-05-1999 L2000 FM *020 †18

MARSHALL, Stephanie Lynne. PO BOX 77096 27109 #036-01-2006 OBG *012

MARTERRE, William Francis. 2933 MAPLEWOOD AVE, STE 4 27103 #051-04-1986 L1994 GS *020 †85

MARTIN, David Franklin. MEDICAL CENTER BLVD, WAKE FOREST U SCH OF MED 27157 #023-07-1982 L1990 ORS OSM *040 †40

MARTIN, Kendra Kathleen. ■ 27104 #036-05-2008 *012

MARTIN, Paul Gray. 175 KIMEL PARK DR 27103 #036-05-1977 L1977 N EM *012

MARTIN, Timothy John. MED CTR BLVD 27157 #051-04-1986 L1991 OPH *020 †35

MARX, Richard Saml. 1381 WESTGATE CENTER DR 27103 #036-05-1974 L1974 ID IM *020 †20

MASCENIK, Thomas Joseph. 175 KIMEL PARK DR, STE 125 27103 #041-09-1974 L1995 N *071 †75 ‡

MASCIELLO, Anthony L. 2932 LYNDHURST AVE 27103 #011-04-1985 L1993 OBG *020 †30 ‡

MASHBURN, Caroline Burns. ■ 27103 #045-01-2005 OBG *012

MASON, Phillip Ross. ■ 27103 #045-04-2008 *012

MASTERS, Shane Christophe. ■ 27127 #012-01-2006 DR *012

MASTROIANNI, Dominick. ■ 27127 #011-04-2007 IM *012

MATERDO, Nobleto Gotilban. ■ 27127 #748-08-1967 L1980 FM *075 †18

MATTERN, Matthew Lawrence. MED CTR BLVD 27157 #422-01-2004 L2008 DR *012

MATTHEWS, Brian Lewis. MEDICAL CENTER BLVD., SCHOOL OF MEDICINE 27157 #036-05-1980 L1982 OTO *020 †45

MATTHEWS, Karen Romaine. 1300 WESTGATE CENTER DR, WESTGATE INTERNAL MEDICINE 27103 #036-05-1981 L1982 IM *020 †20

MATTHEWS, Michelle A. 3333 SILAS CREEK PKWY, INPATIENT PHYSICIANS OF FO 27103 #025-07-1998 L2004 MPD *020 †20

MATTOX, James Dwight. 2990 BETHESDA PL STE 602A 27103 #036-05-1969 L1969 P GP *071 †75

MAXWELL, Kenneth Scruggs. 110 CHARLOIS BLVD, PIEDMONT EAR NOSE & THROAT 27103 #036-01-1989 L1995 OTO *020 †45

MAY, John Scott. MEDICAL CENTER BLVD, DEPT OF OTOLARYNGOLOGY 27157 #036-05-1982 L1983 OTO FPS *020 †45

MAYNARD, Charles Douglas. ■ 27104 #036-05-1959 L1959 DR NR *071 †80,28

MCALLISTER, Beck Deal. ■ 27127 #012-01-2006 ORS *012

MCBRIDE, Allison Shivers. DEPT OF PEDS, MEDICAL CENTER BLVD 27157 #036-01-1999 L2005 PD *020 †55

MCCABE, James Michael. ■ 27101 #847-11-1979 L1981 N P *071 †75

MCCABE, John Michael. 3073 TRENWEST DR, FORSYTH CARDIOLOGY ASSOCS 27103 #051-07-1987 L1999 CD IM *020 †20

MCCAIN, Darla H. 2909 MAPLEWOOD AVE, PEDIATRICS, PLLC 27103 #048-14-1995 L1996 PD *020 †55

MC CAIN, Kenneth Franklin. ■ 27106 #036-01-1960 L1960 A PD *020 †55,03

MC CALL, Charles Emory. MEDICAL CENTER BOULEVARD, SCHOOL OF MEDICINE 27157 #036-05-1961 L1961 IM *020 †20,03

MC CALL, William, Jr. 1381 WESTGATE CENTER DR, AORSYTH INTERNAL MEDICINE 27103 #036-07-1949 L1952 AI IM *071 †20,03

MC CALL, William Vaughn. MED CTR BLVD 27157 #036-07-1984 L1985 **P SME** *020 †75

MC CANDLESS, Danette Gay. MEDICAL CENTER BLVD, DEPT OF PEDIATRICS 27157 #038-43-1995 L2002 **MG** *020

MCCARTHY, Lezah Pagels. ■ 27103 #036-08-2006 L2007 **PTH** *012

MCCARTHY, Sean Christophe. 301 S HAWTHORNE RD, WAKE FOREST UNIV SCH OF ME 27103 #036-05-2006 L2007 **IM** *020

MC CLOUD, Willard L. ■ 27105 #047-07-1948 L1952 **OBG GP** *020

MC CLOUD, Willard L, Jr. 620 CHARLOIS AVE 27101 #047-07-1977 L1980 **OPH** *020

MCCLUNEY, Richard Allen. ■ 27107 #047-06-2005 **AN** *012

MC CONVILLE, Joseph F. 3333 SILAS CREEK PKWY 27103 #030-06-1978 L1983 **AN EM** *020 †05 ‡

MC CORMACK, Joseph Gerard. BOWMAN GREY MED SCH, DEPT MED 27103 #539-04-1972 L1979 **IG ID** *020

MC CUNNIFF, Ann Jones. 3333 SILAS CREEK PKWY, DEPT RAD ONCOLOGY 27103 #012-01-1981 L1983 **RO** *020 †80

MC CUNNIFF, Dennis Edward. 2932 LYNDHURST AVE 27103 #012-01-1981 L1983 **OBG GO** *020 †30

MC CUTCHEN, Thomas M V. MEDICAL CENTER BLVD 27157 #036-05-1995 L2003 **NS** *020 †05

MCCUTHEON, Debra Reid. ■ 27106 #045-04-2007 **AN** *012

MC DONAGH, Anne Mary. ■ 27104 #036-01-1988 L1991 **FM** *074 †18

MC DONALD, Penelope Jane. 3333 SILAS CREEK PKWY, OF FORSYT 27103 #036-08-1989 L1991 **IM** *020 †20

MCDOUGAL-CHUKWUMAH, Letiti. ■ 27127 #036-05-2008 *012

MC GANN, Paul Eugene. MEDICAL CENTER BLVD, DEPT OF INTERNAL MEDICINE 27157 #067-01-1981 L1995 **IM** *020 †20

MC GEE MESA, Maria V. ■ 27106 #847-03-1974 *100

MCGEHEE, Blake Eugene. ■ 27104 #048-02-2005 L2008 **DR** *012

MCGINNIS, Henderson D. MEDICAL CENTER BLVD 27157 #055-02-2001 L2004 **EM ESM** *020 †16

MC GOWEN, Timothy Wade. 170 KIMEL PARK DR 27103 #008-01-1986 L1992 **ORS** *020 †40

MCGOWEN, Tobin A. MEDICAL CENTER BOULEVARD 27157 #048-16-2002 L2003 **PAN** *020 †05

MCGUIRT, William F, Jr. 110 CHARLOIS BLVD, PIEDMONT EAR, NOSE, AND TH 27103 #036-01-1989 L1995 **OTO PDO** *020 †45

MC GUIRT, Wm Frederick. MEDICAL CENTER BLVD, WFUHS DEPT OTOLARYNGOLOGY 27157 #036-05-1968 L1968 **OTO** *030 †45

MCINTIRE, Lisa Michelle. ■ 27103 #021-06-2005 **OPH** *012

MC KEE, Marcia Lynn. WAKE FOREST MEDICAL SCHOOL, DEPT OF PEDIATRICS 27157 #027-01-1981 L1989 **PD** *020 †55

MCKIMMIE, Ryan Lee. ■ 27106 #036-05-2006 **IM** *012

MC KINLEY, Alexander C. ■ 27106 #065-05-1958 L1989 **AN** *071 †05

MC KINLEY, Phillip Howard. 2025 FRONTIS PLAZA BLVD, WINSTON SALEM 27103 #021-01-1972 L1976 **OPH** *020 †35

MC KONE, Robert Clair. MEDICAL CENTER BLVD 27157 #036-05-1958 L1958 **PDC PD** *071 †55

MC LAUGHLIN, Charles A. ■ 27103 #036-05-2003 L2004 **DR** *012

MC LEAN, James Martin. 3333 SILAS CREEK PKWY, WHITAKER REHABILITATION CE 27103 #036-01-1989 L1993 **PM** *020 †60

MC LEAN, Thomas Williams. MEDICAL CENTER BLVD, WAKE FOREST UNIV SCHOOL OF 27157 #045-01-1990 L1998 **PD PHO** *020 †55

MCLORIE, Gordon A. 140 CHARLOIS BLVD 27103 #065-01-1969 L2006 **U UP** *020 †95 ‡

MC MANUS, John Marcus. 3333 SILAS CREEK PKWY 27103 #036-08-1995 L1996 **FM** *020 †18

MC MICHAEL, Amy Jo. MEDICAL CENTER BLVD, DEPT OF DERMATOLOGY 27157 #041-01-1990 L1994 **D** *020 †15

MC MULLEN, Kevin Patrick. MED CTR BLVD 27157 #026-08-1994 L1999 **RO** *020 †80

MC NATT, Stephen S. ■ 27106 #048-02-1994 L2008 **GS** *020 †85

MC NEIL, Cheryl Lynn. MEDICAL CENTER BLVD, WAKE FOREST UNIV SCHL OF M 27157 #036-05-1995 L1996 **N** *020 †75

MC NEIL, Quincy A, Jr. 1900 S HAWTHORNE RD, STE 162 27103 #036-05-1969 L1969 **GYN** *020 †30

MCNEILL, Elena. ■ 27103 #913-11-2000 *100

MC PHERSON, Edgar L, IV. 3333 SILAS CREEK PKWY 27103 #045-01-1995 L2001 **EM** *020 †16

MC PHERSON, Holly M. 1364 WESTGATE CENTER DR, PIEDMONT 27103 #045-01-1996 L2001 **AI** *020 †55,03

MEADORS, Michael Craig. 3333 SILAS CREEK PKWY, INFECTIOUS DISEASE SPECIAL 27103 #021-05-1978 L2001 **ID** *020 †20

MEANS, Robert Lee. ■ 27106 #036-05-1947 L1948 **GS** *071 †85

MEANS, William Elbert. 3333 SILAS CREEK PKWY, FORSYTH MED CTR 27103 #036-05-1974 L1974 **CD IM** *020 †20

MEBRAHTU, Semret Tadesse. 250 CHARLOIS BLVD 27103 #051-01-2003 L2006 **IM** *020 †20

MEIS, Paul Jean. MEDICAL CENTER BLVD, DEPT OF OB-GYN 27157 #018-03-1959 L1977 **OBS OBG** *050 †30

MELIN, Susan Anitra. MEDICAL CTR BLVD, WFU SCH OF MED 27157 #036-05-1985 L1988 **ON HEM** *020 †20

MELOY, Thomas Stuart. 160 KIMEL FOREST DR, STE 100 27103 #036-05-1985 L1989 **PME AN** *020 †05

MELVIN, Eric Joe. 3333 SILAS CREEK PKWY 27103 #036-05-2001 L2002 **IM** *020

MEREDITH, Jay Wayne. MEDICAL CENTER BLVD, WAKE FOREST UNIV SCHL OF M 27157 #036-05-1978 L1979 **TRS TS** *020 †85,90

MEREDITH, Jesse Hedgepeth. MED CTR BLVD 27157 #038-06-1951 L1951 **GS TS** *071 †85,90

MERRELL, Matthew Thomas. ■ 27101 #036-05-2008 *012

MERRILL, David Caswell. MEDICAL CENTER BLVD, WAKE FOREST U, SCHL OF MED 27157 #056-06-1987 L1997 **OBG** *020 †30

MERTZ, Heather Lee. MEDICAL CENTER BLVD, DEPT. OF OBSTETRICS & GYN 27157 #055-01-1995 L1999 **OBG** *020

MESEN, Tolga Berlo. ■ 27103 #036-05-2008 *012

MESSICK, Catherine Sue. MED CTR BLVD 27157 #036-01-1981 L1985 **IMG GYN** *020 †20

METCALF, Douglas Lee. 1900 S HAWTHORNE RD, STE 652 27103 #036-05-1976 L1976 **RHU** *020 †20

MEYER, David Davis. 175 KIMEL PARK DR, STE 125 27103 #036-05-1969 L1969 **N** *020

MEZGER, Kyle Lee. WAKE FOREST U BAPTIST MED, DEPT OF INT MED 27157 #048-16-2003 L2007 **AN** *012 †20

MICHAEL, Davonia Nicole. WAKE FOREST UNIV SCHL MED, DEPT OF PATHOLOGY 27157 #036-01-2001 L2003 **PTH** *020 †50

MIDDLETON, Joseph Lemuel. 3333 SILAS CREEK PKWY 27103 #036-05-1982 L1989 **AN** *020 †05

MILES, Erin Oflynn. ■ 27127 #021-05-2005 **PD** *100

MILES, Matthew Charles. ■ 27127 #021-05-2005 L2006 **IM** *012

MILLER, Aaron Michael. OF MED, WAKE FOREST UNIV SCH 27157 #016-11-2004 L2007 **N** *012

MILLER, Antonius A. MEDICAL CENTER BOULEVARD, WAKE FOREST UNIV SCHL OF M 27157 #409-25-1977 L2000 **ON HEM** *020

MILLER, Ashley Clark. ■ 27127 #035-48-2004 **FM** *020 †18

MILLER, Brigitte Eva. MEDICAL CENTER BLVD, WAKE FOREST UNIV HLTH SCI 27157 #409-25-1977 L2000 **OBG GO** *040 †30

MILLER, Chadwick David. MEDICAL CENTER BLVD 27157 #038-44-2000 L2003 **EM** *020 †16

MILLER, David Philip, Jr. MEDICAL CENTER BLVD, HEALTH SCIENCES 27157 #041-01-1996 L2000 **IM** *040 †20

MILLER, Drew Wilson. MEDICAL CENTER BLVD 27157 #016-06-2006 **D** *012

MILLER, Henry Shelton. MEDICAL CENTER BLVD, WAKE FOREST UNIV SCHOOL OF 27157 #036-05-1954 L1954 **CD IM** *020 †20

MILLER, Lewis Mccoy, III. ■ 27103 #012-22-2003 **CHN** *012

MILLER, Norman Eric. BOWMAN GRAY MED SCHOOL 27103 #917-08-1968 L1988 **END IM** *030

MILLER, Preston R, III. MED CTR BLVD 27157 #036-05-1993 L2001 **CCS** *020 †85

MILLER, Scott Alan. MEDICAL CENTER BLVD, WAKE FOREST UNIV SCHL MED 27157 #026-04-1997 L2004 **AN** *020 †05

MILLER, Stacey Michelle. ■ 27127 #001-06-2007 **IM** *012

MILLMAN, Franklyn Milton. MEDICAL CENTER BLVD, FL 8 27157 #005-02-1967 L1994 **A PUD** *020 †03,20

MIMS, Alice Scott. 1200 N MARTN LTHR KNG JR, DOWNTOWN HEALTH PLAZA 27101 #045-01-2005 L2007 **IM** *012

MIMS, Grover Ray, III. ■ 27104 #036-05-1966 L1966 **AN** *071 †05

MIMS, James Whitman. MED CTR BLVD 27157 #036-01-1995 L2000 **OTO** *020 †45

MIMS, Jaqueline Heder. 2927 LYNDHURST AVE, LYNDHURST GYNECOLOGIC ASSO 27103 #036-01-1994 L1998 **OBG** *020 †30

MINDEL, Eugene D. ■ 27104 #010-01-1960 L1997 **P CHP** *020 †75

MIRANDA, Emelda G. MED CTR BLVD, NC BAPTIST HOSP 27157 #748-10-1990 **PD** *020 †55

MISHRA, Girish. MED CTR BLVD 27157 #028-03-1992 L2001 **GE** *020 †20

MISHRA, Nila Madhab. MED CTR BLVD 27157 #496-05-1994 L2000 **RHU** *012

MITCHELL, Mark Anthony. 3821 FORRESTGATE DR, WINSTON-SALEM CARDIOLOGY A 27103 #033-06-1990 L1998 **CD** *020 †20

MITCHELL, Sandra Elaine. 3333 SILAS CREEK PKWY 27103 #038-41-1985 L2002 **RO** *020 †80

MIYAZAKI, Doug Wayne. 114 CHARLOIS BLVD, WINSTON-SALEM WOMANCARE PA 27103 #036-05-1990 L1993 **OBG** *020 †30

MOBLEY, Jessica Leigh. ■ 27101 #051-01-2007 **AN** *012

MODARRESS, John. ■ 27106 #517-01-1952 L1992 **GS** *071 †85

MOFFET, Cynthia Ann. 101 HOSPICE LN, HOSPICE & PALLIUTIVE CARE 27103 #011-02-1990 L2006 **FM** *020 †18

MOHLER, Steven Lloyd. ■ 27104 #038-40-1990 L1998 **DR** *012 †16

MOLNAR, Istvan. MED CTR BLVD 27157 #473-01-1991 L2000 **HO** *020 †20

MOLNAR, Joseph Andrew. MED CTR BLVD 27157 #038-40-1977 L1994 **HS AN** *020 †65

MONDI, Kelley Velinda. ■ 27103 #036-05-2005 L2008 **FP** *012

MONDI, Matthew Michael. MEDICAL CENTER BLVD, 5TH FL WATLINGTON HALL 27157 #036-01-2001 L2004 **GS** *020

MONJAZEB, Arta Monir. DEPT OF RADIATION ONCOLOGY, WAKE FOREST UNIV SCHOOL OF 27157 #036-05-2005 **RO** *012

MONROE, Anna Genevieve. ■ 27101 #027-01-2006 **EM** *012

MONROE, Charles Timothy. ■ 27106 #036-01-1980 L1981 **PHP** *074 †55

MONROE, John Howard. ■ 27104 #024-01-1947 L1947 **GYN OBS** *071 †30

MONROE, Lanny Lee, Jr. 1930 PEACE HAVEN RD 27106 #027-01-2001 L2006 **PD** *020 †55

MONTGOMERY, Richard Lewis. 3333 SILAS CREEK PKWY, EMERGENCY DEPARTMENT 27103 #036-05-1980 L1981 **EM** *020 †16

MONTGOMERY, Wm Gardener. 140 KIMEL PARK DR 27103 #036-05-1952 L1952 **U** *062 †95

MOODY, Brad Robert. ■ 27127 #001-06-2005 **GS** *012

MOODY, Dixon Mc Guire. MEDICAL CENTER BLVD, WAKE FOREST UNIV SCH OF ME 27157 #048-12-1963 L1974 **DR RNR** *020 †80

MOORE, Mary Patricia. 1 MEDICAL CENTER BOULEVARD 27157 #047-20-2003 L2007 **CHP** *012

MOORE, Phillip Schmitz. ■ 27103 #036-05-2002 **GS** *012

MOORE, Wendy Colleen. MEDICAL CENTER BLVD, DIV OF PULMONARY & CRIT CA 27157 #023-01-1991 L2000 **PUD CCM** *020 †20

MOORE, William Nicholas. ■ 27103 #051-01-2006 L2008 **EM** *012

MOORE, William Scott. 730 HIGHLAND OAKS DR, STE 103 27103 #041-14-1978 L1979 **NEP** *020 †20

MOORMAN, Drew Sumner. ■ 27104 #012-22-2005 L2008 **PD** *012

MOOSE, Beverly Dawn. 3333 SILAS CREEK PKWY, DEPT OF RADIATION ONCOLOGY 27103 #036-05-1990 L1996 **RO** *020 †80

MOOSSAVI, Shahriar. MEDICAL CENTER BLVD, DIV OF NEPHROLOGY 27157 #409-20-1994 L2002 **NEP** *020 †20

MORGAN, Gary Lon, Jr. 5010 PETERS CREEK PKWY, FREIDBERG FAMILY MEDICINE 27127 #036-05-1992 L1995 **FM** *020 †18

MORGAN, Joel Clarence. 2827 LYNDHURST AVE 27103 #036-05-1978 L1979 **TS** *020 †85,90

MORGAN, M Ken, II. 400 JONESTOWN RD 27104 #036-05-1980 L1982 **FM** *020 †18

MORRIS, Padraig Pearse. MED CTR BLVD 27157 #036-05-1983 L1998 **RNR** *020 †75,80

MORRIS, Peter Eugene. MED CTR BLVD 27157 #035-20-1985 L1999 **PUD IM** *020 †20

MORROW, Phillip Ray, Jr. MEDICAL CENTER BLVD, FL 8 27157 #036-05-1994 L1995 **IM** *020 †20

MOTEW, Stephen Joel. 3333 SILAS CREEK PKWY 27103 #016-11-1992 L2000 **VS** *020 †85

MOU, Steven Shi-Tsen. MED CTR BLVD 27157 #038-40-1995 L2002 **CCP** *020 †55

MOUNTJOY, John Robt. MED CTR BLVD 27157 #010-01-1966 L1974 **OTO** *020 †45

MOYA, Frank Joseph. 2025 FRONTIS PLAZA BLVD, WINSTON SALEM 27103 #008-01-1997 L2001 **OPH** *020 †35

MOYER, Donna B. 2808 MAPLEWOOD AVE 27103 #036-05-1979 L1999 **PD** *020 †55

MOYER, Frank Rabe. 100 ROBINHOOD MEDICAL PLZ 27106 #036-05-1978 L2004 **FM** *020 †18

MOYLE, Megan Christine. 190 KIMEL PARK DR, OUTPATIENT CLINIC 27103 #012-05-1999 L2002 **IM** *020 †20

MOZINGO, Willis Scott. ■ 27114 #051-04-2008 *012

MUELLER, John Collet. 190 KIMEL PARK DR 27103 #024-07-1964 L1971 **IM DIA** *020 †20

MURPHY, Daniel Wm. 1901 S HAWTHORNE RD, STE 310 27103 #038-41-1981 L1982 **GE** *020 †20

MURPHY, Martin James. 250 CHARLOIS BLVD, WINSTON-SALEM HEALTH CARE 27103 #035-45-1988 L1991 **IM** *020 †20

MURPHY, Nancy L. 250 CHARLOIS BLVD 27103 #035-45-1988 L1991 **IM** *020 †20

MURPHY, Sean Michael. 3333 SILAS CREEK PKWY 27103 #027-01-1996 L1998 **PCC** *020 †20

MURRAY, Gayle Monica. ■ 27103 #035-15-2005 **PD** *012

MURRAY, Nial Patrick. ■ 27104 #539-03-1954 L1982 **AN** *071 †05

MUTTAGI, Vasudha P. MEDICAL CENTER BLVD, MEDICAL CENTER BLVD 27157 #495-01-1991 L2004 **IM** *020 †55

MUTTON, Thomas Paul. 3001 MAPLEWOOD AVE, ARDMORE MED BLDG 27103 #036-05-1973 L1973 **GS EM** *020 †85

MYERS, Leticia Shawn. 1900 S HAWTHORNE RD, STE 480A 27103 #036-05-1997 L2000 **PD** *020 †55

MYERS, Wendell Stephen. MEDICAL CENTER BOULEVARD, WAKE FOREST UNIVERSITY BAP 27157 #036-05-1990 L1992 **DR** *020 †80

MYRACLE, John Hobart. 250 CHARLOIS BLVD 27103 #039-01-1974 L1978 **PD PDC** *030 †55

MYTON, Suzette Noella. WFU SCHOOL OF MED, DEPT OF ANESTHESIOLOGY 27157 #038-45-2005 **AN** *012

NADKARNI, Milan D. MED CTR BLVD 27157 #496-38-1982 L1997 **PD PEM** *020 †55

NADLER, Jaclyn Sheri. BOX 2263, MEDICAL CENTER BLVD 27157 #011-02-2005 L2006 **IM** *012

NAGARAJ, Shashi Kumar. MED CTR BLVD 27157 #495-37-1983 L1997 **PN** *020 †55

NAGESWARAN, Savithri. WAKE FOREST UNIV SCH MED, DEPT OF PEDIATRICS 27157 #495-59-1989 L2003 **PD** *050 †55,70

NAGGAR, Hany. ■ 27127 #012-01-2007 **IM** *012

NAGLE, Pamela Cochran. MEDICAL CENTER BLVD, DEPT OF ANESTHESIOLOGY 27157 #036-05-1999 L2000 **AN** *100 †55,05

NAGY, Stephen Stanley. 2821 MAPLEWOOD AVE, HAWTHORNE EYE ASSOCIATES, 27103 #036-05-1994 L1998 **OPH** *020 †35

NAKAGAWA, Thomas Alan. MED CTR BLVD 27157 #048-15-1986 L2002 **CCP PD** *020 †55

NAMAK, Shahla Yousif. MEDICAL CENTER BOULEVARD, DEPT OF FAMILY MEDICINE 27157 #528-02-1984 L2005 **FM** *020 †18

NANTON, Jaleema Regine. ■ 27106 #036-05-2008 *012

NASTASI, Kent Jos. 1372 WESTGATE CENTER DR, ASSOCIATES 27103 #021-05-1991 L1997 **IM** *020 †20,55,03

NEFF, Lucas Paul. ■ 27157 #047-20-2006 L2007 **GS** *012

NEISON, David P. MED CTR BLVD, WAKE FOREST UNIV 27157 #048-14-2006 **EM** *012

NELSON, H Vard. ■ 27106 #028-78-1954, ▲ L1954 *071

NELSON, Kenneth Edward. 3333 SILAS CREEK PKWY 27103 #048-14-1992 L1996 **AN** *020 †05

NELSON, Lewis Henry, III. 1928 VIRGINIA RD 27104 #036-05-1970 L1970 **OBG** *030 †30

NELSON, Mark Harvey. 750 HIGHLAND OAKS DR, STE 100 27103 #033-06-1982 L1988 **OPH OS** *020 †35

NELSON, Matthew Ryan. ■ 27127 #018-03-2005 L2006 **IM** *012

NEWSOME, Albert Ray. 1381 WESTGATE CENTER DR 27103 #036-01-1961 L1961 **CD IM** *071 †20

NEWSOME, George Burgwyn. 140 KIMEL PARK DR 27103 #036-05-1989 L1994 **U** *020 †95

NEWTON, Christopher D. ■ 27103 #048-16-2004 L2007 **DR** *012

NEWTON, Jimmie Isaac. 3333 SILAS CREEK PKWY 27103 #036-01-1964 L2003 **GYN** *020 †30

NEWTON, William B, III. ■ 27127 #045-01-2001 L2004 **GS** *012

NICASTRO, Joseph Francis. 300 S HAWTHORNE RD 27103 #056-06-1969 L1973 **ORS** *020 †40

NICHOLS, Margaret Kitt. ■ 27106 #035-45-1987 L1988 **GPM** *020 †70

NICHOLS, Virginia Guest. 1 MEDICAL CENTER BLVD, PEDIATRICS BOWMAN GRAY 27157 #045-01-1984 L1987 **NPM PD** *020 †55

NICKLAS, Edward Wilson, II. 755 HIGHLAND OAKS DR, STE 201 27103 #036-08-1996 L2005 **END** *020 †20

NICKS, Bret Anthony. MED CTR BLVD 27157 #054-04-2001 L2004 **EM** *020 †16

NIFONG, Kimberly Ragsdale. 5350 S MAIN ST 27107 #036-05-2000 L2002 **FM** *020 †18

NIFONG, Ted James. 5350 S MAIN ST 27107 #036-05-1987 L1988 **FM** *020 †18

NOGO, Adnan. 190 KIMEL PARK DR, OUTPATIENT CLINIC 27103 #957-08-1987 L2006 **FM** *100 †18

NOLAN, Robert Earl. ■ 27106 #038-06-1955 L1960 **GS VS** *071 †85

NOMEIR, Abdel-Mohsen Amin. MED CTR BLVD 27157 #915-03-1952 L1972 **CD IM** *020 †20

NORMAN, Calvin Haines. ■ 27106 #010-03-1956 L1962 **GP R** *020 †80

NTIM, William Ofori. MEDICAL CENTER BLVD, WAKE FOREST UNIVERSITY SCH 27157 #412-01-1992 L2005 **CD** *020 †20

NUNEZ, Marina. ■ 27157 #847-11-1988 L2006 **ID** *100

NYCUM, Lawrence Ross. 1010 BETHESDA CT 27103 #036-01-1990 L1995 **GO** *020 †30

NYINAKU-YEBOAH, Phyllis K. 3333 SILAS CREEK PKWY 27103 #412-01-2000 L2005 **IM** *020 †20

OAKS, Timothy Eugene. 5TH FLOOR, WATLINGTON HALL, WAKE FOREST UNIVERSITY 27157 #041-14-1984 L1993 **TS CD** *020 †85,90

OBER, Karl Patrick. MEDICAL CENTER BLVD 27157 #011-03-1974 L1976 **END IM** *040 †20

O'BRIEN, David Reese, Jr. 3333 SILAS CREEK PKWY 27103 #017-20-1991 L2000 **PM PMM** *020 †60

O'BRIEN, Francis X, Jr. MEDICAL CENTER BLVD, FL 8 27157 #041-13-1985 L1998 **IM** *020 †20 ‡

O'BRIEN, James Jos. MED CTR BLVD 27157 #051-04-1983 L1991 **AN PD** *020 †55,05

O'BRIEN, Mary Claire. MED CTR BLVD 27157 #041-13-1985 L1998 **EM** *012 †16

O'DONOVAN, Cormac A. MEDCIAL CENTER BOULEVARD, WFUSM DEPT NEUROLOGY 27157 #539-05-1985 L1995 **N** *020 †75

O'FLAHERTY, Joseph Thos. BOWAN GRAY SCH MED DPT/IM 27103 #041-13-1972 L1981 **HEM GP** *050 †20

OHAR, Jill Ann. MED CTR BLVD 27157 #041-07-1977 L2002 **IM PUD** *050 †20

OHL, Christopher Alan. 100 MEDICAL CENTER DRIVE, WAKE FOREST UNIVERSITY 27157 #056-05-1986 L1996 **ID IM** *040 †20

OLIPHANT, Michael. MED CTR BLVD 27157 #035-20-1967 L1974 **R OS** *020 †80

OLSEN, Kathryn Marie. MED CTR BLVD, WAKE FOREST U BAPTIST M C 27157 #063-01-2004 L2008 **DR** *012

OLULADE, Abisola Adebola. ■ 27104 #036-05-2008 *012

OLYMPIO, Michael Allen. MEDICAL CENTER BLVD, DEPT OF ANESTHESIA 27157 #011-03-1982 L1984 **AN** *020 †05

O'MEARA, Thomas Michael. 1959 PEACE HAVEN RD, # 321 27106 #050-02-1984 L1999 **EM** *020 †18

ONAFUYE, Rasheed Adeyinka. MED CTR BLVD 27157 #913-12-1997 **P** *012

OPITZ, Brian Anthony. ■ 27127 #031-01-2007 **EM** *012

ORBOCK, Jacob Alexander. 250 CHARLOIS BLVD 27103 #041-02-1962 L1979 **CD IM** *020 †20

ORLI, Julie. ■ 27106 #759-10-1976 L1988 **P IM** *020 †75

O'ROURKE, Kenneth Stuart. MEDICAL CENTER BLVD, WAKE FOREST SCHOOL OF MEDI 27157 #010-01-1983 L1992 **RHU IM** *020 †20

ORR, Liston Anderson. 3155 MAPLEWOOD AVE, FORSYTH RADIOLOGICAL ASSOC 27103 #036-08-1987 L1992 **NM DR** *020 †80,28

ORTEGA, Victor Enrique. OF MED, WAKE FOREST UNIV SCH 27157 #042-02-2002 L2006 **PCC** *012 †20

OSBORNE, Jody Neil. WAKE FOREST U BAPTIST MED, MEDICAL CENTER BLVD 27157 #036-08-2001 L2002 **EM** *020 †16

O'SHEA, Thomas M D, Jr. WAKE FORREST UNIV SCH MED, DEPT PEDS BLAINS MED SCH B 27157 #036-01-1980 L1982 **NPM EM** *020 †55,20

OTT, David James. MEDICAL CENTER BLVD 27157 #025-01-1971 L1972 **DR NM** *020 †80

OUTLAW, William Marcus. ■ 27106 #011-03-2001 L2004 **GE** *100 †20

OVERHOLT, Candi Cashen. ■ 27127 #047-06-2006 L2007 **IM** *012

OWEN, John. MED CTR BLVD 27157 #065-10-1974 L1989 **HEM IM** *040

OWEN, Medge Denise. 95 W 32ND ST, R J REYNOLDS TOBACCO COMPA 27105 #019-02-1989 L1994 **AN** *020 †05

PAHOR, Marco. MEDICAL CENTER BLVD, STICHT BLDG 27157 #561-23-1980 L1999 **IMG** *030

PAITSEL, Brian Wayne. ■ 27127 #036-05-2004 L2008 **AN** *012

PALAVECINO, Elizabeth Leo. MED CTR BLVD 27157 #231-01-1980 L2003 **CLP MM** *020 †50

PALMER, William, Jr. 3333 SILAS CREEK PKWY 27103 #035-06-1990 L2002 **PM** *020

PALMES, Guy Kevin. MEDICAL CENTER BLVD 27157 #045-07-1990 L1998 **CHP** *020 †75

PANNELL, Christa Raneeida. 799 HICKORY TREE RD 27127 #023-01-1999 L2003 **FM** *020 †55

PAPADONIKOLAKIS, Anastasio. ■ 27104 #418-04-1999 **ORS** *012

PARK, Christopher Ashley. 1 MEDICAL CENTER BLVD 27157 #001-02-2001 L2007 **PS** *020

PARK, Elizabeth Arnold. ■ 27103 #001-02-2003 **DR** *012

PARKE, Charles William Ke. 160 KIMEL FOREST DR, STE 250 27103 #495-11-1961 L1999 **CD IM** *020 †20

PARKER, Peter Emens. 2933 MAPLEWOOD AVE, STE 4 27103 #038-40-1960 L1966 **GS** *020 †85

PARKS, Graham Eric. ■ 27106 #045-04-2006 **PTH** *012

PARKS, Lenore Yvonne. MEDICAL CENTER BLVD, DEPT OF PEDS WFUSM 27157 #036-08-1990 L1992 **PD** *040 †55

PARSONS, Amy Carol. ■ 27106 #047-20-2005 **PTH** *012

PARSONS, Linn H. 300 S HAWTHORNE RD 27103 #036-01-1976 L1976 **OBG** *020 †30

PASCUAL, Rodolfo Marshall. MED CTR BLVD 27157 #041-02-1994 L2003 **IM PCC** *050 †20

PASHAYAN, Mark Albert. 3746 VEST MILL RD, WESTGATE EXECUTIVE CTR 27103 #036-05-1978 L1995 **PD** *020 †55

PASSMAN, Corey Matthew. ■ 27104 #001-02-2002 L2007 **U** *100

PATEL, Amar Prabodh. 27101 #036-05-2008 *012

PATEL, Arpita Vikram. ■ 27103 #001-06-2005 **N** *012

PATEL, Bhavin Naren. ■ 27103 #005-19-2006 **GS** *012

PATEL, Hirenkumar Babubha. MED CTR BLVD 27157 #422-01-2002 L2008 **NPM** *012 †55

PATEL, Shomeet Vikram. ■ 27103 #496-41-2002 L2007 **IM** *020 †20

PATTERSON, Richard Bruce. ■ 27106 #036-05-1955 L1955 **PHO HEM** *071 †55

PATTON, William Rudd. 3155 MAPLEWOOD AVE, FORSYTH RADIOLOGICAL ASSOC 27103 #051-04-1996 L2005 **RNR** *020 †80

PAUCA, Alfredo L. MEDICAL CENTER BOULEVARD, SCHOOL OF MEDICINE 27157 #737-01-1958 L1977 **AN** *071 †55

PAYNTER, Robert M, Jr. 1351 WESTGATE CENTER DR 27103 #036-05-1998 L2001 **PD** *020 †55

PEACOCK, James Edward, Jr. MEDICAL CENTER BLVD, SCHOOL OF MEDICINE 27157 #036-01-1975 L1979 **ID IM** *020 †20

PEACOCK, Jeffrey Edward. ■ 27104 #036-05-2008 *012

PEARCE, Daniel Jenkins. MEDICAL CENTER BLVD 27157 #036-05-2002 L2004 **D** *012

PEARCE, Jeffrey David. MEDICAL CENTER BLVD, HOUSE STAFF OFFICE 27157 #011-03-2000 L2002 **VS** *012

PEARCY, Walter Curtis. 3073 TRENWEST DR 27103 #045-04-1987 L1994 **CD** *020 †20

PEARL, Allison Lauren. MEDICAL CENTER BLVD, DEPT OF RADIOLOGY 27157 #031-01-2001 L2003 **DR** *020 †20

PECK, Arika Leone. ■ 27103 #036-05-2008 *012

PEDLEY, Carolyn Frances. MED CTR BLVD 27157 #036-07-1977 L1979 **IM** *020 †20

PEGRAM, Paul Saml, Jr. MEDICAL CENTER BLVD, SCHOOL OF MEDICINE 27157 #036-05-1970 L1970 **ID** *040 †20

PENCE, Jill C. 755 HIGHLAND OAKS DR, STE 102 27103 #036-05-1984 L1987 **IM** *020 †20

PENKAR, Suresh Jagannath. 145 KIMEL PARK DR, STE 300 27103 #496-38-1970 L1976 **AN PMM** *020 †05

PENNELL, Timothy Clinard. MEDICAL CENTER BLVD, BOWMAN GRAY SCH OF MED 27157 #036-05-1960 L1960 **GS TS** *071 †85

PENRY, James Kiffin. BOWMAN GRAY SCH MED NEUR 27103 #036-05-1955 L1955 **N CHN** *071 †75

PEPPER, Francis Dewitt. ■ 27106 #036-01-1956 L1956 **R OS** *071 †80

PERAL, Lindsay Seawright. 100 ROBINHOOD MEDICAL PLZ 27106 #036-05-2001 L2003 **FM** *020 †18

PERKINS, Louis Allen. ■ 27106 #045-04-2003 L2008 **SP** *012

PERRY, Joseph Todd. 600 HIGHLAND OAKS DR 27103 #036-05-1996 L1997 **FM** *020 †18

PERTILE, Rachel Oneill. 190 KIMEL PARK DR, VETERANS AFFAIRS OUTPATIEN 27103 #045-04-2000 L2002 **FM** *020 †18

PERUMPILLICHIRA, James Jo. MEDICAL CENTER BLVD, WAKE FOREST UNIVERSITY HEA 27157 #495-44-1994 L2005 *100

PETERS, Donald Walter. MEDICAL CENTER BLVD 27157 #036-01-1982 L1984 **P** *020 †75

PETERS, Randy Alan. 1830 S HAWTHORNE RD, SALEM GASTROENTEROLOGY ASS 27103 #051-01-1982 L1987 **GE IM** *020 †20

PETERS, Stephen Paul. 4510 CHINABERRY LN 27106 #041-12-1978 L2003 **PUD AI** *050 †20 ‡

PETERS, Thomas Geo. 725 HIGHLAND AVE 27101 #008-01-1963 L1984 **CHP P** *030

PETERS, Timothy Ross. MEDICAL CENTER BOULEVARD, WAKE FOREST UNIVERSITY 27157 #008-01-1996 L2007 **PDI** *020 †55

PETERSON, Celeste Knight. MEDICAL CNTR BLVD 27157 #049-01-1993 L1995 **IM** *020 †20

PETROZZA, Patricia Harper. MEDICAL CENTER BLVD, WAKE FOREST UNIVERSITY 27157 #041-02-1978 L1984 **AN MDM** *020 †05

PETTUS, Joseph Atkins, IV. DEPT OF UROLOGY, MEDICAL CENTER BLVD 27157 #001-02-2000 L2007 **U** *100

PETTY, John Kenneth. MEDICAL CENTER BOULEVARD, DEPT OF GENERAL SURGERY, W 27157 #036-01-1997 L2005 **PDS** *100 †85

PETTY, William Jeffrey. MEDICAL CENTER BLVD, WAKE FOREST UNIVERSITY SCH 27157 #036-01-1998 L2005 **HO** *020 †20

PHAN, Anh-Danh Thi. WAKE FOREST UNIV EYE CT, MEDICAL CENTER BLVD 27157 #010-03-1999 L2006 **OPH** *020 †35

PHAN, Thai Tien. 1321 ASHLEYBROOK LN, ASHLEYBROOK CLINIC PA 27103 #941-02-1972 L1995 **FM** *020 †75 ‡

PHILLIPPI, Paul Jasper. 3333 SILAS CREEK PKWY 27103 #047-06-1956 L1965 **IM NEP** *071 †20

PHILLIPS, Christopher J. 3333 SILAS CREEK PKWY, INPATIENT PHYSICIANS FORSY 27103 #021-06-2003 L2006 **IM** *020 †20

PHILLIPS, Ernest Paul, Jr. 186 KIMEL PARK DR 27103 #011-03-1978 L1979 **IM CD** *020 †20

PHILLIPS, Wesley Fletcher. 1950 S HAWTHORNE RD 27103 #036-05-1962 L1962 **FM** *071 †18

PHIPPS, Carl Spencer. 850 YORKSHIRE RD 27106 #036-01-1962 L1962 END IM *071 †20

PHIPPS, John Dickson. 730 HIGHLAND OAKS DR, STE 202 27103 #036-01-1993 L1995 END *020 †20

PIAZZA, Michael John. 861 WATSON AVE 27103 #036-05-2003 L2006 IM *020 †20

PICHARDO, Rita. MEDICAL CENTER BLVD, DEPT OF DERM 27157 #308-03-1985 L2005 D DMP *020

PIEDE, John Allen. ■ 27127 #012-01-2006 IM *012

PIERCE, Angela Gail. MED C, WAKE FOREST UNIV BAPTIST 27157 #045-01-2007 FP *012

PIERCE, Helen Elizabeth. ■ 27103 #036-05-2003 L2007 IM *020 †20

PIERRE, Frantz Eli. ■ 27104 #036-05-2006 P *012

PIERSON, Eric David. MEDICAL CENTER BLVD, DEPARTMENT OF MEDICINE, NE 27157 #051-07-2002 L2007 NEP *020 †20

PIKULA, Louis, Jr. 3333 SILAS CREEK PKWY 27103 #036-05-1961 L1961 NS *071 †25

PILAND, Monroe Gordon. ■ 27101 #036-05-1977 L1979 *075

PINDER, Julie M. 200 ROBINHOOD MEDICAL PLZ, PLAZA DR 27106 #036-05-1994 L1996 PD *020 †55

PINKERTON, Gregory Nolan. 3333 SILAS CREEK PKWY, FORSYTH MEMORIAL HOSPITAL 27103 #023-01-1977 L1994 IM IMG *020 †20

PINYAN, Clark William. 175 KIMEL PARK DR, STE 100 27103 #001-02-1998 L2000 CN *020 †75

PITOVSKI, Dimitri Zivko. MEDICAL CENTER BLVD., WAKE FOREST MEDICAL SCHOOL 27157 #957-04-1986 L2001 OTO ALI *020

PITTAWAY, Donald Edward. 3333 BROOKVIEW HILLS BLVD, STE 105 27103 #021-06-1977 L1983 REN GYN *020 †30

PITTS, Shannon Yvette. DEPT OF PSYCHIATRY, WAKE FOREST UNIV SCH OF ME 27157 #047-20-2004 P *012

PIVOR, Mitchell. 1930 PEACE HAVEN RD 27106 #021-01-1983 L1998 PD *030 †55

PLIKAITIS, Christina M. ■ 27103 #016-11-2003 PS *012

PLONK, Drew Patterson. ■ 27104 #036-05-2006 OTO *012

PLONK, George Webb. MEDICAL CENTER BLVD 27157 #036-05-1973 L1973 GS VS *020 †85

POEHLING, Gary Geo. 131 MILLER ST 27103 #056-06-1968 L1976 ORS *020 †40

POEHLING, Katherine Anne. MEDICAL CENTER BLVD, DEPT OF PEDS/WFU MED CTR 27157 #036-05-1995 L2007 PD *050 †55

POLLAK, Michael Jos. 725 HIGHLAND AVE 27101 #051-04-1968 L1974 OBG *020 †30

POLLARD, Harold C, III. 2927 LYNDHURST AVE, LYNDHURST GYNECOLOGIC ASSO 27103 #036-01-1973 L1974 OBG *020 †30

POLLOCK, Frank Edward. BOWMAN GRAY SCHOOL OF MED, DEPT OF ORTHOPAEDIC SURG 27157 #038-40-1954 L1957 ORS OS *071 †40

POLLOCK, Jeffrey Michael. ■ 27103 #001-06-2001 L2005 RNR *012 †80

POMBO, Mathew William. BOULEVARD, BOX, MEDICAL CENTER 27157 #012-01-2002 L2007 OSM *012

POMPER, Gregory Jay. MED CTR BLVD, PATHOLOGY DEPT 27157 #041-12-1993 L2001 BBK *020 †50

PONDER, Philip Wade. 114 CHARLOIS BLVD, WINSTON-SALEM WOMANCARE, P 27103 #036-01-1990 L1992 OBG *020 †30

PORCELLI, Peter John, Jr. MED CTR BLVD 27157 #033-05-1985 L1990 NPM PD *020 †55

PORTER, John Arthur H. 3333 BROOKVIEW HILLS BLVD, STE 104 27103 #065-05-1971 L1998 N *020 †75

PORTER, Justin Ross. ■ 27127 #039-01-2008 *012

POTTS, Stephen Bradley. 110 CHARLOIS BLVD 27103 #036-07-1991 L1993 OTO *020 †45

POWELL, Bayard Lowery. MEDICAL CENTER BLVD, CANCER CTR OF WAKE FOREST 27157 #036-01-1980 L1981 ON HEM *020 †20

POWELL, Glen Ellis. ■ 27103 #020-02-2004 L2008 OBG *012

POWELL, Myron Sheavictor. ■ 27127 #036-08-2005 GS *012

POWERS, Alexander K. ■ 27103 #011-04-2002 NS *012

POWERS, James Nichols. ■ 27107 #047-06-2004 ID *012

POYNTER, David Jeffrey. ■ 27103 #036-05-2008 *012

PRANIKOFF, Thomas. MEDICAL CENTER BLVD, DEPT OF SURGERY 27157 #024-07-1988 L1997 PDS CCS *020 †85

PRELI, Robert Bruno. 186 KIMEL PARK DR, WINSTON-SALEM CARDIOLOGY A 27103 #036-05-1999 L2000 IC CD *020 †20

PRIME, Darryl Dwayne. MEDICAL CENTER BLVD, INTERNAL MEDICINE-CARDIOLO 27157 #001-02-2002 L2006 CD *012 †20

PRINCE, Sarah Lind. 1920 WEST FIRST STREET 27103 #038-45-1998 L1999 FM *020 †18

PROUT, Heather Michelle. ■ 27103 #036-05-2008 *012

PRUETT, Dennis Derwood. 3734 REYNOLDA RD, OLDTOWN IMMEDIATE CARE PA 27106 #036-05-1956 L1956 FM *020

PUGH, Raeford T, Jr. 250 CHARLOIS BLVD 27103 #036-08-1985 L1988 P *020 †75

PULASKI, Edwin Thos. 1817 GREENBRIER RD 27104 #041-01-1970 L1996 DR *020 †80

PULASKI, Sherry L. 1817 GREENBRIER RD 27104 #005-12-1970 L1998 DR *020 †80

PULLIAM, Thomas Jackson. MEDICAL CENTER BLVD 27157 #036-05-1984 L1985 GE IM *030 †20

PYLANT, Andrew O. MEDICAL CENTER BOULEVARD, DEPT. OF EMERGENCY MEDICIN 27157 #021-06-2004 L2005 EM *020

QUIGLEY, Jill Andrea. ■ 27127 #028-03-2005 FP *012

QUINN-BOGARD, Ann L. 2825 LYNDHURST AVE, STE 103 27103 #056-06-1974 L1979 OTO *020 †45

RABEN, Milton. 300 S HAWTHORNE RD 27103 #024-07-1959 L1964 RO R *071 †80

RABER, Michael Robert. ■ 27104 #036-05-2008 *012

RABIL, William Edmond. 1950 S HAWTHORNE RD 27103 #051-01-1946 L1946 GS *071

RACKLEY, James Wayne. ■ 27103 #047-06-1955 L1976 PD ON *071 †55

RAGONESI, Peter Brian. 1381 WESTGATE CENTER DR 27103 #051-01-1990 L2007 IM *020 †20 ‡

RAHBAR, Laila. 301 S HAWTHORNE RD, WAKE FOREST UNIV SCH OF ME 27103 #036-05-2006 L2006 IM *012

RAINES, Karen Hazel. WAKE FOREST UNIV SCH OF MD, DEPT OF PEDIATRICS 27157 #036-05-1984 L1985 PDC PD *020 †55

RAINEY, David Yotham. 200 ROBINHOOD MEDICAL PLZ 27106 #012-01-1984 L1986 PD ADL *020 †55

RAMOS, Rommel N. 190 KIMEL PARK DR, DEPT OF MENTAL HLTH & BEHA 27103 #748-01-1989 L2005 P *020 †75

RAPP, Derek Alexandre. ■ 27103 #036-05-2008 *012

RAU, Bruce Wm. 2990 BETHESDA PL, STE 602A 27103 #028-03-1972 L1978 P *020 †75

RAUCK, Richard Lee. 145 KIMEL PARK DR 27103 #036-05-1982 L1986 PME AN *040 †05

RAWLINGS, Charles Edward. 426 OLD SALEM RD 27101 #036-07-1982 L1991 NS *020 †25

RAY, Ritz Clyde, Jr. 275 EXECUTIVE PARK BLVD, STE 604 27103 #036-07-1961 L1961 CHP P *020 †55,75

REED, John William. WAKE FOREST UNIV EYE CTR 27157 #036-05-1962 L1962 OPH *071 †35

REES, Catherine Jane. MEDICAL CENTER BLVD, WFUBMC OTOLARYNGOLOGY 27157 #036-05-2001 L2004 OTO *020 †45

REESE, William Mobley, Jr. ■ 27127 #045-04-2004 L2007 AN *012

REGAN, John David. OF MED., WAKE FOREST UNIV. SCH. 27157 #036-01-1987 L1993 VIR *020 †20

REH, Allison Carrie. ■ 27127 #041-14-2005 L2008 PD *012

REID, Charles Derek. 3333 SILAS CREEK PKWY 27103 #036-05-2001 L2005 AN *020 †05

REID, Charles Fredric. 140 KIMEL PARK DR 27103 #036-05-1974 L1977 U *020 †95

REID, Richard Harold. 3155 MAPLEWOOD AVE, FORSYTH RADIOLOGICAL ASSOC 27103 #036-05-1982 L1984 DR *020 †80

REIFLER, Burton Victor. MEDICAL CENTER BLVD 27157 #012-05-1969 L1987 P PYG *030 †75

REQUARTH, Jay Anthony. DEPT OF RADIOLOGY, WAKE FOREST V 27157 #003-01-1986 L2005 AN *100 †85,90

REUHLAND, Richard Gene. 2932 LYNDHURST AVE 27103 #047-20-1982 L1986 OBG *020 †30

REYNOLDS, Erica Bronwen. 1200 N MARTN LTHR KNG JR, DOWNTOWN HEALTH PLAZA 27101 #051-07-2004 L2007 PD *020 †55

REYNOLDS, John Edward. SCHOOL OF MEDICINE, WAKE FOREST UNIVERSITY 27157 #005-06-1992 L2002 AN *020 †05

REYNOLDS, Jon Wellington. ■ 27104 #036-01-2002 L2003 AN *100 †05

REYNOLDS, Joyce H Hinson. 2135 NEW WALKERTOWN RD, COMMUNITY CARE CENTER/CENT 27101 #036-05-1952 L1952 EM *071

REYNOLDS, Patrick Shawn. MED CTR BLVD, DEPT. OF DIAGNOSTIC NEUROL 27157 #047-05-1991 L1996 N *020 †75

RHINEHART, Kenneth B. 160 KIMEL FOREST DR, STE 250 27103 #028-02-1978 L1985 CD *020 †20

RHOADES, Vade G. 1900 S HAWTHORNE RD, FORSYTH MED PARK #S 110 27103 #036-05-1960 L1960 P OM *020 †15

RICE, David Graybeal. 1900 S HAWTHORNE RD, PEDIATRICS 27103 #036-05-1985 L1987 PD *020 †55

RICE, William Yates, III. MEDICAL CENTER BLVD, 8TH FLOOR CSB 27157 #036-05-1989 L1990 IM *020 †20

RICHARD, Jacob Raymond. ■ 27101 #041-12-2005 U *012

RICHARDS, Amber Michele. ■ 27127 #023-01-2005 EM *012

RICHARDS, David Chichang. MEDICAL CENTER BOULEVARD 27157 #012-05-2003 L2004 PMM *012

RICHARDS, Frederick, II. MED CTR BLVD 27157 #045-01-1964 L1965 ON HEM *071 †20

RICHARDSON, Charles Delwy. ■ 27103 #036-05-2008 *012

RICHASON, Noah Casey. ■ 27103 #011-04-2007 P *012

RIEDY, Gerard. MEDICAL CENTER BLVD 27157 #007-02-1997 L1999 RNR *100 †80

RIEKER, Robert Paul. 145 KIMEL PARK DR, STE 300 27103 #024-07-1966 L1974 AN PDC *071 †55,05

RIEMER, Ellen Carrie. MED CTR BLVD 27157 #550-02-1997 L2003 FOP *020 †50

RIGGS, Gregory Scott. ■ 27127 #021-05-2008 *012

RIPPEL, Christopher Andre. ■ 27127 #041-12-2008 *012

RIRIE, Douglas Gordon. MEDICAL CENTER BLVD, BOWMAN GRAY SCHOOL OF MEDI 27157 #036-01-1990 L1991 AN *020 †05

RITCHIE, John Edward. 170 KIMEL PARK DR 27103 #035-15-1980 L1990 ORS OSM *020 †40

ROACH, John Grover, III. 105 VEST MILL CIR 27103 #036-05-1977 L1977 FM *020 †18

ROBACH, Eric Michael. MEDICAL CENTER BLVD, WFUBMC 27157 #012-01-2002 L2005 IM *100 †20

ROBERTS, David Henry. 1365 WESTGATE CENTER DR, STE K1 27103 #004-01-1973 L2001 DR PDR *020 †80

ROBIE, Peter Wm. 1930 PEACE HAVEN RD 27106 #048-04-1976 L1977 IM *020 †20

ROBINSON, Eddie Tyclus. ■ 27102 #047-07-1963 L1965 OS OPH *071

ROBINSON, Ellen Carr. ■ 27104 #020-12-2001 L2003 PD *020 †55

ROBINSON, James Elbert. ■ 27106 #016-06-1953 L1958 ORS *071 †40

ROBINSON, Killian. MED CTR BLVD 27157 #539-03-1978 L2000 CD *020 †20

ROBINSON, Nicolas Edward. 2915 LYNDHURST AVE, SALEM SURGICAL ASSOCIATES, 27103 #020-12-2001 L2007 CRS *012

ROCCO, Michael Vito. MEDICAL CENTER BLVD, DEPT OF MED SECT ON NEPHLY 27157 #047-05-1985 L1991 NEP IM *020 †20

ROGERS, J William. 1351 WESTGATE CENTER DR, FORSYTH PEDIATRICS PA 27103 #036-05-1958 L1958 OPH *071 †35

ROGERS, Jack Marrell. 300 S HAWTHORNE RD, DEPT PSYCH 27103 #036-05-1958 L1958 P N *071 †75

ROGERS, James Michael. 1351 WESTGATE CENTER DR 27103 #036-05-1971 L1971 PD *020 †55

ROGERS, Jeffrey. MEDICAL CENTER BLVD, WAKE FOREST UNIV DEPT GS 27157 #035-46-1990 L2005 TTS GS *020 †85

ROHR, Michael Snell. 300 S HAWTHORNE RD, DEPARTMENT OF SURGERY 27103 #021-01-1967 L1989 TTS GS *020 †85

ROLLINS, Curtis Edward. MEDICAL CENTER BLVD, DEPT OF PSYCHIATRY 27157 #045-01-1992 L2005 P *012

ROMERO, Angelica. MED C, WAKE FOREST UNIV BAPTIST 27157 #048-14-2007 FP *012

ROSE, Donald R, Jr. 755 HIGHLAND OAKS DR, STE 201 27103 #036-01-1993 L1996 END *020 †20

ROSEN, Robert Dean. 2805 LYNDHURST AVE, ARDMORE FAMILY PRACTICE 27103 #041-12-1979 L1980 FM OBS *020 †18

ROSENBAUM, Daryl Alan. MEDICAL CENTER BLVD, DEPT OF FAMILY MEDICINE 27157 #036-05-1997 L2000 FM *020 †18

ROSENBLEETH, Robin Brando. ■ 27103 #036-05-2004 AN *012

ROSENQUIST, Peter Bechan. MEDICAL CENTER BLVD 27157 #030-05-1987 L1991 P *020 †75

ROSS, Dennis Warren. ■ 27104 #005-02-1974 L1978 PTH HMP *071 †50

ROSS, Gregory A. MEDICAL CENTER BLVD 27157 #011-02-1996 L2003 CCP *020 †55

ROSS, Michael Marshall. ■ 27103 #036-05-2006 PD *012

ROSS, Robert Mitchell. 1401 OLD MILL CIR STE A 27103 #041-09-1974 L1981 AI *020 †55,03

ROSS, Vernon Horace. MEDICAL CENTER BLVD 27157 #047-07-1979 L1993 AN *040 †05

ROSSI, Peter John. 1810 ELIZABETH AVE 27103 #025-07-1997 L2004 RO *100 †80

ROUFAIL, Walter Michel. MEDICAL CENTER BLVD 27157 #915-02-1957 L1966 GE IM *040 †20

ROUSTER-STEVENS, Kelly An. 1 MEDICAL CENTER BLVD 27157 #038-41-2000 L2006 PD *040 †55

ROUX, Jennifer Leigh. 145 KIMEL PARK DR, STE 330 27103 #023-01-2003 L2004 PMM *012

ROWLEY, Christopher Patri. ■ 27103 #036-05-2006 IM *012

ROWLEY, Vincent Brent. ■ 27127 #011-04-2005 L2008 DR *012

ROY, Chandra Elizabeth. MEDICAL CENTER BLVD, WAKE FOREST UNIV HEALTH SC 27157 #038-06-1995 L2006 OPH *020 †35

ROY, Raymond Clyde. MED CTR BLVD 27157 #021-01-1974 L1978 **AN** *030 †05

ROYSTER, Roger Lee. MEDICAL CENTER BLVD, DEPT OF ANESTH 27157 #036-05-1975 L1976 **CCM AN** *020 †20,05

RUBIN, Bruce Kalman. MEDICAL CENTER BLVD 27157 #021-01-1979 L1997 **PDP** *020 †55

RUBLE, Wade Eugene. 27104 #051-04-1963 L1966 **GP IM** *071

RUCH, David Simms. MEDICAL CENTER BLVD, DEPT ORTHO 27157 #036-05-1988 L1990 **HS** *020 †40

RUDISAILE, Sarah Noel. ■ 27127 #028-46-1999 L2002 **DMP** *012 †18,50

RUFTY, Alfred Jackson, Jr. 180 KIMEL PARK DR, STE 110 27103 #021-05-1961 L1969 **CD IM** *071 †20

RUIZ, Jimmy. ■ 27127 #016-45-2004 L2005 **IM** *100 †20

RUPERTO, Cornelio R. MEDICAL CENTER BLVD 27157 #011-04-2003 L2006 **CHP** *012

RUSH, Ashley Noel. 27103 #036-05-2005 **OBG** *012

RUSS, Mitchell Allen. ■ 27103 #028-02-1969 L1971 **DR** *071 †80

RUSSELL, Wilson Glover. 3333 SILAS CREEK PKWY 27103 #047-05-1974 L1980 **PTH** *030 †50

SABIO, Hernan. MED CTR BLVD 27157 #042-01-1970 L2001 **PD PHO** *020 †55

SACONN, Paul Anthony. 301 S HAWTHORNE RD, WAKE FOREST UNIV SCH OF ME 27103 #036-05-2004 **RO** *012

SAGERMAN, Paul James. MEDICAL CENTER BLVD, DEPT OF PEDIATRICS 27157 #035-06-1994 L2002 **PD** *020 †55

SAILER, Voyta. 3333 SILAS CREEK PKWY 27103 #045-04-1989 L1992 **IM** *020 †20

SALAMEH, Nabil Peter. ■ 27103 #036-05-2007 **AN** *012

SALIBA, David Lee, II. WFU SCHOOL OF MED, DEPT OF ANESTHESIOLOGY 27157 #039-01-2001 L2003 **AN** *012

SALISU, Adamu. DEPT OF PSYCHIATRY, WAKE FOREST UNIV SCH OF ME 27157 #913-06-1998 L2005 **P** *100

SALIZZONI, Laura Anne. MEDICAL CENTER BLVD 27157 #010-01-1993 L1997 **AN** *020

SAM, Maria Caridad. MEDICAL CENTER BLVD, DEPT OF NEUROLOGY 27157 #042-02-1989 L1996 **N** *020 †75

SAMANT, Jyoti Sachin. ■ 27103 #496-44-2001 L2004 **ID** *012 †20

SAMAROPOULOS, Xanthia Fal. ■ 27103 #051-04-2007 **IM** *012

SANCRANT, James. 3155 MAPLEWOOD AVE 27103 #038-75-2001, ▲ L2004 **DR** *020 †80

SANDERFORD, James L, Jr. 185 KIMEL PARK DR, STE 100 27103 #036-01-1978 L1980 **NM DR** *020 †80,28

SANDERS, David Melville. DEPT OF ANESTHESIOLOGY, MEDICAL CENTER BOULEVARD 27157 #036-05-2004 L2007 **AN** *012

SANDERS, Ellen Chance. ■ 27103 #036-05-2004 **OPH** *012

SANDERS, Terry Gene. ■ 27104 #047-06-2005 L2008 **EM** *012

SANDIFER, John Pettey. ■ 27103 #027-01-2005 L2007 **EM** *012

SANE, Aneysa Christine. MEDICAL CENTER BLVD 27157 #036-07-1986 L1988 **AI** *040 †20,03

SANE, David Chester. MEDICAL CENTER BLVD, WFU SCHOOL OF MEDICINE 27157 #036-07-1983 L1985 **CD IM** *050 †20

SANGUEZA, Omar Pastor. MED CTR BLVD 27157 #847-08-1979 L2000 **DMP** *020 †50

SANTOS, Cesar Cruz. MEDICAL CENTER BLVD, WAKE FOREST UNIV SCH OF ME 27157 #748-08-1982 L1989 **CHN PD** *020 †55,75

SANTOS, Renato Ma. MEDICAL CENTER BLVD, WAKE FOREST UNIV SCHL OF M 27157 #018-03-1990 L1994 **CD** *020 †20

SAPP, Amy Caroline. 3722 VEST MILL RD 27103 #036-05-1995 L1998 **FM** *020 †18

SARAN, Anita Michelle. MEDICAL CENTER BLVD, WAKE FOREST UNIVERSITY HEA 27157 #035-03-1997 L2005 **NEP** *020 †20

SATKO, Scott Gregory. 1 MEDICAL CENTER BLVD, NEPHROLOGY SECTION WFUBMC 27157 #051-01-1994 L1995 **NEP** *020

SATTERFIELD, William H. 3817 FORRESTGATE DR, ASSOCIATES 27103 #036-05-1998 L2004 **ORS** *100 †40

SATTERWHITE, William M, III. 2001 TODAYS WOMAN AVE 27105 #036-05-1997 L1998 **PD** *020 †55

SATTERWHITE, Wm Madison. 1900 S HAWTHORNE RD # 480, PARK 27103 #036-07-1958 L1958 **OTO** *071 †45

SAUER, Ryan Nathan. OF MED, WAKE FOREST UNIV SCH 27157 #017-20-2006 L2007 **DR** *012

SAVAGE, Paul David. MEDICAL CENTER BLVD, WAKE FOREST UNIV SCH MED 27157 #024-07-1981 L1989 **ON IM** *050 †20

SAYERS, Daniel Garvin. 3966 HUDDINGTON CT 27106 #038-40-1977 L1978 **EM** *020 †16

SAYERS, William Floyd. 186 KIMEL PARK DR 27103 #036-01-1965 L1965 **PD** *020 †55

SCANNELL, Michael. 3333 SILAS CREEK PKWY 27103 #654-01-1998 L2002 **AN** *020 †05

SCHAEFER, Eric Scott. ■ 27157 #038-43-2003 L2006 **HO** *012 †20

SCHARLING, Eric Stuart. 3155 MAPLEWOOD AVE 27103 #036-01-1985 L1987 **DR** *020 †80

SCHERER, Kerri Renee. 2932 LYNDHURST AVE 27103 #036-05-1999 L2002 **OBG** *020 †30

SCHILLER, Herbert Miles. ■ 27106 #036-05-1968 L1968 **PTH PCP** *020 †50 ‡

SCHKOLNE, Benzion. 3333 SILAS CREEK PKWY 27103 #836-02-1972 L1979 **AN** *020 †05

SCHMID, Herman Ernest. 147 COLUMBINE DR 27106 #016-11-1955 L1969 **FPG** *020 †18

SCHMITT, Karen Elizabeth. ■ 27101 #036-05-2008 *012

SCHMUNK, Gayle Marie. ■ 27127 #036-01-2006 **IM** *012

SCHNEIDER, Andrew Mark. 2901 MAPLEWOOD AVE 27103 #051-04-1991 L1992 **PS** *020 †85,65

SCHREINER, David Thos. 1930 PEACE HAVEN RD, AEGIS/PEACEHAVEN 27106 #035-45-1980 L1996 **IM** *020 †20

SCHULTZ, John Loesch. ■ 27104 #036-05-1961 L1961 **DR NM** *020 †80,28

SCHWARTZ, Arnold Alton. 1710 S HAWTHORNE RD 27103 #020-12-1973 L1977 **OPH** *020 †35 ‡

SCHWARTZ, Earl. BOWMAN GRAY SCHL MED EM 27157 #036-05-1974 L1977 **EM** *071 †16

SCHWARTZ, Robert Paul. MED CTR BLVD 27157 #011-03-1968 L1969 **PD PDE** *020 †55

SCIBELLI, Stephen Scott. 27127 #045-01-2003 **NS** *012

SCOTT, Georgia Lea. 3333 SILAS CREEK PKWY, INPATIENT PHYSICIANS OF FO 27103 #036-01-2001 L2004 **HOS** *012

SCOTT, Michele Lea. MEDICAL CENTER BLVD, WAKE FOREST UNIV EYE CTR 27157 #041-15-2004 L2008 **OPH** *012

SCOTTI, Stephen Douglas. 27106 #010-01-1987 L1988 **DR** *075 †80

SCUDERI, Phillip Edward. MEDICAL CENTER BLVD, BOWMAN GRAY SCH OF MEDICINE 27157 #036-05-1978 L1979 **AN CCA** *020 †05 ‡

SEALE, Julie Elizabeth. ■ 27103 #012-01-2007 **PD** *012

SEARS, Judith Di Rocco. 3333 SILAS CREEK PKWY, DEPT OF RADIATION ONCOLOGY 27103 #036-05-1990 L1993 **RO** *020 †80

SEAUX, Leroy David. 1492 RYMCO DR 27103 #047-05-1991 L1995 **N** *020 †75

SEIDENSTICKER, Anne Linn. ■ 27104 #036-05-2008 *012

SELMAN, Larkin Leo. 3155 MAPLEWOOD AVE 27103 #001-02-1977 L1991 **DR** *020 †80

SELNA, Mark Jos. 2085 FRONTIS PLAZA BLVD, OF NC, INC 27103 #051-01-1987 L1998 **PD** *020 †55

SELTZER, Barry Robt. 250 CHARLOIS BLVD 27103 #048-12-1986 L1993 **IM IMG** *020 †20

SEMBLE, Elliott Lowell. 755 HIGHLAND OAKS DR, BOX 24325 27103 #165-04-1975 L1981 **RHU IM** *020 †20

SEMCHYSHYN, Taras Michael. 2025 FRONTIS PLAZA BLVD, WINSTON SALEM 27103 #047-05-1998 L2002 **IM** *020 †35

SETTY, Janaki Ram. 3641 WESTGATE CENTER CIR 27103 #495-09-1962 L1974 **IM IMG** *020 †18

SEVILLA, Maria-Dorina C. 3880 VEST MILL RD STE 100, PHYSICIANS ELDER CARE 27103 #748-01-1979 L1993 **IM IMG** *020 †20

SHAH, Bansidhar Parbhulal. 3030 TRENWEST DR 27103 #495-23-1963 L1971 **GS** *020 †85

SHAH, Mahim. ■ 27103 #054-04-2006 **PD** *012

SHAH, Ripal Nitin. ■ 27103 #045-01-2006 L2006 **DR** *012

SHAH, Sumati B. 3030 TRENWEST DR 27103 #495-22-1971 L1978 **GP** *074

SHASHI, Vandana. MED CTR BLVD 27157 #495-37-1982 L1997 **PD** *020 †55,19

SHAW, Edward Gus. MEDICAL CENTER BLVD, DEPT OF RADIATION ONCOLOGY 27157 #016-01-1983 L1995 **RO** *030 †80

SHAW, Kathryn Ann. 301 S HAWTHORNE RD, WAKE FOREST UNIV SCH OF ME 27103 #036-05-2006 L2006 **EM** *012

SHAW, Megan Allison. ■ 27101 #036-05-2008 *012

SHEALY, Ronald Bernard. 110 CHARLOIS BLVD, PIEDMONT EAR, NOSE, & THRO 27103 #045-01-1975 L1980 **OTO** *020 †45

SHEEHAN, Lisa Marie. ■ 27127 #036-05-2005 L2008 **P** *012

SHELBURNE, David Mathisen. ■ 27127 #036-05-2008 *012

SHELTON, John Albert, Jr. 1424 ARROWOOD CT 27104 #036-05-1980 L1981 **FM FSM** *020 †18

SHEN, Jian. 600 HIGHLAND OAKS DR 27103 #035-20-2002 L2003 **ORS** *012

SHEN, Joan. 250 CHARLOIS BLVD, WINSTON SALEM HEALTHCARE 27103 #041-12-1984 L2003 **OBG** *020 †30

SHEN, Perry. MEDICAL CENTER BLVD, DEPT GEN SURGY, SEC SURG O 27157 #005-06-1992 L2000 **GS SO** *020 †85

SHENOY, Rajeev Narayan. MEDICAL CENTER BLVD, SECT ON NEPH 27157 #045-01-2003 L2005 **NEP** *012 †20

SHEPARD, Claudia Prichard. MED CTR BLVD 27157 #036-05-1989 L1990 **P** *020 †75

SHEPARD, Gregg Christian. MED C, WAKE FOREST UNIV BAPTIST 27157 #047-06-2002 L2004 **HO** *012

SHERERTZ, Elizabeth Fritz. 1400 WESTGATE CENTER DR, STE 200 27103 #051-01-1978 L1988 **D** *012 †15

SHERERTZ, Robert Jackson. MEDICAL CENTER BLVD, SCHOOL OF MEDICINE 27157 #051-01-1976 L1979 **ID OS** *050 †20

SHETTY, Avinash Kunjan. MEDICAL CENTER BLVD, SCHOOL OF MEDICINE 27157 #498-38-1989 L2001 **PD** *020 †55

SHIELD, Christian Edward. ■ 27104 #051-04-2004 L2004 **DR** *012

SHIELDS, John Shepherd. ■ 27127 #051-01-2006 **ORS** *012

SHIFERAW, Beletshachew. ■ 27106 #366-01-1983 **IMG** *020

SHIH, Albert Sheau Wei. 3333 SILAS CREEK PKWY 27103 #038-41-1996 L1999 **IM** *020 †20

SHILS, Maurice Edward. ■ 27104 #035-19-1958 **NTR IM** *072

SHILT, Jeffrey Scott. MEDICAL CENTER BLVD, DEPT OF ORTHOPAEDICS 27157 #028-46-1992 L1999 **ORS** *020 †40

SHIN, Haewon. 301 S HAWTHORNE RD, WAKE FOREST UNIV SCH OF ME 27103 #036-05-2006 **N** *012

SHINER, Erin K. ■ 27104 #048-15-2007 **IM** *012

SHIRK, Arianna Mclain. 301 S HAWTHORNE RD, WAKE FOREST UNIV SCH OF ME 27103 #036-05-2007 **PD** *012

SHRIMANKER, Nevin Mahendr. ■ 27103 #036-05-2004 L2007 **AN** *012

SHUPING, Martha Woodhams. 1400 MILLGATE DR 27103 #036-05-1984 L1988 **P** *020

SHUTE, Kevin Barry. ■ 27127 #036-05-2005 **AN** *012

SIGAL, Barry Wm. 3333 SILAS CREEK PKWY 27103 #012-01-1982 L1987 **PUD PCC** *020 †20

SIKES, Charles Van, III. ■ 27104 #036-08-2006 **ORS** *012

SILKSTONE, Margaret Lynn. 1900 S HAWTHORNE RD, PEDIATRICS 27103 #036-08-2003 L2004 **PD** *020 †55

SIMMONS, David Norman, Jr. ■ 27103 #036-05-2005 L2008 **EM** *012

SIMMONS, Tony Wm. MEDICAL CENTER BLVD., BOWMAN GRAY SCH OF MEDICIN 27157 #038-06-1979 L1992 **CD IM** *020 †20

SIMON, Jimmy L. MEDICAL CENTER BLVD, DEPT OF PEDS WFUSM 27157 #005-02-1955 L1973 **PD** *040 †20

SIMPSON, Ellie Elizabeth. ■ 27101 #036-05-2008 *012

SIMPSON, Eugene Myers. 3333 SILAS CREEK PKWY, FORSYTH MED CTR 27103 #036-05-1973 L1973 **PD** *071 †55

SIMPSON, Marcus B. MED CTR BLVD 27157 #036-01-1972 L1981 **BBK CLP** *030 †50

SIMPSON, Martha Kilby. 1900 S HAWTHORNE RD, PEDIATRICS 27103 #036-05-1988 L1989 **PD** *020 †55

SIMPSON, Thomas Edward. 1950 S HAWTHORNE RD 27103 #036-05-1957 L1957 **GS CRS** *020 †85

SIMSTEIN, Rebecca Stott. ■ 27106 #036-05-2006 L2006 **GS** *100

SINAL, Sara A Hendricks. MEDICAL CENTER BLVD, DEPT OF PEDS 27157 #036-01-1971 L1971 **PD** *040 †55

SINGER, Lawrence Robt. 1132 CHESTER RD 27104 #010-01-1954 L1979 **OBG** *071 †30

SINGH, Sonal. MEDICAL CENTRE BLVD, WAKE FOREST UNIV HLTH SCI 27157 #495-15-1999 L2005 **IM** *020

SINGLETON, Amy H. 600 HIGHLAND OAKS DR 27103 #036-08-1999 L2002 **P** *012 †16

SINK, Kaycee Michelle. 1 MEDICAL CENTER BLVD, WAKE FOREST U BAPTIST M C 27157 #005-02-1998 L2004 **IMG** *050 †20

SINTHUSEK, Chirapa S. 730 HIGHLAND OAKS DR, STE 101 27103 #891-03-1970 L1973 **IM DIA** *020 †20

SIPOS, Jennifer Anne. MEDICAL CENTER BLVD. 27157 #036-05-1999 L2002 **END** *100 †20

SKELTON, Joseph Arnold. ■ 27106 #047-06-1999 L2007 **PG** *100 †55

SKYLES, Jason Kimbrough. ■ 27103 #028-34-2005 **DR** *012

SLAUGHTER, Thomas F. MEDICAL CENTER BLVD 27157 #036-07-1987 L1991 **AN** *020 †05 ‡

SLUSHER, M Madison. WAKE FOREST UNIV. EYE CTR, MEDICAL CENTER BLVD. 27157 #020-12-1964 L1973 **OPH** *020 †35

SMISHEK, Matthew J. ■ 27103 #048-14-2000 L2001 **AN** *100

SMITH, Alexis Deana. ■ 27101 #036-05-2008 *012

SMITH, Brian Stanley. ■ 27106 #045-01-2001 L2008 **GE** *012

SMITH, Bryan Greene. ■ 27103 #036-05-2005 L2007 **P** *012

SMITH, Claude A. 3333 SILAS CREEK PKWY 27103 #041-02-1953 L1953 **R OS** *071 †80

SMITH, David Lawrence. ■ 27127 #051-01-2004 L2007 **DR** *012

SMITH, Jennifer Green. DEPT OB/GYN, MEDICAL CENTER BOULEVARD 27157 #036-05-2001 L2005 **OBG** *100

SMITH, John Jos, III. 140 CHARLOIS BLVD 27103 #010-02-1983 L2006 **U** *020 †95
SMITH, Landon Ensign. ■ 27127 #048-02-2007 **IM** *012
SMITH, Michael Vincentcun. ■ 27103 #004-01-2005 **OBG** *012
SMITH, Nat E. ■ 27104 #012-01-1949 L1976 **IM** *071
SMITH, Steven Wayne. 3333 SILAS CREEK PKWY 27103 #051-07-1992 L1993 **EM** *020 †16
SMITH, Timothy Earl. MEDICAL CENTER BLVD, DEPT OF ANESTHESIOLOGY 27157 #036-05-1994 L1995 **AN** *020 †05
SMITH, William George. ■ 27103 #036-01-2005 **IM** *012
SODEMAN, Julia Marie. ■ 27103 #048-12-2007 *012
SOHEILI, Kambiz C. 190 KIMEL PARK DR, VA WS OUTPATIENT CLINIC 27103 #016-11-2001 L2006 **IMG** *100 †20
SOHMER, Marcus F, Jr. ■ 27104 #036-05-1952 L1952 **IM GE** *071 †20
SOKOLOSKY, Mitchell C. MED CTR BLVD 27157 #055-01-1992 L1994 **EM** *020 †16
SOLLENBERGER, Michael Joe. 3080 TRENWEST DR 27103 #010-02-1979 L1989 **IM** *020 †20
SOO, Victoria. ■ 27127 #036-05-2006 **GS** *100
SOPER, Herbert Alva. 145 CORBRIDGE LN 27106 #004-01-1960 L1967 **GYN** *020 †30
SORIANO, Clinton R. 1901 S HAWTHORNE RD # 340 27103 #748-10-1969 L1977 **GS TS** *020
SOUTHARD, John Kelton, Jr. 1345 WESTGATE CENTER DR, STE B 27103 #024-05-1967 L1973 **D** *020 †15
SPANGLER, John Given. MED CTR BLVD 27157 #036-01-1986 L1987 **FM GPM** *040 †70,18
SPANGLER, Kevin Martin. 3155 MAPLEWOOD AVE 27103 #036-05-1993 L1994 **RNR** *020 †80
SPANGLER, Thomas Clayton. 3817 FORRESTGATE DR 27103 #036-01-1984 L1989 **ORS** *020 †40
SPARE, Stephen Vigneron. 3333 SILAS CREEK PKWY 27103 #024-07-1972 L1975 **END IM** *071 †20
SPENCER, David Mc Caughey. 765 HIGHLAND OAKS DR, STE 100 27103 #039-01-1987 L1994 **D OS** *020 †55,15
SPENCER, James Craig. 400 JONESTOWN RD 27104 #056-06-1984 L1987 **FM** *020 †18
SPENCER, Richard L, Jr. 3309 HEALY DR STE A 27103 #051-04-1960 L1965 **P** *020 †75
SPENCER, William Jos. ■ 27106 #036-05-1961 L1962 **CD IM** *071 †20
SPILLMANN, Celia Morse. 4410 PROVIDENCE LN, STE I 27106 #027-01-1981 L1990 **GP** *020
SPILLMANN, Scott Jos. MEDICAL CENTER BOULEVARD, WAKE FOREST UNIVERSITY BAP 27157 #027-01-1982 L1990 **OM GP** *020 †70
SPIVEY, David Lee. 245 CHARLOIS BLVD, STE C 27103 #036-01-1981 L1986 **APM** *020 †05
SPONGBERG, Christopher Ni. ■ 27107 #036-05-2004 L2006 **P** *100
SPRAGUE, David Hugh. MED CTR BLVD 27157 #035-03-1969 L1978 **AN** *020 †05
SPRINGS, Harold Leon, III. ■ 27127 #051-01-2007 **IM** *012
SPUDIS, Edward Verhines. ■ 27106 #023-01-1953 L1959 **N** *071
SQUIRE, Sarah. ■ 27103 #043-01-2006 **RO** *012
STAAB, Edward Vincent. MEDICAL CENTER BLVD 27157 #026-04-1961 L1973 **R NM** *072 †80,28 ‡
STABILE, Kathryne Judith. ■ 27106 #041-15-2006 **ORS** *012
STABLER, Carey Vastine. 190 KIMEL PARK DR, VETERANS ADMIN. OUTPATIENT 27103 #004-01-1962 L1973 **GP EM** *020
STACEY, Richard Brandon. ■ 27103 #001-06-2004 L2008 **IM** *100 †20
STALVEY, Christopher F. MEDICAL CENTER BOULEVARD, DEPARTMENT OF ANESTHESIOLO 27157 #018-75-2003, ▲ L2007 **PMM** *012
STAMEY, Charles Claud. 1930 PEACE HAVEN RD 27106 #024-01-1953 L1953 **PD** *071 †55
STANGER, Brett Kendall. ■ 27127 #012-01-2006 **AN** *012
STANTON, Constance Ann. MED CTR BLVD 27157 #048-04-1981 L1989 **NP N** *020 †50
STARR, Christopher Jenn. ■ 27127 #036-05-2008 *012
STEADMAN, Brent Thomas. ■ 27127 #012-01-2005 L2007 **DR** *012
STEELE, Kathryn Marie. ■ 27104 #036-05-2008 *012
STEFANESCU, Sergiu E M. MEDICAL CENTER BLVD, GENERAL INTERNAL MEDICINE 27157 #781-04-1991 L2003 **IM** *020 †20
STEFFEN, Scott Taylor. 3155 MAPLEWOOD AVE 27103 #011-03-1999 L2001 **DR** *020 †80
STELZER, Diane Marie. ■ 27101 #028-03-1983 L1984 **FM** *020 †18
STEPHENS, Granada Shalane. 7811 N POINT BLVD, PRIMECARE NORTHPOINT 27106 #036-05-2002 L2005 **FM** *020 †18
STEPHENS, Wayland Chad. 2990 BETHESDA PL, STE 602A 27103 #036-07-1980 L1983 **P FM** *020 †75,18
STEPHENSON, Richard Chas. 101 HOSPICE LN 27103 #023-01-1975 L2000 **IM PLM** *020 †20
STEVENS, Edwin Andrew. OF MED, WAKE FOREST UNIV SCH 27157 #012-01-2004 **NS** *012
STEWART, Douglas Wayne. 730 HIGHLAND OAKS DR, STE 103 27103 #041-14-1978 L1983 **NEP IM** *020 †20
STEWART, John Edward. 3155 MAPLEWOOD AVE 27103 #051-04-2000 L2005 **DR** *020 †80
STEWART, John Hubert, IV. MEDICAL CENTER BLVD, SURGERY 27157 #010-03-1995 L2004 **GS SO** *020 †85
STEWART, William Paschal. 2909 MAPLEWOOD AVE 27103 #036-05-1995 L1998 **PD** *020 †55
STIEBER, Volker W. 3333 SILAS CREEK PKWY, DEPT OF RADIATION ONCOLOGY 27103 #005-12-1994 L2000 **RO** *020 †80 ‡
STILLE, Kristen Camille. ■ 27103 #007-02-2007 **OBG** *012
STINSON, Charles Stephen. 3333 SILAS CREEK PKWY 27103 #036-01-1983 L1984 **IM** *020 †20
STOECKEL, William Todd. 4811 STONY CREEK LN 27127 #038-41-2002 L2007 **PS** *012
STOKES, Margaret Massee. ■ 27127 #036-05-2007 **PD** *012
STONE, Brian Douglass. 1372 WESTGATE CENTER DR, ALLERGY PARTNERS OF THE PI 27103 #012-01-1985 L1990 **AI PD** *020 †55,03
STONE, Gale. MEDICAL CENTER BLVD 27157 #036-05-1976 L1976 **PD** *020 †55
STOPYRA, Jason Patrick. MEDICAL CTR BLVD, WAKE FOREST UNIV BAPT MED 27157 #035-06-2000 L2001 **EM** *020 †16
STOREY, Jonathan Ashe. OF MED, WAKE FOREST UNIV SCH 27157 #011-04-2003 **HO** *012 †20
STORY, Lloyd Jerrell. 755 HIGHLAND OAKS DR, STE 102 27103 #047-06-1961 L1965 **IM CD** *020
STRATTA, Robert Jos. MEDICAL CENTER BLVD, DEPT OF GENERAL SURGERY 27157 #016-02-1980 L2001 **TTS GS** *020 †85
STREER, Nathan Paul. OF MED, WAKE FOREST UNIV SCH 27157 #012-01-2002 L2008 **HO** *012 †20
STRICKLAND, Robert Allen. MEDICAL CENTER BLVD 27157 #019-02-1977 L2002 **AN CCA** *020 †05
STRINGER, Llewellyn W, Jr. 121 POLO RD 27105 #051-04-1966 L1971 **PUD AN** *020 †05
STUART, Carole Maxwell. PO BOX 7386, WAKE FOREST UNIV STU HLTH 27109 #040-02-1966 L1971 **FM PD** *020 †55
STUART, Saml Patrick, Jr. 2933 MAPLEWOOD AVE, STE 4 27103 #036-01-1985 L1986 **GS VS** *020 †85
STUBBS, Allston J, Jr. 140 KIMEL PARK DR 27103 #036-07-1967 L1967 **U** *020 †85,95
STUGART, Ricky Howard. 100 ROBINHOOD MEDICAL PLZ 27106 #051-01-1984 L1996 **FM** *020 †18
STURGILL, Stephanie B. 250 CHARLOIS BLVD, WINSTON-SALEM HEALTHCARE 27103 #036-01-2001 L2007 **D** *020 †15
STURGILL, William Hugh. 175 KIMEL PARK DR, DEPT OF DERMATOLOGY 27103 #036-01-1998 L1999 **D** *020 †15
STURKIE, Henry Ray. ■ 27104 #001-02-1955 L1964 **GYN** *071 †30
SUDA, Russell Raymond. 250 CHARLOIS BLVD, WINSTON SALEM HEALTHCARE 27103 #028-34-1978 L2003 **OBG ATP** *020 †50,30
SUGG, Norman Keith. 3333 SILAS CREEK PKWY 27103 #036-05-1979 L1983 **PTH** *020 †50
SUGG, Rebecca L M. 2025 FRONTIS PLAZA BLVD, STE 120 27103 #001-02-2000 L2007 **RNR** *100 †75
SULLIVAN, Christopher A. MEDICAL CENTER BOULEVARD, WAKE FOREST UNIVERSITY HEA 27157 #010-01-1993 L2005 **OTO** *020 †45
SULLIVAN, Toby M. 3333 SILAS CREEK PKWY 27103 #048-15-2002 L2005 **EM** *020
SUMMER, Leigh Ringer. ■ 27106 #036-08-1995 L2003 **FM** *020
SUMMEY, Joycelyn Louise. ■ 27105 #036-08-1995 **OBG** *100
SUMNER, Thomas Edward. MEDICAL CENTER BLVD 27157 #035-45-1968 L1976 **PDR PD** *020 †80,55
SUSCO, Benjamin Mark. ■ 27127 #055-01-2007 **IM** *012
SUTTON, Brian Joseph. ■ 27106 #051-07-2007 **PTH** *012
SUTTON, Homer G. 3333 SILAS CREEK PKWY 27103 #036-05-1953 L1953 **FM** *071 †18
SWAN, Kevin Roy. ■ 27127 #021-06-2005 **OPH** *012
SWEASEY, Thomas Allen. MEDICAL CENTER BLVD 27157 #038-41-1985 L2001 **NS** *020 †25
SWEENEY, John Thomas. MED CTR BLVD 27157 #055-02-1995 L2002 **GE** *020 †20
SWIFT, Catherine Baker. ■ 27103 #045-04-2006 L2008 **IM** *012
SYKOLA, Amanda Cook. ■ 27101 #036-05-2000 L2002 **PDC** *100
SZEWCZYK, Marcia Burkart. ■ 27104 #016-43-1980 L1982 **FM** *071 †18
TABOR, Charles Gordon. 190 KIMEL PARK DR, VETS ASSOC OPC 27103 #036-05-1954 L1954 **IM EM** *020
TACKETT, Amy Elizabeth. ■ 27103 #036-05-2006 **AN** *012
TAFT, Charles Van. 170 KIMEL PARK DR 27103 #036-07-1968 L1968 **ORS** *020 †40
TAGHIZADEH, Behzad. 160 KIMEL FOREST DR, STE 250 27103 #422-01-1995 L2003 **CD** *020 †20
TARA, Charles Saml. 2821 MAPLEWOOD AVE 27103 #050-02-1969 L1970 **OPH** *071 †35
TARLETON, Gregory Paul. 3010 MAPLEWOOD AVE, STE 106 27103 #012-01-1999 L2001 **EM** *020 †16
TATE, David Harrison. 3333 SILAS CREEK PKWY 27103 #036-05-1965 L1965 **PD** *071 †55
TATTER, Stephen Bradley. MED CTR BLVD 27157 #035-20-1990 L1997 **NS** *020 †25
TAWIL, Ghassan. ■ 27106 #875-02-1994 L2005 **CCM** *012 †20
TAYLOR, Benjamin Franklin. ■ 27103 #036-05-1984 **P** *100
TAYLOR, Blucher E. 3333 SILAS CREEK PKWY 27103 #036-05-1963 L1963 **OBG** *071 †30
TAYLOR, Charis Prichard. ■ 27127 #045-04-2006 **IM** *012
TAYLOR, Cullen Andrew. 3333 SILAS CREEK PKWY 27103 #041-09-1998 L2003 **PTH** *020 †50
TAYLOR, Sarah Lynn. MEDICAL CENTER BLVD, WAKE FOREST UNIVERSITY DEP 27157 #018-03-2002 L2005 **FM D** *020 †18 ‡
TCHELEPI, Hisham Ahmad Ab. MEDICAL CENTER BLVD, DEPT OF RADIOLOGY-MEADS HA 27157 #913-93-1986 L2006 **DR** *100
TEASDALL, Kathy J. 2825 LYNDHURST AVE, STE 103 27103 #027-01-1983 L1994 **OTO** *020 †45
TEASDALL, Robert Douglas. MEDICAL CENTER BLVD, DEPT OF ORTHOPAEDICS 27157 #025-07-1986 L1993 **ORS OFA** *020 †40
TEBEJE, Legesse Fulla. 2085 FRONTIS PLAZA BLVD, NOVANT HEALTH INC 27103 #366-01-1988 L1999 **IM** *020 †20
TEGELER, Chas Herman, IV. MEDICAL CENTER BLVD., WAKE FOREST UNIV. SCH. OF 27157 #028-46-1979 L1989 **N IM** *020 †20,75
TEGELER, Debra Renee. 250 CHARLOIS BLVD, WINSTON-SALEM HEALTH CARE 27103 #028-46-1984 L1989 **HEM ON** *020 †20
TEMAS, Gregory. 725 HIGHLAND OAKS DR, STE 101 27103 #038-06-1987 L1991 **OPH** *020 †35
TEMPLETON, Leah Carol. ANESTHESIOLOGY MED CTR BL, WAKE FOREST UNIV SCHOOL OF 27157 #036-05-1999 L2004 **PAN** *020 †05
TEMPLETON, Thomas Wesley. MEDICAL CENTER BLVD 27157 #036-05-1999 L2004 **PAN** *020 †05
TEMPLON, Norman A, Jr. 1930 PEACE HAVEN RD, AEGIS URGENT CARE CTR 27106 #051-04-1961 L1963 **EM** *071
TENNILLE, Marguerite T. 3333 SILAS CREEK PKWY 27103 #036-05-1980 L1983 **PD** *020 †55
TERRELL, Kenyetta R W. ■ 27104 #026-08-2004 **IM** *012
TESTA, Lisa Danielle. MED CTR BLVD 27157 #047-05-1990 L1994 **AN** *020 †05
TETTAMANTI, Hugo Atilio. 2928 MAPLEWOOD AVE 27103 #132-02-1965 L1972 **NEP IM** *020 †20
THAKKAR, Nilima P. MEDICAL CENTER BOULEVARD 27157 #496-21-1998 L2004 **CHP** *020 †75
THARP, Amy Marie. PATHOLOGY DEPT WAKE FORES, UNIV BPT CTR MED CTR BLVD 27157 #035-09-2001 L2003 **PTH** *100 †50
THOHAN, Vinay. MEDICAL CENTER BLVD, WFU BAPTIST MEDICAL CENTER 27157 #023-01-1995 L2006 **CD** *020 †20
THOMAS, Anita J. MEDICAL CENTER DRIVE 27157 #020-02-1980 L2003 **NR** *100 †80,28
THOMAS, Caroline Sheffiel. ■ 27106 #036-05-2007 **PD** *012
THOMAS, John Andrew. 3333 SILAS CREEK PKWY, FORSYTH HOSPITAL - OB ANES 27103 #016-11-1993 L1998 **AN** *020 †05
THOMAS, John Barham R. 105 VEST MILL CIR 27103 #036-05-1976 L1977 **FM** *020 †18
THOMAS, Megan Ray. ■ 27127 #036-08-2006 L2007 **FP** *012
THOMASON, R Bradley, III. 3333 SILAS CREEK PKWY 27103 #036-05-1984 L1986 **VS GS** *020 †85
THOMPSON, Christopher A. 2932 LYNDHURST AVE 27103 #051-01-2001 L2005 **OBG** *020 †30
THOMPSON, James Thomas, II. 1 MEDICAL CTR BLVD, DEPT OF PLASTIC & 27157 #027-01-1998 L1999 **PS GS** *100 †85,65
THOMPSON, Nicholas Carl. ■ 27104 #018-03-2007 **AN** *012
THORNE, Mark Taft. 2933 MAPLEWOOD AVE, STE 4 27103 #035-09-1983 L1991 **GS** *020 †85
THORNE, Nyree K. ■ 27104 #035-15-2001 L2007 **GE** *100
THORNTON, Heath Crumpler. MEDICAL CENTER BOULEVARD, WFU SCHOOL OF MEDICINE 27157 #051-04-2000 L2003 **FSM** *020 †18
THOTAKURA, Rajakumar. 125 ASHLEYBROOK LN 27103 #495-50-1981 L1993 **CHP PD** *020 †75
THOTAKURA, Umalakshmi K. 125 ASHLEY BROOK SQ, WINSTON PSYCHIATRIC ASSOC 27103 #495-50-1983 L1993 **CHP** *020 †75
TILLMAN, Bryan Walter. MEDICAL CENTER BOULEVARD, DEPT OF SURGERY 27157 #001-02-2001 L2006 **VS** *012 †85

■ = Address Information Privacy Protected

TINNEY, Qionna Mariel. PO BOX 7510 27109 #036-01-2006 L2007 **P** *012

TOBIN, Joseph R. MEDICAL CENTER BLVD, WAKE FOREST UNIV SCH OF ME 27157 #035-15-1983 L1993 **PD CCP** *020 †55,05

TOBORG, Robert Theodore. 3333 BROOKVIEW HILLS BLVD, STE 204 27103 #018-03-1998 L1999 **FM** *020 †18

TODD, Jason Wyatt. 160 CHARLOIS BLVD, NORTHEAST NEUROLOGY 27103 #012-01-1998 L2004 **N OS** *020 †75

TOLMIE, John Duncan. 300 S HAWTHORNE RD 27103 #067-01-1959 L1970 **AN** *040 †05

TOMBERLIN, Kenneth Guy. 3817 FORRESTGATE DR 27103 #036-05-1960 L1960 **ORS** *071 †40

TONG, Chuanyao. MED CTR BLVD 27157 #243-16-1983 L1999 **AN** *020 †05

TOOLE, James F. MEDICAL CENTER BOULEVARD, WAKE FOREST UNIV SCH OF ME 27157 #035-20-1949 L1962 **N** *030 †20,75

TORRES, Amaryllis V. 190 KIMEL PARK DR, W-S VA OUTPATIENT CLINIC 27103 #847-02-1978 L1990 **IM** *020

TORTI, Frank Michael. MEDICAL CENTER BLVD, OF WAKE FOREST UNIVERSITY 27157 #024-01-1974 L1994 **ON IM** *050 †20

TOTH-BAGI, Aniko. 3333 SILAS CREEK PKWY 27103 #473-01-1991 L2001 **IM HOS** *020 †20

TOWNSEND, David Leon. ■ 27127 #012-01-2005 L2007 **IM** *012

TRACY, Michael Richard. ■ 27127 #041-01-2003 L2008 **ORS** *012

TRAUNERO, Justin Ryan. ■ 27104 #036-05-2007 **AN** *012

TRAVER, Michael Arthur. ■ 27103 #025-07-2003 **U** *012

TRIDICO, Trina Insook. ■ 27107 #036-05-2005 **FP** *012

TRILLO, Alberto. BOWMAN GRAY SCH MED PTH 27103 #649-01-1967 L1979 **PTH** *020 †50

TRIVEDI, Apurva Navin. ■ 27103 #001-06-2005 L2008 **IM** *012

TROOST, Bradley Todd. MEDICAL CENTER BLVD, DEPT NEURO 27157 #024-01-1963 L1983 **N OPH** *040 †75

TROWELL, Amy Rebecca. 250 CHARLOIS BLVD 27103 #012-01-1972 L1975 **PD PHO** *020 †55

TRUJILLO, Jaime E. 3080 TRENWEST DR 27103 #264-03-1972 L1977 **IM END** *020 †20

TU, Likun. 3333 BROOKVIEW HILLS BLVD, STE 207 27103 #028-34-1998 L2000 **NEP** *020 †20

TUCKER, Scott Leming. 1345 WESTGATE CENTER DR #A 27103 #028-03-1982 L1983 **PS** *020 †65

TUREBYLU, Raghu Ramappa. CHILDREN'S HOSPITAL, BRENNER 27157 #495-72-1991 L2006 **NPM** *040

TURNER, Charles Siewers. 3333 SILAS CREEK PKWY 27103 #036-05-1970 L1970 **PDS GS** *020 †85

TURNER, Henry Catlett. BOWMAN GRAY SCHOOL OF MED 27157 #036-01-1962 L1962 **AN** *020 †05

TURNER, Samuel Jefferyraf. ■ 27127 #036-05-2005 L2007 **IM** *012

TYLER, Holly Kristina. ■ 27127 #036-05-2008 *012

UNDERDAL, Robert Gorder. ■ 27104 #036-05-1956 L1956 **ORS** *072 †40

UPDAW, Robert James. ■ 27127 #038-43-2005 **IM** *012

URBANIC, James John. ■ 27103 #045-01-2003 L2008 **RO** *012

USSERY, Brandy Lee. ■ 27103 #004-01-2006 **FP** *012

UTTERBACK, Reem Samir. 2453 JEFFERSON AVE 27103 #036-05-2000 L2004 **CHP** *020 ‡

VACHHARAJANI, Tushar J. MEDICAL CENTER BLVD., WAKE FOREST UNIVERSITY HEA 27157 #495-01-1986 L2006 **IM** *020 †20

VACHHARAJANI, Vidula T. MEDICAL CENTER BLVD, ASST PROF, CRIT CARE, DEPT 27157 #495-01-1989 L2006 **CCM** *020 †20

VAFAI, Mohamed. BOWMAN GRAY MED CTR 27103 #517-03-1968 **CHP PD** *100

VAIDYA, Rakeschandra S. 190 KIMEL PARK DR 27103 #495-23-1992 L2006 **IM** *020 †20

VALAORAS, Thomas Geo. 245 CHARLOIS BLVD 27103 #012-01-1992 L1996 **OBG** *020 †30

VALLA, Rebecca Suzanne. 915 W 4TH ST 27101 #033-05-1986 L1992 **P** *020 †75

VAN CLEVE, Horatio P. ■ 27106 #026-04-1944 L1975 **FM D** *071 †18

VANNOY, Tammie Frazier. 2808 MAPLEWOOD AVE 27103 #036-05-1995 L1998 **PD** *020 †55

VAN ZANDT, Keith Bergen. 100 ROBINHOOD MEDICAL PLZ 27106 #036-05-1980 L1987 **FM** *020 †18

VARBAN, Oliver Adrian. ■ 27127 #036-05-2005 **GS** *012

VARNELL, Robert Martin. 3155 MAPLEWOOD AVE, TRIAD RADIOLOGY 27103 #047-06-1983 L1990 **VIR** *020 †80

VELEZ, Ramon. MEDICAL CENTER BLVD, WAKE FOREST UNIV MED SCHOO 27157 #035-19-1970 L1976 **IM** *040 †20

VENABLE, Christine Leann. ■ 27103 #036-05-2007 **AN** *012

VERMILLION, Scot Stanley. 3155 MAPLEWOOD AVE, FORSYTH RADIOLOGICAL ASSOC 27103 #047-06-1990 L1996 **DR** *020 †80

VILLEPONTEAUX, Reginald. 3333 SILAS CREEK PKWY, FORSYTH MEDICAL CENTER—IP 27103 #045-01-1980 L1986 **IM** *020 †20

VREELAND, Walling Douglas. 5740 PHILLIPS BRIDGE RD 27104 #036-05-1955 L1955 **GP** *071

VROOMAN, Peter S, Jr. 3333 SILAS CREEK PKWY 27103 #047-07-1988 L1989 **EM** *020 †16

WADE, Stephen Bradley. MEDICAL CENTER BLVD, WAKE FOREST UNIVERSITY 27157 #048-14-2003 L2006 **NPM** *012 †55

WAGNER, Barbara R Curran. ■ 27103 #035-03-1965 L1969 **PD** *071 †55

WAGNER, Chad Martin. MEDICAL CENTER BOULEVARD, WAKE FOREST DEPARTMENT OF 27157 #036-05-2004 L2007 **FSM** *012 †18

WAGNER, Jaime Stephen. ■ 27101 #051-75-2007, ▲ *012

WAGONER, Gwendolyn Field. 110 CHARLOIS BLVD, PIEDMONT EAR NOSE AND THRO 27103 #036-05-2002 L2007 **OTO** *020

WAHLA, Ali Saeed. MED CTR BLVD, BAPTIST MED CTR-PULM CARE 27157 #704-25-2001 L2006 **PCC** *012 †20

WALKER, Francis O'Neill. MEDICAL CENTER BLVD, WAKE FOREST UNIVERSITY SCH 27157 #017-20-1978 L1984 **N** *050 †75

WALKIEWICZ, Thomas Walter. ■ 27103 #031-01-2001 L2006 **RNR** *012 †80

WALL, Amy Barta. 1214 REYNOLDA RD, STE A 27104 #036-05-1994 L1998 **OPH** *020 †35

WALLACE, Amyjo. 2808 MAPLEWOOD AVE 27103 #001-06-2003 L2006 **PD** *020 †55

WALLEY, Bruce Douglas. 2827 LYNDHURST AVE 27103 #036-05-1974 L1974 **TS** *020 †85,90

WALLIN, Jordan Lee. ■ 27127 #010-01-2007 **OTO** *012

WALTER, Keith Andrew. MEDICAL CENTER BLVD, WAKE FOREST UNIV EYE CTR 27157 #036-07-1991 L1996 **OPH IM** *020 †35

WALTERS, Alicia Catherine. ■ 27127 #038-43-2006 **FP** *012

WALTERS, Emily Peay. ■ 27103 #036-05-2008 *012

WANG, Bing. ■ 27104 #048-04-2003 **DR** *012

WANNENBURG, Thomas. MEDICAL CENTER BLVD, DEPT OF CARDIOLOGY 27157 #836-04-1982 L1991 **CD** *020 †20

WARD, Joshua Quayle. ■ 27127 #051-04-2007 **AN** *012

WARD, William Goode. MEDICAL CENTER BLVD, DEPT OF ORTHOPAEDIC SURGER 27157 #036-07-1978 L1980 **ORS OS** *020 †40

WARNER, Benjamin Welton. DEPT OF PEDIATRICS, MED CTR BLVD 27157 #036-05-2006 **PD** *012

WARNER, Rebecca Elizabeth. ■ 27104 #028-34-2007 **GS** *012

WASHBURN, Lisa Katheryn. MEDICAL CENTER BLVD, WAKE FOREST SCHOOL OF MEDI 27157 #036-05-1987 L1993 **PD NPM** *050 †55

WATERER, Ronald Patton. 3333 SILAS CREEK PKWY 27103 #027-01-1989 L1993 **AN** *020 †05

WATERS, Gregory Stiegler. MEDICAL CENTER BOULEVARD, WAKE FOREST UNIVERSITY BAP 27157 #036-08-1990 L1997 **GS CRS** *020 †10,85

WATKINS, Franklin Shields. ■ 27157 #047-06-2002 L2006 **IMG** *100 †20

WATKINS, Raquel Suzanne. MED CTR BLVD 27157 #023-01-1996 L1999 **AI** *020 †20

WATSON, Nat Erskine, Jr. MED CTR BLVD 27157 #045-01-1966 L1972 **NM IM** *071 †28,20

WATTS, Lester Earl. MED CTR BLVD 27157 #036-05-1957 L1957 **CD IM** *071 †20

WEAVER, Frederick Brown. 250 CHARLOIS BLVD, WINSTON-SALEM HLTH CARE PL 27103 #036-05-1963 L1963 **IM** *020

WEAVER, Richard G. MED CTR BLVD 27157 #028-02-1947 L1953 **OPH** *072 †35

WEAVER, Richard Grey. BOWMAN GRAY SCH MED OPH 27106 #036-05-1977 L1977 **OPH** *020 †35

WEBB, Lawrence Xavier. MED CTR BLVD 27157 #041-13-1978 L1979 **ORS OTR** *020 †40

WEBER, Glenda F Hartness. 3333 SILAS CREEK PKWY, FORSYTH MEMORIAL HOSP 27103 #036-05-1965 L1965 **PTH** *020 †50

WEEKS, Duke Byron. MEDICAL CENTER BLVD, BOWMAN GRAY DEPT ANES 27157 #036-05-1965 L1965 **AN** *020 †05

WEEKS, Landon Earl. 2025 FRONTIS PLAZA BLVD, DIGESTIVE HEALTH SPECIALIS 27103 #051-04-1973 L1974 **GE** *020 †20

WEICKER, Michael A. OF MED, WAKE FOREST UNIV SCH 27157 #035-01-2006 **NS** *012

WEINBERG, Richard Barry. 391 TECHNOLOGY WAY, WAKE FOREST UNIV SCH MEDIC 27157 #023-07-1975 L1990 **GE IM** *050 †20

WEISS, Larry Lister. 1950 S HAWTHORNE RD 27103 #038-40-1958 L1962 **OPH** *071 †35

WELCH, Earl Parks. 3333 SILAS CREEK PKWY 27103 #036-01-1957 L1957 **GS TS** *071 †85

WELCH, Martha Carroll. ■ 27101 #036-08-2006 L2006 **FP** *012

WELCH, Meredith Lynn. ■ 27127 #012-01-2005 L2008 **IM** *012

WELLER, Robert Stephen. MED CTR BLVD 27157 #016-06-1979 L1997 **AN** *040 †05

WELLMAN, Nicole Lynn. ■ 27103 #036-05-2004 L2007 **PD** *020 †55

WELLS, Gretchen Lois. MED CTR BLVD 27157 #001-02-1994 L1995 **CD** *020 †20

WENTWORTH, Stacy. ■ 27103 #036-05-2004 L2007 **RO** *012

WERLE, David Michael. ■ 27106 #036-05-2006 **GS** *012

WEST, Paul James. 725 HIGHLAND AVE, DAY MARK RECOVERY SERV INC 27101 #305-01-1999 L2003 **CHP** *020 †75

WEST, Thomas Graham. DP OF RADI. 2ND FLOOR, MEEDS BLV 27157 #036-05-2001 L2005 **RNR** *012 †80

WESTCOTT, Carl Jos. MED CTR BLVD 27157 #041-09-1991 L1997 **GS** *020 †85

WESTON, Jonathan Dunbar. 495 N CLEVELAND AVE 27101 #035-45-1975 L1979 **OBG** *020 †30

WHATLEY, James Bushnell. 3333 SILAS CREEK PKWY, FORSYTH MEDICAL CENTER 27103 #001-02-2004 L2007 **IM** *020 †20

WHELAN, Deborah Moscal. MED CTR BLVD 27157 #021-05-1990 L1991 **AN** *020 †05

WHITE, Anne L. 3000 BETHESDA PL, STE 601 & 602 27103 #017-20-1980 L2005 **D** *020 †18

WHITE, Charles Jared. ■ 27103 #012-01-2007 **EM** *012

WHITE, Douglas Rector. MED CTR BLVD 27157 #016-02-1967 L1974 **ON HEM** *020 †20

WHITE THOMASON, Jason W. 3333 SILAS CREEK PKWY 27103 #036-05-1997 L2004 **PCC** *100 †20

WHITLOCK, Patrick William. ■ 27103 #041-15-2005 **ORS** *012

WIESLER, Ethan Ron. MED CTR BLVD 27157 #036-05-1994 L1996 **HS** *020 †40

WILCOX, Cari Lyn. ■ 27104 #018-03-2007 *012

WILE, Geoffrey Eugene. WFUBMC DEPT OF RADIOLOGY 27157 #047-06-2002 L2005 **DR** *100 †80

WILE, Laura Michelle. 1381 WESTGATE CENTER DR 27103 #047-06-2003 L2005 **IM** *020 †20

WILFRET, David Andrew. MEDICAL CENTER BLVD, WAKE FOREST UNIV PEDS 27157 #011-03-2001 L2006 **PDI** *100 †55

WILKE, Ann Robinson. 250 CHARLOIS BLVD 27103 #023-01-1965 L2002 **CD IM** *020 †20

WILKERSON, Wade Richard. ■ 27103 #036-05-2005 **DR** *012

WILKIN, Aimee Maree. MED CTR BLVD 27157 #048-02-1994 L2001 **ID** *020 †20

WILKINSON, John Ross. ■ 27104 #023-01-1952 L1952 **FM EM** *071

WILLIAMS, Barry Niel. 3000 BETHESDA PL, STE 801 27103 #036-05-1983 L1985 **P** *020 †75

WILLIAMS, Daniel Walter. MEDICAL CENTER BLVD., WAKE FOREST UNIV. SCH. OF 27157 #036-01-1984 L1985 **RNR DR** *020 †80

WILLIAMS, Robert Lee. 1351 WESTGATE CENTER DR 27103 #036-07-1975 L1979 **PD** *020 †55

WILLIAMS, S Clay, Jr. ■ 27106 #041-01-1945 L1946 **IM** *071 †20

WILLIAMS, Susan Jean. MED CTR BLVD 27157 #036-01-1980 L1981 **FM** *020 †18

WILLIAMSON, Christal E. ■ 27127 #048-16-2003 L2006 **HO** *012 †20

WILLIAMSON, Jeff Douglas. STICHT AGING CENTER, WAKE FOREST UNIV 27157 #012-01-1986 L1997 **IMG EM** *040 †20

WILLIFORD, Phillip Mabon. WAKE FOREST UNIV HLTH SCNC, DEPT OF DERM 27157 #036-01-1981 L1982 **DS D** *020 †20,15

WILLINGHAM, Mark Cauthen. MED CTR BLVD 27157 #045-01-1969 L1997 **ATP** *050

WILSON, Benjamin Lewis. 600 HIGHLAND OAKS DR 27103 #036-01-2003 L2005 **FM** *020 †18

WILSON, Charles Steven. 3333 SILAS CREEK PKWY, FORSYTH INPATIENT PHYSICIA 27103 #047-05-1984 L1996 **IM** *020 †20

WILSON, John Allen, Jr. MEDICAL CENTER BLVD, WAKE FOREST U/BAPTIST M C 27157 #041-02-1982 L1993 **NS** *020 †25 ‡

WILSON, Jonathan Lee. MED C, WAKE FOREST UNIV BAPTIST 27157 #055-01-2007 **GS** *012

WILSON, Scott Douglas. 131 MILLER ST, WAKE FOREST UNIV HEALTH SV 27103 #036-05-1986 L2006 **OMO ORS** *020 †40

WINSLOW, James Elbert, III. MED CTR BLVD 27157 #036-01-1999 L2001 **EM** *020 †16

WINTER, Jerald Luke. 2201 GASTON ST 27103 #036-05-1995 L1997 **PTH** *100 †18,50

WINTER, Stephen Bradley. ■ 27127 #048-14-2007 **ORS** *012

WINTERS, Daniel. 3333 SILAS CREEK PKWY 27103 #035-45-1980 L1982 **AN** *020 †05

WISEMAN, Jane Elizabeth. MED C, WAKE FOREST UNIV BAPTIST 27157 #055-02-2007 **FP** *012

WITTMER, Steven Philip. 3333 BROOKVIEW HILLS BLVD, STE 207 27103 #016-45-1981 L1994 **IM** *020 †20

WOFFORD, James Lucius. MEDICAL CTR BLVD IM DEPT, WAKE FOREST UNIV BAP MED 27157 #027-01-1985 L1987 **IM IMG** *020 †20

WOLFE, John Richard. 1381 WESTGATE CENTER DR, FORSYTH INTERNAL MEDICINE 27103 #051-04-1967 L1974 **RHU IM** *020 †20

WOLFF, Thomas Vincent. 3333 SILAS CREEK PKWY 27103 #041-14-1986 L1987 **IM** *020 †20

WOOD, Benjamin Chadwick. ■ 27103 #036-05-2007 **GS** *012

WOOD, Dana Renee. ■ 27103 #036-05-2008 *012

WOOD, Elizabeth Michelle. ■ 27127 #001-06-2007 **IM** *012

■ = Address Information Privacy Protected

WOOD, Jeyhan Suzan. ■ 27104 #048-02-2007 **GS** *012
WOODRUFF, Ralph Dutton. MEDICAL CENTER BLVD-PATH, WAKE FOREST UNIV SCH MED 27157 #041-02-1965 L1979 **ATP CLP** *020 †50
WOODS, Kristy Freeman. MED CTR BLVD 27157 #021-01-1981 L2003 **IM** *020 †20
WORF, Richard Chas. 105 VEST MILL CIR 27103 #036-01-1978 L1979 **FM** *020 †18
WORKMAN, Claude Raymond. 3333 SILAS CREEK PKWY 27103 #023-12-1990 L1992 **VS** *020 †85
WORKMAN, Richard H, Jr. 725 HIGHLAND AVE, DAYMARK 27101 #036-05-1981 L1986 **P IM** *020 †75
WRIGHT, John Herman, Jr. 185 KIMEL PARK DR, STE 201 27103 #036-01-1968 L1968 **PS HS** *020 †85,65
WRIGHT, Stephen Carter, Jr. ■ 27157 #024-05-2000 L2005 **OTO** *100
WU, Wallace Chi-Li. BOWMAN GARY SCH OF MED 27103 #462-01-1966 L1974 **GE IM** *020 †20
WUERTZER, Scott David. ■ 27103 #001-06-2002 L2007 **MSR** *012 †80
WYMER, Antoinette. 201 EXECUTIVE PARK BLVD, BLUE RIDGE MED ASSOC., RLL 27103 #010-02-1979 L1989 **IM** *050 †20
WYNECOFF, Debra Renee. ■ 27105 #036-01-1983 L1993 **FM OM** *075
YALCINKAYA, Tamer M. MEDICAL CENTER BOULEVARD, WAKE FOREST UNIVERSITY HEA 27157 #902-10-1983 L2005 **REN OBG** *020 †30
YANAGI, Hidetaka. INFECTIOUS DISEASES, SECTION ON 27157 #572-03-1994 **ID** *012
YANG, Lucie Lingning. ■ 27103 #005-02-2004 L2007 **DR** *100
YARBORO, Seth Robert. PO BOX 8183 27109 #036-01-2007 **ORS** *012
YASUNAGA, Judith April. ■ 27103 #016-45-2004 L2007 **IM** *100 †20
YE, Qing Brenda. ■ 27157 #036-07-2002 **DR** *012
YEATTS, Robert Patrick. MEDICAL CENTER BLVD., WAKE FOREST UNIV EYE CENTE 27157 #036-05-1978 L1979 **OPH OS** *020 †35
YELVERTON, Christopher B. MEDICAL CENTER BLVD 27157 #048-15-2003 **D** *012
YENTZER, Brad Alan. ■ 27101 #041-02-2006 L2007 **TY** *012
YESTER, Amy Theresa. ■ 27106 #055-01-2006 **OBG** *012
YESTER, Marc Alan. ■ 27106 #055-01-2006 **PD** *012
YETTER, Matt Francis. 2825 LYNDHURST AVE, STE 103 27103 #030-05-1986 L2003 **OTO HNS** *020 †45 ‡
YODER, Jonathan Scott. MEDICAL CENTER BLVD, DEPAT OF FAMILY MEDICINE 27157 #036-05-2004 L2006 **FSM** *012 †18
YOON, Vivienne Sojee. ■ 27101 #048-02-2006 **IM** *012
YOPP, James Dennis. ■ 27106 #036-05-1966 L1966 **CD IM** *071 †20
YOSIPOVITCH, Gil. MED CTR BLVD 27157 #550-02-1989 L2002 **D** *020
YOUNG, Sarah Wistran. ■ 27106 #035-15-2005 **IM** *012
YOUNG, Trudye Awanaha. 27114 #012-21-1998 L1999 **GS** *020
YOUNG, Yorke Douglas. ■ 27127 #047-20-2005 **PTH** *012
YOUNGER, Ernest Deed. 27104 #036-01-1975 L1976 **IM** *075
YOUNT, Ernest H, III. 27104 #048-14-1983 L1985 **FM** *020 †18
YOUNT, Lindsay Shuford. PO BOX 8861 27109 #051-01-2006 L2006 **IM** *012
YOW, Richard Baxter. 250 CHARLOIS BLVD, WINSTON-SALEM HEALTH CARE 27103 #036-01-1981 L1991 **DR** *020 †80
YUENGEL, Christine A. 1900 S HAWTHORNE RD, STE 614 27103 #033-06-1984 L1996 **D** *075 †15
YUSON, Carlo Pilapil. 1900 S HAWTHORNE RD # 358 27103 #748-01-1969 L1976 **N OS** *020 †75
ZAGORIA, Ronald Jay. MEDICAL CENTER BLVD DPT DR, WAKE FOREST UNIV SCH MED 27157 #023-01-1983 L1984 **DR VIR** *020 †80 ‡
ZAMMIT, Robert Paul. 406 FORSYTH MEDICAL PARK 27103 #030-06-1956 L1967 **OBG** *071
ZANNIS, John. ■ 27127 #038-41-2004 **PS** *012
ZEKAN, Patricia Joan. 250 CHARLOIS BLVD 27103 #055-01-1978 L1980 **IM ON** *020 †20
ZELMAN, Stacie Jean. MEDICAL CENTER BLVD, DEPARTMENT OF EMERGENCY ME 27157 #036-01-1999 L2001 **EM** *020 †16
ZHANG, Lin. ■ 27157 #243-70-1988 L2004 **HO** *100 †20
ZHANG, Xishan. MED CENTER BLVD, WAKE FOREST U BAPT MED CTR 27157 #243-45-1984 L2005 **N** *100
ZHAO, Larry. ■ 27103 #036-05-2008 *012
ZIEL, Carol Jean. 2025 FRONTIS PLAZA BLVD, WINSTON SALEM 27103 #020-12-1987 L1999 **OPH** *020 †35
ZINN, Jacqueline Ellen. ■ 27104 #016-11-2003 L2007 **PM** *100
ZUB, David William. ■ 27103 #028-03-2005 L2008 **AN** *012

WINTERVILLE – PITT

BADWAN, Wafa Rawhi. ■ 28590 #036-08-2005 **IM** *012
BERRO, Joseph Benjamin. ■ 28590 #051-07-2006 **EM** *012
BLAIR, Elizabeth Ivey. 4024A OLD TAR RD 28590 #036-01-1988 L1990 **PD** *020 †55
BRADSHAW, Louise Annette. 4024A OLD TAR RD, OUR CHILDREN'S CLINIC 28590 #036-08-1987 L1988 **NPM** *020 †55
CAHILL, Timothy James. 711 ASHLEY MEADOWS DR 28590 #654-01-2001 L2004 **EM** *020 †20
CHAMBERLAIN, Andrea Chris. ■ 28590 #024-05-2003 L2007 **P** *012
CIMO, Christine Louise. ■ 28590 #045-01-2007 **OBG** *012
CORBETT, Timothy Mark. ■ 28590 #036-08-2007 **FP** *012
DAR, Moahad Saeed. ■ 28590 #036-08-1999 L2002 **END** *100 †20 ‡
DAWSON, Brian Christopher. ■ 28590 #036-08-2006 L2008 **EM** *012
DAWSON, Mary H. ■ 28590 #036-08-2006 **FP** *012
DE GUZMAN, Jocelyn May. ■ 28590 #047-06-2006 **EM** *012
DESPRES, Maureen. ■ 28590 #024-16-2005 **MPD** *012
DURHAM, Christopher Alan. ■ 28590 #048-14-2007 **GS** *012
EHRMANN, David Charles. ■ 28590 #036-08-2007 **FP** *012
ELDRIDGE, David Lewis. ■ 28590 #055-02-2000 L2005 **PD** *100 †55
FLETCHER, James Colin. ■ 28590 #012-01-2007 **OBG** *012
FOUSHEE, Jennifer Paige. ■ 28590 #036-08-2007 **IM** *012
FOWLKES, William Mortimer. 4427 SURREY MEADOWS DR 28590 #036-01-2000 L2002 **EM** *100
FUH, Richard Beng. 28590 #409-15-1999 L2007 **PHO** *100 †55
GARCIA, Paul. ■ 28590 #036-08-2000 L2003 **OS** *020 †20,75 ‡
GREEN, William Harris. ■ 28590 #047-20-2006 **D** *012
GUERRA, Carlos Octavio. ■ 28590 #737-01-2001 **ID** *012 †20
HAAG LEDERER, Alejandro F. ■ 28590 #264-12-1984 **FP** *012
HAMPSHIRE, Katherine Robi. ■ 28590 #047-20-2007 **PD** *012

HERNANDEZ, Nancy. ■ 28590 #264-21-2000 **IM** *100
HOLLADAY, Nathan B. ■ 28590 #048-12-2007 *012
HOWARD, Omar Hashim. ■ 28590 #012-21-2006 **P** *012
JOHN, Nadyah Janine. ■ 28590 #010-03-2005 **P** *012
JOHNS, Cynthia Ruth. ■ 28590 #036-08-2008 *012
JOHNSON, Reuben Dempsey. ■ 28590 #010-03-2002 L2007 **OS** *100 †20
JONES, Paul Bernard. ■ 28590 #047-07-2003 **GS** *012
KALEKA, Gurjeet. ■ 28590 #063-01-2003 L2003 **GS** *012
KARKUT, Christopher John. ■ 28590 #036-08-2006 **IM** *012
KENNY, Bernadette M. ■ 28590 #539-04-1995 L1998 **IM** *020 †20
KODROFF, Michael Barry. 390 BAYWOOD DR # 2 28590 #041-02-1967 L1984 **R PDR** *071 †80
LAMBERT, Joseph Alan. ■ 28590 #055-02-2006 **EM** *012
LANDRY, Ronald Charles. ■ 28590 #051-04-1994 L1996 **EM** *020 †16
LIM, Heang Muy. ■ 28590 #036-08-2008 **IM** *012
MARNEY, Nicholas James. ■ 28590 #035-15-2005 L2007 **EM** *012
MAYES, Nicholas Dean. ■ 28590 #036-08-2008 *012
MC GUFFIN, Tabitha Dawn. ■ 28590 #055-01-2003 **OBG** *100
MCNABB, Amanda Renee. ■ 28590 #036-08-2008 *012
MEARA, Michael Paul. ■ 28590 #047-20-2007 **GS** *012
MURPHY, Meena Patel. 4796 OLD TAR RD 28590 #036-08-1995 L1999 **IM** *020 †20
NEVEROV, Nikita Igorevich. ■ 28590 #913-06-1984 L2008 **NEP** *100
NEVEROVA, Maria Vasylievn. ■ 28590 #913-06-1985 L2007 **IM** *012
OTHMAN, Islam Mohamed. ■ 28590 #104-01-2004 L2007 **CD** *012 †20
PAGE, Angela Marie. ■ 28590 #045-04-2004 **OBG** *012
PARK, Hyunsoon Edie. ■ 28590 #036-08-1994 L2002 **P** *020
PAULK, Eric Michael. ■ 28590 #012-01-2006 L2008 **EM** *012
PLONK, Timothy Matthew. ■ 28590 #036-05-2007 **EM** *012
PRIVETTE, Crystal Goodwin. ■ 28590 #036-08-2004 L2007 **OBG** *012
QUAN, Walter, Jr. ■ 28590 #038-40-1986 L2005 **IM** *020 †20
RAMIREZ PEREZ, Beatriz Eu. ■ 28590 #935-01-1998 **IM** *012
REYES-AVILA, Ruben. ■ 28590 #275-02-1986 L2006 **HO** *012 †20
ROBERTS, Leah Fox. ■ 28590 #051-01-2005 **OBG** *100
ROBERTSON, Jeremy Ray. ■ 28590 #001-02-2006 **EM** *012
SAMTANI, Jai-Gurmukh Kish. ■ 28590 #496-22-2005 **FP** *012
SAQIB, Saira. ■ 28590 #704-21-1996 **P** *100
SAUNDERS, Courtney Brooke. ■ 28590 #055-02-2006 **MEM** *012
SCHIMING, Rachel Andrea. ■ 28590 #026-04-2004 L2008 **EM** *012
SIMON, Alexa N. ■ 28590 #010-02-2008 *012
SOLBERG, Heidi Marie. ■ 28590 #041-15-2006 **EM** *012
STEWART, Angela G. 4024A OLD TAR RD 28590 #016-01-1980 L1981 **PD** *020 †55
STOKES, Babatunde Louis. ■ 28590 #023-01-2005 **PTH** *012
SUTTON, Jill Marie. ■ 28590 #036-08-2006 **OBG** *012
THOMAS, Kevin Robert. ■ 28590 #045-04-2004 L2007 **PTH** *012
THOMAS, Sandra Parrish. ■ 28590 #045-04-2004 L2007 **PTH** *012
TURNER, Robert C. 4796 OLD TAR RD 28590 #016-11-1974 L1979 **IM** *020 †20
VIOLA, Gemma Lao. ■ 28590 #748-19-1989 L1998 **AI** *020 †55
WAQAS, Muhammad. ■ 28590 #704-01-2002 L2007 **IM** *020 †20
WATSON, Derek Philip. ■ 28590 #036-08-2004 L2008 **PM** *012
WILDEMAN, Miriam E. ■ 28590 #041-14-1979 L1991 **NS GS** *020
WOOD, Judy Carol Wheat. ■ 28590 #047-06-1969 L2004 **PD** *020 †55 ‡
WRIGHT, Marion Edward, Jr. ■ 28590 #036-01-2002 L2007 **P** *012
ZHOU, Fan. ■ 28590 #243-03-1997 **FP** *012

WINTON – HERTFORD

BROZZETTI, Kelly Ann. ■ 27986 #035-15-2005 **DR** *012

WOODLAND – NORTHAMPTON

SHEAR, Morris. 103 HAZEL ST 27897 #036-08-1985 L1989 **FM EM** *075

WRIGHTSVILLE BEACH – NEW HANOVER

ALSINA, George Anthony. 18 BAHAMA DR, BOX 1038 28480 #024-05-1994 L2003 **NS** *020
CROCKER, William Daniel. PO BOX 674 28480 #036-01-2006 **AN** *012
LYNCH, John Franklin, Jr. ■ 28480 #041-02-1944 L1944 **PD** *071 †55
NIXON, Wm Preston, Jr. 2 JASMINE CT 28480 #051-04-1968 L1971 **IM NEP** *020 †20
REITER, Richard Martin. ■ 28480 #010-03-1970 L1986 **GS IM** *071 †85

YADKINVILLE – YADKIN

ABDULSALAM, Farah Zeshan. 108 S STATE ST, BLUE RIDGE CARDIOLOGY AND 27055 #495-04-2000 L2004 **IM** *012
BRANDON, Henry Allen, Jr. 1905 OLD US 421 HWY W 27055 #036-05-1970 L1970 **EM IM** *020 †20 ‡
HIATT, Wilks Otho, Jr. PO BOX 115 27055 #036-07-1943 L1974 **PHP PD** *071 †55
HILL, Cathy June. 624 W MAIN ST, P O BOX 68 27055 #036-01-1983 L1986 **FM** *020 †18
HUGHES, Carlisle Bee, Jr. 625 W MAIN ST 27055 #051-04-1940 L1951 **GS GP** *071
LONG, Thomas Smither. 624 W MAIN ST 27055 #036-05-1975 L1975 **FM AM** *020 †18
MC GRATH, James Stuart. 624 W MAIN ST 27055 #021-01-1980 L1982 **FM** *020 †18
PORCHEY, Carl Jos. 624 W MAIN ST, P O BOX 68 27055 #028-02-1972 L1974 **IM** *020 †20 ‡
WILLIAMS, Joan Reback. 305 E LEE AVE 27055 #036-01-1985 L1986 **FM** *020
WILLIAMS, John Taylor. 305 E LEE AVE, YADKIN MEDICAL ASSOCIATES 27055 #036-01-1984 L1986 **FM** *020
ZIGLAR, Jerry Thos. 305 E LEE AVE 27055 #036-05-1979 L1981 **IM** *020 †20

YANCEYVILLE – CASWELL

STARLING, James F, Jr. 1702 NC HIGHWAY 86 N 27379 #036-05-1967 L1967 **IM NEP** *020 †20

YOUNGSVILLE – FRANKLIN

CORPENING, Albert Newton. PO BOX 158 27596 #036-05-1955 L1955 **FM** *020 †18
HAMILTON, Byron Bruce. ■ 27596 #035-15-1959 L1962 **PM OS** *071
LIGHTNER, Virginia Ann. 82 WHEATON DR 27596 #036-07-1982 L1983 **D** *020 †15

ZEBULON – WAKE

BANKS, Kenneth. 319 HOSPITAL RD 27597 #036-01-1973 L1973 **FM** *020 †18
BIRD, Kimberly Coates. 535 W GANNON AVE 27597 #036-01-1996 L1997 **PCC SME** *020 †20
BLAKE, Gerald Wayne. 535 W GANNON AVE 27597 #036-01-1967 L1967 **IM ID** *020 †20
BRIDGES, Eugene Drew. 1002 DOGWOOD DR, EASTERN REGIONAL CENTER 27597 #036-01-1975 L1978 **P** *020
CAMPBELL, Elizabeth Anne. 535 W GANNON AVE 27597 #019-02-1991 L1993 **IM** *020 †20
ESHELMAN, Thomas Carl. ■ 27597 #036-05-1967 L1969 **R** *071 †80
GEORGE, Pazhayidathe K. 323 HOSPITAL RD 27597 #495-31-1964 L1983 **IM GE** *020 †20
HWANG, Yinnan Gary. 1303 WATER PLANT RD 27597 #244-05-1970 L1984 **FM PTH** *020 †50
JENKINS, Charles S P. 319 HOSPITAL RD 27597 #035-06-1989 L1992 **IM** *071 ‡
MACLANG, Guy Ruedas. 903 N ARENDELL AVE 27597 #748-01-1990 L2006 **IM** *020 †20

MC CORD, Marcella Taylor. 1002 DOGWOOD DR 27597 #036-01-1992 L1995 **FM** *020 †18
MC LAIN, Lee Wm, Jr. 535 W GANNON AVE 27597 #036-07-1961 L1961 **N** *020 †75
RAJAGOPALAN, Shrinivas. 535 W GANNON AVE 27597 #036-07-1987 L1990 **PTH** *020 †50
ROGERS, Bruce Wm. 304 PONY RD, ZEBULON FAMILY MEDICINE 27597 #041-07-1982 L2007 **FM EM** *020 †18
SCANLAN, James Geo. 535 W GANNON AVE 27597 #016-06-1973 L1980 **CD IM** *020 †20
SEDWITZ, Joseph L. 321 HOSPITAL RD 27597 #051-01-1951 L1961 **GS GYN** *071 †85
SZPAK, Cheryl Anne. 535 W GANNON AVE 27597 #048-12-1977 L1977 **ATP OS** *020 †50
TODD, Meshia Quinelle. ■ 27597 #024-05-2008 *012
WEST, Shelly Lorraine. 301 HOSPITAL RD, WAKELON INTERNAL MEDICINE 27597 #036-08-1997 L2000 **IM** *020 †20

ZIONVILLE – WATAUGA

ESTES, John Eugene. ■ 28698 #036-01-1973 L1973 *020

ZIRCONIA – HENDERSON

BROADBENT, Margaret H. 21 CAMP GREYSTONE LN 28790 #020-02-1989 L1994 **PD** *020 †55
CLINTON, Howard L, Jr. 509 MINE GAP RD 28790 #012-05-1973 L1977 **EM OM** *020 †18

ASHLEY – MCINTOSH

IQBAL, Mohsin. PO BOX 450 58413 #704-01-2000 L2004 **IM** *020
OSTROWSKI, Susan A M. 612 CENTER AVE N 58413 #035-03-1974 L1989 **FM** *020 †18 ‡
TINSATUL, Udom. 612 CENTER AVE N, ASHLEY CLINIC 58413 #891-01-1967 L1977
  GS GP *020 †85

BEACH – GOLDEN VALLEY

MARAVILLA, Restituto, Jr. PO BOX 398, GOLDEN VALLEY MED CENTER 58621
  #748-01-1967 L1976 **GP R** *075
RIBAS-MARAVILLA, Teresita. ■ 58621 #748-01-1968 **GP AN** *020

BELCOURT – ROLETTE

AZURE, Vernon Donald. PO BOX 160 58316 #037-01-1988 L1990 **FM** *020 †18
GAID, Evangeline Signey. PO BOX 160, TURTLE MTN IHS HOSP 58316 #748-08-1973 L1993
  FM *020 †18
HENRY, Patty Kristal. PO BOX 160, BELCOURT HOSPITAL 58316 #038-41-1995 L1997
  OBG *020
MOHAMMED, Ahmed Hashim. PO BOX 160 58316 #915-04-1987 L1995 **IM** *020
WALKER, Thomas Stuart. ■ 58316 #037-01-1995 L1996 **IM** *020

BEULAH – MERCER

GARMAN, Aaron Michael. 1312 HIGHWAY 49 N 58523 #037-01-1996 L1997 **FM** *020 †18
GWINN, David M. 600 3RD AVE NW 58523 #046-01-1977 L1981 **IM EM** *074 †20
KASPARI, Thomas D. 1312 HIGHWAY 49 N 58523 #037-01-1996 L1997 **FM** *020 †18
KLINDWORTH, Jacinta T. 1312 HIGHWAY 49 N, CCCHC 58523 #060-01-1999 L2001
  FM *020 †18 ‡

BISMARCK – BURLEIGH

ADDUCCI, Christopher J. 401 N 9TH ST, MID DAKOTA CLINIC PC 58501 #016-43-1986 1991
  U *020 †95
AHMED, Bilal. 401 N 9TH ST, MID DAKOTA CLINIC PC 58501 #704-02-1982 L1998 **END** *020 †20
AKHTER, Jaweed. COTTONWOOD LOOP 58501 #917-04-1984 L2000 **IM END** *020 †20
ALEXANDER, Alan Wade. 900 E BROADWAY AVE 58501 #047-06-1995 L2002 **P** *100
AL-JAYOUSSI, Randa N. 300 N 7TH ST 58501 #575-02-1996 L2002 **IM** *020 †20
ALTRINGER, William E. 401 N 9TH ST, MID DAKOTA CLINIC PC 58501 #037-01-1990 L1995
  GS *020 †85
AMIN, Bipin Raojibhai. 401 N 9TH ST, MID DAKOTA CLINIC PC 58501 #495-85-1981 L1988
  IM HO *020 †20
ANDERSEN, Jeffrey Ben. 515 E BROADWAY AVE 58501 #037-01-2005 L2005 **FP** *012
APPERT, David Leo. 2700 STATE ST, MID DAKOTA DERMLGC SURG CT 58503
  #037-01-2000 L2000 **PRD** *020 †15
ARAZI, Richard. 315 N WASHINGTON ST 58501 #016-11-1969 L1980 **N CN** *020 †75
AYYOUBI, M Tayyeb. ■ 58503 #118-01-1986 L2005 **PTH** *020 †50
BAKKE, Rebecca Jo. ■ 58503 #037-01-2007 L2007 **PD** *012
BATHURST, Robert Marks. 900 E BROADWAY AVE 58501 #007-02-1971 L2001 **EM AN** *020 †16
BECKER, Ricky Clark. 1500 INTERCHANGE AVE, STE 100 58501 #037-01-1992 L1993
  PS *020 †65
BECKWITH, Jennifer Amber. 515 E BROADWAY AVE 58501 #037-01-2006 L2006 **FP** *012
BELANGER, Eric. 900 E BROADWAY AVE 58501 #067-03-1993 L2005 **NS** *020 †25
BERGLUND, Douglas D. 300 N 7TH ST 58501 #028-34-1987 L1994 **CRS GS** *020 †85,10
BETTING, Gary R. 515 E BROADWAY AVE, UND FAMILY PRACT CTR 58501 #037-01-1993 L1994
  FM *030 †18
BETTING, Susan Patricia. 3318 N 14TH ST, MEDCENTER ONE WALK IN CLIN 58503
  #037-01-1994 L1995 **FM** *020 †18
BLAKE, Lloyd William. 900 E BROADWAY AVE, CUMBERLAND LUNG ASTHMA SLE 58501
  #035-48-1993 L2004 **PCC SME** *020 †20
BLANCHARD, Joel Hubert. 300 N 7TH ST, MEDCENTER ONE Q&R CLINIC 58501
  #068-01-1981 L1991 **EM** *020 †18
BONET, Jorge Federico. 300 N 7TH ST 58501 #132-09-1973 L2001 *020
BOOTH, Allen Michael. 310 N 10TH ST, ST ALEXIUS HEART & LUNG 58501 #023-07-1977 L1989
  TS *020 †85,90
BORROWMAN, Terri Ann. 2700 STATE ST, GATEWAY DERMATOLOGY 58503
  #017-20-1997 L2000 **DMP** *020 †15
BOSSORT, James Bradley. 300 N 7TH ST 58501 #060-02-1990 L1999 **FM** *020 †18
BOTSFORD, John D. 2700 STATE ST, MID DAKOTA CLINIC 58503 #037-01-1993 L1994
  FM *020 †18
BOUTROUS, Attas, II. 600 N 9TH ST, BISMARCK SURGICAL ASSOCIAT 58501
  #037-01-1989 L1993 **AN PME** *020 †05
BOYKO, Kimber Melroy. 222 N 7TH ST, BOX 5505 58501 #005-12-1987 L1993 **GS** *020 †85
BRADLEY, Shannon S. 401 N 9TH ST 58501 #037-01-1996 L2000 **OBG** *020 †30
BROWN, Michael Ray. 310 N 10TH ST, ST ALEXIUS HEART & LUNG 58501 #037-01-1992 L2000
  TS *020 †90,85
BRUDERER, Brent Pymm. 225 N 7TH ST, 5TH FL 58501 #028-46-1982 L1994 **GS** *020 †85
BUCKINGHAM, William M. 515 E BROADWAY AVE 58501 #036-05-1951 L1952 **FM** *072 †18
BUELL, Brad R. 810 E ROSSER AVE STE 401 58501 #037-01-1977 L1978 **OTO HNS** *020 †45
BURY, Janice Marie. 401 N 9TH ST, MID DAKOTA CLINIC PC 58501 #037-01-1990 L1994
  OBG *020 †30
BURY, Robert John. 401 N 9TH ST, MID DAKOTA CLINIC PC 58501 #048-04-1975 L1979
  OBG *020 †30
BUSCEMI, Michael Frank. 300 N 7TH ST 58501 #010-01-1962 L1973 **U** *071 †95
CAIN, William Henry. 232 N 7TH ST, Q & R CLINIC 58501 #026-04-1981 L1985 **DR** *020 †80
CANHAM, Susan Ann. ■ 58503 #062-01-1978 L1994 **FM** *020
CANTWELL, Denise Cynthia. 1136 W DIVIDE AVE, MEDCENTER ONE/Q&R CLINIC 58501
  #038-45-1991 L2005 **IM** *020 †20
CAPAN, Michael Perez. 401 N 9TH ST, ARCHWAY MENTAL HEALTH 58501 #305-01-2000 L2004
  P *020

CARLSON, Hugh Scott. 311 N 9TH ST, HEART & LUNG CLINIC 58501 #046-01-1988 L1992
  AN *020 †05
CARRIEDO, Rodolfo C. 222 N 7TH ST, Q & R CLINIC 58501 #748-01-1949 L1975 **IM FM** *071
CHINTALPURI, Shashwita. 515 E BROADWAY AVE, CTR FOR FAMILY MEDICINEBIS 58501
  #496-26-2002 L2007 **FP** *012
CHRISTIANSON, Thomas Heil. ■ 58504 #048-12-1958 L1975 **ORS** *020 †40
CHRISTOPHER, Terence G C. 900 E BROADWAY AVE 58501 #352-07-1956 L1998
  IM NEP *020 †20
CLEARY, Joseph W. ■ 58501 #021-05-1949 L1956 **OBG OS** *071 †30
CLEARY, William Francis. 310 N 10TH ST, ST ALEXIUS HEART & LUNG 58501
  #030-06-1987 L1991 **AN CCA** *020 †05
CONNELL, Guy J. 300 N 7TH ST, BISMARCK EM ASSOC 58501 #037-01-1997 L2000
  EM *020 †16
CONNELL, Joan Marie. 515 1/2 E BROADWAY AVE, STE 106 58501 #007-02-1998 L2002
  PD *020 †55
COQUILLA, Beatriz H. 2700 STATE ST, GATEWAY DERMATOLOGY 58503 #748-01-1974 L2004
  D *020 †15
CORNATZER, Wm Eugene, Jr. 225 N 7TH ST, 2ND FLOOR UNITED BANK BUIL 58501
  #034-01-1981 L1985 **D** *020 †15
COSGRAVE, Peter M G. 300 N 7TH ST, MEDCENTER ONE HEALTH SYSTE 58501
  #539-05-1970 L1997 *100
CRUICKSHANK, Royston R. 300 N 7TH ST, MEDCENTER ONE HEALTH SYSTE 58501
  #308-11-1987 L1998 **P** *020
CRUZ, Emilio Louis, III. 222 N 7TH ST, MEDCENTER ONE Q & R CLINIC 58501
  #008-01-1978 L2007 **N OPH** *020 †75
DAHL, Brian Phillip. ■ 58503 #037-01-2008 *012
DAHL, Phillip O. 900 E BROADWAY AVE 58501 #016-06-1951 L1952 **IM** *071 †20
DAHMEN, Anne Katherine. ■ 58503 #037-01-2005 *100
DAHMEN, Kevin Robert. 401 N 9TH ST, ARCHWAY MENTAL HEALTH 58501 #005-06-1998 L2003
  CHP *020 †75
DANIELSON, Christopher J. 414 N 7TH ST, WOMENS MEDICAL CENTER 58501
  #037-01-2003 L2007 **OBG** *020
DASILVA, Lawrence Jos. 300 N 7TH ST 58501 #035-45-1989 L1993 **IM** *020 †20
DATZ, Kurt G. 811 E INTERSTATE AVE 58503 #041-77-1991, ▲ L1997 **IM** *020 †20
DAUGELIENE, Lina. 515 E BROADWAY AVE, CTR FOR FAMILY MEDICINEBIS 58501
  #913-96-1992 L2006 **FP** *012
DELAP, Susan Eileen. 1237 W DIVIDE AVE STE 5, WEST CENTRAL HUMAN SERVICE 58501
  #037-01-1995 L2001 **P** *020 †75
DHAR, Pradeep. 515 E BROADWAY AVE 58501 #496-46-1997 L2004 **FM** *020
DIBBELL, David G, Jr. 414 N 7TH ST 58501 #056-05-1981 L2004 **PS** *020 †85,65
DIEDE, Stanley Theodore. 310 N 10TH ST, ST ALEXIUS HEART & LUNG 58501
  #005-12-1974 L1980 **CD IM** *020 †20
DINYER, George Robt. 300 N 7TH ST 58501 #016-01-1973 L1976 **D FM** *071 †18,15
DODIN, Emad M. 300 N 7TH ST 58501 #575-01-1987 L1996 **CD** *020 †20
DORNACKER, Angela S. 3318 N 14TH ST, MEDCENTER ONE WALK IN CLIN 58503
  #037-01-1994 L1995 **FM** *020 †18
DORNACKER, Jon E. 515 E BROADWAY AVE 58501 #037-01-2002 L2002 **FM** *100
DUNNIGAN, Earl Jos. 401 N 9TH ST 58501 #037-01-1983 L1985 **NEP IM** *020 †20
DUNNIGAN, Ralph T. 900 E BROADWAY AVE, ST. ALEXIUS MED. CENTER 58501
  #037-01-1989 L1993 **N** *020 †75
DWELLE, Terry L. 803 N 5TH ST 58501 #028-34-1975 L1978 **GPM PD** *020 †55
EBEL, Gerd Dieter. 222 N 7TH ST 58501 #409-12-1961 L1973 **GP** *071 ‡
EBERTZ, J Mark. 2700 STATE ST, GATEWAY DERMATOLOGY 58503 #037-01-1982 L1986
  D *020 †15
EGGERT, Douglas K. 300 N 7TH ST, MED CENTER ONE 58501 #037-01-1985 L1989
  PM *020 †60
ELLINGSON, Frederick Thos. 300 N 7TH ST 58501 #026-04-1962 L1968 **OPH** *071 †35
ELLISON, Wesley Alan. 3502 FRANKLIN AVE 58503 #049-01-1994 L1999 **PTH** *020 †50
EMERY, Russell James. 2830 N WASHINGTON ST 58503 #037-01-1982 L1983
  FM FPG *020 †18
ERICKSTAD, John Albert. 401 N 9TH ST, MID DAKOTA CLINIC PC 58501 #037-01-1976 L1978
  FM *020 †16,18
ERICKSTAD, Mark Anders. 401 N 9TH ST, MID DAKOTA CLINIC PC 58501 #056-06-1979 L1980
  IM *020 †20
ESHOO, Norman Saml. 310 N 10TH ST, ST ALEXIUS HEART & LUNG 58501 #065-05-1974 L1981
  CD IM *020 †20
FAGAN, James. ■ 58504 #065-05-1971 **EM** *020
FAIRBAIRN, Thomas David. 300 N 7TH ST 58501 #065-05-1972 L1977 **EM** *020 †16
FIECHTNER, Marcus Mathias. 225 N 7TH ST 58501 #016-06-1965 L1970 **OTO** *020 †45
FIELD, David Richard. 414 N 7TH ST 58501 #001-06-1983 L1984 **FM** *020 †18
FINKIELMAN, Javier Daniel. 900 E BROADWAY AVE, SAINT ALEXIUS MEDICAL CENT 58501
  #132-01-1990 L2005 **CCM** *020 †20
FISHER, Catherine P. 300 N 7TH ST, MEDCENTER ONE HEALTH SYSTE 58501
  #037-01-1990 L1992 **PTH** *020 †50
FITZPATRICK, Patrick J. 230 E DIVIDE AVE 58501 #539-04-1968 L1973 **OPH** *071 †35
FOGARTY, Edward Francis. 222 N 7TH ST, Q & R CLINIC 58501 #030-05-1998 L2003
  DR *020 †80
FORTE-PATHROFF, Denise. 225 N 7TH ST, STE B 58501 #024-07-1982 L1986 **D** *020 †15
FORTNEY, Aaron C. 3119 N 14TH ST 58503 #037-01-1999 L2003 **OPH** *020 †35
FORTNEY, Mike S. 810 E ROSSER AVE, STE 201 58501 #037-01-1996 L2002 **DR** *020 †80
FOSTER, Keith Gerald. 515 1/2 E BROADWAY AVE #106 58501 #056-06-1947 L1953
  IM ADM *071 †20
FRANK, Walter Ernst. 300 N 7TH ST, MED CENTER ONE 58501 #561-01-1974 L1979
  CD *020 †20
FREDRICKSON, Ward Darwin. 3502 FRANKLIN AVE 58503 #018-03-1980 L1985 **PTH** *020 †50
FREE, Madeline L. 300 N 7TH ST, MEDCENTER ONE HEALTH SYSTE 58501 #654-01-1986 L1994
  P *020
FREY, Kory A. 401 N 9TH ST, ARCHWAY MENTAL HEALTH 58501 #037-01-1999 L2004
  CHP P *020 †75
FRICKE, Roger Wm. ■ 58501 #047-05-1958 L1958 **IM** *071 †20
FROELICH, Joy. ■ 58503 #037-01-2008 *012
FYFE, Alistair Gordon M. 300 N 7TH ST, MED CENTER ONE 58501 #061-01-1983 L1994 *020
FYFE, Ian Cameron M. 300 N 7TH ST, MED CENTER ONE HEALTH SYST 58501
  #061-01-1987 L1999 *020
GATTEY, Philip Heath. 225 N 7TH ST 58501 #068-01-1980 L1994 **ORS** *020
GAYTON, David J. 900 E BROADWAY AVE, ST ALEXIUS MEDICAL CENTER 58501
  #037-01-1990 L1996 **EM** *020 †16

GILANI, Syed Furqan. 515 E BROADWAY AVE, CTR FOR FAMILY MEDICINEBIS 58501 #704-20-2004 L2006 **GS** *012

GIRARD, Scott Bernard. 401 N 9TH ST 58501 #041-13-1964 L1969 **GS OS** *071

GODFREAD, Ernest Norman. 310 N 9TH ST 58501 #037-01-1977 L1982 **ORS** *071 †40

GOECKE, Scott Allan. 3130 MANITOBA LN 58503 #037-01-1997 L1998 **FM** *020 †18

GOKIM, Gualberto C, Jr. 222 N 7TH ST, QUAIN AND RAMSTAD CLINIC 58501 #748-01-1961 L1972 **GE IM** *020

GOKIM, Rizalina N. 620 N 9TH ST, EYE CLINIC OF NORTH DAKOTA 58501 #748-01-1957 L1972 **OPH** *071

GOLDSTEIN, Heidi Jane. 900 E BROADWAY AVE 58501 #035-08-1991 L2007 **PM** *020 †60

GONUGUNTLA, Anuradha. 515 E BROADWAY AVE, CTR FOR FAMILY MEDICINEBIS 58501 #496-01-1999 L2007 **FP** *012

GONZALEZ, Gilberto. 222 N 7TH ST, Q & R CLINIC 58501 #649-02-1953 L1970 **GS TS** *071 †85

GOODMAN, Patrick Brian. 414 N 7TH ST, MEDCENTER ONE MENTAL HEALT 58501 #037-01-1989 L1991 **P** *020 †75

GOURNEAU, Linda Fay. ■ 58501 #037-01-1989 L1990 **FM** *020 †18

GRENZ, Donald H. 401 N 9TH ST, MID DAKOTA CLINIC 58501 #037-01-1997 L1999 **IM** *020 †20

GRORUD, Jane Ann. 222 N 7TH ST, Q AND R CLINIC 58501 #037-01-1987 L1990 **PD** *020 †55

GRUBE, Thomas James. 3119 N 14TH ST 58501 #046-01-1997 L2002 **OPH** *020 †35

GRUBY, Raymond Stanley. 1120 COLLEGE DR, STE 100 58501 #048-13-1972 L1977 **ORS** *071 †40

GRUVER, Daniel Isaiah. 8500 CREEKSIDE DR, GRUVER CLINIC 58504 #048-12-1961 L1984 **PS FPS** *020 †65

GUANZON, Marie. ■ 58503 #748-02-1996 L2003 **AI** *020 †20,03

GUANZON, Ricardo Alfonso. 515 E BROADWAY AVE, CTR FOR FAMILY MEDICINEBIS 58501 #748-10-2000 L2007 **FP** *012

HAALAND, Robin M. 414 N 7TH ST 58501 #037-01-1992 L1997 **CHP P** *020 †75

HAGAN, John Jos, III. 115 W CENTURY AVE STE B, AESTHETIC CENTER 58503 #024-05-1991 L2000 **IM** *020 †20

HAMAR, Steven Kendall. 401 N 9TH ST, MID DAKOTA CLINIC PC 58501 #048-04-1974 L1978 **GS VS** *020 †85

HAPPEL, Keith Richard. 401 N 9TH ST 58501 #917-21-1972 L1995 **IM** *020 †20

HASSAN, Syed Fahim Ul. 900 E BROADWAY AVE, NEPHROLOGY CLINIC 58501 #704-02-1982 L1999 **NEP IM** *020 †20

HAYNES, Benn Allen. 414 N 7TH ST 58501 #047-06-1966 L1994 **P** *020 †95,75

HEBERT, Brian Joseph. 401 N 9TH ST, MID DAKOTA CLINIC 58501 #037-01-1999 L2001 **IM** *020 †20

HELWIG, Nicholas Jay. 2700 STATE ST STE A5, VA CBOC GATEWAY MALL 58503 #030-05-1996 L1999 **IM** *020 †20

HENKE, Melissa Jo. 300 N 7TH ST, MEDCENTER ONE HEALTH SYSTE 58501 #037-01-2002 L2005 **OS** *020

HERTZ, Dwight J. 222 N 7TH ST, Q & R CLINC 58501 #037-01-1984 L1989 **PTH PCP** *020 †50

HETLAND, Bruce Milton. 401 N 9TH ST, MID DAKOTA CLINIC PC 58501 #048-12-1975 L1979 **IM IMG** *020 †20

HIEB, Robert Eugene. ■ 58504 #049-01-1965 L1966 **TS** *020 †85,90

HILL, Emiliya Spartakovna. 515 E BROADWAY AVE, CTR FOR FAMILY MEDICINEBIS 58501 #913-29-1981 L2006 **FP** *012

HILTS, George Henry, III. 222 N 7TH ST 58501 #037-01-1980 L1981 **OPH** *020 †35

HOLMEN, John Harold. 810 E ROSSER AVE, STE 201 58501 #037-01-1996 L2000 **DR** *020 †80

HONEYCUTT, Darcy Adaire. 810 E ROSSER AVE, MEDICAL ARTS BLDG #303 58501 #048-02-1985 L1997 **PS GS** *020 †85,65

HOSTETTER, Jeffrey E. 515 E BROADWAY AVE, UND FAMILY PRACTICE CENTER 58501 #054-04-2000 L2001 **FM** *020 †18 ‡

HUBER, Cheryl Edith. 414 N 7TH ST, MEDCENTER ONE HEALTH SYSTE 58501 #045-04-1989 L1996 **P** *020 †20

HUGHES, James Andrews. 310 N 10TH ST, ST ALEXIUS HEART & LUNG 58501 #041-01-1974 L1980 **PUD IM** *020 †20

HYDER, Syed Shiraz. 900 E BROADWAY AVE, ST ALEXIUS MEDICAL CENTER 58501 #704-02-1982 L1996 **N** *020 †75

HYLAND, Glen Ray. 500 N 8TH ST, BISMARCK CANCER CENTER 58501 #016-06-1973 L1976 **RO** *020 †80

IRAVANI, Mansureh S. 3117 N 14TH ST, ORAL SURG CTR OF BISMARCK 58503 #038-06-1996 L2002 **GS** *020

IVERSON, Christie A. 414 N 7TH ST 58501 #037-01-1991 L1992 **OBG** *020 †30

JAIN, Sunanda. 900 E BROADWAY AVE, ST ALEXIUS HOSP 58501 #495-30-1994 L2002 **NEP** *020 †20

JANKOVIAK, Michael David. 310 N 10TH ST, ST ALEXIUS HEART & LUNG 58501 #007-02-1998 L2002 **AN** *020 †05

JENNINGS, Robert Lowell. 409 N 9TH ST BOX 5538, MID DAKOTA CLINIC 58501 #050-02-1963 L1965 **GP PD** *071 †18

JOHNSON, Gary Neil. 900 E BROADWAY AVE 58501 #061-01-1969 L1978 **AN PME** *020 †05

JOHNSON, Kenneth J. 222 N 7TH ST, Q & R CLINIC 58501 #026-04-1944 L1951 **A IM** *071

JOHNSON, Marlin John E. 222 N 7TH ST BOX 5505, QUAIN 3 RAMSTAD CLINIC 58501 #030-05-1945 L1951 **IM** *071 †20

JOHNSON, Steven R. 401 N 9TH ST, MID DAKOTA CLINIC PC 58501 #037-01-1993 L1998 **GS** *020 †85

JOHNSON, Terry Max. 401 N 9TH ST, ARCHWAY MENTAL HEALTH 58501 #037-01-1981 L1987 **P** *020 †75

JONDAHL, Paul Eric. 401 N 9TH ST, MID DAKOTA CLINIC PC 58501 #037-01-1988 L1989 **FM** *020 †18

JUHALA, Curtis Alfred. 401 N 9TH ST, MID DAKOTA CLINIC 58501 #048-12-1967 L1978 **PS HS** *071 †65

KANTHAIAH, Kuraguntla. UNIV ND AFFIL HOSP 58501 #495-11-1947 **GS NS** *071

KATHAWALA, Mustafa. 401 N 9TH ST, MID DAKOTA CLINIC 58501 #495-74-1994 L2002 **GE IM** *020 †20

KAUSHIK, Prashant. 900 E BROADWAY AVE 58501 #495-36-1993 L2006 **IM** *020 †20

KAUSHIK, Richa. 515 E BROADWAY AVE, CTR FOR FAMILY MEDICINEBIS 58501 #496-07-1994 L2007 **FP** *012

KAVLIE, Gaylord Jerome. 401 N 9TH ST, MID DAKOTA CLINIC PC 58501 #037-01-1979 L1984 **GS** *020 †85

KHAN, Irfan Ahmad. 900 E BROADWAY AVE 58501 #704-02-1978 L2003 **IM** *020 †20

KIHTIR, Sena A. 300 N 7TH ST, MEDCENTER ONE HEALTH SYSTE 58501 #902-10-1990 L2000 **APM** *020 †20,05

KIHTIR, Tugrul. 300 N 7TH ST, MEDCENTER ONE HEALTH SYSTE 58501 #902-10-1985 L2000 **PS GS** *020 †85,65

KIJPITTAYARIT, Supha. 900 E BROADWAY AVE 58501 #891-04-1998 L2007 **ID** *020

KILLEN, Shelley Anne. 900 E BROADWAY AVE, ST ALEXIUS 58501 #054-04-1990 L2000 **PM SCI** *020 †60

KILZER, Ralph Leon. ■ 58503 #056-01-1966 L1971 **ORS** *020 †40

KLEIN, Scott Anthony. 310 N 10TH ST, ST ALEXIUS HEART & LUNG 58501 #037-01-1987 L1992 **AN** *020 †05

KNUDSEN, Henry David. 646 COTTONWOOD LOOP 58504 #026-04-1963 L1969 **R NM** *071 †80,28

KNUDSON, Joshua John. ■ 58504 #037-01-2008 *012

KNUDSON, Paul Bernhard. 828 KIRKWOOD MALL, MID DAKOTA CLINIC 58504 #037-01-1976 L1977 **FM ADM** *020 †18

KNUTSON, Ronald M. 311 N 9TH ST 58501 #037-01-1985 L1989 **AN** *020 †05

KOLEILAT, Issam. ■ 58504 #035-03-2008 *012

KOLEILAT, Nadim. 900 E BROADWAY AVE 58501 #605-02-1982 L1998 **U TTS** *020 †95

KORANTENG ADDO, F E. 300 W CENTURY AVE 58503 #412-01-1973 L1991 **ON HEM** *020 †20

KOSIAK, Donald John. 3318 N 14TH ST, MEDCENTER CLINIC 58503 #037-01-1979 L1980 **GP** *020

KOTRAPU, Niran. 401 N 9TH ST 58501 #891-02-1965 L1972 **PD PDC** *071 †55

KOZEL, Lisa Lynn. 401 N 9TH ST, MID DAKOTA CLINIC 58501 #030-06-1993 L1996 **PD** *020 †55

KOZEL, William Jos. 900 E BROADWAY AVE 58501 #026-04-1956 L1975 **R** *071 †80

KRALJIC, Steven Gerard. 900 E BROADWAY AVE 58501 #030-06-2000 L2006 **U** *020

KRIEM, Jamal. 401 N 9TH ST, DEPARTMENT OF PEDIATRICS 58501 #875-01-2003 L2008 **PD** *020

KRIENGKRAIRUT, Siriwan. 900 E BROADWAY AVE 58501 #891-02-1978 L1991 **CHN PD** *020 †75,55

KRIENGKRAIRUT, Somsak. 310 N 10TH ST, ST ALEXIUS HEART & LUNG 58501 #891-02-1978 L1991 **PUD CCM** *020 †20

KRUSE, Kenyon Wade. 300 N 7TH ST, MEDCENTER ONE, INC. 58501 #037-01-2001 L2005 **AN** *020 †05

KUKREJA, Ravi. 515 E BROADWAY AVE, CTR FOR FAMILY MEDICINEBIS 58501 #496-61-1998 L2007 **FP** *012

KUMAR, Parag. 222 N 7TH ST, O E R CLINIC 58501 #495-73-1987 L2000 **PD** *020 †55

KWITKA, George. 300 N 7TH ST 58501 #748-11-1978 L1992 **AN** *020 †05

LAMBRECHT, Craig Jonathan. 300 N 7TH ST, MED CTR ONE 58501 #037-01-1987 L1988 **EM PHP** *020 †16

LAMPMAN, James Henry. 900 E BROADWAY AVE, ARTHRITIS CLINIC 58501 #038-06-1974 L1985 **RHU IM** *020 †20

LARSON, James Bruce. 222 N 7TH ST 58501 #016-06-1966 L1987 **A IM** *020 †20,03

LASKOWSKI, Edward J. ■ 58503 #028-34-1942 L1949 **OS** *072

LASZEWSKI, Linda Jean. 310 N 10TH ST, ST ALEXIUS HEART & LUNG 58501 #018-03-1985 L1991 **AN** *020 †05

LASZEWSKI, Michael John. 3502 FRANKLIN AVE 58503 #018-03-1985 L1991 **PTH HMP** *020 †50

LAWSON, Rong. 515 E BROADWAY AVE, CTR FOR FAMILY MEDICINEBIS 58501 #243-62-1993 L2007 **FP** *012

LEINGANG, Gordon D. 630 BUCKSKIN AVE 58503 #018-75-1991, ▲ L1994 **EM GP** *020

LINDELOW, Jill. ■ 58504 #037-01-2008 *012

LINDELOW, O Victor. 401 N 9TH ST 58501 #041-01-1951 L1955 **IM** *071 †20

LINZ, Laurie J. 3502 FRANKLIN AVE 58503 #037-01-1989 L1991 **PTH** *020 †50

LITCHFIELD, Douglas W. 222 N 7TH ST 58501 #030-06-1989 L1993 **OPH** *020 †35

LO, Lim Che. 310 N 10TH ST, ST ALEXIUS HEART & LUNG 58501 #244-01-1975 L1979 **AN** *020 †05

LONGIE, Kelly B. 515 E BROADWAY AVE 58501 #037-01-2005 L2005 **FP** *012

LONGIE, Kevin B. 515 E BROADWAY AVE 58501 #037-01-2005 L2005 **FP** *012

LORENZ, Kevin Michael. 620 N 9TH ST, THE EYE CLINIC OF NORTH DA 58501 #028-34-1987 L1995 **OPH OS** *020 †35

LOUIE, Raymond. 300 N 7TH ST 58501 #038-43-1979 L2001 **AN GP** *020

LOVEN, Roger Ray. 310 N 10TH ST, ST ALEXIUS HEART & LUNG 58501 #037-01-1981 L1984 **AN CCA** *020 †05

LUGER, Joseph Ambrose, Jr. 401 N 9TH ST 58501 #037-01-1985 L1986 **D FM** *020 †15

LUNN, Gerry Michael. 300 N 7TH ST, MEDCENTER ONE HEALTH SYSTE 58501 #037-01-1977 L1978 **IM** *020 †20

MAALIKI, Salem Naji. 222 N 7TH ST, Q & R CLINIC 58501 #422-01-1987 L2000 **CD IM** *020 †20

MACDONALD, Neil A. ■ 58503 #016-11-1946 L1949 **GP OBG** *071

MACK, David Roland. 401 N 9TH ST, ARCHWAY MENTAL HEALTH 58501 #665-01-2001 L2001 **P** *020 †75

MAGILL, Thomas Roland. 900 E BROADWAY AVE 58501 #037-01-1990 L1994 **EM** *020 †16

MAKARIE, George Youssef. 1815 SCHAFER ST 58501 #330-04-1958 L1973 **AN PUD** *071

MARTIN, Carol Kent. 300 N 7TH ST, MEDCENTER ONE/Q & R CLINIC 58501 #054-04-1973 L1995 **ID** *020 †20

MARTIRE, Michael Paul. 121 W CENTURY AVE, SPINE AND PAIN CENTER P.C. 58503 #016-11-1986 L1990 **FP** *020 †60

MASSELLO, William, III. ■ 58503 #048-12-1972 L2007 **PTH GS** *020 †50

MATHESON, Thomas Blair. 300 N 7TH ST 58501 #039-01-1988 L1998 **FM GS** *020 †18 ‡

MATHIEU, Maryse Marie Jac. 310 N 10TH ST, ST ALEXIUS HEART & LUNG 58501 #067-03-1989 L2006 *100

MCCANN, Michelle Lynn. ■ 58501 #037-01-2008 *012

MC CULLOUGH, Sarah Jean. 900 E BROADWAY AVE 58501 #037-01-1998 L2002 **EM** *020 †16

MC DONOUGH, Denise M. 1040 TACOMA AVE, THE FAMILY DOCTORS 58504 #037-01-1995 L1996 **FM** *020 †18

MC DONOUGH, Stephen Lyle. 300 N 7TH ST, MEDCENTER ONE/Q & R CLINIC 58501 #026-04-1977 L1980 **PD** *020 †55

MC INTEE, Michael John. 300 N 7TH ST, MEDCENTER ONE HEALTH SYSTE 58501 #030-06-1994 L1999 **DR** *020 †80

MC KENZIE, Gerard M. 222 N 7TH ST, ORTHOPEDIC CENTER 58501 #061-01-1977 L1984 **ORS** *020 †40

MEEKER, Chris Alan. ■ 58504 #037-01-1997 L2007 **EM** *020 †16

MEHDIRATTA, Atam Jeet. 401 N 9TH ST, MID DAKOTA CLINIC 58501 #495-45-1976 L1990 **GE IM** *020 †20

MENDOZA, Pedro German. 300 W CENTURY AVE 58503 #042-03-1980 L1987 **PUD** *050 †20

MICKELSON, Kevin Scott. 900 E BROADWAY AVE, ST. ALEXIUS MEDICAL CENTER 58501 #037-01-1983 L1986 **EM** *020 †16

MILLER, Brenda L. 1040 TACOMA AVE, BISMARCK FAMILY CLINIC SOU 58504 #037-01-1995 L1996 **FM** *020 †18

MIZELL, George Robt. ■ 58502 #045-04-1989 L1996 **FOP** *020 †50

MOEN, Douglas Lee. 2830 N WASHINGTON ST, FAMILY MEDICAL CTR 58503 #037-01-1985 L1986 **FM EM** *020 †18

MOEN, Rj. ■ 58503 #037-01-2000 L2001 **FM** *020 †18

MONASKY, Mark Stephen. 900 E BROADWAY AVE 58501 #035-01-1982 L1993 **NS LM** *020 †25

MONTZ, Charles Robt. 3203 N WASHINGTON STREET 58503 #018-03-1948 L1955 **OBG** *071 †30

MOORE, Michael R. 310 N 9TH ST, BONE & JOINT CENTER PC 58501 #023-07-1984 L2000 **OSS** *020 †40

MORGAN, Margaret E Forke. 1251 E HIGHLAND ACRES RD 58501 #062-01-1959 L1969 **AN PUD** *075 †05

MOSES, James J. ■ 58501 #036-05-1951 L1952 **U** *071 †95

MURPHY, Louise A. 2700 STATE ST, GATEWAY DERMATOLOGY 58503 #037-01-1986 L1987 **FM** *020 †18

MUSCHA, Bennie W. 515 E BROADWAY AVE, UND FAMILY PRACTICE CTR 58501 #037-01-1992 L1993 **FM** *020 †18

NEUMANN, Nicholas Henry. 310 N 10TH ST, ST ALEXIUS HEART & LUNG 58501 #025-07-1974 L1980 **PUD CCM** *040 †20

NICHOLAS, Hunter Adrian. 1515 HARMON AVE 58501 #024-05-1991 L2001 **IM** *075

NOISYHAWK, Lynelle N. 515 E BROADWAY AVE 58501 #046-01-2003 L2004 **FM** *020

NORDSTROM, Kathleen Ann. 500 N 8TH ST, BISMARCK CANCER CENTER 58501 #005-18-1988 L2001 **RO** *020 †80

NYBAKKEN, Richard Calvin. 222 N 7TH ST 58501 #005-19-1977 L1998 **DR** *020 †80

OATFIELD, Robert Gregory. 310 N 10TH ST, ST ALEXIUS HEART & LUNG 58501 #016-43-1971 L1981 **CD AM** *020 †20

OBREGON, Kathryn E. 828 KIRKWOOD MALL 58504 #037-01-1985 L1994 **PD** *020 †55

OBRITSCH, Jerry Michael. 401 N 9TH ST, MID DAKOTA CLINIC PC 58501 #037-01-1987 L1990 **OBG** *020 †30 ‡

OCEJO MORENO, Rafael. 900 E BROADWAY AVE 58501 #649-01-1972 L1996 **PD NPM** *020 †55

O'KEEFE, Norbert John. ■ 58501 #026-04-1955 L1967 **R** *072 †80

OLDENBURGER, Derek. 401 N 9TH ST, MID DAKOTA CLINIC 58501 #005-14-1971 L1974 **IM GE** *071 †20

OLSON, Le Roy Curtis. 600 S 2ND ST, WEST CENTRAL HSC 58504 #037-01-1976 L1982 **PHP P** *020 †70

ORCHARD, Jeff L. 2700 STATE ST, GATEWAY DERMATOLOGY 58503 #037-01-1982 L1983 **FM EM** *020 †18

ORCHARD, Welland J, Jr. ■ 58503 #007-02-1953 L1954 **GP GS** *072

O'REGAN, David John. 300 N 7TH ST, MED CENTER ONE HEALTH SYST 58501 #068-01-1988 L2001 **ORS OSM** *020

ORSER, Shari Louise. 900 E BROADWAY AVE 58501 #037-01-1977 L1979 **OBG** *020 †30

PANDEY, Jay. 515 E BROADWAY AVE, CTR FOR FAMILY MEDICINEBIS 58501 #495-41-2003 L2005 **FP** *012

PANSEGRAU, Timothy L. 222 N 7TH ST 58501 #048-12-1989 L2004 **TS VS** *020 †85,90

PATEL, Mahesh Natu. 900 E BROADWAY AVE 58501 #495-23-1985 L1996 **NPM** *020 †55

PATEL, Niral Rajesh. 515 E BROADWAY AVE, CTR FOR FAMILY MEDICINEBIS 58501 #496-36-2004 L2006 **FP** *012

PATHROFF, Robert Alan. 225 N 7TH ST, UNITED BANK BUILDING 58501 #024-07-1982 L1987 **U GS** *020 †95

PAULO, Monica Therese. 310 N 10TH ST, ST ALEXIUS HEART & LUNG 58501 #028-34-1985 L1994 **PUD IM** *020 †20

PAULSON, Rick L. 115 W CENTURY AVE STE B, SURGERY, P C 58503 #037-01-1988 L1996 **PS FPS** *020 †65

PEDERSEN, Chad Allan. ■ 58501 #037-01-2008 *012

PENDEM, Shanthan. 900 E BROADWAY AVE, ST. ALEXIUS MEDICAL CENTER 58501 #495-65-2004 L2007 **CCM** *020 ‡

PENGILLY, David J. 1040 TACOMA AVE 58504 #037-01-1992 L1993 **FM** *020 †18

PERKEREWICZ, Kathleen M. 414 N 7TH ST 58501 #037-01-1999 L2003 **OBG** *020 †30

PETERSON, Douglas Ray. 810 E ROSSER AVE STE 201, CENTRAL DAKOTA RADIOLOGIST 58501 #037-01-1981 L1985 **DR** *020 †80

PETERSON, Gregory Scott. 222 N 7TH ST, BONE SPINE SPORTS CTR 58501 #024-07-1981 L1986 **PM PMM** *020 †60

PETERSON, Lynne Schmid. 225 N 7TH ST 58501 #021-01-1990 L1996 **RHU IM** *020 †20

PFEIFLE, Delano Milton. 222 N 7TH ST, QUAIN 3 RAMSTAD CLINIC 58501 #016-06-1959 L1964 **IM ON** *071

PHOOSHKOORU, Vijayarama R. 401 N 9TH ST 58501 #496-01-1998 L2007 **HO** *020 †20

PICKARD, Stephen Paul. 600 E BOULEVARD AVE, DEPT 301 58505 #020-02-1982 L2003 **PHP** *050 †20

PIYAMAHUNT, Arkapol. 310 N 10TH ST, ST ALEXIUS HEART & LUNG 58501 #891-04-1980 L1990 **AI IM** *020 †20,03

PRICE, Tyler Cole. ■ 58501 #037-01-2008 *012

QUAST, Michael Lor. 414 N 7TH ST, MEDCENTER ONE 58501 #005-12-1997 L2002 **AN PME** *020 †05

QUISNO, Jacqueline Elaine. 515 E BROADWAY AVE, UND FAMILY PRACTICE CENTER 58501 #054-04-1999 L2000 **FM** *020 †18

RAGLAND, James B. 1100 WEISS AVE, REGIONAL NEUROLOGICAL CENT 58503 #495-04-1976 L1987 **N P** *020 †75

RAINWATER, Leslie Mark. 900 E BROADWAY AVE 58501 #026-08-1984 L1998 **U** *020 †95

RAMOS, Pablo. ■ 58501 #649-01-1953 L1963 **R** *071 †80

RAUTA, Olimpia. 515 E BROADWAY AVE, UND FAMILY PRACTICE CENTER 58501 #781-01-1992 L2003 **FM** *100 †18

RAUTA, Radu Leonid. 222 N 7TH ST, MEDCENTER ONE Q & R CLINIC 58501 #781-01-1992 L2002 **IM** *020 †20

RAYYAN, Yaser Mohammed. 300 N 7TH ST 58501 #575-01-1992 L2002 **GE** *020 †20

REICHERT, Henry L, Jr. 900 E BROADWAY AVE 58501 #056-06-1966 L1970 **OPH** *071 †35

REMER, Elsa Maria. 200 E MAIN AVE, STE 101 58501 #037-01-1986 L1989 **P** *020 †75

RENTON, Douglas J. 222 N 7TH ST, MEDCENTER ONE Q&R CLINIC 58501 #037-01-2002 L2002 **GE** *012 †20

RENTON, Stanley Mill. 300 N 7TH ST, EMERGENCY ROOM 58501 #919-03-1968 L1976 **EM** *020 †16

REYNOLDS, John. 222 N 7TH ST, MEDCENTER ONE/Q & R CLINIC 58501 #024-01-1949 L1954 **IM HEM** *071 †20

REYNOLDS, John Terry. 300 N 7TH ST 58501 #016-01-1984 L1996 **HO HEM** *020 †20

RIECKE, William Chas. 900 E BROADWAY AVE 58501 #021-01-1959 L1964 **PDA PD** *020 †55

RISING SUN, Zane Collins. 515 E BROADWAY AVE, FAMILY PRACTICE CENTER 58501 #037-01-1997 L1999 *020

RODACKER, Mark Wade. ■ 58501 #037-01-1997 L2004 **PTH** *020 †50

ROLLER, Benedict. 900 E BROADWAY AVE, ST ALEXIUS MEDICAL CENTER 58501 #037-01-1980 L1983 **EM** *020 †16

ROSWICK, Robert Jos. 2700 STATE ST, GATEWAY DERMATOLOGY 58503 #037-01-1984 L1985 **FM** *020 †18 ‡

RUSSELL, Sean Steven. 300 N 7TH ST, MEDCENTER ONE 58501 #056-06-1988 L1996 **TS** *020 †85,90

SAMRAH, Shaher Mohammed. 300 N 7TH ST, MEDOENTER ONE HLTH SYSTEMS 58501 #575-02-1995 L2004 **PCC** *020 †20

SAMUELSON, Albert Frank. ■ 58501 #038-41-1956 L1957 **P** *071

SANATHANA MURTHY, M G. 310 N 10TH ST, ST ALEXIUS HEART & LUNG 58501 #495-33-1972 L1979 **ICE CD** *020 †20

SAQIB, Azim. 222 N 7TH ST, MEDCENTER ONE Q&R CLINIC 58501 #704-16-1981 L2008 **IM CD** *020 †20

SARRIGIANNIDIS, Andreas. 222 N 7TH ST, Q & R CLINIC 58501 #418-02-1987 L2004 **PCC SME** *020 †20

SCARLETT, Robert K. 401 N 9TH ST 58501 #068-01-1968 L1980 **OBG** *020 †30

SCHAFER, Pamela R. 418 E BROADWAY AVE 58501 #037-01-1979 L1981 **P** *020 †75

SCHERR, Steven J. 401 N 9TH ST, MID DAKOTA CLINIC PC 58501 #037-01-1990 L1991 **FM** *020 †18 ‡

SCHIRADO, Michael Anthony. 810 E ROSSER AVE, CENTRAL DAKOTA RADIOLOGY 58501 #037-01-1995 L1998 **DR** *020 †80

SCHMIT, Michael L. 401 N 9TH ST, MID DAKOTA CLINIC PC 58501 #037-01-1999 L2001 **GS** *020 †85

SCHWARTZ, Julie Mae. 401 N 9TH ST, MID DAKOTA CLINIC PC 58501 #037-01-1988 L1991 **IM** *020

SEIBEL, Melissa Marie. 222 N 7TH ST, MEDCENTER ONE Q&R CLINIC 58501 #026-04-2004 L2007 **PD** *100

SEIFERT, Shelly A. 828 KIRKWOOD MALL 58504 #037-01-1996 L1997 **FM** *020 †18 ‡

SERABE, Baruti Maathali. 222 N 7TH ST 58501 #024-07-1987 L1998 **PHO PD** *020 †20,55

SETH, Vinod Kumar. 210 S 12TH ST 58504 #495-30-1970 L1989 **ID PUD** *020 †20

SEVERN, Charles Burton. 900 E BROADWAY AVE, ST ALEXIUS HOSPITAL 58501 #030-05-1976 L1979 **NPM** *020

SEVIGNY, Karen R. 900 E BROADWAY AVE 58501 #037-01-1993 L2000 **NPM** *020 †55

SHARP, Cindy Kaye. PO BOX 997, 900 E BROADWAY 58502 #027-01-1992 L2004 **NEP** *020 †20

SMITH, Clyde Leroy. ■ 58503 #026-04-1943 L1954 **GP GS** *071

SMITH, Craig Donald. 310 N 10TH ST 58501 #037-01-1989 L2007 **AN** *020 †18

SMITH, Jeffrey Alan. 2830 N WASHINGTON ST 58503 #037-01-1985 L1986 **FM EM** *020 †18

SMITH, Stuart T. 1040 TACOMA AVE 58504 #037-01-1992 L1993 **FM** *020 †18

SONGSIRIDEJ, Nowarat. 900 E BROADWAY AVE, ARTHRITIS CLINIC 58501 #891-02-1978 L1990 **RHU IM** *020 †20

SPAGNOLIA, Thomas N. 222 N 7TH ST, MED CENTER ONE 58501 #028-03-1984 L1997 **NS** *020 †25

SPOTTS, Steven Douglas. 401 N 9TH ST, MID DAKOTA CLINIC PC 58501 #037-01-1981 L1986 **OTO** *020 †45

SPRIGGS, Nigeria M. PO BOX 5525, 300 N 7TH ST 58506 #012-21-1997 L2000 **EM** *020 †16

STAKES, Kearney James, II. 300 N 7TH ST, MEDCENTER ONE 58501 #021-05-1999 L2005 **EM** *020 †16

STANLEY, John George. 416 N 6TH ST 58501 #025-07-2003 L2007 **OMF** *020

STEIN, Sherry Lynn. 1040 TACOMA AVE 58504 #037-01-2002 L2002 **FM** *020 †18

STENGL, Thomas Alan. ■ 58503 #026-04-1958 L1958 **OTO** *071 †45

SUNDBERG, Elizabeth E. 900 E BROADWAY AVE, ST. ALEXIUS CLINICS 58501 #040-02-1986 L2002 **NEP IM** *020 †20

SWENSON, Wayne Morris. 222 N 7TH ST 58501 #024-01-1961 L1966 **CD GS** *071 †85

TAN, Aquilino O. 300 N 7TH ST 58501 #748-01-1962 L1998 **AN** *020 †05

TANGEDAHL, Guy P. 515 E BROADWAY AVE, UND FAMILY PRACTICE CTR 58501 #037-01-1982 L1983 **FM** *020 †18

TANOUS, Robert. 2700 STATE ST, MID DAKOTA CLINIC 58503 #018-75-1994, ▲ L1997 **IM** *020 †20

TELLO, Abel Ernesto. 222 N 7TH ST, 5505 58501 #715-01-1969 L1978 **IM NEP** *020 †20

TELLO, Anthony Michael. 222 N 7TH ST 58501 #308-07-1982 L1988 **IM CCM** *040 †20

TELLO, Ronald Dean. 222 N 7TH ST, QUAIN & RAMSTAD CLINIC 58501 #037-01-1976 L1977 **IM** *020 †20

THOMAS, Mathew R. 401 N 9TH ST, MID DAKOTA CLINIC PC 58501 #495-08-1971 L1985 **ON IM** *020 †20

THOMPSON, Eric Michael. 2830 N WASHINGTON ST, FAMILY MEDICAL CENTER NORT 58503 #037-01-1999 L2002 **FM** *020 †18

TINCHER, Michelle Renee. 2830 N WASHINGTON ST, MEDCENTER ONE HEALTH SYSTE 58503 #037-01-1995 L1996 **FM** *020 †18

TWARDOWSKI, Radomysl M. 222 N 7TH ST 58501 #028-03-1986 L1994 **CD IM** *020 †20

TWOGOOD, Todd A. 222 N 7TH ST 58501 #037-01-1994 L1997 **PD** *020 †55

UY, James John Te. ■ 58503 #748-02-1995 L2003 **IM** *020 †20

VAN NORMAN, Alan Stuart. 300 N 7TH ST, MEDCENTER ONE HEALTH SYSTE 58501 #026-08-1985 L1998 **NS** *020 †25

VELANDER, Alan James. ■ 58504 #026-04-1965 L1973 **U** *071 †95

VILELLA-GONZALEZ, Luis S. PO BOX 1251 58502 #042-04-1988 L2003 **PM** *030

VINEY, Jeanette Maude. 222 N 7TH ST 58501 #056-05-1986 L1991 **GS** *020 †85

VOIGT, Matthew Leo. ■ 58501 #037-01-2008 *012

VOLK, Charles Robert. 222 N 7TH ST 58501 #037-01-1976 L1981 **OPH** *020 †35

WAGH, Moshe. 300 N 7TH ST, DEPT OF ANESTHESIA 58501 #308-07-1982 L1985 **AN** *020 †20

WALDSCHMIDT, Wm Duane. 221 N 5TH ST 58501 #005-11-1954 L1959 **GS TS** *020

WENTZ, Robert Morris. 300 N 7TH ST, MEDCENTER ONE Q & R CLNC 58501 #019-02-1971 L1974 **PD** *020 †55

WHITE, Peter Lawrence. 310 N 10TH ST, HEART & LUNG CLINIC 58501 #016-11-1976 L1986 **AN CCM** *020 †20,05

WILEY, Jose Manuel. 310 N 10TH ST, ST ALEXIUS HEART & LUNG 58501 #042-03-1994 L2006 **IC** *020

WILLIAMS, Edward Hanford. 310 N 10TH ST, ST ALEXIUS HEART & LUNG 58501 #041-01-1969 L1981 **TS GS** *020 †85,90

WILLIS, Karin Kristine. 515 E BROADWAY AVE, UND CENTER FOR FAMILY MEDI 58501 #037-01-2005 L2005 **FP** *012

WILSON, Herbert J. ■ 58501 #024-07-1950 L1953 **FM PHP** *071

WINDSOR, John Herbert. 310 N 10TH ST, ST ALEXIUS HEART & LUNG 58501 #011-75-1989, ▲ L1998 **CD IM** *020

WINK, Sue Karen. 225 N 7TH ST 58501 #048-13-1984 L1996 **OTO** *020 †45

WITT, John M. 1000 E ROSSER AVE 58501 #037-01-1982 L1987 **OBG** *020 †30

WONGJIRAD, Chatree. 900 E BROADWAY AVE 58501 #891-01-1969 L1985 **N** *020 †75

WOODARD, Chris Owen. PO BOX 2698, HEART & LUNG CLINIC 58502 #021-06-1986 L2004 **CD CCM** *020 †20 ‡

WOODROW, Peter Andrew. 300 N 7TH ST, MEDCENTER ONE / Q + R CLIN 58501 #068-01-1969 L1994 **OBG** *020

WYMAN, Allen Eugene. 401 N 9TH ST, MID DAKOTA CLINIC PC 58501 #048-15-1974 L1977 **FM** *020 †18

WYNKOOP, Walker Alan. 225 N 7TH ST, BONE SPINE SPORTS CLINIC 58501 #016-43-1985 L2006 **ORS OM** *020 †40

YAQUB, Sumera. 515 E BROADWAY AVE, CTR FOR FAMILY MEDICINEBIS 58501 #704-09-1995 L2004 **FM** *100

ZACHER, Carla Jean. 828 KIRKWOOD MALL, MID DAKOTA CLINIC 58504 #037-01-1996 L1999 **PD** *020 †55

ZAIDI, Syed Waseem A. 401 N 9TH ST, MID DAKOTA CLNIC 58501 #704-16-1990 L2001 **IM** *020 †20

ZIMMER, Stevan Doyle. 1312 BAYVIEW CT 58504 #026-04-1981 L2005 **CD IM** *020 †20

BOTTINEAU — BOTTINEAU

HASSAN, Imran. 316 OHMER ST, ST ANDREW'S HEALTH CENTER 58318 #704-05-1996 L2004 **IM** *020

KIHLE, Kenneth Wm. 314 OHMER ST 58318 #019-02-1959 L1960 **GP** *020

MILLER, C Robt. 322 4TH ST W, BOTTINEAU CLINIC 58318 #030-05-1960 L1961 **A R** *071 †18

BOWMAN — BOWMAN

CHENG, Joseph Liang-Cheng. 14 6TH AVE SW 58623 #385-02-1958 L1980 **GP GS** *020

LANCHBURY, Forrest Dwight. 14 6TH AVE SW 58623 #023-12-1993 L2006 **GP** *020

THOM, Robert Chas. TRI STATE CLINIC 58623 #067-01-1955 L1957 **FM FPG** *071 †18

BURLINGTON — WARD

GRAY, Thomas Kevin. ■ 58722 #037-01-2002 L2002 **FM** *020 †18

CANDO — TOWNER

SAWCHUK, John. ■ 58324 #062-01-1958 L1966 **FM GS** *071

CARRINGTON — FOSTER

GEIER, Rick John. 820 5TH ST N 58421 #037-01-1977 L1978 **GP** *020

PAGE, Michael J. 800 4TH ST N, CARRINGTON HEALTH CENTER S 58421 #037-01-1997 L1998 **FM** *020 †18

SCHAFFER, Todd Wayne. 800 4TH ST N, CARRINGTON HEALTH CENTER 58421 #037-01-2002 L2002 **FM** *020 †18

SHEPARD, Richard. 800 4TH ST N 58421 #026-04-1955 L1989 **GS ORS** *071 †85

CASSELTON — CASS

DOMM, Bruce L. 5 9TH AVE N 58012 #037-01-1985 L1986 **FM** *020 †18

CAVALIER — PEMBINA

ABUL-KHOUDOUD, Hassan R. 301 MOUNTAIN ST E, P O BOX 380 58220 #605-01-1995 L1999 **FM** *020 †18 ‡

DARIDO, Elias Fouad. 301 MOUNTAIN ST E 58220 #605-01-2001 L2007 **GS** *020 †85

KRATCHA, Lynn C. 201 E 3RD AVE S, ALTRU CLC CAVALIER POB 40 58220 #037-01-1994 L1995 **FM OBG** *020 †18

LARSON, Eric John. 201 E 3RD AVE S 58220 #062-01-1958 L1965 **GP** *020

SUMRA, Kulvinder Singh. 301 MOUNTAIN ST E, P O BOX 380 58220 #495-03-1976 L1983 **FM FSM** *020 †18

TAREEN, Jamil-Ur-Rahman. PO BOX 40, 201 E THIRD AVE S 58220 #704-04-1962 L1974 **GS FM** *020 †18

THOMPSON, Susan Joan. 201 E 3RD AVE S, ATLAN CLINIC CAVALIER 58220 #037-01-1996 L1998 **IM** *020

CENTER — OLIVER

GULLICKSON, Nicole. ■ 58530 #037-01-2008 L2008 *012

COOPERSTOWN — GRIGGS

GEIER, David Carl. ■ 58425 #005-12-2000 L2003 **FM** *020 †18

RAMAIYA, Janaksinh Khimji. PO BOX 250 58425 #919-05-1961 L1977 **FM PP** *071 †18

SARPAL, Lakhbir Singh. 1200 ROBERTS AVE NE 58425 #495-03-1963 L1985 **GP** *020

WINSTON, Rohini Ruth. 1200 ROBERTS AVE NE, COOPERSTOWN MED CTR 58425 #496-07-1988 L1996 **IMG** *020 †18

CROSBY — DIVIDE

EVANS, Patrick Jos. ■ 58730 #021-05-1989 L1997 **FM** *020 †18

TSUTSKIRIDZE, Ivane A. ■ 58730 #913-23-1995 L2004 **IM** *020

DEVILS LAKE — RAMSEY

BELLUK, Bradley Peter. 1001 7TH ST NE 58301 #062-01-1989 L1992 **GS** *020 †85

BHARATH, Somasundaram. 1001 7TH ST NE 58301 #495-16-1972 L1980 **IM GE** *020

BITTNER, Heidi M. 1031 7TH ST NE 58301 #037-01-1991 L1992 **FM** *020 †18

CLINKENBEARD, James R. 200 HIGHWAY 2 W, BOX 650 58301 #046-01-1984 L1985 **P** *020

CORBETT, Thomas Conner. 1001 7TH ST NE 58301 #062-01-1973 L1975 **IM GP** *020 ‡

DANNENBERG, Lee Lawrence. 1031 7TH ST NE 58301 #056-05-1969 L1992 **OPH** *020

DILLARD, Dorothy. ■ 58301 #048-02-1976 L1976 **OBG GP** *071

DOWNS, Jacqueline Leonia. 1031 7TH ST NE 58301 #035-46-1993 L1996 **IM EM** *020

FETTERLY, Paul John T. 1001 7TH ST NE 58301 #065-06-1974 L1996 **FM OBS** *020

GREVES, Douglas Leslie. 1031 7TH ST NE 58301 #062-01-1973 L1977 **FM** *020 †18

JOHNSON, Richard Earl. 1031 7TH ST NE 58301 #056-05-1974 L1981 **R OS** *020 †80

LAPP, Gregory Carl. 1001 7TH ST NE 58301 #056-05-1993 L2001 **GS** *020 †45

MC BANE, Robert Donald. ■ 58301 #062-01-1955 L1956 **FM** *071 †18

MONTANIEL, Necito L. 1031 7TH ST NE 58301 #748-08-1959 L1978 **FM IM** *020

MORALEDA, Roberto Antonio. 1001 7TH ST NE, ALTRU CLINIC LAKE REGUM 58301 #748-01-1987 L1996 **IM** *020 †20

PETTY, Russell Warren. 425 COLLEGE DR S STE 14, DEVILS LAKE COMM CLNC 58301 #048-12-1974 L1977 **FM PD** *020

RADA, Delfin Argano. 1031 7TH ST NE 58301 #748-01-1969 L1973 **IM GP** *020

RAYER, Anthony L. 425 COLLEGE DR S, STE 14 58301 #026-04-1966 L1987 **FM EM** *020 †18

SCHAEFER, Frederick L. 1031 7TH ST NE 58301 #038-41-1956 L1987 **OBG** *071 †30

SCHROEDER, James Gordon. 1031 7TH ST NE, MERCY HOSPITAL 58301 #016-11-1969 L1973 **DR OS** *020 †80

TALUSAN, Annabelle B. 1001 7TH ST NE 58301 #748-01-1985 L1998 **IM** *020

TURKULA, William John. ■ 58301 #062-01-1955 **FM GP** *071 †18

WAYMAN, Derek Clifford. 1001 7TH ST NE 58301 #037-01-2003 L2003 **FM** *020 †18

ZETTERMAN, David Kent. 1001 7TH ST NE 58301 #030-05-1995 L2005 **FM FPG** *020 †18

DICKINSON — STARK

ALLEN, William R, Jr. 10914 33M ST SW 58601 #019-02-1978 L2003 **DR** *020 †80 ‡

ANDERSON, Patricia Susan. 938 2ND AVE W 58601 #030-06-1986 L1996 **IM PD** *020

ARNOLD, Thomas Francis. 638 2ND AVE W 58601 #037-01-1984 L1988 **OBG** *020 †30 ‡

BERGER, Timothy John. ■ 58602 #016-43-1974 L1986 **IM** *020 †20

BROOKE, James Murray. 30 7TH ST W 58601 #054-04-1975 L1988 **GS TS** *020 †85

CASSIDY, Michael L. 33 9TH ST W 58601 #068-01-1985 L1997 **FM** *020

CONRADSON, Leonard Lane. 968 18TH ST W 58601 #025-07-1971 L1996 **P** *020 †75

COOMBE, Walter Thos, Jr. 30 7TH ST W 58601 #030-05-1982 L2002 **OTO HNS** *020 †45

CUSIC, Robert Leeroy. 33 9TH ST W 58601 #007-02-1982 L1983 **EM** *020 †16

DAS, Arunava. 827 19TH ST E 58601 #495-32-1969 L2002 **ORS** *020

DUKART, Ralph John. ■ 58601 #025-07-1943 L1947 **FM** *071

FLANAGAN, Mark Steve. 33 9TH ST W 58601 #005-19-2002 L2007 **GS** *020 †85

HANEWALD, Walter Compton. 9TH & SIMS 58601 #035-03-1954 L1972 **GP** *071

HINRICHS, Mark Peter. 33 9TH ST W 58601 #037-01-1978 L1979 **IM** *020 †20

HUGHES, Heather L. 33 9TH ST W 58601 #037-01-2001 L2005 **FM** *020 †18

ISACKSON, Ronald Dwain. 109 7TH ST W, DAKOTA BONE & JOINT 58601 #041-07-1977 L2004 **ORS** *020 †40

KOMOROWSKA, Danuta. 33 9TH ST W 58601 #759-11-1973 L1989 **FM** *020 †18

KUYLEN, David Andrew. 30 7TH ST W 58601 #037-01-2004 L2007 **EM** *020

LARSEN, Harlan Clifton. 33 9TH ST W, GREAT PLAINS CLINIC PC 58601 #004-01-1948 L1949 **GP OBG** *071

LEIDENIX, Monte John. 30 7TH ST W 58601 #037-01-1992 L1997 **OPH** *020 †35

MILLER, Bruce Lawrence. 938 2ND AVE W 58601 #024-01-1964 L1992 **GS TS** *020 †85

OHARA, Brian Edward. 33 9TH ST W 58601 #037-01-1985 L1989 **IM** *020,55

OKSA, Amy. 938 2ND AVE W, DICKINSON CLC 58601 #035-45-1988 L1991 **PD** *020 †55

OLIN, Bruce Wade. 33 9TH ST W 58601 #037-01-1985 L1989 **IM** *020 †20

PETERSON, Gary Dayle. 938 2ND AVE W 58601 #012-01-1969 L1977 **GP** *020 †55

RASHID, Syed Qaiser. 30 7TH ST W, CARE 58601 #495-24-1957 L1983 **P** *020

RATHGEBER, Cory Edmund. 33 9TH ST W 58601 #068-01-1995 L2006 **FM** *020 †18

RINN, David Allen. ■ 58601 #036-05-1962 L1964 **FM GS** *075 †18

ROWED, Robert Bayly. 30 7TH ST W 58601 #062-01-1941 **EM** *020

SAMUY, Narciso. 614 1ST AVE W 58601 #748-01-1970 L1980 **AN** *071

SAWCHUK, Andrew C. ■ 58601 #037-01-1969 L1966 **IM GS** *072

SEVERSON, Sherman Wayne. PULVER HALL DSC CAMPUS 58601 #048-13-1971 L1975 **P** *020

SHERMAN, Kamille Bachmeie. 938 2ND AVE W, DICKINSON CLINIC - MEDCENT 58601 #037-01-1999 L2001 **FM** *020 †18

SKAGER, Tanya Lynn. 30 7TH ST W 58601 #037-01-2001 L2002 **FM** *020 †18

SWENSON, Sheldon Lance. 30 7TH ST W 58601 #037-01-1982 L1983 **EM** *020

TEMPLETON, Thomas Robt. 938 2ND AVE W, MEDCENTER ONE HEALTH SYS 58601 #034-01-1979 L1991 **FM OM** *020 ‡

THOMAS, Jack Gordon, Jr. 938 2ND AVE W 58601 #040-02-1976 L1984 **FM** *020 †18

WILLIAMS, James Mckinley. 30 7TH ST W 58601 #038-06-1986 L2007 **OTO HNS** *020

WOLF, Dennis Elmer. 33 9TH ST W 58601 #056-05-1962 L1965 **FM FPG** *020 †18

DUNSEITH — ROLETTE

KIDD, Pamela Karen. ■ 58329 #016-11-1977 L2004 **OBG** *020 †30

MATRIANO LIM, Damian Uy. SAN HAVEN STATE HOSP 58329 #748-07-1965 **GP** *020

ELGIN — GRANT

JOHNSON, Craig Alan. 601 EAST ST N 58533 #037-01-1982 L1986 **PTH** *020 †50

ELLENDALE — DICKEY

MAC DOUGALL, James Brian. 240 MAIN ST, AVERA UNITED CLINIC 58436 #038-40-1985 L1991 **ORS** *020 †40

POTLURI, Rajendra Choudar. 141 MAIN ST 58436 #496-01-1994 L2002 **CCM** *020 †20

REISENAUER, Justin Joseph. ■ 58436 #037-01-2008 *012

FARGO — CASS

ABADIR, Gebrial Iskander. 1919 ELM ST N, UND DEPT OF NEUROSCIENCE 58102 #915-02-1968 L2003 **P** *100

ABBOTT, David Warren. 1919 ELM ST N 58102 #021-01-1973 L1977 **P** *040 †75

ABDULLAH, Ahmed. 3280 20TH ST S, PLASTIC SURGERY INST PC 58104 #016-06-1985 L1993 **PS GS** *020 †85,65 ‡

ABDULLAH, Kay Marie. 3280 20TH ST S 58104 #017-20-1988 L1993 **GS** *020 †85

ADABALA, Jaya Lakshmi. MEDICAL EDUCATION, UND RESIDENCY-MERITCARE HE 58122 #495-58-2004 L2006 **IM** *012

AGGARWAL, Ajay. 2101 ELM ST N, PULM DIV, VA MEDICAL CENTE 58102 #495-36-1996 L2001 **PCC** *020 †20

AGNEW, Robert Fletcher. 737 BROADWAY N, MERITCARE MEDICAL GROUP 58102 #035-15-1964 L1973 **TS GS** *071 †85,90

AGNIHOTRI, Adheesh. 720 4TH ST N, MERITCARE HOSPITAL 58122 #496-43-1999 L2004 **IM** *020

AHLIN, Thomas Dahl. 736 BROADWAY, MERITCARE CLINIC BEMIDJI 58122 #034-01-1973 L1978 **NEP** *020 †20

AKGUL, Fetih. 1919 ELM ST N, UND DEPT OF NEUROSCIENCE 58102 #902-07-1985 L2003 **P** *020

AKKERMAN, Dave Shelton. 3902 13TH AVE S 58103 #046-01-1986 L1987 **FM** *020 †18

ALBERTO, Neville M. 801 BROADWAY N 58102 #496-15-1991 L2001 **IM** *020 †20

ALKHALAF, Abdulhamid H. 736 BROADWAY N 58102 #875-01-1983 L2005 **ID** *020 †20

ALONTO, Augusto Mateo. 736 BROADWAY N 58102 #016-11-1999 L2001 **ID** *020 †20

ALTAF, Waseem. 801 BROADWAY N 58102 #704-02-1989 L2001 **NPM** *020 †55

ALTENBURG, Bernard Martin. 801 BROADWAY N 58102 #056-06-1965 L1970 **AN** *071 †05

ANDERSON, Christopher Edw. ■ 58103 #037-01-2008 L2008 *012

ARAVAPALLI, Aruna. MEDICAL EDUCATION, UND RESIDENCY-MERITCARE HE 58122 #496-24-1998 L2006 **IM** *012

ARUSELL, Robert Marshall. 820 4TH ST N 58102 #037-01-1976 L1977 **RO IM** *020 †20,80

ASHEIM, Jason Michael. 801 BROADWAY N 58102 #026-04-2001 L2006 **RNR** *020 †80

ASHLEY, Lynn Elizabeth. 2101 ELM ST N, VA MEDICAL CENTER 58102 #037-01-1995 L1998 **FM** *020 †18 ‡

ASHRAF, Usman. 1919 ELM ST N, UND DEPT OF NEUROSCIENCE 58102 #704-01-1999 L2007 **P** *012

ASKEW, R Mark. 2301 25TH ST S, ORTHOPAEDIC ASSOCIATES OF 58103 #037-01-1981 L1986 **ORS** *020 †40

ASLESON, Bruce Allen. 801 BROADWAY N 58102 #026-04-1970 L1977 **DR** *020 †80

AUSTIN, William Robt. 737 BROADWAY N 58102 #037-01-1978 L1980 **DR** *020 †80

BADER, Michael Thos. 737 BROADWAY N 58102 #048-04-1981 L1986 **GE IM** *020 †20

BAGAN, Steven Michael. 4344 20TH AVE SW 58103 #048-04-1976 L1980 **OPH** *020 †35

BAILEY, David Alexander. 2400 32ND AVE S 58103 #038-41-1999 L2005 **HS GS** *020

BAILLY, Richard Craig. 700 1ST AVE S, MERITCARE NEUROSCIENCE 58103 #026-04-1970 L1976 **N CN** *020 †75

BAIRD, John Robt. 401 3RD AVE N 58102 #028-02-1978 L1979 **FM FOP** *020 †18

BALDWIN, Jerry Jos. 737 BROADWAY N, MERITCARE 58122 #026-04-1972 L1975 **PTH** *020 †50

BANDE, Dinesh. PO BOX MC, MERITCARE MC #170 58122 #495-62-2005 L2008 *012

BARKER, Kyle. ■ 58104 #037-01-2008 *012

BARNARD, Donald Max. ■ 58104 #016-11-1947 L1948 **END IM** *071 †20

BARTH, Eric Baier. 2611 12TH ST S 58103 #035-06-1959 L1966 **IM PUD** *071 †20

BATRA, Sandeep. 801 BROADWAY N 58102 #496-09-1993 L2007 **PHO** *020 †55

BAUGH, John R, Jr. 3000 32ND AVE S, INNOVIS HEALTH 58103 #048-13-1996 L2005 **FM** *020 †18

BAUMGARDNER, David Paul. 2400 32ND AVE S, SOUTHPOINT CLINIC 58103 #038-40-1970 L1975 **IM** *071 †20

BEARD, David Matthew. 3270 20TH ST S 58104 #018-03-1992 L2002 **HS** *020 †40

BEAUCLAIR, John G. 3838 12TH AVE N, SERVICES 58102 #037-01-1984 L1985 **OM** *020 †18

BECKER, William Kirby. 2101 ELM ST N, CHIEF OF STAFF 58102 #026-04-1976 L1992 **GS CCM** *020 †85

BELANGER, Mary Crissler. 737 BROADWAY N 58102 #037-01-2000 L2007 **IM** *020 †20 ‡

BELIZARIO, Francisco Y. 1702 UNIVERSITY DR S, TRINITY HEALTH CENTER WEST 58103 #748-02-1971 L2002 **OTO** *020 †45

BELKNAP, Burton Stone. 1702 UNIVERSITY DR S, DAKOTA CLINIC LTD 58103 #018-03-1970 L1980 **D** *020 †15

BENJAMIN, Charles Ira. 3280 20TH ST S 58104 #026-04-1965 L1991 **PS GS** *020 †65,85

BENZ, Becky Kim. 801 BROADWAY N 58102 #037-01-2001 L2007 **RNR** *020 †80

BERG, Laura Ann. 1919 ELM ST N 58102 #037-01-2004 L2004 **P** *012

BERGER, Walter J. 2101 ELM ST N, VA MEDICAL CENTER - FARGO 58102 #037-01-1992 L1997 **CHP** *020 †75

BERGLUND, Howard T. 2301 25TH ST S, ORTHOPAEDIC ASSOCIATES OF 58103 #037-01-1988 L1994 **ORS** *020 †40

BERGSTROM, Lance Kim. 827 28TH ST SW, STE B 58103 #026-04-1991 L1995 **OPH PO** *020 †35

BERNDT, Steven Delwood. 801 BROADWAY N 58102 #037-01-1986 L1996 **AN PME** *020 †05

BERRY, Spencer D. 2400 32ND AVE S 58103 #048-04-1984 L1996 **FM** *020 †18

BEXELL, Jan M. 3000 32ND AVE S, DAKOTA CLINIC 58103 #037-01-1990 L2005 **OBG** *020 †30

BHORA, Milapchand Ajay Ku. 801 BROADWAY N 58102 #495-73-1999 L2006 **IM** *020 †20

BIANCO, Michelle K. 737 BROADWAY N 58102 #037-01-2001 L2006 **PTH** *100 †50

BIEGLER, Peter, III. ■ 58103 #037-01-2007 L2007 **TY** *012

BIER, Dennis Earl. 820 4TH ST N, ROGER MARIS CANCER CENTER 58122 #043-01-1984 L1996 **RO** *020 †80

BILSTAD, Paul Robert. 801 BROADWAY N 58102 #037-01-1998 L2001 **EM** *020 †16

BJERKE, Gregory Jon. 801 BROADWAY N 58102 #030-06-1979 L1980 **EM IM** *020 †20,16

BJORGAARD, Barry Allan. 3000 32ND AVE SW 58103 #060-01-1982 L1990 *020

BLAINE, Richard W. ■ 58102 #018-03-1967 L1969 **D** *071 †15

BLAUFUSS, Mark Chas. 801 BROADWAY N 58102 #028-02-1978 L1984 **PD GE** *020 †55

BLEHM, David Milton. 801 BROADWAY N 58102 #037-01-1981 L1985 **PD** *020 †55

BLEHM, Julie Ann. 736 BROADWAY N 58102 #037-01-1981 L1985 **IM DIA** *030 †20

BLOCK, Terry N. 1702 UNIVERSITY DR S, INNOVIS HEALTH 58103 #037-01-1986 L1990 **P** *020 †75

BOYLE, Jeffrey Glen. 737 BROADWAY N 58102 #049-01-1990 L2008 **OBG** *020 †30

BRICKNER, Derek Michael. ■ 58103 #037-01-2008 *012

BRIGGS, Michael Steven. 3000 32ND AVE SW 58103 #021-06-1976 L1992 **PUD IM** *020 †20

BRIGGS, Steven Eugene. 801 BROADWAY N 58102 #037-01-2000 L2006 **GS CCS** *020 †85

BRO, Walter Chas. 801 BROADWAY N 58102 #005-12-1975 L1981 **OBG** *020 †30

BRONSON-BAUM, Natalya Yur. 1919 ELM ST N, UND DEPT OF NEUROSCIENCE 58102 #913-83-1980 L2002 **P** *020

BRUNSVOLD, Robert Allen. 801 BROADWAY N 58102 #007-02-1975 L1985 **AN GS** *020 †85,05

BUETTNER, Ann M. ■ 58103 #016-01-1977 L1981 **IM** *020 †20

BURD, Ronald Miles. 1702 S UNIVERSITY DR, MERIT CARE SOUTH UNIVERSIT 58122 #049-01-1982 L1986 **P** *020 †75

BURDINE, Jim. 801 BROADWAY N 58102 #048-04-1985 L2003 **TS** *020 †85,90

BURNS, Joseph T. 3000 32ND AVE SW, EMERGENCY DEPARTMENT 58103 #037-01-1993 L1994 **FM EM** *020 †18

BURTNETT, Lawana Marie. ■ 58103 #019-02-1995 L2007 **P** *020 †75

BURTON, Devone Nelson. PO BOX MC, HLTH SYSTEM 58122 #049-01-2007 L2007 **TY** *012

CABO CHAN, Alberto V. 1702 UNIVERSITY DR S, DAKOTA CLINIC, LTD 58103 #748-01-1993 L2004 **END** *020 †20

CAILLIER, Rebecca L. 700 1ST AVE S 58103 #037-01-2003 L2003 **N** *020

CAIRNS, Anne Marie. 1702 UNIVERSITY DR S, DAKOTA CLINIC, LTD. 58103 #065-10-1992 L1998 **FM** *020 †18

CAPEK, Josef Richard. 2710 BROADWAY N, NORTHPORT SHOPPING CTR 58102 #286-04-1959 L1973 **FM EM** *071 †18

CARCOANA, Claudia. 2101 ELM ST N, VA MEDICAL CENTER 58102 #781-01-1988 L1996 **P** *020 †75

CARCOANA, Olivia V. 2688 MEADOW CREEK CIR S, ANESTHESIA ASSOCIATES,LTD. 58104 #781-01-1985 L1999 **AN** *020 †05

CARD, Charlene Connie O. 2601 BROADWAY N 58102 #026-04-1995 L1997 **FM** *020 †18

CARLISLE, Bruce Mitchell. 100 4TH ST S STE 604 58103 #037-01-1976 L1977 **IM** *020

CARLSEN, Donald Arthur. 4510 13TH AVE S, NORIDIAN MUTUAL INC CO 58121 #041-13-1957 L1964 **FM MDM** *030

CARLSON, David Chas. 1702 UNIVERSITY DR S, DAKOTA CLINIC LTD 58103 #026-04-1978 L1981 **IM** *020 †20

CARLSON, David Lee. 1702 UNIVERSITY DR S, DAKOTA CLINIC PSYCH 58103 #037-01-1991 L1992 **P** *020 †75

CARPENTER, James Royal. 737 BROADWAY N, MERITCARE MEDICAL GROUP 58102 #040-02-1969 L1975 **RHU IM** *071 †20

CARSON, Janine Henning. 801 BROADWAY N 58102 #037-01-1986 L1997 **DR** *020 †80

CARSON, John Paul. 1702 UNIVERSITY DR S, DAKOTA CLINIC, LTD. 58103 #038-41-1962 L1969 **ID IM** *071

CARSON, Paul James. 736 BROADWAY N 58102 #037-01-1986 L1996 **ID** *020 †20

CATALAN, Janice M Nicklay. ■ 58104 #037-01-1994 L2005 **NPM** *020 †55

CATALAN, Richard Lee. 737 BROADWAY N 58102 #041-13-1992 L2006 **DR** *020 †80

CHAKRAVORTY, Bhaswati. 306 4TH ST N, FAMILY HEALTH CARE CTR 58102 #495-38-1974 L2001 **FM** *020 †18

CHAKRAVORTY, Utpal. 3000 32ND AVE S 58103 #495-78-1972 L1996 **FM A** *020 †18

CHALASANI, Rao. 2301 25TH ST S, INSTITUTE FOR SPECIAL SURG 58103 #495-50-1991 L1996 **AN** *020 †05

CHANDRASHEKARAN, Satish. 801 BROADWAY N 58102 #495-62-1997 L2004 **IM** *020

CHAUDHARY, Vijay. PO BOX MC, MERITCARE MEDICAL CTR #170 58122 #496-09-2002 L2005 **IM** *012

CHAVOUR, Sudhir Kumar. 801 BROADWAY N 58102 #495-21-2000 L2003 **IM** *020 †20

CHEMITI, Gopalkrishna P. 737 BROADWAY N 58102 #495-21-1990 L2003 **NEP** *020 †20

CHEN, Stanley Jian. 2624 9TH AVE S 58103 #243-45-1985 L2003 **P** *020

CHERIAN, Mathew Amprayil. 801 BROADWAY N 58102 #495-27-2000 L2003 **IM** *020 †20

CHERVENKOFF, Steven. ■ 58102 #198-01-1987 L1996 **IM** *020 †20

CHERVENKOFF, Vassil J. ■ 58102 #198-01-1987 L1999 **TS** *020

CHRISTENSEN, Steffen. 1111 HARWOOD DR S 58104 #018-03-1973 L1977 **REN OBG** *020 †30 ‡

CHRISTOFERSON, Lee A, Jr. 1702 UNIVERSITY DR S, DAKOTA CLINIC LTD 58103 #037-01-1976 L1981 **ORS** *020 †40

CLAPP, Allison Jean. ■ 58103 #037-01-2008 *012

CLARDY, David Jerome. 801 BROADWAY N 58102 #028-02-1977 L1990 **CD** *020 †20

CLEMENSON, Steven Glenn. 737 BROADWAY, MERITCARE BROADWAY CLINIC 58122 #028-34-1984 L2004 **IM CD** *020 †20

CLINKENBEARD, David Lee. 2624 9TH AVE S 58103 #028-34-1986 L1987 **P** *020

CLUTTER, David Jos. 3000 32ND AVE S, DAKOTA CLINIC LTD INNOVIS 58103 #007-02-1979 L1986 **PD NPM** *020 †55 ‡

COFFEY, James H. 737 BROADWAY N, MENTAL HEALTH DEPARTMENT 58102 #030-05-1953 L1962 **PTH** *071 †50

COLLITON, Patrick Allen. 510 4TH ST S 58103 #021-01-1959 L1968 **OPH** *071 †35

COOPER, Mark Carlyle. 1702 UNIVERSITY DR S, DAKOTA CLINIC LTD 58103 #025-07-1986 L1990 **RO** *020 †80

COOPER, Robert Ian. 2704 BROADWAY N STE C, DBA FARGO DISABILITY EVALU 58102 #917-24-1968 L1992 **PM PMM** *020 †60

COWAN, Hugh Ben. ■ 58102 #065-01-1975 L1976 **FM IM** *020

COX, David Boyd. ■ 58103 #007-02-2004 L2004 **GS** *012

CRAGO, Charles Arthur. 4344 20TH AVE S, STE 2 58103 #001-02-1982 L2002 **OS** *020

CRARY, John Lamb. 801 BROADWAY N 58102 #026-04-1969 L1976 **CD IM** *020 †20

CRAYCHEE, Walter Albert. ■ 58102 #041-13-1945 L1946 **GP** *072

CROWE, Christopher Howard. 1702 UNIVERSITY DR S, DAKOTA CLINIC, LTD. 58103 #051-07-1985 L1993 **DR** *020 †80

CROWLEY, Lana R. 1720 S UNIVERSITY 58103 #037-01-1985 L1986 **FM** *020 †18

CUNNINGHAM, Edwin Arthur. ■ 58103 #016-06-1962 L1970 **OS PTH** *071 †50

CZERNEK, Peter. 720 4TH ST N, MERIT CARE HOSP 58122 #759-09-1965 L1983 **IM** *020 †20

DADA, Farooq Mohammad. 3065 40TH AVE SW UNIT A 58104 #704-02-1990 L2003 **PYG ADP** *020 †75

DAHL, Stephanie Kay. 1111 HARWOOD DR S 58104 #037-01-1999 L2004 **REN OBG** *020 †30

DALAN, Danilo A. 100 4TH ST S STE 302 58103 #037-01-1987 L1989 **AI** *020 †20,03

DAMLE, Ajit. 801 BROADWAY N 58102 #495-28-1974 L1989 **TS** *020

DANDO, Carl Frederick. 3115 UNIVERSITY DR S, DRIVE SOUTH 58103 #041-12-1985 L2005 **IM** *020 †20

DANGERFIELD, Jon D. 801 BROADWAY N 58102 #037-01-1992 L1996 **OBG** *020 †30

DANIELS, Steven. 801 BROADWAY N 58102 #028-03-1987 L1991 **AN** *020

DANIELSON, Byron David. 1919 ELM ST N, DEPT OF MEDICINE 58102 #026-04-1966 L1976 **NEP IM** *020 †20

DE BOEL, Stefan L. 801 BROADWAY N 58102 #165-06-1981 L1991 **CD IM** *020 †20

DEES, Brian Kenneth. 3000 32ND AVE S, INNOVIS HEALTH 58103 #037-01-1996 L2003 **GS** *020 †85

DESCHAMPS, Suzanne M. 600 4TH ST S, MERITCARE CLNC ISLAND PA 58103 #065-01-1994 L1997 **FM** *020 †18

DESHPANDE, Nikhil. 737 BROADWAY N 58102 #495-85-1993 L1999 **GE** *020 †20

DICKSON, Jonathan Lee. 801 BROADWAY N 58102 #018-03-1973 L1980 **CD IC** *020 †20

DRAGE, David Charles. 801 BROADWAY N 58102 #056-06-1993 L2003 **EM** *020

DUCKETT, William Douglas. 720 4TH ST N, MERITCARE HOSPITAL 58122 #004-01-1970 L2002 **AN** *020 †05

DUFF, Martha S K. 737 BROADWAY N 58102 #003-01-1998 L2007 **GS** *100 †80
DUVAL, David L. 801 BROADWAY N 58122 #016-06-1962 L1970 **CD IM** *020 †20
EASH, Galen Jay. 2701 13TH AVE S, FARGO CLINC SOUTH WEST 58103 #041-02-1965 L1966 **GP** *071 †18
EHLEN, Matt John. ■ 58102 #021-01-1956 L1957 **OS CD** *072 †20
EICHLER, Marc Edward. ■ 58103 #028-02-1988 L1997 **NS** *020 †25
EL-ZIND, Samira H. 801 BROADWAY N 58102 #915-02-1984 L2004 **CHN** *020 †75
ENGBERG, Roger D. ■ 58103 #040-02-1957 L1958 **ORS** *071
ESPEJO, Napoleon Robanini. 306 4TH ST N 58102 #737-01-1990 L1998 **FM** *020 †18
FABER, Kevin Michael. 1717 UNIVERSITY DR S 58103 #028-03-2002 L2006 **N** *100 †75
FAHSSI, Mohamed Lamine. 720 4TH ST N, MERIT CARE HOSPITAL 58122 #125-01-1974 L1997 **TS** *020
FAUST, Elizabeth Ann. 1720 UNIVERSITY DR S 58103 #018-03-1985 L1989 **P** *020 †75
FENSTAD, Eric Ryan. ■ 58104 #037-01-2008 L2008 *012
FERCHO, Calvin K. 510 4TH ST S 58103 #016-06-1952 L1955 **OPH** *071 †35
FIEBIGER, Siri Johnson. 3000 32ND AVE S, DAKOTA CLINIC, LTD INNOV 58103 #037-01-1985 L1990 **OBG** *020 †30
FINDLEY, Alfonso C. 1702 UNIVERSITY DR S, DAKOTA CLINIC, LTD 58103 #610-01-1978 L2002 **DR NM** *020 †80
FISCHER, Eunah Kang. 2400 32ND AVE S 58103 #032-01-1996 L2001 **IMG** *020 †20
FISCHER, Keith Jerome. 3000 32ND AVE S, INNOVIS HOSPITAL 58103 #037-01-1996 L1999 **FM** *020 †18 ‡
FISCHER, Kenneth J. 100 4TH ST S 58103 #037-01-1996 L2001 **P** *020 †75
FISHER, Christina. 801 BROADWAY N 58102 #781-01-1985 L2003 **AN PME** *020 †05
FISHER, Mark Frederick. 737 BROADWAY N 58102 #023-01-1979 L1984 **R NM** *020 †28,80
FITZGERALD, David Anthony. 3000 32ND AVE S, DAKOTA CLINIC LTD INNOVI 58103 #012-05-1970 L2000 **N OS** *020 †75
FLACH, David Bruce. 2400 32ND AVE S 58103 #037-01-1981 L1985 **D** *020 †15
FLEISSNER, Rachel M. 2902 UNIVERSITY DR S 58103 #917-29-1987 L1998 **CHP** *020 †75
FORNACE, Albert Joseph. 100 35TH AVE NE 58102 #041-77-1944, ▲ L1957 **CD** *071
FREDERICK, James Alan. ■ 58102 #026-04-1972 L1984 **IM** *020 †20
FRISK, James Le Ondis. 2700 12TH AVE SW, STE D 58103 #038-40-1969 L1970 **OTO SME** *020 †45
GABA, Anu Goel. 820 4TH ST N 58102 #495-27-1990 L2004 **HO** *020 †20
GABA, Vijay Kumar. 801 BROADWAY N 58102 #496-09-1985 L2004 **AN** *020 †05 ‡
GAFFREY, John Chas. ■ 58102 #037-01-1977 **IM** *020
GAGNEJA, Arvinder Pal Sin. 1919 ELM ST N, UND DEPT OF NEUROSCIENCE 58102 #495-10-1996 L2006 **P** *012
GALICH, Anton Nikolaevich. 3000 32ND AVE S, DAKOTA CLINIC, LTD/INNOVIS 58103 #913-05-1996 L2006 **U** *020 †95
GARNAAS, Karen Reinke. 700 1ST AVE S, NEUROLOGY NEUROSCIENCE CLI 58103 #026-08-1990 L1995 **N** *020 †75
GARRITY, Stephen Patrick. 737 BROADWAY N, MERICARE MEDICAL GROUP 58102 #026-04-1990 L1995 **DR** *020 †80
GETZ-KLEIMAN, Linda L. 3902 13TH AVE S, DAKOTA CLINIC WEST ACRES 58103 #026-04-1975 L1988 **PD** *020 †55
GHAZI, Majid. 1720 UNIVERSITY DR S, PAIN CLINIC 58103 #409-34-1994 L2004 **AN PMM** *020 †05
GHAZI, Stefanie S. 3000 32ND AVE S, INNOVIS HEALTH/DAKOTA CLIN 58103 #037-01-2000 L2004 **OBG** *020 ‡
GIDDINGS, Kate Michael. 306 FOREST AVE 58102 #037-01-2007 **OBG** *012
GILBERTSON, Roger Lyle. 801 BROADWAY NORTH 58122 #026-04-1963 L1972 **R NM** *020 †80
GISH, David Brent. 1919 ELM ST N 58102 #665-01-2003 L2003 **P** *020
GLASNER, Gregory C. 3000 32ND AVE S, DAKOTA CLINIC LTD INNOVI 58103 #037-01-1990 L1994 **OBG** *020 †30
GLOWER, Martha Elizabeth. 1702 UNIVERSITY DR S 58103 #016-02-1990 L1994 **D** *020 †15
GLUNBERG, Steven Kent. 801 BROADWAY N 58102 #028-02-1981 L1982 **FM** *020 †18 ‡
GOFF, John R. ■ 58103 #035-45-1951 L1954 **OPH** *071 †35
GOGINENI, Srikanth. 720 4TH ST N, MERITCARE MED CENTER 58122 #496-24-2002 L2007 **IM** *012
GOLDENBERG, Jacob Alan. 737 BROADWAY N, MERITCARE MEDICAL GROUP 58102 #062-01-1987 L1997 **DR** *020 †80
GOLI, Sunil K. 700 1ST AVE S 58103 #495-65-1996 L2003 **N** *020 †75
GONZALES, Michael F. 1720 UNIVERSITY DR S 58103 #016-06-1975 L2003 **PM** *075 †60
GOSWAMI, Arundhati Bikash. 720 4TH ST N, MERITCARE MEDICAL CENTER 58122 #495-28-1999 L2004 **AN** *012
GRAFF, Arne Harlan. 100 4TH ST S, STE 410 58103 #037-01-1981 L1984 **FM** *100 †18
GRIDER, John Harold. ■ 58104 #028-79-2007, ▲ L2007 **GS** *012
GRIFFIN, David M. 801 BROADWAY N 58102 #037-01-1991 L1992 **FM** *020 †18
GRIMM, Carol Jean. 737 BROADWAY, MERIT CARE CLINIC 58122 #014-01-1984 L1987 **GP** *020
GRIMM, Terrence Earl. 737 BROADWAY N 58102 #014-01-1975 L1985 **PTH** *020 †50 ‡
GRIMMETT, Garfield M, Jr. 3000 32ND AVE S, DAKOTA CLINIC, LTD INNOV 58103 #010-03-1972 L2001 **CD IM** *020 †20
GROSS, Gerald Gerard. 820 4TH ST NORTH 58122 #037-01-1987 L1994 **ON HEM** *020 †20
GROSZ, David Elwood. 100 4TH ST S, STE 612 58103 #037-01-1980 L1984 **OPH** *020 †35
GUDURU, Prabhakar Rao. 2101 ELM ST N, VA MEDICAL CENTER 58102 #495-57-1980 L1998 **IM** *020 †20
GUNDERSON, Aaron Charles. 801 BROADWAY N 58102 #037-01-1999 L2002 **PD** *020 †55
GUPTA, Mahendra Kumar. 1702 UNIVERSITY DR S, DAKOTA CLINIC 58103 #495-30-1989 L2002 **HO IM** *020 †20
GUPTA, Parul. 2101 ELM ST N, DEPARTMENT OF VETERANS AFF 58102 #496-04-1992 L2003 **IMG IM** *020 †20
GURRAM, Murali Krishna. PO BOX MC, MERITCARE MED CTR #170 58122 #495-11-2004 L2007 **IM** *012
HAAGENSON, Lori Jo. ■ 58102 #037-01-2006 L2006 **P** *012
HAASBEEK, Jeffrey Frank. 2400 32ND AVE S, MERITCARE CLINIC SOUTHPOIN 58103 #062-01-1984 L1991 **OP** *020 †40
HAGE-NASSAR, George T. 737 BROADWAY N 58102 #605-03-1997 L2006 **GE** *100 †20
HAIDER, Nadeem. 1720 UNIVERSITY DR S 58103 #704-09-1989 L1994 **P** *020 †75
HAIDER, Naveed. 1702 UNIVERSITY DR S, MERITCARE SOUTH UNIVERSITY 58103 #704-09-1987 L1999 **P** *020 †75
HAJEK, Philip T. 2624 9TH AVE S 58103 #016-43-1977 L1982 **P N** *020 †75
HALL, Katherine S. 737 BROADWAY, MERITCARE CLINIC 58122 #037-01-2000 L2001 **IM** *020
HALLANGER-JOHNSON, Julie. 2400 32ND AVE S 58103 #037-01-2000 L2006 **END** *100 †20
HAMILTON, Clif Struthers. ■ 58103 #030-05-1957 L1970 **TS** *071 †85,90
HANDA, Geeta. 1389 ELM CIR N 58102 #496-07-1989 L2005 **P** *012
HANDA, Kushal Kumar. 801 BROADWAY N 58102 #917-07-1986 L1998 **IM CD** *020 †20
HANEKOM, David Stephanus. 2400 32ND AVE S, MERITLANE SOUTH POINTE 58103 #836-01-1987 L1999 **IM** *020 †20
HANISCH, Stefanie Ulrike. 100 4TH ST S 58103 #836-03-1994 L2003 **CHP** *020 †75
HANSON, Thomas Lawrence. 100 4TH ST S, STE 612 58103 #007-02-1979 L1983 **OPH** *020 †35
HAO, Weimin. 801 BROADWAY N 58102 #243-47-1984 L1998 **IM** *020 †20
HARRIS, Hoadley Howe. 3280 20TH ST S, PLAINS MEDICAL CLNC 58104 #018-03-1982 L1985 **FM** *020 †18
HARTZ, Charles Richard. 736 BROADWAY N 58102 #010-01-1970 L1979 **ORS** *075 †40
HASAN, Syed Mahmood Ul. 100 4TH ST S 58103 #704-28-2000 **IM** *012
HASAN, Umbreen. 2400 32ND AVE S 58103 #704-25-1996 L2007 **RHU** *020 †20
HATLESTAD, Preston Joshua. ■ 58104 #037-01-2008 *012
HAUER, Darko. 801 BROADWAY N 58102 #957-01-1987 L2003 **IM** *020 †20
HAUGEN, Gregory Michael. 801 BROADWAY N 58122 #037-01-2000 L2003 **EM** *020 †16
HAUGEN, Joel Ross. 1720 UNIVERSITY DR S 58103 #026-04-1979 L1982 **FM** *020 †18
HAUGO, Amie Christine. 600 4TH ST S 58103 #037-01-2004 L2008 **FM** *020
HAYNIE, Gary Donald. 4642 AMBER VALLEY PKWY S, RETINA ASSOCIATES, PC. 58104 #007-02-1982 L1993 **OPH IM** *020 †20,35
HAZZARD, Marion Powell. 2400 32ND AVE S 58103 #004-01-1968 L2003 **ORS** *020 †40
HELLA, Brent Matthew. 1707 GOLD DR S 58103 #037-01-1996 L2000 **IM** *020 †20
HENRY, Lisa Leah. 1919 ELM ST N, 09MED 58102 #037-01-2000 L2001 **IM** *020
HEPPER, Kenneth Norman. 737 BROADWAY N 58102 #016-06-1966 L1970 **IM** *020 †20
HEROLD, Daniel Wilfred. 225 4TH AVE N, FARGO MEPS 58102 #026-04-1981 L1982 **FM** *020 †18
HERZOG, Thomas Le Roy. 801 BROADWAY N 58102 #037-01-1979 L1983 **OBG** *020 †30
HEUPEL, Alden Richard. ■ 58102 #054-04-1960 L1961 **PTH** *071 †50
HIEB, Edwin Orville. ■ 58103 #016-11-1947 L1948 **IM** *071 †20
HINTZ, Warren J. 801 BROADWAY N 58102 #037-01-1986 L1987 **IM** *020 †20
HOAG, Ray Alan. ■ 58102 #037-01-1981 L1985 **OBG** *020 †30
HOGUE, Roger Steven. 3115 UNIVERSITY DR S, STE 1 58103 #005-11-1992 L2005 **PHL** *020
HOLM, Mary Kaye. 3000 32ND AVE S, DAKOTA CLINIC AT INNOVIS 58103 #046-01-1990 L1994 **OBG** *020 †30
HOLTEN, Erik Britten. 737 BROADWAY N 58102 #026-04-1991 L1994 **IM** *020 †20
HONL, Beth Ann. 4141 31ST AVE S STE 103, DERMATOLOGY ASSOCIATES, PC 58104 #037-01-1993 L1994 **D** *020 †15
HOPE, Brian Daeseong. ■ 58104 #037-01-2008 *012
HOUGHTON, James Francis. 1720 UNIVERSITY DR S 58103 #023-01-1947 L1948 **IM CD** *020
HOWELL, Louis Michael. 801 BROADWAY N 58102 #010-02-1966 L1973 **GS** *020 †85
HUHN, Paul Allen. 2101 ELM ST N, VA HOSP 58102 #026-04-1969 L1976 **IM P** *020 †20
HUND, Morris Alan. 100 4TH ST S 58103 #019-02-1985 L1989 **P** *020 †75
HUNT, Daniel Stacey. 3000 32ND AVE S, INNOVIS HEALTH 58103 #049-01-1986 L1989 **EM** *020 †16
HUNTER, Cornelius M. ■ 58104 #025-07-1939 L1945 **OS GP** *071
HUSHKA, Doug James. 801 BROADWAY N 58102 #037-01-1988 L1989 **FM** *020 †18
HUTCHISON, John Winans. 700 1ST AVE S 58103 #005-15-1972 L1996 **NS** *020 †25
HUTCHISON, William K. 2701 13TH AVE S 58103 #017-20-2001 L2008 **PD** *020 †55
HVIDSTON, Andrew James. 2301 25TH ST S, ORTHOPEDIC ASSOCIATES OF 58103 #026-04-1984 L1989 **ORS** *020 †40
ILLOVSZKY FARKAS, Susan. 801 BROADWAY N 58102 #473-01-1982 L2005 **CD** *020 †20
INAYATULLAH, Seema. PO BOX MC, MERITCARE MC #170 58122 #704-09-2003 L2008 *100
INDERGAARD, Patrick John. 801 BROADWAY N 58102 #037-01-1993 L1997 **AN** *020 †05
INGEBRETSON, Mark Chester. 2101 ELM ST N 58102 #037-01-1981 L1983 **IM** *020
IVERS, Robert Ralph. 700 1ST AVE S 58103 #016-06-1955 L1956 **N** *071 †75
IVERSON, Godela Reisig. 1702 S UNIV DR, DAKOTA CLINIC LTD 58103 #047-05-1968 L1973 **ID IM** *071 †20
IWEN, George Wm. 2101 ELM ST N 58102 #056-05-1947 L1979 **GS TS** *071 †85,90
JADAAN, Atef Ajilevich. 2101 ELM ST N 58102 #913-06-1996 L2005 **IM** *020 †20
JALIL, Sajid. 737 BROADWAY N 58102 #704-25-1990 L1995 **GE** *020 †20
JAMIESON, John. 3626 EVERGREEN RD N 58102 #803-05-1950 L1971 **P** *071 †75
JANGDA, Hameeda Aslam. 1919 ELM ST N, UND DEPT OF NEUROSCIENCE 58102 #704-02-1991 L2002 **P** *020 †75
JAYARAMAIAH, Poornima. RESIDENCY-MERITCARE HEALTH, UND 58122 #496-21-2003 L2004 **IM** *100 †20
JENSEN, Mark Olof. 2101 ELM ST N, VA MEDICAL CENTER 58102 #026-04-1978 L1984 **GS SO** *040 †85
JOHNSON, George Magnus. 1919 ELM ST N, UND MEDICAL EDUCATION CENT 58102 #054-04-1960 L1965 **PD DIA** *020 †55
JOHNSON, James Fred. 2301 25TH ST S STE 1 58103 #014-01-1975 L1976 **ORS** *020 †40
JOHNSON, Max Ray. 2345 25TH ST S 58103 #037-01-1982 L1987 **OPH** *020 †35
JOHNSON, Philip Q. 2301 25TH ST S, ORTHOPAEDIC ASSOCIATES OF 58103 #037-01-1984 L1991 **ORS OSM** *020 †40
JOHNSON, Robert Melvin. 700 1ST AVE S, NEUROSCIENCE CLINIC 58103 #062-01-1964 L1971 **NS** *071 †25
JOHNSON, Ronald Lynn. 2101 ELM ST N, VA MEDICAL CENTER 58102 #026-04-1979 L1980 **IM** *020 ‡
JOHNSON, Steven R. 1711 GOLD DR, STE 160 58103 #037-01-1992 L1993 **FM** *020 †18
JOHNSON, Therese. 1711 GOLD DR, STE 160 58103 #037-01-1991 L1992 **FM** *020 †18
JOHNSON, Walter Sanfrid. 1702 UNIVERSITY DR S, DAKOTA CLINIC LTD 58103 #037-01-1978 L1979 **IM** *040 †20
JONES, Jenifer Elisabeth. 3000 32ND AVE S 58103 #422-01-2000 L2004 **PD** *020 †55
JORDAN, Andrew A, Jr. 1717 UNIVERSITY DR S 58103 #054-04-1980 L1981 **OPH** *020 †18,35
JORDHEIM, Robert Phillips. 737 BROADWAY N 58102 #016-06-1954 L1961 **IM** *071 †20
JOSHI, Sheetal Rashmikant. 1919 ELM ST N 58102 #496-48-2000 L2005 **P** *012
JOST, Aaron Daniel. 801 BROADWAY N 58102 #037-01-2001 L2004 **PD** *020 †55
JUSTESEN, Chad R. 801 BROADWAY N 58102 #037-01-1993 L2002 **NS** *020
KALE, Suniti. ■ 58103 #495-45-1984 **APM** *100
KANA, Dale Curtis. 2701 13TH AVE S, MERITCARE CLINIC SW 58103 #019-02-1959 L1960 **FM** *071 †18
KANTAK, Anand Giottam. 801 BROADWAY N 58102 #496-15-1975 L1988 **AI PDP** *020 †55,03
KANTAK, Sunita Anand. 801 BROADWAY N 58102 #496-15-1975 L1988 **PD** *020 †55
KAOUS, Shahid Mehmood. 1919 ELM ST N, UND DEPT OF NEUROSCIENCE 58102 #704-15-1984 L2005 **P** *012
KARAZ, Samy S. 1717 UNIVERSITY DR S 58103 #915-02-1976 L1986 **P** *020 †75
KAREEM, Sohail. 801 BROADWAY N 58102 #704-02-1999 L2003 **IM** *020 †20

■ = Address Information Privacy Protected

KARIM, Mohammad Imtiaz. PO BOX MC, MERITCARE MEDICAL CENTER # 58122 #160-01-1992 L2004 **IM** *020

KARLINS, Nathaniel Louis. 737 BROADWAY N 58102 #028-02-1975 L1991 **DR RNR** *020 †80

KASPARI, Jon Kevin. 737 BROADWAY N, MERITCARE MEDICAL GROUP 58102 #037-01-1979 L1980 **PTH** *062 †50

KAVANAUGH, Gerald John. ■ 58102 #016-06-1954 L1956 **CD IM** *072 †20

KAZI, Noor Ahmed. 1919 ELM ST N, UND DEPT OF NEUROSCIENCE 58102 #704-17-1980 L2005 **P** *012

KEATING, John Jeffrey. 720 4TH ST N 58122 #026-04-1971 L1978 **RO NM** *020 †80,28

KELLY, Edward Leslie. 510 4TH ST S 58103 #305-01-1992 L2001 **PFP P** *020 †75

KELLY, Kimberly Rae. 2400 32ND AVE S 58103 #037-01-1984 L1989 **D** *071 †15

KEMPF, Thomas Wayne. 1702 UNIVERSITY DR S, DAKOTA CLINIC LTD 58103 #037-01-1978 L1979 **IM** *020 †20

KENIEN, Alan Geo. 801 BROADWAY N 58102 #035-15-1972 L1977 **PD PDE** *020 †55

KENNEDY, Gary John. 600 4TH ST S 58103 #026-04-1979 L1990 **FM** *020 †18

KENNEY, Emmet Michael, Jr. 720 4TH ST N 58122 #030-06-1986 L1995 **CHP P** *030 †75

KENNINGER, Randall A. 2400 32ND AVE S 58103 #037-01-1994 L1995 **FM** *020 †18

KETTERLING, Rhonda Lynae. 736 BROADWAY N 58102 #037-01-1979 L1980 **IM IMG** *030 †20

KEUP, Christine Marie. ■ 58104 #037-01-2008 *012

KHAN, Aliya Aziz. 3201 23RD AVE S UNIT L 58103 #704-26-2001 L2006 **P** *012

KHAN, Hasrat. 801 BROADWAY N 58102 #368-01-1989 L2007 **CCM IM** *020 †20

KHAN, Irfan Ali. 3000 32ND AVE S 58103 #704-09-1997 L2007 **IM PCC** *020

KHAN, Zaki Hussain. RESIDENCY-MERITCARE HEALTH, UND 58122 #704-29-2002 L2007 **IM** *012

KHASHAEI, Sepehr. 2101 ELM ST N, MEDICAL AND REGIONAL OFC C 58102 #654-01-1997 L2000 **IM** *020 †20

KHERALLAH, Mazen. 801 BROADWAY N 58102 #875-01-1987 L2003 **CCM** *020 †20

KIDDER, Anne E. 2710 BROADWAY N, DAKOTA CLINIC, LTD. 58102 #037-01-1994 L1996 **FM** *020 †18

KIPPEN, Neil Ralph. 737 BROADWAY N 58102 #062-01-1948 L1971 **FM GS** *071

KLAVA, William Norbert. 801 BROADWAY N 58102 #037-01-1981 L1984 **PM OS** *020 †60

KLEIMAN, Theodore Wm. 3902 13TH AVE S, DAKOTA CLINIC WEST ACRES 58103 #035-19-1971 L1995 **PD** *020 †55

KLOSTER, Ronald Martin. 737 BROADWAY N 58102 #019-02-1958 L1959 **FM** *071 †18

KLOSTERMAN, Bruce Jerome. 801 BROADWAY N 58102 #037-01-1989 L1990 **EM** *020 †18 ‡

KNUTSON, Cynthia Marie. 700 1ST AVE S 58103 #047-07-1985 L1989 **N** *020 †75

KNUTSON, Jeffrey Irwin. 3000 32ND AVE S, DAKOTA CLC AT INNOVIS 58103 #026-04-1978 L1985 **TS** *020 †85,90

KOBRINSKY, Nathan Lewis. 801 BROADWAY N 58102 #062-01-1976 L1991 **PD** *020 †55

KOH, Robert Seinmyint. 2101 ELM ST N, FARGO VA MED CTR 58102 #209-01-1991 L2001 **IM** *020 †20

KOLARS, James Jos. 3620 EVERGREEN RD N 58102 #030-06-1971 L1974 **OBG** *071 †30

KOOYER, Kurt Wm. 3290 20TH ST S 58104 #025-12-1990 L2002 **IM PD** *020 †55,20

KORIMILLI, Vijay Lakshman. 801 BROADWAY N 58102 #496-35-2000 L2004 **IM** *020 †20

KORTUM, Cynthia Lee. 1711 GOLD DR, STE 160 58103 #030-06-1980 L1989 **FM** *020 †18

KOSKI, Charles Gust. 3838 12TH AVE N 58102 #026-04-1964 L1974 **OM TRS** *071 †25

KOUBA, Craig Robt. 801 BROADWAY N 58102 #018-03-1979 L1984 **CD IM** *020 †20

KRASNIEWSKA, Lidia. 801 BROADWAY N 58102 #913-69-1978 L1988 **PD** *020 †55

KREMER, Marnie Jo. ■ 58103 #023-01-2008 *012

KROETSCH, Corey John. ■ 58104 #037-01-2006 L2006 **GS** *012

KROPF, Donald Leon. 801 BROADWAY N 58102 #018-03-1982 L2008 **AN** *020 †05

KUBALAK, Gary Michael. 801 BROADWAY N 58102 #056-05-1983 L1993 **GS VS** *020 †85

KUHLMANN, Craig Francis. 2710 BROADWAY N, DAKOTA CLNC NORTHPORT 58102 #038-40-1983 L1987 **FM FSM** *020 †18

LAGLER, Regis Gary. 801 BROADWAY N 58102 #028-34-1980 L2004 **CCM** *020 †20 ‡

LAKO-ADAMSON, Heidi Jill. 801 BROADWAY N 58102 #037-01-2004 L2007 **EM** *020

LAMB, Donald Leonard. 100 4TH ST S 58103 #049-01-1956 L1963 **PS GS** *071 †85,65

LAMB, Donald R. 1507 UNIVERSITY DR S, LAMB PLASTIC SURG CTR PC 58103 #049-01-1984 L1985 **PS** *040 †85,65

LANG, Darin Wade. 2400 32ND AVE S 58103 #037-01-2001 L2005 **IM IMG** *020

LANTZ, James Philip. 3000 32ND AVE S 58103 #026-04-1965 L1972 **AN** *020 †05

LANTZ, Steven William. 3000 32ND AVE SW 58103 #037-01-1998 L2003 **ORS** *020 †40

LARAWAY, Richard Robt. 2101 ELM ST N, C/O VETERANS ADMINISTRATIO 58102 #037-01-1980 L1981 **IM** *020 †20

LARSEN, Paul Dennis. ■ 58102 #005-11-1970 L1973 **IM LM** *075 †20

LARSON, Leland Junior. 737 BROADWAY N 58102 #019-02-1960 L1966 **DR RO** *020 †80

LASS, Roland Nelson. 2101 ELM ST N, FARGO VA HOSP -LAB 58102 #024-07-1974 L1975 **PTH** *062 †50

LA VENUTA, Ferdinand. 3000 32ND AVE SW 58103 #035-09-1963 L1972 **OTO** *071 †45

LAYAWEN, Aselo O. 801 BROADWAY N 58102 #748-10-1993 L2003 **IM VM** *100 †20

LEE, Rodney John. 1517 32ND AVE S, RAPIDCARE URGENT CARE 58103 #026-04-1996 L1997 **FM** *020 †18

LEE, Shao Chyi. 2601 BROADWAY N, MERITCARE SOUTH UNIVERSITY 58102 #067-01-1994 L2004 **FM EM** *020 †18

LEITCH, John Malcolm. 820 4TH ST N, MERITCARE ROGER MARIS CNCR 58122 #034-01-1973 L1991 **ON HEM** *020 †20

LEON, Zelko. 100 4TH ST S 58103 #957-02-1978 L1991 **P** *020 †75

LEONHARDT, Eric Westfall. 510 4TH ST S, PRAIRIE ST JOHNS 58103 #028-78-2001, ▲ L2006 **CHP** *020

LESSARD, Julie Lynn. 737 BROADWAY N 58102 #037-01-1997 L2003 **PTH** *020 †50

LESSARD, Richard Jos. ■ 58104 #026-04-1955 L1986 **FM AM** *071 †18

LESTEBERG, Keith Gilbert. 801 BROADWAY N 58102 #030-06-1977 L1981 **OBG** *020 †30

LEVITSKI-HEIKKILA, Teresa. 737 BROADWAY N 58102 #759-04-1999 L2001 **NEP** *020 †20

LEVITT, Ralph. 820 4TH ST NORTH 58122 #016-06-1973 L1979 **ON HEM** *020 †20

LEWIS, David Stephen. 2701 13TH AVE S 58103 #037-01-1978 L2005 **PD** *020 †55

LIBI, Bernadette Uy. ■ 58104 #748-01-1963 L1971 **AN PUD** *071

LIBI, Dionisio Teng. ■ 58104 #748-01-1960 L1971 **OTO HNS** *071 †45

LIEN, David J. 2400 32ND AVE S 58103 #037-01-2001 L2004 **FM** *020 †18

LILLESTOL, Michael John. 1707 GOLD DR S 58103 #026-04-1974 L1983 **IM** *020 †20

LIND, Jackson William. 2301 25TH ST S, STE I 58103 #036-05-1962 L1963 **P ADM** *020

LINDQUIST, Kurt Dwight. 2101 ELM ST N, VA MEDICAL CTR 58102 #016-01-1977 L1984 **GS** *020 †85

LINDQUIST, Linda B. 2101 ELM ST N, ROUTE # 112 58102 #016-11-1978 L1984 **GS** *040 †85

LINDQUIST, Paul Jeffery. 736 BROADWAY N 58102 #026-04-1984 L1988 **PM** *020 †60

LO, Tze Shien. 2101 ELM ST N, VA MED CTR 58102 #572-12-1985 L2001 **ID** *020 †20

LONGHURST, Claire Frances. ■ 58104 #037-01-2008 *012

LOPEZ, David Javier. ■ 58102 #026-04-1995 L2006 **P** *020

LOWE, Harold Mason. 1702 UNIVERSITY DR S, DAKOTA CLINIC 58103 #019-02-1958 L2001 **CD IM** *071 †20

LUCHT, Kamilla Lee. 2701 13TH AVE S 58103 #037-01-2003 L2006 **PD** *020

LUDWIG, Rodney Allan. 1707 GOLD DR, STE 101 58103 #037-01-1978 L1979 **IM EM** *020 †20

LUGER, Patrick A. 737 BROADWAY N, MERITCARE MEDICAL GROUP 58102 #037-01-1995 L1996 **IM** *020 †20

LUNDE, Lara Nicole. 2400 32ND AVE S 58103 #040-02-2000 L2003 **FM** *020 †18 ‡

LUNDEEN, Mark Allen. 2301 25TH ST S, ORTHOPAEDIC ASSOCIATES OF 58103 #048-12-1975 L1980 **ORS** *020 †40

LUZ, Aileen L. 2601 BROADWAY N 58102 #748-08-1992 L2002 **FM** *020 †18

LWIN, Htwe Htwe. 2101 ELM ST N, DEPT. OF VETERAN AFFAIRS 58102 #209-01-1991 L2001 **IM** *020 †20

LYSTAD, Jeffrey K. 801 BROADWAY N 58102 #037-01-1992 L1996 **EM** *020 †16

MACAULAY, Warren L. ■ 58102 #026-04-1943 L1943 **D** *071 †15

MADERA, George Jos. 3000 32ND AVE S, CARDIOLOGY - 4TH FLOOR 58103 #005-11-1977 L2007 **CD IM** *020 †20

MAGID, D Riva Bernstein. 737 BROADWAY N 58102 #041-07-1988 L2004 **AN** *020 †05

MAGURA, Connie Anne. 1720 UNIVERSITY DR S 58103 #062-01-1978 L1995 **FM** *020 †18

MAHALE, Adit Shrikrishna. 736 BROADWAY N 58102 #495-17-1997 L2004 **NEP** *020 †20

MAHONEY, Timothy James. 3000 32ND AVE S, INNOVIS HEALTH LLC 58103 #024-07-1974 L1975 **GS VS** *020 †85

MAINGI, Chetan Prakash. 2400 32ND AVE S 58103 #041-13-1998 L2006 **D** *100 †15

MALIK, Asif Raza. 1919 ELM ST N, UNIV ND DEPT PSYCH 58102 #704-21-2000 L2002 **P** *100 †75

MALTRY, Emile, Jr. ■ 58103 #021-01-1937 L1937 **U** *071 †95

MANESIS, John George. 737 BROADWAY N 58102 #030-06-1962 L1974 **R** *071 †20,80

MARCH, Barrie Leethem. 4801 AMBER VALLEY PKWY S, PRACS INSTITUTE, LTD 58104 #024-07-1968 L1979 **IM PHM** *062 †20

MARI, Justo Leon. ■ 58103 #748-01-1953 L1961 **FM** *071

MARSDEN, Richard James. 737 BROADWAY N, MERITCARE MEDICAL GROUP 58102 #048-15-1974 L1976 **R** *020 †80

MARSH, Julie A. 737 BROADWAY N, MERITCARE MEDICAL GROUP 58102 #037-01-1994 L1999 **PTH** *020 †50

MARTIN, J Tyler. 1711 GOLD DR, STE 160 58103 #030-05-1986 L1987 **ID PD** *020 †55

MARTIN, Tracy J. 1711 GOLD DR 58103 #037-01-1988 L1989 **FM** *020 †18

MARTINO, Robert Michael. 3838 12TH AVE N, SERVICES 58102 #030-06-1990 L1999 **FM FSM** *020 †18

MARTSCHING, Sandra Lee. 3000 32ND AVE S, URGENT CARE 58103 #037-01-1999 L2000 **FM** *020 †18

MARUBBIO, A Thos, Jr. 737 BROADWAY N 58102 #035-01-1960 L1978 **GE IM** *020 †20

MASON, Craig Mark. 2345 25TH ST S 58103 #008-01-1979 L2002 **OPH** *020 †35

MASTEL, Glenn A. 737 BROADWAY N 58102 #037-01-1990 L1991 **FM** *020 †18

MATHISON, Mark A. ■ 58103 #026-04-1965 L1979 **U** *071 †95

MATHISON, Susan M. 2700 12TH AVE SW, STE D 58103 #048-12-1990 L1997 **OTO FPS** *020 †45

MATTHEES, Donald John. 3000 32ND AVE S, DAKOTA CLINIC LTD INNOVIS 58103 #026-04-1977 L1981 **PUD CCM** *020 †20

MATTHYS, Gary A. 2301 25TH ST S STE I, MATTHYS ORTHOPAEDIC CENTER 58103 #037-01-1994 L2000 **ORS** *020 †40

MATZKE, Thomas Jarrad. 2400 32ND AVE S 58103 #037-01-2001 L2005 **D** *020 †15

MAUSBACH, Thomas Wm. DAKOTA CLIN/BOX 6001 58108 #048-04-1973 L1976 **PD** *020 †55

MAW, Soe Soe. 2101 ELM ST N 58102 #209-01-1990 L2000 **IM** *020 †20

MAYFIELD JORGENSEN, Michel. 100 4TH ST S 58103 #030-05-2001 L2006 **P** *020

MBOUNI ESSOMBA, Marie. 801 BROADWAY N 58102 #217-01-1993 L2002 **AN** *020 †05 ‡

MC LEAN, Andrew. 2624 9TH AVE S 58103 #037-01-1987 L1992 **P** *020 †75

MCNAB, Brian Douglas. 100 4TH ST S # 604 58103 #068-01-1990 L1999 **PUD** *100 †20

MC NAMARA, David Richard. 736 BROADWAY N 58102 #016-43-1996 L2006 **ID** *020 †20

MENDEZ, Alejandro. 801 BROADWAY N 58102 #231-03-1988 L2003 **NS** *020

MENDOZA, Eusebio Reyes. 100 4TH ST S 58103 #748-07-1955 L1971 **IM** *072

MICKELSON, Daniel G. 737 BROADWAY N, MERITCARE MEDICAL CENTER 58102 #037-01-1984 L1989 **DR** *030 †80

MICKELSON, Margaret T. 801 BROADWAY N 58102 #026-04-1994 L1998 **OBG** *020 †30

MIKS, George Martin. 512 1ST AVE N, RED RIVER WOMEN'S CLINIC 58102 #056-06-1963 L1981 **FM GP** *020 †18

MILES, James Verner, Jr. 1702 UNIVERSITY DR S 58103 #041-01-1947 L1949 **PD** *020 †55

MILLER, Ron Harold. 801 BROADWAY N 58102 #018-03-1971 L1977 **PD IM** *020 †55

MISTRY, Bhanu Odedra. 2400 32ND AVE S 58103 #496-01-1989 L2001 **IM** *020 †20

MISTRY, Bhargav Mangaldas. 801 BROADWAY N 58102 #496-01-1985 L2000 **GS TTS** *020 †85

MITCHELL, James Edward. 100 4TH ST S, STE 204 58103 #016-06-1972 L1996 **P** *050 †75

MITCHELL, Steven L. 737 BROADWAY N, MERITCARE MEDICAL GROUP 58102 #037-01-1982 L1983 **RNR DR** *020 †80

MOE, Jason Thomas. 1720 UNIVERSITY DR S 58103 #037-01-1998 L1999 **FM** *020 †18

MOHIUDDIN, Mohammed Taj. PO BOX 9678 58106 #495-65-1972 L1979 **AN** *020 †05

MONSON, Timothy Paul. 801 BROADWAY N 58102 #046-01-1982 L1987 **GS** *020 †18,85

MONTGOMERY, Robert C. 801 BROADWAY N 58102 #018-03-1960 L1967 **PD MDM** *020 †55

MOORE, Thomas Aquinas. 2101 ELM ST N 58102 #021-05-1959 L1995 **CHP ADP** *020

MOPARTY, Visweswara R. 600 4TH ST S FP CTR 58103 #495-50-1976 **FM** *100

MORAGHAN, Thomas Jos. 2400 32ND AVE S 58103 #037-01-1989 L2004 **END IM** *020 †20

MORALES, Ralph E. ■ 58103 #308-02-1985 L2008 **CD IM** *020 †20

MULDER, Jeffrey Donaldson. 600 4TH ST S, EASTEN CLINIC 58103 #060-01-1992 L1996 **FM** *100 †18

MUNOZ, Juan Manuel. 2400 32ND AVE S 58103 #737-01-1970 L1976 **END NTR** *020 †20

MUNSHI, Miraj-U-Din. ■ 58103 #495-04-1963 L1999 **IM** *100 †20

MUSACCHIA, Thomas X. 2101 ELM ST N, VETERANS HOSPITAL 58102 #028-03-1980 L1987 **GS VS** *020 †85

MUTCHLER, Scott Bradley. 3000 32ND AVE S, DAKOTA CLINIC, LTD INNOVI 58103 #011-02-1976 L1988 **PD CCP** *020 †55

MUTHYALA, Suneetha. 720 4TH ST N 58122 #495-58-2000 L2007 **IM** *012

MYUNG, Chang Ryul. 801 BROADWAY N 58102 #583-22-1989 L2003 **AN** *020 †05 ‡

NAGALLA, Srikanth. RESIDENCY-MERITCARE HEALTH, UND 58122 #495-04-2001 L2004 **HO** *012 †20

NAGPAL, Vandana. 3000 32ND AVE SW 58103 #495-43-1997 L2004 **IM** *020 †20

NAKASATO GUEVARA, Yuri. 2400 32ND AVE S 58103 #737-06-1995 L2007 **FPG** *020 †20

NAMILE, Shanti Sree. PO BOX MC, MERITCARE MEDICAL CENTER # 58122 #495-65-2003 L2007 **IM** *012
NAMMOUR, Fadel Elias. 3000 32ND AVE SW 58103 #605-02-1995 L2002 **GE** *020 †20
NASEER, Osama Bin. 1720 UNIVERSITY DR S 58103 #704-20-1995 L2002 **FM UCM** *020 †18
NEKKANTI, Sonie. 801 BROADWAY N 58102 #495-11-1997 L2003 **AN** *020 †05 ‡
NELSEN, Matthew John. 2301 25TH ST S, ORTHOPAEDIC ASSOCIATES OF 58103 #037-01-1997 L2003 **ORS** *020 †40
NELSON, Bruce Allen. 1717 UNIVERSITY DR S 58103 #028-02-1975 L1979 **OPH** *071 †35 ‡
NELSON, Roald Allen. VA MED CTR 58102 #018-03-1958 L1981 **PUD IM** *040 †20
NELSON, Stephen Neale. 801 BROADWAY N 58102 #019-02-1979 L1990 **NPM** *020 †55
NELSON, Susan Kay. 600 4TH ST S 58103 #037-01-1994 L1996 **FM OBS** *020 †18
NESS, Mary Margo. ■ 58104 #037-01-2008 *012
NEUMANN, James Leslie. 1707 GOLD DR S 58103 #037-01-1995 L1996 **IM** *020 †20
NEWMAN, David William. ■ 58102 #037-01-2007 L2007 *012
NEWMAN, Roxanne Vera. 801 BROADWAY N 58102 #038-44-1986 L1993 **GS** *020 †90,85
NEWMAN, William Peter. 737 BROADWAY N 58102 #048-13-1974 L1981 **END** *020 †20
NGUYEN, Son Thanh. 3000 32ND AVE S, DAKOTA CLINIC 58103 #048-13-1994 L2001 **U** *020 †95
NICHOLS, Ned B. 404 8TH ST S 58103 #026-04-1963 L1993 **IM ID** *030 †20
NOAH, Thomas Anthony. 737 BROADWAY N, MERITCARE MEDICAL GROUP 58102 #037-01-1992 L1998 **U** *020 †95
NORBERG, Alonna K. 100 4TH ST S, STE 410 58103 #037-01-1996 L2002 **PEM** *020 †55
NORBERG, Jon David. 3270 20TH ST S 58104 #037-01-1996 L2002 **ORS HS** *020 †40
NOUR EL-DEEN, Hatem Ahmed. 510 4TH ST S, PRAIRIE ST. JOHN'S CLINIC 58103 #915-02-1993 L2003 **P** *020 †75
NUNES, Richard Julian. ■ 58103 #005-19-1998 L2008 **CHP** *020 †75
NYHUS, Curtis Carl. 1720 UNIVERSITY DR S 58103 #037-01-1977 L1980 **FM** *020 †18
OANCIA, Tammy Lynne. 100 4TH ST S # 604 58103 #060-02-1994 L1999 **IM** *100 †20
OBOH-WEILKE, Aruoriwo M. 1702 UNIVERSITY DR S 58103 #033-06-1997 L2004 **OPH** *020 †35
O'HEARN, Jerome Wm. ■ 58102 #026-04-1956 L1963 **OTO** *071 †45
OHRT, Harry Allan. ■ 58104 #062-01-1949 L1949 **R** *071
OLAFSON, Richard Arlan. ■ 58103 #041-01-1959 L1965 **NS** *071 †25
OLIN, Ronald. 737 BROADWAY N 58102 #062-01-1959 L1960 **IM** *071
OLIVER, Donald Cross. ■ 58104 #803-03-1954 L1971 **GP** *071
OLSON, Robert Jos, Jr. 100 4TH ST S 58103 #037-01-1985 L1989 **P PYG** *020 †75
OPGRANDE, John Donald. 2301 25TH ST S, STE G 58103 #019-02-1967 L1974 **HS ORS** *020 †40
ORSON, Gregory Glen. 737 BROADWAY N 58102 #026-08-1983 L1988 **ORS** *020 †40
ORTMEIER, Thomas C. 737 BROADWAY N, MERITCARE MEDICAL GROUP 58102 #046-01-1996 L2000 **PTH** *020 †50
OSTLIE, Daniel Keith. 2400 32ND AVE S 58103 #046-01-1996 L2001 **ISM** *020 †18
OTERO-CAGIDE, Manuel R. 801 BROADWAY N 58102 #649-01-1979 L1990 **CD ICE** *020 †20
OUANO, Francisco V. 737 BROADWAY N 58102 #748-11-1964 L1991 **R** *020
PARKS, J Scott. 801 BROADWAY N 58102 #037-01-1988 L1991 **EM** *020 †16
PARVATHAREDDY, Vishnupriya. 2400 32ND AVE S 58103 #495-62-1991 L2003 **IM** *020 †20
PASYA, Suresh Kumar Reddy. 801 BROADWAY N 58102 #495-21-2000 L2007 **IM** *100 †20
PATRON, Roberto L. 3000 32ND AVE S, DAKOTA CLINIC LTD 58103 #264-04-1992 L2000 **ID** *020 †20
PATWA, Premal Rajnibhai. 1919 ELM ST N, UND DEPT OF NEUROSCIENCE 58102 #495-22-1996 L2006 **P** *012
PEARSON, Joanne Margaret. 218 15TH AVE N 58102 #026-04-1972 L1984 **CHP P** *020 †75
PEARSON, Patricia George. 801 BROADWAY N 58102 #005-12-1988 L1992 **AN PME** *020 †05
PERENCEVIC, Boris. 3000 32ND AVE S, DAKOTA CLINIC 58103 #957-01-1972 L2002 **AN** *020 †05
PETERS, Shannon Marie. ■ 58104 #037-01-2008 *012
PETERSON, Jeffrey A. 3290 20TH ST S, STE A 58104 #037-01-1991 L1992 **FM** *020 †18
PHADKE, Gautam Mukund. PO BOX MC, MERITCARE MEDICAL CENTER # 58122 #496-46-2001 L2006 **IM** *012
PIATT, Bruce Eric. 3000 32ND AVE S, DAKOTA CLINIC, LTD. INNO 58103 #007-02-1989 L1997 **OSM** *020 †40
PIERCE, Christopher Loren. 801 BROADWAY N 58102 #037-01-1995 L1996 **ICE** *020 †20
PITTS, Bruce Gordon. 737 BROADWAY N 58102 #041-01-1976 L1979 **IM GP** *030 †20
POINDEXTER, Marlin H, Jr. ■ 58102 #019-02-1938 L1945 **PD** *071 †55
PORTER, William Calvin. 100 4TH ST S, STE 418 58103 #048-13-1983 L1988 **OTO** *020 †45
POST, Gregory John. 737 BROADWAY N 58102 #055-01-1974 L1979 **U** *075 †95
PRAMHUS, C Gary. 4344 20TH AVE SW 58103 #016-06-1969 L1977 **OPH** *020 †35
PROANO, Maritza. 737 BROADWAY N 58102 #035-01-1984 L2006 **GE IM** *020 †20
PROMERSBERGER, Eric R. 737 BROADWAY N, MERITCARE MEDICAL GROUP 58102 #037-01-1995 L2000 **DR** *020 †80
PULLEN, Samantha Kae. ■ 58102 #037-01-2007 L2007 **TY** *012
QADIR, Abdul. 1919 ELM ST N 58102 #704-02-2001 L2004 **P** *012
QARNI, Ahmer Hussain. 4474 23RD AVE S, STE M 58104 #704-02-1990 L1999 **NEP** *020 †20
RADKE-HELLA, Michelle M. 1711 GOLD DR S, STE 160 58103 #037-01-1997 L2000 **FM** *020 †18
RADTKE, Wallace Edward. 801 BROADWAY N 58102 #030-05-1970 L1976 **CD IM** *020 †20
RAGAN, John Jos. 3000 32ND AVE SW 58103 #035-09-1990 L2002 **CD** *020 †20
RAJENDER, Settihalli. 3000 32ND AVE SW, DAKOTA CLINIC AT INNOVIS 58103 #495-52-1981 L1997 **GE** *020 †20
RAMLO, John Hale. ■ 58106 #056-05-1960 L1971 **OTO HNS** *071 †45
RASOOL VALI, Zulfikar Ali. 1919 ELM ST N, UND DEPT OF NEUROSCIENCE 58102 #495-74-1988 L2004 **P** *012
RATNASAMY, D M Daniel. ■ 58104 #495-16-1953 L1974 **GP PD** *071 †55
RAU, Keith D. 1702 UNIVERSITY DR S, DAKOTA CLINIC LTD 58103 #037-01-1983 L1984 **IM** *020 †20
RAUM, Jennifer Diane. 2400 32ND AVE S 58103 #037-01-2001 L2001 **IM** *020
REYNOLDS, Jeffrey Carl. 737 BROADWAY N 58102 #019-02-1964 L1987 **OTO HNS** *020 †45
RICE, Jon Richard. 4510 13TH AVE SW, BC/BS OF ND 58121 #048-13-1972 L1975 **MDM FM** *030 †18
RODENBIKER, Harold T, Jr. 100 4TH ST S STE 612 58103 #003-01-1980 L1984 **OPH** *020 †35
RODGERS-RIEGER, Eleana Ro. 737 BROADWAY N 58102 #037-01-2003 L2007 **PTH** *020
ROE, James Burton. 2400 32ND AVE S 58103 #005-15-1972 L2004 **ORS** *040 †40
ROEMBACH, Jeanine L. 100 4TH ST S 58103 #019-02-1975 L1997 **CHP P** *020 †75
ROERS, Stacy Lee. ■ 58104 #037-01-2008 *012
ROESLER, Sean E. 2400 32ND AVE S, MERITCARE SOUTHPOINTE 58103 #037-01-1998 L1999 **FM** *020 †18
ROHLA, Richard Allen. 1702 UNIVERSITY DR S 58103 #037-01-1979 L1980 **FM** *020 †18
RONDEAU, Denise M. 801 BROADWAY N 58102 #037-01-1994 L2002 **OBG** *020 †30
RONDEAU, Jeffrey Allen. 801 BROADWAY N 58102 #023-12-1994 L2004 **OBG** *020 †30
ROSTAD, Christina Terese. 2400 32ND AVE S, MERITCARE S POINTE 58103 #037-01-1995 L1997 **FM** *020 †18
RUGGABER, Garren Carlton. 4415 OAKCREEK DR S 58104 #056-06-1974 L1991 **DR** *020 †80
RUSSELL, Howard Linward. 1702 UNIVERSITY DR S, DAKOTA CLINIC, LTD. 58103 #036-01-1978 L1986 **HO ON** *020 †20
SABERI, Akiko. 2101 ELM ST N 58102 #572-47-1970 L1981 **PTH** *020 †50
SALAMANCA, Jose E. ■ 58103 #748-10-1965 L1974 **R NM** *020
SAMPSON, Jerome Matthew. 1702 UNIVERSITY DR S 58103 #048-04-1978 L1982 **DR** *062 †80
SAMPSON, Steven M. 1720 UNIVERSITY DR S, MERITCARE SOUTH UNIVERSITY 58103 #037-01-1993 L1994 **EM** *020 †18
SANAULLAH, Mohamed. 801 BROADWAY N 58102 #496-27-1998 L2003 **IM** *020
SANDA, Janelle Christine. 737 BROADWAY N, FARGO CLINIC LTD 58102 #037-01-1981 L1984 **IM** *020 †20
SAPIEGA, Vytautas. 801 BROADWAY N 58102 #913-49-1995 L2003 **CCP** *020 †55
SAPIEGIENE, Lina. 801 BROADWAY N 58102 #913-49-1995 L2003 **NPM** *020 †55
SARDA, Rakshak. 801 BROADWAY N 58102 #495-55-1992 L2005 **CD** *020 †20
SAUTER, Brian Alexander. 3000 32ND AVE SW, DAKOTA CLINIC LTD 58103 #016-43-1994 L2002 **EM** *020 †16
SCHAFF, Troy Cordell. 801 BROADWAY N 58102 #026-04-1996 L1999 **EM** *020 †16
SCHELL, Debra Ann. 720 4TH ST N, MERITCARE MED CTR 58122 #037-01-1997 L1998 **IM** *020 †20
SCHENCK, Jason Merle. 3000 32ND AVE S, DAKOTA CLINIC/INNOVIS HOSP 58103 #037-01-2003 L2006 **EM** *020 †16
SCHLECHT, Kristina Angel. 2710 BROADWAY N, NORTHPORT SHOPPING CENTER 58102 #037-01-1996 L1997 **FM** *020 †18
SCHLOSSER, Michael J. 801 BROADWAY N 58102 #037-01-1987 L1988 **EM** *020 †18
SCHOCK, Joel F. 3280 20TH ST S, PLAINS MEDICAL CTR 58104 #037-01-1982 L1983 **FM** *020 †18
SEBONEGO, Mpho Peter. 720 4TH ST N 58122 #305-01-2002 L2002 **IM** *100 †20
SEE, Jay Kwan. 801 BROADWAY N 58102 #748-10-1992 L2007 **ID IM** *020 †20
SEN, Kaushik. 1702 UNIVERSITY DR S 58103 #495-39-1988 L2001 **HO** *020 †20
SEPE, Frank Jos. 737 BROADWAY N, FARGO CLINIC 58102 #037-01-1984 L1987 **IM** *020 †20
SETTERBERG, Maryjane. 6245 16TH ST S 58104 #037-01-2000 L2001 **IM** *020
SHAFFER, Tracie M. ■ 58103 #037-01-2002 L2002 **FM** *020 †18
SHAHIRA, Eram. 801 BROADWAY N 58102 #495-21-2003 L2004 **IM** *020 †20
SHAIKH, Muhammed Akhtar. 2101 ELM ST N, VA HOSPITAL 58102 #704-16-1989 L2001 **IM** *020 †20
SHAKER, Mohammad Reza. 737 BROADWAY N 58102 #048-04-1994 L2000 **OTO** *020 †45
SHAMDAS, Glenn. 2101 ELM ST N, 11C-O 58102 #847-21-1980 L1993 **HEM ON** *020 †20
SHANAAH, Almothana Mahmou. 801 BROADWAY N 58102 #575-02-1997 L2006 **CCM** *100 †20
SHARMA, Sanjeev Kumar. ■ 58103 #495-03-1989 L1997 **P** *020
SHASH, Taysir. 801 BROADWAY N 58102 #286-05-1990 L2007 **NPM** *020 †55
SHELDON, Michael Scott. 1702 UNIVERSITY DR S, DAKOTA CLINIC, LTD. 58103 #037-01-1992 L1996 **IM** *020 †20
SHELDON, Peggy Ann. 736 BROADWAY, MERITCARE MED GRP 58122 #037-01-1979 L1980 **IM** *020 †20
SHER, Mos. 3000 32ND AVE S 58103 #517-01-1961 L2003 **TS GS** *020 †85,90
SHOOK, Dale Ray. 2301 25TH ST S, INDEPENDENT RADIOLOGY SERV 58103 #024-07-1972 L1976 **R** *020 †80
SHOOK, Lester Dale. ■ 58103 #016-11-1947 L1948 **R** *071 †80
SHOOK, Robert Jay. 2301 25TH ST S 58103 #037-01-1979 L1983 **R** *020
SHUJA, Khawaja Fauzia. ■ 58103 #704-02-1999 L2004 **IM** *020 †20
SIEMENS, Charlotte Anne. 2624 9TH AVE S 58103 #019-02-1987 L1992 **CHP** *020 †75
SIKKINK, Kari Newquist. 3000 32ND AVE S, URGENT CARE 58103 #026-04-1989 L2001 **FM** *020 †18
SIMPAO, Louella Pineda. 2101 ELM ST N, FARGO VA MEDICAL CENTER 58102 #748-10-1992 L2003 **CHP** *062
SIMPSON, Michael Blair. 2400 32ND AVE S 58103 #016-06-1985 L2006 **ORS** *020 †40
SKOGEN, Jeffrey Wayne. ■ 58102 #026-04-2000 L2006 **NEP** *100
SLECKMAN, Joseph Brian. 1702 UNIVERSITY DR S, DAKOTA CLINIC LTD 58103 #165-07-1978 L1983 **RHU IM** *020 †20
SMEGO, Raymond A, Jr. ■ 58102 #033-05-1978 L2002 **ID IM** *050 †20
SNOW, Denise Suzanne. 820 4TH ST N 58102 #026-08-1996 L2004 **HO** *020 †20
SOINE, Lesley Anne. 1800 21ST AVE S 58103 #037-01-2000 L2005 **OTO FPS** *020 †45
SOLLOM, Dennis Gene. 1702 UNIVERSITY DR S, INNOVIS HEALTH 58103 #037-01-1980 L1986 **PM** *020 †60
SOMPUR VASANTHKUMAR, Sushi. 1919 ELM ST N, UND DEPT OF NEUROSCIENCE 58102 #495-09-2005 L2007 **P** *012
SONDREAL, Philip Steen. 3290 20TH ST S STE A, URGENT MEDICINE ASSOCIATES 58104 #037-01-1988 L1989 **FM** *020 †18
SORGEN, Irving David. 2701 13TH AVE S, MERITCARE CLINIC SOUTHWEST 58103 #047-06-1965 L1972 **OPH** *071 †35
SORNSON, Michael David. 3000 32ND AVE S 58103 #054-04-1998 L2008 **AN** *020
SPELLMAN, Stephen Jos. 737 BROADWAY N, MERITCARE MEDICAL GROUP 58102 #067-01-1971 L1977 **GE IM** *020 †20
SPIES, Harold W. ■ 58103 #010-01-1946 L1947 **OM IM** *071
SPRENGER, Craig Randall. 737 BROADWAY N, MENTAL HEALTH DEPARTMENT 58102 #037-01-1992 L1995 **IM** *020 †20
SPUR, John. ■ 58102 #154-01-1951 L1984 **GS** *071
SPURBECK, George Headley. ■ 58102 #056-06-1944 L1945 **IM** *030
SRIVATSA, Sanjay Surath. 3000 32ND AVE S, MCFARLAND CLINIC,PC 58103 #917-03-1987 L2007 **CD IC** *020 †20
STAAHL, Gustav Edmund, Jr. 1702 UNIVERSITY DR S, INNOVIS HEALTH 58103 #016-43-1971 L1977 **AN CCA** *020 †05 ‡
STALLMAN, Donald J. 737 BROADWAY N, MERITCARE MEDICAL GROUP 58102 #037-01-1989 L1996 **DR** *020 †80,28
STANLEY, Jeffrey John. 737 BROADWAY N, 737 BROADWAY 58102 #016-11-1993 L2003 **OTO** *020 †45
STANLEY, Kate Peterson. 801 BROADWAY N 58102 #018-03-1997 L2003 **NPM** *020 †55
STARR, Daniel Curtis. PO BOX MC, MERITCARE MEDICAL CENTER # 58122 #037-01-2006 L2006 **IM** *012
STAVENGER, Jeffrey Paul. 2301 25TH ST S, ORTHOPAEDIC ASSOCIATES OF 58103 #046-01-1979 L1984 **ORS** *020 †40

■ = Address Information Privacy Protected

STEEN, Preston Douglas. 820 4TH ST NORTH 58122 #026-04-1984 L1990 **HO PLM** *020 †20
STEVENS, Charles A, Jr. ■ 58103 #035-20-1953 L1964 **OBG GP** *071 †30
STEWART, W John. 2400 32ND AVE S 58103 #037-01-1977 L1980 **IM** *020 †20
STIRLING, Lisa Ann. ■ 58103 #026-04-2007 L2007 **TY** *012
STOE, Anne H. 2624 9TH AVE S 58103 #023-01-1980 L1981 **P** *020 †18,75
STORM, Waldemar George. 801 BROADWAY N 58102 #037-01-1980 L1986 **CCP** *020 †55
STOVER, David Allen. 801 BROADWAY N 58102 #026-04-1994 L2000 **GS** *020 †85
STOY, Sean Patrick. ■ 58103 #037-01-2008 *012
STRINDEN, Steven Paul. 414 8TH AVE S 58103 #016-43-1978 L1983 **U** *020 †95
STRINDEN, Thomas I. 1717 UNIVERSITY DR S 58103 #037-01-1988 L1995 **OPH** *020 †35
STROMSTAD, Stephen Arnold. 801 BROADWAY N 58102 #048-04-1975 L1980 **VS GS** *020 †85
STRONG, Jennifer Ann. 2400 32ND AVE S 58103 #037-01-2002 L2006 **FM** *020 †18
SUBBARAYAN, Sreevidya Kan. PO BOX MC, MERITCARE MEDICAL CENTER # 58122
    #496-35-2001 L2005 **IM** *012
SWAMI, Swati Sunil. 737 BROADWAY N 58102 #495-17-1988 L2004 **AN** *020
SWENSEN, Eric Carl. 1919 ELM ST N, UNIVERSITY OF NORTH DAKOTA 58102
    #037-01-2002 L2002 **P** *020
TADROS, Nader Boulos. 3000 32ND AVE S, INNOVIS HOSPITAL 58103 #915-02-1971 L1988
    TS *020 †85,90
TADROS, Sherine Wahba. ■ 58104 #915-04-1985 L2000 **IM** *020 †20
TAHERI, Arezoo. 300 MAIN AVE STE 303, FARGO GASTOENTEROLOGY AND 58103
    #517-08-1982 L1993 **IM GE** *020 †20
TALBOT, James Milton. 737 BROADWAY N, BOX 2067 58102 #030-05-1970 L1972 **FM** *020
TAMMINEEDI, Srinivas. 801 BROADWAY N 58102 #495-11-1996 L2003 **AN** *020 †05 ‡
TATE, John Michael. 820 N 4TH ST 58122 #037-01-1991 L2000 **HO** *020 †20
TAYLOR, Joseph Cree. 1702 UNIVERSITY DR S, DAKOTA CLINIC 58103 #038-41-1967 L2003
    U GS *071 †95
TEEGAVARAPU, Purnima Srav. PO BOX MC, MERITCARE MEDICAL CENTER # 58122
    #495-73-2002 L2007 **IM** *012
TEIGEN, Corey Lee. 801 BROADWAY N 58102 #023-07-1990 L1995 **VIR DR** *020 †80
TELLO-SKJERSETH, Christina. ■ 58103 #037-01-2007 L2007 **TY** *012
TERSTRIEP, Shelby A. 820 4TH ST N 58102 #028-46-2001 L2007 **IM** *100
TESKE, Owen Garth. 801 BROADWAY N 58102 #037-01-1980 L1981 **EM** *040 †16
THEIGE, David J. 801 BROADWAY N 58102 #037-01-1985 L1987 **IM** *020 †20
THOMAS, John Martin. 1701 38TH ST S, HOSPICE OF THE RED RIVER V 58103
    #026-04-1972 L1973 **FM PLM** *020 †18
THOMPSON, George R. PO BOX 2067 58107 #025-01-1946 L1948 **OBG** *071 †30
THOMPSON, Jody Rochele. 737 BROADWAY N 58102 #037-01-1997 L2000 **IM** *020 †20
THOMPSON, Stanley Dean. 737 BROADWAY N 58102 #041-01-1959 L1960 **DR** *071 †80
THURLOW, Brenda K. 801 BROADWAY N 58102 #037-01-1999 L2003 **PD** *020 †55
TIESZEN, Mark Jos. 801 BROADWAY N 58102 #046-01-1988 L1993 **CCM** *020 †20
TIGHT, Robert Raymond. 736 BROADWAY N, BROADWAY HLTH CTR #51 58102
    #035-45-1967 L1981 **ID IM** *020 †20
TILCHEN, Eugene Jos. 2101 ELM ST N 58102 #025-07-1975 L1976 **ON** *020 †20
TILLISCH, Janet Sturgeon. 3000 32ND AVE S, DAKOTA CLINIC LTD INNOVI 58103
    #019-02-1975 L1979 **PD PHO** *020 †20
TILLOTSON, Joan Nesmith. P B 5313 NDSU STUD HTH CTR 58105 #035-20-1956 L1968
    OS *071
TINGUELY, Stephen Jos. 801 BROADWAY N 58102 #037-01-1978 L1981 **PD** *020 †55
TINJUM, John Michael. ■ 58103 #030-06-2007 L2007 **TY** *012
TIONGSON, Christopher H. 801 BROADWAY N 58102 #037-01-1993 L2002 **PD** *020 †55
TOUMEH, Mohamed Samir. ■ 58104 #875-02-1990 L2005 **IM** *012
TRAN, De Quang. 2101 ELM ST N STE 112, FARGO V A MED CTR 58102 #030-01-1995 L2007
    CRS GS *020 †85 ‡
TRAYNOR, Michael D. 801 BROADWAY N 58102 #037-01-1986 L1993 **GS** *020 †85
TSEN, David Weiching. 1702 UNIVERSITY DR S 58103 #048-13-1988 L1993 **OTO** *020 †45
TWOBEARS, Shantell M. 300 MAIN AVE STE 200, RED RIVER FAMILY MEDICINE 58103
    #037-01-1996 L1997 **FM** *020 †18
UPPALA, Saritha. 1919 ELM ST N, UND DEPT OF NEUROSCIENCE 58102 #495-98-2000 L2007
    P *012
URAL, William F. ■ 58103 #041-01-1966 L1967 **U** *020 †95
VAN EERDEN, Peter. 737 BROADWAY N 58102 #041-07-1992 L2008 **OBG MFM** *020 †30
VAN GELOVEN LYTLE, F. 3000 32ND AVE S, DAKOTA CLINIC/INNOVIS HEAL 58103
    #660-04-1976 L2007 **ORS** *020 †40
VICK, Sarah Jean. 801 BROADWAY N 58122 #037-01-2001 L2001 **PD** *020 †55
VIJAYALAKSHMI, Bangalore. 1702 UNIVERSITY DR S, DAKOTA CLINIC S UNIV 58103
    #496-39-1995 L2004 **PM** *020 †60
VILENSKI, Leonid. 801 BROADWAY N 58102 #654-01-1999 L2001 **IM** *020 †20
VINYCH, John Victor. 1702 UNIVERSITY DR S, DAKOTA CLINIC LTD 58103 #007-02-1988 L1995
    AN *020 †05
VIRDEE, Harjinder Kaur. 2704 BROADWAY N STE C 58102 #917-04-1977 L1992 **P PFP** *020 †75
VO, Timothy Thanh. 2101 ELM ST N, VAMC 58102 #942-01-1978 L1996 **P** *020 †75
VOLK, James Anthony. 801 BROADWAY N 58102 #037-01-1984 L1997 **IM** *075 †20
VON RUEDEN, Michelle M. 3027 23RD AVE S, UNIT C 58103 #037-01-1983 L1985
    FM EM *020 †18
VOTAVA, Henry John. 737 BROADWAY N 58102 #028-02-1976 L1979 **PTH** *020 †50 ‡
WAGNER, James Steven. 3000 32ND AVE S, DAKOTA CLINIC, LTD. INNOV 58103
    #026-08-1983 L1990 **GS VS** *020 †85 ‡
WAGNER, Philip Carl. 801 BROADWAY N 58102 #056-06-1967 L1974 **R** *020
WAGNER, Todd Emmit. ■ 58103 #037-01-2008 *012
WALKER, Debra J. 306 4TH ST N 58102 #026-04-1984 L1985 **FM** *020 †18
WEBER, Ian C. 2400 32ND AVE S 58103 #048-13-2000 L2007 **ORS** *020
WEINER, Michael Julian. 737 BROADWAY N, FARGO CLINIC 58102 #038-41-1972 L1978
    DR VIR *020 †80
WELLE, Patrick Jos. 2701 13TH AVE S, MERITCARE CLINIC SW 58103 #016-11-1979 L1983
    PD NPM *020 †55
WELLER, Maria L. PO BOX MC, MERITCARE HEALTH SYS 58122 #037-01-1990 L2003
    PD *020 †55
WELLS, Orvis Merlin. 3000 32ND AVE S, DAKOTA CLINIC LTD 58103 #038-41-1966 L1989
    OBG *020 †20
WESSMAN, Kari Huseby. 801 BROADWAY N 58102 #026-04-1992 L1996 **OBG** *020 †30
WIEST, David Lee. 2301 25TH ST S, ORTHOPAEDIC ASSOCIATES OF 58103 #025-01-1981 L1986
    ORS *020 †40
WIEST, Eric. ■ 58103 #037-01-2008 *012
WIISANEN, Ronald Evert. 600 4TH ST S 58103 #026-04-1978 L1979 **FM** *020 †18

WYNNE, Joshua. 801 BROADWAY N 58102 #024-05-1971 L2005 **CD IM** *020 †20
YADLAPALLI, Swarna Latha. 3000 32ND AVE S, INNOVIS URGENT CARE CLINIC 58103
    #495-50-1994 L2000 **FM** *020 †18
YALAMANCHILI, Lalitha. 100 4TH ST S, PROF BLDG STE 309 58103 #495-50-1979 L1983
    IM *020 †20
YALAMANCHILI, Prasad S. 100 4TH ST S STE 205 58103 #495-21-1974 L1983 **AN** *020
YEW, Haseong. 2601 UNIVERSITY DR N 58102 #583-02-1978 L1988 **FM EM** *075 †18
YOHE, Mark Gregory. 720 4TH ST N, MERITCARE MED CTR 58122 #665-01-2005 L2005 **IM** *012
YOUCK, Lila Virginia. 600 4TH ST S 58103 #068-01-1964 **FM** *020 †18
YVORCHUK, Wm Alexander. 3270 20TH ST S, PLASTIC SURGERY INSTITUTE 58104
    #067-01-1981 L2004 **PS HS** *020 †65,85
ZIMNY, Matthew Henry. ■ 58104 #037-01-2008 *012
ZOGG, Donald Louis. 737 BROADWAY N, MERIT CARE MEDICAL GROUP 58102
    #028-34-1981 L1982 **GE IM** *020 †20
ZOUAIN, Nicolas Georges. 820 4TH ST N, MERITCARE ROGER HARIS CANC 58122
    #605-02-1998 L2005 **IM** *020 †20,80

FORT RANSOM – RANSOM

THORFINNSON, Hugh Dennis. ■ 58033 #016-11-1956 L1963 **GS** *071 †85

FORT TOTTEN – BENSON

GAID, Emmanuel A. ■ 58335 #748-09-1969 L1986 **FM** *020

FORT YATES – SIOUX

ORTIZ, Angel Rafael. PO BOX J, USPH SVS INDIANA HOSPITAL 58538 #308-01-1967 L1975
    GS *020
ROLDAN-MARTINEZ, Pedro A. PO BOX J 58538 #042-04-1991 L1995 **FM IM** *020 †18

GARDNER – CASS

BURNS, Karl F, Jr. ■ 58036 #038-41-1952 L1952 **GP** *071 †18

GARRISON – MCLEAN

CARLSON, Joseph W. 437 3RD AVE SE, BONE & JOINT CENTER 58540 #037-01-1989 L1994
    ORS *020 †40
CULLY, Gregory Peter. ■ 58540 #060-01-1972 L1995 *100
FOX, Abe Lewis, Jr. ■ 58540 #026-04-1963 L1982 **PTH** *071 †50
HARCHENKO, Vern Allen. 437 3RD AVE SE, GARRISON FAMILY CLINIC 58540
    #422-01-1994 L1997 **FM** *020 †18
LEONARD, Kermit. 407 3RD AVE SE 58540 #030-05-1946 L1961 **FM** *072 †18

GLEN ULLIN – MORTON

HSU, George S. 602 E ASH AVE, GLEN ULLIN/ELGIN CLINICS 58631 #037-01-1984 L1985
    FM *020 †18

GRAFTON – WALSH

ANCHETA, Silvestre Moises. ■ 58237 #748-01-1960 *074
CHEEMA, Gurnam Singh. 164 W 13TH ST 58237 #495-03-1975 L1987 **OBG** *020 †30
HAFEEZ, Abdul. 155 W 14TH ST, GRAFTON FAMILY CLN 58237 #704-04-1965 L1975
    FM IM *020 †18 ‡
KOTNIK, Anthony James. 155 W 14TH ST 58237 #026-04-1973 L1982 **FM** *020 †18
OMOTUNDE, Joshua Olusesan. 164 W 13TH ST, UNITY MEDICAL CENTER 58237
    #690-01-1986 L1996 **FM** *020 †18
OMOTUNDE, Olukayode Saml. 164 W 13TH ST, GRAFTON FAMILY CLINIC 58237
    #690-01-1970 L1989 **GP GS** *020 †18
SCHEFLO, Myron Wayne. ■ 58237 #030-05-1961 L1963 **GP** *071 †18
VITUMS, Arvids. 333 EASTERN AVE # 40 58237 #594-01-1933 **IM GP** *071

GRAND FORKS – GRAND FORKS

AAFEDT, Bradley Chas. 1000 S COLUMBIA RD 58201 #026-04-1990 L1995 **DR** *020 †80
ADAMS, Eddie L. 3035 DEMERS AVE, VALLEY BONE & JOINT CLINIC 58201 #037-01-1984 L1991
    ORS GS *020 †40
AFZAL, Adeel. 501 N COLUMBIA RD 58203 #704-02-2001 L2005 **IM** *020
ALLEN, Jon W. 1000 S COLUMBIA RD 58201 #037-01-1984 L1987 **IM** *040 †20
ANTONENKO, David Ronald. 1000 S COLUMBIA RD 58201 #060-01-1968 L1990 **GS TRS** *020
APOLINARIO-DUALAN, Aileen. ■ 58201 #748-02-1992 L1994 **PD** *020 †55
AVERY, Karilyn Kay. 1000 S COLUMBIA RD 58201 #037-01-2002 L2005 **PD** *020 †55
BAIG, Mirza Mukarram Ali. 501 N COLUMBIA RD 58203 #495-73-2002 **IM** *012
BAKKE, Eric L. 1380 S COLUMBIA RD, MEDICINE CENTER 58201 #037-01-1988 L1989
    FM *020 †18
BANSAL, Arvind Kumar. 1000 S COLUMBIA RD 58201 #495-29-1997 L2007 **PCC** *020 †20
BANSAL, Ashok Kumar. 4732 RIVER OAKS CIR 58201 #496-14-1980 L1990 **P PYG** *020 †75
BARCOME, Donald Francis. 3035 DEMERS AVE 58201 #056-05-1954 L1965 **PM** *020 †60
BEHERA, Sandhya Rani. 501 N COLUMBIA RD 58203 #495-79-1998 L2006 *100
BERG, Jonathan Henry. 2401 DEMERS AVE 58201 #026-04-1982 L1984 **FM** *020 †18
BLANCHARD, Richelle Melan. ■ 58201 #037-01-2008 *012
BOE, Christopher Thomas. 1200 S COLUMBIA RD, ALTRU HOSPITAL 58201
    #037-01-1997 L1998 **EM** *020 †16
BREITWIESER, Wayne Ralph. 1000 S COLUMBIA RD 58201 #018-03-1972 L1978
    PCC CCM *020 †20

BRIGGS, Brian Thomas. 3035 DEMERS AVE, VLY BONE & JOINT CLNC 58201 #068-01-1974 L1979 **ORS** *020 †40

BROCKMAN, Ronald J. 1000 S COLUMBIA RD, ATTRU CLINIC 58201 #041-02-1982 L1994 **OPH** *020 †35

BROSSEAU, James Dean. 1000 S COLUMBIA RD, ALTRU CLINIC 58201 #026-04-1970 L1972 **IM DIA** *020 †20

BROWN, Christina Ann. ■ 58203 #037-01-2007 L2007 **FP** *012

BROWN, Michael R. 1000 S COLUMBIA RD 58201 #037-01-1982 L1983 **OBG** *020 †30

BULS, Justin Michael. 725 HAMLINE ST, G.F.F.M.R. 58203 #037-01-2004 L2004 **FM** *100 †18

BYRON, Eugene Blaine. 1000 S COLUMBIA RD 58201 #048-13-1971 L1972 **GP** *020 †18

CALIN, Cristina. 1380 S COLUMBIA RD, MEDICINE CENTER 58201 #781-01-1995 L2003 **FM** *020 †18

CANFIELD, Wesley Kenneth. 2420 2ND AVE N 58203 #035-15-1976 L1981 **NTR PD** *050

CAOILI, Henri R. 1300 S COLUMBIA RD, ALTRU REHABILITATION CENTE 58201 #748-10-1993 L2002 **PM** *020 †60

CARTER, Francis Mark. 1200 S COLUMBIA RD, ALTRU HEALTH SYSTEM 58201 #917-07-1969 L1977 **NTR CCM** *071 †18

CHAN, Paul Jung-Kuei. 1380 S COLUMBIA RD, MEDICINE CENTER 58201 #187-19-1988 L2002 **FM** *020 †18 ‡

CHARETTE, Scott Duane. 1000 S COLUMBIA RD 58201 #037-01-1993 L1994 **GS VS** *020 †85

CHEATHAM, Christopher M. 725 HAMLINE ST 58203 #020-12-1998 L2002 **FM** *020 †18

CHEBACLO, Mohamed. 1000 S COLUMBIA RD, P O BOX 6003 58201 #165-01-1982 L2001 **CD IM** *020 †20

CHELLIAH, Noah N. 1191 S COLUMBIA RD 58201 #495-27-1974 L1982 **IM CD** *020 †20

CHENG, Shihshiang. ■ 58203 #104-01-2005 L2007 **FP** *012

CHRISTENSON, Mark J. 2891 2ND AVE N STOP 9038 58202 #037-01-1994 L1995 **FM** *020 †18

CHU, Anthony Gerard. 1000 S COLUMBIA RD, ALTRU CLINIC 58201 #026-04-1978 L1984 **GE** *020 †20

CLARK, Rodney Geo. ■ 58201 #016-11-1948 L1958 **OBG** *071 †30

CLAYBURGH, Bennie J. 1300 S COLUMBIA RD 58201 #041-13-1949 L1956 **ORS OAR** *071 †40

CLAYBURGH, Robert Henry. 3035 DEMERS AVE, VALLEY BONE & JOINT CLNC 58201 #028-02-1978 L1984 **ORS HS** *020 †40

CONSING, Raul Peralta. 1000 S COLUMBIA RD, ALIRU HEALTH SYSTEM 58201 #748-02-1985 L2000 **IM** *020

COOK-SHIMANEK, Margaret K. ■ 58201 #037-01-2008 L2008 *012

COOLEY, Albert Marvin. 1200 S COLUMBIA RD 58201 #016-06-1971 L1973 **PTH** *040 †50

CROW, Judson Lewis. 1000 S COLUMBIA RD 58201 #004-01-1961 L1982 **PS GS** *020 †85,65

DAILEY, Walter Chas. ■ 58201 #016-01-1939 L1940 **GP IM** *071

DALLUM, Bernie James, Jr. 1000 S COLUMBIA RD 58201 #026-04-1996 L2000 **DR** *020

DALMI, Attila. 1200 S COLUMBIA RD, MEDICAL STAFF OFFICE 58201 #473-04-1995 L2002 **IM** *020 †20

DAMLE, Jayant Shripad. 1200 S COLUMBIA RD, ALTRU HOSPITAL 58201 #495-28-1971 L1979 **AN** *020 †05

DAMMEYER, Matthew John. ■ 58201 #026-04-2006 L2006 **FP** *012

DE BELTZ, Donald John. 1000 S COLUMBIA RD 58201 #026-04-1992 L1997 **GS** *020 †85

DEERE, Joshua Richard. 725 HAMLINE ST 58203 #037-01-2006 L2006 **FP** *012

DE GUZMAN, Magnolia Kabig. 725 HAMLINE ST, G.F.F.M.R. 58203 #748-10-2002 L2004 **FM** *020 †18

DENTCHEV, Todor N. 960 S COLUMBIA RD 58201 #198-01-1984 L2001 **OM HEM** *020 †20

DEVIG, Patrick Marvin. 1000 S COLUMBIA RD 58201 #019-02-1971 L1981 **TS GS** *020 †85,90

DEWING, Bree December. PO BOX 9037, DEPT OF SURGERY 58202 #665-01-2007 L2007 **GS** *012

DIEPOLDER BROWN, Ann K. 1200 S COLUMBIA RD 58201 #037-01-1989 L1991 **PTH** *020 †50

DORAIS, Jessie Ashley. ■ 58201 #016-11-2007 **OBG** *012

DORRITY, Renae Lea. 725 HAMLINE ST 58203 #037-01-2006 L2006 **FP** *012

DUNAMALYAN, Aida. 501 N COLUMBIA RD, UNIV OF ND SCH MED & HLTH 58203 #913-38-1973 L2002 **P** *020

ECKARDT, Gerald William. ■ 58203 #037-01-2008 *012

EICKMAN, Jeffrey John. 1380 S COLUMBIA RD, MEDICINE CENTER 58201 #037-01-1997 L1998 **FM** *020 †18

ELLINGTON, Christopher Ma. PO BOX 9037, UND DEPT OF SURGERY 58202 #143-11-2007 L2007 **GS** *012

ERICKSON, Keith J. 1451 44TH AVE S 58201 #037-01-1990 L1991 **P** *020

EVANS, Douglas Gerard. 1101 S COLUMBIA RD STE B, THE KIDNEY & HYPERTENSION 58201 #035-08-1990 L2001 **CD** *020 †20

EVANS, Harold W. 1000 S COLUMBIA RD, GRAND FORKS CLINIC LTD 58201 #035-20-1949 L1958 **IM PUD** *071 †20

FASBENDER, James Robt. 1200 S COLUMBIA RD 58201 #056-06-1982 L1983 **EM** *020 †18

FEDYSZYN, Carl John. 1343 S 38TH ST, CARL JOHN FEDYSZYN MD PC 58201 #040-02-1994 L1995 **FM** *020 †18 ‡

FELDMAN, Ellen Kay. 860 S COLUMBIA RD 58201 #041-02-1983 L1997 **CHP** *020

FLEEKER-TREUER, Jody B. 1000 S COLUMBIA RD 58201 #037-01-1996 L2001 **DR** *020 †80

FLEISSNER, Paul. 1300 S COLUMBIA RD, OCCUPATIONAL MEDICINE CLIN 58201 #033-06-1990 L1998 **FM** *020 †18

FORTIN, Jeannine Marie. 1200 S COLUMBIA RD, ALTRU CLINIC 58201 #062-01-1985 L2004 **FM** *020 †18

FUNK, Peter Anthony. 1380 S COLUMBIA RD, ALTRU HLTH SYSTEM FAMILY M 58201 #056-06-1979 L1991 **FM GS** *020 †18

GASIOROWSKI, Luke. 501 N COLUMBIA RD, UNIV OF N DAKOTA DEPT SURG 58202 #759-04-1996 L2002 **GS** *100

GAUL, Gerald Neufeld. 3035 DEMERS AVE 58201 #026-08-1985 L1989 **OPH** *020 †35

GAUL, Joanne Neufeld. 1380 S COLUMBIA RD, MEDICINE CENTER 58201 #026-08-1989 L1990 **FM** *020 †18

GEDDES, Jeffrey Robert. 1200 S COLUMBIA RD, ALTRU HOSPITAL 58201 #037-01-2003 L2006 **EM** *020 †16

GELDERLOOS, Irminne. ■ 58203 #037-01-2008 *012

GHANI, Nasimul. 1000 S COLUMBIA RD 58201 #160-01-1984 L2005 **NEP** *020 †20

GOLOYOGO, Ferdinand Morco. 725 HAMLINE ST, UND FAMILY PRATICE CENTER 58203 #748-10-1998 L2001 **FM** *100

GOMEZ, Yvonne L. 1380 S COLUMBIA RD, MEDICINE CENTER 58201 #037-01-1994 L1996 **FM** *020 †18

GREEK, Greg D. 725 HAMLINE ST, FAMILY PRACTICE RESIDENCY 58203 #037-01-1985 L1986 **FM** *020 †18

GREWAL, Surinder K. 1200 S COLUMBIA RD 58201 #495-92-1981 L1997 **FM** *020 †18

GRISSOM, Douglas William. 1380 S COLUMBIA RD, MEDICINE CENTER 58201 #026-04-2001 L2005 **FM** *020 †18

GUPTA, Chhavi. 501 N COLUMBIA RD 58203 #495-05-2001 L2005 **IM** *012

HALVORSON, Larry Orville. 725 HAMLINE ST, FAMILY PRACTICE RESIDENCY 58203 #037-01-1976 L1977 **FM** *040 †18

HAPE, Robin Todd. 1000 S COLUMBIA RD 58201 #037-01-2002 L2002 **GS** *020 †85

HARRIS, Joel David. 501 N COLUMBIA RD, UNIV OF N.D. SCH OF MED& H 58203 #026-04-2005 L2005 **GS** *012

HAUG, Jonathan Samuel. 1200 S COLUMBIA RD 58201 #037-01-2001 L2005 **AN** *020 †05

HAUG, William Otto, Jr. ■ 58201 #026-04-1999 L2007 **FSM** *100 †18

HEINLEY, Timothy M. 1200 S COLUMBIA RD # 6002 58201 #037-01-1988 L1989 **FM** *020 †18

HILL, Steven M. 725 HAMLINE ST 58203 #037-01-1990 L1991 **P** *020 †75

HOEFS, Tana S Setness. 1000 S COLUMBIA RD 58201 #046-01-1998 L2002 **OBG** *020

HOGGARTH, Bernard Jerome. 1000 S COLUMBIA RD, ALTRU PEDIATRICS 58201 #018-03-1974 L1977 **PD** *020 †55

HOOD, Larissa Lyn. 1000 S COLUMBIA RD 58201 #030-05-1990 L1997 **DR** *020 †80

HOSKULDSSON, Torfi Thorke. 501 N COLUMBIA RD 58203 #484-01-2001 L2005 **GS** *012

HOVET, Charlotte Galegher. 1200 S COLUMBIA RD 58201 #007-02-1983 L1984 **FM** *020 †18

HUNDLEY, Michelle Denise. 725 HAMLINE ST, CTR FOR FAMILY MEDICINEG F 58203 #104-01-2004 L2005 **FP** *012

IGNACIO, Iris Diana. 725 HAMLINE ST, G.F.F.M.R. 58203 #748-10-2002 L2005 **FP** *012

IVERSON, Dianne L. 1200 S COLUMBIA RD 58201 #037-01-1981 L1983 **PTH** *020 †50

JACOB, Cindy Sara. 725 HAMLINE ST, G.F.F.M.R. 58203 #894-01-2003 L2005 **FP** *012

JACOBSEN, John Joy. 1000 S COLUMBIA RD 58201 #030-05-1977 L2006 **PD AI** *020 †55,03

JAMSA TOLLEFSON, Lisa J. ■ 58201 #037-01-2006 L2006 **FP** *012

JARZEMBOWSKI, Tomasz Mare. 725 HAMLINE ST 58203 #759-18-2001 L2005 **FP** *012

JENSEN, Warren Craig. UNIVERSITY AT TULANE, UND AEROSPACE 58201 #005-02-1982 L1983 **AM** *020 †70

JESSEN, Kristen B. 1000 S COLUMBIA RD 58201 #051-01-2000 L2006 **N** *020 †75

JOHNSON, Eric Lind. 1380 S COLUMBIA RD, MEDICINE CENTER 58201 #030-05-1989 L1990 **DIA FM** *020 †18

JOHNSON, Joel Lantz. 1200 S COLUMBIA RD 58201 #037-01-1977 L1978 **EM** *020 †16

JOHNSON, Mandi Lynn. 725 HAMLINE ST 58203 #037-01-2007 L2007 **FP** *012

JOHNSON, Robert Alan. 1300 S COLUMBIA RD 58201 #037-01-1976 L1981 **ORS** *020 †40

KARLSTAD, Gary Leroy. 3035 DEMERS AVE 58201 #026-04-1972 L1978 **OPH** *071 †35

KARTHAM, Sunil Kumar Redd. ■ 58201 #496-23-2002 L2007 **IM** *012 †20

KEEGAN, Gerald Thos. 1200 S COLUMBIA RD 58201 #035-20-1967 L2004 **U** *020 †95

KERBESHIAN, Jacob, Jr. 151 S 4TH ST STE 401, NORTHEAST HUMAN SERVICE CE 58201 #035-45-1970 L1977 **CHP P** *020 †75 ‡

KHOSLA, Seema. 1000 S COLUMBIA RD 58201 #759-01-1999 L2005 **PCC** *020 †20

KHOT, Khandurao Bhanudas. 501 N COLUMBIA RD 58203 #496-38-2002 L2006 **IM** *012

KLEVAY, Leslie Michael. ■ 58201 #056-05-1960 L1973 **NTR IM** *071

KNECHT, Tony A. 5825 PINEHURST CT 58201 #037-01-1994 L1996 **FM** *020 †18

KOLTES EDWARDS, Renee M. 1200 S COLUMBIA RD 58201 #018-03-2001 L2001 **AN** *020 †05

KONZAKJONES, M K. 725 HAMLINE ST, FAMILY PRACTICE RESIDENCY 58203 #037-01-1992 L1993 **FM** *020 †18

KOOTURU, Sri Vardhan Redd. 501 N COLUMBIA RD, UNIV OF ND SCH MED & HLTH 58203 #495-65-2003 L2006 **IM** *012

KRUGER, Michael Steven. 3035 DEMERS AVE 58201 #037-01-2003 L2003 **FSM** *020 †18

KURIHARA, Wallace Katsumi. 1000 S COLUMBIA RD 58201 #040-02-1971 L1992 **VS GS** *020 †85

LACHANCE, Deborah Lynne. 1000 S COLUMBIA RD 58201 #060-02-1993 L1999 *020 †30

LA LONDE, John Barrett. 1000 S COLUMBIA RD, GRAND FORKS CLINIC LTD 58201 #026-04-1960 L1969 **GS** *071 †85

LAMBIE, John Arthur. 1000 S COLUMBIA RD, GRAND FORKS CLINIC 58201 #041-01-1958 L1962 **IM MDM** *071 †20

LANGLOIS, Tricia Jean. 1000 S COLUMBIA RD 58201 #048-02-1993 L2004 **IMG** *020 †20

LAQUA, Patricia Lynn. 3000 N 32ND ST, DAKOTA CLINIC, LTD. 58203 #037-01-2003 L2003 **FM** *020 †18

LEICHTER, Eric Samuel. 1200 S COLUMBIA RD 58201 #051-04-1997 L2004 **U** *020 †95 ‡

LESSARD, James Allan. 3035 DEMERS AVE 58201 #016-45-1975 L1978 **RHU IM** *020 †20 ‡

LI, Haikun. 725 HAMLINE ST, G.F.F.M.R. 58203 #243-16-1985 L2005 **FP** *012

LINDGREN, Christopher. ■ 58201 #037-01-2008 *012

LORBER, Julie Phillips. 501 N COLUMBIA RD 58203 #665-01-2004 L2004 **GS** *012

LUNN, Eric Ryan. 1000 S COLUMBIA RD, ALTRO HLTH SYS 58201 #045-04-1984 L1987 **PD** *020 †55

LYSNE, Dwight Howard. 1451 44TH AVE S, STADTER CENTER 58201 #026-04-1982 L1987 **CHP ADL** *020 †75 ‡

LYSTE, Derek. ■ 58201 #037-01-2007 L2007 **FP** *012

MACCOLL, Colin Scott. 1000 S COLUMBIA RD 58201 #068-01-1986 L1999 **GS** *020 †85

MANN, Wm Stewart Fraser. 725 HAMLINE ST, FAMILY PRACTICE RESIDENCY 58203 #919-05-1964 L1976 **FM** *030 †18

MANSOUROV, Ramil. ■ 58201 #305-01-1998 L2003 **FM** *020 †18

MARTIN, Candelaria Cynthi. 725 HAMLINE ST 58203 #037-01-2004 L2004 **FM OBS** *020 †18

MARTINSON, Erling D. 2024 UNIVERSITY AVE, MARTINSON MED SVC 58203 #037-01-1983 L1984 **FM** *020

MARTSOLF, John Timothy. 501 N COLUMBIA RD, MS 9037 58202 #041-02-1970 L1978 **CG PD** *040 †19 ‡

MASA, Cedric B. 1451 44TH AVE S, STE 121D 58201 #748-01-1989 L2006 **FM** *020 †18

MC CANN, La Vaun Marie. 1200 S COLUMBIA RD 58201 #037-01-1987 L1988 **IM** *020 †20

MC KINNON, William G. 3925 BELMONT RD 58201 #037-01-1983 L1985 **FM EM** *020 †18 ‡

MEREDITH, Wm Christie. 860 RAINDALE CT 58201 #062-01-1955 L1956 **GP** *020

MICHALSKI, Tomasz Jarosla. 725 HAMLINE ST, G.F.F.M.R. 58203 #759-01-2003 L2005 **FP** *012

MIDGARDEN, Kristi J. 1451 44TH AVE S 58201 #037-01-1997 L1998 **FM** *020 †18

MILLETTE, Keith W. 1380 S COLUMBIA RD, MEDICINE CENTER 58201 #037-01-1987 L1988 **FM OBS** *020 †18

MOORE, Patrick Frank. 1380 S COLUMBIA RD, MEDICINE CENTER 58201 #037-01-1976 L1977 **FM** *020 †18

MUDIREDDY, Uma M R. 1000 S COLUMBIA RD 58201 #495-57-1992 L2003 **PCC** *020 †20 ‡

MUIDERMAN, Anthony Kevin. 3165 DEMERS AVE, ALTRU DEMERS CLINIC 58201 #025-07-1990 L2007 **PS** *020 †65

MUUS, John Harold. 3165 DEMERS AVE 58201 #036-05-1966 L1980 **D** *020 †18,15

NAGPAL, Avish. ■ 58203 #496-59-2003 L2007 **IM** *012

NALLACHERU, Srikanth. 501 N COLUMBIA RD 58203 #496-35-2001 L2005 **IM** *012

NASIROV, Teimour Amrah. 501 N COLUMBIA RD, P O BOX 9037 58202 #422-01-2000 L2002 **TS** *012 †85

NELSON, William C. ■ 58201 #026-04-1948 L1957 **IM GE** *071

■ = Address Information Privacy Protected

NOSIK, Stanislav Semenovi. 501 N COLUMBIA RD 58203 #913-09-1999 L2005 **GS** *012

NOYES, William Richard. 1451 44TH AVE S STE E 58201 #037-01-1989 L1994 **RO** *020 †80

NWAKAMMA-OKORO, Ngozi O. 1451 44TH AVE S, STE E 58201 #690-09-1987 L2002 **HO IM** *020 †20

NYGARD, Shane D. 1380 S COLUMBIA RD, MEDICINE CENTER 58201 #037-01-1985 L1986 **FM** *020 †18

OBREGON, Heather Klokstad. 1380 S COLUMBIA RD, MEDICINE CENTER 58201 #037-01-1993 L1995 **FM** *020 †18

OLIVAS, Terry Paul. 1000 S COLUMBIA RD 58201 #031-01-1997 L2006 **TS** *020 †85,90

OLSON, James Richard. ■ 58201 #016-06-1959 L1962 **OPH** *071

OMDAHL, Bonnie Belle. 1000 S COLUMBIA RD, ALTRU HEALTH SYSTEMS 58201 #046-01-1995 L1999 **DR** *020 †80

ONYEKA, Ikechukwu Chinedu. 1200 S COLUMBIA RD, ALTRU HEALTH SYSTEM 58201 #690-04-1991 L2004 **IM** *100

OSPINA, Julian Andres. PO BOX 9037 58202 #264-05-1995 L2003 **GS** *100

OSTLIE, Jane. ■ 58201 #037-01-2008 *012

PANICO, Kevin Gerard. 960 S COLUMBIA RD 58201 #048-12-1998 L2005 **HO** *020 †20

PANSEGRAU, Duane Francis. 1395 S COLUMBIA RD #A 302 58201 #018-03-1956 L1966 **GS** *071 †85

PARIKH, Jitendra Rajendra. 1200 COLUMBIA RD 58201 #496-38-1977 L1984 **AN** *020

PARIKH, Vinita Jitendra. ■ 58201 #030-06-2005 L2005 **AN** *012

PAULSON, Rolf Richard. 1000 S COLUMBIA RD 58201 #026-04-1975 L1984 **IM VM** *020 †20

PENUGONDA, Bapanaiah. 3697 21ST AVE S, SOUTH COLUMBIA ROAD 1300 58201 #495-11-1970 L1992 **AN** *020 †05

PETERSEN, Troy Richard. ■ 58201 #030-05-2001 L2004 **GS** *020

PETERSON, Kirsten Dawn. 1000 S COLUMBIA RD 58201 #037-01-1987 L1990 **IM** *040 †20

PETERSON, Mark Gregory. 1451 44TH AVE S STE E 58201 #037-01-1989 L1996 **FM** *020 †18

PETERSON, Timothy Aaron. 1451 44TH AVE S, STE 121D 58201 #062-01-1992 L1997 *020 †18

PETTIT, Ross Edward. 2812 17TH AVE S STE D 58201 #028-34-1972 L1979 **N CHN** *020 †55,75

PHILPOT, Heidi Jo Erickso. 725 HAMLINE ST, FAMILY PRACTICE RESIDENCY 58203 #037-01-2003 L2003 **FM** *020 †18

PIERCE, Karin L. ■ 58201 #037-01-2006 L2006 **FP** *012

PITCHER, Harrison T. 1000 S COLUMBIA RD, ALTRU HOSPITAL 58201 #065-06-1985 L2006 **TS** *020 †85,90

PODDUTURU, Vikram Reddy. 1000 S COLUMBIA RD, ATTN:JEAN KELLER 58201 #495-65-1997 L2006 **PM** *020 †60

POLOVITZ, Thomas Michael. 1380 S COLUMBIA RD, MEDICINE CENTER 58201 #037-01-1977 L1978 **FM** *020 †18

PULAGAM, Srinivas Reddy. 1200 S COLUMBIA RD 58201 #495-21-2000 L2006 **IM** *020 †20

RABADI, Khaled Mazen. 1451 44TH AVE S, STE D 58201 #575-01-1992 L1997 **NEP** *020 †20

RAMIREZ, Hernan. ■ 58202 #264-05-1970 **PTH** *020 †50

RAYMOND, Jon Francis. 1200 S COLUMBIA RD, ALTRU HOSP 58201 #037-01-1989 L1990 **EM FM** *020 †18

RAYMOND, Laura Ann. 1200 S COLUMBIA RD 58201 #037-01-1989 L1993 **HMP** *020 †50

REDDY, Bhavananda Thootku. 1200 S COLUMBIA RD 58201 #495-57-1986 L2001 **IM** *020

RICHARDS, Robert Norman. 1200 S COLUMBIA RD 58201 #041-01-1958 L1969 **ORS** *071 †40

RICHARDSON, Rita Marie. 1000 S COLUMBIA RD, ALTRU CLINIC - MAIN 58201 #017-20-1995 L1999 **N** *020 †75

ROED, James Richard. 725 HAMLINE ST, GF FAMILY MED RESIDENCY 58203 #037-01-1997 L1998 **FM** *020 †18

ROLLER, Matthew J. 1000 S COLUMBIA RD 58201 #037-01-2002 L2006 **CN** *100

ROW, Jeffrey H. 1451 44TH AVE S 58201 #037-01-1997 L2000 **P** *020

ROXAS, Rodrigo Changco. 725 HAMLINE ST, FAMILY MEDICINE PRGRM 58203 #748-01-2003 L2007 **FP** *012

RYAN, Casey James. 1000 S COLUMBIA RD 58201 #007-02-1975 L1978 **END IM** *020 †20

SAMARAWEERA, Ravinda. ■ 58203 #037-01-2008 *012

SANJAY, Bangarulingam Y. 1200 S COLUMBIA RD 58201 #495-09-1996 L2003 **IM** *020 †20

SCHALL, David M. 3035 DEMERS AVE 58201 #037-01-1997 L2002 **ORS** *020 †40

SCHANZENBACH, Stewart H. 1200 S COLUMBIA RD 58201 #037-01-2000 L2003 **EM** *020

SCHAUER, Roger Williams. PO BOX 9037, UNIVERSITY OF NORTH DAKOTA 58202 #025-07-1971 L1974 **FM** *040 †18

SCHMELKA, Daniel Damian. 1000 S COLUMBIA RD, GRAND FORKS CLINIC 58201 #065-09-1963 L1977 **NS** *020 †25

SCHREINER, Shawn A. 1200 S COLUMBIA RD 58201 #037-01-1994 L2002 **DR RNR** *020 †80

SCHULTZ, Steven Edward. 3375 DEMERS AVE 58201 #046-01-1981 L1988 **U GS** *020

SCHUSTER, Michael Robert. ■ 58203 #037-01-2001 L2006 **AN** *020 †05

SCHWENDER, Frank Thomas. 1300 S COLUMBIA RD, ALTRU HEALTH SYSTEM 58201 #408-14-1995 L2001 **ICE** *100 †20

SCZEPANSKI, Mark Lee. 3035 DEMERS AVE, NORTH DAKOTA EYE CLNC 58201 #037-01-1996 L2000 **OPH** *020 †35

SENS, Mary Ann. 501 N COLUMBIA RD 58203 #045-01-1981 L2002 **PTH FOP** *040 †50

SEVERUD, Robin K. 1200 S COLUMBIA RD 58201 #037-01-2001 L2001 **AN** *020 †05

SHAH, Muhammad A A. 3740 30TH AVE S, STE 310 58201 #704-04-1994 L2004 **P** *020 †75

SHELTON, Frank J. 1000 S COLUMBIA RD 58201 #023-12-1986 L2007 **PD** *020 †55

SIEGEL, Mark. 1000 S COLUMBIA RD 58201 #005-14-1973 L1978 **GS** *020 †85

SKARI, Brad. ■ 58203 #037-01-2007 L2007 **FP** *012

SKJOLDEN, Jessica Ann. 725 HAMLINE ST 58203 #037-01-2007 L2007 **FP** *012

SMITH, Randall J. 1200 S COLUMBIA RD, ALTRU HOSPITAL 58201 #056-05-1995 L2004 **VIR** *020 †80

SMYSER, Gerald S. 1200 S COLUMBIA RD, ALTRU HOSP 58201 #041-13-1977 L1983 **RNR VIR** *020 †80 ‡

SOBUS, Kerstin M. 1300 S COLUMBIA RD 58201 #037-01-1987 L1997 **PM** *020 †60

SOINE, Leslie Ann. 1000 S COLUMBIA RD 58201 #007-02-1971 L1976 **DR** *020

SONDROL, Lori Ann. 1000 S COLUMBIA RD 58201 #037-01-1989 L1993 **PD** *020 †55

SOPHER, Roger Louis. UNIVERSITY STATION 58201 #023-07-1962 L1988 **PTH CLP** *071 †50

STICCA, Robert Peter. 1000 S COLUMBIA RD 58201 #008-02-1984 L1992 **SO GS** *020 †85 ‡

STUDENY, Simon. 501 N COLUMBIA RD 58203 #286-02-1997 L2005 **FP** *012

SUNDLING, Roger Raymond. ■ 58201 #026-04-1974 L1975 **FM** *075

SVEDJAN-WALZ, Hayley Jill. 1380 S COLUMBIA RD, MEDICINE CENTER 58201 #037-01-1994 L1995 **FM** *020 †18

SWANK, Colleen Marie. 1200 S COLUMBIA RD 58201 #037-01-1997 L2000 **PD** *020 †55

SWANSON, Keith Eric. 1200 S COLUMBIA RD, ALTRU HOSPITAL 58201 #037-01-2001 L2005 **GE** *100

SWENSON, John Andrew. UNIVERSITY OF ND, STUDENT HEALTH SERVICE 58201 #030-05-1954 L1955 **IM** *072 †18

TEMPLE, Kevin John. 1200 S COLUMBIA RD, ALTRU HOSPITAL 58201 #038-45-2000 L2005 **ETX EM** *012

TESSMANN, Paul B. 501 N COLUMBIA RD, UDSURGERY 58203 #037-01-2003 L2003 **GS** *012

THOMPSON, Joff Garfield. 3035 DEMERS AVE, STE 3 58201 #036-07-1994 L2001 **ORS** *020 †40

THOMPSON, Robert Allen. 1000 S COLUMBIA RD 58201 #037-01-1985 L1992 **AI MDM** *020 †20,03

TORGERSON, Leslie Al. 1200 S COLUMBIA RD 58201 #028-02-1966 L1974 **PTH** *020 †50

TROTTIER, Rory D. 1451 44TH AVE S 58201 #037-01-1991 L1999 **OBG** *020

UMHAUER, Sandra Anderson. 1000 S COLUMBIA RD, DEPT OF OB-GYN 58201 #020-12-1995 L1999 **OBG** *020 †30

VAN LOOY, James Wm. 1000 S COLUMBIA RD, GRAND FORKS CLINIC LTD 58201 #025-07-1974 L1977 **PD** *030 †55

VASIREDDY, Sri Krishna. 501 N COLUMBIA RD, UNIV OF ND SCH MED & HLTH 58203 #495-57-2002 L2006 **IM** *012

WALSH, Daniel John. 1000 S COLUMBIA RD 58201 #016-11-1991 L1997 **HO** *020 †20

WALZ, Joel D. 1380 S COLUMBIA RD, ALTRU 58201 #037-01-1994 L1995 **FM** *020 †18

WARNER, Robert Craig. ■ 58201 #030-05-1955 L1966 **IM DIA** *071

WASDAHL, Walter Arling. U OF N DAK SCH OF MED PTH 58202 #067-01-1954 L1955 **PTH OS** *071 †50

WEILAND, Timothy Louis. 1200 S COLUMBIA RD 58201 #026-08-1988 L1994 **PTH** *020 †50

WEISER, Steven Joseph. 1300 S COLUMBIA RD, ALTRU HEALTH SYSTEM 58201 #062-01-1993 L1999 **EM** *020

WILDEY, Brian Mathew. 1200 S COLUMBIA RD 58201 #034-01-2003 L2007 **OBG** *100

WILLARDSON, James Donald. 1200 S COLUMBIA RD, ALTRU HOSPITAL 58201 #037-01-1998 L1999 **IM** *020 †20

WILSON, H David. 501 N COLUMBIA RD, UND SCHOOL OF MEDICINE AND 58202 #028-34-1966 L1995 **PDI PD** *030 †55

WINCHESTER, Marshall B. 960 S COLUMBIA RD 58201 #025-07-1983 L2004 **RO** *020

WOOD, Kathleen A. 3598 MEADOW DR 58201 #026-04-1975 L1984 **DR** *020

WOODS, Benjamin Gordon. ■ 58201 #049-01-2008 *012

WOODWARD, George. 1000 S COLUMBIA RD 58201 #028-46-1983 L2001 **N** *020 †75

WROBLEWSKI, Robert Lee. 501 N COLUMBIA RD 58203 #026-04-2003 L2003 **GS** *012

YALAMANCHILI, Neelima. 501 N COLUMBIA RD, UNIV OF ND SCH MED & HLTH 58203 #495-99-2003 L2006 **IM** *012

YOUNGDAHL, Antoinette L. 1380 S COLUMBIA RD, ALTRU FAMILY MEDICINE CENT 58201 #026-04-2002 L2005 **FM** *020 †18

YOUNGS, John Nelson. 1000 S COLUMBIA RD 58201 #041-13-1966 L1970 **OTO** *071 †45

ZAKS, William John. 2219 S 36TH ST 58201 #051-01-1987 L1996 **END** *020 †20

ZELEWSKI, Susan Kaye. 1000 S COLUMBIA RD 58201 #048-04-2001 L2004 **PD** *020 †55

ZELLER, Darrell Eugene. 1116 S 22ND ST, 1000 S. COLUMBIA RD. 58201 #019-02-1974 L2001 **OBG** *020 †30

GRAND FORKS AIR FORCE BASE – GRAND FORKS

ARNHOLT, Jonathan Luke. 1599 J ST, 319 MDG 58205 #023-12-2002 L2003 **OTO** *012

CLELAND, Esperanza Soleda. ■ 58204 #037-01-2007 **IM** *012

GIVENS, Howard Richard. 1599 J ST, GRAND FORKS AFB ND 58205 #020-12-1999 L2001 **FM** *020 †18

HARDWICK, Tracy Elizabeth. 1599 J ST, ATTN: CREDENTIAL OFFICE 58205 #023-12-2003 L2005 *100 †18

HIBBERT, John David. 1599 J ST, 319 MDG 58205 #010-03-1970 L1971 **GS GP** *030 †85

JOHNSTON, Joshua Ross. 1599 J ST, ATTN: CREDENTIAL OFFICE 58205 #018-03-2004 L2004 **FM** *100

KULUND, Daniel Nicholas. 1599 J ST, 319TH MEDICAL GROUP 58205 #010-01-1968 L1970 **ORS** *020 †40

PALECEK, Paul Charles. 1599 J ST, FAMILY MEDICINE 58205 #026-04-2002 L2002 **FM** *020 †18

WONG, Emily B. ■ 58204 #023-12-2005 **FM** *100

HARVEY – WELLS

COVINGTON, David Ralph. 325 BREWSTER ST E, ST ALOISIUS MEDICAL CENTER 58341 #352-07-1961 L1971 **GP** *071

LINDEMANN, Alan Rienhard. ■ 58341 #037-01-1977 L1984 **OBG** *075 †30

NYHUS, Charles Donald. 922 LINCOLN AVE 58341 #037-01-1979 L1980 **FM** *020 †18

THURMANN, Hiltrud. 922 LINCOLN AVE 58341 #409-40-1994 L1997 **IM** *020 †20

HATTON – TRAILL

JONAS, Roxanne Lynn. ■ 58240 #037-01-2000 L2002 **FM** *020

HAZEN – MERCER

GEHRING, Armand Wm. 517 8TH AVE NE 58545 #026-04-1965 L1979 **GP PTH** *020 †50

HUTCHENS, Thomas Pinckney. 510 8TH AVE NE 58545 #012-05-1979 L1987 **OBG** *020 †30

JENSEN, Warren Robt. ■ 58545 #016-06-1954 L1957 **FM GS** *071 †18

KENNEDY, Roger Franklin. 846 45TH AVE NW LOT 10 58545 #030-05-1963 L1971 **NS** *020 †25

LARSEN, David Harold. 521 8TH AVE NE, BONE & JOINT CENTER 58545 #018-75-1978, ▲ L1990 **GP** *020

YARLOTT, Melvin A, Jr. 510 8TH AVE NE 58545 #007-02-1970 L1993 **GS ON** *020 †85

HETTINGER – ADAMS

BERG, Vanessa Victoria. ■ 58639 #046-01-2003 L2007 **FM** *020 †18

BOPP, Timothy John. 1000 HIGHWAY 12, BONE & JOINT CENTER 58639 #028-03-1988 L1993 **ORS** *020 †40

DAHL, Charles Phillip. 1000 HIGHWAY 12, BONE & JOINT CENTER 58639 #048-12-1976 L1981 **ORS** *050 †40

ELDER, William Cowden. 1100 HIGHWAY 12 58639 #028-02-1970 L1974 **GS** *020 †85

GROSSMAN, Robert Edwin. 1100 HIGHWAY 12 58639 #007-02-1973 L1974 **FM** *020 †18

HOULE, Catherine E. 1100 HIGHWAY 12 58639 #018-03-1988 L1989 **FM** *020 †18

JACOBSEN, Thomas Eric. 1100 HIGHWAY 12, WEST RIVER HEATH CLINICS 58639 #041-01-1965 L1967 FM *020 †18

KETTERLING, Ellen L. 1100 HIGHWAY 12 58639 #028-34-1981 L1984 PD *020 †55

KRISTY, Mark Stephen. 1000 HIGHWAY 12, DEPT OF RADIOLOGY 58639 #016-11-1990 L1995 DR R *020 †80

MACK, Terrance Richard. 1100 HIGHWAY 12 58639 #007-02-1972 L1973 FM *020 †18

MATTSON, Joseph Morris. 1000 HIGHWAY 12 58639 #054-04-1965 L1968 FPG FM *020 †18

PIERCE, Troy Darin. 1000 HIGHWAY 12, BONE & JOINT CENTER 58639 #037-01-1991 L1997 ORS HS *020 †40

SAILER, Gerald Theodore. HETTINGER CLINIC 58639 #048-04-1961 L1963 GP GS *030 †18

THORNGREN, Frank Allen. 1100 HIGHWAY 12 58639 #026-04-1973 L2001 FM EM *020 †18

WALKER, Laura Louise. 1100 HIGHWAY 12, WEST RIVER REGIONAL MED CE 58639 #060-02-1995 L1998 FM *020 †18

HILLSBORO — TRAILL

JUELSON, Timothy John. ■ 58045 #037-01-2005 L2007 ORS *012

JAMESTOWN — STUTSMAN

AMIN, Damayanti Arun. 1702 5TH AVE NE, DAMAYANTI A AMIN MD 58401 #495-20-1973 L1994 CHP *020

ARCHULETA, Laura Z. 401 3RD ST SE, DAKOTA CLINIC 58401 #030-06-2001 L2004 FM *020

BROADHEAD, Alan John. 2605 CIRCLE DR, NORTH DAKOTA STATE HOSP 58401 #917-22-1962 L1990 P *020 †75

CANHAM, William Douglas. 300 2ND AVE NE 58401 #064-01-1974 L1994 ORS *020 †40

CURTIS, Philip Bowen. 419 5TH ST NE 58401 #038-40-1955 L1963 U NEP *020

DAYAP, Felicisimo D. 1624 23RD ST S E 58402 #748-07-1957 P *020

ERNSTER, Dale Jon. 401 3RD ST SE, DAKOTA CLINIC 58401 #026-04-1981 L1982 FM FPG *020 †18

GEIER, Debra A. 300 2ND AVE NE 58401 #037-01-2001 L2001 IM *020

GOWRAVARAM, Sridevi. 904 5TH AVE NE 58401 #495-65-1995 L2006 PD *020 †55

HIPP, John Adam. 419 5TH ST NE 58401 #067-01-1972 L1973 PTH BBK *020 †50

HOGGARTH, Tonia L. 300 2ND AVE NE 58401 #037-01-1997 L1998 FM *020 †18

HOLZWARTH, Ryan L. 904 5TH AVE NE 58401 #037-01-2002 L2002 D *020 †15

JOHNSON, Larry Edward. 300 2ND AVE NE, MEDCENTER ONE HEALTH SYSTE 58401 #001-02-1976 L1981 FM *020 †18

JYSTAD, Philip Nathan. 419 5TH ST NE, JAMESTOWN HOSPITAL 58401 #026-04-1988 L1989 FM *020 †18

KHOKHA, Inder Vir. ■ 58401 #495-29-1975 L2003 GS VS *020 †85

KOTTKE, Dennis Boyd. PO BOX 476 58402 #026-04-1968 L1988 P *071

LARSEN, Raymond Lloyd. 916 5TH AVE NE 58401 #005-12-1973 L1976 OPH *020 †35

MAIER, Steven Clark. 904 5TH AVE NE, MERITCARE CLINIC 58401 #037-01-1979 L1984 GS *020 †85

MARDIROSIAN, Ardashir. 401 3RD ST SE, DAKOTA CLINIC LTD JAMESTOW 58401 #396-06-1970 L1975 ORS *071

MATHISON, David Milo. 300 2ND AVE NE 58401 #037-01-1997 L1998 FM *020 †18

MC MILLAN, William K. 904 5TH AVE NE 58401 #048-04-1984 L1987 FM *020 †18

MUHS, David M. 904 5TH AVE NE 58401 #037-01-1985 L1988 FM *020 †18

MUTCHLER, Michael Robt. 904 5TH AVE NE, MERITCARE CLINIC JAMESTOWN 58401 #037-01-1985 L1988 IM *020 †18

OLESTAD, Marie S. PO BOX 1122 58402 #037-01-1979 L1980 ORS *020 †40

PELTON, Charles Leonard. 904 5TH AVE NE, MERITCARE CLINIC JAMESTOWN 58401 #019-02-1970 L1999 FM OBS *020 †18

PRYATEL, William Benj, Jr. 2605 CIRCLE DR, NORTH DAKOTA STATE HOSPITA 58401 #048-13-1975 L1989 P *020 †75

PUNZALAN, Calixto Paredes. 1624 23RD ST S E 58402 #748-01-1957 L1980 P *071

QUANRUD, Myra J. 401 3RD ST SE, DAKOTA CLINIC 58401 #037-01-1990 L1994 PD *020 †55

ROBLES, Maria Diana E. 2605 CIRCLE DR, NORTH DAKOTA STATE HOSPITA 58401 #748-29-1988 L2000 CHP P *020 †75

ROWE, Scott Conrad. 401 3RD ST SE 58401 #026-04-1982 L1983 FM *020 †18

RYOU, Man He. 2605 CIRCLE DR 58401 #583-03-1965 P N *020

TEVINGTON, Kathryn M. 2605 CIRCLE DR, NORTH DAKOTA STATE HOSPITA 58401 #048-13-1994 L2002 P *020 †75

TONI, Conrad Richard. 904 5TH AVE NE 58401 #062-01-1972 L1978 U *020 †95

TORRANCE, James Robin. 401 3RD ST SE, BOX 1980 58401 #037-01-1988 L1989 FM *020 †18

TRINIDAD, Nicasio Cruz. 2605 CIRCLE DR, NORTH DAKOTA STATE HOSPITA 58401 #748-07-1961 L1983 P *071

VAN VALKENBURG, Daisy R. 2605 CIRCLE DR, NORTH DAKOTA STATE HOSPITA 58401 #018-03-1978 L2002 P *020 †75

WELLS, Robert Charles. 904 5TH AVE NE 58401 #032-01-1998 L1999 FM *020 †18

YABUT, Eduardo Pelayo. 520 3RD ST NW, SOUTH CENTRAL HUMAN SERVIC 58401 #748-01-1991 L2002 P *020 †75

KENMARE — WARD

MALHOMME, Bernard Emile. ■ 58746 #062-01-1955 L1977 GP *020

SABIITI, Jesse Mugisha. ■ 58746 #905-02-2004 L2007 IM *020 †20

LAMOURE — LAMOURE

VANGERUD, Paul Thorvold. 107 2ND AVE NE, MERITCARE CLINICS 58458 #019-02-1959 L1960 GP *071

LANGDON — CAVALIER

CHEBERIAK, Teresa. 903 2ND ST, CLINIC 58249 #068-01-1988 L1996 OS *075

FASHORO, Olatubosun Babas. 901 2ND ST 58249 #690-02-1992 L2003 IM *020 †20

GOODLIFFE, Enrique Arturo. 601 8TH AVE 58249 #132-01-1966 L1974 GP GS *071

MARSH, Peter Edward Wm. 901 2ND ST 58249 #917-06-1964 L1976 FM *020

LIDGERWOOD — RICHLAND

HARANATH, Sai Prashanth. 21 WILEY AVE S, SOUTHEAST MEDICAL CENTER 58053 #495-59-1998 L2002 IM *020 †20

LINTON — EMMONS

ABRAMOVITH, Paula. 511 E ELM AVE, LINTON MEDICAL CENTER 58552 #187-18-1983 L2006 FM *020 †18

FAITH, Glenn Carter. 518 N BROADWAY ST, BOX 850 58552 #016-06-1959 L1975 GP PTH *020 †50

OLIVEIRA-FILHO, Edgar K. 511 E ELM AVE, LINTON MEDICAL CENTER 58552 #187-02-1973 L2001 GP EM *020

WAGNER, Ronald Lynn. 511 E ELM AVE, LINTON MEDICAL CENTER 58552 #037-01-1978 L1979 FM *020 †18

ZIMMERMAN, Rodney Leon. 515 N BROADWAY ST 58552 #037-01-1977 L1981 FM *020 †18 ‡

LISBON — RANSOM

FERNANDEZ, Oscar Octavio. 102 11TH AVE W, SOUTHEAST MEDICAL CENTER 58054 #305-01-1981 L1992 GS *020 †18

LEWIS, Asle Kingsley. 819 MAIN ST 58054 #016-11-1944 L1948 FM *071 †18

LOPERENA, Rudolf. 819 MAIN ST, DAKOTA CLINIC-LISBON 58054 #409-33-1989 L1998 FM *020

ROISE, Douglas A. 905 MAIN ST 58054 #037-01-1982 L1983 PTH *020 †50

SHEETS, Barbara Ann. 10 9TH AVE E, BOX 1049 58054 #041-09-1982 L1983 GP *020

SWANGER, Carroll E. 1400 ROSE ST 58054 #018-03-1952 L1982 R *071 †80

MADDOCK — BENSON

BEST, Lyle G. 301 ROOSEVELT AVE 58348 #035-46-1974 L1978 FM *030 †18

SEILER, Hubert Leo. 301 ROOSEVELT AVE 58348 #018-03-1972 L1973 FM *020 †18

SELLAND, Brian L. 301 ROOSEVELT AVE 58348 #037-01-1987 L1994 FM *020 †18

MANDAN — MORTON

ADDY, Boyd Frederick. 2008 TWIN CITY DR 58554 #062-01-1977 L1978 FM *020

BAKER, Biron D. 1000 18TH ST NW 58554 #037-01-1995 L1996 FM *020 †18

BELZER-CURL, Gretchen G. 910 18TH ST NW 58554 #037-01-1996 L1997 FM *040 †18

BOYUM, Lowell Everett. ■ 58554 #048-04-1945 GP *071

CAVE, Jeffrey Ronald. 4809 INLET BAY DR 58554 #654-01-1999 L2003 AN *020 †05 ‡

DAVILA, Cynthia. ■ 58554 #037-01-2004 L2007 PD *020

FOLKERS, Kevin F. 910 18TH ST NW, QUAIN & RAMSTAD CLINIC PC 58554 #037-01-1985 L1986 FM *020 †18

HOOVESTOL, Ryan Arthur. ■ 58554 #037-01-2008 *012

JOHNSON, Anthony T. 102 MANDAN AVE 58554 #037-01-1994 L1995 FM *020 †18

KLEIN, Dale Albert. 910 18TH ST NW 58554 #037-01-1982 L1983 FM *020 †18

LANGE, Darwin K. 910 18TH ST NW 58554 #037-01-1982 L1984 FM *020 †18

MC CULLOUGH, William F. 2200 PIRATES LOOP SE, UNIT 207 58554 #007-02-1952 L1955 DR AM *071 †80

MORGAN, Riffat Farid. 4708 S BAY DR SE 58554 #330-04-1957 L1969 AN CCM *071 †05

PODOLL, Lee Norem. ■ 58554 #056-05-1964 L1977 DR NM *020 †50,80

SCHERBER, Holly Lynn. ■ 58554 #037-01-2008 *012

SUNGA, Conrado. 109 1ST ST NW 58554 #748-01-1962 L1971 GS FM *020

THORSON, Thomas A. 102 MANDAN AVE, Q & R MANDAN CLINIC EAST 58554 #037-01-1988 L1989 FM *020 †18

MAYVILLE — TRAILL

LANGE, Marsha M. 730 MAIN ST E 58257 #025-07-1987 L1989 FM *020 †18

LITTLE, James Mc Nair. 730 MAIN ST E 58257 #026-04-1954 L1955 GP *071

MEHUS, James G. 730 MAIN ST E 58257 #037-01-2000 L2004 MPD *020

PENN, Jeremiah Jon. 730 MAIN ST E 58257 #046-01-2002 L2002 FM *020 †18

MERCER — MCLEAN

MILLER, Stephanie. ■ 58559 #037-01-2007 L2007 IM *012

MICHIGAN — NELSON

HAGEN, Boyd Nathan. PO BOX 290 58259 #055-01-1970 L1971 GP *020

MINOT — WARD

AILSBY, Ronald L. 400 BURDICK EXPY E, MEDICAL ARTS CLINIC, P.C. 58701 #068-01-1969 L1996 ORS *020

AIN, Quara Tul. 1201 11TH AVE SW, FAMILY MEDICINE PRGRM 58701 #704-01-2003 L2007 FP *012

AKHTAR, Saeed. 20 BURDICK EXPY W STE 6 58701 #704-16-1983 L2007 U *020 †95

ANUEBUNWA, Theodore Okwud. 831 S BROADWAY STE 104, TRINITY HEALTH CTR-TOWN & 58701 #690-12-1996 L2007 IM *020 †20

ARYAL, Suima. 1201 11TH AVE SW 58701 #672-03-2004 L2006 FP *012

BEATY, James Robt. 1 BURDICK EXPY W 58701 #051-01-1960 L1987 EM PD *071 †55,16

BEHMANESH, Sharareh. 1201 11TH AVE SW 58701 #517-01-1990 L2006 FP *012

BENAISSA, Rafik. 101 3RD AVE SW, STE 101 58701 #065-09-1990 L2000 ORS *020 †40

BERCIER, Paula J. ■ 58703 #037-01-1992 L1994 FM *020 †18

BIERENBAUM, Robert. PO BOX 5020 58702 #035-03-1978 L1996 GS IM *020

BILLINGS, David Allen. 400 BURDICK EXPY E 58701 #037-01-1992 L1996 OBG *020 †30 ‡

BLAND, James Henry. 116 1ST ST SW 58701 #051-07-1983 L1989 **P PYG** *075 †75
BOUCHARD-KINDY, Evelyne. 120 BURDICK EXPY E 58701 #067-02-1989 L1998 **OPH** *020 †35
BRANTL, Rylan. ■ 58701 #037-01-2008 *012
BRIGGS, Brian Earl. ■ 58701 #026-04-1954 L1955 **NTR** *075 †18
CADWALADER, Ann Marie. 1 BURDICK EXPY W 58701 #028-02-1984 L1988 **PD** *020 †55
CALL, James Edmund, Jr. 1 BURDICK EXPY W 58701 #030-05-1970 L2005 **R** *020 †80
CASHMORE, Robert Wm. 1 BURDICK EXPY W 58701 #026-04-1965 L1983 **PTH DMP** *030 †50
CHIKWENDU, Valentine C. 400 BURDICK EXPY E 58701 #690-04-1981 L2005 **CD** *020 †20
COLLINS, Kevin Basil. 831 S BROADWAY 58701 #039-01-1992 L1999 **RO** *020 †80
COLON DE JESUS, Manuel. 101 3RD AVE SW, STE 101 58701 #042-02-1997 L2004 **AN** *020 †05
CORPUS, Eduardo Tojino. 1408 20TH AVE SW STE 7, VEIN CARE CLINICS 58701 #748-10-1971 L1986 **GS** *020
DALLOLIO, Michael John. 1900 8TH AVE SE, TRINITY HEALTH CTR-RIVERSI 58701 #035-09-1999 L2008 **ADP** *020
DANIELS, Frank J. 1 BURDICK EXPY W, RADIOLOGY DEPARTMENT 58701 #660-03-1977 L2004 **DR** *020 †80
DE JONG, Ann. 1201 11TH AVE SW 58701 #305-01-2005 L2006 **FP** *012
DIAS, Asitha Ravinda. 1201 11TH AVE SW, CENTER FOR FAMILY MEDICINE 58701 #220-01-2002 L2005 **FP** *012
DILLAS, Maya. 1 BURDICK EXPY W 58701 #957-08-1988 L2001 **IM** *020 †20
DIRI, Erdal. 400 BURDICK EXPY E, TRINITY HEALTH CTR-MED.ART 58701 #902-07-1988 L2002 **IM** *020 †20
DORMONT, Richard E. 400 BURDICK EXPY E 58701 #008-01-1940 L1954 **PD** *020 †55
DRAGICEVIC, Todor Tode. 1900 8TH AVE SE 58701 #957-01-1987 L2006 **P** *020 †75
EARNSHAW, Peter Howard. 3RD ST AND BURDICK EXPWY S 58701 #917-23-1976 L1984 **ORS** *020 †40
EL-HOYEK, Georges Maurice. 1301 11TH AVE SW 58701 #605-03-2004 L2007 **FP** *012
FARAH, Samir Ibrahim. 20 BURDICK EXPY W STE 500 58701 #915-03-1962 L1977 **END IM** *020 †20
FIFE, Todd Allen. 831 S BROADWAY, STE 104 58701 #305-01-2000 L2001 **FM** *020 †18
FISCHBACH, Arie Leonard. 400 BURDICK EXPY E 58701 #165-03-1970 L1983 **OBG** *020 †30
FLICKINGER, Dale Bertram. 400 BURDICK EXPY E, MEDICAL ARTS CLINIC PC 58701 #038-40-1954 L1960 **GS OS** *072 †85
FREIBERG, Paul H. 307 5TH AVE SE STE 303 58701 #165-07-1967 L1987 **ON HEM** *020 †20
GASSER, Charles R. 101 3RD AVE SW, STE 101 58701 #034-01-1982 L2002 **OTO HNS** *020 †45
GEE, Quinn. 1 BURDICK EXPY W, TRINITY HOSPITAL 58701 #243-40-1982 L2002 **AN** *020 †05
GIBSON, David Kurt. 1900 8TH AVE SE, TRINITY HEALTH CENTER 58701 #068-01-1997 L2002 *020 †75
GOKEY, Susan Flickinger. 1 BURDICK EXPY W 58701 #037-01-1981 L1982 **EM** *020 †16
GONZALEZ, Karen Santos. 1201 11TH AVE SW, CENTER FOR FAMILY MEDICINE 58701 #748-10-1998 L2002 **FM** *020 †18
GRUBB, Merritt Byron. 400 BURDICK EXPY E 58701 #017-20-1967 L1973 **D GP** *020 †15
GUINTO, Cesar Habito. 400 BURDICK EXPY E, TRINITY HEALTH CENTER 58701 #748-02-1994 L2002 **ID IM** *020 †20
GUTIERREZ GARCIA, Francisc. 1 BURDICK EXPY W 58701 #649-14-1982 L2003 **FM** *100 †18
HADDON, Margaret J. 1 BURDICK EXPY W, TRINITY HOSPITAL 58701 #016-42-1984 L2007 **PDR DR** *020 †80
HAMILTON, Robert Austin. 1201 11TH AVE SW, CENTER FOR FAMILY MEDICINE 58701 #039-01-2003 L2005 **FP** *012
HANJANI, Farzodd Edward. 1 BURDICK EXPY W 58701 #041-15-2002 L2007 **DR** *020 †80
HANKINS, Robert E. 400 BURDICK EXPY E, THE FAMILY PHYSICIANS 58701 #016-43-1950 L1953 **FM A** *071 †18
HART, Mark Bennett. 1600 2ND AVE SW, BONE & JOINT CENTER MINOT 58701 #037-01-1980 L1985 **ORS** *020 †40
HE, Chaoying. 1 BURDICK EXPY W 58701 #243-76-1982 L2000 **AN** *020 †05
HEGGE, Ryan Kelly. ■ 58701 #037-01-2008 *012
HEIDORN, Guenther H. ■ 58703 #041-13-1948 L1959 **CD IM** *071 †20
HOLLAND, Michael John. 400 BURDICK EXPY E, MEDICAL ARTS CLINIC P.C 58701 #026-04-1975 L1978 **PD PDA** *020 †55
HUNTER, Jennifer Lynn. 831 S BROADWAY, STE 109 58701 #036-07-1994 L1998 **D** *020 †15
JANSEN, Wayne L. 1 BURDICK EXPY W, TRINITY HEALTH DEPT OF PAT 58701 #037-01-1978 L1983 **PTH** *020 †50
JETHWA, Ratilal Nathalal. 20 BURDICK EXPY W, STE 302 58701 #495-44-1974 L1983 **FM EM** *020 †18,16
JONES, Frederick W. 400 BURDICK EXPY E 58701 #028-46-1978 L2004 **PD AM** *020 †55
JOSHI, Ravindra Pandurang. 101 3RD AVE SW, STE 101 58701 #496-38-1984 L2000 *020
KAMBA, Thompson Togarepi. 1 BURDICK EXPY W 58701 #775-01-1993 L2006 **DR NR** *020 †80
KARMY, Grigory. PO BOX 1489 58702 #062-01-1992 L1996 **OS** *020
KECK, Stanley Walter. ■ 58703 #016-06-1955 L1956 **ORS** *071 †40
KHAN, Adnan Sikander. 1201 11TH AVE SW, CENTER FOR FAMILY MEDICINE 58701 #759-12-2004 L2004 **FM** *020
KHAN, Mohamed Ibrahim. 20 BURDICK EXPY W, STE 401 58701 #068-01-1963 L1995 **NS** *071
KIESSLING, Jay Jerome. 101 3RD AVE SW, STE 101 58701 #165-08-1984 L2003 **GS VS** *020 †85
KINDY, Alexander S. 101 3RD AVE SW, STE 101 58701 #060-01-1987 L1998 **ORS** *020 †40
KNUTSON, Scott Eric. 1 BURDICK EXPY W, TRINITY HEALTH 58701 #046-01-1997 L1998 **EM FM** *020 †18
KROHN, Kimberly T. 1201 11TH AVE SW 58701 #037-01-1996 L1997 **FM** *040 †18 ‡
LAMMERS, Jeffrey Michael. ■ 58703 #023-12-2002 L2004 **P** *020
LANGAGER, Tyrone O. ■ 58701 #030-05-1973 L1974 **FM GP** *071 †18
LEE, Kon-Hweii. 20 BURDICK EXPY W STE 203, TRINITY PROF BLDG 58701 #244-02-1970 L1976 **N** *072
LEE, William Alexander. 101 3RD AVE SW, STE 202 58701 #062-01-1964 L1971 **OPH** *020 †35
LEWIS, Scott Bradford. 1 BURDICK EXPY W 58701 #049-01-1990 L1996 **DR** *020 †80
LIM, Alan F H. 20 BURDICK EXPY W, STE 202 58701 #062-01-1967 L1974 **U** *020 †95
LONDON, Carl Bezaleel. ■ 58701 #041-09-1945 L1948 **OBG** *071 †30
LOPEZ, Francisco. 345 1ST AVE NW 58703 #847-09-1951 L1978 **RO DR** *020 †80
LOVE, James Thos, Jr. 101 3RD AVE SW, STE 101 58701 #036-01-1964 L2002 **OTO** *020 †45
LUTZ, Dennis Jos. 831 S BROADWAY STE 101 58701 #035-20-1973 L1979 **OBG** *020 †30 ‡
MAC DONALD, David Leslie. ■ 58701 #917-01-1967 L1976 **OBG** *075 †30
MACHADO, Ricardo. 1 BURDICK EXPY W 58701 #042-01-1993 L2004 **EM** *020 †16
MADLAND, William Thomas. 400 BURDICK EXPY E 58701 #034-01-1996 L2003 **OBG** *020 †30
MADZIWA, Felistas Hazvine. 831 S BROADWAY, STE 104 58701 #775-01-1994 L2007 **IM** *020
MAKONI, Stephen Neil Chiw. 831 S BROADWAY 58701 #775-01-1991 L2006 **HO** *020 †20
MARTINSEN, Wayne L. ■ 58701 #037-01-1994 L1996 **P** *020 †75
MATTERN, Dawn Dann. 101 3RD AVE SW, STE 101 58701 #037-01-1997 L1998 **FSM FM** *020 †18
MATTSON, Steven R. 831 S BROADWAY, STE 102 58701 #025-12-1982 L1985 **PD IM** *020 †20,55
MAYER, Monica May. 1 BURDICK EXPY W 58701 #037-01-1995 L1999 **FM** *020
MC CORMICK, Duncan Skye. 400 BURDICK EXPY E 58701 #065-01-1987 L1989 **ALI** *020 †20,03
MCCOY, Andrew Colin. 1201 11TH AVE SW 58701 #037-01-2007 L2007 **GS** *012
MC KENZIE, Jacquelyn K. 1 BURDICK EXPY W 58701 #046-01-1990 L1996 **PTH** *020
MEHTA, Rajnikant Liladhar. 315 MAIN ST S STE 102 58701 #495-39-1972 L1981 **PM GP** *020
MOHAMMED, Abrar Alvi. ■ 58701 #495-27-2001 L2004 **IM** *100 †20
MOILAN, Melissa. 400 BURDICK EXPY E 58701 #046-01-1987 L1994 **PD** *020 †55
MORRIS, Warren Patrick. 20 BURDICK EXPY W, STE 202 58701 #065-09-1986 L1991 *020
MOSTAD, Mary T. 400 BURDICK EXPY E, TRINITY HEALTH CENTER-MEDI 58701 #037-01-1990 L1991 **FM** *020 †18
MULLIN, Sarah Lynne. 831 S BROADWAY, STE 104 58701 #026-04-1985 L1986 **FM EM** *020 †18
MUNAWAR, Naureen. ■ 58701 #704-25-2003 L2007 **FP** *012
NARANJA, Imelda T. 1 BURDICK EXPY W 58701 #748-01-1964 L1971 **GP** *062
NASIR, Nabeel. ■ 58701 #704-01-2006 L2007 **FP** *012
NELSON, John Gerard. 1500 UNIVERSITY AVE W, BURDICK JOB CORPS CENTER W 58703 #539-05-1985 L1996 **EM FM** *020 †18
NETO, Manuel V De Costa. 1500 24TH AVE SW, CENTENNIAL MEDICAL CTR 58701 #770-03-1964 L1982 **U** *020 †95
NISA, Nuzhat Un. ■ 58701 #704-20-2000 L2007 **FP** *012
NJOKU, Chinyere Helen. 1201 11TH AVE SW 58701 #665-01-2005 L2006 **FP** *012
NORDELL, Margaret Claire. 831 S BROADWAY 58701 #037-01-1982 L1983 **OBG** *020 †30 ‡
NWAIGWE, Casmiar Ifeanyi. 400 BURDICK EXPY E, TRINITY HEALTH CENTER-MEDI 58701 #690-02-1991 L2007 **ID IM** *020 †20
ODEGARD, Russell Leon. ■ 58703 #019-02-1959 L1960 **FM** *071 †18
OGUAKWA, Ifesinachi Sylvi. 400 BURDICK EXPY E 58701 #690-04-1994 L2007 **FM** *020 †18
OLSON, Burton Gibson. ■ 58701 #026-04-1943 L1952 **OPH** *071 †35
OLSON, Paul David. 1 BURDICK EXPY W, TRINITY HOSPITAL 58701 #018-03-1987 L1988 **EM GE** *020 †18
OSUALA, Friday. 400 BURDICK EXPY E 58701 #690-04-1996 L2006 **PD** *020 †55
PADGETT, Danial R. 1201 11TH AVE SW 58701 #037-01-2005 L2005 **FP** *012
PAPPAS, Sam Geo. 400 BURDICK EXPY E 58701 #047-06-1966 L2007 **U** *020 †95
PERCELL, Robert Lee, Jr. 400 BURDICK EXPY E, HEALTH CENTER-MEDICAL ARTS 58701 #023-07-1996 L2002 **CD** *020 †20
PETERSON, Diana Lynne. 400 BURDICK EXPY E, HEALTH CENTER MEDICAL ARTS 58701 #038-40-1989 L1996 **PD** *020 †55
PETERSON, Myron Delano. 101 3RD AVE SW STE 101, ORTHOPEDIC ASSOCIATES 58701 #016-06-1959 L1962 **ORS** *071 †40
PIERSON, R Warren. ■ 58701 #016-11-1954 L1955 **GS IM** *071
PUGATCH, Bruce Scott. 400 BURDICK EXPY E, HEALTH CENTER MEDICAL ARTS 58701 #748-18-1989 L2006 **IM** *020 †20
RAGHIB, Gunay M. 400 BURDICK EXPY E 58701 #902-01-1957 L1971 **PD PDC** *071 †55
RASMUSSEN, Derek Jack. 1201 11TH AVE SW 58701 #665-01-2006 L2006 **FP** *012
RAUHUT, Medda Michelle. 1 BURDICK EXPY W 58701 #048-04-1996 L2007 **IM** *020 †20
REE, Cheryl Rae. 400 BURDICK EXPY E 58701 #005-12-1985 L1992 **FM EM** *020 †18
REEVE, Howard E. 400 BURDICK EXPY E 58701 #037-01-1986 L1987 **FM** *020 †18
REGMI, Suman Raj. ■ 58701 #672-03-2003 L2007 **FP** *012
REPP, George Mark. 1 BURDICK EXPY W, TRINITY HEALTH 58701 #028-46-1980 L1993 **PTH** *020 †50
RICHARDS, Deidre Lynn. 1900 8TH AVE SE 58701 #038-40-1998 L2005 **P** *020
RICHARDSON, Gale Robt. ■ 58703 #041-13-1945 **PTH** *020 †50
ROACH, Bruce Lawrence. 400 BURDICK EXPY E 58701 #021-06-1986 L2003 **FM** *020 †18
ROTHBERG, Martin Lee. 20 BURDICK EXPY W, STE 301 58701 #054-04-1982 L1992 **TS** *020 †85,90 ‡
SAFFARIAN, Nasser. 20 BURDICK EXPY W, STE 503 58701 #654-01-1985 L2001 **NEP** *020 †20
SANKE, Robert Francis. 120 BURDICK EXPY E 58701 #025-07-1970 L1999 **OPH** *020 †18,35 ‡
SATHER, Jeffrey A. 1 BURDICK EXPY W, TRINITY HOSPITAL 58701 #037-01-1998 L2001 **EM** *020 †16
SCHAFFNER, Carol Marie. 831 S BROADWAY 58701 #046-01-1978 L1982 **OBG** *020
SCHIELD, Laura Beth. 1 BURDICK EXPY W 58701 #045-04-1991 L1996 **CHP P** *020 †75
SCHMIDT, James A. 1 BURDICK EXPY W, TRINITY HOSPITAL 58701 #037-01-2004 L2004 **FM** *020
SCHOENBERG, Stephen John. 1201 11TH AVE SW 58701 #005-11-1990 *100
SCOTT, Earl Dexter. 101 3RD AVE SW, STE 101 58701 #060-01-1977 L2003 **ORS** *020
SHABER, Justin David. 1201 11TH AVE SW 58701 #024-05-2002 L2005 **CD** *012 †20
SHAFER, Justin Alan. 1201 11TH AVE SW, MINOT CENTER FOR FAMILY ME 58701 #305-01-2005 L2006 **FP** *012
SHEEHAN, John Edward. 831 S BROADWAY STE 105, TRINTY FAMILYCARE CENTER 58701 #046-01-1978 L1982 **IM** *020 †20
SHIDYAK, Ghassan. 1 BURDICK EXPY W 58701 #605-01-1989 L2002 **AN CCA** *020 †05
SHIPLEY, Frank Edward. 101 3RD AVE SW, STE 201 58701 #017-20-1973 L1979 **GS TS** *020 †90,85
SIGAUKE, Ellen. 1 BURDICK EXPY W 58701 #775-01-1997 L2006 **PTH** *020 †50
SIYANBADE, Oyetunde O. 101 3RD AVE SW, STE 101 58701 #690-01-1990 L2005 **GS** *020
SMITH, C Milton. 123 1ST ST SW, UNIVERSITY OF NORTH DAKOTA 58701 #048-13-1971 L1972 **FM** *040 †18
SMITH, John Clair. 1 BURDICK EXPY W 58701 #023-07-1954 L1971 **PTH NM** *020 †50,28
STATON, Robert Dennis. 1900 8TH AVE SE 58701 #011-02-1973 L1979 **P CHP** *020 †75
STILLERMAN, Charles Blair. 20 BURDICK EXPY W, STE 401 58701 #016-43-1982 L1995 **NS GS** *020 †25
STRIPE, Stephen Craig. 123 1ST ST SW, U OF ND SCHOOL OF MEDICINE 58701 #030-05-1979 L2003 **FM** *020 †18 ‡
SULIMAN, Faroug Yassin Mo. 20 BURDICK EXPY E, TRINITY HOSPITAL 58701 #848-01-1994 L2007 **IM** *020 †20
SWENSON, Bruce Berg. 400 BURDICK EXPY E, STE 400 58701 #048-12-1974 L1979 **GE IM** *020 †20
SWENSON, Charles Herbert. 400 BURDICK EXPY E 58701 #026-04-1972 L1973 **IM** *020 †20
TALEBDOOST, Farzin. 1 BURDICK EXPY W, TRINITY HEALTH 58701 #422-01-2003 L2004 **FM** *020
TALLEY, Wade Rolland. 1201 11TH AVE SW 58701 #037-01-1995 L1998 **FM** *040 †18

■ = Address Information Privacy Protected

THOMAS-EAPEN, Elizabeth. 1201 11TH AVE SW, UNIVERSITY PHYSICIANS HEAL 58701 #495-31-1991 L2000 **FM** *020 †18

TIN-MAUNG, Brian. 1 BURDICK EXPY W 58701 #209-01-1980 L1994 **AN** *020 †05

TURK, Samir Michel. 400 BURDICK EXPY E, MEDICAL ARTS CLINIC 58701 #539-06-1987 L1994 **CD** *020 †20

TURNEAU, Kelly Jay. 1 BURDICK EXPY W 58701 #654-01-2000 L2001 **IM** *020

TURNER, Ronald Lowe. TRINITY MEDICAL CENTER, DAKOTACARE PHYSICIANS ASSN 58701 #026-04-1981 L1983 **FM EM** *075 †18

UDEKWE, Anthony Anenechuk. 400 BURDICK EXPY E 58701 #690-04-1995 L2004 **PD** *020 †55

UTHUS, David Martin. 101 3RD AVE SW, STE 101 58701 #026-04-1973 L1982 **ORS** *020 †40

VANDALL, Michael Thos. 315 MAIN ST S, STE 205 58701 #037-01-1976 L1981 **OBG** *020 †30

VERHEY, Jeffrey Todd. 20 BURDICK EXPY W, STE 203 58701 #046-01-1990 L1996 **PCC** *020 †20

VLASAK, William Richard. 1201 11TH AVE SW 58701 #305-01-2001 L2001 **FM** *100

WALKER, Marc Robert. ■ 58701 #007-02-2008 †012

WHITMAN, Mark Warren. 315 MAIN ST S STE 101, RADIOLOGY CONSULTANTS P.C. 58701 #037-01-1978 L1982 **DR** *020 †80

WILKIE, Penny Mc Leod. 123 1ST ST SW, MINOT CENTER FOR FAMILY ME 58701 #037-01-1994 L1996 **FM** *020 †18

WILLIAMS, Darrell Peter. 120 BURDICK EXPY E 58701 #047-05-1980 L1984 **OPH** *020 †35

WOHLER, Johnathan Baumann. 1201 11TH AVE SW 58701 #039-01-1992 L2004 **GPM** *020

WOLSKY, Chad Jeremy. 120 BURDICK EXPY E 58701 #037-01-1999 L2003 *020 †35

YALAVARTHI, Prasad Vk. 831 S BROADWAY, CANCER CARE CENTER 58701 #495-50-1979 L2004 **IM ON** *020

YEUNG, Chi Kong. 20 BURDICK EXPY W STE 602 58701 #244-01-1968 L1975 **U NEP** *020 †95

YOUNG, Marcel Percy. 831 S BROADWAY 58701 #037-01-1990 L1991 **FM** *020 †18

ZHANG, Yuanhui. 1105 11TH ST SW 58701 #243-16-1985 L2002 **PD** *020 †60

MINOT AIR FORCE BASE – WARD

AGNER, Dale Roemer. 10 MISSILE AVE, 5 MDG 58705 #023-12-1990 L1992 **FM** *020 †18

AMENT, Aaron Lee. 10 MISSILE AVE, ATTN: CREDENTIAL OFFICE 58705 #305-01-2002 L2002 **FM** *020 †18

BRANDT, Keith Edward. 10 MISSILE AVE, 5 MDG 58705 #017-20-1991 L1992 **GPM AM** *020 †70,18

CARRAHER, June A. ■ 58705 #030-05-1976 L1977 **FM EM** *020 †18

COOP, Christopher Albert. ■ 58705 #023-12-2000 L2002 **AI** *020 †20,03 ‡

FARBER, Susan Lynne. 10 MISSILE AVE, 5TH MEDICAL GROUP 58705 #023-12-1997 L1998 **PD** *020 †55

SIPOS, Peter Thomas. ■ 58705 #023-12-1998 L2001 **GS** *020

SUMMERS, Mark Adam. ■ 58705 #041-02-1996 L1999 **GPM** *020 †70

THOMAS, Elsa. ■ 58704 #041-15-2001 L2001 **IM** *020

TURNEAU, Kevin John. 10 MISSILE AVE, MINOT AFB ND 58705 #010-03-2003 L2004 **GS** *020

WALSH, David Wm. 10 MISSILE AVE, MINOT VA CBOC 58705 #039-01-1971 L1991 **GP** *020

MOHALL – RENVILLE

FAULCONBRIDGE, Albert J. ■ 58761 #067-01-1960 L1971 **FM OPH** *071 †18

GOKAVI, Walter Alfred. 101 4TH AVE SE, BOX 397 58761 #495-27-1954 L1971 **GP GS** *071

NEW ROCKFORD – EDDY

CRAIG, James Michael. 6 8TH ST N 58356 #030-05-1971 L1991 **FM** *020

NEW TOWN – MOUNTRAIL

ARCELAY, Corey Dean. 1 MINNI TOHE DR, MINNE TOHE HEALTH CENTER 58763 #041-09-1987 L2002 **IM** *020

BENNETT, Dietmar H. 31 LITTLE KNIFE 58763 #917-10-1964 L1972 **GP GS** *071

MC RILL, Philip Elijah. 1 MINNI TOHE DR, MINNE-TOHE HEALTH CENTER 58763 #038-40-1992 L2001 **IM** *020 †18

NORTHWOOD – GRAND FORKS

EELKEMA, Robert Cameron. 4 N PARK ST 58267 #054-04-1961 L1965 **FM GPM** *030 †70,18

OAKES – DICKEY

AVULA, Sai Krishna. ■ 58474 #496-40-1994 L2004 **IMG** *020 †20

NAGALA, Rup Kumar. 420 S 7TH ST, SOUTHEAST MEDICAL CENTER 58474 #495-53-1973 L1977 **CCS FM** *020 †18

NAGALA, Vani. 420 S 7TH ST 58474 #495-50-1981 L1982 **IM IMG** *020 †20

TAN, Raymundo Tengki. 420 S 7TH ST, SOUTHEAST MEDICAL CENTER 58474 #748-01-1974 L1982 **R** *020 †80

PARK RIVER – WALSH

JOHNSON, Joel J. ■ 58270 #037-01-1993 L1994 **FM** *020 †18

PILTINGSRUD, Harold R. ■ 58270 #041-13-1943 L1948 **GP OS** *071

POWERS LAKE – BURKE

KOSA, Annamaria M K. ■ 58773 #917-30-1964 L1973 **GS EM** *071

RICHARDTON – STARK

SELPH, Shelley Suzanne. 215 3RD AVE W 58652 #036-01-2001 L2001 **FM** *020 †18

ROLLA – ROLETTE

CID, Lilia. PO BOX 475 58367 #748-02-1978 L2007 **FM** *020 †18

COCAL, Lerdo Martin. 213 2ND AVE NE, PRESENTATION MEDICAL CENTE 58367 #748-10-1978 L2007 **IM** *020

GLASNER, Duane Dale. 213 2ND ST NE 58367 #056-05-1961 L1964 **FM** *071 †18

MEIER, Lowell Bernard. ■ 58367 #007-02-1966 L1970 **FM** *071 †18

RUGBY – PIERCE

ENUBUZOR, Harriet L. 800 3RD AVE SW 58368 #035-45-1990 L2003 **FM** *020 †18

HILTS, George Henry. 800 3RD AVE SW, EYE SPECIALISTS PC 58368 #018-03-1953 L1954 **GP** *071

LEVENE, Susanne. 800 S MAIN AVE, HEART OF AMERICA MEDICAL C 58368 #007-02-1993 L2006 **GS** *020 †85

MC INTYRE, Donald Gordon. 800 3RD AVE SW 58368 #041-01-1959 L1960 **IM PA** *020 †20

OLUMIDE, Babatunde Adewal. 800 3RD AVE SW, JOHNSON CLINIC 58368 #690-02-1997 L2005 **IM** *020 †20

SCHONEBERG, Steven Bruce. 800 3RD AVE SW 58368 #034-01-1983 L1989 **FM** *020 †18

SEDO, Philip Stanley. 800 3RD AVE SW 58368 #019-02-1974 L1976 **FM** *020

VAAGEN, Jeffrey Lee. 800 S MAIN AVE 58368 #037-01-1994 L1995 **IM** *020 †18,20

SAINT THOMAS – PEMBINA

EELKEMA, Herman H. ■ 58276 #026-04-1953 L1959 **DR** *071 †80

STANLEY – MOUNTRAIL

HENINGER, Robert Dennis. 615 6TH ST SE, P O BOX 399 58784 #037-01-2002 L2002 **FM** *020 †18

PATEL, Shashikant C. ■ 58784 #495-20-1965 L1983 **GP PMM** *020

STEELE – KIDDER

DIEHL, Kent A. 110 W BROADWAY 58482 #037-01-1993 L1994 **FM** *020 †18

TIOGA – WILLIAMS

GADE, Swami Prasad. PO BOX 159, TIOGA MEDICAL CENTER 58852 #495-11-2001 L2007 **FM** *020 †18

MANNE, Hari Krishna. 710 N WELO ST 58852 #495-50-1996 L2003 **IM** *020 †20 ‡

PATEL, Ramanbhai Ambalal. TIOGA MEDICAL CLINIC 58852 #495-20-1964 L1973 **FM GS** *020 †18

TURTLE LAKE – MCLEAN

RILLO, Antonio R. ■ 58575 #748-01-1954 L1971 **GP OBG** *020

VALLEY CITY – BARNES

AHMAD, Adeel. 520 CHAUTAUQUA BLVD 58072 #704-21-2000 L2004 **IM** *020

BRAUNAGEL, Bradley A. 520 CHAUTAUQUA BLVD, MERITCARE VALLEY CITY CLIN 58072 #037-01-1987 L1988 **FM** *020 †18

BUHR, James Byron. 520 CHAUTAUQUA BLVD, JAMES B BUHR MD 58072 #026-04-1971 L1980 **FM** *020 †18

GARCIA, Luis Arturo. 520 CHAUTAUQUA BLVD 58072 #649-31-1994 L2000 **GS** *020 †85

GOVEN, Genevieve Michelle. 520 CHAUTAUQUA BLVD 58072 #037-01-1990 L1991 **FM** *020 †18 ‡

GOVEN, John Wm. VALLEY CITY CLINIC 58072 #036-05-1957 L1958 *071

HLAVINKA, Delbert John. 520 CHAUTAUQUA BLVD 58072 #036-05-1961 L1962 **FM** *020 †18

KANDIMALLA, Jithender Red. 520 CHAUTAUQUA BLVD 58072 #495-21-1991 L2002 **GS** *020 †85

KLEIN, Clifford J. ■ 58072 #016-43-1949 L1952 **GP GS** *071

LARSON, Donald Melvin. 520 CHAUTAUQUA BLVD 58072 #036-05-1960 L1968 **N FM** *071 ‡

LUKE, Madeline Zetee. 520 CHAUTAUQUA BLVD 58072 #043-01-1979 L1984 **IM** *020 †20

MACHAYYA, Maletira G. 909 6TH AVE NE 58072 #495-04-1960 L1973 **GS U** *020

MITZEL, Fredrick. 132 4TH AVE NE, DAKOTA CLINIC 58072 #037-01-1981 L1986 **FM FPG** *020 †18

NAGLE, Thomas Duane. 520 CHAUTAUQUA BLVD 58072 #018-03-1972 L1979 **ORS** *020 †40

SCHMITT, John Elmer, Jr. 520 CHAUTAUQUA BLVD 58072 #038-40-1979 L2002 **OTO** *020 †45

THORESON, Glenn Merton. 520 CHAUTAUQUA BLVD 58072 #019-02-1966 L1969 **FM** *020 †18

ZAIMAN, Herman. 123 3RD ST NE 58072 #047-05-1957 L1978 **R** *071

VELVA – MCHENRY

LARSON, Dana. PO BOX 70, 111 W 1ST ST 58790 #028-02-1970 L1975 **FM** *071 ‡

VOLTAIRE – MCHENRY

COLBY, Karna Del. ■ 58792 #037-01-2004 **PTH** *012

WAHPETON – RICHLAND

BATERINA, Leandro F, Jr. 275 11TH ST S, DAKOTA CLINIC 58075 #748-08-1976 L2001 **FM** *020 †18

CHAMBERS, Robert Tully. 332 2ND AVE N 58075 #065-05-1966 L1995 **GS** *071 †85
DE KREY, John Allen. 614 DAKOTA AVE, MEDICAL ARTS CLINIC 58075 #048-12-1958 L1973 **AN OS** *071 †05
ENGSTROM, David Carl. ■ 58075 #037-01-1976 L1989 **IM** *030 †20
EVANS, Eugene Earl. 275 11TH ST S, DAKOTA CLINIC LTD-WAHPETON 58075 #037-01-1983 L1984 **FM** *075 †18
FRIEDERICHS, Matthew G. 332 2ND AVE N 58075 #037-01-1997 L2003 **OSM** *020 †40
HALVORSON, James Edward. 332 2ND AVE N 58075 #037-01-1980 L1981 **FM** *020 †18
MALKASIAN, Lucy Boghos. 275 11TH ST S 58075 #913-38-1973 L1982 **PD** *020 †55
MAYO, William Michael. 332 2ND AVE N 58075 #037-01-1979 L1980 **FM** *040 †18
MISLAN, Garry Andrew. 332 2ND AVE N, MERITCARE CLNC WAHPETON 58075 #060-02-1974 L1995 **FM** *020 †18
MOHS, Thomas James. 275 11TH ST S 58075 #046-01-1991 L1996 **GS** *020 †85
NYARANDI, Timothy Monari. 332 2ND AVE N 58075 #577-01-2001 L2007 **FM** *020 †18
OSTMO, Robert Parnell. 332 2ND AVE N 58075 #005-02-1982 L1985 **FM** *020 †18
PANKOW, Dawn Kaye. 275 11TH ST S 58075 #037-01-1982 L1985 **FM** *020 †18
STASKO, Andrew John. 332 2ND AVE N 58075 #023-12-1988 L2007 **GS TRS** *020 †85
STENHOUSE, Faine. 332 2ND AVE N, MERITCARE CLINIC 58075 #060-01-1995 L1997 **FM** *020 †18
STRAND, Duane D. 275 11TH ST S 58075 #037-01-1985 L1988 **IM** *020 †20
WALL, Wendell H. 275 11TH ST S 58075 #005-12-1953 L1953 **FM** *071 †18
WASEMILLER, James Preston. 614 DAKOTA AVE 58075 #005-12-1972 L1976 **GS** *020
WASEMILLER, Paul Scot. 275 11TH ST S 58075 #005-12-1982 L1987 **GS** *020 †85

WATFORD CITY — MCKENZIE

GORDON, Terrance Munroe. 525 N MAIN ST, MCKENZIE COUNTY CLINIC 58854 #060-01-1978 L1997 *020
RAMAGE, Gary William. 525 N MAIN ST 58854 #068-01-1990 L1995 **FM** *020

WEST FARGO — CASS

BATCHELLER, April Elizabe. ■ 58078 #037-01-2008 *012
BOROWICZ, Ronald John. 1220 SHEYENNE ST 58078 #026-04-1975 L1976 **FM** *020 †18
DAHL, Bruce Lane. 1220 SHEYENNE ST, MERITCARE CLINIC WEST FARG 58078 #037-01-1976 L1977 **FM** *020 †18 ‡
DRYNAN, John Joseph. ■ 58078 #016-43-1962 L1965 **GYN OBG** *072
GESTON, Robert L. 1220 SHEYENNE ST, WEST FARGO MEDICAL CENTER 58078 #018-03-1960 L1961 **FM** *071 †18
HORDVIK, Marit Karin. 1401 13TH AVE E, DAKOTA CLINIC, LTD. 58078 #037-01-1990 L1992 **FM** *020 †18
HOWDEN, Richard Lorimer. 1401 13TH AVE E 58078 #062-01-1979 L1995 **FM** *020 †18
JACOBSON, David A. 1220 SHEYENNE ST, MERITCARE CLNC WEST FARGO 58078 #037-01-1994 L1996 **FM** *020 †18
LEHER, George Edward. 1401 13TH AVE E 58078 #016-11-1973 L1976 **PD** *020 †55
LENZMEIER, Richard. 1220 SHEYENNE ST, MERITCARE-WEST FARGO 58078 #037-01-1979 L1980 **FM** *020 †18
MC CAMY, Allan Edward. 1220 SHEYENNE ST 58078 #026-04-1976 L2006 **FM** *020 †18
MESTERY, Donald Stephen. 1401 13TH AVE E, DAKOTA CLINIC, LTD. 58078 #062-01-1974 L1987 **IM OS** *071 †20
MORK, Kevin J. ■ 58078 #037-01-1987 L1988 **AN** *020 †05
RAGHIB, Ender Gunay. 325 EDGEWATER DR, PEDIATRIC ARTS CLINIC 58078 #037-01-2000 L2003 **PD** *020 ‡
SHAFFER, Andrew Wesley. ■ 58078 #037-01-2008 *012
VETTER, Richard Thos. 1401 13TH AVE E 58078 #037-01-1988 L1989 **FM** *020 †18
VORA, Rathin Nishikant. 1401 13TH AVE E, INNOVISS HEALTH 58078 #495-01-1998 L2006 **IM** *020 †20,70
WELSH, Megan. ■ 58078 #037-01-2008 *012
WOSICK, William F. ■ 58078 #037-01-1981 L1985 **DR** *020 †80

WILLISTON — WILLIAMS

ADDUCCI, Joseph Edward. 1213 15TH AVE W, BOX 2438 58801 #016-43-1959 L1966 **OBG** *020 †30 ‡

ANDERSON, Wayne Lee. 1213 15TH AVE W STE 200 58801 #037-01-1980 L1982 **GS CRS** *020 †85
BOULTER, Michael James. 1301 15TH AVE W, MERCY HOSPITAL 58801 #021-01-1977 L1986 **EM FM** *020 †16,18
BROWN, Laurie Malcolm. 1301 15TH AVE W, MERCY MEDICAL CENTER 58801 #064-01-1952 L1991 **AN** *071
BRUNSMAN, William Joseph. 1102 MAIN ST 58801 #030-05-1993 L2005 **FM** *020 †18
CANSINO-LIM, Mariquita. 1102 MAIN ST, WESTERN DAKOTA MEDICAL GRO 58801 #748-01-1963 L1973 **GYN GPM** *071
CODE, William Edwin. 1102 MAIN ST 58801 #019-02-1973 L1976 **FM** *020
CONANT, James Edward. ■ 58802 #023-07-1968 L1995 **AN** *020 †05
DAVID, Henry Edward. 1301 15TH AVE W, MERCY MEDICAL CENTER 58801 #028-78-1968, ▲ L2002 **ORS** *020
DAVIES, Edward Hart. 1301 15TH AVE W, MERCY MEDICAL CENTER 58801 #836-02-1967 L2004 **AN** *020 †05
FREISLEBEN-COOK, Lois A. 3 4TH ST E, PO BOX 696 58801 #005-14-1980 L1999 **PD** *020 †55
GREINER, Teresa J. 1301 15TH AVE W, MERCY MEDICAL CENTER 58801 #048-04-1984 L1996 **P** *020 †75
GREWAL, Sarbjit Singh. 1301 15TH AVE W, MERCY HOSP 58801 #539-06-1984 L1994 **EM** *020
HAGAN, Edward J. ■ 58802 #016-01-1942 L1946 *071
HARRISON, Lyle Murray. 1301 15TH AVE W, MERCY MEDICAL CENTER 58801 #049-01-1993 L1997 **RO** *020
HEGGE, Theresa Anne. ■ 58801 #037-01-2008 *012
HERR, John Rudolph. 1213 15TH AVE W 58801 #010-01-1965 L1972 **OPH** *071 †35
ISBISTER, Earl Glen. 1301 15TH AVE W 58801 #067-01-1958 L1961 **U** *020
JASZCZAK, Leszek Julian. 14090 47TH LN NW 58801 #025-07-1993 L1997 **DR** *020 †80
JOHNSON, James Colin. 1102 MAIN ST 58801 #068-01-1976 L1979 **FM** *020
KEATING, Nora Ellen. 1301 15TH AVE W, MERCY HOSPITAL 58801 #037-01-1991 L1992 **FM** *020 †18
KEMP, Robert G. 1213 15TH AVE W, STE 250 58801 #037-01-1992 L1995 **FM** *020 †18
KENNEDY, James Alexander. 1102 MAIN ST 58801 #060-01-1972 L1996 **GP** *020
MAXWELL, John Kevin. ■ 58801 #049-01-1985 L2002 **DR** *020 †80
MC COY, Franklin E. 1301 15TH AVE W, MERCY HOSPITAL 58801 #067-01-1952 L1964 **CLP PTH** *071
MILLER, Cory Russell. 1213 15TH AVE W STE 250, CRAVEN HAGAN CLINIC LTD 58801 #037-01-1985 L1986 **IM** *020 †20
MORIN, Mark Edward. 1213 15TH AVE W STE 260, WILLISTON BASIN 58801 #005-11-1990 L2001 **OPH** *020 †35
NIELSEN, Allan Marc. 1213 15TH AVE W, CRAVEN HAGAN CLINIC LTD 58801 #037-01-1997 L1998 **FM** *020 †18
OLSON, James Harold. 1213 15TH AVE W, STE 260 58801 #037-01-1976 L1990 **OPH** *020 †35
OLSON, M Jerome. ■ 58801 #048-12-1959 L1963 **FM** *071 †18
OLSON, Mark A. 1102 MAIN ST, TRINITY COMM CLINIC 58801 #037-01-1991 L1992 **FM** *020 †18
OLSON, Robert Jos. ■ 58801 #026-04-1957 L1957 **R** *071 †80
RAYMOND, Mark Cooper. 1213 15TH AVE W 58801 #051-07-1987 L2007 **OPH** *020 †35
SHAHIN, Salem Shehadeh. 1301 15TH AVE W 58801 #915-02-1969 L1981 **U** *020 †95
SKJEI, Donald Ellsworth. ■ 58801 #041-13-1946 L1947 **FM PD** *071 †18
SKURDAL, David Nelson. 1301 15TH AVE W 58801 #016-43-1978 L2003 **AN PME** *020
SOLBERG, Sara A. 1213 15TH AVE W STE 220 58801 #037-01-2000 L2004 **OBG** *020
STRINDEN, Dean R. 3016 13TH AVE E, WESTERN DAKOTA MED GROUP P 58801 #007-02-1952 L1953 **GP** *071 †18
TONG, Beverly Jean. 1213 15TH AVE W 58801 #019-02-1997 L2003 **OBG** *020 †30
VIBETO, Brett Kenneth. ■ 58801 #037-01-2000 L2007 **GS** *100
WIENS, Glenn Allen. 1213 15TH AVE W, CRAVEN HAGAN CLINIC LTD 58801 #026-04-1986 L1987 **FM OBS** *020 †18
WILDER, Andrew J. 1102 MAIN ST 58801 #037-01-1997 L1998 **FM** *020 †18
WILDER, Lawrence Lee. 1213 15TH AVE W, CRAVEN HAGAN CLINIC LTD 58801 #026-04-1975 L1976 **FM** *020 †18

WISHEK — MCINTOSH

REAMS, Gary Glenn. 1007 4TH AVE S 58495 #018-03-1971 L1972 **AM** *020

ADA – HARDIN

DAS, Kalyan. 520 W LINCOLN AVE STE D 45810 #160-05-1981 L1998 **IM** *020 †20
DAVIS, Leslie Leon. ■ 45810 #048-02-1997 **OS** *100
KRAMER, John Alan. ■ 45810 #038-40-1938 L1938 **OS GP** *071
ROMANS, Susan Kay. 121 S MAIN ST 45810 #035-15-1982 L1983 **FM** *020 †18

ADENA – JEFFERSON

BANGERA, Divakar S. 211 STATE ROUTE 250 43901 #495-23-1963 L1978 **GP ORS** *020
BLACK, Eric Richard. ■ 43901 #038-40-2005 L2005 **P** *012

AKRON – SUMMIT

ABDALLA, Abdalla Ali. 1 PERKINS SQ, CHILDREN'S HOSPITAL AKRON 44308 #848-01-1982 L2001 **PD CHN** *020 †75
ABDOLLAHIAN, Amir. 444 N MAIN ST 44310 #517-04-1961 L1969 **ORS** *020 †40
ABRAMOVICH, Caroline M. 525 E MARKET ST 44304 #041-12-1996 L1999 **PTH** *020 †50
ABRAMOVICH, Drew Karam. 75 ARCH ST, STE 202 44304 #010-01-1993 L1996 **HO** *020 †20
ABU-MARAQ, Ahmad-Fathi M. 93 W EXCHANGE ST, MAHMOUND 44308 #847-08-1970 L1980 **GP** *020
ABURAHMEH, Samah Khalil. ■ 44304 #575-02-1995 L2002 **PD** *100
ADAMCZYK, Mark John. 300 LOCUST STE 105 44302 #030-06-1999 L2000 **ORS** *100 †40
ADEKUNLE, Emmanuel Olayin. ■ 44313 #023-01-2004 L2004 **PSM** *012
ADY, Michael Scott. 5180 FAWN DR 44319 #038-45-2002 L2002 **EM** *020 †16
AGAMANOLIS, Dimitrios P. 281 LOCUST ST 44302 #418-02-1962 L1972 **NP PTH** *020 †50
AGARWAL, Shanu. 75 ARCH ST, STE 105 44304 #038-44-2000 L2006 **ID** *020 †20
AGNOR, Ross Curtis. 1 PERKINS SQ, MEDICAL CENTER OF AKRON 44308 #038-41-1992 L1995 **AN** *020 †05
AKHTAR, Jabir Kamal. ■ 44307 #661-01-1999 L2002 **FM** *020
ALBAINY, Donald Burton. 789 WHITE POND DR, STE A 44320 #038-45-1988 L1990 **IM** *020 †20
ALBERT, Samuel. 395 E MARKET ST 44304 #035-09-1993 L1998 **OTO** *020 †45
ALBRIGHT, Richard James. 400 WABASH AVE 44307 #017-20-1963 L1967 **R NM** *020 †80,28
ALEXANDER, Ian James. 3975 EMBASSY PKWY, STE 102 44333 #065-06-1978 L1987 **ORS** *071 †40
ALI, Asjad Mahmood. 400 WABASH AVE 44307 #704-04-2001 L2006 **FP** *012
ALLEN, Richard Browning. 400 WABASH AVE, AKRON GENERAL MEDICAL CENT 44307 #038-41-1990 L1994 **RNR** *020 †80
ANAGNOSTOU, Sevasti K. ■ 44313 #038-44-2006 L2006 **OBG** *012
ANDREWS, David Arthur. 300 LOCUST ST, STE 560 44302 #041-12-1982 L1990 **PDS CCM** *020 †85
ANDREWS, James P. 400 WABASH AVE 44307 #038-06-1950 L1950 **PTH** *020 †50
ANDRISH, Shannon Leigh. 1 PERKINS SQ, AKRON CHILDRENS HOSPPEDIAT 44308 #038-40-1999 L1999 **PD** *020 †55
ANSARI, Shaukat Ali. ■ 44313 #496-26-1999 L2003 **CHP** *012
APTE, Nirmala Manohar. 340 S BROADWAY ST, PORTAGE PATH BEHAVIORAL HE 44308 #495-28-1966 L1977 **P** *071 †75
APYNYS, Vytautas. ■ 44320 #427-23-1951 L1960 **OBS GYN** *071
AQUINO, Henedine Suguitan. 1 PERKINS SQ 44308 #748-02-1983 L1990 **PEM** *074 †55
ARDILA, Guillermo Enrique. 444 N MAIN ST 44310 #264-01-1962 *100
ARGUETA, Raphael A. 44320 #305-01-2002 L2005 **FM** *020 †18
ARTHUR, Bruce Wayne. ■ 44313 #038-43-2004 L2004 **MPD** *012
ASHRAF, Muhammad Salman. 400 WABASH AVE, BLDG ACC 44307 #704-02-1999 L2007 **IM** *100
ASIF, Javaria. EDUCATIO400 WABASH, CO MEDICAL 44307 #704-01-2003 L2007 **FP** *012
ASLANIAN, Wahan Socrat. 150 CROSS ST, COMMUNITY SUPPORT NETWORK 44311 #915-02-1971 L1990 **PA** *020 †75
ASSAAD, Wafa. ■ 44307 #605-01-1985 L1992 **IM** *020 †20
ATTALLAH-WASIF, Emad Sami. 400 WABASH AVE, AKRON GENERAL MED CTR 44307 #915-04-2000 L2007 **FP** *012
AWENDER, Herbert Scott. 157 W CEDAR ST, STE 104 44307 #038-41-1989 L1994 **GS** *020 †85
AZIKIWE, Nneka Rachael. 1 PERKINS SQ 44308 #024-01-1997 L2003 **ADL** *020 †55
BAAB, Shad Masters. 1 PERKINS SQ, AKRON CHILDREN'S HOSPITAL 44308 #422-01-2003 L2006 **PEM** *012 †55
BABAI, Sarah. 525 E MARKET ST 44304 #038-44-1997 L1999 **OBG** *020 †30
BACHA, David Eugene. 3975 EMBASSY PKWY STE 101 44333 #038-44-1981 L1982 **RHU IM** *020 †20
BADAL, Joseph John. 2620 RIDGEWOOD RD, ACUTE CARE SPECIALIST 44313 #005-12-1977 L1979 **EM** *020 †16
BAGHERI, Abbas. 995 TIMBERLINE DR 44333 #517-01-1961 L1970 **OBG** *020
BAGHERI, Ali. 995 TIMBERLINE DR 44333 #038-41-2008 *012
BAILEY, Barbara Jean. 571 E TURKEYFOOT LAKE RD, STE A 44319 #038-45-1988 L1989 **FM** *020 †18
BALDONADO, Reginald Pius. 525 E MARKET ST, DEPT OF MED EDUCATION 44304 #748-02-2004 L2006 **FP** *012
BALL, Richard Wm. 1600 E TURKEYFOOT LAKE RD 44312 #055-01-1978 L1979 **PD** *020 †55
BANDI, Rama Krishna Rao. 1037 N MAIN ST, STE B 44310 #495-50-1973 L1979 **GE IM** *020 †20
BANDYOPADHYAY, Tanya. 525 E MARKET ST, DEPT OF OBGYN 44304 #495-39-1990 L2001 **OBG** *020
BARANEK, Robert Allen. 75 ARCH ST STE 412 44304 #038-40-1973 L1973 **TS GS** *020 †85,90
BARE, Rudd Judson. 525 E MARKET ST, SUMMA HEALTH SYSTEM 44304 #038-44-2004 L2004 **EM** *020
BARONE, Bradley Andrew. 525 E MARKET ST, SUMMA HEALTH SYSTEM 44304 #020-12-2004 L2004 **EM** *020
BARTHOLOMAE, Warren Max. ■ 44303 #026-04-1946 L1951 **CD IM** *071 †20
BARTKOWSKI, Henry M. 1 PERKINS SQ, CHMCA #6401 44308 #035-06-1976 L1986 **NS NSP** *020 †25
BARTON, Karen Lee. 1400 S ARLINGTON ST, AKRON COMM HEALTH RESOURCE 44306 #038-44-2002 L2002 **FM** *020 †18
BARWICK, James Franklin. ■ 44313 #036-08-2004 L2004 **ORS** *012
BASHOR, Kendrick Barnett. 880 MULL AVE STE 100 44313 #004-01-1989 L1992 **FM** *020 †18
BATES, James Harold. 1 PARK WEST BLVD STE 310 44320 #038-44-1984 L1986 **OPH N** *020 †35

BAUER, Paula S. 400 WABASH AVE 44307 #025-01-1985 L1990 **PTH** *020 †50
BAVIKATTY, Ramachandra. 444 N MAIN ST 44310 #495-09-1960 L1969 **CD IM** *071 †20
BAZAN, Jose Antonio. 525 E MARKET ST 44304 #038-75-2004, ▲ L2004 **ID** *012 †20
BEDDELL, Gregory Michael. ■ 44312 #038-44-2004 L2004 **GS** *012
BEKLEMISHEVA, Anastasia A. 400 WABASH AVE 44307 #913-72-1996 L2005 **P** *012
BELFER, Mark Harris. 400 WABASH AVE 44307 #018-75-1977, ▲ L1986 **FM** *040 †16
BELL, Robert Harry. 3975 EMBASSY PKWY 44333 #038-41-1979 L1981 **ORS** *020 †40
BENDER, Elizabeth Ann. 75 ARCH ST, STE 406 44304 #038-45-1991 L1997 **GS** *020 †85
BENNETT, Gordon Leslie. 3975 EMBASSY PKWY, CRYSTAL CLINIC, INC 44333 #068-01-1982 L1985 **OAR** *020 †40
BEN-SHACHAR, Giora. 1 PERKINS SQ, CHILDREN'S HOSPITAL OF AKR 44308 #550-01-1968 L1982 **PDC** *020 †55
BENTLEY, Dennis Franklin. 95 ARCH ST, STE 165 44304 #038-41-2000 L2000 **U** *020 †95 ‡
BERZZARINS, Val. ■ 44333 #407-25-1949 L1956 **P** *071
BETHEM, Daniel. 3975 EMBASSY PKWY, STE 102 44333 #041-13-1970 L1973 **OSS** *020 †40
BHALLA, Vivek. ■ 44313 #038-44-2006 L2006 **FP** *012
BHE, Kian Ho. 947 W NIMISILA RD 44319 #506-02-1962 L1973 **GP OS** *020
BHULLER, Komalpreet Kaur. 400 WABASH AVE, AKRON GENERAL MED CTR 44307 #894-01-2004 L2005 **FP** *012
BIANCONI, Walter Bates. ■ 44301 #041-12-1955 L1958 **GP** *020 †18
BILGE-JOHNSON, Sumru Ayse. 400 WABASH AVE, CO AKRON GEN MED CTR-MED E 44307 #902-10-1993 L2003 **CHP** *012
BINDRA, Akhil Pratap. 95 ARCH ST, STE 210 44304 #038-44-1995 L1998 **IM PCC** *020 †20
BIONDI, John Xitco. 3975 EMBASSY PKWY, STE 201 44333 #040-02-1983 L1984 **HS VS** *020 †40
BIRD, Michael Wm. 1 PERKINS SQ, CHILDREN'S HOSP MEDICAL CE 44308 #038-41-1988 L1992 **PEM** *030 †20
BISHOP, Robert Michael. ■ 44313 #012-05-2007 L2007 **PD** *012
BISHOP, Troy William. 55 ARCH ST, INC 44304 #038-44-1994 L1995 **IM** *020 †20
BLACK, John Allen. 1 PARK WEST BLVD, STE 200 44320 #005-14-1985 L1989 **OBG** *020 †30.
BLANDA, Joseph B. 2383 S MAIN ST STE D106 44319 #041-12-1985 L1986 **ORS OSM** *020 †40
BLANDA, Michelle. 525 E MARKET ST # EM, AKRON CITY HOSPITAL 44304 #038-43-1985 L1986 **EM** *050 †16
BOBINSKY, Theodore M. 190 N UNION ST, STE 104 44304 #038-06-1983 L1984 **PME AN** *020 †05
BOBOC, Georgiana. 400 WABASH AVE 44307 #781-02-2003 L2006 **FP** *012
BOGANEY, Anthony Corey. 525 E MARKET ST, SUMMA HEALTH SYSTEM 44304 #041-07-1998 L2000 **GS** *020
BOLLIN, Gary Edward. 224 W EXCHANGE ST, STE 290 44302 #038-40-1980 L1981 **ID IM** *020 †20
BOLOGNA, Raymond Anthony. 95 ARCH ST, STE 165 44304 #038-44-1993 L1994 **U** *020 †95
BOLYARD, Brooks Edward. 525 E MARKET ST 44304 #038-44-1995 L2000 **PTH** *020 †50
BOND, Jess G. 444 N MAIN ST 44310 #038-44-1984 L1984 **OM IM** *062 †20,70
BONDI, Christopher John. ■ 44303 #038-44-2007 L2007 **TY** *012
BONILLA, Hector F. 75 ARCH ST, STE 105 44304 #264-05-1983 L2001 **IM** *020 †20
BONO, Kenneth T. ■ 44319 #033-05-2005 L2005 **ORS** *012
BONTADELLI, Rebecca Leah. ■ 44313 #038-45-2006 L2006 **EM** *012
BOSHKOS, Christopher. 411 E MARKET ST 44304 #038-40-1980 L1981 **NEP IM** *020 †20
BOUCHARD, Lawrence Fidele. 676 S BROADWAY ST, STE 105 44311 #024-07-1980 L1981 **FM** *020 †18
BOWER, John Richmond. 281 LOCUST ST 44302 #027-01-1986 L1986 **PD** *020 †55
BOWERSOX, Natalie Ann. 3636 YELLOW CREEK RD, OF THE RESERVE 44333 #038-43-1999 L2003 **OBG** *020 †30
BOWMAN, Dirk William. ■ 44303 #038-44-2006 L2006 **GS** *012
BOYLE, Kathleen Deminico. ■ 44319 #038-75-2005, ▲ L2005 **GS** *012
BRADFORD, John Chas. 400 WABASH AVE, AKRON GEN MED CTR 44307 #018-75-1978, ▲ L1979 EM *071 †16
BRAR, Ravinder Kaur. 340 S BROADWAY ST, PORTAGE PATH BEHAV HLTH 44308 #495-29-1973 L1979 **P** *020
BREAUX, Fabian Levere. 95 ARCH ST, STE 165 44304 #010-03-1968 L1969 **U** *020 †95
BREAUX, Todd Fabian. 95 ARCH ST STE 1, ADVANCED UROLOGY ASSOCIAT 44304 #038-41-1998 L2000 **U** *020 †95
BREEN, Thomas Robert. 55 ARCH ST, STE 1B 44304 #038-06-2005 L2005 **IM** *012
BRIDEWESER, Wm Buhmair. ■ 44319 #038-40-1961 L1961 **AN OS** *020
BRIES, Andrew David. ■ 44303 #018-03-2005 L2005 **ORS** *012
BRIGGS, Vilma Rose. 1 PARK WEST BLVD, STE 200 44320 #038-44-1991 L1995 **OBG** *020 †30
BROWER, Richard Scott. 20 OLIVE ST STE 200 44310 #024-07-1989 L1986 **ORS** *020 †40
BROWN, Calvin R. 1655 W MARKET ST, STE L 44313 #030-05-1976 L1977 **IM** *020 †18
BROWN, James Jude. 5147 MANCHESTER RD 44319 #038-44-1999 L1999 **FM** *020 †18
BU-ALI, Hanadi Mohammed. ■ 44307 #155-01-1996 L2007 **GS** *012 †85
BUKULMEZ, Hulya. 1 PERKINS SQ, AKRON CHINDRAN'S HOSPITAL 44308 #902-21-1992 L2000 **PPR** *020 †55
BULEN, Kenneth Allen. 400 WABASH AVE 44307 #038-40-1980 L1980 **FM OM** *020 †18
BURDETTE, Robert Dana. 963 GENESEE RD 44303 #016-06-1962 L1963 **CHN N** *071 †55
BURGHARDT, Tyson Clark. ■ 44313 #038-43-2007 L2007 **IM** *012
BURNETTE, Kreg Andrew. ■ 44303 #038-45-2002 L2002 **PEM** *012 †55
BURNSTINE, Robert Alan. 300 LOCUST ST STE 490 44302 #017-20-1972 L1972 **OPH PO** *020 †35
BURTON, Jean Frances. 3636 YELLOW CREEK RD, OF THE RESERVE 44333 #038-44-1985 L1987 **OBG** *020 †30
BUTLER, Thomas Jeffrey. 300 LOCUST ST, STE 540 44302 #056-06-1987 L1996 **PD** *020 †55
BUTTON, Kenneth Franklin. 400 WABASH AVE 44307 #017-20-1970 L1992 **PTH** *030 †50
BYLER, Jamie Marie. ■ 44303 #038-45-2004 L2004 **OBG** *012
CALDWELL, Joseph Martin. 400 WABASH AVE, AKRON GENERAL MED CTR 44307 #025-07-2006 L2006 **ORS** *012
CAMPBELL, John Allen. ■ 44303 #038-06-1941 L1941 **AI GP** *071 †03
CAMPBELL, Lori B. ■ 44305 #038-41-1989 L1993 **OBG** *020 †30
CAMPENSA, Ross Frederick. 263 S BAY DR 44319 #038-44-1986 L1989 **EM** *030 †16
CANILANG, Enrique P. ■ 44313 #748-02-1955 L1972 **PM OS** *071 †60
CANTERBURY, Brian. ■ 44313 #038-44-2004 L2004 **U** *012
CARDONA, Mildred. 1 PARK WEST BLVD, STE 200 44320 #035-08-1989 L1993 **OBG** *020 †30
CARMEN, Kevin Patrick. 44333 #038-44-2007 **EM** *012
CARNE, David Michael. ■ 44313 #040-02-2006 L2006 **GS** *012
CASTANEDA, Joaquin Ahunka. 444 N MAIN ST 44310 #030-06-2002 L2002 **ORS** *020
CASTRO, Jonathan Troadio. 400 WABASH AVE, AKRON GEN MED CTR 44307 #748-02-2001 L2004 **IM** *020

■ = Address Information Privacy Protected

CATING, Monica Therese Ba. 400 WABASH AVE 44307 #748-02-2001 L2003 **IM** *100 †20
CAVANAUGH, Richard K. ■ 44319 #028-34-1951 L1970 **CD IM** *072 †20
CAVENY, Elizabeth Anne. 400 WABASH AVE 44307 #045-01-1977 L1981 **PTH OS** *020 †50
CECILIO, Michael Draganic. 400 WABASH AVE, AKRON GENERAL FAMILY MEDIC 44307 #957-07-2000 L2002 **FM** *100 †18
CERVINO, A Lawrence. 3925 EMBASSY PKWY, STE 300 44333 #035-01-1964 L1974 **PS HS** *020 †85,65
CEVASCO, Robert Danl, Jr. 444 N MAIN ST 44310 #038-06-1978 L1979 **FM** *040 †18
CHA, Stephen Duk. ■ 44308 #038-44-2007 L2007 **PD** *012
CHAHAL, Jaspreet Kaur. 400 WABASH AVE, AKRON GENERAL MED CTR 44307 #661-03-2004 L2004 **FM** *100
CHAND, David Vasant. 4606 BARNSLEIGH DR, 11100 EUCLID AVENUE 44333 #024-01-2000 L2000 **PDI** *100 †55 ‡
CHAND, Erlinda Uy. 444 W EXCHANGE ST, C/O PLANNED PARENTHOOD 44302 #748-01-1963 L1970 **GYN OBG** *071
CHAND, Vasant A. 762 EASTLAND AVE 44305 #495-01-1952 L1966 **IM** *071
CHATURVEDI, Preti Bala. 224 W EXCHANGE ST, STE 330 44302 #038-44-1999 L1999 **NEP** *020 †20
CHAUDRY, Nasir Badar. 400 WABASH AVE 44307 #039-01-2007 L2007 **GS** *012
CHLYSTA, Walter John. 400 WABASH AVE, AKRON GENERAL MEDICAL HOSP 44307 #038-40-1994 L1996 **GS** *020 †85
CHOMO, Diane Lynne. 400 WABASH AVE, BLDG ACC 44307 #038-44-1981 L1984 **IM** *020 †20
CHRISTOPHER, Norman Carl. 1 PERKINS SQ, AKRON CHILDRENS HOSPITAL 44308 #048-14-1985 L1985 **PD** *020 †55
CHU, Emilio C. ■ 44313 #748-01-1968 L1973 **U** *020 †95
CHULIK, John Dale. 157 W CEDAR ST STE 2 44307 #016-43-1971 L1972 **U** *020 †95
CHUNDURI, Anil Kumar. ■ 44307 #496-35-2003 L2005 **IM** *012
CIANCONE, Ann C. 444 N MAIN ST STE 404, OUTPATIENT PSYCHIATRY CLIN 44310 #038-44-1995 L1996 **P** *012 †16
CICHOWSKI, Sara Beth. ■ 44303 #054-04-2004 L2004 **OBG** *012
CILTEA, Daniela. 400 WABASH AVE 44307 #781-01-1996 L2002 **END** *100 †20
CIRALDO, Alfred Vitale. 95 ARCH ST STE 220 44304 #038-40-1979 L1980 **GS** *020 †85
CLARK, John Mark. 1 PERKINS SQ, AKRON CHILDRENS HOSPITAL 44308 #038-44-1991 L1998 **PDC PD** *020 †55
CLARKE, Raymond E. 525 E MARKET ST 44304 #024-05-1974 L1979 **CLP PTH** *020 †50
CLAVECILLA, Leo Demetria. 2040 E MARKET ST 44312 #038-44-1993 L1995 **IM** *020 †20
CLAY, Cheryl Ann. 1 PERKINS SQ, AKRON CHILDREN'S HOSPITAL 44308 #041-12-2005 L2005 **PD** *012
CLEVELAND, Maryjo Lynn. 75 ARCH ST, STE G2 44304 #025-12-1987 L1988 **IMG IM** *020 †20
CLOYD, Gregory Millard. 190 N UNION ST, STE 104 44304 #047-05-1982 L1986 **AN** *020 †05
COCHRAN, Martin Armando. 300 LOCUST ST 44302 #038-44-2002 L2002 **PD** *020 †55
COCHRAN, Steven Lee. 3535 GRANGER RD 44333 #005-19-1973 L1974 **FM IMG** *020 †18
CODY, Derek Gordon. ■ 44307 #038-40-2004 L2004 **PS** *012
COLA, Lynne Marie. 1611 AKRON PENINSULA RD #C 44313 #038-44-1981 L1984 **OBG** *020 †30
COLE, Crystal Jayne. ■ 44312 #038-44-2007 L2007 **FP** *012
COLEMAN, Dwight Dwayne. 340 S BROADWAY ST, PORTAGE PATH BEHAVIORAL HE 44308 #043-01-1993 L1999 **P** *020
COLLINS, Emory J. 1 PERKINS SQ, AKRON CHILDREN'S HOSPITAL 44308 #038-41-1997 L1999 **PG** *020 †55
COLLINS, Michelle Dee. 1 PERKINS SQ, AKRON CHILDRENS HOSPITAL E 44308 #020-12-1997 L2000 **PE** *020 †55
CONGENI, Blaise Leo. 1 PERKINS SQ 44308 #038-40-1973 L1975 **PDI ID** *020 †55
CONGENI, Jonathan Paul. ■ 44333 #038-44-2008 *012
CONGENI, Joseph Anthony. 388 S MAIN ST, MEDICAL CENTER OF AKRON 44311 #038-44-1984 L1986 **PSM PD** *020 †55
CONGER, George T. ■ 44303 #035-20-1953 L1957 **GYN** *071 †30
CONLIN, Kathryn Panis. 400 WABASH AVE 44307 #038-40-1954 L1954 **IM** *020
CONNER, Ronald Curtiss, Jr. ■ 44313 #038-44-2007 L2007 **IM** *012
CONRAD, Daniel Jacob. 1 PERKINS SQ, DEPT OF PEDIATRIC PSYCHIAT 44308 #017-20-1977 L1987 **CHP** *020 †18,75
CONVERSE, Maurice. ■ 44334 #038-40-1955 L1955 **AN** *071
COOK, William Arthur. ■ 44313 #038-40-1955 L1955 **OBG** *071 †30
CORBIT, Christopher K. 400 WABASH AVE, DEPT OF EMERGENCY MEDICINE 44307 #030-05-1999 L1999 **EM** *020 †16
COSBY, Stephen Lee. 1 PERKINS SQ STE 280, AKRON CHILDREN'S HOSPITAL 44308 #038-41-1978 L1985 **CHP P** *020 †75 ‡
COSTELLO, Mary K. 1 PERKINS SQ, CENTER OF AKRON 44308 #038-44-1995 L1996 **PEM PD** *020 †55
COULTMAN, Angela Raquel. ■ 44313 #041-15-2001 L2006 **PD** *020 †55
COURSON, Sladjana. 676 S BROADWAY ST, STE 103 44311 #038-75-1996, ▲ L1999 **PD** *020 †55
CRANE, Patrick Shawn. ■ 44312 #005-12-2006 L2006 **EM** *012
CREMER, Steven A. 999 N MAIN ST 44310 #055-01-1984 L1987 **PM OM** *020 †60
CROCKER, Forrest Will. 2315 MANCHESTER RD 44314 #025-01-1957 L1959 **PD** *071 †55
CROFT, Herbert Earl. ■ 44333 #041-12-1956 L1956 **HEM ON** *071
CROW, John Paul. 300 LOCUST ST, STE 560 44302 #038-44-1985 L1992 **PDS CCS** *020 †85
CULLADO, Michael John. 550 E MARKET ST STE 103 44304 #026-04-1986 L1987 **GS CRS** *020 †85,10
CUSTODIO, Paul Jerome Pal. 400 WABASH AVE 44307 #748-02-2005 L2007 **IM** *012
CUTTER, Christopher Thoma. ■ 44320 #038-40-2006 L2006 **EM** *012
DABBAS, Mohammed. 388 S MAIN ST STE 403 44311 #875-02-1974 L1980 **OBG** *020
DAKE, Timothy William, Jr. ■ 44313 #038-45-2007 L2007 **EM** *012
DALHEIM, Leroy Geo. 1 PERKINS SQ 44308 #035-19-1953 L1955 **PHP PD** *071
DALIRI, Narges. 1 PERKINS SQ 44308 #704-01-1976 L1985 **PEM PD** *020 †55
DALTON, Arthur Benjamin. 95 ARCH ST STE 280 44304 #308-07-1982 L1991 **GS** *020 †85
DALUMPINES, Pierre Andre. 400 WABASH AVE, AKRON GENERAL MED CTR 44307 #748-01-2002 L2006 **FP** *012
DAN, Adrian George. 95 ARCH ST, STE 240 44304 #038-44-2000 L2005 **GS** *020 †85 ‡
DANIEL KEMPF, Ellen Sue. 2 PERKINS SQ, STE 6300 44308 #038-40-1979 L1990 **PD** *020 †55
DANKOFF, Joseph Saml. 95 ARCH ST, STE 165 44304 #041-02-1985 L1987 **U** *020 †95
DARIUSHNIA, Akbar. 777 W MARKET ST 44303 #517-01-1965 L1972 **OBG OS** *020 †30
D'AVELLO, Lori Boothe. 370 E MARKET ST 44304 #038-44-1986 L1988 **PD** *020 †55
DAVIDSON, Elliot B. 400 WABASH AVE 44307 #038-44-1982 L1983 **FM** *040 †18
DAVIS, James Kenneth. 585 WHITE POND DR STE C 44320 #038-40-1980 L1981 **OBG** *020 †30
DAVIS, Joseph Bartlett. 400 WABASH AVE, AKRON GEN MED CTR 44307 #038-75-2006, ▲ L2006 **OBG** *012
DAVIS, Mark Allan. 1 PARK WEST BLVD, STE 200 44320 #038-44-1987 L1988 **OBG** *020 †30
DAVIS, Scott M. 525 E MARKET ST 44304 #016-11-1982 L1984 **EM** *020 †16
DEAN, Dorothy Emma. 85 N SUMMIT ST 44308 #038-43-1993 L1998 **FOP** *020 †50
DEDHIA, Bharesh D. PO BOX 1501, ORIANA HOUSE RIP 44309 #496-38-1989 L1994 **GS** *075
DEEKEN, Amy Hatfield. 525 E MARKET ST 44304 #038-44-2001 L2001 **PTH** *020 †50
DE FREEST, Daphne K. ■ 44319 #035-15-1959 L1963 **FM ADM** *071 †30
DE FREEST, Lynn J. ■ 44319 #035-15-1960 L1964 **ORS** *071 †40
DEIS, Andrea Marie. 1 PERKINS SQ, AKRON 44308 #038-41-1992 L1993 **PD** *020 †55
DELAHUNTY, Carol Marie. 1 PERKINS SQ, NEURO DEVELOPMENTAL CENTER 44308 #051-01-1991 L2004 **PD** *020 †55
DELANEY ELSNER, David Jos. ■ 44313 #028-78-2007, ▲ L2007 *012
DELA PAZ, Tala Maria Alca. 400 WABASH AVE 44307 #748-02-2004 L2006 **IM** *012
DEL GRECO, Kenneth A. ■ 44333 #038-40-1954 L1954 **OM GP** *071
DE LUCIA, Michael Angelo. 3043 SANITARIUM RD 44312 #038-44-1990 L1993 **PD** *020 †55
DEPERRO, Dean J, Sr. 611 W TURKEYFOOT LAKE RD, STE C 44319 #041-77-1995, ▲ L1996 **IM** *020
DE RUBEIS, Michael Alex. 3529 FORTUNA DR 44312 #038-43-1997 L1998 **FM** *020 †18
DESAI, Bharati Ashok. 444 N MAIN ST 44310 #495-17-1970 L1977 **AN** *020 †05
DESAI, Sonia Praful. 400 WABASH AVE, CO AKRON GEN MED CTR-MED E 44307 #496-01-1997 L2001 **FM** *100 †05
DESAI, Tapan Apurva. 525 E MARKET ST, CO SUMMA HLTH SYS-MED EDU 44304 #894-01-2002 L2003 **PCC** *012 †20
DETTLING, John Jos. 566 WHITE POND DR, STE C 44320 #010-02-1954 L1961 **OBG OS** *071 †30
DEVENY, Thomas Clifford. 2779 WALNUT RIDGE RD 44333 #038-43-1986 L1987 **GYN** *030 †30
DEVINE, John B. 676 S BROADWAY ST STE 102, NE OHIO UROGNCLGY CTR 44311 #038-44-1992 L1993 **GYN OS** *020 †30
DEVITOFRANCESCHI, Joseph. ■ 44313 #561-01-1949 L1960 **AN** *075 †05
DI CIOCCIO, Michael. 224 W EXCHANGE ST, STE 360 44302 #038-06-1984 L1984 **AN CCM** *020 †05
DICKEY, Jeffrey Eugene. 1655 W MARKET ST, STE 510 44313 #038-06-1981 L1982 **R** *020 †80
DIETRICH, John Wm. 3975 EMBASSY PKWY STE 201 44333 #025-01-1983 L1989 **HS ORS** *020 †40
DIETZ, Harold W. ■ 44313 #038-41-1951 L1951 **OM AM** *071 †70
DI LUCIANO, Mark Edward. 1 PERKINS SQ 44308 #038-43-1988 L1991 **AN** *020 †05
DIMITRIS, Kelly Catherine. 55 ARCH ST 44304 #038-40-2000 L2000 **EM** *020 †16
DISABATO, John Anthony. 55 ARCH ST, STE 3A 44304 #038-44-1987 L1988 **FM** *020 †18
DI SIMONE, Robt Nicholas. 3333 S ARLINGTON RD 44312 #038-40-1963 L1963 **DR NM** *071 †80,28
DJUNG, Ida I-Giai. ■ 44313 #242-15-1939 L1960 **PTH** *071 †50
DOGRA, Atul. 400 WABASH AVE 44307 #496-67-2003 L2006 **FP** *012
DOLINAK, Joan. ■ 44303 #038-44-2002 L2002 **GS** *012
DONAHUE, Robert Joseph. 190 N UNION ST, STE 104 44304 #056-06-1979 L1982 **AN** *020 †05
DONCALS, Desiree Elaine. 525 E MARKET ST, RADIATION ONCOLOGY PHYSICI 44304 #041-07-1990 L1995 **RO** *020 †80
DONOVAN, Duane Lee. 95 ARCH ST STE 215, AKRON VASCULAR ASSOCIATES, 44304 #038-40-1971 L1971 **VS** *020 †85
DORNER, William, Jr. 1867 W MARKET ST 44313 #038-40-1953 L1953 **D** *071 †15
DOUGHERTY, James Michael. 400 WABASH AVE, AKRON GENERAL MEDICAL CENT 44307 #016-11-1976 L1977 **EM** *020 †16
DUBY, John Chas. 1 PERKINS SQ 44308 #038-40-1979 L1990 **PD** *020 †55
DUGGAL, Anurag. 400 WABASH AVE, AKRON GENERAL MED CTR 44307 #495-43-2001 L2003 **ID** *012 †20
DULLE, David John. 525 E MARKET ST 44304 #038-41-1998 L1999 **FM** *020 †18
DULUC, Salvador Anibal. ■ 44303 #308-01-1959 L1964 **FM** *020
DULYN, Gregor L. ■ 44319 #407-16-1955 L1961 **IM OS** *071
DUPPSTADT, Susan Ann. 1569 VERNON ODOM BLVD, B.S. BONYO & ASSOCIATES 44320 #038-06-1980 L1983 **FM** *020 †18
DY, Jose T. 975 N MAIN ST, HEALTHCARE CENTER PHYSICIA 44310 #748-01-1964 L1974 **IM ON** *020
ECHT, Eve Alison. 400 WABASH AVE, DEPT OF RADIOLOGY 44307 #038-06-1994 L1995 **NR** *020 †80
ECKMAN, Jeffrey Michael. 75 ARCH ST, STE 501 44304 #038-43-1991 L1992 **IM** *020 †20
EDWARD, Deepak P. 75 ARCH ST STE 512, DEPARTMENT OF OPHTHALMOLOG 44304 #495-52-1980 L2007 **OPH** *020 †35
EHRLER, Douglas Michael. 3975 EMBASSY PKWY 44333 #038-45-1993 L1996 **ORS** *020 †40
EIDAHL, Jason Dean. ■ 44303 #037-01-2005 L2005 **EM** *012
EIDE, Erin Lillian. ■ 44303 #046-01-2006 L2006 **PTH** *100
EIPPER, Donald Fred. 444 N MAIN ST, STE 408 44310 #041-02-1964 L1965 **NEP IM** *020 †20
EIWEN, Rebecca Dawn. ■ 44305 #038-44-1994 L1997 **FM** *020 †18
ELAHI, Manzoor E. 150 CROSS ST, COMMUNITY SUPPORT SVCS 44311 #160-02-1989 L2000 **P** *020 †75
ELAHI, Tahmina. 150 CROSS ST, COMMUNITY SUPPORT SERVICES 44311 #160-02-1990 L2000 **P** *020
ELLIS, Cecilia A. 605 N CLEVELAND MASSILN RD, STE A 44333 #018-75-1988, ▲ L1989 **OBG** *020 †30
EL-TAYEB, Babiker O. 224 W EXCHANGE ST, STE 330 44302 #848-01-1981 L1998 **NEP IM** *020 †20
EMCH, Michelle Beata. 400 WABASH AVE 44307 #038-44-2001 L2005 **P** *100
ENGLES, Drew Ronald. 3975 EMBASSY PKWY STE 201 44333 #017-20-1991 L1992 **HS** *020 †40
ENLOW, Mary Kathleen. 300 LOCUST ST, STE 400 44302 #038-06-1985 L1986 **PO** *020 †35
ENLOW, Thomas Chas. 1 PERKINS SQ, CHMCA 44308 #008-02-1985 L1988 **CHN CN** *020 †75
ENRIGHT, Valeria J. ■ 44312 #010-02-1952 L1954 **P OBG** *071
ENRIONE, Maria Annette. 1 PERKINS SQ, DIV OF PEDIATRIC CRITICAL 44308 #038-40-1988 L1989 **CCP** *020 †55
ERK, Vernon O. ■ 44309 #017-20-1945 L1945 **GP GS** *020
ERZURUM, Victor Zafer B. 400 WABASH AVE STE 3500, SUMMIT VASCULAR SPECIALIST 44307 #038-44-1995 L1999 **VS** *020 †85
ESBER, Edward Jos. 570 WHITE POND DR, STE 100 44320 #038-43-1988 L1991 **GE** *020 †20
ESBER, Mary Jane. 1 PERKINS SQ, AKRON 44308 #038-43-1988 L1991 **PD** *020 †55
ESPINAL, Eric Alexei. 75 ARCH ST, STE 407 44304 #038-44-1992 L1999 **TS** *020 †85,90
ESPINAL, Sue Ellen Marie. 3636 YELLOW CREEK RD, OF THE RESERVE 44333 #038-43-1992 L1994 **OBG** *020 †30
ESPINOSA, Aixa Damaris. ■ 44307 #042-02-2000 L2000 **N** *100
ESTEP, Ernest Robt. 1611 AKRON PENINSULA RD #C 44313 #038-40-1967 L1967 **OBG** *071 †30

■ = Address Information Privacy Protected

EVANS, Douglas M. 400 WABASH AVE 44307 #038-06-1952 L1952 **GS OS** *050 †85
EVANS, Michael J. 224 W EXCHANGE ST STE 300 44302 #028-34-1972 L1987 **TS VS** *071 †85,90
EVENSKI, Andrea Jean. ■ 44303 #036-08-2003 L2003 **ORS** *012
EWING, John Whitaker. 2457 COVINGTON RD 44313 #041-12-1964 L1969 **ORS** *020 †40
FAIRTILE, Richard David. 190 N UNION ST, STE 104 44304 #010-02-1989 L1993 **AN** *020 †05
FAIRWEATHER, William H. ■ 44313 #041-01-1942 L1952 **GS** *072 †85
FALTAY, Bela Botond. 224 W EXCHANGE ST, STE 380 44302 #038-44-1998 L1999 **AI** *020 †20,03
FAULKNER, Robert Walter. 525 E MARKET ST, ANNEX 3 44304 #038-40-1976 L1977 **EM** *020 †16
FAYAZI, Behnaz. ■ 44313 #038-40-2001 L2001 **PS** *012 †85
FEDERMAN, Raymond S. 3975 EMBASSY PKWY STE 101 44333 #038-40-1959 L1959 **RHU IM** *071 †20
FEICK, Harriet James. 300 LOCUST ST, STE 540 44302 #038-44-1985 L1986 **NPM PD** *020 †55
FEITL, Julius Anthony. ■ 44303 #038-44-2008 *012
FELTEN, Scott Edward. 400 WABASH AVE, AKRON GENERAL MEDICAL CENT 44307 #030-05-1997 L1998 **EM** *020 †16
FELTRUP, Albert A. 2818 S ARLINGTON RD, STE B 44312 #038-41-1977 L1978 **FM** *020 †18
FENG, Jianfang. 20 OLIVE ST, STE 300 44310 #243-47-1986 L2003 **IM** *020 †20
FENSTER, Michael Scott. 224 W EXCHANGE ST STE 280 44302 #051-04-1990 L2005 **CD** *020 †20
FENTON, Andrew Hadley. 400 WABASH AVE 44307 #038-44-1986 L1987 **GS** *020 †85
FENTON, Cydney Walker. 1 PERKINS SQ, DEPT OF ENDOCRINOLOGY 44308 #024-05-1992 L2005 **PDE** *020 †55
FERAN, Sarah Diane. 1 PERKINS SQ 44308 #038-40-2004 L2004 **PD** *020 †55
FERNER, Gregory Edward. 20 OLIVE ST, STE 300 44310 #038-44-1995 L1996 **IM** *020 †20
FERRERI, Roger Nicholas. PO BOX 1651 44309 #038-06-1980 L1980 **GP OM** *020
FILE, Mary Elizabeth. 444 N MAIN ST 44310 #038-40-1974 L1975 **OPH** *020 †35
FILE, Thomas Mc Donald. 75 ARCH ST STE 105, AKRON INFECTIOUS DISEASE I 44304 #025-01-1972 L1975 **ID** *020 †20
FINK, John Alan. 525 E MARKET ST 44304 #038-40-1980 L1982 **VS GS** *020 †85
FINOCCHIO, Joseph A. 400 WABASH AVE, BLDG ACC 44307 #038-44-1984 L1985 **IM** *020 †20
FITZGERALD, Antonia Losse. 400 WABASH AVE, CO AKRON GEN MED CTR-MED E 44307 #198-01-1990 L2000 **P** *020 †75
FITZGIBBON, James Jos. 300 LOCUST ST STE 350 44302 #025-07-1975 L1977 **PD ADL** *020 †55
FLANAGAN, John Patrick. 444 N MAIN ST 44310 #038-40-1968 L1968 **ORS** *020 †40
FLEISSNER, Paul Raymond. 3975 EMBASSY PKWY, STE 102 44333 #038-40-1984 L1985 **ORS** *020 †40
FLORA, Robert Francis. 95 ARCH ST, STE 220 44304 #038-43-1987 L1988 **GYN** *020 †30
FOLTZ, Douglas Michael. 1655 W MARKET ST, STE 510 44313 #038-44-1993 L2000 **DR** *020
FORBES, Michael Leighton. 1 PERKINS SQ, AKRON CHILDRENS HOSPITAL 44308 #041-12-1990 L2006 **CCP** *020 †55
FORD, Kennard Chandler. 525 E MARKET ST, REHAB UNIT 44304 #038-41-1986 L1989 **PM** *020 †60
FOX, Charles Robt. ■ 44303 #038-40-1953 L1953 **GS** *071 †85
FOX, James Walter. 1 PERKINS SQ, AKRON CHILDREN'S HOSPITAL 44308 #038-41-1999 L2003 **PEM** *100 †20,55
FRANCIS, Stephen J. 444 N MAIN ST STE 310 44310 #024-07-1977 L1979 **ID** *020 †20
FRANKLIN, Aris Wm. 20 S BROADWAY ST 44308 #038-40-1948 L1948 **R** *020 †80
FRATE, Dean Michael. 55 ARCH ST, INC 44304 #038-06-2004 L2004 **IM** *020 †20
FREDETTE, Renay Kristine. 400 WABASH AVE 44307 #005-12-2004 L2005 **FM** *020 †18
FREY, Matthew Scott. ■ 44319 #038-44-2007 L2007 **EM** *012
FRIEBERT, Sarah. 1 PERKINS SQ, CHILDRENS HOSP MED CTR AKR 44308 #038-06-1993 L1996 **PD PHO** *020 †55
FRIEDMAN, Harvey Marshall. 400 WABASH AVE 44307 #038-40-1958 L1958 **N** *020 †75
FRIEDMAN, Norman Mark. 400 WABASH AVE, AKRON NEUROLOGICAL 44307 #038-44-1995 L1996 **N** *020 †20,75
FRYE, Paul E. ■ 44333 #023-01-1946 L1954 **AN** *071 †05
FU, John Chihwa. 20 OLIVE ST, STE 300 44310 #038-44-1999 L1999 **IM** *020 †20
FUENNING, Charles R. 95 ARCH ST STE 210 44304 #060-01-1981 L1983 **PUD CCM** *020 †20
FULTON, Scott Anthony. 570 WHITE POND DR, STE 200 44320 #005-18-1993 L1999 **GE** *020 †20
GACAD, Reynaldo Carlos. 570 WHITE POND DR, STE 200 44320 #748-01-1983 L1992 **GE** *020 †20
GAISIE, Godfrey. 1 PERKINS SQ, DEPT OF RADIOLOGY 44308 #412-01-1972 L1987 **PDR DR** *020 †55,80
GALEHOUSE, George Roberts. 525 E MARKET ST, STE 206 44304 #038-40-1955 L1955 **OBG** *071 †30
GAMBOA, Eric Ortiz. 400 WABASH AVE, AKRON GEN MED CTR 44307 #748-02-2004 L2005 **IM** *012
GANT, Jonathan Allen. ■ 44303 #038-45-2006 L2006 **ORS** *012
GARCIA, Eduardo Enrique. 2620 RIDGEWOOD RD, STE 100 44313 #048-04-1977 L1977 **IM EM** *020 †20
GARCIA-RUBIO, Eduardo. 525 E MARKET ST 44304 #275-01-1953 L1965 **AN** *071
GAYOMALI, Charina Parinas. 55 ARCH ST STE 1A 44304 #748-02-2002 L2003 **IM** *100 †20
GEDEON, Michael Robt. 75 ARCH ST, STE 501 44304 #038-45-1986 L1987 **IM** *020 †20
GEERS, Teresa Anne. 224 W EXCHANGE ST, STE 290 44302 #038-44-1994 L1995 **ID** *020 †20
GERASSIMAKIS, Constance S. 400 WABASH AVE, AKRON GENERAL MEDICAL CENT 44307 #041-02-1979 L1994 **DR** *020 †80
GHARIBEH, Tarek Rashad. 400 WABASH AVE 44307 #575-02-2003 L2005 **IM** *012
GHUMMAN, Preetinder Kaur. 400 WABASH AVE 44307 #495-29-2001 L2005 **FM** *100
GINGO, Anthony Joseph. 525 E MARKET ST 44304 #038-40-1962 L1962 **GP PD** *075
GINGRAS, Gerard Gilles. 400 WABASH AVE 44307 #065-09-1957 L1962 **P** *071
GINTHER, William Henry. 300 LOCUST ST, STE 200 44302 #038-40-1975 L1978 **PD** *020 †55
GIOITTA-TUCKER, Moira. 1 PERKINS SQ 44308 #539-05-1992 L1999 **AN** *020 †05
GIORDANO, Ellen Marie. ■ 44303 #422-01-2007 L2007 **PD** *012
GIORGIO, Gary Thos. 525 E MARKET ST, AKRON CITY HOSP 44304 #038-44-1985 L1986 **EM** *040 †16
GIRARD, Meredith Devoe. 525 E MARKET ST 44304 #023-01-1990 L1993 **IM** *020 †20
GIST, Katja Michelle. ■ 44313 #022-75-2006, ▲ L2006 **PD** *012
GLASS, Ericka Renee. ■ 44307 #038-43-2004 L2004 **ORS** *012
GLENN, Gina Daniele. 444 N MAIN ST 44310 #038-06-2001 L2001 **P** *020
GLICK, Starla June. 1 PERKINS SQ, CHILDREN'S HOSP MED CTR AK 44308 #017-20-1992 L1996 **PDP** *020 †55
GLOVATSKAYA, Galina. 400 WABASH AVE 44307 #913-06-1987 L2003 **IM** *020 †20
GODALE, Heather Rose. ■ 44303 #038-44-2003 L2003 **EM** *020 †16
GODWIN, Jennifer Elizabet. ■ 44310 #038-44-2006 L2006 **OBG** *012
GOLDEN, Eileen Choi. 3636 YELLOW CREEK RD, OF THE RESERVE 44333 #038-43-1997 L1998 **OBG** *020 †30
GOLDMAN, Eileen K. 3535 GRANGER RD 44333 #041-07-1976 L1979 **FM** *020 †18
GOLDMAN, George Edward. 525 E MARKET ST 44304 #041-13-1978 L1979 **EM** *020 †16
GOLESTAN, Yahya. 1 PERKINS SQ, AKRON CHILDRENS HOSP 44308 #517-08-1980 L1988 **PD PE** *020 †55
GONCERO, Grace May. 525 E MARKET ST, DEPT OF MED EDU 44304 #748-10-2002 L2006 **FP** *012
GORJANC, Michael Louis. ■ 44313 #038-06-2004 L2004 **P** *012
GOSKE, James Richard. 3975 EMBASSY PKWY STE 101 44333 #038-40-1974 L1974 **RHU IM** *020 †20
GOSWAMI, Atul S. 1037 N MAIN ST, STE A 44310 #495-89-1973 L1984 **IM** *020
GOULD, Ned Trump. UNIV AKRON HLTH SER 44325 #038-40-1948 L1948 **PD ADL** *071
GRACIANSKY-LENGYEL, Anna. ■ 44313 #409-07-1982 L1985 **GYN** *020 †30
GRADISAR, Ian Martin. ■ 44333 #038-40-2003 L2003 **ORS** *012
GRADISAR, Ivan Albin. 3975 EMBASSY PKWY STE 102 44333 #038-40-1967 L1967 **ORS** *071 †40
GRADISAR, Sara Grace. ■ 44333 #038-40-2002 L2002 **OBG** *100
GRADISEK, Nicole Kristen. ■ 44313 #038-43-2008 *012
GRADISEK, Richard E. 400 WABASH AVE 44307 #016-43-1979 L1982 **EM** *020 †16
GRANT, C Earl. 400 WABASH AVE, CO AKRON GEN MED CTR-MED E 44307 #026-04-1999 L2001 **IM** *100
GRANTHAM, Anne Seniow. 571 E TURKEYFOOT LAKE RD, STE A 44319 #041-12-1988 L1989 **FM** *020 †18
GREEN, Akida Jamal. 525 E MARKET ST 44304 #038-44-2004 L2004 **IM** *020 †20
GREENBERG, Barry Jay. 3975 EMBASSY PKWY, STE 102 44333 #038-41-1967 L1967 **ORS** *020 †40
GREENE, Kathie Tross. 45 GOODYEAR BLVD, GOODYEAR FAMILY MEDICAL CE 44305 #038-44-1990 L1991 **FM** *020 †18
GREENE, Kenneth Allen. 3975 EMBASSY PKWY, STE 102 44333 #038-40-1982 L1983 **ORS** *020 †40
GREGOREK, Michael Jos. 777 W MARKET ST 44303 #041-12-1981 L1984 **IM** *074 †20
GRIFFIN, Janet Louise. 525 E MARKET ST 44304 #055-01-1986 L1992 **OTO HNS** *020 †45
GRIMES, Michael Gordon. 791 WHITE POND DR, STE C 44320 #038-44-1997 L1999 **FM** *020 †18
GROVER, Harold Edward. ■ 44333 #038-40-1958 L1958 **GP FM** *071
GROW, James Foster, Jr. 3535 GRANGER RD 44333 #055-01-1967 L1967 **FM FPG** *030 †18
GROW, Jennifer Laura. 300 LOCUST ST, STE 540 44302 #038-44-1996 L1998 **NPM** *020 †55 ‡
GUERRERO-DUBY, Sara F. 370 E MARKET ST 44304 #038-40-1979 L1990 **PD** *020 †55
GUJARATHI, Parul. 400 WABASH AVE, AKRON GEN MED CTR 44307 #038-44-1999 L2000 **IM** *020 †20
GUNAY-AYGUN, Meral. 1 PERKINS SQ 44308 #902-05-1987 L1999 **PG** *020 †19,55
GUPTA, Adarsh. 1 PERKINS SQ, CHILDRENS HOSP MED CTR AKR 44308 #965-01-1985 L1991 **PD** *020 †55
GUPTA, Sunil N. ■ 44313 #060-01-1989 **OS** *020
GUTIERREZ, Wilson Sy. 400 WABASH AVE 44307 #748-02-2004 L2005 **IM** *012
GUYTON, Daniel Printz. 400 WABASH AVE 44307 #038-06-1975 L1975 **GS** *020 †85
GUYTON, Richard Albert. ■ 44333 #038-06-1947 L1947 **OM IM** *071 †20
HACKENBERG, D Douglas. 370 E MARKET ST 44304 #038-40-1995 L1996 **PD** *020 †55
HAHN, John Michael. 400 WABASH AVE 44307 #016-06-1997 L2000 **OPH** *020 †35
HAIDER, Anzar. 1 PERKINS SQ, DIVISION 44308 #690-02-1981 L1995 **PDE IM** *020 †55
HAJJIRI, Mohmmad Fayez. 400 WABASH AVE 44307 #575-02-2004 L2007 **IM** *012
HALASY, Christopher M. 1400 S ARLINGTON ST # 38 44306 #038-06-1998 L1999 **FM** *020 †18
HAMBLIN, Milton Hercules. 400 WABASH AVE 44307 #047-07-1970 L1974 **OBG** *071 †30
HAMOR, Robert Hunt. 525 E MARKET ST, SUMMA HEALTH SYSTEM 44304 #016-06-1963 L1969 **R** *071 †80
HAMRICH, Lynn Marlene. 75 ARCH ST, STE 002 44304 #038-06-1996 L1997 **FM** *020 †18
HAMZEH, Khaled Walid. 400 WABASH AVE 44307 #917-34-1999 L2003 **GS** *012
HANDLER, Mark Bennet. 1 PERKINS SQ 44308 #064-01-1969 L1974 **PS HS** *020 †65
HANLON, Herbert James. 400 WABASH AVE 44307 #028-34-1962 L1963 **FM EM** *020 †18
HANSEL, John Raymond. 75 ARCH ST, STE 412 44304 #038-40-1963 L1963 **TS GS** *072 †85,90
HAQUE, Ihsan Ul. 95 ARCH ST, STE 130 44304 #704-01-1950 L1958 **CD IM** *020
HAQUE, Javed-Ul. 400 WABASH AVE, DEPT. OF PSYCHIATRY 44307 #704-16-1991 L2000 **P** *020 †75
HAROUNY, Antoine Mansour. ■ 44312 #605-02-1950 L1958 **OM OBG** *071
HARPER, Adolph, Jr. 2569 ROMIG RD STE 201 44320 #027-01-1976 L1980 **OBG** *020
HARTMANN, William Paul. 400 WABASH AVE 44307 #038-44-1999 L2000 **P** *020 †75 ‡
HART-SPICER, Cherie Renee. ■ 44312 #038-44-2005 L2005 **PTH** *012
HATCHETT, Angel Daniel. 55 W WATERLOO RD, LOUIS STOKES VA MED CTR 44319 #308-11-1989 L2003 **P** *020 †75
HATHAWAY, Thomas Russell. 525 E MARKET ST 44304 #025-01-1960 L1966 **R** *071 †80
HAWKINS, Curtis Wayne. 1867 W MARKET ST STE C14 44313 #038-06-1980 L1983 **D** *020 †15
HAZRA, Sandra Virginia. 157 W CEDAR ST STE 215 44307 #067-01-1969 L1979 **HEM ON** *020 †20
HEGAZY, Adham. ■ 44313 #915-04-1982 L1993 **NPM** *020 †55
HEGDE, Vishvas. 525 E MARKET ST 44304 #038-44-1999 L1999 **PD** *020 †55
HEISER, David G. 157 W CEDAR ST 44307 #038-44-1994 L2000 **U** *020 †95
HEMPHILL, Robert J. 777 W MARKET ST 44303 #020-02-1948 L1950 **IM RHU** *071
HENRY, Jed William. ■ 44313 #038-40-2004 L2004 **U** *012
HENSCHEN, Ross Richard. 525 E MARKET ST 44304 #038-44-1981 L1982 **EM CCM** *020 †16
HENTHORNE, William Arthur. 525 E MARKET ST 44304 #038-40-1975 L1975 **PTH PCP** *020 †50
HERBENER, Suzanne E. 150 CROSS ST, COMMUNITY SUPPORT SERVICES 44311 #038-06-1984 L1985 **P** *020
HERBENER, Thomas Edward. 2603 W MARKET ST, STE 110 44313 #041-12-1984 L1990 **DR** *020 †80
HERMANOWSKI, Robert W. 150 CROSS ST 44311 #038-44-1989 L1990 **P PFP** *020 †75
HEROLD, William Hugh. 1 PERKINS SQ 44308 #007-02-1971 L1991 **ATP PTH** *020 †50
HERRINGTON, Gayle M. 400 WABASH AVE, BLDG ACC 44307 #001-02-1995 L1996 **IM** *020 †20
HERSHBERGER, Vernon J. 880 MULL AVE, STE 100 44313 #038-40-1975 L1975 **FM** *020 †18
HETRICK, Thomas Jon. 400 WABASH AVE 44307 #041-02-1976 L1978 **EM** *020 †16
HILL, Michael Forrest. 3043 SANITARIUM RD 44312 #038-43-1982 L1983 **IM** *020 †20

HINES, Richard Michael. 75 ARCH ST STE 002 44304 #041-13-1976 L1977 FM *020 †18

HIRSCHFELD, Stephen Saml. 224 W EXCHANGE ST, STE 360 44302 #038-41-1968 L1968 CD PD *020 †55,05

HIXON, Kathryn O. ■ 44308 #038-44-2006 L2006 PD *012

HLIVKO, Thomas Jos. 525 E MARKET ST 44304 #051-04-1972 L1979 PTH *050 †50

HODSDEN, James Edmund. 400 WABASH AVE, STE 230 44307 #038-40-1976 L1976 CD IM *020 †20

HOLDER, Michael Gordon, Jr. 1 PERKINS SQ 44308 #033-06-1996 L2005 PD PEM *020 †55

HOLLER, Yolanda Faye. 1 PERKINS SQ, CHILDREN'S MED CTR OF AKRO 44308 #016-11-1997 L2003 CHN *020 †55,75 ‡

HOLSINGER, Eva. 3043 SANITARIUM RD, STE 3 44312 #039-01-1999 L1999 PD *020 †55

HONG, Sandra Jessica. 75 ARCH ST, STE 303 44304 #038-40-1993 L1998 IM *020 †20,03

HONG, Susan Marie. 525 E MARKET ST, RADIATION ONCOLOGY DEPT 44304 #038-44-1995 L2000 RO *020 †80

HOOD, Valeri Ann. 1600 E TURKEYFOOT LAKE RD 44312 #038-41-1992 L1994 PD *020 †55

HORATTAS, Mark C. 400 WABASH AVE ACC CTR 44307 #038-44-1985 L1986 GS *020 †85 ‡

HORD, Jeffrey Dale. 1 PERKINS SQ, CHILDREN'S HOSP MEDICAL CE 44308 #020-12-1989 L1990 PHO *020 †55

HOUGHTON, John D. 578 WESTMINSTER CIR 44319 #018-75-2004, ▲ L2004 OBG *012 †50

HOUSTON, Alma Faye. 87 N CANTON RD, CHILD GUIDANCE CENTERS 44305 #004-01-1969 L1981 CHP P *020 †75

HOVAN, Michael James. 190 N UNION ST, STE 104 44304 #038-06-1977 L1980 AN *020 †05

HU, Melody. 525 E MARKET ST, CO SUMMA HLTH SYS-MED EDU 44304 #038-44-2003 L2003 PMM *012

HUANG, Li. 525 E MARKET ST 44304 #243-45-1987 L2006 SP *020

HUBER, Michael Neil. 20 OLIVE ST STE 300 44310 #038-40-1993 L1996 IM *020 †20

HUCK, Patrick Daniel. ■ 44304 #038-44-2006 L2006 GS *012

HUGHES, Gwendolyn Dotts. 525 E MARKET ST STE 1N, CARE PHYS 44304 #036-05-1984 L1989 IM *020 †20

HULL, Robert Bowen. 1 PERKINS SQ, MEDICAL CENTER OF AKRON 44308 #041-13-1979 L2000 PD *020 †55

HULVAT, Gerald Francis. 3696 GRANGER RD 44333 #038-40-1973 L1979 DR *020 †80

HUSAMI, Tarek Wafic. 3875 EMBASSY PKWY, STE 203 44333 #915-04-1980 L1986 PS *020

HUTCHINGS, Timothy Brent. ■ 44313 #005-77-2004, ▲ L2004 AN *071

HUYNH, Anhtuan T. 400 WABASH AVE 44307 #039-79-2005, ▲ L2005 OBG *012

HWANG, John. ■ 44304 #038-44-1954 L1954 AN *100

IBRAHIM, Ahmad K. 55 ARCH ST STE 3A 44304 #067-01-2002 L2004 FM *020 †18

IMAM, Abubakr A. 1 PERKINS SQ, DIVISION OF NEPHROLOGY 44308 #848-01-1991 L2006 PN *020 †55

IMHOFF, Trisha Ann. ■ 44312 #025-07-2006 L2006 FP *012

ISADA, Loretta Roach. 4125 MEDINA RD, STE 208 44333 #038-43-1986 L1988 IM CD *020 †20

IVAN, Todd Michael. 400 WABASH AVE 44307 #038-06-1991 L1992 P *020 †75

IVORY, Dedri Markita. 400 WABASH AVE, DEPT OF MED EDUCATION 44307 #305-01-2006 L2006 IM *012

JACKSON, David Lance. 3529 FORTUNA DR 44312 #038-44-1986 L1987 FM *020 †18

JACKSON, Thomas John. 400 WABASH AVE 44307 #041-02-1964 L1970 R DR *071 †80

JACOB, John. ■ 44313 #038-40-1954 L1954 AN *071

JACOBS, John Francis, Jr. 224 W EXCHANGE ST, STE 330 44302 #051-04-1973 L1978 NEP OS *020 †20

JACOBSTEIN, Mark David. 1 PERKINS SQ, MEDICAL CENTER OF AKRON 44308 #025-01-1976 L1979 PD *020 †55

JACQUES, Andrew Peter. ■ 44313 #038-45-2005 L2005 EM *012

JACQUES, Mindy Michelle. ■ 44313 #038-45-2004 L2004 PEM *012 †55

JACQUET, Joshua Michael. ■ 44307 #038-44-2006 L2006 EM *012

JAGAR, Eric John. 55 W WATERLOO RD 44319 #036-05-1997 L1998 IM *020 †20

JAIN, Rajneesh. 300 LOCUST ST 44302 #495-49-1992 L1999 PD *020 †55

JALEES, Shah Arshaduddin. ■ 44307 #704-02-1990 L2001 P *020 †75

JAMES, Summer Leigh. ■ 44308 #038-44-2002 L2002 OBG *100

JANDA, Jeffrey Jason. 224 W EXCHANGE ST, STE 380 44302 #038-44-1998 L2000 IM *020

JAVORSKY, Thomas Gerard. 224 W EXCHANGE ST, STE 360 44302 #038-45-1990 L1993 AN *020 †05

JEANMAIRE, John Robt. 190 N UNION ST, STE 104 44304 #056-06-1979 L1982 AN *020 †05

JENSEN, Todd Alan. ■ 44312 #030-05-2004 L2004 EM *012

JEWELL, Steven Wm. 312 LOCUST ST, CHILD GUIDANCE & FAM SOLTN 44302 #016-06-1974 L2005 CHP P *020 †75 ‡

JOHNSON, Andre H. 400 WABASH AVE, AKRON GENERAL MED CTR 44307 #035-03-2001 L2001 OSM *020

JOHNSON, Clifford Andrew. 525 E MARKET ST 44304 #030-06-1948 L1954 OM *071

JOHNSON, Jeffrey Scott. ■ 44312 #038-44-2007 L2007 ORS *012

JOHNSON, Jil Marie. ■ 44313 #041-78-2005, ▲ L2005 OBG *012

JOHNSON, Kellie. 1 PARK WEST BLVD, STE 200 44320 #017-20-1990 L1992 OBG *020 †30

JOHNSON, Vijay. 400 WABASH AVE, AKRON GEN MED CTR 44307 #495-35-2001 L2005 IM *012

JONES, Brian Thos. 75 ARCH ST, STE 103 44304 #038-44-1987 L1988 GS OS *085

JONES, Garimah Aisha. 1867 W MARKET ST 44304 #038-44-1998 L1999 IM *020 †20

JONES, Jack Gordon. 1660 AKRON PENINSL RD #101 44313 #038-06-1973 L1975 GS OS *020 †85

JONES, Kerwyn Chas. 300 LOCUST ST, STE 170 44302 #041-07-1992 L2001 OP ORS *020 †40

JONES, Ronald Rex. 55 ARCH ST, INC 44304 #038-43-1979 L1982 IM *020 †20

JOPPERI, Eric Richard-All. 525 E MARKET ST 44304 #038-75-2004, ▲ L2004 IM *020 †20

JOSEPHS, Brian Constantin. ■ 44313 #047-07-2005 L2005 OBG *012

JOURILES, Nicholas John. 400 WABASH AVE, DEPT OF EMERG MED 44307 #038-06-1982 L1987 EM IM *040 †16

JOYCE, Julie Ann. 4880 S MAIN ST, STE 4 44319 #038-44-1994 L1995 PD *020 †55

JUNKO, Jeffrey Todd. 20 OLIVE ST, STE 210 44310 #038-44-2000 L2000 ORS *100

JURSEK, Eugene Stanley. 525 E MARKET ST 44304 #038-40-1958 L1958 OBG *071 †30

JWAYYED, Sharhabeel Musa. 525 E MARKET ST, SUMMA HEALTH SYSTEM 44304 #038-40-1989 L1990 EM *020 †16

KAISER, Elizabeth Anne. ■ 44308 #038-41-2007 L2007 PD *012

KAKARALA, Harish. 224 W EXCHANGE ST STE 380, CRITICAL CARE ASSC INC 44302 #038-44-1996 L2002 PCC *020 †20

KAKUMANU, Vijay. 400 WABASH AVE 44307 #661-02-2005 L2005 IM *012

KAMDAR, Apur Ramesh. 75 ARCH ST, STE 303 44304 #038-44-2001 L2001 CD *012 †20

KAMIENSKI, Robert Wayne. 224 W EXCHANGE ST, STE 300 44302 #018-03-1974 L1975 TS VS *020 †85,90

KANAA'N, Anmar Hashem. 400 WABASH AVE, AKRON GEN MED CTR 44307 #575-02-2004 L2006 IM *012

KANAAN, Zeyad Hashem. 400 WABASH AVE 44307 #575-02-2005 L2007 IM *012

KANDULA, Sushma. ■ 44312 #038-44-2005 L2005 OPH *012

KANG, Peter Lee. ■ 44303 #038-44-2005 L2005 EM *012

KANTAK, Anand Dattatraya. 300 LOCUST ST STE 540 44302 #495-22-1974 L1981 NPM PD *020 †55

KARNANI, Ravi. ■ 44308 #038-44-1996 L1997 IM *020 †20,03

KARTHIKEYAN, Jeyavarna. ■ 44312 #038-44-2006 L2006 IM *100

KASHKARI, Sheila. 525 E MARKET ST DEPT PATH 44304 #495-03-1961 L1971 PTH *040 †50

KASPER, John Andrew. 444 N MAIN ST, ST THOMAS HOSP 44310 #038-44-1986 L1993 P PYG *020 †75

KASTELIC, Joseph Ernest. CHILDRENS HOSP OF AKRON 44308 #028-34-1959 L1962 PD HEM *020 †55

KATIRJI, M K. 215 E WATERLOO RD STE 10 44319 #875-02-1974 L1980 IM *020 †20

KATZ, David. ■ 44333 #038-06-1955 L1955 R *072 †80

KAUH, Bong Suck. 55 ARCH ST, GERIATRICIANS 44304 #583-01-1984 L1989 IM IMG *020 †20

KAWAKITA, Erick Makio. 400 WABASH AVE, AKRON GENERAL MED CTR 44307 #025-07-2006 L2006 ORS *012

KAY, David Beryl. 3975 EMBASSY PKWY, STE 102 44333 #038-43-1980 L1981 ORS *050 †40

KAYANI, Natalie Anastasia. 55 ARCH ST, GERIATRICIANS 44304 #016-11-1995 L2001 IM IMG *020 †20

KAYANI, Thomas Joseph. 525 E MARKET ST 44304 #035-46-1996 L2001 NEP IM *020 †20

KEATON, Brian Francis. 525 E MARKET ST, EMERGENCY DEPARTMENT 44304 #038-43-1979 L1980 EM *020 †16

KECK, Carl Wm. 177 S BROADWAY ST 44308 #038-06-1965 L1965 PHP *071 †70

KEFALAS, Costas H. 570 WHITE POND DR, STE 100 44320 #038-44-1997 L1998 GE *020 †20 ‡

KELLY-LANGEN, Catherine A. 1 PERKINS SQ, PALLIATIVE CARE CTR 44308 #010-02-1996 L2002 PD PLM *020 †55

KEMPE, Jeffrey William. 20 OLIVE ST, STE 300 44310 #654-01-2003 L2003 IM *020 †20

KEMPPAINEN, John William. ■ 44333 #025-07-2007 L2007 ORS *012

KEPLEY, Robert Franklin. 444 N MAIN ST 44310 #038-40-1975 L1976 ORS *020 †40

KEREK, William Balint. 75 ARCH ST, STE 102 44304 #038-40-1976 L1977 IM *020 †20

KERN, Herbert. ■ 44313 #869-05-1954 L1961 P *071

KERR, Julie L. 1 PERKINS SQ 44308 #038-41-1994 L1996 IM *020 †20

KHALIL, Rafik Mounir. 2603 W MARKET ST, RADIOLOGY & IMAGING SERV 44313 #038-40-1990 L1991 DR *020 †80

KHAN, Sameera. 340 S BROADWAY 44308 #704-09-1974 L1990 P *020

KHASSAWNEH, Basheer Y. ■ 44304 #575-02-1993 L1998 PCC *020 †20

KILE, Jeffrey David. 3529 FORTUNA DR, SOUTH CENTRAL FAMILY PHYSI 44312 #038-45-1993 L1996 FM *020 †18

KILLION, Christopher D. 1 PERKINS SQ, MEDICAL CENTER OF AKRON 44308 #041-15-2001 L2006 PEM *012 †55

KIM, Albert Byoungsang. 95 ARCH ST, STE 210 44304 #038-44-1997 L1998 PCC *020 †20

KIM, Won. 400 WABASH AVE 44307 #583-10-2001 L2003 MPD *020

KIMBERLY, David R. 554 WHITE POND DR STE B 44320 #030-05-1996 L2002 GS *020

KING, Toni Michele. 444 N MAIN ST STE 306 44310 #038-44-1989 L1991 END *020 †20

KIRK, Jos Michael. 224 W EXCHANGE ST STE 36, SUITE 360 44302 #671-01-1980 L1985 AN *020 †20

KIRKPATRICK, Marcus Scott. ■ 44302 #038-40-2007 L2007 ORS *012

KISHORE, Rajeev. 215 W BOWERY ST, STE 4500 44308 #495-36-1973 L1978 PDA PD *020 †55,03

KLATT, Walter Allan. 3614 MANCHESTER RD, STE 101 44319 #038-40-1990 L1993 IM *020 †20

KLEIN, Jeffrey J. 1755 W MARKET ST 44313 #038-41-1973 L1974 IM ID *020 †20

KLEIN, Robert Louis. 300 LOCUST ST, STE 560 44302 #056-06-1966 L1967 PDS *020 †85

KLEJKA, James Patrick. 525 E MARKET ST, REHAB UNIT 44304 #038-40-1989 L1991 PM *020 †60

KLIMO, Lynn Marie. 444 N MAIN ST STE 408, SUMMA PSYCHIATRY ASSOCIATE 44310 #038-06-2000 L2001 P *020 †75

KLIMSA, Ivan. ■ 44333 #286-04-1962 L1973 OPH *071 †35

KLINE, Jennifer A. ■ 44313 #038-43-2006 L2006 EM *012

KLINE-KRAMMES, Sarah E. ■ 44320 #038-41-2006 L2006 PD *012

KLONK, Christopher J. 3975 EMBASSY PKWY, STE 102 44333 #038-44-1987 L1989 PP *012 †40

KLOSS, Joseph Leo. 400 WABASH AVE 44307 #028-34-1957 L1959 D PD *020 †55,15

KOELKER, Cynthia. 213 MASSILLON RD 44312 #038-06-1983 L1984 FM *020 †18

KOENIG, Joseph Michael. 75 ARCH ST, STE 202 44304 #038-40-1985 L1986 HEM ON *020 †20

KOENIG, Michael Gilbert. 1 PERKINS SQ, CENTER OF AKRON 44308 #035-09-1998 L2004 PDP *100 †55

KOENIG, Teresa. 55 ARCH ST, INC 44304 #038-40-1985 L1986 IM *040 †20

KOKOMOOR, Franklin Wesley. 300 LOCUST ST STE 500 44302 #011-03-1977 L1981 NPM PD *020 †55

KOLAKALUR, Sripriya Doss. 20 OLIVE ST, STE 300 44310 #495-59-2001 L2004 IM *020 †20

KOLARIK, Doug Bryan. ■ 44303 #038-44-2004 L2004 IM *020 †20

KONDOVSKI, Josif. ■ 44313 #957-02-1960 L1966 R *071 †80

KORDELSKI, Cynthia Anne. 1280 ASHWOOD RD 44312 #038-44-1995 L1999 PDR *020

KORNICK, Jeffrey Jonathan. 2603 W MARKET ST, STE 110 44313 #038-43-1987 L1993 DR *020 †80

KORYTKOWSKI, Paul Jos. 224 W EXCHANGE ST STE 360 44302 #035-06-1977 L1980 AN *020 †05

KOTHA, Kavitha. ■ 44308 #038-44-2006 L2006 PD *012

KOUFOS, Alex. 281 LOCUST ST, CHILDREN'S MED CTR OF AKRON 44302 #038-40-1978 L1981 PD HEM *050 †55

KOUSAIE, Frank Michael. 3975 EMBASSY PKWY STE 202A 44333 #038-40-1956 L1956 AN IM *020 †05

KOVACEVICH, Gregory Janko. 500 PORTAGE LAKES DR, STE B 44319 #038-44-1995 L1997 OBG *020 †30

KOVALCIK, Jason Benjamin. 1 PERKINS SQ, 500 GYPSY LANE 44308 #038-44-1998 L2000 PD *020 †55

KRAUS, Henry. ■ 44303 #038-06-1947 L1947 IM CD *071 †20

KRAUS, Jane Merrill. ■ 44313 #036-07-1948 L1971 PTH OS *075

KRAUS, William G. ■ 44313 #038-06-1945 L1945 ORS OS *071

KRAYNACK, Nathan Charles. 1 PERKINS SQ, ROBERT T STONE RESP CTR 44308 #010-02-1997 L1998 PDP *020 †55

KRETCHMER, Kenneth Ronald. 95 ARCH ST, STE 100 44304 #038-06-1975 L1976 PUD IM *020 †20

KRISHEN, Adarsh Edwin. 55 ARCH ST STE 3A, FAM PRAC CTR OF AKRON 44304 #038-44-1986 L1987 FM *020 †18

■ = Address Information Privacy Protected

KUERBITZ, Steven James. 1 PERKINS SQ, OF AKRON 44308 #025-07-1984 L1995 PHO PD *020 †55

KULASEKARAN, T. 300 LOCUST ST, STE 460 44302 #495-27-1966 L1981 CHN PD *020 †55,75

KULASEKARAN, Vishnu. ■ 44313 #038-41-2008 *012

KUMAR, Raman. ■ 44312 #030-06-2005 L2005 GS *012

KUMER, Kimberly Dawn. 1953 STANSBERRY CIR 44313 #038-44-1997 L1998 P *020 †75

KURMAN, Andrew Jay. 400 WABASH AVE, AKRON GENERAL RADIOLOGY 44307 #035-03-1980 L1986 RNR R *020 †80

KURTZ, William Jason. ■ 44301 #037-01-2004 L2004 ORS *012

KUTNICK, Steven Lee. 395 E MARKET ST 44304 #025-01-1971 L1978 OTO FPS *020 †45

LABABIDI, Tony G. 2092 WEDGEWOOD DR 44312 #038-75-2001, ▲ L2001 AN *020 †05

LADEN, Nathaniel Seth. 224 W EXCHANGE ST STE 14 44302 #038-43-1988 L1997 TS *020 †90,85

LAL, Manohar. ■ 44313 #495-41-1966 L1971 OBG OS *071 †30

LAL, Tanmay Girish. 525 EAST AVE 44304 #495-17-1993 L2000 GS *020 †85

LALJI, Ronil S. 75 ARCH ST, AKRON CITY HOSPITAL 44304 #060-01-1993 L1996 IM *100

LAMKIN, Barry Chas. 4125 MEDINA RD STE 200, HEALTH AND WELLNESS CENTER 44333 #025-01-1975 L1981 D *020 †15

LANE, John Richard. 1 PERKINS SQ, CHILDREN'S HOSP MED CTR/AK 44308 #047-05-1989 L1993 PDC *020 †20,55

LANGKAMP, Diane Louise. 1 PERKINS SQ, AKRON CHILDRENS HOSP 44308 #035-45-1981 L1992 PD *050 †55

LANOY, Reynerio Sepe. 400 WABASH AVE, AKRON GEN MED CTR 44307 #748-27-1997 L2004 IM *020 †20

LANTZOUNI, Eleni. 1 PERKINS SQ 44308 #418-01-1991 L2000 ADL PD *020 †55

LASKOVSKI, Jovan Riste. ■ 44313 #038-44-2006 L2006 ORS *012

LAWRENCE, Henry Steven. 1260 INDEPENDENCE AVE, OHIO PERMANENTE MED GRP 44310 #028-34-1978 L1980 PD PEM *020 †55

LAZAR, Andrew Evan. 411 E MARKET ST 44304 #025-07-1998 L2002 NEP *020 †20

LAZZERINI, Frank Domenico. ■ 44303 #038-44-2006 L2006 FP *012

LEANO, Ann Marie. 95 ARCH ST, STE 210 44304 #041-07-1993 L2000 PCC *020 †20

LECAT, Paul Jacques. 400 WABASH AVE 44307 #035-06-1989 L1992 IM PD *020 †20,55

LEE, Christine I. 224 W EXCHANGE ST STE 300 44302 #038-75-1993, ▲ L1994 NEP *020

LEE, Jai Hoon. 75 ARCH ST STE 407 44304 #035-06-1984 L1990 TS *020 †85,90

LEE, Kwangshin. 1 PERKINS SQ 44308 #583-02-1964 L1972 AN *071 †05

LEE, Timothy John. 1 PERKINS SQ, DEPT OF EMERGENCY MEDICINE 44308 #038-43-2000 L2002 PEM *100 †55

LEE, Young Hun. 525 E MARKET ST, SUMMA HEALTH SYSTEM 44304 #038-44-1998 L2000 PCC *100 †20

LEEDY, Marvin Eugene. 150 SPRINGSIDE DR, STE 225B 44333 #038-40-1970 L1970 OPH *020 †35

LEHMAN, Christie Melby. ■ 44333 #038-40-2005 L2005 PM *012

LEHMAN, James A, Jr. 300 LOCUST ST, STE 590 44302 #041-02-1961 L1964 PS HNS *020 †85,65 ‡

LEVIN, Solomon Elias. 400 WABASH AVE 44307 #836-01-1950 PDC OS *020

LEVINE, Mark Roger. 400 WABASH AVE 44307 #041-09-1965 L1966 OPH OS *020 †35

LEWANDOWSKI, Phillip J. 3975 EMBASSY PKWY, CRYSTAL CLINIC, INC 44333 #038-40-1990 L1991 ORS *020 †40

LEWIS, James Michael. 1 PERKINS SQ 44308 #038-40-1964 L1964 PS *071 †65

LI, Richard Lichuan. 525 E MARKET ST, DEPT OF MED EDUCATION 44304 #243-71-1984 L2006 IM *100

LIBERTIN, Nicholas, II. 1600 E TURKEYFOOT LAKE RD 44312 #038-44-1986 L1987 PD *075 †55

LICHTEN, Gary Dan. 157 W CEDAR ST, STE 201 44307 #038-40-1973 L1975 D IM *020 †20,15

LICHTENBERGER, Erik Jacob. 1260 INDEPENDENCE AVE 44310 #014-01-1985 L1987 GS *020 †30

LIEBELT, Robert Arthur. 400 WABASH AVE 44307 #048-04-1958 L1975 ADM *040

LIN, Chieh Hsin. 400 WABASH AVE 44307 #654-01-2002 L2003 IM *100 †18

LIN, Tsun Hsin. 300 LOCUST ST, STE 540 44302 #244-04-1969 L1974 NPM PD *020 †55

LISTERMAN, Peter Murphy. 525 E MARKET ST, EMERGENCY DEPARTMENT 44304 #038-43-1991 L1994 EM *020 †16

LISY, Todd Alan. 4880 S MAIN ST, STE 4 44319 #038-44-1997 L1998 MPD *020 †20,55

LITMAN, George Irving. 400 WABASH AVE 44307 #024-05-1964 L1972 CD IM *030 †20

LLAMAS, Katrina De Castro. 400 WABASH AVE 44307 #748-17-2004 L2007 FP *012

LOBODA, Michael Steven. 224 W EXCHANGE ST, STE 360 44302 #038-06-1997 L1999 AN *020 †05

LOCASTRO, Anthony Jos. 300 LOCUST ST, STE 400 44302 #038-44-1986 L1987 OPH OS *020 †35

LOCKWOOD, Ramona Esther. 1 PERKINS SQ 44308 #051-07-1994 L1995 PD *020 †55

LOFGREN, Samuel David. 525 E MARKET ST 44304 #028-02-2001 L2001 EM *020 †16

LOFTUS, Martin Frank. 3800 EMBASSY PKWY, STE 300 44333 #014-01-1977 L1978 FM *020 †18

LOIUDICE, Thomas Anthony. 224 W EXCHANGE ST STE 410, AKRON GASTRO ASSOCS INC 44302 #016-76-1972, ▲ L1974 GE NTR *020 †20,18

LONG, Ruby Janel. ■ 44319 #017-20-2006 L2006 EM *012

LONSDORF, William Kevin. 2818 S ARLINGTON RD, STE B 44312 #038-43-1976 L1977 FM *020 †18

LOU, Ching Yun. 3593 S ARLINGTON RD, STE C 44312 #244-06-1971 L1979 CRS *020 †10,85

LOUD, Keith John. 388 S MAIN ST, MEDICAL CENTER OF AKRON 44311 #067-01-1996 L2004 ADL PSM *020 †55

LOUGHRY, C Wm. 525 E MARKET ST 44304 #038-40-1950 L1950 GS *071 †85

LOUISIN, Victor John. 400 WABASH AVE, AKRON GENERAL MEDICAL CENT 44307 #038-41-1967 L1967 DR *020 †80

LUGO, Manuel, Jr. 1 PERKINS SQ, CO CHILDREN S HOSP-MED EDU 44308 #038-40-1999 L2001 PD *020 †55

LUKOWSKI, David Eric. 400 WABASH AVE, MEDICAL CENTER 44307 #055-01-2005 L2005 ORS *012

MABEE, Grant Wm. 1 PARK WEST BLVD, STE 200 44320 #065-05-1963 L1965 GE IM *071 †20

MACKAN, Michael Dale. 525 E MARKET ST 44304 #038-40-1975 L1975 FM *020 †16

MACRITCHIE, Ellen C. 1 PERKINS SQ, MEDICAL EDUCATION DEPARTME 44308 #038-45-2003 L2003 PD *020 †55

MADALIN, Karla Jeanne. 4125 MEDINA RD, STE 211 44333 #048-04-1981 L1983 N *020 †75

MAGER, Thomas George. 935 MORNINGSTAR DR 44307 #038-40-2001 L2001 EM *020 †16

MAGOLINE, Alfred Jos, Jr. 400 WABASH AVE 44307 #038-06-1961 L1961 OTO HNS *071 †45

MAJORS, David Christopher. ■ 44313 #038-43-2007 L2007 IM *012

MAKATI, Samir Ashok. ■ 44313 #038-44-2006 L2006 IM *012

MAKKAR, Hitesh. 95 ARCH ST, STE 210 44304 #038-44-1994 L1995 PCC *020 †20

MALHOTRA, Vivek. 1 PERKINS SQ, DEPT OF PICU 44308 #495-83-1986 L1997 CCP *020 †55

MALIK, Hassan. 1755 W MARKET ST 44313 #305-01-1997 L2000 IM *020 †20

MALLAH, Albert Hartley. 400 WABASH AVE 44307 #665-01-2001 L2002 IM *100

MANNEH, Nabil Abu. 525 E MARKET ST 44304 #550-01-1965 L1974 GS *020

MANNING, Neal Robt. 3043 SANITARIUM RD 44312 #038-40-1992 L1994 IM *020 †20

MARCHETTA, Ross Frank, II. 3636 YELLOW CREEK RD, OF THE RESERVE 44333 #038-41-1986 L1987 OBG *020 †30

MARHEFKA, Marcia L. 1 PERKINS SQ 44308 #038-40-2001 L2001 PD *100 †55

MARK, Julie A. 789 WHITE POND DR, STE A 44320 #038-44-1996 L1997 D *020 †15

MARK, Thomas Edward. 190 N UNION ST, STE 104 44304 #038-44-1994 L1996 AN *020 †05

MARKOVICH, Renee Lynn. 400 WABASH AVE 44307 #038-44-1994 L1996 FM *072 †20

MARLEY, Robert Alan. 400 WABASH AVE, STE 372 44307 #036-05-1981 L1986 GS *020 †85

MARQUART, Chris Dorr. 1450 FIRESTONE PKWY STE F, CONCCENTRA MEDICAL CTR 44301 #056-05-1971 L1980 FM *020 †16

MARQUINEZ, Frederick P. 224 W EXCHANGE ST, STE 310 44302 #038-44-1985 L1991 ON IM *020 †20

MARRERO, Luis Gilberto. ■ 44303 #649-01-1956 L1963 D *071

MARSICO, Robert Edward. 1867 W MARKET ST, STE C2 44313 #038-40-1961 L1961 D *071 †15

MARSICO, Robt Edward, Jr. 1867 W MARKET ST, FAIRWAY CTR STE C-2 44313 #038-40-1991 L1993 D *020 †15

MARTIN, Bradley R. 525 E MARKET ST 44304 #055-02-1983 L1984 CCM IM *020 †20

MARTINO, Carl Richard. 400 WABASH AVE, AKRON GENERAL MED CTR 44307 #038-06-1980 L1982 DR *020 †80

MARTIN-SHULTZ, Kenneth G. UNIV AKRON INST BIO MED 44325 #038-43-1980 OS PHP *040

MASEELALL, Erwin Arvind. 75 ARCH ST STE 501 44304 #495-01-1971 L1976 IM *020 †20

MASIN, Jeffrey Scott. 300 LOCUST ST STE 100 44302 #023-01-1991 L1996 OTO PDO *020 †45

MASSANYI, Eric Zoltan. ■ 44303 #038-44-2006 L2006 U *012

MASSAU, Sharon Diane. 444 N MAIN ST 44310 #038-44-1983 L1984 P *020 †75

MATHIAS, Daniel Webster. 55 ARCH ST STE 3B 44304 #038-06-1948 L1949 OPH *071 †35

MATOS, Estanislao Antonio. 20 OLIVE ST, STE 401 44310 #308-01-1961 L1967 IM *020 †20

MATTHEWS, Mark Alan. 5147 MANCHESTER RD, COMMUNITY HLTH CARE/MANCHE 44319 #038-45-1989 L1990 FM *020 †18

MAXWELL, Catherine Sue. 55 ARCH ST, GERIATRICIANS 44304 #028-34-1978 L1980 IMG IM *020 †20 ‡

MAY, Maryann Christine. 177 S BROADWAY ST, AKRON HEALTH DEPT 44308 #038-43-1979 L1980 PD *020 †55

MAY, Richard Eugene, Jr. 411 E MARKET ST 44304 #038-40-1987 L1988 NEP *020 †20

MCBENNETT, Kimberly Ann. 400 WABASH AVE, BLDG ACC 44307 #038-44-2001 L2001 MPD *020 †20

MC BRIDE, John Thos. 1 PERKINS SQ 44308 #038-06-1971 L1999 PUD PDP *020 †55

MC BRIDE, Margaret S C. 1 PERKINS SQ, AKRON, DIV OF CHILD NEUROL 44308 #038-06-1971 L1999 CHN PD *020 †55,75

MC COLLUM, Mark O. 300 LOCUST ST STE 560 44302 #048-13-1995 L2002 PDS *020 †85

MC CORMACK-PFEFFER, M. 676 S BROADWAY ST, STE 103 44311 #038-44-1992 L1994 PD *020 †55

MC COY, Don W. 123 E WATERLOO RD 44319 #035-09-1951 L1952 FM *071 †18

MC COY, Michael Donald. ■ 44313 #038-06-1960 L1960 PTH *071 †50

MC CUE, Ralph William. 3925 EMBASSY PKWY 44333 #055-01-1976 L1977 ORS HS *020 †40

MC DANIEL, Margaret Sue. 1 PERKINS SQ 44308 #038-44-2002 L2002 PD *020

MC DERMOTT, Janet L. 1621 FLICKINGER RD 44312 #016-43-1982 L1990 IMG IM *020

MCGOLDRICK, Katherine Bri. 400 WABASH AVE 44307 #041-78-2005, ▲ L2005 OBG *012

MCGRIEVY, Nancy Jean. ■ 44333 #495-19-2006 L2006 OBG *012

MC KNIGHT, Eric Joseph. 1 PARK WEST BLVD, STE 200 44320 #038-41-1998 L2002 OBG *020 †30

MC MAHON, Daniel Robt. 300 LOCUST ST STE 260 44302 #038-40-1988 L1990 UP U *020 †95

MC MULLEN, Mary Jo. 400 WABASH AVE 44307 #038-40-1976 L1977 EM *020 †16

MC NALLY, Shannon Marie. 20 OLIVE ST 44310 #038-44-1997 L1999 IM *020 †18

MC NATT, Joshua Matthew. ■ 44312 #038-44-2004 L2004 FM *020 †18

MCQUOWN, Mary Colleen. ■ 44313 #038-44-2005 L2005 EM *012

MC ROBERTS, Mark Richard. 3043 SANITARIUM RD 44312 #038-41-1981 L1983 IM *020 †20

MCSHANNIC, Joseph Robert. 525 E MARKET ST 44304 #038-43-1990 L1991 VS *020 †85

MECKLER, David. 370 E MARKET ST 44304 #041-02-1959 L1961 PD *071 †55

MEDVEDEFF, Mark Andre. ■ 44303 #038-40-1976 L1976 EM FM *030 †16

MEHTA, Nirmal. 444 N MAIN ST 44310 #060-01-1992 OS *100 †80

MEHTA, Vinayak Trambaklal. 400 WABASH AVE, AKRON GEN MED CTR DEPT PAT 44307 #495-38-1954 L1972 PTH CLP *071 †50

MELBY, Arne, III. 3975 EMBASSY PKWY, STE 102 44333 #038-40-1973 L1975 ORS *020 †40

MELIAN, Jose Maria. 656 W MARKET ST 44303 #847-02-1955 L1965 OPH *071

MENASSA, Maximilien Emile. ■ 44313 #330-03-1953 L1967 P *071 †75

MENCL, Francis Rene. 525 E MARKET ST 44304 #038-44-1990 L1991 EM *020 †16

MENDISE, Thomas Joseph. 493 CANTON RD 44312 #422-01-2001 L2003 OBG *020 †30

MERCADO, Francis Amado Di. 400 WABASH AVE, AKRON GEN MED CTR 44307 #748-02-2003 L2005 IM *012

MERCADO, Margaret Gutierr. 400 WABASH AVE, AKRON GENERAL MED CTR 44307 #748-02-1999 L2005 FP *012

MEREDICK, Richard B. 400 WABASH AVE, AKRON GENERAL MED CTR 44307 #041-12-2002 L2002 ORS *100

MILLER, Charles J, Jr. ■ 44313 #038-06-1945 L1945 DR *071 †80

MILLER, David Allen. 95 ARCH ST, STE 210 44304 #038-44-1985 L1986 IM *020 †20

MILLER, Eric Thomas. ■ 44319 #038-44-2003 L2003 ORS *012

MILLER, Hugh James. 130 W EXCHANGE ST, SURGICAL & MED NEUR ASSOC 44302 #025-07-1981 L1985 N *020 †75

MILLER, Kevin Scott. 444 N MAIN ST, STE 306 44310 #038-40-1998 L1999 END *020 †20

MILLER, Louise Ann. 224 W EXCHANGE ST STE 330 44302 #007-02-1996 L2001 PD *020 †55

MILLER, Stephen F, III. 326 LOCUST ST 44302 #016-11-1997 L2000 PSM *020 †55

MILLS, Belinda Maria. 281 LOCUST ST 44302 #305-01-2006 L2006 PD *012

MILO, Anton Gregory. 395 E MARKET ST 44304 #038-40-1993 L1994 OTO HNS *020 †45

MILO, Anton Polykron. ■ 44333 #038-40-1960 L1960 OTO HNS *071 †45

MINHAS, Meha. ■ 44321 #495-03-2001 L2006 IM *012

MINOR, David Cragar. 113 AMBASSADOR CT 44312 #004-01-1981 L1983 PHP *075

MINOR, Stacie Ann. 676 S BROADWAY ST, STE 103 44311 #038-40-1999 L1999 PD *020 †55

MIR, Raafia. ■ 44303 #038-45-2006 L2006 FP *012

MITCHELL, David Michael. 400 WABASH AVE, BLDG ACC 44307 #016-11-1998 L2005 IM *020 †20

MITCHELL, Ronald B. ■ 44313 #021-01-1951 L1953 **OBG** *071 †30
MITCHELL, Steve Z. 190 N UNION ST, STE 104 44304 #035-03-1979 L1982 **AN** *020 †05
MITSTIFER, Jack Henry. 400 WABASH AVE, AKRON GENERAL MEDICAL CENT 44307 #041-01-1992 L2000 **EM** *020 †16
MOATS, William Emerald. 444 N MAIN ST # 3 44310 #038-40-1962 L1962 **FM GP** *020 †18
MOAWAD, John Atef. 95 ARCH ST, STE 215 44304 #016-02-1993 L2001 **VS** *020 †85
MOAWAD, Stephanie Anne. 95 ARCH ST, STE 215 44304 #038-43-2003 L2003 **PD** *020 †55
MOE, James T. ■ 44303 #037-01-2005 L2005 **EM** *012
MONTAGNESE, Miguel Daniel. ■ 44310 #038-43-2003 L2003 **GS** *012
MONTE, James Roger. 493 CANTON RD, PARAGON HEALTH ASSOC 44312 #038-40-1989 L1990 **OBG** *020 †30
MONTEITH, Jeffrey Randall. ■ 44312 #038-44-2006 L2006 **IM** *012
MONTGOMERY, David. 1 PARK WEST BLVD, STE 200 44320 #051-07-1977 L1978 **OBG** *020 †30
MONTINOLA, Antonio B. 10 PENFIELD AVE 44310 #748-08-1964 L1974 **P** *020 †16
MOONEY, Kenneth Edward. 395 E MARKET ST 44304 #041-01-1982 L1987 **OTO HNS** *020 †45
MOORE, Jeffrey Lee. 400 WABASH AVE 44307 #038-40-1982 L1986 **P** *020 †75
MOORE, Randy D. 1002 SNOWFALL SPUR # A 44313 #068-01-1990 *100
MOORHEAD, Colin Stuart. 470 WHITE POND DR, STE 100 44320 #038-44-1998 L1999 **IM** *020 †20
MOORHEAD, Kelly L. 470 WHITE POND DR, STE 100 44320 #038-45-1996 L1997 **IM** *020 †20
MOORSTEIN, Benjamin. 400 WABASH AVE 44307 #025-01-1943 L1949 **P** *072 †75
MORAN, Rocio Tarvin. 1 PERKINS SQ, DEPT OF PEDIATRICS 44308 #038-06-2000 L2000 **OS** *100 †55,19
MORETUZZO, Richard W. 525 E MARKET ST 44304 #035-06-1977 L1978 **REN GYN** *020 †30
MOROCCO, Michael Dominic. 444 N MAIN ST, STE 306 44310 #038-40-1997 L2000 **END** *020 †20
MORTIER, George Peter. 444 N MAIN ST 44310 #065-09-1955 L1960 **OBG OS** *075 †30
MOSER, James Michael. 177 S BROADWAY ST, AKRON HEALTH DEPARTMENT 44308 #020-12-1977 L1983 **PHP IM** *030 †20,70
MOSES, Douglas Edward. 1 PERKINS SQ 44308 #038-44-1995 L1996 **PD** *020 †55
MOSTOW, Eliot Nathan. 157 W CEDAR ST STE 101 44307 #038-40-1985 L1993 **D** *020 †15
MOWAD, Eugene Michael. 1 PERKINS SQ, CHILDREN'S HOSP MED CTR OF 44308 #041-12-1990 L1994 **PD** *020 †55
MOYEN, Farhana Rahman. 820 CANTON RD 44312 #160-02-1983 L1998 **IM** *020
MUAKKASSA, Farid Fuad. 400 WABASH AVE, DEPT SURG 44307 #605-01-1983 L1993 **GS CCS** *020 †85
MUAKKASSA, Kamel F. 157 W CEDAR ST, STE 203 44307 #605-01-1974 L1984 **NS** *020 †25
MUBASHIR, Bashar Ahmad. 224 W EXCHANGE ST, STE 310 44302 #704-04-1967 L1973 **HO IM** *020 †20
MUCITELLI, Diane Rose. 400 WABASH AVE 44307 #561-01-1982 L1989 **ATP CLP** *040 †50
MULLEN, Patricia Alice. 400 WABASH AVE, ACC 4TH FLOOR 44307 #041-07-1978 L1980 **IM** *020 †20
MULLIGAN, Daniel Dale. ■ 44313 #038-43-2005 L2005 **U** *012
MUNETZ, Mark Richard. 100 W CEDAR ST STE 300, SUMMIT COUNTY ADM BROAD 44307 #041-01-1976 L1989 **P** *030 †75
MUNIYAPPA, Pramodha. 525 E MARKET ST, C/O SUMMA HLTH SYS-MED EDU 44304 #038-44-2002 L2002 **PG** *012
MURNANE, Laura B.. 400 WABASH AVE 44307 #305-01-2007 L2007 **IM** *012
MURPHY, Dale Patterson. 55 ARCH ST, INC 44304 #038-40-1971 L1971 **IM** *030 †20
MURPHY, John James. ■ 44313 #016-43-1954 L1954 **IM** *071
MURPHY, William Raymond. 525 E MARKET ST 44304 #010-01-1955 L1957 **IM** *071 †20
MURRAY, Gail Alary. ■ 44313 #068-01-1975 L1983 **GS IM** *020
MURRAY, Mary Katherine. 3925 EMBASSY PKWY STE 275 44333 #038-45-1998 L1999 **GS** *020 †85
MURRAY, Richard W. 150 CROSS ST 44311 #038-41-1949 L1977 **P** *071 †75
MURRAY, Timothy C. 224 W EXCHANGE ST, STE 380 44302 #060-01-1984 L1988 **CCM IM** *020 †20
MURRAY, Travis Norman. 444 N MAIN ST 44310 #056-06-2003 L2003 **ORS** *012
MUSSER, Howard Oliver. ■ 44333 #041-01-1940 L1941 **AN** *071 †05
MYERS, Joseph Paul. 75 ARCH ST STE 105, PROFESSIONAL CTR NORTH 44304 #038-40-1975 L1977 **ID IM** *020 †20
NACKES, Nick Emmanuel. 525 E MARKET ST # 1N 44304 #038-41-1987 L1989 **CCM IM** *020 †20
NAFFAA, Lena Nassif. 1 PERKINS SQ, AKRON CHILDRENS HOSPITAL 44308 #605-03-1998 L2003 **PDR NR** *100
NAGASHIMA-WHALEN, Lauren. 4125 MEDINA RD, STE 200A 44333 #038-06-1989 L1992 **D DMP** *020 †15
NAIR, Bhavana Rajeev. 400 WABASH AVE, AKRON GEN MED CTR 44307 #495-31-1997 L2005 **IM** *020
NANKERVIS, George Arthur. 1 PERKINS SQ 44308 #035-45-1962 L1968 **PD ID** *030 †55
NAQVI, Syed Shaji Raza. 400 WABASH AVE 44307 #704-02-2001 L2004 **FP** *020 †20
NARD, James Albert. 1 PERKINS SQ, CHILDREN'S HOSP MED CTR OF 44308 #041-02-1984 L1988 **PD** *020 †55
NASH, David Michael. 95 ARCH ST, STE 250 44304 #038-44-1992 L1993 **OBG** *020 †30
NASRALLAH, Phillip F. 300 LOCUST ST STE 260 44302 #038-40-1971 L1971 **U PD** *020 †95
NATARAJAN, Shanmuga S. 400 WABASH AVE, CO AKRON GEN MED CTR-MED E 44307 #035-09-1998 L2000 **MPD** *012
NEGI, Lakshman Singh. 676 S BROADWAY ST, STE 105 44311 #038-40-1988 L1989 **FM** *020 †18
NEHER, Jeffrey Ray. 1037 N MAIN ST, STE B 44310 #038-40-1993 L1995 **GE** *020 †20
NEIMAN, Leon. 120 W BOWERY ST 44308 #038-40-1959 L1959 **OTO A** *020 †45
NELSON, Donald S. ■ 44313 #010-01-1950 L1953 **A PD** *071 †05
NELSON, George Clifford. 2620 RIDGEWOOD RD, STE 100 44313 #048-02-1957 L1957 **GS OS** *020 †85
NELSON, Holly Reid. ■ 44313 #038-43-2003 L2003 **DR** *012
NELSON, Jason Martin. 1485 WESTVALE AVE 44313 #020-02-2000 L2000 **EM** *020 †16 ‡
NELSON, Marc Erik. 300 LOCUST ST, STE 150 44302 #038-40-1997 **OTO** *020 †45
NEMER, Rasheed Faouzi. 577 GRANT ST 44311 #308-03-1986 L1994 **IM** *020
NEMER, Waleed Fawzi. 1134 BROWN ST STE 1A 44301 #915-03-1981 L1985 **IM CCM** *020 †20
NETZLEY, Robert Glenn. 400 WABASH AVE 44307 #038-44-1981 L1984 **TS VS** *020 †85,90
NG, Swee F. 525 E MARKET ST, SUMMA HEALTH SYSTEM 44304 #060-02-2003 L2004 **FM** *020 †20
NGUYEN, Dang-Khoa Quoc. 525 E MARKET ST 44304 #038-44-2004 L2004 **IM** *020 †20
NGUYEN, Hoai-Nghia. 1069 KENMORE BLVD 44314 #011-02-1993 L1997 **MPD** *020 †20,55
NGUYEN, Vinh-Truyen Quoc. ■ 44303 #038-40-2003 L2004 **IM** *020 †20

NICELY, Alfred Lorenz. 2241 COTTONWOOD CIR 44312 #038-40-1961 L1961 **OPH** *071 †35
NIELSON, Jeffrey Arthur. ■ 44313 #049-01-2003 L2004 **EM** *100
NIERTIT, Amy Katherine. ■ 44320 #035-06-2007 L2007 **EM** *012
NJOKU, Charles C. 390 S PORTAGE PATH 44320 #047-07-1979 L1983 **GS** *020
NJUS, Nina Maria. 3975 EMBASSY PKWY STE 201 44333 #018-03-1980 L1986 **HS ORS** *020 †40
NOBLE, Jeffrey Steven. 3975 EMBASSY PKWY, STE 102 44333 #018-03-1986 L1989 **ORS** *020 †40
NOEL, Curtis Robert. 3975 EMBASSY PKWY 44333 #030-05-2000 L2000 **ORS** *100
NORMAN, Robert Elwood, Jr. 444 N MAIN ST 44310 #055-01-1975 L1976 **IM IMG** *020
NOVAK, Pamela Eileen. 300 LOCUST ST 44302 #036-07-1975 L1982 **PD** *020 †55
NOVAK, Robert Wm. 1 PERKINS SQ, CHILDRENS HOSP DEPT PATH 44308 #036-07-1975 L1982 **PP PD** *020 †55,50 ‡
NTUKOGU, Kenechukwu Okwuc. ■ 44313 #038-40-2005 L2005 **IM** *012
NUNNALLY, Lucy Ann. 869 E MARKET ST 44305 #036-01-1979 L1991 **GYN** *020 †30
OCHS, Steven Edward. 157 W CEDAR ST 44307 #019-02-1993 L2004 **U** *020 †95
ODDI, Michael Anthony. 224 W EXCHANGE ST, STE 300 44302 #038-40-1972 L1972 **TS VS** *020 †85,90
O'DELL, Harry W. 400 WABASH AVE 44307 #017-20-1944 L1950 **ORS** *071 †40
O'DELL, Nancy Elaine. 1 PERKINS SQ 44308 #039-01-1988 L2001 **AN** *020 †05
OEY KUNTARAF, Andrea Lare. ■ 44312 #005-12-2006 L2006 **OBG** *012
OGONEK, Joseph Anthony. 400 WABASH AVE 44307. #056-06-1962 L1963 **FM** *071 †18
OKINO, Blaine Mitsuyuki. ■ 44313 #014-01-2006 L2006 **EM** *012
OKON, Roseline Ekaette. 1 PERKINS SQ, PEDIATRIC PSY 44308 #690-06-1993 L2006 **CHP** *100 †75
OLIN, Annette Corinne. 400 WABASH AVE 44307 #166-02-2002 L2003 **IM** *100
OLOYA, Acen Waraidzo. 1 PERKINS SQ, STE 390-1 44308 #038-44-2003 L2005 **PD** *100
OMLOR, Gregory J. 1 PERKINS SQ # PUD, CHILDREN HOSP MED CTR 44308 #038-43-1987 L1988 **PDP** *020 †55
ONEILL, Hugh Aloysius. ■ 44313 #038-40-2005 L2005 **FP** *012
ONG, Cesar Lee. 1 PERKINS SQ 44308 #748-10-1987 L2006 **PDR** *100
ONTELL-SILVERMAN, Sheryl. 190 N UNION ST, STE 104 44304 #038-06-1984 L1985 **AN** *020 †05
OOI, Say-Tat. 400 WABASH AVE, CO AKRON GEN HOSP-MED EDU 44307 #064-01-2000 L2000 **ID** *100 †20 ‡
OPRITZA, Andrew. 444 N MAIN ST 44310 #038-40-1954 L1954 **IM** *071 †20
ORLINO, Artemio L, Jr. 361 E WATERLOO RD 44319 #748-01-1970 L1976 **PTH** *020
OROS, Michael Joseph. 400 WABASH AVE, PSYCHIATRIC RESIDENT CLINI 44307 #041-12-2004 L2005 **P** *012
OROSZ, Jim Frederick. 525 E MARKET ST, STE 290 MEDICAL II 44304 #025-07-1976 L1983 **FM** *030 †18
OSHEA, Maura Kathleen. 605 N CLEVELAND MASSILN RD, STE A 44333 #047-05-1996 L2001 **OBG** *020 †30
OSOTEO, Rafael Pascua, Jr. 361 E WATERLOO RD 44319 #748-01-1969 L1973 **FM** *020 †18
PADIYAR, Nandita Krishna. 45 GOODYEAR BLVD 44305 #496-26-1997 L2001 **FM** *020 †18
PANKEY, Jan Marylee. 1 PERKINS SQ, AKRON CHILDREN'S HOSPITAL 44308 #003-01-1986 L2007 **AN** *020 †18,05
PANZNER, Margaret Patton. 55 W WATERLOO RD, AKRON OUTPATIENT CLINIC 44319 #038-43-1976 L1977 **FM FPG** *020 †18
PAPAS, Nicholas H. 1 PARK WEST BLVD, STE 350 44320 #038-44-1986 L1992 **PS HS** *020 †85,65
PAPOURAS, William Chris. 400 WABASH AVE 44307 #038-43-1996 L1997 **GS** *020 †85
PARANJAPE, Charudutt Nara. 400 WABASH AVE, AKRON GEN MED CTR 44307 #495-28-1995 L2001 **GS** *012
PARAS, Dwight Jonathan. 444 N MAIN ST 44310 #060-02-1989 L1991 **FM** *020 †18
PARENTI, Linda Ann. 605 N CLEVELAND MASSILN RD, STE A 44333 #038-40-1972 L1972 **OBG OS** *020 †30
PARK, Chandler H. 400 WABASH AVE, AKRON GEN MED CTR. 44307 #020-02-2007 L2007 **TY** *012
PARKER, Donald Lee. 75 ARCH ST STE 206 44304 #016-06-1960 L1964 **NEP IM** *071 †20
PARKER, Michael George. 1 PARK WEST BLVD, STE 350 44320 #016-11-1978 L1983 **PS GS** *020 †85,65
PARKER, Steven Bradford. 20 OLIVE ST, STE 300 44310 #055-01-2003 L2003 **IM** *100 †20
PARMAR, Deepti. 1260 INDEPENDENCE AVE 44310 #495-29-1995 L2004 **FPG** *020 †18
PARMAR, Rajinder. 1037 N MAIN ST, STE B 44310 #495-03-1989 L2004 **GE** *020 †20
PASSERO, Michael A. 95 ARCH ST, STE 210 44304 #043-01-2000 L2007 **SME IM** *020 †20
PATEL, Biren Manu. 300 LOCUST ST STE 260 44302 #041-13-2001 L2001 **U** *020 †95
PATEL, Chandrakant R. 1 PERKINS SQ, CENTER OF AKRON 44308 #495-23-1984 L1991 **PDC** *020 †55
PATEL, Divyansu Dhirendra. 400 WABASH AVE 44307 #665-01-2004 L2005 **P** *012
PATEL, Mehool Anil. 75 ARCH ST, STE 202 44304 #038-44-1998 L1999 **HO** *020 †20
PATEL, Nirali H. 281 LOCUST ST 44302 #495-37-2003 L2005 **PD** *012 †20
PATTERSON, Richard D, Jr. 3342 N MARTADALE DR 44333 #038-41-1992 L1995 **DR** *020 †80
PATTERSON, Richard David. 400 WABASH AVE 44307 #038-40-1961 L1961 **R** *071 †80
PATTON, Donna Felice. 1 PERKINS SQ, OF AKRON/DIV HEMOTOLOGY-ON 44308 #038-43-1979 L2000 **PHO** *020 †55
PAYNE, Jennifer Eileen. 75 ARCH ST, STE 202 44304 #041-12-1997 L2000 **HO** *020 †20
PAYNE, Lawrence N. 525 E MARKET ST 44305 #055-01-1983 L1984 **EM** *020 †16
PEDERSEN, John Carl. 1 PARK WEST BLVD, STE 350 44320 #025-07-1991 L1996 **PS HS** *020 †85,65
PEDERSEN, Sejal V. 3636 YELLOW CREEK RD, OF THE RESERVE 44333 #038-44-1994 L1997 **OBG** *020 †30
PENNINGTON, Gary Alan. 3925 EMBASSY PKWY, SUITE300 44333 #020-12-1985 L1987 **PS HS** *020 †85,65
PENNZA, Paul Thos. 20 OLIVE ST, STE 300 44310 #038-40-1978 L1978 **FM** *020 †16,18
PERERA, Ruwan Trevor. 400 WABASH AVE 44307 #661-03-2004 L2004 **FM** *100
PERO, Kathleen Ann. 282 W BOWERY ST, FAMILY BEHAVIORAL HEALTH 44307 #038-40-1991 L1992 **P** *020 †75
PERRY, Jessica Rae. ■ 44313 #015-01-2005 L2005 **OBG** *012
PERSAUD, Andre. 1 PERKINS SQ, AKRON CHILDREN'S HOSPITAL 44308 #035-15-2000 L2004 **PEM** *100 †55
PESSIN, Joshua Paul. ■ 44313 #016-01-2003 L2003 **GS** *012
PETER, Charles Arno. 1 PARK WEST BLVD, STE 150 44320 #028-34-1966 L1967 **OPH** *072 †35
PETER, David John. 400 WABASH AVE, AKRON GENERAL MEDICAL CENT 44307 #038-41-1987 L1989 **EM PLM** *020 †16
PETERSEN, Jason Dayne. 400 WABASH AVE, CO AKRON GEN MED CTR-MED E 44307 #018-03-2003 L2003 **PS** *012

■ = Address Information Privacy Protected

PETERSON, Gregory Alan. 150 CROSS ST 44311 #038-40-1978 L1978 **P** *020 †75
PETRINEC, Drazen. 525 E MARKET ST 44304 #038-44-1989 L1990 **VS** *020 †85
PETTAY, James Buell, II. 300 LOCUST ST 44304 #038-40-2000 L2000 **PD** *020 †55
PFISTER, Eugene Wm. 400 WABASH AVE, BLDG ACC 44307 #038-40-1977 L1977
   IM IMG *020 †20
PHILLIPS, James Edgar. 468 E MARKET ST, STE C 44304 #038-40-1986 L1987 **IM** *020 †20
PHILLIPS, Leonard V. 2106 BRAEWICK CIR 44313 #017-20-1946 L1952 **CD IM** *071 †20
PHILLIPS, Melodie A. 1867 W MARKET ST, STE B3 44313 #038-44-1984 L1985
   IM PD *020 †20,55
PHINNEY, Melinda Sue. 411 E MARKET ST 44304 #038-43-1989 L1990 **NEP IM** *020 †20
PIDHORODECKYJ, Nykolai V. 444 N MAIN ST 44310 #028-03-1997 L2000 **ADP** *020
PIERCE, Bradley Arthur. 400 WABASH AVE, AKRON GENERAL MED CTR 44307
   #038-06-2006 L2006 **ORS** *012
PIROZZI, Philomena D. 3535 GRANGER RD 44333 #038-06-1980 L1983 **FM** *020 †18
PITTINGER, Lori. 400 WABASH AVE 44307 #041-07-1989 L2001 **P** *020 †75
PITTINGER, Timothy P. 300 LOCUST ST, STE 560 44302 #041-01-1990 L1999 **PDS** *020 †85
PITTS, Andrew Todd. ■ 44313 #022-75-2006, ▲ L2006 **PD** *012
PLAZZO, Lisa A. 525 E MARKET ST 44304 #051-01-1982 L1984 **EM** *020 †16
PLOTNER, Alisha Nicole. ■ 44313 #038-44-2008 *012
POA, Helen Olga. 400 WABASH AVE 44307 #418-02-1991 **FM** *100
POBLETE, Jose Enrique. 75 ARCH ST, STE 105 44304 #010-03-2001 L2001 **ID** *100 †20
POLDNEFF, Ludmila. 1 PERKINS SQ 44308 #913-15-1976 L1988 **PD** *020 †55
POLING, Jeff Lee. 20 OLIVE ST, STE 300 44310 #055-01-1978 L1981 **IM** *020 †20
POLISETTY, Sudhir. ■ 44308 #038-44-2007 L2007 **IM** *012
POLLAUF, Laura Ann. 1 PERKINS SQ 44308 #038-43-1993 L1997 **PD PEM** *020 †55
POONIA, Roopinder Singh. ■ 44398 #496-03-2001 L2003 **NEP** *012 †20
POPE, John Francis. 1 PERKINS SQ, AKRON, DEPT OF CRICITCAL C 44308 #038-06-1985 L1989
   PD *020 †55
PORTER, Joel Arden. 95 ARCH ST, STE 150 44304 #038-40-1981 L1982 **GS CRS** *020 †10,85
POTTER, Joseph Leo. CHILDREN'S HOSP OF AKRON 44308 #038-06-1962 L1963
   PCH CLP *062
POULSON, John Thos. 251 E MILL ST 44308 #010-03-1954 L1955 **AN** *071
POWELL, Angela Teresa. 400 WABASH AVE 44307 #038-40-1989 L1994 **PCP** *020 †50
POWELL, Keith Richardson. 1 PERKINS SQ, CHILD HOSP MC OF AKRON 44308
   #028-34-1971 L1998 **PD ID** *071 †55
PRATT, Charles Edward. 75 ARCH ST, STE 102 44304 #038-40-1956 L1956 **IM CD** *020
PREWITT, Erin Marie. ■ 44313 #038-40-2007 L2007 **ORS** *012
QUEEN-WILLIAMS, Heather E. 150 CROSS ST, COMMUNITY SUPPORT SERVICES 44311
   #038-45-1991 L1994 **P** *020 †75
RADWANY, Julia Baron. 55 ARCH ST, INC 44304 #038-41-1983 L1986 **IM** *020 †20
RADWANY, Steven Michael. 55 ARCH ST, INC 44304 #038-41-1983 L1986 **IM** *020 †20
RAJAPPANNAIR, Lakshmi Lee. 525 E MARKET ST, SUMMA HLTH SYS 44304
   #495-31-1991 L2002 **HMP** *012 †50
RAJIAH, Sam Emerson. 900 MULL AVE 44313 #495-42-1960 L1973 **P** *020 †75
RAO, Sheela Mocherla. 762 EASTLAND AVE 44305 #496-07-1976 L1995 **PD** *020 †55
RAY, Nancy Louise. 190 N UNION ST, STE 104 44304 #049-01-1985 L1988 **AN OBG** *020 †05
RAY, Susan M. 411 E MARKET ST 44304 #038-44-1984 L1986 **NEP IM** *020 †20
RAZACK, Suban Mohamed. 1134 BROWN ST STE 2A 44301 #495-16-1967 L1978 **IM** *020 †20
REED, Sally J Pastorelle. 3333 S ARLINGTON RD 44312 #047-13-1965 L1968 **DR** *020 †80
REEDUS, Derrick Lamar. ■ 44302 #038-44-2002 L2002 **U** *012
REES, Wilson David. ■ 44333 #038-40-1948 L1948 **R** *071 †80
REGULA, Douglas Allen. 224 W EXCHANGE ST, STE 360 44302 #038-40-1973 L1973
   AN *020 †05
REGULA, Eric Harold. ■ 44303 #038-40-2007 L2007 **IM** *012
REHMAN, Saif Ur. 444 N MAIN ST 44310 #704-02-1990 L1995 **NEP** *020 †20
REHMAN, Saif Ur. 874 ROBINWOOD HILLS DR 44333 #704-05-1981 L2000 **HO IM** *020 †20
REHMAN, Waqas. ■ 44333 #038-44-2007 L2007 **IM** *012
REHMUS, James Martin. 1 PERKINS SQ, CHILDRENS HOSPITAL OF AKRO 44308
   #025-01-1981 L1986 **PD** *040 †55
REILLY, Thomas John, Jr. 3975 EMBASSY PKWY STE 201 44333 #038-41-1979 L1982
   HS *020 †40
REODICA, Alex Michael. 525 E MARKET ST, DEPARTMENT OF 44304 #038-44-2003 L2003
   EM *020
REODICA, Renato E. 444 N MAIN ST 44310 #748-01-1962 L1972 **GS** *020
REPKO, Thomas Alan. 95 ARCH ST STE 120, THE SURGICAL EYE CARE CTR 44304
   #038-40-1982 L1982 **OPH** *020 †35
RETIKAS, Demetrios Geo. ■ 44303 #418-01-1951 L1959 **OBG** *071
REYNOLDS, Charles Wesley. 209 CARROLL ST RM 116, CENTER FOR NURSING CLINIC 44325
   #041-13-1953 L1958 **END IM** *020 †20
REYNOLDS, William Ward. 525 E MARKET ST 44304 #036-05-1947 L1952 **IM** *071
RHEE, Margaret Ellen. 1 PARK WEST BLVD, STE 200 44320 #038-06-1995 L1997 **OBG** *020 †30
RICE, Timothy Best. 702 E MARKET ST, COMMUNITY HEALTH CENTER 44305
   #048-02-1971 L1974 **IM** *020
RICH, Michael Wallace. 55 ARCH ST, INC 44304 #038-43-1990 L1991 **IM** *040 †20
RICHMAN, Steven Aaron. 1700 W MARKET ST, # 315 44313 #038-45-1997 L1999 **FM** *020 †18
RICHTER, David E. 471 N CLEVELAND MASSILN RD 44333 #143-02-1974 L1983 **RHU IM** *020
RIEMENSCHNEIDER, B J. 1 PERKINS SQ 44308 #038-43-1992 L1996 **APM** *020 †05
RILEY, Patrick Michael, Jr. ■ 44333 #038-44-2008 *012
RILEY, William James. 1 PERKINS SQ, AKRON CHILDREN'S HOSPITAL 44308
   #020-12-1971 L2005 **PDE PTH** *020 †55
RINI, Darryl Rosario. 2603 W MARKET ST STE 110, RADIOLOGY IMAGING 44313
   #038-43-1986 L1990 **DR** *020 †20
RITZMAN, Stacy Lyn. ■ 44333 #038-40-2000 L2000 **AN** *100 †05
RITZMAN, Todd Forrest. 1 PERKINS SQ 44308 #038-40-2000 L2001 **ORS** *020
RIVERA, Mercedes Yadao. 400 WABASH AVE, AKRON GEN MED CTR 44307 #748-02-2001
   IM *012
RIVERA, Rowena Engracia F. 1 PERKINS SQ, DEPT OF NEUROLOGY 44308
   #748-01-1989 L2003 **CHN PD** *020 †55,75
ROBERTSON, Ted Emmons. 75 ARCH ST, STE 401 44304 #038-40-1963 L1963 **OBG** *020 †30
ROBINSON, Haynes B, Jr. 1 PERKINS SQ 44308 #038-40-1962 L1962 **PTH MG** *020 †50,55,19
ROBINSON, Raymond Everett. 839 E MARKET ST, AKRON'S WOMEN'S MEDICAL GR 44305
   #047-07-1971 L1973 **OBG** *020 †30
RODERS, Mark Kevin. 75 ARCH ST, STE 407 44304 #038-06-1982 L1983 **VS GS** *075 †85
RODGERS, Andrea E. ■ 44303 #038-44-1993 L1995 **EM** *020 †16
RODRIGUEZ, Eric Joseph. 55 W WATERLOO RD 44319 #038-06-1995 L1996 **IM** *020 †20

ROE, Duane Clinton. 570 WHITE POND DR, STE 100 44320 #038-40-1972 L1972
   GE IM *020 †20 ‡
ROMAN, Marvin Flores. 400 WABASH AVE, AKRON GENERAL MED CTR 44307
   #748-02-2004 L2005 **FP** *012
ROMISHER, Stephen Chas. 400 WABASH AVE 44307 #038-40-1986 L1987 **EM** *020 †16
ROSHETSKY, Lisa Marie. ■ 44333 #038-44-2006 L2006 **IM** *100
ROSS, Charles Edmund. 75 ARCH ST STE 202 44304 #055-01-1966 L1971 **GP** *020
ROTHERMEL, Wm Shannon. 3333 S ARLINGTON RD 44312 #041-02-1944 L1949 **R** *071 †80
ROUSE SCHARSCHMIDT, A. ■ 44313 #038-44-2003 L2003 **OBG** *012
ROY, Bijon Kumar. ■ 44333 #495-18-1967 L1976 **R OS** *020 †80
ROZENBOM, Carlos Victor. 3333 S ARLINGTON RD 44312 #132-01-1969 L1977 **RO** *020 †80
RUBIN, Carrie. 3043 SANITARIUM RD, STE 3 44312 #037-01-1993 L1997 **PD** *020 †55
RUBIN, Evelyn Arias. 400 WABASH AVE, AKRON GEN MED CTR 44307 #748-02-2004 L2006
   IM *012
RUBIN, Mike D. 1 PERKINS SQ, DEPT OF RADIOLOGY 44308 #037-01-1993 L2001
   PDR DR *020 †80
RUIZ DE LUZURIAGA, Arlene. ■ 44333 #036-07-2003 L2007 **D** *020
RUIZ DELUZURIAGA, Brian. ■ 44333 #036-07-2003 L2005 **DR** *012
RUSSELL, Shellie A. 1 PERKINS SQ 44308 #056-06-1988 L2000 **PD** *020 †55
RYAN, Stephanie Philomena. 1 PERKINS SQ 44308 #539-03-1982 L1994 **PDR VIR** *020 †80
SABELLA, Paula. 300 LOCUST ST 44302 #038-44-1989 L1991 **PD** *020 †55
SACHDEVA, Aadesh. 400 WABASH AVE, BLDG ACC 44307 #495-29-2000 L2004 **IM** *020 †20
SACHDEVA, Saru. 400 WABASH AVE 44307 #495-03-2003 L2007 **IM** *012
SAHGAL, Suneet. 1 PERKINS SQ, NEURODEVELOPMENTAL CENTER 44308 #016-06-1997 L2006
   PM *020 †60,55
SAHOTA, Simranjot. 400 WABASH AVE 44307 #496-07-2004 L2007 **IM** *012
SAKOL, Marvin J. 628 W MARKET ST 44303 #038-40-1950 L1950 **IM ON** *020 †20
SALAY, Elizabeth Mary. 1260 INDEPENDENCE AVE, KAISER PERMANENTE 44310
   #038-41-1997 L2000 **IM** *020 †20
SALEM, James Kenneth. 75 ARCH ST, RM 301 44304 #038-44-1988 L1990 **END IM** *020 †20
SALVINO, Richard Mark. 570 WHITE POND DR, STE 200 44320 #038-43-1998 L1999
   GE *020 †20
SALVINO, Roberto P. 75 ARCH ST, AKRON CITY HOSPITAL 44304 #748-10-1989 L1997
   ID *100 †20
SAND, Nina. 1 PERKINS SQ 44308 #067-01-1996 L2004 **PD** *020 †55
SANDERS, Douglas W. ■ 44313 #041-01-1951 L1956 **IM** *071
SANDERSON, Jeffrey David. 525 E MARKET ST, REHAB UNIT 44304 #038-40-1998 L1999
   PM *020 †60
SANELLI, Victoria Lynn. 444 N MAIN ST, CENTER FOR AKRON PSYCHIATR 44310
   #038-44-1996 L1997 **P** *020 †75
SARBAH, Steedman Ackah. 1037 N MAIN ST STE B, CONSULTANTS INC 44310
   #775-01-1991 L1995 **GE** *020 †20
SARGEANT, Lori Kompanik. 525 E MARKET ST 44304 #038-44-1989 L1990 **EM** *020 †16
SATARIANO, Daniel Wm. 224 W EXCHANGE STE 360 44302 #038-06-1984 L1987
   AN *020 †05
SAVAN, Carole Ann. 676 S BROADWAY ST, STE 105 44311 #038-44-1981 L1983 **FM** *020 †18
SAVELLI, Stephanie Lynn. 1 PERKINS SQ, DEPARTMENT OF HEMATOLOGY/O 44308
   #035-06-1999 L1999 **PHO** *100 †55
SAVITSKI, Jennifer Lee. 145 S PERSHING AVE 44313 #047-20-2001 L2001 **OBG** *020 †30
SAWAN, Eugene Donald. ■ 44313 #028-34-1965 L1966 **OBG** *071 †30
SAWHNEY, Vishal. 400 WABASH AVE, AKRON GEN MED CTR 44307 #496-03-2003 L2005
   IM *012
SAXENA, Samir. 20 OLIVE ST STE 300 44310 #306-01-1997 L1999 **IM** *020 †20
SCALERA, Nikole Marie. ■ 44305 #038-45-2005 L2005 **IM** *012
SCANTLING, Molly Kramer. 224 W EXCHANGE ST, STE 100 44302 #038-41-1991 L1994
   IM *020 †20
SCHAAD-WALSH, Michele. 1 PERKINS SQ 44308 #038-40-1997 L2000 **PD** *020 †55
SCHAAL, Robert James. 20 OLIVE ST, STE 300 44310 #038-41-1995 L1996 **IM** *020 †20
SCHARSCHMIDT, Thomas John. 444 N MAIN ST, DEPT OF ORTHOPAEDICS 44310
   #038-44-2003 L2003 **ORS** *012
SCHLUETER, Thos Mc Master. 75 ARCH ST STE 405 44304 #038-41-1957 L1957
   GS IM *071 †85
SCHMIDLIN, Thomas Michael. 400 WABASH AVE, DEPT OF RADIOLOGY 44307
   #001-02-1976 L1977 **DR FM** *020 †80,18
SCHMITT, Scott Alan. 340 S BROADWAY 44308 #041-12-1988 L1998 **P** *020 †75
SCHOTT, Edward Chas. ■ 44333 #038-06-1954 L1954 **OPH** *071 †35
SCHRADER, William Chas. 300 LOCUST ST, STE 170 44302 #038-41-1983 L1986 **OP** *020 †40
SCHUCKMAN, Hugh A. 525 E MARKET ST 44304 #047-06-1978 L1979 **EM IM** *020 †20,16
SCHUH, Paul David. 676 S BROADWAY 44311 #038-44-1992 L1993 **PD** *020 †55
SCHWARTZ, Eileen Meryl. 150 CROSS ST 44311 #035-06-1990 L1992 **P** *020 †75
SCHWARZE, Karl Douglas. 224 W EXCHANGE ST STE 330 44302 #025-07-1981 L1989
   NEP IM *020 †20
SCOTT, Edward Demond. 525 E MARKET ST, STE 290 44304 #038-45-2001 L2002
   FM *100 †18 ‡
SCOTT, Emily Gale. 1 PERKINS SQ 44308 #038-44-2000 L2000 **PEM** *100 †55
SCROCCO, John David. 55 ARCH ST, STE 1A 44304 #038-44-2005 L2005 **IM** *012
SCROGGINS, Timothy Allen. 45 GOODYEAR BLVD 44305 #048-02-1992 L2001 **FM** *020 †18
SEGUIN, Francois Wilfrid. 370 E MARKET ST 44304 #067-01-1965 L1966 **PD** *071 †55
SELIGA, Rose Mary. 224 W EXCHANGE ST, STE 330 44302 #038-44-1986 L1988
   NEP IM *020 †20
SHAFFER, Lawrence Alfred. 1600 E TURKEYFOOT LAKE RD 44312 #041-02-1979 L1982
   PD *020 †55
SHAH, Deepak Arvind. 1400 S ARLINGTON ST, UNIT 38 44306 #038-44-1995 L1996
   FM *020 †18
SHAH, Dipti Jayantilal. 1260 INDEPENDENCE AVE, KAISER PERMANENTE 44310
   #495-76-1980 L1984 **IM** *020 †20
SHAH, Nilesh. 20 OLIVE ST STE 201 44310 #038-40-1998 L1999 **FSM** *020 †18
SHAHEEN, William Frank. 570 WHITE POND DR, STE 100 44320 #038-06-2000 L2006
   GE *020 †20
SHAKOORI, Shanaz. ■ 44333 #308-03-1981 **GS** *020
SHAPIRO, Howard David. 400 WABASH AVE, STE 260POB 44307 #035-03-1970 L1971
   N SME *020 †75
SHAPIRO, Sharon. 44333 #035-03-1980 L1986 **AN** *020 †05
SHARP, William Vern. 75 ARCH ST, STE 407 44304 #038-40-1958 L1958 **VS GS** *071 †85

OHIO

AKRON

SHAUB, Ted Franklin. 95 ARCH ST, STE 300 44304 #038-43-1983 L1984 **CD IM** *020 †20
SHAW, Christopher Scott. ■ 44301 #038-40-2002 L2002 **IM** *012
SHAW, Jeffrey Henry. 1 PERKINS SQ 44308 #038-06-2005 L2005 **PD** *012
SHEERS, Titus Gaylord. 400 WABASH AVE, BLDG ACC 44307 #054-04-1991 L1992 **MPD PD** *020 †20,55
SHIELDS, Earl Francis. 185 W CEDAR ST, STE 407 44307 #023-01-1959 L1960 **TS** *071 †85,90
SHILL, Martin. 570 WHITE POND DR, STE 200 44320 #836-01-1982 L1991 **GE IM** *020 †20
SHIN, Joong-Ho. 20 OLIVE ST, STE 300 44310 #038-40-1993 L1994 **IM** *020 †20
SHIN, Paul Chas. 87 SPRINGSIDE DR STE A 44333 #038-43-1990 L1991 **APM** *020 †05
SHIREY, Pamela Sue. 400 WABASH AVE 44307 #041-02-1984 L1989 **P PHP** *020 †75
SHONDEL, Susan Marie. 1 PARK WEST BLVD, STE 200 44320 #038-40-1999 L2003 **OBG** *020 †30
SHORTEN, Scott Douglas. 400 WABASH AVE 44307 #038-44-1981 L1985 **PTH** *020 †50
SHUNDRY, Stacy Ann. 41 ARCH ST, STE 521 44304 #038-44-2006 L2006 **EM** *012
SIEN, Stefan Yiuman. 525 E MARKET ST 44304 #005-76-2005, ▲ L2005 **IM** *100
SIEW, Darrick. ■ 44313 #038-40-2002 L2003 **PD** *020
SIGEL, Jessica Lefton. 525 E MARKET ST 44304 #038-06-1996 L1998 **PTH** *020 †50
SIGNS, Denise Juna. 224 W EXCHANGE ST, STE 290 44302 #038-40-1982 L1983 **ID IM** *020 †20
SINGH, Amarpreet Dosanjh. 300 LOCUST ST, STE 490 44302 #025-07-2000 L2001 **OPH** *100 †35
SINGH, Hardeep. 400 WABASH AVE, DEPT OF MED EDU 44307 #495-29-2000 L2006 **P** *012
SIRACKI, Vladimir Walter. ■ 44313 #038-43-1987 L1990 **CCM** *020 †20
SKOBLAR, Richard Steven. 1655 W MARKET ST STE 510 44313 #024-07-1971 L1975 **DR** *020 †80
SLEZAK, Frederick Andrew. 95 ARCH ST, STE 150 44304 #038-40-1978 L1978 **CRS GS** *020 †10,85
SLIPKA-MARINOS, Gina Mari. 400 WABASH AVE, AKRON GEN MED CTR 44307 #308-03-2001 L2003 **IM** *020 †20
SMARTNICK, Anthony Robt. 400 WABASH AVE, CENTER FOR AKRON PSYCHIATR 44307 #010-02-1986 L1990 **P** *020 †75
SMELCER, Philip John. ■ 44313 #047-06-2005 L2005 **OBG** *012
SMITH, Buel S. ■ 44333 #041-01-1952 L1954 **ORS** *071 †40
SMITH, Gregory Mathew. 400 WABASH AVE 44307 #038-43-1999 L1999 **EM** *020 †16
SMITH, H Vaughn. 525 E MARKET ST 44304 #041-13-1948 L1949 **GP** *071
SMITH, Mark Alan. 731 CANTON RD 44312 #038-43-1982 L1983 **IM** *020 †20
SMITH, Michael Allyn. 45 GOODYEAR BLVD 44305 #035-06-1976 L2008 **FM** *020 †18
SMITH, Philip Cooper. 1 PERKINS SQ 44308 #026-04-1987 L1998 **PCS** *020 †85,90
SMITH, Sarah A. ■ 44313 #018-75-2007, ▲ L2007 **OBG** *012
SMUCKER, William Darrell. 75 ARCH ST STE 001 44304 #038-06-1978 L1980 **FM FPG** *040 †18
SMURAWA, Troy Michael. 1 PERKINS SQ 44308 #048-13-1991 L1994 **PD PSM** *020 †55
SNYDER, Donald Curtiss. ■ 44313 #038-06-1936 L1936 **GYN** *071 †30
SOBHANIE, Mohammad Mahdee. ■ 44333 #038-44-2008 *012
SOBIESKI, Robert Leonard. 300 LOCUST ST, STE 200 44302 #028-34-1968 L1969 **PD** *020 †55
SOLARO, Lori Reed. 300 LOCUST ST, STE 280 44302 #038-41-1992 L1998 **CHP** *020 †75
SOLINGER, Dianne Lyn. 400 WABASH AVE 44307 #037-01-1979 L1981 **IM** *020
SONG, Michael Francis. 696 CANTON RD 44312 #583-10-1963 L1973 **UCM EM** *020 †30
SPARHAWK, Geo Roger, Jr. 444 N MAIN ST, STE 408 44310 #038-06-1976 L1977 **P** *020 †75
SPEAKMAN, Eric Douglas. 400 WABASH AVE, DEPT OF PATHOLOGY 44307 #051-01-1992 L1997 **PTH** *020 †50
SPEAR, Kevin Allen. 95 ARCH ST, STE 165 44304 #038-43-1989 L1991 **U OS** *020 †95
SPECHT, Elizabeth M. 1 PERKINS SQ, CHILDRENS HOSP AKRON 44308 #038-40-1977 L1977 **PD** *040 †55
SPECHT, Frederick Alan. 400 WABASH AVE, AKRON GENERAL MEDICAL CENT 44307 #038-40-1977 L1980 **IM IMG** *020 †20
SPECTOR, Michael Lew. 1 PERKINS SQ 44308 #038-06-1976 L1978 **PCS GS** *020 †85,90
SPELTZ, Jessica Grace. ■ 44313 #047-07-2008 *012
SPERLING, David Mark. 75 ARCH ST, STE 002 44304 #038-44-1985 L2001 **FM** *020 †18 ‡
SREENIVASAN, Vembar V. 1 PERKINS SQ 44308 #495-09-1958 L1971 **PDC** *071 †55
STANFORD, Cheryl Rogers. ■ 44305 #045-01-2003 L2003 **FM** *100 †18
STEELE, Mark Andrew. 1 PERKINS SQ, CHILDRENS HOSP MED CTR PAT 44308 #055-01-1994 L1998 **PP** *020 †50
STEELE, Robert James. 95 ARCH ST, STE 350 44304 #065-05-1970 L1976 **CD** *020
STEER, Sheila Hollinger. 525 E MARKET ST, DEPT OF EM SUMMA 44304 #038-44-1984 L1985 **EM** *020 †16
STEIN, Sara Lynn. 340 S BROADWAY ST 44308 #038-06-1988 L1989 **P** *050 †75
STEINREICH, Otto Selick. 444 N MAIN ST 44310 #051-04-1938 L1947 **GS PS** *071 †85
STEPHENS, Kathleen Diane. 2116 PILGRIM WAY 44313 #038-41-1978 L1981 **CD IM** *020 †20
STERMAN, Bruce Martin. 1 PERKINS SQ 44308 #038-40-1985 L1987 **OTO FPS** *020 †45
STEWART, Diana Lee. 55 ARCH ST, INC 44304 #038-44-1987 L1989 **IM** *020 †20
STEWART, John Wm, Jr. 400 WABASH AVE, AKRON MATERNAL FETAL MED S 44307 #038-41-1987 L1991 **OBG MFM** *020 †30
STIFFLER, Kirk Alan. 525 E MARKET ST, SUMMA HEALTH SYSTEM 44304 #038-44-1994 L1995 **EM** *020 †16
STINE, Thomas Donald. 493 CANTON RD 44312 #041-02-1956 L1963 **OBG** *020 †30
STOCKER, Patrick Jos. 224 W EXCHANGE ST STE 300 44302 #038-44-1981 L1983 **TS** *020 †85,90
STONE, Robert Theodore. 300 LOCUST ST 44302 #038-40-1961 L1961 **PD PG** *020 †55
STONESTREET, Matthew Jose. ■ 44313 #038-44-2007 L2007 **GS** *012
STOWBUN, Lydia Tkatsch. ■ 44313 #913-05-1943 L1959 **FM** *071 †18
STREBY, Keri Ann. ■ 44303 #038-44-2008 *012
STRECK, Richard James. 400 WABASH AVE, AKRON GEN HOSPITAL 44307 #011-02-1980 L1982 **IM MDM** *030 †20
SULLIVAN, Christopher P. 75 ARCH ST STE 301 44304 #038-40-1979 L1980 **END IM** *020 †20
SUNDHEIMER, R Neil. 789 WHITE POND DR, STE B 44320 #038-06-1994 **FPS OS** *020
SUNOO, Edward S. 1 PERKINS SQ 44308 #583-02-1964 L1970 **AN PUD** *020 †05
SUNOO, Helen Paik. ■ 44333 #583-08-1965 L1974 **AN** *074
SURYADEVARA, Durga. 400 WABASH AVE, CO AKRON GEN MED CTR-MED E 44307 #654-01-1998 L2000 **P** *020
SUTTLES, Shivonne Nacole. ■ 44304 #038-44-2008 *012
SWANSON, Kenneth Francis. 1 PERKINS SQ 44308 #016-11-1960 L1964 **R PDR** *020
SWEENEY, Katherine Jane. ■ 44313 #038-41-2004 L2004 **PD** *020 †55
SWEET, David Brian. 55 ARCH ST, INC 44304 #038-40-1977 L1977 **IM** *040 †20
SYMMONDS, Catharine I. 1 PERKINS SQ 44308 #038-06-2004 L2004 **PD** *012 †55
SZILAGY, David M. 525 E MARKET ST STE 1N, AT AKRON CITY HOSPITAL 44304 #038-75-1990, ▲ L1991 **CCM IM** *020 †20
TABET, Muriel. 525 E MARKET ST 44304 #305-01-2007 L2007 **OBG** *012
TADDEO, James Clifford. 1 PERKINS SQ 44308 #038-40-1973 L1973 **PD** *020 †55
TALAIZADEH, M. 1 PERKINS SQ 44308 #517-06-1970 L1983 **PD PHO** *020 †55
TALIWAL, Rajiv Vishnu. 20 OLIVE ST STE 200 44310 #033-06-1995 L2001 **OSS** *020 †40
TALMAGE, Lance Allen, Jr. 224 W EXCHANGE ST, STE 360 44302 #038-40-1991 L1993 **AN** *020 †05
TAN, Luis Yap Yatco. 762 EASTLAND AVE 44305 #748-01-1965 L1972 **GS** *020
TAN, Michael James. 75 ARCH ST, STE 105 44304 #038-44-1999 L1999 **ID** *020 †20 ‡
TAN, Stephanie Ng. 55 ARCH ST, INC 44304 #038-44-1994 L1995 **IM** *040 †20
TANG, Cathy. 444 N MAIN ST 44310 #068-01-1983 **IM** *100
TANG, Te-Hsien. 3593 S ARLINGTON RD 44312 #244-06-1972 L1978 **FM** *020
TANPHAICHITR, Natthavat. 224 W EXCHANGE ST, STE 330 44302 #038-44-1994 L1995 **NEP** *020 †20
TANTRI, Devi Prasad. 1 PARK WEST BLVD, STE 350 44320 #495-09-1963 L1977 **PS** *020 †85,65
TAREEN, Basir Urrehman. 400 WABASH AVE, C/O AKRON GEN MED CTR-MED 44307 #037-01-2002 L2002 **U** *100
TARMOHAMED, Zubeida A. 525 E MARKET ST 44304 #704-02-1980 **P** *020
TARR, Jennifer M.. 55 ARCH ST STE 1B 44304 #038-44-2004 L2004 **IM** *020 †20
TASNIN, Rokeya. 400 WABASH AVE, DEPT OF MED EDU 44307 #160-02-2001 L2006 **P** *012
TAYLOR, Matthew Shawn. 3593 S ARLINGTON RD, STE D 44312 #004-01-1996 L1997 **IM** *020 †20
TAYLOR, Roxanne Lynell. ■ 44308 #038-41-2006 L2006 **PD** *012
TAZUDEEN, Wahid Abdul. 400 WABASH AVE, DEPT MED 44307 #041-15-2006 L2007 **IM** *012
TEERMANN, Gabriele Emma. 525 E MARKET ST 44304 #836-01-1990 L2003 **PTH** *100 †50
TEWARI, Sanjiv. 224 W EXCHANGE ST, STE 380 44302 #060-01-1991 L1993 **PCC** *020 †20
TEWART, Sanjiv. 224 W EXCHANGE ST 44302 #060-01-1991 **PUD** *020
THOMPSON, Edward Herbert. 20 OLIVE ST, STE 401 44310 #055-01-1965 L1965 **ORS** *071 †40
THOMPSON, Robert Eugene. ■ 44313 #016-06-1959 L1960 **OPH** *071 †35
THOMPSON, Steven Michael. 525 E MARKET ST 44304 #038-44-2001 L2001 **PTH** *020 †50
THOMPSON, Thomas R. 4125 MEDINA RD STE 200C, NETWORK HEALTH SPECIALISTS 44333 #028-34-1977 L1978 **ORS HS** *020 †40
THONG, Aileen. ■ 44313 #624-01-1972 L1977 **PD** *020 †55
TIMMONS, Gerald Dean. 300 LOCUST ST, STE 460 44302 #017-20-1956 L1964 **CHN** *020 †75
TIPTON, Kyle David. 190 N UNION ST, INC 44304 #038-44-1987 L1996 **AN** *020 †05
TIRODKER, Urmila Hari. 1 PERKINS SQ, DIV OF CRITICAL CARE 44308 #495-17-1993 L2003 **CCP** *020 †55
TOEPPEN-SPRIGG, Barbara. 1144 E MARKET ST, D108H 44316 #038-06-1977 L1978 **FM** *020 †70,18
TOOR, Fawzia Ashfaq. 1 PERKINS SQ, DEPT OF PEDIATRIC PSYCHIAT 44308 #704-02-1979 L2000 **CHP** *020
TORREGOSA, Hope Lao. 525 E MARKET ST 44304 #748-02-2005 L2007 **IM** *012
TOTH, Mary. 1 PERKINS SQ, RHEUMATOLOGY DEPT 44308 #038-44-1988 L1991 **RHU PD** *020 †20,55
TREVINO, Sylvia Deyanira. ■ 44313 #016-11-2007 L2007 **GS** *012
TROCHELMAN, Ralph Douglas. 75 ARCH ST, STE 202 44304 #038-41-1982 L1983 **ON IM** *020 †20
TROTTER, Johnny Ray. 1085 WEXFORD CT 44312 #010-01-2002 L2005 **GS** *100
TSAI, Margaret. 55 ARCH ST, STE 1B 44304 #038-44-2003 L2003 **RHU** *012
TSAI, Tsung-Tso. 400 WABASH AVE 44307 #748-02-2004 L2007 **IM** *012
TSENG, Tony H. ■ 44304 #038-41-2002 L2002 **AN** *100 †05
TUCKER, Elrie Christian. 1 PERKINS SQ 44308 #539-05-1992 L1997 **PAN AN** *020 †05
TUGAOEN, Jocelyn Theresa. 525 E MARKET ST, CO SUMMA HLTH SYS-MED EDU 44304 #038-40-2002 L2002 **IM** *020 †20
TULISIAK, Terrence Geo. 16761 S PARK CENTER 44316 #038-40-1977 L1978 **CD IM** *020 †20
TUNNELL, Le Roy. ■ 44313 #038-06-1955 L1955 **OPH** *062 †35
TWITCHELL, Kathryn Joann. ■ 44314 #038-40-2004 L2004 **OBG** *012
ULMER, Chad Winfield. ■ 44303 #038-40-2005 L2005 **EM** *012
UNDERWOOD, Ingrid Margot. 525 E MARKET ST DEPT ROTAT 44304 #038-44-1991 *100
UNROE, Kathleen Ann. ■ 44313 #038-40-2005 **IM** *012
UPP, Linda Lee. 75 ARCH ST STE B1 44304 #038-45-1987 L1988 **OBG** *020 †30
URSO, Frank Phillip. ■ 44313 #011-02-1962 L1971 **PTH IM** *020 †50,20
VANASDALE, Sara Ellen. 400 WABASH AVE, AKRON GENERAL MED CTR 44307 #038-75-2004, ▲ L2004 **OBG** *012
VAN BUREN, George. ■ 44313 #041-01-1939 L1942 **PD** *020 †85
VANDEVELDE, Jennifer Rae. ■ 44313 #041-78-2007, ▲ L2007 **OBG** *012
VAN DEVERE, Chris Allen. ■ 44333 #010-02-1965 L1965 **CHP** *071 †75
VAN FOSSEN, John Maynard. ■ 44313 #038-40-1959 L1959 **FM** *071 †18
VAN FOSSEN, Victoria L. 95 ARCH ST, STE 280 44304 #038-44-1991 L1992 **GS** *020 †85
VAN FOSSEN, Wesley Hugh. ■ 44333 #038-40-1962 L1962 **U** *071 †95
VARGO, Susan Marie. 370 E MARKET ST 44304 #038-43-1984 L1986 **PD** *020 †55
VARLEY, Joseph David. 444 N MAIN ST, DEPT PSYCHIATRY/ST THOMAS 44310 #038-40-1987 L1989 **P** *020 †75
VAUGHAN, Maureen C. 1 PERKINS SQ, AKRON CHLDRNS HOSP 44308 #041-02-1994 L2004 **PEM** *100 †55
VENKATARAMANI, Arjun. 570 WHITE POND DR 44320 #495-37-1990 L1999 **GE HEP** *020 †20
VENTOSA, Jose A. 45 GOODYEAR BLVD 44305 #042-02-1982 L1988 **IM** *020 †20
VERBECK, Stephen R. 95 ARCH ST, STE 270 44304 #041-02-1980 L1981 **IM** *020 †20
VERMA, Bipin Bihari. 725 E MARKET ST, HEALTH CTR 44305 #495-15-1954 L1974 **P IM** *020
VERMA, Monica. ■ 44312 #004-01-2005 L2005 **OPH** *012
VINES, Amanda E. 400 WABASH AVE 44307 #038-44-1998 L2002 **P** *020 †75
VIRATA, A Gerard C. 3867 W MARKET ST, PMB 265 44333 #748-10-1986 L1996 **IM** *020
VISITACION, Mark Paul Mac. 400 WABASH AVE 44307 #748-11-2003 L2006 **IM** *012
VOLLMAN, John Hubert. 300 LOCUST ST STE 540 44302 #038-41-1969 L1974 **NPM** *071 †55
VORA, Pankil Jayantilal. 762 EASTLAND AVE, INTERNAL MEDICINE OFFICE P 44305 #495-22-1979 L1992 **IM** *020 †20
WAGNER, Douglas Scott. 1 PARK WEST BLVD, STE 350 44320 #038-40-1981 L1982 **PS** *020 †85,65
WAICKMAN, Michael John. 544 WHITE POND DR STE B 44320 #038-06-1985 L1990 **AI IM** *020 †20,03
WAIGHT, David J. 1 PERKINS SQ, CENTER OF AKRON 44308 #018-03-1991 L2003 **PDC** *020 †55
WAKE, Vince T. 400 WABASH AVE, AKRON GENERAL MED CTR 44307 #038-44-2002 L2002 **ORS** *020
WALDMAN, Rachel Lynn. ■ 44313 #038-40-2005 L2005 **IM** *012
WALKER, Lewis H. ■ 44313 #017-20-1944 L1950 **PDA A** *071 †55,03

■ = Address Information Privacy Protected

WALLACE, Julie A. 470 WHITE POND DR, STE 100 44320 #038-45-1996 L1997 **FM** *020 †18
WALLINGTON, Charlyce J. 1600 E TURKEYFOOT LAKE RD 44312 #038-40-1995 L1996 **PD** *020 †55
WALLIS, Nicole Marie. 1 PERKINS SQ, EMERGENCY SERVICES 44308 #038-40-2004 L2004 **PEM** *012
WARD, Catherine Hanna. 1 PERKINS SQ, AKRON CHILDREN'S HOSPITAL 44308 #048-02-1999 L2005 **PD** *100 †55,19
WARMUS, Joanne Maria. 2818 S ARLINGTON RD 44312 #038-43-1981 L1983 **PD EM** *020 †55
WARNER, Elliott Bruce. 312 LOCUST ST, AKRON CHILD GUIDANCE CTR 44302 #035-15-1983 L1993 **CHP** *071
WATERBROOK, Stephen Kento. ■ 44313 #005-12-2004 L2004 **GS** *012
WATKINS, David Allen. 224 W EXCHANGE ST STE 290 44302 #038-44-1987 L1989 **ID IM** *020 †20
WATKINS, Richard Ryan. 224 W EXCHANGE ST, STE 290 44302 #654-01-2001 L2006 **ID** *020
WEAR, Kyle James. 55 W WATERLOO RD, VETERANS ADMINISTRATION—A 44319 #028-46-1990 L1992 **IM** *020 †20
WEBER, John Lawrence. 370 E MARKET ST 44304 #038-44-1988 L1990 **PD** *020 †55
WEGRYN, John David. 95 ARCH ST 44304 #038-43-1994 L1996 **U** *020 †95
WEGRYN, John Francis R. ■ 44333 #056-06-1959 L1964 **U** *071 †95
WEIGAND, John Victor. 525 E MARKET ST, DEPT EMER 44304 #010-02-1974 L1976 **EM** *020 †16
WEIL, Harvey Jerome. 525 E MARKET ST 44304 #038-06-1968 L1968 **OBG** *020 †30
WEINER, Dennis Stuart. 300 LOCUST ST STE 160 44302 #038-40-1963 L1963 **ORS OP** *020 †40
WEINER, Scott David. 20 OLIVE ST, STE 201 44310 #038-41-1986 L1987 **ORS OTR** *020 †40
WEINGART, Jon Ledman. 130 W EXCHANGE ST 44302 #038-06-1961 L1961 **N** *071 †75
WEINSTEIN, Cynthia Link. 525 N CLEVELAND MASSILN RD, STE 203 44333 #038-06-1984 L1985 **FM** *020 †18
WELKO, Jeffrey Richard. 400 WABASH AVE 44307 #038-40-1983 L1985 **CCM IM** *020 †20
WENDORF, Richard Joseph. 1 PERKINS SQ, AKRONS CHILDRENS HOSPITAL 44308 #016-45-1993 L2006 **CCP** *020 †55
WENGER, Olivia Kay. 1 PERKINS SQ, CHMCA DEPT OF MEDICAL EDUC 44308 #035-46-2004 L2004 **PD** *100 †55
WEST, Dixy Lee. 444 N MAIN ST 44310 #060-01-1980 **DR IM** *100
WHITE, Harold A. 400 WABASH AVE, DEPT OF RADIOLOGY 44307 #038-44-1984 L1991 **DR VIR** *020 †80
WHITE, Kimberly Ann. 1 PARK WEST BLVD, STE 200 44320 #038-41-1987 L1991 **OBG** *020 †30
WHITE, Peter Cooper, Jr. 1 PERKINS SQ, AKRON CHILDRENS HOSP 44308 #016-02-1981 L1987 **PD** *020 †55
WHITE, Ralph Peter. 4125 MEDINA RD, STE 200 A B & C 44333 #016-06-1972 L1974 **PUD IM** *020 †20 ‡
WILBER, Scott Terrance. 525 E MARKET ST, (AKRON CITY HOSPITAL) 44304 #038-44-1993 L1994 **EM** *020 †16
WILCOX, Philip Gary. 1655 W MARKET ST, STE 305 44313 #017-20-1980 L1981 **ORS OSM** *020 †40
WILFORD, Rex D. 55 ARCH ST STE 1B, SUMMA HEALTH SYSTEM INC 44304 #038-75-2003, ▲ L2003 **IM** *100 †20
WILKE, Todd Thomas. 444 N MAIN ST, STE 404 44310 #038-41-2003 L2004 **P** *020
WILKERSON, James Eastman. 95 ARCH ST, STE 170 44304 #055-01-1964 L1969 **U** *020 †95
WILLIAMS, Gary Brian. 75 ARCH ST 44304 #038-40-1972 L1973 **GS** *020 †85
WILLIAMSON, Jay Curtis. 55 ARCH ST 44304 #038-40-1973 L1973 **FM** *030 †18
WILLIS, Karen Christine. 1 PERKINS SQ, AKRON CHILDREN'S HOSPITAL 44308 #038-41-2002 L2006 **PD** *100 †55
WILSON, Caroline Louise. 525 E MARKET ST, DEPT OF EMERGENCY MEDICINE 44304 #038-06-1975 L1978 **EM FM** *020 †16
WILSON, James Allen. 525 E MARKET ST, STE 1 44304 #038-43-1989 L1990 **CCM IM** *020 †20
WILSON, James Earl. 525 E MARKET ST 44304 #038-41-1965 L1965 **EM IM** *030 †20
WINKHART, Bradly Paul. 444 N MAIN ST 44304 #038-45-1994 L1996 **P** *020 †20
WINOT, Scott David. 525 E MARKET ST, DEPT OF MED EDUCATION 44304 #305-01-2006 L2006 **EM** *012
WOELKER, Jennifer Ursula. 1 PERKINS SQ, DEPT EMERGENCY MEDICINE 44308 #056-05-1997 L1998 **PEM** *100 †55
WOJCIK, Joseph. 676 S BROADWAY 44311 #065-09-1956 L1961 **IM** *072 †20
WOJNO, William Clement. 3975 EMBASSY PKWY STE 101 44333 #038-41-1979 L1989 **RHU IM** *020 †20
WONG, Henry T. 190 N UNION ST, UNION POINT - SUITE #104 44304 #748-01-1964 L1972 **AN** *020
WOODRUFF, Todd E. 1 PARK WEST BLVD, STE 310 44320 #017-20-1979 L1984 **OPH** *020 †35
WORKMAN, Robert Gerald. 400 WABASH AVE 44307 #012-05-1969 L1972 **R** *020 †80
WRIGHT, Cyrene E. ■ 44306 #016-42-2005 L2005 **OBG** *012
WRIGHT, Dennis Jos. 400 WABASH AVE, STE 3500 44307 #038-44-1982 L1984 **VS** *020 †85
WRIGHT, Ian Charles. 190 N UNION ST STE 104, INC. AKRON 44304 #038-44-1996 L1999 **AN** *020 †05
WU, Ying Teh. 945 W NIMISILA RD 44319 #244-04-1969 L1974 **FM** *020 †18
WUESCHER, Christian Andre. ■ 44333 #038-43-2007 L2007 **TY** *012
WYERS, Robert Arnold. 2008 LARCHMONT RD 44313 #004-01-1960 L1974 **OTO** *071 †45
WYNESKI, Holly Kay. ■ 44319 #038-44-2003 L2003 **U** *012
WYNESKI, Matthew John. ■ 44319 #038-44-2003 L2003 **PG** *012 †55
YEAKLEY, William Robt. 1 PARK WEST BLVD, STE 150 44320 #038-06-1976 L1977 **OPH** *020 †35
YEROPOLI, Dean Rocco. ■ 44313 #038-44-2006 L2006 **IM** *012
YOUNG, Allison Murray. ■ 44301 #038-40-2007 L2007 **PTH** *012
YOUNG SZALAY, Melissa D. 3925 EMBASSY PKWY, STE 200 44333 #038-40-1994 L1995 **HS ORS** *020 †40
YOUNIS, Bishr Mohammed. 400 WABASH AVE, DEPT OF MED EDU 44307 #575-02-2004 L2006 **IM** *012
ZAFIRAU, William James. 75 ARCH ST, STE G2 44304 #038-40-2000 L2000 **FPG** *020 †18
ZAHN, Richard Carter. 130 W EXCHANGE ST 44302 #038-40-1961 L1961 **NS** *071 †25
ZANG, Jie. 400 WABASH AVE 44307 #243-47-1992 L2004 **IM** *020 †20
ZARAA, Adel Sleiman. 585 WHITE POND DR, STE E 44320 #473-01-1979 L1991 **P** *020 †75
ZARCONI, Joseph. 411 E MARKET ST 44304 #038-44-1981 L1982 **NEP IM** *040 †20
ZELLERS, Gordon Lee. 150 SPRINGSIDE DR, STE 225B 44333 #011-04-1984 L1985 **EM OM** *016
ZESCHUK, Gregory P. 444 N MAIN ST 44301 #060-01-1992 L1996 **OS** *100
ZIEROTT-WIEDE, Ute. ■ 44313 #409-21-1963 **PD** *100
ZOGRAFAKIS, John G. 95 ARCH ST, STE 240 44304 #028-34-1998 L2000 **GS AS** *020 †85
ZOUMBERAKIS, Erick. 400 WABASH AVE, CO AKRON GEN MED CTR-MED E 44307 #038-40-2003 L2003 **EM** *100

ZWART, Jeffrey Brian. 1 PARK WEST BLVD, STE 200 44320 #017-20-1997 L2001 **OBG** *020 †30

ALBANY – ATHENS

BAUMGARTEL, Wolfhard. PO BOX 218, 5243 WASHINGTON ST 45710 #407-20-1949 L1955 **GP** *071
MOYSAENKO, Valeriy. ■ 45710 #038-40-1971 L1971 **GS** *020 †85

ALEXANDRIA – LICKING

CRAIG, Robert Bruce, Jr. ■ 43001 #028-34-1979 L1986 **ATP OS** *074 †50

ALLIANCE – STARK

ARCHER, Linette Octavia. 264 E RICE 44601 #038-40-1999 L1999 **EM** *020 †16
BASCH, John Steven. 200 E STATE ST, ALLIANCE MEDICAL ASSOCIATE 44601 #016-45-1992 L1993 **EM** *020 †16
BASIT, Abdul. 200 W STATE ST 44601 #704-20-1987 L2000 **CCM** *020 †20
BHARGAVA, Pramod Anand. 270 E STATE ST, STE 100 44601 #495-76-1984 L2003 **IM NEP** *020 †20
BLACK, Bradford Thos. 885 S SAWBURG AVE, STE 105 44601 #004-01-1984 L1989 **U IM** *020 †95
BONAVITA, Gregory Joseph. 270 E STATE ST, CARDIOVASCULAR 44601 #033-06-1986 L1994 **ICE CD** *020 †20
CARTER, Donald Ellas, Jr. 149 E SIMPSON ST 44601 #041-09-1974 L1975 **FM** *020 †18
COGSWELL, Terrence Louis. 270 E STATE ST, CARDIOVASCULAR 44601 #017-20-1980 L1985 **IM** *020 †20
CORTESE, Ferdinando. 885 S SAWBURG AVE, STE 110 44601 #561-10-1972 L1986 **ON HEM** *020 †20
DE JULIUS, Angela J. 405 S LINDEN AVE, STE 210 44601 #038-41-1993 L1996 **FM** *020 †18 ‡
DENNING, Stephen Mitchell. 270 E STATE ST, CARDIOVASCULAR 44601 #036-07-1980 L1996 **CD IM** *020 †20
DE PERALTA, Claudio A. 1207 W STATE ST, STE C 44601 #748-02-1981 L1996 **GS TS** *020 †85
DINTIMAN, Peter Evans. 210 E STATE ST 44601 #007-02-1981 L1982 **U** *075 †95
DOPIRAK, Milan Richard. 270 E STATE ST, CARDIOVASCULAR 44601 #038-43-1973 L1974 **CD IM** *020 †20
DORFMAN, Daniel Marc. 2462 W STATE ST, ORTHOPAEDIC 44601 #038-40-1985 L1989 **PM** *020 †60
EICHNER, William Malcolm. 1640 S UNION AVE 44601 #038-43-1982 L1983 **FM** *020
FABRE, Carlos Eduardo. 270 E STATE ST, CARDIOVASCULAR 44601 #264-04-1967 L1975 **CD IM** *020 †20
FITZELLE, David Thornton. 264 E RICE ST 44601 #035-45-1947 L1953 **IM** *071
FLOURAS, Katherine. 264 E RICE ST 44601 #003-01-1991 L2002 **AN CCA** *020 †05
FOSTER, Carl Jos, Jr. 264 E RICE ST, ANESTHESIA ASSOC OF ALLIAN 44601 #041-13-1987 L1998 **AN** *020 †05
FRIEDLANDER, Ira Ray. 270 E STATE ST, CARDIOVASCULAR 44601 #036-01-1979 L1991 **ICE CD** *020 †20
FUJIMOTO, Luiz Kiyoshi. 270 E STATE ST, STE 240 44601 #187-11-1972 L1996 **GS VS** *020 †85
GALFORD, Roberta E. 264 E RICE ST 44601 #055-01-1981 L1991 **AN IM** *020 †20,05
GARTON, John Riley. 270 E STATE ST, STE 100 44601 #038-44-1992 L1997 **NEP** *020 †20
GEORGE, Craig Wm. 264 E RICE ST 44601 #041-01-1957 L1958 **OPH** *071 †35
GORDON, Barry Mark. 720 W STATE ST 44601 #038-40-1981 L1982 **EM** *020 †16
GRIFF, Franklin Wolfe. 270 E STATE ST, CARDIOVASCULAR 44601 #041-13-1969 L1976 **CD IM** *020 †20
GRUBB, Mark Richard. 2462 W STATE ST 44601 #038-40-1989 L2002 **ORS** *020 †40
HAISS, Annemarie. ■ 44601 #407-16-1951 L1961 **GP** *071
HAYWOOD, Michele Tempe. 975 S SAWBURG AVE, SURGERY ALLIANCE 44601 #041-01-1994 L1998 **AN** *020 †05
HILL, John Warren. 270 E STATE ST, STE G120 44601 #025-07-1985 L1997 **AN IM** *020 †05
HOSTETTLER, Mark Eugene. 75 GLAMORGAN ST, STE 107 44601 #038-44-1984 L1985 **IM** *020 †20
JAHDI, Eloisa H. 200 E STATE ST 44601 #748-01-1978 L1987 **HEM PTH** *040 †50
KANAGY, David Alan. 1401 S ARCH AVE, CARNATION CLINIC INC 44601 #038-40-1992 L1997 **OTO** *020 †45
KIBLER, Daniel Andrew. 264 E RICE ST 44601 #038-40-1955 L1955 **FM R** *071
KIKO, Danielle Sherree. ■ 44601 #038-44-2006 L2006 **OBG** *012
KING, Christopher M. 985 S SAWBURG AVE, OHIO EYE ALLIANCE INC 44601 #038-40-1961 L1961 **OPH** *071 †35
KNELL, Leonard Gene. 2462 W STATE ST 44601 #038-06-1967 L1967 **ORS** *071 †40
KRUPKO, Thomas Andrew. 2461 W STATE ST, STE C 44601 #038-40-1980 L1983 **ORS** *020 †40
KUENTZ, Duane Chas. 149 E SIMPSON ST 44601 #038-41-1977 L1980 **FM** *020 †18
LAKRITZ, Amy Claire. 1826 S ARCH AVE 44601 #056-05-1991 L1995 **PD** *020 †55
LAO, Andres Baguio, Jr. 75 GLAMORGAN ST, STE 103 44601 #748-01-1965 L1973 **IM** *020 †20
LAVINDER, Julie. 200 E STATE ST, ALLIANCE COMMUNITY HOSPITA 44601 #038-45-1996 L1997 **FM** *020 †18
LONDON, Michael David. 2462 W STATE ST, ORTHOPAEDIC 44601 #016-02-1982 L1987 **ORS** *020 †40
LUKEZ, Frank A. 1111 S ARCH AVE 44601 #561-11-1956 L1960 **PD PHP** *020
MANUDHANE, Pradeep K. 1207 W STATE ST, STE M 44601 #038-44-1987 L1988 **P** *020 †75
MARCELO, Teresita Calibag. 131 W STATE ST 44601 #748-01-1959 L1973 **GP** *020
MC GRADY, Michael L. 149 E SIMPSON ST, FAMILY MED CTR OF ALLIANCE 44601 #038-43-1974 L1975 **FM** *020 †18
MITCHELL, Daniel Ray. 200 E STATE ST, NEO SURG ASSOC INC 44601 #038-06-1990 L1999 **GS** *020 †18
MITCHELL, Edward Lee. 264 E RICE ST 44601 #038-06-1958 L1958 **GS** *071 †85
MKPARU, Fidelis Okechukwu. 2565 S UNION AVE 44601 #407-07-1987 L1994 **CD IM** *020 †20
MUNGO, David Victor. 1401 S ARCH AVE, CARNATION CLINIC INC 44601 #035-45-1995 L1999 **ORS** *020 †40
NASH, Larry Kevin. 200 E STATE ST 44601 #038-44-1983 L1984 **IM** *020 †20
ODEAR, Craig Scott. 270 E STATE ST STE G1, ALLIANCE 44601 #038-40-1995 L1999 **OBG** *020 †30 ‡
PALUTSIS, Roger Stanley. 1401 S ARCH AVE, CARNATION CLINIC INC 44601 #016-01-1985 L1992 **OSM** *020 †40

PARK, John S. 270 E STATE ST STE G110 44601 #038-44-1989 L1990 **GE IM** *020 †20

PAULOWSKI, John J. 270 E STATE ST, CARDIOVASCULAR 44601 #038-44-1987 L1992 **CD IM** *020 †20

PEDERZOLLI, Andrew Steven. ■ 44601 #038-40-2008 *012

PEDERZOLLI, Ann Cecilia. ■ 44601 #038-40-2005 L2005 **DR** *100

PICKETT, David Lee. 1207 W STATE ST 44601 #051-01-1955 L1967 **OTO OS** *071 †45

PODUGU, Radha Ramana. 270 E STATE ST, CARDIOVASCULAR 44601 #495-65-1984 L1997 **CD** *020 †20

REED, Robert Calvin. 1207 W STATE ST, STE E 44601 #041-13-1965 L1969 **OTO** *071 †45

RENCH, Thomas Eugene. 264 E RICE ST 44601 #038-43-1995 L1996 **EM** *020 †16

RHEE, Judith Youkyung. 1826 S ARCH AVE, CHILDRENS CLINIC 44601 #038-44-1995 L1998 **PD** *020 †55

RICH, Mark Jonathan. 270 E STATE ST, STE G100 44601 #011-02-2001 L2001 **OBG** *020

ROBINSON, David Glen. 270 E STATE ST, STE G100 44601 #038-40-1979 L1980 **OBG** *020 †30

ROHOLT, Philip Christian. 985 S SAWBURG AVE, OHIO EYE ALLIANCE INC 44601 #026-04-1979 L1980 **OPH** *020 †35

ROSEDALE, Raymond S, Jr. 1207 W STATE ST 44601 #016-43-1958 L1961 **OTO** *071 †45

SATTI, Srinivasa D. 270 E STATE ST, CARDIOVASCULAR 44601 #035-03-1994 L1996 **CD** *020 †20

SCHWEIKERT, Jana Frances. 1826 S ARCH AVE, CHILDRENS CLINIC 44601 #038-45-1995 L1996 **PD** *020 †55

SCOLIERI, Michael Joseph. 885 S SAWBURG AVE, STE 105 44601 #041-12-1995 L1996 **U** *020 †95

SINGH, Kusum. 2011 GLAMORGAN ST 44601 #495-30-1984 L1991 **FM** *020 †18

SINGH, Ritu Devendra. 1826 S ARCH AVE, CHILDRENS CLINIC 44601 #495-20-1992 L2000 **PD** *020 †55

STIFF, Christopher Allyn. 885 S SAWBURG AVE, STE 105 44601 #038-44-1991 L1997 **U** *020 †95

TEGTMEIER, Terrence E. 270 E STATE ST, CARDIOVASCULAR 44601 #016-11-1976 L1981 **CD** *020 †20

THOMPSON, John Eric. 270 E STATE ST, PREMIER HEALTH ASSOCIATES 44601 #038-44-1989 L1992 **IM CCM** *020 †20

WHITE, Robert Tressel. 264 E RICE ST 44601 #023-07-1952 L1958 **OBG** *071

WIGGINS, S Lata. 1826 S ARCH AVE, CHILDRENS CLINIC 44601 #368-01-1974 L1980 **PD** *020

WITMER, Enos James. 1826 S ARCH AVE, CHILDRENS CLINIC 44601 #051-01-1969 L1972 **PD** *020 †55

ZUMBAR, Zachary Matthew. ■ 44601 #038-40-2006 L2006 **TY** *012

AMELIA — CLERMONT

ANAYA, Baltazar G. 43 E MAIN ST, CLERMONT COUNSELING CENTER 45102 #649-02-1954 L1964 **P** *020

BRODERICK, William Gerard. 1126 W OHIO PIKE 45102 #038-41-1993 L1994 **PD** *020 †55

GUPTA, Manju. 1324 STATE RTE 125 DR #101 45102 #496-07-1973 L1980 **PD** *020 †55

GUPTA, Rakesh Kumar. 1324 STATE RTE 125 DR #101 45102 #495-29-1973 L1979 **CD IM** *020 †20

KALE, Sharatkumar Vishnu. 1010 OHIO PKE 45102 #495-01-1964 L1976 **U AN** *020

MUIR, Katherine Mitchell. 1126 W OHIO PIKE 45102 #025-07-2003 L2003 **PD** *020 †55

NATARAJAN, Tarakad V. 43 E MAIN ST, CLERMONT COUNSELING CTR 45102 #495-57-1974 L1978 **IM P** *020

REINHART, Meri Lej. 1126 W OHIO PIKE 45102 #038-41-1995 L1997 **PD** *020 †55

RIDEL, Keith Richard. ■ 45102 #038-41-2005 L2005 **CHN** *012

SALUKE, Ann Marie. 1126 W OHIO PIKE 45102 #038-41-1980 L1981 **PD** *020 †55

SANTANGELO, Joseph David. 1126 W OHIO PIKE 45102 #038-06-1998 L1999 **PD** *020 †55

SARKAR, Nabarun. 1324 STATE RTE 125 DR, STE 101 45102 #495-02-1987 L1997 **IM** *020 †20

WHITE, Laura Kellum. 1126 W OHIO PIKE 45102 #038-41-1996 L1997 **PD** *020 †55

AMHERST — LORAIN

AYAD, Sabry Salama. 254 CLEVELAND AVE 44001 #915-03-1990 L1996 **AN PME** *020 †05

BOGOEVSKI, Vasil Mike. ■ 44001 #957-04-1961 L1967 **FM** *071

BRABENDER, Wayne. 155 N LEAVITT RD STE 201 44001 #038-41-1978 L1983 **IM ID** *020 †20

BRUGGER, Gerold E. ■ 44001 #407-19-1951 L1962 **NS** *071 †25

BUTREY, Peter A. 254 CLEVELAND AVE 44001 #016-76-1959, ▲ L1960 **GP** *071

CALABRESE, Jennifer A. 101 COOPER FOSTER PARK RD 44001 #038-44-1998 L1999 **FM** *020 †18

CARISSIMI, Ronald Chas. 101 COOPER FOSTER PARK RD 44001 #038-45-1989 L1992 **FM** *020 †18

CHOBAN, Michael Jos. 254 CLEVELAND AVE 44001 #038-06-1986 L1986 **AN** *020 †05

DE BIN, John Augustus. 254 CLEVELAND AVE 44001 #035-03-1994 L1998 **APM** *020 †05

DITTO, Steven Richard. 254 CLEVELAND AVE 44001 #038-40-1984 L1985 **AN** *020 †05

DOBROW, David Alan. ■ 44001 #051-01-1965 L1967 **PTH** *071 †50

HAQUE, Quazi M Nesarul. 254 CLEVELAND AVE 44001 #160-06-1989 L2003 **APM** *100 ‡

HOFSTRA, Richard Manville. 254 CLEVELAND AVE 44001 #025-01-1990 L1994 **AN** *020 †05

HUGUNIN, Ralph A. 254 CLEVELAND AVE 44001 #056-06-1981 L2000 **AN FM** *020 †18,05

JAGETIA, Anil. 254 CLEVELAND AVE 44001 #038-44-1993 L1994 **AN** *020 †05

KAPLAN, Gordon David. 254 CLEVELAND AVE 44001 #035-08-1990 L1993 **FM EM** *020 †18

KIM, John Il-Chung. 254 CLEVELAND AVE 44001 #917-25-1981 L1988 **AN CCA** *020 †05

KROSKY, Cathy Ann. 254 CLEVELAND AVE 44001 #038-43-1977 L1978 **FM IM** *020 †18

LYDON, Joseph Francis, Jr. 254 CLEVELAND AVE 44001 #038-06-1986 L1988 **AN** *020 †05

MC EACHERN, John Edward. 576 N LEAVITT RD 44001 #038-06-1989 L1996 **IM** *030

MORONI, Rosemary. 530 N LEAVITT RD 44001 #028-02-1974 L1984 **OTO A** *020

NOVELLO, Augustine Jos. ■ 44001 #561-17-1936 L1938 **GP OM** *071

O'SHEA, Katherine. ■ 44001 #038-43-1989 L1994 **EM** *020

RAHMAN, Salman. ■ 44001 #704-02-1989 L2004 **IM** *012

REED, William Davis. ■ 44001 #041-13-1958 L1959 **R OS** *071 †80

SHAH, Chirag Jayantilal. 254 CLEVELAND AVE 44001 #495-48-1989 L1994 **AN** *020 †05

SHAH, Pankaj Devshibhai. 254 CLEVELAND AVE 44001 #496-38-1974 L1979 **AN** *040

SISON, Demostenes R. 254 CLEVELAND AVE 44001 #748-02-1961 L1975 **GS** *020 †85

SOCHA, Eugene M. ■ 44001 #056-06-1951 L1953 **AN GP** *071

SUICO, Vivian. 343 TENNEY AVE 44001 #748-11-1972 L1981 **IM** *020 ‡

SZOLLOSY, Frank F, Jr. 1170 CLEVELAND AVE, A 44001 #422-01-1988 L1993 **PD ID** *020

VLASIE, Valeriu Dan. 254 CLEVELAND AVE 44001 #781-02-1991 L2002 **AN** *020 †05

WEBBER, Freeman Burton. ■ 44001 #064-01-1949 L1970 **GS TS** *071 †85

WHITE, Richard Bruce. 101 COOPER FOSTER PARK RD 44001 #038-45-1992 L1994 **FM** *020 †18

WHITTED, Glenn Elliott. 550 N LEAVITT RD, AMHERST ORTHOPAEDIC SURGEO 44001 #038-43-1986 L1992 **ORS OAR** *020 †40

YOOD, Carl Michael. 415 CANDY LN 44001 #008-01-1967 L1974 **GS** *071 †85

ANDERSON — HAMILTON

PACHMAYER, Brian S. 7500 STATE RD, MERCY ANDERSON 45255 #038-40-1998 L2000 **IM** *020 †20

ANNA — SHELBY

VASKO, Matthew Scott. 104 DIAMOND DR, ANNA FFAMILY PRACTICE 45302 #038-43-2003 L2003 **FM** *020 †18

ANSONIA — DARKE

FOX, Kenneth Lee. 201 W ELROY ANSONIA RD 45303 #038-43-1997 L2000 **FM** *020 †18

LENOX, Bobby C, Jr. 201 W ANSONIA ELROY RD 45303 #028-78-1990, ▲ L1992 **FM** *020 †18

ANTWERP — PAULDING

WILEY, Todd Michael. 422 W RIVER ST 45813 #045-04-1999 L2001 **FM** *020 †18

ARCANUM — DARKE

GURRAM, Ashakiran Reddy. 702 N MAIN ST 45304 #495-50-1989 L2000 **IM** *020 †20

RIFFELL, Douglas Alan. 702 N MAIN ST 45304 #038-45-1982 L1983 **FM** *020 †18

SAMPSON, Shane Timothy. 702 N MAIN ST, STE 1 45304 #017-20-1989 L1992 **FM** *020 †18

ARCHBOLD — FULTON

BOWMAN, Randall J. 121 WESTFIELD DR, MIDWEST COMMUNITY HEALTH A 43502 #051-04-1983 L1986 **IM** *020 †20

CHRISTOPHER, Beatrice N. 121 WESTFIELD DR, STE 4 43502 #495-42-1970 L1984 **AN** *020

DAYOUB, Nael L. 121 WESTFIELD DR 43502 #875-01-1982 L1998 **FM** *020 †18

EBERSOLE, Robert A. 405 E LUTZ RD 43502 #041-02-1952 L1952 **GP** *071

FRITZ, Kevin Gerard. 121 WESTFIELD DR, STE 1 43502 #017-20-1992 L2007 **GS** *020 †85

HARRISON, Charles Mc Cann. 121 W FIELD DR 43502 #025-01-1966 L1973 **GS SO** *071 †85

JOHNSON, Larry Wayne. ■ 43502 #018-03-1973 L1991 **FM EM** *020 †18

KRUEGER, Joseph Scott. 121 WESTFIELD DR, MIDWEST COMMUNITY HEALTH A 43502 #038-43-1985 L1988 **IM** *020 †20

LEHMAN, Eric John. 121 WESTFIELD DR, ARCHBOLD MEDICAL GROUP 43502 #038-40-1986 L1987 **FM** *020 †18

LEHMAN, Keith Jay. 121 WESTFIELD DR, ARCHBOLD MED GRP 43502 #038-40-1979 L1980 **FM** *020 †18

RIVERA, Lenin. ■ 43502 #847-03-1960 L1967 **OS GP** *071

ROW, Jason Powers. 121 WESTFIELD DR, STE 1 43502 #038-40-1998 L1999 **FM** *020 †18

THEOBALD, Caryn C. 121 WESTFIELD DR STE 1, MIDWEST COMMUNITY HEALTH A 43502 #038-40-2000 L2000 **FM** *020 †18

YODER, Rick Lee. 121 WESTFIELD DR, STE 1 43502 #038-40-1996 L1997 **FM** *020 †18

ARLINGTON — HANCOCK

WALTON, Michael Eric. PO BOX 319 45814 #038-43-1989 L1990 **FM** *020 †18

ASHLAND — ASHLAND

ALLIE, Shana Lynn. ■ 44805 #016-42-2004 L2007 **PD** *020 †55

ALLMAN, James Richard. 934 CENTER ST 44805 #030-06-1989 L1990 **OBG** *020 †30

BECKNER, John W. 1126 COTTAGE ST 44805 #038-44-1993 L1994 **P** *020

BEKKAM, Naveen Kumar Redd. 1025 CENTER ST, SAMARITAN HOSPITAL 44805 #495-21-2001 L2006 **IM** *100 †20

BENTLEY, James David. 1025 CENTER ST 44805 #038-06-1989 L1990 **PTH PCP** *020 †50

BENTLEY, Katherine H. 350 HILLCREST DR 44805 #038-06-1989 L1990 **PD** *020 †55

BERNHARD, Matthew Cole. 45 AMBERWOOD PKWY 44805 #038-40-1995 L2000 **ORS** *020 †40

BHATTA, Bhubanesh Kumar. 350 HILLCREST DR 44805 #672-01-1998 L2007 **PDC** *012 †55

BOYD, Christopher David. 2109 CLAREMONT AVE 44805 #038-40-1997 L1998 **FM** *020 †18

BRECHBUHLER, Wayne S. 934 CENTER ST 44805 #038-40-1969 L1969 **ORS** *071 †40

BRUNICARDI, Mario Oreste. 45 AMBERWOOD PKWY 44805 #038-40-1995 L1996 **FM** *020 †18

CHALFANT, Henry Chas. ■ 44805 #038-06-1954 L1954 **FM AN** *071

CHALFANT, Vera Clem. ■ 44805 #038-06-1954 L1954 **PD** *071

COWDEN, Deborah Ream. 119 SLOAN AVE, ASHLAND CARE CENTER 44805 #038-45-1991 L1993 **FM** *020 †18 ‡

CULLEN, William Bryan. 1025 CENTER ST 44805 #038-44-1986 L1987 **EM FM** *020 †18

DAKSHINAMURTHI, Arumugham. 350 HILLCREST DR 44805 #495-16-1964 L1974 **PD NPM** *071 †55

DAUGHERTY, Daniel Reif. 1941 BANEY RD S 44805 #038-40-1974 L1974 **FM** *020 †18

DAVIS, Robert Burns. 1025 CENTER ST, C/O SAMARITAN HOSP 44805 #033-05-1970 L1971 **GE IM** *020 †20

EMERY, William Markley. ■ 44805 #038-06-1958 L1958 **GS GP** *071

FRIESEN, Steven Lee. 1522 CLAREMONT AVE 44805 #011-04-1999 L1999 **PD** *020 †55

FURNESS, Patrick Terrance. 2109 CLAREMONT AVE 44805 #041-09-1998 L1999 **FM** *020 †18

GOGATE, Leelawati B. ■ 44805 #495-20-1963 L1978 **PTH** *071 †50

GRIMES, Mark Lynn. 1025 CENTER ST 44805 #038-45-2000 L2000 **EM** *020 †16

GUPTA, Mohinder Kumar. 21 SUGARBUSH CT 44805 #495-29-1966 L1977 **OPH** *020 †35 ‡

HAMERNIK, Patti Ann. 350 HILLCREST DR, CHILDREN'S HOSP PHYSICIAN 44805 #035-06-1996 L2003 **PD** *020 †55
HENRY, Brian David. 2305 STATE ROUTE 603 44805 #038-41-2008 *012
HESS, Katherine A. 1941 BANEY RD S 44805 #038-43-1977 L1980 **IM** *020 ‡
IRVINE, Jack Edward. 350 HILLCREST DR 44805 #019-02-1959 L1961 **FM** *071
JAIN, Shashi B. 1025 CENTER ST 44805 #495-30-1977 L1995 **PTH** *020 †50
JARACH, Mazen. ■ 44805 #875-01-2002 L2004 **IM** *020 †20
JENTES, John Phillip. 1025 CENTER ST 44805 #038-40-1974 L1974 **FM** *020 †18
JONES, Julie O. 2021 BANEY RD S STE B 44805 #038-45-1995 L1996 **FM** *020 †18
KANG, Chungkil Lewis. 934 CENTER ST 44805 #583-10-1967 L1976 **FM OM** *020
KODZ, Irena Cheslavovna. 2111 CLAREMONT AVE, MEDICINE, INC 44805 #913-32-1987 L1997 **IM** *020 †20
KRISHNAMURTHI, K C. 1941 BANEY RD S 44805 #495-36-1964 L1971 **U GS** *020 †85,95
LEE, Jae Kwan. 1025 CENTER ST 44805 #583-01-1959 L1971 **PTH** *071 †50
LEE, Jae-Kyu. 1025 CENTER ST 44805 #583-09-1964 L1974 **DR NM** *020 †28,80
MAC DONALD, Mary Carey. 350 HILLCREST DR 44805 #010-02-1986 L1998 **GS CCS** *020 †85
MALHOTRA, Arvind Kumar. 1025 CENTER ST 44805 #495-36-1975 L1983 **DR** *020 †80
MARTIN, Michael Allen. 1025 CENTER ST 44805 #038-41-1991 L1993 **AN** *020 †05
MC CARTHY, Mary Dianne. ■ 44805 #038-06-1966 L1967 **IM ID** *020 †20
MC DANIEL, Matthew David. 1025 CENTER ST 44805 #038-43-1993 L1995 **NS** *020
MOONEY, Laurie A. 1025 CENTER ST 44805 #038-40-1992 L1993 **PUD SME** *020 †20
MURRAY, Colleen Jeanette. 1522 CLAREMONT AVE 44805 #038-43-1997 L2000 **PD** *020 †55
MYERS, Philip Everett. 350 HILLCREST DR 44805 #038-41-1977 L1982 **GS** *071 †85
OLSON, Brad Allen. 1522 CLAREMONT AVE, 1522 CLAREMONT AVE 44805 #051-07-1995 L1998 **PD** *020 †55
PATEL, Sharmishtha J. ■ 44805 #495-22-1965 L1983 **FM** *071 †18
PECK, John Willard, II. 2212 MIFFLIN AVE, STE 230 44805 #038-40-1997 L1999 **U** *020 †95
POWELL, James Robert. 1025 CENTER ST 44805 #041-02-1982 L2007 **PUD IM** *020 †20
RABER, Danielle Nichole. 1941 BANEY RD S, PRACTICE, INC 44805 #038-45-1994 L1996 **PD** *020
RABER, Douglas Lee. 1941 BANEY RD S 44805 #038-45-1993 L1994 **FM** *020 †18
RIVERA, Apollo Sabile. 854 TWO RD 713 R3 44805 #748-01-1965 L1980 **EM** *020 †16
ROSS, Shannan Christie. 934 CENTER ST 44805 #038-44-1999 L2003 **OBG** *020 †30
SCHECODNIC, Heidi Lee. 350 HILLCREST DR 44805 #038-43-1999 L1999 **IM** *020
SHIKARY, Abbas K. 53 SUGARBUSH CT 44805 #496-38-1971 L1976 **OBG** *020 †50,30
SHIN, Young Chan. 1025 CENTER ST 44805 #583-02-1969 L1976 **IM** *020 †20
SNYDER, Roger Owen. 1941 BANEY RD S 44805 #038-44-1983 L1984 **FM** *020 †18
STEIN, Andrew Michael. 2212 MIFFLIN AVE, STE 130 44805 #038-40-1991 L1995 **OTO A** *020 †45
STEINHAUSER, Raymond Paul. 1025 CENTER ST 44805 #041-12-1985 L1989 **AN GP** *020 †05
STENCEL, Michael David. 2109 CLAREMONT AVE 44805 #038-45-1983 L1984 **FM** *020 †18
TAVALLAEE, Mehrdad M. 2021 BANEY RD S, STE A 44805 #517-04-1995 L2001 **IM** *020 †20
TORSKI, John Stephen. 1025 CENTER ST 44805 #038-41-1979 L1983 **EM IM** *020
VORE, Vernon William, II. 1941 BANEY RD S, PRACTICE, INC 44805 #038-40-1974 L1976 **FM** *020 †18
WOLFE, James R. 45 AMBERWOOD PKWY, MID OHIO PAINCARE 44805 #038-40-1989 L1991 **PMM AN** *020 †20,05
YODER, Stephen Allen. 934 CENTER ST 44805 #038-40-1977 L1982 **ORS** *020 †40
ZARRABI, Faranak. 2030 STONE BROOK CIR, SAMARITAN REGIONAL HEALTH 44805 #517-12-1995 L2005 **IM** *020

ASHLEY – DELAWARE

TINCHER, Larry Melvin, Jr. ■ 43003 #038-40-1994 L1995 **FM** *020 †18

ASHTABULA – ASHTABULA

AJIT, Sarbjot Singh. 2801 C CT, COMMUNITY COUNSELLING CENT 44004 #496-21-1998 L2006 **P** *020
ALTIER, Samuel L. ■ 44004 #038-40-1951 L1951 **AN GP** *071
AVRAM, Tiberiu Simion. 524 W 24TH ST 44004 #781-01-2000 L2002 **OBG** *020
BENE, Gabriella. 3129 STATE RD 44004 #473-03-1986 L2002 **PD** *100 †55
BOUTSICARIS, Peter S. 2422 LAKE AVE 44004 #038-44-1981 L1989 **GS** *020 †85
BRACE, Kenneth Howard. 2420 LAKE RD W 44004 #038-40-1961 L1961 **GP OM** *071
CABELIN, Mark Anthony. 2422 LAKE AVE 44004 #024-05-1993 L2006 **U** *020 †95
CARRILLO, Edward Anthony. 5026 N RIDGE W 44004 #005-14-1979 L1980 **FM OM** *020 †18
CHILLCOTT, James H T. 430 W 25TH ST 44004 #065-05-1981 L1992 **FM EM** *020 †18
CHO, James Namjae. 2420 LAKE AVE 44004 #583-04-1966 L1975 **CD IM** *020 †20
CHOI, Suk Kon. 2422 LAKE AVE 44004 #583-06-1971 L1977 **GP** *020
CHOURE, Jayant Sakharam. 4200 PARK AVE 44004 #496-30-1997 L2000 **CHP** *020 †75 ‡
COVERT, Donn Farrar. ■ 44004 #038-06-1947 L1947 **PUD IM** *071
DE CATO, Alfred Ralph. 2420 LAKE AVE 44004 #041-02-1958 L1959 **GS GP** *071
DEVULAPALLI, Krishna. 2801 C CT, COMMUNITY COUNSELING CTR 44004 #495-21-1978 L1994 **P CHP** *020
DLWGOSH, Robert Alan. 2422 LAKE AVE 44004 #038-41-1989 L1991 **IM** *020 †20
DOBOSIEWICZ, Stephen T. 600 STATE RD, STE 166 44004 #041-12-1980 L1993 **EM FM** *020 †18,16
D'SILVA, Orlando Antonio. 1111 LAKE AVE 44004 #495-52-1973 L1982 **IM NEP** *020 †20
EDWARDS, Bonnie Lynn. 2422 LAKE AVE 44004 #065-01-1977 L1994 **FM** *020
EIPPERT, Glenn E. 2422 LAKE AVE 44004 #038-41-1963 L1963 **FM** *020
EL-SAYEGH, Samar Said. 4200 PARK AVE FL 2 44004 #605-01-1997 L2000 **P** *020 †75
GUERINI, Debra S. 2420 LAKE AVE 44004 #038-44-1991 L1993 **IM** *020 †20
GUIDO, Bruce Philip. 420 W 24TH ST 44004 #055-01-1980 L1986 **D** *020 †15
HOSSAIN, Mohmood T. ■ 44004 #160-02-1960 L1972 **CD IM** *071 †20
HUANG, Shin Ee. 2709 LAKE AVE 44004 #385-04-1967 L1972 **OBG** *020 †30
KIM, Choong Hong. 2825 LAKE AVE 44004 #583-01-1968 L1975 **IM** *020
KIM, Jong Gu. 2221 E PROSPECT RD 44004 #583-04-1959 L1972 **OTO** *020 †45
KONDRU, Ashok V. 2112 LAKE AVE 44004 #495-11-1975 L1992 **GE IM** *020 †20
KRAJEC, Richard Lee Geo. 2422 LAKE AVE 44004 #016-43-1980 L1983 **FM PLM** *020 †18
LAZARESCU, Dan. 524 W 24TH ST 44004 #422-01-1989 L1996 **OBG** *020 †30
LEE, Almon Seenam. 2143 W PROSPECT RD 44004 #583-10-1966 L1976 **IM NEP** *020 †20
LEE, Mario Alexander. 2422 LAKE AVE 44004 #035-46-1999 L2006 **ORS** *020 †40
LEE, Samuel Sang Joon. 2420 LAKE AVE, ACMC 44004 #583-04-1967 L1973 **AN** *020
MAK, Matthew Tai-Hung. 2728 LAKE AVE 44004 #869-07-1973 L1980 **OPH** *020 †35
MALLEIS, Ronald James. 1230 LAKE AVE 44004 #025-07-1970 L1971 **IM** *020 †20
MARCUS, Adel Badir. ■ 44004 #915-02-1965 L1976 **U** *071 †95
MATEO, Gilda I. 2422 LAKE AVE, ASHTABULA CLINIC 44004 #308-02-1982 L1993 **PD** *040 †55
MILLER, Doris P. 2422 LAKE AVE 44004 #038-40-1984 L1987 **PD** *020 †55
MIRANDO, Denise Maureen. 2422 LAKE AVE 44004 #038-06-1991 L1993 **OPH** *020 †35
MIRANDO, William Skippon. 2420 LAKE AVE 44004 #038-06-1989 L1990 **D** *020 †15
MOLINOFF, Arthur Wm. 2422 LAKE AVE 44004 #165-06-1978 L1984 **IM PUD** *020 †20
NOLAN, J Richard. 925 E 26TH ST, # A-209 44004 #028-34-1945 L1948 **ORS** *071 †40
PATEL, Anil Ganpatbhai. 1184 LAKE AVE 44004 #495-22-1982 L1992 **PTH** *020
POSCH, John Nicholas. 2422 LAKE AVE 44004 #008-01-1972 L1973 **ORS** *020 †40
RAGHUPATHY, Kade N. 1527 W 19TH ST 44004 #495-33-1969 L1975 **PD** *020 †55
RAMACHANDRAN, C K. 1230 LAKE AVE 44004 #495-04-1963 L1974 **ORS** *071 †40
RAMACHANDRAN, Saraswathi. 2401 N RIDGE E 44004 #495-04-1967 L1975 **AN** *071
RAVI, Raveendra Bubu. 2422 LAKE AVE 44004 #495-58-1972 L1977 **U** *020
REDMON, Maria. 1230 LAKE AVE, ASHTABULA VA CLINIC 44004 #654-01-1990 L1997 **IM** *075 †20 ‡
SEEDS, William Asa. 2893 N RIDGE E, ASHTABULA SURGERY CENTER 44004 #038-41-1990 L1996 **ORS** *020 †40
SHELBY, Reginald W. PO BOX 1172 44005 #047-07-1950 L1957 **GS GP** *071 †85
SOLOMON, Daniel Leonard. 2420 LAKE AVE, ASHTABULA COUNTY MEDICAL C 44004 #038-41-1985 L1986 **AN** *020 †05
STACHELEK, Conrad James. 2412 LAKE AVE, CENTER 44004 #008-02-1986 L1993 **RO** *020 †80
SUNMONU, Yisa Babawande. 2422 LAKE AVE 44004 #690-02-1990 L2003 **PUD IM** *020 †20
TALIH, Farid Ramzi. 2420 LAKE AVE 44004 #605-01-2001 L2002 **SME** *100 †75
TIDD, Harmon O. ■ 44004 #038-06-1951 L1951 **FM** *071
VARANASI, Anju Bhargavi. 2420 LAKE AVE 44004 #495-61-1999 L2007 **FM** *020 †18
VARGHAI, Mohammad Ali. 2412 LAKE AVE, THE REGIONAL CANCER CENTER 44004 #517-01-1971 L1986 **HO IM** *020 †20
WARREN, Anne Elizabeth. 345 RODGERS PL 44004 #014-01-1979 L1980 **P PYG** *020 †75
WASYLENKI, Morris. ■ 44004 #065-01-1953 L1964 **GS** *071 †85
WELLS, Stephen Curtis. 2422 LAKE AVE, ASHTABULA CLNC INC 44004 #065-01-1976 L1994 **GP** *020
WIESE, Edward Andrew Tony. 2422 LAKE AVE, ASHTABULA CLINIC, INC. 44004 #065-06-1991 L1995 **IM** *020 †20
WILKINSON, Archie Scott. 2736 LAKE AVE 44004 #038-45-1982 L1983 **FM EM** *020 †18
WOO, Chong-Kyoo. 2210 S RIDGE E 44004 #583-09-1966 L1974 **OBG GP** *020 †30
WOO, Theodore Jinsoo. ■ 44004 #038-43-2008 *012

ATHENS – ATHENS

AHMED, Imtiaz. 65 HOSPITAL DR 45701 #160-06-1979 L1995 **CD IM** *020 †20
ALMOHAILEB, Fahad M. ■ 45701 #797-01-1985 L1997 **RNR** *100
BATCHELOR, Allison Jay. GERIATRICS CLINICS, PARKS HALL 45701 #038-43-1985 L1996 **IMG IM** *020 †20
BROWN, Elizabeth Lois. ■ 45701 #054-04-2008 *012
CALNON, Dennis Arthur. 65 HOSPITAL DR 45701 #041-14-1990 L1998 **CD IM** *020 †20
CANDELA, Richard John. 65 HOSPITAL DR 45701 #038-40-1972 L1972 **CD** *071 †20
CHANDNA, Jalaj. 55 HOSPITAL DR, OBLENESS MEMORIAL HOSPITAL 45701 #690-04-1990 L1996 **IM** *020 †20 ‡
CHEN, George. 55 HOSPITAL DR, O'BLENESS HOSPITAL 45701 #035-48-1994 L2004 **APM** *020 †05
CHICKOS RAMOSO, Rosemary. ■ 45701 #038-75-2007, ▲ *012
CHINTALA, Sudarshan. ■ 45701 #495-21-1972 **P** *075
CONJEEVARAM, Geetha. 101 S SHAFER ST 45701 #495-37-1992 L2000 **IM** *020 †20
CORDINGLEY, Gary Edward. 75 HOSPITAL DR STE 360 45701 #036-07-1977 L1983 **N P** *020 †75
CROCI, Henry Geo. 75 HOSPITAL DR, STE 110 45701 #038-40-1965 L1965 **OPH** *071 †35
CUNNINGHAM, John Dennis. 2 HEALTH CENTER DR 45701 #038-40-1976 L1977 **OS GYN** *020
DODRILL, Craig. 55 HOSPITAL DR 45701 #038-44-1997 L1998 **OPH** *020 †35
DOPKINS, Jane Ellery. 75 HOSPITAL DR, STE 260 45701 #035-06-1998 L1999 **GYN OBS** *020 †30
FOOKS, Henry, Jr. 224 COLUMBUS RD 45701 #038-41-1983 L2006 **U** *020 †95
FREEMAN, Julian Jay. 101 S SHAFER ST 45701 #016-11-1972 L1999 **IM N** *062 †20
FRUTH, Beryl Rose. 510B W UNION ST 45701 #038-40-1977 L1978 **FM** *020 †18
GASKELL, J Richard. 530 W UNION ST, STE B 45701 #041-12-1964 L1970 **PD** *020 †55
GAU, Jen-Tzer. 253 GROSVENOR ST, DEPT GERIATRIC MED 45701 #244-05-1990 L2001 **IMG** *020 †20
GAWANDE, Atmaram S. 265 W UNION ST 45701 #495-19-1961 L1973 **U** *020 †85,95
GEORGE, Peter Bippus. 65 HOSPITAL DR 45701 #038-40-1994 L1995 **CD** *020 †20
GOSWAMI-GAWANDE, Sushila. 265 W UNION ST 45701 #495-22-1962 L1973 **PD BBK** *075
GOULDER, Eric Alan. 65 HOSPITAL DR 45701 #038-40-1976 L1978 **CD IM** *020 †20
GREWAL, Karanvir Singh. 65 HOSPITAL DR 45701 #038-44-1990 L1991 **CD** *020 †20
JOHNSON, James Howard. 100 HOSPITAL DR 45701 #028-02-1971 L1993 **GP** *020
JONES, Bruce Alan. 100 HOSPITAL DR 45701 #038-40-1971 L1972 **P** *020 †75
KATTA, Sreenivasulu. 100 HOSPITAL DR, ATHENS MENTAL HLTH CTR 45701 #496-01-1972 **P** *020
KIDWELL, Gregory Alan. 65 HOSPITAL DR 45701 #038-40-1979 L1982 **ICE** *020 †20
KINNARD, Philip David. 444 W UNION ST, RIVERSIDE PROFFESIONAL BLD 45701 #038-41-1958 L1958 **GS** *071 †85
KLEMAN, James Michael. 65 HOSPITAL DR 45701 #023-01-1987 L1994 **ICE CD** *020 †20
KOHARA, Dai. ■ 45701 #038-75-2007, ▲ L2007 *012
KRONER, John F, Jr. 55 HOSPITAL DR 45701 #016-43-1962 L1964 **OBG** *071 †30
LANUZA-COX, Fe Garcia. ■ 45701 #748-01-1958 **P** *020
LINK, Arthur Joseph. 63 1/2 S COURT ST 45701 #028-78-1960, ▲ L1971 **GP** *071
MAYNARD, Lance M. ■ 45701 #038-75-2007, ▲ L2007 *012
MC ADOO, Jeffrey Floyd. 75 HOSPITAL DR STE 110, ATHENS INC 45701 #038-40-1987 L1988 **OPH** *020 †35
MC GEE, Mark Fletcher. 100 HOSPITAL DR, HEALTHCARE 45701 #038-40-1989 L1996 **P** *020 †75
MICKUNAS, Patricia B. 100 HOSPITAL DR 45701 #038-45-1999 L2000 **P** *020
MILLER, Steven Michael. 75 HOSPITAL DR, STE 380 45701 #038-41-1995 L2005 **ORS** *020 †40

MILLESEN, Gwendolyn Joy. 55 HOSPITAL DR, OBLENESS MEMORIAL HOSPITAL 45701 #008-02-1987 L2000 **EM** *020 †16

MOLEA, John Samuel. GROSVENOR HALL 45701 #018-75-1959, ▲ L1960 **GP** *071

MURPHY, Terence J. 224 COLUMBUS RD, HOLZER CLINIC INC 45701 #305-01-1987 L2007 **IM ON** *020 †20

NEELY, Travis Robert. 224 COLUMBUS RD, HOLZER CLINIC 45701 #038-06-2000 L2002 **PD** *100 †55

NELSON, Marjorie Ellen. GROSVENOR HALL DPT FAM MED 45701 #017-20-1964 L1977 **GPM PHP** *040 †70

NELSON, Steven Donald. 65 HOSPITAL DR 45701 #038-40-1981 L1987 **ICE CD** *020 †20

NESBITT, Neal James. 75 HOSPITAL DR STE 310 45701 #005-14-1976 L1993 **GS** *020 †85

NOWAK, Felicia V. ■ 45701 #028-02-1978 L1980 **END** *050

ORTMAN, John Phillip. 100 S SHAFER ST 45701 #025-12-1975 L1977 **GP** *020 ‡

PATEL, Halesh Murigeppa. 530 W UNION ST STE C 45701 #495-09-1971 L1986 **IM ON** *020 †20

PAXTON, Bruce Robt. 444 W UNION ST, EYE PHYS & SURG ATHENS INC 45701 #038-40-1964 L1964 **OPH** *071 †35

RAJAN, Sathya P. 90 HOSPITAL DR, TRI COUNTY MENTAL HEALTH C 45701 #495-04-1988 L2007 **P** *020 †75

RIGHI, Susan Patricia. 2 HEALTH CENTER DR 45701 #020-02-1978 L2001 **PHP OM** *020 †70,18

ROTHSTEIN, Mark Terry. 101 S SHAFER ST 45701 #035-08-1973 L1974 **FM** *020 †18

SAMMONS, Dawn. ■ 45701 #038-75-2003, ▲ L2003 **D** *100

SCHWARTZ, Frank Lee. 115 W GREEN DR, UNIVERSITY MEDICAL ASSOCIA 45701 #055-01-1978 L1989 **END IM** *020 †20

SHANMUGHAM, Muthia. 55 HOSPITAL DR, OBLENESS MEM HOSP 45701 #495-53-1969 L1981 **IM AN** *020 †05

SHEETS, Jared Andrew. 224 COLUMBUS RD 45701 #038-40-1997 L1998 **MPD** *020 †20,55

SHELTON, Penny L. 224 COLUMBUS RD 45701 #016-01-1996 L2003 **GPM** *020 †70 ‡

SMALLING, Charles Ronald. 224 COLUMBUS RD 45701 #047-20-1997 L2006 **D AM** *020 †15

STARZYK, Pawel. ■ 45701 #038-40-2005 L2006 **IM** *100

WEI, Eileen Ning-Jen Sun. 45701 #242-30-1950 **PD** *074

WOOD, Wheaton Bissell. 100 HOSPITAL DR, APPALACHIAN BHVRL HLTH SYS 45701 #035-15-1989 L1999 **P ADP** *020 †75

WRIGHT, Curtiss. 100 HOSPITAL DR 45701 #028-78-1976, ▲ L2006 **P CHP** *020 †75

YAKUBOV, Steven Jos. 65 HOSPITAL DR 45701 #038-44-1985 L1986 **CD IC** *020 †20

YELLAMRAJU, Asha. 510 W UNION ST 45701 #495-65-1993 L2002 **IM** *100 †20

YELLAMRAJU, Umamahesh. 101 S SHAFER ST 45701 #495-65-1993 L1998 **IM** *020 †20

ATTICA – SENECA

LIEM, Tik Tjong. 23 COOK DR 44807 #385-02-1968 L1974 **GS GP** *075

ATWATER – PORTAGE

TRAISTER, Russell Scott. 2106 STATE ROUTE 44 44201 #041-12-2008 *012

AURORA – PORTAGE

ASTORGA, Alex Michael. ■ 44202 #005-15-1962 L1975 **FM** *071 †18

BARRETT, Thomas J. ■ 44202 #016-43-1947 L1947 **GYN** *071

BRANDEN, Charles M. ■ 44202 #038-06-1953 L1953 **GYN** *071 †30

CASTNER, Casey Jean. ■ 44202 #038-44-2008 *012

CHHEDA, Niketa Jagdish. 700 WALDEN PL 44202 #496-25-1992 L2007 **FM** *020 †18

CORFIAS, Stephen Peter. 211 S CHILLICOTHE RD 44202 #038-43-1995 L1998 **FM** *020 †18

CUSTODIO, David Eugene. ■ 44202 #038-43-1988 L1990 **EM** *020 †16

DEMYAN, Natalie Michele. 700 WALDEN PL 44202 #038-43-1995 L1996 **IM** *020 †20

DOMBROWSKI, Nicole. ■ 44202 #038-75-2005, ▲ L2005 **IM** *012

EVANS, Doris Anita. 700 WALDEN PL 44202 #038-06-1968 L1968 **PD CD** *020 †55

FADER, Alfred. ■ 44202 #016-42-1954 L1955 **R NM** *071 †80

FAYEN, John Dempsey. ■ 44202 #016-02-1984 L1984 **ID IM** *020 †20

FERRIS, Clarence Craig. ■ 44202 #649-33-1977 L1980 **IM** *020 †20

KLEINMAN, Gary Alan. ■ 44202 #016-42-1972 L1973 **IM** *020 †20

LOPEZ-MATA, Nilda B. ■ 44202 #748-01-1951 L1960 **IM** *071

MORGAN-MINOTT, Melodie. 515 CLUB DR 44202 #035-09-1980 L1981 **P** *020 †75

POTOCNIK-WELSH, Nancy L. 162 TIMBERLANE DR 44202 #038-43-1996 L2001 **P** *020 †

REYES, Octubre Ayran. ■ 44202 #748-01-1954 L1967 **OM EM** *071

SCALI, Henry Anthony. ■ 44202 #038-06-1957 L1957 **CHP P** *020 †

SVEHLA, Joseph Ludwig. 889 N AURORA RD # 79 44202 #028-34-1946 L1947 **AN** *071

TELLALIAN-ADAMS, Sarah A. 700 WALDEN PL 44202 #038-41-1993 L1996 **PD** *020 †55

WAITMAN, Amy E. ■ 44202 #028-46-1999 L1999 **GS** *020 †85

WHITE, Christopher Robert. 615 LEN CT 44202 #035-06-1993 L1998 **EM** *020 †16

AUSTINBURG – ASHTABULA

FARMER, James Prentice. ■ 44010 #038-06-1954 L1954 **R** *071 †80

AUSTINTOWN – MAHONING

BROWN, John Willock, Jr. 44515 #041-12-1943 L1954 **OM TRS** *071

CRANS, Charles Alexis. 20 OHLTOWN RD 44515 #041-12-1962 L1969 **GS** *071 †85

JOSHI, Manish. 1300 S CANFIELD NILES RD, STE 4 44515 #495-22-1990 L1996 **IM** *100 †20

KELEMAN, Richelle Leigh. 25 N CANFIELD NILES RD, STE 160 44515 #038-44-2000 L2000 **PD** *020 †55 ‡

KENNEDY, David Mark. 1450 S CANFIELD NILES RD 44515 #038-45-1989 L1990 **IM** *020 †20

KHAN, Muhammad Iqbal. 704 JAVIT CT 44515 #704-04-1968 L1979 **PD** *020 †75

KHOOBLALL, Necklall. 253 S CANFIELD NILES RD 44515 #539-06-1980 L1991 **IM** *020 †20

LIANG FOK, Maria Mu-Lien. 325 S CANFIELD NILES RD 44515 #242-21-1942 L1959 **GP** *072

MC ELROY, John Brian. 60 N CANFIELD NILES RD, STE 700 44515 #028-46-1980 L1983 **U EM** *095

MUSSELMAN, Paul W, II. 60 N CANFIELD NILES RD, STE 700 44515 #038-44-1982 L1985 **U** *020 †95

NORD, Richard Griffin. 60 N CANFIELD NILES RD, STE 700 44515 #041-14-1986 L1992 **U** *020 †95

ORTEGA PEREZ, Scotty Rami. ■ 44515 #319-06-2003 L2006 **FP** *012

PICKLOW, Thomas Michael. 60 N CANFIELD NILES RD, STE 700 44515 #038-40-1987 L1992 **U** *020 †95

RAY, Glenn William. 6252 MAHONING AVE, DEPT OF EMERGENCY MEDICINE 44515 #038-40-1997 L1998 **EM FM** *020 †18 ‡

SWAIN, Steve Michael. 1450 S CANFIELD NILES RD 44515 #038-44-2002 L2002 **FM** *020 †18

WAGLEY, Craig A. 5437 MAHONING AVE 44515 #038-06-1996 L1997 **GS** *020

WATANAKUNAKORN, Paul W. 20 OHLTOWN RD 44515 #038-44-1998 L1999 **IM** *020 †20

AVON – LORAIN

ALAM, Ehsan. ■ 44011 #704-01-1997 L2004 **PM** *100

ASTLEY, Brendan Joseph. ■ 44011 #038-43-2003 L2003 **AN** *012

ATKINS, John H. ■ 44011 #041-09-1943 L1944 **OBG** *071 †30

BAAR, Joseph. ■ 44011 #065-06-1984 L2006 **HO** *020 †20

BESCAK, Kenneth John. 1220 MOORE RD STE B 44011 #038-40-1973 L1973 **CD IM** *020 †20

BHATNAGAR, Mamta. ■ 44011 #496-07-2001 L2002 **IMG** *100 †20

BLANKENSHIP, Danny C. 1220 MOORE RD STE B, NORTH OHIO HEART CENTER, I 44011 #055-01-1986 L1987 **IC CD** *020 †20

BROWN, Cynthia Lynn. ■ 44011 #038-43-1989 L1991 **AN** *020 †05

BUTREY, Charles Michael. 1480 CENTER RD, STE A 44011 #038-45-1988 L1989 **FM** *020 †18

CARANDANG, Jennifer M. 2535 HALE ST 44011 #038-06-1997 L1998 **MPD** *020 †55,20

CARBONE, Kenneth J. 1480 CENTER RD 44011 #038-75-1985, ▲ L1986 **FM** *020 †18

CHO, Donald I. 1220 MOORE RD, STE B 44011 #038-45-1995 L2001 **CD** *020 †20

CHOI, Myung Ja. ■ 44011 #583-08-1968 L1972 **P** *074

DAMM, William Alfred. 37460 HARVEST AVE, AVON PHYSICIANS 44011 #038-40-1996 L1997 **IM** *020 †20

DOMINGO, Godofredo Dizon. ■ 44011 #748-01-1957 L1964 **GS** *071 †85

ELYADERANI, Mehrun K. 1502 TRAVELERS PT 44011 #030-06-1992 L1994 **ORS** *020 †40

ESCOLAS, John W. 1480 CENTER RD, STE A 44011 #038-75-1986, ▲ L1987 **FM** *020 †18

FARNER, Paula Mary. 36595 DETROIT RD 44011 #038-41-1982 L1982 **PD NPM** *020 †55

FERGUS, Nathan Patrick. ■ 44011 #038-45-2007 **PD** *012

FOLLEY, Candace Anne. 1480 CENTER RD 44011 #038-44-1991 L1992 **FM** *020 †18

GOSKY, Garry Alan. 36901 AMERICAN WAY, CCF AVON POINTE 44011 #038-40-1972 L1972 **PD PHP** *020 †55

GROSEL, Gary Michael. 36901 AMERICAN WAY 44011 #038-45-1990 L1991 **OBG** *020 †30

HOLDEN, Darlene Margareta. ■ 44011 #012-22-2003 L2004 **DR** *012

HORWOOD, Raymond Louis. 1502 TRAVELERS PT 44011 #038-06-1981 L1982 **ORS** *020 †40

JACOBS, Katherine Anne. 36505 DETROIT RD 44011 #055-01-1982 L1985 **OPH** *020 †35

KACIR, Matthew Aaron. 2535 HALE ST 44011 #038-41-2001 L2001 **PD** *020 †55

KOPSCH, Paul J. ■ 44011 #035-08-1948 L1951 **PHP AN** *071 †05

KUMAR, Manjusha. ■ 44011 #496-28-1994 L1999 **IM** *020 †20

LEMBERG, Alison Denny. 36901 AMERICAN WAY, STE A 44011 #047-20-1999 L2003 **OBG** *020

LEW, Michael Minyoung. 1502 TRAVELERS PT 44011 #038-44-1988 L1993 **ORS** *020 †40

MAHAJAN, Darshan. 1997 HEALTHWAY DR, STE 203 44011 #495-03-1973 L1980 **N** *020 †75

MAHESHWER, Conjeevaram B. 1502 TRAVELERS PT 44011 #495-04-1985 L1998 **ORS OAR** *020 †40

MARR, Edgar Rainer-Maria. 36465 DETROIT RD 44011 #409-37-1985 L1993 **IM** *020 †20

MARR, Liselotte A. 36465 DETROIT RD 44011 #407-10-1949 L1965 **GP GYN** *071

MARR, Valentine C. 36465 DETROIT RD 44011 #407-10-1946 L1964 **D GP** *071

MARR, Valerie Roswitha. 36465 DETROIT RD 44011 #409-32-1982 L1982 **IM** *100

MARTINEZ, Manuel Andres. 1502 TRAVELERS PT 44011 #010-02-1982 L1987 **ORS** *020 †40

MEADOWS, Telly Ali. ■ 44011 #012-05-2002 L2005 **OS** *012 †20

MENDOZA, Jose Estrella. ■ 44011 #748-08-1988 L1994 **IM** *020 †20

MOORE, Stephen Lee. 1220 MOORE RD 44011 #028-78-1983, ▲ L1987 **ICE CD** *020

MUNOZ, Fernando X. 1220 MOORE RD, STE B 44011 #308-03-1986 L1990 **CD** *020 †20

MYERS, James Harry. 2535 HALE ST 44011 #036-05-1975 L1977 **END IM** *020 †20

NGUYEN, Christina Rae. ■ 44011 #038-44-2006 L2006 **PD** *012

NOVOTNY, David Allen. 36855 AMERICAN WAY, STE 2D 44011 #038-43-1988 L1989 **PS** *020 †65

OLARIU, Niculina Rodica. 1997 HEALTHWAY DR 44011 #781-05-1979 L2000 **IM** *020 †20

PACHECO, Ted Raymond. 1220 MOORE RD STE B, NORTH OHIO HEART CENTER, I 44011 #030-06-1988 L1993 **CD IM** *020 †20

PARIKH, Sanjay R. 1997 HEALTHWAY DR, STE 203 44011 #495-23-1984 L1992 **CHN** *020 †75

PATEL, Dhruvkumar R. 1997 HEALTHWAY DR, STE 203 44011 #495-37-1983 L1997 **N** *020 †75

PATEL, Rahul S. ■ 44011 #039-79-2007, ▲ L2007 **P** *012

PERHALA, Robert Stephan. 36855 AMERICAN WAY STE A, NORTHRN OHIO ARTHRITIC CTR 44011 #038-40-1985 L1987 **RHU** *020 †20

PILESKI, Cassandra Marie. 36711 AMERICAN WAY 44011 #038-43-1988 L1989 **IM** *020 †20

PRABHAKARAN, Anbazhagan. ■ 44011 #495-16-1995 L2004 **IM** *100 †20

RAMAHI, Alfida Jamil. 1220 MOORE RD STE B, OHIO MEDICAL GROUP 44011 #605-01-1982 L1989 **OBG U** *020 †30

REINHOLD, Jean S. 36901 AMERICAN WAY, STE A 44011 #038-06-1990 L1991 **OBG** *020 †30

REYES, Roland J. 1997 HEALTHWAY DR STE 203 44011 #038-44-1986 L1991 **PS HS** *020 †85,65

RICHARDSON, William S. 2535 HALE ST, STE A 44011 #048-12-1993 L1997 **IM** *020 †20

RICHENDOLLAR, Bill G. ■ 44011 #038-40-2005 L2005 **PTH** *012

SAFI, Bassel. ■ 44011 #875-01-1972 L1978 **VS** *020 †85

SCHMOTZER, Stacy Ann. 1220 MOORE RD, STE B 44011 #038-45-2002 L2002 **FM** *020 †18

SENTER, Shaun Randolph. ■ 44011 #016-01-2004 L2007 **IM** *020

SHELDON, William Scott. 1220 MOORE RD, STE B 44011 #038-75-1988, ▲ L1996 **CD** *020 †20

SINGH, Poonam. ■ 44011 #495-37-1997 **P** *100

SMITH, Duret Stanford. 1502 TRAVELERS PT 44011 #035-06-1977 L1982 **HS ORS** *020 †40

SMITH, Terry Ronald. ■ 44011 #004-01-1980 L1980 **IM** *020 †20

STEPHENS, Amy Louise. 36901 AMERICAN WAY, STE A 44011 #024-07-1992 L1997 **OBG** *020 †30

STRIMBU, Victor Paul. 1502 TRAVELERS PT 44011 #038-06-1985 L1988 **ORS** *020 †40

STRONSKY, David Lee. ■ 44011 #028-34-1968 L2005 **ORS OTR** *020 †40

SUNDARAM, Rajendran. 1997 HEALTHWAY DR, SUPERIOR MEDICAL CARE 44011 #495-59-1987 L1997 **IM** *020 †20

TADROSS, Nabil Adib. 36901 AMERICAN WAY, CLEVELAND CLINIC REG CTR 44011 #915-03-1985 L1997 **IM** *020 †20

■ = Address Information Privacy Protected

TRABOULSSI, Mourhaf. 1220 MOORE RD STE B, NORTH OHIO HEART CENTER, I 44011 #875-01-1983 L1997 **CD IM** *020 †20
VACANTE, Michael. 1220 MOORE RD STE B, NORTH OHIO HEART CENTER, I 44011 #018-75-1981, ▲ L1984 **CD IM** *020 †20
VAN KEULS, Nancy D. 36901 AMERICAN WAY, AVON POINTE 44011 #038-40-1988 L1993 **PD** *020 †55
WATTAR, Abdul Rahman. 1220 MOORE RD, STE B 44011 #875-02-1988 L1993 **CD** *020 †20
ZANOTTI, Salena. 36901 AMERICAN WAY, STE A 44011 #041-14-1997 L2003 **OBG** *020 †30

AVON LAKE – LORAIN

ABOU-HAIDAR, Said Naaman. 223 MILLER RD # A 44012 #605-01-1985 L1988 **P** *020 †75
AKBAR, Khalid. 450 AVON BELDEN RD, CHP PEDIATRIC PHYSICIANS 44012 #704-02-1987 L1999 **PD** *020 †55
ALMHANA, Diab Mfrej. 223 MILLER RD 44012 #875-01-1994 L1999 **P** *020 †75
BARTLEY, Charles P. ■ 44012 #020-02-1949 L1961 **ORS** *071 †40
BAUGHMAN, William Christo. ■ 44012 #047-05-2004 L2004 **DR** *012
BRILL, Jack Jos. 228 MILLER RD, JACK J BRILL DO INC 44012 #041-77-1953, ▲ L1954 **FM** *071
CHEN, Henry Y. 32926 LAKE RD 44012 #385-01-1965 L1972 **OBG GP** *020 ‡
COLLINS, Carol Fundak. 650 MILLER RD, FORD MOTOR COMPANY 44012 #005-19-1980 L1993 **IM OM** *020 †70
COSTIN, John August, III. ■ 44012 #038-06-2002 L2002 **GS** *020
COZMIN, Lavinia M. 450 AVON BELDEN RD, AVON LAKES PHYSICIANS 44012 #781-01-1982 L1995 **IM** *020 †20
DE OLIVEIRA, Daniel D. 32818 WALKER RD # 172 44012 #187-06-1990 L2003 **TS** *020 †85
DRAKE, Natalie Lynne. ■ 44012 #039-01-1998 L2006 **OBG** *020 †30
EICKHOLT, Kimberly Ann. ■ 44012 #038-44-2005 L2005 **PTH** *012
FERRATO, Peter J. ■ 44012 #038-06-1946 L1946 **TS GS** *071 †85,90
HAUSROD, Richard Vincent. ■ 44012 #038-45-2003 L2005 **EM** *100 †16
JELDEN, Gwynn L. 32292 PINEHURST DR 44012 #028-03-1968 L1968 **RO** *030 †80
JONES, Kelly Patrick. ■ 44012 #820-02-2006 L2007 **AN** *012
JOSEF, Demetrio M. 650 MILLER RD 44012 #748-01-1944 L1963 **OM** *071
KRAJCIK, Robert John. 400 BOUNTY WAY 44012 #038-43-1982 L1985 **FM** *020 †18
KREWSON, Thomas Dale. ■ 44012 #038-06-2007 L2007 **DR** *012
LAFFINEUSE, Laura Walsh. ■ 44012 #023-01-2001 L2005 **OBG** *100
LLEWELLYN, Beth Megan. ■ 44012 #038-06-1990 L1991 **DR** *020 †80
MALICDEM, Maria Lourdes T. ■ 44012 #748-01-1992 L1996 **IM** *020 †20
MIRZA-MOHAMMADI, Ali. 450 AVON BELDEN RD 44012 #409-38-1998 L2005 **IMG** *020 †20
NUGENT, Myrna M Plantilla. 650 MILLER RD, OHAP MEDICAL 44012 #748-01-1957 L1966 **OM AN** *071
PANDIT, Vidya Mukul. 32730 WALKER RD STE H 44012 #495-01-1988 L1999 **IM** *020 †20
POBLETE, J Vicente P. 32730 WALKER RD STE F1, AESTHITICS WITHIN 44012 #051-01-1987 L1995 **PS EM** *020 †85,65
POBLETE, Vicente F, Jr. 32720 WALKER RD, # F1 44012 #748-02-1960 L1986 **OBG OS** *020
RICHARDSON, Monique Ann. 32730 WALKER RD, STE H 44012 #048-12-1993 L1997 **FM** *020 †18
RISH, Michael Joseph. 32730 WALKER RD, STE H 44012 #038-43-1994 L1996 **FM** *020 †18
SIMON, James Franics. ■ 44012 #016-43-1998 L2007 **NEP** *100 †20
SINCLAIR, William. ■ 44012 #035-01-1943 L1949 **PTH** *071 †50
SITABKHAN, Rayeka M. 32730 WALKER RD, STE H 44012 #495-01-1972 L1981 **PD** *020 †55
SMITH, Brian. ■ 44012 #038-44-1993 L1994 **GS** *020
SMITH, Thomas Geo. 33398 WALKER RD 44012 #038-40-1973 L1973 **PD** *020 †55
SMITH, Thomas Leonard. ■ 44012 #016-43-1939 L1939 **OTO A** *071 †45
ST MARIE, Michael Gene. ■ 44012 #649-14-1976 L1992 **OM EM** *020 †16
SWEENEY, Michael Thomas. ■ 44012 #016-02-2005 L2005 **MEM** *012
SZENTENDREY, Karoly. ■ 44012 #038-40-1958 L1958 **R** *071 †80
TRZECIAK, Antoni. ■ 44012 #407-16-1951 L1956 **IM** *071
UHL, Justin Nelson. ■ 44012 #038-06-2007 L2007 **MPD** *012
WELSH, Todd Samuel. 655 LAKESIDE DR, 1555 LONG POND ROAD 44012 #008-02-1999 L2006 **EM** *020 †16 ‡
WOJTASIEWICZ, Anna M. ■ 44012 #759-01-1982 L1985 **FM** *020 †18
YASIN, Sabha. 33186 FAIRPORT DR 44012 #495-51-1997 L2001 **IM** *020 †20

AVONDALE – HAMILTON

HEUBI, James Edward. 3333 BURNET AVE, CHILDRENS HOSPITAL 45229 #017-20-1973 L1979 **PD** *020 †55

BALTIMORE – FAIRFIELD

MEHRA, Tarun. 1055 W MARKET ST STE H 43105 #495-59-1988 L1999 **IM** *020 †20
MILLER, Steven Craig. ■ 43105 #020-12-1973 L1974 **FM** *071 †18
SCHELLHASE, Jill Ann. 1055 W MARKET ST, STE H 43105 #038-40-1988 L1990 **FM** *020 †18

BARBERTON – SUMMIT

ADJAN, Marwan. 970 S AZALEA BLVD 44203 #875-02-1973 L1977 **IM GP** *020 †20
AHMED, Shameem Mohammed. 201 5TH ST NE, STE 2 44203 #495-21-1981 L1989 **IM GE** *020 †20
ALVARADO, Leopoldo A, Jr. 155 5TH ST NE, BARBERTON CITIZENS HOSPITA 44203 #748-01-1969 L1982 **GS** *020
ANSLOVAR, Joseph Anthony. ■ 44203 #067-01-1964 L1965 **OS PD** *071
AYOUB, Anna Marie. 631 E BAIRD AVE 44203 #016-11-2002 L2002 **IM** *020 †20
BARTLETT, Glenn Hughes. ■ 44203 #012-01-1974 L1981 **FM** *020 †18
BEYENE, Yekalo Tsehai. 155 5TH ST NE, DEPT OF MED EDU 44203 #305-01-2002 L2006 *100
BHULLAR, Karamjit Singh. 155 5TH ST NE 44203 #496-04-1983 L2003 **IM** *020 †20
BISCONTI, Nicholas, Jr. 201 5TH ST NE, STE 10 44203 #038-44-1985 L1986 **GS** *020 †85
BLACK, Glenn Raymond. 103 5TH ST SE STE Q 44203 #038-40-1973 L1974 **IM** *020 †20
BLAIR, Amber Dawn. 155 5TH ST NE 44203 #038-44-2004 L2004 **FM** *020 †18
BORGES, Paulo Miguel. 155 5TH ST NE, BARBERTON CITIZENS HOSP 44203 #422-01-2005 L2005 **FP** *012
BUCKLEY, Sheryl Lea. 155 5TH ST NE, DEPT ANESTH-BARBERTON CH 44203 #041-07-1972 L1973 **AN** *071 †05
BUDDING, Carlos Alfredo. 101 5TH ST SE STE A 44203 #132-02-1966 L1979 **GS** *020 †85
BUNDY, Robert Virgil, Jr. 155 5TH ST NE 44203 #561-01-1984 L1988 **IM IMG** *020
CASINO, Alfredo Valdez. 101 5TH ST SE STE L 44203 #748-01-1958 L1967 **GS GE** *020 †85
CHANG, Yilan L. 155 5TH ST NE, DEPT OF PATHOLOGY 44203 #243-47-1987 L2000 **PTH PCP** *020 †50
CHATURVEDI, Laxmi Narayan. 155 5TH ST N E TUSCORA PK 44203 #495-19-1959 L1972 **EM PD** *071
COLEMAN, Paul Donald. 107 5TH ST SE STE 9 44203 #019-02-1984 L1985 **FM** *020 †18
COLLUM, Nichole Elizabeth. 62 CONSERVATORY DR 44203 #038-44-2003 L2003 **PD** *020 †55
COTTERMAN, Richard Gale. 101 5TH ST SE STE A 44203 #038-40-1954 L1954 **AN** *071 †05
CROCKER, Norman Lloyd. 155 5TH ST NE, DEPT OF RAD 44203 #038-44-1985 L1990 **DR** *020 †80
DAR, Mohmad Akram. 91 5TH ST SE 44203 #495-15-1969 L1979 **PUD IM** *020 †20
DEBSKI, Robert Frank. 201 5TH ST NE STE 8 44203 #041-13-1976 L1983 **TS** *020 †85,90
DERGANC, Metka. 155 5TH ST NE 44203 #957-03-1970 *100
DONOHOO, Roger Vernon. 155 5TH ST NE 44203 #038-43-1981 L1982 **PTH** *020 †50
DWYER, Jennifer Nelle. 62 CONSERVATORY DR, STE A 44203 #038-40-1996 L1997 **PD** *020 †55
EDWARDS, Jonathan Lee. 155 5TH ST NE 44203 #038-41-1999 L1999 **FM** *020 †18
ELEY, James Allen. 62 CONSERVATORY DR, STE B 44203 #038-44-1988 L1989 **FM** *071 †18
ELIAS, Jon Andrew. 155 5TH ST NE 44203 #038-40-1989 L1990 **FM EM** *020 †18
FARKAS, Stephen Andrew. 155 5TH ST NE 44203 #038-40-1973 L1974 **ID IM** *030 †20
FLICKINGER, Nancy Louise. 155 5TH ST NE 44203 #038-44-1981 L1984 **FM** *040 †18
FORSYTH, Kevin James. 101 5TH ST SE, STE J 44203 #305-01-1986 L1995 **OM IM** *020
GANNON, Timothy Leo. 105 5TH ST SE 44203 #025-12-2000 L2000 **P** *020 †75
HAAS, Andrew John, Jr. 155 5TH ST NE 44203 #016-43-1977 L1982 **HO** *020 †20
HAILEMARIAM, Michael Team. 155 5TH ST NE, BARBERTON CITIZENS HOSP 44203 #665-01-2001 L2005 **FM** *020 †18
HAKIM, Roger Edmond. 256 NORTON AVE 44203 #330-01-1955 L1966 **GP OM** *020
HALL, Daniel Lee. 201 5TH ST NE, STE 6 44203 #055-02-1984 L1985 **OBG** *020 †30
HANZEL, Frank R. ■ 44203 #038-41-1950 L1950 **FM** *071
HAQUE, Ihsan Ul. 201 5TH ST NE, STE 18 44203 #704-01-1976 L1982 **CD IM** *020 †20
HINES, Robert Michael. 201 5TH ST NE, STE 15 44203 #038-40-1983 L1983 **PUD CCM** *020 †20
HUSAIN, Iftekhar. 91 5TH ST SE 44203 #496-14-1980 L1993 **PUD IM** *020 †20
IBRAHIM, Islam Mohamed. 91 5TH ST SE 44203 #915-02-1988 L1998 **CCM** *020 †20
JASH, Satkari. 3334 E TUSCARAWAS EXT 44203 #495-39-1960 L1974 **IM GP** *020 †20
KARIMIAN, Hojatollah. 103 5TH ST SE, STE R 44203 #517-01-1971 L1981 **CD IM** *020 †20
KEITH, David K. 28 CONSERVATORY DR, STE B 44203 #038-75-1997, ▲ L1999 **FM** *020 †18
KENNEDY, James Patrick. 566 ROBINSON AVE STE 400 44203 #038-44-1984 L1985 **ORS TRS** *020 †40
KHAN, Mohamad Afzal. 155 5TH ST NE 44203 #495-51-1971 **GP** *100
KIM, John Myoung Koo. 1115 WOOSTER RD W 44203 #583-10-1967 L1975 **FM GP** *020
KROLL, Harry H V. ■ 44203 #065-05-1938 L1957 **IM** *071
LEE, Yoon Suk. 155 5TH ST N E TUSCORA PK 44203 #583-01-1948 L1973 **FM** *071
LEES, Michelle J. 155 5TH ST NE, BARBERTON AREA FAMILY PRAC 44203 #038-43-2002 L2002 **FM** *020 †18
LEW, Sanghwan. 155 5TH ST NE 44203 #583-02-1957 L1966 **AN OS** *071 †05
LIEDERBACH, Christopher T. 87 CONSERVATORY DR, STE A 44203 #038-40-1994 L1997 **GS** *020
LISHNEVSKI, Diana. 155 5TH ST NE 44203 #473-03-2003 L2005 **FP** *012
LONGSDORF, Katherine Anne. 155 5TH ST NE 44203 #038-44-2000 L2000 **FM** *020 †18
LUA, Joseph N. 155 5TH ST NE, PATH DEPT BARBERTON HOSP 44203 #748-02-1966 L1973 **PTH** *062 †50
MALEK, Roushdy Wissa. 101 5TH ST SE STE K 44203 #330-02-1955 L1970 **OPH OS** *020 †35
MATTY, Teresa Maria. 101 5TH ST SE STE B 44203 #759-01-1969 L1974 **IM** *020
MAYORS, Dean John. 201 5TH ST NE STE 10, SUITE 10 44203 #038-40-1976 L1976 **GS** *020 †85
MC ANLIS, John Geo. 101 5TH ST SE 44203 #038-40-1959 L1959 **GS** *020 †85
MC DONALD, Michael Xavier. 62 CONSERVATORY DR, STE A 44203 #017-20-1982 L1984 **PD** *020 †55
MCDONNELL, Kevin Christop. ■ 44203 #038-41-2007 L2007 **TY** *012
MCKITTY, Nadia Jonelle. 155 5TH ST NE, DEPT OF MED EDU 44203 #654-01-2003 L2006 *100
MIDHA, Sunita. 201 5TH ST NE STE 4, TUSCORA PK PROFESSIONAL CE 44203 #496-07-1983 L1993 **END** *020 †20
MILLER, Joel Brian. 155 5TH ST N E TUSCORA PK 44203 #023-01-1974 L1980 **PTH** *020 †50
MINICH, Diane Marie. 86 CONSERVATORY DR, STE B 44203 #038-43-1984 L1985 **FM** *020 †18
MIR, Ghulam Nabi. 201 5TH ST NE STE 2 44203 #495-51-1970 L1980 **GE** *020 †20
MITHIPATI, Vanilakshmi. 155 5TH ST NE, DEPT OF FAMILY PRACTICE 44203 #495-11-2001 L2004 **FP** *012
MORRIS, Edward F. 480 W TUSCARAWAS AVE 44203 #038-06-1949 L1949 **R** *071 †80
MOSKOVITZ, David Allen. 105 5TH ST SE, STE 6 44203 #038-06-1971 L1976 **P** *020 †75
MOYENUDDIN, Munshi. 155 5TH ST NE, BARBERTON CITIZENS HOSPITA 44203 #160-06-1975 L2000 **ID** *020
MUSTAFA, Masroor. 91 5TH ST SE 44203 #495-51-1991 L1996 **IM PCC** *020 †20
NAIDU, Loushaana. 155 5TH ST NE 44203 #665-01-2002 L2002 **IM** *012
NGUYEN, Nhut Cao Binh. 155 5TH ST NE 44203 #654-01-2001 L2003 **FM** *100 †18
NOVAK, Laura Leeson. 155 5TH ST NE 44203 #038-40-1980 L1983 **FM** *020 †18
OKEKE, Ifeoma Roseline. 103 5TH ST SE, BARBERTON CANCER CARE LLC 44203 #690-04-1991 L2006 **HO** *020 †18,20
PAMFILIE, Jennifer M. 101 5TH ST SE, STE G 44203 #038-44-1995 L1996 **FM** *020 †18
PAPOURAS, Julia L. 62 CONSERVATORY DR, STE A 44203 #038-43-1996 L1997 **PD** *020 †55
PAPPAS, Paul Nick. 155 5TH ST N E TUSCORA PK 44203 #017-20-1958 L1959 **GP** *071
PARK, Youn Wook. 105 5TH ST SE STE 4 44203 #583-01-1971 L1979 **OTO HNS** *020 †45
PARKER, Mark Edgar. 155 5TH ST NE 44203 #035-03-1977 L1983 **PTH** *020 †50
PATEL, Kanubhai R. 103 5TH ST SE S-T 44203 #495-22-1962 L1972 **GS** *020
PATEL, Vimal Babubhai. 155 5TH ST NE, DEPT OF MED EDU 44203 #654-01-2005 L2006 *100
PATEL, Vimalkumar Ramchan. 155 5TH ST NE 44203 #495-48-2001 L2004 **FM** *100 †18
PATEL, Yogeshwar Ashokkum. 155 5TH ST NE, BARBERTON CITIZENS HOSP 44203 #495-23-2002 L2005 **FP** *012
PETRUS, John Jos. 201 5TH ST NE, STE 3 44203 #038-44-1984 L1985 **HEM ON** *020 †20
QADIR, Manzoor. 3939 CLEVELAND MASSILLN RD 44203 #704-21-1986 L1996 **GE** *020 †20
RAMESH, Vidya. 155 5TH ST NE, DEPT OF MED EDUI 44203 #654-01-2004 L2006 *100

■ = Address Information Privacy Protected

REDDY, Aparna Nukala. 155 5TH ST NE, DEPT OF FAMILY PRAC 44203 #305-01-2004 L2004 IM *012

REHMUS, Esther Hoogland. 201 5TH ST NE, STE 3 44203 #025-01-1981 L1987 ON HEM *020 †20

RICHARD, James Randall. 155 5TH ST NE 44203 #038-41-1979 L1980 **FM EM** *040 †16,18

RUZICS, Thomas Francis. 201 5TH ST NE STE 6 44203 #308-03-1983 L1988 **OBG** *020 †30 ‡

SAKLECHA, Falgu R. 155 5TH ST NE 6TH FL, REHAB MED PARTNERS LLC 44203 #038-44-1994 L1995 **PM** *020 †60

SCARCELLA, Robert Geo. 101 5TH ST SE E 44203 #038-06-1974 L1975 **GS** *020 †85

SCHMITT, William Michael. 155 5TH ST NE 44203 #016-43-1970 L1981 **FM IMG** *040 †18

SESAY, Michael. 155 5TH ST NE 44203 #473-03-2000 L2004 **FM** *100 †18

SHKOLNIK, Alexandra. 155 5TH ST NE 44203 #407-16-1948 L1958 **R NM** *071 †80

SOFUOGLU, Muzaffer. 101 5TH ST SE STE A 44203 #902-03-1951 L1968 **OTO OS** *045

SPRANCE, Lee Anne. 155 5TH ST NE, PARKVIEW CTR 44203 #035-09-1985 L1994 **GS OS** *020 †85

STARKEY, Jeffrey Todd. 31 CONSERVATORY DR 44203 #017-20-1989 L1993 **OPH** *020 †35

STEMPLE, Kurtis Neal. 72 5TH ST SE, STE A 44203 #038-44-2001 L2001 **ORS** *020

SUDIMAK, Vincent Louis. ■ 44203 #038-44-2007 L2007 **GS** *012

SWORNIOWSKI, Teddy. 566 ROBINSON AVE, STE 200 44203 #065-01-1961 L1971 **OBG** *071 †30

TAJ, Syed S. 91 5TH ST SE 44203 #495-15-1969 L1984 **IM** *020 †20

TALIWAL, Ruchi. 101 5TH ST SE, STE G 44203 #495-43-1999 L2001 **FM** *020 †18

THUESTAD, Ola Andreas. 155 5TH ST NE, DEPT OF MED EDUCATION 44203 #473-03-2002 L2006 **FP** *012

TRAN, Khiem Quoc. 155 5TH ST NE 44203 #665-01-2002 L2005 **FP** *012

TRUMP, Kristin Jeannine. 290 5TH ST NE, COMMUNITY HLTH CARE/BARBER 44203 #035-46-1995 L1996 **FM** *020 †18

WEHLING, Don Wesley. 201 5TH ST NE, STE 12 44203 #038-40-1958 L1958 **AN** *071 †05

WU, Peter Yee-Tun. 742 WISTERIA DR 44203 #385-03-1968 L1974 **DR NM** *020 †80

YASSINE, Zouhair C. 101 5TH ST SE, STE J 44203 #605-02-1951 L1958 **ORS** *071 †40

ZHANG, Qiwen. 155 5TH ST NE, BARBERTON ANESTHESIA CARE 44203 #243-65-1982 L2000 **AN** *020 †05

BARNESVILLE — BELMONT

BAUM, Michael Raymond. 100 HOSPITAL DR STE 103 43713 #038-40-1979 L1979 **GS** *020 †85

BROCKWELL, Janet Marjorie. 639 W MAIN ST 43713 #038-43-1974 L1976 **IM EM** *020

DEAN, Wendy Kay. 639 W MAIN ST 43713 #055-02-1993 L1995 **EM** *100 †18

GERST, Mary Ellen. 639 W MAIN ST, BARNESVILLE HOSP ASSOCIATI 43713 #038-40-1978 L1978 **FM EM** *020 †18

KHAN, Abdullah. 639 W MAIN ST 43713 #704-09-1980 L1997 **IM EM** *020 †20

LEE-WOOD, Russell S. 101 E MAIN ST 43713 #422-01-1992 L1995 **FM** *020 †18

MONTE DE RAMOS, Calvin B. 100 HOSPITAL DR STE 203, BELMONT PROFESSIONAL ASSOC 43713 #748-07-1956 L1965 **FM** *020

NARKEVIC, Carol Ann. 639 W MAIN ST 43713 #041-02-1979 L1982 **FM** *020 †18

PATCHA, Himalaya. 101 E MAIN ST 43713 #495-70-1979 L1993 **IM** *020 †20

REDDY, K N Sampangirama. 639 W MAIN ST 43713 #495-33-1972 L1978 **EM** *020

SAMUEL, Aaron James. 100 HOSPITAL DR STE 202 43713 #495-42-1966 L1979 **IM** *020

SOURI, Pratap Kumar. 100 HOSPITAL DR STE 201 43713 #495-27-1963 L1973 **IM** *020 †20

BATAVIA — CLERMONT

ALAWADHI, Husain A. ■ 45103 #155-01-1992 L1999 **ID** *100 †20 ‡

ALTENAU, Ted Richard. 3000 HOSPITAL DR 45103 #038-45-1982 L1985 **EM** *020 †16

AQUINO, Nestor Amoranto. 3000 HOSPITAL DR 45103 #748-01-1971 L1976 **AN** *020 †05

BARNES, Jimmie Cline. 3000 HOSPITAL DR 45103 #038-41-1969 L1969 **R** *020 †80

BARNES, Stephen Edward. 3000 HOSPITAL DR 45103 #038-41-1996 L2001 **DR** *020 †80

BAUMAN, Douglas Harold. ■ 45103 #038-41-2005 L2005 **IM** *012

BORNOVALI, Seref. 2055 HOSPITAL DR, STE 300 45103 #902-07-1990 L2000 **IM** *020 †20 ‡

BUDDHEV, Rekha Harilal. 2400 CLERMONT CENTER DR, BOX 103 45103 #495-22-1962 L1976 **PD** *020 †55

CARDELLA, Richard George. 3000 HOSPITAL DR 45103 #016-11-1978 L1984 **R** *020 †20,80

CARSON, Robert John. 3020 HOSPITAL DR, STE 250 45103 #056-06-1969 L1970 **PD** *071 †55

CHANG, Roger Kaidi. 2245 BAUER RD, STE A 45103 #038-40-1998 L2005 **FM** *020 †18

CUSUMANO, Patricia. 2245 BAUER RD STE A, BATAVIA FAMILY PRACTICE 45103 #016-42-1986 L1989 **FM** *020 †18

DAVIS, James Alvin. ■ 45103 #020-12-1999 L1999 **NEP** *020 †20

ESMAILI, Saeed. 3000 HOSPITAL DR 45103 #517-01-1966 L1978 **TS GS** *020 †85

FARBER, Sheldon. 3000 HOSPITAL DR 45103 #038-41-1958 L1958 **AN OS** *071 †05

FAROOQUI, Mohammed H. 1981 FRONT WHEEL DR, BATAVIA TRANSMISSIONS LLC 45103 #495-65-1969 L1995 **FM** *020 †20

FERNANDEZ, Lisa Margarita. ■ 45103 #042-02-2005 L2005 **P** *012

FITZPATRICK, Timothy J. ■ 45103 #038-41-1985 L1990 **EM** *075 †16

FORMAN, Joel Benjamin. 3020 HOSPITAL DR, STE 270 45103 #038-40-1996 L2005 **CD** *020 †20

GEORGE, Ene Georgina. 2245 BAUER RD, STE A 45103 #690-07-1991 L2000 **OBG** *020 †30

GO, Annabelle Lim. 3000 HOSPITAL DR 45103 #748-11-1972 L1980 **AN** *071

GO, Rolando Fabi. 3000 HOSPITAL DR, STE 235 45103 #038-41-1970 L1970 **OTO FPS** *020 †45

GRAHAM, Larry Anthony. 3000 HOSPITAL DR 45103 #020-02-1988 L1989 **CHP P** *020 †75

HARIHARAN, Parameswaran. 2055 HOSPITAL DR, STE 300 45103 #495-21-1991 L1995 **IM** *020 †20

HAWRYSCHUK, Michael Chris. ■ 45103 #035-06-2006 L2006 **AN** *012

HONTANOSAS, Jesus C. 2055 HOSPITAL DR, STE 335 45103 #748-11-1971 L1979 **GS** *020 †85

JONES, Stewart R, II. 3000 HOSPITAL DR 45103 #038-41-1970 L1970 **GS VS** *020 †85

LAMBERT, Robert Wayne. 3000 HOSPITAL DR 45103 #038-43-1986 L1987 **EM** *020 †16

LONG, Nathan Blazer. 3000 HOSPITAL DR 45103 #038-41-2002 L2003 **DR** *020 †80

MASSOUD, Paul Jos. 3000 HOSPITAL DR, STE 240 45103 #038-41-1989 L1992 **IM** *020 †20

MC CABE, Kevin Jos. 2245 BAUER RD STE A 45103 #038-40-1984 L1985 **FM** *020 †18

MC KIMM, Douglas James. 3000 HOSPITAL DR 45103 #005-11-1980 L1982 **GPM** *020 †70,16

MEHTA, Ila N. 3000 HOSPITAL DR 45103 #495-48-1968 L1977 **PTH OBG** *020 †50

MOSTAFA, Ahmed Elsayed O. 3020 HOSPITAL DR, STE 210 45103 #915-03-1993 L2000 **IM** *020

MULLA OSSMANN, Omar. 3020 HOSPITAL DR, CLERMONT MERCY HOSPITAL 45103 #409-15-1994 L2004 **N** *020

MYERS, Ronald Elwood. ■ 45103 #016-02-1956 L1981 **N OBG** *030

PATEL, Natvarlal L. 2055 HOSPITAL DR, STE 300 45103 #495-75-1969 L1974 **IM** *020 †20

PEREZ, Herminio Luis. 2245 BAUER RD, STE A 45103 #025-12-1985 L1990 **FM** *020 †18

PFALZGRAF, Philip A, Jr. 3000 HOSPITAL DR 45103 #038-41-1961 L1961 **FM GP** *071

PHILIP, Jeffrey Scott. 3000 HOSPITAL DR 45103 #038-40-1989 L1993 **AN MDM** *020 †05

RAO, Shoba. 2245 BAUER RD, DBA BATAVIA FAMILY PRACTIC 45103 #495-75-1987 L2000 **FM** *020 †18

ROUSSEAU, Michel Blaise. 3020 HOSPITAL DR, STE 270 45103 #061-01-1990 L1992 **U** *020 †95

SACHDEVA, Manish. 2055 HOSPITAL DR, STE 300 45103 #495-45-1996 L1999 **IM** *020 †20

SAVOY, John Albert. ■ 45103 #035-03-1964 L1965 **NS OS** *071 †25

SCHILLING, Jonathan Willi. ■ 45103 #038-41-2007 L2007 **GS** *012

SEAMAN, Joseph Carey. ■ 45103 #038-45-2004 L2004 **IM** *020 †20

SHIFF, Brian Mathew. 2055 HOSPITAL DR, STE 355 45103 #038-43-1993 L1998 **GS VS** *020 †85

STEVENS, Barry Scott. 3000 HOSPITAL DR 45103 #021-06-1990 L2004 **DR** *020 †80

TCHAKMAKOFF, George D. ■ 45103 #407-07-1948 L1954 **ORS TRS** *072 †40

THOMPSON, Matthew J. ■ 45103 #919-05-1989 L1998 **FM** *020 †18

VICKERY, Diane Marilynn. 2245 BAUER RD, STE A 45103 #012-01-1976 L1979 **P** *020 †75

VU, Kimanh Thi. 2245 BAUER RD, STE A 45103 #038-40-1996 L2002 **FM** *020 †18

WAHLBRINK, Robert A. 3000 HOSPITAL DR 45103 #020-12-1985 L1989 **DR** *020 †80

WELLS, Gregg Anderson. 3000 HOSPITAL DR 45103 #016-11-1984 L1987 **DR** *020 †80

BATH — SUMMIT

BORODAJKO, Lubomir. ■ 44210 #759-02-1942 L1960 **AN OS** *020

LEMMON, James Francis. ■ 44210 #038-06-1943 L1943 **OTO A** *071 †45

SOMPLE, John Mark. 2682 IRA ROAD 44210 #038-45-1984 L1985 **EM** *075 †16

BAY VILLAGE — CUYAHOGA

BAIRD, Terry Michael. 30313 PROVINCETOWN LN 44140 #038-41-1983 L1987 **NPM** *050 †55

BOWMAN, Melissa Christine. ■ 44140 #038-40-2005 L2005 **PTH** *012

DI GREGORIO, Delia Maria. ■ 44140 #132-01-1964 L1972 **PD HEM** *072 †55

DODGE, Emily Katharine. ■ 44140 #038-06-2006 L2006 **EM** *012

ERLANDSON, Marion E. ■ 44140 #038-06-1950 L1950 **PD** *071 †55

EVENHOUSE, Matthew Henry. 28917 NORTHFIELD RD, BAY VILLAGE 44140 #041-15-2001 L2001 **EM** *020 †16

FERRY, Amanda Catherine. ■ 44140 #038-06-1997 L1999 **OBG** *020 †30

HOEFFLER, Dennis F. ■ 44140 #041-12-1957 L1982 **OM GPM** *072 †55,70

HUNT, Andrew Warren. ■ 44140 #038-40-2006 L2006 **P** *012

IBRAHIM, Victor Mounir. ■ 44140 #038-06-2005 L2007 **PM** *012

LEE, Mi Kyung. ■ 44140 #583-08-1964 L1985 **CHP P** *020

LOCHNER, Sarah Anne. ■ 44140 #048-02-1991 L1997 **IM** *020 †20

MAPUS, Renee Karen. ■ 44140 #038-43-2004 L2007 **IM** *100 †20

NAGEOTTE, Catherine Ann. ■ 44140 #038-44-1985 L1986 **CHP P** *020 †75

PARAS, Thomas Peter. ■ 44140 #418-01-1953 L1959 **TS CD** *020

PETERJOHN, Harlan R. ■ 44140 #038-06-1953 L1953 **PTH** *071 †50

RICHARDS, Robert Ralph. ■ 44140 #038-06-1938 L1938 **GS EM** *071

SCHAEKEL, Melissa Marie. ■ 44140 #023-07-2004 L2006 **P** *012

ZALUD, Lee Donald. 29514 LAKE RD 44140 #038-43-1988 L1989 **IM** *020 †20

BEACHWOOD — CUYAHOGA

ABDEL-AZIZ, Khaled Farid. ■ 44122 #915-05-1995 L2006 **U** *100

ABELSON, Tom Isaac. 26900 CEDAR RD STE 315S, CLEVELAND CLINIC BCHWD 44122 #038-06-1976 L1977 **OTO** *020 †45

ABOUSSOUAN, Loutfi S. 26900 CEDAR RD 44122 #605-01-1986 L1991 **PCC SME** *020 †20

ADAN, Francoise. 20600 CHAGRIN BLVD STE 702 44122 #165-01-1984 L1994 **P** *020 †75

ADHAMI, M Talal M. 26900 CEDAR RD 44122 #605-01-1992 L1995 **IM** *020 †20

AKHTAR-ZAIDI, Syed Jawed. 4180 WARRENSVILL CNTR RD R, BLD A 3RD FLOOR 44122 #704-17-1980 L1995 **PM** *020 †60

ALAM, Daniel Syed. 26900 CEDAR RD 44122 #023-07-1996 L2002 **OTO** *020 †45

ALHADDAD, Sawsan T. 26900 CEDAR RD, STE 30N 44122 #528-01-1973 L1982 **AN** *020 †05

ALLEN, Mark Lynn. 4110 WARRENSVILLE CENTR RD, A-241 44122 #019-02-1980 L1992 **AN OS** *020 †05

ALPERIN, Leonard J. ■ 44122 #038-06-1942 L1942 **PD** *071 †55

AMDUR, Donald Stanley. ■ 44122 #038-40-1978 L1978 **IM** *020

ANDERSON, Thomas Edward. 26900 CEDAR RD, STE 305S 44122 #018-03-1977 L1982 **ORS OSM** *020 †40

ARCHER, Bernard Thos. 3355 RICHMOND RD 44122 #018-03-1960 L1965 **R** *071 †80

ARMSTRONG, Douglas Gordon. 3909 ORANGE PL, STE 3200 44122 #065-10-1982 L2003 **ORS** *020 †40

ATTARAN, Hashem. 4009 E ASH LN 44122 #517-05-1962 L1973 **IM** *020 †20

AUSTIN, Cynthia Milee. 26900 CEDAR RD, STE 200S 44122 #010-01-1979 L1982 **REN OBG** *020 †20

BABIC, Maja. ■ 44122 #957-02-1998 L2005 **ID** *100

BADALYAN, Seda. 4200 WARRENSVILLE CENTR RD, STE 340 44122 #913-38-1997 L2002 *020 †20

BAKER, Everett B. ■ 44122 #024-07-1952 L1978 **EM OS** *030 †85

BAL, Baljit Singh. 26900 CEDAR RD, STE 26N 44122 #038-15-1990 L1997 **IM** *020 †20

BALLOCK, Robert Tracy. 26900 CEDAR RD 44122 #024-01-1984 L1994 **ORS** *020 †40

BASS, Steven N. 3609 PARK EAST DR, STE 207 44122 #035-20-1976 L1979 **ID IM** *020 †20

BASTANI, Bijan. 3733 PARK EAST DR, CONSULTANTS 44122 #038-51-1974 L1983 **P** *020 †75

BATRA, Sukhpreet Singh. 26900 CEDAR RD 44122 #028-03-1997 L2002 **OTO** *020 †45

BENNETT, Angela Miller. 4200 WARRENSVILL CNTR RD R, SOUTH POINTE HOSPITAL BLDG 44122 #038-06-2000 L2000 **FM** *020 †18

BERIE, Diane Catherine. 3690 ORANGE PL, STE 410 44122 #038-40-1995 L1996 **P** *020

BERNIE, Stephen Ross. 24300 CHAGRIN BLVD, STE 210 44122 #038-40-1966 L1966 **GP OPH** *020

BEYTAS, Erol Martin. 24675 WOODSIDE LN 44122 #047-05-1981 L1992 **NM NR** *020 †80,28

BHARDWAJ, Elvira L. 4200 WARRENSVILLE CENTR RD, STE 122 44122 #748-01-1955 L1973 **EM FM** *071 †18,16

BHULLAR, Davinder. ■ 44122 #495-29-1996 **IM** *100 †20

BILLOWITZ, Aaron Theodore. 3690 ORANGE PL 44122 #024-05-1966 L1968 **P** *020 †75

BOCKOVEN, John Robt. 23250 CHAGRIN BLVD, STE 325 44122 #038-43-1991 L1997 **PDC** *020 †55

BONNET, David Macnaughtan. 3909 ORANGE PL STE 2500 44122 #055-01-1998 L2000 **MPD** *020 †20

BONOMO, Rita Marie. 3909 ORANGE PL, STE 2400 44122 #038-06-1989 L1991 **IM** *020 †20

BORG, Bryson Dale. ■ 44122 #041-14-2000 L2000 **RNR** *020 †80

BORUKH, Elena. 26900 CEDAR RD STE 26N 44122 #913-79-1978 L1996 **IM** *020 †20

BOYD, Theresa Elaine. 23250 CHAGRIN BLVD, STE 130 44122 #038-43-1988 L1991 **PD ADL** *020 †55

BOYLE, Ivy Roberta Bock. 23230 CHAGRIN BLVD, BLDG 3 44122 #035-45-1969 L1970 **CHP P** *020 †75

BRAHMS, Malcolm A. 3755 ORANGE PL, STE 101 44122 #038-06-1950 L1950 **ORS OS** *071 †40

BRENNER, Robert Scott. 3733 PARK EAST DR 44122 #038-40-1969 L1969 **END IM** *020 †20

BRICKEL, Arthur C J. ■ 44122 #028-34-1966 L1973 **N** *075 †75

BRINDZA, Deborah. 3609 PARK EAST DR 44122 #038-41-1984 L1987 **PD** *020 †55

BRODKEY, Jerald Steven. 24755 CHAGRIN BLVD 44122 #030-05-1960 L1969 **NS OS** *071 †25

BROOK, Marvin Gerald. PARKWAY MEDICAL CNTR 44122 #038-41-1947 L1947 **PYA P** *072

BROOKS, Dennis Bruce. 26900 CEDAR RD 44122 #038-06-1963 L1963 **ORS** *071 †40

BUONAIUTO, Salvatore Jose. ■ 44122 #422-01-2004 L2007 **PDC** *012

BYKOV, Victor. 3355 RICHMOND RD, STE 221 44122 #051-07-1993 L1995 **DR** *020 †80

CAHAN, Clement. 23310 WENDOVER DR 44122 #550-02-1981 L1988 **PUD CCM** *020 †20

CAMPBELL, Kristine M. 23230 CHAGRIN BLVD, STE 350 44122 #038-06-1988 L1989 **P** *040 †75

CARMAN, Toni Louise. 3733 PARK EAST DR, CONSULTANTS 44122 #010-02-1976 L1985 **P** *020 †75

CARROL, Anne Mc Donald. 23250 CHAGRIN BLVD STE 150 44122 #038-06-1988 L1990 **IM** *020 †20

CASTRO, Oscar M. ■ 44122 #748-01-1968 L1978 **GS GP** *020

CEICYS, Victor Alphonse. 3355 RICHMOND RD, STE 221 44122 #038-06-1976 L1977 **DR** *020 †80

CHAVINSON, Jill Diane. 3909 ORANGE PL, STE 2100 44122 #038-06-1996 L1999 **IM** *020 †20

COBB, Pamela Key. 25825 SCIENCE PARK DR, STE 300 44122 #004-01-1978 L1989 **FM** *020 †18

COBB, Sandra Louise. 26900 CEDAR RD, STE 26N 44122 #038-06-1980 L1981 **IM** *020 †20

COCONCEA, Nicoleta. 24200 CHAGRIN BLVD, STE 126 44122 #781-01-1986 L1998 **P PYG** *020 †75

COHN, Bruce Theodore. 3755 ORANGE PL 44122 #038-06-1981 L1984 **ORS** *020 †40

COMROV, Elana. ■ 44122 #035-46-2003 L2003 **PD** *100 †55

COOPERMAN, Daniel Roy. 3909 ORANGE PL, STE 2300 44122 #016-02-1974 L1987 **ORS** *020 †40

COTTA, Claudiu Vasile. ■ 44122 #781-05-1994 L2007 **HMP** *100 †50

CRUZ, Natasha Ria E. 3909 ORANGE PL, STE 2100 44122 #748-10-1995 L2005 **FM** *020 †18

DARVIN, Howard Ira. 3609 PARK EAST DR, STE 104 44122 #010-03-1982 L1988 **GS** *020 †85

DAVIES, Ryan Nicholas. ■ 44122 #016-76-2007, ▲ L2007 *012

DAVIS, Carrie Beth. 23250 CHAGRIN BLVD, STE 440 COMMERCE PARK BLDG 44122 #038-06-1987 L1987 **OPH** *020 †35

DENNIS, Bradley Anthony. 24755 CHAGRIN BLVD, PREMIER WMNS HLTH INC #345 44122 #041-01-1975 L1979 **OBG** *020 †30

DEOSKAR, Dhananjay Shripa. ■ 44122 #495-85-1990 L2006 **NPM** *012

DESAI, Anand Bharat. ■ 44122 #038-06-2007 L2007 **TY** *012

DIAMOND, Alan Sloan. 23625 COMMERCE PARK # 204, FRANKLIN & SEIDELMANN INC 44122 #061-01-1987 L2006 **RNR** *020 †80

DINNER, Melvyn I. 5 NANTUCKET CT 44122 #836-01-1965 L1976 **PS** *020 †65

DJOHAN, Risal Satiaputra. 26900 CEDAR RD 44122 #016-42-1994 L2002 **PS** *020 †85,65

DONLEY, Brian Gerard. 26900 CEDAR RD 44122 #025-01-1990 L1996 **ORS** *020 †40

DUGGAN, Patricia Ann. 4110 WARRENSVILLE CENTR RD, CLEVELAND VASCULAR INSTITU 44122 #038-43-1995 L2000 **VS** *020 †85

DURDEN, Faith Marie. 3690 ORANGE PL, STE 300 44122 #038-06-1989 L1991 **D** *020 †15

DUTTON, Edward Navarro. 3461 WARRENSVILLE CENTR RD, STE 205 44122 #038-06-1974 L1981 **P GP** *020

ECKSTEIN, Michael Brad. 3909 ORANGE PL, STE 2400 44122 #035-09-1975 L1976 **IM** *020 †20

ELLEN, Mark M. ■ 44122 #407-15-1951 L1956 **AN** *071

EPELMAN, Slava. ■ 44122 #060-02-2005 L2005 **IM** *012

EPPELL, Beth Anne. ■ 44122 #028-02-1993 L1994 **FM** *020 †18

EPPIG, Michael Dennis. 3619 PARK EAST DR STE 318 44122 #038-06-1977 L1982 **OSS** *020 †40

EPSTEIN, Howard Gregg. 26900 CEDAR RD, STE 325 44122 #038-06-1979 L1982 **RHU IM** *020 †20

EZIGBO, Bernard Kenechukw. ■ 44122 #690-04-1996 L2007 **IM** *100 †20

FALL, Christine. 3909 ORANGE PL, STE 2400 44122 #038-06-1998 L2000 **IM** *071 †20

FEDELE, Gregory Malcolm. 25201 CHAGRIN BLVD, STE 180 44122 #038-41-1991 L1996 **PS** *020 †65

FEINLEIB, Steven Elliot. 26900 CEDAR RD, CCF BEACHWOOD 44122 #023-01-1997 L1999 **IM** *020 †20

FEUDO, Scott Christopher. 3909 ORANGE PL, STE 2400 44122 #038-41-1990 L1992 **IM** *020 †20

FINE, Aaron Jerome. ■ 44122 #038-06-1954 L1954 **A** *071 †03

FINKE, Heather Cathleen. ■ 44122 #038-43-2000 L2000 **DR** *100 †80

FOLEY, Conrad Bruce. 26900 CEDAR RD, STE 27N 44122 #011-03-1984 L1987 **PD** *020 †55

FOLEY, Tina Marie. ■ 44122 #027-01-1990 L2005 **N** *020 †75

FRANKEL, Leonard. ■ 44122 #038-40-1936 L1936 **IM** *071 †20

FREYLE, Hanna Bathia. ■ 44122 #264-04-1995 L2006 **ID** *100 †20

FRIEDMAN, Darci H. 23250 MERCANTILE RD 44122 #038-40-2001 L2007 **IM** *020 †20

FUREY, Christopher Geo. 3909 ORANGE PL, STE 3200 44122 #038-06-1991 L1992 **ORS** *020 †40

GANDHI, Sanjay. ■ 44122 #495-45-1996 L2005 **CD** *100 †20 ‡

GARDNER, Gretchen Kay. 24200 CHAGRIN BLVD 44122 #038-06-1991 L1994 **P** *020 †75

GAROFALO, Thomas Edward. 26900 CEDAR RD STE 32N 44122 #041-12-1992 L1996 **CRS GS** *020 †85,10

GATHA, Harilal Gokaldas. ■ 44122 #495-22-1957 L1973 **FM GS** *071 †18

GEIER, Peter Jones. 23811 CHAGRIN BLVD, STE 310 44122 #038-41-1984 L1986 **CHP** *020 †75

GEYER, Pamela Kay. 3909 ORANGE PL STE 2500 44122 #038-41-1980 L1982 **IM** *020 †20

GILMORE, Allison. 3909 ORANGE PL, STE 3200 44122 #038-06-1994 L1995 **ORS** *020 †40

GOJI, Nega Ali. 3609 PARK EAST DR # 20, ID CONSULTANTS INC 44122 #366-01-1994 L2006 **IM ID** *020 †20

GOLDFARB, James Morris. 26900 CEDAR RD, STE 200S 44122 #038-40-1973 L1974 **REN OBG** *020 †20

GOLDMAN, Sara Gail. 24800 HIGHPOINT RD, STE B 44122 #035-08-1996 L2000 **P** *020 †75

GOLDMAN, Steven Andrew. 3619 PARK EAST DR STE 303 44122 #041-12-1993 L1999 **PS** *020 †45,65

GOLUB, Joshua Adam. ■ 44122 #038-43-2003 L2004 **DR** *012

GOODFELLOW, Donald Bruce. 3909 ORANGE PL, STE 3200 44122 #038-06-1977 L1978 **ORS OSM** *012

GOODMAN, Kenneth Ira. 26900 CEDAR RD STE 22, CLEVELAND CLINIC BEACHWOOD 44122 #038-45-1988 L1989 **FM** *020 †18

GOPINATH, Anil. ■ 44122 #495-53-1997 L2005 **SME** *012

GREENSPAN, Gary Allan. 4200 WARRENSVILL CNTR RD R 44122 #231-01-1982 L1986 **IM** *020 †20

GRUSENMEYER, Michael Jos. 3909 ORANGE PL, STE 2100 44122 #025-07-1979 L1983 **FM EM** *020 †16,18

GUPTA, Geeta. 4200 WARRENSVILLE CENTR RD, STE 353 44122 #495-03-1981 L1988 **IM** *020 †20

HALL, Ryan Chaloner Winto. ■ 44122 #010-02-2003 L2007 **PFP** *012

HAMID, Mohamed A. 24755 CHAGRIN BLVD STE 310, CLEVE HEARING & BALANCE CT 44122 #038-06-1994 L1995 **OTO NO** *020

HANDEL, Jeremy David. ■ 44122 #011-03-2002 L2007 **VIR** *012 †80

HART, David Joseph. 3909 ORANGE PL 44122 #054-04-1997 L2004 **NS** *020

HART, James Lee. ■ 44122 #038-06-1974 L1974 **PYA P** *071 †75

HASAN, Samia. 23230 CHAGRIN BLVD 44122 #023-01-1992 L1996 **P** *020 †75

HAUSER, Michael Stuart. 23250 CHAGRIN BLVD, STE 205 44122 #024-16-1983 L1986 **OS** *040

HAZEN, Jacalyn Weissman. 26900 CEDAR RD, STE 27N 44122 #028-02-1989 L1997 **PD** *020 †55

HELFAND, Robert Fred. 26900 CEDAR RD 44122 #038-06-1984 L1988 **AN IM** *020 †20,05

HENDRICKS, Leonard D. 25450 FAIRMOUNT BLVD 44122 #056-05-1979 L1982 **EM LM** *062 †16

HERTZER, John Leslie. 23240 CHAGRIN BLVD, BEACHWOOD COMMERCE PARK 4 44122 #038-43-1994 L1997 **CHP** *020 †75

HERTZER, Julie Anne. 3733 PARK EAST DR, STE 102 44122 #017-20-1994 L1997 **PD** *020 †55

HEYMAN, Tonya Sheree. 3609 PARK EAST DR, STE 210 44122 #038-06-1982 L1986 **GYN** *020 †30

HIRSH, Alan Mathew. 3909 ORANGE PL, STE 2400 44122 #016-11-1985 L1991 **IM** *020 †20

HIRSHMAN, Judith Lynn. 23250 CHAGRIN BLVD STE 310 44122 #038-06-1988 L1991 **P PFP** *020 †75

HOLLAND, Joel Barry. 26900 CEDAR RD 44122 #035-45-1977 L1982 **CD IM** *020 †20

HORWITZ, Samuel J. ■ 44122 #836-02-1953 L1967 **CHN PD** *071 †55,75

HOU, Yanlin. ■ 44122 #243-21-1986 L2000 **PM** *100 †60

HULL, Tracy Lynn. 26900 CEDAR RD 44122 #038-40-1986 L1991 **GS** *020 †85,10

IANNOTTI, Joseph Patrick. 26900 CEDAR RD, STE 305S 44122 #016-06-1979 L2000 **ORS** *020 †40

IMMERMAN, Ronald Stuart. 3517 HAMPTON RD 44122 #038-06-1981 L1982 **P** *020

INTINI, Anselma. ■ 44122 #561-23-1994 L2002 **CD** *012 †20

JAHAMY, Houssein David. 3609 PARK EAST DR, STE 207 44122 #913-16-1996 L2001 **ID** *020 †20

JANG, Sunguk. ■ 44122 #023-01-1999 L2006 **GE** *020 †20

JASSANI, Majida Nakib. 26900 CEDAR RD 44122 #528-01-1960 L1969 **OBG DR** *020 †30

JONES, Jace Stephen. 26900 CEDAR RD, STE 305S 44122 #004-01-1986 L1999 **U** *020 †95

JONES, Pythias Damon. 3645 WARRENSVILL CNTR RD R 44122 #038-06-1980 L1982 **P** *020 †75

KAGAN, Michael Iosif. ■ 44122 #913-09-1988 L1999 **IM UCM** *020 †20

KANJ, Mohamed Hani. ■ 44122 #605-01-1997 L2002 **ICE** *100 †20

KANTER, Myron F. ■ 44122 #038-06-1939 L1939 **GS** *071

KARK, Elizabeth Coe. ■ 44122 #024-01-1971 L1974 **D** *020 †15

KASHYAP, Vikram Shantaram. 26900 CEDAR RD, STE 32N 44122 #041-02-1990 L2003 **VS GS** *020 †85

KAUR, Navneet. 3733 PARK EAST DR, CONSULTANTS 44122 #495-05-1983 L2000 **CHP P** *020

KELLER, Julie Catherine. 3909 ORANGE PL STE 21, SUITE 2100 44122 #038-06-1996 L1998 **FM** *020 †18

KENDIS, Daniel Roger. ■ 44122 #041-12-1976 L1979 **AN** *075 †20

KESELMAN, Irena. ■ 44122 #913-16-1987 L2003 **P** *100

KHALAFI, Kamal. 4180 WARRENSVILLE CENTR RD, STE 120 44122 #902-05-1992 L1998 **IM** *100 †20

KHODADAI, Omid. ■ 44122 #005-18-2004 L2005 **AN** *012

KIBBE, Peter Sherwin. 3461 WARRENSVILLE CENTR RD, STE 303 44122 #038-06-1977 L1980 **IM EM** *020 †20

KILMARTIN, Ellen M. 3733 PARK EAST DR, CONSULTANTS 44122 #010-02-1986 L1988 **CHP** *020 †75

KING, Richard M. 3985 WARRENSVILLE CENTR RD 44122 #038-40-1978 L1979 **IM IMG** *020 †20

KIRSH, Brian Marshall. 3700 PARK EAST DR, STE 100 44122 #038-43-1991 L1992 **GE** *020 †20

KIWI, Robert. 26900 CEDAR RD, STE 200S 44122 #836-02-1968 L1978 **OBG NPM** *020 †30

KLARFELD, Jonathan Eric. 23250 MERCANTILE RD 44122 #035-20-1978 L1980 **IM AN** *020 †20

KLEINMAN, Jeffrey David. 4110 WARRENSVILL CNTR RD R, SOUTHPOINTE HOSPITAL 44122 #038-45-1995 L1996 **DR** *020 †80

KLEINMAN, Leonard A. 26600 GEORGE ZEIGER DR, STE D-21 44122 #038-40-1943 L1944 **IM** *071 †20

KOC, Omer Naci. 26900 CEDAR RD, ONCOLOGY-BEACHWOOD 44122 #902-07-1987 L1991 **ON** *020 †20

KOCHARIAN, Edward. 4100 WARRENSVILLE CENTR RD 44122 #913-38-1989 L1997 **IM** *020 †20

KOLETSKY, Richard J. 23250 CHAGRIN BLVD # 1, COMMERCE PARK FIVE 44122 #038-06-1975 L1976 **END ID** *020 †20

KOYFMAN, Shlomo Asher. ■ 44122 #008-01-2006 L2006 **RO** *012

KRANTZ, David Jay. 3601 GREEN RD, STE 316 44122 #038-43-1990 L1992 **AN** *020 †05

KRIWINSKY, Jan. 3690 ORANGE PL, STE 100 44122 #038-40-1984 L1985 **PD PEM** *020 †55

KUMAR, Prashanth Vasantha. ■ 44122 #025-07-2003 L2003 **NEP** *012 †20

KUMAR, Priya Ajit. ■ 44122 #495-15-2007 L2007 **AN** *020 †05

KURZBAUER, Robert. 4200 WARRENSVILL CENTR RD 44122 #038-06-1949 L1949 **IM FM** *071

KWON, Kong Young. 3355 RICHMOND RD BLDG A, STE 225 44122 #583-01-1967 L1974 **P** *071 †75

KWON, Suk Chan. 3498 COURTLAND RD 44122 #583-04-1966 L1973 **R** *020 †80

■ = Address Information Privacy Protected

LANE, Modish Jean. 23250 CHAGRIN BLVD, BLDG #5 - SUITE 110 44122 #025-12-1980 L1983 GE *020 †20

LANTSBERG, Igor A. 4200 WARRENSVILLE CENTR RD, STE 344 44122 #913-06-1961 L1978 IM A *020

LARSON-ODE, Katie Marie. ■ 44122 #056-05-2005 L2005 PD *012

LASCH, James R. 24755 CHAGRIN BLVD, STE 235 44122 #038-06-1953 L1953 GS *071 †85

LAVIN, Arthur. 3733 PARK EAST DR, STE 102 44122 #038-40-1979 L1990 PD NPM *020 †55

LEBEDEVA, Zinaida L. 23210 CHAGRIN BLVD, STE 400 44122 #913-01-1982 L1999 P *020

LEEMING, Rosemary Ann. 3909 ORANGE PL, STE 4400 44122 #041-09-1983 L1986 GS *020 †85

LEFTON, Eva Ray. 16 DEERFIELD LN 44122 #038-40-1963 L1963 IM IMG *020

LEIZMAN, Daniel Jay. 23250 MERCANTILE RD 44122 #038-40-1988 L1992 ORS PM *020 †60

LERNER, Raisa A. 4200 WARRENSVILLE CENTR RD, STE 215 44122 #913-81-1972 L1978 IM *020 †20

LEVER, David Saml. 26900 CEDAR RD 44122 #010-01-1980 L1982 GE IM *020 †20

LEVINE, Stephen Barrett. 23230 CHAGRIN BLVD STE 350 44122 #038-06-1967 L1967 P *020 †75

LEVITAN-GERSON, Deborah. 3909 ORANGE PL, STE 4500 44122 #024-01-1977 L1983 OBG *020 †30

LEVITIN, Abraham. 23266 WENDOVER DR 44122 #035-08-1991 L1997 DR VIR *020 †80

LEVY, Lawrence Richmond. 26900 CEDAR RD, STE 305S 44122 #038-06-1961 L1961 GO *020 †20

LIEBESKIND, Amy. 23625 COMMERCE PARK, STE 204 44122 #008-01-1998 L2007 OBG *100 †80

LINDEN, Milton. ■ 44122 #016-11-1946 L1951 GYN *071 †30

LIPOLD, Laura Dorr. 26900 CEDAR RD STE 22N 44122 #035-03-1997 L1998 FM *020 †18 ‡

LISBONA, Hanna Huguette. 26900 CEDAR RD, STE 200S 44122 #550-03-1980 L1985 OBG *020 †20

LISSAUER, Jack Steven. 3700 PARK EAST DR STE 100 44122 #023-01-1971 L1975 GE IM *020 †20

LOCK, Joseph Chas. 26900 CEDAR RD, STE 305S 44122 #038-43-1975 L1977 PD *020 †55

LOWRIE, Bruce. 23250 CHAGRIN BLVD, STE 150 44122 #038-06-1985 L1986 IMG IM *020 †20

LUCAS, Armand E. 26900 CEDAR RD 44122 #032-01-1977 L1988 PS GS *020 †65

MACKNIN, Carol Hyman. 23230 CHAGRIN BLVD, STE 845 44122 #038-06-1985 L1989 P *020 †75

MADHUN, Zuhayr T. 23250 CHAGRIN BLVD STE 201 44122 #605-01-1987 L1990 IM END *020 †20

MAKKAR, Vinit Kumar. 26900 CEDAR RD STE 305 44122 #038-44-1989 L1990 HEM *020 †20

MAKOS, George Stavros. ■ 44122 #418-01-1970 L1988 TS *020 †85,90

MANDAPAT, Aimee Luna. ■ 44122 #038-40-2005 L2005 IM *012

MANDEL, Morris Jack. ■ 44122 #038-40-1957 L1957 IM CD *071 †20

MANOLACHE, Mihaela Roxana. 4200 WARRENSVILLE CENTR RD 44122 #781-04-1985 L2001 IM *100 †20

MARCOTTY, Andreas. 25101 CHAGRIN BLVD, STE 150 44122 #025-07-1978 L1983 PO OPH *020 †35

MARCUS, Randall Evan. 3909 ORANGE PL, STE 3200 44122 #021-05-1975 L1976 ORS *020 †40

MARKS, Jeffrey Michael. 3909 ORANGE PL, STE 4300 44122 #024-07-1987 L1990 GS *020 †85

MARKS, Kenneth Edward. 26900 CEDAR RD 44122 #038-06-1970 L1972 ORS *020 †40

MARS, Harold. 3609 PARK EAST DR STE 517 44122 #067-01-1960 L1971 N *020

MASSIEN, Scott Louis. 3909 ORANGE PL, UHHS CHAGRIN HGHLDS MED CT 44122 #038-06-2001 L2002 IM *020 †20

MC CLELLAND, Chas Quinn. ■ 44122 #038-06-1946 L1946 PD OS *071 †55

MC CRACKEN, Gaylee. 3909 ORANGE PL, STE 2300 44122 #038-06-1999 L1999 IM *020

MC ELROY, Tara Maria. 26900 CEDAR RD, CLEVELAND CLINIC FOUNDATIO 44122 #038-44-1999 L1999 OBG *020 †30

MENDLOVIC, Daniel Bernard. 3733 PARK EAST DR, STE 105 44122 #038-40-1986 L1988 END DIA *020 †20

MICHEL, Beno. 23200 CHAGRIN BLVD STE 350, COMMERCE PARK FIVE 44122 #869-04-1962 L1969 D OS *020 †15

MICHELOW, Bryan Jos. 3733 PARK EAST DR, STE 107 44122 #836-01-1979 L1991 PS CS *020 †65

MILLER, Darryl. 26900 CEDAR RD, STE 18N 44122 #836-02-1994 L1999 CD *020 †20

MILLINER, Lynn Helen. ■ 44122 #038-06-1999 L1999 PD *020 †55

MILLSTEIN, Michael Edward. 25101 CHAGRIN BLVD, SIGNATURE SQUARE 44122 #041-01-1986 L1988 OPH *020 †35

MILNER, Louise Dennis. 25875 SCIENCE PARK DR, AC116 44122 #038-06-2001 L2001 DR *020 †80

MOORE, Michael E. 26900 CEDAR RD 44122 #033-06-1980 L1990 ORS GS *020 †40

MOOSALLY, Allison Jo. 26900 CEDAR RD, STE 320 44122 #041-15-2002 L2002 D *012 †15

MOSKOWITZ, Roland Wallace. 3609 PARK EAST DR STE 307N 44122 #041-13-1953 L1962 RHU IM *050 †20

MUISE, Kevin Lewis. 26900 CEDAR RD, STE 210 44122 #024-05-1986 L1989 OBG *020 †30

NASRALLAH, Mona Phillipe. ■ 44122 #605-01-1995 L2000 MPD *020 †20,55

NATHAN, Erika Ann. 24200 CHAGRIN BLVD 44122 #038-43-1995 L1996 P *020 †75

NATHAN, Jennifer Eileen. ■ 44122 #038-43-2004 L2004 DR *012

NEGRON, Larissa Rosana. ■ 44122 #042-01-2004 L2007 PD *020 †55

NUDELMAN, Harry. ■ 44122 #038-06-1956 L1956 PD *072 †55

OKAFOR, Emmanuel C. 23250 CHAGRIN BLVD STE 110 44122 #690-04-1978 L1987 GE IM *020 †20

PALLAS, James. 23230 CHAGRIN BLVD STE 350 44122 #038-41-1990 L1992 P *020 †75

PANDYA, Chirag Maheshbhai. ■ 44122 #496-41-2003 L2004 PCC *012 †20

PARKER, Lydia Urbassik. 3733 PARK EAST DR, STE 104 44122 #038-06-1988 L1989 D *020 †15

PATEL, Nilesh Prahlad. ■ 44122 #036-05-2001 L2007 PCP *100 †50

PATEL, Preethi. ■ 44122 #495-37-2002 L2006 IM *100 †20

PATEL, Priti Bachubhai. 23625 COMMERCE PARK # 204, FRANKEL SEIDELMANN RAD GRP 44122 #473-01-2001 L2006 DR *020 †80

PATEL, Sanjiv Shashikawt. ■ 44122 #917-23-1990 L1996 IM *020 †20

PATTERSON, James A. 25875 SCIENCE PARK DR, AC 116 44122 #035-06-1969 L1970 R *062 †20

PERSKY, James Michael. 3609 PARK EAST DR, STE 104 44122 #038-06-1983 L1985 VS GS *020 †85

PESKIN, Barry David. 26900 CEDAR RD, STE 200S 44122 #836-01-1984 L1990 OBG *020 †30

PESKIN, Julian Leon. 26900 CEDAR RD STE 200S, CLEVELAND OB/GYN SPECIALTI 44122 #836-01-1984 L1990 OBG *020 †30

PETER-WOHL, Sigal. 4020 HEMLOCK CIR 44122 #550-03-1996 L1998 PD *020 †55

PETROFF, Nina. 23250 CHAGRIN BLVD, STE 350 44122 #913-06-1978 L1984 D PTH *020 †50,15

PICKLOW, Francis Edward. 25003 DUFFIELD RD 44122 #038-40-1957 L1957 OM LM *020

PODL, Tod Roger. 26900 CEDAR RD, STE 22N 44122 #038-06-1996 L1997 FM *020 †18

POLIAKOVA, Marina. ■ 44122 #913-09-1979 L1999 IM *020 †20

POLLACK, Michael J. ■ 44122 #035-46-2001 L2001 GE *100

POPE, Thomas Lee. 23625 COMMERCE PARK, STE 204 44122 #036-01-1978 L2005 DR R *020 †80

POTASH, Howard. 3355 RICHMOND RD, STE 221 44122 #041-09-1983 L1988 R *062 †80

POWELL, Emilia Luisa. 24755 CHAGRIN BLVD, STE 235 44122 #038-06-1988 L1989 P *074 †75

QUINTINI, Cristiano. ■ 44122 #561-01-1999 L2006 GS TTS *020

RABBAT, Mark George. ■ 44122 #025-12-2005 L2005 IM *012

RAJAGOPALAN, Sudha. ■ 44122 #495-04-1997 L2000 PAN *020 †05

RAMOS-ESTEBAN, Jerome Cha. ■ 44122 #649-14-2000 L2006 OPH *020

RANJAN, Rakesh. 3690 ORANGE PL 44122 #495-54-1986 L1992 P *020 †75

RAO, Revati Arjun. ■ 44122 #422-01-1997 L2005 IM *020

RAO, Sudhakar Surapaneni. 26900 CEDAR RD, STE 200S 44122 #038-06-1992 L1993 OBG *020 †30

REEP, Peggy J. 23625 COMMERCE PARK, STE 204 44122 #037-01-1989 L1999 DR *020 †80

REMZI, Feza Huseyin. 26900 CEDAR RD 44122 #902-05-1989 L1995 CRS GS *020 †85,10

RESNICK, Lee Aaron. 3909 ORANGE PL 44122 #038-06-1997 L1999 FM *020 †18

REYES, Bettina Grace. 3690 ORANGE PL, STE 100 44122 #038-43-1990 L1993 PD *020 †55

RICHARDSON, Robert Frank. 4110 WARRENSVILLE CENTR RD 44122 #038-06-1994 L1995 N *020 †75

RITCHEY, Arthur Francis. ■ 44122 #038-41-1943 L1944 CHP PTH *072

RIZK, Magdi Shafik. 3619 PARK EAST DR STE 313, PARKWAY MEDICAL BLDG #313 44122 #915-04-1960 L1974 P PFP *020 †75

ROCCO, Michael Benj. 26900 CEDAR RD, BEACHWOOD CARDIOLOGY 44122 #036-07-1980 L1988 CD IM *020 †20

ROCKER, Laura Hannah. 3733 PARK EAST DR, CONSULTANTS 44122 #038-40-1980 L1991 CHP P *020 †15

RODA, James Jos. 3355 RICHMOND RD 44122 #038-40-1957 L1957 R *071 †80

RODRIGUEZ, Barbara M. 21625 CHAGRIN BLVD, STE 200 44122 #038-06-1980 L1983 P *020 †75

ROSEN, Kathleen Routier. ■ 44122 #051-07-1980 L2006 AN CCM *075 †05

ROSENBERG, Jennifer T. 26900 CEDAR RD, STE 200 44122 #038-06-1987 L1989 PD *020 †75

ROSENBLATT, Ellen A. ■ 44122 #038-06-1987 L1991 P *020

ROSENTHAL, Alan Howard. 3690 ORANGE PL, STE 100 44122 #038-06-1983 L1985 PD PSM *020 †55

ROSS, Melvin B. 28001 CHAGRIN BLVD, MELVIN B ROSS INC 44122 #038-06-1953 L1953 P *075 †75

ROSSIO, Robert James. 25201 CHAGRIN BLVD STE 160, BEACHWOOD, LLC 44122 #038-40-1981 L1983 PS GS *020 †65,85

RUGGIERO-DELLITURRI, M. ■ 44122 #035-08-1990 L2006 DR *020 †80

RUKIN, Deborah Jeanne. ■ 44122 #024-07-1996 L1997 CHN *020

RUSSELL, Evan Todd. ■ 44122 #038-41-2007 L2007 IM *012

SAKS, John Benj. 26900 CEDAR RD 44122 #038-40-1978 L1978 DR *020 †80

SALGADO, Christopher John. ■ 44122 #010-02-1995 L2008 PS *020 †65

SANDHU, Madhupal Kaur. ■ 44122 #496-21-2002 L2007 AN *012

SANDHU, Satinderpal Kaur. 6 CHELSEA CT, METROHEALTH MEDICAL CENTER 44122 #033-05-1988 L1997 IMG IM *020 †20

SANDHU, Satnam Singh. 4200 WARRENSVILLE CENTR RD, RR 210 44122 #495-03-1985 L1991 NEP IM *020 †20

SANTAMARIA, Adrian A. ■ 44122 #048-14-2003 L2007 SME *012

SARANGI, Premjit. ■ 44122 #495-98-1996 L2007 AN *100

SAYEGH, Touhama. 3909 ORANGE PL, STE 2400 44122 #875-01-1979 L1988 IM *020 †20

SAZGARI, Reza Seid. 23625 COMMERCE PARK 44122 #025-07-1999 L2007 DR *100 †80

SCHARF, Victor. ■ 44122 #038-06-1954 L1954 CRS GS *071 †85,10

SCHNUR, Gary Arnold. 26900 CEDAR RD 44122 #035-03-1979 L1988 ON HEM *020 †20

SCHUBACH, Margaret B. ■ 44122 #957-03-1952 L1965 PD *020 †55

SCOTT, Cary Chas. 4110 WARRENSVILL CNTR RD R, SOUTH POINTE HOSPITAL - ER 44122 #038-40-1983 L1986 GS *020

SEITZ, William Henry, Jr. 26900 CEDAR RD, STE 305 44122 #035-01-1979 L1985 ORS HS *020 †40

SEQUEIRA, Thomas M. 3609 PARK EAST DR, STE 114 44122 #495-52-1970 L1976 CD IM *020 †20

SHAARAOUI, Mustaphasahim. 3715 WARRENSVIL CNTR RD #5 44122 #605-01-1999 L2000 IM *020

SHAH, Manjula A. 3355 RICHMOND RD, STE 225 44122 #495-22-1961 L1972 P *020 †75

SHARMA, Mithlesh Chandra. 3401 ENTERPRISE PKWY, RETINA ASSOCIATES OF 44122 #495-49-1982 L2004 OPH *020 †35

SHEKAR, Raja. 3609 PARK EAST DR STE 207 44122 #495-09-1969 L1982 ID IM *020 †20

SHERMAN, Alla. 3609 PARK EAST DR STE 418 44122 #913-15-1981 L1995 PD *020 †55

SHOAG, Mark Benj. ■ 44122 #008-01-1981 L1983 IM *020 †20

SIDDIQUI, Faisalanis. ■ 44122 #704-02-1991 AN *100

SIOSON, Eulogio Rosario. 4200 WARRENSVILLE CENTR RD, BLDG A 44122 #748-07-1963 L1973 IM IMG *030 †20

SOBEL, Marvin Howard. 26000 GEORGE ZEIGER DR 44122 #038-40-1948 L1948 GP *071

SOLOMON, Ellen Renee. ■ 44122 #050-02-2007 L2007 OBG *012

STARKS, David Charles. ■ 44122 #025-01-2005 L2005 OBG *012

STAUFFER, Anthony Edward. ■ 44122 #060-01-1976 L2004 DR *020 †80

STEARNS, Eliz Lambert. 24300 CHAGRIN BLVD, STE 109 44122 #035-01-1942 L1949 CHP *071

STEINBERG, Laura Frances. 23210 CHAGRIN BLVD STE 400, NORTHEAST OHIO HEALTH SVCS 44122 #038-06-2001 L2001 P PYA *020 †75 ‡

STEPHENSON, Janette Marie. 3909 ORANGE PL STE 4500 44122 #038-06-1994 L1998 OBG *020 †30

STOCKFISH, Hyman Meyer. 3609 PARK EAST DR 44122 #038-40-1957 L1957 IM *020 †20

STULTZ, Todd Walker. 26900 CEDAR RD 44122 #038-44-1996 L1998 DR RNR *020 †80

SYKORA, Glenn Fredric. 3355 RICHMOND RD STE 221, DRS HILL & THOMAS CO. 44122 #041-12-1963 L1966 R RNR *020 †80

TAVILL, Anthony Sydney. 26900 CEDAR RD, STE 305S 44122 #917-08-1960 L1976 GE *020

TAXMAN, Thomas Louis. 3609 PARK EAST DR STE 210 44122 #020-05-1980 L1984 GE PD *020 †55

TECUTA, Mihaela Mirela. 27060 CEDAR RD # 509 BLD 44122 #781-01-1996 L2005 AN *100

TESTON, Lois Jane. 3909 ORANGE PL, STE 1100 44122 #038-06-1996 L1997 HO *020 †20

THIGPEN, Yolanda Annette. 24755 CHAGRIN BLVD, STE 345 44122 #047-07-1991 L1995 OBG *020

THOMPSON, George Harman. 3909 ORANGE PL, STE 3200 44122 #039-01-1970 L1978 PDS ORS *020 †40

THYNNE, Arthur Mervyn. 3355 RICHMOND RD 44122 #917-28-1969 L1978 **R** *071 †80

TOBIAS, Samuel. 26900 CEDAR RD 44122 #649-01-1990 L2001 *020

TRANGLE, Kevin Larry. 3609 PARK EAST DR, STE 202N 44122 #026-04-1978 L1984 OM IM *020 †20,70

TSE-XIE, William Wei-Ning. ■ 44122 #243-21-1986 L2004 **ON** *020 †20

TUNG, Rebecca Clare. 26900 CEDAR RD 44122 #016-06-1996 L2000 **D** *020 †15

VALLABHANENI, Rajendra. ■ 44122 #495-99-1990 L2001 **IM CD** *020 †20

VARMA, Kalpana. ■ 44122 #495-47-1980 L2000 **AN** *020 †05

VARNER, Arthur Emmet. 23250 MERCANTILE RD, ALLERGY DIAGNOSTICS 44122 #038-40-1992 L1993 **AI IM** *020 †20,03 ‡

VICTOROFF, Brian Nicholas. 3909 ORANGE PL, UNIVERSITY CHAGRIN HIGHLAN 44122 #038-06-1986 L1986 **ORS OSM** *020 †40

VILLANUEVA, Ronald O. 3695 GREEN RD 44122 #748-01-1959 L1971 **GS GP** *020

VILLEGAS-VILLANUEVA, R. 4200 WARRENSVILLE CENTR RD, STE 380 44122 #748-01-1962 L1971 **PD P** *062 †55

VIZY, Barbara Bates. 3690 ORANGE PL STE 230 44122 #038-40-1991 L1992 **FM** *020 †18

WALLER, Todd Steven. 4200 WARRENSVILLE CENTR RD, STE 271 44122 #005-14-1977 L1986 **HNS AI** *020 †45

WANG, Huijian. ■ 44122 #243-16-1994 L2007 **ICE CD** *020 †20

WARREN, Van Duren. 3909 ORANGE PL STE 3, UNIV HOSPITALS HEALTH SYST 44122 #038-40-1985 L1990 **IM RHU** *020 †20

WEBB, Charles Garrick. 4200 WARRENSVILLE CENTR RD, WEBB MED STE 390 BLDG A 44122 #005-06-1974 L1995 **FM OM** *020

WEIDENTHAL, Daniel Tilles. 25700 SCIENCE PARK DR, STE 190 44122 #038-06-1958 L1958 **OPH** *020 †35

WEINBERGER, Richard Fred. 3690 ORANGE PL, STE 230 44122 #012-05-1981 L1983 **FM IMG** *020 †18

WEISS, Phillip Herman. 26900 CEDAR RD, STE 125 44122 #038-06-1967 L1967 **R NM** *071 †28,80

WEXBERG, Steven Sanford. 26900 CEDAR RD 44122 #038-06-1981 L1982 **PD** *020 †55

WHITE, Eugene Albert. 3355 RICHMOND RD 44122 #038-06-1965 L1966 **R RNR** *071 †80

WHITE, Judith A. 26900 CEDAR RD, STE 315S 44122 #024-16-1989 L2003 **OTO** *020 †45

WIEDER, Devorah Rydzinski. ■ 44122 #041-01-2005 L2005 **OBG** *042

WILKES, Gary Mason. 23811 CHAGRIN BLVD STE 170 44122 #038-41-1981 L1983 **P** *020

WOLF, Brooke Sue Matthews. 3690 ORANGE PL STE 430, NORTH COAST MENTAL HEALTH 44122 #041-13-1972 L1976 **P** *040 †75

WOLF, Sanford Robert. 23210 CHAGRIN BLVD STE 300, ONE COMMERCE PARK 44122 #025-01-1962 L1988 **P** *020 †75

WOLFE, Keith Jeremy. ■ 44122 #038-41-2006 L2007 **DR** *012

WOLINSKY, Emanuel. ■ 44122 #035-20-1941 L1963 **ID MM** *071

WU, James Shihkong. 26900 CEDAR RD 44122 #028-02-1986 L1994 **CRS** *020 †85,10

WU, Willis Michael. ■ 44122 #023-01-2004 L2007 **IM** *012 †20

YASINOW, Eric Martin. 3909 ORANGE PL, STE 2400 44122 #038-06-1983 L1984 **IM** *020 †20

YETMAN, Randall J. 26900 CEDAR RD 44122 #011-02-1975 L1983 **PS HS** *020 †65

YOKIEL, Jerome Bernard. 3755 ORANGE PL, STE 103 44122 #038-45-1988 L1989 **AN PME** *020 †05

ZEISSLER, Renate Hare. ■ 44122 #407-06-1954 L1964 **PM** *071 †60

ZERVOS, Athanasios. ■ 44122 #418-01-1993 L1994 **OPH** *020 †35

ZETZER, Stuart Irwin. 3619 PARK EAST DR, STE 316 44122 #038-06-1972 L1972 **P** *020

ZIMMERMAN, Robert James. ■ 44122 #038-41-1945 L1945 **EM** *071

ZOBER, Jerry Martin. 29425 CHAGRIN BLVD, STE 301 44122 #030-06-1974 L1975 **P** *020 †75

BEAVERCREEK — GREENE

AFANEH, Zuhair. ■ 45434 #575-02-1993 L2006 **IM** *020 †20

AMISOLA, Rogelio Virgilio. 2322 LAKEVIEW DR, PRIMED PHYSICIANS 45431 #748-10-1992 L2004 **ADL** *012

ASKEW, Gail Tari. 3359 KEMP RD, STE 250B 45431 #038-45-1989 L1990 **FM** *020 †18

BEAN, Stacey B. ■ 45431 #045-01-1999 L2003 **FM** *020 †18

BEECHY, Christopher Rober. ■ 45431 #038-45-2007 L2007 **GS** *012

BELISLE, Adelle Lynn. ■ 45431 #050-02-2001 L2001 **ORS** *020

BJORNSTAD, Bryan. 3359 KEMP RD, STE 230 45431 #038-41-1997 L2007 **CN** *020 †75

BROCKMAN, Matthew Robert. ■ 45431 #016-06-2006 *012

BUCHHOLZ, Ryan Matthew. 3606 KING HENRY DR 45431 #038-45-2004 L2004 **MPD** *012

BULLINGER, Katie Leigh. ■ 45431 #038-45-2008 *012

CHAKRABARTI, Anindita. ■ 45431 #038-45-2008 *012

CURTIS, Bryan Christopher. ■ 45431 #023-12-2003 L2003 **GS** *012

DESAI, Usha Priyakant. 38 WOODCROFT TRL, XENIA PATHOLOGY LABORATORY 45430 #495-22-1969 L1983 **PTH** *050

DILLON, Richard Terrence. 3617 DAYTON XENIA RD, PED CARDIO OF DAYTON INC 45432 #024-07-1973 L1976 **PDC PD** *020 †55

DINES, Megan. ■ 45431 #038-45-2008 *012

DOAK, Scott Alan. 220 DANERN DR 45430 #038-40-1991 L1992 **EM** *020 †16

EDWARDS, Debra Gale. ■ 45434 #055-02-2006 L2006 **EM** *012

ENGEL, Michael Edward. 1244 MEADOW BRIDGE DR, STE 100 45434 #038-41-1992 L1995 **FM** *020 †18

ETTINGER, David Jay. 3359 KEMP RD, STE 200 45431 #550-02-1981 L1993 **PS HS** *020 †65

FORD, Robert Marshall. ■ 45430 #005-12-2007 L2007 **TY** *012

GALVIN, Susan Catherine. 3359 KEMP RD STE 250B, FAMILY PRACTICE PHYSICIAN 45431 #035-03-1998 L2007 **FM** *020 †18

GELFORD, Krista Glynne. 2476 DAYTON XENIA RD 45434 #005-12-1985 L1990 **PD** *020 †55

GLOWIENKA, Paul R. 2358 LAKEVIEW DR, STE A 45431 #023-12-1983 L2002 **END** *020 †20

GREEN, Reginique Leonetta. 3359 KEMP RD 45431 #030-06-1994 L1998 **FM** *020 †18

HAMILTON, Joshua A. ■ 45431 #048-16-2008 *012

HORNBACK, William Leslie. ■ 45431 #038-02-2005 L2005 **GS** *012

HORTON, Lauren Kyle. ■ 45431 #038-45-2008 *012

HUMPHREY, Stephen Strong. 2145 N FAIRFIELD RD STE B 45431 #008-01-1978 L1983 **U GS** *020 †95

JEFFERS, Amy Marie. ■ 45431 #038-45-2008 *012

JONAS, Arthur Patrick. 2633 COMMONS BLVD, FAMILY HEALTH CONNECTIONS, 45431 #038-40-1976 L1978 **FM** *020 †18

KALNINS, Aris Gotholds. ■ 45431 #038-45-2008 *012

KIM, Tony S. ■ 45434 #023-12-1999 L2001 **FM AM** *020 †18

KING, Erin E. 3588 OLD OAKS DR 45431 #038-45-2008 *012

KIROVSKI, Emil. 3371 KEMP RD, GMH URGENT CARE 45431 #957-04-1984 L1998 **IM** *020 †20

LAUB, James L. 2510 COMMONS BLVD, BEAVERCREEK HEALTH CTR STE 45431 #016-76-1985, ▲ L2004 **OMM AM** *020 †20

LIAUGMINAS, Alexander. ■ 45434 #038-43-2008 *012

LINK, Emily Elizabeth. ■ 45431 #038-06-2008 *012

MALL, Ryan Howard. ■ 45431 #495-65-1997 L2000 **IM** *020 †20

MEZOFF, Ethan Andrew. ■ 45431 #038-45-2008 *012

MIDDLETON, Molly C. ■ 45430 #038-41-2007 L2007 **FP** *012

NISENOFF, Carolina Debora. ■ 45431 #035-15-2003 L2004 **P** *012

OWEN, Rory G. PO BOX 340372 45434 #048-12-1991 L1993 **GPM** *020 †70,18

PANDYA, Himani Som. ■ 45431 #038-45-2008 *012

PAPAIOANNOU, Glen. 2282 BLUEWING DR 45431 #005-12-2001 L2002 **HO** *012 †20

PENCE, Jack Reese, II. 2145 N FAIRFIELD RD STE B, SURGEONS, INC 45431 #038-06-1976 L1979 **U** *020 †95

PESHKE, Julia Denise. ■ 45431 #038-45-2008 *012

PINA, Desiderio. 2542 KING CHARLES ST, STE D 45431 #308-13-1992 L2003 **GP NUP** *020 †75,03,55 ‡

QUIGLEY, Patrick Robert. 2950 WHITE WATER CT, P O BOX 340605 45431 #019-02-1994 L1996 **OM GPM** *020 †70

RAJ KRISHNAMURTHY, Vidya. ■ 45431 #496-20-2003 L2006 **IM** *012

RAMIREZ, Peter Armando. 3121 EVELYN DR, STE 110 45434 #005-14-1987 L1989 **P** *020 †75 ‡

RAWLINS, Michael Logan. ■ 45431 #051-07-2006 L2006 **GS** *012

REDHU, Richa. ■ 45431 #495-55-2002 L2005 **IM** *012

REES, Andrew Gregory. ■ 45431 #023-12-2005 L2005 **P** *012

RINGLE, Mark Allison. 1244 MEADOW BRIDGE DR, STE 100 45434 #038-40-1984 L1986 **FM** *020 †18

RINI, Elizabeth Ann. ■ 45431 #016-43-2007 L2007 **IM** *012

SCHWARZ, Eric Randel. ■ 45431 #025-07-1984 L1989 **DR** *020 †20

SENS, Beth Ann. ■ 45431 #038-45-2007 **FP** *012

SIEBUHR, Karl Frank. ■ 45431 #038-45-2004 L2004 **ORS** *012

SIKORA, Jeremy Michael. ■ 45434 #038-44-2004 L2004 **PD** *020 †55

STULL, Adrian Kenneth. ■ 45434 #023-12-2000 L2005 **EM** *012

SUROWIEC, Richard Joseph. ■ 45434 #038-34-2006 L2006 **MPD** *012

TAXTER, Alysha Jo. ■ 45431 #038-45-2008 *012

THOMAS, James Joseph. 2322 LAKEVIEW DR 45431 #023-12-1996 L2007 **FM** *020 †18

TILLE, Katherine Suzanne. ■ 45431 #028-34-2005 L2005 **PD** *012

TOWERS, Geoffrey David. ■ 45434 #049-01-1995 L2004 **OBG** *020 †30

VANBUREN, Mindy Marie. ■ 45431 #038-45-2008 *012

WAITE, Christina G. 722 N FAIRFIELD RD STE 200 45434 #038-45-1999 L2000 **P** *020 †75

WALBROEHL, Gordon S. 3438 OHARA DR 45434 #033-05-1972 L1978 **FM** *040 †18

WARDDEMO, Pamela Phyllis. ■ 45434 #046-01-2008 *012

WEHRI, Katherine Ann. ■ 45431 #038-45-2008 *012

WEISER, Jeffrey Wm. ■ 45434 #055-01-1991 L1993 **CHP P** *020 †75

WINGATE, Katherine H. 3140 DAYTON XENIA RD, STE C 45434 #038-45-1991 L1993 **PD** *020 †55

WIRK, M Alam. 2620 LANTZ RD 45434 #704-01-1971 L1976 **R** *071 †80

YUAN-LING, Yu Ru. 1337 HANES RD 45434 #242-26-1946 L1957 **PD** *071 †55

ZACHARIAS, Dawn Michele. 3121 EVELYN DR, STE 100 45434 #038-43-1999 L1999 **AI IM** *020 †20,03

BEDFORD — CUYAHOGA

ABBASS, Julia Milman. 25580 AURORA RD 44146 #038-06-1994 L1996 **DR** *020 †80

ABDEL-AZIZ, Khaled A. 6 COLUMBUS ST 44146 #915-04-1983 L1996 **IM** *020

ALEXANDER-COOK, Lydia. 19999 ROCKSIDE RD 44146 #035-15-1984 L1986 **PD** *020 †55

ALI, Syed Jaffer. 12 COLUMBUS ST 44146 #495-21-1964 L1974 **TS GP** *020 †85

ASLANIAN, Erika Andre. 44 BLAINE AVE 44146 #913-38-1961 L1988 **AN** *071

AZEM, Haitham Mouaid. 88 CENTER RD 44146 #875-01-1979 L1988 **IM** *020 †20

BAFNA, Mohanlal. 25 TARBELL AVE 44146 #495-30-1960 L1971 **IM** *020 †20

BERNER, Jerome J. 7730 FIRST PL 44146 #041-02-1952 L1960 **PTH** *071 †50

BINSTOCK, Martine. 19999 ROCKSIDE RD 44146 #396-32-1985 L1995 **IM** *020 †20

BLAIR, Jean Elaine. 7730 FIRST PL, STE A 44146 #038-44-2002 L2002 **PTH** *100 †50

BRISKIN, Toby Judith. 19999 ROCKSIDE RD 44146 #041-09-1976 L1979 **IM** *020 †20

BURGIN, Diane Carol. 22750 ROCKSIDE RD, UNIVERSITY PREMIER PEDIATR 44146 #038-06-1980 L1985 **PD** *020 †55

CHENG, Wanli. 7730 FIRST PL, STE A 44146 #243-52-1985 L2000 **PTH** *100

COLLANTES, Virgilio T. 44 BLAINE AVE 44146 #748-01-1952 L1964 **IM** *071

CRIHFIELD, Kimberly Sue. 22750 ROCKSIDE RD 44146 #038-40-1994 L1999 **IM** *020 †20

DAVIS, Jacqueline Karen. 44 BLAINE AVE, BEDFORD MEDICAL CENTER 44146 #032-01-1993 L2000 **AN** *020

DAWOUD, Amir Saleeb. 44 BLAINE AVE, U.H.H.S. BEDFORD MED CENTE 44146 #915-03-1981 L1994 **APM** *020 †05

DELAHAY, Joan Esther. 19999 ROCKSIDE RD 44146 #005-11-1973 L1991 **PD** *020 †55

DINES, Philipp. 44 BLAINE AVE 44146 #038-06-1984 L1985 **P PYG** *020 †75

FEDAK, Michael John. 19999 ROCKSIDE RD 44146 #038-34-1983 L1986 **PD** *020 †55

FRANCESCHINI, Lelio G. 44 BLAINE AVE 44146 #561-17-1956 L1964 **IM CD** *071

GASCOIGNE, George B. 22750 ROCKSIDE RD STE 210 44146 #038-41-1973 L1995 **PD EM** *020 †55

GEOGHEGAN, Thomas G. ■ 44146 #035-06-1953 L1956 **GP** *071

GRAMLICH, Terry Lee. 7730 FIRST PL, STE A 44146 #055-01-1986 L1990 **PTH** *020 †75

GRIMES, Steven Lee. 44 BLAINE AVE, EMERGENCY DEPT. 44146 #007-02-1992 L1994 **IM** *020 †20

GROSSMAN, Dennis. 88 CENTER RD, STE 280 44146 #038-06-1983 L1987 **IM** *020 †20

HADDAD, Ghassan Fares. 88 CENTER RD, STE 130 44146 #605-01-1985 L2001 **IM** *020 †20

HILAL, Marwan Antoine. 88 CENTER RD STE 250 44146 #875-01-1979 L1986 **IM EM** *020 †20

HOLLANDSWORTH, Kimberly. 7730 FIRST PL, STE A 44146 #055-01-1991 L1995 **D DMP** *020 †15

KATZIN, William Effron. 7730 FIRST PL, STE A 44146 #038-06-1983 L1983 **ATP CLP** *020 †50

KOLODNY, Scott William. 44 BLAINE AVE 44146 #048-14-1996 L1999 **DR** *020

LENOX, Madeleine Marie. 22750 ROCKSIDE RD, UNIVERSITY MEDNET 44146 #033-06-1988 L1993 **OTO** *020 †45

LEVY, Matthew Eric. 50 BLAINE AVE, STE 2300 44146 #038-06-1990 L1994 **ORS** *020 †40

LU, Ghai Chun. 22750 ROCKSIDE RD, MEDICINE 44146 #495-13-1986 L1993 **IM** *020 †20
LUCZEK, Philomena E I. 88 CENTER RD, STE 340 44146 #165-04-1963 L1965 **P** *071 †75
MARK, Matthew Michael. 50 BLAINE AVE STE 2200 44146 #038-44-1997 L1998 **FM** *020 †18
MC PHERSON, Geo Leverne. 19999 ROCKSIDE RD 44146 #025-01-1973 L1976 **PD** *020 †55
MITCHELL, Wendy Mae. ■ 44146 #016-11-2005 L2005 **AN** *012
MOSS, Kenneth Steven. 88 CENTER RD, STE 100 44146 #028-02-1976 L1977
  AN PME *020 †05
MOUFAWAD, Sami Elias. 50 BLAINE AVE STE 2300, BEDFORD MEDICAL CTR 44146
  #605-03-1994 L2000 **APM PM** *020 †60
MUELLER, Henry Martin. 44 BLAINE AVE 44146 #035-09-1964 L1988 **OBG** *020 †30
OBI, Gabriel Nnaemeka. 19999 ROCKSIDE RD 44146 #038-43-1989 L1990 **IM** *020 †20
PATEL, Kanaiyalal M. 44 BLAINE AVE 44146 #495-23-1964 L1977 **PTH** *030 †50
PATIL, Ashok Sitaram. 5311 NORTHFIELD RD 44146 #495-20-1971 1986 **OM IM** *020 †70
PETRAS, Robert Edward. 7730 FIRST PL STE A 44146 #038-40-1978 L1981 **PTH** *020 †50
PILLAI, Latha Raj. 22750 ROCKSIDE RD, MEDICINE 44146 #495-01-1979 L1988 **IM** *020 †20
PIZARRO, Mariano Q. 44 BLAINE AVE 44146 #748-01-1957 L1968 **GP IM** *020
ROTH, Mark Allan. 19999 ROCKSIDE RD 44146 #038-40-1977 L1978 **IM** *020 †20
SALAMON, Robert John. 50 BLAINE AVE 44146 #038-06-1978 L1979 **PS** *020 †65
SCHAFFER, Suzanne. 22750 ROCKSIDE RD, MEDICINE 44146 #016-02-1981 L1987 **IM** *020 †20
SKUGOR, Blazenka. 22750 ROCKSIDE RD, MEDICINE 44146 #957-01-1988 L2004 **IM** *100 †20
SONG, Grace. 50 BLAINE AVE STE 2200 44146 #038-44-2000 L2000 **FM** *020 †18
SUKOL, Roxanne Breines. 22750 ROCKSIDE RD, MEDICINE 44146 #038-06-1995 L1996
  IM *020 †20
THAKER, Niranjana Shah. 88 CENTER RD STE 250 44146 #495-22-1964 L1978 **OBG** *020 †30
TINIO, Joaquin Fernando. 19999 ROCKSIDE RD 44146 #035-45-1989 L1995 **IM** *020 †20
TIRGAN, Mohammad Ali. 88 CENTER RD STE 210 44146 #517-01-1971 1986
  ON HEM *020 †20
TUMA, Augustine Lavelle. 88 CENTER RD STE # 200 44146 #690-02-1981 L1998 **IM** *020 †20
VESOULIS, Zissis. 7730 FIRST PL, STE A 44146 #038-43-1980 L1991 **PTH PCP** *062 †50
VIBHAKAR, Nilla S. 19999 ROCKSIDE RD 44146 #495-17-1974 L1983 **PD** *020 †55

BELLAIRE – BELMONT

ANGHIE, A C G A. 3200 BELMONT ST, HEALTH GUARD 43906 #220-01-1967 L1975
  IM PUD *020 †20
BAILER, William J. 4697 HARRISON ST 43906 #038-45-1991 L1996 **GS** *020 †85
BHULLAR, Satinder Singh. 3000 GUERNSEY ST, BELMONT COMMUNITY HEALTH C 43906
  #495-29-1966 L1972 **GP** *020 †18
BRAUTIGAN, Frederick B. 4697 HARRISON ST 43906 #055-02-1995 L1999 **FM EM** *020 †18
CANDARI, Justito M. 57620 48TH ST, BELLVIEW HGTS 43906 #748-10-1974 L1984 **AN** *020
GONZALES, Bienvenido L. 4697 HARRISON ST, EMERGENCY DEPARTMENT 43906
  #748-11-1969 L1974 **IM EM** *020 †20
HECETA, Wilmer Gao-Ay. 4697 HARRISON ST 43906 #748-10-1961 L1974 **GS TS** *020 †85,90
JEAN, Chit-Kui. 3000 GUERNSEY ST 43906 #385-03-1959 L1966 **PD PDA** *020 †20
MUSUNURI, Maheshwar R. 3000 GUERNSEY ST, BELMONT COMMUNITY HLTH CEN 43906
  #495-65-1980 L1996 **IM** *020 †20
NEPOMUCENO, Ruben A. 4697 HARRISON ST 43906 #748-01-1959 L1970 **FM GP** *020 ‡
PATEL, Chaganlal N. 3000 GUERNSEY ST 43906 #495-21-1963 L1973 **FM EM** *020 †18
SOHN, Keith Yong. 4697 HARRISON ST 43906 #583-02-1961 L1971 **PD** *071 †55
STEINBERG, Michael Lewis. 3000 GUERNSEY ST 43906 #561-17-1983 L1990
  AI PD *020 †55,03
SUTANDI, Harlan. 4697 HARRISON ST 43906 #506-01-1964 L1976 **OBG** *020 †30
WEIDMAN, Paul Daniel. 3000 GUERNSEY ST, STE 27 43906 #055-01-2001 L2004 **FM** *020 †18
WILLIAMS, Joseph Lewis. 3000 GUERNSEY ST 43906 #035-45-1956 L1960 **GP** *020 †18

BELLBROOK – GREENE

ATIQ, Rafay. 3170 MILL POND DR 45305 #704-02-1997 L2002 **P** *020 †75 ‡
BUCK, Nathan S.. ■ 45305 #038-45-2008 *012
BUCKREUS, James Wm. 4403 STATE ROUTE 725, STE A 45305 #038-41-1979 L1980
  OBG *020 †30
CHHUON, Pat. ■ 45305 #003-01-2005 L2005 **EM** *012
FABER, Jason Richard. ■ 45305 #038-45-2008 *012
FOSTER, James Eugene, Jr. 4403 W FRANKLIN ST, STE D 45305 #038-43-1991 1992
  FM *020 †18
GOLDENBERG, Kim. 1078 PAXON DR 45305 #035-03-1979 L1981 **IM** *030 †20
HEINEMEYER FOSTER, Lisa K. 4403 W FRANKLIN ST, STE D 45305 #038-43-1990 L1992
  FM *020 †18
HEMMELGARN, Lori Marie. 4403 STATE ROUTE 725, STE A 45305 #038-41-1989 L1990
  OBG *020 †30
JAYAKUMAR, Arun Guru. ■ 45305 #038-40-2000 **NEP** *020 †20
KOLODZIK, Joan Marie. 1108 PAXON CT 45305 #038-45-1986 L1987 **EM** *020 †16
NARTKER, John R, Jr. ■ 45305 #038-45-1982 L1983 **FM** *020 †18
REYNOLDS, Mark Edward. 4301B STATE ROUTE 725, BELLBROOK PSYCHIATRIC SVCS 45305
  #038-45-1988 L1989 **P** *020 †75
RUSSELL, Shane Todd. ■ 45305 #021-01-1998 L2005 **U** *020 †95
SCHAFFER, Mark Stephen. 2971 RISING SPRING CT 45305 #038-40-1977 L1978 **PD** *020 †55
SCHAFFRINNA, Michael Geo. ■ 45305 #040-02-1983 L2007 **ADL PD** *020
SONGER, Douglas Arthur. 4301 STATE ROUTE 725, STE B 45305 #038-41-1992 L1994
  P *020 †75

BELLEFONTAINE – LOGAN

ANDERSON, Robert Chris. 2221 TIMBER TRL 43311 #038-40-1971 L1979 **ORS** *020 †40
BICKLER-BLUTH, Michelle E. 212 IRVING AVE STE B 43311 #028-02-1987 L1991 **IM** *020 †20
BOUCHARD, Raymond David. 412 E COLUMBUS AVE 43311 #062-01-1982 L1996 **GP** *020
BRAIG, Kristen Theobald. 2211 TIMBER TRL 43311 #038-40-2000 L2000 **FM** *020 †18
COLLINS, Mark Edward. 205 E PALMER RD 43311 #038-45-1988 L1992 **UCM EM** *020
DAVIS, Robert H. 205 E PALMER RD 43311 #030-05-1977 L1979 **PTH** *020 †50
DIXON, Evan Willis. 205 E PALMER RD 43311 #038-40-1967 L1969 **CD PUD** *020
DUNN, Janet Christine. 118 DOWELL AVE 43311 #038-45-1986 L1997 **PD** *020 †55
FRANKLIN, Thomas Craig. 2221 TIMBER TRL 43311 #038-40-1974 L1975 **ORS** *020 †40

FULMER, Gregg S. 2231 TIMBER TRL, MAD RIVER MEDICAL SPECIALT 43311
  #654-01-1997 L2002 **IM** *020 †20
GOYAL, Kimmy. ■ 43311 #661-03-2007 2007 **FP** *012
GRABER, Rodney Curtis. 2220 TIMBER TRL, CARDIOLOGY ASSOCIATES OF 43311
  #038-43-1993 L1996 **CD** *020 †20
GROSS, Maria Livia. 205 E PALMER RD 43311 #781-04-1986 L2000 **IM** *020 †20
GUST, Amy Walters. ■ 43311 #038-40-2005 L2005 **FP** *012
HERFORD, Therese H. 205 E PALMER RD, DEPT OF RADIOLOGY 43311 #041-07-1975 L1976
  DR *020 †20
HODDINOTT, Boyd Clifford. 2211 TIMBER TRL 43311 #065-06-1968 L1994 **GP FSM** *020
HOOLEY, Paul E. 205 E PALMER RD 43311 #017-20-1953 L1954 **FM** *071 †18
HOOLEY, Steven Paul. 705 N MADRIVER ST 43311 #038-40-1977 L1978 **GE FM** *020 †18
HOUSER, William Arthur. 2220 TIMBER TRL, CARDIOLOGY ASSOCIATES OF 43311
  #038-40-1990 L1993 **CD** *020 †20
KIM, Bong Oh. 205 E PALMER RD 43311 #583-05-1938 L1969 **PTH GP** *071 †50
LORENZ, Frederick Stephen. 116 DOWELL AVE, AND THROAT 43311 #021-01-1980 L2004
  OTO A *020 †45
MALONE, Annette Hardy. 205 E PALMER RD, CORPORATE HEALTH SERVICES 43311
  #038-41-1980 L1983 **FM OM** *020 †18
MANN, Cheryl Ann. 205 E PALMER RD 43311 #038-45-1994 L1996 **FM** *020 †18
MEYER, Jay Edward. 205 E PALMER RD 43311 #038-40-1977 L1977 **OBG** *020 †30
MURRAY, Laura Louise. 2231 TIMBER TRL 43311 #036-01-1994 L1995 **IM** *020 †20
NARDUCCI, Audrey Ann. 114 DOWELL AVE 43311 #014-01-1986 L2007 **GS** *020 †85
O'CONNOR, John C. 2211 TIMBER TRL 43311 #038-43-1993 L1994 **FM** *020 †18
PARSONS, Herbert Lynn. 116 DOWELL AVE 43311 #021-01-1969 L1982 **GS** *020 †85 ‡
PENN, Gerald M. 205 E PALMER RD, PATHOLOGY CENTER INC. 43311 #038-40-1964 L1964
  PTH HMP *020 †50
REAL, Margaret Anne. 212 IRVING AVE, STE D 43311 #016-11-1965 L1989 **CD IM** *071 †20
SEMAAN, Hassan B. 205 E PALMER RD, BELLEFONTAINE RADIOLOGIST 43311
  #875-03-1990 L1999 **DR** *020 †80
SHIVA PRASAD, Mabbu G. 2210 TIMBER TRL, LOGAN FAM MED CTR 43311
  #495-98-1983 L1997 **FM P** *020 †75,18 ‡
STOLTZFUS, Winfred E. 2231 TIMBER TRL 43311 #034-01-1984 L1993 **IM** *020 †20
TEREBUH, Boris Milan. 212 IRVING AVE STE D, MUSCULOSKELETAL CENTER 43311
  #038-43-1993 L1994 **PM** *020 †60
TEREBUH, Josip. 205 E PALMER RD 43311 #660-02-1958 L1963 **OPH** *030
TRAUL, Richard Snyder. 212 BENT PINES CT 43311 #038-40-1965 L1965 **AN OS** *020 †05
VARIAN, Grant Karl. 2231 TIMBER TRL, MAD RIVER INTERNAL MED INC 43311
  #038-40-1971 L1971 **IM** *030 †20
WETZEL, Scott Curtis. ■ 43311 #025-07-1981 L1999 **OBG** *020 †30
ZOX, Sherry Beth. 205 E PALMER RD, MARY RUTAR HOSP/RADIOLOGY 43311
  #038-40-1976 L1978 **DR** *020

BELLEVUE – SANDUSKY

ABDELMOTALEB, Abeer Ibrah. ■ 44811 #915-04-1993 L2004 **OBG** *100
ABOU CHAKRA, Iman. 5433 STATE ROUTE 113, ADVANCED NEUROLOGIC ASSOCI 44811
  #875-01-1983 L2000 **PM** *020 †60 ‡
ALDA, Rugen Mabalay. 813 NORTHWEST ST, BLDG C 44811 #038-44-1997 L1998 **FM** *020 †18
ALT-COAN, Amy Christina. 1255 W MAIN ST STE A 44811 #038-43-1996 L1997
  MPD *020 †20,55
AMBURN, Orville Rene. 250 CASTALIA ST, STE G 44811 #038-43-1972 L1982 **FM GP** *020
BALL, Theodore Raymond. 1255 W MAIN ST, STE A 44811 #038-40-1960 L1960 **GP** *020
BAUER, Brendan W. 5433 STATE ROUTE 113 44811 #038-43-1998 L2000 **N** *020 †75
BAUER, William Rudolph. 5433 STATE ROUTE 113 44811 #539-02-1965 L1967 **N IM** *020 †75
BENEDICT, Steven. 5433 STATE ROUTE 113, ADVANCED NEUROLOGIC ASSOC. 44811
  #038-43-1997 L1998 **N** *020 †75
BERRY, Daniel Braxton, II. 813 NORTHWEST ST, BLDG C 44811 #045-01-1995 L2001
  IM *020 †20
BERRY, James Richard. 185 AIGLER BLVD W 44811 #038-40-1977 L1978 **ORS** *020 †40
BROWN, Ronald N, Jr. 1400 W MAIN ST 44811 #025-01-1990 L1995 **OPH** *020 †35
COLIZOLI, Joseph Ernest. 1400 W MAIN ST 44811 #038-06-1973 L1975 **AN** *020 †05
COLL, Robert Ray. 1991 W MAIN ST STE A 44811 #038-40-1984 L1985 **IM** *020 †20
DANNER, Nicole. 5433 STATE ROUTE 113, ADVANCED NEUROLOGIC ASSOC 44811
  #038-75-2001, ▲ L2001 *020
FELTER, Michael Jos. 185 AIGLER BLVD W 44811 #038-40-1978 L1979 **ORS** *020 †40
HEMEYER, Edward Jos. 521 N SANDUSKY ST STE B 44811 #038-45-1987 L1990 **FM** *020 †18
HOY, Douglas Michael. 1265 W MAIN ST, STE A 44811 #038-45-1991 L1992 **FM** *020 †18
JUDKINS, Richard Friden. 811 NORTHWEST ST 44811 #024-05-1963 L1988 **OTO NO** *071 †45
KAINE, Patricia Ann. ■ 44811 #038-45-1982 L1984 **FM** *071 †18
KARASIK, Gregory B. 1400 W MAIN ST, STE A 44811 #913-01-1982 L1995 **OBG** *020 †30
KENDALL, Richard Lee. 811 NORTHWEST ST, BELLEVUE HOSPITAL 44811 #038-40-1990 L1991
  EM *020 †16
KEREKES, Jill Marie. 1971 W MAIN ST, STE A 44811 #038-40-2001 L2005 **MPD** *020 †55,20
KNIGHT, Kim Edward. 521 N SANDUSKY ST, STE A 44811 #038-41-1982 L1984
  FM OBS *020 †18
KOMOROWSKI, Frank Stanley. 1355 W MAIN ST, STE D 44811 #847-10-1979 L1990
  GYN GP *020 †30
LESLIE, Michael Joseph. 5433 STATE ROUTE 113 44811 #038-43-1996 L2000 **N** *020 †75
MORROW, Matthew Edward. 185 AIGLER BLVD W 44811 #030-06-1990 L1995 **RHU** *020 †20
OLEXA, Thomas Anthony. 185 AIGLER BLVD W 44811 #038-43-1995 L1999 **ORS** *020 †40
RALOFSKY, Louis William. 813 NORTHWEST ST, BLDG C 44811 #038-45-1996 L1997
  FM *020 †18
RALOFSKY, Michele L. 813 NORTHWEST ST, BLDG C 44811 #038-45-1996 L1997 **FM** *020 †18
RAVIN, James Gordon. 1400 W MAIN ST 44811 #025-01-1968 L1970 **OPH** *020 †35
REICHENBACH, D J. 1991 W MAIN ST 44811 #025-01-1961 L1965 **IM** *071
SMITH, Mark Richard. 811 NORTHWEST ST, BELLEVUE HOSPITAL 44811
  #561-17-1980 L1983 *020
STEWART, James Franklin. 1400 W MAIN ST, THE BELLEVUE HOSPITAL 44811
  #038-43-1990 L1994 **AN** *020 †05
TIMMIS, Hilary Houghton. 1255 W MAIN ST, STE B 44811 #036-01-1994 L1999 **OTO** *020 †45
WALL, Mary Jean. 251 EUCLID AVE 44811 #041-09-1982 L1989 **DR** *020 †80
WONG, Kam Ming. 185 AIGLER BLVD W 44811 #038-06-1986 L1987 **ORS** *020 †40
ZIMMERMAN, John L. ■ 44811 #025-01-1951 L1953 **PTH OS** *020 †50

■ = Address Information Privacy Protected

BELLVILLE – RICHLAND

CURTISS, Charles Francis. ■ 44813 #038-40-1944 L1944 **GP** *071

BELMONT – BELMONT

COTTERMAN, George Michael. 66840 BELMONT MORRISTWN RD 43718 #038-40-1973 L1974
FM *020 †18
DURKALSKI, Joseph M. 66840 BELMONT MORRISTWN RD, MORRISTOWN CLINIC 43718
#055-75-1991, ▲ L1994 **FM** *020 †18
HALL, Joseph Edward. ■ 43718 #038-41-2008 *012
YAVELAK, William James. ■ 43718 #038-43-2002 L2004 **FM** *020 †18

BELOIT – MAHONING

CORALLO, David J. 18586 5TH ST 44609 #035-75-1995, ▲ L1998 **D DS** *020
ST JOHN, David Scott. ■ 44609 #038-44-2005 L2005 **DR** *012

BELPRE – WASHINGTON

COOK, Teri Liane. 125 LEE ST 45714 #055-01-2000 L2005 **MPD** *020
GUANZON, Noel Araneta. ■ 45714 #748-01-1970 L1994 **GP** *075
KEMP, James A. ■ 45714 #012-01-1952 L1961 **HEM PHP** *071 †20
MAIJUB, A Gabriel. 204 STONE RD 45714 #308-03-1980 L1996 **FM GP** *020 †18
MEYERS, Gregory Scott. 809 FARSON AVE, UNIT 107 45714 #005-15-1988 L2003
DR RNR *020 †80
PALAZZO, Kurt James. 809 FARSON AVE STE 1, PHYSICIANS, LLC 45714 #038-40-1990 L1994
FM *020 †18
POWDERLY, Brian. 301 SAINT ANDREWS BLVD 45714 #539-04-1979 L1999 **FM IMG** *020 †18
REYES, Charles Wesley. 308 MAIN ST 45714 #055-01-1976 L1987 **IM** *020
SAMS, Robert Eugene. 2515 WASHINGTON BLVD 45714 #055-01-1965 L1969 **P** *020
STRAIGHT, Heather. 610 WASHINGTON BLVD 45714 #055-75-2002, ▲ L2007 **FM** *020
WARREN, Penelope Ruth. ■ 45714 #038-40-1972 L1972 **FM** *071
WATSON, Richard Wm. 204 STONE RD 45714 #038-43-1992 L1996 **FM** *020 †18

BEREA – CUYAHOGA

BAKER, Garrard Edward. ■ 44017 #048-02-1997 L1998 **NR** *100
BLANKFIELD, Robert Peter. 201 FRONT ST STE 101 44017 #038-06-1984 L1985 **FM** *020 †18
CHANG, Kau-Wun. 347 FRONT ST 44017 #244-05-1968 L1976 **PD** *020
CHOUDHARY, Sanjay Kumar. 276 W BAGLEY RD 44017 #496-14-1991 L2000 **IM** *020 †20
CROUSE, Micah Shawn. 44017 #654-01-2006 L2006 **FP** *012
DEHN, Helmut Max. 3 BEREA COMMONS, # 285 44017 #051-04-1939 L1946 **PD PDA** *071 †55
DIMACULANGAN, Lucina R. ■ 44017 #748-01-1955 L1965 **AN** *071
ETUK, Blessing Godwin. ■ 44017 #033-06-1996 L2007 **RO** *020 †80
GOLDSCHMIDT, Rhoda Yvonne. 201 FRONT ST, STE 103 44017 #038-06-1996 L2000
OBG *020 †30
JOSHI, Atul. 276 W BAGLEY RD 44017 #495-41-1991 L1997 **IM** *020 †20
KITAGAWA, Gregory Y. 201 FRONT ST, STE 103 44017 #038-40-1998 L1999 **OBG** *020 †30
MCLONEY, Mark Allen. 398 W BAGLEY RD 44017 #038-43-1989 L1991 **FM** *020 †18
SHARMA, Sandeep Kumar. 201 FRONT ST, STE 103 44017 #065-06-1993 L1998 **OBG** *020
TIGERT, Scott Stephen. 201 FRONT ST, STE 103 44017 #065-01-1989 L1994 **OBG** *020 †30
TROY, Nicole Christine. 853 W BAGLEY RD 44017 #038-44-2002 L2002 **FM** *020 †18

BERGHOLZ – JEFFERSON

MILLS, James Harold. 1251 TOWNSHIP ROAD 263 43908 #038-40-1978 L1979
EM FM *020 †18,16

BERLIN – HOLMES

BOYD, Kim Edward. 4897 W MAIN ST 44610 #038-40-1975 L1976 **FM** *020 †18
MULLET, Maurice Eugene. PO BOX 260 44610 #038-40-1963 L1963 **PHP FM** *071

BERLIN CENTER – MAHONING

KIRKPATRICK, Kelly Jo. 44401 #038-44-2007 L2007 **FP** *012
LAMBERT, James Arthur. 44401 #038-06-1966 L1966 **OTO** *071 †45

BETHEL – CLERMONT

BAKER, Robert Alan. 201 S UNION ST 45106 #025-01-1958 L1965 **GS FM** *020 †85
BRINTZENHOFF, Rita Anne. ■ 45106 #038-41-2007 **GS** *012
EVERSON, Curtis Bryon. 525 W PLANE ST 45106 #038-45-1988 L1992 **IM PD** *020
KAYA, James Naoto. 3088 ANGEL DR, MERCY MED ASSOC 45106 #038-41-1981 L1983
IM *020 †20
MC FAWN, Briana Lynn. 3088 ANGEL DR 45106 #038-40-1998 L2002 **IM** *020 †20
MENDOZA, Antonio P. ■ 45106 #748-08-1961 L1970 **FM** *071
MENDOZA, Araceli Reyes. ■ 45106 #748-01-1954 L1970 **PD OS** *074 †55
PATTERSON, Brad Scott. 210 N UNION ST, BROWN CTY REG HLTHCARE 45106
#038-45-2001 L2004 **FM** *020 †18
SARAH, Amal. 3088 ANGEL DR, MERCY MEDICAL ASSOCIATES 45106 #875-03-1995 L2000
FM *020 †18 ‡

BEVERLY – WASHINGTON

WHITACRE, Victor Calvin. PO BOX 188 45715 #038-40-1946 L1946 **GP PHP** *071

BEXLEY – FRANKLIN

CIUREA, Alexandru I. 43209 #781-03-1950 L1975 **P** *072
DARWIN, Beverly A Sumner. 43209 #036-07-1986 L1991 **D** *020 †15
EPSTEIN, Clara Raquel. 2691 E MAIN ST, STE 101 43209 #016-42-1996 L2003 **NS OS** *020
GRISCHKAN, Jonathan Marc. 43209 #038-06-2005 L2005 **OTO** *012
HERSHENSON, Jared Adam. ■ 43209 #028-02-2004 L2007 **PD** *100 †55
IOREMBER, Franca Mngu. ■ 43209 #690-07-1992 L2005 **PD** *100
MILLER, Jerad Paul. ■ 43209 #030-05-2002 L2002 **CRS** *012 †85
ROSS-DOLEN, Mary Martin. ■ 43209 #035-46-1992 L2002 **CHP P** *071 †75
SNIDERMAN, Michael Isaac. ■ 43209 #038-43-2006 L2006 **AN** *012

BLACKLICK – FRANKLIN

BENDER, Stephen Patrick. ■ 43004 #038-40-2004 L2004 **AN** *012
BERGER, Allan Myron. ■ 43004 #016-42-1954 L1961 **OPH** *071 †35
CALLOWAY, Tiffany Nicole. ■ 43004 #038-40-2004 L2004 **PM** *012
CAMPBELL, Shannon M. ▲ L2006 **D** *012
FARUQUI, Azhar Masood A. ■ 43004 #704-02-1971 L1974 **CD** *040 †20
HWANG, Kiu-Won. 2289 COB TAIL WAY 43004 #583-04-1967 L1977 **AN** *020 †05
LOPEZ, Jesse G, III. ■ 43004 #034-01-2001 L2001 **AN** *020 †05
LOVE-WALKER, Gina M. 7340 E BROAD ST STE B, PHYSICIANS 43004 #038-45-1993 L1994
IM *020
MC NUTT, Emily Suzanne. 7974 WINDSOME CT 43004 #045-01-2003 L2003 **EM** *020 †16
MOHANDAS, Elizabeth. ■ 43004 #495-16-1975 L1984 **AN** *074 †05
NARCELLES, Andrew Millan. 7340 E BROAD ST, STE B 43004 #038-40-1999 L1999
FM *020 †18
NDUAGUBA, Emanuel C. ■ 43004 #038-43-2001 L2002 **FM** *100
NDUAGUBA, John C. ■ 43004 #038-45-1982 L1983 **EM IM** *020 †16
RAMSEY, Shavonne T. ■ 43004 #041-12-2003 L2003 **OBG** *100
RESNICK, Kimberly Erin. ■ 43004 #038-06-2003 L2003 **OBG** *100
RUDY, Russell Michael. 7257 HAVENS RD 43004 #038-40-1982 L1983 **EM** *020 †16
RUSSELL, Nathaniel Duane. ■ 43004 #038-06-1997 L2003 **FM** *020 †18
TANCEVSKI, Aleksandar. ■ 43004 #038-41-2008 *012
TSAI, Shane Francis. ■ 43004 #025-01-2001 L2005 **PDC** *012 †20,55
WADHWA, Rajiv. 6405 HAVENS RD 43004 #495-45-1985 L1994 **IM** *020 †20
ZYLBERBERG, Rachel Haya. 7340 E BROAD ST 43004 #038-40-1981 L1981 **PD NPM** *020 †55

BLANCHESTER – CLINTON

BANKSTON, Laurie Ann. 849 CHERRY ST, BLANCHESTER MEDICAL SERVIC 45107
#038-45-1999 L2000 **FM** *020 †18
BOSTER, Richard Brian. ■ 45107 #055-02-1989 L1990 **IM** *020 †20
LARUFFA, Catherine. 700 S BROADWAY ST 45107 #654-01-1986 L1991 **FM** *020 †18 ‡
LA RUFFA, Cesare Anthony. 700 S BROADWAY ST 45107 #561-08-1951 L1959 **GP GS** *020
MAGOWAN, Simon Henry. 700 S BROADWAY ST, CATHERINE LARUFFA MD INC 45107
#919-03-1984 L1988 **FM** *020 †18
MOORE, Robert Wm. 849 CHERRY ST 45107 #038-40-1984 L1986 **FM PD** *020 †18
WEBER, Steven Raymond. 849 CHERRY ST 45107 #038-45-1990 L1993 **FM** *020 †18

BLOOMINGDALE – JEFFERSON

CURRENT, James Van. 6243 STATE HIGHWAY 646 43910 #038-06-1962 L1962 **IM** *071 †20

BLUE ASH – HAMILTON

KADAKIA, Parool Mayur. 4260 GLENDALE MILFORD RD, STE 101 45242 #035-48-1995 L1998
IM *020 †20
KHAN, Faisal Mahmood. ■ 45236 #704-25-2002 L2004 **CD** *012 †20
MARKOVICH, John Christoph. ■ 45209 #038-41-2008 *012
RISSOVER, Jay Elliott. 4260 GLENDALE MILFORD RD, STE 101 45242 #038-43-1984 L1986
IM *020 †20
TIPPETT, Aletha Wissler. 10274 ALLIANCE RD 45242 #038-41-1997 L1998 **FM PME** *020 †18

BLUFFTON – ALLEN

AVILA, James Ybanez. 139 GARAU ST, BLANCHARD VALLEY BLUFFTON 45817
#748-09-1977 L1995 **AN** *020
BROWN, Desrene Kerryann. ■ 45817 #033-05-1995 L1999 **OBG** *020 †30
CHAPPELL, Louis Terry. 122 THURMAN ST 45817 #025-01-1969 L1971 **FM NTR** *020 †18
CRIBLEZ, Lance Patrick. 139 GARAU ST 45817 #038-45-2001 L2001 **FM** *020 †18
DAGANI, Jacob. 139 GARAU ST 45817 #048-02-1977 L1992 **OBG GP** *020 †30
HOTMIRE, Darrel. 132 GARAU ST, BLUFFTON FAMILY PRACTICE, 45817 #038-75-1996, ▲ L1998
FM *020
MC CARTHY, Mary Evans. 161 GARAU ST, P O BOX 126 45817 #038-40-1990 L1991
FM *020 †18
SHELLY, Howard Myers. 132 GARAU ST 45817 #016-11-1956 L1957 **GP** *071
SULLIVAN, Murray Glen. 139 GARAU ST, BLANCHARD VALLEY HOSPITAL 45817
#028-46-1991 L1993 **EM** *020
YOUNG-DAVIES, Cara Louise. ■ 45817 #038-43-2008 *012

BOARDMAN – MAHONING

ALLISON, Bennie W. ■ 44512 #047-07-1981 L1983 **IM** *020
ANSEVIN, Carl Franklin. 7417 SOUTH AVE 44512 #038-40-1974 L1975 **N** *020 †75
ARMILE, James A. 8262 SOUTH AVE 44512 #041-78-1997, ▲ L1998 **D** *020
AU, Samuel Poriza. 8401 MARKET ST, BOARDMAN CAMPUS CANCER CEN 44512
#005-19-1995 L2002 **RO** *020 †80
BAIR, Booker Ted. 6505 MARKET ST, BLDG C 44512 #038-44-2001 L2001 **PD** *020 †55

BAUTISTA, Manuel Antonio. 960 WINDHAM CT 44512 #308-05-1993 L2007 **CCM** *020 †20

BERNY, James Jos. 7986 SPARTAN DR, ASSOCIATES IN ANESTHESIOLO 44512 #051-04-1979 L1989 **AN** *020 †05

BONIFACE, James Eugene. 835 MCKAY CT, STE 100 44512 #038-43-1990 L1991 **ORS** *020 †40

BONIFACE, Raymond John. 835 MCKAY CT STE 100 44512 #038-06-1982 L1988 **ORS** *020 †40

COLLA, Ralph Wm. 1011 BOARDMAN CANFIELD RD 44512 #038-04-1973 L1973 **OBG** *020 †30

CORTEZ, Orlando Pastor, Jr. ■ 44512 #038-43-2008 *012

DASS, Bhagwan. 1240 BOARDMAN CANFIELD RD, STE 1 44512 #495-51-1989 L2000 **IM** *020 †20

DE MARIO, Chas Lawrence. 7600 SOUTHERN BLVD, STE 1 44512 #041-13-1978 L1984 **OBG** *040 †18,30

DUDDELLA, Padmaja. 901 TRAILWOOD DR 44512 #495-57-1991 L1999 **IM** *020 †20

EBERLY, Leroy Richard. 6505 MARKET ST, BLDG C 44512 #038-43-1997 L1999 **PD** *020 †55

EBERT, Daniel Mark. 6505 MARKET ST, OFC 204 44512 #038-45-1992 L1999 **HS GS** *020 †85

ECONOMUS, Constantine G. 6505 MARKET ST STE C111 44512 #038-40-1994 L1995 **OBG** *020 †30

EL-AZEEM, Sayed Abd. 8170 SOUTH AVE 44512 #915-02-1982 L1995 **OBG** *020 †20,30

EL-HAYEK, Antoine Toufic. 1111 BOARDMAN CANFIELD RD 44512 #605-03-1989 L1992 **OBG** *020 †30

FILDES, Mark David. 250 DEBARTOLO PL STE 2750 44512 #028-34-1976 L1979 **IC CD** *020 †20

GIANNINI, A James. 721 BOARDMAN POLAND RD 44512 #041-12-1974 L1978 **P** *020

GOLDSTEIN, Lawrence Scott. 960 WINDHAM CT 44512 #035-15-1991 L1992 **PCC** *020 †20

GRAY, Sharmane Marie. ■ 44512 #018-03-1999 L2006 **FP** *012 ‡

HAKKI, Naser Kazem. ■ 44512 #422-01-2006 L2006 **IM** *012

HEFFNER, Jeremy James. ■ 44512 #038-41-2006 L2006 **GS** *012

HELDMAN, Irene Katherine. 1265 BOARDMAN CANFIELD RD 44512 #041-02-1986 L2000 **PM** *020 †20,60

HOUSER, William L, Jr. 250 DEBARTOLO PL STE 1510 44512 #038-44-1984 L1985 **AI PDA** *020 †55,03

ISKANDER, Nazih Sabah. 914 TRAILWOOD DR, PENNSYLVANIA PAIN MANAGEME 44512 #915-05-1987 L2004 **PM PME** *100 †60

KING, Steven Alphonso. 5600 MARKET ST STE 10, CENTER FOR BEHAVIORAL HEAL 44512 #016-01-1982 L1983 **P** *020 †75

KOCZWARA, Jeffrey M. ■ 44512 #038-44-1997 *100

KONYA, Meredith Leigh. ■ 44512 #038-44-2006 L2006 **PM** *012

LABIB, Nefertiti. 755 BOARDMAN CANFLD RD #H2 44512 #915-02-1970 L1981 **P** *020

LLOYD, Amy Allison. ■ 44512 #665-01-2007 L2007 **GS** *012

LUCHEY, Adam Michael. ■ 44512 #038-44-2008 *012

MANSOUR, Waleed Nasr. 810 BOARDMAN CANFIELD RD 44512 #305-01-1998 L2000 **IM** *020 †20

MARCHAND, Tiffany Dawn. ■ 44512 #820-02-2006 L2007 **GS** *012

MARTINEZ, Jorge Arturo. 755 BOARDMAN CANFIELD RD 44512 #649-03-1976 L1984 **PME** *020

MATHUR, Pradeep. 955 WINDHAM CT, STE 2 44512 #495-45-1982 L1990 **CHP P** *020 †75

MC KEE, Victor Jos. 8401 MARKET ST 44512 #649-14-1981 L1988 **FM EM** *020 †18

MENDEZ, Consuelo A. 1280 BOARDMAN CANFIELD RD 44512 #042-01-1984 L1986 **IM** *020 †20

MORRONE, Carmen Valdes. 1100 BOARDMAN CANFIELD RD, APT 46B 44512 #308-13-1999 L2004 **PD** *020

PADUBIDRI, Rekha Arvind. 725 BOARDMAN CANFIELD RD, STE J2 44512 #496-39-1984 L2001 **IM** *020

PAOLONE, Vincent Anthony. 7010 SOUTH AVE, STE 7 44512 #038-40-1992 L1994 **P** *020 †75

PRIZANT, Ronald Jos. 7525 CALIFORNIA AVE 44512 #041-13-1985 L1990 **AN** *020 †05

SALOMON, Jack Berry. ■ 44512 #025-07-1971 L1972 **IM GP** *020 †20

SETHI, Manu. 7525 CALIFORNIA AVE, SOUTHWOODS ANESTHESIA, INC 44512 #038-41-1996 L1997 **AN** *020 †05

SHAH, Jyotindra Prataprai. 1026 BOARDMAN CANFIELD RD 44512 #495-01-1967 L1974 **IM** *020

SLUSHER, Lloyd Earl. 888 BOARDMAN CANFIELD RD, BLDG S-1 44512 #038-41-1970 L1970 **DR** *020 †80

SMITH, Melinda Kathrine. 6505 MARKET ST, CATHERINE E MOLLOY & SMITH 44512 #037-01-1987 L1989 **OBG** *020 †30

SPIRTOS, George. 7355 CALIFORNIA AVE # 101 44512 #038-44-1984 L1988 **GS** *020 †85

STOVER, Anne Mc Pherren. 250 DEBARTOLO PL STE 1650, LIVING WELL FMLY PRAC INC 44512 #039-05-1988 L1990 **FM** *020 †18

TUROCY, Francis Michael. 755 BOARDMAN CANFIELD RD, SOUTH BRIDGE WEST 44512 #038-45-1982 L1983 **FM EM** *020 †18

VIJAYAKUMAR, Anu. 1100 BOARDMAN CANFIELD RD 44512 #495-99-2000 L2004 **IM** *020 †20

WASSEF, Cybele Amin. 725 BOARDMAN CANFIELD RD, BLDG A 44512 #915-02-1970 L1986 **IM PM** *020 †60

WINCHESTER, Tara Danielle. 1111 BOARDMAN CANFIELD RD, ADVANCED WOMEN'S CARE, INC 44512 #055-75-1999, ▲ L1999 **OBG** *020 †30

ZIEMAK, Anita. ■ 44512 #038-06-1982 L1983 **EM** *020 †16

BOLIVAR — TUSCARAWAS

HIESTAND, Matthew Ernest. 10724 STATE ROUTE 212 NE 44612 #038-43-1994 L1996 **MPD** *020 †20,55

HILLYER, Mark Andrew. 10724 STATE ROUTE 212 NE 44612 #038-44-2001 L2001 **FM** *020

BOWERSTON — HARRISON

CARDEN, Edward Thos. ■ 44695 #041-02-1966 L1984 **OTO FPS** *071 †45

BOWLING GREEN — WOOD

ABOWD, Michael C. 970 W WOOSTER ST, RM 221 43402 #038-43-2000 L2005 **OPH** *020 †35

AHMED, Mohammed K. 960 W WOOSTER ST, STE 207 43402 #495-21-1970 L1981 **PD** *072

AHMED, Syeda Shameem. 960 W WOOSTER ST STE 216 43402 #495-57-1973 L1978 **PD** *020 †55

ANDRESHAK, Thomas Guido. 960 W WOOSTER ST, STE 110 43402 #016-42-1987 L1991 **ORS** *020 †40

ATWELL, David Mitchell. 960 W WOOSTER ST 43402 #038-40-1975 L1975 **PUD IM** *020 †20

BARKER, Richard David. 970 W WOOSTER ST, RM 222 43402 #038-41-1973 L1974 **ORS OSM** *020 †40

BARKER-MERRILL, Lisa C. 1215 RIDGEWOOD DR, STE B 43402 #038-43-2002 L2002 **FM** *020 †20

BASS, Nancy Elizabeth. 755 HASKINS RD 43402 #422-01-1999 L2000 **OBG** *020 †30 ‡

BAUTISTA, Maria Helen G. 960 W WOOSTER ST, MARIAN HELEN BAUTISTA 43402 #748-01-1963 L1973 **GP OBG** *020

BELL, David Wayne. 1037 CONNEAUT AVE, # 206 43402 #064-01-1972 L1995 **FM** *020

BELLIAN, David Paul. 1045 KLOTZ RD 43402 #038-43-1996 L1997 **P** *020 †75

BIESZCZAD, Jacob Ethan. ■ 43402 #038-43-2007 L2007 **TY** *012

BRANT, Zhanna Akimovna. UNIV HEALTH CENTER, BOWLING GREEN STATE 43402 #913-07-1970 L1984 **FM** *020

BROWN, David Wallace. 960 W WOOSTER ST, STE 111 43402 #038-40-1979 L1981 **HEM ON** *020 †20

CALCAMUGGIO, Lyle T. 970 WOOSTER ST, RM 130 43402 #038-43-1989 L1990 **OBG** *020 †30

CHAPMAN, Richard Samuel. RIDGE STREET, BOWLING GREEN STATE UNIVER 43403 #038-43-1997 L1999 **FM** *020 †18

CONRAD-PEATEE, Marjorie E. ■ 43402 #041-09-1946 L1965 **GP** *071

DAWLEY, Daniel Marvin. 970 W WOOSTER ST, RM 130 43402 #038-40-1979 L1980 **IM** *020 †20

DE LA SERNA, Manuel L, Jr. 960 W WOOSTER ST 43402 #748-01-1963 L1973 **U** *020 †95

DESMOND, Robert Raymond. BOWLING GREEN STATE UNIVER, STUDENT HEALTH CENTER 43403 #016-43-1961 L1962 **GP** *020

DEVANY, John. 960 W WOOSTER ST, STE 211 43402 #038-40-1955 L1955 **OTO** *071 †45

DILLON, William Irving. 1037 CONNEAUT AVE, STE 201 43402 #025-01-1988 L1992 **D** *020 †15

DOMINI, Teresita C T. STUDENT HEALTH CENTER, BOWLING GREEN STATE UNIVER 43403 #748-01-1970 L1974 **FM** *020

EGELMAN, Glenn. RIDGE STREET, BGSU STUDENT HEALTH SERV 43403 #035-45-1991 L2004 **IM** *030 †20

FEEMAN, William E, Jr. 640 S WINTERGARDEN RD 43402 #038-40-1970 L1970 **FM GPM** *020

GARCIA, Josefina Paz. 1039 HASKINS RD 43402 #748-10-1965 L1971 **OBG** *020

GENSON, Charles Carter. ■ 43402 #038-43-2000 L2000 **DR** *100 †80

GLADDEN, Merrill Lee, Jr. 970 W WOOSTER ST, RM 222 43402 #038-40-1992 L2004 **ORS HS** *020 †40

GLENN, Jeffrey Charles. 960 W WOOSTER ST, STE 110 43402 #038-75-1997, ▲ L1998 **ORS OAR** *020

GORDON, Jessica Lauren. ■ 43402 #038-45-2008 *012

GUERRA, Jose, Jr. 950 W WOOSTER ST, WOOD COUNTY HOSPITAL 43402 #038-40-1975 L1984 **DR** *020 †80

HEIZELMAN, Robert Joseph. RIDGE ST, BOWLING GREEN STATE UNIVER 43403 #038-43-2002 L2003 **FM** *100 †18

HESS, Douglas Sterling. 950 W WOOSTER ST 43402 #038-40-1959 L1959 **GS** *071

HESS, Douglas Wm. 640 S WINTERGARDEN RD 43402 #038-40-1981 L1981 **GS** *020 †85

HESS, Luana Jane. 950 W WOOSTER ST, WOOD COUNTY HOSPITAL 43402 #038-43-1979 L1980 **EM GP** *020 †12

HICKS, Carol Jane. 755 HASKINS RD, WOOD COUNTY WOMEN'S CARE I 43402 #038-41-1984 L1985 **FM** *020 †20

HORRIGAN, Elizabeth Ann. 1215 RIDGEWOOD DR, STE B 43402 #038-43-1997 L1998 **FM** *020 †18 ‡

KALU, Uchenna Peter. 950 W WOOSTER ST 43402 #690-06-1995 L2007 **IM IMG** *020 †20

KAPLAN, Joshua E. 950 W WOOSTER ST 43402 #035-08-1971 L1985 **IM EM** *030 †20

KETTINGER, James Jude. 1001 E WOOSTER ST, HEALTH SERVICES 43403 #038-40-1984 L1985 **FM EM** *020 †18

KIM, Woong Suh. 960 W WOOSTER ST 43402 #583-01-1965 L1972 **IM** *071

KUEBECK, Edelbert Jos. 1052 W WOOSTER ST 43402 #038-40-1979 L1980 **FM** *020 †18 ‡

LALOR, Peter F.. ■ 43402 #539-06-2001 L2002 **GS OS** *020 †85

LANE, Brian Francis. 960 W WOOSTER ST, STE 116 43402 #024-07-1988 L2005 **GS** *020 †85

LEGGAT, Ian Thomas. 755 HASKINS RD 43402 #919-05-1976 L2005 **OBG** *020 †30

LEMON, Michael John. 960 W WOOSTER ST STE 105 43402 #038-40-1985 L1986 **PD** *020 †55

LIGHTFOOT, John Kevin. 950 W WOOSTER ST, EMERGENCY DEPT. 43402 #035-15-1997 L2006 **EM** *020 †16

MAHMOOD, Hafiz Khalid. 960 W WOOSTER ST, BOX 463 43402 #704-21-1981 L1994 **N** *020

MC CARTHY, Rodney William. 970 W WOOSTER ST, RM 221 43402 #067-01-1973 L1979 **OPH PS** *020 †35

MIKO, Benjamin Alexander. 113 E BACK BAY RD 43402 #024-05-2006 L2008 **IM** *012

MIKSANEK, Bryan Keith. 950 W WOOSTER ST 43402 #016-45-1990 L1991 **FM** *040 †16

MILBRODT, Thomas Orian. 960 W WOOSTER ST, STE 101 43402 #038-43-1978 L1981 **IM** *020 †20

MILLER, David G. 725 HASKINS RD 43402 #038-40-1956 L1956 **OBG** *071 †30

MILLER, Ronald Charles, Jr. 960 W WOOSTER ST, STE 205 43402 #038-43-1996 L1997 **IM** *020 †20

MIR, Khawaja Sajid Ahmad. ■ 43402 #704-04-1999 L2007 **IM** *020 †20

NARAYANRAO, Vijayarajan. 950 W WOOSTER ST, WOOD COUNTY HOSPITAL 43402 #495-09-2001 L2007 **IM** *020 †20

NOCETI-DUNPHY, Stephanie. 960 W WOOSTER ST STE 105 43402 #041-02-1998 L1999 **PD** *020

NOFTZ, Jeffrey Bentley, II. 1039 HASKINS RD 43402 #038-43-2001 L2003 **FM** *020 †18 ‡

OVERHULSE, Paul R. ■ 43402 #023-07-1951 L1956 **GS GP** *071 †85

PACIO, Wilfredo. 950 W WOOSTER ST 43402 #748-01-1968 L1972 **PTH** *020 †50

POPLAVSKY, Konstantin. 628 HICKORY CT 43402 #913-69-1962 L1986 **R DR** *020 †80

POWER, Kenneth Harrison. 970 W WOOSTER ST, RM 130 43402 #063-01-1996 L2006 **PLM FM** *020

RHEE, Robert Kwanung. 1221 RIDGEWOOD DR, STE A 43402 #038-43-1995 L1999 **OPH** *020 †35

ROSS, John A. 1221 RIDGEWOOD DR, STE A 43402 #047-07-1979 L1992 **OBG** *020 †30

SANCHEZ, Rogelio Aborot. 960 W WOOSTER ST 43402 #748-07-1965 L1972 **FM EM** *020

SHAWBERRY, Patricia Ann. 970 W WOOSTER ST RM 124, PSYCHOLOGICAL RESOURCES LT 43402 #038-43-1999 L1999 **P** *020

SHEHATA, Said Ahmed H. 960 W WOOSTER ST 43402 #915-03-1963 L1975 **GS VS** *020 †85

SIDIQ, Mohammad. 1039 HASKINS RD UNIT A 43402 #704-09-1966 L1972 **IM CD** *020 †20

SMITH, Albert Wright, III. 515 BROWNWOOD CT, 515 BROWNWOOD CT 43402 #038-41-1968 L1968 **FM** *020

SMITH, Jay Leslie. 1072 N MAIN ST 43402 #038-40-1979 L1979 **AN** *020 †05

SOKOLOSKI, Steven Neil. 960 W WOOSTER ST, STE 110 43402 #038-43-1991 L1996 **ORS** *020 †40

STEPHENS, Jeffery Nelson. 970 W WOOSTER ST, RM 221 43402 #038-43-1999 L2005 **OPH** *020 †35 ‡

■ = Address Information Privacy Protected

TAM, Richard Ceenan. 970 W WOOSTER ST RM 224 43402 #028-02-1999 L2000
OPH IM *020 †35
TAMLYN, Todd R. 960 W WOOSTER ST STE 208 43402 #037-01-1992 L1994 GS *020 †85
TAYLOR, Jay Bradley. 950 W WOOSTER ST 43402 #038-45-1999 L1999 EM *020 †16
TAYLOR, Lynn Marie. ■ 43402 #038-45-1998 L1999 PD *020 †55
TEITLEBAUM, Phillip B. 950 W WOOSTER ST 43402 #038-40-1973 L1976 AN *020 †05
THOMAS, Sherri Ann. 960 W WOOSTER ST STE 105 43402 #038-43-1996 L1997 PD *020 †55
TRIMPEY, Randy Alan. 1039 HASKINS RD, BOWLING GREEN CLINIC INC 43402
#038-43-2001 L2001 FSM *020 †18
WAHEED, Adil Muhammad. 950 W WOOSTER ST 43402 #704-15-2000 L2007 IM *020 †20
WALSH, Richard Peter. 960 W WOOSTER ST, STE 115 43402 #038-43-1981 L1983 FM *020 †18
WOJCIECHOWSKI, Edward J. 1413 TURNBERRY CT 43402 #038-43-1996 L1997 FM *020 †18 ‡
WOJCIECHOWSKI, Thos Edwin. 970 W WOOSTER ST, RM 130 43402 #025-07-1975 L1976
FM *020 †18
ZICK, David Gerald. 1010 N PROSPECT ST 43402 #025-01-1983 L1985 P *020 †75

BRATENAHL – CUYAHOGA

ANDERSON, Rollin John. 292 CORNING DR 44108 #038-40-1960 L1960 AN *020 †05
BHATTI, Sokun Ky. ■ 44108 #041-02-2004 L2004 IM *100 †20
DATT, Stuart Balfour. ■ 44108 #049-01-1956 L1964 IM *020 †20
EIBEN, Robert Michael. ■ 44108 #038-06-1946 L1946 CHN PD *071 †55
HERMANN, Robert Ewald. ■ 44108 #038-02-1954 L1959 GS *071 †85
MALBASA, Christi Lynn. ■ 44108 #038-06-2006 L2006 AN *012
TULSYAN, Nirman. ■ 44108 #033-05-1999 L2004 GS *020

BRECKSVILLE – CUYAHOGA

AHMED, Manzoor. ■ 44141 #704-09-1995 L1999 RNR *020 †80
AHMED, Md Mahbood. 10000 BRECKSVILLE RD, VA MEDICAL CENTER,BRECKSVI 44141
#160-06-1989 L2003 PYG *020
APOLONIO, Domingo Guillen. 10000 BRECKSVILLE RD 44141 #748-01-1948 L1972
OPH OTO *071
APOLONIO, Ferdinand Emman. ■ 44141 #748-20-2002 L2005 FP *012
APOLONIO, Gloria C V. ■ 44141 #748-01-1953 L1970 P GP *020
AUSTRIA, Alfredo Austria. ■ 44141 #748-07-1955 L1965 GS *020
BANSAL, Manish. ■ 44141 #495-20-1998 L2007 PDC *012 †55
BARKOUKIS, Athanasius M. ■ 44141 #418-01-1935 L1944 GP *071
BAYLOR, Lauren Ashley. ■ 44141 #028-02-2007 IM *012
BENDER, Martha J. ■ 44141 #041-07-1951 L1952 PUD IM *071 †20
BENISH, William Arthur. 10000 BRECKSVILLE VA HOSP 44141
#025-01-1982 L1994 IM *020 †20
BIRCHALL, Curtis Lee. 6896 W SNOWVILLE RD, UNIV EMER SPEC, INC 44141
#038-43-1976 L1977 EM *072 †16
BLANK, David John. 10000 BRECKSVILLE RD 44141 #038-43-1996 L1998 P *020 †75
BOND, Linda Christine. 10000 BRECKSVILLE RD, BRECKSVILLE VA HOSP 44141
#038-44-1986 L1995 P *040 †75
BRAVO, Lulette Tricia Ca. ■ 44141 #748-02-2001 L2003 IM *100 †20
CHEN, Peijun. 10000 BRECKSVILLE RD, PSYCH SVC 161A(B) 44141 #243-16-1984 L2006
P PYG *100 †75
CHERNIV, Alexander. ■ 44141 #913-22-1942 L1960 PTH *071
CHESTER, Carol Susan. ■ 44141 #038-06-1967 L1967 N *071 †75
CORWIN, Michael Thomas. ■ 44141 #038-06-2004 L2004 DR *012
DE JESUS, Rosalinda H. 10000 BRECKSVILLE RD 44141 #748-08-1965 L1972 GP *020
DHILLON, Jaspinder Singh. ■ 44141 #305-01-2004 L2006 FPG *012
DHILLON, Robin K. 10100 BRECKSVILLE RD 44141 #041-09-1986 L2000 GS OS *071 †85
DISPENZA, Thomas Charles. ■ 44141 #041-12-2005 L2005 PD *012
DOMINGUEZ, Miguel A. ■ 44141 #649-01-1955 L1964 PTH *020 †50
ELHAJ, Omar. 10000 BRECKSVILLE RD, PSYCHIATRY SERVICES 44141 #875-01-1995 L2002
ADP PYG *030
ELKHALIFA, Mohamed Y. ■ 44141 #848-01-1981 L1990 PTH *020 †50
FARAG, Rosemary Robert G. ■ 44141 #915-04-1990 L2000 PCP *020 †20
FISSELL, William Henry, IV. ■ 44141 #038-06-1998 L2000 NEP *020 †20
FRYMIER, Robert Clarence. 10000 BRECKSVILLE RD, RMEC 44141 #038-40-1958 L1958 P *030
GALANTERNIK, Edward Oscar. ■ 44141 #041-12-1962 L1974 OPH *020
GERARDO, Ernesto A. 6909 ROYALTON RD, STE 304 44141 #748-01-1981 L1983 PD *020 †55
GERARDO, Ernesto Montano. 10000 BRECKSVILLE RD 44141 #748-01-1954 L1966 GP P *020
GERARDO, Patria Gutay. ■ 44141 #748-01-1981 L1987 IM IMG *020 †20
GLORIOSO, Nancy Dollete. ■ 44141 #748-08-1963 L1973 IM *020
GOTTL, Frederick Eugen. ■ 44141 #473-01-1925 L1964 *074
GOYER, Peter Francis, Jr. 10000 BRECKSVILLE RD 44141 #023-07-1974 L1989
NM P *030 †75,28
HANNA, James Lawrence. ■ 44141 #038-06-1945 L1945 DR *071 †80
HASMAN, Michael Thomas. 10000 BRECKSVILLE RD 44141 #038-43-2003 L2003 FM *100 †18
HIREMATH, Girish K. ■ 44141 #038-44-2002 L2002 NS *012
HUANG, Cynthia Paradies. 6909 ROYALTON RD STE 20 44141 #035-46-1985 L1990
D IM *020 †15
JASKIW, George Eugene. 10000 BRECKSVILLE RD, CLEVELAND VAMC 44141
#065-01-1980 L1990 P *020 †75
KAUSCH, Otto. 10000 BRECKSVILLE RD, VA BRECKSVILLE-VARC 44141 #023-07-1985 L1991
P PFP *020
KHAWAM, Elias Albert. 10000 BRECKSVILLE RD, L S CLEVELAND VAMC 44141
#875-01-1991 L2000 P *100 †75
KIM, James. ■ 44141 #025-01-2007 L2007 TY *012
KIM, Kong Keun. ■ 44141 #583-02-1955 L1976 P GP *071
KNAPPENBERGER, George F. 10000 BRECKSVILLE RD, VETERANS AFFAIRS MED CTR 44141
#041-12-1985 L2000 IM PD *020 †20,55
KONICKI, Paul Eric. 10000 BRECKSVILLE RD, 116A B 44141 #026-04-1983 L1990 P *020 †75
KREMSDORF, Robin Amy. ■ 44141 #038-06-2004 L2004 MPD *012
LANKERANI, Mohammed Reza. 6930 TREELINE DR, STE G 44141 #517-03-1966 L1973
PTH *071 †50
LEVY, Michelle Lynn. 6909 ROYALTON RD 44141 #038-06-1992 L1995 PD *020 †55
MARQUA, Sybille. 10000 BRECKSVILLE RD, VA MEDICAL CENTER 44141 #409-22-1983 L1994
P *020 †75

MARSH, Loralee. 8223 BRECKSVILLE RD, LOWER LEVEL 44141 #016-11-1976 L1981
CHP *020 †75
MATTHEWS, Laurel Ann. ■ 44141 #038-41-1981 L1992 GS OS *075
MIDIS, Milton Panos. ■ 44141 #051-04-1986 L1991 AN GS *020 †05
MIHALEK, John Charles. 10000 BRECKSVILLE RD, BRECKSVILLE VA HOSPITAL 44141
#422-01-2002 L2003 P *020
MOHAMED, Rihab Ibrahim. 6802 HIDDEN LAKE TRL 44141 #848-03-1989 L2003 CHP *012
MYSLENSKI, Maya Czosnyka. ■ 44141 #759-17-1995 L2000 PD *020 †55
NAM, Kyung Hee. 10000 BRECKSVILLE RD #117B, CLEVELAND VA HOSP 44141
#583-03-1971 L1979 PM *020 †60
ONDER, Baran Mete. ■ 44141 #038-06-2007 L2007 FP *012
ORTIZ, Ernesto De Guzman. ■ 44141 #748-08-1957 L1968 GP *020
ORTIZ, Iluminada Garcia. ■ 44141 #748-01-1957 L1971 GP *020
PARADISE, Joseph Robt. ■ 44141 #028-34-1948 L1949 GS OM *072 †85
POTTS, Kathryn Nancy Duta. ■ 44141 #038-06-1952 L1952 GP PD *071
PRASAD, Sudhamani. ■ 44141 #495-33-1970 L1979 FM ATP *020 †50
PROCTOR, Monica Haller. 10000 BRECKSVILLE RD, B51A 44141 #038-43-1991 L1996
P *020 †75 ‡
RAM, Dasarathi. ■ 44141 #495-13-1959 L1972 R *071 †80
RAMUNDO, Maria Lisa. ■ 44141 #038-41-1988 L1990 PD *020 †55
REYES-JANDI, Zenaida V. 10000 BRECKSVILLE RD 44141 #748-02-1966 L1972 IM *020
SAHAI, Purbi Surya. ■ 44141 #038-44-2005 L2005 MPD *100
SALEWSKI, Carol Ann. 6909 ROYALTON RD, BRECK MC 44141 #038-06-1990 L1991
IM *020 †20
SCHWARTZ, Richard Matthew. 6930 TREELINE DR, STE G 44141 #041-12-1970 L1977
PTH DMP *020 †50
SINGH, Gurdeep. ■ 44141 #495-45-1968 L1976 NEP IM *071 †20
STERN, Denise Ingrid. 6909 ROYALTON RD, STE 101 44141 #038-44-1999 L2000 IM *020
THAKURIA, Pranjal. ■ 44141 #038-06-2004 L2004 OPH *012
USMANI, Arif Suhail. 6930 TREELINE DR, STE G 44141 #915-09-1985 L2000 PTH *020 †50
VELLANKI, Indira Devi. 10000 BRECKSVILLE RD, VA MED CTR 44141 #495-50-1977 L1983
AN *020 †20
VERGARA, Marcelino M. ■ 44141 #748-01-1950 OPH OTO *020
WHALEN, Christopher C. 8457 WHITEWOOD RD 44141 #038-06-1984 L1985 ID IM *020 †20
WU, Joyce Spring. 7416 W CROSS CREEK TRL 44141 #038-44-1997 L1998 EM *020 †16
YAP, Celia. 10096 FITZWATER RD 44141 #748-02-1968 L1972 R *020 †80

BRIDGEPORT – BELMONT

KALLA, Ahmed Hasan. ■ 43912 #495-30-1961 L1978 CRS GS *071 †85,10
LAZO, Fausto Jose. 55741 NATIONAL RD 43912 #649-14-1975 L1979 FM FPG *020 †18 ‡
LAZO, Sharon Lee. 55741 NATIONAL RD 43912 #649-14-1975 L1979 FM *020 †18
PARK, William Favre. 56104 NATIONAL RD 43912 #023-01-1946 L1965 OPH *071 †35
PINSKY, Sheldon T. 57640 N ELEANOR ST 43912 #038-40-1951 L1951 GP IM *020
SHAW-NIEVES, Carmel C. 300 HOWARD ST, STE 4 43912 #010-02-1984 L1993 FM *020

BRISTOLVILLE – TRUMBULL

OMALIA, Kelly Kirsten. 6265 STATE ROUTE 45 44402 #038-40-1996 L1997 FM *020 †18 ‡

BROADVIEW HEIGHTS – CUYAHOGA

AHMED, Hossam Kamel. ■ 44147 #915-11-1992 L2007 NR *020
BELLEZA, Anastacio A. ■ 44147 #748-02-1953 L1967 AS GP *075
BLADES, Deborah A. 1 EAGLE VALLEY CT 44147 #038-06-1986 L1986 NS *020 †25
BOLINAO, Engracia I. ■ 44147 #748-08-1962 CHP P *020
CASTRO, Alan Santillan. 1374 APPLE VALLEY CT 44147 #748-10-1990 L1995 P *020 †75
COLLINS, Caroline Jennife. ■ 44147 #038-43-2008 *012
CORDLE, Andrew Christophe. ■ 44147 #038-06-2007 L2007 ORS *012
CRUSE, Lauren Mary. ■ 44147 #038-41-2008 *012
D'AMICO, Joseph A. ■ 44147 #038-06-1982 L1984 IM AN *071 †20,05
DASARATHY, Srinivasan. 8732 BRECKENRIDGE OVAL 44147 #495-53-1984 L1999 GE *020 †20
DONICH, Dawn Eileen. 2001 E ROYALTON RD 44147 #038-44-1989 L1991 DR *020 †80
FRAGATOS, Peter. 1 EAGLE VALLEY CT 44147 #065-09-1965 L2003 NS PMM *020
GALLAGHER, Susan Anne. 2001 E ROYALTON RD 44147 #038-40-1978 L1981 IM *020 †20
GUJRAL, Rajnish Mohan. 3421 MAGNOLIA WAY 44147 #495-01-1994 L1999 IM *020 †20
HERRMANN PELAGALLI, Kristi. 1000 W WALLINGS RD STE C 44147 #038-44-1994 L1998
OBG *020 †30
JACOBS, Howard Steven. 500 E ROYALTON RD, STE 100 44147 #010-01-1978 L1980
PD *020 †55
JAKUBOWYCZ, Alexander. 8352 WINDSOR WAY 44147 #847-04-1963 L1970 RO OS *071 †80
JOHN, Binu V. ■ 44147 #495-27-1998 L2005 GE *012
KING, Christine Kline. 2001 E ROYALTON RD 44147 #038-06-1985 L1985 FM *020 †18
KOMROVSKY, Boris. 303 E ROYALTON RD 44147 #033-05-1979 L1980 OPH EM *020 †35
KUMAR, Sanjay. 1682 KENDAL DR 44147 #048-02-1991 L1992 CD *020 †20
KUMAR, Sanjay. ■ 44147 #495-14-1995 L2000 IM *020 †20
LANG, Mark Andrew. 2001 E ROYALTON RD 44147 #038-45-1995 L1997 FM *020 †18
LE, Ngocminh Dang. ■ 44147 #041-15-2005 L2005 CHN *012
LISCH, Nancy Jayne. 500 E ROYALTON RD 44147 #035-06-1988 L1990 PD *020 †55
LONTOC, Rodolfo Maravilla. ■ 44147 #748-07-1948 L1967 DR NM *071
MACKEY-SAWYER, Michelle L. 2001 E ROYALTON RD 44147 #038-40-1995 L1996 FM *020 †18
MARCY, Jennifer Christina. 500 E ROYALTON RD STE 100 44147 #038-43-2004 L2004
PD *020 †55
MARMASH-JAKUBOWYCZ, Marta. ■ 44147 #065-05-1998 L2001 ID *020 †20
MERHEB, Maya Georges. ■ 44147 #038-43-2005 L2005 IM *012
MOOD, Girish R. ■ 44147 #496-39-1995 L2002 IM *020 †20
MUDE, Jagdish L. ■ 44147 #038-44-1983 L1999 P *020
NG, Vincent Yuhin. ■ 44147 #038-40-2007 L2007 ORS *012
QUINN, Megan Murphy. ■ 44147 #016-43-2006 L2006 AN *012
RAMBASEK, James Francis. 303 E ROYALTON RD 44147 #038-06-1970 L1971 OPH *020 †35
RASLAN, Abdulhassib. ■ 44147 #915-04-1981 L1993 OBG *020 †30
RAWAL, Ish. 329 LEXINGTON CIR 44147 #495-74-2003 L2003 IM *020 †20

ROJAS VILLEGAS, Cesar H. 1 EAGLE VALLEY CT 44147 #132-08-1967 L1984 **NS NM** *075
RUDDY, Jennifer Rose. ■ 44147 #038-40-2003 L2003 **PDP** *012 †55
SALWAN, Fayiz A. ■ 44147 #605-01-1959 L1966 **GS SO** *071 †85
SHAH, Jayanti Virpal. ■ 44147 #495-53-1979 L1983 **PD** *020 †55
SHALL, Jeffrey Fain. 1 EAGLE VALLEY CT, STE 101 44147 #038-40-1984 L1989 **ORS** *020 †40
SHARMA, Girishwar. ■ 44147 #495-29-1992 L2000 **PCP** *020
SINGH, Aakash Deep. ■ 44147 #038-44-2002 L2002 **DR** *020 †80
SNEARLY, Roland Glenn. ■ 44147 #017-20-1959 L1972 **EM GS** *071 †85,16
SORIN, Wendy Ann. 303 E ROYALTON RD 44147 #041-01-1983 L1988 **OPH** *071 †35
SRYVALIN, Alejo. ■ 44147 #726-01-1956 L1969 **OS GS** *020 †85
STEVENS, Joanne Kay. 6640 HARRIS RD 44147 #038-06-1993 L1995 **P** *020
TANNOUS, George. 1088 OLD ROYALWOOD RD 44147 #038-41-2008 *012
TORRES, Augusto Javier. ■ 44147 #038-43-1999 AM L1999 **AN** *100 †05
WEINGART, Jason Timothy. ■ 44147 #038-43-2008 *012
WHITE, C Conner, Jr. 500 E ROYALTON RD, STE 100 44147 #038-40-1962 L1962 **FM** *071 †18
YEH, Lloyd Rongkung. 500 E ROYALTON RD, STE 100 44147 #016-06-1996 L1999 **PD** *020 †55
ZACHARY, Ihor Geo. 303 E ROYALTON RD 44147 #008-01-1967 L1970 **OPH** *020 †35
ZELIS, John J. 2107 STONEY RUN CIR 44147 #038-44-1991 L1992 **GS** *020 †85
ZGRABIK, Michael James. 303 E ROYALTON RD 44147 #024-01-1983 L1987 **OPH** *020 †35

BROOK PARK – CUYAHOGA

ANLOAGUE, Pedro Creer, Jr. 14401 SNOW RD, SW URGICARE BROOKPARK CTR 44142 #748-02-1963 L1972 **GP EM** *072
FETTERMAN, Timothy James. 14401 SNOW RD, STE 106 44142 #038-45-1995 L1996 **FM** *020 †18
HONG, John Joonpyo. 15400 SNOW RD 44142 #583-02-1964 L1972 **GP AS** *072
HONG, Rosamond Szyhee. 15400 SNOW RD STE 2 44142 #040-02-1995 L1997 **IM** *020
KEPPLER, Louis. 15900 SNOW RD, STE 200 44142 #028-34-1978 L1983 **ORS OSS** *020 †40
SCARCELLA, Joseph Bernard. 15900 SNOW RD, STE 600 44142 #038-06-1988 L1989 **ORS** *020 †40
THYAGARAJAN, Purnima. ■ 44142 #038-44-2000 L2003 **DBP** *100 †55
TORRES, Vicente J V. 14401 SNOW RD, SOUTH WEST URGICARE 44142 #748-01-1964 L1975 **GPM OM** *020

BROOKFIELD – TRUMBULL

D'AMORE, Amanto Primo. 7264 WARREN SHARON RD 44403 #038-40-1933 L1933 **FPG** *071
GARRIOTT, John Collin. 671 EDGEWOOD DR SE, JAMESON MEMORIAL HOSPITAL 44403 #017-20-1965 L1973 **DR** *020 †80
POMPURA, Patricia Ann. 7264 WARREN SHARON RD, STE 105 44403 #038-44-1994 L1996 **IM** *020 †20
VATURI, Shani. 7264 WARREN SHARON RD 44403 #038-45-1990 L1991 **FM** *020 †18

BROOKLYN – CUYAHOGA

AGEMA, Ryan James. ■ 44144 #025-07-2007 L2007 **EM** *012
ANTHONY, David George. ■ 44144 #038-40-2003 L2003 **CCA** *012
BENHACENE, Assia. ■ 44144 #125-05-1986 L2000 **AN** *020 †05
DEEB, Khaleel. 7575 NORTHCLIFF AVE, STE 304 44144 #875-01-1981 L1990 **FM** *020 †18
DETWILER, Lawrence Alfred. 7575 NORTHCLIFF AVE, STE 102 44144 #038-40-1976 L1979 **IM** *020 †20
HILTON, Pamela Kay. 7575 NORTHCLIFF AVE, STE 307 44144 #038-40-1983 L1985 **IM** *020 †20
KLOVNING, Jason John. ■ 44144 #056-05-2003 L2006 **GS** *012
KOEPKE, Charles Robert. 7575 NORTHCLIFF AVE 44144 #038-06-1997 L1999 **IM** *020 †20
KOEPKE, Keith Robt. 7575 NORTHCLIFF AVE, RIDGEPARK MEDICAL ASSOC., 44144 #038-41-1969 L1969 **IM CD** *020
KUMAR, Suresh. 7575 NORTHCLIFF AVE, STE 103 44144 #495-04-1981 L1990 **N IM** *020 †75
LONERGAN, J Michael. 4758 RIDGE RD, STE 274 44144 #048-13-1976 L1977 **CCP EM** *020 †55,16
MARKOVIC, Michael Andrew. ■ 44144 #038-06-2006 L2006 **DR** *012
MEDIDAS, Rogelia B. 7003 MEMPHIS AVE 44144 #748-09-1966 L1972 **IM** *020 †20
MEHRA, Maneesh Lal. ■ 44144 #305-01-2007 L2007 **IM** *012
SILVERMAN, Michael Steven. 7575 NORTHCLIFF AVE, STE 400 44144 #041-09-1982 L1988 **IM NEP** *030 †20

BROOKVILLE – MONTGOMERY

AHMED, Salva B. 950 SALEM ST 45309 #038-45-1994 L1996 **FM** *020 †18
DAVIS-BROWN, Susan F. 950 SALEM ST 45309 #038-41-1993 L1997 **MPD** *020 †55,20
MARSIDI, Irene. 515 W WESTBROOK RD 45309 #165-04-1976 L1983 **PD** *020 †55
MERGLER, Kristin Suzanne. ■ 45309 #038-45-2007 L2007 **PD** *012
MOLFENTER, Gerald Alfred. 515 W WESTBROOK RD 45309 #038-41-1962 L1962 **PD** *020 †55
PELSOR, Donald August. 515 W WESTBROOK RD 45309 #017-20-1975 L1979 **PDE PD** *020 †55
STUDEBAKER, Jeffrey B. 98 MOSIER PKWY 45309 #038-40-1979 L1980 **FM** *020 †18
STUDEBAKER, Matthew Scott. 98 MOSIER PKWY 45309 #038-40-1999 L1999 **FM** *020 †18
WHARTON, Donald Paul. 950 SALEM ST 45309 #038-45-1989 L1991 **FM** *020 †18

BRUNSWICK – MEDINA

BASSETT, Michael Dale. ■ 44212 #038-43-2006 L2006 **IM** *012
BREWER, Joann Lucy. 3812 CENTER RD 44212 #038-40-1992 L1993 **PD** *020 †55
BRUNO, Lawrence Paul. 3724 CENTER RD STE 105 44212 #038-40-1982 L1983 **ORS** *020 †40
CAIN, Robert Allen. 3724 CENTER RD STE 100, BRUNSWICK FAMILY HLTH CTR 44212 #038-43-1987 L1988 **FM OM** *020 †18
CARRUOZZO, Michele. 3812 CENTER RD 44212 #038-44-1987 L1989 **PD** *020 †55
CHUGHTAI, Humayun. 629 MARKS RD, UNIT E 44212 #704-04-1976 L1999 **P** *020
COLEMAN, Joshua Francis. ■ 44212 #038-06-2007 L2007 **PTH** *012
COOK, Mark. 32 CLEARWATER DR 44212 #041-78-2003, ▲ L2003 **NEP** *012 †20

EHLERT, Michael Joseph. ■ 44212 #038-06-2007 *012
HEMPEL, Joanne Marie. 3812 CENTER RD, STE 100 44212 #038-06-1974 L1977 **PD** *020 †55
HOSTETLER, Daniel Donovan. 3812 CENTER RD 44212 #038-06-1959 L1959 **PD DIA** *020 †55
HUANG, An-Jen. 3724 CENTER RD, STE 102 44212 #244-04-1979 L1985 **CD** *020 †20
IAHN, Paul Harold. ■ 44212 #038-44-1969 L1969 **P GP** *020 †75
KUCHYNSKI, Marie. 3812 CENTER RD, STE 106 44212 #038-06-1990 L1991 **RHU IM** *020 †20
KUO, Su Chiao. 3724 CENTER RD, STE 102 44212 #244-04-1979 L1985 **IM** *020 †20
KUSCHNIR, Konstantin R. 1212 PEARL RD 44212 #038-40-1974 L1974 **ORS** *020
LAMOTHE, Comoche. ■ 44212 #440-01-1974 **P** *100
LEE, Carolyn Kaye. 3724 CENTER RD 44212 #038-06-1975 L1978 **R DR** *062 †80
LITTMAN, James Steven. 3724 CENTER RD 44212 #038-40-1987 L1991 **DR VIR** *020 †80
MC COURT, Laurel Ann. 3724 CENTER RD, BRUNSWICK IMMED CARE CTR 44212 #038-44-1981 L1983 **FM** *020 †18
MCNEELEY, Sean Michael. 3574 CENTER RD 44212 #038-43-1996 L1997 **FM** *020 †18
MEACHAM, Mark Howard. 3724 CENTER RD, STE 100 44212 #038-43-1990 L1991 **FM** *020 †18
MILLER, Timothy Ray. 3724 CENTER RD, STE 100 44212 #038-44-1995 L1996 **FM** *020 †18
PATEL, Ashwinkumar N. 3801 CENTER RD, TRI-COUNTY ONCOLOGY 44212 #495-23-1980 L1987 **RO** *020
PERSTIN, Elizabeth. ■ 44212 #913-33-1990 L2000 **IM** *020
POTTSCHMIDT, Steven A. 3724 CENTER RD 44212 #017-20-1990 L1991 **FM** *020 †18
SEE, Lily A. 1839 PEARL RD, 1839 PEARL RD A-101 44212 #748-01-1965 L1971 **PD PTH** *020 †50,55
SPRENG, Jeannette P. 1212 PEARL RD 44212 #038-43-1984 L1985 **FM** *020 †18
TIRRI, Angelo. 3724 CENTER RD 44212 #561-08-1954 L1967 **OBG OS** *020
TOTH, John David. 3812 CENTER RD 44212 #038-40-2003 L2003 **PD** *020 †55
TRUDEAU, John P. 3812 CENTER RD 44212 #016-43-1982 L1984 **PD** *020 †55
TULISIAK, Thomas Lee. 3724 CENTER RD STE 100 44212 #038-43-1980 L1981 **FM** *020 †18
WALKER, David Cameron. 3812 CENTER RD 44212 #038-06-1980 L1992 **PD** *050 †55,19
WILLIAMS, Marc Semyan. 3724 CENTER RD STE 100 44212 #038-40-1984 L1985 **FM** *020 †18

BRYAN – WILLIAMS

AFIFI, Mahmoud. 442 W HIGH ST, MIDWEST COMMUNITY HEALTH A 43506 #915-04-1983 L1999 **HO** *020 †20
AL-KHALEEFA, Adnan Abdoh. 442 W HIGH ST 43506 #704-02-1975 L1979 **OBG** *020 †30
BELL, Clarence A, Jr. 442 W HIGH ST 43506 #038-43-1977 L1978 **FM** *020 †18
CARRICO, Virgil Norman. 442 W HIGH ST, BRYAN MEDICAL GROUP 43506 #017-20-1966 L1970 **FM** *071 †18
CHAO, Darren Dayuan. 433 W HIGH ST 43506 #060-02-1994 L2000 **DR** *020 †80
CONRAD, Diane. 442 W HIGH ST 43506 #038-06-1979 L1980 **FM** *020 †18
DIAZ-PEREDA, Lamberto. 442 W HIGH ST 43506 #649-03-1972 L1976 **IM END** *020 †20
DODDIPATLA, Sarveswara R. 442 W HIGH ST 43506 #495-11-1972 L1977 **GS GP** *071 †85
FINK, Kimberly Lynn. 442 W HIGH ST 43506 #038-40-1999 L1999 **PD** *020 †55
GALUPO, Pedrito Apoong. 324 W HIGH ST 43506 #748-08-1962 L1971 **GS GP** *020 †85
GROTHAUS, Matthew C. 442 W HIGH ST 43506 #038-43-2001 L2001 **HS** *020
HARVEY, William Dow. 442 W HIGH ST 43506 #048-12-1976 L1977 **GS** *020 †85
HESS, Richard Lynn. 442 W HIGH ST, BRYAN MEDICAL GROUP 43506 #055-01-1967 L1972 **PD PDA** *020 †55
HICKS, Kerry Lee. 442 W HIGH ST, BRYAN MEDICAL GROUP, INC 43506 #038-41-1992 L1995 **OBG** *020 †30
HOOK, Bruce Alfred. 433 W HIGH ST, COMMUNITY HOSP OF WILLIAMS 43506 #836-01-1978 L1993 **TS GS** *020 †85
JACKSON, Allen Gene. ■ 43506 #038-40-1961 L1961 **PD** *071 †55
JACOBS, Misty Dawn. ■ 43506 #038-43-2005 L2005 **PTH** *012
KANNEY, Robert Oscar, Jr. 442 W HIGH ST 43506 #038-43-1979 L1980 **FM** *020 †18 ‡
KEIL, Shannon Michelle. 410 W HIGH ST, CHWG LAB 43506 #038-43-2001 L2001 *020
KENNEDY, Larry Malcolm. 442 W HIGH ST 43506 #038-02-1989 L1995 **PM** *020 †60
KOLOVICH, Kevin James. 442 W HIGH ST, MIDWEST COMMUNITY HEALTH A 43506 #038-40-1981 L1982 **ORS** *020 †40
KOZDEMBA, Teresa Ann. ■ 43506 #025-12-1998 L2007 **EM** *020 †16
MEYER, Raymond Kederick. 442 W HIGH ST 43506 #038-06-1979 L1980 **FM** *020 †18
MOATS, John Edwin. ■ 43506 #038-41-1961 L1961 **FM AN** *071 †18
NAGEL, Frederick John. ■ 43506 #038-43-1973 L1975 **FM** *071 †20
PAK, Michael Milan. 524 W HIGH ST, RADIATION ONCOLOGY CENTER 43506 #016-42-1992 L2000 **RO** *020 †80
POLE, Michael Jos. 433 W HIGH ST, DEPARTMENT OF RADIOLOGY 43506 #038-45-1991 L1995 **DR** *020 †80
REDDY, Damodar Kutur. 442 W HIGH ST 43506 #495-57-1973 L1978 **AN** *020 †05
REDDY, Kesireddy Damoder. 442 W HIGH ST 43506 #495-65-1972 L1991 **IM** *020 †20,25
ROEBUCK, David Michael. 433 W HIGH ST, BRYAN COMM HOSP 43506 #025-01-1967 L1977 **DR** *020
SAUBER, Michael Jos. 442 W HIGH ST 43506 #038-41-1978 L1979 **FM** *020 †18
SHARMA, Usha. 433 W HIGH ST, DEPT OF RADIOLOGY 43506 #495-64-1974 L1985 **DR** *020 †80
SHARROCK, Robert Earl. 442 W HIGH ST 43506 #023-01-1971 L1977 **FM EM** *020 †18 ‡
SMETHURST, Patricia Ann. 442 W HIGH ST, ATTN ADMINISTRATION 43506 #038-40-1982 L1984 **PD** *020 †55
SROA, Hardev Singh. 442 W HIGH ST, MIDWEST COMMUNITY HEALTH A 43506 #495-36-1976 L1996 **PD SME** *020 †55
STALTER, Marvin Dale. 442 W HIGH ST 43506 #038-43-1998 L1999 **FM** *020 †18
TANTOCO, Almario Ramos. 442 W HIGH ST 43506 #748-11-1973 L1980 **OBG EM** *020 †30
TANTOCO, Luvenia Estrada. 442 W HIGH ST 43506 #748-11-1973 L1980 **PD** *020 †55
TOKUNAGA, Yoshinori. 433 W HIGH ST, WELLNESS CENTERS 43506 #572-07-1957 L1972 **PTH** *020 †50
WALZ, Carl Nicholas. 442 W HIGH ST 43506 #038-43-1974 L1975 **FM** *020 †18

BUCYRUS – CRAWFORD

AUCHARD, Virgil Allen. ■ 44820 #038-40-1959 L1959 **GP OS** *071
BLAIR, Keith David. 725 N SANDUSKY AVE 44820 #017-20-1973 L1974 **FM GYN** *020 †18
BOWERS, Vicki Elizabeth. 140 HILL ST, STE A 44820 #038-43-1999 L2002 **FM** *020 †18
BOWERSOCK, George Wesley. ■ 44820 #038-40-1959 L1959 **GP AN** *071
FRAZIER, Ronald Dayle. 725 N SANDUSKY AVE 44820 #038-40-1978 L1983 **CD** *020

■ = Address Information Privacy Protected

IDE, Carl John. ■ 44820 #038-40-1944 L1944 **GP FM** *071
IVANAUSKAS, Saulius. 629 N SANDUSKY AVE 44820 #913-96-1988 L1999 **FM** *020 †18
KHAWAJA, Waseem A. 629 N SANDUSKY AVE 44820 #704-01-1988 L1996 **EM IM** *020 †20 ‡
KURTZ, John Kiess. 629 N SANDUSKY AVE 44820 #023-07-1962 L1963 **IM HEM** *071
LANDES, Michael David. 512 HILL ST 44820 #038-40-1987 L1989 **FM** *020 †18
LEWIS, Lawrence Alfred. 629 N SANDUSKY AVE 44820 #065-01-1984 L1995 **EM** *020 ‡
LYON, Ralph L. 2356 QUAKER RD 44820 #016-76-1979, ▲ L1980 **GP** *020
MILLER, David Ronald. 629 N SANDUSKY AVE 44820 #038-41-1974 L1974 **U** *020
MORTERA, Gloria H. 629 N SANDUSKY AVE 44820 #748-02-1952 L1968 **PD** *020
SHIN, Dong Wook. 725 N SANDUSKY AVE 44820 #583-03-1963 L1978 **OBG** *020
SOLT, Robert Lee, Jr. 629 N SANDUSKY AVE 44820 #038-40-1957 L1957 **GS OS** *071 †85 ‡
STRICKLAND, R Todd. 139 GAIUS ST 44820 #038-43-1993 L1995 **MPD ADM** *020 †20
STRICKLAND, Rebecca Lee. 139 GAIUS ST 44820 #038-43-1997 L2003 **PLM IMG** *020 †20
WENNER, Donald R. ■ 44820 #038-40-1944 L1944 **GP AN** *071

BURBANK – WAYNE

SCHULZ, Robert E. ■ 44214 #041-02-1949 L1957 **CLP PTH** *071 †50

BUTLER – RICHLAND

REED, Esther Elizabeth. 46 W ELM ST 44822 #025-07-1943 L1945 **GP** *071

BYESVILLE – GUERNSEY

ROTH, Barbara Kay. 205 SENECA AVE 43723 #035-09-1975 L1989 **FM OBG** *020

CADIZ – HARRISON

ABDULLAH, Mohammed Najeeb. 951 E MARKET ST 43907 #875-01-1975 L1985 **END IM** *071
KUZIAK, John Dennis. 951 E MARKET ST 43907 #038-40-1967 L1967 **IM CD** *020
LOOBY, Robert Gary. 951 E MARKET ST 43907 #033-05-1973 L1983 **FM** *020 †18
MODI, Ajit Singh. ■ 43907 #495-20-1961 L1972 **EM GP** *020
MURTHY, Anandhi N. 943 E MARKET ST 43907 #495-59-1976 L1995 **GS EM** *020 †85
PECAR, Janez. 951 E MARKET ST 43907 #957-03-1970 L1992 **IM** *020 †20
SHAFFER, David. 951 E MARKET ST, HARRISON COMMUNITY HOSPITA 43907 #654-01-1989 L1992 **GS** *020 †85
SHAH, Nalini Hasmukh. 951 E MARKET ST 43907 #495-28-1966 L1973 **PTH** *030 †50
SISCU, Haralambie. 951 E MARKET ST, HARRISON COMMUNITY HOSPITA 43907 #781-01-1996 L2001 **FM** *020 †18 ‡
TABBAH, Isam. 943 E MARKET ST 43907 #875-01-1971 L1975 **GP GS** *020
TABBAH, Sammy M. PO BOX 322 43907 #038-44-2007 L2007 **OBG** *012

CALCUTTA – COLUMBIANA

DUGAN, Thomas Matthew, Jr. 15303 STATE ROUTE 170 43920 #041-12-1977 L1995 **N** *020 †75

CALDWELL – NOBLE

ASHCRAFT, David Clinton. 111 WEST ST, ASHCRAFT CLINIC INC 43724 #028-79-1974, ▲ L1976 **FM OS** *071
COX, Frederick Manson. ■ 43724 #038-40-1957 L1957 **FM PHP** *071 †18
JENKINS, John Benjamin. 304 MAIN ST 43724 #005-17-1962 L1975 *075
MURRAY, Thomas Douglas. 317 WEST ST 43724 #051-01-1979 L2000 **FM ADM** *020 †18 ‡

CAMBRIDGE – GUERNSEY

AL-QUAIMI, Muhammad J. 1200 CLARK ST 43725 #584-01-1989 L2004 **OP** *020 †40
ALTEN, Kevin Wayne. 1210 CLARK ST 43725 #038-40-1993 L1994 **OBG** *020 †30
ANTALIS, John James. 1210 NEAL DR 43725 #038-40-1989 L1990 **OPH** *020 †35
APEL, Clarence Raymond. ■ 43725 #038-40-1952 L1952 **GP FM** *071 †18
BINKIEWICZ, Joseph Arthur. 1210 CLARK ST 43725 #055-01-1996 L1997 **OBG** *020 †30
CHENDRAJ, Bilimagga V. 1515 MAPLE DR 43725 #495-52-1967 L1973 **IM CD** *020
CHLOVECHOK, James David. 216 HIGHLAND AVE 43725 #038-40-1987 L1988 **EM IM** *020 †16
CONAWAY, Earl E, Jr. 1198 CLARK ST 43725 #038-43-1983 L1984 **FM** *020
CONAWAY, Earl Edwin. 1198 CLARK ST 43725 #038-06-1941 L1941 **GP** *072 †18
CUDDEBACK, Barbara. 66737 OLD 21 RD 43725 #012-01-2002 L2002 **P** *020 †75
DAY, Richard Graham. 1325 CLARK ST 43725 #038-06-1980 L1980 **FM** *020
DAYTON, Michelle Suzanne. 1341 CLARK ST, MEDICAL CENTER 43725 #038-45-1996 L1997 **EM** *020 †16
DYCOCO, Edna. 1341 CLARK ST 43725 #748-01-1969 L1988 **PD** *020
EDDY, Andrew D. 1341 CLARK ST, SOUTHEASTERN MED 43725 #038-44-1983 L1984 **EM IM** *020 †20,16
FERN, Stewart Adam. 2500 JOHN GLENN HWY, SCI SIX COUNTY INC. 43725 #748-09-1976 L1991 **P EM** *020
FISHER, Thomas E. 7297 JOHN GLENN HWY 43725 #038-06-1999 L1999 **GS** *020
FLANIGAN, Jackson L. 100 CLARK CT, SOUTHEASTERN OHIO PHYS 43725 #055-02-1986 L1991 **GS** *020 †85
GAINOR, Patricia A. 1115 CLARK ST, OHIO PSYCHIATRIC 43725 #055-01-1986 L1997 **CHP** *020 †75
GHOLL, John Bernard. 813 STEUBENVILLE AVE, CAMBRIDGE ENT & ALLERGY 43725 #023-01-1984 L2003 **OTO** *020 †45
GOGGIN, Joseph Thos. 1515 MAPLE DR 43725 #010-02-1959 L1963 **IM** *020 †20
GOGGIN, Mark Thomas. 1515 MAPLE DR 43725 #038-45-1994 L1995 **MPD** *020 †20,55
GOGGIN, Patrick David. 1515 MAPLE DR 43725 #038-41-1998 L1999 **IM** *020 †20
HATWALKAR, Shrikant M. COUNTY RD 35 N 43725 #495-19-1962 L1980 **P ADP** *020 †75
HOLLOWAY, Thomas Craig. ■ 43725 #038-40-1982 L1983 **AN GP** *020 †16
JACHE, Heidi. 2007 E WHEELING AVE, THOMPKINS CHILD & ADOL SER 43725 #056-06-1982 L1987 **CHP P** *020 †75

KELLER, James Wesley. 1341 CLARK ST 43725 #038-40-1961 L1961 **MDM** *030 †85
KELLUM, Jesse B. 1341 CLARK ST 43725 #024-01-1951 L1956 **GS** *071 †85
KNAUER, Quentin Frederick. 1341 CLARK ST 43725 #038-06-1958 L1966 **GS EM** *071 †85
KOLLENGODE, Sivaram R. 1350 CLARK ST 43725 #495-73-1969 L1994 **FM** *020 †18
LALL, Shobha Uttam. 1432 CLARK ST 43725 #495-01-1968 L1976 **PD** *020 †55
LEE, Simon. COUNTY RD 35 N, DEPT PSYCH 43725 #244-02-1965 L1978 **P** *100
LESLIE, Clark James. 100 CLARK CT, SOUTHEASTERN OHIO PHYS 43725 #038-40-1992 L1997 **GS** *020 †85
MAHAYRI, Eyad. 1350 CLARK ST 43725 #781-01-1985 L1996 **PUD CCM** *020 †20
MASSULLO-SCHUBERT, Sandra. 9259 CADIZ RD 43725 #038-44-1992 L1994 **MPD** *020 †55
MAXIMO, Clifford Bautista. 1200 CLARK ST 43725 #038-44-1994 L1996 **U** *020 †95
MAXIMO, Zosimo Tan. 1200 CLARK ST 43725 #748-01-1963 L1972 **U** *020 †95
MILLER, Howard D. ■ 43725 #038-06-1952 L1952 **FM** *071
NAU, Melissa Ann. 10095 BRICK CHURCH RD 43725 #038-45-1994 L1999 **FM** *020 †18
NOCHE, Emmanuel Dimatulac. 1327 CLARK ST 43725 #748-01-1963 L1975 **OTO** *020
OJEDELE, Kayode Ayodele T. 1515 MAPLE DR 43725 #690-01-1988 L2000 **IM** *020 †20 ‡
POWERS, J Michael. 1431 CLARK ST, CENTER, DEPT OF ANESTHESIO 43725 #030-05-1984 L1997 **AN** *020 †05
RANGASWAMY, Billimagga V. 1515 MAPLE DR 43725 #495-33-1966 L1975 **PD** *020 †55
RANGWANI, Mukesh R. 1115 CLARK ST, OHIO PSYCHIATRIC 43725 #704-08-1982 L1995 **P** *020
RASS, Amjad Al. 61353 SOUTHGATE RD, STE 5 43725 #875-01-1989 L1999 **IM** *020 †20
REDDY, Gurijala N. 1410 CLARK ST, CAMBRIDGE REGIONAL CANCER 43725 #495-57-1968 L1981 **RO** *020 †80
REED, Suzanne Michelle. ■ 43725 #038-40-2006 L2006 **PD** *012
ROUTSON, Gary Wayne. 1175 S 13TH ST 43725 #038-40-1975 L1975 **ORS** *020 †40
RUSH, Douglas Allen. 1515 MAPLE DR 43725 #038-41-1998 L2002 **MPD** *020 †20,55
SARAP, Michael Duke. 100 CLARK CT, SOUTHEASTERN OHIO PHYS 43725 #038-41-1982 L1986 **GS VS** *020 †85
SAYAT, Jose Nilo Macaraig. 64975 OLD 21 RD 43725 #748-01-1967 L1973 **GS** *020
SAYEGH, Michael Foad. 61353 SOUTHGATE RD 43725 #875-01-1986 L2005 **AN PME** *020 †05
SHARAN, Vishwa Mohan. 1410 CLARK ST 43725 #495-15-1967 L1980 **RO** *071 †80
SLABINSKI, Carmencita B. ■ 43725 #038-44-1992 L1993 **IM** *020 †20
SLABINSKI, Mark Stanley. 67043 OLD 21 RD, EMP TRUST 43725 #038-44-1992 L1995 **EM** *020 †16
SNYDER, Dayle Owen. ■ 43725 #016-11-1958 L1964 **GS** *071
SPROUT, Kelly Lynn. 2500 JOHN GLENN HWY RO 43725 #038-40-1995 L1997 **P** *020 †75
SRIKANTIAH, Akkihebbal R. 9884 CADIZ RD 43725 #495-09-1961 L1976 **OPH** *020 †35
STANSBURY, Stephen W. 1337 CLARK ST BOX 1176 43725 #036-07-1975 L1983 **FM** *020 †18
STONER, Brady B. 749 WHEELING AVE 43725 #038-40-1971 L1971 **AN** *020 †05
SWAN, Thomas De Selm. ■ 43725 #016-06-1955 L1957 **FM PHP** *071 †18
THAMBURAJ, Vimala. 66737 OLD 21 RD, APPALACHIAN BEHAVRL HLTH 43725 #495-27-1971 L1977 **FM** *020
TINANA, Andres M. PO BOX 724 43725 #748-01-1966 L1976 **AN** *020
TOMPKINS, Harry H. ■ 43725 #048-12-1951 L1971 **DR NM** *071 †80
TORMA, James A. 1341 CLARK ST, SOUTHEAST OHIO REG MED CEN 43725 #048-13-1992 L1994 **AN** *020 †05
TRIPATHI, Prabha R. 66737 OLD 21 RD, CAMBRIDGE P HOSPITAL 43725 #495-05-1964 L1977 **P** *071 †75
TRIPATHI, Rajkishore R. 1515 MAPLE DR 43725 #495-17-1966 L1973 **CD IM** *020
VAISHNAV, Pratik Mayur. ■ 43725 #495-48-1996 L2006 **FM** *100
VAKA, Sreeramulu Reddy. 66737 OLD 21 RD, CARE / ODMH 43725 #496-01-1982 L2000 **P** *020
VORA, Shashikant Maganlal. 1452 CLARK ST 43725 #496-38-1974 L1971 **AN** *020 †20
VORA, Sonali Shashi. ■ 43725 #038-44-2007 *012
WRIGHT, Paul Christopher. 1210 CLARK ST 43725 #038-43-1994 L1996 **OBG** *020 †30
YANES, Marwan. 1341 CLARK ST 43725 #875-01-1971 L1975 **EM** *020 †16
ZEIDAN, Trisha Lynn. ■ 43725 #038-40-2004 L2004 **END** *012 †20

CAMPBELL – MAHONING

FIORINI, Richard J. 315 STRUTHERS LIBERTY RD 44405 #028-78-1967, ▲ L1968 *071
GAETANO, Themelina Barker. ■ 44405 #038-45-2002 L2003 **PD** *100
VUKSTA, Michael J. ■ 44405 #038-45-1988 L1992 *020

CANAL FULTON – STARK

HITE, Amy Ann. 8841 VANDERGRIFF AVE NW 44614 #038-44-1999 L2000 **IM** *020 †20
ISON, Rodney Keith. 944 CHERRY ST E 44614 #020-12-1983 L1984 **FM GE** *020 †18
NAIR, Ajay. 944 CHERRY ST E 44614 #038-44-1996 L1997 **FM** *020 †18
RUCKI, Pamela A. 944 CHERRY ST E 44614 #038-43-1985 L1986 **FM** *020 †18
WALTERS, Michelle Dawn. ■ 44614 #038-44-2008 *012

CANAL WINCHESTER – FRANKLIN

ANDERSON, Geoffrey M. 11925 LITHOPOLIS RD NW, TRI-COUNTY FAMILY PHYSICIA 43110 #038-40-1989 L1991 **FM** *020 †18
CASTRUITA, Jesus Jose. 43110 #026-04-1977 L1998 **AN GP** *020
CRAMER, Timothy Jay. 3618 GENDER RD # 117, CLEVELAND CLINIC FOUNDATIO 43110 #004-01-1990 L1998 **DR** *020 †80
ESTIS, Herbert Ray. 43110 #025-01-1976 L1977 **FM** *020 †18
FRANZ, Robin Lynn. 11925 LITHOPOLIS RD NW, UPPR LEVEL 43110 #007-02-2003 L2003 **FM** *020 †18
HARRIS, Melissa Dianna. 11925 LITHOPOLIS RD NW, UPPR LEVEL 43110 #038-43-1998 L1999 **FM** *020 †18
HARVEY, Karah Ann. ■ 43110 #038-45-2008 *012
HERDMAN, Marc Reid. ■ 43110 #038-40-2000 L2000 **EM** *020 †16
KIMPTON, Mark Troy. 11925 LITHOPOLIS RD NW, UPPR LEVEL 43110 #305-01-1993 L1997 **FM** *020 †18
KIRKBRIDE, Jill Lynn. ■ 43110 #038-45-2000 L2004 **MPD** *020
LAMB, Jarom Frederick. ■ 43110 #038-40-2007 L2007 **GS** *012
LEGG, Duncan Eric. 11925 LITHOPOLIS RD NW, UPPR LEVEL 43110 #016-11-1984 L1985 **FM** *020 †18
ONWE, Charles Nwode. 3618 GENDER RD # 213 43110 #690-01-1991 L2004 **IM** *020 †20

PHILLIPS, Scott Richey. 11925 LITHOPOLIS RD NW, UPPR LEVEL 43110 #038-41-1974 L1975 FM *020 †18

PRINCE, Clifton J. ■ 43110 #047-07-1999 L2000 FM *020

QUINLIN, Teresa Ellen. 28 E WATERLOO ST 43110 #038-45-1984 L1985 FM *020 †18

SMITH, Myron Ray. ■ 43110 #038-40-1954 L1954 NS *071 †25

TURNER, Ross P. ■ 43110 #038-75-2004, ▲ L2004 AN *100

WARD-KIMPTON, Audre L. 11925 LITHOPOLIS RD NW 43110 #305-01-1994 L2000 PTH *100

WYNKOOP, Barbara Mcquaid. 6441 WINCHESTER BLVD, CANAL WINCHESTER FAM HLTH 43110 #038-40-1988 L1989 FM *020 †18

CANFIELD – MAHONING

AGNESI, Nicholas F. 3869 STARRS CENTRE DR 44406 #038-44-1984 L1987 GS *020

ALBANI, Thomas E, Jr. 6715 TIPPECANOE RD, STE E101 44406 #038-40-1981 L1982 FM *020 †18 ‡

ANDERSON, John James. ■ 44406 #038-41-1956 L1956 PD *071 †55

ARNOTT, Jon Wm. 450 E MAIN ST 44406 #308-03-1987 L1990 IM *020 †20

AWAD, Marie Linda. ■ 44406 #038-44-2007 L2007 GS *012

BACANI, Roberto A. 3645 STUTZ DR 44406 #748-10-1961 L1969 NEP IM *020

BAIRD, Jennifer M. 4139 BOARDMAN CANFIELD RD 44406 #055-01-1995 L1996 OBG *020 †30

BAL, Rajpreet Kaur. ■ 44406 #038-44-2002 L2002 APM *100

BARTELS, William Tod. 459 LISBON ST 44406 #038-44-1990 L1992 FM *020 †18 ‡

BARTON, Daniel Patrick. 3685 STUTZ DR 44406 #038-40-1997 L1999 MPD *020

BASILE, Simon A. 3623 MERCEDES PL 44406 #056-06-1963 L1967 IM CD *020

BOBOVNYIK, Denise Louise. 3660 STUTZ DR STE 102, PRIMARY CARE SPECIALISTS, 44406 #038-44-1985 L1986 FM *020 †18

BOULOS, Anthony Michael. ■ 44406 #038-44-2008 *012

BRAR, Jasdip Singh. ■ 44406 #305-01-2005 L2005 IM *012

CHAHINE, Antoine Emile. 3695 BOARDMAN CANFIELD RD 44406 #605-01-1986 L1988 ON IM *020 †20

CHIU, Yau-Too, Jr. 3768 BOARDMAN CANFIELD RD 44406 #385-03-1962 L1969 PS HS *020 †85,65 ‡

CROWE, Stephen Nathaniel. ■ 44406 #012-01-1998 L2004 FM *020 †18

CUTTICA, Robert J. 6470 TIPPECANOE RD, RR 224 44406 #035-08-1968 L1976 ORS IM *020

DAY, Xuan-Trang Thi. ■ 44406 #007-02-1997 L2003 IM *020 †20

DEWAN, Sanjeev. 3645 STUTZ DR 44406 #067-01-1984 L1991 OPH *020 †35

DIETZ, George Henry. 3694 STARRS CENTRE DR 44406 #035-08-1954 L1961 PS *071 †65

DOMINGO, Narciso Calaucay. 3821 STARRS CENTRE DR, STE B 44406 #748-01-1965 L1972 AI PD *020 †55,03

FRIEDRICH, Fredrick A. ■ 44406 #010-01-1946 L1948 FM *071 †18

GALOSE, Michael Carmen. ■ 44406 #038-40-1956 L1956 FM PD *020 †18

GARFINKLE, Paul Andrew. 3645 STUTZ DR 44406 #041-02-1993 L1998 OPH *020 †35

GARG, Sudershan Kumar. 3695 BOARDMAN CANFIELD RD 44406 #495-03-1962 L1975 ON HEM *020 †20

GARRITANO, Daniel. 4139 BOARDMAN CANFIELD RD, STE 2 44406 #038-44-1981 L1982 PS HS *020 †85,65

GATEWOOD, Paul Douglas. 5395 BAY HILL DR 44406 #055-01-1970 L1971 OBG *020 †30

GELETKA, Susan Mary. 9275 W CALLA RD, MINERS MEDICAL CENTER 44406 #041-02-1980 L1983 DR *020 †80

GERSHKOWITZ, Robert Scott. 7368 TIPPECANOE RD, STE 330 44406 #038-43-1994 L1995 EM *016

GREENBAUM, Arthur M. ■ 44406 #035-46-1982 L1988 RO *020

GROSS, Eric Todd. 6674 TIPPECANOE RD, STE 1 44406 #038-44-1995 L1996 PM *020 †60

HARKEY, Gregory Lawrence. ■ 44406 #038-44-2007 L2007 DR *012

HECHT, Bryan Reid. 6674 TIPPECANOE RD STE 3 44406 #038-44-1981 L1983 REN OBG *020 †30

HO, Paul. ■ 44406 #028-34-1972 L1973 IM *020

JAMISON, James Patrick. 6470 TIPPECANOE RD 44406 #036-05-1990 L1997 ORS OAR *020 †40

JONES, Daniel Fuller. ■ 44406 #050-02-2002 L2005 PTH *012

JOSEPH, Thomas Anthony. 6470 TIPPECANOE RD 44406 #038-40-1996 L1998 OSM *020 †40

KALAVSKY, Steven Mark. 6715 TIPPECANOE RD, BLDG E STE 201 44406 #008-01-1969 L1976 CHN *020 †55,75

KERRIGAN, James Thos. 6470 TIPPECANOE RD 44406 #038-43-1982 L1988 ORS *020 †40

KRISHNAN, Unni Eledath. 3695 BOARDMAN CANFIELD RD, BLOOD & CANCER CENTER 44406 #495-53-1972 L1977 HEM ON *020 †20

LAKHANI, Prabhudas R. 3798 SPERONE DR 44406 #495-38-1959 L1974 IM *020 †20

LEHRER, Richard Aaron. 3645 STUTZ DR 44406 #035-47-1988 L1993 OPH *020 †35

LEWIS, Robert D. 4139 BOARDMAN CANFIELD RD, STE 2 44406 #016-11-1989 L1991 PS HS *020 †85,65

MANSOUR, Huwaida E. 4000 MONTEREALE DR 44406 #305-01-1998 L2000 OM *020 †55

MASSULLO, Edmund Anthony. ■ 44406 #028-34-1947 L1948 VS TS *072

MILLER, Patricia Ann. ■ 44406 #041-07-1968 L1975 IM *020

MORCOS, Roy Nicolas. 45 MANOR HILL DR, STE 300 44406 #605-01-1980 L1985 FM REN *020 †18 ‡

MORGAN, Scott David. ■ 44406 #038-44-1993 L1994 FM *020 †18

NEWTON, Charles C. 3685 VILLA ROSA DR 44406 #306-01-1985 L2001 PD PE *020 †55

ORR, Robert Joseph. 3685 STUTZ DR 44406 #038-44-1996 L1997 NEP *020

PAGANO, Trina Marie. 4139 BOARDMAN CANFIELD RD 44406 #038-40-1989 L1990 OBG *020 †30

PATEL, Niranjan Nanalal. 6674 TIPPECANOE RD STE 6 44406 #496-38-1975 L1982 GS EM *020 †85

POWELL, Derek Scott. ■ 44406 #038-43-2008 *012

SCHWENDEMAN, Leslie Jon. 6470 TIPPECANOE RD, YOUNGSTOWN ORTHOPAEDIC ASS 44406 #038-40-1990 L1996 HS *020 †40

SHEIK, Saba Lateef-Khan. ■ 44406 #422-01-2004 L2004 IM *100

SHIU, Albert Tak-Yee. 4038 SAINT ANDREWS CT 44406 #016-43-1965 L1989 OBG *040 †30

SHORTEN, Edward Arthur. ■ 44406 #038-06-1943 L1944 GS *071 †85

SMYTHE, Richard L. ■ 44406 #024-01-1950 L1955 GS *071 †85

SOLMEN, James David, Jr. 6470 TIPPECANOE RD 44406 #038-40-1992 L1995 ORS OS *020 †40

STEFKO, Joseph Michael. 74 OAK TREE DR 44406 #038-45-1989 L1995 ORS OSM *020 †40

TOLEN, Dianna. 4133 BOARDMAN CANFIELD RD, KIDS FIRST PEDIATRIC CARE 44406 #038-44-1995 L1996 PD *020 †55

VASSILAROS-SARMA, Maria G. ■ 44406 #418-01-1983 L1988 IM *020

WEST COFFEE, Carla Sumiko. ■ 44406 #016-42-2006 L2006 GS *012

YOUNG, Scott Douglas. 3645 STUTZ DR 44406 #038-40-2003 L2007 GE *012 †20

ZINNI, Gregory Stephen. 540 E MAIN ST 44406 #038-40-1982 L1983 FM *020 †18

CANTON – STARK

ABOOD, Samuel N. 2600 6TH ST SW 44710 #038-40-1952 L1952 GP OS *071

ABOU RJEILY, Charbel Meh. 2600 6TH ST SW, DEPT MED 44710 #605-03-2004 L2007 IM *012

ABUZAKHM, Sonia Marie. ■ 44703 #038-44-2007 L2007 IM *012

ADAMS, Daniel Wilcox. 5000 HIGBEE AVE NW 44718 #035-20-1959 L1967 OBG *071 †30

AGARWALA, Krishna Prasad. 4168 HOLIDAY ST NW 44718 #495-34-1961 L1973 IM *020 †20

AHMAD, Mirza Nasir. 4782 MUNSON ST NW 44718 #704-01-1965 L1974 PS HS *020 †65

AHMED, Farooq. 3688 DRESSLER RD NW, TRICOUNTY HEMATOLOGY & 44718 #704-01-1967 L1973 ON HEM *020 †20

AHMED, Syed Viqar. ■ 44708 #704-01-1985 *100

AHN, Joseph Hisuck. 1445 HARRISON AVE NW, STE 101 44708 #583-01-1967 L1977 OBG *020 †30

AIELLO, Michael Richard. 2600 6TH ST SW, RADIOLOGY ASSOCIATES OF 44710 #035-15-1976 L2001 DR *020 †80

AL-ABBOUSY, Fadhil Khalil. 2815 TUSCARAWAS ST W 44708 #528-01-1955 L1969 PD *020 †55

ALASYALI, Aziz. 1320 TIMKEN MERCY DR NW 44708 #902-01-1951 L1966 IM FM *020

ALBERTSON, Steven. 2600 TUSCARAWAS ST W, STE 620 44708 #035-08-1988 L1990 CRS GS *020 †85,10

ALBERTUCCI, Mario. ■ 44718 #561-17-1981 L1999 TS *020 †90,85

ALJABERI, Mohamed M. 4105 HOLIDAY ST NW, NEUROCARE CENTER INC 44718 #875-02-1982 L1992 N *020 †75

ALLAMPATI, Sanath Kumar. 2600 6TH ST SW, DEPT OF GME 44710 #496-01-2001 L2005 IM *012

ALLISON, Randy Guy. 44709 #038-44-2007 L2007 ORS *012

ANDALORO, Rebecca Lynne. 3666 CLEVELAND AVE SW 44707 #038-44-2001 L2001 FM *020 †18

ANDRADE FLOR, Guillermo. ■ 44714 #847-04-1965 L1977 EM *020

ANDREFSKY, John Charles. 2600 6TH ST SW 44710 #041-09-1990 L1994 N NS *020 †75

ANDREOZZI, John Chas. 2421 13TH ST NW 44708 #030-06-1974 L1975 ADM GP *020

ARMINEOUS, Anthony George. 1320 MERCY DR NW, PAIN MANAGEMENT DEPT 44708 #915-04-1987 L2004 IM *012

ARONICA, Josephine Clara. 5850 FULTON DR NW 44718 #041-07-1964 L1966 OS *020

ARONSON, Brian A. 1320 MERCY DR NW 44708 #016-06-1990 L2004 VIR *020 †80

ARORA, Manoj Kumar. 1445 HARRISON AVE NW, # 305 44708 #495-75-1973 L1981 OBG GP *020

ARORA, Neelam. 1445 HARRISON AVE NW # 306 44708 #496-07-1973 L1982 PD *020 †55

ARORA, Rakesh Kumar. 4760 BELPAR ST NW, O,MI ORTHPEDS INC 44718 #495-05-1970 L1982 ORS *020 †40

ARRIETA GARCIA, Carlos Em. 2600 6TH ST SW 44710 #264-12-2001 L2007 IM *012

ARSUAGA-SANTANA, Rafael E. 4160 HOLIDAY ST NW 44718 #042-01-1979 L1980 RHU IG *020 †20

ASFOURA, Jehad Yusuf. 4689 FULTON DR NW 44718 #875-01-1980 L1989 NEP IM *020 †20

ASSAAD, Manal. 1320 MERCY DR NW 44708 #038-44-1994 L1998 OPH *020 †35

ATIENZA, Allan. 2600 6TH ST SW 44710 #038-43-1994 L1995 EM *020 †16

AVENIDO, Miguel Manalo. ■ 44708 #748-01-1953 L1966 R *075

BACHMEIER, James A. 4665 DOUGLAS CIR NW 44718 #037-01-1991 L1994 AN *020 †05

BACHRACH, Eric Lawrence. 2600 7TH ST SW, AULTMAN FAMILY PRACTICE RE 44708 #654-01-2005 L2005 FP *012

BACKUS, Donna Jean. 2920 MARKET AVE N 44714 #038-44-1996 L1999 PD *020 †55

BAGNOLI, Dominic J, Jr. 4535 DRESSLER RD NW 44708 #038-45-1990 L1991 EM *030 †16

BAINBRIDGE-COSS, Susan L. ■ 44708 #038-06-1989 L1991 IM *020

BAKER, Roger Edwin. 4151 HOLIDAY ST NW 44718 #038-44-1973 L1973 GYN *030 †30

BANEZ, Ofelia Gatchalian. ■ 44718 #748-01-1958 L1969 PD GP *071 †55

BANEZ, Ramon Virata. 733 MARKET AVE S 44702 #748-01-1952 L1966 GP *071

BANO, Saira. ■ 44704 #704-01-1996 L2003 FM *020 †20

BARCHIESI, Barbara Joan. 2600 TUSCARAWAS ST W # 200 44708 #041-09-1987 L1994 OPH *020 †35

BASISTA, Robert Leonard. 2600 6TH ST SW, RADIOLOGY ASSOCIATES OF 44710 #038-43-1975 L1977 DR *020 †80

BASKAR, Govindasamy. 2815 TUSCARAWAS ST W, STARK PEDIATRICS 44708 #495-16-1986 L1987 PD *020 †55

BATHIJA, Jagdesh S. 4665 DOUGLAS CIR NW, STE 101 44718 #495-01-1968 L1975 AN *071 †05

BATHIJA, Pushpa J. 4565 DRESSLER RD NW, STE 111 44718 #495-09-1966 L1974 END IM *020 †20

BATIZY, Arpad G. 1320 MERCY DR NW 44708 #473-01-1977 L1982 EM IM *020 †16

BAUM, Elizabeth. 1320 TIMKEN MERCY DR NW 44708 #038-44-1984 L1985 IM CD *040 †20

BAUTISTA, Marcianito A. 4677 FULTON DR NW 44718 #748-08-1965 L1971 PS GS *020 †65

BAXTER, Kirkman Graves. 2600 6TH ST SW, RADIOLOGY ASSOCIATES OF 44710 #019-02-1983 L1999 DR NM *020 †80,28

BAZZOLI, Hiram John. 205 15TH ST NW 44703 #028-34-1943 L1944 GS GP *072

BAZZOLI, Victor Hiram. 2600 6TH ST SW 44708 #028-34-1968 L1972 OBG *020 †30

BELLALA, Ravi Kiran. ■ 44718 #495-11-2000 L2006 IM *012

BELLEZA, James Neil. 1320 MERCY DR NW 44708 #038-44-1989 L1990 EM *020 †16

BENMESSAOUD ZAHIR, Nisrine. 2600 6TH ST SW 44708 #913-06-2001 L2005 OBG *012

BENSON, Don Michael. ■ 44705 #010-02-1965 L1966 AN *071 †05

BENSON, Robert Malcolm. 2425 13TH ST NW 44708 #035-06-1967 L1974 PDE PD *020

BERBAUM, Mark Wm. 4527 EVERHARD RD NW 44718 #056-06-1980 L1988 D *020 †15

BERG, Thomas Peter. 2600 6TH ST SW 44710 #028-34-1970 L1973 PD *071

BERGER, Bernhard. 1455 HARRISON AVE NW 44708 #051-01-1973 L1977 OBG *020 †30

BERTMAN, Stan. 3030 TUSCARAWAS ST W 44708 #056-06-1974 L1975 IM *020

BESHARA, Edmund Francis. 315 TUSCARAWAS ST W, STE 400 44702 #020-02-1940 L1940 P *072

BETKERUR, Mangala V. 1320 MERCY DR NW 44708 #495-35-1974 L1981 PD NPM *020 †55

BETKERUR, Vasant Nagappa. 2600 TUSCARAWAS ST W, STE 400 44708 #495-72-1972 L1981 U *020 †85

BHACHAWAT, Virendra Kumar. 1455 HARRISON AVE NW, STE 202 44708 #495-20-1961 L1972 FM *020 †18

BHATT, Asmeen. ■ 44708 #496-46-2000 L2007 **IM** *012
BHATT, Sandeep Dhananjay. ■ 44708 #496-46-2000 L2007 **IM** *012
BHAVSAR, Anil Shashikant. ■ 44708 #055-01-2008 *012
BLAGRAVE, Troy Alex. ■ 44720 #038-43-2005 L2005 **DR** *012
BLOCKER, Douglas Lyle. 4575 EVERHARD RD NW 44718 #038-40-1973 L1974
PD PDA *020 †55
BLOCKER, William Phillip. 4160 HOLIDAY ST NW 44718 #055-01-1975 L1976 **RHU** *020 †20
BOGGS, Leo R, Jr. 4535 DRESSLER RD NW, EMERGENCY MEDICINE PHYSICI 44718
#055-02-1983 L1989 **EM** *020 †16
BOLYARD, Jennifer Lynn. 2600 6TH ST SW, ASST PROG DIR INTER MED PR 44710
#038-44-1994 L1996 **IM** *020 †20
BORTH, Dean Wyland. 2600 6TH ST SW 44710 #046-01-1978 L1979 **GS** *020 †85
BOSACK, Douglas Paul. ■ 44718 #038-41-1978 L1983 **CD** *020
BOTTI, John D. 1330 TIMKEN MERCY DR NW 44708 #041-01-1952 L1957 **GS** *071 †85
BRANDAU, David Ray. 2600 6TH ST SW 44710 #038-40-1976 L1976 **OBG** *020 †30
BRECKBILL, Samuel Colby. ■ 44714 #038-40-2000 L2000 *062
BRISTER, Evelyn Clark. 5000 HIGBEE AVE NW, STARK COUNTY WOMEN'S CLINI 44718
#038-44-1994 L1995 **OBG** *020 †30
BROIDA, Robert I. 4535 DRESSLER RD NW, EMP LEGAL DEPT 44718 #038-43-1981 L1982
EM LM *030 †16
BUCUR, John. ■ 44703 #781-03-1950 L1960 **IM END** *071
BURKHOLDER, James D. 4105 HOLIDAY ST NW 44718 #038-40-1964 **N** *020 †75
BURR, Barbara Ann. 2600 6TH ST SW, RADIOLOGY ASSOCIATES OF 44710
#023-12-1988 L2000 **DR** *020 †80
CAIN, George Franklin. 1320 TIMKEN MERCY DR NW 44708 #041-12-1945 L1946 **FM** *071
CALDWELL, Linda Cheryl. 1320 MERCY DR NW 44708 #038-40-1987 L1990 **EM** *020 †16
CANDAGE, Raymond Lester. 2600 TUSCARAWAS ST W, STE 300 44708 #038-40-1975 L1978
ORS OP *020 †40
CARDON, Grant. ■ 44711 #065-06-1984 L1999 **FM** *100
CARUSO, Saverio. ■ 44718 #561-20-1955 L1961 **P** *071 †75
CASANOVA, Jose Maria. 4105 HOLIDAY ST NW, P O BOX 35006 44718 #847-04-1983 L1995
N *020 †75
CASPER, Kelly Lynne. 2920 MARKET AVE N 44714 #038-41-1999 L1999 **PD** *020 †55
CECIL, Mark Lewis. 4760 BELPAR ST NW, ORTHOPAEDIC 44718 #038-45-1990 L1991
ORS U *020 †40
CHAE, Jin. ■ 44718 #583-02-1965 L1978 **FM EM** *020
CHAHIN, Chadi. 2600 SIXTH ST SW, AULTMAN HOSPITAL 44710 #875-01-1997 L2001
VIR *020 †80
CHALFANT, Marshall Lee. 2600 6TH ST SW, AULTMAN HOSPITAL 44710 #038-06-1988 L1990
DR NR *020 †80
CHASIN, Stacie Laurel. ■ 44708 #654-01-2006 L2006 **IM** *012
CHEN, Xiaoyan. ■ 44708 #243-92-1998 L2007 **IM** *012
CHICATELLI, Paul Douglas. 1320 MERCY DR NW 44708 #016-43-1967 L1968 **PHP ADL** *020
CHIDURALA, Ram Mohan. ■ 44708 #495-11-2000 L2007 **IM** *012
CHIMALAKONDA, Ravi Kumar. ■ 44708 #495-65-2000 L2004 **IM** *100 †20
CHITRABANU, B. 1470 E VALENTINE CIR NW 44708 #496-07-1966 L1979 **OBG** *020 †30
CHO, Yvette M. 2600 SIXTH ST SW, OHIO HOSP BASED PHY CORP 44710 #038-44-1993 L1994
AN *020
CHONG, Eng Seng Chua. 420 MARKET AVE N 44702 #748-01-1964 L1972 **GS** *071
CHOUDHRY, Iqbal Ahmad. 4848 HIGBEE AVE NW 44718 #704-01-1968 L1974 **PD PDC** *020 †55
CHRIST, Benno Karl. ■ 44714 #409-19-1993 **IM** *100
CHRISTENSEN, Greg Austin. 1320 MERCY DR NW, MERCY MED CENTER, STARK CT 44708
#016-43-1985 L1986 **FSM** *020 †18
CHRYSSOS, Antonios E. 1330 MERCY DR NW, STE 502 44708 #418-01-1982 L1989
TS GS *020 †85,90
CHUGHTAI, Sajid-Ul-Qayyum. 3030 TUSCARAWAS ST W 44708 #704-01-1966 L1973
TS GS *071 †85,90
CHUKWUMERIJE, Agatha A. 1930 FULTON RD NW, # 101 44709 #690-01-1984 L1994
IM *020 †20
CISNEROS, Gerardo. 601 CLEVELAND AVE NW 44702 #649-52-1994 L1999 **IM** *020 †20
CLARK, James Matthew. 2600 6TH ST SW, DEPT OF MED EUDUCATION 44710
#661-02-2006 L2006 **OBG** *012
CLARK, Rebecca Sue. 2600 6TH ST SW 44710 #038-44-1990 L1991 **EM** *020 †16
CLARK, William Gilbert. 2600 6TH ST SW 44710 #038-43-1993 L1994 **EM** *020 †16
COBLENTZ, Timothy Ray. 2600 TUSCARAWAS ST W, STE 400 44708 #038-40-1998 L2003
U *020 †95
COGGINS, Mark Edward. 2600 TUSCARAWAS ST W, STSTE 300 44708 #055-02-1987 L1993
ORS OSS *020 †40
COHEN, Lawrence Edward. 4360 FULTON DR NW 44718 #038-40-1971 L1971 **GE IM** *020 †20
COHEN, Terry L. 2600 6TH ST SW, RADIOLOGY ASSOCIATES OF 44710 #016-42-1973 L1977
R *020 †80,28
CONGENI, Jeffrey Leo. 2600 TUSCARAWAS ST W, CANTON OPTHALMOLOGY 44708
#038-44-1993 L1994 **OPH** *020 †35
COOPER, Richard Alan. 2425 13TH ST NW 44708 #308-03-1984 L1988 **IM** *020 †20
COSENTINO, Christine M. 2600 6TH ST SW, RADIOLOGY ASSOCIATES OF 44710
#038-44-1989 L1991 **DR** *020 †80
CRANER, Delbert Edwin. 2600 6TH ST SW 44710 #038-40-1962 L1962 **AN** *071 †05
CROCK, Ronald Dean. 1320 MERCY DR NW, NEOUCOM AFFIL HOSP 44708
#038-44-1992 L1994 **IM** *040 †20
CURD, Gerald Louis. ■ 44709 #038-44-2005 L2005 **OBG** *012
CURRIER, David Scott. 2600 SIXTH ST SW, BASED PHYSICIANS 44710 #038-44-1992 L1993
AN *020 †05
DAN, Michael David. 1320 MERCY DR NW 44708 #065-01-1984 L1999 **NS** *040 †25
DASH, Surendra Nath. 1330 MERCY DR NW, STE 522 44708 #495-13-1962 L1973
TS VS *071 †85,90
DAVIS, Janae Marie. 2600 6TH ST SW, CO AULTMAN HOSP-MED EDU DE 44710
#038-44-2002 L2002 **OBG** *100
DAVIS, Steven Edward. 2600 6TH ST SW, ER DEPARTMENT 44710 #038-41-1998 L1999
EM *020 †16
DECAMPS, Sarah. 2600 6TH ST SW, PEDIATRIC AND PERINATOLOGY 44710
#308-02-1989 L1997 **PD** *020 †55
DECOY, Donald Lee. 1330 MERCY DR NW, STE 418 44708 #038-43-1988 L1989 **PCC** *020 †20
DE HAAS, Edward Douglas. ■ 44714 #038-40-1966 L1966 **EM GP** *020
DE LA CRUZ, Edgar R. 2600 6TH ST SW 44710 #748-01-1973 L1979 **OBG** *020 †30
DE LONG, Victoria Y. 919 2ND ST NE, CHILD AND ADOLESCENT SERVI 44704
#025-12-1986 L1991 **CHP** *020 †75

DIETER, Kevin Fred. 2821 WOODLAWN AVE NW 44708 #038-44-1985 L1986 **FM PLM** *020 †18
DOMINGO, Albert Tunji. 128 WERTZ AVE NW, STE B 44708 #010-03-1982 L1983
OBG IM *020 †30
DONALD, Daryl Lykell. 2600 6TH ST SW, ER DEPARTMENT 44710 #047-06-1991 L1992
EM *020 †16
DONICH, Dane John. 1330 MERCY DR NW, STE 402 44708 #038-44-1992 L1997 **NS** *020 †25
DOUGLASS, Brenda Hilty. 2600 6TH ST SW, PERINATAL AND PEDIATRIC SE 44710
#038-06-1989 L1995 **NPM PD** *020 †55
DOWELL, Harold Richard. ■ 44718 #038-40-1956 L1956 **FM EM** *071
DOYLE, Michael Francis. 1320 MERCY DR NW 44708 #539-04-1970 L1989 **PTH** *020 †50
DURISHIN, Catherine Marie. 4088 HOLIDAY ST NW 44718 #038-44-1999 L1999 **IM** *020 †20
EAST, Glenn Edward. 2600 7TH ST NW 44710 #038-41-1959 L1959 **FM** *071 †18
EL-BADEWI, Mounir. 1717 CLEVELAND AVE NW 44703 #038-44-1994 L1996 **AN** *020
EL-CHARIF, Maria Amer. 4340 FULTON DR NW, PHOENIX DERMATOLOGY 44718
#605-01-1989 L1996 **D** *020 †15
EL GHAMRY SABE, Ahmed A. 1320 MERCY DR NW, MERCY MEDICAL CTR 44708
#915-02-1979 L1995 **CD IM** *020 †20
ELLIS, Rodney. 2600 6TH ST SW, STARK RADIATION ONCOLOGY 44710 #038-44-1992 L1993
RO *020 †80
ERHARDT, Christopher A. 1320 MERCY DR NW 44708 #038-06-1995 L1997 **PCP PTH** *020 †50
ERICKSON, Robert C. 4650 HILLS AND DALES RD NW, STE 200 44708 #047-05-1972 L1980
ORS *020 †40
ERUO, Frederick U. 2525 13TH ST NW, STE 102 44708 #690-04-1988 L2004 **OBG** *020 ‡
ESCOBAR, Rossini Amon. 2600 6TH ST SW 44710 #422-01-2007 L2007 **TY** *012
ESGUERRA, Jorge V. 2600 6TH ST SW, RADIOLOGY ASSOCIATES OF 44710
#748-08-1964 L1978 **RNR DR** *020 †80
FABIAN, Vladimir. 4535 DRESSLER RD NW, HMG 44718 #286-13-1988 L2002 **IM** *020
FAHMY, Nabil Abdel-Aziz M. 4360 FULTON DR NW, STE B 44718 #915-04-1989 L1994
GE IM *020 †20
FARQUHARSON, Robert Roy. 4535 DRESSLER RD NW, EMERGENCY MEDICINE PHYS 44718
#041-02-1976 L1979 **EM** *020 †16
FATTAH, Shakir Mahmood. ■ 44714 #528-01-1960 L1972 **CD IM** *075
FAZEKAS-GRUBB, Nancy N. ■ 44718 #038-40-1989 L1990 **FM** *020 †18
FIEGENSCHUH, Wm H, Jr. 1320 MERCY DR NW, MERCY MEDICAL CTR 44708
#016-06-1973 L1974 **ADM** *020 †85
FIKE, John Adam. 120 DARTMOUTH AVE SW, MANSARD MEDICAL ASSOCS INC 44710
#038-06-1966 L1966 **IM** *071 †20
FIORENTINO, Julia M. 2600 7TH ST SW 44710 #038-44-1994 L1997 **IM** *020 †20
FIORENTINO, Marcantonio. 128 WERTZ AVE NW, STE C 44708 #035-08-1991 L1997
ID *020 †20
FITZ, George Robt, II. 2600 6TH ST SW 44710 #038-40-1961 L1961 **OBG** *020 †30
FLADEN, Todd Douglas. 1330 MERCY DR NW, STE 310 44708 #038-40-1977 L1981
OPH *020 †35
FOOTE HUTH, Jose Edward. 1806 MT VERNON BLVD NW 44709 #038-44-1992 L1998
PTH *020 †50
FOX, Monte. 4240 MUNSON ST NW, STE C 44718 #011-75-1988, ▲ L1991 **D** *020
FRANK, Michael. 4535 DRESSLER RD NW 44718 #038-06-1974 L1975 **LM EM** *030 †16
FRATCZAK, Slawomir M. 1320 MERCY DR NW 44708 #759-09-1985 L1997 **IM** *020 †20
FREELS, Michael Wayne. 1320 MERCY DR NW 44708 #048-14-2000 L2000 **DR** *020 †80
GALANG, Lamberto Trinidad. ■ 44721 #038-40-2001 L2001 **IM** *012
GALAYDA, Theresa Anne. 4319 HILLS AND DALES RD NW 44708 #038-44-2002 L2002
FM *020 †18
GASHASH, H John. 2725 LINCOLN ST E 44707 #875-01-1972 L1977 **FM** *020 †50
GEIHSLER, James Danl. 2600 6TH ST SW, RADIOLOGY ASSOCIATES OF 44710
#016-11-1979 L1981 **DR VIR** *020 †80
GERSTEN, Mark H. 1320 MERCY DR NW, EMERGENCY DEPARTMENT 44708
#017-20-1988 L1989 **EM** *020 †16
GESMUNDO, Clarissa Jara. 2600 7TH ST SW, AULTMAN FAMILY PRACTICE RE 44710
#665-01-2005 L2005 **FP** *012
GHOFRANI, Mohsen. ■ 44710 #517-08-1999 L2003 **DR** *100 †80
GIANCOLA, Katherine Cecil. ■ 44708 #038-44-2006 L2006 **FP** *012
GILBERT, Gene Max. 1455 HARRISON AVE NW, NORTH BLDG STE 207 44708
#035-45-1967 L1967 **CHP P** *020 †75
GILES-SWEATT, Dauphine R. 2600 6TH ST SW 44710 #041-12-1996 L2000 **DR** *020 †80
GILL, Prabhcharan Preet. 2600 SIXTH ST SW 44710 #577-01-1979 L1990 **OBS** *040 †30
GIVEN, John T. 4048 DRESSLER RD NW 44718 #024-16-1978 L1984 **AI PUD** *020 †20,03
GOETZ, Patricia L. 800 MARKET AVE N STE 1150 44702 #041-12-1974 L1988 **CHP P** *030 †75
GOLDMAN, Brad Stewart. 2600 6TH ST SW 44710 #035-08-1992 L1998 **EM** *020 †16
GOMEZ-MUGURUZA, Maria T. ■ 44718 #847-06-1980 L2001 **PD** *020 †55
GONZALEZ, Raul Emilio. 1320 MERCY DR NW 44708 #275-01-1957 L1964 **P** *020
GOVIL, Harsh. 4650 HILLS AND DALES RD NW 44708 #495-84-2000 L2003 **PM PME** *020 †20
GOYAL, Manish. 2600 6TH ST SW, RADIOLOGY ASSOCIATES OF 44710 #495-45-1986 L1998
DR *020 †80
GRACEY, Janel Louise. 2600 6TH ST SW 44710 #305-01-2005 L2005 **FP** *012
GRAHAM, Jonathan Donald. 1320 MERCY DR NW 44708 #045-01-1983 L1985 **EM IM** *020 †20
GRIFFITHS, Victoria F. 2600 6TH ST SW, RADIOLOGY ASSOCIATES OF 44710
#038-41-1993 L2003 **DR** *020 †80
GUDENA, Vinay Kumar. 2600 SIXTH ST SW, INTERNAL MEDICINE 44710 #495-11-2000 L2002
HO *012 †20
GUDIPATI, Madhuri Reddy. 2600 6TH ST SW, DEPT OF MEDICAL EDUCATION 44710
#495-62-2001 L2005 **IM** *012
GUDLA, Jyothi D. 733 MARKET AVE S, VA CANTON 44702 #495-65-1996 L2003 **IMG** *020 †20
GUNAWARDENA, Yamani Sheev. 4535 DRESSLER RD NW, HOSPITALIST MANAGEMENT
GRO 44718 #220-02-1996 L2005 **IM** *020
GURNEY, Michael Sumner. 2726 FULTON DR NW, GASTROENTEROLOGY 44718
#036-01-1979 L1996 **GE IM** *020 †20
GUTLOVE, David Paul. 4665 DOUGLAS CIR NW, STE 101 44718 #010-02-1985 L1995
APM AN *020 †05 ‡
GYALAI, Joseph K. 3996 FULTON DR NW, NORTHWEST 44718 #407-16-1948 L1955 **GP** *071
HAAS, Mandal Brian. 1320 TIMKEN MERCY DR NW 44708 #038-45-1995 L1996 **FM** *020 †18
HADID, Anna Elizabeth. 1320 MERCY DR NW 44708 #654-01-2001 L2001 **IM** *040
HADID, Jabr Eskander. ■ 44709 #104-01-2005 L2006 **IM** *012
HAIDER, Tauseef. 2600 7TH ST SW 44710 #704-21-1996 L2001 **FM** *020
HALL, Roy Louis. 4665 DOUGLAS CIR NW, STE 101 44718 #038-06-1991 L1992 **AN** *020 †05
HAMDAN, Firas M A. 4466 FULTON DR NW, CARDIOLOGY ONE 44718 #605-01-1989 L1992
ICE CD *020 †20

HAMILTON, Robert, III. 128 WERTZ AVE NW, STE A 44708 #010-03-1974 L1981 **OBG** *020

HAMRICK, Ginger Annette. 2600 6TH ST SW, CANTON AULTMAN EMERGENCY P. 44710 #038-44-1990 L1991 **EM** *020 †16

HANLEY, Edward J, Jr. 100 30TH ST NW, STE 102 44709 #038-06-1945 L1945 **ORS** *071 †40

HARDING, Neil David. 2205 TUSCARAWAS ST E 44707 #038-45-1983 L1985 **IM** *020 †20

HAROLD, Suzanne Michelle. 4634 HILLS AND DALES RD NW 44708 #305-01-2001 L2001 **END** *020

HARRIS, Randall James. 1330 MERCY DR NW, STE 418 44708 #038-40-1989 L1990 **PUD CCM** *020 †20

HATCHER, Mark Wilson. 2600 6TH ST SW, ER DEPARTMENT 44710 #017-20-1990 L1991 **EM** *020 †16

HAUT, Mitchell. 1455 HARRISON AVE NW, STE105 44708 #035-47-1984 L1987 **ON HO** *020 †20

HAYEK, Fredrick Charbel. 4909 MUNSON ST NW, P O BOX 35546 44718 #561-17-1980 L1983 **IM** *020 †20

HICKEY, Ann Marie. ■ 44708 #038-40-1995 L1996 **PM** *100

HILAND, Thomas William. 2600 TUSCARAWAS ST W, STE 500 44708 #038-41-2002 L2002 **IM** *020 †20

HILL, Edward A. ■ 44708 #038-40-1944 L1944 **FM** *071 †18

HILL, Kevin Kenneth. 201 DUEBER AVE SW 44706 #038-43-1995 L1997 **IM** *020 †20

HIRSCH, Steven Craig. 4466 FULTON DR NW, CARDIOLOGY ONE INC 44718 #038-40-1982 L1985 **CD IM** *020 †20

HISSONG, Samuel Lowell. 2600 6TH ST SW, RADIOLOGY ASSOCIATES OF 44710 #038-40-1967 L1967 **DR OS** *020 †80

HOFSTETER, Grace. ■ 44708 #023-01-1950 L1951 **CD IM** *071

HOLLAWAY, Stacey. 4810 MUNSON ST NW 44718 #038-44-1990 L1991 **IM** *020 †55,20

HOOVER, Thomas Henry. 5000 HIGBEE AVE NW, STARK COUNTY WOMEN'S CLINI 44718 #035-20-1947 L1953 **OBG** *071 †30

HOPKINS, Michael Patrick. 2600 6TH ST SW, GYNECOLOGIC ONCOLOGISTS 44710 #038-06-1980 L1981 **GO GYN** *020 †30

HOPPE, Jason Matthew. 2600 6TH ST SW 44710 #018-75-2004, ▲ L2004 **OBG** *012

HOPPES, William Leonard. 1330 TIMKEN MERCY DR NW, TIMKEN MERCY HOSPITA STE#3 44708 #038-06-1965 L1965 **ID IM** *040

HOSSAIN, Quazi A. 4535 DRESSLER RD NW, HOSPITALISTS MANAGEMENT GR 44718 #160-02-1985 L1999 **IM** *020 †20

HRICS, Paul David. 2600 6TH ST SW 44710 #038-06-1993 L1994 **EM** *020 †16

IGLESIAS, Arthur Jesus. 2600 6TH ST SW 44710 #654-01-2004 L2005 **RO** *012

IMMESOETE, Phillip Arthur, Jr. ■ 44708 #016-11-2001 L2004 **NS** *100

INDORF, Amy Susan. 1320 MERCY DR NW, 2ND FL MERCY HALL 44708 #038-44-1987 L1988 **ID** *020 †20

IQBAL, Amjad. 4240 MUNSON ST NW STE B 44718 #020-02-1983 L2004 **IM CD** *020 †20

JAFRI, A Khatib. 1320 MERCY DR NW 44708 #704-02-1989 L1997 **PTH MM** *020 †50

JAGADEESAN, Jagada. 4884 HIGBEE AVE NW STE 101 44718 #495-16-1965 L1975 **OBG** *020 †30

JAGADISH, Sunitha. 5000 HIGBEE AVE NW 44718 #495-04-1991 L2001 **OBG** *020

JANAMANCHI, Varalakshmi. ■ 44708 #495-37-2000 L2007 **IM** *012

JANAS, George John. 1320 MERCY DR NW 44708 #038-43-1994 L1995 **IM** *020 †20,16

JANOWICZ, Janine Louise. 1320 MERCY DR NW 44708 #038-44-1986 L1989 **IM** *020 †20

JAYARAMAN, Latha Manivann. 2600 6TH ST SW 44710 #496-39-1996 L2005 **IM** *012

JEUN, Kong Ryeul. 304 15TH ST NE 44714 #583-10-1968 L1976 **P** *040 †75

JOHNS, James Dean. 211 15TH ST NW 44703 #038-41-1982 L1983 **FM** *020 †18 ‡

JOHNS, Martin Paul. 4665 DOUGLAS CIR NW, STE 101 44718 #038-44-2001 L2001 **AN** *020 †05

JOHNSON, Randy Michael. 4535 DRESSLER RD NW, EMP 44718 #038-43-2003 L2006 **EM** *020 †16

JOHNSTON-LEDFORD, Alexis. 2600 6TH ST SW 44710 #038-75-2004, ▲ L2004 **OBG** *012

KAEBERLEIN, Frank. 1320 MERCY DR NW, MERCY MED CTR DEPT EMERG 44708 #038-44-1989 L1990 **EM** *020 †16

KAFUUMA, Roland Kato. 2600 6TH ST SW 44710 #905-01-2000 L2005 **IM** *012

KAMEN, Alan Ralph. 2600 TUSCARAWAS ST W 44708 #038-40-1963 L1963 **CD IM** *072 †20

KANG, Hyung Wook. PO BOX 36959, 4760 BELPAR ST NW 44735 #583-02-1965 L1971 **ORS** *020 †40

KANKANALA, Suresh Babu. 2600 6TH ST SW 44710 #495-11-1998 L2006 **IM** *012

KANTARAS, Marla Ann. 4575 EVERHARD RD NW 44718 #038-44-1995 L1997 **PD** *020 †55

KARAKULA, Satheesh Reddy. 2600 SIXTH ST SW, DEPT OF MED EDUCATION 44710 #495-62-2002 L2006 **IM** *012

KARLEN, John Richard. 2600 6TH ST SW, GYNECOLOGIC ONCOLOGISTS 44710 #016-06-1969 L1974 **GO GYN** *020 †20

KARNS, Laurence Joel. 800 MCKINLEY AVE NW 44703 #038-40-1985 L1986 **OPH D** *020 †35

KEFALAS, George Harry. 2600 TUSCARAWAS ST W, STE 100 44708 #038-44-1999 L1999 **PCC** *020 †20

KELLERMEYER, Robert Wm. 2600 6TH ST SW, AULTMAN HOSP 44710 #038-06-1955 L1955 **ON HEM** *030 †20

KELLEY, Kevin John. 4689 FULTON DR NW, KIDNEY & HYPERTSN CNSLTS 44718 #038-40-1997 L1998 **NEP IM** *020 †20

KELLING, James Stephen. 1320 MERCY DR NW 44708 #038-06-1977 L1979 **PUD IM** *020 †20

KELLY, Steven Mark. 2600 6TH ST SW 44710 #038-06-1993 L2001 **GS** *020 †85

KENDIS, Betsy Lynn. 4575 STEPHENS CIR NW 44718 #038-41-1993 L1996 **MPD** *020 †55,20

KENNEDY, Kay Wm. 5000 HIGBEE AVE NW 44718 #056-06-1946 L1950 **GYN** *071 †30

KENNY-FORTNER, Laura A. 2600 6TH ST SW 44710 #038-43-1996 L2000 **OBG** *020 †20

KHAN, Mushtaq Ahmad. 4761 HIGBEE AVE NW 44718 #704-01-1966 L1974 **D DMP** *020 †50,15

KHAN, Raza A. 2600 6TH ST SW 44710 #704-21-1986 L2002 **ON HEM** *020 †20

KHAYYAT, Ghassan Fuad. 1330 MERCY DR NW, STE 402 44708 #605-01-1969 L1976 **NS** *020 †25

KHETARPAL, Sanjiv. 4665 BELPAR ST NW, P O BOX 36329 44718 #495-45-1980 L1992 **GE IM** *020 †20

KHIMJI, Tasneem Naushad. 1320 MERCY DR NW 44708 #038-06-1987 L1989 **DR N** *020 †80

KHULLAR, Sanjiv Kumar. 4665 BELPAR ST NW, BOX 36329 44718 #495-45-1981 L1999 **GE IM** *020 †20

KILDUFF, James F, Jr. ■ 44708 #028-34-1945 L1948 **GYN** *071 †30

KILKENNY, Timothy John. 2600 SIXTH ST SW, HARTER 266 44710 #020-12-1994 L1996 **PD** *020 †55

KIM, Benedict Y. 2600 6TH ST SW, RADIOLOGY ASSOCIATES OF 44710 #025-76-1994, ▲ L1996 **NR NM** *020 †80,28

KIMBELL, David Bruce. 4080 HOLIDAY ST NW 44718 #038-41-1996 L1998 **IM** *020 †20

KINAST, Morris. 4105 HOLIDAY ST NW, P O BOX 35006 44718 #038-41-1974 L1976 **CHN** *020 †55,75

KING, James Francis. 4360 FULTON DR NW, STE B 44718 #028-34-1961 L1962 **GE IM** *020 †20

KING, William Davies. 214 DARTMOUTH AVE SW 44710 #038-06-1947 L1947 **OTO OPH** *071

KINNEY, Thomas Jackson. 2600 SIXTH ST SW, DEPT OF EMERGENCY MED 44710 #041-07-1979 L1980 **EM** *020 †16

KLEIN, Paul. 4148 HOLIDAY ST NW 44718 #035-46-1971 L1975 **GS** *020 †85

KLING-TIPTON, Kelly Lynn. 2600 6TH ST SW 44710 #654-01-2006 L2006 **IM** *012

KLOEHN, Gregory Charles. 2600 6TH ST SW, STE A2-710 44710 #847-11-1991 L2000 **CD** *020 †20

KMETZ, George Wesley. 2600 TUSCARAWAS ST W, STE 400 44708 #017-20-1970 L1971 **U** *020 †95

KOLARIK, Louise Anne. 2600 6TH ST SW, DEPT OF MED EDUCATION 44710 #917-13-2005 L2006 **FP** *012

KOMMAREDDI, N Rao. 733 MARKET AVE S, CANTON VA OUT PT CLINIC 44702 #495-46-1964 L1977 **P** *020

KORABLEVA, Irina B. 4634 HILLS AND DALES RD NW, NORTHEAST OHIO ENDOCRINOLO 44708 #913-01-1988 L1999 **END IM** *020 †20

KORKOR, Khalil Bichara. 4124 MUNSON ST NW 44718 #875-01-1975 L1981 **GE IM** *020 †20 ‡

KORTE, George Jos. 2600 TUSCARAWAS ST W # 300 44708 #025-01-1961 L1966 **ORS** *071 †40

KOTHARI, Madhubala Atul. 5065 CARDINGTON GRN CIR NW 44718 #495-20-1974 L1984 **P** *020 †75

KRAUS, Charles Thos. 2600 TUSCARAWAS ST W, STE 400 44708 #038-06-1975 L1976 **U** *020 †85,95

KREW, Michael Andrew. 2600 6TH ST SW, AULTMAN HOSP 44710 #016-06-1982 L1986 **MFM OBG** *020 †30

KRISHNA, Arvind Yogeshwar. 4565 DRESSLER RD NW, STE 111 44718 #495-45-1985 L1995 **END IM** *020 †20

KRISHNA SETTY, B N. 2600 6TH ST SW, RADIOLOGY ASSOCIATES OF 44710 #495-09-1966 L1973 **R** *020 †80,28

KRIVETZKY, Joann. 5000 HIGBEE AVE NW 44718 #038-06-1993 L1997 **OBG** *020 †30

KUMAR, Praveen. 1445 HARRISON AVE NW, STE 200 44708 #495-09-1978 L1994 **IM** *020 †20

KUNGLE, Jennifer L. 4575 EVERHARD RD NW 44718 #038-44-1995 L1996 **PD** *020 †55

KUSENTHIRAN, Sri Kasthuri. EDUCATIO2600 SIXTH, CO MEDICAL 44710 #665-01-2007 L2007 **FP** *012

LAH, John S. 1330 TIMKEN MERCY DR NW 44708 #583-02-1950 L1971 **IM HEM** *020 †20

LAHHAM, Mohamad Kamel. 4884 HIGBEE AVE NW 44718 #875-01-1959 L1967 **IM** *072

LAZCANO, Antonio Maria. 2600 6TH ST SW, ER DEPARTMENT 44710 #056-05-1982 L1983 **EM** *020 †16

LEPSKY, Steven Lawrence. 2600 6TH ST SW 44710 #038-44-1990 L1991 **EM** *020 †20,16

LEVITT, Michelle. 4575 EVERHARD RD NW 44718 #038-44-1994 L1995 **PD** *020 †55

LEWIS, Norman. 1320 TIMKEN MERCY DR NW 44708 #038-06-1942 L1942 **GYN** *071 †30

LIBERTIN, Andrew Geo. 2600 6TH ST SW 44710 #038-40-1985 L1987 **GE PD** *020 †20,55

LINZ, David Neel. 2600 6TH ST SW 44710 #038-44-1989 L1990 **GS** *020 †85

LINZ, Michael Howard. 2425 13TH ST NW 44708 #038-44-1984 L1985 **IM** *020 †20

LIU, Wen-Shin. 4889 MUNSON ST NW 44718 #244-02-1968 L1987 **AN** *020 †05 ‡

LOHN, Barbara Claire. 832 MCKINLEY AVE NW, CRISIS INTERVENTION & RECO 44703 #038-06-1994 L1999 **P** *020

LUCIANO, William Nicholas. ■ 44714 #305-01-2007 L2007 **PD** *012

LUNGOCIU, Nicholas N. 1320 TIMKEN MERCY DR NW 44708 #038-40-1959 L1959 **R PDR** *071 †55,80

LYNCH, Michael John. 5545 FOXCHASE AVE NW 44718 #038-44-2003 L2003 **AN** *020 †20

MACHER, Jerry Irving. 730 MCKINLEY AVE NW 44703 #035-09-1976 L1977 **OPH** *020 †35

MADER, Anju G. 4575 STEPHENS CIR NW, 1320 MERCY DRIVE NW 44718 #038-44-1992 L1995 **PD** *020 †20

MADER, Michael Thos. 2600 6TH ST SW, RADIOLOGY ASSOCIATES OF 44710 #038-44-1992 L1996 **DR** *020 †80

MAGOON, Elbert Hendrik. 1330 MERCY DR NW, STE 310 44708 #024-01-1974 L1982 **OPH** *020 †35

MAGOON, Martha Wasson. 2600 6TH ST SW 44710 #024-01-1975 L1982 **NPM PD** *020 †55

MAGUIRE, Pamela. 1320 MERCY DR NW 44708 #016-42-1978 L1982 **R** *020 †80

MAIORIELLO, Richard P. 2600 6TH ST SW 44710 #041-02-1964 L1979 **OTO FPS** *020 †45

MALACKANY, Natasha M. ■ 44708 #038-75-2007, ▲ L2007 *012

MALHOTRA, Shishuka. 2600 TUSCARAWAS ST W, STE 120 44708 #495-20-1995 L2000 **P** *020 †75

MALIK, Rajesh K. 1320 MERCY DR NW 44708 #495-45-1987 L2001 **NPM** *020 †55

MALOSKY, Steven Anthony. 2600 6TH ST SW, STE A2-710 44710 #041-01-1990 L2004 **CD** *020 †20

MAMOUNAS, Eleftherios P. 2600 6TH ST SW, AULTMAN HOSPITAL 44710 #418-01-1983 L1997 **GS SO** *020 †85

MANNS, Robert Lawrence. 2600 TUSCARAWAS ST W # 300 44708 #041-12-1954 L1962 **ORS** *071 †40

MANOHAR, Murli. 4942 HIGBEE AVE NW STE E 44718 #065-05-1976 L1978 **IM ID** *020 ‡

MANUSZAK, Paul Raymond. 2600 6TH ST SW 44710 #038-43-1974 L1977 **ON HEM** *020 †20

MARKARIAN, Georges Zohrab. 1330 MERCY DR NW, STE 402 44708 #038-40-1994 L2000 **NS** *020 †25

MARKOWITZ, Steven Linn. 4535 DRESSLER RD NW 44708 #038-40-1987 L1988 **EM** *020 †16

MARRA, Gregory I. ■ 44721 #305-01-2007 L2007 **OBG** *012

MARTELLO, Alfred John. 4889 MUNSON ST NW 44718 #038-40-1991 L1995 **AN** *020 †05

MARTIN, David Albert. 4160 HOLIDAY ST NW 44718 #041-14-1976 L1981 **RHU IM** *020 †20

MARTINO, Luis Jorge. 2600 TUSCARAWAS ST W, STE 500 44708 #308-11-1988 L1996 **IM** *020 †20

MARTYN, Nick. 2600 7TH ST SW, AULTMAN FAMILY MEDICINE RE 44710 #913-07-1987 L2006 **FP** *012

MARVIN, Michael James. 3730 WHIPPLE AVE NW # 400 44718 #017-20-1981 L1983 **EM OM** *020 †16

MATTHEWS, Lee Anne. 2600 TUSCARAWAS ST W, STE 400 44708 #023-01-1991 L1996 **U** *020 †95

MAYCON, Zev Randy. 4665 BELPAR ST NW 44718 #033-06-1992 L1997 **GE** *020 †20

MCDANIEL, Timothy Eugene. 2600 6TH ST SW, MATERNAL FETAL MEDICINE 44710 #422-01-1997 L2000 **OBG** *020 †30

MC DONOUGH, Geoffrey S. 2600 6TH ST SW, ER DEPARTMENT 44710 #035-15-1981 L1983 **EM** *020 †16

MC KENNEY, Bradley Allen. 1320 MERCY DR NW 44708 #038-44-1984 L1985 **EM FM** *020 †18

MC MAHON, Raymond John. ■ 44718 #056-06-1955 L1956 **IM OS** *071

MC VEY, John R. ■ 44708 #038-06-1953 L1953 **AN** *071 †05

MELDON, Stephen Wm. 4535 DRESSLER RD NW, EMERGENCY MEDICINE PHYSICI 44718 #038-41-1986 L1993 **EM** *020 †16

MENDIOLA, Joseph Anthony. 1320 MERCY DR NW 44708 #038-44-1999 L2000 **DR** *020 †80

MERCER, Susan E. 2600 7TH ST SW 44710 #035-06-1980 L1983 **FM** *040 †18

MERTES, Lori Lynn. 2600 SIXTH ST SW, AULTMAN HOSPITAL 44710 #038-43-1994 L1996 **IM** *030 †20

MERZ, Robert Hans. ■ 44708 #038-40-1956 L1956 **AN** *071

MEYERHOEFER, Frederick P. ■ 44721 #038-06-1961 L1961 **OS PD** *071 †55

MEYERHOEFER, Todd A. 2600 TUSCARAWAS ST W, STE 620 44708 #038-44-1986 L1990 **GS** *020 †85

MICHAEL, Alexander, III. 4760 BELPAR ST NW, ORTHOPAEDIC 44718 #021-01-1979 L1979 **ORS** *020 †40

MIHANOVIC, Jos Zvonimir. ■ 44709 #561-01-1950 L1956 **IM CD** *071

MIKHAIL, Mounir N. ■ 44718 #915-04-1979 L1993 **AN** *020 †05

MILLER, Jeffrey Bennett. 2600 TUSCARAWAS ST W, STE 100 44708 #561-01-1976 L1982 **PUD CCM** *020 †20

MILLER, Robert Baer. 2600 TUSCARAWAS ST W, STE 100 44708 #012-05-1966 L1972 **PUD CCM** *020 †20

MODUTHAGAM, Asunta. EDUCATIO2600 SIXTH, CO MEDICAL 44710 #654-01-2006 L2007 **FP** *012

MONTASERKOOHSARI, Anoushir. 2600 6TH ST SW, DEPT RAD 44710 #517-11-1993 L2007 **DR** *012

MONTGOMERY, David Miguel. 403 CLARENDON AVE NW 44708 #038-41-1966 L1966 **IM HEM** *020

MOONEY, Stephen Breck. 2600 TUSCARAWAS ST W, INC 44708 #038-44-1995 L1998 **OBG REN** *030 †30

MORESEA, Brigitta Anne. 4575 STEPHENS CIR NW 44718 #041-12-1993 L1997 **PD** *020 †55

MORESEA, George Alan, III. 4665 DOUGLAS CIR NW # 101, STARK COUNTY ANESTHESIA 44718 #041-12-1993 L1997 **AN** *020 †05

MORGAN, Richard Larry. 2600 6TH ST SW, AULTMAN HOSP DEPT OF PATH 44710 #038-40-1993 L1997 **PTH HMP** *020 †50

MORMAN, Steven Robert. 4677 FULTON DR NW 44718 #038-40-1996 L1997 **AI** *020 †55,03

MOTZ, Michael John. 4575 EVERHARD RD NW 44718 #038-44-1989 L1990 **PD** *020 †55

MURPHY, William David. 1320 MERCY DR NW 44708 #038-43-1985 L1989 **DR** *020 †80

MUSA, Roger. 2600 SIXTH ST SW, DEPT OF GME 44710 #665-01-2005 L2005 **FP** *012

MUZYCZKA, Jaroslaw. 1320 TIMKEN MERCY DR NW 44708 #407-16-1949 L1956 **IM** *071

NADAS, John Adalbert. 1330 MERCY DR NW STE 220 44708 #036-07-1974 L1984 **P** *020 †75 ‡

NAFZIGER, Ned A. 4105 HOLIDAY ST NW 44718 #038-06-1988 L1991 **PM** *020 †60

NAGAJOTHI, Nagaprasad. 4875 HIGBEE AVE NW, GABRAIL CANCER CENTER 44718 #495-59-1999 L2005 **HO** *100 †20

NAM, Kun Woo. 100 30TH ST NW STE 103 44709 #583-01-1971 L1980 **IM EM** *020

NAMKUNG, Yun. 4535 DRESSLER RD NW 44718 #422-01-2000 L2004 **IM** *020 †20

NASHAWATI, Eyad. 2600 TUSCARAWAS ST W # 100 44708 #875-01-1984 L1987 **PCC SME** *020 †20

NAZINITSKY, Kenneth Jan. 2600 6TH ST SW, RADIOLOGY ASSOCIATES OF 44710 #035-08-1984 L1988 **R DR** *020 †80

NEAL, James Matthew. 2600 TUSCARAWAS ST W, STE 400 44708 #017-20-1965 L1973 **U** *071 †95

NEDROW, Ann. AULTMANN HOSP 44710 #007-02-1978 **DR** *100

NEWELL, Charles Conklin. ■ 44710 #010-01-1946 L1951 **IM** *071 †18

NIJMEH, Ruba Wadei. 2600 6TH ST SW 44710 #575-01-1997 L2005 **IM** *012

NKANGINIEME, Ikemefuna A. 4450 BELDEN VILLAGE ST NW, STE 215 44718 #690-04-1983 L2000 **P** *020 †75

NOOKA, Ajay Kumar. 2600 6TH ST SW, DEPT OF MED EDUCATION 44710 #495-11-2000 L2005 **IM** *012

NOVOA, Roberto. 2600 6TH ST SW 44710 #042-01-1977 L1988 **TS** *020 †85,90

NOVOA, Roberto Andres. 5050 PLAIN CENTER AVE NE 44714 #024-01-2008 *012

NUCHIKAT, Patrath Suresh. 2600 TUSCARAWAS ST W 44708 #495-01-1967 L1972 **NEP IM** *020 †20

OLOYA, Richard Ogaba. 2600 6TH ST SW RM 268 44710 #917-02-1971 L1989 **NPM PD** *020 †55

ONG, Marino Gesulga. 2600 6TH ST SW 44710 #748-11-1964 L1972 **PTH PCP** *020 †50

ONUORA, Cosmas Onwudiwe. 4775 HIGBEE AVE NW 44718 #047-07-1985 L1990 **OBG** *020 †30

OPRANDI, Allison M. 2600 6TH ST SW 44710 #038-43-1986 L1987 **FM** *030 †18

ORIJA, Abiodun Ayodele. ■ 44708 #422-01-2005 L2006 **IM** *012

O TOOLE, Timothy Martin. 2600 6TH ST SW, ER DEPARTMENT 44710 #016-42-1987 L1988 **EM** *020 †16

OVIEDO, Gina Joanne. ■ 44721 #038-44-2008 *012

OZA, Rajnikant V. 2600 6TH ST SW 44710 #495-23-1975 L1979 **PTH** *020 †50

PACKER, Robert Bruce. 1330 TIMKEN MERCY DR NW 44708 #038-06-1964 L1965 **PUD CCM** *020 †20

PACKO, David Chas. 4535 DRESSLER RD NW 44718 #038-40-1989 L1990 **EM** *020 †16

PALMERT, Mark Raney. 1320 MERCY DR NW 44708 #038-06-1992 L2001 **PD END** *072 †55

PAN, Jeffrey Tai. 2600 6TH ST SW 44710 #422-01-2004 L2004 **AN** *012

PARK, Bae Woo. ■ 44718 #583-04-1959 L1977 **AN** *071

PARK, Woo Sam. 201 DUEBER AVE SW 44706 #583-02-1960 L1971 **GS** *071 †85

PASCALE, Sabatino P. 1330 MERCY DR NW 44708 #422 44708 #561-10-1952 L1960 **GYN** *020 †30

PASSERINI, Stephen M. 2600 SIXTH ST SW 44710 #038-40-2001 L2001 **DR** *020 †80

PATEL, Hardik Ishverlal. 2600 7TH ST SW, AULTMAN FAMILY MEDICINE RE 44710 #305-01-2006 L2006 **FP** *012

PATEL, Indravadan P. 1330 TIMKEN MERCY DR NW, INDRAVADAN P PATEL MD INC 44708 #495-01-1966 L1977 **HEM ON** *071

PATEL, Kanubhai Chunibhai. 3745 WHIPPLE AVE NW, STE A 44718 #495-23-1971 L1976 **P** *020

PATEL, Neil Pravin. ■ 44710 #305-01-1998 L2000 **PM** *100 †60

PATEL, Soudamini Mulay. ■ 44718 #495-17-1964 L1980 **OTO** *020

PATEL, Suresbhai Ambalal. 3745 WHIPPLE AVE NW, STE A 44718 #495-23-1971 L1982 **P CHP** *020 †75

PATIBANDLA, Sujana Kumari. 4186 HOLIDAY ST NW 44718 #495-11-1970 L1982 **OBG** *020 †30

PATIL, Preeti Hemanagouda. 2600 6TH ST SW, DEPT OF MED EDU 44710 #495-99-2004 L2006 **IM** *012

PATILANO, Richard Romero, Jr. ■ 44708 #748-01-1996 L2007 **IM** *012

PATNAIK, Bireswar. 1320 MERCY DR NW 44708 #495-13-1967 L1975 **GS VS** *020 †85

PATTON, Melissa Sue. 5000 HIGBEE AVE NW 44718 #038-75-1998, ▲ L2000 **OBG** *020

PAUL, Bipin C. ■ 44718 #495-27-1984 L2000 **IM** *020 †20

PAUSKAR, Privi Praveen. 2600 7TH ST SW, AULTMAN PHYSICIAN CENTER 44710 #495-44-1997 L2003 **IM** *100

PENG, Bob. ■ 44718 #422-01-2007 L2007 **OBG** *012

PFEIFFER, Herbert. ■ 44708 #407-20-1955 L1963 **PTH** *071 †50

PHILLIPS, Danny Michael. 4535 DRESSLER RD NW, EMER MEDIANE PHYSICIANS 44718 #055-02-1987 L1988 **EM** *020 †16

PHOEY, Valdeline Irma. 2600 SIXTH ST SW, DEPT OF MED EDU 44710 #665-01-2006 L2006 **FP** *012

PICA, Katherine Joy L. 3001 TREESIDE ST NW 44709 #748-02-1985 L2000 **IMG IM** *020 †20

PIELSTICK, Kristi Lee. 4889 MUNSON ST NW 44718 #038-44-1984 L1986 **AN IM** *020 †20,05

PODUGU, Radha. 2600 TUSCARAWAS ST W, STE 500 44708 #496-24-1991 L1997 **IM** *020 †20

POTDAR, Santosh. ■ 44708 #495-75-1979 L2007 **GS** *020 †85

POULTON, Thomas B. 2600 6TH ST SW, RADIOLOGY ASSOCIATES OF 44710 #011-02-1979 L1980 **DR FM** *020 †80,18

POWELL, Michael Danl. 2725 LINCOLN ST E 44707 #010-03-1979 L1981 **PD EM** *030

PRAKASH, Rohit. 255 DUEBER AVE SW 44706 #495-36-1985 L1989 **IM** *020 †20

PREM, Jeffrey Thomas. 1445 HARRISON AVE NW, STE 103 44708 #038-45-1994 L1997 **GS** *071 †85

PRODAFIKAS, John. 2600 6TH ST SW, STE A2-710 44718 #024-07-1993 L2003 **CD** *020 †20

PROWE, Gary. 2920 MARKET AVE N 44714 #407-02-1953 L1956 **PDA PD** *071 †55

PUPPALA, Neha. ■ 44720 #038-44-2008 *012

PUTERBAUGH, Myron Randall. ■ 44718 #038-41-1962 L1962 **RO** *071 †80

RAJAN, James Melvin. 4689 FULTON DR NW 44718 #305-01-2001 L2001 **NEP** *100 †20

RAJAN, Meena R. 2600 6TH ST SW 44710 #495-08-2000 L2005 **IM** *012

RAJARATNAM, Mohan. 1320 MERCY DR NW 44708 #060-01-1993 L1995 **EM** *020 †20,16

RAMAIAH, Priyabala. 1455 HARRISON AVE NW, STE 200 44708 #496-07-1988 L1992 **OBG** *020 †20

RAMALINGAM, S Raja. 2600 6TH ST SW, AULTMAN HOSPITAL 44710 #495-16-1963 L1972 **EM IM** *020 †20,16

RAMEY, Russell Lawrence. 1330 MERCY DR NW, STE 222 44708 #038-43-1989 L1992 **GS** *020 †85

RASHID, Tasnim Quaser. 2600 6TH ST SW, CANTON MED EDUC FNDN 44710 #160-03-1982 L2004 **IM** *100

RAVAL, Vikram. 2600 6TH ST SW, RADIOLOGY ASSOCIATES OF 44710 #495-22-1968 L1975 **R DR** *020 †80

RAVISHANKAR, Venkatesan. 4612 TUSCARAWAS ST W, INTERNAL MEDICINE 44708 #495-04-1977 L1997 **IM** *020 †20

REICHERT, Richard Jos. 2626 FULTON DR NW 44718 #038-43-1981 L1982 **OM FM** *020 †70,18

REYNOLDS, Ronald Kerry. 4535 DRESSLER RD NW, EMP CREDENTIALING 44718 #017-20-1983 L1983 **EM** *020 †16

RICH, Jason Lowell. 4410 EXECUTIVE CIR NW, RICH HEALTH AND WELLNESS 44718 #038-40-1999 L2000 **FM** *020 †30

RICH, Michael Anthony. 304 15TH ST NE 44714 #038-43-1990 L1993 **P** *020 †75

RICHARDS, Paul M. 4665 DOUGLAS CIR NW # 101, STARK COUNTY ANESTHESIA I 44718 #038-75-1992, ▲ L1993 **AN** *020 †05

RICHARDSON, Shoshone A. 5154 FULTON DR NW, STARK COUNTY EMERGENCY PHY 44718 #038-40-2002 L2002 **EM** *020 †16

RIESTER, John Norman. 2600 TUSCARAWAS ST W, SUITE300 44708 #035-15-1979 L1985 **ORS** *020 †40

RIGGS, Karin Tuve. 4575 STEPHENS CIR NW 44718 #038-44-1988 L1990 **MPD PD** *020 †55,20

ROBERTS, Breeze Baker. ■ 44718 #038-44-2005 L2005 **OBG** *012

ROBINSON, Thomas Dean. 4535 DRESSLER RD NW 44718 #038-40-1975 L1975 **OBG** *020 †30

RODRIGUEZ, Craig Paul. 2600 6TH ST SW, DEPT OF RADIOLOGY 44710 #016-11-2001 L2005 **DR** *012

ROGERS, Jennifer Lee. ■ 44714 #305-01-2007 L2007 **OBG** *012

ROMAN, Frankie. 4774 MUNSON ST NW, STE 100 44718 #042-01-1984 L1992 **SME** *020 †20

ROONEY, Christopher M. 2600 SIXTH ST SW 44710 #038-44-2000 L2000 **OBG** *020

ROONEY, Dina Kathleen. 3688 DRESSLER RD NW, TRICOUNTY HEMATOLOGY & 44718 #038-40-1989 L1997 **HO** *020 †20

ROSE, Barry Steven. 2600 6TH ST SW, RADIOLOGY ASSOCIATES OF 44710 #023-01-1976 L1977 **DR VIR** *020 †80

ROSENBERG, Leon Harris. 4105 HOLIDAY ST NW 44718 #043-01-1975 L1982 **N** *020 †75

ROSENBLATT, Arnold Mark. 2600 TUSCARAWAS ST W 44708 #024-07-1963 L1967 **IM** *020 †20

ROSKOS, Erin Rose. ■ 44714 #038-44-2007 L2007 **EM** *012

ROVNER, Allen J. 2600 6TH ST SW, RADIOLOGY ASSOCIATES OF 44710 #024-05-1971 L1977 **R** *020 †80

ROZARIO, Catherine. 2600 7TH ST SW, AULTMAN FAMILY MEDICINE RE 44710 #305-01-2006 L2006 **FP** *012

RUBIN, Patricia Jane. 2600 6TH ST SW 44710 #038-45-1988 L1989 **CD IM** *020 †20

RUDICK, Alan. 1330 MERCY DR NW, STE 418 44708 #018-75-1981, ▲ L1989 **PCC SME** *020

RUDICK, James Howard. 4765 HIGBEE AVE NW 44718 #038-41-1976 L1977 **END IM** *020 †20

RUIZ, Roberto Emilio. ■ 44718 #132-02-1956 L1967 **FOP PTH** *062 †50

RUSNAK, Ronald Robt, Jr. 2600 SIXTH ST SW, AUHMAN HOSPITAL, CAEP 44710 #038-43-1987 L1988 **EM** *020 †16

RUSS, Elizabeth Ann. 2600 6TH ST SW, DEPT OF MED EDUCATION 44710 #654-01-2006 L2006 **DR** *012

RUSSELL, Donald Lee. 2600 6TH ST SW 44710 #038-40-1981 L1981 **IM CD** *020 †20

SAADEY, Jos Anthony, Jr. 2600 TUSCARAWAS ST W, STE 620 44708 #038-40-1991 L1996 **GS** *020 †85

SAAVEDRA, Juan Carlos. ■ 44710 #319-08-2003 L2005 **OBG** *012

SABOTA, Robert William. 201 DUEBER AVE SW 44706 #038-44-1993 L1995 **IM** *020 †20

SADDLETON, Michael John. 3730 WHIPPLE AVE NW, STE 400 44718 #068-01-1974 L1978 **OM OS** *020 †16

SAKLECHA, Akhil. 2600 6TH ST SW, ER DEPARTMENT 44710 #038-44-1994 L1995 **EM** *020 †16

SALES, Gary Nelson. 2421 13TH ST NW 44708 #038-45-1988 L1989 **P PFP** *020 †75

SALTARELLI, Matthew G. 2600 6TH ST SW, AULTMAN HOSPITAL 44710 #035-06-1990 L1995 **PTH** *020 †50

SANDHU, Aqeel Akram. 2600 SIXTH ST SW, HEART CARE LLC 44710 #704-01-1987 L2001 **TS VS** *020 †85,90

SANDS, Steven Fletcher. 2600 6TH ST SW, RADIOLOGY ASSOCIATES OF 44710 #016-42-1981 L1989 **DR NR** *020 †80

SANOFSKY, Stephen Jay. 2600 SIXTH ST SW 44710 #028-02-1980 L1992 **TS CD** *020 †85,90

SANWARDEKER, Milind B. 4850 HIGBEE AVE NW 44718 #495-28-1968 L1975 **IM OS** *020 †20

SAYOC, Alexis S. 2600 6TH ST SW, RADIOLOGY ASSOCIATES OF 44710 #748-02-1967 L1973 **R VIR** *020 †80

SAYOC, Lisa Marie. 4677 FULTON DR NW 44718 #038-44-1997 L1998 **D** *020 †15

SCHLEICH, Carl Thos. 5000 HIGBEE AVE NW, 5000 HIGBEE AVE NW 44718 #038-40-1984 L1986 **OBG** *020 †30

SCHMOTZER, James A, Jr. 2600 6TH ST SW 44710 #038-06-1984 L1984 **HEM ON** *020 †20

SCHWARTZ, Richard L. 2550 INVERNESS PKWY NW 44708 #035-01-1973 L1982 **VS TS** *071 †85
SEDA-OLMO, Norbert Jose. 2600 SIXTH ST SW, AFFILIATED HOSPS-NEOUCO 44710 #042-02-2002 L2004 **DR** *100
SENGER, Kathleen Ann. 2600 6TH ST SW 44710 #038-43-1988 L1993 **IM PLM** *040 †20
SERRI, Geneiso Armando. 2600 6TH ST SW, ER DEPARTMENT 44710 #038-44-1987 L1988 **EM** *020 †16
SETH, Ajay Kumar. 4650 HILLS AND DALES RD NW 44708 #056-06-1998 L2000 **ORS** *020 †40
SHAH, Akbar S. 2600 6TH ST SW, STE A2-710 44710 #704-25-1989 L1999 **CD IM** *020 †20
SHAH, Nadia. ■ 44708 #038-44-2007 **GS** *012
SHAH, Sanjay Natavarlal. 2600 6TH ST SW, RADIOLOGY ASSOCIATES OF 44710 #495-23-1965 L1974 **R** *062 †80,28
SHAH, Vinodbala Sanjay. 2600 6TH ST SW 44710 #495-22-1968 L1981 **P** *020 †75
SHAH, Zaheer Akber. 4665 DOUGLAS CIR NW 44718 #704-02-1972 L1978 **PS HS** *020 †85,65
SHAHEEN, Louis Geo. 2600 TUSCARAWAS ST W, STE 500 44708 #038-40-1986 L1987 **IM** *020 †20
SHARMA, Vinod. 4974 HIGBEE AVE NW, STE 206 44718 #495-55-1965 L1984 **P** *020 †75
SHEIKH, Parwaiz. 2600 SIXTH ST SW, VA OUTPATIENT CLINIC 44710 #704-02-1986 L2001 **IM** *020 †20
SHEROCK, Nicholas E, Jr. 2600 6TH ST SW 44710 #038-75-1989, ▲ L1990 **OBG** *020 †30
SHIPLEY, Margaret Bae S. ■ 44718 #035-45-1942 L1944 **PD** *071 †55
SHOTELERSUK, Voravan. 2600 6TH ST SW, CANTON AFFILIATED HOSP 44710 #891-01-1995 L2000 **PDR** *020 †80
SHUBERT, Ronald Anthony. 3501 TUSCARAWAS ST W 44708 #038-06-1965 L1965 **IM ID** *020 †20 ‡
SHUKLA, Vinayak. 2600 6TH ST SW 44710 #496-02-2000 L2005 **IM** *012
SHUNDRY, Nicholas Philip. ■ 44709 #038-44-2007 L2007 **EM** *012
SHWE, Myint Myint. 2600 6TH ST SW 44710 #209-01-1981 L2006 **FP** *012
SICARD, Fausto Antonio. 1320 MERCY DR NW 44708 #038-44-1988 L1992 **D** *020 †15
SINGH, Anil Chadanand. 2600 6TH ST SW 44710 #305-01-2001 L2001 **CCM** *012
SKIBBENS, Richard V. COLUMBIA MERCY MC 44708 #041-12-1949 L1955 **R** *071 †80
SMITH, Alison Simona. 2600 6TH ST SW, RADIOLOGY ASSOCIATES OF 44710 #038-43-1981 L1982 **RNR EM** *020 †80
SMITH, Charles Edward. 4565 DRESSLER RD NW, STE 111 44718 #038-41-1969 L1969 **END IM** *020 †20
SMITH, Clarence V. 4565 DRESSLER RD NW 44718 #038-41-1942 L1942 **IM DIA** *072
SMITH, David W. 1320 TIMKEN MERCY DR NW 44708 #028-79-1962, ▲ L1962 **ORS** *071
SMITH, Gerald Edward. 2600 6TH ST SW 44710 #038-06-1964 L1964 **GE IM** *071 †20
SMITH, Lane Robert. ■ 44721 #038-43-2007 L2007 **FP** *012
SMITH, Russell Campbell. 4665 DOUGLAS CIR NW, STE 101 44718 #065-05-1981 L1985 **AN** *020 †05
SMITH, Steven Donis. 2600 6TH ST SW 44710 #038-44-1984 L1985 **FM** *020 †18
SOBOWALE, Adeyemi O. 1330 MERCY DR NW, MERCY MED CTR 44708 #690-02-1982 L1998 **NPM** *020 †55
SOEHNLEN, Michael William. 2600 SIXTH ST SW, AULTMAN HOSPITAL 44710 #038-41-2000 L2000 **DR** *100 †80
SOMASUNDARAM, A. 1470 E VALENTINE CIR NW 44708 #495-04-1961 L1977 **GE HEP** *020 †20
SONI, Prasanna L. 1900 FULTON RD NW 44709 #495-19-1970 L1974 **ORS** *020 †40
SOTO, C. Elizabeth. 2600 6TH ST SW, DEPT OF MED EDUCATION 44710 #305-01-2006 L2006 **FP** *012
SOTO, Luis. 4689 FULTON DR NW 44718 #042-03-1988 L1991 **NEP** *020 †20
SOTO, Luis Felipe. 4689 FULTON DR NW, CONSULTANTS, INC 44718 #429-01-1980 L1981 **IM CD** *020 †20
SPANGLER, Robert Theodore. 1330 MERCY DR NW, STE 520 44708 #028-34-1972 L1977 **GS** *020 †85
SPOHN, Gregory John. 4575 EVERHARD RD NW 44718 #028-34-1979 L1984 **PD** *020 †55
SPRIGGS, David Wm. 1320 MERCY DR NW, MERCY MEDICAL CENTER 44708 #038-40-1974 L1974 **DR CD** *020 †80
STABHOLZ, Thaddeus. 1320 TIMKEN MERCY DR NW 44708 #050-02-1953 L1954 **GP** *072
STACHEL, David Craig. 1445 HARRISON AVE NW, STE 202 44708 #038-43-1984 L1987 **IM** *020 †20
STACHEL, Mark Carless. 1330 MERCY DR NW, STE 318 44708 #154-07-1985 L1990 **IM** *020
STALKER, Andrew Phillip. 4105 HOLIDAY ST NW, P O BOX 35006 44718 #038-40-1997 L2000 **N** *020 †75
STARCHER, Randall Scott. 5000 HIGBEE AVE NW, 5000 HIGBEE AVENUE NW 44718 #038-44-1993 L1997 **OBG** *020 †30
STASIAK, Steven Richard. 211 15TH ST NW, TICE, INC 44703 #038-44-1991 L1994 **FM** *020 †18
STEPHENS, Paul Andrew. 2600 6TH ST SW 44710 #038-44-2003 L2003 **EM** *020 †16
STERN, Sharon Griffith. 4889 MUNSON ST NW 44718 #038-06-1985 L1988 **AN CCM** *020 †05
STIRES, David Brian. 4884 HIGBEE AVE NW, HOLIDAY PROFESSIONAL BLDG 44718 #038-40-1970 L1970 **GS** *020 †85
STRICKLAND, Britni Leigh. ■ 44718 #038-44-2008 *012
STUHLMILLER, Sam David. 2600 6TH ST SW, RADIOLOGY ASSOCIATES OF 44710 #038-44-1992 L1996 **VIR** *020 †80
SUMMERSON, Stanley Ford. 5000 HIGBEE AVE NW, STARK COUNTY WOMENS CLNC 44718 #041-12-1967 L1974 **OBG** *071 †30
SUTTON, John David. 4319 HILLS AND DALES RD NW 44708 #038-44-1993 L1994 **FM** *040 †18
SWEITZER, Kirby Lee. 1330 MERCY DR NW, STE 319 44708 #038-43-1986 L1992 **CRS GS** *020 †10,85
SWISHER, Benjamin Joel. 4465 FULTON DR NW, STE 100 44718 #038-44-1999 L2000 **FM** *020 †18
TABET, Bechara. 1455 HARRISON AVE NW, STE 200 44708 #605-02-1972 L1995 **U** *020 †95
TABET, Jean-Claude Marie. 2600 TUSCARAWAS ST W, STE 540 44708 #038-40-1980 L1980 **NS** *020 †25
TALUG, Eser. 4076B HOLIDAY ST NW 44718 #902-10-1974 L1990 **IM** *020 †20
TANTIWONGKOSI, Bundhit. 2600 6TH ST SW 44710 #891-02-1999 L2004 **DR** *012
TAWIL, Mark Tawfik. 1330 MERCY DR NW, STE 502 44708 #605-01-1983 L1990 **TS GS** *020 †85,90
THAKKAR, Mahendra K. 1320 MERCY DR NW 44708 #495-22-1965 L1973 **IM CD** *020 †20
THAKORE, Nimish Jayandra. 4105 HOLIDAY ST NW, METROHEALTH MEDICAL CENTER 44718 #495-76-1987 L1998 **CN** *020 †75
THOMAS, Joseph Paul. 1445 HARRISON AVE NW, STE 200 44708 #038-06-1959 L1959 **IM CD** *020
THOMPSON, John F. 5260 FULTON DR NW 44718 #041-02-1950 L1953 **OM GP** *071
THOTTAM, Johnson J. 4800 HIGBEE AVE NW 44718 #495-63-1970 L1974 **PS** *020 †65
TIRMONIA, Virgil. 1330 TIMKN MRCY DR NW #517 44708 #038-40-1956 L1956 **IM** *071
TOPCUOGLU, Hasan Necdet. 2600 6TH ST SW, RADIOLOGY ASSOCIATES OF 44710 #902-03-1955 L1966 **R** *020 †80
TREHAN, Shruti Chopra. 2600 6TH ST SW 44710 #496-38-1992 L1998 **HO** *020 †20
TSAI, John Chen. 4466 FULTON DR NW, CARDIOLOGY ONE, INC 44718 #038-40-1987 L1989 **CD** *020 †20
TUCKER, Elmo Glenn. 4535 DRESSLER RD NW 44718 #024-05-1984 L1988 **EM** *020
TUDOSIE, Mioara. 2600 TUSCARAWAS ST W # 640 44708 #781-01-1977 L1992 **IM** *020 †20
TURGEON, Paul William. 1330 MERCY DR NW, STE 310 44708 #038-43-1984 L1989 **OPH** *020 †35
U, Nilar. ■ 44710 #654-01-2001 L2003 **FM** *020
UTLAK, David Jos. 4455 DRESSLER RD NW 44718 #038-40-1978 L1979 **CD IM** *020 †20
VAIDYA, Achal Madhav. 4160 HOLIDAY ST NW 44718 #496-38-1993 L1998 **RHU IM** *020 †20
VANCE, Sara Lynne. ■ 44721 #038-44-2003 L2003 **OBG** *020
VAN EPPS, Kenneth Allen. 2725 LINCOLN ST E 44707 #047-06-1969 L1971 **IM** *020
VAN NESS, Michael Moore. 2726 FULTON DR NW, GASTROENTEROLOGY 44718 #051-01-1979 L1988 **GE IM** *020 †20
VARIAN, Dean Wade. 2600 6TH ST SW, ER DEPARTMENT 44710 #038-40-1973 L1974 **EM AM** *020 †16
VAZQUEZ, Roger Lee. 2600 6TH ST SW 44710 #038-44-1985 L1995 **NPM PD** *020 †55
VEG, Andrew. ■ 44708 #038-40-1953 L1953 **AN** *071 †05
VELLANKI, R Rao. 2600 6TH ST SW 44710 #495-16-1958 L1972 **PTH BBK** *071 †50
VEMULAPALLI, Sunitha. 2600 SIXTH ST SW, MORNING STAR HEM/ONC ASSOC 44710 #495-50-1995 L2004 **HO** *020 †20
VERA, Chido Dorothy. EDUCATIO2600 SIXTH, CO MEDICAL 44710 #422-01-2007 L2007 **TY** *012
VILLAPANDO, Aurora B. ■ 44708 #748-01-1962 L1970 **AN** *020
VILLARREAL, Carlos. ■ 44710 #649-14-1951 *075
VOLK, Barbara Helen. 4810 MUNSON ST NW 44718 #038-44-1984 L1985 **IM PD** *020 †20,55
WAIBEL, Paul Charlton. 2600 6TH ST SW 44710 #041-09-1973 L1978 **GE IM** *071 †20
WAKULCHIK, Stephen David. 2600 7TH ST SW 44710 #038-06-1982 L1991 **FM** *040 †18
WALLACE, William Raymond. 2600 6TH ST SW, RADIOLOGY ASSOCIATES OF 44710 #038-06-1976 L1980 **R** *020 †80
WALSH, Edward Jos. 1320 MERCY DR NW, MERCY MED CTR RAD ONCOLOGY 44708 #038-06-1988 L1989 **RO** *020 †80
WANG, Nina. 2600 6TH ST SW, DEPT PATH 44710 #209-01-1970 L1980 **HEM PTH** *020
WASEF, Atef Fahim. 2600 6TH ST SW, AULTMAN HOSPTIAL 44710 #915-04-1986 L2001 **AN** *020 †05
WASHINGTON, William John. 4105 HOLIDAY ST NW 44718 #038-41-1992 L1994 **PM** *020 †60
WEAVER, E Merle Metzger. ■ 44718 #041-12-1938 L1939 **PD OBG** *071
WEEMAN, Kisa Ewing. 2600 SIXTH ST SW 44710 #038-40-1989 L1995 **HO IM** *020 †20
WEIL, Richard Mark. 1320 MERCY DR NW 44708 #038-44-1987 L1988 **FM** *020 †18
WEINBERG, Stephanie Ann. 5000 HIGBEE AVE NW 44718 #038-44-1984 L1985 **OBG** *020 †30
WEINER, Mark Alan. 2600 TUSCARAWAS ST W # 520 44708 #056-05-1989 L1995 **NS** *020 †25
WEINFELD, Irwin J. 1320 MERCY DR NW, MERCY NEONATOLOGY 44708 #035-08-1968 L1975 **NPM** *020 †55
WEINSTOCK, Frank Joseph. 2600 TUSCARAWAS ST W, CANTON OPTHALMOLOGY 44708 #035-15-1960 L1961 **OPH** *020 †35
WELCH, Paul Wiley. 1320 MERCY DR NW 44708 #047-05-1966 L1968 **ORS** *020 †40
WERSTLER, Keith Brian. 4319 HILLS AND DALES RD NW 44708 #038-40-1991 L1993 **FM** *040 †18
WHITE, William Barton. 4535 DRESSLER RD NW 44718 #005-06-1979 L1984 **EM** *020 †16
WIETECHA, Kevin G. 4634 HILLS AND DALES RD NW 44708 #025-76-1991, ▲ L1995 **END IM** *020
WILSON, James Richard. 2600 6TH ST SW 44710 #038-43-1994 L1996 **OBG** *020 †30
WILT, Edward Gregory. 1320 TIMKEN MERCY DR NW 44708 #649-19-1957 L1964 **PTH FOP** *071 †50
WITHNELL, Philip Leigh. 2600 7TH ST SW 44710 #038-45-1995 L1996 **FM** *020 †18
WOLF, Bruce Howard. 2600 6TH ST SW, RADIOLOGY ASSOCIATES OF 44710 #038-06-1966 L1966 **DR NM** *020 †80,28
WONG, Paul Wingcheung. 2600 6TH ST SW, RADIOLOGY ASSOCIATES OF 44710 #028-34-1994 L2002 **PDR** *020 †80
WORRALL, Martin Andrew. 4690 MUNSON ST NW 44718 #008-02-1993 L2006 **OPH** *020 †35
WYCHANKO, Naomi Ann. 4151 HOLIDAY ST NW 44718 #037-01-1998 L1999 **OBG** *020 †30
XU, Xiaofei. 2425 13TH ST NW 44708 #243-52-1986 L1998 **IM** *020 †20
YAGHOOTI, Ali Reza. ■ 44708 #517-01-1959 L1966 **AN** *072
YEE, Briana Danielle. EDUCATIO2600 SIXTH, CO MEDICAL 44710 #665-01-2007 L2007 **FP** *012
YOUNG, James Scott, Jr. 2600 6TH ST SW, AULTMAN HOSP 44710 #038-41-1969 L1969 **GS** *020 †85
YOUNUS, Asif. 2815 TUSCARAWAS ST W, STARK PEDIATRICS, INC. 44708 #704-02-1990 L1999 **PN** *020 †55
YUNG, Kenny Shing. 2726 FULTON DR NW, GASTROENTEROLOGY 44718 #038-06-1998 L2004 **GE** *100 †20
YUT, Joseph Peter. 210 DUEBER AVE SW 44706 #010-01-1957 L1960 **OTO** *020 †45
ZAGST, Jeffrey S. 2600 SIXTH ST SW, OHIO HOSPITAL BASED PHYS C 44710 #016-43-1999 L1999 **AN** *020 †05 ‡
ZAIDI, Adnan Raza. 2600 6TH ST SW STE A2-710 44710 #704-01-1975 L1980 **CD IM** *020 †20
ZAIDI, Samina. 2600 TUSCARAWAS ST W, STE 120 44708 #704-01-1975 L1983 **P** *020 †75
ZAKI, Muhammad. 1330 MERCY DR NW STE 508 44708 #539-06-1990 L2003 **GE** *020 †20
ZALDIVAR, Guillermo. 1320 MERCY DR NW 44708 #132-02-1963 L1971 **R** *020 †80
ZHOU, Min. 2600 6TH ST SW 44710 #243-49-1987 L2006 **IM** *012
ZIEGLER, James R. 2600 6TH ST SW, CANTON MED EDUC FOUND 44710 #038-40-1973 L1973 **PUD IM** *020 †20
ZIMMERMAN, Donald M. 2600 6TH ST SW 44710 #038-40-1976 L1976 **IM EM** *020 †20
ZORKO, Michael Francis. 2600 6TH ST SW, ER DEPARTMENT 44710 #038-40-1981 L1982 **EM** *020 †16
ZSOM, Lajos. 2600 TUSCARAWAS ST W # 160, RENAL CONSULTANTS, INC 44708 #473-01-1991 L2005 **NEP** *020 †20
ZUCKER, Jamie Lee. 1320 MERCY DR NW 44708 #038-06-1984 L1984 **OPH FPS** *020 †35
ZURICK, Andrew Martin. 2600 SIXTH ST SW, DEPT. OF ANESTHESIA/AULTMA 44710 #033-05-1973 L1974 **AN** *020 †05

CARBON HILL – HOCKING

DEVOL, Marjorie Daisy. ■ 43111 #038-43-2003 L2006 **FM** *020 †18

■ = Address Information Privacy Protected

CARDINGTON – MORROW

LEE, William K. 117 E MAIN ST 43315 #583-06-1965 L1977 **FM GP** *020

CAREY – WYANDOT

HUSTON, Talmadge Ray. ■ 43316 #038-06-1946 L1946 **FM** *071
KAUFFMAN, Dwight Allen. 120 W SOUTH ST 43316 #026-04-1970 L2003 **FM** *020 †18
MAZZA, August C. 120 W SOUTH ST, CAREY MEDICAL CENTER 43316 #038-41-1951 L1951 **FM** *072 †18
ZIEGLER, John Patrick. 120 W SOUTH ST 43316 #020-12-1989 L1990 **FM** *020 †18

CARLISLE – WARREN

NESTOR, Anne Katharine. 300 BUSINESS PKWY 45005 #047-06-1989 L1991 **FM** *020 †18
STEVENS, Jewel A. 300 BUSINESS PKWY 45005 #005-12-1977 L1978 **FM** *020 †18

CARROLL – FAIRFIELD

LYNCH, Michele Suzanne. ■ 43112 #038-06-1992 L1993 **IM** *020

CARROLLTON – CARROLL

BISSELL, Nan Marie. 264 S LISBON ST, BOX 338 44615 #038-40-1974 L1974 **GP A** *071
MAFFETT, Jack Lewis. 264 S LISBON ST 44615 #038-41-1958 L1958 **FM PHP** *071 †18
MORTAZAVI, Kayvaan M. 1020 TRUMP RD NW 44615 #654-01-1996 L1998 **FM** *020 †18
STINE, Walter Scott. 1040 TRUMP RD NW, STE B 44615 #010-01-1977 L1986 **FM** *020 †18
STONE, John P. 125 CANTON RD NW 44615 #023-01-1971 L1989 **FM PM** *020 †18
WATSON, Thomas William. 125 CANTON RD NW, ORTHOPAEDIC 44615 #038-44-1990 L1994 **ORS** *020 †40

CEDARVILLE – GREENE

ANKENMAN, Eliz L Zigler. ■ 45314 #038-41-1959 L1959 **GP** *074
BROOKS, Beverly Joy. ■ 45314 #038-44-1989 L1997 **FM EM** *020 †18
GARRETT, Matthew Richard. 251 N MAIN ST # 3020 45314 #038-06-2007 L2007 **OTO** *012
SIDDALL, Allison Marie. 251 N MAIN ST # 5398 45314 #016-43-2007 **TY** *012
STEINGASS, Katherine Joy. 251 N MAIN ST # 5531 45314 #038-43-2006 L2006 **PD** *012
SULLIVAN, Dennis Michael. 251 N MAIN ST, CEDARVILLE UNIVERSITY 45314 #038-06-1978 L1980 **GS** *020 †85

CELINA – MERCER

AMARAN, Preetha. ■ 45822 #038-44-2001 L2001 **IM** *020
AMARAN, Thangaraj. 950 S MAIN ST 45822 #495-42-1971 L1981 **U GS** *020 †95
BAYTION, Carlos Macias. 8250 ST RTE 703, NORTWOOD, BOX 32 45822 #748-08-1961 L1974 **GP GS** *071
BRUAL, Rolando Sarmiento. ■ 45822 #748-01-1957 L1968 **IM PUD** *071
DABIS, Nazih J. 329 E MARKET ST 45822 #915-02-1970 L1980 **PD NPM** *020 †55
FOX, Donald R. ■ 45822 #041-13-1952 L1953 **GP** *071 †18
GUTTA, Jayanth Kumar. 950 S MAIN ST, STE 3 45822 #495-58-1981 L2005 **CCM PUD** *020 †20
HOLLERAN, Neal Evan. 208 S MAIN ST 45822 #038-40-1970 L1979 **IM** *020
JAARA, Farouk Mohammed F. 666 N ASH ST 45822 #915-04-1972 L1981 **CD IM** *050 †20
JOSEY, Michael C. 801 PRO DR, JTDMH CELINA MEDICAL CENTE 45822 #064-01-1989 L1995 *020
KEMMLER, James E. 123 HAMILTON ST 45822 #016-11-1990 L1998 **U** *020 †40
KESSELRING, Richard Allen. 950 S MAIN ST, STE 8 45822 #055-02-1989 L1994 **OBG** *020 †30
LACUESTA, Marden B. 718 E WAYNE ST 45822 #748-11-1968 L1979 **GS GP** *020
MASSER, Philip Ray. PO BOX 420, 724 E WAYNE ST 45822 #038-43-1981 L1983 **FM** *020 †18
MC MANES, Joseph Mathew. ■ 45822 #038-40-1960 L1960 **GP** *071
OTIS, James John. 111 N WALNUT ST 45822 #038-41-1940 **GP GS** *071
RHEE, Gil John. 950 S MAIN ST, STE 10 45822 #583-06-1969 L1983 **OBG** *020 †30
SATYANARAYANA, Malavalli. 1005 N MAIN ST 45822 #495-09-1973 L1980 **IM CD** *020 †20
SATYANARAYANA, Shanthi. 255 E 2 45822 #495-99-1978 L1984 **IM GP** *020 †20
SWARTS, Karen. 801 PRO DR 45822 #038-40-1998 L2004 **PD** *020 †55
THRESHER, Alison Jean. 950 S MAIN ST, STE 7 45822 #011-02-1975 L2001 **OBG** *020 †30
WHITE, Peter R. 801 PRO DR 45822 #064-01-1974 L1997 **GP A** *020
ZIEGENBUSCH, Kenneth H. ■ 45822 #038-41-1955 L1955 **DR** *071

CENTERBURG – KNOX

HALL, Nathan Christopher. ■ 43011 #038-41-2000 L2004 **NM** *020 †28
MARTINSON, Ron Tsuyoshi. 4581 COLUMBUS RD 43011 #014-01-1998 L1999 **FM** *020 †18
MITCHEM, Jonathan Bower. ■ 43011 #038-40-2007 L2007 **GS** *012

CENTERVILLE – MONTGOMERY

ADAM, Wynn Wygal. 1997 MIAMISBURG CENTRVL RD 45459 #041-02-1977 L1978 **DR** *020 †80
AYRES, William Bliss. ■ 45459 #016-06-1941 L1941 **GP** *071
BALAKRISHNAN, Dheepa. 330 N MAIN ST 45459 #038-44-2001 L2001 **OBG** *020 †30
BALWALLY, Atul Nandakumar. 255 N MAIN ST 45459 #038-41-1988 L1996 **OTO** *020 †45
BATCHRA, Nandita. ■ 45459 #065-01-1993 L2007 **OTO** *020 †45
BAUMANN, Berta H. 232 WALNUT GROVE DR O 45458 #038-40-1979 L1985 **DR NM** *030 †80,28
BEEGAN, James Gregory. 1975 MIAMISBURG CENTRVL RD 45459 #038-40-1991 L1992 **PM** *020 †60
BHAT, Maryann Pollock. 101 S MAIN ST 45458 #038-41-1989 L1990 **FM** *020 †18

BOYLES, John H, Jr. 7076 CORPORATE WAY 45459 #016-06-1960 L1960 **OTO A** *020 †45
BRADY, Colin Martin. ■ 45459 #038-40-2006 **GS** *012
BRITTAIN, Rick Lee. 7707 PARAGON RD STE 106 45459 #038-45-1993 L1998 **DR** *020 †80
BUDIAMAL MATHAI, Lita R. 1997 MIAMISBURG CENTRVL RD 45459 #506-03-1972 L1982 **AN PME** *020 †05 ‡
CASWELL, Jolinda Lee. 896 S MAIN ST 45458 #038-40-1976 L1977 **FM** *020 †18
CATA, Anne Charters. 6520 ACRO CT 45459 #038-41-1988 L1990 **PD** *020 †55
CRIBBS, Katherine A. 63 MEETING HOUSE RD 45459 #038-45-2004 L2004 **MPD** *012
DITTOE, Nathaniel Joseph. ■ 45459 #038-45-2004 L2004 **IM** *012 †20
DOEPKER, Matthew Patrick. ■ 45458 #038-45-2008 *012
DOUCETTE, David Jos. 6438 WILMINGTON PIKE, STE 300 45459 #005-12-1982 L1992 **OBG EM** *020 †30
EISENHUT, Randy. 6520 ACRO CT 45459 #019-02-1988 L1989 **PD** *020 †55
FREY, Jennifer Lynn. ■ 45458 #038-45-2007 L2007 **OBG** *012
GAMADIA, Kaywan Dinyar. ■ 45458 #028-79-2007, ▲ L2007 *012
GERLINGER, Lawton C, Jr. 450 N MAIN ST 45459 #038-40-1963 L1963 **D** *071 †15
GOLDENBERG, Robert A. 255 N MAIN ST 45459 #020-02-1968 L1972 **NO** *020 †45
ISAAK, Edahn Joshua. ■ 45458 #011-04-1991 L2007 **PTH BBK** *030 †50
IZU, Brent Seiji. ■ 45458 #023-12-2004 L2004 **GS** *012
JACKSON, Rosalind Joy. 6611 CLYO RD STE B 45459 #038-45-1995 L1996 **OBG** *020 †30
JONES, Christie Leigh. ■ 45458 #001-06-2007 L2007 **GS** *012
KAISER, Lisa Lee. 896 S MAIN ST 45458 #038-45-2004 L2004 **FM** *020 †18
KANE, Naomi Marlene. 7707 PARAGON RD STE 106 45459 #035-09-1983 L1996 **DR** *020 †80
KELLAWAN, Karl K, II. 400 N MAIN ST STE D 45459 #005-12-1982 L1988 **D** *020 †15
KOHLS, Gregory Stephen. 600 HEARTLAND TRCE 45458 #038-41-2008 *012
LAUBENTHAL, Amanda K. ■ 45459 #038-75-2007, ▲ L2007 *012
LEISRING, Jeffrey Michael. 101 S MAIN ST STE D, CENTERVILLE HEALTH CARE 45458 #038-40-1984 L1985 **FM** *020 †18
LIM, Jennifer Michele. ■ 45458 #028-34-2007 L2007 **EM** *012
LIN, Jain I. ■ 45458 #385-01-1964 L1979 **PTH** *071 †50
LUNA, Raymond. 896 S MAIN ST 45458 #038-45-1996 L1997 **FM** *020 †18
MARTIN, Derrick John. 8940 KINGSWICH DR, SUITE 105 45458 #566-01-1977 L1990 **GS EM** *020 †85
MCAFEE, Jacob Seth. ■ 45458 #038-45-2008 *012
MC CARTHY, John F, III. 896 S MAIN ST 45458 #038-41-1986 L1987 **FM** *020 †18
MOELL, Ann Trzaska. 6611 CLYO RD, RAHN HILLS MEDICAL GROUP 45459 #038-40-1988 L1990 **FM** *020 †18
MONTGOMERY, Keith Allen. ■ 45459 #028-34-2004 L2004 **P** *012
MOREY, Anjali K. 255 N MAIN ST 45459 #005-15-1998 L2004 **GE** *100 †20
NAVAYOGARAJAH, Shahila. ■ 45459 #220-03-1995 L2000 **IM** *020 †20
OKEKE, Vivian Chizoba. ■ 45458 #759-04-2003 L2005 **IM** *012
OWUSU-DEKYI, Kwabena. 6520 ACRO CT, PRIMED PHYSICIANS 45459 #017-20-1995 L1996 **FM** *020 †18
PALMER, D Greg. 6720 LOOP RD, SURGERY CENTER, INC. 45459 #038-45-1982 L1985 **D PD** *020 †55,15
PATEL-BRITTAIN, Bhairavi. 6438 WILMINGTON PIKE, STE 300 45459 #038-45-1994 L1998 **OBG** *020 †30
PAUIG, Maximo Malana. 5716 PRICE HILL PL 45459 #748-01-1944 L1974 **P CHP** *020
RICHARDS, Cynthia J. 1159 LYONS RD 45458 #046-01-1989 L1996 **CHP** *020 †75
RICHARDS, Michael F. ■ 45458 #020-02-1994 L1997 **FM AM** *020 †18
ROGERS, William Evered. ■ 45458 #017-20-1971 L1977 **IM NM** *020 †20,28
ROMER, Douglas Edward. 6520 ACRO CT, PRIMED PHYSICIANS 45459 #028-34-1982 L1983 **FM** *020 †18
RONCALLO, Paolo Gino. ■ 45458 #011-04-2001 L2003 **ADL** *020 †55
RUEHLE, James Allan. 330 N MAIN ST 45459 #025-01-1973 L1975 **GYN** *020 †30
RUSH, William Joseph A. ■ 45459 #038-45-2003 L2006 **OBG** *020
SCHAFFER, Robert Randall. 330 N MAIN ST, STE 101-102 45459 #005-12-1986 L1987 **FM** *020 †18 ‡
SCHEUFLER, Tara Jolene. ■ 45458 #041-78-2002, ▲ L2007 **FM HOS** *020 †18
SCOTT-TOMLISON, Tasha N. 216 BRANCH CREEK CT 45458 #038-41-2001 L2001 **FM** *100 †18
SESSLAR, Christopher J. 6627 CENTERVILLE BSNS PKWY 45459 #038-45-1996 L1997 **FM** *020 †18
SETSER, Charles Adam. 7073 CLYO RD, 7707 PARAGON RD SUITE 101 45459 #038-40-1998 L1999 **IM** *020 †20
SHARAT, Kalvakota. 400 N MAIN ST, STE B 45459 #495-65-1969 L1980 **U** *020 †95
SHARMA, Vibhavasu. 1989 MIAMISBURG CENTRVL RD, JOSLIN DIABETES STE 304 45459 #495-45-1998 L2006 **END** *020 †20
SHAW, Jeffrey Brian. 597 BANBURY RD 45459 #038-40-1985 L1986 **FM** *020 †18
STOUFFER, Mark Harold. ■ 45458 #056-06-2007 L2007 **ORS** *012
STRATTON, Harold C. 1550 YANKEE PARK PL, STE A 45458 #010-03-1955 L1957 **GP** *020
THAMBIPILLAI, G. 6728 LOOP RD, STE 304 45459 #539-05-1995 L2007 **IM** *020 †20
THEIN, Walter. 330 N MAIN ST 45459 #132-01-1959 L1970 **OBG** *071 †30
THESING, Michael Joseph. 330 N MAIN ST, 330 N MAIN ST 45459 #038-41-1986 L1989 **OBG** *020 †30
THOMAS, Joseph Daniel. ■ 45459 #038-41-2008 *012
THOME, Judene Marie. 6520 ACRO CT 45459 #056-06-1989 L1990 **PD** *020 †55
TURNER, William J. 255 N MAIN ST 45459 #041-01-1992 L1998 **OTO** *020 †45
UDREA, Petre. 1975 MIAMISBURG CENTRVL RD 45459 #038-45-1995 L1996 **N** *020
VAN JURA, Jodi Lynne. 1512 YANKEE PARK PL 45458 #038-45-1999 L1999 **FM** *020 †18
VARGHESE, Sanju Andrew. 1989 MIAMISBURG CENTRVL RD 45459 #422-01-2000 L2006 **NEP** *020 †20
WALD, Steven Lewis. ■ 45459 #030-05-1975 L1999 **NS** *020 †25
WOOTON, Amy Noel. 330 N MAIN ST, STE 101102 45459 #038-45-2002 L2002 **FM** *020 †18
YALAMANCHILI, Kiranmai. ■ 45459 #495-57-2001 L2007 **IM** *100 †20
ZELLER, Charles Joseph. 7076 CORPORATE WAY 45459 #038-75-1998, ▲ L1999 **OTO FPS** *020

CHAGRIN FALLS – CUYAHOGA

ABUNYEWA, Charles. 15401 SUFFOLK LN, GLENVILLE HEALTH FOUNDATIO 44022 #412-01-1997 L2000 **IM** *100 †20 ‡
AHN, Ho. ■ 44022 #583-02-1970 L1980 **AN GS** *020
BAKOS, Leslie. 115 E SUMMIT ST 44022 #473-01-1954 L1964 **P** *020
BATTLES, Heather Anne. ■ 44022 #038-43-2006 L2006 **PD** *012

■ = Address Information Privacy Protected

BERKELEY, Barbara Ellen. 5192 CHILLICOTHE RD, STE 104 44022 #035-48-1980 L1987 IM *020 †20
BLOOMFIELD, Richard A. ■ 44022 #041-12-1949 L1949 PD *020 †55
BOWE, David Alan. 63 WALNUT ST 44022 #038-44-1984 L1988 IM PD *020 †55,20
BRUNER, Harlan Jason. ■ 44022 #035-01-2002 L2004 NS *012
BUCKLAN, Bruce Eric. 551 E WASHINGTON ST 44022 #038-40-1981 L1983 AN *020 †05
CHEN, Yong. 551 E WASHINGTON ST CF10, CHAGRIN FALLS FAMILY HLTH 44022 #243-45-1982 L1997 IM *020 †20
CHERNETZKY, John. 115 E SUMMIT ST 44022 #407-13-1944 L1959 P *072
CICEK, Wendy T. 5291 CHILLICOTHE RD, STE 101 44022 #038-06-1998 L2000 FM *020 †18
CINTI, Edde. 551 E WASHINGTON ST 44022 #869-05-1967 L1969 IM NEP *020 †20
COFFEY, Michael David. 180 KENTON RD 44022 #038-40-1993 L1999 DR *020 †80
COLLINS, Thomas Edward, Jr. 50 FAIRFAX DR 44022 #028-34-1993 L1995 EM *020 †16
CUSUMANO, Philip Anthony. 551 E WASHINGTON ST 44022 #038-45-1983 L1984 IM OM *020 †20
DAYNEKA, Andrew David. 551 E WASHINGTON ST 44022 #065-05-1987 L1999 *020
DE MARCO, Victor Jos. ■ 44022 #038-06-1966 L1966 DR *020 †80
DUCHESNEAU, Paul M. ■ 44022 #024-05-1952 L1960 RNR OS *071 †80
GOTA, Marius Pompei. ■ 44022 #781-03-1989 L2002 CCA *020 †05
HAMLER, Scott Thomas. 551 E WASHINGTON ST 44022 #038-43-2003 L2003 FM *020 †18
HERGENROEDER, Patrick T. 34 W WASHINGTON ST 44022 #010-02-1974 L1975 ORS HS *020 †40
JULIANO, Erin Elizabeth. 551 E WASHINGTON ST, CLEVELAND CLNC CHAGRIN FLS 44022 #035-15-2002 L2004 IM *020 †18
KALE, Neelima Jayavant. 5192 CHILLICOTHE RD 44022 #039-01-1996 L1998 FM *020 †18
KANVINDE, Mangesh H. 15 WILDING CHASE, P O BOX 224 44022 #039-01-1997 L1999 DR *020
KERLEK, Anna Jaquay. ■ 44022 #038-41-2006 L2007 P *012
KING, Kathleen Patricia. ■ 44022 #035-46-1983 L1988 FM *020 †18
KITCHEN, Alfred Geo E. 551 E WASHINGTON ST 44022 #065-05-1973 L1977 CD IM *075
KORNBLUTH, Irwin. ■ 44022 #067-01-1961 L1964 OBG *071 †30
KRUDY, Catherine. ■ 44022 #473-01-1944 L1960 P *071
LEE, Shin Jae. ■ 44022 #583-02-1972 L1976 P *020
LINDBLAD, Robert Walter. 38355 CHAGRIN BLVD 44022 #038-41-1981 L1988 EM *020 †16
LINGL, Friedrich Albert. ■ 44022 #407-16-1952 L1960 P OS *072 †75
LONEY, James W. ■ 44022 #038-06-1950 L1950 OM PUD *071 †20
LONG, Donald Eugene, Jr. ■ 44022 #038-40-1978 L1979 IM GE *020 †20
LUDWIG, Elizabeth Norris. 38355 CHAGRIN BLVD 44022 #038-41-1981 L1983 OPH *020
MADAN-MOHAN, Gayatri. ■ 44022 #495-16-1984 L2000 PTH *020 †30
MAKLEY, John Thos. ■ 44022 #038-41-1961 L1961 ORS OMO *071 †40
METZ, Karl V. 5192 CHILLICOTHE RD, STE 104 44022 #055-01-1964 L1991 ORS *020 †40
MICHAEL, Nancy Barrington. ■ 44022 #038-06-1950 L1950 CHP *071
MIRFENDERESKI, Seyed A. ■ 44022 #902-05-1993 L1997 IM *020 †20
MISTHOS, Maria. 1265 BELL RD 44022 #035-19-1987 L2003 IM *020 †20
MOBASSERI, Jafar. ■ 44022 #517-05-1964 L1972 R RO *071 †80
OGBOGU, Christopher Ibe. 29399 N HILLTOP RD 44022 #033-06-1982 L1993 IM *020 †20
PARK, Ellen Sunjoo. ■ 44022 #051-04-2000 L2006 DR *100 †80
PENSIERO, Donald Allen. ■ 44022 #038-40-1957 L1957 IM CD *071 †20
POLSTER, Amy Melissa. 551 E WASHINGTON ST, DERMATOLOGY/CF10 44022 #038-06-1999 L2000 D *020 †15
PONSKY, Jeffrey L. ■ 44022 #038-06-1971 L1973 GS *020 †85
QUEDDING-PIZARRO, Maria A. 551 E WASHINGTON ST 44022 #748-10-1991 L1999 IM *020
RIMMERMAN, Maria Simon. 2635 SOM CENTER RD 44022 #038-06-1987 L1993 PTH *020 †50,20
ROOD, Mark N. 5192 CHILLICOTHE RD, STE 101 44022 #038-41-1985 L1987 FM *020 †18
ROSENBAUM, Arthur Elihu. ■ 44022 #011-02-1962 L1987 RNR R *020 †80
RUBINSTEIN, Lee I. ■ 44022 #038-06-1953 L1953 GYN *020 †30
SAMPLINER, James Edward. ■ 44022 #038-06-1963 L1963 GS *071 †85
SAVRIN, Ronald A. 235 JACKSON DR 44022 #035-15-1974 L1975 VS *040 †85
SCHMITT, Ilana Levenson. 29450 N HILLTOP RD 44022 #038-06-1988 L1992 PD *020 †15
SIMON, Helge Ulrich. ■ 44022 #035-01-1995 L2001 ICE *020 †20
TAHIR, Mohammad Imran. ■ 44022 #704-01-1989 L1997 IM *020 †20
TARR, Jesse Edwin. 19 E BELMEADOW LN 44022 #038-40-1955 L1955 IM *071 †20
VART, Gary Richard. ■ 44022 #051-01-1959 L1966 OBG *075 †30
WALD, David Nathan. ■ 44022 #038-06-2005 L2005 PTH *012
WALTZ, Gary Woosley. 115 E SUMMIT ST 44022 #038-06-1979 L1979 P PA *020 †75
WEINERT, Dayna May. 175 GREY FOX RUN 44022 #038-06-1982 L1993 DR PDR *020 †80
WIRTZ, Christina Martin. 5192 CHILLICOTHE RD, S RUSSELL MED CTR 44022 #038-40-1981 L1981 DR *020 †80
YUNUS, Samina Y. 551 E WASHINGTON ST, CLEVELAND CLINIC ,CHAGRIN 44022 #495-53-1990 L2005 FM *020 †18

CHAGRIN FALLS – GEAUGA

ALEXANDER, Alan Russel. 17747 CHILLICOTHE RD 44023 #038-06-1956 L1956 PD *071 †55
BLOSER, Dieter. ■ 44023 #038-06-1970 L1970 DR *071 †80
BRAHMANANDAM, Vikram Madd. ■ 44023 #041-12-2007 L2007 *012
BUCHANAN, Kelly V. 8185 E WASHINGTON ST, STE 1A 44023 #038-06-1996 L1999 OBG *020 †30
CAMERON, Robert Bruce. 8185 E WASHINGTON ST, STE 2 44023 #038-06-1979 L1979 MPD GE *020 †20 ‡
ECSY, Laszlo. ■ 44023 #473-01-1952 L1962 P *020 †75
ELSAWY, Tarek. 17747 CHILLICOTHE RD, STE 203A 44023 #038-06-1991 L1994 IM *020 †20
FIKTER, William Pasan. 17747 CHILLICOTHE RD, STE 202 44023 #038-44-1990 L1992 P CHP *020
FORD, Mary Means. ■ 44023 #038-06-1952 L1955 PD OM *071
GRCEVICH, Stephen. 8401 CHAGRIN RD STE 14B 44023 #038-44-1986 L1989 CHP P *020 †75
GRUEN, Thomas Chas. 8185 E WASHINGTON ST 44023 #038-41-1966 L1966 IM *071 †20
ILIEVA, Antoaneta Ivanova. 8185 E WASHINGTON ST, STE 1 44023 #198-01-1989 L2000 IM *020 †20
IRWIN, John Rankin. 8401 CHAGRIN RD, STE 19 44023 #038-06-1985 L1987 LM *075
JEROMIN, Gerald Anthony. ■ 44023 #038-43-1990 L1991 EM *020 †16
JEROMIN, Jennifer Joan. ■ 44023 #038-43-1992 L1994 EM *020 †16
KATSMAN, Helen. 17747 CHILLICOTHE RD, CENTER 44023 #913-77-1983 L1997 IM *020 †20
KEARY, Jonathan Stephen. ■ 44023 #038-06-2008 *012

KHALIL, Naguib Tewfik. 17747 CHILLICOTHE RD, CENTER 44023 #915-02-1950 L1972 PD IM *020
KING, Scott John. ■ 44023 #038-41-2006 L2007 DR *012
LAZARUS, Jeffrey Edward. 8185 E WASHINGTON ST 44023 #016-01-1978 L1981 PD *020 †55
LEIZMAN, Jonathan. 17747 CHILLICOTHE RD, CENTER 44023 #038-40-1997 L1998 FM *020
MALLAK, Kathryn Anne. ■ 44023 #025-01-1990 L1994 AN *020 †05
MASON, Laura Elaine. ■ 44023 #035-45-1985 L1997 PD ADL *020 †55
MEKHAIL, Ruth Ibrahim. ■ 44023 #915-04-1980 PTH *100
MOEN, Robert Chas. ■ 44023 #054-04-1979 L1980 IG PD *050 †55,03
MULLEN, Lori Shoos. 8185 E WASHINGTON ST, BAINBRIDGE HEALTH CENTER 44023 #038-06-1994 L1996 OBG *020 †30
MURPHY, Mary Rita. 7754 COUNTRY LN 44023 #035-06-1990 L1999 PD *020 †55
O'MALLEY, Charles M, Jr. ■ 44023 #038-41-1988 L1994 DR *020 †80
OZSOYOGLU, Aliye Aysegul. ■ 44023 #038-06-2006 L2006 DR *012
PARADIS, Carmen Ann Marie. ■ 44023 #060-01-1974 L1979 PS HS *071 †65
PASSODELIS, William E. 188 WOODSONG WAY 44023 #055-02-1992 L1994 DR *020 †80
PATEL, Sandeep Bhikhu. 17747 CHILLICOTHE RD 44023 #759-06-2003 L2003 IM *020 †20
PIZARRO, James T. 8185 E WASHINGTON ST 44023 #748-10-1991 L1995 IM *020
PLESEC, Thomas Panella. ■ 44023 #038-44-2004 L2004 PTH *012
RIEMENSCHNEIDER, Thomas A. ■ 44023 #035-15-1964 L1982 PDC *071 †55
ROWANE, William Anthony. 8401 CHAGRIN RD STE 1 44023 #041-09-1983 L1987 CHP P *020 †75
ROZMAN, Raymond Wm. 8185 E WASHINGTON ST, # 2 44023 #038-06-1984 L1986 IM GE *020 †20
SHAFFER, Mark Baylies, Jr. 8185 E WASHINGTON ST 44023 #038-06-1959 L1959 IM *071
SHAPIRO, Eric Jos. 8185 E WASHINGTON ST, STE 2 44023 #038-06-1985 L1986 GE IM *020 †20
SMITH, Kristen Alaine. ■ 44023 #038-41-2006 L2006 N *012
STEMAR, Andrew Michael. 17747 CHILLICOTHE RD, CENTER 44023 #759-01-1987 L1996 PUD IM HEM *012
STRASSMAN, Selig S. ■ 44023 #041-09-1951 L1953 PD ADL *071 †55
STRICKLAND, Susan Kay. ■ 44023 #038-44-1990 L1993 PD *075 †55
USIS, Paula Bekeny. 8185 E WASHINGTON ST STE 8 44023 #038-06-1995 L1997 OBG *020 †30
WONGCHAOWART, Boonlieng. ■ 44023 #572-58-1972 L1977 PTH *020 †50

CHARDON – GEAUGA

ABADIR, Kamal Faltas. 13207 RAVENNA RD 44024 #915-04-1911 L1978 AN *020
AHUJA, Samir. 13207 RAVENNA RD, OBGYN 44024 #065-01-1989 L1995 OBG *020 †30
ANDREANI, Natalina N. 13170 RAVENNA RD, ST 116 44024 #038-43-1995 L1997 OBG *020 †30
ANOUCHI, Yoel Shlomo. 13241 RAVENNA RD 44024 #024-05-1982 L1983 ORS OAR *020 †40
ANSARI, Mohammad. 13221 RAVENNA RD 44024 #517-05-1964 L1977 IM HEM *071 †20
BARNETT-RICO, Marian. 13207 RAVENNA RD 44024 #305-01-1983 L1992 EM IM *020 †20
BELLAMY, Robert Edgar. ■ 44024 #035-01-1973 L1974 GS *020
BINDER, Hertha F. 12793 TAYLOR WELLS RD 44024 #154-07-1950 L1961 OPH *071 †35
BINDER, Rudolf Florian. 12793 TAYLOR WELLS RD 44024 #154-07-1950 L1962 OPH *020 †35
CAMERON, John Jeffery. 13170 RAVENNA RD, STE 116 44024 #038-06-1984 L1985 OBG *020 †30
CARLSON, Melanie Lynn. 13221 RAVENNA RD, STE 8 44024 #038-45-1998 L1999 FM *020 †18
CHARTRAND, Kevin Michael. 13221 RAVENNA RD, SUITE9 44024 #035-06-1984 L1987 FM OM *020 †18
CHRISTIAN, Horace D, II. 13170 RAVENNA RD, STE 202 44024 #041-12-1986 L1988 GS *020 †85
COLEMAN, Robert S, Jr. 13207 RAVENNA RD, ATTN MEDICAL STAFF OFFICE 44024 #305-01-1995 L1999 IM *020 †20
COSTELLO, Frank Jerome. 13207 RAVENNA RD 44024 #038-45-1991 L1993 AN CCA *020 †05
COURTRIGHT, Anne Comfort. PO BOX 694, 117 SOUTH ST # 209 44024 #039-01-1951 L1951 P *071
DI MARCO, Anthony F. 13221 RAVENNA RD STE 9 44024 #024-07-1974 L1977 PUD IM *050 †20
DOBYNS, Brown M. ■ 44024 #023-07-1939 L1951 GS *071 †85
DREBOTY, Daria Marie. ■ 44024 #038-41-2001 L2004 FM *100 †18
DUANGJAK, Patrawadee. 13207 RAVENNA RD, UHHS GEAUGA REG HOSP PATH 44024 #891-01-1965 L1973 ATP PCP *020 †50
DUANGJAK, Vichai. 12475 HOSPITAL DR 44024 #891-01-1965 L1972 OBG *020 †30
FAILINGER, Ann Louise. 13241 RAVENNA RD, CHESTERLAND PEDIATRICS 44024 #047-05-1993 L2001 PD *020 †55
GHOSE, Manash Kumar. 12340 BASS LAKE RD 44024 #495-38-1952 L1971 NEP IM *020 †20
GOTTLOB, Milford Errol. 13221 RAVENNA RD STE 3 44024 #038-40-1963 L1963 D *020 †15
HALAWA, Abdul. 13170 RAVENNA RD, STE 206 44024 #575-01-1988 L1993 ID *020 †20
IZAR-BRISENO, Sergio. 13207 RAVENNA RD, GEAUGA HOSPITAL 44024 #649-01-1962 L1975 AN *020
JAHANGIRI, Sudy Elizabeth. ■ 44024 #038-44-2008 *012
JAWA, Prem Sagar. 13170 RAVENNA RD 44024 #495-29-1965 L1974 U *020 †95
JONES, Gail Ellen. ■ 44024 #038-06-1996 L1997 FM *020 †18 ‡
KAGAN, Evgenia. 13207 RAVENNA RD, UNIV HOSP GEAUGA MEDICAL C 44024 #913-12-1998 L1998 IM *020
KAKISH, Robert Stephen. 115 WILSON MILLS RD 44024 #028-34-1978 L1982 IM *020 †20
KELLIS, George John. 100 7TH AVE 44024 #038-40-1984 L1985 ORS *020 †40
KHAITAN, Leena. 13207 RAVENNA RD 44024 #038-06-1995 L2006 GS *020 †85
KNIGHT, Karen Hankins. 12340 BASS LAKE RD 44024 #025-12-1996 L2000 PM *020 †60
KRALIK, John J. 13170 RAVENNA RD 44024 #041-01-1949 L1949 GS VS *020 †85
LEE, Jung Min. 13221 RAVENNA RD 44024 #583-01-1960 L1968 PD *020 †55,20
LEE, Seungkwon. 150 7TH AVE STE 210 44024 #041-12-1986 L1991 GS *020 †85
LOOMIS, Gordon R. ■ 44024 #028-34-1951 L1955 P NTR *071
LUMAPAS, Arminda Lim. 13207 RAVENNA RD, GEAUGA HOSPITAL SPECIALTY 44024 #055-01-2002 L2002 RHU *100 †20
MACKLIN, Martin. 13207 RAVENNA RD, GEAVGA REGIONAL HOSPITAL 44024 #038-06-1977 L1978 P ADM *030 †75
MADDEN, Maria Theresa. 150 7TH AVE, STE 210 44024 #038-45-1988 L1990 GS GE *020 †85
MARSHALL, Craig Edan. ■ 44024 #038-05-2001 L2005 FM *020 †18
MASUOKA, Kayoshi. ■ 44024 #038-40-1958 L1958 FM *071 †18
MC NAMARA, Patricia Ann. 13207 RAVENNA RD, OBGYN 44024 #038-06-1986 L1986 OBG *020 †30
MORITZ, John Bradley. 13221 RAVENNA RD, STE 8 44024 #004-01-1984 L1988 FM *020 †18

OCA, Oscar Santa Cruz. 13346 RAVENNA RD, OSCAR S OCA MD INC 44024 #748-01-1953 L1961 **GS CD** *071
OH, James Jaihoon. ■ 44024 #056-05-1990 L1992 **AN** *020 †05
O'HARA, Janet Lynn. 150 7TH AVE 44024 #038-44-1984 L1988 **IM PD** *020 †20,55
ONDREJKA, John Jos. 510 5TH AVE 44024 #038-43-1985 L1987 **IM EM** *020
PAWLICKI, Matthew Bernard. 150 7TH AVE, STE 110 44024 #038-45-2001 L2003 **FM** *020 †18
PRIMC, Michael Joseph. ■ 44024 #038-06-1995 L1999 **P** *020 †75
RAMACCIATO, Angelo Mario. 13207 RAVENNA RD 44024 #561-10-1957 L1965 **AN** *071
RAZMJOUEI, Karim. 12340 BASS LAKE RD, HEATHER HILL HOSP. AND REH 44024 #561-06-1990 L2000 **IM** *020 †20
RITROVATO, James. ■ 44024 #561-12-1951 L1960 **GP** *071
ROM, Michael E. 13170 RAVENNA RD STE 204 44024 #836-01-1984 L1991 **OPH** *020 †35 ‡
ROSENBERG, Samuel. 13241 RAVENNA RD 44024 #649-01-1984 L1986 **APM IM** *020 †20,05
RUN, Tocky Landerway. ■ 44024 #244-04-1970 L1975 **IM GP** *020
SCHULTE, James Jos. 510 5TH AVE, PRIMEHEALTH FAMILY PHYS 44024 #016-06-1982 L1993 **FM** *020 †18
SINKS, Peter B. 10221 MULBERRY RD 44024 #038-06-1985 L1985 **RHU IM** *020 †20
SMITH, David Gilbert. 100 7TH AVE, STE 222 44024 #038-44-1991 L1993 **CD** *020 †20
STEWART, Robert Denison. 12340 BASS LAKE RD 44024 #005-11-1969 L1970 **ORS GS** *071 †40
SUNDARARAJAN, Krishnan. 100 7TH AVE, STE 222 44024 #495-96-1988 L1993 **CD** *020 †20
SWARUP, Namita. 13170 RAVENNA RD, STE 118 44024 #690-01-1989 L2002 **PD** *020 †55
URBANCIC, John Milan. 13221 RAVENNA RD, STE 8 44024 #051-01-1995 L1996 **FM** *020 †18
VUCETIC, Henry Emil. ■ 44024 #055-01-2007 L2007 **AN** *012
WENZ, Margie Ellen. 13170 RAVENNA RD 44024 #038-06-1985 L1989 **OBG** *020 †30
WIELAND, Ralph Gazell. 13170 RAVENNA RD, STE 206 44024 #041-01-1956 L1957 **IM END** *020 †20
YOON, Sai Byung. 470 CENTER ST 44024 #583-01-1959 L1970 **R** *071 †80
ZIMMER, Scott Michael. 13241 RAVENNA RD 44024 #038-45-1998 L1999 **HS** *020 †40
ZIMMERMAN, Robert J. 13207 RAVENNA RD 44024 #048-13-1996 L1997 **EM** *020 †16
ZNIDARSIC, Robert Mark. 510 5TH AVE, PRIMEHEALTH CHARDON FAM PR 44024 #038-43-1995 L1996 **FM** *020 †18

CHESAPEAKE – LAWRENCE

ALI, Rizwan. 717 3RD AVE 45619 #704-02-1989 L2000 **P** *020
MORFORD, Warren Newton. RT 1 BOX 421 45619 #020-02-1957 L1958 **P** *071
OXLEY, Kimberly Ann. 717 3RD AVE 45619 #055-02-1994 L1997 **PD** *020 †55
SMITH, Robert Geo. ■ 45619 #038-40-1954 L1954 **ORS** *071 †40
WATSON-GRAY, Kathie Lynn. 717 3RD AVE 45619 #041-12-1995 L1998 **FM** *020 †18

CHESTERLAND – GEAUGA

BENNETT, Ana Elodia. ■ 44026 #715-01-1988 L2003 **PTH** *020 †50
COUTINHO, Maria-Josefa P. 8055 MAYFIELD RD, STE 106 44026 #495-28-1985 L1990 **PN PD** *020 †55
CUONZO, Richard Anton. ■ 44026 #047-06-1944 L1945 **GS PS** *071 †85
DEV-RAMAN, Simret Kaur. 8055 MAYFIELD RD, STE 107 44026 #759-06-2000 L2005 **FM** *020 †18
FAKULT, Sandra M. 8055 MAYFIELD RD, STE 101 44026 #038-06-1994 L1996 **IM** *020 †20
GAMERMAN, Larisa L. 8254 MAYFIELD RD 44026 #913-27-1992 L2002 **IM** *100 †20
GARDNER, Robert Earl. ■ 44026 #038-40-1948 L1948 **GP OBG** *071
GODDARD, Donald Jos. 8055 MAYFIELD RD # 107, STE 107 44026 #038-06-1990 L1992 **FM** *020 †18
GYURGYIK, L. ■ 44026 #038-44-1986 L1987 **OPH** *071 †35
HAULER, Joseph. ■ 44026 #781-05-1956 L1971 **GP** *071
LORENZO, Reuben Suguitan. ■ 44026 #748-07-1953 L1965 **DR RO** *071
METTEE, Thomas Muther. 12714 OPALOCKA DR 44026 #035-45-1968 L1978 **GP PD** *020 †55,18
MILLER, Michael Jay. 8254 MAYFIELD RD, CHESTERLAND INTERNAL MED A 44026 #038-40-1984 L1985 **IM** *020 †20
PATCHIN, Donald M. ■ 44026 #038-41-1960 L1960 **GP** *071
PHELPS, Thomas Edwin. 8055 MAYFIELD RD, STE 106 44026 #038-40-1984 L1988 **PD** *020 †55
TEPPER, Deborah E. ■ 44026 #054-04-1995 L2008 **IM** *020 †20
WANG, Elaine F Petigura. ■ 44026 #462-01-1973 L1977 **PTH** *020 †50
WEISS, Judith Harriet. 8055 MAYFIELD RD, STE 107 44026 #038-44-1983 L1985 **FM** *020 †18
WOLLAM-HUHN, Nancy Lee. 8055 MAYFIELD RD STE 105 44026 #038-06-1982 L1985 **OBG** *020 †30

CHILLICOTHE – ROSS

ABDULRAHMAN, Ossama. 4437 STATE ROUTE 159, STE 125 45601 #875-01-1983 L2006 **CD** *020 †20
ADEVA, Aurora Yusay. ■ 45601 #748-01-1954 L1967 **PM** *071
ADEVA, Dolores Guimiera. ■ 45601 #748-01-1946 L1969 **GP OS** *072
ADLER, Roger Todd. 50 N PLAZA BLVD 45601 #016-42-1995 L2000 **OPH** *020
ANNADURAI, Dharman. 17273 STATE ROUTE 104 45601 #495-42-1968 L1974 **IM PUD** *020
BAKER, Ethelbert Jackson. 4439 STATE ROUTE 159, STE 130 45601 #048-13-1986 L1995 **TS GS** *020 †85,90
BALLERENE, Ellen Wilcox. 4449 STATE ROUTE 159, BOX 6179 45601 #010-02-1999 L1999 **P** *100
BEAM, Wayne W, Jr. 60 CAPITAL DR 45601 #012-05-1988 L1995 **FM** *020 †18 ‡
BENNETT, Joseph Carl. 311 CALDWELL ST, CENTER 45601 #038-40-1973 L1973 **IM** *020 †20
BERGER, Brad Zale. 455 SHAWNEE LN 45601 #016-06-1990 L1995 **CHP** *020 †75
BERNO, Jack Chas, Jr. 4437 STATE ROUTE 159, STE 270 45601 #038-43-1979 L1982 **IM** *020 †20
BHATTACHARYA, Debashish K. 272 HOSPITAL RD, NEUROLOGY AND PMR 45601 #496-38-1978 L1995 **PAN PME** *020 †05
BHATTACHARYYA, Debasish. 4437 STATE ROUTE 159, STE G25 45601 #004-01-2002 L2006 **N** *020 †75
BLUMBERG, Lara. 100 N WALNUT ST 45601 #665-01-2000 L2000 **FM** *020 †18 ‡
BLUTH, Lester Irwin. 4461 STATE ROUTE 159 45601 #035-19-1976 L1981 **AN CCA** *020 †05

BOLL, George Wm. 4439 STATE ROUTE 159, STE 160 45601 #038-06-1959 L1981 **GS VS** *071 †85
BULLOCK, Jennifer Zane. 3 HEALTH DR 45601 #038-40-2000 L2000 **AI** *020 †55,03
BULLOCK, Joseph Daniel. 3 HEALTH DR 45601 #038-40-1967 L1967 **AI** *020 †55,03
CALDWELL, Joseph Grimes. 17273 STATE ROUTE 104, VA MEDICAL CENTER 45601 #038-40-1964 L1964 **END IM** *030 †20
CARROLL, Brendan Thos. 17273 STATE ROUTE 104, DEPT OF PSYCHIATRY #116A 45601 #038-43-1987 L1991 **P PFP** *020
CHAWLA, Jyoti Rai. 272 HOSPITAL RD 45601 #021-01-1995 L2003 **IM** *020 †20
CHEN, Wenfu. 3 MEDICAL DR 45601 #385-01-1968 L1976 **OTO** *020 †45
CHINNAPPAN, Bhuvaneswari. 17273 STATE ROUTE 104, VA MEDICAL CTR 45601 #495-94-1977 L2002 **IM** *020 †20
CHITLURI, Jaisree Rani. 17273 STATE ROUTE 104, VAMC 45601 #495-11-1976 L1980 **OPH** *020 †35
CHOICE, Denee Roberts. 4455 STATE ROUTE 159 45601 #038-43-1994 L1995 **PM PME** *020 †60
CHOICE, Young Sun. ADENA REGIONAL MED CTR, DEPR RAD 45601 #583-03-1964 L1973 **DR** *020 †55,80
CHOWDHURY, Mahbub. ■ 45601 #160-02-1966 L1979 **IM** *071
COLLINS, Jason J. 100 N WALNUT ST 45601 #305-01-2004 L2004 **FM** *020 †18
COPPEL, Lewis W. 272 HOSPITAL RD 45601 #025-01-1946 L1949 **FM** *071 †18
CRAWFORD, John Eric. 1049 WESTERN AVE 45601 #038-45-1990 L1993 **FM** *020 †18
DELGROSSO, Edward Anthony. ■ 45601 #038-40-1987 L2001 **DR** *020 †80
DEMICK, Stephen Edward. 159 E 2ND ST, SOUTHERN OHIO EYE ASSOC 45601 #016-11-1988 L1990 **OPH** *020 †35
DESAI, Bindu Thakorbhai. 4439 STATE ROUTE 159, STE 130 45601 #496-38-1971 L1994 **N OS** *020 †75
DEWAR, Jennifer Marie. 60 CAPITAL DR 45601 #038-44-2001 L2006 **FM** *020 †18
DIEKROGER, James Edward. ■ 45601 #038-40-2008 *012
DURBIN, Richard Jos. 272 HOSPITAL RD 45601 #038-45-1984 L1985 **IM** *020 †20
EGOLF, Jay S. 50 N PLAZA BLVD 45601 #041-02-2000 L2003 **OPH** *020 †35 ‡
ESSELSTEIN, Robert W. 455 SHAWNEE LN 45601 #038-43-1990 L1992 **FM** *071 †18
EVANS, John Denoon. 159 E 2ND ST 45601 #038-40-1996 L2001 **OPH** *020 †35
EVANS, Karen Cheryl. 4439 STATE ROUTE 159 45601 #038-40-1998 L1999 **FM** *020 †60
FANNING, Wm James, IV. 4439 STATE ROUTE 159, STE 130 45601 #038-40-1979 L1981 **TS** *020 †20,85,90
FIELDS, Charles Mitchell. 4457 STATE ROUTE 159 45601 #038-40-1980 L1980 **ORS OSM** *020
FINE, Robert Lewis. PO BOX 5500 45601 #038-40-1974 **P** *074
FLEISCHER, Stephen. 4439 STATE ROUTE 159 # G10 45601 #035-01-1951 L1955 **PD** *020 †55
FLEMING, James Edward, Jr. ■ 45601 #038-06-1989 L1991 **ORS** *020 †40
FOLZENLOGEN, Douglas J. 4437 STATE ROUTE 159, STE 115 45601 #038-41-1994 L1998 **IM** *020 †20
FRAZIER, Ellis. 272 HOSPITAL RD 45601 #020-12-1984 L1985 **FM** *020 †18
FRICK, Lawrence Paul. 60 CAPITAL DR 45601 #038-41-1991 L1992 **FM** *020 †18
GABIS, John Anthony. 100 N WALNUT ST 45601 #038-45-1987 L1988 **FM** *072 †18
GANGADHARAPPA, Rame G. VET ADMIN MED CTR 45601 #495-38-1959 L1972 **IM** *030
GBARUK, Kombian. 4439 STATE ROUTE 159, STE 150 45601 #412-02-2000 L2003 **IM** *020 †20
GHANY, Neil Christopher. 4439 STATE ROUTE 159, ADENA HEALTH SYSTEM 45601 #035-08-1999 L2005 **HS** *020
GIBBONS, Richard Earl. 17273 STATE ROUTE 104 #11G, R E GIBBONS MD VA MED CTR 45601 #041-01-1961 L1986 **OBG GP** *020 †30
GORDON, Stephanie L. 17273 STATE ROUTE 104, BLUE TEAM 45601 #038-45-1994 L1997 **FM** *020 †18
HAMILL, John Mark. 4449 STATE ROUTE 159, SCIOTO PAINT VLY MENTAL HL 45601 #019-02-1987 L1988 **P** *020 †75
HAMMOND, James E. ■ 45601 #048-04-2000 L2005 **DR** *020 †80
HAN, Kyoung Soo. 17273 STATE ROUTE 104, MEDICAL CENTER 45601 #583-02-1973 L1991 **PM** *020 †60
HARKINS, Keith John. 5474 EGYPT PIKE, NA 45601 #054-04-1990 L1991 **EM** *020 †16
HASKINS, William Lee. ■ 45601 #017-20-1956 L1966 **IM** *030
HAUGEN, Mark David. 60 CAPITAL DR 45601 #030-06-2000 L2003 **FM** *020 †18
HERLLIHY, Jennifer Regan. 4439 STATE ROUTE 159, STE G70 45601 #017-20-1994 L1995 **OBG** *020 †30
HEWITT, Robert Benton. 17273 STATE ROUTE 104, CHILLICOTHE VA MEDICAL CTR 45601 #038-40-1963 L1963 **GP** *020 †80
HICKMAN, Max Roy. ■ 45601 #038-41-1960 L1960 **GS ORS** *071 †85
HILL, Gayle Alaine. 4439 STATE ROUTE 159, STE G70 45601 #038-41-1999 L2003 **OBG** *020
HILL, Jeffrey Charles. 272 HOSPITAL RD, ADENA REGIONAL MEDICAL CEN 45601 #021-05-1994 L1998 **OM IM** *020 †70
HO, Jimmy. 272 HOSPITAL RD 45601 #024-07-1976 L1993 **DR** *020 †80
HUME, Dale Allyn. 272 HOSPITAL RD 45601 #038-43-1987 L1992 **DR** *020 †80
HUSPEN, Richard. 455 SHAWNEE LN 45601 #018-75-2000, ▲ L2000 **P** *020 †75
IRANI, Sohrab Rustom. 4439 STATE ROUTE 159 # 24 45601 #495-96-1969 L1993 **OBG** *020 †30 ‡
JALBUENA, Numeriano M. 8 MEDICAL DR 45601 #748-01-1966 L1973 **U** *020
JANE-WIT, Saeree. 17273 STATE ROUTE 104 45601 #891-03-1969 L1977 **IM** *020 †20
JENISON, Gary Lynn. 80 STAR DR 45601 #021-05-1989 L1995 **OTO HNS** *020
JETTY, Lois Bharathi. 4439 STATE ROUTE 159 # G10 45601 #495-65-1986 L1995 **PD** *020 †55
JETTY, Sathish V. 4439 STATE ROUTE 159 # G10, PEDIATRIC GROUP 45601 #495-65-1986 L1993 **PD** *020 †55
JOSEPH, Chryshantha S R. 17273 STATE ROUTE 104 45601 #220-04-1984 L2000 **IM** *020 †20
KENNEDY, Richard Dean. 55 CENTENNIAL BLVD 45601 #038-45-2000 L2000 **IMG** *100
KING, Gideon Lee. 100 N WALNUT ST, PICKAWAY-ROSS FAMILY PRAC 45601 #019-02-2001 L2004 **FM** *020 †80
KLINGLER, Eugene La Rue. ■ 45601 #024-07-1958 L1979 **IM NEP** *030
KLISOVIC, Dino D. 159 E 2ND ST 45601 #957-01-1994 L2000 **OPH** *100 †35
KUNZ, Jerry Martin, Jr. 6 MEDICAL DR 45601 #038-40-1996 L1997 **FM GE** *020 †75
LAPURGA, John Palaganas. 272 HOSPITAL RD, ADENE REG MEDICAL CENTER 45601 #038-43-1993 L1995 **AN** *020 †85
LEE, Judy Kuanyao. 100 N WALNUT ST 45601 #028-34-1998 L2004 **END IM** *020 †20
LEE, Nam Hi. ■ 45601 #583-08-1960 **P** *071
LEE, Robert Tae. 100 N WALNUT ST 45601 #038-45-1994 L1998 **AN** *020
LEE, Young Soon. 122 E WATER ST BOX 490 45601 #583-02-1957 L1976 **ORS** *071
LI, Siyun. 4439 STATE ROUTE 159, STE 130 45601 #243-46-1985 L2006 **CN** *100
LOPEZ, Ronald Lee. 4439 STATE ROUTE 159, STE 120 45601 #004-01-1984 L1988 **OBG** *020 †30

MAC CARTER, Paul F, Jr. 60 CAPITAL DR 45601 #038-41-1953 L1953 **FM** *071 †18

MAGBAG, Emmanuel A. 8 MEDICAL DR 45601 #748-01-1965 L1973 **U** *020 †95

MAKINO, Ryoji. 17273 STATE ROUTE 104, VA MEDICAL CTR 45601 #572-29-1969 L1973 **P CHP** *030 †75

MANAZER, James Randall. 4439 STATE ROUTE 159, STE 130 45601 #049-01-1999 L2006 **GS** *020 †85

MANCHESTER, Stephen Lee. 1049 WESTERN AVE 45601 #038-45-1988 L1989 **FM** *020 †18

MANNING, Roy Eugene. 311 CALDWELL ST, CENTER 45601 #038-40-1957 L1957 **OBG** *020 †30

MC CALLUM, Kristine. 1049 WESTERN AVE, FAMILY HEALTHCARE INC 45601 #016-43-1996 L1997 **FM** *020 †18

MC CALLUM, Scott Jeffrey. 4439 STATE ROUTE 159, STE G10 45601 #016-43-1996 L1997 **PD** *020 †55

MC KEE, Steve Edward. 272 HOSPITAL RD 45601 #038-40-1988 L1990 **EM** *020 †18

MC KELL, David. ■ 45601 #038-41-1953 L1953 **FM** *071 †18

MC KELL, Joseph S. 174 W MAIN ST BOX 328 45601 #007-02-1953 L1956 **FM** *020 †18

MC NEIL, Donald Lauchlin. 3 HEALTH DR 45601 #060-01-1974 L1986 **AI RHU** *020 †03,20

MEDLIN, Douglas Anthony. ■ 45601 #036-07-1973 L1979 **IM** *020 †20

MIDDENDORF, Donald F. 4439 STATE ROUTE 159, STE 200 45601 #038-40-1974 L1974 **NEP IM** *020 †20

MILLER, Randall Lee. 4439 STATE ROUTE 159, STE 130 45601 #028-02-1980 L1987 **TS GS** *85,90

MOWRY, Jennifer Marie. 60 CAPITAL DR 45601 #038-40-2000 L2003 **FM** *020 †18

MURTHY, Chitluri M. 17273 STATE ROUTE 104 45601 #495-50-1969 L1973 **P** *020 †75

NAFZIGER, J Calvin. 17273 STATE ROUTE 104 45601 #024-01-1968 L1996 **P** *020 †75

NAIR, Krishnankutty S. 17273 STATE ROUTE 104, VA MEDICAL CENTER 45601 #495-31-1969 L1998 **P** *020

NAUMOVSKI, Zoran. 626 CENTRAL CTR 45601 #038-40-1996 L1997 **MPD** *020 †20,55

NOEL, Alan De Mesa. 100 N WALNUT ST 45601 #748-01-1986 L1999 **FM** *020 †18

O'DONNELL, Timothy P. 4447 STATE ROUTE 159 45601 #010-02-1997 L2003 **GS CRS** *020 †85,10

OOMMEN, Thomas. 17273 STATE ROUTE 104, ACOS AMB CARE (11C) 45601 #495-98-1978 L1985 **IM** *020 †20

OTTEN, Carl Edward. 272 HOSPITAL RD 45601 #017-20-1981 L1999 **OM AM** *020 †70

PANEK, Henry Francis. ■ 45601 #008-01-1968 L1977 **OPH EM** *020 †35

PEDICELLI, Gabriele. 272 HOSPITAL RD, MEDICAL CENTER HOSP 45601 #067-06-1983 L1992 *020 †80

PEREZ, Cara E. 55 CENTENNIAL BLVD, ADENA HEALTH CENTER 45601 #038-40-1998 L2002 **AN** *05

PIERCE, Harvey James, III. 1049 WESTERN AVE 45601 #038-40-1978 L1979 **EM OM** *020 †18,16

POJE, Joanne. 4461 STATE ROUTE 159, STE E 45601 #561-25-1981 L2000 **OBG** *020 †30

POUDEL, Damodar. 272 HOSPITAL RD 45601 #672-01-1997 L2001 **FM** *020 †18

PRIOR, Phillip Edwin. 4439 STATE ROUTE 159 # 130 45601 #038-40-1986 L1988 **FM GS** *020 †18

QURAISHI, Sabir Mohammad. 272 HOSPITAL RD 45601 #495-12-1987 L1997 **IM** *020 †20

RAMIREZ, Jose Angel. ■ 45601 #649-14-2000 L2001 **FM** *100

ROLFES, Richard James. 1200 N BRIDGE ST 45601 #038-40-1986 L1989 **DR NR** *020 †80

ROONEY, Richard Craig. 2422 PLYLEYS LN 45601 #038-41-1967 L1967 **GS** *020 †85,90

SAXENA, Kamala. 11 MEDICAL DR 45601 #495-21-1968 L1977 **PD** *020 †85

SCHUMACHER, Patrick D. 50 N PLAZA BLVD 45601 #038-40-2001 L2001 **OPH** *020 †35

SEGNITZ, Herbert. 713 BUCKEYE ST 45601 #020-12-1989 L1990 **FM** *020 †18

SEIDENSTICKER, John F. 100 N WALNUT ST 45601 #038-06-1961 L1961 **IM END** *020 †20

SHAFIQ, Mohammad Parsa. 17273 STATE ROUTE 104 # 13 45601 #118-01-1981 L1998 **IMG** *020 †20

SHARMA, Suman Chandra. 1049 WESTERN AVE 45601 #672-01-1996 L2005 **FM** *020

SHAW, Allen David. 60 CAPITAL DR 45601 #038-45-1988 L1989 **FM** *020 †18

SHEVERINI, James Alan. PO BOX 711, 17273 ST RT 104 45601 #517-01-1962 L1979 **TS CD** *020 †85,90

SHY, Kathy Elaine. 4449 STATE ROUTE 159, SCIOTO PAINT VALLEY MHC 45601 #038-40-1981 L1985 **P** *020 †75

SINNING, Herbert Martin. 4447 STATE ROUTE 159 45601 #041-13-1984 L1990 **GS TRS** *020

SKRENTNER, Pamela Susan. 4439 STATE ROUTE 159, CENTER OB-GYN ASSOC INC 45601 #025-01-1974 L1990 **OBG** *020 †30

SMITH, Byron Delford. 272 HOSPITAL RD, LABORATORY MEDICAL CENTER 45601 #017-20-1972 L1980 **PTH** *020 †50

SMITH, David Eugene. 4439 STATE ROUTE 159, STE 210 45601 #038-40-1970 L1970 **IM GE** *020 †20

SORENSEN, Richard Lee. ■ 45601 #016-42-1981 L1992 **AN EM** *071 †05

STRAUCH, William Bradley. 4437 STATE ROUTE 159, STE G15 45601 #055-01-2003 L2007 **FSM** *020 †18

SWANK, Robert Elmer. 272 HOSPITAL RD 45601 #038-40-1945 L1945 **GP AN** *071

TANDON, Tarun. 272 HOSPITAL RD 45601 #041-14-1998 L2006 **AN** *020

TANEDO, Pablito V. 606 OVERLOOK HEIGHTS LN 45601 #748-01-1952 L1965 **GS TS** *071

TUCKER, Kirk Michael. 4439 STATE ROUTE 159, STE 150 45601 #038-40-2000 L2000 **IM** *020

UCCI, John. 1049 WESTERN AVE 45601 #654-01-1999 L2004 **FM** *020 †18

VANVOORHIS, Randall David. 4439 STATE ROUTE 159, STE 150 45601 #038-40-1997 L1999 **IM** *020 †20

VENKANNA, Kanna. VAMC CHILLICOTHE 45601 #495-21-1971 L1993 **IM IMG** *020 †20

VILLARREAL, Kathleen S. 55 CENTENNIAL BLVD, ADENA REG MED CTR URGENT 45601 #038-43-1993 L1997 **MPD** *020 †20,55

WANG, Joseph M. 272 HOSPITAL RD, ADENA MEDICAL CENTER 45601 #244-05-1978 L2003 **RO** *020 †80

WILLS, Laura Sue. ■ 45601 #038-43-2007 L2007 **PD** *012

WU, Yunpeng. 4439 STATE ROUTE 159, STE 150 45601 #243-16-1988 L2007 **IM** *020 †20

YEN, Cheng-Chung. 183 E WATER ST 45601 #385-02-1966 L1972 **GYN** *071 †30

ZISKOWSKI, John Jos. 272 HOSPITAL RD 45601 #561-01-1977 L1986 **PTH** *020 †50

CINCINNATI – CLERMONT

AFMAN, Chad Evart. ■ 45244 #025-07-2002 L2002 **PDO** *012

BORCHERS, Deborah Ann. 4357 FERGUSON DR, STE 150 45245 #020-12-1983 L1985 **PD OS** *020 †55

BRAHMAMDAM, Ranga Sai. 4452 EASTGATE BLVD, STE 107 45245 #495-50-1986 L1997 **ON** *020 †20

BRESLIN, Kevin Jos. 4421 EASTGATE BLVD, STE 300 45245 #038-45-1985 L1986 **FM** *020 †18

BUERGER, Leopold Franz. ■ 45245 #407-33-1954 L1963 **PTH FOP** *020 †50

BYRNES, John Edward. 7175 TREERIDGE DR 45245 #024-16-1986 L1992 **EM** *020 †16

CAOILI, Elena S. 473 OLD STATE ROUTE 74, STE 4 45244 #748-07-1977 L1993 **FM** *020 †18

CHAMBERLIN, Michael. 4371 FERGUSON DR 45245 #016-11-1996 L2000 **PD** *020 †55

CRAVEN, Thomas Francis. 3045 WILLIAMS CREEK DR 45244 #028-34-1970 L1974 **DR** *071 †80

CRIPE, Linda Heidel. 2300 SHIMMERING BAY LN 45244 #018-03-1987 L1999 **PDC** *020 †55 ‡

DAVIDSON, Amberly Lynn. ■ 45244 #038-45-2007 L2007 **OBG** *012

DAVIDSON, Raymond Lee. 4867 RUMPKE RD 45244 #038-40-1960 L1960 **GP** *020 †20

DOYNE, Emanuel Oury. 4371 FERGUSON DR 45245 #047-05-1971 L1974 **PD** *020 †55

DUFFY, James Matthew. ■ 45245 #038-41-2006 L2006 **AN** *012

DWIVEDI, Nageshwar P. ■ 45244 #495-49-1963 L1973 **CRS OS** *071 †85

DYEHOUSE, Karyn Marie. 4578 E TECH DR, - 45245 #038-41-2001 L2001 **HO** *020

ENCARNACION, Orlando Jose, Jr. ■ 45245 #035-06-2006 L2006 **EM** *012

EVANKO, Michelle. ■ 45245 #016-11-1996 L1999 **EM** *020 †16

FORRISTAL, Thomas Jos. 4420 AICHOLTZ RD 45245 #038-41-1965 L1965 **PD** *071 †55

GARCIA-DUARTE, Alejandro. ■ 45244 #847-04-1955 L1963 **IM CD** *075

GARNICA, Tomas Santos. 5000 VILLAGE DR 45244 #847-04-1962 L1966 **R** *071 †80

HAMMILL, Adrienne Marie. ■ 45245 #048-12-2004 L2004 **PHO** *012

HASSAN, Noor Ul. 872 OHIO PIKE 45245 #495-33-1962 L1971 **EM NS** *020

HOENES, Holly Anne. ■ 45244 #012-22-2007 L2007 **PD** *012

HOFFMANN, Clifford Oscar. ■ 45244 #038-43-1984 L1988 **AN** *020 †05

HOLLAND, Elizabeth Y. 4452 EASTGATE BLVD, STE 305 45245 #045-01-1995 L1998 **OPH** *020 †35

HOPEWELL, William Scott. 817A EASTGATE SOUTH DR, NETWORK 45245 #035-01-1958 L1991 **IM CD** *071 †20

JASKIEWICZ, Julie Ann. 4357 FERGUSON DR, STE 150 45245 #051-01-1984 L1992 **PD** *020 †55

JINER, Kristina Renee. ■ 45245 #038-41-2008 *012

KALE, Minal Sharatkumar. ■ 45244 #038-41-2006 **IM** *012

KIM, Pamina S. ■ 45244 #008-01-2003 L2007 **IM** *100 †20

KREITEL, K Derek. ■ 45244 #038-41-2005 L2005 **DR** *012

KROEGER, Daniel Raymond. 4371 FERGUSON DR 45245 #038-43-1987 L1989 **PD** *020 †55

KURIAN, Chiramal P. 6620 CLOUGH PIKE 45244 #495-44-1984 L2002 **IM** *020 †20

LA FON, Everette Darr, Jr. ■ 45244 #047-06-1983 L2004 **EM** *100 †70

LE, Chuc Phuc. 4452 EASTGATE BLVD 45245 #020-02-1992 L1996 **FM** *020 †18

LEE, Bienvenido Sy. 4415 AICHOLTZ RD 45245 #748-11-1971 L1977 **AN PME** *020

LOPEZ, Marvin Jose. 6620 CLOUGH PIKE 45244 #038-40-1996 L2002 **GE** *020 †20

LYND, Sean William. 796 OLD STATE ROUTE 74 45243 #038-41-1993 L1995 **IM** *020 †20

MARRS, James Michael. ■ 45244 #038-41-1969 L1969 **D** *071 †15 ‡

MAST, Samantha Howard. ■ 45245 #038-45-2004 L2004 **OBG** *012

MENSAH, George Tetteh. 4357 FERGUSON DR, STE 210 45245 #610-01-1983 L1990 **OBG** *020 †30

MEYERS, Thomas Earl. 796 OLD STATE ROUTE 74, STE 100 45245 #038-43-1986 L1987 **IM AN** *020 †20

MILLER, William Clifford. 6620 CLOUGH PIKE 45244 #038-41-1972 L1972 **IM NEP** *020 †20

MORAND, Thomas Michael. 4415 AICHOLTZ RD 45245 #038-41-1978 L1979 **RO** *020 †80

NATHAN, Jaimie David. ■ 45244 #008-01-1998 L2005 **PDS** *100

NGUYEN, Tommy Bao Truong. ■ 45244 #305-01-2005 L2006 **AN** *012

PELTIER, Chris Jon. 4371 FERGUSON DR 45245 #038-41-1995 L1999 **PD** *020 †55

PICKUP, Tiffany Lee. ■ 45244 #038-41-2006 L2006 **D** *012

PLUNKETT, Jim Bob. 4452 EASTGATE BLVD, STE 302 45245 #038-41-1977 L1980 **OBG** *020 †30

RAINS, Stephanie Lynn. ■ 45244 #025-07-2007 L2007 **PD** *012

RAJ, Phulchand Prithvi. ■ 45245 #495-09-1958 L1979 **AN** *040 †05

RATHOD, Hardas Lakha. 473 CINCINNATI BATAVI PIKE 45244 #495-23-1970 L1979 **GS VS** *020 †85

RICHARD, Jennifer Blair. 4371 FERGUSON DR 45245 #038-41-1995 L1997 **PD** *020 †55

ROACH, Harry Collins. ■ 45245 #038-41-1961 L1961 **GYN** *071 †30

ROBERTS, Steven Evan. 4355 FERGUSON DR STE 270, CLERMONT CBOC 45245 #038-06-1994 L1998 **IM** *020 †20

ROJAS, Alvaro. 4452 EASTGATE BLVD STE 107 45245 #264-01-1964 L1973 **OBG** *020

RUBIO, Eva Ilse. ■ 45244 #051-07-2001 L2004 **DR** *100 †80

SANTANGELO, Megan Marie. 4357 FERGUSON DR, STE 150 45245 #038-06-1998 L1999 **PD** *020 †55

SCHLESINGER, A. ■ 45244 #660-03-1958 L1959 **DR** *071 †80

SCHULMAN, Robert Wm. ■ 45245 #038-41-1974 L1975 **P PYA** *020 †75

SCOTT, Robert Augustine T. 3590 ROUND BOTTOM RD, PMB 128899 45244 #024-01-1964 L1965 **N** *020 †75

SHAH, Tushar Ashvin. ■ 45244 #495-17-2002 L2004 **NPM** *012

SHEHATA, Wagih M. 4415 AICHOLTZ RD 45245 #330-02-1964 L1972 **RO** *075 †80 ‡

SHENG, Yu-Hwa Peter. 4578 E TECH DR STE 202, HEMATOLOGY-MED ONCOLOGY 45245 #244-02-1978 L1982 **ON OS** *020 †20

SHREVE, Eric William. ■ 45244 #038-41-2006 L2007 **U** *012

SHREY, Daniel Walter. ■ 45244 #038-41-2008 *012

STRUB, William Martin. ■ 45244 #038-41-2001 L2001 **DR** *100 †80

SUMME, Lisa Mikulcik. ■ 45244 #020-02-1991 L1995 **IM** *020 †20

SUYEMOTO, Dorothy H B. ■ 45244 #025-01-1949 L1950 **EM** *072

SYZEK, Thomas Edward. ■ 45244 #038-40-1979 L1980 **EM FM** *020 †18,16

VALENTIN, Francisco C. ■ 45245 #748-08-1964 L1976 **ORS** *012

WALLACE, Jessica Marie. ■ 45244 #056-06-2007 L2007 **OBG** *012

WARE, Stephanie Marie. 5740 LENGWOOD DR 45244 #038-41-1997 L2004 **MG** *020 †19,55

WELDEN, Scott Robert. 872 OHIO PIKE, EASTSIDE URGENT CARE 45245 #038-41-1997 L1998 **EM** *030 †16

WHITE, Daniel Robt. 4415 AICHOLTZ RD 45245 #038-41-1985 L1989 **RO** *020 †80

WILLIAMS, Donald Rae. 473 OLD STATE ROUTE 74 # 4 45244 #020-02-1974 L1977 **GP** *020

YOST, Catherine Leigh. 4371 FERGUSON DR 45245 #021-05-1983 L1986 **PD** *020 †55

ZUCK, Thomas Frank. ■ 45244 #041-09-1963 L1969 **BBK PTH** *071 †50

CINCINNATI – HAMILTON

AASHISH, Anunaya. 4777 E GALBRAITH RD 45236 #496-35-2001 L2005 **IM** *012

ABABNEH, Osama Hamid. 231 ALBERTS WAY 45267 #575-01-1997 L2004 *100

■ = Address Information Privacy Protected

ABBOTTSMITH, Chas Wisdom. 2123 AUBURN AVE, STE 136 45219 #067-01-1963 L1966 CD IM *020 †20

ABBOY, Chandar. 2123 AUBURN AVE, STE 401 45219 #495-04-2001 L2002 PCC *012 †20

ABDALLAH, Mouhamad Hasan. 234 GOODMAN ST 45267 #605-01-2003 L2005 IM *012

ABDOLMOHAMMADI, Alireza. 375 DIXMYTH AVE 45220 #517-08-2001 L2007 IM *012

ABDULLA, Farah Rukhsana. ■ 45208 #038-44-2004 L2004 D *012

ABIRACHED, Jose. ■ 45236 #649-02-1954 OBG *071

ABONIA, Juan Pablo. 3333 BURNET AVE, ML7028 45229 #035-06-1997 L2004 AI *020 †55,03 ‡

ABRAHAMSON, Ira A. 105 W 4TH ST STE 719 45202 #038-41-1948 L1948 OPH *071 †35

ABRAHAMSON, Richard Ira. 105 W 4TH ST, STE 719 45202 #038-41-1987 L1991 OPH *020 †35

ABRAMS-CONNERS, Lori M. 2139 AUBURN AVE, DEPT 1104 45219 #038-41-1998 L1999 *020 †12

ABRUZZO, Todd. 234 GOODMAN ST 0761, UNIVERSITY RADIOLOGY ASSOC 45267 #035-08-1991 L2004 RNR *020 †80

ABSALON, Michael Joseph. 3333 BURNET AVE 45229 #040-02-1998 L2005 PHO *020 †55

ABUNKU, Orduen. 2139 AUBURN AVE, NUCLEAR MED DEPT 45219 #690-03-1984 L1998 GP NM *020

ACEBEDO, Erich Glenn Cust. 375 DIXMYTH AVE 45220 #748-19-2000 L2006 IM *012

ACH, F Jay. 10475 READING RD 45241 #038-41-1950 L1950 FM OM *071 †18

ACKDOE, Emmit F. 2635 HIGHLAND AVE 45219 #902-01-1956 L1964 P N *071

ACTON, James Douglas. 3333 BURNET AVE, C5 45229 #016-11-1993 L1999 PDP *020 †55

ACTON, Sarah Ann. 3333 BURNET AVE 45229 #038-41-2005 L2005 PD *012

ADAMS, Brian Burke. 222 PIEDMONT AVE, STE 5300 45219 #008-01-1995 L1999 D *020 †15

ADAMS, Denise Martin. 3333 BURNET AVE, MLC 7015 45229 #010-02-1988 L2003 PHO *020 †55

ADAMS, Heather Renee. 3333 BURNET AVE, CHILDRENS HOSP MED CTR 45229 #016-76-2007, ▲ L2007 CPP *012

ADAMS, John Mark. ■ 45219 #036-08-2007 L2007 IM *012

ADEOYE, Opeolu Makanju. 234 GOODMAN ST 45219 #041-12-2002 L2002 EM *100 †16

ADHIKARI, Tara Joshi. ■ 45208 #672-02-2000 L2008 IM *012

ADKINS, Bryan Eugene. 151 W GALBRAITH RD 45216 #038-41-1993 L1995 FM *020 †18

ADLER, Caleb Matthew. 231 ALBERT SABIN WAY 45267 #041-02-1991 L1999 P *050 †75

ADLER, Elena. 3333 BURNET AVE 45229 #021-05-1976 L1984 AN *020 †55,05

ADOLPH, Robert J. 222 PIEDMONT AVE STE 6000 45219 #016-11-1952 L1962 CD IM *020 †20

ADORNETTO, Jenny L. 3333 BURNET AVE 45229 #038-41-2002 L2002 PE *020

AGABEGI, Steven Soheil. 231 ALBERT SABIN WAY, UNIV OF CINCINNATI MED CTR 45267 #041-13-2002 L2002 OSS *012

AGBOMI, Elemi John E. PO BOX 58521 45258 #004-01-1995 FM *100

AGLORIA, Maliha. 3200 BURNET AVE 45229 #704-29-2001 L2004 IM *100 †20

AGUILAR SAENZ, Carlos Arm. 2139 AUBURN AVE, CHRIST HOSP 45219 #176-01-1998 L2006 IM *012

AHMAD, Muhammad Riaz. 1 NEUMANN WAY 45215 #704-05-1985 L1999 IM *020 †70

AHMED, Aman. 619 OAK ST 45206 #495-65-1992 L1995 IM *020 †20

AHMED, Kashif. ■ 45208 #012-01-2005 L2005 IM *012

AHMED, Sameer Zia. 4777 E GALBRAITH RD, DEPT OF INT MED 45236 #704-02-2002 L2005 IM *012

AHMED, Samina. 375 DIXMYTH AVE 45220 #704-01-1983 L2005 PD *020 †55

AHMED, Syed N. 231 ALBERT SABIN WAY, UNIV OF CINCINNATI 45267 #704-02-1992 L1995 CD *020 †75

AHMED, Waqas. 4777 E GALBRAITH RD, DEPT OF GME 45236 #704-01-2005 L2006 IM *012

AHRENS, Kirsten Gail. 3333 BURNET AVE, DEPT OF EMERGERCY MEDICINE 45229 #038-41-1994 L1996 PD *020 †55

AIR, Ellen Louise. ■ 45226 #038-41-2004 L2004 NS *012

AKHUTINA, Maria Vladimiro. 375 DIXMYTH AVE 45220 #913-69-2002 L2006 IM *012

AKINBI, Henry Toyin. 3333 BURNET AVE, CINCINNATI CHILDREN'S HOSP 45229 #690-05-1980 L1995 NPM *050 †55

AKRAM, Mudassir. 375 DIXMYTH AVE 45220 #704-01-2001 L2005 IM *012

ALABDULRAZZAK, Motaz. 3333 BURNET AVE, DEPT OF MED EDU 45229 #875-01-1996 L2005 *100

ALALAMI, Achir Ahmad Mahe. 375 DIXMYTH AVE 45220 #902-05-2002 IM *012

ALAM, Masroor. 7520 STATE RD 45255 #704-02-1990 L1994 AN PME *020 †05

ALAM, Rukhsana Shah. ■ 45249 #495-05-1975 L1984 IM *020 †20

ALAM, Shumyle. 3333 BURNET AVE STE 3400, DIV OF UROLOGY RM450 45229 #051-04-1999 L2005 UP *020

ALAMIN, Khosrow. 3131 QUEEN CITY AVE 45238 #517-01-1957 L1966 PTH *020 †50

AL-ANSARI, Essam Mahmoud. 2915 CLIFTON AVE 45220 #797-02-1996 L2006 PCC *100 †20

AL-ASSAAD, Ali Nihad. 231 ALBERT SABIN WAY, CARDIOVASCULAR DISEASES 45267 #875-02-1989 L1994 CD *020 †20

ALBANO, Anthony. ■ 45255 #024-16-1986 L1994 EM *020 †16

ALBAYYARI, Hassan M. 619 OAK ST, BETHESDA HOSP 45206 #539-06-1990 FM *100

ALBERS, Christopher Micha. ■ 45212 #038-41-2006 L2006 IM *012

ALBERS, John Edward. 130 NOVNER DR 45219 #038-41-1955 L1955 TS *071 †85,90

ALBIEZ, Fritz Walter. 45220 #407-19-1950 L1955 D *071

ALBRIGHT, Robert Edwin. 5053 WOOSTER RD, ONCOLOGY HEMATOLOGY CARE I 45226 #041-14-1979 L1990 N ON *020 †75

ALBRINCK, Anne Patricia. 8221 CORNELL RD, STE 420 45249 #038-41-1996 L1997 OBG *020 †30

ALDERSON, Theresa Rose. 10663 MONTGOMERY RD, ASSOCIATES 45242 #017-20-1995 L1998 PHO *020 †55

ALEXANDER, Brandi Nicole. ■ 45216 #038-41-2007 L2007 PD *012

ALEXANDER, Elizabeth S. 375 DIXMYTH AVE, GOOD SAMARITAN HOSPITAL 45220 #038-41-1976 L1979 DR *020 †80

ALEXANDER, J Wesley. 231 ALBERT SABIN WAY, ML 0558 45267 #048-02-1957 L1959 GS TTS *020 †85,90

ALEXANDER, Marc Albert. 6350 GLENWAY AVE 45211 #038-41-1981 L1983 IM *020 †20

ALEXANDER, Shana Ryan. 3333 BURNET AVE, CINCINNATI CHILDREN'S HOSP 45229 #038-41-2005 L2005 PD *012

ALFARO, Raul Daniel. 3200 VINE ST, VA HOSPITAL 45220 #737-01-1951 L1962 IM *050

ALFIDI, Mary Margaret. 7500 STATE RD 45255 #038-06-1991 L1992 DR *020 †80

ALGENIO, Jose Gamo. 3131 QUEEN CITY AVE 45238 #748-01-1962 L1969 AN *020

AL-GHAWI, Hayma. DEPT OF PATHOLOGY, UNIV OF CINCINNATI MED CTR 45267 #875-01-2001 L2005 PTH *012

ALHALLAQ, Yousif Abdulrao. 4777 E GALBRAITH RD, DEPT OF MED EDU 45236 #575-01-2003 L2006 IM *012

ALI, Amir Sheikh. ■ 45243 #704-01-1971 L1977 NEP IM *020 †20

ALI, Asad Syed. 4777 E GALBRAITH RD 45236 #035-09-1997 L1999 IM *020 †20

ALI, Sadia. 234 GOODMAN ST 45267 #704-25-2003 L2005 IM *012

ALINO, Lito Del Rosario. 11490 SPRINGFIELD PIKE 45246 #748-09-1966 L1978 AN *020

AL-KHADRA, Ayman Samih. 45236 #797-02-1989 L1996 ICE CD *012

AL-KHADRA, Eman Samih. 3333 BURNET AVE, CHILDRENS HOSP 45229 #797-02-1996 L2006 PDP *050 †55 ‡

ALLEN, Bruce Howard. 2752 ERIE AVE 45208 #020-02-1975 L1976 OBG *020 †30

ALLEN, James Mc Intosh. ■ 45202 #038-41-1974 L1979 CD IM *020 †20

ALLEN, Sheryl Elaine. 3333 BURNET AVE, DIV OF EMERGENCY MED, OSB- 45229 #017-20-1992 L1998 PD *020 †55

ALLEN, Steven Ray. 3333 BURNET AVE, BLDG C 45229 #011-03-2000 L2000 GS *012

ALLENDOERFER-FERNA, Ruth. 151 W GALBRAITH RD, DRAKE CENTER 45216 #409-33-1983 L2000 IM *020 †55

ALONSO-KATZOWITZ, Julie S. ■ 45206 #047-05-2005 L2005 CPP *012

ALRABADI, Anmar Naser. 375 DIXMYTH AVE 45220 #575-02-2002 L2005 IM *012

AL-SAYYAD, Mohammed Jalal. 3333 BURNET AVE, CO CHILDREN S HOSP-PED DEP 45229 #797-02-1992 L2000 ORS *020

ALSPAUGH, Jonathan Paul. 234 GOODMAN ST, ML 0761 45267 #038-41-1976 L1978 DR *020 †80

ALTMAN, Alan Paul. 8221 CORNELL RD, STE 420 45249 #038-41-1987 L1988 OBG *020 †30

ALUNDAY, Robertpaul Limjo. ■ 45208 #038-41-2008 *012

AMATA, Andrew Oghenekaro. 234 GOODMAN ST, CO UNIV HOSPS-MED EDU DEPT 45219 #690-01-1983 L2000 APM *100

AMBE, Aparna Pradeep. 1253 KEMPER MEADOW DR 45240 #496-15-1993 L1999 IM *020 †20

AMEND, Kenneth Gordon. 5939 COLERAIN AVE 45239 #056-06-1968 L1971 OPH *020 †35

AMIN, Raouf Samy. 3333 BURNET AVE, CCHMC 45229 #915-04-1978 L1982 PDP PD *050 †55

AMIS, James Anthony. 3219 CLIFTON AVE, STE 300 45220 #048-12-1980 L1985 ORS *030 †40

AMOILS, Sandra. 6400 E GALBRAITH RD 45236 #836-01-1982 L1994 FM *020 †18 ‡

AMOILS, Steven L. 6400 E GALBRAITH RD 45236 #836-01-1982 L1990 FM PME *020 †18

AMONGERO, Flavio Jose. 2825 BURNET AVE 45219 #132-02-1956 L1965 TS GS *071 †85,90

AMRIEN-NOLL, Jean. 8044 MONTGOMERY RD, STE 155 45236 #051-07-1983 L1991 OPH *020 †35

ANADKAT, Tara Devi. ■ 45202 #038-41-2007 L2007 PD *012

ANADOL, Deniz. 3333 BURNET AVE, CO CHILDREN S HOSP-MED EDU 45229 #902-05-1991 L2000 *100

ANDERSEN, Nancy Pamela. 231 BETHESDA AVE DEPT ANES, UNIV CINCINNATI MED CTR 45229 #024-05-1981 L1993 AN *020 †55

ANDERSON, Aaron Stevens. ■ 45230 #038-41-2008 *012

ANDERSON, Debra Sue. 7691 5 MILE RD, CINCINNATI 45230 #038-41-1983 L1984 D IM *020 †15

ANDERSON, Donald Roger. ■ 45249 #025-07-1975 L1984 AN *020 †05

ANDERSON, Heidi Kristina. 3333 BURNET AVE, 7TH FLOOR, PEDIATRIC RESID 45229 #036-05-1998 L1999 D PD *020 †55,15

ANDERSON, Jaclyn Marie. ■ 45209 #038-41-2004 L2004 PD *020

ANDERSON, Jeffrey Bruce. 3333 BURNET AVE, ML 2003 45229 #049-01-2002 L2006 PDC *012 †55

ANDERSON, Tari Smith. 71 E HOLLISTER ST 45219 #038-45-1988 L1989 GYN *020 †30

ANDOLINA, Mark Thomas. 45236 #016-43-2006 L2006 IM *012

ANDREW-JAJA, Aya Dawn. ■ 45208 #038-41-2005 L2007 IM *012

ANDREWS, Charles Martin. ■ 45219 #038-41-2008 *012

ANDREWS, John S, Jr. EDEN AT ALBERT SABIN WAY, HOLMES HOSPITAL/RM 1007 45267 #038-06-1973 L1977 OM IM *030 †20,70 ‡

ANDREWS, Lizy. 10475 MONTGOMERY RD, STE 4- 45242 #495-31-1983 L2003 OBG *020

ANDREWS, Margaret Ellen. 3652 SHAW AVE 45208 #010-01-1975 L1981 PD PDA *020 †55

ANDREWS, Michelle. 10663 MONTGOMERY RD, CIN SPORTS MED & ORTHOPAE 45242 #041-09-1985 L1990 ORS GS *020 †40

ANJARI, Tarek. 3158 GLENMORE AVE, STE B 45211 #875-01-1993 L2003 IM *020

ANNENBERG, Alan Jon. 4030 SMITH RD, CARDIAC VASCULAR & 45209 #038-40-1982 L1983 VS *020 †85

ANNESS, Stuart Harold. 3267 WESTBOURNE DR 45248 #038-41-1978 L1979 OPH *020 †35 ‡

ANSWINI, Geoffrey Albert. 2123 AUBURN AVE, STE 136 45219 #041-13-1996 L2003 TS *020 †85,90

ANTHENELLI, Robt Michael. 3200 VINE ST # 116-A, VET AFFAIRS MC 45220 #023-07-1986 L1988 P ADP *050 †75

ANTHONY, James Jos. 10550 MONTGOMERY RD, STE 33 45242 #038-41-1970 L1970 N *020 †75

ANTON, Christopher Gerard. 3333 BURNET AVE 5031, DEPARTMENT OF RADIOLOGY 45229 #055-02-1993 L1997 PDR *020 †80

ANTONCHAK, Marc A. ■ 45209 #038-44-2004 L2004 RHU *012 †20

AQUINO, Neal Joseph. ■ 45215 #038-41-2001 L2001 EM *020

ARANI, Ali Ghiseri. 420 SPRINGFIELD PIKE, STE H 45215 #517-01-1965 L1977 CD IM *071 †20

ARANT, Sarah Meghan. ■ 45212 #047-06-2006 L2006 PD *012

ARAR, Hisham Hassan. 2450 KIPLING AVE, STE 109 45239 #038-41-1993 L1995 OPH *020 †35

ARCHDEACON, Michael T. 231 ALBERT SABIN WAY 0, DEPT. OF ORTHOPAEDIC SURGE 45267 #038-40-1993 L1995 ORS *020 †40

ARCUINO, Rogelio F. ■ 45249 #748-11-1966 L1988 GS GP *020

AREND, Lois Johanna. UNIV OF CINCINNATI, DEPT OF PATH PO BOX 670529 45267 #025-12-1992 L2004 ATP *020 †50

ARENT, Robin Jo. 3333 BURNET AVE, DEPT OF EMERGENCY MEDICINE 45229 #035-06-1994 L1999 PD PE *020 †55

ARGO, David Brent. 6480 HARRISON AVE, STE 201 45247 #047-06-1998 L2005 OSM ORS *020 †40

ARIF, Farhan Ahmad. 2139 AUBURN AVE 45219 #704-20-2005 L2006 IM *012

ARIF, Imran. 231 ALBERT SABIN WAY, CARDIOLOGY DIV 45267 #704-01-1994 L2007 IC *012 †20

ARISTEGUIETA, Carlos A. ■ 45217 #270-02-1991 L2002 GPM *020 †70,18

ARJMAND, Ellis Mir. 3333 BURNET AVE, DEPT OF PEDIATRIC/OTOLARYN 45229 #016-06-1986 L2004 OTO PDO *020 †45

ARNOLD, Kenneth James. 1219 MORTS PASS 45215 #041-02-1985 L1986 EM *020 †16

ARNOLD, Lesley Mussio. 222 PIEDMONT AVE, STE 8 45219 #038-41-1986 L1990 P *020 †75

ARON, Bernard Steven. 234 GOODMAN ST, STE 0054 45219 #035-19-1957 L1969 RO ON *071 †80

ARONSON, Lori Anne. 3333 BURNET AVE, DEPT. OF ANESTHESIOLOGY 45229 #016-11-1994 L1995 PAN PD *020 †55,05

ARONSTEIN, William Seth. 45246 #023-07-1986 L1999 IM FM *020 †20

ARTHUR, Todd Michael. 3333 BURNET AVE, DIV OF NEUROLOGY 45229 #038-41-1999 L2005 CHN CN *100 †55,75

ARYA, Kraisith. 4777 E GALBRAITH RD, JEWISH HOSPITAL 45236 #748-21-1990 L1997 NEP *020 †20

ARYA, Maziar David. 3219 CLIFTON AVE STE 400, C/O CREDENTIALING 45220 #055-01-1996 L1998 CD *020 †20

ASBURY, Taylor. PO BOX 19070, UNIVERSITY MEDICAL ARTS BL 45219 #038-41-1949 L1949 OPH *071 †35

ASFOUR, Mohammad Walid. ■ 45248 #875-01-1979 L1985 N *020 †75

ASGHAR, Sheba. ■ 45219 #704-25-2000 L2007 IM *100

ASHBROOK, Lauren Michelle. ■ 45220 #038-41-2008 *012

ASHER, Anthony John. 7500 STATE RD 45255 #038-41-1986 L1987 DR *062 †80

ASHOUIAN, Nasrin. ■ 45215 #035-46-2005 L2005 IM *012

ASHWORTH, Ming E. 8000 5 MILE RD, STE 250 45230 #038-43-1990 L1992 FM *020 †18

ASIF, Sadiya. 1401 STEFFEN AVE, LINCOLN HEIGHTS 45215 #495-37-1977 L1986 PD *020 †55

ASLAM, Muhammad. 234 GOODMAN ST, STE 0559 45219 #704-01-1992 L2000 PYG *020 †75

ASOJO, Oluyomi Adebola. 231 ALBERT, CO PATHOLOGY DEPT 45267 #690-01-2002 L2007 PTH *012

ASSA'AD, Amal Halim. 3333 BURNET AVE 45229 #915-04-1978 L1992 AI *020 †20,55,03

ASUNCION, Romeo Realica. 2006 MORNINGRIDGE DR 45211 #748-08-1967 GS *020

ATHOTA, Krishna Prasad. 231 ALBERT SABIN WAY, ML 0558 45267 #038-43-2001 L2007 CCS *012

ATIQ, Muslim. ■ 45267 #704-25-2002 L2004 IM *100 †20

ATKINSON, Matthew Riley. ■ 45267 #038-41-2002 L2002 GE *012 †20

ATLURI, K Pratha. 10475 READING RD, STE 201 45241 #495-94-1990 L1999 IM *020 †20

ATLURI, Sairam Lakshmi. 7655 5 MILE RD, STE 117 45230 #495-65-1991 L1995 APM *020 †05

ATTAR, Ahmad. 10496 MONTGOMERY RD, STE 208 45242 #875-01-1972 L1979 GE IM *020

ATTARI, Mehran. ■ 45236 #517-01-1994 L2004 ICE *020 †20

ATTERBURY, Margaret R. 5818 MADISON RD, CINCINNATI HEALTH DEPT 45227 #016-11-1982 L1989 OM IM *020 †20,70

ATWELL, Tanika Rae. ■ 45236 #020-02-2004 L2004 OBG *012

AUBUCHON, Mira. 2123 AUBURN AVE, STE A44 45219 #016-06-1998 L2005 OBG *020 †30

AUGER, Katherine Ann. ■ 45220 #001-02-2005 L2005 PD *012

AUGSBURGER, James Jay. SABIN WAY, EDEN AVE & ALBERT 45267 #038-41-1974 L1976 OPH SO *020 †35

AUKERMAN, Kevin Allen. 7500 STATE RD 45255 #038-41-1988 L1991 R *020 †80

AUNG, Thet Han. 375 DIXMYTH AVE 45220 #308-13-2005 L2006 IM *012

AUNG, Thu Han. 375 DIXMYTH AVE, MEDICAL EDUCATION DEPARTME 45220 #308-13-2003 L2004 IM HOS *012 †20

AUSDENMOORE, Robert Wm. 3333 BURNET AVE, OSB5 45229 #038-41-1957 L1957 AI PD *071 †55,03

AUSTIN, Joe Newby, Jr. 3219 CLIFTON AVE STE 325 45220 #047-06-1983 L1991 NEP IM *020 †20

AUSTIN, Orson Jude. 1295 KEMPER MEADOW DR 45240 #047-07-1988 L1990 FM *020 †18

AUTRY, Anne Cravitz. 3333 BURNET AVE 45229 #025-01-1977 L1978 PD *020 †55

AUVIL, Dallas Gregory. 58 E HOLLISTER ST 45219 #038-06-1986 L1986 P GS *020 †75

AVERY, William Jos. 8074 BEECHMONT AVE 45255 #038-41-1963 L1963 OBG *071 †30

AVISSAR, Uri. ■ 45208 #035-45-2001 L2004 GE *100

AWADALLA, Sherif Geo. 3805 EDWARDS RD STE 450 45209 #038-41-1981 L1985 REN OBG *020 †30

AYE PE, Nant Anita. ■ 45239 #209-01-1969 L1980 GP *020

AYLWARD, Shawn Christophe. ■ 45230 #016-45-2005 L2005 CHN *012

AYRE, Karen June. ■ 45220 #038-41-2008 *012

AZIZKHAN, Richard Geo. 3333 BURNET AVE, CHILDREN'S HOSP MEDICAL CT 45229 #041-14-1976 L1999 PDS CCS *020 †85

BABAOFF, Arash. 3130 HIGHLAND AVE, PROTEIN EXPRESS 45219 #025-01-1994 L1996 PD *075 †55

BABAR, Nabila S. 2446 KIPLING AVE 45239 #704-21-1988 L1994 IM *020 †20

BABBITT, David Gerard. 2123 AUBURN AVE, STE 624 45219 #038-45-1983 L1985 CD IC *020

BABCOCK, Diane K S. 3300 ELLAND AVE # RAD, CHILDRENS HOSPITAL 45229 #016-06-1970 L1971 PDR *020 †80

BABCOCK, John Reed. 2123 AUBURN AVE # 321 45219 #016-06-1970 L1971 U *020 †95

BABEL, Charles Lewis. CINCINNATI GEN HOSP PATH 45229 #035-15-1974 PTH *020

BACH, Bernd Bruno. 2915 CLIFTON AVE, GROUP HEALTH ASSOCIATES 45220 #407-23-1957 L1968 IM CD *071

BACKELJAUW, Philippe F. 3333 BURNET AVE, DIV OF PED ENDOCRINOLOGY 45229 #165-02-1986 L1990 PDE PD *020 †18

BACON, John Patrick. 55 PROGRESS PL 45246 #038-40-1991 L1992 PD *020 †55

BACON, William Thos. ■ 45215 #038-40-1943 L1943 FM *071 †18

BADIE, Nicole Christina. ■ 45220 #038-41-2008 *012

BADREDDINE, Hana M. 311 STRAIGHT ST, DEACONESS ARTHRITIS CENTER 45219 #605-01-1988 L1998 RHU GP *020 †20

BAGAMERY, Nancy Sue. 3006 PORTSMOUTH AVE 45208 #038-41-1983 L1986 PD *020 †55

BAGGISH, Michael Simeon. 375 DIXMYTH AVE, DEPT OB 45220 #020-02-1961 L1993 OBG PTH *020 †30

BAI, Brian Chong. 45243 #308-03-2000 L2005 FP *012

BAILEY, John Kevin. 222 PIEDMONT AVE, STE 200 45219 #038-41-1993 L1995 GS *020 †85

BAILEY, Kimberly Anne. ■ 45243 #038-41-1980 L1981 IM *050 †20

BAILEY, Warren Weston. 3300 ELLAND AVE # CDS, CHILDRENS HOSPITAL 45229 #024-07-1970 L1982 TS *020 †85,90

BAIN, Kathleen Suzanne. 3333 BURNET AVE, CINCINNATI CHILDREN'S HOSP 45229 #038-45-1993 L1997 PD *020 †55

BAJAJ, Anureet Kaur. 222 PIEDMONT AVE, STE 7200 45267 #041-12-1996 L2004 PS *020 †65

BAJAJ, Vina Ramchand. 7810 5 MILE RD 45230 #496-38-1971 L1984 END IM *020 †20

BAKER, Raymond Chas. 3333 BURNET AVE, CINCINNATI CHILDRENS HOSP 45229 #038-40-1971 L1979 PD *020 †55

BAKHSH, Adel Abdullah. ■ 45267 #797-02-1989 L2000 GS *100 †85

BAKKAR, Rania Mohamed. DEPT OF PATHOLOGY, UNIV OF CINCINNATI MED CTR 45267 #915-02-2002 L2005 PTH *012

BAKRLI, Hussam. ■ 45208 #875-01-1987 L1992 CHN *100 †55

BALASA, Vinod V. 3333 BURNET AVE, CINCINNATI CHILDREN'S HOSP 45229 #496-21-1992 L1996 PHO *012

BALDWIN, Nicole Renee. 11238 CORNELL PARK DR 45242 #038-41-2003 L2003 PD *020 †55

BALISTRERI, William F. 3333 BURNET AVE, CHILDRENS HOSP MED CTR 45229 #035-06-1970 L1978 PG HEP *020 †55

BALKO, Michael Gregory. 3159 EDEN AVE 45219 #020-02-1983 L1991 FOP PTH *020 †50

BALKOWIEC, Katarzyna B. 3333 BURNET AVE, DIVISION OF EMERGENCY MEDI 45229 #759-03-1991 L1997 PD *020 †55

BALL, Molly Katherine. 3333 BURNET AVE, CHILDREN'S HOSP MED CTR 45229 #047-05-2005 L2005 PD *012

BALL, William Slaughter, Jr. 3300 ELLAND AVE # RAD, CHILDRENS HOSPITAL 45229 #021-01-1974 L1984 DR *020 †80,55

BALLARD, Edgar Thos. CHILDRENS HOSP 45229 #011-03-1965 L1971 ATP PP *062 †55,50

BALLARD, Jeanne La Croix. 2139 AUBURN AVE 45219 #041-07-1965 L1971 PD NPM *020 †55

BALLESTER, John Michael. 234 GOODMAN ST, STE 0769 45219 #019-02-1994 L2001 EM IM *020 †16,20

BALUYOT, Sabino T, Jr. 5049 CROOKSHANK RD, STE 202 45238 #748-01-1963 L1972 OTO HNS *020 †45

BALZ, George P. 250 WM HOWARD TAFT RD 45219 #016-11-1952 L1958 RHU *071

BANDA, Ramzi Wadi. 231 BETHESDA AVE 45229 #605-01-1980 L1983 N *020 †75

BANDLAMUDI, Govardhana R. 234 GOODMAN ST 45267 #495-50-1980 L2000 PYG *100

BANERJEE, Eboo. ■ 45215 #209-01-1957 L1983 PD *071 †55

BAO, Liming. CINCINNATI CHILD MED CTR, MEDICAL GENETICS 45229 #243-16-1985 MG *050 †19

BARBARA, Mark J. 5576 GLENWAY AVE 45238 #020-12-1982 L1986 P *020 †75

BARCZAK, Sylvester Martin. 4623 WESLEY AVE, STE C 45212 #020-02-1975 L1977 EM IM *030 †16

BARDEN, Tom Preston. 234 GOODMAN ST 45267 #017-20-1958 L1968 OBG MFM *071 †30

BARE, Kathleen U. 3803 HAUCK RD 45241 #038-41-1979 L1979 OBG *020 †30

BARKER, Gail Austing. 3001 HIGHLAND AVE, STE E 45219 #038-41-1980 L1983 P *020 †75

BARKER, Matthew Alderson. ■ 45219 #046-01-2002 L2006 OBG *100

BARKER, Megan Jane. ■ 45223 #038-41-2008 *012

BARLOW, Courtenay Brook. 3333 BURNET AVE 45229 #054-04-2005 L2005 PD *012

BARNES, Alfonso Eduardo. 9030 MONTGOMERY RD 45242 #847-10-1969 L1979 GO GYN *020 †30

BARNES, Daniel Bernard. 672 NEEB RD 45233 #020-12-1996 L1999 FM *020 †18

BARNES, Stephen Leonard. 231 ALBERT SABIN WAY, ML 0558 45267 #001-02-1997 L2004 CCS *020 †85

BARNETT, Jalynn Ann. 311 ALBERT SABIN WAY, CENTRAL CLINIC 45229 #020-12-2004 L2004 P *012

BARNETT, Sean Jeffrey. ■ 45238 #038-45-2000 L2007 PDS *012

BARNHORN, Robert Wm. 8074 BEECHMONT AVE STE C 45255 #038-41-1975 L1975 OBG *020 †30

BARON, Sherry Lee. ■ 45220 #038-06-1982 L1982 OM IM *020 †20,70

BARREAU, Jose Gerardo. 9403 KENWOOD RD, STE B120 45242 #308-03-1999 L2000 HO *020 †20

BARRERE, David Miles. 2123 AUBURN AVE 45219 #038-40-1994 L1995 OBG *020 †30

BARRETT, Amanda Bettine. ■ 45239 #025-12-2002 L2002 MPD *100 †20,55

BARRETT, Jera Anne. 3200 VINE ST, DEPT OF VETERANS AFFAIRS 45220 #038-44-1990 L1994 P *071 †75

BARRETT, William Lannon. 234 GOODMAN ST 45219 #038-41-1987 L1988 RO GS *020 †80

BARRETTE, Erica C. ■ 45215 #056-05-2004 L2007 OBG *012

BARRON, David Robt. 9844 REDHILL DR 45242 #010-01-1979 L1981 DMP *062 †15

BARRY, Curtis Tran. 231 ALBERT SABIN WAY, DIVISION OF DIGESTIVE DISE 45267 #024-05-2003 L2007 GE *012 †20

BARTHOLOMEW, Julie Anne. 3333 BURNET AVE 45229 #665-01-2006 L2006 PD *012

BARTISH, Lawrence Andrew. 2450 KIPLING AVE, STE G03 45239 #038-40-1982 L1987 GS *020 †85

BARTLETT, Sarah Elizabeth. ■ 45208 #020-02-2004 L2004 OBG *012

BARTMAN, Thomas. 3333 BURNET AVE, MLC 7009 45229 #041-13-1996 L2003 NPM *020 †55

BARZMAN, Drew Harris. 3333 BURNET AVE, MLC 3014 45229 #035-06-1997 L2001 CHP *020 †75

BASIL, Jack Broadwater. 3219 CLIFTON AVE, STE 225 45220 #038-40-1993 L2004 OBG *020 †30

BASKAKOVA, Alla V. 3200 VINE ST, CINCINNATI VA MEDICAL CENT 45220 #913-69-1987 L2004 CHP *100

BASKIN, Henry Jackson, Jr. 3333 BURNET AVE, DEPT OF RADIOLOGY 45229 #045-01-2001 L2006 PDR *100 †80

BASSETTE, Caesar S, Jr. ■ 45220 #010-03-1951 L1956 OBG FM *071

BASSIN, Benjamin Scott. ■ 45208 #025-01-2005 L2005 EM *012

BATAILLE, Feguens Joseph. ■ 45220 #041-12-2006 L2007 IM *012

BATALDEN, Karin Beth. ■ 45208 #026-08-2006 L2006 PD *012

BATEMAN, Joseph Neal. 3306 RUTHER AVE, ALLIANCE PRIMARY CARE 45220 #041-02-1987 L1987 FM *020 †18

BATES, Michael David. 3333 BURNET AVE, PED GASTROENTEROLOGY & NUT 45229 #036-07-1992 L1993 PG PD *020 †55

BATH, Richard Kent. 10500 MONTGOMERY RD 45242 #038-41-1954 L1954 IM *050 †20

BATSEL-THOMAS, Sandra Dee. 6764 SIEBERN AVE 45236 #020-12-2002 L2002 CHP *020 †75

BAUER, Karen Ann. 151 W GALBRAITH RD, DRAKE CENTER 45216 #038-41-1983 L1984 PUD CCM *020 †20

BAUGHMAN, Robert Phillip. 231 ALBERT SABIN WAY 45267 #038-06-1977 L1978 PUD IM *020 †20

BAUMAN, Wayne Emerson. 10496 MONTGOMERY RD 45242 #065-06-1971 L1978 D IM *020 †15

BAUMGARTNER, N R, Jr. 1040 SAINT PAUL PL 45202 #038-41-1960 L1960 R *071 †80,55

BAUS, Joseph Edward. ■ 45208 #038-40-2006 L2006 EM *012

BAUSHER, Judith Ann. 3333 BURNET AVE 45229 #011-03-1975 L1980 PD *040 †55

BAWANI, Shahab Zare. ■ 45267 #517-05-1982 L2000 IM *100

BAXTER, Clarke Wm. 4760 RED BANK RD, STE 104 45227 #038-40-1981 L1986 FM *020 †18

BAXTER, Malcolm Stephen. 231 ALBERT SABIN WAY, MAIL LOCATION 0769 45267 #038-41-1989 L1990 EM *020 †16

BAYER, Todd Matthew. 4030 SMITH RD, STE 300 45209 #016-11-1991 L1992 VS *012 †85

BAYKO, Ryan Lee. 4411 MONTGOMERY RD, STE 400 45212 #038-41-2006 L2006 FP *012

BAYNHAM, Marian Stapleton. 7400 JAGER CT 45230 #020-12-1986 L1989 PD *020 †55

BEAL, Daniel Michael. 3200 VINE ST, A-924 45220 #038-40-1975 L2004 P *020 †75

BECHHOLD, Rebecca G. 4350 MALSBARY RD, STE 208 45242 #020-02-1978 L1979 ON HEM *020 †20

BECK, Amy Denise. ■ 45209 #038-41-2003 L2003 DR *012

BECK, Andrew Finkel. ■ 45243 #041-12-2006 L2006 PD *012

BECK, David Christopher. ■ 45211 #038-41-2001 L2003 PCC *020

BECK, Stephen Craig. 800 COMPTON RD STE 31 45231 #018-03-1975 L1976 CHP P *020 †75

BECK, Stephen Richard. 7500 STATE RD, MERCY HOSPITAL ANDERSON 45255 #038-41-1992 L1994 IM *020 †20

BECKER, Janson Robb. 4750 E GALBRAITH RD, STE 207 45236 #038-41-1985 L1987 IM GP *020 †20

■ = Address Information Privacy Protected

BECKES, Angela B. 375 DIXMYTH AVE, GOOD SAMARITAN HOSPITAL 45220 #012-05-1994 L1996 **DR** *020 †80

BECKES, Kirt Aron. 500 E BUSINESS WAY 45241 #017-20-1991 L1996 **AN** *020 †05

BECKMAN, Daniel Robt. 375 DIXMYTH AVE 45220 #035-06-1974 L1987 **PTH** *020 †18,50

BECKMAN, Emily Louise. ■ 45267 #012-05-2006 L2007 **IM** *012

BECKMEYER, William Peter. 2446 KIPLING AVE, MERCY MOUNT AIRY HOSPITAL 45239 #038-41-1987 L1994 **AN** *05

BEDOLLA, Gabriela Maria. ■ 45267 #048-13-2000 L2000 **PTH** *020 †50

BEDOYA APRAEZ, Ivan Dario. 400 WABASH AVENUE 45236 #264-06-2003 L2007 **IM** *012

BEDSOLE, Russell Lee. 231 ALBERT SABIN WAY, RM6603 45267 #001-02-2000 L2001 **IM** *020

BEEKMAN, Robt Harold, III. 3333 BURNET AVE, DIVISION OF CARDIOLOGY 45229 #036-07-1976 L1982 **PDC PD** *020

BEG, Muhammad Shaalan. ■ 45219 #704-25-2003 L2005 **IM** *012

BEHRENS, Scott Arthur. 8000 5 MILE RD, THE OHIO HEART & VASCULAR 45230 #038-41-1984 L1985 **CD IM** *020

BEHRMAN, Douglas Frank. 415 STRAIGHT ST, DEACONESS HOSPITAL 45219 #035-46-1990 L1996 **IM** *020

BEITER, Elizabeth Ann. 4411 MONTGOMERY RD, STE 400 45212 #038-41-2006 L2006 **FP** *012

BEITER, Patrick Allen. 4411 MONTGOMERY RD, STE 200 45212 #038-41-2004 L2004 **FSM** *012 †18

BEKAL, Pradeepkumar. 1207 SPRINGFIELD PIKE 45215 #495-04-1984 L1994 **GE IM** *020 †20

BELAGAJE, Samir Rama. ■ 45208 #017-20-2004 L2004 **N** *012

BELAGAJE, Sudhir Rama. ■ 45267 #017-20-2006 L2006 **ORS** *012

BELL, Gina Simone. 2830 VICTORY PKWY, STE 140 45206 #016-42-2003 L2007 **OBG** *100

BELL, Howard Lee. 7527 STATE RD STE A 45255 #038-40-1981 L1981 **OPH EM** *020 †35

BELL, Jason Howard. 234 GOODMAN ST, PAVILION A, 2ND FLOOR 45219 #038-41-2005 L2005 **OPH** *012

BELL, Stephen Josh. 12115 SHERATON LN, CO CINCI SPORTS MEDORTHO C 45246 #048-12-1997 L2003 **ORS** *020 †40

BELL, Stephen Lester. 1150 W 8TH ST, STE 120 45203 #038-40-1973 L1973 **OM EM** *020 †16,70

BELL, Thomas Edwin. 231 ALBERT SABIN WAY, CINCINNATI COLLEGE MEDICIN 45267 #038-41-1964 L1964 **U** *020 †95

BELLAMAH, Howard Ferris. 2139 AUBURN AVE 45219 #038-41-1954 L1954 **GS** *071 †85

BELLAMY, Charles Duane. 3155 GLENDALE MILFORD RD, CINCINNATI EVENDALE SURG 45241 #038-41-1985 L1989 **AN** *020 †05

BELLET, Paul Sanders. 3333 BURNET AVE, CHILDRENS HOSP MED CTR 45229 #035-45-1971 L1972 **PD** *040 †55

BELMONT MONTEVERDE, Talia. 3333 BURNET AVE, CHILDREN'S HOSPITAL MEDICA 45229 #737-06-2005 L2007 **PD** *012

BENDER, Melissa Ann. 2139 AUBURN AVE, DEPT FM 45219 #017-20-2007 L2007 **FP** *012

BENDER, Thomas Arthur. 3345 WHITFIELD AVE 45220 #038-41-1977 L1977 **ORS EM** *020 †40

BENEDETTO, Charles V. ■ 45208 #021-05-1986 L1991 **AN** *020

BENEDICT, Michael Andrew. 231 ALBERT SABIN WAY, ML 0535 DEPT INT MED 45267 #038-41-1994 L2003 **IM PD** *020,55

BENEDICT, Wendy Brandt. 2139 AUBURN AVE, MOB SUITE A 28 45219 #051-01-1994 L1999 **IM** *040 †20

BENNETT, Aurora Jorge. 222 PIEDMONT AVE, STE 8500 MEDICAL ARTS BLDG 45219 #038-40-1986 L1988 **P CHP** *020 †75

BENNETT, Berkeley Lynn. 3333 BURNET AVE 45229 #005-12-1999 L2006 **PEM** *100

BENNETT, Dale Winston. 2123 AUBURN AVE, STE 108 45219 #020-12-1964 L1971 **U** *071 †95

BENNETT, Nitza M. 7495 STATE RD 45255 #042-01-1966 L1971 **PD PN** *020 †55

BENNETT, Robert James. 2859 BOUDINOT AVE, STE 107 45238 #038-41-1992 L1994 **FM** *020 †18

BENNETT, Stephen Garrett. 2123 AUBURN AVE, STE 108 45219 #038-40-1996 L1997 **U** *020 †95

BENSON, D Woodrow. 3333 BURNET AVE, DIVISION OF CARDIOLOGY-OSB 45229 #036-07-1972 L2001 **PDC** *020

BENSON, Paul Andrew Scott. 3333 BURNET AVE, MCL 4000 45229 #016-01-2000 L2006 **ADL PD** *020 †55

BENTON, Corning. ■ 45227 #067-01-1959 L1964 **PDR** *071 †80

BENZA, Robert. 7850 CAMARGO RD 45243 #038-41-1990 L1991 **OPH** *020 †35

BENZING, George. 3333 BURNET AVE, CHILDRENS HOSP 45229 #038-41-1958 L1958 **CCP PDC** *020 †55

BERBERICH, Norbert J, III. 7500 STATE RD, CARE CONSULTANTS MERCY 45255 #020-02-1989 L1990 **AN PME** *020 †05

BERENSON, A David. ■ 45241 #024-07-1960 L1963 **OM FM** *071 †70,18

BERG, Douglas Benjamin. ■ 45242 #038-43-2007 L2007 **GS** *012

BERG, Stephen Michael. 9330 KENWOOD RD 45242 #038-41-1981 L1982 **IM IMG** *020 †20

BERGER, Jose M. 3723 HAUCK RD, PLASTIC RECNSTRCTV SURG 45241 #396-31-1980 L1987 **PS HS** *071 †65

BERGER, Omer Gene. CHILDRENS HOSPITAL 45229 #038-41-1963 L1963 **PD** *020 †55

BERGER, Thomas Stanley. 3219 CLIFTON AVE, STE 110 45220 #038-41-1965 L1965 **NS** *020 †25

BERGMANN, Mark Thos. 2859 BOUDINOT AVE 45238 #038-45-1982 L1983 **OPH** *020 †35

BERGQUIST, Lynn Marie. 2980 ERIE AVE 45208 #025-07-1994 L2000 **IM** *020 †20

BERKOWITZ, David Victor. 1275 E KEMPER RD 45246 #038-41-1970 L1970 **SME P** *020 †75

BERKOWITZ, Drora. ■ 45242 #550-03-1984 L1992 *020

BERMAN, Jerome Richard. ■ 45208 #038-41-1944 L1944 **GE IM** *071 †20

BERNARD, Aaron William. 231 ALBERT SABIN WAY, DEPARTMENT OF EMERG MED 45267 #035-48-2003 L2003 **EM** *100

BERNARD, Bruce Patrick. 4676 COLUMBIA PKWY R-10 45226 #039-01-1982 L1982 **OM** *020 †05

BERNFELD, Jonathan A. 8265 MELLON DR 45242 #038-41-1975 L2000 **PYG** *020 †20

BERNHEISEL, Christopher R. 2123 AUBURN AVE STE 340, THE CHRIST HOSP FAM MED 45219 #038-41-2002 L2002 **FM** *040 †18

BERNIE, William Allen. 4545 CREEK RD 45242 #038-41-1963 L1963 **GS SO** *050 †85

BERNINGER, Howard G. 10500 MONTGOMERY RD 45242 #038-41-1949 L1949 **FM** *071 †18

BERNSTEIN, David I. 8444 WINTON RD 45231 #035-06-1977 L1983 **ID PD** *050 †55

BERNSTEIN, David Isaac. 9275 MONTGOMERY RD 45242 #038-41-1977 L1979 **AI IM** *020 †20,03

BERNSTEIN, I Leonard. 9275 MONTGOMERY RD 45242 #038-41-1949 L1949 **ALI IM** *020 †20,03

BERNSTEIN, Jonathan Abram. 9275 MONTGOMERY RD 45242 #038-41-1985 L1986 **AI IM** *020 †20,03

BERNSTEIN, Joseph E. 5819 CHEVIOT RD 45247 #016-42-1983 L1989 **DR** *080 †80

BERNSTEIN, Tamar. 3333 BURNET AVE, OSB-5 45229 #550-02-1987 **CCP** *100

BERRY, Ravi Bhushan. 375 DIXMYTH AVE 45220 #495-03-1968 L1978 **P PYG** *020 †75

BETHEL, Monique. ■ 45220 #038-41-2006 L2006 **GS** *100

BETTER, Elaine S. 4422 CARVER WOODS DR 45242 #035-06-1977 L1984 **P CHP** *020 †75

BETTS, Jeffrey Brian. 6600 DRAKE RD, JEFFREY BETTS MD 45243 #055-02-1991 L1995 **DR PDR** *020 †80

BEVER, Anne Marie. 7400 JAGER CT 45230 #038-45-1996 L2006 **PD** *020 †55

BEYER, Amanda. ■ 45237 #407-33-1954 L1968 **D** *071

BEZERRA, Jorge A. 3333 BURNET AVE 45229 #187-16-1984 L1990 **PD** *075 †55

BHABHRA, Ruchi. CO MEDICAL EDUCATION DEPT, THE CHRIST HOSPITAL 45219 #496-02-2000 L2007 **IM** *012

BHAGWAT, Ajit R. 521 MARTIN LUTHER KING DR, APT 24B QUEEN CTY APTS 45220 #495-56-1984 L1994 **CD** *020 †20

BHAGWAT, Vinaya Ajit. ■ 45243 #495-56-1986 L1994 **IM** *020 †20

BHALA, Balmukund Bansilal. U-CINCINNATI HOSP 45267 #495-19-1972 *100

BHAMIDIPATY, Sunita V. ■ 45267 #010-01-1999 L2003 **AN** *012

BHANDARI, Manish Sidhraj. 10506 MONTGOMERY RD 45242 #024-01-1996 L2005 **HO** *020 †20

BHANDARI, Sadhana. 24 COMPTON RD, STE 205 45216 #495-51-1980 L1985 **IM IMG** *020 †20

BHANGOO, Sukminder Singh. 200 NORTHLAND BLVD 45246 #495-03-1971 L1973 **AN** *020 †05

BHARDWAJ, Kaushal Kumar. 9019 COLERAIN AVE, GROESBECK MEDICAL & LONGEV 45251 #496-02-1971 L1983 **IM** *020

BHARGAVA, Manoj. 12115 SHERATON LN, & ORTHOPEDIC CENTER 45246 #065-01-1992 L2000 **OSM** *100

BHARGAVA, Reena. 231 ALBERT SABIN WAY, DEPT OF SURGERY 45267 #065-06-1999 L2004 *100

BHASKARAN, Jayapandian. 5520 CHEVIOT RD 45247 #495-59-1968 L1978 **HO HEM** *020 †20

BHATI, Anant Ram. 10190 SPRINGFIELD PIKE 45215 #495-30-1965 L1974 **OBG** *030 †30

BHATKI, Leah. 3333 BURNET AVE 45229 #005-02-2002 L2007 **PAN** *012

BHATLA, Deepika. 3333 BURNET AVE 45229 #496-07-1992 L2004 **PHO** *100 †55

BHATT, Shabari Sanat. ■ 45249 #038-40-2007 L2007 **IM** *012

BHATTACHARYA, Sarbori R. 631 MAIN ST 45202 #038-41-1996 L1999 **P** *020

BHUTTA, Rajal Pravin. 200 NORTHLAND BLVD 45246 #495-17-1968 L1977 **AN** *020 †05

BIALICK, Howard Allan. 1219 MORTS PASS 45215 #025-07-1982 L1990 **EM** *020 †16

BIBB, Mary H. 2567 ERIE AVE 45208 #016-11-1969 L1978 **P** *020 †75

BIBB, Richard Edward. 3001 HIGHLAND AVE 45219 #047-05-1959 L1963 **P PYA** *071 †75

BIBLER, Lindsay Wilson. 8040 HOSBROOK RD STE 100 45236 #016-06-1980 L1983 **OPH** *020 †35

BIBLER, Mark Richard. 222 PIEDMONT AVE, STE 6000 45219 #016-06-1980 L1984 **ID** *030 †20

BIDDINGER, Paul Williams. 234 GOODMAN ST 45219 #038-41-1979 L1986 **ATP FOP** *020

BIELEKOVA, Bibiana. 222 PIEDMONT AVE, STE 3200 45219 #286-03-1993 L2005 **N** *050 †75

BIELIAUSKAS, Danute G. ■ 45251 #407-14-1945 L1958 **FM** *071

BIERBRAUER, Karin Sabine. 3333 BURNET AVE, ML-2016 45229 #045-01-1984 L2004 **NS NSP** *020 †25

BIGGS, John Theodore. ■ 45208 #038-40-1992 L1993 **AN** *020 *05

BIGHAM, Michael Theodore. 3333 BURNET AVE, ML 2005 45229 #038-43-2002 L2002 **CCP** *012 †55

BILL, Jeffrey Paul. 5314 DELHI AVE 45238 #038-45-2003 L2005 **FM** *020 †18

BILLMIRE, David Arch. 3333 BURNET AVE 2020, CINCINNATI CHILDRENS HOSPI 45229 #038-40-1975 L1975 **PS GS** *020 †85,65

BILLMIRE, M Elaine. 9070 WINTON RD 45231 #038-40-1975 L1975 **PD** *020 †55

BILLOCK, Nanci Jo. 375 DIXMYTH AVE 45220 #665-01-2007 L2007 **OBG** *012

BILLS, Gordon Lee. 10500 MONTGOMERY RD, BETHESDA NORTH 45242 #038-40-1980 L1980 **PTH** *020 †50

BINA, Shashi. 1101 SUMMIT RD 45237 #495-41-1967 L1978 **P** *020

BINDER, Stephanie Audrey. 3333 BURNET AVE 45229 #412-01-2000 L2006 **NPM** *012 †55

BINGHAM, Harry James. 5535 MONTGOMERY RD 45212 #038-41-1947 L1947 **FM** *071

BINGHAM, James Gault. 5535 MONTGOMERY RD 45212 #038-41-1978 L1978 **IM** *020 †20

BIRD, Stephen G. 9070 WINTON RD 45231 #038-41-1983 L1987 **PD** *020 †55

BIREN, Paula. 2800 WINSLOW AVE STE 104 45206 #407-23-1951 L1955 **P** *071

BIRO, Frank M. 3333 BURNET AVE 45229 #024-01-1979 L1984 **ADL MFM** *020 †20,55

BISCOTTI, Matthew Robert. ■ 45227 #038-41-2006 L2006 **IM** *012

BISMAYER, John Adam. 199 WILLIAM HOWARD TAFT RD, STE 101 45219 #016-11-1971 L1973 **ON IM** *020 †20

BISMUTH, Bella. ■ 45227 #035-48-2003 L2006 **PG** *012 †55

BISSLER, John Jos. 3333 BURNET AVE - 7022, FOUNDATION #5 45229 #038-44-1985 L1988 **PD PN** *050 †55

BIXEL, Carl Adrian. 3200 VINE ST, VETERANS ADMIN MED CTR 45220 #038-41-1985 L1987 **IM** *020 †20

BJORNSON, Henry Stephen. 250 WILLIAM HOWARD TAFT RD, FL 2 45219 #038-41-1974 L1976 **ID IM** *062

BLACKLIDGE, Melodie Gayle. 2915 CLIFTON AVE 45220 #038-41-1986 L1987 **PD** *020 †55

BLACKNEY, Kevin Allen. ■ 45215 #038-34-2007 L2007 **IM** *012

BLADES, Mary Diane. 5310 RAPID RUN RD, STE 101 45238 #038-41-1993 L1994 **IM** *020 †20

BLADES, Nancy. ■ 45248 #023-01-1951 L1952 **GP** *072

BLAND, Pamela Cornelia. ■ 45209 #010-03-2002 L2002 **PAN** *020

BLANEY, Donald John. ■ 45233 #025-01-1957 L1961 **D** *071 †15

BLATMAN, Hal Saml. 10653 TECHWOOD CIR, STE 101 45242 #041-07-1980 L1982 **PMM OM** *020 †70

BLATT, Norman Howard. 7661 MONTGOMERY RD 45236 #038-41-1947 L1947 **PD PDA** *071 †55

BLATT, Stephen Patrick. 330 STRAIGHT ST, STE 400 45219 #038-41-1985 L1988 **ID IM** *020 †20

BLISS, Robert Thos. 3200 VINE ST 45220 #038-41-1957 L1957 **OS** *071

BLITZER, Bennett Lloyd. 2123 AUBURN AVE STE 107 45219 #008-01-1973 L1982 **GE IM** *020 †20

BLOMKALNS, Andra Leah. 231 ALBERT SABIN WAY, DEPT EMERGENCY MEDICINE ML 45267 #021-06-1997 L1998 **EM** *020 †16

BLONIGEN, Brian Joseph. ■ 45226 #056-06-2004 L2005 **RO** *012

BLOOMER, Jeffrey Brian. 4760 E GALBRAITH RD 45236 #038-41-1977 L1978 **PUD** *020 †20

BLOOMFIELD, Saul Solomon. 234 GOODMAN ST 45267 #869-04-1953 L1981 **PA IM** *071

BLOUNT, Robert J. 134 WM HOWARD TAFT RD 45219 #023-07-1999 L1999 **MPD** *100 †20,55

BLOUSTEIN, Paul A. 4777 E GALBRAITH RD, CLINICAL LABORATORY 45236 #035-19-1967 L1969 **ATP** *071 †50

BLUM, Barry Alan. 375 DIXMYTH AVE, GOOD SAMARITAN HOSPITAL 45220 #023-01-1968 L1975 **DR** *020

BLUMENTHAL, Barry. 55 PROGRESS PL 45246 #836-02-1968 L1988 **OBG** *020 †30

BLUST, Michael William. 231 ALBERT SABIN WAY, STE ML531 45267 #038-41-1996 L2005 **AN** *020 †05

BLYTHE, Marguerite M. 4903 VINE ST, PRACTICAL PSYCHIATRY 45217 #038-41-1985 L1985 **PYG P** *020 †75

BOAT, Thomas Frederick. 3333 BURNET AVE, CHILDREN'S HOSP MED CTR 45229 #018-03-1966 L1971 **PD PDP** *030 †55

BOBBITT, David Bradley. 5049 CROOKSHANK RD, STE 202 45238 #038-41-1997 L2000 **OTO** *020 †45

BOBBITT, Ralph Carter. 7629 KENWOOD RD 45236 #038-41-1965 L1965 **AI** *020 †55,03

BOBBITT, Ralph Carter, Jr. 7629 KENWOOD RD 45236 #038-41-1999 L2002 **AI** *020 †20,03

BOBULA, Steven Mark. ■ 45247 #038-45-2005 L2005 **IM** *012

BOEHMER, Reinhard Hansi. 234 GOODMAN ST 45267 #836-03-1982 *020

BOFINGER, Karl Kurt. ■ 45230 #028-34-1963 L1965 **PD** *071 †55

BOFINGER, Mary Kessis. ELLAND & BETHESDA AVES, CHILDRENS HOSP 45229 #038-41-1964 L1964 **CG PD** *071 †55,19

BOGAT, Erick. 234 GOODMAN ST, UNIV CINCINNATI HOSP 45267 #409-12-1985 **IM** *100

BOGEN, Kimberly Ann. ■ 45209 #038-43-2007 L2007 **OBG** *012

BOGIN, Ruben A. 11877 MASON MONTGOMERY RD 45249 #913-29-1983 L2000 *100

BOHINSKI, Robert John. 7691 5 MILE RD, STE 305 45230 #038-41-1996 L1997 **NS** *020 †25

BOIMAN, Richard E. 3219 CLIFTON AVE STE 100 45220 #038-41-1949 L1949 **OBG** *071 †30

BOLAND, Rachael Eve. 2139 AUBURN AVE, STE 6162 45219 #038-41-2003 L2003 **IM** *020

BOLDT, Gregory Blair. 1219 MORTS PASS 45215 #039-01-1991 L1994 **EM** *020 †16

BOLLEPALLI, Sureka. 3333 BURNET AVE, DEPT ENDO 45229 #422-01-2003 L2006 **PDE** *012 †55

BOND, Graeme Randall. 3333 BURNET AVE, DIV EMER MED 45229 #028-34-1980 L1999 **PEM PDT** *020 †55,16

BONDOC, Alexander Joseph. 231 ALBERT SABIN WAY, UC DEPT OF SURGERY 45267 #025-01-2005 L2005 **GS** *012

BONDOC, Antonio Sibal. 3352 JEFFERSON AVE 45220 #748-01-1957 L1969 **GP IM** *020

BONGIOVANNI, Gail Lucile. 4260 GLENDALE MILFORD RD, STE 101 45242 #038-06-1977 L1982 **GE IM** *040 †20

BONIFACE, Kenneth Jos. 3131 QUEEN CITY AVE, ST FRANCIS-ST GEORGE HOSPI 45238 #045-01-1975 L1978 **EM** *020 †16

BONIFACE, William R. 231 BETHESDA AVE 45229 #028-02-1953 L1960 **P N** *071

BONNAIG, Nicolas Simon. ■ 45248 #047-07-2008 *012

BONOMO, Jordan Bradley. ■ 45243 #043-01-2003 L2003 **EM** *100

BOPPANA, Swapna. 2139 AUBURN AVE 45219 #495-37-2000 L2007 **IM** *012

BORCHERDING, Janet Ann. 4623 WESLEY AVE, STE G 45212 #038-41-1977 L1978 **PD** *020 †65

BORDEN, Jonathan Alan. 10550 MONTGOMERY RD, STE 33 45242 #008-01-1988 L2004 **NS** *020 †25

BORDER, William Lewis M. 3333 BURNET AVE, CINCINNATI CHILDRENS HOSPI 45229 #836-02-1993 L1999 **PDC** *020 †55

BOREN, Gregory Greene. 3131 QUEEN CITY AVE 45238 #038-41-1968 L1968 **PTH** *020 †50

BORT, Leslie Ann. 234 GOODMAN ST 45267 #649-14-1981 L1987 **FM** *074

BORT, Thaddeus Michael. 6331 GLENWAY AVE 45211 #649-14-1981 L1985 **FM** *020 †18

BORZOTTA, Anthony Peter. 10498 MONTGOMERY RD, STE A 45242 #010-02-1978 L1985 **GS TRS** *020 †85

BOSHELL, Bill Hunter. ■ 45209 #055-02-2003 L2005 **DR** *012

BOSQUES, Glendaliz. ■ 45219 #042-01-2003 L2007 **RPM** *012

BOSSERT, John Edward. 2139 AUBURN AVE, CHRIST HOSPITAL 45219 #047-05-1967 L1968 **GS** *071 †85

BOUGHABA, Dolly Albert. 222 PIEDMONT AVE, STE 3200 45219 #605-03-1994 L2000 **N** *020 †75

BOULTON, Bryon James. ■ 45220 #038-41-2002 L2003 **GS** *012

BOURG, Donald Jos. 45224 #025-01-1937 L1954 **CHP P** *040 †55,70,75

BOUVAY, Kamali Letitia. 3333 BURNET AVE, DIVISION OF EMERGENCY MEDI 45229 #041-13-2005 L2005 **PD** *012

BOVE, Kevin Emil. 3333 BURNET AVE, DEPT PATH 45229 #035-06-1961 L1963 **PP** *020 †50

BOWDEN, Jennifer Marie. 3333 BURNET AVE, CHILDRENS HOSP 45229 #025-12-2007 L2007 **CPP** *012

BOWEN, Daniel Clifford. 11317 SPRINGFIELD PIKE 45246 #038-45-1989 L1991 **OBG** *020

BOWERS, Walter Thos, II. 3131 HARVEY AVE STE 204 45229 #025-01-1975 L1976 **OBG** *020

BOWERSOX, Jon Chas. ■ 45202 #005-06-1984 L2003 **VS GS** *030 †85

BOWLES, Brian Ira. 7710 READING RD STE 120 45237 #041-12-1974 L1975 **PD** *020

BOWLING, Marcia C. 199 WILLIAM HOWARD TAFT RD 45219 #024-16-1978 L1986 **GYN ON** *020 †30

BOXER, Peter Alan. 1101 SUMMIT RD, CLINICAL ADMIN SUMMIT BEH 45237 #035-08-1980 L1982 **P OM** *020 †75,70

BOYD, Deborah Ann. 3333 BURNET AVE, CHILDRENS' HOSPITAL MED CT 45229 #038-41-1982 L1983 **PD** *020 †55

BOYD, Kellie Linee. 10475 READING RD, STE 20 45241 #038-41-2001 L2001 **FM** *020 †18

BOYLE, Janet Margaret. 231 ALBERT SABIN WAY, ML 0585 45267 #918-01-1997 L2000 *020 †20

BOZIAN, Richard C. 222 PIEDMONT AVE STE 6000, UNIVERSITY MED ARTS BLDG 45219 #035-03-1950 L1963 **NTR IM** *071 †20

BRACKEN, Robert Bruce. 231 ALBERT SABIN WAY, UNIV OF CINCINNATI MED CEN 45267 #062-01-1966 L1981 **U ON** *020 †95

BRADEN, Jana Holmes. 2123 AUBURN AVE 45219 #020-12-1988 L1989 **LM** *020 †20

BRADFORD, Ray Tully. 8041 HOSBROOK RD 45236 #038-41-1948 L1948 **OPH LM** *071 †35

BRADLEY, Robert Graydon. 2123 AUBURN AVE, STE 310 45219 #038-41-1998 L2000 **GS** *020 †85

BRADY, Kim. 375 DIXMYTH AVE 45220 #048-04-1980 L1990 **OBG MFM** *020 †30

BRADY, Patrick Wharton. 3333 BURNET AVE, CINCINNATI CHILDREN'S HOSP 45229 #028-02-2003 L2003 **PD** *100 †55

BRADY, Rebecca Charlene. 3333 BURNET AVE, CINCINNATI CHILDREN'S HOSP 45229 #020-12-1988 L1992 **PDI ID** *050 †20,55

BRAEUNING, Mary Patricia. 5819 CHEVIOT RD 45247 #038-41-1988 L2000 **DR** *020 †80

BRALEY, Susan E. 234 GOODMAN ST, STE 0054 45219 #038-41-1986 L1991 **R** *020 †80

BRAMEL, Jene E. 3011 GLOSS AVE 45213 #038-41-1999 L1999 **PD** *020 †55

BRAMLAGE, William Arthur. 9200 MONTGOMERY RD, STE A 45242 #038-41-1968 L1968 **DR** *071 †80

BRAMY, Dove Thierry. ■ 45246 #038-41-1993 L2000 **BBK** *100 †50

BRANDTS, Nichole Lee. 820 DELTA AVE 45226 #038-44-1996 L1998 **FM P** *020 †18,75

BRANNAN, John James. 6480 HARRISON AVE, SPORTS MEDICINE 45247 #038-43-1991 L1995 **PM PRS** *020 †60

BRANTLEY, Elise Fowler. ■ 45236 #039-01-2005 L2005 **D** *012

BRANTLEY, Richard Scott. 5920 COLERAIN AVE 45239 #038-41-1993 L1994 **IM** *020

BRANTLEY, Steven Paul. ■ 45236 #020-12-2005 L2005 **ORS** *012

BRATCHER, Glenn Omer. 222 PIEDMONT AVE STE 5200 45219 #056-06-1961 L1962 **OTO PDO** *030 †45

BRAUN, Karl Bruce. 7794 5 MILE RD, STE 200 45230 #038-41-1981 L1983 **U** *020 †95

BRAUN, Margaret Corless. 6331 GLENWAY AVE 45211 #038-41-2001 L2004 **FM** *020 †18

BRAVERMAN, Paula Karen. 3333 BURNET AVE, MAIL LOCATION 4000 ADOL MD 45229 #008-01-1982 L1985 **ADL PD** *020 †55

BRAVERMAN, Timothy S. 311 STRAIGHT ST 45219 #026-04-1983 L2001 **HMP PTH** *020 †50

BRAVO, Miguel Carlos. 3333 BURNET AVE 45229 #748-02-1995 L2004 *100

BREDESTEGE, Deborah Smith. 10475 MONTGOMERY RD 45242 #038-41-2005 L2005 **OBG** *012

BREECH, Lesley Louise. 3333 BURNET AVE, ML 4000 45229 #038-40-1994 L2004 **OBG** *020 †30

BREITWESER, James Allen. ■ 45220 #026-04-1973 L1974 **DR PD** *030 †55,80

BRENEMAN, Debra Lynn. 222 PIEDMONT AVE, STE 100 45219 #018-03-1981 L1985 **D** *020 †15

BRENGLE, Douglas Crocker. 3805 EDWARDS RD 45209 #038-41-1981 L1990 **IM** *020 †20

BRESCIA, Aaron Isaac. ■ 45211 #038-43-2004 L2004 **OTO** *012

BREVARD, Theresa Anne. ■ 45240 #048-14-1976 L1979 **PD** *071

BREWER, Bradley Glenn. ■ 45230 #020-02-2007 L2007 *012

BREWER, Stephen Leslie. 2123 AUBURN AVE # 321 45219 #020-02-1980 L1988 **U OS** *020 †95

BRIDENBAUGH, Diann Hurd. 3223 ALBERT SABIN WAY, STE 1200 45267 #038-41-1990 L1991 **AN** *020

BRIDENBAUGH, Phillip Owen. 3223 ALBERT SABIN WAY, STE 1200 45267 #030-05-1960 L1977 **AN** *020 †05

BRIDGES, Kathleen F. ■ 45230 #038-41-2003 L2003 **IM** *100

BRIESCHKE, Martin Anthony. ■ 45211 #038-41-2005 L2005 **AN** *012

BRILAKIS, Harilaos S. 1945 CEI DR 45242 #418-01-1997 L2002 **IM** *020 †35 ‡

BRILLI, Richard John. 3333 BURNET AVE, DIVISION OF CRITICAL CARE 45229 #011-04-1976 L1977 **PD CCP** *020 †55

BRINKMAN, William Bernard. 391 OREGON ST 45202 #028-34-1999 L2003 **PD** *020 †55

BRISKER, Allan. ■ 45247 #038-41-1954 L1954 **FM IM** *071

BRITIGAN, Bradley Edward. 3130 HIGHLAND AVE, STE 0557 45219 #005-06-1980 L2004 **ID IM** *050 †20

BRITTO, Maria Teresa. 3333 BURNET AVE, DEPT ADOLESCENT MED 45229 #051-01-1987 L1995 **ADL MPD** *020 †20,55

BROADNAX, Stanley Eugene. 2139 AUBURN AVE 45219 #025-01-1974 L1977 **PHP IM** *075

BROADNAX, Walter Geo. 111 WELLINGTON PL, STE 64 45219 #051-07-1984 L1990 **NS** *020

BRODERICK, Joseph Paul. 2139 AUBURN AVE 45219 #038-41-1982 L1987 **N** *050 †75

BRODERICK, Thomas Michael. 2123 AUBURN AVE, STE 136 45219 #038-41-1983 L1989 **CD IM** *020 †20

BRODERICK, Timothy John. 231 ALBERT SABIN WAY, UNIVERSITY OF CINCINNATI M 45267 #038-41-1990 L2003 **GS** *020 †85

BRODY, Alan Saml. 3331 BURNET AVE, CHILDRENS HOSP X RAY DEPT 45229 #035-46-1980 L1986 **R PD** *020 †80,55

BRODY, Terri Lynn. 3200 VINE ST, VA HOSPITAL 45220 #038-41-1982 L1984 **IM** *020 †20

BRODZINSKI, Holly E. 3333 BURNET AVE, DIVISIO OF EMERGENCY MEDIC 45229 #036-05-2003 L2006 **PEM** *012 †55

BROKAW, Susan Ann. ■ 45243 #017-20-1980 L1988 **PTH** *020 †50

BROMLEY, Joel Jay. ■ 45208 #017-20-1981 L1988 **AN OS** *020 †20

BROMWICH, Matthew Alexand. 3333 BURNET AVE #065-05-2002 L2007 **PDO** *012

BROOK, Barry Allen. 4750 E GALBRAITH RD, STE 207 45236 #038-41-1983 L1986 **IM** *020 †20

BROOKS, Crystal Yvonne. ■ 45202 #036-04-2007 L2007 **PD** *012

BROOMALL, David Lee. 8245 NORTH CREEK DR, GROUP HEALTH ASS 45236 #020-02-1979 L1983 **D** *020 †55

BROSE, Edward Louis, III. 500 E BUSINESS WAY 45241 #038-45-1986 L1987 **AN** *020 †05

BROTT, Edwin T. 2208 SOUTH RD 45233 #048-13-1989 L1991 **AN** *020 †05

BROUN, Edward Randolph. 199 WILLIAM HOWARD TAFT RD, STE 101 45219 #028-34-1982 L1996 **HEM ON** *020 †20

BROWN, Alex James. 4777 E GALBRAITH RD 45236 #047-20-2005 L2006 **IM** *012

BROWN, Anthony Woodley. 10550 MONTGOMERY RD, STE 12 45242 #422-01-1995 L1997 **FM** *020 †18

BROWN, Clyde Dennis. 10945 REED HARTMN HWY #209 45242 #038-06-1979 L1979 **OTO OM** *020

BROWN, Courtney Marie. 2475 W GALBRAITH RD # A, QUEEN CITY PHYSICIANS, GRO 45239 #041-13-2005 L2005 **IM** *020

BROWN, Edward Richard. 5275 WINNESTE AVE 45232 #038-41-1962 L1962 **GP** *020

BROWN, Elizabeth Halcyon. 3006 PORTSMOUTH AVE 45208 #051-01-1980 L1981 **PD** *020 †55

BROWN, George E. 2139 AUBURN AVE, THE CHRIST HOSPITAL 45219 #026-04-1939 L1957 **IM CD** *071 †20

BROWN, Kelly Ann. ■ 45238 #038-41-2005 L2005 **FP** *012

BROWN, Mary Patrice. 3333 BURNET AVE, HOPSITAL ANESTHESIA 45229 #017-20-1982 L1991 **AN PD** *020 †55,05

BROWN, Nicole Marie. ■ 45242 #038-41-2006 L2006 **MPD** *012

BROWN, Thomas Andrew. 5819 CHEVIOT RD 45247 #038-41-1998 L2000 **RNR** *020 †80

BROWNE, James M, II. ■ 45223 #038-41-1992 L1997 **DR** *020 †80

BRUBAKER, Ronald. 311 STRAIGHT ST 45219 #319-03-1983 L1990 **PTH** *020 †50

BRUCE, Jeremy Edward. 4044 MCLEAN DR, MEDICINE SPECIALISTS LLC 45255 #038-41-2000 L2000 **HO** *020 †20 ‡

BRUEGGEMANN, Martin Wm. 2123 AUBURN AVE STE 242 45219 #038-41-1966 L1966 **PUD IM** *020 †20

BRUMFIELD, Jeffrey Thomas. 6353 GLENGARIFF DR 45230 #020-12-1996 L2004 **CD** *020 †20

BRUMM, Celia May Nelson. ■ 45208 #038-41-1941 **OS** *071

BRUNNER, Hermine Isabella. 3333 BURNET AVE, DIVISION OF RHEUMATOLOGY 45229 #409-16-1987 L2000 **PPR** *020 †55

BRUNO, Rodolfo Q. 2859 BOUDINOT AVE, STE 311 45238 #748-08-1963 L1970 **GS VS** *020

BRUNS, Bernard Bruce. 2475 W GALBRAITH RD 45239 #038-41-1959 L1959 **PD** *071 †55

BRUNS, Gregg Raymond. 1219 MORTS PASS 45215 #038-41-1988 L1990 **EM** *020 †16

BRUNS, James Robert. ■ 45208 #038-41-2004 L2005 **AN** *012

BRUNS, Janet Sue. 3200 VINE ST 45220 #038-41-1997 L2000 **PM** *020 †60

BRUNS, John David. 2475 W GALBRAITH RD, STE A 45239 #028-34-1998 L2002 **PD** *020 †55

BRUNSMAN, Tom Harry. ■ 45215 #038-41-1956 L1956 **OBG** *071 †30

BRUSH, Richard Walter. 130 WELLINGTON PL 45219 #038-40-1958 L1958 **P U** *020 †75

BRUSS, Jon Brian. ■ 45208 #034-01-1986 L1990 **ID PD** *020 †55

■ = Address Information Privacy Protected

BRY, Kristina Mirja. 3333 BURNET AVE, CHILDREN'S HOSPITAL MED CE 45229 #374-01-1983 L1999 **NPM** *020 †55

BRYAN, Yvon Jos. 3333 BURNET AVE, MLC 2001 45229 #048-14-1989 L1993 **AN** *020 †05 ‡

BRYANT, Sean Montgomery. 234 GOODMAN ST, STE 0769 45219 #038-45-1998 L1999 **EM** *020 †16

BUCKLEY, Donald Chas. 4030 SMITH RD, CARDIAC VASCULAR & 45209 #003-01-1982 L1984 **TS** *020 †90,85

BUCKLEY, William Roy, Jr. 7810 5 MILE RD 45230 #047-07-1989 L1992 **OBG** *020 †30

BUCUVALAS, John C. 3333 BURNET AVE, CHILDREN'S HOSP MED CTR 45229 #024-01-1978 L1982 **GE PD** *050 †55

BUCY, Emily Evelyn. 6 ALBERT PL 45227 #038-41-1993 L1997 **P** *020 †75

BUDDE, Leanne Sterbank. 199 WILLIAM HOWARD TAFT RD 45219 #038-41-1999 L1999 **HO** *020 †20

BUDDE, Richard B, Jr. 5819 CHEVIOT RD, THE CHRIST HOSPITAL 45247 #038-41-1984 L1989 **DR VIR** *020 †80

BUDDE, Richard Bernard. 506 OAK ST 45219 #028-34-1955 L1961 **NS** *071 †25

BUDDHDEV, Chandulal N. 9200 MONTGOMERY RD 45242 #495-22-1962 L1976 **IM IMG** *020 †20

BUDEV, Hari N. 8245 NORTHCREEK DR 45236 #495-22-1960 L1975 **GYN** *020 †30

BUDHANI, Irfan Bahadurali. 234 GOODMAN ST 45267 #704-25-2001 L2003 **IM** *100 †20

BUDKE, Kevin Thos. 9070 WINTON RD 45231 #038-45-1983 L1984 **IM** *020 †20

BUECHLER, Jonathan Wood. ■ 45208 #038-41-2008 *012

BUFFINGTON, Philip Jay. 7794 5 MILE RD, STE 200 45230 #038-41-1984 L1985 **U** *020 †95

BUI, Hai Xuan. 3200 VINE ST, VA MED CTR-DEPT PATH (113) 45220 #941-01-1978 L1992 **ATP PTH** *020 †50

BUJAK-AARON, Carol Ann. 375 DIXMYTH AVE, GOOD SAMARITAN HOSPITAL 45220 #665-01-2002 L2006 **AN** *020 †05

BUKA, Theodore E. 3200 BURNET AVE 45229 #038-41-1949 L1949 **OPH** *071 †35

BULAS, Robert Victor. 2139 AUBURN AVE, STE 102 45219 #038-40-1989 L1993 **DR** *020 †80

BULCAO, Christian Farr. UNIVERSITY HOSP, INC, DEPT SURG 45267 #067-01-2002 L2002 **GS** *012

BULLARD, Newton Hudson. 47 E HOLLISTER ST 45219 #038-41-1976 L1977 **IM** *020 †20

BURCH, Thomas Gregory. 2450 KIPLING AVE, STE 109 45239 #047-06-1981 L1986 **OPH N** *020 †35

BURCO, Katie Daily. ■ 45208 #040-02-2002 L2006 **PG** *012 †55

BURGER, Andrew J. 231 ALBERT SABIN WAY, ML0542 45267 #041-12-1978 L2007 **CD IM** *020 †20

BURGER, Mary R Fleet. 9942 FORESTGLEN DR 45242 #041-12-1978 L2007 **PD PHP** *050 †55

BURGER, Robert Richard. 6480 HARRISON AVE, SPORTS MEDICINE 45247 #038-41-1985 L1991 **ORS OSM** *020 †40

BURGESS, Elizabeth J. 10500 MONTGOMERY RD, DEPT OF ANESTHESIOLOGY 45242 #020-12-1990 L1991 **AN** *020 †05

BURKART, Collin Michael. ■ 45211 #038-41-2005 L2005 **OTO** *012

BURKE, Miles Jos. 10475 MONTGOMERY RD, STE 4F 45242 #003-01-1974 L1979 **PO OPH** *020 †35

BURKET, Robert L. ■ 45218 #038-41-1950 L1950 **OBG OS** *071 †30

BURKHARDT, Mary Carol. ■ 45236 #038-41-2007 L2007 **PD** *012

BURKHART, Bradd Gregory. ■ 45208 #023-01-2002 L2006 **ORS** *012

BURNS, Karen Cristly. 3333 BURNET AVE, MLC 7015 45229 #041-13-1999 L2005 **PHO** *100 †55

BURNS, Lisa Ann. ■ 45209 #016-43-2002 L2007 **PCC** *012 †55,20

BURROUGHS, Jefferson Mark. 2123 AUBURN AVE, STE 624 45219 #038-41-1984 L1990 **CD IM** *020 †20

BURROUGHS, Lee Francis. 663 ANDERSON FERRY RD, WEST SIDE PEDIATRICS INC 45238 #038-41-1969 L1969 **PD** *020 †55

BURROW, Thomas Andrew. 3333 BURNET AVE, MLC 4006 45229 #004-01-2003 L2003 **PMG** *012 †55

BURROWS, Christine Marie. 3130 HIGHLAND AVE, STE 0557 45219 #051-01-1996 L1997 **MPD** *020 †20,55

BURTON, Linda Lee. ■ 45243 #038-41-1966 L1966 **PTH** *020 †50

BURTON, Matthew Franklin. 2915 CLIFTON AVE, GROUP HEALTH ASSOCIATES 45220 #038-44-1981 L1983 **RHU IM** *020 †20

BURWINKEL, Alan Geo. 5636 BRIDGETOWN RD STE G 45248 #038-41-1978 L1980 **D** *020 †15

BUSACCO, Bradley. 7495 STATE RD STE 325, SEVEN HILLS WOMENS HLTH CT 45255 #011-03-1979 L1982 **GYN** *020 †30

BUSAM, Matthew Lee. 3301 WESTBOURNE DR 45248 #047-05-2001 L2007 **OSM** *100

BUSAM, Paul A. ■ 45231 #038-41-1953 L1953 **GP** *071

BUSTOS, Shila Shamim. 3333 BURNET AVE 45229 #025-07-2001 L2001 **PD** *020 †55

BUTLER, Andrew Shine. 231 ALBERT SABIN WAY, P O BOX 670769 45267 #028-02-2004 L2004 **EM** *012

BUTLER, Karyn Leigh. 231 ALBERT SABIN WAY, ML 0558 45267 #012-21-1986 L2004 **TRS CCS** *020 †85

BUTLER, Michael James. 7117 FOWLER AVE 45243 #038-40-1964 L1964 **OTO** *020 †45 ‡

BUTTERFIELD, Jennifer L. 4750 E GALBRAITH RD, STE 215 45236 #038-43-1996 L1998 **PS CS** *020 †65

BUTTERFIELD, Spencer L. 7663 5 MILE RD, STE 140 45230 #035-03-1973 L2005 **ORS** *020 †40

BYK, Dmitry. 1101 SUMMIT RD 45237 #422-01-2002 L2005 **P PFP** *020

BYRD, Angela Sherell. ■ 45208 #036-07-2005 L2005 **PD** *012

BYRNES, Abigail Beth. 231 ALBERT SABIN WAY 0, UNIV. OF CINCINNATI MED.CE 45267 #038-41-2002 L2002 **HO** *012 †20

CABANAS, Victor Yambing. 2446 KIPLING AVE 45239 #748-09-1966 L1974 **PTH** *075 †50

CAGIANNOS, Catherine. 231 ALBERT SABIN WAY #2567, DIVISION OF VASCULAR SURGE 45267 #065-06-1992 L2003 **VS** *100 †85

CAHILL, Tanya Erin. 3333 BURNET AVE, CINCINNATI CHILDREN'S HOSP 45229 #038-41-2000 L2000 **NPM** *100 †55

CAILLAT, Alexandre Willia. ■ 45242 #038-45-2005 L2005 **GS** *100

CAIRNS, Bryan Mitchell. PS231 ALBERT, CO DEPARTMENT OF 45267 #038-40-2006 L2006 **FPP** *012

CA JACOB, Daniel Emerson. 2915 CLIFTON AVE, GROUP HEALTH ASSOCIATES 45220 #038-41-1981 L1986 **OTO HNS** *020 †45

CALDEMEYER, Robt Durward. 24 COMPTON RD, STE 205 45216 #051-04-1982 L1985 **FM** *020 †18

CALDWELL, Esly Saml. 2230 AUBURN AVE 45219 #010-03-1964 L1978 **IM HEM** *020 †20,18

CALFEE, Archna. 3333 BURNET AVE, CINCINNATI CHILDRENS HOSP 45229 #028-02-2001 L2006 **PD** *020 †55

CALIGARIS, Joseph Thayer. 9403 KENWOOD RD, STE A130 45242 #024-05-1983 L1984 **OBG** *020 †30

CALLARD, Geo Melancthon. 2139 AUBURN AVE 45219 #023-07-1960 L1972 **TS CD** *062 †85,90

CALLIRGOS, Marco Antonio. 375 DIXMYTH AVE, GOOD SAMARITAN HOSPITAL 45220 #737-01-1993 L2000 **IM** *020 †20

CALVERT, Geoffrey Mc Call. 234 GOODMAN ST 45267 #038-45-1983 L1987 **IM OM** *050 †20,70

CALVO GARCIA, Maria Azuce. 3333 BURNET AVE, CINN CHILDRENS HOSP MED CE 45229 #847-13-1989 L2002 **PDR** *020 †80

CALVO SAINZ, Ignacio Feli. ■ 45219 #176-01-1999 L2005 **IM** *012

CAMINITI, Deanna Dorothy. 6480 HARRISON AVE, STE 300 45247 #038-41-2002 L2002 **OBG** *020 †30

CAMPBELL, Grady Benton. 2727 MADISON RD STE 208 45209 #012-05-1972 L1974 **PUD IM** *020 †20

CAMPBELL, John William. ■ 45243 #024-05-2003 L2003 **EM** *100

CAMPBELL, Kathleen Marie. 3333 BURNET AVE 45229 #047-06-1997 L1999 **PG** *020 †55

CAMPBELL, Pamela Ann. 3333 BURNET AVE 45229 #028-34-1985 L2000 **CHP** *020 †75

CAMPINHA-BACOTE, Dexter L. 205 W 4TH ST, STE 1000 45202 #043-01-1982 L1988 **FM** *030 †18

CAMPION, Eric Michael. ■ 45220 #025-01-2006 L2006 **GS** *012

CAMUS, Florence. 234 GOODMAN ST 45267 #396-12-1984 **END** *020

CANADA, Nettie Mae. 3200 VINE ST 45220 #038-41-1981 L1981 **IM** *020 †20

CANCELAS PEREZ, Jose Anto. 3130 HIGHLAND AVE, HOXWORTH BLOOD CENTER 45267 #847-13-1990 L2002 *100

CANERIS, Onassis Anthony. 10550 MONTGOMERY RD, STE 33 45242 #038-41-1989 L2004 **N** *020 †75

CANESTRI, Felix Raul. ■ 45242 #132-03-1965 L1977 **GS VS** *071 †85

CANOS, Eleanor Jalipa. 234 GOODMAN ST, STE 0531 45219 #748-02-1971 L1978 **AN** *050 †05

CANOS, Hilda Jalipa. 4966 GLENWAY AVE STE 104 45238 #748-02-1972 L1981 **IM NEP** *020

CANOS, Michael Richard. 6708 VERDE RIDGE DR 45247 #010-01-2003 L2003 **END** *012 †20

CANTOR, Lauren Elizabeth. ■ 45209 #025-01-2007 L2007 **PD** *012

CANTOR, Lisa Marie. 1207 SPRINGFIELD PIKE 45215 #038-41-1995 **FM** *020 †75,18

CANTOR, Robert Michael. 234 GOODMAN ST, STE 0054 45219 #561-16-1977 L1986 **DR** *020 †80

CANTRELL, Varon Edward. ■ 45231 #017-20-2005 L2005 **MPD** *012

CAPLES, Pete Ledley. 608 READING RD, STE B 45202 #051-01-1971 L1976 **CD IM** *020 †20

CAPURRO, Nico. 4044 MCLEAN DR 45255 #561-10-1954 L1959 **GS** *071

CAPUTO, Mark Edward. 8638 OLD STONE CT 45249 #038-40-1989 L2000 **EM** *020 †16

CARBONARO, Damiano Santo. ■ 45230 #016-42-2004 L2004 **EM** *012

CARDEN, Wade Douglas. 2016 EDGECLIFF PT 45206 #008-01-1968 L1970 **AN** *020 †05

CARDI, Michael Anthony. 2123 AUBURN AVE STE 404 45219 #024-01-1977 L1984 **NEP** *020 †20

CARDONE, C Chris. 3789 COUNTRY CLUB PL 45208 #038-41-1988 L1990 **AN IM** *020 †05

CARDONE, John Scott. 2859 BOUDINOT AVE, STE 307 45238 #038-41-1988 L1989 **D** *020 †15

CARDONE, Mary Theresa. 6045 BRIDGETOWN RD 45248 #038-41-1988 L1989 **IM** *020 †20

CARDOSI, John F. 3806 EASTERN AVE, G MCAULEY HEALTH CTR 45226 #038-41-1953 L1953 **FM** *020 †18

CARDOSI, Michael Peter. 500 E BUSINESS WAY 45241 #020-12-1997 L2000 **AN** *020 †05

CARE, Marguerite Mary. 3333 BURNET AVE, DEPARTMENT OF RADIOLOGY 45229 #030-06-1993 L1998 **PDR** *020 †80

CAREY, James Peele. 10577 MONTGOMERY RD 45242 #055-01-1979 L1984 **PS GS** *020 †85,65

CARINGI, Vincent Francesc. ■ 45220 #038-41-2007 L2007 **P** *012

CARLETON, Steven Craig. 231 ALBERT SABIN WAY, UNIVERSITY HOSPITAL 45267 #038-41-1987 L1989 **EM** *020 †16

CARLSON, Marilyn Ruth. 3724 MONETS LN 45241 #038-06-1988 L1990 **IM** *020 †20

CARNEY, William Paul. 3001 HIGHLAND AVE, STE E 45219 #016-06-1966 L1969 **P** *020 †75

CAROTHERS, Chas Olmsted. 250 WM H TAFT RD, STE 210 45219 #024-01-1946 L1954 **ORS** *071 †40

CAROTHERS, Gary Gordon. 8044 MONTGOMERY RD STE 155 45236 #038-41-1965 L1965 **OPH** *071 †35 ‡

CAROTHERS, Thomas Abbott. 2100 SHERMAN AVE, STE 105 45212 #038-41-1972 L1978 **ORS LM** *020 †40

CARPENTER, Craig. 231 ALBERT SABIN WAY, ML#0559 45267 #038-41-2001 L2001 **CHP** *020

CARPENTER, M Lavenia B. 231 ALBERT SABIN WAY, DEPARTMENT OF OB/GYN 45267 #047-06-1992 L1996 **OBG** *020 †30

CARR, Douglas Edward. 231 ALBERT SABIN WAY, ML 0558 45267 #017-20-1987 L1998 **CCS** *100 †85

CARR, Stanley Harrison. 2450 KIPLING AVE, STE 201 45239 #038-40-1986 L1994 **OBG** *020 †30

CARR, Tara Belur. ■ 45241 #495-09-1978 L1985 **P** *020 †75

CARRAN, Todd Stephen. 3306 RUTHER AVE, UNIV FAMILY MEDICINE CENTE 45220 #020-12-1991 L1996 **FM** *020 †18

CARRIER, Laurie Anne. 2123 AUBURN AVE, UC FAMILY MEDICINE RESID 45219 #539-03-2004 L2004 **FPP** *012

CARRIGAN, Terrence James. 6350 GLENWAY AVE 45211 #038-41-1972 L1972 **IM** *020 †20

CARROLL, Mark Geoffry. ■ 45230 #038-41-1956 L1956 **GS OS** *020 †85

CARRUTHERS, Donald Peter. 2915 CLIFTON AVE 45220 #305-01-1998 L2000 **PM** *020 †60

CARSON, J Turner. 9686 CINCINNATI COLUMBS RD 45241 #038-41-1978 L1979 **IM NTR** *020

CARSON, Shawn Michael. 2139 AUBURN AVE 45219 #038-43-2002 L2006 **AN** *100

CARSON, Steven Corliss. 3155 GLENDALE MILFORD RD, CINCINNATI EVENDALE SURG 45241 #016-42-1976 L1977 **AN** *020 †16,05

CARTER, Todd E. ■ 45208 #048-15-1991 L1993 **CCA** *020 †05

CASE, Brian Warren. ■ 45267 #005-12-2000 L2000 **GPM** *020 †70

CASILE, Eligio Osea, Jr. ■ 45239 #748-08-1959 L1980 **AN** *072

CASPER, Joseph M. 10500 MONTGOMERY RD 45242 #038-41-1950 L1950 **AN** *071 †05

CASPER, Keith Andrew. ■ 45208 #038-41-2003 L2003 **OTO** *012

CASPER, Michelle Lynn. ■ 45208 #038-41-2003 L2003 **RO** *012

CASSADY, Harold A. 3006 PORTSMOUTH AVE 45208 #038-41-1941 **PD OS** *071 †55

CASSIDY-VU, Lisa Anne. 1207 SPRINGFIELD PIKE 45215 #038-41-2002 L2006 **FM** *020 †18

CASTILLA, Elias Augusto. 10500 MONTGOMERY RD, DEPT PATH 45242 #264-09-1995 L2000 **PTH** *020 †50

CASTILLO, Heidi Adele. 3333 BURNET AVE, MLC 4002 45229 #049-01-2001 L2002 **DBP** *012 †55

CASTILLO, Jonathan. ■ 45213 #049-01-2001 L2002 **PD** *100 †55

CASTRO, Dalys Eneida. 3100 VINE ST, CINCIINNATI, VA MEDICAL CE 45219 #715-01-1993 L2003 **RNR** *100 †80

CAVALIERI, Anthony John. ■ 45267 #025-07-2006 L2006 **P** *012

CAVALLO, Anita. 3333 BURNET AVE, CHILDREN'S HOSP MED CTR 45229 #187-04-1964 L1973 **PD** *020 †55

■ = Address Information Privacy Protected

CAVALLO, Tito. 234 GOODMAN ST, UNIVERSITY HOSPITAL 45267 #187-04-1963 L1992 PTH *071 †50

CELMER, Meagan Ohaire. ■ 45208 #038-41-2008 *012

CEPELA, Mark Allen. 2859 BOUDINOT AVE, STE 308 45238 #025-01-1984 L1991 OPH *020 †35

CERIMELE, Joseph Michael. ■ 45208 #038-41-2008 *012

CERULLO, Michael A. 231 ALBERT SABIN WAY, ML 0559 45267 #028-34-2000 L2005 P *020

CETINKAYA, Altug. 231 A;BERT WAY, DEPT OF OPHTHALMOLOGY 45267 #902-05-1998 L2006 *100

CHA, Peter Shin. 500 E BUSINESS WAY, STE A 45241 #038-41-1998 L1999 ORS *020 †40

CHAALALA, Chiraz. NE231 ALBERT, CO DEPARTMENT OF 45267 #067-06-1996 L2004 *100

CHADEHUMBE, Madeline Ange. 3333 BURNET AVE, HOSP MED 45229 #775-01-2000 L2004 CHN *020 †55

CHADWELL, Christopher Lee. 2139 AUBURN AVE, DEPT 1104 45219 #038-41-1998 L1999 IM *020 †20

CHAILLET, James Robt, Jr. 2915 CLIFTON AVE 45220 #023-01-1975 L2002 FM *020 †18

CHAMBERS, Albert Alan. 234 GOODMAN ST, STE 0054 45219 #038-41-1964 L1964 R RNR *020 †80

CHAMBERS, Patricia Lea. 3333 BURNET AVE, ML C5021 45229 #041-13-2001 L2004 PEM *100 †55

CHAN, Christine Margaret. 3333 BURNET AVE 2008, CINCINNATI CHILDREN'S HOSP 45229 #047-05-2004 L2004 PD *100 †55

CHAN, Kerwin. ■ 45227 #016-42-2007 L2007 IM *012

CHAN, Roy Kinwai. ■ 45240 #020-12-2008 *012

CHANDLER, Paul Tivis. 9393 FIELDS ERTEL RD 45249 #012-05-1968 L1976 IM DIA *020 †20

CHANDRA, Saurabh. EDUCATION DEPARTME, CO MEDICAL 45219 #495-67-1992 L2006 *100

CHANDRAKANTAN, Arvind. 3333 BURNET AVE, HOSP MED 45229 #496-23-2000 L2007 PAN *012

CHANG, Chunghun George. ■ 45220 #035-09-2000 L2005 PTH *012

CHANG, Edward Yangru. 5535 MONTGOMERY RD 45212 #038-41-1996 L1997 IM *020 †20

CHANG, Wantsu. ■ 45267 #041-14-2007 L2007 EM *012

CHANG, William. 375 DIXMYTH AVE, GOOD SAMARITAN HOSP 45220 #026-04-1966 L1975 DR PD *071 †55,80

CHANIN, Matthew P. 7309 OSCEOLA DR 45243 #048-13-2001 L2006 DR *020 †80

CHANNAN, Gitanjli. 3805 EDWARDS RD, STE 300 45209 #060-01-1993 L1996 FM *020 †18

CHANTILAS, Lydia Duarte. 2139 AUBURN AVE, ANESTHESIA ASSOC OF CINCIN 45219 #847-03-1988 L1995 AN PAN *020 †05

CHARI, Sunita Vedantum. 231 BETHESDA AVE, P O BOX 670585 45267 #038-40-1990 L1993 NEP *020 †20

CHARLES, Richard Henry. 3200 BURNET AVE 45229 #038-41-1961 L1961 IM CD *075

CHARVAT, Kathleen Ann. 3333 BURNET AVE, CIN CTR FOR DEVELOP DISORD 45229 #038-41-1985 L1988 OS PD *020 †55

CHASE, Dustin Andrew. ■ 45267 #038-41-2005 L2005 IM *012

CHASE, Margaret Ann. 3333 BURNET AVE 45229 #051-07-2000 L2000 CCP *100

CHATMAN, Robyn Fortner. 10498 MONTGOMERY RD, STE H 45242 #038-43-1994 L1997 FM *020 †18

CHAUHAN, Gagneet. ■ 45241 #495-29-1998 L2002 END *100 †20

CHAUHAN, Shailendra S. 231 ALBERT SABIN WAY, MC 0595 45267 #038-41-1998 L2001 GE *040 †20

CHAVEZ, Jose Luis. 3380 ERIE AVE, STE 100 45208 #649-01-1972 L1979 OM EM *062 †16

CHEEMA, Faisal Nawaz. 4777 E GALBRAITH RD 45236 #704-02-2001 L2003 IM *020 †20

CHEKAN, Lisa Bourque. 4215 SMITH RD 45209 #010-01-1997 L2000 PD *020 †55

CHEN, Jim Yunfei. ■ 45231 #038-41-2006 L2006 AN *012

CHEN, Yee-Wen Kacy. 2001 ANDERSON FERRY RD, GROUP HEALTH ASSOCIATES 45238 #035-06-1991 L1994 PD *020 †55

CHENG, Carlos Kenneth. 234 GOODMAN ST, STE 0559 45219 #038-41-1998 L2000 P *020 †75

CHENG, Hsin-Chuan. ■ 45243 #385-04-1966 L1975 GS *020

CHERNAUSEK, Steven Dwight. 3300 ELLAND AVE # END, CHILDRENS HOSPITAL 45229 #026-04-1976 L1982 PDE PD *050 †55

CHERNESKY, Marianne Kenck. 5 E LIBERTY ST, CROSSROAD HEALTH CENTER 45202 #048-12-2003 L2006 FM *020 †18

CHETTY, Bhakta Viziam. UC COLLEGE OF MEDICINE, DEPT OF DERMATOLOGY 45267 #495-11-1950 D *040

CHEWNING, John Barkley. ■ 45243 #041-01-1946 L1949 OS *071

CHHABRA, Manpreet Singh. 3333 BURNET AVE, DEPT OF MED EDUCATION 45229 #495-36-2001 L2006 IM *012

CHICCHON, Douglas E. 308 READING RD, FL 1B 45202 #737-01-1966 L1973 GS *020 †85

CHIDIPOTHU, Chitra. ■ 45243 #495-62-1999 L2006 IM *100 †20

CHIMA, Ranjit Singh. 3333 BURNET AVE 45229 #495-01-1996 L2002 CCP *100 †55

CHIN, Cindy Nengchi. ■ 45209 #047-05-2006 L2006 PD *012

CHINI, Barbara Ann. 3333 BURNET AVE, DEPT OF PULMONOLOGY CHMC 45229 #047-05-1990 L1994 PDP *020 †55

CHIRLIN, Paul Jerome. 11360 SPRINGFIELD PIKE 45246 #035-06-1977 L1981 PD *020 †55

CHO, Gerald Jeungil. ■ 45219 #038-41-2008 *012

CHOE, Kyuran Ann. 234 GOODMAN ST, STE 0054 45219 #024-16-1987 L1994 DR NR *020 †80

CHOI, Carol Minkyung. 222 PIEDMONT AVE, STE 5100 45219 #038-41-1994 L1995 OBG *020 †30

CHOICE, Sean Karl. 222 PIEDMONT AVE, MEDICAL ARTS BLDG 45219 #038-43-1994 L1995 DR *020 †80

CHOKSHI, Manish Mahendra. 4631 RIDGE AVE 45209 #038-06-1994 L2004 GE *020 †20

CHONG, Zhang. 2368 VICTORY PKWY, STE 501 45206 #243-46-1983 L2000 AN *020 †05

CHOO, Daniel Insung. 3333 BURNET AVE, DEPT OTOLARY 45229 #035-15-1989 L1998 OTO *020 †45

CHOQUETTE, Monique Lauren. 3333 BURNET AVE, CHILDRENS HOSP MED CTR 45229 #024-05-2006 L2006 PD *012

CHOUDHRI, Tina. ■ 45219 #038-41-2008 *012

CHOUDHURY, Sambhu Nath. 375 DIXMYTH AVE 45220 #041-02-1992 L1998 OP ORS *020 †40

CHOUTKA, Ondrej. 2139 AUBURN AVE 45219 #917-09-2002 L2004 NS *012

CHRIST, Matthew Harold. ■ 45238 #038-41-2008 *012

CHRISTIAN, Karen Kay. 3001 HIGHLAND AVE 45219 #026-04-1979 L1993 CHP *020 †75

CHRISTIE, Celia D C. 3300 ELLAND AVE, CHILDRENS HOSPITAL 45229 #566-01-1979 L1990 PD ID *020 †55

CHRISTOPHER, Brenda J. ■ 45219 #047-20-2005 L2005 IM *012

CHRONIS, Alex John. 2139 AUBURN AVE, STE 102 45219 #047-06-1975 L1988 DR *020 †80

CHUA, Michael Stephen. 3333 BURNET AVE, CINCINNATI CHILDREN'S HOSP 45229 #020-02-1999 L1999 PD *020 †55

CHUANG, Ryan. ■ 45223 #024-01-2004 L2004 EM *012

CHUGHTAI, Saba Atiq. 222 PIEDMONT AVE, STE 8 45219 #704-21-1988 L2003 P *020 †75

CHUN, Andrew Byungsuk. 8245 NORTHCREEK DR 45236 #041-02-1991 L1999 GE IM *020 †20

CHUN, Galen Foohock. 375 DIXMYTH AVE, DEPT OF RADIOLOGY 45220 #028-34-1993 L1998 DR *020 †80

CHUN, Sooyun. 2925 VERNON PL, STE 100 45219 #035-20-2001 L2004 GE *020

CHUNDURI, Jaideep. 6480 HARRISON AVE, SPORTS MEDICINE 45247 #038-44-1997 L2003 OSS ORS *020 †40

CHUNG, Eugene Sejin. 2454 KIPLING AVE, STE G20 45239 #024-16-1990 L2000 CD IM *020 †20

CHUNG, Pei Chang. ■ 45208 #028-46-2004 L2004 GS *012

CHUNG, Sora. ■ 45206 #043-01-2007 L2007 EM *012

CHUNG, Yunjo. 5889 COLERAIN AVE 45239 #583-03-1963 L1971 OBG *020 †30

CIANCIOLO, Eli Robert. ■ 45209 #038-41-2004 L2004 AN *012

CIANCIOLO, Frank Wm. ■ 45243 #038-41-1960 L1960 FM OM *071 †18

CILINGIROGLU, Mehmet. ■ 45219 #902-05-1993 L2008 IC *020 †20

CIONNI, Anthony Steven. 375 DIXMYTH AVE, STE 64 45203 #038-41-1982 L1985 AN *020 †05

CIONNI, Joseph Dominic. 3300 ELLAND AVE, CHILDRENS HOSPITAL 45229 #041-02-1957 L1960 PD *020 †20

CIONNI, Robert Jos. 1945 CEI DR 45242 #038-41-1985 L1989 OPH OS *020 †35

CIRASOLE, Donna Marie. 2123 AUBURN AVE, STE 724 45219 #035-47-1990 L2003 OBG *072 †30

CIRULLI, Christopher. 4700 SMITH RD 45212 #020-12-1982 L1984 U GS *020 †95

CLABO, Kathryn Michelle. ■ 45227 #047-05-2007 L2007 PD *012

CLAES, Donna Jean. ■ 45230 #028-03-2004 L2004 PD *100 †55

CLARK, Elizabeth Ann. 3219 CLIFTON AVE, STE 125 45220 #038-41-1982 L1984 OBG *020 †30

CLARK, Keith T. 400 BROADWAY ST 45202 #020-12-1981 L1989 OS EM *030 †16

CLAYBON, Louis Edward. 7520 STATE RD 45255 #016-06-1976 L1980 AN CCM *020 †05

CLAYDON, Charles Robert. 4130 DRY RIDGE RD 45252 #038-41-1998 L1999 FM *020 †18

CLEMENT, Jeannine Denise. 10050 MONTGOMERY RD, # 290 45242 #038-41-1985 L1986 OM IM *062 †70

CLEVES, G Stephen. 2753 ERIE AVE, 1ST FL 45208 #038-41-1988 L1990 IM *020 †20

CLYNE, David Hyett. 2123 AUBURN AVE STE 434 45219 #143-02-1963 L2004 NEP IM *020 †20

CNOTA, James Frank, II. 3333 BURNET AVE, THE HEART CTR CINTI CHILDS 45229 #021-01-1995 L2000 PDC PD *020 †55

COBB, Janet White. 2702 E KEMPER RD 45241 #020-12-1990 L1991 IM *020 †20

COBERLY, Leann. 231 ALBERT SABIN WAY, UNIV OF CIN COLLEGE OF MED 45267 #038-41-1989 L1992 IM *020 †20

COCHRAN, Kevin Joseph. 2123 AUBURN AVE, STE 624 45219 #016-11-1994 L2006 IC CD *020 †20

CODISPOTI, Christopher D. ■ 45208 #038-41-2003 L2006 AI *012 †20

CODY, Matthew Robert. ■ 45249 #038-44-2006 L2007 IM *012

CODY, Robert L. 10506 MONTGOMERY RD 45242 #020-02-1980 L1991 IM HO *020 †20

COHEN, John S. 1945 CEI DR 45242 #020-02-1968 L1971 OPH OS *020 †35

COHEN, Loren Hillel. 4600 WESLEY AVE STE B 45212 #018-03-1969 L1980 NEP IM *020 †20

COHEN, Mitchell Bruce. 3333 BURNET AVE, CIN CHILD HOSP MED CTR 45229 #035-47-1977 L1982 GE PD *050 †55

COHEN, Paul Lawrence. 506 OAK ST 45219 #023-07-1996 L1997 NS *020 †25

COHEN, Robert M. 3125 EDEN AVE RM 1331, THE VONTZ CENTER 45267 #035-45-1978 L1984 END DIA *050 †20

COHEN, Sidney. 259 HILLTOP LN 45215 #038-41-1957 L1957 CD IM *020 †20

COHEN, William. 234 GOODMAN ST 45230 #038-40-1955 L1955 D *020 †15

COITH, Robert Lahuis, Jr. 10525 MONTGOMERY RD 45242 #038-41-1977 L1979 CD *020 †20

COLBERT, Robert Allen. 3333 BURNET AVE, DIV OF RHEUMATOLOGY, ML401 45229 #035-45-1987 L1992 PD RHU *020 †55

COLDIRON, Brett Malcolm. 3024 BURNET AVE 45219 #020-12-1982 L1983 D *020 †20,15

COLE, James Walton. 2060 READING RD, STE 170 45202 #007-02-1990 L1996 RNR *020 †80

COLEMAN, Kristi Marie. ■ 45206 #038-41-2008 *012

COLEMAN, Rachael Annette. 8146 HAMILTON AVE 45231 #038-43-1998 L1999 MPD *020 †20 ‡

COLLAR, Ryan Mitchell. ■ 45255 #038-41-2006 L2006 OTO *012

COLLINS, Charles Wm. 311 ALBERT SABIN WAY 45229 #038-43-1985 L1988 CHP P *020 †75

COLLINS, Craig Hays. 3155 GLENDALE MILFORD RD, CINCINNATI EVENDALE SURG 45241 #020-02-1979 L1982 AN *020 †05

COLLINS, Dana Maureen. ■ 45267 #016-06-2004 L2004 PM *012

COLLINS, Douglas Paul. 2446 KIPLING AVE, UCMERCY-FRAN MT AIRY HOSPF 45239 #038-45-1998 L2000 FM *020 †18

COLLINS, Francis Martin. 463 OHIO PIKE, STE 300 45255 #016-02-1975 L1978 IM END *020 †20

COLLINS, Jacqueline. 231 BETHESDA AVE 0559, DEPT OF PSYCHIATRY 45267 #038-43-1986 L1987 P PD *020 †75

COLLINS, James Jacob. 3333 BURNET AVE 5018, CHILDREN'S HOSPITAL 45229 #038-41-2004 L2004 PD *100

COLLINS, John Mark. 3155 GLENDALE MILFORD RD, CINCINNATI EVENDALE SURG 45241 #038-41-1978 L1984 AN IM *020 †20,05

COLLINS, Kimberly Kay. 3333 BURNET AVE, DIV OF EMERG MED 45229 #056-05-1997 L1999 PD *020 †55

COLLINS, Margaret Helen. 3333 BURNET AVE, MLC 1010 B 4.180 45229 #010-02-1977 L1999 ATP PP *020 †50 ‡

COLLINS, Robert Henry. 2700 ASHLAND AVE 45206 #038-41-1976 L1982 GS VS *020 †85

COLLINS, Sean Patrick. 234 GOODMAN ST, STE 0769 45219 #056-05-1997 L1998 EM *020 †16

COLLISON, Edgar King. 375 DIXMYTH AVE, GOOD SAMARITAN HOSPITAL 45220 #539-06-2004 L2004 GS *012

COLMAN, Pamela Jane Brown. ■ 45208 #065-01-1978 L1988 *020

COLOMBEL, George Irvine. 130 WELLINGTON PL 45219 #016-06-1962 L1968 P CHP *020 †75

COLON, Vicente Franklin. 10500 MONTGOMERY RD 45242 #030-05-1963 L1977 FM *071 †18

COLOSIMO, Angelo Joseph. 311 STRAIGHT ST 45219 #035-19-1984 L1991 ORS OSM *020 †40

COLUMBUS, Karen Schatz. 375 DIXMYTH AVE, DONNA STAHL MD INC 45220 #035-46-1985 L1990 GS *020 †85

COLUMBUS, Michael Joseph. 4850 RED BANK RD, FL 2 45227 #041-02-1985 L1992 PS *020 †85,65

COMPAAN, Pearl Joan. ■ 45220 #025-01-1964 L1970 RO ON *071 †80

CONDO, Sarah Lynn. 375 DIXMYTH AVE, TRI-HEALTH MED CTR 45220 #011-75-2006, ▲ L2006 OBG *012

CONDORODIS, Constandinos. ■ 45243 #038-41-1960 L1960 GYN *071 †30

CONKEL, Steven Edward. 4777 E GALBRAITH RD 45236 #422-01-2002 L2002 GS *020 †85

CONNELLY, Beverly L. 3333 BURNET AVE, CINCI CHILDRENS MLC 5019 45229 #012-01-1979 L1982 ID PD *040 †55

CONRAD, Paul J, Jr. 3825 GLENWAY AVE 45205 #038-41-1951 L1951 **GP** *071

CONSTANTINOU, Panayiota N. ■ 45208 #418-01-1988 L1993 **PD ID** *020 †55

CONYERS, Emmett. ■ 45213 #047-07-1959 L1962 **IM CD** *071

COOK, Hillary Ann. ■ 45216 #038-41-2007 L2007 **PD** *012

COOK, Mica Watts. ■ 45206 #048-04-2005 L2005 **AN** *012

COOK, Patricia Evon. 8000 5 MILE RD 45230 #036-05-1978 L1979 **FM** *020 †18

COOK, Thomas Kevin. ■ 45267 #048-02-2005 L2005 **PS** *012

COOK, William Haymond. 4030 SMITH RD, CARDIAC VASCULAR & 45209 #036-05-1995 L2002 **TS** *020 †85,90

COOLEY, Steven Chas. 5680 BRIDGETOWN RD, ALLIANCE PRIMARY CARE 45248 #051-04-1991 L1996 **IM** *020 †20

COOPER, Emmett Geo. 125 WM HOWARD TAFT RD 45219 #010-03-1972 L1976 **P** *020 †75

COOPER, Matthew Lawrence. ■ 45212 #038-41-2007 L2007 **TY** *012

COORS, Raymond B, Jr. 6040 HARRISON AVE 45248 #038-41-1976 L1977 **OTO HNS** *020 †45

COPELAND, Kristen Adele. 3333 BURNET AVE, MLC 7035 45229 #001-02-1999 L1999 **PD EM** *020 †55

COPPAGE, Kristen Hummel. 375 DIXMYTH AVE, GOOD SAMARITAN HOSP 45220 #020-12-1998 L1999 **MFM OBG** *020

CORATHERS, Sarah Dawn. 234 GOODMAN ST, DEPT. OF INTERNAL MEDICINE 45219 #038-45-2002 L2002 **END** *012 †55,20

CORCEGA, Jose Arocena. ■ 45240 #748-01-1955 **P** *020

CORCORAN, Helen Lucille. 7500 STATE RD 45255 #039-01-1980 L1981 **DR GP** *020 †80

CORDELL, Alan Spencer. 2450 KIPLING AVE, STE 101 45239 #020-02-1973 L1975 **U** *020 †95

CORGAN, Robert Leo. 234 GOODMAN ST 45267 #020-12-1983 L1985 **EM** *020 †18

CORNELIUS, Rebecca Sue. 234 GOODMAN ST, UNIV OF CINTI DEPT OF RADI 45267 #038-40-1985 L1990 **RNR R** *020 †18

CORNISH-VERMAIRE, Deborah. 3333 BURNET AVE, DEPT OF ANESTHESIA 45229 #020-02-1990 L2006 **AN PAN** *020 †05

CORNWELL, James Robt, Jr. 5819 CHEVIOT RD 45247 #038-41-1983 L1989 **DR** *020 †80

CORSER, Bruce Clayton. 4460 RED BANK RD, STE 210 45227 #035-15-1980 L1981 **IM PUD** *020 †20

CORTEZ, Armando Abel. 2450 KIPLING AVE, STE G9 45239 #566-01-1971 L1978 **OBG EM** *071 †30

CORWIN, James Gerard. 2752 ERIE AVE STE 5 45208 #028-03-1989 L1990 **IM** *020 †20

CORWIN, Jeanne Marie. 10475 READING RD STE 307 45241 #038-41-1991 L1993 **OBG** *020 †30

COSTA MORON, Adalgiza Ele. 375 DIXMYTH AVE 45220 #264-12-1995 L2007 **IM** *012

COSTANDI, Youssef Tewfik. 6350 GLENWAY AVE, STE 201 45211 #330-04-1955 L1973 **U** *020 †95

COSTANTINI, Carey Henry. 7520 STATE RD 45255 #038-40-1981 L1981 **AN** *020 †05

COSTANTINI, Joseph. ■ 45236 #561-17-1946 L1955 **AN IM** *071

COSTEA, Alexandru Lonel. 3200 VINE ST, STE 111D 45220 #781-01-1997 L2006 **ICE** *020 †05

COTTINGHAM, Elizabeth M. 222 PIEDMONT AVE, STE 8 45219 #020-02-1991 L1997 **CHP** *020 †75

COTTONGIM, Toni Leslie. 2859 BOUDINOT AVE, STE 107 45238 #020-02-1994 L1997 **FM** *020 †18

COX, Joseph Allen. ■ 45243 #038-41-1962 L1964 **PDS OS** *020 †85

COX, Justin Andrew. UNIV OF CINCINNATI MED CTR, DIV OF UROLOGY 45267 #020-02-2007 L2007 **U** *012

COX, William Randall. 10550 MONTGOMERY RD, STE 12 45242 #038-40-1993 L1994 **FM** *020 †18 ‡

COYNE, James Timothy, Jr. 7857 MARTIN ST 45231 #038-43-1997 L2000 **AN** *020 †05 ‡

CRACE, Phillip Parker. ■ 45224 #020-12-2003 L2003 **GS** *012

CRAFTON, William Boyd. 2123 AUBURN AVE, STE 242 45219 #051-04-1982 L1987 **GS TS** *020 †85

CRAIG, Arthur Jay. 3805 EDWARDS RD, STE 300 45209 #025-07-1990 L1993 **HO** *020 †20

CRAIG, Diane Bills. 1232 W KEMPER RD # 241 45240 #038-45-1983 L1995 **IM PD** *020 †20,55

CRAIG, Jeffrey Lee. 3805 EDWARDS RD 45209 #020-02-1991 L1992 **IM** *020 †20

CRANE, Rebecca Lynn. ■ 45229 #016-11-1999 L2009 **PD** *020

CRANLEY, James Peter. 5049 CROOKSHANK RD, STE 202 45238 #038-41-1980 L1981 **GE IM** *020 †20

CRANLEY, Robert David. 3747 W FORK RD 45247 #038-41-1982 L1984 **VS GS** *020 †85

CRAVEN, Jeffrey Alan. 311 STRAIGHT ST, EMERGENCY DEPARTMENT 45219 #038-41-1976 L1977 **IM** *020 †20,16

CRAWFORD, Alvin Howell. 3333 BURNET AVE, BLD C3 / ML 2017 45229 #047-06-1964 L1978 **ORS PD** *020 †40

CREMER-NICOLI, Guillermo. 2446 KIPLING AVE 45239 #737-01-1963 L1991 **IM END** *020 †20

CREW, Carl Leon, Jr. 124 E MCMILLAN ST 45219 #038-41-1972 L1972 **P** *020 †75 ‡

CRIMMINS, Nancy Abigail. 3333 BURNET AVE, ENDOCRINOLOGY MLC 7012 45229 #017-20-2000 L2000 **PDE** *100 †55

CRIPE, Timothy Peter. 3333 BURNET AVE, HEMATOLOGY/ONCOLOGY 45229 #018-03-1989 L1999 **PD** *020 †20

CRISALLI, Joseph Adrian. 3333 BURNET AVE 45229 #012-05-2002 L2002 **PDP** *012 †55

CRISPEN, Melvin Floyd. 7520 STATE RD 45255 #020-12-1984 L1985 **AN** *020 †05

CROALL, Gail Borgatti. 55 PROGRESS PL, GROUP HEALTH ASSOCIATES 45246 #051-04-1981 L1984 **PD** *020 †55

CROMBLEHOLME, Timothy M. 3333 BURNET AVE, CINCINNATI CHILDREN'S HOSP 45229 #024-07-1984 L2004 **PDS** *020 †85

CRONE, Kerry Ray. 3333 BURNET AVE, MLC 2016 45229 #038-41-1978 L1985 **NS** *020 †25

CROOG, Alexander Samuel. 538 OAK ST, #200 MARY S STERN HAND FND 45219 #051-01-2001 L2006 **HS** *020

CROSS, Andrew Walker. 10700 MONTGOMERY RD, STE 150 45242 #047-20-2001 L2007 **HS** *020

CROSSMAN, Michael Wm. 3333 BURNET AVE 45229 #028-34-1986 L1988 **NPM** *050 †55

CROTEAU, Lynn Marie. 7810 5 MILE RD 45230 #041-01-1984 L1988 **PD** *020 †55

CROTTY, Eric Joseph. 3333 BURNET AVE, DEPT OF RADIO 45229 #539-02-1990 L2000 **PDR** *020 †80

CROWE, David Robert. ■ 45267 #038-41-2007 L2007 **D** *012

CRUMPTON, Marilyn E. 45241 #001-02-1974 L2007 **PHP PD** *074 †55

CRUZ, Jeremia Erguiza. ■ 45211 #748-01-1961 **IM OBG** *075

CRUZ JIMENEZ, Maireni Ric. 375 DIXMYTH AVE 45220 #308-13-2003 L2006 **IM** *012

CRUZ-NOVO, M Elena. 7207 WOOSTER PIKE # 302 45227 #035-09-1980 L1988 **OS AN** *071 †05

CUALING, Hernani Del M. ■ 45243 #038-41-1962 L1964 **PDS OS** *020 †85... 748-02-1978 L1992 **PTH** *020 †50

CUDZILO, Corey James. UNIV OF CINCINNATI, DEPT OF INTERNAL MEDICINE 45267 #047-06-2007 L2007 **MPD** *012

CUNNINGHAM, Claire Angela. ■ 45219 #023-01-2008 *012

CUNNINGHAM, Kyle William. ■ 45219 #038-41-2008 *012

CURELL, James Hobson. 234 GOODMAN ST, STE 0559 45219 #038-41-1987 L1991 **P** *020 †75

CURRAN, Michael Griffith. 3140 LEGACY TRCE 45255 #025-12-1993 L2004 **GS** *020 †85 ‡

CURRY, Richard Charles, III. 45202 #038-43-2007 L2007 *012

CURRY, Trace William. 330 STRAIGHT ST, STE 330 45219 #047-05-1993 L1998 **GS** *020 †85

CURT, Bradford August. ■ 45267 #012-05-2003 L2003 **NS** *012

CURTISS, Mary Anne. 3200 VINE ST, 8TH FL 45220 #038-41-1985 L1986 **ADM FM** *020 †18

CUSI, Maria Victoria P. ■ 45208 #748-19-1987 L1996 **PTH** *020

CUSTER, John Vernon. 672 NEEB RD 45233 #038-41-1960 L1960 **FM** *020 †18

CUTFIELD, Wayne Stephen. 3300 ELLAND AVE, CHILDRENS HOSPITAL 45229 #671-02-1983 **PDE** *020

CZAIKOWSKI, Adam John. ■ 45209 #038-41-2008 *012

CZARNECKI, John Peter. 2841 BOUDINOT AVE, STE 304 45238 #016-06-1995 L2001 **IM GE** *020 †20

CZECH, Kimberly Ann. ■ 45202 #016-01-2002 L2005 **PN** *012 †55

DADDABBO, Anna Marie. 3306 RUTHER AVE, ALLIANCE PRIMARY CARE 45220 #038-45-1985 L1986 **FM** *020 †18 ‡

DADDABBO, Joseph Gerard. 12055 SHERATON LN 45246 #036-05-1987 L1988 **D GP** *020 †15 ‡

DAGENBACH, Joseph Richard. 2123 AUBURN AVE, STE 440 45219 #038-41-1996 L2000 **IM** *020 †20

DAGGY, Matthew William. 4411 MONTGOMERY RD, STE 206 45212 #038-45-2003 L2003 **FM FSM** *020 †18

DAHAR, Irfan Ahmed. 4030 MOUNT CARMEL TOBSC RD 45255 #704-08-1988 L1999 **PYG** *020

DAILEY, Calley Nicole. ■ 45219 #038-41-2008 *012

DAILEY, Stephen William. 6350 GLENWAY AVE 45211 #041-02-1993 L1998 **HS** *020 †40

DAINES, Cori Sanders. 3333 BURNET AVE, PULMONARY MEDICINE, ML 202 45229 #028-34-1993 L1999 **PDP PD** *020 †55

DAJANI, Karim. ■ 45202 #539-03-2004 L2004 **FPG** *012 †20

DAJANI, Zeina Ahmadwalid. ■ 45206 #024-05-2007 L2007 **D** *012

DALE, Shannon Evelyn. ■ 45243 #019-02-2005 L2005 **N** *012

D'ALESSIO, David Andrew. 3130 HIGHLAND AVE, STE 0557 45219 #056-05-1983 L1999 **END** *020 †20

DALIA, Deanna Asad. 3155 GLENDALE MILFORD RD, CINCINNATI EVENDALE SURG 45241 #038-40-1992 L1993 **AN** *020 †05

DALLMAN, Elizabeth M. 1207 SPRINGFIELD PIKE, WYOMING 45215 #038-41-1998 L1999 **IM** *020 †20

DALTON, William Jack, II. 7865 IVYGATE LN, BETHESDA HOSPITAL 45242 #038-41-1967 L1967 **AN** *020 †05

DAMA, Sunil Kumar. 2123 AUBURN AVE, STE 401 45219 #495-21-1993 L2002 **PCC** *020 †20

DAMMEL, Richard Milton. 5 W GALBRAITH RD 45246 #038-41-1975 L1976 **IM CD** *020 †20

DANG, Bich Ngoc. ■ 45212 #048-12-2003 L2006 **IM** *050 †20

DANIELS, John Preston. 4652 HAMILTON AVE 45223 #038-41-1995 L1996 **PD** *020 †55,75

DANIELYAN, Arman. 231 ALBERT, CO PSYCHIATRY DEPT 45267 #913-38-1992 L2007 **P** *012

DAOUD, Ingrid Maria H. 11238 CORNELL PARK DR 45242 #407-10-1963 L1975 **PD ADL** *020 †55

DASENBROCK, Raymond Jos. 7810 5 MILE RD 45230 #038-41-1967 L1967 **PD** *020 †55

DATO, Mark Edward. 3333 BURNET AVE 45229 #016-42-1991 L1994 **PDP** *020 †55

DAUGHERTY, Joseph F, III. 2230 AUBURN AVE 45219 #020-02-1974 L1976 **IM OS** *020 †20

DAUN, Michael E. 2055 READING RD, STE 210 45202 #049-01-1987 L1997 **OPH** *020 †35

DAUPLAISE, Derrick John. ■ 45212 #011-04-2004 L2004 **CCP** *012

D'AURIA, John Jos. 3200 VINE ST, CINCINNATI VAMC 45220 #041-01-1980 L1983 **AN PME** *020 †05

DAVENPORT, Agena Renee. ■ 45211 #038-41-2008 *012

DAVIDSON, Katharine Elisa. ■ 45220 #038-41-2008 *012

DAVIES, Stella M. 3333 BURNET AVE, AVENUE, MLC 7015 45229 #917-04-1981 L2002 **PHO** *020

DAVIN, Jeffrey Scott. 11125 KENWOOD RD, BETHESDA CARE 45242 #027-01-1983 L1987 **OM** *020 †70

DAVIN, Vincent Ambrose. 1295 KEMPER MEADOW DR, UNIVERSITY FAMILY PHYS FOR 45240 #038-41-1964 L1964 **OBG** *020 †30

DAVIS, Bradley Rice. 2123 AUBURN AVE, STE 524 45219 #035-06-1996 L1999 **CRS** *020 †85,10

DAVIS, Cherrica Tishonda. 231 ALBERT SABIN WAY 45267 #025-07-2002 L2002 **MPD** *020 †20,55

DAVIS, Denise Hampton. 9549 MONTGOMERY RD, 1ST FL 45242 #038-43-1980 L1990 **OBG** *020 †30

DAVIS, Dianne L. 2139 AUBURN AVE, C/O THE CHRIST HOSP-MED ED 45219 #020-02-2001 L2001 **DR** *012

DAVIS, Kenneth, Jr. 231 ALBERT SABIN WAY, WAY ML0558 45267 #028-34-1976 L1984 **GS CCS** *040 †85

DAVIS, Lesley Joy. ■ 45240 #038-41-2008 *012

DAVIS, Mary Helen. 7810 5 MILE RD 45230 #020-02-1982 L1983 **P** *020 †75

DAVIS, Marybeth. 7810 5 MILE RD, GROUP HEALTH ASSOCIATES 45230 #020-02-1992 L2006 **IM** *020 †20

DAVIS, Reginald Htodd, III. ■ 45219 #054-04-2007 L2007 **EM** *012

DAVIS, Renee Ann. 234 GOODMAN ST, STE 0531 45219 #030-05-1990 L1992 **AN** *020 †05

DAVISON, James Fredrick. 12103 SHERATON LN 45246 #028-34-1972 L1973 **U** *020 †95

DAVITT, Sean Paul. 12124 SHERATON LN 45246 #005-19-1998 L2002 **OPH** *020 †35

DAVREN, John Wm. 4600 MCAULEY PL, 6TH FL 45242 #038-41-1976 L1977 **FM** *030 †18

DAWODU, Adekunle Hakeem. 3333 BURNET AVE 5041, CINCINNATI CHILDRENS HOSP 45229 #690-01-1968 **PD NPM** *030

DAWSON, Patrick James. ■ 45227 #056-05-2004 L2004 **OBG** *012

DAWSON, Rank O, Jr. 2859 BOUDINOT AVE STE 305 45238 #038-41-1982 L1982 **HS PS** *074 †65

DAY, James Albert. 8000 5 MILE RD, STE 305 45230 #038-40-1984 L1985 **IM** *020 †20

DAY, Scottie Brian. 3333 BURNET AVE, CHILDREN'S HOSPITAL 45229 #020-12-2002 L2006 **CCP** *012

DEAK, Andrew John. 3248 WESTBOURNE DR 45248 #038-41-1971 L1973 **GE IM** *020 †20

DE ALARCON, Alessandro. 3333 BURNET AVE, CINCINNATI CHILDREN'S HOSP 45229 #051-04-2001 L2006 **PDO** *012 †45

DEAN, Helen. ■ 45205 #748-07-1956 L1959 **GP IM** *020

DEATON, Lois Lucinda. 222 PIEDMONT AVE, STE 3400 45219 #038-41-1991 L1995 **PM** *020 †60

DEBLASIO, Dominick John. 10700 MONTGOMERY RD, STE 100 45242 #038-41-2001 L2001 **PD** *020 †55

DE BLASIS, Nancy Mac Leod. 8245 NORTHCREEK DR 45236 #038-41-1981 L1982 **PD** *020 †55

DE BROSSE, Quintin Jos. ■ 45242 #038-41-1947 L1947 **OBG** *071 †30
DECANIO, Raymond Enrique. ■ 45219 #038-41-2006 L2006 **DR** *012
DE COURTEN-MYERS, G. 234 GOODMAN ST 45219 #869-07-1974 L1983 **NP** *062
DEEPE, George Saml. 3200 VINE ST, STE 111D 45220 #038-41-1976 L1980 **ID** *050 †20
DE FOOR, William R, Jr. 3333 BURNET AVE, DIV OF PEDIATRIC UROLOGY 45229 #020-12-1996 L2001 **UP** *020 †95
DE FOREST, Ralph E. ■ 45236 #025-07-1943 L1944 **PM OS** *071 †60
DE GRAUW, Ton Johannes. 3333 BURNET AVE, DEPT OF PEDIATRIC NEUROLOG 45229 #660-05-1979 L1985 **N** *020 †75
DEGREG, Joanne Elizabeth. 2136 W 8TH ST 45204 #038-41-1986 L1988 **IMG** *020 †18
DE GUIA, Gabriel. 3200 BURNET AVE 45229 #748-07-1964 L1976 **GP** *020
DEHNER, Benjamin Lawrence. ■ 45267 #038-41-2005 L2005 **U** *012
DEHOOP, Thomas Art. 222 PIEDMONT AVE, STE 5100 45219 #056-06-1990 L1993 **OBG** *020 †30
DE LAAT, Cynthia Anne. 3300 ELLAND AVE, CHILDRENS HOSPITAL 45229 #038-41-1981 L1982 **PD PHO** *020 †55
DELAMERCED, Amador S. 5757 GLENWAY AVE, GLENWAY FAMILY MEDICINE 45238 #748-02-1987 L1993 **IM** *020 †20
DELAUNE, Samuel John, Jr. 3333 BURNET AVE, DEPT OF PEDIATRICS 45229 #048-02-2006 L2006 **PD** *012
DEL BELLO, Melissa P. 231 ALBERT SABIN WAY, ML 559 45267 #035-45-1995 L1996 **CHP** *020 †75
DELEDDA, John Matthew. 2139 AUBURN AVE, STE 0769 45219 #025-01-1999 L1999 **EM** *020 †16
DELGADO, Sergio V, Jr. 3333 BURNET AVE 45229 #649-02-1981 L2002 **CHP PYA** *020 †75
DELLINGER, Cindy Lee. 4460 RED BANK RD 45227 #038-41-1986 L1987 **OBG** *020 †30
DELORENZO, Gregory Jos. 2001 ANDERSON FERRY RD 45238 #038-40-1987 L1988 **RHU IM** *020 †20
DE LOS RIOS LA ROSA, Felip. MEDICIN231 ALBERT, CO INTERNAL 45267 #737-06-2005 L2007 **N** *012
DELWORTH, Mark Gerard. 7794 5 MILE RD, STE 200 45230 #019-02-1988 L1995 **U** *020 †95
DE MARCO, David John. 3248 WESTBOURNE DR, THE FAMILY MEDICAL GROUP 45248 #038-40-2002 L2005 **FM** *100 †18
DENNEY, Amanda Marie. 3130 HIGHLAND AVE, STE 0557 45219 #038-45-2000 L2001 **END** *020 †20
DENSON, Lee A, III. 3333 BURNET AVE 45229 #051-04-1993 L2003 **PG** *020 †55
DENT, Catherine Louise. 3333 BURNET AVE, DIVISION OF CARDIOLOGY/MLC 45229 #028-46-1991 L2001 **PDC** *020 †55
DENTLER, Michael Donald. ■ 45239 #038-41-2008 *012
DEORAH, Sundeep. ■ 45267 #495-36-2000 L2006 **U** *012
DEPALMA-DUERSCH, Jennifer. 663 ANDERSON FERRY RD, PEDIATRICIAN - WEST SIDE P 45238 #038-40-2005 L2005 **PD** *012
DEPIORE, James Jerald. 7400 JAGER CT 45230 #038-43-1990 L1991 **PD** *020 †55
DEPOWELL, John Joseph. ■ 45267 #038-41-2006 L2006 **NS** *012
DERBY, Elizabeth Ann. ■ 45219 #041-13-2002 L2003 **OPH** *012
DERICKSON, Theresa Marie. 55 PROGRESS PL 45246 #038-41-2003 L2003 **PD** *020 †55
DERROW, Amy Elise. ■ 45209 #036-05-2004 L2004 **D** *012
DESAI, Rasesh Rohitbhai. CO MEDICAL EDUCATIO, CHILDREN'S HOSPITAL MEDICA 45229 #495-76-1999 L2007 **OSS** *012
DETTERLINE, Alvin James. 10663 MONTGOMERY RD, CINCINNATI SPORTSMEDICINE 45242 #017-20-2002 L2006 **ORS** *020
DETTERLINE, Stephanie Ami. ■ 45208 #017-20-2002 L2007 **IM** *020 †20
DEUTSCH, Gail Hope. 3333 BURNET AVE, MLC 1010 45229 #016-02-1993 L2002 **PTH** *020 †50
DEUTSCH, Mark David. 11135 MONTGOMERY RD 45249 #038-41-1991 L1993 **OTO** *020 †45
DEVANY, Vola L. 3333 BURNET AVE 45229 #038-40-1980 L1992 **AN PD** *020 †55,05
DEVARAJAN, Prasad. 3333 BURNET AVE, CINCINNATI CHILDREN'S HOSP 45229 #495-96-1983 L2003 **PN PD** *020 †55
DE VEGA, Maria Del Rosari. 4411 MONTGOMERY RD, STE 200 45212 #270-02-2002 L2006 **FP** *012
DEVINE, Christopher J. 2055 READING RD, STE 210 45202 #016-06-1992 L1998 **OPH** *072 †35
DEVITT, James J, Jr. 311 STRAIGHT ST 45219 #038-41-1988 L1994 **PTH HMP** *020 †50
DEVORE, James Wilford, Jr. ■ 45267 #038-41-2007 L2007 **IM** *012
DE VORE, Richard Alan. 8221 CORNELL RD 45249 #038-41-1984 L1989 **OTO** *020 †45
DE WITT, Thomas Gebhard. 3333 BURNET AVE, CHILDRENS HOSPITAL MED CTR 45229 #035-45-1976 L1995 **PD** *030 †55
DHAMIJA, Ashima. ■ 45236 #038-41-2008 *012
DHANRAJ, David Nathaniel. 375 DIXMYTH AVE 45220 #017-20-1999 L1999 **OBG** *020 †30
DHARAMSI, Nafisa. 3333 BURNET AVE, CO CHILDREN S HOSP-MED EDU 45229 #060-02-1998 L2003 **UP** *100
DHEENAN, Shekar. 7794 5 MILE RD, STE 200 45230 #038-43-1992 L1999 **U** *020 †95
DICKENS, Sandra E. 4600 WESLEY AVE, STE N 45212 #038-41-1991 L1994 **IM** *020 †20
DICKERSON, Rachel Anne. ■ 45230 #048-02-2008 *012
DICKHONER, William H. 2651 OBSERVATORY AVE 45208 #038-41-1980 L1985 **VS GS** *020 †85
DICKIE, Belinda. 3333 BURNET AVE, DEPT OF MED EDUCATION 45229 #065-01-1998 L2006 *100
DICKINSON, Timothy Dale. 7520 STATE RD 45255 #055-02-1992 L1996 **AN** *020 †05
DICKSON, John M. 3333 BURNET AVE 2018, DEPT PED OTO 45229 #061-01-2002 L2007 **PDO** *012
DIEHL, Dina Renee. ■ 45208 #041-77-2003, ▲ L2003 **IM** *020 †20
DIEHL, John William. 4411 MONTGOMERY RD STE 200, BETHESDA FAMILY PRACTICE 45212 #038-41-2004 L2004 **FSM** *012
DIERS, Tiffiny Leigh. 231 ALBERT SABIN WAY, INTERNAL MEDICINE/UNIV. OF 45267 #036-07-1997 L1998 **MPD** *020 †55,20
DIGGINS, John James. 311 ALBERT SABIN WAY, CENTRAL CLINIC 45229 #038-41-2003 L2003 **CPP** *012
DIGIULIO, Gregg Albert. 3333 BURNET AVE, CHILDREN'S HOSPITAL MED CT 45229 #041-12-1986 L1989 **PEM** *020 †55
DIGNAN, Peter St John. 3333 BURNET AVE 45229 #671-01-1957 L1975 **PD** *071 †55,19
DILLARD, Charles Overton. 2600 STRATFORD AVE 45219 #047-07-1961 L1967 **IM RHU** *020
DILLER, Philip M. 1295 KEMPER MEADOW DR 45240 #016-02-1988 L1990 **FM** *020 †18
DILLON, Anne Colleen. 8000 5 MILE RD, STE 210 45230 #038-45-1991 L1992 **FM** *020 †18
DIMACULANGAN, Jarrel P. ■ 45223 #748-01-1964 L1975 **AN** *020
DIMASI, Mary Kathleen. ■ 45213 #030-05-2002 L2002 **PD** *100
DINERMAN, Michael. ■ 45220 #038-41-2005 *100
DINERSTEIN, Robert Jos. 2110 E GALBRAITH RD 45237 #016-02-1976 **OS** *050
DINOPOULOS, Argirios. 3333 BURNET AVE, CO CHILDREN S HOSP-NEUROLO 45229 #418-01-1989 L2000 **CN** *020

DIRKES, Wm Eugene, Jr. 2139 AUBURN AVE 45219 #038-41-1984 L1985 **PLM PME** *030 †05
DIVINE, Jon G. 3333 BURNET AVE, MLC-10001 45229 #048-02-1993 L1996 **FM FSM** *020 †18
DIXON, Bradley Patton. 3333 BURNET AVE, CINCINNATI CHILDREN'S HOSP 45229 #047-06-1999 L1999 **PN** *100 †55
DIXON, Estrelita Annette. 231 ALBERT SABIN WAY, RM 6603 45267 #010-03-1989 L1992 **IM** *020 †20
DIXON, Jedediah Richard. 400 WABASH AVENUE 45236 #917-09-2001 L2007 **IM** *012
DIXON, Sheree Jones. 7011 BEECH HOLLOW DR 45236 #012-01-1982 L1987 **P CHP** *020
DIXON, Teabra Ahnee. ■ 45240 #038-41-2004 L2007 **IM** *100
DJAFARI, Paria. 375 DIXMYTH AVE 45220 #104-01-2003 L2005 **FP** *012
D'LIMA, Reynold Rodney M. ■ 45238 #495-52-1987 L1997 **FM** *020 †18
DLUGOSZ, Heather Heintz. ■ 45212 #038-41-2005 L2005 **P** *012
DMELLO, Sharon Louise. 3333 BURNET AVE, CHILDRENS HOSP MED CTR 45229 #033-05-2004 L2007 **PG** *012 †55
DO, Twee Thi. 3353 BURNET AVE ML2017, CHILDRENS HOSPITAL MED CTR 45229 #018-03-1993 L1999 **OP** *020 †40
DOBBS, Michael David. 3333 BURNET AVE, ML 5018 45229 #003-01-2005 L2005 **PD** *012
DOBROGORSKI, Olga Johanna. 3217 CLIFTON AVE DEPT PATH 45220 #407-04-1950 L1957 **PTH** *071 †50
DOLAN, Damian Francis. 11490 SPRINGFIELD PIKE 45246 #011-02-1986 L1990 **AN** *020 †05
DOLAN, Lawrence Michael. 3333 BURNET AVE, CHILDREN'S HOSPITAL MED CE 45229 #005-14-1976 L1983 **DIA PDE** *050 †55
DOLENSKY, Diane Joan. 463 OHIO PIKE, STE 300 45255 #038-43-1993 L1996 **IM** *020 †20
DONALDSON, Angela Moneak. ■ 45211 #038-41-2008 *012
DONALDSON, Archie Robt. ■ 45229 #010-03-1964 L1965 **OBG** *020
DONALDSON, Virginia H. 3300 ELLAND AVE, CHILDRENS HOSPITAL 45229 #050-02-1951 L1958 **OS HEM** *050 †55
DONATH, Alexander Stephen. 7763 MONTGOMERY RD 45236 #038-41-2001 L2007 **OTO** *020 †45
DONATH, Werner Ernst. ■ 45226 #407-07-1953 L1957 **PTH** *071 †50
DONEPUDI, Radhika. 140 W KEMPER RD 45246 #495-21-1989 L1996 **FM** *020 †18
DONHAM, Benjamin Powelson. ■ 45202 #012-05-2004 L2004 **EM** *012
DONLEY, Diane R Kramer. 3333 BURNET AVE, ML 7009 45229 #021-01-1984 L1990 **PD** *020 †55
DONNELLY, Lane Francis. 3333 BURNET AVE, DEPT OF RADIOLOGY - MLC 50 45229 #038-41-1990 L1992 **PDR** *020 †80
DONNELLY, Walter E, Jr. 6331 GLENWAY AVE 45211 #035-20-1982 L1984 **FM** *020 †18
DONOHUE, Marianne. 310 TERRACE AVE, STE 101 45220 #038-43-1984 L1986 **OBG** *075 †30
DONOVAN, Edward Francis. 3333 BURNET AVE 45229 #005-14-1971 L1977 **NPM PD** *020 †55
DONOVAN, James Ryan, Jr. 3217 CLIFTON AVE 45220 #038-43-1981 L1982 **OM IM** *075 †20,70
DONOVAN, Robert Paul. 3550 WASHINGTON AVE, CENTER FOR RESPITE CARE IN 45229 #038-43-1979 L1980 **FM** *020 †18
DONOVAN, Stuart Lee. 2123 AUBURN AVE, STE 231 45219 #038-45-1986 L1991 **GS VS** *020 †85
DORLAC, Gina R. 231 ALBERT SABIN WAY, ML 0558 45267 #023-12-1989 L2007 **CCM PUD** *020 †20
DORLAC, Warren Chas. ■ 45208 #023-12-1989 L2008 **CCS TRS** *020 †85
DORN, Charlotte Lynn. 7520 STATE RD 45255 #038-41-1994 L1999 **AN** *020 †05
DORN, Gerald W, II. 222 PIEDMONT AVE, STE 1200 45219 #045-01-1981 L1990 **CD IM** *020 †20
DOUGHTY, Lesley Ann. 3333 BURNET AVE ML2005, CRITICAL CARE MEDICINE 45229 #032-01-1988 L2005 **CCP** *020 †55
DOWLING, Brian Patrick. 231 ALBERT SABIN WAY, DEPARTMENT OF PSYCHIATRY 45267 #038-41-2001 L2001 **P** *020 †75
DOWNEY, Kathleen Ann. 1207 SPRINGFIELD PIKE 45215 #041-12-1979 L1982 **FM** *020 †18
DOYLE, Patricia Mary. ■ 45233 #038-40-1959 L1959 **OS** *071 †05
DRAKE, Betsy Ann. 4411 MONTGOMERY RD, STE 400 45212 #038-41-2006 L2006 **FP** *012
DRAKE, David Francis. 8000 5 MILE RD, STE 310 45230 #038-41-1969 L1969 **CD IM** *020 †20
DRANOVE, Jason Eric. 3333 BURNET AVE, CO CHILDREN S HOSP-MED EDU 45229 #012-01-2003 L2003 **PG** *012 †55
DRAPER, David James. 231 ALBERT SABIN WAY 5, THE UNIVERSITY HOSPITAL 45267 #038-41-2003 L2003 **HO** *012 †20
DRASNIN, Jeffrey Alan. 2711 MADISON RD 45209 #038-41-1997 L1998 **PD** *020 †55
DRASNIN, Ronald. 2711 MADISON RD 45209 #038-41-1960 L1965 **PD** *020 †55
DRAUD, Kimberly Sue. 375 DIXMYTH AVE 45220 #020-12-1998 L2005 **DR** *020 †80
DRAZNIK, Michael Robt. 10500 MONTGOMERY RD 45242 #038-41-1978 L1979 **OBG** *020 †30
DRESKIN, O Herman. 3200 BURNET AVE 45229 #010-01-1941 L1949 **IM HEM** *071 †20
DROESSLER, Paul Thomas. 4314 HAIGHT AVE 45223 #038-41-2003 L2003 **P** *100
DROSICK, David Randolph. 4350 MALSBARY RD 45242 #055-01-1985 L1991 **IM HEM** *020 †20
DRURY, Timothy William, II. ■ 45230 #020-02-2003 L2005 **IM** *100
DRURY, Timothy Wm. 2446 KIPLING AVE 45239 #020-02-1984 L1985 **EM** *020 †16
DRYER, Peter David. ■ 45267 #038-43-2006 L2006 **IM** *012
DRYER, Thomas Adolph. 4130 DRY RIDGE RD 45252 #038-41-1979 L1982 **FM OBS** *020 †18
D'SOUZA, Leo. 325 LAFAYETTE AVE 45220 #654-01-1981 L1993 **PTH** *020
DSOUZA, Sharon Annunciata. 10700 MONTGOMERY RD, STE 100 45242 #038-45-1997 L1998 **PD** *020 †55
DUBIN, Neil Stanford. 58 E HOLLISTER ST 45219 #045-01-1977 L1979 **P** *020 †75
DUFFEY, William C. 234 GOODMAN ST, ML0761 45267 #038-41-1950 L1950 **R NM** *071 †80,28
DUFFY, James Paul. 375 DIXMYTH AVE 45220 #038-41-1971 L1971 **ORS OSM** *020 †40
DUKE, Don Dewindle, Jr. ■ 45208 #047-06-1987 L1988 **GP EM** *020 †16
DUKER, Andrew P. 222 PIEDMONT AVE, STE 3200 45219 #038-43-2001 L2001 **N** *020
DUKES-DOBOS, Francis N. ■ 45237 #473-01-1951 **OM** *050
DUMA, Elena Anne. 3333 BURNET AVE, CHILDREN'S HOSP MEDICAL CE 45229 #047-06-1991 L1993 **PD PEM** *020 †55
DUMBADZE, Igor. 6350 GLENWAY AVE, STE 201 45211 #038-41-1973 L1974 **U** *020 †95
DUMBAULD, Steven La Mar. 3219 CLIFTON AVE STE 325 45220 #038-43-1975 L1976 **NEP IM** *020 †20
DUMONT, Francis Emile. 1060 NIMITZVIEW DR, STE 210 45230 #038-41-1990 L1991 **FM** *020 †18
DUNKIN, Bradley Steven. ■ 45243 #020-02-2007 L2007 **ORS** *012
DUNLEVY, Hillary Ann. ■ 45220 #038-41-2008 *012
DUNN, Corwin R. 2123 AUBURN AVE 45219 #016-11-1964 L1966 **ID IM** *020 †20
DUNN, Deborah Droder. ■ 45248 #038-41-1980 L1981 **GP PMM** *020
DUNN, Edward James. 2139 AUBURN AVE 45219 #025-07-1973 L1980 **TS** *071 †85,90
DUNSIETH, Neal William, Jr. 231 ALBERT SABIN WAY 055, PO BOX 670559 45267 #041-14-1993 L1996 **PFP** *100 †75

DUNSKER, Stewart Ben. 551 ABILENE TRL, MAY FIELD CLINIC 45215 #038-41-1960 L1960 NS *020 †25

DUPLECHAN, Lester Sherman. 6480 HARRISON AVE, SPORTS MEDICINE 45247 #005-14-1990 L1998 PM PME *020 †60

DURAND, Malia Skye. ■ 45249 #016-06-2007 L2007 IM *012

DURANT, Denise Megan. 538 OAK ST, STE 200 45219 #023-07-2001 L2006 HS *020

DURHAM, Kristine Marie. 4777 E GALBRAITH RD 45236 #038-41-1997 L2000 IM *020 †20

DURRANI, Abubakar Atiq. 3333 BURNET AVE, ML 2017 45229 #704-22-1991 L2000 ORS *020 †40

DUVALL, William Ercel. 2139 AUBURN AVE, DEPT 1104 45219 #020-12-1978 L1979 AN *020 †05

DUWEL, John Jeremiah. ■ 45230 #028-34-1970 L1970 GS *020

DWIVEDI, Leela Choudhary. 8595 BEECHMONT AVE STE 200 45255 #495-49-1963 L1976 OBG *020 †30

DYER, Damian Rohan. UNIV OF CINCINNATI MED CTR, DEPT OF SURGERY 45267 #020-02-2004 L2004 GS *100

EADY, Caroline Elizabeth. ■ 45229 #038-41-2006 L2006 EM *012

EAGEN, Emily Margaret. 3333 BURNET AVE, CO CHILDREN S HOSP-MED EDU 45229 #038-41-2001 L2003 CCP *100 †55

EARHART, William Thos. 375 DIXMYTH AVE, OBSTETRIC ANESTHESIA 45220 #038-40-1975 L1978 AN *020

EARLEY, Neal N. 2123 AUBURN AVE STE 242 45219 #038-41-1943 L1944 GS *071 †85

EATON, Jennifer Dorothy. ■ 45209 #038-41-2007 L2007 P *012

EBENS, Christen Layne. ■ 45211 #016-11-2006 L2007 PD *012

EBERSOLD, Donald K. 6350 E GALBRAITH RD 45236 #038-41-1953 L1953 FM *072 †18

EBY, Robert Stephen. 2450 KIPLING AVE STE 108 45239 #038-40-1978 L1980 FM *020 †18

ECHARTEA GONZALEZ, Jaime. 3333 BURNET AVE 45229 #649-30-2001 L2006 PD *012

ECKERT, Daniel Clark. 231 ALBERT SABIN WAY, UNIVERSITY HOSPITAL MEDICI 45267 #038-41-2001 L2001 CD *012

ECKMAN, Mark Harris. 234 GOODMAN ST 45267 #035-03-1981 L1999 IM OS *030 †20

EDE, Mitchell. 441 VINE ST STE 1005 45202 #021-01-1945 L1952 D OS *020 †15

EDGAR, Courtney Leann. ■ 45213 #036-08-2006 L2006 MPD *012

EDLIN, Philip. ■ 45206 #038-41-1947 L1947 GE IM *071 †20

EDWARDS, John Dudley. 305 CRESCENT AVE 45215 #016-01-1982 L1997 VS GS *020 †85

EDWARDS, Valerie Lloyd. 1525 ELM ST 45202 #016-11-1985 L1989 PD *020 †55

EE, Looi Cheng. 3333 BURNET AVE, CHILDRENS HOSP MED CTR 45229 #143-06-1985 L2000 PG *100

EFFAT, Mohamed Ahmed. 231 ALBERT SABIN WAY, DIV OF CARDIOLOGY 45267 #915-02-1984 L2005 IC *100 †20

EFTEKHARI, Nahid. ■ 45249 #016-45-2004 L2004 OBG *012

EGER, Charles Hubert. 175 W GALBRAITH RD 45216 #038-44-1983 L1984 IM MDM *020 †20

EGGERMAN, Kevin Wm. 3506 BOUDINOT AVE, # 100 45211 #028-34-1990 L1995 CHP *020

EGHTESADY, Pirooz. 3333 BURNET AVE, CHILDREN'S HOSP MED CTR CI 45229 #005-14-1993 L2002 TS *020 †90,85

EGNER, Carol Lynn. 6480 HARRISON AVE, STE 300 45247 #038-43-1981 L1983 OBG *020 †30

EILER, Janis Elaine. 2752 ERIE AVE STE 5 45208 #017-20-1981 L1986 IM LM *020 †20

EISELE, Sandra Adams. 6350 GLENWAY AVE 45211 #016-06-1979 L1984 ORS OFA *020 †40 ‡

EISEN, Drore. 7691 5 MILE RD, CINCINNATI 45230 #051-04-1986 L1990 D *020 †10

EISENTROUT, Craig Alan. 10496 MONTGOMERY RD, STE 103 45242 #038-41-1982 L1983 PUD CCM *020 †20

EISSA, Moustafa. ■ 45211 #915-09-1978 NEP *020

ELDER, Deborah Ann. 3333 BURNET AVE 45229 #020-12-1995 L2001 PDE *020 †55

ELDER, Nancy Caroline. 1207 SPRINGFIELD PIKE 45215 #026-04-1983 L2001 FM *020 †18

ELFAR, John Claude. 538 OAK ST STE 200, SURGERY FND 45219 #024-01-2002 L2006 HSO *012

EL-HOUJAIRY, Joseph Zaki. 2139 AUBURN AVE 45219 #913-35-1999 L2005 IM *012

ELIAS, Sami Victor. 619 OAK ST, CO BETHESDA HOSP-MED EDU D 45206 #396-39-1997 L2000 FM *100

ELICKER, Edward Robt. 4700 SMITH RD 45212 #038-41-1969 L1969 U *020 †95

ELKEEB, Dena Mohamed S.A.. ■ 45230 #613-02-1993 L2004 PD *100 †55

EL-KHATIB, Mahmuud Talib. 231 ALBERT SABIN WAY 45267 #913-15-1981 L1991 NEP *020 †20

ELLIS, Corey James. 305 CRESCENT AVE, WFPC/UNIVERSTY 45215 #038-41-2002 L2002 PSM *020 †18

ELLIS, Frank E. 3308 JEFFERSON AVE 45220 #038-41-1953 L1953 GS *020 †85

ELLIS, Lora Elizabeth. 3333 BURNET AVE 45229 #038-41-2002 L2002 PD *020 †55

ELLIS, Robert Victor, II. 1207 SPRINGFIELD PIKE 45215 #038-41-2002 L2002 FM *020 †18

ELLURU, Ravindhra G. 231 ALBERT SABIN WAY, ML0528 45267 #048-12-1996 L2001 PDO *020 †45

ELSASS, Thomas Robert. ■ 45215 #038-41-2003 L2007 AN *020

EMBI, Colleen Sheridan. 9670 KENWOOD RD 45242 #011-04-1997 L2000 DMP *020

EMBI, Peter Joseph. 231 ALBERT SABIN WAY, UNIVERSITY OF CINCINNATI 45267 #011-04-1997 L2002 RHU *020 †20

EMERY, Callie G Rogers. ■ 45242 #048-12-2002 L2003 CPP *012

EMERY, Kathleen H. 3333 BURNET AVE 45229 #016-43-1982 L1989 DR PD *020 †80

ENANY, Nasreldin Mohamed. 234 GOODMAN AVE ML-0764, DEPT OF ANESTHESIA 45267 #915-03-1981 L2001 APM *100 †05

ENGEL, Carol Brown. 3333 BURNET AVE 45229 #005-19-1997 L1999 OS *020 †55,75

ENGELHARDT, Robert J, Jr. 6350 GLENWAY AVE, STE 300 45211 #038-41-1996 L1997 PD *020 †55

ENGEN, Rachel Marie. ■ 45202 #028-02-2008 *012

ENGLENDER, Steven J. 3101 BURNET AVE, CINCINNATI HLTH DEPT 45229 #038-06-1973 L2000 PHP PD *030 †70

ENGLERT, James J. 7835 REMINGTON RD 45242 #038-41-1952 L1952 PD *071 †55

ENRIQUEZ, Jessica C. 8146 HAMILTON AVE, LINCOLN HEIGHTS 45231 #748-01-1961 L1973 FM OS *020

ENTIS, Gregory Neil. 10496 MONTGOMERY RD, STE 207 45242 #028-02-1974 L1976 AI PDA *020 †55,03

ENZER, Charles Hart. 4220 ROSE HILL AVE 45229 #035-09-1964 L1969 P CHP *020 †75

EPPLEY, Christopher Alan. 4411 MONTGOMERY RD STE 206, BETHESDA HOSPITAL 45212 #038-41-2002 L2002 FM *020 †18

EPSTEIN, Tolly Goldberg. ■ 45242 #017-20-2003 L2007 AI IM *100 †20

ERICKSON, Nissa Ingrid. 3333 BURNET AVE, CO CHILDRENS S MED CTR-MED 45229 #026-04-2000 L2003 PG *100 †55 ‡

ERNST, Jennifer Marie. ■ 45236 #038-41-2003 L2003 MPD *100 †20,55

ERNST, Robert James. 5819 CHEVIOT RD 45247 #038-41-1987 L1992 DR *020 †80

ESHUN, Francis Kwabena. 3333 BURNET AVE, MLC 7015 45229 #412-01-1996 L2005 PHO *012 †55

ESINDUY, Canan Besime. 151 W GALBRAITH RD, DRAKE CENTER 45216 #038-43-1998 L1999 IM *020 †18

ESMAILI, Neama. 7810 5 MILE RD 45230 #038-40-2004 L2004 FM *020 †18

ESPAY, Alberto Javier. 222 PIEDMONT AVE, STE 3200 45219 #935-01-1994 L2005 N *020 ‡

ESSELL, James Herbert. 199 WILLIAM HOWARD TAFT RD, STE 101 45219 #038-41-1985 L1987 HO ON *020 †20

ESSELL, Scott Kurt. 1219 MORTS PASS 45215 #038-41-1989 L1992 EM *020 †16

ESTERLE, Teresa Marie. 663 ANDERSON FERRY RD, WEST SIDE PEDIATRICS 45238 #047-05-1995 L1996 PD *020 †55

ESTES, Robin. 10496 MONTGOMERY RD, STE 106 45242 #016-11-1978 L1983 NEP *020 †20

EVANS, Arthur T, III. 3333 BURNET AVE 45229 #038-41-1974 L1974 OBG MFM *020 †30

EVANS, Burton Warren. 2123 AUBURN AVE, # 200 45219 #038-41-1962 L1962 CRS GS *071 †85

EVANS, Gregory Edward. ■ 45249 #038-41-2008 *012

EVANS, Jamie Lorraine. ■ 45220 #041-12-2008 *012

EVANS, Kristin Marie. ■ 45230 #038-41-2008 *012

EVANS, Linda Clemmons. 10475 MONTGOMERY RD STE 1C 45242 #038-41-1988 L1989 OBG *020 †30 ‡

EVANS, Richard Harold. 3155 GLENDALE MILFORD RD, CINCINNATI EVENDALE SURG 45241 #038-41-1955 L1955 AN FPG *072 †05

EVANS, Thomas Miller. 7500 STATE RD 45255 #038-41-1959 L1959 OBG *071 †30

EVENSON, Eric T. 5299 SPRING GROVE AVE, RM 2506 45217 #026-08-1976 L2002 OM PHP *030 †70

EVERHARD, Janet Schulz. 7655 5 MILE RD, STE 212 45230 #016-43-1989 L1992 GYN *020

EYAL, Ori. 3333 BURNET AVE 45229 #550-02-1998 L2002 PDE *100

FABREY, David Christopher. 9292 COMPTON SQUARE DR #24 45231 #038-40-1973 L1977 FM *020

FACKLER, Jon Richard. 11135 MONTGOMERY RD 45249 #038-43-1986 L1988 OBG *020 †30

FAGIN, James A. 222 PIEDMONT AVE, STE 6000 45219 #132-01-1973 L1995 END IM *050 †20

FAIK BARAK PETERS, Mhroos. 2139 AUBURN AVE 45219 #915-04-1997 L2005 FP *012

FAIN, Michael Anthony. ■ 45208 #012-01-1980 L1981 EM *020 †16

FALCIGLIA, Horacio Sergio. 3217 CLIFTON AVE DEPT PED 45220 #132-01-1968 L1976 NPM PD *020

FALCIGLIA, Mercedes. 3125 EDEN AVE, UC MEDICAL CTR-ENDOCRINOLO 45267 #038-41-1997 L1999 END *020 †20

FALCONE, Richard A, Jr. 231 ALBERT SABIN WAY 05 45267 #035-19-1995 L1997 PDS *020 †85

FALKNER, Charles Fredrick. 1101 SUMMIT RD 45237 #062-01-1952 L1960 P OS *071

FALLAT, David Michael. 5837 HAMILTON AVE 45224 #038-41-1991 L1992 P *020 †20

FARHEY, Yolanda Daniela. 231 ALBERT SABIN WAY 45267 #781-01-1983 L1996 RHU IM *020 †20

FARNEJAD, Farshad. 4777 E GALBRAITH RD, CO MEDICAL 45236 #422-01-2007 L2007 GS *012

FARNUM, James Brotherton. 375 DIXMYTH AVE, GOOD SAM HOSP DEPT OF PATH 45220 #016-11-1974 L1990 ATP PCP *062 †50

FARRELL, Helen Mavourneen. 234 GOODMAN ST 45267 #539-03-2006 L2007 P *012

FARRELL, Michael Kevin. 3333 BURNET AVE, CHILDRENS HOSP MED CTR 45229 #041-02-1970 L1974 PG NTR *030 †55

FAUL, Robert Louis. 11155 KENWOOD RD, UNIT1 45242 #028-02-1972 L1976 GS *020 †85

FAULKNER, James Donald. 1945 CEI DR 45242 #038-41-1966 L1966 OPH OS *020 †35

FAULKNER, William Joe. 1945 CEI DR 45242 #020-02-1976 L1980 OPH OS *020 †35 ‡

FAVORITO, Honora Heffner. 311 STRAIGHT ST 45219 #035-06-1993 L2000 PTH *020 †50

FAVORITO, Paul Joseph. 6350 GLENWAY AVE 45211 #035-06-1993 L1998 OSM ORS *020 †40

FAZLANI, Naveed Anjum. 2450 KIPLING AVE, STE 204 45239 #704-02-1989 L1995 IM *020 †20

FEALY, Jessica Lynne. ■ 45239 #038-41-2008 *012

FECTEAU, Annie Helene. ■ 45226 #067-01-1988 L1996 GS *020 †85

FEDDERS, David Leo. 1 W 4TH ST STE 2250 45202 #028-34-1969 L1972 P *020 †75

FEGELMAN, Elliott Jay. 4760 E GALBRAITH, STE 108 45236 #038-45-1988 L1991 GS *020 †85

FEGHALI, Edouard Amine. 2139 AUBURN AVE 45219 #605-02-1972 L1977 OBG *020 †30

FEGHALI, George Maurice. 3219 CLIFTON AVE, STE 215 45220 #561-11-1980 L1985 IM *030 †20

FEIGELSON, Howard H. 234 GOODMAN ST, ML0761 45267 #038-41-1950 L1950 R NM *071 †80,28

FEIMAN, David Maurice. 3101 BURNET AVE, C/O MEDICAL DIRECTOR CINN 45229 #038-06-1969 L1969 P CHP *020 †75,55

FEINBERG, Judith. 3223 ALBERT SABIN WAY, STE 405 45267 #016-01-1979 L1995 ID IM *050 †20

FELD, Ellen W. 8231 CORNELL RD, ASSOCIATES IN WOMENS 45249 #035-08-1982 L1985 OBG *020

FELDHAUS, Omer John. 375 DIXMYTH AVE 45220 #038-41-1948 L1948 GP OS *020

FELDKAMP, Rachel Marie. ■ 45243 #038-40-2006 L2006 PD *012

FELDMAN, Debra Miriam. ■ 45208 #016-42-1986 L1995 EM *020 †16

FELDMAN, Michael Ian. 9403 KENWOOD RD STE B100, KENWOOD PROF BLDG 45242 #038-41-1973 L1973 D *020

FELIPE-MORALES, Javier A. 2450 KIPLING AVE, STE 105 45239 #847-04-1969 L1982 U *020 †95

FENNIMORE, Irina Anatolye. 375 DIXMYTH AVE, TRI-HEALTH MED CTR 45220 #913-83-1993 L2004 OBG *012

FENOGLIO-PREISER, Cecilia. 231 ALBERT SABIN WAY, UNIVERSITY OF CINCINNATI 45267 #010-02-1969 L1990 PTH OBG *062 †50

FEQUIERE, Pierre Richard. ■ 45230 #440-01-1998 L2005 CHN *012 †55

FERGUSON, Bryce Lyman. ■ 45230 #049-01-2005 L2005 MPD *012

FERIOLI, Simona. 231 ALBERT, INTERNAL MEDICINE DEPT 45267 #561-01-2005 L2007 N *012

FERMANN, Gregory Jos. 2139 AUBURN AVE, STE 0769 45219 #038-41-1992 L1996 EM *020 †16

FERNANDEZ, Francisco Javi. ■ 45208 #010-01-2006 L2006 EM *012

FERNANDEZ-ULLOA, Mariano. 234 GOODMAN ST, STE 0054 45219 #924-01-1967 L1976 NM *020 †28

FERREE, Bret Allen. 8000 5 MILE RD, STE 112 45230 #038-41-1986 L1991 ORS *020 †40

FERRERI, Nicholas Alexand. ■ 45242 #038-41-2008 *012

FICHTENBAUM, Carl Jack. 231 ALBERT SABIN WAY, PO 670405 45267 #028-46-1985 L1999 ID IM *050 †55,20

FIDELHOLTZ, James Ira. 6103 HAMILTON AVE 45224 #038-41-1972 L1972 IM IMG *020 †20

FIEDLER, Michael Joseph. 7500 STATE RD, CARE CONSULTANTS MERCY 45255 #038-41-2001 L2001 AN *020

FIEHRER, Kevin Douglas. 4422 CARVER WOODS DR, STE 100 45242 #038-45-1984 L1986 FM *020 †18

FILAK, Andrew Thos, Jr. 3333 BURNET AVE 45229 #010-01-1978 L1979 FM EM *040 †18

FILARDO, Thomas Wesley. ■ 45241 #016-11-1971 L1989 FM *062 †18

FILIPOVICH, Alexandra. 3333 BURNET AVE, DIV OF HERMATOLOGY/ONCOLOG 45229 #026-04-1974 L1996 OS IG *050 †55

FINER, Saul. ■ 45202 #038-41-1945 L1945 GP *071

FINK, Richard Wm, Jr. 6350 GLENWAY AVE, STE 205 45211 #038-41-1971 L1971 OBG *020 †30

FINKE, John Elsbernd. 3724 SAINT LAWRENCE AVE 45205 #028-34-1954 L1955 FM *020

FINKE, Teresa Bernadette. 3333 BURNET AVE, MLC 11013 45229 #020-02-2003 L2007 MPD *020 †55

FINKELMAN, Fred Douglass. BOX 670563, OF MED IMMUNOL PO 45267 #008-01-1971 L1995 RHU IM *050 †20

FINLAY, Robert Dawson. 3130 HIGHLAND AVE, STE 0557 45219 #038-45-1997 L1999 IM *020 †20

FINN, Thomas E. 6350 GLENWAY AVE 45211 #038-41-1951 L1951 OBG *071

FINNEY, Susan Newsom. 2475 W GALBRAITH RD # A, QUEEN CITY PHYS 45239 #001-02-1984 L1987 PD *020 †55

FINTON, Paula Jeanne. 375 DIXMYTH AVE 45220 #104-01-2007 L2007 IM *012

FIORITO, Frank Nunzio. 1219 MORTS PASS 45215 #038-45-2000 L2000 EM *020 †16

FIRESTEIN, Scott Lawrence. 2001 ANDERSON FERRY RD, GROUP HEALTH ASSOCIATES-OB 45238 #028-34-1993 L1995 OBG *020 †30

FIRESTONE, Melvin Martin. 2915 CLIFTON AVE 45220 #008-01-1975 L1977 IM *020 †20

FIROR, Hugh Valentine. ■ 45249 #023-01-1953 L1981 PDS *040 †85

FIROR, Thomas Russell. 9925 FORESTGLEN DR, TOM FIROR 45242 #038-41-1987 L1989 IM *020 †20

FISCHER, Carl Geo, Jr. 3300 ELLAND AVE # ANES, CHILDRENS HOSPITAL 45229 #035-45-1965 L1966 AN *071 †05

FISCHER, Danny Benj. 3219 CLIFTON AVE, STE 325 45220 #065-09-1985 L1991 NEP *020 †20

FISCHER, Donald C. ■ 45243 #028-34-1951 L1953 OS IM *071 †20

FISCHER, Ian Thomas. 234 GOODMAN ST, DEPT RAD 45267 #039-01-2005 L2006 DR *012

FISCHER, Thomas Jos. 375 DIXMYTH AVE 45220 #038-41-1971 L1971 AI PD *020 †55,03

FISHER, David Carl. 2753 ERIE AVE 45208 #038-40-1990 L1993 IM *020 †20

FISHER, Edward Gregory. 10547 MONTGOMERY RD, STE 400 45242 #016-43-1964 L1971 ORS *020 †40

FISHMAN, Melvin B. ■ 45229 #038-41-1941 L1941 GS *071

FISK, Jean Ann. 2139 AUBURN AVE 45219 #038-41-1980 L1983 GYN OBS *075 †30

FITZ, Anne M Basarrate. 3333 BURNET AVE, CINCINNATI CHILDREN'S HOSP 45229 #047-06-1993 L1996 PD *020 †55

FIX, Annmarie. 7495 STATE RD *55 45255 #038-45-1996 L1997 PD *020 †55

FIXLER, Z Chas. 3120 BURNET AVE, STE 302 45229 #869-05-1951 L1954 D *020 †15 ‡

FLAHERTY, Matthew Leonard. 222 PIEDMONT AVE, STE 3200 45219 #019-02-1999 L2003 N *100 †75

FLASPOHLER, Louis Edward. 2100 SHERMAN AVE, STE 110 45212 #038-41-1997 L2000 RHU *020 †20

FLECK, Robert Jos, Jr. 3333 BURNET AVE, CCHMC-MLC 5031 45229 #026-04-1991 L2000 PDR *020 †80

FLEGE, John Blain. 231 ALBERT SABIN WAY, ML 0558 45267 #038-41-1954 L1954 TS *072 †85,90

FLEISCH, Sheryl Brynne. ■ 45227 #047-05-2008 *012

FLEISCHMAN, Meyer Jack. 3200 BURNET AVE 45229 #038-41-1946 L1946 OBG *020

FLEITES, Rafael. 9200 MONTGOMERY RD, STE 3A 45242 #275-03-1990 L1998 IM *020 †20

FLEMING, Richard Bahr. ■ 45226 #038-41-1959 L1961 OTO A *071 †45

FLENNER, Timothy Joseph. 7500 STATE RD 45255 #038-41-1979 L1980 PM *020 †60

FLESSA, Herbert C. BETHESDA AVE M2562, COLLEGE OF MED 45267 #038-41-1952 L1952 OS HEM *020 †20

FLETCHER, Derek Douglas. 9206 HUNTERS CREEK DR 45242 #038-45-2002 L2002 PD *020 †55

FLETCHER, Paula Darlene. 45246 #022-12-1971 L1983 IM END *020 †20

FLIMAN, Henry J. 8221 CORNELL RD, STE 420 45249 #550-02-1974 L1978 OBG *020 †30

FLOREZ, Francis Xavier. 2454 KIPLING AVE, STE 120 45239 #038-06-1985 L1988 ORS *020 †40

FLOREZ, Raul. 2841 BOUDINOT AVE, FREIBERG ORTHOPAEDIC AND 45238 #264-01-1950 L1957 ORS *072 †40

FLYNN, Freeda J. 4623 WESLEY AVE, STE P 45212 #020-02-1991 L1994 FM *020 †18 ‡

FOAD, Baher Salem Ibrahim. 7730 MONTGOMERY RD, STE 200 45236 #330-04-1964 L1972 RHU IM *020 †20,03

FOAD, Mohab Baher. 222 PIEDMONT AVE STE 2200 45219 #038-41-1999 L1999 HS ORS *020 †40

FOAD, Mona Salem. 7730 MONTGOMERY RD, 2ND FL 45236 #038-41-1998 L2002 D *020 †15

FOAD, Wafaa A R. 7730 MONTGOMERY RD, STE 200 45236 #915-04-1964 L1980 IM *020

FODOR, Daniel Wade. DEPT. OF RADIOLOGY, UNIVERSITY OF CINCINNATI 45267 #016-42-2001 L2002 DR *100 †80

FODOR, Kim Marie. 7825 LAUREL AVE 45243 #010-01-1996 L2002 IM *020 †20

FOERTMEYER, Charles Henry. ■ 45240 #038-41-1942 L1942 IM *071

FOGEL, Kevin Morrow. 45267 #038-41-1999 L1999 PCC *100

FOLEY, Ian Michael. ■ 45212 #038-43-2006 L2006 OBG *012

FOLT, Jason Robert. ■ 45212 #038-41-2008 *012

FOOTE, David William. ■ 45212 #038-40-2006 L2006 IM *012

FORBES, Kathleen Lee. 619 OAK ST, TRIHEALTH 45206 #038-43-1987 L1990 FM *030 †18

FORD, Kanti Ranu. ■ 45237 #005-14-1998 L2005 ADL *012 †18

FORD, Starr, Jr. 2139 AUBURN AVE, # 234 45219 #038-41-1961 L1962 IM END *071 †20

FORD-CRAWFORD, Lisa D. 7162 READING RD, 12 FL 45237 #038-41-1991 L1997 P *020

FOREMAN, Mark Jonathan. ■ 45219 #005-06-2007 L2007 MPD *012

FORRESTER, Jacob Justen. 311 ALBERT SABIN WAY 45229 #038-41-2004 L2004 P *012

FORSTON, Stanley Rodes, Jr. ■ 45226 #020-12-1975 L1977 PD *030 †55

FORTUNA, Robert Brian. 234 GOODMAN ST 45219 #045-01-2001 L2002 DR *100 †80

FORTUNO, Salvador Z. ■ 45252 #748-01-1953 L1980 GP *071

FORUHARI, Farzin. 3158 GLENMORE AVE 45211 #011-03-1998 L2000 MPD *020 †20,55

FOSTER, Bernard Bouldin. 3001 HIGHLAND AVE, STE E 45219 #067-01-1965 L1966 P PYA *020 †75

FOSTER, Keith Douglas. 3333 BURNET AVE 45229 #038-45-1988 L1989 CHP *020 †75

FOSTER, Kirk William. 231 ALBERT SABIN WAY 45267 #023-01-1997 L2004 PTH *020 †50

FOULADI, Maryam. 3333 BURNET AVE, MAIL LOCATION: 7015 45229 #065-01-1991 L1998 PD *020 †55

FOUNDAS, Semele. 4760 E GALBRAITH RD # 108 45236 #055-01-1984 L1987 GS *071 †85

FOUNTAIN, Jamie Korin. ■ 45202 #035-03-2006 L2006 PD *012

FOUYAS, Ioannis. ■ 45267 #418-01-1988 L2000 *100

FOX, Constance. 58 E HOLLISTER ST 45219 #007-02-1972 L1975 P *020 †75

FOX, John P. 11234 CORNELL PARK DR 45242 #038-41-1953 L1953 GP *020 †70

FOX, Matthew. 3200 BURNET AVE 45229 #550-04-2004 L2004 DR *012

FOX, Oran Danl. 6480 HARRISON AVE, SPORTS MEDICINE 45247 #038-40-1974 L1974 ORS *020 †40

FOX, Sarah Elizabeth. ■ 45249 #038-41-2008 *012

FOY, Richard Rodney. 4623 WESLEY AVE, STE P 45212 #038-45-1985 L1987 FM *020 †18

FRAME, Peter Timothy. SABIN WAY, EDEN AVE & ALBERT 45267 #038-41-1969 L1969 ID IM *020 †20

FRANKLIN, Daniel Allen. 3380 ERIE AVE, STE 16 45208 #038-41-1966 L1966 EM IM *020 †20,16

FRANKOWSKI, Amy Ann. 175 W GALBRAITH RD 45216 #038-40-1990 L1991 IM *020 †20

FRANZ, David Neal. 3333 BURNET AVE, CHILDRENS HOSP-NEUROLOGY 45229 #038-40-1985 L1986 CHN *020 †75,55

FRAZIER, Larita Linette. 155 TRI COUNTY PKWY, STE 240 45246 #038-41-1989 L1992 FM *020 †18

FRECKA, James Thos. 4750 E GALBRAITH RD, STE 206 45236 #038-41-1988 L1994 IM *020 †20

FRECKMAN, Herman A F. ■ 45215 #038-41-1938 ON *071

FREDERICK, Kenneth A J. ■ 45224 #038-41-1949 L1949 FM FPG *072 †18

FREE, Noel Karl. 3001 HIGHLAND AVE, STE E 45219 #036-01-1972 L1977 P PYA *020 †75

FREEDMAN, Jerald Neil. 3020 BURNET AVE 45242 #038-41-1973 L1974 DR VIR *020 †85

FREEMAN, Andrew Glen. 3223 EDEN AVE ML #0458, CENTER FOR OCCUPATIONAL HL 45267 #005-18-1986 L1995 GPM GP *020 †70

FREEMAN, Stephanie. 375 DIXMYTH AVE, ATT: MEDICAL EDUCATION 45220 #913-50-1997 L2007 OBG *012

FREEMAN, Timothy Duane. 3306 RUTHER AVE, CLIFTON-CORRYVILLE 45220 #038-41-1984 L1986 FM *020 †18

FREESE, Michael Eugene, Jr. 2135 DANA AVE, STE 210 45207 #038-41-1996 L1997 IM *020 †20

FREIBERG, Richard Albert. 9825 KENWOOD RD, STE 200 45242 #024-01-1957 L1959 ORS *071 †40

FRENCH, Michelle L. 4370 MALSBARY RD, STE 100 45242 #038-41-1987 L1989 PD *020 †55

FRENCK, Robert Wilson, Jr. ■ 45236 #048-14-1981 L2006 PD ID *050 †55

FREY, Gregory Alan. 4700 SMITH RD 45212 #020-02-1977 L1978 U *020 †95

FREY, Raymond Terrell. 375 DIXMYTH AVE 45220 #038-41-1973 L1974 DR VIR *020 †80

FRIAS, Mayra Yokasta. 8245 NORTHCREEK DR 45236 #308-03-1988 L2000 IM *020 †20

FRIDRIKSSON, Jon Hilmar. 3333 BURNET AVE, DEPARTMENT OF PEDIATRICS 45229 #484-01-1988 L1993 NPM *020 †55

FRIED, Peter Ronald. 4777 E GALBRAITH RD 45236 #051-04-1981 L1988 RO *020 †80

FRIEDEMAN, Elliott M. 106 WELLINGTON PL 45219 #011-03-1972 L1976 P CHP *020 †75

FRIEDLAND, Leonard Ross. 3333 BURNET AVE 45229 #035-47-1987 L1992 PD PEM *020 †55

FRIEDMAN, Stewart Jay. 2123 AUBURN AVE, STE 528 45219 #038-41-1978 L1982 OBG *030 †30

FRIEDRICH, Andrew D. 231 ALBERT SABIN WAY, DEPT OFANESTHESIA 45267 #035-45-1995 L2005 CCA *020 †05

FRIEDSTROM, Scott Roy. 330 STRAIGHT ST 45219 #040-02-1979 L1999 ID *020 †20

FRIEMOTH, Jerry Alan. 1295 KEMPER MEADOW DR 45240 #038-40-1974 L1974 FM *040 †18

FRIEND, Kerri Leigh. ■ 45219 #038-41-2008 *012

FRIMER, David Stephen. 24 COMPTON RD, STE 205 45216 #065-01-1972 L1979 FM *020

FRISCH, Amy Lynn. ■ 45208 #020-12-2006 L2006 PD *012

FRITZ, Deborah Ann. 10550 MONTGOMERY RD STE 23 45242 #020-02-1982 L1983 RHU *020 †20

FRITZHAND, Martin Danl. 2825 BURNET AVE 45219 #035-08-1967 L1969 OM LM *020 †95

FROEHLICH, Kurt Wm. 10475 MONTGOMERY RD STE 3A 45242 #038-41-1992 L1993 OBG *020 †30

FROEHLICH, Tanya E. 3333 BURNET AVE, MLC 4002 45229 #008-01-1999 L2002 DBP *100 †55

FROELICH, Sebastien Charl. 231 ALBERT, DEPT OF NEUROLOGICAL SURGE 45267 #396-08-2002 L2005 *100

FROSCHAUER, Wm Edward, Jr. 2915 CLIFTON AVE, GROUP HEALTH ASSOCIATES 45220 #038-41-1971 L1971 IM *020

FRY, Gregory John. 500 E BUSINESS WAY 45241 #038-41-1986 L1990 AN PME *020 †05

FRY, Richard Jos. 2915 CLIFTON AVE, GROUP HEALTH ASSOCIATES 45220 #038-43-1979 L1983 OBG *020 †30

FU, Lily. ■ 45267 #048-02-2002 L2003 DR *020 †80

FUHS, John Chas. 2139 AUBURN AVE 45219 #038-41-1945 L1945 OPH *071 †35

FULKERSON, Patricia Chand. ■ 45209 #038-41-2007 L2007 PD *012

FULLER, Nancy Suzanne. 231 ALBERT SABIN WAY, PSYCHIATRY AND 45267 #045-01-2001 L2006 PFP *012 †75

FUNCH, Matthew James. ■ 45208 #055-02-2008 *012

FUNK, Daniel Allen. 3950 RED BANK RD 45227 #038-41-1981 L1986 ORS *020 †40

FURBY, John Edward. 7655 5 MILE RD 45230 #016-11-1982 L1985 OS PD *020

FURER, Jerald Allen. 8221 CORNELL RD, STE 420 45249 #038-41-1977 L1978 OBG *020 †30

GABRIEL-SHENOUDA, Samira. CINCINN GEN HOSP, DEPT PATH 45229 #915-04-1969 L1976 PTH *020 †50

GAINES, Juanita Hall. 4623 WESLEY AVE, STE P 45212 #038-41-1979 L1982 IM *020 †20

GAITONDE, Krishnanath Dat. 231 ALBERT SABIN WAY, ML 0589 UROLOGY 45267 #496-15-1994 L2004 *100

GAITONDE, Shrawan. UNIV OF CINCINNATI MED CTR, DEPT OF SURGERY 45267 #048-16-2007 L2007 GS *012

GALARZA, Marcelo. UNIV OF CINCINNATI, PO BOX 670510 45267 #132-07-1996 L2001 NS *100

GALE, Melvin S. 2123 AUBURN AVE # 303 45219 #035-08-1969 L1971 P PYG *020 †75

GALL, Ronald Marcel. 2475 W GALBRAITH RD 45239 #038-41-1977 L1978 IM *020 †20

GALLA, John Halm. 3130 HIGHLAND AVE, STE 0557 45219 #035-20-1967 L1989 NEP IM *072 †20

GALLAGHER, John Michael. 6480 HARRISON AVE, SPORTS MEDICINE 45247 #038-41-1978 L1981 ORS *020 †40

GALLAGHER, Mary Deegan. 3130 HIGHLAND AVE, STE 0557 45219 #030-05-1996 L1999 IM *020 †20

GALLAWAY, Mary Ann. ■ 45211 #038-41-2007 L2007 FP *012

GALLENSTEIN, Edwin Elmer. 6240 HAMILTON AVE 45224 #038-41-1955 L1955 GP *020

GALLOWAY, Elizabeth M. 3333 BURNET AVE, CCHMC ML2005 45229 #046-01-2002 L2005 CCP *012

GALLOWAY, Marc Tomas. 3301 WESTBOURNE DR 45248 #036-07-1984 L1989 ORS OSM *020 †40

■ = Address Information Privacy Protected

GAMMON, Steven Ray. ■ 45231 #028-34-2006 L2006 **ORS** *012
GANDOLA, Carl Davidson. 3917 SPRING GROVE AVE, NORTHSIDE HEALTH CENTER 45223 #038-06-1976 L1979 **IM IMG** *020 †20
GANDRA, Sushmitha. ■ 45236 #495-57-2000 L2004 **NEP** *012 †20
GANESH, Thiyagarajan. 375 DIXMYTH AVE 45220 #495-94-2001 L2005 **IM** *012
GAPEN, Cynthia Lisabeth. 375 DIXMYTH AVE, NEONATOLOGY 45220 #038-41-1985 L1990 **PTH IM** *020 †50
GARCIA, Victor Franco. 3333 BURNET AVE, OSB-3 PEDIATRIC SURGERY 45229 #041-01-1974 L1990 **PDS GS** *020 †85
GARCIA-DUARTE, Olga C. 8000 5 MILE RD, STE 103 45230 #847-03-1982 L1987 **IM EM** *020
GARDNER, Sandy Lynn. 3219 CLIFTON AVE STE 230 45220 #019-02-1996 L1997 **OBG** *020 †30
GARFIELD, James. 10475 READING RD STE 401 45241 #038-41-1954 L1954 **IM** *071 †20
GARG, Rajeev Kumar. ■ 45267 #048-12-2002 L2002 **AN** *020 †05
GARIN-LAFLAM, Monica Paz. 3333 BURNET AVE, PEDIATRIC GASTROENTEROLOGY 45229 #011-02-2001 L2004 **PG** *100
GARLAPATI, Vamsi Krishna. 231 ALBERT SABIN WAY 55 45267 #495-50-1995 L2003 **P** *020
GARRETT, Jeffrey Vernon. 231 ALBERT SABIN WAY, SECTION OF CARDIOTHORACIC 45267 #039-01-2000 L2005 **TS** *012 †85
GARRISON, Jonathan Cross. 8220 NORTHCREEK DR STE 11D 45236 #038-41-1982 L1987 **CHP P** *020
GARRO, Aris Charles. 3333 BURNET AVE, CO CHILDREN S HOSP-MED EDU 45229 #047-05-2001 L2001 **PEM** *020 †55
GARVEY, James Mc Brayer. 2123 AUBURN AVE, STE 520 45219 #035-01-1954 L1957 **IM CD** *071 †20
GARVIN, Edward Ralph. 3006 PORTSMOUTH AVE 45208 #038-41-1994 L2006 **PD** *020 †55
GARZA, Jose Miguel. 3333 BURNET AVE, CHILDRENS HOSP MED CTR 45229 #649-13-2003 L2004 **PG** *012 †55
GASKILL, Mary Frances. 234 GOODMAN ST, STE 0054 45219 #038-41-1983 L1985 **DR** *020 †80
GASS, Margery L S. 222 PIEDMONT AVE, STE 5100 45219 #038-41-1980 L1983 **GYN** *020 †30
GATES, William Harold. 4767 N BEND RD 45211 #038-41-1966 L1966 **IM EM** *072
GATTA, Prakash. 231 ALBERT SABIN WAY, DEPT OF SURGERY 45267 #496-38-2000 L2007 **GS** *020
GAUSE, Levi Nathan. ■ 45231 #001-06-2005 L2005 **ORS** *012
GAW, Eusebio Tiu. 2450 KIPLING AVE, STE 112A 45239 #748-01-1962 L1969 **HS GS** *020 †85
GAYOL, Ester Azarcon. 3036 WOODBURN AVE 45206 #748-08-1961 L1970 **PD ADL** *020 †55
GAYOL, Eusebio N. ■ 45211 #748-01-1957 L1969 **GP** *071
GEBHARDT, Brian Stephen. ■ 45233 #038-41-2003 L2003 **AN** *020
GEERAERTS, Frans L. 2446 KIPLING AVE 45239 #165-02-1959 L1964 **P** *072 †75
GEERS, Ryan Theodore. ■ 45209 #038-45-2007 L2007 **EM** *012
GEIER, Rodney Phelps. 7500 STATE RD 45255 #038-41-1984 L1988 **RO** *020 †80
GEIS, Gary Lee. 3333 BURNET AVE 45229 #038-41-1997 L2001 **PEM PD** *020 †55
GELBART, Howard. 184 E MCMILLAN ST 45219 #020-02-1969 L1975 **OBG** *020 †30
GELDMACHER, Randy Jay. 3200 BURNET AVE 45229 #654-01-2007 L2007 **GS** *012
GELFAND, Michael Jos. 3333 BURNET AVE 45229 #005-11-1971 L1974 **NM PD** *020 †28,55
GELKE, Ann Roberta Huser. ■ 45220 #038-41-1970 L1970 **CHP P** *020
GELLER, James Ian. 3333 BURNET AVE, DIV OF HEMATOLOGY / ONCOLO 45229 #550-02-1997 L2004 **PHO** *100 †55 ‡
GELMAN, Larisa. 151 W GALBRAITH RD 45216 #913-18-1981 L1997 **IM** *020 †20
GELMAN, Lev. 4871 PROSPERITY PL 45238 #913-18-1979 L1995 **IM** *020 †20
GELMAN, Sheila Claire. ■ 45237 #038-41-1980 L1987 **IM IMG** *020 †20
GENDELMAN, Arthur V. 7426 JAGER CT 45230 #038-41-1978 L1979 **IM** *020 †20
GENNARI, Lisa Carol. 8231 CORNELL RD, STE 320 45249 #028-46-1992 L1993 **OBG** *020 †30
GENSLER, Fredrick. 106 WELLINGTON PL 45219 #035-06-1970 L1973 **P** *020 †75
GENTRY, Kristen Marie. CINCINNATI M, UNIV HOSP-UNIV OF 45267 #038-40-2006 L2006 **P** *012
GEORGE, Alex. ■ 45238 #048-04-2005 L2005 **PD** *012
GEORGE, Rebecca. 10500 MONTGOMERY RD 45242 #495-96-1971 L1975 **PTH CLP** *020 †50
GERACIOTI, Thomas D, Jr. 3200 VINE ST 45220 #038-41-1983 L1993 **P** *050 †75
GERAGHTY, Sheela Rath. 3333 BURNET AVE, MLC 7035 45229 #038-41-1995 L1999 **PD** *020 †55
GERBER, Michael Allen. 3333 BURNET AVE, CHILDRENS HOSP MED CTR 45229 #008-01-1974 L2001 **PD ID** *020 †55
GERDES, Deborah Ann. 2727 MADISON RD STE 208 45209 #038-41-1999 L1999 **IM** *020 †20
GERHARDT, William John. ■ 45224 #038-41-1954 L1954 **PD** *071 †55
GERKE, Robert Anthony. 5535 MONTGOMERY RD 45212 #038-41-1990 L1992 **IM** *020 †20
GERSCH, Karen Ann. ■ 45226 #036-08-1998 L2007 **TS** *100
GERSON, Jennifer Whitney. 4350 MALSBARY RD, STE 208 45242 #038-41-1988 L1989 **RO** *020 †80
GERSON, Myron Craig. 3130 HIGHLAND AVE, STE 0557 45219 #017-20-1972 L1979 **CD IM** *040 †20
GERSTNER, Stephen Francis. 6040 HARRISON AVE 45248 #038-41-1974 L1975 **OTO** *071 †45
GESELL, Laurie Beth. 231 ALBERT SABIN WAY - M, MED C 45267 #033-05-1991 L1993 **EM ETX** *020 †16
GETACHEW, Mekasha Mike. ■ 45243 #005-02-1991 L2004 **DR** *020 †80
GHANI, Rasheed. 3515 BOUDINOT AVE 45211 #704-02-1961 L1977 **FM PD** *020
GHASTINE, Michel P. 6045 BRIDGETOWN RD 45248 #605-02-1990 L2001 **GE** *020 †20
GHAZI, Freidoon. 3219 CLIFTON AVE, STE 400 45220 #517-08-1977 L1984 **CD IM** *020 †20
GHIAUR, Elena Diana. ■ 45219 #781-01-2001 L2003 **IM** *020 †20
GHIAUR, Gabriel A. 2139 AUBURN AVE 45219 #781-01-2001 L2006 **IM** *012
GHORY, Ann Clark. 7495 STATE RD 45255 #038-40-1976 L1976 **AI PDA** *020 †55,03
GHORY, Patricia K. 7495 STATE RD, STE 350 45255 #038-41-1980 L1985 **AI PD** *020 †55,03
GHOSN, Saad J. 3200 VINE ST, VAMC/PATH & LAB MED (113) 45220 #605-01-1974 L1988 **PTH PCH** *020 †50
GIANNELLA, Ralph Aroune. 3130 HIGHLAND AVE, STE 0557 45219 #035-03-1965 L1980 **GE IM** *020 †20
GIANNOUTSOS, Ioannis. 234 GOODMAN ST 45267 #836-02-1987 **PTH** *100
GIBBONEY, Lawrence Jos. ■ 45215 #038-41-1942 L1942 **DR** *071 †80
GIBBONS, Joseph Gerard. 3333 BURNET AVE 45229 #038-40-1980 L1987 **PD** *020 †55
GIBBONS, Mary Elizabeth. 375 DIXMYTH AVE, GOOD SAMARITAN HOSPITAL 45220 #038-45-2001 L2006 **AN** *020 †05
GIBLER, Walter Brian. 231 ALBERT SABIN WAY ML076 45267 #047-05-1981 L1982 **EM** *030 †16
GIESEL, Roger Gresham. 7655 5 MILE RD 45230 #038-41-1954 L1954 **PD A** *071 †55
GIESLER, Caitlin Mc Aneny. ■ 45202 #048-14-2002 L2002 **CD** *012 †20
GIESLER, Eric J. ■ 45267 #048-14-2002 L2002 **U** *100
GIGLIA, Joseph Saml. 231 ALBERT SABIN WAY #2567 45267 #035-06-1989 L1998 **VS CCS** *020 †85
GILAD, Elyahu. 3333 BURNET AVE, OSB-5 45229 #550-01-1986 **CCP** *100
GILBERT, Donald Lawrence. 2015 MILLS AVE, DEPT OF NEUROLOGY, 45212 #025-01-1993 L1998 **CHN** *020 †75
GILBERTSON, Lesley Irene. 234 GOODMAN ST, STE 0531 45219 #041-12-1983 L2004 **AN IM** *020 †05
GILDAY, Elizabeth Carolyn. ■ 45204 #038-41-2006 L2006 **P** *012
GILDENBLATT, Daryl L. 10506 MONTGOMERY RD # 302 45242 #038-40-1980 L1983 **OBG** *020 †30 ‡
GILINSKY, Norman Harris. 6350 E GALBRAITH RD 45236 #836-02-1973 L1991 **GE IM** *020 †20
GILLEN, John Bernard, Sr. 7850 CAMARGO RD 45243 #038-41-1962 L1962 **OPH** *020 †35,18
GILLINGHAM, Paul Muir. ■ 45215 #005-02-1968 L1974 **CHP P** *020 †75
GILLIS, David Henry. ■ 45255 #047-07-1971 L1973 **ORS LM** *075
GINSBURG, Marshall. 231 BETHESDA AVE, DEPT PSYCHIATRY COLLEGE OF 45267 #016-11-1954 L1960 **P** *071 †75
GIRARD, Rita Maureen. 2446 KIPLING AVE, PROVIDENCE HOSPITAL RESIDE 45239 #025-01-1993 L1995 **FM** *020 †18
GIRARDI, Janna Ruthe. ■ 45215 #038-45-2008 *012
GITTELMAN, Michael Aron. 3333 BURNET AVE, CHILDREN HOSP MED CTR 45229 #041-07-1994 L1997 **PEM PD** *020 †55
GITTENS, Esther Mahabee. 3333 BURNET AVE 45229 #035-08-1992 L1996 **PD PEM** *020 †55
GIULIANO, John Sebastian. 3333 BURNET AVE, DEPT PEDIATRIC CRITICAL CA 45229 #010-01-2002 L2005 **CCP** *012 †55
GIULITTO, Carmella Helen. 330 STRAIGHT ST, STE 210 45219 #038-43-1986 L1991 **IM** *020 †20
GIVAN, Gordon Victor. ■ 45209 #038-41-2008 *012
GLASER, Richard Stephen. 10496 MONTGOMERY RD # 101 45242 #025-07-1971 L1972 **TS CD** *020 †85,90
GLASS, David Neville. 3333 BURNET AVE, PAV E2.270 45229 #917-01-1965 L1988 *020
GLASS, Todd Farryl. 3333 BURNET AVE 45229 #051-04-1989 L1998 **PD** *020 †55
GLASSMAN, Alan Danl. 2841 BOUDINOT AVE, STE 200 45238 #038-41-1976 L1986 **CD IM** *020 †20
GLASSMAN, Victor Philip. 4760 E GALBRAITH RD, STE 203 45236 #038-41-1969 L1969 **IM NEP** *020 †20
GLAUSER, Tracy Andrew. 3333 BURNET AVE, CHILDRENS HOSP DEPT NEUR 45229 #041-02-1985 L1992 **CHN N** *020 †75,55
GLEICH, Lyon Lance. 4620 WESLEY AVE, MEDPACE INC 45212 #035-08-1989 L1994 **ON OTO** *050 †45
GLOSTER, Angelique Devold. 375 DIXMYTH AVE 45220 #012-21-1989 L1994 **PD** *020 †55
GLOSTER, Hugh Morris, Jr. 4460 RED BANK RD, STE 130 45227 #012-01-1989 L1994 **D** *020 †15
GLUCKMAN, Jack Louis. 222 PIEDMONT AVE, STE 5200 45219 #836-02-1967 L1978 **OTO HNS** *020 †45
GLUECK, Charles Jonathan. 3200 BURNET AVE, CHOLESTEROL CENTER ABC BLD 45229 #038-06-1964 L1964 **CD END** *050
GOCKERMAN, Amy Lynn. 151 W GALBRAITH RD 45216 #036-01-1998 L1999 **IM** *020 †20
GODBY, Nicholas Adam. ■ 45236 #020-12-2008 *012
GODDARD, Mark Jos. 151 W GALBRAITH RD, PM&R SOUTH PAVILION 45216 #038-41-1983 L1986 **PM N** *020 †60
GODOFSKY, Alan Arnold. 7500 STATE RD, CARE CONSULTANTS MERCY 45255 #021-01-1983 L1986 **AN** *020 †05
GOEBEL, Jens W D. 3333 BURNET AVE, MLC 7022, CHILDRENS HOSP M 45229 #409-10-1990 L2003 **PN PD** *020 †55
GOEL, Jasleen Kaur. 3333 BURNET AVE, DEPT OF ANESTHESIOLOGY 45229 #496-07-1982 L1998 **PD** *020 †55
GOEL, Sharad. 3219 CLIFTON AVE STE 325 45220 #495-45-1982 L1998 **NEP** *020 †20
GOEL, Tarun K. 3308 JEFFERSON AVE 45220 #496-02-1971 L1980 **AS GS** *020 †85
GOEL, Vijender Nath. P2446 KIPLING AVE 45239 #495-30-1961 L1977 **FM PD** *071 †55
GOH, Ten Suan. ■ 45219 #825-01-1971 **PD** *050 †55
GOLDBERG, Grigory. 500 E BUSINESS WAY, SPORTS MEDICINE 45241 #035-08-2000 L2007 **ORS** *100
GOLDBERG, Stephen Jay. 4777 E GALBRAITH RD, JEWISH HOSP MEDICAL CENTE 45236 #016-42-1967 L1970 **GE HEP** *040 †20
GOLDFARB, Richard S. 2450 KIPLING AVE STE 108 45239 #038-41-1985 L1990 **MPD PD** *020 †20,55
GOLDMAN, Frederick M. 3120 BURNET AVE APT 4040 45229 #038-41-1936 **IM** *020 †20
GOLDSBERRY, Sara Helen. 234 GOODMAN ST 45219 #038-41-1996 L1999 **IM** *020 †20
GOLDSCHNEIDER, Kenneth R. 3333 BURNET AVE, DEPT OF ANESTHESIA 45229 #008-02-1991 L1999 **AN PME** *020 †05,55
GOLDSMITH, Richard J. 3200 VINE ST, 7 E VA MC 45220 #038-41-1977 L1980 **ADM** *020 †75
GOLLOBIN, Glenn Stephen. 3155 GLENDALE MILFORD RD, CINCINNATI EVENDALE SURG 45241 #028-02-1977 L1985 **AN IM** *020 †20,05 ‡
GOLTER, Lowell Emmitt. ■ 45215 #038-41-1946 L1946 **IM** *071
GOMAA, Ahmed E. 4676 COLUMBIA PKWY, MS R-17 45226 #915-03-1977 L2004 **IM OM** *020 †70
GOMEZ, Ana Maria. ■ 45267 #264-13-1984 L2000 *020 †50
GOMEZ, Francisco Javier. 231 ALBERT SABIN WAY 45267 #264-03-1989 L1995 **ID IM** *020 †20
GONZALES, Susan Violet. 1525 ELM ST 45202 #737-01-1993 L1998 **IM** *020 †20
GONZALEZ, Aurora. ■ 45202 #649-31-1985 L2000 **DR** *020 †80
GONZALEZ DEL REY, Javier. ELLAND AND BETHESDA AVE, DIV EM MED 45229 #308-02-1983 L1988 **PD** *020 †55
GOODMAN, Arlene Michelle. ■ 45227 #036-05-2004 L2007 **PSM** *012 †55
GOODMAN, Michael David. ■ 45208 #038-41-2005 L2005 **GS** *012
GOODMAN, Richard Paul. 330 STRAIGHT ST, STE 400 45219 #038-06-1990 L2001 **IM** *020 †20
GORANTLA, Radhika. 234 GOODMAN ST, DEPT RAD 45267 #016-11-2006 L2007 **DR** *012
GORELIK, Mark. ■ 45227 #047-05-2005 L2005 **PD** *012
GORHAM, Marian Jean. 7520 STATE RD 45255 #055-02-1986 L1988 **AN** *020 †05
GORMAN, Douglas Scott. 12053 BROOKWAY DR, BD CERTIFIED INTERNAL MED 45240 #028-02-1992 L1997 **IM** *020 †20
GORMAN, Kerry Elizabeth. 3333 BURNET AVE 5018, CHILDREN'S HOSPITAL 45229 #016-42-2004 L2004 **PD** *100 †55
GOSKE, Marilyn J. 3333 BURNET AVE, DEPT OF RADIOLOGY 45229 #008-02-1977 L1986 **PDR DR** *020 †80
GOSSARD, Ted William. 7175 BEECHMONT AVE, CARE-FOREST HILLS 45230 #038-41-1997 L1998 **FM** *020 †18
GOSSMANN, Martin W. 2430 FAIRVIEW AVE 45219 #409-05-1985 **P** *100
GOTTESMAN, Brent Evan. ■ 45208 #024-07-2005 L2005 **EM** *012
GOTTLIEBSON, William Mark. 3333 BURNET AVE, CIN CHLDRN HOSP MED CTR 45229 #021-01-1992 L2003 **PDC** *020 †55

■ = Address Information Privacy Protected

GOTTSCHLICH, Gregory Mark. 311 STRAIGHT ST 45219 #038-40-1982 L1983 AI IM *020 †20,03

GOTWALS, Clayton Kulp. 3001 HIGHLAND AVE, STE E 45219 #041-13-1966 L1971 PYA P *020 †75

GOULDIN, Catherine Wright. 3333 BURNET AVE, EMERGENCY MED DIV ML2008 45229 #051-04-1985 L1988 PD *020 †55

GOVIL, Amit. 231 ALBERT SABIN WAY, M.L. 0585 NEPHROLOGY 45267 #495-45-1994 L2000 NEP *020 †20

GOYAL, Prakash Chand. 10192 SPRINGFIELD PIKE 45215 #495-30-1958 L1974 PUD IM *020 †20

GRABOWSKI, Gregory Alex. 3333 BURNET AVE, S 45229 #026-04-1974 L1992 PD *020 †55,19

GRACANIN, Ludmila Maria. 2841 BLUE ROCK RD 45239 #038-43-1990 L1993 IM *020 †20

GRACANIN, Vlado. 2841 BLUE ROCK RD 45239 #154-02-1954 L1961 CD IM *071 †20

GRAD, Edward Alphonse, Jr. 311 STRAIGHT ST 45219 #038-41-1959 L1959 FM OM *071 †18

GRAD, Marjorie Ann. 5343 HAMILTON AVE, # RAL-40 45244 #038-41-1947 L1947 FM GYN *071

GRAF, Russell Arthur. 500 E BUSINESS WAY 45241 #020-02-1992 L1996 AN *020 †05

GRAF, William Richey. ■ 45208 #038-41-1945 L1945 OBG *071 †30

GRAFF, Jason Paul. 4139 WESLEY AVE, STE J 45210 #037-01-2000 L2000 FPG *020 †20

GRAHAM, J Robt. 3223 EDEN AVE, HEALTH PRO BLDG STE 141 45267 #019-02-1970 L1975 FM OS *020

GRAHAM, Thomas Brent. 3333 BURNET AVE, CHILDREN'S HOSPITAL MEDCEN 45229 #047-05-1992 L1996 PD PPR *020 †55

GRANDE, Andrew Walker. ■ 45267 #026-04-2003 L2003 NS *012

GRANDHI, Nav K. 9403 KENWOOD RD, STE 208 45242 #495-39-1985 L1990 GE *020 †20

GRANDOMINICO, Jodi Marie. ■ 45212 #038-41-2006 L2006 IM *012

GRANNAN, Kevin Jos. 2915 CLIFTON AVE, GROUP HEALTH ASSOCIATES 45220 #038-40-1982 L1985 GS *020 †85

GRANT, Oyebukola Ajike. 3101 BURNET AVE, STE 116 45229 #041-15-2003 L2007 PD *020

GRASS, Jeffrey Ira. 8000 5 MILE RD, STE 105 45230 #041-12-1995 L1996 RO *020 †80

GRAVELY, Chandra Yvette. 10700 MONTGOMERY RD, STE 311 45242 #012-21-1989 L1991 OBG *020 †30

GRAWE, Brian Michael. ■ 45208 #038-41-2008 *012

GRAY, Lisa Kaplan. ■ 45242 #038-41-2007 L2007 P *012

GRAY, Michael Eric. ■ 45242 #038-41-2007 L2007 IM *012

GREEN, Debora Jones. ■ 45208 #019-02-1975 L1979 IM EM *075

GREEN, Franklin Myles. 4777 E GALBRAITH RD, OBSTETRIC ANESTHESIA ASSOC 45236 #025-01-1982 L1985 AN *020 †30

GREEN, Jennifer Ach. 2123 AUBURN AVE STE 5 45219 #038-41-1997 L1998 OBG *020 †30

GREEN, Julianne Vernadett. 3333 BURNET AVE, CHILDRENS HOSP MED CTR 45229 #020-02-2006 L2006 PD *012

GREEN, Stuart Aaron. P.O. BOX 670564, UNIV OF CINC, 231 BETHESDA 45267 #047-06-1988 L1993 PUD CCM *012

GREEN, Thomas Eugene. 7631 CHEVIOT RD 45247 #038-45-1986 L1987 FM *020 †18

GREENBERG, Bruce Alan. 4750 E GALBRAITH RD, STE 207 45236 #017-20-1973 L1976 IM *020

GREENBERG, James Morris. 3333 BURNET AVE, DIV OF PULMONARY BIOLOGY 45229 #016-11-1981 L1991 NPM *020 †55

GREENBLUM, David Nathan. ■ 45243 #051-04-1976 L1980 P *020 †75

GREENERT, Stacey. 632 VINE ST STE 327 45202 #038-41-1966 L1966 A FM *020

GREENFIELD, David Jay. 2841 BOUDINOT AVE, FREIBERG ORTHOPAEDIC AND 45238 #035-15-1968 L1969 ORS *020 †40

GREENWALD, Dawn Iris. 7691 5 MILE RD, CINCINNATI 45230 #035-03-1979 L1987 D *020 †15

GREFF, Linda Joy. 1945 CEI DR 45242 #038-40-1985 L1991 OPH OS *020 †35

GREGG, Richard Van. 3155 GLENDALE MILFORD RD, CINCINNATI EVENDALE SURG 45241 #020-02-1981 L1985 PMM AN *020 †05

GREGORIE, Daniel A. 655 EDEN PARK DR, STE 400 45202 #024-07-1975 L1990 OS IM *030 †20

GREGORY, Robert Edward. 2001 ANDERSON FERRY RD 45238 #038-41-1955 L1955 PD *020 †55

GREINER, Alson Lee. 2139 AUBURN AVE 45219 #005-02-1967 L1976 NS *020 †25

GREINWALD, John H, Jr. 222 PIEDMONT AVE, FL 5 45219 #045-01-1987 L2000 OTO *020 †45

GREIWE, Raymond Michael. ■ 45223 #011-04-2004 L2004 ORS *012

GRIES, Gary Edward. 6211 SALEM RD, ANDERSON TWP FIRE ANDRESCU 45230 #038-43-1979 L1981 EM *020 †16

GRIFFIN, George D J. 5754 BRIDGETOWN RD 45248 #038-41-1975 L1975 ORS *020 †40

GRIFFIN, George Danl Jos. 5754 BRIDGETOWN RD 45248 #016-43-1947 L1956 GS OS *071 †85

GRIFFIN, Thomas Andrew. 3333 BURNET AVE, MLC 4010 45229 #038-06-1991 L1992 PPR *050 †54

GRIFFITH, David Olswells. 5400 KENNEDY AVE, PROSCAN IMAGING 45213 #048-12-1984 L1994 DR *020 †80

GRIFFITH, John F. 3200 BURNET AVE, HEALTH ALLIANCE 45229 #068-01-1958 L2000 CHN PD *030 †55

GRIM, Harley Alfred. 8234 WINTON RD STE 250 45231 #038-41-1979 L1981 OBG *020 †30

GRIMM, Thomas Wendell. 9030 MONTGOMERY RD 45242 #038-41-1983 L1986 FM *020 †18

GRINFELD, Evgueni. 619 OAK ST, TRIHEALTH INC 45206 #913-06-1994 L2005 IM *100 †20

GRINVALSKY, Henry T. 222 PIEDMONT AVE, STE 3200 45219 #048-15-1975 L1979 N OS *071 †75

GRISE, Erin Mcdonough. ■ 45213 #016-06-2004 L2004 EM *012

GRISEL, Jedidiah James. ■ 45267 #048-16-2006 L2006 OTO *012

GROBER, Robert A. 7500 STATE RD 45255 #010-01-1982 L1984 FM *020 †18

GROH, Lynda Michelle. 3155 GLENDALE MILFORD RD, CINCINNATI EVENDALE SURG 45241 #038-40-1991 L1992 APM AN *020 †05

GROM, Alexei Alexei. 3333 BURNET AVE 45229 #913-69-1986 L1999 PD *020 †55

GROSS, Carey K. ■ 45206 #028-78-2006, ▲ L2006 OBG *012

GROTH, David Henry. 602 MAIN ST 45202 #008-01-1962 L1969 PTH *030 †50

GRUBBS, Andrew David. 619 OAK ST 45202 #038-41-1983 L1983 IM *020 †20

GRUBBS, David Alan. ■ 45233 #038-41-1968 L1968 FM *071 †18

GRUBBS, Peter Alan. 3223 ALBERT SABIN WAY, STE 405 45267 #038-41-1985 L1986 ID *020 †20

GRUBER, James T. ■ 45242 #038-41-1951 L1951 GP *071

GRUBER, Lauren Elizabeth. ■ 45226 #035-06-2007 L2007 PD *012

GRULEE, Mary Eileen. 3333 BURNET AVE 45229 #038-41-2000 L2000 PD *020

GRUNENWALD, Paul W. 3130 HIGHLAND AVE, STE 0557 45219 #041-12-1960 L1969 CD IM *040 †20

GRUNWALDT, Lorelei J. ■ 45208 #035-15-2001 L2006 PS *012 †85

GRUPP, Jacqueline Martha. 3333 BURNET AVE, EMERGENCY MEDICINE OSB 4 45229 #038-41-1990 L1998 PD *020 †55

GRUPPO, Ralph Angelo. 3333 BURNET AVE, MAILSTOP 7015 45229 #023-07-1967 L1974 HEM PD *020 †55

GUADAGNO, Gina Maria. 234 GOODMAN ST 45267 #654-01-1995 L2000 P *020 †75

GUANCIALE, Anthony F. 222 PIEDMONT AVE STE 2200 45219 #038-43-1989 L1991 ORS OSS *020 †40

GUENTHER, Joseph Michael. 3747 W FORK RD 45247 #025-01-1987 L2001 GS SO *020 †85

GUIMARAES, Carolina Valdu. 3333 BURNET AVE, DEPT OF MED EDUCATION 45229 #187-73-2002 L2006 PDR *012

GUIOT, Amy Beth. 3333 BURNET AVE, CINCINNATI CHILDRENS HOSP 45229 #038-06-1993 L2003 PD *020 †55 ‡

GUITRON ROIG, Julian. ■ 45212 #649-01-2002 L2007 TS *012

GUL, Maryam. 234 GOODMAN ST 45267 #704-25-2003 L2006 IM *012

GUNDERSON, Donald Edward. ■ 45208 #030-06-1956 L1963 R NM *071 †80,28

GUNTER, Joel Brent. 3333 BURNET AVE, DEPT OF ANESTHESIA 45229 #039-01-1982 L1992 AN PD *020 †05

GUNZENHAUSER, Leslie F. 3155 GLENDALE MILFORD RD, CINCINNATI EVENDALE SURG 45241 #038-40-1977 L1979 AN IM *020 †20,05

GUPTA, Babu Venkatesh. 106 WELLINGTON PL 45219 #038-41-1990 L1994 P *020 †75

GUPTA, Chetan. 375 DIXMYTH AVE, DEPT OF MED EDUCATION 45220 #665-02-2006 L2006 FP *012

GUPTA, Madhukar. 10506 MONTGOMERY RD, STE 504 45242 #495-41-1984 L2003 ICE *020 †20

GUPTA, Shalini. 10600 MONTGOMERY RD, STE 301 45242 #024-01-1996 L2000 D *020

GUPTA, Shelly Rani. ■ 45230 #038-44-2006 L2006 IM *012

GUPTA, Shilpa. ■ 45236 #496-20-1999 L2005 PDE *012 †55

GUREASKO, Michael Allan. 2123 AUBURN AVE, STE 415 45219 #016-42-1969 L1970 P ADM *020 †75

GUR-LAVI, Joy Gabriella. ■ 45229 #028-02-2002 L2002 PD *100

GURNEY, Craig William. ■ 45230 #018-03-2008 *012

GUSTIN, Byron Wm. 415 STRAIGHT ST, STE 300 45219 #038-41-1970 L1970 CD *020 †20

GUTBEZAHL, Cary David. 9830 MISTYMORN LN, TRIVISTA HLTH CARE GROUP I 45242 #041-02-1978 L1994 GP BBK *030 †50

GUTKOWSKI, S Lenoard. ■ 45211 #056-06-1972 L2000 AN EM *020 †05

GUTMAN, Amy Rebecca. ■ 45247 #665-01-2002 L2007 EM *012

GUTTMAN, Alan Lee. 2642 KIPLING AVE 45239 #038-40-1962 L1962 OTO *071

GUZMAN, Florencia Riel. 12053 SHERATON LN BLDG 5 45246 #748-01-1965 L1974 OBG *020

GYLYS-MORIN, Victoria. 3333 BURNET AVE, CHILDREN'S HOSPITAL MED CE 45229 #041-01-1985 L1993 PDR *020 †80

HAAFF, Eric Orval. 10550 MONTGOMERY RD, STE 22 45242 #017-20-1981 L1987 U *020 †95

HAAS, Kara Lyn. 4545 CREEK RD, ML 23 45242 #021-01-1984 L2000 GS *040 †85

HABEL, Todd David. 608 READING RD, STE D 45202 #038-43-1991 L1997 PD *020 †55

HABERMAN, Beth Ellen. 3333 BURNET AVE, DEPT OF PEDIATRICS 45229 #020-02-1993 L1994 NPM *020 †55

HABLI, Mounira Adnan. ■ 45211 #605-01-1998 L2006 OBG *100

HACKENBERG-BAUER, Petra H. 7400 JAGER CT 45230 #038-45-1991 L1993 PD *020 †55

HACKETT, Edward F, Jr. 9157 MONTGOMERY RD STE 206 45242 #038-40-1967 L1967 P *020 †75

HACKETT, Timothy Robert. ■ 45237 #038-43-2004 L2004 GS *012

HACKWORTH, Joe Nathan. 3219 CLIFTON AVE 45220 #001-02-1975 L1976 CD IM *020 †20

HAFFNER, Frederick D. 3333 BURNET AVE 45229 #035-20-1944 L1946 PD *071 †55

HAGAMAN, Jared Travis. 231 ALBERT SABIN WAY 45267 #038-41-2004 L2004 IM *012 †20

HAGEN, Ann. ■ 45241 #038-06-1983 L1983 *074

HAGENAUER, Fedor. 3001 HIGHLAND AVE 45219 #957-01-1949 L1960 PYA CHP *071 †75

HAGENDORF, Benjamin Ari. ■ 45219 #011-04-2000 L2007 GS *020

HAGERMAN, Nancy Sokal. 3333 BURNET AVE 2001, CINCINNATI CHILDRENS HOSP 45229 #036-05-2001 L2005 PAN *100 †05

HAGGERTY, Michael Francis. 10550 MONTGOMERY RD, STE 15 45242 #038-41-1986 L1988 VIR DR *020 †80

HAGLUND, Lisa Ann. 231 ALBERT SABIN WAY ML056 45267 #016-02-1985 L1991 ID IM *020 †20

HAJJAR, Fuad. 375 DIXMYTH AVE 45220 #875-01-1994 L1999 PCC *012 †20

HALES, Thomas Ross. 4676 COLUMBIA PKWY, R 9 45226 #038-06-1983 L1987 OM IM *050 †20,70

HALL, Gregory Alan. 5946 BEACRAFT AVE 45213 #038-41-2000 L2000 EM *020 †16

HALL, John M. ■ 45229 #035-06-1971 L1976 P PYA *020 †75

HALL, Kent Nelson. 6904 MURRAY AVE, RESCUE DISTRICT 45227 #035-15-1981 L1987 EM *020 †16

HALLINAN, Barbara E. 3333 BURNET AVE, CCHMC, DIV OF CHILD NEUROL 45229 #038-41-2001 L2001 CHN *020 †55,75

HALLMAN, Gilbert Daryl. 2446 KIPLING AVE, MERCY MT AIRY HOSPITAL 45239 #020-02-1980 L1992 DR *020 †80

HALPIN, John Albert. 8044 MONTGOMERY RD, STE 155 45236 #020-12-1969 L1974 OPH *035

HALPIN, Michael S. 8044 MONTGOMERY RD, STE 155 45236 #020-12-1975 L1978 OPH *035

HALSTED, Mark Jonathan. 3333 BURNET AVE, DEPT OF RADIO 45229 #008-01-1993 L1999 PDR *020 †80

HALTER, Elaine Ann. ■ 45206 #038-41-2008 *012

HALTON, Lori Clark. ■ 45208 #020-02-2004 L2004 DR *012

HALVONIK, Michael John. 10496 MONTGOMERY RD, PULMONARY CONSLTS 45242 #035-03-1981 L1983 PUD PCC *020 †20

HAMAD, Joseph Frederick. 8245 NORTHCREEK DR, GROUP HEALTH ASSOCIATES 45236 #038-40-1982 L1983 IM *020 †20

HAMBROOK, John Thomas. 3333 BURNET AVE, MLC 2003 45229 #056-06-2003 L2006 PDC *012

HAMDI, Mohamad Abdallah. PO BOX 670526, DEPT OF OB/GYN 45267 #605-04-2002 L2007 OBG *012

HAMED, Osama H. M.. 375 DIXMYTH AVE, DEPT OF MED EDU 45220 #575-01-2003 L2005 *100

HAMIDINIA, Ahmad. 231 ALBERT SABIN WAY, ML 0558 45267 #517-04-1970 L1989 U *020 †95

HAMILTON, Bruce Abbott. 330 STRAIGHT ST, STE 400 45219 #038-41-1978 L1978 ID *075 †20

HAMILTON, Jenny Marie. 9302 TOWNE SQUARE AVE 45242 #038-06-1987 L1987 OPH *020 †35

HAMLING, Alexander Michae. 3333 BURNET AVE, DEPT OF PEDIATRICS 45229 #041-13-2006 L2006 PD *012

HAMMASH, Muhannad M. 3015 CLIFTON AVE 45220 #575-01-1994 L1999 IM *020 †20

HAMMEL, Richard Robt. 11530 REED HARTMAN HWY, PROCTER & GAMBLE COMPANY 45241 #017-20-1984 L1993 OM PTX *030 †70

HAMMERLI, Mark P. 240 BETHESDA AVE 45229 #869-05-1978 **PDC** *020
HAN, Peggy Kim. ■ 45220 #038-41-2008 *012
HANAGAN, John Robt. ■ 45249 #033-05-1969 L1970 **ON IM** *030
HANCHER, Douglas Lowe. 212 W SHARON RD 45246 #038-06-1985 L1985 **FM** *020 †18
HAND, Dwight Everett. 231 ALBERT SABIN WAY, ML 0558 45267 #016-02-1988 L2008 **TS** *100
HANDLETON, Michael R. 6825 WOOSTER PIKE 45227 #038-41-1989 L1990 **FM** *020 †18
HANDWERGER, Stuart. 3333 BURNET AVE, CHILDRENS HOSP 45229 #023-01-1964 L1991 **PDE PD** *040 †55
HANENSON, Irwin B. 231 BETHESDA AVE 557 45267 #035-19-1946 L1955 **OS IM** *071
HANKIN, James David. ■ 45202 #038-41-1992 L2006 **DR VIR** *020 †80
HANSEL, Cindy Marie. 10700 MONTGOMERY RD, STE 311 45242 #038-45-1993 L1996 **OBG** *020 †30
HANSON, Pamela J. 5920 COLERAIN AVE 45239 #026-04-1982 L1984 **FM** *020 †18
HANUMANTHU, Sai Kumar. 3219 CLIFTON AVE, STE 400 45220 #001-02-1995 L2001 **CD** *020 †20
HAQ, Nisar Fatima. 5275 WINNESTE AVE, WINTON HILLS MEDICAL CENTR 45232 #704-16-1986 L1997 **IM** *020 †20
HAQ, Syed Zubair. 2450 KIPLING AVE, STE G1 45239 #704-02-1983 L1988 **CD IM** *020 †20
HAQUE, Mofiz. 4777 E GALBRAITH RD, THE JEWISH HOSPITAL 45236 #043-01-1996 L2003 **IM** *020 †20
HARDEBECK, Margaret Mary. 2142 ALPINE PL, STE 100 45206 #020-02-1981 L1982 **FM** *020 †18
HARDIE, Jennifer B. 3333 BURNET AVE, ML#7009 45229 #048-12-1993 L1995 **PD** *020 †55
HARDIE, William David. 3333 BURNET AVE, PULMONARY MEDICINE 45229 #047-05-1990 L1991 **PDP** *020 †55
HARDIN, Matthew Evan. 3130 HIGHLAND AVE, STE 0557 45219 #038-45-1996 L1997 **MPD** *020 †20,55
HARDING, Kristen L. 6480 HARRISON AVE 45247 #038-45-1997 L2007 **FM** *020 †18
HARDING, Mark Allen. 3747 W FORK RD 45247 #038-45-1997 L2003 **GS VS** *020 †85
HARDING, Warren Gamaliel. 6350 GLENWAY AVE 45211 #005-12-1967 L1975 **ORS OSM** *020 †40
HARMYCH, Brian M. ■ 45230 #038-45-2007 L2007 **OTO** *012
HARRIS, Debra S. 3200 VINE ST, 116A 45220 #016-11-1979 L2004 **P** *050 †75
HARRIS, Irwin. ■ 45242 #016-11-1957 L1958 **TS VS** *071 †85,90
HARRIS, J D. ■ 45227 #038-06-1981 L1981 **N** *071
HARRIS, Leonard. 3300 ELLAND AVE, CHILDRENS HOSPITAL 45229 #035-19-1949 L1959 **CHP P** *020 †55,75
HARRIS, Richard Ekman. 3333 BURNET AVE, CHILDRENS HOSP CHRF 2385 45229 #051-01-1973 L1979 **PHO IG** *020 †55
HARRIS, Samuel. ■ 45242 #038-02-1936 L1936 **GP** *071
HARRIS, Stewart M, Jr. 1000 SYCAMORE ST 45202 #038-41-1978 L1980 **P CHP** *020
HARRIS, Thorold D. 2368 VICTORY PKWY, STE 501 45206 #049-01-1957 L1989 **AN GS** *020
HARRIS, William Edward. 7500 STATE RD 45255 #038-40-1992 L1995 **AN** *020 †05
HARRISON, Donald Carey. 3130 HIGHLAND AVE, STE 0557 45219 #001-02-1958 L1986 **CD IM** *030 †20
HARRISON, Wayne Lynn. ■ 45208 #012-01-1978 L1988 **CHP P** *020
HARSH, Claudia Elizabeth. 6400 E GALBRAITH RD 45236 #038-41-1985 L1986 **OBG** *020 †30
HART, Catherine Kay. ■ 45206 #026-04-2005 L2005 **OTO** *012
HART, Steven Paul. 234 GOODMAN ST 665X, HOXWORTH CENTER 2ND FLOOR 45219 #028-34-2003 L2003 **MPD** *100 †20,55
HARTFORD, James Thos. 10550 MONTGOMERY RD STE 20 45242 #030-05-1973 L1980 **P IMG** *020 †75
HARTFORD, Madelon. 10550 MONTGOMERY RD #NO-20 45242 #917-05-1967 L1983 **P** *020
HARTMAN, Kimberly Corrine. ■ 45208 #025-07-2007 L2007 **PPM** *012
HARTMAN, Rachel Lynn. ■ 45238 #038-45-2005 L2005 **PD** *012
HARTMAN, Rae E. ■ 45206 #038-41-1949 L1949 **FM** *071 †18
HARTMANN, Reid Arthur. 3200 VINE ST 45220 #038-44-2004 L2004 **FM** *020 †18
HASAN, Samer Saadat. 3301 WESTBOURNE DR 45248 #047-05-1994 L2000 **ORS** *020 †40
HASL, Robert John. ■ 45211 #038-41-1963 L1963 **GS AS** *071 †85
HASSAN, Mohammed. 375 DIXMYTH AVE, GOOD SAMARITAN HOSPITAL 45220 #038-13-2002 L2003 **GS** *012
HASSOUN, Joseph Ken. 311 STRAIGHT ST, DEACONESS HOSPITAL 45219 #016-02-1984 L2000 **AN IM** *020 †20,05
HASTIE, Mindy Fine. 4750 E GALBRAITH RD, STE 207 45236 #038-41-1983 L1985 **IM** *020 †20
HATER, Michael Anthony. 1945 CEI DR 45242 #038-41-1993 L1998 **OPH** *020 †35
HATTEMER, Charles Ryan. 2123 AUBURN AVE, STE 624 45219 #038-06-1985 L1988 **CD** *020 †20
HATTENDORF, O Warren. ■ 45209 #038-41-1942 L1942 **OM GP** *071
HAUXWELL, Justin. ■ 45238 #019-02-2004 L2004 **FPP** *012
HAVERKOS, Stephen Douglas. 55 PROGRESS PL 45246 #038-40-1982 L1985 **ORS** *020 †40
HAWAYEK, Lana Habib. 4460 RED BANK RD, STE 130 45227 #605-01-1999 L2001 **D DS** *020 †15
HAWES, Jenny Grace. ■ 45202 #038-41-2002 L2002 **GS** *012
HAWKINS, Clifford Matthew. ■ 45217 #025-12-2007 L2007 **TY** *012
HAWKINS, Harold H, Jr. 5400 KENNEDY AVE 45213 #016-43-1974 L1979 **R** *075 †80
HAWKINS, James Robt. 415 STRAIGHT ST, # 301 45219 #038-41-1971 L1972 **P** *020 †75
HAWKINS, John Michael. 58 E HOLLISTER ST 45219 #056-06-1991 L1993 **P** *020 †75
HAWLEY, Donald Kohl. 250 WILLIAM HOWARD TAFT RD, INTERNAL MEDICINE PHYS INC 45219 #038-41-1947 L1947 **IM** *071 †20
HAWLEY, Douglas Key. 199 WILLIAM HOWARD TAFT RD 45219 #038-41-1979 L1980 **HO IM** *020 †20
HAY, Donald Lee. 7500 STATE RD 45255 #020-02-1984 L1989 **OBG REN** *020
HAYNER, Christopher E. 2915 CLIFTON AVE, GROUP HEALTH ASSOCIATES 45220 #055-02-1987 L1990 **PUD CCM** *020 †20
HAZEN, Jack. ■ 45237 #038-41-1957 L1957 **FM** *071
HAZEN, Joseph Phillip. 6331 GLENWAY AVE 45211 #038-06-1990 L1991 **FM** *020 †18
HE, Ming. 5400 KENNEDY AVE, PROSCAN IMAGING 45213 #038-41-2001 L2001 **NM** *020
HEAD, Jonathan Hayes. 8958 BLUE ASH RD 45242 #038-41-1973 L1973 **IM GE** *075
HEARST, Matthew James. 231 ALBERT SABIN WAY, ML 0528 45267 #012-01-2002 L2002 **NO** *012
HEATH, Robert Burch. 2800 WINSLOW AVE, STE 300 45206 #016-11-1978 L1982 **ORS** *075 †40
HEATON, Charles Lloyd. 3130 HIGHLAND AVE, DEPT OF DERMATOLOGY G126 45267 #048-04-1961 L1978 **D OS** *020 †15 ‡
HEBBELER - CLARK, Renee S. ■ 45238 #654-01-2004 L2004 **ID** *012 †20
HEFFELFINGER, Sue Carol. 234 GOODMAN ST 45219 #012-05-1984 L1991 **PTH** *020 †50
HEIDI, Melissa A. ■ 45248 #047-06-2004 L2004 **OBG** *012
HEIDT, Robert Saml. 6350 GLENWAY AVE 45211 #020-02-1948 L1950 **ORS OSM** *071 †40
HEIL, William E. 311 STRAIGHT ST 45219 #038-41-1952 L1952 **GP** *071
HEILE, Michael Kenneth. 6331 GLENWAY AVE 45211 #038-41-1994 L1997 **FM** *020 †18
HEIMANN DE BUYS, Paige An. 2139 AUBURN AVE 45219 #038-41-2000 L2000 **RHU** *020 †20
HEIMBROCK, Donald J. ■ 45267 #038-41-1953 L1953 **R** *071 †80
HEIMLICH, Henry Jay. 311 STRAIGHT ST 45219 #035-20-1943 L1969 **TS GS** *071 †85,90
HEIN, Elizabeth Anne. 3333 BURNET AVE, DEPT OF ANESTHESIA OSB3 45229 #038-43-1993 L1996 **AN** *020 †05
HEIS, Peggy Ann. 3325 GLENMORE AVE 45211 #038-41-1991 L1992 **OBG** *020 †30
HEIS, Stephen Dale. 8000 5 MILE RD, STE 340 45230 #038-41-1980 L1981 **PM** *020 †60
HEITNER, Alan David. ■ 45243 #051-04-1973 L1974 **EM** *020 †16
HEITSCH, Laura Elaina. ■ 45267 #016-11-2005 L2005 **EM** *012
HELD, John Stanley. 2123 AUBURN AVE, STE 624 45219 #038-40-1973 L1974 **CD IM** *020 †20
HELD, Justin David. ■ 45226 #038-41-2008 *012
HELLMANN, Gail Marie. 909 SYCAMORE ST STE 4 45202 #038-41-1983 L1985 **P PFP** *020 †75
HELLMANN, Joseph Richard. 2123 AUBURN AVE, STE 209 45219 #038-41-1987 L1987 **OTO** *020 †45
HELLMANN, Raymond Henry. 330 STRAIGHT ST, STE 301 45219 #038-41-1976 L1977 **IM IMG** *020 †20
HELLMANN, Robert James. 8245 NORTHCREEK DR, GROUP HEALTH ASSOCIATES 45236 #038-41-1983 L1985 **IM** *020 †20
HELM, David Arthur. 9260 MONTGOMERY RD, # 8A 45242 #025-07-1970 L1976 **P** *020 †75
HELM, Robert Albert. ■ 45220 #038-41-1945 L1945 **CD IM** *071 †20
HELMICK, John Robt. 375 DIXMYTH AVE, 6TH FL 45220 #038-41-1985 L1990 **AN** *020 †05
HELMICK, Ryan Alexander. ■ 45208 #038-40-2007 L2007 **GS** *012
HELMRICH, Dwight Ernst. 1219 MORTS PASS 45215 #028-34-1986 L1987 **EM** *020 †16
HELMSWORTH, James A. ■ 45226 #041-01-1939 L1943 **TS** *071
HELMY, Tarek A. 231 ALBERT SABIN WAY, ML 0542 45267 #915-02-1991 L2006 **CD** *020 †20
HELTON, Kathy Jane. 3333 BURNET AVE, DEPARTMENT OF RADIOLOGY 45229 #027-01-1997 L2002 **PDR** *020 †80
HELTON, Robert Allen. 375 DIXMYTH AVE 45220 #038-41-1960 L1960 **AN OS** *071
HELTON, Sally H. 3155 GLENDALE MILFORD RD, CINCINNATI EVENDALE SURG 45241 #048-02-1981 L1984 **AN** *020 †05
HEMMER, Richard Allen. 8059 ASHLEY VIEW DR, 8059 ASHLEY VIEW DRIVE 45227 #020-02-1978 L1991 **EM** *020 †16
HENKE, Timothy James. 375 DIXMYTH AVE, DEPT OF EMERGENCY MED 45220 #038-41-1994 L1998 **EM** *020 †16
HENLEY, John David. 234 GOODMAN ST, STE 0501 45219 #017-20-1990 L2007 **PTH** *020 †50
HENNEY, Jane Ellen. ■ 45267 #017-20-1973 L1973 **ON IM** *030
HENRY, George Morrison. ■ 45241 #004-01-1960 L1960 **N IM** *020 †20
HENTHORN, Richard W. 2123 AUBURN AVE, STE 624 45219 #038-40-1976 L1979 **CD IM** *020 †20
HERD, Colin. 10050 MONTGOMERY RD, STE 308 45242 #065-01-1983 L1992 **FM PD** *020 †18
HERFEL, Charles Vos. 375 DIXMYTH AVE 45220 #020-12-2002 L2002 **DR** *020 †80
HERFEL, Lee Underwood. 1219 MORTS PASS 45215 #020-12-1996 L2000 **EM** *020 †16
HERGENROTHER, John Shea. 3219 CLIFTON AVE STE 325 45220 #038-44-1997 L1998 **NEP** *020 †20
HERMAN, Jerome Herbert. 231 BETHESDA AVE 45229 #023-01-1960 L1969 **RHU IM** *040
HERMAN, Roger William. 7400 JAGER SOUTHHAMPTON SQ 45230 #016-11-1973 L1976 **PD** *020 †55
HERMANN, Leanne Marie. ■ 45220 #038-41-2007 L2007 **OBG** *012
HERNANDEZ, Lydia Esther. 375 DIXMYTH AVE, DONNA STAHL MD INC 45220 #038-45-1989 L1991 **GS** *020 †85
HEROLD, John Anthony, III. 375 DIXMYTH AVE, OBSTETRIC ANESTHESIA 45220 #020-02-1985 L1988 **AN** *020 †05
HERSHEY, Andrew Dean. 3333 BURNET AVE, CHILDRENS MED CTR DEPT N 45229 #028-02-1992 L1997 **CHN PD** *020 †75
HERTZFELD, Kara Stahl. ■ 45227 #038-41-2005 L2005 **RO** *012
HERTZMAN, Bernard Lee. 10475 READING RD, STE 206 45241 #038-41-1969 L1969 **U** *020 †95
HERZOG, Walter Henry. 2852 BOUDINOT AVE 45238 #038-41-1964 L1964 **CD IM** *020 †20
HESHMAT, Samy Mamdouh Moh. 3333 BURNET AVE, CHILDRENS HOSP MED CTR 45229 #915-04-2000 L2006 **UP** *012
HESS, David Don. 3248 WESTBOURNE DR 45248 #038-40-1984 L1986 **GE IM** *020 †20
HESS, Evelyn Victorine. UNIV CINCINNATI MED CTR, ML 563 MSB 45267 #539-04-1949 L1965 **RHU IM** *040
HESS, Jeffery Elwood. 11530 REED HARTMAN HWY, RM C1W10 45241 #038-44-1991 L1992 **GPM** *020 †18,70
HEUKER, Sonja. 6331 GLENWAY AVE 45211 #038-43-2001 L2005 **FM** *020 †18
HEWITT, Katherine Denise. 71 E HOLLISTER ST 45219 #038-40-1981 L1982 **GYN OS** *020 †30
HEYDARIAN, Haleh C. ■ 45236 #055-02-2002 L2002 **PDC** *012 †55
HEYMAN, Richard Benjamin. 752 WAYCROSS RD 45240 #035-01-1973 L1976 **PD ADL** *020 †55
HEYSE, Phillip Bradford. ■ 45238 #038-41-2008 *012
HICKERT, Maureen Colette. 2621 VICTORY PKWY 45206 #019-02-1989 L1993 **P** *020 †75
HICKEY, Francis James. 7810 5 MILE RD 45230 #038-41-1984 L1986 **PD OS** *020 †55
HIGGINS, Edwin L F. ■ 45239 #038-41-1941 L1950 **D** *071 †15
HILDEBRAND, Jay Alan. ■ 45208 #016-01-2006 L2006 **IM** *012
HILL, James Korey. 11340 MONTGOMERY RD, STE 208 45249 #038-40-1994 L1995 **IM** *020 †20
HILL, Jeffery Michael. ■ 45202 #038-41-2008 *012
HILL, Mary Clare. 234 GOODMAN ST, STE 0531 45219 #038-41-1988 L1991 **AN** *020 †05
HILLARD, William E. 79 E HOLLISTER ST 45219 #038-41-1951 L1951 **P N** *072
HILLMAN, Jennifer Bahr. 3333 BURNET AVE, CINCINNATI CHILDRENS HOSPI 45229 #028-03-2001 L2001 **ADL** *012 †20,55
HILLMAN, Noah Harold. ■ 45236 #028-03-2001 L2001 **NPM** *100 †55
HILTZ, Robert Emmett. 7794 5 MILE RD, STE 280 45230 #020-02-1989 L1994 **RHU** *020 †20
HINCKLEY, William Richard. 2139 AUBURN AVE, STE 0769 45219 #017-20-2000 L2000 **EM** *020 †16
HINES, Dirk Roderick. 4130 DRY RIDGE RD 45252 #038-41-1993 L1994 **FM** *020 †18
HINTON, Andrea Cooke. 375 DIXMYTH AVE 45220 #045-01-1998 L2002 **OBG** *020
HINTON, John T. 615 ELSINORE PL STE 9 45202 #028-79-1977, ▲ L1977 **FM EM** *020
HINTON, Robert Bruce, Jr. 3333 BURNET AVE, CIN CHILD HOSP DIV CARDIO 45229 #045-01-1999 L2002 **PDC** *100 †55
HINZE, Claas Heinrich. 3333 BURNET AVE, CO CHILDREN S HOSP-MED EDU 45229 #409-40-2002 L2003 **PPR** *012 †55

HIRATZKA, Loren Forrest. 4030 SMITH RD, CARDIAC VASCULAR & 45209 #018-03-1970 L1986 **TS** *020 †85,90
HIRSCH, Russel. ■ 45236 #836-02-1988 L2002 **PDC** *020 †55
HIRSH, Paul David. 8000 5 MILE RD, STE 102 45230 #038-06-1976 L1977 **CD IM** *020 †20
HIRTH, Ronald Daniel. ■ 45233 #038-45-2005 L2007 **OBG** *012
HO, Ching. 4760 E GALBRAITH RD, STE 208 45236 #038-41-1984 L1985 **GS OS** *020 †85
HOATH, Steven Bradley. 231 BETHESDA AVE DEPT PD 45229 #005-14-1976 L1984 **NPM PD** *020 †55
HOBAN, Rebecca Ann. ■ 45202 #017-20-2006 L2006 **PD** *012
HOBART, Julie Ann. 2450 KIPLING AVE STE 108, WESTERN FAMILY PHYSICIANS 45239 #038-40-1995 L1996 **FM** *020 †18
HOBEIKA, Claude Pierre. 6527 COLERAIN AVE 45239 #330-03-1959 L1968 **OTO NO** *071 †45
HOBLER, Scott Carlson. 4360 COOPER RD, STE 303 45242 #038-43-1993 L1995 **GS** *020 †85
HOBOHM, Herman Karl. 3801 HAUCK RD 45241 #038-45-1980 L1981 **EM FM** *020
HOCHBERG, Isidor. ■ 45211 #154-02-1954 L1962 **GP CD** *020
HOCHWALT, James Michael. 2135 DANA AVE, STE 210 45207 #038-41-1988 L1989 **IM** *020 †20
HODGES, Marytena B. 11238 CORNELL PARK DR, NORTHEAST CINCINNATI PED A 45242 #020-12-1991 L1994 **PD** *020 †55
HOELZLE, Mark Richard. 305 CRESCENT AVE 45215 #038-41-2003 L2003 **FPG** *020 †18
HOFFMAN, Richard A. 201 E 5TH ST, STE 2200 45202 #038-41-1942 L1942 **OPH OS** *071 †35
HOFFMANN, Karol Alexander. 3200 BURNET AVE, JEWISH HOSPITAL 45229 #154-07-1954 L1962 **PME AN** *071 †05
HOFMANN, Glen Emery. 10506 MONTGOMERY RD, STE 303 45242 #020-02-1983 L1984 **REN** *020 †30
HOFMANN, William Bradley. 11135 MONTGOMERY RD 45249 #038-41-1958 L1958 **OTO HNS** *071 †45
HOGG, Stephen P. 2730 OBSERVATORY AVE 45208 #020-02-1944 L1948 **OTO OS** *071 †45
HOGYA, Paul Timothy. 1219 MORTS PASS 45215 #038-06-1986 L1989 **EM** *020 †16
HOLBERT, Michael Ray. 9525 KENWOOD RD STE 1 45242 #038-41-2005 L2005 **OBG** *012
HOLDITCH, Lawrence S. 3917 SPRING GROVE AVE 45223 #038-40-1981 L1984 **IM** *020 †20
HOLLAND, Carolyn Kluwe. 231 ALBERT SABIN WAY 1505, UNIV OF CINCINNATI MED CEN 45267 #051-07-2003 L2003 **PEM** *012
HOLLAND, Katherine Dana. 3333 BURNET AVE, DEPT OF NEUROLOGY 45229 #028-02-1991 L2000 **CHN** *020 †75
HOLMES, Jeffrey Alan. ■ 45208 #047-05-2004 L2004 **EM** *012
HOLMES, Pamela Deirdre. ■ 45220 #038-41-2006 L2006 **PD** *012
HOLT, Andrew Foy. 7153 SILVER CREST DR 45236 #048-12-2000 L2003 **GE** *020 †20
HOLTEN, Keith Bryan. 1295 KEMPER MEADOW DR 45240 #020-02-1981 L1982 **FM** *020 †18
HOLUBECK, Laurie Ann. 11360 SPRINGFIELD PIKE, SPRINGDALE-MASON PEDS 45246 #014-01-1990 L1996 **PD** *020 †55
HOLUBECK, Thomas John. 1413 LINN ST 45214 #038-41-1989 L1996 **PD** *020 †55
HOLZAPFEL, Allison Mac Gr. 8044 MONTGOMERY RD, STE 230 45236 #020-02-1999 L2004 **FPS OTO** *020 †45 ‡
HONG, Changgi. 231 BETHESDA AVE 45229 #583-02-1961 L1975 **NEP IM** *040 †20
HONIG, Richard Gordon. 3001 HIGHLAND AVE, STE E 45219 #035-03-1971 L1974 **CHP P** *020 †75
HOODIN, Asher Oliver. ■ 45237 #038-40-1958 L1958 **U** *072
HOOGSTRATEN, Barth. ■ 45206 #660-01-1955 L1981 **ON** *071
HOOKER, Edmond A, II. 3800 VICTORY PKWY 45207 #051-07-1985 L1998 **EM** *020 †16
HOOPER, David Kimball. 3333 BURNET AVE 45229 #049-01-2003 L2003 **PN** *012 †55
HOPKIN, Robert James. 3333 BURNET AVE 45229 #031-01-1990 L1994 **MG PD** *020 †19,55
HOPKINS, Brandon Scott. ■ 45208 #047-20-2007 L2007 **OTO** *012
HOPKINS, Sarah Elizabeth. ■ 45213 #004-01-2004 L2004 **CHN** *012
HOR, Kan Nam. ■ 45212 #016-11-2000 L2003 **PDC** *100 †55
HORN, Joyce Lee. 3219 CLIFTON AVE, STE 125 45220 #025-01-1983 L1984 **OBG** *020 †30
HORNE, Dale Scott. 10550 MONTGOMERY RD, STE 33 45242 #028-02-1990 L2006 **NS** *020 †25
HORNSBY, Christopher Wayn. ■ 45267 #143-05-1983 L2000 **OPH** *100
HORTON, Edward S, Jr. 10550 MONTGOMERY RD, STE 15 45242 #050-02-1984 L1996 **DR RNR** *020 †80
HORWITZ, Harry. 2800 WINSLOW AVE, RIVERHILLS HEALTHCARE INC 45206 #917-20-1950 L1965 **ON RO** *071 †80
HOSMER, Kathleen Anne. ■ 45209 #025-07-2005 L2005 **EM** *012
HOSU, Liana Gabriela. ■ 45208 #781-03-1995 L2000 **PAN** *100 †05 ‡
HOUGH, Paul Smith. 2600 STRATFORD AVE, STE 101 45219 #047-07-1944 L1954 **IM OS** *071
HOUK, John Lawrence. 3652 WERK RD 45248 #038-41-1965 L1965 **RHU OM** *020 †20
HOWARD, David Geo. 7815 BEECHMONT AVE 45255 #038-41-1980 L1981 **OPH** *020 †35
HOWELL, Gail A Henninger. 4600 WESLEY AVE, STE N 45212 #011-02-1969 L1971 **GP** *020
HOWELL, Jonathan Christia. 3333 BURNET AVE, CINCINNATI CHILDREN'S HOSP 45229 #017-20-2005 L2005 **PD** *012
HOWIE, Betty Lynn. 1171 ADAMS ST 45215 #038-40-1980 L1983 **PD** *020 †55
HOWINGTON, John Anthony. 231 ALBERT SABIN WAY, UNIV SURGICAL GRP OF CINCI 45267 #047-06-1989 L1999 **TS** *020 †85,90 ‡
HSIEH, Ron James. 8060 MONTGOMERY RD STE 302 45236 #025-12-1978 L1982 **DIA IM** *020
HSU, Colleen Yuhong Xu. ■ 45243 #243-76-1988 L2003 **IM** *020 †20
HUANG, Jennifer Hsinping. UNIV OF CINCINNATI, DEPT OF INTERNAL MEDICINE 45267 #019-02-2007 L2007 **MPD** *012
HUANG, Kai. ■ 45239 #038-41-2008 *012
HUANG, Rae-Chi. 3333 BURNET AVE, CO CHILDREN S HOSP-MED EDU 45229 #143-06-1995 L2002 *100
HUANG, Shaoming. 6725 MIAMI AVE 45243 #243-47-1982 L1999 **NEP** *020 †20
HUBBARD, Carol Jean. 1000 SYCAMORE ST, HAMILTON COUNTY JUSTICE CE 45202 #038-45-1982 L1985 **FM** *020 †18
HUBER, Brian Matthew. ■ 45238 #038-41-2008 *012
HUBER, Carrie Lynn. ■ 45238 #020-02-2006 L2006 **OBG** *012
HUBER, Tammy Jo. 1095 NIMITZVIEW DR, STE 401 45230 #038-44-1991 L1993 **P** *020 †75
HUDAK, Donald Thomas. 1945 CEI DR, CINCINNATI EYE INSTITUTE 45242 #038-44-1997 L2000 **OPH FPS** *020 †35
HUDEPOHL, Nathan Joseph. ■ 45233 #024-07-2006 L2006 **EM** *012
HUELSMAN, David Anthony. 375 DIXMYTH AVE, GOOD SAMARITAN HOSP, RADIO 45220 #038-41-1996 L1998 **DR** *020 †80
HUESING, John Anthony. 6829 WOOSTER PIKE 45227 #038-41-1960 L1960 **OBG** *071 †30
HUESMAN, Alvin Anthony. 3131 QUEEN CITY AVE 45238 #038-41-1962 L1962 **FM** *071 †18
HUEY, James Maurice, Jr. 3200 VINE ST, DEPT OF AMBULATORY MED 45220 #020-02-1980 L1981 **IM** *020 †20
HUEZO, Karen Lissette. ■ 45267 #021-05-2004 L2004 **GS** *012
HUFFMAN, Lynn C. 231 ALBERT SABIN WAY, ML 0558 DEPT SURGERY 45267 #025-01-2001 L2001 **GS** *012
HUG, George R. ELLAND & BETHESDA AVE, CHILDRENS HOSP MED CTR 45229 #869-07-1957 L1967 **PD** *050 †55
HUG, Katherine. 10550 MONTGOMERY RD, STE 15 45242 #038-41-1998 L2005 **DR IM** *020 †80
HUGGINS, Jennifer Lynn. 3333 BURNET AVE, ML 4010 45229 #019-02-1984 L2005 **PPR** *100 †20,55,03
HUGHES, Arthur Lee. 3285 WESTBOURNE DR 45248 #023-01-1967 L1975 **N** *020 †75
HULL, Sarah Berno. ■ 45220 #038-41-2004 L2004 **AN** *012
HULON, Walter Culton. 5299 SPRING GROVE AVE, PROCTOR APT GAMBLE 45217 #001-02-1967 L1990 **OM AM** *020 †70
HUMMEL, Robert P, Jr. 222 PIEDMONT AVE, HASSELGREN PER-OLOF 45219 #038-41-1951 L1951 **GS OS** *071 †85
HUMMEL, Robert Paul, III. 4850 RED BANK RD, FL 2 45227 #038-41-1988 L1990 **PS** *020 †65,65
HUMMEL, Trent Ryan. ■ 45215 #038-41-2001 L2001 **PHO** *100 †55
HUMPHRIES, Dennis Victor. 12061 SHERATON LN 45246 #038-41-1967 L1967 **FM** *020
HUNTER, Monica Greis. 608 READING RD, STE B 45202 #020-02-1995 L1996 **CD** *020 †20
HUNTER, Robert Scott. 4965 GLENWAY AVE 45238 #038-41-1977 L1978 **PD** *020 †55
HUNTER, Yvette D Casey. 5275 WINNESTE AVE 45232 #010-03-1978 L1981 **PD** *020 †55
HUPPERT, Jill Suzanne. 3333 BURNET AVE, ADOLMED ML4000 45229 #028-02-1985 L1986 **OBG ADL** *050 †30
HURD, Robert Edward. 3844 VICTORY PKWY, XAVIER UNIV 45207 #030-06-1978 L2003 **END IM** *074 †20
HURT, Amber Renee. ■ 45206 #020-02-2005 L2005 **GS** *012
HURTUBISE, Monica Yung. ■ 45220 #038-41-2008 *012
HUSCHART, Joseph Andrew. 425 FARRELL CT 45233 #038-45-1993 L1996 **IM** *020 †20
HUSSAIN, Sayed Tahir. 4777 E GALBRAITH RD, MEDICAL STAFF OFFICE 45236 #704-25-1996 L2005 **CD** *012 †20
HUSSEINZADEH, Heideh Lynn. ■ 45220 #038-41-2008 *012
HUSSEINZADEH, Nader. 231 ALBERT SABIN WAY, DEPT OF OBSTETRICS AND GYN 45267 #517-08-1971 L1983 **GO GYN** *020 †30
HUSTED, Thomas Lee. 231 ALBERT SABIN WAY, ML0558 45267 #025-07-1994 L2001 **GS** *020
HUTCHINS, Matthew George. 2123 AUBURN AVE, STE 624 45219 #038-41-1994 L1995 **CD IM** *020 †20
HUTCHINS, Robert Karl. 2859 BOUDINOT AVE, STE 211 45238 #016-11-1982 L1987 **OPH** *020 †35
HUTSON, John Clinton. 10500 MONTGOMERY RD, 6TH FL 45242 #020-12-1999 L2006 **IM** *020 †20
HUTTON, John James, Jr. 231 BETHESDA AVE, UNIV OF CINCINNATI 45267 #024-01-1964 L1984 **IM HO** *050 †20
HUTTON, John Stafford. ■ 45243 #038-41-1998 L2002 **PD** *012
HYLTON, Everton. ■ 45215 #759-09-1986 L1995 **PDE** *100 †55
IACUONE, John Jos. ■ 45251 #017-20-1973 L1976 **PD PHO** *030 †55
IARUSSI, Anthony Michael. ■ 45230 #038-41-2005 L2005 **AN** *012
IBRAHIM, Nasrien Ezzeldin. ■ 45242 #038-41-2008 *012
IGNATOW, Stanley Bernard. 2139 AUBURN AVE, STE 102 45219 #020-02-1970 L1977 **DR NR** *020 †80
IITAKA, Kikuo. 3300 ELLAND AVE # NEP, CHILDRENS HOSPITAL 45229 #572-20-1971 **NEP PD** *050 †55
IMAM, Nabeel Muhammad. 375 DIXMYTH AVE, DEPT OF MED EDU 45220 #704-02-2001 L2006 **IM** *012
IMWALLE, Lauren Elizabeth. ■ 45226 #038-41-2008 *012
IMWALLE, Susan Marie. 234 GOODMAN ST 0761, DEPT OF RADIOLOGY, UNIV OF 45267 #038-41-1998 L2000 **DR** *100 †80
INABA, Michiko. ■ 45202 #572-57-1997 L2005 **IM** *012
INGBERG, Robert Louis. 3333 BURNET AVE 45229 #038-41-1964 L1964 **PD PDP** *071 †55
INGE, Thomas Harris. 3333 BURNET AVE, MLC 2023 45229 #051-04-1993 L2000 **PDS** *020 †85
INGRAHAM, Angela Margaret. ■ 45230 #016-43-2006 L2006 **GS** *012
IONNA, Stephen Lawrence. 8260 NORTHCREEK DR, STE 310 45236 #038-41-1985 L1985 **GE IM** *020 †20
IPPISCH, Holly Marie. 3333 BURNET AVE, BLDG C-2003 45229 #038-45-1997 L2001 **PDC** *020 †55
IQBAL, Fizzah. 234 GOODMAN ST 45267 #704-02-2003 L2006 **IM** *012
IRELAND, Gene E. 4850 RED BANK RD, 1 PLASTIC SURGERY CENTER 45227 #008-02-1975 L1976 **PS OS** *020 †65
IRETON, Candace Lynn. 1295 KEMPER MEADOW DR 45240 #016-06-1994 L2001 **FM** *020 †18
IRVIN, Ronald Kent. 10600 MONTGOMERY RD, STE 300 45242 #038-41-1966 L1966 **PD** *020 †55
ISAAC, Gregory Lee. 7810 5 MILE RD 45230 #038-41-1980 L1983 **FM** *020 †18
ISAACSOHN, Jonathan. 4620 WESLEY AVE 45212 #836-02-1977 L1991 **CD** *020 †20
ISENHART, Craig Eric. 311 STRAIGHT ST 45219 #017-20-1987 L1993 **PTH HMP** *020 †50
ISLAM, Md Wahidul. 12029 SHERATON LN 45246 #160-02-1992 L2000 **IM** *020 †20
ISTAPHANOUS, George Karee. 3333 BURNET AVE 45229 #422-01-2002 L2003 **PAN** *100 †05
ITZKOWITZ, Maralyn M. 2915 CLIFTON AVE 45220 #039-01-1978 L1979 **FM** *020 †18
IVEY, Tom Dexter. 2123 AUBURN AVE, STE 136 45219 #056-05-1970 L1988 **TS** *020 †85,90
IYER, Meenakshi Nagarajan. 2139 AUBURN AVE 45219 #496-01-2004 L2005 **IM** *012
IYER, Srikant. 3333 BURNET AVE, ML # 2008 45229 #036-01-1997 L1998 **PEM** *100 †55
IYER, Vivek Shankar. 2139 AUBURN AVE, ANESTHESIA DEPARTMENT 45219 #038-41-2002 L2007 **APM** *020
IZADNIA, Fariba. 3333 BURNET AVE, CHILDRENS HOSP MED CTR 45229 #517-05-1988 L1999 **PD** *100
IZHAR, Amir. 3219 CLIFTON AVE, SUITE325 45220 #704-02-1990 L1998 **NEP** *020 †20
JABIN, M Kathryn. 5049 CROOKSHANK RD, STE 102 45238 #038-41-1990 L1992 **OBG** *020 †30
JACKSON, Elizabeth Connor. 3333 BURNET AVE, DEPT OF NEPHROLOGY/MLC-702 45229 #051-01-1978 L2003 **PN** *020 †55
JACKSON, Sharon. ■ 45267 #047-07-2005 L2005 **GS** *012
JACKSON, Wendy Ann. 3333 BURNET AVE 45229 #671-02-1990 L2000 **PDE** *100
JACOB, Robert Steven. 3155 GLENDALE MILFORD RD, CINCINNATI EVENDALE SURG 45241 #038-41-1987 L1990 **AN GS** *020 †05
JACOB, Susan. ■ 45242 #495-01-1974 L1989 **FM** *100 †18
JACOBS, Donald Seyler. 10700 MONTGOMERY RD, STE 100 45242 #023-07-1972 L1978 **OPH** *020 †35
JACOBS, John Alan. ■ 45242 #917-03-1958 L1974 **AN** *071
JACOBSON, Eugene Donald. ■ 45219 #050-02-1955 L1961 **GE** *071
JACOBSON, Leonard. 7770 COOPER RD 45242 #035-06-1964 L1968 **OPH** *020 †35

■ = Address Information Privacy Protected

JACOBSON, Roy Hardy. 1207 SPRINGFIELD PIKE 45215 #038-41-1995 L1996 **FM** *020 †18

JACOBUS, Christian H. 231 ALBERT SABIN WAY, UC MEDICAL CENTER 45267 #011-02-2003 L2003 **EM** *100

JACQUEMIN, John Brian. 2841 BOUDINOT AVE, FREIBERG ORTHOPAEDIC AND 45238 #038-41-1996 L2004 **ORS** *020 †40

JAEKLE, Ronald Kenneth. 3333 BURNET AVE 45229 #047-06-1985 L1991 **MFM OBG** *020 †30

JAFFE, Murray Sherwood. 3120 BURNET AVE 45229 #038-41-1948 L1948 **GS** *071 †85

JAFRI, Mubeen Akhtar. ■ 45224 #051-07-2002 L2002 **GS** *012

JAGTAP, Shyamala. 10495 MONTGOMERY RD, STE 17 45242 #495-33-1988 L1996 **IM ID** *020 †20

JAIN, Nimisha. ■ 45220 #038-41-2008 *012

JAIN, Viral Virendra. 3333 BURNET AVE, DEPT OF MED EDU 45229 #495-22-1999 L2006 **OSS** *012

JAKUBOWSKI, Martin. 2139 AUBURN AVE, DEPT OF FAMILY MEDICINE 45219 #759-18-2003 L2005 **FP** *012

JALILVAND, Masoud. 3131 QUEEN CITY AVE, MERCY FRANCISCAN HOSPITAL 45238 #517-06-1991 L2006 **IM** *012

JAMES, Jeanne Marie. 3333 BURNET AVE 45229 #055-01-1987 L1995 **PDC** *050 †55

JAMES, Shaka Pazhachira. ■ 45226 #038-41-2007 L2007 **IM** *012

JAMES, Thomas Israel. 231 ALBERT SABIN WAY 45267 #038-41-2004 L2004 **AN** *012

JAMIESON, William Malcolm. 2123 AUBURN AVE, STE 104 45219 #038-40-1973 L1974 **GYN** *020 †30

JANNERFELDT, Eric Robt. 4676 COLUMBIA PKWY, NIOSH, HETAB 45226 #858-02-1972 L1982 **OM** *030 †70

JANQUART, Neal Joseph. 3131 QUEEN CITY AVE 45238 #056-05-2000 L2004 **AN** *020 †05 ‡

JANSEN, Donald Henry. 9030 MONTGOMERY RD 45242 #038-41-1959 L1959 **OPH PS** *020 †35

JANSON, Jerome N. 1960 MADISON RD, # 119 45206 #028-34-1940 L1945 **GP IM** *071

JANSZEN, Iveta Alexandra. 3155 GLENDALE MILFORD RD, CINCINNATI EVENDALE SURG 45241 #038-41-1992 L1996 **AN** *020 †05

JANSZEN, James Norbert. 3155 GLENDALE MILFORD RD, CINCINNATI EVENDALE SURG 45241 #020-12-1984 L1987 **AN GS** *020 †05

JARAMILLO-DE LA TORRE, Jor. 231 ALBERT, DEPT OF NEUROLOGICAL SURG 45267 #649-52-1999 L2005 *100

JAUCH, Edward Charles. 234 GOODMAN ST, STE 0769 45219 #038-41-1993 L1995 **EM** *020 †16

JAVAID, Sunbal Zamani. 2123 AUBURN AVE, STE 724 45219 #038-41-2001 L2001 **OBG** *020

JAWAID, Kashif. 234 GOODMAN ST 45267 #704-25-2001 L2003 **IM** *100

JAWEED, Saif. 8044 MONTGOMERY RD, STE 155 45236 #038-43-1998 L2000 **OPH** *020 †35

JAWORSKI, Paul Gregor. ■ 45215 #038-41-1987 *100

JAZIEH, Abdul-Rahman. 234 GOODMAN ST ML0501, BARRETT CANCER CENTER 45267 #875-01-1988 L2000 **ON HEM** *020 †20

JAZY, Foroogh Kananie. 3217 CLIFTON AVE, RADIATION ONCOLOGY DEPT 45229 #517-06-1968 L1973 **RO** *020 †80

JEAN, Marina Entran. ■ 45267 #016-06-1997 L2002 **GS** *100

JEFFERSON, Lena Lachelle. ■ 45267 #038-41-2002 L2002 **P** *100

JENIKE, Frank Thos. 2123 AUBURN AVE, STE 624 45219 #038-41-1968 L1968 **CD IM** *020 †20

JENKINS, Frederick G, Jr. 311 STRAIGHT ST STE 301 45219 #047-07-1976 L1978 **CD IM** *020 †20

JENKINS, Timothy Jos. 7500 STATE RD 45255 #056-05-1990 L1991 **DR** *020 †80

JENNINGS, Mark Richard. 3747 W FORK RD 45247 #038-06-2000 L2001 **GS** *020 †85

JENNINGS, Michael Robert. 2139 AUBURN AVE 45219 #038-41-1982 L1983 **IM** *020 †20

JERARDI, Karen Elizabeth. ■ 45243 #041-12-2006 L2006 **PD** *012

JETT, Roy, Jr. ■ 45241 #038-41-1956 L1956 **A AM** *071

JEYARAMAN, Anuradha. 2139 AUBURN AVE 45219 #495-42-2001 L2005 **IM** *012

JIANG, Jiazhong. 3131 QUEEN CITY AVE 45238 #243-47-1992 L2003 **PTH HMP** *020 †50

JIMENEZ RODRIGUEZ, Manuel. 375 DIXMYTH AVE 45220 #275-03-1989 L2006 **IM** *012

JOBALIA, Karen Amy. 2446 KIPLING AVE, PROVIDENCE HOSPITAL 45239 #038-41-1990 L1991 **DR** *020 †80

JOBE, Alan Hall. 3333 BURNET AVE, CHILDRENS HOSP MED CTR 45229 #005-18-1973 L1997 **NPM PD** *050 †55

JODELE, Sonata. 3333 BURNET AVE, MLC 7015 45229 #913-49-1994 L2004 **PHO PD** *020 †55

JODICKE, Cristiano Dias. & GYNE2, CO DEPT. OF OBSTETRICS 45267 #187-01-2001 L2004 **OBG** *012

JOFFE, Stephen Neal. 7840 MONTGOMERY RD UNIT 3 45236 #836-01-1967 L1980 **GS** *020

JOHANNIGMAN, Jay Albert. 6350 E GALBRAITH RD 45236 #038-06-1983 L1988 **TRS CCM** *020 †85

JOHNSON, James H. 8245 NORTHCREEK DR, GROUP HEALTH ASSOCIATES 45236 #041-02-1956 L1957 **PM** *071

JOHNSON, Jennifer Jean. 130 WELLINGTON PL 45219 #038-41-1973 L1975 **CHP P** *020 †75

JOHNSON, Kay Ann. 3130 HIGHLAND AVE, STE 0557 45219 #038-43-1987 L1988 **IM ID** *020 †20

JOHNSON, Kimberly Ann. ■ 45240 #038-06-1983 L1984 **FM** *020

JOHNSON, Laurie Heather. 3333 BURNET AVE, ML2008 45229 #036-08-2000 L2003 **PEM** *100 †55

JOHNSON, Mark Clayton. 3333 BURNET AVE 45229 #038-43-2003 L2006 **CHP** *012

JOHNSON, Marleen Cousins. 234 GOODMAN ST, DEPARTMENT OF EMERGENCY ME 45267 #028-02-1997 L1998 **EM** *020 †16

JOHNSON, Monique Delana. 234 GOODMAN ST DEPT PED 45267 #036-01-1997 **PD** *100

JOHNSON, Neil David. 3333 BURNET AVE, DEPT OF RADIO 45229 #143-02-1976 L1991 **PDR PD** *020 †80

JOHNSON, Rhonda Moore. 3333 BURNET AVE 45229 #041-14-1982 L1983 **PD MDM** *030 †55

JOHNSON, Robert Ryn. ■ 45209 #038-41-2007 L2007 **IM** *012

JOHNSTON, Henry Coulter. 234 GOODMAN ST, STE 0531 45219 #038-41-1975 L1976 **AN** *020

JOHNSTON, Joseph Andrew. 222 PIEDMONT AVE, STE 4100 45219 #028-03-1996 L1997 **MPD** *020 †20,55

JOHNSTON, Peirce Wood. ■ 45206 #038-41-2007 L2007 **P** *012

JOHNSTONE, Harold Evan. 629 OAK ST STE 105 45206 #038-41-1961 L1961 **OBG** *071 †30

JOHNSTONE, Robert Ellis. ■ 45208 #050-02-1943 L1951 **OBG** *071 †30

JOINER, Clinton Hubert. 3333 BURNET AVE 45229 #036-07-1977 L1988 **NPM PHO** *050 †55

JOLIAT, Lisa M. 4460 RED BANK RD 45227 #038-41-1993 L1995 **IM** *020 †20

JOLSON, Richard Alan. 1201 EDGECLIFF PL 45206 #020-02-1955 L1960 **ORS** *071 †40

JOLSON, Robert Scott. 2841 BOUDINOT AVE, FREIBERG ORTHOPAEDIC AND 45238 #038-41-1986 L1990 **ORS** *020

JONAS, Mark Edward. 4760 E GALBRAITH RD, STE 107 45236 #035-08-1990 L1998 **GE IM** *020 †20

JONES, Blaise Vincent. 3333 BURNET AVE, RADIOLOGY DEPARTMENT 45229 #010-02-1988 L1989 **PDR RNR** *020 †80

JONES, Brett Asher. ■ 45219 #001-02-2004 L2004 **EM** *012

JONES, Camille Arnel. ■ 45208 #038-06-1982 L1984 **GPM IM** *030 †20,70

JONES, Charla Screll. ■ 45267 #038-41-2006 L2006 **P** *012

JONES, Edmund Weber. 7960 BLOME RD 45243 #038-41-1961 L1961 **GS AS** *071 †85

JONES, Elizabeth Morley. ■ 45206 #038-43-2006 L2006 **IM** *012

JONES, Evelyn. 3333 BURNET AVE, ML 7009 45229 #038-45-1992 L1995 **PD** *020 †55

JONES, Jill Shawn. 4411 MONTGOMERY RD STE 206, BETHESDA HOSPITAL 45212 #020-12-1994 L1996 **FM** *020 †30,18

JONES, William Warren. ■ 45229 #020-02-1957 L1964 **OM** *071

JORDAN, Earl Farrar. 830 MAIN ST STE 500 45202 #038-41-1957 L1957 **NS** *075 †25

JORDAN, Kathryn Anne. ■ 45242 #023-01-2005 L2005 **MPD** *012

JORDAN, Michael Brian. 3333 BURNET AVE, ML-7038 45229 #048-12-1993 L2004 **PHO** *020 †55

JOSEPH, Evelyn Claire. 3006 PORTSMOUTH AVE 45208 #038-41-1982 L1983 **PD** *020 †55

JOSEPH, James Michael. 5400 KENNEDY AVE, PROSCAN READING SERVICES 45213 #038-40-1998 L2005 **DR** *020 †80

JOSEPH, Kevin James. 231 ALBERT SABIN WAY 45267 #047-05-2001 L2001 **EM** *020 †16

JOSEPH, Patricia Maxwell. 231 ALBERT SABIN WAY 45267 #047-06-1984 L1999 **PDP CCM** *020,55

JOSEPH, Rajesh Abraham. 3248 WESTBOURNE DR 45248 #038-44-1998 L1999 **GE** *020

JOSEPHS, Sean Alan. 234 GOODMAN ST, P O BOX 670764 45219 #025-12-2001 L2002 **CCA** *020 †05

JOSHI, Deepak. 2139 AUBURN AVE 45219 #672-04-2003 L2006 **IM** *012

JOU, Jingfang F. 3333 BURNET AVE, CHILDREN'S HOSPITAL 45229 #048-13-2002 L2006 **PAN** *020 †20

JOVIC, Jasmina. 3200 VINE ST 45220 #957-07-1981 L1995 **IM** *020 †20

JOVICIC, Sasa Sreten. 4027 EASTERN AVE, EAST END HEALTH CENTER 45226 #495-02-1984 L1999 **IM** *020 †20

JUERGENS, Christopher W. 4360 COOPER RD, STE 303 45242 #038-41-1992 L1995 **GS** *020 †85

JUNG, Edward Mathias. 2123 AUBURN AVE, STE 331 45219 #038-41-1988 L1990 **IM** *020 †20

JUNGERWIRTH, Steven. 11450 GROOMS RD, PROCTER & GAMBLE PHARM 45242 #041-09-1994 L2001 **ID IM** *020 †20

JUNGST, Elizabeth Jane. ■ 45243 #011-03-2005 L2005 **IM** *012

JURELL, Kathleen C. 6200 PFEIFFER RD STE 3, 3RD FLOOR 45242 #048-04-1991 L1992 **PM** *020 †60

JURELL, Kim Richard. 2925 VERNON PL, STE 100 45219 #017-20-1990 L1996 **GE** *020 †20

JUSTIN, Michael. 1577A GOODMAN AVE 45219 #040-01-1972 L1973 **ORS OSS** *020 †40

JUTTE, Donald L. 7495 STATE RD, STE 325 45255 #038-41-1979 L1984 **PS GS** *071 †65

JUYAL, Malini. 400 WABASH AVENUE 45236 #473-04-2006 L2007 **IM** *012

KABALIN, Thomas Jos. 3333 BURNET AVE, DEPT OF ANESTHESIA 45229 #010-02-1989 L2002 **AN** *020 †05

KABBOUCHE, Marielle A. 3333 BURNET AVE, MLC 2015 45229 #605-02-1993 L2000 **PD** *020 †75

KADE, Roslyn K. 71 E HOLLISTER ST 45219 #038-41-1985 L1987 **GYN GP** *020

KADIVAR, Bahram. 10475 MONTGOMERY RD, STE 1B 45242 #517-06-1962 L1970 **PS** *071 †85,65

KAGAN, Richard Jeffrey. 3229 BURNET AVE, SHRINERS HOSPITALS FOR CHI 45229 #028-34-1974 L1988 **GS OS** *020 †85

KAHL, James Bennett. 7770 COOPER RD, STE 10 45242 #041-09-1958 L1965 **PS HS** *020 †65

KAHN, Alfred, III. 2123 AUBURN AVE, STE 201 45219 #004-01-1972 L1973 **ORS OSS** *020 †40

KAHN, Eric. 3200 BURNET AVE 45229 #836-02-1956 L1970 **OBG OS** *071 †30

KAHN, Isaac I. 135 GARFIELD PL 45202 #660-03-1958 L1966 **IM OS** *071

KAHN, Jessica Spira. 3333 BURNET AVE, CHLDRNS HOSP ADOLESCENT CL 45229 #024-01-1992 L1999 **PD ADL** *020 †55

KAHN, Robert Steven. 3333 BURNET AVE # PEDS, CHILDRENS HOSP MED CTR 45229 #047-05-1992 L1999 **PD** *020 †55

KAISER, Donald Raymond. ■ 45238 #038-41-1954 L1954 **OBG PTH** *071 †30

KAKARLAPUDI, Ganesh Venka. ■ 45236 #030-06-2004 L2004 **GE** *012 †20

KAKUMANU, Anil Kumar. CO MEDICAL EDUCATION DEPT, THE CHRIST HOSPITAL 45219 #495-50-2002 L2007 **IM** *012

KALE, Vasudha Sharatkumar. 375 DIXMYTH AVE, OBSTETRIC ANESTHESIA 45220 #495-17-1968 L1977 **AN** *020 †05

KALFA, Theodosia A. 3333 BURNET AVE, CHILDRENS HOSP HEM ONC 45229 #418-02-1990 L2003 **PHO** *050 †55

KALIDINDI, Venkat Krishna. 3200 BURNET AVE 45229 #495-21-2000 L2005 **IM** *012

KALINYAK, Karen Ann. 3333 BURNET AVE, STE 201 45219 #041-13-1977 L1984 **HEM ON** *020 †55

KALLAPUR, Suhas G. 3333 BURNET AVE 45229 #496-38-1985 L1991 **NPM PD** *050 †55

KALLENBERG, Richard Bruce. 55 PROGRESS PL, GROUP HEALTH ASSOCIATES 45246 #038-41-1983 L1984 **IM** *020

KALRA, Maninder. 3333 BURNET AVE, CHILDREN'S HOSPITAL-PULMON 45229 #495-43-1991 L2000 **PDP** *020 †55

KALTENSTADLER, Kristin Li. ■ 45239 #028-03-2006 L2006 **PD** *012

KAM, Justus Hungching. ■ 45219 #012-05-2006 L2006 **CPP** *012

KAMAL YOUSSEF, Ashraf Sam. UNIV OF CINCINNATI, PO BOX 670515 45267 #915-04-1991 L2001 **NS** *100

KAMATH, Suresh. 231 ALBERT SABIN WAY RM G2, UC MEDICAL CENTRAL 45267 #495-33-1988 L2002 **NEP IM** *040 †20

KAMBELOS, Peter J. 4767 NORTH BEND RD 45211 #020-02-1993 L1995 **IM GP** *020 †20

KAMDAR, Kala Yogesh. ■ 45267 #020-02-2000 L2000 **PHO** *012

KAMINSKI, Brian Jonathan. 1219 MORTS PASS 45215 #036-07-2001 L2004 **EM** *020 †16

KAMINSKI, Nancy Karen. 2135 DANA AVE, STE 210 45207 #038-41-1986 L1987 **IM** *020 †20

KAMNITZER, Sophie. ■ 45208 #869-02-1953 L1960 **P** *071

KAMP, Elizabeth Hoyt. ■ 45211 #018-03-2005 L2005 **EM** *100

KANAGARAJAN, Karthikeyan. 2123 AUBURN AVE, STE 401 45219 #495-42-1993 L2006 **CCM** *100 †20 ‡

KANE, Sean Kelly. ■ 45267 #016-11-2002 L2002 **AN** *020

KANERIA, Rakeshkumar M. 234 GOODMAN ST 45267 #495-22-1997 L2000 **P** *020 †75 ‡

KANT, Adrien Jean. ■ 45229 #035-03-2000 L2007 **GS** *100

KANT, Kotagal Shashi. 222 PIEDMONT AVE, STE 1200 45219 #495-36-1970 L1976 **NEP IM** *020 †20

KANU, Eneni Hazel. 3301 BEEKMAN ST 45225 #690-07-1984 L1993 **PD** *020 †55

KAPLAN, Deborah Elizabeth. ■ 45267 #008-01-2007 L2007 **PM** *012

KAPLAN, Heather Cecille. 3333 BURNET AVE, ML 7009 45229 #016-06-2001 L2007 **NPM** *100 †55

KAPLAN, Jennifer Melissa. 3333 BURNET AVE, CINCINNATI CHILDREN'S HOSP 45229 #038-41-1999 L2002 **CCP** *100 †55

KAPLAN, Marcia Joan. 3001 HIGHLAND AVE, STE E 45219 #048-12-1982 L1986 **P N** *020 †75

KAPLAN, Stanley M. 231 ALBERT SABIN WAY, COLLEGE OF MEDICINE 45267 #038-41-1946 L1946 **P PYA** *020

KAPP, Bethany Meredith. ■ 45267 #021-01-2006 L2006 **EM** *012

KAPUR, Sangita. ■ 45255 #496-09-1991 L2003 **DR** *100 †80

KARACHRISTOS, Andreas. ■ 45267 #418-05-1987 L2005 **GS** *100 †85

KARACOSTAS, Velissarios. 3333 BURNET AVE, CHILD & ADOLESCENT PSYCHI 45229 #051-07-1997 L2003 **CHP** *020 †75

KARATZA, Ekaterini C. 1945 CEI DR 45242 #418-06-1992 L2005 **OPH** *020 †35

KAREV, Milla. 8000 KENWOOD RD 45236 #913-86-1987 L1998 **IMG IM** *020 †20

KARLEN, Heather Noel. ■ 45227 #038-41-2000 *100

KARLOSKY, Loran Edward. ■ 45241 #020-12-2008 *012

KARP, Christopher L. 3333 BURNET AVE, TCHRF 1566, CHILDREN'S HOS 45229 #036-01-1986 L2001 **IM ID** *020 †20

KARRAM, Michael. 10506 MONTGOMERY RD, STE 201 45242 #915-02-1979 L1984 **OBG GP** *020 †30

KARRAM, Mickey Mohamed. 3219 CLIFTON AVE, STE 100 45220 #915-02-1982 L1986 **GYN OBG** *020 †30

KARTAL, John Paul. ■ 45229 #869-05-1951 L1959 **IM** *071

KASCKOW, John W. 4903 VINE ST 45217 #035-45-1987 L1995 **P** *020 †75

KASHYAP, Vikas. 494 NEEB RD 45233 #038-41-1985 L1987 **IM GS** *020 †20

KATTAN, Kenneth. 234 GOODMAN ST, STE 0054 45219 #550-01-1953 L1967 **DR R** *072 †80,28

KATZ, Eliezer. ■ 45248 #550-01-1979 L1984 **GS** *020

KATZ, Michael Edward. 9312 WINTON RD 45231 #033-05-1973 L1974 **OBG** *020 †30

KATZ, Molly Ann. 71 E HOLLISTER ST 45219 #038-43-1977 L1981 **GYN** *020 †30

KAUFMAN, Adam Henry. 222 PIEDMONT AVE, STE 1700 45219 #038-41-1987 L1993 **OPH** *020 †35

KAUFMAN, Enrique Norberto. 2825 BURNET AVE 45219 #132-01-1958 L1972 **P** *075 †75

KAUFMAN, Kyle. 234 GOODMAN ST, DEPT IM & PEDS 45219 #038-41-2006 L2006 **MPD** *012

KAUFMAN, Sarah. ■ 45242 #007-02-1982 L1985 **GP** *020

KAUFMANN, Kristiana Renee. ■ 45224 #025-07-2005 L2005 **EM** *012

KAUKAB, Zahida Parveen. 1038 CAREW TOWER 45202 #704-01-1969 L1978 **IM** *020 †20

KAUL, Ajay. 3333 BURNET AVE, CHILDREN'S HOSPITAL MED CE 45229 #495-47-1986 L1996 **PD** *020 †55

KAUL, Pamposh Darbari. 3223 ALBERT SABIN WAY, STE 405 45267 #495-51-1987 L1997 **ID** *020 †20

KAUL, Saroj. ■ 45220 #495-34-1956 L1980 **OBG PD** *020

KAVINSKY, Jeanne Krekeler. 222 PIEDMONT AVE STE 6000 45219 #038-41-1984 L1986 **IM** *020 †20

KAWAMOTO, Melody M. 4676 COLUMBIA PKWY MS R-10 45226 #014-01-1980 L1983 **OM IM** *050 †20,70

KAY, Rena Lynn Victor. 3001 HIGHLAND AVE, STE E 45219 #023-01-1971 L1971 **P PYA** *020 †75

KAY, William Aaron. 231 ALBERT SABIN WAY # 5, UNIVERSITY OF CINCINNATI 45267 #017-20-2004 L2004 **MPD** *012

KAZIOR, Richard John. 10496 MONTGOMERY RD, STE 212 45242 #041-14-1980 L1985 **OBG** *020 †30 ‡

KECK, Paul E, Jr. 231 ALBERT SABIN WAY ML559, COLLEGE OF MEDICINE 45267 #035-47-1983 L1991 **P** *020 †75

KEEFE, John Michael. ■ 45208 #038-41-1975 L1979 **EM IM** *071 †20,16

KEEGAN, Brian Jay. 4777 E GALBRAITH RD, DEPT O F MED EDUCATION 45236 #665-01-2006 L2006 *100

KEGLER, James L. 629 OAK ST 45206 #038-41-1975 L1976 **FM** *075 †18

KEHRES, Mark Gerard. 4623 WESLEY AVE, STE C 45212 #038-41-1987 L1990 **IM** *020

KELLAM, Mark Edward. 415 GREENWELL AVE 45238 #054-04-1996 L1999 **EM** *020 †16

KELLER, James David. 3801 HAUCK RD 45241 #016-02-1984 L1986 **OM LM** *020 †70

KELLEY, Scott R. ■ 45242 #020-12-2006 L2006 **GS** *012

KELLEY, Todd Christopher. ■ 45208 #016-11-2003 L2003 **ORS** *012

KELLEY, William Robt. 1525 ELM ST, C/O EMPLOYEE SERVICE HEALT 45202 #038-41-1965 L1965 **IM GP** *020

KELLOGG, Frank W. ■ 45243 #025-01-1946 L1953 **PD** *020

KELLY, Elizabeth Anne. 222 PIEDMONT AVE, STE 5100 45219 #038-41-1984 L1991 **OBG** *020 †30

KELLY, Nancy. 7655 5 MILE RD STE 101 45230 #007-02-1986 L1991 **PD** *020 †55

KELLY, Patrick Francis. 3333 BURNET AVE, CINCINNATI CHILDRENS HOSPI 45229 #023-01-1991 L2002 **PHO** *020 †55

KELMAN, Jay Paul. 1945 CEI DR, CINCINNATI EYE INSTITUTE 45242 #038-41-1972 L1976 **OPH** *020 †35

KEMMER, Nyingi Munanyo. 231 ALBERT SABIN WAY, ML 0595 45267 #690-13-1991 L2004 **GE** *020 †20

KEMPCZINSKI, Richard F. 234 BETHESDA AVE, DEPT SURG 45229 #024-01-1967 L1979 **VS CD** *020 †85

KEMPER, Robert A. ■ 45206 #020-02-1950 L1952 **OPH** *071 †35

KEMPFE, Konrad Max. 566 8 MILE RD 45255 #407-12-1963 L1970 **OBG** *071 †30

KENKEL, Henry F. 7631 CHEVIOT RD, UNIT2 45247 #038-41-1978 L1981 **P** *020 †75

KENKEL, Henry Jos. 2446 KIPLING AVE 45239 #038-41-1954 L1954 **NM R** *020 †28

KENNEALY, James Andrew. 3248 WESTBOURNE DR 45248 #038-41-1971 L1971 **PUD IM** *020 †20

KENNEBECK, Greg Duane. 222 PIEDMONT AVE, STE 6000 45219 #016-06-1997 L2002 **IM** *020 †20

KENNEBECK, Stephanie S. 3333 BURNET AVE, DEPT PED EM MED MLC 2008 45229 #016-06-1996 L2002 **PEM** *020 †55

KENNEDY, John Charles. 231 ALBERT SABIN WAY, BOX 0559 45267 #038-40-1993 L1994 **P PFP** *020 †75

KENNEDY, Monica Margaret. 7495 STATE RD, STE 340 45255 #038-43-1984 L1986 **P** *020 †75

KENNEY, Barbara A Breden. 2136 W 8TH ST, PRICE HILL CENTER 45204 #038-41-1967 L1967 **PD** *071 †55

KENNEY, Louis Thos. 3917 SPRING GROVE AVE, NORTHSIDE HEALTH CENTER 45223 #038-41-1967 L1967 **PD** *020 †55

KENNY, Alan Patrick. 3333 BURNET AVE, CINCINNATI CHILDREN'S HOSP 45229 #035-45-2002 L2005 **NPM** *012 †55

KENNY, Michael Robt. ■ 45236 #038-41-1986 L1988 **PTH GS** *020 †50

KENT, Charlotte Pelham. CINCINN U MED CTR PUD DIS 45267 #919-03-1976 **PUD** *050

KEPNER, Julie Ann. ■ 45255 #038-41-2004 L2004 **P** *012

KERCSMAR, Carolyn M. 3333 BURNET AVE, DIV OF PULMONARY MED 45229 #038-06-1978 L1981 **PDP** *020 †55

KEREIAKES, Dean James. 2123 AUBURN AVE, STE 136 45219 #038-41-1978 L1984 **CD** *050 †20

KEREIAKES, Thomas James. 2123 AUBURN AVE, STE 209 45219 #038-41-1980 L1985 **OTO HNS** *020 †45

KERLAKIAN, George M. 2915 CLIFTON AVE 45220 #605-02-1981 L1984 **GS VS** *020 †85

KERMODE-JADEED, Kathryn E. ■ 45236 #038-41-2001 L2001 **MPD** *100

KERR, Hanan. 3219 CLIFTON AVE, STE 400 45220 #038-40-1989 L1994 **CD** *020 †20

KERR, Stewart Matthew. ■ 45246 #023-12-1998 L2003 **ORS** *100

KERREY, Benjamin Thomas. 3333 BURNET AVE, CINCINNATI CHILDREN'S HOSP 45229 #030-05-2002 L2002 **PEM** *012

KERSTEN, Jennifer Lee. 2139 AUBURN AVE, STE 102 45219 #018-03-1978 L1985 **DR** *020 †80

KERSTINE, Richard S. 1945 CEI DR, CINCINNATI EYE INSTITUTE 45242 #020-02-1958 L1965 **OPH** *020 †35

KESAV, Prashanth R. 6045 BRIDGETOWN RD 45248 #495-98-1992 L1998 **IM** *020 †20

KESSEL, Sol L. ■ 45229 #038-41-1941 **U** *071

KESSELRING, Audrey Anne. ■ 45202 #038-41-2007 L2007 **PS** *012

KESSLER, Daniel Lee. 10495 MONTGOMERY RD, STE 20 45242 #025-01-1977 L1985 **U** *020 †95

KESSLER, Margaret F. 2139 AUBURN AVE 45219 #038-41-1951 L1951 **IM** *075

KESSLER, Megan Lee. 3219 CLIFTON AVE, STE 125 45220 #038-41-1992 L1993 **OBG** *020 †30

KESTERSON, David Marc. 2450 KIPLING AVE 45239 #038-41-1971 L1971 **GS** *071 †85

KEVAN, Emily Nelson. ■ 45236 #026-04-2004 L2007 **PG** *012 †55

KEYES, Robert Scott. ■ 45227 #038-41-2000 L2000 **FPG** *020 †20

KEYS, Michael Arnold. 415 STRAIGHT ST STE 403 45219 #038-41-1983 L1985 **P PYG** *020 †75

KEYS, Richard H, Jr. 12103 SHERATON LN 45246 #047-06-1970 L1971 **U** *020 †95

KHAJA, Aslam Mohammed. 45267 #038-44-2001 L2002 **VN** *100

KHAJA, Faizuddin Muhammed. ■ 45208 #038-44-2006 L2006 **OPH** *012

KHALIL, Amin Youssef. 231 ALBERT SABIN WAY, STE ML531 45267 #915-03-1990 L1999 **IM** *020 †20

KHALILY, Cyma. 8624 WINTON RD STE A 45231 #038-40-1986 L1990 **P PFP** *020 †75

KHALILY, Hooshang. 8686 WINTON RD 45231 #517-01-1960 L1972 **P CHP** *072

KHAN, Amber Rasheed. 234 GOODMAN ST 45267 #704-25-2003 L2006 **IM** *012

KHAN, Hafiz Sarfraz Ahmad. CO INTERNAL MEDICIN, UNIV CINCINNATI COMUNIV HO 45267 #704-25-2003 L2007 **IM** *012

KHAN, Irum. 234 GOODMAN ST 45267 #704-25-2003 L2005 **IM** *012

KHAN, Muhammad A. 4600 WESLEY AVE STE B 45212 #704-02-1996 L2004 **NEP IMG** *020 †20

KHAN, Muhammad Asim. 6725 MIAMI AVE 45243 #704-01-1965 L1973 **RHU IM** *040 †20

KHAN, Najma Samad. 1966 ANDERSON FERRY RD, # 1 45238 #704-06-1969 L1984 **IM** *020 †20

KHAN, Rashid Masood. 2450 KIPLING AVE, STE 204 45239 #704-22-1983 L1995 **IM** *020 †20

KHAN, Shagufta Asifa. 234 GOODMAN ST, STE 0501 45219 #704-02-1990 L2005 **PTH** *020 †50

KHAN, Shah-Naz Hayat. ■ 45248 #704-20-1989 L2006 **NS** *100

KHAN, Yasser Anwar. ■ 45267 #065-10-1997 L2002 *100

KHAN, Zahida. ■ 45219 #041-12-2008 *012

KHATANA, Anup Kanji. 1945 CEI DR 45242 #025-07-1991 L2000 **OPH** *020 †35

KHATRI, Pooja. 222 PIEDMONT AVE, STE 3200 45219 #016-11-2000 L2004 **VN** *020 †75

KHATRI, Rakesh. 231 ALBERT SABIN WAY, UNIVERSITY OF CINCINNATI 45267 #496-29-2001 L2005 **N** *012

KHATRI, Reshma Rakesh. ■ 45236 #496-29-2001 L2005 *100 †55

KHERA, Oner Ali. ■ 45208 #010-01-2005 L2005 **ORS** *012

KHODADAD, Rhazes Kevin. 2130 SINTON AVE 45206 #654-01-1998 L2000 **IM** *020 †20

KHOLODENKO, Yana A. 7825 LAUREL AVE 45243 #038-41-2002 L2002 **IM** *020

KHOSLA, Nandini Nayar. 7654 MONTGOMERY RD 45236 #496-07-1966 L1982 **P N** *020 †75

KHURANA HERSHEY, Gurjit. 3333 BURNET AVE, CHILDRENS HOSP MED CTR 45229 #028-02-1992 L1997 **PDA AI** *020 †03,55

KIBELBEK, Michael John. 3333 BURNET AVE 45229 #040-02-1979 L1998 **PAN PD** *020 †55,05

KIEFHABER, Thomas Ray. 10700 MONTGOMERY RD, STE 150 45242 #038-41-1980 L1982 **HS** *020 †40

KIELY, Charles Edward, Jr. ■ 45220 #038-41-1947 L1947 **IM HEM** *071 †20

KIESLER, H Joseph, Jr. 1295 KEMPER MEADOW DR, UNIVERSITY FAM PHYSICIANS 45240 #038-41-1994 L1995 **FM** *040 †18

KIGHTLINGER, Alan Rigby. ■ 45220 #038-41-1963 L1963 **ORS HS** *071 †40

KILGORE, April Elaine. ■ 45208 #055-02-2004 L2006 **PDI** *012 †55

KIM, Charles Chungson. ■ 45218 #143-11-2000 L2005 **PCC** *012 †20

KIM, Cheryl Kyung. ■ 45209 #025-01-2007 L2007 **MPD** *012

KIM, Daniel. 375 DIXMYTH AVE, GOOD SAMARITAN HOSPITAL 45220 #005-12-2001 L2006 **VS** *012

KIM, Dong-Sik. 231 ALBERT WAY, DEPT OF SURGERY 45267 #583-03-1996 L2006 *100

KIM, Edward S. 3333 BURNET AVE, DIV OF CARDIO MAIL ST 2003 45229 #038-40-2000 L2003 **PDC** *100 †55

KIM, Haejin. 45240 #038-41-2004 L2004 **IM** *100 †20

KIM, Hee K.. 3333 BURNET AVE 45229 #583-03-1999 **PDR** *012

KIM, Hyon Jeong. ■ 45230 #026-04-2007 *012

KIM, Ku Jung. 2446 KIPLING AVE 45239 #583-10-1975 L1982 **AN** *020

KIM, Kyu-Hwan. 6557 GRACELY DR 45233 #583-01-1963 L1978 **GS GP** *020

KIM, On Ja. 2139 AUBURN AVE, THE CHRIST HOSPITAL 45219 #583-02-1953 L1972 **ATP** *071 †50

KIM, Sang-Hee Bernadette. 2139 AUBURN AVE 45219 #583-08-1960 L1975 **ON IM** *020 †20

KIM, Sung Soo. 9600 COLERAIN AVE STE 410 45251 #583-09-1961 L1971 **OS** *020 †85

KIM, Young Ghon. ■ 45208 #583-02-1967 L1974 **AN** *071 †05

KIMBALL, Thomas Richard. 3333 BURNET AVE, CHILDRENS HOSP MED CTR 45229 #035-19-1982 L1988 **PDC PD** *020 †55

KINDEL, Elmore A, Jr. ■ 45243 #038-41-1958 L1958 **D OM** *071 †15

KINDEL, Robert Matthew. 2450 KIPLING AVE 45239 #038-41-1993 L1999 **GE** *020 †20

KINDEL, Steven James. ■ 45209 #038-40-2003 L2003 **PDC** *012 †55

KINDEL, Susan Elizabeth. 9670 KENWOOD RD 45242 #038-41-1986 L1991 **DMP** *062 †15

KINDEL, Tammy Lyn. ■ 45209 #038-40-2005 L2007 **GS** *012

KINDER, Brent Wayne. 231 ALBERT SABIN WAY, DIVISION OF PULMONARY, CRI 45267 #012-05-2000 L2007 **IM** *100 †20

KING, Brooke Anne. ■ 45213 #056-06-2004 L2004 **NPM** *012 †55

KING, Lionel R. ■ 45243 #020-02-1952 L1953 **NEP END** *071 †20

KINGMA, Pamela Beth. 3333 BURNET AVE, CIN CHILDRENS HOSP MED CTR 45229 #047-05-2000 L2000 **PD PEM** *020 †55

KINGMA, Paul Scot. 3333 BURNET AVE, DEPARTMENT OF NEONATOLOGY 45229 #047-05-2000 L2000 **NPM** *100 †55

KINKARTZ, Jason Daniel. ■ 45219 #025-12-2006 L2006 **ORS** *012

KINNETT, Douglas Gene. 3333 BURNET AVE, BLDG E 2310 CCHMC 45229 #038-41-1988 L1989 **PM PD** *020 †60,55

■ = Address Information Privacy Protected

KIRBY, Jerry Neal. 2123 AUBURN AVE # NO-301 45219 #038-41-1977 L1979 **OPH** *020 †35

KIRCHER, Christopher. 5400 KENNEDY AVE, PROSCAN IMAGING&LIVING LON 45213 #017-20-1973 L1977 **N PHM** *050 †75

KIRCHNER, Donald Bruce. 5299 SPRING GROVE AVE, RM 2S32 - MAILBOX 25 45217 #041-12-1974 L1995 **OM IM** *030 †20,70

KIRK, Patrick Gerard. 2123 AUBURN AVE, # 201 45219 #016-01-1985 L1991 **OAR OTR** *020 †40

KIRKENDALL, Eric Steven. 3325 BISHOP ST 45220 #038-41-2003 L2003 **PD** *100 †55

KIRKHAM, Lea Neely. 11238 CORNELL PARK DR 45242 #020-12-1994 L1997 **PD** *020 †20

KIRKHAM, Mark Miller. 2123 AUBURN AVE, STE 624 45219 #020-12-1992 L1998 **CD** *020 †20

KIRKLAND, Clem Ryan. ■ 45208 #038-44-2005 L2005 **D** *012

KIRKPATRICK, David D, III. 7502 STATE RD, STE 1180 45255 #038-06-1981 L1986 **GS VS** *020 †85

KIRN, Julius. ■ 45215 #038-41-1986 L1988 **FM OS** *020 †18

KIRSH, Gary Michael. 10475 READING RD, STE 206 45241 #016-02-1984 L1988 **U** *020 †95

KIRSH, Marvin. 5920 COLERAIN AVE 45239 #045-01-1957 L1962 **GP OS** *020

KIRWAN, Kelley Anne. 7655 5 MILE RD 45230 #020-02-1984 L1989 **PD** *020 †55

KISSEL, David Jos. 7500 STATE RD 45255 #038-41-1981 L1984 **PM** *020 †60

KITZMILLER, Karl Wm. 9403 KENWOOD RD STE B100, SUITE B-100 45242 #038-41-1960 L1960 **D OS** *020 †15

KIWAN, Rabee Abdelraouf. 3217 CLIFTON AVE, GOOD SAMARITAN HOSP 45220 #605-01-2001 L2002 **FPG** *100 †20

KLAFTER, Andrew Bennett. 222 PIEDMONT AVE, STE 8 45219 #035-06-1996 L2000 **P** *020 †75

KLATTE, Paul B. 4966 GLENWAY AVE 45238 #038-41-1951 L1951 **U** *071 †95

KLEEMAN, Steven Douglas. 375 DIXMYTH AVE, 8TH FL 45220 #038-41-1994 L1995 **OBG** *020 †30

KLEIER, Ruth Sharon. 9670 KENWOOD RD 45242 #020-12-1987 L1992 **DMP** *020 †15 ‡

KLEIMEYER, Ted Allen. 3131 QUEEN CITY AVE 45238 #038-41-1978 L1980 **DR NM** *020 †80

KLEIN, David Jay. 3333 BURNET AVE, CHILDRENS HOSP/CIN 45229 #035-46-1977 L1992 **PN PD** *050 †55

KLEIN, Jillian Ann. ■ 45239 #038-41-2005 L2005 **PD** *012

KLEIN, Judith A Gleser. ■ 45201 #017-20-1971 **P** *020

KLEIN, Jules Isaac. ■ 45206 #038-41-1939 L1941 **PD** *071 †55

KLEIN, Linda Diana. 311 STRAIGHT ST 45219 #038-41-1981 L1982 **P** *020 †75

KLEIN, Melissa Dawn. 3333 BURNET AVE, MLC 2011 45229 #035-03-1995 L1996 **PD** *020 †55

KLEIN, William Bernard. 6460 HARRISON AVE, STE 201 45247 #038-41-1996 L2000 **FSM** *020 †18

KLEINFELDER, James S. 7810 5 MILE RD 45230 #045-01-1980 L1982 **FM** *020 †18

KLEINMAN, Jerome J. 4422 CARVER WOODS DR 45242 #020-02-1968 L1971 **CHP P** *020

KLINE-FATH, Beth Marie. 3333 BURNET AVE, CINTI CHILDREN'S HOSP RADI 45229 #038-41-1989 L1993 **PDR** *020 †80

KLINGENBERG, Ralph H. ■ 45241 #038-41-1950 L1950 **OM** *071

KLOPP, Richard Gerard. 6045 BRIDGETOWN RD 45248 #038-41-1975 L1977 **IM** *020 †20

KLUGER, Carrie Zwerdling. 7661 MONTGOMERY RD 45236 #422-01-1984 L1994 **PD PDC** *020 †55

KLYOP, Gerald Wayne. 3200 BURNET AVE RM 56 45229 #038-41-1977 L1978 **PM** *020 †60

KNABE, Peter Gerald. 10550 MONTGOMERY RD, STE 15 45242 #038-43-1990 L1991 **DR** *020 †80

KNEPLER, James Lee, Jr. 231 ALBERT SABIN WAY, ML 0564 45267 #038-40-1994 L1995 **PCC** *020 †20

KNEZEVIC, Slavko. 2446 KIPLING AVE 45239 #957-01-1953 L1970 **IM CD** *020 †20

KNILANS, Timothy Kevin. 3333 BURNET AVE, DIVISION OF CARDIOLOGY (OS 45229 #038-41-1983 L1986 **PDC ICE** *020 †55

KNIPPER, Tara Donice. 2915 CLIFTON AVE 45220 #020-02-1999 L2000 **OBG** *020 †30

KNISELY, Jan Perry. 2139 AUBURN AVE 45219 #038-41-1977 L1978 **AN IM** *020 †05

KNOCHEL, Kurt. 1219 MORTS PASS 45215 #017-20-1988 L1991 **EM** *020 †16

KNOX, Sarah Margaret. 3001 HIGHLAND AVE, STE B 45219 #038-41-1980 L1980 **P PYA** *020

KO, Carlyn Yeongsook. ■ 45215 #016-42-1995 L2004 **EM** *020 †16

KOCH, Bernadette Lu. 3333 BURNET AVE, CHILDREN'S HOSP MED CTR 45229 #038-41-1987 L1988 **PDR** *020 †80

KOCH, Marcella Ann. ■ 45208 #038-41-2004 L2004 **NS** *012

KOCHARLA, Lakshmi Padma. 231 ALBERT SABIN WAY, ML 0563 45229 #495-50-2000 L2006 **RHU** *012 †20

KOCOSHIS, Samuel Angelus. 3333 BURNET AVE, CHILDRENS HOSPITAL MEDICAL 45229 #056-06-1973 L2000 **PG PD** *040 †55

KODE, Hima D. 222 PIEDMONT AVE, STE 8500 45219 #038-44-1993 L1998 **P ADP** *020 †75

KODE, Ramesh. 1945 CEI DR 45242 #038-41-1992 L1996 **OPH** *020 †35 ‡

KOEHLER, Alison. 234 GOODMAN ST 45219 #035-06-1991 L1992 **PTH** *020 †50

KOENIG, Matthias Werner. 3333 BURNET AVE, DEPT OF ANESTHESIOLOGY 45229 #409-15-1996 L2005 **PAN** *020

KOGAN, Jillene M. ■ 45242 #016-11-2001 L2001 **OS** *100 †55,19

KOHLI, Rohit. 3333 BURNET AVE 45229 #495-73-1999 L2007 **PG HEP** *100 †55

KOHLS, Regina Anne. 6331 GLENWAY AVE 45211 #038-40-1991 L1994 **FM** *020 †18 ‡

KOHN, Edward Ira. 3001 HIGHLAND AVE, STE E 45219 #035-01-1975 L1977 **P PYA** *020 †75

KOHUT, Robert Michael, Jr. ■ 45212 #038-41-2008 *012

KOLB, Dennis Michael. 10498 MONTGOMERY RD, STE A 45242 #038-41-1992 L1993 **IM** *020 †20

KOMOROSKI, Eva Maria. 3917 SPRING GROVE AVE 45223 #038-06-1984 L1985 **PD EM** *020 †55

KONDASH, Joy Ann. ■ 45248 #038-41-1987 L1988 **FM** *074

KONDASH, Stephen Thos. 2841 BOUDINOT AVE, STE 300 45238 #038-41-1987 L1991 **OPH IM** *020 †35

KONERMAN, Harry J. 3536 EDWARDS RD, HARRY J KONERMAN & JAMES P 45208 #016-43-1946 L1947 **IM OS** *072

KONERU, Madhavi. ■ 45242 #495-65-1997 L2005 **NPM** *012 †55

KOO, Julie Christie. 3306 RUTHER AVE 45220 #038-41-1997 L1998 **FM** *020 †18

KOOY, Neil Warren. 3333 BURNET AVE 45229 #047-05-1987 L1999 **CCP PD** *050 †55

KOPELOFF, Nicholas, Jr. ■ 45213 #035-46-1966 L1971 **IM** *020

KOPPENHOEFER, Ron Michael. 8333 MONTGOMERY RD 45236 #038-41-1973 L1974 **PM** *020 †60

KORELITZ, Joel Leonard. 4760 E GALBRAITH RD, STE 108 45236 #038-41-1975 L1975 **GS** *020 †85

KORFHAGEN, Thomas Richard. 3333 BURNET AVE, CHILDREN'S HOSPITAL MED CT 45229 #038-41-1981 L1983 **PD MG** *050 †75

KORTEKAMP, Gerard Edward. 2123 AUBURN AVE, STE 331 45219 #038-41-1982 L1983 **IM** *020 †20

KOSELKA, Helen Katherine. 3219 CLIFTON AVE, STE 215 45220 #016-06-1987 L1995 **IM NM** *020 †28,20

KOSHARSKIY, Boleslav. 3333 BURNET AVE, CO CHILDREN S HOSP-MED EDU 45229 #409-33-1997 L2002 **APM** *020 †05

KOTAGAL, Uma Raman. 3333 BURNET AVE, CHMC DEPT OF HEALTH POLICY 45229 #495-01-1971 L1976 **NPM PD** *050 †55

KOTCHER, Peter Giles. 3200 VINE ST, CINCINNATI VAMC/MHC 45220 #021-06-1976 L1978 **P PYA** *030 †75

KOTHEGAL, Harischandir P. 3308 JEFFERSON AVE 45220 #495-09-1977 L1983 **U** *020 †95

KOTTE, J Harold. 400 BROADWAY ST # 10 45202 #038-41-1938 **CD IM** *072 †20

KOTWAL, Renu. 222 PIEDMONT AVE, STE 8 45219 #496-17-1987 L2002 **P** *020 †75

KOURIE, Michel Ange. 463 OHIO PIKE, STE 300 45255 #308-02-1989 L1998 **IM** *020 †20

KOVILAM, Oormila P. 234 GOODMAN ST 45219 #495-37-1981 L1995 **OBG** *020 †30

KOWAL, Norman Edward. US EPA HLTH EFF RES LAB 45268 #055-01-1977 **PHP** *030

KOWATCH, Robert Anthony. 3333 BURNET AVE, CHILDRENS HOSPITAL MEDICAL 45229 #016-42-1980 L2000 **P** *020 †75

KRALOVIC, Stephen Michael. 231 BETHESDA AVE 0560, DIV OF INFECTIOUS DIS/INT 45267 #038-43-1989 L1991 **ID** *020 †20

KRAMER, Lisa Ann. ■ 45242 #038-41-2004 L2004 **U** *012

KRAMER, Michael John. 9250 BLUE ASH RD 45242 #038-41-1975 L1975 **NS** *020 †25

KRAMER, Susan Marie. 9900 CARVER RD STE 10 45242 #038-40-1985 L2001 **FM** *020 †18

KRAUS, Steven Jay. 3333 BURNET AVE, CHILD HOSP CINCI DEP RADIO 45229 #051-04-1992 L1999 **PDR** *020 †80

KRAUSE, Julie Anne. 3131 QUEEN CITY AVE 45238 #038-41-1998 L1999 **IM** *020 †20

KRAVETZ, Russell Stuart. 5525 MARIE AVE 45248 #038-41-1954 L1954 **P** *020 †75

KRAVETZ, Todd Michael. 5525 MARIE AVE 45248 #038-43-1993 L1995 **IM** *020 †20

KRAYTERMAN, Galina. 9200 MONTGOMERY RD STE A 45242 #913-33-1990 L2000 **IM** *020 †20

KREBS, Heidi Jane. 924 WAYCROSS RD, LINCLON HEIGHTS HEALTH 45240 #038-43-2003 L2006 **FM** *020 †18

KREEGER, Michael Colasurd. ■ 45267 #038-41-2002 L2002 **DR** *012

KREEGER, Renee Nierman. 3333 BURNET AVE 45229 #038-41-2003 L2003 **PAN** *012

KREINDLER, David Michael. 231 BETHESDA AVE, U CINCINNATI COLL OF MED 45229 #038-41-1995 *100

KREINDLER, James Jacob. 7625 COLERAIN AVE, STE E 45239 #038-41-1975 L1975 **PDA AI** *020

KREINDLER, Michael S. 2625 COLERAIN AVE STE D, C/O KREINDLER MED ASSOC 45214 #038-41-1967 L1967 **A IG** *020

KREINES, Kenneth. 4360 COOPER RD 45242 #038-41-1956 L1956 **DIA END** *020 †20

KREINES, Michael David. 1207 SPRINGFIELD PIKE 45215 #038-41-1983 L1989 **GE** *020 †20

KREJSA, Douglas Charles. 231 BETHESDA AVE, M L 0529 45229 #038-06-1993 L1996 **EM** *020 †16

KREMCHEK, Timothy Edward. 6480 HARRISON AVE, SPORTS MEDICINE 45247 #038-41-1986 L1987 **ORS OSM** *020 †40

KRESSEL, Amy Beth. 3223 ALBERT SABIN WAY, STE 405 45267 #016-06-1989 L1997 **ID** *020 †20

KREYLING, George Henry. 6350 GLENWAY AVE 45211 #038-41-1963 L1963 **IM** *020 †20

KRICK, David Howard. 7794 5 MILE RD, STE 100 45230 #038-41-1972 L1972 **U** *020 †95

KRIMERMAN, Naum S. 3200 BURNET AVE, 1 RIDGEWAY 45229 #913-50-1984 L1998 **IM** *020 †20

KRISHNAMOORTHY, Kumaresh. D231 ALBERT, OTOLARYNGOLOGY 45267 #496-32-1996 L2006 *100

KRISHNAN, Shoba S. 2711 MADISON RD 45209 #495-96-1986 L1992 **PD PEM** *020 †55

KROCKER TUSKAN, Maria. 3259 ELLAND AVE 45267 #450-02-1954 L1959 **CHP P** *020

KRONE, Karen Lynn. 231 ALBERT SABIN WAY, DEPT. OF ANESTH COLLEGE OF 45267 #038-41-1982 L1983 **AN** *062 †05

KRONE, Robert E. ■ 45242 #038-41-1950 L1950 **FM** *071

KRONE, Robert Emil, Jr. 8260 NORTHCREEK DR, STE 310 45236 #038-41-1979 L1979 **GE IM** *020 †20

KRUEGER, Darcy Andrew. 3333 BURNET AVE, C/O CHILDREN'S HOSP-MED ED 45229 #028-34-2002 L2002 **CHN** *100

KRUIS, Steven E. 375 DIXMYTH AVE 45220 #016-76-1993, ▲ L2002 **DR** *020 †80

KRUMMEN, Donna Marie. 10615 MONTGOMERY RD, STE 201 45242 #038-41-1992 L1995 **PS** *020 †85,65 ‡

KRUPP, Seth Samuel. ■ 45206 #016-02-2005 L2006 **EM** *012

KUAN, Chia-Yi. 3333 BURNET AVE 45229 #244-02-1989 *100

KUAN, Lisa Wylin. 8146 HAMILTON AVE, MOUNT HEALTHY FAMILY PRACT 45231 #025-12-1989 L1992 **PD NPM** *020 †55

KUBALA, Ginger Sadler. 10550 MONTGOMERY RD, STE 12 45242 #038-43-1987 L1988 **FM** *020 †18 ‡

KUBY, Mark Benj. 4750 E GALBRAITH RD, STE 207 45236 #038-41-1974 L1979 **IM ID** *020 †20

KUDCHADKER, Nivedit Ajay. ■ 45267 #496-15-2001 L2004 **MPD** *100

KUEHNLE, Leonard W. 2915 CLIFTON AVE 45220 #056-06-1946 L1947 **OBG** *071

KUHN, Benjamin Robert. ■ 45236 #041-77-2005, ▲ L2005 **PG** *012

KUHN, Brian Allen. ■ 45248 #030-06-2004 L2004 **GS** *012

KUHN, Eric Jos. 2859 BOUDINOT AVE, STE 206 45238 #016-43-1985 L1993 **U GS** *020 †20

KUHN, Howard F. ■ 45246 #038-41-1941 **FM** *071

KUKIELKA, Gilbert Leon. 4760 E GALBRAITH RD, STE 205 45236 #270-01-1983 L1999 **CD IC** *020 †20

KUKRETI, Asha. ■ 45206 #496-07-1966 L1984 *020

KULKARNI, Anuradha V. 4777 E GALBRAITH RD, JEWISH HOSP-ANESTH DEPT 45236 #495-19-1972 L1982 **AN** *020 †05

KULKARNI, Vinayak Shankar. 3200 BURNET AVE 45229 #495-56-1970 L1982 **GE IM** *020 †20

KULWIN, Dwight Robt. 3219 CLIFTON AVE STE 110, CINCINNATI EYE INSTITUTE 45220 #016-02-1973 L1979 **OPH** *020 †35

KUMAR, Ashok. 10496 MONTGOMERY RD, STE 204 45242 #495-15-1977 L1993 **CRS** *020 †85,10

KUMAR, Manoj Koyamparamba. 3333 BURNET AVE 45267 #495-44-1989 L2002 **PDO** *100

KUMAR, Seena Manoj. ■ 45267 #495-80-1995 L2002 **SP** *100 †50

KUMAR, Sunil. 45202 #704-16-1988 **GS** *100

KUMBALA, Damodar Reddy. 4777 E GALBRAITH RD 45236 #496-31-1996 L2002 **IM** *020 †20

KUNKEL, Robert Louis, Jr. 4411 MONTGOMERY RD, STE 200 45212 #649-14-1982 L1986 **FM** *020 †18

KUNTZ, Charles David. 222 PIEDMONT AVE STE 3100 45219 #038-06-1991 L2000 **NS** *020 †25

KUNTZ, Charles Henne. 10550 MONTGOMERY RD, STE 15 45242 #038-41-1963 L1963 **R** *020 †80

KUROKAWA, Ryu. ■ 45267 #572-20-1995 L2000 *100

■ = Address Information Privacy Protected

KURTH, Charles Dean. 3333 BURNET AVE, CHILDRENS HOSPITAL MEDICAL 45229 #056-05-1982 L2002 **AN PD** *020 †55,05

KURTZMAN, Lawrence Craig. 4850 RED BANK RD, FL 2 45227 #041-09-1981 L1989 **PS** *020 †65

KUSCHNIR, Susan Marie. 231 ALBERT SABIN WAY 45267 #038-41-2003 L2005 **CHP** *012

KUSHNER, Jonathan Paige. 9275 MONTGOMERY RD, STE 100 45242 #010-01-1981 L2002 **GE NTR** *020 †20

KUY, Daniel G. 8044 MONTGOMERY RD, STE 230 45236 #869-07-1986 L1997 **PS** *020 †85,65

KUYKENDAL, Robert Lee. 820 DELTA AVE 45226 #036-01-1971 L1974 **P** *020 †75

LABOWSKY, Christine. 10700 MONTGOMERY RD, STE 101 45242 #038-41-1975 L1977 **PD** *020 †55

LACKEMANN, George Walter. 425 OAK ST 45219 #038-41-1983 L1987 **P** *020 †75

LACKER, Robert David. 7835 REMINGTON RD 45242 #038-40-1978 L1982 **PD** *020 †55

LACUESTAKIMMEL, Nanette N. ■ 45209 #038-41-2008 *012

LACY, Karen Kay. ■ 45248 #038-43-1987 L1988 **FM** *071 †18

LACY, Peter David. 3333 BURNET AVE, CO CHILDREN S MED CTR-MED 45229 #539-03-1989 L2000 **PD OTO** *100

LADLE, Brian Hansen. ■ 45255 #023-07-2007 L2007 **PD** *012

LAFLAM, Paul Frederick. 234 GOODMAN ST, UNIVERSITY HOSPITAL 45219 #011-02-2003 L2004 **NEP** *012 †20

LA FRANCONI, Paula J. 55 PROGRESS PL 45246 #409-32-1985 L1990 **IM** *020 †20

LAHAM, Ailee Mark. ■ 45230 #038-41-2008 *012

LA HUE, Dale James. 6045 BRIDGETOWN RD 45248 #038-43-1984 L1985 **IM** *020 †20

LA MARRE, Thomas David, Jr. 330 STRAIGHT ST, STE 400 45219 #038-40-1996 L1997 **ID** *020 †20

LAMB, Clarence Eugene, Jr. 8146 HAMILTON AVE, LINCOLN HEIGHTS 45231 #038-41-1979 L1980 **GYN OBS** *020 †30

LAMB, Melinda Nicole. ■ 45242 #026-08-2004 L2006 **GS** *012

LAMBECK, Tah Chance. ■ 45209 #038-41-2008 *012

LAMBERS, Donna Sue. 375 DIXMYTH AVE, GOOD SAMARITAN SETON CTR 45220 #038-41-1990 L1992 **OBG MFM** *020 †30

LAMPHERE, Benjamin Gordon. ■ 45208 #025-12-2005 L2005 **MPD** *012

LAMPING, Richard Jos. 9400 READING RD 45215 #038-40-1960 L1960 **GP** *071

LAMPING-ARAR, Kathleen Jo. 3006 PORTSMOUTH AVE 45208 #038-41-1993 L1996 **PD** *020 †55

LAMPKIN, Beatrice C. 3300 ELLAND AVE, CHILDRENS HOSPITAL 45229 #001-02-1960 L1966 **PHO OS** *040 †55

LAMPKIN, Jonathan Traylor. 234 GOODMAN ST 07, UNIV CINCINNATI COMRADIOLO 45219 #027-01-2002 L2002 **DR** *100 †80

LANARD, Bruce James. 7500 STATE RD 45255 #041-02-1965 L1985 **PTH** *020 †50

LANCASTER, Scott B. ■ 45238 #048-78-2006, ▲ L2006 **IM** *012

LANE, Joseph A. 3200 BURNET AVE 45229 #038-41-1944 L1944 **OTO** *072 †45

LANG, James Edward. 4260 GLENDALE MILFORD RD, STE 202 45242 #038-41-1985 L1986 **IM** *020 †20 ‡

LANG, Tara Renee. ■ 45209 #056-05-2004 L2007 **NPM** *012 †55

LANG, Wayne Thos. 234 GOODMAN ST 45267 #020-02-1984 L1996 **P** *100

LANGE, Robert J G. ■ 45232 #020-12-1971 L1978 **P CHP** *075 †18,75

LANGENDERFER, Rachel Ann. 440 RAY NORRISH DR 45246 #051-01-1995 L1996 **OBG** *020 †30

LANGHEIM, Steven Terence. 2136 W 8TH ST 45204 #038-41-1972 L1973 **PD** *020 †55

LANPHEAR, Bruce P. 3333 BURNET AVE 45229 #028-46-1986 L1988 **GPM** *020 †70

LANPHEAR, Nancy E. 3333 BURNET AVE, CHILDREN'S HOSP MEDICAL CE 45229 #028-46-1987 L1990 **PD OS** *050 †55

LAOR, Tal. 3333 BURNET AVE, CHILDREN'S HOSPITAL MED CE 45229 #024-01-1986 L1998 **PDR** *020 †80

LAOR, Yehuda G. ■ 45243 #869-07-1957 L1964 **RO NM** *071 †80,28

LAOR, Yona Shifra. ■ 45243 #869-07-1956 L1964 **OS** *074

LARASON, Carrie Jean. 3333 BURNET AVE 45229 #038-41-2001 L2002 **PD** *020 †55

LARKIN, Lisa Conrad. 4460 RED BANK RD, STE 100 45227 #008-01-1988 L1991 **IM** *020 †20

LARMA, Joel Daniel. ■ 45220 #021-01-2003 L2007 **OBG** *020

LARRABEE, Hollynn L. 231 ALBERT SABIN WAY 45267 #041-12-2001 L2001 **EM** *020 †16

LARSON, Craig Robert. ■ 45209 #035-75-2004, ▲ L2004 **GS** *012

LARSON, Edwin Robt. 9200 MONTGOMERY RD STE 8A 45242 #020-02-1973 L1977 **P** *020

LASKIN, Benjamin Lewis. ■ 45208 #023-01-2005 L2005 **PD** *012

LATIMORE, Larry J. ■ 45213 #025-12-1973 *071

LAURICELLA, Christopher. 375 DIXMYTH AVE 45220 #038-75-2001, ▲ L2001 *020

LAURY, Darcey Lynette. ■ 45219 #038-41-2005 L2005 **MPD** *012

LAUTMAN, Lee Paul. 2915 CLIFTON AVE, GROUP HEALTH ASSOCIATES 45220 #038-45-1986 L1992 **OBG** *020 †30

LAVERY, Adrian Paul. 3333 BURNET AVE, ML 7009 45229 #051-07-2001 L2005 **NPM** *012 †55

LAVIGNE, Ruth Faye. 234 GOODMAN ST, STE 0054 45219 #038-41-2000 L2000 **RO** *040 †80

LAWHON, Steven Michael. 2139 AUBURN AVE 45219 #020-02-1976 L1977 **ORS OP** *020 †40

LAWRENCE, John Patrick. 234 GOODMAN ST, STE 0531 45219 #028-34-1994 L1999 **AN** *020 †05

LAWSON, Brenda. 1401 STEFFEN AVE 45215 #038-45-1993 L1995 **IM** *020

LAWSON, Marva Lynn. 311 ALBERT SABIN WAY 45229 #038-41-1994 L1999 **P** *020

LAXTON, Alenna Brynae. ■ 45237 #020-12-2004 L2004 **OTO** *012

LAZARON, Lisbeth Mary. 2450 KIPLING AVE 45239 #016-01-1983 L1989 **FM** *020 †18

LE, Phuong Nhan. 222 PIEDMONT AVE, STE 4100 45219 #012-01-1991 L1992 **IM** *020 †20,55

LE, Theodore Toan. 231 ALBERT SABIN WAY, ML-0212 45267 #005-19-1994 L1995 **ORS** *020 †40

LEACH, James L. 10550 MONTGOMERY RD, STE 15 45242 #038-41-1990 L1991 **DR** *020 †80

LEACH, Sabrina S. 234 GOODMAN ST, STE 0769 45219 #038-41-1990 L1991 **EM** *020 †16

LEADBETTER, Michael G. 4850 RED BANK RD, 1 PLASTIC SURGERY CENTER 45227 #038-40-1974 L1977 **PS FPS** *020 †65

LEANZA, Joseph R. 11360 SPRINGFIELD PIKE 45246 #038-43-1999 L2002 **PD** *020 †55

LEAVELL, Walter Fairchild. ■ 45241 #047-07-1964 L1976 **OS IM** *071

LECHNER, Mark Frederick. ■ 45229 #038-41-2008 *012

LE COULTRE, Claude P. 240 BETHESDA AVE 45229 #869-04-1969 L1981 **PDS** *020

LEDER, Wilfried. 10506 MONTGOMERY RD 45242 #038-41-1970 L1970 **ON IM** *020 †20

LEDFORD, Diana Marie. ■ 45227 #038-41-2006 L2006 **AN** *012

LEDYARD, Holly Kristine. 231 ALBERT SABIN WAY ML0769, DEPT OF EMERG MED 45267 #038-41-2002 L2002 **EM OS** *020 †16

LEE, Andy Chunhao. ■ 45231 #038-41-2005 L2005 **AN** *012

LEE, Arthur Francis. 6350 GLENWAY AVE 45211 #038-41-1982 L1983 **ORS OSM** *020 †40

LEE, Bae Suk. ■ 45241 #583-01-1956 L1975 **AN** *071

LEE, Cheryl Linda. ■ 45242 #016-06-1983 L1984 **EM** *020 †16

LEE, Chin Tai. 10550 MONTGOMERY RD, STE 33 45242 #385-02-1967 L1974 **NS** *020 †25

LEE, Cindy S C. ■ 45242 #385-02-1967 L1974 **AN** *020

LEE, David Sungkiew. ■ 45209 #025-01-2007 L2007 **MPD** *012

LEE, Gerald Bell. ■ 45236 #038-06-2003 **PD** *012 †55

LEE, Ik Sung. 3333 BURNET AVE, DEPARTMENT OF ANESTHESIA, 45229 #583-04-1968 L1975 **AN PD** *020 †05

LEE, Kenneth. 13054 COOPERMEADOW LN 45242 #038-41-2008 *012

LEE, Ki Hyeong. 3333 BURNET AVE, CCH MEDICAL CENTER 45229 #583-02-1990 L2006 **CHN** *020 †75

LEE, Kun II. 375 DIXMYTH AVE, OBSTETRIC ANESTHESIA 45220 #583-02-1968 L1983 **AN** *020

LEE, Lisa Ann. 3333 BURNET AVE 45229 #038-41-1993 L1996 **PDC** *020 †55

LEE, Olivia Tien. ■ 45208 #038-41-2008 *012

LEE, Paikky. ■ 45255 #583-02-1958 L1969 **AN PME** *071 †05

LEE, Su-Ju. 5819 CHEVIOT RD, PROFESSIONAL RADIOLOGY 45247 #038-41-1985 L1989 **DR** *020 †80

LEE, Tsz Leung. 3333 BURNET AVE, CO CHILDREN S HOSP-MED EDU 45229 #462-01-1992 L2002 *100

LEENELLETT, Elizabeth E. 234 GOODMAN ST, STE 0769 45219 #025-01-1995 L1996 **EM** *016

LEE-ROBINSON, Ayse L. 10700 MONTGOMERY RD, STE 110 45242 #038-41-1982 L1983 **PM** *020 †60

LEHMAN, Laura Lee. ■ 45206 #038-41-2006 L2006 **PD** *012

LEHMANN, Corinne E. 3130 HIGHLAND AVE, STE 0557 45219 #038-41-1993 L1996 **ADL AMI** *020 †55,20

LEIBOLD, John Louis. 10550 MONTGOMERY RD, STE 15 45242 #038-41-1983 L1985 **R RNR** *020 †80

LEININGER, Brian E. 231 ALBERT SABIN WAY, ML 0558 45267 #028-03-1998 L2007 **CCS** *012 †85

LEISGANG, John Jos. 5525 MARIE AVE 45248 #038-41-1980 L1980 **IM** *020 †20

LEKAN, Thomas James. 3155 GLENDALE MILFORD RD, CINCINNATI EVENDALE SURG 45241 #038-06-1982 L1983 **AN** *020 †05

LEKSON, Jeffrey Thos. 3200 VINE ST, V.A. MEDICAL CENTER 45220 #038-41-1989 L1994 **IM** *020 †20

LEKSON, Suzanne Loesch. 5575 CHEVIOT RD 45247 #038-41-1989 L1999 **MPD EM** *020 †20,55

LE MASTERS, Margaret Mary. 3219 CLIFTON AVE, STE 125 45220 #038-41-1982 L1982 **OBG** *020 †30

LEMBERG, Bradley Maurice. 752 WAYCROSS RD 45240 #038-41-1969 L1969 **OTO HNS** *020 †45

LEMING, Philip Deering. 10506 MONTGOMERY RD 45242 #020-02-1975 L1977 **ON HEM** *020 †20

LEMPERT, Hamilton H. 9150 WINTON RD 45231 #035-46-1992 L1994 **EM** *020 †16

LENCHITZ, Bernard. 8146 HAMILTON AVE, LINCOLN HEIGHTS 45231 #033-06-1985 L1988 **IM** *020 †20

LENKAUSKAS, Edmundas. ■ 45208 #407-10-1948 L1958 **OTO OS** *020

LENKAUSKAS, Siga M. 10700 MONTGOMERY RD, STE 100 45242 #038-41-1988 L1992 **PD** *020 †55

LENOBEL, Robert S. 5819 CHEVIOT RD 45247 #028-03-1975 L1980 **R NR** *020 †80

LENZ, Kellene Maria. 5575 CHEVIOT RD 45247 #038-41-1994 L1995 **FM** *020 †18

LEONARD, David Gregory. 222 PIEDMONT AVE, STE 8500 45219 #038-41-2000 L2000 **P** *020 †75

LEONARD, James Robt. 6350 GLENWAY AVE 45211 #038-41-1981 L1983 **ORS** *020 †40

LEONIS, Mike Anthony. 3333 BURNET AVE, CHILDREN'S HOSPITAL MEDICA 45229 #028-02-1996 L2000 **PG** *020 †55

LERHAUPT, Karen E. 4750 E GALBRAITH RD, STE 105 45236 #038-40-1999 L2000 **OPH** *020 †35

LE ROITH, Derek. ■ 45267 #836-02-1967 L1983 **END DIA** *050 †20

LESINSKI, Stanley G. 11135 MONTGOMERY RD 45249 #025-01-1966 L1974 **NO** *020 †45

LESLIE, Nancy Doan. 3333 BURNET AVE, DIV OF HUMAN GENETICS 45229 #028-02-1979 L1983 **MG PD** *020 †55,19

LESSURE, Alfred P. 9232 DEERCROSS PKWY 45236 #038-41-1955 L1955 **DR** *020 †80

LESTER, Tiffany Rachel. ■ 45206 #038-41-2008 *012

LESTINA, Lisa Suzanne. 4760 E GALBRAITH RD, STE 107 45236 #016-06-1995 L2001 **GE** *020 †20

LETICA, Ljubica Helen. 1219 MORTS PASS 45215 #025-07-1991 L1994 **EM** *020 †16

LETSCHER, Robert Michael. 7911 EUCLID AVE 45243 #038-40-1988 L1989 **FM** *020 †18

LETT, Sarah Katharine. ■ 45208 #408-02-2004 L2004 **MPD** *012

LEUENBERGER, Kurt Paul, Jr. 2450 KIPLING AVE, STE 111 45239 #038-40-2000 L2000 **IM** *020

LEVICK, Elizabeth Horn. 4350 MALSBARY RD, STE 208 45242 #038-43-1984 L1990 **RO DR** *020 †80

LEVIN, Jerrold Mayer. 3918 E GALBRAITH RD, EYE CARE CENTER OF CINCINN 45236 #038-41-1967 L1967 **OPH** *020 †35

LEVIN, Ronald Stewart. 3333 BURNET AVE 45229 #038-41-1973 L1975 **PD** *020 †55

LEVINE, Isaac J. 6770 FAIR ACRES LN 45213 #030-05-1949 L1951 **IM PUD** *071 †20

LEVINE, Mark Allen. 2123 AUBURN AVE 45219 #038-41-1985 L1989 **OBG** *075 †30

LEVINSON, Joseph E. 222 PIEDMONT AVE, ELYSE E LOWER 45219 #038-41-1944 L1944 **RHU IM** *071

LEVITAS, John R. 400 MARTIN LUTHER KNG DR E 45229 #016-06-1949 L1950 **ORS** *071 †40

LEVITT, Marc Aaron. 3333 BURNET AVE, MAIL LOCATION 2023 45229 #035-46-1993 L2005 **PDS** *020 †20

LEVY, Richard Carl. 234 GOODMAN ST # 769 45267 #020-02-1972 L1974 **EM** *071 †16

LEVY, Richard Leon. 4777 E GALBRAITH RD 45236 #038-41-1969 L1969 **RO IM** *020 †20,80

LEWIS, Christopher Todd. 3306 RUTHER AVE 45220 #038-41-2000 L2000 **FM** *020 †18

LEWIS, David F, Jr. 234 GOODMAN ST 45219 #021-06-1985 L2007 **OBG** *020 †30

LEWIS, H Paul. 10550 MONTGOMERY RD, STE 33 45242 #035-09-1960 L1966 **NS** *020 †25

LEWIS, Jaime Dawn. ■ 45230 #038-41-2004 L2004 **GS** *012

LEWIS, Lisa Susan. 3333 BURNET AVE, OSB-4, C H M C DIV EMERGENCY MED 45229 #041-01-1985 L1992 **PEM** *040 †55

LEWIS, Marthe Getoor. ■ 45227 #017-20-1997 *100

LEWIS, Sarah Ann. 8245 NORTHCREEK DR 45236 #038-44-2000 L2000 **OBG** *020

LEWIS, Stephen. 10525 MONTGOMERY RD 45242 #017-20-1989 L1996 **CD IM** *020 †20

LEWIS, Timothy Joseph. 231 ALBERT SABIN WAY, OF GEN INT MED C/O PEG SCH 45267 #025-07-1998 L2000 **FPG** *020 †20

LI, Chao. ■ 45255 #243-72-1997 L2007 **OBG** *012

■ = Address Information Privacy Protected

LI, Jolly Thos. 3155 GLENDALE MILFORD RD, CINCINNATI EVENDALE SURG 45241 #038-44-1988 L1993 **AN** *020 †05

LI, Maureen. 111 WELLINGTON PL 45219 #243-47-1986 L2000 **CN** *020 †75

LIANG, Warren Min. 231 ALBERT SABIN WAY, MAIL LOCATION 559 45267 #005-19-1977 L1981 **P CHP** *040 †75

LICHTENBERG, Ann Carolyn. 4370 MALSBARY RD, STE 100 45242 #038-41-1967 L1967 **PD** *071 †55

LICHTENSTEIN, Philip K. 24 COMPTON RD, STE 205 45216 #047-05-1976 L1979 **PD GE** *020 †55

LIERL, Michelle Brennan. 3333 BURNET AVE, ALLERGY IMMUNOLOGY ML2021 45229 #020-12-1979 L1986 **AI PDP** *020 †55,03

LIFSHITZ, Jarrad Neil. 1219 MORTS PASS 45215 #422-01-2002 L2005 **EM** *020 †16

LIGHT, Irwin Jos. 3333 BURNET AVE, CINCI CHILDRENS HOSP MED C 45229 #067-01-1959 L1975 **NPM PD** *030 †55

LIKE, Anne Claudette. 375 DIXMYTH AVE 45202 #038-41-1990 L1992 **OM IM** *020 †70,20

LILLY, Soma Irani. 538 OAK ST STE 200 45219 #038-44-2000 L2006 **HS** *020

LIM, Lynne Hsueh Yee. 3333 BURNET AVE 45229 #825-01-1992 L2001 **PDO** *100

LIN, Chuni John. 3000 E SHARON RD, PLANT 45241 #016-42-1986 L1987 **IM OM** *020 †20

LIN, Show Whei. ■ 45243 #244-02-1975 L1997 **ADP** *072 †75

LIN, Tsung-Her. 3217 CLIFTON AVE, GOOD SAMARITAN HOSPITAL 45220 #385-04-1967 L1972 **AN PUD** *020 †05

LINAM, Leann Eggers. 3333 BURNET AVE, CINCINNATI CHILDREN'S HOSP 45229 #047-06-2000 L2001 **PDR** *100 †80

LINAM, William Matthew. 3333 BURNET AVE, DIVISION OF INFECTIOUS DIS 45229 #047-06-2001 L2001 **PDI** *012 †55

LIND, Leonard Jay. 234 GOODMAN ST, STE 0531 45219 #035-47-1976 L1992 **AN CCM** *020 †05

LINDENFELD, Thomas Nelson. 3301 WESTBOURNE DR 45248 #025-01-1978 L1984 **ORS** *020 †40 ‡

LINDQUIST, Harley D. ■ 45220 #035-06-1953 L1963 **PTH FOP** *071 †50

LINDSEY, Sommer Eryn. ■ 45226 #038-41-2008 *012

LINDSLEY, Andrew Warren. ■ 45268 #017-20-2007 L2007 *012

LINDY, Jacob David. 3001 HIGHLAND AVE, STE E 45219 #035-01-1963 L1967 **P** *020

LINK, Dana Thompson. 3333 BURNET AVE, DIVISION OF OTOLARYNGOLOGY 45229 #028-46-1991 L1997 **PDO** *020 †16

LINNEMANN, Calvin C, Jr. 5885 GRAVES LAKE DR, UNIV OF CINCINNATI MED CEN 45243 #036-07-1965 L1972 **ID IM** *071 †20

LINZ, Douglas Henry. 11129 KENWOOD RD 45242 #025-01-1977 L1985 **OM IM** *020 †20,70

LINZ, John Christopher. 6350 GLENWAY AVE 45211 #038-41-1993 L1999 **ORS** *020 †40

LIPPE, Joyce Elayne. ■ 45209 #031-01-2006 L2006 **MPD** *012

LIPPERT, Raymond J. 5920 COLERAIN AVE 45239 #038-41-1949 L1949 **EM** *072

LIPPERT, Wayne Arthur. 2123 AUBURN AVE, STE 122 45219 #038-41-1969 L1969 **GYN** *020 †30

LIPSCOMB, Eric Lamont. 45236 #038-40-2007 L2007 **AN** *012

LIPSTEIN, Hadassah. ■ 45237 #550-03-2001 L2007 **DR** *100 †80

LITTLE, Iris Gutmark. ■ 45215 #023-07-2004 L2004 **PDE** *012 †55

LITTLE, Kevin James. ■ 45215 #023-07-2004 L2004 **ORS** *012

LITWIN, Allen. 10500 MONTGOMERY RD 45242 #038-41-1957 L1957 **AI ALI** *071 †03,20

LIU, John Kwokin. 3236 BURNET AVE 45229 #038-43-1988 *020

LIVINGSTON, Jeffrey C. 3333 BURNET AVE 45229 #051-04-1991 L2004 **MFM OBG** *020 †30

LOCASTO, Donald Anthony. 2139 AUBURN AVE, STE 0769 45219 #033-06-1996 L2001 **EM IM** *020 †16

LOCKEY, James Edward. 3223 EDEN AVE, UNIV OV CINCINNATI 45267 #041-13-1972 L1979 **OM PUD** *050 †20,70

LOCKWOOD, Pamela Jane. 4240 HUNT RD 45242 #038-41-1977 L1980 **P CHP** *020 †75 ‡

LODOLO, Mauro. 400 OAK ST 45229 #561-15-1982 L2002 **CHN** *100

LOEPKE, Andreas. 3333 BURNET AVE - ML2001, CHILDREN'S HOSPITAL MED CT 45229 #409-25-1994 L2003 **AN** *020 †05

LOEWENSTINE, Virginia. 2245 GILBERT AVE STE 400 45206 #038-43-1987 L1988 **OM FM** *020 †18

LOEWY, Andrew. 4760 E GALBRAITH RD, STE 217 45236 #143-03-1969 L1974 **IM** *020 †20

LOFTISS, Carrie Monica. 400 WABASH AVENUE 45236 #665-01-2007 L2007 **IM** *012

LOFTUS, Abby Elizabeth. ■ 45211 #038-41-2008 *012

LOGAN, Douglas Kent. 2123 AUBURN AVE, STE 144 45219 #038-41-1976 L1979 **IM** *071 †20

LOGAN-COLLINS, Jocelyn M. ■ 45267 #016-06-2003 L2003 **GS** *012

LOGEMAN, Jay Paul. 10500 MONTGOMERY RD 45242 #038-06-1984 L1985 **GS** *020 †85

LOGGIE, Jennifer M H. 3300 ELLAND AVE, CHILDRENS HOSPITAL 45229 #836-01-1959 L1976 **PD OS** *071

LOHR, Joann Marie. 6350 GLENWAY AVE, STE 208 45211 #056-05-1983 L1991 **GS VS** *020 †85

LOHRE, Margaret Susan. 9549 MONTGOMERY RD, STE 100 45242 #020-02-1978 L1979 **IM** *020 †16

LOMAS, Ben. 3200 VINE ST, PSYCHIATRY DEPARTMENT 116A 45220 #005-06-1962 L1979 **P PYA** *030 †75

LONG, Amy Lyn. ■ 45230 #055-01-2005 L2006 **OBG** *012

LONG, Daniel Edward. 2139 AUBURN AVE, STE 102 45219 #038-41-1995 L1997 **DR** *020 †80

LONG, Don Scott. 2915 CLIFTON AVE, 2ND FL 45220 #038-40-2000 L2000 **PM** *020 †60 ‡

LOON, Martin Harvey. 375 DIXMYTH AVE, OBSTETRIC ANESTHESIA 45220 #836-02-1969 L1979 **AN** *020 †05

LOPEZ, Alfonso Perez. 500 E BUSINESS WAY 45241 #016-43-1978 L1981 **AN IM** *020 †20,05

LORTS, Angela. ■ 45213 #030-06-1998 L2002 **PDC** *020 †55

LOSINIECKI, Andrew John. ■ 45209 #017-20-2005 L2005 **NS** *012

LOTZ, Douglas Richard. ■ 45211 #048-02-2004 L2004 **MPD** *012

LOUDERMILK, M Katherine. 3333 BURNET AVE, CINCINNATI CHILDRENS HOSPI 45229 #038-41-1988 L1990 **PD** *020 †55 ‡

LOUGHREY, John Richard. 2450 KIPLING AVE, STE G02 45239 #038-41-1971 L1971 **GE IM** *020 †20 ‡

LOUIS, Michelle Yee. 375 DIXMYTH AVE, GOOD SAM HOSP FAC MED CTR 45220 #038-41-1995 L1999 **IM** *020 †20

LOVE, Daniel Curtis. 12124 SHERATON LN 45246 #038-41-1982 L1986 **OPH** *020 †35

LOVELL, Daniel Joe. 3300 ELLAND AVE # 159, CHILDRENS HOSPITAL 45229 #019-02-1978 L1984 **RHU PD** *020 †55

LOVETT, William Bernard. 2800 WINSLOW AVE STE 412, INC 45206 #038-43-1988 L1989 **EM** *020 †16

LOWE, Gerald Franklin. 7500 STATE RD 45255 #010-01-1956 L1961 **FM** *020 †18

LOWENHAUPT, Rosalin W. 234 GOODMAN ST 45267 #242-07-1944 **OS** *050

LOWER, Elyse Ellen. 199 WILLIAM HOWARD TAFT RD 45219 #038-41-1981 L1983 **HEM IM** *020 †20

LU, Qing. ■ 45242 #243-16-1988 L1994 **SP** *020 †50

LU, Sunny Yang. 311 MARTIN LUTHER KING DR 45220 #243-69-1982 L1996 **P** *020

LUBOW, Jeffrey Mark. ■ 45220 #034-01-2004 L2004 **OBG** *012

LUBOW, Robert Edward. 3001 HIGHLAND AVE, STE E 45219 #035-08-1965 L1971 **P** *020 †75

LUCAS, Frederick Vance, Jr. 234 GOODMAN ST, STE 0501 45219 #028-03-1975 L1977 **PTH CLP** *020 †50

LUCAS, Johna Doing. 71 E HOLLISTER ST 45219 #028-03-1976 L1978 **OBG** *020 †30

LUCAS, Marvin Howard. 4750 E GALBRAITH RD, STE 207 45236 #038-41-1989 L1992 **IM NM** *020 †28,20

LUCAS, Patricia Jane. ■ 45255 #038-41-1960 L1960 **GP GYN** *071

LUCKHAUPT, Sara Elizabeth. INST FOR HEALTH POLICY, BOX 670840 HLTH SVCS RES 45267 #038-40-2002 L2002 **IM** *100 †70

LUCKY, Anne Weissman. 7691 5 MILE RD, CINCINNATI 45230 #008-01-1970 L1983 **D PDE** *020 †55,15

LUCKY, Paul Andrew. 7691 5 MILE RD 45230 #008-01-1972 L1983 **D RHU** *020 †20,15

LUEBBERS, Mark Jos. 400 BROADWAY ST 45202 #038-41-1984 L1985 **IM** *020 †20

LUESSEN, Eric Craig. 4623 WESLEY AVE, STE C 45212 #038-41-1981 L1983 **IM** *020 †20,70

LUGGEN, Michael Edmund. 231 ALBERT SABIN WAY, UNIVERSITY OF CINCINNATI 45267 #035-01-1974 L1977 **RHU IM** *020 †20

LUKAC, Ivan. 375 DIXMYTH AVE 45220 #957-01-1969 L1975 **IM UCM** *020

LUKE, Robert Geo. 231 ALBERT SABIN WAY, ML 557 45267 #803-05-1959 L1988 **IM NEP** *040

LUKIN, Andrea Jeanette. ■ 45208 #038-41-1996 L2000 **D** *020

LUKIN, Robert Roy. 234 GOODMAN ST, STE 0054 45219 #038-41-1965 L1965 **R RNR** *030 †80

LUM, Ted Michael. 2825 BURNET AVE 45219 #038-43-1980 L1984 **OBG** *020 †30

LUMPKIN, Houston L, III. 2123 AUBURN AVE, STE 331 45219 #041-12-1974 L1975 **GYN** *020 †30

LUND, Andrew David. ■ 45219 #038-41-2008 *012

LUNDBERG, Thomas Geo. 11340 MONTGOMERY RD, STE 208 45249 #038-41-1989 L1992 **IM** *020 †20

LUNDEEN, Andrea Marie. ■ 45209 #030-06-2007 L2007 **GS** *012

LUNDGREN, Janell Erae. PO BOX 19176 45219 #035-06-2002 L2002 **FM** *100

LUNDQUIST, Christopher A. ■ 45267 #047-05-2006 L2006 **GS** *012

LUO, Guangju. 231 ALBERT WAY, DEPT OF PATHOLOGY 45267 #243-01-1984 L2006 **PTH** *020

LURIA, Joseph Walter. 3333 BURNET AVE 2008, EMERGENCY MEDICINE 45229 #038-41-1989 L1993 **EM** *020 †20

LURIE, Max L. 3120 BURNET AVE, 301 JEWISH HOSPITAL PROF B 45229 #038-41-1943 L1944 **P N** *071

LUSTIG, David Alan. 2915 CLIFTON AVE 45220 #038-41-1985 L1987 **IM** *020 †20

LUTZ, James Thos. 4460 MONTGOMERY RD 45212 #038-45-1986 L1988 **OM FM** *020 †18,70

LUTZ, John Peter. ■ 45238 #038-40-1976 L1977 **P** *020 †75

LYKINS, Jane Eleanor. ■ 45230 #056-05-1996 L2004 **FM** *020 †18

LYNCH, Matthew Clyde. ■ 45227 #035-45-2005 L2005 **N** *012

LYONS, Christopher Babak. ■ 45219 #038-41-2008 *012

LYONS, Jefferson Morton. 2734 MARKBREIT 45209 #051-07-2000 L2000 **TS** *012 †85

LYONS, Michael Steffen. 2139 AUBURN AVE, STE 0769 45219 #036-07-1998 L1999 **EM** *050 †16

LYONS, Richard Arthur. ■ 45219 #869-04-1966 **PM** *020

LYONS, Sara Worcester. 2123 AUBURN AVE, STE 528 45219 #038-41-2000 L2002 **OBG** *020

MAAMARI, Micheline J. 663 ANDERSON FERRY RD, WEST SIDE PEDIATRICS INC 45238 #605-01-1993 L1996 **PD** *020 †55

MAC ALLISTER-SJOERDSMA, F. ■ 45243 #025-01-1950 L1979 **P OS** *071

MACAVEI, Sorina Momeu. 463 OHIO PIKE, STE 300 45255 #781-05-1996 L2001 **IM** *020

MACCALLUM, Patricia L. 3333 BURNET AVE, CHILDREN'S HOSPITAL MED CE 45229 #065-06-1995 L2000 **OTO** *020 †45

MACCARONE, Gina Liore. ■ 45219 #038-41-2007 L2007 **GS** *012

MACHERET, Leonid. 12087 SHERATON LN 45246 #913-99-1977 L1987 **GP OS** *020

MACHUCA, Jennifer Lynn. ■ 45211 #038-43-2004 L2004 **FP** *012

MACK, Elizabeth Hayes. 3333 BURNET AVE, MEDICAL CENTER 45229 #045-04-2003 L2006 **CCP** *012 †55

MAC LEOD, John Adams. 3001 HIGHLAND AVE, STE E 45219 #024-01-1948 L1953 **PYA** *020 †75

MACPHERSON, Colin R. 231 BETHESDA AVE, LM 0714 45267 #836-02-1946 L1960 **BBK CLP** *030 †50

MACZKO, Karen Marie. 130 WELLINGTON PL 45219 #025-07-1980 L1984 **CHP P** *020 †75

MADDIPATI, Murali Krishna. 400 WABASH AVENUE 45236 #495-21-2001 L2001 **IM** *012

MADDUKURI, Vinaya Chandra. 234 GOODMAN ST, MAIL LOCATION 0535 45219 #495-21-1998 L2006 **IM** *100 †20

MADDUX, Brian Neil. 111 WELLINGTON PL 45219 #048-12-1992 L1997 **N** *020 †75

MADHAV, Taruna Jethanand. ■ 45209 #016-06-2004 L2004 **ORS** *012

MAEDER, Michael Chas. 2727 MADISON RD, STE 208 45209 #038-40-1971 L1971 **END IM** *020 †20

MAERCKS, Rian Adam. ■ 45212 #036-07-2003 L2003 **PS** *012

MAGENHEIM, Douglas Alan. 9050 MONTGOMERY RD, STE B 45242 #038-41-1988 L1989 **IM MDM** *020 †20

MAGGIO, Michael Ignatius. 3308 JEFFERSON AVE 45220 #016-43-1982 L1983 **U** *020 †95

MAHAJAN, Aparna Madhukar. 231 ALBERT, CO PATHOLOGY DEPT 45267 #495-01-2000 L2007 **PTH** *012

MAHALINGAM, Krishnamurthi. 11155 KENWOOD RD 45242 #495-66-1970 L1974 **GS VS** *020 †85

MAHALINGAM, Sudha. 5049 CROOKSHANK RD, STE G5 45238 #495-65-1975 L1980 **RO** *020 †80

MAHASETH, Hemchandra. 231 ALBERT WAY, DEPT OF INTERAL MED 45267 #759-03-2000 L2007 **IM** *020

MAHER, James Frederick. 5520 CHEVIOT RD, ONCOLOGY PARTNERS NETWORK 45247 #039-01-1997 L1998 **HO IM** *020 †20

MAHMOUD, Mohamed Abdou. 3333 BURNET AVE, PEDIATRIC ANESTHESIA DEPT 45229 #915-04-1995 L2002 **PAN** *100 †05

MAHONEY, Mary Catherine. 234 GOODMAN ST, STE 0054 45219 #038-41-1983 L1986 **DR** *020 †80

MAIER, John Eyman. ■ 45243 #041-13-1961 L1962 **AN** *071 †05

MAILLER-SAVAGE, Erica Ann. ■ 45267 #038-45-2004 L2004 **D** *012

MAJOR, Stephen Douglas. ■ 45212 #038-43-2007 L2007 **IM** *012

MAK, Grace Zee. 234 GOODMAN ST 45267 #048-04-2000 L2000 **GS** *100 †85

MAKLEY, Amy Teres. ■ 45243 #038-41-2005 L2005 **GS** *012

MAKOROFF, Kathi Lynn. 3333 BURNET AVE, CINCINNATI CHILDREN'S HOSP 45229 #041-12-1994 L1997 **PD** *020 †55

MALDON, Kevin Robt. DEACONESS HOSP 45219 #917-25-1963 **PD** *020

MALDONADO, Arturo Rafael. ■ 45231 #033-05-1999 L2004 **GS** *100
MALEMPATI, Srikanth. ■ 45208 #422-01-2003 L2006 **IM** *020 †20
MALIK, Amina. ■ 45242 #038-41-2008 *012
MALIK, Anuj Subhash Chand. 3200 BURNET AVE 45229 #496-48-2001 L2005 **IM** *012
MALIK, Inayatullah Khan. 10550 MONTGOMERY RD, STE 22 45242 #704-01-1963 L1971 **U** *020 †95
MALIK, Junaid S. 10496 MONTGOMERY RD # 103, PULMONARY CONS INC 45242 #654-01-1998 L2000 **PCC** *020 †20
MALIK, Mohammad Sadruddin. ■ 45241 #915-05-1983 L1999 **PYG** *100 ‡
MALIK, Punam. 3333 BURNET AVE, MAIL LOCATION 7013 45229 #496-07-1988 L1996 **PHO** *020 †55
MALIK, Zaiba. 9302 TOWNE SQUARE AVE 45242 #011-02-2001 L2006 **OPH** *020 †35
MALINOWSKI, Laurel Ann. 3333 BURNET AVE, HOSP MED 45229 #056-05-2004 L2006 **CHN** *012
MALLICK, Shahla. 2915 CLIFTON AVE 45219 #704-02-1989 L1996 **PCC** *020 †20
MALONE, Roderick Angus. 375 DIXMYTH AVE 45220 #016-43-1961 L1970 **AN** *071 †05
MALONEY, Michael Jerome. 3001 HIGHLAND AVE, STE E 45219 #023-01-1971 L1975 **CHP** **P** *020 †75
MALONEY, Thomas Brennan. 2001 ANDERSON FERRY RD 45238 #055-02-1984 L1986 **PD** *020 †55
MALTZ, Robert. 11135 MONTGOMERY RD, # LL 45249 #038-41-1962 L1962 **OTO** **FPS** *020 †45
MANDEL, Keith Evan. 3333 BURNET AVE 45229 #041-12-1990 L2001 **PD** *030 †55
MANDELL-BROWN, Mark K. 10735 MONTGOMERY RD 45242 #038-41-1980 L1988 **OTO** **FPS** *020 †45
MANDERS, Jennifer Bryna. 4460 RED BANK RD, STE 120 45227 #016-42-1999 L2005 **SO** **GS** *020 †85
MANDYBUR, George Timothy. 222 PIEDMONT AVE STE 3100, UNIVERSITY MED ARTS BLDG 45219 #038-41-1990 L2004 **NS** *020 †25
MANDYBUR, Thaddeus Ian. U C MED CTR /PATH 529 45267 #759-09-1954 L1970 **NP** **PTH** *030 †50
MANEGOLD, Mark Andrew. 2450 KIPLING AVE, STE 104 45239 #038-40-1982 L1985 **GE** *020 †20
MANETAVAT, Narong. 5049 CROOKSHANK RD, STE 202 45238 #891-02-1962 L1975 **GS** *020 †55
MANFROY, Dawn Marie. 3333 BURNET AVE, DEPT OF EMERGENCY MEDICINE 45229 #047-05-1998 L1999 **PD** *020 †55
MANFROY, Pierre Paul. 11238 CORNELL PARK DR, NORTHEAST CINCINNATI PED A 45242 #047-05-1997 L1999 **PD** *020 †55
MANGAL, Ajay Kumar. 436 RAY NORRISH DR 45246 #018-03-1984 L1986 **OTO** *020 †45
MANGAL, Mamta. 436 RAY NORRISH DR 45246 #495-01-1987 L1991 **IM** *020 †20
MANGAT, Devinder Singh. 8044 MONTGOMERY RD, STE 230 45236 #020-12-1973 L1981 **PS** **OTO** *020 †45
MANGU, Padma. 8245 NORTHCREEK DR 45236 #495-56-1991 L1996 **END** **IM** *020 †20
MANLEY, Mark David. 3155 GLENDALE MILFORD RD, CINCINNATI EVENDALE SURG 45241 #038-41-1988 L1989 **AN** *020 †05
MANN, Ravinder Singh. 234 GOODMAN ST 45267 #495-75-1980 L1995 **P** *020
MANNAVA, Prabhavathy. 234 GOODMAN ST 45267 #495-21-1973 L1982 **P** **N** *020 †75
MANNAVA, Sriram. ■ 45249 #038-44-2005 L2006 **DR** *012
MANNAVA, Vallabhai Patel. 2600 STRATFORD AVE STE 101 45219 #495-65-1975 L1980 **PM** **EM** *020 †60
MANNING, Peter Bruce. 3333 BURNET AVE, DEPT OF CARDIOTHORACIC SUR 45229 #025-01-1982 L1996 **PDS** **TS** *020 †90,85
MANNING-COURTNEY, P. M. 3333 BURNET AVE, MEDICAL CENTER, PAVILION-2 45229 #038-41-1991 L1994 **PD** *020 †55
MANNION, Brian Alfred. 2727 MADISON RD, STE 400 45209 #035-19-1991 L1997 **ON** *020 †20
MANSON, Neil Anderson. 2125 AUBURN AVE STE 624 45219 #064-01-1999 L2004 **OSS** *100
MANSOUR, Mona Elizabeth. 3333 BURNET AVE, ML 2011 45229 #038-41-1992 L1996 **PD** *030 †55
MANYET, Rebecca Braun. 8260 NORTHCREEK DR 45236 #038-41-1995 L1997 **PM** *100
MARAAN, Benjamin Manalo. 2450 KIPLING AVE, STE 112A 45239 #748-01-1957 L1969 **TS** *071
MARABOYINA, Sanjay. ■ 45208 #038-41-2007 L2007 **IM** *012
MARATHE, Umesh Suresh. 7495 STATE RD, STE 200 45255 #036-07-1996 L2007 **OTO** *020 †45
MARCHESAN, Werther G. ■ 45230 #187-04-1964 L1973 **PS** *020
MARCHESCHI, Edward A. 6350 GLENWAY AVE 45211 #038-41-1997 L1999 **FSM** *020 †20
MARCOTTE, Michael Paul. 375 DIXMYTH AVE 45220 #038-43-1991 L1992 **MFM** **OBG** *020 †30
MARCUS, David Lynn. 1219 MORTS PASS 45215 #038-41-1976 L1977 **EM** **FM** *020 †18,16
MARCUS, Irving. ■ 45222 #143-01-1951 L1958 **AN** *071
MARGOLIN, E Gordon. UNIV OF CINCINNATI, DEPT OF GEN INT MED ML0535 45267 #030-05-1947 L1955 **IM** **IMG** *040 †20
MARGOLIN, Harold N. 3200 BURNET AVE 45229 #030-05-1951 L1955 **CCM** *072 †80
MARGOLIS, Charles Frank. 1207 SPRINGFIELD PIKE 45215 #036-01-1974 L1977 **FM** *020 †18
MARGOLIS, Jennifer A S. 1207 SPRINGFIELD PIKE 45215 #036-01-1974 L1977 **PD** *020 †55
MARIC, Alma Mustafa. 8250 KENWOOD CROSSING WAY, STE 205 45236 #957-08-1981 L1999 **PD** *020 †55
MARINAKIS, Vasiliki. ■ 45212 #038-41-1992 L1993 **IM** *020 †20
MARINO, Bradley Scott. 3333 BURNET AVE, ML 2003 45229 #024-01-1994 L2007 **CCP** **PDC** *020 †55
MARKHAM, Larry Wayne. 3333 BURNET AVE 45229 #047-20-1996 L2001 **PDC** *020 †20,55
MARKLAY, Jennifer Marie. 8245 NORTHCREEK DR 45236 #038-41-1995 L1996 **IM** *020 †20
MARLER, Jennifer J. 3333 BURNET AVE, CTR 45229 #067-01-1989 L2003 **PS** *020
MARSDEN, Brent David. ■ 45249 #016-45-2004 L2004 **GS** *012
MARSH, Maurice Delbert. ■ 45202 #018-03-1939 L1943 **IM** **CD** *071 †20
MARSH, Rebecca Arehart. ■ 45230 #016-01-2003 L2006 **PD** *100 †55
MARTIN, Angela. 222 PIEDMONT AVE, STE 3200 45219 #041-14-1999 L1999 **N** *020 †75
MARTIN, Colin Alex. ■ 45267 #025-07-2003 L2003 **GS** *012
MARTIN, Frederick Thos. C3131 QUEEN CITY AVE 45238 #038-41-1953 L1953 **FM** *071
MARTIN, Kurtis Wayne. 6355 E KEMPER RD, STE 100 45241 #020-12-1986 L1992 **PS** *020 †65
MARTIN, Lester W. 3333 BURNET AVE 45229 #024-01-1949 L1957 **PDS** *071 †85
MARTIN, Mary Margaret. ■ 45202 #038-40-1948 L1948 **RHU** *071 †85,65
MARTIN, Vincent Thos. 231 ALBERT SABIN WAY, DEPT OF INTERNAL MEDICINE 45267 #038-41-1984 L1985 **IM** *020 †20
MARTIN, William Albert. 3219 CLIFTON AVE, STE 400 45220 #038-41-1998 L1999 **IC** *020 †20
MARTIN, William Jos. 231 ALBERT SABIN WAY, PO BOX 670557 45267 #026-04-1974 L2002 **IM** **PUD** *030 †20
MARTINEK, Edward Francis. 5819 CHEVIOT RD 45247 #025-01-1990 L1996 **RNR** **VIR** *020 †80
MARTINEZ, Jose O. 3328 WESTBOURNE DR 45248 #748-01-1956 L1977 **IM** **PME** *020

MARTIN HAWVER, Lisa R. ■ 45267 #028-46-2001 L2007 **GS** *020 †85
MARTINI, Sharyl Rene. ■ 45267 #048-04-2004 L2007 **N** *012
MARTY, Theodore S, III. 175 W GALBRAITH RD 45216 #038-40-1986 L1989 **IM** *020 †20
MARURI, Srilakshmi. 3502 BOUDINOT AVE 45211 #495-50-1993 L1997 **IM** *020
MARVEL, Nathaniel T. 311 STRAIGHT ST 45219 #847-13-1981 L1984 **P** **IMG** *020 †75
MARWAN, Ahmed Marwan Ibra. 3333 BURNET AVE, DEPT OF MED EDU 45229 #915-04-2000 L2006 **GS** *100
MASHNY, John Michael. 10525 MONTGOMERY RD 45242 #038-41-1991 L1997 **CD** *020 †20
MASIH, Ashish Kumar. MED CTR-NEU, UNIV OF CINCINNATI 45267 #820-02-2005 L2007 **N** *012
MASINENI, Sreeharsha Nara. 231 ALBERT, CO PATHOLOGY DEPT 45267 #495-98-2000 L2007 **PTH** *012
MASON, Karen Jane. 3333 BURNET AVE, MLC 4002 45229 #023-01-1993 L2004 **PD** *020 †55
MASSA, Scott John. 425 FARRELL CT 45233 #038-40-1984 L1985 **IM** **IMG** *020 †20
MASSION, Charles Geo. 2139 AUBURN AVE 45219 #007-02-1953 L1977 **CLP** *071 †50
MASSOUD, Jennifer Estep. 775 DIXMYTH AVE., EMERGENCY DEPT. 45220 #038-41-1989 L1992 **EM** *016
MASSOUD, Joseph D. 375 DIXMYTH AVE 45220 #038-41-1955 L1955 **P** *071 †75
MASTERS, James Jos. 4760 E GALBRAITH RD, STE 109 45236 #017-20-1971 L1980 **DR** *020 †80
MASTERSON, Brian Michael. 231 ALBERT SABIN WAY, PSYCHIATRY AND 45267 #038-41-2003 L2003 **PFP** *012
MASUKAWA, Teruo. 9922 FORESTGLEN DR, CINCINNATI 45242 #572-04-1952 L1980 **OBG** *020
MATACIA, Gina Marie. ■ 45208 #038-41-2006 L2006 **IM** *012
MATHEW, Sajini. ■ 45236 #495-37-1992 L2003 **PTH** *020 †50
MATHIAS, Charles Gordon. 2001 ANDERSON FERRY RD 45238 #067-01-1972 L1985 **D** **IM** *020 †20,15
MATHIEU, Alix. 2368 VICTORY PKWY, STE 501 45206 #440-01-1963 L1980 **AN** *020 †05
MATHIS, Bradley Randall. 222 PIEDMONT AVE, STE 1200 45219 #038-41-1995 L1996 **IM** *020 †20
MATIAS, Mary T. 3333 BURNET AVE 45229 #043-01-2001 L2001 **OS** *100
MATTA, Mahendra Kumar. 10496 MONTGOMERY RD, STE 204 45242 #495-45-1970 L1978 **CRS** **PRO** *020 †85,10
MATTER, Jean-Paul. 200 NORTHLAND BLVD, ANESTHESIA GROUP PRACTICE 45246 #396-08-1983 L1986 **AN** *020 †05
MATTHEIS, Philip John. 3333 BURNET AVE, CINCINNATI CHILDRENS' HOSP 45229 #046-01-1988 L2006 **PD** *020 †55
MATTHEWS, Kathleen. 311 STRAIGHT ST 45219 #010-02-1978 L1990 **PTH** *020 †50
MATTHYS, Laura Anne. ■ 45208 #047-06-2001 L2001 **OBG** *020 †30
MATTINGLY, Jason Ross. 5575 CHEVIOT RD, EASTGATE FAMILY PRACTICE 45247 #017-20-1999 L2005 **FM** *020 †18
MATTISON, Kira. ■ 45267 #038-06-2006 L2006 **OBG** *012
MATUNIS, Suzanne Frances. 9403 KENWOOD RD, STE C208 45242 #041-02-1986 L1994 **FM** *020 †18
MATUSKA, Robert Anthony. ■ 45233 #038-41-1948 L1948 **GS** *071 †85
MATVEY, Shari Ann. 500 E BUSINESS WAY 45241 #038-41-1987 L1991 **AN** **PME** *020 †05
MAUGHLIN, Melanie Denise. 231 ALBERT SABIN WAY, ML-0531 45267 #023-07-1987 L2003 **AN** *020 †05
MAURER, Carter John. 12115 SHERATON LN, CO CINCI SPORTS MED-MED ED 45246 #036-07-2000 L2003 **ORS** *020
MAVI, Jagroop Kaur. ■ 45219 #038-41-2008 *012
MAXON, Harry Russell, III. 222 PIEDMONT AVE, STE 1600 45219 #021-01-1967 L1972 **NM** **END** *071 †20,28 ‡
MAYBODI, Leila. ■ 45236 #010-01-2004 L2004 **N** *012
MAYER, Kristine L. 234 GOODMAN ST 796, C/O UNIVERSITY HOSPS-MED E 45219 #062-01-1996 L2000 **OPH** *100 †35
MAYER, Matthew Percypatri. ■ 45242 #038-41-2005 L2005 **PPM** *012
MAYNARD, Thomas Curry. 8000 5 MILE RD, STE 112 45230 #004-01-1979 L1984 **GS** **VS** *020 †85
MAYOUE, Mark Patrick. 3259 ELLAND AVENUE 45267 #020-02-1987 L1991 **P** *020
MAYR, Judith A Kopfstein. ■ 45230 #038-41-1966 L1966 **GP** *020
MAZE, Seymour S. 231 BETHESDA AVE, UNIV OF CINCINNATI MED CTR 45267 #836-02-1973 L1988 **CD** *020 †20
MAZHARI, Amir. ■ 45267 #025-07-1999 L2001 **N** *100 †75
MAZRAESHAHI, Reza M. 231 ALBERT SABIN WAY, U OF CINCINNATI 45267 #517-01-1994 L2007 **CD** *012
MAZUR, Wojciech. 2123 AUBURN AVE, STE 136 45219 #759-04-1991 L2002 **CD** *020 †20
MAZWI, Mjaye Leslie. 3333 BURNET AVE 45229 #775-01-2003 L2005 **PD** *012
MC ADORY, Louis Elliott. ■ 45206 #051-04-2002 L2002 **DR** *012
MC ANDREW, Mark Richard. 375 DIXMYTH AVE, ATTN MEDICAL STAFF OFFICE 45220 #020-12-1994 L1999 **GS** *020 †85
MC ANDREW, Michael Edward. 375 DIXMYTH AVE, ATTN MEDICAL STAFF OFFICE 45220 #020-12-1990 L1998 **GS** *020 †85
MC ANENEY, Constance M. 3333 BURNET AVE, CHILDRENS HOSP OSB 4 45229 #010-02-1986 L1991 **PD** *020 †55
MC AULIFFE, John J, III. 3333 BURNET AVE, DEPARTMENT OF ANESTHESIA O 45229 #067-01-1977 L1985 **AN** **PD** *020 †55,05
MC CALL, John Edward. 3229 BURNET AVE, MED STAFF OFC SHRINERS HOS 45229 #038-41-1982 L1983 **PAN** **CCP** *020 †05
MCCALLA, Chad David. 3333 BURNET AVE, CHILDRENS HOSP MED CTR 45229 #038-41-2005 L2005 **PD** *012
MC CARREN, Timothy John. 6331 GLENWAY AVE 45211 #038-41-1977 L1978 **FM** *020 †18
MC CARTHY, Charles Eugene. 45211 #038-41-1962 L1963 **R** *071 †80
MC CARTHY, David E. ■ 45224 #038-41-1951 L1951 **CHP** **P** *071
MC CLAINE, Rebecca Jane. ■ 45213 #036-07-2005 L2005 **GS** *012
MC CLELLAN, Marvin. ■ 45247 #038-41-1943 L1944 **PD** **OS** *071 †55
MC CLELLAN, Michael M. 2135 DANA AVE, STE 210 45208 #038-41-1988 L1989 **IM** *020 †20
MC CLUSKEY, Cornelia Mary. 2123 AUBURN AVE 45219 #038-41-2000 L2000 **RO** *020
MC CONNELL, Charles Thoma. 375 DIXMYTH AVE, DEPT OF RADIOLOGY 45220 #038-40-1988 L1991 **DR** *020 †80
MC CONVILLE, Brian J. 231 BETHESDA AVE, ROOM #7258 DEPARTMENT OF P 45267 #671-01-1957 L1984 **CHP** **P** *050 †75
MC CONVILLE, Fiona Claire. 231 BETHESDA AVE, U CINCINNATI COLL OF MED 45229 #038-41-1998 *100
MC CONVILLE, Janice M. 8245 N CREEK DR 45236 #671-01-1959 L1984 **PD** *071 †55
MC CORKLE, Marilyn Rousey. ■ 45237 #038-41-1956 L1956 **GP** *075
MC CORMACK, Francis X. 222 PIEDMONT AVE, STE 1200 45219 #048-02-1982 L1994 **IM** **PUD** *050 †20

MC CORMICK, Betsy Alynn. 2830 VICTORY PKWY, STE 140 45206 #038-43-2001 L2001 OBG REN *020 †30

MC COY, Malinda Margaret. 9459 MONTGOMERY RD, STE 100 45242 #038-41-1987 L1988 IM *020 †20

MCCOY, Terrence Francis. 7525 STATE RD STE B 45255 #016-11-1988 L1989 IM *020 †20

MC CULLOUGH, Mary Ellen. 5525 MARIE AVE 45248 #038-41-1994 L1995 HO *020 †20

MC CULLOUGH, Patrick J. 151 W GALBRAITH RD 45216 #038-41-1994 L1995 IM *020 †20

MCCUNE, Sara Huegli. ■ 45231 #030-06-2004 L2004 MPD *012

MCDANIEL, Janice Diane. ■ 45215 #038-41-2007 L2007 IM *012

MC DANIEL, Jerry Hayes. 375 GLENSPRINGS DR, STE 410 45246 #038-40-1979 L1982 PD *020

MC DANIEL, Thomas Carlyle. ■ 45216 #028-78-1953, ▲ L1954 GP *071

MCDONALD, Mark Robert. ■ 45208 #056-06-2007 L2007 P *012

MC DONALD, Patrick Edward. 1095 NIMITZVIEW DR STE 104 45230 #017-20-1998 L2000 P *020

MC DONOUGH, John Jos. 10700 MONTGOMERY RD, STE 150 45242 #038-41-1968 L1968 HS GS *020 †85

MC DONOUGH, Nancy K. 7810 5 MILE RD 45230 #038-41-1987 L1989 PM *020 †60

MC ELROY, Susan Lynn. 222 PIEDMONT AVE, STE 8 45219 #035-20-1983 L1991 P *020 †75

MC ELROY-MARCUS, Susan. 4753 CORNELL RD 45241 #020-02-1983 L1985 IM *020 †20

MC ENERY, Paul Thos. 3333 BURNET AVE, CHILD HOSP MED CNTR 45229 #016-43-1965 L1969 PN PD *020 †55

MC ERLANE, Albert David. ■ 45208 #038-41-1954 L1954 OS GP *075

MCEWAN, Amy Jennifer. ■ 45231 #012-05-2006 L2006 IM *012

MC GILL, Alisa Ostendorf. 3333 BURNET AVE, ML 7009 45229 #038-41-1990 L1991 PD *020 †55

MC GOVERN, Mark Edward. 7400 JAGER CT, SOUTHAMPTON SQUARE 45230 #030-06-1968 L1973 PD *020 †55

MC GRATH, Marianne. 8260 NORTHCREEK DR STE 380 45236 #020-12-1968 L1970 P CHP *020 †55

MC GRAW, Dennis Wilentz. 231 ALBERT SABIN WAY, PULMONARY DIV MS 0564 45267 #027-01-1986 L1998 PUD *020 †20

MC GRAW, Megan Lee. 3333 BURNET AVE 45229 #038-41-2003 L2003 PD *100 †55

MC HENRY, Christine L. 3333 BURNET AVE, CIN CHILD HOSP MED CTR 45229 #041-12-1977 L1978 PD *040 †55

MC HENRY, Lee. ■ 45248 #038-41-1954 L1954 IM *071 †20

MC HENRY, Marshall. 105 W 4TH ST, STE 707 45202 #038-41-1980 L1981 IM PUD *020 †20

MC INTYRE, Benjamin C. ■ 45208 #045-04-2003 L2003 GS *012

MC KENNA, Peter James. 10577 MONTGOMERY RD 45242 #038-41-1985 L1988 PDS *020 †85,65

MCKIBBEN, Julie Marie. ■ 45249 #024-05-2002 L2008 IM *020

MC KINNON, Hugh West. 26 W M L KING DR 45268 #051-01-1977 PHP GPM *030

MC LAIN, Clarence Reid. 222 PIEDMONT AVE, STE 5100 45219 #036-01-1955 L1966 OBG *075 †30

MC LAUGHLIN, Matthew M. 6350 GLENWAY AVE, STE 401 45211 #038-40-1989 L1990 PM *020 †60

MC LAURIN, Robert Love. 250 WILLIAM HOWARD TAFT RD 45219 #024-01-1944 L1953 NS N *071 †25

MCLEAN, Kelly Marie. 231 ALBERT SABIN WAY, ML 0558 45229 #025-01-2001 L2001 GS *012

MCLIN, Valerie Anne. 3333 BURNET AVE, CHILD HOSP MED CTR 45229 #869-04-1996 L2001 PG *100

MC MAHON, Mary Anne. 3333 BURNET AVE, CHMC, PAV 2310 45229 #038-41-1992 L1994 OS PM *020 †60,55

MCMASTERS, Richard Louis. ■ 45229 #048-04-1994 L2004 PP HMP *020 †50

MCMULLAN, Jason Thomas. 45217 #045-01-2004 L2004 EM *012

MCNAMEE, Megan Kathleen. ■ 45208 #038-41-2005 L2005 P *012

MC NEILL, Oxford Redmond. 8044 MONTGOMERY RD 45236 #065-01-1959 L1965 ORS HS *071 †40

MC PHERSON, Christopher M. 2123 AUBURN AVE, STE 441 45219 #019-02-1998 L1999 NS *020

MC TIGHE, Martin Louis. 6480 HARRISON AVE, SPORTS MEDICINE 45247 #038-41-1971 L1971 ORS *020 †40

MC WILLIAMS, Frank Ed. 2139 AUBURN AVE, STE 102 45219 #048-04-1973 L1979 DR *020 †80

MECHLEY, Amy Jo. 6311 GLENWAY AVE, PARTNERS IN HEALTH, PSC 45211 #038-41-1995 L1998 FM OBS *020 †18

MECHLIN, Maggie Win. ■ 45243 #038-41-2006 L2006 AN *012

MECOLI, Marc Daniel. ■ 45209 #038-41-2008 *012

MEDINA, Fausto P Vasquez. 1000 SYCAMORE ST 45202 #737-01-1965 L1970 IM CD *020

MEDINA, Luis Santiago. 3333 BURNET AVE 45229 #264-16-1987 L1997 PDR *020 †80

MEDIODIA, Manuel H, Jr. C3131 QUEEN CITY AVE 45238 #748-01-1953 L1966 FM *020

MEDIWALA, Rahul Navin. 231 GOODMAN ST 45219 #048-04-2000 L2000 NEP *020 †20

MEEKER, Hayden E. 10122 WOODFERN WAY 45242 #038-41-1972 L1972 GE IM *020

MEESE, Ernest H. 5049 CROOKSHANK RD STE 202 45238 #035-06-1954 L1965 TS GS *020 †85,90

MEGOIS, Lee Stephen. 7500 STATE RD, CARE CONSULTANTS MERCY 45255 #038-41-1978 L1983 AN *020 †05

MEHTA, Anjali Hemu. 2139 AUBURN AVE 45219 #104-01-2007 L2007 IM *012

MEHTA, Deepak Kumar. 3333 BURNET AVE, CHILDRENS HOSP MED CTR 45229 #495-99-1994 L2005 PDO *012

MEHTA, Monal Arun. 1525 ELM ST 45202 #038-41-1992 L1993 IM *020 †20

MEHTA, Parindaapurva. 3333 BURNET AVE, MLC 7015, CCHMC 45229 #496-38-1995 L2002 PHO *100 †55

MEHTA, Sudha Arun. 3101 BURNET AVE 45229 #495-22-1964 L1973 PTH BBK *020 †50

MEHTER, Ariff Ahmed. 1525 ELM ST 45202 #020-02-1994 L1997 FM OM *020 †18

MEIER, George Henry, III. 231 ALBERT SABIN WAY, DIV VASCULAR SURG 45229 #012-05-1980 L2007 VS GS *020 †85

MEIER, Matthew John. ■ 45208 #038-41-2006 L2006 D *012

MEIERAN, Sharon Elizabeth. 231 ALBERT SABIN WAY, DEPT EMERGENCY MEDICINE 45267 #005-02-2002 L2002 EM *100 †16

MEINERS, Louis Pierre. 4624 RUNNINGFAWN DR 45247 #038-41-1971 L1971 OBG *020 †30

MEJIA, Juan Carlos. 375 DIXMYTH AVE - 7TH, GOOD SAMARITAN HOSPITAL 45220 #308-02-1990 L1999 IM *020 †20

MELAMPY, C Nelson. 3333 BURNET AVE 45229 #038-06-1950 L1950 AN *071 †05

MELANSON, Maria Jolanta. 222 PIEDMONT AVE, STE 3200 45219 #759-03-1989 L1998 N *020 †75

MELLOR-HEINEKE, Sabine. 3333 BURNET AVE 45229 #409-38-2001 L2004 PHO *012

MELTON, Kristin Ruth. 3333 BURNET AVE # 7009, CINCINNATI CHILDREN'S HOSP 45229 #030-05-1995 L2000 NPM PD *020 †55

MELVIN, David Boyd. 222 PIEDMONT AVE, STE 200 45219 #047-06-1967 L1979 TS *050 †85,90

MELVIN, Howard D. 3120 BURNET AVE, STE 303 45219 #047-07-1977 L1985 OPH *020

MENA CANTO, Rafael. 3333 BURNET AVE 45229 #308-13-2003 L2005 PD *012

MENDEL, Sandra Gayle. 3333 BURNET AVE 45229 #038-43-1981 L1985 IM PD *020 †20,55

MENDENHALL, Charles Lee. 3200 VINE ST 151F, VA MEDICAL CENTER 45220 #030-05-1956 L1973 HEP IM *020

MENDES, Tony Adewale. ■ 45220 #010-03-1974 FM *100

MENDEZ, Fernando L, Jr. ■ 45208 #06-19-1946 L1957 PUD OS *072 †85,90

MENDI, Ramit. ■ 45236 #016-11-2002 L2007 DR *100 †80

MENDI, Resham Ramit. ■ 45236 #016-06-2003 L2007 DR *100

MENDOZA, Nina Castro. 2123 AUBURN AVE, STE 434 45219 #748-01-1964 L1973 NEP IM *020 †20

MENEFEE, Max Gene. 5757 GLENWAY AVE 45238 #035-15-1961 L1981 FM *071

MENKE, Rosemary Kay. 3643 RUSSELL AVE 45208 #051-04-1986 L1990 OBG *020 †30

MERANUS, James Moss. 375 DIXMYTH AVE 45220 #038-06-1986 L1986 DR *020 †80

MEREDITH, J Stephen. 9157 MONTGOMERY RD STE 206 45242 #038-41-1964 L1964 P *020 †75

MERHAR, Gary Louis. 2446 KIPLING AVE, MERCY HOSPITAL MOUNT AIRY 45239 #038-41-1978 L1980 DR *020 †80

MERHAR, Stephanie Lynne. 3333 BURNET AVE, NEONATOLOGY 45229 #041-01-2005 L2005 PD *012

MERLING, Jeffrey William. 9030 MONTGOMERY RD 45242 #038-45-1999 L1999 FM *020 †18

MERRELL, James Allyn. ■ 45251 #038-40-2003 L2003 OTO *012

MERRILL, Walter Hilson. 231 ALBERT SABIN WAY, MAIL LOCATION 0558 45267 #023-07-1974 L2002 CD GS *020 †85,90

MERROW, Arnold Carl. 3333 BURNET AVE, DEPT. OF RADIOLOGY, ML 503 45229 #001-02-2001 L2006 PDR *100 †80

MERWIN, Susan Louise. 4422 CARVER WOODS DR 45242 #047-05-1976 L1980 P CHP *020 †75

MERZ, Donald. ■ 45249 #038-40-1966 L1966 IM *071 †20

MERZ, Matthew Michael. 8260 NORTHCREEK DR, GROUP HEALTH ASSOCIATES 45236 #038-41-1995 L1996 IM PM *020 †60

MESH, Charles Leslie. 4030 SMITH RD, CARDIAC VASCULAR & 45209 #038-41-1984 L1992 VS *020 †85

MESSER, Jennifer Anne. 7829 LAUREL AVE 45243 #038-41-2004 L2004 FM *020 †18

METHERD, Warren Lee. 8221 CORNELL RD, STE 420 45249 #038-41-1982 L1985 OBG *020 †30

METZ, Kelly Allred. ■ 45242 #038-41-2004 L2004 PD *020 †55

METZGER, Paul Vincent. ■ 45202 #038-41-2004 L2007 EM *100

METZGER, Ray Joseph. 425 FARRELL CT 45233 #038-41-1998 L1999 IM *020 †20

METZLER, Adam Vincent. ■ 45206 #038-41-2007 L2007 ORS *012

MEYER, Christopher Glenn. ■ 45242 #038-41-1999 L1999 GS *020 †85

MEYER, Cristopher Andrew. 234 GOODMAN ST, STE 0054 45219 #028-02-1987 L1988 DR *020 †80

MEYER, Kevin Carl. 1219 MORTS PASS, QUALIFIED EMERGENCY SPEC, 45215 #038-45-1997 L2000 EM *020 †16

MEYER, Mark John. 3333 BURNET AVE, DEPT OF ANESTHESIA 45229 #038-41-1998 L2000 PAN *100 †05

MEYER, Mary Catherine. ■ 45249 #038-06-1979 L1981 PD *020 †55

MEYER, Richard Alan. CHILDRENS HOSP 45229 #038-41-1964 L1964 PDC *050 †55

MEYER, Richard Louis. 5520 CHEVIOT RD 45247 #028-34-1959 L1964 ON IM *071 †20

MEYER, Roger Vincent. 6480 HARRISON AVE STE 100 45247 #038-41-1968 L1968 ORS *071 †40

MEYERS, Ann Levine. ■ 45220 #038-41-1978 L1979 GP *020

MEYERS, Marie Willke. 2753 ERIE AVE, 1ST FL 45208 #038-41-1979 L1981 IM *075

MEYERS, Stephen Michael. 2123 AUBURN AVE, STE 624 45219 #038-41-1997 L2000 CD *020 †20

MEYN, Malcolm Anthony, Jr. 330 STRAIGHT ST STE 311 45219 #021-01-1965 L1976 ORS *075 †40

MICHAEL, Mark. 10495 MONTGOMERY RD STE 24 45242 #915-03-1977 L1985 AI PD *020 †55,03

MICHAUD, Linda Joyce. 3333 BURNET AVE 45229 #054-04-1982 L1997 PM PD *020 †55,60

MICHELFELDER, Erik C. 3333 BURNET AVE, CHILDRENS HOSPITAL MED CTR 45229 #041-14-1990 L1998 PDC *020 †55 ‡

MICKELSON, Judith Kay. 3219 CLIFTON AVE, STE 400 45220 #048-04-1978 L2000 CD IM *050 †20

MIDAY, Karen Kallberg. ■ 45208 #038-40-1975 L1975 P *020 †75

MIDAY, Robert Kallberg. ■ 45208 #038-40-1975 L1975 PHM OM *050 †70

MIDDAUGH, Deborah Ann. 11125 KENWOOD RD, BETHESDA CARE - BLUE ASH 45242 #025-01-1977 L1985 OM IM *020 †20,70

MIDDLETON, Gregory S. 3333 BURNET AVE, DEPT OF PEDS 45229 #003-01-2006 L2006 PD *012

MIETHKE, Alexander Gerhar. 3333 BURNET AVE 45229 #408-30-2000 L2002 PG *012

MIKKELSEN, Erik Johan. 3333 BURNET AVE 45229 #056-06-2004 L2007 CCP *012 †55

MILAN, Stacey Anne. ■ 45267 #041-13-2004 L2004 GS *100

MILES, Lili. 3333 BURNET AVE 45229 #243-45-1986 L2000 PP *100 †50

MILITANTE-HILVANO, Ayes T. 231 ALBERT SABIN WAY, STE ML531 45267 #748-11-1990 L2003 AN *020 †20

MILLARD, Justin Michael. 200 NORTHLAND BLVD 45246 #038-41-2003 L2006 AN *020

MILLER, Brian Scott. 7500 STATE RD 45255 #038-43-1991 L1994 OBG *020 †30

MILLER, Charlene Alison. ■ 45247 #035-15-1996 L2002 EM *016

MILLER, Charles Dale. 6350 GLENWAY AVE 45211 #038-40-1978 L1987 ORS *020 †40

MILLER, E Huxley, Jr. 2915 CLIFTON AVE 45220 #024-07-1977 L1982 ID IM *020 †20

MILLER, Edward Henderson. 9795 FOX HOLLOW LN 45243 #038-41-1961 L1961 ORS *020 †40

MILLER, Henrietta Marie. 4001 ROSSLYN DR # A2 45209 #038-41-1935 PD *071

MILLER, Katherine Marie. 45230 #038-41-2004 L2004 END *012 †20

MILLER, Nicholas Paul. ■ 45219 #017-20-2007 L2007 IM *012

MILLER, Rachel J. 3333 BURNET AVE, ML 4000 45229 #037-01-2002 L2006 OBG *100

MILLER, Sandra Louise. 2123 AUBURN AVE, STE 442 45219 #036-01-1991 L2000 CCS GS *020 †85

MILLER, Sean Anthony. 231 ALBERT SABIN WAY 45267 #038-41-1998 L1999 IM *020 †20

MILLER, Shannon Corey. ■ 45249 #038-40-1992 L1993 P ADM *020 †75

MILLER, Sharon Christine. 4360 COOPER RD 45242 #038-41-1997 L1999 END *020 †20

MILLER, Teresa Lynn. 45230 #020-12-2005 L2005 P *012

MILLER, Timothy John. 375 DIXMYTH AVE, DEPT RADIOLOGY 45220 #038-41-1987 L1992 RNR R *020 †80

MINDRUM, Gordon M. 2123 AUBURN AVE 45219 #018-03-1950 L1955 **ADP** *071 †20

MINEVICH, Eugene A. 3333 BURNET AVE, CH PROCTOR 5 45229 #913-71-1985 L1993 **U** *020 †95

MINHAS, Imran Tasleem. 231 ALBERT SABIN WAY 45267 #748-21-2000 L2002 **FPG** *020 †18

MINHAS, Rajbir S. 2841 BOUDINOT AVE, FREIBERG ORTHOPAEDIC AND 45238 #495-03-1987 L2002 **IM** *020 †20

MINHAS, Tasleem Ahmed. 6480 HARRISON AVE, STE 100 45247 #704-01-1957 L1971 **ORS OSM** *020 †40

MIRKOPULOS, Nicholas S. 10547 MONTGOMERY RD, STE 400 45242 #038-41-1983 L1985 **ORS** *020 †40

MIRZA, Farooq Ahmad. 2123 AUBURN AVE, # 400 45219 #704-01-1974 L1979 **GS VS** *020 †85

MITAN, Laurie Ann. 3333 BURNET AVE 45229 #030-06-1990 L1999 **ADL PD** *020 †55

MITCHELL, Ashley Lyn. ■ 45217 #041-00-2007 L2007 **OBG** *012

MITSNEFES, Mark M. 3333 BURNET AVE, ML-7022 45229 #913-36-1985 L1998 **PN** *020 †55

MITTIGA, Heather Leigh. ■ 45208 #038-06-2001 L2005 **PHO** *012 †55

MITTIGA, Matthew Robert. 3333 BURNET AVE 2008, DIVISION OF EMERGENCY MEDI 45229 #038-06-2001 L2001 **PEM** *012 †55

MITTS, Donald Louis. 2123 AUBURN AVE, STE 136 45219 #020-12-1971 L1977 **TS** *020 †85,90

MIZUKAWA, Benjamin Eiji. ■ 45255 #049-01-2004 L2004 **PHO** *012

MO, Jun Qin. ■ 45215 #243-43-1987 L2000 **PP** *020 †50

MOAK, James Hutchcraft. 234 GOODMAN ST, STE 0769 45219 #027-01-1999 L2003 **EM** *020 †16

MODI, Vipul Ramesh. 234 GOODMAN ST, DEPT OF RADIOLOGY 45267 #038-06-2005 L2005 **DR** *012

MOELLMAN, Joseph John. 234 GOODMAN ST, STE 0769 45219 #038-41-1992 L1995 **EM** *020 †16

MOGA, Michael-Alice. ■ 45239 #026-08-2002 L2005 **PDC** *012 †55

MOGILISHETTY, Gautham. ■ 45209 #495-21-1994 L2004 **NEP** *020 †20

MOHAMED, Ismail Sidky. 3333 BURNET AVE, CO CHILDREN S HOSP-MED EDU 45229 #915-03-1989 L2002 **CN** *020 †55,75

MOHLMAN, Yvonne Michele. 3494 READING RD 45229 #038-41-1958 L1958 **FM PD** *020

MOHMAND, Hashim Khan. 231 ALBERT SABIN WAY, GENERAL INTERNAL MEDICINE 45267 #704-09-1999 L2005 **IM** *100 †20

MOLLERAN, Virginia Marie. 234 GOODMAN ST, STE 0054 45219 #038-41-1993 L1997 **DR** *020 †80

MOLLOY, Cynthia Ann. 3333 BURNET AVE 45229 #038-41-1983 L1985 **PD** *020 †55

MOLNAR, Courtney Anne. 820 DELTA AVE 45226 #038-41-2002 L2002 **P** *020 †75

MOLNAR, James Martin. 8261 CORNELL RD STE 630, CINCINNATI PAIN MGMNT CONS 45249 #038-40-1982 L1985 **AN IM** *020 †20,05

MONCRIEF, Terri Michele. ■ 45240 #028-02-2006 L2006 **PD** *012

MONDESI GARRIDO, Jose Mig. ■ 45236 #038-13-2003 L2005 **IM** *012

MONDSCHEIN, Joshua Keith. ■ 45219 #011-02-2006 L2006 **OTO** *012

MONGEY, Anne-Barbara M. 305 CRESCENT AVE 45215 #539-04-1981 L1991 **RHU IM** *020 †20

MONNIG, William Bernard. 4700 SMITH RD, STE 4 45212 #038-41-1969 L1969 **U** *020 †95

MONROE, Beverly Ann. ■ 45243 #035-03-1978 L1982 **PTH** *020 †50

MONROE, Kevin Dale. 311 STRAIGHT ST 45219 #021-05-1978 L1991 **PTH** *020 †50

MONTAG, David Jos. 8245 NORTHCREEK DR 45236 #038-41-1986 L1987 **IM** *020 †20

MONTAUK, Susan Louisa. 1295 KEMPER MEADOW DR 45240 #038-40-1984 L1985 **FM ADL** *020 †18

MONTVILLE, Christopher P. 2123 AUBURN AVE STE A44, CTR FOR REPRODUCTIVE HEALT 45219 #054-04-2002 L2006 **OBG** *100

MOODY, Douglas Clay. 9030 MONTGOMERY RD 45242 #038-41-1985 L1988 **FM** *020 †18

MOORE, Brett Wm. 7500 STATE RD, MERCY ANDERSON HOSPITAL 45255 #038-41-1990 L1991 **IM** *020 †20

MOORE, Kevin John. 11490 SPRINGFIELD PIKE 45238 #038-40-1991 L1992 **AN** *020 †05

MOORE, Matthew John. 234 GOODMAN ST # 0761, UNIV HOSPITAL DEPT OF RADI 45219 #017-20-1999 L2004 **DR** *020 †10

MOOSBRUGGER, Emily Ashwor. ■ 45208 #038-41-2006 L2006 **D** *012

MOQEETH, Syed A. 151 W GALBRAITH RD 45216 #495-65-1991 L1994 **IMG** *020 †20

MORAD, David Michael, Jr. 7810 5 MILE RD 45230 #038-41-1978 L1984 **OTO FPS** *020 †45

MORAITES, Richard Stephen. 7717 MONTGOMERY RD 45236 #038-41-1956 L1956 **D** *020 †15

MORALES RAMOS, Humberto C. ■ 45229 #737-01-2000 L2007 **RNR** *012

MORAN, William Jos. 375 GLENSPRINGS DR 45246 #017-20-1958 L1969 **OBG** *071 †30

MOREIRA, Katheryn M. 234 GOODMAN ST, STE C-237 45219 #038-41-2000 L2000 **OBG** *020 †30

MOREIRA, Nora E. 10495 MONTGOMERY RD STE 15 45242 #176-03-1969 L1972 **IM** *020 †20

MOREIRA, Rodolfo Julio. 9403 KENWOOD RD, STE B200 45242 #176-03-1969 L1972 **GS VS** *020 †85

MORGAN, Michael Andrew. 7691 5 MILE RD, CINCINNATI 45230 #036-01-1995 L1999 **D** *020 †15

MORGAN, Xolti. ■ 45219 #001-02-2007 L2007 **IM** *012

MORGAN CAREY, Patricia. 3130 HIGHLAND AVE, HOXWORTH BLOOD CENTER 45267 #055-01-1979 L1983 **BBK FM** *075 †50

MORGESON, Jeffrey Scott. 1207 SPRINGFIELD PIKE 45215 #038-41-2003 L2003 **FM** *100 †18

MORILLO-DELERME, J. 3333 BURNET AVE, ML 2001 45229 #042-03-1981 L2003 **AN GS** *020 †05

MORIN, Richard P. 4360 COOPER RD, STE 303 45242 #056-06-1978 L1981 **GS VS** *020 †85

MORITA, Diego. 3333 BURNET AVE ML2015, CINCINNATI CHILDREN'S HOSP 45229 #132-01-1992 L2000 **CHN** *020

MOROVIC, Anamarija. 231 ALBERT ST, DEPT OF PATHOLOGY 45267 #957-01-2004 L2006 **PTH** *012

MORRIS, Richard Howard. 2446 KIPLING AVE 45239 #038-41-1956 L1956 **FM** *071

MORRISON, Sarah Wright. 58 E HOLLISTER ST 45219 #038-41-1994 L1995 **CHP** *020 †75

MOSBACHER, Marc Rene. 8000 5 MILE RD STE 105 45230 #035-01-1997 L2002 **RO** *020 †80

MOSES, Steven James. 375 DIXMYTH AVE 45220 #017-20-1997 **GS** *100

MOSHER, James Leslie. 3155 GLENDALE MILFORD RD, CINCINNATI EVENDALE SURG 45241 #038-43-1988 L1992 **AN** *020 †05

MOSKO, Mary Kuzma. 9403 KENWOOD RD, STE C208 45242 #038-41-1994 L1995 **FM** *020 †18

MOSKOWITZ, Myron. 234 GOODMAN ST 0054 45219 #038-41-1958 L1958 **R IM** *071 †80

MOSS, Joshua Parker. ■ 45226 #047-05-2002 L2007 **HSO** *012

MOSS, Quinton Eugene. 231 ALBERT SABIN WAY, P O BOX 670559 45267 #051-07-1999 L1999 **P** *020 †18,75

MOSTER, Lynn Stephanie. ■ 45241 #038-40-1993 L1997 **AN** *020 †05

MOTLEY, Jenny. 3333 BURNET AVE, CHMC-DIV OF EMERGENCY MEDI 45229 #011-02-1997 L1998 **PD** *020 †55

MOTLEY, William Walker. 3333 BURNET AVE, MAIL LOCATION 4008 45229 #011-02-1997 L1998 **OPH PO** *020 †35

MOUCH, David E. 7631 CHEVIOT RD 45247 #038-43-1984 L1985 **FM** *020 †18

MOULTON, Jonathan S. 234 GOODMAN ST 45219 #038-41-1982 L1985 **DR** *020 †80

MOULTON, Regine M. 7809 LAUREL AVE STE 11 45243 #407-02-1963 L1974 **FM** *020 †18 ‡

MOUNAJJED, Taofic. 231 ALBERT ST 45267 #875-01-2004 L2005 **PTH** *012

MOUNLA-SAKKAL, Maysa. ■ 45242 #875-02-1984 *020

MOUSSA, Hind Nadim. GYNECOLOGY DE2, CO OBSTETRICS & 45267 #605-01-2003 L2004 **OBG** *012

MOUSSAVIAN, Seyed. 9200 MONTGOMERY RD, STE 18A 45242 #517-01-1969 L1977 **GE NTR** *020

MOWERY, Clifford Scott. 4750 E GALBRAITH RD, STE 207 45236 #038-41-1984 L1985 **IM** *020 †20

MOY, Justin Randolph. ■ 45233 #038-41-2004 L2005 *020

MOYER, Mary Susan. 3333 BURNET AVE, MEDICAL CENTER 45229 #041-14-1979 L1983 **PG** *020 †55

MRUS, Joseph M. 3130 HIGHLAND AVE, STE 0557 45219 #048-14-1994 L1995 **MPD OS** *050 †20,55

MUCENSKI, Cathleen Minges. 7520 STATE RD 45255 #038-41-1989 L1990 **AN CCA** *020 †05 ‡

MUCK, Patrick Edward. 3219 CLIFTON AVE, STE 215 45220 #041-09-1996 L1997 **VS** *020 †85

MUELLER, Caroline V. 234 GOODMAN ST 665X, HOXWORTH CENTER, 2ND FLOOR 45219 #038-41-1990 L1991 **IM** *040 †20,55

MUELLER, Stephen David. 3200 BURNET AVE, 1 RIDGEWAY 45229 #038-41-1979 L1980 **IMG IM** *020 †20

MUELLER, Thomas Wm. 2001 ANDERSON FERRY RD 45238 #038-40-1980 L1988 **IM** *020 †20

MUELLER, Tracy Elisabeth. ■ 45267 #038-41-2003 L2003 **P** *100

MUETHING, Stephen Edward. 3333 BURNET AVE, GEN PEDS # 2011 45229 #038-41-1984 L1988 **PD** *020 †55

MUHLEMAN, Albert F, Jr. 3200 VINE ST, HEM/ONC SEC 111D 45220 #038-41-1965 L1965 **IM HO** *040 †20

MUKHDOMI, Gulam Jeelani. 231 ALBERT SABIN WAY, STE ML531 45267 #495-51-1976 L2003 **AN** *020

MUKKADA, Thresiamma A. 7520 STATE RD 45255 #495-63-1967 L1975 **AN** *020 †05

MULDERIG, James Kevin. 9084 WINTON RD 45231 #038-40-1985 L1986 **P** *020 †75

MULLER, Lars Ulf Werner. 3333 BURNET AVE, CHILDRENS HOSP MED CTR 45229 #409-25-2002 L2003 **PHO** *012 †55

MULLINS, Eric Scott. 3333 BURNET AVE, MLC 7015 45229 #028-03-2001 L2004 **PHO** *100 †55

MULLINS, Tanya Kowalczyk. ■ 45242 #045-01-2001 L2004 **ADL** *100 †55

MULVANEY, William P. ■ 45231 #016-43-1946 L1947 **U** *071 †95

MUMMA, Jonathan David. 7810 5 MILE RD 45230 #038-41-1990 L1991 **PD** *020 †55

MUNDA TABUSSO, Rino. 231 ALBERT SABIN WAY, ML0558 45267 #737-06-1967 L1974 **AS CD** *020 †85

MUNIZ-HELM, Mayra L. 2223 AUBURN AVE 45219 #042-01-1991 L1995 **P** *020

MUNJAL, Jitender. 3200 BURNET AVE 45229 #495-45-1999 L2004 **IM** *100 †20

MUNTEL, Emily Elizabeth. ■ 45267 #038-41-2006 L2006 **IM** *012

MURDICK, Sara Margaret. ■ 45211 #038-41-2007 L2007 **PD** *012

MURRAY, Robert Leslie, Jr. 8245 NORTHCREEK DR 45236 #020-12-1991 L1995 **OBG** *020 †30

MURRAY, Sara Lesley. 7520 STATE RD 45255 #038-41-1995 L1996 **AN** *020 †05

MURTAUGH, Thomas Isaiah. 2454 KIPLING AVE, STE 207 45239 #041-12-1989 L1998 **CD IM** *020 †20

MUSGRAVE, Elizabeth Mc El. 3333 BURNET AVE, CO CHILDREN S MED CTR-MED 45229 #045-01-2003 L2003 **PD** *100 †55

MUSGRAVE, Ethan Joseph. 3333 BURNET AVE, CINCINNATI CHILDREN'S HOSP 45229 #045-01-2003 L2003 **CHP** *012

MUSKAT, Peter Clark. 222 PIEDMONT AVE, STE 200 45219 #023-12-1984 L2004 **GS** *020 †85

MUSOLINO, Tammy Renee. 55 PROGRESS PL 45246 #038-45-2000 L2000 **PM** *100 †60 ‡

MUSSMAN, Adam Barrs. 5819 CHEVIOT RD, PROFESSIONAL RADIOLOGY 45247 #038-41-2002 L2002 **DR** *012

MUTASIM, Diya F. 222 PIEDMONT AVE, STE 5300 45219 #605-01-1979 L1990 **D** *020 †15

MUTEMA, George Kimbugwe. 234 GOODMAN ST, UNIVERSITY HOSPITAL 45267 #905-01-1989 L2000 **SP** *020 †50

MUTEMA, Nandawula. 5818 MADISON RD 45227 #495-98-1992 L1997 **IM** *020 †20

MUTHUNAYAGAM, Newton Pack. UNIV OF CINTI, DEPT OF GASTLGY/INT MED 45267 #495-31-1996 L2005 **GE** *012 †20

MYER, Charles Monroe. ■ 45208 #038-45-2006 L2006 **OTO** *012

MYER, Charles Monroe, III. 3333 BURNET AVE, DEPT OF OTOLARYNGOLOGY 45229 #001-02-1978 L1980 **OTO** *020 †45

MYERS, Kasiani Christina. ■ 45224 #038-06-2004 L2004 **PHO** *012 †55

NABER, William John. 231 ALBERT SABIN WAY - ML, P O BOX 670729 45267 #038-41-1993 L1996 **EM** *020 †16

NACOPOULOS, Joanna C. 3333 BURNET AVE 45229 #041-12-2002 L2005 **PD** *100 †55

NADAKAV, George Ignatius. 4777 E GALBRAITH RD, DEPT OF MED EDUCATION 45236 #473-04-2005 L2006 **IM** *012

NADER-SEPAHI, Ali. ■ 45242 #917-25-1991 L2000 *100

NADLER, Arthur Wm. ■ 45251 #038-41-1944 L1944 **IM** *071

NAGAVI, Amir Sean. ■ 45243 #038-41-2008 *012

NAGESPARAN, Sathya. 10500 MONTGOMERY RD 45242 #422-01-1994 L1997 **IM** *020 †20

NAHM, Soonze. ■ 45215 #583-03-1959 L1976 **GP PTH** *071 †50

NAIR, Rajalakshmi Rajagop. ■ 45206 #421-05-2004 L2004 **GS** *012

NAJEED, Anjum Fatima. 375 DIXMYTH AVE 45220 #496-27-2002 L2007 **IM** *012

NAKATOMI, Hirofumi. ■ 45267 #572-03-1993 L2004 *012

NALABOLU, Dasharathram R. ■ 45219 #567-15-1973 L1984 **AN PME** *075

NALABOLU, Harsha Reddy. ■ 45219 #038-41-2008 *012

NAMAKY, Devin Dadyar. ■ 45236 #038-41-2007 L2007 **OBG** *012

NANDAGOPAL, Jayasree Jaya. 3333 BURNET AVE, MLC 3014 45229 #495-17-1996 L2003 **CHP** *100 †75

NAQVI, Fizza Fatima. CO INTERNAL MEDICIN, UNIV CINCINNATI COMUNIV HO 45267 #704-25-2004 L2007 **IM** *012

NAQVI, Imran Raza. 4777 E GALBRAITH RD, DEPT OF MED EDUCATION 45236 #665-01-2006 L2006 **IM** *012

NARAYAN, Tina M. 7495 STATE RD, CINTI CHILDRENS OPA #355 45255 #495-27-1978 L2002 **CHN** *020 †55,75

NARENDRAN, Vivek. 3333 BURNET AVE 45229 #496-39-1985 L1998 **NPM** *020 †55

NARTKER, David James. 9403 KENWOOD RD, STE D203 45242 #038-41-1989 L1990 **IM** *020 †20

NASCIMENTO, Carmosino C. 151 W GALBRAITH RD 45216 #187-06-1955 L1967 **CD IM** *071

NASH, Barry Patrick. 3200 BURNET AVE 45229 #422-01-2001 L2004 **IM** *100

NASH, Brian Curtis. 7810 5 MILE RD 45230 #045-04-1990 L1992 **D** *020 †15

NASRALLAH, Henry A. 231 ALBERT SABIN WAY, UNIV OF CINCINNATI MED CTR 45267 #605-01-1972 L1985 **P PA** *050 †75

NASSER, Michael Philip. 3333 BURNET AVE, DEPT OF RADIOLOGY - MLC 50 45229 #051-04-2000 L2005 **PDR** *100 †80

NASSIF, Zeidan Merhij. ■ 45236 #306-01-1987 L1993 **PDE PD** *020 †55

NATARAJAN, Niranjana. ■ 45209 #028-41-2008 *012

NATARAJAN, Sakunthala. 10500 MONTGOMERY RD, BETHESDA NORTH HOSPITAL 45242 #495-57-1975 L1981 **PTH** *020

NATESA SUBRAMANIAN, Kavith. 2139 AUBURN AVE 45219 #495-42-2001 L2006 **IM** *012

NATH, Amaresh R. 3200 VINE ST, STE 111D 45220 #495-96-1979 L1997 **PCC** †20

NATHAN, Amy Taylor. 3333 BURNET AVE, MLC #7038 45229 #008-01-1998 L2005 **NPM** *100 †55

NATTIN, Monique Allyson. 7495 STATE RD 45255 #038-41-1995 L1998 **PD** *020 †55

NAUSS, Michael David. ■ 45227 #025-01-2004 L2004 **EM** *012

NAVANEETHAN, Udayakumar. CO INTERNAL MEDICIN, UNIV CINCINNATI COMUNID HO 45267 #495-42-2003 L2007 **IM** *012

NAWAZ, Sarah Akhter. 820 DELTA AVE 45226 #038-41-1990 L1994 **P** *020 †75

NAYAK, Premanand Kumbla. 6350 GLENWAY AVE 45211 #495-37-1960 L1980 **ORS** *020

NAYAK, Rajeshri P. 2368 VICTORY PKWY 45206 #038-41-1991 L1995 **AN** *020 †05

NAYAK, Suresh. 6350 GLENWAY AVE 45211 #038-41-1989 L1994 **ORS** *020 †40

NAZ, Tehmina. 231 ALBERT SABIN WAY, ML 0542 45267 #704-01-1988 L2005 **CD** *020

NAZEK, Mohammad Khoder. 311 STRAIGHT ST 45219 #575-01-1982 L1989 **PTH** *020 †50

NEAL, Amy Marie. 2450 KIPLING AVE 45239 #038-45-2001 L2001 **FM** *020 †18

NEAL, Keith Scott. 3217 CLIFTON AVE, GOOD SAMARITAN HOSPITAL 45220 #020-12-1986 L1990 **EM** *100

NEAL, Kenneth Wayne, Jr. 9275 MONTGOMERY RD, STE 100 45242 #047-07-2000 L2004 **D** *100 †15

NEBERT, Daniel Walter. 3333 BURNET AVE #040-02-1964 L1993 **OS PD** *050

NEEDHAM, Brett Jos. 2139 AUBURN AVE 45219 #038-40-1984 L1985 **IM PA** *075

NEEL, Robert Walton, IV. 222 PIEDMONT AVE, STE 3200 45219 #038-41-2000 L2000 **CN** *020 †75

NEELY, Lydia A E. ■ 45237 #748-01-1944 L1960 **GP** *075

NEFF, Ann G. 4460 RED BANK RD, STE 130 45227 #038-44-1993 L2004 **D** *100 †35,15

NEFF, Guy W. 9275 MONTGOMERY RD, STE 100 45242 #038-44-1992 L1993 **GE IM** *020 †20

NEIDICH, Marci Jill. ■ 45219 #016-01-2007 L2007 *012

NEIROUZ, Yvette Aziza. 7810 5 MILE RD 45230 #038-41-2003 L2003 **IM** *020 †20

NEISS, Daniel Paul. ■ 45213 #038-41-2008 *012

NELSON, Daniel Alan. 3333 BURNET AVE #039-01-1985 L1997 **P CHP** *020 †75

NELSON, Elbert John Thos. 222 PIEDMONT AVE, STE 5100 45219 #047-07-1967 L1971 **OBG** *020 †30

NELSON, Erik Bertil. 231 ALBERT SABIN WAY, DEPT OF PSYCHIATRY/MAIL #5 45267 #038-41-1992 L1995 **P** *020 †75

NELSON, Naveena. 3200 BURNET AVE 45229 #496-23-1994 L2003 **IMG** *020 †20

NEMETH, Nicole Marie. ■ 45240 #038-41-2007 L2007 **ORS** *012

NESTOK, Blake Richard. 311 STRAIGHT ST 45219 #011-02-1985 L1992 **PTH PCP** *020 †50

NEUS, Steven Eugene. 7500 STATE RD 45255 #020-12-1991 L1994 **FM** *020 †18

NEUSS, Michael Norbert. 4350 MALSBARY RD, STE 208 45242 #036-07-1979 L1985 **ON HEM** *020 †20

NEWMAN, Lawrence Jay. 10597 MONTGOMERY RD, STE 200 45242 #025-01-1976 L1977 **PDA AI** *020 †55,03

NEWMAN, Robert Mark. 1101 SUMMIT RD, SUMMIT BEHAVIORAL HEALTHCA 45237 #020-12-1991 L1993 **P** *020 †75

NEWMARK, Kenneth J. 3219 CLIFTON AVE, STE 325 45220 #020-02-1967 L1972 **NEP** *020 †20

NEWTON, Michael Allen. 234 GOODMAN ST 45267 #016-11-1974 L1975 **P** *020 †75

NG, Silvania Cristina. 10495 MONTGOMERY RD, INFECTIOUS DISEASE 45242 #187-07-1981 L1992 **ID IM** *020 †20

NG, Vicky. 3333 BURNET AVE, CHILDRENS HOSP MED CTR 45229 #065-01-1993 L2000 **PG** *020 †55

NG, Willie Alfonso. 3330 ERIE AVE 45208 #187-07-1981 L1990 **PD PDC** *020 †55

NGU, Monica Ngocman. 8000 5 MILE RD, STE 250 45230 #038-45-1995 L1997 **M** *020 †20

NGUYEN, Douglas Long. ■ 45219 #038-41-2008 L2008 **U** *072

NGUYEN, Thomas Anh. ■ 45220 #048-04-1992 L2000 **U** *072

NGUYEN, Thomas Toan. 4777 E GALBRAITH RD, JEWISH HOSP 45236 #305-01-2003 L2004 *020 †20

NICHOLAS, Sharon Sue. 7810 5 MILE RD 45230 #038-41-1985 L1995 **IM** *020 †20

NICHOLS, Christopher W. 222 PIEDMONT AVE, STE 3200 45219 #041-15-2002 L2006 **VN** *100

NICOLAS, Joseph Anselm. 222 PIEDMONT AVE, STE 3200 45219 #038-41-1989 L1991 **N** *020 †75

NICOLAS, Tomas Ocampo. ■ 45243 #748-01-1957 L1973 **PTH FM** *071 †50

NIEHAUS, Ferdinand Jos. 3131 QUEEN CITY AVE 45238 #056-06-1963 L1964 **FM OS** *020 †18

NIEHAUS, Robert W. 3330 ERIE AVE 45208 #035-09-1950 L1952 **PD PDA** *071 †55

NIELSEN, David Bryce. 234 GOODMAN ST 0761, DEPT OF RADIOLOGY, UNIV OF 45267 #030-06-1997 L2000 **PDR** *020 †80

NIEMAN, Melinda Ann. 231 ALBERT SABIN WAY 45267 #038-41-2000 L2000 **P** *100

NIEMES, William John. 422 RAY NORRISH DR, # 2 45246 #038-41-1974 L1979 **AI PD** *020 †55,03

NIEMEYER, Lee Edward. ■ 45255 #038-45-2007 L2007 **FP** *012

NIESEN, Edmond H, Jr. 19 GARFIELD PL STE 208 45202 #038-41-1943 L1944 **IM CD** *071

NIKIFOROV, Yuri E. 231 ALBERT SABIN WAY 45267 #913-32-1985 L1999 **PTH** *020 †50

NIKLINSKI, Waldemar T. 231 ALBERT SABIN WAY, ACADEMIC PATHOLOGY ASSOC I 45267 #759-11-1981 L2002 **PTH** *100 †18,50

NISHINAKA, Kazuyuki. 3333 BURNET AVE PW-5SE, CHILDREN'S HOSP MED CTR 45229 #572-53-1990 L2002 **UP** *100

NISHIYAMA, Hiroshi. 234 GOODMAN ST, STE 0054 45219 #572-32-1959 L1972 **NM PDC** *020 †28

NIX, Gregory Scott. 4777 E GALBRAITH RD 45236 #305-01-1999 L1999 **IM** *020 †20

NIZNY, Melvyn Mandell. 3001 HIGHLAND AVE, STE E 45219 #038-41-1964 L1964 **P PFP** *020 †75

NOBUNAGA, Austin Isao. 231 ALBERT SABIN WAY, PHYS MED & REHAB 45267 #025-01-1985 L1989 **PM PHP** *020 †60

NOFFSINGER, Amy Elisabeth. PO BOX 670529, UNIVERSITY OF CINCINNATI 45267 #038-41-1989 L1993 **PTH** *020 †50

NOFZIGER, Donald Lee. 3333 BURNET AVE 45229 #038-41-1965 L1965 **PD OS** *072

NOGUEIRA, Thomas Edward. 2139 AUBURN AVE, STE 102 45219 #038-41-1992 L1999 **DR EM** *020 †80

NOH, Kyung Mee. 2060 READING RD, STE 170 45202 #035-45-1988 L1995 **VIR** *020 †80

NOH, Paul. 3333 BURNET AVE 5037, CINCINNATI CHILDRENS 45229 #041-02-1998 L2007 **UP** *100 †95

NORBY, Ellen Heinrichs. 2475 W GALBRAITH RD STE A, LTD-GROESBECK PEDIATRICS 45239 #026-04-1987 L1990 **PD** *020 †55

NORDLUND, Michael Lenart. 1945 CEI DR 45242 #038-41-1996 L2000 **OPH** *020 †35

NORRIS, Mark Douglas. ■ 45230 #026-08-2003 L2003 **MPD** *100 †20,55

NORTON, James Henry, Jr. 45243 #023-07-1960 L1983 **PTH** *071 †50

NOSCHANG, Raymond Louis. ■ 45236 #038-41-1985 L1989 **IM** *020

NOSS, Michael Jos. 11500 NORTHLAKE DR, STE 320 45249 #038-41-1989 L1990 **FM** *020 †18

NOWAK, Jeffrey Edward. 3333 BURNET AVE, MLC-2005 45229 #012-05-2000 L2007 **CCP** *012 †55

NOYES, Frank Roberts. 3301 WESTBOURNE DR 45248 #010-01-1966 L1975 **ORS OSM** *020 †40

NUGENT, Michael Allen. 231 ALBERT SABIN WAY, INSTITUTE FOR PSYCHIATRY A 45267 #039-01-2001 L2005 **P** *100

NUNLIST-YOUNG, Donald G. 2567 ERIE AVE 45208 #035-45-1972 L1976 **FM** *020 †18

NUNNALLY, Mark Edwin. 3333 BURNET AVE, CO CHILDREN S HOSP MED CTR 45229 #054-04-1998 L2001 **CCA** *100 †05

NURRE, John William, II. 6040 HARRISON AVE 45248 #038-41-1983 L1986 **OTO HNS** *020 †45

NURRE, Theresa Aurand. 6350 GLENWAY AVE 45211 #038-41-1982 L1985 **IM** *020 †20

NUTHAKKI, Prasanth. 4777 E GALBRAITH RD, DEPT OF MED EDUCATION 45236 #305-01-2006 L2006 **PM** *012

NUTINI, Andrew John. 5310 RAPID RUN RD, STE 101 45238 #020-02-1984 L1985 **IM** *020 †20

NYLUND, Cade Mccoy. ■ 45242 #023-12-2004 L2007 **PG** *012 †55

OBEIDAT, Moutasem Mohamma. 3333 BURNET AVE, CHILDRENS HOSP MED CTR 45229 #575-01-1997 L2004 **OP** *100

OBERDOERSTER, Michael P. 5837 HAMILTON AVE 45224 #038-43-1984 L1985 **P PYG** *030 †75

OBICI, Silvana. ■ 45215 #561-31-1981 L2006 **IM** *100

OBLINGER, Phillip F. 7205 MIAMI AVE, MADEIRA & INDIAN HILL RES 45243 #051-01-1982 L1983 **EM** *020 †16

O'BRIEN, David Patrick, IV. 2123 AUBURN AVE, STE 524 45219 #012-05-1997 L1999 **CRS** *020 †85,10

OBRIEN, Hope Lorraine. ■ 45267 #038-41-2005 L2005 **N** *012

O'BRIEN, Patricia Olivia. ■ 45217 #011-03-2005 L2005 **PD** *012

O'BRIEN, Robyn Lynn. 10498 MONTGOMERY RD, STE A 45242 #038-45-1994 L1995 **IM** *020 †20

O'BRIEN, Shannon Denise. ■ 45209 #048-13-2002 L2002 **PS** *012

O'CONNOR, Katherine Ellen. ■ 45219 #025-01-1957 L1965 **CHP** *071

OELTGEN, Ryan Christopher. 231 ALBERT SABIN WAY, U OF CINCINNATI/CARDIOLOGY 45267 #038-41-2002 L2006 **CD** *012 †20

OESTREICH, Alan Emil. 3300 ELLAND AVE # RAD, CHILDRENS HOSPITAL 45229 #023-07-1965 L1979 **PDR DR** *020 †20

OFFENBERGER, John Brett. 820 DELTA AVE 45226 #038-41-1985 L1989 **CHP P** *020 †75

OFFERMAN, Shannon Therese. ■ 45208 #056-06-2006 L2007 **RO** *012

OGBURN, Casey Andrew. ■ 45231 #422-01-2006 L2006 **OBG** *012

OGBURN, Jean Marie. 3333 BURNET AVE 45229 #020-02-1990 L1993 **PEM** *020 †55

OGG, Cari Ann. 4760 E GALBRAITH RD, STE 108 45236 #038-45-2001 L2001 **GS** *020 †85

O'HARA, Sara Marie. 3333 BURNET AVE # RAD, CHILDRENS HOSP MED CTR 45229 #010-02-1988 L1993 **PDR NM** *020 †80

OHLBAUM, Karen Beth. 3200 VINE ST 45220 #017-20-1978 L1978 **IM CD** *020 †20

OHMER, Richard James. 4592 MONTGOMERY RD 45212 #038-41-1996 L1998 **FM** *020 †18

OHR, Matthew Paul. ■ 45243 #038-45-2004 L2004 **OPH** *012

OIKAWA, Jeanne Hiroko. ■ 45243 #038-43-1979 L1986 **ID** *020 †20

OIKAWA, Yoichi. ■ 45243 #038-41-1954 L1954 **GE IM** *071 †20

OJEDA-FOURNIER, Haydee. ■ 45208 #038-41-2000 L2000 **DR** *100 †80

OKRAGLY, Richard Anthony. 4411 MONTGOMERY RD STE 200 45212 #038-44-2000 L2004 **FSM** *020 †18 ‡

OKUM, Eric Jason. ■ 45242 #038-40-1996 L2004 **TS** *020 †85,90

OKUNADE, Mausi Abosede. 3200 BURNET AVE, SUITE 1 RIDGEWAY 1 45229 #690-01-1982 L2000 **FM IMG** *020 †18

OLANDA, Eliseo Ayroso. ■ 45225 #748-01-1953 L1987 *075

OLANO, Geronimo Estrada. ■ 45248 #748-07-1952 **GP** *062

OLDT, Mary Ruth. ■ 45223 #038-06-1935 L1935 **PTH** *071 †50

OLINGER, Charles Penick. ■ 45220 #051-01-1957 L1962 **N** *071

OLIVER, Gary Wayne, Jr. 9844 REDHILL DR 45242 #035-46-1993 L1999 **DMP** *020 †10

OLIVER, Richard Gerard. 7520 STATE RD 45255 #020-02-1987 L1997 **AN** *020 †05

OLLENDORFF, Arthur T. 222 PIEDMONT AVE, STE 5100 45219 #016-06-1993 L1997 **OBG** *020 †30

OLOWOOKERE, Ayodele Olawa. 375 DIXMYTH AVE, DEPT OF MED EDUCATION 45220 #690-05-1992 L2006 **OBG** *012

O'NEAL, Emmett Gene. 1413 LINN ST 45214 #020-02-1977 L1978 **U OS** *020 †95

O'NEIL, John Christian. 3421 BROOKLINE AVE, 1S 45220 #038-44-2008 *012

ONYEACHOLEM, Ifeanyichuk. ■ 45208 #038-41-2008 *012

OOSTVEEN, Robert James. ■ 45239 #025-12-2003 L2004 **DR** *012

OPPENHEIMER, S Gevelber. CHILDRENS HOSP 45229 #038-06-1958 L1958 **PD OS** *040 †55

ORABELLA, Christopher M. 2123 AUBURN AVE # 401 45219 #038-40-1991 L1992 **PCC IM** *020 †20

OREJUELA, Ausberto A. 7017 VINE ST 45216 #737-01-1958 L1972 **GP GS** *072

ORLANDO, Marc Patrick. 2915 CLIFTON AVE 45220 #038-41-1993 L1994 **IM** *020 †20,60

ORNSTEIN, Anna. 231 BETHESDA AVE 45229 #407-10-1952 L1956 **P CHP** *040 †75

ORR, Robert Hamner, III. ■ 45229 #038-41-2004 *100

OSBORNE, Robert Mitchell. 8000 5 MILE RD, STE 305 45230 #038-41-1986 L1987 **IM** *020 †20

OSCHERWITZ, Morris Geo. 3001 HIGHLAND AVE 45219 #038-41-1963 L1963 **PYA P** *071 †75

OSHER, James Matthew. ■ 45208 #038-41-2008 *012

OSHER, Sanford Stuart. 10495 MONTGOMERY RD STE 14 45242 #038-41-1982 L1987 **OBG GYN** *020 †30

OSINBOWALE, Abraham O. 318 E UNIVERSITY AVE 45219 #690-01-1975 L1983 **IM OM** *020 †70

OSTERHAGE, Dorothy A. 311 STRAIGHT ST 45219 #020-02-1989 L1994 **PTH** *020 †50

OSTERHOLT, Dawn Michelle. ■ 45208 #038-06-2006 L2007 **MPD** *012

OSTERLUND, Mary Elizabeth. 234 GOODMAN ST, STE 0769 45219 #010-02-1996 L1997 **EM** *071 †16

OSTLING, Lauren Rose. ■ 45233 #038-41-2008 *012

OSTROWSKI, Lawrence G. 1101 SUMMIT RD 45237 #025-07-1977 L1991 **P CHP** *030 †75

O'SULLIVAN, Michael G. ■ 45202 #539-02-1983 **NS** *100

OSWALD, Marcus Paul. 12124 SHERATON LN 45246 #028-34-1976 L1980 **DR** *020 †80
O'TOOLE, Jennifer Kathryn. ■ 45255 #035-06-2003 L2003 **MPD** *100 †55
OTREMBIAK, James John. 3333 BURNET AVE 45229 #016-11-1980 L1981 **PD** *020 †55
OTT, Joseph Lee. ■ 45211 #038-41-2008 *012
OTTEN, Edward Jos. 2139 AUBURN AVE, STE 0769 45219 #038-41-1977 L1978
   EM PD *020 †16 ‡
OWEN, Scott James. 10550 MONTGOMERY RD, STE 15 45242 #038-06-1992 L1993
   DR *020 †80
OWENS, Lloyd Edgar. 7809 LAUREL AVE STE 11 45243 #038-41-1954 L1954 **FM** *071
OWENS, O'Dell. 2421 AUBURN AVE 45219 #008-01-1976 L1982 **REN OBG** *020 †30
OZDEMIR, Evren. 234 GOODMAN ST 0796, UNIV HOSP OFFICE GME 45219 #902-05-1992 L2000
   HO *100
PACHARN, Preeyacha. 3333 BURNET AVE 45229 #891-03-1994 L2007 **PDR** *012
PADILLA, Benita S. ■ 45229 #748-02-1983 **NEP** *100
PAGANI, Luis Felix. 111 WELLINGTON RD 45219 #132-04-1963 L1974 **NRN ADM** *020 †75,16 ‡
PAGE, Elena Hernandez. 4676 COLUMBIA PKWY, MAILSTOPR-10 45226 #020-12-1988 L1997
   OM *050 †70
PAHREN, Kenneth Jude. 1219 MORTS PASS 45215 #038-45-1985 L1987 **EM CCM** *020 †18
PAI, Savita Kiran. ■ 45206 #011-05-2007 L2007 **IM** *012
PAI, Umeshraya T. 234 GOODMAN ST 0531 45219 #495-37-1963 L1980 **AN** *020 †05
PAIDY, Samata Reddy. 231 ALBERT SABIN WAY 0, DEPT. OF ANESTHESIA 45229
   #496-01-1998 L2001 **AN** *020 †05
PAIK, Eugene. 45219 #017-20-2001 L2002 **VIR** *012 †80
PAJARI, Karen Louise. ■ 45241 #026-04-1965 L1972 **P** *020 †75
PAJOOHI, Fariba. P.O. BOX 670526, UNIVERSITY OF CINCINNATI M 45267 #517-08-1995 L2006
   OBG *012
PAKRASHI, Tarita. 231 ALBERT WAY, UNIV OF CINCINNATI 45267 #495-17-2004 L2006
   OBG *010
PALASCAK, Joseph Edward. 222 PIEDMONT AVE, STE 1200 45219 #041-02-1968 L1981
   HEM IM *020 †20
PALERMO, Gerald Anthony. 2475 W GALBRAITH RD 45239 #038-41-1972 L1972 **IM** *020 †20
PALKOVACS, Elizabeth Mary. ■ 45208 #038-41-2005 L2006 **OPH** *012
PALMER, Kenneth Eugene. 2123 AUBURN AVE, STE 724 45219 #038-41-1971 L1971
   GYN *020 †30
PALUMBO, Joseph. 3333 BURNET AVE, CHILDREN'S HOSP MEDICAL CT 45229
   #041-14-1993 L1996 **PHO** *020 †55
PALUMBO, Todd Nicholas. 231 ALBERT SABIN WAY, MSB/ M.L. 0559 45267
   #038-06-2004 L2004 **P** *012
PAN, Brian Shenta. ■ 45267 #030-06-2004 L2004 **PS** *012
PANCHAL, Mahendra Jagjiva. 9886 HUMPHREY RD, MT.AIRY MEDICAL IMAGING 45242
   #496-38-1983 L2003 **R MSR** *020 †80
PANCIOLI, Arthur Martin. 231 ALBERT SABIN WAY, UNIV OF CINCINNATI MED CEN 45267
   #025-01-1991 L1994 **EM** *020 †16
PANCOAST, John Richard. 234 GOODMAN ST 45219 #038-41-1973 L1973 **ON HEM** *020 †20
PANDALAI, Prakash K. 231 ALBERT SABIN WAY, ML#0558 45267 #038-45-2001 L2001 **GS** *012
PANDALAI, Soumya Lakshmi. ■ 45241 #038-44-2005 **MPD** *012
PANGALOS, Vincent Themis. 375 DIXMYTH AVE, GOOD SAMARITAN HOSPITAL 45220
   #051-04-1990 L1993 **EM** *016
PANKE, Elizabeth Solarski. 375 DIXMYTH AVE 45220 #038-41-1984 L1986 **CLP** *050
PANKE, Thomas Walter. 375 DIXMYTH AVE, GOOD SAMARITAN HOSP 45220
   #035-45-1970 L1971 **PTH HMP** *030 †50
PANOS, Ralph J. 3200 VINE ST, STE 111D 45220 #043-01-1983 L2004 **PUD CCM** *020 †20
PAPANNA, Ranganath. 4777 E GALBRAITH RD 45236, DEPT INTERNAL MED 45236
   #496-22-1999 L2001 **IM** *100
PAPPAS, John Milton. 8260 NORTHCREEK DR STE 110 45236 #418-01-1958 L1963 **IM** *071
PAPPAS, Zoe. 151 W GALBRAITH RD 45216 #418-01-1951 L1965 **PTH OS** *020 †50
PARADIES, Karen M. ■ 45267 #035-15-2000 L2000 **P** *100
PARAMESWARAN, Lalitha. 3200 BURNET AVE, 1 RIDGEWAY 45229 #495-21-1992 L1996
   FPG *020 †20
PARIKH, Samir Piyush. 234 GOODMAN ST, UNIVERSITY HOSP 45267 #048-04-2002 L2002
   NS *012
PARIKH, Shital Navnitbhai. 3333 BURNET AVE, ML 2017 45229 #495-76-1997 L2001
   ORS OSM *020
PARIS, Michael David. 8220 N CREEK DR 45236 #035-09-1967 L1973 **P** *020 †75
PARK, John M. ■ 45248 #030-05-2005 L2005 **GS** *012
PARK, Richard Eldon. 7520 STATE RD 45255 #038-41-1969 L1969 **AN CCA** *020 †05
PARK, Steven Earl. 4030 SMITH RD, CARDIAC VASCULAR & 45209 #016-02-1985 L1993
   TS *020 †85,90
PARK, Su-Kil. ■ 45243 #583-02-1982 **NEP** *020
PARK, Theodore Taeshik. 2123 AUBURN AVE, CO FAMILY PRACTICE 45219 #016-06-2004 L2004
   FM *100
PARKER, Jeffrey David. 2121 HERRICK AVE 45208 #038-41-1974 L1974 **CCM LM** *071 ‡
PARKER, Tammy Marie. ■ 45208 #038-45-2005 L2005 **OBG** *012
PARKER, Thomas John. 2915 CLIFTON AVE 45220 #038-41-1978 L1989 **PUD** *020 †20
PARKS, Jenny Lee. 2711 MADISON RD 45209 #038-41-1993 L1996 **PD** *020 †55
PARLIN, John Andrew, III. 1495 MOON VALLEY LN 45230 #038-41-1969 L1969 **R** *020 †80
PAROBECK, Deanna Lynne. 10475 READING RD STE 307, FOR WOMEN, INC 45241
   #038-41-1983 L1984 **OBG** *020 †30
PARROTT, C Leonard, Jr. ■ 45229 #012-05-1977 L1981 **PTH FOP** *020 †50
PARTHASARATHI, Niranjana. 3130 HIGHLAND AVE, STE 0557 45219 #051-04-1988 L1991
   IM *040 †20
PARTRIDGE, Suzanne Marie. ■ 45213 #038-43-2002 L2002 **HO** *012 †20
PASSO, Murray Howard. 3333 BURNET AVE, CHILDRENS HOSP 45229 #017-20-1974 L1989
   PPR PD *020 †55
PASTERNAK, Brad Alan. 3333 BURNET AVE, MLC 2010 45229 #550-02-2002 L2005
   PG *012 †55
PATEL, Jay Rajni. 400 WABASH AVENUE 45236 #495-37-2006 L2007 **IM** *012
PATEL, Manish N. 3333 BURNET AVE, DEPT OF RADIOLOGY/MCL 5031 45229 #028-78-1999,
   ▲ L2004 **PDR** *020 †80
PATEL, Manisha Ami. 4030 SMITH RD, CARDIAC VASCULAR & 45209 #050-02-1994 L2002
   TS *020 †85,90
PATEL, Sapan Mayank. ■ 45230 #041-12-2006 L2006 **MPD** *012
PATEL, Umakant Kalidas. 7502 GRIFFIN DR 45237 #496-15-1981 L1986 **IM** *020 †20
PATHAK, Sanjeev. 3333 BURNET AVE D3014, C CHILDRENS HOSP MED CTR 45229
   #495-36-1992 L1999 **CHP** *020 †75
PATHMARAJAH, Rajaratnam. ■ 45249 #220-04-1998 L2003 **IM** *020 †20

PATHMARAJAH, Sivani. ■ 45249 #220-04-1998 L2003 **IM** *020 †20
PATIL, Ninad Mohan. 231 ALBERT WAY, DEPT OF PATHOLOGY 45267 #496-38-2001 L2006
   PTH *012
PATIL, Reena Dhanda. ■ 45243 #016-11-1998 L2007 **OTO** *012
PATIL, Sadanand. 234 GOODMAN ST RM 2009, U.C. MED CTR. BARRET CANC 45219
   #495-35-1991 L1997 **HO IM** *020 †20
PATINO, Mario. ■ 45236 #264-05-1996 L2002 **PAN** *012
PATKAR, Jayant Pundlik. 3300 ELLAND AVE # ANES, CHILDRENS HOSPITAL 45229
   #496-38-1965 L1976 **AN PD** *020
PATRICK, Edward Alfred. 311 STRAIGHT ST 45219 #017-20-1974 L1976 **EM FM** *050 †16
PATTERSON, Bonnie Jean. CINCINNATI CTR DEVLPMT DIS 45229 #017-20-1970 L1981
   PD OS *020 †55
PATTERSON, Larry Todd. 3333 BURNET AVE, CHILDRENS HOSP MEDICAL CEN 45229
   #041-14-1984 L1986 **PN PD** *050 †55
PATTERSON, Mary Deffner. 3333 BURNET AVE, CHILDRENS HOSP MEDICAL CEN 45229
   #041-14-1984 L1986 **PD PEM** *050 †55
PAUL, John Wade. 311 STRAIGHT ST, DEACONESS HOSP EMER DEPT 45219
   #001-02-1978 L1980 **EM** *020
PAUL, William T F. 3217 CLIFTON AVE, GOOD SAMARITAN HOSP 45220 #047-06-1947 L1947
   GS *071
PAULS, Rachel Nicole. 375 DIXMYTH AVE 45220 #062-01-1998 L2003 **OBG** *020
PAUPOO, Arasen Avinash Vi. ■ 45267 #917-03-2002 L2005 **OBG** *100
PAWAR, Swaroop Abhimanyoo. 375 DIXMYTH AVE 45220 #495-28-2002 L2007 **IM** *012
PAYNE, Jack E. ■ 45224 #038-41-1951 L1951 **GP** *071
PAYNE, Stephen Russell. 3805 EDWARDS RD, STE 300 45209 #038-41-1978 L1978 **IM** *020 †20
PEAKE, Paula Lightfoot. 8000 5 MILE RD STE 250 45230 #036-07-2000 L2000 **FM** *020 †18
PECLET, Maria Alonso. 3333 BURNET AVE, DIV OF PEDIATRIC SURGERY 45229
   #041-01-1982 L1991 **GS** *020 †85
PEDDI, Venkat Ram. 222 PIEDMONT AVE, STE 1200 45219 #495-65-1986 L1995 **NEP** *020 †20
PEEDEN, Kathryn Margaret. 8000 5 MILE RD, STE 210 45230 #038-41-2001 L2004 **FM** *020
PEERLESS, Alter Gerson. 9403 KENWOOD RD, STE C204 45242 #038-41-1973 L1978
   OTO *45
PEERLESS, Brian Jeffrey. ■ 45208 #038-41-2000 L2003 **FM** *100 †18
PEIRSON, Ryan Patrick. 1101 SUMMIT RD, SUMMIT BEHAVIORAL HEALTH 45237
   #054-04-2002 L2007 **PFP** *100
PELC, Nancy Jo. 1127 FEHL LN 45231 #016-11-1988 L1990 **D** *020 †15
PELLETIER, Maureen M. 5400 KENNEDY AVE 45213 #024-07-1984 L1990 **GYN OBS** *020 †30
PEMBAUR, Berthold Jos. 8245 NORTHCREEK DR, GROUP HEALTH ASSOCIATES 45236
   #154-02-1975 L1980 **IM** *020 †20
PEMBAUR, Bertold Jos. 2915 CLIFTON AVE, GROUP HEALTH ASSOCIATES 45220
   #154-02-1945 L1957 **FM IM** *071
PENA, Alberto. 3333 BURNET AVE, CCH MEDICAL CENTER 45229 #649-05-1963 L2006
   PDS *020
PENA AYALA, Esteban. ■ 45241 #319-08-2001 L2005 **IM** *020
PENA SALAZAR, Adolfo Mois. 4777 E GALBRAITH RD 45236 #737-01-2000 L2005 **IM** *012
PENIX, Arnold Ray. 8044 MONTGOMERY RD, STE 100 45236 #021-01-1977 L1989
   ORS *020 †40
PENMETSA, Ashok. 2123 AUBURN AVE STE 440, CARDIOVASCULAR CONSULTANTS 45219
   #496-09-1983 L1990 **CD IM** *020 †20
PENNYWELL, John Barrett. ■ 45225 #038-41-1992 **IM** *100
PENSAK, Myles Luther. 222 PIEDMONT AVE, STE 5200 45219 #035-09-1978 L1984
   OTO *040 †45
PENTIUK, Scott Patrick. ■ 45229 #038-41-2002 L2002 **PG** *012
PERALTA, Ferdinand R. 228 BERWOOD DR 45243 #748-08-1973 *020
PERALTA SOLER, Alejandro. 9844 REDHILL DR, RICHFIELD LAB 45242 #132-02-1979 L2006
   ATP DMP *020 †50
PERENTESIS, John Peter. 3333 BURNET AVE, ML 7015 DEPT HEM/OMC 45229
   #025-01-1980 L2002 **PHO** *050 †55
PEREZ, Stephen Wayne. 1219 MORTS PASS 45215 #038-41-1992 L1995 **EM** *020 †16
PEREZ-ALVIAR, Felicitas G. 375 DIXMYTH AVE, OBSTETRIC ANESTHESIA 45220
   #748-01-1963 L1974 **AN** *020
PERI, Miriam Yaffa. 2475 W GALBRAITH RD, STE A 45239 #001-02-1993 L1994 **PD** *020 †55
PERKINS, Alison Jean. ■ 45213 #041-02-2004 L2004 **MPD** *012
PERLER-TOMBOLY, Samuel E. 231 BETHESDA AVE RM 1509, CENTER 45267
   #038-41-1988 L2002 **EM** *020 †16
PERLMAN, Aaron Wm. ■ 45267 #067-03-1942 L1943 **ORS** *071 †40
PERLMAN, Steve Jay. 3200 BURNET AVE 45229 #038-43-1980 L1986 **DR R** *020 †80
PERLMAN, Susan Welch. 4360 COOPER RD, STE 301 45242 #038-43-1979 L1986 **IM** *071 †20
PERLSTEIN, Paul Harris. 3333 BURNET AVE 45229 #049-01-1962 L1964 **NPM PD** *050 †55
PERMAN, Marissa Jill. ■ 45208 #023-01-2005 L2005 **PD** *012
PERME, Charles Mccrory. 234 GOODMAN ST, STE 0054 45219 #038-41-1990 L1992
   DR *020 †80
PERO, Mary Beth. 2750 BEEKMAN ST, HEALTH CENTER 45225 #038-40-1992 L1996
   PD *020 †20
PERRINO, Frank Dominic. 4411 MONTGOMERY RD STE 201 45212 #038-40-1981 L1981
   FM IMG *020 †18
PERSINGER, Courtney Payne. 10550 MONTGOMERY RD 45242 #051-04-1957 L1962
   U *071 †95
PERSON, Allison Krisna. ■ 45229 #038-41-2008 *012
PERSON, Patsy Linn. 3006 PORTSMOUTH AVE 45208 #017-20-1973 L1977 **PD** *071 †55
PERSSON, Perjohan Holger. ■ 45239 #038-41-2002 L2002 **VS** *012
PERUMAL, Venkatachalapathy. 3333 BURNET AVE 45229 #495-33-1988 L2005 **OP** *100
PERUMBETI, Ajaychandra. ■ 45208 #038-44-2001 L2006 **PHO** *012 †55
PESCHIERA, Juan Luis. 10901 REED HARTMAN HWY, STE 300 45242 #737-06-1980 L1984
   GS TRS *020 †85
PETELENZ, Kasia M. ■ 45220 #038-06-2003 L2003 **PAN** *012
PETERS, Jayanthi N. 3001 HIGHLAND AVE, STE E 45219 #068-01-1993 L2004 **P** *020 †75
PETERS, Marianne B. 7981 BEECHMONT AVE 45255 #473-01-1990 L1996 **IM** *020
PETERSEN, Michael Richard. 1945 CEI DR, CINCINNATI EYE INSTITUTE 45242
   #011-02-1986 L1992 **OPH** *020 †35
PETERSON, Kathryn P. 11238 CORNELL PARK DR 45242 #038-41-1988 L1989 **PD** *020 †55
PETINIOT, Lisa Kay. ■ 45242 #056-05-2001 L2001 **PPR** *012 †55
PETROCY, Pamela Joan. 2841 BOUDINOT AVE STE 202 45238 #038-40-1999 L2004 **ORS** *020
PETROSOVA, Natalia. 3333 BURNET AVE, CO CHILDREN S HOSP MED EDU 45229
   #913-15-1982 L2002 **AN** *020 †05
PETROVIC, Olga Maria. 8952 WINTON RD 45231 #038-40-1974 L1977 **RHU** *020 †20

PETROZE, Robin Theresa. ■ 45220 #038-41-2008 *012
PETTIGREW, Hugh Wm. 23 E HOLLISTER ST 45219 #047-05-1973 L1974 **CHP** *020 †75
PFEIFER, Jonathan Charles. ■ 45267 #038-41-2004 L2004 **CHP** *012
PFISTER, Howard F Carl. ■ 45243 #038-41-1943 L1943 **GS CRS** *071 †85
PFLUM, Joseph John. 4750 E GALBRAITH RD, STE 207 45236 #038-45-1986 L1987 **FM** *020 †18
PHELAN, Kieran J, III. 3333 BURNET AVE, EFFECT 45229 #016-06-1991 L1998 **CCP** *020 †55
PHELPS, Allison Michael. ■ 45236 #020-02-2008 *012
PHILIP, Abraham. 10500 MONTGOMERY RD, BETHESDA NORTH HOSPITAL 45242 #495-01-1981 L1984 **PTH PCP** *020 †50
PHILIP, Joyce Mary. 1253 KEMPER MEADOW DR 45240 #495-08-1983 L1990 **IM IMG** *020 †20
PHILIP, Lori Renee. 11135 MONTGOMERY RD 45249 #041-02-1989 L1993 **OBG** *020 †30
PHILLIPS, Christine Lynn. ■ 45242 #017-20-2002 L2006 **PHO** *012 †55
PHILLIPS, Margaret Dean. 5400 KENNEDY AVE, PROSCAN IMAGING 45213 #024-05-1983 L1996 **DR** *020 †20,80
PHILLIPS, Tonya M. 3333 BURNET AVE, MEDICAL CENTER MLC2015 45229 #004-01-1991 L2003 **PD** *020 †75
PIATTI, Andres Matias. ■ 45224 #132-02-2001 L2006 **IM** *012
PIERCE, Stephen. 2368 VICTORY PKWY, STE 501 45206 #649-14-1981 L1985 **AN** *020
PIETRONI, Patrick C. ■ 45220 #917-23-1966 L1979 **FM** *040
PILGER, Pamela Ann. 10475 READING RD, STE 209 45241 #038-41-1995 L1997 **MPD** *020 †20,55
PILJANGENTLE, Alyssa Anne. ■ 45242 #038-41-2004 L2004 **DBP** *012
PILLAI, Vandhana Mohan. 2139 AUBURN AVE 45219 #422-01-2007 L2007 **IM** *012
PILLOW, Deborah Rae. 10500 MONTGOMERY RD 45242 #038-45-1987 L1988 **FM** *020 †18
PINDER, Leeya Fatima. ■ 45267 #045-01-2005 L2005 **OBG** *012
PINHAS-HAMIEL, Orit. ■ 45249 #550-02-1987 **PDE PD** *100
PINKERTON, Lynne E. 4676 COLUMBIA PKWY R-15, NIOSH 45226 #019-02-1988 L1994 **OM** *020 †70,20
PINTO, Ian Glen. 231 ALBERT SABIN WAY 05 45267 #496-55-2002 L2006 **IM** *020 †20
PIRKO, Istvan. 222 PIEDMONT AVE, STE 3200 45219 #473-04-1995 L1999 **N** *020 †75
PISARSKA, Marta. 375 DIXMYTH AVE, GOOD SAMARITAN HOSP 45220 #759-06-1990 L2001 **P** *100
PITMAN, Benjamin Douglas. ■ 45227 #038-41-2008 *012
PLATT, Kevin Tsuneda. 1219 MORTS PASS, QESI 45215 #038-40-2001 L2004 **EM** *020 †16
PLEATMAN, Clifford Wayne. 7500 STATE RD, MERCY HOSPITAL ANDERSON 45255 #038-41-1981 L1984 **R** *020 †80
PLECHA, Christine Ellen. 2123 AUBURN AVE, STE 724 45219 #038-06-1985 L1987 **GYN** *030
PLETTNER, James Page. 6350 GLENWAY AVE 45211 #038-41-1980 L1985 **HS GS** *040 †85
PLISKIN, Marc J. 2450 KIPLING AVE, STE 101 45239 #041-77-1983, ▲ L1991 **U** *020 †95
PLOY-SONG-SANG, Sunantha. 2139 AUBURN AVE, THE CHRIST HOSPITAL ONCOLO 45219 #891-02-1967 L1975 **RO ON** *020 †20
POBST, Lori Jean. ■ 45208 #026-08-2007 L2007 **PD** *012
PODORE, Peter Chas. 8250 KENWOOD CROSSING WAY, STE 225 45236 #035-45-1977 L1982 **VS GS** *020 †85
POINDEXTER, Gary Lee. ■ 45237 #011-03-1978 L1983 **NEP IM** *020
POLANCO, Gerardo B. ■ 45230 #041-13-1950 L1962 **PTH PCP** *071 †50
POLASKY, Nathan. 1409 WESTERN AVE, CINCINNATI JOB CORPS CENTE 45214 #038-41-1953 L1953 **IM** *020
POLASKY, Saul Hyman. ■ 45201 #038-41-1954 L1954 **IM** *071 †20
POLICASTRO, Michael A. 231 ALBERT SABIN WAY RM 15 45267 #038-45-2001 L2001 **EM** *020 †16
POLLANDT, Sebastian Wilhe. 231 ALBERT, INTERNAL MEDICINE 45267 #409-46-2003 L2007 **N** *012
POLLOCK, Judson Bradford. 6725 MIAMI AVE 45243 #038-41-2000 L2003 **NEP** *020
POLONSKY, Sheldon Mark. 8245 NORTH CREEK DR 45236 #056-05-1988 L1990 **PD** *020 †55
POLSTER, Darrell Martin. 3131 QUEEN CITY AVE, DEPT AN 45238 #038-44-1992 L2004 **AN** *020 †05
POLZIN, William James. 375 DIXMYTH AVE 45220 #056-06-1983 L1992 **MFM OBG** *020 †30 ‡
POMERANTZ, Wendy Jane. 3333 BURNET AVE # OSB-4 45229 #048-12-1992 L1995 **PD PEM** *020 †55
PONKSHE, Ajay Bhalchandra. 3333 BURNET AVE, CINCINNATI CHILDREN'S HOSP 45229 #495-14-1991 L2005 **PD** *020 †55
POOL, Charles Edward, Jr. ■ 45267 #038-41-2007 L2007 **AN** *012
POON, James. 1577 GOODMAN AVE # B 45224 #028-34-1953 L1954 **OPH** *071 †35
POON, Philip James. 1577 GOODMAN AVE B 45224 #038-40-1976 L1976 **OPH** *020 †35
POPA, Thomas Octavian. 7426 JAGER CT 45230 #038-41-1978 L1979 **IM** *020 †20
POPKEN, John Frederick. 5049 CROOKSHANK RD, WESTERN HILLS RAD INC 45238 #028-34-1954 L1956 **R NM** *071 †80
POPP, Martin Blaine. 2123 AUBURN AVE STE 420 45219 #041-01-1968 L1969 **GS SO** *020 †85
PORDY, Michael Gregory. 4760 E GALBRAITH RD, STE 114 45236 #028-34-1976 L1979 **RHU IM** *020 †20
PORNOY, Geoffrey Alan. 2915 CLIFTON AVE 45220 #038-41-1987 L1991 **IM EM** *020 †20
PORNOY, Robert Arthur. ■ 45231 #275-01-1955 L1960 **OTO OS** *020 †45
PORRAS-RUEDA, Beatriz H. 9670 KENWOOD RD 45242 #264-12-1988 L1999 **PTH** *020 †50
PORTER, Tama. ■ 45267 #038-06-2007 L2007 **IM** *012
POSTMA, Brian Stephen. 3333 BURNET AVE 45229 #038-41-2005 L2005 **PD** *012
POTOCKI, Lance De Witt. ■ 45217 #023-01-1981 L1983 **FM** *075 †18
POTTER, Rachel Ann. ■ 45242 #038-41-2007 L2007 **FP** *012
POTTSCHMIDT, John David. 2123 AUBURN AVE STE 404 45219 #038-41-1960 L1960 **OBG** *071 †19
POWELL, Erik Scott. 3306 RUTHER AVE, ALLIANCE PRIMARY CARE 45220 #038-41-1987 L1988 **FM** *020 †18
POWELL, James Hayes. 11370 REED HARTMAN HWY 45241 #035-20-1978 L1983 **PA GP** *030
POWELL, Susan Elizabeth. ■ 45208 #055-02-2005 L2005 **OBG** *012
POWERS, Patricia Lee. 5 E LIBERTY ST, CROSSROAD HEALTH CENTER 45202 #038-41-1989 L1992 **FM** *020 †18
POWERS, Thomas Henry. 3333 BURNET AVE 45229 #028-34-1959 L1963 **OPH** *071 †35
POYNTER, Mark Thomas. 3219 CLIFTON AVE, STE 215 45220 #017-20-1997 L2000 **GS** *020 †85
PRADA, Carlos Enrique. 3333 BURNET AVE, CHILDRENS HOSP MED CTR 45229 #264-09-2003 L2006 **PMG** *012
PRAGALOS, Antoinette. 2123 AUBURN AVE, STE 334 45219 #038-43-1993 L1994 **IM** *020 †20
PRAGER, Jeremy David. ■ 45208 #028-02-2003 L2005 **OTO** *012

PRAKASH, Priya Saraswathi. ■ 45209 #038-41-2008 *012
PRAMUK, Laurel Anne. 8245 NORTHCREEK DR, KENWOOD OFFICE 45236 #007-02-1998 L2007 **PD** *020 †55
PRANIKOFF, Joel David. 2123 AUBURN AVE, STE 528 45219 #038-41-1987 L1989 **OBG** *030
PRASAD, Chandra Gurunadha. 6045 BRIDGETOWN RD 45248 #495-98-1974 L1981 **IM** *020 †20
PRASAD, Jwala S P. 3155 GLENDALE MILFORD RD, CINCINNATI EVENDALE SURG 45241 #495-09-1975 L1982 **AN OS** *020 †05
PRASAD, Rajesh K. ■ 45267 #038-41-2002 L2002 **U** *012
PRAVDA, Marvin. ■ 45242 #035-08-1963 L1966 **P** *071 †75
PRENGER, Casey Custer. ■ 45231 #038-41-2005 L2005 **IM** *012
PRESTON, Robert Hidy. ■ 45206 #038-41-1946 L1946 **D** *071 †15
PRESTRIDGE, Adrienne L. 3333 BURNET AVE 45229 #051-07-1998 L2001 **PDP** *020 †55
PRETORIUS, Harold Thos. 7124 MIAMI AVE, STE C 45243 #035-19-1976 L1988 **IM END** *020 †20,28
PREVITE, Joseph P. 3333 BURNET AVE, ML-2001 45229 #055-01-1989 L2003 **PAN** *020 †05
PRIETO, Inma Concepcion. 3801 HAUCK RD, STE A 45241 #847-15-1984 L1990 **IM** *020 †20
PRITCHARD, James Clay. 8060 MONTGOMERY RD, STE 305 45236 #038-41-1982 L1983 **IM** *020 †20
PRITTS, Sarah Dahlgren. 1207 SPRINGFIELD PIKE 45215 #016-06-1996 L1997 **FM** *020 †18 ‡
PRITTS, Timothy Alan. 222 PIEDMONT AVE, STE 200 45219 #016-06-1995 L1997 **GS CCS** *020 †85
PRIVITERA, Michael D, Jr. UNIV CINCINNATI ML 525, DETP NEUROLOGY 45267 #035-15-1980 L1986 **N OS** *030 †75
PROFFITT, Aaron Michael. ■ 45255 #038-41-2008 *012
PROTZER, William Richard. 222 PIEDMONT AVE, MEDICAL ARTS BLDG 45219 #023-12-1980 L1991 **DR OS** *020 †80
PRUDEN, Carla Maria. 3333 BURNET AVE 45229 #024-07-2004 L2007 **PEM** *012
PRUIS, Dirk Thos. 8044 MONTGOMERY RD, STE 100 45236 #017-20-1980 L1986 **ORS OAR** *020 †40
PRUITT, David William. 3333 BURNET AVE, MLC 4009 45229 #016-43-1998 L2000 **PM** *020 †60
PRYOR, Chester C, II. 2828 HIGHLAND AVE 45219 #010-03-1955 L1956 **OPH** *020 †35
PSCHESANG, Benjamin P. 2139 AUBURN AVE, STE 102 45219 #038-41-1998 L2000 **DR** *020 †80
PUCHALSKI, Jonathan T. 3333 BURNET AVE 45229 #038-45-1998 L1999 **PDP** *100 †20,55
PUGH, John Anthony. ■ 45240 #024-05-2007 L2007 *012
PULLEN, Shayla L. 2915 CLIFTON AVE 45220 #010-03-2003 L2003 **FM** *020 †18
PURI, Vanshipal Singh. 935A MONASTERY ST 45202 #038-44-1999 L1999 **IC** *020 †20
PUTERBAUGH, Douglas E. 6825 WOOSTER PIKE 45227 #038-41-1981 L1983 **FM** *020 †18 ‡
PUTNAM, Frank Wm, Jr. 3333 BURNET AVE, ML 3008 45229 #017-20-1975 L2000 **P** *050 †75
PUTNAM, Philip Eugene. 3333 BURNET AVE, CHILDREN'S HOSP MED CTR 45229 #025-01-1984 L1999 **PG** *050 †55
PUTTMANN, Ambrose Anthony. 2859 BOUDINOT AVE STE 101 45238 #038-41-1983 L1987 **OBG** *020 †30
PUTTMANN, William R. ■ 45238 #038-41-1950 L1950 **GYN** *071 †30
PYLES, Derek Brandon. ■ 45230 #038-41-2008 *012
QUADRI, Khaja H Mujtaba. ■ 45241 #704-02-1986 L1989 **IM** *020 †20
QUINLAN, John Gilmary. 231 ALBERT SABIN WAY, UNIV OF CINCINNATI HOSP 45267 #016-11-1980 L1987 **N** *040 †75
QURESHI, Majid Ahmad. 3515 WERK RD 45248 #704-01-1956 L1966 **GS HS** *071 †85
RABIE, Fouad Mohamed. ■ 45229 #330-02-1957 L1971 **OBG** *075
RABKIN, Elizabeth Joy. 231 BETHESDA AVE # 535 45229 #038-41-1985 L1987 **IM** *020 †20
RACADIO, John Miras. 3333 BURNET AVE 45229 #038-41-1992 L1993 **PDR** *072 †80
RACADIO, Judy M. 231 BETHESDA AVE, UNIV HOSPITAL 45267 #038-41-1992 L1994 **EM** *020 †16
RADIN, Donald Irving. 2825 BURNET AVE 45219 #038-41-1954 L1954 **IM END** *072 †20
RADLEY, Thomas Justin. ■ 45243 #038-41-1942 L1942 **ORS** *071 †40
RAETZKE, Bradley Dennis. ■ 45219 #038-41-2008 *012
RAFFERTY, Janice F. 2123 AUBURN AVE, UNIV SURGICAL GRP OF CINCI 45219 #038-40-1988 L1990 **CRS** *020 †85,10
RAHIM, Kim Andre. 234 GOODMAN ST, STE 0054 45219 #038-41-1989 L1993 **DR** *020 †80
RAHNER, David Paul. 5 E LIBERTY ST, CROSSROAD HEALTH CTR 45202 #038-41-1989 L1992 **FM** *020 †18
RAHUSEN, Frans. 231 BETHESDA AVE, M L 0529 45229 #660-02-1988 L1994 **GS** *100 †85
RAI, Fasi. ■ 45267 #496-27-1998 L2001 **N** *100
RAINES, Robert Arnold, Jr. 6350 GLENWAY AVE 45211 #038-41-1993 L1999 **ORS** *020 †40
RAITHEL, Donald James. 3155 GLENDALE MILFORD RD, CINCINNATI EVENDALE SURG 45241 #016-06-1985 L1989 **AN** *020 †05
RAJA, Ali Shahbaz. 234 GOODMAN AVE 45219 #036-07-2004 L2004 **EM** *012
RAJASEKHAR, Lakkaraj. 2866 BOUDINOT AVE 45238 #495-21-1969 L1980 **CD IM** *020 †20
RAMAMOORTHY, Suriya. 375 DIXMYTH AVE, OBSTETRIC ANESTHESIA 45220 #495-04-1975 L1982 **AN** *020 †05
RAMAMURTHY, Mahesh Babu. 3333 BURNET AVE 45229 #496-01-1989 L2000 **PDP** *100
RAMAN, Rachna. CO MEDICAL EDUCATION DEPT, THE CHRIST HOSPITAL 45219 #495-15-2005 L2007 **IM** *012
RAMASWAMY, Geetha. 4903 VINE ST 45217 #495-09-1983 L1987 **P** *020 †75
RAMLO-HALSTED, Barbara A. 3130 HIGHLAND AVE, STE 0557 45219 #008-01-1993 L2000 **END IM** *020 †20
RAMPRASAD, Krishnamurthy. 2925 VERNON PL, STE 100 45219 #495-04-1975 L1980 **GE** *020 †20
RAMPRASAD, Rajeshwari G. ■ 45242 #495-09-1977 **PTH** *100
RAMSINGH, Harvinder Singh. ■ 45208 #012-01-2004 L2004 **AN** *012
RAMSINGH, Kulwant K. ■ 45243 #495-47-1971 L1996 **NM** *012
RANDOLPH, Leonard M, Jr. 4600 MCAULEY PL 6TH FL, MERCY HEALTH PARTNERS 45242 #047-07-1972 L1978 **GS EM** *030 †85
RANESES, Dante Savilla. 5944 COLERAIN AVE 45239 #748-01-1978 L1996 **IM** *020 †20
RANGEL, Josefa Maria. 3333 BURNET AVE, MS 5041 45229 #005-11-1996 L2005 **IM** *020 †20
RANGWALA, Fatima A. ■ 45241 #038-41-2005 **IM** *012
RANK, Allison Ann. ■ 45255 #038-41-2002 L2002 **PDC** *012
RANKER, John Otto. UNIV OF CINCINNATI, DEPT OF INT MED 45267 #038-41-2003 L2004 **NEP** *012
RASHID, Nauman Waheed. ■ 45227 #047-07-2006 L2007 **IM** *012
RASHKIN, Mitchell Carl. 3130 HIGHLAND AVE, STE 0557 45219 #025-01-1977 L1978 **CCM PUD** *020 †20
RATH, Angela Marie. ■ 45247 #038-41-2007 L2007 **PD** *012

RATH, Kellie Susan. ■ 45212 #038-41-2006 L2006 **OBG** *012
RATH, Ranjit. 4030 SMITH RD, CARDIAC VASCULAR & 45209 #495-13-1962 L1971 **TS** *020 †85,90
RATHOD, Asha H. ■ 45243 #495-22-1968 L1979 **AN** *020
RATLEDGE, H Willis. ■ 45238 #025-01-1946 L1954 **U** *071 †95
RAUB, Jeffrey Bryan. 2915 CLIFTON AVE 45220 #038-43-1990 L1991 **AI** *020 †03,55
RAUH, Joseph Louis. 3300 ELLAND AVE, CHILDRENS HOSPITAL 45229 #038-41-1955 L1955 **ADL PD** *030 †55
RAVE, Norman Louis. 3219 CLIFTON AVE, STE 230 45220 #038-41-1959 L1959 **GYN** *072 †30
RAVERT, Brian Lee. ■ 45220 #038-40-2006 L2006 **DR** *012
RAVISUDHIR, Ravinuthala V. 10196 SPRINGFIELD PIKE 45215 #495-58-1990 L2004 **GE** *020 †20
RAWAL, Bishal Bahadur. 4777 E GALBRAITH RD, DEPT OF MED EDU 45236 #672-03-2005 L2006 **IM** *012
RAY, Malia Anne. ■ 45242 #020-12-2005 L2005 **MPD** *012
RAYBORN, Jeffrey Michael. ■ 45241 #038-41-2005 L2005 **FP** *012
RAY CHAUDHURY, Abhik. 3200 VINE ST, STE 111D 45220 #495-32-1979 L2001 **NP** *020 †50
RAZAVI, Seid Ali. 3219 CLIFTON AVE STE 400 45220 #517-05-1971 L1978 **CD IM** *020 †20
REAVIS, Stephanie Lysette. 3333 BURNET AVE, ML 2008 45229 #051-07-2002 L2005 **PEM** *012
RECHT, Matthew Hamilton. 3219 CLIFTON AVE, STE 215 45220 #025-07-2000 L2001 **VS** *020 †85
RECHTIN, Robert Michael. 7810 5 MILE RD 45230 #020-02-1984 L1985 **IM** *020 †20
REDDY, Gudimetla S. ■ 45219 #495-11-1971 L1981 **FM** *020 †55
REDDY, Jaya Pottapu. 311 STRAIGHT ST 45219 #495-62-1971 L1981 **IM** *020 †20
REDDY, Likith Vootukuru. 222 PIEDMONT AVE, STE 200 45219 #048-12-2000 L2003 **GS** *020
REDDY, Marpadga P. 1728 CHASE AVE 45223 #495-57-1967 L1974 **EM IM** *020
REDDY, Neha Bandaru. ■ 45220 #038-41-2008 *012
REDDY, Nenuka Dargani. 375 DIXMYTH AVE, TRI-HEALTH MED CTR 45220 #748-10-1998 L2004 **FPG** *012 †20
REDDY, Pramod Puli. 3333 BURNET AVE 45229 #495-50-1990 L2001 **U GS** *020 †95
REDDY, Radha Bhimavarapu. 234 GOODMAN ST 45219 #038-40-1998 L2004 **OBG** *020 †30
REDINGTON, Thos John, Jr. 1401 STEFFEN AVE 45215 #038-40-1987 L1989 **IM** *020 †20
REED, Amy J. 231 ALBERT SABIN WAY 0 45267 #056-05-1994 L2002 **VS** *020 †85
REED, David Craig. 3219 CLIFTON AVE STE 400 45220 #038-41-1981 L1988 **CD IM** *020 †20
REED, James Christopher. 3333 BURNET AVE, CHILDREN'S HOSP MEDCTR 45229 #021-01-1999 L2007 **CHP** *012
REED, Jennifer Lynn. 3333 BURNET AVE, DIV OF EMERG MED ML2008 45229 #038-41-1998 L2000 **PD PE** *020 †55
REED, Michael Floren. 231 ALBERT SABIN WAY, ML 0558 45267 #024-01-1991 L2002 **TS** *020 †85,90
REED, Robert Lewis. 111 WELLINGTON PL 45219 #038-41-1966 L1966 **N** *020 †75
REEVES, Scott Douglas. 3333 BURNET AVE, DIV OF EMERGENCY MED - OSB 45229 #017-20-1990 L1993 **PD** *020 †55
REGE, Pramod Raghunath. ■ 45220 #495-28-1956 L1971 **U** *071 †95
REICHARD, Jeffrey Dawson. 8000 5 MILE RD, STE 102 45230 #038-40-1997 L1999 **FM** *020 †20
REID, Erin Michelle. ■ 45208 #038-41-2008 *012
REID, Leon Asbury, III. 4631 RIDGE AVE, STE A 45209 #047-07-1974 L1980 **OPH** *020 †35
REID, Vincent Junior. 231 BETHESDA AVE, U CINCINNATI COLL OF MED 45229 #038-41-1999 **GS** *100
REIDY, Caroline M. 3333 BURNET AVE 45229 #038-41-1993 L1996 **PD** *020 †55
REIF, Max. 3130 HIGHLAND AVE, STE 0557 45219 #869-05-1973 L1990 **NEP IM** *020 †20
REILLY, Daniel G. 10700 MONTGOMERY RD, STE 150 45242 #038-41-1986 L1992 **HS ORS** *020 †40
REILLY, Eugene Wm. 7631 CHEVIOT RD 45247 #038-41-1991 L1992 **FM** *020 †18
REILLY, Gerard Paul. 5049 CROOKSHANK RD, STE 102 45238 #038-41-1988 L1989 **OBG** *020 †30
REILLY, Kevin Eugene. 6350 GLENWAY AVE 45211 #038-41-1990 L1995 **ORS** *020 †40
REILMAN, Linda Louise. 5819 CHEVIOT RD 45247 #038-40-1984 L1984 **DR RNR** *020 †80
REINHART, Glenn Alan. 8250 KENWOOD CROSSING WAY, STE 200 45236 #016-06-1988 L1999 **ORS OSM** *020 †40
REINHART, Shawn Stephen. 5819 CHEVIOT RD 45247 #038-40-1993 L1997 **DR** *020 †80
REISING, Jos Martin, III. 231 BETHESDA AVE 45229 #038-40-1980 L1985 **TS CD** *020 †90,85
REITZ, Julia Delehanty. 5837 HAMILTON AVE 45224 #019-02-2001 L2002 **FM** *100 †18
RENDER, Marta Louise. 3200 VINE ST, 111F 45220 #020-12-1979 L1986 **PUD IM** *020 †20
REPASKE, David Roy. 3333 BURNET AVE, CENTER 45229 #047-05-1985 L1992 **PDE END** *020 †55
RETZINGER, Gregory Scott. 234 GOODMAN ST 45219 #016-02-1983 L1993 **PTH** *020 †50
REULAND, George Terence. 2450 KIPLING AVE, STE 112A 45239 #038-41-1971 L1972 **PUD IM** *020 †20
REUSS, Raymond Thos. 2001 ANDERSON FERRY RD, GROUP HEALTH ASSOCIATES 45238 #038-45-1992 L1993 **IM** *020 †20
REUTER, John Henry. 3333 BURNET AVE 45229 #038-41-1976 L1980 **NPM** *050 †55
REVILLA, Fredy Jesus. DEPT. OF NEUROLOGY, ML0525, 260 STETSON STREET, SUITE 45267 #737-06-1993 L2003 **N** *020 †75
REVIS, Brian Lee. ■ 45211 #038-41-2006 L2006 **IM** *012
REYES, Alvaro. 2450 KIPLING AVE, STE 110 45239 #264-01-1983 L1998 **NEP** *020 †20
REYNOLDS, Kasey Aileen. ■ 45206 #038-41-2007 L2007 **OBG** *012
REYNOLDS, Melissa Gale. ■ 45209 #048-04-2007 L2007 **PD** *012
REZAEI, Ario. ■ 45215 #025-01-2004 L2005 **DR** *012
RHOAD, Robert Clark. 6350 GLENWAY AVE 45211 #041-01-1993 L1999 **HS ORS** *020 †40
RHOADES, Torre Henderson. ■ 45267 #038-41-2003 L2003 **GS** *100
RIBIER, Andrea Christina. 311 ALBERT SABIN WAY 45229 #025-01-2004 L2004 **CPP** *012
RICE, James Fenton. ■ 45239 #038-41-1959 L1959 **FM** *071
RICE, Richard Bankhardt. 7520 STATE RD 45255 #020-12-1983 L1988 **AN** *020 †05
RICE, Sharice Natasha. UNIV OF CINCINNATI, DEPT OF INTERNAL MEDICINE 45267 #036-01-2007 L2007 **MPD** *012
RICE, Ward Richard. 3333 BURNET AVE, CHILDREN'S HOSP MEDICAL CE 45229 #016-02-1978 L1981 **NPM PD** *050 †55
RICER, Ricky Edwin. 1207 SPRINGFIELD PIKE 45215 #038-40-1978 L1985 **FM GP** *020 †18
RICHARDS, Catherine Ann. 234 GOODMAN ST, STE 0054 45219 #038-41-1991 L1995 **DR** *020 †80
RICHARDSON, Kenrick S. 1413 LINN ST 45214 #038-41-1997 L1998 **IM** *020 †20
RICHARDSON, Reuben. 10500 MONTGOMERY RD 45242 #047-07-1950 L1953 **PD FM** *075
RICHBURG-WHITFIELD, V. 2475 W GALBRAITH RD, STE A 45239 #038-41-1998 L2000 **PD** *020 †55
RICHTAND, Neil Mark. 231 ALBERT SABIN WAY 0559, UNIV OF CINCINNATI PSYCH 45267 #047-05-1987 L1994 **P OS** *020 †75
RICHTER, Gresham Thomas. 3333 BURNET AVE 2018, CINCINNATI CHILDRENS HOSPI 45229 #007-02-2001 L2006 **PDO** *012 †45
RICHTER, Ralph W. 5049 CROOKSHANK RD 45238 #038-41-1953 L1953 **ORS** *071
RICHTER, Randy Chas. 3131 QUEEN CITY AVE 45238 #038-41-1988 L1994 **AN** *020 †05
RICHTER, Robert Bernard. 4777 E GALBRAITH RD, THE JEWISH HOSPITAL 45236 #038-41-1988 L1991 **PM** *020 †60
RICHTER, Ronald Jos. 2446 KIPLING AVE 45239 #038-41-1989 L1992 **AN** *020
RIDDLE, Sarah Whitt. 3333 BURNET AVE, HOUSESTAFF OFFICE 45229 #023-07-2001 L2001 **PD** *100 †55
RIEDEL, Richard D. 3710 PAXTON AVE 45209 #020-02-1968 L1970 **OPH** *071 †35
RIEGEL, Timothy Mark. 3229 BURNET AVE, SHRINERS BURNS HOSP 45229 #060-02-1997 L2002 **PS CCS** *020
RIEGLER, Sandra Lee. 3130 HIGHLAND AVE, STE 0557 45219 #038-41-1973 L1973 **IM** *020 †20
RIELEY, Margaret Burton. 3333 BURNET AVE, CINCINNATI CHILDREN'S HOSP 45229 #063-01-2004 L2007 **MG** *012 †55
RILEY, Nancy. 10475 READING RD, STE 20 45241 #028-46-1994 L1996 **MPD PD** *020 †20,55
RILL, Brian Kieth. 10663 MONTGOMERY RD 45242 #025-07-2001 L2005 **ORS** *020
RINALA, Grace Lampa Sta. 500 E BUSINESS WAY 45241 #748-01-1965 L1974 **AN IM** *020
RINALA, Sara Gage. 10475 READING RD, STE 307 45241 #038-45-2004 L2004 **OBG** *012
RINALDI, Christopher Aldo. 3333 BURNET AVE, CO CHILDREN S HOSP-MED EDU 45229 #917-19-1990 L2001 **CD** *100
RINDERKNECHT, Andrea S. 3333 BURNET AVE 45229 #043-01-2003 L2003 **PEM** *012 †55
RINGENBACH, Raymond M. 3012 GLENMORE AVE 45238 #038-41-1971 L1971 **D** *020 †15
RINGER, Andrew Joel. 222 PIEDMONT AVE STE 3100 45219 #016-11-1993 L2001 **NS** *020 †25
RINGGENBERG, Ewa H. 8060 MONTGOMERY RD 45236 #759-08-1961 L1975 **OBG** *020 †30
RINSKY, Mark Joel. 8340 SPRINGVALLEY DR 45236 #038-41-1973 L1974 **D** *020 †15
RIOS, Juan M. 3217 CLIFTON AVE, GOOD SAMARITAN HOSP 45220 #649-01-1984 **IM** *075
RISMA, Isidro Betonio. ■ 45241 #748-07-1954 L1970 **GP** *071
RISMA, Isidro Glenn. 2751 O'VARSITY WAY, UNIVERSITY OF CINCINNATI 45221 #038-40-1992 L1994 **FM** *020 †18
RISMA, Kimberly Ann. 3333 BURNET AVE 2000, CINCINNATI CHILDRENS HOSP 45229 #038-06-1997 L1999 **AI** *050 †03,55
RISSOVER, Janalee Krick. 8000 5 MILE RD STE 340 45230 #038-43-1985 L1988 **PM** *020 †60
RISTAGNO, Ross Louis. 2139 AUBURN AVE 45219 #025-01-1979 L1986 **VIR** *020 †20,80
RITCHISON, Andrew John. ■ 45216 #017-20-2003 L2003 **GS** *012
RITZI, Robert William. 2139 AUBURN AVE 45219 #038-41-1962 L1962 **AN** *071 †05
RIVERA, Alfredo. 4460 RED BANK RD, STE 200 45227 #748-01-1989 L1995 **PYG P** *020 †75
RIVERA, Emmanuel V. 5920 COLERAIN AVE 45239 #748-01-1988 L2000 **FPG** *020 †18
ROACH, Alan Edward. ■ 45227 #038-41-2008 *012
ROBBINS, Andrew F, Jr. 4760 RED BANK RD, STE 108 45227 #038-41-1973 L1974 **OPH** *020 †35
ROBERSON, Charles A. 10663 MONTGOMERY RD, CINCINNATI SPORTSMEDICINE 45242 #035-15-1993 L2005 **OSM** *100
ROBERTS, Alice Amanda. 9844 REDHILL DR 45242 #035-45-1999 L2005 **PTH DMP** *020
ROBERTS, Christopher M. 7432 JAGER CT 45230 #038-41-1995 L1997 **IM** *020 †20
ROBERTS, John Mark, V. 2123 AUBURN AVE, STE 201 45219 #038-41-1980 L1985 **ORS** *020 †40
ROBERTS, Kristin Marie. 212 W SHARON RD 45246 #038-41-2000 L2003 **FM** *020 †18
ROBERTS, Mable Moy. 2123 AUBURN AVE, STE 724 45219 #038-06-1994 L1998 **OBG** *020 †30
ROBERTS, Thomas Courtney. 5 E LIBERTY ST 45202 #038-40-1990 L1992 **FM** *020 †18
ROBERTSHAW, Daniel Franci. ■ 45236 #038-41-2008 *012
ROBERTSON, Jaime Clayton. 231 ALBERT SABIN WAY 45267 #039-01-2001 L2001 **ID** *100
ROBERTSON, Saml Thos, III. 3001 HIGHLAND AVE, STE E 45219 #038-06-1979 L1982 **P PYA** *020
ROBINSON, Alaba Devonne. ■ 45211 #056-05-2002 L2002 **MPD** *020
ROBINSON, Allan Harvey. 752 WAYCROSS RD 45240 #038-41-1967 L1967 **PD** *020 †55
ROBINSON, Bryce Robert. 231 ALBERT SABIN WAY, DIVISION OF TRAUMA & CRITI 45267 #038-41-2001 L2006 **CCS** *100
ROBINSON, John Jos, Jr. 9070 WINTON RD 45231 #038-41-1974 L1974 **PD NPM** *020 †55
ROBINSON, John Randal. 4030 SMITH RD, CARDIAC VASCULAR & 45209 #048-12-1978 L1989 **TS VS** *020 †85,90
ROBINSON, Suzanne. ■ 45255 #038-41-2004 L2004 **AN** *012
ROBINSON, Wilson Scout, Jr. ■ 45208 #047-06-2006 L2006 **PD** *012
ROBINSON-SMITH, Toni M. 231 ALBERT SABIN WAY 45267 #041-12-1986 L1998 **ATP PCP** *020 †50
ROBLES, Rosa Maria. 10495 MONTGOMERY RD, STE 15 45242 #847-12-1981 L1990 **IM** *020 †20
ROCHE, Conal Daniel. ■ 45226 #038-41-2008 *012
RODGERS, Jared David. 3200 VINE ST 45220 #001-02-1984 L1985 **IM** *020 †20
RODRIGUES, Renee S. 5444 ERIE STATION LN # 1 45227 #048-04-2002 L2005 **DBP** *012 †55
RODRIGUEZ, Dirk Isaias. ■ 45208 #042-02-1981 L2007 **GS VS** *020 †85
RODRIGUEZ, Ernesto. 375 DIXMYTH AVE, OBSTETRIC ANESTHESIA 45220 #042-03-1988 L1990 **AN PME** *020 †05
RODRIGUEZ, Nelia Dacuycuy. 2446 KIPLING AVE 45239 #748-11-1967 L1976 **PTH** *020 †50
RODRIGUEZ, Sarah Marie. ■ 45211 #038-41-2007 L2007 **PD** *012
ROEDERSHEIMER, Rebecca A. 2859 BOUDINOT AVE, STE 206 45238 #038-41-2003 L2003 **U** *012
ROESEL, Gwen Choi. 2752 ERIE AVE 45208 #038-41-2003 L2003 **U** *012
ROESER, Eve Lauren. 10700 MONTGOMERY RD, STE 100 45242 #035-15-1991 L1995 **PD** *020 †55
ROEVER, Harold D. ■ 45208 #038-41-1952 L1952 **PTH OS** *074
ROGERS, Lynn Marie. 1104 KUERTZMILL DR 45249 #038-40-1986 L1990 **AN** *020 †05
ROGERS, Paul Jos. 2123 AUBURN AVE, STE 624 45219 #016-06-1981 L1990 **CD IM** *020 †20
ROHATGI, Reina. DEPT OF PSYCHIATRY, UNIV HOSPITAL-UNIV OF CINC 45267 #495-37-1994 L1999 **P** *100
ROHDE, Jack Frank. ■ 45249 #038-41-1947 L1947 **IM** *071
ROHNER, Deborah Jo. ■ 45209 #038-41-2007 L2007 **AN** *012
ROHS, Amy Marie. KETTERING G-18/ P.O.BOX 67, 3223 EDEN AVE. 45267 #038-43-1998 L1999 **GPM** *100 †20
ROHS, Anne Elizabeth. ■ 45215 #038-40-2007 **P** *012
ROHS, Robert Gregory. 375 DIXMYTH AVE # 1035-1 45220 #030-05-1975 L1991 **P PYG** *020 †75
ROJAS, Antonio Alirio. 425 FARRELL CT 45233 #654-01-1998 L2000 **IM** *020 †20

■ = Address Information Privacy Protected

ROLFES, Donald B, Jr. 375 DIXMYTH AVE, NEONATOLOGY 45220 #038-41-1979 L1984 PTH *020 †50

ROLFES, Ernst Gerth. 7793 COLERAIN AVE 45239 #038-41-1956 L1956 PD *071 †55

ROMAN, Brion Wain. 7520 STATE RD 45255 #038-41-1999 L2003 AN *020 †05

RONAN-BENTLE, Sarah E. 231 ALBERT SABIN WAY 45267 #038-41-2001 L2001 EM *020 †16

RORICK, Marvin H, III. 10550 MONTGOMERY RD, STE 33 45242 #038-41-1984 L1985 N IM *020 †75 ‡

ROSAL, Dionisia Caoile. 2446 KIPLING AVE, PROVIDENCE HOSPITAL 45239 #748-01-1962 L1976 GP IM *020

ROSALES, Carlos Alberto. ■ 45209 #041-12-2002 L2007 VS *012

ROSARIO, Michelle. GYN231 ALBERT, CO OBSTETRICS & 45267 #042-01-2004 L2004 OBG *012

ROSE, Douglas Frederick. 3333 BURNET AVE OSB-5, CHILDRENS HOSPITAL MEDICAL 45229 #038-06-1977 L1979 N PD *020 †75,55

ROSE, Geoffrey Andrew. 2475 W GALBRAITH RD 45239 #759-01-2000 L2000 IM *020 ‡

ROSE, Susan Rogers. 3333 BURNET AVE 45229 #038-06-1980 L2000 PDE *020 †55

ROSELLE, Gary Alan. 3200 VINE ST, MEDICAL SERVICE 111 45220 #038-40-1973 L1973 IM ID *020 †20

ROSENBERG, Lee Sander. 3200 BURNET AVE 45229 #024-01-1943 L1947 DR *071 †80

ROSENBLATT, Arthur Allen. ■ 45208 #047-05-1972 L1973 OTO FPS *020 †45

ROSENTHAL, Jonathan David. 3120 BURNET AVE STE 301 45229 #038-41-1965 L1965 P *020

ROSENTHAL, Montiel Teresa. 3333 BURNET AVE 45229 #038-41-1986 L1989 FM OBS *020 †18

ROSERO, Marciano A, Jr. ■ 45237 #748-01-1954 L1964 GP GS *020

ROSING, Joanna Lee. ■ 45247 #038-41-2008 *012

ROSNER, Isador Kenneth. ■ 45236 #041-09-1932 L1933 IM *071

ROSNER, Steven A. 2450 KIPLING AVE, STE 202 45239 #041-09-1978 L1982 D *020 †15

ROSS, Courtney Renee. ■ 45239 #038-41-2007 L2007 AN *012

ROSS, Micaela. 311 STRAIGHT ST 45219 #036-05-2001 L2007 HMP *100 †50

ROSSI, Rocco Anthony. ■ 45212 #038-41-2006 L2006 OBG *012

ROST, Raymond Clifford, Jr. 5819 CHEVIOT RD 45247 #038-41-1979 L1981 DR *020 †80

ROTH, Andrew M. 2841 BOUDINOT AVE, FREIBERG ORTHOPAEDIC AND 45238 #020-12-1974 L1976 ORS *020 †40

ROTH, Daniel Jeremy. 7432 JAGER CT 45230 #025-01-1995 L1999 IM *020 †20

ROTH, Eli Meyer. 2230 AUBURN AVE, LEVEL B 45219 #038-41-1976 L1977 CD IM *020 †20

ROTH, Jeffrey Louis. 375 DIXMYTH AVE, OBSTETRIC ANESTHESIA 45220 #011-02-1978 L1983 AN *020 †05

ROTHENBERG, Florence. 3130 HIGHLAND AVE, STE 0557 45219 #048-12-1991 L1997 CD *020 †20

ROTHENBERG, Marc Elliot. 3333 BURNET AVE, CHILDRENS HSP MED CTR 45229 #024-01-1990 L1997 AI *050 †55,03

ROUAN, Gregory Wayne. 231 ALBERT SABIN WAY, DEPT OF INTERNAL MEDICINE 45267 #038-41-1980 L1981 IM *062 †20

ROUMELIOTIS, Athanasios A. ■ 45267 #418-01-1989 L2000 OPH *100

ROUSE-RAINES, Deborah A. 7300 BEECHMONT AVE, CINCINNATI GYNECOLOGY SPEC 45230 #038-41-1993 L1999 OBG *020 †30

ROUSSEAU, James Harry. ■ 45208 #008-02-2007 L2007 IM *012

ROVETTO, Pedro Alejandro. 234 GOODMAN ST DEPT PTH, UNIV OF CINN MS 529 45267 #264-05-1976 L1986 BBK PTH *020

ROVNER, Leon (Leonid). 4777 E GALBRAITH RD, DEPT OF GME 45236 #913-96-2003 L2006 IM *012

ROWE, Christopher Cornell. 58 E HOLLISTER ST 45219 #038-41-1984 L1985 P *020 †75

ROY, Suresh. ■ 45236 #495-22-1961 L1971 PTH *020 †50

ROY-CHAUDHURY, Prabir. 231 ALBERT SABIN WAY, DIV OF NEPHROLOGY (MSBG251 45267 #495-73-1985 L1997 IM NEP *020 †20

ROZEN, Michael Jay. 7800 COOPER RD, NEHDC 45242 #038-40-1967 L1967 ORS *020 †40

RUBENSTEIN, Eli. 2350 AUBURN AVE 45219 #038-41-1946 L1946 R NM *072 †80,28 ‡

RUBIN, Jon Scott. 234 GOODMAN ST, STE 0054 45219 #038-41-1997 L2000 DR *020 †80

RUBIN, Robert. ■ 45249 #913-79-1990 L1999 IM *020 †20

RUBINSTEIN, Jack Herbert. 541 LUDLOW AVE 45220 #024-01-1952 L1956 PD *030 †55

RUCHHOFT, Elizabeth A. 10475 READING RD, STE 307 45241 #038-41-1991 L1996 OBG *020 †30

RUCKNAGEL, Donald Louis. 3300 ELLAND AVE # MED, CHILDRENS HOSPITAL 45229 #028-02-1954 L1997 IM PD *050 †19

RUDDY, Richard M. 3300 ELLAND AVE, CHILDRENS HOSPITAL 45229 #010-02-1976 L1991 PEM CCM *030 †55

RUDEMILLER, Mark Wm. 2859 BOUDINOT, STE 107 45238 #038-41-1980 L1982 FM P *020 †20

RUDEMILLER, Michael E. 10500 MONTGOMERY RD 45242 #038-41-1988 L1989 IM *020 †20

RUDEMILLER, William B, Jr. 2859 BOUDINOT, STE 107 45238 #056-06-1948 L1949 FM OM *071 †18

RUDICH, Steven Mark. 2139 AUBURN AVE 45219 #035-47-1989 L2002 GS TTS *020 †85

RUDOLPH, Jeffrey Alan. 3333 BURNET AVE, CHILDRENS HOSP MED CTR 45229 #041-12-1994 L1997 PG *020 †55

RUDOLPH, Priya. 5310 RAPID RUN RD, STE 202 45238 #495-94-1992 L2004 HO *020 †20

RUEHLMAN, Peter Geo. 199 WILLIAM HOWARD TAFT RD 45219 #038-41-1978 L1980 ON HEM *020 †20

RUFFING, Debra Marie. ■ 45220 #038-41-1994 *100

RUFNER, Deborah Kay. 55 PROGRESS PL, GROUP HEALTH ASSOCIATES 45246 #038-40-1975 L1980 PD *020 †55

RUFO, Rogelio Bulatao. 11438 LEBANON RD, STE G 45241 #748-01-1964 L1973 FM *020 †18

RUGH, Walter Bunn. 7500 STATE RD 45255 #038-41-1947 L1947 OBG *071 †30

RUHALTER, Aaron. 4545 CREEK RD, ML 86 45242 #869-04-1956 L1958 GS *071 †85

RUHNKE, Christopher James. 6350 GLENWAY AVE 45211 #833-06-1991 L1992 ORS *020 †40 ‡

RUKSENAS, Audrius. 4260 GLENDALE MILFORD RD, GCIM 45242 #913-49-1993 L1998 IM *020 †20

RUKSENIENE, Indre. 8220 NORTH CREEK DR, STE 110 45236 #913-49-1993 L1999 P *020 †75

RUNK, Dianne Marie. 375 DIXMYTH AVE, DONNA STAHL MD INC 45220 #038-41-1993 L1995 GS *020 †85

RUNYON, John P, Jr. 2123 AUBURN AVE STE 136 45219 #020-12-1983 L1985 CD *020 †20

RUPP, Paul Jos. 5575 CHEVIOT RD 45247 #038-45-1990 L1992 FM *020 †18

RUSCHULTE, Amy Renee. 2450 KIPLING AVE STE 108, WESTERN FAMILY PHYSICIANS 45239 #038-45-1998 L1999 FM *020 †18

RUSK, Aimee Johnson. 410 REILY RD 45215 #409-24-1985 L1988 P *020 †75

RUSNAK, Rima Nasrallah. 3333 BURNET AVE, CHILDREN'S HOSPITAL 45229 #047-05-2002 L2002 PD *100 †55

RUSSELL, Joseph Chas. 7794 5 MILE RD 45230 #020-12-1972 L1973 OS VM *030 †20

RUSSELL, Joseph Erwin. ■ 45238 #028-34-1957 L1958 FM *071 †18

RUTTER, Meilan Marianne. 3333 BURNET AVE, CINCINNATI CHILDREN'S HOSP 45229 #917-18-1987 L2000 PD *020 †55

RUTTER, Michael J. 3333 BURNET AVE, DEPT OF PEDIATRIC 45229 #671-02-1987 L2000 PDO *020 †55

RUWE, Elizabeth Anne. GYNECOLOGY DE, CO OBSTETRICS & 45267 #038-41-2004 L2004 OBG *012

RYAN, Richard Jos. 2139 AUBURN AVE, STE 0769 45267 #035-09-1990 L1991 EM *020 †16

RYAN, Thomas Daniel. ■ 45219 #001-02-2005 L2006 PD *012

RYCKMAN, Frederick Chas. 3333 BURNET AVE 45229 #025-01-1977 L1984 PDS TTS *020 †85

SAAD, Ali Ghazi. ■ 45267 #605-03-1998 L2000 PP *100 †50

SAAL, Howard Max. 3333 BURNET AVE, MC 4006 45229 #025-07-1979 L1993 MG PD *020 †19,55

SABA, Alexander Khamis. 2450 KIPLING AVE 45239 #038-41-1988 L1990 GS *020 †85

SABA, Khamis Alexander. 1559 W NORTH BEND RD 45224 #605-01-1953 L1961 GS CRS *020 †85

SABIN, Sarah Jane. 2859 BOUDINOT AVE, STE 101 45238 #020-02-1998 L1999 OBG *020 †30

SABO, Leslie John. ■ 45233 #473-03-1955 L1963 OTO *071 †45

SABOUR, Sarmad. ■ 45206 #048-13-2005 L2005 OTO *012

SACHAR, Raj Mohan. 375 DIXMYTH AVE, OBSTETRIC ANESTHESIA 45220 #495-45-1980 L1992 AN *020 †05

SACHER, Ronald Alan. 3130 HIGHLAND AVE 45267 #836-01-1969 L2001 HEM BBK *020

SACHS, Ronald Allen. 58 E HOLLISTER ST 45219 #038-41-1980 L1984 P ADP *020 †75

SAEED, Zahid Ahmad. 1380 COMPTON RD 45231 #704-09-1976 L2001 IM GE *020 †20

SAENGER, Eugene Lange. 234 GOODMAN ST 45267 #038-41-1942 L1942 NM R *071 †80,28

SAFDAR, Shahzad. 2925 VERNON PL, STE 302 45219 #704-01-1983 L1998 NP IM *020 †20

SAFDI, Alan Victor. 2925 VERNON PL, STE 1 45219 #038-41-1978 L1981 GE IM *020 †20

SAFDI, Michael Andrew. 4760 E GALBRAITH RD, STE 107 45236 #038-41-1975 L1978 GE IM *020 †20

SAGCAL, Anna Carmela Ponc. ■ 45229 #748-02-2002 L2007 PPR *012 †55

SAGHIR, Syed Shariq Ahmad. ■ 45249 #495-15-2000 L2003 IM *020 †20

SAHA, Madhumita. 4750 E GALBRAITH RD, STE 103 45236 #495-39-1982 L1999 IM CD *020 †20

SAHAY, Alok. 222 PIEDMONT AVE STE 3200 45219 #495-30-1984 L1999 N OS *020 †75

SAHEBJAMI, Hamid. 231 BETHESDA AVE RM 7511, PULMONARY/CRITICAL CARE ME 45267 #517-01-1964 L1977 PUD IM *071 †20

SAJJAD, Tahir. 3219 CLIFTON AVE, STE 325 45220 #704-01-1989 L2001 NEP *020 †20

SAKKAL, Saad Al. ■ 45242 #875-01-1972 L1983 END IM *020 †20

SALADIN, Thomas Anthony. 375 DIXMYTH AVE 45220 #038-41-1959 L1959 IM GE *040 †20

SALDANA-GAUTIER, Luis R. 234 GOODMAN ST 45219 #042-01-1961 L1965 MFM OBG *020 †30

SALEH, Nael Ali. ■ 45202 #038-43-2006 L2006 IM *012

SALEHI, Marzieh. 3125 EDEN AVE, ENDOCRINOLOGY DIVISION 45219 #517-01-1994 L2004 IM *020 †20

SALEM, Anthony Joseph. 2139 AUBURN AVE 45219 #038-41-1962 L1962 IM PUD *020 †20

SALIBA, Jose Antonio. 375 DIXMYTH AVE, CO GOOD SAM HOSP - MED EDU 45220 #935-06-1995 L2001 IM *020

SALLEE, Floyd Randy. 3333 BURNET AVE, DEPT PSYCHIATRY/CHILD HOSP 45229 #016-45-1978 L1998 P PA *050 †75

SALUD, Leo Gerardo Hocbo. PO BOX 670515, UNIV OF CINCINNATI 45267 #748-01-1990 L2003 NS *020

SAMAAN, Saad. 3200 VINE ST, VAMC 45220 #875-01-1985 L1996 PTH PCP *020 †50

SAMAAN, Zeina Marcho. 3333 BURNET AVE, CHILDREN HOSP MED CTR 45229 #875-01-1985 L1996 PD *020 †55

SAMAHA, Antoine Labib. 3219 CLIFTON AVE, STE 325 45220 #605-02-1993 L1999 IM NEP *020 †20

SAMMARCO, Giacomo James. 311 STRAIGHT ST, CINCINNATI SPORTS MED & OR 45219 #021-01-1965 L1968 ORS OFA *020 †40

SAMMARCO, Vincent James. 3301 WESTBOURNE DR 45248 #038-06-1993 L1998 OFA ORS *020 †40

SAMOL, John Michael. 5049 CROOKSHANK RD, STE 102 45238 #038-41-2001 L2001 OBG *020

SAMOL, Nancy B. 3333 BURNET AVE, DEPT. OF ANESTHESIA, ML 20 45229 #038-41-2002 L2002 PAN *012

SAMPANG, Benjamin Mallari. 7520 STATE RD 45255 #748-10-1965 L1985 AN *020

SAMPANG, Suzanne Josafat. 3333 BURNET AVE, MLC 6015 45229 #748-10-1997 L2000 CHP P *020 †75

SAMPSON, Kevin Blair. 12115 SHERATON LN 45246 #550-02-2001 L2005 HSO *012

SAMS, Laura Ann. 231 BETHESDA AVE, 4010 MEDICAL SCI BLDG., #5 45267 #020-12-1988 L1992 N IM *020 †75

SAMSON, Charles Michael. ■ 45208 #054-04-2003 L2006 PG *012 †55

SAMUEL, Jibin Valiyaveett. 3200 BURNET AVE 45229 #495-37-2003 L2005 AN *012

SAMUELS, Paul Jason. 3333 BURNET AVE, DEPT ANEST ML0531 45229 #035-19-1987 L1994 AN PD *020 †05,55

SANDERS, Richard J. ■ 45242 #396-02-1981 L1984 FM *020 †18

SANDHU, Anita. ■ 45243 #496-07-1989 L1994 END *074 †20

SANGHAVI, Amy. 3333 BURNET AVE 7012, HOSP MED 45229 #422-01-2004 L2007 PDE *012 †55

SANGHVI, Vijay Ratital. 3200 BURNET AVE 45229 #495-22-1962 L1972 CD IM *020

SANGVAI, Gangadhar D. 3131 QUEEN CITY AVE 45238 #495-56-1966 L1973 GS *020 †05

SANKAR, Anila Pillai. 2139 AUBURN AVE 45219 #496-20-1999 L2007 IM *012

SANKAR, Mannadimangalam Y. 4460 MONTGOMERY RD, BETHESDA CARE NORWOOD 45227 #495-42-1959 L1986 OM *071

SANTA INES, Carols Jr. 3333 BURNET AVE 45229 #038-41-1969 L1969 PD *020 †55

SANTANGELO, Richard G. 3333 BURNET AVE 45229 #038-41-1969 L1969 PD *020 †55

SANTIPRABHOB, Jeerunda. 3333 BURNET AVE 45229 #891-02-1994 L1999 PDE *100 †55

SANYASI, Raju Sagi. 311 STRAIGHT ST 45219 #495-11-1960 L1971 P GP *072

SAOUDIAN, Mahnaz. 231 ALBERT SABIN WAY, ML 0563 45229 #517-13-1998 L2007 RHU *012 †20

SARAF, Smita Anil. 10196 SPRINGFIELD PIKE 45215 #496-25-1996 L2003 FM *020

SARAFZADEH, Shaden. ■ 45219 #038-41-2008 *012

SARANGA, Vita Paran. ■ 45219 #038-41-2008 *012

SAREMBOCK, Ian Jos. 2123 AUBURN AVE, STE 136 45219 #836-01-1975 L2007 CD IM *020 †20

SARGENT, Scott Lee. 7500 STATE RD 45255 #038-40-1983 L1986 PTH NR *020

SARIC, Amra. DEPT OF PHYS MED/REHAB, UNIV HOSPITAL-UNIV OF CINC 45267 #957-08-1987 L2000 PM *100 †60

SARKAR, Nibar Kumar. 5340 CLOVER LEAF LN 45239 #495-32-1961 L1972 **IM GE** *020 †20

SAUL, Thomas Glenn. 4020 SMITH RD 45209 #038-41-1974 **NS GS** *040 †25

SAUNDERS, Douglas Alan. 4750 E GALBRAITH RD, STE 207 45236 #038-41-1987 L1989 **IM** *020 †20

SAVAGE, Christopher Rober. ■ 45227 #038-45-2004 L2004 **OTO** *012

SAWNANI, Hemant. 3333 BURNET AVE # 2021, DIVISION OF PULMONARY MED 45229 #496-38-1996 L2007 **SME** *012 †55 ‡

SAWYER, William Procter. 11714 US ROUTE 42 45241 #038-41-1982 L1982 **FM** *020 †18

SAX, Sharon Ann. 5525 MARIE AVE 45248 #038-41-1987 L1989 **IM** *020 †20

SAXENA, Sydney Suresh. 3200 VINE ST, VA MEDICAL CENTER 45220 #020-12-1999 L2000 **IM** *100 †20

SCHAEN, Michael David. 3200 BURNET AVE 45229 #038-41-1965 L1965 **DR** *071 †80

SCHAENGOLD, Robert L. 55 PROGRESS PL 45246 #056-05-1986 L1994 **PD** *020 †55

SCHAFFIELD, Mark Jerome. ■ 45255 #020-12-1974 L1980 **EM** *020 †55,16

SCHAFFZIN, Joshua K. ■ 45229 #038-41-2002 L2002 **PD** *100

SCHAIBLE, Pamela Hughes. 1380 COMPTON RD 45231 #038-41-1993 L1995 **FM** *020 †18

SCHAINOST, Diane M. 7691 5 MILE RD, STE 215 45230 #048-02-1985 L1990 **OTO A** *020 †45

SCHANTZ, R Matthew. 311 STRAIGHT ST 45219 #038-40-1988 L1990 **AN** *020 †05

SCHAPIRO, Mark B. 3333 BURNET AVE, CHILDREN'S HOSP MED CTR 45229 #047-06-1976 L2000 **N PD** *020 †55,75

SCHAROLD, Frank J, Jr. ■ 45248 #038-41-1953 L1953 **ADM FM** *071 †18

SCHAUER, Daniel Patrick. 231 ALBERT SABIN WAY, ML 0535 45267 #038-41-1999 L1999 **IM** *020 †20

SCHEIBER, Michael David. 3805 EDWARDS RD STE 450 45209 #005-02-1990 L1996 **OBG** *020 †30

SCHELER, Jennifer Lynn. 234 GOODMAN ST 0761, OF C 45267 #020-02-2000 L2000 **NR** *100 †80

SCHELLER, Chad Douglas. 3200 BURNET AVE, JEWISH HOSP OF CINCINNATI 45229 #422-01-2006 **GS** *012

SCHELLHAS, Helmut F G. 3219 CLIFTON AVE, STE 225 45220 #407-05-1959 L1971 **GO OBG** *020 †30

SCHIFF, Gilbert Martin. 3333 BURNET AVE, CH 1 RM 1337 45229 #038-41-1957 L1958 **IM ID** *050

SCHIFF, Robert Cleveland. 4370 MALSBARY RD, PEDIATRIC ASSOC OF 45242 #038-41-1981 L1982 **PD** *020 †55

SCHIFFER, Renate J. 415 STRAIGHT ST 45219 #409-10-1962 L1974 **IM PUD** *020

SCHLAUDECKER, Elizabeth P. 3333 BURNET AVE, CINCINNATI CHILDREN'S HOSP 45229 #038-41-2003 L2003 **PD** *100 †15

SCHLAUDECKER, Jeffrey D. 1295 KEMPER MEADOW DR, UNIVERSITY FAMILY PHYSICIA 45240 #038-41-2003 L2003 **FPG** *100 †18

SCHLOSS, Edward Janszen. 2123 AUBURN AVE, STE 136 45219 #016-06-1989 L1995 **ICE CD** *020 †20

SCHLUETER, David Edward. 9500 KENWOOD RD 45242 #038-41-1975 L1975 **FM OM** *020 †18

SCHLUETER, Elmer. 10500 MONTGOMERY RD 45242 #038-41-1948 L1948 **FM** *071 †18

SCHLUETER, Francis J. 375 DIXMYTH AVE, DEPT OF RADIOLOGY 45220 #038-41-1990 L1996 **VIR** *020 †20

SCHMELTZER, Paul Andrew. 234 GOODMAN ST, UH/UCCOM 45219 #010-02-2003 L2007 **IM** *012 †20

SCHMERLER, Michael. 10550 MONTGOMERY RD, STE 33 45242 #016-06-1973 L1977 **N** *020 †20,75 ‡

SCHMID, Rita Ann. ■ 45209 #017-20-2006 L2006 **IM** *012

SCHMIDT, Carl Jacob. 10500 MONTGOMERY RD 45242 #020-02-1964 L1965 **OM FM** *071

SCHMIDT, Marlene J. 8000 5 MILE RD STE 21 45230 #038-41-1986 L1988 **CHP P** *020 †75

SCHMIDT, Richard Thos F. 724 LAFAYETTE AVE 45220 #038-41-1943 L1944 **OBG** *071 †30

SCHMIDT, Rosemary Estelle. 3300 ELLAND AVE, CHILDRENS HOSPITAL 45229 #028-34-1956 L1957 **PD** *071 †55

SCHMIDT, Thomas Edmund. 500 E BUSINESS WAY 45241 #038-41-1987 L1991 **AN** *020 †05

SCHMITT, Christopher B. 2123 AUBURN AVE, STE 401 45219 #038-41-1998 L1999 **PCC** *020 †20

SCHMITT, Philip John. 3200 VINE ST, MEDICAL CENTER 45220 #028-02-1979 L1995 **IM** *020 †85,20

SCHMITZ, Elizabeth Ann. ■ 45247 #038-41-2008 *012

SCHMULEWITZ, Nathan. 231 ALBERT SABIN WAY, ML-0595 45267 #035-01-1996 L2005 **GE** *020 †20

SCHNEEBERGER, Eric W. 231 ALBERT SABIN WAY, P O BOX 670558 45267 #836-02-1980 L2000 **TS** *020

SCHNEIDER, David Brian. 2139 AUBURN AVE 45219 #020-12-2001 L2001 **IM** *100

SCHNEIDER, Eli Irwin. ■ 45242 #038-41-1952 L1952 **GP OBG** *072

SCHNEIDER, Giselle Martin. 3333 BURNET AVE, MEDICAL CENTER 45229 #020-02-2000 L2003 **ADL** *100 †55 ‡

SCHNEIDER, Harold Joel. ■ 45226 #038-41-1947 L1947 **R** *071 †80

SCHNEIDER, Jeffrey Lee. 9403 KENWOOD RD, STE D203 45242 #038-41-1984 L1987 **IM IMG** *020 †20

SCHNEIDER, Margaret J. 311 STRAIGHT ST 45219 #038-41-1940 **GP** *071

SCHNEIDER, Thomas Jay. 4760 E GALBRAITH RD # 111 45236 #038-43-1982 L1990 **PUD IM** *020 †20

SCHNETZER, Joann Renee. ■ 45208 #018-03-2004 L2004 **IM** *100

SCHNUR, Walter. ■ 45231 #143-02-1955 L1957 **FM FPG** *071

SCHONFELD, David J. 3333 BURNET AVE, M.L.C. 4002 45229 #024-05-1983 L2005 **PD** *050 †55

SCHOOLFIELD, Lydia Ruth. ■ 45208 #038-43-1990 L1992 **EM** *020 †12

SCHOR, David Pineles. 3333 BURNET AVE, DEV BEHAVIORAL PEDS-CCHMC 45229 #038-06-1975 L1978 **PHP PD** *020 †55 ‡

SCHORR, David Michael. 1219 MORTS PASS 45215 #051-04-1998 L2003 **EM** *020

SCHORR, Martin Richard. 2139 AUBURN AVE 45219 #038-41-1961 L1961 **AN** *071 †05

SCHORRY, Elizabeth Kolks. 3333 BURNET AVE 45229 #025-01-1982 L1985 **PD MG** *020 †19,55

SCHOTT, Louis Jos. 2055 READING RD, STE 210 45202 #038-40-1986 L1992 **OPH** *020 †35

SCHRAGER, Jeffrey Andrew. 231 ALBERT SABIN WAY 45267 #032-01-1990 L2005 **HMP** *020 †50

SCHRAND, Mark Edward. 330 STRAIGHT ST, STE 210 45219 #038-45-1985 L1986 **IM** *020 †20

SCHREIBER, J Tracy. 231 BETHESDA AVE, M L 0529 45229 #028-34-1958 L1961 **TS** *071 †85,90

SCHREINER, Albert W, III. 2139 AUBURN AVE 45219 #038-41-1949 L1949 **IM HEM** *072 †20

SCHRICHTEN, James Edward. ■ 45202 #038-41-1997 L1998 **EM** *020 †16

SCHRIMPF, Thomas Michael. 5630 BRIDGETOWN RD STE 4 45248 #016-43-1977 L1978 **OTO FPS** *020 †45 ‡

SCHRODER, John Raymond. 2139 AUBURN AVE, THE CHRIST HOSPITAL 45219 #038-41-1987 L1988 **IM** *020 †20

SCHROER, Melissa Lynne. 5314 DELHI AVE, STE 1 45238 #020-02-1991 L1994 **FM** *020 †18

SCHUBERT, Charles John. 333 BURNET AVE 45229 #038-41-1983 L1985 **PD** *020 †55

SCHUBERT, William K. 3333 BURNET AVE 45229 #038-41-1952 L1952 **PD GE** *071 †55

SCHUERMANN, Jill E. 2123 AUBURN AVE, STE A28 45219 #020-12-1992 L1993 **IM** *020 †20

SCHUERMANN, Matthew G. 6239 CHEVIOT RD 45247 #038-41-1992 L1993 **IM** *020 †20

SCHULER, Jeffrey Michael. 375 DIXMYTH AVE 45220 #038-41-1984 L1987 **OM GPM** *020 †70

SCHULTZ, Raymond Aubrey. 5340 RAPID RUN RD 45238 #038-41-1975 L1976 **OPH** *020 †35

SCHURDAK, Robert Jos A. 11317 SPRINGFIELD PIKE 45246 #038-41-1959 L1959 **FM** *071

SCHUTTE, Teresa June. 2139 AUBURN AVE 45219 #038-43-1994 L1997 **OBG** *020 †30

SCHWAB, Louis. 5725 DRAGON WAY, STE 105 45227 #024-01-1944 L1953 **PD OS** *071 †55

SCHWARTZ, Bernard Robt. 4700 SMITH RD 45212 #021-01-1982 L1982 **U** *020 †95

SCHWARTZ, David Bruce. 10506 MONTGOMERY RD, STE 204 45242 #025-01-1978 L1979 **OBG** *020 †30

SCHWARTZ, David Coleman. 3300 ELLAND AVE # CARD, CHILDRENS HOSPITAL 45229 #038-41-1961 L1961 **PDC PD** *071 †55

SCHWARTZ, Hamilton Parker. 3333 BURNET AVE, CHILDREN'S HOSPITAL MED CE 45229 #041-02-1999 L1999 **PEM** *100 †55

SCHWARTZ, Martin. 151 W GALBRAITH RD 45216 #035-09-1975 L1985 **IM IMG** *020 †20

SCHWARTZ, Steven Michael. 3333 BURNET AVE, CHILDRENS HOSP MED CTR 45229 #025-07-1988 L1996 **PDC** *020 †55

SCHWEITZER, Edmund H. 2100 SHERMAN AVE, STE 105 45212 #038-41-1972 L1972 **ORS** *020 †40

SCHWEMLEIN, George Alan. 7300 BEECHMONT AVE 45230 #038-41-1975 L1975 **GYN** *071 †30

SCHWETSCHENAU, Eric L. 11135 MONTGOMERY RD 45249 #038-41-1996 L2001 **OTO** *020 †45 ‡

SCHWETSCHENAU, Paul Robt. 10550 MONTGOMERY RD, STE 33 45242 #028-34-1967 L1975 **NS** *020 †25

SCOTT, Christopher Dean. ■ 45206 #051-01-2007 L2007 **GS** *012

SCOTT, David Adam. ■ 45219 #017-20-2007 L2007 **IM** *012

SCOTT, Ian. 6048 LOCKARD AVE 45230 #352-07-1950 L1967 **OS CD** *030

SCOTT, Mark Jos. 2123 AUBURN AVE, STE 401 45219 #038-40-1986 L1992 **CCM** *020 †20

SCURRY, Mia Lynn. 3333 BURNET AVE, ML 5018 45229 #041-12-1994 L1998 **PEM** *020 †55

SEAMAN, Danielle Marie. ■ 45226 #038-06-2005 L2005 **DR** *012

SEDACCA, Carl Meyer. 10600 MONTGOMERY RD, STE 200 45242 #038-41-1955 L1955 **GE IM** *072

SEGAL, Joseph Jay. 151 W GALBRAITH RD 45216 #017-20-1976 L1976 **IM ID** *040 †20

SEGHAL, Mandi M. 3306 RUTHER AVE 45220 #001-06-2001 L2004 **FPG** *020 †18

SEHGAL, Nirmala. 800 COMPTON RD 45231 #496-07-1974 L1983 **FM** *020 †18

SEIBERT, Joseph John. 672 NEEB RD 45233 #038-41-1998 L1999 **FM** *020 †18

SEILSTAD, Kay Helen. 9670 KENWOOD RD 45242 #049-01-1987 L2004 **DMP PCP** *020 †50

SEIWERT, Vincent Jos. 2446 KIPLING AVE 45239 #038-41-1944 L1944 **CD NM** *071 †28

SEKAR, Priya. ■ 45206 #016-42-2002 L2005 **PDC** *012

SELIGMAN, Roslyn. 231 ALBERT SABIN WAY, P O BOX 670559 45267 #012-01-1961 L1964 **P CHP** *040 †75

SELLARS, Elizabeth Ann. ■ 45227 #004-01-2007 L2007 **PMG** *012

SELTZER, David Alan. 3520 ARBORCREST CT 45236 #038-41-1974 L1975 **P** *020 †75

SELTZER, Kimberly A. 2001 ANDERSON FERRY RD 45238 #038-40-1993 L1995 **IM** *020 †20

SELZER, Jack D. 10495 MONTGOMERY RD, STE 26 45242 #038-41-1953 L1953 **PRO** *071

SEMERTZIDES, John N. 11147 MONTGOMERY RD, STE 200 45249 #418-02-1978 L1985 **GS** *020 †85

SENCHENKOV, Alex. ■ 45236 #913-05-1993 L2000 **PS HNS** *100 †85 ‡

SENSER, Kenneth David. 48 E HOLLISTER ST 45219 #038-41-1982 L1986 **P** *020

SERBER, Julia Frances. ■ 45209 #023-01-2008 *012

SEROTA, Gretchen Olympia. 619 OAK ST # 645 45206 #038-41-1993 L1994 **IMG** *020 †20

SERRONE, Joe. UNIV OF CINCINNATI, PO BOX 670515 45267 #028-46-2007 L2007 **NS** *012

SESHIAH, Puvinarayanan. 3219 CLIFTON AVE, STE 400 45220 #495-04-1995 L1999 **CD IC** *020 †20

SETHI, Hanish. 231 ALBERT SABIN WAY 45267 #495-30-1992 L2000 **P** *020 †75

SETLIK, Jennifer. 3333 BURNET AVE ML2008, CINCINNATI CHILDREN'S HOSP 45229 #016-11-2003 L2006 **PEM** *012 †55

SEVERYN, Edward Jan. 4044 MCLEAN DR, EASTERN CINTI IM SPECIALIS 45255 #028-34-1980 L1983 **IM** *020 †20

SEWARD, Thomas Gordon. 10550 MONTGOMERY RD, STE 15 45242 #038-41-1981 L1982 **R** *020 †80

SHA, Edward Chihchou. 3219 CLIFTON AVE STE 325 45220 #016-06-1997 L2003 **NEP IM** *020 †20 ‡

SHABBIR, Asim. 2450 KIPLING AVE, STE 204 45239 #704-02-1989 L1995 **PD** *020 †55

SHACKLEFORD, April Michel. ■ 45255 #055-01-2005 L2005 **EM** *012

SHACKSON, James Brian. 619 OAK ST, 6TH FLOOR SOUTH, #657 45206 #038-44-1988 L1991 **PYG P** *020 †75

SHAFFER, Dorothy Peirce. 3836 READING RD 45229 #038-06-1993 L1996 **IM** *020 †20

SHAFFER, Kelly Lynne. UNIV OF CINCINNATI, PO BOX 670515 45267 #047-05-2007 L2007 **NS** *012

SHAFTEL, Lee David. 2841 BOUDINOT AVE, FREIBERG ORTHOPAEDIC AND 45238 #016-42-1975 L1976 **ORS** *020 †40

SHAH, Bhanukumar C. 311 STRAIGHT ST 45219 #496-38-1968 L1975 **GS DS** *020 †85

SHAH, Hassan Ali. 234 GOODMAN ST 45267 #704-25-2002 L2005 **OPH** *012

SHAH, Mahmud. 7502 GRIFFIN DR 45237 #704-01-1967 L1972 **IM ID** *020 †20

SHAH, Ojas Niranjan. 45267 #051-04-2007 L2007 **OTO** *012

SHAH, Poornima Bipin. ■ 45230 #495-22-1968 **PTH** *100

SHAH, Pushpa Nutan. 2100 SHERMAN AVE STE 115, VISITING PHYS ASSOC 45212 #495-22-1970 L1992 **IM** *020 †20

SHAH, Romin Bharat. 4777 E GALBRAITH RD 45236 #422-01-2004 L2005 **IM** *012

SHAH, Steven. 3012 GLENMORE AVE STE 106 45238 #495-01-1955 L1971 **OBG** *071 †30

SHAHBABIAN, Set. 3285 WESTBOURNE DR 45248 #517-01-1969 L1980 **NS** *020 †25

SHAHEEN, Mazen Hussein. 234 GOODMAN ST, INTERNAL MEDICINE DEPT 45219 #605-01-2003 L2004 **IM** *020 †20

SHAKKOTTAI, Padmanabha P. 2123 AUBURN AVE, STE 401 45219 #005-06-1999 L2006 **PCC** *020 †20

SHAKOOR, Tariq. 10600 MONTGOMERY RD, STE 200 45242 #704-02-1978 L1983 **GE HEP** *020 †20

SHANI, Hezekiah G P. 3120 BURNET AVE, STE 401 45229 #905-01-1970 L1986 **TS VS** *071 †85,90

SHANK, Reed Albert, III. 2123 AUBURN AVE, STE 108 45219 #038-41-1984 L1986 **U** *020 †95

SHANLEY, Dean John. 10550 MONTGOMERY RD, STE 15 45242 #041-77-1986, ▲ L1998 **DR** *020 †80

SHAPIRO, Robert Allan. 3333 BURNET AVE, CHILDREN'S HOSP MED CENTER 45229 #016-11-1979 L1984 **PD EM** *020 †55

SHARMA, Ramesh Chandra. 311 STRAIGHT ST, DEACONESS HOSPITAL 45219 #308-07-1981 L2003 **EM IM** *020

SHARMA, Yogesh. 2001 ANDERSON FERRY RD, GROUP HEALTH ASSOCIATES 45238 #495-45-1988 L2007 **IM** *020 †20

SHARP, Laura Ann. 7175 BEECHMONT AVE, CARE-FOREST HILLS 45230 #038-45-1996 L1997 **FM** *020 †18

SHARP, Susan Elizabeth. ■ 45236 #025-01-2001 L2002 **PDR** *100 †80

SHAUGHNESSY, Elizabeth A. 231 ALBERT SABIN WAY, ML # 0558 45267 #016-11-1985 L1997 **GS SO** *020 †85

SHAUGHNESSY, Erin Elizabe. 3333 BURNET AVE, CCHMC HOUSE STAFF OFC 45229 #036-07-2005 L2005 **PD** *012

SHAW, George Jerome, III. 231 ALBERT SABIN WAY, DEPT OF EMERGENCY MEDICINE 45267 #010-02-1997 L1998 **EM** *020 †16

SHAW, James Kent. 3001 HIGHLAND AVE STE F 45219 #038-41-1963 L1963 **P PYA** *071

SHAY, Brian Francis. 4700 SMITH RD 45212 #047-05-1997 L2003 **U** *020 †95

SHEA, Patrick John. 10506 MONTGOMERY RD, STE 504 45242 #025-01-1980 L1989 **CD IM** *020 †20

SHEATT, Mohammad Aiman. 10490 MONTGOMERY RD, STE 103 45242 #875-02-1997 L2005 **PCC** *020 †20

SHEETS, Warren Kaven. ■ 45208 #038-43-1981 **P** *100

SHEGOG, Don Roy. 791 E MCMILLAN ST 45206 #010-03-1968 L1970 **DR GP** *020

SHELDON, Curtis Allan. 3333 BURNET AVE 45229 #005-18-1976 L1986 **UP PDS** *020 †95,85

SHELDON, Murray B, Jr. ■ 45208 #036-07-1945 L1952 **CD IM** *020 †20

SHELY, Elizabeth Ann. 2915 CLIFTON AVE, GROUP HEALTH ASSOCIATES 45220 #025-07-1982 L1984 **PD PN** *020 †55

SHENAI, Ravindranath N. 10196 SPRINGFIELD PIKE 45215 #495-37-1958 L1972 **FM P** *071

SHENAI, Usha R. 10196 SPRINGFIELD PIKE 45215 #038-41-1988 L1990 **FM** *020 †18

SHENG, George Gang. 231 ALBERT SABIN WAY 05, OF CI 45267 #047-05-2002 L2002 **GS** *012

SHERIDAN, Rachel Miceli. 45243 #187-45-2001 L2004 **PTH** *012

SHERMAN, Kenneth Eliot. 231 ALBERT SABIN WAY, UNIV OF CINCINNATI MED CEN 45267 #010-01-1985 L1994 **GE IM** *050 †20

SHERMAN, Marc O. 222 PIEDMONT AVE STE 3400, UNIV REHABILITATION INC 45267 #048-04-1990 L1995 **PM** *020 †60

SHETH, Anita P. 3333 BURNET AVE, DEPT OF DERMATOLOGY-SEC 45229 #005-02-1986 L1993 **D** *020 †15

SHETH, Pranav B. 222 PIEDMONT AVE, STE 2300 45219 #038-41-1992 L1994 **D** *020 †15

SHETTY, Roshni. 3317 GLENMORE AVE 45211 #021-01-1998 L2000 **IM** *020 †20

SHETTY, Vishwanath M. 3317 GLENMORE AVE 45211 #495-37-1962 L1972 **IM OS** *020

SHIELDS, George Seamon. ■ 45246 #035-20-1952 L1961 **IMG IM** *071

SHIN, Thomas Woo. ■ 45267 #025-01-2003 L2003 **GS** *012

SHIPLEY, Ralph Taylor, III. 234 GOODMAN ST, STE 0054 45219 #035-45-1979 L1984 **DR** *040 †80

SHIZUKUDA, Yukitaka. ■ 45236 #572-53-1986 L2006 **CD** *020 †20

SHOCKLEY, John R. 2123 AUBURN AVE STE 520 45219 #038-45-1994 L1995 **IM GP** *020 †20

SHOLITON, Marilyn M Cohen. 3120 BURNET AVE STE 305 45229 #038-41-1961 L1961 **P OS** *020 †75

SHON, Alyssa Soyoung. 12127 CRESTFIELD CT 45249 #038-44-2007 **IM** *012

SHONFIELD, Lee Jules. 4422 CARVER WOODS DR 45242 #038-41-1971 **P CHP** *020 †75

SHONK, Richard Francis. 7440 WOOD MEADOW DR, DR. RICHARD SHONK, MD 45243 #038-06-1978 L1979 **FM MDM** *030 †18

SHOTT, Sally Richard. 3333 BURNET AVE 2018, CHILDREN'S HOSP. MED. CTR. 45229 #038-41-1982 L1987 **OTO PDO** *020 †45

SHROFF, Neha Mahesh. ■ 45233 #047-05-2006 L2006 **EM** *100

SHUBECK, Frank. ■ 45241 #025-01-1953 L1975 **GYN P** *050 †30

SHUGAR, Michael Joseph. 1219 MORTS PASS 45215 #045-01-1995 L1997 **EM** *020 †16

SHUKLA, Aman. ■ 45267 #495-43-2001 L2004 **IM** *100

SHUKLA, Chittaranjanbhai. 3200 VINE ST 8TH FL 45220 #495-23-1978 L2000 **ADP** *020

SHUMRICK, Donald Albert. 222 PEIDMONT 5TH FLOOR 45267 #026-04-1957 L1966 **HNS OTO** *071 †45

SHUMRICK, Kathryn Klein. 2830 VICTORY PKWY, STE 100 45206 #038-41-1986 L1991 **DR NM** *020 †80

SHUMRICK, Kevin Albert. 231 ALBERT SABIN WAY, DEPT OF OTOLARYNGOLOGY 45267 #038-41-1979 L1985 **OTO FPS** *020 †45

SHUTTER, Lori Anne. 506 OAK ST, MAYFIELD CLINIC 45219 #012-05-1990 L2003 **N** *020 †75

SHYBUT, George Theodore. 6350 GLENWAY AVE 45211 #016-02-1976 L1989 **ORS OS** *020 †40

SIA, Arturo Lee. 7520 STATE RD 45255 #748-01-1972 L1985 **AN** *020

SIBAI, Baha'Uddin. 231 BETHESDA AVE, P O BOX 670526 45267 #605-01-1973 L2000 **MFM OBG** *020 †30

SIDDIQI, Sam. 375 DIXMYTH AVE, GOOD SAMARITAN HOSPITAL 45220 #035-09-2001 L2005 **OBG** *100

SIDDIQI, Tariq Ahmed. 2123 AUBURN AVE, STE 115 45219 #704-01-1975 L1981 **MFM OBG** *020 †30

SIDDIQUI, Anwer H. 10495 MONTGOMERY RD, INFECTIOUS DISEASE 45242 #704-02-1987 L1995 **ID** *020 †20

SIDDIQUI, Usman Ahmed. 2450 KIPLING AVE STE 10, SUITE 104 45239 #308-11-1984 L1995 **N OS** *020 †75

SIEBENALER, Jean Anne. 5420 N BEND RD, WESTERN FAMILY PHYSICIANS 45247 #056-05-1982 L1991 **FM PD** *020 †18

SIEGEL, Mark Girard. 3301 WESTBOURNE DR 45248 #024-05-1977 L1981 **ORS** *020 †40

SIEPLINGA, Kira Rae. 3333 BURNET AVE, CHILDREN's HOSPITAL 45229 #025-01-2004 L2005 **PD** *012

SIFRI, Edmond Gerasmus. 5914 GLENWAY AVE 45238 #605-01-1956 L1968 **PDA PD** *020 †55,03

SIFRI, George David. 425 FARRELL CT 45233 #038-40-1990 L1993 **IM** *020 †20

SIFRI, Michael David. 2745 ANDERSON FERRY RD 45238 #038-41-1991 L1996 **OPH** *020

SIKES, Clayton Reid, Jr. 2123 AUBURN AVE, STE 520 45219 #038-41-1947 L1947 **IM CD** *071 †20

SILBERSTEIN, Edward B. 234 GOODMAN ST STE G026, MONT REID PAVILION 45219 #024-01-1962 L1966 **ON NM** *020 †28,20

SILVER, David William. ■ 45209 #016-02-2007 L2007 **EM** *012

SILVERMAN, Deborah R. 3101 BURNET AVE 45229 #035-15-1977 L1982 **FM ADL** *020 †18

SILVERSTEIN, Irvin S. 900 ADAMS XING, STE 9200 45202 #038-41-1951 L1951 **GP** *020 †18

SIMAKAJORNBOON, Narong. 3333 BURNET AVE, DIV OF PULMONARY MEDICINE 45229 #891-02-1992 L2006 **PDP PD** *040 †55

SIMKO, Stephen James. 3333 BURNET AVE, MLC 11013 45229 #012-01-2004 L2007 **PD** *100 †55

SIMMONS, Jeffrey Michael. 3333 BURNET AVE, ML 2011 45229 #036-05-2000 L2000 **PD** *020 †20

SIMON, David Leo. 234 GOODMAN ST 45267 #038-41-1948 L1948 **IM CD** *071

SIMON, Gene Ayson. 5815 BRIDGETOWN RD 45248 #748-07-1955 L1967 **GP** *071

SIMON, Nancy Louise. 4350 MALSBARY RD, STE 208 45242 #025-01-1978 L1989 **GO** *020 †30

SIMPSON, Emily Mitchell. 10495 MONTGOMERY RD, STE 17 45242 #001-02-2002 L2008 **ID** *020 †20

SINGER, Leonard Joshua. 234 GOODMAN ST 45267 #035-09-1980 L1983 **MDM** *071 †65

SINGERMAN, Janice. 3001 HIGHLAND AVE, STE E 45219 #038-41-1977 L1978 **CHP IMG** *020 †18,75

SINGH, Anisha. 9200 MONTGOMERY RD, STE 3A 45242 #495-23-1995 L2000 **IM** *020 †20

SINGH, Jagdeep. 234 GOODMAN ST 45267 #539-06-2005 L2005 **IM** *012

SINGH, Kuldip K. 9200 MONTGOMERY RD, STE 16A 45242 #495-03-1967 L1976 **P** *020 †75

SINGH, Manpreet Kaur. 3333 BURNET AVE, C/O CHILDRENS HOSPITAL-MED 45229 #025-12-2002 L2002 **CPP** *012

SINGH, Navkaran Bhagwant. 6350 GLENWAY AVE, STE 205 45211 #038-40-1989 L1991 **OBG** *020 †30

SINGH, Priti Bosski. 3333 BURNET AVE, CO CHILDREN S HOSP-MED EDU 45229 #495-37-2000 L2003 **AN** *100

SINGH, Rajinder Pal. 3219 CLIFTON AVE, STE 400 45220 #495-29-1992 L2007 **ICE** *020 †20

SINGH, Ram Surat. 2446 KIPLING AVE 45239 #495-15-1958 L1972 **N IM** *020

SINGH, Sareena. ■ 45226 #038-41-2008 *012

SINGH, Satwant. 222 PIEDMONT AVE, STE 1200 45219 #495-03-1963 L1975 **NEP IM** *020 †20

SINGSTOCK, Brian David. 11490 SPRINGFIELD PIKE, SCROGGINS INFORMATION SERV 45246 #038-40-1999 L2000 **AN** *020 †05

SINHA, Arvind Kumar. 2139 AUBURN AVE, CHRIST HOSPMED EDUC DEPT 45219 #495-54-1975 L2000 **NM** *100

SINKFIELD, Brandi A. ■ 45246 #038-06-2007 L2007 **AN** *012

SIRKIN, Joseph. 3131 HARVEY AVE, STE 201 45229 #038-41-1962 L1962 **OTO A** *071 †45

SIVARUBAN, Kaveri. 8139 BEECHMONT AVE, THE ANDERSON 45255 #220-04-1994 L2003 **IM** *020 †20

SIVASUBRAMANIAM, Devaki. ■ 45219 #495-94-1995 L2005 **HO** *012

SKALE, Brian Taylor. 3219 CLIFTON AVE STE 400 45220 #038-41-1978 L1984 **CD** *020 †20

SKILLICORN, Brian Jeffrey. 5819 CHEVIOT RD 45247 #038-41-2000 L2001 **DR** *020 †80

SKUROW, Richard Howard. 752 WAYCROSS RD 45240 #012-05-1975 L1976 **OTO** *020 †45

SLAGLE, Kirby Marsh. 3200 VINE ST, ML113 45220 #038-41-1994 L1998 **PTH** *020 †50

SLAGLE, Robert Gordon. 10577 MONTGOMERY RD 45242 #038-40-1960 L1961 **PS** *071 †65

SLATTERY, Nancy Jo. 4010 N BEND RD STE 200 45211 #038-40-1993 L1996 **IM** *020 †20

SLAUGHTER, Jonathan Lee. 3333 BURNET AVE, DIVISION OF NEONATOLOGY 45229 #036-05-2004 L2007 **NPM** *012 †55

SLONE, Leah Ann. 8220 NORTHCREEK DR STE 110 45236 #020-12-1990 L1992 **CHP** *020 †75

SMALL, Jonathan. 8050 HOSBROOK RD STE 402 45236 #035-06-1977 L1979 **P N** *020 †75

SMITH, Andrew Michael. 231 ALBERT SABIN WAY 0, UNIV OF CINCINNATI, IMMUNO 45267 #016-06-2001 L2001 **AI** *100 †20,03

SMITH, Christopher Jay. 5535 MONTGOMERY RD 45212 #020-02-1988 L1990 **IM** *020 †20

SMITH, Corwin Mansell. 10494 MONTGOMERY RD 45242 #038-41-1964 L1964 **OPH OS** *020 †35

SMITH, Denise Renee. ■ 45241 #005-19-2004 L2004 **D** *012

SMITH, Edwin Townsend. 4623 WESLEY AVE STE P 45212 #038-41-1966 L1966 **IM CD** *020

SMITH, Emery Vernon. 8725 BLOME RD 45243 #038-41-1941 L1941 **IM CD** *071

SMITH, Eric Peter. 3300 ELLAND AVE, CHILDRENS HOSPITAL 45229 #036-07-1979 L1988 **PDE** *075

SMITH, Franklin O, III. 3333 BURNET AVE, HEMATOLOGY ONCOLOGY 45229 #045-04-1984 L2002 **PHO PD** *020 †55

SMITH, Helen M. 2139 AUBURN AVE 45219 #068-01-1958 L1964 **AN OS** *020

SMITH, Jason Aaron. 2454 KIPLING AVE STE G20, THE OHIO HEART & VASCULAR 45239 #038-41-1997 L1999 **CD** *020 †20

SMITH, Jennifer Marie. ■ 45236 #020-02-2007 L2007 **PD** *012

SMITH, John Michael. 4030 SMITH RD, CARDIAC VASCULAR & 45209 #020-02-1989 L1994 **TS** *020 †85,90

SMITH, Kelly J. 3333 BURNET AVE, CO CHILDREN S HOSP-MED EDU 45229 #048-13-2000 L2004 **PDP** *020

SMITH, Kenneth Lamont. 1219 MORTS PASS 45215 #045-01-1974 L1984 **EM** *020 †16

SMITH, Kurt Arnold. ■ 45230 #024-01-2005 L2005 **EM** *012

SMITH, Linda Jane. ■ 45231 #048-02-1967 L1972 **N** *020 †15

SMITH, Marsha Jean. 1413 LINN ST 45214 #025-01-1977 L1979 **GP** *020

SMITH, Michael Robt. 8000 5 MILE RD, STE 310 45230 #038-41-1969 L1969 **CD IM** *020 †20

SMITH, Peter James. 5400 KENNEDY AVE 45213 #143-02-1986 **DR** *020

SMITH, Robert. 231 BETHESDA AVE, U.C. COLLEGE OF MEDICINE 45267 #539-03-1945 L1976 **FM** *020

SMITH, Robert Clifton. 7691 5 MILE RD 45230 #038-41-1975 L1978 **IM** *020 †20

SMITH, Roger Dean. 234 GOODMAN ST, STE 0501 45219 #035-09-1958 L1972 **ATP ID** *040 †50

SMITH, Ronald Evolee, Jr. 55 PROGRESS PL, GROUP HEALTH ASSOCIATES 45246 #038-41-1996 L1997 **IM** *020 †20

SMITH, Victor Raeburn. 2475 W GALBRAITH RD, STE A 45239 #020-12-1972 L1973 **PD** *020 †55

SMITH, Wiley Rufus, Jr. 5400 EDALBERT DR, ST JOSEPH ORPHANAGE 45239 #021-01-1952 L1961 **CHP P** *030 †75

SMITH, William David. 5525 MARIE AVE 45248 #038-41-1985 L1987 **IM** *020 †20

SMOTHERS, Chandrea Darcel. 3333 BURNET AVE, DEPT OF RADIOLOGY 45229 #036-07-1995 L1999 **PDR** *020 †80

SMUCKER, Douglas Ronald. 1207 SPRINGFIELD PIKE 45215 #038-43-1984 L1985 **GPM** *020 †70,18

SMULIAN, Alan Geo. 3200 VINE ST, STE 111D 45220 #836-01-1980 L1990 **ID** *050 †20

SMYTH, Paul Gregory. 702 TWEED AVE 45226 #038-40-1999 L1999 **CN** *062 †75

SMYTH, Robert James. 2730 OBSERVATORY AVE 45208 #038-41-1973 L1974 **OTO FPS** *020 †45

SNOOK, Curtis Pendleton. 234 GOODMAN ST 769, DEPT OF EMERGENCY MEDICINE 45267 #035-01-1987 L1990 **ETX EM** *020

SNYDER, Mark Alan. 6350 GLENWAY AVE 45211 #038-41-1979 L1980 **ORS OAR** *020 †40

SNYDER, Richard Herschel. 231 ALBERT SABIN WAY, STE 6065 45267 #047-07-1979 L2007 **IM CCM** *020 †20

SO, Mathew Jeremiah. ■ 45219 #026-08-2007 L2007 **IM** *012

SOBANDE, Patrick Olamidot. 3333 BURNET AVE, MLC 2021 45229 #690-14-1997 L2005 **PDP** *012 †55

SOBEL, Lawrence Dean. 234 GOODMAN ST, STE 0054 45219 #038-40-1985 L1992 **DR IM** *020 †80

SOBOLEWSKI, Brad Andrew. ■ 45227 #041-12-2004 L2004 **PD** *012 †55

SOBOLEWSKI, Kerri Beth. ■ 45227 #038-41-2005 L2005 **PD** *012

SOBOLEWSKI, Thomas Paul. 500 E BUSINESS WAY 45241 #056-05-1993 L1996 **AN** *020 *05

SOCHACKI, Arthur Andrzej. 1101 SUMMIT RD, AND CSN SBH 45237 #759-10-1966 L1998 **P** *020 †75

SOHAIL, Samina. 2450 KIPLING AVE, STE 204 45239 #028-34-2000 L2000 **FM** *020

SOHN, Haekyon Roh. ■ 45220 #583-06-1952 L1971 **GP** *071

SOLAN, Patrick Donovan. ■ 45226 #035-06-2007 L2007 **GS** *012

SOLEIMANI, Manoocher. 231 ALBERT SABIN WAY, MEDICAL CENTER 45267 #517-05-1978 L1995 **NEP** *012

SOLER, Ximena. 3333 BURNET AVE, MLC 2001 45229 #264-04-1997 L2003 **PAN** *05

SOLIMAN, Peter Kamal Fara. 2139 AUBURN AVE, DEPT FM 45219 #915-02-2002 L2007 **FP** *012

SOLOMKIN, Joseph Sherman. 222 PIEDMONT AVE, STE 200 45219 #035-46-1970 L1981 **GS ID** *020 †85

SOMERA, Marta Fontanilla. ■ 45252 #748-07-1966 L1983 **AN GS** *020

SOMMERKAMP, T Greg. 10700 MONTGOMERY RD, STE 150 45242 #020-12-1985 L1995 **HS ORS** *020 †40

SOMOZA, Arthur David. 231 ALBERT WAY, DEPT OF PATHOLOGY 45267 #665-02-2006 L2006 **PTH** *012

SOMOZA, Eugene Cesar. 3200 VINE ST, VA MEDICAL CENTER 45220 #847-13-1980 L1984 **P** *020 †75

SOMOZA, Melinda F. 3200 VINE ST, CINCINNATI VA MEDICAL CENT 45220 #037-01-1997 L2006 **FM** *020 †18

SOMSAK, Denise Anne. 3333 BURNET AVE, ML 9011 45229 #038-40-1997 L1998 **PD** *020 †55

SONG, Hyun Min. ■ 45213 #035-09-1998 L2006 **DR** *020 †80

SONG, Richard Sung. ■ 45219 #016-11-2003 L2006 **GE** *012 †20

SONNIER, Dennis Irving, Jr. ■ 45209 #021-05-2007 L2007 **GS** *012

SONNIER, Loretta Ann. ■ 45209 #021-05-2006 L2006 **CPP** *012

SORGER, Joel Irwin. 6350 GLENWAY AVE 45211 #051-04-1991 L1993 **ORS** *020 †40

SORGER, Kathy Peccatiello. 3333 BURNET AVE, MAIL LOCATION 7009 45229 #051-04-1991 L1993 **PD** *020 †55

SOROKHAN, Vasyl. 2123 AUBURN AVE, CO FAMILY PRACTICE 45219 #913-86-1999 L2007 **FP** *012

SORSCHER, Jonathan Stuart. 4411 MONTGOMERY RD, STE 200 45212 #025-07-1990 L1991 **FM** *020

SORSCHER, Robert Brian. 119 RITCHIE AVE 45215 #038-41-1990 L1996 **CHP** *020 †75

SORTER, Michael Thos. 3333 BURNET AVE 45229 #038-41-1985 L1987 **CHP P** *020 †75

SOSNOWSKI, James Peter. 8221 CORNELL RD, STE 420 45249 #033-06-1992 L1993 **OBG** *020 †30

SOSTOK, Michael Anthony. 222 PIEDMONT AVE, STE 6000 45219 #041-02-1984 L1987 **IM** *020 †20

SOTOS, Michelle Ilya. 2915 CLIFTON AVE 45220 #759-04-1999 L2000 **IM** *020 †20

SOUTHALL, Lenzy Gerard. ■ 45237 #038-06-1982 L1984 **IM** *020

SOUTHAMMAKOSANE, Cathy An. 3333 BURNET AVE, CHILDRENS HOSP MED CTR 45229 #010-01-2007 L2007 **CPP** *012

SOUTULLO, Cesar A. 231 ALBERT SABIN WAY 45267 #847-04-1989 L1998 **CHP** *020

SPACCARELLI, Paul Anthony. 7721 MONTGOMERY RD 45236 #038-41-1966 L1966 **OBG** *020 †30

SPAEDY, Melanie Ann. 9070 WINTON RD 45231 #030-06-1985 L1988 **IM** *020 †20

SPAETH, James Philip. 3333 BURNET AVE 45229 #051-01-1993 L1998 **AN PAN** *020 †05

SPAETH, James Thos. 3333 BURNET AVE 45229 #038-40-1978 L1981 **PD** *020 †55

SPAIN, Jeffry Alan. 8060 MONTGOMERY RD STE 101 45236 #038-41-1979 L1989 **PME AN** *020 *05

SPANIER, Adam Jason. 3333 BURNET AVE 45229 #021-05-2000 L2000 **PD** *100 †55

SPANOS, Stephen Paul. ■ 45267 #020-02-2005 L2005 **AN** *012

SPARNALL, Jo Ann. 3200 VINE ST 45220 #038-41-2000 L2000 **IM** *020 †20

SPATA, Jennifer Ricer. ■ 45249 #038-41-2005 L2005 **FP** *012

SPAULDING, Abbot Gregory. 222 PIEDMONT AVE, STE 1500 45219 #028-34-1959 L1965 **OPH PTH** *071 †35

SPECKNER, Eric Edward. ■ 45209 #047-06-2006 L2006 **OPH** *012

SPELLMAN, Kathleen M. 3333 BURNET AVE 45229 #035-20-1943 L1961 **ADL** *072

SPICER, Robert Louis. 3333 BURNET AVE 45229 #016-01-1977 L1999 **PDC** *040 †55

SPIESS, Libbey Mary. 6350 GLENWAY AVE, STE 300 45211 #038-41-1992 L1993 **PD** *020 †55

SPIGARELLI, Michael G. 3333 BURNET AVE ML4000, DIV OF ADOLESCENT MEDICINE 45229 #025-01-1996 L2000 **MPD** *020 †20,55

SPINNATO, Joseph Anthony, II. 231 ALBERT SABIN WAY 45267 #020-02-1974 L2000 **MFM OBG** *020 †30

SPITZ, Harold Bernard. 234 GOODMAN ST, STE 0054 45219 #038-41-1956 L1956 **DR** *040 †80

SPONAUGLE, Jim Harper. 11490 SPRINGFIELD PIKE 45246 #055-01-1982 L2002 **AN** *020 †20,05

SPORE, Jan Wybesse. 4750 E GALBRAITH RD, STE 206 45236 #038-41-1979 L1982 **IM** *020 †20

SPREEN, Steven Arthur. 111 WELLINGTON PL, JOHN R BABCOCK 45219 #038-41-1968 L1968 **U** *071 †95

SRIKIATKHACHORN, Anon. 3333 BURNET AVE, OSB-3, CHMCC 45229 #891-03-1984 L1999 **AI PD** *050 †55,03

SRINIVASA, Mandyam K. 10260 ALLIANCE RD STE 160 45242 #495-33-1971 L1977 **AN** *020 *05

SRIVASTAVA, Adrash Kumar. ■ 45255 #038-45-2007 **MEM** *012

SRIVASTAVA, Amit. ■ 45216 #038-44-2002 L2002 **CD** *012 †20

SRIVASTAVA, Manish Girish. 9200 MONTGOMERY RD STE 3A 45242 #495-23-1992 L2000 **IMG** *020 †20

SRIVUTHANA, Keyrati. 3333 BURNET AVE, CHILDREN'S HOSPITAL MEDICA 45229 #891-01-1990 L1994 **PDE PD** *100 †55

SROGA, Julie Marie. ■ 45213 #038-45-2003 L2006 **OBG** *012

STAAT, Mary Allen. 3333 BURNET AVE, DIV OF INFECTIOUS DISEASES 45229 #020-12-1986 L1995 **GPM** *020 †70,55

STACHOWICZ, Rafal Zbignie. ■ 45219 #038-41-2007 L2007 **ORS** *012

STACKPOLE, Kristin M. 3333 BURNET AVE, CINCINNATI CHILDRENS HOSPI 45229 #023-01-1999 L1999 **PD** *020 †55

STADLER, Laura Patricia. 3333 BURNET AVE MLC5019, CINCINNATI CHILDREN'S HOSP 45229 #020-02-2000 L2003 **PDI** *020 †55 ‡

STADNIK, John Clifton. 1219 MORTS PASS 45215 #025-07-1992 L1995 **EM** *020 †16

STAEHLING, Dawn Danielle. 415 GREENWELL AVE, QUALIFIED EMERGENCY SPECIA 45238 #038-45-2003 L2006 **EM** *020 †16

STAGAMAN, Joseph Harry. ■ 45242 #028-34-1948 L1950 **FM** *071 †18

STAGAMAN, Martha Mary. 10498 MONTGOMERY RD, STE H 45242 #038-41-1997 L1998 **IM** *020 †20

STAHL, Donna Laura. 4850 RED BANK RD, DONNA STAHL MD INC 45227 #018-03-1971 L1973 **GS** *020 †85

STALETS, Erika Lynn. 3333 BURNET AVE ML2005 45229 #016-45-2001 L2006 **CCP** *012 †20,55

STAMATIS, Tom Alex. ■ 45220 #038-41-2008 *012

STAMLER, Eric Franklin. 6350 GLENWAY AVE STE 205 45211 #038-41-1985 L1988 **OBG** *020 †30

STANDLEY, Jeffrey Clay. 5819 CHEVIOT RD, STE B 45247 #038-41-1978 L1983 **DR** *020 †80

STANEK, Jerzy W. 234 GOODMAN ST 45219 #759-01-1968 L1994 **PTH** *020 †50

STANFIELD, Denver Thos. 6350 GLENWAY AVE 45211 #038-41-1985 L1989 **ORS OSM** *020 †40

STANFORD, Sharon L. 222 PIEDMONT AVE, STE 8 45219 #038-41-1999 L2000 **FM P** *020 †18,75

STANISIC, Slobodan Milan. 10506 MONTGOMERY RD 45242 #017-20-1995 L1996 **HO** *020 †20

STATHAM, Melissa Mc Carty. ■ 45208 #020-02-2003 L2003 **OTO** *012

STATILE, Angela M. ■ 45230 #051-07-2006 L2006 **PD** *012

STATILE, Christopher Jose. ■ 45230 #051-07-2006 L2006 **PD** *012

STATMAN, Norman Marvin. ■ 45241 #038-41-1957 L1957 **IM** *020 †20

STATTON, Jeremy Oneal. 4701 CREEK RD, STE 110 45242 #020-02-2003 L2007 **ORS** *012

STAUBACH, Lawrence B, II. ■ 45242 #038-41-1981 L1982 **PHM OS** *062

STAUBACH, Rebecca Lynn. ■ 45242 #038-41-2007 **EM** *012

STAVA, Michael William. NEURORADIOLOGY FELLOWSHIP, THE UNIV HOSP 45267 #020-12-1996 L2007 **RNR** *012 †16,80

STEELE, John Lewis. 1701 LLANFAIR AVE, # 227 45224 #038-41-1946 L1946 **FM** *071

STEELE, Paul Edward. 234 GOODMAN ST, UNIVERSITY HOSPITAL 45267 #028-46-1978 L1988 **CLP** *020 †50

STEFFEN, Michelle Marie. 3333 BURNET AVE, DIVISION OF EMERGENCY MEDI 45229 #020-02-2001 L2001 **PD** *020 †55

STEFFEN, Timothy Howard. 7175 BEECHMONT AVE, CARE-FOREST HILLS 45230 #038-41-2000 L2000 **FM** *020 †20

STEGMAN, Bryan Keith. 6145 SHEED RD 45247 #038-41-1991 L1995 **GS** *071 †85

STEHR, Wolfgang. ■ 45227 #409-19-1997 L2002 **GS** *012

STEICHEN, Jean J. 231 ALBERT SABIN WAY, PO 670541 45267 #396-06-1968 L1977 **NPM PD** *050 †55

STEIN, Debra Michelle. 7888 MITCHELL FARM LN 45242 #035-03-1995 L2001 **PD** *020 †55

STEIN, Evan Albert. 4685 FOREST AVE, STE B 45212 #836-01-1970 L1977 **CD CLP** *050

STEIN, Judith Nan. ■ 45208 #024-01-1979 L1980 **DR** *071 †80

STEIN, Robert Alan. 3020 BURNET AVE 45219 #038-41-1947 L1947 **IM** *020

STEINBERG, Scott Hymson. 11238 CORNELL PARK DR 45242 #020-02-1992 L1995 **PD** *020 †55

STEINBERG, Stuart Allen. 10496 MONTGOMERY RD, STE 104 45242 #038-41-1970 L1972 **CD IM** *020 †20

STEINBRUNNER, Erin Marie. ■ 45229 #038-41-2007 *012

STEINEGGER, Cathleen M. 3333 BURNET AVE, CHILDREN'S HOSPITAL MED CT 45229 #030-05-1998 L1999 **ADL** *100 †55

STEINER, John Clifton. ■ 45255 #041-02-1965 L1966 **N FM** *071 †75

STEINHOFF, Mark C. 3333 BURNET AVE, MLC 5041 45229 #016-02-1973 L1976 **PD ID** *050 †55

STEINKAMP, Steven L. 7520 STATE RD 45255 #038-41-1985 L1987 **AN** *020 *05

STEINMETZ, Ryan Daniel. 2452 KIPLING AVE 45239 #038-41-2002 L2002 **RO** *020

STELLA, Caroline. 2830 VICTORY PKWY, STE 140 45206 #748-08-1995 L2005 **OBG** *020

STEMMERMANN, Grant N. 234 GOODMAN ST 45219 #067-01-1943 L1992 **ATP OS** *072 †50

STEPHANIDES, Steven Louis. 234 GOODMAN ST, STE 0769 45219 #024-01-1998 L1999 **EM** *020 †16

STEPHENS, Gregory Wm. 2123 AUBURN AVE STE 404 45219 #020-12-1979 L1986 **NEP IM** *020 †20

STEPHENS, Gretel C. 3159 EDEN AVE 45219 #047-06-1974 L2005 **FOP PTH** *020 †50 ‡

STEPHENS, Lorraine Ann. 4411 MONTGOMERY RD, STE 200 45212 #038-45-1989 L1991 **FM** *020 †18

STEPHENS, Walter Kenneth. 2751 O'VARSITY WAY RM 339C, UNIV HEALTH SERVICES 45221 #017-20-1974 L1975 **OM OS** *020 †70

STERN, David Mark. 231 ALBERT SABIN WAY 45267 #024-01-1978 L2006 **HEM** *020 †20

STERN, Kathleen Shirley. ■ 45236 #024-01-1978 L2006 **OPH** *020 †35

STERN, Peter Joseph. 231 ALBERT SABIN WAY, UC COLLEGE OF MEDICINE 45267 #028-02-1970 L1978 **ORS HS** *062 †40

STERNFELD, David Charles. 231 BETHESDA AVE 45267 #038-41-1999 L1999 **EM** *020 †16

STETTLER, Brian Arthur. 231 ALBERT SABIN WAY, DEPT OF EMERGENCY MEDICINE 45267 #038-40-2000 L2000 **EM** *020 †16

STEVENS, Justin Dale. ■ 45239 #038-41-2008 *012

STEVENSON, Richard Jean. 2222 BURNET AVE, CHILDREN'S HOSP MED CTR 45219 #038-41-1973 L1973 **PDS** *020 †85

STEVENSON, Stefanie Lynn. 2415 AUBURN AVE, NEIGHBORHOOD HEALTH CARE 45219 #023-07-1998 L1999 **FM** *020 †20

STEWART, Cheryl Ann. 234 GOODMAN ST, STE 0054 45219 #041-07-1975 L1980 **DR RNR** *020 †80

STEWART, Douglas Paul. 3155 GLENDALE MILFORD RD, CINCINNATI EVENDALE SURG 45241 #038-06-1987 L1987 **AN** *020 †05

STEWART, Gary Lawrence. 151 W GALBRAITH RD, STE 2100 45216 #038-41-1993 L1994 **IM** *020 †60

STEWART, James Paul. 4472 W 8TH ST 45238 #038-41-1954 L1954 **IM** *071

STEWART, Robert L. ■ 45208 #017-20-1944 L1961 **PYA P** *072

STEWART, Terri Lee. 2123 AUBURN AVE, STE 136 45219 #038-44-1990 L1992 **CD** *020 †20

ST GEORGE, Elmer Chas. 24 COMPTON RD, E C SAINT GEORGE JR 45216 #028-34-1957 L1961 **GP** *071 †18

STIENE, Henry Albert. 6480 HARRISON AVE, SPORTS MEDICINE 45247 #038-41-1986 L1987 **IM ISM** *020 †20

STIENS, Jean C. ■ 45220 #038-41-1959 L1959 **P GPM** *071

STILZ, Richard John. 3155 GLENDALE MILFORD RD, CINCINNATI EVENDALE SURG 45241 #017-20-1974 L1977 **AN** *020 †05

STINEHELFER, Susan Estell. ■ 45206 #036-01-2005 L2005 **D** *012

STINGER, Randolph Charles. 7124 MIAMI AVE 45243 #038-41-1981 L1982 **OBG** *020 †30

STONER, Theodore R, Jr. 4812 VINE ST STE 303 45217 #038-41-1961 L1961 **AN** *071 †05

STOOPS, Jean Todd. ■ 45215 #017-20-1942 L1942 **GP DR** *071

STORROW, Alan Bruce. 231 ALBERT SABIN WAY, UNIVERSITY OF CINCINNATI 45267 #038-41-1989 L1990 **EM** *050 †16

STORRS, Bruce G. 375 DIXMYTH AVE, GOOD SAMARITAN HOSP 45220 #021-01-1984 L1993 **PTH HMP** *020 †50

STRADER, Bryan Philip. 10498 MONTGOMERY RD, STE A 45242 #020-12-1998 L1999 **IM** *020 †20

STRAIT, Richard Thos. 3333 BURNET AVE 7038, DIV OF EMERGENCY MED 45229 #038-41-1989 L1991 **PEM** *050 †15

STRAKOWSKI, Stephen M. 231 ALBERT SABIN WAY 45267 #047-05-1988 L1992 **P** *050 †75

STRASSER, Edward S. 2852 BOUDINOT AVE, STE 203 45238 #038-41-1948 L1948 **GS CD** *071 †85

STRASSER, Marcie Diane. 8250 WINTON RD, STE 103 45231 #035-08-1988 L1989 **PD** *020 †55

STRAUSBAUGH, Steve. 3130 HIGHLAND AVE, STE 0557 45219 #038-40-1996 L2000 **PCC** *020 †20

STRAUSS, Edmund. 375 DIXMYTH AVE 45220 #154-07-1953 L1956 **IM** *071

STRAYER, Jonathan Robt. 151 W GALBRAITH RD, STE 2100 45216 #038-41-1988 L2003 **PM** *020 †60

STRETCHER, Denise M. 4360 COOPER RD STE 200 45242 #038-45-1991 L1992 **FM** *020 †18

STRICK, Susan Renee. 6350 GLENWAY AVE, STE 300 45211 #038-41-1994 L1996 **PD** *020 †55

STRIET, Jeffrey Thomas. ■ 45233 #038-40-2006 L2006 **IM** *012

STRIET, Stephanie Locaput. 5680 BRIDGETOWN RD 45248 #038-41-2002 L2002 **IM** *020 †18

STRIFE, Janet R Lang. 3333 BURNET AVE 5031 45229 #033-05-1968 L1973 **PDR CD** *020 †80

STRIKE, Holly. 3333 BURNET AVE 45229 #038-41-2003 L2006 **NPM** *012 †55

STRIKER, Theodore. 3333 BURNET AVE, MED CENTER/DEPT OF ANESTH 45229 #038-41-1962 L1962 **AN** *020 †05

STROHM, Angelika. 3333 BURNET AVE, CO CHILDREN S HOSP-MED EDU 45229 #409-36-1997 L2003 **PAN** *020 †05

STRONG, Maria Adele. 3200 VINE ST 45220 #035-08-1954 L1968 **R** *020 †80

STRUB, Robert John. 2139 AUBURN AVE, THE CHRIST HOSPITAL 45219 #038-41-1972 L1972 **OBG MDM** *020 †30

SUAREZ, Guillermo M. ■ 45208 #016-42-2007 L2007 **EM** *012

SUBAUSTE, Carlos Jorge. 231 BETHESDA AVE, P O BOX 670560 45267 #737-06-1983 L1997 **IM** *020 †20

SUCHOCKI, Andrew Gary. ■ 45202 #038-40-2006 L2006 **FP** *012

SUCHOSKI, Anthony Joseph. 375 DIXMYTH AVE 45220 #748-15-2000 L2005 **FP** *012

SUDARSHAN, Gururau. 8261 CORNELL RD, STE 630 45249 #495-45-1981 L1996 **AN** *020 †05

SUDER, Garfield Louis. ■ 45255 #038-06-1946 L1946 **PHP** *071 †95

SUGARMAN, Sigmund Robt. 2123 AUBURN AVE, STE 108 45219 #038-41-1968 L1968 **U** *020 †95

SUH, Andrew Dong. ■ 45241 #025-01-2005 L2008 **AN** *012

SUKIN, Craig Alan. 3219 CLIFTON AVE STE 400, CARDIOLOGY ASSOC.OF CINTI, 45220 #036-07-1988 L1997 **CD** *020 †20

SULLIVAN, Denise Leanne. 3333 BURNET AVE, DEPT OF ANESTHESIA 45229 #048-12-2003 L2007 **PAN** *012

SULLIVAN, John Jos. 11135 MONTGOMERY RD 45249 #038-41-1989 L1990 **OBG** *020

SULLIVAN, Raymond James. 7520 STATE RD 45255 #035-15-1985 L1988 **AN** *020 †05

SULTAN, Tariq. 5920 COLERAIN AVE 45239 #704-02-1987 L1997 **IM** *020 †20

SUMIDA, Suzanne H. 8260 NORTHCREEK DR STE 380 45236 #038-41-1995 L1996 **CHP** *020 †75

SUMME, Christopher Louis. 311 STRAIGHT ST, BETHESDA NORTH HOSPITAL 45219 #020-02-1977 L1996 **GS FM** *020 †18

SUMME, Robert Bernard. 2123 AUBURN AVE 45219 #020-02-1991 L1995 **RO** *020 †80

SUN, Andrew Yuanmin. 2915 CLIFTON AVE 45220 #243-58-1985 L2000 **IM** *020 †20

SUNA, Lester Ellis. 2123 AUBURN AVE, STE 624 45219 #038-06-1983 L1983 **CD** *020 †20

SUNDARARAJAN, Vanitha. UNIV OF CINCINNATI MED CTR, DEPT OF PATHOLOGY 45267 #496-32-1993 L2001 **PTH** *100 †10

SUNTAY, Alfredo Soco. 375 DIXMYTH AVE 45220 #748-01-1953 L1972 **FM** *020 †18

SUNTAY, Priscila Jacinto. 3200 BURNET AVE 45229 #748-01-1954 L1976 **AN** *020

SURDULESCU, Victoria. 222 PIEDMONT AVE, STE 6000 45219 #781-01-1992 L1996 **PCC SME** *020 †20

SUSKIND, Raymond Robt. COLL OF MED KETTERING LAB 45267 #035-08-1943 L1949 **OM D** *071 †15

SUSMAN, Jeffrey Louis. 1207 SPRINGFIELD PIKE 45215 #032-01-1981 L1999 **FM FPG** *020 †18

SUSSMAN, Jeffrey Jay. 3200 VINE ST, SURGERY OFFICE, VAMC CINCI 45220 #005-14-1988 L1997 **SO GS** *020 †20

SUTHERELL, Jamie Scott. ■ 45208 #038-43-2002 L2006 **PDC** *012 †55

SUTHERLAND, Betty Steele. 3300 ELLAND AVE, CHILDRENS HOSPITAL 45229 #041-01-1950 L1956 **PD OS** *071 †55

SUTHERLAND, James M. ■ 45208 #016-02-1950 L1956 **PD** *071 †55

SUTLER, Denise Weathers. 6350 GLENWAY AVE, STE 205 45211 #020-02-1998 L1999 **OBG** *020 †30

SUTTON, Mary E. 3333 BURNET AVE, NEUROLOGY, MLC 2015 45229 #035-45-1989 L1997 **CHN** *020 †55,75 ‡

SUTTON, Steven A. 10597 MONTGOMERY RD, STE 200 45242 #048-12-1998 L1999 **AI** *020 †55,03

SWANK, Michael Lawson. 2841 BOUDINOT AVE, FREIBERG ORTHOPAEDIC AND 45238 #016-06-1987 L1993 **ORS** *020 †40

SWANSON, Patrick Gale. 9200 MONTGOMERY RD, STE C11AA 45242 #016-11-1988 L1989 **CHP P** *020 †75

SWARTZEL, Robert Lee, Jr. 2825 BURNET AVE, STE 422 45219 #038-41-1977 L1979 **PM** *020 †60

SWAY, Daniel Henry. 6540 WINTON RD 45224 #038-41-1968 L1968 **FM** *020

SWEATT, Hemella Lydia. 9844 REDHILL DR 45242 #010-03-1991 L1998 **D** *020 †50

SWEENEY, Christopher D. 10475 READING RD, STE 209 45241 #025-07-1978 L1981 **FM** *020 †18

SWEENEY, Gregory Dean. 7500 STATE RD, ATTN DEPT OF MEDICAL AFFAI 45255 #020-12-1987 L2003 **EM** *020 †18,16

SWEENEY, Paul David. 1634 CENTRAL PKWY 45202 #038-41-1957 L1957 **IM DIA** *071 †20

SYED, Aitizaz Uddin. 3333 BURNET AVE, CHILDRENS' HOSP/CARDIOTHOR 45229 #704-24-1986 L2001 *100

SYFERT, Sandra Marie. 5 E LIBERTY ST 45202 #038-41-1992 L2001 **FM** *020 †18

SYLVIA, Frederic Roger, Jr. ■ 45243 #023-12-1998 L2002 **ORS** *020 †40

SZABOVA, Alexandra. 3333 BURNET AVE, PAIN MANAGEMENT DIVISION 45229 #286-03-1995 L2000 **PAN** *100 †05

SZCZEPANSKI, Karen Elias. 3333 BURNET AVE, ML 2008 45229 #017-20-1998 L1999 **PD** *020 †55

SZCZYKUTOWICZ, Pawel M. 4260 GLENDALE MILFORD RD, STE 202 45242 #759-06-1995 L2000 **IM** *020 †20

SZMYD, Susan Marie. 9302 TOWNE SQUARE AVE, CHILDRENS EYE PHYS 45242 #016-06-1979 L1984 **OPH PO** *020 †35

SZUMLAS, Gregory Allan. 3333 BURNET AVE, GEN PEDS MLC 2011 45229 #018-03-1991 L1994 **PD** *020 †55

TABRIZI, Hassan. ■ 45249 #038-45-1989 L1991 **IM** *020 †20

TAKETANI, Tsuyoshi. 231 ALBERT SABIN WAY, DEPT OF SURG CTR FOR SURG 45267 #572-03-1996 L2004 *100

TAMAI, Junichi. 3333 BURNET AVE, MLC 2017 45229 #035-01-1996 L2002 **ORS PD** *020 †40

TAMBYRAJA, Rabindra R. 3333 BURNET AVE 45229 #038-06-2004 L2005 **CPP** *012

TAMI, Thomas Allen. 55 PROGRESS PL 45246 #028-34-1979 L1992 **OTO** *020 †45

TAN, Ernesto Compendio. 4373 BRIDGETOWN RD 45211 #748-01-1969 L1982 **EM GP** *020

TANAKA, Shiro N. ■ 45249 #572-01-1960 L1969 **OM** *071 †70

TANAKA, Tomoko. 3333 BURNET AVE, CHILDREN HOSP 45229 #572-60-1993 L2002 **NS** *012

TANDOC, Mariano Zabala. ■ 45249 #748-01-1951 L1968 **GP EM** *071

TANDON, Nalini. 375 DIXMYTH AVE, 6TH FL 45220 #495-05-1966 L1976 **AN** *020 †05

TANDON, Som Nath. 3551 SPRINGDALE RD 45251 #495-05-1963 L1976 **PS** *020 †65

TANSY, Aaron Patrick. ■ 45243 #038-06-2005 L2005 **N** *012

TANTE-TAKOUGANG, Prudence. 6350 GLENWAY AVE 45211 #038-41-2000 L2000 **IM** *020 ‡

TAPAY, Nicholas John. 375 DIXMYTH AVE #473-01-1952 L1962 **A PD** *071 †55,03

TAPP, Loren Cheri. 4676 COLUMBIA PKWY R-10, NATL INST OCCUPTLN SAF-HLT 45226 #020-12-1986 L1993 **OM GP** *050 †70

TAYLOR, Brook Louise. 3333 BURNET AVE, CHILDRENS HOSP MED CTR 45229 #001-02-2006 L2006 **PD** *012

TAYLOR, Curtis W. 2600 STRATFORD AVE STE 100 45219 #024-07-1976 L1992 **IM** *020 †20

TAYLOR, Glenn Matthew. 5819 CHEVIOT RD 45247 #038-41-1994 L1998 **VIR R** *020 †80

TAYLOR, Janice Abigail. 45230 #038-40-2003 L2003 **GS** *012

TAYLOR, Sally Louise. 800 COMPTON RD STE 9204 45231 #055-01-1965 L1966 **FM FPG** *020 †18

TAYLOR, Tamara Shunta. ■ 45208 #038-06-2007 L2007 **PD** *012

TECSON, Josephine. 3200 BURNET AVE 45229 #748-10-1988 **PM IM** *100

TEDFORD, William L. 3001 HIGHLAND AVE 45219 #038-45-1986 L1989 **CHP P** *020 †75

TEGTMEIER, Todd Alan. 8000 5 MILE RD, STE 210 45230 #038-41-1993 L2000 **FM** *020 †18 ‡

TEKULVE, Kristyn Jennifer. ■ 45236 #017-20-2008 *012

TEMIZER, Dogan H. 3219 CLIFTON AVE, STE 400 45220 #038-40-1985 L1995 **CD IM** *020 †20

TEMPLIN, Elizabeth Ann. 3333 BURNET AVE 45229 #036-05-2001 L2001 **PD** *020 †55

TENCZA, Christian Thomas. 231 ALBERT SABIN WAY # 0, DEPT OF INTERNAL MEDICINE 45267 #038-41-2004 L2004 **PCC** *012

TENCZA, Kara Ann. 3333 BURNET AVE, MLC 5018 45229 #038-41-2004 L2004 **PD** *020 †55

TENKMAN, Allegra Rose. ■ 45231 #038-41-2008 *012

TENKMAN, Lawrence Robert. 260 STETSON AVE. STE 5300, UNIVERSITY OF CINCINNATI S 45267 #038-40-2006 L2006 **OPH** *012

TENNEY, Jeffrey Russell. 3333 BURNET AVE, CHILDRENS HOSP MED CTR 45229 #024-16-2006 L2006 **PD** *012

TENOEVER, George Jos. 375 DIXMYTH AVE 45220 #028-34-1948 L1950 **IM** *071

TEPE, Kenneth Edward. 10050 MONTGOMERY RD # 284 45242 #038-41-1975 L1977 **P** *020

TERRELL, Amani Shama. ■ 45215 #048-12-2005 L2005 **PD** *012

TERRY, Aaron Wade. 3200 BURNET AVE 45229 #422-01-2007 L2007 **GS** *012

TETIRICK, Bruce Lyle. 10495 MONTGOMERY RD, STE 29 45242 #038-41-1978 L1978 **OBG** *020 †30

TEVAR, Amit. 222 PIEDMONT AVE, STE 200 45219 #028-46-1998 L2004 **GS** *020 †85

THACKER, Mihir Mohan. 3333 BURNET AVE 45229 #496-38-1996 L2001 **OMO** *100

THAKAR, Charuhas Vinay. 11650 CURRIER LN UNIT E 45249 #496-42-1996 L2000 **NEP** *020 †20

THALER, Robert Jos, Jr. 4010 NORTH BEND RD, STE 200 45211 #038-41-1978 L1979 **IM** *020 †20

THENGAMPALLIL, Abraham L. ■ 45267 #035-08-2004 L2004 **OS** *100

THEODOSOPOULOS, Philip. 222 PIEDMONT AVE, STE 310 45219 #005-11-1996 L2003 **NS** *020 †25

THIBODEAUX, Louis Chas. 11155 KENWOOD RD 45242 #021-05-1991 L1992 **GS VS** *020 †85

THIE, Jennifer Lynn. 4430 CARVER WOODS DR, STE 125 45242 #038-41-1978 L1978 **GYN REN** *020 †30

THIND, Gurpreet Kaur. 7810 5 MILE RD 45230 #047-05-1997 L1998 **PD** *020 †55

THIRUGNANAM, Omdevasena. 4411 MONTGOMERY RD, STE 200 45212 #496-70-2001 L2006 **FP** *012

THOLKING, John Henry. 10535 MONTGOMERY RD 45242 #038-41-1971 L1971 **PD** *071

THOMAS, Anil Oommen. ■ 45220 #038-41-2008 *012

THOMAS, Cameron Walker. 3333 BURNET AVE, HOSP MED 45229 #007-02-2005 L2005 **CHN** *012

THOMAS, Donald R. 10500 MONTGOMERY RD 45242 #038-41-1953 L1953 **OM FM** *071

THOMAS, Gloria Jean. 7770 COOPER RD, STE 9 45242 #005-06-1980 L1985 **PS** *020 †85,65

THOMAS, James Harold. 3001 HIGHLAND AVE, STE E 45219 #038-41-1976 L1977 **P PYA** *020 †75

THOMAS, Mark Joseph. 231 ALBERT SABIN WAY, P O BOX 670558 45267 #008-02-1996 L2003 **TTS OS** *020

THOMAS, Michael Anthony. 2123 AUBURN AVE, STE A44 45219 #016-11-1984 L1988 **REN OBG** *020 †30

THOMAS, Michael Evan. ■ 45206 #038-41-2007 L2007 **IM** *012

THOMAS, Ryan Michael. ■ 45206 #016-43-2003 L2003 **GS** *012

THOMAS, Sandra Delores. ■ 45227 #038-40-1988 *100

THOMPSON, Amy Michelle. 222 PIEDMONT AVE, STE 5100 45219 #001-06-1999 L2007 **OBG** *100 †30

THOMPSON, Brian Carson. ■ 45213 #038-41-1983 *050

THOMPSON, Carl Gordon, Jr. ■ 45215 #038-41-1947 L1947 **IM HEM** *071 †20

THOMPSON, Jonathan Richar. ■ 45267 #038-41-2006 L2006 **GS** *012

THOMSON, Joanna Elaine. ■ 45236 #028-34-2008 *012

THOMSON, Paul Eugene. ■ 45247 #047-05-1985 L1987 **RHU IM** *020 †20

THORESEN, Christopher Jon. 4600 WESLEY AVE, STE D 45212 #056-05-1986 L1989 **CD IM** *020 †20

THORPE, Joseph Edward. 10500 MONTGOMERY RD 45242 #038-40-1978 L1978 **PUD CCM** *020 †20

THRESS, Timothy James. 8074 BEECHMONT AVE 45255 #038-40-1982 L1983 **OBG** *020 †30

THUNDATHIL, Raju Varghese. ■ 45242 #020-12-1998 L2000 *100

THUSS-PATTERSON, Ingeborg. ■ 45220 #038-41-1950 L1950 **OS FM** *071

TIAO, Gregory Ming. 3333 BURNET AVE, MLC2023 45229 #016-11-1990 L1993 **PDS** *020 †85

TIGAR, Tommy Ray. 2139 AUBURN AVE, THE CHRIST HOSPITAL 45219 #038-41-1996 L1998 **IM** *020 †20

TILLEMA, Jan-Mendelt. 3333 BURNET AVE, DEPT OF MED EDUCATION 45229 #660-05-2005 L2006 **PD** *012

TIMANI, Shereen Saad Khal. 9275 MONTGOMERY RD, STE 100 45242 #605-01-1998 L2003 **DMP** *012 †15

TIMM, Nathan Lowell. 3333 BURNET AVE, MEDICAL CENTER 45229 #018-03-1997 L2000 **PD** *020 †55

TIMPERMAN, Walter Wm. 1 BENGALS DR, CINCINNATI BENGALS, INC. 45204 #038-41-1957 L1957 **GS** *071 †85

TINKER, E Charles. 1219 MORTS PASS 45215 #038-45-1999 L2003 **EM** *020 †16

TINKLE, Bradley Thomas. 3333 BURNET AVE, MLC 4006 45229 #017-20-1999 L1999 **OS** *100 †55,19

TITCHENER, James L. CENTRAL PSYCH CLN 45267 #036-07-1949 L1953 **PYA P** *071 †75

TOBIAS, Barbara Bowman. 1207 SPRINGFIELD PIKE, STE 54 # A 45215 #038-41-1987 L1988 **FM ADL** *020 †18

TOBIAS, Brian. 375 DIXMYTH AVE, OBSTETRIC ANESTHESIA 45220 #836-02-1966 L1979 **AN** *020 †05

TOBIAS, Jonathan. 234 GOODMAN ST, STE 0501 45219 #005-19-1998 L2000 **FOP** *020 †50

TOBLER, William Donn. 7691 5 MILE RD, STE 305 45230 #038-41-1978 L1978 **NS** *020 †25

TOBLER, William Donn, Jr. ■ 45226 #038-41-2008 *012

TODD, Joseph Chapman. 2123 AUBURN AVE STE 140 45219 #024-01-1958 L1964 **TS** *071 †85,90

TODD, Michael Ulland. 212 W SHARON RD 45246 #038-41-1993 L1996 **FM** *020 †18

TODD, Samuel P, Jr. ■ 45226 #038-41-1949 L1949 **ORS** *020 †40

TODD, Thomas Ulland. 212 W SHARON RD 45246 #038-41-1958 L1958 **FM** *071 †18

TOEBBE, Frank Andrew. 2139 AUBURN AVE 45219 #020-02-1989 L1995 **IM** *020 †20

TOEPFER, Nicholas John. ■ 45208 #038-41-2008 *012

TOJO, James. 1525 ELM ST 45202 #038-41-1955 L1955 **OM GS** *020

TOLENTINO, Jonathan Lee. ■ 45213 #012-01-2006 L2006 **MPD** *012

TOLLACK, John L. 2915 CLIFTON AVE, GROUP HEALTH ASSOCIATES 45220 #038-41-1974 L1979 **EM** *020

TOLTZIS, Robert Joshua. 625 EDEN PARK DR STE 340, CINCINNATI HEART GROUP INC 45202 #041-09-1974 L1982 **CD PDC** *020 †20

TOMASSON, Jon. 3333 BURNET AVE, DEPT OF ANESTHESIOLOGY 45229 #484-01-1997 L2006 **PAN** *100 †50

TOMASZEWSKI, Mara Diane. ■ 45206 #038-41-2005 L2006 **FP** *012

TOMER, Gitit. 3333 BURNET AVE 2010, PEDIATRIC GASTRO & HEPATOL 45229 #550-02-1995 L2005 **PG PD** *020 †55

TOMER, Yaron. 3130 HIGHLAND AVE, STE 0557 45219 #550-02-1984 L2005 **END IM** *050 †20

TOMSICK, Scott David. ■ 45267 #038-41-2004 L2004 **DR** *012

TOMSICK, Thomas Adolph. 234 GOODMAN ST, STE 0054 45219 #028-34-1970 L1971 **R** *020 †80

TOMSON, Sue Ellen. 3333 BURNET AVE, ML 2005 45229 #017-20-1997 L1998 **CCP** *020 †55

TONDOW, David, Jr. 3219 CLIFTON AVE, STE 400 45220 #010-02-1970 L1977 **CD IM** *020 †20

TONG, Jenny. 3125 EDIN AVE STE 1331 45267 #243-77-1990 L2008 **END** *020 †20

TONNE, Brian Michael. ■ 45233 #038-41-2006 L2006 **ORS** *012

TOPALA, Alexander George. ■ 45247 #038-41-2005 L2006 **AN** *012

TOWBIN, Alexander Justin. 3333 BURNET AVE 45229 #038-41-2002 L2002 **PDR** *012 †80

TRACY, Linda Marie. 7691 5 MILE RD 45230 #038-43-1979 L1982 **FM** *020 †18

TRAIFOROS, Eleftherios D. 2139 AUBURN AVE, STE 102 45219 #418-01-1968 L1973 **DR** *020 †80

TRAIFOROS, James Terry. 2139 AUBURN AVE, STE 102 45219 #038-41-1999 L2005 **VIR** *020 †80

TRAMUTA, Daniel Anthony. 311 STRAIGHT ST, STE 301 45219 #038-40-1992 L1993 **CD** *020 †20

TRAPNELL, Bruce Colston. 222 PIEDMONT AVE, STE 1200 45219 #023-01-1984 L1998 **PUD** *050 †20

TRAXEL-WANG, Erica Joy. 3333 BURNET AVE, CHILDRENS HOSP MED CTR 45229 #048-04-2002 L2007 **UP** *012

TREON, Brian Malcolm. 1219 MORTS PASS 45215 #038-41-1994 L1997 **EM** *020 †16

TRICE, Laura May. 4750 WESLEY AVE, STE J 45212 #038-41-1995 L1996 **IM IMG** *020 †20

TRIMARCO, Thomas Walter. 45226 #035-06-2007 L2007 **EM** *012

TRIMBLE, Atitaya Than. ■ 45237 #020-12-2005 L2005 **FP** *012

TRINIDAD, Adriano C, Jr. 7114 PIPPIN RD 45239 #748-07-1953 L1968 **EM GP** *071

TROENDLE, August James. 4620 WESLEY AVE, MEDPACE INC 45212 #023-01-1983 L1992 **CD PA** *050

TROJANOVICH, Christopher. 45236 #007-02-2004 L2004 **IM** *020

TROTT, Alexander Thos. 2139 AUBURN AVE, STE 0769 45219 #038-41-1972 L1972 **EM** *020 †16

TROUP, Stanley B. 231 BETHESDA AVE # 562 45229 #026-04-1950 L1975 **IM HEM** *062 †20

TROUT, Douglas Bruce. 4676 COLUMBIA PKWY, MAILSTOP R-12 45226 #041-01-1989 L1992 **OM IM** *050 †70,20

TROY, Raymond George. 3333 BURNET AVE, CINCINNATI CHILDREN'S HOSP 45229 #028-34-1999 L1999 **OS** *020 †75

TRUFANT, Samuel A. 3939 ERIE AVE 45208 #021-01-1943 L1950 **N P** *071 †75

TRUJILLO FALLA, Alfonso. 318 E UNIVERSITY AVE, PRIMARY CARE OF CINCINNATI 45219 #264-01-1963 L1974 **GS GP** *020 †85

TRUONG, Bryan Nguyen. ■ 45208 #048-02-2007 L2007 **IM** *012

TSAI, Tobias Jungming. ■ 45202 #023-07-2005 L2006 **PPM** *012

TSANG, Reginald Chun-Nau. ELLAND & BETHESDA AVES, CHILDRENS HOSP 45229 #462-01-1964 L1969 **NPM PD** *030 †50

TSANG, Vivian Gawai. ■ 45267 #016-11-2003 L2004 **FM** *100

TSEVAT, Joel. 3130 HIGHLAND AVE, STE 0557 45219 #048-13-1983 L1995 **IM** *050 †20

TSUANG, Mark Min-Tsong. 2123 AUBURN AVE 45219 #244-05-1972 L1979 **U** *020 †95

TSUANG, Wayne Mark. ■ 45243 #016-02-2007 L2007 **IM** *012

TSUEI, Betty Janet. 222 PIEDMONT AVE, STE 200 45219 #038-41-1989 L1994 **CCS** *020 †85

TUCKER, Angela Una. 10498 MONTGOMERY RD, STE H 45242 #038-41-2004 L2004 **FM** *020 †18

TUCKER, David Neil. 7527 STATE RD, STE A 45255 #035-20-1966 L1973 **OPH** *020 †35

TURKI, Jamal A. ■ 45240 #575-01-1982 L1994 **PCC** *100 †20

TURNER, Joseph Sheridan. ■ 45238 #038-41-2008 *012

TURNER, Matthew Joseph. ■ 45215 #038-41-2007 L2007 **D** *012

TURPIN, Brian Keith. ■ 45224 #028-78-2006, ▲ L2006 **PD** *012

TUSKAN, Ivan. 5889 COLERAIN AVE 45239 #957-01-1943 L1953 **OBG OS** *020 †30

TUSSEY, Rocio Guadalupe. 2139 AUBURN AVE 45219 #649-44-1992 L2005 **FP** *012

TUTTLE, Ann Abeel. 8261 CORNELL RD STE 630, CINCINNATI PAIN MGMNT CONS 45249 #038-41-1988 L1992 **AN** *020 †05

TWEET, Matthew Lee. ■ 45230 #038-41-2005 L2005 **ORS** *012

TYLER, Tana Corliisha. ■ 45249 #036-01-2003 L2007 **PAN** *012

TYMITZ, Kevin Michael. ■ 45211 #038-43-2005 L2005 **GS** *012

UDOM, Lawrence Ekan. ■ 45267 #035-03-2005 L2005 **FPP** *012

UDSTUEN, Gavin James. 234 GOODMAN ST, STE 0054 45219 #038-41-1995 L1996 **RNR** *020 †80

UEDA, Kazuhiro. ■ 45267 #572-36-1966 L1976 **PTH PD** *050 †50

UETA, Ikuya. 3333 BURNET AVE # OSB-5 45229 #572-05-1991 **CCP** *100 †55

UGWU, Obinna Raphael. 3159 EDEN AVE, HAMILTON COUNTY CORONER'S 45219 #690-04-1991 L2000 **PTH** *100

UNAKA, Ndidi Ifeoma. ■ 45202 #025-01-2007 L2007 **PD** *012

UNGER, Lawrence Martin. 3200 BURNET AVE DEPT PATH 45229 #028-02-1963 L1968 **PTH** *071 †50

UNTERTHINER, Rudi Allen. ■ 45231 #060-01-1967 L1971 **PS** *020 †65

URBINA, Elaine Mott. 3333 BURNET AVE, CINCINNATI CHILDS HOSP 45229 #012-01-1988 L2003 **PDC PD** *050 †55

URRIQUIA, Esthela M. 1413 LINN ST 45214 #748-01-1964 L1972 **IM** *020 †20

USMANI, Ahsan Imran. 10945 REED HARTMAN HWY, STE 219 45242 #422-01-2000 L2006 **APM** *020 †05

UWIERA, Trina. 3333 BURNET AVE 45229 #068-01-2000 L2005 **PDO** *100

VADHVA, Mukta. 3333 BURNET AVE, CO CHILDREN S HOSP-GRAD ME 45229 #495-77-1989 L2000 **OP** *100

VAGAL, Achala Sameer. ■ 45267 #495-01-1994 L2003 *020 †80

VAGO, John Francis. 311 STRAIGHT ST 45219 #038-40-1982 L1988 **PM PHP** *020 †50

VAIDYANATHAN, Chandra S. 2123 AUBURN AVE, STE 334 45219 #495-16-1988 L1996 **IM** *020 †20

VALENTIN, Francis C. 6350 GLENWAY AVE 45211 #055-01-1996 L2002 **PM** *020 †60

VALENTIN, Harriet Hadley. 3333 BURNET AVE, CINCINNATI CHILDRENS HOSPI 45229 #055-01-1997 L2002 **DBP** *100 †55

VALENTO, Matthew John. ■ 45208 #035-19-2005 L2005 **EM** *012

VALENZUELA, Yunuen Manuel. 231 ALBERT SABIN WAY 05, OF CI 45267 #041-12-2002 L2002 **GS** *100

VALIDO, Richard Guillermo. 8231 CORNELL RD, STE 320 45249 #038-45-1987 L1989 **OBG** *020 †30

VALLE, Gianfranco. 4767 N BEND RD 45211 #649-14-1985 L1997 **IMG** *020 †20

VAN AMERONGEN, Derek. ■ 45241 #016-01-1979 L1996 **OBG** *020 †30

VANCE, David James. 8000 5 MILE RD, STE 305 45230 #038-41-1978 L1979 **IM** *020 †20

VANDE KAPPELLE, R Peter, Jr. 3333 BURNET AVE, CO CHILDREN S HOSP-MED EDU 45229 #041-02-2003 L2003 **PDC** *012 †55

VAN DER BEL-KAHN, J. ■ 45267 #660-03-1955 L1967 **PTH** *040 †50

VAN DEUSEN, Reed William. 2901 VEAZEY AVE 45238 #038-41-2002 L2002 **MPD** *020 †20,55

VAN GILSE, William Victor. 2139 AUBURN AVE, STE 722 45219 #038-40-1975 L1980 **GS** *020 †85

VANGINKEL, David. 3333 BURNET AVE 45229 #018-03-1962 L1964 **PD** *020 †55

VAN HOOK, Catherine L. 222 PIEDMONT AVE, STE 5100 45219 #048-02-1987 L2007 **OBG** *020 †30

VAN HOOK, James Warren. ■ 45267 #021-06-1982 L2007 **MFM CCA** *040 †30

VAN LEEUWEN, Eugene Jos. 58 E HOLLISTER ST 45219 #038-43-1986 L1987 **P CHP** *020 †75

VAN ZILE, Jonathan Wm. 234 GOODMAN ST, STE 0769 45219 #045-01-1982 L1986 **IM** *020 †20,16

VARDAKA, Marianna C. 4760 E GALBRAITH RD, STE 200 45236 #418-01-1981 L1989 **OBG GS** *020 †30

VARGHAI, Houman. ■ 45220 #038-41-2008 *012

VARGHESE, Samuel. ■ 45242 #496-38-1973 L1984 **OTO OS** *020 †45

VARGUS-ADAMS, Jilda N. 3333 BURNET AVE, PEDS REHAB MLC 4009 45229 #008-01-1995 L1996 **PME PD** *050 †60,55

VARLEY, Gary Alan. 1945 CEI DR 45242 #025-01-1984 L1989 **OPH OS** *020 †35

VARTZELIS, Georgios. 3333 BURNET AVE, DEPT OF MED EDUCATION 45229 #418-01-1995 L2006 *100

VARUGHESE, Anna Mary. 3333 BURNET AVE 2001, CHILDREN'S HOSP MEDICAL CE 45229 #495-11-1985 L1996 **AN** *020 †05

VAS, Marianne B. ■ 45208 #050-02-1961 L1969 **AN** *071 †05

VASQUEZ GARAGATTI, Raul. 375 DIXMYTH AVE 45220 #737-10-2004 L2007 **IM** *012

VASSILYADI, Michael. 3333 BURNET AVE, CHILDRENS HOSP 45229 #067-01-1990 L1996 **NS** *020 †25

VAUGHAN, Brian Newell. 3155 GLENDALE MILFORD RD, CINCINNATI EVENDALE SURG 45241 #010-02-2001 L2005 **AN** *020 †05

VAUGHN, Mattie Lou. 2603 UNIVERSITY CT 45219 #025-01-1973 L1977 **OBG** *075

VEERAREDDY, Rakesh Reddy. 4777 E GALBRAITH RD, DEPT OF INTERNAL MEDICINE 45236 #495-73-1999 L2002 **IM** *020 †20

VEHR, Geraldine Marie. 2123 AUBURN AVE, STE 331 45219 #038-41-2001 L2001 **IM** *020

VELARDE, Jorge Juan. ■ 45208 #023-01-2006 L2006 **PD** *012

VELURY, Vijaya Saradhi. 231 ALBERT SABIN WAY #3057, DIVISION OF CARDIOLOGY 45267 #495-65-1988 L2007 **IC** *100 †20

VEMANA, Goutham. ■ 45220 #038-41-2007 L2007 **U** *012

VENARD, Elizabeth Marie. 6480 HARRISON AVE, STE 300 45247 #020-02-1997 L1998 **OBG** *020 †30

VENKATESWARAN, Prema. 234 GOODMAN ST, STE 0531 45219 #495-04-1968 L1980 **AN** *020

VENNEMEYER, John Jos. 7400 JAGER CT 45230 #038-41-1985 L1988 **PD** *020 †55

VERMA, Kedar Nath. 1101 SUMMIT RD 45237 #495-47-1964 L1978 **IM ADM** *020 †20

VERMA, Sadhna. 234 GOODMAN ST, STE 0054 45219 #020-02-1992 L1994 **DR** *020 †80

VESPER, Lee Jos. 1127 FEHL LN 45230 #038-41-1961 L1961 **D** *020 †15

VESTER, Samuel Russell. 4030 SMITH RD, CARDIAC VASCULAR & 45209 #038-41-1983 L1991 **TS VS** *020 †85,90

VICKERS, Leroy. 330 STRAIGHT ST, STRATFORD FAM PRAC STE 102 45219 #038-41-1972 L1972 **FM** *020 †18 ‡

VIDWAN, Navjyot Kaur. 3333 BURNET AVE 45229 #539-04-2004 L2004 **PDI** *012

VIJAYASEKARAN, Shyan. 3333 BURNET AVE 45229 #143-06-1994 L2004 **PDO** *100

VILLACIS, Cynthia Huyck. 3036 WOODBURN AVE 45206 #038-45-1990 L2004 **FM** *020 †16

VILLANUEVA, T T Guilas. 3921 MONTGOMERY RD, DNA ANALYSIS INC 45212 #748-01-1954 L1999 **PTH IM** *020 †50

VILLENA, Nestor R. 5596 GLENWAY AVE 45238 #748-01-1964 L1971 **IM NEP** *020

VILTER, Richard W. 222 PIEDMONT AVE STE 6000 45219 #024-01-1937 L1937 **IM HEM** *072 †20

VISWALINGAM, Kalvarayan A. ■ 45249 #495-16-1965 L1980 **N EM** *072

VIVIAN, Rodney Elgar. 8000 5 MILE RD STE 240 45230 #038-41-1975 L1977 **CHP P** *020 †75

VOGEL, Daniel Andrew. 5642 HAMILTON AVE 45224 #056-06-1998 L2000 **CHP** *100

VOLCK, Brian Edward. 3130 HIGHLAND AVE, STE 0557 45219 #028-02-1985 L1987 **PD** *020 †55

VOMACKA, Henry J. ■ 45251 #035-08-1940 L1941 **AN** *071

VONDERBRINK, Richard H. 9030 MONTGOMERY RD, MONTGOMERY FAMILY MEDICINE 45242 #038-41-1995 L1996 **FM** *020 †18

VONLEHMDEN, Sarah Beth. ■ 45226 #038-41-2008 *012

VOORHEES, Holly Lee. 2139 AUBURN AVE, DEPT OF ANESTHESIOLOGY 45219 #038-41-2002 L2006 **AN** *100

VOSS, Deward Henry. 375 DIXMYTH AVE 45220 #028-03-1983 L1996 **MFM OBG** *020 †30

VOSSMEYER, Michael Thos. 3333 BURNET AVE, DIV OF GENERAL&COMM PEDIAT 45229 #020-12-1979 L1981 **PD** *040 †55

VOURAZERIS, Jason Duane. ■ 45202 #038-41-2008 *012

VRISHABHENDRA, Leela H. 7810 5 MILE RD, GROUP HEALTH ASSOCIATES 45230 #496-35-1992 L2000 **IM** *020 †20

VROMEN, Amos. ■ 45242 #550-01-1985 **PDS** *100

VU, Doan Ngo. 234 GOODMAN ST 761, UNIV HOSP OF CINCINNATI 45219 #038-41-1983 L1987 **DR** *020 †80

VU, Mai Thanh. ■ 45211 #038-41-2008 *012

VU, Thuhuong Ngo. ■ 45206 #038-41-2005 L2005 **P** *012

WABNITZ, Steven Alan. 400 BROADWAY ST, MS 26 45202 #038-45-1982 L1983 **IM OS** *020 †20

WACHENDORF, Judith Marie. 4790 RED BANK EXPY, STE 212 45227 #038-41-1988 L1990 **PM** *020 †60

WACKSMAN, Stanley Jerome. 3020 BURNET AVE 45219 #038-41-1962 L1962 **IM HEM** *071

WADIH, George E. 311 STRAIGHT ST 45219 #875-03-1982 L2001 **ATP OS** *020 †50 ‡

WAGNER, George Grieshaber. 3131 QUEEN CITY AVE 45238 #021-05-1976 L1987 **NM PDE** *020 †55,80,28

WAGNER, Lars Martin. 3333 BURNET AVE, MLC 7015 45229 #020-12-1991 L2003 **PHO** *020 †55

WAGNER, Lauren Elizabeth. ■ 45247 #038-41-2008 *012

WAGONER, Lynne Elizabeth. 2123 AUBURN AVE, STE 624 45219 #036-08-1986 L1994 **CD** *020 †20

WAISSBLUTH, Alvaro Danl. 4760 E GALBRAITH RD # 20, GREATER CINCINNATI CARDIOV 45236 #038-40-1992 L1999 **CD** *020 †20

WAISSBLUTH, George. 2925 VERNON PL, STE 100 45219 #231-01-1964 L1975 **GE IG** *020 †20

WAITE, Henry Chester. 7817 COOPER RD STE C 45242 #021-05-1977 L1977 **P CHP** *020 †75

WAKEFIELD, Peter Brock. ■ 45227 #038-41-1967 L1967 **GP** *071

WALDER, Erich William. 2460 KIPLING AVE, STE 204 45239 #038-41-1998 L2000 **PCC** *012 †20

WALKER, Donald Eli. ■ 45242 #038-06-1958 L1958 **IM CD** *071 †20

WALKER, Nita Williams. 3130 HIGHLAND AVE, STE 0557 45219 #012-01-1988 L1991 **IM** *020 †20

WALKER, Roosevelt. 222 PIEDMONT AVE, STE 4000 45219 #020-02-1981 L1986 **OBG** *020 †30

WALL, Arthur A, III. 234 GOODMAN ST, STE 0769 45219 #038-41-1993 L1998 **OS EM** *020 †20,16

WALL, Eric James. 3333 BURNET AVE, BLD C3 / ML 2017 45229 #005-18-1986 L1993 **OP OSM** *020 †40

WALL, Jennifer Lindsay. ■ 45267 #038-41-2004 L2004 **ID** *012

WALL, Sheila Teresa. 375 DIXMYTH AVE 45220 #007-02-1978 L1980 **P** *020 †75

WALLACE, Christine Marie. 55 PROGRESS PL, GHA 45246 #028-46-1992 L1994 **IM PD** *020 †55,20

WALLACE, Erin Elizabeth. ■ 45227 #038-41-2005 L2005 **PD** *012

WALLACE, Waymon Leland. 2450 KIPLING AVE, STE 204 45239 #038-45-1995 L1996 *020

WALLER, Paul Alberto. 1253 KEMPER MEADOW DR, STE 250 45240 #038-41-1987 L1989 **FM** *020 †18

WALLER, Theodore John. 10506 MONTGOMERY RD # 504, C/O THE OHIO HEART & VASCU 45242 #038-41-1980 L1980 **ICE CD** *020 †20

WALLER, Yelandra May. 1253 KEMPER MEADOW DR, STE 250 45240 #038-41-1988 L1991 **FM** *020 †18

WALLHAUSSER, Lorena Jane. 1101 SUMMIT RD, SUMMIT BEHAVIORAL HEALTHCA 45237 #038-45-1991 L1993 **P** *020 †75

WALLIHAN, Daniel Brown. ■ 45242 #017-20-2001 L2006 **DR** *012

WALSH, William E, Jr. 7500 STATE RD 45255 #038-41-1983 L1983 **PM** *020 †60

WALSON, Philip David. 3333 BURNET AVE, MLC 7004 45229 #005-02-1969 L1981 **PA PD** *050 †55

WALTER, Lorene Louise. 58 E HOLLISTER ST 45219 #056-06-1991 L1992 **P** *040 †75

WALTHER, Angela Mary. ■ 45239 #038-40-1989 L1991 **FM** *075

WALZER, Peter Dugliss. 231 BETHESDA AVE 45229 #035-03-1968 L1981 **ID IM** *050 †20

WAND, Austin. 234 GOODMAN ST, STE 0054 45219 #038-41-1972 L2000 **DR OS** *020 †80

WANG, Jiang. DEPT OF PATHOLOGY, UNIV OF CINCINNATI MED CTR 45267 #243-38-1985 L2004 **PTH** *100

WANG, Kuoying. 10495 MONTGOMERY RD, INFECTIOUS DISEASE 45242 #035-09-1990 L1994 **ID IM** *020 †20

WANG, Ping. 231 ALBERT SABIN WAY, ML0531 45267 #243-45-1987 L2000 **AN** *020 †05

WANG, Shuhe. UNIV OF CINCINNATI MED CTR, DEPT OF PATHOLOGY 45267 #243-71-1982 L2001 **PTH** *100 ‡

WANG, Sunny Meichun. ■ 45213 #036-07-2007 L2007 **EM** *012

WANG, Yanfeng. ■ 45231 #036-05-2007 L2007 **IM** *012

WANG, Zhaohui. 375 DIXMYTH AVE 45220 #243-48-1992 L2007 **IM** *012

WANIGASOORIYA, Don. ■ 45243 #220-01-1979 L2002 **APM** *100

WARD, David Truman. 7500 STATE RD 45255 #028-34-1994 L2006 **GS VS** *020 †85

WARD, Jacqueline Suzanne. 175 W GALBRAITH RD, ALLIANCE PRIMARY CARE 45216 #038-40-1996 L1997 **HO** *020 †20

WARD, Laura Placke. 3333 BURNET AVE ML7009, DEPARTMENT OF NEONATOLOGY 45229 #028-34-1994 L2001 **NPM** *020 †55

WARD, Michael Jeffrey. ■ 45209 #012-05-2006 L2006 **EM** *012

WARDEN, Robert James. 2123 AUBURN AVE, STE 334 45219 #038-43-1993 L1994 **IM** *020 †20

WARE, Avis E. 2123 AUBURN AVE # 630 45219 #038-41-1992 L1993 **RHU** *020 †20

WARM, Eric Jay. 231 ALBERT SABIN WAY, ML 0535 45267 #038-41-1993 L1996 **IM** *020 †20

WARNER, Barbara Ann. 375 DIXMYTH AVE 45220 #038-41-1975 L1977 **P** *020 †75

WARNER, Petra Maria. 2123 AUBURN AVE, STE 115 45219 #016-43-1994 L2000 **GS** *020 †85

WARNICK, Ronald Eugene. 222 PIEDMONT AVE, STE 3100 45219 #035-45-1982 L1991 **NS SO** *020 †25

WARNICK, Stephen Joseph, Jr. ■ 45206 #025-01-2007 L2007 **FPP** *012

WARREN, Galen Richard. 2752 ERIE AVE 45208 #038-40-1967 L1967 **U** *020 †95

WARRIER, Kavita Shanker. 3333 BURNET AVE, CO CHILDREN S HOSP-MED EDU 45229 #028-02-2003 L2003 **PD** *020 †55

WARRIER, Manoj Rajkumar. 3333 BURNET AVE, MEDICAL CENTER MLC 7028 45229 #020-02-1998 L2004 **AI** *020 †20,55,03

WARRINGTON, Chevone Renee. ■ 45220 #038-41-2008 *012

WARSHAW, Gregg Alan. 231 ALBERT SABIN WAY, P O BOX 670504 45267 #025-01-1976 L1985 **FM FPG** *040 †18

WARTH, Irvin. 400 MARTIN LUTHER KNG DR E 45229 #038-41-1946 L1946 **ORS** *071

WASHINGTON, Israel. 2911 READING RD 45206 #001-02-1974 L1976 **OBG** *020 †30

WASSENAAR, Elizabeth S. ■ 45227 #041-02-2008 *012

WATERHOUSE, David Michael. 4350 MALSBARY RD, STE 208 45242 #024-16-1985 L1993 **HEM ON** *020 †20

WATERS, Anne Boat. 3333 BURNET AVE, DEPT OF ANESTHESIA 45229 #036-01-1997 L1999 **PAN** *100 †05

WATKINS, Yulonda. 2920 SCIOTO 2ND FL, UNIVERSITY HEALTH CTR-UC 45221 #004-01-1983 L1995 **OM** *020 †20

WATSON, Richard John. 8000 5 MILE RD, STE 340 45230 #038-40-1971 L1971 **PM** *020 †60

WATTS, Nelson Barnett. 222 PIEDMONT AVE STE 4300, OSTEOPOROSIS CENTER 45219 #036-01-1969 L2001 **END IM** *020 †20 ‡

WAYNE, Donald Louis. 4760 E GALBRAITH RD, STE 205 45236 #016-42-1983 L1985 **CD** *020 †20

WAYNE, Leo. 7825 LAUREL AVE 45243 #038-41-1952 L1952 **IM HEM** *020 †20

WEAVER, Brian Dewayne. 5819 CHEVIOT RD 45247 #038-41-1990 L1991 **DR** *020 †80

WEAVER, Donald John, Jr. ■ 45219 #036-01-2003 L2006 **PN** *012 †55

WEAVER, Elizabeth Anne. 2139 AUBURN AVE, STE 102 45219 #038-43-1993 L2003 **DR** *020 †20

WEAVER, Glenn Morrison. 2123 AUBURN AVE # 311 45219 #038-41-1945 L1945 **P PFP** *020 †75 ‡

WEBB, Barry Warren. 212 W SHARON RD 45246 #038-41-1974 L1977 **FM** *020 †18

WEBB, Cheryle Branch. 3131 HARVEY AVE, STE 201 45229 #011-03-1977 L1981 **END IM** *020 †20

WEBB, Daniel Barnes. ■ 45208 #001-02-2006 L2006 **NS** *012

WEBB, Michael Douglas. 4411 MONTGOMERY RD, STE 200 45212 #038-43-1978 L1985 **END IM** *020 †20

WEBB, Pamela Joyce. 200 NORTHLAND BLVD 45246 #020-12-1975 L1978 **AN** *020

WEBB, Thomas Stephen. 3130 HIGHLAND AVE, STE 0557 45219 #035-45-1992 L1994 **IM PD** *020 †55,20

WEBB, Timothy John Harvey. 234 GOODMAN ST, STE 0531 45219 #048-13-1980 L1996 **AN** *020 †20

WEBER, Daniel Jos. 820 DELTA AVE 45226 #038-41-1974 L1974 **P** *020

WEBER, Frederick H, Jr. 222 PIEDMONT AVE, STE 1200 45219 #024-07-1983 L1986 **GE** *020 †20

WEBER, Georg Franz. ■ 45249 #409-20-1988 **CLP IM** *050

WEBER, James Lawrence. 7500 STATE RD 45255 #038-41-1980 L1980 **DR** *020 †80

WEBER, Joseph Timothy. ■ 45240 #038-40-2005 L2005 **IM** *012

WEBER, Kevin Patrick. ■ 45202 #038-41-2001 L2001 **NM** *020 †80,28 ‡

WEBSTER, Charles Thomas. 1295 KEMPER MEADOW DR 45240 #038-41-1997 L2000 **FM** *020 †18

WEBSTER, Warren Richmond. 2727 MADISON RD STE 208 45209 #038-41-1970 L1970 **IM** *020 †20

WEDIG, Henry Elmer, Jr. 7500 STATE RD 45255 #038-41-1956 L1956 **FM** *071 †18

WEDIG, Kathryn Ellen. 375 DIXMYTH AVE, GOOD SAMARITAN HOSP 45220 #038-41-1978 L1980 **NPM PD** *020 †55

WEESNER, Robert Eliot. 3200 VINE ST # 111GI 45220 #017-20-1972 L1974 **GE IM** *040 †20

WEHRMAN, Sally R. 7655 5 MILE RD STE 101 45230 #028-34-1974 L1974 **PD** *020

WEICHERT, Kathryn Ann. 234 GOODMAN ST 45219 #038-41-1972 L1972 **RO ON** *020 †80

WEIDNER, Norbert Jos. 3333 BURNET AVE, DEPARTMENT OF ANESTHESIA O 45229 #041-13-1975 L1977 **EM PD** *020 †55,05

WEIL, Eric Joel. 3333 BURNET AVE, ML 5018 45229 #016-02-2004 L2004 **PD** *100 †55

WEIMANN, Richard Lester. 2450 KIPLING AVE STE 205 45239 #038-41-1971 L1974 **ORS** *020 †40

WEINBERG, Susan G. 8500 OLD CARRIAGE TRL 45242 #038-06-1976 L1978 **DR** *020 †80

WEINSTEIN-NUSSBAUM, Sue. 3805 EDWARDS RD STE 566 45209 #038-41-1986 L1988 **OS** *030

WEINTRAUB, Neal Lee. 231 ALBERT SABIN WAY ML05, UNIVERSITY OF CINCINNATI 45267 #021-01-1984 L2006 **CD** *020 †20

WEISENBERGER, Gary Jos. 2001 ANDERSON FERRY RD 45238 #038-41-1982 L1984 **PD** *020 †55

WEISENBERGER, Ronald Jos. 10600 MONTGOMERY RD # 100 45242 #038-41-1975 L1975 **GE IM** *020 †20

WEISFELDER, Philip Lars. 2139 AUBURN AVE, HOSPITALISTS OF MT AUBURN 45219 #038-41-1997 L1998 **IM** *020 †20

WEISKITTEL, David Gerard. 7829 LAUREL AVE 45243 #038-40-1986 L1987 **FM** *020 †18

WEISS, Kenneth Lee. 234 GOODMAN ST, ML0762 DEPT RADIOLOGY 45267 #025-01-1981 L1985 **RNR** *020 †80

WEISS, Mark A. 375 DIXMYTH AVE 45220 #010-02-1971 L1977 **ATP** *020 †50

WELCH, Michael Craig. 6350 GLENWAY AVE 45211 #038-40-1973 L1973 **ORS** *020 †40

WELLER, James Francis. 10500 MONTGOMERY RD 45242 #023-07-1998 L2003 **AN** *020 †05

WELLING, Richard Edward. 3219 CLIFTON AVE, STE 100 45220 #038-41-1966 L1966 **GS VS** *040 †85

WELLS, Robert Stacy. 7500 STATE RD, CARE CONSULTANTS MERCY 45255 #020-12-1987 L2001 **AN** *020 †05

WELLS, Victoria Elizabeth. 8875 SPOOKY RIDGE LN, SOTENI INTERNATIONAL 45242 #038-06-1980 L1989 **PHP OM** *040 †70

WELSH, George Franklin. 6200 PFEIFFER RD, STE 320 45242 #024-01-1966 L1976 **PS AM** *020 †85,65 ‡

WELTMAN, Robert. 10506 MONTGOMERY RD, STE 402 45242 #035-19-1978 L1987 **GP D** *020 †15

WELTON, Scott Thomas. 871 EIGHT MILE RD 45255 #048-16-1997 L2002 **DR** *020 †80

WENDEL, James Schoelles. 2123 AUBURN AVE, STE 724 45219 #038-41-1982 L1983 **OBG** *020 †30

WENDEL, Richard Geo. 2450 KIPLING AVE 45239 #038-41-1961 L1961 **U** *071 †95

WENG, Eric Lee. ■ 45267 #038-41-2003 L2003 **PTH** *100

WENSTRUP, Richard J, Jr. 3333 BURNET AVE, ML 4006 45229 #038-41-1978 L1993 **PD ADL** *020 †55,19

WERNER, Robert Blair. 330 STRAIGHT ST, STE 201 45219 #038-41-1979 L1983 OPH *020 †35

WERNKE, Suzanne Marie. 3130 HIGHLAND AVE, STE 0557 45219 #038-41-1988 L1989 IM *020 †20

WESS, Mark Louis. 231 ALBERT SABIN WAY, MAIL LOCATION 670535 45267 #038-41-1989 L1991 IM *020 †20

WESSELKAMPER, Kristen R. ■ 45255 #038-41-2000 L2000 CHN *100 †75

WEST, Clark D. 3333 BURNET AVE, CHILDRENS HOSP MED CTR 45229 #025-01-1943 L1953 PN DR *050

WEST, Constance Elizabeth. 3333 BURNET AVE # 4, CHILDRENS HOSP MED CTR 45229 #024-16-1986 L1993 OPH *020 †35

WEST, David Vinh. 234 GOODMAN ST ML076, UNIV OF CINCINNATIRADIOLOG 45219 #038-41-1999 L1999 DR *020 †80

WESTERMANN, Cindy Denese. 2139 AUBURN AVE, CHRIST HOSP DEPY PTH 45219 #038-41-1985 L1990 PTH GS *020 †50

WESTRY, Jeanie Anne. ■ 45249 #036-07-1983 L1991 PD *020 †55

WETZLER, Karin Margaret. 8245 NORTHCREEK DR 45236 #038-40-1988 L1990 PD *020 †55

WEXLER, Laura Gail Fooner. 3200 VINE ST 45220 #028-02-1971 L1987 CD *040 †20

WHALEN, Daniel A. ■ 45213 #038-41-1945 L1945 AN EM *071 †05

WHALEN, John Kevin. 4623 WESLEY AVE, STE P 45212 #038-43-1994 L1997 FM *020 †18

WHANG, David Dean. 4760 E GALBRAITH RD, STE 205 45236 #039-01-1985 L1992 CD IM *020 †20

WHEELER, Derek Scott. 3333 BURNET AVE, DIV OF CRITICAL CARE MEDIC 45229 #017-20-1994 L2000 CCP *020 †55

WHITAKER, Anthony R, Sr. 231 ALBERT SABIN WAY 0, UNIVERSITY HOSPITAL 45267 #025-12-2001 L2001 PFP *020 †18

WHITAKER, Stephen Howard. ■ 45208 #047-05-1977 L1979 N PD *075

WHITAKER, Winnie Tung. 3333 BURNET AVE ML2008, CHILDREN'S HOSPITAL 45229 #048-13-2001 L2001 PEM *100 †55

WHITE, Christine Mary. ■ 45208 #028-03-2004 L2004 PD *012 †55

WHITE, Christopher. ■ 45217 #016-45-2003 L2003 FPP P *012 ‡

WHITE, David K. 5819 CHEVIOT RD, PROFESSIONAL RADIOLOGY 45247 #048-13-1992 L2000 RNR *020 †80

WHITE, Lydia Ann. ■ 45209 #047-05-2006 L2006 ORS *012

WHITE, William Wallace. ■ 45243 #036-01-1955 L1964 R *071 †80

WHITE, Zandra Janelle. ■ 45220 #038-41-2005 *100

WHITE-ARCHER, Margaret A. 2750 BEEKMAN ST 45225 #047-06-1991 L1993 PD *020 †55

WHITMAN, Roy M. CINCINNATI UNV HOSP, DEPT PSYCH 45267 #017-20-1946 L1957 P PYA *071 †75

WHITMER, Jeffrey Thos. 2139 AUBURN AVE 45219 #041-14-1977 L1981 CD END *071 ‡

WHITSETT, Jeffrey Allen. 3300 ELLAND AVE # NEON, CHILDRENS HOSPITAL 45229 #035-01-1973 L1978 NPM *050 †55

WHITTAKER, Dorothy J. ■ 45246 #038-41-1951 L1951 AN PHP *020 †05

WHITTEN, Robert Ray, Jr. 7810 5 MILE RD 45230 #055-01-1980 L1981 PM FM *020 †60,18

WHITTINGTON, Cheryl V. 9200 MONTGOMERY RD BLDG H, MONTGOMERY STATION 45242 #024-07-1973 L1979 D OM *071 †15

WIDDICE, Eleanor Austin. 3333 BURNET AVE, CHILDRENS HEALTH MEDCL CTR 45229 #054-04-2000 L2006 ADL *100 †55

WIERS, Kristina Marie. 3333 BURNET AVE, ML 4010 45229 #305-01-2002 L2006 PPR *012

WIERWILLE, Ann C Southard. 3001 HIGHLAND AVE, STE E 45219 #038-41-1962 L1962 P PYA *020 †85

WIERWILLE, George Herman. 7655 5 MILE RD, STE 117 45230 #038-41-1962 L1962 OBG *071 †30

WIKENHEISER-BROKAMP, Kathr. 234 GOODMAN ST 45219 #038-41-1996 L2003 ATP *020 †50

WILBORN, Amy Tanner. 3333 BURNET AVE, CHILDREN'S HOSPITAL 45229 #051-04-2000 L2000 PAN *100 †55,05

WILBURN, Rochelle Denise. 231 ALBERT SABIN WAY, CO UNIV CINCI C.O.M.-OB-GY 45267 #016-11-2003 L2003 OBG *020

WILDMAN, Walter B, II. 2139 AUBURN AVE 45219 #035-19-1947 L1952 AN *071 †05

WILEY, Susan Elizabeth. 3333 BURNET AVE, CCHMC 45229 #038-41-1994 L1995 PD *020 †55

WILHELMY, Oscar. 11490 SPRINGFIELD PIKE 45246 #407-21-1946 L1957 GP OS *071

WILKIN, James Henry. 3200 VINE ST, VA HOSPITAL 45220 #038-40-1969 L1969 CD IM *020 †20

WILLGING, Jay Paul. 3333 BURNET AVE, DEPT OF OTOLARYNGOLOGY 45229 #038-41-1985 L1990 OTO PDO *020 †45

WILLIAMS, Arthur Burton. 3200 VINE ST, MEDICAL CENTE 45220 #016-01-1994 L1996 GS *020 †85

WILLIAMS, Cheau Eugene. 375 DIXMYTH AVE, C/O MEDICAL EDUCATION 45220 #305-01-2005 L2007 OBG *012

WILLIAMS, David Allan. 3333 BURNET AVE, MLC 7013 45229 #017-20-1979 L1980 PHO *050 †55

WILLIAMS, David Symmes. 311 STRAIGHT ST 45219 #038-41-1979 L1980 IM OS *030 †20

WILLIAMS, James Douglas. 4700 SMITH RD 45212 #017-20-1974 L1975 U *020 †95

WILLIAMS, Jill Marie. ■ 45255 #020-02-1989 L1990 AN *020 †05,55

WILLIAMS, John Arthur. 663 ANDERSON FERRY RD 45238 #038-41-1959 L1959 PD *020 †55

WILLIAMS, Nicole Renee. 8280 MONTGOMERY RD, STE 206 45236 #038-40-1996 L1999 FM *020 †18

WILLIAMS, Richard Bryan. 4850 RED BANK RD, FL 2 45227 #020-12-1981 L1986 PS HS *020 †85,65

WILLIAMS, Timothy C. 4360 COOPER RD 45242 #038-41-1978 L1979 END IM *020 †20

WILLIAMS-ARYA, Pamela H. 400 MARTIN LUTHER KNG DR E 45229 #055-01-1996 L1997 PD *020 †55

WILLIE, Katrina L. ■ 45206 #048-04-2005 L2005 PD *012

WILLING, Michael Joseph. 4777 E GALBRAITH RD, JEWISH HOSP ED 45236 #028-34-1997 L1998 EM *020 †16

WILLIS, Carol Lee. 2810 BURNET AVE STE V 45219 #025-12-1977 L1979 P CHP *020 †75

WILLIS, Craig Benjamin. 2841 BOUDINOT AVE, FREIBERG ORTHOPAEDIC AND 45238 #025-01-1995 L2000 HS ORS *020 †40

WILLIS, James Barry. 2841 BOUDINOT AVE, FREIBERG ORTHOPAEDIC AND 45238 #025-01-1965 L1966 ORS HS *020 †40

WILLKE, John Chas. 1821 W GALBRAITH RD 45239 #038-41-1948 L1948 FM OS *030

WILLMOTT, William Clay. UNIV OF CINCINNATI, DEPT OF INT MED 45267 #020-02-2002 L2002 PCC *012 †20

WILLOUGHBY, Christopher B. ■ 45202 #021-01-2005 L2005 EM *012

WILSON, Amy Colleen. 3333 BURNET AVE 7022 45229 #023-07-2003 L2003 PN *012 †55

WILSON, David Gene. 8000 5 MILE RD, STE 305 45230 #038-43-1976 L1977 IM *020 †20

WILSON, Ernest Roy. 1534 DALTON AVE 45214 #352-11-1951 L1954 OM FM *071

WILSON, Geo Garland, III. ■ 45220 #051-01-1974 L1975 OTO FPS *020 †45

WILSON, James Miller, III. 4030 SMITH RD, CARDIAC VASCULAR & 45209 #036-07-1971 L1980 TS GS *071 †85,90

WILSON, John Homer. 3219 CLIFTON AVE STE 400 45220 #038-43-1980 L1981 CD IM *020 †20

WILSON, Melinda Kay. 2060 READING RD, STE 170 45202 #038-41-1988 L1993 DR *020 †80

WILSON, Stephen Edwin. 234 GOODMAN ST 66SX, HOXWORTH CENTER 2ND FLOOR 45219 #038-40-1998 L2000 MPD EP *050 †20,55

WILT, Allison Elaine. 2139 AUBURN AVE 45219 #020-02-1999 L2001 PS *020

WILTSE, David Wm. 3248 WESTBOURNE DR 45248 #008-01-1975 L1976 P IM *020 †20

WINE, Todd Michael. ■ 45226 #047-05-2003 L2003 OTO *012

WINHOLT, Jeffrey Wayne. 311 STRAIGHT ST, DEPT ANESTHESIOLOGY 45219 #038-43-1985 L1989 AN *075

WINHUSEN, Stephen Martin. 2859 BOUDINOT AVE, STE 107 45238 #038-41-1991 L1996 FM *020 †18

WINIARSKA, Magdalena Anna. 3200 BURNET AVE 45229 #759-06-2000 L2004 IM *100 †20

WINSTON, Fredrick Benj. 2285 BANNING RD 45239 #021-05-1965 L1970 ORS *075 †40

WINTZINGER, Roland G. ■ 45233 #038-41-1949 L1949 R *071 †80

WIOT, Jerome F. 234 GOODMAN ST 45219 #038-41-1953 L1953 DR *040 †80

WISSMAN, Robert David. 234 GOODMAN ST, STE 0054 45219 #038-40-1991 L2003 DR *020 †80

WITSKEN, Matthew Gerard. 7500 STATE RD 45255 #038-41-1997 L1998 IM *020 †20

WITTE, David Paul. CINCINNATI CHILD HSP PATH 45229 #038-41-1979 L1985 ATP *050 †50

WITTKUGEL, Eric Peter. 3333 BURNET AVE, CHILDRENS HOSP MLC 2001 45229 #035-06-1983 L1989 PAN PD *020 †55,05

WOHLGETHAN, Judith A E. ■ 45255 #038-41-1974 L1974 P IMG *020 †75

WOLF, Bradley Rex. 11877 MASON MONTGOMERY RD 45249 #017-20-1980 L1985 OS EM *016

WOLF, John Wm. 6480 HARRISON AVE, SPORTS MEDICINE 45247 #041-01-1968 L1980 ORS AM *020 †40

WOLF, Richard E. ■ 45208 #041-01-1939 L1943 PD *072 †55

WOLTERMAN, Robert Matthew. ML0535 - RM 6603, 231 ALBERT SABIN WAY 45267 #038-45-1998 L2000 MPD *020 †20,55

WOLUJEWICZ, Michael. ■ 45227 #038-41-2007 L2007 IM *012

WONES, Robert Gordon. 222 PIEDMONT AVE, STE 6000 45219 #038-41-1980 L1983 IM *030 †20

WONG, Brenda Lai Ying. 3333 BURNET AVE, CHMC 45229 #825-01-1980 L1998 CHN *020 †75

WONG, Hector Raul. 3333 BURNET AVE, CHILDRE'S HOSPITAL MEDICAL 45229 #033-06-1989 L1995 CCP *020 †55

WONG, Kwan-Yuen. 4370 MALSBARY RD, STE 100 45242 #462-01-1963 L1974 HEM ON *071 †55

WONG, Peter Kai. 8000 5 MILE RD, STE 250 45230 #038-45-1992 L1995 FM *020 †18

WONNELL, Dirk Mitchell. 2450 KIPLING AVE, STE 101 45239 #017-20-1982 L1988 U *020 †95

WOOD, Michael David. 2123 AUBURN AVE, STE 209 45219 #038-41-1979 L1983 OTO A *020 †45

WOOD, Sharon Ann. 2314 AUBURN AVE 45219 #025-12-2001 L2001 FM *020

WOODLE, Ervin Steve. 222 PIEDMONT AVE, STE 200 45219 #048-02-1980 L1999 OS GS *020 †85

WOODS, Scott Edward. 4411 MONTGOMERY RD, STE 200 45212 #038-41-1987 L1988 FM *020 †18

WOOLDRIDGE, Jamie Lynn. 3333 BURNET AVE, PULMONARY MEDICINE CCHMC 45229 #017-20-1995 L2002 PDP *020 †55

WOOLFORD, Elizabeth Ann. 6400 E GALBRAITH RD, MEDICINE 45236 #038-43-1988 L1999 FM *020 †18

WOOTEN, Virgil Dale. 10475 MONTGOMERY RD, STE 1D 45242 #004-01-1980 L1998 SME *020 †75

WOOTTEN, Christopher Todd. ■ 45208 #048-04-2002 L2007 PDO *012

WORKMAN, Mark B. 2859 BOUDINOT AVE, SUTIE 311 45238 #056-06-1973 L1982 CD *020 †20

WRIGHT, Christopher M. 2450 KIPLING AVE, STE G01 45239 #038-41-1999 L1999 IM *020 †20

WRIGHT, Creighton Bolter. 4030 SMITH RD, CARDIAC VASCULAR & 45209 #036-07-1965 L1981 VS TS *020 †85,90

WRIGHT, Dave Allen. 3155 GLENDALE MILFORD RD, CINCINNATI EVENDALE SURG 45241 #049-01-1989 L1993 AN *020 †05

WRIGHT, Maria B. 4460 RED BANK RD, STE 100 45227 #028-02-1993 L1995 IM *020 †20

WRIGHT, Stewart West. 231 BETHESDA AVE, UNIV CINCINNATI 45229 #028-02-1993 L1995 EM *020 †16

WRIGHT, Thomas L. 222 PIEDMONT AVE STE 6000 45219 #028-02-1953 L1961 IM ON *071 †20

WU, Geraldine Nada. 7124 MIAMI AVE STE D 45243 #036-01-1974 L1983 P *020 †75

WU, John Kang-Min. 3333 BURNET AVE 45229 #462-01-1980 L1987 PHO PD *020 †55

WU, Steve Wei. 3333 BURNET AVE, CO CHILDREN S HOSP-MED EDU 45229 #047-05-2003 L2003 CHN *012

WU, Tai-Wei. 3333 BURNET AVE, CHILDREN'S HOSPITAL MEDICA 45229 #748-31-2006 L2007 PD *012

WU, William C. UNIV OF CINCINNATI MED CTR, DEPT OF SURGERY 45267 #016-01-2007 L2007 GS *012

WULSIN, John Hager. ■ 45242 #035-45-1944 L1948 GS *071 †85

WULSIN, Lawson Reed. 231 ALBERT SABIN WAY, ML 559 45267 #038-41-1979 L1986 P *040 †75

WUNDER, Steve Scott. 2915 CLIFTON AVE 45220 #038-41-1980 L1980 PM *020 †60

WURZBACHER, Constance Ann. 3219 CLIFTON AVE, STE 125 45220 #038-41-2001 L2001 OBG *020

WYATT, Lindy M. 7013 CLEARWOOD CT 45236 #038-41-1993 L1997 N *062 †75

WYLER, Carl Iglauer. ■ 45209 #038-41-1938 IM *072 †20

WYRICK, John Dwight. 231 ALBERT SABIN WAY, RM 5709, MAIL LOC 0212 45267 #038-45-1984 L1985 OTR HS *020 †20

XANTHAKOS, Stavra A. 3333 BURNET AVE, CHILDRENS HOSPITAL MED CTR 45229 #036-07-1997 L1999 PG *100 †55

YADLAPALLI, Naga Ganesh. 231 ALBERT SABIN WAY, MSB RM G259 45267 #495-50-1987 L2000 MPD *020 †20,55

YAKUBOFF, Kevin Paul. 3229 BURNET AVE, SHRINERS BURNS HOSPITAL 45229 #038-34-1977 L1986 HS PS *020 †65,85

YAMAGUCHI, Ben T, Jr. 2139 AUBURN AVE, DEPT PATH 45219 #038-41-1960 L1960 PTH *020 †50

YANG, Lisa. 8245 NORTHCREEK DR 45236 #017-20-1988 L1989 OBG *020 †30

YANG, Wonseok. ■ 45219 #583-02-1987 NEP *100

YASIN, Zahida. 234 GOODMAN ST RM 2009, BARRETT CANCER CENTER 45219 #704-02-1976 L1997 ON *020 †20

YAZIGI, Nada Anis. 3333 BURNET AVE, TION C#4CHILDREN'S HOSP ME 45229 #605-02-1987 L1995 **PG** *020 †55

YEE, Leslie Mitchell. 2 PROCTER AND GAMBLE PLZ, PROCTER AND GAMBLE COMPANY 45202 #038-41-1979 L1990 **OM PHP** *030 †70

YEH, David Dinh. ■ 45267 #028-34-1999 L1999 **NS** *020

YEH, Kelly W. ■ 45229 #038-41-2008 *012

YEUNG, Evan Kaiyuen. 3333 BURNET AVE, EMERGENCY DEPARTMENT 45229 #025-01-1996 L1997 **PD** *020 *55

YI, Michael Sunghun. 3130 HIGHLAND AVE, STE 0557 45219 #051-04-1995 L1999 **MPD PD** *020 †20,55

YICK, Andrew Van. ■ 45231 #011-04-2007 L2007 **EM** *012

YIP, Chee Chew. ■ 45267 #825-01-1991 L2001 **OPH** *100

YOO, Andrew Cha. UNIV OF CINCINNATI MED CTR, DEPT OF SURGERY 45267 #048-12-2007 L2007 **GS** *012

YOO, Ho Hyun. 3217 CLIFTON AVE, GOOD SAMARITAN HOSPITAL 45220 #008-01-1996 L2004 **EM** *020 †16

YOO, Joyce Eunmee. 3200 VINE ST, CINCINNATI VA MED CTR 45220 #005-12-1993 L1998 **IM** *020

YORK, Virginia Victoria. ■ 45205 #038-45-2008 *012

YOST, Theresa Marie. 4370 MALSBARY RD, PEDIATRIC ASSOC OF 45242 #038-41-1999 L2002 **PD** *020 †55

YOUKILIS, Abbie Gail. 2915 CLIFTON AVE 45220 #038-45-1996 L1997 **IM** *020 †20

YOUKILIS, Marvyn Herschel. 10506 MONTGOMERY RD, STE 301 45242 #038-41-1964 L1964 **OBG** *071 †30 ‡

YOUNG, Brian Wesley. 6125 DALEVIEW RD 45247 #036-05-1985 L1987 **IM** *075

YOUNG, Christopher M. 2123 AUBURN AVE, DEPARTMENT OF INT MEDICINE 45219 #020-02-2001 L2001 **IM** *020

YOUNG, Katherine Suzanne. ■ 45211 #041-14-2006 L2006 **PD** *012

YOUNG, Lisa Rosenthal. 3333 BURNET AVE 45229 #036-07-1997 L2001 **PCC** *100 †20,55

YOUNGER, Bruce. 2752 ERIE AVE 45208 #026-04-1977 L1981 **D** *020 †15

YOUNUS, Shahnaz. 705 READING RD 45267 #902-19-1994 L2000 **P** *020 †75 ‡

YOUSUF, Farheen. ■ 45267 #704-02-2001 L2002 **END** *100 †20

YOUSUF, Mian Atif. 231 ALBERT WAY, DEPT OF INTERNAL MED 45267 #704-25-2004 L2006 **IM** *012

YU, Wei. 3333 BURNET AVE, CO CHILDREN S HOSP-MED EDU 45229 #243-43-1983 L2001 **AN** *100

YU, Zhongxin. 3333 BURNET AVE, CHILDRENS HOSP MED CTR 45229 #243-32-1983 L2007 **PP** *012 †50

YUELLIG, Thomas Ries. 5310 RAPID RUN RD, STE 101 45238 #038-41-1985 L1986 **IM** *020 †20

ZAACKS, Philip Louis. 2871 FAIR ACRES DR 45213 #836-02-1962 L1977 **AN PME** *020

ZABBATINO, Salvatore M. ■ 45242 #308-11-1985 **PA** *050

ZACKARY, Maher Jeffrey Sa. 375 DIXMYTH AVE 45220 #915-05-2002 L2005 **AN** *012

ZADIKOFF, Colin M. 2450 KIPLING AVE, STE 103 45239 #836-01-1968 L1982 **N PD** *020 †75

ZAHEER, Misbah. 375 DIXMYTH AVE 45220 #704-20-2004 L2007 **IM** *012

ZAKARIA, Mhd Tarek. ■ 45246 #875-01-1998 L2003 **IM** *012

ZAKE, Abigail Frein. ■ 45267 #038-41-2007 L2007 **MPD** *012

ZAKEM, Stuart Alan. 10498 MONTGOMERY RD, STE A 45242 #038-45-1983 L1984 **IM** *020 †20

ZALTA, Alan Harold. STE 1700, 222 PIEDMONT AVE 45267 #048-14-1978 L1984 **OPH OS** *020 †35

ZALZAL, Marcelle. 3012 GLENMORE AVE, STE 101 45238 #605-02-1962 L1988 **D** *020

ZAMMIT, Christopher Georg. ■ 45236 #035-09-2008 *012

ZAMOR, Philippe Jude. 231 ALBERT SABIN WAY, ML 0595 45267 #024-05-2000 L2007 **GE** *012 †20

ZANGRANDO, David Duane. 7520 STATE RD 45255 #038-06-1991 L1995 **AN** *020 †05

ZARATE, Yuri Alexander. 3333 BURNET AVE 45229 #264-09-2003 L2004 **PMG** *012

ZDENEK, K Anusuya. ■ 45249 #495-04-1954 L1988 **FM** *020 †18

ZEBUHR, Carleen Amy. ■ 45206 #041-13-2005 L2005 **PD** *012

ZEFF, Lawrence Alan. 2841 BOUDINOT AVE, FREIBERG ORTHOPAEDIC AND 45238 #038-40-1986 L1986 **PM** *020 †60

ZEIGLER, Daryl Ned. 3200 VINE ST # 117, VETERANS AFFAIRS MEDICAL C 45220 #041-09-1979 L1987 **PM MDM** *071 †60

ZEISLER, Jonathan Andrew. 234 GOODMAN ST 45219 #035-48-2002 L2005 **OBG** *020 †30

ZELLER, John Edward. 2139 AUBURN AVE DEPT MED 45219 #028-02-1975 L1977 **IM** *020

ZELLNER, David Carl. 222 PIEDMONT AVE, STE 6000 SIUTE 4100 45219 #038-06-1955 L1955 **ON IM** *071 †20

ZELLNER, Karen Sue. 119 RITCHIE AVE 45215 #038-41-1990 L1996 **CHP** *020 †75

ZENNI, Gregory Chas. 4030 SMITH RD, CARDIAC VASCULAR & 45209 #028-34-1986 L1993 **VS GS** *020 †85

ZERHUSEN, John R. 4767 N BEND RD 45211 #020-02-1965 L1971 **CD IM** *020

ZETTEL, Kent Robert, II. ■ 45220 #038-41-2008 *012

ZHU, Yongyi. 231 ALBERT SABIN WAY, STE ML531 45267 #243-16-1984 L2000 **APM AN** *020

ZIEGLER, Mark Christopher. 7500 STATE RD, CARE CONSULTANTS MERCY 45255 #038-41-1994 L1995 **AN** *020 †05

ZIMMER, Michelle Hoerlein. 3333 BURNET AVE, DIV OF DEVELOPMENTAL DISAB 45229 #038-41-1994 L2005 **PD** *020 †18

ZIMMERMAN, Matthew Jason. 231 ALBERT SABIN WAY, DIV OF CARDIOLOGY 45267 #020-02-2001 L2005 **CD** *012

ZIMMERMAN, Tamela. 311 STRAIGHT ST, DEACONESS E.R. 45219 #038-41-1984 L1985 **EM IM** *020 †20

ZIMMERMANN, Anthony Geo. 7520 STATE RD 45255 #047-06-1991 L2000 **AN** *020 †05

ZIMMERMANN, Nives. 3333 BURNET AVE, DIV OF ALL & IMMUN 45229 #957-01-1995 *100

ZINK, Jeffrey Michael. 1945 CEI DR 45242 #041-01-2001 L2006 **OPH** *100 †35

ZIPFEL, David Kirk. 10506 MONTGOMERY RD, STE 101 45242 #038-41-1967 L1967 **PSH PS** *020 †45

ZIPKIN, Jeffrey Warren. 10475 READING RD, STE 206 45241 #038-40-1977 L1980 **U GP** *020 †95

ZISKO, John Patrick. 6350 GLENWAY AVE 45211 #038-41-1993 L1996 **FM FSM** *020 †18

ZISKO, Terri Lynn. 6331 GLENWAY AVE 45211 #038-41-1993 L1996 **FM** *020 †18 ‡

ZIV, Francine Anne. 6103 HAMILTON AVE 45224 #035-46-1992 L1996 **PM** *020

ZOBAY, Allen Jos. 2475 W GALBRAITH RD, STE C 45239 #016-43-1969 L1970 **IM GS** *020

ZOOROB, Dani George. G231 ALBERT, CO OBSTETRICS AND 45267 #605-01-2002 L2007 **OBG** *012

ZORICH, Nora Lee. 11450 GROOMS RD, PROCTER & GAMBLE PHARM 45242 #016-11-1984 L1989 **PA OBG** *050

ZUCKER, Michele Leigh. 3333 BURNET AVE 4000 45229 #016-42-1998 L2004 **PD ADL** *020 †55

ZUCKER, Stephen David. 9275 MONTGOMERY RD, STE 100 45242 #024-01-1985 L1998 **GE IM** *050 †20

ZUMKHAWALA, Ashvin R. 11490 SPRINGFIELD PIKE 45246 #495-22-1969 L1974 **AN** *020 †18

ZUMKHAWALA, Dolar Ashvin. 5920 COLERAIN AVE 45239 #495-76-1968 L1977 **GP OBG** *020

ZUN, Sook Im. 2441 MOERLEIN AVE 45219 #583-03-1973 L1980 **FM** *020 †18

ZUO, Li. ■ 45242 #243-01-1982 L2002 **AI** *012

ZUREIKAT, Yousef Jamal. 3333 BURNET AVE, CO CHILDREN S MED CTR-MED 45229 #575-01-1987 L2000 **TS** *100

ZUSAN, Erin Ann. 375 DIXMYTH AVE, GOOD SAMARITAN HOSPITAL 45220 #017-20-2004 L2004 **GS** *012

ZWERGEL, Kenneth John. 6350 GLENWAY AVE, STE 300 45211 #038-45-1990 L1991 **PD** *020 †55

CIRCLEVILLE – PICKAWAY

ALKIRE, Nancy Lynn. 140 MORRIS RD 43113 #049-01-2000 L2000 **IM** *020 †18

ALVAREZ, Carlos Barriere. 147 PINCKNEY ST 43113 #649-01-1948 L1959 **GS OM** *072 †85

ANDERSON, Francis W. ■ 43113 #038-40-1941 L1941 **GP** *072

ARBOGAST, Joy Diane. 600 N PICKAWAY ST 43113 #038-43-1990 L1991 **OBG** *020 †30

BARR, Jayne Anne. 600 N PICKAWAY ST 43113 #055-02-1990 L1991 **IM PD** *020 †55,20

BOHLEN, John Gregory. 600 N PICKAWAY ST 43113 #038-40-1980 L1981 **FM FPG** *020 †18

BOLENDER, Vernon G. 610 NORTHRIDGE RD 43113 #038-43-1977 L1978 **FM** *020 †18

BOONE, Gregory Michael. 600 N PICKAWAY ST, STE 203 43113 #038-45-1984 L1985 **GS** *020 †85

BORY, Jeff L. 600 N PICKAWAY ST 43113 #038-43-1989 L1993 **DR** *020 †80

BRODY, Andrea Lynn. 210 SHARON RD, STE A 43113 #038-40-1995 L1996 **FM** *020 †18

CHOUEIRI, Mark Anthony. 210 SHARON RD 43113 #055-01-1995 L2000 **GS** *020 †85

COOK, Kenneth Saml. 1170 N COURT ST 43113 #047-07-1986 L1999 **GPM** *072

COTTON, Bradford Wendell. ■ 43113 #038-40-1991 L1992 **EM** *020 †16

EVANS, William Edwin. ■ 43113 #038-40-1961 L1961 **VS GS** *071 †85

FRANK, Kevin Dale. 140 MORRIS RD 43113 #038-45-1998 L1999 **FM** *020 †18

GERON, Michael Edward. 140 MORRIS RD 43113 #030-06-1973 L1975 **FM** *020 †18

GILLEN, Gary Lee. 131 LEWIS AVE 43113 #038-41-1973 L1973 **FM MDM** *020 †18

GIRI, Praveen Kumar. 600 N PICKAWAY ST, SUITE 5 NOECKER BLDG 43113 #495-52-1979 L1988 **N** *020

GOLDFARB, David Benj. 600 N PICKAWAY ST 43113 #038-44-1991 L1994 **OBG** *020 †30

GRONBACH, Kort Matthew. ■ 43113 #305-01-2001 L2001 **APM** *020 †05

HEDGES, Charles Richard. 610 NORTHRIDGE RD 43113 #047-06-1967 L1967 **FM OM** *020 †18

HEDGES, Jasper M. 610 NORTHRIDGE RD 43113 #038-40-1941 L1941 **FM OM** *072 †18

IANNI, Daniel J. 130 MORRIS RD 43113 #033-75-1986, ▲ L1994 **GS** *020

ISKRA-STEVENSON, Linda A. 210 SHARON RD, STE A 43113 #038-40-1995 L1996 **PD** *020 †55

JENKINS, Brian Robert. PO BOX 578, 610 NORTHRIDGE RD 43113 #038-40-1995 L1996 **FM** *020 †18

LEFKOWITZ, Michael Scott. 130 MORRIS RD 43113 #038-41-1988 L1989 **ORS** *020 †40

LINDSAY, Kelly Elizabeth. 600 N PICKAWAY ST, GROVE CITY PHYSICAL MEDICI 43113 #665-01-2000 L2001 *020 †60

LOW, Aaron Ay-Lunn. 210 SHARON RD, STE A 43113 #065-06-1994 L1996 **FM** *020

LUTZ, Emily Eileen. ■ 43113 #038-40-1959 L1959 **GYN** *071 †30

MADHAVEN, Jaswant. 600 N PICKAWAY ST 43113 #495-31-1986 L2000 **CRS** *020 †85,10

MAHER, Mir-M F. 600 N PICKAWAY ST, BERGER HOSPITAL 43113 #118-01-1977 L1995 **AN** *020

MASON, Thomas Owen. 600 N PICKAWAY ST 43113 #038-40-1984 L1985 **DR** *020 †80

MC COY, Robert Hampshire. 1180 N COURT ST 43113 #038-40-1958 L1958 **GP** *020

MOSLEY, James Arthur. 610 NORTHRIDGE RD 43113 #038-40-1985 L1986 **FM** *020 †18

MUELLER, Robert W. 130 MORRIS RD 43113 #023-07-1988 L1999 **ORS** *020 †40 ‡

NAIR, Gopinath A V. 600 N PICKAWAY ST 43113 #649-76-1976 L1990 **IM** *020

NUNNALLY, Ian Patrick. 600 N PICKAWAY ST, STE 203 43113 #039-01-1998 L2005 **GS** *020 †85

PADMANABHAN, Anantha. 600 N PICKAWAY ST 43113 #495-73-1978 L1989 **CRS** *020 †85,10

REIS, Gretchen. 1171 N COURT ST 43113 #048-04-1993 L2005 **FM** *020 †18

RHINEHART, Stephen Nels. 140 MORRIS RD 43113 #038-45-1994 L1996 **FM** *020 †18

ROACH, Ralph Warren. 600 N PICKAWAY ST 43113 #038-43-1975 L1978 **FM** *020 †18

SARDO, James Joseph. 600 N PICKAWAY ST, STE 5 43113 #017-20-1993 L1998 **PM** *020 †60

SATTAR, Farooq. 210 SHARON RD 43113 #704-01-1996 L2004 **PCC** *020 †20

SINGH, Yadwinder. 210 SHARON RD STE D, PICKAWAY HEALTH SERVICES 43113 #495-03-1991 L1997 **IM** *020 †20

STERKOWICZ, Jerzy. 600 N PICKAWAY ST, STE 102 43113 #759-12-1996 L2004 **CD** *020 †20

TRIVEDI, Tapaswini A. 600 N PICKAWAY ST, STE 204 43113 #308-11-1986 L1999 **IM** *020

CLARKSBURG – ROSS

STINSON, Byron. 729 DOGTOWN RD 43115 #038-40-1950 L1950 **P AM** *020 †75

CLAYTON – MONTGOMERY

MANNARINO, Frank Peter. 1250 NATIONAL RD 45315 #038-41-1976 L1981 **ORS** *020 †40

MOTE, Evelyn Renee. 1250 NATIONAL RD, STE 400 45315 #038-40-1990 L1991 **FM** *020 †18

SANDHIR, Bihu. 1250 NATIONAL RD STE 700, ENGLEWOOD HLTH CT 45315 #496-21-1991 L1996 **IM** *020 †20

SMITH, Robert Walter. ■ 45315 #016-06-1955 L1956 **FM** *072

STAHLER, John Chas. ■ 45315 #038-40-1946 L1946 **AN** *071 †05

CLEVELAND – CUYAHOGA

AACH, Richard David. 10900 EUCLID AVE, T308 SCHOOL OF MEDICINE 44106 #028-02-1959 L1989 **IM GE** *030 †20

ABADIE, Sebastian. ■ 44126 #132-03-1994 L2007 **GE** *012 †20

ABASHIDZE, Teah A. 13951 TERRACE RD, MERIDIA HURON HOSPITAL 44112 #912-02-1997 L2001 **IM** *100

ABDALLA, Mohamed Ahmed. 9500 EUCLID AVE 44106 #915-02-1996 L2000 **AN** *020 †05

ABDALLAH, Ghassan. 7225 OLD OAK BLVD, STE A210 44130 #038-43-1997 L1998 **FM** *020 †18

ABDALLAH, Karen Lyn. 7225 OLD OAK BLVD, STE A210 44130 #038-06-1994 L1995 **FM** *020 †18

ABDEL AZIZ, Hiba Mohamed. 11100 EUCLID AVE, CO UNIV HOSPS-RESIDENCY OF 44106 #539-06-1999 L2003 **GS** *012

ABDEL KARIM, Nagla Fawzy. 18101 LORAIN AVE, CO FAIRVIEW HLTH SYS-INT M 44111 #915-02-1993 L2003 **HO** *012 †20

ABDELMALAK, Basem Badie. 9500 EUCLID AVE E-31 44195 #915-09-1992 L1998 **AN CCA** *020 †05

ABDELMALAK, Joseph Badie. 9500 EUCLID AVE, CLEVELAND CLINIC FOUNDATIO 44195 #915-05-1983 L2006 **AN** *012

ABDELMANNAN, Dima Kamal. 18101 LORAIN AVE 44111 #916-01-2000 L2003 **END** *012 †20

ABDELMISIH, Sherif R. 9500 EUCLID AVE, DEPT OF GEN SURGERY 44195 #041-02-2003 L2003 **GS** *012

ABDELNAEM, Esamelden Sala. 9500 EUCLID AVE, CLEVELAND CLINIC FNDN 44195 #915-10-1992 L2004 **AN** *012

ABDEL RAHIM, Adli Osman. 11100 EUCLID AVE 44106 #848-01-1990 L2006 **NPM** *012

ABD ESSAMAD, Hasan. 11100 EUCLID AVE 44106 #605-01-2003 L2005 **OBG** *012

ABDOU, Amgad William. 9500 EUCLID AVE, C/O CCF-GRAD MED EDU DEPT- 44195 #915-04-1995 L2001 **AN** *100 †05

ABDULIAN, Michael Hovig. 11100 EUCLID AVE, UNIV HOSPS - CASE MED CTR 44106 #021-01-2007 L2007 **ORS** *012

ABDUL-KARIM, Fadi Wm. 11400 EUCLID AVE STE 100 44106 #605-01-1979 L1986 **PTH** *040 †50

ABELLO, Remigio Lozada. 5500 S MARGINAL RD, CONCENTRA HEALTH SERVICES 44103 #748-01-1955 L1969 **GP OM** *020

ABI SALEH, Wajdy J. 9500 EUCLID AVE 44195 #605-02-1989 L1994 **PCC** *100 †20

ABONYI, Eugenia Ukamaka. 2500 METROHEALTH DR 44109 #913-84-1990 L2003 **CHP** *012

ABOUASSALY, Robert. 11100 EUCLID AVE 44106 #067-01-2002 L2002 **U** *012

ABOU ASSI, Hiba Najib. 11100 EUCLID AVE, DEPT OF INTERNAL MED 44106 #605-01-2004 L2005 **IM** *012

ABOU EL FADL, Mohamed Has. 18101 LORAIN AVE, FAIRVIEW HOSPITAL 44111 #915-03-2003 L2007 **IM** *012

ABOUELSOUD, Mahmoud M E. 3609 PARK EAST DR # 207NOR 44122 #915-03-1977 L1985 **PD** *020 †55

ABOU HASSAN, Nada. 11100 EUCLID AVE 44106 #605-03-2003 L2007 **IM** *012

ABOUL FETTOUH, Hazem Ibra. 9500 EUCLID AVE, CLEVELAND CLINIC FOUNDATIO 44195 #915-02-1992 L2000 **U** *100

ABOU RESLAN, Walid Fadlal. 9500 EUCLID AVE BOX HB6 44195 #605-01-1994 *100

ABRAHAM, Shiny Mary. CO GME - NA23, CLEVELAND CLINIC FOUNDATIO 44195 #495-37-2003 L2007 **P** *012

ABRAHAMSON, Jon Kenneth. 20800 WESTGATE MALL, NORTH COAST PEDIATRICS 44126 #025-01-1982 L1985 **PD** *020 †55

ABRAKSIA, Samir. ■ 44124 #875-01-1984 L1991 **ON** *020 †20

ABRAMS, Marc Alan. 2322 E 22ND ST STE 102 44115 #038-06-1980 L1981 **OPH** *020 †35

ABSI, Ahmed Almohanad. 9500 EUCLID AVE, R 35 44195 #875-02-1999 L2000 **HO** *100 †20

ABUDAYYEH, Ahmad Mohammad. 9500 EUCLID AVE 44195 #528-03-1987 *100

ABUGHALI, Nazha Fawzi. 2500 METROHEALTH DR, RM H423 44109 #605-01-1986 L1991 **PD ID** *020 †55

ABU HAZEEM, Anas Abdel Ha. 9500 EUCLID AVE, CLEVELAND CLINIC FOUNDATIO 44195 #575-02-2004 L2006 **PD** *012

ABU JAWDEH, Bassam Giryes. 2500 METROHEALTH DR, METROHEALTH MED CTR 44109 #605-01-2003 L2004 **NEP** *012 †20

ABU QARE, Abdul-Elah Yous. 2351 E 22ND ST, C/O ST.VINCENT CHAR-MED ED 44115 #575-01-1996 L2001 **IM** *100 †20

ABU-RAJAB TAMIMI, Tarek I. 9500 EUCLID AVE 44195 #575-01-2003 L2005 **IM** *012

ABU-SHAWEESH, Jalal M. 11100 EUCLID AVE, RB&C 44106 #575-01-1989 L1995 **NPM** *020 †55

ACEVEDO, Monica Andrea. 9500 EUCLID AVE, # 500 44195 #231-03-1990 L2000 *100

ACHANTI, Prasad Baby R. 18101 LORAIN AVE, NEONATOLOGIST 44111 #495-50-1976 L1986 **PD NPM** *020 †55

ACHANTI, Vijayalakshmi. 20800 WESTGATE MALL, STE 400 44126 #495-50-1976 L1986 **PD** *020 †55

ACHESON, Louise Seymour. 11100 EUCLID AVE, STE 1200 44106 #024-01-1976 L1984 **FM FPG** *050 †18

ACHKAR, Edgar. 9500 EUCLID AVE, MC S40 44195 #605-02-1963 L1976 **GE** *020 †20

ACHKAR, Jean-Paul. DESK A30, DEPT OF GASTROENTEROLOGY 44195 #038-06-1991 L1992 **IM GE** *020 †20

ACRA, Patricia Elena. 9500 EUCLID AVE, CLEVELAND CLINIC FNDN 44195 #308-02-1989 L1994 **PD** *020 †55

ADAL, Karim A. 9500 EUCLID AVE, DESK A-81 44195 #017-20-1989 L1995 **ID IM** *020 †20

ADAM, Mahmoud. 6780 MAYFIELD RD 44124 #875-01-1963 L1971 **CD IM** *020 †20

ADAMEK, Peter Michael. 11100 EUCLID AVE 44106 #038-45-1988 L1989 **AN PME** *020 †05 ‡

ADAMICH, Robert L T. ■ 44107 #038-06-1949 L1949 **GS** *071

ADAMIDOU, Fotini. 9500 EUCLID AVE, DEPT BIOMEDICAL ENG-ND20 44195 #418-02-1988 L2002 **END** *071

ADAMS, Angela B. ■ 44105 #030-06-1945 L1946 **IM** *071

ADAMS, William Randolph. ■ 44106 #024-01-1943 L1951 **PYA OS** *020 †75

ADEDIPE, Adebowale A. 11201 SHAKER BLVD STE 338 44104 #690-01-1983 L1993 **PD** *020 †55

ADELMAN, Christopher Lee. 2351 E 22ND ST, ROSARY HALL 44115 #039-01-1978 L1987 **ADM EM** *020 †16

ADELSTEIN, David Jos. 9500 EUCLID AVE, DESK R35 44195 #035-19-1975 L1977 **ON HEM** *020 †20

ADER, Richard Steven. 6707 POWERS BLVD, STE 205 44129 #038-06-1975 L1979 **CD** *050 †20

ADHVARYU, Hareendra G. 7215 OLD OAK BLVD STE A418 44130 #495-22-1969 L1976 **P N** *020

ADHVARYU, Neela Hareendra. 7215 OLD OAK BLVD STE A418 44130 #495-22-1971 L1982 **PD EM** *020

ADI, Ahmad Maher. 9500 EUCLID AVE 44195 #875-01-1988 L1994 **AN** *020 †05

ADUAKO, Cecilia Dyllis Bo. 13951 TERRACE RD 44112 #412-01-2003 L2004 **IM** *020 †20

ADUR, Anjali Prabhakar. 9500 EUCLID AVE, LAKESIDE BLDG. - ROOM 2032 44106 #496-38-1974 L1980 **AN FM** *020 †05

ADURY, Kamala Sundari. 9500 EUCLID AVE, CO CCF-GRAD MED EDU DEPT-N 44195 #495-79-2000 L2004 **P** *100

ADUSUMILLI, Surendranath. 25678 WOODPATH TRL, WESTLAKE 44145 #495-58-1969 L1981 **AN** *020

ADUSUMILLI, Swattantra L. ■ 44145 #495-50-1970 L1983 *100

AEDER, Mark Irwin. 11100 EUCLID AVE, DEPARTMENT OF SURGERY 44106 #028-02-1980 L1984 **GS TTS** *020 †85

AFONJA, Abdu-Rauf Abiodun. 7255 OLD OAK BLVD, STE C111 44130 #690-01-1970 L1978 **ORS** *020 †40

AGARWAL, Sajat. 2500 METROHEALTH DR 44109 #495-45-2002 L2006 **IM** *012

AGARWAL, Saket. 9500 EUCLID AVE 44195 #495-36-1996 L2004 *100

AGDINAOAY, Caridad C. 13916 EUCLID AVE 44112 #748-07-1955 L1971 **IM** *020

AGDINAOAY, Saturnino F. 13916 EUCLID AVE 44112 #748-08-1957 L1978 **GP OS** *020

AGHEL, Arash. 9500 EUCLID AVE, CLEVELAND CLINIC FOUNDATIO 44195 #517-04-2006 L2006 **IM** *012

AGLE, David Patton. 11100 EUCLID AVE, DEPT OF PSYCHIATRY 44106 #067-01-1957 L1962 **P PYA** *040 †75

AGRA, Ruben Tagala. 3361 E 55TH ST 44127 #748-08-1962 L1972 **AN** *020

AGRAWAL, Saurabh. ■ 44195 #187-70-2001 L2005 **IM GS** *012

AGUILERA, Richard Glenn G. SUPPOR2500 METROH, CO RESIDENCY 44109 #748-01-2000 L2007 **PM** *012

AGUSTINES, Manuel Ramirez. ■ 44128 #748-02-1966 L1973 **IM GE** *020

AHLUWALIA, Manmeet Singh. 18101 LORAIN AVE, FAIRVIEW HOSP 44111 #495-45-2001 L2003 **ON** *012 †20

AHMAD, Muzaffar. 9500 EUCLID AVE A, CLEVELAND CLINIC 44195 #495-51-1965 L1972 **PUD IM** *020 †20

AHMAD, Najeh Muhammad. 2500 METROHEALTH DR, CO METRO HLTH MED CTR-RES 44109 #875-01-1995 L2002 **FM** *020 †18

AHMAD, Tasneen Pasha. ■ 44145 #704-02-1982 *100

AHMADINIA, Kasra. ■ 44114 #025-01-2007 L2007 **ORS** *012

AHMED, Ehab Ibrahim. 2500 METROHEALTH DR 44109 #915-03-1976 L2000 **PD** *020 †55

AHMED, Farooq Masood. 2500 METROHEALTH DR, DEPT OF GERIATRICS 44109 #496-27-1997 L2006 **FM** *100 †18

AHMED, Mansoor. 7050 ENGLE RD, STE 101 44130 #704-01-1980 L1992 **PUD CCM** *020 †20

AHMED, Qasim. 3395 SCRANTON RD, DEPT PATH 44109 #704-01-1985 L1994 **PTH** *100 †50

AHMED, Razia Ali. 850 COLUMBIA RD, STE 200 44145 #495-33-1969 L1985 **P** *020

AHMED, Syed Erfan. 1708 SOUTHPOINT DR 44109 #704-16-1990 L2003 **P** *020 †75

AHMED, Tosaddaq. 11100 EUCLID AVE 44106 #160-02-1980 L1995 **IM IMG** *020 †20

AHMED, Yahya Mohamed Huss. 18101 LORAIN AVE, FAIRVIEW HOSPITAL 44111 #915-02-2003 L2007 **IM** *012

AHMED, Ziad Taher M. 11100 EUCLID AVE, UNIV HOSP OF CLEVELAND 44106 #528-03-1977 L1997 **N** *020 †75

AHN, Nicholas Utchan. 1100 EUCLID AVE, STE HAN5043 44115 #024-01-1996 L2005 **OSS ORS** *020 †40

AJIBEKOV, Timour Abitovic. 2500 METROHEALTH DR, METRO HEALTH MED CTR 44109 #913-84-1998 L2006 **NPM** *012

AKHAVAN, Sam. 11100 EUCLID AVE, HANNA 6TH FL 44106 #016-06-2001 L2001 **ORS** *100

AKHTAR, Roomana. 2351 E 22ND ST, ST VINCENT CHARITY HOSPITA 44115 #704-20-1996 L2002 **IM** *020 †20

AKINSOOTO, Shola Victor. 2500 METROHEALTH DR 44109 #690-08-1991 **FM** *100

AKOUM, Fadi Husayn. 11100 EUCLID AVE 44106 #605-01-1999 L2003 **NEP IM** *012 †20

AKUNDI, Aruna. 1729 FULTON RD 44113 #021-05-2000 L2006 **EM** *020 †16

AL-ABOUSI, May Hikmat. 12100 SUPERIOR AVE 44106 #528-01-1989 L1996 **IM** *020 †20

ALAEDEEN, Diya Ihsan. 11100 EUCLID AVE 44106 #017-20-2001 L2001 **GS** *012

ALAGARSAMY, Jayanthi. 11201 SHAKER BLVD 44104 #495-04-1993 L1997 **IM** *020 †20

ALAHMAD, Alaa. 13951 TERRACE RD 44112 #875-01-1998 L2003 **IM** *100 †20

AL AITI, Mohamad Amer. 18101 LORAIN AVE 44111 #875-01-2002 L2005 **IM** *012

ALAM, Uzma. 2500 METROHEALTH DR 44109 #308-13-1997 L1999 **DR** *020 †80

AL AMMARY, Fawaz Saeed Om. 2500 METROHEALTH DR 44109 #915-02-1999 L2004 **IM** *100 †20

ALASFAR, Fahad Saud. ■ 44195 #584-01-1994 L2004 **VS** *020 †85

AL ASHHAB, Aiham. 2351 E 22ND ST, DEPT OF MED EDU 44115 #875-01-2001 L2005 **IM** *012

AL - ASHKAR, Feyrouz Tano. 9500 EUCLID AVE, CLEVELAND CLN A50 44195 #305-01-2000 L2000 **RHU** *012

ALBAINY, Victor Elias. 7007 POWERS BLVD 44129 #308-01-1961 L1970 **ORS** *020

ALBANI, Barbara Jean. 9500 EUCLID AVE BOX 208 44195 #010-02-1997 L1999 **DR** *100 †75,80

ALDANA, Alejandro M, Jr. ■ 44441 #748-01-1956 L1967 **GP GS** *071

ALDANA, Benigno Roque, III. 1730 W 25TH ST, DEPT OF ANESTH 44113 #748-02-1983 L1990 **AN** *020 †05

ALDAOUD, Feras. 18101 LORAIN AVE, FAIRVIEW HOSPITAL 44111 #875-03-2006 L2007 **IM** *012

ALEGRIA, Marco Antonio. 9500 EUCLID AVE, TT32 44195 #649-05-1983 **N** *100

ALESSEH, Hassan. 2500 METROHEALTH DR 44109 #875-01-1993 L1999 **NPM** *020 †55

ALEXANDER, Christine Ann. 2500 METROHEALTH DR, BELL GREVE BUILDING 44109 #038-40-1992 L1997 **FM** *020 †18

ALEXANDER, John J. 2500 METROHEALTH DR, METROHEALTH MEDICAL CENTER 44109 #041-12-1978 L1984 **TS** *020 †85

ALEXANDREANU, Iulia Const. 9500 EUCLID AVE, C/O CCF - GRAD MED EDU DEP 44195 #781-01-1997 L2001 **IM** *100 †05

ALEXOPOULOS, Andreas V. 9500 EUCLID AVE, CLEVELAND CLINIC FOUNDATIO 44195 #418-01-1993 L2002 **CN** *100 †75

ALFIREVIC, Andrej. 9500 EUCLID AVE 44195 #957-01-1997 L2000 **AN** *020 †05

ALFRED, Karl Sverre. 2351 E 22ND ST 44115 #035-08-1942 L1950 **ORS** *071 †40

AL-GHOUL, Mohammed Salah. 9500 EUCLID AVE, CO CCF-GRAD MED EDU DEPT-N 44195 #575-01-1999 L2001 **GS** *012

ALGUR, Ece. 9500 EUCLID AVE 44195 #902-10-1991 L2004 *100

ALHADDAD, Adil Hussain. 9500 EUCLID AVE 44195 #528-01-1978 L2000 **AN** *020 †05

AL-HADDAD, Ali Ghalib. 18901 LAKE SHORE BLVD 44119 #528-01-1973 L1982 **EM IM** *020 †20,16

AL-HARIRI, Adham Bassam. 11100 EUCLID AVE, CO UNIV HOSPS-RESIDENCY OF 44106 #605-01-2001 L2002 **IM** *100

ALI, Mohammed Abbas. CO RESIDENCY OFFICE, UNIVERSITY HOSPITALS CASE 44106 #496-27-2000 L2007 **IM** *012

ALI, Rabie Rafat. 2500 METROHEALTH DR 44109 #495-21-1974 L1996 **FM** *100

ALI, Reyadh Salman. ■ 44195 #915-04-1999 L2007 **PCC** *012

ALIYARI ZENOOZ, Navid. 11100 EUCLID AVE, UNIVERSITY HOSPITALS OF CL 44106 #517-01-2000 L2004 **DR** *012

AL KADDOUMI, Bashir Faris. 9500 EUCLID AVE, CLEVELAND CLINIC FOUNDATIO 44195 #575-01-2004 L2006 **IM** *012

AL-KAISI, Nadia K. 2074 ABINGTON RD 44106 #528-01-1978 L1986 **PTH** *020 †50

ALKHOURI, Naim. PED GASTRO/NUTRITION, DEPT OF 44195 #875-01-2001 L2007 **PG** *012 †20,55

ALLADA, Venkata Naga Rama. 13951 TERRACE RD, DEPT OF GME 44112 #495-11-2003 L2005 **IM** *012

ALLAM, Sridhar Reddy. 9500 EUCLID AVE, DEPT OF GME 44195 #495-11-2003 L2005 **IM** *012

ALLAMANENI, Shyam Sunder. 9500 EUCLID AVE, CLEVELAND CLINIC FNDN 44195 #495-21-1998 L2004 **GS** *012

ALLAREDDY, Veerajalandhar. 2500 METROHEALTH DR, METROHEALTH MED CTR 44109 #495-59-2002 L2004 **MPD** *012

ALLEGRETTI, Amy Elizabeth. 2500 METROHEALTH DR 44109 #017-20-2002 L2002 **EM** *020 †16

ALLEN, Brian Christopher. 9500 EUCLID AVE, CLINIC FOUNDATION 44195 #056-06-2004 L2006 **DR** *012

ALLEN, Valerie Theresa. 15201 EUCLID AVE 44112 #038-06-1994 L1997 **MPD** *040

ALLENDE, Daniela Soledad. CO GME - NA23 9500 EUCLID, CLEVELAND CLINIC FOUNDATIO 44195 #132-11-2001 L2006 **PTH** *012

ALLOCCO, Frances Theresa. 1215 W 110TH ST, # 306 44102 #016-02-2002 L2002 **GS** *012

ALLYN, Wilfred Earl, Jr. ■ 44122 #035-09-1940 L1941 **GP FM** *071

ALMAARAWI, Mohammad. 18101 LORAIN AVE, DEPT OF INTERNAL MED 44111 #875-01-2002 L2003 **IM** *100

AL-MARRAWI, Mhd Yaser. 7007 POWERS BLVD 44129 #875-01-1995 L2003 **IM** *020 †20

ALMASLAMANI, Yousuf. 9500 EUCLID AVE, CO CCF-GRAD MED EDU DEPT-N 44195 #539-06-1988 L2000 **U** *100

AL-MHANNA, Khaldoun Najib. ■ 44106 #875-01-1994 L2005 **HO** *012 †20

AL MOASIS, Ghassan. 2322 E 22ND ST STE 210 44115 #875-01-1976 L1984 **TS GS** *020 †85,90

AL-MUHAIZEA, Mohammad A. ■ 44195 #797-01-1993 L2000 **CHN** *100 †55,75

AL-NIMR, Amer Omar. 11100 EUCLID AVE 3RD, FLOOR LAKESIDE, 44106 #605-01-2002 L2003 **MPD** *012 †55

ALOMRAN, Mohammed Shaker. 11100 EUCLID AVE RM 3018, CO UNIV HOSPS-RESIDENCY OF 44106 #155-01-1995 L2003 *020

ALRAIES, M Chadi Mowfak. 2351 E 22ND ST, DEPT OF MED EDUCATION 44115 #875-02-2002 L2005 **IM** *012

ALRAIYES, Abdul Hamid Mow. 2351 E 22ND ST, DEPT OF MED EDU 44115 #875-02-2001 L2006 *100

AL-RUZZEH, Sharif Mohamed. ■ 44115 #915-02-1994 L2007 **GS** *012

AL SHAER, Adnan Mohammad. 2351 E 22ND ST, DEPT OF MED EDU 44115 #575-02-1999 L2006 *100

AL-SHEKHLEE, Amer Kassim. 11100 EUCLID AVE 44106 #528-01-1991 L1999 **N** *020 †75

AL SOLAIMAN, Firas. 9500 EUCLID AVE, C/O CCF-GRAD MED EDU DEPT- 44195 #875-02-2000 L2002 **IM** *100 †20

ALTON, John Anthony. 7255 OLD OAK BLVD, STE C202 44130 #038-40-1992 L1996 **OBG** *020 †30

ALTOSE, Brenda Rachel. ■ 44118 #038-06-2005 L2005 **CHP** *012

ALTOSE, Michael Dov. 11100 EUCLID AVE, BOLWELL 2400 44106 #038-06-2004 L2004 **AN** *012

ALTOSE, Murray David. 10701 EAST BLVD 44106 #062-01-1965 L1977 **IM PUD** *030 †20

ALURU, Radhalakshmi Devi. 2500 METROHEALTH DR, METROHEALTH MED CTR-RES SU 44109 #495-50-1998 L2000 **IM** *020 †20

ALVARADO, Nannette. 11100 EUCLID AVE, RADIOLOGY DEPARTMENT 44106 #042-02-1994 L2002 **UCM** *020 †80

ALVAREZ-TOSTADO, Javier A. 9500 EUCLID AVE, CLEVELAND CLINIC FOUNDATIO 44195 #649-31-1997 L2005 *100

ALZOUBI, Hassan. 18099 LORAIN AVE, # 508 44111 #875-01-1998 L2001 **IM** *020

AMANULLAH, Jamaluddin Fai. 6559 WILSON MILLS RD, STE 106A 44143 #496-14-1994 L2001 *020

AMENT, Albert Erik. 2074 ABINGTON RD, DEPT RAD 44106 #154-01-1970 L1976 **R** *020 †80

AMIN, Jaina Indu. 11100 EUCLID AVE, UNIV HOSPS OF CLEVELAND 44106 #017-20-2006 L2006 **P** *012

AMIN, Shalin Jitendra. CLINIC FOUNDATION, CLEVELAND 44195 #024-07-2003 L2004 **DR** *012

AMINI, Mohammad Reza. 9500 EUCLID AVE 44195 #517-01-2000 L2006 **IM** *012

AMIR, Jacob. ■ 44120 #550-01-1960 L1976 **ON HEM** *020 †20

AMIRI, Loabat. 2500 METROHEALTH DR, DEPT OF GME 44109 #517-08-1997 L2006 **IM** *012

AMIRLAK, Bardia. 11100 EUCLID AVE, UNIV HOSP OF CLEVELAND 44106 #308-13-1999 L2007 **PS** *012

AMIRNENI, Vamsee Krishna. 2351 E 22ND ST, DEPT OF MED ED 44115 #495-50-2000 L2005 **IM** *012

AMIT, Guy. 2500 METROHEALTH DR, DEPT OF GME 44109 #550-01-1995 L2006 **ICE** *012

AMOFAH, Rosemary. ■ 44106 #010-03-1995 L2000 **PD** *020 †55

ANAND, Lokanathan. 2351 E 22ND ST, ST VINCENT CHARITY 44115 #495-16-1993 L2003 **IM** *020 †20

ANANDAMURTHY, Balaram. 18101 LORAIN AVE, DEPT OF INTERNAL MED 44111 #496-35-1998 L2005 **IM** *012

ANCHALA, Krishnapriya. 11100 EUCLID AVE, CHILDRENS HOSP-PEDIATRICS 44106 #028-02-1998 L2000 **PD** *020 †55

ANDERS, Peter A Zalewski. 26314 CENTER RIDGE RD 44145 #759-03-1996 L2000 **IM** *020 †20

ANDERSON, Carryn Marie. ■ 44118 #048-02-2003 L2003 **RO** *012

ANDERSON, Eric. 9500 EUCLID AVE, DESK E-19 44195 #038-06-1984 L1984 **EM** *020 †16

ANDERSON, James Morley. 11400 EUCLID AVE STE 100 44106 #038-06-1976 L1979 **PTH** *040

ANDERSON, James Robert. 11100 EUCLID AVE HH-610, ORTHOPAEDIC SURGERY 44106 #048-12-1999 L2005 **HS ORS** *020 †40

ANDERSON, James Stephen. 2500 METROHEALTH DR, STE H910 44109 #005-15-1986 L1992 **NS** *020 †25

ANDERSON, Michael E. 9500 EUCLID AVE 44195 #038-06-1985 L1986 **OBG** *020 †30

ANDERSON, Michael Robt. 2500 METROHEALTH DR 44109 #038-06-1990 L1993 **CCP** *020 †55

ANDERSON, Spencer Hoyt. 9500 EUCLID AVE 44195 #025-07-1981 L1985 **DR** *020 †80

ANDERSON, Wilfred L. ■ 44118 #028-02-1974 L1975 **OS** *075

ANDO, Makoto. 9500 EUCLID AVE, CO CCF-GRAD MED EDU DEPT-N 44195 #572-01-1991 L2000 *100

ANDRADE ORTIZ, Werner Alf. ■ 44118 #429-02-2001 L2005 **GS** *012

ANDREJIC, Anthony. 9500 EUCLID AVE, CLEVELAND CLINIC/MED ED NA 44195 #305-01-1996 L2000 **GS** *100

ANDRESEN, Steven Ware. 9500 EUCLID AVE, DESK R 35 44195 #018-75-1978, ▲ L1979 **IM HEM** *020 †20

ANDREWS, Herbert. ■ 44104 #012-05-1965 L1971 **GS OS** *071 †40

ANDRISH, Jack Taylor. 9500 EUCLID AVE, DESK A-41 44195 #019-02-1969 L1977 **ORS** *020 †40

ANGEL, Mark Eric. 6770 MAYFIELD RD, STE 205 44124 #836-01-1981 L1994 **IC CD** *020 †20

ANGELOV, Lilyana. 9500 EUCLID AVE 80, CLEVELAND CLINIC FOUNDATIO 44195 #065-01-1992 L2002 *020

ANGERMEIER, Kenneth Wayne. 9500 EUCLID AVE, STE 100 44195 #017-20-1985 L1989 **U** *020 †95

ANGHELOIU, Viorel. 13951 TERRACE RD, DEPT OF GME 44112 #781-08-1999 L2005 **IM** *012

ANGLEA, Joy Sharon. PO BOX 308011 44130 #051-01-1981 L2005 **FM** *030 †18

ANHALT, John Paul. 11100 EUCLID AVE, UNIV. HOSPITALS OF CLEVELA 44106 #028-02-1972 L1998 **CLP** *030 †50

ANIL, Sunitha. 2500 METROHEALTH DR, CO METROHEALTH MED CTR-RES 44109 #496-34-1996 L2003 **MPD** *100

ANIS ABDEL LATIF, Khaled. 9500 EUCLID AVE 44195 #915-06-2003 L2005 **N** *012

ANJUM, Amina. 2351 E 22ND ST, DEPT OF MEDICAL EDUCATION 44115 #704-06-2000 L2005 **IM** *012

ANKENEY, Jay Lloyd. 2074 ABINGTON RD 44106 #038-06-1945 L1945 **TS** *071 †85,90

ANKU, Vincent Danl. 19250 BAGLEY RD, STE 107 44130 #035-20-1969 L1972 **ON HEM** *020 †20

ANNABLE, William Lawrence. 1611 S GREEN RD, ASSOCIATES 44121 #041-01-1971 L1973 **OPH** *020 †35

ANSELMI, Lora Jo. 5955 RIDGE RD 44129 #025-01-1989 L1991 **P** *020

ANSEVIN, Carl Daniel. 11100 EUCLID AVE RM 3018, CO UNIV HOSPS-RESIDENCY OF 44106 #038-45-2003 L2003 **N** *020

ANSLEY, William Geo. SUNNY ACRES HOSP 44122 #038-41-1954 L1954 **IM** *071

ANTENUCCI, Christina M. 2500 METROHEALTH DR 44109 #024-01-1995 L1999 **FM** *020 †18

ANTEOLA, Edmundo Mappala. 805 COLUMBIA RD STE 101 44145 #748-01-1965 L1973 **PUD IM** *020 †20

ANTHONY, Donald D. CASE WESTERN RESERVE U SCH 44106 #038-06-1958 L1958 **ON GE** *050

ANTHONY, Mary Elizabeth. 6115 POWERS BLVD, STE 100 44129 #038-75-1998, ▲ L2000 *020

ANTONELLI, Giuseppe. 6789 RIDGE RD, STE 108 44129 #132-01-1974 L1980 **RHU IM** *020

ANWARUDDIN, Saif. ■ 44195 #024-16-2002 L2005 **CD** *012 †20

APONTE, Carlos Julio. 18099 LORAIN AVE, ST 208 44111 #264-01-1968 L1975 **RHU IM** *020 †20

APOSTOLAKIS, John T. 9500 EUCLID AVE 44195 #041-01-1988 L1997 **AN** *020 †05

APPACHI, Elumalai. 9500 EUCLID AVE 44195 #495-16-1993 L1997 **CCP** *020 †55

APPACHI, Mala. 6770 MAYFIELD RD # 236, MAYFIELD HEIGHTS 44124 #495-16-1985 L2000 **PD** *020 †55

APPAU, Kweku. ■ 44120 #038-45-2005 L2005 **IM** *100

APPLEBAUM, Hillorie Ann. 3927 W MEADOW LN 44122 #038-43-1981 L1985 **PD** *020 †55

ARAFAH, Bahauddin Mahmdud. 2074 ABINGTON RD 44106 #605-01-1976 L1980 **END IM** *050 †20

ARAIN, Faisal Daud. 9500 EUCLID AVE 44195 #704-20-1997 L2002 **AN** *100 †05

AREFIN, Faruq Nurul. 2500 METROHEALTH DR, METROHEALTH MED CTRINT MED 44109 #160-02-1990 L1999 **IM** *100

ARELLI, Vineesha. ■ 44114 #028-03-2007 L2007 **IM** *012

ARENA, Roberto. 9500 EUCLID AVE, CLEVELAND CLINIC 44195 #561-12-1996 L2004 **PTH** *012

ARGALIOUS, Maged Youssef. 9500 EUCLID AVE E-31, THE CLEVELAND CLINIC 44195 #915-02-1992 L2000 **AN** *020 †05

ARGEKAR, Ashok Waman. 7007 POWERS BLVD 44129 #495-01-1969 L1977 **GS GP** *030 ‡

ARMADA, Philip C. 3395 SCRANTON RD, METRO LIFE-FLIGHT 44109 #025-07-1987 L1998 **EM** *020 †16

ARNOLD, James Edward. 11100 EUCLID AVE, LAKESIDE 4500 44106 #048-13-1977 L1987 **PDO** *040 †45

ARNSON, Douglas Scott. 4400 RENAISSANCE PKWY, STE L 44128 #038-40-1986 L1988 **DR** *020 †80

ARON, Anirudh. 13951 TERRACE RD 44112 #496-43-1999 L2005 **IM** *012

ARON, David C. 10701 EAST BLVD, EDUCATION OFFICE 14W 44106 #035-01-1975 L1981 **END IM** *030 †20

ARON, Monish. 9500 EUCLID AVE, DEPT OF GME 44195 #495-12-1991 L2005 **U** *100

ARONICA, Mark Anthony. 9500 EUCLID AVE, ALLERGY/IMMUNOLOGY C22 44195 #035-06-1991 L2001 **AI PCC** *020 †20,03

ARONSON, Sarah Cymry. 11100 EUCLID AVE, MATHER PAVILLION 1716 44106 #043-01-1987 L2001 **AN** *012 †75,18

ARORA, Catherine Dowe. 18099 LORAIN AVE, INC 44111 #038-06-1994 L1996 **PD** *020 †55

ARORA, Harendra. 9500 EUCLID AVE, MAIL CODE E-31 44195 #495-45-1991 L2007 **AN** *020

ARRABI, Walid. 12000 MCCRACKEN RD 44125 #913-92-1983 L1991 **IM** *020 †20

ARRUDA, Maria Janine L. 9500 EUCLID AVE 44195 #187-07-1984 L2003 **PDC** *020

ARRUDA, Mauricio Silveira. 9500 EUCLID AVE - F15, CLEVELAND CLINIC FOUNDATIO 44195 #187-86-1984 L2003 **IM** *020 †20

ARSHAD, Saaima. 18101 LORAIN AVE, FAIRVIEW HOSPITAL 44111 #704-20-2005 L2007 **IM** *012

ARSHAM, Kenneth Lee. 23250 CHAGRIN BLVD STE 450 44122 #010-02-1979 L1983 **PS HS** *020 †65

ARTZ, J Sheldon. 6780 MAYFIELD RD 44124 #021-01-1967 L1968 **PS** *020 †65

ARUMUGAM, Chitra. 2500 METROHEALTH DR, DEPT OF RESIDENCY SUPPORT 44109 #496-23-1995 L2006 **PD** *012

ASADUZZAMAN, S. M.. 2500 METROHEALTH DR 44109 #160-05-1995 L2006 **IM** *012

ASANTE, Donald Darko. 13951 TERRACE RD, DEPT OF GME 44112 #412-02-2004 L2006 **IM** *012

ASH, Lori Louise. 9500 EUCLID AVE A111, CLEVELAND CLINIC FOUNDATIO 44195 #038-44-1991 L1994 **PG** *020 †55

ASHAI, Nuzhat. 9500 EUCLID AVE 44195 #704-01-1983 L1990 **IM NEP** *020 †20

ASHBY, Arlan Marcus Caine. ■ 44195 #026-08-1996 L2004 **OBG** *020 †30

ASHBY-VINCENT, Karen L. 5850 LANDERBROOK DR, STE 3 44124 #038-06-1988 L1992 **OBG** *020 †30

ASHLEY, Kellan Elizabeth. ■ 44114 #027-01-2002 L2006 **CD** *012 †20

ASHRAF, Syed Parvez. 6559 WILSON MILLS RD, STE 106A 44143 #495-15-1992 L1998 **IM** *020 †20

ASHWATH, Mahi Lakshmi. 11100 EUCLID AVE, HARVEY HOUSE 415 44106 #495-21-1999 L2004 **CD** *012

ASKARI, Arman Teimouri. 9500 EUCLID AVE F15, THE CLEVELAND CLINIC FOUND 44195 #038-06-1997 L2001 **CD** *020 †20

ASSAF, Hasan Mohammad. PO BOX 77097 44107 #605-01-1981 L1984 **PTH PCP** *020 †50

ASTREIKA, Vera. 2500 METROHEALTH DR 44109 #912-05-1997 L2005 **P** *012

ATALLAH, Sylvana Latif Ha. 18101 LORAIN AVE 44111 #915-02-1995 L2004 **IM** *020 †20

ATANASKOVA, Natasha. ■ 44118 #026-08-2007 L2007 **D** *012

ATAYA, Khalid Mohammad. 2500 METROHEALTH DR, DEPT OB 44109 #605-01-1979 L1989 **REN OBG** *050 †20

ATIEMO, Humphrey Odei. 9500 EUCLID AVE A100 44195 #023-01-1999 L2005 **U** *020

ATIK, Fernando Antibas. 9500 EUCLID AVE, C/O CCF-GRAD MED EDU DEPT- 44195 #187-67-1995 L2002 *020

ATKINSON, Lisa Ann. 12200 FAIRHILL RD 44120 #055-02-1988 L1994 **IMG** *020 †20

ATLURI, Dileep Kumar. 2500 METROHEALTH DR, METROHEALTH MED CTR 44109 #495-65-2002 L2005 **IM** *012

ATREJA, Ashish. 9500 EUCLID AVE, DESK A91 44195 #495-36-1999 L2001 **IM** *100

ATTARAN, Marjan. 9500 EUCLID AVE, DEPT OF OB/GYN - A/81 44195 #038-44-1988 L1991 **OBG** *020 †30

AUCEJO, Federico Natalio. 9500 EUCLID AVE, DESK A110 44195 #132-11-1998 L2005 *100

AUCKLEY, Dennis Herbert. 2500 METROHEALTH DR 44109 #017-20-1990 L1998 PUD CCM *020 †20

AUGUSTINE, Joshua James. 10701 EAST BLVD, DEPT OF NEPHROLOGY 44106 #025-01-1997 L2001 IM *020 †20

AULAKH, Lakyntiew Patsha. 11100 EUCLID AVE, DEPARTMENT OF PSYCHIATRY 44106 #495-18-1991 L2001 PYG *100 †75

AULETTA, Jeffery James. 11100 EUCLID AVE, UNIVERSITY HOSP OF CLEVELA 44106 #038-06-1996 L1997 PHO *020 †55

AURON-GOMEZ, Ari. 2500 METROHEALTH DR, CO METROHEALTH MED CTR-RES 44109 #649-01-2001 L2001 PN *020 †55

AURON-GOMEZ, Moises. 2500 METROHEALTH DR H52 44109 #649-01-1999 L2003 MPD *100 †20,55

AUSENBACHS, Anita. ■ 44138 #594-01-1943 L1952 RHU *030

AVENDANO, Virgilio A. ■ 44141 #748-01-1956 L1967 IM *020

AVERBOOK, Bruce Jeffrey. 2500 METROHEALTH DR, METROHEALTH MEDICAL CENTER 44109 #010-01-1983 L1993 GS SO *020 †85

AVERY, Ann K. 2500 METROHEALTH DR, C-2001 44109 #038-06-1994 L1997 ID *020 †20

AVERY, Robin K. 9500 EUCLID AVE, DESK S32 CLEVELAND CLINIC 44195 #024-01-1985 L1993 ID *020 †20

AVITSIAN, Rafi. 9500 EUCLID AVE E-31, CLEVELAND CLINIC 44195 #517-01-1994 L2000 AN *020 †05 ‡

AWAIS, George M. 9500 EUCLID AVE, #EE40 EMERITUS OFC 44195 #065-01-1960 L1967 OBG *071 †30

AYACHE, Mirna Bahij. 9500 EUCLID AVE 44195 #605-01-2004 L2005 IM *012

AYANLEKE, Omobayonle Mosa. 2351 E 22ND ST, DEPT OF MED EDU 44115 #690-01-1999 L2006 *100

AYDIN, Huseyin Nail. 9500 EUCLID AVE, C/O CCF-GRAD MED EDU DEPT- 44195 #902-10-1996 L2003 GS *012

AYDIN, Naz Bige. 9500 EUCLID AVE, CLEVELAND CLINIC FOUNDATIO 44195 #902-19-1996 L2005 *012

AYOUB, Basim Ayoub. 18101 LORAIN AVE, DEPT OF INTERNAL MED 44111 #915-02-2001 L2006 IM *012

AYOUB, Walaa Ayoub Gabra. 18101 LORAIN AVE, FAIRVIEW HOSPITAL 44111 #915-02-1995 L2007 IM *012

AYYAD, Alaeddin Mohammad. ■ 44195 #038-40-2006 L2006 IM *012

AZAR, Ann Mary. 14055 CEDAR RD, STE A6 44118 #165-03-1979 L1985 IM *020 †20

AZIZ, Adel Mofeed. 18101 LORAIN AVE 44111 #915-02-1974 L1986 AN CCA *020 †05

AZIZ, Fekri Ramzi. 9500 EUCLID AVE 44195 #330-02-1963 L1975 AN IM *020 †05

AZIZ, Mervat Zaky. 29000 CENTER RIDGE RD 44145 #915-02-1976 L1989 PD *020 †55

BAAKLINI, Samia Chatta. 960 CLAGUE RD, STE 3201 44145 #875-01-1981 L1992 IM *020 †20

BABAKHANLOU, Pejman. ■ 44143 #056-06-2005 L2005 GS *012

BABU, Benson Abbi. ■ 44195 #473-04-2003 L2004 IM *100 †20

BABU, Mayukh. ■ 44106 #038-44-2003 L2003 DR *012

BABU, Vinay Gutti. 10900 EUCLID AVE, DEPT OF OPTHALMONOLOGY 44106 #041-14-2004 L2005 OPH *012

BACCALA, Angelo Angelino. 9500 EUCLID AVE, CO CCF-GRAD MED EDU DEPT-N 44195 #023-07-2002 L2002 U *012

BACEVICE, Ann Mary. 11100 EUCLID AVE 44106 #038-06-1999 L1999 PEM *100 †55

BACH, John Alexander. ■ 44113 #038-41-2005 L2005 GS *012

BACIK, Ronald John. 4269 PEARL RD, STE 311 44109 #016-06-1972 L1973 PUD PCC *020 †20

BACNIS-ABOLA, Maria T. 9500 EUCLID AVE, TT32 44195 #748-02-1986 VS *020

BADRI, Rafal A. 14100 CEDAR RD, STE 350 44121 #528-01-1976 L1984 GP D *020 †85

BAE, Charles Joonghie. 9500 EUCLID AVE, CLEVELAND CLINIC SLEEP CTR 44195 #010-02-1988 L2001 N SME *020 †75

BAE, Seong Gon. 18101 LORAIN AVE, FAIRVIEW GEN HOSP 44111 #011-04-2005 L2007 GS *012

BAELE, Henry R. 11100 EUCLID AVE 44106 #017-20-1980 L1983 VS GS *020 †85

BAETZ-GREENWALT, Barbara. 9500 EUCLID AVE 44195 #038-06-1979 L1981 ID PD *020 †55

BAEZA, Cristian Rafael. 9500 EUCLID AVE, CO CCF-GRAD MED EDU DEPT-N 44195 #231-01-1995 L2000 *020

BAFNA, Shamik. 2740 CARNEGIE AVE, CLEVELAND EYE CLNC 44115 #025-01-1992 L2007 OPH *020 †35

BAGAI, Rajesh Kumar. 11100 EUCLID AVE 44106 #038-44-2000 L2000 HO *020 †20

BAHLER, Robert Clyde. 2500 METROHEALTH DR 44109 #038-06-1961 L1965 CD IM *020 †20

BAHLIS, Nizar Jack. 11100 EUCLID AVE, IRELAND CANCER CENTER 44106 #605-02-1995 L2002 HO *100 †20

BAHNER, Jennifer Dawn. ■ 44118 #056-05-2006 L2006 IM *012

BAHNIWAL, Charanjit S. 9500 EUCLID AVE, DEPT OF ANESTHESIA 44195 #495-29-1980 L2000 AN *020 †05

BAHU, Suhail George. 9500 EUCLID AVE, DEPT OF GME 44195 #539-03-2005 L2006 IM *012

BAI, Indira M. 1730 W 25TH ST, LUTHERAN HOSPITAL 44113 #495-63-1970 L1974 PTH D *020 †50

BAIG, Mirza Khurrum. 9500 EUCLID AVE, CLEVELAND CLINIC FNDN 44195 #704-02-1989 CRS *100

BAILIN, Charles Martin. 26250 EUCLID AVE STE 203 44132 #038-06-1969 L1969 GYN *020 †30

BAILIN, Philip Lawrence. 9500 EUCLID AVE, DEPT DERM 44195 #016-06-1968 L1971 D DMP *020 †15

BAILIT, Jennifer Lynne. 2500 METROHEALTH DR 44109 #024-07-1994 L2002 OBG *020 †30

BAIN, Mark Douglas. ■ 44195 #010-02-2004 L2004 NS *012

BAISHNAB, Radha Raman. 14861 CHEROKEE TRL, FRCPC 44130 #704-03-1963 L1970 IM CD *020

BAJWA, Jawad Ahmad. 9500 EUCLID AVE 31, CENTER FOR NEUOGOLY RESERV 44195 #704-01-1999 L2006 N *100

BAJWA, Momena Khalid. 2500 METROHEALTH DR, DEPT OF MED/PEDS 44109 #305-01-2007 L2007 MPD *012

BAJWA, Nadia Massod. 9500 EUCLID AVE, CLEVELAND CLINIC FOUNDATIO 44195 #038-44-2001 L2001 PD *020 †55

BAJZER, Christopher T. 9500 EUCLID AVE, DESK F25 44195 #025-07-1990 L1994 CD *020 †20

BAKDASH, Tarif. 11100 EUCLID AVE, RAINBOW BABIES & CHILDREN 44106 #875-01-1988 L1998 CHN *020 †55,75

BAKER, Mark Early. 9500 EUCLID AVE, CLEVELAND CLINIC 44195 #016-43-1978 L1994 DR *020 †20

BAKER, Saul P. 2111 ACACIA PARK DR 44124 #038-40-1953 L1953 IMG CD *071

BAKER, Stephen Edward. ■ 44103 #004-01-2006 L2006 PTH *012

BAKHOS, Charles Tanos. 9500 EUCLID AVE, CO CCF-GRAD MED EDU DEPT-N 44195 #605-02-2001 L2002 GS *012

BAKHRU, Mihir Ramesh. 9500 EUCLID AVE, CLEVELAND CLINIC FOUNDATIO 44195 #422-01-2004 L2004 IM *100 †20

BAKHRU, Ritu. 11100 EUCLID AVE 44106 #661-03-2004 L2005 FP *012

BAKHTIARI, Nabi. 9500 EUCLID AVE 44195 #539-03-1992 L2004 FP *012

BAKSHI, Anuradha. 18200 LORAIN AVE, DEPT OF FAMILY PRACTICE 44111 #539-06-2001 L2006 FP *012

BALA, Endrit. 9500 EUCLID AVE, CLEVELAND CLINIC FOUNDATIO 44195 #120-01-2001 L2006 *100

BALAJI, Harigopal N. 6789 RIDGE RD, INC 44129 #495-16-1988 L1999 IM *020 †20

BALASUBRAMANIAN, Vijayalak. 2351 E 22ND ST 44115 #495-59-1999 L2004 IM *100 †20

BALEY, Jill Elizabeth. 2101 ADELBERT RD 44106 #038-41-1976 L1979 NPM PD *020 †55

BALIGA, Christopher Sures. 11100 EUCLID AVE, UNIV HOSP OF CLEVELAND 44106 #495-37-2002 L2005 IM *012

BALINA, Cynthia Kraus. 2500 METROHEALTH DR # A1, THE METROHEALTH SYSTEM 44109 #038-41-2001 L2001 IM IMG *020

BALIS, George P. 9500 EUCLID AVE, FOUNDATION A/40 44195 #418-01-1975 L1979 ORS *020 †40

BALL, Philippe Georges. ■ 44119 #055-02-2005 L2005 AN *012

BALL, Steven Scott. 9500 EUCLID AVE, HEAD AND NECK INSTITUTE 44195 #038-40-1996 L2001 OTO *020 †45

BALLARD, Lester Arthur. 9500 EUCLID AVE 44195 #038-40-1955 L1955 GYN *071 †30

BALLIN, Mitchell Irving. 2500 METROHEALTH DR 44109 #550-02-2001 L2001 IM *020 †20

BALLO, Frances. 29125 CHAGRIN BLVD, STE 110 44122 #038-06-1988 L1995 D *020 †55,15

BALLOU, Stanley Paul. 2500 METROHEALTH DR 44109 #041-12-1973 L1974 RHU *040 †20

BALRAJ, Elizabeth K. 11001 CEDAR AVE FL 4 44195 #495-27-1963 L1972 FOP *020 †50

BALSELLS, Francisco. ■ 44145 #429-02-1989 PG *020 †55

BALTAGI, Sirine Abdallah. 9500 EUCLID AVE 44195 #605-01-2004 L2005 PD *012

BAMBA, Sonya. ■ 44115 #028-34-2007 *012

BAMFORD, Cynthia C. 9500 EUCLID AVE 44195 #038-06-1990 L1991 N *020 †75

BANAGA, Paraluman B. 18697 BAGLEY RD 44130 #748-10-1972 L1978 GP *020

BANAGA, Rogelio Ainza. ■ 44129 #748-10-1969 L1979 AN OS *020

BANAS, David Allan. 2500 METROHEALTH DR 44109 #038-40-2003 L2003 AMF *020 †18

BANGAYAN, Norberto M. 4269 PEARL RD STE 208 44109 #748-10-1964 L1972 CD *020

BANGERT, Barbara Ann. 11100 EUCLID AVE, STE 2600 44106 #051-07-1986 L1991 RNR *020 †80

BANKER, Betty Quarrier. 1708 AIKEN AVE 44109 #035-03-1950 L1970 NP N *040 †75

BANKS, Michael Alan. 7255 OLD OAK BLVD, STE C405 44130 #038-06-1992 L1993 ORS *020 †40

BANO, Fasahat. 2351 E 22ND ST, DEPT OF MED EDU 44115 #704-02-1990 L2006 *100

BANOZIC, Richard Michael. 2500 E 22ND ST, 2ND FL 44115 #038-06-1991 L1994 IM *020 †20

BANSAL, Rashmi Malay. 11311 SHAKER BLVD RM 4135 44104 #495-56-1990 IM *100

BANSAL, Ridhi. 2500 METROH, CO RESIDENCY 44109 #495-43-2003 L2007 P *012

BANSAL, Samiksha. CLEVELAND CLINIC, 900 EUCLID AVE 44195 #495-77-1999 GS *012

BANSAL, Vipin Kumar. ■ 44114 #654-01-2001 L2005 PAN *012

BAPTISTA, Bernard Agustin. 11100 EUCLID AVE, LKS 3018 44106 #748-01-1993 L2002 PD *100

BAQUET-SIMPSON, Alena M. 8333 ROCKSIDE DR, STE 200 44125 #047-07-1983 L1998 FM *030 †18 ‡

BARAKAT, Mazen Ahmad. 2500 METROHEALTH DR 44109 #305-01-2004 L2005 MPD *012

BARANWAL, Seema. 9500 EUCLID AVE, DESK S-70 44195 #025-01-1994 L2004 IM *020 †20

BARBACCI, Joanne C. 6780 MAYFIELD RD 44124 #038-40-1983 L1986 OBG GP *020 †30

BARBAR, Maha I. 9500 EUCLID AVE, CLEVELAND CLINIC FNDN 44195 #575-01-1989 L1998 PG *100 †55

BARBASTEFANO ARAGON, Juan. ■ 44195 #264-05-1999 L2005 IM *012

BARBER, Ashley Elizabeth. ■ 44118 #038-45-2006 L2006 IM *012

BARBER, Matthew Don. 9500 EUCLID AVE 44195 #041-02-1994 L2001 OBG *020 †30

BARBU, Anca Maria. 11100 EUCLID AVE, DEPT. OF SURGERY 44106 #041-15-2004 L2004 OTO *012

BARCENA BLANCH, Julio And. 2074 ABINGTON RD 44106 #264-04-1999 L2002 CD *012

BARDHAN, Bonny. 2500 METROHEALTH DR, METROHEALTH MED CTR 44109 #495-02-1997 L2001 PD *020 †55

BARICH, Donald Peter. 11100 EUCLID AVE, UNIV PRIM CARE PRACT 44106 #016-11-1965 L1966 PD MDM *030 †55

BARINGER, David Chas. 9500 EUCLID AVE, DESK A80 44195 #038-40-1978 L1983 GS TRS *020 †85

BARKOUKIS, Michael Thos. 6900 PEARL RD STE 200, SOUTHWEST UROLOGY 44130 #038-06-1977 L1981 U *020 †95

BARNES, Arthur. 9500 EUCLID AVE 44195 #024-05-1955 L1957 AN *030 †05

BARNES, David Shields. 9500 EUCLID AVE, CLEVELAND CLINIC 44195 #036-01-1981 L1986 GE *020 †20

BARNETT, Gene Henry. 9500 EUCLID AVE, CLEVELAND CLINIC HOSPDESK 44195 #038-06-1980 L1986 NS *020 †25

BARNETT, Timothy Raymond. 20455 LORAIN RD STE 353 44126 #038-40-1996 L1997 GS *020 †85

BARON, Mira. 3619 PARK EAST DR STE 109 44122 #913-89-1970 L1981 IM *050

BARON VON MAYDELL, Bernhar. 9500 EUCLID AVE, CO CCF-GRAD MED EDU DEPT-N 44195 #409-16-1996 L2000 CN *100

BARR, Sudipa B. 9500 EUCLID AVE M-73, CLEVELAND CLINIC FOUNDATIO 44195 #038-44-2002 L2002 PDE *020 †55

BARRETT, Conor Dominic. 9500 EUCLID AVE, DEPT OF GME 44195 #539-02-1999 L2006 *100

BARRETT, James Patrick. ■ 44111 #028-34-1955 L1956 P GS *020 †85

BARRON, Bernard. ■ 44122 #038-40-1958 L1958 IM *020

BARROW, Betty Jean. 2500 METROHEALTH DR 44109 #038-06-1990 L1994 RO *020 †80

BARRY, Jill Marie. 27100 CHARDON RD, INC 44143 #025-12-1989 L1991 IM *020 †20

BAR-SHAIN, David Solomon. 2500 METROHEALTH DR, METROHEALTH MEDICAL CENTER 44109 #038-06-1995 L1996 PD *020 †55

BARSOUM, Kamal Nosseir. 9500 EUCLID AVE 44195 #915-04-1962 L1973 AN PUD *071 †05

BARTONE, Tracy Marie. 11100 EUCLID AVE 44106 #665-01-1999 L1999 CCA *100

BARUCH, Yaacov. 2500 METROHEALTH DR, CO METROHEALTH MED CTRRES 44109 #550-03-1977 L2000 *100

BASA, Arturo Simon. 6900 PEARL RD, # 2 44130 #748-08-1963 L1971 U GS *020 †95

BASALI, Ayman Harris. 9500 EUCLID AVE, CLEVELAND CLINIC FOUND 44195 #915-02-1986 L1997 PME AN *020 †05

BASCOM, Daphne Ayn. 11100 EUCLID AVE, OF OTOLARYNGOLOGY, HEAD & 44106 #041-12-1996 L2002 OTO *020 †45

BASH, Norman. 5187 MAYFIELD RD, STE 102 44124 #038-40-1952 L1952 FM *071 †18

BASHIAN, Gregory Garo. F-15, C/O LOIS ADAMSKI, 9500 EUCLID AVENUE 44195 #023-07-2000 L2004 ICE *012 †20

BASHOUR, Charles Allen. 9500 EUCLID AVE, M/C G58 44195 #048-12-1987 L1996 **TS CCS** *020 †85

BASHOUR, Fadi S. 7575 NORTHCLIFF AVE, STE 200 44144 #875-01-1989 L1993 **OBG** *020 †20,30

BASKIN, Jonathan Z. 11100 EUCLID AVE, DEPT OF OTO HNS STED 4500 44106 #035-19-1998 L2004 **OTO FPS** *020 †45

BASS, Jonathan. 2475 E 22ND ST, STE 611 44115 #038-41-1979 L1980 **D DMP** *020 †15

BASS, Nancy Ellyn. 11100 EUCLID AVE 44106 #038-06-1987 L1987

BATAL, Omar Abdulhamid. 9500 EUCLID AVE 44195 #605-01-2006 L2007 **IM** *012

BATES, Craig Guy. 2500 METROHEALTH DR 44109 #036-01-2001 L2001 **EM** *020 †16

BATIZY, Lehel G. 12301 SNOW RD 44130 #473-01-1991 L1995 **IM** *020 †20

BATTON, Angela Lynn. 2500 METROHEALTH DR, DEPT OF EMGY MED BG-360 44109 #016-43-2002 L2005 **EM** *020 †16

BATTON, Beau Jacob. 11100 EUCLID AVE, DEPT. NEONATOLOGY, RB&C HO 44106 #016-43-2002 L2005 **NPM** *012 †55

BAUER, Dorota Ewa. 1730 W 25TH ST 44113 #759-10-1991 L1997 **IM** *020 †20

BAUER, Roberta E. 2801 MARTIN LTHR KNG JR DR, CCCHR 44104 #041-12-1978 L1988 **PD** *020 †55

BAUER, Thomas Wm. 9500 EUCLID AVE, MS L25 44195 #030-05-1979 L1983 **PTH** *020 †50

BAUSE, George Stephen. 5247 WILSON MILLS RD # 282 44143 #023-07-1981 L1992 **AN PMM** *071 †05

BAUTISTA, Irene Hilario. 18697 BAGLEY RD 44130 #748-08-1971 L1983 **PD** *020 †55

BAUTISTA, Jocelyn Fortes. 9500 EUCLID AVE S51, CLEVELAND CLIN-DEPT NEURO 44195 #028-02-1995 L1999 **CN N** *020 †70

BAUTISTA, Remigio L, Jr. 4310 SAINT CLAIR 44103 #748-01-1969 L1974 **GS** *020 †85

BAVRY, Anthony Alexander. 9500 EUCLID AVE # 605 44195 #011-03-1998 L2003 **IC** *012 †20

BAYAR, Emel. 9500 EUCLID AVE, CCF PEDS HEM ONC S35 44195 #902-10-1972 L1990 **PHO PD** *050 †55

BAZ, Rachid Chafic. 9500 EUCLID AVE 44195 #605-01-2000 L2001 **HO** *100

BEACHY, Nathan Ray. 4071 LEE RD, STE 260 44128 #038-45-1987 L1989 **FM** *020 †18

BEACHY, Rochele Miller. 2500 METROHEALTH DR 44109 #038-45-1986 L1987 **FM** *020 †18

BEBAWY, Edward Samir. ■ 44115 #038-06-2001 L2003 **IM** *020

BECK, Carol Weisman. ■ 44122 #012-01-1978 L1980 **PD** *074 †55

BECK, Rose Chu. DEPT PATH DESK L25 44195 #038-06-2001 L2001 **HMP** *100 †50

BECKER, Jeffery Michael. 2500 METROHEALTH DR, METROHEALTH MEDICAL CENTER 44109 #038-06-1996 L1997 **IM** *020 †20

BECKER, Maier. 18599 LAKE SHORE BLVD, UNIVERSITY MEDNET 44119 #035-46-1990 L1992 **END** *020 †20

BECKFORD, Ian George. 6835 BROADWAY AVE 44105 #038-06-1998 L1999 **FM** *020 †18

BECKFORD, Rita Deattrea. 4071 LEE RD, STE 260 44128 #038-06-1998 L1999 **FM** *020 †18

BEDAIWY, Mohamed Ali. 2500 METROHEALTH DR, CO METROHEALTH MED CTR-RES 44109 #915-05-1993 L2003 **OBG** *012

BEDDOW, Timothy Donald. 2500 METROHEALTH DR 44109 #037-01-1978 L1987 **PTH BBK** *020 †50

BEECHER, Benjamin Robert. 11100 EUCLID AVE 44106 #018-03-2006 L2006 **ORS** *012

BEG, Nuzhat Rais. ■ 44124 #704-06-1966 L1979 **P** *100

BEG, Rais Ahmad. 2449 CEDARWOOD RD, CARDIO VESCULAR SURGEON 44124 #704-09-1966 L1971 **TS VS** *020 †85,90

BEGLEY, James Jos. 2500 METROHEALTH DR, DEPT OF PM & R 44109 #030-06-1990 L1994 **PM** *020 †60

BEHMER, Maryellen. 3838 W 150TH ST 44111 #038-40-1988 L1991 **IM** *020 †20

BEHZADI, Nejad. ■ 44140 #517-01-1957 L1965 **AN** *071

BEJANISHVILI, Tamar Y. 730 SOM CENTER RD 44143 #913-23-1997 L2000 **IM** *020 †20

BEKKERMAN, Yelena. 13951 TERRACE RD 44112 #913-47-1999 L2004 **IM** *100 †20

BELINSON, Jerome Leslie. 9500 EUCLID AVE A/81, CLEVELAND CLINIC FOUNDATIO 44195 #028-03-1968 L1990 **GO GYN** *020 †30

BELL, Gordon R. 9500 EUCLID AVE, CLEVELAND CLINIC FOUNDATIO 44195 #065-09-1977 L1978 **ORS** *020 †40

BELL, Julie Reynolds. ■ 44118 #020-02-2005 L2005 **AN** *012

BELLIN, Sandra Lee. 29001 CEDAR RD, BEACHWOOD OB GYN INC 44124 #038-06-1987 L1987 **OBG** *020 †30

BELLON, Errol Manfred. 2500 METROHEALTH DR, METROHEALTH MD CTR DPT RAD 44109 #836-12-1961 L1968 **R DR** *030 †80

BELTON, Michael John. 18101 LORAIN AVE, CO FAIRVIEW HOSPITAL-SURGE 44111 #038-06-2002 L2002 **GS** *020

BENMEIR, Aviv. 2351 E 22ND ST 44115 #038-06-1996 L1997 **GS** *020 †85

BENNETT, Mary Frances. 11100 EUCLID AVE, RESIDENCY OFFICE 44106 #539-02-1999 L2006 *100

BENNETT, Robert Franklin. ■ 44115 #038-06-1946 L1946 **N** *020 †20

BENNETT, Shirley Lynn. 7255 OLD OAK BLVD, STE C202 44130 #038-06-1987 L1987 **OBG** *020 †30

BENNINGER, Michael S. 9500 EUCLID AVE A-71, CLEVELAND CLINIC 44195 #038-06-1983 L1987 **OTO** *020 †45

BENSON, Jerrel Ward. 2500 METROHEALTH DR, DEPT OF SURGERY 44109 #023-07-1948 L1953 **GS** *071 †85

BENYO, Robert Bruce. 6780 MAYFIELD RD 44124 #028-34-1965 L1967 **PTH IM** *020 †50

BENZEL, Edward Chas. 9500 EUCLID AVE, CLEVELAND CLINIC DEPT OF N 44195 #056-06-1975 L1999 **NS SCI** *020 †25

BERBER, Eren. 9500 EUCLID AVE, STE A80 44195 #902-10-1994 L2000 **GS** *020 †85

BERGER, Benjamin. 11100 EUCLID AVE 44106 #038-40-1942 L1942 **IM N** *071 †20

BERGER, Melvin. 11100 EUCLID AVE, RAINBOW BABIES DEPT PEDS 44106 #038-06-1976 L1984 **IG AI** *050 †55,03

BERGER, Nathan Allen. 10900 EUCLID AVE, CASE WESTERN RESERVE UNIV 44106 #041-09-1966 L1983 **ON HEM** *030

BERGFELD, John Albert. 9500 EUCLID AVE, STE E21 44195 #041-13-1964 L1966 **ORS OS** *020 †40

BERGFELD, Wilma L Fowler. 9500 EUCLID AVE - A61, DEPT OF DERMATOLOGY 44195 #041-13-1964 L1966 **D DMP** *020 †15 ‡

BERIS, Alexandra. 13951 TERRACE RD, HURON HOSPITAL 44112 #781-01-1991 L1998 **IM** *020 †20

BERKELHAMER, Maura Carol. 11100 EUCLID AVE 44106 #016-01-1988 L2000 **PD** *020 †55,05

BERKOWITZ, Mark S. 1730 W 25TH ST # 3200, LUTHERAN MEDICAL ARTS BLDG 44113 #035-09-1978 L1983 **ORS** *020 †40

BERMAN, Brian Wm. 11100 EUCLID AVE, RAINBOW BABIES & CHILD HOS 44106 #041-13-1975 L1980 **PD PHO** *020 †55

BERMAN, Leonard Solomon. 6803 MAYFIELD RD, STE 106 44124 #038-06-1972 L1972 **DR** *020 †80

BERMAN, Norman E. ■ 44120 #010-02-1945 L1950 **RO R** *071 †80

BERMAS, Kristina Wong. 13951 TERRACE RD 44112 #305-01-2007 L2007 **GS** *012

BERMEL, Robert Anthony. 9500 EUCLID AVE, CO CCF-GRAD MED EDU DEPT-N 44195 #035-06-2003 L2003 **N** *100

BERNARD, Steven Lowell. 2500 METROHEALTH DR, DEPARTMENT OF SURGERY 44109 #038-06-1986 L1986 **PS HS** *020 †85,65

BERNITSAS, Evanthia. 11100 EUCLID AVE, DEPT. OF NEUROLOGY 44106 #418-02-1990 L2004 **N** *012

BERTE, Michael Thos. 6900 PEARL RD STE 200, SOUTHWEST UROLOGY 44130 #017-20-1980 L1986 **U** *020 †95

BERTIN, Vincent James. 18660 BAGLEY RD 44130 #038-41-1978 L1980 **VS** *030 †85

BESHARA, Hani Moheeb. 18101 LORAIN AVE 44111 #915-03-2001 L2005 **IM** *012

BETHOUX, Francois Andre. 9500 EUCLID AVE, THE MELLEN CENTER/UIO 44195 #396-09-1990 L2000 **PM** *012

BEVEN, Edwin Geo. 9500 EUCLID AVE, CLEVELAND CLINIC EE-40 44195 #067-01-1956 L1964 **VS** *071 †85

BEVERLEY, Laurel Ann. 12301 SNOW RD, MERRIMACK VALLEY ORTHOPAED 44130 #024-05-1997 L2002 **ORS** *020 †40

BHADRA, Eva Lillian. 8300 HOUGH AVE, NEON 44103 #495-32-1981 L1995 **PD** *020 †55

BHALLA, Rakesh. 18101 LORAIN AVE, FAIRVIEW HOSPITAL 44111 #496-09-1981 L1996 **IM** *020 †20

BHANDARY, Sujatha Panambo. 9500 EUCLID AVE 44195 #496-35-1994 L2005 **AN** *012

BHARDWAJ, Ajay. 18200 LORAIN AVE, DEPT RADIOLOGY 44111 #496-09-1988 L2007 **DR** *012

BHARGAVA, Ajay. 9500 EUCLID AVE F15, CLEVELAND CLNC FOUNDATION 44195 #495-36-1987 L2005 **CD** *020 †20

BHARGAVA, Mandeep. 9500 EUCLID AVE, DESK F-15 44195 #495-45-1991 L2002 **ICE CD** *020

BHAT, Pradeep Krishna. CO RESIDENCY SUPPORT, METROHEALTH MEDICAL CENTER 44109 #495-09-1997 L2007 **IM** *012

BHATT, Deepak. 9500 EUCLID AVE F25, CLEVELAND CLC 44195 #035-20-1993 L2000 **IC CD** *020 †20

BHATT, Jyoti Jatin. 18599 LAKE SHORE BLVD 44119 #496-38-1980 L1993 **IM** *020 †20

BHATTA, Nivedita. 9500 EUCLID AVE, C/O CCF-GRAD MED EDU DEPT- 44195 #028-34-2000 L2002 **U** *100

BHATTACHARYA, Sujit. 2500 METROHEALTH DR 44109 #495-39-1993 L2006 **IM** *012

BHATTI, Naeem. ■ 44108 #041-15-2004 L2004 **AN** *012

BHAVANI, Sekar S. 9500 EUCLID AVE 44195 #495-23-1977 L1986 **AN** *012

BHAVNANI, Sanjeev. 12301 SNOW RD, KAISER PERMANENTE MOB 44130 #495-28-1983 L2001 **IM** *020 †20

BHIDE, Suwarna Ashok. 9500 EUCLID AVE, CLEVELAND CLINIC FOUNDATIO 44195 #495-83-1991 L2006 **AN** *012

BHIMANI, Jayantilal D. 2709 FRANKLIN BLVD, FL 2E 44145 #495-48-1981 L1994 **IM** *020 †20

BHINDER, Harchitwant Sing. 2500 METROHEALTH DR 44109 #305-01-2006 L2007 **IM** *012

BIAGIOTTI, David. ■ 44130 #132-02-1966 L1978 **AN** *071

BIBEVSKI, Steven. ■ 44115 #038-06-2004 L2004 **GS** *012

BICKEL, Brent Alan. ■ 44102 #038-40-2002 L2002 **HSO** *012

BIDARI, Afshin. 11100 EUCLID AVE, RESIDENCY PROGRAM DEPARTME 44106 #517-08-1993 L2005 **IM** *012

BIGG, Margaret Mary. CDU E14, 8500 EUCLID AVE 44195 #038-40-1994 L1995 **FM** *020 †18

BIGORNIA, Lina Alvero. 2351 E 22ND ST 44115 #748-01-1962 L1977 **AN** *071 †05

BILENKER, Robert Marc. 2500 METROHEALTH DR 44109 #033-05-1967 L1969 **PD** *071 †55

BILFIELD, Laurence Henry. 1730 W 25TH ST, # 128 44113 #038-06-1980 L1981 **ORS** *020 †40

BILIC, Joseph Peter. 574 E 200TH ST 44119 #957-02-1967 L1972 **IM** *020

BILLINGS, Steven Douglas. 9500 EUCLID AVE, L25 44195 #017-20-1995 L2007 **DMP** *020 †50

BINA, Pouya. CO RESIDENCY SUPPORT, METROHEALTH MEDICAL CENTER 44109 #665-01-2006 L2007 **IM** *012

BINDER, Louis Stewart. 2500 METROHEALTH DR, METROHEALTH MEDICAL CENTER 44109 #026-04-1980 L1999 **EM** *020 †16

BINGAMAN, William Emanuel. 9500 EUCLID AVE, CLEVELAND CLINIC 44195 #041-13-1990 L1995 **NS** *020 †25

BIRDI, Shiva. 9500 EUCLID AVE, CO CCF-GRAD MED EDU DEPT-N 44195 #038-40-2003 L2003 **CCA** *012

BIRGISSON, Sigurbjorn. 3395 SCRANTON RD 44109 #484-01-1989 L1993 **GE** *100 †20

BIRNKRANT, David Jonathan. 2500 METROHEALTH DR, METROHEALTH MEDICAL CENTER 44109 #008-01-1985 L1988 **PDP** *020 †55

BISCOTTI, Charles Vincent. 9500 EUCLID AVE, CLEVELAND CLINIC FOUNDATIO 44195 #038-06-1983 L1983 **PTH** *062 †50

BISHAI, Adel Ragheb. 9500 EUCLID AVE 44195 #915-04-1982 L2004 **AN** *020

BISHOP, Edward Jacob. 7255 OLD OAK BLVD, STE 408 44130 #038-41-1947 L1947 **NS** *072 †25

BITAR, Naila. 11100 EUCLID AVE 44106 #067-01-2007 L2007 **PD** *012

BITTENCE, Jessica H. 6420 YORK RD 44130 #038-06-40-1994 L1995 **FM** *020 †18

BITZAN, Joseph L. 5109 BROADWAY AVE STE 205 44127 #028-34-1951 L1952 **GS ORS** *071 †85

BLACK, James Edward. 11100 EUCLID AVE, MAILSTOP-HMP 5099 44106 #038-06-2003 L2004 **IM** *100

BLACKBURN, Bradley Arthur. 4330 W 150TH ST 44135 #035-47-1981 L1986 **DR** *020 †80

BLACKHAM, Kristine Ann. 11106 EUCLID AVE, DEPT OF RADIOLOGY 44106 #038-06-1999 L1999 **RNR** *020 †80

BLACKSTONE, Eugene Hubert. 9500 EUCLID AVE, DESK JJ40 44195 #016-02-1966 L1998 **CD PUD** *050

BLAHA, Steven Carl. 9500 EUCLID AVE, BLDG E 44195 #038-43-1995 L1996 **EM** *020 †16

BLAIR, Henry Frank. 6780 MAYFIELD RD, DEPT RADIATION ONCOLOGY 44124 #038-41-1986 L1987 **RO IM** *020 †80

BLANCO, Carlos Javier. 11100 EUCLID AVE 44106 #176-06-2003 L2008 **PDC** *012 †55

BLANTON, Ronald Edward. 2109 ADELBERT RD 44106 #038-06-1979 L1982 **IM** *050 †20

BLAUT, Andrew Paul. 9500 EUCLID AVE 44195 #038-44-2004 L2004 **AN** *012

BLEDSOE, Brian Anthony. ■ 44114 #047-06-2004 L2004 **AN** *012

BLICKER, Jamie Zack. 9500 EUCLID AVE, DEPT OF ER MED STE E-19 44195 #067-01-1999 L2004 **EM** *020 †16

BLIGH-GLOVER, William Z. ■ 44120 #038-06-1995 L1997 **PTH** *020

BLITZ, Arie. 1110 EUCLID AVE, FL 6227 44115 #035-46-1989 L2005 **GS** *020 †90,85

BLOCH, Edward Henry. CASE WESTERN RESERVE U MED 44106 #047-06-1945 L1945 **CD ID** *071

BLOCHOWIAK, Patricia Ann. ■ 44112 #056-05-1978 L1992 **FM** *020 †18

BLOOM, Henry Robt. 20620 N PARK BLVD, STE 208 44118 #038-06-1973 L1976 **FM** *020 †18

BLOOM, Jeffrey Norman. 5850 LANDERBROOK DR, STE 240 44124 #035-19-1972 L2007 OPH PO *020 †35

BLUM, Adam Howell. 11100 EUCLID AVE, STE 2600 44106 #038-43-1990 L1992 VIR DR *020 †80

BLUMENTHAL, David Evan. 2500 METROHEALTH DR, METROHEALTH MEDICAL CENTER 44109 #028-02-1983 L1997 RHU *020 †20

BLUMENTHAL, Harold Leslie. 3619 PARK EAST DR 44122 #041-02-1959 L1960 D *020 †15 ‡

BLUMER, Jeffrey Lee. 11100 EUCLID AVE, RM RB&C3131 44106 #038-06-1979 L1981 CCP PA *030 †55

BLYUMIN, Nella. 18697 BAGLEY RD, SOUTHWEST GENERAL HEALTH C 44130 #913-15-1988 L1999 PD *020 †55

BOADA, Enrique. 2074 ABINGTON RD ORTH SURG 44106 #847-01-1972 L1980 ORS *100 †40

BOAPIMP, Pimpawan. 13951 TERRACE RD, MERIDIA HURON HOSP 44112 #891-08-1995 L2000 ID *100 †20

BOBAK, David Allan. 11100 EUCLID AVE, FOLEY BLDG/RM 303 44106 #038-40-1980 L1983 ID IM *050 †20

BOBYLEV, Matvey V. 9500 EUCLID AVE BOX 134 44195 #913-15-1988 L2000 APM *020 †05

BOCCIA, Joseph Anthony. 11311 SHAKER BLVD, DEPARTMENT OF PATHOLOGY 44104 #035-20-1965 L1967 PTH *020 †50

BODA, Stephen Andrew. 1283 E 17TH ST 44114 #781-05-1963 PTH *100

BODICHARLA, Rajasekhar. 9500 EUCLID AVE, CLEVELAND CLINIC FOUNDATIO 44195 #495-65-1999 L2007 PD *012

BODNER, Donald Roger. 11100 EUCLID AVE, RM 2500 44106 #017-20-1979 L1979 U GS *020 †95

BODOR, Frank. 18099 LORAIN AVE, STE 141 44111 #957-01-1955 L1970 PD *071 †55

BODZIAK, Kenneth Alan. 11100 EUCLID AVE 44106 #038-41-1987 L2001 OS NEP *020 †20

BOGAN, Kimberley. ■ 44108 #038-43-1993 L2003 P *100

BOHL, William Reinert. 1730 W 25TH ST, STE 3200 44113 #038-06-1972 L1973 ORS GP *020 †40

BOHLMAN, Henry Hubert. 11100 EUCLID AVE 44106 #023-01-1964 L1972 ORS *040 †40

BOHN, Timothy Peter. 18101 LORAIN AVE 44111 #038-43-1991 L1994 IM *020 †20

BOIERU, Cristiana Miriam. 18099 LORAIN AVE, STE 441 44111 #781-01-1981 L1986 RHU IM *020 †20 ‡

BOISSY, Adrienne Renee. 9500 EUCLID AVE U-10, CCF MELLEN CENTER 44195 #041-14-2002 L2002 N *100 †75

BOKAR, Joseph A. 11100 EUCLID AVE 44106 #038-06-1990 L1991 ON *020 †05

BOLDEN, Norman. 4330 W 150TH ST 44135 #024-01-1988 L1990 AN *020 †05

BOLISETTY, Bhaskara P. 1708 SOUTHPOINT DR, NORTH COAST BEHAVIORAL HEA 44109 #495-50-1982 L1992 IM *020 †20

BOLWELL, Brian James. 9500 EUCLID AVE, # R32 44195 #038-06-1981 L1981 HO IM *020 †20

BOMEISL, Philip Edwin. 11100 EUCLID AVE 44106 #011-75-2004, ▲ L2004 PCP *012

BONCHER, Nicholas Anthony. ■ 44113 #025-01-2006 L2006 GS *012

BONILLA, Maria Fernanda. 9500 EUCLID AVE, CLEVELAND CLINIC FNDN 44195 #264-05-1999 L2004 IM *100 †20

BONNY, Andrea Elena. 2500 METROHEALTH DR, OF ADOL HLTH 44109 #028-02-1994 L1997 PD ADL *020 †55

BONOMO, Robert Anthony. 10701 EAST BLVD, LOUIS STOKES VETERANS AFFA 44106 #038-06-1983 L1983 ID *020 †20

BOOHER, Delbert Lowell. 9500 EUCLID AVE, DESK A-81 44195 #038-40-1963 L1963 GYN OBS *071 †30

BOOM, Willem Henry. 2109 ADELBERT RD, 10TH FL 44106 #035-45-1979 L1988 IM *020 †20

BOONCHALERMVICHIAN, Chaiya. 13951 TERRACE RD 44112 #891-01-1998 L2005 IM *100

BOONGIRD, Atthaporn. 9500 EUCLID AVE, C/O CCF-GRAD MED EDU DEPT- 44195 #891-01-1996 L2002 NS *020

BOONGIRD, Chitima. 1170 EUCLID AVE 44115 #891-01-1996 L2001 IMG *100 †18

BOONYAPISIT, Kanokwan. 9500 EUCLID AVE, CLEVELAND CLINIC 44195 #891-02-1994 L2000 CN *100 †75

BOOTH, Bradley. 11100 EUCLID AVE, UNIV HOSPITALS OF CLEVELAN 44106 #065-09-2000 L2005 PFP *100 †75

BOOTH, Christine N. 9500 EUCLID AVE, # L25 DEPT PATH 44195 #016-43-1997 L1999 PCP ATP *020 †50

BOPPANA, Haritha. 18697 BAGLEY RD, SW GENERAL HEALTH CTR 44130 #495-21-1995 L2006 IM *020 †20

BOPPANA, Raghu Babu. 2500 METROHEALTH DR, DEPT OF RESIDENCY SUPPORT 44109 #495-21-1996 L2006 MPD *012

BORDEN, Ernest Carleton. 9500 EUCLID AVE R40, TAUSSIG CANCER CENTER 44195 #036-07-1966 L1999 ON HEM *030 †20 ‡

BORISON, Daniel I. 6770 MAYFIELD RD # 320 44124 #035-19-1987 L1988 GS *020 †85

BORKOWSKI, Gregory Peter. 9500 EUCLID AVE, CLEVELAND CLINIC HOSPITAL 44195 #041-02-1971 L1976 R IM *020 †80

BORKOWSKI, Raymond G. 9500 EUCLID AVE 44195 #041-02-1989 L1994 AN *020 †05

BORNEMAN, Karen. 1983 E 24TH ST # 503 44115 #024-12-1979 L1982 FM *020 †18

BORUS, Joseph Samuel. 1611 S GREEN RD, STE 35 44121 #051-04-2001 L2001 PD *020 †55

BORZOVA, Vera Valerievna. 18101 LORAIN AVE, DEPT OF PEDIATRICS 44111 #913-66-1993 L2003 AN *100 †55

BOSE, Reena. 2500 METROHEALTH DR, METROHEALTH MEDICAL CTRRES 44109 #496-07-2000 L2002 IM *100 †20

BOSWELL, April Atkins. 12301 SNOW RD 44130 #038-06-2003 L2003 D *020

BOSWELL, Michael Darnell. 2500 METROHEALTH DR, CO METROHEALTH MED CTR-RES 44109 #010-03-2001 L2001 NEP *020

BOTEZ, Gabriela Irina. 9500 EUCLID AVE, CLEVELAND CLINIC FOUNDATIO 44195 #781-02-2002 L2006 PD *012

BOTHAM, Mark Judson. 6707 POWERS BLVD STE 303, DIV OF CARDIOTHORACIC SURG 44129 #035-20-1979 L1990 TS *020 †85,90

BOTHE, Denise Annette. 10524 EUCLID AVE STE 3150, WALKER CENTER WLK 6038 44106 #035-15-1993 L1997 PD *020 †18

BOTTI, Robert Ernest, Jr. 6770 MAYFIELD RD, STE 205 44124 #038-06-1985 L1985 CD IM *020 †20

BOTTROS, John Joseph. ■ 44113 #035-15-2005 L2005 ORS *012

BOTT-SILVERMAN, Corinne. 9500 EUCLID AVE 44195 #028-34-1979 L1985 CD *040 †20

BOUDREAUX, Benjamin J. ■ 44113 #021-05-2001 L2006 PS *012

BOULIS, Nicholas Matthew. 9500 EUCLID AVE, NB20 44195 #024-01-1994 L2001 NS *020 †25

BOUMPHREY, Francis Robt. 9500 EUCLID AVE, DESK A-81 44195 #917-29-1971 L1979 ORS *020 †40

BOURAOUI-KAROUI, Amor. 2525 E 22ND ST 44115 #869-05-1963 L1999 CHP P *020

BOURDAKOS, Demetrios. 9500 EUCLID AVE 44195 #418-02-1984 L1992 CCA *020 †05

BOURDAKOS, Gregory. 9500 EUCLID AVE 44195 #418-01-1985 L1993 CCA IM *020

BOUTROS, Rami A. 9500 EUCLID AVE 44195 #875-01-1989 L1993 PD *020 †55

BOWERFIND, Edgar S, Jr. 2074 ABINGTON RD 44106 #038-06-1949 L1949 IM *020 †20

BOXER, Rebecca Sue. 11100 EUCLID AVE, UNIVERSITY HOSPITALS 44106 #041-01-1997 L2000 IMG *020 †20

BOXERBAUM, Bernard. ■ 44124 #038-40-1956 L1956 PD ID *071 †55

BOYLE, Gerard John. 9500 EUCLID AVE, MAIL CODE M-40 44195 #035-08-1987 L2004 PDC PD *020 †55

BOYLE, James Martin. 2351 E 22ND ST 44115 #035-45-1969 L1970 GE IM *020 †20

BRADLEY, Karen. 20525 CENTER RIDGE RD, STE 606 44116 #016-43-1978 L1984 P FM *020 †75

BRADLEY, Linda Darlene. 9500 EUCLID AVE, DESK A81 44195 #038-41-1981 L1983 OBG *040 †30

BRAHMANANDAM, Maddikunta. 5109 BROADWAY AVE, ST MICHAEL MEDICAL ARTS BL 44127 #495-36-1964 L1977 IM *020

BRAHMBHATT, Rameshbhai J. 21851 CENTER RIDGE RD, STE 200 44116 #495-23-1973 L1979 CD IM *020 †20

BRAINARD, Jennifer Ann. 9500 EUCLID AVE 44195 #038-40-1994 L1997 PTH *020 †50

BRALLIAR, Thomas Boynton. 9500 EUCLID AVE # E31, CLEVELAND CLC FNTDN 44195 #047-06-1968 L1970 AN *020 †05

BRAND, Lisa Rachael. 2816 E 116TH ST, METROHEALTH BUCKEYE HLT CT 44120 #038-06-1989 L1991 PD *020

BRANDT, Christopher P. 2500 METROHEALTH DR 44109 #038-06-1984 L1984 GS TRS *020 †85

BRANNIGAN, Ann Elizabeth. 9500 EUCLID AVE, CO CCF-GRAD MED EDU DEPT-N 44195 #539-04-1993 L2002 *100

BRAR, Saroj Bala. 4255 PEARL RD, MEDICAL ARTS BUILDING #105 44109 #496-07-1965 L1982 P *020

BRAUN, Ryan Edgar. 11100 EUCLID AVE 44106 #016-42-2004 L2004 AN *012

BRAUN, William Eugene. 9500 EUCLID AVE # A51 44195 #010-02-1959 L1960 NEP IG *020 †20

BRAVER, Yvonne Jeanette. 9500 EUCLID AVE 44195 #012-05-1996 L2000 IM *020 †20

BRAVO, Emmanuel L. 9500 EUCLID AVE, DESK A51 44195 #748-10-1961 L1971 END IM *020 †20

BRAWNER, Johnny Aliac. 18697 BAGLEY RD 44130 #748-02-1967 L1976 GS GP *072 †85

BRAY, Patrick Garnett. 2322 E 22ND ST 44115 #036-01-1975 L1987 OM PHP *020 †70

BRAYLEY, Jason Dean. ■ 44195 #005-12-2001 L2007 FM *020 †18

BREITENBACH, Daniel A. 13916 CEDAR RD 44118 #038-40-1982 L1984 IM GP *020

BRELL, Joanna M. 11100 EUCLID AVE, LAKESIDE 1200 44106 #048-14-1992 L1994 HO *020

BREMS, John Jos. 9500 EUCLID AVE, CLEVELAND CLINIC FOUNDATIO 44195 #010-02-1978 L1979 ORS *020 †40

BRENNAN, James Nicolas. 11100 EUCLID AVE, STE 2600 44106 #017-20-1970 L1972 DR *020 †80

BRENNAN, Sandra Brigid. 9500 EUCLID AVE, CLEVELAND CLNC FOUNDATION 44195 #539-04-1998 L2006 IM *100

BRETHAUER, Stacy Alan. 9500 EUCLID AVE # A80, CLEVELAMD CLC FNDT-SURGERY 44195 #023-12-1993 L2005 GS *020 †85

BRIEKE, Andreas. 9500 EUCLID AVE 44195 #409-16-1996 L2000 CD *020 †20

BRINDLE, Allison Wentwort. 9500 EUCLID AVE, DESK A-120 44195 #023-01-2001 L2006 PD *020 †55

BRIONES, Berta. 2351 E 22ND ST, STE 306 44115 #270-02-1988 L1993 EM PCC *020 †20

BRISKIN, Susannah M. 11100 EUCLID AVE, RBC MAILSTOP 6081 44106 #035-45-1999 L1999 PSM PD *020 †55 ‡

BRITTENUM, Donald Fulton. ■ 44122 #047-07-1961 L1967 TS GS *062 †85,90

BROADNAX, Jeremy Phillipp. ■ 44118 #038-06-2008 *012

BROCCO, Karen Jean. 2500 METROHEALTH DR 44109 #041-07-1974 L1975 P *020 †75

BROCK, Daniel Joseph. 11100 EUCLID AVE 44106 #038-43-2006 L2006 FP *012

BROJMOHUN, Archana Devi. 11100 EUCLID AVE 44106 #473-04-2006 L2007 P *012

BRONIATOWSKI, Michael. 2351 E 22ND ST, HEALTH CTR 44115 #396-06-1969 L1979 OTO HNS *020 †45

BRONNER, Mary Patricia. 9500 EUCLID AVE 44195 #041-01-1989 L2003 PTH *020 †50

BRONSON, David Leigh. 9500 EUCLID AVE, CLEVELAND CLINIC - A91 44195 #050-02-1973 L1992 IM *030 †20

BROOKER, Craig Alan. 9500 EUCLID AVE, DEPT OF GME 44195 #539-04-2006 L2006 N *012

BROOKS, Elizabeth Brown. 11100 EUCLID AVE, DIV PEDS RHEUMATOLOGY 44106 #038-06-1993 L2005 RHU IM *020 †20

BROOKS, Peter J. 99 NORTHLINE CIR 44119 #065-01-1979 L1991 ORS *020 †40

BROOKS, Suzanne Nichole. ■ 44195 #038-40-2005 L2005 GS *012

BROUHARD, Ben Herman. 2500 METROHEALTH DR, MEDICAL CENTER 44109 #017-20-1972 L1988 PN *020 †55

BROWER, David Jeffrey. ■ 44112 #011-02-2007 L2007 GS *012

BROWN, Bert Matt. 5400 TRANSPORTATION BLVD, STE 8 44125 #038-41-1983 L1988 OTO *020 †45

BROWN, Calvin Christopher. ■ 44121 #038-06-2005 L2005 IM *012

BROWN, Edward Southard. 11311 SHAKER BLVD 44104 #008-01-1943 L1944 GS EM *071

BROWN, Homer Wesley. 18697 BAGLEY RD 44130 #038-41-1969 L1969 PD *020 †55

BROWN-HARRISON, Mary C. 11100 EUCLID AVE, UNIV HOSP CASE CNT 44106 #051-01-1989 L1999 PD *020 †55

BROWNING, Kara Helene. 9500 EUCLID AVE, DESK A91 44195 #038-06-1996 L1997 IM ISM *020 †20

BRUGGER, Thomas C. 2040 ABINGTON RD 44106 #056-05-1953 L1959 CHP P *030 †75

BRUN, Carlos Antonio. TT22 - NSVAD, 9500 EUCLID AVE 44195 #038-44-2001 L2005 CCM *012 †20

BRUNER, Julia Elizabeth. 6835 BROADWAY AVE 44105 #016-01-2001 L2001 FM *020 †18

BRUNER, William Evans, II. 1611 S GREEN RD, ASSOCIATES 44121 #038-06-1975 L1976 OPH *020 †35

BRUNEY, Francisca Claudia. ■ 44102 #665-01-2005 L2005 FP *012

BRUNKEN, Richard. 9500 EUCLID AVE, DEPT OF NUCLEAR MEDICINE/G 44195 #030-05-1978 L1994 NM CD *020 †20,28

BRYANT, Roosevelt, III. ■ 44195 #024-05-1999 L2004 GS *100

BRZEZINSKI, Aaron. 9500 EUCLID AVE, DESK A-30 44195 #649-01-1981 L1992 GE *020 †20

BSHARA, Ibrahim. 3665 W 117TH ST 44111 #875-02-1980 L1992 IM NM *020 †20

BUCHINSKY, Roy Marc. 5850 LANDERBROOK DR, STE 100 44124 #836-01-1989 L1995 IM *020 †20

BUDD, Francis Xavier. ■ 44129 #028-34-1930 L1931 OPH *071

BUDD, George Thos. 9500 EUCLID AVE, CLEVELAND CLINIC DESK R35 44195 #019-02-1977 L1979 ON HEM *050 †20

BUDD, John Henry. ■ 44111 #064-01-1933 L1936 GP OBG *071

BUDUR, Kumaraswamy. ION 9500 EUCLID AVENUE, P57 CLEVELAND CLINIC FOUND 44195 #495-72-1996 L2001 **CN** *100 †75

BUENAVENTURA, Michaela A. ■ 44106 #012-01-2001 L2001 **PDE** *100 †55

BUENCAMINO, Maria Clarind. 9500 EUCLID AVE, DEPT OF GME 44195 #748-01-2002 L2005 **IM** *012

BUENDIA, Elena Catindig. 2358 PROFESSOR AVE 44113 #748-01-1959 L1983 **FM** *071

BUI, Kimmie Lu. 9500 EUCLID AVE, DEPT OF RADIOLOGY, HB6 44195 #010-01-2003 L2004 **DR** *012

BUITRAGO BLANCO, Manuel M. 9500 EUCLID AVE, CLEVELAND CLINIC FOUNDATIO 44195 #264-04-2000 L2006 **N** *012

BUKOWSKI, Ronald Mathew. 9500 EUCLID AVE, STE 100 44195 #016-06-1967 L1968 **ON HEM** *020 †20

BUKUTS, James Thomas. 5955 RIDGE RD 44129 #038-43-1993 L1998 **P** *020 †75

BULLARD, David Scott. 2500 METROHEALTH DR 44109 #038-41-1998 L1999 **EM** *020 †16

BUNYARD, Matthew Phillip. 9500 EUCLID AVE A-50, CCF DIVISION OF RHEUMATOLO 44195 #038-43-1987 L1990 **RHU** *020 †20

BUNYE, Ernesto Cabales. 12645 PEARL RD 44136 #748-01-1970 L1976 **PD ADL** *020

BURDICK, Michael Joseph. ■ 44113 #051-04-2005 L2006 **RO** *012

BURDJALOV, Vladimir F. 9500 EUCLID AVE, CLEVELAND CLINIC FOUNDATIO 44195 #913-15-1988 L2002 **NPM** *020 †55

BURGESS, Richard Clement. 9500 EUCLID AVE, DEPT OF NEUROLOGY 44195 #038-06-1977 L1978 **CN N** *020

BURKE, Carol Ann. 9500 EUCLID AVE, DESK A-30 44195 #038-40-1988 L1989 **GE IM** *020 †20

BURKONS, David Max. 1611 S GREEN RD, STE 204 44121 #025-01-1973 L1977 **OBG** *020 †30

BURMA, Gerald Melvin. 6707 POWERS BLVD, STE 205 44129 #038-06-1978 L1979 **CD** *020 †20

BURNEY, Edward N. 11100 EUCLID AVE 44106 #038-06-1978 L1979 **OPH** *020 †35

BURRELL, Lydia Lambe. 1611 S GREEN RD 44121 #051-01-1992 L1995 **IM** *020 †20

BURVAL, Daniel Joseph. 9500 EUCLID AVE, CO CCF-GRAD MED EDU DEPT-N 44195 #055-01-2001 L2001 **ORS** *020

BUSH, Edward Sergins. 2475 M L K JR DR 44120 #038-06-1958 L1958 **P** *020 †75

BUSHER, Maureen Mildred. 2500 METROHEALTH DR 44109 #041-12-2002 L2002 **OBG** *100

BUSQUETS, Ana Cristina. 2500 METROHEALTH DR, DEPARTMENT OF DERMATOLOGY 44109 #016-06-2001 L2001 **D** *020 †15

BUTLER, Brett Alan. 9500 EUCLID AVE BOX 71 44195 #038-41-1997 L2000 **GS** *100 †85

BUTT, Ishrat Jehan. ■ 44136 #704-06-1975 L1984 **PTH** *020 †50

BUTT, Saud. 2500 METROHEALTH DR, CO METROHEALTH MED CTR-RES 44109 #038-43-2003 L2003 **NEP** *012 †20

BUTTRAM, Cheryl Lynn. 2500 METROHEALTH DR 44109 #047-20-2000 L2003 **NEP** *100 †20

BUZATU, Alexander. 18101 LORAIN AVE 44111 #781-01-1966 L1983 **AN OS** *071

BUZATU, Theodora. 1 MOUNT SINAI DR 44106 #781-01-1967 L1988 **PD** *071

BYBEL, Bohdan. 9500 EUCLID AVE GB3, CLEVELAND CLIN FOUNDATION 44195 #062-01-1990 L1999 **NM** *020 †28

BYRD-LANE, Gerri Tobytha. 12301 SNOW RD 44130 #035-20-1978 L1979 **GE** *020 †20

BYRNES, Nina Agnes. 9500 EUCLID AVE BOX 545 44195 #539-03-1996 *100

C, Anand. 2500 METROHEALTH DR 44109 #496-39-1999 L2005 **IM** *012

CACHO BOWMAN, Carolyn P. 11100 EUCLID AVE, LAKESIDE 8130 44106 #010-03-1984 L1990 **NEP IM** *020 †20

CADESKY, Alan S. 11100 EUCLID AVE, STE 1200 44106 #065-01-1978 L1996 **FM** *020 †18

CAI, Dan Xiaodan. 2500 METROHEALTH DR, METROHEALTH MEDICAL CENTER 44109 #243-21-1982 L2000 **NP ATP** *020 †50

CAI, Olivia Xu Ye. 9500 EUCLID AVE, CLEVELAND CLINIC FOUNDATIO 44195 #243-52-1985 L2005 **IM** *020 †20

CAI, Rongsheng. 9500 EUCLID AVE, DEPT OF GME 44195 #243-73-1985 L2006 *100

CAIRO, Dana Lynn. 9500 EUCLID AVE, CLEVELAND CLINIC 44195 #036-07-2006 L2006 **PTH** *012

CAKULEV, Ivan Toma. 11100 EUCLID AVE, UNIVERSITY HOSPITALS OF CL 44106 #957-04-1992 L2002 **ICE** *020 †20

CALABRESE, Joseph Richard. 11400 EUCLID AVE STE 200 44106 #038-40-1980 L1981 **P** *020 †75

CALIMON, Zenaida Cruz. ■ 44147 #748-01-1956 L1976 **P** *020

CALLAHAN, Thomas Daniel. 9500 EUCLID AVE, DEPT OF CARDIOLOGY - F15 44195 #051-07-1999 L2003 **ICE** *012 †20

CAMERON, Marte. ■ 44195 #539-06-1999 L2000 **IM** *100 †20

CAMPBELL, Catherine Watki. 2322 E 22ND ST, CHARITY HOSPITAL 44115 #038-44-1983 L1984 **FM** *020 †18,70

CAMPBELL, James Wiley. 2500 METROHEALTH DR, DEPATEMENT OF FAMILY MEDIC 44109 #038-41-1984 L1987 **FM FPG** *020 †18

CAMPBELL, Jennifer Carole. ■ 44118 #048-15-2003 L2007 **OBG** *100

CAMPBELL, John Patrick. 9500 EUCLID AVE A-11, CLEVELAND CLINIC 44195 #041-14-1972 L1973 **GPM IM** *020 †20

CAMPBELL, Maibritt. 2500 METROHEALTH DR, DEPARTMENT OF RADIOLOGY 44109 #038-41-2001 L2002 **AR** *020 †80

CAMPBELL, Patricia. 2500 METROHEALTH DR 44109 #068-01-1985 L1990 **IMG IM** *020 †20 ‡

CAMPBELL, Steven Chas. 9500 EUCLID AVE, STE 100 44195 #016-02-1989 L1991 **U** *020 †95

CAMPO-IGLESIAS, Manuel A. 2500 METROHEALTH DR 44109 #308-03-1982 L1995 **NPM** *020

CAMSARI, Ulas Mehmet. 9500 EUCLID AVE, CLEVELAND CLNC 44195 #902-04-2003 L2006 **P** *012

CANADAY, David Hinman. 10900 EUCLID AVE, BRB 1010B 44106 #028-02-1992 L1995 **ID** *020 †20

CANES, David. ■ 44113 #035-20-2001 L2007 **U** *100

CANNADY, Steven Bernard. ■ 44121 #038-40-2002 L2002 **OTO** *012

CANNON, Vernon Terence. 11100 EUCLID AVE, CO UNIV HOSPS-RESIDENCY OF 44106 #033-06-2002 L2003 **OBG** *100

CANO, Javier. 2012 W 25TH ST, STE 507 44113 #649-01-1953 L1959 **AN GP** *020

CANTERBURY, Bryan S. 2500 METROHEALTH DR 44109 #143-11-2005 L2006 **EM** *012

CANTILLON, Daniel James. 9500 EUCLID AVE 44195 #010-02-2003 L2006 **CD** *012 †20

CANTONI, James Dennis. 7007 POWERS BLVD 44129 #041-09-1978 L1990 **AN** *020 †05

CAPDEVILLE, Michelle J. 9500 EUCLID AVE, THE CLEVELAND CLINIC FOUND 44195 #005-02-1989 L1992 **AN** *020 †05

CAPPAERT, William Edward. 2500 METROHEALTH DR 44109 #016-43-1962 L1967 **OPH N** *040 †35

CAPULONG, Edwin Leano. 9500 EUCLID AVE C21, CENTER FOR SPINE HEALTH 44195 #748-16-1993 L2002 **PM** *020 †60 ‡

CARAS, Maria Alexandra. 11100 EUCLID AVE, DEPARTMENT OF SURGERY 44106 #028-02-1980 L1982 **IM** *020 †20

CARAVELLA, Louis P, Jr. 21375 LORAIN RD, FAIRVIEW EYE CENTER 44126 #028-34-1974 L1975 **OPH** *020 †35

CAREY, John Joseph. 9500 EUCLID AVE, A50/DEPT RHEUMATIC DISEASE 44195 #539-04-1993 L2003 **RHU** *020

CAREY, William Dahill. 9500 EUCLID AVE, CLINIC CENTER 44195 #024-07-1968 L1976 **HEP GE** *020 †20

CARIL, Sarah Marie. 2500 METROHEALTH DR 44109 #038-06-2001 L2001 **OBG** *020 †30

CARL, John Chas. 11100 EUCLID AVE MS 6006, RAINBOW BABIES & CHILDRN'S 44106 #010-01-1985 L1986 **PDP PD** *020 †55

CARLIN, Susan Marie. 2500 METROHEALTH DR, METRO HLTH MED CTR 44109 #038-40-1980 L1984 **PD** *020 †55

CARLOS, Antonio A. ■ 44116 #748-01-1957 L1972 **GS GP** *020 †85

CARLSON, Roland David. 850 BRAINARD RD, HIGHLAND MEDICAL CENTER 44143 #035-20-1958 L1960 **OPH AM** *071 †35

CARMAN, Teresa Lynn. 9500 EUCLID AVE # S-60, VASCULAR MEDICINE 44195 #038-40-1992 L1998 **VM IM** *020 †20

CARNEY, James Francis. 18660 BAGLEY RD, STE 204 44130 #055-01-1966 L1970 **D DMP** *020 †15

CARNEY, Sherri Lynn. 2351 E 22ND ST 44115 #748-09-2000 L2001 **IM** *020

CARO, Mildred E. 2500 E 79TH ST 44104 #042-02-1984 L1988 **PUD GS** *020

CARR, Mianda Cheree. 2500 METROHEALTH DR, DEPT OF OB/GYN 44109 #016-11-2004 L2004 **OBG** *012

CARRIGAN, Thomas Paul. ■ 44121 #019-02-2005 L2005 **IM** *012

CARRILLO, Romulo Zacarias. ■ 44130 #748-01-1948 L1961 **OM GPM** *071

CARROLL, Marion Eileen. 11100 EUCLID AVE, UNIV HOSP OF CLEVELAND 44106 #038-06-1989 L1990 **PD** *020 †16

CARRUTHERS, Kirk A. 11100 EUCLID AVE, UNIV HOSPS OF CLEVELAND 44106 #012-21-2006 L2006 **P** *012

CARSON, Dwight K. 15201 EUCLID AVE 44112 #047-07-1977 L1983 **FM** *020 †18

CARTER, Christine Anne. ■ 44195 #038-06-2002 L2002 **PG** *012 †55

CARTER, John Robt. 2074 ABINGTON RD, DEPT OF PATHOLOGY 44106 #035-45-1943 L1967 **ATP ORS** *040 †70

CARTER, Joseph Benj. 2500 METROHEALTH DR, DEPARTMENT OF OTOLARYNGOLO 44109 #026-04-1974 L1980 **OTO** *020 †45

CARTER, Melissa Ann. ■ 44121 #038-44-2006 L2006 **AN** *012

CARVALHO, Alex Franco De. 9500 EUCLID AVE, DEPT OF ORTHO SPORTS MED 44195 #187-48-1994 L2004 **OSM** *012

CASCORBI, Helmut Freimund. 11100 EUCLID AVE 44106 #407-16-1957 L1971 **AN OS** *040 †05

CASERTA, Laura Ann. 11100 EUCLID AVE 44106 #038-06-1998 L2000 **PD** *020 †55

CASTELLANOS VASQUEZ, Jaime. 2500 METROHEALTH DR, C/O METROHEALTH MED CTR-RE 44109 #132-01-1998 L2003 **IM** *100 †20

CASTILLO, Carlos Alberto. ■ 44128 #132-01-1964 L1970 **EM** *020

CASTRO, Constancia Torres. 8300 HOUGH AVE 44103 #748-01-1967 L1976 **PD** *020 †55

CASTRO, Leonidas. ■ 44114 #264-01-1950 L1969 **RO** *072 †80

CASTRO, Pilar Eugenia. 9500 EUCLID AVE, CLEVELAND CLINIC FOUNDATIO 44195 #264-05-2000 L2002 **PAN** *012

CATA, Juan Pablo. 9500 EUCLID AVE, CLEVELAND CLINIC FOUNDATIO 44195 #132-09-1997 L2005 **AN** *012

CATACUTAN, Thadeo Garcia. 9500 EUCLID AVE 44195 #748-01-2000 L2003 **IM** *020 †20

CATALANO, Patrick Michael. 2500 METROHEALTH DR, DEPT OB/GYN A-211 44109 #050-02-1975 L1989 **OBS MFM** *050 †30

CATALANO, Richard Fabian. 12000 MCCRACKEN RD, STE 460 44125 #035-03-1948 L1952 **IM** *071

CATANA, Mircea Ilie. 18099 LORAIN AVE STE 250 44111 #781-03-1969 L1982 **PS HS** *071 †65

CATARDO, Marcello. 9500 EUCLID AVE, CLEVELAND CLINIC FOUNDATIO 44195 #187-12-1997 L2005 *100

CATER, Grace Nicolas. 5208 MEMPHIS AVE 44144 #055-01-1984 L1987 **CD** *020 †20

CAVEY, Carol Meredith. 2900 DETROIT AVE 44113 #038-06-1982 L1982 **P** *020

CAYCE, Kimberly. ■ 44106 #028-46-2002 L2004 **P** *012

CEBUL, Randall Dale. 2500 METROHEALTH DR, METRO HEALTH MED CTR 44109 #008-01-1976 L1987 **IM** *050 †20

CELESTIN, Carmel Audrey. 9500 EUCLID AVE, CLEVELAND CLINIC FOUNDATIO 44195 #010-03-2002 L2006 **IM** *020 †20

CELZO, Ma Florence Intia. 9500 EUCLID AVE, CLEVELAND CLINIC FOUNDATIO 44195 #748-02-1999 L2006 **IM** *012

CERALDI, Bernard A. 18101 LORAIN AVE 44111 #038-06-1942 L1942 **GS** *071 †85

CERNY, Cathleen Anne. 11100 EUCLID AVE, C/O UNIV HOSPS-RESIDECNY O 44106 #038-41-2001 L2001 **PFP** *100 †75

CERQUEIRA, Manuel D. 9500 EUCLID AVE, DEPT OF NUCLEAR MED (GB3) 44195 #035-19-1976 L2004 **CD NM** *020 †20,28

CERVANTES IBANEZ, Sebastia. 9500 EUCLID AVE, DEPT OF GME 44195 #847-11-2001 L2006 *100

CESPON, Ruben Regis. ■ 44106 #748-10-1983 L1999 **ADP** *100

CEVASCO, Nathaniel Charte. 9500 EUCLID AVE, A-61 44195 #038-06-2006 L2006 **D** *012

CHA, Sigmund. 12000 MCCRACKEN RD 44125 #583-01-1964 L1971 **P** *020 †75

CHA, Young Rhee. 12000 MCCRACKEN RD, MARY MOUNT MEDICAL 44125 #583-08-1965 L1972 **PD** *020 †55

CHACKO, Leena. 13951 TERRACE RD, MERIDIA HURON HOSPITAL 44112 #496-35-1990 L2002 **IMG** *012 †18

CHADHA, Shivani. 9500 EUCLID AVE, DEPT OF GME 44195 #422-01-2006 L2006 **AN** *012

CHAE, John. 2500 METROHEALTH DR, METROHEALTH MED CTR 44109 #033-05-1990 L1994 **PM** *050 †60

CHAGOYA-BELLO, Juan Carlo. 9500 EUCLID AVE, CO CCF-GRAD MED EDU DEPT-N 44195 #649-05-1993 L2003 *020

CHAHINE, Lama Maryrose. 9500 EUCLID AVE, CLEVELAND CLINIC FOUNDATIO 44195 #605-01-2005 L2006 **N** *012

CHAIBAN, Joumana Tannous. 10900 EUCLID AVE, UNIVERSITY HOSPITALS 44106 #605-02-2000 L2006 **IM** *012

CHAITOFF, Jeffrey Alan. 6563 WILSON MILLS RD, STE 104 44143 #038-40-1973 L1973 **IM RHU** *020 †20

CHAK, Amitabh. 11100 EUCLID AVE 44106 #035-01-1984 L1991 **IM GE** *050 †20

CHAKRABARTI, Atreyi. 9500 EUCLID AVE BOX S32 44195 #495-47-1991 L2006 **FP** *012 †20

CHAMPAGNE, Bradley J. 11100 EUCLID AVE, LAKESIDE 7TH FLOOR 44106 #035-15-2000 L2006 **GS** *020 †85,10

CHAN, Terence Si-Chung. 9500 EUCLID AVE, CO CCF - GRAD MED EDU DEPT 44195 #056-06-2001 L2001 **IM** *020

CHAND, Bipan. 9500 EUCLID AVE BOX A80 44195 #028-46-1996 L2000 **GS** *020 †85

CHAND, Deepa H. 9500 EUCLID AVE, MAILCODE A120 44195 #028-46-1996 L1998 **PN** *020 †55

CHANDAR, Krishan. 11100 EUCLID AVE, UNIVERSITY HOSPITALS 44106 #495-08-1961 L1976 **N** *071 †75

CHANDRA, Rajesh. 11100 EUCLID AVE, HARVEY HOUSE 409 44106 #495-15-1990 L1999 **IM** *072 †20

CHANDRA-PRAKASH, Aparna. 12301 SNOW RD, KAISER PERMAMENTE 44130 #495-65-1993 L2006 **IM** *020 †20

CHANE, Afaf. 12301 SNOW RD 44130 #875-01-1979 L1989 **PTH** *020 †50

CHANG, Anthony Jules. 4330 W 150TH ST 44135 #016-11-1992 L1995 **AN** *020 †05

CHANG, Lowell. 9500 EUCLID AVE, CLINIC FOUNDATION 44195 #016-01-2005 L2005 **IM** *012

CHANGARATH VIJAYAN, Anil. CO RESIDENCY SUPPORT, METROHEALTH MEDICAL CENTER 44109 #495-16-1997 L2007 **IM** *012

CHAO, Jason. 11100 EUCLID AVE, STE 1200 44106 #016-06-1979 L1982 **FM** *020 †18

CHAO, Samuel Tay. 9500 EUCLID AVE, DESK T28 44195 #038-06-2001 L2001 **RO** *100 †80

CHAO, Victor Tar-Toong. 9500 EUCLID AVE, CLEVELAND CLINIC FOUNDATIO 44195 #825-01-1993 L2006 *062

CHAOUKI, Khaled Shawki. 6780 MAYFIELD RD 44124 #875-01-1965 L1974 **AN** *020 †05

CHAPA, Jeff Balaji. 11100 EUCLID AVE, MACDONALD WOMENS HOSPITAL 44106 #028-34-1996 L1999 **MG** *020 †19,30

CHAPMAN, Jeff Thos. 9500 EUCLID AVE, DESK A90 44195 #028-02-1992 L2000 **PCC** *020 †20

CHAPMAN, Mark Stephen. 1611 S GREEN RD, STE 237 44121 #038-06-1982 L1985 **OBG** *020 †30

CHAPNICK, Rebekah Maxine. 2500 METROHEALTH DR, DEPT OF INTERNAL MEDICINE 44109 #038-06-1994 L2004 **IM** *020 †20

CHARBEL, Samer Charbel. 9500 EUCLID AVE, C/O CCF-INTERNAL MEDICINE 44195 #605-02-2002 L2003 **GE** *012 †20

CHARI, Narmada. 3783 W 117TH ST, INDUSTRIAL CLINIC 44111 #495-21-1958 L1983 **PM** *020

CHARI, Vedantum R. 13951 TERRACE RD 44112 #495-21-1958 L1979 **GS** *020 †85

CHARLES, Ronald Andre. ■ 44195 #035-20-2007 L2007 **GS** *012

CHATTERJEE, Soumya. 9500 EUCLID AVE, CCF DEPT OF RHEUMATIC AND 44195 #495-02-1986 L2004 **RHU** *020 †20

CHAU, Chuong John. ■ 44113 #038-06-2004 L2004 **AN** *012

CHAUDHARY, Meena Dalsang. ■ 44106 #041-13-2000 L2002 **OPH** *020 †35

CHAUDHRY, Asif Ali. 18200 LORAIN AVE, CANCER CTR 44111 #704-01-1964 L1971 **ON IM** *020 †20

CHAUDHRY, Naeem Al-Khaliq. 2500 METROHEALTH DR, METRO HEALTH MEDICAL CTR 44109 #690-07-1986 L2004 **PD** *100 †55

CHAVAN, Arti Dilip. 9500 EUCLID AVE, CLINIC FOUNDATION 44195 #496-60-2003 L2004 **IM** *100 †20

CHAWLA, Ashish. 12301 SNOW RD, CLEVELAND CLINIC FOUNDATIO 44130 #019-02-1997 L2004 **GE** *020 †20

CHELIMSKY, Thomas Chas. 11100 EUCLID AVE, CASE MEDICAL CENTER 44106 #028-02-1983 L1990 **N IM** *020 †20,75

CHEMALI, Kamal Raymond. 9500 EUCLID AVE, DEPT OF NEUROLOGY S-90 44195 #605-03-1994 L1998 **N** *020 †75

CHEN, Andrew. UNIVERSITY HOSP DEPT MED 44106 #041-02-2005 L2005 **IM** *012

CHEN, Chichiung. 9500 EUCLID AVE A81, OBSTETRICS AND GYNECOLOGY 44195 #017-20-2001 L2005 **OBG** *100 †30

CHEN, Elliott Ho. ■ 44118 #041-13-1998 L2007 **PS** *100 †85

CHEN, Evan. 2500 METROHEALTH DR, METROHEALTH MED CTR 44109 #051-04-2005 L2006 **AN** *012

CHEN, Julie Tsulee. ■ 44195 #023-01-2004 L2005 **NS** *012

CHEN, Michael Kaiyan. 11100 EUCLID AVE, DEPT OF FAMILY MEDICINE 44106 #023-01-2006 L2006 **FP** *012

CHEN, William Chunying. ■ 44115 #035-19-2006 L2007 **RO** *012

CHEN, Zhen Yu. 11100 EUCLID AVE, CO UNIV HOSPS-RESIDENT OFF 44106 #243-48-1984 L2001 **PTH** *100

CHENG, Jianguo. 9500 EUCLID AVE, DEPT OF PAIN MGMT 44195 #243-32-1983 L2006 **AN PME** *020 †05

CHENG CHING, Esteban. ■ 44195 #270-01-2002 L2007 **N** *012 †20

CHEONG, Lai Leng. 9500 EUCLID AVE, TT32 44195 #825-01-1985 **D** *020

CHERACCI, Ugo. 7007 POWERS BLVD 44129 #561-11-1955 L1962 **AN** *071

CHERIAN, Neil. T33, PROG OF VESTIBULAR & BALAN 44195 #035-08-1996 L2000 **N** *020 †75

CHERIYAN, Luke Lohan K. 1730 W 25TH ST, LUTHERAN HOSPITAL 44113 #495-27-1974 L1985 **AN** *020

CHERULLO, Edward Ernest. 11100 EUCLID AVE, MS 5046 44106 #028-34-1997 L1999 **U** *020 †95

CHERULLO, Lisa Marie. 6780 MAYFIELD RD 44124 #028-34-1997 L1999 **PD** *020 †55

CHEUNG, Bonnie Wai-Wah. 11100 EUCLID AVE, DEPT OB 44106 #005-06-2000 L2004 **OBG** *020

CHEW, Derek Peng Beng. 9500 EUCLID AVE 44195 #143-02-1992 L1999 *100

CHHABRA, Nipun. ■ 44106 #010-01-2007 L2007 **OTO** *012

CHIDIAC, Rita M. ■ 44106 #605-01-1992 L1996 **END** *100 †20

CHIESA VOTTERO, Andres Ga. ■ 44195 #132-07-1994 L2000 **SP** *100 †50

CHIGARAPALLI, Sukesh. ■ 44122 #495-70-1986 **GS** *100

CHIKWENDU, Obiageli Chiaz. ■ 44102 #690-04-2004 L2007 **IM** *012

CHILCOTE, Wm August, Jr. ■ 44124 #038-41-1978 L1979 **R** *020 †80

CHIM, Harvey Wei Ming. 11100 EUCLID AVE 44106 #825-01-2002 L2007 **PS** *012

CHIMPIRI, Annapurneswara. 9500 EUCLID AVE, CLEVELAND CLINIC FOUNDATIO 44195 #495-58-1995 L2005 *100

CHIN, Melvyn Jow Yang. 2500 METROHEALTH DR 44109 #665-01-2005 L2006 **IM** *100

CHIN, Stephanie Elaine. ■ 44120 #035-06-2006 L2006 **PD** *012

CHING, Chi Keong. 9500 EUCLID AVE, CLEVELAND CLINIC FOUNDATIO 44195 #825-01-1995 L2006 *100

CHING, Eiza Lyn Ong. 9500 EUCLID AVE, CLEVELAND CLINIC FOUNDATIO 44195 #748-01-2000 L2003 **AI** *012 †20

CHING, Lina Miriam. ■ 44195 #016-42-2005 L2005 **IM** *012

CHINNAPPA, Priya. 11311 SHAKER BLVD, RM 4135 44104 #495-37-1997 L1999 **END IM** *100 †20

CHIONG, Ignacio. ■ 44114 #016-11-2006 L2006 **DR** *012

CHIRIBAU, Mona Iuliana. CO RESIDENCY SUPPORT, METROHEALTH MEDICAL CENTER 44109 #781-02-2002 L2007 **IM** *012

CHITRAVAS, Numthip. 11100 EUCLID AVE, UNIVERSITY HOSPITALS 44106 #891-04-1999 L2007 **IM** *012

CHIU QUEVEDO, Jorge Ferna. 9500 EUCLID AVE, CO CCF-GRAD MED EDU DEPT-N 44195 #429-02-1997 L2003 *020

CHMIEL, James Francis. 2101 ADELBERT RD, STE 3001 44106 #025-01-1991 L1995 **PDP** *020 †55

CHMIELEWSKI, Richard M. 2351 E 22ND ST 44115 #041-01-1977 L1980 **ID IM** *020 †20

CHO, Edward Inntae. ■ 44195 #008-01-2004 L2004 **OTO** *012

CHO, Sunghee Leslie. 9500 EUCLID AVE C51, CLEVELAND CLINIC FOUNDATIO 44195 #016-02-1994 L2000 **CD IC** *020 †20

CHOE, Juno. ■ 44103 #054-04-2005 L2006 **RO** *012

CHOI, Cecilia Mi-Young. 2500 METROHEALTH DR 44109 #665-02-2004 L2004 **HO** *012 †20

CHOI, Ihn Shick. 18101 LORAIN AVE 44111 #583-04-1966 L1971 **AN** *020 †05

CHOI, Michael Insup. 2500 METROHEALTH DR 44109 #422-01-2007 L2007 **PTH** *012

CHOLITKUL, Suteevan. 13951 TERRACE RD, CO MER HURON HOSP-INT MED 44112 #891-02-2000 L2004 **IMG** *012 †20

CHOLITKUL, Suwitda. 13951 TERRACE RD, CO MER HURON HOSP-INT MED 44112 #891-02-2000 L2004 **IMG** *012 †20

CHOOLJIAN, David Mcavoy. ■ 44120 #047-05-2007 L2007 **IM** *012

CHOU, Samuel Shi-Ming. 9500 EUCLID AVE 44195 #385-02-1957 L1981 **NP NS** *071

CHOUDHARY, Chirag. ■ 44195 #496-35-2002 L2006 **PCC** *012 †20

CHOUKSEY, Akhilesh Kumar. 11100 EUCLID AVE, RM 504 / MAILSTOP 6008B 44106 #495-47-1985 L2002 **PD** *020 †03,55

CHOUNG, Soung Whoa. 7007 POWERS BLVD 44129 #583-01-1972 L1977 **FM** *020

CHOURE, Anuja Gautam. 9500 EUCLID AVE 44195 #495-17-2004 L2007 **IM** *012

CHOURE, Gautam Sakharam. ■ 44195 #496-30-2001 L2006 **IM** *012

CHOW, Brian Davidwaifun. ■ 44118 #038-06-2005 L2005 **MPD** *012

CHOW, Chen Hoe. 9500 EUCLID AVE 44195 #064-01-2005 L2005 **IM** *012

CHOW, Michael Ming-Lee. 9500 EUCLID AVE, DEPT OF GME 44195 #065-05-1994 L2002 *100 †25

CHOWDHRY, Aqeel Ahmad. ■ 44195 #016-06-2004 L2005 **DR** *012

CHOWDHRY, Manorama Singh. 9500 EUCLID AVE, C/O CCF-GRAD MED EDU DEPT- 44195 #495-30-1989 L2003 **AN** *012

CHOWDHRY, Shakeel Ahmad. ■ 44103 #010-02-2005 L2005 **NS** *012

CHRISMAN-KHAWAM, Leanne M. 11100 EUCLID AVE, CWRU-DEPT OF FAMILY MEDICI 44106 #040-02-1993 L2001 **FM** *020 †18

CHRISTIAN, Michael Oliver. 6780 MAYFIELD RD, HILLCREST HOSPITAL 44124 #035-20-1975 L1982 **DR** *020 †80

CHRISTIE, Richard Ernest. 2351 E 22ND ST W325 44115 #028-34-1961 L1962 **IM PUD** *040 †20,18

CHRISTOFFERSON, Ryan D. 9500 EUCLID AVE, BOX 606 44195 #048-12-2001 L2004 **IC** *012

CHTEINGARDT, Irina I. 6770 MAYFIELD RD # 425 44124 #913-06-1995 L2000 **IM** *100 †20

CHU, Kimberly Erin. ■ 44106 #041-12-2002 L2007 **PTH** *100 †50

CHUA, Joselita Uy. 2103 CLARK AVE 44109 #748-26-1987 L2000 **P** *020 †75

CHUANG, Hsuan-Hung. 9500 EUCLID AVE 44195 #825-01-1994 L2004 *100

CHUANG, Janet Shawchen. 11100 EUCLID AVE, UNIV HOSP 44106 #038-40-2007 L2007 **PD** *012

CHUNG, Benjamin Inbeh. 9500 EUCLID AVE, A100 44195 #041-02-1999 L2005 **U** *100 †95

CHUNG, Brian Jaehoon. ■ 44121 #036-01-2002 L2002 **OTO** *012

CHUNG, Hyung Rewl. ■ 44124 #583-01-1964 L1976 **GP IMG** *020

CHUNG, Jeffrey Yauhuei. 9500 EUCLID AVE I-13, COLE EYE INSTITUTE 44195 #035-06-2002 L2006 **OPH** *012 †35

CHUNG, Mina Kay. 9500 EUCLID AVE, DEPT OF CARDIOLOGY - F15 44195 #028-02-1983 L1993 **ICE CD** *020 †20

CHUNG, Moon Ja. 2500 METROHEALTH DR 44109 #583-08-1966 L1972 **PTH** *020 †50

CHUNG, Roy Fwu Shen. 2500 METROHEALTH DR 44109 #539-02-2002 L2004 **IM** *100

CHUONG, Diana Dai. ■ 44106 #010-02-2000 L2007 **OTO** *100 †45

CHURCH, James Michael. 9500 EUCLID AVE, # A-30 44195 #671-02-1973 L1985 **CRS** *020

CHURGIN, Samara Spring. ■ 44114 #010-01-2001 L2007 **PS** *012

CHUTKAY, Indrani Shreekan. 2351 E 22ND ST, DEPT OF INTERNAL MED 44115 #495-65-1999 L2005 **IM** *012

CIANFLOCCO, Alfred James. 99 NORTHLINE CIR STE 100, DEPT OF ORTHOPAEDIC SURGER 44119 #036-05-1976 L1982 **FM OS** *020 †18

CIASCHINI, Michael Walter. 9500 EUCLID AVE, C/O CCF-GRAD MED EDU DEPT- 44195 #041-01-2000 L2000 **MSR** *012 †80

CIEZKI, Jay Phillip. 9500 EUCLID AVE 44195 #056-06-1991 L1995 **RO** *020 †80

CIGAGNA, Rosalia. ■ 44131 #041-07-1949 L1950 **AN** *071 †05

CINGLE, Kimberly Ann. 12301 SNOW RD 44130 #038-06-1995 L1999 **OPH** *020 †35

CISARIK, Paul Marian. 2500 METROHEALTH DR, METROHEALTH MED CTR 44109 #422-01-2005 L2005 **IM** *012

CIVIC, Kimberly Rae. 9500 EUCLID AVE A-120, GENERAL PEDIATRICS 44195 #038-44-2003 L2003 **PD** *020

CLAIR, Daniel Gerard. 9500 EUCLID AVE, DESK S-40 44195 #051-01-1986 L1998 **VS** *020 †85

CLARK, Brian Albert. 9500 EUCLID AVE, DEPT OF EMERGENCY MEDICINE 44195 #040-02-1986 L1992 **OBG MG** *020 †19,30

CLARK, Christopher T. 18101 LORAIN AVE, DEPARTMENT OF PATHOLOGY 44111 #036-08-1991 L1997 **PTH** *020 †50

CLARK, Deborah Yvette. 12100 SUPERIOR AVE 44106 #038-06-1988 L1990 **OBG** *020 †30

CLARK, Gary Steven. 2500 METROHEALTH DR, DEPT PHYS MED & REHAB 44109 #041-02-1975 L2001 **PM MDM** *030 †60

CLARK, Kevin Robt. 11100 EUCLID AVE 44106 #038-45-1986 L1989 **ADP** *020 †18

CLARK, Malcolm John. 2500 METROHEALTH DR 44109 #671-01-1977 L1986 **IM N** *020

CLARK, Walter J. 8300 HOUGH AVE 44103 #010-03-1978 L1988 **IM** *020 †20

CLAYMAN, Julie Ann. 11100 EUCLID AVE 44106 #038-06-1966 L1966 **TS** *020 †85,90

CLAYTON, Warren Floyd, Jr. 9500 EUCLID AVE, A91 44195 #001-02-2003 L2003 **IM** *100 †20

CLEGG, Kathleen Anne. 11100 EUCLID AVE 44106 #038-06-1989 L1991 **P** *020 †75

CLEMENTE LARRANAGA, J. 18099 LORAIN AVE STE 316 44111 #737-01-1967 L1977 **IM NEP** *020 †20

CLEVELAND, Wm Bingham. ■ 44106 #038-06-1943 L1944 **GS** *072

CLEVES BAYON, Catalina. 13660 FAIRHILL RD, APT 302 44120 #264-21-2003 L2006 **PD** *100 †55

CLIFFORD, Bradley Thomas. ■ 44121 #038-43-2006 L2006 **IM** *012

CLIFFORD, Celia Anne Lori. 9500 EUCLID AVE BOX 443 44195 #143-08-1990 L2001 *100

CLOUGH, John David. 9500 EUCLID AVE, CLEVELAND CLC W14 44195 #010-01-1965 L1966 **RHU IG** *030 †20

CLOUGH, John M. 600 SUPERIOR AVE E, STE 2100 44114 #038-06-1951 L1951 **ORS OS** *071 †40

CMOLIK, Brian Lawrence. 10701 EAST BLVD SURG SVC, LOUIS STOKES VAMC 44106 #038-44-1985 L1993 **TS** *020 †85,90

COBB, Kendalle. 99 NORTHLINE CIR 44119 #010-01-1996 L2004 **FM** *020 †18

COBURN, Donald James. 18599 LAKE SHORE BLVD 44119 #028-34-1945 L1946 **GS TS** *071 †85

7480

■ = Address Information Privacy Protected

COCCO, Amy Elizabeth. ■ 44122 #038-06-2002 L2002 **HMP** *100 †50
COCHRAN, Richard Kenneth. 2351 E 22ND ST 44115 #017-20-1978 L1982 **PTH** *020 †50
COCIERU, Andrei. 9500 EUCLID AVE 44106 #913-50-1998 L2005 **GS** *100
COCKERILLE, Laurence L. 4229 PEARL RD 44109 #051-01-1959 L1964 **D** *071 †15
COE, Bonita. 9500 EUCLID AVE 44195 #010-03-1994 L1996 **IM** *020 †20
COFFEY, Anne Hope. 11100 EUCLID AVE, STE 2600 44106 #038-06-1994 L1996 **DR** *020 †80
COFFEY, Sheila Ann. 9500 EUCLID AVE 44106 #038-06-1990 L1992 **PDR** *020 †80
COFFMAN, Kathy Lee. 9500 EUCLID AVE, THE CLEVELAND CLINIC FOUND 44195 #025-07-1983 L2007 **P** *020 †75
COGAN, Elizabeth Anne. 9500 EUCLID AVE # MED-P39, CLEVELAND CLNC FOUNDATION 44195 #539-04-1997 **IM** *100
COHEN, Alan R. 11100 EUCLID AVE, 5TH FL 44106 #035-20-1978 L1994 **NS** *020 †25
COHEN, Bruce Howard. 9500 EUCLID AVE, DEPT OF EMERGENCY MEDICINE 44195 #035-46-1982 L1989 **CHN N** *020 †55,55
COHEN, David Wayne. ■ 44102 #038-43-2003 L2003 **PTH** *100 †50
COHEN, Herschel. 1 MOUNT SINAI DR 44106 #028-34-1941 L1943 **IM CD** *071 †20
COHEN, James Harrison. 18901 LAKE SHORE BLVD 44119 #020-12-1981 L1982 **IM EM** *020 †20
COHEN, Jamie Neil. 7255 OLD OAK BLVD, ASSOCIATES 44130 #064-01-1997 L2005 *020 †20
COHEN, Jeffrey Alan. 9500 EUCLID AVE 44195 #016-02-1980 L1994 **N** *020 †75
COHEN, Mark Lloyd. 11400 EUCLID AVE STE 100 44106 #035-20-1983 L1986 **IM PTH** *020 †50
COHEN, Nir. 11100 EUCLID AVE 3018, CO UNIV HOSPS-RESIDENCY OF 44106 #550-02-1991 L2000 *100
COHEN, Rosana E. 11400 EUCLID AVE STE 100 44106 #187-03-1981 L1987 **PTH** *020 †50
COHEN, Sidney Mace. 18599 LAKE SHORE BLVD, UNIVERSITY MEDNET 44119 #008-01-1959 L1964 **U** *071 †95
COHN, Peter Jochim. ■ 44124 #038-40-1959 L1959 **GS VS** *071 †85
COHN, Robert Copley. 2500 METROHEALTH DR, DEPT PEDIATRICS 44109 #024-05-1982 L1985 **PDP PD** *020 †55
COKLEY, Cherise Lenee. ■ 44102 #028-34-2004 L2004 **OBG** *012
COLE, George W, Jr. ■ 44113 #008-01-1994 L2007 **TS** *012
COLE, Monroe. 11100 EUCLID AVE, UNIV HOSPITALS CLEVELAND 44106 #010-02-1957 L1970 **N** *071 †75
COLEMAN, Nichelle Diane. ■ 44120 #038-06-2001 L2001 **IM** *020 †20
COLETTA, John Eugene. 6770 MAYFIELD RD # 423 44124 #041-12-1960 L1961 **IM** *071 †18
COLLIN, Marc F. 2500 METROHEALTH DR 44109 #016-43-1979 L1989 **NPM PD** *020 †55
COLLINS, Atif Bendanieli. ■ 44106 #038-06-2006 L2007 **OPH** *012
COLLINS, Gregory Bruce. 9500 EUCLID AVE 44195 #038-40-1970 L1970 **P ADP** *020 †75
COLLINS, Nicole Renee. ■ 44120 #016-45-2007 L2007 **GS** *012
COLLINS, Stephen Douglas. ■ 44106 #038-06-1984 L1990 **N IM** *020 †75
COMO, John Joseph. 2500 METROHEALTH DR, DEPARTMENT OF 44109 #033-06-1995 L2003 **GS CCS** *020 †85
CONKLIN, Jeffrey Bryan. 2500 METROHEALTH DR, C/O METROHEALTH MED CTR-RE 44109 #035-06-2002 L2002 **MPD** *020 †20,55
CONNELL, Cindylou F. 11100 EUCLID AVE, UNIV HOSPS CLEVELAND 44106 #038-40-1988 L1992 **ON** *020 †20
CONNORS, Alfred Francis, Jr. 2500 METROHEALTH DR, METROHEALTH MEDICAL CENTER 44109 #038-43-1974 L1975 **CCM PUD** *040 †20
CONOMY, John Paul. 2709 FRANKLIN BLVD 44113 #028-34-1964 L1965 **N LM** *020 †75
CONOVER, Pamela Taylor. 29000 CENTER RIDGE RD, ST JOHN W SHORE HOSP 44145 #038-06-1987 L1987 **PTH** *020 †20
CONVERSE, Chas Franklin. 2633 COLCHESTER RD 44106 #035-15-1967 L1968 **PS** *071 †85,65
CONVERY, Ellen Patricia. ■ 44106 #038-06-2007 L2007 **AN** *012
CONWAY, Katharine Marie. 44109 #038-45-2005 L2005 **FP** *012
CONWELL, Stephanie H. 18101 LORAIN AVE 44111 #038-41-1987 L1988 **EM** *020 †16
COOK, James Robert. 9500 EUCLID AVE 44195 #038-02-1998 L2003 **HMP** *020 †50
COOK, Lloyd Matthew. 7963 EUCLID AVE 44103 #035-15-1983 L1986 **IM** *020 †20
COOK, Sebastian Anthony. 6780 MAYFIELD RD 44124 #028-34-1967 L1971 **R NM** *020 †80
COOKE, Kenneth Robt. 2103 CORNELL RD RM 6524, WOLSTEIN RESEARCH BLDG 6FL 44106 #033-06-1990 L2008 **PHO PD** *020 †55
COOLEY, Roger Scott. ■ 44145 #038-43-2004 L2004 **AN** *012
COONEY, Matthew Morrissey. 11100 EUCLID AVE, UNIVERSITY HOSPITALS OF CL 44106 #038-06-1998 L2000 **HO** *020 †20
COOPER, Antonio. 2500 METROHEALTH DR 44109 #038-06-1984 L1990 **AN IM** *020 †20,05
COOPER, Brenda Carol. 11100 EUCLID AVE 44106 #023-07-1984 L1989 **ON IM** *020 †20
COOPER, Gregory Scott. 11100 EUCLID AVE 44106 #041-01-1986 L1988 **GE IM** *020 †20
COOPER, Kevin D. 11100 EUCLID AVE # 3516, UNIV HOSP CLEVELAND DEPT D 44106 #011-03-1977 L1995 **D IG** *030 †15
COOPER, Kevin Lee. 2351 E 22ND ST 44115 #038-40-1984 L1989 **PTH** *020 †50 ‡
COOPER, Mark Jeffrey. 11100 EUCLID AVE 44106 #023-07-1982 L1990 **ON** *050 †20
COOPER, Scott Evan. 9500 EUCLID AVE 44195 #035-01-1995 L2001 **N** *020 †75
COPELAN, Edward A. 9500 EUCLID AVE 44106 #024-07-1977 L1980 **HEM IM** *020 †20
COPELAND, Laura Lee. 9500 EUCLID AVE E-19, CLEV CLINIC EMERGENCY DEPT 44195 #038-40-2001 L2001 **EM** *020 †16
COPELAND, Ronald Louis. 1001 LAKESIDE AVE E, STE 1200 44114 #038-41-1977 L1977 **GS** *020 †85
COPPEDGE, Everette P, Jr. ■ 44120 #038-06-1943 L1943 **FM GS** *071 †18
CORDASCO, Edward M. 9500 EUCLID AVE, # EE40 44195 #010-02-1949 L1952 **PUD IM** *071 †20
CORDIER, Jennifer Rose. ■ 44195 #010-02-2005 L2005 **PD** *012
CORNELIO FLORES, Oscar Al. 18101 LORAIN AVE 44111 #737-01-2000 L2005 **FP** *012
CORPUS, Peter Andrew. 11100 EUCLID AVE, UNIV HOSPS OF CLEVELAND 44106 #038-40-2005 L2005 **P** *012
CORPUZ, Nancy Ann. ■ 44195 #038-43-2006 L2006 **PTH** *012
CORRADI, Richard Bryon. 2500 METROHEALTH DR, UNIV HOSP 44106 #035-45-1960 L1961 **P** *020 †20
CORRIGAN, Mary Virginia. 2500 METROHEALTH DR, FAMILY PRACTICE DEPARTMENT 44109 #038-41-1990 L1992 **FPG FM** *020 †18
CORRIVEAU, Michael Lee. 2345 MURRAY HILL RD, 330 B 44106 #056-06-1979 L1990 **IM** *020 †20
CORSO, Jorge Eduard. THE CLEVELAND CLINIC, DEPT OF VASCULAR SURGERY 44195 #012-01-2002 L2007 **VS** *012
CORTAS, Tania Elie. 11100 EUCLID AVE - R, CO UNIV HOSPS-RESIDENCY OF 44106 #605-01-2001 L2001 **HO** *100
CORTEVILLE, Jane E. 2500 METROHEALTH DR, DEPT OF OB-GYN 44109 #028-02-1983 L1998 **OBG MG** *020 †19,30
CORVO, Antoinette. 9500 EUCLID AVE, DEPT OF ANESTHESIOLOGY/E31 44195 #067-01-1994 L2000 *020

CORWIN, Robert Gilbert. 7155 PEARL RD 44130 #038-06-1968 L1968 **D IM** *020 †15
CORZO MOODY, Alfonso. ■ 44135 #649-01-1950 L1965 **P** *071
COSBY, Paul Wilson. 7123 PEARL RD, STE 201 44130 #005-19-1973 L1981 **EM GP** *072 †16 ‡
COSGROVE, Delos M, III. 9500 EUCLID AVE 44195 #051-01-1966 L1975 **TS** *020 †85,90
COSSOY, Michael Bryan. 9500 EUCLID AVE, DEPT OF GME 44195 #065-06-1999 L2004 *103
COSTALDI, Mark Eric. ■ 44114 #028-34-2006 L2006 **PTH** *012
COSTANTINI, Ottorino. 2500 METROHEALTH DR, HAMANN 3D FLOOR H-334 44109 #035-19-1989 L1991 **CD IM** *020 †20
COSTARELLA, Bruce R. 21000 BROOKPARK RD, MS 15-5 44135 #038-45-1991 L1992 **FM UCM** *020 †18
COSTIN, John August. 9500 EUCLID AVE 44195 #038-06-1975 L1976 **OPH** *020 †35
COTRONEO, John. 9500 EUCLID AVE 44195 #143-02-1995 L2003 *020
COTTON, Claire E. ■ 44121 #028-34-1950 L1951 **IM** *071
COUDSI, Ayman. 7255 OLD OAK BLVD 44130 #875-01-1972 L1977 **PD** *020 †55
COVER, Lindsay Brianne. ■ 44121 #007-02-2007 L2007 **AN** *012
COVIELLO, James Michael. 1611 S GREEN RD 44121 #038-40-1994 L1996 **IM** *020 †20
COVIN, Antoinette Barbara. ■ 44120 #038-06-2006 L2006 **AN** *012
COVINGTON, Edward C, Jr. 9500 EUCLID AVE, CLEVELAND CLINIC DEPT OF P 44195 #047-06-1970 L1979 **PMM P** *020 †75
COX, Diethra Diane. 2816 E 116TH ST, BUCKEYE METROHEALTH MEDICA 44120 #047-07-1982 L1986 **IM** *020 †20
COX, John Osborne. 5900 CARGO RD, WHOLE HEALTH MANAGEMENT CL 44135 #065-06-1970 L1996 **GP** *020 †18
COYNE, Cathleen Ann. 18099 LORAIN AVE, INC 44111 #038-43-1990 L1993 **PD** *020 †55
CRABTREE, Robert Hugh. 19250 BAGLEY RD 44130 #038-40-1975 L1976 **PTH HEM** *020 †50
CRACIUN, Atanase Romeu. 3619 PARK EAST DR 44122 #781-01-1973 L1981 **N GP** *020 †75
CRACIUN, Horia Liviu. 12301 SNOW RD 44130 #781-01-1982 L1997 **P** *020 †75
CRAVEN, Daniel Ince. 2101 ADELBERT RD, STE 3001 44106 #038-06-1993 L1996 **PD PDP** *020 †55
CRAWFORD, Joseph Arden. 11100 EUCLID AVE, UNIV HOSP OF CLEVELAND 44106 #010-01-1971 L1978 **NM DR** *020 †80,28
CREASEY, Graham Harold. 2550 METROHEALTH DR 44109 #919-03-1972 L1992 *020
CRIPE-MAMIE, Chantal. 2500 METROHEALTH DR, CO METRO HLTH MED CTR-RES 44109 #869-01-1992 L2001 **NPM** *100
CROLLICK, Jill Susan. ■ 44122 #041-02-1981 L1982 **D** *071 †15
CROMER, Barbara Ann. 2500 METROHEALTH DR 44109 #038-40-1977 L1980 **ADL PD** *020 †55
CROOK, Robert Edward. 2500 METROHEALTH DR 44109 #038-43-2005 L2005 **IM** *012
CROWE, Carol A Cooper. 2500 METROHEALTH DR, METROHEALTH MEDICAL CENTER 44109 #028-34-1972 L1975 **PD** *020 †55,19
CROWE, Joseph Patrick, Jr. 9500 EUCLID AVE, DESK A-80 44195 #038-06-1978 L1980 **GS** *020 †85
CROWELL, Trevor Adam. ■ 44118 #005-06-2008 *012
CRUM, Edward Dewey. 2500 METROHEALTH DR, METRO HEALTH MEDICAL CENTE 44109 #038-06-1965 L1965 **ON HEM** *020 †20
CRUZ, Nilsa Lizette. 9500 EUCLID AVE, # TT32 44195 #042-02-1992 L2006 **CCP** *100
CRUZ, Wilfredo A. 19250 BAGLEY RD, STE 101 44130 #748-01-1960 L1971 **AN** *020
CRUZ CORREA, Miguel Angel. 9500 EUCLID AVE, DEPT OF GME 44195 #264-04-1984 L2005 **AN** *012
CRUZ-KNIGHT, Wanda Enid. ■ 44121 #038-06-1997 L2007 **FM** *020 †18 ‡
CUA, John V. 18101 LORAIN AVE 44111 #748-08-1966 L1972 **IM** *020
CUFF, Steven Christopher. 2226 WARRENSVILL CNTR RD R 44118 #038-40-2003 L2003 **PSM** *012 †55
CUI, Lixin. 2500 METROHEALTH DR, DEPARTMENT OF PM&R 44109 #243-03-1991 L2000 **PM** *020 †60
CULVER, James E, Jr. 9500 EUCLID AVE, CLEVELAND CLINIC FOUND 44195 #035-01-1965 L1974 **ORS HS** *071 †40
CUMMINGS, Jennifer Eiko. 9500 EUCLID AVE, F-15 44195 #038-44-1997 L1998 **ICE** *100 †20
CUMMINGS, Kenneth Clark. 9500 EUCLID AVE, MAILCODE E-30 44195 #028-02-2001 L2004 **AN** *100 †05
CUNAGIN, James Ferrel. 1611 S GREEN RD, STE LL06 44121 #038-41-1999 L1999 **P FM** *020 †18,75
CUPALA, Homai J. 18697 BAGLEY RD 44130 #495-23-1965 L1975 **P** *020 †75
CUPALA, Jitendra B. 18697 BAGLEY RD 44130 #495-23-1970 L1977 **P** *020 †75
CURLEY, Catherine Anne. 2550 METROHEALTH DR 44109 #038-06-1993 L1994 **IM** *020 †20
CURTIN, Ronan John. 9500 EUCLID AVE, CARDIOVASCLR MED DESK F15 44195 #539-02-1995 L2005 **CD** *100
CUSI, Esther Florencia. ■ 44120 #748-19-1991 **IM** *100 †20
CUTARELLI, Marina Laura. 6681 RIDGE RD, STE 404 44129 #038-43-1989 L1991 **IM** *020 †20
CYDULKA, Rita Kay. 2500 METROHEALTH DR, RM BG3-68 44109 #016-06-1980 L1989 **EM IM** *040 †20,16
CYMBOR, Susan L Tebich. 9500 EUCLID AVE E-31, CCF - DEPT OF GENERAL ANES 44195 #759-01-1988 L2003 **AN** *020 †05
CYWINSKI, Jacek Boguslaw. 9500 EUCLID AVE, CLEVELAND CLINIC FOUNDATIO 44195 #759-10-1993 L2000 **AN** *020 †05
CZEISLER, Barry Michael. ■ 44106 #038-06-2008 *012
CZEPAK, Bohdan Robert. 1730 W 25TH ST 44113 #409-16-1970 L1977 **PS HS** *020 †65
CZORNYJ, Ivan. 1912 W 73RD ST 44102 #407-04-1947 L1956 **GP** *071
DABB, Barbara Fieldhouse. 11100 EUCLID AVE 44106 #038-06-1974 L1976 **AN** *020 †05
DABRAMO, Catherine Victor. 44135 #038-45-2005 L2005 **EM** *012
DACHA, Harinathrao R. 1001 LAKESIDE AVE E, STE 1200 44114 #495-21-1974 L1981 **PUD IM** *020 †20
DAHBAR, Mazen. 18101 LORAIN AVE, DEPT OF INTERNAL MED 44111 #875-01-2005 L2006 **IM** *012
DAHDAH, Nagib S. 2500 METROHEALTH DR, DEPT OF PEDIATRICS 44109 #605-02-1988 L1996 **PDC** *020 †55
DAHL-GROVE, Deanna Lynn. 11100 EUCLID AVE, UNIV HOSP OF CLEVELAND 44106 #038-06-1990 L1992 **PE PD** *040 †55
DAHMS, Beverly Barrett. 11100 EUCLID AVE 44106 #035-08-1968 L1978 **PP ATP** *020 †55,50
DAKIN, Theodora Letta P. ■ 44106 #010-01-1943 L1944 **GP** *071
DALAL, Tejas Ajay. 11100 EUCLID AVE, ATTN: CYNTHIA PATENA 44106 #050-02-2005 L2006 **DR** *012
DALE, Roman Michael. 1730 W 25TH ST STE 233A 44113 #065-01-1978 L1995 *020
DALOUK, Khidir Abdelmonei. 2500 METROHEALTH DR 44109 #848-01-1999 L2007 **IM** *012
DALY, Ryan Patrick. 9500 EUCLID AVE, CLEVELAND CLINIC 44195 #024-05-2002 L2005 **CD** *012 †12
D'AMICO, Louis. 9500 EUCLID AVE, STE 100 44195 #041-09-1973 L1976 **U** *020 †95

DAMIS, Marina. 11100 EUCLID AVE RM 3018, CO UNIV HOSPS-RESIDENCY OF 44106 #422-01-1997 L2002 **PYG** *100

DAMTEW, Belai. ■ 44130 #366-01-1976 L1985 **ID IM** *020 †20

DANESE, Rossana Diana. 11100 EUCLID AVE, CWRU DEPT OF MEDICINE 44106 #038-43-1986 L1989 **END** *020 †20

DANESHGARI, Firouz. 9500 EUCLID AVE, STE 100 44195 #517-01-1983 L2001 **U GS** *020 †95

DANIEL, Thomas Mallon. 2074 ABINGTON RD, DEPT MED 44106 #024-01-1955 L1958 **PUD IM** *050 †20

DANNUG-BASUG, Carmen B. 2500 METROHEALTH DR 44109 #748-01-1955 L1972 **IM CD** *071

DANZIGER-ISAKOV, Lara Ann. 9500 EUCLID AVE S25, CLEV CLINIC CHILDREN'S HOS 44195 #038-06-1997 L1998 **PD** *020 †55

DAOUD, Emad Wasfy Rizk. 1730 W 25TH ST, LUTHERAN HOSP 44113 #915-04-1976 L1993 **AN PMM** *020 †05

DAOUD, Mohammad Othman. ■ 44145 #575-01-1991 L1996 **END** *020 †20

DAOUD, Shaza. 18101 LORAIN AVE, FAIRVIEW GEN 44111 #875-01-1996 L2006 **IM** *012

DAPRANO, Joseph Kennedy. 11100 SAINT CLAIR AVE 44108 #038-06-1993 L1995 **IM** *020 †20,55

DAR, Asaf Ali. 3878 ROCKY RIVER DR 44111 #704-01-1971 L1980 **CD IM** *020 †20

DAR, Gohar Habib. 9500 EUCLID AVE G/3, CLEVELAND CLINIC FOUNDATIO 44195 #704-24-1992 L2000 **CCA** *020 †05

DAREJEH, Zahra. 11100 EUCLID AVE 44106 #517-05-1996 L2005 **IM** *020

DAROFF, Robert Barry. 11100 EUCLID AVE, STE 5512 44106 #041-01-1961 L1980 **N OS** *072 †75

DARR, Khalid Bashir. 5510 PEARL RD, STE 205 44129 #704-01-1963 L1971 **FM TS** *020 †85

DASARATHY, Jaividhya. 2500 METROHEALTH DR, METROHEALTH MEDICAL CENTER 44109 #495-42-1991 L2000 **FM** *020 †18 ‡

DASHEFSKY, Larry Howard. 6803 MAYFIELD RD STE 409 44124 #062-01-1981 L1987 **N CN** *020 †75

DA SILVA, Geni. ■ 44108 #187-12-1958 **P** *062

DASKAL, Allan Naftali. 2500 METROHEALTH DR, METROHEALTH MED CTR 44109 #035-46-2007 L2007 **IM** *012

DATTA, Mihir Kanti. 18599 LAKE SHORE BLVD, UNIVERSITY MEDNET 44119 #495-02-1954 L1973 **PTH** *020 †16

DAUT, Gregory Allen. ■ 44106 #038-06-2008 *012

DAVEIGA, Sigrid Payne. ■ 44195 #016-43-2003 L2007 **AI** *012 †55

DAVESSAR, Nitin. 7255 OLD OAK BLVD, STE 205 44130 #043-01-1991 L1998 **GE** *020 †20

DAVID, Laura Jean. 1611 S GREEN RD STE 216 44121 #028-02-1978 L1980 **OBG NPM** *020 †30

DAVID SELWYN JEYARAJ, Darw. ■ 44109 #495-95-1999 L2002 **CD** *012

DAVIDSON, Brooke Lauren. ■ 44106 #021-01-2006 L2006 **PD** *012

DAVIDSON, Eleanor Warnock. 2145 ADELBERT RD 44106 #025-01-1979 L1985 **IM NEP** *030 †20

DAVIDSON, Jon Craig. 9500 EUCLID AVE, DEPARTMENT OF RADIOLOGY HB 44195 #041-02-1995 L2000 **DR** *020 †80

DAVIES-JOHNS, Teresa J. 9500 EUCLID AVE BOX 184 44195 #038-44-1996 L2000 **RO** *020

DAVIS, Ajuah Ora. 2801 MARTIN LTHR KNG JR DR 44104 #016-06-1992 L2000 **PDE** *020 †55

DAVIS, Alan Wayne. 9500 EUCLID AVE 44195 #038-45-1984 L1988 **ORS** *020 †40

DAVIS, Beth Rachel. ■ 44113 #038-45-2008 *012

DAVIS, Bryan R. 2500 METROHEALTH DR, CLEVELAND METROPOLITAN HOS 44109 #041-01-1967 L1974 **D IM** *020 †15

DAVIS, Esa Matius. 11100 EUCLID AVE, FAMILY MED CTR 1200 BOLWEL 44106 #033-05-1997 L2003 **FM EM** *050 †18

DAVIS, Joan L Tenzel. 6559 WILSON MILLS RD 44143 #038-06-1975 L1976 **U** *071 †95

DAVIS, Maryellen S. 8223 BRECKSVILLE RD LL 44141 #041-01-1967 L1974 **CHP P** *020 †75

DAVIS, Mellar Pilgrim. 9500 EUCLID AVE, PALLIATIVE CARE DEPT 44195 #038-40-1977 L1977 **HEM ON** *020 †20

DAVIS, Michael Charles. ■ 44120 #038-06-2008 *012

DAVIS, Pamela Harris. 4330 W 150TH ST 44135 #038-45-1984 L1985 **D IM** *020 †20,15

DAVIS, Stephen J. 9500 EUCLID AVE, DEPT OF PEDI CRITICAL CARE 44195 #050-02-1989 L1996 **CCP** *020 †55

DAWSON, Andrea Ellen. 9500 EUCLID AVE 44195 #049-01-1985 L1998 **PTH** *020 †50

DAWSON, Dawn Marie. 11100 EUCLID AVE 44106 #051-07-1989 L1995 **PTH** *020 †50

DAWSON, Neal Von. 2500 METROHEALTH DR, RM -R239A 44109 #028-03-1976 L1982 **IM EP** *050 †20

DAYAL, Anuradha. ■ 44113 #038-43-2007 L2007 **PD** *012

DEAL, Chad Logan. 9500 EUCLID AVE, DEPT RHEUMATOLOGY A-50 44195 #004-01-1977 L1984 **RHU** *020 †20

DEAN, Clayton Loyal. ■ 44102 #041-02-2003 L2003 **ORS** *012

DEARBORN, Dorr Gellatly. 2101 ADELBERT RD, STE 3001 44106 #026-04-1970 L1974 **PDP PUD** *050 †55

DEARMIN, Mary Stacia. 6780 MAYFIELD RD 44124 #038-06-1995 L1997 **PD** *020 †55

DE BAZ, Petros Danl. 11100 EUCLID AVE, STE 2600 44106 #561-11-1972 L1981 **DR OS** *020 †80

DE BERNARDO, Robert L. 11100 EUCLID AVE, DIVISION GYN/ONCOLOGY 44106 #041-13-1997 L2004 **GO** *020 †20

DE BOER, Glenn Edward. 9500 EUCLID AVE #P-21-PEDI, CLEVELAND CLINIC 44195 #038-06-1970 L1974 **IM** *075

DEBS, Michael E. ■ 44114 #198-01-1987 L1993 **IM** *020 †20

DE CARVALHO, Alexandre B. ■ 44195 #187-09-1979 L2005 **PUD IM** *020 †20

DECHANT, Hallie Kerstin. 2500 METROHEALTH DR, METRO HEALTH MEDICAL CENTE 44109 #023-07-1984 L1984 **IM** *020 †20

DECHANT, Sarah Anne. 10701 EAST BLVD, LOUIS SSTOKES VAMC 44106 #010-02-1997 L2001 **IM** *020 †20

DECKER, Barry. ■ 44106 #035-19-1952 L1958 **PHP RHU** *030 †20

DECKER, Brooke Kathleen. ■ 44106 #038-06-2007 L2007 **IM** *012

DEEHRING, Randall Craig. 29000 CENTER RIDGE RD 44145 #016-42-1972 L1975 **EM** *020 †16

DEFANTE, Maria Margarita. 11100 EUCLID AVE RM 3018, CO UNIV HOSPS-RESIDENCY OF 44106 #016-42-2003 L2003 **AN** *020

DE FAZIO, John Louis. 2105 ADELBERT RD, DEPT OF REPRODOCTIVE 44106 #010-02-1977 L1983 **OBG END** *020 †30

DE GEORGIA, Michael Allan. 9500 EUCLID AVE S80, DEPT OF NEUROLOGY 44195 #038-44-1989 L1999 **N** *020 †20,75

DEGOLIA, Peter Alexander. 2500 METROHEALTH DR, METROHEALTH SYSTEM 44109 #016-01-1990 L1991 **IMG FPG** *020 †18

DE GUISE, Michele. 9500 EUCLID AVE, CO CCF-GRAD MED EDU DEPT 44195 #067-02-1986 L2000 *100

DE GUZMAN, Ramon Ramirez. 10701 EAST BLVD, CLEVELAND VA MED CTR 44106 #748-20-1985 L2006 **RNR** *020

DE GUZMAN, Raquel Pallasi. 11100 EUCLID AVE 44106 #748-21-2003 L2006 **FM** *100

DEHAAN, Karl. 1 INFINITY CORPORT CNTR DR, NORTH SHORE 44125 #409-33-1972 L1975 **GE IM** *020 †20

DEITCHER, Steven Robt. 9500 EUCLID AVE, DEPT OF VASCULAR MEDICINE/ 44195 #016-06-1988 L1993 **HO** *020 †20

DE JOY, Samuel J. 4330 W 150TH ST 44135 #038-06-1997 L1999 **AN** *020 †05

DE LA CRUZ, Tomas I. 18099 LORAIN AVE # 30, FAIRVIEW HOSP PYS CENTER 44111 #308-01-1955 L1964 **GS GP** *071

DELANEY, Conor Patrick. 11100 EUCLID AVE, CASE MEDICAL CENTER 44106 #539-04-1989 L2000 **CRS** *020

DELANEY, Miriam Frances. 9500 EUCLID AVE, A50/DEPT OF RHEUM 44195 #539-02-1991 L2003 **END** *050 †20

DE LEON, Brigida M. 7007 POWERS BLVD 44129 #748-08-1964 L1977 **AN** *020

DEL GIUDICE, Ennio. ■ 44106 #561-10-1973 **CHN** *020

DELL, Katherine Mac Rae. 11100 EUCLID AVE 44106 #024-01-1992 L1998 **PN PD** *050 †55

DELL, Michael S. 11100 EUCLID AVE, RAINBOW BABIES & CHILDREN' 44106 #024-01-1992 L1998 **PD** *020 †55

DEL MAR, Raoul Borromeo. 11100 EUCLID AVE RM 3018 44106 #748-19-1991 L2002 **PD** *020 †55

DELOS REYES, Christina M. 11100 EUCLID AVE, UNIV HOSPS OF CLEVELAND/PS 44106 #038-44-1996 L1998 **P** *020 †75

DEL RIO, Richard Albert. 11100 EUCLID AVE, WEARN BUILDING 247 44106 #038-06-2001 L2003 **GE** *020 †20

DEMIAN, Yousef Kamal A. 18101 LORAIN AVE 44111 #330-03-1958 L1969 **AN CCA** *071

DE MIO, Phillip C. 1 MOUNT SINAI DR 44106 #038-06-1984 L1987 **EM GPM** *020 †16

DEMIRJIAN, Sevag Garabet. 9500 EUCLID AVE, A51 44195 #605-01-2000 L2001 **IM** *020

DEMMY, Nicholas. 5109 BROADWAY AVE STE 408 44127 #023-01-1950 L1956 **P N** *071

DENNIS, Vincent Wm. 9500 EUCLID AVE, DESK A101/DEPT OF NEPH & H 44195 #010-02-1966 L1992 **NEP IM** *050 †20

DENT, Arlene Elizabeth. 11100 EUCLID AVE, PED DISEASE RM 487 44106 #017-20-1999 L1999 **PD PDI** *050 †55

DEO, Aparna Arun. 2500 METROHEALTH DR, METROHEALTH MED CTR 44109 #495-17-2001 L2004 **MPD** *012

DEOGAONKAR, Anupa Milind. 9500 EUCLID AVE, DEPT OF GME 44195 #495-83-1989 L2005 **AN** *012

DEOGAONKAR, Milind Shashi. 9500 EUCLID AVE, CLEVELAND CLINIC FOUNDATIO 44195 #495-83-1989 L2005 *100

DEOGRACIAS, Franco B. 5706 TURNEY RD 44125 #748-07-1966 L1978 **GS** *020

DE OREO, Gerard A, Jr. 9500 EUCLID AVE 44195 #038-06-1967 L1967 **U** *020 †95

DE POMPEI, Lambert Nick. 8413 LAKE AVE 44102 #649-01-1950 L1955 **OM FM** *075

DEPP, Edward B. 127 PUBLIC SQ STE 4900 44114 #041-12-1943 L1948 **AN** *020 †05

DEPTA, Jeremiah Peter. ■ 44114 #016-42-2006 L2006 **IM** *012

DERGHAM, Lena. 1730 W 25TH ST, ATTENTION: ADMINISTRATION 44113 #875-01-1999 L2005 **IM PLM** *020 †12

DEROCHE, Amy Baxi. ■ 44195 #028-34-2005 L2005 **AN** *012

DESAI, Krishna Mahesh. ■ 44143 #038-41-2008 *012

DESAI, Mihir Mahesh. 9500 EUCLID AVE, 44195 #495-76-1993 L2001 *020

DESAI, Milind Yagnesh. 9500 EUCLID AVE, DESK F-15 44195 #495-76-1994 L2005 **CD** *020 †20

DESAI, Neelesh R. 6707 POWERS BLVD, STE 205 44129 #496-38-1978 L1982 **CD IM** *020 †20

DESHAZER, Charlie. ■ 44115 #016-11-1984 L2006 **IM** *020

DESHMUKH, Avinash Shankar. 7550 LUCERNE DR, STE 405 44130 #495-28-1961 L1973 **U** *071 †95

DE SILVA, Dona Piyaseeli. 2351 E 22ND ST 44115 #220-01-1968 **PTH** *100

DE SWART, Robert Johan. 18101 LORAIN AVE 44111 #660-07-1987 L1992 **OP ORS** *020 †40

DEUCHER, Michael Francis. 7255 OLD OAK BLVD, ASSOCIATES 44130 #038-40-1994 L1995 **CD IM** *020 †20

DEUNGRIA, Joseph Michael. 9500 EUCLID AVE E-31 44195 #028-46-1995 L2000 **AN** *020

DEUTSCHMAN, Daniel Allen. 7255 OLD OAK BLVD, STE 302 44130 #038-06-1963 L1963 **P ADM** *020 †75

DEVARAJAN, Jagan. 9500 EUCLID AVE, CLEVELAND CLINIC FOUNDATIO 44195 #495-66-1999 L2006 **AN** *012

DEVEREAUX, Michael Wm. 11100 EUCLID AVE, STE 5512 44106 #048-04-1968 L1977 **N** *020 †75

DE VILLIERS, Pierre Anton. 9500 EUCLID AVEDESK G30, DEPT OF CARDIO/ANESTHESIA 44195 #836-04-1982 L1997 **AN** *020 †05

DE WOLFE, Victor Geo. 9500 EUCLID AVE 44195 #035-01-1943 L1949 **CD IM** *072 †20

DEZELON, Lynn Celeste. 2500 METROHEALTH DR, DEPT OF 44109 #038-06-1992 L1993 **EM** *020 †16

DHALIWAL, Sukhdeep S. ■ 44120 #038-06-2006 L2006 *012

DHAM, Gitika. 2351 E 22ND ST, DEPT OF MEDICAL EDUCATION 44115 #495-45-2001 L2005 **IM** *012

DHARMANI, Aarti Ashok. ■ 44115 #025-01-2004 L2004 **OBG** *012

DHAWAN, Vikram. 18101 LORAIN AVE 44111 #496-09-2000 L2002 **CCA** *100 †20

DHRUVA, Tanvee Uday. 2500 METROHEALTH DR 44109 #495-76-1982 L2005 **FP** *012

DIAB, Dima Lutfi. 9500 EUCLID AVE, DEPT OF ENDOCRINOLOGY / A5 44195 #605-01-2002 L2003 **IM** *100 †20

DIAB, Isam Abdulkader. 18660 BAGLEY RD, PHASE 2, STE 102B 44130 #875-02-1978 L1990 **RHU** *020 †20

DIAB, Rand. 11100 EUCLID AVE, DEPT OPHTHALMOLOGY 44106 #016-11-1999 L2000 **OPH** *020 †35

DIAZ, Alberto Noel. 2500 METROHEALTH DR 44109 #737-06-1994 L2002 **IM CD** *020 †20

DIAZ, Arturo H. 14519 DETROIT AVE 44107 #748-01-1968 L1978 **GS** *020 †85

DIAZ GOMEZ, Jose Luis. 9500 EUCLID AVE 44195 #264-13-1995 L2004 **AN** *012

DIAZ GUZMAN ZAVALA, Enriqu. 9500 EUCLID AVE, CLEVELAND CLNC FNDN 44195 #649-30-1999 L2003 **PCC** *012 †20

DICKMAN, Elliott Roy. 5885 LANDERBROOK DR 44124 #035-46-1976 L1980 **ON HEM** *020 †20

DICKSON, Douglas Darko. 11100 EUCLID AVE, UNIV HOSPS OF CLEVELAND 44106 #010-03-2005 L2005 **ORS** *012

DIEHL, Beate. 9500 EUCLID AVE 44195 #409-37-1992 L2000 **CN N** *020 †75

DIERKER, Le Roy Jos, Jr. 2500 METROHEALTH DR, METROHEALTH MEDICAL CENTER 44109 #018-03-1968 L1976 **MFM OBG** *062 †30

DIETZ, David Wecker. 9500 EUCLID AVE A30 44195 #041-02-1993 L1996 **CRS** *020 †85,10

DIETZ, Irene Cihon. 2500 METROHEALTH DR, METROHEALTH MEDICAL CENTER 44109 #038-41-1987 L1990 **PD** *020 †55

DIETZ, Jill R. 9500 EUCLID AVE, # A80 44195 #041-02-1993 L1998 **GS** *020 †85

DIETZ, Michelle Kristeen. 2500 METROHEALTH DR, RM A-109 44109 #018-03-1999 L1999 **FPG** *020 †20

■ = Address Information Privacy Protected

DI FIORE, John A. 2500 METROHEALTH DR 44109 #030-06-1943 L1960 **CD IM** *071 †20
DIFIORE, John Wm. 9500 EUCLID AVE, DEPT OF PEDIATRIC SURGERY/ 44195 #035-01-1988 L1998 **PDS** *020 †85
DIGGS, Jessica Carmelita. ■ 44106 #038-06-2008 *012
DIJKSTRA, Jacob Willem E. 9500 EUCLID AVE, CLEVELAND CLINIC FOUNDATIO 44195 #660-02-1971 L1984 **D** *020 †15
DILLON, Steven Douglas. 2450 DERBYSHIRE RD, # 449 44106 #025-12-2006 L2006 **AN** *012
DIMANCHE, Marieeliza. ■ 44106 #038-06-2008 *012
DIMAS, Alexios Peter. 9500 EUCLID AVE 44195 #418-01-1976 L1988 **CD IM** *020 †20
DIMEFF, Robert Jos. ONE CLINIC CENTER, 9500 EUCLID AVE., DESK A41 44195 #038-44-1985 L1989 **ORS FM** *020 †18
DIMOV, Vesselin Vassilev. 9500 EUCLID AVE S70, CLEVELAND CLINIC 44195 #198-01-1996 L2002 **IM** *020 †20
DINAVAHI, Lakshman Kumar. 13951 TERRACE RD 44112 #495-58-2000 L2005 **IM** *012
DINCHMAN, Kurt H. 2500 METROHEALTH DR, STE H947 44109 #038-40-1987 L1993 **U** *020 †95
DING, Philip Dieuming. ■ 44106 #060-01-2001 L2007 **GS** *100
DINICOLA, Kathleen Marie. 11100 EUCLID AVE 44106 #038-40-2004 L2004 **PD** *100 †55
DISCH, Jno J. 2500 METROHEALTH DR, DEPOT OF EMERG 44109 #038-06-2001 L2001 **EM** *020 †16 ‡
DISTAD, Richard Cleveland. 29800 BAINBRIDGE RD 44139 #038-40-1955 L1955 **PD** *020 †55
DISTELHORST, Clark Wm. CASE WESTERN RES HOSP HEM 44106 #038-40-1971 L1971 **HEM ON** *050 †20
DIULUS, Carrie A. 9500 EUCLID AVE, # A41 44195 #038-44-1999 L1999 **ORS** *012
DIWADKAR, Gouri B. ■ 44106 #024-07-2003 L2007 **OBG** *100
DIWAN, Rajni V. 1001 LAKESIDE AVE E, STE 1200 44114 #495-03-1956 L1979 **R NM** *020 †80
DIWAN, Vasudeo Govind. 10701 EAST BLVD 44106 #495-21-1951 L1978 **RO** *020 †80
DIXIT, Rahul. ■ 44106 #023-01-2004 L2004 **IM** *100 †20
DIXIT, Varun. 18101 LORAIN AVE, DEPT OF SURGERY 44111 #495-30-2000 L2007 **GS** *012
DJIGBENOU, Daignon Ruthan. 2500 METROHEALTH DR 44109 #038-43-2006 L2006 **IM** *012
D'NETTO, Marita. 9500 EUCLID AVE M31 44195 #495-04-1983 L2002 **NPM** *020 †55
DO, Anh Phuong. 9500 EUCLID AVE A120, CHILDREN'S HOSPITAL 44195 #065-01-1993 L1999 **PD** *020 †55
DO, Dieu Thuc. 2307 W 14TH ST 44113 #941-01-1966 L1980 **GP** *020
DOBLER, Kimberly Katherin. ■ 44135 #038-40-2006 L2006 **FP** *012
DOBRYANSKY, Michael. ■ 44114 #035-19-1999 L2005 **PS** *100
DOCTOR, Marguertie D. 13301 MILES AVE 44105 #038-06-1991 L1997 **OBG** *020
DODIG, Milan. 2500 METROHEALTH DR 44109 #957-01-1989 L1999 **GE** *020 †20
DOERSHUK, Carl Frederick. 11100 EUCLID AVE 44106 #038-06-1956 L1956 **PUD PD** *071 †55
DOLAK, James Alexander. 9500 EUCLID AVE, SIOLOGY/E31 44195 #038-06-1991 L2001 **AN** *020 †05
DOLEGA, Christopher J. 7225 OLD OAK BLVD STE 2 44130 #038-06-1998 L1999 **FM** *020 †18
DOLINAR, Teresa Marie. 2074 ABINGTON ROAD, UNIV HOSPS OF CLEVELAND 44106 #038-06-1993 L1995 **IM IMG** *020 †20
DOLL, Mary M. ■ 44120 #016-06-1966 L1969 **PD FM** *071
DONAHUE, John Kevin. 2500 METROHEALTH DR, RAMMELKAMP 653 44109 #028-02-1992 L2005 **ICE** *020 †20
DONNELLY, Gertrude C. ■ 44126 #038-06-1934 L1934 **GP** *071
D'ONOFRIO, Mary M. 1708 SOUTHPOINT DR, HEALTHCARE 44109 #038-44-2001 L2001 **FM** *020 †18
DONOHUE, Lee Terese. ■ 44106 #038-41-2007 L2007 **PD** *012
DONSKEY, Curtis Jos. 10701 EAST BLVD, LOUIS STOKES VA MEDICAL CE 44106 #056-06-1990 L1995 **ID** *020 †20
DOODEH-ASKARI, Ali. 11100 EUCLID AVE, FOLEY BLDG ROOM 201 44106 #517-01-1966 L1972 **RHU IM** *020 †20
DOROSTI, Khosrow. 9500 EUCLID AVE, MC F25 44195 #517-01-1967 L1972 **CD** *020 †20
DOROSTKAR, Parvin C. 11100 EUCLID AVE 44106 #031-01-1987 L1999 **PDC** *020 †55
DORSEY, Steven Timothy. 9500 EUCLID AVE, CLEVELAND CLINIC FOUNDATIO 44195 #038-40-1997 L1999 **EM** *020 †16
DOSHI, Krupa Bakulesh. 9500 EUCLID AVE A/53 44195 #496-38-2001 L2006 **IM** *100 †20
DOTA, Anthony Patrick, III. ■ 44113 #038-43-2007 L2007 **IM** *012
DOTHEY, Chantal I M G. 2500 METROHEALTH DR, METROHEALTH MED CTR/RM R-2 44109 #165-01-1981 L1988 **PD NPM** *040 †55
DOUGLAS, Janice Electa. 10900 EUCLID AVE, LAKESIDE HOSP ENDOCR/HYPER 44106 #047-07-1968 L1976 **END** *050
DOULL, James Angus, Jr. 2460 FAIRMOUNT BLVD STE 30 44106 #051-01-1954 L1959 **P PYA** *020
DOURADO, Claudia Mattos D. 11100 EUCLID AVE 44106 #187-01-1992 L2002 **HO** *020 †20
DOVICH, Tracy Palumbo. 9500 EUCLID AVE, E31 44195 #038-44-2002 L2002 **AN** *020 †05
DOWDELL, William Francis. 4229 PEARL RD 44109 #041-02-1944 L1948 **IM** *071
DOWDEN, Richard. 6770 MAYFIELD RD STE 410 44124 #067-01-1968 L1979 **PS GS** *020 †85,65
DOWLATI, Afshin. 11100 EUCLID AVE, DIVISION OF HEMATOLOGY/ONC 44106 #165-03-1992 L1999 **ON HO** *020 †20
DOWNES, Katharine A. 11100 EUCLID AVE, DEPT OF PATHOLOGY 44106 #038-06-1997 L1999 **BBK CLP** *020 †50
DOWNEY, Ross Andrew. 9500 EUCLID AVE, DESK F15 44195 #032-01-2000 L2004 **ICE** *012 †20 ‡
DOWNS, Brandon Howard. ■ 44195 #005-12-2000 L2005 **ORS** *100
DOYLE, D John. 9500 EUCLID AVE, DEPT OF ANESTHESIOLOGY 44195 #065-01-1982 L2002 **AN** *020 †05
DRAHOTUSKY-DODIG, Tatjana. 2500 METROHEALTH DR 44109 #957-01-1990 L2007 **P** *012
DRAKE, Richard Dennis. 9500 EUCLID AVE A81, CLEVELAND CLINICE 44195 #017-20-1983 L1987 **PTH PP** *020 †50
DRAWZ, Paul Englund. 11100 EUCLID AVE 44106 #026-04-2003 L2003 **IM** *020 †20
DRAZDIK, Janeen Marie. 18200 LORAIN AVE 44111 #038-06-1996 L1998 **FM** *020 †18
DREICER, Robert. 9500 EUCLID AVE, STE 100 44195 #048-14-1983 L1999 **ON IM** *020 †20
DRESHAJ, Ismail A. 11100 EUCLID AVE, UH, HARVEY HOUSE # 415 44106 #957-09-1975 L2001 **IM** *020
DREWS, Freddy B. 11100 EUCLID AVE, DEPT OF RADIOLOGY 44106 #264-03-1973 L2001 **DR GS** *020
DREYFUSS, Michael. ■ 44120 #038-06-1961 L1961 **OS** *050
DRISCOL, Meredith E. 300 E 185TH ST, HOSPICE OF THE WESTERN RES 44119 #017-20-1989 L1999 **HO** *020 †20
DRISCOL, Thomas Edson. 2109 ADELBERT RD 44106 #038-06-1957 L1957 **CD IM** *071
DROGELL, Kristin Marie. ■ 44134 #038-43-2007 L2007 **EM** *012
DROUBI, Basem. 20997 LORAIN RD, W 210 LORAIN MED BLDG 44126 #875-01-1973 L1977 **TS GS** *020 †85
DRUMMOND, Katherine L. 9500 EUCLID AVE, DESK A-81 44195 #038-06-1989 L1990 **DR** *020 †80
DUA, Susheel. 9500 EUCLID AVE C-25 44195 #495-76-1997 L2001 **AN** *100 †05
DUA, Veena. ■ 44147 #495-77-1974 *100
DUBCHUK, Natalya. 2074 ABINGTON RD 44106 #913-89-1990 L2002 **OBG** *100
DUBRIA, Quirino A, Jr. 18697 BAGLEY RD 44130 #748-01-1969 L1976 **GP PD** *020
DUCHESNEAU, Renate Halley. 11100 EUCLID AVE # 2600 44106 #024-07-1953 L1961 **DR** *071 †80
DUCLOS, Alain Jean. 9500 EUCLID AVE, DEPT OF GME 44195 #067-02-2000 L2005 *100
DUDENEY, Michael Sean. ■ 44195 #539-06-1989 L2000 *100
DUERINCKX, Andre Jozef. 2500 METROHEALTH DR 44109 #011-02-1986 L2007 **DR CD** *020 †80 ‡
DULDNER, John Eric, Jr. 2500 METROHEALTH DR 44109 #038-41-1993 L1994 **EM** *020 †16
DUMAS, Susan Dakin. 11100 EUCLID AVE 44106 #038-06-1993 L1994 **AN** *020 †05
DUMICZ, Piotr. ■ 44106 #035-48-1999 L2004 **TS** *020 †85
DUMITRIU, Bogdan. 9500 EUCLID AVE 44195 #781-01-2000 L2007 **IM** *012
DUMONT, Eric Daniel. 9500 EUCLID AVE, CLEVELAND CLINIC FOUNDATIO 44195 #067-02-1998 L2004 *100
DUMPE, Jarrod Edward. ■ 44121 #012-01-2006 L2007 **ORS** *012
DUNCAN, Brian Wayne. 2801 MARTIN LTHR KNG JR DR 44104 #017-20-1985 L2001 **PDS** *072 †85,90
DUNCAN, Charles H. 29000 CENTER RIDGE RD 44145 #038-06-1975 L1978 **IM** *020
DUNDERDALE-HAZELTON, I. 1 MOUNT SINAI DR 44106 #352-05-1959 L1974 **OS NTR** *020
DUNIFER, Charles De Leon. 11311 SHAKER BLVD, DEPT ANES 44104 #748-01-1970 L1976 **AN GS** *075
DUNLAP, Mark E. 2500 METROHEALTH DR, METROHEALTH MEDICAL CENTER 44109 #047-06-1982 L1989 **CD IM** *020 †20
DUNN, Jonathan Edward. 2500 METROHEALTH DR 44109 #396-28-1983 L1986 **P ADM** *030 †75
DUNN, Richard Lynwood. 9500 EUCLID AVE, DESK A-81 44195 #038-06-1959 L1959 **GPM IM** *020
DUONG, Hien Kim. 740 W SUPERIOR AVE, STE 209 44113 #025-01-2004 L2007 **HO** *012 †20
DUPPS, William, Jr. 9500 EUCLID AVE, I-32 44195 #038-40-2000 L2004 **OPH** *020 †35
DURAN CASTILLO, Marina Ya. 7835 NORMANDIE BLVD, APT E46 44130 #649-01-2003 L2004 **MPD** *012
DURBIN, Michael Denis. 8301 DETROIT AVE 44102 #038-06-1990 L1992 **P** *020
DUTERTE, Emmanuelle Jacqu. 2500 METROHEALTH DR, CO METROHEALTH MED CTR-RES 44109 #748-17-2000 L2004 **P** *012
DVORETSKY, Philip Marvin. 9500 EUCLID AVE, DEPT ANATOMIC PATH L-25 44195 #035-45-1976 L2002 **OS PTH** *020 †50
DWEIK, Raed Abdul-Rahim. 9500 EUCLID AVE A90, CLEVELAND CLINIC 44195 #575-01-1988 L1993 **PCC** *020 †20
DWORKEN, Harvey Jos. 11100 EUCLID AVE 44106 #038-06-1944 L1944 **GE IM** *072 †20
DY, Lungee Go. 6681 RIDGE RD 44129 #748-02-1958 L1966 **IM** *071
DYER, Kimberly Lynne. ■ 44118 #038-06-2003 L2003 **PDE** *012 †55
DYSON, Senait W. 11100 EUCLID AVE 44106 #012-21-2000 L2000 **D** *020 †15
DZIWIS, Carolyn M. 2500 METROHEALTH DR 44109 #035-45-1982 L1987 **IMG** *020 †20
EAGLETON, Matthew J. 9500 EUCLID AVE, DEPT. OF VASCULAR SURGERY/ 44195 #035-45-1994 L2002 **VS** *020 †85
EAPEN, Babu Manathra. 7255 OLD OAK BLVD, STE C106 44130 #495-63-1983 L1990 **PUD** *020 †20
EAPEN, Sara Shoba. 27155 CHARDON RD 44143 #039-05-1986 L1987 **IM PD** *020 †20,55
EASTWOOD, Douglas Wm. 11100 EUCLID AVE 44106 #018-03-1943 L1972 **AN** *072 †05
EASTWOOD, Gregory Lindsay. 10900 EUCLID AVE, INAMORI CTR FOR ETHICS 44106 #038-06-1966 L1966 **GE IM** *071 †20
EBERHARDT, Joshua Miller. 9500 EUCLID AVE A30 44195 #056-05-2002 L2007 **CRS** *012 †85
EBERLEIN, David Arthur. 18200 LORAIN AVE 44111 #038-06-1983 L1985 **FM OBS** *020 †18
EBERSBACHER, Donald James. 5850 LANDERBROOK DR, STE 100 44124 #308-11-1983 L1992 **IM** *020 †20
EBRAHIM, Lilian Veronica. 9500 EUCLID AVE, # P57 44195 #496-38-1975 L1979 **P** *020 †75
EBRAHIM, Zeyd Yusuf. 9500 EUCLID AVE, # E31 44195 #496-38-1975 L1979 **AN** *020 †05
ECCLES-JAMES, Ked N. ■ 44115 #409-23-1976 L2000 **IM** *020
ECHEVARRIA, Michelle Ann. 2500 METROHEALTH DR, C/O METRO HLTH MED CTR-RES 44109 #016-06-2002 L2002 **EM** *100 †16
ECKSTEIN, Margaret Ann. 18599 LAKE SHORE BLVD 44119 #018-03-1978 L1982 **IM** *020 †20
ECONOMO, Nicholas. ■ 44111 #418-02-1954 L1961 **GS** *071
ECONOMOU, Peter Gregory. 4229 PEARL RD 44109 #418-01-1953 L1958 **GP GS** *071
EDELMAN, Kenneth Everett. 2500 METROHEALTH DR 44109 #038-40-1994 L1995 **OBG** *020 †30
EDGELL, Randall Clive. 9500 EUCLID AVE, DEPT OF NEUROLOGY / S91 44195 #048-04-2000 L2004 **VN** *100 †75
EDMAN, Jennifer C. ■ 44111 #035-45-2000 L2000 **ADL** *012 †18
EDWARDS, Amy Marie. 2500 METROHEALTH DR 44109 #550-04-2007 L2007 **PD** *012
EDWARDS, James Jos. 5500 RIDGE RD, STE 208 44129 #010-02-1974 L1974 **OPH** *020 †35
EFFRON, Barry Allan. 11100 EUCLID AVE 44106 #038-40-1978 L1982 **CD IM** *020 †20
EFFRON, David. 2500 METROHEALTH DR, DEPT OF EMERGENCY MEDICINE 44109 #038-41-1980 L1980 **EM IM** *020 †16
EFFRON, Lorri. 12301 SNOW RD, DEPT OF OPHTHALMOLOGY 44130 #038-40-1979 L1980 **OPH** *020 †35
EGHOBAMIEN, Donald Eghosa. 27100 CHARDON RD, INC 44143 #690-06-1991 L1999 **IM** *020 †20
EGHTESAD, Bijan. 9500 EUCLID AVE, DESK A110 44195 #517-05-1978 L2004 **GS TTS** *040
EHRENBERG, Stacey. ■ 44118 #038-43-2006 L2006 **OBG** *012
EIGNER, Edwin Harvey. 1611 S GREEN RD STE 306B, CLEVELAND EYE SPECIALIST 44121 #038-06-1954 L1954 **OPH** *020 †35
EINSTADTER, Douglas. 2500 METROHEALTH DR, DEPARTMENT OF MEDICINE, R2 44109 #016-11-1986 L1987 **IM** *050 †20
EINSTEIN, David Marc. 9500 EUCLID AVE, DESK HB6 44195 #038-06-1978 L1979 **DR** *020 †80
EISEN, Jaime. 4242 LORAIN AVE, DEPT VETERANS AFFAIRS 44113 #264-04-1977 L1988 **IM** *020 †20
EISEN, Matthew Steven. 2500 METROHEALTH DR, METROHEALTH MEDICAL CENTER 44109 #038-06-1991 L1992 **IM** *020 †20
EISENBERG, Henry Wm. 2121 EUCLID AVE, CLEVELAND STATE UNIV HLTH 44115 #035-01-1968 L1969 **MDM** *020 †10,85
EISENSTAT, Michael Saul. 5187 MAYFIELD RD, STE 11 44124 #065-05-1963 L1968 **CRS GS** *071 †85

■ = Address Information Privacy Protected

EISNER, Leo. ■ 44118 #035-08-1962 L1992 **FPG GP** *071 †18

EITEL, Janice Ruth. ■ 44118 #028-02-1992 L1993 **EM** *020 †16

EKSTEIN, Laurie Susan. 4242 LORAIN AVE 44113 #024-05-1991 L1994 **PD** *020 †55

EL ALI, Mazen. ■ 44106 #605-01-2006 L2007 **IM** *012

ELAMM, Joelle. 11100 EUCLID AVE, UNIVERSITY HOSPITALS CASE 44106 #605-01-2006 L2007 **IM** *012

EL ASSY, Saeed Mohmed Ref. 11100 EUCLID AVE RM 3018, CO UNIV HOSP-RESIDENCY OFF 44106 #915-04-1994 L2001 **TS** *100

EL-ATASSI, Rafel Shawki. 18099 LORAIN AVE 44111 #915-04-1982 L1987 **CD IM** *020 †20

EL-ATAT, Fadi Ahmed. 12000 MCCRACKEN RD, STE 460 44125 #605-01-1999 L2007 **IC** *020 †20

ELAYI, Samy Claude. 9500 EUCLID AVE, CLEVELAND CLINIC 44195 #396-12-2001 L2005 **CD** *020 †20

EL BADAWY, Emad Hamdy. 1730 W 25TH ST, STE 1100 44113 #915-02-1998 L2000 **IM** *020 †20 ‡

EL BEJJANI, Dalia Elias. 11100 EUCLID AVE 44106 #605-01-2000 L2002 **ID** *100

EL DABH, Cherine H F. 9500 EUCLID AVE 44195 #915-02-1981 L1988 **AN** *020 †05

ELDER, Jack S. 5850 LANDERBROOK DR 44124 #039-01-1976 L1986 **UP U** *020 †95

ELDER, Kareem. 15322 SAINT CLAIR AVE 44110 #035-48-2002 L2002 **IM** *020 †20

ELDRIDGE, Wendell Craig. 2500 METROHEALTH DR, METROHEALTH MEDICAL CENTER 44109 #038-40-2004 L2004 **FP** *012

ELEFF, Eric Stephen. 1730 W 25TH ST, LUTHERAN HOSPITAL 44113 #038-06-1984 L1989 **OPH FM** *020 †35

ELESSAWIE, Magda Abdel H. STA VINCENT CHAR HSP PATH 44115 #915-04-1969 **PTH** *020

ELGUDIN, Yakov Lvovich. 10701 EAST BLVD, SURGERY (112) 44106 #913-66-1989 L2002 **TS** *020 †85,90

ELIACHAR, Isaac. 9500 EUCLID AVE, THE CLEVELAND CLINIC FOUND 44195 #550-01-1963 L1985 **OTO** *020

ELINZANO, Heinrich D. 9500 EUCLID AVE, TAUSSIG CANCER CENTER / R2 44195 #748-02-1992 L2006 **N** *020 †75

ELKASSABANY, Nabil Mohame. ■ 44195 #915-03-1993 L2002 **AN** *020

EL-KHAIRI, Shukri M F. 12000 MCCRACKEN RD, STE 214 44125 #915-04-1967 L1976 **GS** *020 †85

ELKHAMRA, Omar Youssef. 18101 LORAIN AVE, FAIRVIEW HOSPITAL 44111 #605-04-2005 L2007 **IM** *012

ELKHOURY, Gaby Salim. 6835 BROADWAY AVE 44105 #605-01-1995 L1998 **FM** *020 †18

ELKHWAD, Mohammed Osman E. 2500 METROHEALTH DR, C/O METROHEALTH MED CTR 44109 #848-01-1993 L2001 **NPM** *100 †55

ELLICK, Lawrence Robt. 2475 MARTIN LTHR KNG JR DR 44120 #038-40-1957 L1957 **GYN** *071 †30

ELLIOTT, John M. 9500 EUCLID AVE 44195 #671-01-1979 **CD** *020

ELLIS, Dianne Lynne. 11100 EUCLID AVE 44106 #016-43-1987 L1991 **PD** *020

ELLIS, Lloyd Harris, Jr. ■ 44139 #038-06-1970 L1972 **EM** *040 †16

ELLIS, Stephen Geoffrey. 9500 EUCLID AVE, CLEVELAND CLIN FOUN DESK F 44195 #005-14-1978 L1991 **CD EM** *040 †20

ELMAHDY, Amr Hamid. 600 SUPERIOR AVE E # 2100 44114 #915-08-1976 L1984 **AN** *071

EL-MALLAH, Wael Mohamed. 2500 METROHEALTH DR 44109 #915-04-1994 L2005 **MPD** *012

EL-MALLAWANY, Nader Kim. ■ 44124 #038-43-2003 L2003 **PHO** *012

EL-MEANAWY, Ashraf. 2500 METROHEALTH DR 44109 #915-02-1981 L1996 **NEP** *100 †20

EL-SAID, Ahmed Galal. 9500 EUCLID AVE, CO CCF-GRAD MED EDU DEPT-N 44195 #915-02-1993 L2000 **IM** *020

ELSAKR, Hany. CLEVELAND CLINIC FNDN, DEPT PED 44106 #915-02-1975 **PD** *100

ELSHARKAWY, Hesham Abdela. 9500 EUCLID AVE, DEPT OF GME 44195 #915-03-2000 L2005 **AN** *012

ELSHEIKH, Ibrahim Siddig. 2500 METROHEALTH DR, METROHEALTH MED CTR 44109 #308-13-2005 L2006 **PD** *012

ELSON, Robert Bruce. 2500 METROHEALTH DR 44109 #035-46-1982 L1983 **FM OS** *050 †18

ELTOMEY, Atef Abdelhafez. 18099 LORAIN AVE, STE 425 44111 #915-07-1973 L1984 **NS** *020 †25

ELUEZE, Ifeanyi Emmanuel. 7963 EUCLID AVE 44103 #690-01-1980 L1997 **IM** *020 †20

ELYAN, Mazen. 2500 METROHEALTH DR 44109 #875-01-1998 L2002 **IM** *100 †20

EL ZAWAWY, Hossam Ahmed B. ■ 44195 #915-04-1997 L2007 **RHU** *012 †20

EMANCIPATOR, Steven N. 11400 EUCLID AVE STE 100 44106 #043-01-1977 L1982 **PTH IG** *050 †50

EMBURY, Ruth A. 2609 FRANKLIN BLVD 44113 #038-06-1967 L1967 **GS OM** *071

EMCH, Todd Michael. 9500 EUCLID AVE, SEC OF NEURORADIOLOGY - L1 44195 #038-44-2000 L2000 **RNR** *100 †80

EMERMAN, Charles Louis. 2500 METROHEALTH DR 44109 #038-43-1979 L1982 **EM** *030 †16

EMERY, Jonathan David. 9500 EUCLID AVE, DEPT OF OB/GYN - M66 44195 #038-06-1994 L1995 **OBG** *020 †30

EMERY, Sanford Emil. 11100 EUCLID AVE, UNIV HOSPITALS OF CLEVE 44106 #036-07-1981 L1986 **ORS** *020 †40

EMETAROM, Nnamdi B. ■ 44111 #550-01-1970 L1974 **OBG** *020 †30

ENCOMIENDA, Renato P. 2500 METROHEALTH DR 44109 #748-01-1954 L1971 **AN** *020

ENDERS, Patrick Danl. 6009 LANDERHAVEN DR STE F, LANDERHAVEN OFFICE PLAZA 44124 #038-41-1973 L1976 **P PYA** *030 †75

ENG, Charis Euli. 9500 EUCLID AVE, GENOMIC MEDICINE INST NE50 44195 #016-02-1988 L1998 **OS ON** *020 †20

ENG, Philip Cher Tiew. 9500 EUCLID AVE, CLEVELAND CLINIC FNDN 44195 #825-01-1984 **CCM PUD** *020

ENGEL, Scott Jeffrey. PLASTIC SURGERY, A60-DEPT OF 44195 #041-02-2002 L2007 **PS** *020

ENGINEER, Rakesh Shirish. 9500 EUCLID AVE, CLEVELAND CLINIC FOUNDATIO 44195 #038-40-1996 L2001 **EM** *020 †16

ENGLUND, Kristin Anne. 9500 EUCLID AVE 44195 #038-41-1990 L1997 **ID** *020 †20

ENRIQUE, Nelida Rocha. 7211 BROADWAY AVE 44105 #748-01-1959 L1971 **GP** *020

ENRIQUE, Romeo C. 9195 AVERY RD 44147 #748-01-1959 L1973 **GS GP** *071

ENRIQUEZ, Louie Anthony. ■ 44118 #008-01-2003 L2003 **DR** *012

ENTRESS, Anthony Hilmer. 9500 EUCLID AVE DEPT AN 44195 #917-22-1968 L1978 **AN PDC** *020

EPSTEIN, David Carlin. ■ 44124 #016-42-1976 L2006 **GS EM** *020 †16

EPSTEIN, Donald Leslie. 1450 SOM CENTER RD STE 28 44124 #033-05-1972 L1977 **PCC PUD** *020

EPSTEIN, James Grover. 18660 BAGLEY RD, BLDG 2 44130 #038-06-1981 L1983 **IM** *020 †20

EPSTEIN, Samuel Stanley. CASE WESTERN RES U SCH MED 44106 #352-07-1950 **GPM** *050

ERCAN, Sina. ■ 44195 #902-19-1993 L2002 **TS** *100

ERDELYI, Gyula Jos Chas. ■ 44107 #473-02-1940 L1959 **OBG GP** *071

ERDOGAN, Okan. ■ 44106 #902-07-1991 **ICE** *100

ERENBERG, Francine Gail. 11100 EUCLID AVE, PED CARDIO MS6011 44106 #038-06-1991 L1992 **PDC PD** *020 †55

ERENBERG, Gerald. 9500 EUCLID AVE 44195 #016-11-1962 L1976 **CHN** *020 †55,75

ERFAN, Ayesha. 2351 E 22ND ST, ST VINCENT CHARITY 44115 #704-06-1992 L2003 **IM** *020 †20

ERZURUM, Serpil Cemile. 9500 EUCLID AVE, DESK NC22 44195 #038-44-1983 L1985 **PUD IM** *020 †20

ESAKKY, Rajalakshmi. 13951 TERRACE RD, HURON HOSP - CLEVELAND CLI 44112 #495-95-1997 L2004 **IM** *100

ESFANDIARI, Shahpour. 9500 EUCLID AVE, G68 CLEVELAND CLINIC 44195 #517-01-1967 L1976 **CCA AN** *062 †05

ESHELMAN, Joseph Chalice. 5500 S MARGINAL RD, CONCENTRA MEDICAL CENTER 44103 #023-01-1984 L1987 **OM** *020 †55

ESHETU, Tadesse. 9500 EUCLID AVE, CLINIC FOUNDATION 44195 #038-06-2005 L2006 **DR** *012

ESHO, Adetokunbo Olusanmi. 18697 BAGLEY RD 44130 #690-02-1994 L1999 **IM** *020 †20

ESKINAZI, Victoria. 11100 EUCLID AVE 44106 #038-06-1990 L1991 **AN** *020 †05

ESMAIL, Najwa S. 9500 EUCLID AVE 44195 #065-01-2000 **DMP** *012

ESPER, Frank Peter. 11100 EUCLID AVE, UNIVERSITY HOSPITAL 44106 #038-06-1998 L2005 **PDI** *100 †55

ESPOSITO, Andrew Alberto. 11100 EUCLID AVE, DEPT OF OPHTHALMOLOGY 44106 #038-06-2004 L2004 **OPH** *012

ESSANDOH, Michael Kojo. ■ 44106 #041-14-2005 L2005 **AN** *012

ESTAFANOUS, Fawzy George. 9500 EUCLID AVE 44106 #330-04-1961 L1972 **AN** *062

ESTFAN, Bassam Nedal. 9500 EUCLID AVE, CO CCF-GRAD MED EDU DEPT-N 44195 #875-01-1998 L2003 **IM** *100 †20

ESTRIN, Yuriy Mikhailovic. 9500 EUCLID AVE, C/O CCF-GRAD MED EDU DEPT- 44195 #913-01-1995 L2002 **AN** *020

ESTRINA, Olga Vladimizovn. 321 ROYAL OAK BLVD 44143 #913-09-1995 L2002 **CHP** *020

EU, Kong Weng. 9500 EUCLID AVE, TT32 44195 #825-01-1986 **CRS** *020

EVANGELISTA, Edith Harrow. 18660 BAGLEY RD, STE 302 44130 #748-01-1962 L1971 **IM RHU** *020

EVANGELISTA, Merlita B. 18101 LORAIN AVE, FAIRVIEW HOSPITAL 44111 #748-07-1963 L1978 **PD** *071 †55

EVANS, Judith Anne. 29001 CEDAR RD, BEACHWOOD OB GYN INC 44124 #038-06-1980 L1983 **GYN REN** *020 †30

EVANS, Mark. 6681 RIDGE RD, STE 205 44129 #038-06-1995 L1997 **PD** *020 †55 ‡

EVANS, Wilma Anita Mc Vey. ■ 44106 #035-03-1943 L1961 **IM** *071

EVERSMAN, George Stephen. ■ 44116 #038-41-1988 L1991 **EM** *020 †20,16

EVERSMAN, Lynne Adrain. 11100 EUCLID AVE 44106 #038-41-1988 L1991 **PEM PD** *020 †55

EZZIDDIN, Abdalla. 6770 MAYFIELD RD # 333 44124 #875-01-1969 L1974 **CD IM** *020 †20

FABABE, Kelly Lee. 18200 LORAIN AVE 44111 #041-14-2003 L2003 **FM** *020 †18

FABER, Cristiano Nicoletti. 9500 EUCLID AVE, CO CCF-GRAD MED EDU DEPT-N 44195 #187-17-1994 L2000 *100

FABIEN, Andre Maurice. 11100 EUCLID AVE, HARVEY HOUSE: ROOM 415 44106 #038-06-2003 L2003 **IM** *100 †20

FACTORA, Faithnatal Fagel. ■ 44195 #016-06-2006 L2006 **AN** *012

FACTORA, Ronan Mangcucang. 99 NORTHLINE CIR 44119 #038-40-2000 L2003 **IMG** *020 †20

FAHIM, Ahmed. CO RESIDENCY SUPPORT, METROHEALTH MEDICAL CENTER 44109 #704-05-2000 L2007 *100

FAIMAN, Charles. DESK A-53 9500 EUCLID AVE, CLEVELAND CLINIC FOUNDATIO 44195 #062-01-1962 L1992 **END** *020

FAIMAN, Gregg H. 5850 LANDERBROOK DR, STE 100 44124 #062-01-1994 L1999 **END** *020 †20

FAIRBANKS, Kyrsten Del. 9500 EUCLID AVE A-31, CLEVELAND CLINIC FOUNDATIO 44195 #028-02-1998 L2004 **GE** *020 †20

FAIRLEY, Patrick Hugh. 29000 CENTER RIDGE RD 44145 #010-02-1981 L1986 **EM IM** *020 †16

FAJOBI, Olufunke Omobola. 6835 BROADWAY AVE, METROHEALTH MED CTR 44105 #690-02-1995 L2000 **P** *040 †75 ‡

FALCK-YTTER, Corinna D. 2500 METROHEALTH DR, METROHEALTH MEDICAL CENTER 44109 #409-44-1992 L1999 **IM** *020 †20

FALCK-YTTER, Yngve T. 10701 EAST BLVD, LOIS STOKES VA MED CTR 44106 #409-44-1995 L1998 **GE** *020 †20

FALCONE, Tatiana Alexandr. 9500 EUCLID AVE, DEPT OF PSYCHIATRY P57 44195 #264-13-1996 L2002 **CHP** *100

FALCONE, Tomasso. 9500 EUCLID AVE, CLEVELAND CLINIC FOUNADTIO 44195 #067-01-1981 L1994 **REN OBG** *020 †30

FALK, Gary Warren. 9500 EUCLID AVE, DESK A-31 CLEVELAND CLINIC 44195 #035-45-1980 L1986 **GE IM** *020 †20

FALLON, Wm Francis, Jr. 2500 METROHEALTH DR, METROHLTH MED CTR 44109 #024-16-1976 L1993 **TRS GS** *020 †85

FALOLA, Joy Oluwatoyin. ■ 44121 #048-12-2006 L2006 **OTO** *012

FANAROFF, Avroy Arnold. 11100 EUCLID AVE - PEDS, RAINBOW BABIES &CHILD HOSP 44106 #836-01-1960 L1972 **PD NPM** *062 †55

FANAROFF, Jonathan Mark. 11100 EUCLID AVE, NEONATOLOGY 44106 #038-06-1998 L2000 **NPM PD** *020 †55

FANG, Jim Chentson. 11100 EUCLID AVE, UNIV HOSP CLEVELAND CARDIO 44106 #036-07-1988 L2006 **CD** *020 †20

FARACI, Rosalie Celeste. 20800 WESTGATE MALL, NORTH COAST PEDIATRICS 44126 #038-06-1967 L1967 **PD** *020 †55

FARAG, Ehab Samir Aziz. 9500 EUCLID AVE, CLEVELAND CLINIC FOUNDATIO 44195 #915-04-1986 L1999 **AN** *050 †05

FARAG, Hany Latif Moufid. 18101 LORAIN AVE, DEPT OF INTERNAL MED 44111 #915-02-2002 L2006 **IM** *012

FARAH, Michel Geo. 2074 ABINGTON RD MED 44106 #605-01-1970 L1974 **CD IM** *020 †20

FARAJIPOUR, Arezou. 11100 EUCLID AVE, RESIDENCY OFFICE 44106 #038-06-1998 L2000 **DR** *020

FARESS, Jihane Abdelmassi. 11100 EUCLID AVE, CO UNIV HOSPS-RESIDENCY OF 44106 #605-02-1999 L2003 **PCC** *100 †20

FARHA, Samar Youssef. 9500 EUCLID AVE A90, CLINIC FOUNDATION 44195 #605-01-2000 L2004 **PCC** *100

FARHADI, Saeid. ■ 44120 #305-01-2000 L2003 **CN** *012

FARHADIAN, Elaheh. 13951 TERRACE RD, HURON HOSP - CLEVELAND CLI 44112 #517-08-1998 L2004 **IM** *100

FARID, Ibrahim S. 9500 EUCLID AVE 44195 #915-04-1993 L1999 **PAN** *020 †05

FARION, Dmytro. 5604 MEMPHIS AVE 44144 #407-16-1950 L1955 **GP** *071

FARMER, James Jos Ivan. ■ 44126 #065-09-1954 L1957 **IM OM** *071
FARMER, Keri K. ■ 44103 #048-04-2005 L2005 **PD** *012
FAROOQI, Muhammad S. 10654 LORAIN AVE 44111 #704-01-1964 L1972 **FM IMG** *020 †18
FARRELL, Ruth Morgan. 9500 EUCLID AVE, DEPT OF BIOETHICS 44195 #038-06-2000 L2001 **OBG** *100
FARROKHI, Farnoosh. 18101 LORAIN AVE, FAIRVIEW HOSPITAL 44111 #517-12-2002 L2007 **IM** *012
FARVER, Carol Frances. 9500 EUCLID AVE 44195 #008-01-1985 L1993 **PTH** *020 †50
FATHI, Robert Babak. 9500 EUCLID AVE 44195 #143-05-1995 L2003 *020
FATICA, Richard Anthony. 9500 EUCLID AVE, DESK A101 44195 #051-04-1993 L2000 **NEP** *020 †20
FATTAL, Omar Abdulrazzak. 9500 EUCLID AVE, STE 57 44195 #605-01-1999 L2001 **P** *020 †75
FAULHABER, Peter Francis. 11100 EUCLID AVE, STE 2600 44106 #016-43-1990 L1992 **DR** *020 †80
FAULX, Ashley L. 10701 EAST BLVD, VA HOSP WADE PARK DIV 44106 #041-13-1997 L1999 **GE** *100 †12
FAULX, Michael David. 11100 EUCLID AVE, MAIL STOP 5038 44106 #041-13-1997 L2000 **CD** *100 †20
FAX, Aviva Lieber. 2500 METROHEALTH DR 44109 #550-02-2005 L2006 **PD** *100
FAX, Daniel Josiah. 11100 EUCLID AVE 44106 #550-02-2005 L2005 **PD** *012
FAYADH, Dhafir A. 18099 LORAIN AVE STE 304 44111 #528-01-1958 L1972 **PD** *071 †55
FAZIO, Victor W. 9500 EUCLID AVE # A30 44195 #143-03-1965 L1974 **CRS GS** *020 †10
FEARNHEAD, Nicola Shan. CO GME-NA23 9500 EUCLID, CLEVELAND CLINIC FOUNDATIO 44195 #917-09-1993 L2005 *100
FEDORKO, Ladislav. 18660 BAGLEY RD # 301, INC. 44130 #286-07-1970 L1997 **FM** *020 †18
FEIGHAN, John English. 12000 MCCRACKEN RD, STE 251 44125 #038-06-1991 L1992 **ORS OFA** *020 †40
FEINBERG, Lisa Andrea. 9500 EUCLID AVE, DESK A111 44195 #038-43-1999 L1999 **PG** *100 †55
FEJA, Kristina Nora. 2500 METROHEALTH DR, CO METROHEALTH MED CTR-RES 44109 #473-01-1996 L2000 **PDI** *100 †55
FELDMAN, Aaron Edward. 6770 MAYFIELD RD, STE 205 44124 #028-02-1965 L1966 **CD IM** *020 †20
FELDMAN, Edward Saml. 2816 E 116TH ST 44120 #035-01-1977 L1981 **IM GE** *020 †20
FELDMAN, Marc A. 9500 EUCLID AVE, THE CLEVELAND CLINIC, E-31 44195 #023-07-1984 L1998 **AN** *020 †05
FELDMAN, Ron Jacob. ■ 44102 #045-01-2005 L2005 **D** *012
FELDSTEIN, Ariel E. ■ 44143 #132-01-1997 L2004 **PG** *100 †55
FELVER, Michael Edward. 9500 EUCLID AVE, CLEVELAND CLINIC / A91 44195 #010-01-1987 L1992 **IM** *020 †20
FENG, Bing Huan. ■ 44114 #048-04-2003 L2007 **AN** *100
FENG, Lu-Jean. 1730 W 25TH ST 44113 #008-01-1979 L1987 **PS** *020 †65
FERENCZI, Katalin. 11100 EUCLID AVE 44106 #473-01-1992 L2004 **D** *012
FERGANY, Amr Farouk. 9500 EUCLID AVE, STE 100 44195 #915-02-1986 L1998 **U** *020 †95
FERGUSON, David Roy. 2500 METROHEALTH DR 44109 #067-01-1967 L1976 **GE IM** *020 †20
FERNANDEZ, James M.. 2500 METROHEALTH DR, METROHEALTH MED CTR 44109 #038-06-2006 L2006 **IM** *012
FERNANDEZ FAITH, Esteban. 950 EUCLID AVE 44195 #270-01-2004 L2006 **D** *012
FERNANDO, Michael Praveen. ■ 44195 #035-09-2005 L2005 **AN** *012
FERRER, Bonifacio H. 5599 PEARL RD, BONIFACIO FERRER FAM PRAC 44129 #748-01-1959 L1967 **FM GP** *071
FERRERI, Raymond N. ■ 44124 #038-06-1944 L1944 **P** *071 †75
FERRINI, Vincent Frank. 127 PUBLIC SQ, STE 2400 44114 #038-45-1994 L1995 **EM** *020 †16
FESKO, Yuri Anthony. 2500 METROHEALTH DR 44109 #038-06-1999 L1999 **HO** *100 †20
FIELDS, Allen Drew. ■ 44110 #038-06-2001 L2005 **P** *020
FIERRA, Jeffrey James. 2012 W 25TH ST, STE 601 44113 #038-40-1969 L1969 **R** *020
FIGLER, Richard Allen. 9500 EUCLID AVE, DEPARTMENT OF ORTHOPEDICS 44195 #038-06-1996 L2006 **FSM** *020 †18
FINDLING, Robert Lawrence. 11100 EUCLID AVE 44106 #051-04-1987 L1992 **CHP PD** *050 †75,55
FINE, Jeffrey Louis. 9500 EUCLID AVE BOX L25 44195 #038-40-2000 L2000 **PTH** *100 †50
FINELLI, Antonio. 9500 EUCLID AVE 44195 #065-01-1996 L2003 *020
FINET, Jose Emanuel. 2500 METROHEALTH DR 44109 #132-11-2005 L2006 **IM** *012
FINIGAN, James Hanna. 11100 EUCLID AVE, INTERNAL MEDICINE 44106 #035-45-1999 L1999 **PCC** *100 †20
FINIZIA, Anthony Joseph. 5208 MEMPHIS AVE 44144 #038-45-2000 L2000 **MPD** *020
FINK, Daniel Lyon. 11100 EUCLID AVE, DEPT PEDIATRIC CARD 44106 #005-06-1984 L1986 **PDC** *100 †55
FINK, Eli. 3395 SCRANTON RD, DEPT REHAB 44109 #038-05-1993 L1994 **PM** *020
FINKELHOR, Robert Steven. 2500 METROHEALTH DR, METROHEALTH MEDICAL CENTER 44109 #041-02-1978 L1981 **CD EM** *040 †20
FINLEY, James. 2500 METROHEALTH DR, METROHEALTH MEDICAL CENTER 44109 #028-34-1984 L1989 **PUD CCM** *020 †20
FIOCCHI, Claudio. 9500 EUCLID AVE, THE CLEVELAND CLINIC FOUND 44195 #187-31-1969 L1977 **GE** *050 †20
FIOCCHI, Midori Funayama. 1730 W 25TH ST 44113 #187-31-1969 L1979 **P PYA** *020 †75
FISHER, Charles Jack, Jr. 9500 EUCLID AVE, DESK A-81 44195 #025-12-1973 L1986 **EM CCM** *030 †20,16
FISHER, Fred Lawrence. 18099 LORAIN AVE # NO-329 44111 #038-06-1957 L1957 **IM** *071 †20
FISHER, John Roberts, III. 11100 EUCLID AVE 44106 #038-06-1964 L1964 **P** *062
FISHER, Steven Andrew. 2103 CORNELL RD, 4533 WOLSTEIN BLDG 44106 #041-01-1986 L1994 **IM** *020 †20
FISHER, Thomas Michael. 9500 EUCLID AVE # TT32 44195 #409-07-1988 L1988 **HO** *100
FISHLEDER, Andrew Jay. 9500 EUCLID AVE, CLEVELAND CLNC FOUNDATION 44195 #025-01-1978 L1981 **PTH** *030 †50
FISHMAN, David Jay. 26250 EUCLID AVE, STE 711 44132 #041-01-1975 L1976 **ON HEM** *020 †20
FISSELL, Rachel Burdick. 9500 EUCLID AVE A-51, NEPHROLOGY & HYPERTENSION 44195 #023-01-1996 L2007 **IM NEP** *074 †20
FITZGERALD, Elaine J. 2500 E 79TH ST 44104 #035-03-1983 L1984 **PD** *074 †55
FITZMAURICE, Maryann. 11100 EUCLID AVE, PATHOLOGY ASSOC OF UNIV HO 44106 #038-06-1983 L1987 **PTH** *050 †50
FITZSIMONS, Brian Charles. 9500 EUCLID AVE, E-30 DEPT OF GEN ANESTH 44195 #038-40-1999 L1999 **AN** *020 †05
FLAGG, Aron. ■ 44195 #016-42-2005 L2005 **PD** *012
FLAGG, Douglas Nathan. 1611 S GREEN RD 44121 #038-43-1986 L1988 **RHU IM** *020 †20

FLAMM, Scott Danl. 9500 EUCLID AVE MC-HB6, DIVISION OF RADIOLOGY 44195 #010-01-1988 L1994 **DR CD** *020 †80
FLECHNER, Stuart Marc. 9500 EUCLID AVE, UROLOGICAL INST A110 44195 #005-14-1975 L1993 **U GS** *020 †95
FLECK, Douglas Carlisle. 2226 WARRENSVILL CNTR RD R 44118 #038-06-2001 L2001 **PD** *020 †55
FLEMING, Barbara J Herman. 10701 EAST BLVD 44106 #024-05-1969 L1970 **IM END** *030 †20
FLEMING, Ronald Burton. ■ 44143 #038-06-1958 L1958 **IM ADM** *071 †20
FLORES, Angela Therese C.. 9500 EUCLID AVE 44195 #748-10-1997 L2005 **PD** *012
FLYNN, Michael John. 9500 EUCLID AVE, CLEVELAND CLINIC FNDN 44195 #539-03-1993 L2006 **TS** *012
FLYNN, Stephen Patrick. 18200 LORAIN AVE 44111 #041-02-1972 L1983 **FM** *030 †18
FOERSTNER, James Emmett. 18099 LORAIN AVE, STE 429 SUSITE 429 44111 #028-34-1955 L1957 **GS GP** *071 †85
FOLCH, Erik Eduardo. 9500 EUCLID AVE, CLEVELAND CLINIC FOUNDATIO 44195 #649-01-2000 L2006 **PCC** *012 †20
FOLEY, Joseph Michael. UNIVERSITY HOSPITALS 44104 #024-01-1941 L1961 **N IMG** *071 †75
FONG, Michael William. 11100 EUCLID AVE, CO UNIV HOSPS-RESIDENCY OF 44106 #038-41-2001 L2001 **CD** *100 †20
FORCIER, Paul Gerard. 11100 EUCLID AVE 44106 #051-01-1982 L1983 **OS ORS** *020 †40
FORD, Amasa B. C WESTERN RES UNIV EPID 44106 #024-01-1950 L1953 **IMG** *071 †20
FORD, Harold Warren. 3609 PARK EAST DR # 207NOR 44122 #010-03-1948 L1953 **PD** *071 †55
FORDE, Wayne Alonzo. 2500 METROHEALTH DR, DEPT OF FAMILY PRACTICE 44109 #035-06-1989 L1997 **FM** *020 †18
FORREST, Carl Lewis. 11100 EUCLID AVE, UNIVERSITY ANESTHESIOLOGIS 44106 #035-48-1985 L1993 **AN** *020 †05
FORSYTHE, William E, III. 9500 EUCLID AVE, STE 100 44195 #010-01-1967 L1968 **U** *020 †95
FORTICH SERJE, Karol Enri. 11100 EUCLID AVE 44106 #264-12-1988 L2005 **IM** *012
FOSS, Joseph F. 9500 EUCLID AVE, DEPT GEN ANESTHESIA E31 44195 #043-01-1985 L2006 **AN PA** *050 †05
FOSS, Richard Howard. 12000 MCCRACKEN RD STE 252 44125 #025-01-1955 L1961 **OPH** *071 †35
FOUAD-TARAZI, Fetnat M. 9500 EUCLID AVE, DEPT OF CARDIOLOGY F15 44195 #915-02-1965 L1978 **CD OS** *020 ‡
FOWLER, Adele Renee. 9500 EUCLID AVE, DEPT OF GENERAL MEDICINE/A 44195 #025-07-1997 L2001 **IM** *020 †20
FOWLER, Hudson D, II. 18599 LAKE SHORE BLVD 44119 #041-13-1938 L1939 **GS** *071
FOX, David Laurence. 6115 POWERS BLVD, STE 204 44129 #038-06-1987 L1988 **P** *020 †75
FOX, Robert James. 9500 EUCLID AVE U-10, CLEVELAND CLINIC FOUNDATIO 44195 #023-07-1996 L2000 **N** *020 †75
FOX, Stanley Lowell. 464 RICHMOND RD STE 101 44143 #038-40-1964 L1964 **D ID** *020 †15 ‡
FRAGASSI, Philip Alan. 2816 E 116TH ST, METROHEALTH BUCKEYE CENTER 44120 #045-04-1991 L1994 **PD** *020 †55
FRANCIS, Gary Stuart. 9500 EUCLID AVE, DESK F 15 DEPT CARDIOLOGY 44195 #030-06-1969 L1997 **CD** *020 †20
FRANCIS, Neelamkavil Smit. 18101 LORAIN AVE, DEPT OF INTERNAL MED 44111 #496-31-2001 L2006 **IM** *012
FRANCO, Kathleen Susan N. 9500 EUCLID AVE # P57 44195 #038-43-1975 L1978 **P CHP** *020 †75
FRANCO-CERECEDA, Anders. 9500 EUCLID AVE, CO CCF-GRAD MED EDU DEPT-N 44195 #858-02-1990 L2000 **TS** *100
FRANCO-VELOZ, Irving De J. 9500 EUCLID AVE, MC F25 44195 #308-01-1964 L1971 **CD** *020
FRANCY, Scott Alan. 2801 MARTIN LTHR KNG JR DR 44104 #038-40-1990 L1998 **PD** *020 †55
FRANK, Scott Howard. 1611 S GREEN RD, STE LL06 44121 #025-01-1979 L1982 **FM** *020 †18
FRANK, Thomas Martin. 2500 METROHEALTH DR 44109 #038-06-1985 L1985 **OBG** *020 †30
FRANKEL, Mark Henry. 1730 W 25TH ST 44113 #038-40-1968 L1968 **P PYG** *020 †75
FRANKEL, Melissa Beth. 11100 EUCLID AVE, DEPT. OF RADIOLOGY 44106 #038-45-1987 L1988 **DR** *020 †80
FRANKEL, Michael Henry. 12000 MCCRACKEN RD, GASTROENTEROLOGY 44125 #038-40-1975 L1978 **GE IM** *020 †20
FRANKMANN, Donald Bender. 11100 EUCLID AVE 44106 #038-06-1960 L1963 **AN** *075 †05
FRANTSUZOV, Julia. 2801 MARTIN LTHR KNG JR DR 44104 #913-15-1989 L2002 **PD** *020 †55
FRASER, John G. 11100 EUCLID AVE 44106 #041-09-1951 L1964 **AN** *040 †05
FRASER, Thomas Gilbert. 9500 EUCLID AVE, DIV OF INFECTIOUS DISEASE/ 44195 #016-06-1994 L1996 **ID** *020 †20
FRATIANNE, Richard Bryan. 2500 METROHEALTH DR 44109 #038-06-1958 L1958 **GS** *020 †85
FREDEBAUGH, Loreal Lynn. 9500 EUCLID AVE # TT32 44195 #038-06-1989 L1995 **CCP** *075
FREDERICK, Sean Adrian. 11100 EUCLID AVE, RAINBOW BABIES & CHILDREN' 44106 #010-03-2002 L2005 **NPM** *012 †55
FREDRICKSON, Eric Roy. 10701 EAST BLVD, MOTION STUDIES LAB 151-W 44106 #019-02-1992 L2001 **N OS** *050
FREEDMAN, Lois Sue. 10701 EAST BLVD 44106 #041-01-1976 L1990 **P PYG** *020 †75
FREEMAN, Deborah Lane. 2816 E 116TH ST, METROHEALTH BUCKEYE HEALTH 44120 #025-12-1977 L1986 **OBG** *020 †30
FREEMAN, Katherine Sandra. ■ 44114 #038-44-2006 L2006 **IM** *012
FREEMAN, Lelabelle C. ■ 44120 #010-03-1949 L1953 **PD** *071
FREIJE IBANEZ, Pablo. 2500 METROHEALTH DR 44109 #847-11-2003 L2005 **P** *012
FREIRE, Maxime Figueiredo. 9500 EUCLID AVE, DEPT OF GME 44195 #187-48-1994 L2006 *100
FRENCH, Dan B. ■ 44118 #048-02-2001 L2007 **U** *020
FRICK, Alexander Parker. ■ 44106 #038-06-2007 *012
FRIDIE-MODLIN, Sheryl A. 11100 EUCLID AVE 44106 #016-06-1987 L1992 **AN** *020 †05
FRIEDLAND, Robert Paul. 11100 EUCLID AVE, STE 5512 44106 #035-47-1973 L1990 **N** *050 †75
FRIEDLANDER, Samuel Louis. 2825 LUDLOW RD, 2ND FL 44120 #051-07-1999 L2000 **AI** *020 †55,20,03
FRIEDMAN, Joshua Baer. 2500 METROHEALTH DR, DIV OF PEDIATRICS 44109 #038-06-2005 L2005 **PD** *012
FRIEDMAN, Judah David. 5885 LANDERBROOK DR 44124 #038-06-2001 L2007 **HO** *020
FRIEDMAN, Neil Roy. 9500 EUCLID AVE, DEPARTMENT OF NEUROLOGY/S7 44195 #836-02-1987 L1998 **CHN** *020 †75,55
FRIEDMAN, Seymour. 14055 CEDAR RD 44118 #038-40-1953 L1953 **IM** *071
FRIESS, Eric Gene. 4242 LORAIN AVE 44113 #038-06-1993 L1994 **FM** *020 †18
FRISOF, Kenneth Bruce. 6835 BROADWAY AVE 44105 #035-19-1972 L1984 **FM** *020 †18
FRITZ, Michael Anthony. 9500 EUCLID AVE, CLINIC FOUNDATION 44195 #038-40-1997 L1999 **OTO FPS** *020
FROIMSON, Mark Ian. 9500 EUCLID AVE A-41 44195 #021-01-1985 L1991 **ORS OSM** *020 †40
FRY, James Henry. 7057 W 130TH ST 44130 #041-13-1948 L1951 **P** *071

FU, Evelyn Xi. ■ 44107 #038-06-2003 L2006 **OPH** *012

FUDURIC, James Edward. 18101 LORAIN AVE 44111 #038-43-1973 L1975 **PD IM** *020 †55

FUENTES, Karel. ■ 44113 #270-02-2000 L2006 **N** *100

FUERTES, Maria Rosa. 9500 EUCLID AVE 44195 #132-01-1993 L2004 **AN** *012

FUERTES, Nabor Juan. 4755 PEARL RD, U.S. 42 44109 #737-01-1951 L1966 **IM** *071

FULLER, Thomas Arthur. 2816 E 116TH ST 44120 #038-06-1971 L1974 **IM IMG** *020 †20

FULMES, Mychailo. ■ 44111 #913-89-1989 L2002 **GS** *012

FULOP, Steven Charles. 2135 COLUMBUS RD UP 44113 #038-06-2002 L2002 **NS** *012

FULTON, Gregory Joseph. 9500 EUCLID AVE, CO CCF-GRAD MED EDU DEPT-N 44195 #539-03-1990 L2002 *100

FULTON, Scott Alexander. 10900 EUCLID AVE, BRB RM1021 44106 #025-07-1989 L1992 **ID IM** *050 †20

FUNG, John Julian. 9500 EUCLID AVE, CLEVELAND CLC DEPT GEN SUR 44195 #016-02-1982 L2004 **GS TTS** *020 †85

FUNG, Kenneth Kuen Wo. 11100 EUCLID AVE # 2600 44106 #244-03-1964 L1979 **DR R** *020 †80

FUREY, Erin James. 11100 EUCLID AVE 44106 #038-06-1989 L1993 **CCA** *020 †05

FUREY, Susan Marie Kane. ■ 44124 #038-06-1989 L1991 **P** *020

FURLAN, Anthony John. 9500 EUCLID AVE, CLEVELAND CLINIC 44195 #016-43-1973 L1974 **N** *020 †75

FURMAN, Lydia Mary. 11100 EUCLID AVE 44106 #038-06-1983 L1990 **PD ADL** *040 †55

FURUKAWA, Bruce. 20637 EMERALD PKWY, CLEVELAND M.E.P.S. 44135 #038-40-1984 L1986 **FM** *074

GABALI, Ali Mahdi. 2500 METROHEALTH DR 44109 #797-03-1996 L2005 **PTH** *012

GABELMAN, Edward Henry. 23250 MERCANTILE RD 44122 #025-01-1966 L1967 **ORS CD** *020 †40 ‡

GABRILOVICH, Mikhail. 11100 EUCLID AVE, PULMONARY AND CRITICAL CAR 44106 #913-93-1995 L2004 **PCC** *012 †20

GACAD, Joji Elazegui. 12100 SUPERIOR AVE 44106 #748-01-1983 L1993 **PD** *020 †20

GADIYARAM, Madhuri Devi. 27100 CHARDON RD, HOSPITALIST-UH RICHMOND HT 44143 #495-70-1997 L2003 **IM** *020 †20

GAITHER, Shayla Kristin. 11100 EUCLID AVE 44106 #010-03-2005 L2005 **AN** *012

GAJWANI, Prashant. 10524 EUCLID AVE, MOOD DISORDERS PROGRAM 44106 #496-02-1996 L2000 **P** *020

GAKHOKIDZE, Maia Levan. 13951 TERRACE RD, HURON HOSP CCHSINTERNAL ME 44112 #912-02-1997 L2000 **IM** *100 †20

GALAN, Gayle. 1730 W 25TH ST 44113 #038-06-1978 L1979 **EM FM** *020 †18,16

GALANG, Cirilo Flores. 812 HURON RD E, STE 520 44115 #748-01-1960 L1968 **PTH P** *071 †50

GALITA, Dan Alexandru. 3395 SCRANTON RD 44109 #781-01-1977 L2003 **PTH FOP** *062

GALLA, John Michael. ■ 44195 #054-04-2002 L2005 **CD** *012 †20

GALLAGHER, Tara Maura. ■ 44145 #038-06-1999 L1999

GALLAGHER, Timothy John. 6707 POWERS BLVD, STE 201 44129 #038-06-1986 L1987 **IM** *020 †20

GALVEZ, Javier Virgilio. 2460 FAIRMOUNT BLVD, STE 212 44106 #737-01-1966 L1975 **CCP** *020 †75

GALWAY, Ursula Ann. 9500 EUCLID AVE, C/O CCF-GRAD MED EDU DEPT- 44195 #539-06-2000 L2001 **CCA** *100 †05

GAMALELDIN, Haissam. 18101 LORAIN AVE, DEPT. OF ANESTHESIOLOGY 44111 #915-04-1993 L2000 **AN** *020 ‡

GAMBETTI, Pier Luigi. 2085 ADELBERT RD, NATL PRIOR DISEASE PATH 44106 #561-01-1959 L1978 **NP PTH** *050

GANDHI, Namita Sharma. 9500 EUCLID AVE 44195 #495-30-1999 L2005 **DR** *020 †80

GANESAN, Santhi. 2500 METROHEALTH DR 44109 #495-66-1990 L2000 **PCP** *020 †50

GANESAN, Srinivasan. 2500 METROHEALTH DR, C/O METRO HLTH MED CTR-RES 44109 #495-72-1995 L2002 **GE** *012

GANGESTAD, Angelina Kay. 5850 LANDERBROOK DR, STE 3 44124 #041-09-1996 L1998 **OBG** *020 †30

GANNON, Angela. ■ 44126 #038-43-2004 L2004 **P** *012

GANS, Richard Evan. 11100 EUCLID AVE, BOWELL #3200 44106 #038-06-1982 L1982 **OPH** *020 †35 ‡

GANTWERKER, Brian Randall. 11100 EUCLID AVE RM 3018, C/O UNIV HOSPS - RESIDENCE 44106 #016-01-2001 L2001 **NS** *012

GANZ, Edward. 11100 EUCLID AVE, UNIV HOSPS DEPT NEUROSURG 44106 #016-02-1967 L1983 **NS** *020 †25

GANZ, Michael Bruce. 6780 MAYFIELD RD, MERIDA HILLCREST HOSP 44124 #041-07-1982 L1991 **NEP IM** *020 †20

GANZHORN, Dann Wm. 300 E 185TH ST 44119 #038-45-1981 L1983 **FM PME** *020 †18

GAO, Keming. 11400 EUCLID AVE, STE 200 44106 #243-07-1985 L2000 **P** *020 ‡

GAO, Xing. ■ 44106 #038-06-2006 L2006 **AN** *012

GAO, Yuehua. ■ 44120 #243-16-1985 *100

GARBER, Rachel Miriam. 1611 S GREEN RD, STE 34 44121 #048-02-1980 L1982 **PD** *020 †55

GARCIA, Jorge Alberto. 9500 EUCLID AVE, STE 100 44195 #264-18-1994 L2004 **HO** *100 †20

GARCIA, Jorge Antonio. 9500 EUCLID AVE R-35, CLEVELAND CLINIC FOUNDATIO 44195 #005-02-1990 L1991 **IM** *020 †20

GARCIA, Pacita E Gabriel. 7007 POWERS BLVD 44129 #748-02-1953 L1969 **AN OS** *020

GARCIA, Ryan Michael. ■ 44121 #010-01-2005 L2005 **ORS** *012

GARCIA-ROBLE, Amelia V. ■ 44133 #748-07-1963 L1973 **EM** *020

GARCIA-TOCA, Manuel. 9500 EUCLID AVE, CLEVELAND CLI - SURG 44195 #649-13-2000 L2003 **GS** *012

GARDNER, John Howland. 1611 S GREEN RD, STE 34 44121 #008-01-1956 L1964 **N IM** *071 †75

GARDNER, Stanley Morris. 24700 CENTER RIDGE RD, PREVENTIVE MEDICINE GROUP 44145 #748-10-1980 L2001 **PD OS** *020 †05

GARG, Vipul Kumar. 2500 METROHEALTH DR, METROHEALTH MED CTR 44109 #305-01-2003 L2003 **PEM** *012

GARLAND, Allan Bruce. 2500 METROHEALTH DR 44109 #016-02-1986 L2001 **CCM PUD** *040 †20

GARRO, Rouba. 2351 E 22ND ST 44115 #875-01-2001 L2003 **PN** *012 †55

GARUDA, Radha Rao. ■ 44120 #495-11-1967 L1975 **AN** *030 †05

GARVIN, Harry Clark. 11201 SHAKER BLVD STE 202 44104 #038-06-1955 L1955 **IM** *071 †20

GASKINS, Sonji Lynette. ■ 44112 #038-06-1992 L1996 **FM** *020 †18

GATZOYLIS, Kostas A. 2074 ADELBERT RD 44106 #418-02-1980 L1986 **IM CD** *020 †20

GAUGLER, Erin. 300 N COMMONS BLVD 44143 #038-41-1997 L2002 **EM** *020 †16

GAUSE, Paul Russell. 11100 EUCLID AVE STE 5128, SPINE DIVISION DEPT OF ORT 44106 #005-14-2002 L2007 **ORS** *100

GAUVIN, Wali. 11100 EUCLID AVE, ROOM 380 -PEDIATRIC CARDIO 44106 #035-15-2000 L2003 **PD** *020

GEERTMAN, Robert Theodore. 2500 METROHEALTH DR # H910 44109 #035-09-1996 L1997 **NS OS** *020

GEISLER, Daniel Phillip. 9500 EUCLID AVE, THE CLEVELAND CLNC 44195 #028-34-1996 L2002 **CRS GS** *020 †85,10

GELEHRTER, George Ludwig. 2500 METROHEALTH DR, METROHEALTH MED CTR 44109 #038-06-1976 L1977 **IMG PLM** *020 †20

GELLER GUMPERTZ, Esti. 6770 MAYFIELD RD # 249 44124 #035-08-1982 L1985 **D** *020 †15

GELLES, Ellen Jill. 2500 METROHEALTH DR 44109 #038-06-1994 L2002 **IM** *020 †20

GELLES, Lisa Nan. 2500 METROHEALTH DR A-109, METRO HEALTH MEDICAL CENTE 44109 #038-06-1989 L1990 **D PD** *020 †15,55

GEMECHU, Fassil Woyessa. 2500 METROHEALTH DR, DEPT OF FAMILY PRACTICE 44109 #286-05-1993 L2000 **FM** *020 †18

GEMMA, Lee William. 2500 METROHEALTH DR, METROHEALTH MED CTR 44109 #038-40-2005 L2005 **IM** *012

GENUTH, Saul Maurice. 10900 EUCLID AVE, CASE WESTERN RESERVE U 44106 #038-06-1957 L1957 **END** *040 †20

GEORGE, Elizabeth Michell. ■ 44106 #028-03-2004 L2004 **IM** *012 †20

GEORGE, Jon Chillikkattil. 11100 EUCLID AVE, DEPT OF CARDIOLOGY 44106 #038-41-2002 L2002 **CD** *012 †20

GEORGE, Kristopher Mahlon. 9500 EUCLID AVE, DEPT OF THORACIC & CARDIO 44195 #025-07-1998 L2005 **TS** *020 †20

GEORGE, Paul H. 18101 LORAIN AVE 44111 #028-34-1949 L1952 **PD** *072

GEORGE, Saby. 9500 EUCLID AVE, TAUSSIG CANCER CENTER 44195 #495-63-1999 L2003 **IM** *050 †20

GEORGE, Samir M. ■ 44124 #915-04-1959 L1976 **D FM** *071

GERACI, Kevin Thos. 1611 S GREEN RD 44121 #038-40-1967 L1967 **IM GE** *020 †20

GERACI, Michele Marie. 6835 BROADWAY AVE 44105 #038-06-1994 L1996 **IM** *020 †20

GERBER, Helmut R. 2065 ADELBERT RD 44106 #407-19-1967 L1973 **AN IM** *020 †05

GERBER, Robert Brian. 15805 PURITAS AVE, OHIO CHEST PHYSICIANS, LTD 44135 #028-46-1995 L2000 **PCC** *020 †20

GERBLICH, Judith. 1422 EUCLID AVE STE 616 44115 #550-02-1972 L1977 **OPH** *020

GERDING, Robert Lewis. 7255 OLD OAK BLVD, STE C411 44130 #038-06-1978 L1983 **GS OS** *020 †85,65

GERKEN, Karen Lowrey. 19250 BAGLEY RD 44130 #038-06-1984 L1987 **PTH** *020 †50

GERSON, Stanton L. 11100 EUCLID AVE, WEARN 151 44106 #024-01-1977 L1983 **HO ON** *030 †20

GERVASI, Lawrence Alfred. 6900 PEARL RD, STE 200 44130 #048-04-1985 L1991 **U** *020 †95

GETAHUN, Berhanu. 2351 E 22ND ST, STE 421W 44115 #366-01-1973 L1983 **IM CLP** *020

GHAFOORI, Sherine Ruth. ■ 44120 #005-02-1999 L2007 **AN** *100 †55,05

GHAITH, Ziad Matanious. ■ 44135 #875-01-1992 **IM** *100

GHALI, Nabil Nashed. ■ 44106 #330-02-1958 L1972 **OBG** *075

GHALY, Mary Mofied Kiroll. 9500 EUCLID AVE 44195 #915-02-1998 L2004 **AN** *012

GHAYURI, Mohammadreza. 11100 EUCLID AVE, UNIV MACDONALD WOMEN'S HOS 44106 #517-05-1998 L2004 **OBG** *100

GHAZOUL, Deborah Marie. 18101 LORAIN AVE 44111 #038-43-1987 L1988 **PD** *020 †55

GHERMAN, Cindy Renee. 18599 LAKE SHORE BLVD 44119 #010-01-1990 L1992 **PD** *020 †55

GHOLAM, Pierre Michel. 11100 EUCLID AVE, UNIV HOSPS OF CLEVELAND 44106 #605-01-1996 L2005 **IM** *020 †20

GHOSH, Debabrata. 9500 EUCLID AVE, DESK571 THE CLEVELAND CLIN 44195 #495-02-1985 L2000 **CHN** *020 †75

GHOSH, Partha Sekhar. 9500 EUCLID AVE, CLEVELAND CLINIC FOUNDATIO 44195 #495-02-1998 L2007 **PD** *012

GIANNATTASIO, Bartolomeo. 7255 OLD OAK BLVD, ASSOCIATES 44130 #561-23-1987 L1998 **CD** *020 †20

GIBBONS, Joseph. 11100 EUCLID AVE, UNIV HOSPITALS OF CLEVELAN 44106 #038-40-1979 L1980 **HEM ON** *040 †20

GIBSON, Sarah. ■ 44195 #036-07-2004 L2004 **PTH** *012

GIDWANI, Gita Prem. 9500 EUCLID AVE, DESK A-81 44195 #495-28-1960 L1970 **GYN PD** *020 †30

GIFFORD, Susan Adelaide. 21000 BROOKPARK RD 44135 #038-06-1984 L1985 **IM** *020 †20

GIGENA, Tomas. 1530 SAINT CLAIR AVE NE 44114 #132-02-1999 L2002 **FM** *100 †18

GILANI, Ramyar. THE CLEVELAND CLINIC, DEPT OF VASCULAR SURGERY 44195 #048-15-2002 L2007 **VS** *012

GILBERT, Leslie Jean. 2322 E 22ND ST STE 302 44115 #038-06-1988 L1989 **VM IM** *020 †20

GILDEA, Thomas Robert. 9500 EUCLID AVE, CRITICAL CARE 44195 #041-09-1996 L2000 **PCC** *020 †20 ‡

GILES, Katherine Elizabet. ■ 44113 #028-34-2008 *012

GILKESON, Robert Chapman. 11100 EUCLID AVE, STE 2600 44106 #038-06-1989 L1996 **DR** *020 †80

GILL, Inderbir S. 9500 EUCLID AVE, STE 100 44195 #495-29-1979 L1997 **U** *020 †95

GILL, Inderjit S. 2500 METROHEALTH DR, 3RD FL 44109 #495-08-1981 L1990 *020

GILL, Namita. ■ 44195 #065-06-2003 L2003 **IM** *100 †20

GILLESPIE, Beth Hengst. ■ 44118 #041-02-2005 L2005 **OPH** *012

GILLESPIE, Christopher O. 4242 LORAIN AVE 44113 #038-45-1998 L2000 **FM** *020 †18

GILLESPIE, Laura Ann. 9500 EUCLID AVE, CLEVELAND CLINIC FOUNDATIO 44195 #038-06-2000 L2000 **PD** *020

GILLIGAN, Timothy David. 9500 EUCLID AVE R-35, CLEVELAND CLINIC TAUSSIG C 44195 #005-11-1996 L2005 **ON IM** *020 †20

GILLINOV, Marc Alan. 9500 EUCLID AVE, DESK F24, DEPT OF CARDIAC 44195 #023-07-1988 L1997 **TS** *020 †85,90

GILREATH, Marcellus Jajua. 16603 HARVARD AVE 44128 #038-41-1988 L1990 **IM** *020 ‡

GINDI, Maurice Yacoub. 9500 EUCLID AVE 44195 #330-02-1956 L1970 **AN** *020

GINGO, Anthony Jos, Jr. 7225 OLD OAK BLVD, STE B314 44130 #038-06-1988 L1990 **OBG** *020 †30

GIRZHEL, Julia. ■ 44106 #038-06-2004 L2004 **OBG** *012

GISSER, Jonathan. 2500 METROHEALTH DR, METROHEALTH MED CTR 44109 #550-03-2001 L2002 **PG** *012 †55

GLASER, Bela. ■ 44122 #409-05-1971 L1975 **IMG** *020

GLASER, Joram. ■ 44122 #550-01-1962 L1973 **PDC** *020

GLAUSER, Jonathan Mark. 2500 METROHEALTH DR 44109 #041-13-1976 L1979 **EM** *030 †16

GLAZER, Dennis Allen. 1001 LAKESIDE AVE E, STE 1200 44114 #038-40-1967 L1967 **ORS** *020 †40

GLAZER, Gwen Karen. 2816 E 116TH ST, HEALTH CENTER 44120 #038-06-1984 L1986 **PD** *020 †55

GLAZER, John Prescott. 9500 EUCLID AVE, DEPT OF PSYCHIATRY 44195 #005-18-1972 L1979 **P PD** *020 †55,75

GLICK, Yitzchak Aryeh I. 9051 CEDAR AVE 44106 #550-01-1991 L1996 **EM** *072 †16
GLIGA, Arina Monica. 17900 JEFFERSON PARK RD, STE 103 44130 #781-03-1975 L1991 **END IM** *020 †20
GLORIOSO, Virgilio C. 2500 METROHEALTH DR 44109 #748-01-1962 L1971 **AN** *020
GLUZ, George Daniel. 5500 S MARGINAL RD 44103 #422-01-1996 L2008 **IM** *020 †20
GLYNN, Alicia Ann. ■ 44118 #037-01-2006 L2006 **MPD** *012
GO, Raymundo Tiu. 9500 EUCLID AVE, DEPT OF NUCLEAR MEDICINE (44195 #748-01-1965 L1980 **NM DR** *020 †28,80
GOBEZIE, Reuben. 11100 EUCLID AVE, HH5043 44106 #024-01-1999 L2006 **ORS** *100
GODARD, Joel White. 6707 POWERS BLVD, STE 205 44129 #038-40-1986 L1995 **CD** *020 †20
GODBOLE, Medha S. 12301 SNOW RD 44130 #495-01-1984 L1995 **PTH** *020 †50
GODFREY, David Michael. ■ 44113 #017-20-2003 L2006 **ORS** *012
GOEL, Anurag. 2500 METROHEALTH DR, DEPT OF RESIDENCY SUPPORT 44109 #495-29-1998 L2006 **IM** *100
GOEL, Nidhi. 2500 METROHEALTH DR 44109 #495-34-2004 L2006 **P** *012
GOEL, Raj. 9500 EUCLID AVE A100 44195 #062-01-2002 L2006 *100
GOGATE, Prema Anil. 10701 EAST BLVD 44106 #495-28-1972 L1976 **PTH OS** *020 †50
GOH, Ping Ping. 9500 EUCLID AVE BOX 189 44195 #825-01-1988 *100
GOHIL, Rahul Ramesh. ■ 44106 #038-06-2003 L2007 **GS** *012
GOLAWALA, Mushfeka Moiz. 9500 EUCLID AVE, CLEVELAND CLINIC FNDN 44195 #496-25-2004 **IM** *012
GOLCHINI, Hassan. 13951 TERRACE RD, DEPT OF INTERNAL MEDICINE 44112 #517-01-1997 L2004 **IM** *100 †20
GOLD, Jay Richard. 14100 CEDAR RD, LUBERT KRAUSE & ASSOCS INC 44121 #038-40-1961 L1961 **R** *020 †80
GOLDBERG, Andrew L. 3132 BREMERTON RD 44124 #023-01-1980 L2001 **DR RNR** *020 †80
GOLDBERG, Daniel Philip. 11100 EUCLID AVE 44106 #016-06-1986 L1995 **PS GS** *020 †85,65
GOLDBERG, Gerald. 1 MOUNT SINAI DR 44106 #065-01-1955 L1958 **AN** *071 †05
GOLDBERG, Jeffrey M. 9500 EUCLID AVE A81, CLEVELAND CLINIC FOUNDATIO 44195 #033-05-1983 L1987 **OBG REN** *020 †30
GOLDBERG, Jonathan L. 11100 EUCLID AVE RM 3018, CO UNIV HOSPS-RESIDENCY OF 44106 #050-02-2002 L2003 **CD** *012 †20
GOLDBERG, Laura Dunn. 2074 ABINGTON RD, UNIV HOSP OF CLEVELAND 44106 #050-02-2002 L2002 **PD** *100 †55
GOLDBERG, Philip Neil. 9500 EUCLID AVE, MAIL CODE BE 11 44195 #020-02-1980 L1982 **OPH** *020 †35
GOLDBERG, Victor. 11100 EUCLID AVE 44106 #035-08-1964 L1965 **ORS** *020 †40
GOLDBLUM, John Reid. 9500 EUCLID AVE 44195 #025-01-1989 L1993 **PTH** *020 †50
GOLDFARB, Beth Rochelle. ■ 44101-13-1986 L1988 **AN** *020
GOLDFARB, David Andrew. 9500 EUCLID AVE, STE 100 44195 #041-13-1985 L1988 **U** *040 †95
GOLDFARB, Johanna. 9500 EUCLID AVE, CLEVELAND CLINIC 44195 #023-07-1974 L1986 **ID PD** *020 †55
GOLDFARB, Nosson Shlomo. 18151 JEFFERSN PRK RD #103 44130 #038-45-1992 L1994 **AI PD** *020 †55
GOLDFEDER, Yael Rena. ■ 44118 #023-01-2003 L2006 **EM** *020
GOLDFINGER, Mark. 11100 EUCLID AVE 44106 #056-06-1990 L1995 **AN** *020 †05
GOLDHIRSCH, Henry. 2460 FAIRMOUNT BLVD 44106 #869-05-1952 L1954 **P OS** *071
GOLDING, Leonard A R. 9500 EUCLID AVE, ND 20 44195 #143-03-1964 L1976 **TS** *020
GOLDMAN, Howard Brian. 6770 MAYFIELD RD, STE 226 44124 #035-46-1991 L1997 **U** *020 †95
GOLDNER, Joshua David. 18101 LORAIN AVE, DEPT OF ANESTHESIOLOGY 44111 #038-40-2000 L2004 **APM** *020 †05
GOLDSTEIN, David J. 1 MOUNT SINAI DR 44106 #025-76-1973, ▲ L1976 **AN** *071
GOLDSTEIN, Jessica Ruth. 2500 METROHEALTH DR 44109 #035-20-2001 L2003 **EM** *020 †16
GOLDSTEIN, Robert Neil. 18599 LAKE SHORE BLVD 44119 #035-20-1996 L1997 **ICE** *100 †20
GOLDSTONE, Jerry. 11100 EUCLID AVE, CASE MEDICAL CTR 44106 #040-02-1965 L1999 **VS GS** *020 †85
GOLDTHWAIT, David A. ■ 44106 #035-01-1945 L1959 **OS ON** *071
GOLOVAN, Ronald Philip. 2709 FRANKLIN BLVD FL 2 44113 #038-45-1989 L1990 **IM** *020 †20
GOLSHAYAN, Ali Reza. ■ 44120 #050-02-2001 L2001 **HO** *100
GOMES, Dominic. 8315 DETROIT AVE 44102 #748-12-1983 L2000 **P** *020
GOMES, Marcelo Pires. 9500 EUCLID AVE 44195 #187-09-1993 L1998 **IM** *020 †20
GOMES, Marcos Emanuel Wor. 9500 EUCLID AVE, CLEVELAND CLINIC FOUNDATIO 44195 #187-25-2000 L2006 **AN** *012
GOMEZ-HERNANDEZ, Carlos M. 9500 EUCLID AVE, CO CCF-GRAD MED EDU DEPT 44195 #847-12-1988 L2000 *100
GONCALVES, Carolina Gomes. 9500 EUCLID AVE, CLEVELAND CLINIC FOUNDATIO 44195 #187-08-2001 L2005 *100
GONG, Michael Chi. 9500 EUCLID AVE A100, GLICKMAN UROOLOGIC FOUNDAT 44195 #016-02-1990 L1999 **U** *020 †95
GONZALES, Agripino C, Jr. 18697 BAGLEY RD 44130 #748-01-1970 L1975 **GS** *020
GONZALEZ, Christopher L. ■ 44113 #035-01-1984 L1987 **ATP** *020 †50
GONZALEZ, Darsham Yussef. 44109 #038-06-2005 L2005 **IM** *012
GONZALEZ, Gonzalo Vicente. 9500 EUCLID AVE, F24 44195 #042-01-1994 L2003 **TS** *100 †85,90
GOOD, Milton Billings. 18099 LORAIN AVE 44111 #017-20-1965 L1969 **N** *071 †75
GOODING, Judith Frances. 2500 METROHEALTH DR 44109 #038-06-1978 L1979 **IMG IM** *071
GOODMAN, Evan Joshua. 5163 BROADWAY AVE 44127 #041-14-1987 L1991 **AN** *020 †05
GOPALAKRISHNA, K V. 18101 LORAIN AVE 44111 #495-09-1965 L1972 **ID IM** *020 †20
GOPINATH, Devi. 44109 #495-31-2001 L2007 **CD** *012
GORDIEV, Katherine Amelia. 9500 EUCLID AVE, CO CCF-GRAD MED EDUDEPT-NA 44195 #143-03-1993 L2003 *020
GORDON, Gregory John. 2500 METROHEALTH DR, METROHEALTH MEDICAL CENTER 44109 #026-04-1975 L1978 **AN PD** *020 †55,05
GORDON, Steven Mark. 9500 EUCLID AVE, CLINIC FOUNDATION 44195 #035-20-1984 L1993 **ID IM** *020 †20
GOREN, Hershel. 9500 EUCLID AVE 44195 #025-07-1964 L1970 **N** *030 †75
GORGUN, Ihya Emre. 9500 EUCLID AVE, THE CLEVELAND CLINIC FOUND 44195 #902-10-1996 L2005 *100
GORI, Abdulla Khan. 2500 METROHEALTH DR 44109 #495-31-1981 L2000 **PD** *020 †55
GORJANC, Mary Margaret. 7255 OLD OAK BLVD, STE C408 44130 #038-45-1981 L1982 **AN** *020 †20
GORLA, Kiranmai. 2500 METROHEALTH DR 44109 #495-11-2002 L2004 **PD** *100 †55
GORNIK, Heather Leah. 9500 EUCLID AVE S60, DEPT. OF CARDIOVASCULAR ME 44195 #016-02-1997 L2005 **CD** *020
GORODESKI, Eiran Zev. 9500 EUCLID AVE, CLEVELAND CLINIC FOUNDATIO 44195 #038-06-2003 L2006 **CD** *012 †20

GORODESKI, Israel Geo. 5850 LANDERBROOK DR, STE 3 44124 #550-02-1973 L1988 *020
GOSNELL, Amy Lyn. ■ 44106 #038-06-2008 *012
GOSWAMI, Dheeraj Kumar. ■ 44106 #051-07-2006 L2006 **PD** *012
GOTTESMAN, Dina Miriam. ■ 44120 #041-01-2006 L2006 **PD** *012
GOTTESMAN, Eleanor Jean H. 2816 E 116TH ST 44120 #125-01-1973 L1986 **PD** *020 †55
GOTTESMAN, Howard Gerald. 2500 METROHEALTH DR, DEPARTMENT OF PSYCHIATRY 44109 #125-01-1973 L1985 **P** *020 †75
GOTTLIEB, Alexandru. 9500 EUCLID AVE, DEPT OF ANESTHESIA 44195 #550-03-1972 L1978 **AN** *020 †05
GOTTSCHLING, Carl Floyd. 11100 EUCLID AVE, UNIV ANESTHESIOLOGISTS, 44106 #005-06-1991 L1995 **AN** *020 †05
GOUBAR, Zinovi Volodymyro. 2500 METROHEALTH DR, METROHEALTH MED CTR 44109 #913-42-1975 L2001 **P** *100
GOULD, Deborah Jean. 11100 EUCLID AVE 44106 #038-06-1973 L1973 **P PYG** *020 †75
GOULDER ABELSON, Abby M. 9500 EUCLID AVE A50, CLEVELAND CLINIC FOUNDATIO 44195 #038-06-1979 L1979 **RHU IM** *020 †20
GOUTMAN, Stephen Aaron. ■ 44106 #016-02-2007 L2007 *012
GOWANS, Laura Kate. 2801 MARTIN LTHR KNG JR DR 44104 #025-07-1997 L2003 **PHO** *020 †55
GOYAL, Kush Kumar. ■ 44124 #038-43-2006 L2007 **GS** *012
GOYAL, Pankaj. 11100 EUCLID AVE, BOLWELL 1200 44106 #495-30-2003 L2007 **FP** *012
GOYAL, Ram Kishan. 26900 CEDAR RD, KRAUSE LUBERT & ASSOCS INC 44122 #495-12-1965 L1980 **RO** *012
GOYAL, Sheela. ■ 44124 #495-11-1967 *074
GRABER, Ellen R. 18099 LORAIN AVE, INC 44111 #038-06-1987 L1987 **PD** *020 †55
GRABER, Raymond Gregory. 11100 EUCLID AVE 44106 #035-06-1984 L1987 **AN** *020 †05
GRABER, Thomas Woodrow. 2351 E 22ND ST 44115 #038-06-1975 L1981 **EM IM** *020 †16
GRAHAM, Debra J. 10701 EAST BLVD DEPT SURG, CLEVELAND VA MED CTR 44106 #041-09-1985 L1987 **GS** *020 †85
GRAHAM, Linda Mae. 9500 EUCLID AVE, CLEVELAND CLNIC FDTN S40 44195 #025-01-1975 L1988 **VS** *020 †85
GRAHAM, Richard Cyril, Jr. 10701 EAST BLVD, VA MEDICAL CENTER 44106 #018-03-1960 L1963 **ID IM** *040 †20
GRANDINETTI, Lisa M. 9500 EUCLID AVE, # A61 44195 #041-15-2004 L2004 **D** *012
GRANT, Richard Edward. 11100 EUCLID AVE DEPT O 44106 #010-03-1976 L1985 **ORS** *020 †40
GRASSO, Adam Wright. 9500 EUCLID AVE, DESK F15 44195 #038-06-2000 L2004 **IM** *100
GRAVES, Stephen Raymond. 11311 SHAKER BLVD 44104 #041-02-1964 L1965 **IM** *071
GRAY, Lawrence Keith. 13951 TERRACE RD 44112 #165-03-1980 L1982 **IM** *020 †20
GRECO, Anthony Alphonso. 18101 LORAIN AVE 44111 #038-06-1960 L1960 **PTH** *071 †50
GRECO, Peter Jos. 3838 W 150TH ST 44111 #024-01-1987 **IM** *020 †20
GREEN, Carolyn. 11100 EUCLID AVE, DEPT PEDIATRIC NEUROLOGY 44106 #025-07-1987 L1993 **CHN** *020 †75
GREEN, Douglas Howard. 1001 LAKESIDE AVE E, STE 1200 44114 #038-43-1991 L1992 **U** *020 †95
GREEN, Hazel Yvonne. 11000 EUCLID AVE, DEPT OF RADIOLOGY 44106 #025-12-1979 L1981 **DR** *020 †80
GREENBERG, David Jeremiah. 50 PUBLIC SQ, STE 1300 44113 #051-04-1947 L1947 **IM PTH** *071 †20
GREENBERG, Roy Kenneth. 9500 EUCLID AVE, CLEVELAND CLINIC FOONDATIO 44195 #038-41-1992 L1999 **GS** *020 †85
GREENE, Andrew Benjamin. ■ 44114 #035-01-2006 L2007 **OPH GS** *012
GREENE, Brenda Sue. 9500 EUCLID AVE 44195 #038-45-1985 L1986 **AN IM** *020 †05
GREENE, Lloyd Howard. 11100 EUCLID AVE, LKS 5038 44106 #035-19-1987 L1989 **CD** *020 †20
GREENFIELD, Marjorie Lisa. 5850 LANDERBROOK DR, STE 3 44124 #038-06-1983 L1986 **OBG** *020 †30
GREENSMITH, Latoya Andrec. ■ 44106 #038-06-2007 L2007 **PD** *012
GREENSPAN, Neil Sanford. 11400 EUCLID AVE STE 100 44106 #041-01-1981 L1986 **OS CLP** *050
GREER, Steven Franklin. ■ 44121 #036-05-2003 L2003 **GS** *100
GREGORY, Jolee Henri. 2500 E 79TH ST 44104 #047-07-1986 L2003 **PD** *020 †55,20 ‡
GREICIUS, Francis A. 25001 EMERY RD, STE 100 44128 #038-06-1972 L1976 **R** *020 †80
GRETTER, Brock John. ■ 44195 #038-40-2002 L2002 **AN** *020 †05
GRETTER, Thomas Edward. 9500 EUCLID AVE, S91 44195 #041-01-1960 L1966 **N** *020 †75
GRIESMER, Brendan Clark. 30680 BAINBRIDGE RD 44139 #038-06-2003 L2006 **IM** *100 †20
GRIFFIN, Brian P. DESK F- 15, 9500 EUCLID CLINIC 44195 #539-05-1979 L1993 **CD** *020 †20
GRIGORESCU, Bogdan Andrei. ■ 44195 #539-04-2000 L2004 **OBG** *100
GRIGORYEVA, Irina. 11100 EUCLID AVE, UNIV HOSP 44106 #023-01-2003 L2003 **U** *012
GRIGSBY, Joel Kent. ■ 44121 #019-02-2007 L2007 **AN** *012
GRINBERG, Anna. ■ 44106 #038-40-2005 L2005 **PD** *012
GRINBLATT, Michael Steven. 6770 MAYFIELD RD, STE 205 44124 #038-40-1982 L1985 **CD** *075 †20
GRIPSHOVER, Barbara Marie. 11100 EUCLID AVE, UNIV HOSPS CLEVELAND 44106 #047-05-1987 L1990 **ID IM** *020 †20
GRISCHKAN, David M. 24025 COMMERCE PARK 44122 #067-01-1974 L1979 **GS** *020 †85
GROMMES, Christian. 11100 EUCLID AVE, UNIV HOSP OF CLEVELAND 44106 #409-39-2000 L2005 **N** *012
GROSSMAN, Gerald E. 11100 EUCLID AVE, STE 5512 44106 #038-06-1977 L1983 **N** *020 †75
GROSSMAN, Morton. 29001 CEDAR RD, STE 200 44124 #869-02-1958 L1961 **IM IMG** *071
GROTEWOLD, Gisela. 11100 EUCLID AVE, RAINBOW BABIES AND CHILDRE 44106 #132-01-1988 L1991 **PG** *020 †55
GROTTE, Lee Bryan. 5399 MAYFIELD RD 44124 #038-06-1980 L1980 **GP** *020
GROUP, Marguerite Marie. 17300 S PARK BLVD, 5555 TRANSPORTATION BLVD 44120 #038-06-1985 L1985 **AN** *020 †20
GROVES, Megan Testa. ■ 44120 #038-06-2007 L2007 **P** *012
GRUBE, Amy Rebecca. 11100 EUCLID AVE, UNIVERSITY HOSPITALS HEALT 44106 #038-40-1999 L2003 **PD** *020 †55
GRUZDYS, Vitoldas. 11203 FAIRHILL RD 44104 #616-01-1943 L1951 **GP** *072
GUDAVALLI, Ravindra. 9500 EUCLID AVE A90 44195 #495-21-2001 L2007 **PCC** *012 †20
GUERRERO, Dubert Medina. 11100 EUCLID AVE 44106 #748-02-2002 L2004 **ID** *012 †20
GUETTA, Victor. 9500 EUCLID AVE # 628, CLEVELAND CLNC FNDATN 44195 #550-04-1986 **CD** *020
GUGLIOTTI, David Vincent. 9500 EUCLID AVE 44195 #038-40-1996 L1999 **IM** *020 †20
GUIAO, Ramon T. ■ 44126 #748-02-1962 L1969 **FM** *071 †85
GUILLERMO, Reynaldo F. 1370 ONTARIO ST STE 450 44113 #748-01-1966 L1977 **RO DR** *071
GUIRGUIS, Wafiek Adeib. 18101 LORAIN AVE 44111 #915-03-1960 L1982 **AN CCM** *071 †05

GULAB, Bobby Asif. 2500 METROHEALTH DR 44109 #305-01-2005 L2006 **MPD** *100
GULATI, Ish Kumar. 2500 METROHEALTH DR 44109 #495-44-2000 L2005 **PD** *012
GULATI, Kapil. 6559 WILSON MILLS RD, STE 106A 44143 #495-45-2001 L2004 **IM** *100 †20
GULATI, Reema. 2500 METROHEALTH DR, METROHEALTH MED CTR 44109 #495-45-2002 L2005 **PD** *012
GUMABAO-FLORES, Susan G. 1730 W 25TH ST, LUTHERAN MEDICAL CENTER 44113 #748-01-1973 L1980 **IM OM** *020
GUNAWARDENA, Diyana R. 2500 METROHEALTH DR 44109 #038-06-1994 L1997 **FPG** *020 †20
GUNDAPANENI, Ramesh-C. 7255 OLD OAK BLVD, STE 209 44130 #496-01-1971 L1977 **IM** *020 †20
GUNDROO, Rubina. 9500 EUCLID AVE 44195 #495-07-2004 L2007 **P** *012
GUPTA, Ajay. 2801 MARTIN LTHR KNG JR DR 44104 #495-03-1988 L1998 **CHN CN** *020 †55,75
GUPTA, Avneesh. 2500 METROHEALTH DR 44109 #495-45-1997 L2005 **PTH** *012
GUPTA, Deepak. 9500 EUCLID AVE, CLEVELAND CLIN-ANESTHESIA- 44195 #041-07-1992 L1996 **AN** *020 †05
GUPTA, Mona. 13951 TERRACE RD, MERIDIA HURON HOSP 44112 #496-07-1995 L2002 **IMG** *100 †20
GUPTA, Rajendra P. 6688 RIDGE RD, RAJENDRA GUPTA MD INC 44129 #495-20-1963 L1976 **PCC IM** *071 †20
GUPTA, Sandeep. 9500 EUCLID AVE, CLEVELAND CLNC 44195 #050-02-2000 L2000 **TS** *012 †85
GUPTA, Usha. 19999 ROCKSIDE RD 44146 #496-02-1971 L1982 **OBG GS** *020 †30,55
GURD, Alan Robt. 9500 EUCLID AVE, A41 CLEVELAND CLINIC 44195 #918-01-1964 L1978 **ORS** *020 †40
GURD, David Peter. 9500 EUCLID AVE, CLEVELAND CLINIC FOUNDATIO 44195 #038-40-2000 L2000 **OP** *020
GURLEY, Jerold Paul. 7215 OLD OAK BLVD, STE A421 44130 #038-43-1989 L1994 **OSS** *020 †40
GURSAL, Kemal. ■ 44126 #902-03-1954 L1961 **IM** *071
GURUPRASAD, Khodanpur C. 12000 MCCRACKEN RD STE 460 44125 #495-33-1981 L1991 **CD IM** *020 †20
GUTGSELL, Terence Lee. 9500 EUCLID AVE, DEPT OF HEMATOLOGY/ONCOLOG 44195 #020-12-1972 L2007 **IM** *020 †20
GUTIERREZ, Yezid. 11100 EUCLID AVE 44106 #264-06-1962 L1975 **OS PTH** *071
GUTMAN, Froncie Alan. 9500 EUCLID AVE, DESK A-81 44195 #025-01-1960 L1969 **OPH** *071 †35
GUTTA, Ravi Chandra. 9500 EUCLID AVE 44195 #495-11-2002 L2006 **IM** *012
GUYURON, Bahman. 29017 CEDAR RD 44124 #517-01-1971 L1979 **PS** *020 †85,65
GYVES, Michael Thos. 11100 EUCLID AVE, STE 1200 44106 #035-20-1968 L1975 **OBG MFM** *020 †30
HA, Byeong Keun. 2500 METROHEALTH DR, METROHEALTH MED CTR 44109 #583-02-1990 L2004 **PTH** *012
HAAGA, John Robt. 11100 EUCLID AVE, STE 2600 44106 #038-40-1970 L1970 **DR** *020 †80
HAAS, Adam Jacob. 11100 EUCLID AVE, DEPT OF ANESTHESIOLOGY 44106 #038-06-1999 L1999 **PTH** *100 †05
HAAS, Edwin Nicholas. ■ 44126 #028-34-1958 L1960 **U** *071 †95
HAAS, Judith Conroy. 2500 METROHEALTH DR, METROHEALTH MEDICAL CENTER 44109 #038-06-1990 L1992 **AN** *020 †05
HACHWI, Rami Nazem. 11100 EUCLID AVE, BOLWELL 270 DEPT OF NEMOLO 44106 #875-01-1992 L2003 **N** *100 †75
HACK, Maureen. 1110 EUCLID AVE, RAINBOW BABIES & CHILDRENS 44115 #836-03-1960 L1977 **NPM** *050 †55
HACKETT, James W, II. ■ 44113 #038-41-2002 L2002 **AN** *020 †05
HADAM, Valerie. ■ 44118 #038-40-2002 L2002 **END** *012 †20
HADDAD, Abdo Salmoun. 5900 EUCLIDE AVE R40 44195 #875-03-1993 L2004 **HO** *012 †20
HADDAD, Fady Fayez. 9500 EUCLID AVE, CO CCF-GRAD MED EDU DEPT-N 44195 #605-02-1991 L2004 *020
HADDAD, Nada F. 2500 METROHEALTH DR, METRO HEALTH MEDICAL CENTE 44109 #605-02-1988 L1993 **CCP** *020 †55
HADDAD, Samar G. 5208 MEMPHIS AVE, METROHEALTH BROOKLYN 44144 #875-01-1989 L1993 **PD** *020
HADLEY, Wyatt Lee. ■ 44118 #018-03-2005 L2006 **DR** *012
HAFTKOWYCZ, Erast John. 18099 LORAIN AVE 44111 #035-45-1983 L1985 **OBG** *020 †30
HAGERTY, Robert Daniel. 2500 METROHEALTH DR, # BG-3 DEPT EM 44109 #003-01-2004 L2004 **EM** *020
HAGHPANAH, Sepideh. 2500 METROHEALTH DR 44109 #517-05-1995 L2003 **PM** *100
HAHN, David Y. 11100 EUCLID AVE, UNIVERSITY HOSPITALS CASE 44106 #038-44-1995 L1996 **P** *020 †75
HAHN, Joseph Francis. 9500 EUCLID AVE 44195 #051-01-1968 L1976 **NS** *030 †25
HAHN-SPORZYNSKI, Jadwiga. ■ 44143 #759-03-1951 L1968 **P OPH** *071
HAIDER, Masoom Abbas. 2540 N MORELAND BLVD 44120 #065-09-1986 L1994 **DR** *020 †80
HAIDER, Syed Shabbir. ■ 44115 #704-01-1999 L2005 **PCC** *012 †20
HAIMES, Jonathan L. PO BOX 18529 44118 #038-41-1992 L1994 **OBG** *020 †30
HAJJAFAR, Layla. ■ 44114 #038-44-2001 L2001 **GE** *012
HAJJ ALI, Rula Adel. 99 NORTHLINE CIR 44119 #605-01-1993 L2000 **RHU** *020 †20
HALABI, Ali S. 5316 BROADWAY AVE 44127 #875-01-1973 L1980 **GS GP** *020
HALAT, Shams Khalil. 11100 EUCLID AVE, CO UNIV HOSPS-RESIDENCY SU 44106 #605-01-2001 L2003 **PTH** *012
HALL, Gregory Lafayette. 11201 SHAKER BLVD, STE 328 44104 #038-43-1991 L1992 **IM** *020 †20
HALL, Harry Calvin. ■ 44130 #005-15-1962 L1975 **GP** *071
HALL, Philip Wells. 2109 ADELBERT RD, CASE WESTERN RESERVE UNIV 44106 #038-06-1955 L1955 **NEP IM** *040
HALL, Phillip Marvin. 9500 EUCLID AVE, # A101 44195 #038-40-1965 L1965 **NEP IM** *020 †20
HALLAK, Laura. 2500 METROHEALTH DR 44109 #649-33-2000 L2005 **FP** *012
HALLAK, Nicholas Yaacoub. 2500 METROHEALTH DR 44109 #306-01-2003 L2004 **OBG** *012
HALLE, Austin A, III. 11100 EUCLID AVE, UNIVERSITY HOSPITALS 44106 #047-06-1982 L2005 **CD IM** *020 †20
HALLER, Robert John. 25001 EMERY RD, STE 100 44128 #038-06-1988 L1990 **DR** *020 †80
HALLEY, Carmel Mary. 9500 EUCLID AVE, CO CCF-GRAD MED EDU DEPT-N 44195 #539-04-1999 L2001 **IM** *100
HALLEY, Heber Myron. 7225 OLD OAK BLVD 44130 #038-06-1957 L1957 **OBG** *071
HALL MENNES, Mary C. 11100 EUCLID AVE, UHHS DEPT OF PSYCH 44106 #038-06-2000 L2007 **CHP** *020
HALLORAN, Christian C. 11100 EUCLID AVE, BHC5064 44106 #038-06-2003 L2006 **EM** *100 †16

HALLOWELL, Peter Thomas. 11100 EUCLID AVE, UNIVERSITY HOSP. OF CLEVEL 44106 #010-03-1994 L1996 **GS** *020 †85
HAMADE, Haya Maged. 11100 EUCLID AVE 44106 #605-01-2005 L2006 **PD** *012
HAMBOULIDES, Christos P. ■ 44120 #418-01-1966 L1974 **IM NEP** *020
HAMDAN, Ayad Riad. 11100 EUCLID AVE, UNIV HOSP OF CLEVELAND 44106 #605-01-2003 L2005 **IM** *012
HAMID, Nauman. 2500 METROHEALTH DR 44109 #305-01-2007 L2007 **IM** *012
HAMIEH, Tarek S. 9500 EUCLID AVE, MEDICINE/ S-70 44195 #305-01-2003 L2007 **IM** *020
HAMMARBERG, Larry Donald. 18697 BAGLEY RD 44130 #041-09-1962 L1966 **TS** *071
HAMMER, Donald Frank. EUCLID A, CLEVELAND CLINIC 950 44195 #038-40-1978 L1979 **CD IM** *020 †20
HAMMOND, Bethanie Rae. CLEVELAND CLINIC FDN, DEPT OF DIAGNOSTIC RAD HB6 44195 #020-02-2005 L2007 **DR** *012
HAMMOND, Louis Eugene. 11201 SHAKER BLVD, STE 240 44104 #010-03-1957 L1961 **OBG OS** *030
HAMMOND-MONTIER, Carolyn. ■ 44120 #010-03-1949 L1957 **P FM** *072
HAMOGEORGAKIS, Themistokl. 11100 EUCLID AVE, UNIV HOSPITALS OF CLEVELAN 44106 #418-01-1992 L2000 **TS** *085,90
HAMPEL, Nehemia. 14100 CEDAR RD STE 130, WATERSTOWN MED 44121 #550-01-1969 L1978 **U** *020 †95
HAMRAHIAN, Amir Hekmat. 9500 EUCLID AVE, DEPT OF ENDOCRINOLOGY, DIA 44195 #902-05-1991 L1997 **END** *020 †20
HAMROCK, David Joseph. 9500 EUCLID AVE, DEPT OF DERMATOLOGY 44195 #038-43-1999 L1999 **D** *020 †15 ‡
HAMZA, Nashaat Sobhi. ■ 44123 #915-07-1986 L1999 **IM ID** *020 †20
HAN, Anne. ■ 44114 #035-01-2007 L2007 **IM** *012
HANAOKA, Beatriz Yae. 9500 EUCLID AVE 44195 #187-04-2004 L2005 **IM** *012
HANCOCK, Mary Ellen. 2500 METROHEALTH DR, METRO HLTH MED DEPT EMERG 44109 #038-06-1993 L1994 **EM** *020 †16
HANCOCK, Robert Arthur. ■ 44133 #038-06-1992 L1993 **EM** *020 †16
HANICAK, John Edward. 11709 LORAIN AVE, CLEVELAND OHIO 44111 44111 #038-45-1999 L1999 **FM** *020 †18
HANIFF, Imraan. ■ 44139 #305-01-1988 L1993 **PUD** *020 †20
HANNA, Dina Saad Makram. 9500 EUCLID AVE 44106 #915-02-1994 L2001 **AN** *100 †05
HANNA, Haifa. 6770 MAYFIELD RD # 333 44124 #875-01-1964 L1972 **NEP IM** *020
HANNA, Joseph Patrick. 5208 MEMPHIS AVE 44144 #038-41-1988 L1989 **N** *020 †75
HANNA, Mazen Andrew. 9500 EUCLID AVE, 2627 FENWICK RD 44195 #038-40-1998 L2002 **CD** *100 †20
HANNA, Waad. 11100 EUCLID AVE, DEPT RAD 44106 #028-34-2006 L2007 **DR** *012
HANNAHOE, Brigid Mary. 9500 EUCLID AVE L25 44195 #035-06-2001 L2001 **PTH** *020 †50
HANSEL, Donna Jaworsky. 9500 EUCLID AVE, STE L25 44195 #023-07-2001 L2006 **PTH** *020 †50
HAR, Aileen Frances. 9500 EUCLID AVE, DEPT OF PEDIATRICS 44195 #539-06-2005 L2005 **PD** *012
HARDACRE, Jeffrey Max. 11100 EUCLID AVE, UNIVERSITY HOSPITALS CASE 44106 #036-07-1996 L2003 **GS** *020 †85
HARDACRE, Jon Allan. 12000 MCCRACKEN RD STE 251 44125 #038-40-1964 L1964 **ORS** *071 †40
HARDERS, Maureen Storen. 4330 W 150TH ST 44135 #025-07-1990 L1998 **AN** *020 †05
HARDING, Clifford Vincent. 11400 EUCLID AVE STE 100 44106 #028-02-1985 L1993 **ATP IG** *050
HARDY, Brian Thomas. ■ 44113 #051-01-2003 L2003 **ORS** *012
HARE, Donald Eugene. ■ 44142 #407-05-1956 L1961 **IM PDE** *020
HARIA, Chandravadan Damji. 7215 OLD OAK BLVD, STE A414 44130 #495-01-1966 L1976 **OTO HNS** *020 †45
HARIDAS, Manjunath. 11100 EUCLID AVE 44106 #496-39-2000 L2007 **GS** *012
HARKEY, Paul Peter. 2500 METROHEALTH DR 44109 #038-43-2005 L2005 **DR** *012
HARLAN, Richard Curtis. 10654 LORAIN AVE, WESTOWN PHYSICIAN CENTER 44111 #038-06-1991 L1993 **OBG** *020 †30
HARPELL, Gabrielle Lee. 11100 EUCLID AVE, UNIV HOSP 44106 #041-15-2007 L2007 **PD** *012
HARR, Sidney Beauvard, Jr. ■ 44120 #040-02-1974 L1976 **EM** *020
HARRAZ, Madiha El-Sayed. 9500 EUCLID AVE 44195 #330-03-1969 **ATP CLP** *020
HARRINGTON, Michael D. 2500 METROHEALTH DR, INTERNAL MEDICINE 44109 #038-40-1994 L1995 **IM IMG** *020 †20
HARRIS, Allan Harvey. 4200 WARRENSVILLE CENTR RD, STE 420 44122 #011-02-1959 L1963 **CD IM** *020
HARRIS, Andrew Christophe. ■ 44195 #038-06-2005 L2005 **PD** *012
HARRIS, C Martin. 9500 EUCLID AVE H18, CLEVELAND CLINIC FOUNDATIO 44195 #041-01-1982 L1996 **IM** *040 †20
HARRIS, Christopher E. 3100 WOOSTER RD 44116 #038-40-1981 L1982 **OPH** *020 †35
HARRIS, James. 1 INFINITY CORPORT CNTR DR, NORTH SHORE 44125 #038-40-1976 L1978 **GE IM** *020 †20
HARRIS, Mariel Ann. 12200 FAIRHILL RD, 3RD FL 44120 #016-02-1977 L1987 **IM** *020 †20
HARRIS, Mark Joseph. 18697 BAGLEY RD, SOUTHWEST GENERAL HEALTH C 44130 #038-43-2004 L2004 **EM** *100
HARRIS, Michael Andrew. 2500 METROHEALTH DR, METROHEALTH MC REHAB PAV 44109 #035-08-1987 L1992 **PM** *020 †60
HARRIS, Wm Theophilus. 6780 MAYFIELD RD 44124 #041-13-1958 L1979 **OBG** *071 †30
HARRISON, Alexander Marc. 2801 MARTIN LTHR KNG JR DR 44104 #032-01-1990 L1999 **CCP** *020 †55
HARRY, Onengiya. ■ 44106 #036-05-2008 *012
HART, Meeghan Anne. 2101 ADELBERT RD, STE 3001 44106 #035-06-1996 L2000 **PDP** *020
HART, William Roy. 9500 EUCLID AVE, L-21 44195 #025-01-1965 L1981 **PTH** *071 †50
HARTE, Brian Jeffrey. 9500 EUCLID AVE S70, CLEVELAND CLINIC FOUNDATIO 44195 #041-01-1996 L2004 **IM** *020 †20
HARTKE, David Marc. 11100 EUCLID AVE 44106 #012-05-2002 L2002 **U** *012
HARTKE, Lopa Patel. 11100 EUCLID AVE, C/O UNIV HOSPS-RESIDENCY O 44106 #012-05-2002 L2002 **PDC** *012 †20,55
HARTLEY, John Edward. 9500 EUCLID AVE, C/O CCF-GRAD MED DEPT- 44195 #917-32-1990 L2000 **CRS** *100
HARTWELL, Shattuck W, Jr. 9500 EUCLID AVE 44195 #025-01-1954 L1963 **PS** *071 †65
HARWELL, Carla Michelle. 8819 QUINCY AVE 44106 #038-41-1995 L1998 **IM** *020 †20
HASHI, Mohamed Jama. 18200 LORAIN AVE, DEPT OF FAMILY PRAC 44111 #561-31-1993 L2004 **FM** *020 †18
HASHIMOTO, Koji. 9500 EUCLID AVE, DEPT OF GME 44195 #572-12-1995 L2006 *100

HASHKES, Philip Joseph. 9500 EUCLID AVE, CLEVELAND CLINIC FOUNDATIO 44195 #550-01-1988 L1996 **PPR** *020

HASSAN, Manal Ismail. 9500 EUCLID AVE 44195 #915-02-1985 L2000 **AN** *020

HASSAN, Medhat Omar. 10701 EAST BLVD 44106 #915-02-1961 L1982 **PTH** *020 †50

HATHWAY, Denzil. ■ 44116 #352-01-1959 L1969 **PTH OS** *071 †50

HATTERS-FRIEDMAN, S J. 11100 EUCLID AVE, HANNA PAVILION 44106 #038-06-1999 L1999 **PFP** *020

HAUK-PETRIGALLA, Maria. ■ 44129 #957-01-1947 L1970 **GP PTH** *071 †50

HAUSE-WARDEGA, Katarzyna. 2322 E 22ND ST, STE 200 44115 #759-10-1993 L1999 **IM** *020 †20

HAWI, Riem. 9500 EUCLID AVE 44195 #409-38-2004 L2007 **IM** *012

HAWTHORN, Brendan Andrew. 2500 METROHEALTH DR, CO METROHEALTH MED CTR-RES 44109 #047-06-2003 L2003 **EM** *020

HAWWA, Abdu George. 12000 MCCRACKEN RD, STE 460 44125 #605-01-1977 L1984 **CD IM** *020 †20

HAXHIU-ERHARDT, Lendita. 2500 METROHEALTH DR, 8TH FL 44109 #957-09-1989 L1999 **P** *020 †75

HAYDEN, Stephen Peter. 9500 EUCLID AVE, CLEVELAND CLINICFOUNDATION 44195 #917-25-1968 L1980 **IM PUD** *020 †20

HAYEK, Selim Michel. 11100 EUCLID AVE, UNIV HOSPS OFCLEVELAND 44106 #605-01-1991 L1996 **APM** *020 †05

HAYNE, Gregory Walter. 7575 NORTHCLIFF AVE 44144 #038-06-1984 L1985 **IM** *020 †20

HAYNESWORTH, Dominic Todd. ■ 44121 #024-07-1979 L1981 **GS** *020 †16

HAZEN, Stanley Leon. 9500 EUCLID AVE, NC10 44195 #028-02-1992 L1997 **END** *020 †20

HAZLETT, David Damion, Jr. 11200 EUCLID AVE 44106 #038-41-2001 L2001 **DR** *100 †80

HEADEN, David Jerome. 13301 MILES 44105 #038-06-1991 L1992 **IM** *020 †20

HEATHER, John Andrew. 11400 EUCLID AVE STE 200, MOOD DISORDERS PROGRAM 44106 #035-06-1992 L1996 **P** *020 †20

HEBBAR, Ramnath Balakrish. 2500 METROHEALTH DR, METRO HEALTH MEDICAL CENTE 44109 #495-99-1998 L2004 **IM** *100 †20

HEBERT, Chris John. 9500 EUCLID AVE, CLEVELAND CLINIC FOUNDATIO 44195 #038-40-1992 L1999 **IM** *020 †20

HEBERT, Katherine Anne. 11100 EUCLID AVE, UNIV HOSP 44106 #025-07-2007 L2007 **PD** *012

HECHT, Carrie Rose. ■ 44114 #025-07-2007 L2007 **EM** *012

HECHT, Yehuda Ervin. ■ 44121 #550-02-1979 L1987 *100

HECKER, Michelle Theresa. 2500 METROHEALTH DR, RM C-2001 44109 #016-02-1990 L1992 **ID** *020 †20

HEDRICK, David Paul. 6707 POWERS BLVD, STE 205 44129 #038-06-1999 L1999 **IC** *100 †20

HEEGER, Peter Scott. 9500 EUCLID AVE, NB30 44195 #041-01-1984 L1993 **IM NEP** *020 †20

HEGARTY, Joel Mcclay. 18697 BAGLEY RD, SOUTHWEST ANESTHESIOLOGY G 44130 #038-06-1989 L1990 **AN** *020 †05

HEGARTY, Nicholas John. 9500 EUCLID AVE, CLEVELAND CLINIC FOUNDATIO 44195 #539-02-1992 L2005 *100

HEGDE, Shura Sanjiv. 6780 MAYFIELD RD 44124 #913-89-1983 L1995 **P** *020 †75

HEGERFELDT, Yael. 2500 METROHEALTH DR, CO METROHEALTH MED CTR-RES 44109 #409-44-2001 L2002 **HO** *012 †20

HEGGIE, Alfred Dineley. RAINBOW BABIES HOSP 44106 #035-45-1956 L1963 **PD ID** *040 †55

HEIPLE, Kingsbury Graff. 2074 ABINGTON RD 44106 #016-02-1953 L1958 **ORS HS** *071 †40

HELFAND, Marion Skalweit. 10701 EAST BLVD, VA MEDICAL CTR 44106 #038-06-1996 L1997 **ID** *020 †20

HELFAND, Toby Scheintaub. 1611 S GREEN RD, STE 56 44121 #038-06-1957 L1957 **D** *071 †15

HELFGOTT, Roberta L K. 9500 EUCLID AVE 44195 #010-01-1972 L2002 **DR** *071

HELLERSTEIN, Elizabeth L. 1611 S GREEN RD, STE 35 44121 #038-06-1991 L1992 **PD** *020 †55

HELLERSTEIN, Mary Feil. ■ 44106 #038-06-1949 L1949 **PD** *040

HELM, Nicola Alger. 2500 METROHEALTH DR, METRO HEALTH MEDICAL CENTE 44109 #308-10-1987 L1992 **IM** *020 †20

HELMI, Hany Medhat. 2500 METROHEALTH DR, METROHEALTH MED CTR 44109 #820-02-2005 L2005 **PM** *012

HELOU, Joe. ■ 44195 #065-09-1991 L2000 *020

HELPER, Stephen Dunn. 29001 CEDAR RD, STE 519 44124 #038-06-1983 L1984 **ORS** *020 †40

HEMMINGSEN, Evelyn Morley. ■ 44135 #038-06-2008 **FP** *012

HENDERSON, John Michael. 9500 EUCLID AVE, E32 DIV SURG 44195 #803-02-1969 L1992 **GS** *020

HENDRICKSON, Marissa Anne. ■ 44118 #038-06-2001 L2001 **PEM** *012 †55

HENDRICKSON, Mark F. 9500 EUCLID AVE, SECTION A40 44195 #010-02-1985 L1995 **HS PS** *020 †85,65

HENDRYX, Paula Victoria. 2500 METROHEALTH DR, RM G231F 44109 #038-44-1987 L1989 **OBG** *020 †30

HENG, Daniel. 11477 MAYFIELD RD, APT 902 44106 #060-02-2002 L2007 **HO** *100

HENNEIN, Hani A. 11100 EUCLID AVE STE 380, RAINBOW BABIES & CHILDREN' 44106 #016-43-1984 L2001 **PDS CD** *020 †90,85

HENNESSEY, Tara M. 2500 METROHEALTH DR 44109 #035-03-1998 L2000 **FPG** *020 †20

HENNING, Janelle Louise. 18200 LORAIN AVE 44111 #038-06-2003 L2003 **FM** *100 †18

HENRICKS, Walter Henry. 9500 EUCLID AVE 44195 #025-01-1991 L1997 **PTH OS** *020 †50

HENRY, Catherine Ann. 9500 EUCLID AVE, 871 44195 #025-07-1985 L1994 **IM OS** *020 †20

HERCBERGS, Aleck Arje. 18200 LORAIN AVE 44111 #836-02-1967 L1991 **DR** *020 †80

HERESI DAVILA, Gustavo Ad. ■ 44195 #737-05-2000 L2005 **PCC** *012 †20

HERIOT, Alexander Graham. 9500 EUCLID AVE, CO CCF-GRAD MED EDU DEPT-N 44195 #917-03-1991 L2003 *020

HERNANDEZ, Katya Miroslav. ■ 44114 #016-11-2005 L2005 **AN** *012

HERNANDEZ, Rose Aileen. 2900 DETROIT AVE, RECOVERY RESOURCES 44113 #048-02-1993 L1997 **P PFP** *020 †75

HERRAN, Maria Isabel. 11100 EUCLID AVE 44106 #042-01-1977 L1990 **PD** *020 †55

HERRON, Charles Andrew. 11100 SAINT CLAIR AVE 44108 #038-06-1962 L1962 **IM GPM** *071

HERTS, Brian R. 9500 EUCLID AVE, STE 100 44195 #041-01-1987 L1992 **DR** *020 †80

HERTZER, Norman Ray. 9500 EUCLID AVE, EMERITUS OFFICES EE-40 44195 #017-20-1967 L1976 **VS** *050 †85

HEUPLER, Frederick A, Jr. 9500 EUCLID AVE, CLEVELAND CLINIC 44195 #041-01-1963 L1966 **CD** *020 †20

HEUR, Jin H. 11100 EUCLID AVE 44106 #005-14-1999 L1999 **PD** *020 †55

HEUR, Martin Junmin. ■ 44195 #038-41-2004 L2004 **OPH** *012

HEVI, Delali Kodzo. 13951 TERRACE RD 44112 #412-01-2003 L2005 **IM** *012

HEYEN, Francoise. 9500 EUCLID AVE BOX 550 44195 #067-02-1981 **CRS** *020 †85

HEYKA, Robert Jos. 9500 EUCLID AVE, CLEVELAND CLINIC 44195 #025-07-1981 L1986 **IM NEP** *020 †20

HEYSE, Walter Erich. 18660 BAGLEY RD 44130 #038-40-1955 L1955 **ORS** *020 †40

HIBBS, Anna Maria. 2101 ADELBERT RD 44106 #041-01-2000 L2006 **PD** *020 †55 ‡

HIGGINS, Thomas Francis. 18101 LORAIN AVE, FAIRVIEW HOSPITAL 44111 #038-06-1985 L1990 **EM** *020 †16

HIGHAM, Susan. 2500 METROHEALTH DR, METROHEALTH MEDICAL CENTER 44109 #041-07-1977 L1980 **IM END** *020 †20

HIJAZ, Adonis Khezaee. 9500 EUCLID AVE, CLEVELAND CLINIC FOUNDATIO 44195 #605-01-1995 L2002 *020

HILA, Sorana. 9500 EUCLID AVE, CLEVELAND CLINIC FOUNDATIO 44195 #781-05-1992 L2002 **IM** *100 †20

HILDEBRANDT, Gerhard Carl. 11100 EUCLID AVE 44106 #409-32-1997 **PD** *012

HILEMAN, Craig Michael. 7123 PEARL RD, STE 201 44130 #038-44-2003 L2005 **FM** *020 †18

HILL, Elizaeth Beu. 6559 WILSON MILLS RD, STE 102 44143 #038-06-1977 L1979 **PD** *074 †55,75

HILL, Richard Ray. 2900 DETROIT AVE 44113 #038-06-1992 L1994 **P ADM** *020

HILLIER, Sherry Ann. 25001 EMERY RD STE 100, DRS. HILL & THOMAS CO. 44128 #038-06-1992 L1997 **DR** *020 †20

HINDEN, Ira. 9500 EUCLID AVE 44195 #035-06-1965 L1966 **FM** *020 †18 ‡

HIONIS, Marinos D. 25701 N LAKELAND BLVD 44132 #418-01-1958 L1965 **OPH** *071

HIROSE, Kenzo. 9500 EUCLID AVE, DESK A-110 44195 #024-01-1999 L2006 **GS** *020

HIRSCH, Christina Susanne. 10900 EUCLID AVE, CWRU DIV INF DISEASES 44106 #409-20-1987 L1992 **IM** *050 †20

HIRSCHFELD, Seth Nelson. 11100 EUCLID AVE 44106 #038-06-1971 L1973 **PD PDA** *020 †55

HIRSCHMANN, Hans. 2065 ADELBERT RD 44106 #869-01-1934 *050

HIRSH, Alex Todd. 6551 WILSON MILLS RD, STE 101 44143 #038-40-1998 L2002 **D** *020 †15

HIRSH, Fred Stanley. 6551 WILSON MILLS RD, STE 101 44143 #038-40-1972 L1972 **D** *020 †15

HIRT, Nada Mahmoud. 9500 EUCLID AVE # TT32 44195 #605-01-1988 **AN** *100

HISAMOCHI, Kunikazu. 9500 EUCLID AVE, C/O CCF-GRAD MED EDU DEPT- 44195 #572-09-1988 L2000 **PDC** *100

HISAMUDDIN, Kola. 2500 METROHEALTH DR, METROHEALTH MED CTR 44109 #495-99-1994 L2003 **GE** *012 †20

HIZON, Raul Pagsanjan. 1708 SOUTHPOINT DR, CARE 44109 #748-10-1992 L2001 **P** *020

HO, Simon G. ■ 44195 #016-11-2002 L2006 **AN** *100

HOBAN, Jeremy Charles. 9500 EUCLID AVE, CLEVELAND CLINIC FOUNDATIO 44195 #038-43-1999 L1999 **CCA** *020 †05

HOBAN, Monica Garcia. 2500 METROHEALTH DR, A-109 44109 #038-43-1999 L1999 **PD** *020 †55

HOBART, Michael Gray. 9500 EUCLID AVE, DESK A-81 44195 #060-01-1990 L1998 *020

HOBBS, Robert Edward. 9500 EUCLID AVE, CLEVELAND CLINIC F-25 44195 #041-02-1974 L1977 **CD IM** *020 †20

HODGMAN, James Ranck. 9500 EUCLID AVE, MS F15 44195 #025-01-1959 L1966 **CD IM** *071 †20

HOELTGE, Gerald Adrian. 9500 EUCLID AVE, CLEVELAND CLINIC FOUND 44195 #038-06-1917 L1967 **BBK CLP** *100 †50

HOFFER, Seth Alan. 11100 EUCLID AVE, C/O UNIV HOSPS-NEUROSURGER 44106 #035-45-2001 L2001 **NS** *012

HOFFMAN, Byron K. 21755 BROOKPARK RD 44126 #038-06-1953 L1953 **ORS GS** *071 †40

HOFFMAN, Gary Stuart. CLEVELAND CLINIC A50, DEPT OF RHEUMATIC & 44195 #051-04-1971 L1992 **RHU** *030 †20

HOFFMAN, Robert D, II. 11400 EUCLID AVE STE 100 44106 #023-07-1984 L1992 **ATP** *020 †20

HOFFMANN, Gerhard. ■ 44113 #869-02-1934 L1949 **P** *071

HOIT, Brian D. 11100 EUCLID AVE 44106 #016-11-1979 L1988 **CD IM** *050 †20

HOLAN, Jane Elizabeth. 11100 EUCLID AVE, DEPT OF PEDIATRICS 44106 #028-34-1979 L1986 **PD** *020 †55

HOLMES, Laura Lee. 9500 EUCLID AVE 44195 #041-13-1988 L1990 **IM** *020 †20

HOLT, Joseph Paynter. CASE WESTERN UNIV, DEPT OBG 44106 #020-02-1936 L1936 **OS** *050

HOLZBACH, R Thomas, Jr. 9500 EUCLID AVE, CLEVELAND CLINIC 44195 #038-06-1955 L1955 **GE IM** *071 †20

HOLZHEIMER, Richard E. 18599 LAKE SHORE BLVD, UNIVERSITY MEDNET 44119 #038-40-1965 L1965 **OBG** *071 †20

HONARI, Golara. ■ 44124 #517-11-1999 L2001 **IM** *020 †20

HONDA, Kord Shuji. 11100 EUCLID AVE, BOLWELL 3109 44106 #005-02-1999 L2006 **DMP** *100 †20,15

HONG, Raymond Sungwan. 11100 EUCLID AVE, UHHS/CWRU 44106 #038-44-1996 L2002 **RHU** *020 †20

HONGALGI, Krishnakumar Du. 2500 METROHEALTH DR 44109 #495-35-1997 L2004 **NEP** *012 †20

HOOD, Carrie Nicole. ■ 44111 #016-11-2008 *012

HOOGWERF, Byron James. 9500 EUCLID AVE 44195 #026-04-1971 L1985 **END IM** *020 †20

HOPPEL, Charles Leslie. 10701 EAST BLVD 44106 #028-34-1962 L1971 **PA IM** *050 †20

HOREJS, David Jos. 25001 EMERY RD, STE 100 44128 #038-41-1984 L1990 **DR** *020 †20

HORENSTEIN, Craig Israel. 9500 EUCLID AVE, C/O CCF-GRAD MED EDU DEPT- 44195 #035-19-2003 L2003 **DR** *012

HORN, Christopher Martin. ■ 44121 #025-07-2005 L2005 **N** *012

HORN, Rebecca Blank. ■ 44106 #041-13-2003 L2003 **GS** *100

HORNICK, Thomas Richard. 12000 FAIRHILL RD 44106 #023-01-1983 L1986 **IMG** *020 †20

HOROWITZ, Andrew I. ■ 44118 #043-01-2007 L2007 **GS** *012

HOROWITZ, Karen Ruth. 11100 EUCLID AVE, UNIVERSITY HOSPITALS OF CL 44106 #035-06-1983 L1986 **DIA IM** *020 †20

HORVATH, Edward Philip. 10701 EAST BLVD 44106 #038-40-1971 L1971 **OM IM** *020 †20,70

HORWITZ, Leonard Jos. 9500 EUCLID AVE, R 35 44195 #035-46-1977 L1989 **ON HEM** *020 †20

HORWITZ, Ralph Irving. 10900 EUCLID AVE 44106 #041-14-1973 L2003 **IM** *050 †20

HOSCHAR, Aaron Philip. ■ 44195 #041-15-2000 L2000 **PTH** *100 †50

HOSKINS, Lansing C. 10701 EAST BLVD, LOUIS STOKES VA MED CTR 44106 #035-45-1954 L1964 **GE IM** *050 †20

HOU, Betty Whitshuan. 18200 LORAIN AVE 44111 #016-06-1999 L1999 **GS** *020

HOUSE, Jonathan David. 18200 LORAIN AVE 44111 #017-20-2002 L2002 **AN** *100

HOUSER, Harold B. CASE W RESRV UNIV SC MED 44106 #017-20-1944 L1958 **GPM IM** *050 †20

HOUSER, Steven Michael. 4330 W 150TH ST 44135 #038-40-1993 L1996 **OTO A** *020 †45

HOWARD, Michael William. 9500 EUCLID AVE, CO CCF-GRAD MED EDU DEPT-N 44195 #231-03-1992 L2000 *100

HOWARD, Randy. 2500 METROHEALTH DR, METROHEALTH MED CTR 44109 #020-12-1999 L1999 **GE** *020 †20

HOYEN, Harry Alexander. 2500 METROHEALTH DR, RM H629 44109 #056-06-1992 L1994 **ORS** *020 †40

■ = Address Information Privacy Protected

HOYT, Charles Russell. 7225 OLD OAK BLVD 44130 #748-08-1966 L1970 **GPM FSM** *020

HRICIK, Donald Edward. 11100 EUCLID AVE 44106 #010-02-1977 L1982 **IM NEP** *020 †20

HRINCZENKO, Borys Walter. 2500 METROHEALTH DR, CANCER CARE PAVILION 44109 #035-08-1992 L2004 **HEM HO** *050 †20

HRUBY, Ferdinand Joseph H. 3461 WARRENSVILLE CENTR RD 44122 #010-02-1943 L1943 **IM END** *071 †20

HSEU, Anne Feng. ■ 44113 #016-06-2007 L2007 **OTO** *012

HSI, Eric Darryl. 9500 EUCLID AVE 44195 #025-01-1990 L1997 **HMP** *020 †50

HSIA, Augusto Tan, Jr. 9500 EUCLID AVE # C21, SPINE INSTITUTE 44195 #748-16-1993 L2000 **RHU IM** *020 †20

HSICH, Eileen. 9500 EUCLID AVE F-25, CLEVELAND CLINIC FNDTN 44195 #023-07-1994 L2004 **CD** *020 †20

HSICH, Gary Evan. 9500 EUCLID AVE, S 51 44195 #023-07-1996 L2004 **CHN** *020

HSIEH, Fred. 9500 EUCLID AVE, ALLERGY SECTION / C22 44195 #043-01-1995 L2001 **AI IM** *020 †20,03

HSU, Daniel Pierce. 11100 EUCLID AVE, STE 2600 44106 #012-01-1999 L1999 **RNR** *020 †80

HSU, John Tseng-Tung. 2074 ABINGTON RD, DEPT OF RADIOLOGY 44106 #385-03-1957 L1991 **R** *020 †80

HU, Yin Chih. ■ 44106 #016-42-2004 L2004 **NS** *012

HUANG, Alex Yeechen. 11100 EUCLID AVE, MS: 6054 44106 #023-07-1997 L2007 **PHO IG** *050 †55

HUANG, Deren. 5566 ELM HILL DR 44195 #243-58-1986 L2004 **N** *012

HUANG, Jerry Iming. 11100 EUCLID AVE, CO UNIV HOSPS-RESIDENCY OF 44106 #005-14-2001 L2001 **HSO** *012

HUANG, Jiunn Shyong. ■ 44124 #244-02-1970 L1974 **AN** *071 †05

HUANG, Julie Chahuey. 9500 EUCLID AVE, DEPT OF CARDIOLOGY / F15 44195 #023-07-1991 L2001 **IM** *020 †20

HUANG, Lennox Hungchia. 11100 EUCLID AVE 44106 #065-01-1997 L2000 **CCP** *020 †55

HUANG, Shu Quey. 3395 SCRANTON RD 44109 #244-02-1970 L1974 **PM R** *020 †60

HUANG, Steve Shihlin. 9500 EUCLID AVE, DEPARTMENT OF NUCLEAR MEDI 44195 #041-01-2003 L2007 **NM** *100 †28

HUANG, Suber S. 11100 EUCLID AVE, WEARN 646 44106 #035-46-1985 L1990 **OPH** *020 †35

HUDEC, John A. 4229 PEARL RD 44109 #010-02-1944 L1945 **GP GS** *071

HUGHES, Gordon B. 9500 EUCLID AVE A-71, CLEVELAND CLINIC 44195 #038-06-1974 L1976 **OTO** *020 †45

HUGHES, Robert Francis. ■ 44130 #539-02-1959 L1961 **OBG OBS** *071

HUHN, Ronald G. 4949 GALAXY PKWY, STE U 44128 #030-06-1976 L1987 **PTH** *020 †50

HULL, Alan Lawrence. 9500 EUCLID AVE, CLEVELAND CLINIC/E13 44195 #038-06-1996 L1997 **IM** *040 †20

HUNT, Jennifer Leigh. 9500 EUCLID AVE 44195 #041-01-1997 L2005 **PTH** *020 †50

HUNTER, Maria Jean. 10900 EUCLID AVE, CWRU HEALTH SERVICES 44106 #038-40-1993 L1995 **IM** *020 †20

HUNTER, William Lee. ■ 44106 #010-03-1967 L1972 **R** *020

HUPERTZ, Vera Frantsov. 9500 EUCLID AVE A111, CLEVELAND CLINIC FNDTATIO 44195 #035-45-1982 L1984 **GE PD** *020 †55

HURD, William Ward. 11100 EUCLID AVE, MAC 5034 44106 #001-02-1979 L1980 **OBG REN** *030 †30

HURLEY-KUNZ, Maja Elisabe. 9500 EUCLID AVE, CO CCF-GRAD MED EDU DEPT-N 44195 #869-05-1989 L2001 *100

HUSAIN, Khawaja Omair. 2500 METROHEALTH DR, METROHEALTH MED CTR 44109 #704-01-1997 L2004 **IM** *012

HUSSAIN, Junaid Akhtar. 11100 EUCLID AVE, UNIV HOSP OF CLEVELAND 44106 #704-02-2001 L2007 **CHP** *012

HUSSAIN, Rafiq A. 15008 LORAIN AVE 44111 #704-02-1962 L1972 **NEP CCM** *020

HUSSAIN, Sarah Khalid. 9500 EUCLID AVE, CLEVELAND CLINIC FNDTATIO 44195 #704-25-2004 L2006 **IM** *012

HUSSAIN, Syed Tarique. 9500 EUCLID AVE, CLEVELAND CLINIC FNDTATIO 44195 #495-36-1998 L2006 *100

HUSSAIN, Tanveer. 3929 ROCKY RIVER DR, CENTER FOR FAM AND CHILDRE 44111 #704-02-1990 L1998 **P CHP** *020 †75

HUSSEIN, Hassan. 18101 LORAIN AVE, DEPT OF INTERNAL MED 44111 #875-01-2005 L2006 *100

HUSSNY, Sayed M. ■ 44124 #330-03-1956 L1972 **OBG IM** *072

HUSTEY, Fredric Michael. 9500 EUCLID AVE, CLEVELAND CLINIC FOUNDATIO 44195 #038-40-1994 L1996 **EM** *020 †16

HUTCHINSON, Richard C. ■ 44102 #024-01-1958 L1967 **P** *071 †75

HUTSON, Phyllis Anne C. ■ 44110 #038-06-1976 L1977 **PD OS** *020 †55

HUTZLER, Jeffery Conway. 9500 EUCLID AVE, P57 44195 #038-40-1969 L1969 **P** *071 †75

IAMPHONGSAI, Seree. 11100 EUCLID AVE, C/O UNIV HOSP-RESIDENCY OF 44106 #891-02-1998 L2003 **PS** *012

IANNOTTI, Christopher Ant. ■ 44195 #028-34-2004 L2004 **NS** *012

IBEN, Sabine Claudia. 9500 EUCLID AVE, CLEVELAND CLINIC FOUNDATIO 44195 #409-37-1993 L1996 **NPM PD** *020 †55 ‡

IBRAHIM, Andra Elizabeth. 9500 EUCLID AVE, G-30 DEPT & CARDIOTHORACIC 44195 #026-04-1990 L2001 **AN CCA** *020 †05

IBRAHIM, Osama Ahmed Abde. 11100 EUCLID AVE 44106 #915-04-1995 L2004 **CD** *100 †20

IBRAHIM, Rim Said Mohamed. 11100 EUCLID AVE 44106 #915-04-1996 L2001 **CHP** *100 †75

IBRAHIM, Said Aidid. 11100 EUCLID AVE 44106 #038-06-1993 L1996 **IM** *020 †20

IBRAHIM, Sally Monir. 9500 EUCLID AVE, FA20 44195 #048-02-2003 L2003 **SME** *012

IBRAHIM, Samuel Assad Ami. CO GME - NA23, CLEVELAND CLINIC FOUNDATIO 44195 #915-04-2001 L2007 **GS** *012

IDITOIU, Cristian Stefan. 18101 LORAIN AVE, FAIRVIEW HOSPITAL 44111 #781-03-1995 L2000 **AN** *020 †05 ‡

IDRISS, Nauras Nizar. 9500 EUCLID AVE, CO CCF-GRAD MED DEPT-NA23 44195 #654-01-1994 L2000 **AN** *100

IDURU, Venkata Satish. 2500 METROHEALTH DR, METROHEALTH MED CTR 44109 #495-11-1999 L2004 **GE** *012 †20

IFTIKHAR, Imran Hasan. 18101 LORAIN AVE, FAIRVIEW HOSPITAL 44111 #704-20-2004 L2005 **IM** *012

IGNACIO-FRANCISCO, Meade. 13301 MILES AVE 44105 #748-02-1978 L1996 **PD** *020 †55

IKOMI, Jolomi Tubogbanimi. 9500 EUCLID AVE, DEPT OF GME 44195 #690-01-2002 L2006 **P** *012

ILASLAN, Hakan. 99 NORTHLINE CIR 44119 #902-19-1994 L2002 **DR** *020 †80

ILER, Mark Alan. 9500 EUCLID AVE, C/O CARDIOLOGY FELLOWSHIP, 44195 #038-40-1999 L2003 **IM** *020 †20

INDURU, Raghava Reddy. 2351 E 22ND ST, DEPT OF MEDICAL EDUCATION 44115 #495-37-2001 L2005 **IM** *012

INFELD, Michael David. 2500 METROHEALTH DR 44109 #016-11-1983 L1986 **IM PUD** *050 †20

INKLEY, Scott R. 2074 ABINGTON RD 44106 #038-06-1945 L1945 **IM PUD** *071 †20

INTON, Maria Rica Garcia. 9500 EUCLID AVE, DEPT OF GEN ANESTHESIA E-3 44195 #748-10-1992 L2000 **AN** *020 †05

INTRALAWAN, Daranee. 11100 EUCLID AVE, BOLWELL 1200 44106 #891-02-2002 L2007 **FP** *012

IONESCU, Daniel. 2500 METROHEALTH DR, DEPARTMENT OF PSYCHIATRY 44109 #781-03-1998 L2007 *100 †75

IOVI, Mihaela Ruxandra. 2351 E 22ND ST, STE 3W 44115 #781-04-1999 L2006 **IM** *100

IQBAL, Saima. 2351 E 22ND ST, DEPT OF MED EDU 44115 #704-06-2001 L2006 *100

IREFIN, Samuel Adesoji. 9500 EUCLID AVE 44195 #028-34-1988 L1994 **AN CCA** *020 †05

ISA, E Tomas Jorge. 1708 SOUTHPOINT DR 44109 #275-01-1956 L1962 **P IM** *072

ISAACSON, J Harry. 9500 EUCLID AVE # A91, CLEVELAND CLINIC FOUNDATIO 44195 #025-01-1984 L1993 **IM** *020 †20

ISADA, Carlos Manuel. 9500 EUCLID AVE, CLEVELAND CLINIC FOUNDATIO 44195 #035-06-1986 L1989 **IM** *020 †20

ISAKOV, Raymond. 9500 EUCLID AVE, A-60 44195 #016-42-1998 L2001 **PS** *100 †85,65

ISAKOV, Terence. 5187 MAYFIELD RD 44124 #836-03-1964 L1978 **FM** *020 †18

ISARIYAWONGSE, Justin Pra. ■ 44106 #038-40-2005 L2005 **GS** *012

ISENBERG, Gerard. 11100 EUCLID AVE, WRN 242 44106 #016-06-1990 L1994 **GE IM** *020 †20

ISHIYAMA, Susan Yuri. 11401 LORAIN AVE 44111 #038-40-1993 L2001 **CHP** *020 †75

ISIGUZO, Obinna Gift. 6780 MAYFIELD RD 44124 #690-04-1990 L2000 **CD IM** *020 †20

ISLAM, Ali. 9500 EUCLID AVE, CLEVELAND CLINIC FOUNDATI 44195 #065-01-1999 L2004 *100

ISLAM, Andrew Shafik. ■ 44120 #038-06-2003 L2003 **ORS** *012

ISRAELI, Rafi Michael. 11100 EUCLID AVE, CASE MEDICAL CENTER 44106 #035-46-2002 L2007 **OS** *100 †20

ISTRATE, Claudia Gineta. 2322 E 22ND ST STE 305, ASSOC. INC. 44115 #781-01-1993 L2001 **IM** *020 †20

ITANO, Hideki. 9500 EUCLID AVE, CO CCF-GRAD MED EDU DEPT-N 44195 #572-77-1990 L2001 **TS** *100

ITIN, Ilia. 9500 EUCLID AVE, STAFF NEUROLOGIST MOVEMENT 44195 #422-01-1999 L2006 **N** *020 †75

IYIER, Nithya. 9500 EUCLID AVE A90 44195 #495-16-2000 L2007 **PCC** *012 †20

IZANEC, James Jos. 12000 MCCRACKEN RD, STE 351 44125 #038-06-1971 L1977 **OBG** *071 †30

IZUMI, Kosuke. CO RESIDENCY OFFICE, UNIVERSITY HOSPITALS 44106 #572-20-2003 L2007 **PMG** *012

IZUTANI, Hironori. 9500 EUCLID AVE, CO CCF-GRAD MED EDU DEPT-N 44195 #572-83-1988 L2001 **TS** *100

JAAFAR, Randa. ■ 44106 #025-07-2007 L2007 **AN** *012

JABER, Wael A. 9500 EUCLID AVE #605-01-1992 L1998 **CD** *020 †20

JACKSON, Carl Ernest. 1464 E 105TH ST, STE 301 44106 #010-03-1987 L1988 **GS** *020 †85

JACKSON, Charles Lee. 9500 EUCLID AVE, STE A100 44195 #025-01-1982 L1985 **U** *020 †95

JACKSON, Edgar B, Jr. 11100 EUCLID AVE 44106 #038-06-1966 L1966 **IM** *071 †20

JACOB, Miriam Sara. ■ 44121 #051-01-2003 L2007 **IM** *100 †20

JACOBS, Avrum Gerson. 6770 MAYFIELD RD, STE 205 44124 #023-07-2001 L2007 **CD** *020

JACOBS, Ernest C. 9500 EUCLID AVE, DESK A-81 44195 #042-12-1982 L1986 *062

JACOBS, Gretta Hazel. 11100 EUCLID AVE, DEPT OF PATHLGY 44106 #836-01-1972 L1984 **ATP** *020 †50

JACOBS, Irwin. 2500 METROHEALTH DR, METROHEALTH MED CTR-PEDS 44109 #005-11-1966 L1967 **CHN PD** *020 †55,75

JACOBS, Larry Judah. 6770 MAYFIELD RD, STE 205 44124 #035-19-1974 L1990 **CD ICE** *020 †20

JACOBS, Michael Roy. 11100 EUCLID AVE, DEPT OF PATHOLOGY 44106 #836-01-1971 L1981 **CLP MM** *030

JACOBSEN, Chad Thomas. 11100 EUCLID AVE 44106 #048-12-1997 L2000 **PHO** *020 †55

JACOBSOHN, James Semeon. ■ 44120 #038-06-1960 L1960 **P** *071

JACOBSON, Robert Paul. 25001 EMERY RD, STE 100 44128 #038-40-1972 L1972 **DR** *062 †80

JACONO, Frank Joseph, III. 11100 EUCLID AVE, DIV. PULMONARY/CCM 44106 #028-02-1998 L2000 **PCC** *020 †20

JAFFER, Amir Kader. 9500 EUCLID AVE, DEPT GEN INTERNAL MEDICINE 44195 #024-05-1994 L1997 **IM** *020 †20

JAFFER, Sukaina. ■ 44114 #495-85-1987 L2003 **IM** *020 †20

JAGADEESH, Shobha. 2500 METROHEALTH DR, METRO HEALTH MEDICAL CENTE 44109 #496-22-2000 L2004 **IM** *100 †20

JAHAN, Ali E. 9500 EUCLID AVE, SURGICAL ICU / G61 44195 #025-01-1992 L1997 **AN** *020 †05

JAHED, Ayda. 9500 EUCLID AVE, DESK A91 44195 #517-08-1999 L2006 **IMG** *020 †20

JAHNIGEN, Dennis Wm. ■ 44195 #038-40-1975 L1986 **IMG IM** *020 †20

JAIN, Alka. ■ 44109 #496-10-1993 L2000 **FM** *100

JAIN, Alok Kumar. 2500 METROHEALTH DR 44109 #496-39-1996 L2003 **GE** *012 †20

JAIN, Anil Kantilal. 9500 EUCLID AVE 191, CLEVELAND CLINIC 44195 #016-06-1995 L1996 **IM** *020 †20

JAIN, Priya. ■ 44120 #038-06-2001 L2001 **HO** *012

JAIN, Rajat Kumar. ■ 44120 #038-40-2006 L2006 **MPD** *012

JAIN, Siddharth Vinod. 2500 METROHEALTH DR 44109 #496-36-2003 L2007 **PD** *012

JAIN, Steven Roshan. ■ 44120 #038-06-2001 L2001 **IC** *012

JAIN, Sudhanshu. 18101 LORAIN AVE, FAIRVIEW HOSPITAL 44111 #496-09-1999 L2004 **IM** *020 †20

JAIN, Vikas. 2500 METROHEALTH DR, METRO HEALTH MED CTR 44109 #495-45-1997 L2007 **DR** *012

JAISHANKAR, Vidhyalakshmi. 1100 EUCLID AVE, DEPT OF CHILD & ADOLESC 44115 #495-04-1999 L2004 **CHP** *100 †75

JAKOB, John Andrew. 11100 EUCLID AVE, DEPT OF INTERNAL MEDICINE 44106 #035-01-2005 L2005 **IM** *012

JAMES, Erica Michelle. ■ 44106 #011-02-2004 L2007 **FM** *100 †18

JAMES, Karen Bertha. ONE CLINIC CENTER, CLEVELAND CLINIC DESK F25 44195 #041-09-1982 L1983 **CD IM** *020 †20

JAMES, Neena M. ■ 44113 #024-05-2004 L2007 **RHU** *012 †20

JANA, William Salim. 27633 BASSETT RD 44145 #308-01-1960 L1966 **IM RHU** *020 †20

JANAKIRAM, Murali. CO RESIDENCY SUPPORT, METROHEALTH MEDICAL CENTER 44109 #495-04-2003 L2007 **IM** *012

JANDI, Jorge T. ■ 44133 #748-08-1962 L1972 **IM** *071

JANICKI, Thomas Ignacy. 1611 S GREEN RD, STE 237 44121 #759-10-1974 L1978 **OBG** *020 †30

JANKOWSKI, Jason Thomas. ■ 44102 #038-40-2002 L2002 **U** *012

JANUS, Annette. 11100 EUCLID AVE, HANNA HOUSE 5TH FL 44106 #759-18-2003 L2004 **NMN** *012

JATKAR, Tejas Arun. 11100 EUCLID AVE, UNIV HOSP 44106 #041-13-2006 L2007 **DR** *012

JATLA, Sridhar. 11100 EUCLID AVE 44106 #041-02-2002 L2003 **P** *020

JAWORSKI, Hanna Christine. ■ 44121 #012-05-2005 L2005 **PD** *012

JAWORSKY, Christine. 2500 METROHEALTH DR, DEPT OF DERMATOLOGY 44109 #016-11-1982 L1993 **D PTH** *020 †15

JAYAVANT, Arun Manohar. 9500 EUCLID AVE 44195 #495-17-1957 L1972 **OBG** *071 †30

JAYAWEERA, Manonitha. 1708 SOUTHPOINT DR, NORTHCOAST BEHAVIORAL HEAL 44109 #220-01-1978 L2000 **P** *020 †75 ‡

JEANCLAUDE, Jessie M. 10701 EAST BLVD, SURGERY 112-W 44106 #035-01-1989 L2001 **VS** *020 †85

JEEVANANDAM, Devi P. ■ 44106 #198-01-1992 **CD** *050

JEFFERSON, Brian Keith. 9500 EUCLID AVE, CO CCF-GRAD MED EDUD EPT-N 44195 #047-05-1998 L2001 **IC** *020 †20

JEHA, Lara Emile. 9500 EUCLID AVE, STE 572 44195 #605-01-1999 L2000 **CN** *100

JELOVSEK, John Eric. A 81, 9500 EUCLID AVE 44195 #047-20-1999 L2003 **GYN OBG** *020 †30

JENG, Bennie Hau. 9500 EUCLID AVE I-32, CLEVELAND CLINIC FOUNDATIO 44195 #041-01-1998 L2000 **OPH** *020 †35

JENG, Linda Jo Bone. 10524 EUCLID AVE, 6TH FL 44106 #041-01-1998 L2000 **CMG MG** *062 †55,19

JENKINS, Kenneth W, II. 9500 EUCLID AVE 44195 #038-43-1992 L1993 **EM** *020 †16

JENKINS, Rima Janine. 2074 ABINGTON RD DEPT PED 44106 #041-01-1989 **PD** *100

JENKINS, Trevor Lawrence. ■ 44106 #038-06-2006 **IM** *012

JENNINGS, Constance Ann. 9500 EUCLID AVE 44195 #026-08-1985 L1996 **PUD CCM** *020 †20

JENNINGS, Denise Cecile. 12100 SUPERIOR AVE 44106 #038-40-1981 L1982 **OBG** *020

JEONG, Jinyoung. 9500 EUCLID AVE, CLEVELAND CLINIC FOUNDATIO 44195 #583-10-1991 L2006 *100

JERIC, William H. 2475 E BLVD 44120 #038-06-1943 L1943 **GS** *020

JETHVA, Natwarlal M. 18660 BAGLEY RD, STE 102B 44130 #495-22-1972 L1982 **IM IMG** *020 †20

JETTY, Prasad. 9500 EUCLID AVE, DEPT OF GME 44195 #067-01-1999 L2005 *100

JHANDIR, Muhammad Faisal. 2500 METROHEALTH DR, METROHEALTH MED CTR 44109 #704-25-1998 L2000 **IM** *100 †20

JHEE, Marianne Tudtud. 11100 EUCLID AVE, UNIVERSITY HOSP CASE MEDIC 44106 #016-11-2005 L2006 **P** *012

JIMERSON, Andrew. 11811 SHAKER BLVD STE 330 44120 #038-06-1976 L1977 **IM** *020

JIN, Xian Wen. 9500 EUCLID AVE, BLDG S-70 44195 #243-16-1982 L1996 **IM** *020 †20 ‡

JINKS, Jeffrey Harvey. 6770 MAYFIELD RD STE 310 44124 #038-43-1987 L1988 **PD** *020 †55

JINN, Jung Kee. ■ 44441 #583-03-1964 L1971 **AN PMM** *071 †05

JIROUT, Martin. 9500 EUCLID AVE 44106 #286-13-1999 **PTH** *012

JOHANN, Donald Joseph, Jr. 2500 METROHEALTH DR, CO METROHEALTH MED CTR-RES 44109 #038-06-1994 L2000 **ON** *012 †20

JOHNSON, Anthony Mark. ■ 44139 #038-06-1996 L2002 **DR** *012

JOHNSON, Clayborne B, Jr. ■ 44104 #038-06-1976 L1977 **GP** *075

JOHNSON, Eva Rajki. 11100 EUCLID AVE, RAP CLINIC 44106 #038-06-2000 L2000 **PD** *020 †55

JOHNSON, John Leland. 11100 EUCLID AVE, DIV OF INF DISEASES 44106 #041-12-1981 L1987 **CCM PUD** *020 †20

JOHNSON, Mark Thomas. 11100 EUCLID AVE, UNIV HOSPITALS OF CLEVELAN 44106 #038-06-1998 L1999 **OS** *020 †55,19

JOHNSON, Michael David. ■ 44106 #035-01-2003 L2003 **GS** *012

JOHNSON, Nicole Marie. ■ 44119 #038-06-2001 L2002 **CCP** *012 †55

JOHNSON, Toni Love. 6835 BROADWAY AVE 44105 #025-01-1991 L1994 **P** *020 †75

JOHNSON, Wendy Lynn. ■ 44114 #038-40-1995 L1998 **FM** *020 †18

JOHNSTON, Douglas Ross. 9500 EUCLID AVE H35, CLEVELAND CLINIC FND 44195 #024-01-1998 L2005 **TS** *012 †85

JOHNSTON, Olwyn Klara. 9500 EUCLID AVE BOX 452 44195 #539-04-1996 *100

JOINER, Charles M. ■ 44102 #038-06-1980 L1983 **EM** *020 †16

JOIS-BILOWICH, Preeti. 9500 EUCLID AVE E-19, CLEVELAND CLINIC FOUNDATIO 44195 #011-02-2003 L2006 **EM** *100 †16

JOKHIO, Muhammad Ilyas. 1001 LAKESIDE AVE E, STE 1200 44114 #704-08-1969 L1976 **IM PUD** *020 †20

JONES, David Charles. 2500 METROHEALTH DR, DEPARMENT OF MEDICINE 44109 #056-06-2003 L2003 **IM** *100

JONES, James Crothers. ■ 44104 #038-06-1948 L1948 **GS** *071 †85

JONES, Morgan Herancourt. 9500 EUCLID AVE 44195 #038-40-1999 L2005 **ORS OSM** *020 †40

JONES, Penola Phyllis. 13930 EUCLID AVE 44112 #048-12-1980 L1984 **OBG** *020 †30

JONES, Robert, II. 9500 EUCLID AVE 44195 #038-44-1994 L1996 **FM** *020 †18

JONES, Robert Stanley, Jr. 11100 EUCLID AVE, UNIVERSITY HOSPITALS CLEVE 44106 #035-08-1999 L2004 **NM** *020 †28

JONES, Stephen Edward. 9500 EUCLID AVE U-15, CLEVELAND CLINIC FOUNDATIO 44195 #024-07-2001 L2007 **RNR** *100 †80

JONSYN, Gerald Hubert. 29000 CENTER RIDGE RD 44145 #409-10-1974 L1981 **CCA** *100

JORDAN, Roderick Bernard. 11100 EUCLID AVE, RBMC 122 44106 #038-06-1982 L1983 **PS** *020 †65

JORGENSEN, Fred M. 18200 LORAIN AVE 44111 #038-43-1981 L1984 **FM** *020 †18

JOSEPH, Shelley Ann. ■ 44113 #048-14-2007 L2007 **IM** *012

JOSEPHSON, Richard A. 11100 EUCLID AVE, U HOSPITALS 44106 #035-19-1982 L1988 **CD IM** *020 †20

JOSHI, Raja. 9500 EUCLID AVE, CLEVELAND CLINIC FOUNDATIO 44195 #495-12-1995 L2001 *020

JOSHI, Vinod Shankar. 9500 EUCLID AVE E31, CCF-DEPT OF ANESTHESIOLOGY 44195 #495-30-1968 L1978 **AN** *020

JOUMA, Bashar. 1730 W 25TH ST 44113 #875-01-1991 L2000 **CCA** *020 †05

JOY, Edward Gerard. ■ 44118 #016-42-2002 L2007 **ORS** *020

JOY, Matthew Alan. 2500 METROHEALTH DR, METRO HEALTH MED CNTR 44109 #038-40-1991 L1992 **AN CCA** *020 †05

JOY, Samuel John. 18101 LORAIN AVE 44111 #038-40-1959 L1959 **OBG** *071 †30

JOYCE, Katherine May. ■ 44113 #038-45-2007 L2007 **PD** *012

JOYCE, Kelly L W. 1611 S GREEN RD, STE 35 44121 #038-06-1995 L1996 **PD** *020 †55

JOYCE, Michael Jos. 9500 EUCLID AVE A41, CLEVELAND CLINIC FOUNDATIO 44195 #020-02-1976 L1983 **ORS** *020 †40

JOYCE, Myles Richard. ■ 44118 #539-05-1997 L2007 **CRS** *012

JOYNER, Joseph Todd. 2500 METROHEALTH DR, DEPT OF MEDICINE-MHMC 44109 #654-01-1999 L1999 **IM** *020 †20

JUAN, Norberto L. 11009 DETROIT AVE 44102 #748-07-1965 L1976 **GP** *020

JUBRAN, Fuad Youssef. 9500 EUCLID AVE, CLEVELAND CLINIC FOUNDATIO 44195 #605-01-1964 L1977 **CD IM** *020 †20

JUDGE, Nancy Elizabeth. 11100 EUCLID AVE, STE 1200 44106 #024-16-1977 L1978 **OBG** *020 †30

JUGUILON, Alejandro. 7007 POWERS BLVD 44129 #748-01-1956 L1967 **GP GS** *071

JUHANT, Frank. 12000 MCCRACKEN RD STE 252 44125 #038-40-1974 L1980 **OPH** *020 †35

JULIANO, Justin James. 9500 EUCLID AVE, DESK T-28 44195 #035-15-2002 L2004 **RO** *020

JUMP, Robin L. ■ 44106 #038-06-2004 L2004 **ID** *012 †20

JUODENAS, Edmundas. 18021 MARCELLA RD # 1-3 44119 #616-01-1940 L1951 **GP** *072

JURATLI, Sham. 2500 METROHEALTH DR, CO METROHEALTH MED CTR-RES 44109 #875-01-1996 L2000 **GPM** *100 †18,70

JURJUS, George Jamil. 10701 EAST BLVD, CLEVELAND VAMC 44106 #605-01-1985 L1988 **P** *020 †75

JUVELEKIAN, Georges S. 9500 EUCLID AVE, DESK A90 44195 #605-01-1993 L2001 **PCC** *100 †20

KABBARA, Abdallah Issam. 2500 METROHEALTH DR 44109 #654-01-1998 L1999 **AN** *020 †05

KAESGEN, Anne Katherine. ■ 44126 #038-40-2005 L2005 **FP** *012

KAFFEN, Sheldon. 4200 WARRENSVILLE CENTR RD, STE 451 44122 #038-06-1958 L1958 **ORS** *020 †40

KAFOREY, Neal Alan. 12301 SNOW RD, KAISER PERMANENTE OF OHIO 44130 #038-41-1981 L1982 **EM** *020 †16

KAIMAN, Harold. 4180 WARRENSVILLE CENTR RD 44122 #030-05-1967 L1973 **DR NM** *020 †80,28

KAISER, Peter Kazuo. 9500 EUCLID AVE, DIV OF OPHTHALMOLOGY A31 44195 #024-01-1992 L1997 **OPH** *020 †35

KAKUMANI, Praveena Lakshm. ■ 44195 #495-58-1999 L2006 **RHU** *012 †20

KALADY, Matthew Frank. 9500 EUCLID AVE A-30, CLEVELAND CLINIC FOUNDATIO 44195 #036-07-1998 L2005 **GS** *100 †85,10

KALADY, Skyler Elizabeth. 9500 EUCLID AVE, - M73 44195 #036-01-2000 L2005 **PD** *020 †55

KALAHASTI, Priya. 9500 EUCLID AVE, DESK A51, CLEVELAND CLINIC 44195 #495-70-1994 L2000 **IM** *020

KALAHASTI, Vidyasagar. 9500 EUCLID AVE, DESK F15 DEPT OF CARDIOLOG 44195 #495-70-1994 L2000 **IM CD** *020 †20

KALAMANGALAM, Giridhar Pa. 9500 EUCLID AVE, CLEVELAND CLINIC FOUNDATIO 44195 #495-53-1989 L2003 **CN** *020

KALAYCIOGLU, Matt Etem. 9500 EUCLID AVE 44195 #055-01-1988 L1990 **HEM** *020 †20

KALAYJIAN, Robert Chas. 2500 METROHEALTH DR 44109 #024-07-1982 L1988 **ID IM** *020 †20

KALE, Hemangi Parag. 2500 METROHEALTH DR 44109 #495-22-1990 L1999 **GE** *020 †20

KALEPU, Anand Rao. 7007 POWERS BLVD 44129 #495-53-1975 L1984 **TS GS** *020

KALEPU, Sudheera. 2351 E 22ND ST, ST VINCENT CHARITY 44115 #495-58-1993 L2003 **IM** *020 †20

KALFAS, Iain H. 9500 EUCLID AVE, CLEVELAND CLINIC FOUNDATIO 44195 #038-44-1982 L1983 **NS** *020 †25

KALHAN, Santosh Balbir. 9500 EUCLID AVE, # E31 44195 #495-36-1965 L1974 **AN PD** *020 †05

KALHAN, Satish Chander. 2500 METROHEALTH DR 44109 #495-36-1964 L1973 **PD NPM** *050 †55

KALHAN, Sujata. #44122 #496-07-1987 L1996 **IM** *020 †20

KALIDINDI, Srinivasa Raju. 18101 LORAIN AVE, C/O FAIRVIEW HLTH SYS-INT 44111 #495-21-1998 L2003 **IM** *100 †20

KALINOWSKI, Valerie E. 9500 EUCLID AVE S10A, CARE MEDICINE 44195 #010-01-2001 L2007 **CCP** *020 †55

KALLA, Arpita. 11100 EUCLID AVE, DEPT OF PEDIATRICS 44106 #917-10-2001 L2006 **PD** *012

KAMATH, Sameer Shantaram. 2500 METROHEALTH DR, METROHEALTH MED CTR 44109 #495-17-1997 L2002 **CCP** *012 †55

KAMBAMPATI, Vikram. 11100 EUCLID AVE, UNIV HOSP OF CLEVELAND 44106 #041-12-2005 L2005 **P** *012

KAMEN, Sheldon D. 12000 MCCRACKEN RD, STE 101 44125 #038-40-1960 L1960 **OPH** *071 †35

KAMINSKI, Peggy Ann. 2226 WARRENSVILL CNTR RD R 44118 #038-43-1982 L1988 **PD** *020 †55

KAMIONKOWSKI, Mario David. 12000 MCCRACKEN RD, GASTROENTEROLOGY 44125 #132-01-1958 L1964 **GE IM** *020 †20

KAMMERMAN, Teresa Martha. 5850 LANDERBROOK DR, STE 220 44124 #038-06-1987 L1987 **PD** *020 †55

KAMOGA, Gilbert-Roy Buken. CO RESIDENCY OFFICE, UNIVERSITY HOSPITALS 44106 #905-03-2006 L2006 **IM** *012

KAMPANI, Shanta Nair. 4255 PEARL RD, STE 401 44109 #495-27-1964 L1972 **GS GP** *020

KANDA, Mona Kabisa. ■ 44195 #010-01-2006 L2006 **AN** *012

KANDASAMY, Rajesh Kumar. RM 3018, CO RESIDENCY OFFICE 44109 #495-59-1998 L2007 **IM** *012

KANDIL, Enas S. 9500 EUCLID AVE, RESIDENCY PROGRAM 44195 #915-02-1996 L2000 **APM** *020 †05

KANDIL, Sherif Hamdy. 9500 EUCLID AVE 44106 #915-04-1994 L2000 **AN** *100 †05

KANDULA, Prasada Rao. 2351 E 22ND ST 44115 #495-98-1974 L1985 **DR** *020

KANE, Sarah Marie. ■ 44113 #041-15-2005 L2005 **OBG** *012

KANESHIRO, David Kei. ■ 44121 #016-11-2006 L2006 **PTH** *012

KANG, Hui Suk. ■ 44106 #048-15-2003 L2003 **PMM** *012

KANG, Preet Singh. 10701 EAST BLVD, RADIOLOGY SERVICE 114W 44106 #495-45-1992 L2002 **R VIR** *020

KANG, Tyler Yutai. 9500 EUCLID AVE, R 35 44195 #005-06-2001 L2005 **HO** *012

KANKAM, Charity. 5109 BROADWAY AVE, STE 310 44127 #065-01-1971 L1990 **IM NEP** *030

KANNE, Jeffrey Paul. 9500 EUCLID AVE, # HB 6 44195 #012-05-2000 L2006 **DR** *100 †80 ‡

KANNER, Andrew Ariye. 9500 EUCLID AVE, CO CCF-GRAD MED EDU DEPT-N 44195 #869-01-1992 L2000 *100

KANSAL, Sunil Chandra. 18820 BAGLEY RD STE 106 44130 #495-67-1968 L1981 **IM** *020 †20

KANTOR, Gareth Simon. 11100 EUCLID AVE 44106 #836-02-1984 L1994 **AN MDM** *020 †05

KAO, Amy Wanju. ■ 44113 #038-40-2005 L2006 **DR** *012

KAOUK, Jihad Hussein. 9500 EUCLID AVE, STE 100 44195 #605-01-1993 L2000 **U** *020

KAPADIA, Jyotika Gautam. 19250 BAGLEY RD, STE 101 44130 #495-76-1971 L1982 **AN** *020

KAPADIA, Manasvee S. 2351 E 22ND ST, DEPT. OF OPHTHALMOLOGY 44115 #495-76-1993 L2000 **OPH** *020 †35

KAPADIA, Samir R. 9500 EUCLID AVE F-25, CLEVELAND CLINIC 44195 #495-76-1990 L1996 **CD** *020 †20

KAPLAN, Barbara Sue. 9500 EUCLID AVE A111, CLEVELAND CLINIC FOUNDATIO 44195 #038-41-1978 L1983 **PD PG** *020 †55

KAPLAN, David Ray. 2085 ADELBERT RD 44106 #016-02-1980 L1984 **ILI OS** *050

KAPLAN, Samuel Brett. 11100 EUCLID AVE, BOLWELL 1200 44106 #550-03-2007 L2007 **FP** *012

KAPOOR, Gopalkrishna R. 16111 LORAIN AVE 44111 #495-23-1972 L1979 **IM** *020 †20
KAPOOR, Rajeev. 9500 EUCLID AVE A91, CLEVELAND CLINIC 44195 #496-02-1998 L2006 **IM** *100 †20
KAPOOR, Rupa. 11100 EUCLID AVE, UNIV HOSP 44106 #048-13-2007 L2007 **PD** *012
KAPPUS, Jane Christine. 18099 LORAIN AVE 44111 #038-06-1979 L1982 **OBG** *020 †30
KAPUR, Anand. ■ 44111 #033-06-2003 L2003 **FSM** *020 †18
KAPUR, Gaurav. 1730 W 25TH ST 44113 #495-90-1994 L2002 **PM** *020 †60
KAPURAL, Leonardo. 9500 EUCLID AVE C-25, PAIN MANAGEMENT CLEVELAND 44195 #957-01-1990 L1999 **APM** *020 †05
KAPURAL, Miranda. 9500 EUCLID AVE, CLEVELAND CLINIC FOUNDATIO 44195 #957-01-1996 L2006 **AN** *012
KARAI, Laszlo. ■ 44195 #473-02-1994 L2007 **DMP** *012 †50
KARAKAS, Sabiha P. 9500 EUCLID AVE HB6, THE CLEVELAND CLINIC 44195 #902-05-1991 L2006 **DR** *020 †80
KARAKASIS, Christopher Jo. ■ 44143 #038-40-2008 L012
KARAPETIAN, Armine. ■ 44124 #005-02-2005 **U** *012
KARHA, Juhana Kristian. ■ 44120 #016-06-2000 L2003 **IC** *012 †20
KARIMI, Mohsen. 11100 EUCLID AVE STE 380 44106 #017-20-1996 L2007 **GS PCS** *020 †85,90
KARIMPIL, Joseph Jacob. 763 E 200TH ST 44119 #495-31-1973 L1980 **IM** *020
KARIV, Yehuda. 9500 EUCLID AVE, DEPT OF GME 44195 #550-01-1999 L2006 *100
KARLAKUNTI, Chandrashekar. 9500 EUCLID AVE, CLEVELAND CLINIC FOUNDATIO 44195 #496-02-1991 L1997 **IM** *020 †05
KARNS, Daniel James. 6115 POWERS BLVD, STE 100 44129 #038-43-1987 L1991 **ORS OSM** *020 †40
KARNS, Robert Earl. 1370 ONTARIO ST STE 450 44113 #041-02-1950 L1987 **DR** *071 †80
KARODY, Vijender Rao. 2500 METROHEALTH DR, DEPT OF RESIDENCY SUPPORT 44109 #495-21-1997 L2005 **PD** *012
KARRI, Lavanya Venkata La. 2500 METROHEALTH DR 44109 #495-11-1999 L2006 **FP** *012
KARRI, Saraswathi Venkata. 9500 EUCLID AVE 44106 #495-21-1994 L2002 **AN** *100
KARROUM, Rami Edward. 9500 EUCLID AVE, C/O CCF-GRAD MED EDU DEPT- 44195 #915-04-1995 L2002 **PAN** *012
KASS, Lawrence. 2500 METROHEALTH DR 44109 #016-02-1964 L1966 **HEM PTH** *030 †20
KASSABIAN, Sirvart. 2500 METROHEALTH DR 44109 #166-02-2002 L2007 **PD** *012
KASSEN, Julian. 1001 LAKESIDE AVE E 44114 #012-05-1942 L1949 **IM OS** *071
KATCHER, Jerald. 5885 LANDERBROOK DR 44124 #038-41-1993 L1997 **RO** *020 †80
KATIGBAK, Edgardo B. 805 COLUMBIA RD STE 102 44145 #748-02-1957 L1965 **OBG** *071 †30
KATIRJI, Bashar. 11100 EUCLID AVE, STE 5512 44106 #875-02-1977 L1983 **N CN** *020 †75
KATYAL, Sumit K. ■ 44195 #038-44-2005 L2005 **AN** *012
KATZ, Cheryl Lynne. 1250 SUPERIOR AVE E 44114 #504-04-1991 L2001 **FM** *020 †18
KATZ, Jeffry Adam. 11100 EUCLID AVE, UNIV HOSPS CLEVELAND 44106 #038-06-1987 L1994 **GE IM** *020 †20
KATZ, Michael Jay. CASE WESTERN RESERVE U 44106 #038-06-1979 *040
KATZ, Tyler Jessica. ■ 44124 #038-06-2002 L2007 **OBG** *100 †30
KATZAN, Cynthia Mary. 7123 PEARL RD STE 201, TEAMHEALTH MIDWEST 44130 #038-06-1996 L2000 **EM** *020 †16
KATZAN, Irene Louise. 2500 METROHEALTH DR, RAMMELKAMP BLDG 44109 #038-40-1993 L1998 **N** *050 †75
KAUFFMAN, Erick Roman. 2358 PROFESSOR AVE, NEIGHBORHOOD FAMILY 44113 #041-12-1997 L2000 **FM** *020 †18
KAUFMAN, Barbara R H. 29525 CHAGRIN BLVD STE 302 44122 #062-01-1950 L1952 **P PD** *071 †55
KAUFMAN, Benjamin. 2074 ABINGTON RD 44106 #038-40-1952 L1952 **R** *020 †80
KAUFMAN, Bram Robt. 2500 METROHEALTH DR # H953, METROHEALTH MED CTR 44109 #038-06-1987 L1987 **PS** *020 †85,65
KAUSHAL, Nina. 30680 BAINBRIDGE RD, PHYSICIAN STAFFING INC 44139 #305-01-1995 L2000 **IM** *020 †20
KAVLICH, John James, Jr. 11311 SHAKER BLVD 44104 #038-45-1987 L1988 **EM GP** *020
KAW, Roop K. 9500 EUCLID AVE - M80-22, DEPT OF GENERAL INTERNAL M 44195 #495-51-1988 L2001 **IM** *020 †20
KAWASE, Isamu. 9500 EUCLID AVE, CO CCF-GRAD MED EDU DEPT-N 44195 #572-76-1999 L2002 *100
KAY, Marsha Helen. 9500 EUCLID AVE A111, CLEVELAND CLINIC FOUND 44195 #038-44-1986 L1988 **PG PD** *020 †55
KAY, Robert. 9500 EUCLID AVE, STE A100 44195 #005-14-1971 L1980 **U** *020 †95
KAY, William Ezra. 14100 CEDAR RD, STE 300 44121 #010-03-1973 L1978 **DR** *075
KAYANJA, Harriet Kose. 11100 EUCLID AVE, UNIVERSITY HOSPITALS 44106 #905-03-1996 L2007 **IM** *012
KAZA, Venu. 2074 ABINGTON RD DEPT IM 44106 #038-06-1991 **OPH** *100
KAZDAN, David. 10701 EAST BLVD 11A-W, CLEVELAND VA MC 44106 #038-41-1985 L1985 **AN** *020 †05
KAZURA, James Walter. 2109 ADELBERT RD DEPT MED 44106 #038-40-1972 L1978 **ID IM** *040 †20
KEA, Karen Elizabeth. 2816 E 116TH ST 44120 #038-06-1989 L1991 **IM** *020
KEATING, Catherine Emily. 11100 EUCLID AVE 44106 #038-06-1977 L1980 **FM** *020 †20
KEATING, Louise Jacobacci. 3747 EUCLID AVE 44115 #025-01-1949 L1954 **BBK** *030
KEATING, Robert Jos. 18820 BAGLEY RD STE 102 44130 #036-05-1989 L1990 **FM FSM** *020 †18
KEATON, Daniel Brian. 11100 EUCLID AVE, UNIV HOSP OF CLEVELAND 44106 #305-01-2003 L2003 **FPP** *012
KEDIA, Kailash Ram. 19250 BAGLEY RD, STE 107 44130 #495-24-1969 L1976 **U** *020 †95
KEEFE, John Patrick. 29001 CEDAR RD STE 620 44124 #041-02-1961 L1967 **GYN** *020 †30
KEEYAPAJ, Worasak. 9500 EUCLID AVE, DEPT OF GME 44195 #891-01-2001 L2006 **AN** *012
KEFER, John Christopher. 9500 EUCLID AVE, CO CCF-GRAD MED EDU DEPT-N 44195 #016-43-2003 L2003 **U** *012
KEIDL, Claudia Marie. 11100 EUCLID AVE, RAINBOW BABIES & CHILDRENS 44106 #056-06-1991 L1995 **PDI** *020 †55
KEILER, Susan Ann. 11100 EUCLID AVE, UNIV HOSP 44106 #016-11-2006 L2006 **D** *012
KEITH, Michael Warren. 4330 W 150TH ST 44135 #038-40-1973 L1973 **HS ORS** *020 †40
KELKAR, Manohar Shankar. 33355 STATION ST 44139 #495-01-1961 L1972 **FM GYN** *075 †18
KELLER, Kimberly Joy. 2500 METROHEALTH DR, CO METROHEALTH MED CTR-RAD 44109 #021-01-1999 L2000 **DR** *020
KELLEY, Brendan. 9500 EUCLID AVE, C/O CCF-GRAD MED EDU DEPT- 44195 #038-40-2002 L2002 **N** *012
KELLNER, Patricia Jean. 14100 CEDAR RD, STE 320 44121 #008-01-1983 L1985 **FM PD** *020 †18
KELLY, Clay Matthew. 4330 W 150TH ST 44135 #030-06-1987 L1991 **PM OS** *020 †60

KELLY, Denis. 9500 EUCLID AVE, CO CCF-GRAD MED EDU-NA23 44195 #539-04-1990 L2000 *100
KELLY, Dympna Mary. 9500 EUCLID AVE #A80, CLEVELAND CLC DEPT GEN SUR 44189 #539-04-1983 L2005 *020
KELLY, Michael Edward. 9500 EUCLID AVE S80, DEPT OF NEUROSURGERY 44195 #068-01-1999 L2006 *071
KELLY, Peter John. 9500 EUCLID AVE, CLEVELAND CLINIC FOUNDATIO 44195 #539-02-1997 L2006 *100
KELLY, Robert Boland. 18200 LORAIN AVE, CENTER FOR FAMILY MEDICINE 44111 #051-01-1980 L1983 **FM** *050 †18
KELSO, Rebecca Lynn. 9500 EUCLID AVE # 540, CLEVELAND CLINIC VASC SURG 44195 #036-01-2001 L2007 **VS** *020 †85
KEMP, David Eric. 11400 EUCLID AVE STE 200, CASE WESTERN RESERVE UNIV 44106 #038-44-2002 L2006 **P** *050 †75
KEMPE, Kazuo. 9500 EUCLID AVE 44195 #030-06-1990 L1992 **IM** *020
KENAGY, David Neil. 2801 MARTIN LTHR KNG JR DR, CHILDREN'S HOSP FOR REHABI 44104 #041-02-1981 L1988 **PN** *020 †55 ‡
KENDIS, Loren Saml. 6555 WILSON MILLS RD, STE 103 44143 #041-12-1979 L1981 **IM** *020 †20
KENNELL, John Hawks. 2101 ADELBERT RD 44106 #035-45-1946 L1952 **PD** *050 †55
KENT, Lawrence Tambling. 1611 S GREEN RD, STE 260 44121 #038-06-1974 L1977 **RHU** *012
KERAMATI, Akbar. 12000 MCCRACKEN RD STE 250 44125 #517-05-1973 L1982 **GS** *020 †85
KERMAN, Keith M. 5900 LANDERBROOK DR # 200 44124 #043-01-1984 L1985 **IM** *062 †20
KERN, Elizabeth F O. 2109 ADELBERT RD RM 437, CASE WESTERN RESERVE UNIV 44106 #048-12-1999 L2001 **NEP DIA** *020 †20
KERN, Jeffrey Alan. 11100 EUCLID AVE, WEARN BLDG RM 616 44106 #056-05-1979 L2000 **PUD IM** *020 †20
KERR, Douglas Stuart. 11100 EUCLID AVE, UNIV HOSPITALS OF CLEVELAN 44106 #038-06-1965 L1974 **OS DIA** *050 †55
KERWIN, Kevin J. 18697 BAGLEY RD 44130 #038-43-1997 L2003 **ON** *020 †20
KESKINEN, Rosemary Sato. 9500 EUCLID AVE 44195 #038-06-1978 L1979 **D** *020 †15
KESSLER, Joel David. 30680 BAINBRIDGE RD, COMMUNITY HOSPITALISTS 44139 #035-46-2002 L2002 **IM** *100
KEST, Layton M. 6803 MAYFIELD RD STE 418 44124 #016-06-1954 L1958 **U** *071 †95
KEYS, Thomas Frederick. 9500 EUCLID AVE, MAIL CODE-S32 44195 #016-06-1963 L1983 **ID IM** *071 †20
KHADERI, Saira Aijaz. 9500 EUCLID AVE, CLINIC FOUNDATION 44195 #048-02-2005 L2005 **IM** *012
KHADILKAR, Vidula C. 5162 BROADWAY AVE, STE 4 44127 #495-28-1985 L1995 **PD** *020 †55
KHADOUR, Fadi Hikmat. 2351 E 22ND ST, C/O ST VINCENT CHAR-MED ED 44115 #528-01-1987 L2002 **IM** *020 †20
KHAIRALLAH, Philip A. 9500 EUCLID AVE 44195 #035-01-1951 L1957 **OS PA** *071
KHALIL, Al-Amin A. 11100 EUCLID AVE, LKS 5007 44106 #915-02-1980 L1995 **APM** *020 †05
KHALIL, Amer Khalil Ahmad. 9500 EUCLID AVE S80, CLEVELAND CLINIC 44195 #575-01-2002 L2007 **NS** *012
KHAN, Abrar. 9500 EUCLID AVE, DEPT. OF SURGERY, DIVISION 44195 #067-01-1989 L2007 **GS** *020 †85
KHAN, Asma Tehniat. 2500 METROHEALTH DR 44109 #048-15-2006 L2006 **PD** *012
KHAN, Bilquis Farooq. 15322 SAINT CLAIR AVE 44110 #495-65-1968 L1987 **PD** *020 †55
KHAN, Fahd. ■ 44108 #038-44-2004 L2004 **NS** *012
KHAN, Galena. RESIDENT MAILBOX, CLEVELAND CLINIC FDN 44195 #539-04-2006 L2006 **IM** *012
KHAN, Javaad. 2500 METROHEALTH DR 44109 #308-13-2000 L2001 **SME** *012
KHAN, Kashif Zehanet. 2500 METROHEALTH DR, METROHEALTH MEDICAL CENTER 44109 #308-13-1999 L2001 **IM** *100 †20 ‡
KHAN, Mehreen Malik. 11100 EUCLID AVE, DEPT OF GME 44106 #704-21-2004 L2006 **IM** *012
KHAN, Mohammad. 9500 EUCLID AVE, STE F25 44195 #704-08-1991 L2001 **IM** *020
KHAN, Mohammad Halim. 18101 LORAIN AVE, FAIRVIEW HLTH SYSTEM 44111 #704-02-1982 L2002 **GS** *100
KHAN, Mufeedulla. 7123 PEARL RD STE 201, TEAM HEALTH MIDWEST 44130 #308-11-1986 L2000 **ADP ADM** *020 †18 ‡
KHAN, Naveed Ahmed. ■ 44106 #051-07-2007 L2007 **GS** *012
KHAN, Ossam. 9500 EUCLID AVE, CLEVELAND CLINIC FNDN 44195 #704-25-2001 L2004 **IM** *100
KHAN, Sara. 9500 EUCLID AVE, CLEVELAND CLINIC FOUNDATIO 44195 #704-25-2004 L2006 **N** *012
KHAN, Tariq Jamil Ahmad. 2500 METROHEALTH DR, ENDOCRINOLOGY DEPT 44109 #704-20-1988 L2001 **END** *012
KHANDEKAR, Prakash K. 6803 MAYFIELD RD 44124 #495-20-1962 L1971 **D** *020 †15
KHANDELWAL, Anand Vardhan. 18697 BAGLEY RD 44130 #495-54-1977 L1984 **IM PUD** *020 †20
KHANNA, Gaurav. 2500 METROHEALTH DR, METROHEALTH MED CTR 44109 #495-45-2003 L2007 **PCC** *012 †20
KHANTWAL JOSHI, Reena. 9500 EUCLID AVE 44195 #496-10-1998 L2004 *020
KHARBANDA, Monica. 2500 METROHEALTH DR, C/O RESIDENCY SUPPORT 44109 #495-43-2005 L2006 **MPD** *012
KHASAWNEH, Mohamad Khair. 2351 E 22ND ST, ST.VINCENT HOSPITAL 44115 #575-02-1999 L2003 **IM** *020 †20
KHASAWNEH, Wasim Abdelrah. 2500 METROHEALTH DR, METROHEALTH MED CTR 44109 #575-02-2000 L2006 **NPM** *012
KHASSAWNEH, Mohammad Y. 18697 BAGLEY RD 44130 #575-02-1994 L1998 **NPM** *100 †55
KHATIB, Omar Faisal. 9500 EUCLID AVE 44195 #575-01-2006 L2007 **IM** *012
KHATIB, Reem. 9500 EUCLID AVE 44195 #056-05-1999 L1999 **AN CCA** *100 †05
KHATIBI, Parisa. ■ 44124 #517-29-1997 L2006 **IM** *020 †20
KHATRI, Jaikirshan J. 7255 OLD OAK BLVD, C-208 44130 #038-44-1997 L2006 **IC** *020 †20
KHIANI, Vijay Shyam. 11100 EUCLID AVE, DEPT IM 44106 #016-11-2005 L2005 **IM** *012
KHIYAMI, Amer Madani. 2500 METROHEALTH DR, METROHEALTH PATHOLOGY DEPT 44109 #875-01-1981 L1988 **PTH PCP** *020 †50
KHOOBLALL, Khemlall. 6731 RIDGE RD, STE 303 44129 #539-04-1964 L1980 **CD IM** *020
KHORIATY, Rami Naim. 9500 EUCLID AVE 44195 #605-01-2005 L2006 **IM** *012
KHOSA, Sandeep Singh. 2500 METROHEALTH DR 44109 #665-01-2007 L2007 **IM** *012
KHOSLA, Manmohan Krishan. 20800 WESTGATE MALL, STE 510 44126 #495-73-1978 L1987 **PD** *020 †55
KHOURY, Fadi Raymond. 2500 METROHEALTH DR, G240 44109 #038-06-1996 L1998 **OBG** *020 †30

■ = Address Information Privacy Protected

KHOURY, Wael. 6780 MAYFIELD RD 44124 #875-01-1975 L1978 **CD IM** *020 †20

KIATCHOOSAKUN, Pakaphan. 11100 EUCLID AVE 3018, CO UNIV HOSPS-RESIDENCY OF 44106 #891-05-1989 L2000 **NPM** *100

KIDD, Jennifer Roberts. 10900 EUCLID AVE, UNIVERSITY HEALTH SERVICE 44106 #025-01-1990 L1994 **IM** *030 †20

KIEFER, Harry Kinser. 4242 LORAIN AVE 44113 #016-11-1976 L1980 **PD** *020 †55

KIEGER, Edward Frank, II. 5109 BROADWAY AVE, STE 204 44127 #024-01-1957 L1964 **VS GS** *020 †85

KIEHN, Clifford L. ■ 44120 #025-01-1941 L1946 **PS** *071 †65

KIENZLE, Thomas Craven. 1 MOUNT SINAI DR 44106 #016-06-1993 **ORS** *100

KIKANO, George E. 1611 S GREEN RD, STE LL06 44121 #605-01-1986 L1990 **FM** *020 †18

KIM, Alice Inja. 9500 EUCLID AVE, DESK S32 44195 #038-44-1997 L1999 **ID** *020 †20

KIM, Esther Sungah. ■ 44106 #025-07-2003 L2006 **NPM** *012 †55

KIM, Eugene. ■ 44195 #038-06-2006 L2007 **AN** *012

KIM, Hyunmi. ■ 44195 #583-08-1989 L2006 **CN** *100 †75

KIM, Julian Anthony. 11100 EUCLID AVE, UNIV HOSP HLTH SYM 44106 #038-43-1986 L1993 **GS** *020 †85

KIM, Mi Rim. 9500 EUCLID AVE, DEPT OF CARDIOLOGY, F-25 44195 #583-01-1986 **END** *100

KIM, Sanghee. 11100 EUCLID AVE, UNIV HOSP 44106 #016-11-2007 L2007 **PD** *012

KIM, Soo Hyun. ■ 44195 #036-07-2002 L2005 **CD** *012 †20

KIM, Tikhon. 9500 EUCLID AVE 44195 #913-29-1970 L1999 **AN** *020

KIMBO, Florence Vidzem. 2500 METROHEALTH DR 44109 #217-01-1986 L2002 **CHP** *020 †75

KIMMEL, Susan Elizabeth. 11400 EUCLID AVE 44106 #038-43-1986 L1990 **P** *020 †75

KING, Christopher Lee. 2103 CORNELL RD, CWRU 44106 #025-01-1984 L1991 **IM ID** *050 †20

KING, Drue, Jr. ■ 44106 #024-07-1950 L1953 **IM OM** *071

KING, Mary Anne. 25001 EMERY RD STE 100 44128 #038-41-1978 L1980 **DR NM** *020 †80

KING, Peter A. 9051 CEDAR AVE 44106 #035-06-1975 L1976 **EM** *020 †16

KINNARD, Margaret Fern. 11100 EUCLID AVE 44106 #035-45-1988 L1998 **GE IM** *020 †20

KINNEY, Sam Emerson. DESK A-71, 9200 EUCLID AVENUE 44195 #038-06-1964 L1964 **NO OTO** *020 †45

KINSELLA, Timothy James. 11100 EUCLID AVE, CASE WESTERN RESERVE 44106 #035-45-1974 L1998 **IM** *020 †20,80

KIOUS, Alfred Gus. 13951 TERRACE RD 44112 #038-06-1977 L1978 **FM** *030 †18

KIRAN, Ravi Pokala. 9500 EUCLID AVE, CO CCF-GRAD MED EDU DEPT-N 44195 #495-21-1993 L2002 **CRS** *100 †85

KIRILCUK, Jana Daria. 11100 EUCLID AVE 44106 #286-02-1966 L1975 **AN** *020

KIRILCUK, Vladimir. 2074 ABINGTON RD 44106 #286-03-1950 L1975 **AN** *071

KIRKPATRICK, Kellie Lynn. ■ 44113 #038-44-2007 L2007 **EM** *012

KIRSCH, Alla Jodidio. 6559 WILSON MILLS RD # 107 44143 #035-19-1985 L1988 **FM** *020 †18

KIRSCHENBAUM, Donn Wm. 2500 METROHEALTH DR 44109 #020-02-1976 L1977 **DR NM** *040 †80

KIRSCHMAN, Jeffrey C. 12301 SNOW RD, PARMA MEDICAL CENTER 44130 #047-06-1993 L1994 **OM** *020 †70,18

KISER, William Sites. 5163 BROADWAY AVE 44127 #023-01-1953 L1964 **U** *071 †95

KISTANGARI, Gaurav. 18101 LORAIN AVE 44111 #495-21-2003 L2005 **IM** *012

KISTEMAKER, Aaron Rick. 11100 EUCLID AVE, HARVEY HOUSE ROOM 415 44106 #038-41-2003 L2003 **IM** *100 †20

KLATZKO, Neal Jay. 18697 BAGLEY RD 44130 #038-41-1968 L1968 **EM IM** *020 †20,16

KLEIN, Allan. 9500 EUCLID AVE, THE CLEVELAND CLINIC FOUND 44195 #067-01-1981 L1988 **CD IM** *020 †20

KLEIN, Christian Scott. 11100 EUCLID AVE, DEPT OF OPTH 44106 #035-15-2002 L2003 **OPH** *020

KLEIN, Eric Alan. 9500 EUCLID AVE, STE 100 44195 #041-12-1981 L1984 **U** *020 †95

KLEIN, Le Roy. 2074 ABINGTON RD DEPT ORTH 44106 #038-06-1965 L1965 **OS ORS** *050

KLEIN, Leonard Ross. 18697 BAGLEY RD, SOUTHWEST GENERAL 44130 #038-44-1987 L1989 **AN** *020 †05

KLEIN, Steven Michael. 29001 CEDAR RD STE 518, BEACHWOOD OB/GYN INC 44124 #038-40-1969 L1969 **OBG REN** *020 †30 ‡

KLEIN, Susan Kerins. 11100 EUCLID AVE 44106 #041-12-1981 L1989 **CHN PD** *075 †55,75

KLEMENCIC, Sarah Elizabet. ■ 44111 #038-06-2007 L2007 **EM** *012

KLEMME, Jay Carl. 11100 EUCLID AVE, UNIVERSITY HOSP OF CLEVELA 44106 #016-06-1979 L1985 **D OM** *020 †70,15

KLENK, Elizabeth Ellen. ■ 44130 #038-41-1996 L2000 **HO** *020

KLINE, Adam Michael. 2500 METROHEALTH DR 44109 #305-01-2005 L2005 **IM** *012

KLINE, Loan Trinh. 2500 METROHEALTH DR 44109 #305-01-2005 L2006 **PD** *012

KLUG, Rose Gubitosi. 11100 EUCLID AVE, RBC 6004 44106 #028-02-1999 L2000 **PDE** *100 †55

KNASEL, Anne H Lowe. 9700 ROCKSIDE RD, STE 115 44125 #024-05-1968 L1987 **PD** *071 †55

KNAUER, Kent Alan. 3909 ORANGE PL STE 2300 44122 #020-12-1975 L1984 **IM AI** *020 †20,03

KNOLL, Karen Chedvah. ■ 44118 #038-06-1989 *100

KNOPF, Simon Lee. ■ 44118 #038-06-1996 L2000 **GS TRS** *020 †85

KNOTHE, Ulf. 99 NORTHLINE CIR 44119 #869-02-1992 L2002 *020

KNOTT, Philip Daniel. ■ 44120 #005-18-2000 L2000 **OTO** *100 †45

KO, James Hyongjae. 9500 EUCLID AVE FA20, SLEEP DISORDERS CENTER/CLE 44195 #041-02-2002 L2007 **SME** *012

KOCH, Colleen Gorman. 9500 EUCLID AVE, (G-58) CLEVELAND CLINIC 44195 #038-41-1987 L1992 **AN** *020

KOCH, James Michael. 2322 E 22ND ST, STE 302 44115 #038-41-1985 L1987 **CD IM** *020 †20

KOCHHAR, Romeen. CLE CLINIC FNDTN, R35 FELLOWS OFFICE 44195 #041-07-1997 L2001 **IM** *020 †20

KODISH, Eric D. 9500 EUCLID AVE, BIOETHICSNAIO 44195 #038-44-1986 L1993 **PHO** *020 †55

KOEHLER, Matthew Paul. 7225 OLD OAK BLVD STE B3 44130 #038-43-1980 L1983 **OPH** *020 †35

KOH, Heajeoung Elizabeth. ■ 44113 #048-16-2007 L2007 **EM** *012

KOH, Poh-Koon. 9500 EUCLID AVE, CLEVELAND CLINIC FOUNDATIO 44195 #825-01-1996 L2006 *100

KOHN, Amitai Zion. 11100 EUCLID AVE, RAINBOW BABIES AND CHILDRE 44106 #550-03-2002 L2005 **NPM** *012 †55

KOHN, Howard D. ■ 44124 #038-06-1942 L1942 **OPH** *071 †35

KOHRMAN, Deborah Jan. 2500 METROHEALTH DR 44109 #038-06-1985 L1987 **PD** *100

KOLLUS, Helen Marie. 2500 METROHEALTH DR 44109 #038-41-2000 L2000 **IM** *020

KOMINSKY, Alan H. 9500 EUCLID AVE A71 44195 #041-13-1985 L1993 **OTO** *020 †45

KONDAPALLI, Prasadarao. 18099 LORAIN AVE, STE 14 44111 #495-11-1969 L1978 **PUD IM** *020

KONDOW, Alexander Jos. 2500 METROHEALTH DR, METRO HEALTH MEDICAL CENTE 44109 #038-06-1984 L1987 **DR** *020 †80

KONGTHONG, Nerissa V. 1925 SAINT CLAIR AVE NE, # K 44114 #748-01-1963 L1974 **PD** *020 †55

KONIARCZYK, Michael Paul. ■ 44113 #035-15-2007 L2007 **MPD** *012

KONSTAN, Michael Wm. 2101 ADELBERT RD, STE 3001 44106 #038-06-1982 L1982 **PUD PD** *050 †55

KONTI, Jon Andrew. 11100 EUCLID AVE, DEPT OPH 44106 #038-41-2006 L2006 **OPH** *012

KOO, Anna Ping-Yun. 9500 EUCLID AVE, RHEUMATIC & IMMUNOLOGIC DI 44195 #033-05-1978 L1980 **OS RHU** *020 †20

KOO, Bon Chul. 25001 EMERY RD, STE 100 44128 #583-04-1970 L1979 **DR** *020 †80

KOO, Brian Bon-Jeong. 10701 EAST BLVD, DEPARTMENT OF NEUROLOGY 44106 #024-07-2001 L2005 **CN** *100 †75

KOOLWIJK, Irene. 9500 EUCLID AVE, `44195 #660-03-2003 L2006 **PD** *012

KOONTZ, Daniel Wesley. 11100 EUCLID AVE, DEPARTMENT OF NEUROLOGY 44106 #012-01-2001 L2001 **CN** *100 †75

KOPLAS, Monica Carolina. ■ 44195 #026-04-2004 L2005 **DR** *012

KOPYEVA, Tatyana Mikhailo. 9500 EUCLID AVE, CLEVELAND CLINIC FOUNDATIO 44195 #913-06-1987 L2000 **AN** *020 †05

KORI, Umakant Rachappa. ■ 44113 #051-07-2006 L2007 **FP** *012

KORMAN, Neil J. 11100 EUCLID AVE, DEPT OF DEMTLGY UNIV HOSP 44106 #038-06-1984 L1985 **D** *020 †15

KORSAH, Nana Nyarko. 2500 METROHEALTH DR, DEPT OF MEDICINE 44109 #038-45-2004 L2004 **IM** *100 †20

KOSDROSKY, Martin Anthony. 6900 PEARL RD, STE 200 44130 #038-43-1994 L2002 **U GS** *020 †95

KOSTENKO, Olga. 9500 EUCLID AVE, CLEVELAND CLINIC FOUNDATIO 44195 #913-98-1996 L2006 **P** *012

KOTAGAL, Prakash. DESK S-51, 9500 EUCLID AVE, CLEVELAND CLINIC FOUNDATIO 44195 #495-53-1980 L1988 **PD N** *012 †20

KOTHARI, Shakuntala. 9500 EUCLID AVE, S-70 44195 #028-46-1993 L1994 **IM** *020 †20

KOUBEISSI, Mohamad Zakari. 11100 EUCLID AVE, HANNA HOUSE ROOO 544 44106 #605-01-1999 L2006 **CN** *100 †75

KOVACEVIC, Olga. 18181 PEARL RD, STE B202 44136 #038-45-1994 L1995 **FM** *020 †18

KOVACH, Ralph John. 9700 GARFIELD BLVD 44125 #016-43-1953 L1953 **ORS** *020 †40

KOVALENKO, Oleg Georgievi. 11100 EUCLID AVE 44106 #913-10-1996 L2005 **PDC** *012

KOVES, Gabor. 13951 TERRACE RD, HURON ROAD HOSP-INTERNAL M 44112 #473-03-1993 L2000 **IM** *100 †20

KOWAL, Jerome. 10900 EUCLID AVE, DEANS OFFICE T110 SCH MED 44106 #023-07-1956 L1970 **IMG END** *020 †20

KOWALSKI, Timothy Felix. 300 N COMMONS BLVD 44143 #025-01-1983 L1989 **PUD CCM** *020 †20

KOZOKOFF, Norman J. 1 MOUNT SINAI DR 44106 #016-43-1949 L1955 **IM** *071 †20

KRAENZLER, Erik John. 9500 EUCLID AVE 44195 #056-06-1983 L1988 **AN CCA** *020 †05

KRAJEWSKI, Dorota Anna. 9500 EUCLID AVE, CLEVELAND CLINIC FNDN 44195 #759-18-2006 L2006 **IM** *012

KRAJEWSKI, Leonard Paul. 9500 EUCLID AVE DEPT SURG, S-40 44195 #041-09-1973 L1975 **VS GS** *020 †85

KRAKOVITZ, Paul Rabin. 9500 EUCLID AVE, A71 44195 #017-20-1997 L2002 **OTO** *020

KRALL, Joseph I. 11100 EUCLID AVE, UNIV HOSPITALS OF CLEVELAN 44106 #035-06-1965 L1968 **DR** *020 †20

KRAMER, Amanda Marie. ■ 44118 #023-01-2007 L2007 **PD** *012

KRAMER, Bradley Robert. 11100 EUCLID AVE, UNIV HOSP 44106 #023-01-2007 L2007 **PD** *012

KRAMER, Daniel A. 5850 LANDERBROOK DR, STE 220 44124 #035-03-1971 L1973 **PD** *020 †55

KRAMER, John Robt, Jr. 9500 EUCLID AVE, THE CLINIC CENTER 44195 #051-01-1969 L1971 **CD IM** *020

KRANYAK, Margaret Sue. 18200 LORAIN AVE 44111 #038-41-1984 L1991 **RO** *020 †80

KRASNEY, Ronald Howard. 11100 EUCLID AVE 44106 #051-01-1979 L1983 **OPH** *020 †35

KRASUSKI, Richard Andrew. 9500 EUCLID AENUE DESK F15, CARDIOVASCULAR MEDICINE 44195 #024-01-1994 L2005 **CD IM** *020 †20

KRAUSE, Marycatheri L. 2500 METROHEALTH DR, METROHEALTH MEDICAL CENTER 44109 #038-06-1984 L1991 **IM** *075

KRAVITZ, Alan Eric. 6780 MAYFIELD RD 44124 #041-02-1969 L1975 **CD IM** *020 †20

KRCIK, James Anthony. 9500 EUCLID AVE, CCF 44195 #016-45-1994 L1999 **ORS** *012 †20,55

KREBS, Viktor Erik. 9500 EUCLID AVE 44195 #038-40-1992 L1997 **ORS** *020 †40

KREINER, Allison Elizabet. ■ 44106 #038-06-2008 *012

KREYMERMAN, Peter A. 9500 EUCLID AVE, DEPT OF PLASTIC SURGERY - 44195 #038-41-2001 L2001 **PS** *012

KRIEG, Alexys Ranee. ■ 44118 #038-06-2008 *012

KRIEGER, Derk Wolfgang. 9500 EUCLID AVE, CLEVELAND CLINIC FOUNDATIO 44195 #409-39-1984 L1998 *020

KRIEGER, Silke. 9500 EUCLID AVE 91, GENERAL INTERNAL MEDICINE 44195 #409-10-1994 L2000 **IM** *020 †20

KRIEGLER, Jennifer S. 9500 EUCLID AVE T33 44195 #035-06-1976 L1980 **N PMM** *020 †75

KRISHNA, Jyoti. 9500 EUCLID AVE FA-20, CLEVELAND CLINIC 44195 #495-45-1988 L2007 **PD** *020 †55

KRISHNAMURTHI, Swetha. 11100 EUCLID AVE, C/O UNIV HOSPS-RESIDENCY O 44106 #495-45-1995 L2002 **PD** *100

KRISHNAMURTHI, Venkatesh. 9500 EUCLID AVE, STE 100 44195 #038-06-1993 L1995 **U** *020 †95

KRISHNAN, Sudhir. 2500 METROHEALTH DR, DEPT OF RESIDENCY SUPPORT 44109 #496-44-2000 L2006 **IM** *012

KRISHNAN, Vidya. 2500 METROHEALTH DR, BG3-37 44109 #025-01-1999 L2007 **PCC** *100 †20

KRISHNANEY, Ajit Ashok. 9500 EUCLID AVE, THE CLEVELAND CLINIC FOUND 44195 #056-05-1999 L1999 **NS** *100

KRISHNASWAMY, Amar. ■ 44195 #008-01-2003 L2006 **CD** *012 †20

KROEN, Collin David. 9500 EUCLID AVE, MAIL STOP A72 44195 #017-20-1997 L2000 **IM** *020 †20

KROFINA, Mark Emil. 2500 METROHEALTH DR, METROHEALTH MEDICAL CENTER 44109 #038-06-1996 L1997 **FM** *020 †18

KROH, Matthew Duane. CLINIC FOUNDATION, CLEVELAND 44195 #035-47-2002 L2002 **GS** *100 †85

KRUEGER, Ronald Robt. 9500 EUCLID AVE, I/32 44195 #033-05-1987 L1998 **OPH OS** *020 †35

KRUMMEN, Paul Jerome. ■ 44120 #038-40-2003 L2005 **AN** *012

KRUPKIN, Richard Scott. 4450 SAINT CLAIR AVE 44103 #422-01-1993 L1997 **PM OM** *020 †60

KUENZLER, Rebecca Mc Carr. 9500 EUCLID AVE, CLEVELAND CLINIC FOUNDATIO 44195 #038-43-2000 L2000 **CN** *100 †75

KUFEL, Mark Francis. 12301 SNOW RD, PARMA MEDICAL CENTER 44130 #038-44-1990 L1994 **OBG** *020 †30

■ = Address Information Privacy Protected

KUHEL, Alan Gilbert. 9500 EUCLID AVE 44195 #025-07-1987 L1991 **AN** *020 †05

KUIVILA, Thomas E. 9500 EUCLID AVE, A41 CLEVELAND CLINIC 44195 #040-02-1983 L1991 **OP** *020 †40

KUJAWA, Mary Jean. 11400 EUCLID AVE 44106 #038-06-1990 L1991 **P** *020 †75

KUKREJA, Navrajan. 1 BRATENAHL PL STE 6 44108 #495-45-1983 L1997 **CCA AN** *020 †05

KUKUNOOR, Rajesh Naidu. 9500 EUCLID AVE R35 44195 #495-21-1994 L2002 **HO** *020 †20

KULLMAN, Valeria Sue. ■ 44130 #055-01-1967 L1984 **R** *071 †80

KUMAR, Ajay. 9500 EUCLID AVE # A-13, CLEVELAND CLINIC 44195 #496-39-1996 L2001 **IM** *100 †20

KUMAR, Deepak. 2500 METROHEALTH DR, RM 249 44109 #496-09-1986 L1998 **PD NPM** *020 †55

KUMAR, Mary L. 2500 METROHEALTH DR, RM H423 44109 #038-06-1967 L1967 **PD ID** *072 †55

KUMAR, P K Unni. 18660 BAGLEY RD, STE 501 44130 #495-31-1962 L1970 **GE IM** *020 †20

KUMAR, Praneet. 9500 EUCLID AVE 44195 #038-38-2003 L2007 **IM** *012

KUMAR, Sunita. 11100 EUCLID AVE, DEPT OF PSYCHIATRY 44106 #495-15-1991 L2000 **P** *020

KUMARAVEL, Arthi. 9500 EUCLID AVE 44195 #496-32-2005 L2007 **IM** *012

KUMBHANI, Dharam Jaydeep. ■ 44114 #495-01-2002 L2007 **IM** *100 †20

KUNDRANDA, Madappa Nanaya. 18101 LORAIN AVE, DEPT OF INTERNAL MED 44111 #496-34-2000 L2006 **IM** *012

KUNDRANDA, Roshni Madappa. 18101 LORAIN AVE 44111 #495-37-2000 L2003 **IM** *020 †20

KUNDTZ, Ewald E, III. 18101 LORAIN AVE 44111 #038-06-1989 L1990 **IM** *020 †20

KUNGL, Martin John. 18697 BAGLEY RD, DEPARTMENT OF ANESTHESIA 44130 #038-40-1991 L1992 **AN** *020 †05

KUNHI VEEDU, Hari Prasad. 9500 EUCLID AVE, DEPT OF GME 44195 #495-44-1989 L2006 **IM** *012

KUNKEL, Robert Scott, Jr. 9500 EUCLID AVE, NEUROLOGY T 33 44195 #041-12-1960 L1960 **OS IM** *020 †20

KUNKEL, Thomas John, Jr. 11100 EUCLID AVE 44106 #038-41-1990 L1991 **CCA** *020 †05,16

KUNOS, Charles Andrew. 11100 EUCLID AVE B181, UNIVERSITY HOSP/RADIATON O 44106 #038-06-2001 L2001 **RO** *100

KUNTJORO, Ivandrito. 9500 EUCLID AVE, CLEVELAND CLINIC FNDN 44195 #506-02-2001 L2006 **IM** *012

KUO, Jana. ■ 44120 #010-01-2005 L2005 **OPH** *012

KUO, Meiying. 11100 EUCLID AVE, C/O UNIV HOSPS-RESIDENCY O 44106 #048-16-2002 L2002 **GS** *100 †85

KUPCZAK, Bohdan. 2001 CROCKER RD, STE 650 44145 #154-02-1966 L1973 **OBG** *020 †30

KUPPALA, Venkata Sasidhar. 9500 EUCLID AVE, CLEVELAND CLINIC FOUNDATIO 44195 #495-58-1998 L2005 **NPM** *012

KURPAD, Shekar N S. 11100 EUCLID AVE 3018, CO UNIV HOSPS-RESIDENCY OF 44106 #495-33-1991 L2000 **NS** *020 †25

KURSH, Elroy Donald. 9500 EUCLID AVE, STE 100 44195 #038-40-1963 L1963 **U** *020 †85,95

KURUP, Ramachandra. 4269 PEARL RD 44109 #495-04-1959 L1969 **GS** *071 †85

KURZ, Sebastian Gerhard. 11100 EUCLID AVE, UNIVERSITY HOSPITALS 44106 #409-20-2004 L2007 **IM** *012

KUSHNER, Irving. 2500 METROHEALTH DR, METROHEALTH MEDICAL CENTER 44109 #028-02-1954 L1958 **RHU IM** *062 †20

KUSHNIR, Ori. 730 SOM CENTER RD, STE 340 44143 #550-02-1984 L1991 **OBG OS** *020 †30

KUTELIA, Rajden. 13951 TERRACE RD, MERIDA HURON HOSP 44112 #912-02-1997 L2001 **IM** *100

KUYN, Erik Olphert. 2500 METROHEALTH DR 44109 #422-01-2004 L2004 **PM** *012

KWAK, Yun Sik. ■ 44145 #583-04-1961 L1975 **CLP PCH** *040 †50

KWOK, Pauline. 18101 LORAIN AVE, FAIRVIEW HOSPITAL 44111 #020-12-1994 L1999 **DR NM** *020 †80,28

KWON, Deborah H. ■ 44103 #025-01-2002 L2005 **CD** *012 †20

KWON, Eunji. ■ 44114 #041-01-2005 L2006 **D** *012

KWON, Ki Ho. 10701 EAST BLVD 44106 #583-04-1966 L1971 **PTH** *020 †50

KWONG, Shu Keung. 9500 EUCLID AVE BOX 577 44195 #462-01-1988 *100

KYEI, Joseph Oforiwaa. ■ 44195 #038-06-2006 L2006 **D** *012

KYPRIANOU, Annette Marie. 4330 W 150TH ST 44135 #038-44-1992 L1996 **GE** *020 †20

KYRKOS, Spiros Gregory. 26410 CENTER RIDGE RD 44145 #418-01-1954 L1964 **FM** *071

LABABEDE, Omar. 9500 EUCLID AVE HB6, CLEVELAND CLINIC FOUNDATIO 44195 #875-01-1992 L2000 **R OS** *020 †80

LABASTILLE, Joseph Y. 2500 E 79TH ST, METROHEALTH CLEMENT CENTER 44104 #440-01-1974 L1999 **FM** *020 †18

LA BEAUD, Angelle Desiree. 11100 EUCLID AVE, C/O UNIV HOSPS-MED EDU DEP 44106 #056-06-2000 L2000 **PD** *100 †55

LACEY, Stephen Henderson. 1611 S GREEN RD STE 27 44121 #038-40-1969 L1969 **ORS HS** *020 †40

LACHEY, Bradley Justin. 9500 EUCLID AVE, CO CCF-GRAD MED EDU DEPT-N 44195 #038-45-1999 L2003 **PTH** *020

LACHHWANI, Deepak K. 9500 EUCLID AVE, MS 51 44195 #495-49-1991 L2000 **N** *020 †55,75

LACHHWANI, Maria Del P. 3518 W 25TH ST 44109 #264-05-1989 L2002 **CHP** *012

LAGAZZI GARROS, Luigi Fab. 9500 EUCLID AVE, CLEVELAND CLINIC FOUNDATIO 44195 #231-01-1995 L2005 *100

LAGMAN, Ruth L. HEMOLOGY/ONCOLOGY R35, CLEVELAND CLINIC FOUNDATIO 44195 #748-01-1986 L1999 **IM PLM** *020 †20

LAGUNZAD, Simplicio Pabro. ■ 44195 #748-01-1950 *071

LAHAM, Riad. 9500 EUCLID AVE 44195 #875-01-1980 L1984 **AN** *074 †05

LAHORRA, Ignacio Garcia. 11100 EUCLID AVE 44106 #748-01-1954 L1963 **GP GS** *071

LAHORRA, Joseph Anthony. 6707 POWERS BLVD STE 303, DIV OF CARDIOTHORACIC SURG 44129 #023-07-1988 L1997 **TS** *020 †85,90

LAHUD, Luis Armando. 2500 METROHEALTH DR A-107, METROHEALTH MED CTR/ANESTH 44109 #341-04-2000 L2002 **AN** *100

LAI, Keith Kaytar. 9500 EUCLID AVE L25, CLEVELAND CLINIC 44195 #028-34-2007 L2007 **PTH** *012

LAI, Kwok Keung Thoma. 1 MOUNT SINAI DR DEPT MED 44106 #462-01-1989 L1989 **IM** *020

LAI, Yih-Wen. 9500 EUCLID AVE, STE 100 44195 #244-03-1965 L1978 **U** *020 †95

LAKIN, Milton Maxwell. 9500 EUCLID AVE, STE 100 44195 #016-02-1972 L1974 **IM HEM** *020 †20

LALLI, Lorenzo Saturnino. 18099 LORAIN AVE, STE 14 44111 #561-01-1984 L1987 **IM** *020 †20

LALUK, Michael Alexander. 6688 RIDGE RD STE 1105 44129 #561-17-1979 L1983 **IM** *020 †20

LAM, Buh-Khanh. ■ 44195 #067-01-1994 L2000 *100

LAM, Cathy Tse-Fun. 9500 EUCLID AVE, C/O CCF-GRAD MED DEPT- 44195 #462-01-1992 L2000 **ICE** *100

LAM, Mildred. 2500 METROHEALTH DR 44109 #038-06-1973 L1975 **NEP** *050 †20

LAM, Trung Minh. ■ 44113 #019-02-2007 L2007 **IM** *012

LAM, Yui Ming. 9500 EUCLID AVE, CO CCF-GRAD MED EDU DEPT-N 44195 #462-01-1992 L2000 **CD** *100

LAMARRE, Eric Donald. ■ 44121 #041-14-2005 L2005 **OTO** *012

LAMB, Steven Alan. 18099 LORAIN AVE, STE 141 44111 #016-11-1979 L1984 **U** *020 †95

LAMBERT, Lisa Marie. 3929 ROCKY RIVER DR, CENTER FOR FAMILIES & CHIL 44111 #038-44-1995 L1996 **P** *012

LAMBERT, Renee Susanne. 10701 EAST BLVD 44106 #038-41-2001 L2001 **IM** *020

LAMM, Michael Emanuel. 2085 ADELBERT RD 44106 #035-45-1959 L1981 **ATP** *050 †50

LAMPERT, Elmer Graham. 12000 MCCRACKEN RD, STE 465 44125 #016-42-1972 L1975 **CRS** *071 †85,10

LAMPERT, Virginia. 11100 EUCLID AVE 44106 #016-42-1972 L1975 **DR** *020 †80

LANCIONE, Raymond Robert, Jr. 2500 METROHEALTH DR, DIV OF OPHTHALMOLOGY 44109 #041-12-1996 L2000 **OPH** *020 †35

LANCIONI, Christina L. 11100 EUCLID AVE, RAINBOW BABIES & CHILDREN' 44106 #041-01-2006 L2006 **PDI** *012 †55

LANDEN, Katherine Evans. 2500 METROHEALTH DR 44109 #038-06-2005 L2005 **EM** *012

LANDERS, Steven Howard. 11100 EUCLID AVE 44106 #038-06-2003 L2004 **IMG** *012 †18

LANDO, Ane Vibeke. CASE WESTRN RES U SCH MED 44106 #038-06-1987 *020

LANDRY, Beverly L. 13301 MILES AVE 44105 #024-05-1976 L1988 **PD** *020 †55

LANE, Brian Robert. 9500 EUCLID AVE, GLICKMAN UROLOGICAL AND KI 44195 #025-01-2002 L2002 **U** *012

LANE, Geoffrey Kevin. 9500 EUCLID AVE, CLEVELAND CLINIC 44195 #143-03-1987 L1999 **PDC** *100

LANE, James, Jr. 6780 MAYFIELD RD 44124 #035-20-1978 L1979 **CD IM** *020 †20

LANE, Juanita. ■ 44120 #038-06-1994 **P** *100

LANE, Kenneth. 2500 METROHEALTH DR, CANCER CARE PAVILLON 44109 #025-12-1975 L1980 **RO** *020 †80

LANG, David Michael. 9500 EUCLID AVE, ALLERGY C22 44195 #025-01-1980 L2002 **AI IM** *020 †20,03

LANG, Richard Stephen. 9500 EUCLID AVE, DESK A-11 44195 #038-41-1979 L1980 **IM GPM** *020 †20,70

LANGE, Christoph G M. 11100 EUCLID AVE, UNIV HOSPSMED EDUCATION DE 44106 #409-44-1994 L2000 **ID** *100

LANGER, Nathan Ernest. 11100 EUCLID AVE, UNIV HOSP OF CLEVELAND 44106 #017-20-2005 L2005 **IM** *012

LANGEVIN, Claude-Jean. ■ 44113 #035-20-2004 L2007 **PS** *012

LANGFORD, Carol Anne. 9500 EUCLID AVE A50, CLEVELAND CLINIC FOUNDATIO 44195 #005-14-1987 L2004 **RHU** *020 †20

LANGSTON, Roger H S. 9500 EUCLID AVE, CLEVELAND CLINIC I32 44195 #067-01-1965 L1974 **OPH** *020 †35

LANNING, John Thos, Jr. 2351 E 22ND ST # AL 44115 #038-40-1960 L1960 **NEP IM** *020

LANZIERI, Chas Frederick. 11100 EUCLID AVE, STE 2600 44106 #035-09-1978 L1985 **DR** *020 †80

LAPEYROLERIE, Jeffrey C. 19250 BAGLEY RD, STE 107 44130 #035-20-1986 L1992 **U GS** *020 †95

LAPINSKI, James Edward. ■ 44118 #038-40-2007 L2007 **PTH** *012

LARCHIAN, William Aram. 9500 EUCLID AVE, STE 100 44195 #024-05-1984 L1997 **U SO** *012

LARRIGAN, John Reynolds. 9500 EUCLID AVE, VASC & INTERVENT RADIO 44195 #062-01-1996 L2001 *100

LASCANO, Martin Eduardo. 9500 EUCLID AVE M82 44195 #264-05-1999 L2001 **IM NEP** *020 †20

LASH, David Chase. 7225 OLD OAK BLVD, STE A210 44130 #038-43-1984 L1985 **FM** *020 †18

LASHGARI-SAEGH, Shamsi. 1730 W 25TH ST, MEDICAL ARTS BLDG. RM 1100 44113 #517-01-1968 L1980 **PM** *020 †60

LASHIN, Ossama Mamdouh Mo. 11100 EUCLID AVE, DEPT OF INTERNAL MEDICINE 44106 #915-04-1995 L2004 **END** *012

LASHNER, Bret Auerbach. 9500 EUCLID AVE, DESK A30 44195 #035-19-1980 L1992 **GE** *020 †20

LASKEY, Sara Lehman. 2500 METROHEALTH DR, METROHEALTH MEDICAL CENTER 44109 #038-06-2004 L2004 **EM** *100

LASSAR, Tom Albert. 11100 EUCLID AVE, UNIV HOSP CLEVELAND 44106 #028-34-1977 L1988 **CD IM** *020 †20

LATHWELL, Margaret Janet. 2500 E 79TH ST 44104 #041-07-1983 L1986 **FM** *020 †18

LATIFI, Samir Q. 2074 ABINGTON RD, UNIVERSITY HOSPS 44106 #917-23-1990 L1997 **CCP** *100 †55

LATSON, Larry Allen. 2801 MARTIN LTHR KNG JR DR 44104 #048-04-1976 L1993 **PDC CCP** *020 †55

LAUER, Michael S. 9500 EUCLID AVE, CLEVELAND CLINIC FOUNDATIO 44195 #035-03-1985 L1993 **CD IM** *020 †20

LAUGHLIN, Mary Joan. 11100 EUCLID AVE, CASE WESTERN RESERVE UNIV 44106 #035-06-1988 L1998 **ON** *020 †20

LAURENCIC, Djurdjica. 9500 EUCLID AVE, C/O CCF-GRAD MED DEPT- 44195 #957-02-1995 L2001 **PYM** *100 †75

LAVERTU, Pierre. 11100 EUCLID AVE, UNIV HOSPITALS CASE MEDICA 44106 #067-02-1976 L1983 **OTO HNS** *020 †45

LAVERY, Aleksandyr W. 11100 EUCLID AVE, DEPT. OF NEUROSURGERY 44106 #056-06-2000 L2000 **NS** *012

LAVIN, Thomas Jos. 9500 EUCLID AVE, DESK A-81 44195 #038-40-1960 L1960 **AN** *071 †05

LAWAS, Francisco Laudato. ■ 44130 #748-02-1953 L1964 **AN** *071 †05

LAWRENCE, Ann Elizabeth. ■ 44113 #038-44-2004 L2004 **AN** *012

LAWTON, Jeffrey Nathan. 9500 EUCLID AVE # A40 44195 #025-01-1993 L2002 **ORS HS** *020 †20

LAZARONY, Robert Jos. 4229 PEARL RD 44109 #056-06-1967 L1968 **DR** *071 †80

LAZARUS, Hillard Michael. 11100 EUCLID AVE 44106 #035-45-1974 L1975 **ON HEM** *050 †20

LAZARYAN, Aleksandr. 9500 EUCLID AVE, DEPT OF GME 44195 #913-38-1997 L2006 **IM** *012

LAZBIN, Marina. 2500 METROHEALTH DR 44109 #913-16-1989 L2003 **PD** *100 †55

LAZEBNIK, Rina. 11100 EUCLID AVE 44106 #550-02-1975 L1989 **PD ADM** *020 †55

LE, Tien Viet. ■ 44195 #011-04-2004 L2004 **NS** *012

LEA, Ethan Scott. ■ 44125 #038-06-2008 *012

LEAK, Byron Christopher. 2500 METROHEALTH DR, CO METROHEALTH MED CTR-RES 44109 #038-06-2002 L2003 **AN** *100

LEAR, Aaron Michael. 11100 EUCLID AVE, FAMILY MEDICINE-BOLWELL CL 44106 #038-40-2003 L2003 **FSM** *020 †18

LEBRON, Roberto. 3569 RIDGE RD, NEIGHBORHOOD FAMILY 44102 #042-01-1997 L2005 **FM** *020 †18

LECHNER, Roseanna Marie. 2500 METROHEALTH DR 44109 #038-06-1988 L1990 **NS** *020 †25
LECKY, Kerry Anne. 11100 EUCLID AVE RM 3018, CO UNIV HOSPS-RESIDENCY OF 44106 #041-15-2003 L2003 **FP** *012
LEDERER, Joan Alice. 2460 FAIRMOUNT BLVD, STE 320 44106 #025-12-1984 L1990 **CHP** *020 †75
LEDERMAN, Michael M. 2074 ABINGTON RD INF DIS 44106 #035-47-1974 L1980 **ID IM** *050 †20
LEDERMAN, Richard J. 9500 EUCLID AVE # S-91 44195 #035-06-1966 L1973 **N OS** *020 †75
LEDTKE, Christopher Steve. 9500 EUCLID AVE 44195 #654-01-2007 L2007 **IM** *012
LEE, Ae-Ja Son. 11100 SAINT CLAIR AVE 44108 #583-01-1966 L1972 **PD** *020 †55
LEE, Amy Faye. 12000 MCCRACKEN RD, STE 351 44125 #038-44-1988 L1990 **PHP** *030 †70
LEE, Benjamin. ■ 44106 #038-06-2008 *012
LEE, Brian Jen. ■ 44118 #041-01-2005 L2005 **OPH** *012
LEE, Byron Hinglung. ■ 44120 #023-07-2007 L2007 **GS** *012
LEE, Chi Hoon. 6803 MAYFIELD RD, STE 519 44124 #583-02-1969 L1979 **PTH** *020 †50
LEE, Chin Wook. 11100 SAINT CLAIR AVE 44108 #583-01-1966 L1971 **IM** *020
LEE, Chun-Kyu. 6100 W CREEK RD, ROCKSIDE RADIOLOGY INC 44131 #583-06-1956 L1975 **P** *071
LEE, Currie. ■ 44106 #016-11-2006 L2007 **AN** *012
LEE, Dae Kyu. 9500 EUCLID AVE, CO CCF-GRAD MED EDU DEPT-N 44195 #583-02-1995 L2003 *020
LEE, Hasoon. 25001 EMERY RD, STE 100 44128 #583-12-1973 L1977 **DR** *020 †80
LEE, Jennifer Kim. ■ 44118 #035-45-2008 *012
LEE, John C. 11100 EUCLID AVE, CASE WESTERN RESERVE 44106 #035-46-1999 L1999 **CCS** *100
LEE, Joung Hoon. 9500 EUCLID AVE R20, CLEVELAND CLINIC FOUNDTN 44195 #005-06-1986 L1993 **NS** *020 †25
LEE, Katherine Bo. 9500 EUCLID AVE, A10 44195 #038-44-1990 L1993 **IM** *020 †20
LEE, Ke Suk. 9500 EUCLID AVE 44195 #583-02-1973 L1980 **AN** *020 †05
LEE, Kyu-Duck. 18099 LORAIN AVE, STE 541 44111 #583-01-1963 L1970 **CD IM** *071
LEE, Michael Chung. ■ 44195 #016-06-2006 L2006 **U** *012
LEE, Pyng. 9500 EUCLID AVE, CO CCF-GRAD MED EU DEPT-NA 44195 #825-01-1990 L2000 *100
LEE, Richard Garrett. ■ 44121 #030-06-2003 L2003 **OTO** *012
LEE, Roger Paul. 9500 EUCLID AVE, CLEVELAND CLC DEPT RADIO 44195 #033-05-2000 L2006 **MSR** *100 †80
LEE, Sang Soon. 26025 BROADWAY AVE 44146 #583-03-1956 L1978 **FM** *020
LEE, Sara Hirschfeld. 3948 W MEADOW LN 44122 #038-06-2001 L2001 **ADL** *020 †55
LEE, Teng Chun. 11100 EUCLID AVE 44106 #028-02-1999 L1999 **TS** *012
LEE, Una Jeanie. ■ 44195 #005-11-2003 L2004 *100
LEE, Walter Tsong. 9500 EUCLID AVE A71, CLEVELAND CLINIC 44195 #010-01-1999 L1999 **HNS OTO** *050 †45
LEE, Weng-Hon. 9500 EUCLID AVE, TT32 44195 #539-06-1992 **IM** *100
LEE, Yann-Jinn. ■ 44121 #244-04-1977 **PDE** *020
LEEN, Hans. ■ 44101 #385-02-1950 L1962 **AN** *071
LEGRAND, Susan Buchanan. 9500 EUCLID AVE, R 35 44195 #045-04-1983 L1998 **OS ON** *020 †20
LEGUIZAMON, Mario Cesar. 6688 RIDGE RD STE 1230 44129 #132-02-1964 L1971 **IM CD** *071
LEHNER, Thomas Stephen. 1001 LAKESIDE AVE E, STE 1000 44114 #038-44-1982 L1983 **FM** *020 †18 ‡
LEHOUX, Juan Manuel. 9500 EUCLID AVE, CLEVELAND CLINIC FOUNDATIO 44195 #308-04-2003 L2006 **GS** *012
LEIGH, R John. 11100 EUCLID AVE, STE 5512 44106 #917-04-1970 L1983 **N OPH** *020 †75
LEMYRE, Martin Stephen. 2500 METROHEALTH DR 44109 #665-01-2006 L2006 **IM** *012
LENHARD, Amanda Hymel. 30680 BAINBRIDGE RD, COMMUNITY HOSPITALISTS 44139 #038-06-2002 L2002 **IM** *100 †20
LENKOSKI, L Douglas. 11100 EUCLID AVE 44106 #038-06-1953 L1953 **P** *072
LENNON, Anne Marie. 9500 EUCLID AVE 44195 #539-06-1996 *100
LEON-RUIZ, Elias Nicolas. 11100 EUCLID AVE 44106 #319-03-1969 L1979 **AN CD** *020 †05
LEOTTA, Eros. 9500 EUCLID AVE, CLEVELAND CLINIC FOUNDATIO 44195 #561-20-1990 L2006 *100
LERNER, Alan Jay. 11100 EUCLID AVE, STE 5512 44106 #035-20-1987 L1989 **N IMG** *020 †75
LERNER, Allan N. ■ 44120 #038-06-1962 L1963 **DR VIR** *020 †80
LERNER, Phillip Irwin. 11100 EUCLID AVE 44106 #038-06-1958 L1958 **ID IM** *071
LESITSKY, Marc Andrew. 19250 BAGLEY RD 44130 #041-14-1993 L1996 **CCA** *020 †05
LESLIE, Hugh J, Jr. 1611 S GREEN RD, STE 35 44121 #038-06-1949 L1949 **PD** *071 †55
LESTER, Harvey Alan. 29525 CHAGRIN BLVD, STE 107 44122 #016-42-1961 L1962 **OPH OS** *020 †35
LETSINGER, Darrin Blane. ■ 44106 #021-05-2003 L2007 **AN** *100
LETSINGER, Kelly Ryder. ■ 44106 #021-05-2003 L2007 **IM** *100 †20
LEU, James Alfred. 2500 E 79TH ST, FOR FAMILY HEALTH CARE 44104 #038-06-1963 L1963 **PD** *020
LEUNG, Cynthia G. 2500 METROHEALTH DR, DEPT OF EMERGENCY MEDICINE 44109 #041-15-2003 L2003 **EM** *100 †16
LEUNG, Dominic Yiu Cheong. 9500 EUCLID AVE 44195 #462-01-1984 L1996 **CD** *020
LEUNG, Steven Hin-Chiu. ■ 44106 #038-06-2007 L2007 **GS** *012
LEVER, Harry Miles. 9500 EUCLID AVE, DESK F15 44195 #041-12-1971 L1978 **CD** *020 †20
LEVESQUE, Gilles, Jr. ■ 44120 #067-06-1980 **NPM PD** *020
LEVIEN, Michael Gerald. 9500 EUCLID AVE S20, CLEVELAND CLINIC FOUNDATION 44195 #011-02-1972 L1989 **HEM PD** *050 †55
LEVIN, Jared Stephen. 6789 RIDGE RD, STE 100 44129 #025-01-1995 L2001 **OSM** *020 †40
LEVIN, Kerry Hartley. 9500 EUCLID AVE, CLEVELAND CLINIC 44195 #023-07-1977 L1984 **N CN** *020 †75
LEVIN, Lora Bartolet. 11100 EUCLID AVE 44106 #041-01-1995 L2001 **AN** *020 †05
LEVINE, Michael Alan. 9500 EUCLID AVE, DIV OF PEDIATRICS, LRI SD2 44195 #041-09-1976 L2003 **END IM** *050 †20
LEVINE, Ralph J. ■ 44102 #038-06-1978 L1987 **IM** *071
LEW, Ronald Dean. 10701 EAST BLVD 44106 #016-43-1972 L1984 **DR** *020 †80
LEW, Thomas Wing Kit. ■ 44120 #038-06-1985 **AN** *100
LEWANDOWSKI, Ernest A. 5706 TURNEY RD, EASTSIDE PHYSICIANS INC 44125 #005-15-1962 L1975 **GP** *075
LEWIS, Brenda Sue. 9500 EUCLID AVE, E31 44195 #038-75-1981, ▲ L1982 **AN** *020 †05
LEWIS, Carol Elaine. ■ 44113 #024-07-1988 L1991 **P** *020
LEWIS, Hilel. 9500 EUCLID AVE, OPHTH I30 44195 #649-31-1979 L1993 **OPH** *020 †35
LEWIS, Michael Robin. 18101 LORAIN AVE 44111 #654-01-2005 L2005 **FP** *012

LEWIS, Richard Phelps. 9500 EUCLID AVE, THE CLEVELAND CLINIC 44195 #040-02-1961 L1969 **CD IM** *020 †20
LEWIS, William Robt. 2500 METROHEALTH DR, METROHEALTH MEDICAL CTR 44109 #038-40-1986 L1989 **CD IM** *020 †20
LEYES, Manuel. 9500 EUCLID AVE 44195 #847-11-1991 L1999 **OSM** *100
LI, Charles Shuhang. 6681 RIDGE RD STE 303 44129 #028-34-1957 L1961 **PS HS** *071 †85,65
LI, Li. 11100 EUCLID AVE, STE 1200 44106 #243-52-1986 L2000 **FM** *020 †18
LI, Morgan Kuangtsu. ■ 44113 #035-15-2006 L2006 **EM** *012
LI, Xiaxin. 11100 EUCLID AVE 44106 #243-74-1983 L2004 **PHO** *012 †55
LIAM, Beng Lin. 9500 EUCLID AVE 44195 #825-01-1984 **PUD** *100
LIAMBEIS, John. ■ 44124 #038-06-1952 L1952 **IM** *071 †20
LICATA, Angelo Anthony. 9500 EUCLID AVE 44195 #035-45-1973 L1982 **END DIA** *020 †20
LICHTIN, Alan Eli. 9500 EUCLID AVE, DESK R-35 44195 #038-41-1980 L1982 **HO IM** *020 †20
LICINA, Michael Geo. 9500 EUCLID AVE, CLINIC 44195 #041-12-1980 L1988 **AN CCA** *020 †05
LIDESTRI, Paula Ann. 9500 EUCLID AVE C21 44195 #035-09-2001 L2005 **PM** *020 †60
LIDSKY, Karen Beth. 11100 EUCLID AVE 44106 #038-06-1993 L1996 **CCP** *020 †55
LIE, Kevin Theodore. 11100 EUCLID AVE, STE 2600 44106 #143-11-2001 L2002 **DR** *100 †80
LIE, Sutek. 11100 EUCLID AVE 44106 #385-02-1967 L1971 **DR NR** *020 †80
LIEBLING, David Seth. ■ 44139 #035-20-1971 L1975 **P** *020 †75
LIEBMAN, Jerome. 2103 ADELBERT RD 44106 #024-01-1955 L1960 **PDC PD** *040 †55
LIETMAN, Steven Andrew. 9500 EUCLID AVE A41, CCF DEPT OF ORTHOPAEDICS 44195 #032-01-1988 L2003 **OMO** *020 †40
LIEW, Yin Ping. ■ 44195 #539-04-1999 L2004 **IM** *100
LIGUORI, Chiara. 9500 EUCLID AVE, DIV OF CARDIOLOGY F/15 44195 #561-31-1986 L2005 **CD** *020 †20
LIKAVEC, Matt John. 2500 METROHEALTH DR 44109 #024-01-1974 L1975 **NS** *020 †25
LIM, Chong Hee. ■ 44106 #825-01-1990 L2000 *100
LIM, Kathleen Jade Del Ca. 9500 EUCLID AVE, CLEVELAND CLINIC FOUNDATIO 44195 #748-11-2002 L2006 **IM** *012
LIM, Li Ling. CLEVELAND CLINIC, DEPT OF NEUROLOGY 44195 #825-01-1992 L2000 **N** *020 †75
LIM, Roger Michael Ison. 9500 EUCLID AVE, CO CCF-GRAD MED EDU DEPT-N 44195 #811-01-1986 L2000 *100
LIM, Yee Juan So. 9500 EUCLID AVE 44195 #748-01-1961 L1974 **CD** *071
LIM, Yeong-Phang. 9500 EUCLID AVE, DEPT OF GME 44195 #917-03-1992 L2005 *100
LIMRUNGSIKUL, Anchalee. 11100 EUCLID AVE 44106 #891-04-1996 L2007 **NPM** *012
LIN, Eugene Weijen. 2500 METROHEALTH DR 44109 #055-02-2000 L2006 **PM** *100
LIN, George Her-Ching. 4229 PEARL RD 44109 #385-02-1965 L1972 **OBG GP** *075 †30
LIN, Jia. 9500 EUCLID AVE 44195 #243-47-1995 L2000 **AN** *020 †05
LIN, Vicki Y. 11100 EUCLID AVE 44106 #016-06-1999 L2000 **OPH** *100 †35
LIN, Wen-An. 18599 LAKE SHORE BLVD 44119 #244-05-1975 L1985 **IM** *020 †20
LIN, Yih Chang Chen. 9500 EUCLID AVE 44195 #748-01-2004 L2007 **IM** *012
LINA, Agnes Alice. 11100 EUCLID AVE, UHC DEPT OF ANESTHESIOLOGY 44106 #038-40-1974 L1974 **AN GS** *020 †05
LINARES TAPIA, Guillermo. 9500 EUCLID AVE, CO CCF-GRAD MED EDU DEPT-N 44195 #649-52-2003 L2004 **N** *012
LINCOFF, Abraham Michael. 9500 EUCLID AVE, F-25 44195 #023-07-1986 L1993 **IC CD** *020 †20
LINDAN, Olgierd. ■ 44121 #759-04-1937 L1963 **IM** *071
LINDEN, Philip Aaron. 11100 EUCLID AVE, MAIL STOP 5011 44106 #041-01-1992 L2007 **TS** *020 †85,90
LINDES, Conrad. 7225 OLD OAK BLVD, STE A210 44130 #041-02-1974 L1975 **FM EM** *020 †18
LINDHEIM, Nora Joan. 2500 METROHEALTH DR, METROHEALTH MEDICAL CENTER 44109 #038-06-1983 L1986 **IM** *020 †20
LINDNER, Daniel J. 9500 EUCLID AVE 44195 #010-02-1981 L1982 **GS** *075
LINDSAY, Carol Andrea. 9500 EUCLID AVE 44195 #016-06-1990 L1991 **OBG MFM** *020 †30
LINDT, Hans A. 1370 ONTARIO ST STE 450 44113 #407-25-1955 L1966 **DR** *071 †80
LING, Alexander. ■ 44140 #028-02-1944 L1950 **NS** *071 †25
LIPMAN, Jeremy M. ■ 44118 #041-15-2004 L2004 **GS** *012
LISAN, Ronald Martin. 2500 METROHEALTH DR, HOSPITAL DEPT OF ANESTHESI 44109 #008-01-1985 L1990 **AN** *020 †05
LISGARIS, Michelle Vallos. 2061 CORNELL RD 44106 #038-06-1995 L1997 **IM ID** *020 †20
LISTINSKY, Catherine. 2085 ADELBERT RD, PATHOLOGY INST 211C 44106 #016-02-1978 L2003 **PTH HMP** *020 †50 ‡
LISTINSKY, Jay John. A-10, 9500 EUCLID AVENUE, CLEVELAND CLINIC FOUNDATIO 44195 #016-02-1982 L2003 **DR** *020 †80
LITAKER, David Glenn. 1 CLINIC CTR 44195 #036-07-1984 L1992 **IM** *020 †20
LITMANOVITZ, Ita. ■ 44122 #550-01-1981 L1992 **NPM** *020
LITT, Jerome Z. 3619 PARK EAST DR 44122 #016-42-1951 L1953 **D** *020
LITTLE, Sherard Gregory-H. CO GME-NA23 9500 EUCLID, CLEVELAND CLINIC FOUNDATIO 44195 #566-01-1999 L2005 *100
LITTNER, Yoav. 11100 EUCLID AVE, DEPT NEONATOLOGY 44106 #550-03-1999 L2004 **NPM** *020
LIU, Eugene Weikang. ■ 44106 #038-06-2008 *012
LIU, James H. 5850 LANDERBROOK DR, STE 3 44124 #038-40-1977 L1988 **OBG REN** *020 †30
LIU, James Kaichen. ■ 44115 #038-06-2006 L2006 **NS** *012
LIU, Jinbo. 11100 EUCLID AVE RM 3018, CO UNIV HOSPS-RESIDENCY OF 44106 #243-85-1983 L2003 *100
LIU, Nathaniel Tetze. ■ 44113 #038-06-2007 L2007 **GS** *012
LIU, Raymond Wei. ■ 44118 #023-07-2004 L2004 **ORS** *012
LIU, Sheng. 2500 METROHEALTH DR, METROHEALTH DEPT FMLY PRAC 44109 #243-69-1991 L2000 **FM FPG** *020 †18 ‡
LIU, Wendy Wei. 9500 EUCLID AVE 44195 #243-47-1990 L2000 **PTH** *020 †50
LIU, Xuehui. 11100 EUCLID AVE RM 3018, CO UNIV HOSPS-RESIDENCY OF 44106 #243-47-1984 L2003 **FM** *100
LIU, Yao-Chang. 2500 METROHEALTH DR 44109 #244-05-1981 L1991 **PTH** *020 †50
LIU, Zejin. 19250 BAGLEY RD 44130 #243-03-1996 L1999 **PTH** *020 †50
LLERENA, Luis Alberto. 18099 LORAIN AVE # 533 44111 #737-01-1963 L1978 **END IM** *071 †20
LO, Percy Hsu. 11100 EUCLID AVE, UNIV HOSP OF CLEVELAND 44106 #056-05-1996 L1999 **PS** *020 †85
LO, Wilbur Howard. ■ 44143 #038-43-1991 **PTH** *100
LOBO, Bjorn Mark. ■ 44195 #038-44-2007 L2007 **NS** *012
LOCALA, Joseph A. P57 CCF 44195 #041-13-1990 L1994 **P** *020 †75
LOCKWOOD, Daniel Sprague. ■ 44122 #038-06-2003 L2003 **DR** *012
LODDENKEMPER, Tobias. 9500 EUCLID AVE, C/O CCF-GRAD MED EDUD EPT- 44195 #409-24-1999 L2003 **CHN** *012

LODHI, Wajahat Ali Khan. 2500 METROHEALTH DR, C/O RESIDENCY SUPPORT 44109 #496-27-1998 L2006 **FP** *012
LOEB, Sheldon. 11201 SHAKER BLVD 44104 #016-42-1953 L1953 **P** *071
LONDON, Alan Eric. 9500 EUCLID AVE, H-18 44195 #038-43-1979 L1995 **FM** *030 †18
LONG, Bruce D. 1730 W 25TH ST # 1200 44113 #016-11-1978 L1980 **RHU OS** *020 †20
LONTOC, Malaya Villaroman. ■ 44147 #748-07-1955 L1969 **AN** *020
LONZER, Mary Deborah A. 2801 MARTIN LTHR KNG JR DR 44104 #041-14-1990 L1991 **PD** *020 †55
LOOMIS, Kristina Lynn. ■ 44108 #038-41-2007 L2007 **OBG** *012
LOOP, Floyd D. 9500 EUCLID AVE 44195 #010-01-1962 L1971 **TS GS** *030 †85,90
LOPEZ, Christine Poblete. 9500 EUCLID AVE, A61 DEPT OF DERM 44195 #035-47-1995 L2000 **D GS** *020 †15
LOPEZ, Javier. 5158 BROADWAY AVE 44127 #264-03-1957 L1963 **GS** *020 †85
LOPEZ, Karim Habib. 2500 METROHEALTH DR, DEPARTMENT OF GERIATRICS 44109 #038-06-1992 L1994 **FM** *020 †18
LOPEZ BUSTINDUY, Amaya. ■ 44106 #847-04-2000 L2007 **PDI** *012 †55
LOPEZ-GONZALEZ, Miguel An. CO GME - NA23 9500 EUCLID, CLEVELAND CLINIC FOUNDATIO 44195 #649-12-1999 L2005 *100
LOPEZ-VALLE, Hilda Ruth. 11100 EUCLID AVE 3018, CO UNIV HOSPS-RESIDENCY OF 44106 #649-04-1980 L2000 **PCP** *020 †50
LO PRESTI, Charles A. 6789 RIDGE RD, STE 100 44129 #038-06-1980 L1985 **ORS** *020 †40
LOPRESTI, Michael Anthony. 6789 RIDGE RD, STE 100 44129 #038-06-1987 L1991 **ORS GS** *020 †40
LORBER, Richard Owen. 2801 MARTIN LTHR KNG JR DR 44104 #056-06-1990 L2002 **PDC** *020 †55
LOSEY, Theodore James. ■ 44106 #005-12-2006 L2006 **EM** *012
LOTT, David G. 9500 EUCLID AVE A71, CLEVELAND CLINIC HEAD AND 44195 #018-03-2004 L2004 **OTO** *012
LOTTO, Michelle Lynn. 9500 EUCLID AVE 44195 #056-05-1996 L1999 **AN** *020 †05
LOUIS, Gregory John. 2322 E 22ND ST, STE 307 44115 #038-41-1983 L1985 **OPH GP** *020 †35
LOVE, Allan Shelton. 12301 SNOW RD 44130 #035-03-1987 L1993 **U GS** *020 †95
LOVICH-SAPOLA, Jessica A. 2500 METROHEALTH DR 44109 #038-44-2001 L2001 **AN** *100 †05
LOVOFF, Mary Weidle. 9500 EUCLID AVE 44195 #038-06-1950 L1950 **PD** *071
LOWDER, Careen. 9500 EUCLID AVE I32, CLEVELAND CLINIC FOUNDATIO 44195 #038-06-1978 L1995 **OPH** *040 †35
LOWE, Boris Shew Hee. 9500 EUCLID AVE, CLEVELAND CLINIC FOUNDATIO 44195 #671-02-1996 L2005 *100
LOWE, John Burton. 10900 EUCLID AVE, DEPARTMENT OF PATHOLOGY 44106 #049-01-1980 L2005 **CLP** *050 †50
LOWE, Robert Michael. ■ 44106 #054-04-2004 L2004 **PD** *020
LOWENTHAL, Gilbert, Jr. 9500 EUCLID AVE 44195 #035-01-1964 L1976 **IM** *020 †20
LOWENTHAL, Rebecca. 6835 BROADWAY AVE, METROHEALTH - BROADWAY CLI 44115 #023-07-2002 L2002 **FM** *020 †18
LOWRIE, Lia H. 11100 EUCLID AVE, DEPT PED 44106 #038-06-1984 L1985 **CCP PD** *020 †55
LOWTHER, Abigail Lynch. ■ 44106 #038-06-2007 L2007 **FP** *012
LOY, Maria Jocelyn V. 2500 METROHEALTH DR 44109 #038-01-1991 L1999 **PAN AN** *020 †05
LOZANO, Sara Patricia. 9500 EUCLID AVE 44195 #264-05-1992 L1999 *020 †05
LU, Kurt Quoc. 11100 EUCLID AVE, DEPT O/DERM*LAKESIDE 3500 44106 #035-45-2002 L2005 **D** *012
LUBIN, Alan. 730 SOM CENTER RD, STE 305 44143 #038-40-1963 L1963 **HO IM** *020 †20
LUCAS, Elizabeth Jane. ■ 44113 #038-45-2006 L2006 **MPD** *012
LUCIANO, Angel Abad. ■ 44109 #042-01-2001 L2004 **NPM** *012 †55
LUCIANO, Mark Gregory. 9500 EUCLID AVE, DEPT OF EMERGENCY MEDICINE 44195 #016-02-1985 L1993 **NS** *020 †25
LUDERS, Jurgen Christian. 9500 EUCLID AVE, C/O CCF-GRAD MED EDU DEPT 44195 #016-02-1998 L1999 **NS** *020
LUDGIN, J Richard. ■ 44120 #010-01-1979 L1982 **IM NEP** *030
LUKACS, Peter Mihaly. 11100 EUCLID AVE, CO UNIV HOSPS-RESIDENCY OF 44106 #473-03-1990 L2003 **N** *100
LUKENS, Thomas Walter. 2500 METROHEALTH DR 44109 #016-02-1980 L1985 **EM IM** *020 †20,16
LUMANLAN, Annie Juico. 1001 LAKESIDE AVE E, STE 1200 44114 #748-02-1964 L1974 **PM PD** *020 †60
LUNA, Vicente A, Jr. 1708 SOUTHPOINT DR, CLEVELAND PSYCHIATRIC INST 44109 #748-01-1970 L1987 **P** *020
LUND, Cheryl Marie. ■ 44115 #422-01-2004 L2007 **IM** *012
LUONG, Amber U. 9500 EUCLID AVE, CLEVELAND CLINIC FOUNDATIO 44195 #048-12-2002 L2007 **OTO** *020
LURIA, Myron Harold. 11311 SHAKER BLVD 44104 #028-34-1959 L1968 **CD IM** *020 †20
LURIA, Sanford Stanly. 6770 MAYFIELD RD # 226 44124 #038-41-1983 L1964 **U** *020 †95
LUTZ, Gabriele Klara. 9500 EUCLID AVE, TT32 44195 #409-44-1989 **N** *100
LYDEN, Sean Patrick. 9500 EUCLID AVE, MC 5A0 44195 #038-41-1993 L2001 **GS** *020 †85
LYNCH, Andrew Craig. 9500 EUCLID AVE, CO CCF-GRAD MED EDU DEPT-N 44195 #671-01-1991 L2002 *100
LYNCH, Gwendolyn Faye. 11100 EUCLID AVE, HANNA HOUST 5TH FL 44106 #038-40-1990 L2000 **N** *020 †75
LYNCH, Melanie Ann. 11100 EUCLID AVE 44106 #038-40-2000 L2000 **GS** *100
LYON, Aldona Thomas. 2351 E 22ND ST 44115 #041-07-1955 L1956 **AN** *071 †05
LYONS, Janice A. 11100 EUCLID AVE, UNIV HOSP OF RAD/ONC 44106 #016-11-1995 L1996 **RO** *020 †80
LYSTAD, Lisa Douglass. 23250 CHAGRIN BLVD STE 440 44122 #024-07-1987 L1991 **OPH OS** *020 †35
LYTLE, Bruce W. 9500 EUCLID AVE F24, CLEVELAND CLINIC FOUNDATIO 44195 #024-01-1971 L1978 **TS** *020 †85,90
MA, Patrick Chi Chung. 10900 EUCLID AVE, CASE WESTERN RESERVE UNIV 44106 #065-01-1994 L2005 **HO** *100 †20
MAAG, Jennifer Ann. 9500 EUCLID AVE 44195 #038-44-2002 L2002 **HMP** *020 †50
MAAN, Jasmine. 2500 METROHEALTH DR 44109 #494-23-2004 L2005 **P** *012
MACE, Sharon Elizabeth. 9500 EUCLID AVE E-19, DEPT OF EMERGENCY MEDICINE 44195 #035-15-1975 L1977 **EM PD** *020 †55,16
MACHADO, Andre Guelman Go. 9500 EUCLID AVE 44195 #187-04-1997 L2004 *020
MACHADO, Grenville J. 1001 LAKESIDE AVE E, STE 1200 44114 #495-01-1977 L1995 **FM** *020 †18
MACHANDA, Katie Eileen. 2500 METROHEALTH DR 44109 #019-02-2001 L2001 **MPD** *100 †55,20
MACHANDA, Sean. 3569 RIDGE RD, NEIGHBORHOOD FAMILY 44102 #065-06-2001 L2001 **FM** *020 †18

MACHUZAK, Michael Shawn. 9500 EUCLID AVE, CRITICAL CARE MED 44195 #041-15-1999 L2006 **PCC** *020 †20
MACIEJEWSKI, Jaroslaw P. R40 9500 EUCLID AVENUE, CLEVELAND CLINIC CANCER CT 44195 #408-30-1990 L2001 **HEM** *020 †20
MACINTYRE, Elizabeth P. 2322 E 22ND ST STE 202 44115 #038-06-1976 L1980 **GE IM** *020 †20
MACIUNAS, Robert J. 11100 EUCLID AVE, DEPT OF NEUROSURGERY 44106 #016-11-1980 L2000 **NS** *020 †25
MACKALL, Judith Anne. 11100 EUCLID AVE, DEPT CARDIOLOGY 44106 #038-45-1987 L1992 **CD** *020 †20
MACKLIS, Roger Milton. 9500 EUCLID AVE, DESK T 28. 44195 #024-01-1983 L1993 **RO** *020 †80
MACKNIN, Michael Larry. 9500 EUCLID AVE, DEPT OF PEDIATRICS/A120 44195 #024-01-1975 L1980 **PD** *020 †55
MAC LENNAN, Gregory Thos. 2085 ADELBERT RD, INST OF PATHOLOGY 44106 #062-01-1971 L1995 **ATP U** *020 †95,50
MADAN, Nitin. 9500 EUCLID AVE, CLEVELAND CLINIC FOUNDATIO 44195 #495-45-2003 L2006 **PD** *012 †20
MADAN MOHAN, Sri Krishna. 7255 OLD OAK BLVD, ASSOCIATES 44130 #495-16-1983 L1997 **CD** *020 †20
MADDEN, Jessica Whelan. 11100 EUCLID AVE, UNIV HOSP OF CLEVELAND 44106 #038-40-2003 L2006 **NPM** *012 †55
MADER, Scott Lawrence. 11100 EUCLID AVE 44106 #038-06-1981 L1986 **IMG** *030 †20
MADHWAL, Surabhi. 9500 EUCLID AVE, CLEVELAND CLINIC FOUNDATIO 44195 #495-84-1999 L2006 **IM** *012
MAGA, Joni Marie. 2500 METROHEALTH DR, METRO HEALTH MEDICAL CENTE 44109 #038-44-2002 L2003 **AN** *100 †05
MAGAURAN, Claire Ellen. 9500 EUCLID AVE S-32, DEPT OF INFECTIOUS DISEASE 44195 #539-06-2001 L2004 **IM** *100
MAGEN, Andrea Bernice. 9500 EUCLID AVE, CLEVELAND CLINIC FOUNDATIO 44195 #041-02-1986 L1997 **DR** *020 †80
MAGIERA, Michael David. ■ 44106 #025-07-2004 L2004 **CHP** *012
MAGI-GALLUZZI, Cristina. 9500 EUCLID AVE, STE 100 44195 #561-27-1990 L2002 **PTH** *020 †50
MAGILL, Ari Benyehuda. ■ 44130 #048-12-2007 L2007 **PD** *012
MAGISANO, James. 18099 LORAIN AVE STE 508 44111 #038-41-1957 L1957 **GS** *071 †85
MAGLIOLA, Ronald John, Jr. ■ 44115 #017-20-2002 L2002 **MPD** *100 †55,20
MAGNUSON, David Kurt. 9500 EUCLID AVE, CHILDREN'S HOSPITAL-CLEVEL 44195 #026-04-1984 L1998 **PDS** *020 †85
MAGOULIAS, Constance D. 4071 LEE RD, STE 260 44128 #025-01-1980 L1983 **FM** *020 †18
MAGPOC, Leopoldo Aguilar. 7449 STATE RD 44134 #748-01-1953 L1960 **GP GS** *071
MAGREY, Marina Nighat. 5208 MEMPHIS AVE, METRO HLT BROOKLYN 44144 #495-51-1991 L1996 **RHU** *012 †20
MAHADEVAN, Arul. 9500 EUCLID AVE, DESK T-28 44195 #495-59-1988 L2002 **RO** *020 †80
MAHADEVAPPA, Manjunath Ch. 18101 LORAIN AVE 44111 #495-09-2001 L2005 **IM** *012
MAHAJAN, Dipti. CO GME - NA23 9500 EUCLID, CLEVELAND CLINIC FOUNDATIO 44195 #495-45-2002 L2007 **PTH** *012
MAHAJAN, Subhash Chander. 7215 OLD OAK BLVD STE A312 44130 #495-29-1972 L1977 **GE** *020
MAHAJAN, Suresh Kumar. 7255 OLD OAK BLVD STE C1 44130 #495-08-1982 L1989 **GE IM** *020 †20
MAHBOOBI, Ramatia. 9500 EUCLID AVE, DEPT OF GME 44195 #517-01-2000 L2006 *100
MAHER, Samir Mohamed. 9500 EUCLID AVE, CO CCF-GRAD MED DEU DEPT-N 44195 #915-08-1975 L2000 *100
MAHFOUD, Youssef. 9500 EUCLID AVE 44106 #605-02-2002 L2004 **P** *012
MAHLAY, Taras. 7255 OLD OAK BLVD, STE 209 44130 #038-43-1989 L1991 **IM** *020 †20
MAHMOUD-AHMED, Ashraf Sha. 9500 EUCLID AVE, CO CCF-GRAD MED EDU DEPT-N 44195 #915-04-1990 L2001 **RO** *100
MAHON, Niall Gerard. 9500 EUCLID AVE, CO CCF-GRAD MED EDU DEPT-N 44195 #539-05-1991 L2000 *100
MAHONEY, Thomas Wm, Jr. 18101 LORAIN AVE 44111 #010-02-1955 L1958 **OBG OS** *100
MAIER, Vanessa Farrell. ■ 44118 #038-06-2004 L2007 **FM** *100 †18
MAJMUDAR, Amit Himanshu. 11100 EUCLID AVE, ATTN CYNTHIA PATENA 44106 #038-44-2003 L2003 **DR** *012
MAJMUDAR, Smita Himanshu. ■ 44143 #495-48-1974 L1984 **FM EM** *020
MAK, Koon Hou. 9500 EUCLID AVE, DEPT CARD 44195 #825-01-1985 **CD** *020
MAKARY, Laila Farouk. 9500 EUCLID AVE 44106 #915-02-1991 L2000 **AN** *020 †05
MAKKAR, Rohit. ■ 44195 #038-43-2005 L2005 **IM** *012
MAL, Niladri. 11100 EUCLID AVE, UNIVERSITY HOSPITALS 44106 #495-38-1998 L2006 **IM** *012
MALANGONI, Mark Alan. 2500 METROHEALTH DR, METROHEALTH MED CTR 44109 #017-20-1975 L1990 **GS CCS** *020 †85
MALEC, Melanie Jo. 11100 EUCLID AVE DEPT FP 44106 #025-12-2006 L2006 **FP** *012
MALGIERI, James Anthony. 6770 MAYFIELD RD, STE 22 44124 #010-02-1979 L1980 **GS** *020 †85
MALIK, Amara Taimur. 9500 EUCLID AVE 44106 #704-25-2001 L2003 **GS** *012
MALIK, Numaan Farid. 9500 EUCLID AVE 44195 #704-25-2003 L2006 **IM** *012
MALKAMAKI, Daniel Markku. 4071 LEE RD, STE 260 44128 #038-45-1997 L2001 **PM** *020 †60
MALLAWI, Yaseen Mohammed. 9500 EUCLID AVE 44195 #797-03-1988 *100
MALLETT, David Lincoln. 17406 ROYALTON RD 44136 #038-06-1956 L1956 **IM** *071 †20
MALLIK, Mridula. 5162 BROADWAY AVE, STE 1 44127 #160-03-1965 L1977 **PD ADL** *020
MALONE, Charles A. ■ 44108 #035-20-1953 L1975 **CHP P** *040
MALONE, Donald A, Jr. 9500 EUCLID AVE, DESK P68 44195 #038-44-1985 L1989 **P** *020 †75
MALONE, Kevin James. 2500 METROHEALTH DR, DEPT OF ORS 44109 #038-41-2001 L2007 **HS** *100
MALUF, Noble Suydam R. ■ 44107 #024-01-1946 L1974 **GS U** *050 †95,85
MALY, Yulia. 9500 EUCLID AVE 44195 #913-21-1991 L2000 **APM** *012
MAMOUN, Ihsan Irfan. 9500 EUCLID AVE 44195 #575-02-2004 L2006 **DR** *012
MAMOUN, Negmeldeen Fathy. 9500 EUCLID AVE, CO CCF-GRAD EDU DEPT-NA23 44195 #915-02-1996 L2003 **AN** *012
MANAPAT, Adrian E. 9500 EUCLID AVE 44195 #748-02-1984 **TS** *020
MANDA, Sudhir. 9500 EUCLID AVE 44195 #495-65-2002 L2005 **IM** *012
MANDALAKAS, Anna Maria. 11100 EUCLID AVE, MS6003 44106 #041-09-1994 L1994 **PD** *020 †55
MANDAPAT, Aida Luna. 4229 PEARL RD 44109 #748-08-1963 L1975 **PD GP** *020 †55
MANDEL, David Ralph. 6551 WILSON MILLS RD 44143 #038-41-1977 L1978 **RHU IM** *020 †20
MANDEL, Morris Meyer. 9500 EUCLID AVE 44195 #038-40-1981 L1984 **AN** *020 †05
MANDELL, Brian Franklin. 9500 EUCLID AVE 44195 #035-19-1980 L1993 **RHU IM** *020 †20

■ = Address Information Privacy Protected

MANDELL, Walter Alan. 10701 EAST BLVD 44106 #035-46-1965 L1966 P *020 †75

MANDIGA, Rahul. ■ 44106 #024-07-2007 L2007 IM *012

MANECKSHANA, Bejon Temus. ■ 44195 #033-05-2003 L2003 GS *012

MANEKER, Amy Jill. 11100 EUCLID AVE 44106 #041-01-1988 L1992 PD PE *020 †55

MANGEL, Jeffrey Mark. 2500 METROHEALTH DR, METROHEALTH MEDICAL CENTER 44109 #067-01-1994 L2000 OBG *020 †30

MANGLA, Pawan K. 6780 MAYFIELD RD 44124 #495-29-1974 L1983 GS EM *020

MANI, Jayanthi. ■ 44195 #496-38-1991 L2003 CN *020

MANJI, Zain. ■ 44106 #035-47-2008 *012

MANLAPAZ, Mariel R. 9500 EUCLID AVE, CARDIOTHORACIC ANESTHESIA 44195 #005-15-2000 L2000 AN *100 †05

MANN, Ajitpal Singh. 11100 EUCLID AVE, DEPARTMENT OF MEDICINE 44106 #495-29-2000 L2006 PCC *012 †20

MANNE, Mahesh Babu. ■ 44195 #495-21-2002 L2005 IM *012

MANNING, Marybeth. 18101 LORAIN AVE, FAIRVIEW HOSP 44111 #038-06-1987 L1989 IM *020 †20

MANNIX, Marin Kay. ■ 44118 #016-06-2006 L2006 AN *012

MANSON, Greg Vaughan. ■ 44113 #038-43-2006 L2006 IM *012

MANSOUR, Edward Geo. 2500 METROHEALTH DR 44109 #605-01-1961 L1970 ON GS *020 †85

MANZANO, Carlos G. 7007 POWERS BLVD 44129 #649-01-1957 L1959 AN *071

MANZON, Katherine. 2500 METROHEALTH DR 44109 #035-08-1977 L1979 EM IM *020 †20,16

MAQBOOL, Sabba. 9500 EUCLID AVE, CLEVELAND CLINIC HOSP 44195 #495-77-2001 L2003 GE *012 †20

MARAS, Zvonimir Ivan. ■ 44124 #407-10-1959 L1963 R *020 †80

MARCELO, Fidela Callanta. 4507 CLARK AVE 44102 #748-07-1956 L1982 GP *071

MARCH, Randal Edward. 6770 MAYFIELD RD 44124 #038-06-1983 L1983 OPH *020 †35

MARCHANT, Kandice Kottke. 9500 EUCLID AVE 44195 #038-06-1986 L1990 PTH *020 †50

MARCINIAK, Donn Alan. ■ 44109 #038-06-2004 L2004 AN *012

MARCU, Marina Simona. 1730 W 25TH ST, STE 1100 44113 #781-01-1997 L2001 ID *020 †20

MARGOLIS, Ron. ■ 44195 #035-20-2004 L2005 OPH *012

MARINO, Lucyndia Rose. 11100 EUCLID AVE, CI CENTER CWRU 44106 #038-06-1977 L1992 GE PD *050 †55

MARKAKIS, Dorothea A. 9500 EUCLID AVE E-31, DEPT OF PEDIATRIC ANESTHES 44195 #023-07-1986 L1997 AN *020 †05

MARKHAM, Thomas Newton. 4450 SAINT CLAIR AVE 44103 #028-34-1960 L1984 OM PHP *020 †70

MARKO, Nicholas Frank. ■ 44118 #010-01-2005 L2005 NS *012

MARKOWITZ, Alan Harvey. 1110 EUCLID AVE, DIV CARD SURG 44115 #035-03-1970 L1974 TS *020 †85,90

MARKOWITZ, Allan Stuart. 11100 EUCLID AVE 44106 #035-46-1974 L1975 OPH *071 †35

MARKOWITZ, Sanford David. 11100 EUCLID AVE, UNIV HOSPS OF CLEV ONCOLOG 44106 #008-01-1980 L1987 ON IM *020 †20

MARKS, Constance A. 9500 EUCLID AVE, C/O CCF-GRAD MED EDU DEPT- 44195 #024-01-2001 L2001 U *100

MARKS, Theodore Nathan. 9500 EUCLID AVE, DIV OF ANESTHESIOLOGY 44195 #038-06-1992 L1999 AN *020 †20

MARMOLYA, Gary Allen. 11100 EUCLID AVE 44106 #038-06-1976 L1977 R DR *020 †80

MARONIAN, Nicole C. 11100 EUCLID AVE, LKS 5045 44106 #035-45-1991 L2004 OTO *020 †45

MAROO, Anjli. 18099 LORAIN AVE 44111 #024-01-1998 L2001 IC *020 †20

MAROO, Prafulchandra V. 18099 LORAIN AVE 44111 #495-01-1968 L1973 IC CD *020 †20

MAROUF, Mohamad Azmi. 1464 E 105TH ST STE 201 44106 #848-03-1991 L1998 IM *020 †20

MARR, Ilona Alexandra. ■ 44145 #038-43-1991 L1995 AN *020 †05

MARRERO, Francisco Jose. ■ 44118 #024-16-2002 L2002 GE *012 †20

MARRIE, Ruth Ann. 9500 EUCLID AVE, CLEVELAND CLINIC-MELLEN CE 44195 #064-01-1996 L2001 N *020 †75

MARSH, Dale Hobert. 1110 EUCLID AVE, CLEVELAND 44115 #038-43-1992 L2000 TS *020 †85,90

MARSH, Lonnie, II. 16603 HARVARD AVE 44128 #038-06-1974 L1975 IM IMG *020

MARSH, Sybil Kathleen. 11100 EUCLID AVE, STE 1200 44106 #065-10-1986 L1991 ADM *040 †18

MARSHALL, James Smith. 2074 ABINGTON RD 44106 #035-01-1948 L1964 END ON *071

MARSHALL, John Bruce. 2351 E 22ND ST, ST VINCENT CHARITY HOSP 44115 #025-07-1968 L1973 GE IM *020 †20

MARSHALL, Sylvia Florence. 9700 GARFIELD BLVD, GARFIELD HEIGHTS 44125 #495-43-1962 L1980 IMG IM *020

MARSOLAIS, Ernest Byron. 10701 EAST BLVD STE B270, ANESTHESIA PAIN CENTER 44106 #018-03-1963 L1970 PME PM *020 †40

MARSSAS ALAULAQI, Abdullah. 9500 EUCLID AVE, CLEVELAND CLINIC FOUNDATIO 44195 #797-01-1992 L2006 *100

MARTIN, Adam Samuel. 11100 EUCLID AVE, C/O UNIV HOSPS-RESIDENCY O 44106 #020-12-2002 L2002 GS *020 †85

MARTIN, David Owen. 9500 EUCLID AVE, DESK F-15 44195 #001-02-1992 L2001 ICE *020 †20

MARTIN, Felix J. ■ 44120 #847-04-1960 L1973 EM *020 †16

MARTIN, John Craig. 6780 MAYFIELD RD 44124 #064-01-1965 L1967 SO GE *020

MARTIN, Joseph Michael. 6707 POWERS BLVD, STE 205 44129 #038-45-1997 L1998 CD *100 †20

MARTIN, Pamela A. 1730 W 25TH ST, MEDICAL ARTS BLDG 44113 #051-04-1986 L1989 GS *020 †85

MARTIN, Richard John. 2101 ADELBERT RD 44106 #143-03-1970 L1976 PD *050 †55

MARTINEZ, Jorge Alvaro Go. 9500 EUCLID AVE, CO CCF - GRAD MED EDU DEPT 44195 #187-04-1994 L2001 NS *012

MARTINEZ, Luciano Antonio. 27633 BASSETT RD 44145 #308-01-1954 L1972 GS *020

MARTINEZ, Michael Edwin. 11100 EUCLID AVE, UNIVERSITY HOSP OF CLEVELA 44106 #038-06-2000 L2000 DR *100 †80

MARTIRENA, Margarita Emil. CO GME-NA23 9500 EUCLID, CLEVELAND CLINIC FOUNDATIO 44195 #924-01-1993 L2005 AN *012

MARTYN, Shari. 11100 EUCLID AVE, BOWELL #3200 44106 #038-06-1979 L1979 OPH *020 †35 ‡

MASARYK, Thomas John. 9500 EUCLID AVE L10, CLEVELAND CLINIC FOUNDATIO 44195 #038-43-1981 L1982 DR *020 †80

MASCARENHAS, Loyola J. 6559 WILSON MILLS RD, STE 106A 44143 #495-21-1960 L1970 OS *020 †85

MASIMASI, Nziavake. 9500 EUCLID AVE, BLDG A-10 44195 #001-02-2003 L2006 IM *100

MASON, David Park. 9500 EUCLID AVE, DESK F24 44195 #038-01-1994 L2004 GS *020 †85,90

MASON, Katherine E. 2500 METROHEALTH DR 44109 #043-01-1992 L1995 CCP *020 †55

MASON, Theodore. 8300 HOUGH AVE, HOUGH HEALTH CTR 44103 #047-07-1961 L1965 OBG EM *071 †30

MASRI, Tony Joseph. ■ 44113 #038-43-2007 L2007 IM *012

MASSIER, Anamaria. 18101 LORAIN AVE 44111 #781-01-1998 L2005 IM *012

MASSIER, Christian George. 13951 TERRACE RD, DEPT OF SURGERY 44112 #781-01-1999 L2004 GS *012

MASSIE-STORY, Mary E. 6835 BROADWAY AVE 44105 #038-06-1996 L1999 FM *020 †18 ‡

MASSOOMI, Sayed Vahab. 18697 BAGLEY RD 44130 #517-01-1966 L1998 OBG *020 †30

MASSOUD, Omar Ibrahim. 2500 METROHEALTH DR, METROHEALTH MEDICAL CENTER 44109 #915-02-1981 L2001 GE *012

MAST, William Asbury. 6801 MAYFIELD RD 44124 #035-45-1958 L1963 ORS *071 †40

MASTER, Daniel Lee. 11100 EUCLID AVE 44106 #008-02-2006 L2006 ORS *012

MASTERS, Christie Lynn. ■ 44106 #028-03-2008 *012

MASTERSON, Martin L. 4229 PEARL RD 44109 #539-05-1975 L1988 CD *020 †20

MASTRACCI, Tara Marie. ■ 44120 #065-10-2000 VS *012

MATA, Antonio S. 1445 W 9TH ST 44113 #748-01-1952 L1967 GP GS *020

MATEJCZYK, Mary-Blair. 9500 EUCLID AVE, DESK A41 44195 #041-07-1975 L1981 ORS *020 †40

MATGOURANIS, Peter Martin. 11100 EUCLID AVE 44106 #038-06-1985 L1986 AN *020 †05

MATHAVAN, Rajeev Kumar. 2500 METROHEALTH DR 44109 #495-99-1995 L2000 FPG *020 †20 ‡

MATHEWS, Manu. 9500 EUCLID AVE, CO GME-NA23 9 44195 #495-52-2000 L2004 P *012

MATHIVANAN, Vidya. 18101 LORAIN AVE, DEPT OF INTERNAL MED 44111 #495-04-1998 L2004 IM *012

MATHUR, Piyush. 9500 EUCLID AVE, DEPT OF CRITICAL CARE 44195 #495-73-1999 L2001 CCA *100 †05

MATSUMOTO, Riki. 9500 EUCLID AVE, CO CCF-GRAD MED EDU DEPT-N 44195 #572-01-1994 L2000 *100

MATTHEWS, Allison Mclauri. ■ 44195 #038-06-2006 L2006 PD *012

MATTHEWS, Florence M K. ■ 44120 #038-04-1946 L1946 P *071

MATZEN, Richard Norman. 9500 EUCLID AVE 44195 #041-01-1954 L1982 IM PUD *071

MAURER, Janet Rae. 9500 EUCLID AVE, DESK A-81 44195 #026-04-1976 L1995 PUD IM *040 †20

MAURER, Walter Glenn. 9500 EUCLID AVE E3-31, DEPT. OF GENERAL ANESTHE 44195 #038-40-1977 L1983 AN IM *020 †20,05

MAURTUA, Marco Antonio. 9500 EUCLID AVE 44195 #132-01-1993 L2000 *020 †05

MAVINKURVE, Gaurav Gajana. ■ 44195 #023-07-2005 L2005 NS *012

MAVISSAKALIAN, Matig R. 11100 EUCLID AVE, U HOSP OF CLEVELAND DEPT P 44106 #605-01-1969 L1986 P *020 †75

MAWAD, Maurice R. 9500 EUCLID AVE F24, DEPT OF THORACIC/CARDIO SU 44195 #028-34-1992 L2003 TS *020 †85,90

MAWHORTER, Steven Dwight. 9500 EUCLID AVE, CLEV CLC DEPT INF DISEASE 44195 #036-07-1984 L1989 ID IM *020 †20,55

MAXEY, Stephen Stone. ■ 44118 #051-04-1961 L1978 EM GP *071

MAXWELL, John Scott. 2500 METROHEALTH DR, DEPT. OF MEDICINE/METROHEA 44109 #028-34-1978 L1980 GE IM *020 †20

MAY, Michael Edward. 2500 METROHEALTH DR 44109 #008-01-1980 L1985 ID EM *020 †20,16

MAYER, Mark Edward. 9500 EUCLID AVE, DESK A91 44195 #016-11-1982 L1991 IM *020 †20

MAYER, Robert E. 18697 BAGLEY RD 44130 #038-40-1948 L1949 OBG FM *072 †30

MAYERS, Douglas Bruce. 6780 MAYFIELD RD 44124 #028-02-1977 L1978 AN *020 †05

MAYOCK, Robert Thos. 9500 EUCLID AVE 44195 #038-06-1981 L1984 IM *020 †20

MAYS, Mary Ann. 9500 EUCLID AVE, THE CLEVELAND CLINIC T33 44195 #038-43-1993 L1998 N *020 †75

MAYTIN, Edward Vincent. 9500 EUCLID AVE ND-20, MOLECULAR DERM LAB 44195 #035-45-1985 L2000 D *050 †15

MAZKALNINS, John. 6681 RIDGE RD 44129 #407-24-1951 L1955 P CHP *074

MAZZONE, Peter J. 9500 EUCLID AVE A90, DEPT OF PULM ALL & CRCTL 44195 #065-06-1994 L1997 PCC *020 †20

MBANEFO, Charles Oseloka. 11201 SHAKER BLVD 44104 #917-21-1970 L1985 IM NEP *020 †20

MC ACHRAN, Sarah E. 9500 EUCLID AVE A-100, CLEVELAND CLINIC 44195 #047-05-2000 L2000 U *100

MC ALISTER, Hugh F. 9500 EUCLID AVE 44195 #671-02-1980 CD *020

MCANDREW, Christopher Mic. ■ 44118 #047-06-2004 L2004 ORS *012

MC BRIDE, Nancy Riley. 21245 LORAIN RD STE 206 44126 #038-06-1987 L1987 END IM *020 †20

MC BURNEY, Richard C. 7225 OLD OAK BLVD, STE A210 44130 #038-06-1973 L1978 FM *020 †18

MC CAMPBELL, Ernest J. 13815 KINSMAN RD 44120 #010-03-1943 L1946 GP OS *071

MC CARTHY, Joan Mary. 8300 HOUGH AVE 44103 #539-04-1949 L1969 PD OS *020

MC CLURE, Mallory Leslie. 27100 CHARDON RD, INC 44143 #051-01-1997 L2000 CD *020 †20

MC COLLOM, Andrea Dawn. ■ 44138 #007-02-1992 L1997 FOP *020 †50

MCCOMSEY, Grace. 11100 EUCLID AVE 44106 #605-02-1989 L1993 ID *020 †55,20

MC CORKLE, Lois Pake. 2074 ABINGTON RD 44106 #038-06-1951 L1951 OS *050 †19

MC CORMICK, William E. 9500 EUCLID AVE 44195 #035-45-1997 L2000 NS *020 †25

MC COY, Blane William. 18660 BAGLEY RD, STE 102 44130 #028-34-1977 L1978 ORS HS *020 †40

MC COY, Christopher David. 11100 EUCLID AVE, CO UNIV HOSP-RESIDENCY OFF 44106 #038-41-2003 L2003 CD *012 †20

MC CRAE, Keith Randall. 10900 EUCLID AVE, DIVISION HEMATHOLOGY ONCOL 44106 #036-07-1982 L1999 HEM ON *050 †20

MC CREERY, Laurie Sampson. 2500 METROHEALTH DR, METROHEALTH MEDICAL CENTER 44109 #038-06-1995 L1996 IM *020

MC CULLOUGH, Arthur Jos. 3395 SCRANTON RD, DEPT MED 44109 #035-15-1974 L1980 GE IM *050 †20

MC CUMBER, Charlotte C. 6780 MAYFIELD RD 44124 #038-06-1997 L1998 PD *020 †55

MC DAVID, Lolita Maria. 11100 EUCLID AVE, RAINBOW BABIES&CLDS HOSP 44106 #038-06-1979 L1982 PD *030 †55

MCDIVIT, Anna Mercedes. 9500 EUCLID AVE 44195 #143-03-2006 L2007 IM *012

MC DONALD, Amy Ann. 2500 METROHEALTH DR 44109 #017-20-1996 L1998 GS *020 †85

MC DONNELL, Matthew C. 6707 POWERS BLVD, STE 202 44129 #038-43-1986 L1990 OTO *020 †45

MC DOWELL, Karen Margaret. 9500 EUCLID AVE, DESK A111 44195 #041-13-1990 L1993 PDP PD *020 †55

MC EVOY, Robert Jude. 29000 CENTER RIDGE RD 44145 #028-34-1946 L1952 PD *071 †55

MC FARLANE, Michael James. 3395 SCRANTON RD DEPT MED 44109 #019-02-1978 L1988 IM *030 †20

MC GOWAN, Nicolle K. 9500 EUCLID AVE 44195 #038-43-1997 L1999 P *020 †75

MC GRATH, Tory Lawrence. 9500 EUCLID AVE, MAIL CODE G-30 44195 #005-18-2002 L2002 AN *020 †05

MCHAOURAB, Ali Sobhi. 10701 EAST BLVD, 11A (W) 44106 #605-01-1995 L2006 APM *020 †05

MC HENRY, Christopher R. 2500 METROHEALTH DR 44109 #038-44-1984 L1990 GS PDS *020 †85

MC HUGH, Michael John. 2801 MARTIN LTHR KNG JR DR 44104 #038-06-1975 L1978 CCP *020 †55

MC KEE, Keith. ■ 44118 #025-07-2001 L2007 PM *020

MC KEE, Sharon Elaine. ■ 44106 #038-06-1996 L1997 PD *020 †55

MC KENZIE, Kay Quaintance. 1611 S GREEN RD STE 302 44121 #038-06-1975 L1975 P PYA *020 †75

MC KINLEY, Derrick Scott. ■ 44143 #028-02-1995 *100

MC KINLEY, Elizabeth Dorr. 2500 METROHEALTH DR, 242 RAMMELKAMP BLDG 44109 #038-06-1987 L1989 IM OS *020 †20

MC LAIN, Robert Felix. 9500 EUCLID AVE, DEPART OF ORTHOPAEDIC-A41 44195 #005-19-1984 L1997 OSS *020 †40

MC LAUGHLIN, Daniel John. 18099 LORAIN AVE, STE 14 44111 #038-40-1984 L1990 VS GS *020 †85

MC LAUGHLIN, Thomas Chas. 11100 EUCLID AVE 44106 #035-45-1965 L1966 ORS OSM *020 †40

MC LENNAN, Devon Brooke. ■ 44118 #038-06-2004 L2004 PM *012

MC MANUS, Matthew Francis. ■ 44120 #041-01-2005 L2007 PTH *012

MCMULLIN, Ann Marie. 9500 EUCLID AVE 44195 #016-11-1992 L2003 EM *020 †16

MC MULLIN, Nolan Dee. 9500 EUCLID AVE, DEPT EMG MED DESK E19 44195 #054-04-2000 L2000 EM *020

MC NAMARA, Marilyn H. 18697 BAGLEY RD, SOUTHWEST GEN HC 44130 #035-45-1974 L1977 CCS VS *030 †85

MC NAMARA, Michael Jr. 2500 METROHEALTH DR 44109 #038-43-1979 L1980 DR EM *020 †80

MC NAMARA, Nora Kathleen. 11100 EUCLID AVE 44106 #038-40-1994 L1999 P *020 †75

MC QUARRIE, Irvine Gray. 2119 ABINGTON RD 44106 #035-20-1965 L1981 NS TRS *050 †25

MCWILLIAMS, Laurie France. ■ 44195 #016-42-2004 L2004 N *012

MEACHAM, Gordon C. ■ 44106 #023-07-1945 L1951 IM *071 †20

MEDALIE, Daniel Alexander. 11100 EUCLID AVE, UNIVERSITY PLASTIC SURGERY 44106 #035-20-1991 L2002 PS *020 †65

MEDARAMETLA, Madhuri. 11100 EUCLID AVE 44106 #496-01-1998 L2002 CHP *020

MEDINA, Trinidad M. ■ 44130 #748-01-1992 L1997 PD *100 †55

MEDINA ZULUAGA, Hector Ma. 9500 EUCLID AVE, C/O CCF-GRAD MED EDU DEPT- 44195 #264-04-1999 L2002 CD *012 †20

MEE, Roger B B. 9500 EUCLID AVE 44195 #671-01-1968 L1993 TS *020

MEGERIAN, Cliff Andrew. 11100 EUCLID AVE, DEPT OF OTOLARYNGOLOGY/HD 44106 #025-01-1988 L2002 NO OTO *020 †45

MEGNA, Jose Maria. ■ 44113 #726-01-1978 L2004 NPM *020

MEHRA, Reena. 9500 EUCLID AVE BOX A90 44195 #038-44-1996 L1999 PCC *020 †20

MEHTA, Adi E. 9500 EUCLID AVE A53 44195 #065-06-1974 L1993 IM *020 †20

MEHTA, Aditi. 11100 EUCLID AVE, CO UNIV HOSPS 44106 #496-05-2000 L2003 CHP *012

MEHTA, Atul Chandrakant. 9500 EUCLID AVE 44195 #495-76-1974 L1981 PUD IM *020 †20

MEHTA, Gita. 29001 CEDAR RD STE 300 44124 #495-45-1973 L1982 OBG R *020 †30

MEHTA, Lina. 11100 EUCLID AVE, STE 2600 44106 #038-44-1994 L1998 NR *020 †80

MEHTA, Madhusudan P. 19250 BAGLEY RD 44130 #495-48-1966 L1976 PTH *020 †50

MEHTA, Neil Bipinchandra. A-91 9500 EUCLID AVE, CLEVELAND CLINIC FOUNDATIO 44195 #495-76-1987 L1995 IM *020 †20

MEHTA, Nishit. ■ 44113 #025-01-2006 L2006 EM *012

MEHTA, Rajendra Kumar. 6407 SAINT CLAIR AVE 44103 #495-30-1969 L1987 CD IM *020 †20

MEHTA, Sudhir Ken. 2500 METROHEALTH DR 44109 #495-05-1969 L1978 PDC PD *020 †55

MEHTA, Usha. 13301 MILES AVE, NEON HEALTH SERVICES,INC. 44105 #495-30-1974 L1999 IM *020 †20

MEI, Matthew. ■ 44106 #038-06-2007 IM *012

MEINE, Jon Gerrit. OF DERMATOLOGY, A61 DEPARTMENT 44195 #018-03-1994 L1998 DS D *020 †15

MEISLER, David Mark. 9500 EUCLID AVE, I32 44195 #038-40-1976 L1982 OPH *020 †35

MEJIA, Melvin Samson. 2500 METROHEALTH DR A-1, METROHEALTH MEDICAL CENTER 44109 #748-10-1994 L2000 SCI *100 †60

MEKHAIL, Nagy Abdelmalek. 9500 EUCLID AVE C-25, THE CLEVELAND CLINIC FOUND 44195 #915-04-1975 L1992 AN PME *020 †05

MEKHAIL, Tarek Moris. 9500 EUCLID AVE, FOUNDATION 44195 #915-02-1984 L1998 IM *020 †20

MEKURIA, Sara Mekonnen. 9500 EUCLID AVE, DEPT OF GME 44195 #366-01-2004 L2006 IM *012

MELAMUD, Mark. 29001 CEDAR RD, STE 430 44124 #913-69-1967 L1986 GE IM *020 †20

MELARAGNO, Mark Jos. 18101 LORAIN AVE 44111 #038-40-1990 L1995 PCP *020 †50

MELNICK, Martin Leonard. 11203 FAIRHILL RD 44104 #409-10-1964 L1975 IM EM *071 †16

MELTON, Alton L, Jr. 9500 EUCLID AVE, CLEV CLINIC FOUNDATION A-7 44195 #036-01-1982 L1988 PDA AI *020 †55,03

MELTON, Tia Meychelle. 27155 CHARDON RD, STE 106 44143 #038-41-1993 L1994 OBG *020 †30

MEMMESHEIMER, Christian A. ■ 44120 #409-21-1994 L1999 IM *020 †20

MENDEZ, Jose Ysrael. 2500 METROHEALTH DR 44109 #935-02-1992 L2007 P *012

MENDEZ, Matthew M. ■ 44106 #038-06-2003 *100

MENDEZ, Zoraida A. 1611 S GREEN RD, STE 34 44121 #308-02-1984 L1988 HEM *020

MENDLOVIC, Samuel Michael. 6780 MAYFIELD RD 44124 #154-02-1952 L1957 IM *071

MENEZES, Krishe. 9500 EUCLID AVE 44195 #496-15-1994 L2006 N *012

MENGES, Hermann. 1611 S GREEN RD, STE 213 44121 #038-06-1957 L1957 IM CD *020 †20

MENON, Venugopal. 9500 EUCLID AVE, DEPT CARDIOVASCULAR MED 44195 #495-53-1989 L2005 CD IM *020 †20

MERCER, Brian Mackenzie. 2500 METROHEALTH DR 44109 #065-09-1983 L2000 MFM OBG *020 †30

MERCHANT, Zahra Mehboob. 2500 METROHEALTH DR 44109 #820-02-2005 L2005 PM *012

MERELLI, Francisco. 9500 EUCLID AVE, C/O CCF-GRAD MED EDU DEPT- 44195 #561-23-1983 L2002 *020

MERIDORES, Tessy. 18099 LORAIN AVE, STE 533 44111 #748-08-1982 L1993 IM *020 †20

MERLINO, Amy Allyn. 2500 METROHEALTH DR, METROHEALTH MEDICAL CENTER 44109 #038-06-2000 L2000 OBG MFM *020

MERLINO, James I. 2500 METROHEALTH DR, H-920 44109 #038-06-1997 L1999 CRS *020 †85,10

MERSOL, Valentin Francis. 5400 TRANSPORTATION BLVD, STE 8 44125 #016-43-1959 L1959 OTO A *020 †45

MERTENS, Renato A. 9500 EUCLID AVE, CO CCF-GRAD MED UED DEPT-N 44195 #231-03-1987 L2000 VS *100

MERUGU, Srinivas Reddy. 2322 E 22ND ST 44115 #495-21-1997 L2000 IM *020

MESIHA, Mena Mounir. ■ 44113 #035-08-2006 L2006 ORS *012

MESNER, Oded. 11100 EUCLID AVE RM 3018, CO UNIV HOSPS-RESIDENCY OF 44106 #550-01-1997 L2003 NPM *100

MESSINEO, Daniela Giulia. 9500 EUCLID AVE, M73 44195 #038-40-1998 L2000 PD *020 †55

MESSINGER-RAPPORT, B. 9500 EUCLID AVE, SECT'N OF GERIATRICS, DESK 44195 #038-06-1989 L1995 IM IMG *020 †20

MESUBI, Olurotimi Olorunf. 2500 METROHEALTH DR, RESIDENCY SUPPORT 44109 #690-08-1998 L2006 MPD *012

METZ, Claudia. 2026 MURRAY HILL RD STE 10 44106 #024-01-1978 L1980 P *020 †75

MEULET, John Eric. 9500 EUCLID AVE, CLEVELAND CLINIC 44195 #143-05-1998 L2006 *100

MEYER, William Andrew. 4229 PEARL RD 44109 #020-12-1994 L1996 EM *100

MEYERS, Anne Elizabeth. 11100 EUCLID AVE 44106 #038-43-1988 L1992 AN *020 †05

MEYERS, Mariana Laura. 11100 EUCLID AVE 44106 #132-04-2000 L2003 DR *012

MEYERSON, Howard Jay. 11400 EUCLID AVE STE 100 44106 #038-06-1987 L1987 HMP PTH *020 †50

MEYYAZHAGAN, Swarnalatha. 11100 EUCLID AVE 44106 #495-42-1985 L1999 IM *020 †20

MHANNA, Maroun J. 2500 METROHEALTH DR 44109 #605-02-1989 L1995 CCP NPM *020 †55

MIAN, Somia Zia. 2500 METROHEALTH DR, METROHEALTH MED CTR 44109 #033-05-2001 L2001 GE *100

MICHELSON, Edward Allen. 11100 EUCLID AVE, DEPT OF EMER MED BOLWELL37 44106 #028-02-1982 L2002 EM IM *040 †20,16

MICHENER, Chad Michael. 9500 EUCLID AVE, DEPT OF OB/GYN-DESK A81 44195 #038-45-1997 L1998 GO GYN *020

MICHENER, William M. CLEVELAND CLINIC 44195 #024-07-1955 L1961 GE PD *072 †55

MICHOTA, Franklin Arthur. E13/9500 EUCLID AVENUE 44195 #038-40-1993 L1994 IM *020 †20

MICULA-GONDEK, Weronika A. 11100 EUCLID AVE 44106 #759-12-2003 L2007 P *012

MIEDLER, John David. 11100 EUCLID AVE, DEPT OF PATHOLOGY 44106 #025-01-2005 L2005 PTH *012

MIGUEL, Ruben Asis. 7575 NORTHCLIFF AVE # 102 44144 #649-01-1965 L1972 RHU *020

MIHALJEVIC, Tomislav. 9500 EUCLID AVE, CLEVELAND CLINIC 44195 #957-01-1989 L2004 TS TTS *020 †85,90

MIKAMI, Hiroshi. ■ 44124 #572-55-1974 OS *100

MIKKILINENI, Haritha. 13951 TERRACE RD 44112 #495-99-2003 L2003 IM *100 †20

MIKOLAENKO, Irina. 9500 EUCLID AVE 44195 #913-86-1992 L2006 NP *020 †50

MILAS, Kresimira M. 9500 EUCLID AVE, CLEVELAND CLC-DPT SURG/A80 44195 #048-14-1994 L2002 GS *020

MILES, Jeffrey Douglas. 11100 EUCLID AVE, DEPT OF NEUROLOGY 44106 #005-06-2002 L2003 N *012

MILGRAM, Laura Jane Head. 2101 ADELBERT RD, STE 3001 44106 #038-06-1992 L1993 PDP *020 †55

MILICEVIC, Jure. 13951 TERRACE RD 44112 #957-01-1955 L1975 OBG CD *071

MILLAN, Monica Scheiding. 9500 EUCLID AVE, CLEVELAND CLINIC FOUNDATIO 44195 #847-08-1996 L2005 *100

MILLAR, Ronald A. 9500 EUCLID AVE 44195 #919-03-1947 L1979 AN *071

MILLER, Brian. 17700 LORAIN AVE 44111 #165-04-1960 L1961 GP *020

MILLER, Charles Michael. 9500 EUCLID AVE A110, CLEVELAND CLINIC 44195 #035-41-1978 L2004 GS *020 †85

MILLER, Charlotte K Buck. 11100 EUCLID AVE 44106 #038-06-1970 L1973 IMG IM *030 †20

MILLER, Daniel William. 11100 EUCLID AVE, DEPT OF NUROLOGY 44106 #038-40-1998 L2000 N *020 †75

MILLER, David Gordon. 8300 HOUGH AVE, TOTAL HLTH CARE 44103 #038-06-1957 L1957 IM GPM *030

MILLER, Frank Piersoll. 11001 CEDAR AVE 44106 #038-06-1993 L1994 FOP PTH *020 †50

MILLER, Jacqueline Ann. 11100 EUCLID AVE 44106 #038-06-1977 L1978 P PYA *020 †75

MILLER, Janine D'Amelio. 11100 EUCLID AVE 44106 #422-01-2003 L2005 D *012

MILLER, Jonathan Paul. 11100 EUCLID AVE 44106 #038-06-2002 L2002 NS *012

MILLER, Lawrence Alan. ■ 44106 #035-46-2005 L2005 IM *012

MILLER, Mary Louise. 2500 METROHEALTH DR, METROHEALTH MEDICAL CENTER 44109 #038-06-1980 L1981 P *020 †75

MILLER, Noah L. 11100 EUCLID AVE, UNIV HOSP DEPT OF PSYCH 44106 #038-44-2001 L2001 CHP *020 †75

MILLER, Richard Tyler. 10701 EAST BLVD, LOUIS STOKES VAMC 111K 44106 #038-06-1980 L2002 IM *020 †20

MILLER, Robin Lynn. ■ 44120 #038-41-1979 L1983 IM ON *020 †20

MILLER, Rolf Fredrick. 6741 RIDGE RD 44129 #407-23-1943 L1955 D A *020

MILLS, William Robert. 2500 METROHEALTH DR, CO METRO HLTH MED CTR-RES 44109 #038-06-2002 L2002 IM *100 †20

MILNER, Michael Mark. 33165 SOLON RD 44139 #020-02-1984 L1986 IM *020 †20

MILNER, Sherry Davidson. 33165 SOLON RD 44139 #020-02-1984 L1987 PD *020 †55

MINAI, Beena Ahmed. 11100 EUCLID AVE, UNIV HOSP OF CLEVELAND 44106 #704-02-1998 L2005 FP *020 †20

MINAI, Omar A. 9500 EUCLID AVE, CLEVELAND CLINIC FOUND 44195 #704-25-1990 L1996 PCC SME *020 †20

MINARI, Afaf Michel. 9500 EUCLID AVE, MED EDUCATION NA23 44195 #605-03-1994 L2000 ID *100

MINEFF, George. 4229 PEARL RD 44109 #407-16-1944 L1955 IMG IM *020 †20

MINIACI, Anthony. 9500 EUCLID AVE, DESK A-41 44195 #065-06-1982 L2003 ORS *020

MINZTER, Beth Hillary. 9500 EUCLID AVE, CLEVELAND CLINIC/C25 44195 #003-01-1988 L2007 AN PME *020 †05

MIRA AVENDANO, Isabel Cri. CO RESIDENCY OFFICE, UNIVERSITY HOSPITALS CASE 44106 #264-08-1995 L2007 IM *012

MIRABELLI, Jorge Luis A. 11100 EUCLID AVE, HANNA HSE 538 44106 #132-03-1985 L2000 N *071

MIRALDI, Floro Deo. 11100 EUCLID AVE, UNIV HOSPS OF CLEVE 44106 #038-06-1970 L1971 NM *071 †28

MIRANDA, Cyndee Cruz. 9500 EUCLID AVE S-32, CLEVELAND CLINIC FNDN 44195 #748-02-2001 L2003 ID *012 †20

MIRANDA, Dalmacio L, Jr. 8413 LAKE AVE 44102 #748-09-1966 L1980 GP *020

MIRANDA, Samuel Patrick. 11100 EUCLID AVE, DEPT OF ANESTHESIA 44106 #038-43-1995 L1996 AN *020 †05

MIRELES-CABODEVILA, Eduard. 9500 EUCLID AVE, CO CCF-GRAD MED EDU DEPT-N 44195 #649-13-2000 L2004 PCC *012 †20

MIRODON, Radu B. 1001 LAKESIDE AVE E, STE 1200 44114 #781-01-1994 L2000 IM *020 †20

■ = Address Information Privacy Protected

MIRZA, Agni. 13951 TERRACE RD, HURON HOSP - CLEVELAND CLI 44112 #286-07-2000 L2004 IM *100 †20

MIRZOYAN, Gagik. ■ 44111 #913-37-1997 L2007 IM *012

MISAK, James Edward. 4242 LORAIN AVE, THOMAS MCCAFFERTY HEALTH C 44113 #016-06-1983 L1990 FM *020 †18

MISHRA, Aparajita. 18200 LORAIN AVE, DEPT OF FAMILY PRACTICE 44111 #496-05-2004 L2006 FP *012

MISHRA, Leenu. 9500 EUCLID AVE, CLEVELAND CLNC 44195 #496-05-2001 L2006 CHP *012

MISKOVSKY, Shana Nicole. 11100 EUCLID AVE, DEPARTMENT OF 44106 #041-12-1997 L2000 ORS *020 †40

MISRA, Subhasis. ■ 44126 #495-13-1999 L2005 GS *012

MISRA, Vivek. ■ 44195 #495-37-2000 L2007 N *012

MISRA-HEBERT, Anita Diana. 9500 EUCLID AVE A50 44195 #038-40-1992 L1999 IM *020 †20

MISTRY, Manjula Vijay. 9500 EUCLID AVE 44195 #495-57-1976 L1982 AN *020

MISTRY, Vijay Govindkant. 6780 MAYFIELD RD 44124 #495-17-1970 L1978 CD IM *050 †20

MITCHELL, Anna Louise. 11100 EUCLID AVE, LAKESIDE 1500 44106 #025-01-1996 L2004 MG PD *050 †19,55

MITRA, Sudeshna. 9500 EUCLID AVE, C/O CCF-GRAD MED EDU DEPT- 44195 #495-02-1990 L2000 PD *100 †55

MIYATAKE, Tsukasa. 9500 EUCLID AVE, CO CCF-GRAD MED EDU DEPT-N 44195 #572-29-1989 L2000 *100

MOALLEM, Moayyed. 2500 METROHEALTH DR 44109 #875-01-2001 L2002 PCC *012 †20

MOAWAD, Heidi. 11100 EUCLID AVE, DEPT OF NEUROLOGY 44106 #038-06-1995 L2001 N *012

MOAWAD, Nashat S. 11100 EUCLID AVE, UHHS - DEPT OF OB/GYN 44106 #915-02-1998 L2001 OBG *012 †18 ‡

MOBASSERI, Keyhan M. 5162 BROADWAY AVE, STE 5 44127 #517-05-1966 L1972 OBG *020

MODADUGU, Anand. 2500 METROHEALTH DR, METROHEALTH MED CTR 44109 #496-24-1999 L2004 IM *100 †20

MODI, Raju. 6707 POWERS BLVD, STE 205 44129 #038-44-1991 L1998 CD *020 †20

MODIC, Mark Louis. 7255 OLD OAK BLVD, STE C412 44130 #038-06-1982 L1983 GE *020 †20

MODLIN, Charles Stanley. 9500 EUCLID AVE, STE 100 44195 #016-06-1987 L1993 U TTS *020 †95

MODRYKAMIEN, Ariel Marcel. ■ 44195 #132-11-1998 L2007 PCC *012 †20

MOELLER, Chaim Meir. ■ 44118 #023-01-2007 L2007 IM *012

MOFFA, Donald Anthony, Jr. 9500 EUCLID AVE E-19 44195 #038-40-1990 L1994 EM *020 †16

MOGHBELLI, Meisam Hossein. 9500 EUCLID AVE 44195 #517-06-2004 L2006 IM *012

MOHAMED, Armin. CLEVELAND CLI FNDN 44106 #143-03-1990 CN *100

MOHAMMAD, Amal Othman. 9500 EUCLID AVE 44195 #575-01-2004 L2007 IM *012

MOHEET, Asma Mahavash. ■ 44113 #028-46-2004 L2004 N *012

MOHIDEEN, Amina. 9500 EUCLID AVE, CLEVELAND CLINIC 44195 #495-31-1996 L2003 AN *020 †05

MOHR, Franziska. 9500 EUCLID AVE, PEDIATRIC GASTROENTEROLOGY 44195 #409-12-1997 L2001 PG *020 †55

MOINUDDIN, Mahmood. 4229 PEARL RD, DEACONESS HOSPITAL 44109 #495-21-1958 L1967 IM PUD *071 †20

MOIR, Thomas Wm. 2074 ABINGTON RD, UNIV HOSP OF CLEVELAND 44106 #035-45-1948 L1952 CD IM *071 †20

MOLINARI-ZUZEK, Marina B. 6780 MAYFIELD RD, HILLCREST HOSP PED ER 44124 #038-43-1988 L1991 PD PEM *020 †55

MOLLOY, Eleanor Joan. 11100 EUCLID AVE RM 3018, CO UNIV HOSPS-RESIDENCY OF 44106 #539-02-1993 L2003 NPM *100

MOMEN, Muhammad Nurul. 1708 SOUTHPOINT DR, SYSTEM CLEVELAND CAMPUS 44109 #160-04-1982 L2002 CHP *100

MONNIER, Vincent Michel. CASE WESTERN RESERV UNIV 44106 #869-01-1972 L1984 CLP PCH *050 †50

MONTAGUE, Drogo K. 9500 EUCLID AVE, STE 100 44195 #025-01-1968 L1971 U *020 †95

MONTENEGRO, Hugo D. 2074 ABINGTON RD 44195 #737-03-1966 L1975 PUD IM *020 †20

MONTGOMERY, Lynda Gay. 10900 EUCLID AVE 44106 #041-01-1996 L2002 FM *020 †18

MONTGOMERY, William Henry, Jr. 9500 EUCLID AVE A41 44195 #014-01-2001 L2006 ORS *100

MOODLEY, Amaran. 9500 EUCLID AVE, DEPT OF GME 44195 #836-02-2001 L2006 PD *012

MOODLEY, Jayavani. 9500 EUCLID AVE, CLEVELAND CLNC FNDN 44195 #836-02-2002 L2006 IM *012

MOODLEY, Sangithan. 18101 LORAIN AVE 44111 #836-05-1972 L1985 MFM OBG *020 †30

MOON, Ho-Seong. 12200 FAIRHILL RD 44120 #583-01-1986 IMG *100

MOONEY, Colin James. ■ 44113 #056-05-2005 L2005 IM *012

MOORE, Courtenay Kathryn. 9500 EUCLID AVE, STE 100 44195 #035-03-1999 L2004 U *020 †95

MOORE, Halle Foster. 9500 EUCLID AVE R35, CLEVELAND CLINIC 44195 #038-06-1993 L1999 HO *020 †20

MOORE, James Clarence. 9500 EUCLID AVE, DESK A-81 44195 #047-07-1974 L1976 IM *071

MOORE, John James C, II. 2500 METROHEALTH DR 44109 #051-01-1976 L1979 NPM *040 †55

MOORE, Laurice R Bargas. 2500 METROHEALTH DR, METROHEALTH MED CTR 44109 #305-01-2000 L2001 PD *020

MOORE, Patricia Hughes. 11100 EUCLID AVE, STE 1200 44106 #024-01-1974 L1988 FM *020 †18

MOORE, Timothy Alan. 2500 METROHEALTH DR, METROHEALTH MEDICAL CENTER 44109 #038-45-1998 L2000 ORS OSS *020 †40

MOORE, Timothy Eugene. 11100 EUCLID AVE, DEPT OF RADIOLOGY 44106 #038-41-1998 L1999 DR *020 †80

MORALES, Amelia Elena. ■ 44114 #036-08-2005 L2005 MPD *100

MORANT, Victor Anselmo. 9500 EUCLID AVE, ONE CLINIC CENTER DESK F-1 44195 #016-06-1969 L1973 CD IM *071

MORAVEC, William D. ■ 44116 #028-34-1975 L1986 OBG *020 †30

MOREIRA, Andrea Arnaud. 9500 EUCLID AVE, DEPT OF GME 44195 #187-20-1992 L2006 *100

MORGAN, Michelle Jimenez. 18697 BAGLEY RD 44130 #038-40-1989 L1992 AN *020 †05

MORGAN, Philip Glennon. 11100 EUCLID AVE, DEPT. OF ANESTHESIOLOGY 44106 #007-02-1980 L1986 AN *050 †05

MORIKAWA, Masahiro. 11100 EUCLID AVE, STE 1200 44106 #572-49-1987 L1996 FM *020 †18 ‡

MORILLO, Miguel Angel. 9500 EUCLID AVE, CLEVELAND CLINIC FNDN 44195 #935-01-1995 L2005 IM *020 †20

MORNINGSTAR, Wm Albert. PO BOX 94721 44101 #041-12-1942 L1949 PTH CLP *071 †50

MORRA, Nariman Kamal. 10114 NANFORD RD 44102 #875-01-1996 L2005 IM *012

MORRIS, William Herbert. 9500 EUCLID AVE, ML-S 70 44195 #038-06-2003 L2004 IM *020 †20

MORRISON, Colin Myles. 9500 EUCLID AVE, DEPT OF GME 44195 #539-03-1994 L2006 *100

MORSCHER, Arnold. 11709 LORAIN AVE 44111 #154-01-1950 L1954 FM *071 †18

MORSCHER, Arnold Hans. 2500 METROHEALTH DR, METROHEALTH MED CTR 44109 #038-40-1985 L1986 AN IM *020 †05

MORTIMER, Joanne Clarage. 11100 EUCLID AVE, UNIVERSITY HOSPITALS OF CL 44106 #034-01-1975 L1986 PD *020 †55

MORTON, Jay Dennis. 1611 S GREEN RD 44121 #023-07-1964 L1966 IM NEP *020 †20

MOSES, Joseph David. 18099 LORAIN AVE STE 450 44111 #038-06-1974 L1975 GE IM *020 †20

MOSKOWITZ, Shaye Isaac. 9500 EUCLID AVE, CCF/DEPT NEUROSURGERY-S80 44195 #035-08-2001 L2001 ES *012

MOSQUEDA, Eric Nuneza. 2101 ADELBERT RD 44106 #748-15-1993 L2005 NPM *020 †55

MOSSAD, Emad Beniameen. 9500 EUCLID AVE, DEPT OF CARDIOTHORACIC 44195 #915-02-1985 L1992 AN CD *020 †05

MOSSAD, Sherif Beniameen. 9500 EUCLID AVE, CLEVELAND CLINIC FND. 44195 #915-02-1987 L1993 ID *020 †20

MOSTAFAVI, Kian. 11100 EUCLID AVE, UNIV HOSP CLEVELANDSURGERY 44106 #305-01-1998 L2000 VS GS *020 †85

MOSTOW, Nelson David. 7255 OLD OAK BLVD, ASSOCIATES 44130 #038-06-1975 L1976 CD IM *020 †20

MOTTA, Antonino Orazio. 12300 MCCRACKEN RD, MARMOUNT HOSPITAL 44125 #038-06-1982 L1986 R DR *020 †80

MOTTA, Pablo. 1730 W 25TH ST 44113 #924-01-1993 L2000 AN *020 †05

MOUL, Danielle Kathleen. ■ 44113 #023-01-2002 L2003 D *012

MOUNIR, Loran Alfy. 9500 EUCLID AVE E-3, DEPT OF GENERAL ANESTH 44195 #915-02-1997 L2000 PAN *100 †05

MOUNTANTONAKIS, Stavros E. ■ 44195 #418-07-2000 L2004 CD *012 †20

MOUNTS, Troy Isaac. 11100 EUCLID AVE, UNIV HOSPS - CASE MED CTR 44106 #047-06-2007 L2007 ORS *012

MOURAD, Ronda. ■ 44113 #038-06-2002 L2002 IM *100 †20

MOUSSA, Basel. 20997 LORAIN RD 44126 #875-01-1985 L1996 CD PD *020 †55,20

MOUSSAVAND, Samaresh. 11100 EUCLID AVE, UNIVERSITY HOSPITALS OF CL 44106 #409-32-1993 L2000 CHP P *020

MOUSTAPHA, Walid Ahmed. 9500 EUCLID AVE, CO CCF-GRAD MED EDU DEPT-N 44195 #915-04-1993 L2001 *100

MROZ, Thomas Edward. 9500 EUCLID AVE 44195 #038-06-1997 L2003 ORS *020 †40

MUEENUDDIN, Mian. 12301 SNOW RD 44130 #704-01-1972 L1999 PTH *020 †50

MUEHRCKE, Cecile Sweeney. ■ 44119 #016-11-1978 L1980 IM *074 †20

MUGHARBIL, Anas M. 18697 BAGLEY RD 44130 #605-01-1984 L1995 ON *020 †20

MUHAMMAD, Kamran Ijaz. 9500 EUCLID AVE, DESK F-15 44195 #024-16-2002 L2006 CD *012 †20

MUKHERJEE, Ratan Kumar. 18099 LORAIN AVE, STE 420 44111 #495-02-1961 L1974 IM *020

MUKUNDA, Beejadi N. 6559 WILSON MILLS RD, STE 106A 44143 #495-35-1992 L1998 IM *020 †20

MULDER, Sarah Christine. 9500 EUCLID AVE 44195 #025-12-2004 L2004 PD *020 †55

MULGAOKAR, Girish Diwakar. 11100 EUCLID AVE 44106 #496-38-1975 L1980 AN *020 †05

MULLEN, Heather. 4242 LORAIN AVE, FAMILY PRAC 44113 #038-06-1999 L1999 FM *020 †18

MULLEN, Kevin Daniel. 2500 METROHEALTH DR, METROHEALTH MEDICAL CENTER 44109 #539-04-1976 L1981 GE IM *050 †20

MULLENS, Wilfried Agnes M. 9500 EUCLID AVE, CLEVELAND CLINIC FOUNDATIO 44195 #165-04-1999 L2006 *100

MULLIGAN, Paula Bocsor. 960 CLAGUE RD, STE 1850 44145 #473-01-1950 L1961 PD *071

MULTANI, Amy Girish. ■ 44113 #035-03-2005 MPD *012

MULVIHILL, Niall. 9500 EUCLID AVE 44195 #539-04-1992 IM *100

MUMTAZ, Muhammad A. 9500 EUCLID AVE M-41, PEDS. & CONG. HEART SURGER 44195 #704-01-1989 L2000 TS *020 †85,90

MURAKAMI, Masato. 9500 EUCLID AVE 44195 #572-28-1976 RHU *100

MURPHY, Aisling Mary. 11100 EUCLID AVE 44106 #539-06-2002 L2006 OBG *012

MURPHY, James Edward. 11100 EUCLID AVE 44106 #041-14-2006 L2006 ORS *012

MURPHY, John R. 11100 EUCLID AVE, UNIVERSITY HOSPITALS 44106 #038-06-1951 L1951 HEM ON *071

MURPHY, Pamala Jawan. 19999 ROCKSIDE RD 44146 #038-06-1978 L1978 IM *020 †20

MURPHY, Ross Thomas. 9500 EUCLID AVE 44195 #539-06-1993 L2004 *020

MURPHY, Thomas Aquinas. 2500 METROHEALTH DR 44109 #028-02-1978 L1981 END IM *020 †20

MURRAY, Brian Eamon. 9500 EUCLID AVE, DESK A-81 44195 #539-04-1992 L1997 CN *020 †75

MURRAY, John Gerard. ■ 44106 #539-05-1987 L1995 *020

MURRAY, Patrick Kevin. 2500 METROHEALTH DR, METROHEALTH MEDICAL CENTER 44109 #035-48-1974 L1984 PM IM *030 †20,60

MURTHY, Sreenivasa P S. 2121 ADELBERT RD 44106 #495-09-1959 L1965 PTH FOP *062 †50

MURTHY, Sudish. 9500 EUCLID AVE, CULAR SURGERY/F24 44195 #035-01-1992 L1999 TS *020 †85,90

MUSCA, Albert Anthony A. ■ 44108 #038-06-1961 L1961 GS GP *071 †85,50

MUSCHLER, Geo Frederick. 9500 EUCLID AVE, DEPT ORTHO SURGERY A41 44195 #016-06-1981 L1988 OAR ORS *020 †40

MUSHTAQ, Nadia. 2351 E 22ND ST 44115 #704-21-1997 L2002 *100

MUSLIMANI, Alaa. 18101 LORAIN AVE 44111 #875-02-1997 L2004 IM *020 †20

MUSTAFA, Khader Nimer. ■ 44144 #575-01-1981 L1992 RHU *020 †20

MUTNAL, Amar Basavaraj. 11100 EUCLID AVE 44106 #025-01-2006 L2006 ORS *012

MUZINA, David John. 9500 EUCLID AVE, CLEVELAND CLINIC FOUNDATIO 44195 #038-06-1993 L1994 P *020 †75

MUZINA, Kathryn Snow. 2351 E 22ND ST, PSYC EMERG DEPT-SVCH 44115 #038-06-1993 L1994 P *020 †75

MYERS, Andrew Hanauer. 11100 EUCLID AVE, STE 2600 44106 #038-06-1991 L1995 DR *020 †80

MYERS, Melissa Terry. 2500 METROHEALTH DR, DEPARTMENT OF RADIOLOGY 44109 #008-01-1989 L1995 DR *020 †80

MYERS, Ross Elliott. 11100 EUCLID AVE 44106 #038-44-2004 L2004 PD *100 †55

MYHRE, Ulf. 9500 EUCLID AVE, CO CCF-GRAD MED EDU DEPT-N 44195 #539-06-1984 L2001 *100

MYTON-CRAIG, Kaye A. 2775 S MORELAND BLVD # 201 44120 #038-45-1991 L1994 IM *020

MZHAVANADZE, Patman Zurab. 13951 TERRACE RD, DEPT OF INTERNAL MED 44112 #912-02-2001 L2005 IM *012

NAASAN, Georges Raja. 11100 EUCLID AVE, UNIVERSITY HOSPITALS CASE 44106 #605-01-2006 L2007 IM *012

NADIMPALLI, Deepa Raju. 2500 METROHEALTH DR, CO RESIDENCY 44109 #496-23-2003 L2007 P *012

NAEEM, Rabia. ■ 44120 #704-25-1999 L2006 **PD** *100 †55
NAFF, George Bluford. 10701 EAST BLVD, DEPT MED 44106 #051-01-1957 L1965 **NEP IM** *030
NAGEEB, Fady Safwat. 9500 EUCLID AVE, C/O CCF-GRAD MED EDU DEPT- 44195 #915-04-1990 L2002 **PMM** *012
NAGEM, Hassan Ali. 9500 EUCLID AVE, DEPT OF GME 44195 #915-03-2000 L2006 *100
NAGPAL, Dheeraj. 9500 EUCLID AVE, DEPT OF ANESTHESIOLOGY 44195 #496-09-1995 L2005 **PAN** *100
NAGUIB, Hossam Saad. 29000 CENTER RIDGE RD 44145 #915-02-1991 L1998 **IM** *020 †20
NAGY, Bethanne. ■ 44195 #041-14-2004 L2004 **PD** *020 †55
NAGY, Denis. ■ 44106 #038-06-2001 **GS** *100
NAHIGIAN, Stanley Haig. 29001 CEDAR RD STE 519 44124 #038-40-1957 L1957 **HS** *071 †40
NAIK, Nimesh Harish. ■ 44102 #965-01-2002 L2005 **IM** *012
NAIR, Deepu S. ■ 44106 #028-02-2001 L2005 **CD** *012
NAIR, Dileep. 9500 EUCLID AVE, DEPT OF NEUROLOGY-DESK S-5 44195 #038-44-1993 L1995 **CN** *020 †75
NAIR, Rashmi Thottathil. 9500 EUCLID AVE HB6 44195 #495-53-1997 L2005 **AR** *020
NAIR, Ravi Narayan. 2074 ABINGTON CD 44106 #495-17-1978 L1984 **CD IM** *020 †20
NAJARIAN, Brian C. ■ 44113 #025-07-2003 L2006 **ORS** *012
NAJARIAN, Sandra Lynn. 2500 METROHEALTH DR 44109 #025-01-1995 L1996 **EM** *020 †16
NAJI, Abdul Fattah. 5163 BROADWAY AVE, ST ALEXIS HOSPITAL 44127 #528-01-1946 L1963 **PTH** *075 †50
NAJM, Imad M. 9500 EUCLID AVE 44195 #605-02-1988 L1996 **N** *020 †75
NAKAGAWA, Shunichi. 9500 EUCLID AVE, CLEVELAND CLINIC FOUNDATIO 44195 #572-29-1997 L2005 **IM** *012
NAKAMOTO, Satoru. 9500 EUCLID AVE, DESK A-81 44195 #572-31-1951 L1961 **NEP IM** *020
NAKANO, Toshihide. 9500 EUCLID AVE, C/O CCF-GRAD MED EDU DEPT- 44195 #572-12-1991 L2002 *020
NALLY, Joseph Vahey, Jr. 9500 EUCLID AVE 44195 #038-40-1975 L1976 **NEP IM** *050 †20
NAMBIAR, Pradeep Manikoth. DEPT. OF CARDIAC SURGERY,, CLEVELAND CLINIC FOUNDATIO 44195 #495-73-1984 L2005 **TS** *100
NAMCHAISIRI, Jule. ■ 44121 #891-01-1991 L2000 **TS** *100
NANAVATI, Shailesh R. 15644 MADISON AVE STE 206 44107 #495-22-1970 L1979 **PD** *020
NANDA, Ashish. ■ 44120 #495-43-2001 L2007 **VN** *012
NANDI, Sumon. ■ 44103 #035-19-2004 L2004 **ORS** *012
NANDIGAM, Veerendra. 1 MOUNT SINAI DR 44106 #495-50-1970 L1979 **GS VS** *020 †85
NAPIERKOWSKI, Daniel E. 9500 EUCLID AVE 44195 #041-12-1986 L1990 **AN OS** *020 †05
NARA, Andrew Richard. 2074 ABINGTON RD DEPT MED 44106 #038-06-1976 L1979 **CD IM** *020 †20
NARAGHIPOUR, Hossein. 7215 OLD OAK BLVD, STE A411 44130 #517-06-1958 L1969 **TS VS** *071 †85,90
NARICHANIA, Dilip Bhailal. 7215 OLD OAK BLVD, STE A414 44130 #495-97-1977 L1985 **GS** *020 †85
NARVAJA, Helen Lawas. 18101 LORAIN AVE 44111 #748-08-1966 L1974 **PD PHO** *020 †55
NASH, Clyde Lester, Jr. 2500 METROHEALTH DR, DEPT ORTHO 44109 #038-06-1962 L1964 **ORS OSS** *020 †40
NASHED, Hanan. 1730 W 25TH ST 44113 #875-01-1990 L1995 **PD** *020 †55
NASO, Arabi. 2500 METROHEALTH DR, DIV OF CARDIOLOGY 44109 #875-01-1993 L1998 **IM** *020 †20
NASR, Vivian Fayek. 9500 EUCLID AVE, CLEVELAND CLINIC FOUNDATIO 44195 #915-02-1992 L2001 **AN** *020 †05
NASSIF, Rita Mae Perko. 2351 E 22ND ST 44115 #038-40-1962 L1962 **FM IM** *071 †18
NATAL, Luz Ivette. ■ 44195 #042-01-2005 L2005 **PD** *012
NATALE, Maria Eugenia. 11100 EUCLID AVE, LKS 3018 44106 #132-01-1995 L2002 *100
NATESAN, C.N.S.. 27100 CHARDON RD, INC 44143 #495-04-1994 L2001 **IM** *020 †20
NATESAN, Nandhitha. 11100 EUCLID AVE, CRITICAL CARE 44106 #496-23-2003 L2003 **PCC** *012 †20
NATOWICZ, Marvin Roy. 9500 EUCLID AVE S-71, DEPT OF NEUROLOGY 44195 #028-02-1983 L2000 **PTH** *020 †50,19
NATURALE, Richard Timothy. 11100 EUCLID AVE, DEPT OF PATHOLOGY 44106 #038-41-2005 L2005 **PTH** *012
NAUGHTON, Paul Joseph. 9500 EUCLID AVE, DEPT OF CARDIOTHORACIC ANE 44195 #539-05-1990 L2000 *100
NAVADEH, Alireza. 9500 EUCLID AVE, THE CLEVELAND CLINIC FOUND 44195 #517-01-1995 L2000 **AN** *100 †05
NAVARE, Teja Makarand. 2500 METROHEALTH DR, C/O METROHEALTH MED CTR-RE 44109 #495-96-1995 L2002 **HO** *100
NAVIA, Jose Luis. 9500 EUCLID AVE, DESK F-25 44195 #132-03-1984 L2001 **TS** *020
NAVRACRUZ, Lisa Christine. 1530 SAINT CLAIR AVE NE, CARE ALLIANCE 44114 #005-11-2000 L2000 **FM** *020 †18
NAWAR, Rita N. 11100 EUCLID AVE 44106 #605-03-1998 L2004 **END** *100
NAYAK, Hemanta Kumar. 12301 SNOW RD 44130 #495-79-1977 L1990 **IM** *020 †20
NAYLOR, Douglas Falconer. 9500 EUDLID AVE / ML G68, AND CRITICAL CARE MEDICINE 44195 #038-43-1983 L1986 **GS CCS** *020 †85
NEARMAN, Howard Sloman. 11100 EUCLID AVE 44106 #038-06-1976 L1977 **AN CCA** *020 †05
NEARY, Paul Christopher. ■ 44195 #539-02-1992 L2003 **CRS** *100
NEDOROST, Susan Lynn. 11100 EUCLID AVE 44106 #038-06-1987 L1989 **D** *020 †15
NEELEY, Roy Curtis. ■ 44121 #011-04-2003 L2003 **AN** *012
NEF, Patrick Chinedu. 9500 EUCLID AVE, CO CCF-GRAD MED EDU DEPT-N 44195 #539-06-2000 L2001 **NEP** *012
NEGREA, Lavinia Aura. 11100 EUCLID AVE, UNIV HOSPITALS OF CLEVELAN 44106 #781-03-1983 L1997 **NEP IM** *050 †20
NEILSON, Derek Edmund. 11100 EUCLID AVE, LAKESIDE 1500 44106 #040-02-1998 L1999 **MG PD** *020 †55,19
NELSON, Coveda Tanya. 9500 EUCLID AVE 44195 #038-45-1989 L1990 **AN** *020 †05
NELSON, Richard Arnold. 7123 PEARL RD, STE 201 44130 #038-43-1985 L1988 **EM** *020 †16
NEME, Silvia Beatriz. 9500 EUCLID AVE 44195 #132-02-1995 L2004 **N** *012
NEMEC, Carolyn Frances. 9500 EUCLID AVE A-10 44195 #038-43-1985 L1986 **GS** *018
NEMESLAKI, Judith R. 11100 EUCLID AVE 44106 #407-19-1962 L1986 **ON HEM** *074 †55
NEMUNAITIS, Greg Allen. 2500 METROHEALTH DR, METROHEALTH MEDICAL CENTER 44109 #038-06-1985 L1989 **PM** *075 †60
NENTO, Daniel Edgardo. 9500 EUCLID AVE, DEPT OF GME 44195 #132-06-1998 L2006 *100
NERI, German L, Jr. 14601 DETROIT AVE, STE 730 44107 #748-01-1962 L1970 **IM CD** *072 †20
NEUBECK, Peter. 9500 EUCLID AVE, CO CCF-GRAD MED EDU DEPT-N 44195 #409-16-1998 L2000 *100
NEUMAN, Michael Robt. 1 MOUNT SINAI DR DEPT MED 44106 #038-06-1974 L1974 **IM** *100
NEUMANN, Donald Richard. 9500 EUCLID AVE, THE CLEVELAND CLINIC FOUND 44195 #038-45-1980 L1983 **DR** *071 †80

NEUMANN, Klaus H. 20997 LORAIN RD 44126 #407-33-1956 L1964 **IM PUD** *071
NEW, Erica Maria. 3100 EUCLID AVE 44115 #035-20-1988 L1991 **P** *020 †75
NEWCOMB, Deborah Lynn. ■ 44195 #011-02-2006 L2006 **AN** *012
NEWMAN, Arthur Jerome. 11100 EUCLID AVE 44106 #035-19-1948 L1951 **PD RHU** *020 †55
NEWMAN, James Stuart. 9500 EUCLID AVE 44195 #038-06-1984 L1991 **VIR R** *020 †80
NEYMAN, Margarita N. 2801 MARTIN LTHR KNG JR DR, JR. DR 44104 #913-15-1988 L1997 **PD** *020 †55
NG, Henry Hinglun. 2500 METROHEALTH DR, METRO HLTH MED INT MED PED 44109 #025-12-2001 L2001 **MPD** *100 †20,55
NG, Kenneth Kwan Chung. 9500 EUCLID AVE, CO CCF-GRAD MED EDU DEPT-N 44195 #825-01-1992 L2002 **CD** *100
NGUYEN, Carvell Tran. 9500 EUCLID AVE A100 44195 #005-06-2004 L2004 **U** *012
NGUYEN, Dennis Huu-Luyen. ■ 44113 #005-02-2004 L2005 **D** *012
NGUYEN, Kenny. 2500 METROHEALTH DR 44109 #305-01-2004 L2004 **PD** *020
NGUYEN, Mike Minh. 9500 EUCLID AVE A100, CLEVELAND CLINIC FOUNDATIO 44195 #005-19-2000 L2006 **U** *020
NGUYEN, Mike S. ■ 44106 #038-06-2008 *012
NGUYEN, Thuyanh. ■ 44118 #051-01-2007 L2007 **AN** *012
NICE, Timothy James. 6770 MAYFIELD RD, # 449 44124 #016-43-1973 L1974 **ORS** *020 †40
NICHOLS, David Paul. ■ 44106 #028-03-2001 L2004 **PDP** *012 †20,55
NICHOLSON, Cameron Lee. 9500 EUCLID AVE, C/O CCF-GRAD MED EDU DEPT- 44195 #038-40-2002 L2002 **PD** *100 †55
NICHOLSON, Kimberly Ann. M 73, 9500 EUCLID AVE 44195 #038-40-2001 L2001 **PD UCM** *020 †55
NICKEL, Stewart Newman. 21755 BROOKPARK RD, QUADAX 44126 #025-01-1955 L1965 **CD IM** *071 †20
NICKELS, John Harvey. 2307 W 14TH ST 44113 #042-03-1981 L1985 **PME AN** *020
NICKERSON, Paul Edwin. 4568 MAYFIELD RD STE 104 44121 #016-06-1966 L1974 **IM IMG** *020 †20
NICKLAS, Jeffrey Scott. 7816 DORVER AVE 44105 #038-06-1990 L1994 **AN** *012
NICOLA, Sami Fouad I. 2307 W 14TH ST 44113 #915-02-1958 L1975 **GS N** *040 †85
NICOLACAKIS, Kathrin. 2500 METROHEALTH DR, METROHEALTH MEDICAL CENTER 44109 #038-40-1989 L1991 **PUD CCM** *020 †20
NIELSEN, Craig David. 3605 INGLESIDE RD, 9500 EUCLID AVENUE 44195 #050-02-1994 L1996 **IM** *020 †20
NIEMI, Timothy Alan. 7123 PEARL RD, STE 201 44130 #038-06-1982 L1986 **GS OS** *020 †16
NIEVES, Lucybeth. ■ 44114 #042-01-2002 L2006 **OBG** *012
NIEZGODA, Julie Jan. 9500 EUCLID AVE, CLEVELAND CLINIC FOUNDATIO 44195 #038-40-1985 L1988 **AN PD** *020 †05,55
NIGRO, Kelly Grove. 11100 EUCLID AVE, UNIV HOSP OF CLEV PATH DPT 44106 #038-06-2002 L2002 **PCP** *020 †50
NIGRO, Samuel Angelo. 11100 EUCLID AVE 44106 #028-34-1961 L1965 **CHP P** *020 †75
NIJHAWAN, Sheetal. 13951 TERRACE RD 44112 #496-39-2003 L2005 **GS** *012
NINGEGOWDA, Lokesh Basava. C-25, DEPARTMENT OF PAIN M 44195 #496-35-1996 L2001 **AN** *100
NINTCHEFF, Peter. 11351 PEARL RD 44136 #010-01-1964 L1965 **OPH** *020 †35
NISAR, Mohamed I. 3540 RIDGE RD 44102 #495-37-1962 L1976 **IM** *020
NISSEN, Steven Evan. 9500 EUCLID AVE, CLEVELAND CLINIC F15 CVMED 44195 #025-01-1978 L1992 **CD** *020 †20
NIYAKORN, Gerayu. ■ 44103 #019-02-2007 L2007 **AN** *012
NOAISEH, Ghaith. 9500 EUCLID AVE, DESK S-70 44195 #875-03-2002 L2004 **IM** *100 †20
NOBLE, Mark Jeffrey. 9500 EUCLID AVE, STE 100 44195 #025-01-1975 L1977 **U** *020 †95 ‡
NOCHOMOVITZ, Michael Leon. 11100 EUCLID AVE, HUMPHREY BLDG #1633 44106 #836-02-1973 L1979 **PUD IM** *030 †20
NOCK, Charles John. 11100 EUCLID AVE, DEPT OF MED HEMATOLOGY-ONC 44106 #038-41-2001 L2001 **ON IM** *020 †20
NOCK, Mary Lynn. 2101 ADELBERT RD 44106 #038-41-1997 L1999 **NPM** *020 †55
NOELLER, Thomas Paul. 2500 METROHEALTH DR, DEPT OF EMERG MED 44109 #025-01-1994 L1995 **EM** *020 †16
NOERENBERG, Annemarie O. 11100 EUCLID AVE, UNIVERSITY HOSPITALS 44106 #407-33-1964 L1972 **AN** *020 †05
NOFFSINGER, Stephen G. 1708 SOUTHPOINT DR 44109 #038-44-1987 L1988 **P PFP** *020 †75
NOGUERA, Edward. CLEVELAND CLI FNDN, DEPT ANES 44195 #264-01-1997 L2002 **CCA** *012
NOLAN, Shelia Mary. 10701 EAST BLVD, CENTER 44106 #060-02-1976 L1983 **P IM** *020 †20,75
NONEVSKI, Ilche Teodore. 11100 EUCLID AVE, C/O UNIV HOSPS-RESIDENCY O 44106 #038-41-2002 L2002 **GE** *012 †20
NOOR, Saira. 9500 EUCLID AVE, MAIL CODE S70 44195 #704-02-1999 L2005 **IM** *020 †20
NORCIA, Matthew Patrick. 11100 EUCLID AVE, UNIV HOSPITALS OF CLEVELAN 44106 #038-06-1991 L1994 **CCA** *020 †05
NORITZ, Garey. 2500 METROHEALTH DR, METROHEALTH MEDICAL CENTER 44109 #043-01-1999 L1999 **NDP MPD** *020 †20,55
NORMAN, Bruce E. 1001 LAKESIDE AVE E STE 12, NORTH POINT TOWERD 44114 #065-05-1974 L2001 **OBG** *020 †20
NORRIS, Gregory Sheldon. 2500 METROHEALTH DR, RM K152 44109 #409-33-1978 L1982 **IM** *020 †20
NORTON, Dora Louise. 3100 EUCLID AVE, POSITIVE EDUCATION PROGRAM 44115 #038-44-2000 L2006 **CHP** *020 †75
NOUR ABDALLA, Sherif Gama. 11100 EUCLID AVE, STE 2600 44106 #915-02-1992 L2004 *020 †80
NOURALDIN, Muhamed H. 1730 W 25TH ST, STE 1000 44113 #875-01-1991 L1996 **IM IMG** *020 †20
NOVAC, Viorica. ■ 44111 #781-03-1952 **GP** *074
NOVAK, Joshua Daniel. 11100 EUCLID AVE, CO UNIV HOSPS-RESIDENCY OF 44106 #035-06-2003 L2003 **GE** *012 †20
NOVAK, Louis John. 5885 LANDERBROOK DR 44124 #038-06-1970 L1970 **RO R** *020 †80
NOVAK, William Jospeh, Jr. 9500 EUCLID AVE, CLEVELAND CLINIC NEUROLOGY 44195 #038-45-2002 L2006 **SME** *100
NOVICK, Andrew Carl. 9500 EUCLID AVE, STE 100 44195 #067-01-1972 L1977 **U** *020 †95
NOWACEK, D Virgene Graham. ■ 44118 #038-06-1961 L1961 **PD A** *020 †55
NOWAK, Richard John. 6000 PARKLAND BLVD, QUALCHOICE INC 44124 #035-45-1946 L1954 **OBG** *071 †30
NUGENT, Zoe Sara. 9500 EUCLID AVE 44195 #917-34-2004 *100
NUNEZ-HOYO, Marisol. 11100 EUCLID AVE, STE 2600 44106 #042-01-1979 L1982 **DR GS** *020 †80
NURKO, Saul. 9500 EUCLID AVE, CLEVELAND CLINIC A-51 44195 #649-01-1987 L1994 **NEP** *020 †20

■ = Address Information Privacy Protected

N. V., Ahsan Moosa. 9500 EUCLID AVE, CLEVELAND CLINIC FNDN 44195 #495-66-2004 L2006 **CHN** *012

NWANKWO, Uchebike Nnagozi. ■ 44114 #025-07-2007 L2007 **MPD** *012

NWAOKAFOR, Felix C. 8300 HOUGH AVE 44103 #690-01-1980 L2000 **IM** *020 †20

NYALAKONDA, Kavita. ■ 44106 #035-06-2004 L2004 **IM** *012 †20

NYBERG, Eric Mackenzie. ■ 44120 #038-06-2004 L2004 **DR** *012

OAKLEY, Thomas Kelley. 2500 METROHEALTH DR 44109 #038-40-1956 L1956 **R** *071 †80

O'BEIRNE, Thomas J. 3395 SCRANTON RD 44109 #539-06-1947 L1977 **DR** *020

O'BELL, John Chas. 18101 LORAIN AVE 44111 #038-06-1969 L1970 **NPM PD** *075 †55

OBER, Scott K. 10701 EAST BLVD, VA MED CTR DEPT MED 44106 #038-44-1989 L1995 **IM P** *020 †20

OBIAS, Vincent James. 11100 EUCLID AVE 44106 #051-04-1999 L2004 **CRS GS** *020 †85

O'BRIEN, Angela. 9500 EUCLID AVE # IM-P39, CLEVELAND CLNC FOUNDATION 44195 #539-04-1997 **IM** *100

O'BRIEN, Keith Osmond. ■ 44112 #012-21-1999 L1999 **IM** *020 †20

O'BRIEN, Timothy Edwin. 2500 METROHEALTH DR, METROHEALTH MEDICAL CENTER 44109 #035-45-1989 L1992 **HO** *020 †20

O'BRIEN, William John. 5555 TRANSPORTATION BLVD, STE D 44125 #056-06-1985 L1989 **GS** *020 †85

OCAMPO, Dalisay Torrijos. ■ 44129 #748-08-1953 L1975 **GP** *071

OCCHIONERO, Scot Joseph. 18099 LORAIN AVE, INC 44111 #038-06-1986 L1986 **PD** *020 †55

OCLOO, Agbeko Carlos Kwes. 9500 EUCLID AVE, DEPT OF GME 44195 #412-01-1996 L2006 *100

OCONER JAVIER, Aleli S. 5162 BROADWAY AVE 44127 #748-01-1957 L1968 **AN OS** *074

O'DAY, Carla. 18901 LAKE SHORE DR 44119 #038-06-1979 L1979 **GS** *020 †20

O'DONNELL, Colm Patrick F. N 44106 #539-04-1996 **IM** *100

O'DONNELL, James K, Jr. 11100 EUCLID AVE 44106 #038-40-1973 L1974 **NM IM** *020 †28

O'DONOVAN, Peter Barry. 9500 EUCLID AVE, CLEVELAND CLINIC 44195 #539-04-1974 L1974 **DR** *020 †80

OESTERMEYER, Carl F, III. 1127 CARNEGIE AVE 44115 #038-06-1961 L1973 **PHP OS** *071

OETHINGER, Margret Doroth. 9500 EUCLID AVE, CLEVELAND CLINIC 44195 #409-36-1987 L2006 **PTH** *100 †50

OGAN, Nicholas. 7123 PEARL RD 44130 #038-06-1974 L1976 **EM** *020 †16

OGBOGU, Princess Uzoamaka. 11100 EUCLID AVE 44106 #038-44-2000 L2002 **AI** *020

OGHLAKIAN, Roger Ohanes. CO MEDICAL EDUCATIO11100 E, UNIV HOSPS 44106 #605-01-2004 L2006 **N** *012

OGRINC, Lawrence B. 6414 SAINT CLAIR AVE 44103 #016-43-1952 L1952 **IM** *071

OGUNDE, Olumuyiwa E. 11100 EUCLID AVE RM 3018, CO UNIV HOSPS-RESIDENCY OF 44106 #690-02-1990 L2001 **CCP** *100

OGUNLESI, Olusegun Ademol. ■ 44112 #690-01-1997 L2003 **ID** *012 †20

OGUNWALE, Ben Opeyemi. 838 OVERLOOK RIDGE DR 44109 #913-12-1995 L2000 **GE** *012 †20

O'HARA, Jerome F, Jr. 9500 EUCLID AVE, STE 100 44195 #038-43-1987 L1991 **AN** *020 †05

O'HARA, Patrick J. 9500 EUCLID AVE, DEPARTMENT OF VASCULAR SUR 44195 #024-05-1971 L1979 **VS GS** *020 †85

OKAFOR, Chidi Celestine. 2351 E 22ND ST, DEPT OF MED EDU 44115 #690-04-2002 L2006 *100

OKAMOTO, Barbara Kazuko. 12301 SNOW RD 44130 #041-07-1979 L1995 **GS** *074 †85

OKERE, Isidore Chimezie. 11100 EUCLID AVE, DEPT OF MED EDU 44106 #690-02-1999 L2006 **IM** *012

OKEREKE, Ikenna Chidume. 9500 EUCLID AVE BOX 755 44195 #028-02-1999 L1999 **TS** *012

OKOH, Samuel Kofi Osei. 18101 LORAIN AVE, DEPT OF INTERNAL MED 44111 #412-01-2003 L2005 **IM** *012

OKOLIE, Collins Nwabudike. 11100 EUCLID AVE, CASE WESTERN RESERVE UNIV 44106 #033-05-2006 L2006 **IM** *012

OLANSKY, Leann. 9500 EUCLID AVE A53, DEPT OF ENDOCRINOLOGY 44195 #012-05-1976 L2006 **END IM** *040 †20

O'LEARY, Emmeline M. ■ 44121 #025-07-2003 L2003 **AN** *100

OLESKY HILEMAN, Corrilynn. ■ 44118 #038-44-2003 L2006 **ID** *012 †20

OLIVEIRA, Eduardo Infante. 9500 EUCLID AVE, CLEVELAND CLINIC FOUNDATION 44195 #770-02-1999 L2006 *100

OLIVEIRA, Leonardo Protas. 9500 EUCLID AVE 44195 #187-13-2007 L2007 **IM** *012

OLIVERA, Arturo Alejandro. 2900 DETROIT AVE, RECOVERY RESOURCES 44113 #737-01-1963 L1977 **P** *071 †75

OLNESS, Karen Norma. 11100 EUCLID AVE, MAILSTOP 6038 44106 #026-04-1961 L1987 **PD OS** *040 †55

OLOWE, Kayode Olusegun. 200 FOX HOLLOW DR 44124 #035-20-2000 L2004 **GE** *012 †20

OLSEN, Bjorn Thomas. ■ 44118 #016-01-2007 L2007 **AN** *012

OLYNYK, Maryanne S. ■ 44120 #038-44-1985 L1990 **OM IM** *075

O'MALLEY, Kiaram Joseph. ■ 44122 #539-06-1990 **N** *020

ONDERS, Raymond Peter. 11100 EUCLID AVE 44106 #038-44-1988 L1990 **GS AS** *020 †85

O'NEILL, James Oliver. 11100 EUCLID AVE, LKS 3018 44106 #539-04-1995 L2002 *100

O'NEILL, Sean Matthew. 9500 EUCLID AVE 44195 #539-02-1992 L2004 *020

ONG, Hean Yee. 9500 EUCLID AVE, CLEVELAND CLINIC FOUNDATIO 44195 #918-01-1994 L2006 *100

ONG, Hian Tat. 9500 EUCLID AVE BOX S71 44195 #825-01-1987 *100

ONTANEDA, Daniel. ■ 44195 #319-08-2004 L2006 **N** *012

ONWUKA-SMARTY, Sylvester. 2500 METROHEALTH DR, METROHEALTH MED CTR 44109 #690-10-1994 L2001 **PFP** *100 †75

OOI, Boon Swee. 9500 EUCLID AVE, C/O CCF-GRAD MED EDU DEPT- 44195 #825-01-1992 L2001 **CRS** *100

ORAVEC, Dubravka C. 2500 METROHEALTH DR 44109 #957-01-1971 L1983 **R** *020

ORAZULIKE, Chidubem Nnaem. ■ 44143 #038-43-2007 L2007 **EM** *012

ORDONEZ, Maria Pilar A. 2400 ORANGE AVE 44101 #748-07-1962 L1976 **GP** *062

ORENCIA, Anthony J. 2351 E 22ND ST, ST VINCENTS CHARITY HOSP 44115 #748-01-1983 L2000 **IM** *020

ORIJA, Israel Babajide. ■ 44195 #690-02-1990 L2000 **IM** *020 †20

ORLINO, Patricia Ann. 2500 METROHEALTH DR, C/O METROHEALTH MED CTR-RE 44109 #038-40-2000 L2000 **DR** *100 †80

ORNT, Daniel Burrows. 10900 EUCLID AVE BRB110, CASE WESTERN SCHOOL OF MED 44106 #035-45-1976 L2003 **NEP PN** *040 †20

ORRINGER, Agnes Tibor. ■ 44124 #011-02-1974 L1977 **PD** *074

ORRINGER, Carl Edward. 5850 LANDERBROOK DR, STE 100 44124 #011-02-1974 L1992 **CD IM** *020 †20

ORTEGA, Bienvenido D. 5500 RIDGE RD, STE 213 44129 #748-10-1963 L1972 **NS GS** *020 †25

ORTIZ, Jose De Jesus. 11100 EUCLID AVE, DIVISION OF CARDIOLOGY 44106 #264-12-1985 L1996 **CD** *020 †20

OSEMOTA, Simeon Usifo. 11100 EUCLID AVE, BOLWELL 1200 44106 #913-12-2005 L2007 **FP** *012

OSHEA, Robert Stephen. 11100 EUCLID AVE., CLEVELAND CLIN 9500 EUCLID AVE 44195 #035-45-1988 L1998 **GE PHP** *020 †20

OSHODI, Ganiyu. 2500 METROHEALTH DR, DIV OF CARDIO, HEART AND V 44109 #690-05-1992 L2005 **CD** *012 †20

OSINBOWALE, Olusegun O. ■ 44121 #038-41-2001 L2001 **IM** *100 †18,20

OSMAN, Mohammed Najeeb. 11100 EUCLID AVE, DIV OF CRDLGY UNIV HOSP 44106 #495-80-1988 L2002 **CD** *012 †20

OSORIO OVALLES, Federico. ■ 44195 #264-16-1997 L2004 **AN** *012

OSTER, Howard Steven. 11100 EUCLID AVE 44106 #038-06-1996 L1997 **IM** *020 †20

O'TOOLE, Elizabeth Ellen. 2500 METROHEALTH DR, METROHEALTH MEDICAL CENTER 44109 #038-06-1988 L1989 **IMG** *020 †20

O'TOOLE, Orna Terese Mary. 9500 EUCLID AVE, CO CCF-GRAD MED EDU DEPT-N 44195 #539-04-1998 L2000 *100

OTT, Patrick Alexander. 11100 EUCLID AVE RM 3018, CO UNIV HOSPS-RESIDENCY OF 44106 #409-16-1996 L2002 **HO** *012

OURIEL, Kenneth. 9500 EUCLID AVE, DESK NO E32 44195 #016-02-1981 L1998 **VS** *020 †85

OVERLY, Tjuan Lee. ■ 44113 #020-12-1999 L2003 **IC** *012 †20

OWENS, Douglas Blair. 25001 EMERY RD, STE 100 44128 #038-06-1983 L1987 **DR** *020 †80

OWENS, Francis Joseph, Sr. 9500 EUCLID AVE STE EE43 44195 #038-40-1944 L1944 **GE IM** *071 †20

OWUSU, Cynthia. 11100 EUCLID AVE, DIVISION OF HEMATOLOGY-ONC 44106 #412-02-1992 L2006 **HO** *012 †20

OZA, Sudhir Ramchandra. 16111 LORAIN AVE 44111 #495-23-1973 L1980 **PD IM** *020 †20,55

PACE, Stanley Carter. ■ 44120 #038-06-2007 L2007 **PTH** *012

PACHIKARA, Anita Josephin. 2500 METROHEALTH DR 44109 #305-01-2006 L2007 **PD** *012

PACHIKARA, Ninon James. ■ 44195 #001-06-2005 L2005 **CHN** *012

PACKER, Clifford Decatur. 10701 EAST BLVD 44106 #038-06-1988 L1991 **IM** *020 †20

PACZAS, Michael Richard. ■ 44114 #425-01-2004 L2004 **ORS** *012

PADIA, Siddharth Ashok. CLINIC FOUNDATION, CLEVELAND 44195 #023-07-2003 L2004 **DR** *012

PADIYAR, Aparna. 2500 METROHEALTH DR R43 44109 #025-01-2000 L2003 **NEP** *100 †20

PADMANABHAN, Ravindran Ar. 9500 EUCLID AVE, DEPT OF INF DIS/S32 44195 #496-34-1994 L2001 **ID** *100 †20 ‡

PAEZ, Armando Philip Sang. 12940 FAIRHILL RD 44120 #748-01-2000 L2001 **ID** *020

PAGANINI, Emil Presley. 9500 EUCLID AVE 44195 #561-01-1972 L1979 **NEP IM** *030 †20

PAGANO, Gary T. 11100 EUCLID AVE 44106 #038-06-1975 L1978 **P IM** *020 †20,75

PAGEDAR, Nitin Ajitkumar. 11100 EUCLID AVE, LKS 3018 44106 #038-06-2002 L2002 **OTO** *100

PAGEDAR, Saroj A. 18101 LORAIN AVE 44111 #495-96-1970 L1977 **PD** *020 †55

PAI, Anil Raghav. 1730 W 25TH ST 44113 #495-01-1988 L1998 **IM** *072 †20

PAI, Seema. ■ 44106 #038-43-2008 *012

PAIK, In-Ki. 9500 EUCLID AVE BOX 69 44195 #583-02-1972 **OS** *020

PAIK, Paul K. ■ 44118 #035-20-2005 L2008 **IM** *012

PALEKAR, Sanjay Sakharam. 1001 LAKESIDE AVE E, STE 1200 44114 #496-38-1972 L1981 **ORS** *020 †40

PALFREYMAN, Eric Joseph. ■ 44118 #049-01-2007 L2007 **IM** *012

PALLAKI, Muralidhar. 10701 EAST BLVD, SECTION OF GERIATRICS 44106 #495-33-1988 L1993 **IMG PLM** *020 †20

PALMER, Jeffrey Steven. 9500 EUCLID AVE, STE 100 44195 #035-46-1992 L2001 **U UP** *072 †95

PALMER, Robert Marshall. 9500 EUCLID AVE, CLEVELAND CLINIC FOUNDATIO 44195 #025-01-1971 L1986 **IMG IM** *030 †20

PALMIERI, Anthony G. 5163 BROADWAY AVE 44127 #028-34-1937 L1938 **GP TRS** *072

PALOMAKI, Jacob Frederick. 13040 EDGEWATER DR 44107 #038-06-1967 L1967 **OBG** *071 †30

PALOMAKI, Joan Carol. 1730 W 25TH ST STE 15, LUTHERAN HOSPITAL 44113 #038-06-1972 L1973 **GS** *071 †85

PALWAI, Aishwarya. 2500 METROHEALTH DR 44109 #495-65-1999 L2005 **PCC** *012 †20

PAL-WAL, Elena. 2801 MARTIN LTHR KNG JR DR, HOSP FOR REHABILITATION 44104 #913-04-1993 L1998 **PD** *020 †55

PAN, Andrew Beng Siong. 9500 EUCLID AVE 44195 #825-01-1991 L2000 *100

PANDE, Aman. 2500 METROHEALTH DR, CO METROHEALTH MED CTR-RES 44109 #496-09-1999 L2002 **PCC** *012 †20

PANDEY, Aradhana. ■ 44144 #495-30-2001 *100

PANDEY, Vishal. 2500 METROHEALTH DR, METROHEALTH MED CTR 44109 #496-02-1998 L2003 **NPM** *100

PANDIT, Mukul Gangadhar. 11201 SHAKER BLVD, STE 102A 44104 #495-01-1983 L1997 **IM** *020 †20

PANDRANGI, Vasu. 29101 HEALTH CAMPUS DR, STE 250 44145 #495-11-1971 L1980 **PS** *020 †85,65

PANDYA, Rajul. 9500 EUCLID AVE, DEPT OF GME 44195 #495-47-1999 L2006 *100

PANIA, Vimla Devi. 7225 OLD OAK BLVD, STE B309 44130 #496-07-1967 L1974 **IM** *020 †20

PANIGUTTI, Mark Anthony. 7255 OLD OAK BLVD, STE C405 44130 #038-06-1993 L1994 **ORS** *020 †40

PANUTO, John A, Jr. 5500 RIDGE RD, STE 226 44129 #038-45-1988 L1990 **AI IM** *020 †20,03

PANWAR, Sunil. 9500 EUCLID AVE, CLEVELAND CLINIC 44195 #495-55-1989 L2006 *100

PAPADAKIS, Aphrodite. 2500 METROHEALTH DR, METROHEALTH MEDICAL CENTER 44109 #038-40-1999 L2002 **FM** *020 †18

PAPADOPOL, Narcis Artur. 20201 LORAIN RD 44126 #781-01-1996 L2006 **FP** *012

PAPAKONSTANTINOU, Nicholas. ■ 44113 #025-07-2003 L2006 **ORS** *012

PAPAY, Francis Anthony. 9400 EUCLID AVE, A60 44195 #038-44-1984 L1985 **PS OTO** *020 †45,65

PAPIROVA, Irina Iosifovna. 730 SOM CENTER RD, STE 230 44143 #913-66-1982 L1998 **IM** *020 †20

PAPOUCHADO, Bettina Gabri. 9500 EUCLID AVE 44195 #132-01-1997 L2005 **PTH PCP** *100

PAPPAS, Rita M. 9500 EUCLID AVE, DESK M73 44195 #038-45-2001 L2001 **PD** *020 †55

PARAISO, Marie Fidela R. 9500 EUCLID AVE, STE A81 44195 #017-20-1990 L1992 **OBG** *020 †30

PARAKH, Tehnaz Nawzer. ■ 44102 #038-06-2008 *012

PARAMBI, Joan Annie Della. 11100 EUCLID AVE, UNIV HOSP OF CLEVELAND 44106 #496-23-2005 L2006 **IM** *012

PARAMBIL, Chere Joseph G. 9500 EUCLID AVE, CRITICAL CARE MEDICINE 44195 #473-03-1997 L2006 **PCC** *100

PARAYNO, Maria Lourdes. 11100 EUCLID AVE, DEPT RAD 44106 #021-01-2006 L2007 **DR** *012

PARDO, Luis Alfredo. 9500 EUCLID AVE, C/O CCF-GRAD MED EDU DEPT- 44195 #935-07-1998 L2002 **AN** *100

■ = Address Information Privacy Protected

PARIKH, Aditi Shah. ■ 11100 EUCLID AVE, UNIVERISTY HOSPITALS CASE 44106 #038-06-1999 L2004 **MG** *020 †55,19

PARIKH, Kalpana K. 29000 CENTER RIDGE RD 44145 #495-01-1962 L1982 **P** *075 †75

PARIKH, Mona. 2500 METROHEALTH DR 44109 #422-01-2007 L2007 **IM** *012

PARIKH, Sumit. 9500 EUCLID AVE, CLEVELAND CLINIC, S71 44195 #038-06-1998 L2003 **CHN** *100 †55,75

PARIKH, Vibha Kirit. 4255 PEARL RD STE 206 44109 #495-22-1965 L1973 **OBG** *020 †30

PARK, Amy Josephine. 9500 EUCLID AVE, DESK A81 44195 #035-45-2002 L2006 **OBG** *100

PARK, Chanho H. 2351 E 22ND ST 44115 #583-02-1972 L1978 **PTH** *020 †50

PARK, Hoon. 14055 CEDAR RD 44118 #583-12-1973 L1985 **ON IM** *020 †20

PARK, Hyun Young. 7007 POWERS BLVD 44129 #583-03-1964 L1974 **OBG** *075

PARK, Young Sin. 2351 E 22ND ST 44115 #583-10-1969 L1975 **PTH** *020 †50 ‡

PARKER, Brian Matthew. 9500 EUCLID AVE 44195 #035-06-1992 L1997 **AN** *020 †05

PARKER, Richard Dean. 1 CENTER CT RM A107.1, B108B 44115 #038-40-1981 L1983 **ORS** *020 †40

PARLOW, Susan Robin. 9500 EUCLID AVE, CLEVELAND CLINIC FOUNDATIO 44195 #422-01-2007 L2007 **PD** *012

PARMAR, Harbhajan Singh. 6559 WILSON MILLS RD, STE 106A 44143 #496-20-1996 L2002 **CD** *050 †20

PARRAN, Theodore V, Jr. 2351 E 22ND ST 44115 #038-06-1982 L1988 **IM ADM** *020 †20

PARRA SANCHEZ, Ivan Adolf. 13951 TERRACE RD 44112 #264-11-1998 L2006 **GS** *012

PARRISBALOGUN-COLE, Stefan. ■ 44109 #025-07-2003 L2003 **P** *012 †20

PARRY, Robert Lydon. 5850 LANDERBROOK DR, STE 220 44124 #035-20-1985 L2002 **PDS GS** *020 †85

PARSI, Mansour Aron. 9500 EUCLID AVE A31, CLEVELAND CLNC FOUND 44195 #693-01-1992 L2000 **GE** *020 †20

PASAM, Tresa Philomena. 2500 METROHEALTH DR 44109 #495-50-1983 L2005 **FP** *012

PASCHALL, Velma Lou. 9500 EUCLID AVE, IMMUNOLOGY/ DIV OF PEDI/ A 44195 #047-06-1978 L1986 **AI PD** *020 †55,03

PASHKOVSKAYA, Irina. 9500 EUCLID AVE, CLEVELAND CLINIC FOUNDATIO 44195 #913-41-1988 L2004 **GS** *012 †05

PASHMINI, Nazly. 2500 METROHEALTH DR 44109 #517-01-2001 L2007 **MPD** *012

PATEL, Aashish Pravin. 2500 METROHEALTH DR, METROHEALTH MEDICAL CENTER 44109 #038-43-2000 L2004 **EM** *012

PATEL, Alpeshkumar Bipink. 18101 LORAIN AVE, FAIRVIEW GEN HOSP 44111 #496-42-2003 L2006 **IM** *012

PATEL, Amit Raman. ■ 44113 #038-40-2004 L2004 **U** *012

PATEL, Chhaya Jayram. 7255 OLD OAK BLVD, STE C302 44130 #038-44-2000 L2004 **N** *100 †75 ‡

PATEL, Dipika Mahendra. ■ 44113 #038-45-2008 *012

PATEL, Divya Chadraka. ■ 44114 #028-78-2007, ▲ L2007 **IM** *012

PATEL, Falguni K. 9500 EUCLID AVE, DESK P57 44195 #038-44-2003 L2003 **CHP** *012

PATEL, Janish Jay. ■ 44195 #055-01-2007 L2007 **AN** *012

PATEL, Jigisha Suman. 2500 METROHEALTH DR 44109 #308-13-2002 L2004 **PD** *100

PATEL, Jinesh B. 2500 METROHEALTH DR, METROHEALTH MED CTR 44109 #305-01-2006 L2006 **PTH** *012

PATEL, Maheshkumar P. 1419 W 9TH ST, THE HILLIARD BUILDING, 1ST 44113 #495-37-1966 L1972 **AN GP** *020

PATEL, Mohanlal G. 7255 OLD OAK BLVD, STE 209 44130 #495-01-1971 L1978 **IM** *020 †20

PATEL, Narendra S. 19250 BAGLEY RD, STE 101 44130 #495-22-1974 L1984 **AN** *020 †05

PATEL, Neelam Mahendra. 11100 EUCLID AVE, UNIV HOSP 44106 #041-15-2007 L2007 **PD** *012

PATEL, Reshma Vinod. ■ 44120 #025-07-2004 L2004 **END** *012 †20

PATEL, Rishit Kirit. ■ 44113 #038-44-2005 L2005 **IM** *012

PATEL, Sangita T. 850 BRAINARD RD 44143 #495-76-1989 L1998 **OPH** *020 †35

PATEL, Sanjay Rajnikant. 11100 EUCLID AVE, PULMONARY DIV WEARN 612D 44195 #024-01-1996 L2005 **SME PCC** *050 †20

PATEL, Shefali Sumant. 44130 #038-06-2006 L2006 **IM** *012

PATER, Nina. 6835 BROADWAY AVE 44105 #019-02-1999 L2004 **FM** *020 †18

PATHAK, Anand. ■ 44118 #038-41-2007 L2007 **IM** *012

PATHAL, Kalindi Shridhar. 11100 EUCLID AVE 44106 #495-19-1957 L1973 **AN** *075 †05

PATRICK, Pamela Artise. 2500 METROHEALTH DR, DRIVE A-107 44109 #033-06-1999 L2002 **CCS** *100

PATRICK, Robert Marshall. 9500 EUCLID AVE S70, CLEVELAND CLINIC FOUNDATIO 44195 #038-06-1997 L2005 **IM** *020 †20

PATTERSON, Betsy Anne. ■ 44121 #038-06-2004 L2004 **OBG** *012

PATTERSON, Brendan M. 2500 METROHEALTH DR, DEPT ORTHO 44109 #038-06-1986 L1986 **ORS GS** *020 †40

PATTERSON, Elizabeth Nash. ■ 44106 #038-06-1986 L1986 **IM** *020

PATTERSON, Linda A. 2351 E 22ND ST 315 44115 #016-11-1994 L1996 **GS** *020 †85

PATTERSON, Scott Ellis. 1 MOUNT SINAI DR 44106 #038-40-1983 L1984 **AN LM** *020 †05

PATTIMAKIEL, Lynn Mary. 2351 E 22ND ST, DEPT OF MED EDU 44115 #473-04-2004 L2006 *100

PAUL, Grace Meera. 12301 SNOW RD 44130 #495-09-1959 L1971 **PTH BBK** *071 †50

PAUL, Grace Rebecca. 2500 METROHEALTH DR 44109 #495-27-2000 L2004 **PD** *020 †55

PAUL, Randhir Singh. 18697 BAGLEY RD 44130 #495-49-1978 L1987 **EM PE** *020 †55

PAUL, Robindra K. 11100 EUCLID AVE, DEPARTMENT OF PSYCHIATRY 44106 #035-15-2003 L2007 **PFP** *012

PAVIA, Stephen Vincent. 9500 EUCLID AVE, C/O CCF-GRAD MED EDU-NA23 44195 #143-05-1987 L2000 **ICE** *100

PAVLOVICH, Justin Brana. 44121 #041-12-2003 L2003 **OTO** *012

PAWA, Pratheep. 1730 W 25TH ST, STE 3200 44113 #495-14-1981 L2002 **FM** *100 †18

PAWAR, Baba Govindrao. 2466 W 14TH ST 44113 #495-20-1956 L1966 **GS P** *020

PAWPYSZYN, Demetrius. 4229 PEARL RD 44109 #154-02-1954 L1963 **GP** *072

PAZOOKI, Mohamad. 13951 TERRACE RD BX 96, HURON HOSPITAL INT MED 44112 #517-01-1995 L2005 **IM** *012

PEACOCK, Elizabeth Kay. ■ 44106 #038-06-2008 *012

PEACOCK, Wm Franklin, IV. 9500 EUCLID AVE, DEPT. OF EMERGENCY MED 44195 #025-07-1985 L1994 **EM** *020 †16

PEARLSTEIN, Avram Ellis. 2500 METROHEALTH DR 44109 #038-40-1968 L1968 **R** *020 †80

PEARSE, Iyabode Ayodamola. 2500 METROHEALTH DR, METROHEALTH MEDICAL CENTER 44193 #690-01-1987 L2000 **FM** *020

PEARSON, Carol Ann. ■ 44118 #026-08-2000 L2002 **CHP** *012

PEEREBOOM, David Marc. 9500 EUCLID AVE R33, HEMATOLOGY/MED ONCOLOGY 44195 #051-04-1986 L1989 **ON** *020 †20

PEERLESS, Joel Robt. 2500 METROHEALTH DR 44109 #038-41-1980 L1983 **CCM AN** *020 †20,05

PEIRIS, Shanaka Richard. ■ 44195 #035-45-2004 L2004 **AN** *012

PEKARSKI, Krista Lee. 9500 EUCLID AVE, CLEVELAND CLINIC 44195 #037-01-2006 L2006 **PTH** *012

PELECANOS, Helen Irene. ■ 44120 #038-40-1987 L1988 **IM** *074 †20

PELEG, Gil. 18697 BAGLEY RD 44130 #038-44-1994 L1995 **HO** *020 †20

PELEGRIN, Ralph John. 11100 EUCLID AVE 44106 #056-06-1942 L1942 **PD** *071 †55

PELLEY, Robert James. 9500 EUCLID AVE, R-35 CLEVELAND CLINIC 44195 #038-41-1980 L1982 **ON HEM** *020 †20

PENATE, Oscar Ernesto. ■ 44118 #054-04-2006 L2006 **AN** *012

PENCIU, Florin. ■ 44102 #781-03-1993 L1999 **IM** *100 †20

PENFIELD, Joshua David. 9500 EUCLID AVE 44195 #917-13-2004 L2006 **IM** *012

PENKE, Nicole Amy. ■ 44113 #038-06-2007 L2007 **IM** *012

PENN, Marc Steven. 9500 EUCLID AVE 44195 #038-06-1994 L1995 **CD** *020 †20

PENNELL, Nathan Adam. 9500 EUCLID AVE, R 35 44195 #011-03-2002 L2002 **HO** *020 †20

PENNINGTON, Jeffrey E. 2500 METROHEALTH DR, METRO HEALTH MEDICAL CENTE 44109 #017-20-1991 L1994 **EM** *020 †16

PENROD, Carolyn Elizabeth. 6780 MAYFIELD RD, HILLCREST HOSP PED ER 44124 #038-06-2002 L2002 **PD** *020 †55

PEPPLE, Douglas Albert. ■ 44106 #038-06-2008 *012

PERALI, Hari Krishna Venk. 2500 METROHEALTH DR 44109 #496-22-1995 L2006 **FP** *012

PERALTA, Demetrio L. 12220 YORK RD 44133 #748-07-1957 L1964 **ADL GS** *071

PERALTA, Francisco Marasi, Jr. 9500 EUCLID AVE, CO CCF-GRAD MED EDU DEPT-N 44195 #748-01-1989 L2000 *100

PERALTA, Leo Hector. 1780 E 55TH ST 44103 #748-08-1967 *100

PERALTA, Modesto M, Jr. 9500 EUCLID AVE 44118 #041-04-1964 L1972 **TS VS** *020 †85,90

PEREIRA, Jeremy James. 9500 EUCLID AVE, CO CCF-GRAD MED EDU DEPT-N 44195 #143-02-1989 L2000 *100

PEREZ, Federico. 11100 EUCLID AVE, UNIV HOSP RM 2 44106 #264-05-2001 L2003 **ID** *012 †20

PEREZ-FOURNIER, Marina Mo. 2500 METROHEALTH DR, METROHEALTH MED CTR 44109 #649-13-1998 L2005 **NPM** *012

PEREZ-ZINCER, Fernando. 9500 EUCLID AVE, STE 738 44195 #649-05-1991 L2000 **HO** *100

PERIASAMY, Tamilselvi. ■ 44113 #495-95-1985 L1992 **IM** *020 †20

PERILLA PINEDA, Mauricio. 9500 EUCLID AVE, CO CCF-GRAD MED EDU DEPT-N 44195 #264-11-1981 L2003 **AN** *012

PERKINS, Dwayne Anthony. ■ 44195 #016-11-2005 L2005 **IM** *012

PERNG, Wuu Jau. 18697 BAGLEY RD 44130 #244-05-1967 L1976 **GP** *020

PERRIGO, Earl Stanley. 2500 METROHEALTH DR, METRO HEALTH MED CENTER 44109 #050-02-1969 L1976 **CD IM** *040 †20

PERRY, Dewayde Conniley. 30680 BAINBRIDGE RD 44139 #047-07-1995 L2002 **GS GPM** *020

PERRY, Julian Damon. 9500 EUCLID AVE I-20, COLE EYE INSTITUTE 44195 #035-01-1993 L1999 **OPH** *020 †35

PERRY, Marvin Lee. 7007 POWERS BLVD 44129 #028-34-1958 L1959 **IM GE** *071

PERRYMAN, Brenda Joyce. 1464 E 105TH ST 44106 #038-06-1982 L1982 **IM** *020 †20

PERSE, David Frank. 1730 W 25TH ST # 154 44113 #038-40-1979 L1984 **GS** *020 †85

PESH-IMAM, Taslim. 44145 #407-10-1968 L1976 **IM GE** *020 †20

PETCHER, John D. 7300 STATE RD 44134 #038-06-1950 L1950 **IM** *071

PETERSILGE, Cheryl Ann. 11100 EUCLID AVE 44106 #038-40-1987 L1993 **DR** *020 †80

PETERSON, Jennifer Hope. 9500 EUCLID AVE, M31 DEPT OF NEONATOLOGY 44195 #018-03-1999 L2003 **NPM** *020 †55

PETERSON, Loretta Lydia. 9500 EUCLID AVE, DESK A-81 44195 #025-07-1979 L1984 **PM** *020 †60

PETRACK, Emory Mark. 11100 EUCLID AVE 44106 #035-08-1984 L1992 **PEM** *040 †55

PETRAS, Keith Michael. 11100 EUCLID AVE, CLEVELAND DEPT OF MEDICINE 44106 #041-14-1999 L1999 **NEP** *020 †20

PETRE, John Henry. ■ 44143 #041-02-1946 L1947 **U** *071 †95

PETREA, Dan Lucian. 2351 E 22ND ST, C/O ST VINENCT CHAR/MED ED 44115 #781-01-1995 L2000 **IM** *012

PETRELLI, Mary Panayota. 2500 METROHEALTH DR 44109 #848-01-1960 L1973 **ATP OS** *071 †50

PETRIE, Timothy Gerard. 2500 METROHEALTH DR 44109 #038-06-1992 L1993 **DR** *020

PETROFF, Roman. 730 SOM CENTER RD, STE 230 44143 #913-06-1976 L1982 **IM** *020 †20

PETROSIUTE, Agne. 2500 METROHEALTH DR, DEPT OF RESIDENCY SUPPORT 44109 #913-96-2002 L2005 **PD** *012

PETROZZI, Mariana C. 11100 EUCLID AVE, CLEVELAND 44106 #038-06-1997 L1999 **PCC** *020 †20

PETTERSSON, Gosta Bengt. 9500 EUCLID AVE, # F24 44195 #858-05-1971 L1999 *020

PHAM, Quan Van. 2500 METROHEALTH DR, C/O METROHEALTH MED CTR-RE 44109 #026-04-1999 L2002 **ICE** *100 †20

PHAM, Ramya Murali. 11100 EUCLID AVE 44106 #038-45-2003 L2003 **DR** *012

PHAM, Thu Thien. ■ 44113 #041-01-2005 L2006 **OPH** *012

PHAM, Tong Van. 2500 METROHEALTH DR, METROHEALTH MEDICAL CENTER 44109 #026-04-1999 L2005 **CD** *012 †20

PHANINDRA, Channagiri. ■ 44141 #495-33-1972 L1980 **GS** *020 †85

PHELAN, Michael Patrick. 9500 EUCLID AVE 44195 #035-06-1990 L2001 **EM** *020 †16

PHILIP, Femi. 9500 EUCLID AVE, CLEVELAND CLINIC FOUNDATIO 44195 #836-02-2000 L2006 **IM** *012

PHILIP, Rajiv Thomas. 2500 METROHEALTH DR 44109 #665-01-2007 L2007 **IM** *012

PHILIP, Roland Stephen. ■ 44106 #165-04-1966 L1969 **GS CCS** *071 †85

PHILLIPS, Christopher O. 1701 E 12TH ST, STE 81-W 44114 #023-01-1995 L2004 **IM** *020 †20

PHILLIPS, Karen Patrice. 9500 EUCLID AVE, DEPT of GME 44195 #143-05-1996 L2006 *100

PHILLIPS, Micheal David. 9500 EUCLID AVE, MC: U-15 44195 #035-01-1990 L2002 **RNR** *020 †80

PHILLIPS, Shannon Connor. 9500 EUCLID AVE M73, CLEVELAND CLINIC FOUNDATIO 44195 #035-01-1990 L2003 **PD** *020 †55

PHITAYAKORN, Roy. 11100 EUCLID AVE 44106 #041-12-2002 L2002 **GS** *012

PI, Diana Jochien. 2500 METROHEALTH DR, DEPT INTERNAL MEDICINE 44109 #032-01-1988 L1992 **IM** *020 †20

PICKERING, Sharyl Lynn. 11100 EUCLID AVE, UNIV HOSP CASE MED CTR 44106 #016-11-1980 L1984 **DR** *020 †80

PICKETT, Patrick Myers. ■ 44106 #048-13-2007 L2007 **AN** *012

PIERCE, Gregory. 9500 EUCLID AVE, DEPT OF RADIOLOGY 44195 #041-13-1995 L1996 **VIR** *020 †80

PIEREN, Sara Kane. ■ 44121 #038-40-2006 L2006 **AN** *012

PIETRANGELO, Lee A. 18101 LORAIN AVE, FAIRVIEW HOSPITAL 44111 #038-06-1993 L1994 **IM** *020 †20

PIFER, Matthew Alan. ■ 44103 #038-06-2008 *012

■ = Address Information Privacy Protected

PIGNOLET, Dale Wesley. 18901 LAKE SHORE BLVD 44119 #038-06-1987 L1990 **EM** *020 †16
PIKTEL, Joseph Stephen. 2500 METROHEALTH DR 44109 #038-06-2004 L2004 **EM** *100
PILE, James Craig. 2500 METROHEALTH DR, METROHEALTH MEDICAL CTR 44109 #038-40-1987 L1994 **IM ID** *020 †20
PILIANG, Melissa Ann. 9500 EUCLID AVE, DERMATOLOGY - A-61 44195 #017-20-2001 L2001 **DMP** *100
PILLAI, Dilip Parameshwar. 2500 METROHEALTH DR, HEAR & VASCULAR CTR H 316 44109 #495-53-1985 L2000 **IC** *100 †20
PINA, Ileana L. 11100 EUCLID AVE, LAKESIDE HOSPITAL/3RD FL 44106 #011-02-1976 L2000 **CD IM** *020 †20
PINAULT, Gilles C J. 11100 EUCLID AVE 44106 #067-01-1991 L1994 **VS CCA** *020 †85
PINCHAK, Alfred Cyril. 2500 METROHEALTH DR, METROHEALTH MEDICAL CENTER 44109 #038-06-1973 L1973 **AN** *050 †05
PINCHCOFSKY, Howard Aaron. ■ 44115 #016-01-2005 L2006 **DR** *012
PINE, Richard Wilbur. 18697 BAGLEY RD 44130 #038-06-1973 L1974 **GS CD** *020 †85
PINEDA, John Jos. 6780 MAYFIELD RD 44124 #005-06-1982 L1988 **AN IM** *020 †20,05
PINEYRO TREZZA, Maria Mer. 9500 EUCLID AVE 44195 #924-01-1998 L2005 **END** *100
PINKERTON, Jay Stuart. 5850 LANDERBROOK DR, STE 3 44124 #038-06-1995 L1996 **OBG** *020 †30
PIORO, Erik Paul. 9500 EUCLID AVE, CLEVELAND CLINIC FDN 44195 #060-02-1981 L1994 **PTH** *020 †75
PIORO, Mathilde H. 10701 EAST BLVD 111N, CLEVELAND VA MED CTR 44106 #067-01-1989 L1994 **RHU** *020 †20
PIOTROWICZ, Teresa Maria. 11100 EUCLID AVE, OF CLEVELAND 44106 #759-12-1982 L2004 **ADP** *012
PIRJANIAN, Zareh. 2500 METROHEALTH DR, METROHEALTH MED CTR 44109 #305-01-2006 L2006 **IM** *012
PISHCHIK, Vitaliy. 2351 E 22ND ST, DEPT OF GME 44115 #913-13-1997 L2006 *100
PITAS, Grzegorz Adam. 9500 EUCLID AVE G3, DEPT OF CT ANESTH CCF 44195 #759-04-1989 L2001 **AN** *020 †20
PITT, Sunny Eusun. 9500 EUCLID AVE, DIV OF RADIOLOGY / HB6 44195 #038-44-1992 L2000 **PDR** *020 †80
PITT, Tracy S. 9500 EUCLID AVE, DEPT OF SURGERY 44106 #038-75-2001, ▲ L2002 **GS** *020
PLA, Ramon. ■ 44117 #275-01-1961 L1968 **GP GS** *075
PLATT-HOUSTON, Candis N. 4071 LEE RD, STE 260 44128 #038-06-2000 L2000 **PD** *020 †55 ‡
PLAUTZ, Gregory Edward. 9500 EUCLID AVE, THE CLEVELAND CLINIC S20 44195 #017-20-1984 L1994 **PHO PD** *050 †55
PLECHA, Donna Tasch. 11100 EUCLID AVE, UNIVERSITY HOSPITALS 44106 #038-06-1988 L1990 **DR** †80
PLECHA, Ferdinand Michael. 7255 OLD OAK BLVD, STE C108 44130 #038-06-1987 L1988 **VS** *020 †85
PLERHOPLES, William Alan. 2500 METROHEALTH DR, C/O METROHEALTH MED CTR-RE 44109 #035-45-2002 L2002 **EM** *020
PLOTKIN, Jack. 19201 VILLAVIEW RD 44119 #038-40-1962 L1962 **OPH** *071 †35
POCHIRAJU, Sitarama P R. 16600 W SPRAGUE RD STE 80, VISITING PHYSICIANS ASSOC. 44130 #495-11-1976 L2000 **IM IMG** *020 ‡
POE, Brigid Maureen. 25001 EMERY RD, STE 100 44128 #038-44-1985 L1993 **DR** *020 †80
POGGIO, Emilio Daniel. 9500 EUCLID AVE, DESK A51 44195 #132-07-1993 L2001 **IM NEP** *020 †20
POHL, Marc Alfred. 9500 EUCLID AVE, NEPHROL/HYTN DEPT, GLICKMA 44195 #038-06-1966 L1966 **NEP IM** *020 †20
POHLMAN, Brad L. 9500 EUCLID AVE R35, CLEVELAND CLINIC TAUSSIG C 44195 #017-20-1985 L1993 **HO IM** *020 †20
POLA, Lakshmaiah. 7255 OLD OAK BLVD, STE C412 44130 #495-21-1972 L1977 **GE IM** *020 †20
POLIMENAKOS, Anastasios C. 11100 EUCLID AVE, CO UNIV HOSPS - RESIDENCY 44106 #418-01-1995 L2001 **TS** *020 †85,90
POLLARD, Robert Richard. 4071 LEE RD, STE 260 44128 #038-44-1995 L1998 **OBG** *020 †30
POLLOCK, Harry Winslow. 2500 METROHEALTH DR, # 812B 44109 #038-06-1982 L1982 **P PYA** *020 †75
POLSTER, Daniel Seth. 6115 POWERS BLVD, STE 204 44129 #038-06-1996 L1997 **P** *020 †75
POLSTON, David Wilson. 9500 EUCLID AVE, NEUROMUSCULAR CT S91 44195 #020-02-1999 L2004 **N NMN** *020 †75
POMERANZ, Jerome Raphael. 2475 E 22ND ST STE 611, CLEVELAND SKIN PTH LAB 44115 #024-05-1956 L1965 **D DMP** *020 †15
PONSKY, Lee Evan. 11100 EUCLID AVE, RM 2500 44106 #038-06-1997 L1999 **U** *020 †95
PONSKY, Todd Adam. 11100 EUCLID AVE, RBC 122 44106 #038-06-1999 L2007 **PDS** *100 †85
PONTIUS, Kathryn Inez. ■ 44145 #017-20-1977 L1980 **PTH** *074 †50
POOLOS, Pete Nick. 18099 LORAIN AVE 44111 #012-01-1957 L1963 **NS** *071 †25
POOSTIZADEH, Ahmad. 11100 EUCLID AVE, CO UNIV HOSPS-CARDIOTHORAC 44106 #517-08-1986 L2000 **TS** *020
POPONICK, Janet Marie. 2500 METROHEALTH DR, DEPT OF EMERGENCY MEDICINE 44109 #038-45-1985 L1988 **CCM EM** *020 †20
POPOVICH, Marc John. 9500 EUCLID AVE 44195 #038-40-1985 L1986 **CCA AN** *020 †20,05
POPOVSKY, Julio. 1 MOUNT SINAI DR 44106 #132-01-1960 L1970 **TS** *071 †85,90
POPTIC, Jennifer Marie. 18200 LORAIN AVE, CO FAMILY PRACTICE 44111 #038-43-2005 L2005 **FP** *012
PORTER, Arthur. 6770 MAYFIELD RD # 226 44124 #041-09-1974 L1975 **U** *020 †95
PORTER, Robert Jos. 2351 E 22ND ST 44115 #016-43-1959 L1963 **R NM** *020 †80,28
PORTER, Robert Patrick. 18697 BAGLEY RD, RADIOLOGY DEPARTMENT 44130 #038-43-1988 L1996 **DR** *020 †80
PORUBOVICH, Jeanette S. 7215 OLD OAK BLVD, STE A314 44130 #038-44-1986 L1987 **IM** *020 †20
POST, Anthony Benj. 11100 EUCLID AVE 44106 #038-06-1986 L1987 **GE IM** *071 †20
POST, Susan Esther. 2500 METROHEALTH DR, METRO HEALTH MEDICAL CENTE 44109 #025-12-1995 L1997 **PD** *020 †20
POSTOEV, Angelina. 13951 TERRACE RD, DEPT OF GME 44112 #305-01-2004 L2005 **GS** *012
POTOKAR, Christine Ann. 3525 SCRANTON RD 44109 #038-06-1995 L1996 **IM** *020 †20
POTTER, Paul S. 9500 EUCLID AVE 44195 #048-13-1985 L1997 **AN** *020 †05
POTTS, Aaron Daniel. ■ 44114 #025-07-2006 L2006 **ORS** *012
POTTS, Jeannette Kolis. 9500 EUCLID AVE, STE 100 44195 #038-06-1991 L1994 **GS** *020 †18
POTZMAN, Jennifer Marie. 11100 EUCLID AVE, DEPT OF ANESTHESIOLOGY 44106 #011-02-2006 L2006 **AN** *012
POWELL, Douglas Peter. 13951 TERRACE RD, HURON HOSPITAL - NEONATOLO 44112 #020-02-1968 L1989 **NPM PD** *020 †55
POZUELO, Fatima Maria. 6803 MAYFIELD RD STE 309 44124 #038-45-1995 L1997 **PCC** *020 †20

POZUELO, Leopoldo Jose. 9500 EUCLID AVE 44195 #847-11-1988 L1992 **P IM** *020 †20,75
PRABHAKARAN, Radhai. 9500 EUCLID AVE, CLEVELAND CLINIC FOUNDATIO 44195 #495-04-1997 L2007 **PD** *012
PRADA, Cristian M. 2500 METROHEALTH DR 44109 #781-01-1983 L2000 **AN** *020
PRADHAN, Minal. ■ 44122 #495-01-1957 L1968 **AN GP** *020
PRADITSUWAN, Rungnirand. ■ 44118 #891-02-1982 **IMG** *100
PRATT, Debra A. 18200 LORAIN AVE, 2ND FL 44111 #055-01-1989 L1994 **GS** *020 †85
PRATT, Lindsay L. ■ 44195 #041-02-1953 L1961 **OTO** *020 †45
PRAYSON, Richard Anthony. 9500 EUCLID AVE, CLEVELAND CLNC 44195 #038-06-1988 L1989 **PTH** *020 †50
PREMINGER, Tamar Judith. 9500 EUCLID AVE, PEDCARDIOLOGY M41 44195 #035-09-1986 L1994 **PDC PD** *020 †55
PREMSAGAR, Ishwar Chandra. 9500 EUCLID AVE, CO CCF-GRAD MED EDU DEPT-N 44195 #495-05-1979 L2000 *100
PRESTON, David Channing. 11100 EUCLID AVE, STE 5512 44106 #038-06-1985 L1985 **N IM** *020 †75
PRETLOW, Thos Garrett, II. CASE WESTERN RESERVE PATH 44106 #035-45-1965 L1984 **PTH ON** *050
PREUSS, Otto Paul G. 17876 SAINT CLAIR AVE 44110 #407-19-1945 L1956 **OM** *071
PRICE, Franklin Bruce. 14055 CEDAR RD, STE 200 44118 #038-40-1967 L1967 **HO IM** *020 †20
PRICE, Ronald L. 1611 S GREEN RD STE 306C, UNIV OF OPHTHAL ASSOC 44121 #035-01-1965 L1971 **PO OPH** *071 †35
PRIEBE, Paul Preston. 2500 METROHEALTH DR, H922 44109 #056-06-1973 L1976 **GS OS** *020 †85
PRIETO, Lourdes Rosa. 9500 EUCLID AVE, PEDIATRIC CARDIOLOGY DEPT 44195 #023-07-1987 L1994 **PDC** *020 †55
PRIOLA, Ginna Marie. ■ 44103 #051-07-2007 L2007 **PD** *012
PRITCHARD, Claudene Marie. 9500 EUCLID AVE, E30 44195 #038-43-2002 L2002 **AN** *100 †05
PROCHOROFF, Andre. 2500 METROHEALTH DR, DEPT OF PEDIATRICS 44109 #409-05-1998 L2000 **CHN** *020
PROK, Alan Leroy. 9500 EUCLID AVE BOX L25 44195 #038-06-2000 L2000 **PTH** *100 †50
PROKOPIUS, Michael J. 4330 W 150TH ST 44135 #038-44-1991 L1992 **OPH** *020 †35
PROLOGO, John David. 11100 EUCLID AVE, # 2600 44106 #038-06-1999 L1999 **DR** *020 †80
PROUDFIT, William L. 9500 EUCLID AVE 44195 #024-01-1939 L1946 **CD** *071 †20
PROVENCIO, Javier Jose. 9500 EUCLID AVE, NEUROLOGY/S90 44195 #041-14-1993 L2003 **CCM N** *020 †75,20
PROVITT, Linda Kaye. 11100 EUCLID AVE, UNIV HOSP HANNA PAV BLDG 44106 #038-43-1993 L1999 **P ADP** *100
PRUD'HOMME, Dominique G. 9500 EUCLID AVE, CARDIOTHORACIC ANESTHESIA 44195 #396-21-1985 L1998 **AN** *020 †05
PSARRAS, James P. 2351 E 22ND ST 44115 #038-40-1977 L1981 **P** *020
PUCELL, Anthony Geo. 18660 BAGLEY RD STE 40 44130 #028-34-1973 L1974 **DR PD** *020 †80,55
PUDUNAGAR SUBBIAH, Shanmug. 2500 METROHEALTH DR, METROHEALTH MED CTR 44109 #495-04-1997 L2003 **HO** *012
PUJAZON, Melissa Anne. 11100 EUCLID AVE, C/O UNIV HOSPS-RESIDENCY O 44106 #048-12-2002 L2002 **AN** *100
PUKIS, Vytautas. 13951 TERRACE RD, DEPT OF MED 44112 #913-96-2004 L2006 **IM** *012
PUNDIK, Svetlana. 11100 EUCLID AVE, STE 5512 44106 #038-06-1999 L1999 **N** *020 †75
PUNJABI-DUTTA, Rachna. 9500 EUCLID AVE, DEPT OF REGIONAL RADIOLOGY 44195 #495-01-1992 L1999 **DR** *020 †80
PURUSHOTHAM, Archana. 9500 EUCLID AVE, C/O CCF-GRAD MED EDU DEPT- 44195 #495-53-1994 L2003 **N** *012
PUTHAWALA, Meherunisa A H. ■ 44124 #495-22-1968 L1976 **OBG** *071
PUTKA, Brian Stephen. 2500 METROHEALTH DR 44109 #038-43-2000 L2000 **GE** *100 †20
PUWANANT, Araya. 11100 EUCLID AVE, UNIV HOSP OF CLEVELAND 44106 #891-07-1998 L2005 **N** *012
PWEE, Emily May Li. 13951 TERRACE RD 44112 #539-02-1996 L2002 *100
QADEER, Mohammed Abdul. 9500 EUCLID AVE, A-31 44195 #495-21-1991 L2003 **GE** *012
QASIM, Zaffer Ahmed. 2500 METROHEALTH DR 44109 #704-26-2001 L2005 **IM** *012
QIAN, Ying. ■ 44195 #041-01-2005 L2006 **OPH** *012
QUACH, Michael M. CLEVELAND CLINIC, EPILEPSY CTR/S51 44195 #017-20-2001 L2007 **CN** *012 †55
QUALLICH, Leonard George. 18660 BAGLEY RD, STE 501 44130 #038-41-1973 L1975 **GE IM** *020 †20
QUAN, Kara Jeanine. 2500 METROHEALTH DR 44109 #038-44-1990 L1991 **ICE** *020 †20 ‡
QUANG, Lourdes Falconi. 3167 FULTON RD 44109 #038-44-1994 L2000 **OBG** *020 †30
QUEALY, Kathleen P. 2500 METROHEALTH DR, METROHEALTH MEDICAL CTR 44109 #038-40-1990 L1993 **CD** *020 †20
QUEEN, John Richard, Jr. 9500 EUCLID AVE, DEPT OF EMERGENCY MED, E-1 44195 #038-40-1994 L1999 **EM IM** *020 †16
QUILTY, James Francis, Jr. 2500 METROHEALTH DR, METRO HEALTH MEDICAL CENTE 44109 #028-34-1966 L1971 **OS PD** *030 †55
QUINN, Kathleen May. 2801 MARTIN LTHR KNG JR DR 44104 #024-01-1975 L1982 **CHP P** *020 †75
QUINN, Martin John. 9500 EUCLID AVE, CO CCF-GRAD MED EDU DEPT-N 44195 #539-04-1992 L2000 *100
QURESHI, Athar Mahmood. ■ 44195 #704-25-1996 L2002 **PDC** *100
RAAD, Bassel Fadl. 11100 EUCLID AVE, UNIVERSITY HOSPITALS CASE 44106 #605-01-2003 L2007 **IM** *012
RAAF, Heather Neilson. 11001 CEDAR AVE, CUYAHOGA CTY CORONERS OFC 44106 #038-06-1987 L1991 **FOP PTH** *062 †50
RAAF, John Hart. ■ 44120 #024-01-1970 L1985 **GS SO** *071 †85
RABBI, Jamal Fazal. 18101 LORAIN AVE, CO SURGERY DEPT 44111 #704-09-1999 L2004 **GS** *012
RABETS, John Charles. 9500 EUCLID AVE, STE A100 44195 #041-01-2000 L2000 **U** *100
RABINOWITZ, Laura Osofsky. 12300 MCCRACKEN RD, EMERGENCY DEPT. 44125 #038-06-1991 L1994 **PTH** *020 †50
RABINOWITZ, Martin Zvi. 19250 BAGLEY RD 44130 #035-08-1978 L1982 **PTH** *020 †50
RABOVSKY, Michael Alan. 26900 CEDAR RD STE 22N 44122 #023-01-1981 L1984 **FM** *020 †18
RACKLEY, Raymond Robt. 9500 EUCLID AVE A100, GLICKMAN UROLOGICAL & KIDN 44195 #038-06-1989 L1992 **U** *020 †95
RADDOCK, Michael Louis. 2500 METROHEALTH DR, METROHEALTH MEDICAL CENTER 44109 #005-14-1994 L1999 **FM** *020 †18
RADEBAUGH, David Ellis. 12301 SNOW RD 44130 #038-40-1969 L1969 **DR** *020 †80
RADER, Florian. 2500 METROHEALTH DR 44109 #154-07-2002 L2005 **IM** *012

■ = Address Information Privacy Protected

RADHAKRISHNAN, Kadakkal R. 9500 EUCLID AVE, CLEVELAND CLINIC, A111 44195 #495-31-1992 L2000 **PG** *100 †55
RADHAKRISHNAN, Sunita. 9500 EUCLID AVE, CO CCF-GRAD MED EDU DEPT-N 44195 #495-59-1996 L2003 **OPH** *100
RADIO, James Robt. 2900 DETROIT AVE, RECOVERY RESOURCES 44113 #038-41-1992 L1997 **P** *020 †75
RADIVOYEVITCH, Milan. 2500 METROHEALTH DR 44109 #957-02-1954 L1963 **CLP PTH** *020 †50
RADKOWSKI, Diana. 11100 EUCLID AVE 44106 #024-05-1987 L1993 **OTO** *020 †45
RADU, Liviu Dan. 9500 EUCLID AVE, C/O CCF-GRAD MED EDU DEPT- 44195 #781-05-1996 L2002 **AN** *100
RAE-GRANT, Alexander D. 9500 EUCLID AVE U10, CLEVELAND CLINIC 44195 #065-10-1982 L2007 **N** *020 †75
RAFEY, Mohammad Abdur. 9500 EUCLID AVE A51, NEPHROLOGY/HYPERTENSION 44195 #496-22-1990 L2007 **NEP** *100 †20
RAFFAY, Thomas Michael. ■ 44135 #038-40-2007 L2007 *012
RAFIEI, Shervin. ■ 44112 #517-08-2000 L2002 **DR** *012
RAGHAVAN, Derek. 9500 EUCLID AVE, RM R35 44195 #143-03-1974 L2005 *020
RAHEJA, Deepak. 2307 W 14TH ST, GRACE HOSPITAL 44113 #495-73-1979 L1993 **N** *020 †75
RAHMAN, Faisal Alam. ■ 44195 #038-44-2005 L2005 **AN** *012
RAHMAN, Mirza. 2500 METROHEALTH DR 44109 #035-48-1990 L1995 **FM GPM** *020 †70,18
RAHMAN, Rahim Na. ■ 44110 #038-06-2004 L2004 **AN** *012
RAI, Shankar Man. 9500 EUCLID AVE 44195 #672-01-1986 *100
RAINA, Rupesh. 3500 METRO HEALTH DR, DEPT OF INTERNAL MED/PEDS 44195 #495-05-1998 L2003 **MPD** *100
RAINEY, Jon Marshall. 26250 EUCLID AVE STE 625 44132 #056-06-1980 L1982 **IM IMG** *020 †20
RAISONI, Sapna J.. 9500 EUCLID AVE 44106 #166-02-2000 L2002 **AN** *100
RAITSIS, Valery B. ■ 44143 #913-15-1976 L1983 **IMG GP** *020
RAJ, Chandra Prabha. ■ 44140 #495-13-1971 L1980 **AN GS** *071
RAJ, Prasanta Kumar. 18099 LORAIN AVE, STE 14 44111 #495-13-1972 L1978 **GS** *020 †85
RAJAGOPALAN, Suman. 9500 EUCLID AVE, DEPT OF GME 44195 #496-21-2000 L2006 **AN** *012
RAJEE, Nirmala Kumari. 2500 METROHEALTH DR 44109 #496-39-1988 L2001 **PTH** *100
RAKHIT, Ashis Kumar. 2322 E 22ND ST, STE 305 44115 #495-39-1978 L1990 **CD IM** *020 †20
RAMACHANDRA, Indiresha. 10701 EAST BLVD, STOKES VA MED CTR 44106 #495-33-1992 L2007 **IM CD** *020 †20
RAMACHANDRA, M. 9500 EUCLID AVE, DEPT OF ANESTH E31 44195 #495-94-1990 L2000 **AN** *020 †05
RAMAHI, Amani Ahmad. 11100 EUCLID AVE, UNIV HOSPS OF CLEV 44106 #575-01-1989 L1996 **N** *020 †75
RAMAN, Anand V. S.. ■ 44195 #759-06-2002 L2005 **PDC** *012
RAMASAMY, Kavitha. 2351 E 22ND ST, ST VINCENT CHARITY 44115 #495-42-1998 L2003 **IM** *100
RAMASUBBU, Kumudha. ■ 44195 #409-10-1999 L2000 **CD** *100 †20
RAMIREDDY, Sweeya Reddy. ■ 44195 #496-64-2003 L2007 **IM** *012
RAMIREZ, Haydee Mishel. ■ 44195 #050-02-1999 L2004 **D** *012
RAMIREZ, Maria Rowena Car. 9500 EUCLID AVE, CLEVELAND CLINIC FOUNDATIO 44195 #748-01-2000 L2007 **PD** *012
RAMIREZ GAVIDIA, Jose Rob. 18101 LORAIN AVE, DEPT OF SURGERY 44111 #341-03-2005 L2007 **GS** *012
RAMOS, Bayani N. 4229 PEARL RD 44109 #748-01-1955 L1969 **GS GP** *020
RAMOS, Edita N. 5109 BROADWAY AVE 44127 #748-01-1956 L1975 **PD** *020 †55
RAMOS, Jesus A. 18697 BAGLEY RD 44130 #748-01-1961 L1970 **GS** *020
RAMOS, Roberto Villarama. 1 MOUNT SINAI DR # RADIO 44106 #748-01-1971 **R** *100
RAMSEY, Cyrus A. ■ 44120 #038-06-2006 L2006 **GS** *012
RANA, Divya. 2500 METROHEALTH DR, C/O METROHEALTH MED CTR-RE 44109 #913-92-1999 L2003 **NPM** *012 †55
RANAWAT, Nishant Singh. 11100 EUCLID AVE 44106 #495-30-1998 L2006 **N** *012
RANKIN, George Bain. 1 CLINIC CTR 44195 #038-06-1959 L1959 **GE IM** *071 †20
RANSOHOFF, Richard Milton. 9500 EUCLID AVE, DEPT OF NEUROLOGY 44195 #038-06-1978 L1979 **N** *050 †20,75
RAO, Dinkar V. 6770 MAYFIELD RD STE 223 44124 #495-37-1971 L1977 **OBG** *020 †30
RAO, Kavitha Prakash. 2074 ABINGTON RD 44106 #495-09-1999 L2001 **PTH** *100 †50
RAO, Laxminarayana C. 7255 OLD OAK BLVD, STE 106 44130 #495-09-1968 L1975 **PUD** *020 †20
RAO, Llewelyn John. ■ 44115 #028-34-2004 L2005 **OPH** *012
RAO, Poornima B. 9500 EUCLID AVE, C/O CCF-GRAD MED EDU DEPT- 44195 #035-09-2000 L2000 **GS** *012
RAO, Pravin Kumar. ■ 44195 #023-07-2004 L2004 **U** *012
RAPISUWON, Suthee. CO RESIDENCY OFFICE, UNIVERSITY HOSPITALS 44106 #891-04-2003 L2007 **MDG** *012
RAPKIN, David Scott. 11100 EUCLID AVE 44106 #056-05-1984 L1987 **AN** *020 †05
RASHAD, Fouad A. 3395 SCRANTON RD 44109 #330-04-1955 L1970 **DR** *020 †80
RASHIDI, Arash. 18101 LORAIN AVE 44111 #517-10-1997 L2002 **NEP** *020 †20
RASHIDI, Omid. 2500 METROHEALTH DR, METROHEALTH MED CTR 44109 #517-19-2001 L2005 **FP** *012
RASKIND, Craig Howard. M31, 9500 EUCLID AVE, CLEVELAND CLINIC FOUNDATIO 44195 #035-46-1996 L2002 **NPM** *020 †55
RASMUSSEN, Peter Alan. 9500 EUCLID AVE S-80 44195 #056-05-1991 L1998 **NS RNR** *020 †25
RASTGOUFARD, Aboutaleb. 2351 E 22ND ST 44115 #517-01-1957 L1972 **TS** *020 †85,90
RASTOGI, Vijay. 12100 SUPERIOR AVE 44106 #496-09-1993 L1999 **IMG** *020 †20
RASUL, Shahid. 11311 SHAKER BLVD DEPT MED 44104 #704-02-1990 **IM** *020
RATCHESON, Robert Allan. 11100 EUCLID AVE, 5TH FL 44106 #016-06-1965 L1981 **NS** *072 †25
RATLIFF, Norman B, Jr. 9500 EUCLID AVE 44195 #036-07-1962 L1981 **ATP CD** *071 †50
RATNOFF, Oscar Davis. UNIVERSITY HOSPITALS 44106 #035-01-1939 L1950 **HEM IM** *072 †20
RATTANACHAIYANO, Manee. 1730 W 25TH ST 44113 #891-02-1985 **IM** *100
RAUCH, Julia Kristen. ■ 44106 #038-06-2008 *012
RAVAKHAH, Keyvan. 13951 TERRACE RD, HURON HOSPITAL 44112 #902-05-1992 L1995 **IM PLM** *020 †20 ‡
RAVAS, Rebecca Christine. 11100 EUCLID AVE 44106 #038-43-2000 L2000 **AN** *020 †05
RAVINDRA, Sunay Bangalore. 2500 METROHEALTH DR, METROHEALTH MED CTR 44109 #495-37-2000 L2005 **AN** *012
RAVISHANKAR, K C. 7215 OLD OAK BLVD, A411 44130 #495-52-1979 L1993 **N** *020 †75
RAY, Amy Jo. 11100 EUCLID AVE, C/O UNIV HOSPS-RESIDENCY O 44106 #038-06-2001 L2003 **ID** *100 †20
RAY, Monica. 11100 EUCLID AVE 2ND, UNIVERSITY HOSPITALS 44106 #064-01-1983 L1992 **GE IM** *040 †20
RAYES, Rania. 2074 ABINGTON RD 44106 #875-01-1996 L2000 **HMP** *020 †50
RAYHAN, Kazi Zahir. 2500 METROHEALTH DR, C/O RESIDENCY SUPPORT 44109 #422-01-2005 L2006 **IM** *012
RAZA, Muhammad. 9500 EUCLID AVE, CLEVELAND CLINIC FNDN 44195 #704-01-2001 L2004 **IM** *012
RAZAVI, Amir Hossein. CO RESIDENCY SUPPORT, METROHEALTH MEDICAL CENTER 44109 #665-01-2007 L2007 **IM** *012
RAZAVI, Mehdi. 9500 EUCLID AVE, CLEVELAND CLNC MS F25 44195 #517-06-1957 L1967 **CD IM** *020
RAZI, Ahmad. 2500 METROHEALTH DR, DEPT OF OB/GYN 44109 #517-01-1968 L1975 **OBG ON** *020 †30
RAZIUDDIN, Ahmed. 13951 TERRACE RD 44112 #496-27-2002 L2005 **IM** *012
RAZVI, Samiya. ■ 44106 #495-27-1987 L2007 **PDP** *100 †55
REA, Mark Edward. 2500 METROHEALTH DR, DIV OF CARDIOLOGY 44109 #038-44-2002 L2005 **CD** *012 †20
READERMAN, Irwin Harvey. 6770 MAYFIELD RD # 210 44124 #041-13-1954 L1963 **OTO** *071 †45
REDAHAN, Anita Patricia. 2816 E 116TH ST, METROHEALTH BUCKEYE HEALTH 44120 #539-04-1976 L1982 **IM** *020 †20
REDDEN, Pamela Lynne. 12100 SUPERIOR AVE 44106 #010-03-1978 L1981 **IM** *020 †20
REDDY, Aditya Gollakistag. 2500 METROHEALTH DR, METROHEALTH MEDICAL CENTER 44109 #422-01-2005 L2005 **AN** *012
REDDY, Allareddy Raghaven. 2500 METROHEALTH DR, METROHEALTH MED CTR 44109 #495-11-1984 L2003 **IM** *020 †20
REDDY, Anantha Bizwar. 9500 EUCLID AVE, THE CLEVELAND CLINIC 44195 #495-21-1986 L1999 **PM** *020 †60
REDDY, Anita J. 9500 EUCLID AVE, DESK A-90 44195 #048-13-2001 L2007 **PCC** *100
REDDY, Geetha Nukalapati. ■ 44106 #495-04-1981 **IM** *100
REDDY, Laxma G. ■ 44120 #495-65-1979 **IM** *100
REDDY, Sujana Karra. 11100 EUCLID AVE, FOLEY BLDG, 2ND FLOOR 44106 #047-06-2003 L2003 **RHU** *012 †20
REDDY, Vishala. 10701 EAST BLVD 44106 #495-58-1978 L2002 **NM** *100 †28
REDLINE, Raymond Wayne. 2085 ADELBERT RD 44106 #024-05-1979 L1990 **OBG PTH** *020 †50
REDLINE, Susan. 2074 ABINGTON RD 44106 #024-05-1979 L1981 **PUD CCM** *020 †20
REED, Mona Lee. 11201 SHAKER BLVD 44104 #038-06-1982 L1984 **CD IM** *020 †20
REEP, Michael David. 18660 BAGLEY RD, STE 204 44130 #038-43-1997 L1998 **D DS** *020 †15
REESE, Jada Jnene. ■ 44195 #047-07-2004 L2005 **AN** *012
REHM, Susan J. 9500 EUCLID AVE 44195 #030-05-1978 L1981 **ID IM** *020 †20
REICHSMAN, Ann. 3569 RIDGE RD, NEIGHBORHOOD FAMILY 44102 #035-08-1977 L1979 **FM** *020 †18
REID, Isaac Marshall. 13301 MILES AVE 44105 #047-07-1959 L1968 **PD** *020 †55
REID, Janet Russell. 9500 EUCLID AVE, CLEVELAND CLIN CHILDREN'S 44195 #065-05-1987 L1999 **PDR** *020 †80
REIDER, Mitchell William. 1611 S GREEN RD, STE 237 44121 #038-06-1997 L1999 **OBG** *020 †30
REINHART, William James. 11100 EUCLID AVE, DEPARTMENT OF OPHTHALMOLOG 44106 #038-06-1968 L1968 **OPH** *020 †35
REISMAN, John. 2322 E 22ND ST, STE 202 44115 #165-04-1978 L1982 **HEM IM** *020 †20
REMER, Erica Ellen. ■ 44122 #035-06-1985 L1994 **EM** *020 †16
REMER, Erick Marc. 9500 EUCLID AVE, DEPT OF RADIOLOGY-A21 44195 #025-01-1988 L1994 **DR** *020 †80
REMZI, Berna. 9500 EUCLID AVE, DEPT OF DERM - MC A61 44195 #902-05-1990 L2000 **D** *020
RENSEL, Mary Rita. 9500 EUCLID AVE, MELLEN CENTER U-10 44195 #038-43-1992 L1995 **N IG** *020 †75
RESCH, Timothy Andrew. 9500 EUCLID AVE 44195 #858-01-1999 L2004 *100
RESNICK, Phillip Jacob. 11100 EUCLID AVE 44106 #038-06-1963 L1963 **P** *040 †75
RETIZOS, Nelin Briones. 4229 PEARL RD 44109 #748-10-1964 L1976 **P** *071
REU, Frederic Joel. 9500 EUCLID AVE, C/O CCF-GRAD MED EDU DEPT- 44195 #409-19-1998 L2000 **IM** *020
REVAK, Conrad S. 9500 EUCLID AVE 44195 #041-12-1966 L1989 **R** *071 †80
REVENAUGH, Peter Charles. 9500 EUCLID AVE, NECK I 44195 #035-06-2007 L2007 **OTO** *012
REYDMAN, Melvin Maxwell. 1 MOUNT SINAI DR 44106 #056-05-1944 L1946 **TS VS** *071 †85,90
REYES, Bernardo Taboco. 29001 CEDAR RD 44124 #748-01-1961 L1973 **AN** *071
REYES, Karl Michael Gutie. 9500 EUCLID AVE, DEPT OF GME 44195 #748-10-1999 L2006 *100
REYES, Wilfrido Cristobal. 3665 W 117TH ST 44111 #748-08-1965 L1974 **AN** *020
REYNOLDS, Daniel Fryett. 8300 HOUGH AVE 44103 #038-40-1957 L1957 **FM EM** *071 †18
REYNOLDS, Harry Lewis, Jr. 11100 EUCLID AVE 44106 #038-06-1986 L1986 **CRS GS** *020 †85,10
REZA, Mohammad. 18697 BAGLEY RD 44130 #496-09-1980 L1999 **IM** *020 †20
REZAEE, Rod Peter. 11100 EUCLID AVE, DEPT OTO-HNS 44106 #038-40-1996 L1997 **OTO HNS** *020 †45
REZAEE, Roya Lissa. 18697 BAGLEY RD 44130 #038-43-1995 L2004 **OBG** *020 †30
REZAI, Ali Reza. 9500 EUCLID AVE, DESK S31 44195 #005-06-1990 L2000 **NS** *020 †25
REZAYE-GOLKAR, Reza. ■ 44128 #517-01-1960 L1972 **TS GS** *071
RHEAULT, Michel. 9500 EUCLID AVE, CLEVELAND CLINIC FOUNDATIO 44195 #067-03-2001 L2006 *100
RHEE, Katherine Sungeun. 11100 EUCLID AVE, C/O UNIV HOSPS-RESIDENCY O 44106 #043-01-2002 L2002 **U** *012
RIAD, Samy Magdy. 2500 METROHEALTH DR, METROHEALTH MED CTR 44109 #915-04-2003 L2004 **MPD** *012
RIAD IBRAHIM ELGAMMAA, Iha. 9500 EUCLID AVE, C/O CCF-GRAD MED EDU DEPT- 44195 #915-04-1995 L2001 **PAN** *100 †05
RICANATI, Edmond Solomon. 11717 EUCLID AVE 44106 #396-04-1961 L1969 **NEP IM** *020
RICANATI, Elizabeth H. 9500 EUCLID AVE RM A10, CLEVELAND CLINIC FOUNDATIO 44195 #038-06-1997 L1998 **IM** *020 †20
RICANATI, Steven Asher. 2500 METROHEALTH DR, BG-315 44109 #038-06-1995 L2001 **IM** *020 †20
RICAURTE, Basma. 18101 LORAIN AVE, FAIRVIEW GENERAL HOSPITAL 44111 #797-01-1990 L2000 **PCC** *012 †20
RICE, Brenda Lynn. 9500 EUCLID AVE, DEPT OF INTERNAL MED 44195 #539-03-2005 L2005 **IM** *012
RICE, Janet Lynn. 9500 EUCLID AVE 44195 #038-43-1978 L1983 **OBG** *020 †30
RICE, Louis Bernard. 10701 EAST BLVD, VA MED CTR 44106 #035-01-1983 L1990 **ID IM** *020 †20

■ = Address Information Privacy Protected

RICE, Thomas Wm. 9500 EUCLID AVE 44195 #065-01-1978 L1986 **GS** *020 †85,90

RICH, Candace Ann Hammel. 29000 CENTER RIDGE RD, ST JOHN WEST SHORE HOSPITA 44145 #025-07-1973 L1977 **PTH** *020 †50 ‡

RICHARDS, Yoleetah Christ. 4763 WALFORD RD, # 4 44128 #038-41-2008 *012

RICHARDSON, Kenneth Lamar. 2500 METROHEALTH DR, C/O METROHEALTH MED CTR-RE 44109 #032-01-1997 L2000 **FPG** *100

RICKSON, David Parker. ■ 44140 #038-06-1989 L1993 **NS EM** *020

RIDGEWAY, Beri Melissa. 9500 EUCLID AVE, DESK A-81 44195 #005-02-2002 L2006 **OBG** *100

RIFKA, Mona Gabriel. 9500 EUCLID AVE, CLEVELAND CLINIC FOUNDATIO 44195 #605-01-1988 L1998 **NPM PD** *020 †55

RIHANI, Muhamad Raed. 9500 EUCLID AVE 44195 #875-01-1993 L1999 **AN** *020 †05

RILEY, Alyssa Ann. 9500 EUCLID AVE 44195 #038-40-2004 L2004 **PD** *100 †55

RILEY, David E. 11100 EUCLID AVE 44106 #067-01-1981 L1985 **N** *020 †75

RINCON, Gustavo. 9500 EUCLID AVE, # F25 44195 #264-01-1964 L1972 **CD IM** *020 †20

RINGEL, Roman Adam. 7255 OLD OAK BLVD, C-112 44130 #038-06-1977 L1981 **PS HS** *020 †65

RINI, Brian Ignatius. 9500 EUCLID AVE, STE 100 44195 #038-40-1995 L2005 **HO** *020 †20

RISIUS, Barbara Feldick. 9500 EUCLID AVE HB6 44195 #018-03-1975 L1979 **DR** *020 †80

RITCHEY, R Michael, Jr. 9500 EUCLID AVE, E31 44195 #038-43-1989 L1990 **AN** *020 †05

RIVERA, Alfonso Pedro. 9500 EUCLID AVE, RADIOLOGY DEPT - RC35 44195 #041-01-1996 L2006 **DR** *020 †80

RIVERA, Alicia B. 3768 ROCKY RIVER DR, STE 287 44111 #748-02-1958 L1976 **OBG** *020

RIVERA, Rene Javier. ■ 44114 #035-20-2004 L2007 **IM** *100 †20

RIVERA-REYES, Brenda Mari. 11100 EUCLID AVE, UNIV HOSP 44106 #038-06-2007 L2007 **PD** *012

RIZI, Helen Lidia. 3909 ORANGE PL STE 2500 44122 #038-06-1982 L1986 **IM** *020 †20

RIZK, Assad E. 6780 MAYFIELD RD 44124 #875-01-1969 L1981 **CD** *020 †20

RIZK, Nabila. 10701 EAST BLVD 44106 #330-02-1968 L1973 **P** *020

RIZK, Nesrine Afif. 2500 METROHEALTH DR, CO METRO HLTH MED CTR-RES 44109 #605-01-2001 L2002 **ID** *100 †20

RIZK, Ruba Khalil. 9500 EUCLID AVE 44195 #605-01-2003 L2005 **PD** *012

RIZKALLAH, Elie. 2500 METROHEALTH DR, PEDIATRICS METROHEALTH MED 44109 #605-02-1986 L2000 **CHN** *020 †55,75

RIZZO, Christopher Paul. 2500 METROHEALTH DR, PEDIATRIC H455 44109 #038-44-1985 L1987 **PD ID** *030 †55

RO, Eliot Sunho. 11100 EUCLID AVE 44106 #038-06-2003 L2003 **AN** *012

ROBALINO, Silvia Marisol. ■ 44113 #270-02-2001 L2007 **IM** *020 †20

ROBBIN, Mark Richard. 11100 EUCLID AVE, UNIVERSITY HOSPITALS RADIO 44106 #005-06-1992 L1997 **DR** *020 †80

ROBBINS, Norman. CASE WESTERN SCH MED 44106 #024-01-1959 **OS** *050

ROBERTS, David Gordon. 2500 METROHEALTH DR, DEPT OF PEDS 44109 #025-07-1984 L1987 **PD** *020 †55

ROBERTS, Jeff John. 29000 CENTER RIDGE RD 44145 #038-06-1985 L1985 **ORS OSS** *020 †40 ‡

ROBINSON, Edweana Maria. 10515 CARNEGIE AVE 44106 #038-06-1981 L1981 **DR** *075

ROBINSON, Howard Henry. ■ 44195 #008-02-2006 L2006 **AN** *012

ROBINSON, Jenice A. 11100 EUCLID AVE, DEPT. OF NEUROLOGY 44106 #038-41-2000 L2000 **N** *100 †75

ROBINSON, Maria Rosa. ■ 44113 #041-14-2003 L2005 **D** *012

ROBINSON, Monique. 4071 LEE RD, STE 260 44128 #038-06-1999 L1999 **FM** *020 †18

ROBINSON, Patrick Norman. 9500 EUCLID AVE 44106 #067-02-1996 L2001 **CRS** *100

ROBINSON, Tanisha Orriana. ■ 44195 #023-01-2007 L2007 **AN** *012

ROBKE, Jason Michael. 11100 EUCLID AVE, FL 6206 44106 #038-43-1997 L2004 **TS GS** *020 †85,90

ROBLE, Dominador B. ■ 44133 #748-07-1963 *100

ROBLE, Sharon Lynn. 11100 EUCLID AVE, UNIVERSITY HOSPITALS OF CL 44106 #025-12-2001 L2001 **CD** *012 †20,55

ROBSON, Carl Adrian. 1468 E 55TH ST 44103 #038-06-1966 L1969 **FM** *020 †18

ROCHELLE, Robert E L. 3461 WARRENSVIL CNTR RD #R 44122 #038-06-1949 L1950 **OM GP** *071

ROCHON, Paul John. ■ 44106 #021-05-2004 L2006 **IM** *100

ROCK, Lisa Moreschi. 11100 EUCLID AVE 44106 #041-07-1992 L1994 **GS** *020 †85

ROCKWOOD, Edward Jos. 9500 EUCLID AVE I-32, CLEVELAND CLINIC FOUNDATIO 44195 #035-06-1980 L1981 **OPH** *020 †35

RODGERS, Mark Stewart. 11100 EUCLID AVE, UNIV HOSPITALS OF CLEVELAN 44106 #041-02-1992 L1995 **NP** *062 †50

RODGERS, Steven Richard. 4660 HINCKLEY IND PKWY 44109 #038-06-1989 L1991 **FM** *020 †18

RODKEY, Mark Lee. 6780 MAYFIELD RD 44124 #025-07-1990 L1992 **PEM PD** *020 †55

RODRIGUEZ, Benigno. 2061 CORNELL RD, FOLEY BLDG 4TH FL 44106 #264-04-1990 L2000 **ID** *050

RODRIGUEZ, Carlos Luis. 9500 EUCLID AVE, CLEVELAND CLINIC FOUNDATIO 44195 #048-13-1994 L2005 **CN** *100 †75

RODRIGUEZ, Cristina Pagui. 9500 EUCLID AVE, CO CCF-GRAD MED EDU DEPT-N 44195 #748-02-2001 L2002 **HO** *012 †20

RODRIGUEZ, Luis Leonardo. 9500 EUCLID AVE, CARDIOLOGY DESK 15 44195 #935-02-1979 L1994 *020

RODRIGUEZ, Ricardo Jorge. 2101 ADELBERT RD 44106 #132-01-1980 L1991 **NPM** *020 †55

RODRIGUEZ, Shellyanne H. ■ 44195 #041-14-2003 L2005 **AN** *100

RODRIGUEZ, Victorio C. 5163 BROADWAY AVE 44127 #748-08-1966 L1971 **FM** *020

RODRIGUEZ-AGRA, Lolita. 3361 E 55TH ST 44127 #748-08-1962 L1972 **FM** *020 †18

RODRIGUEZ-ANTUNEZ, A. UNIVERSITY HOSPITALS 44106 #847-03-1951 L1964 **RO R** *071 †80

RODRIGUEZ-TRIAS, Juan. ■ 44107 #020-02-1949 L1953 **P** *071 †75

RODRIGUEZ VILLAMIZAR, John. CO GME - NA23, CLEVELAND CLINIC FOUNDATIO 44195 #935-01-2004 L2007 **GS** *012

ROE, Jane Kirkwood. 7255 OLD OAK BLVD, STE C408 44130 #038-43-1979 L1982 **IM** *075 †20

ROESSMANN, Uros. 2085 ADELBERT RD 44106 #038-06-1957 L1957 **NP** *040 †50

ROFAIEL, George. 9500 EUCLID AVE, CLEVELAND CLINIC FNDN 44195 #915-02-2002 L2004 **GS** *012

ROFFI, Marco. 9500 EUCLID AVE, CLEVELAND CLINIC 44195 #869-02-1991 L2000 *100

ROGERS, Douglas Geo. 9500 EUCLID AVE, CLEVELAND CLINIC A-120 44195 #016-42-1974 L1991 **DIA PDE** *020 †55

ROGERS, Gregory Jos. 7255 OLD OAK BLVD, STE C108 44130 #038-40-1981 L1983 **VS** *020 †85

ROGERS, Heesun Jeon. 2500 METROHEALTH DR, METROHEALTH MED CTR 44109 #583-08-1988 L2004 **PTH** *012

ROHATGI, Nidhi. 2351 E 22ND ST, DEPT OF MED EDUCATION 44115 #495-45-2002 L2006 *100

ROHENY, Nader Seyed. 6731 RIDGE RD, STE 302 44129 #517-01-1988 L1993 **IM** *020 †55

ROIZEN, Michael Fredric. 9500 EUCLID AVE, E-30 44195 #005-02-1971 L2005 **AN PA** *020,05

ROIZEN, Nancy Mrazek. 11100 EUCLID AVE - 6038, RAINBOW BABIES & CHILD HSP 44106 #024-07-1972 L2005 **PD** *020 †55

ROLSTON, Mike Karee. 9500 EUCLID AVE, GENERAL INTERNAL MED/A91 44195 #495-27-1973 L2001 **IM GE** *020 †20

ROLSTON, Raj Kamal. 2351 E 22ND ST 44115 #495-27-1972 L2003 **PCP** *020 †50

ROMBERG, Henry Chas. 4180 WARRENSVILLE CENTR RD 44122 #038-06-1967 L1967 **IM GP** *075

ROME, Ellen Sue. 9500 EUCLID AVE A120, CLEVELAND CLINIC FOUNDATIO 44195 #038-06-1988 L1994 **PD** *020 †55

ROMOSER, Kristin Joan. 9500 EUCLID AVE 44195 #038-43-1985 **N** *020

RONA, Sabine. 9500 EUCLID AVE, CO CCF-GRAD MED EDU DEPT-N 44195 #561-17-1994 L2000 *100

RONIS, Robert Jeremy. 11100 EUCLID AVE 44106 #038-06-1982 L1982 **P PHP** *030 †75

ROSACE, Regina Pisaneschi. ■ 44143 #038-44-1989 L1993 **PD** *020 †55

ROSE, Peter Graham. 9500 EUCLID AVE, A8100 44195 #024-05-1981 L1983 **GO OBG** *020 †30

ROSELLI, Eric Ercole. 9500 EUCLID AVE, DESK F24 44195 #016-43-1997 L1999 **TS** *100 †85,90

ROSEN, Carol Lynn. 11400 EUCLID AVE, MAIL STOP 6083 44106 #016-11-1976 L1999 **SCI PD** *050 †55

ROSEN, Ryan. 2500 METROHEALTH DR 44109 #104-01-2007 L2007 **PM** *012

ROSENBAUM, Arthur Louis. ■ 44106 #038-06-1958 L1958 **PYA** *020 †75

ROSENBAUM, David S. 2500 METROHEALTH DR, METROHEALTH MEDICAL CENTER 44109 #016-11-1983 L1991 **IM CD** *020 †20

ROSENBERG, Arlene S. 2475 E 22ND ST STE 611 44115 #011-04-1995 L2003 **DMP** *020 †50

ROSENBERG, David Michael. 3909 ORANGE PL STE 2300 44122 #038-06-1974 L1979 **PUD IM** *020 †20,70

ROSENBERG, Jeffrey Steven. 2500 METROHEALTH DR 44109 #016-06-1987 L2003 **IM** *020 †20

ROSENBERG, Lewis Arthur. ■ 44121 #038-06-2007 L2007 **IM** *012

ROSENFIELD, Allan Oliver. 11201 SHAKER BLVD 44104 #035-47-1981 L1982 **IM** *020 †20

ROSENFIELD, Amy Lora. ■ 44118 #038-06-1991 L1992 **IM** *062 †20

ROSENSTEIN, Alix Leslie. 2500 METROHEALTH DR 44109 #028-02-2000 L2000 **EM** *020 †16

ROSENSTEIN, Lilia. 6780 MAYFIELD RD 44124 #913-69-1972 L1982 **PD ADL** *020

ROSENTHAL, Geoffrey Lahn. 9500 EUCLID AVE -M41 44195 #023-01-1992 L2002 **PDC CCP** *020 †75

ROSENTHAL, Melvin Stanley. 11311 SHAKER BLVD 44104 #010-01-1952 L1962 **IM ID** *071

ROSENTHAL, Miriam B. 11100 EUCLID AVE 44106 #010-01-1953 L1962 **P** *020 †75

ROSENTHAL, Noah. 11100 EUCLID AVE 44106 #038-06-2004 L2006 **CD** *012 †20

ROSENZWEIG, Arnold Irwin. 18599 LAKE SHORE BLVD 44119 #041-01-1957 L1964 **HEM HO** *071

ROSNER, Itzhak Aavi. 2073 ABINGTON RD 44106 #038-06-1975 L1976 **RHU** *050 †20

ROSS, Jonathan Harry. 9500 EUCLID AVE, STE A100 44195 #025-01-1986 L1989 **U UP** *020 †95

ROSS, Kristi Renee. 11100 EUCLID AVE, RBC 3001 PEDIATRIC PULMONO 44106 #051-01-2000 L2000 **PDP** *100 †55

ROSSI, Mirela Roxana. 464 RICHMOND RD, STE 102 44143 #781-04-1993 L2003 **IM** *020 †20

ROSS-SHELTON, Carrie. 21000 BROOKPARK RD MS15-5, NASA GLENN RESEARCH CENTER 44135 #038-06-1980 L1982 **IM** *020

ROTEMBERG, Silvia Cristin. 9500 EUCLID AVE, DESK A60 44195 #187-67-1993 L2000 **PS** *012 †65

ROTH, David Lawrence. 6555 WILSON MILLS RD 44143 #041-12-1998 L2000 **IM** *020 †20

ROTH, Joy Lederman. 9500 EUCLID AVE, DEPT OF ANESTHESIOLOGY/E30 44195 #038-06-1994 L1999 **AN** *020

ROTHCHILD, Ellen Newman. ■ 44106 #035-01-1955 L1958 **P CHP** *020 †75

ROTHCHILD, Irving. 2065 ADELBERT RD 44106 #038-40-1954 L1955 **OS** *071

ROTHCHILD, Kevin Bradley. 9500 EUCLID AVE, CO CCF-GRAD MED EDU DEPT-N 44195 #038-40-1997 L2003 **GS** *100

ROTHFUSZ, Eric Ralph. 9500 EUCLID AVE, DEPT OF ANES # E30 44195 #038-06-1984 L1988 **AN** *020 †05

ROTHNER, A David. 9500 EUCLID AVE, DEPT OF EMERGENCY MEDICINE 44195 #016-11-1965 L1973 **CHN N** *020 †55,75

ROTHSTEIN, Fred Craig. 11100 EUCLID AVE 44106 #016-42-1976 L1981 **GE PD** *020 †55

ROUKOZ, Henri Salim. 9500 EUCLID AVE 44195 #605-02-2004 L2005 **M** *012

ROUTHOUSKA, Shannon Brown. 11100 EUCLID AVE, DEPT OF DERMATOLOGY 44143 #035-15-2003 L2004 **D** *012

ROUTMAN, Sherri Linda. ■ 44143 #038-06-1979 L1981 **DR** *075 †80

ROWBOTTOM, James Richard. 11100 EUCLID AVE 44106 #038-41-1987 L1988 **AN CCA** *020 †05

ROWE, David J. ■ 44120 #035-03-2001 L2007 **PS** *100

ROWEN, Howard Earl, Jr. 1611 S GREEN RD, STE O34 44121 #038-06-1960 L1960 **CD IM** *062 †20

ROWLAND, Vernon. 2432 KENILWORTH RD 44106 #024-01-1946 L1950 **P** *071 †75

ROY, Kausik. 2500 METROHEALTH DR 44109 #665-01-2005 L2005 **IM** *012

ROY, Sukumar. 5183 LEE RD 44137 #704-03-1957 L1969 **GP GS** *075 †85

ROYYURU, Durga Rajyasree. 2500 METROHEALTH DR, DEPT OF INT MED 44109 #495-21-1995 L2005 **FP** *012

ROZATI, Fatemeh. 9500 EUCLID AVE 44195 #517-08-2004 L2007 **IM** *012

ROZSA, John Theodore. 12100 SUPERIOR AVE 44106 #010-03-1978 L1980 **OBG** *020

RUBAI, Amal S. 11100 EUCLID AVE, UNIVERSITY HOSP OF CLEVELA 44106 #528-01-1991 L2000 **ADP** *100 †10

RUBIN, Brian Paul. ■ 44106 #035-20-1995 L2006 **PTH** *020 †50

RUBIN, Darrell Casimir. ■ 44121 #038-06-2006 L2006 **IM** *012

RUDA, James Michael. 44103 #041-14-2005 L2005 **OTO** *012

RUDA VEGA, Pablo Federico. 9500 EUCLID AVE, CO CCF-GRAD MED EDU DEPT-N 44195 #132-01-1993 L2001 *100

RUDICK, Richard Alan. 9500 EUCLID AVE, JJ36 44195 #038-06-1975 L1986 **N OS** *050 †20,75

RUDISILL, Robert M. CLEVELAND CLINIC, DEPT OF ANESTHESIOLOGY 44106 #021-05-1951 L1972 **AN** *012

RUEDA, Mauricio. 9500 EUCLID AVE, CLEVELAND CLINIC FOUNDATIO 44195 #264-03-1991 L2005 *100

RUEDRICH, Stephen L. 2500 METROHEALTH DR 44109 #038-40-1976 L1977 **P PYG** *020 †75 ‡

RUGGLES, Richard L. 11201 SHAKER BLVD 44104 #038-06-1944 L1944 **OTO A** *071 †45

RUN, Sheila N. 9500 EUCLID AVE 44195 #561-01-1970 L1980 **AN** *020

RUNSEWE, Babajide Olutosi. 2500 METROHEALTH DR, METROHEALTH MED CTR 44109 #690-01-1982 L2004 **FPG** *012 †18

RUPERT, Terra Brooke. ■ 44124 #038-06-2007 L2007 **PD** *012

RUSCHHAUPT, William F. 9500 EUCLID AVE, MC S60 44195 #041-12-1972 L1978 **CD IM** *020 †20

RUSSELL, Amanda Marie. ■ 44144 #039-01-2006 L2006 **IM** *012

RUSSELL, Debra Ann. 2351 E 22ND ST 44115 #038-41-1985 L1985 **EM** *020 †16

RUSSELL, K Mitchell. 9500 EUCLID AVE, CLEVELAND CLINIC FOUNDATIO 44195 #017-20-1999 L2001 **IM** *020 †20

RUSSELL, Sarah Beth. ■ 44109 #039-01-2006 L2006 **AN** *012

RUSSO, Nicholas Anthony. ■ 44129 #025-01-2004 L2004 **AN** *012

RUTHERFORD, Isobel. 9500 EUCLID AVE, DESK A-81 44195 #065-05-1957 L1978 **CLP MM** *071 †50

RYAN, David Anthony. 2500 METROHEALTH DR 44109 #038-06-2003 L2003 **PMM** *012

RYAN, Edward C. ■ 44115 #028-34-1951 L1952 **NS GS** *071

RYAN, John Mark. ■ 44118 #038-06-2005 L2005 **ORS** *012

RYAN, Martin Jerome. 2816 E 116TH ST 44120 #047-06-1985 L1988 **IM** *020 †20

RYAN, Thomas Anthony. 9500 EUCLID AVE, CLEVELAND CLINIC 44195 #539-03-1982 L1994 **CCA** *020

RYBAK, James Jos. 7123 PEARL RD STE 201 44130 #038-40-1968 L1968 **EM OM** *030 †16,18

RYCKMAN, Joseph Victor. 9500 EUCLID AVE, # E31 44195 #005-12-1978 L1982 **AN** *020 †05

RYZIJ, Orest Miron. 7007 POWERS BLVD 44129 #407-02-1951 L1959 **GS VS** *050

RZEPKA, Daniel. 18599 LAKE SHORE BLVD 44119 #016-06-1979 L1983 **OBG** *020 †30

RZEWNICKI, Robert Edward. 2322 E 22ND ST STE 306 44115 #008-02-1976 L1979 **RHU IM** *020 †20

SAAD, Eduardo Benchimol. 9500 EUCLID AVE, DESK FIR CLEV CLINIC FNDTN 44195 #187-03-1997 L2001 *020

SAAD, Georges Jos. 4269 PEARL RD, 4269 PEARL RD 300 44109 #605-02-1969 L1976 **VS GS** *020 †85

SAAD, Ramsey Nabil. 9500 EUCLID AVE 44195 #915-02-2001 L2004 **AN** *012

SAADE, Jimmy Youssef. 2500 METROHEALTH DR, METROHEALTH MEDICAL CENTER 44109 #003-01-2005 L2005 **EM** *012

SAADI, Hussein F. 1 CLINIC CTR 44195 #605-01-1985 L1989 **IM END** *020 †20

SAALOUKE, Zein. 5850 LANDERBROOK DR, STE 301 44124 #875-01-1979 L1992 **PD** *020 †55

SAARINEN, Ulla Maria. 2074 ABINGTON RD 44106 #374-01-1969 L1985 **PHO** *050

SABANEGH, Edmund S, Jr. 9500 EUCLID AVE, STE 100 44195 #051-01-1985 L2006 **U GS** *020 †95

SABBAGH, Ahmad Firas. 13951 TERRACE RD 44112 #875-02-1999 L2004 **IM** *100 †20

SABBAGH, Emile Issa. 7901 DETROIT AVE, STE 205 44102 #875-03-1994 L2000 **IM IMG** *020 †20 ‡

SABBAGH, Yaman. 9500 EUCLID AVE 44195 #875-02-2004 L2005 **GS** *012

SABELLA, Camille. 9500 EUCLID AVE, DIV OF PEDS S25 44195 #038-44-1987 L1989 **PD PDI** *020 †55

SABER, Wael Sherif M. 9500 EUCLID AVE 44195 #915-04-1995 L2000 **HEM** *012 †20

SABHARWAL, Vivek. 9500 EUCLID AVE G61-70, DEPT OF ANESTHESIOLOGY 44195 #495-99-1991 L2000 **AN** *020 †05

SABIK, Ellen Mayer. 9500 EUCLID AVE 44195 #024-01-1988 L1997 **CD** *020 †20

SABIK, Joseph Frank. 9500 EUCLID AVE, DESK F 25 44195 #024-01-1987 L1996 **TS** *020 †85,90

SABIO, Andres Refelino. 11201 SHAKER BLVD STE 144 44104 #748-01-1957 L1969 **GP OS** *071

SABLE, Henry Zodoc. CASE WESTERN RESERVE UNIV 44106 #065-01-1943 **OS** *071

SABOGAL, Jaime Miguel. 12301 SNOW RD 44130 #737-01-1975 L1982 **ORS** *020 †40

SACHAR, Ravish. CLEVELAND CLINIC FNDTN, DESK F-25 44195 #005-06-1996 L2000 **CD** *020 †20

SACHDEVA, Reecha. ■ 44124 #010-01-2007 *012

SADE, Burak. 9500 EUCLID AVE, CLEVELAND CLINIC FOUNDATIO 44195 #902-20-1995 L2004 **NS** *020

SADLER, Laurie Susan. 2351 E 22ND ST, ST VINCENT CHARITY HOSP 44115 #038-41-1988 L1990 **IM OS** *050 †20

SADLON, Stephanie Jane. 2500 METROHEALTH DR, H522 44109 #038-40-1990 L1996 **IM PD** *020 †55,20

SAEED, Haleema. 13951 TERRACE RD, MERIDIA HURON HOSPITAL 44112 #704-25-1999 L2002 **PD** *100

SAEED, Pasha Mustafa. 9500 EUCLID AVE C25, PAIN MANAGEMENT DEPARTMENT 44195 #704-16-1985 L1998 **AN** *020 †05

SAEGH, Samad. 1730 W 25TH ST, STE 1000 44113 #517-05-1963 L1973 **IM GE** *020 †20

SAFA, Maryam Banou. 2500 METROHEALTH DR 44109 #517-06-1990 L2002 **FM** *100 †18

SAFAVI, Arash. ■ 44106 #517-08-2004 L2007 **GS** *012

SAFDER, Manzoor Hussain. ■ 44134 #308-13-2004 L2006 **FP** *012

SAFFOLD, Oscar Elmwood. 2475 E 22ND ST 44115 #047-07-1967 L1969 **D** *020 †15

SAFRAN, Ori. 9500 EUCLID AVE, CLEVELAND CLINIC FOUNDATIO 44195 #550-04-1990 L2002 *100

SAGAR, Stephen Melville. 11100 EUCLID AVE, UNIV HOSPITALS 44106 #024-01-1972 L1997 **N IM** *050 †20,75

SAHADEVAN, Jayakumar. 11100 EUCLID AVE 44106 #496-01-1985 L1998 **CD** *020 †20

SAHGAL, Vinod. 11100 EUCLID AVE, DEPT PHY & REHAB HAN 6020 44106 #495-08-1960 L1971 **N PM** *020 †60

SAHI, Hina. 9500 EUCLID AVE, STE A91 44195 #495-45-1998 L2004 **PCC** *100

SAHNI, Rajiv. 2351 E 22ND ST 44115 #495-45-2001 L2004 **ID** *012 †20

SAIKIA, Satyaki. 2351 E 22ND ST 44115 #495-78-1995 L1999 **IM** *075

SAINI, Sonia. 9500 EUCLID AVE, CLEVELAND CLINIC FOUNDATIO 44195 #495-43-1997 L2006 **AN** *012

SAITO, Hidehiko. LAKESIDE HOSP, DEPT MED 44106 #572-47-1963 L1976 **ON HEM** *050 †20

SAJATOVIC, Martha. 11100 EUCLID AVE, DEPT OF PSYCHIATRY 44106 #038-43-1986 L1988 **P** *020 †75

SAKER, Firas Ahmad. 2101 ADELBERT RD 44106 #875-01-1986 L1993 **NPM** *020 †55 ‡

SAKR ESA, Wael Moustafa A. 9500 EUCLID AVE, CLEVELAND CLINIC FOUND 44195 #915-04-1995 L2002 **AN** *012

SALAM, Maher. 1730 W 25TH ST, C/O ADMINISTRATION OFFICE 44113 #875-01-1999 L2003 **IM** *020 †20

SALAMA, Sherif Aziz. 9500 EUCLID AVE, CLEVELAN CLINIC FOUNDATION 44195 #915-04-1985 L1996 **APM** *020 †05

SALAMON, Francis Toma. ■ 44118 #550-02-1975 **PUD IM** *020

SALAMON, Samuel M. 2322 E 22ND ST STE 30 44115 #035-46-1977 L1985 **OPH OS** *020 †35 ‡

SALATA, Robert Andrew. 11100 EUCLID AVE 44106 #038-06-1979 L1979 **ID IM** *050 †20

SALAZAR-SALAZAR, Fortino. 9500 EUCLID AVE, DEPT OF GME 44195 #649-52-1997 L2004 *100

SALE, Shiva Murthy. 9500 EUCLID AVE G-30, CLEVELAND CLINIC FOUNDATIO 44195 #495-09-1997 L2001 **AN** *100 †05

SALEM, Charbel Antoine. 9500 EUCLID AVE 44195 #605-01-2005 L2006 **IM** *012

SALGADO, Antonio V S E. CLEVELAND CLNIC FNDN NEUR 44106 #770-02-1980 L1986 **N** *020 †75

SALIGAN, Josephine. 9500 EUCLID AVE, C/O CCF-GRAD MED EDU DEPT- 44195 #748-11-1985 L2000 **ICE** *100

SALMAN, Lubna. 2351 E 22ND ST 44115 #704-02-1990 L2003 **IM** *020

SALTZMAN, Joel Nathan. 5885 LANDERBROOK DR 44124 #038-40-1997 L1998 **HO** *020 †20

SALUAN, Paul Maron. 9500 EUCLID AVE, DESK A 41 ORTHOPAEDICS 44195 #038-06-1993 L1995 **OP OSM** *020 †40 ‡

SAMAAN, Muhannad. 2351 E 22ND ST, DEPT OF MED EDU 44115 #875-01-2001 L2005 **IM** *012

SAMAME, Peter E. ■ 44130 #737-01-1958 L1966 **GS GP** *071

SAMANDARI, Faramarz. 2351 E 22ND ST 44115 #517-03-1959 **OTO** *020

SAMPLASKI, Mary Katherine. ■ 44195 #010-01-2005 L2005 **U** *012

SAMPLES, Stephen D. 9500 EUCLID AVE, DEPT OF NEUROLOGY 44195 #048-13-1997 L2000 **N** *020

SAMUEL, George. 9500 EUCLID AVE BOX 422 44195 #067-01-1995 L2000 **PCC** *100 †20

SAMUEL, Samuel Wadie. 9500 EUCLID AVE 44195 #915-04-1997 L2000 **APM** *020 †05

SAMUEL, Vasundaran Sriniv. OFFICE11100 EUCLI, CO RESIDENCY 44106 #495-95-1983 L2005 *100

SAMUSIS, Stasys P. ■ 44107 #409-16-1954 **GP** *020

SAMUY, Nichole Pilotin. 11100 EUCLID AVE, DEPT OF PEDIATRICS 44106 #001-02-2005 L2005 **PD** *012

SANABRIA, Juan Ramon. 11100 EUCLID AVE, LAKESIDE 7306 44106 #264-10-1985 L2001 **TTS GS** *050

SANAGUSTIN, Hermites M. ■ 44140 #748-01-1962 L1971 **GS GP** *071

SANAKA, Madhusudhan Rao. ■ 44136 #495-21-1994 L1999 **GE** *020 †20,55

SANBORN, Sharon Lynn. ■ 44135 #038-06-2002 L2005 **HO** *012 †20

SANCHEZ, Josefina Guzman. 11925 PEARL RD STE 401 44136 #748-10-1964 L1972 **GP** *100

SANCHEZ, Julian Alfredo. ■ 44106 #024-07-2003 L2006 **GS** *012

SANDADI, Samith. 11100 EUCLID AVE, WOMEN'S HOSP 44106 #011-02-2006 L2006 **OBG** *012

SANDHU, Amolak Singh. 2500 METROHEALTH DR, CO METROHEALTH MED CTR-MED 44109 #495-43-2002 L2003 **MPD** *020

SANDHU, Harkeet Singh. 18101 LORAIN AVE, FAIRVIEW HLTH SYSTEM 44111 #495-43-2003 L2005 **IM** *012

SANDHU, Roopinder Kaur. 2500 METROHEALTH DR, CO METRO HLTH MED CTR-RES 44109 #305-01-2002 L2002 **CD** *012 †20

SANDHU, Rupinder Jeet Sin. 13951 TERRACE RD, DEPT OF MED EDU 44112 #495-01-2001 L2005 **IM** *012

SANDIGE, Heidi Linda. ■ 44106 #028-02-2005 L2005 **PD** *012

SANFORD, Steve. 4660 HINCKLEY INDSTRL PKWY 44109 #048-04-1974 L1985 **IM** *020 †20,70

SANGANI, Bindu N. 9500 EUCLID AVE E13, CLEVELAND CLINIC FOUNDATIO 44195 #025-07-1996 L2000 **IM** *012 †20

SANII, Kamrooz. 9500 EUCLID AVE A 100, GLICKMAN UROLOGY INSTITUTE 44195 #517-05-1973 L2007 **U** *020 †95

SANITATO, John Joseph. 18101 LORAIN AVE 44111 #038-40-1962 L1962 **IM** *072

SANITATO, John Joseph, Jr. 11100 EUCLID AVE, UNIV HOSPS OF CLEVELAND 44106 #038-40-1997 L1998 **PYG** *020

SANKAR, Roopa Devi. 8300 HOUGH AVE 44103 #495-33-1984 L1991 **IM** *020 †20

SANTACRUZ NIETO, Jose Fer. ■ 44195 #649-14-2002 L2004 **PCC** *012 †20

SANTIAGO, Edgardo V. 29000 CENTER RIDGE RD 44145 #748-01-1962 L1968 **IM RHU** *071

SANTO DOMINGO, Diana. 18101 LORAIN AVE 44111 #422-01-2004 L2005 **FM** *100

SANTOS, Ivan Mark. ■ 44115 #038-43-2006 L2006 **EM** *012

SANTOS, Susan Kovacs. 2500 METROHEALTH DR, DEPT PEDS 44109 #038-41-1996 L1999 **PD** *020 †55

SANTOSCOY, Carlos. ■ 44106 #649-07-1980 L1987 **PTH** *100

SANTOSO, Mohammad Alfa F. 9500 EUCLID AVE, C/O CCF-GRAD MED EDU DEPT- 44195 #624-02-1989 L2003 **TS** *100

SAPATNEKAR, Suneeti. 3747 EUCLID AVE 44115 #495-28-1986 L1998 **BBK PTH** *020 †50

SAPPATI BIYYANI, Raja She. 2500 METROHEALTH DR, METROHEALTH MEDICAL CENTER 44109 #496-01-2001 L2003 **IM** *020

SARAC, Timur Paul. 9500 EUCLID AVE 540, THE CLEVELAND CLINIC 44195 #035-06-1990 L1999 **VS** *020 †85

SARALAYA, Sparsha. 18101 LORAIN AVE, FAIRVIEW HOSPITAL 44111 #496-59-2004 L2007 **IM** *012

SARAN, Monica Kaur. 9500 EUCLID AVE 44195 #495-43-2005 L2005 **P** *012

SARASA, Jose. 6370 YORK RD STE 111 44130 #847-06-1950 L1964 **P GP** *072

SARAVANAN, Balaji. 9500 EUCLID AVE 44195 #495-16-1994 L2005 **P** *100

SARDESAI, Mahesh P. ■ 44113 #016-02-2003 L2003 **AN** *012

SARKEES, Michael Lazaro. 9500 EUCLID AVE, DEPT OF GME 44195 #654-01-2006 L2006 **IM** *012

SARKIS, Rani. 9500 EUCLID AVE 44195 #605-01-2006 L2007 **IM** *012

SARMIENTO, Ramon Salvosa. 12301 SNOW RD 44130 #748-10-1978 L1988 **GS** *020 †85

SAROJINI, Jonnalagadda S. ■ 44133 #495-04-1955 L1981 **P** *071

SAROUF MAALOUF, Majed You. ■ 44195 #605-02-2002 L2007 **GS** *012

SARWANI, Nabeel Imtiaz. 9500 EUCLID AVE, CO CCF-GRAD MED EDU DEPT-N 44195 #155-01-1997 L2004 *020

SASS, Morton. 14055 CEDAR RD 44118 #038-40-1950 L1950 **IM** *072

SATING, Robert Jos. 29000 CENTER RIDGE RD 44145 #028-34-1968 L1969 **OPH** *020 †35

SAUDYE, Hammad Ahmed. ■ 44113 #016-11-2006 L2006 **IM** *012

SAUL, James Todd. 6681 RIDGE RD, STE 404 44129 #038-43-1989 L1991 **IM** *020 †20

SAUNDERS, Sharon E. 12200 FAIRHILL RD 44120 #038-40-1982 L1985 **IM** *020 †20

SAUTO, James William, Jr. 18901 LAKE SHORE BLVD 44119 #038-45-2000 L2000 **EM** *020 †16 ‡

SAVAGE, Robert Mitchell. 9500 EUCLID AVE, THE CLEVELAND CLINIC 44195 #036-07-1976 L1990 **CCA CD** *020 †05

SAVON, Summer Patricia. ■ 44118 #038-43-2003 **P** *100

SAVVIDES, Panayiotis S. 11100 EUCLID AVE 44106 #418-01-1986 L2003 **HO** *020 †20

SAW, Jacqueline. 9500 EUCLID AVE, CO CCF-GRAD MED EDU DEPT-N 44195 #065-09-1996 L2002 **IC** *100 †20

SAWADY, Joram. 2500 METROHEALTH DR 44109 #550-02-1978 L1989 **PTH PCP** *020 †50

SAWHNY, Bhupinder Singh. 7255 OLD OAK BLVD, STE C305 44130 #495-73-1973 L1982 **NS** *020 †25

SAWKAR, Sudhas R. 2500 METROHEALTH DR 44109 #495-35-1973 L1978 **AN** *020 †05

SAWYER, Mark David. ■ 44106 #051-01-2004 L2004 **U** *012

SAWYER, Robert Newell, Jr. 2500 METROHEALTH DR, METROHEALTH MED CTR 44109 #038-06-1988 L1989 **NRN** *020 †75

SAX, Janet Berman. ■ 44120 #038-06-1953 L1953 **PD CD** *071 †55

SAXTON, Jerrold Phillip. 9500 EUCLID AVE, MAIL STOP T28 44195 #047-07-1972 L1983 R *020 †80

SAYEED, Mohammed Rehan. ■ 44195 #495-04-1995 L2005 *020

SAYLES, Stephen Fred. 2500 METROHEALTH DR 44109 #035-06-2005 L2005 **EM** *012

SAYYED KASSEM, Laure. 11100 EUCLID AVE, UNIV HOSP OF CLEVELAND 44106 #605-01-2005 L2006 **IM** *012

SCHACHAT, Andrew Peter. 9500 EUCLID AVE, MAIL STOP I-30, COLE EYE 44195 #023-07-1979 L2006 **OPH** *020 †35

SCHAEFER, Aida S. ■ 44138 #748-01-1954 L1973 **PTH PCP** *020

SCHAEFER, Michael P. 2500 METROHEALTH DR 44109 #038-40-1998 L2004 **PM PRS** *020 †60

SCHAEFFER, Christopher J. 9500 EUCLID AVE, MAIL CODE HB6 44195 #038-41-2003 L2003 **DR** *012

SCHAFER, Irwin A. 2500 METROHEALTH DR, METROHEALTH MED CTR 44109 #041-12-1953 L1967 **PD OS** *071 †55,19

SCHAFFER, Jonathan L. 9500 EUCLID AVE A41, CLEVELAND CLINIC FOUNDATIO 44195 #038-06-1984 L2001 **ORS** *020 †40

SCHARF, Andrew Michael. 25001 EMERY RD, STE 100 44128 #038-06-1994 L1995 **DR** *020 †80

SCHARF, Leonard Alfred. 11100 EUCLID AVE 44106 #025-01-1959 L1962 **PD** *020 †55

SCHARFSTEIN, Jonathan S. 6780 MAYFIELD RD 44124 #041-01-1987 L1994 **CD** *020 †20

SCHARFSTEIN, Suzanne K. 2500 METROHEALTH DR 44109 #041-01-1987 L1994 **PD** *020 †55

SCHARPF, Joseph. 9500 EUCLID AVE, CLEVELAND CLINIC FOUNDATIO 44195 #038-40-1998 L2000 **OTO** *020 †45

SCHAUER, Philip R. 9500 EUCLID AVE A80, CLEVELAND CLINIC FOUNDATIO 44195 #048-04-1986 L2005 **GS** *020 †85

SCHECHTER, Amy Beth. 1071 EAST BLVD, LOUIS STOKES CLEV DVA MED 44108 #038-06-1998 L1999 **IM** *020

SCHECHTER, J Michael. 23250 CHAGRIN BLVD, STE 310 44122 #038-40-1989 L1991 P *075 †75

SCHEETZ, Raymond John, Jr. 9500 EUCLID AVE, CLEVELAND CLINIC 44195 #038-40-1968 L1968 **RHU IM** *020 †20

SCHELLING, Jeffrey Robt. 2500 METROHEALTH DR, RM R-425 44109 #038-06-1985 L1985 **NEP IM** *020 †20

SCHERMER, Donald Richard. 6803 MAYFIELD RD, STE 510 44124 #025-01-1963 L1964 D *020 †15

SCHICKENDANTZ, Mark S. 2709 FRANKLIN BLVD 44113 #028-34-1986 L1988 **ORS OSM** *020 †40

SCHIETZELT, John Alfred. 2159 WOOSTER RD # NO-37 44116 #018-03-1948 L1959 **GS** *071 †85

SCHILS, Jean Pierre. 9500 EUCLID AVE, CLEVELAND CLINIC FOUNDATIO 44195 #165-01-1980 L1990 *020

SCHINABECK, Anne Lyren. 11100 EUCLID AVE 44106 #038-06-1997 L1999 **PD** *020

SCHINDLER, Kim Marie. 9500 EUCLID AVE, C/O CCF-GRAD MED EDU DEPT- 44195 #035-06-2002 L2003 **DR** *100 †80

SCHLENK, Richard Paul. 9500 EUCLID AVE S80, THE SPINE CENTER 44195 #033-05-1995 L2002 **NS** *020

SCHLESINGER, Rachel E. ■ 44124 #016-01-2003 L2007 **AN** *100

SCHMAIER, Alvin Harold. 10900 EUCLID AVE, WR32-130 44106 #051-04-1974 L2006 **HEM ON** *050 †20

SCHMIDT, Kristen Lee. 2500 METROHEALTH DR, METROHEALTH 44109 #038-40-2001 L2001 **EM** *020 †16

SCHMITT, Michael Craig. 18901 LAKE SHORE BLVD 44119 #038-40-1978 L1978 **EM OM** *020 †16

SCHMITT, Steven Karl. 9500 EUCLID AVE, S32 CLEVELAND CLINIC 44195 #038-41-1988 L1990 **IM** *020 †20

SCHNALL, Adrian Michael. 1611 S GREEN RD, STE 065 44121 #008-01-1969 L1970 **IM END** *020 †20

SCHNASER, Erik Allen. ■ 44113 #031-01-2007 L2007 **ORS** *012

SCHNEEWEIS, Stanley Ira. 6555 WILSON MILLS RD, STE 103 44143 #035-08-1962 L1963 **IM** *071 †20

SCHNEIDER, Martin Louis. 6770 MAYFIELD RD 44124 #010-03-1970 L1971 **OBG** *071 †30

SCHNELL, David Jos. 2500 METROHEALTH DR 44109 #038-06-1990 L1991 **CD** *020 †20

SCHNELL, John Edward. 2500 METROHEALTH DR 44109 #038-06-1989 L1991 **PM** *020 †60

SCHOENFIELD, Lynn R. 9500 EUCLID AVE 44195 #038-43-1982 L1989 **PTH** *020 †50

SCHOENHAGEN, Paul. 9500 EUCLID AVE, RADIOLOGY H6-6 44195 #409-15-1992 L1998 **IM CD** *020 †20

SCHOENWALD, Peter Klaus. 9500 EUCLID AVE 44195 #038-06-1981 L1983 **AN** *020 †20

SCHOPF, Carrie R Krewson. 14519 DETROIT AVE 44107 #016-02-1964 L1977 **FM PHP** *020

SCHREIBER, Eric Robt. 9500 EUCLID AVE, BREAST IMAGING SECTION / A 44195 #035-19-1978 L2006 **DR VIR** *020 †80

SCHREIBER, Helmut. 2351 E 22ND ST, # 3W 44115 #038-40-1970 L1970 **GS** *020 †85

SCHREIBER, Lawrence Jos. ■ 44143 #038-06-1959 L1959 **CHP P** *071

SCHREIBER, Martin Jos. 9500 EUCLID AVE, A51 44195 #038-06-1976 L1979 **NEP IM** *020 †20

SCHRICKER, Mary E. 11100 EUCLID AVE 44106 #016-06-1984 L1985 **PD ID** *074 †55

SCHROCK, Jon William. 2500 METROHEALTH DR 44109 #038-40-1999 L1999 **EM** *020 †16

SCHROEDER, Carsten. ■ 44118 #409-32-1996 L2005 **TS** *012

SCHUBECK, Dianne. 5208 MEMPHIS AVE 44144 #038-06-1989 L1990 **OBG** *020 †30

SCHUBERT, Armin. 9500 EUCLID AVE E31, CLEVELAND CLINIC FOUNDATIO 44195 #035-01-1980 L1988 **AN CCM** *020 †05

SCHUBERT, Daniel S P. 2500 METROHEALTH DR H81, METROHEALTH MEDICAL CENTER 44109 #035-06-1965 L1972 **P** *020 †75

SCHUERMEYER, Isabel N. 11100 EUCLID AVE, C/O UNIV HOSPS - RESIDENCY 44106 #038-41-2000 L2001 **P** *020 †75

SCHUERMEYER, Joseph. ■ 44143 #038-43-2008 L2008 *012

SCHULAK, James Andrew. 11100 EUCLID AVE, CASE MEDICAL CENTER 44106 #016-02-1974 L1985 **GS** *020 †85

SCHULER, Sarah Lynn. 9500 EUCLID AVE C15, CLEVELAND CLINIC FOUNDATIO 44195 #033-05-2001 L2005 **PM** *020 †60

SCHULTE, Elaine Elizabeth. 9500 EUCLID AVE 120, THE CLEVELAND CLINIC 44195 #035-03-1988 L2007 **PD PM** *020 †55

SCHULTE, Mark Everett. 11100 EUCLID AVE 44106 #305-01-2003 L2004 **RHU** *012 †20

SCHULTZ, David W. 1730 W 25TH ST 44113 #038-06-1953 L1953 **IM CD** *071

SCHUMACHER, Mariah Ann. 11100 EUCLID AVE, DEPT OPH 44106 #042-02-2006 L2007 **OPH** *012

SCHUMAN, Jeannine Michell. 11100 EUCLID AVE, DEPT OF PEDIATRICS 44106 #028-34-2006 L2006 **PD** *012

SCHWANDT, Anita. 2500 METROHEALTH DR, METROHEALTH MEDICAL CENTER 44109 #038-40-1996 L1997 **IM** *012 †30

SCHWARTZ, Dagan. 7123 PEARL RD STE 201, ATTN: LINDA FURBEE 44130 #550-01-1990 L1997 **EM** *020 †16

SCHWARTZ, Ilze Knezinskis. 18599 LAKE SHORE BLVD, UNIVERSITY MEDNET 44119 #024-07-1961 L1967 **P** *020

SCHWARTZ, Michael Scott. ■ 44195 #041-14-2001 L2001 **PDP** *100 †55

SCHWARTZ, Randall Scott. 730 SOM CENTER RD, STE 230 44143 #038-43-1987 L1990 **IM** *020 †20

SCHWARTZ, Richard Abram. ■ 44108 #024-07-1961 L1967 **P** *071 †75

SCHWARTZMAN, Raul Alejand. 2351 E 22ND ST, CO ST VINCENT CHAR-MED EDU 44115 #132-01-1989 L2003 **CD** *012 †20

SCHWEID, Daniel Edson. 2460 FAIRMOUNT BLVD STE 20, HEIGHTS MEDICAL BUILDING 44106 #038-06-1965 L1965 **P** *020 †75

SCHWEIKERT, Robert Alan. 9500 EUCLID AVE, CLEVELAND CLINIC 44195 #038-43-1990 L1991 **ICE CD** *020 †20

SCHWERSENSKI, Jeffrey. 6780 MAYFIELD RD, SPECIAL CARE NURSERY-HILLC 44124 #836-02-1973 L1990 **NPM PD** *020 †55

SCIARROTTA, Joseph. 2500 METROHEALTH DR 44109 #038-06-1959 L1959 **OBG** *072 †30

SCOLNICK, Alan Morton. 1 MOUNT SINAI DR 44106 #038-41-1964 L1964 **OBG** *071 †30

SCOTT, Bryan Eder. 9500 EUCLID AVE, CLEVELAND CLINIC 44195 #035-06-2000 L2006 **DR** *020 †80

SCOTT, David Lee. 11100 EUCLID AVE, UNIV HOSPS OF CLEVELAND 44106 #038-06-1982 L2006 **P** *012

SCOTT, William C. 12402 BUCKEYE RD 44120 #010-03-1949 L1955 **PD** *020

SCULL, Stephen James. ■ 44143 #035-06-2007 L2007 **EM** *012

SCULLY, Stephen Joseph. CO GME-NA23 9500 EUCLID, CLEVELAND CLINIC FOUNDATIO 44195 #539-04-2004 L2004 *100

SEARS, Jonathan Eliot. 9500 EUCLID AVE, COLE EYE INST/ CLEVELAND C 44195 #008-01-1992 L1998 **OPH** *020 †35

SEBALLOS, Raul John. 9500 EUCLID AVE, DESK A-11 44195 #038-43-1988 L1990 **IM PCC** *020 †20

SEBALLOS, Rosalinda D. 7007 POWERS BLVD 44129 #748-08-1961 L1972 **AN GP** *020 †05

SECHLER, James Lester. 6707 POWERS BLVD, STE 205 44129 #041-02-1980 L1983 **CD IM** *020 †20

SEDENSKY, Margaret Mary. 11100 EUCLID AVE 44106 #007-02-1980 L1986 **GS** *050 †05

SEDKI, Emad Adel Kamal. 18101 LORAIN AVE, FAIRVIEW HOSPITAL 44111 #915-03-2003 L2007 **IM** *012

SEDLOCK, David Joseph. 9500 EUCLID AVE 44195 #041-15-1999 L1999 **PCP** *100 †50

SEDOR, John Reid. 2500 METROHEALTH DR, METROHEALTH MEDICAL CENTER 44109 #051-01-1978 L1980 **NEP IM** *030 †20

SEEHOLZER, Eileen Louise. 2500 METROHEALTH DR, METROHEALTH MEDICAL CENTER 44109 #038-06-1995 L1997 **IM** *020 †20

SEFFO, Firas. 1730 W 25TH ST, DEPT OF MEDICINE 44113 #875-02-1996 L2000 *100 †20 ‡

SEFTEL, Allen Donald. 11100 EUCLID AVE, DEPT OF UROLOGY 44106 #035-08-1984 L1988 U *020 †95

SEGRAVES, Robert Taylor. 2500 METROHEALTH DR, MHMC PSYCHIATRY 44109 #047-05-1971 L1986 **P** *020 †75 ‡

SEGHAL, Ashwini. 2500 METROHEALTH DR, METRO HEALTH MEDICAL CENTE 44109 #024-01-1986 L1993 **NEP IM** *020 †20

SEIDMAN, Michael Joshua. 6835 BROADWAY AVE 44105 #038-06-1997 L2000 **FM** *020 †18

SEIF, John Seifeldeen Att. 9500 EUCLID AVE 44195 #915-02-2002 L2005 **AN** *012

SEKERES, Mikkael Aaron. 9500 EUCLID AVE R35, THE CLEVELAND CLINIC FOUND 44195 #041-01-1996 L2002 **HO** *020 †20

SELA, Ron. CO RESIDENCY OFFICE, UNIVERSITY HOSPITALS 44106 #550-03-1996 L2007 **ICE** *012

SELIGMAN, Stanley Fred. 11001 CEDAR AVE, CUYAHOGA CNTY CORONERS OFF 44106 #935-02-1981 L1988 **FOP** *050

SELIM, Mostafa Ahmed. 2500 METROHEALTH DR, METROHEALTH MED CTR 44109 #915-02-1959 L1970 **GO GYN** *071 †30

SELKIRK, Stephen Michael. 11100 EUCLID AVE, NAEUROLOGY HANNA HOUSE 5TH 44106 #035-06-2002 L2003 **N** *100

SELVARAJ, Soundiah. 1730 W 25TH ST, LUTHERN HOSPITAL 44113 #495-42-1961 L1973 **IM** *071 †20

SEMAAN, Maroun Tanus. 11100 EUCLID AVE, C/O UNIV HOSPS-RESIDENCY O 44106 #605-02-1999 L2002 **OTO** *100

SEMAJ, Flamur Xhemal. 18101 LORAIN AVE 44111 #120-01-1993 L2004 **DR** *012

SEMASKIENE, Ruta. 18101 LORAIN AVE, DEPT OF INTERNAL MED 44111 #913-96-2002 L2005 **IM** *012

SENDERS, Shelly David. 2226 WARRENSVILL CNTR RD R 44118 #035-46-1983 L1986 **PD** *020 †55

SENG, Cynthia D. 10701 EAST BLVD 44106 #038-44-1984 L1987 **P** *020 †75

SENINGEN, Aimee Elizabeth. 11100 EUCLID AVE, CO UNIV HOSPS-RESIDENCY OF 44106 #041-13-2003 L2003 **ADL** *100 †55

SENTHILKUMAR, Hemalatha C. 2500 METROHEALTH DR, METROHEALTH MED CTR 44109 #495-04-1991 L2004 **FM** *100 †18

SENTHILVEL, Egambaram. 2500 METROHEALTH DR 44109 #495-16-1992 L2006 **FP** *012

SEO, Yuji. 13951 TERRACE RD, MERIDIA HURON HOSP 44112 #572-16-1993 L2001 **RO** *012

SEQUEIRA, Elizabeth Anne. 2500 METROHEALTH DR 44109 #023-01-1992 L1996 **FM** *020 †18

SERSIG, Beth Brandt. 10900 EUCLID AVE, CWRU HEALTH SVC 44106 #038-06-1984 L1984 **FM** *020 †18

SESSLER, Daniel Ira. 9500 EUCLID AVE P77 44195 #035-01-1980 L2005 **AN PD** *050 †55,05

SETHI, Akhil. 9500 EUCLID AVE 44195 #496-03-2001 L2005 **P** *012

SETHI, Raminder Singh. ■ 44125 #495-29-1994 **IM** *100

SETRAKIAN, Sebouh. 2085 ADELBERT RD DEPT PATH 44106 #165-01-1983 L1991 **PTH** *020 †50

SEWELL, Mark Fuller. 2500 METROHEALTH DR, METROHEALTH MEDICAL CENTER 44109 #023-12-1999 L2003 **OBG** *020 †30

SEYED TOTONCHI, Seyed Ali. 11100 EUCLID AVE, C/O UNIV HOSPS-RESIDENCY O 44106 #517-03-2000 L2003 **PS** *012

SFEIR, David Mark. 18697 BAGLEY RD, DEPARTMENT OF ANESTHESIOLO 44130 #038-40-1993 L1998 **APM** *020 †05

SFERRY, Carl Anthony. 8333 ROCKSIDE RD, ANTHEM BLUE CROSS & B SHLD 44125 #016-06-1976 L1979 **IM** *062 †20

SFILIGOJ, Matthew Joseph. 2500 METROHEALTH DR 44109 #038-41-2003 L2003 **DR** *012

SHABAN, Iyad Adel. 6780 MAYFIELD RD 44124 #875-01-1972 L1978 **PUD IM** *020 †20

SHAD, Fariha. 18101 LORAIN AVE, DEPT OF INTERNAL MED 44111 #704-27-2001 L2005 **IM** *012

SHADMEHR, Mohammad Behgam. 9500 EUCLID AVE, CO CCF-GRAD MED EDU DEPT-N 44195 #517-08-1993 L2003 **GS** *100

SHAFER, William H. 9500 EUCLID AVE, # A91 44195 #038-41-1952 L1952 **IM GE** *071 †20

SHAFFER, John Wade. 11100 EUCLID AVE 44106 #023-01-1969 L1977 **ORS HS** *020 †40

SHAFIE, Ahmed Hassan Moha. 9500 EUCLID AVE, C/O CCF-GRAD MED EDU DEPT- 44195 #915-04-1993 L2001 **AN** *100

SHAFRON, Melvin. 26900 CEDAR RD, MELVIN SHAFRON COLOMBI 44122 #024-01-1956 L1957 **NS** *071 †25

SHAH, Ajit C. 7215 OLD OAK BLVD, STE 4101 44130 #495-23-1967 L1980 **IM** *020 †45

SHAH, Ajit Dhimantlal. 3865 ROCKY RIVER DR 44111 #495-22-1967 L1986 **OTO HNS** *020

SHAH, Ankur S. ■ 44106 #028-34-2007 L2007 **IM** *012

SHAH, Arvindkumar R. 5162 BROADWAY AVE STE 3, CLEVELAND OHIO 44127 44127 #495-22-1957 L1971 **CD IM** *020 †20

SHAH, Avani Bharat. 18660 BAGLEY RD, STE 407 44130 #495-22-1978 L1988 **PD** *020 †55

SHAH, Bindu Bipin. ■ 44106 #028-46-2006 L2006 **IM** *012

SHAH, Chintan Bakulbhai. ■ 44114 #495-76-2003 L2007 **FP** *012

SHAH, Devang Maheshkumar. 9500 EUCLID AVE 44106 #496-39-1998 L2001 **AN** *100 †05

SHAH, Gaurang Subodhbhai. 9500 EUCLID AVE, GLICKMAN UROLOGICAL INSTIT 44195 #495-76-1984 L2006 **U** *020

SHAH, Jay Rajendra. 11100 EUCLID AVE, DEPT OTO 44106 #016-01-2007 L2007 **OTO** *012

SHAH, Jaya Ramesh. 11100 EUCLID AVE 44106 #495-01-1964 L1971 **PD** *020 †55

SHAH, Kevin Naresh. ■ 44114 #041-15-2007 L2007 **GS** *012

SHAH, Manish Dhiraj. ■ 44120 #028-06-2005 L2005 **IM** *012

SHAH, Nirav R. 2500 METROHEALTH DR, METRO HEALTH MEDICAL CENTE 44109 #665-01-2004 L2004 **GE** *012 †20

SHAH, Rajiv Rasik. 2500 METROHEALTH DR, DEPT OF RADIOLOGY 44109 #016-42-1990 L1991 **DR RNR** *020 †80

SHAH, Reshma. 11100 EUCLID AVE 44106 #041-09-1997 L2000 **PD** *020 †55

SHAH, Shahnaz Z. 6780 MAYFIELD RD 44124 #704-02-1979 L1995 **PDR** *020 †80

SHAH, Shashikant P. 9700 GARFIELD BLVD, STE 105 44125 #495-01-1965 L1971 **PD** *020 †55

SHAH, Tehmeena. - 346, INTERNAL MEDICINE RESIDENC 44195 #704-01-2001 L2003 **CD** *012 †20

SHAH, Tushar Kantilal. 6999 FRY RD 44130 #495-17-1992 L2001 **IM** *020 †20

SHAH, Usman Shahid. 2500 METROHEALTH DR 44109 #305-01-2005 L2005 **IM** *012

SHAH, Yogesh Gambhirlal. 18101 LORAIN AVE DEPT OBG, PERINATAL MED RM 345 44111 #495-17-1973 L1989 **NPM OBG** *020 †30

SHAH, Zahid Riaz. 2500 METROHEALTH DR 44109 #704-01-1970 L1977 **DR** *020 †80

SHAHAMATPOUR, Ahmad. 4229 PEARL RD, STE 405 44109 #517-06-1969 L1976 **IM CD** *020

SHAHED, Mohamad Mamdouh. 4330 W 150TH ST 44135 #875-02-1996 L2000 **IMG** *020 †20

SHAHEEN, Philip. 9500 EUCLID AVE R35, THE CLEVELAND CLINIC FOUND 44195 #875-01-1997 L2000 **IM** *100 †20

SHAIKH, Ali Nawaz. 21851 CENTER RIDGE RD, STE 109 44116 #704-08-1958 L1971 **CD IM** *020 †20

SHAIKH, Farhat. 2500 METROHEALTH DR, MED PEDS 44109 #305-01-2004 L2004 **MPD** *012

SHAKIBA, Khashayar. 2500 METROHEALTH DR 44109 #517-08-1998 L2004 **OBG** *020

SHAKOOR, Hasan. ■ 44120 #704-25-1999 L2005 **PCC** *012 †20

SHALLENBERGER, David W. ■ 44115 #038-06-1938 L1938 **IM** *071

SHALODI, Abdel Wahab D. 2500 METROHEALTH DR 44109 #915-04-1967 L1979 **OBG** *020 †30

SHAMAKIAN, Carol Sue. 25001 EMERY RD STE 100, DRS. HILL & THOMAS CO. 44128 #038-06-1994 L1995 **DR** *020

SHAMAN, Ziad Samir Jamil. 2500 METROHEALTH DR 44109 #422-01-2000 L2000 **PCC** *100 †20 ‡

SHAMIR, Dan. 18099 LORAIN AVE, STE 525 44111 #038-40-1989 L1990 **PM** *020 †60

SHANK, Daniel Jos. 3838 W 150TH ST 44111 #038-41-1991 L1992 **FM** *020 †18

SHANKARAN, Usha. 19250 BAGLEY RD STE 101 44130 #495-33-1969 L1974 **AN** *020

SHANKARAN, Vijay. ■ 44124 #028-02-2002 *100

SHANMUGASUNDARAM, V A. MARY MOUNT HOSP, DEPT IM 44125 #495-04-1960 L1978 **OS** *020

SHANNON, Nilda Bulacan P. CLEVELAND CL FNDN CARD 44106 #748-01-1959 L1978 **AN** *071

SHAPIRO, Barbara Ellen. 11100 EUCLID AVE, STE 5512 44106 #011-02-1985 L1998 **N IM** *020 †75

SHAPIRO, Daniel J. 9500 EUCLID AVE, CLEVELAND CLINIC FD 44195 #035-03-1950 L1951 **PD** *071 †55

SHAPIRO, Marc Andrew. 9500 EUCLID AVE, DESK R35 44195 #038-43-2001 L2007 **HO** *100

SHAPIRO, Robert Alan. 9500 EUCLID AVE, STE A100 44195 #038-40-1967 L1967 **U** *020 †95

SHARA, Richard Lee. 1001 LAKESIDE AVE E, NORTH POINT TOWER 44114 #038-43-1979 L1980 **EM** *020 †16

SHARMA, Joy Vashisht. ■ 44113 #051-04-2002 L2007 **HSO** *012

SHARMA, Nidhi. ■ 44120 #495-73-2006 **DR** *012

SHARMA, Priyanka. 2351 E 22ND ST, ST VINCENT CHARITY 44115 #495-45-2001 L2003 **IM** *100 †20

SHARMA, Rakesh. 9500 EUCLID AVE, STE 100 44195 #038-45-1996 L1998 **IM** *020 †20

SHARMA, Ramakant. 2500 METROHEALTH DR 44109 #496-03-1992 L2006 **IM** *012

SHARMA, Sanjeev Kumar. 7215 OLD OAK BLVD, A-410 44130 #003-01-1990 L2006 **TS** *020 †85,90

SHARMA, Trilok Chandra. 7255 OLD OAK BLVD, ASSOCIATES 44130 #495-45-1974 L1981 **CD IC** *020 †20

SHARP, Sherrie Lynn. 9500 EUCLID AVE # P57 44195 #024-05-2003 L2003 **CHP** *012

SHATILA, Ahmad H. 18660 BAGLEY RD 44130 #605-01-1970 L1976 **GS SO** *020 †85

SHATNAWEI, Abdullah Sulei. 18101 LORAIN AVE 44111 #575-02-2000 L2002 **IM** *100 †20 ‡

SHAUGHNESSY, Michael Paul. 1611 S GREEN RD, ASSOCIATES 44121 #038-43-1997 L2000 **OPH** *020 †35

SHAWI, Joseph. 18599 LAKE SHORE BLVD 44119 #875-01-1981 L1992 **OBG GS** *020 †30

SHAY, Steven Seth. CLINIC FOUNDATION, CLEVELAND 44195 #036-05-1973 L1992 **GE IM** *020 †20

SHEDDA, Susan Michelle. 9500 EUCLID AVE, CLEVELAND CLINIC FOUNDATIO 44195 #143-02-1996 L2006 *100

SHEELER, Leslie Robt. 12000 MCCRACKEN RD, INNOVA ENDOCRINOLOGY 44125 #038-40-1971 L1971 **END IM** *071 †20

SHEIN, Alan Howard. ■ 44124 #041-07-1983 L1991 **GP ADM** *020

SHEIN, Steven Lewis. ■ 44113 #038-06-2005 L2005 **PD** *012

SHELDON, William Caldwell. 1 CLINIC CTR 44195 #016-06-1957 L1962 **CD IM** *071 †20

SHEN, Bo. 9500 EUCLID AVE, DESK A30 DEPT OF GASTROENT 44195 #243-54-1982 L2000 **GE** *020 †20

SHEN, Hong. 1730 W 25TH ST 4A, PAIN MGMT CTR 44113 #243-78-1984 L2000 **PM** *020 †60

SHEN, Paul Medal. 9500 EUCLID AVE H35, CLEVELAND CLINIC FOUNDATIO 44195 #506-06-1996 L2000 **TS** *100

SHENAI, Nisha Ann. ■ 44114 #495-65-2004 **IM** *012

SHENAI, Shaila Marie. CLEVELAND CLINIC FDN, DEPT OF GERIATRIC MED A91 44195 #495-65-2002 L2007 **IMG** *012

SHENOY, Smitha V. ■ 44106 #048-13-2006 L2006 **AN** *012

SHEPARD, Lee Saml. 2500 METROHEALTH DR 44109 #016-11-1973 L1975 **AN** *020 †05

SHEPLAN, Lawrence James. CLINIC FOUNDATION, CLEVELAND 44195 #042-01-2007 L2007 **RO** *012

SHER, Theodore Harvey. 1611 S GREEN RD, THEODORE HARVEY SHER 44121 #035-08-1974 L1979 **AI PDA** *020 †55,03

SHERMAN, Sanford Jay. 25130 PENSHURST DR 44122 #038-06-1982 L1982 **OPH** *020

SHERMAN, Vadim. 9500 EUCLID AVE M61 44195 #065-06-2000 L2005 **GS** *100 †85

SHETE, Mona Manohar. 18101 LORAIN AVE 44111 #495-28-1991 L2005 **GS** *100

SHETH, Madhusudan T. 16173 LIBBY RD 44137 #495-22-1965 L1975 **FM GP** *020

SHEYKHOLESLAMI, Kianoush. 11100 EUCLID AVE, UNIV HOSP CLEVE-DEPT OTO 44106 #517-23-1996 L2004 **OTO** *012

SHIELDS, Robt Warren, Jr. 9500 EUCLID AVE, CLEVELAND CLNC DEPT NEURO 44195 #011-02-1974 L1975 **N** *020 †75

SHIH, David Chunming. 2500 METROHEALTH DR, METROHEALTH MED CTR 44109 #028-02-2000 L2004 **GPM** *100 †70

SHIN, Janet J. 7215 OLD OAK BLVD STE A416 44130 #583-04-1967 L1975 **PM** *020 †60

SHINTRE, Lata. 11100 EUCLID AVE, MAILSTOP MATHEW HOUSE 6019 44106 #495-06-2001 L2002 **IM** *020 †55,20

SHINTRE, Niranjan Jayant. 11100 EUCLID AVE, C/O UNIV HOSPS-RESIDENCY O 44106 #495-06-2001 L2003 **GS** *012

SHIOTA, Takahiro. 9500 EUCLID AVE, CARDIOLOGY F15 44195 #572-03-1983 L2000 **CD OS** *020

SHIREY, Earl K. CLEVELAND CLININ FOUND 44195 #041-12-1952 L1955 **CD IM** *071 †20

SHIRIF, Khalid Mahmoud. ■ 44195 #026-04-1997 L2006 **PS** *100

SHIVADAS, Anita. 9500 EUCLID AVE, CO CCF-GRAD MED EDU DEPT-N 44195 #495-59-1998 L2003 **IM** *100 †20

SHIYAB, Ala Mohamed Abdel. 13951 TERRACE RD 44112 #575-02-2001 L2004 **GS** *012

SHOAB, Sulaiman Syed. 9500 EUCLID AVE, CLEVELAND CLINIC FOUNDATIO 44195 #704-09-1985 L2005 **IM** *012

SHOJANIA, Abdol H. SUNNY ACRES HOSP 44106 #517-01-1956 L1960 *020

SHOLLENBERGER, Lee Ann. 805 COLUMBIA RD STE 106 44145 #038-40-1988 L1989 **PD** *020 †55

SHOOK, Steven James. 9500 EUCLID AVE, S90 44195 #038-40-2002 L2002 *100 †75

SHOSKES, Daniel Arthur. 9500 EUCLID AVE, STE 100 44195 #065-01-1985 L2005 **U OS** *020

SHOTWELL, Arlington, Jr. ■ 44108 #026-04-1977 L1990 **DR IM** *075

SHREEVATSA, Ajai. 11100 EUCLID AVE, GENERAL INTERNAL MEDICINE 44106 #496-22-1999 L2005 **IM** *100 †20

SHRESTHA, Nabin Kumar. 9500 EUCLID AVE, S-32 44195 #495-45-1995 L2000 **ID** *020 †20

SHRESTHA, Rabin Kumar. 9500 EUCLID AVE, MICROBIOLOGY DEPARTMENT 44195 #495-45-1997 L2000 **ID** *100 †20

SHRESTHA, Rajeet. 2500 METROHEALTH DR, DEPT OF PSYCHIATRY 44109 #704-04-2001 L2004 **P** *012

SHRIKANTHAN, Sankaran. 9500 EUCLID AVE GB-3, DEPT OF NUCLEAR MEDICINE 44195 #495-33-1991 L2006 **NM** *100 †20,28

SHROYER, Jeffrey Britten. 12000 MCCRACKEN RD, STE 251 44125 #038-06-1986 L1986 **ORS** *020 †40

SHTEYNGARTS, Ann Riana. 9500 EUCLID AVE 44195 #038-40-1999 L1999 **D** *100

SHTULL, Kiva Y. 34208 AURORA RD 44139 #038-06-1984 L1984 **EM** *020 †16

SHTYBEL, Wayne Wesley. 9500 EUCLID AVE 44195 #060-01-1983 **N** *020 †75

SHUCK, Jerry Mark. 11100 EUCLID AVE, DEPT OF SURGERY 44106 #038-41-1959 L1959 **GS TRS** *040 †85,90

SHUMYATCHER, Yana. 2500 METROHEALTH DR, METROHEALTH MEDICAL CENTER 44109 #913-82-1989 L2002 **PD** *020

SHUPE, Erik W. 11100 EUCLID AVE 44106 #039-79-2005, ▲ L2005 **AN** *012

SIDAGAM, Vasu. 11100 EUCLID AVE, HARVEY HOUSE RM 415 44106 #496-24-1994 L2001 **IM** *020

SIDDIQUI, Nazema Yusuf. ■ 44109 #025-01-2001 L2002 **OBG** *100

SIDHU, Kamaljit Kaur. 2500 METROHEALTH DR 44109 #665-01-2006 L2006 **PM** *012

SIDHU, Kanwaljit. 4330 W 150TH ST 44135 #495-08-1979 L1990 **AN PD** *020 †05

SIDHU, Navneet K.. CLEVELAND CLI FNDN, DEPT PSYCH 44195 #495-10-1998 L2002 **P** *020

SIDHU, Ramandeep Singh. 18101 LORAIN AVE 44111 #495-17-1999 L2003 **GS** *012

SIDHU, Tejbir Singh. 4330 W 150TH ST 44135 #495-08-1979 L1988 **AN** *020 †05

SIDOR, Tim Andrew. 6900 PEARL RD STE 200 44130 #038-06-1977 L1977 **U** *020 †95

SIEBEN, Louise Alice. 3838 W 150TH ST, METROHEALTH WEST PARK MEDI 44111 #028-34-1988 L1991 **IM PD** *020 †55,20

SIEGEL, Christopher T. 11100 EUCLID AVE, UNIV HOSPITALS OF CLEVELAN 44106 #041-02-1989 L1999 **GS TTS** *020 †85

SIEGEL, Howard Sheldon. 2475 E 22ND ST, CENTRAL MEDICAL ARTS 44115 #023-01-1957 L1961 **OPH** *020 †35

SIEMIONOW, Krzysztof Bory. 9500 EUCLID AVE, C/O CCF-GRAD MED EDU DEPT- 44195 #759-18-2003 L2003 **ORS** *012

SIEMIONOW, Maria. 9500 EUCLID AVE # A60, THE CLEVELAND CLIN FOUNDAT 44195 #759-04-1974 L1999 **PS** *040

SIERK, Anne Elizabeth. 29000 CENTER RIDGE RD, ST JOHN W SHORE HOSP 44145 #035-03-1982 L1988 **PTH PCP** *020 †50

SIEVERS, Corey James. 2500 METROHEALTH DR, METROHEALTH MED CTR 44109 #305-01-2005 L2005 **IM** *012

SIFF, Jonathan Edward. 2500 METROHEALTH DR, DEPT OF EMERGENCY MEDICINE 44109 #038-41-1995 L1996 **EM** *020 †16

SIGLOW, James Edward. 1 MOUNT SINAI DR 44106 #038-44-1986 L1989 **FM** *020 †18

SIGNER, Benjamin. 25001 EMERY RD, STE 100 44128 #038-41-1982 L1984 **DR VIR** *020 †80

SIH, Marvin. 11100 EUCLID AVE, UNIVERSITY HOSPITALS 44106 #748-02-2005 L2007 **IM** *012

SIKON, Andrea. 9500 EUCLID AVE 44195 #038-44-1997 L2000 **IM** *020 †20

SILA, Cathy Ann. 9500 EUCLID AVE, CLEVELAND CLINIC 44195 #038-06-1981 L1983 **N** *020 †75

SILVEIRA, Diosely Castro. CLEVELAND CLINIC, EPILEPSY CTR/S51 44195 #187-40-1983 L2007 **CN** *012

SILVER, Bernard Jason. 9500 EUCLID AVE, CLEVELAND CLC FNDTN 44195 #025-01-1975 L1982 **HEM IM** *020 †20

SILVER, Marcia Rochelle. 2500 METROHEALTH DR, METROHEALTH MED CTR 44109 #023-07-1975 L1986 **NEP IM** *020 †20

SILVER, Richard Frank. 10900 EUCLID AVE, BIOMEDICAL RESEARCH BLDG # 44106 #010-01-1987 L1993 **ID REN** *020 †20

SILVERMAN, Paula. 11100 EUCLID AVE, MAILSTOP BHC 5055 44106 #038-06-1981 L1984 **ON IM** *020 †20

SILVERSTEIN, Roy Lee. 9500 EUCLID AVE, DEPT OF CELL BIOLOGY - NC1 44195 #012-05-1979 L2004 **HEM ON** *020

SIMMONS, Harry Dady, Jr. 11002 DETROIT AVE, C T I T 44102 #035-08-1977 L1993 **GP ATP** *020 †50

SIMMONS, Peter Matthew. 9500 EUCLID AVE, CO CCF-GRAD MED EDU DEPT-N 44195 #017-20-2002 L2003 **DR** *100 †80

SIMON, Howard. 3395 SCRANTON RD 44109 #038-41-1967 L1967 **IM** *020 †20

SIMON, Judith Ellen. 2500 METROHEALTH DR, DEPARTMENT OF RADIOLOGY 44109 #038-40-1982 L1985 **DR RNR** *020 †80

SIMONCIC, Rudolph Jos. ■ 44119 #028-34-1971 L1980 **DR** *020

SIMPFENDORFER, Claus S. 9500 EUCLID AVE, CO CCF-GRAD MED EDU DEPT-N 44195 #038-43-2002 L2003 **MSR** *012 †80

SIMPFENDORFER, Conrad. 9500 EUCLID AVE 44195 #231-03-1971 L1981 **CD IC** *020 †20

SIMPFENDORFER, Conrad H. 9500 EUCLID AVE, A80 44195 #041-02-1999 L2000 **GS** *100 †85

SIMPSON, Kim Elise. 11100 EUCLID AVE 44106 #038-06-1998 L1999 **PD** *020 †55

SINGER, Nora G. 11100 EUCLID AVE 44106 #035-03-1987 L1997 **RHU PD** *020 †55,20

SINGER, Sanford Bernard. 2500 METROHEALTH DR, DEPARTMENT OF PEDIATRICS 44109 #748-01-1973 L1978 **PD** *020

SINGH, Annapurna. 11100 EUCLID AVE, DEPT OF OPHTH LKS 4110 44106 #495-73-1981 L2003 **OPH** *020 †35

SINGH, Aparajita. 9500 EUCLID AVE, CLEVELAND CLINIC FOUNDATIO 44195 #495-36-2004 L2005 **IM** *012

SINGH, Artaj. 2163 PAYNE AVE, THE HOMELESS 44114 #065-10-1985 L1997 **GP** *020

SINGH, Arun Dev. 9500 EUCLID AVE I3-129, CLEVELAND CLINIC FOUNDATIO 44195 #495-53-1984 L2003 **OPH** *020 †35

SINGH, Gurmeet. 9500 EUCLID AVE, CO CCF-GRAD MED EDU DEPT-N 44195 #060-01-1992 L2000 *020

SINGH, Joseph Udai. 10701 EAST BLVD 44106 #038-44-2004 L2004 **IM** *020 †20

SINGH, Kuldeep. 4269 PEARL RD 44109 #495-03-1970 L1975 **GS EM** *020 †85

SINGH, Mamta Kailash. 2500 METROHEALTH DR, BG 310 44109 #048-12-1994 L1996 **IM** *040 †20

SINGH, Mandeep. 11100 EUCLID AVE, CO UNIV HOSPS-RECIDENCY OF 44106 #016-06-2003 L2003 **U** *012

SINGH, Neena. 2074 ABINGTON RD 44106 #495-45-1980 L1994 **CLP** *020

SINGH, Ram Nath. 6688 RIDGE RD, STE 1420 44129 #495-41-1963 L1974 **CD** *020

SINGH, Vaishali M. 9500 EUCLID AVE, BLDG S70 44195 #035-08-1996 L2002 **IM** *020 †20

SINNOTT, Michael Peter. CO GME - NA23 9500 EUCLID, CLEVELAND CLINIC FOUNDATIO 44195 #539-04-2006 L2007 **PTH** *012

SIOMIN, Vitaly Eugene. 9500 EUCLID AVE, CO CCF-GRAD MED EDU DEPT-N 44195 #913-06-1994 L2002 **NS** *012

SIPAHI, Ilke. 9500 EUCLID AVE, CLEVELAND CLINIC FOUNDATIO 44195 #902-07-1998 L2006 *100

SIPERSTEIN, Allan Eric. 9500 EUCLID AVE, CLEVELAND CLNC DEPT GS 44195 #048-12-1983 L1999 **GS** *020 †85

SIRINVARAVONG, Sirinart. 13951 TERRACE RD, HURON HOSPITAL 44112 #891-02-2004 L2007 **IM** *012

SIRKIN, Jonathan William. 9500 EUCLID AVE 44195 #035-06-1996 L2001 **CHP** *020 †75

SIROY, Alan Edwin. ■ 44120 #016-45-2007 L2008 **IM** *100

SIVAK, Michael Valerian. 11100 EUCLID AVE WEARN2, UNIV HOSPS OF CLEVELAND 44106 #041-09-1969 L1971 **GE IM** *020 †20

SIVARAMAN, Padmapriya. 11100 EUCLID AVE, UNIVERSITY HOSPITALS CASE 44106 #495-37-2001 L2007 **IM** *012

SIVASHANKARAN, S. 11100 EUCLID AVE, UNIV HOSPITALS OF CLEVELAN 44106 #495-54-1971 L1979 **AN** *020 †05

SIVIT, Carlos Jesus. 11100 EUCLID AVE, STE 2600 44106 #051-01-1981 L1995 **PDR PD** *020 †80,55

SIWIK, Ernest S. 11100 EUCLID AVE, RBC 380C PED CARDIOLOGY 44106 #025-07-1989 L1992 **PDC** *012

SIWIK, Ronald Anthony. 12000 MCCRACKEN RD 44125 #025-01-1966 L1969 **R** *071 †80

SKAZNIK-WIKIEL, Malgorzata. 2500 METROHEALTH DR 44109 #759-03-2002 L2006 **OBG** *012

SKELLY, Cynthia Danielle. 11100 EUCLID AVE, UNIV HOSP 44106 #041-13-2004 L2007 **NPM** *012 †55

SKITZKI, Joseph J. ■ 44106 #041-14-1999 L1999 **GS** *100 †85

SKOURI, Hadi Naji. 9500 EUCLID AVE, DEPT OF GME 44195 #605-01-1998 L2006 *100

SKRHA, Joseph W. ■ 44127 #016-43-1951 L1951 **FM** *071

SKRINSKA, Algirdas Julius. 18660 BAGLEY RD, STE 407 44130 #038-40-1978 L1979 **PD** *020 †55

SKUGOR, Mario. 9500 EUCLID AVE, A53 44195 #957-01-1986 L2000 **END** *020 †20

SKVAZA, Helen. 2322 E 22ND ST STE 305 44115 #957-05-1970 L1975 **CD IM** *020 †20

SLAVIN, Lee Peter. 955 W SAINT CLAR AVE #1816 44113 #308-06-1980 L1996 **GS** *020 †85

SLAVIN, Thomas Paul. ■ 44113 #011-04-2005 L2005 **PD** *012

SLOAN, Mandeep A. 11100 EUCLID AVE 525, UNIVERSITY HOSPITAL CASE M 44106 #024-01-1990 L2006 **NS ON** *020 †25

SMACHLO, Kathy Anne. 10900 EUCLID AVE, CWRU 44106 #035-20-1980 L1984 **IM** *020 †20

SMEDIRA, Holly J. 9500 EUCLID AVE 44195 #005-02-1988 L1994 **IM** *020 †20

SMEDIRA, Nicholas G. 9500 EUCLID AVE 44195 #035-45-1984 L1994 **TS TRS** *020 †85,90

SMIRNOFF, George. 1250 SUPERIOR AVE E 44114 #038-06-1971 L1971 **FM** *075 †18

SMITH, Aaron Robt. 1001 LAKESIDE AVE E, STE 1200 44114 #038-41-1988 L1989 **EM** *020 †16

SMITH, Andrew Dennis. 9500 EUCLID AVE, RADIOLOGY - HB6 44195 #038-43-2004 L2004 **DR** *012

SMITH, Andrew Malvern. 9500 EUCLID AVE, CO CCF-GRAD MED EDU DEPT-N 44195 #917-32-1991 L2003 *100

SMITH, Brenda Joyce. 2816 E 116TH ST, METROHEALTH BUCKEYE CENTER 44120 #010-03-1978 L1979 **IM** *020

SMITH, Charles Kent. 10900 EUCLID AVE, DEPT OF FAMILY MEDICINE 44106 #016-06-1963 L1988 **FM IM** *040 †20,18 ‡

SMITH, Dennis Harold. 2500 METROHEALTH DR 44109 #019-02-1958 L1963 **OBG P** *071 †30,75

SMITH, Diarmuid. 9500 EUCLID AVE, MAILBOX 390 44195 #539-04-1994 **IM** *100

SMITH, Ethel Elizabethan. 2500 E 22ND ST, VISITING NURSE ASSOCIATION 44115 #038-06-1992 L1996 **FPG** *100 †18

SMITH, Jennifer Susan. ■ 44143 #038-44-2003 L2003 **IM** *020

SMITH, Kelly Maureen. ■ 44130 #041-01-2008 *012

SMITH, Michael Chas. 11100 EUCLID AVE 44106 #038-40-1971 L1971 **NEP IM** *020 †20

SMITH, Michael Patrick. 9500 EUCLID AVE, GENERAL ANESTHESIA - E31 44195 #038-44-1989 L1993 **AN** *050 †05

SMITH, Regina Yvonne. 9500 EUCLID AVE # TT32 44195 #005-14-1993 **P** *100

SMITH, Scott Drew. 9500 EUCLID AVE, COLE EYE INST/DEPT OF OPHT 44195 #008-01-1990 L2000 **OPH** *050 †35

SMITH, Tamara. 9500 EUCLID AVE, DESK A-81 44195 #038-44-1993 L1998 **PTH** *020 †50

SMITH, Todd Ian. 11100 EUCLID AVE, LK 5029 44106 #038-45-2004 L2004 **IM** *012

SMOOT, Ernest Anthony, Jr. 12100 SUPERIOR AVE 44106 #048-12-1991 L1995 **PD** *020 †55

S. N., Sandesh Chakravart. 18101 LORAIN AVE, FAIRVIEW HOSPITAL 44111 #496-35-2000 L2004 **MG** *012

SNEARLY, Martha Damaske. 12301 SNOW RD 44130 #025-07-1970 L1971 **OPH** *020 †35

SNELL, Michael Robert. 11100 EUCLID AVE 44106 #038-06-2002 L2006 **HO** *100

SNIDER, Hope Henneke. ■ 44120 #024-01-1962 L1969 **PHP GPM** *030 †70

SO, Felisberto Samia. 4229 PEARL RD 44109 #764-01-1964 L1973 **GS GP** *020

SOBECKS, Ronald Michael. 9500 EUCLID AVE R35, DEPT HEMATOLOGIC ONCOLOGY 44195 #038-06-1993 L1995 **HO** *020 †20

SODERSTRUM, William Kent. 1 ERIEVIEW PLZ 44114 #016-02-1981 L1983 **IM** *020 †20,70

SODHI, Manica. 13951 TERRACE RD 44112 #495-96-2001 L2003 **PCC** *012 †20

SOEI, Yu Lan. ■ 44106 #660-03-1990 **IM** *100

SOGG, Alan Jay. 6770 MAYFIELD RD, STE 210 44124 #038-41-1957 L1957 **OTO AI** *020 †45

SOGOR, Laszlo. 3500 LORAIN AVE, STE 400 44113 #038-06-1978 L1979 **OBG** *020 †30

SOKOLOW, Andrew Garrett. 11100 EUCLID AVE 44106 #035-06-2005 L2005 **PD** *012

SOKOVS, Irma Berta. 2307 W 14TH ST 44113 #594-01-1943 L1962 **AN** *072

SOLA, Srikanth. 9500 EUCLID AVE, DESK F15 44195 #020-02-1998 L2005 **CD** *020 †20

SOLARES RIVERA, Clementino. 9500 EUCLID AVE, C/O CCF-GRAD MED EDU DEPT- 44195 #429-02-2000 L2002 **OTO** *012

SOLDES, Oliver S. 9500 EUCLID AVE, CLEVELAND CLINIC 44195 #043-01-1993 L2001 **PDS** *020 †85

SOLE, Kristina Baker. 9500 EUCLID AVE, A81 44195 #032-01-1997 L2000 **OBG** *020 †30

SOLIMAN, Charles Evan. ■ 44115 #039-01-2007 L2007 **GS** *012

SOLIMAN, Marcos Maher. 9500 EUCLID AVE 44195 #915-03-2001 L2003 **AN** *012

SOLOMON, Todd Daniel. 6555 WILSON MILLS RD, STE 103 44143 #038-40-1996 L1997 **IM** *020 †20

SOLOMON-SETO, Lynn. 9500 EUCLID AVE, DEPT OF CARDIOTHORACIC SUR 44195 #041-02-1986 L2004 **TS** *020 †85,90

SOLOVERA, Maria Eliana Ro. 9500 EUCLID AVE, CLEVELAND CLINIC FOUNDATIO 44195 #231-03-1997 L2003 *020

SOLTESZ, Edward Greg. 9500 EUCLID AVE, DEPT OF CARDIOVASCULAR AND 44195 #024-01-1998 L2006 **TS** *020 †85

SOLTYS, Ingrid Tomanova. 2074 ABINGTON RD 44106 #286-03-1991 L2002 **PD** *100

SOLYMOS, Maria Bucsai. ■ 44124 #473-01-1944 L1961 **P** *071

SOMACH, Stephen Conrad. 2475 E 22ND ST, NUMBER 611 44115 #011-04-1987 L1995 **D DMP** *020 †20,15

SOMANADER, Theodore D S. 9500 EUCLID AVE 44195 #220-02-1972 L1978 **AN** *020 †05

SON, Julia. 2500 METROHEALTH DR, DEPT OF FAMILY MEDICINE 44109 #035-47-2000 L2000 **FM** *020 †18

SON-HING, Jochen. 11100 EUCLID AVE, DEPT OF ORTHOPAEDICS 44106 #061-01-2000 L2005 **ORS** *020

SONPAL, Indukumar M. 11201 SHAKER BLVD 44104 #496-38-1969 L1974 **GS TRS** *020 †85

SONTICH, John Kurt. 2500 METROHEALTH DR, DEPT OF ORTHOPAEDICS 44109 #038-41-1987 L1992 **ORS** *020 †40

SOOD, Ajay. 11100 EUCLID AVE 5030, UNIV HOSP OF CLEVELAND 44106 #495-36-1984 L2001 **IM END** *020 †20

SOOD, Apra. 9500 EUCLID AVE, CLEVELAND CLINIC 44195 #495-90-1989 L2002 **D** *100 †15

SOOD, Pratima. ■ 44106 #104-01-2007 L2007 **IM** *012

SOOD, Sanjeev. 3395 SCRANTON RD 44109 #495-29-1982 **FM** *100

SOONG, Wen Chih. 6681 RIDGE RD 44129 #244-02-1951 L1975 **PD** *071 †55

SOPKO, Joseph Anthony. 2351 E 22ND ST, STE 306 44115 #024-07-1974 L1979 **PUD CCM** *020 †20

SOREMEKUN, Maurice A. 8819 QUINCY AVE 44106 #025-01-1974 L1978 **OBG** *020 †30

SORENSEN, Kelly Loren. 2085 ADELBERT RD 44106 #016-06-1976 L1981 **PTH** *020 †50

SORIA, Roberto R. 11100 EUCLID AVE 44106 #319-03-1983 L1995 **P ADM** *020

SOURIANARAYANANE, Achuthan. 2500 METROHEALTH DR, METROHEALTH MED CTR 44109 #495-53-1989 L2004 **IM** *100 †20

SOUTHERN, Brian Derris. 11100 EUCLID AVE 44106 #001-02-2003 L2004 **IM** *012

SOWMYA, Basavatti Madappa. 18101 LORAIN AVE 44111 #495-09-2001 L2006 **IM** *012

SPAGNO, Anthony A. ■ 44130 #035-06-1953 L1956 **P** *075

SPAGNUOLO, Philip Jos. 3395 SCRANTON RD 44109 #041-01-1973 L1975 **IM ID** *071 †20

SPAGNUOLO, Sara Townley. 9500 EUCLID AVE, CLEVELAND CLINIC FOUNDATIO 44195 #038-06-1975 L1979 **AN** *020 †05

SPAIN, James Williamson. 9500 EUCLID AVE, DESK HB6 44195 #035-06-1994 L1998 **VIR** *020

SPALDING, Steven James. 9500 EUCLID AVE, IMMUNOLOGIC DI 44195 #038-45-2001 L2006 **PPR** *100 †55

SPANER, Donald Kevin. 6780 MAYFIELD RD 44124 #038-06-1991 L1992 **EM** *020 †16

SPANO, Kenneth Andrew. 18599 LAKE SHORE BLVD 44119 #010-01-1968 L1975 **GS VS** *071 †85

SPEAGLE, Lewis E. 18200 LORAIN AVE, FAIRVIEW GENERAL HOSPITAL 44111 #036-01-1977 L1978 **FM** *075 †18

SPEARS, Roderick Carlyle. 9500 EUCLID AVE, T-33 44195 #025-07-1999 L1999 **N** *020 ‡

SPECH, Anthony F. 2475 E 22ND ST 44115 #038-06-1950 L1950 **GS GP** *072 †85

SPENCE, Liam Dominic. 9500 EUCLID AVE, CLEVELAND CLINIC/RADIOLOGY 44195 #918-01-1987 L1997 **VIR** *020 †80

SPENCER, David Colin. 2500 METROHEALTH DR 44109 #836-02-1974 **ID IM** *012

SPERO, Michael. 18599 LAKE SHORE BLVD 44119 #035-46-1975 L1978 **END IM** *020 †20

SPIEGEL, Alan Baron. ■ 44118 #023-01-2007 L2007 **PD** *012

SPINELLI, Linda Maria. 2500 METROHEALTH DR 44109 #038-43-1995 L1997 **IM** *020 †20

SPIRO, Timothy Peter. 18200 LORAIN AVE, FAIRVIEW HOSPITAL 44111 #143-06-1974 L1995 **ON HEM** *020 †20

SPLAWSKI, Judy Buckman. 11100 EUCLID AVE, RAINBOW BABIES & CHILDS HS 44106 #016-11-1977 L2001 **PG PD** *020 †55

SPOONHOWER, Kimberly Ann. 11100 EUCLID AVE 44106 #038-06-2001 L2001 **PDP** *100 †55

SPRING, Gottfried Karl. 21625 CHAGRIN BLVD 44122 #154-07-1962 L1967 **P** *030 †75

SPROAT, Laura Anne. ■ 44115 #041-01-2005 L2006 **OBG** *012

■ = Address Information Privacy Protected

SPROAT, Lisa Ostrosky. 9500 EUCLID AVE, CLEVELAND CLINIC FOUNDATIO 44195 #050-02-2000 L2005 **HO** *012 †20

SPURNEY, Robert Venman. ■ 44118 #038-06-1955 L1955 **OPH** *071 †35

SRIDHARAN, Sudhakar T. 9500 EUCLID AVE, CRILE BLDG 44195 #495-04-1986 L1997 **RHU** *020 †20

SRIKIJVILAIKUL, Teeradej. 9500 EUCLID AVE, CO CCF-GRAD MED EDU DEPT-N 44195 #891-01-1988 L2002 *100

SRINIVAS, Titte R. 9500 EUCLID AVE A51, DIV OF NEPHROLOGY 44195 #495-36-1988 L2007 **IM NEP** *020 †20

SRINIVASAN, Deepa. ■ 44122 #495-44-1994 L2000 **CD** *100 †20

SRIRAM, Chenni Shreeniwaz. 9500 EUCLID AVE, CLEVELAND CLINIC FOUNDATIO 44195 #496-09-1999 L2007 **PD** *012

SRIVASTAVA, Sunita Devi. 6770 MAYFIELD RD, STE 22 44124 #035-15-1991 L2000 **GS** *020 †85

STAGER, Margaret Morey. 2500 METROHEALTH DR, DEPT PEDS 44109 #035-06-1988 L1990 **PD ADL** *020 †55

STAGNO, Paul A. 18101 LORAIN AVE 44111 #038-40-1983 L1985 **PTH** *020 †50

STAGNO, Susan Jorve. 10524 EUCLID AVE, DEPT OF PSYCHIATRY 44106 #037-01-1981 L1982 **P** *020 †75

STAHL, John Saml. 11100 EUCLID AVE, DEPT NEUROLOGY,UNIV HOSP C 44106 #035-19-1992 L1996 **N** *050 †75

STALLION, Anthony. 2801 MARTIN LTHR KNG JR DR 44104 #025-01-1987 L1990 **PDS** *020 †85

STALOCH, Michael Anthony. 9500 EUCLID AVE 44195 #048-14-2001 L2002 **DR** *100 †80

STAMBLER, Bruce S. 11100 EUCLID AVE, UNIVERSITY HOSP 44106 #036-07-1984 L1998 **ICE CD** *020 †20

STANESCU, Roxana Marina. 27155 CHARDON RD, STE 205 44143 #781-01-1983 L1998 **IM** *020 †20

STANFORD, Ralph Edward. 11100 EUCLID AVE, DEPT ORTH SURG 44106 #143-10-1988 L2000 **OSS** *100

STANGE, Kurt Charles. 11100 EUCLID AVE, STE 1200 44106 #035-03-1983 L1988 **FM GPM** *020 †70,18

STANKAITIS, Jonas. 6780 MAYFIELD RD 44124 #616-01-1937 L1953 **GP FM** *071

STANSBREY, Robert John. 11100 EUCLID AVE 44106 #038-44-1991 L1995 **CHP** *020 †75

STANSIFER, Libbie Louise. ■ 44121 #038-06-2004 L2004 **CHP** *012 †55

STANTON-HICKS, Michael D. 9500 EUCLID AVE, THE CLEVE CLINIC FOUNDATIO 44195 #143-01-1962 L1989 **PME AN** *020

STARLING, Randall Carson. 9500 EUCLID AVE, CLEVELAND CLINIC FOUNDATIO 44195 #041-13-1981 L1986 **IM** *020 †20

STARR, Norman J. 9500 EUCLID AVE # G30 44195 #017-20-1968 L1979 **AN** *020 †05

STAUGAITIS, Susan Mary. 9500 EUCLID AVE 44195 #035-19-1992 L1997 **NP** *050 †50

STEARNS, Kim. 2709 FRANKLIN BLVD STE 6E, HORIZON ORTHOPEDIC 44113 #038-44-1985 L1986 **ORS** *020 †40

STECK, Willard Duewall. 9500 EUCLID AVE, CLEVELAND CLINIC 44195 #048-02-1954 L1971 **D DMP** *075 †15

STECKNER, Karen Lynne. 9500 EUCLID AVE, E31 44195 #065-06-1989 L1993 **AN PME** *020 †05

STEEL, Malcolm Charles. 9500 EUCLID AVE, CO CCF-GRAD MED EDU DEPT-N 44195 #143-02-1991 L2001 *100

STEELE, Elizabeth Ann. 2500 METROHEALTH DR, DEPT. ANESTHESIA 44109 #036-01-2000 L2004 **AN** *020 †05

STEFANCIN, John Joseph. ■ 44124 #038-43-2002 L2002 **ORS** *012

STEFANIK, Thomas Jos. ■ 44130 #038-40-1964 L1964 **OTO AI** *071 †45

STEFANO, Gregory Thomas. 10701 EAST BLVD 44106 #038-41-2004 L2004 **IM** *020

STEFFEE, Arthur David. 2709 FRANKLIN BLVD, HORIZON ORTHOPEDIC 44113 #067-01-1960 L1966 **OSS OAR** *071 †40

STEFFEN, Rita Marie. 9500 EUCLID AVE, DESK A-111 44195 #038-44-1983 L1984 **PG IM** *020 †20,55

STEGAWSKI, Christopher A. ■ 44145 #759-03-1973 L1980 **AN GP** *020 †05

STEIGER, David Alan. 25001 EMERY RD, STE 100 44128 #038-06-1981 L1984 **R** *020 †80

STEIGER, Ezra. 9500 EUCLID AVE, DESK A80 44195 #038-40-1966 L1966 **GS** *020 †85

STEIN, Jeremiah. ■ 44118 #035-46-1983 L1985 **PHO HEM** *020 †55

STEIN, Richard Edward. 1611 S GREEN RD 44121 #047-06-1999 L1999 **IM** *020 †20

STEIN, Robert Jeffrey. 9500 EUCLID AVE A100, CLEVELAND CLINIC GLICKMAN 44195 #041-01-2000 L2006 **U** *100

STEINBERG, Joel Stuart. 11100 EUCLID AVE 44106 #012-05-1958 L1967 **P IM** *020 †75,20

STEINBERG, Marta C. 11001 CEDAR AVE, CUYAHOGA COUNTY CORONER'S 44106 #012-05-1960 L1970 **FOP N** *020 †75

STEINEMANN, Thomas L. 4330 W 150TH ST 44135 #038-43-1985 L1999 **OPH** *020 †35

STEINER, Howard A. 10701 EAST BLVD 44106 #028-02-1938 L1946 **R NM** *071 †80

STEINMETZ, Michael P. 9500 EUCLID AVE, SPINE INSTITUTE 44198 #048-15-1998 L2000 **NS** *100

STELLATO, Thomas A. 11100 EUCLID AVE 44106 #010-02-1975 L1976 **GS** *020 †85

STEMPEL, Kevin B. 2500 METROHEALTH DR 44109 #035-48-1981 L1999 **DR** *020 †80

STEPHANY, Brian Richard. 9500 EUCLID AVE, CLEVELAND CLINIC FOUNDATIO 44195 #038-40-1999 L2002 **IM** *020 †20

STEPHENS, Debbie Marie. ■ 44114 #028-78-2007, ▲ L2007 *012

STEPHENS, Donald C, III. 2500 METROHEALTH DR 44109 #038-41-1996 L1997 **OPH** *020 †35

STEPHENSON, Andrew James. 9500 EUCLID AVE, STE 100 44195 #065-06-1997 L2005 **U** *020 †20

STEPKA, Erin Clifford. 18101 LORAIN AVE, NICU 44111 #038-06-1999 L1999 **NPM** *020 †55

STEPP, Kevin James. 2500 METROHEALTH DR, DEPT OB/GYN 44109 #025-07-1998 L1999 **OBG** *020

STERBA, Richard. 9500 EUCLID AVE, PEDIATRIC CARDIOLOGY M-41 44195 #038-40-1974 L1974 **PDC PD** *020 †55

STERIN, William K. ■ 44120 #062-01-1955 L1964 **PTH CLP** *071 †50

STERN, Asha Garg. 11100 EUCLID AVE, BRB 8TH FLOOR ROOM 835 44106 #038-06-1998 L1999 **GPM** *020 †20

STERN, Elizabeth Bennet. 2460 FAIRMOUNT BLVD, STE 210 44106 #038-06-1989 L1991 **P** *020 †75

STERN, Robert C. 11100 EUCLID AVE 44106 #035-46-1963 L1964 **PD PUD** *020 †55

STETZ, Gregory Joseph. 11100 EUCLID AVE 44106 #038-40-2004 L2004 **AN** *012

STEVENS, Tyler Kenneth. 9500 EUCLID AVE, INT MED RESDCY OFFICE 44195 #016-11-1999 L1999 **GE** *020 †20

STEVENSON, Jean Terhune. 2500 METROHEALTH DR, CANCER CENTER 44109 #051-04-1984 L1988 **GS** *020 †85

STEVENSON, Ryan Lloyd. ■ 44106 #038-06-2008 *012

STEWART, Robert Wm. 11100 EUCLID AVE, UNIVERSITY HOSPITALS 44106 #025-07-1974 L1983 **TS TTS** *020 †85,90

STEWART, William James. 9500 EUCLID AVE 44195 #038-41-1977 L1984 **OS CD** *020 †20

STIANCHE, Michael Jos. ■ 44109 #028-34-1960 L1961 **R GP** *020

STICKNEY, D Philip. 1 EAGLE VALLEY CT, STE 101 44147 #038-06-1995 L1996 **ORS** *020 †40

STIEFEL, Usha. 10701 EAST BLVD, INFECTIOUS DISEASE-VAMC 44106 #035-06-1997 L2000 **ID IM** *050 †20

STILLMAN, Mark Jay. 9500 EUCLID AVE, DEPT OF NEUROLOGY/T33 44195 #016-06-1978 L1987 **N PMM** *020 †20,75

STOCCHI, Luca. 9500 EUCLID AVE, DEPT OF COLORECTAL SURGERY 44195 #561-01-1992 L2005 **CRS** *100 †85,10

STOKES, George Gregorg. 1001 LAKESIDE AVE E, STE 1200 44114 #038-45-1984 L1985 **OBG** *020

STOLFI, Vito M. 9500 EUCLID AVE, CLEVELAND CLINIC FNDN 44195 #561-23-1984 **CRS** *100

STOLLER, James Kevin. 9500 EUCLID AVE, # A90 44195 #008-01-1979 L1986 **AN IM** *020 †20

STONE, Lael Anne. 9500 EUCLID AVE, MELLEN CENTER/U10 44195 #048-04-1986 L1998 **N** *020 †20

STONE, Robert S. ■ 44106 #035-08-1950 L1952 **GPM** *071 †50

STORER, John. 3070 MAYFIELD RD 44118 #041-09-1945 L1946 **TS** *071 †85,90

STORK, Eileen Kane. 11100 EUCLID AVE, RB&CH UNIV HOSP 44106 #023-01-1978 L1981 **NPM PD** *020 †55

STORK, John Ernest. 11100 EUCLID AVE 44106 #023-01-1978 L1981 **AN MPD** *020 †20,05,55

STOTTS, Grant. 9500 EUCLID AVE BOX S90 44195 #060-02-1994 L2000 *100

STOUT, Griffin Alexander. ■ 44106 #038-41-2007 L2007 **P** *012

STOVSKY, Mark Danl. 27100 CHARDON RD 44143 #016-06-1991 L1996 **U** *020 †95

STRATTON, Jason Shawhan. ■ 44124 #055-02-2007 L2007 **PTH** *012

STRAUSS, Melvin. 10701 EAST BLVD 44106 #028-02-1967 L1988 **HNS OTO** *071 †45

STRAUSS, Ronald A. 20455 LORAIN RD, STE 73 44126 #035-08-1972 L1975 **A PDA** *020 †55,03

STREEM, David William. 9500 EUCLID AVE # P-57 44195 #038-40-1995 L1997 **P** *020 †75

STREEM, Stevan Brian. 9500 EUCLID AVE, STE A100 44195 #016-11-1975 L1982 **U** *020 †95

STREETER, George Allen. 2500 METROHEALTH DR 44109 #023-07-1942 L1950 **P IM** *071

STRELIOFF, George Donald. 5850 LANDERBROOK DR, STE 200 44124 #068-01-1982 L1985 **FM** *020 †18

STRICKLAND, Jameelah Din. 15322 SAINT CLAIR AVE, NEON 44110 #038-43-1996 L1998 **IM** *020 †20

STRIETER-BOLAND, Cynthia. 18099 LORAIN AVE, INC 44111 #038-06-1987 L1987 **PD** *020 †55

STRINGER, Brenda S. 18151 JEFFERSON PARK RD, STE 103 44130 #038-44-1986 L1989 **IM PD** *020 †20,55

STROHL, Kingman Perkins. 10701 EAST BLVD, 111S(W) VAMC 44106 #016-06-1974 L1980 **PUD IM** *050 †20

STRONG, Scott Arthur. 9500 EUCLID AVE, DEPT. OF COLORECTAL SURGER 44195 #018-03-1985 L1992 **GS** *020 †85,10

STROSAKER, Robyn Heather. 11100 EUCLID AVE 44106 #038-06-2000 L2000 **PD** *020 †55

STROUP, Robert Thos, Jr. 1611 S GREEN RD STE 238 44121 #038-06-1983 L1990 **PS** *020 †65

STROUPE, Howard L, IV. ■ 44120 #028-34-2003 L2007 **AN** *100

STRUS, Maria Lesia. 2500 METROHEALTH DR, METROHEALTH MEDICAL CENTER 44109 #038-06-1999 L1999 **DR** *012 †20,55

STUART, Laurie Ann. 18101 LORAIN AVE 44111 #038-06-1972 L1975 **PD OS** *020

STUHLDREHER, Peter Philip. ■ 44106 #012-05-2008 *012

STULBERG, Bernard Nathan. 1730 W 25TH ST # 4E 44113 #025-01-1974 L1980 **ORS OAR** *020 †40

STULBERG, Jonah James. ■ 44106 #038-06-2008 *012

STUMP, Franklin Anthony. ■ 44102 #038-41-2006 L2006 **P** *012

STUNGYS, Peter. ■ 44143 #616-01-1936 L1962 **OS P** *071

SU, Johnny Guanhan. 11100 EUCLID AVE # 201, DEPT OF MED RHEUMATOLOGY 44106 #038-06-1991 L1999 **IM RHU** *020 †20

SU, Le-Chu. 9500 EUCLID AVE, CLEVELAND CLINIC 44195 #038-06-1988 L1989 **GE IM** *020 †20

SU, Tiffany Shin. ■ 44106 #048-15-2004 L2004 **AN** *012

SUAREZ, Margaret. 2085 ADELBERT RD DEPT PATH 44106 #847-09-1976 L1987 **PTH** *020 †50

SUBBARAO, Kakarrla. 11100 EUCLID AVE, UNIV RADIOLOGISTS CLEVELAN 44106 #495-11-1950 L1973 **DR** *020 †80

SUBBIAH, Vivek. 2500 METROHEALTH DR, MED PEDS H522 44109 #496-23-2002 L2004 **MPD** *012

SUBHAS, Naveen. ■ 44120 #038-40-2000 L2000 **DR** *100 †80

SUBRAMANIAN, Sakthiraj. 2351 E 22ND ST 44115 #496-35-2000 L2004 **IM** *100 †20

SUBRAMANYAN, Suja S. 10701 EAST BLVD, VAMC LOUIS STOKES 44106 #495-44-1966 L1974 **PTH BBK** *020 †50

SUDILOVSKY, Oscar. CASE WESTERN RES U PATH 44106 #132-04-1959 L1976 **PTH** *050

SUH, John H. 9500 EUCLID AVE T28 44195 #011-02-1990 L1991 **RO** *020 †20

SUH, Theodore Tongun. 9500 EUCLID AVE, GERIATRIC MEDICINE, DESK A 44195 #038-41-1998 L2000 **IMG** *020 †20

SULLIVAN, Eugene Jeffrey. 9500 EUCLID AVE, DESK A-81 44195 #023-01-1989 L1995 **PUD** *020 †20

SULTANA, Dilara. 11100 EUCLID AVE RM 3018, CO UNIV HOSPS-RESIDENCY OF 44106 #160-02-1984 L2001 **P** *100

SUMERAUER, Dieter Wilhelm. 18660 BAGLEY RD, BLDG II 44130 #038-06-1997 L1999 **PD** *020 †55

SUN, Manhua. 2500 METROHEALTH DR, CO METROHEALTH MED CTR - R 44109 #243-21-1989 L2001 **ATP PCP** *100 †50

SUNDARARAJAN, Sophia. 11100 EUCLID AVE, STE 5512 44106 #038-06-1995 L1998 **N** *020 †75

SUNDARARAJAN, Sumana. 11100 EUCLID AVE, RAINBOW BABIES AND CHILDRE 44106 #496-07-1990 L2002 **PDE** *100 †55

SUNDARESH, Shailaja. 26250 EUCLID AVE STE 203 44132 #495-33-1970 L1976 **GYN** *020 †30

SUNG, Wai W. 9500 EUCLID AVE, DEPT OF GEN ANESTHESIOLOGY 44195 #462-02-1989 L1998 **AN** *020 †20

SUNSHINE, Jeffrey L. 11100 EUCLID AVE, STE 2600 44106 #038-06-1990 L1991 **RNR** *020 †80

SUPER, Dennis Michael. 2500 METROHEALTH DR, METROHEALTH MEDICAL CENTER 44109 #038-40-1978 L1983 **PD** *020 †55

SUPPES, Frederick Thos. 6803 MAYFIELD RD 44124 #038-06-1956 L1956 **FM** *071 †18

SURESH, Kolli. 10701 EAST BLVD NUC-MED 44106 #495-57-1971 L1980 **NM** *075 †28

SURI, Sanjeev. 9500 EUCLID AVE S70 44195 #495-45-1988 L2001 **IM** *020 †20

SUSAN, Luay Philip. 9500 EUCLID AVE, STE 100 44195 #528-01-1970 L2001 **U** *020 †95

SUSOIU TCACIUC, Daniela. 2322 E 22ND ST, STE 200 44115 #781-01-1996 L2000 **IM** *020 †20

SUSOIU TCACIUC, Ioan Flor. 2351 E 22ND ST, ST VINCENT CHARITY HOSP 44115 #781-01-1996 L2006 **IM** *100

SUTHERLAND, Sharon Ann. 18101 LORAIN AVE 44111 #038-40-1992 L1994 **OBG** *020 †30

SUWAN, Tariq Ziad. 18101 LORAIN AVE, FAIRVIEW HLTH SYSTEM 44111 #575-01-2004 L2005 **DR** *012

SVENSSON, Lars Geo. 9500 EUCLID AVE F24 44195 *836-01-1978 L1992 **TS VS** *020
SWADI, Omar Qareeb. ■ 44195 #528-01-1992 L2000 *100
SWARTZ, Justin Stephen. ■ 44195 #045-04-2001 L2005 **PCC** *012
SWEDEH, Mohamed Ali. 18101 LORAIN AVE #875-01-2001 L2002 **IM** *020 †20 ‡
SWEENEY, Daniel Emmett. 30033 CLEMENS RD 44145 #038-06-1978 L1979 **FM** *020 †18
SWEENEY, Patrick J. 9500 EUCLID AVE, NEUROLOG S91 THE CLEVELAND 44195
#035-06-1964 L1971 **N** *020 †75
SWEETENHAM, John William. 9500 EUCLID AVE R-35, HEMATOLOGY & ONCOLOGY 44195
#917-31-1980 L2005 **HO** *020
SWINDELL, Kim Douglass. CLEVELAND CLC FNDT, PEDIATRIC CHIEF RES 44195
#041-14-2002 L2002 **PDI** *012 †55
SWISHER, Christa Brittany. ■ 44125 #038-06-2007 L2007 **IM** *012
SYED, Aasia K. 2500 METROHEALTH DR, C/O METROHEALTH MED CTR-RE 44109
#704-16-1988 L2003 **P** *100
SYED, Abu Naasir. 18660 BAGLEY RD, SUITE 405 PHASE 2 44130 #704-02-1976 L1984
P *020 †75
SZATHMARY, Eva Ann. 7255 OLD OAK BLVD STE C302 44130 #473-04-1991 L2001 **ID** *020 †20
SZETO, Kwong. 4229 PEARL RD 44109 #243-62-1958 L1977 **GP** *020
SZMULOWICZ, Ursula Maria. 9500 EUCLID AVE A-30, DEPT OF COLORECTAL SURGERY 44195
#035-19-2000 L2006 **CRS** *100 †85,10
TAARNHOJ, Knud Palle. 6780 MAYFIELD RD 44124 #297-01-1945 L1955 **NS** *020
TABAN, Mehran. 9500 EUCLID AVE, CO CCF-GRAD MED EDU DEPT-N 44195
#005-15-2003 L2004 **OPH** *100
TABBAA, Kutaiba. 2500 METROHEALTH DR, DPT. OF ANESTHESIOLOGY 44109
#875-01-1978 L1986 **TS CD** *020 †05
TABORA, Consolacion C. 2351 E 22ND ST 44115 #748-08-1968 L1981 **GP** *020
TADELE, Mahlet. ■ 44103 #038-45-2005 L2008 **IM** *012
TAEGE, Alan Jay. S-32 INFECTIOUS DISEASE, 9500 EUCLID AVE 44195 #028-34-1979 L1997
ID IM *020 †20
TAFARI, Nebiat. 2500 METROHEALTH DR 44109 #605-01-1965 L1997 **PD OS** *020 †55
TAFURI, John Andrew. 18101 LORAIN AVE, DEPT OF EMERGENCY MED 44111
#016-06-1984 L1986 **EM** *020 †16
TAGHIZADEH, Touraj. 7255 OLD OAK BLVD, ASSOCIATES 44130 #051-01-1992 L1998
CD *020 †20
TAGKALIDIS, Peter Panagio. 9500 EUCLID AVE, CO CCF-GRAD MED EDU DEPT-N 44195
#143-02-1991 L2003 *100
TAGLE, Rodrigo Jaime. 9500 EUCLID AVE, CO CCF-GRAD MED EDU DEPT-N 44195
#231-03-1988 L2000 *100
TAHER, Mohammad. 18101 LORAIN AVE, FAIRVIEW HLTH SYSTEM 44111 #875-01-2000 L2004
IM *020 †20
TAHER, Ola Abdelfattah. 11100 EUCLID AVE RM 3018, CO UNIV HOSPS-RESIDENCY OF 44106
#915-02-1989 L2002 **GS** *100
TAHIR, Faiza. 13951 TERRACE RD, HURON HOSPITAL 44112 #704-02-2003 L2007 **IM** *012
TAHIR-FADLALLAH, Adnan H. 11100 EUCLID AVE 44106 #605-01-1984 L1989 **END** *020 †20
TAJ, Zareen. 2500 METROHEALTH DR 44109 #496-27-2001 L2006 **FP** *012
TAKAGAKI, Masami. 9500 EUCLID AVE, CO CCF-GRAD MED EDU DEPT-N 44195
#572-09-1990 L2004 *020
TAKAOKA, Yoshiro. 2500 METROHEALTH DR, CLEVELAND METROPOLITAN GEN 44109
#572-58-1965 L1976 **NS** *071
TALANOW, Roland. 13951 TERRACE RD 44112 #408-09-2001 L2004 **DR** *012
TALBOT, Kathleen Thompson. 7901 DETROIT AVE, STE 340 44102 #038-45-1984 L1986
FPG FM *020 †18
TALIAK, Martin B, Jr. 7225 OLD OAK BLVD 44130 #035-20-1963 L1971 **GS GP** *071 †85
TAMARKIN, Stephen Wayne. 2500 METROHEALTH DR, METRO HEALTH MEDICAL CENTE 44109
#038-43-1988 L1991 **DR** *020 †80
TAMASKAR, Mandakini Y. 3783 W 117TH ST, BELLAIRE MEDICAL CLINIC 44111
#495-47-1966 L1977 **AN** *020
TAMASKAR, Ranjit B. 6559 WILSON MILLS RD, STE 106A 44143 #495-49-1996 L2000
IM *020 †20
TAMASKER, Shobha R. 8300 HOUGH AVE 44103 #495-65-1963 L1973 **OBG** *020 †30
TAMBE, Alan. 1422 EUCLID AVE STE 1504 44115 #605-02-1958 L1967 **CD IM** *071 †20
TAMHANE, Umesh Uday. 2351 E 22ND ST, C/O ST VINCENT CHAR-MED ED 44115
#495-96-1995 L2002 **IMG** *100 †20
TAMIM, Mohammed Morshed N. ■ 44126 #875-01-1986 L2000 **PD** *100 †55
TAMRAKAR, Lina. 13951 TERRACE RD 44112 #672-01-2003 L2006 **IM** *012
TAN, Ann. 9500 EUCLID AVE, DEPT OF INTERNAL MED 44195 #065-06-2004 L2004 **HO** *012 †20
TAN, Carmela D. 9500 EUCLID AVE # L25, CLEVELAND CLINIC FOUND 44195
#748-02-1989 L2005 **PTH** *020 †50
TAN, Eng Huat. 9500 EUCLID AVE, TT32 44195 #825-01-1986 **HO** *100
TAN, Marie Cecilia Yu. CLEVELAND CLI FNDN 44106 #748-10-1994 **P** *100
TANAKA-ESPOSITO, C C. ■ 44106 #028-34-2000 L2000 **CD** *012 †20
TANASE, Diana. 9500 EUCLID AVE, CLEVELAND CLINIC FNDN 44195 #781-03-1995 L2004
N *012
TANCHANCO, Roberto Corder. 9500 EUCLID AVE, DEPT OF GME 44195
#748-10-1995 L2006 *100
TANCINCO, Benj Fernandez. 19250 BAGLEY RD 44130 #748-08-1981 L1983 **PTH** *020 †50
TANCINCO, Benjamin C. 19250 BAGLEY RD 44130 #748-02-1952 L1962 **PTH** *071 †50
TANDON, Mahendra Kumar. ■ 44124 #038-34-1964 L1973 **GS** *075
TANDRA, Usharani V. 2500 METROHEALTH DR, DEPT PM & R - H604 44109 #041-07-1994 L1998
PM *020 †60
TANG, Jenny Poh Lin. ■ 44195 #825-01-1991 L2000 *100
TANG, Peter H L. ■ 44122 #385-03-1959 L1965 **PTH** *071 †50
TANG, Wai Hong Wilson. 9500 EUCLID AVE F25, DEPT CV MED CLEVELAND CLC 44195
#024-01-1996 L2000 **CD IM** *020 †20 ‡
TANG-WAI, Richard. 9500 EUCLID AVE 44195 #067-01-1999 L2005 **CN** *100
TANIO, Sonia Lastimosa. 11009 DETROIT AVE 44102 #748-11-1968 L1981 **GP** *020
TANNER, Jonathan Ryan. 11100 EUCLID AVE, UNIVERSITY HOSP/RADIOLOGY 44106
#038-44-1998 L2000 **DR** *020 †80
TAPDASAN, Rosario Cabuena. ■ 44102 #748-11-1968 L1977 **IM** *020
TARAKJI, Khaldoun George. 9500 EUCLID AVE F 15 44195 #875-01-1998 L2000 **CD** *012
TARAR, Riaz Ahmad. 25001 EMERY RD, STE 100 44128 #704-01-1965 L1973 **R** *020 †80
TARBOX, James A. ■ 44120 #048-15-2005 L2005 **IM** *012
TARDIO, Jerry Chas. 18101 LORAIN AVE 44111 #038-43-1981 L1983 **FM PD** *020 †18
TARR, Robert Wm. 11100 EUCLID AVE, DEPT OF RADIOLOGY UNIV HOS 44106
#023-01-1984 L1990 **R DR** *050 †80
TASSE, James Lee. 18901 LAKE SHORE BLVD 44119 #028-34-1973 L1974 **GS CCS** *020 †16,85

TATEWAKI, Hideki. 9500 EUCLID AVE 44195 #572-12-1993 L2004 *100
TAUTE, Carey Terra. ■ 44121 #016-01-2007 L2007 **PD** *012
TAVAKOLI, Mehran. ■ 44106 #517-01-1991 L2002 **IM** *020 †20
TAVEE, Jinny. 9500 EUCLID AVE S90, NEUROMUSCULAR CENTER 44195 #028-46-1998 L2000
CN *075
TAWNEY, Kathryn M. 5850 LANDERBROOK DR, STE 105 44124 #038-06-1987 L1990
IM *020 †20
TAYLOR, Cynthia. 2026 MURRAY HILL RD STE 10 44106 #051-01-1976 L1981 **P FM** *020 †18,75
TAYLOR, David Owen. 9500 EUCLID AVE 44195 #034-01-1984 L2001 **CD IM** *020 †20
TAYLOR, Harris Chaim. 10701 EAST BLVD, CLEVELAND VET ADMIN HOSP 44106
#016-02-1965 L1968 **END DIA** *040 †20
TAYLOR, Harry Lundy, IV. 11100 EUCLID AVE, DEPT PATH PTH5077 44106 #012-01-1966 L2006
CLP FOP *030 †50
TAYLOR, James Selwyn. 9500 EUCLID AVE 44195 #017-20-1966 L1967 **D OM** *020 †15
TAYLOR, John Michael. ■ 44106 #038-06-2008 *012
TAYLOR, John Victor. 26300 EUCLID AVE STE 624 44132 #017-20-1982 L1985 **RHU IM** *020 †20
TAYLOR, Michael Dee. 18101 LORAIN AVE 44111 #020-02-1999 L1999 **CCS** *020
TAYLOR, Paul Conrad. 9500 EUCLID AVE, CLEVELAND CLINIC 44195 #010-01-1965 L1973
TS *071 †85,90
TCHOU, Patrick Jos. 9500 EUCLID AVE F15, CLEVELAND CLINIC 44195 #038-06-1979 L1981
ICE CD *020 †20
TEKAUTZ, Tanya Marie. 9500 EUCLID AVE, S20 44195 #026-04-1996 L2006 **PHO** *020 †55
TENDULKAR, Rahul Dilip. 9500 EUCLID AVE, DESK T 28 44195 #025-01-2003 L2003 **RO** *012
TENG, Erwey Albert. 11100 EUCLID AVE, C/O UNIV HOSPS-RESIDENCY O 44106
#035-45-2002 L2002 **PCC** *012 †20
TENG, Kathryn Ailing. 9500 EUCLID AVE, DESK S-70 44195 #047-05-1997 L2006 **IM** *020 †20
TEN HOVE, Willem Rogier. CLEVELAND CLI FNDN 44106 #660-03-1992 **IM** *100
TEO, Dennis Ciocson. 9500 EUCLID AVE, CO CCF-GRAD MED EDU DEPT-N 44195
#748-01-1991 L2000 *100
TEO, Swee Guan. 9500 EUCLID AVE, CLEVELAND CLINIC FOUNDATIO 44195
#143-07-1996 L2000 *100
TESAR, George E. 9500 EUCLID AVE, DESK P57 44195 #026-08-1977 L1980 **P IM** *020 †20,75
TETZLAFF, John Edwin. 9500 EUCLID AVE, # E31 44195 #028-34-1979 L1980 **AN** *020 †05
TEWARSON, Ivan P. 12000 MCCRACKEN RD STE 209 44125 #495-27-1953 L1966
GS PDS *071 †85
THACKER, Holly L. 9500 EUCLID AVE, CLEVELAND CLINIC A10 44195 #028-46-1986 L1986
IM *020 †20
THAKORE, Yuan-Hua. 9500 EUCLID AVE 44195 #495-76-1987 L2000 **P** *020 †75
THAKUR, Swati. 18200 LORAIN AVE, DEPARTMENT OF INTERNAL MED 44111
#495-90-1998 L2004 **IM** *020 †20
THAL, Sergio Gustavo. 9500 EUCLID AVE 44195 #132-01-1993 L2004 *100
THAM, Kwang Wei. ■ 44143 #539-02-1995 L1999 **END** *100
THAMILARASAN, Maran. 9500 EUCLID AVE, CLEVELAND CLINIC DESK F15 44195
#025-01-1992 L2000 **CD** *020 †20
THAPAR, Vandana Cherie. 11100 EUCLID AVE 44106 #305-01-2002 L2002 **CCP** *012 †55
THEIL, Karl Stephen. 9500 EUCLID AVE 44195 #038-40-1980 L1983 **HMP CCG** *020 †50
THEKKEURUMBIL, Sanjay Vij. MEREDIA HURON HOSP, DEPT SURG 44112
#665-01-2002 L2002 **GS** *012
THELANDER, Keir James. 18101 LORAIN AVE, DEPT OF SERGERY 44111 #017-20-1999 L1999
GS *020 †85
THEODOS, Gus. 11100 EUCLID AVE RM 3018, CO UNIV HOSPS-RESIDENCY OF 44106
#038-06-2003 L2003 **IM** *020 †20
THIRUMALAI, Sridhar. 13951 TERRACE RD, HURON HOSP - CLEVELAND CLI 44112
#495-59-1999 L2004 **IM** *100 †20
THIRUNAVUKKARASU, Deepapri. 2351 E 22ND ST, DEPT OF MED EDU 44115
#496-69-2004 L2006 *100
THOMAS, Anil Abraham. 9500 EUCLID AVE 44195 #539-06-2004 L2005 **U** *012
THOMAS, Anthony Jos, Jr. 9500 EUCLID AVE, STE 100 44195 #038-41-1969 L1969
U GP *020 †95
THOMAS, Colleen Kim. 9500 EUCLID AVE, CO CCF-GRAD MED EDU DEPT-N 44195
#825-01-1990 L2000 *100
THOMAS, George, Jr. 2063 E 4TH ST, APT 201 44115 #047-05-2001 L2004 **ICE** *012 †20
THOMAS, James David. 9500 EUCLID AVE, DEPT OF CARDIOLOGY, F-15 44195
#024-01-1981 L1992 **CD** *020 †20
THOMAS, James Jos, Jr. 30680 BAINBRIDGE RD, PHYSICIAN STAFFING INC 44139
#038-06-1968 L1968 **OBG** *020 †30
THOMAS, Richard Gilmor. 18660 BAGLEY RD 44130 #038-40-1980 L1982 **OPH** *020 †35
THOMAS, Robert Lloyd. 2500 METROHEALTH DR, CO METROHEALTH MED CTR-RES 44109
#010-03-2003 L2003 **IM** *100
THOMAS, Sandra. ■ 44106 #035-15-2005 L2005 **FP** *012
THOMAS, W David. 18697 BAGLEY RD 44130 #038-44-1992 L1996 **AN** *020 †05
THOMAS-MC CAULEY, Tina. 11100 EUCLID AVE 44106 #016-11-1989 L1992 **N** *075
THOMSEN, Kimberly Kay. 2322 E 22ND ST, STE 201 44115 #011-02-2001 L2004 **RHU** *100
THORISDOTTIR, Anna S. 2500 METROHEALTH DR 44109 #484-01-1984 **IM** *100 †20
THORNE, Christine M. 2351 E 22ND ST, ST VINCENT CHARITY HOSPITA 44115
#038-06-1993 L1994 **OPH** *020
THOTA, Prashanthi N. 9500 EUCLID AVE, DEPT OF GASTROENTEROLOGY,A 44195
#495-65-1995 L2000 **GE** *020 †20 ‡
THYSSERIL, Thomas J. 18051 JEFFERSN PRK RD #106, OAKTREE BEHAVIORAL HEALTH 44130
#495-44-1981 L1995 **P** *020
TIE, Mark Leung H'Sin. 11100 EUCLID AVE, STE 2600 44106 #539-06-1989 L2001 **DR** *020 †80
TIEVSKY, Andrew Leon. 9500 EUCLID AVE, DESK L10-NEURORADIOLOGY 44195
#010-01-1974 L2003 **DR RNR** *020 †80
TIMALA, Rabindra Bhakta. ■ 44195 #672-01-1992 L2004 *020
TIMEN, Sanford Martin. 5400 TRANSPORTATION BLVD, STE 8 44125 #028-02-1974 L1979
OTO *020 †20
TIMLIN, Homa. 2500 METROHEALTH DR 44109 #781-01-1993 L2004 *100
TING, Tracy Veiyie. ■ 44195 #055-01-2002 L2002 **PPR** *012 †55
TIONG, Irving Yong Howe. 9500 EUCLID AVE # MED-P39, CLEVELAND CLNC
FOUNDATION 44195 #067-01-1998 L2000 **IM** *020 †20
TISDALE, Patricia Lee. 12301 SNOW RD, KAISER HOSPITAL 44130 #016-11-1980 L1991
DR NM *020 †28,80
TITUS, Jessica M. ■ 44121 #037-01-2007 L2007 **GS** *012
TIU, Rolando Sindo. 18697 BAGLEY RD, SW GEN HLTH CTR 44130 #748-11-1972 L1980
AN *020 †05
TJOE, Soen Liang. 6803 MAYFIELD RD, STE 412 44124 #385-02-1967 L1973 **CD IM** *020 †20

TO, Richard Go. 9500 EUCLID AVE, CLEVELAND CLINIC FOUNDATIO 44195 #748-02-1995 L1998 IC *100 †20

TO, Thuc D. ■ 44115 #016-42-2007 L2007 IM *012

TOBER, Susan Anne. ■ 44134 #038-45-2008 *012

TODIA, William Jos. 2500 METROHEALTH DR 44109 #038-43-1985 L1990 OBG *020 †30

TOKAREVICH, Aleksej. ■ 44117 #407-10-1954 L1960 P *075

TOKMAKOVA, Rositsa Ivanov. 2351 E 22ND ST, DEPT OF MEDICAL EDUCATION 44115 #198-01-2002 L2005 IM *012

TOKUNAGA, Shigehiko. 9500 EUCLID AVE, CO CCF-GRAD MED EDU DEPT-N 44195 #572-08-1988 L2000 *100

TOLENTINO, Edgardo E. 4269 PEARL RD STE 204 44109 #748-01-1963 L1972 GS GP *071

TOLENTINO, Lutgarda Cruz. 6681 RIDGE RD, STE 302 44129 #748-08-1963 L1976 GP *020

TOLTZIS, Philip Harold. 2500 METROHEALTH DR 44109 #041-01-1978 L1988 CCP *020 †55

TOMAC, Andreas C. ■ 44114 #035-45-2005 L2005 NS *012

TOMASHEFSKI, Joseph F, Jr. 2500 METROHEALTH DR 44109 #038-06-1976 L1976 PTH PUD *020 †50

TOMCIK, Colleen Bevevino. 11100 EUCLID AVE, HAN 5040 44106 #017-20-2003 L2007 N *100

TOMECKI, Kenneth Jos. 9500 EUCLID AVE, CLEVELAND CLNC A61 44195 #035-01-1972 L1980 D *020 †15

TOMOLO, Anne Margaret. 10701 EAST BLVD, CLEVELAND VA MEDICAL CENTE 44106 #038-06-1996 L1998 IM *020 †20

TOMSAK, Robert Leon. 11100 EUCLID AVE, DIV NEURO-OPHTLGY LKSD 320 44106 #038-06-1977 L1979 OPH *020 †35

TOOSI, Zahra. 10701 EAST BLVD, V.A. MEDICAL CENTER 44106 #517-05-1977 L1982 ID IM *050 †20

TORNERIA WILKE, Carlos Al. 2500 METROHEALTH DR 44109 #308-13-2004 L2006 PD *012

TORRES, Augusto. 1730 W 25TH ST 44113 #319-01-1968 L1972 GS *020

TORRES, Jairo Ivan. 11100 EUCLID AVE, DEPT OF OTOLARYNGOLOGY 44106 #264-05-1983 L2002 OTO *012

TORRES, Jose A. 11811 SHAKER BLVD, STE 210 44120 #042-03-1986 L1994 AN PME *020

TORRES-BONILLA, Gisela. 11100 EUCLID AVE, DEPT. OF DERMATOLOGY, LAKE 44106 #024-01-2001 L2003 D *100 †15

TOSCANA, Diego Miguel. 9500 EUCLID AVE 44195 #132-07-1994 L2000 AN *020 †05

TOTTEN, Vicken Y. 11100 EUCLID AVE 44106 #016-43-1978 L2005 EM FM *020 †18,16

TOUB, Julia Beth. ■ 44120 #035-03-2005 L2005 N *012

TOUSI, Babak. 1730 W 25TH ST, LUTHERAN HOSP 44113 #517-01-1997 L2002 IM OS *020 †20

TOUT, Susan E. 7123 PEARL RD, EM PROF SVCS/TM HLTH #201 44130 #055-01-1988 L1990 EM *020 †16

TOWNSEND, Tiffany. 9500 EUCLID AVE, CLEVELAND CLINIC FNDN 44195 #067-01-1999 L2004 CN *100

TRABOULSI, Elias Iskandar. 2801 MARTIN LTHR KNG JR DR 44104 #605-01-1982 L1997 OPH MG *020 †19,35

TRAKS, Elmerice. 2500 METROHEALTH DR 44109 #407-19-1949 L1956 CD IM *071 †20

TRAN, Daniel. ■ 44135 #017-20-2004 L2004 PM *012

TRAN, Kim Thien. ■ 44114 #038-40-2005 L2005 IM *012

TRAN, Michael Ngoc. 2500 METROHEALTH DR, METROHEALTH MED CTR 44109 #665-01-2002 L2006 P *012

TRANG, Tung T. 2500 METROHEALTH DR 44109 #035-45-2000 L2000 OTO *100 †45

TRAVASSOS, Mark Abraham. ■ 44124 #035-20-2004 L2004 PDI *012 †55

TRAYLOR, Michael Dean. 4071 LEE RD, STE 260 44128 #038-41-1990 L1994 PD *020 †55

TREAT, Richard Carter. 18101 LORAIN AVE, FAIRVIEW HOSP 44111 #038-40-1971 L1971 TRS EM *050 †85

TRELKA, Darin Patrick. ■ 44119 #041-15-2002 L2007 PTH *100 †50

TREMBLAY, Alain. 9500 EUCLID AVE, CO CCF-GRAD MED EDU DEPT-N 44195 #067-01-1995 L2000 PCC *100 †20

TRESSER, Nancy. 1771 E 30TH ST 44114 #025-01-1987 L1989 NP MDM *030 †50

TREY, Joan Ellen. 2500 METROHEALTH DR, METROHEALTH MEDICAL CENTER 44109 #038-06-1980 L1983 IM *020 †20

TRIPATHY, Asit Kumar. ■ 44195 #495-13-1994 L2006 CHN *012 †55

TRIPI, Paul Alan. 11100 EUCLID AVE, DEPT OF ANESTHESIOLOGY 44106 #024-01-1987 L1989 AN PD *020 †05,55

TROCME, Stefan Danl. 11100 EUCLID AVE, MAIL STOP 5068 44106 #858-02-1981 L2007 OPH TTS *020 †35

TROMBETTA, Carlos Eduardo. 9500 EUCLID AVE 44195 #935-01-1996 L2004 AN *012

TROST, Leonid Benjamin. A-61 9500 EUCLID AVE 44195 #038-40-2004 L2004 D *012

TROUGHTON, Richard Willia. 9500 EUCLID AVE, CO CCF-GRAD MED EDU DEPT-N 44195 #671-02-1992 L2000 *100

TROUW, Cornelis. 26300 EUCLID AVE 44132 #836-03-1967 L1978 FM *020 †18

TRUCCO, Matteo Maria. ■ 44113 #041-13-2006 L2006 PD *012

TSAI, Eve Chang. 9500 EUCLID AVE 44195 #065-01-1995 L2005 *100

TSAI, James Shih-Kuan. 18101 LORAIN AVE 44111 #385-02-1953 L1970 IM NEP *071

TSAO, Raymond Eric. ■ 44118 #033-06-2002 L2005 HO *012 †20

TSCHEIKUNA, Jamsak. CASE WESTERN RES U AFL HSP 44106 #891-02-1985 PCC *100

TSE-HUSNI, M Elaine. 9500 EUCLID AVE, DESK A50 44195 #024-05-1996 L2005 RHU IM *020 †20

TSENG, Lee. 2500 METROHEALTH DR 44109 #038-44-1992 L1996 DR *020 †80

TSUI, Ping Tim. 9500 EUCLID AVE, TT32 44195 #462-01-1985 L2002 CD *100

TUCKER, Amy Elizabeth. 9500 EUCLID AVE, A-41 44195 #020-02-2000 L2001 ORS *100

TUCKER, Harvey Michael. 11100 EUCLID AVE, LAKESIDE 4TH FLOOR 44106 #041-02-1964 L1975 HNS OTO *020 †45

TUCKER, Leonard C. 6770 MAYFIELD RD # 338 44124 #038-40-1948 L1949 OPH *020 †35

TUFENKJIAN, Krikor. 11100 EUCLID AVE, UNIVERSITY HOSPITALS 44106 #875-02-2003 L2007 IM *012

TUFFUOR, Emmanuel Osei. 1831 FOREST HILLS BLVD # 1 44112 #038-06-1980 L1980 IM *020 †20

TUNGSIRIPAT, Marisa. 9500 EUCLID AVE S-32, DEPT OF INFECTIOUS DISEASE 44195 #028-46-1995 L1998 ID *020 †20

TURAKHIA, Ashwin K. 12301 SNOW RD 44130 #495-20-1984 L1990 IM *020 †20

TURCIOS, Betty. ■ 44129 #451-01-1967 L1977 IM *020

TURELL, David Charles. 9500 EUCLID AVE, M73 44195 #048-16-1996 L2007 PD *020 †55

TURGEON, Karen Larson. 18660 BAGLEY RD, STE 204 44130 #016-06-1985 L1987 D DMP *020 †15

TURK, David Sylvester. 6900 PEARL RD STE 200, SOUTHWEST UROLOGY 44130 #038-43-1994 L1995 U *020 †20

TURNER, Raymond D, IV. 9500 EUCLID AVE, CLEVELAND CLN FNDN 44195 #759-18-2002 L2003 NS *012

TUTHILL, Antoinette Ailee. 9500 EUCLID AVE, CO CCF-GRAD MED EDU DEPT-N 44195 #539-02-1997 L2000 *100

TUTHILL, Ralph James. 9500 EUCLID AVE 44195 #021-01-1969 L1981 ATP DMP *020 †50

TUTHILL, Timothy Martin. 6559 WILSON MILLS RD, STE 106A 44143 #023-07-1966 L1967 IM PUD *020 †20

TUZCU, Emin Murat. 9500 EUCLID AVE F-25, CLEVELAND CLINIC/CARDIOLOG 44195 #902-10-1977 L1992 CD IM *020 †20

TY, Edna Boringot. CLEVELAND CLINIC FNDN, DEPT CHILD NEUR 44106 #748-01-1991 L2000 CHN *100

TYLER, Carl V. 18200 LORAIN AVE, DEPT FM 44111 #038-44-1982 L1986 FM FPG *040 †18

TYLER, Melanie Denise. 13301 MILES AVE 44105 #025-01-1991 L1993 IM *020 †20

TYMCIO, Stephen John. 7225 OLD OAK BLVD, STE A210 44130 #038-40-1974 L1974 FM *020

TYSON, Patrice Jenne. ■ 44118 #030-05-2001 L2007 PG *100 †55

UCHIN, Jeffrey Michael. ■ 44113 #041-12-2006 L2006 PTH *012

UDAYASHANKAR, Solur V. 9500 EUCLID AVE 44195 #495-33-1972 L1982 AN PUD *020 †05

UDOMSAWAENGSUP, Suthep. 9500 EUCLID AVE, CLEVELAND CLINIC FOUNDATIO 44195 #891-01-1996 L2005 *100

UGOKWE, Kenechukwu T. CLINIC FOUNDATION, CLEVELAND 44195 #010-03-2002 L2002 NS *012

UKO, Victor Essien. 9500 EUCLID AVE, CLEVELAND CLINIC FOUNDATIO 44195 #690-02-1997 L2007 PD *012

ULCHAKER, James C. 9500 EUCLID AVE, STE 100 44195 #038-06-1991 L1993 U *020 †95

ULI, Naveen K. 11100 EUCLID AVE, RB & C STE 737 44106 #495-09-1991 L2002 PDE *020 †55

UMAPATHY, Kandasamy. 11311 SHAKER BLVD, RM 4135 44104 #220-01-1986 L1998 IM *020 †20

UNDERWOOD, Donald Arthur. 9500 EUCLID AVE, CLEVELAND CLINIC 44195 #038-06-1975 L1978 CD *020 †20

UNGVARSKY, Richard F. 6707 POWERS BLVD, STE 100 44129 #396-21-1982 L1986 GS *020 †85

UNNITHAN, Jaya Sarojini. 2351 E 22ND ST 44115 #495-31-1989 L2003 IM *100 †20

UNZEK, Samuel. 11100 EUCLID AVE 44106 #649-13-2001 L2003 CD *012 †20

UPCHURCH, Bennie Ray, III. 9500 EUCLID AVE, DESK A30 44195 #018-03-1993 L1994 GE IM *020 †20

UPPALLURI, Murali Rangana. 2351 E 22ND ST, DEPT OF MED EDU 44115 #495-21-1998 L2006 *100

URBAIN, Jean-Luc Claude. 9500 EUCLID AVE 44195 #165-07-1980 L2001 NM IM *020 †28

USMANI, Ali. 9500 EUCLID AVE 44195 #704-02-1999 L2002 IM *020 †20

UTIAN, Wulf H. 5900 LANDERBROOK DR, STE 390 44124 #836-01-1962 L1977 GYN REN *071 †30

UY-KROH, Mary Sia. ■ 44106 #038-06-2006 L2006 OBG *012

VADERA, Sumeet. 9500 EUCLID AVE S80, CLEVELAND CLINIC 44195 #041-02-2007 L2007 NS *012

VAGHELA, Kuldeep. 11100 EUCLID AVE, UNIV HOSP OF CLEVELAND 44106 #665-01-2002 L2003 P *012

VAIDYA, Vijaykumar S. 29000 CENTER RIDGE RD 44145 #495-97-1978 L1989 GS CD *020

VAITKUS, Linas Francis. 7255 OLD OAK BLVD, STE C106 44130 #024-05-1979 L1983 PUD IM *020 †20

VAKKALANKA, Bhanu K.V.V.S. 2500 METROHEALTH DR, METROHEALTH MED CTR 44109 #495-58-1993 L2005 IM *012

VALERA CARDY, Manuel De J. 16215 MADISON AVE 44107 #308-01-1960 L1966 IM *020 †20

VALERIO, Jose E. 9500 EUCLID AVE, CLEVELAND CLINIC FOUNDATIO 44195 #649-14-1994 L2006 *100

VALLEJO, Pedro Bernardo. 5163 BROADWAY AVE 44127 #748-01-1948 L1959 GP *071

VALLIER, Heather Audrey. 2500 METROHEALTH DR, DEPARTMENT OF ORTHOPAEDICS 44109 #005-11-1995 L2001 OTR ORS *020 †40

VAN ANTWERP, Amy D. 11100 EUCLID AVE, CO UNIV HOSPS-RESIDENCY OF 44106 #038-41-1998 L2000 U *020

VAN ANTWERP, Judith M. ■ 44114 #305-01-1998 L2004 GS *020 †05

VANAUKEN, Douglas Paul. 4242 LORAIN AVE 44113 #038-06-1990 L1991 FM *020 †18

VAN BERGEN, Robert Paul. 18101 LORAIN AVE, FAIRVIEW GENERAL HOSP 44111 #038-41-1973 L1974 OS *020 †85,90

VAN BUREN, George Allyn. 11100 EUCLID AVE, STE 1200 44106 #038-44-1985 L1987 OBG MFM *020 †30

VAN DER KUYP, Frits. 2500 METROHEALTH DR 44109 #850-01-1958 L1969 PUD PHP *071 †70

VAN DER SCHAAR, Annelies. 9500 EUCLID AVE, TT32 44195 #660-01-1987 IM *100

VAN DER SCHAAR, Pieter J. 9500 EUCLID AVE, TT32 44195 #660-01-1987 IM *100

VANDERVOORT, Pieter M. 9500 EUCLID AVE 44195 #165-04-1985 L1993 CD *100

VAN DUIN, David. 9500 EUCLID AVE 44195 #660-01-1999 L2007 ID *100 †20 ‡

VAN DYKE, Arthur Edmund. 6770 MAYFIELD RD, STE 205 44124 #033-06-1975 L1977 CD *020 †20

VAN HEECKEREN, Daniel W. 11100 EUCLID AVE 44106 #024-01-1964 L1971 TS CD *020 †85,90

VAN LUNTEREN, Erik. 10701 EAST BLVD 44106 #038-06-1979 L1982 PUD IM *050 †20

VAN MASTRIGT, Irma. ■ 44126 #660-04-1950 L1962 AN OS *012

VARAHAN, Subha Lakshmi. 11100 EUCLID AVE RM 3018, CO UNIV HOSPS RESIDENCY OF 44106 #039-01-2003 L2003 CD *012 †20

VARGAS-WHALE, Raquel Ann. ■ 44114 #048-02-2005 L2005 PD *012

VARGO, John Jos, II. DESK A-30, DEPT. OF GASTROENTEROLOGY/ 44195 #035-45-1985 L1990 GE IM *020 †20

VARGO, Mary Annette. 2500 METROHEALTH DR, METROHEALTH MEDICAL CENTER 44109 #035-45-1985 L1989 PM *020 †60

VARYANI, Nandlal. 19250 BAGLEY RD STE 101, ANESTH CARE OF OHIO 44130 #704-08-1972 L1980 AN CCM *020 †05

VASARHELYI, Zoard Alpar. 9500 EUCLID AVE 44106 #473-01-1999 L2000 AN *100 †20

VASAVADA, Pauravi Shah. 11100 EUCLID AVE, DEPT OF RADIOLOGY 44106 #028-46-1994 L2007 PDR *020 †80

VASAVADA, Sandip Prasan. 9500 EUCLID AVE, STE 100 44195 #038-44-1991 L1992 U *020 †95

VASSIL, Andrew Dean. ■ 44113 #033-06-2005 L2005 RO *012

VASU, Tiberiu. 13099 LORAIN AVE, STE 545 44111 #781-01-1979 L1983 GE IM *020

VATANKHAHI, Shiva. ■ 44143 #517-19-2001 L2006 IM *012

VAZQUEZ, Eduardo D. 4115 BRIDGE AVE # 208 44113 #649-02-1970 L1977 P *020 †75

VEBER, William Fredric. 18101 LORAIN AVE 44111 #038-47-1978 L1982 AN *020

VECCHIONE, Donna Sue. 730 SOM CENTER RD STE 310 44143 #035-48-1985 L1987 GS *020 †85

VEERA, Arun Kumar Reddy. ■ 44130 #495-72-2002 L2006 FP *012

VEERAMACHANENI, Harish. 18200 LORAIN AVE, DEPT OF FAMILY PRACTICE 44111 #496-59-2003 L2006 FP *012

VEGI, Srivalli. 13951 TERRACE RD, CO MER HURON HOSP-INT MED 44112 #495-11-2001 L2004 IMG *012 †20

VEGUNTA, Prasad G K. 30680 BAINBRIDGE RD, PHYSICIAN'S STAFFING INC. 44139 #495-50-1963 L1986 GS *074 †85

VEKSHTEIN, Vladimir I. 6780 MAYFIELD RD #035-19-1984 L1990 CD IM *020 †20

VELAYUDHAN, Plakkat K. 18660 BAGLEY RD, STE 501 44130 #495-44-1970 L1977 GE IM *020 †20

VELEZ, Maria Giselle Sant. 2351 E 22ND ST 44115 #748-02-2000 L2004 IM *020 †20

VELEZ, Vicente Jose Monti. 2351 E 22ND ST 44115 #748-02-2002 L2004 IM *100 †20

VELLOZE, Sabino Jos D. 7255 OLD OAK BLVD, ASSOCIATES 44130 #495-17-1978 L1985 CD IM *020 †20

VELOIRA, Jaime Samonte. 18101 LORAIN AVE 44111 #748-01-1954 L1972 AN *071 †20

VELOSO, Inia Espina. 4229 PEARL RD 44109 #748-11-1964 L1973 IM *020

VELURU, Chandra Sekhar. CO RESIDENCY SUPPORT, METROHEALTH MEDICAL CENTER 44109 #495-62-2002 L2006 IM *012

VEMANA, Srikrishna. 11100 EUCLID AVE 44106 #038-43-2004 L2004 IM *100 †20

VENDELAND, James Lee. 2092 EDENHALL DR 44124 #038-41-1965 L1965 OPH *020 †35

VENER, David F. 9500 EUCLID AVE, MED STAFF OFFICE/EE46 44195 #048-04-1989 L2004 PAN AN *020 †05

VENESY, Deborah Ann. 9500 EUCLID AVE C21, CLEVELAND CLINIC 44195 #038-45-1986 L1987 PM *020 †60

VENGOECHEA BARRIOS, Jaime. CO RESIDENCY OFFICE, UNIVERSITY HOSPITALS 44106 #264-04-2005 L2007 TY *012

VENKATARAMANAN, Sangeetha. 2500 METROHEALTH DR, DEPT OF RESIDENCY SUPPORT 44109 #496-34-2002 L2005 IM *012

VENKATESHAIAH, Lokesh Kum. 2500 METROHEALTH DR 44109 #496-39-2000 L2005 IM *012

VENTENILLA, Aurora C. ■ 44141 #748-07-1963 L1974 P *030 †75

VENUS, Sam John. 2500 METROHEALTH DR 44109 #422-01-2005 L2005 IM *012

VERBEEK, Willem Cornelis. 2500 METROHEALTH DR 44109 #539-06-1996 L1999 PD *100 †55

VERGALES, Jeffrey Eric. ■ 44106 #052-01-2007 L2007 PD *012

VERKA, Lisena Gabriela. 2351 E 22ND ST, DEPT OF MED EDU 44115 #781-03-1991 L2005 IM *012

VERMA, Atul. 9500 EUCLID AVE, DESK F-15 44195 #065-01-1997 L2003 ICE *100

VERMA, Ravi Rajam. 12301 SNOW RD 44130 #495-53-1983 L1994 ON *020 †55,20

VERREES, Margaret Ann. 2500 METROHEALTH DR # A-, METROHEALTH MEDICAL CENTER 44109 #032-01-1998 L2000 NS *012

VERTES, Victor. 1800 E 105TH ST 44106 #038-06-1953 L1953 IM *071 †20

VEXLER, David Paul. 29001 CEDAR RD, BEACHWOOD OB GYN INC 44124 #035-47-1993 L1997 OBG *020 †30

VICTORIO, Maria Cristina. ■ 44120 #748-10-1993 L2001 PD *100

VICTORY, Colleen. ■ 44120 #036-01-1990 L1991 EM *020 †16

VIDETIC, Gregory. CLEVELAND CLINIC FOUNDATIO, RADIATION ONCOLOGY/ T28 44195 #067-01-1986 L2004 RO *100 †80

VIDIMOS, Allison Therese. 9500 EUCLID AVE, DESK A61 44195 #017-20-1985 L1987 D OS *020 †15

VIDOVICH, Nela Abalon. 18101 LORAIN AVE 44111 #748-11-1965 L1978 PD *020

VIDT, Donald Gardner. 9500 EUCLID AVE, DESK A-81 44195 #038-40-1959 L1959 NEP IM *071 †20

VIDU, Dorian Marcel. ■ 44130 #781-01-1982 L1986 IM *075 †20

VIELHABER, Marta Marie. 12301 SNOW RD, PARMA MEDICAL CENTER 44130 #038-06-1980 L1984 AI *012 †55,03

VIENI, Alfio. ■ 44143 #561-12-1950 L1963 AN *020

VIGNOS, Paul J, Jr. 11100 EUCLID AVE 44106 #038-06-1944 L1944 OS IM *072

VIGUERA, Adele Casals. 9500 EUCLID AVE, P57 44195 #032-01-1991 L2007 P *020 †75

VIJAYAKUMAR, Sujaya. 11100 EUCLID AVE, UHHS 44106 #495-95-1986 L2004 FM *100 †18

VILINSKY, Felix. 5850 LANDERBROOK DR, STE 105 44124 #913-65-1974 L1982 IM *020 †20

VILINSKY, Inna. 4400 RENAISSANCE PKWY, STE L 44128 #913-69-1971 L1984 DR *020 †80

VILLALBA, Karen Darlene. 2500 METROHEALTH DR 44109 #038-06-1984 L1984 EM *040 †16

VILLAROSA, Anthony Minard. ■ 44139 #025-07-1992 L1995 EM *020 †16

VILLELLA, Anthony D. 11100 EUCLID AVE, MS 6054 44106 #041-12-1997 L1999 PHO *020 †55

VINYARD, Ronald Weldon. ■ 44120 #040-02-1962 L1969 ORS *072

VISWANATHAN, Sreekanth Ki. 2500 METROH, CO RESIDENCY SUPPORT 44109 #495-44-1998 L2007 PD *012

VITEBSKIY, Sergey A. 10701 EAST BLVD 44106 #012-05-2002 L2002 CD *012 †20

VITEK, Jerrold Lee. 9500 EUCLID AVE NC30, CENTER FOR NEUROLOGICAL RE 44195 #026-04-1984 L2004 N *050 †75

VO, Michelle Le. ■ 44106 #038-06-2008 *012

VOGEL, Donald Louis. 9500 EUCLID AVE, M62-BIRTHING SERVICES 44195 #028-34-1964 L1970 OBG *071 †30

VOGELBAUM, Michael Alan. 9500 EUCLID AVE 44195 #051-01-1992 L1999 NS *020 †25

VOGELIUS, Esben Steenstru. ■ 44106 #033-05-2006 L2006 DR *012

VOGT, David Paul. 9500 EUCLID AVE, CLEVELAND CLINIC 44195 #016-06-1975 L1976 GS *020 †85

VOLK, Marita Ann. 18901 LAKE SHORE BLVD 44119 #038-44-1987 L1988 EM *020 †16

VOLLWEILER, Jason F. 7255 OLD OAK BLVD STE C101 44130 #016-06-1997 L2000 GE IM *020 †20

VOLLWEILER, Jennifer Lisa. 18697 BAGLEY RD 44130 #016-06-1997 L2000 HO *020 †20

VOLSKY, Michael David. ■ 44122 #021-01-1973 L1974 FM OM *020

VON GRUENIGEN, Vivian. 11100 EUCLID AVE, STE 1200 44106 #038-45-1991 L1992 GO *020 †30 ‡

VORA, Niloni Harshad. 9500 EUCLID AVE, DEPT OF PSYCHIATRY 44106 #496-26-1997 L2004 P *100

VORSTER, Sarel Johannes. ■ 44195 #836-03-1987 L2000 NS *100 †25

VOURGANTI, Srinivas. ■ 44118 #038-40-2004 L2004 GS *100

VRABEL, Cynthia Steele. 1744 PAYNE AVE, DEPT OF PSYCHIATRY, UNIV H 44114 #038-06-1992 L1994 P *020 †20

VROBEL, Thomas Raymond. 2500 METROHEALTH DR, RM 314 HAMMAN BLDG 44109 #056-05-1969 L1970 CD IM *040 †20

VUGRINCIC, Cedomil Franjo. ■ 44116 #957-01-1939 L1971 GE IM *072 †20

VUPPALA, Murty S. 1 MOUNT SINAI DR 44106 #495-11-1972 L1978 PD *020 †55

VYAS, Dinesh. ■ 44114 #496-03-1998 L2006 GS *012

VYDYANATHAN, Amaresh. ■ 44195 #495-59-1999 L2004 AN *012

WADHWA, Punit D. 2500 METROHEALTH DR 44109 #495-28-1990 L2000 HO *020 †20

WADIA-BRINK, Farah A. 9500 EUCLID AVE, MAIL CODE: A120 44195 #038-44-2001 L2001 PD *020 †55

WAGGONER, Steven Eugene. 5850 LANDERBROOK DR, STE 3 44124 #054-04-1984 L2002 GO GYN *020 †30

WAGNER, Chad Edward. 9500 EUCLID AVE, G30 44195 #048-14-1998 L2005 CCM *020 †05

WAGNER, Gabriel Arturo. ■ 44102 #038-43-2006 L2006 IM *012

WAGNER, Karl Gordon. 2500 METROHEALTH DR, CO METROHEALTH MED CTR-RES 44109 #665-01-2002 L2003 AN *100

WAGNER, Kimberly Ann. 7225 OLD OAK BLVD, STE A210 44130 #038-43-1998 L2000 FM *020 †18

WAHEED, Nadia Khalida. 9500 EUCLID AVE, COLE EYE INSTITUTE 44195 #704-25-1998 L2006 OPH *100 †35

WAJIDA, Ghousia. 30680 BAINBRIDGE RD, PHYSICIAN STAFFING 44139 #495-21-1998 L2003 IM *020 †20

WAKIM-FLEMING, Jamile. 2500 METROHEALTH DR 44109 #605-02-1982 L1991 GE *020 †20

WALBERT, Tobias. 11100 EUCLID AVE, UNIV HOSP 44106 #408-11-2000 L2004 N *012

WALD, Abigail Beth. 11000 EUCLID AVE, RAINBOW BABIES AND CHILDRE 44106 #038-06-2004 L2004 PD *020 †55

WALDMAN, Sanford. 11000 EUCLID AVE 44106 #038-06-1955 L1955 CHP P *020

WALKER, E Harry. 2500 METROHEALTH DR 44109 #038-41-1979 L1980 IM *030

WALKER, Michael Wm. 9500 EUCLID AVE - A41, DEPT OF ORTHOPAEDIC SURGER 44195 #561-17-1978 L2001 ORS *020 †40

WALKOWIAK, John E. 18101 LORAIN AVE 44111 #028-34-1946 L1946 IM *071 †05

WALLACE, Lee Kimbrough. 9500 EUCLID AVE, DEPT CT ANES/6-30 44195 #001-02-1989 L1994 AN *020 †05

WALLS, Michael Jason. ■ 44195 #020-02-2004 L2004 AN *012

WALSH, Brendan Colleran. ■ 44195 #539-06-2002 L2004 AN *012

WALSH, Chantal Germaine. 3525 SCRANTON RD 44109 #028-34-1996 L1998 IMG *020 †20

WALSH, Ciaran Joseph. 9500 EUCLID AVE 44195 #539-06-1984 CRS *100

WALSH, Michele C. 2101 ADELBERT RD 44106 #038-06-1982 L1985 NPM *050 †55

WALSH, Richard A. 11100 EUCLID AVE, CASE WESTERN RSRV U 44106 #010-02-1972 L1990 CD IM *020 †20

WALSH, Richard Matthew. 9500 EUCLID AVE, DEPT GENERAL SURGERY A80 44195 #056-06-1985 L1991 GS *020 †85

WALSH, Thomas Declan. 9500 EUCLID AVE 44195 #539-04-1971 L1988 OS *030 †20

WALTERS, Gloria. 9500 EUCLID AVE, # E31 44195 #051-07-2001 L2006 AN *020

WALTERS, Mark Douglas. 9500 EUCLID AVE, STE 100 44195 #038-40-1980 L1990 GYN *020 †30

WANG, Carter C. 6803 MAYFIELD RD, STE 412 44124 #038-06-1953 L1956 CD IM *071 †20

WANG, Heng. 1708 SOUTHPOINT DR 44109 #243-57-1983 L2002 PD *020 †55

WANG, Hsien-Chang. 6801 MAYFIELD RD, STE 150 44124 #385-02-1963 L1972 CD IM *071 †20

WANG, Jin. 13951 TERRACE RD 44112 #243-03-2000 IM *012

WANG, Katherine. 11100 EUCLID AVE, DEPT OF PEDIATRICS 44106 #025-01-2005 L2005 PD *012

WANG, Nancy. 11400 EUCLID AVE STE 100 44106 #038-06-1994 L1995 PTH *020 †50

WANG, Wei. 13951 TERRACE RD 44112 #243-45-1996 L2005 IM *012

WANG, Yang. ■ 44113 #041-01-2005 L2006 EM *012

WANG, Yun Min. ■ 44111 #038-06-2006 L2006 GS *012

WANG, Zhiyu. ■ 44120 #243-46-1996 L2006 IM *012

WARD, Melanie Kim. ■ 44106 #005-19-2006 L2006 AN *012

WARM, Theodore R. 11100 EUCLID AVE 44106 #038-06-1957 L1957 CHP P *040 †75

WARREN, Edward Leo. 2500 METROHEALTH DR 44109 #038-06-1987 L1987 PUD *020 †20

WARREN, Gregory Peter. 18697 BAGLEY RD 44130 #038-43-1989 L1995 HO *020 †20

WARSHAWSKY, Ilka Ruth. 9500 EUCLID AVE 44195 #028-02-1996 L2000 CLP *020 †50

WARUINGI, Wambui. 2500 METROHEALTH DR 44109 #577-01-1996 L2005 MPD *012

WASHINGTON, John A. 9500 EUCLID AVE, THE CLEVELAND CLINIC FOUND 44195 #023-07-1961 L1966 CLP *071 †50

WASHINGTON, Wm Jerome. 11100 EUCLID AVE 44106 #038-06-1978 L1979 PD *020 †55

WASMAN, Jay Kevin. 11100 EUCLID AVE, DEPT OF PATH UNIV HOSP CLE 44106 #038-06-1989 L1990 PTH *020 †50

WATERMAN, Jason Joseph. ■ 44120 #038-43-2006 L2006 IM *012

WATERS, Heather Holmes. CLINIC FOUNDATION, CLEVELAND 44195 #038-40-2005 L2007 OTO *012

WATERS, Thomas Andrew. 2500 METROHEALTH DR, DEPARTMENT OF EMERGENCY ME 44109 #038-40-1994 L1995 EM *020 †16

WATERS, Tina Elizabeth. 9500 EUCLID AVE, CLEVELAND CLINIC FOUNDATIO 44195 #038-41-2004 L2004 N *012

WATTS, Brook. ■ 44121 #001-02-2000 L2004 IM *020 †20

WATTS, Gregory Alan. 6770 MAYFIELD RD, STE 210 44124 #038-40-1981 L1983 AI *020 †20,03

WATTS, Joel C. 11100 EUCLID AVE, UNIV HOSP CLEVELAND 44106 #065-06-2003 *100

WATTS, Micah Matthew. ■ 44195 #035-06-2006 L2006 DR *012

WAYNE, Matthew S. 12200 FAIRHILL RD, FOLEY ELOER HEALTH CTR 44120 #038-06-1993 L1995 IMG *020 †20

WAYS, Heather Ann. 3569 RIDGE RD, NEIGHBORHOOD FAMILY 44102 #038-06-1984 L1986 FM *020 †18

WAZIR, Shahid. ■ 44195 #704-09-2001 L2004 CD *012 †20

WAZNI, Oussama Musbah. 9500 EUCLID AVE, C/O CCF-GRAD MED EDU DEPT- 44195 #605-01-1997 L2000 ICE *100 †20

WEATHERHEAD, Arthur Dixon. 9500 EUCLID AVE, CLEVELAND CLINIC FOUNDATIO 44195 #917-20-1945 L1955 P *071 †75

WEBB, Douglas Phillips. 850 BRAINARD RD 44143 #038-40-1982 L1983 OPH EM *020 †35

WEBER, Luke Jeffrey. 9500 EUCLID AVE A30, DEPT OF GASTROENTEROLOGY 44195 #038-40-1997 L1998 GE *020 †20

WEBER, Peter Cy. 9500 EUCLID AVE STE A71, CLEVELAND CLINIC DEPT OF E 44195 #035-03-1988 L2001 OTO NO *020 †45

WEBSTER, Whitney. 11100 EUCLID AVE, UNIV HOSP 44106 #038-06-2007 L2007 PD *012

WEE, Alvin Chan. 2351 E 22ND ST, DEPT OF MEDICAL EDUCATION 44115 #748-01-1997 L2005 IM *100

WEHNER, Tim. 2500 METROHEALTH DR 44109 #409-44-2001 L2002 CN *100 †75

WEIGHT, Steven Aldous. 2500 METROHEALTH DR 44109 #049-01-1984 L1985 OBG *020 †30

WEIL, Andrew Campbell. 9500 EUCLID AVE 44195 #422-01-2007 L2007 IM *012

WEIL, Robert John. ■ 44106 #028-03-1988 L2004 NS *020 †25

WEINBERG, Herman Chas. 6780 MAYFIELD RD 44124 #016-02-1937 L1937 OPH *071 †35

WEINER, Marlene Dovin. ■ 44122 #016-11-1981 *075

WEINSTEIN, Marlene Hana. 11100 EUCLID AVE - BHC5064, EMERGENCY SERVICES 44106 #550-02-1982 L1991 FM *020 †18

WEINSTEIN, Meredith Allen. 2500 METROHEALTH DR 44109 #035-46-1966 L1974 DR *020 †80

WEIRICH, Stephen Arthur. 12201 EUCLID AVE 44106 #035-45-1987 L1987 FM OM *020 †18

WEISBURGER, Michael Chris. ■ 44106 #023-01-2006 L2006 ORS *012

WEISE, Kathryn Louise. 9500 EUCLID AVE, CLEVELAND CLINIC 44195 #036-01-1982 L1982 CCP PD *020 †55

WEISMAN, Thomas. 8333 ROCKSIDE RD # 200 44125 #038-06-1974 L1975 IM MDM *030 †20

WEISS, Alan Mark. 9500 EUCLID AVE, DESK A91 44195 #038-06-1998 L2001 IM *020 †20

WEISS, Anita Helen. 11100 EUCLID AVE, MAIL CODE 6010 44106 #005-02-1987 L1993 CCP *020 †55

WEISS, Michael Aaron. 2109 ADELBERT RD, DEPT BIOCHEMISTRY W427 44106 #024-01-1985 L2005 END IM *050 †20

WEISS, Miriam F. 11100 EUCLID AVE, UNIVERSITY HOSPITALS 44106 #035-46-1973 L1986 NEP IM *071 †20

WEISS, Robert Stanley. 2500 METROHEALTH DR H 44109 #038-41-1968 L1968 P *020 †75

WEISS, Zwi. 2074 ABINGTON RD 44106 #550-03-1975 IMG *020 †75

WELLER, Jay Scott. 9500 EUCLID AVE, MAIL CODE E-30 44195 #016-01-1982 L1986 AN CD *020 †05 ‡

WELLER, Suki Ohk. 2500 METROHEALTH DR, METROHEALTH MEDICAL CENTER 44109 #038-06-2005 L2005 EM *012

WELLMAN, Charles V. 300 E 185TH ST 44119 #016-43-1979 L1982 IM PLM *020 †20

WELLS, Brian Jay. 9500 EUCLID AVE, CLEVELAND CLINIC 44195 #038-45-1999 L2004 FM *050 †18

WENTZ, Susan Wilma. 10900 EUCLID AVE, LOC # 4956 44106 #025-01-1981 L1984 FM *040 †18

WERA, Glenn Don. ■ 44113 #016-11-2003 L2003 ORS *012

WERNER, Sandra Lee. 2500 METROHEALTH DR, METROHEALTH MEDICAL CENTER 44109 #051-04-2000 L2000 EM *020 †16

WERZ, Mary Ann. 11100 EUCLID AVE, DEPT NEUROLOGY 44106 #025-01-1987 L1991 N IM *020 †75

WESOLOWSKI, Robert. ■ 44195 #035-08-2004 L2004 HO *012 †20

WEST, Harvey Jarold. 2500 METROHEALTH DR 44109 #038-40-1969 L1969 R *020 †80

WEST, Sara Gilmer. 11100 EUCLID AVE 44106 #051-01-2003 L2004 P *012

WESTBROOK, Edward Lloyd. 11100 EUCLID AVE, STE 5512 44106 #035-20-1965 L1969 N *020 †75

WESTGARD, Britt Anna. ■ 44106 #038-06-2008 *012

WEXLER, Isaiah David. 11100 EUCLID AVE, UNIV HOSP OF CLEVELAND 44106 #035-19-1983 L1985 PDE PD *020 †75

WHELAN, Patrick. 12301 SNOW RD 44130 #539-04-1988 L1993 PUD *020 †20

WHINNEY, Christopher M. 9500 EUCLID AVE STE S70 44195 #041-07-1996 L2001 IM *020 †20

WHITE, Constance Sturgis. 9500 EUCLID AVE 44195 #041-13-1967 L1968 RHU IM *071

WHITE, Darrell Edward. 2237 CROCKER RD, # 100 44145 #050-02-1986 L1991 OPH *020 †35

WHITE, Desmond Barry. 9500 EUCLID AVE, TT32 44195 #038-54-1992 IM *100

WHITE, Edward Cramer. 7225 OLD OAK BLVD, STE A210 44130 #038-06-1959 L1959 FM GP *071 †18 ‡

WHITE, Robert J. 2500 METROHEALTH DR 44109 #024-01-1953 L1961 NS *071 †25

WHITE, Teresa Rose. 18200 LORAIN AVE, FAIRVIEW HOSPITAL 44111 #038-06-2002 L2002 FM *020 †18

WHITEHOUSE, Peter John. 12200 FAIRHILL RD, RM323C FAIRHILL CTR 44120 #023-07-1976 L1986 N P *030 †75

WHITE-OWEN, Cathy L. 7215 OLD OAK BLVD, STE A311 44130 #012-05-1986 L1988 GS EM *020 †85

WHITESIDE-DE VOS, Julia. 2500 METROHEALTH DR, METRO HEALTH MED CTR 44109 #008-01-1986 L2001 OPH *050 †35

WHITLEY, Jessica Jones. 30680 BAINBRIDGE RD 44139 #038-06-1999 L2002 IM *100 †20

WHITLOW, Patrick Lee. 9500 EUCLID AVE 44195 #036-07-1976 L1986 CD IM *020 †20

WHITMAN, Marvin L. 14100 CEDAR RD STE 330 44121 #038-41-1950 L1950 OBG GYN *071 †30

WHITTLESEY, Diana. 10701 EAST BLVD 44106 #023-07-1975 L1977 TS CD *020 †85,90

WICKLINE, Donald Wayne. ■ 44113 #055-02-2006 L2006 EM *012

WICKREMESEKERA, Agadha Cr. 9500 EUCLID AVE BOX 728 44195 #671-01-1986 *100

WIDZER, Gary Martin. 29001 CEDAR RD, STE 200 44124 #041-12-1968 L1971 IM *020 †20

WIECKOWSKA, Anna. ■ 44195 #067-01-1999 L2004 *100

WIECZOREK, Martin Francis. 27155 CHARDON RD, STE 106 44143 #025-01-1981 L1989 OBG *020 †30

WIEDEMANN, Herbert P. 9500 EUCLID AVE A-90, CLEVELAND CLNC 44195 #035-20-1977 L1984 PUD CCM *020 †20

WIERSMA, Susan Renee. 11100 EUCLID AVE, UNIV HOSP CLEV 44106 #038-06-1984 L1984 PHO PD *020 †55

WIESNER, Georgia Lowrey. 11100 EUCLID AVE # 1500, CTR FOR HUMAN GENETICS 44106 #026-04-1985 L1994 MG IM *050 †20,19

WIEST, Peter Michael. 2500 METROHEALTH DR, METRO HEALTH MEDICAL CENTE 44109 #041-09-1981 L1994 IM *020 †20

WIKIEL, Krzysztof Jan. 11100 EUCLID AVE 44106 #759-03-2002 L2006 GS *012

WILBER, John Howard. 11100 EUCLID AVE, DEPT OF ORTHOPEDIC SRGY 44106 #038-06-1978 L1979 ORS OTR *020 †40

WILBER, Roger Griffin. 2500 METROHEALTH DR, METROHEALTH MEDICAL CENTER 44109 #038-06-1986 L1986 OAR *020 †40

WILDE, Alan Hugh. 1730 W 25TH ST 44113 #041-09-1959 L1966 ORS *020 †40

WILDER, Robert Brent. 2351 E 22ND ST 44115 #038-06-1977 L1978 EM FM *020 †18,16

WILDER, William Thornton. 2709 FRANKLIN BLVD, FAIRVIEW MEDICAL GROUP 44113 #017-20-1955 L1961 IM *071 †20

WILEY, Robert Geo. 2740 CARNEGIE AVE 44115 #051-01-1970 L1975 OPH EM *071 †35

WILEY, William Frank. 2740 CARNEGIE AVE, CLEVELAND EYE CLINIC 44115 #038-43-1998 L2002 OPH *020 †35

WILHELM, John Bernard. 16600 W SPRAGUE RD, STE 225 44130 #038-41-1979 L1981 P *020 †20

WILHELM, Scott Michael. 11100 EUCLID AVE DEPT SRGY, UNIF HOSPS OF CLEVELAND 44106 #038-41-1995 L2000 GS OS *020 †85

WILKE, William Saml. 9500 EUCLID AVE A50, CLEVELAND CLINIC FOUNDATIO 44195 #056-07-1971 L1976 RHU *020

WILKINS, Francesca Amelia. ■ 44114 #027-01-2005 L2005 IM *012

WILKOFF, Bruce Larry. 9500 EUCLID AVE, CLEVELAND CLINIC DESK F15 44195 #038-40-1979 L1982 CD OS *020 †20

WILLEN, Marlene D. 2500 METROHEALTH DR 44109 #038-45-1984 L1987 D *040 †15

WILLIAMS, Barbara Ann. 7255 OLD OAK BLVD, ASSOCIATES 44130 #038-06-1994 L1995 CD *020 †20

WILLIAMS, Brent Richard. ■ 44130 #037-01-2003 L2003 U *012

WILLIAMS, Christina Peder. ■ 44120 #038-06-2004 L2004 GS *012

WILLIAMS, Gary David. 9500 EUCLID AVE, DESK A-120 44195 #038-44-1986 L1989 PD *020 †55

WILLIAMS, Glen Chas. 11201 SHAKER BLVD, STE 328 44104 #038-43-1990 L1992 IM *020 †20

WILLIAMS, James S, Jr. 9500 EUCLID AVE 44195 #035-45-1989 L1995 ORS *020 †40

WILLIAMS, Jerome. 5209 EUCLID AVE 44103 #038-06-1985 L1987 FM *020

WILLIAMS, P Mark. ■ 44108 #041-01-1974 L1976 OBG *020

WILLIAMS, Sherrie Dixon. 2500 METROHEALTH DR, DEPT PULMONRY BELGREVE 3RD 44109 #016-11-1990 L1997 PUD CCM *020 †20

WILLIAMS, Tara Simone. 2500 METROHEALTH DR 44109 #041-12-1999 L2001 PD *020 †55

WILLIAMSON, Mary Elizabet. ■ 44195 #012-01-2005 L2006 OTO *012

WILLIS, Joseph Edward, Jr. 11400 EUCLID AVE STE 100 44106 #539-02-1982 L1993 PTH *020 †50

WILLS, Cheryl Denise. 5247 WILSON MILLS RD 452 44143 #035-15-1991 L1996 CHP PFP *020 †75

WILLS, Eddie, Jr. 32399 PINEBROOK LN, RESEARCH DEPT 44124 #020-12-1976 L1978 PD *020

WILLS, Marketa Michelle. 2351 E 22ND ST 44115 #041-01-2000 L2006 P *062 †75

WILLSON, James Knox V. 11100 EUCLID AVE, 151 WEARN 44106 #001-02-1976 L1987 ON IM *050 †20

WILSON, Erica Janeen. ■ 44143 #038-06-1996 L1999 FOP *020 †50

WILSON, Harry Edward. 18697 BAGLEY RD 44130 #010-01-1958 L1959 P *071 †70

WILSON, Jason David. ■ 44121 #038-06-2003 L2003 NS *012

WILSON, Lance Dean. 2500 METROHEALTH DR 44109 #038-06-1990 L1992 EM *020 †16

WILSON, Marcietta R. 1831 E 81ST ST 44103 #038-75-2000, ▲ L2004 *020

WILSON, Michael Stanley. 11100 EUCLID AVE, UNIV HOSPITALS HEALTH SYST 44106 #021-05-2001 L2006 P *020 †75

WILSON, Milton E. 3554 E 149TH ST 44120 #047-07-1985 L1989 FM *020 †18

WILSON, Patrick Thomas. 11100 EUCLID AVE 44106 #045-01-2003 L2006 PDI *012 †55

WILSON, Richard Dwillis. 2500 METROHEALTH DR 44109 #038-43-2002 L2002 PM *100 †60

WILSON, Steven Eugene. 9500 EUCLID AVE I32, CLEVELAND CLINIC-THE COLE 44195 #005-18-1984 L1995 OPH *020 †35

WILSON, Valerie Margaret. 9500 EUCLID AVE, CLEVELAND CLINIC 44195 #038-06-2000 L2000 EM *020 ‡

WILSON, Wendy Louise. 12201 EUCLID AVE DEPT PM 44106 #038-06-1985 L1987 PM *020 †60

WILSON-COSTELLO, Deanne E. 2101 ADELBERT RD 44106 #038-45-1991 L1994 NPM PD *020 †55 ‡

WIMBISCUS, Molly Michelle. ■ 44113 #047-06-2006 L2006 P *012

WIMPIE, Nina Florence. 18660 BAGLEY RD, STE 200B 44130 #035-03-1979 L1983 PD ADL *020 †55

WINALSKI, Carl Scherman. 9500 EUCLID AVE A21, DIVISION OF RADIOLOGY 44195 #024-07-1984 L1998 DR *020 †80

WINANS, Charles Getty. 9500 EUCLID AVE # A110 44195 #008-01-1993 L2002 GS TTS *020 †85

WINE, Alan Cecil. 3619 PARK EAST DR, STE 211 44122 #038-40-1970 L1970 HEM ON *020 †20

WINER, Norton Andrew. 18599 LAKE SHORE BLVD, UNIVERSITY MEDNET 44119 #056-06-1974 L1978 N *020 †75

WINFIELD, Anna Marie. ■ 44106 #024-07-1998 L2006 MPD *020 †20,55

WINKELMAN, Eugene I. 9500 EUCLID AVE 44195 #025-01-1953 L1962 GE IM *071 †20

WINKELMAN, Marc David. 2500 METROHEALTH DR, METROHEALTH MEDICAL CENTER 44109 #038-06-1978 L1979 N NP *040 †20

WISE, Anne Seymour. 3569 RIDGE RD, NEIGHBORHOOD FAMILY 44102 #041-13-1990 L1995 OM *020 †70,18

WISEMAN, Martin Nurock. 6780 MAYFIELD RD 44124 #917-20-1979 L1990 CD OS *020 †20

WISH, Jay Barry. 11100 EUCLID AVE, DIV NEPHROLOGY 44106 #024-07-1974 L1979 NEP IM *020 †20

WISHAH, Kholoud Khalil. 11100 EUCLID AVE, UNIVERSITY HOSPITALS CLEVE 44106 #575-01-1991 L1999 AI *020 †03,55

WISHNEV, Martin Alan. ■ 44128 #041-02-1963 L1968 GE IM *071 †20

WISNIESKI, Jeffrey Jon. 2500 METROHEALTH DR 44109 #038-06-1971 L1973 IG RHU *050 †20

WITHAM, Terence L. 18051 JEFFERSON PARK RD 44130 #037-01-1996 L2002 CHP *020

WITT, William Jacob. 11100 EUCLID AVE 44106 #038-41-1966 L1966 OTO *020 †45

WIZNITZER, Max. 11100 EUCLID AVE 44106 #016-06-1977 L1979 CHN PD *020 †55,75

WOC-COLBURN, Laila Eugeni. 11100 EUCLID AVE 44106 #429-02-2001 L2007 ID *012 †20

WOLF, Aharon Aviv. 18101 LORAIN AVE 44111 #550-02-2007 L2007 IM *012

WOLF, David Irwin. ■ 44124 #035-19-1964 L1977 OPH *071

WOLFORD, Robert W. 11100 EUCLID AVE, DEPT EMERG MD BOLWELL 3700 44106 #040-02-1984 L2005 EM *020 †18

WOLPAW, Daniel Rick. 10701 EAST BLVD, VA MEDICAL CENTER III (W) 44106 #038-06-1977 L1984 EM IM *020 †20,18,16

WOLPAW, Therese Maran. 2074 ABINGTON RD DEPT MED 44106 #038-06-1988 L1989 RHU *020 †20

WONG, Alfred Leung-Wing. 12301 SNOW RD 44130 #017-20-1976 L1979 IM *020 †20

WONG, Hsienyean. 9500 EUCLID AVE 44195 #041-12-2001 L2007 DR *100 †80

WONG, John W N. 2085 ADELBERT RD 44106 #065-01-1985 L1994 PTH *050 †50

WONG, King Hwa. 13951 TERRACE RD 44112 #539-02-2004 GS *012

WONG, Kutt Sing. 9500 EUCLID AVE, CO CCF-GRAD MED EDU DEPT-N 44195 #825-01-1991 L2002 CRS *100

WONG, Mary. 2801 MARTIN LTHR KNG JR DR 44104 #042-07-1991 L2000 PD *020 †55

WONG, Milton Chu-Yuan. 7007 POWERS BLVD 44129 #748-10-1984 L1997 IM CCM *020 †20

WONG, Raymond Ching Chiew. 9500 EUCLID AVE, DEPT OF GME 44195 #825-01-1997 L2007 *100

WONG, Richard Chi Kit. 11100 EUCLID AVE, U HOSP DIV GE WEARN 247A 44106 #917-24-1986 L1996 GE *020 †20

WONG, Virginia Louise. 11100 EUCLID AVE, DIV OF VAS SURG UNIV HOSP 44106 #035-08-1995 L2000 VS VIR *020 †85

WONGCHAOWART, Sherri Lynn. 11100 EUCLID AVE, HANNA PAVILLION 44106 #038-44-2002 L2002 P *020 †75

WOO, Byung Hyuck. ■ 44122 #583-02-1960 L1977 R *071 †80

WOO, Jong Moon. 11100 EUCLID AVE 44106 #583-09-1973 L1981 AN *020 †05

WOO, Lynn Lim. 9500 EUCLID AVE, CO CCF-GRAD MED EDU DEPT-N 44195 #018-03-2002 L2002 U *012

WOOD, Benjamin Gray. 9500 EUCLID AVE A71, CLEVELAND CLINIC FOUNDATIO 44195 #060-01-1968 L1976 HNS ON *020 †45

WOOD, Hadley Merrideth. 9500 EUCLID AVE, C/O CCF-GRAD MED EDU DEPT- 44195 #023-07-2003 L2003 U *012

WOODS, Donald Matthew. 11100 EUCLID AVE, C/O UNIV HOSPS-RESIDENCY O 44106 #041-15-1999 L2002 APM *012

WORTHINGTON, Daniel Chas. LL311 SHAKER BLVD 44104 #038-06-1972 L1973 PD ADL *071 †55

WOYSHVILLE, Mark Jos. 18660 BAGLEY RD, BLDG II 44130 #038-41-1989 L1992 P *020 †75

WRIGHT, Jackson Thos., Jr. 11100 EUCLID AVE, # 209 44106 #041-12-1976 L1990 IM *020 †20
WRIGHT, Martha Susan. 11100 EUCLID AVE, RAINBOW BABIES CHLDRNS HOS 44106 #036-07-1984 L1992 PD PEM *040 †55
WRIGHT, Michael Mcbrearty. 2500 METROHEALTH DR, METROHEALTH MEDICAL CENTER 44109 #012-22-2001 L2001 GS *100
WU, Bing. 18101 LORAIN AVE, FAIRVIEW HOSPITAL 44111 #243-03-1984 L2004 CD *012
WU, Carleton. 9500 EUCLID AVE 44195 #038-40-1995 L1999 AN *020 †05
WU, Guiyun. 9500 EUCLID AVE 44195 #243-53-1988 L2003 NM *020 †75,28
WU, Jeffrey Jarjerg. 9500 EUCLID AVE H35 44195 #016-06-1999 L2006 TS *100 †85,90
WU, Jeffrey Kai. 9500 EUCLID AVE, A40 44122 #038-40-2002 L2007 ORS *100
WU, Sue Xiaohua. 9500 EUCLID AVE 44195 #243-64-1982 L2000 AN *020
WUTTE, Cordula Maria. 2500 METROHEALTH DR 44109 #409-44-2005 L2007 MPD *012
WYLLIE, Elaine. 9500 EUCLID AVE, CLEVELAND CLINIC FOUNDATIO 44195 #017-20-1978 L1984 CHN OS *020 †55,75
WYLLIE, Robert. 2801 MARTIN LTHR KNG JR DR 44104 #017-20-1976 L1980 PD *020 †55
WYSE, Aaron Jonathon. ■ 44118 #036-07-2004 L2004 DR *012
WYSE, Denton H. 11100 EUCLID AVE 44106 #038-06-1973 L1973 P PYG *020 †75
XIA, Guohua. 11400 EUCLID AVE STE 200 44106 #243-47-1986 L2007 P *050
XIAO, Zuo-Liang. 9500 EUCLID AVE, THE CLEV 44195 #243-65-1987 L2007 GE *012 †20
XU, Han. 2351 E 22ND ST 44115 #243-16-1982 L1996 PTH *020 †50 ‡
XU, Zhiyuan. 9500 EUCLID AVE, CLEVELAND CLINIC FOUNDATIO 44195 #243-78-1994 L2006 *100
YACOUB, Sawsan Yousif. 2500 METROHEALTH DR, CO METRO HEALTH MED CTR - 44109 #528-03-1982 L2001 FM *020 †18
YADAVALLI, Gopala Krishna. 10701 EAST BLVD 44106 #041-02-1995 L1998 ID *020 †20
YAGAN, Rauf. 3395 SCRANTON RD DEPT RAD 44109 #902-03-1955 L1968 R *020 †80
YAGI-KAURACHI, Noriko. 9500 EUCLID AVE BOX 727 44195 #572-23-1987 *100
YAHYA VARGAS, Javier Fern. 2500 METROHEALTH DR, CO METROHEALTH MED CTR-RES 44109 #737-01-1981 L2001 P *100 †75
YALCINBAS, Yusuf Kenan. 9500 EUCLID AVE, C/O CLEVELAND CLINIC GME/N 44195 #902-07-1989 L2000 *100
YALCINKAYA, Gulgun. 2101 ADELBERT RD 44106 #902-07-1989 L2002 NPM PD *020 †55
YANG, Bin. 9500 EUCLID AVE 44195 #243-38-1982 L2000 PCP *020 †50
YANG, Guang. 2500 METROHEALTH DR 44109 #243-47-1989 L2002 PM *020
YANG, Suzanne. 11100 EUCLID AVE, DEPARTMENT OF PSYCHIATRY 44106 #005-02-1998 L2006 P *020
YAO, Qin. 2101 ADELBERT RD 44106 #243-52-1992 L2000 PD NPM *020 †55
YAP, Tsiao Yi. 9500 EUCLID AVE, CO CCF-GRAD MED EDU DEPT-N 44195 #067-01-2003 L2003 *100
YARED, Jean-Pierre Pierre. 9500 EUCLID AVE DEPT CD 44195 #605-01-1977 L1987 AN CCA *020 †05
YATES, Veronica Klus. 200 PUBLIC SQ, STE 4 44114 #056-06-1956 L1985 OM GPM *072
YATSU, Jeffrey Wayne. 3800 W 143RD ST, PPG INDUSTRIES 44111 #038-40-1973 L1973 IM PHP *020 †20
YAZBEK, Andre. ■ 44134 #605-02-1963 GE OS *071
YEE, Albert Juang Ming. 2500 METROHEALTH DR 44109 #065-01-1992 L1999 *020 †40
YEO, Kee Thai. 11100 EUCLID AVE 44106 #067-01-2004 L2005 PD *012
YERKEY, Michael Wayne. 9500 EUCLID AVE, CLEVELAND CLINIC 44195 #008-01-1998 L2004 ICE *012 †20
YERMAL, Sooraj Gopal. 18101 LORAIN AVE, DEPT OF INTERNAL MED 44111 #496-59-1995 L2006 IM *100
YETSKO, Richard A. ■ 44134 #016-43-1979 L1980 IM *020 †20,16
YOMTOVIAN, Roslyn Ann K. 11400 EUCLID AVE STE 100 44106 #028-02-1974 L1988 PTH BBK *020 †50
YONAN, Sameh Rizkallah. 9500 EUCLID AVE, CLEVELAND CLN FNDN 44195 #915-04-1995 L2000 AN *100 †05
YOO, Ji Won. ■ 44106 #583-03-2000 L2005 IM *012
YOO, Sook Kyung. 11203 FAIRHILL RD 44104 #583-03-1949 L1971 AN *020
YOON, Helen Zinn. 9500 EUCLID AVE 44195 #033-06-1995 L1996 NPM *020 †55
YOON, Young Sun. 18599 LAKE SHORE BLVD, UNIVERSITY MEDNET 44119 #583-06-1966 L1976 DR IM *020 †80
YOSHIDA, Sean H. 9500 EUCLID AVE, CO CCF-GRAD MED EDU DEPT-N 44195 #061-01-1991 L2000 DR *100 †80
YOUNG, Christopher W. 18101 LORAIN AVE FAM PR 44111 #038-41-1996 L1997 FM *020 †18
YOUNG, Diane Louise. 9500 EUCLID AVE 44195 #041-07-1979 L1982 OBG *020 †30
YOUNG, James Benard. 9500 EUCLID AVE, DIVISION OF MEDICINE T13 44195 #048-04-1974 L1995 CD IM *020 †20
YOUNG, Jess Ray. 9500 EUCLID AVE, CLEVELAND CLINIC 44195 #028-34-1955 L1956 CD IM *071 †20
YOUNG, Peter Christopher. 1110 EUCLID AVE, BOLWELL 5038B 44115 #017-20-1993 L1997 DR *020 †80
YOUNGNER, Stuart James. 11100 EUCLID AVE, UNIVERSITY HOSPITALS 44106 #038-06-1970 L1972 P *020 †75
YOUNGSTROM, Paul Clarence. 9500 EUCLID AVE 44195 #067-01-1976 L1977 AN *020 †05
YOUSFI, Samer. ■ 44135 #875-01-2001 L2005 NPM *012 †55
YOUSSEF, George Nagy N. 9500 EUCLID AVE P21, CLEVELAND CLINIC FOUNDATIO 44195 #915-02-1992 L2000 AN *020 †05
YOUSSEFI, Mojtaba E. 2500 METROHEALTH DR 44109 #038-44-1989 L1990 IM *020 †20
YOWLER, Charles Jos. 2500 METROHEALTH DR 44109 #030-06-1977 L1996 GS CCS *020 †85
YU, Jae-Hak. ■ 44140 #583-13-1985 L2000 ADP *012
YU, Steve Pyong. 11100 EUCLID AVE, WOMEN'S HOSP 44106 #422-01-2004 L2005 OBG *012
YUE, Cheung Cho. 2500 METROHEALTH DR, DEPT OF MEDICINE 44109 #035-45-1978 L1980 IM RHU *020 †20,50
YUEN, Ho-Wang. ■ 44113 #056-06-2005 L2005 EM *012
YUH, Song Lim. 5162 BROADWAY AVE, STE 3 44127 #583-03-1972 L1978 GP PTH *020 †50
YULISH, Barry Shayle. ■ 44124 #038-41-1958 L1958 PDR *071 †80
YURICK, Robert S. 14601 DETROIT AVE, STE 640 44107 #038-40-1960 L1960 ORS *020 †40
ZABAKHIDZE, Ekaterina. 13951 TERRACE RD 44112 #912-02-1998 L2003 IM *100 †20
ZABALA, Reynaldo Tuang. 14519 DETROIT AVE 44107 #748-08-1970 L1979 GS CCS *020
ZABALA, Susan Soto. ■ 44145 #748-30-1970 L1982 GP *020
ZACHARIAH, Manorama. 6780 MAYFIELD RD 44124 #495-04-1969 L1994 OBG *020 †30
ZAHARINA, Mia. ■ 44195 #038-44-2003 L2005 P *012
ZAHKA, Kenneth Geo. 11100 EUCLID AVE, RAINBOW BABIES & CHILDREN' 44106 #023-07-1975 L1990 PDC PD *020 †55
ZAHNISER, Mark Howard. 19250 BAGLEY RD 44130 #038-43-1990 L1994 AN CCA *020 †05 ‡

ZAHR, Firas Elie. 9500 EUCLID AVE, DEPT OF GME 44106 #875-01-2002 L2005 IM *012
ZAIA, William I. 9500 EUCLID AVE, DEPT. OF NEONATOLOGY/M31 44195 #528-01-1968 L1988 NPM PD *020 †55
ZAIZAFOUN, Manaf. ■ 44111 #875-03-2001 L2005 IM *012
ZAK, John F. 7232 PEARL RD 44130 #038-06-1996 L1997 GS *100
ZAKAIB, John Salem. CLINIC FOUNDATION, CLEVELAND 44195 #051-04-1999 L2003 ICE *012 †20
ZAKARIA, Asma. ■ 44195 #704-25-2001 L2007 *100
ZAKHARY, Wasefy Hanna. 9500 EUCLID AVE, CO CCF-GRAD MED EDU DEPT-N 44195 #915-05-1978 L2003 AN *020
ZAKY, Ahmed Fathy. ■ 44106 #915-03-1997 L2007 CCA *100
ZAKY, Sherif Shawky. 9500 EUCLID AVE, CLEVELAND CLINIC FOUND 44195 #915-04-1995 L2001 AN *012
ZANGMEISTER, John M. 11709 LORAIN AVE 44111 #038-40-1983 L1984 FM *020 †18
ZANNONI, Jean S. 4732 PEARL RD, STE 1 44109 #583-03-1958 L1983 FM *020
ZARA, Barbara Yousif. 673 ALPHA DR STE C, ANNASHEE CORPORATION 44143 #528-02-1977 L1995 P *020
ZARAGOZA, Miguel V, Jr. 12301 SNOW RD, 17083 HUNTING MEADOWS 44130 #748-01-1965 L1965 GP *020
ZARKOWSKI, Paul A. 2500 METROHEALTH DR, METROHEALTH MED CTRRESIDEN 44109 #665-01-1997 L2000 N *020 †75
ZARLINGO, Thomas Jos. 18099 LORAIN AVE STE 345, DEPARTMENT OF OB GYN 44111 #038-43-1980 L1982 MFM OBG *020 †30
ZAWANEH, Michael S. 11100 EUCLID AVE, LAKESIDE 3113, CARDIOLOGY 44106 #011-03-2002 L2002 CD *012 †20
ZAWORSKI, Norman W. ■ 44125 #038-06-1944 L1944 IM *071
ZEIN, Nizar. 9500 EUCLID AVE A31, THE CLEVELAND CLINIC 44195 #875-03-1986 L2002 GE MPD *020 †20,55
ZEITOUNI, Mohammed Omar. 3609 PARK EAST DR, UNIVERSITY PHYSICIANS INC 44122 #605-01-1987 L1989 CCM PUD *020 †20
ZELCH, James Vern. 4400 RENAISSANCE PKWY, REGIONAL MRI 44128 #038-40-1966 L1968 DR *020 †80
ZELIN, Mira Borisovna. 2500 METROHEALTH DR, METROHEALTH MED CTR 44109 #913-82-1987 PM *012
ZELIN, Steve Ira. 9500 EUCLID AVE NA23, CLEVELAND CLINIC-ANESTHESI 44195 #038-40-2002 L2002 PAN *100 †05
ZELITSKY, Vladimir. 1001 LAKESIDE AVE E, STE 1200 44114 #913-07-1970 L1983 OTO *020
ZEWAIL, Aly Mohamed Aly. 2500 METROHEALTH DR, DEPT OF GERIATICS 44109 #915-02-1997 L2006 FPG *020 †18
ZHANG, Jianping. 9500 EUCLID AVE 44195 #243-48-1988 L2005 P *012
ZHANG, Ming. 11110 EUCLID AVE 44106 #243-72-1992 L2004 CD *012
ZHAO, Jinhua. 10701 EAST BLVD, LOUIS STOKES VA MEDICAL CE 44106 #243-92-1987 L2007 NEP *020 †20
ZHAO, Xiangyang. 2500 METROHEALTH DR 44109 #243-92-1993 L2006 P *012
ZHOU, Jianhong. 2500 METROHEALTH DR, C/O METROHEALTH MED CTR-RE 44109 #243-48-1988 L2003 PCP *012 †50
ZHOU, Lan. 9500 EUCLID AVE S90 44195 #243-16-1989 L2003 CN *020 †75
ZHOU, Ming. 9500 EUCLID AVE, STE L25 44195 #243-16-1989 L2003 PTH *020 †50
ZHU, Hui. 11100 EUCLID AVE 44106 #036-07-1999 L2005 U *020
ZICKAFOOSE, Joseph Scott. 11100 EUCLID AVE 44106 #038-06-2004 L2004 PD *100 †55
ZIELINSKI, Kathleen Mary. 1611 S GREEN RD, ASSOCIATES 44121 #038-45-2001 L2001 OPH *020 †35
ZIEMBICKI, Jenny Ann. 2500 METROHEALTH DR, DEPT OF SURGERY 44109 #041-13-2000 L2000 CCS *012 †85
ZIMMERMAN, Robert S. 9500 EUCLID AVE, A53 44195 #023-07-1981 L2000 END IM *020 †20
ZIMMERMAN, Teresa Nelson. 11100 EUCLID AVE, RB & C RM 737 44106 #038-45-1981 L2001 PDE DIA *020 †55
ZINN, Arthur Brian. 11100 EUCLID AVE, UNIVERSITY HOSPITALS OF CL 44106 #038-06-1976 L1982 CG CBG *020 †19
ZINN, Stephen Blake. 29425 CHAGRIN BLVD STE 301 44122 #038-06-1970 L1971 P CHP *020 †20
ZINS, James Edward. 9500 EUCLID AVE, DEAK A60 44195 #041-01-1974 L1983 PS *020 †85,65
ZIPP, Thomas Marc. 4071 LEE RD, STE 260 44128 #038-41-1977 L1978 NEP IM *020 †20
ZIPPE, Craig Donald. 9500 EUCLID AVE, CLEVELAND CLINIC FOUNDATIO 44195 #016-01-1980 L1994 U ORS *020 †95
ZIPPERT, Albert M. 2351 E 22ND ST 44115 #038-06-1953 L1953 GS *072 †85
ZIRAFI, Christine M. 7255 OLD OAK BLVD, STE C302 44130 #038-44-1982 L1989 CD *020 †20
ZIRKIN, Howard J. 1001 LAKESIDE AVE E, STE 1200 44114 #025-07-1968 L1975 PTH *020 †50
ZIVIC, Miodrag Vitomir. 13951 TERRACE RD, MERIDIA HURON HOSP 44112 #957-06-1995 L2002 *100 †20
ZNIDARSIC, Adolph Francis. 15621 WATERLOO RD 44110 #016-43-1955 L1958 GS GP *020
ZSAKO, Steven. 18599 LAKE SHORE BLVD 44119 #407-21-1958 L1959 IM *071
ZUCCARO, Gregory Donald. 9500 EUCLID AVE, A30 44195 #035-06-1983 L1988 GE IM *020 †20
ZUCKER, Boruch. 11100 EUCLID AVE 44106 #047-06-2000 L2000 ICE *012 †20
ZULUAGA TORO, Tania. CO GME-NA23 9, CLEVELAND CLINIC FNDN L25 44195 #264-05-2002 L2004 PTH *012
ZURA, Andrew Michael. 9500 EUCLID AVE, THE CLEVELAND CLINIC FOUND 44195 #025-07-1992 L1996 AN *020 †05
ZURCHER, Vickie Lee. 10527 EUCLID AVE # FL6 44106 #038-41-1982 L1986 CG PD *074 †55,19
ZUTSHI, Massarat. 9500 EUCLID AVE 44195 #495-01-1982 L2004 CRS *020
ZUZEK, Ryan William. 9051 CEDAR AVE 44106 #539-05-2002 L2002 CD *012 †20
ZWICKER, Jocelyn C. 9500 EUCLID AVE BOX 181 44195 #065-01-1997 L2000 N *100 †75

CLEVELAND HEIGHTS – CUYAHOGA

ABBAS, Farouk A. 10 SEVERANCE CIR, 1H 44118 #875-01-1980 L1984 OPH IM *075 †20,35
ABDULKADIR, Ahmet. 10 SEVERANCE CIR 44118 #902-10-1972 L1990 TS GS *020 †85,90
ACQUAH, David C H. 50 SEVERANCE CIR 44118 #412-01-1973 L1991 DR NM *020 †80
ADAMS, David Harris. 5 SEVERANCE CIR STE 318 44118 #024-01-1978 L1980 OPH GP *020 †35
ADAMS, Ronald Albert. 10 SEVERANCE CIR 44118 #038-41-1981 L1983 IM *020 †20
ADIJA, Akinyi A. ■ 44118 #035-47-1998 L2004 PD *020

ALCORN, Robert Watson. 2812 FAIRMOUNT BLVD STE 32 44118 #038-06-1970 L1971 P *075 †75

ALEXANDER, Sarah Weeks. 11100 EUCLID AVE, HOSP/DIV PEDI HEMATOLOGY O 44106 #024-01-1994 L2001 PHO *020 †55

ALI, Jafer. ■ 44118 #038-44-2006 L2006 AN *012

ALLE, Darshana. ■ 44118 #038-44-2005 L2005 IM *012

ALMEIDA-CHEN, Gracie Mari. ■ 44118 #035-08-2004 L2004 AN *012

ALTMAN, Andrew Louis. 10 SEVERANCE CIR 44118 #035-06-1995 L1996 U *020 †95

AMERI, Nahid. 10 SEVERANCE CIR 44118 #517-04-1971 L1990 CHP P *020 †75

ANCHETA, Priscilla I. 5 SEVERANCE CIR, STE 416 44118 #748-01-1962 L1962 PD GP *020 †55

ANDERSON, Ingrid Mcdowell. ■ 44118 #016-11-2007 L2007 PD *012

ANTHONY, Donald D. ■ 44112 #038-06-1993 L1994 RHU *020 †20

ANTHONY, Ryan Andrew. ■ 44118 #035-45-2006 L2006 IM *012

APPLEBAUM, David Leslie. ■ 44118 #038-43-1978 L1979 IM EM *020 †20,16

APTE, Susan M. ■ 44106 #495-96-1973 L1979 CCS *100 †85

ARETAKIS, Kari Ann. ■ 44106 #016-06-2007 L2007 GS *012

ARMENTROUT, Rachel Ayne. ■ 44118 #038-06-2008 *012

ARMIJO, Bryan Stapp. ■ 44118 #003-01-2005 L2005 PS *012

ARMITAGE, Keith Barclay. 12600 CEDAR RD, CASE MEDICAL SCHOOL 44106 #007-02-1986 L1988 IM *040 †20

ARMSTRONG, Delilah. 10 SEVERANCE CIR 44118 #005-14-1985 L1998 IM *020 †20

ATTAYA, Shariff H. ■ 44118 #016-11-2005 L2007 IM *012

AYMAT, Fernando. 10 SEVERANCE CIR 44118 #847-04-1962 L1977 N *075 †75

AZAM, Salman Mohammed. ■ 44118 #025-07-2005 L2005 IM *012

AZAR, Nami Ramzi. 11100 EUCLID AVE, DEPARTEMENT OF RADIOLOGY 44106 #875-02-1991 L1999 DR *020 †80

AZOK, Jill Stacy. ■ 44118 #038-06-2005 L2005 PD *012

BARK, Charles Martyn. ■ 44106 #035-46-2004 L2004 IM *100 †20

BARR, Paul Michael. 11100 EUCLID AVE, DIV HEMATOLOGY ONCOLOGY 44106 #038-44-2000 L2000 HO *100 †20

BAUER, Andrew Michael. ■ 44118 #016-11-2007 L2007 GS *012

BEARER, Cynthia Frances. 11100 EUCLID AVE, RM 3100 44106 #023-07-1983 L1992 NPM PD *050 †55

BECK, Thomas Russell. ■ 44118 #035-20-1975 L1976 IM NEP *050 †20

BEDIENT, Carrie Elizabeth. ■ 44106 #003-01-2008 *012

BHAKTA, Shyam. ■ 44118 #025-07-2000 L2000 IC *012

BHOLA, Monika. 11100 EUCLID AVE, DEPT OF PEDIATRICS 44106 #495-08-1986 L2004 NPM *020 †55

BLACK, Jane Beth. 10 SEVERANCE CIR 44118 #035-15-1985 L1988 PD *020 †55

BLAKE-GUMBS, Lyla. 11100 EUCLID AVE, DEPT. OF FAMILY MEDICINE 44106 #041-09-1997 L2004 FM *020 †18

BOCIRNEA, Cristina. ■ 44118 #035-45-1994 L2007 IM *020 †20

BOLLINGER, Kathryn E. ■ 44118 #056-06-2003 L2004 OPH *100

BOUCHARD, Denis. ■ 44121 #067-01-1992 L2000 *100

BOUTRY, Mireille Gernaine. 11100 EUCLID AVE, RAINBOW BABIES & CHILDRN'S 44106 #165-01-1976 L1990 PD OS *020 †55

BOWES-DAVIS, Pamela Zoe. 2101 ADELBERT RD, RAINBOW BABIES & CHILDRENS 44106 #036-07-1974 L1981 PD PUD *030 †20,55

BRADFORD, Dorothy A. 5 SEVERANCE CIR, STE 107 44118 #026-04-1980 L1984 IM *020 †20

BRENNER, Barry Evan. 3495 SHANNON RD, DEPT OF EMERGENCY MEDICINE 44118 #051-04-1974 L1976 IM EM *020 †20,16

BREWSTER, Deborah Lynn. ■ 44118 #038-45-2007 L2007 P *012

BROWN, Billy Lee. 5 SEVERANCE CIR 44118 #038-06-1917 L1978 IM *020

BROWN, James Robt. 10 SEVERANCE CIR 44118 #038-43-1975 L1978 IM *020

BURNS, Arthur Eugene. ■ 44106 #047-07-1946 L1949 PD *071 †55

BURRAGE, Lindsay Catherin. ■ 44106 #038-06-2008 *012

BUSBY, Katherine Ann. ■ 44118 #038-43-2006 L2006 P *012

BYRAMJEE, Aspi Minoo. 10 SEVERANCE CIR 44118 #539-06-1969 L1974 GS VS *020 †85

CAIMI, Paolo Fabrizio. ■ 44106 #231-03-2002 L2007 HO *012 †20

CAMASSO, Karen Ann. 11100 EUCLID AVE, HOSPITAL, DEPT OF PEDIATRI 44106 #041-13-1991 L1995 PD PE *040 †55

CARR, Cassandra Lee. ■ 44106 #038-06-1999 PTH *100

CARRENO, Mar. ■ 44106 #847-11-1992 L1999 *100

CARTER, Jeffrey Walstrom. ■ 44106 #035-06-2007 L2007 GS *012

CATANZARO, Jason Robert. ■ 44118 #041-13-2008 *012

CATTON, Alexander Josef. ■ 44118 #016-11-2005 L2005 AN *012

CHAN, Eric Jonathan. ■ 44118 #038-44-2006 L2006 IM *012

CHANDRA, Sunandana. ■ 44118 #025-12-2008 *012

CHANG, Peter Chung-Wen. ■ 44118 #065-06-2004 L2004 NEP *012 †20

CHEN, Michael Roy. ■ 44118 #016-06-2004 L2004 ORS *012

CHEN, Yongjin. 10900 EUCLID AVE, DEPT OF FAMILY MEDICINE 44106 #243-47-1990 L2006 FPG *020

CHOWDHURY, Punam. ■ 44118 #010-03-2004 L2004 IM *020 †20

CHUNG, Elizabeth Soohee L. ■ 44118 #038-06-2008 *012

CLEMENT, Patrick Anthony. 2862 BERKSHIRE RD 44118 #038-41-1958 L1958 FM *071

COLOMBI, Benedict Joseph. 11100 EUCLID AVE, UNIVERSITY HOSPITALS OF CL 44106 #038-06-1968 L1968 NS *020 †25

CONNOR, Michael Joseph, Jr. ■ 44118 #012-01-2003 L2007 MPD *100 †55

COP, Vladislav. 5 SEVERANCE CIR, STE 215 44118 #957-01-1959 L1969 GP *071

CREAMER, Johnbuck Daniel. ■ 44118 #038-06-2006 L2006 IM *012

CUMMING, Wm Stevenson. ■ 44118 #038-06-1956 L1956 IM NEP *020

CUMMINGS, Linda C. 11100 EUCLID AVE, DIV OF GASTROENTEROLOGY 44106 #028-02-2001 L2005 GE *012 †20

CUTTLER, Leona. 2101 ADELBERT RD, RM 790 44106 #067-01-1975 L1990 PDE *050 †55

DAVIS, Ira David. 11100 EUCLID AVE, STE 787 44106 #026-04-1984 L1986 PN PD *020 †55

DE JESUS, Aurora T. 10 SEVERANCE CIR 44118 #748-01-1962 L1973 PD PM *020 †55

DEMEL, Karin Petra. 10 SEVERANCE CIR, STE 2H 44118 #038-41-1992 L2001 CD *020 †20

DESCHENES, Geoffrey Ronal. ■ 44106 #041-02-2005 L2005 OTO *012

DEVERA, Wylie Craig. ■ 44106 #005-12-2007 L2007 GS *012

D'HUE, Joel Oliver. 5 SEVERANCE CIR, STE 401 44118 #012-05-1976 L1977 OTO *020 †45

DILLARD, Peter Harrison S. ■ 44118 #035-03-1977 L1981 OM EM *020 †70

DININNY, David R. 11100 EUCLID AVE, UNIVERSITY HOSPITALS 44118 #038-06-1988 L1990 CCA *020 †05

DISCOLO, Christopher M. ■ 44121 #035-08-1999 L1999 OTO *020 †45

DOUMIT, Jhony Youssef. ■ 44118 #605-01-2001 L2002 GE *012 †20

DUGAN, Mark Christopher. ■ 44106 #003-01-2008 *012

DUMFORD, Donald Marvin, III. ■ 44106 #038-45-2006 L2006 IM *012

EGAR, John Wells. ■ 44118 #038-06-1989 L2005 IM *012

EINSTEIN, Douglas Bennett. 11100 EUCLID AVE, ONCOLOGY, LERNER B-181 44106 #035-46-1996 L2001 RO *020 †80

EL-TOUKHY, Essam Ali. 2107 COVENTRY RD 44118 #915-02-1989 *100

EROKWU-MBANEFO, Evelyn. 5 SEVERANCE CIR STE 514 44118 #038-41-1980 L1982 IM *020 †20

EUBANKS, Jason David. 11100 EUCLID AVE 44106 #038-06-2003 L2003 ORS *012

EVEC, Adam D. 11100 EUCLID AVE, DEPARTMENT OF ANESTHESIOLO 44106 #028-78-2003, ▲ L2003 AN *020

EWALD, Sabrina. ■ 44118 #038-41-1995 L1996 PD *100

FAIRLEY, Jessica Kathleen. ■ 44118 #010-02-2003 L2007 ID *012 †55

FARROW, Lutul Dashaun. ■ 44118 #038-06-2002 L2002 GS *100

FERNANDES, Timothy Martin. 3522 MONTICELLO BLVD 44121 #038-41-2006 L2006 IM *012

FERNANDO, Josephine. 10 SEVERANCE CIR, KAISER PERMANENTE 44118 #495-42-1968 L1976 EM IM *020 †16

FIRDAUS, Rashda. 5 SEVERANCE CIR, STE 207 44118 #704-01-1973 L1979 DR *020

FITZGERALD, Steven John. ■ 44121 #021-01-2004 L2004 ORS *012

FLYCKT, Rebecca Lynn. ■ 44118 #038-06-2006 L2006 OBG *012

FORCIER, Beverly C. ■ 44106 #051-01-1982 L1985 OPH *071 †35

FOSTER, Charles Bartlett. ■ 44118 #038-06-1991 L2006 PDI *020 †55

FRIEDMAN, Daniel. ■ 44106 #038-06-2003 L2007 N *100

FUKUHARA, Toru. ■ 44118 #572-09-1989 L1999 NS *100

GAGE, Earl Anthony, Jr. ■ 44118 #048-12-2001 L2007 PS *012 †85

GAJEWSKI, Timothy C. 10 SEVERANCE CIR, CLEVELAND HTS MEDICAL CENT 44118 #065-05-1985 L1992 ORS *020 †40

GARCIA, Reinaldo Naveiro. ■ 44118 #264-04-1996 L2005 PG *020 †55

GARTRELL, Benjamin Adam. ■ 44106 #016-06-2005 L2005 IM *012

GEELAN-HANSEN, Katie R. ■ 44118 #018-03-2005 L2005 OTO *012

GEHANI, Neal Chandurpal. ■ 44118 #035-03-2007 L2007 OTO *012

GEORGE, Craig Rudolph. 10701 EAST BLVD, DEPARTMENT OF RADIOLOGY 44106 #038-40-1974 L1974 DR *020 †80

GEORGES, George Chukri. ■ 44121 #605-01-1990 L1993 PUD *020 †20

GETTY, Patrick John. 11100 EUCLID AVE, DEPT OF ORTHOPAEDICS/5043 44106 #016-02-1991 L1999 ORS *012 †20

GIBBS, Melonie C. 10 SEVERANCE CIR 44118 #038-06-1979 L1979 OBG *020 †30

GILLESPIE, Robert James. ■ 44118 #041-02-2005 L2005 ORS *012

GILPIN, David Allen. ■ 44118 #047-06-2006 L2006 OTO *012

GOEL, Rishi Kumar. ■ 44118 #010-01-2003 L2003 NS *012

GOEL, Sachin Sudhir Kumar. ■ 44118 #496-38-2003 L2005 IM *012 †20

GOLDBERG, Brian Keith. ■ 44106 #035-19-2003 L2007 PM *100

GOMES, Amanda Melissa. ■ 44106 #028-34-2008 *012

GOOMBER, Roger. ■ 44118 #038-43-2007 L2007 AN *012

GORDON, Julian Allan. 14100 CEDAR RD, STE 130 44121 #023-01-1970 L1977 U *020 †95

GORDON, Zachary L. ■ 44106 #038-06-2007 L2007 ORS *012

GOTHE, Barbara. ■ 44118 #407-24-1964 L1978 PUD IM *071 †20

GOYAL, Monisha. 11100 EUCLID AVE, MAILSTOP 6090 44106 #001-02-1991 L1998 CHN *020 †55,75

GRASS, Jeffrey Albert. 11100 EUCLID AVE, DEPT OFANESTHESIOLOGY 44106 #050-02-1986 L1994 AN *020 †05

GRAYSON, Patricia S. 10 SEVERANCE CIR 44118 #038-40-1974 L1975 IM *020

GREEN, Albert Michael. 10 SEVERANCE CIR, OHIO KAISER-PERMANENTE MED 44118 #035-09-1979 L1984 PTH OBG *020 †30

GREENBERG, Lior Jacob. ■ 44118 #550-03-2002 L2007 ID *012

GREENSPAN, Sammy Anna. ■ 44106 #035-08-1986 L1992 PD *020 †55

GRISWOLD, Katherine Jane. ■ 44106 #016-06-2006 L2006 PD *012

GUERCH, Meziane Abdeslam. 2300 OVERLOOK RD, APT 420 44106 #125-01-1987 L2004 N *012

GUERRA, Lazaro. ■ 44121 #270-01-1971 L1974 ORS *075

GULATI, Alka Kumari. ■ 44118 #038-44-2005 L2005 PD *012

HACKER, Lisa Marie. 11100 EUCLID AVE, RM 3018 44106 #665-01-2001 L2001 CCA *100 †05

HADISANTOSO, Antonius S. 50 SEVERANCE CIR 44118 #506-05-1974 L1981 OBG *020 †30

HALDAR, Saptarsi. 2103 CORNELL RD, WOLSTEIN RES BLDG RM 4-525 44106 #023-07-2000 L2006 CD *050 †20

HANOUNEH, Ibrahim. ■ 44118 #875-03-2003 L2007 IM *012

HARRIS, Frederick David. 5 SEVERANCE CIR, STE 505 44118 #038-06-1985 L1985 IM *020 †20

HARRIS-HAYWOOD, Sonja M. 11100 EUCLID AVE, 1200 BOLWELL HEALTH CENTER 44106 #033-05-1997 L2004 FM *020 †18

HART, Jane Lee. ■ 44118 #038-06-1993 L1996 IM *071 †20

HARTH, Karem Clementina. ■ 44106 #035-48-2006 L2006 GS *012

HARTMAN, Herbert A III. ■ 44118 #030-05-2006 L2006 IM *012

HDEIB, Alia Mousa. ■ 44118 #023-07-2006 L2006 NS *012

HEIMANN, Brent Richard. ■ 44106 #056-05-2006 L2006 IM *012

HEJAL, Rana Bashir. 11100 EUCLID AVE, AND CRITICAL CARE MEDICINE 44106 #605-01-1988 L1992 PUD *020 †20

HEKMAN, James Michael. 10 SEVERANCE CIR, KAISER PERMANENTE 44118 #016-02-2000 L2006 IM *020 †20

HENRY, Lilia Margaret. 10 SEVERANCE CIR # 802 44118 #038-06-1994 L1995 IM *020 †20

HILL, James Adam. ■ 44118 #005-12-2005 L2005 PD *012

HOWEY, Jill Lynn. ■ 44121 #025-12-2003 L2003 CCP *012 †55

HUBBARD, Matthew Owen. ■ 44118 #035-45-2006 L2006 GS *012

INGELMO, Christopher Pere. ■ 44106 #016-06-2004 L2007 IM *100

INTZES, Stefanos. ■ 44106 #063-01-2004 L2007 PHO *012 †55

JAKOB, Harriet Anne. 10 SEVERANCE CIR 44118 #038-40-1990 L1994 IM *020 †20

JAKOB, Herbert Gerhard. ■ 44118 #038-40-1956 L1956 GS *071 †85

JAMES, Alvin Curtis. ■ 44118 #028-02-2007 L2007 EM *012

JARCHOW, Andrea Marie. ■ 44121 #036-08-2004 L2004 OTO *012

JASPER, John Jay. 11100 EUCLID AVE, DEPT OF SURGERY 44106 #026-04-1996 L1998 GS *020 †85

JAWAS, Ali Mohammed. ■ 44118 #539-06-1991 GS *100

JEFFERY, Annita Nikole. ■ 44118 #038-06-2008 *012

JIN, Zhuo. ■ 44106 #038-41-2004 L2004 GS *012

JUSKENAS, Nellie K. ■ 44118 #616-01-1943 L1956 AN *071 †05

KAHRIMAN, Mustafa. 10701 EAST BLVD, MED CTR, NEUROLOGY MAIL ST 44106 #902-22-1988 L2003 N CN *020 †75

KALE, Parag P. 11100 EUCLID AVE, HEALTH SYSTEM 44106 #496-38-1989 L1996 **CD** *020 †20

KANG, David Eugene. ■ 44121 #036-07-2007 L2007 **GS** *012

KAPLAN, Ludmila Nikolaevn. 5 SEVERANCE CIR STE 304, 5 44118 #913-39-1985 L2001 **IM** *020 †20

KARIMLOO, Zahra. 11100 EUCLID AVE, UNIVERSITY HOSPITALS CASE 44106 #517-10-2002 L2004 **VIR** *100

KATZ, Daniel E. ■ 44106 #038-06-1988 L1991 **PTH DR** *075 †50

KATZ, Leonard Gerson. 5 SEVERANCE CIR STE 410 44118 #038-40-1957 L1957 **D** *020

KEILER, Louis Charles, III. ■ 44106 #011-06-2003 L2004 **RO** *012

KELLON, Donald James. 2124 LAMBERTON RD 44118 #038-40-1956 L1956 **P** *030 †75

KESSLER, Margaret Ann. ■ 44118 #038-44-2005 L2005 **D** *012

KHOSLA, Arjun. ■ 44106 #038-06-2008 *012

KIM, Jenny Jiyun. 2660 EUCLID HEIGHTS BLVD, STE 208W 44106 #005-06-2004 L2007 **HO** *012 †20

KIM, Karen Chunguhn. ■ 44106 #005-11-2005 L2005 **IM** *012

KIM, Paul Keetae. ■ 44121 #027-01-2001 L2007 **NS** *100

KIM, Yuli Young. ■ 44106 #051-01-2001 L2005 **CD** *012 †20

KING, Charles Harding. ■ 44118 #035-08-1978 L1982 **IM ID** *050 †20

KIRBY, Karen Clarice. 3309 WASHINGTON BLVD 44118 #010-03-1994 L2000 *020

KIRILMAZ, Ata. 12479 CEDAR RD 44106 #902-22-1989 **ICE** *100

KLEIN, Nina Louise. 11100 EUCLID AVE, CLEVELAND 44106 #038-06-1988 L1990 **DR** *020 †80

KNAUSS, Thomas Clayton. 10701 EAST BLVD, MEDICAL CENTER 44106 #025-01-1976 L1985 **NEP IM** *050 †20

KO, Alvin Bryant. ■ 44118 #041-12-2005 L2005 **OTO** *012

KO, Timothy Yeetak. 11100 EUCLID AVE 44106 #038-44-2003 L2003 **PMM** *012

KOON, Henry B, Jr. ■ 44106 #027-01-1994 L2002 **IM** *020 †20

KRAAY, Matthew Jos. 11100 EUCLID AVE, DEPT OF ORTHOPAEDICS 44106 #025-07-1983 L1984 **ORS** *020 †40

KRAJEWSKI, Colleen Michel. ■ 44118 #041-12-2007 L2007 **OBG** *012

KRAUSE, Franklin Danl. 5 SEVERANCE CIR STE 808, ARTS BLDG. 44118 #035-45-1963 L1966 **IM PUD** *020 †20

KRUITHOFF, Keith Leonard. 10 SEVERANCE CIR 44118 #024-16-1989 L1994 **CD** *020 †20

KUHN, Matthew Thomas. ■ 44121 #038-43-2004 L2004 **PTH** *012

KUSUMA, Shashidhar. ■ 44118 #012-01-1998 L2004 **OTO** *100 †45,65

LAI, Thomas Tze Jen. 11100 EUCLID AVE, DEPT OF PEDIATRICS/DIV OF 44106 #024-05-2003 L2006 **NPM** *012 †55

LANGLIE, Jean Karen. 10 SEVERANCE CIR 44118 #038-06-1984 L1986 **IM** *020 †20

LASS, Jonathan Hershel. 11100 EUCLID AVE, D 44106 #024-05-1973 L1979 **OPH** *030 †35

LAVOIE-L'ALLIER, Philippe. ■ 44118 #067-06-1992 L2000 *100

LAZEBNIK, Noam. 11100 EUCLID AVE, AVE, (MAC-5034) 44106 #550-02-1975 L1988 **OBG** *020 †19

LEE, Debra Pinkston. ■ 44118 #041-01-2005 L2005 **PD** *012

LEIZMAN, Debra Sue. 11100 EUCLID AVE, UNIVERSITY HOSPITAL 44106 #038-41-1987 L1988 **IM** *020 †20

LEONARD, Ethan Gabriel. 11100 EUCLID AVE RM 487, PEDIATRIC INFECTIOUS DISEA 44106 #038-06-1996 L1997 **PDI** *020 †55

LESNEFSKY, Edward Jos, Jr. 10701 EAST BLVD, LOUIS STOKES CLEVELAND VAM 44106 #056-05-1981 L1990 **CD IM** *020 †20

LEUKHARDT, William Herman. ■ 44118 #038-43-2006 L2006 **GS** *012

LEVIN, Trevor Z. 3101 MAYFIELD RD 44118 #836-01-1983 L1995 **GP PM** *020 †60

LIGHTBODY, Richard Alden. 2264 N SAINT JAMES PKWY, SIDE ENTRANCE 44106 #038-06-1977 L1978 **P N** *050 †75

LIGON, Antonio Ramon Chan. ■ 44118 #748-01-2002 L2005 **IM** *012

LIPSCOMBE, Jennifer Bridg. ■ 44118 #067-01-1996 L2004 *020

LI PUMA, Joseph Peter. 11100 EUCLID AVE, DEPT OF RADIOLOGY 44106 #035-15-1974 L1975 **DR VIR** *020 †80

LO, Kar-Ming. ■ 44118 #038-44-1996 L2004 **PCC** *020 †20

LUBIN, Jeffrey Scott. 11100 EUCLID AVE, BOLWELL 3700 44106 #033-06-1998 L2004 **EM** *020 †16

LUBITZ, Deborah Sue. 3811 KIRKWOOD RD 44121 #012-05-1983 L1989 **PD EM** *020 †55

LUDERS, Hans. 11100 EUCLID AVE, UNIV HOSPS DEPT OF NEU 44106 #231-03-1966 L1979 **N** *030 †75

LYNN, David. ■ 44121 #035-45-1989 L1992 **MPD** *020 †55,20

MACKEL, Audley M, III. 5 SEVERANCE CIR STE 609 44118 #047-07-1981 L1988 **ORS** *020 †40

MACKLEY, Heath Brandon. ■ 44121 #041-01-2002 L2002 **RO** *100

MAHANNA, Elizabeth Brady. ■ 44106 #048-12-2007 L2007 **GS** *012

MANSOUR, John Souheil. ■ 44106 #038-06-2006 L2006 **IM** *012

MARIAPPURAM, Valsamma J. 10 SEVERANCE CIR 44118 #495-80-1978 L1991 **IM** *020 †20

MARTIN, Charles, III. ■ 44118 #038-06-2003 L2003 **DR** *012

MARTIN, Patricia Margaret. 2460 FAIRMOUNT BLVD # 302 44106 #143-03-1970 L1974 **PYA P** *020 †75

MATHEW, Raichal Thomas. 10 SEVERANCE CIR 44118 #495-31-1977 L1984 **PD** *020 †55

MATHIS, Laura Marie. ■ 44118 #017-20-2006 L2006 **D** *012

MATTEOTTI, Ronald. ■ 44118 #869-01-1994 L2006 **GS** *012

MAYUGA, Kenneth Aguilar. ■ 44118 #016-11-2005 L2005 **IM** *012

MC CANDLESS, Shawn Edward. 11100 EUCLID AVE, LAKESIDE 1500 44106 #041-13-1988 L1998 **MG CBG** *050 †19,55

MCCORMICK, Nicole Catheri. ■ 44106 #008-02-2007 L2007 **OTO** *012

MC EWEN, Ewen Currier. ■ 44118 #038-06-1980 L1981 **EM** *020 †16

MC GEE, Michael Francis. ■ 44106 #041-15-2003 L2003 **GS** *012

MC INTYRE, Patrick James. 11100 EUCLID AVE, DIVISION OF PAIN MEDICINE 44106 #038-41-2001 L2001 **AN** *100 †05

MC KINLEY, Yvonne Hurt. 50 SEVERANCE CIR, DEPT OF DERMATOLOGY 44118 #020-12-1993 L1997 **D** *020

MCVOY, Molly Kathleen. 11100 EUCLID AVE 44106 #038-41-2005 L2005 **P** *012

MEDOF, Melvin Edward. 2085 ADELBERT RD, CASE WESTERN UNIV 44106 #005-06-1969 L1985 **RHU IM** *050 †20

MEEK, Lisa Elain. 2905 E OVERLOOK RD 44118 #038-40-1985 L1989 **IMG IM** *020 †20

MELTON-MEAUX, Genevieve B. ■ 44106 #023-07-2000 L2007 **CRS** *012 †85

MENON, Aiyappan. 10 SEVERANCE CIR 44118 #495-75-1983 L1991 **NEP** *020 †20

MENYAH, Daniel Kingsford. 5 SEVERANCE CIR STE 709 44118 #412-01-1972 L1978 **IM** *020 †20

MERCADO-DEAN, Maria-G. 11100 EUCLID AVE, RM B937 44106 #042-01-1982 L2005 **PDR PD** *040 †55,80

MESSERSCHMITT, Patrick Ja. ■ 44118 #038-41-2005 L2005 **ORS** *012

MIDAMBA, Fatuma Nabuti. 5 SEVERANCE CIR STE 304 44118 #902-19-1992 L1997 **IM** *020 †20

MILLER, Martha Jane. 11100 EUCLID AVE, HOSPITAL 44106 #005-06-1977 L1982 **NPM PD** *020 †55

MILLER, Sanford Allen. 5 SEVERANCE CIR, STE 510 44118 #038-41-1969 L1969 **NEP OS** *020 †20

MILLET, Dan. 50 SEVERANCE CIR 44118 #550-01-1971 L1978 **OTO** *020

MITCHELL, Jamie Canders. ■ 44112 #010-02-2000 L2007 **GS** *020 †85

MOHAN, Sanjay Ram. ■ 44118 #041-14-2004 L2004 **IM** *100

MOON, Michael. ■ 44106 #062-01-1997 L2005 *100

MORAN, Timothy John. ■ 44121 #026-04-2004 L2004 **AN** *012

MORI, Ryan Lee. ■ 44118 #041-12-2007 L2007 **GS** *012

MOSS, Milton Jay. 10 SEVERANCE CIR 44118 #038-06-1960 L1960 **ORS** *071 †40

MOSTOW, Ann Baskiewicz. 10 SEVERANCE CIR 44118 #038-06-1979 L1980 **CD IM** *020 †20

MUNYON, Charles Nelson. ■ 44106 #041-01-2007 L2007 **GS** *012

NAGAIAH, Govardhanan. 11100 EUCLID AVE, HARVEY HOUSE 44106 #495-66-1996 L2006 **IM** *020 †20

NAKAMOTO, Dean Akira. 11100 EUCLID AVE, DEPT OF RADIOLOGY 44106 #038-06-1987 L1987 **R** *020 †80

NAZ, Sofia Yusuf. ■ 44118 #917-24-2001 L2004 **AN** *012

NEELEY, Maya Kamath. ■ 44121 #011-02-2003 L2003 **PD** *020

NEUHAUSER, Elinor Toaz. ■ 44118 #035-20-1965 L1980 **PHP PD** *072

NICHOLSON, Oscar, Jr. 5 SEVERANCE CIR, STE 215 44118 #041-12-1986 L1988 **GS EM** *020 †85

NOWICKI, Edward Richard. ■ 44106 #041-02-1966 L1967 **TS TRS** *020 †85,90

OKADA, Haruko Catherine. ■ 44106 #038-06-2008 *012

OLDENBURG, Frederick P. ■ 44118 #038-06-2002 L2002 **ORS** *012

OMAR, Omar Adel. 10701 EAST BLVD, LOUIS STOKES CLEVELAND VA 44106 #915-04-1994 L2000 **AN** *020 †05

ONWUZULIKE, Kaine Chamber. ■ 44118 #038-06-2006 **NS** *012

OWEN, Virginia L. ■ 44118 #038-06-1950 L1950 **PD** *071

PACKER, Sam. ■ 44118 #038-06-1950 L1950 **OS GS** *071 †85

PADRINO, Susan Leonor. 11100 EUCLID AVE, HPV 5080 44106 #023-01-1999 L2004 **OS** *100

PAI, Aarthi Ajith. ■ 44118 #038-43-2004 L2004 **PDP** *012

PATEL, Rishi Rajnikant. ■ 44118 #038-06-2003 **D** *012

PEATROSS, Tracey Kim. 1667 IVYDALE RD 44118 #038-06-1997 L1999 **OBG** *020 †30

PERERA, Ganesha Boniface. ■ 44118 #041-15-2000 L2006 **VS** *012 †85

PEREZ, Alejandro. ■ 44118 #035-46-2005 L2005 **D** *012

PERSONS, Marjie Lynn. 11100 EUCLID AVE, UNIV HOSPITALS OF CLEVELAN 44106 #035-15-1980 L1988 **GS** *020 †85

PETERSILGE, William John. 11100 EUCLID AVE, DEPARTMENT OF 44106 #038-40-1987 L1989 **ORS OAR** *020 †40

PETERSON, Frank R, II. 2200 SURREY ST 44106 #038-45-1988 L1995 **AN** *075

PEYTON-COOK, Jacqueline. 5 SEVERANCE CIR, STE 401 44118 #038-06-1983 L1987 **OBG** *020 †30

PLAS, Jeffrey Chas. 10701 EAST BLVD, DEPT. OF VETERANS AFFAIRS 44106 #038-44-1986 L1987 **P** *020 †75

POMPILI, Vincent John. 11100 EUCLID AVE, DIV OF CARDIOVASCULAR MEDI 44106 #038-06-1988 L1999 **CD IM** *020 †20

POONYAGARIYAGORN, Hataya. ■ 44118 #035-46-2005 L2005 **IM** *012

POWELL, Gregory Scott. 11100 EUCLID AVE ML3313, WEARN 247 44106 #035-03-2000 L2000 **GE** *020 †20

PREBIS, James Wm. 11100 EUCLID AVE, DIVISION OF NEPHROLOGY 44106 #020-12-1973 L1992 **PN PD** *020 †20

QUANG, Larry S. 11100 EUCLID AVE, DIV OF PEDIATIC PHARMACOLO 44106 #038-44-1995 L2003 **PEM** *100 †55

RAJ MOHAN, Paspulati. 11100 EUCLID AVE, BOLWELL HEALTH CENTER #260 44106 #495-21-1982 L2002 *020

RANDA, Jessica Helena. ■ 44118 #038-06-2008 **IM** *012

REEG, Rachel Dickhoff. ■ 44118 #054-04-2005 L2005 **IM** *012

REINER, Neil Eugene. 2577 OVERLOOK RD 44106 #038-06-1974 L1977 **ID IM** *040 †20

ROBINSON, Shenandoah. 11100 EUCLID AVE, CASE WESTERN RESERVE UNIV 44106 #016-06-1991 L1999 **NS** *020 †25

ROSE, Jerri Anne. ■ 44118 #047-06-2003 L2003 **PEM** *012 †55

ROSE, Johnie. ■ 44118 #047-06-2003 L2003 **IM** *100

ROSENBERG, Paul Haim. 50 SEVERANCE CIR, 3RD FLOOR ADMINISTRATION 44118 #067-01-1971 L1977 **IM ID** *020 †20

ROSNECK, James Thomas. ■ 44121 #038-45-2002 L2002 **ORS** *012

ROSS, Allison Clare. ■ 44112 #041-12-2002 L2002 **PDI** *012 †55

ROY, Anita. ■ 44118 #038-40-2006 L2006 **PD** *012

RYDER, Stephen Woodbury. 9051 CEDAR AVE, EMERGENCY SERVICES DEPARTM 44106 #038-06-1975 L1978 **EM IM** *020 †20

SAADEH, Wasim. 10 SEVERANCE CIR 44118 #875-01-1990 L1998 **PD** *020 †55

SACHDEVA, Mandi Popovich. ■ 44118 #038-40-2004 L2004 **D** *012

SACHS, Peter Bell. 11100 EUCLID AVE, UNIV HOSPS OF CLEVELAND 44106 #024-01-1983 L1986 **DR IM** *020 †20,80

SACKMAN, Vernon Eugene. 10 SEVERANCE CIR 44118 #028-03-1973 L1975 **D** *020 †15

SAMPLINER, John W. 10701 EAST BLVD, VETERANS AFFAIRS MEDICAL C 44106 #038-06-1974 L1978 **DR** *020 †80

SANDHAUS, Linda M. 11100 EUCLID AVE, HOSPITALS OF CLEVELAND 44106 #035-19-1978 L1995 **PTH HEM** *020 †50

SARAN, Avtar Singh. 10 SEVERANCE CIR, KAISER PERMANETE 44118 #495-03-1972 L1977 **P** *020 †75

SATYAPRIYA, Anand Aditya. ■ 44106 #038-06-2007 L2007 **AN** *012

SCALZI, Lisabeth Victoria. 11100 EUCLID AVE STE 504, HOSPIAL 44106 #035-03-1994 L2002 **RHU** *020 †20,55

SCHEID, Andrea Theresa. ■ 44118 #025-07-2007 L2007 **PD** *012

SCHER, Mark Steven. 11100 EUCLID AVE, DEPT OF PEDIATRIC NEUROLOG 44106 #035-08-1976 L1997 **CHN PD** *050 †75,55

SCHULTZ, Brett Alison. ■ 44118 #028-78-2005, ▲ L2005 **OBG** *012

SCHWACHTER, Marc. ■ 44106 #038-06-1997 L2001 **OBG** *020

SELMAN, Warren Richard. 11100 EUCLID AVE, DEPARTMENT OF NEUROSURGERY 44106 #038-06-1977 L1978 **NS GS** *020 †25

SERRET, Marc Anthony. ■ 44118 #056-04-2005 L2005 **PS** *012

SETH, Rahul. ■ 44106 #035-45-2006 L2006 **OTO** *012

SETO, Robert Scott. ■ 44118 #041-09-1972 L1974 **TS** *071

SHAH, Sejal H. ■ 44118 #016-06-2005 L2005 **PD** *012

SHANDS, Philip Ronald. 10 SEVERANCE CIR, KAISER PERMANENTE 44118 #038-40-1984 L1985 OPH *020 †35

SHENK, Robert Ritchie. 11100 EUCLID AVE, UNIV HOSPITALS 44106 #038-06-1978 L1979 GS *020 †85

SHER, Andrew Craig. ■ 44106 #038-06-2007 L2007 IM *012

SHETH, Sandeep Madhusudan. 11100 EUCLID AVE, HP-2 44106 #038-44-2001 L2001 CHP *020

SHIPCHANDLER, Taha Zoher. ■ 44106 #017-20-2003 L2003 OTO *012

SHUFFER, Phillip Michael. 10 SEVERANCE CIR, KAISER PERMANENTE 44118 #030-06-1988 L1996 OBG *020 †30

SLEPIAN, Jacob Zeiger. 5 SEVERANCE CIR, STE 304 44118 #561-01-1968 L2005 OTO A *020 †45

SMITH, Curtis West. 5 SEVERANCE CIR, STE 304 44118 #038-06-1977 L1982 ORS *020

SMITH, David Mathias. 44121 #035-09-2007 L2007 GS *012

SOADWA, Kakra Achiaa. ■ 44118 #041-12-2008 *012

SOUSA, Consuelo Maria. ■ 44118 #010-03-1958 L1965 PD PHP *071 †55

SPECH, Richard Alan. 5 SEVERANCE CIR STE 510 44118 #038-40-1988 L1994 NEP *020 †20

SPLICHAL, Katherine Mary. ■ 44121 #037-01-2008 *012

SPRECHER, Robert Carroll. 11100 EUCLID AVE, PEDIATRIC OTOLARYNGOLOGY 44106 #011-03-1989 L1995 OTO *020 †45

STEFFEE, William Pierce. ■ 44106 #041-01-1961 L1981 NTR IM *071 †20

STEGMOYER, Robert John. 10 SEVERANCE CIR 44118 #041-14-1981 L1985 OTO *020 †45

STEINHILBER, Richard M. ■ 44118 #041-09-1945 L1945 P *071 †75

STEPHENS, Susan Ellen. 5 SEVERANCE CIR, STE 609 44118 #041-01-1986 L1987 GS ORS *020 †40

STEPHENS, Timothy L, Jr. 5 SEVERANCE CIR 44118 #010-03-1961 L1965 ORS *071 †40

STERNS, Jordan Ben. ■ 44118 #028-34-1991 L1992 RO *012

STICKNEY, Carolyn Ann. ■ 44118 #038-06-2004 L2004 MPD *012

STORMORKEN, Anne G. 3100 COLERIDGE RD, UNIVERSITY HOSPITALS OF CL 44118 #061-01-1988 L1998 CCP *020 †55

STRAINIC, James Paul. ■ 44118 #038-41-2002 L2003 PDC *012

SU, Dennis Lien-Hsun. ■ 44106 #422-01-2002 L2007 VS *012 †85

SUBRAMANIAN, Vairavan Sar. ■ 44121 #040-04-2005 L2005 U *012

SUNG, Joanne Jooyeon. ■ 44106 #035-19-2005 L2006 D *012

SWARTZ, Edina Cseh. ■ 44118 #045-04-2002 L2006 AI *100 †20,03

TAN, Chee-Kiat. ■ 44118 #825-01-1984 HEM *100

TANAGHO, Youssef Samir. ■ 44118 #032-01-2005 L2005 U *012

TEN, Irina Sergejevna. 11100 EUCLID AVE, DEPT OF PEDIATRICS 44106 #913-32-1997 L2004 CCP *100 †55

THOMSON, Jodi Michelle. ■ 44118 #038-06-2008 *012

TICHAVAKUNDA, Akari. 3486 MAYFIELD RD 44118 #038-41-1987 L1993 PD *020

TIMOFTE, Irina Liliana. 13951 TERRACE RD, HURON HOSPITAL 44112 #781-01-2003 L2004 IM *100 †20

TINMAN, Daniel Phineas. 2656 HAMPSHIRE RD, CLEVELAND HEIGHTS 44106 #041-07-1975 L1976 OM *020 †70

TOMFORD, J Walton. 3145 FAIRMOUNT BLVD 44118 #023-07-1975 L1977 ID *020 †20

TORRES, Alexander. ■ 44118 #665-02-2004 L2007 RHU *012

TROWBRIDGE, Victoria M. ■ 44118 #038-06-1981 L1982 OBG *075

TUCKER, Howard Jerome. 5 SEVERANCE CIR, STE 304 44118 #038-40-1947 L1947 N CHN *071 †75

TUCKER, Sara Ethel Siegel. ■ 44118 #035-01-1958 L1959 PYA P *020 †75

VAKIL, Nakul. ■ 44106 #035-48-2006 L2006 S *012

VAN HEECKEREN, Willem Jan. ■ 44121 #038-06-2002 L2003 HO *100

VISIONI, Anthony James. ■ 44118 #035-08-2008 *012

VOGT, Beth Ann. 11100 EUCLID AVE, RAINBOW BABIES&CHILDRENS H 44106 #041-12-1988 L1994 PN *020 †55

VOLTZ, Donald Michael. 11100 EUCLID AVE, DEPT OF ANESTHESIA 44106 #056-05-1996 L1999 AN *020 †05

VRICELLA, Gino Joseph. ■ 44118 #028-03-2006 L2006 GS *012

VRICELLA, Laura Kathryn. ■ 44118 #028-03-2006 L2006 OBG *012

VROOMAN, Bruce Martin. ■ 44106 #051-07-2003 L2007 PMM *012

VU, Hongha Thi. ■ 44118 #028-02-2007 L2007 IM *012

WALDO, Albert Leon. 11100 EUCLID AVE, UNIV HOSP CASE MEDICAL CEN 44106 #035-08-1962 L1986 CD IM *050 †20

WALDRON, Sean Robert. ■ 44121 #033-06-2005 L2005 ORS *012

WALKER, Chrisopher Adam. ■ 44106 #038-06-2007 L2007 IM *012

WALLACE, David. 2220 WOODMERE DR 44106 #047-07-1952 L1957 GYN *071

WALTER, Benjamin Lee. 2331 S OVERLOOK RD 44106 #041-15-1999 L2004 N *020 †75

WANG, Yiping. 10 SEVERANCE CIR, OHIO PERMANENTE MEDICAL GR 44118 #243-03-1990 L1999 IM *020 †20

WANG-PETERMAN, Jenny Jing. ■ 44106 #038-06-2008 *012

WARMAN, Matthew Lloyd. 10900 EUCLID AVE, CASE WESTERN RESERVE UNIV 44106 #035-20-1982 L1995 OS PD *050 †55,19

WASON, Irwin Thomas. 50 SEVERANCE CIR 44118 #209-01-1957 L1970 OBG *071 †30

WATTERS, R Brad. 10 SEVERANCE CIR, OHIO PERMANENTE MEDICAL GR 44118 #038-06-1979 L1982 IM *020 †20

WEBSTER, Leslie T, Jr. ■ 44106 #024-01-1948 L1955 PA *050 †20

WEHRUM, Paul A. 5 SEVERANCE CIR STE 7, SEVERANCE MED ART BLDG 44118 #005-15-1962 L1975 *071

WEINBERGER, Bradley Charl. ■ 44118 #028-02-2005 L2005 PD *012

WEISS, Amanda Kay. 11100 EUCLID AVE, UNIVERSITY HOSP. OF CLEVEL 44106 #010-01-1997 L2003 FSM *020 †55

WIEDER, William Thos. 10 SEVERANCE CIR 44118 #041-12-1968 L1972 PD *020 †55

WILLIAMS, Erin Scott. ■ 44118 #048-14-2005 L2005 AN *012

WILLIAMS, George W. ■ 44118 #048-04-2005 L2005 AN *012

WOOD, John Holmes. 10 SEVERANCE CIR 44118 #065-09-1987 L1994 ORS *020 †40

YBARRA, Juan Munoz. ■ 44106 #847-12-1989 END *012

YEANEY, Natalie Krista. 11100 EUCLID AVE, MAILSTOP 6010 44106 #041-02-1995 L1998 NPM *020 †55

YOHANN, Molly Mc Mahon. 11100 EUCLID AVE, DEPT OF RADIOLOGY / BSH 50 44106 #038-06-1993 L1997 DR *020 †80

YONG-SENG, Tan. ■ 44118 #825-01-1984 TS *020

YOO, Estelle Sukyung. ■ 44118 #048-06-2007 L2007 GS *012

YOUNG, Benjamin Patrick. 3793 MONTEVISTA RD 44121 #038-06-2004 L2006 PCC *012

ZAGAR, Timothy Michael. ■ 44106 #035-47-2006 L2007 RO *012

ZEIN, Claudia Ortiz. 10701 EAST BLVD, GI SECTION, 111E(W) 44106 #308-02-1993 L2002 GE *020 †20 ‡

ZETS, Andrea S. 10 SEVERANCE CIR 44118 #038-44-1989 L1991 PD *020 †55

ZOLTANSKI, Joan Margaret. ■ 44118 #038-06-2003 L2003 CCP *012

CLEVES – HAMILTON

BURWINKEL, Mary Margaret. ■ 45002 #038-41-1981 L1982 FM *020

BUSCHUR, Michael Everett. ■ 45002 #038-06-2006 L2006 IM *012

CLIFTON – GREENE

POTTS, Rebecca Elizabeth. ■ 45316 #038-45-1992 L1994 IM *020 †20

CLINTON – SUMMIT

DUNHAM, Victor Edward. ■ 44216 #038-44-1985 L1986 FM EM *071 †18

JOURDEN, Michael John. ■ 44216 #038-06-2008 *012

ORLANDI, Marc Anthony. ■ 44216 #038-44-1991 L1992 AN *020 †05

PATEL, Roma Chandrakant. ■ 44216 #038-45-2001 L2001 AN *020

SU, Shwu Jen. ■ 44216 #244-04-1972 L1977 GP *020

CLOVERDALE – PUTNAM

BURGEI, Teresa Jean. ■ 45827 #038-44-2008 *012

KLIR, Wesley Adam. ■ 45827 #038-06-1997 L1998 FM *020 †18

SCHROEDER, Jennifer Renee. ■ 45827 #038-45-2008 *012

CLYDE – SANDUSKY

AONA, Francis Keamakui. 819 N MAIN ST 43410 #014-01-1984 L1985 FM *020 †18

BROWN, Jennifer Lynn. 455 W MCPHERSON HWY 43410 #038-45-2005 PD *012

FANNING, James Edward. 509 W MCPHERSON HWY, STE A 43410 #038-40-1993 L1994 HO *020 †20

GRAHAM, Susan Joy. 402 W MCPHERSON HWY 43410 #065-10-1983 L1994 GP *020

HOHMAN, Jennifer G. 420 W MCPHERSON HWY, STE D 43410 #038-44-1998 L1999 FM *020 †18

LAWRENCE, Elbert David. 420 W MCPHERSON HWY 43410 #005-06-1956 L1975 GS *071

LOBINS, Raymond L. 509 W MCPHERSON HWY, STE A 43410 #018-75-2000, ▲ L2006 HO *020 †20 ‡

REEVES, Robert S, Jr. 420 W MCPHERSON HWY 43410 #038-43-1981 L1984 FM OBG *075 †18

ROSHON, Steven Gale. 509 W MCPHERSON HWY, STE A 43410 #038-40-1978 L1979 ON IM *020 †20

COAL GROVE – LAWRENCE

TSAI, Peter. 205 MARION PIKE 45638 #001-02-1998 L2004 GP FM *020

TSAI, Tahsiung. 205 MARION PIKE 45638 #385-04-1966 L2006 GYN *030 †30

COLDWATER – MERCER

ALBERS, Robert Wm. 407 S OAK ST, COLDWATER MEDICAL INC 45828 #038-41-1959 L1959 FM *071

FISHBEIN, Donn S. 800 W MAIN ST 45828 #041-02-1981 L1991 PTH EM *020 †50

HEINRICHS, Timothy Arnold. 407 S OAK ST 45828 #038-45-1986 L1987 FM FOP *020 †18

KNAPSCHAEFER, Gina Marie. ■ 45828 #038-40-2006 L2006 PD *012

LEE, Lisa Jeewon. 800 W MAIN ST 45828 #038-43-1995 L2001 DR *020 †80

NAVEAU, John Jos. 407 S OAK ST, COLDWATER MED INC 45828 #038-40-1980 L1981 FM *020 †18

NEELATI, Venkatarao. 800 W MAIN ST 45828 #495-58-1983 L1995 AN *020 †05

PENNINGTON, Cecil Eugene. ■ 45828 #020-02-1958 L1959 AN FM *071 †18

RANGA, Puttagunta. 800 W MAIN ST 45828 #495-50-1973 L1980 CD IM *020 †20

COLUMBIA STATION – LORAIN

JOHNSTON, Kent Harry. ■ 44028 #024-01-1961 L1963 GS TTS *071 †85

COLUMBIANA – COLUMBIANA

AMORN, Melissa Marie. ■ 44408 #038-44-2006 L2006 OTO *012

AMORN, Y. ■ 44408 #891-01-1970 L1975 GE DIA *020 †20

CROWL, Lori Anne. 258 STATE ROUTE 14, STE A 44408 #038-44-1995 L1997 FM *020 †18

EVANS, Mark Howard. 258 STATE ROUTE 14, STE A 44408 #038-06-1980 L1987 FM *020 †18

GOIST, Kevin Joseph. ■ 44408 #055-01-2007 L2007 IM *012

MASHBURN, Medford Benny. 913 STATE ROUTE 46 44408 #038-44-1997 L1999 FM *020 †18

COLUMBUS – DELAWARE

ABELLA, Antonio Rosa. ■ 43240 #748-01-1968 L1973 GP *020

AKUSOBA, Arinze Echezona. ■ 43240 #308-11-1999 L2006 IM *020 †20

AYERS, Leona Bell Weston. 2001 POLARIS PKWY, RM 2046 43240 #036-07-1967 L1969 CLP ATP *040 †50

AZIZ, Haroon Akhtar. 1120 POLARIS PKWY, STE 120 43240 #704-01-1970 L1977 PS HS *020 †65,85

BASTON, Catherine Flickin. ■ 43240 #045-04-2006 L2006 OPH *012

BOYLE, Sandra Lee Tabor. 8947 ANTARES AVE 43240 #055-02-1983 L1985 PD *020 †55

CARR, Richard Dean. 1080 POLARIS PKWY, CENTER FOR SURGICAL DERMAT 43240 #038-40-1954 L1954 **D IM** *071 †20,15 ‡

CORRADINE-TORRES, Martha. 1120 POLARIS PKWY 43240 #264-05-1988 L1997 **IM** *020 †20

DESHPANDE, Kedar Krishna. 1080 POLARIS PKWY, STE 200 43240 #654-01-1998 L2000 **PM** *020 †60

GIRAGOS, Jumana Camille. 8947 ANTARES AVE 43240 #036-01-1998 L2001 **PD** *020 †55

HILL, Joshua Hayden. ■ 43240 #038-45-2003 L2003 **GS** *012

PATEL, Chandrahas Bhagubh. ■ 43240 #759-12-2001 L2006 **TS** *012

RAY, S A. 1070 POLARIS PKWY, STE 120 43240 #017-20-1986 L1989 **IM** *020 †20

SCHWAAB, Jillian Leigh. ■ 43240 #056-06-2004 L2005 **EM** *012

TOLANI, Olugbenga Felix. 1120 POLARIS PKWY, STE 210 43240 #690-02-1990 L2004 **IM** *020

COLUMBUS – FRANKLIN

ABDEL-RAHMAN, Mohamed Hel. 410 W 10TH AVE 43210 #915-02-1990 L2004 *020

ABEREGG, Scott K. 473 W 12TH AVE, 201 DAVIS HEART LUNG RESEA 43210 #038-40-1998 L2005 **PCC** *100 †20

ABIB, Mohamed H. 2415 DEEWOOD DR STE B 43229 #830-01-1980 L2000 **FM** *020 †18

ABRAHAM, William Tober. 473 W 12TH AVE RM 110P, DIV OF CV MED 43210 #024-01-1986 L1997 **CD IM** *020 †20

ABRAMOVITZ, Fred Martin. 6100 E MAIN ST, STE 101 43213 #038-40-1973 L1973 **OBG** *020 †30

ABRAMS, Kamilah Marie. 4480 REFUGEE RD, STE 120 43232 #038-44-2003 L2003 **FM** *020 †18

ABRAMS, Kristen Kamille. 1670 UPHAM DR 43210 #005-12-2004 L2004 **P** *012

ACCETTA, Peter Anthony. 3535 OLENTANGY RIVER RD 43214 #038-41-1979 L1985 **PTH** *020 †50

ACHENBACH, Sarah Elizabet. 370 W 9TH AVE, 200A MEILING HALL 43210 #038-40-2006 L2006 **OBG** *012

ADAMO, James Paul. 3545 OLENTANGY RIVER RD, RR 201 43214 #016-11-1984 L1986 **PUD CCM** *020 †20

ADAMS, Anna Marie. 410 W 10TH AVE 43210 #038-40-1981 *020

ADAMS, Van Lee. ■ 43230 #055-02-2005 L2005 **MPD** *012

ADAMSON, Wallace Cobner. 4278 INDIANOLA AVE 43214 #038-40-1982 L1983 **FM OS** *020 †18

ADENUGA, Olufemi Michael. 793 W STATE ST 43222 #690-01-2001 L2006 **IM** *012

ADKINS, Justin Gregory. ■ 43215 #055-02-2008 *012

ADLER, Brent Hale. 700 CHILDRENS DR, DEPT OF RADIOLOGY 43205 #025-01-1989 L1997 **PDR** *020 †80

ADMANE, Vaishali Shailesh. 793 W STATE ST, MT CARMEL MED CTR 43222 #496-53-1997 L2004 **IM** *100

ADRION, William Robt. 2514 SUMMIT ST 43202 #038-40-1963 L1963 **FM LM** *020 †18

ADVANI, Sunil. 473 W 12TH AVE, STE 200 43210 #038-40-1999 L2000 **IC** *012 †20,55

AFSHAR, Farhad. 410 W 10TH AVE, DEPT SURG 43210 #917-25-1967 L1984 **NS** *100

AFZAL, Syed Mujtiba. 410 W 10TH AVE 43210 #704-02-1987 L2005 **FP** *012

AGABALYAN, Bela. 1301 N HIGH ST 43201 #913-38-1973 L1992 **CHP IM** *020

AGARWAL, Anil Kumar. 1654 UPHAM DR, NEPHROLOGY 43210 #496-10-1980 L1994 **NEP** *040 †20

AGIUS, Lawrence M. ■ 43220 #627-01-1975 L1985 **PTH N** *020 †50

AGNESE, Doreen Marie. 410 W 10TH AVE 43210 #033-06-1993 L2001 **GS** *020 †85

AGNONE, Charlotte Marie. 111 S GRANT AVE 43215 #038-40-1990 L1991 **OPH** *020 †35

AGRA, Anthony Dean. 51 S SOUDER AVE, FIRST FLOOR 43222 #038-45-1995 L1997 **NEP** *020 †20

AGRAWAL, Amit. 456 W 10TH AVE STE 4A 43210 #016-06-1993 L1998 **OTO HNS** *020 †45

AGUILAR, Pedro Soberanis. 285 E STATE ST, STE 515 43215 #649-06-1972 L1981 **CRS GS** *020 †10,85

AGUILERA-BARRANTES, Irene. 410 W 10TH AVE, OH STATE UNIV HOSP 43210 #270-02-1999 L2004 **PTH** *012

AGUIRRE, Augusto. 3535 OLENTANGY RIVER RD, LABORATORY DEPARTMENT 43214 #264-06-1962 L1968 **CLP PTH** *071 †50

AHARONY, Lea. 410 W 10TH AVE 43210 #550-03-1984 **FM** *020

AHMAD, Mohammad. 1615 FISHINGER RD 43221 #704-09-1970 L1994 **IM** *020 †20 ‡

AHMED, Mohammed I. 1430 S HIGH ST, MEDICAL ARTS BLDG 43207 #495-65-1983 L1992 **IM** *020 †20

AHMED, Nasra Mohamed Haji. 2231 N HIGH ST, RARDIN FAMILY 43201 #561-17-1996 L2005 **FP** *012

AHMED, Rownak. 1301 N HIGH ST 43201 #160-01-1984 L1998 **P** *020

AHSAN, Abul Kalam Mohamma. 456 W 10TH AVE, 4510 CRAMBLETT HALL 43210 #160-04-1995 L2004 **IMG** *012

AKHTAR, Muhammad N. 2440 DAWNLIGHT AVE, ROSEMONT CENTER 43211 #704-02-1985 L1999 **CHP PD** *020 †75

AKIN, Emin Baris. 1375 PERRY ST, C/O OSU HOSPS-MED EDU DEPT 43201 #902-03-1995 L2001 *100

AKUSOBA, Martin O. 1990 HARMON AVE, CORRECTIONS MEDICAL CENTER 43223 #690-04-1983 L1994 **IM** *020 †20

ALASYALI, Evsen. 16 W LONG ST, SOUTH EAST, INC 43215 #902-03-1972 L1997 **P** *020

ALBARRACIN, Narciso S, Jr. 1087 DENNISON AVE, 1ST FL 43201 #748-02-1960 L1972 **PTH HEM** *071 †50

ALBERT, Nick Charles. 370 S 5TH ST, STE 612/512 43215 #038-40-1962 L1962 **FM GP** *071

AL-DAHHAK, Roula. 1087 DENNISON AVE 43201 #875-01-1993 L2001 **N** *020 †75

ALDRICH, William Thos, Jr. 793 W STATE ST 43222 #005-12-1974 L1976 **P** *075

ALDRINK, Jennifer Hall. ■ 43206 #036-08-2000 L2007 **PDS** *012 †85

ALEXANDER, Jeffrey Lodge. 793 W STATE ST, MOB #3 43222 #055-02-2002 L2003 **P** *020

ALEXIS, Thomas Ray. 4310 CLIME RD N, STE B 43228 #038-40-1974 L1974 **IM** *020 †20

ALGHOTHANI, Nora. ■ 43220 #038-40-2008 *012

ALI, Mohamed Bushaala. ■ 43235 #613-01-1977 L1985 **ID HEM** *020 †20

ALI, Naeem Akhtar. 473 W 12TH AVE 43210 #038-40-1996 L1997 **PCC SME** *050 †20

ALI, Rehan Husain. 285 E STATE ST STE 670, GRANT MED CTR 43215 #661-02-2002 L2006 **FP** *012

ALKHOURY, Razan. 579 S YEARLING RD, CHILDREN CLOSE TOHOME 43213 #875-01-1983 L1994 **PD** *020 †55

ALLAMAN, Aimee Ann. ■ 43201 #038-45-2005 L2005 **IM** *100

ALLEN, David E. 6164 CLEVELAND AVE, REHABILITATION CARE GROUP 43231 #038-45-1983 L1984 **EM IM** *020

ALLEN, Elizabeth D. 700 CHILDRENS DR 43205 #038-40-1985 L1987 **PDP PD** *020 †55

ALLEN, Hugh D. 700 CHILDRENS DR 43205 #038-41-1966 L1966 **PDC** *020 †55

ALLEN, Jacinda Marie. 3555 OLENTANGY RIVER RD, STE 1080 43214 #038-45-2002 L2002 **IM** *020

ALLEN, James N, Jr. 473 W 12TH AVE, 201 HEART LUNG INSTITUTE 43210 #038-40-1984 L1988 **PUD CCM** *040 †20

ALLEN, John Geoffrey. 3535 OLENTANGY RIVER RD, STE 5310 43214 #038-40-1986 L1988 **OPH** *020 †35

ALLEN, Steven Jeffrey. 700 CHILDRENS DR, COLUMBUS CHILDREN'S HOSP 43205 #048-02-1977 L2007 **CCA AN** *020 †05

ALLENBY, Patricia Ann. 6001 E BROAD ST 43213 #016-06-1983 L1988 **PTH** *020 †50

ALLENIUS, Arnold O. 1020 DENNISON AVE 43201 #041-77-1960, ▲ L1961 **GP** *071

ALMONEY, Robert Wilson, Jr. 3535 OLENTANGY RIVER RD 43214 #038-40-1966 L1966 **END IM** *020 †20

ALPERT, Seth Adam. 555 S 18TH ST, STE 6D 43205 #010-01-1997 L2005 **U** *020 †95

ALSABUR, Idris Kazeem. 391 WOODLAND AVE, 4850 EAST MAIN STREET 43203 #038-40-2004 L2005 **FM** *100

ALTMAN, Jerold Henry. 785 E BROAD ST 43205 #038-41-1963 L1963 **P** *020

ALTURA, Rachel Allison. 700 CHILDRENS DR, HEMATOLOGY/ONCOLOGY 43205 #028-02-1992 L1999 **PHO** *020 †55

AMANN, Corey Michael. ■ 43204 #038-45-2006 L2006 **FP** *012

AMIGO, Roger G. 5131 BEACON HILL RD, STE 220 43228 #038-75-1989, ▲ L1990 **U** *020

AMIN, Anish Krupesh. ■ 43201 #038-40-2006 L2006 **IM** *012

AMIR, Muhammad Wasif. 3525 OLENTANGY RIVER RD, STE 4330 43214 #704-01-1993 L2004 **IM** *100 †20

AMMIRATI, Mario Pio A B D. ■ 43210 #561-10-1977 L2005 **NS** *020 †25

AMPONSAH, Akua Abrafi. 700 CHILDRENS DR, AMBULATORY SERVICES 43205 #025-07-2003 L2007 **PD** *100

AMR, Khaled Labib. 700 CHILDRENS DR 43205 #915-04-1986 L2005 **PAN** *020 ‡

ANANTH, Uma. 4845 KNIGHTSBRIDGE BLVD, STE 220 43214 #495-83-1975 L1990 **OBG** *020 †30

ANDERSON, Bernadette Rose. 6096 E MAIN ST, STE 102 43213 #038-43-2000 L2000 **FM** *020 †18 ‡

ANDERSON, Clark Lawrence. 480 W 9TH AVE RM 2054, DIV OF IMMUNOLOGY 43210 #016-02-1964 L1986 **IG IM** *050

ANDERSON, Craig Warren. 285 E STATE ST, STE 520 43215 #038-40-1976 L1976 **NPM PD** *020 †55

ANDERSON, Kevin James. 7630 RIVERS EDGE DR 43235 #038-40-1987 L1989 **IM** *020 †20

ANDERSON, Samuel Ray. 500 THOMAS LN STE 3G, TALLO & ASSOCS 43214 #038-41-1997 L2002 **END** *020 †20

ANDERSON, Wendy Kathleen. 700 CHILDRENS DR, AMBULATORY PEDIATRICS 43205 #010-03-1997 L2000 **PD** *020 †55

ANDREONI, Kenneth A. 1654 UPHAM DR # 361, OHIO STATE UNIV MED CTR 43210 #008-01-1988 L1996 **GS TTS** *020 †85

ANDREWS, Heather Fallon. ■ 43220 #038-44-2006 L2006 **OBG** *012

ANDREWS, Madeleine Jean. 1631 NW PROFESSIONAL PLZ, STE 107 43220 #038-40-1980 L1980 **AN** *020 †05

ANDREWS, Martin John. 1110 BEECHER XING N, STE B 43230 #056-06-1990 L1995 **PME AN** *020 †05

ANDRITSOS, Michael James. 410 W 10TH AVE, N416 43210 #048-15-1999 L2006 **AN** *020 †05

ANGELOS, Mark Gus. 1654 UPHAM DR 43210 #049-01-1982 L1983 **EM CCM** *050 †16

ANGOURAS, Dimitrios. 1375 PERRY ST RM 5, CO OSU HOSPS-MED EDU DEPT 43201 #418-01-1990 L2000 *100

ANNINGER, William Victor. 1375 PERRY ST, CO OSU HOSPS-CORP CRED OFC 43201 #032-01-2001 L2002 **OPH** *100 †35

ANNIS, Christopher Michae. ■ 43228 #016-11-2006 L2006 **AN** *012

ANNIS, Christy Lynn. ■ 43228 #016-11-2006 L2006 **EM** *012

ANSEL, Ann Zoretic. 3535 OLENTANGY RIVER RD 43214 #038-43-1988 L1990 **D** *020 †15

ANTENUCCI, John F. 6001 E BROAD ST, MT CARMEL E HOSPITAL 43213 #038-75-1985, ▲ L1986 **AN** *020 †05

ANTONOPLOS, Anthony Peter. ■ 43204 #038-41-2002 L2002 **DR** *020 †80

APSELOFF, Glen. 5084 GRAVES HALL, OHIO STATE UNIVERSITY 43210 #038-40-1986 L1987 **OBG** *020

ARAUJO, Julio Cesar. 370 W 9TH AVE, OH STATE U COLL OF MED 43210 #038-40-2000 L2003 **NEP** *100 †20

ARCE, Erick A. 931 CHATHAM LN, NEUROLOGICAL ASSOCIATES, I 43221 #409-15-1990 L1998 **N** *020 †75

ARCHIBALD, Sarah Elizabet. 700 CHILDRENS DR, UNIV OF WA SOM GME RM C212 43205 #054-04-2002 L2002 **PD** *020 †55

ARCINIEGA, Juan Carlos. ■ 43215 #935-04-2004 *100

AREHART, Patrice Torres. 543 TAYLOR AVE 43203 #308-01-1979 L1987 **P** *030

ARGUS, Michael Brandon. 1654 UPHAM DR, 167 MEANS HALL 43210 #038-41-2002 L2002 **EM** *020 †16

ARING, Ann Marie. 697 THOMAS LN, RIVERSIDE FAM PRACTICE 43214 #038-40-1993 L1994 **FM** *020 †18

ARMEN, Scott Bradley. 321 MARSHALL PSGE, 1654 UPHAM DRIVE 43215 #038-40-2000 L2000 **CCS** *100 †85 ‡

ARNETT, Amy Michele. 700 CHILDRENS DR, CHILDRENS HOSPITAL-EMERGEN 43205 #038-41-1989 L2001 **PEM** *020 †55

ARNETT, Shalin E. ■ 43221 #028-78-2006, ▲ L2006 *012

ARNOLD, John H. 3525 OLENTANGY RIVER RD, STE 5320 43214 #038-40-1986 L1994 **TS CCS** *020 †85,90

ARNOLD, Mark Wm. 410 W 10TH AVE # N737 43210 #035-19-1983 L1988 **CRS** *020 †10,85

ARORA, Amit. 3535 OLENTANGY RIVER RD, MED ED DEPT 43214 #038-44-2005 L2005 **GS** *012

ARORA, Samir. 99 N BRICE RD, STE 260 43213 #495-37-1991 L2001 **FM** *020 †18

AROS, Brian Christopher. ■ 43221 #038-40-2001 L2007 **OSM** *012

ARROYO-SCOTOLIFF, H A. 2643 SUMMIT ST 43202 #847-10-1961 L1992 **PD** *020 †55

ARTHUR, Lindsay Grier, III. 700 CHILDRENS DR, ED 379 43205 #041-02-1998 L2004 **PDS** *100 †85

ARTMAN, Sarah Louise. 410 W 10TH AVE 43210 #038-40-1987 L1989 **OBG** *020 †30

ASADI MOGHADDAM, Kaveh. 2050 KENNY RD 43221 #409-20-2002 L2005 **NS** *012

ASHCRAFT, Cregg Duaine. 410 W 10TH AVE 43210 #017-20-1996 L1998 **MPD** *020 †20

ASHTON, Nicola Stuart. 4821 ROBERTS RD 43228 #005-12-1964 L1969 **GP** *071

ASIM, Saira. 3535 OLENTANGY RIVER RD 43214 #704-06-2005 L2007 **IM** *012

ASLO, Abdulkarim H. 1670 UPHAM DR, OSU HOSPS/PSYCHIATRY 43210 #781-01-1982 L2000 **P** *100

ASSOR, Dieter. 793 W STATE ST 43222 #407-07-1957 L1968 **PTH** *071 †50

ASTOR, Todd Loren. 700 CHILDRENS DR, PULMONARY MEDICINE 43205 #010-01-1997 L2004 PCC *100 †20

ASTUDILLO CORDOVA, Juan A. ■ 43228 #319-02-2003 L2005 GS *100

ATHENS, William John. ■ 43221 #041-77-1957, ▲ L1958 FM *071 †18

ATKIN, Joan F. 700 CHILDRENS DR 43205 #014-01-1978 L2001 CG OS *020 †55,19

ATTAMAN, Jill Amanda. ■ 43214 #025-12-2003 L2003 OBG *100

AUGOSTINI, Ralph Sayre. 473 W 12TH AVE STE 200, OSU DIV OF CARDIO MED 43210 #035-06-1990 L1999 ICE CD *020 †20

AUKERMAN, Glen Frederick. 2000 KENNY RD 43221 #038-40-1964 L1964 FM PHP *020 †18 ‡

AUSTIN, Kimberly Bradshaw. 793 W STATE ST, CO MT CARMEL MED CTR-MED E 43222 #055-02-2001 L2001 FM *020 †18

AVALOS, Belinda Rene. 2001 TREMONT RD 43221 #038-40-1980 L1981 HEM IM *020 †20

AWAN, Farrukh Tauseef. 410 W 10TH AVE, DIV OF HEMATOLOGY/ONCOLOGY 43210 #704-25-2001 L2006 HO *012 †20

AWAN, Hisham Muzaffar. ■ 43219 #025-07-2004 L2006 ORS *012

AYAD, Onsy S. 700 CHILDRENS DR 43205 #915-03-1984 L1998 CCP *020 †55

AYOUBI, Ali. ■ 43215 #017-20-2003 L2006 CD *012 †20

AYUB, Raheela. 793 W STATE ST, MT CARMEL MED CTR 43222 #704-09-1999 L2004 FM *100

AZIZ, Khwaja Abdul. PO BOX 20070 43220 #704-01-1954 L1975 IM CD *020

BACKES, Carl Hubert. ■ 43212 #038-45-2006 L2006 PD *012

BACKES, Floortje Antoinet. ■ 43221 #660-02-2004 L2005 OBG *012

BADGWELL, Brian Dean. 1654 UPHAM DR, 321 MEANS HALL 43210 #048-16-1999 L2000 GS *100 †85

BAEHR, Michael Chas. 535 OFFICENTER PL, STE A 43230 #038-40-1982 L1983 FM OS *020 †18 ‡

BAGENSTOSE, Abner Harvey. 4830 KNIGHTSBRIDGE BLVD 43214 #038-40-1974 L1974 AI IM †20,03

BAGENSTOSE, Scott Elder. 4830 KNIGHTSBRIDGE BLVD, STE C 43214 #038-41-1999 L2002 AI *020 †20,03

BAHNER, David Paul. 1654 UPHAM DR 43210 #038-41-1995 L1996 EM *020 †16

BAHNSON, Robert Roy. 456 W 10TH AVE, DIV OF UROLOGY 43210 #024-07-1979 L1996 U *020 †95

BAILEY, Shawn Carrol. 2975 DONNYLANE BLVD, COMMUNITY MEDICINE CLINIC 43235 #038-40-2001 L2001 IM *020

BAILY, William Blair. 79 E STATE ST 43215 #038-06-1935 L1936 CD GPM *075

BAIOCCHI, Robert Alan. 410 W 10TH AVE 43210 #038-40-1999 L2000 HO *100 †20

BAIRD, Ian Mc Nicoll. 3555 OLENTANGY RIVER RD, STE 3020 43214 #803-02-1969 L1973 ID IM *020 †20

BAIRD, James N, Jr. 3555 OLENTANGY RIVER RD, STE 3070 43214 #038-40-1966 L1966 MDM GYN *071 †30

BAIRD, Michael Alleyne. 410 W 10TH AVE, N201 DOAN HALL 43210 #038-40-1996 L1999 GE *020 †20

BAISDEN, Beth Ann. 285 E STATE ST, STE 520 43215 #012-01-1989 L2007 NPM *020 †55

BAKER, Kathryn Renee. 456 W 10TH AVE, OSU - 5251 CRAMBLETT HALL 43210 #047-20-2004 L2005 OPH *012

BAKER, Kenneth Weinrandow. 423 E TOWN ST, CAPITOL CITY CARDIOLOGY 43215 #011-02-1992 L1994 CD *020 †20

BAKER, Kristina J. 700 CHILDRENS DR, CHILDREN'S HOSPITAL, ED #2 43205 #038-45-2001 L2004 PEM *100 †55

BAKER, Norman Doug. 262 NEIL AVE, OPHTHALMIC SURGEONS & 43215 #038-40-1982 L1983 OPH *020 †35

BAKER, Norman Henry. 931 CHATHAM LN 43221 #038-40-1954 L1954 TS *071 †85,90

BAKER, Peter B, III. 700 CHILDRENS DR, COLUMBUS CHILDRENS HOSP 43205 #038-40-1978 L1979 PTH *020 †50

BAKKE, Andrew Lars. ■ 43214 #037-01-2006 L2007 EM *012

BAKKER, Richard Gerrit. ■ 43214 #055-01-2006 L2006 IM *012

BALALOSKI, Steven Petar. 4030 EASTON STA, STE 200 43219 #038-40-1993 L1994 OBG *020 †20

BALCERZAK, Stanley P, Jr. 410 W 10TH AVE, DIV HEMATOLOGY & ONCOLOGY 43210 #023-01-1955 L1955 ON HEM *071 †20

BALINT, Jane Penelope. 700 CHILDRENS DR, PEDIATRIC GASTROENTEROLOGY 43205 #035-03-1989 L1992 PG PD *020 †55

BALL, Alton Jacob, Jr. 2231 N HIGH ST 43201 #038-41-1977 L1984 FM OM *020 †18,70

BALL, Erin Elizabeth. ■ 43214 #038-40-2008 *012

BALTES, Edward Joseph. 1171 FAIRWAY BLVD, FAIRWAY FAMILY PHYSICIANS 43213 #038-40-1974 L1975 FM *020 †18

BALUCH, John David. 500 E MAIN ST STE 200 43215 #041-12-1984 L1993 U *020 †95

BAMBACH, Dennis Frank. 3555 OLENTANGY RIVER RD 43214 #038-40-1981 L1983 EM *020 †16

BANG, Michael E. 3525 OLENTANGY RIVER RD, STE 4330 43214 #035-15-2000 L2000 IM *100 †20

BANKS, Joseph Henry, Jr. 700 CHILDRENS DR 43205 #038-40-1965 L1965 PD *020 †55

BANSAL, Atul. 793 W STATE ST, CO MT CARMEL HLTH-MED EDU 43222 #654-01-2000 L2000 IM *100

BAPNA, Sumit. ■ 43235 #038-44-2003 L2003 OTO *012

BAPTISTA BAEZA, Jose L. 456 W 10TH AVE 43210 #847-04-1983 FM *020

BARBARA, David M, Jr. 2200 DORSET RD 43221 #020-12-1979 L2003 GS *020 †85

BARBOZA, Ricardo. 6200 CLEVELAND AVE, COLUMBUS RADIOLOGY CORP 43231 #737-06-1976 L1992 VIR GP *020 †80

BARDALES, Richard Mark. 423 E TOWN ST, STE 1000 43215 #041-14-1991 L1998 CD *020 †20

BARENDS, Fredrik Simon. ■ 43213 #660-04-1950 L1955 FM *071

BARKER, Raymond E. ■ 43221 #038-40-1953 L1953 CD IM *071 †20

BARKER, Samantha J. ■ 43214 #060-01-2001 L2006 DR *100

BARKER, William Dale. 4605 SAWMILL RD 43220 #038-40-1970 L1970 ORS *020 †40

BARNARD, John Allman, III. 700 CHILDRENS DR, WA 2011 43205 #027-01-1980 L2000 GE PD *020 †55

BARNES, Chadwick Edward. ■ 43210 #038-44-2006 L2006 IM *012

BARNES, Francis Edward J. 3360 TREMONT RD STE 2 43221 #065-06-1960 L1967 GS TRS *020 †85

BARNES, James Allen. 1560 S HIGH ST 43207 #038-40-1996 L1997 FM *020 †18

BARNES, James Erle. 3555 OLENTANGY BLVD 43214 #038-40-1955 L1955 NS *071 †25

BARNES, Sean Benjamin. 410 W 10TH AVE, OH STATE UNIV HOSP 43210 #038-44-2007 L2007 IM *012

BARNES-MULLETT, Carrie Je. 700 CHILDRENS DR 43205 #055-01-2003 L2003 PD *020 †55

BARNETT, Gary Edward. 410 W 10TH AVE, STE 310 43210 #035-03-1970 L1971 PTH *020 †50

BARNETT, George Wm. 270 S GRANT AVE 43215 #038-40-1978 L1980 FM IMG *020 †18

BARNEY, Vernon James. 111 S GRANT AVE, GRANT MEDICAL CENTER 43215 #034-01-1991 L1995 AN *020 †05

BARRESI, Vincent. 5975 E BROAD ST, STE 305 43213 #035-08-1965 L1979 CD IM *020 †20

BARRETT, Gregory Alan. 4885 OLENTANGY RIVER RD, RD 2-10 43214 #038-40-1978 L1978 PD *020 †55

BARRETT, Thomas William. 720 E BROAD ST 43215 #038-40-1996 L1997 IM *020 †20

BARSKY, Sanford Howard. 1645 NEIL AVE 43210 #041-12-1974 L2005 PTH *020 †50

BARSON, William Jos. 700 CHILDRENS DR 43205 #038-40-1975 L1975 PD ID *020 †55

BARTELS, Melissa Jean. 555 S 18TH ST, CHILDREN'S HOSPITAL 43205 #038-40-1999 L1999 PD *100 †55

BARTH, Rolf Frederick. 1645 NEIL AVE, 165 HAMILTON HALL-PATH DEP 43210 #035-01-1964 L1979 PTH OS *050 †50

BARTHOLOMEW, Dennis Wm. 700 CHILDRENS DR, CHILDREN'S HOSPITAL/TIMKEN 43205 #016-06-1980 L1998 PD *020 †55,19

BARTLEY, Robert Earl, III. 700 E BROAD ST, SPCLZD ORTHO & SPORT MED 43215 #041-01-1987 L1992 ORS *020 †40

BARTZ, John Kuonlet. ■ 43221 #008-01-1976 L1999 P CHP *071 †75

BARUA, Eric Amit. ■ 43206 #041-02-2005 L2006 AN *012

BARUA, Pierre Sumit. 3555 OLENTANGY RIVER RD, STE 1080 43214 #759-12-2000 L2002 IM *020 †20

BASARAN, Mehmet Gokhan. 5877 CLEVELAND AVE 43231 #012-05-1983 L1988 AI PDA *020 †55,03

BASOBAS, Liberato Batin. 1515 E BROAD ST 43205 #748-01-1957 L1978 P GP *020 †80

BATES, Barry Francis. 1430 S HIGH ST 43207 #025-01-1966 L1993 DR P *020 †80

BATES, Carlton Matthew. 700 CHILDRENS DR, W490 43205 #038-40-1991 L1992 PN *050 †55

BATES, David Gregory. 700 CHILDRENS DR 43205 #024-07-1986 L1998 PDR *020 †50

BATES, Kimberly Carter. 1609 NORTHWEST BLVD 43212 #038-40-1999 L2006 MPD *020 †20,55

BATES, William Jos. 1000 URLIN AVE STE 20 43212 #010-03-1973 L1974 P *020 †75

BATHINI, Deepika. 1492 E BROAD ST, WEST ANNEX MODULAR UNIT. 43205 #495-21-1996 L2008 IM *020 †20

BATISKY, Donald Lee. 700 CHILDRENS DR, CHILDREN HOSP 43205 #038-43-1987 L1988 PN *040 †55

BATLEY, Rosalind Jane. 700 CHILDRENS DR 43205 #038-40-1977 L1980 PM OS *020 †55,60

BATTERSON, Robert Edward. ■ 43220 #038-40-1954 L1954 PD *071 †55

BAUER, Constance J. 5200 W BROAD ST, CENTRAL OHIO RADIATION 43228 #038-40-1987 L1990 RO *020 †80

BAUER, Elizabeth Bromert. 700 CHILDRENS DR 43205 #030-05-2002 L2004 PD *100 †55

BAUER, Michael Shawn. ■ 43214 #030-05-2004 L2004 GS *012

BAUGH, David Leon. ■ 43201 #038-40-2008 *012

BAUGHMAN, Thomas Hugh. 1211 E WHITTIER ST 43206 #038-40-1982 L1984 GP LM *020

BAUJAN, Melissa Ann. 866 W BROAD ST 43222 #028-34-1993 L1996 RNR *020 †80

BAUM, Rebecca A. 700 CHILDRENS DR, TIMKEN HALL / 3C 43205 #041-01-1996 L2006 DBP *012 †55

BAUM, Walter. ■ 43209 #035-19-1943 L1950 IM *071

BAUMGARTNER, Richard L. 3400 KENNY RD 43221 #038-06-1958 L1958 P CHP *020

BAYOUMY, Mohamed S. 700 CHILDRENS DR, COLUMBUS CHILDREN'S HOSPIT 43205 #915-09-1985 L1999 PHO *020 †55

BAYTION, Michael Carlos. 370 W 9TH AVE, OH STATE U COLL OF MED 43210 #038-40-2003 GS *012

BAZELLA, Corinne Ann. 410 W 10TH AVE, MEANS HALL 5TH FLOOR 43210 #041-12-2004 L2004 OBG *012

BAZERBASHI, Marwan. 1430 S HIGH ST 43207 #875-01-1972 L1979 GS GP *020 †85

BEAN, Herbert Eugene. 3535 OLENTANGY RIVER RD 43214 #038-40-1955 L1955 AN *075

BEARD, Jennifer Kiko. 1975 GUILFORD RD 43221 #038-44-1997 L1998 IM *020 †20

BEATHLER, John E, Jr. 4825 KNIGHTSBRIDGE BLVD 43214 #038-45-1995 L1997 IM *020 †20

BEATTIE, James F, Jr. 750 MT CARMEL MALL, STE 100 43222 #038-40-1981 L1983 OBG *020 †30

BEAVER, Wayne Lee. 777 W STATE ST, STE 302 43222 #017-20-1968 L1979 CD IM *071 †20

BECHER, Brian Michael. 3545 OLENTANGY RIVER RD 43214 #016-11-1985 L1987 OBG *020

BECHTEL, Mark Allen. 5965 E BROAD ST, STE 290 43213 #017-20-1977 L1981 D *020 †15

BECK, Catherine Elizabeth. ■ 43214 #038-40-2008 *012

BECKER, Mark John. 5200 W BROAD ST, CENTRAL OHIO RADIATION 43228 #041-07-1989 L1994 RO *072 †80

BEDNAREK, Pavla. 793 W STATE ST, MT CARMEL HLTH SYS-MED ED 43222 #286-05-1991 L2001 IM *020 †20

BEEBE, Allan Carlisle. 479 PARSONS AVE 43215 #016-06-1983 L1989 OP ORS *020 †40

BEECH, Amy L. ■ 43209 #038-44-1990 L1994 PD *020

BEECH, Douglas Winston. 2740 E MAIN ST 43209 #038-44-1990 L1992 P *020 †75

BEERY, Paul Richard, II. ■ 43220 #038-40-1999 L2000 GS *020 †85

BEHNKE, Stephen James. 3525 OLENTANGY RIVER RD, STE 4330 43214 #020-02-2000 L2003 IM *100 †20

BEHRENDT, Nicholas John. 1654 UPHAM DR, OHIO STATE UNIV MED 43210 #030-05-2006 L2006 OBG *012

BEHRENS, Brent Conrad. 810 JASONWAY AVE, STE A 43214 #056-05-1976 L1985 ON IM *020 †20

BELFIORI, Philip Thos. ■ 43220 #056-05-1969 L1970 P *071

BELJIN, Milos. ■ 43222 #038-45-2006 L2006 IM *100

BELL, George Edwin. 111 S GRANT AVE 43215 #038-40-1947 L1947 OS IM *072

BELL, Jeffrey Geo. 500 THOMAS LN 43214 #038-40-1975 L1978 GO OBG *020 †30

BELLISARI, Gregory Ernest. ■ 43221 #038-40-2005 L2005 ORS *012

BENDRE, Pradnya Suhas. 700 CHILDRENS DR, CHILDREN'S HOSP 43205 #495-83-1989 L2002 *100

BENEDETTI, Constantino. 300 W 10TH AVE STE 51 43210 #561-17-1971 L1990 PLM AN *020

BENES, Susan Carleton. 262 NEIL AVE, STE 210 43215 #041-07-1975 L1981 OPH N *020 †35

BENJAMIN, David. 320 W 10TH AVE, DIV OF HEMATOLOGY/ONCOLOGY 43210 #550-01-1975 L1990 HEM ON *020

BENJAMIN, Mariam. 500 THOMAS LN, STE 3G 43214 #915-04-1993 L2007 IM *020 †20

BENNETT, Adrienne Louise. 456 W 10TH AVE, DEPT OF INTERNAL MEDICINE 43210 #008-01-1992 L2005 IM OS *020 †20

BENNETT, Anita Sofia. ■ 43220 #035-15-1990 L1994 IM *020

BENNETT, John David. 2240 N BANK DR, UPPR 43220 #038-40-1990 L1994 AN *020 †05

BENNETT, Robert Paul. 262 NEIL AVE, STE 320 43215 #038-40-1975 L1975 OPH *020 †35

BENNETT, William Fred. 410 W 10TH AVE, DEPT OF RADIOLOGY 43210 #038-40-1977 L1977 DR *020 †80

BEN-SHACHAR, Enbar. 1375 PERRY ST 5T, CO OSU HOSPS-MED EDU DEPT 43201 #550-01-1992 L2001 *100

BENSON, Ryo Eun-Choi. 5100 W BROAD ST 43228 #017-20-1987 L1990 **DR** *074 †80

BERAN, Leann Cari. 285 E STATE ST, STE 300 43215 #030-05-1999 L2004 **GS** *020 †85

BERAN, Matthew Craig. ■ 43219 #038-40-2006 L2006 **ORS** *012

BERARDUCCI, Albert L, Jr. 3535 OLENTANGY RIVER RD 43214 #035-19-1975 L1987 **N** *020 †75

BERG, Luciana Elisa. 641 N HIGH ST, APT 4 43215 #038-06-2001 L2004 **PD** *020 †55

BERGER, Bryan Kenneth. ■ 43201 #038-40-2007 L2007 **IM** *012

BERGER, Philip David. 1560 S HIGH ST 43207 #038-43-1996 L1998 **FM** *020 †18

BERGER, Stephen Miles. 745 W STATE ST, STE 600 43222 #035-01-1965 L1972 **CD IM** *071 †20

BERGESE, Sergio Daniel. 410 W 10TH AVE R 429, THE OHIO UNIV 43210 #132-02-1988 L1999 **AN** *020 †05

BERGGREN, Ronald Bernard. 3555 OLENTANGY BLVD 43214 #041-01-1957 L1965 **PS** *071 †85,65

BERHANE, Menna. 285 E STATE ST STE 6, EDUC DEPT 43215 #041-13-1998 L2006 **FP** *012

BERKMAN, Robert Allen. ■ 43209 #035-03-1972 L1980 **U** *071 †95

BERLET, Gregory Charles. 6200 CLEVELAND AVE 43231 #060-02-1992 L1999 **ORS** *020 †40

BERLINER, Scott Robt. 6001 E BROAD ST 43213 #038-40-1990 L1991 **AN PME** *020 †05

BERMUDEZ, Armand Anthony. 3535 OLENTANGY RIVER RD, STE 3070 43214 #038-45-1995 L1997 **IM** *020 †20

BERNACKI, Brad Lang. 370 W 9TH AVE, OH STATE U COLL OF MED 43210 #038-40-2000 L2000 **ORS** *020

BERSAGEL, Eric John. 793 W STATE ST 43222 #028-02-1985 L1986 **IM** *020

BERTANI, Leanne Mcdonald. 3535 OLENTANGY RIVER RD 43214 #038-40-1985 L1985 **FM** *020 †18

BESECKER, Beth Yvonne. 473 W 12TH AVE, 201 DHLRI 43210 #038-43-2001 L2001 **PCC** *100

BESNER, Gail Ellen. 555 S 18TH ST, CHILDRENS SURGICAL 43205 #038-41-1982 L1991 **PDS** *020 †20

BEST, James Leroy. 3535 OLENTANGY RIVER RD 43214 #038-41-1955 L1955 **AN** *071 †05

BEST, Thomas Michael. 2050 KENNY RD, FL 3 43221 #065-06-1988 L2005 **FM FSM** *020 †18

BESTER, Stefanie Riego. 700 CHILDRENS DR 43205 #038-40-2003 L2003 **PD** *020 †55

BETKERUR, Anupama Vasant. ■ 43220 #038-40-2005 L2005 **OPH** *012

BETTESWORTH, Jacob Gale. ■ 43212 #028-78-2007, ▲ L2007 **TY** *012

BETTS, Robert Kenneth. 793 W STATE ST 43222 #038-40-1986 L1987 **AN** *020 †05

BETZ, Melissa Lynn. 700 CHILDRENS DR 43205 #038-45-2006 L2006 **PD** *012

BEYER, John Baxter. 3974 KARL RD 43224 #038-40-1963 L1963 **GP IM** *020

BEYNEN, Agatha Sophia. 815 W BROAD ST 43222 #038-41-1997 L1998 **IM** *020 †20

BHALLA, Munish Kumar. ■ 43215 #665-01-2003 L2003 **IM** *020 †20

BHASIN, Romi. 5965 E BROAD ST, BLDG 5 43213 #035-48-1997 L2002 **END** *020 †20

BHATT, Nitin Yogendra. 473 W 12TH AVE, 201 HLRI 43210 #038-40-1995 L1997 **PCC** *020 †20

BHATT, Udayan Yogendra. 1654 UPHAM DR, NEPHROLOGY 43210 #038-40-1995 L1997 **NEP** *020 †20

BHETWAL, Narayan Prasad. 2231 N HIGH ST 43201 #704-15-1995 L2004 **FM** *020 †18

BIBER, Jennifer Lynn. ■ 43220 #038-40-2008 L2008 **PD** *012

BICKETT, Melissa Mae. ■ 43201 #038-40-2008 L2008 **IM** *012

BIELAWSKA, Iwona M. 700 CHILDRENS DR 43205 #759-09-1990 L2002 **AN** *020

BILLER, Elizabeth Ann. ■ 43230 #041-12-2006 L2006 **PTH** *012

BILLINGS, Charles Edgar. ■ 43212 #035-19-1953 L1958 **AM OM** *071 †70

BING, Arthur Gan Hok. 3600 OLENTANGY RIVER RD, STE 480 43214 #506-05-1963 L1973 **PS HS** *020 †65

BINKLEY, Philip Frederick. 473 W 12TH AVE, STE 110 43210 #038-40-1979 L1981 **CD IM** *050 †20

BINKOVITZ, Larry Alan. 700 CHILDRENS DR 43205 #038-40-1984 L1993 **DR OBG** *020 †80

BIRCK, Herbert Georg. 555 S 18TH ST STE 6B 43205 #407-10-1948 L1957 **PD** *020 †45

BIRINYI, Frank. 750 MOUNT CARMEL MALL 43222 #038-06-1983 L1985 **EM** *020 †16

BIRNBAUM, Brian Fredrick. 700 CHILDRENS DR, ED 650A 43205 #007-02-2006 L2006 **MPD** *012

BISCA, Basil V. ■ 43220 #035-09-1954 L1955 **OBG** *071 †30

BISHOP, Julie Young. 2050 KENNY RD, STE 3300 43221 #035-20-1997 L2000 **ORS** *020 †40

BISSELL, Michael Gilbert. 410 W 10TH AVE 43210 #005-11-1975 L1997 **CLP PHP** *030 †50

BISUTTI, Michelle Louise. ■ 43230 #654-01-2003 L2006 **ESM** *020

BITTNER, Stephen Jon. ■ 43214 #016-02-1973 L1975 **P** *020 †55,75

BLACK, Cynthia J. 6495 E BROAD ST 43213 #038-06-1988 L1989 **PD** *020 †55

BLACK, Joshua Dale. ■ 43220 #030-05-2007 L2007 **MPD** *012

BLACK, Richard Alan. 5151 REED RD, STE 128C 43220 #036-05-1978 L1994 **CHP OPH** *020 †35,75

BLACKBURN, Shelley Lynn. 4626 SAWMILL RD 43220 #038-40-1987 L1988 **FM** *020 †18

BLACKFORD, James Mitchell. ■ 43235 #038-40-1964 L1964 **TS CD** *071 †85,90

BLACKMAN, John David. 500 E MAIN ST, STE 100 43215 #033-06-1984 L1987 **END IM** *020

BLAIR, Charmaine Melissa. 3433 AGLER RD, STE 1100 43219 #038-40-1994 L1997 **IM** *020 †20

BLAIR, John Goldsberry. 111 S GRANT AVE 43215 #038-40-1992 L1994 **AN** *020 †05

BLAIR, Scott Cameron. 810 JASONWAY AVE, STE A 43214 #038-43-1986 L1992 **ON HEM** *020 †20

BLAKE, Kathleen Degroft. ■ 43221 #038-43-2004 L2004 **PD** *100 †55

BLAKE, Michael John. 6001 E BROAD ST 43213 #038-40-1984 L1986 **AN IM** *020 †20,05

BLAKE, Sarah E. 410 W 10TH AVE, MEDICAL CENTER 43210 #038-40-2001 L2001 **APM** *020

BLAKELY, Keith Allen. 6200 CLEVELAND AVE 43231 #038-41-1984 L1985 **FM** *020 †18

BLAKEMAN, Henry Clay, Jr. ■ 43201 #038-40-1980 L1981 *020

BLANCHONG, Carol Ann. 700 CHILDRENS DR 43205 #038-44-1993 L1994 **PHO** *020 †55

BLANK, Christopher W. 1161 BETHEL RD, STE 101 43220 #038-41-1991 L1994 **P** *030 †75

BLANK, Harley Myron. 5969 E BROAD ST STE 301 43213 #038-40-1964 L1964 **OBG** *020

BLAZEK, James Virgil. 3525 OLENTANGY RIVER RD, STE 5360 43214 #018-03-1956 L1967 **R NM** *071 †80,28

BLAZER, Kimberly Kay. ■ 43220 #038-40-2008 L2008 **PD** *012

BLINT, Andy Jay. ■ 43206 #056-06-2002 L2007 **ORS** *020

BLOCH, William Evan. 3555 OLENTANGY RIVER RD, STE 4020 43214 #016-42-1987 L2006 **U** *020 †95

BLOOD, Jeffrey Ray. 51 S SOUDER AVE, THIRD FLOOR 43222 #038-40-1980 L1981 **PM OM** *020 †60

BLOOMFIELD, Clara Derber. 320 W 10TH AVE, STE A455 43210 #016-02-1968 L1997 **ON IM** *050 †20

BLOOMFIELD, Ronald James. 745 W STATE ST, STE 610 43222 #038-41-1984 L1985 **IM** *020 †20

BLOOMSTON, Paul Mark. 410 W 10TH AVE, N924 DOAN HALL 43210 #011-04-1997 L2004 **GS** *020 †85

BLOSE, Ralph Dennis. 6075 E BROAD ST 43213 #038-40-1968 L1968 **OBG** *020 †30

BLOSSER, Thomas Laurence. 3311 TREMONT RD, STE 101 43221 #038-40-1981 L1982 **FM FSM** *020 †18

BLOSSOM, Geoffrey Barton. 3555 OLENTANGY RIVER RD, # 2070 43214 #038-43-1988 L1996 **TS VS** *020 †85,90

BLUM, Kristie. 320 W 10TH AVE, B324 STARLING LOVING HALL 43210 #011-02-1997 L2003 **HO IM** *020 †20

BLUM, William George, III. 310 W 10TH AVE, B310 STARLING LOVING HALL 43210 #012-01-1997 L2003 **HO IM** *020 †20

BLUMENFELD, Michael L. 456 W 10TH AVE, STE 2B 43210 #038-40-1985 L1986 **OBG** *020 †30

BLUMENKRANTZ, Miriam. 700 CHILDRENS DR 43205 #067-01-1994 L2003 **PP** *100

BOBBA, Sharda Karuturi. 393 E TOWN ST, STE 228 43215 #495-58-1970 L1980 **P** *020 †75

BOCK, Joseph John. 3535 OLENTANGY RIVER RD 43214 #038-40-1957 L1957 **HS ORS** *071 †40

BOES, Thomas Joseph. 3545 OLENTANGY RIVER RD, RIVERSIDE PULMONARY 43214 #038-40-1981 L1982 **PUD IM** *020 †20

BOESEL, Carl Press. 700 CHILDRENS DR 43205 #038-41-1966 L1966 **ATP NP** *020 †50

BOGUCKI, Benjamin Anthony. ■ 43201 #038-40-2008 L2008 *012

BOGUCKI, Jennifer Marie. ■ 43201 #038-40-2008 L2008 *012

BOHL, Robert Daniel. 750 MT CARMEL MALL, STE 350 43222 #038-06-1974 L1975 **U** *020 †95 ‡

BOHL, Robert Wm. ■ 43221 #038-40-1945 L1945 **IM CD** *071

BOKOR, Andrew Brian. 6100 E MAIN ST, STE 112 43213 #038-40-1992 L1995 **OBG** *020 †30

BOLES, E Thos, Jr. 700 CHILDRENS DR 43205 #024-01-1945 L1950 **PDS** *071 †85

BOLTON, Eileen Carol. 7400 HUNTINGTON PARK DR 43235 #038-41-1989 L1990 **PD** *020 †55

BOLZ, William Scott. 3555 OLENTANGY RIVER RD, STE 201 43214 #038-40-1964 L1964 **ORS** *020 †40

BOMBACH, Jaren Douglas. 1405 DUBLIN RD 43215 #038-40-1975 L1975 **ORS** *020 †40

BOMMARAJU, Kalki. ■ 43215 #038-40-2008 L2008 *012

BONA, Susan Jean. 410 W 10TH AVE DEPT PTH 43210 #038-40-1985 L1990 **DMP** *020 †50

BONSU, Bema K. 700 CHILDRENS DR, RM ED459 43205 #412-01-1990 L1999 **PD** *020 †55

BONTA, Joseph Anthony. 3555 OLENTANGY RIVER RD 43214 #035-20-1948 L1955 **GS OS** *071 †85

BONTA, Marco Jos. 3535 OLENTANGY RIVER RD, ATTN: OPERATING ROOM 43214 #038-43-1982 L1983 **VS GS** *020 †85

BONZA, Sarah Hope. 1495 VIRGINIA AVE 43212 #038-40-2004 L2004 **FM** *100

BOOK, Nicole Marie. ■ 43221 #038-43-2005 L2005 **OBG** *012

BOONE, Shelley Kay. 480 MEDICAL CENTER DR, OHIO STATE UNIVERSITY 43210 #041-12-2003 L2004 **PM** *020

BOPE, Edward Tharp. 797 THOMAS LN 43214 #038-40-1976 L1976 **FM** *020 †18

BORCHERS, Glen Gerard. 543 TAYLOR AVE 43203 #038-40-1990 L1991 **GE** *020 †20

BORCHERS, James Robert. 2050 KENNY RD 43221 #038-44-2000 L2000 **FSM** *020 †18 ‡

BORCHERS, Justine. 1601 W BROAD ST, COLUMBUS DEVELOPMENTAL CTR 43222 #016-06-1953 L1956 **PD** *020 †55

BORCHERS, Susan Denise. 7630 RIVERS EDGE DR 43235 #038-40-1990 L1991 **PUD IM** *020 †20

BORDERS, Robert W. ■ 43215 #019-02-1949 L1953 **AN** *071 †05

BORKOWSKI, Lisa Marie. 262 NEIL AVE, STE 220 43215 #025-12-1995 L2004 **OPH OS** *020 †35

BORLAND, Bryan L. ■ 43214 #038-41-2002 L2002 **DR** *100 †80

BORNMAN, Lynette Suzanne. 3535 OLENTANGY RIVER RD 43214 #038-06-1999 L2005 **PTH** *020 †50

BOSCHEE, Pamela F. ■ 43230 #037-01-1988 L2004 **FM** *100

BOSTER, Aaron Lee. 456 W 10TH AVE, STE 1C 43210 #038-41-2002 L2005 **OS** *012 †75

BOTIC, Zoran Bozidar. 2626 E BROAD ST 43209 #957-02-1974 L1983 **AN** *020 †05

BOTTI, Anne Mc Rae. ■ 43220 #010-01-1991 L2004 **PD** *012

BOUDINOT, Wanda C. 4885 OLENTANGY RIVER RD, STE E2-10 43214 #038-43-1985 L1987 **PD** *020 †55

BOUDOULAS, Olga. 4185 MUMFORD CT 43220 #418-02-1970 L1986 **D** *020 †15

BOUE, Daniel Robt. ■ 43235 #026-04-1991 L1997 **PTH PP** *020 †50

BOULTER, Daniel Jeffrey. ■ 43210 #038-40-2007 L2007 **TY** *012

BOUREKAS, Eric Christ. 1654 UPHAM DR, 623 MEANS HALL/RAD DEPT 43210 #038-41-1989 L1993 **RNR** *020 †80

BOURONCLE, Bertha Augusta. 320 W 10TH AVE, O.S.U. 43210 #737-01-1948 L1955 **HEM ON** *071

BOWDEN, Sasigarn A. 700 CHILDRENS DR, DIV OF ENDOCRINOLOGY 43205 #891-03-1990 L1998 **PDE** *020 †55

BOWEN, Jonathan Morris. ■ 43220 #038-40-2006 L2006 **EM** *012

BOWMAN, Mary Jo Alice. 700 CHILDRENS DR, HOSPITAL 43205 #056-06-1986 L1987 **PD PEM** *020 †55

BOWYER, Brian Lance. 480 MEDICAL CENTER DR, DODD HALL 43210 #038-40-1984 L1985 **PM PRS** *020 †60

BOYD, Andrew James. ■ 43229 #038-40-2005 L2005 **FP** *012

BOYD, Casey Allison. ■ 43201 #038-40-2008 L2008 *012

BOYLE, Brendan Michael. ■ 43228 #038-40-2004 L2004 **PG** *012 †55

BOYLE, Elizabeth Ann. ■ 43204 #038-40-2008 L2008 *012

BOYLE, Joseph Robt. 3535 OLENTANGY RIVER RD 43214 #035-15-1943 L1952 **GP PUD** *071

BOYLE, Kenneth Andrew, Jr. 3525 OLENTANGY RIVER RD, STE 200 43214 #038-40-1993 L1994 **OPH** *035

BOYSE, Kathryn Elise. 456 W 10TH AVE, 7131 CRAMBLETT HALL 43210 #038-40-2005 L2006 **D** *012

BRACHMAN, Shael. 456 W 10TH AVE, 4510 CRAMBLETT HALL 43210 #024-07-1999 L2006 **IM** *020 †20

BRADLEY, John Franklin. 51 N HIGH ST, 4TH FL 43215 #011-04-1982 L1983 **AMI EM** *030 †18

BRADY, Michael Thos. 700 CHILDRENS DR, AB 7048 43205 #041-02-1977 L1981 **ID PD** *020 †55

BRADY, Thomas Francis. 793 W STATE ST, INTERNAL MEDICINE, MEDICAL 43222 #038-45-2004 L2004 **IM** *020 †20

BRAND, Edward Jay. 777 W STATE ST, OHIO GASTROENTEROLOGY 43222 #041-12-1974 L1979 **GE** *020 †20

BRANDES, Norman S. 6230 BUSCH BLVD STE 310 43229 #047-06-1950 L1956 **P PYA** *071 †75

BRANDT, David Saml. 3120 E MAIN ST 43209 #038-40-1966 L1966 **IM PUD** *020 †20

BRANDT, Edward Chas. ■ 43235 #038-40-1924 L1924 **GP GS** *071

BRAUNER, Mark Edward. 410 W 10TH AVE 43210 #038-75-2005, ▲ L2005 **EM** *012

BRAVENDER, Terrill Dennis. 700 CHILDRENS DR, ADOLECENT MEDS 43205 #025-01-1992 L1996 **ADL PD** *020 †55

BREECE, Richard Harold. ■ 43235 #035-19-1948 L1949 **GP** *071

BRENNAN, John Kelley. 6001 E BROAD ST 43213 #038-40-1971 L1971 **IM** *020 †20

BRENNAN, Timothy David. 1654 UPHAM DR, 202 MEANS HALL (OSU) 43210 #038-41-2003 L2003 **CD** *012 †20

BRESSLER, Franklin Duane. 111 S GRANT AVE 43215 #017-20-1958 L1962 **OBG** *020 †30

BRIDGER, Matthew Anthony. 223 E TOWN ST 43215 #036-08-1985 L1988 **FM** *020 †18

BRIGGS, John Richard. ■ 43209 #038-06-1959 L1959 **ORS** *071 †40

BRIGGS, William Eugene. 3600 OLENTANGY RIVER RD, COLUMBUS MAMO CTR INC 43214 #038-40-1952 L1952 **R DR** *020 †80

BRIGHT, Darrin Lee. 3705 OLENTANGY RIVER RD 43214 #038-44-1997 L1998 **FSM** *020 †18

BRILL, David Dean. 4626 SAWMILL RD 43220 #038-45-2003 L2003 **FM** *020 †18

BRIN, Margarita. 4850 E MAIN ST 43213 #038-45-2003 L2003 **FM** *020 †18

BRINGARDNER, Benjamin D. 700 CHILDRENS DR 43205 #038-34-2000 L2000 **PCC** *100

BRINKMAN, Vincent Eugene. 370 W 9TH AVE, OH STATE U COLL OF MED 43210 #038-40-2001 L2001 **CD** *012

BRIONES, Rodolfo. ■ 43206 #748-07-1967 **IM** *020

BRITTSAN, Angela Gail. 473 W 12TH AVE, STE 200 43210 #038-41-2004 L2004 **CD** *012 †20

BROGAN, Martha Anne Bacon. 866 W BROAD ST 43222 #038-40-1982 L1986 **DR** *020 †80

BROGAN, Michael Dale. 1211 DUBLIN RD, FL 2 43215 #038-40-1978 L1981 **GE IM** *020 †20

BRONER, Cynthia W. 700 CHILDRENS DR 43205 #011-04-1979 L1989 **CCM PD** *075

BRONSTEIN, Herbert Alan. 5877 CLEVELAND AVE 43231 #038-40-1960 L1960 **AI IM** *020 ‡

BROOKS, Juliana H J. 5689 WALNUT VIEW BLVD 43230 #038-40-1982 L1985 **AN** *020 †05

BROSE, Christine Marie. ■ 43201 #038-40-2008 *012

BROWER, Marc Charles. 111 S GRANT AVE, 3RD FL 43215 #035-45-1998 L2005 **AN** *020 †05

BROWN, Christopher Gene. 1654 UPHAM DR, NEPHROLOGY 43210 #036-01-2001 L2001 **NEP** *100

BROWN, Dan. 3535 OLENTANGY RIVER RD 43214 #038-40-1978 L1979 **OPH EM** *020 †35

BROWN, David Hugh. 500 THOMAS LN, STE 3C 43214 #038-43-1997 L1998 **U** *020 †95

BROWN, Donald Lewis. 855 W MOUND ST, C/O FRANLKIN CTY CHILD SVC 43223 #038-40-1966 L1966 **CHP P** *020 †75

BROWN, Erica Renee. ■ 43229 #056-05-2005 L2006 **EM** *012

BROWN, Lloyd Garth. 316A MARSHALL PSGE, OHIO STATE UNIV 43215 #035-45-2002 L2003 **GS** *012

BROWN, Mark Sherman. 270 E TOWN ST 43215 #038-40-1980 L1987 **OBG** *020 †30

BROWN, Rachel Elizabeth. 700 CHILDRENS DR, ATTN: DIV. OF NEONATOLOGY 43205 #038-45-2000 L2006 **NPM** *100 †55

BROWN, Robert Theodore. 700 CHILDRENS DR 43205 #041-13-1971 L1982 **ADL PD** *040 †55

BROWN, Steven Randall. 4775 KNIGHTSBRIDGE BLVD, STE 207 43214 #038-45-1998 L1999 **PD IM** *020 †55

BROWN, Theresa Luken. 941 CHATHAM LN STE 205 43221 #038-40-1991 L1992 **IM** *020 †20

BROWNELL, Mark David. 3535 OLENTANGY RIVER RD 43214 #035-15-1980 L1987 **ATP CLP** *020 †50

BROWNING-SHAW, Ann C. 2200 W BROAD ST, TWIN VALLEY BEHAVIORAL HEA 43223 #038-40-1979 L1989 **IM** *020 †20

BROWNLEE, Thomas Robt. 3555 OLENTANGY RIVER RD 43214 #038-40-1963 L1963 **D** *071 †15

BROYLES, John Thos. 1904 BETHEL RD 43220 #038-40-1976 L1976 **FM** *020 †18

BRUCE, Robert A, Jr. 85 MCNAUGHTEN RD 43213 #045-01-1973 L1974 **OPH** *020 †35

BRUMMEL, Nathan Edward. 410 W 10TH AVE, DEPT OF IM 43210 #028-03-2005 L2005 **IM** *012

BRUNO CALIMLIM, Theresa. ■ 43235 #038-40-2004 L2004 **PM** *012

BRUNS, Aaron Scott. 473 W 12TH AVE, 201 DHLRI 43210 #017-20-2003 L2006 **PCC** *012 †20

BRUSH, Darryl Jon. 5965 E BROAD ST, STE 230 43213 #038-40-1992 L1996 **P** *020 †75

BRYANT, Jason Andrew. 410 W 10TH AVE, 416 DOAN HALL OSU MED CENT 43210 #038-44-2001 L2001 **PAN** *100 †05

BUBOLZ, Beth A. ■ 43214 #048-14-1989 L2006 **PDC PD** *020 †55

BUCHANAN, Larry Michael. 750 MOUNT CARMEL MALL, STE 300 43222 #038-40-1971 L1971 **EM** *020

BUCK, David Paul. 797 THOMAS LN 43214 #055-01-2000 L2000 **FM** *040 †18 ‡

BUDAY, Stephen Jos Geo. 50 MCNAUGHTEN RD, STE 200 43213 #038-40-1969 L1969 **GS** *020 †85

BUDIN, Lee Eric. 6096 E MAIN ST, STE 112 43213 #038-40-1990 L1991 **PD** *020 †55

BUDKE, Gail Marie. 2050 KENNY RD, STE 2400 43221 #030-06-2004 L2004 **IM** *100 †20

BUELL, Joanna May. 1654 UPHAM DR, OHIO STATE UNIV MED CTR 43210 #001-02-2006 L2006 **OBG** *012

BULLARD, Jessica Taylor. ■ 43232 #026-04-2003 L2004 **OBG** *012

BULLOCK, Thomas Robt. 750 MOUNT CARMEL MALL 43222 #010-01-1979 L1980 **EM** *020 †16

BUMGARDNER, Ginny Li. 770 KINNEAR RD, STE 100 43212 #051-01-1983 L1993 **TTS GS** *020 †85

BUONI, William Gerard. 6150 E BROAD ST, 2ND FL 43213 #038-40-1982 L1983 **FM** *020 †18

BURAK, William Edward, Jr. 410 W 10TH AVE, 908 DOAN HALL 43210 #041-02-1987 L1992 **SO** *020 †85

BURDGE, Jeremy John. 3732 OLENTANGY RIVER RD, STE C 43214 #038-40-1975 L1978 **PS** *020 †85,65

BURGERS, John Kevin. 3555 OLENTANGY RIVER RD, STE 4020 43214 #023-07-1984 L1990 **U GS** *020 †95

BURKETT, Amy Marie. 1654 UPHAM DR, MEANS HALL 5TH FLOOR 43210 #038-44-2003 L2003 **OBG** *100

BURKHART, Jennifer Ellen. ■ 43235 #038-40-2005 L2005 **IM** *012

BURKHART, John A. 340 E TOWN ST, PHYSICAL MEDICINE 43215 #038-40-1968 L1968 **PM** *071 †60

BURKHART, Timothy Martin. ■ 43235 #038-40-2003 L2007 **PM** *012

BURLON, Daniel T. 100 N MURRAY HILL RD 43228 #028-79-1970, ▲ L1970 **IM** *020

BURMAN, Jerome. 992 LORNABERRY LN 43213 #038-40-1958 L1958 **GP IM** *071

BURNETT, Trever Michael. 410 W 10TH AVE, OH STATE UNIV HOSPS 43210 #049-01-2002 L2007 **MPD** *012

BURNICH, John Jeffrey. 793 W STATE ST 43222 #038-40-1982 L1983 **IM** *020 †20

BURNS, John R, Jr. ■ 43216 #038-40-1982 L1982 **IM CCM** *020 †20

BURNS, Kathryn Ann. ■ 43215 #038-06-1985 L1988 **P PFP** *020 †75

BUSH, Charles Ralph. 3525 OLENTANGY RIVER RD 43214 #038-40-1974 L1976 **TS VS** *020 †85,90

BUSHEK, Stephen. 1495 MORSE RD STE 207 43229 #038-40-1978 L1978 **FM FPG** *020 †18

BUSSER, Amber Rae. 2050 KENNY RD, C/O CORP CREDENTIALING 43221 #041-78-2007, ▲ L2007 **P** *012

BUSTER, Ward P. 931 CHATHAM LN, STE 200 43221 #018-75-1997, ▲ L2003 **NS** *020

BUTCHER, Mary Beth. 41 S HIGH ST STE 25, RIVERSIDE PHYSICIAN CTR 43215 #055-02-1983 L1984 **FM** *020 †18

BYLAW, Bethany Dawn. ■ 43220 #038-40-2005 L2005 **FP** *012

CABARON-DOLOR, Melinda C. 3535 OLENTANGY RIVER RD 43214 #748-11-1963 L1971 **PTH BBK** *020 †50

CACIOPPO, Carrie Elizabet. 555 S 18TH ST 43205 #038-40-2003 L2006 **PD** *020 †55

CAFFARATTI, Angela Rose. ■ 43235 #031-01-2000 L2000 **FM** *020 †18

CAHILL, Kenneth Vern. 262 NEIL AVE, OPHTHALMIC SURGEONS & 43215 #038-40-1979 L1983 **OPH PSH** *020 †35

CAIN, Brian Kristian. ■ 43214 #038-40-2003 L2003 **MPD** *020 †55

CAIN, George Patrick. 1492 E BROAD ST, DEPT OF ORTHOPAEDICS 43205 #016-43-1970 L1974 **DR** *020 †20

CALDERON-MORENO, Leticia. 370 W 9TH AVE, OH STATE U COLL OF MED 43210 #038-40-2002 L2002 **FM** *020 †18

CALDWELL, Craig Brian. 2240 N BANK DR, UPPR 43220 #041-14-1977 L1985 **AN** *020 †05

CALDWELL, David Mckean. 4606 SAWMILL RD 43220 #038-40-1997 L1998 **AN** *020 †05

CALDWELL, James Hudson. 410 W 10TH AVE, N213 DOAN HALL 43210 #038-40-1963 L1963 **GE IM** *020 †20

CALDWELL, Nicole Vansteyn. 700 CHILDRENS DR, PEDIATRIC RESIDENCY OFFICE 43205 #038-40-2003 L2003 **PD** *020 †55

CALDWELL, Patricia B. 473 W 12TH AVE, STE 200 43210 #036-07-1971 L1972 **CD IM** *020 †20

CALIGIURI, Jeanne Lynn. 500 THOMAS LN, STE 3G 43214 #038-40-2000 L2000 **IM** *020

CALIGIURI, Michael A, Jr. 320 W 10TH AVE, 458A STARLING LOVING HALL 43210 #005-11-1983 L1999 **HO IM** *020 †20

CAMBIER, Denise Marie. 750 MT CARMEL MALL STE 250 43222 #038-41-1994 L1999 **N CN** *020 †75

CAMBIER, Gregory Scot. 700 CHILDRENS DR 43205 #038-45-1993 L1997 **PAN** *020 †05

CAMERLENGO, Leon Jos. 2240 N BANK DR, UPPR 43220 #045-01-1985 L1989 **AN** *020 †05

CAMERON, Seema Chauhan. 111 S GRANT AVE, GRANT MEDICAL CENTER 43215 #496-51-1998 L2007 **FP** *012

CAMPAGNI, Michael Andrew. 6001 E BROAD ST 43213 #038-40-1989 L1993 **AN** *020 †05

CAMPBELL, Albert James. 285 E STATE ST, STE 620 43215 #028-03-1983 L1986 **GS AS** *020 †85

CAMPBELL, Jennifer H. 6096 E MAIN ST, STE 112 43213 #041-12-1995 L1999 **PD** *020 †55

CAMPBELL, John David. 2240 N BANK DR, UPPR 43220 #041-12-1995 L1999 **AN** *020 †05

CAMPBELL, Matthew Leslie. 793 W STATE ST 43222 #038-40-2003 L2003 **GS** *012

CAMPO, John Vincent. 1670 UPHAM DR STE 465 43210 #041-01-1982 L2006 **CHP P** *020 †55,75

CANDAGE, Raymond Lester. ■ 43221 #024-07-1947 L1962 **IM CD** *020

CANIANO, Donna Anne. 555 S 18TH ST, CHILDRENS SURGICAL 43205 #035-03-1976 L1981 **PDS** *040 †85

CANNON, Patricia Ann. 6075 CLEVELAND AVE, STE 100 43231 #036-07-1977 L1982 **PD PN** *020 †55

CANOWITZ, Stephen Mark. 5969 E BROAD ST 43213 #038-43-1994 L1995 **MPD** *020 †20,55

CANTRELL, Julie Ann. 1250 DEARBORN DR, MEDICAL & WELLNESS CENTER 43085 #038-40-1992 L1993 **FM** *020 †18

CANTZLER, Ryan Michael. 750 MOUNT CARMEL MALL, STE 300 43222 #017-20-2002 L2005 **EM** *020 †16

CAPERS, Quinn, IV. 423 E TOWN ST, STE 1000 43215 #038-40-1991 L2004 **CD** *020 †20

CAPUTO, Renee Marie. 745 W STATE ST STE 550A 43222 #038-44-1987 L1993 **OBG U** *020 †30

CARAGINE, Louis P, Jr. 410 W 10TH AVE, N1021 DOAN 43210 #010-02-1992 L2004 **NS OS** *020 †25

CAREY, Jeffrey Michael. 750 MT CARMEL MALL, STE 350 43222 #038-43-1996 L2003 **U GYN** *020 †95 ‡

CARLOS, Jennifer B. 5072 REED RD, MEDICINE 43220 #016-11-1993 L1994 **PD** *020 †55

CARLSON, Matthew Jerome. ■ 43207 #030-05-2007 L2007 **OBG** *012

CARMONA, Monica Maria. 793 W STATE ST, C/O MT CARMEL HOSPITAL-MED 43222 #264-04-1995 L2002 **IM** *100 †20

CARROLL, William Emil, II. 285 E STATE ST STE 430 43215 #038-43-1995 L1996 **N** *020 †75

CARSON, William Edgar, III. 410 W 10TH AVE 43210 #005-06-1986 L1997 **GS** *020 †85

CARTABUKE, Richard S. 930 BETHEL RD, OHIO SURGERY CENTER 43214 #035-15-1984 L1988 **AN** *020 †05

CASAVANT, Marcel Jos. 700 CHILDRENS DR, PHARA/TOY 43205 #024-16-1990 L1992 **ETX EM** *020 †16

CASHMAN, John W. ■ 43209 #016-02-1946 L1971 **PHP** *071

CASSADY, James Donald, Jr. 697 THOMAS LN, RIVERSIDE FAMILY PRACTICE 43214 #038-45-1999 L1999 **FPG** *020 †18

CASSELL, Robert Theodore. ■ 43209 #869-04-1954 L1958 **IM RHU** *071

CASSIDY, Steven Chas. 700 CHILDRENS DR, CHILDREN'S HOSPITAL 43205 #035-08-1983 L1989 **PDC PD** *020 †55

CASTILE, Robert Glenn. 700 CHILDRENS DR, CHILDRENS HOSP 43205 #023-01-1973 L1992 **PDP PD** *020 †55

CASTROP, Julie Anne. 1833 PARSONS AVE 43207 #038-43-1988 L1991 **PD** *020 †55

CATALAND, Samuel. 456 W 10TH AVE 43210 #038-40-1965 L1965 **END IM** *071 †20

CATALAND, Spero Rick. 320 W 10TH AVE, DIV OF HEM/ONC 43210 #038-40-1994 L1995 **HO** *020 †20

CATIGNANI, Karen Marie. 410 W 10TH AVE 43210 #038-44-2003 L2006 **IM** *100 †20

CATTON, Mark Douglas. 111 S GRANT AVE, 3RD FL 43215 #038-40-1994 L1996 **AN** *020 †05

CAULIN-GLASER, Teresa L. 3535 OLENTANGY RIVER RD, MCCONNELL HEART HEALTH CEN 43214 #038-06-1987 L2002 **CD** *020 †20

CERILLI, G James. 410 W 10TH AVE 43210 #023-07-1958 L1967 **GS OS** *071 †85

CHAKERES, Donald Wm. 1654 UPHAM DR, 630 MEANS HALL 43210 #038-40-1975 L1975 **R RNR** *020 †80

CHALMERS, Julie Ann. 3400 OLENTANGY RIVER RD, STE 150 43202 #038-40-1992 L1993 **IM** *020 †20

CHAMBERS, Bryan Thomas. 793 W STATE ST, MOUNT CARMEL MEDICAL CENTE 43222 #041-13-2001 L2001 **ORS** *100

CHAMBERS, Lowell W. 777 W STATE ST, METRO SURGERY, SUITE 501 43222 #020-12-1996 L1997 **GS** *020 †85

CHAMBERS, Michelle C. 4900 GETTYSBURG RD 43220 #025-07-1982 L1990 **D** *020 †15

CHAMBERS, Terrence Michae. ■ 43212 #010-03-2004 L2004 **DR** *012

CHAN, David Punsek. 700 CHILDRENS DR, CHILDRENS HOSP CARDIO 43205 #025-07-1986 L1992 **PDC PD** *020 †55

CHAN, Michael Alan. 750 MOUNT CARMEL MALL, STE 220 43222 #025-07-1982 L1989 **P** *020 †75 ‡

CHANDNANI, Vijay Prem. 866 W BROAD ST 43222 #038-40-1984 L1985 **R** *020 †80

CHANDRASEKARAN, Suchitra. ■ 43216 #016-06-2007 L2007 **OBG** *012

CHANG, Susie. 456 W 10TH AVE, 5TH FL 43210 #038-40-2001 L2001 **OPH** *020 †35

CHAPMAN, Kenneth J, Jr. 3535 OLENTANGY RIVER RD 43214 #047-06-1953 L1957 **GYN** *071

CHARLES, Christina Lynn. 750 MOUNT CARMEL MALL, STE 100 43222 #038-40-1999 L1999 **OBG** *020 †30

CHATTERJEE, Amit Kumar. 456 W 10TH AVE, RM 4510 43210 #035-09-2003 L2006 **IM** *100 †20

CHAUDHARI, Alok Mohan. 370 W 9TH AVE, OH STATE U COLL OF MED 43210 #038-40-2002 L2002 **NS** *012

CHAUDHARI, Monika. 700 CHILDRENS DR, DIVISION OF ENDOCRINOLOGY 43205 #038-44-1995 L2001 **PDE** *020 †55

CHAUHAN, Anupama. 1073 BLUFFPOINT DR 43235 #038-44-2002 L2002 **IM** *100 †20

CHAWLA, Rakesh Ricky. 777 W STATE ST, 3FL STE 302 43222 #041-02-1994 L1995 **IM IC** *020 †20

CHEATHAM, John P. 700 CHILDRENS DR, THE HEART CTR CHILDS HOSP 43205 #039-01-1976 L2002 **PDC PD** *020 †55

CHEEK, John Arthur. 4488 W BROAD ST 43228 #038-40-1982 L1982 **EM OS** *075

CHEEK, Shannon Marie. ■ 43201 #038-40-2008 *012

CHELLINI, Jerry Walter. 5100 W BROAD ST 43228 #038-75-2003, ▲ L2003 **NEP** *012

CHEN, Chaur-Shong. 1636 NORTHWEST BLVD 43212 #018-75-1992, ▲ L1993 **GP** *020

CHEN, Feng. 1547 W BROAD ST 43222 #243-52-1982 L1998 **IM** *020 †20

CHEN, Jing Xuan. 285 E STATE ST, STE 460 43215 #243-95-1983 L2002 **AN** *020

CHEN, Li Chuen. ■ 43220 #385-03-1955 L1975 **P** *071 †75

CHEN, Mao-Hsiung. 111 S GRANT AVE 43215 #385-02-1965 L1971 **CD IM** *020 †20

CHEN, Richard. ■ 43204 #038-40-2008 *012

CHENEY, Nick A. ■ 43228 #038-75-2007, ▲ L2007 *012

CHERNICK, Edward Michael. 7630 RIVERS EDGE DR 43235 #038-40-1981 L1982 **IM CD** *020

CHERUKURI, Sreehari. 7630 RIVERS EDGE DR 43235 #038-44-1998 L2001 **IM** *020 †20

CHESS, Robert Lewis. 410 W 10TH AVE, STE 310 43210 #047-05-1979 L1983 **PTH** *020 †50

CHIANG, Tendy. ■ 43201 #038-40-2007 L2007 **OTO** *012

CHICOINE, Louis Gustave. 700 CHILDRENS DR, CHILDREN'S HOSPITAL 43205 #048-02-1990 L2004 **NPM** *020 †55

CHIDESTER, Kara Elizabeth. 697 THOMAS LN 43214 #038-40-2004 L2004 **FM** *020 †18

CHIDESTER, Sara Janine. ■ 43201 #038-40-2008 *012

CHIDIAC, Tarek. 3100 PLAZA PROPERTIES BLVD 43219 #605-02-1990 L1993 **HO IM** *020 †20

CHILDS, Adam Marcellos. 370 W 9TH AVE, 200A MEILING HALL 43210 #038-40-2006 L2006 **FP** *012

CHINN, William Michael. 745 W STATE ST, STE 510 43222 #038-40-1969 L1969 **PUD IM** *020 †20

CHIRRAVURI, Venkatesh. 3525 OLENTANGY RIVER RD, STE 4330 43214 #495-21-1991 L2004 *020

CHIRUMAMILLA, Sree. 700 CHILDRENS DR, CHILDRENS HOSPITAL 43205 #422-01-1996 L2003 **CCP** *020 †55

CHITTARI, Lalitha Macharo. 1492 E BROAD ST 43205 #495-62-1998 L2005 **IM** *020 †20

CHITTIPROLU, Jagan. 16 W LONG ST, SOUTH EAST, INC. 43215 #495-58-1979 L1994 **P** *020 †75

CHO, Chin U. 5965 E BROAD ST, STE 330 43213 #048-02-1995 L1997 **U** *020

CHO, Chuck C. 5200 W BROAD ST, CENTRAL OHIO RADIATION 43228 #583-02-1975 L1984 **RO** *020 †20

CHOBAN, Patricia Smith. 750 MT CARMEL MALL, STE 200 43222 #038-06-1983 L1991 **GS CCS** *020 †85

CHOHAN, Mohammad A. 4506 SAWMILL RD 43220 #704-01-1962 L1972 **AN** *071 †05

CHOI, Haemi. 2050 KENNY RD STE 3100, OSU SPORTS MED CTR 43221 #305-01-2004 L2005 **FSM** *012 †18

CHOI, Jin Kook. 6001 E BROAD ST 43213 #583-01-1964 L1972 **AN** *020 †05

CHOI, Kwang-Taik. 6001 E BROAD ST, MT CARMEL EAST HOSPITAL 43213 #583-02-1970 L1983 **AN** *020 †05

CHOI-PEARSON, Ryo Chong. 1875 MILLIKIN RD 43210 #017-20-1984 L1987 **OBG** *020 †30

CHOLKERI, Vismai. 3535 OLENTANGY RIVER RD 43214 #038-44-2004 L2004 **FSM** *012 †18

CHOSY, Robert F. 3535 OLENTANGY BLVD 43214 #038-40-1959 L1959 **OBG** *072 †30

CHOUNG, Kilwha. 793 W STATE ST 43222 #583-02-1965 L1972 **AN** *020 †05

CHOW, Wen-Shiung. 1211 DUBLIN RD, COLUMBUS ARTHRITIS CENTER 43215 #038-40-1989 L1990 **RHU IM** *020 †20

CHOWDHURY, Lucia. 5100 W BROAD ST, ICU 43228 #781-01-1985 L2002 **CCM PCC** *020 †20

CHRISTENSON, Paul J. 500 E MAIN ST STE 220 43215 #049-01-1976 L2001 **U** *020 †95

CHRISTIAN, Beth Ann. 89 E JEFFREY PL 43214 #038-40-2002 L2002 **HO** *012 †20

CHRISTIAN-TAYLOR, Janice. 600 W SPRING ST 43215 #038-45-1999 L1999 **PD** *020

CHRISTMAN, Jennifer Ann. ■ 43230 #038-43-2004 L2004 **GS** *012

CHRISTOFIDES, Elena A. 94 W 3RD AVE 43201 #038-40-1995 L1996 **END** *020 †20

CHRISTOFORIDIS, A J. 1654 UPHAM DR, 630 MEANS HALL 43210 #418-01-1949 L1962 **DR** *071 †80

CHRISTOFORIDIS, Greg A. 1654 UPHAM DR, 627 MEANS HALL 43210 #038-40-1990 L1998 **RNR** *020 †80

CHRISTOFORIDIS, John B. 456 W 10TH AVE, BOBBI TODD 43210 #038-40-1991 L1999 **OPH** *020 †35

CHRISTY, Jonathan Michael. ■ 43212 #055-01-2008 *012

CHUANG, John. ■ 43204 #305-01-2004 L2005 **FP** *012

CHUN, Esther. 4606 SAWMILL RD 43220 #024-07-1994 L1999 **AN** *020 †05

CHUN, Linda Eunkyung. 2000 KENNY RD 43221 #041-12-1980 L1994 **AN IM** *020 †20,05

CHUN, Linda Eunkyung. 2000 KENNY RD 43221 #038-40-2002 L2002 **MPD** *100 †20,55

CHUNG, Carol Y. 3545 OLENTANGY RIVER RD, STE 220 43214 #038-40-1986 L1989 **P** *020 †75

CHUNG, Jason Hyun. 410 W 10TH AVE, THE OHIO STATE UNIVERSITY 43210 #038-40-2004 L2005 **AN** *012

CHUNG, John Woojune. 370 W 9TH AVE, OH STATE U COLL OF MED 43210 #038-40-1998 L2001 **PHO** *020 †55

CHUNG, Joshua Suah. ■ 43204 #305-12-2007 L2007 **GS** *012

CHURCHILL, Cynthia M. 1515 E BROAD ST 43205 #038-43-1981 L1985 **P PYG** *020 †75

CHURCHILL, Susan E. ■ 43214 #024-16-1986 L1987 **EM** *020 †16

CIBULA, Jean Ellen. 5340 E MAIN ST, STE 100 43213 #038-06-1991 L2000 **N CN** *020 †75

CIOC, Adina Mihaela. 410 W 10TH AVE, CO OSU HOSPS-MED ED DEPT 43210 #781-06-1995 L2000 **HMP** *012 †50

CIOFANI, Kim Raney. 3535 OLENTANGY RIVER RD, RIVERSIDE METHODIST HOSPIT 43214 #038-06-1997 L2001 **EM** *020 †16

CIOLLI, Glenn Anthony. 750 MOUNT CARMEL MALL 43222 #038-40-1977 L1978 **EM IM** *020,16

CIOS, Jacquelyne Susan. ■ 43235 #038-40-2004 L2004 **N** *012

CLAIRMONT, Albert Clement. 480 W 9TH AVE, DODD HALL 43210 #566-01-1974 L1981 **PM** *020 †55,60

CLARK, Robert Nelson. ■ 43220 #041-01-1964 L1978 **ORS** *020 †40

CLARK, Robert Wesley. 1430 S HIGH ST 43207 #038-40-1972 L1974 **N** *020 †75

CLARKE, Charles David. ■ 43201 #038-40-2008 *012

CLARKE, James Westover. ■ 43214 #038-40-2004 L2004 **RO** *012

CLARKSON, Peter Martin. ■ 43221 #038-40-1998 *100

CLARY, Richard Henry. 717 W TOWN ST 43222 #038-40-1970 L1970 **P** *020 †16,75

CLAUSEN, Kathryn M Pearce. 370 W 9TH AVE, 260 MEILING HALL 43210 #038-40-1966 L1966 **ATP** *040 †50

CLAXTON, Elizabeth Anne. 700 CHILDRENS DR 43205 #031-01-1997 L2001 **PEM** *020 †55

CLAYBON, Marcie Ann. ■ 43212 #038-40-2008 *012

CLEMENCY, Karen Alice. 1020 DENNISON AVE, SECOND FLOOR 43201 #047-05-1985 L1986 **GP** *020

CLINCHOT, Daniel Michael. 480 W 9TH AVE, STE 1025 43210 #035-15-1988 L1990 **PM** *020 †60

CLINTON, Carol. 6100 CHANNINGWAY BLVD, STE 505 43232 #038-40-1990 L1991 **EM** *020 †16

CLINTON, Steven Kelly. 320 W 10TH AVE, A434 STARLING-LOVING HALL 43210 #016-11-1984 L1998 **ON IM** *050 †20

COBOURN, Svitlana. 6001 E BROAD ST, MT CARMEL EAST MEDICAL CEN 43213 #913-05-1991 L2002 **IM** *100 †20

COCCIA, Maria Regina. 80 AVONDALE AVE 43222 #038-40-1983 L1986 **ID CCM** *020 †20

COFFMAN, John Carl. ■ 43204 #047-06-2006 L2006 **AN** *012

COHEN, Daniel Michael. 700 CHILDRENS DR, EMERGENCY MEDICINE 43205 #008-02-1987 L1991 **PE** *020 †55

COHEN, Jonathon Brett. ■ 43221 #011-03-2007 L2007 **IM** *012

COHEN, P. Aryeh. ■ 43209 #550-02-2000 L2007 **TS** *100

COHEN, Scott David. 4677 E MAIN ST 43213 #011-02-2001 L2004 **NEP** *012

COHN, David Elliot. 320 W 10TH AVE, M-210 STARLING LOVING HALL 43210 #010-02-1994 L2001 **OBG** *020 †30

COHN, Evan Barton. 750 MT CARMEL MALL, STE 350 43222 #016-06-1993 L2001 **U** *020 †95

COLACHIS, Sam Constantine. 480 MEDICAL CENTER DR, DODD HALL/DAVIS CENTER 43210 #005-06-1984 L1985 **PM** *020 †60

COLE, Arthur Neil. 750 MOUNT CARMEL MALL, STE 230 43222 #010-03-1981 L1985 **NS** *020 †25 ‡

COLEGATE, Bradford Geo. 1875 MILLIKIN RD 43210 #038-40-1978 L1979 **FM** *020 †18

COLEMAN, Carl Richard. 3600 OLENTANGY RIVER RD #B 43214 #016-06-1954 L1955 **ORS** *071 †40

COLEMAN, Katherine Elizab. 697 THOMAS LN 43214 #038-40-2006 L2006 **FP** *012

COLEMAN, Thomas Hewitt. 3555 OLENTANGY RIVER RD 43214 #038-40-1972 L1973 **AI PN** *020 †55,03

COLE-SEDIVY, Deborah L. 3260 W HENDERSON RD, STE 100 43220 #038-75-1986, ▲ L1986 **FM** *020 †18

COLEY, Brian Douglas. 700 CHILDRENS DR, DEPT OF RADIOLOGY 43205 #005-18-1987 L1993 **PDR R** *020 †80

COLLER, Kristen Sladek. ■ 43220 #047-20-2002 L2007 **IM** *020 †20

COLLER, Zachary Vincent. ■ 43220 #028-34-2000 L2007 **IM** *100 †20

COLLING, Landon James. ■ 43221 #016-45-2006 L2006 **OPH** *012

COLLINS, Elizabeth Marieb. ■ 43235 #038-40-2007 *012

COLLINS, Erin Ann. ■ 43204 #026-04-2006 L2006 **OBG** *012

COLLINS, Meredith Suzanne. ■ 43201 #038-40-2008 *012

COLLINS, Valerie Denise. ■ 43229 #035-01-2007 L2007 **IM** *012

COLLINS, Vincent Ricardo. 700 CHILDRENS DR, CHILDRENS HOSP 43205 #041-01-1976 L1992 **P PD** *020 †75

COLLIS, George Nicholas. ■ 43213 #038-40-2006 L2006 **GS** *012

COLMAN, Kymberly Tsai. 700 CHILDRENS DR DEPT OF, EMERGENCY MED, C/O ABBIE D 43205 #048-16-2002 L2005 **PEM** *012 †55

COLOMBO, David Foster. 1654 UPHAM DR, 561 MEANS HALL 43210 #038-40-1993 L1997 **OBG MFM** *020 †30

COLOMBO, James Bradford. 500 E MAIN ST, STE 220 43215 #038-43-2001 L2001 **U** *020 †95

COMAS, Theodore C. 456 W 10TH AVE, WILLIAM H HAVENER EYE CTR 43210 #038-40-2001 L2001 **FM** *020

COMFORT, Gregory Bigham, Jr. ■ 43221 #038-40-2008 *012

COMISAR, Bruce Rodney, Jr. 323 E TOWN ST 43215 #038-41-1994 L2000 **OSM ORS** *020 †40

COMTE, Timothy James. ■ 43214 #038-41-2007 L2007 **EM** *012

CONAWAY, Michael David. 3535 OLENTANGY RIVER RD 43214 #038-43-1993 L1994 **IM** *020 †20

CONDON, David Lawrence. 86 N WILSON RD 43204 #038-40-1987 L1990 **IM OM** *020

CONDON, John F. ■ 43214 #030-06-1953 L1954 **IM A** *071 †20

CONGBALAY, Maria Paz C. ■ 43235 #748-01-1961 L1975 **BBK CLP** *020

CONGBALAY, Rolando C. 985 W 3RD AVE 43212 #748-01-1964 L1971 **NEP IM** *071 †20

CONKLIN, Jacob Ezra. 7630 RIVERS EDGE DR 43235 #038-40-2005 L2005 **IM** *012

CONNELL, George F. ■ 43235 #065-01-1957 L1967 **AN** *071 †05

CONNELL, George Raymond. 111 S GRANT AVE, GRANT ANESTHESIA ASSOCIATE 43215 #051-07-1989 L1993 **AN** *020 †05

CONNOR, Patricia. 453 WATERBURY CT, PEDIATRIC & ADOLESCENT 43230 #038-40-1986 L1988 **PD** *020 †55

COOK, Brian William. ■ 43214 #017-20-2004 L2004 **OBG** *012

COOK, Charles Howard. 4830 KNIGHTSBRIDGE BLVD, STE J 43214 #038-40-1991 L1992 **GS** *020 †85

COOK, Harold Eugene, III. 2050 KENNY RD, 7TH FL 43221 #041-12-1980 L1994 **AN IM** *020 †20,05

COOK, Mary Veronica. 3555 OLENTANGY RIVER RD, STE 1080 43214 #030-06-1984 L2001 **IM** *020 †20

COOK, Paul Albert. 3400 OLENTANGY RIVER RD, STE 200 43202 #038-44-1991 L1993 **ORS** *020 †40

COOK, Stephen Christopher. 700 CHILDRENS DR, CHILDREN'S HOSPITAL 43205 #024-05-1997 L2001 **PDC** *100 †20,55

COOKE, Glen Eric. 1654 UPHAM DR, DIV. OF CARDIOLOGY -MEANS 43210 #038-43-1990 L1993 **CD** *020 †20

COONEY, Michael John. 719 W TOWN ST 43222 #038-40-1970 L1970 **IM** *020 †20

COOPER, Michael Patrick. 246 N HIGH ST 8TH FL 43215 #025-12-2003 L2003 **FM** *062 †18

COOPER, Minton Truitt. 410 W 10TH AVE, RM N1050 43210 #051-01-2003 L2003 **ORS** *012

COOPER, Richard Preston. 3525 OLENTANGY RIVER RD, STE 5360 43214 #007-02-1995 L2007 **DR** *020 †80

COOPER, Robert Winston. 130 S DAVIS AVE, STE 203 43222 #038-40-1970 L1970 **GS** *020 †85

COOPER-FENSKE, Carrie Ann. ■ 43212 #038-40-2008 *012

COOPERMAN, Marc. 1492 E BROAD ST STE 1300 43205 #005-11-1973 L1977 **GS** *020 †85

COOPERRIDER, Jon Herbert. 2500 CORPORATE EXCHANGE DR 43231 #038-40-1963 L1963 **FM AN** *071 †18

COPELAND, Larry James. 1654 UPHAM DR, STE 505 43210 #065-06-1973 L1988 **GO GYN** *020 †30

COPLEY, Larae Meschelle. 370 W 9TH AVE, OH STATE U COLL OF MED 43210 #038-40-2006 L2006 **P** *012

■ = Address Information Privacy Protected

CORDASCO, Edward M, Jr. 3545 OLENTANGY RIVER RD, RIVERSIDE PULMONARY 43214 #041-77-1984, ▲ L1985 **PUD CCM** *020 †20

CORDERO, Leandro. 410 W 10TH AVE, N118 DOAN HALL PEDIATRICS 43210 #132-01-1959 L1972 **PD** *020 †55

CORDES, Kimberly Dawn. ■ 43222 #028-46-2000 L2000 **EM** *100 †16

CORPUS, Lolita Umali. ■ 43220 #748-01-1958 L1972 **P** *071

CORRIDORE, Marco. ■ 43220 #025-01-2001 L2007 **PAN** *100 †05

CORRIVEAU, Sarah Joy. 285 E STATE ST, STE 520 43215 #056-06-1979 L1991 **NPM PD** *020 †55

COSTA, Stephanie Wellman. 1315 W LANE AVE 43221 #038-40-1994 L1995 **OBG** *020 †30

COSTLOW, Kathleen Ann. 453 WATERBURY CT, PEDIATRIC & ADOLESCENT 43230 #038-45-1998 L2000 **PD** *020 †55

COTTON, William Herbert. 700 CHILDRENS DR, AMBULATORY PEDIATRICS NATL 43205 #038-41-1981 L1984 **PD EM** *020 †55

COTTRELL, Daryl Ann. 500 THOMAS LN STE 2C, COMMUNITY MEDICINE 43214 #038-40-1986 L1988 **END** *020 †20

COULTER, James Morgan. 4808 N HIGH ST 43214 #038-40-1956 L1956 **FM** *071 †18

COUNTS, George Washington. 410 W 10TH AVE 43210 #018-03-1965 L1966 **ID IM** *030 †20

COURY, Daniel Lee. 700 CHILDRENS DR 43205 #047-06-1978 L1983 **PD** *040 †55

COWAN, Walter Elliott. ■ 43202 #020-02-1969 L1972 **P N** *071

COX, William Anthony. 520 KING AVE, FRANKLIN COUNTY CORONERS 43201 #041-13-1967 L1978 **FOP NP** *020 †50

COZZARELLI, Cellini J. 520 KING AVE 43201 #319-03-1956 **PTH** *020

CRAENEN, Josefa Maria. 700 CHILDRENS DR #165-04-1960 L1968 **PDC OS** *020 †55

CRAIG, Elson Leroy. 456 W 10TH AVE 43210 #038-40-1966 L1966 **OPH** *071 †35

CRAMBLETT, Henry G. 456 W 10TH AVE, 1024 CRAMBLETT HALL 43210 #038-41-1953 L1953 **PD ID** *071 †55

CRANDALL, Wallace Vernon. 700 CHILDRENS DR, COLUMBUS CHILDREN'S HOSPIT 43205 #049-01-1994 L2000 **PG** *020 †55

CRANE, Robert Sellers, III. 2231 N HIGH ST 43201 #038-43-1977 L1977 **FM** *020 †18

CRAW, John Rich. ■ 43220 #038-40-2008 *012

CRAWFORD, John P. ■ 43221 #038-40-1949 L1949 **GS TS** *072 †85

CRAWFORD, Regina Denise. 320 W 10TH AVE, B304 STARLING LOVING HALL 43210 #038-41-2000 L2003 **IM** *020 †20

CRAWLEY, Matthew Dale. ■ 43203 #038-40-2001 L2001 **FM** *100

CRESTANELLO, Juan Antonio. 410 W 10TH AVE, 8 N DOAN HALL 43210 #924-01-1991 L2004 **TS** *020 †85,90

CRIDEN, Marc Robert. 456 W 10TH AVE, CRAMBLETT HALL 43210 #041-02-2001 L2002 **OPH** *020 †35

CRISTALES, Quirico G. 1289 E LIVINGSTON AVE, LIVINGSTON LOCKBOURNE AVE 43205 #748-07-1966 L1984 **GP** *020

CRNKOVICH, Mark Jos. 3535 OLENTANGY RIVER RD 43214 #038-41-1980 L1985 **RO** *020 †80

CROCKETT, Andrew Owen. ■ 43202 #049-01-2005 L2005 **GS** *012

CROFT, Ann Marie. 1021 COUNTRY CLUB RD, STE A 43213 #038-40-1987 L1988 **PD** *020 †55

CRONAU, Holly Riedel. 456 W 10TH AVE, RM B 43210 #038-40-1985 L1986 **FM** *020 †18

CROUSER, Elliott David. 473 W 12TH AVE, 201F HLRIANS HALL 43210 #038-43-1989 L1992 **PCC** *020 †20

CROWE, Debra Lowery. 700 CHILDRENS DR 43214 #021-06-1980 L1980 **PD** *020 †55

CRUZ, Julio C. ■ 43202 #737-01-1963 L1983 **AN OS** *071 †05

CSETRI, Csaba Ferenc. 1555 BETHEL RD 43220 #473-02-1956 L1961 **P** *071

CUA, Clifford Lee. 700 CHILDRENS DR, CHILDREN'S HOSPITAL 43205 #017-20-1997 L1999 **PDC** *020 †55

CUMMINS, Elizabeth A. 3535 OLENTANGY RIVER RD 43214 #038-40-1991 L1993 **OBG** *020 †30

CUMMINS, James. 3535 OLENTANGY RIVER RD 43214 #038-40-1999 L1999 **P PYG** *100 †75

CUNIN, Kathryn Ann. ■ 43212 #038-40-2005 L2005 **IM** *012

CUNNINGHAM, Dennis John. 700 CHILDRENS DR, ED 583 43205 #033-06-1996 L2002 **PDI** *020 †55

CUNNINGHAM, Jerome James. 410 W 10TH AVE, DEPT RAD 43210 #011-03-1965 L1983 **DR** *071 †80

CUNNINGHAM, John Wm. 4660 ROBERTS RD 43228 #038-40-1969 L1969 **OM GPM** *020 †16,70

CUNNINGHAM, Melissa Sue. ■ 43085 #038-40-2007 L2007 **FP** *012

CUNNINGHAM, Michael F. 941 CHATHAM LN, STE 110 43221 #038-40-1992 L1994 **U** *020 †95

CURREN, Camilla. 1609 NORTHWEST BLVD, OSU INTERNAL MED & PEDS 43212 #038-40-1989 L1991 **IM PD** *020 †55,20

CURTIS, Boyd Delanor. 6465 E BROAD ST, STE D 43213 #038-40-1988 L1990 **IM** *020 †20

CYRAN, Katherine Maria. 1550 KENNY RD, WENDT-BRISTOL DIAGNOSTIC 43212 #020-02-1990 L1995 **DR RNR** *020 †80

CZAPLICKI, Anthony Peter, III. ■ 43221 #017-20-2007 L2007 **ORS** *012

CZERWINSKI, Peter. 111 S GRANT AVE 3RD FL, ANESTHESIA 43215 #038-40-1992 L1993 **AN** *020 †05

CZERWINSKI, Romana. 2200 W BROAD ST 43223 #759-03-1954 L1975 **P** *020 †75

CZYZ, Craig. ■ 43201 #041-77-2003, ▲ L2004 **OPH** *100 ‡

DAAB-KRZYKOWSKI, Susan R. 4808 N HIGH ST 43214 #038-40-1997 L1999 **FM** *020 †18

D'ADDARIO, Stephen F. 150 TAYLOR STATION RD, STE 250 43213 #035-15-2002 L2007 **PRD** *020 †15

DAGAM, Jeannette Chary. 410 W 10TH AVE, OH STATE UNIV HOSP 43210 #028-78-2006, ▲ L2006 **P** *012

DAHL, Mark Robt. 2240 N BANK DR, UPPR 43220 #038-40-1982 L1985 **AN** *020 †05

DAHMER, Diane Gomez. ■ 43235 #016-01-1978 L1981 **PD** *020 †55

DAIGA, David A. ■ 43201 #038-40-2008 *012

DAIRO, Olamide Olatunji. 700 CHILDRENS DR 43205 #690-01-1988 L2000 **AN** *020 †05

DALTON, Ryan Eric. 410 W 10TH AVE, OHIO STATE UNIVERSITY 43210 #038-40-2000 L2000 **IM** *020 †05

DANG, Khanh Vinh. 1151 BETHEL RD, STE 201 43220 #038-40-1992 L1993 **IM** *020 †20

DANG, Nghia Chinh. ■ 43220 #005-18-2003 L2004 **DR** *012

DANG, Toan Tran. ■ 43212 #038-40-2008 *012

DANGEL, Matthew Edwin. 456 W 10TH AVE 43210 #038-40-1977 L1978 **OPH** *020 †35

DANIELS, Curt John. 473 W 12TH AVE, 249 DHLRI 43210 #038-40-1991 L1992 **CD PD** *020 †20,55

DAOUD, Emile Georges. 473 W 12TH AVE, DHLRI, STE 200 43210 #038-41-1988 L1997 **CD IM** *020 †20

DAPPEN, Nathan Nale. 2240 N BANK DR, UPPR 43220 #018-03-1972 L1983 **AN** *020 †05

DARABI, Kamruz. ■ 43201 #409-39-2003 L2007 **D** *012

DARIUSHNIA, Sean Robert. 1066 MICHIGAN AVE 43201 #038-40-2001 L2001 **VIR** *012 †80

DARRELLFIELDS, Charlene M. ■ 43219 #038-40-2007 L2007 **FP** *012

DARWIN, Robert Howard. 866 W BROAD ST 43222 #036-07-1986 L1991 **DR** *020 †80

DAS, Mohan. 1654 UPHAM DR, # N325 43210 #495-16-1975 L1983 **VS CD** *020 †85

DAS, Subinoy. 456 W 10TH AVE STE 4A, OSU MEDICAL CENTER 43210 #051-01-2001 L2006 **OTO** *020 †45

DASGUPTA, Asok. 2760 AIRPORT DR STE 120, ASSOCIATES INC 43219 #495-39-1984 L1996 **PCC** *020 †20

DASHKO, Peter M. 2339 CLEVELAND AVE 43211 #038-75-1983, ▲ L1984 **FM GS** *071

DASKALOV, Tanya Nichole. ■ 43214 #038-40-2005 L2005 *100

DAVAKIS, Stephen Michael. 3400 OLENTANGY RIVER RD, STE 150 43202 #038-40-1987 L1988 **IM** *020 †20

DAVE, Amitkumar V. 793 W STATE ST, MT CARMEL MED CTR 43222 #759-06-2005 L2005 **IM** *012

DAVE, Pranav. 3525 OLENTANGY RIVER RD, STE 5360 43214 #041-14-2000 L2006 **DR** *100 †80

DAVENPORT, Jason Rennard. 1492 E BROAD ST, STE 1302 43205 #025-07-2000 L2004 **FSM** *020 †18 ‡

DAVIDO, Helen Theresa. 410 W 10TH AVE, OHIO STATE UNIV HOSP 43210 #041-12-2002 L2002 **CCS** *012

DAVIDORF, Frederick H. 456 W 10TH AVE STE 5B 43210 #038-40-1965 L1965 **OPH** *020 †35

DAVIDSON, Horace B, Jr. ■ 43214 #038-40-1960 L1960 **PTH** *071 †50

DAVIDSON, Patricia J. 700 CHILDRENS DR 43205 #038-41-1981 L1984 **AN PD** *020 †55,05

DAVIES, Dwight Howard. ■ 43231 #038-40-1945 L1945 **OM FM** *072

DAVIES, Elizabeth Ann. 1654 UPHAM DR, 357 MEANS HALL 43210 #038-44-1983 L1986 **TTS** *020 †85

DAVIS, Denise L. 543 TAYLOR AVE 43203 #016-45-1994 L1996 **PM** *020 †60

DAVIS, Galen Hubert. 5320 E MAIN ST STE 800 43213 #038-40-1958 L1958 **IM OS** *020

DAVIS, Gary Myron. 2200 W BROAD ST 43223 #038-40-1984 L1986 **P** *020 †75

DAVIS, John Raymond. 410 W 10TH AVE, UNIV HOSPITALS DIV. OF NUC 43210 #038-40-1967 L1967 **NM** *020 †28

DAVIS, Labronz Crenelle. 2782 W BROAD ST, HILLTOP FAMILY HEALTH 43204 #038-43-1996 L1999 **FM** *020 †18

DAVIS, Lee Roy. 4830 KNIGHTSBRIDGE BLVD, STE A 43214 #038-40-1973 L1973 **CD IM** *020 †20

DAVIS, Margaret Dorian. 3555 OLENTANGY RIVER RD, PEDIATRIX MED GRP STE 3050 43214 #038-40-1983 L1984 **NPM** *020 †55

DAVIS, Michael Paul. ■ 43221 #038-45-2003 L2003 **CD** *012 †20

DAVIS, Norman. 5975 E BROAD ST STE 201 43213 #038-40-1962 L1962 **A** *071

DAVIS, Tiffany Eul. 3525 OLENTANGY RIVER RD, STE 6350 43214 #038-43-2002 L2002 **OBG** *020 †55

DAVISON, Brian Lynn. 85 MCNAUGHTEN RD 43213 #018-03-1990 L1997 **OTR ORS** *020 †40

DAWOOD, Maha Munir. 5131 BEACON HILL RD, STE 210 43228 #575-01-1993 L2006 **IM** *020 †20

DAWSON, Emily Catherine. ■ 43215 #016-43-2004 L2007 **PEM** *012 †55

DEASY, Ryan Foster. 370 W 9TH AVE, OH STATE U COLL OF MED 43210 #038-40-2002 L2002 **OPH** *100 †35

DECKER, Gregory Harry. 3535 OLENTANGY RIVER RD 43214 #038-40-1982 L1983 **EM** *020 †16

DEEP, Don Patrick. 3555 OLENTANGY RIVER RD, STE 1080 43214 #038-44-1994 L1996 **IM** *020 †20

DEIBEL, Amy Elizabeth. 700 CHILDRENS DR 43205 #038-40-1998 L1999 **PD** *020 †55

DE LAPA, Joseph Michael, II. ■ 43204 #038-40-2004 L2004 **AN** *012

DELAVERIS, Steven Leo. 7630 RIVERS EDGE DR 43235 #016-76-1979, ▲ L1980 **FM OM** *020 ‡

DE LEON, Andre Mikael. 410 W 10TH AVE 43210 #305-01-2006 L2007 **FP** *012

DE LEON, Eric Orlando. 2240 N BANK DR, UPPR 43220 #011-04-1981 L1988 **AN** *020 †05

DELEVIE, Raymond Mark. 85 E GAY ST, STE 705 43215 #038-40-1991 *100

DELGADO, Mariel. ■ 43228 #042-01-2003 L2004 **NS** *012

DEL MEDICO, Valerie Jo. 4897 KARL RD, N COMM COUNSELING INC 43229 #038-40-1988 L1989 **CHP** *020

DE LOS REYES, Emily C. 700 CHILDRENS DR, DEPT CHILD NEUROLOGY 43205 #748-10-1985 L2003 **CHN** *020 †75,55

DE LOS SANTOS, Edith T. 543 TAYLOR AVE, VA OUTPATIENT CLINIC 43203 #748-01-1980 L1989 **IM END** *020

DELPHIA, Maureen Annette. 51 S SOUDER AVE, STE 2B 43222 #021-01-1987 L1987 **N** *020 †75

DELPHIA, Michael John. 4885 OLENTANGY RIVER RD 43214 #038-40-1976 L1976 **IM** *020 †20

DEL ROSARIO, Antonio J. 849 HARMON AVE 43223 #748-01-1964 L1971 **PD OS** *020

DEMARCO, Kristen Marie. 370 W 9TH AVE, OH STATE U COLL OF MED 43210 #038-40-2002 L2002 *100

DEMORAES, Francisco B. 1515 E BROAD ST 43205 #187-03-1965 L1996 **P** *020

DE MUTH, David Wallis. 92 NORTHWOODS BLVD 43235 #038-40-1962 L1962 **P** *020 †75

DE MUTH, Gary Ellis. ■ 43228 #038-40-1964 L1964 **GP OS** *062

DENNY, Sarah Anne. 700 CHILDRENS DR, UNIV OF WA SOM GME RM C212 43205 #038-45-2004 L2007 **PD** *020 †55

DERCK, James W. 750 MOUNT CARMEL MALL 43222 #038-40-1979 L1980 **EM** *020 †16

DE RENNE, Lawrence Alfred. 410 W 10TH AVE, OH STATE UNIV MED CTR 43210 #017-20-1973 L1998 **PTH** *020 †50

DERROW, Solomon Zvi. ■ 43210 #038-40-2001 L2001 **DR** *020 †80

DESAI, Aashish Pravin. 793 W STATE ST, MT CARMEL MED CTR 43222 #665-02-2006 L2006 **IM** *012

DESAI, Kalpna Satish. 543 TAYLOR AVE 43203 #495-76-1969 L1981 **GP** *020

DESCHENES, Denise. 1640 NEIL AVE 4TH FL, YOUNKIN SUCCESS CTR 43201 #038-40-1989 L1991 **P** *020 †75

DE VERTEUIL, Virginia A. 453 WATERBURY CT, PEDIATRIC & ADOLESCENT 43230 #038-40-1982 L1983 **PD** *020 †55

DEVINE, Steven Michael. 320 W 10TH AVE, B411 STARLING LOVING HALL 43210 #024-16-1987 L2005 **ON** *020 †20

DE VOE, Keith, Jr. 3555 OLENTANGY RIVER RD, STE 3070 43214 #038-40-1955 L1955 **GYN** *072 †30

DEVOE, Stephen John. 3545 OLENTANGY RVR RD #114 43214 #038-40-1969 L1969 **OBG MFM** *020 †30

DEVORE, Elise Rene. 700 CHILDRENS DR, CHILDREN'S HOSPITAL 43205 #018-03-2000 L2007 **ADL** *100 †55

DEVULAPALLY, Kiran Kumar. 473 W 12TH AVE, 201 DHLRI 43210 #495-65-1995 L2001 **PCC** *012 †20

DHAWALE, Praveena V. 1495 MORSE RD 43229 #017-20-2001 L2001 **PD** *020 †55

DHAWALE, Ravi Shrikrishna. 500 THOMAS LN, STE 3G 43214 #017-20-2001 L2001 **END** *020

DHAYANANDHAN, Christi Pri. 370 W 9TH AVE, 254 MEILING HALL 43210 #038-40-2008 *012

DHILLON, Lena. 111 S GRANT AVE 43215 #495-43-2001 L2003 **P** *100

DIAB, Andrew George. ■ 43212 #038-40-2008 *012

■ = Address Information Privacy Protected

DIAB, Mohammad Samir. 793 W STATE ST, MT CARMEL WEST 43222 #038-44-2004 L2004
D *012

DIAKOFF, Elizabeth Anne. 456 W 10TH AVE 43210 #038-43-1999 L1999 IM *020 †20

DIAZ, Philip Tomas. 473 W 12TH AVE, RM 201 43210 #041-14-1986 L1989 PUD *050 †20

DICK, Michael Richard. 1654 UPHAM DR, 146 MEANS HALL 43210 #038-40-1989 L1990
CCS EM *020 †16

DICKENS, Dale Raywood. ■ 43220 #038-40-1945 L1945 GS *071 †85

DICKERSON, Jennifer Ann. 473 W 12TH AVE, STE 200 43210 #038-45-2001 L2001 CD *100

DICKERSON, Kevin Michael. 4885 OLENTANGY RIVER RD, # 2-10 43214 #012-01-1997 L1998
PD *020 †55

DICKEY, Douglas James. 7400 HUNTINGTON PARK DR, STE 200 43235 #038-43-1992 L1993
FM *020 †18

DIECKHOFF, John C, Jr. 793 W STATE ST, MOUNT CARMEL WEST 43222 #038-45-2003 L2004
IM *012 †20

DIEDERICHS, Henry August. 941 N HIGH ST 43201 #023-01-1955 L1964 PTH *071 †95

DIEDRICH, Wm Arnold, Jr. 5100 W BROAD ST 43228 #035-03-1979 L2006 PTH *020 †50

DIEHL, Jason James. 2050 KENNY RD, FL 3 43221 #038-40-2000 L2000 FSM *020 †18

DIETRICH, Ann Marie. 700 CHILDRENS DR, EMERGENCY MEDICINE 43205 #038-44-1985 L1987
PD PEM *020 †55

DIETSCH, John Donald. ■ 43214 #038-40-1960 L1960 AN OS *071 †05

DIJKSTRA, Margit Cecile. 3781 S HIGH ST, COLUMBUS NEIGHBORHOOD HEAL 43207
#038-40-2004 L2004 FM *020

DILLHOFF, Mary Colter. 316A MARSHALL PSGE, OHIO STATE UNIV 43215 #038-41-2005 L2005
GS *012

DIMITRIS, Craig Nick. ■ 43204 #038-40-2008 *012

DIMITRIS, Kirk Douglas. 793 W STATE ST, CO MT CARMEL HOSP-MED EDU 43222
#038-40-2003 L2003 ORS *012

DIMITROVA, Galina T. 410 W 10TH AVE, DOAN HALL N416 43210 #198-03-1990 L2000
AN *05

DIN, Anwar U. 423 E TOWN ST, STE 1000 43215 #690-02-1981 L1998 CD NC *020 †20

DINGLE, Jack. 262 NEIL AVE, STE 420 43215 #038-40-1972 L1972 OPH *020 †35

DINGLE, Thomas John. ■ 43221 #038-40-2004 L2005 OPH *012

DI ORIO, Douglas James. 3705 OLENTANGY RIVER RD, STE 260 43214 #038-40-1994 L1995
FSM *020 †18

DI ORIO, Mary Seit. ■ 43220 #038-40-1994 L1995 GPM *020 †18,70

DIPIETRA, John. 5969 E BROAD ST 43213 #561-11-1986 L1994 IM PD *020 †20

DI SALVO, Rebecca R. 755 THOMAS LN 43214 #038-40-1986 L1987 IM *030 †20

DIXON, Meredith Christine. ■ 43212 #038-40-2008 *012

DOBSON, Janet Louise. 41 S HIGH ST 30TH FL 43215 #038-43-1980 L1984 LM PTH *062 †50

DOBYNS, Mary Meredith. 2200 W BROAD ST 43223 #038-06-1973 L1973 P CHP *020 †75

DODDS, Stephen Howard. 750 MOUNT CARMEL MALL 43222 #035-01-1993 L1994
EM *020 †16

DODSON, Edward Eugene. 456 W 10TH AVE, THE OHIO ST UNIV, UHC 4024 43210
#051-01-1989 L1996 OTO *020 †45

DOGRA, Simmi. 700 CHILDRENS DR, CHILDREN'S HOSPITAL 43205 #038-44-1996 L1997
PD *020 †55

DOLEH, Tarick Yunes. ■ 43201 #038-40-2008 *012

DOLOR, F Robert G. 500 E MAIN ST, STE 100 43215 #748-10-1963 L1971 IM CD *020

DOMINGO, Carlos Bansuelo. 43230 #017-20-2001 L2001 CCS *100

DOMINGUEZ, Edward Paul. 3545 OLENTANGY RIVER RD, STE 525 43214 #038-40-2000 L2000
GS *085

DONNALLY, Michael Robert. 1654 UPHAM DR, 202 MEANS HALL 43210 #038-43-2004 L2004
IM *100 †20

DONNELLY, Dustin James. ■ 43220 #038-40-2008 *012

DONNER, Jessica Lynn. ■ 43221 #038-40-2007 L2007 OBG *012

DONNERBERG, Roy L. 51 S SOUDER AVE 43222 #038-41-1950 L1950 IMG PUD *071 †20

DONO, Francis Vincent. 180 E BROAD ST 43215 #038-75-1958, ▲ L1959 OBG GS *020

DONOFRIO, Mark Michael. 410 W 10TH AVE, DEPT OF ORTHOPEDIS 43210
#041-15-1999 L1999 ORS *020 †40

DONOVAN, James Patrick. ■ 43212 #038-41-2007 L2007 GS *012

DONOVAN, Lorna Ferguson. 453 WATERBURY CT, PEDIATRIC & ADOLESCENT 43230
#038-40-1985 L1987 PD *020 †55

DONTHI, Rajesh Ramamurthy. 700 CHILDRENS DR 43205 #038-43-2001 L2001 PD *100 †55

DONTHIREDDY, Kavitha Redd. ■ 43230 #495-21-1998 L2007 ON *100 †20

DONTHIREDDY, Shilpa. ■ 43230 #496-22-2000 L2005 IM *100 †20

DOODY, Dennis Michael. 170 NORTHWOODS BLVD 43235 #038-40-1974 L1974
PD ADL *020 †55

DOOLITTLE, Kenneth H. ■ 43212 #035-45-1956 L1960 U *071 †95

DORAN, Trisha Annette. 1654 UPHAM DR, 215 MEANS HALL 43210 #038-40-2002 L2002
GE *012 †20

DORGAN, James Quinn, Jr. 111 S GRANT AVE 43215 #038-40-1961 L1961 GPM PM *020

DOSHI, Amit Arvind. 473 W 12TH AVE, STE 200 43210 #665-01-2000 L2003 CD *012 †20

DOSSETT, Lee M. 410 W 10TH AVE, 209 MEANS HALL 43210 #020-12-2006 L2006 IM *012

DOSUNMU, Eniolami Omowunm. ■ 43201 #038-40-2008 *012

DOUGHERTY, Dana Lynn. 150 TAYLOR STATION RD, STE 140 43213 #028-34-2000 L2003
FM *020 †18 ‡

DOWLING, Todd Michael. 262 NEIL AVE, STE 500 43215 #038-40-1991 L1995 AN *020 †05

DOWNEY, Charles Michael. 4488 W BROAD ST 43228 #038-40-1966 L1966 FM *071 †18

DOYLE, Patrick Brian. 3180 E BROAD ST 43209 #038-40-1982 L1983 FM *020

DRAGO, Stefano P. 410 W 10TH AVE 43210 #561-17-1986 GS *020

DRAKE, Jaclyn M. 207 MEANS HALL, OHIO STATE UNIV MED CTR 43210 #038-75-2007,
▲ L2007 IM *012

DRAKE, Melanie Renee. 3555 OLENTANGY RIVER RD, STE 1080 43214 #038-44-2003 L2003
IM *020

DRAKE, Miles Edward. 1654 UPHAM DR, 407 MEANS HALL 43210 #036-07-1977 L1982
N OS *020

DREES, David Michael. 777 W STATE ST 43222 #038-40-1985 L1991 DR *020 †80

DRENNEN, Erica Rae. 1654 UPHAM DR, OHIO STATE UNIV MED CTR 43210
#038-40-2007 L2007 OBG *012

DREW, Kathryn. ■ 43221 #038-40-1977 L1977 IM *020 †20

DREYER, Jeffrey Randall. 750 MOUNT CARMEL MALL, STE 300 43222 #038-40-1985 L1986
EM FM *020 †18,16

DROBNY, Eric David. 1496 OLD HENDERSON RD 43220 #038-40-1994 L1995 EM *020 †16

DROSS, Ingeborg C Patrylo. ■ 43201 #407-20-1944 L1969 IM GP *072

DROSS, Vasilios P. 543 TAYLOR AVE 43203 #418-01-1947 L1964 FM EM *071 †18

DRSTVENSEK, John Andrew. 3535 OLENTANGY RIVER RD 43214 #038-40-1976 L1976
EM OM *020 †16

DRUHAN, Stephen Michael. 700 CHILDRENS DR, DEPT OF RADIOLOGY, A1010 43205
#038-41-2000 L2000 PDR *020 †80

DUBEY, Praveen. 3535 OLENTANGY RIVER RD, METHODIST HOSPITAL 43214
#038-44-1991 L1992 RO *020 †20,80

DUBIN, Alex Raymond. 6495 E BROAD ST STE A 43213 #038-40-1966 L1966 PD *020 †55

DUFF, Steven Barron. 3555 OLENTANGY RIVER RD, STE 2060 43214 #038-41-1981 L1988
TS *020 †85,90

DUFFEY, Michelle Lea. 700 CHILDRENS DR, COLUMBUS CHILDREN'S HOSPIT 43205
#038-45-1999 L1999 PD *020 †55

DUFFY, Joseph Stephen, Jr. ■ 43214 #038-43-2008 *012

DUGAN, Christine Louise. 555 S 18TH ST 43205 #017-20-2005 L2005 PD *012

DUHIGG, Daniel James. 1670 UPHAM DR, 3RD FL ADULT UNIT 43210 #028-78-2005, ▲ L2005
P *012

DULL, Bradley D. ■ 43212 #036-05-2007 L2007 GS *012

DUNFEE, Heather Christie. 410 W 10TH AVE 43210 #038-75-2005, ▲ L2005 AN *012

DUNGAN, Kathleen Marie. 456 W 10TH AVE 43210 #038-40-2001 L2006 END *020 †20

DURAN, Robert Jackson. 410 W 10TH AVE 43210 #039-01-1947 L1956 HS PS *071 †65

DURBIN, John C. 700 CHILDRENS DR, CHILDREN'S HOSPITAL 43205
#033-06-1989 L1997 PTH *020 †50

DURBIN, Robert Allen. 259 TAYLOR STATION RD, INC 43213 #038-40-1976 L1976 ORS *020 †40

DURBIN, Thomas Christophe. 793 W STATE ST, EDUCATION DEPT. 43222 #038-40-2006 L2006
ORS *012

DURNWALD, Celeste P. 1654 UPHAM DR, MEANS HALL 43210 #038-44-1997 L2000
OBG *020 †30

DURRANI, Samedyar Irfan. 793 W STATE ST 43222 #038-41-2005 L2005 GS *012

DUSSEAU, Joseph Patrick. 2231 N HIGH ST, OSU RARDIN FAM PRACTICE 43201
#038-40-2000 L2003 FM *020 †18

DUSSEAU, Paul David. 3311 TREMONT RD 43221 #038-40-1974 L1974 FM *020 †18

DUTKIEWICZ, Radoslaw M. ■ 43228 #056-05-2003 L2003 IM *100

DUZIK, Emily Ann. 3535 OLENTANGY RIVER RD 43214 #018-75-2005, ▲ L2005 IM *012

DYER, Jennifer Shine. ■ 43202 #048-13-2000 L2006 PDE *100 †55

DYSON, Kristie Yancy. ■ 43235 #038-41-2007 L2007 OBG *012

DZODZOMENYO, Samuel. 700 CHILDRENS DR, DEPT OF NEUROLOGY 43205
#412-02-1996 L1996 CHN *020 †75

EAKIN, Jeff Lewis. 410 W 10TH AVE, OH STATE UNIV HOSP 43210 #038-40-2006 L2006 GS *012

EARLY, Richard Edwin. 793 W STATE ST 43222 #038-40-1981 L1983 FM ADL *050 †18

EASTERDAY, Mark Andrew. 793 W STATE ST 43222 #038-45-1995 L1996 IM *020 †18,20

EATON, Antoinette Parisi. 700 CHILDRENS DR, COLUMBUS CHILDRENS HOSP 43205
#041-07-1956 L1957 PD *062 †55

EATON, Lynne Antoinette. 4775 KNIGHTSBRIDGE BLVD, STE 103 43214 #041-07-1988 L1990
OBG *020 †30

ECHAVARRIA CANO, Maria La. 410 W 10TH AVE 43210 #132-09-1997 L2007 OBG *012 ·

ECK, Heather Christine. 111 S GRANT AVE, 3RD FL 43215 #038-44-2000 L2000 AN *020

ECKER, Robert Arthur. 4885 OLENTANGY RIVER RD, STE 2-50 43214 #038-43-1978 L1980
IM *020 †18

ECKLAR, George Patrick. 1547 W BROAD ST, METROWEST FAMILY HEALTH 43222
#038-40-1975 L1976 IM *020 †20

EDGIN, Richard Alan. 85 MCNAUGHTEN RD STE 320, OHIO GASTROENTEROLOGY 43213
#048-15-1976 L1977 GE *020 †20

EDISON, James Austin. 777 W STATE ST, OHIO GASTROENTEROLOGY 43222
#038-41-1990 L1992 GE *020 †20

EDWARDS, Christine C. ■ 43221 #055-01-1990 L1995 OS *012

EGAN, Matthew Jay. 700 CHILDRENS DR, COLUMBUS CHILDRENS HOSP 43205 #035-15-2004 L2007
PDC *012 †55

EICKHOLT, John Lewis, III. 7811 FLINT RD, STE C 43235 #038-40-1977 L1978 N SME *020 †75

EIGINGER, Ann Margaret. 1492 E BROAD ST, OSU EAST HOSPITAL 43205 #038-44-1992 L1993
EM *020 †16

ELAM, Mary Jane. 1875 MILLIKIN RD, STUDENT HEALTH SERVICES 43210 #025-07-1985 L1986
FM OS *020 †18

EL-BASH, Omar Ahmad. ■ 43214 #915-05-1971 L1978 U *020 †95

ELBIAADI, Anne. ■ 43215 #016-42-2004 L2005 OPH *012

ELFALLAH, Khaled Elmabruk. 1375 PERRY ST 5TH FL, RM 526 43201 #613-02-2000 L2002
GS *100

ELKHAMMAS, Elmahdi A. 1654 UPHAM DR, 3RD FLOOR MEANS HALL 43210
#613-01-1977 L1985 GS TTS *020 †85

ELKHATIB, Imad Mouin. ■ 43210 #038-41-2007 IM *012

ELLINGWOOD, Beth Leah. 6495 E BROAD ST, STE A 43213 #038-40-1998 L1999 PD *020 †55

ELLIS, Jennifer Watters. 2231 N HIGH ST 43201 #016-43-1998 L1999 FM *020 †18

ELLIS, Robert Charles. 2250 NORTHBANK DR 43220 #038-40-1959 L1959 OPH *071 †35

ELLISON, Bradley Scott. ■ 43212 #036-01-2003 L2003 ORS *012

ELLISON, Edwin C. 327 MARSHALL PSGE, 1654 UPHAM DR 43215 #056-06-1976 L1977
GS GE *020 †85

ELMARAGHY, Charles Albert. 456 W 10TH AVE, 4A EAR NOSE AND THROAT CLI 43210
#038-40-2000 L2000 OTO *020 †20

EL SAYED AWAD, Hamdy M. 410 W 10TH AVE, N-146 DOAN HALL 43210 #915-09-1983 L1997
AN *020 †05

EL-SHAMMAA, Emile Nabil. 1654 UPHAM DR 43210 #036-07-1994 L1995 EM GP *020 †16

ELSHARYDAH, Ahmad M. 2050 KENNY RD, OHIO STATE SPINE CENTER 43221
#875-01-1990 L2006 APM *100 †20

ELSHEIKH, Bakri Hassan. 1654 UPHAM DR, 473 MEANS HALL 43210 #848-01-1991 L2000
N *020 †75

ELTON, Scott Wentworth. 700 CHILDRENS DR 43205 #041-12-1994 L1996 NS *020 †25

ELWOOD, Patrick Clay. 5825 WESTBOURNE AVE 43213 #030-05-1975 L2000 HEM ON *050 †20

EL-ZAHARNA, Ramy Mohamed. 111 S GRANT AVE 43215 #286-12-2000 L2005 FP *012

EMLICH, William F, Jr. 4930 W BROAD ST STE 4 43228 #038-75-1986, ▲ L1987 GE HEP *020

ENELI, Ihuoma Uchechi. 700 CHILDRENS DR, CENTER FOR HLTH WEIGHT 43205
#690-04-1989 L2006 PD *020 †55 ‡

ENGELMAN, Mark Richard. ■ 43212 #038-40-1973 L1973 EM *020 †16

ENGLEHART, Thomas W. 793 W STATE ST, MOUNT CARMEL MEDICAL CENTE 43222
#038-45-1994 L1995 AN *020 †18

ENRILE, Benedicta G. 700 CHILDRENS DR, TIMKEN BLDG RM G351 PEDS 43205
#748-01-1962 L1972 PD OS *020 †55

EPITROPOULOS, Alice T. 262 NEIL AVE, OPHTHALMIC SURGEONS & 43215
#038-40-1989 L1990 OPH *020 †35

EPSTEIN, Avrom David. 262 NEIL AVE, STE 440 43215 #038-40-1980 L1994 OPH *020 †35,75

ERDEY, Richard Andrew. 5965 E BROAD ST, STE 490 43213 #051-04-1984 L1991 OPH *020 †35

ERDMAN, Steven Henry. 700 CHILDRENS DR, THE OHIO STATE UNIVERSITY 43205 #049-01-1981 L2000 **PD GE** *020 †55
ERTER, Jack William. ■ 43202 #045-01-2004 L2007 **HO** *012
ERWIN, Elizabeth Anne. ■ 43205 #038-41-1997 L1998 **PD** *020 †55,03
ESCOBAR, Patricia. 3535 OLENTANGY RIVER RD, INTENSIVE CARE UNIT 43214 #264-02-1981 L1992 **AN IM** *020 †20
ESKIN, Steven James. 3535 OLENTANGY RIVER RD, DEPT OF EMERGENCY MED 43214 #035-03-1985 L1986 **EM** *040 †16
ESPINOSA, Allan Vigarny. 410 W 10TH AVE 43210 #682-04-2003 L2007 **IM** *012
ESSIG, Garth Fredric. 456 W 10TH AVE, STE 2B 43210 #038-40-1961 L1961 **OBG** *020 †30
ESSIG, Leroy William, II. 473 W 12TH AVE, 201 HLRI 43210 #038-40-1999 L1999 **PCC** *100 †20
ESTELLE, Kimberly Anne. ■ 43209 #038-40-2006 L2006 **IM** *012
ESTERLINE, William James. 85 MCNAUGHTEN RD, STE 110 43213 #008-01-1986 L1992 **TS** *020 †85,90
EVANS, David Clay. ■ 43214 #036-07-2006 L2006 **GS** *012
EVANS, Erik W. 280 E TOWN ST, STE C 43215 #016-06-2001 L2006 **GS** *020
EVANS, Kenneth Wynne. 410 W 10TH AVE 43210 #062-01-2004 L2006 **DR** *100
EVANS, Mark Alan. 3724 OLENTANGY BLVD 43214 #038-40-1984 L1985 **FM FPG** *020 †18
EVANS, R R. 5657 GODOWN RD 43235 #035-09-1974 L1983 **AN** *020 †05
EVANS, Thomas Wm. 280 E TOWN ST, STE C 43215 #038-40-1969 L1969 **FPS EM** *020
EVERHART, Larry Stewart. 730 MT AIRYSHIRE BLVD, STE A 43235 #038-40-1973 L1973 **IM** *020 †20
EVERHART, Richard L. ■ 43214 #038-40-1941 L1941 **GP** *071
EVERHART-MC DONALD, M A. 1010 BETHEL RD 43214 #038-40-1984 L1985 **PM OS** *020 †60
EWING, John David. ■ 43204 #038-40-2006 L2006 **EM** *012
EXLINE, Matthew C. 1654 UPHAM DR 43210 #031-01-2000 L2000 **PCC SME** *050 †20
EZELL, Harry Eugene, Jr. 777 W STATE ST 43222 #047-05-1944 L1947 **OBG** *071 †30
EZZIDDIN, Omar. ■ 43214 #038-40-2008 *012
EZZIE, Michael Elias. 473 W 12TH AVE, 201 DHLRI 43210 #038-40-2001 L2001 **PCC** *012
EZZIE, Mollie Kristin. 1654 UPHAM DR, MEANS HALL RM 539 43210 #038-40-2001 L2001 **OBG** *100 †30
FABIA, Renata Bronislawa. 555 S 18TH ST, CHILDRENS SURGICAL 43205 #759-12-1985 L2000 **GS** *020 †85
FABIAN, Matthew Joseph. ■ 43221 #047-06-2003 L2003 **AN** *012
FADA, Robert Alan. 323 E TOWN ST, SPORTS MEDICINE GRANT, INC 43215 #041-12-1991 L1996 **ORS** *020 †40
FAGAN, J Barry. 745 W STATE ST, STE 510 43222 #038-40-1984 L1988 **PUD** *020 †20
FAHEY, Patrick Jos. 2231 N HIGH ST, C/O RARDIN FAMILY PRACTICE 43201 #016-11-1975 L1976 **FM** *040 †18
FALCONE, Robert Edward. 111 S GRANT AVE, # 2 43215 #038-40-1976 L1977 **GS TRS** *030 †85
FALLON, Timothy James. 51 S SOUDER AVE 43222 #038-40-1967 L1967 **PM** *071 †60
FAN, Lisha. 1654 UPHAM DR, 630 MEANS HALL 43210 #243-02-1983 L2000 **RO** *100
FANKHAUSER, Richard Allen. 815 W BROAD ST STE 300 43222 #038-40-1977 L1978 **ORS** *020 †40
FARBER, Sanders Merton. 150 TAYLOR STATION RD, STE 150 43213 #038-40-1960 L1960 **OPH** *020 †35
FARDAL, Patrick Michael. 520 KING AVE 43201 #056-05-1973 L1977 **FOP PTH** *062 †50
FARHAN, Joman Ishaq. ■ 43235 #575-01-1988 L1999 **IM** *020 †20
FARINA, Ralph Albert, Jr. 930 BETHEL RD, OHIO SURGERY CTR 43214 #038-44-1988 L1991 **AN** *020 †05
FARNER, Staci Dawn. ■ 43214 #028-34-2004 L2004 **OBG** *012
FAROOKI, Shella. 6200 CLEVELAND AVE, COLUMBUS RADIOLOGY CORP 43231 #035-46-1994 L2000 **DR** *020 †80
FAROOKI, Zia Ul Qamar. 700 CHILDRENS DR, ST JOHN HOSPITAL & MEDICAL 43205 #704-01-1965 L2007 **PDC PD** *020 †55
FAROOQUI, Asim Ashraf. 2200 W BROAD ST, TWIN VALLEY BEHAVIORAL HEA 43223 #704-16-1989 L1996 **P** *020 †75
FARRAR, Britten Alison. ■ 43215 #038-40-2004 L2004 **IM** *100
FARRAR, William Blair. 300 W 10TH AVE 43210 #051-01-1975 L1976 **SO HNS** *040 †85
FARRELL, Matthew James. ■ 43201 #038-40-2008 *012
FARYMAN, Sheila Ann. 370 W 9TH AVE, OH STATE U COLL OF MED 43210 #038-40-2002 L2002 **IM** *100 †20
FARYNA, Alice. 770 KINNEAR RD 43212 #035-45-1957 L1958 **RHU IM** *071 †20
FASS, Robert Jerome. 456 W 10TH AVE, 4715 UNIV HOSP CLNC 43210 #024-07-1964 L1967 **ID IM** *050 †20
FATE, Troy David. 4882 E MAIN ST, STE 200 43213 #038-43-2001 L2007 **FM** *020
FATHALA, Ahmed Labib. ■ 43228 #915-03-1991 L2006 **IM** *020 †20,28
FAUST, Russell Allen. 700 CHILDRENS DR, COLUBUS CHILDRENS HOSP 43205 #026-04-1992 L2006 **OTO** *020 †45
FEDEL, Gina Marie. 700 CHILDRENS DR 43205 #041-07-1986 L1997 **AN CCM** *020 †05
FEDERER, Harold Wm. ■ 43230 #038-40-1943 L1943 **GP** *071
FEDORCHAK, Arlene Marie. ■ 43220 #038-40-1987 L1990 **IM** *071 †20
FEIBEL, Jonathan Barnett. 1405 DUBLIN RD 43215 #038-40-1995 L1996 **OFA ORS** *020 †40
FELDMAN, David Seth. 473 W 12TH AVE, STE 200 43210 #012-01-1994 L2003 **CD** *020 †20
FELTES, Timothy Francis. 700 CHILDRENS DR, COLUMBUS CHILDREN'S HOSPIT 43205 #038-43-1980 L1986 **PDC** *020 †55
FENNER, Melissa Kelly. 1654 UPHAM DR, 165 MEANS HALL 43210 #038-41-1999 L1999 **EM** *020 †16
FERGUSON, Ronald Morris. 1654 UPHAM DR, 363 MEANS HALL 43210 #028-02-1971 L1982 **TTS GS** *040 †85
FERNALD, Willard B. 1021 COUNTRY CLUB RD, STE A 43213 #024-01-1951 L1955 **PD** *071 †55
FERNANDEZ MELENDEZ, Karen. ■ 43221 #429-02-2001 L2006 **PHO** *012 †55
FERNANDEZ-PIZZI, Alex. 740 E 17TH AVE, C/O OHIO STATE HWY PATROL 43211 #847-10-1974 L1980 **OM GS** *020 †85,70
FERRANTE, Mark Anthony. ■ 43232 #011-04-1989 L2007 **N** *020 †75
FERRIS, William Edmund. 962 S FRONT ST, SOUTH FRONT FAMILY HEALTH 43206 #038-41-1956 L1956 **FM** *071 †18
FETKO, Mark. 6001 E BROAD ST 43213 #038-40-1986 L1988 **AN PMM** *020 †05
FETTMAN, Mark Saml. 4700 REED RD, STE A 43220 #038-40-1973 L1990 **P CHP** *020 †75
FIALA, Joseph Francis. 7400 HUNTINGTON PARK DR 43235 #038-40-1988 L1989 **PD** *020 †55
FICCO, Ryan Patrick. ■ 43201 #038-40-2008 *012
FIELD, Robert Louis. 1440 HAWTHORNE AVE 43203 #045-01-1980 L1981 **RO** *020
FIGURA, Andrew Thomas. 1087 DENNISON AVE 43201 #041-15-1999 L2004 **RO RO** *012
FILIATRAUT, Arthur Z. 410 W 10TH AVE 43210 #016-43-1970 L1973 **DR** *020 †80
FINCK, Samuel A. ■ 43228 #038-75-2004, ▲ L2004 **ORS** *012
FINK, Colleen Anne. 793 W STATE ST, MT CARMEL MED CTR 43222 #665-01-2005 L2005 **IM** *012
FINNIE, Douglas Gordon. 4310 CLIME RD STE B 43228 #038-40-1975 L1975 **IM** *020 †20 ‡
FIRSTENBERG, Michael Sol. ■ 43212 #038-06-1996 L1998 **GS** *100 †85,90
FISCHER, Richard Alan. 1405 DUBLIN RD, SURGEONS, INC 43215 #050-02-1980 L1991 **ORS** *020 †40
FISHER, David Joshua. 700 CHILDRENS DR 43205 #024-07-1974 L1995 **OS PDC** *030 †55
FISHER, Mason Gordon. 316A MARSHALL PSGE, OHIO STATE UNIV 43215 #038-40-2003 L2003 **GS** *012
FISHER, Megan Christine. ■ 43221 #038-40-2006 L2006 **GS** *012
FITCH, Jill Alison. 700 CHILDRENS DR, ED-354/CRITICAL CARE 43205 #038-44-1992 L1995 **CCP** *020 †55,20
FITCH, Robert Dine. 4850 E MAIN ST 43213 #038-45-1987 L1989 **FM** *020 †18
FITCH, Teresa M. 4850 E MAIN ST 43213 #038-40-1999 L1999 **FM** *020 †18
FLANIGAN, David Clint. ■ 43235 #018-03-1998 L2004 **OSM** *020 †40
FLEAGLE, Jessica M. ■ 43235 #038-75-2007, ▲ L2007 *012
FLEMING, Gloria Penelope. 456 W 10TH AVE 43210 #035-15-1994 L2005 **OPH** *020 †35
FLEMING, Kelly Jeanne. 697 THOMAS LN, RIVERSIDE FAMILY PRACTICE 43214 #038-40-2004 L2004 **FM** *100 †18
FLEMING, Mark Stephen. 130 S DAVIS AVE STE 101 43222 #021-01-1980 L1989 **NS** *075 †25
FLOOD, Joseph. 497 E TOWN ST STE 230 43215 #010-02-1979 L1984 **RHU** *020 †20
FLORES, Arthur. ■ 43201 #038-40-1998 L2000 **FM** *020 †18
FOERSCHLER, Derek L. ■ 43228 #003-75-2007, ▲ L2007 **AN** *012
FOLEY, Kristin Michelle. 3525 OLENTANGY RIVER RD, STE 5360 43214 #028-02-2000 L2007 **DR** *100 †80
FOLEY, Ryan Patrick. ■ 43201 #038-06-2006 L2007 **ORS** *012
FOLIANO, Laura. 410 W 10TH AVE 43210 #038-43-1988 L1990 **FM** *020 †18
FOLK, Robert Lee. 200 MCILING HALL, 370 W 9TH AVE 43210 #038-40-1960 L1960 **IM END** *071 †20
FONTANA, Mary Elizabeth. 473 W 12TH AVE 43210 #038-40-1966 L1966 **CD** *040 †20
FOOR, John Stephen. 4300 CLIME RD, STE A 43228 #038-40-1999 L2000 **GS** *020 †85
FORD, Carla Denise. ■ 43204 #038-40-2005 L2005 **OPH** *012
FORD, Larry Creed. 1654 UPHAM DR, 202 MEANS HALL 43210 #038-40-2005 L2005 **IM** *012
FORD, Meghan Elizabeth. ■ 43201 #038-40-2008 *012
FORGUE, Wesley Vincent. 285 E STATE ST, STE 360 43215 #048-12-1975 L1981 **NEP IM** *020 †20
FORREST, Lowell Arick. 456 W 10TH AVE, STE 4A 43210 #038-40-1988 L1993 **OTO** *020 †45
FORSTER, Meghan Rebecca. ■ 43201 #038-41-2004 L2004 **GS** *012
FORSTHOEFEL, Kevin F. 410 W 1OTH AVE, DEPT PATHOLOGY 43201 #038-41-1987 L1988 **PTH** *020 †50
FORSYTHE, Robert Cumming. 4885 OLENTANGY RIVER RD, STE 2-10 43214 #018-03-1977 L1981 **PD AI** *020 †55,03
FORTUNE, Brett Emerson. 1654 UPHAM DR, 202 MEANS HALL 43210 #036-05-2004 L2004 **IM** *100 †20
FOSNAUGH, Neil Ray. 3535 OLENTANGY RIVER RD 43214 #038-40-1976 L1976 **EM FM** *020 †18,16
FOSS, Peter Forrest. 5131 BEACON HILL RD, STE 320 43228 #038-75-1985, ▲ L1986 **IM** *020
FOSTER, James Carlton. ■ 43228 #038-40-2006 L2006 **IM** *012
FOSTER, Jenniene Lynn. 410 W 10TH AVE, OHIO STATE UNIVERSITY HOSP 43210 #038-40-2002 L2002 **AN** *020 †05
FOSTER, Jessica E A. 700 CHILDRENS DR, PEDI DIV 43205 #019-02-2001 L2007 **PD DBP** *020 †55
FOSTER, Jill Annette. 262 NEIL AVE, OPHTHALMIC SURGEONS & 43215 #016-11-1986 L1992 **OPH FPS** *020 †35
FOSTER, Sidney Vincent. ■ 43221 #038-40-1962 L1962 **FM** *071 †18
FOUZAS, Ioannis Paul. 410 W 10TH AVE 43210 #418-02-1990 *100
FOWLER, Jeffrey Mccabe. 1654 UPHAM DR 5TH FL, DEPT OBGYN MEANS HALL 43210 #016-06-1985 L1987 **GO GYN** *020 †30
FOWLER, Terry Ty. ■ 43215 #025-07-2005 L2005 **ORS** *012
FOX, Charity Craver. 473 W 12TH AVE, 201 DAVIS HEART LUNG RESEA 43210 #023-01-1978 L1991 **AI IM** *020 †20,03
FOX, David Brian. 3555 OLENTANGY RIVER RD, STE 3030 43214 #038-40-1989 L1990 **MFM OBG** *020 †30
FOX, Jason Hilton. 6200 CLEVELAND AVE, COLUMBUS RADIOLOGY CORP 43231 #038-43-1996 L2004 **DR** *020 †80
FOX, Thomas Edward. ■ 43221 #038-40-1940 L1940 **R** *071 †80
FRAIR, Ellin C. 2760 AIRPORT DR, STE 100 43219 #012-05-1992 L1996 **IM** *020 †20
FRAKER, Theodore D'Eston. 473 W 12TH AVE, 2ND FLOOR HLRI 43210 #038-40-1973 L1974 **CD IM** *030 †20
FRANCIS, Patricia Ann. 1830 BETHEL RD STE C 43220 #025-07-1987 L1988 **PD** *020 †55
FRANCO, Veronica. 473 W 12TH AVE, OHIO STATE UNIVERSITY 43210 #737-06-1998 L2007 **CD** *100 †20
FRANK, Erin Christine. 410 W 10TH AVE, DEPT IM 43210 #028-34-2007 L2007 **IM** *012
FRANK, Megan Sellman. ■ 43209 #038-40-2004 L2004 **FM** *020 †18
FRANKEL, Wendy Lynne. 1645 NEIL AVE 43210 #025-01-1988 L1997 **PTH** *020 †50
FRANKLIN, Brock Allen. ■ 43206 #016-11-2006 L2006 **EM** *012
FRANKLIN, Lewis T. ■ 43220 #018-03-1951 L1952 **AN** *071 †05
FRANZ, Michael Lloyd. 3535 OLENTANGY RIVER RD 43214 #038-40-1971 L1971 **A PD** *020 †55,03
FRANZ, Randall William. 285 E STATE ST, STE 260 43215 #038-45-1992 L1994 **VS GS** *020 †85
FRASER, Nikkiya Marie. ■ 43210 #038-41-2003 L2006 **ID** *012 †20
FRAZER, Dana Marie. 285 E STATE ST STE 620 43215 #038-45-1996 L1997 **GS** *020 †85
FRAZIER, Warren Joshua. 700 CHILDRENS DR 43205 #055-02-2001 L2001 **CCP** *012 †55
FREEDY, Lucy V Rawlings. 1654 UPHAM DR, 630 MEANS HALL 43210 #036-07-1957 L1959 **DR NM** *020 †80
FREEDY, Robert J. 505 KING AVE, HEALTH SERVICES DEPT 43201 #038-40-1960 L1960 **OM FM** *071
FREELAND, Richard Alan. 2200 W BROAD ST 43223 #028-34-1978 L1989 **P** *020 †75
FREIMER, Earl Howard. ■ 43209 #035-15-1955 L1968 **ID IM** *071
FREIMER, Miriam Laura. 1654 UPHAM DR, RM 425 MEANS HALL 43210 #038-40-1985 L1992 **N** *020 †75
FRENCH, Bruce Green. 285 E STATE ST, STE 500 43215 #024-16-1992 L1997 **ORS OTR** *020 †40
FRENO, Janet Ann. ■ 43220 #038-40-1968 L1968 **PD** *020 †55
FREY, Diana Maria. 770 JASONWAY AVE STE G2 43214 #038-45-1998 L2000 **IM** *020 †20

■ = Address Information Privacy Protected

FRID, David Joshua. 2050 KENNY RD 43221 #023-01-1984 L1994 **CD PHP** *020 †20

FRIDAY, Dorothy Ann. 4300 CLIME RD, STE 130 43228 #038-40-1991 L1992 **OBG** *020 †30

FRIEDMAN, Barry Marvin. 2050 KENNY RD, STE 2400 43221 #038-40-1972 L1972 **IM** *040 †20

FRIEDMAN, Chad Isaac. 3535 OLENTANGY RIVER RD 43214 #016-02-1975 L1977 **REN** *020 †30

FRIEDMAN, Roger Alan. 5877 CLEVELAND AVE 43231 #038-40-1977 L1982 **AI PD** *020 †55,03

FRIES, Richard Bruce, II. 1375 PERRY ST 5TH FL, C/O OSU HOSPS-MED EDU DEPT 43201 #038-41-2001 L2001 **VS** *020 †20

FRY, Donald L. 400 W 12TH AVE 43210 #024-01-1949 L1951 **CD** *050

FRYCZKOWSKI, Andrzej W. 410 W 10TH AVE, DEPT OPH 43210 #759-09-1962 **OPH HNS** *050

FRYE, Thomas Robt. 700 CHILDRENS DR, DEPT RAD 43205 #038-40-1954 L1954 **PDR DR** *020 †80

FU, Eugene Yinghaw. 3525 OLENTANGY RIVER RD, STE 6300 43214 #038-40-1991 L1992 **CD ICE** *020 †20

FUGATE, Lisa P. 130 S CASSADY AVE 43209 #038-40-1989 L1991 **PHP** *020 †60

FUHRMAN, Susan Adela. 3535 OLENTANGY RIVER RD, RIVERSIDE METHODIST HOSP 43214 #025-01-1978 L1993 **PTH PCH** *030 †50

FULLAM, William Thomas. ■ 43214 #038-40-2003 L2003 **AN** *100

FULLER, Leta. 700 CHILDRENS DR, CHILDREN'S HOSPITAL-NEONAT 43205 #038-40-1996 L1997 **NPM** *020 †55

FULOP, James Peter. 931 CHATHAM LN, STE 200 43221 #038-40-1994 L1995 **N** *020 †75

FULTS-GANEY, Kristen Ann. 3525 OLENTANGY RIVER RD, STE 5360 43214 #023-12-1996 L2006 **DR** *020 †80

FUNG, Bonita R. ■ 43209 #068-01-1988 L2004 **PP** *100 †50

FURUTA, Wilmer Kenichi. 111 S GRANT AVE 43215 #038-40-1968 L1968 **CHP P** *020

GABLE, Thomas Andrew. 262 NEIL AVE, STE 500 43215 #038-40-1991 L1992 **AN** *020 †05

GABRIEL, Paul W. 1492 E BROAD ST, DEPT OF ORTHOPAEDICS 43205 #012-05-1980 L1985 **EM** *020 †16

GADDAM, Venkatarama Reddy. 1492 E BROAD ST, STE 1401 43205 #495-65-1995 L2004 **IC** *020 †20 ‡

GADEK, James Edward. 1655 UPHAM DR 43210 #035-20-1972 L1982 **IM PUD** *075 †03

GAETA, Santo Anthony. 3545 OLENTANGY BLVD 43214 #038-45-1987 L1988 **IM** *020

GAEUMAN, John Victor. 505 KING AVE, MEDICAL DEPT 43201 #038-40-1958 L1958 **OM IM** *030 †70,20

GAGE, Anita Marie. 1087 DENNISON AVE 43201 #041-13-1989 L1989 **EM** *020 †16

GAGLANI, Rajendrakumari R. 1495 MORSE RD 43229 #495-23-1979 L1982 **PD PEM** *020 †55

GAHBAUER, Reinhard. 300 W 10TH AVE 43210 #409-16-1971 L1983 **RO** *020 †80

GAISER, Ronda Marie. 3525 OLENTANGY RIVER RD 43214 #038-06-1993 L1996 **OBG** *020 †30

GALANI, Ruple Jayantilal. 473 W 12TH AVE, HEART LUNG RESEARCH INSTIT 43210 #038-43-2002 L2006 **CD** *012 †20

GALANTI-BERGESE, Marta A. 1211 DUBLIN RD, FL 2 43215 #132-02-1993 L1999 **GE** *020 †20

GALANTOWICZ, Mark Edward. 700 CHILDRENS DR 43205 #035-20-1987 L2002 **TS PD** *020 †85,90

GALLAGHER, Marjorie C. 4603 N HIGH ST 43214 #038-40-1973 L1973 **P** *020 †75

GALLEN, Joseph Michael. 3469 E LIVINGSTON AVE 43227 #038-40-1943 L1943 **GYN** *075

GALLINA, Kelly Ann. 456 W 10TH AVE 43201 #038-44-2003 L2003 **D** *020 †15

GALLOWAY, Gloria Matilda. 700 CHILDRENS DR, DEPT OF NEUROLOGY 43205 #422-01-1987 L1998 **N CN** *020 †75

GALUSICK, Joseph Anthony. ■ 43214 #038-45-1997 **FM** *100

GAMBLA, Michael Thomas. 3555 OLENTANGY RIVER RD, STE 4020 43214 #016-01-1996 L1997 **U** *020 †95

GAMS, Richard A. 410 W 10TH AVE 43210 #035-08-1960 L1986 **HEM ON** *020 †20

GANDHI, Rajiv Jay. 3525 OLENTANGY RIVER RD, CENTRAL OHIO HOSPITALISTS, 43214 #016-11-2004 L2007 **IM** *020

GANGASANI, Ashish. ■ 43230 #495-36-1997 L2007 **ICE** *012 †20

GANTE, Helmut. 3535 OLENTANGY RIVER RD 43214 #407-22-1949 L1955 **CD IM** *071

GANTT, Donald L. 3535 OLENTANGY RIVER RD 43214 #038-44-1949 L1949 **GYN** *071

GARABIS, Francisco A, IV. 1430 S HIGH ST, STE 100 43207 #038-40-2000 L2000 **FM** *020 †18

GARBARINO, Judson Payne. 1636 KING AVE 43212 #047-06-2002 L2002 **EM** *100 †16

GARCIA, Teodora Medina. 543 TAYLOR AVE, VA OUTPATIENT CLINIC 43203 #748-01-1956 L1974 **P OBS** *071

GARDNER, Edmond Walter. 1495 MORSE RD STE 312 43229 #038-40-1962 L1962 **D** *071 †15

GARLOCK, Adam Paul. ■ 43228 #038-40-2008 *012

GARNER, Walton Richard. 1375 PERRY ST 43201 #038-40-1962 L1962 **OM AM** *071 †70

GARUDA, Rina Shah. 7630 RIVERS EDGE DR 43235 #038-44-1997 L2007 **FM** *020 †18

GARUDA, Sanjay Rao. 3820 OLENTANGY RIVER RD, OHIO GASTROENTEROLOGY 43214 #038-44-1998 L2005 **GE** *020 †20

GARZON, Ramiro. ■ 43221 #132-02-1994 L2005 **IM** *100 †20

GASIOROVA, Magdalena. 793 W STATE ST 43222 #759-12-2001 L2006 **IM** *012

GASTALDO, Joseph Michael. 3555 OLENTANGY RIVER RD, STE 3020 43214 #038-45-1996 L1997 **ID** *020 †20

GATENS, Paul Francis, Jr. 745 W STATE ST, STE 700 43222 #028-03-1969 L1981 **PM** *071 †60

GAUTHIER, Jerome Laurier. 3535 OLENTANGY RIVER RD 43214 #065-09-1954 L1959 **AN OS** *071 †05

GAVIN, Thomas Jos. 1654 UPHAM DR 43210 #041-02-1990 L1991 **EM** *020 †16

GEARHART, Bruce Earl. 3555 OLENTANGY RIVER RD, STE 2050 43214 #001-02-1995 L2000 **DR** *020 †80

GEBHART, Don Edward. 700 CHILDRENS DR 43205 #038-41-1964 L1964 **OTO MDM** *030 †45

GEESE, James Wesley. 4605 SAWMILL RD 43220 #038-41-1999 L1999 **AN** *020 †05

GEGAS, Bill G, Jr. 1250 DEARBORN DR 43085 #038-40-1984 L1984 **FM** *020 †18

GEISE, Andrea Janelle. 410 W 10TH AVE, OH STATE UNIV HOSP 43210 #038-75-2006, ▲ L2006 **N** *012

GELFIUS, Carl Dane. ■ 43230 #038-40-2004 L2004 **PM** *012

GENDREAU, Roger Michael. 505 KING AVE 43201 #038-40-1981 L1981 *050

GENTILE, Steven Clark. 750 MOUNT CARMEL MALL 43222 #017-20-1985 L1987 **IM** *020 †20

GEORGE, Christopher S. 810 JASONWAY AVE 43214 #038-41-1991 L1993 **HO** *020 †20

GEORGE, Jack Melvin. 410 W 10TH AVE # N1111 43210 #038-40-1958 L1958 **END IM** *071 †20

GEORGE, Teresa Marie. 500 THOMAS LN, COMMUNITY MEDICINE DEPARTM 43214 #038-41-1991 L1993 **RHU** *020 †20

GERACE, Ann. 3545 OLENTANGY RIVER RD, RIVERSIDE EYE PHYS & SURG 43214 #041-07-1972 L1974 **OPH** *071 †35

GERBER, Nicholas. ■ 43235 #143-03-1958 L1978 **IM PA** *020 †55

GERHARDT, Mark Allen. 410 W 10TH AVE, N-146 DOAN HALL 43210 #025-01-1992 L1998 **AN** *020 †05

GERLACH, Jennifer Elizabe. ■ 43228 #038-45-2005 L2005 **PD** *012

GERMAK, John Andrew. 700 CHILDRENS DR, CHILDREN'S HOSPITAL 43205 #016-43-1974 L2000 **PDE PD** *050 †55

GEROULAKOS, George. 410 W 10TH AVE, DN N708 43210 #418-01-1981 **VS** *100

GEST, Alfred Louis. 700 CHILDRENS DR, SECTION OF NEONATOLOGY 43205 #048-04-1976 L2004 **NPM PD** *020 †20

GETZ, Bradley Scott. 111 S GRANT AVE, DEPT OF ANESTHESIOLOGY 43215 #038-40-1985 L1987 **AN** *020 †20,05

GEWIRTZ, Amy Siegel. 410 W 10TH AVE, STE 310 43210 #038-41-1990 L1994 **PTH** *020 †50

GEWIRTZ, Yaffa Rachael. 700 CHILDRENS DR, EMERGENCY MEDICINE CHILDRE 43205 #038-41-1998 L2004 **PEM** *100 †55

GHALLY, Philip Sobhy. 793 W STATE ST 43222 #665-02-2004 L2006 **IM** *012

GHANI, Ahmed M. 1492 E BROAD ST 43205 #915-02-1975 L1989 **HO** *020 †20

GHARIBSHAHI, Shahram. ■ 43235 #517-12-2002 L2006 **N** *012

GHAZARIAN, Gohar Vrejovna. 793 W STATE ST, MOUNT CARMEL HEALTH SYSTEM 43222 #913-38-1997 L2004 **IM** *012

GIAMMAR, David Robert. 5965 E BROAD ST, STE 120 43213 #038-44-1996 L1999 **CRS** *020 †85,10

GIANAKOPOULOS, George J. 3555 OLENTANGY RIVER RD, STE 3020 43214 #038-40-1985 L1986 **ID IM** *020 †20

GIANAKOPOULOS, William P. 340 E TOWN ST STE 7-200 43215 #038-45-1987 L1991 **U** *020 †95

GIANNETTO, Francine A. 4605 SAWMILL RD, STE 102 43220 #038-44-1997 L1998 **IM** *020 †20

GIANNONE, Peter John, Jr. 700 CHILDRENS DR, COLUMBUS CHILDRENS HOSPITA 43205 #035-15-1996 L2002 **NPM** *020 †55

GIBBONS, Gregory David. 3820 OLENTANGY RIVER RD, OHIO GASTROENTEROLOGY 43214 #055-01-1979 L1980 **GE IM** *020 †20

GICHNER, Lisa Ann. 700 CHILDRENS DR 43205 #036-07-1982 L1990 **PD** *020 †55

GIERSCH, Jennifer Ann. 150 TAYLOR STATION RD, STE 140 43213 #038-44-1984 L1985 **FM** *020 †18

GILBERT, Monica Claire. 700 CHILDRENS DR, C/O CHILDREN S HOSP-MED ED 43205 #038-40-2003 L2003 **PD** *020 †20

GILCHRIST, Richard Holmes. 700 CHILDRENS DR, TIMKEN HALL 2ND FL H2K 43205 #038-40-1995 L1997 **PD** *020 †75,55

GILES, Mariann Brown. 2000 KENNY RD 43221 #038-40-1995 L1996 **FM** *020 †18

GILL, Kirandeep Kaur. ■ 43212 #028-78-2006, ▲ L2006 **MPD** *012

GILLERAN, Jason Patrick. 456 W 10TH AVE, 4980 UNIV HOSP CLINICS 43210 #025-07-1998 L2005 **U** *100 †95

GILLISON-DAWSON, E Alexis. 2200 W BROAD ST 43223 #041-12-1979 L1983 **IM** *030

GINGRICH, Curtis Lee. 797 THOMAS LN 43214 #038-40-1992 L1993 **FM** *020 †18

GIRAY, Saim. ■ 43235 #902-01-1953 L1963 **P** *071

GLASGOW, Karen Ann. 500 THOMAS LN, C/O COMMUNITY MEDICINE 43214 #035-06-1976 L1977 **IM OS** *020 †20

GLASSMAN, Andrew H. 4850 E MAIN ST, HEALTH CENTER 43213 #038-43-1979 L1980 **ORS** *030 †40

GLATZ, Dennis Michael. 1654 UPHAM DR, 635 MEANS HALL 43210 #055-01-2002 L2003 **DR** *100 †80

GLATZ, Stephen Matthew. 340 E TOWN ST, STE 7-500 43215 #055-01-2002 L2008 **GS** *100 †85

GLEESON, Sean Patrick. 111 S GRANT AVE, GRANT MEDICAL CENTER 43215 #041-01-1993 L1999 **PD** *020 †55

GNANASEKARAN, Gowrishankar. 2050 KENNY RD, STE 2400 43221 #496-45-1999 L2004 **IMG** *012 †20

GODDARD, Mini Bansal. 815 W BROAD ST, STE 300 43222 #016-43-1991 L1994 **PM PME** *020 †60

GODZIK, Natalie Jo. ■ 43204 #038-45-2004 L2004 **FM** *100

GOFF, John Paul. 3535 OLENTANGY RIVER RD 43214 #038-40-1964 L1964 **OBG MDM** *071 †30

GOFF, Thomas Leslie. 473 W 12TH AVE, SUITE 200 DAVIS HEART & LU 43210 #020-12-2002 L2005 **CD** *012 †20

GOIST, Melissa Marie. 456 W 10TH AVE, STE 2B 43210 #038-43-2000 L2000 **OBG** *020 †30

GOLAN, Jeff. ■ 43212 #067-01-2001 L2006 **NS** *012

GOLDBERG, Donald. 3545 OLENTANGY RIVER RD, STE 428 43214 #036-07-1958 L1963 **P PYA** *020

GOLDBERG, Edward Aron. 99 N BRICE RD, EASTSIDE SLEEP DIAGNOSTIC 43213 #038-40-2002 L2007 **PM** *020

GOLDBERG, Jack Leon. ■ 43213 #038-40-1956 L1956 **OPH** *071 †35

GOLDBERG, Robert Fromme. 497 E TOWN ST 43215 #035-09-1948 L1948 **OS END** *072 †20

GOLDBLATT, Matthew Isaac. 4830 KNIGHTSBRIDGE BLVD, STE J 43214 #056-06-1997 L2004 **GS** *020 †85

GOLDENBERG, Neal Evan. ■ 43202 #038-40-2007 *012

GOLDENSTEIN, Leonard A. ■ 43202 #038-40-2008 *012

GOLDMAN, Ernesto. 410 W 10TH AVE N-431, OHIO STATE UNIVERSITY HOSP 43210 #132-04-1966 L1981 **AN** *020 †05

GOLDMEIER, Maynard. 3245 E LIVINGSTON AVE 43227 #038-40-1959 L1959 **IM PUD** *020

GOLDSTEIN, Morton Irving. 270 E CAMPUS VIEW BLVD, WORTHINGTON RADIOLOGY 43235 #035-15-1958 L1961 **R** *071 †80

GOLEMAN, Martha Jane. 700 CHILDRENS DR, CHILDRENS HOSPITAL CPAS 43205 #038-40-1982 L1984 **PD** *020 †55

GOLLAPUDY, Radhika. 1301 N HIGH ST 43201 #495-21-1990 L1998 **P** *020

GOMEZ, Liliana. ■ 43235 #264-11-1995 L2006 **FP** *012

GOODLIVE, Thomas William. 3705 OLENTANGY RIVER RD, STE 100 43214 #038-43-1996 L1997 **CD** *020 †20

GOODMAN, Jaime Terner. 4605 SAWMILL RD 43220 #038-40-2005 L2005 **IM** *012

GOODMAN, Joseph H. 410 W 10TH AVE, N 911 DIVISION OF NEUROSUR 43210 #036-01-1971 L1973 **NS** *020 †25

GOODMAN, Julian Jacob. ■ 43204 #038-40-2007 L2007 **IM** *012

GOODSON, Leroy Beverly. 1000 E BROAD ST 43205 #025-01-1959 L1959 **FM** *020 †18

GOOREY, Louis Jos R. 700 CHILDRENS DR 43205 #038-40-1957 L1957 **PD MDM** *071

GORA, Alan Gerard. 750 MOUNT CARMEL MALL 43222 #016-43-1992 L1993 **EM** *020 †16

GORDILLO, Gayle Marietta. 4830 KNIGHTSBRIDGE BLVD, SURGERY 43214 #038-40-1990 L1996 **PS** *020 †65

GORDON, Jeffrey Paul. 111 S GRANT AVE 43215 #038-40-1984 L1986 **IM** *040 †20

GORFINKEL, H Joel. 745 W STATE ST 43222 #016-11-1965 L1978 **CD** *020 †20 ‡

GORGAS, Diane Lynn. 1654 UPHAM DR, 166 MEANS HALL 43210 #038-06-1990 L1992 **EM** *020 †16

GORTY, Sree Rama Chandra. 793 W STATE ST, MOUNT CARMEL MEDICAL CENTE 43222 #495-21-1967 L1983 **AN** *020 †05

GOST, Dena J. 1640 NEIL AVE, YOUNKIN SUCCESS CENTER, 4L 43201 #038-40-1997 L1999 **P** *020 †75

GOTTESMAN, Martin Jay. 931 CHATHAM LN, STE 101 43221 #038-40-1977 L1977 ORS *020 †40

GOULDER, Norman Ernest. ■ 43219 #024-01-1940 L1946 CD IM *071 †20

GOWDA, Chandre C. 1336 E MAIN ST 43205 #495-37-1980 L2004 FM *020 †18

GOWDA, Charan. 43220 #036-07-2004 L2005 ORS *012

GOY, Robert Brett. 2050 KENNY RD, ATTN: ANNE SMITH 43221 #018-75-2007, ▲ L2007 AN *012

GOYAL, Mili Patel. 3555 OLENTANGY RIVER RD, STE 1080 43214 #016-11-2004 L2007 IM *020 †20

GOYLE, Ashu K. ■ 43201 #038-75-2002, ▲ L2002 AN *100 †05

GRACE, Ted Wm. 1875 MILLIKIN RD, WILCE STUDENT HEALTH CTR 43210 #038-40-1976 L1976 FM IM *030 †20,70,18

GRAHAM, Bruce William. 5969 E BROAD ST, STE 202 43213 #038-40-1974 L1981 CD *020 †20

GRAHAM, Jacqueline Marie. 410 W 10TH AVE, OSUMC- DEPT. OF ANESTHESIO 43210 #056-05-2003 L2004 AN *020

GRAINGER, Andrew Vincent. 810 JASONWAY AVE, STE A 43214 #030-06-1997 L1999 HO IM *020 †20

GRAMANN, William John. 4825 KNIGHTSBRIDGE BLVD 43214 #051-04-1984 L1985 IM *020 †20

GRANDINETTI, Paul Jos. 6465 E BROAD ST, STE D 43213 #055-02-1990 L1996 IM *071 †20

GRANT, Rebecca Lynne. ■ 43220 #038-40-2008 *012

GRAUER, Allison Christine. ■ 43204 #038-40-2007 L2007 MPD *012

GRAVLEE, Glenn Page. 410 W 10TH AVE, DEPT OF ANESTHESIOLOGY 43210 #016-06-1974 L1999 AN *020 †05

GRAY, Anna Christine. 5072 REED RD, MEDICINE 43220 #038-40-2000 L2000 PD *020 †55

GRAY, Linda S. 480 W 9TH AVE, DAVIS MEDICAL RESEARCH CEN 43210 #055-01-1983 L1990 RHU IM *020 †20

GRECO, Carol Jean. 1315 W LANE AVE 43221 #038-40-1987 L1988 OBG *020 †30

GRECULA, John Christopher. 300 W 10TH AVE, UNIVERSITY RADIATION 43210 #038-44-1987 L1988 RO *020 †80

GREEGOR, David Haynie. ■ 43212 #038-40-1941 L1941 IM OS *071 †20

GREEN, Harold Neil. 150 TAYLOR STATION RD, STE 300 43213 #038-40-1991 L1993 OBG *020 †30

GREEN, John Willock. 340 E TOWN ST, STE 8-550 43215 #038-40-2000 L2000 FM *020 †18

GREEN, Marvin Gene. 1492 E BROAD ST 43205 #038-40-1964 L1964 IM *020

GREENE, Lawrence Stanley. ■ 43213 #035-06-1954 L2002 GE IM *071 †20

GREGORY, Ian Walter. ■ 43220 #352-03-1948 L1964 P *071 †75

GRENADE, Cassandra Natali. ■ 43223 #038-40-2008 *012

GRIFFIN, Jessica Marie. ■ 43206 #028-34-2005 L2005 PD *012

GRIFFIN, Omega Joi. ■ 43219 #038-40-2003 L2005 AN *012

GRIFFITH, Robert Fleming. 750 MOUNT CARMEL MALL 43222 #028-02-1982 L1989 EM IM *040 †20,16

GRIGORIEVA, Anastassia. ■ 43202 #038-40-2007 L2007 TY *012

GRIMES, Jaison Allen. ■ 43212 #038-40-2008 *012

GRONER, Jonathan Ira. 700 CHILDRENS DR # ED341 43205 #016-06-1984 L1991 PDS *020 †85

GRONER, Judith. 700 CHILDRENS DR 43205 #035-46-1977 L1986 PD *020 †55

GROSS, Thomas Gene. 700 CHILDRENS DR, CHILDREN'S HOSPITAL 43205 #030-05-1988 L1998 PHO PD *020 †55

GROSSKINSKY, Clemens M. 4830 KNIGHTSBRIDGE BLVD, STE E 43214 #035-08-1988 L1994 REN *030 †30

GUDURI, Sridhar. 99 N BRICE RD, STE 140 43213 #495-65-1995 L2002 AI *020 †20,03

GUENTERBERG, Kristan Davi. 410 W 10TH AVE, 316-A MEANS HALL 43210 #005-12-2005 L2005 GS *012

GUERRERO, Jesus Lopez. ■ 43220 #847-04-1946 L1980 PD *071 †55

GUERTIN, Michael Gerard. 930 BETHEL RD 43214 #025-07-1988 L1991 AN *020 †05

GUINN, Vincent Lee. 3433 AGLER RD, STE 2400 43219 #038-40-1984 L1991 CD IM *020 †20

GUIRGIS, Hossam. 1670 UPHAM DR, OSU HARDING HOSPITAL 43210 #915-02-1997 L2006 P *100 †75

GUMINA, Richard Jose. 473 W 12TH AVE, HLRI, SUITE 200 43210 #056-06-1997 L2006 IC *100 †20

GUMMER, Richard Lynn, II. 3555 OLENTANGY RIVER RD, STE 1080 43214 #038-43-1999 L2003 MPD *020 †20

GUNKA, Vit Bohumil. 410 W 10TH AVE, DEPT OF ANESTHESIOLOGY 43210 #286-05-1990 L1998 AN *020 †05

GUNSOREK, Lisa Marie. 3535 OLENTANGY RIVER RD 43214 #038-43-1996 L1997 IM *020

GUPTA, Akash. 4300 CLIME RD, STE 100 43228 #038-06-2000 L2000 OTO *020 †45

GUPTA, Bhagwandas. 410 W 10TH AVE, O.S.U. HOSPITAL 43210 #495-65-1970 L1981 AN *020 †20

GUPTA, Esha Angeline. ■ 43221 #038-44-2008 *012

GUPTA, Manya Jyoti. 859 OLD WOODS RD 43235 #038-41-2008 *012

GUPTA, Piyush. 1833 PARSONS AVE 43207 #495-20-2000 L2001 IM *020

GUPTA, Shivani. 370 W 9TH AVE, 200A MEILING HALL 43210 #038-40-2006 L2006 OPH *012

GUPTA, Somil Ashok. 697 THOMAS LN 43214 #495-28-1999 L2004 FPG *012 †18

GUPTA, Suresh Chander. 5100 W BROAD ST, DOCTOR'S HOSPITAL WEST 43228 #495-03-1975 L1980 AN *020 †05

GUPTA, Uma. 700 CHILDRENS DR, CHILDRENS HOSPITAL 43205 #495-41-1973 L1980 PD EM *020 †55

GURRAM, Nandkishore. 410 W 10TH AVE 43210 #495-21-1984 L1995 CD *100 †20

GUTHRIE, Julie Ann. 5151 REED RD, STE 128C 43220 #038-40-1988 L1989 P *020 †75

GUTHRIE, Robert Miller. 376 W 10TH AVE, HEALTH SCI LIB 43210 #023-01-1974 L1982 IM FM *020 †20,18

GUTIERREZ, Camilo Enrique. 700 E COLUMBUS ST 43206 #264-21-1999 L2005 PEM *012 †55

GUTIERREZ, Elena Sophia. ■ 43208 #018-03-2006 L2006 NS *012

GUTIERREZ, Tamara Lea. 2231 N HIGH ST 43201 #038-06-2002 L2005 FM *020 †18

GUTMANN, Becky M. 410 W 10TH AVE, DEPT OF ANESTHESIOLOGY 43210 #038-06-1987 L1987 AN *020 †20

GUTTERMAN, Lorence Armon. 74 S ROOSEVELT AVE 43209 #051-04-1964 L1965 HEM *020 †20

GUY, Gregory Eugene. 1654 UPHAM DR, 630 MEANS HALL 43210 #038-41-1982 L1992 VIR R *020 †80

GUY, Jerry Thos. 410 W 10TH AVE 43210 #038-40-1965 L1965 HEM ON *020 †20

GUYTON, John Donald. 745 W STATE ST STE 7 43222 #041-13-1954 L1961 PM OS *020 †60

GWYNNE, Peter Holford. ■ 43214 #352-11-1955 L1961 P *075 †75

HAAS, Garrie J, Jr. 3705 OLENTANGY RIVER RD, STE 100 43214 #055-02-1983 L1985 CD IM *020 †20

HAASE, Jennifer Anne. 4919 DIERKER RD 43220 #038-40-2002 L2002 PD *020

HABASH, Nabil A. 793 W STATE ST 43222 #036-01-2003 L2003 PS *012

HABIB, Pamela Asma. ■ 43215 #038-40-2007 L2007 TY *012

HABIB, Paula Ayesha. 2321 ASCHINGER BLVD 43212 #038-40-2004 L2005 DR *012

HABIB, Phillip James. 410 W 10TH AVE, DEPT OF INTERNAL MEDICINE 43210 #038-44-2006 L2006 IM *012

HACKETT, Kevin Joseph. 921B JASONWAY AVE 43214 #038-41-1979 L1980 OBG *020 †30

HACKMAN, Mark Allen. 5969 E BROAD ST, 2ND FL 43213 #038-43-1982 L1983 IM *020 †20

HACKSHAW, Kevin Victor. 480 W 9TH AVE, STE 2050 43210 #048-04-1983 L1990 RHU IM *020 †20

HADDAD, Nabil Jamil. 1654 UPHAM DR, NEPHROLOGY 43210 #913-97-1981 L1995 NEP IM *020 †20

HADEN, Allison Oley. 410 W 10TH AVE, HOSPITALISTS 43210 #055-01-2000 L2007 IM *020 †20

HADEN, Douglas William. ■ 43235 #055-01-2001 L2007 PCC *100 †20

HADZIAHMETOVIC, Mersiha. ■ 43235 #038-40-2007 L2007 TY *012

HAGAN, Benjamin Nti. 599 S HAMILTON RD 43213 #412-02-1992 L2002 IM *020 †20

HAHN, Andrea Leigh. ■ 43201 #038-40-2008 *012

HAHN, Seong Hack. 793 W STATE ST 43222 #583-02-1964 L1973 AN *020 †05

HAIDAR, Atteqa. 793 W STATE ST, MT CARMEL HOSP-MED EDU 43222 #704-21-1997 L2003 IM *020 †20

HAILE, Daniel Minasse. 4155 CLAIRMONT RD, 4155 CLAIRMONT RD. 43220 #023-07-1985 L1996 AN GS *020 †05

HAINS, David Sullivan. ■ 43204 #017-20-2004 L2004 PD *100 †55

HAJINAZARIAN, Melkon. 285 E STATE ST, STE 360 43215 #605-01-1986 L1990 NEP IM *020 †20

HALAS, Evan J. 1555 BETHEL RD 43220 #473-01-1948 L1961 P *020

HALE, Alice Ann. 16 W LONG ST, SOUTHEAST INC 43215 #038-40-1983 L1984 P PFP *020 †75

HALE, Arthur Lewellen. 285 E STATE ST STE 670 43215 #038-40-2004 L2004 FM *100

HALEY, Earl Gregory. ■ 43218 #038-45-2008 *012

HALL, Charles William, Jr. 931 CHATHAM LN, STE 200 43221 #038-41-2000 L2005 N *100 †75

HALL, Jeffrey Adam. 974 BETHEL RD, STE A 43214 #038-40-1998 L2004 OTO *020

HALL, Kelly Fleming. 1405 S HIGH ST, MAIN 43204 #038-40-1997 L2004 FM OBG *020 †18

HALL, Mark William. 700 CHILDRENS DR, CHILDREN'S HOSP PEDIATRIC 43205 #051-01-1994 L2002 CCP *020 †55

HALLE, Mark Thos. 1515 E BROAD ST 43205 #056-05-1987 L1989 P *020

HALLET, Michael Benj. 5969 E BROAD ST STE 301 43213 #038-41-1978 L1979 U *020 †95

HALLET, Robert L. ■ 43209 #036-07-1949 L1955 OBG *071 †20

HALLEY, David Keysmith. 4560 N HIGH ST 43214 #038-40-1967 L1967 ORS *020 †40

HALPERN, Barry. 285 E STATE ST, STE 520 43215 #038-40-1981 L2005 NPM *020 †55

HALPERN, Pinchas. 410 W 10TH AVE, N429 DOAN HALL 43210 #550-02-1983 CCM AN *100

HAMADANI, Sayed Mehdi Hus. ■ 43209 #704-01-2001 L2006 HO *012 †20

HAMAMURA, Edward Tsu-Yen. ■ 43220 #028-34-2005 L2005 MPD *100

HAMELBERG, William. ■ 43204 #038-40-1948 L1949 AN *071 †05

HAMILTON, Charles Harold. 840 MICHIGAN AVE, HAMILTON MD'S INC 43215 #038-40-1954 L1954 CRS *071 †10

HAMILTON, Charles Laxton. ■ 43223 #056-05-2004 L2005 AN *012

HAMILTON, James Francis. 1975 GUILFORD RD 43221 #038-40-1965 L1965 D *020 †15

HAMILTON, Lisa Ann. 750 MOUNT CARMEL MALL 43222 #038-40-1989 L1990 EM FM *020 †18

HAMMAR, Matthew. ■ 43235 #038-75-2005, ▲ L2005 IM *012

HAMMOND, Sue. 410 W 10TH AVE 43210 #005-19-1982 L1986 PTH *020 †50

HAMOUDI, Ala Bakir. 700 CHILDRENS DR, DEPT PATH 43205 #528-01-1961 L1972 PTH *020 †55

HAMOUDI, Ayser Chalabi. 1480 GRANDVIEW AVE, GRANDVIEW FAMILY MEDICAL C 43212 #528-01-1967 L1972 FM ATP *020 †50,18

HAMPTON, Rebecca Ruth. 700 CHILDRENS DR, CHILDREN'S HOSPITAL 43205 #016-01-2000 L2003 PEM *100 †55

HANNA, Maged Fouad. 100 N MURRAY HILL RD 43228 #038-40-1988 L1989 FM *075 †18

HANNALLAH, David. 85 MCNAUGHTEN RD, STE 200 43213 #028-02-2000 L2007 ORS *020

HANNUN, Ghaleb Ali Mosleh. 4300 CLIME RD, STE C 43228 #915-02-1969 L1979 VS *020 †85

HANSEN, Nancy Beth. 700 CHILDRENS DR 43205 #047-06-1978 L1983 NPM PD *020 †55

HANSON, Ryan Paul. 1875 MILLIKIN RD, THE OHIO STATE UNIVERSITY 43210 #038-40-1995 L1996 IM *020 †18

HANYAK, John Paul. 6004 CLEVELAND AVE 43231 #038-40-1985 L1986 IM IMG *071

HAPKE, Barbara Lynn. 1654 UPHAM DR, 146 MEANS HALL 43210 #034-01-2003 L2003 EM *100 †16

HAPPEL, Lynn Christina. ■ 43212 #028-46-2002 L2007 GS *020 †85

HAQUE, Malika Hakim. 700 CHILDRENS DR, COLUMBUS CHILDRENS HOSP 43205 #495-16-1967 L1971 PD *050 †55

HAQUE, Mohammad Farhan. 3525 OLENTANGY RIVER RD, STE 4330 43214 #704-26-2003 L2007 IM *020

HARBRECHT, Jeffrey Bernard. 500 THOMAS LN, STE 3C 43214 #020-02-1986 L1993 U *020 †95

HARD, Wes F. 100 N MURRAY HILL RD 43228 #038-40-1982 L1982 FM FPG *020 †18

HARDER, Thomas Peter. 4830 KNIGHTSBRIDGE BLVD, STE J 43214 #038-40-1989 L1992 RHU *020

HARDIN, Dana Sue. 700 CHILDRENS DR, ENDOCRINOLOGY DEPARTMENT 43205 #017-20-1986 L2006 PDE PD *050 †55

HARI, Jayeshkumar. 6200 CLEVELAND AVE, COLUMBUS RADIOLOGY CORP 43231 #017-20-1995 L2000 VIR *020 †80

HARI, Sunil Baju. ■ 43201 #038-40-2008 *012

HARPER, Levi Keith. ■ 43235 #020-12-2007 L2007 FP *012

HARRIGAL, Michael Joseph. 3535 OLENTANGY RIVER RD 43214 #038-40-2005 L2005 IM *012

HARRIS, Angela Marie. 700 CHILDRENS DR 43205 #038-40-1998 L1999 PEM *020 †55

HARRIS, George L, Jr. 2231 N HIGH ST RM 205, OHIO STATE UNIV 43201 #038-40-2000 L2000 FM *100

HARRIS, Jesse David. 4845 KNIGHTSBRIDGE BLVD, STE 100 43214 #038-40-1984 L1986 IM P *020 †20

HARRIS, Joshua David. 410 W 10TH AVE 43210 #038-40-2006 L2006 ORS *012

HARRIS, Randall Edward. 320 W 10TH AVE, STARLING LOVING M-116 43210 #030-05-1983 L1990 GPM BBK *050 †50,70

HARROLD, Bradley Richard. 473 W 12TH AVE, 201 DHLRI 43210 #038-40-2001 L2001 PCC *020 †20

HART, Brandon Jay. ■ 43221 #049-01-2006 L2006 MPD *012

HART, David Tamunotonye. 473 W 12TH AVE, 2ND FLOOR HLRI 43210 #690-01-1982 L2003 CD *020 †20

HART, Mary C Dillin. 545 S 18TH ST STE 240 43205 #018-03-1983 L1986 OTO *020 †45

HART, Sheri Lyn. 1654 UPHAM DR, 424 MEANS HALL 43210 #038-40-2000 L2000 N *100 †75

HARTER, Ronald Lee. 410 W 10TH AVE, N-417 DOAN HALL 43210 #038-40-1989 L1994 AN *020 †05

HARTLEY, Anne Katharine. ■ 43215 #016-01-2005 L2005 *100
HARTMAN, Jennifer Jill. 393 E TOWN ST, OUTPATIENT MEDICAL CLINIC 43215
#038-40-2003 L2003 **FM** *020 †18
HARTMAN, William Ryan. 543 TAYLOR AVE, DEPT OF VETERANS AFFAIRS 43203
#038-40-1995 L1999 **P** *020 †75
HARTRANFT, Thomas Howard. 4300 CLIME RD, STE A 43228 #038-40-1969 L1969
VS GS *071 †85
HARTT, Gregory T. 1654 UPHAM DR, 167 MEANS HALL 43210 #038-40-2003 L2003
EM *100 †16
HARTZ, Clinton Albert. 410 W 10TH AVE 43210 #104-01-2007 L2007 **FP** *012
HARZMAN, Alan Eldon. 410 W 10TH AVE, N717 DOAN HALL 43210 #028-02-2001 L2007
CRS *020
HASAN, Ayesha Khalid. 473 W 12TH AVE, DHLRI SUITE 200 43210 #055-01-1999 L2005
CD *100 †20
HASAN, Mazen Mohammad. 2050 KENNY RD 43221 #875-01-1998 L2005 *100
HASHMI, Shereen. 8000 RAVINES EDGE CT, STE 202 43235 #704-06-1984 L1992 **RHU** *020 †20
HASWAH, Neda Saleh. ■ 43202 #016-11-2008 *012
HAUBERT, Lisa Marie. ■ 43201 #038-40-2006 L2006 **GS** *012
HAUDENSCHILT, Ronald J. 5770 KARL RD 43229 #038-40-1984 L1987 **FM** *020 †18
HAUERSPERGER, Karla R. 700 CHILDRENS DR, CHILDRENS HOSPITAL COLUMBU 43205
#036-01-1991 L1992 **PD PEM** *020 †55
HAUSER, Walter Henry. 85 MCNAUGHTEN RD 43213 #038-40-1958 L1958 **ORS** *020 †40
HAUSWIRTH, David William. 1654 UPHAM DR, OHIO STATE UNIVERSITY 43210
#038-43-1999 L2000 **AI** *100 †20,55,03
HAWKER, Kathleen Susan. 2050 KENNY RD, STE 2250 43221 #065-10-1983 L2006 **P** *020 †75
HAWLEY, Jeffrey Robert. ■ 43215 #038-40-2005 L2005 **DR** *012
HAWLEY, Miles Patten. 1654 UPHAM DR, 202 MEANS HALL 43210 #038-41-2006 L2006 **IM** *012
HAWLEY, Philip Caldwell. 111 S GRANT AVE, RESPIRATORY THERAPY 43215
#036-07-1975 L1977 **PCC IM** *020 †20
HAYES, Patrick R. 3535 OLENTANGY RIVER RD, EMERGENCY SERVICES 43214
#035-06-1976 L1977 **N** *020 †20
HAYNES, Patricia E. 285 E STATE ST STE 670, GRANT MED CTR 43215 #305-01-2005 L2006
FP *012
HAYS, Michael J. ■ 43235 #038-44-2008 *012
HAZEY, Jeffrey Wallace. 410 W 10TH AVE, N724 DOAN HALL 43210 #038-06-1992 L1993
GS *020 †85
HEAD, Danamarie Elizabeth. ■ 43215 #038-40-2008 *012
HEARNE, Dean Wm. 456 W 10TH AVE, # 4731 43210 #051-04-1991 L1993 **D** *020 †15
HEBAN, Paul Thos. 5969 E BROAD ST, STE 307 43213 #038-40-1977 L1980 **IM EM** *020 †20
HEBERT, Lee Alois. 1654 UPHAM DR, NEPHROLOGY 43210 #056-06-1962 L1979 **NEP** *062 †20
HEDRICK, Sterling Wm. 1515 E BROAD ST 43205 #038-40-1973 L1976 **RHU IM** *020 †20
HEEREMA, Bret Douglas. 793 W STATE ST, CO MT CARMEL HOSP-MED EDU 43222
#017-20-2003 L2003 *100
HEFLIN, Jonathan Willis. ■ 43224 #038-45-2008 *012
HEILMAN, Robert Lynn. 750 MOUNT CARMEL MALL, STE 300 43222 #038-40-1972 L1972
EM *020 †16
HEINTZ, John Stephen. 1117 W 1ST AVE 43212 #038-40-1985 L1986 **IM PD** *020 †20,55
HEINTZELMAN, Kurt Wm. 1990 HARMON AVE 43223 #038-40-1988 L2001 **P** *020
HEINY, Lawrence Perry. 453 WATERBURY CT, PEDIATRIC & ADOLESCENT 43230
#056-06-1971 L1973 **PD** *020 †55
HEIRONIMUS, James David. ■ 43204 #056-06-1977 L1979 **IM NM** *071 †20,28
HELMINIAK, Brandy Lynn. 1654 UPHAM DR 43210 #035-06-1999 L1999 **EM** *020 †16
HELMRATH, Thomas Anthony. 2500 SULLIVANT AVE 43204 #028-34-1962 L1980
PD NPM *020 †55
HENDERSHOT, Andrew Jennin. ■ 43204 #038-40-2005 L2005 **OPH** *012
HENDERSON, Scott Keith. 4606 SAWMILL RD 43220 #016-11-1982 L1986 **AN** *105
HENION, Wallace Fetter. ■ 43221 #038-06-1956 L1959 **PD** *071
HENNIGAN, Christine Ann. 4605 SAWMILL RD, STE 102 43220 #024-16-1992 L1996
OBG *020 †30
HENRIQUES, Rena. 41 S HIGH ST STE 25 43215 #038-44-1998 L2000 **IM** *020 †20
HENRY, Dianne Elizabeth. ■ 43201 #038-40-2008 *012
HENRY, Jon Clifford. ■ 43235 #038-40-2008 *012
HENRY, Mitchell Lane. 1654 UPHAM DR, 347 MEANS HALL 43210 #030-05-1979 L1980
GS TTS *020 †85
HENRY, Robert J. ■ 43206 #038-40-1943 L1943 **GP** *071
HENSELER, Karol Ann. 700 CHILDRENS DR, CHILDERENS HOSPITAL AMBULA 43205
#038-40-1993 L1994 **PD** *020 †55
HERBEI, Andreea Simona. 285 E STATE ST, GRANT MEDICAL CENTER 43215
#781-04-1999 L2007 **FM** *020 †18
HERBERT, Mark Thos. 2970 W BROAD ST 43204 #038-44-1985 L1986 **ID IM** *020 †20
HERCEG, Milan Bender. 4605 SAWMILL RD 43220 #038-40-1998 L1999 **ORS** *020 †40
HERMAN, Gail Ellen. 700 CHILDRENS DR RM W403, NATIONWIDE CHILDREN'S RES 43205
#036-07-1981 L1996 **MG PD** *020 †55,19
HERMAN, Grace Gales. ■ 43221 #035-01-1949 **OM** *071
HERMAN, Kim R.. 793 W STATE ST, MT CARMEL MED CTR 43222 #130-01-2003 L2005 **FP** *012
HERNANDEZ, Pablo David. 1670 UPHAM DR 43210 #042-01-1994 L1998 **P** *020 †75
HERSH, Joshua Adam. 1670 UPHAM DR 43210 #038-40-2000 L2000 **P** *020 †75
HERSHFIELD, Robert. 5969 E BROAD ST, STE 200 43213 #008-01-1978 L1979 **IM** *020 †20
HERZOG, Alysia Courtot. 111 S GRANT AVE, 285 EAST STATE STREET STE. 43215
#038-06-1999 L1999 **FM** *020 †18
HEVEZI, Louis William. 3555 OLENTANGY RIVER RD, STE 1080 43214 #038-45-2003 L2005
IM *020 †20
HEYER, Geoffrey Lyle. 700 CHILDRENS DR, PEDIATRIC NEUROLOGY 43205
#035-01-2000 L2001 **CHN** *020
HICKEY, Scott Ewing. 700 CHILDRENS DR, CHILDREN'S HOSP 43205 #020-02-2004 L2004
MG *012 †55
HICKEY, Susan Jean Werts. ■ 43221 #038-40-1981 L1983 *030
HICKS, William James. 2050 KENNY RD, RM 904 43221 #041-12-1974 L1975 **ON HEM** *020 †20
HICKS-GRAHAM, Shari. 393 E TOWN ST, STE 229 43215 #041-12-2000 L2005 **D** *020 †15
HIESTAND, Brian Charles. 1654 UPHAM DR, 149 MEANS HALL 43210 #038-40-1998 L1999
EM *050 †16
HIGBEE, John Wilson. ■ 43235 #038-40-1964 L1964 **OPH** *071 †35
HIGGINS, Gloria Christine. 700 CHILDRENS DR, CHILDREN'S HOSPITAL 43205
#035-46-1983 L1999 **PPR** *050 †55
HILL, Cindi Lynn. ■ 43202 #038-40-1991 L1992 **FM** *030 †18
HILL, James Richard. 3535 OLENTANGY RIVER RD 43214 #007-02-1959 L1963
PTH BBK *071 †50

HILL, Lanetta Marie. 370 W 9TH AVE, OH STATE U COLL OF MED 43210 #038-40-2003 L2004
FM *100
HILL, Marisa Eve. 410 W 10TH AVE, 207 MEANS HALL 43210 #038-41-2005 L2005 **IM** *012
HILLMAN, Barry Sidney. 5975 E BROAD ST 43213 #038-40-1959 L1959 **OTO HNS** *071
HILTBRAND, Jeffery Bruce. 4300 CLIME RD, STE 100 43228 #038-40-1984 L1989
OTO *020 †45
HILTY, Milo Duane. 700 CHILDRENS DR 43205 #038-40-1965 L1965 **ID PD** *074 †55
HINDY, Stacey Robbyn. 316A MARSHALL PSGE, OHIO STATE UNIV 43215 #038-40-2005 L2005
GS *012
HINGSBERGEN, Elizabeth A. 700 CHILDRENS DR 43205 #028-02-1985 L1990 **DR** *020 †80
HINKLE, Philip Edward. 3535 OLENTANGY RIVER RD 43214 #038-40-1976 L1976
PYG P *020 †75
HINRICHS, Victor Herman. 941 N HIGH ST 43201 #038-41-1960 L1960 **PTH** *071 †50
HIRSCHL, Robert Alex. ■ 43228 #038-40-2004 L2004 **NS** *012
HIRSELJ, Daniel Aaron. 700 CHILDRENS DR, CHILDRENS HOSP 43205 #038-40-2001 L2007
UP *012
HIRSH, David Kessler. 456 W 10TH AVE 5TH FL, OSU EYE PHYSICIANS & SURGE 43210
#035-46-1984 L2004 **OPH N** *020 †35
HIRSH, Jennifer Lauren. ■ 43201 #038-40-2002 L2002 **N** *020
HIRSHBERG, James Asher. ■ 43206 #025-01-2003 L2005 **EM** *012
HITCHCOCK, Charles L. 700 ACKERMAN RD, STE 380 43202 #038-40-1983 L1993
PTH *020 †50
HO, George Tseng. 500 E MAIN ST, STE 220 43215 #016-06-1988 L1994 **U** *020 †95
HOCKENBERRY, Scott Edward. 285 E STATE ST, STE 620 43215 #038-44-1989 L1994
GS TRS *020 †85
HODGES, Ellen Elizabeth. ■ 43206 #048-14-2007 L2007 **EM** *012
HOEL, Elizabeth Lauren. 1654 UPHAM DR, OHIO STATE UNIV MED CTR 43210
#026-04-2006 L2006 **OBG** *012
HOENIG, Eric Paul. ■ 43212 #038-40-1994 L1996 **IM** *020 †20
HOFFBUHR, Cory Neil. ■ 43201 #038-40-2008 *012
HOFFMAN, Jeffrey Marc. 700 CHILDRENS DR, CHILDREN'S HOSPITAL 43205
#041-02-1990 L1995 **PEM** *020 †55
HOFFMAN, Robert Paul. 700 CHILDRENS DR, CHILDRENS HOSP ED 544 43205
#038-40-1981 L1983 **PDE** *040 †55
HOFFMAN, Timothy Michael. 700 CHILDRENS DR, DIV OF CARDLGY 43205
#055-01-1992 L2002 **PDC PD** *020 †55
HOFFMANN, Stephen Paul. 473 W 12TH AVE, 201 HLRI 43210 #038-41-1989 L1991
PCC IM *020 †20
HOFMEISTER, Craig C. ■ 43221 #038-40-1999 L2006 **HO** *100 †20
HOFMEISTER, Joseph Konrad. 810 JASONWAY AVE STE A, COLUMBUS ONCOOGY
ASSOCIATE 43214 #041-12-1994 L1997 **HO IM** *020 †20
HOFMEISTER, Marietta A. 4605 SAWMILL RD STE 102 43220 #041-12-1995 L1997 **IM** *020 †20
HOGAN, Mark Jos. 700 CHILDRENS DR 43205 #038-41-1989 L1991 **DR** *020 †80
HOHMANN, John Edward. 410 W 10TH AVE 43210 #038-40-1967 L1967 **AN** *020 †05 ‡
HOISINGTON-STABILE, Amy B. 829 BETHEL RD STE 311 43214 #038-45-2001 L2001
CHP *020 †75
HOLBROOK, Amanda Lee. ■ 43221 #038-45-2004 L2004 *100 †20
HOLBROOK, Walter A. ■ 43221 #038-40-1953 L1953 **FM** *071 †19
HOLLAND, Cynthia Marie. 700 CHILDRENS DR 43205 #016-02-1994 L2000 **PD ADL** *040 †55
HOLLAND, Gregory Carl. 750 MT CARMEL MALL, STE 390 43222 #038-40-1987 L1988
PS *020 †85,65
HOLLENBACH, John Robt. 793 W STATE ST 43222 #038-40-1982 L1985 **IM** *020 †20
HOLLERN, Kristine Peet. 1930 CROWN PARK CT, FAMILY MEDICINE NORTH 43235
#038-40-1992 L1993 **FM** *020 †18
HOLLIDAY, Scott Ashton. 700 CHILDRENS DR, DEPT OF AMBULATORY PEDIATR 43205
#038-40-1994 L1995 **MPD PD** *020 †20,55
HOLLINGSWORTH, Patricia F. 3900 E LIVINGSTON AVE 43227 #018-03-1985 L1991
FM OS *020 †18
HOLLINRAKE, Elizabeth Mar. 1654 UPHAM DR, OHIO STATE UNIV MED CTR 43210
#018-03-2007 L2007 **OBG** *012
HOLMAN, Todd Aron. 410 W 10TH AVE 43210 #038-40-1996 L1997 **PEM** *100 †18
HOLTZAPFEL, Seth Edward. 4885 OLENTANGY RIVER RD, STE 250 43214 #038-45-1994 L1995
IM *020 †20
HOLTZLANDER, Jeffrey D. 700 CHILDRENS DR 43205 #038-40-2002 L2002 **PD** *020 †55
HONDA, Nicholas Paul. 3555 OLENTANGY RIVER RD, STE 1080 43214 #038-44-2004 L2004
IM HOS *100 †20
HONEGGER, Jonathan Robert. 456 W 10TH AVE, 202 MEANS HALL 43210 #017-20-2000 L2000
PDI *012 †20,55
HOOPES, Andrea Jeanne. ■ 43215 #038-40-2008 *012
HOPKIN, Mark S. 2231 N HIGH ST RM 205, OHIO STATE UNIV 43201 #038-40-2000 L2000
FM *100
HOPKINS, Daria Janiece. ■ 43224 #038-41-2007 L2007 **IM** *012
HOPPES, Tyler Cameron. ■ 43212 #038-45-2008 *012
HOSIER, Don Miller. 700 CHILDRENS DR 43205 #038-40-1947 L1947 **PDC PD** *071 †55
HOSSAIN, Fatima. 793 W STATE ST, MT CARMEL MED CTR 43222 #160-04-1997 L2004
IM *100 †20
HOSTETLER, Sarah Grim. ■ 43202 #038-40-2008 *012
HOSTETLER, Todd Landon. ■ 43202 #038-40-2004 L2004 **MPD** *012
HOTHEM, Elijah Allen. ■ 43220 #038-44-2005 L2005 **ORS** *012
HOU, Yueping. ■ 43220 #019-02-2007 L2007 **TY** *012
HOUSER, Laura Lynn. 150 TAYLOR STATION RD, STE 300 43213 #038-40-1993 L1997
OBG *020 †30
HOUSTON, Thomas Price. 3773 OLENTANGY RIVER RD, MCCONNELL HEART HLTH CTR 43214
#027-01-1977 L1981 **FM** *030 †18
HOWARD, Michael Stockton. 793 W STATE ST, CO MT CARMEL HOSP-MED EDU 43222
#019-02-2003 L2003 **ORS** *012
HOWER, Olivia Chu. 5925 CLEVELAND AVE 43231 #038-40-1994 L1995 **FM** *020 †18 ‡
HSIAO, Yunsheng. ■ 43235 #038-40-2007 L2007 **FP** *012
HUA, Trieu Phuc. 535 OFFICENTER PL, STE A 43230 #038-40-1993 L1994 **FM** *020 †18
HUANG, Cheng Cheng. 410 W 10TH AVE 43210 #243-58-1986 L2007 **PTH** *012
HUANG, Michael K. 3525 OLENTANGY RIVER RD, STE 4330 43214 #038-44-1997 L1999
IM *020 †20
HUBBLE, Jean Pintar. 1581 DODD DR, STE 371 43210 #019-02-1983 L1988 **N** *020 †75
HUBER, David Francis. 259 TAYLOR STATION RD, INC 43213 #038-40-1980 L1982
ORS *020 †40
HUDAK, Christine Diane. 797 THOMAS LN 43214 #038-40-1991 L1992 **FM** *040 †18

HUEBERT, Candace Ann. ■ 43204 #030-05-2006 L2006 **IM** *012
HUEBERT, Ty Douglas. 410 W 10TH AVE, DEPT OF INTERNAL MEDICINE 43210 #030-05-2006 L2006 **IM** *012
HUESTIS, Robert David. 862 S 3RD ST 43206 #038-40-1970 L1970 **CHP P** *040 †75
HUET, Jason Daniel. ■ 43215 #038-40-2004 L2004 **PCC** *012
HUHEEY, Marilyn Jane. 1335 DUBLIN RD, STE 25A 43215 #020-12-1970 L1971 **OPH GP** *020 †35
HULL, Walter Baird. 456 W 10TH AVE, STE 2B 43210 #048-04-1963 L1973 **OBG GP** *020 †30
HUMMEL, John David. 473 W 12TH AVE, DHLRI, STE 200 43210 #051-01-1987 L1994 **ICE IM** *020 †20
HUMPHREY, Benj Carlisle. 445 HUTCHINSON AVE STE 300 43235 #020-12-1973 L1974 **FM MDM** *030 †18
HUNDLEY, Andrew Franklin. 1654 UPHAM DR, 565 MEANS HALL 5TH FL 43210 #048-12-1998 L2005 **OBG** *020 †30
HUNT, David Francis. 6001 E BROAD ST 43213 #038-45-1982 L1983 **IM** *020 †20
HUNT, Justin Tyler. ■ 43220 #038-40-2008 *012
HUNT, William Garrett. 700 CHILDRENS DR, ED-584 43205 #007-02-1997 L2004 **PDI** *020 †55
HUNTER, Billy Ray. 1670 UPHAM DR, OSU/UMC NEURSCIENCE FACLTY 43210 #036-01-1976 L1990 **P** *040 †75
HUNTER, Douglas Dean. 2929 KENNY RD, STE 160 43221 #038-40-1984 L1985 **FM** *020 †18
HUNTER, Jessica Blaire. 2975 DONNYLANE BLVD 43235 #038-43-2003 L2003 **IM** *020 †20
HUNTER, Roger John. 2240 N BANK DR, UPPR 43220 #025-01-1982 L1986 **AN IM** *020 †20,05
HUNTER, William Ward, Jr. 1654 UPHAM DR, 630 MEANS HALL 43210 #038-40-1973 L1976 **R NM** *020 †28
HURA, Donald Eugene. 50 MCNAUGHTEN RD, STE 200 43213 #038-45-1984 L1985 **GS** *020 †85
HURD, Brooks Harding. ■ 43215 #024-05-1942 L1954 **PTH** *071 †50
HURST, Elizabeth E. 5151 REED RD 43220 #038-43-1985 L1986 **P** *020 †75
HURST, Mark Andrew. 2200 W BROAD ST, TWIN VALLEY BEHAV HEALTH 43223 #038-43-1985 L1986 **P ADP** *030 †75
HURT, Jason D. 320 W 10TH AVE, M-210 STARLING-LOVING 43210 #048-15-2004 L2007 **OBG** *012
HUSTAK, Erik Christopher. ■ 43205 #038-40-2008 *012
HUTMAN, Burton Simson. 793 W STATE ST, MT CARMEL MEDICAL CENTERS 43222 #041-12-1960 L1961 **P** *020
HYMAS, Joseph Clark. ■ 43221 #038-40-2007 L2007 **MPD** *012
IAMS, Andrew Jay. ■ 43221 #038-41-2005 L2005 **PM** *012
IAMS, Jay Donald. 1654 UPHAM DR, 561 MEANS HL OH ST UNIV 43210 #056-05-1972 L1977 **MFM OBG** *050 †30
IBRAHIM, Waleed. ■ 43235 #915-03-1988 L2002 **DR** *100 †80
IMBODEN, Lester E. 642 CHAFFIN RDG 43214 #038-40-1950 L1950 **AN AM** *071 †05 ‡
IMM, Amy Ann. 3545 OLENTANGY RIVER RD, RIVERSIDE PULMONARY 43214 #038-40-1988 L1989 **CCM** *020 †20
ING, Steven Wai. 1581 DODD DR, 491 MCCAMPBELL HALL 43210 #035-19-1993 L2005 **END** *020 †20
INGLIS, Robert M. 717 NEIL AVE APT 512 43215 #038-40-1938 L1938 **GYN** *071 †30
INGRAHAM, Susan Elizabeth. ■ 43206 #038-41-2004 L2004 **PD** *100 †55
INNES, Jeffrey Thomas. 285 E STATE ST, STE 620 43215 #005-19-1981 L1983 **GS** *020 †85
IRAM, Durdana. 700 CHILDRENS DR, CHILDREN'S HOSPTIAL COLUMB 43205 #704-09-1990 L1997 **PDP** *020 †55
IRENE, Richard Thomas. 974 BETHEL RD, STE A 43214 #035-06-1979 L1986 **OTO** *020 †45
IRWIN, Anna Isakov. ■ 43204 #038-40-2007 L2007 **IM** *012
IRWIN, Terry Lee. 4830 KNIGHTSBRIDGE BLVD, STE A 43214 #038-40-1973 L1973 **IM** *020 †20
ISLAM, Shaheen U. 473 W 12TH AVE, 201 HEART AND LUNG INST. 43210 #160-03-1988 L2005 **PCC** *100 †20
ISLER, Brian Milton. 85 MCNAUGHTEN RD, OHIO GASTROENTEROLOGY 43213 #038-43-1996 L1997 **GE IM** *020 †20
IWENOFU, Obiajulu Hans. ■ 43221 #690-04-1995 L2007 **SP** *100 †50
IYENGAR, Kavita. ■ 43220 #038-45-2006 L2006 **ORS** *012
IYENGAR, Srinivas. 473 W 12TH AVE, 2ND FLOOR DHLRI 43210 #305-01-2000 L2000 **CD** *020
JABBOUR, Saad M. ■ 43215 #875-02-1990 L1999 **FM** *100
JACABAN, Pureza Deocales. 1336 E MAIN ST 43205 #748-08-1963 L1974 **GP** *020
JACKSON, Aurelia J. 700 CHILDRENS DR, DEPT OF AMBULATORY PEDIATR 43205 #038-43-1995 L1997 **PD** *020 †55
JACKSON, Benita Marie. 320 W 10TH AVE, OSU SCH PUBLIC HLTH 43210 #010-03-1982 L1991 **PHP IM** *040 †70
JACKSON, Edward F, Jr. 1450 HAWTHORNE AVE 43203 #038-40-1968 L1968 **IM** *020 †20
JACKSON, Elizabeth I. 543 TAYLOR AVE, VA OUTPATIENT CLINIC 43203 #028-34-1975 L1976 **P** *020 †75
JACKSON, Jermaine M. 2188 RIVER RUN TRCE 43235 #047-06-2001 L2001 **PCC** *012
JACKSON, Rebecca Dorothy. 456 W 10TH AVE 43210 #038-40-1978 L1979 **IM END** *050 †20
JACKSON, Samantha Mary. 410 W 10TH AVE, 207 MEANS HALL 43210 #038-40-2004 L2004 **IM** *012
JACKSON, Sharon Lynn. ■ 43203 #025-07-1994 **OBG** *020
JACOB, Abraham. 456 W 10TH AVE RM 4024B, 456 W 10TH AVE ROOM 4024B 43210 #025-01-1997 L2004 **NO** *100 †45
JACQUEMIN, Shawn Paul. 1021 COUNTRY CLUB RD STE A, PEDIATRIC ASSOCIATES 43213 #038-40-2002 L2002 **PD** *020 †55
JACQUES, Richard Henry. ■ 43214 #041-02-1938 L1945 **IM RHU** *071 †20
JADCHERLA, Sudarshan R. 700 CHILDRENS DR, DEPT OF PEDIATRICS-NEONATO 43205 #495-65-1982 L2002 **NPM PD** *020 †55
JAGGI, Preeti. 700 CHILDRENS DR, ED 583 43205 #038-40-1999 L2006 **PDI** *100 †55
JAIN, Sanjay Kumar. 1654 UPHAM DR, OHIO ST 609 MEANS HALL 43210 #038-44-1996 L2002 **R** *020 †80
JAKDA, Ahmed Ibrahim. 2231 N HIGH ST 43201 #665-01-2003 L2003 **FM** *100 †18
JAKDA, Almas. 410 W 10TH AVE 43210 #665-01-2004 L2005 **FP** *012
JALBUENA, Tracy Lynn. ■ 43201 #036-01-2006 L2006 **EM** *012
JAMIL, Altaf. 700 CHILDRENS DR, CHILDRENS HOSP/HEM/ONC 43205 #704-09-1988 L1997 **PD** *020 †55
JAMMU, Balpreet Singh. ■ 43235 #025-07-1994 L1997 **FM** *020 †18
JAN, Solomon A.. ■ 43215 #305-01-2004 L2005 **FP** *012
JANECZEK, Curtis Lee. ■ 43231 #038-40-1982 L1984 *020
JANKE, Igor Edward. 1670 UPHAM DR, PSYCHIATRY 43210 #038-44-1985 L1994 **P** *040 †75
JASTI, Ramesh Babu. 543 TAYLOR AVE, CHALMERS WYLIE 43203 #025-07-1992 L2007 **P** *020 †75
JASYS, Irene. ■ 43215 #616-01-1944 L1952 **OS** *071
JATANA, Kris R.. 456 W 10TH AVE, 4100 UNIV HOSP CLINIC 43210 #038-44-2004 L2004 **OTO** *012
JAYANTHI, Venkata R. 700 CHILDRENS DR, COLUMBUS CHILDREN'S HOSPIT 43205 #038-40-1987 L1994 **U** *020 †95
JAYANTI, Kameshwari. 410 W 10TH AVE 43210 #495-49-1980 L1990 **P** *020
JAYANTI, Subbarao. 793 W STATE ST 43222 #495-11-1974 L1981 **AN** *020 †05
JEFFERS, Phillip Dean. 3535 OLENTANGY RIVER RD 43214 #038-40-1973 L1973 **ORS** *020 †40
JEFFERSON, Alfred Blair. 1829 E LONG ST 43203 #047-07-1955 L1956 **OBG** *071 †30
JENKINS, Carol S. 7400 HUNTINGTON PARK DR, STE 100 43235 #038-40-1992 L1995 **OBG** *020 †30
JENKINS, Craig Steven. 4606 SAWMILL RD 43220 #038-40-1979 L1980 **AN** *020 †20,05
JENKINS, Kevin Russell. 2240 N BANK DR, UPPR 43220 #038-41-1998 L2003 **AN** *020 †05
JENNINGS, Michael Robt. 3773 OLENTANGY RIVER RD, MC CONNELL HEART HLTH CTR 43214 #038-06-1972 L1975 **IM CD** *020 †20
JENSEN, Jasmin Sue. ■ 43228 #049-01-2006 L2006 **MPD** *012
JEPPESEN, Kelly Marvin. ■ 43220 #038-40-2008 *012
JHAVERI, Monika Piyush. 793 W STATE ST, DEPT OF MED EDU 43222 #305-01-2005 L2006 **IM** *012
JHAVERI, Shefali Nishit. 6001 E BROAD ST, ATTN MEDICAL STAFF OFFICE 43213 #496-38-1993 L2000 **IM** *020 †20
JIMENEZ, Rafael Enrique. ■ 43210 #270-01-1991 L2005 **PTH** *100 †50
JIPA, Daniela Elena. 4310 CLIME RD, STE B 43228 #781-01-1992 L2001 **IM** *020 †20
JIPA, Mihai. 1180 E MAIN ST 43205 #781-01-1991 L1997 **IM** *020 †20
JOCHEM, Gustav Gottfried. 3400 OLENTANGY RIVER RD, STE 150 43202 #407-10-1952 L1959 **IM** *071
JOCHEM, Victor Josef. 3820 OLENTANGY RIVER RD, OHIO GASTROENTEROLOGY 43214 #038-41-1987 L1990 **IM** *020 †20
JOHANSEN, Michael Edward. ■ 43202 #038-40-2008 *012
JOHNSON, A John. 2 MIRANOVA PL, STE 390 43215 #496-16-1984 L1995 **P MDM** *030
JOHNSON, Charles Felzen. 700 CHILDRENS DR, CHLDRN HOSP-CHILD & FAM AD 43205 #005-14-1961 L1981 **OS PD** *071 †55
JOHNSON, Derrick Elliott. ■ 43224 #038-41-2004 L2004 **IM** *100 †20
JOHNSON, Emily Jane. 697 THOMAS LN 43214 #038-45-2005 L2005 **FP** *012
JOHNSON, Ernest W. 480 MEDICAL CENTER DR, STE 1025 43210 #038-40-1952 L1952 **PM** *020 †60
JOHNSON, James Bradford. ■ 43220 #038-40-1986 L1989 **DR** *075 †80
JOHNSON, John Constantine. 866 W BROAD ST 43222 #038-40-1965 L1965 **DR** *072 †80
JOHNSON, Philip R, Jr. 700 CHILDRENS DR 43205 #036-01-1980 L1991 **ID** *050 †55
JONAS, Philip Clayton. ■ 43206 #038-44-2006 L2006 **IM** *012
JONAUS, Lawrence Jos, Jr. 2240 N BANK DR, UPPR 43220 #056-05-1995 L1999 **AN** *020 †05
JONAUS, Sarah Ann. 5969 E BROAD ST, STE 200 43213 #056-05-1996 L1999 **IM** *020 †20
JONES, Angela Vachon. 700 CHILDRENS DR, ATTN: CHIEF RESIDENTS 43205 #038-43-2003 L2003 **PD** *100 †55
JONES, Daniel Alan. 1699 W LANE AVE 43221 #005-12-1989 L1993 **N** *020 †75
JONES, David Edward. 3131 W BROAD ST 43204 #270-03-1999 L2000 **FM** *100
JONES, David Ray. 5100 W BROAD ST, DOCTORS HOSPITAL EMERGENCY 43228 #036-08-1990 L1992 **EM GS** *020 †16
JONES, Debra R S. 1620 E BROAD ST, PARK TOWERS 43203 #038-40-1984 L1989 **P** *020
JONES, E Paul. ■ 43227 #038-40-1977 L1979 **OBG** *020
JONES, Edna Marie. 1727 BETHEL RD 43220 #038-40-1981 L1982 **FM ADM** *020 †18
JONES, George F. ■ 43214 #038-41-1939 **R** *071 †80
JONES, Grant Lloyd. 2050 KENNY RD, OSU SPORTS MEDICINE CENTER 43221 #038-40-1992 L1994 **OSM** *020 †40
JONES, Jeffrey Alan. ■ 43201 #025-01-2000 L2006 **ON** *020 †20
JONES, Julie M. 4300 CLIME RD, STE 130 43228 #038-40-1993 L1996 **OBG** *020 †30
JONES, Lynne A. 400 E TOWN ST, STE 210 43215 #010-03-1972 L1973 **FM** *030
JONES, Matthew Lawrence. 340 E TOWN ST, STE 8-550 43215 #038-40-2003 L2003 **HOS** *020 †18
JONES, Natalie Beckman. 410 W 10TH AVE, 316-A MEANS HALL 43210 #038-40-2004 L2004 **GS** *012
JONES, Sheree Lynn. 6096 E MAIN ST, ST 102 43213 #038-43-1999 L2000 **FM** *020 †18
JONES, Virginia Haller. 246 N HIGH ST, OHIO DEPARTMENT OF HEALTH 43215 #041-14-1980 L1984 **PHP PD** *020 †55
JORDAN, Kim M. 500 THOMAS LN, COMMUNITY MEDICINE DEPARTM 43214 #055-02-1982 L1991 **IM IMG** *040 †20
JORDAN, Lee Workman. 3535 OLENTANGY RIVER RD, RIVERSIDE METHODIST HOSPIT 43214 #047-05-1981 L2007 **CD IM** *020 †20
JOSEPH, Anthony J. 3040 RIVERSIDE DR, STE 224 43221 #038-40-1977 L1977 **EM OS** *062 †18,16
JOSEPH, Joseph. 6111 E BROAD ST 43213 #654-01-1999 L2000 **IM** *100 †20
JOSEPH, Michael Henry. 700 CHILDRENS DR, DEPT OF ANESTHESIOLOGY 43205 #030-06-1993 L2007 **PD** *020 †55
JOSEPH, Suja A. 700 CHILDRENS DR, DEPT. OF PEDIATRIC NEUROLO 43205 #624-01-1988 L1995 **CHN** *020 †75,55
JOSHI, Kamal Kant. 340 E TOWN ST STE 7-200 43215 #495-03-1971 L1980 **U** *020 †95
JOSTPILLE, Fanree Marie. 700 CHILDRENS DR, ATTN: MEDICAL STAFF 43205 #038-41-2000 L2000 **PD** *020 †55
JULKA, Abhishek. ■ 43212 #038-40-2008 *012
KABIRU, Wanjiku Joan. 1654 UPHAM DR, 546 MEANS HALL 43210 #047-07-1997 L2004 **OBG** *020 †30
KADEMIAN, Monique Elise. ■ 43209 #038-40-2004 L2004 **D** *012
KAEDING, Christopher C. 1847 NEIL AVE, OSU MCCORKLE TRAINING ROOM 43210 #016-06-1983 L1990 **ORS** *020 †40
KAEVEL, Jorn. 793 W STATE ST, DEPT OF MED EDUCATION 43222 #409-21-1999 L2007 *100
KAHN, Eric Lee. 1455 S 4TH ST 43207 #038-40-1982 L1990 **P** *020
KAHWASH, Eiad Badie. 1375 PERRY ST 5TH FL, CO OSU HOSPS-MEDICAL ED DE 43201 #875-02-1991 L2000 **BBK** *100 †50
KAHWASH, Samir B. 1645 NEIL AVE 43210 #875-01-1983 L1992 **HMP PP** *020 †50
KAIDE, Colin Graham. 1654 UPHAM DR, RM 146 43210 #016-11-1993 L1994 **EM** *020 †16
KAITZ, Ellen S. 700 CHILDRENS DR, PHYSICAL MEDICINE & REHAB 43205 #024-16-1987 L1997 **PM PD** *020 †60
KAKABADZE, Shalva V. 1492 E BROAD ST, STE 1302 43205 #913-23-1994 L2000 **FM** *020 †18
KAKOS, Gerard Stephen. 300 E TOWN ST 43215 #038-40-1967 L1967 **TS** *020 †85,90
KALATHOOR, Sasi R. 700 CHILDRENS DR, DEPT OF ANESTHESIOLOGY 43205 #012-01-1989 L1992 **AN** *020 †05 ‡
KALBFLEISCH, Steven Jack. 473 W 12TH AVE, DHLRI - SUITE 200 43210 #025-01-1986 L1993 **CD IM** *020 †20

■ = Address Information Privacy Protected

KALLIAFAS, Stavros D. 410 W 10TH AVE, OHIO STATE UNIVERSITY 43210 #418-01-1986 L1993 **VS** *020 †85

KALPATTHI, Ramasubramanian. 700 CHILDRENS DR, CHILDREN'S HOSPITAL 43205 #495-66-1996 L2003 **PHO** *100 †55

KALRA, Rajeev Kumar. ■ 43215 #661-03-2004 L2006 **FP** *012

KALYANAM, Ram Chandran. 1670 UPHAM DR 43210 #041-02-1993 L2006 **P** *020

KAMADANA, Swapna. ■ 43220 #038-40-2005 L2005 **IM** *012

KANG, Dong-Kyoo Richard. 555 S 18TH ST STE 2A, CHILDRENS PED OTOLARYNGOLO 43205 #024-05-1980 L2003 **OTO PDO** *040 †45 ‡

KANG, Katherine Jane. 370 W 9TH AVE, 254 MEILING HALL 43210 #038-40-2008 *012

KANG, Shin Suk. ■ 43235 #583-01-1971 L1986 **AN PME** *071 †05

KANKANALA, Ramana Reddy. 410 W 10TH AVE 43210 #495-65-2004 L2007 **FP** *012

KANOOR, Sachidanandan P. 543 TAYLOR AVE, CLINIC 43203 #495-62-1971 L1995 **IM** *020 †20

KANTER, Stuart J. 6150 E BROAD ST, GERIATRIC PHYSICIAN ASSOCI 43213 #016-76-2000, ▲ L2000 **FPG FM** *020 †18

KANTHARIA, Bharat K. 473 W 12TH AVE, 2ND FL - HLRI 43210 #496-38-1980 L2005 **ICE** *020 †20

KANTOR, Seth Mason. 480 W 9TH AVE, OHIO STATE UNIV DIV OF IMM 43210 #035-45-1975 L1983 **RHU IM** *030 †20

KAO, Ruey Horng. ■ 43235 #038-40-2005 *100

KAPETANSKY, Frederick M. 262 NEIL AVE, STE 310 43215 #025-01-1957 L1958 **OPH** *020 †35

KAPLAN, Marvin. 5969 E BROAD ST, FL 2 43213 #803-05-1968 L1970 **IM** *020

KAPOOR, Ritu. ■ 43215 #010-01-2003 L2008 **AN** *100

KARAS, Chris Sotere. ■ 43220 #038-40-2003 L2003 **NS** *012

KARAYANNACOS, Panayotis E. ■ 43212 #410-01-1960 **TS GS** *050

KARLEN, Matthew Robert. 1654 UPHAM DR, 630 MEANS HALL 43210 #038-41-2000 L2000 **DR** *100 †80

KARNE, Rajaram Jivaji. 456 W 10TH AVE 43210 #495-82-1988 L2005 **END** *020 †20

KAROL, Seth Evan. ■ 43235 #038-40-2008 *012

KAROLIN, Stella Helene. 793 W STATE ST 43222 #407-07-1950 L1961 **P** *071 †75

KARPENKO, Matthew J. 410 W 10TH AVE, DIV OF HEMATOLOGY ONCOLOGY 43210 #041-78-2002, ▲ L2005 **HO** *012 †20

KASSICIEH, Victor N. 5100 W BROAD ST 43228 #028-79-1967, ▲ L1968 **GP** *071

KATAKI, Maria. 1654 UPHAM DR, 467 MEANS HALL 43210 #418-01-1989 L2003 **N** *020

KATPADI, Manmohankrishna. 1492 E BROAD ST # 1201 43205 #495-33-1985 L1996 **CD** *020 †20

KATULA, Douglas Alan. 4845 OLENTANGY RIVER RD, STE 210 43214 #038-40-1989 L1990 **IM** *020 †20

KATZ, Allen Charles. 3525 OLENTANGY RIVER RD, STE 5360 43214 #016-11-1993 L2007 **DR** *020 †80

KATZ, Charles Meyer. 941 CHATHAM LN 43221 #041-12-1968 L1970 **END DIA** *020 †20

KATZ, Gary Robert. 1654 UPHAM DR, MEANS HALL 165 43210 #038-43-1998 L1999 **EM** *020 †16

KATZ, Marshall Gene. 175 S 3RD ST STE 1200 43215 #025-07-1973 L1974 **IM MDM** *020

KATZ, Schmuel. 410 W 10TH AVE 43210 #550-01-1969 **PD** *100

KATZ, Sherman Allen. 410 W 10TH AVE, HALL N708 43210 #038-40-1973 L1976 **VS VIR** *020 †85

KATZ, Steven Edward. 456 W 10TH AVE 43210 #038-40-1990 L1991 **OPH** *020 †35

KAUFMAN, Paul Nathan. 6001 E BROAD ST 43213 #025-07-1986 L1988 **U** *020 †95

KAVANAGH, Marsha Cheung. 262 NEIL AVE, STE 430 43215 #024-01-2001 L2006 **OPH** *100

KAYE, Peter Max. 111 S GRANT AVE, GRANT MED CTR 43215 #016-42-2002 L2007 **CRS** *012 †85

KAYLOR, Terry Randall. 410 W 10TH AVE, N 201 DOAN HALL 43210 #038-41-2002 L2002 **GE** *012 †20

KAZI, Imtiaz Uddin. 1460 S HIGH ST, SOUTHWOOD FAMILY PRACTICE 43207 #160-02-1977 L1993 **FM PHP** *020 †18

KEAN, John Ray. 259 TAYLOR STATION RD, INC. 43213 #041-13-1974 L1975 **OP** *020 †40

KEDER, Lisa Margret. 1654 UPHAM DR, RM 522 43210 #038-40-1989 L1995 **OBG** *020 †30

KEELING, Thomas Callendar. 685 BRYDEN RD 43205 #038-40-1995 L1996 **ID** *020 †20

KEGLER, Kevin Grant. 111 S GRANT AVE 43215 #038-40-1997 L2000 **OPH** *020 †35

KEITH, Jason Christopher. 50 MCNAUGHTEN RD, STE 200 43213 #038-40-1995 L1996 **GS** *020 †85

KEITH, Paul Fancher. 500 THOMAS LN, COMMUNITY MEDICINE CLINIC 43214 #035-09-1960 L1962 **IM** *071

KELEGAMA, Anandanee Diluk. 285 E STATE ST STE 6, EDUC DEPT 43215 #104-01-2005 L2006 **FP** *012

KELLAR, Matthew Vinton. 750 MOUNT CARMEL MALL 43222 #038-40-1997 L1998 **EM** *020 †16

KELLER, Martin D. 410 W 10TH AVE 43210 #035-20-1952 L1957 **GPM IM** *071 †70

KELLER, Tara Ressallat. 115 W MAIN ST # 1103 43215 #038-40-1997 *100

KELLEY, Amy Rickly. 770 JASONWAY AVE, STE 1A 43214 #038-43-1989 L1991 **IM** *020 †20

KELLEY, Brian Scott. 3045 OLENTANGY RIVER RD, PROFESSIONALS/WOMEN'S HLTH 43202 #038-40-1996 L1997 **OBG** *020 †30

KELLEY, Curtin Gregg. 262 NEIL AVE, STE 320 43215 #038-40-1977 L1983 **OPH** *020 †35

KELLEY, Michael Timothy. 1166 DUBLIN RD 43215 #038-41-1981 L1982 **OM PTX** *030 †16,70

KELLY, David Robt. 456 CLINIC DR DEPT OTO 43210 #038-40-1965 L1965 **OTO HNS** *071 †45

KELLY, Garrett Tyler. 410 W 10TH AVE, N-146 DOAN HALL 43210 #038-06-1993 L1996 **AN** *020 †05

KELLY, Sean Gerard. ■ 43221 #038-40-2007 L2007 **MPD** *012

KELLY, William Brian. 793 W STATE ST 4TH FL, MT CARMEL MED CTR-ANESTHES 43222 #031-01-1987 L1992 **AN** *020 †05

KELSTEN, Martin Lee. 111 S GRANT AVE, DEPT OF PATHOLOGY GRANT HO 43215 #018-03-1982 L1989 **PTH PCP** *020 †50

KEMP, William Robt. 5965 E BROAD ST, STE 420 43213 #041-13-1981 L2003 **NS GS** *020 †25

KENDRA, Kari Lynn. 320 W 10TH AVE, B415 STARLING LOVING HALL 43210 #016-01-1990 L2001 **ON** *020 †20

KENDRICK, Ronald Edward. 3050 OLENTANGY RIVER RD, STE 2010 43214 #038-06-1961 L1961 **ORS** *071 †40

KENNARD, Elizabeth Ann. 4830 KNIGHTSBRIDGE BLVD, STE E 43214 #038-06-1986 L1988 **REN OBG** *020 †30

KENNEDY, George Mitchell. 3545 OLENTANGY RIVER RD, STE 525 43214 #055-01-1988 L1993 **GS** *020 †85

KENNEDY, Melanie J S. 410 W 10TH AVE, ROOM 310 DOAN HALL 43210 #038-40-1968 L1969 **BBK CLP** *030 †50

KENNEY, Brian David. 555 S 18TH ST, CHILDRENS SURGICAL 43205 #038-43-1983 L1984 **PDS TRS** *040 †85

KENYON, Robert Earl, Jr. 750 MT CARMEL MALL, STE 300 43222 #051-01-1974 L2004 **EM IM** *020 †20,16

KERLIN, Bryce Andrew. 700 CHILDRENS DR, DIV OF HEM/ONC ED 557 43205 #056-06-1996 L2004 **PHO PD** *012 †55

KERNER, Bruce Alan. 5965 E BROAD ST, STE 120 43213 #016-42-1984 L1990 **CRS** *020 †85,10

KERNER, Todd Eric. ■ 43228 #032-01-2003 L2005 **PM** *012

KERNS, Katrina Sue. ■ 43204 #038-40-2007 L2007 *012

KERSHAH, Sharif Mohamed. ■ 43220 #038-43-2005 L2005 **DR** *012

KEY, Craig. 1654 UPHAM DR, 146 MEANS HALL 43210 #038-43-1992 L2000 **EM** *020 †16

KEYASHIAN, Peyman. ■ 43201 #038-40-2008 *012

KEYES, Jeffrey Scott. ■ 43203 #036-01-2006 L2006 **PD** *012

KEYHANI-ROFAGHA, Sedigheh. 410 W 10TH AVE, STE 310 43210 #517-01-1971 L1983 **PTH** *030 †50

KHABIRI, Hooman. 1654 UPHAM DR, DEPT/ RADIOLOGY 43210 #038-40-1990 L1992 **R VIR** *020 †80

KHAIRY, Raed Nabil. ■ 43202 #575-01-2000 L2002 **ID IMG** *012 †20

KHAMAG, Abdussalam A. ■ 43220 #613-01-1977 L1985 **GS** *020

KHAN, Meena Sadaf. 3535 OLENTANGY RIVER RD, CO RIVERSIDE METHODIST-MED 43214 #038-40-2003 L2003 **N** *012

KHAN, Muhammad Nadeem. 1430 S HIGH ST, URGENT CARE PLUS 43207 #704-09-1992 L1996 **IM** *020 †20

KHAN, Nadeem. 700 CHILDRENS DR 43205 #704-16-1984 L1998 **CCP** *020 †55

KHAN, Raheel Ahmad. 410 W 10TH AVE 43210 #041-78-2004, ▲ L2004 **P** *012

KHANDELWAL, Sorabh. 1654 UPHAM DR, 170A MEANS HALL 43210 #038-40-1995 L1997 **EM** *020 †16

KHANDUJA, Karamjit Singh. 4310 CLIME RD, STE C 43228 #495-01-1980 L1983 **CRS** *020 †10,85

KHARAT, Varsha Ramdas. 340 E TOWN ST STE 8-550, GRANT MEDICAL CENTER,ATT-W 43215 #495-28-1995 L2003 **NEP** *012 †20

KHAWAJA, Raheela A. 1581 DODD DR 43210 #704-01-1984 L1999 **END** *020 †20

KHAYAT, Rami Nicolas. 473 W 12TH AVE, 201 DAVIS HEART & LUNG INS 43210 #875-03-1994 L2003 **PCC** *020 †20

KHOURY, Paneez. ■ 43210 #016-11-2005 L2005 **IM** *012

KHUHRO, Abdul Latif. 700 CHILDRENS DR, CHILDRENS HOSPITAL 43205 #704-16-1985 L2002 **CN CHN** *020 †55,75

KIACZ, Mary Lynn. 1875 MILLIKIN RD 43210 #038-40-1979 L1980 **IM EM** *020

KIEFER, Thomas Andrew. 500 E MAIN ST, STE 110 43215 #038-40-1980 L1981 **AI PD** *020 †55,03

KIEHL, Samuel Jacob, III. 410 W 10TH AVE 43210 #038-40-1971 L1971 **EM** *030 †16

KIKTA, Donald Gregory, Jr. 370 W 9TH AVE, 200A MEILING HALL 43210 #038-40-2006 L2006 **IM** *012

KILLIAN, Valerie Nanagas. ■ 43201 #038-41-2000 L2000 **EM** *020 †16

KIM, Chang Zoon. 111 S GRANT AVE, GRANT MEDICAL CENTER 43215 #583-10-1967 L1974 **AN** *020 †05

KIM, Daniel Jinwoo. ■ 43202 #038-40-2008 *012

KIM, Dongmin. 2200 W BROAD ST, COLUMBUS CAMPUS 43223 #583-02-1967 L1979 **P** *020 †75

KIM, Edward Young. 300 W 10TH AVE, RM 072A 43210 #038-06-2001 L2001 **RO** *100

KIM, Grace Z. 245 TAYLOR STATION RD 43213 #583-08-1963 L1975 **OPH** *020 †35

KIM, Inah. 370 W 9TH AVE, 200A MEILING HALL 43210 #038-40-2008 *012

KIM, James Koohwan. 410 W 10TH AVE, N214 DOAN HALL 43210 #038-45-1995 L1997 **GE** *020 †20

KIM, John H. 16 W LONG ST, HUMAN RESOURCES DEPT 43215 #583-04-1986 L1997 **P** *100

KIM, John Sangho. 1275 OLENTANGY RIVER RD, STE 10 43212 #038-40-1989 L1992 **PCC PUD** *020 †20

KIM, Kenneth Hyunchung. ■ 43221 #038-43-2005 L2005 **OBG** *012

KIM, Liza Sunmin. ■ 43235 #010-01-2003 L2003 **PS** *012

KING, Denis Renz. 555 S 18TH ST, CHILDRENS SURGICAL 43205 #041-09-1969 L1972 **PDS GS** *020 †85

KING, Harry Stephen. 111 S GRANT AVE 43215 #038-40-1974 L1974 **IM** *020 †20

KING, John Paul. 700 CHILDRENS DR 43205 #539-02-1955 L1958 **PD AM** *075

KING, Mark Alan. 1654 UPHAM DR, 630 MEANS HALL 43210 #038-40-1986 L1990 **DR IM** *020 †80

KING, Samuel Jerome. 410 W 10TH AVE, OH STATE UNIV HOSP 43210 #020-02-2006 L2007 **AN** *012

KING, Sonia Lean. 4606 SAWMILL RD 43220 #017-20-1995 L1999 **AN** *020 †05

KINGTON, Joseph Kevin. 3545 OLENTANGY RIVER RD, STE 114 43214 #038-40-1985 L1989 **OBG** *020 †30

KIRK, Paul Christian. 456 W 10TH AVE 43210 #038-40-1985 L1985 **FM OM** *020 †18

KIRKBY, Stephen Edward. 410 W 10TH AVE 43210 #041-14-2001 L2001 **PCC** *012 †20,55

KIRKENDALL, Dean Alan. 3954 NEWHALL RD 43220 #038-40-1983 L1984 **P** *020 †75

KIRSCHNER, Lawrence S. 456 W 10TH AVE 43210 #035-46-1993 L2002 **END IM** *050 †20

KISNER, Jennifer Lynn. 750 MOUNT CARMEL MALL, MALSTE 200 43222 #038-40-1999 L2000 **GS** *020 †85

KISSEL, John Thos. 456 W 10TH AVE STE 1200B, OHIO STATE UNIVERSITY HOSP 43210 #016-06-1978 L1983 **N** *012 †20

KLAGES, Reynold E, Jr. 793 W STATE ST 43222 #038-40-1949 L1949 **IM CD** *071

KLAIMAN, Miriam Holly. 1375 PERRY ST 5T, CO OSU HOSPS-MED EDU DEPT 43201 #026-04-1997 L2000 **N** *012

KLAMAR, Jan Edward. 479 PARSONS AVE 43215 #038-40-1988 L1990 **ORS** *020 †40

KLAMAR, John Andrew. 4885 OLENTANGY RIVER RD, STE 250 43214 #035-03-1963 L1964 **PD** *071 †55

KLAMAR, Karl Wagner. 700 CHILDRENS DR, RM ED477 43205 #038-43-1993 L2003 **PM PD** *020 †60

KLAMERUS, Justin F. 1654 UPHAM DR, 202 MEANS HALL 43210 #025-12-2003 L2003 **ON** *012 †20

KLATTE, Emily Terese. 1654 UPHAM DR, OHIO STATE UNIV MED CTR 43210 #038-40-2002 L2002 **N** *100 †75

KLAUS, Andrew Peter. 423 E TOWN ST, STE 1000 43215 #016-06-1966 L1972 **CD IM** *020 †20

KLAUS, Jennifer Lynne. 685 BRYDEN RD, INFECTIOUS DISEASE CONSULT 43205 #038-40-1999 L1999 **ID** *020 †20

KLAUSNER, Todd Stuart. 866 W BROAD ST 43222 #038-43-1998 L2003 **DR** *020 †80

KLECKER, Rosemary Jordan. ■ 43235 #010-01-1997 L2000 **DR NS** *020 †80

KLEIN, James A. 85 MCNAUGHTEN RD, INC 43213 #020-12-1981 L1983 **PUD PCC** *020 †20

KLEIN, James Eduard. 111 S GRANT AVE 43215 #038-43-1989 L1990 **EM** *020 †16

KLINEFELTER, Ryan Dale. 410 W 10TH AVE, DEPT OF ORTHOPAEDICS 43210 #038-40-1997 L2000 **HS** *020 †40

KLINGELE, Kevin Edward. 259 TAYLOR STATION RD 43213 #038-40-1996 L2002 **ORS** *020 †40

KLISOVIC, Marko Ivo. 150 TAYLOR STATION RD 43213 #957-01-2000 L2004 **OBG** *012

KLISOVIC, Rebecca. 320 W 10TH AVE, B401 STARLING LOVING HALL 43210 #038-40-1997 L2001 **HO IM** *020 †20

KLOMFASS, Matthias T. 410 W 10TH AVE 43210 #409-36-1999 L2000 **FM** *020 †18

KLOOS, Richard Thos. 456 W 10TH AVE 43210 #038-06-1989 L1991 **END NM** *020 †20,28

KLOSTERMAN, Howard D. 410 W 10TH AVE 43210 #016-43-1963 L1964 **R** *040 †80

KNAPP, Jennifer S. 1670 UPHAM DR 43210 #011-75-2005, ▲ L2005 **P** *012

KNAPP, Mark Hayward. 3100 PLAZA PROPERTIES BLVD 43210 #038-41-1997 L2000 **HO** *020 †20

KNELLINGER, Andrea Erin. ■ 43235 #038-40-2005 L2005 **OPH** *012

KNIGHT, Charles Thos. 370 W 9TH AVE BOX 881 43210 #038-40-1988 *020

KNIGHT, Douglas Reid. 700 CHILDRENS DR, CHILDRENS HOSP DEPT CARD 43205 #038-40-1966 L1966 **OM PD** *040

KNIGHT, James Roland. ■ 43212 #026-08-2005 L2005 **MPD** *012

KNOPP, Alois. 1654 UPHAM DR, 630 MEANS HALL 43210 #409-10-1958 **R** *020

KNUDSEN, Bodo Egon. 456 W 10TH AVE, DEPT OF UROLOGY 43210 #062-01-1997 L2005 **U** *100 †95

KNUTSON, Douglas James. 2231 N HIGH ST, RARDIN FAMILY PRACTICE 43201 #038-40-1993 L1994 **FM** *020 †18

KOBAISY, Omaima. 410 W 10TH AVE 43210 #308-13-2003 L2005 **FP** *012

KOBUS, Raymond J, Jr. 3400 OLENTANGY RIVER RD, STE 200 43202 #038-45-1984 L1985 **ORS HS** *020 †40

KOCAK, Ergun. 1654 UPHAM DR, 316 MEANS HALL 43210 #038-40-2000 L2000 **PS** *012

KOCAR, Diana Elizabeth. ■ 43201 #038-40-2008 *012

KOCH, Jean-Paul. 410 W 10TH AVE, DEPT SURG 43210 #869-05-1976 **GS** *100

KOEGEL, Lawrence, Jr. 6001 E BROAD ST 43213 #038-06-1978 L1979 **OTO** *020 †45

KOEHL, Edward Rowe. ■ 43212 #048-12-2002 L2004 **DR** *012

KOELLING, Heather C. 2020 KENNY RD 43221 #035-15-1993 L1994 **OPH** *020 †35

KOERNER, Mark Alan. 111 S GRANT AVE 43215 #018-03-1978 L1982 **OBG** *020 †30

KOESTERS, Irene Paparizos. 4775 KNIGHTSBRIDGE BLVD, STE 207 43214 #038-40-2001 L2001 **PD** *020 †55

KOESTERS, Stephen Craig. 1609 NORTHWEST BLVD, OSU INTERNAL MEDICINE 43212 #038-40-1998 L1999 **MPD** *020 †20,55 ‡

KOESTNER, Adelaide Wilma. ■ 43220 #407-16-1950 L1964 **PTH** *075 †50

KOFF, Stephen Andrew. 700 CHILDRENS DR, EDUCATION BLDG ED 343 43205 #036-07-1969 L1982 **U PD** *020 †95

KOIZUMI, Hisako. 473 W 12TH AVE 43210 #572-16-1965 L1976 **CHP P** *020 †75

KOKMEYER, Daniel Theodore. ■ 43214 #038-40-2008 *012

KOLB, Boris. ■ 43220 #407-16-1952 L1957 **P OS** *020

KOLB, Stephen James. ■ 43214 #048-14-1998 L2007 **N** *020

KOLETAR, Susan Lynn. 410 W 10TH AVE, N1135 DOAN HALL 43210 #055-01-1983 L1986 **ID IM** *050 †20

KOLIBASH, Albert Jos, Jr. 1654 UPHAM DR, MEANS HALL-601 43210 #055-01-1967 L1973 **CD** *020 †20

KOLODZIK, Stephen Ned. 51 S SOUDER AVE 43222 #038-40-1972 L1973 **ORS** *020 †40

KOLOVICH, Gregory Paul. ■ 43215 #038-40-2008 *012

KOMMAREDDY, Gargeyi. 285 E STATE ST, STE 667 43215 #495-21-1999 L2005 **IM** *020 †20

KONCZAL, Laura Lee. 700 CHILDRENS DR, DEPARTMENT OF GENETICS 43205 #038-45-2003 L2003 **MG** *012 †55

KONERU, Lata. 1299 OLENTANGY RIVER RD, STE B 43212 #495-35-1993 L1997 **IM** *020 †20

KONFALA, Rita Marie. 3781 S HIGH ST 43207 #038-40-1986 L1987 **IM PD** *020 †20,55

KONG, Jerome M. 793 W STATE ST, MT CARMEL WEST HOSP 43222 #048-04-1998 L2001 **IM** *100 †20 ‡

KONTRAS, Stella B. 1430 S HIGH ST 2ND FL, HEALTHCARE MANAGEMENT 43207 #038-40-1953 L1953 **CHP** *020

KOPECHEK, Jack Anthony. 1390 CLEVELAND AVE STE 201 43211 #038-40-1984 L1985 **PD** *020 †55

KOPP, Amy Michelle. 456 W 10TH AVE, 5TH FLOOR - ATTN: BOBBI TO 43210 #038-40-2002 L2002 **OPH** *100 †35

KOPP, Benjamin Taylor. ■ 43235 #038-40-2006 L2006 **PD** *012

KORANYI, Katalin. 700 CHILDRENS DR 43205 #737-06-1970 L1973 **PD** *020 †55

KORB, Allan Richard. 648 KENILWORTH CT 43230 #038-40-1955 L1955 **P N** *071

KORMAN, Benjamin Douglas. ■ 43214 #038-40-2008 *012

KORYTKO, Timothy Paul. ■ 43204 #038-06-2005 L2006 **RO** *012

KOSNIK, Edward James. 700 CHILDRENS DR 43205 #023-01-1969 L1971 **NS NSP** *020 †25

KOSTYK, Sandra K. 1581 DODD DR, MCCAMPBELL HALL 371 43210 #016-02-1985 L1998 **N** *050 †75

KOTHARI, Rajul Mukund. ■ 43212 #016-11-2004 L2004 **OBG** *012

KOURLAS, Peter James. 810 JASONWAY AVE, STE A 43214 #038-40-1995 L1996 **HO** *020 †20

KOVACH, Paul Anton. 745 W STATE ST, STE 520 43222 #038-06-2000 L2005 **NEP** *020 †20 ‡

KOVAL, John Stephen. 6001 E BROAD ST, MOUNT CARMEL EAST HOSPITAL 43213 #055-01-1983 L1999 **AN PME** *020 †05

KOVALASKE, Michelle Anne. 3535 OLENTANGY RIVER RD 43214 #038-43-2005 L2005 **IM** *012

KOVALCHIN, John David. 700 CHILDRENS DR, EDUCATION BLDG 616 43205 #038-44-1989 L1990 **PDC** *020 †55

KOVER, Alan Jos. 410 W 10TH AVE, N-146 DOAN HALL 43210 #038-45-1986 L1987 **AN CCM** *020 †05

KRAMER, Thomas Wm. 5969 E BROAD ST # S-404 43213 #038-40-1983 L1983 **GE IM** *020 †20

KRAUT, Eric Harvey. 320 W 10TH AVE 43210 #041-13-1972 L1975 **HEM ON** *040 †20

KRAVEC, Thomas Francis. ■ 43220 #016-06-1969 L1970 **AN** *020 †05

KREINBRINK, Ronald Matthe. ■ 43201 #038-40-2008 *012

KREUTER, Michael Robert. ■ 43214 #038-43-2004 L2004 **AN** *012

KREUTZER, Ernest F, Jr. 1169 MILLCREEK LN 43220 #016-42-1981 L1985 **AN CCM** *020 †05

KRIECHBAUM, Karmon Leigh. 1654 UPHAM DR, MEANS HALL 5TH FLOOR 43210 #038-40-2005 L2005 **OBG** *012

KRIEGER, Jennifer Anne. ■ 43228 #038-43-2004 L2004 **PD** *100 †55

KRIETEMEYER, Laura Ann. 410 W 10TH AVE 43210 #038-40-1992 L1996 **N** *072

KROUSTOS, Constantine N. 456 W 10TH AVE, # 3D 43210 #038-40-2003 L2003 **END** *012 †20

KRUEGER, Justin Keith. 370 W 9TH AVE, OH STATE U COLL OF MED 43210 #038-40-2001 L2001 **MPD** *100 †20,55

KUEBLER, John Philip. 810 JASONWAY AVE STE A, COLUMBUS ONCOLOGY ASSOC,IN 43214 #038-06-1977 L1979 **ON IM** *020 †20

KUENZLI, Valerie J. ■ 43212 #038-45-2006 L2006 **FP** *012

KUHNER, Ross Jacob. 700 CHILDRENS DR, DEPT. OF EMERGENCY MEDICIN 43205 #038-41-2003 L2006 **PEM** *012 †55

KUHR, Lora. ■ 43220 #016-06-1972 L1974 **OPH** *071 †35

KULWICKI, Aaron D. 793 W STATE ST, MOUNT CARMEL 43222 #038-43-2003 L2003 **GS** *012

KUMAR, Vasantha K. 1930 CROWN PARK CT 43235 #495-42-1976 L1999 **AN PMM** *020 †05

KUMLER, Ellen Kehres. 6495 E BROAD ST, EASTGLEN PEDIATRICS, INC. 43213 #038-41-1995 L2000 **PD** *020 †55

KUMLER, Karl William, II. 815 W BROAD ST, STE 300 43222 #038-40-1967 L1967 **ORS OSM** *020 †40

KUMLER, Karl William, III. 815 W BROAD ST, STE 300 43222 #038-41-1995 L1997 **ORS OSM** *020 †40

KUNIN, Calvin M. 320 W 10TH AVE 43210 #035-20-1953 L1979 **IM ID** *050 †20

KUNZ, Albert Lynn. ■ 43214 #017-20-1959 L1963 **OS GP** *050

KURIAKOSE, Rosalie Ann. 2575 W BROAD ST 43204 #038-43-1993 L2000 **FM** *020 †18

KURPITA, Ruslana Vasylivn. 2000 KENNY RD 43221 #913-89-1998 L2005 **FP** *012

KURUP, Madhuri. 150 TAYLOR STATION RD, STE 300 43213 #495-31-1986 L2001 **OBG** *020 †30

KURZER, Scott Alan. 65 HIGHVIEW BLVD 43207 #056-06-1996 L2005 **FM** *020 †18

KUSEK, Kyle David. 43202 #030-05-2003 L2006 **PG** *012 †55

KUSUMI, Rodney Kent. 685 BRYDEN RD 43205 #038-41-1975 L1976 **IM ID** *020 †20

KUTAYLI, Ziad Nour. ■ 43214 #046-01-2001 L2001 **CCS** *100

KUZMA, Mary Kay. 700 CHILDRENS DR 43205 #038-44-1986 L1987 **PD** *020 †55

KWAK, John N. 3525 OLENTANGY RIVER RD, STE 4330 43214 #038-44-1994 L1995 **IM** *020 †20

LACKEY, Rachel Courtney. ■ 43221 #017-20-2006 L2008 *100

LAFONT, Beth Galyn. ■ 43201 #025-01-2006 L2006 **OBG** *012

LAGMAY, Joanne Pigues. 700 CHILDRENS DR, 5TH FL 43205 #748-02-2002 L2006 **PHO** *012 †55

LAGOSKI, Megan Bethany. ■ 43206 #016-11-2006 L2006 **PD** *012

LA HUE, David Scott. 4825 KNIGHTSBRIDGE BLVD 43214 #038-44-1981 L1983 **IM** *020 †20

LAKE, Heather Michelle. ■ 43206 #018-75-2004, ▲ L2007 *100

LAKHI, Rani Amarlal. 85 PHILLIPI RD 43228 #495-01-1967 L1975 **EM** *020 †16

LALONE, Katy Ann. ■ 43204 #038-40-2008 *012

LAMB, James Francis. 2050 KENNY RD STE 2402, OSU INTERNAL MEDICINE AT M 43221 #041-09-1984 L1990 **IM** *020 †20

LAMBERT, David Reed. 456 W 10TH AVE, RM 4731 43210 #038-40-1981 L1982 **D DS** *020 †15

LAMOUR, Richard Joseph. ■ 43212 #038-40-2008 *012

LAMPRECHT, Richard Wm. 793 W STATE ST 43222 #038-40-1957 L1957 **OBG** *020 †30

LANDON, Mark Bruce. 2050 KENNY RD 6TH FL 43221 #035-20-1980 L1987 **MFM OBG** *040 †30

LANE, Margaret Mary. ■ 43221 #016-11-1943 L1947 **OS** *071

LANE, Sandra Evelyn. 2200 PINEBROOK RD 43220 #038-40-1984 L1985 **FSM OS** *020 †18

LANEY, Joseph Scott. 85 MCNAUGHTEN RD, STE 320 43213 #038-40-1981 L1982 **GE** *020 †20

LANG, Christopher Timothy. 1654 UPHAM DR, 5TH FL & MEANS HALL 43210 #035-06-2002 L2002 **OBG MFM** *100 †30

LANG, David Frank. 5340 E MAIN ST, STE 100 43213 #041-07-1991 L1998 **N CN** *020 †75

LANG, Frederick David. 4606 SAWMILL RD 43220 #038-43-1974 L1979 **AN GS** *020 †05

LANGAN, Michael Scott. 2050 KENNY RD, STE 2400 43221 #038-40-2004 L2004 **IM** *100 †20

LANGE, Tishana Roxanne. 1299 OLENTANGY RIVER RD, STE B 43212 #038-44-1999 L1999 **FM** *020 †18

LANGERMAN, Fawn Michelle. ■ 43201 #038-40-2008 *012

LAPUZ, Miguel H S, Jr. 543 TAYLOR AVE, COLUMBUS HOSP 43203 #748-02-1982 L1987 **IM NEP** *030 †20

LA ROE, Rebecca Ruth. 6001 E BROAD ST 43213 #038-40-1992 L1996 **AN** *020 †05

LAROQUE, Barbara. 1500 E 17TH AVE, ST STEPHEN'S HEALTH CENTER 43219 #038-44-1996 L1997 **MPD** *020 †20,55

LAROSA, Joseph Lawrence. 6200 CLEVELAND AVE, COLUMBUS RADIOLOGY CORP 43231 #038-40-1982 L1984 **DR RO** *020 †20

LARRICK, Robert B. ■ 43212 #045-01-1949 L1952 **ORS** *071 †40

LARRIMER, John Navin. 6100 E MAIN ST, STE 102 43213 #038-40-1972 L1972 **END IM** *020 †20

LARRIMER, Nye Richard. 340 E TOWN ST, STE 8-300 43215 #038-40-1963 L1963 **ON IM** *020 †20

LARSON, Alexander Jay. ■ 43220 #038-40-2008 *012

LARSON, Douglas Glen. ■ 43220 #038-40-2008 *012

LARSON, Jeremy Todd. 700 CHILDRENS DR, SECT OF EMGY MED 43205 #041-12-1994 L1997 **PEM PD** *020 †55

LASKY, Larry Charles. 700 ACKERMAN RD, STE 380 43202 #025-01-1976 L1993 **BBK CLP** *020 †50

LATIF, Maria Rustam. 410 W 10TH AVE 43210 #704-24-2001 L2006 **FP** *012

LAUSA, Ralph D. ■ 43235 #038-40-1953 L1953 **FM** *071 †18

LAVERY, Daniel Philip. ■ 43204 #038-40-2008 *012

LAVERY, Hugh Joseph. ■ 43206 #008-02-2004 L2004 **U** *012

LAW, Jonathan Hoyin. ■ 43212 #038-40-2008 *012

LAW, Richard Marion. ■ 43220 #038-40-2008 *012

LAWLESS, Christine Eunice. 473 W 12TH AVE, STE 200 43210 #016-43-1977 L2006 **CD IM** *020 †20

LAWRENZ, Anita G. 1144 DUBLIN RD, MOUNT CARMEL HOSPICE 43215 #055-01-1993 L1996 **IM** *020 †20

LAWSON, Victoria Heather. 456 W 10TH AVE, STE 1C 43210 #060-02-1995 L2007 **N** *020 †75

LAWYER, Ruskin B, Jr. 3555 OLENTANGY RIVER RD 43214 #038-40-1966 L1966 **ORS** *020 †40

LAXSON, Leah Carol. 456 W 10TH AVE STE 5 43210 #038-40-1985 L1987 **OPH** *020 †35

LAYNE, Eric Michael. 1670 UPHAM DR 43210 #038-45-2003 L2003 **P** *020

LE, Vu. ■ 43201 #038-40-2008 *012

LEACH, Christina S. 4605 SAWMILL RD, STE 102 43220 #038-40-1998 L2001 **IM** *020 †20

LEACH, Joseph T. ■ 43221 #038-40-1943 L1944 **ORS** *071 †40

LEAK, William David. 99 N BRICE RD, STE 200/270 43213 #036-05-1979 L1980 **PMM AN** *020 †05

LEANZ, Gary Francis. 505 KING AVE, BATTELLE MEMORIAL INSTITUT 43201 #023-07-1975 L1996 **GP OM** *020 †70

LEARMONTH, George James. 3535 OLENTANGY RIVER RD 43214 #024-05-1959 L1963 **P** *020 †75

LEARN, Christopher Philip. 700 CHILDRENS DR, COLUMBUS CHILDREN'S HOSPIT 43205 #024-05-2003 L2007 **PDC** *012

LEATHERMAN, Sue Ann. 2150 AGLER RD, CAPITAL FAMILY HEALTH CTR 43224 #038-40-1978 L1980 **FM** *020 †18

LEBARIO, Anthony Paul. ■ 43201 #038-40-2007 L2007 **GS** *012

LEBECK, Ann Beatrice. 285 E STATE ST STE 670 43215 #305-01-2007 L2007 **FP** *012

LEBEIKO, Carol M Hyslop. 3535 OLENTANGY RIVER RD 43214 #038-40-1963 L1963 **CHP P** *020 †55,75

LEDER, Marc Scott. 700 CHILDRENS DR, CHILDREN'S HOSPITAL 43205 #035-08-1990 L1993 **PEM** *020 †55

LEDER, Mary Ranee. 700 CHILDRENS DR, CHILDRENS HOSP 43205 #038-45-1992 L1993 **PD** *020 †55

LEDFORD, Cynthia H. 1609 NORTHWEST BLVD 43212 #038-40-1992 L1995 **MPD** *020 †20,55

LEE, Anthony Yun. 700 CHILDRENS DR, DEPT CCM 43205 #305-01-1997 L2006 **CCP** *100 †20,55

LEE, Catherine. 1211 DUBLIN RD 43215 #023-07-1975 L1979 **RHU IM** *020 †20

LEE, David C. 5969 E BROAD ST STE 201 43213 #244-05-1970 L1976 **GS AS** *020 †85

LEE, David Kyungjin. 697 THOMAS LN 43214 #038-40-2003 L2003 **FM** *020 †18

LEE, Jay Wook. 1515 E BROAD ST 43205 #583-04-1969 L1978 **P** *020 †75

LEE, Joo Ahn. ■ 43220 #035-03-2004 L2006 **IM** *012

LEE, Joon Ja. 2240 N BANK DR, UPPR 43220 #583-08-1970 L1977 **AN** *020 †05 ‡

LEE, Kenneth Kamkin. ■ 43235 #038-43-1987 L1989 **FM** *020 †18

LEE, Melissa Tsungping. ■ 43220 #038-40-2008 *012

LEE, Rushyuan Jay. ■ 43221 #038-40-2008 *012

LEE, S Christopher. 6200 CLEVELAND AVE, COLUMBUS RADIOLOGY CORP 43231 #583-01-1965 L1970 **DR AR** *040 †80

LEE, Sonia. 793 W STATE ST 43222 #583-10-2002 L2005 **DR** *012

LEE, Sung-Chul. ■ 43214 #583-01-1979 **OPH** *100

LEE, Thomas Hoon. 6200 CLEVELAND AVE, STE 100 43231 #035-01-1987 L1993 **ORS GS** *020 †40

LEE, Weikuo. ■ 43220 #385-03-1955 L1976 **PM** *071 †60

LEFF, John David. 3545 OLENTANGY RIVER RD, STE 525 43214 #038-40-1996 L1997 **GS** *020 †85

LEFKOVITZ, Jeffrey A. 4850 E MAIN ST 43213 #038-45-1988 L1989 **GE IM** *020 †20

LEFKOVITZ, Dana Suzanne. ■ 43220 #038-40-2008 *012

LE GALLO, Robin Denise. ■ 43205 #051-01-1997 L2003 **PTH** *100 †50

LEHMAN, Kristina Marie. 1609 NORTHWEST BLVD 43212 #038-43-2004 L2004 **MPD** *012

LEHMANN, David Michael. 262 NEIL AVE, OPHTHALMIC SURGEONS & 43215 #038-40-1985 L1990 **OPH** *020 †35

LEHV, Michael Saul. 793 W STATE ST 43222 #035-08-1967 L1971 **LM PS** *071 †65

LEIBY, Jane Marie. 810 JASONWAY AVE, COLUMBUS ONCOLOGY ASSOCIAT 43214 #038-40-1979 L1981 **ON HEM** *020 †20

LEIDHEISER, Paul Conrad, Jr. 1930 CROWN PARK CT 43235 #038-40-1976 L1976 **FM EM** *020 †18

LEIER, Carl Victor. 473 W 12TH AVE, DAVIS HLRI 2ND FLR 43210 #030-06-1969 L1971 **CD IM** *040 †20

LEININGER, Robert English. ■ 43221 #038-40-2008 *012

LEITHART, Megan Elizabeth. ■ 43214 #038-43-2007 L2007 *012

LEITHART, Paul W. 793 W STATE ST 43222 #038-40-1948 L1949 **ADM FM** *071

LEITMAN, Reuben H. ■ 43209 #869-05-1951 L1979 **P** *072

LEMAILE-WILLIAMS, M. 240 PARSONS AVE, COLUMBUS PUBLIC HEALTH 43215 #023-01-1998 L2004 **IM** *020

LEMASTER, Linda Ann. 500 THOMAS LN, RIVERSIDE COMMUNITY MEDICI 43214 #038-43-1994 L2000 **IM** *020 †20 ‡

LEMBACH, Richard Geo. 456 W 10TH AVE 43210 #038-40-1968 L1968 **OPH** *020 †35

LEMBACH, Robert Edmund. 2250 N BANK DR, NORTHWEST EYE SURGEONS 43220 #038-40-1968 L1968 **OPH** *020 †35

LENAHAN, Florence C. 1586 E DUBLIN GRANVILLE RD 43229 #038-40-1963 L1963 **GP** *020

LEON, Marino Enrique. ■ 43210 #737-06-1990 L2006 **PTH HMP** *020 †50

LEONARD, Steven Earl. 2231 N HIGH ST 43201 #038-40-1985 L1987 **FM** *020 †18

LEON COLONNA, Jorge Enriq. 410 W 10TH AVE 43210 #264-12-1996 L2005 **PTH** *020 †50

LEPI, Mark Steven. 370 W 9TH AVE, OH STATE U COLL OF MED 43210 #038-40-1999 L1999 **MPD** *020 †20,55

LETSON, Alan Douglas. 456 W 10TH AVE 43210 #038-06-1977 L1979 **OPH** *020 †35

LEUCHTER, Heinrich Jos. ■ 43212 #407-01-1944 L1955 **PHP P** *071 †70

LEVEY, Michael Steven. 866 W BROAD ST 43222 #038-40-1986 L1990 **DR** *020 †80

LEVIN, Douglas Michael. 410 W 10TH AVE 43210 #035-19-1969 L1976 **GE IM** *020 †20

LEVIN, Sheldon Isaac. 1631 NW PROFESSIONAL PLZ, STE 107 43220 #062-01-1979 L1985 **AN** *020 †05

LEVINE, Deborah Abramson. 2050 KENNY RD, STE 2402 43221 #035-08-1992 L1993 **PEM PE** *020 †55

LEVINE, Deborah Allison. 2050 KENNY RD, STE 2400 43221 #035-47-1996 L2007 **IM** *050 †20

LEVY, Alan Bruce. 3545 OLENTANGY RIVER RD 43214 #020-02-1979 L1983 **P** *020 †75

LEVY, Dale Robt. 3525 OLENTANGY RIVER RD, STE 5320 43214 #038-06-1987 L1987 **TS** *020 †90,85

LEWANDOWSKI, George Scott. 3100 PLAZA PROPERTIES BLVD 43219 #038-40-1982 L1982 **GO** *020 †30

LEWE, Robert Foster. 3535 OLENTANGY RIVER RD 43214 #038-40-1987 L1988 **IM** *020 †20

LEWIS, Brian David. ■ 43228 #018-03-2007 L2007 **ORS** *012

LEWIS, Daniel Evans. 6200 CLEVELAND AVE, COLUMBUS RADIOLOGY CORP 43231 #038-40-1960 L1960 **R** *071 †80

LI, Cuizhen. ■ 43220 #243-47-1984 L2007 **SP** *020 †50

LI, Guibin. 793 W STATE ST 43222 #243-36-1983 L2005 **IM** *012

LI, Lin. 410 W 10TH AVE, RM N416 43210 #243-46-1985 L2000 **AN** *020 †05

LI, Yun You. 473 W 12TH AVE, STE 200 43210 #243-38-1985 L2004 **CD** *020

LIBELL, Charles Francis. ■ 43235 #018-75-1959, ▲ L1960 **OPH** *071

LICKLIDER, Samuel D. ■ 43212 #035-20-1957 **OS** *075

LIEPACK, Jerry Glenn. ■ 43209 #041-12-1961 L1961 **FM GP** *062 †18

LILLY, Larry Joe. 3555 OLENTANGY RIVER RD, STE 2020 43214 #038-40-1975 L1976 **GS** *020 †85

LIM, Keun Hee. 543 TAYLOR AVE, COLUMBUS VA OPC 43203 #583-08-1970 L1979 **P** *020 †75

LIM, Kun Boo. 543 TAYLOR AVE 43203 #583-01-1968 L1980 **LM** *020 †20

LIM, Susie. ■ 43215 #038-40-2004 L2004 **OBG** *012

LIMBERT, James Geo. 6001 E BROAD ST 43213 #038-40-1973 L1973 **OPH** *020 †35

LIMPEROS, Richard James. 170 A MEANS HALL, 1654 UPHAM DR 43210 #038-44-2001 L2001 **EM** *100 †16

LIN, Karen Yin. 410 W 10TH AVE, DEPT OF INTERNAL MEDICINE 43210 #035-15-2006 L2006 **IM** *012

LIN, Lien-Ching. 6001 E BROAD ST, MT CARMEL EAST HOSP/RADIOL 43213 #017-20-1984 L1988 **DR NM** *020 †80,28

LIN, Thomas Samuel. 320 W 10TH AVE, THE OHIO STATE UNIVERSITY 43210 #008-01-1995 L2001 **HO** *050 †20

LIN, Yixin. 165 N MURRAY HILL RD, C/O YIXIN LIN, MD 43228 #243-16-1984 L2000 **N** *020 †75

LINDBERG, Kirsten. 480 MEDICAL CENTER DR, DODD HALL 43210 #016-02-2004 L2005 **PM** *012

LINDNER, Lewis Arthur. 1960 W BROAD ST 43223 #038-40-1960 L1960 **P** *030

LINDSEY, David Eugene. 410 W 10TH AVE, N711 DOAN HALL 43210 #038-40-1976 L1978 **CCS** *020 †85

LINEHAN, Ronald Patrick. 1110 BEECHER XING N, STE B 43230 #047-06-1989 L1990 **PME AN** *020 †05

LINGAMNENI, Rajeshwari A. 5770 KARL RD, NORTHTOWNE FAMILY PRACTICE 43229 #495-65-1994 L1999 **FM** *020 †18

LINN, Cady Louise. ■ 43221 #017-20-2005 L2005 **OBG** *012

LIOTTA, Eric Michael. ■ 43201 #038-40-2008 *012

LIPPINCOTT, Christopher K. ■ 43202 #051-01-2006 L2006 **IM** *012

LIPSCOMB, James W. 393 E TOWN ST, STE 212 43215 #038-40-1977 L1978 **FM** *020 †18 ‡

LISCYNESKY, Christina The. ■ 43212 #038-44-2006 L2006 **IM** *012

LISS, Leopold. 456 W 10TH AVE 43210 #407-10-1950 L1960 **N** *072

LISTON, Beth Anne. 370 W 9TH AVE, OH STATE U COLL OF MED 43210 #038-40-2002 L2006 **MPD** *020 †20,55

LITRIZZA, Anne Theresa. 3555 OLENTANGY RIVER RD, STE 1080 43214 #038-45-1993 L1995 **IM** *020 †20

LITSKY, Alan S. ■ 43235 #035-01-1979 L1987 **ORS OS** *050

LITTLETON, Anne Dunnam. 4775 KNIGHTSBRIDGE BLVD, STE 207 43214 #038-40-1987 L1989 **PD** *020 †20

LITTS, Christopher S. 410 W 10TH AVE, DEPT OF ORTHOPAEDIC SURGER 43210 #038-43-1992 L2005 **HS** *020 †85

LITVAK, Ronald. 1170 HENDERSON RD STE 201 43220 #038-40-1964 L1964 **P PFP** *020 †75

LITZINGER, Thomas Clark. ■ 43214 #038-40-2006 L2006 **TY** *012

LIU, James Jingyao. ■ 43202 #243-36-1983 L2005 **PCP** *100

LIU, Jie. 410 W 10TH AVE, OH STATE UNIV HOSP 43210 #243-47-1984 L2005 **N** *012

LIU, Zhenguo. 473 W 12TH AVE # 200 DHLR1, DIV OF CARDIOVASCUTAL MED 43210 #243-76-1984 L2004 **ICE CD** *020 †20

LIVINGSTON, Ryan Edward. ■ 43201 #038-41-2006 **P** *012

LLOYD, Eric Allan. 700 CHILDRENS DR, DEPT OF CRITICAL CARE 43205 #038-44-2001 L2007 **CCP** *100 †55

LO, Simon Shek-Man. 300 W 10TH AVE STE 083, DEPT OF RADIATION MEDICINE 43210 #462-02-1991 L2006 **RO** *020 †80

LO, Warren David. 700 CHILDRENS DR 43205 #016-06-1977 L1985 **PD** *020 †55,75

LOBEL, Jeffrey Stuart. 931 CHATHAM LN, STE 200 43221 #016-42-1997 L2006 **NS** *020

LOCSEY, Steve Michael. 4849 E MAIN ST 43213 #649-14-1986 L1993 **IM** *020

LOGAN, Karen Dugger. 6001 E BROAD ST, DEPT OF ANESTHESIOLOGY 43213 #036-05-1988 L1989 **AN** *020 †05

LOIZOS, Theodore Emmanuel. ■ 43221 #038-40-2005 L2005 **OPH** *012

LOMBARDO, John Anthony. 3705 OLENTANGY RIVER RD, STE 260 43214 #038-40-1977 L1977 **FM FSM** *020 †18

LONDEREE, Gwyn Renee. 4900 GETTYSBURG RD 43220 #038-40-1994 L1995 **D IM** *020 †20,15

LONG, Charles E. ■ 43219 #038-40-1953 L1953 **OS GP** *071

LONG, Frederick Robt. 700 CHILDRENS DR 43205 #008-01-1988 L1995 **PDR** *020 †80

LONG, Joseph Michael. ■ 43235 #038-40-1988 L1990 **AN** *020 †05

LONG, Ricky Lee. 3311 TREMONT RD, STE 101 43221 #038-40-1973 L1974 **FM** *020

LONG, Roland Ellsworth. 3535 OLENTANGY RIVER RD 43214 #038-40-1948 L1948 **D** *071 †15

LONG, Sarah Eliz Brackney. ■ 43229 #038-40-1952 L1952 **IM** *062

LONG, Teresa Charl. 240 PARSONS AVE, COLUMBUS HEALTH DEPT 43215 #005-02-1983 L1986 **PHP GPM** *030 †70

LONGERT, Alan Lloyd. 793 W STATE ST 43222 #038-40-1964 L1964 **ORS** *071 †40

LONGWELL, Charles William, III. 410 W 10TH AVE, OH STATE UNIV HOSP 43210 #028-34-2005 L2006 **N** *012

LOPEZ, Luis Amado. 2941 KENNY RD, STE 110 43221 #682-01-1972 L1983 **AN** *020

LOPEZ, Raul Jose, III. ■ 43221 #038-40-2008 *012

LORA, Rafael Osiris. 700 CHILDRENS DR, DEPT PED 43205 #308-01-1970 **PD HEM** *100

LOTFI-FARD, Basheer. ■ 43221 #038-40-2004 L2004 **P** *012

LOUIS, Louis Benson, IV. 410 W 10TH AVE, N846 DOAN HALL 43210 #011-02-1998 L2005 **TS** *100 †85

LOVE, Charles J. 473 W 12TH AVE, 2ND FLR DHLRI 43210 #041-12-1983 L1984 **ICE CD** *020 †20

LOVE, Jason Edward. 370 W 9TH AVE, OH STATE U COLL OF MED 43210 #038-40-2001 L2001 **HMP** *020 †50

LOVE, Richard Reed. 320 W 10TH AVE, B402 STARLING-LOVING HALL 43210 #038-06-1971 L2004 **ON** *050 †20

LOW, Andrea Jane. 1375 PERRY ST RM 5, CO OSU HOSPS-MED EDU DEPT 43201 #067-01-2000 L2004 **ID** *100 †20

LOWE, Gregory James. ■ 43228 #038-43-2005 L2005 **U** *012

LOWE, Matthew. 410 W 10TH AVE 43210 #038-75-2005, ▲ L2005 **P** *012

LOWE, Robert A. 5100 W BROAD ST, EMERGENCY DEPT 43228 #048-15-1999 L1999 **EM** *020 †16

LOWERY, Howard Wesley. 974 BETHEL RD, OHIO ENT SURGEONS INC 43214 #038-40-1955 L1955 **OTO** *071 †45

LOWERY, James Douglas. 974 BETHEL RD, STE A 43214 #038-40-1986 L1991 **OTO** *020 †45

LOWERY, Lisa Kay. 33 N GRANT AVE STE 150 43215 #038-44-1986 L1994 **OSM ORS** *020 †40

LOWES, Robert Jos. 2240 N BANK DR, UPPR 43220 #038-41-1991 L1998 **AN** *020 †05

LOZANSKI, Gerard. 410 W 10TH AVE, STE 310 43210 #759-04-1987 L1998 **PTH** *020 †50

LTEIF, Ghada N. 1670 UPHAM DR, DEPT OF PSYCHIATRY 43210 #605-01-1989 L1994 **CHP P** *020 †75

LU, Jerry Pingmaw. ■ 43212 #038-40-2008 *012

LUBBERS, Lawrence Michael. 3400 OLENTANGY RIVER RD, STE 200 43202 #020-02-1975 L1976 **HS ORS** *020 †40

LUBOW, Martin. 456 W 10TH AVE 43210 #005-02-1956 L1968 **OS OPH** *050 †35

LUCARELLI, Maria Rose. 473 W 12TH AVE, 201 HLRI 43210 #038-44-1998 L1999 **PCC** *020 †20

LUCAS, Joel Geo. 700 ACKERMAN RD, STE 380 43202 #028-03-1973 L1980 **PTH** *020 †50

LUCAS, Jonathan Tyrone. ■ 43235 #038-41-2004 L2004 **PEM** *012

LUCAS, Leo A. ■ 43201 #869-02-1951 L1955 **IM** *071 †44

LUCE, Wendy Ann. 700 CHILDRENS DR, NATIONWIDE CHILDRENS HOSPI 43205 #038-40-2002 L2002 **MPD** *012 †55

LUCEY, Catherine Reinis. 370 W 9TH AVE, OHIO STATE UNIV CL OF MED 43210 #016-06-1982 L2002 **IM IMG** *040 †20

LUEDKE, Eric Allen. ■ 43215 #056-06-2007 L2007 **GS** *012

LUGANNANI-GUARINO, Carolyn. 4808 N HIGH ST 43214 #038-40-1998 L2000 **FM** *020 †18

■ = Address Information Privacy Protected

LUK, Connie. 3535 OLENTANGY RIVER RD 43214 #061-01-2003 L2003 **AN** *020

LUNDY, Eugene. 1200 BRENTNELL AVE 43219 #038-40-1977 L1993 **OS IM** *030

LUQUETTE, Mark Henry. 700 CHILDRENS DR, CHILDRENS HOSP DEPT PATH 43205 #021-05-1985 L1993 **PTH NP** *020 †50

LUSTBERG, Mark Elliot. ■ 43215 #023-01-2004 L2007 **ID** *012 †20

LUSTBERG, Maryam Beheshti. ■ 43215 #023-01-2003 L2007 **HO** *012 †20

LUTES, Richard Alan. 5340 E MAIN ST 43213 #038-40-1975 L1975 **FM** *040 †18

LUTMAN, Christopher V. 500 THOMAS LN, STE 3B 43214 #038-40-1995 L2003 **OBG** *020 †30

LUTMER, William John. 500 E MAIN ST, CAPITAL PRIMARY CARE 43215 #038-41-1977 L1980 **END** *020 †20

LUTMERDING, Medard R, Jr. 750 MOUNT CARMEL MALL 43222 #038-40-1975 L1976 **EM** *020 †16

LUTTER, Kathleen Quinn. 3555 OLENTANGY RIVER RD, STE 3070 43214 #038-44-1984 L1986 **GYN** *020 †30

LUTTER, Kenneth Stephen. 941 CHATHAM LN, STE 215 43221 #038-44-1984 L1986 **VS** *020 †85

LUTZ, W Beale. ■ 43215 #038-40-1952 L1952 **IM RHU** *071

LYNN, Courtney Melissa. 410 W 10TH AVE, DEPT MED 43210 #038-40-2007 L2007 **IM** *012

LYNN, Deborah Joanne. 2050 KENNY RD, STE 2250 43221 #038-40-1984 L1990 **N IM** *020 †20,75

LYTLE, Larry Howard. 897 BRIARBANK DR 43235 #038-40-1974 L1974 **IM** *020

MA'ANI, Houshang E. ■ 43220 #517-01-1951 L1975 **P EM** *071

MABEE, Christopher Loften. 3820 OLENTANGY RIVER RD, OHIO GASTROENTEROLOGY 43214 #038-40-1992 L1993 **GE** *020 †20

MACEROLLO, Allison Avery. 2231 N HIGH ST 43201 #038-40-1995 L2003 **FM** *020 †18

MACK, Aaron Christopher. 150 TAYLOR STATION RD, STE 150 43213 #038-43-1998 L2002 **OPH** *020 †35

MACK, Joseph Alexander. 3525 OLENTANGY RIVER RD, STE 4330 43214 #038-40-1997 L1998 **IM** *020 †20

MACKESSY, James Patrick. 3180 E BROAD ST 43209 #038-45-1989 L1990 **FM** *020 †18

MACKEY, Caleb Gray. ■ 43220 #038-40-2007 L2007 **IM** *012

MACKLIN, James Edward. 3555 OLENTANGY RIVER RD, STE 3070 43214 #030-06-1977 L1977 **PUD CCM** *020 †20

MAC LEAN, William C, Jr. 625 CLEVELAND AVE 43215 #067-01-1966 L1982 **NTR PD** *062 †55

MACNEALY, Marcus Warrenco. ■ 43220 #038-40-2008

MACWILLIAMS, Bryan Phelps. 1654 UPHAM DR, 146 MEANS HALL 43210 #038-41-2004 L2004 **EM** *020

MAFFETT, Marisa Dreisbach. 3535 OLENTANGY RIVER RD 43214 #038-40-2004 L2004 **OBG** *012

MAFFETT, Scott Augustus. 456 W 10TH AVE 43210 #038-40-2003 L2003 **CD** *012 †20

MAGALANG, Ulysses J. 473 W 12TH AVE, RM 201 43210 #748-02-1983 L2003 **PUD CCM** *020 †20

MAGEE, David James. 6200 CLEVELAND AVE, COLUMBUS RADIOLOGY CORP 43231 #038-40-1985 L1989 **DR** *020 †20

MAGORIEN, Raymond Danl. 2328 CLUB RD 43221 #038-40-1974 L1974 **CD IM** *020 †20

MAHAN, John, Jr. 700 CHILDRENS DR 43205 #041-09-1977 L1984 **PN PD** *040 †55

MAHER, Eileen Gormley. 4775 KNIGHTSBRIDGE BLVD, STE 207 43214 #038-40-1981 L1984 **PD** *020 †55

MAHER, William Edward. 410 W 10TH AVE, DOAN HALL 43210 #038-40-1979 L1981 **PHP ID** *030 †20

MAHMOUD, Akram Hassan. 285 E STATE ST, STE 430 43215 #055-75-1992, ▲ L2003 **NS** *020

MAHOOTI, Sepi. 410 W 10TH AVE 43210 #305-01-2004 L2004 **PTH** *012

MAIER, Megan Marie. ■ 43220 #038-43-2008 *012

MAILLOUX, Jason William. 6495 E BROAD ST, STE A 43213 #025-01-2004 L2004 **PD** *020 †55

MAIN, Thomas Sprague. 974 BETHEL RD, STE A 43214 #038-40-1970 L1970 **OTO** *020 †45

MAINS, William Arthur. 41 S HIGH ST, STE 25 43215 #396-02-1982 L1985 **FM** *020 †18 ‡

MAK, Thomas Alden. 3535 OLENTANGY BLVD 43214 #038-40-1991 L1992 **CHP** *020 †75

MAKONNEN, Girma. ■ 43215 #035-47-2006 L2006 **NS** *012

MALARKEY, William Blair. 480 W 9TH AVE, 2111 E DAVID MED RESEARCH 43210 #041-12-1965 L1966 **ICE END** *020

MALIK, Arvind Mark. 111 S GRANT AVE, ANESTHESIOLOGY CONSULTANTS 43215 #038-44-1990 L1994 **AN IM** *020 †20,05

MALINOWSKI, Mark N. ■ 43212 #041-78-2004, ▲ L2005 **AN** *012

MALLESKE, Daniel Thomas. 700 CHILDRENS DR 43205 #038-44-2000 L2000 **NPM** *012

MALLIK, Gunwant Singh. 285 E STATE ST, STE 430 43215 #017-20-1987 L1996 **NS** *020 †25

MALLORY, Thomas Howard. 720 E BROAD ST 43215 #038-40-1965 L1965 **ORS** *071 †40

MALONE, James Chas. 2240 N BANK DR, UPPR 43220 #038-40-1975 L1989 **AN** *020 †05

MANALOOR, John Jacob. ■ 43205 #017-20-2003 L2003 **PDI** *012 †55

MANDY, George T. 700 CHILDRENS DR 43205 #473-01-1983 L2003 **PD** *020 †55

MANGINO, Julie Ellen. 410 W 10TH AVE, # 1135 43210 #035-08-1989 L1995 **ID** *020 †20

MANI, Aruna. ■ 43215 #038-44-2002 L2002 **HO** *012 †20

MANILCHUK, Andrei V. 1492 E BROAD ST, STE 1102-TOWER 43205 #913-36-1984 L2000 **GS** *020 †85

MANITSAS, Sarah Christine. 1654 UPHAM DR, 202 MEANS HALL 43210 #038-40-2002 L2002 **GE** *012 †20

MANNING, Maura Marie. 794 FRANKLIN AVE 43205 #038-40-1993 L2000 **GS** *020

MANOCHA, Sachida Nand. 4850 E MAIN ST 43213 #495-47-1985 L2001 **APM AN** *020 †05

MANOS, Diane Carol. 2000 KENNY RD 43221 #038-40-1987 L1988 **FM** *020 †20

MANSUKHANI, Tarun Ram. 2231 N HIGH ST RM 205, RARDIN FAMILY PRACTICE CTR 43201 #166-03-2002 L2006 **FP** *012

MANUEL, Timothy Scott. 503 S FRONT ST, STE 230 43215 #038-45-1991 L1993 **EM** *020 †16

MANZANO, Melissa Lynn. 410 W 10TH AVE, DEPT IM 43210 #025-12-2007 L2007 **PM** *012

MARAR, Unni Krishnan. 1492 E BROAD ST, STE 1401 43205 #495-96-1979 L1993 **CD** *020 †20

MARCINIAK, Ellen Terese. ■ 43212 #016-11-2007 L2007 **IM** *012

MARCUCCI, Guido. 320 W 10TH AVE, REAR A437 43210 #561-23-1987 L1997 **HO** *020 †20

MARCUS, Daniel Philip. ■ 43228 #038-41-2005 L2005 **EM** *012

MARCUS, David B. 3535 OLENTANGY RIVER RD, DEPT OF EMERGENCY MEDICINE 43214 #035-45-1998 L2001 **EM** *020 †16

MARGER, Richard Stuart. 6100 E MAIN ST, STE 112 43213 #038-40-1995 L1999 **OBG** *020 †30

MARKHAM, Kara Beth. 1654 UPHAM DR, OHIO STATE UNIVERSITY MEDI 43210 #025-01-2005 L2005 **OBG** *012

MARKOVICH, Stephen E. 697 THOMAS LN, RIVERSIDE FAM PRAC CTR 43214 #038-40-1993 L1994 **FM** *020 †18

MARKOWITZ, Joseph. ■ 43212 #023-01-2007 L2007 *012

MARKS, Jack. 4039 E BROAD ST 43213 #038-40-1953 L1953 **IM** *075 †20

MARQUES, David Rodrigo. 4850 E MAIN ST, GRANT FAMILY PRACTICE 43213 #038-40-1995 L2005 **FM** *040 †18

MARR, Elisabeth Cheney. 7400 HUNTINGTON PARK DR, STE 200 43235 #005-02-1997 L1999 **FM** *020 †18

MARSH, Clay B. 473 W 12TH AVE, 201 HEART AND LUNG INSTITU 43210 #055-01-1985 L1989 **PUD IM** *020 †20

MARSH, William L, Jr. 700 ACKERMAN RD, STE 380 43202 #051-01-1972 L1986 **PTH** *020 †50

MARSHALL, Brian J.. ■ 43221 #654-01-2001 L2001 **EM** *020

MARTIN, Daniel Jos. 1670 UPHAM DR 43210 #028-03-1966 L1967 **P** *020 †75

MARTIN, Daniel Robt. 1654 UPHAM DR, RM 146 43210 #017-20-1983 L1988 **EM IM** *020 †20,16

MARTIN, Douglas David. 300 W 10TH AVE, RADIATION MED RM 088-B 43210 #046-01-1987 L2006 **RO OS** *020 †80

MARTIN, Edward Wright. 300 W 10TH AVE 43210 #047-07-1972 L1973 **AS CRS** *020 †85

MARTIN, Elwood Ray. ■ 43221 #038-40-2003 L2003 **GS** *012

MARTIN, Frances Granger. ■ 43215 #048-02-1955 L1987 **GYN** *072

MARTIN, Jeffrey Thos. ■ 43215 #038-40-1981 L1983 **IM** *075

MARTIN, Larry Christopher. 456 W 10TH AVE 43210 #011-03-1982 L1996 **GS TRS** *020 †85

MARTIN, Laura Therese. 700 CHILDRENS DR, COLUMBUS CHILDREN'S HOSPIT 43205 #038-06-1990 L1991 **PHO PD** *050 †55

MARTIN, Lisa Copenhaver. 700 CHILDRENS DR, RADIOLOGY A 1010 43205 #055-01-1987 L1995 **PDR** *020 †80

MARTIN, Ludmila Katherine. ■ 43220 #038-40-2007 L2007 **IM** *012

MARTIN, Robert Alan. 259 TAYLOR STATION RD, CARDINAL ORTHOPAEDIC INSTI 43213 #038-41-1989 L1995 **ORS** *020 †40

MARTINEZ, Kristi Lynn. ■ 43205 #038-40-2008 *012

MARTINEZ-MONGE, Rafael. 300 W 10TH AVE, 080 JAMES CANCER HOSP 43210 #847-06-1989 *100

MARTINO, John David. 660 CHILDRENS DR 43205 #055-01-1972 L1975 **PAN NS** *040 †05

MARTYN, Michael Dean. 700 CHILDRENS DR 43205 #056-06-1993 L1994 **OTO** *020 †45

MARUNA, Matthew David. ■ 43219 #038-40-2005 L2005 **PD** *012

MASON, Harold Crew. ■ 43235 #038-06-2002 L2002 **FP** *012

MASSICK, Susan Chang. 5965 E BROAD ST, STE 290 43213 #047-05-1997 L2000 **D** *020 †20,15

MASSOOMI, Nima Sayad. 280 E TOWN ST 43215 #047-05-2004 L2007 **OMF** *020

MAST, Maurice Conrad. 500 E MAIN ST, STE 100 43215 #038-40-1982 L1984 **IM** *020 †20

MASTEL, Michael Matthew. ■ 43230 #028-78-1950, ▲ L1951 *071

MASTERS, Kathleen Marie. 750 MOUNT CARMEL MALL, STE 300 43222 #048-13-1984 L1985 **EM** *020

MASTRONARDE, John Guy. 473 W 12TH AVE, DAVIS HEART & LUNG RESEARC 43210 #038-40-1988 L1990 **PCC PD** *020 †20,55

MASTRUSERIO, Dominic N. 941 CHATHAM LN STE 323 43221 #038-41-1991 L1997 **D** *020 †15

MASTRUSERIO, Jennifer J. 5072 REED RD, MEDICINE 43220 #038-41-1991 L1996 **PD** *020 †55

MASYS, John Harold. 1988 WILLOW GLEN LN 43229 #038-40-1968 L1968 **OM IM** *020 †20

MATHARBOOTHAM, Mani. 410 W 10TH AVE N-416, DEPT OF ANESTHESIOLOGY 43210 #495-33-1971 L1983 **AN** *020 †20

MATHIAS, Marc Tyrell. ■ 43201 #038-40-2008 *012

MATHIS, Trevor James. ■ 43220 #038-40-2008 *012

MATKOVIC, Velimir. 480 MEDICAL CENTER DR, DODD HALL 43210 #957-01-1971 L1988 **PM IM** *020 †60

MATRKA, Laura Ann. ■ 43201 #038-41-2006 L2006 **OTO** *012

MATRKA, Paul Jos. ■ 43220 #038-40-1963 L1963 **ORS** *071 †40

MATTINGLY, Chas Vincent. 4830 KNIGHTSBRIDGE BLVD 43214 #056-06-1963 L1969 **IM** *071 †20

MATYAS, John Andrew. 3555 OLENTANGY RIVER RD, COLUMBUS SURGICAL 43214 #038-40-1975 L1978 **GS** *020 †85

MAUGER, Thomas Fredrick. 456 W 10TH AVE, STE 5A 43210 #038-40-1984 L1985 **OPH** *020 †35

MAXWELL, Clarence Leroy. 3535 OLENTANGY RIVER RD 43214 #038-40-1958 L1958 **PS** *071 †65

MAXWELL, Richard Brian. ■ 43212 #038-40-2008 *012

MAY, Charles B. 1550 W 5TH AVE 43212 #028-78-1976, ▲ L1977 **FM** *020

MAY, Eugene Shannon. 3820 OLENTANGY RIVER RD 43214 #038-40-1967 L1967 **GE IM** *071 †20

MAY, Patricia D Gregg. ■ 43214 #038-40-1967 L1967 **CHP P** *071

MAY, Robert Kenneth. 1904 BETHEL RD 43220 #038-40-1976 L1977 **FM** *020 †18

MAY, Steffan John. ■ 43212 #038-40-2007 L2007 **IM** *012

MAY, Susan Jane. 625 CLEVELAND AVE 10521, ABBOTT LABORATORIES 43215 #021-01-1978 L1984 **PD** *020 †55

MAYERSON, Joel Leon. 2050 KENNY RD, STE 3300 43221 #023-07-1994 L1995 **OMO ORS** *020 †40

MAYES, Tara Swisher. 1670 UPHAM DR 43210 #038-40-2005 L2005 **P** *012

MAYMIND, Michael. ■ 43209 #913-16-1975 L1998 **PTH** *020 †50

MAYNARD, Prisca. 6465 E BROAD ST STE D 43213 #038-41-1995 L1999 **MPD** *020 †20,55

MAYR, Nina A R. 300 W 10TH AVE STE 08 43210 #409-16-1985 L2004 **RO** *020 †80

MAZZAFERRI, Ernest Louis. 1655 UPHAM DR, 215 MEANS HALL 43210 #038-40-1962 L1962 **END IM** *071 †20

MAZZAFERRI, Ernest Louis, Jr. 1654 UPHAM DR RM 225, OHIO ST UNIV HOSPINT MED 43210 #038-40-1999 L1999 **IC** *100 †20

MC ALHANY, Christopher D. 473 W 12TH AVE, SUITE 200 DAVIS HLRI 43210 #045-04-2001 L2005 **CD** *012

MCANNENY, Alison. ■ 43206 #041-14-2007 L2007 **GS** *012

MCBEE, Amy D. 285 E STATE ST, STE 520 43215 #028-02-2001 L2001 **NPM** *020 †55

MCBRIDE, Kim Lewis. 700 CHILDRENS DR, RM W410 43205 #068-01-1987 L2004 **MG CBG** *050 †19,55

MC CAFFERTY, Mary Jude. 1670 UPHAM DR, OHIO STATE UNIVERSITY 43210 #038-40-1987 L1989 **P** *020 †75

MCCALLIN, John Patrick, III. ■ 43212 #038-40-2008 *012

MCCALLISTER, Jennifer Wan. 473 W 12TH AVE, 201 DAVIS HEART & LUNG RES 43210 #055-01-2000 L2007 **PCC** *100

MC CAMEY, Kendra Lee. 2231 N HIGH ST 43201 #038-43-2000 L2000 **FM FSM** *020 †18 ‡

MCCARTHY, Alicia Marie. ■ 43235 #017-20-2008 *012

MC CARTHY, Michael Joseph. 370 W 9TH AVE, OH STATE U COLL OF MED 43210 #038-40-2005 L2007 **P** *012

MCCARTHY, Sean Thomas. ■ 43206 #038-43-2008 *012

MCCARTNEY, Michael Sean. 2050 KENNY RD 43221 #038-43-2004 L2007 **FSM** *012 †18

MC CAUGHAN, James Stewart. 111 S GRANT AVE 43215 #041-02-1956 L1965 **TS GS** *020 †85,90

MC CLEAD, Richard E, Jr. 700 CHILDRENS DR 43205 #038-40-1974 L1974 **NPM PD** *050 †55
MC CLELLAN, Derek Armand. 1495 MORSE RD 43229 #038-40-1997 L1998 **PD** *020 †55
MC CLOUD, William Jerry. 5300 E MAIN ST, STE 102 43213 #038-40-1964 L1964 **ORS** *020
MC CONAGHY, John Regis. 1615 FISHINGER RD 43221 #041-12-1989 L1996 **FM** *071 †18
MCCONAHY, Melissa L. ■ 43229 #005-12-2007 L2007 **EM** *012
MC CONNELL, Patrick Ian. ■ 43221 #030-05-1999 L2002 **TS** *012 †85
MCCORMACK, Jennifer Marie. ■ 43206 #037-01-2005 L2005 **PD** *012
MCCORMACK, Steven Eric. 1654 UPHAM DR, 202 MEANS HALL 43210 #037-01-2005 L2005
    IM *012
MCCORMICK, Anna Marie. ■ 43204 #016-45-2006 L2006 **EM** *012
MC COY, Karen Sharrock. 700 CHILDRENS DR 43205 #036-01-1975 L1982 **PUD OS** *050 †55
MCCREA, Michael James. 1654 UPHAM DR, 146 MEANS HALL 43210 #038-43-2004 L2004
    EM *020
MC CREARY, Marvin Raymond. 750 MOUNT CARMEL MALL 43222 #038-40-1997 L1998
    EM *020 †16
MC CULLERS, Meghan Kori. ■ 43214 #017-20-2001 L2007 **PCC** *012 †20
MC DOUGALL, Eric Colin. 1492 E BROAD ST, STE 1302 43205 #060-01-1994 L2007 **ID** *020 †18
MC DOUGLE, Leon. 1492 E BROAD ST, DEPT OF FAMILY MEDICINE 43205 #038-40-1989 L1996
    FM *020 †18
MC DOWELL, Sharon Uhle. 410 W 10TH AVE 43210 #041-13-1990 L2005 **PM** *020 †60
MC FARLAND, Dan Ross. 3525 OLENTANGY RIVER RD, STE 5360 43214 #038-40-1963 L1963
    R NM *020 †80,28
MCGANN, Patrick M.. 3535 OLENTANGY RIVER RD 43214 #820-02-2003 L2003 **GS** *012
MC GARR, Janet Ann. ■ 43221 #016-06-1980 L1990 **ID IM** *012 †20
MC GEE, Hall Thomas, IV. 456 W 10TH AVE, 5TH FL 43210 #051-01-2003 L2004 **OPH** *020
MC GHEE, Paul Timothy. 793 W STATE ST 43222 #038-40-1964 L1964 **GS OS** *071 †85
MC GINNIS, Molly C. 700 CHILDRENS DR 43205 #051-04-2004 L2007 **PG** *012 †55
MC GOWAN, Kathleen A. 3545 OLENTANGY RIVER RD, STE 400 43214 #038-41-1979 L1980
    OPH *020 †35
MC GREGOR, John Michael. 700 ACKERMAN RD STE 650 43202 #018-03-1984 L1985
    NS *020 †25
MC GREGOR, Walter Edward. 3525 OLENTANGY RIVER RD, STE 5320 43214
    #038-44-1994 L2000 **TS** *020 †85,90
MC GWIRE, Bradford Scott. 410 W 10TH AVE, N-1147 DOAN HALL 43210 #016-42-1997 L2004
    ID *020 †20
MC GWIRE, Gerd Brigitta. 700 CHILDRENS DR, COLUMBUS CHILDREN'S HOSPIT 43205
    #016-11-2001 L2006 **PD** *020 †55
MCHUGH, Matthew. 1250 DEARBORN DR 43085 #038-40-1991 L1992 **FM** *020 †18
MC ILROY, Mary Lynn. 700 CHILDRENS DR 43205 #038-40-1975 L1976 **PD** *030 †55
MC KAY, Michael Jos. 111 S GRANT AVE, GRANT MEDICAL CENTER 43215 #017-20-1977 L1981
    AN CCM *040 †05
MCKEE, Jean Eileen. 7400 HUNTINGTON PARK DR, STE 200 43235 #836-01-1993 L1998
    FM *020 †18
MCKIERNAN, Matthew Paul. 410 W 10TH AVE, OH STATE UNIV HOSP 43210
    #305-01-2005 L2005 **AN** *012
MC KINLAY, Robert T. 5957 CLEVELAND AVE, COMPREHENSIVE EYE CARE 43231
    #041-01-1964 L1974 **OPH** *071 †35
MC KINNEY, Colleen J. 370 W 9TH AVE, OH STATE U COLL OF MED 43210 #038-40-1997 L1999
    PD *020 †20
MC KITRICK, Charles J, Jr. 3535 OLENTANGY RIVER RD 43214 #038-40-1946 L1946
    IM *071 †20
MC LAUGHLIN, Douglas J. 700 CHILDRENS DR, PEDIATRICS ACADEMIC ASSCIA 43205
    #028-34-1993 L2001 **PD** *020 †55
MC LAUGHLIN, R Waidner. 1260 N HIGH ST, ST MARKS COMMUMITY HEALTH 43201
    #038-40-1962 L1962 **EM** *071
MCLONEY, Eric Dean. ■ 43228 #038-40-2008 L2008 **EM** *012
MC MAHAN, James David. 4845 KNIGHTSBRIDGE BLVD, STE 230 43214 #040-02-1983 L1988
    PS HS *020 †85,65
MC MAHON, David Earl. 1547 W BROAD ST 43222 #016-02-1978 L1992 **IM** *040 †20
MC MAKEN, David Allen. 2511 OAKSTONE DR 43231 #038-45-1989 L1990 **IM** *020
MC MANUS, Ellen Mary. 700 CHILDRENS DR, CHILDREN'S HOSPITAL 43205
    #010-01-1992 L1999 **PEM** *020 †55
MC NALLY, Cora Frances. 3555 OLENTANGY RIVER RD, STE 3020 43214 #539-03-1991 L1998
    ID *020 †20
MC VICKER, Robt Frederick. 3555 OLENTANGY RIVER RD, STE 2060 43214
    #038-06-1973 L1974 **TS VS** *020 †85,90
MEAGHER, Michael James. 931 CHATHAM LN, STE 200 43221 #038-40-1974 L1981
    NS *020 †25
MECHENBIER, James Arthur. 839 W BROAD ST 43222 #038-40-1970 L1970
    OTO HNS *020 †45
MECKLER, Lowell Courtenay. 2475 E MAIN ST 43209 #038-40-1960 L1960 **IM CD** *020 ‡
MECKSTROTH, Charles V. ■ 43220 #038-40-1947 L1947 **TS** *071 †85,90
MEDIRATTA, Anuj. ■ 43212 #038-40-2008 *012
MEEHAN, Patrick Scott. ■ 43206 #055-01-2005 L2005 **MPD** *012
MEESIG, Deborah Marie. 111 S GRANT AVE 43215 #038-40-1981 L1982 **GS CRS** *030 †85,10
MEFTAH, Laxmi. ■ 43221 #517-01-1962 L1962 **GS U** *071
MEHTA, Laxmi. 473 W 12TH AVE, STE 270 43210 #038-44-1998 L2007 **CD** *020 †20
MEHTA, Madhu. 480 MEDICAL CENTER DR, S-2056 43210 #495-45-1985 L2002 **RHU** *100 †20
MEHTA, Meera Rajesh. 700 CHILDRENS DR, PEDIATRIC RESIDENCY OFFICE 43205
    #038-44-2004 L2004 **PD** *020 †55
MEHTA, Rohit. 473 W 12TH AVE, HLRI- RM 200 43210 #004-01-1999 L1999 **CD** *020 †20
MEHTA, Sanjay B. 285 E STATE ST, STE 500 43215 #495-01-1990 L1996 **OTR** *020
MEHTA, Sheetal. ■ 43231 #016-11-2003 L2007 **D** *100 †15
MEHTA, Vimla. ■ 43214 #495-05-1964 L1990 **FM** *020
MEIER, Jarrell Collin. ■ 43215 #038-40-2008 *012
MEIMARIDIS, Stavros E. ■ 43214 #418-02-1954 L1964 **GP NTR** *020 †50
MEIS, Gregory Michael. 1375 PERRY ST, C/O OSU HOSPS-CORP CRED OF 43201
    #016-76-2002, ▲ L2002 **GE** *012 †20
MEISEL, Jennifer Lynne. ■ 43221 #038-40-2007 L2007 *012
MEISTER, Melissa Remle. ■ 43227 #038-45-2002 L2002 *020
MEJILLA, Jennifer. ■ 43206 #038-75-2007, ▲ L2007 **N** *012
MEKHJIAN, Hagop Sarkis. 410 W 10TH AVE, DOAN HALL RM 130 43210 #605-01-1962 L1970
    GE IM *020 †20
MELARAGNO, Daniel Philip. 3400 OLENTANGY RIVER RD, STE 150 43202 #038-40-1984 L1985
    IM *020 †20
MELARAGNO, Ernest Sam. ■ 43235 #038-40-1958 L1958 **FM** *071

MELBOURNE, Launice Andrea. ■ 43229 #038-40-2008 *012
MELECA, Michael John. 423 E TOWN ST, STE 1000 43215 #038-40-1990 L1993 **CD** *020 †20
MELMED, Sanford Z. 2222 WELCOME PL 43209 #038-41-1983 L1987 **IM EM** *020 †16,20
MELVIN, W Scott. 410 W 10TH AVE, N729 DOAH HALL 43210 #038-43-1987 L1992 **GS** *020 †85
MENCHEN, Lindsey Cassini. ■ 43201 #038-40-2008 *012
MENDELL, Jerry Roy. 700 CHILDRENS DR RM WA3024, COLUMBUS CHILDRENS RSCH
    IN 43205 #048-12-1966 L1972 **N** *050 †75
MENDLIK, Matthew Thomas. 370 W 9TH AVE, OH STATE U COLL OF MED 43210
    #038-40-2007 L2007 *012
MENDOLA, Janet Field. 1115 BETHEL RD, BETHEL PSYCH SVCS 43220 #035-06-1982 L1987
    P *020
MENGESHA, Teferi Getachew. 285 E STATE ST, STE 150 43215 #038-41-1999 L2004
    NEP *020 †20
MENKE, James Alexander. 700 CHILDRENS DR, COLUMBUS CHILDREN'S HOSPIT 43205
    #035-03-1973 L1981 **NPM PD** *050 †55
MENTSER, Mark Irwin. 700 CHILDRENS DR, DIV OF NEPHROLOGY 43205 #038-40-1973 L1978
    PN *020 †55
MERRITT, Russell James. 625 CLEVELAND AVE, RM 105215/N3 ROSS PROD DIV 43215
    #005-15-1972 L1994 **NTR PD** *030 †55
MERRYMAN, Scott Henson. 2231 N HIGH ST, RARDIN FAMILY MEDICINE 43201
    #038-40-1977 L1980 **FM** *020 †18
MERRYMAN, William Barton. ■ 43235 #038-40-1947 L1947 **OBG** *071 †30
MERTZ, Marissa Maia. ■ 43235 #012-05-2006 L2006 **FP** *012
MESSICK, George Mc Dowell. 4919 DIERKER RD 43220 #038-40-1987 L1988 **PD** *020 †55
MESSICK, Richard T. ■ 43221 #038-40-1953 L1953 **IM RHU** *071 †20
MESTEMAKER, Amy Louise. 3595 OLENTANGY RIVER RD, HOMEREACH HOSPICE 43214
    #038-40-1992 L1994 **IM** *020 †20
METZ, Earl Nelson. 410 W 10TH AVE 43210 #036-07-1961 L1968 **IM HEM** *071 †20
MEYER, Bruce Perry. 453 WATERBURY CT, PEDIATRIC & ADOLESCENT 43230
    #038-40-1964 L1964 **PD** *030 †55
MEYER, Harlan David. 866 W BROAD ST 43222 #038-41-1990 L1991 **DR** *020 †80
MEYER, Marty Michael. 1654 UPHAM DR, 202 MEANS HALL 43210 #038-40-2003 L2003
    GE *012 †20
MEYER, Tearle L. 6200 CLEVELAND AVE, COLUMBUS RADIOLOGY CORP 43231
    #038-40-1960 L1960 **R RO** *071 †80
MEYER, Thomas Lloyd. 793 W STATE ST 43222 #016-06-1955 L1959 **ORS** *071 †40
MEYERS, Lori Dawn. 410 W 10TH AVE, N-146 DOAN HALL 43210 #038-40-1995 L1998
    AN *020 †05
MEZGER, Ronald Alfred. ■ 43235 #038-40-1955 L1955 **GP** *071 †18
MICHALSKY, Marc Peter. 555 S 18TH ST, CHILDRENS SURGICAL 43205 #033-05-1992 L1999
    PDS *020 †85
MIDAY, Greg Hamlin. ■ 43212 #038-40-2008 *012
MIGLETS, Andrew Wm, Jr. 456 W 10TH AVE RM 4118 43210 #038-40-1960 L1960
    OTO *071 †45
MIHALOV, Leslie Kay. 700 CHILDRENS DR 43205 #038-43-1984 L1986 **PD** *020 †55
MIKAMI, Dean Jiro. 410 W 10TH AVE, N747 DOAH HALL 43210 #019-02-1997 L2000
    AS GS *020 †85
MIKKILINENI, Himabindu. ■ 43230 #038-40-2008 *012
MIKLOSIK, Stephen. 793 W STATE ST 43222 #065-01-1960 L1965 **AN** *020 †05
MIKOLAJ, Michael Brian. ■ 43220 #038-40-2008 *012
MIKULIK, Zhanna. 1654 UPHAM DR, 209 MEANS HALL 43210 #913-32-1987 L2000
    RHU IM *020 †20
MILANO, Nicholas Jerome. ■ 43201 #038-40-2008 *012
MILER, Veronica. 700 CHILDRENS DR, CHILDS HOSP DEPT OF ANESTH 43205
    #024-07-1981 L1999 **AN PD** *020 †05,55
MILLANA, Rolando T. ■ 43228 #748-09-1972 *100
MILLER, Daniel Lawrence. 3525 OLENTANGY RIVER RD, STE 4330 43214 #038-40-2002 L2002
    IM *020 †20
MILLER, Edward M. 3535 OLENTANGY RIVER RD 43214 #038-40-1953 L1953 **PTH** *071 †50
MILLER, Hans B. 2050 KENNY RD, OHIO STATE SPINE CENTER 43221 #012-22-2000 L2001
    AN *020
MILLER, Kenneth Jos. 1375 CHERRY WAY DR STE 230 43230 #038-45-1982 L1983
    P GP *020 †75
MILLER, Marcus Richard. 750 MT CARMEL MALL STE 200, MID OHIO SURG ASSOC 43222
    #038-45-1998 L1999 **GS** *020 †85
MILLER, Martha Denise. 700 CHILDRENS DR, AMBULATORY PEDS DEPT 43205
    #020-12-1978 L1980 **PD** *020 †55
MILLER, Matthew C. 456 W 10TH AVE, CRAMBLETT MED CLINIC-4A 43210 #035-15-2003 L2003
    OTO *012
MILLER, Michael John. 4830 KNIGHTSBRIDGE BLVD, SURGERY 43214 #024-16-1982 L1987
    PS GS *020 †85,65
MILLER, Michelle Ann. 700 CHILDRENS DR, NATIONWIDE CHILDRENS HOSPI 43205
    #051-04-1992 L1998 **PD PM** *020 †60
MILLER, Randy Robt. 3555 OLENTANGY RIVER RD, STE 3050 43214 #038-40-1980 L1983
    NPM PD *020 †55
MILLER, Roger Alan. 1875 MILLIKIN RD, 120N WILCE CTR 43210 #038-40-1987 L1989
    GPM GP *020 †70
MILLER, Ronald Lee. 3650 OLENTANGY RIVER RD, STE 302 43214 #038-40-1978 L1980
    IM *020 †20
MILLER, Ronald Stanley. 543 TAYLOR AVE, VA CLINIC 43203 #038-06-1971 L1977
    GE HEP *020 †20
MILLER, Roy Robt. ■ 43220 #038-40-1961 L1961 **P OS** *071
MILLER, Scott Michael. 777 W STATE ST, OHIO GASTROENTEROLOGY 43222
    #038-40-1985 L1987 **GE IM** *020 †20
MILLER, Sidney Frederick. 410 W 10TH AVE, DEPT OF SUR N717 DOAN HALL 43210
    #017-20-1968 L1969 **GS OS** *020 †85
MILLER, Timothy Lee. 410 W 10TH AVE, DEPT OF ORTHOPAEDICS 43210 #038-45-2005 L2005
    ORS *012
MILLER, Veronica Yvette. 700 CHILDRENS DR, DEPT ANES 43205 #025-12-2002 L2003 **AN** *020
MILLS, Nicholas Tracy. ■ 43235 #038-40-2007 L2007 **OBG** *012
MILOVICH, Laurie Ahne. ■ 43221 #038-40-2008 *012
MINARCHEK, Joseph. 340 E TOWN ST, STE 7-250 43215 #038-40-1984 L1986 **PS** *020 †65
MINER, Michael Ervin. 410 W 10TH AVE, N1021 DOAN HALL 43210 #019-02-1969 L1989
    NS *030 †25
MINGIONE, Matthew Jacob. 3535 OLENTANGY RIVER RD, STE 3030 43214
    #038-41-1999 L2007 **OBG MFM** *020 †30

■ = Address Information Privacy Protected

MINTZ, Robert Michael. 2240 N BANK DR, UPPR 43220 #051-01-1981 L1985 **AN** *030 †05
MIRSHAK, Monique. 410 W 10TH AVE, 167 MEANS HALL 43210 #035-15-2005 L2005 **EM** *012
MISER, William Frederick. 2231 N HIGH ST, DEPT OF FAMILY MED 43201 #038-40-1982 L1998 **FM FPG** *020 †18
MISHKIND, Michael Harry. ■ 43221 #038-40-1971 L1971 **NEP IM** *071 †20
MITCHELL, Annree Sumner. ■ 43202 #036-08-2005 L2005 **EM** *012
MITCHELL, Christopher All. ■ 43235 #038-40-2008 *012
MITCHELL, Geoffrey C. ■ 43214 #038-43-1981 L1981 **EM** *020 †16
MITCHELL, Howard R, Jr. ■ 43213 #038-40-1952 L1952 **FM GP** *071
MITCHELL, Jerry Wayne, Jr. 745 W STATE ST, STE 550B 43222 #036-01-1997 L2003 **HO** *020 †20
MITCHELL, William Blunt. 6200 CLEVELAND AVE, COLUMBUS RADIOLOGY CORP 43231 #048-12-1994 L2002 **DR VIR** *020 †80
MITCHELL, William Roy. 4506 SAWMILL RD 43220 #005-11-1972 L1977 **AN** *071 †05 ‡
MITSAK, Richard Andrew. 1640 NEIL AVE, RM 438 43201 #038-40-1971 L1971 **P** *020 †75
MITZEL, Jerrod Carl. 793 W STATE ST 43222 #473-02-2005 L2005 **FP** *012
MIZELLE, Katherine M. 700 CHILDRENS DR, CHILDRENS HOSPITAL 43205 #051-01-1992 L2000 **PDC PD** *020 †55
MODI, Achal Pankaj. 316A MARSHALL PSGE, THE OHIO STATE UNIVERSITY 43215 #038-40-2006 L2006 **GS** *012
MOFFA, John Kevin. 4030 W HENDERSON RD 43220 #055-01-1995 L1996 **IM** *020 †20
MOHAMMAD, Yousef Mohammad. 456 W 10TH AVE 43210 #605-01-1989 L2001 **N** *020 †75
MOHARIR, Alok Mukund. ■ 43220 #025-12-2005 L2006 **AN** *012
MOHLER, Lester Ray. 4661 SAWMILL RD 43220 #038-40-1964 L1964 **PS** *071 †65
MOHR, James John. 85 MCNAUGHTEN RD STE 20, OHIO GASTROENTEROLOGY 43213 #038-43-1982 L1984 **GE IM** *020 †20
MOHR, Kurtis Bauer. ■ 43206 #011-04-2007 L2007 **FP** *012
MOHSIN, Syed K. 3535 OLENTANGY RIVER RD 43214 #704-02-1991 L2005 **PTH** *020 †50
MOINZADEH, Nasser. ■ 43220 #517-01-1952 L1983 **OTO HNS** *071
MOISE, Alicia Ann. 700 CHILDRENS DR, OSU CHILDREN'S HOSPITAL 43205 #048-12-1981 L2000 **NPM PD** *020 †55
MOKHTARI, Ali. 3121 W BROAD ST 43204 #517-01-1966 L1973 **GS** *020 †85
MOKHTARI, Mina Rahmani. 3121 W BROAD ST 43204 #517-01-1969 L1977 **FM** *020 †18
MOLEDOR, Jeffery James. 1930 CROWN PARK CT 43235 #038-40-1981 L1981 **FM** *020 †18
MOLEDOR, Julianne Marie. 1930 CROWN PARK CT 43235 #038-40-1981 L1981 **FM EM** *020 †18
MOLENDA, Matthew Alexande. ■ 43215 #038-44-2007 L2007 **D** *012
MONEME, Obinna Ifeanyichu. 410 W 10TH AVE, MEANS HALL RM 473 43210 #038-40-2006 L2006 **N** *012
MONK, J Paul, III. 320 W 10TH AVE, A433B STARLING-LOVING HALL 43210 #038-40-1996 L1999 **HO** *020 †20
MONTEBELLO, Jos Federic. 300 W 10TH AVE, UNIVERSITY RADIATION 43210 #020-12-1978 L1982 **RO** *020 †80
MONTONEY, Mark Robt. 180 E BROAD ST, FL 34 43215 #038-41-1982 L1983 **IM** *020 †20
MOODY, Gina N. ■ 43220 #041-78-2006, ▲ L2006 **IM** *012
MOON, Wong Kyun. 340 E TOWN ST, GRANT MEDICAL CENTER STE 43215 #005-12-1993 L2004 **PS** *020 †85,65
MOORE, Angela. ■ 43223 #055-75-2004, ▲ L2004 **PD** *100
MOORE, Evan Corlee. ■ 43214 #049-01-2005 L2006 **EM** *012
MOORE, Fred Thomas. ■ 43207 #038-40-1962 L1962 **GS OM** *075
MOORE, J Layne. 1654 UPHAM DR, RM 413 43210 #038-45-1987 L1988 **N P** *020 †75
MOORE, Jared Michael. ■ 43201 #038-40-2008 *012
MOORE, Michael Lawrence. 1 W NATIONWIDE BLVD 43215 #038-40-1979 L1979 **IM OS** *071 †20 ‡
MOORE, Nancy C. 543 TAYLOR AVE, VETERANS OUTPATIENT CLINIC 43203 #038-40-1988 L1995 **FM** *020 †18
MOORE, Patrick John. 793 W STATE ST 43222 #028-34-1955 L1970 **TS** *071 †85,90
MOORE, Timothy David. 745 W STATE ST, STE 550B 43222 #041-12-1981 L1994 **ON HEM** *050 †20
MOORE, William Morley. 625 CLEVELAND AVE 43215 #065-05-1962 L1964 **NTR PHP** *030
MOORE-RUFFIN, Jada E. 4850 E MAIN ST 43213 #047-07-1996 L1997 **FM** *020 †18
MOORMA, Karin Hilda. 7400 HUNTINGTON PARK DR, STE 100 43235 #038-40-1986 L1987 **OBG** *020 †30
MORAILLE, Richard. 285 E STATE ST, STE 520 43215 #038-40-1997 L1999 **NPM** *020 †55
MORCOS, John Elias. 4897 KARL RD 43229 #038-40-1968 L1968 **P** *071 †75
MOREL, Jose Bethoven. 2500 SULLIVANT AVE 43204 #308-01-1993 L2002 **IM** *020 †20
MORELLI, Sheryl Lyn. 700 CHILDRENS DR, DEPT OF AMB PED 43205 #038-45-2000 L2001 **PD** *020 †55
MORGAN, Sherri Lynn. 2150 MARBLE CLF OFC PARK P 43215 #038-45-2000 L2000 **FM** *020 †18 ‡
MORMOL, John Lazarus. 6495 E BROAD ST, STE A 43213 #017-20-1960 L1965 **PD** *020 †55
MORRICE, Bryce Ian. 3535 OLENTANGY RIVER RD 43214 #038-41-1978 L1980 **CD IM** *020 †20
MORRIS, Benjamin Nicholas. 410 W 10TH AVE, N416 DOAN HALL 43210 #045-01-2004 L2006 **AN** *012
MORRIS, James Douglas. 777 W STATE ST 43222 #038-40-1966 L1966 **DR GP** *020 †80
MORRIS, Laurie Jean. 370 W 9TH AVE, OH STATE U COLL OF MED 43210 #038-40-2001 L2005 **OBG** *020
MORRIS, William Jos. 3900 E LIVINGSTON AVE 43227 #038-43-1977 L1978 **FM** *020 †18
MORRISON, Andrea Katherin. ■ 43204 #037-01-2007 L2007 *012
MORRISON, Ashton Byrom. ■ 43221 #036-07-1946 L1956 **PTH** *071 †50
MORRISON, Gregory Earle. 5969 E BROAD ST, STE 302 43213 #036-07-1979 L1986 **PS GS** *020 †65
MORRISON, Matthew Joseph. 5072 REED RD 43220 #028-34-1997 L1999 **PD** *020 †55
MORROW, Grant. 700 CHILDRENS DR 43205 #041-01-1959 L1978 **PD** *030 †19,55
MORSE, Thomas Andrew. 3535 OLENTANGY RIVER RD 43214 #038-40-1987 L1987 **EM** *020 †16
MORTAZAVI, Amir. 320 W 10TH AVE, A441 STARLING LOVING HALL 43210 #517-01-1997 L2003 **ON IM** *020 †20
MORTON, Paul Stuart. ■ 43220 #038-40-1959 L1959 **IM** *071 †20
MOSELEY, Ellen Butler D. ■ 43214 #024-05-1951 L1983 **P** *071
MOSES, James Lloyd. 2680 W BROAD ST 43204 #038-06-1973 L1974 **OPH** *020 †35
MOSES, Jonathan Daniel. ■ 43201 #038-40-2005 L2005 **PD** *012
MOSLEY, Dwight Edward. ■ 43204 #038-40-2007 L2007 **GS** *012
MOULIK, Supratik Kumar. ■ 43201 #048-12-2005 L2006 **DR** *012
MOUSA, Hayat. 700 CHILDRENS DR, ED 426 43205 #875-01-1982 L1993 **PG** *020 †55

MOUSER, James Garret. ■ 43212 #038-40-2003 L2003 **OPH** *020
MOWBRAY, John Gladden. 793 W STATE ST, CO MT CARMEL HOSP-MED EDU 43222 #020-02-2002 L2002 **HSO** *012
MROZEK, Ewa. 320 W 10TH AVE, OHIO STATE UNIVERSITY 43210 #759-07-1983 L1999 **HO** *100 †20
MSHIU, Merlyn Elirehema. ■ 43214 #880-01-1989 L2002 **IM** *100 †20
MUCHA, Meredtin Nicole. 3535 OLENTANGY RIVER RD, CO RIVERSIDE METH-MED ED D 43214 #038-45-2003 L2003 **IMG** *100 †20
MUDUNURI, Sunitha Raghava. 1492 E BROAD ST 43205 #495-65-1997 L2003 **IM HOS** *020 †20 ‡
MUELLER, Charles F. 1654 UPHAM DR, 630 MEANS HALL 43210 #038-41-1962 L1962 **DR GP** *071 †80,28
MUELLER, Kathe L L. ■ 43221 #038-41-1966 L1966 **FM** *020 †18
MUES, Adam Christopher. ■ 43214 #030-05-2004 L2004 **U** *012
MULHOLLAND, Mari Beth. 1875 MILLIKIN RD, THE OHIO ST UNIV 43210 #017-20-1978 L1982 **IM** *020 †20
MULLIGAN, Michael G. 3535 OLENTANGY RIVER RD, UPPR 43214 #038-45-1989 L1994 **AN** *020 †05
MULLIN, Bradford Brent. 5965 E BROAD ST, STE 420 43213 #038-40-1988 L1989 **NS** *020 †25
MULLOWNEY-AGRA, Ruth. 2970 W BROAD ST 43204 #028-34-1997 L2000 **ID** *020 †20
MULUMBA, Matia. 2231 N HIGH ST 43201 #305-01-2001 L2002 **FM UCM** *020 †18
MUNDY, William Michael. 111 S GRANT AVE 43215 #038-43-1999 L2004 **FM** *100 †18
MUNEER, Ather. ■ 43229 #704-02-1986 **P** *100
MUNN, Gerald Edward. 5770 KARL RD 43229 #020-02-1963 L1964 **GP EM** *020
MUNSHI, Anuradha. 793 W STATE ST, CO MT CARMEL HOSP-MED EDU 43222 #038-44-2003 L2003 **IM** *020 †20
MURAD, Khalil. 1492 E BROAD ST, WEST ANNEX BUILDING / HMG 43205 #875-01-1997 L2006 **IM** *020 †20 ‡
MURAKAMI, James Walter. 700 CHILDRENS DR, RADIOLOGY K-160 43205 #005-18-1990 L1999 **DR** *020 †80
MURAWSKI, Juanita Marie. 1670 UPHAM DR, OSU HARDING HOSPITAL 43210 #038-40-1981 L1982 **CHP P** *020 †75
MURDEN, Robert Alan. 2050 KENNY RD, STE 2400 43221 #028-03-1977 L1991 **IMG IM** *020 †20
MURPHY, Edward Hal. 5969 E BROAD ST STE 407 43213 #040-02-1958 L1964 **U** *071 †95
MURPHY, Mary Ann. 899 E BROAD ST, 6142219922 43205 #010-02-1986 L1998 **CHP** *020 †75
MURPHY, Michael J. ■ 43221 #041-02-1953 L1954 **GS** *071 †85
MURRAY, Andrew Leight. ■ 43214 #038-40-2008 *012
MURRAY, Robert David. 700 CHILDRENS DR, OHIO STATE UNIVERSITY 43205 #017-20-1979 L1985 **GE PD** *040 †55
MURREY, Douglas Arthur, Jr. ■ 43235 #038-40-2007 L2007 **GS** *012
MURTHY, Sowmya. ■ 43235 #038-44-2006 L2006 **IM** *012
MUSABJI, Aris Miyanji. ■ 43204 #016-43-2002 L2007 **DR** *100 †80
MUSCARELLA, Peter, II. 410 W 10TH AVE 43210 #035-09-1993 L1995 **GS** *020 †85
MUSTILLO, Peter J. 700 CHILDRENS DR, RM ED516 43205 #033-06-1996 L1997 **AI MPD** *020 †20,03,55
MUSTRIC, Steven James. 793 W STATE ST 43222 #038-40-1962 L1962 **R** *020 †80
MUTABAGANI, Khaled Hamed. ■ 43235 #797-02-1988 L1991 **GS** *020 †85
MUTCHLER, Gail Eugene. 3545 OLENTANGY RIVER RD, RIVERSIDE PULMONARY 43214 #038-40-1979 L1979 **PUD IM** *020 †20
MYERS, Joseph H. ■ 43221 #024-01-1952 L1962 **IM CD** *071 †20
MYERS, Julie Ann. ■ 43204 #038-40-2004 L2004 **OPH** *012
MYLES, Ian Antheni. ■ 43235 #007-02-2005 L2005 **IM** *012
MYSIW, Walter Jerry. 480 W 9TH AVE, STE 1025 43210 #038-40-1981 L1982 **PM** *020 †60
MYUNG, Joon Mo. 5969 E BROAD ST STE 300, DISEASE ASSOCIATES 43213 #187-04-1992 L2004 **GE** *020 †20
MYUNG, Yoonmo. 2680 W BROAD ST 43204 #008-01-2000 L2005 **OPH** *100 †35
NADASDY, Tibor. 320 W 10TH AVE 43210 #473-02-1981 L2003 **ATP** *020 †50
NAGARAJ, Usha Deepa. ■ 43212 #038-44-2007 L2007 **TY** *012
NAGARAJAN, Rajaram. 456 W 10TH AVE 43210 #041-07-1995 L2006 **PHO** *020 †55
NAGUIB, Aymen Nabil. 700 CHILDRENS DR 43205 #915-02-1993 L2003 **PAN** *020 †05
NAIK, Apurwa S. 285 E STATE ST, STE 520 43215 #495-21-1991 L2000 **NPM PD** *020 †55
NAJERA, Travis Alexander. ■ 43228 #038-40-2006 L2006 **FP** *012
NAJJAR-EL DAHDAH, Najwa E. 700 CHILDRENS DR, AMBULATORY PEDIATRICS 43205 #605-01-1977 L2000 **PD** *020 †55
NALLURI, Koteswara Rao. 793 W STATE ST, MOUNT CARMEL WEST HOSPITAL 43222 #495-50-1981 L1999 **AN** *040 †05
NANA-SINKAM, Serge P. 473 W 12TH AVE, RM 201 43210 #036-05-1996 L2006 **PCC** *020 †20
NANDYAL, Lauri Erway. 543 TAYLOR AVE 43203 #038-41-1989 L1990 **FM** *020 †18
NANKERVIS, Craig Alan. 700 CHILDRENS DR 43205 #038-43-1988 L1989 **PD** *020 †55
NAPPI, James Francis. 3400 OLENTANGY RIVER RD 3 43202 #038-40-1976 L1976 **HS** *020 †65
NAPRAWA, James Thaddeus. 700 CHILDRENS DR, CHILDREN'S HOSPITAL 43205 #035-08-1996 L2000 **PD** *020 †55
NARULA, Vimal Kumar. 410 W 10TH AVE, UNIV HOSP OHIO STATE UNIV 43210 #055-02-1999 L2005 **GS** *100
NARVEL, Faozan Abdulahad. 455 INDUSTRIAL MILE RD, WESTLAND FAMILY PRACTICE 43228 #495-99-1986 L1997 **FM** *020 †18
NASH, Patricia Lin. 700 CHILDRENS DR, DEPT OF PEDIATRICS 43205 #017-20-1990 L1995 **PD** *020 †55
NASH, Steven Mark. 1654 UPHAM DR, 413 MEANS HALL 43210 #017-20-1990 L1995 **N CN** *020 †75
NATALIE, Jamie Anthony. ■ 43202 #038-40-2005 L2005 **PM** *012
NATARAJAN, Lekshmi. 793 W STATE ST, CO MT CARMEL HOSP-MED EDU 43222 #495-31-2000 L2003 **IM** *020
NAU, Peter Nealey. ■ 43204 #018-03-2006 L2006 **GS** *012
NAUMAN, Mary. 111 S GRANT AVE 43215 #038-40-1978 L1979 **CLP EM** *020 †20
NAUMOFF, Casey Andrew. ■ 43201 #038-40-2008 *012
NDIFE, Anita Nwamaka. 504 HAVENS CORNERS RD 43230 #690-04-1997 L2002 **FM** *020 †18
NECKERS, Andrew Carlyle. 866 W BROAD ST 43222 #038-43-2000 L2005 **DR** *100 †80
NEEDLEMAN, Bradley Jason. 410 W 10TH AVE N723 43210 #035-47-1994 L1999 **GS** *020 †85
NEFF, Joddi Michelle. 3535 OLENTANGY RIVER RD 43214 #038-45-2005 L2005 **IM** *012
NEFF, Ryan Lee. 410 W 10TH AVE, N-924 DOAN HALL 43210 #041-02-2001 L2006 **GS** *020 †85
NEIGER, David Robt. 770 JASONWAY AVE, SICIANS INC 43214 #038-40-1981 L1982 **IM** *020 †20
NEIGER, Rebecca Rupp. 3535 OLENTANGY RIVER RD 43214 #038-44-1981 L1982 **IM** *020 †20
NEKI, Anterpreet Singh. 320 W 10TH AVE B-411, OHIO STATE UNIV MED CTR 43210 #495-45-1986 L1997 **HO IM** *020 †20

NELIN, Leif Danl. 700 CHILDRENS DR, SECTION OF NEONATOLOGY 43205 #011-04-1982 L2003 NPM PD *040 †55

NELSON, Richard Norman. 1654 UPHAM DR, DEPT OF EMERGENCY MED 43210 #038-40-1978 L1979 EM *020 †16

NELTNER, Kurt Anthony. 1492 E BROAD ST 43205 #020-12-1995 L1999 EM *020 †16

NERI, Anthony Steven. 3500 E LIVINGSTON AVE 43227 #048-40-1956 L1956 OBG OS *071 †30

NERVEZ, Remus Treyes. 849 HARMON AVE, 849 HARMON AVENUE 43223 #748-08-1973 L1992 IM PD *020

NEUFELD, Carl Leonard. 1087 DENNISON AVE 43201 #028-78-1955, ▲ L1956 R NM *071 †28

NEWKIRK, Ernest Manley. 3040 N HIGH ST, CAPITAL CARE CENTER 43202 #047-07-1948 L1953 GYN *071 †30

NEWTON, Herbert Bruce. 1654 UPHAM DR 43210 #035-06-1984 L1990 N ON *020 †75

NEWTON, William Allen, Jr. 700 CHILDRENS DR 43205 #025-01-1946 L1952 PD *072 †55,50

NG, Ambrose Tat-Ming. 995 E BROAD ST, AMERICAN RED CROSS 43205 #462-01-1972 L1983 BBK *030 †50

NGAYAN, Ronald Palalay. 410 W 10TH AVE 43210 #654-01-2005 L2007 FP *012

NGUYEN, Keoni. ■ 43215 #028-78-2006, ▲ L2007 D *012

NGUYEN, Van Hung. 700 CHILDRENS DR 43205 #067-02-1992 L2000 PP *100

NGUYEN, Zachary Chat. 111 S GRANT AVE, 3RD FL 43215 #019-02-1992 L2004 AN *020 †05

NICELY, Charles Jon. 3535 OLENTANGY RIVER RD 43214 #038-40-1988 L1993 PTH *020 †50

NICHOLS, Allan Jay. 3525 OLENTANGY RIVER RD, STE 6300 43214 #038-40-1980 L1981 ICE CD *020 †20

NICHOLS, Keith E. 3555 OLENTANGY RIVER RD, COLUMBUS SURGICAL 43214 #038-44-1984 L1987 GS *020 †85

NICHOLSON, Jill Marley. 3535 OLENTANGY RIVER RD, EMGY DEPT 43214 #038-40-1996 L2000 EM *020 †18

NICK, William Verill. 410 W 10TH AVE RM N713 43210 #038-40-1960 L1960 GS FOP *030 †85

NICOL, Kathleen Kennedy. 555 S 18TH ST, STE 4C 43205 #020-02-1993 L1998 PP BBK *020 †50

NIEDERKOHR, Ryan Daniel. ■ 43220 #038-40-2003 L2003 NM *100 †28

NIEDERMIER, Julie Ann. 1670 UPHAM DR, STE 140 43210 #038-40-1995 L1996 P *020 †75

NIKOKIRAKIS, Maria C. ■ 43221 #038-40-2002 L2002 MPD *020 †20,55

NINE, Erik Brandon. ■ 43214 #025-12-2003 L2003 DR *012

NISSIMOV, Norbert. ■ 43235 #198-01-1950 L1972 A *071 †03

NOBLE, Charles W, II. 423 E TOWN ST, STE 1000 43215 #038-43-1985 L1992 CD IM *020 †20

NOBLE, Kathryn Prince. ■ 43220 #038-40-1953 L1953 AN *071 †05

NOLAN, Robert Bernard. ■ 43220 #030-06-1955 L1981 PA *050 †55

NOLTIMIER, Judith Walford. 111 S GRANT AVE #917-04-1964 L1976 PTH *020 †50

NORDER, Emily Elaine. 370 W 9TH AVE, 200A MEILING HALL 43210 #038-40-2006 L2006 IM *012

NORGAN, Reagan Salifu. ■ 43232 #902-07-1998 L2007 PM *020 †18

NORI, Uday Sankar. 1654 UPHAM DR, N210 MEANS HALL 43210 #495-58-1991 L2005 NEP *020 †20

NORRIS, Donald Lee, II. 1654 UPHAM DR, 150 MEANS HALL 43210 #055-02-2000 L2003 EM *100

NORRIS, Ralph B. 105 GREAT SOUTHERN BLVD 43207 #041-13-1962 L1964 OPH *020

NORRIS, Robert Edward. 3191 W BROAD ST 43204 #038-40-1979 L1979 IM *020 †20

NORTH, Phillip Thiele. 2912 S HIGH ST, COLUMBUS SOUTHERN MEDICAL 43207 #016-02-1976 L1988 GS FM *020

NORTON, John A. 2283 OXFORD RD, 410 WEST 10TH AVE 43221 #016-76-2001, ▲ L2002 AN *100 †05

NOTICEWALA, Neelam N. 700 CHILDRENS DR 43205 #038-40-2001 L2001 PD *020 †55

NOTTINGHAM, Dana Ann. 3705 OLENTANGY RIVER RD, STE 260 43214 #038-40-1991 L1992 FM *020 †18

NOVIKOV, Mikhail. 285 E STATE ST, STE 360 43215 #020-12-1997 L1998 NEP *020 †20

NUCKLOS, William Wolff. 254 WOODLAND AVE STE 105 43203 #038-40-1977 L1989 PM PME *020

NUECHTERLEIN, Barry E. 410 W 10TH AVE, OSU DEPT OF ANESTHESIOLOGY 43210 #016-43-2000 L2004 AN *020 †05

NUNLEY, David Ray. 473 W 12TH AVE, OSU / 201 HEART & LUNG INS 43210 #055-02-1985 L1996 PUD IM *020 †20,55

NUOVO, Gerard James. 700 ACKERMAN RD, STE 380 43202 #050-02-1983 L1999 PTH *020 †50

NUOVO, Margaret Alice. 1645 NEIL AVE 43210 #847-13-1980 L1999 PTH *020 †50

NUSS, Kathryn Elise. 700 CHILDRENS DR, CHILDREN'S HOSPITAL 43205 #038-40-1992 L1993 PD PE *020 †55

NUTOR, Perfect Newlove. 410 W 10TH AVE 43210 #412-02-1996 L2005 FP *012

NWOMEH, Benedict C. 555 S 18TH ST, CHILDRENS SURGICAL 43205 #690-02-1986 L2003 GS *020 †85

NYE, Darin Duane. ■ 43201 #038-40-2008 *012

NYESTE, Lawrence Jos. ■ 43221 #038-40-1973 L1973 OBG *071 †30

OBEIDAT, Khaled Ali. 2050 KENNY RD, 212 TOWER 43221 #575-02-1997 L2006 *100

OBRADOVIC, Djuro. ■ 43214 #016-16-1951 L1962 P OBG *075

OBREGON, Pedro Jara, II. 1430 S HIGH ST 43207 #748-08-1960 L1971 GS *072 †85

O'BRIEN, Autumn Mc Intyre. 4775 KNIGHTSBRIDGE BLVD, STE 207 43214 #038-40-1995 L1996 MPD PD *020 †20,55

O'BRIEN, Blaize Andrew. 974 BETHEL RD, STE A 43214 #038-40-1996 L1999 OTO *020 †45

O'BRIEN, James Martin, Jr. 473 W 12TH AVE, 201 HEART AND LUNG INSTITU 43210 #038-40-1996 L1997 PCC *012

O'BRIEN, Kevin Patrick. ■ 43220 #038-40-1990 *100

O'BRIEN, Richard Eugene. 793 W STATE ST 43222 #038-40-1956 L1956 IM PUD *071 †30

O'BRIEN, Sarah Harvey. 700 CHILDRENS DR J141, COLUMBUS CHILDREN'S HOSPIT 43205 #041-12-2000 L2006 PHO *020 †55

OCHOA, Ricardo. 3600 REED RD 43220 #319-02-1973 L1979 DR OS *071 †80

O'DONOVAN, Julie Currie. 700 CHILDRENS DR, DEPARTMENT OF RADIOLOGY 43205 #016-43-1989 L1999 PDR DR *020 †80

O'DWYER, Patrick Jos. 410 W 10TH AVE # N924 43210 #539-02-1979 L1985 ON *020

OEHLER, Jeffrey Curtis. 2250 N BANK DR 43220 #038-40-1988 L1989 OPH *020 †35

OFFEI, Yaw Ayesu. 4384 CLEVELAND AVE 43224 #412-02-1993 L2002 IM *020 †20

OFFUTT, E Jann. 1430 S HIGH ST 43207 #017-20-1978 L1986 FM *020 †18

O'HANDLEY, John G, Jr. 6150 E BROAD ST, MOUNT CARMEL COMMUNITY OUT 43213 #028-03-1972 L1975 FM *020 †18

OHR, Joseph Simmons, Jr. 520 KING AVE, FRANKLIN CTY CORONERS OFC 43201 #422-01-1999 L2005 FOP *100

OKTENER, Haldun Hakki. ■ 43214 #902-01-1952 L1967 TS PUD *071

OKTENER, Semiha. ■ 43214 #902-10-1953 L1973 GP PD *071

OLAH, Erin Michelle. 150 TAYLOR STATION RD, STE 300 43213 #038-45-1999 L2003 OBG *020 †30

OLIVER, Nicole Marie. ■ 43229 #017-20-2005 L2005 OBG *012

OLIX, Melvin Leonard. 3535 OLENTANGY RIVER RD 43214 #038-41-1954 L1954 ORS OS *071 †40

OLSEN, John. 1654 UPHAM DR, 630 MEANS HALL 43210 #035-15-1968 L1976 NR R *020 †80,28

OLSHEFSKI, Randal Scott. 700 CHILDRENS DR, CHILDREN'S HOSPITAL 43205 #041-12-1988 L1989 PHO *050 †55

OLSON, Mary Catherine. ■ 43215 #038-40-2007 L2007 IM *012

OLSON, Richard Sulo. 3535 OLENTANGY RIVER RD 43214 #038-40-1959 L1959 OPH *020 †35

OLSOY, Margaret Mary. ■ 43220 #054-04-1986 L1987 PD *020 †55

O'MAHONEY, Paige L. 700 CHILDRENS DR, COLUMBUS CHILD HOSP 43205 #038-40-2001 L2001 PD *020 †55

O'MALLEY, David Michael. ■ 43209 #025-07-1998 L2000 OBG *020 †30

OMIKUNLE, Adebomi Adeola. ■ 43209 #038-40-2006 L2006 PD *012

O'NEAL, James Franklin. 3535 OLENTANGY RIVER RD, DEPT OF MEDICAL EDUCATION 43214 #055-02-1988 L2003 IM *040 †20

ONO, Minoru. 410 W 10TH AVE, N816 DOAN HALL WEST 43210 #572-03-1987 L2000 *100

OPLATEK, Agnes M. ■ 43221 #016-43-2006 L2006 OTO *012

OPPENHEIM-KNUDSEN, Eunice. 1615 FISHINGER RD, UPPER ARLINGTON 43221 #062-01-1996 L2002 IM *020 †18

OPREMCAK, Colleen Marie. 3535 OLENTANGY BLVD 43214 #038-40-1982 L1983 P *074 †75

O'REILLY, Kevin Patrick. 745 W STATE ST STE 520 43222 #038-40-1996 L2002 NEP IM *020 †20

ORLOUSKY, Sarah Rebecca. ■ 43230 #038-40-2006 L2006 EM *012

OROURKE, Kevin Gerard, Jr. 410 W 10TH AVE, OH STATE UNIV HOSP 43210 #019-02-2007 L2007 EM *012

ORR, Janet Sigler. 6096 E MAIN ST STE 112 43213 #038-40-1991 L1992 PD *020 †55

ORSINELLI, David August. 473 W 12TH AVE, OSU DIVISION OF CARDIOLOGY 43210 #028-34-1983 L1991 CD IM *020 †20

ORT, Erin Marie. 1654 UPHAM DR, 201 MEANS HALL 43210 #038-44-2004 L2004 IM *100 †20

ORTH, Matthew David. 1087 DENNISON AVE 43201 #028-78-2004, ▲ L2004 DR *012

OSAWE, Obosa Nosayaba. 1654 UPHAM DR, OHIO STATE UNIV MED CTR 43210 #035-15-2006 L2006 OBG *012

OSBORNE, Chad Neilson. ■ 43230 #005-18-2007 L2007 FP *012

OSEI, Kwame. 456 W 10TH AVE 43210 #412-01-1976 L1982 END IM *040 †20

O'SHAUGHNESSY, Richard. 410 W 10TH AVE, DEPT OBGYN 43210 #038-40-1973 L1973 OBG MFM *020 †30

OSUAGWU, Ngozi. 5131 BEACON HILL RD, STE 220B 43228 #035-06-1990 L1995 OBG *020 †30

O'SULLIVAN, Brendan J. 793 W STATE ST 43222 #539-04-1946 L1951 AN *071 †05

OTABOR, Iyore Amy. 410 W 10TH AVE, DEPT OF SURGERY 43210 #024-07-2006 L2006 GS *012

OTTERSON, Gregory Alan. 320 W 10TH AVE, DIV OF HEM/ONC 43210 #010-02-1986 L1998 HO IM *020 †20

OTTO, Bradley Alan. ■ 43210 #038-45-2002 L2002 OTO *100

OYORTEY, Michele Armande. 3433 AGLER RD, STE 1300 43219 #038-40-1993 L1998 PD *020

OYSTER, Marlo Norina. 410 W 10TH AVE, DEPARTMENT OF ORTHOPAEDICS 43210 #038-45-2003 L2003 ORS *012

OZ, Abdullah. 6001 E BROAD ST, BLDG 2 43213 #902-10-1985 L2001 IM *020 †20

OZA, Rupal Sharad. 2231 N HIGH ST 43201 #496-36-1998 L2002 FM *020 †18

OZER, Enver. 456 W 10TH AVE, STE 4024 43210 #902-19-1994 L2003 OTO HNS *020

PACE, Robert Joseph. ■ 43201 #038-40-2008 *012

PACKER, Mark Dee. ■ 43220 #023-12-1995 L1996 NO *012 †45

PADAMADAN, Hosi. 1727 BETHEL RD 43220 #495-99-1979 L1996 FM *020 †18

PAES, John Elwood. 1581 DODD DR, 4TH FL MCCAMPBELL HALL 43210 #038-75-2003, ▲ L2003 END *012

PAI, Manju Mizar. ■ 43204 #038-40-2008 *012

PAJER, Kathleen Ann. 700 CHILDRENS DR, CHILDREN'S RESEARCH CTR 43205 #001-06-1982 L1985 P *050 †75

PAK, Yong Cha. 1875 MILLIKIN RD 43210 #583-01-1961 L1975 PD *020 †55

PAKALNIS, Ann. 700 CHILDRENS DR, DEPT PED 43205 #038-43-1982 L1984 N *020 †75

PAL, Subodh. ■ 43205 #422-01-2003 L2003 MPD *020,55

PALLACI, Michael J. 3535 OLENTANGY RIVER RD, RIVERSIDE METHODIST HOSPIT 43214 #035-75-1998, ▲ L2001 EM *020 †18

PALMA, Bernard John, Jr. 2339 CLEVELAND AVE 43211 #028-79-1991, ▲ L1995 FM OMM *020

PALOSKI, Michael. ■ 43228 #038-75-2006, ▲ L2006 *012

PANCHAL, Ashish Raman. ■ 43220 #038-40-2005 L2005 EM *012

PANDYA, Aradhi Urmil. 3555 OLENTANGY RIVER RD, STE 1080 43214 #038-44-2002 L2002 IM *020 †20

PANZNER, Kathryn Margaret. ■ 43221 #038-40-2008 *012

PAPP, Gerard M. ■ 43220 #041-77-1971, ▲ L1972 ORS *071

PAQUELET, Jean Rachelle. 866 W BROAD ST 43222 #038-43-1976 L1979 R *020 †80

PAQUELET, Stephen Edward. 2050 KENNY RD 43221 #038-43-2002 L2002 APM *020 †05

PARA, Michael Francis. 410 W 10TH AVE RM N1143 43210 #038-40-1974 L1980 ID IM *050 †20

PARBHOO, Sitaben Kantilal. 2200 W BROAD ST 43223 #495-22-1966 L1978 GP P *020

PAREDES, Roland-Jake L. 750 MT CARMEL MALL, EMERGENCY SREVICES INC 43222 #038-44-2002 L2005 EM *020 †16

PARGAONKER, Nikhil Makran. 793 W STATE ST, MT CARMEL MED CTR 43222 #305-01-2001 L2002 IM *100

PARISER, Roslyn F. 3545 OLENTANGY RIVER RD, STE 422 43214 #025-01-1943 L1948 P *071 †75

PARISER, Stephen Fellman. 1670 UPHAM DR, ADULT PSYCHIATRY CLINIC 43210 #038-40-1972 L1973 P *020 †75,30

PARK, Edward Young. 1654 UPHAM DR, N210 MEANS HALL 43210 #028-79-2003, ▲ L2004 NEP *012 †20

PARK, Kyung Won. S407 RHODES HALL, 450 W 10TH AVE 43210 #005-18-1985 L1986 AN *020 †05

PARK, Roger Wm. 700 CHILDRENS DR 43205 #025-01-1959 L1960 PD *071 †55

PARKER, Augustus Garland. 85 MCNAUGHTEN RD, STE 310 43213 #038-41-1981 L1981 OBG *020 †30

PARKER, Hallie C. ■ 43206 #038-40-2007 L2007 IM *012

PARKER, Michael Sean. 1080 BEECHER XING N, NORTHEAST OB GYN INC 43230 #038-40-1989 L1991 OBG *020 †30

PARKINSON, Nicholas Gray. 111 S GRANT AVE, GRANT MEDICAL CENTER 43215 #038-40-2001 L2001 FM *020 †18

PARKS, Alan Jos. 150 TAYLOR STATION RD, STE 250 43213 #035-08-1983 L1986 **D** *020 †15
PARKS, Alicia. ■ 43235 #038-75-2005, ▲ L2005 **IM** *012
PARSONS, James Norman. 3535 OLENTANGY RIVER RD 43214 #038-40-1974 L1975 **ID IM** *020 †20
PARSONS, Jonathan Philip. 178 ACTON RD 43214 #038-43-1999 L1999 **PCC** *100 †20
PARSONS, Melissa Margaret. 700 CHILDRENS DR, CHILDRENS HOSPITAL 43205 #038-43-1999 L1999 **PD** *020 †55
PARSONS, Steven Caroll. 4849 E MAIN ST 43213 #038-40-1981 L1983 **GP OM** *020
PASSERINI, David Scott. 866 W BROAD ST 43222 #038-40-2000 L2000 **DR** *100 †80
PATEL, Amit Babu. 700 CHILDRENS DR, CHILDREN'S HOSPITAL 43205 #047-06-1994 L1998 **MPD** *020 †20,55
PATEL, Alpa Vallabh. 3555 OLENTANGY RIVER RD, STE 1080 43214 #759-06-2002 L2002 **IM** *100 †20
PATEL, Ashay Sharad. ■ 43214 #028-78-2003, ▲ L2003 **U** *012
PATEL, Bharat Bhagubhai. 500 E MAIN ST 43215 #495-22-1992 L2001 **NEP** *020 †20
PATEL, Bhavesh Pravin. 793 W STATE ST 43222 #305-01-2005 L2006 **IM** *012
PATEL, Chintan Rajni. 2231 N HIGH ST RM 205, RARDIN FAMILY PRACTICE CTR 43201 #654-01-2004 L2005 **FP** *012
PATEL, Hiren Pravinkumar. 700 CHILDRENS DR, SECTION OF NEPHROLOGY 43205 #026-04-1997 L1998 **PN** *012
PATEL, Jaydeep Vipin. 410 W 10TH AVE 43210 #495-01-2003 L2006 **FP** *012
PATEL, Kanishka Bhalla. 2231 N HIGH ST RM 205, RARDIN FAMILY PRACTICE CTR 43201 #665-01-2004 L2005 **FP** *012
PATEL, Monika. 6465 E BROAD ST, STE D SUBURBAN INTERNL MED 43213 #495-37-1989 L1992 **IM** *020 †20
PATEL, Nisha Nathalal. 692 N PARK ST 43215 #305-01-2001 L2001 **IM HOS** *020
PATEL, Parita. 1492 E BROAD ST, STE 1302 43205 #062-01-1992 L2007 **FM** *020 †18
PATEL, Rajendra C. 423 E TOWN ST, STE 1000 43215 #495-23-1974 L1980 **CD IM** *020 †20
PATEL, Rashmi Ishwar. 750 MT CARMEL MALL, STE 350 43222 #038-41-1994 L1997 **U** *020 †95
PATEL, Shailesh R. 6001 E BROAD ST 43213 #495-37-1989 L1991 **ICE CD** *020 †20
PATEL, Sugat Siddharth. 85 MCNAUGHTEN RD 43213 #038-40-1997 L2003 **OPH OS** *020 †35
PATEL, Trupti Vikram. 1670 UPHAM DR, STE 130 43215 #654-01-1997 L2004 **P PYG** *020 †75
PATEL, Tushar C. 410 W 10TH AVE, N201 DOAN HALL 43210 #919-05-1988 L2006 **HEP GE** *020 †20
PATHAN, Shunaid Muhammad. 793 W STATE ST 43222 #704-08-2002 L2005 **IM** *012
PATRICK, Laura Ellen. 456 W 10TH AVE 43210 #038-40-1998 L2001 **END** *020 †20
PATRICK, Tiffany Lacole. ■ 43212 #038-40-2008 *012
PATTERSON, Cynthia Curren. ■ 43201 #038-40-2005 L2005 **D** *012
PAUL, Carey B. ■ 43213 #041-02-1954 L1955 **FM OS** *071
PAULSON, George Wesley. 3957 LYTHAM CT, MCCAMPBELL HALL, ROOM 371 43220 #036-07-1956 L1967 **N** *062 †75
PAYIND, Gharanai Abdullah. 793 W STATE ST, C/O MT CARMEL HOSP-MED EDU 43222 #305-01-2002 L2003 **IM** *020 †20
PAYNE, Jason Edward. 1654 UPHAM DR, 630 MEANS HALL 43210 #045-01-2003 L2004 **DR** *012
PAYNE, Melissa Anne. 65 HIGHVIEW BLVD 43207 #038-41-1997 L1999 **FM** *020 †18
PEARSON, Gregory David. 4830 KNIGHTSBRIDGE BLVD, SURGERY 43214 #038-40-1998 L1999 **CFS** *020 †65
PEASE, William Stoess. 480 MEDICAL CENTER DR, STE 1018 43215 #038-41-1981 L1982 **PM OS** *030 †60
PEDRICK, Thomas J. 3535 OLENTANGY RIVER RD 43214 #038-41-1981 L1985 **RO** *020 †80
PEERZADE, Sharistha Ibrah. 285 E STATE ST STE 670, GRANT MED CTR 43215 #496-39-2000 L2008 **FP** *012
PEJI, Joyce Choi. 1211 DUBLIN RD, FL 2 43215 #038-40-1998 L1999 **GE** *020 †20
PELLETIER, Ronald Paul. 410 W 10TH AVE 43210 #038-41-1987 L1989 **GS** *020 †85
PEMA, Ann Eaton. 700 CHILDRENS DR, DEPT. OF AMBULATORY PEDIAT 43205 #038-40-1990 L1991 **PD** *020 †55
PEMA, Peter James, Jr. ■ 43220 #041-77-1959, ▲ L1960 **IM** *071
PENA BAEZ, Eneysis Margar. ■ 43204 #308-13-1999 L2005 **NPM** *012
PENG, Charles Yenwei. ■ 43209 #038-40-2008 *012
PENNIMAN, Wright Charles. 223 E TOWN ST, SECOND FLOOR 43215 #018-75-1997, ▲ L2007 **FM OM** *012
PENZA, Sam Lawrence. 320 W 10TH AVE, JAMES CANCER HOSPITAL - 05 43210 #038-40-1989 L1991 **HO HEM** *030 †20
PEPPER, Jeanette Abell. ■ 43220 #038-45-1990 L1992 **IM** *020 †20
PEPPER, Tom Hartwell. 1492 E BROAD ST, TALBOT HALL 43205 #048-04-1970 L1985 **P GP** *020 †75 ‡
PERALTA GARCIA, Feyce Mab. 410 W 10TH AVE 43210 #308-05-2004 L2006 **AN** *012
PERENCEVICH, Eli Nicholas. 94 W 3RD AVE, DRS SETNAR NAGY & ASSOCS 43201 #018-75-1966, ▲ L1966 **PLM** *071
PEREZ, Ernesto Lautaro. 1336 E MAIN ST 43205 #319-01-1949 L1965 **FM** *071
PEREZ, Lesley Ann. ■ 43228 #038-40-2004 L2004 **EM** *020
PERKINS, Robert Harrison. 340 E TOWN ST, PHYSICAL MEDICINE 43215 #038-40-1995 L1996 **PM** *020 †60
PERKINS, Robert Louis. 111 S GRANT AVE 43215 #023-07-1956 L1958 **ID IM** *071 †20
PERNOUD, Cathleen. ■ 43204 #028-34-2004 L2005 **DR** *012
PERRY, Michael Andrew. 6096 E MAIN ST STE 11 43213 #017-20-1990 L1991 **PD** *020 †55
PERUZZI, Pier Paolo. 410 W 10TH AVE 43210 #561-17-2004 L2007 **NS** *012
PESA, Marcus Joseph. 750 MOUNT CARMEL MALL 43222 #038-40-1993 L1995 **EM** *020 †16
PESAVENTO, Todd Edward. 1654 UPHAM DR, NEPHROLOGY 43210 #020-02-1989 L1995 **NEP** *020 †20
PESTRITTO, Vincent Matthe. 456 W 10TH AVE, 4510 CRAMBLETT CLINIC 43210 #041-14-2005 L2008 **IM** *012
PETERS, Sara Beth. 410 W 10TH AVE, O.S.U. MED CTR 43210 #035-15-1991 L2006 **DMP ATP** *020 †50
PETRI, Benita Marie. 2231 N HIGH ST 43201 #055-02-1994 L1997 **FM** *020 †18
PEWITT, E Bradley. 750 MT CARMEL MALL, STE 350 43222 #016-02-1992 L1998 **U** *020 †95
PFEIL, Sheryl Ann. 410 W 10TH AVE, ROOM N216 DOAN HALL 43210 #038-40-1984 L1985 **GE IM** *020 †20
PHAM, John Dunghoang. ■ 43201 #051-04-2005 L2005 **PTH** *012
PHAM, Nhung Samantha. 2131 DAWNLIGHT AVE 43211 #038-45-1995 L1996 **MPD** *020 †20,55
PHAM, Thomas. ■ 43201 #038-41-2007 L2007 **GS** *012
PHILLIPS, Alistair B. 700 CHILDRENS DR, CHILDREN'S HOSPITAL COLUMB 43205 #035-01-1994 L2005 **PCS** *020 †85,90
PHILLIPS, Antonio Marty. 2231 N HIGH ST RM 205, OHIO STATE UNIV 43201 #038-40-2002 L2002 **FM** *100

PHILLIPS, Michelle Lynn. 700 CHILDRENS DR 43205 #028-03-2005 L2005 **PD** *012
PHILLIPS, Pamela Reif. ■ 43209 #035-01-1995 L2005 **PD** *020 †55
PHIPPS, Brian Dale. 4830 KNIGHTSBRIDGE BLVD, STE A 43214 #038-40-1998 L1999 **IM** *020 †20
PICKERING, Robert Rudolph. 85 MCNAUGHTEN RD, INC 43213 #038-45-1986 L1991 **PUD CCM** *020 †20
PICKSTONE, Stephen Mark. 1670 UPHAM DR 43210 #055-02-1995 L1997 **P** *020 †75
PIEPER, Heinz Paul. 333 W 10TH AVE # PHYSIOL 43210 #407-16-1950 *030
PIERO, David Lee. 5975 E BROAD ST, STE 302 43213 #038-40-1971 L1971 **PM** *020 †60
PIETROPAOLO, Domenico. ■ 43204 #038-40-2007 L2007 *012
PINGEL, Christopher James. ■ 43230 #028-34-2007 L2007 *012
PINKHAM, Sandra M. 2170 RIVERSIDE DR 43221 #035-45-1968 L1970 **PD GP** *020 †55
PINTA, Emil Richard. ■ 43235 #038-40-1966 L1966 **P** *020 †75
PINZONE, Joseph Jude. 456 W 10TH AVE 43210 #035-19-1992 L2006 **IM** *020 †20
PIPPIN, Cheryl D Bocook. 700 CHILDRENS DR, CHILDREN'S HOSPITAL 43205 #055-02-1988 L1989 **R** *020 †55
PLEISTER, Irina Shahkhnov. ■ 43202 #056-06-2004 L2004 **GS** *012
PLOTT, Darceilia Tresele. 370 W 9TH AVE, OH STATE U COLL OF MED 43210 #038-40-2002 L2002 **IM** *100 †20
PLOUFFE, Joseph Francis. 410 W 10TH AVE, UNIVERSITY HOSPITAL N-1135 43210 #028-34-1972 L1977 **ID** *040 †20
POEHM, Erika Helen. 99 N BRICE RD STE 300, COLUMBUS SLEEP CONSULTANTS 43213 #473-01-1989 L2006 **N** *020 †75
POHAR, Kamaljeet. 456 W 10TH AVE 43210 #060-01-1993 L2002 **U** *020 †95
POI, Mun Jye. 410 W 10TH AVE 43210 #065-06-2005 L2005 **GS** *012
POKA, Attila. 285 E STATE ST, STE 500 43215 #473-01-1970 L1992 **ORS** *020
POLITI, Joel Roger. 85 MCNAUGHTEN RD 43213 #038-44-1993 L1994 **ORS** *020 †40
POLITI, Julie Owens. 700 CHILDRENS DR, CHILDREN'S HOSPITAL 43205 #038-44-1994 L1995 **PD** *020 †55
POLL, Wayne Lyle. 3555 OLENTANGY RIVER RD, STE 4020 43214 #047-05-1981 L1987 **U** *020 †95
POLLACK, Paul Frederick. ■ 43215 #035-08-1974 L2000 **NPM GE** *062 †55 ‡
POLLYEA, Edward Jay. 1492 E BROAD ST 43205 #016-11-1974 L1976 **IM AI** *020
POLONIA, Danilo. 4850 E MAIN ST 43213 #038-40-1992 L1993 **FM** *020 †18
POLSTER, Louis Robert. 6495 E BROAD ST 43213 #038-40-1968 L1968 **PD** *020 †55
POMERANTS, B J. 340 E TOWN ST, STE 7-500 43215 #038-44-1989 L1992 **GS** *020 †85
PONGONIS, Raymond Marion, Jr. ■ 43221 #038-40-2007 **IM** *012
PONS, Maureen Elizabeth. ■ 43235 #008-02-2007 L2007 **GS** *012
POOL, Joseph Wilson. 6465 E BROAD ST, STE D 43213 #048-13-1998 L1999 **IM** *020 †20
POPP, James Edward. 1405 DUBLIN RD 43215 #038-06-1992 L1993 **HS** *020 †40
PORCELL, Ana Irene. OH STATE UNIV HOSP, DEPT PATH 43210 #715-01-1990 L1998 **PTH** *100 †50
PORCU, Pierluigi. 320 W 10TH AVE, #B407 STARLING LOVING HALL 43210 #561-20-1987 L1999 **HO** *020 †20
PORRES, Paul J. ■ 43221 #038-75-2007, ▲ L2007 *012
PORTER, Alex Tristan. ■ 43220 #038-40-2007 L2007 **IM** *012
PORTMAN, David Jay. 99 N BRICE RD, STE 120 43213 #038-40-1990 L1991 **OBG** *050 †30
PORTMAN, Miriam Davidson. ■ 43209 #038-40-1990 L1992 **GP** *071
PORTMAN, Samuel Louis. 5965 E BROAD ST 43213 #038-40-1960 L1960 **OBG** *071 †30
POST, Linda Louise. 2800 CORPORATE EXCHANGE DR 43231 #038-43-1981 L1983 **FM OBG** *030 †18
POTARAJU, Kameswara P. 1301 N HIGH ST 43201 #495-50-1979 L1998 **P** *020 †75
POTHAST, Jason Lee. ■ 43204 #038-40-2008 *012
POTTER, Carol Jean. 700 CHILDRENS DR 43205 #026-04-1985 L1991 **PD NM** *020 †55
POTTS, Michelle Anne. 43214 #038-45-2006 L2006 **PM** *012
POULOS, Georgann Anetakis. ■ 43219 #038-44-2007 L2007 **D** *012
POULOS, Jeffrey George. 1492 E BROAD ST, OSU HOSPITALS EAST 43205 #038-44-1995 L1996 **IM** *020 †20
POWELL, Dwight Alden. 700 CHILDRENS DR, CHILDRENS HOSP ID STE 577 43205 #016-11-1969 L1979 **PD ID** *020 †55
POWELL, Jennifer Lynn. 700 CHILDRENS DR, ATTN EMERGENCY MEDICINE 43205 #038-45-1999 L1999 **PD** *020
POWERS, James Joseph. 340 E TOWN ST, PHYSICAL MEDICINE 43215 #038-40-1965 L1965 **PM** *020 †60
POWERS, Michael J, II. ■ 43201 #038-40-2008 *012
POZDERAC, Rodney Victor. 1654 UPHAM DR, 630 MEANS HALL 43210 #010-01-1964 L1989 **NM IM** *020 †28,80
PRAKASH, Asha Srirangaraj. 600 W SPRING ST, COLUMBUS NEIGHBORHOOD HEAL 43215 #495-09-1995 L2000 **IM** *020 ‡
PRASAD, Mona R. ■ 43228 #003-75-2001, ▲ L2001 **OBG** *100
PRASAD, Nishant. ■ 43212 #038-40-2008 *012
PRATT, Craig Thorsell. 1144 DUBLIN RD, MOUNT CARMEL HOSPICE 43215 #028-46-1979 L1987 **PLM P** *020 †75
PRENGER, Eric John. 4850 E MAIN ST 43213 #038-40-2004 L2004 **FM** *020 †18
PRESTON, Jon Theodore. 111 S GRANT AVE, GRANT MEDICAL CENTER 43215 #038-40-1987 L1991 **AN GS** *020 †05
PRESTON, Thomas Anthony. 3535 OLENTANGY BLVD 43214 #038-40-1988 L1989 **CCM IM** *020 †20
PRESTON, Thomas Arthur. 3545 OLENTANGY RIVER RD 43214 #041-01-1962 L1963 **CD IM** *071 †20
PRICE, Jonathan James. 700 CHILDRENS DR, SECTION EMG MED CHILD HOSP 43205 #038-40-1979 L1979 **PD** *020
PRICE, Phillip Duane. 5969 E BROAD ST, STE 306 43213 #038-40-1989 L1991 **GS** *020 †85
PRICE, Pliny A. 1430 S HIGH ST 43207 #038-40-1939 L1939 **NS** *071 †75,25
PRINCE, Loren Carter. 111 S GRANT AVE 43215 #038-40-1962 L1962 **AN** *020 †05
PRITCHARD, James Douglas. 810 JASONWAY AVE 43214 #038-40-1967 L1967 **ON** *071 †20
PRITCHETT, Cedric Von. ■ 43232 #038-40-2008 *012
PROCA, Daniela Mihaela. 410 W 10TH AVE, STE 310 43210 #781-01-1992 L1998 **PTH** *020 †50
PRONOLD, Barry John. ■ 43215 #056-06-2007 L2007 **IM** *012
PROSCIAK, Mark Peter. ■ 43214 #422-01-2001 L2008 **GS** *100
PROSEK, Jason Matthew. ■ 43215 #038-40-2007 L2007 **IM** *012
PRZEBINDA, Arthur Zenon. 1375 PERRY ST 5T, CO OSU HOSPS-MED EDU DEPT 43201 #759-01-1997 L2000 **NM** *100
PU, Min. 473 W 12TH AVE, 2ND FL 43210 #243-45-1982 L2000 **CD IM** *020 †20
PUDLO, Nancy Anne. ■ 43235 #017-20-2005 L2005 **PD** *012

PUE, Charles Alan. 1275 OLENTANGY RIVER RD, STE 10 43212 #041-13-1988 L1990 PUD CCM *020 †20

PUGH, Kevin Joseph. 1335 DUBLIN RD 43215 #018-03-1988 L1989 OTR OFA *020 †40

PULEO, William William, II. 340 E TOWN ST, SUITE 8-550, 340 EAST TOWN 43215 #038-06-2003 L2005 IM *100 †20

PULTZ, Andrew Joseph. 3341 E LIVINGSTON AVE, STE D 43227 #038-40-1956 L1956 FM *071 †18

PUNATAR, Ankit Dilip. ■ 43212 #038-40-2008 *012

PYKA, Ronald E. 3535 OLENTANGY BLVD 43214 #048-13-1983 L1993 PTH NP *020 †50

QAMAR, Mehdi Ali. 423 E TOWN ST, STE 1000 43215 #704-05-1988 L2003 IC CD *020 †20

QAZI, Asif Qutub. 6465 E BROAD ST, STE D 43213 #035-08-1993 L2006 IM *020 †20

QUALMAN, Stephen Jay. 700 CHILDRENS DR 43205 #025-01-1979 L1984 PP *030 †50

QUICK, Adam Duret. ■ 43212 #017-20-2002 L2007 N NMN *100

QUICK, Allison Marie. ■ 43212 #050-02-2006 L2007 RO *012

QUILLIN, Alston Mc Clure. 170 NORTHWOODS BLVD 43235 #038-40-1962 L1962 D OS *071

QUILLIN, Andrew Donley. 170 NORTHWOODS BLVD, STE 10 43235 #038-43-1994 L1998 D *020 †15

QUINN, Daniel Patrick. ■ 43221 #017-20-2005 L2005 ORS *012

QURESHI, Absar Ahmed. 2752 CLEVELAND AVE 43224 #704-02-1987 L1998 IM *020 †20

QURESHI, Azeem Abdul. 543 TAYLOR AVE, VET AFFAIR OUT PATIENTS CL 43203 #704-08-1977 L1999 P ADP *020

RACKE, Michael Karl. 1654 UPHAM DR, 445 MEANS HALL 43210 #033-05-1985 L2006 N *020 †20

RADCLIFF, Kendra Lou. ■ 43228 #038-40-2006 L2006 MPD *012

RADECKI, Kevin Michael. 197 PRAIRIECREEK WAY 43213 #030-06-1993 L2001 TS *020 †85,90

RAFFEL, Corey. 700 CHILDRENS DR, DIV OF PD NEUROSURGERY 43205 #005-18-1980 L2000 NS *020 †25

RAGOSIN, Robert Jos. 1654 UPHAM DR, 630 MEANS HALL 43210 #038-40-1968 L1968 R *020 †80

RAGUE, Louis Michael, III. 4606 SAWMILL RD 43220 #035-09-1987 L1990 AN *020 †05

RAHL, Amy Wermuth. 921B JASONWAY AVE 43214 #038-40-1998 L1999 OBG *020 †30

RAHMAN, Syed Mukhlesur. 6200 CLEVELAND AVE, COLUMBUS RADIOLOGY CORP 43231 #160-01-1964 L1977 RO OS *020 †80

RAIG, Ene Therese. ■ 43220 #038-40-2008 *012

RAJAB, Amer. 1654 UPHAM DR 43210 #875-01-1983 L2000 GS TTS *020 †85

RAJASINGHAM, Christiana R. 700 CHILDRENS DR 43205 #035-09-2000 L2000 PEM *100 †55

RAJU, Satesh Kumar. ■ 43204 #654-01-2001 L2002 CCP *012

RAKOWSKY, Alexander T. 700 CHILDRENS DR, RESEARCH INSTITUTE 43205 #041-14-1990 L2004 PD PDI *050 †55

RAMACHANDRAN, Anand. 6100 E MAIN ST STE 1 43213 #038-43-1997 L2001 OPH *020 †35

RAMACHANDRAN, Veena. ■ 43202 #038-40-2008 *012

RAMAN, Subha Venkat. 473 W 12TH AVE, OF CARDIOLOGY 43210 #038-40-1996 L1997 CD *020 †20

RAMAN, Vidya. 700 CHILDRENS DR 43205 #035-03-1996 L2006 AN *020 †55,05 ‡

RAMANATHAN, Nithya. 1670 UPHAM DR 43210 #495-23-1997 L2000 CHP *020 †20

RAMASWAMY, Chakravarthi R. 745 W STATE ST STE 520 43222 #495-59-1984 L2000 NEP IM *020 †20

RAMIREZ, Alvaro. ■ 43235 #264-04-1967 L1972 R *100

RAMIREZ, Nilsa C. 1645 NEIL AVE 43210 #042-01-1985 L2001 ATP CLP *020 †50

RAMMOHAN, Kottil Walappil. 2050 KENNY RD # 2250 43221 #495-04-1969 L1973 N IM *020 †20,75

RAMOS, Caroline Diaz. 4605 SAWMILL RD, STE 102 43220 #038-40-1993 L1996 IM *020 †20

RAMSEY, Michael S. 741 E BROAD ST, NETCARE 43205 #005-76-1998, ▲ L2000 CHP *020 ‡

RAMSINGH, Parshan Singh. 1654 UPHAM DR, DEPT OF RADIOLOGY 43210 #495-19-1973 L1992 NM DR *030 †28,80

RANA, Abid Iqbal. 4850 E MAIN RD, GRANT FAMILY PRATICE 43213 #422-01-2004 L2005 FP *012

RANA, Ankur Rajendersin. ■ 43204 #038-44-2001 L2007 CCS *100

RANDALL, John Gill. ■ 43221 #038-40-1959 L1959 P *075

RANGWANI, Deepika Mukesh. 1875 MILLIKIN RD, SW WILCE STUDENT HEALTH CE 43210 #495-17-1987 L1995 FM *020 †18

RANKIN, Demicha Denise. 410 W 10TH AVE, OH STATE UNIV HOSP 43210 #038-40-2006 L2006 AN *020

RANKINE, Kirk P. 285 E STATE ST, STE 360 43215 #035-15-1998 L1999 NEP *020 †20

RANSBOTTOM, Thomas Craig. 3820 OLENTANGY RIVER RD, OHIO GASTROENTEROLOGY 43214 #038-40-1979 L1982 GE IM *020 †20

RAO, Mohini Sudarshan. 410 W 10TH AVE, OSU HOSPITALS AND CLINICS 43210 #495-21-1988 L2002 AN *020 †05

RAO, Sandeep. ■ 43202 #048-15-2004 L2006 DR *012

RAO, Shweta Sreenivas. 410 W 10TH AVE 43210 #496-21-2005 L2006 FP *012

RAO, Syamala Kandarpa. 1301 N HIGH ST, NORTH CENTRAL MENTAL HLTH 43201 #495-04-1952 L1964 P *071 †75

RAPHAEL, Peter R. 793 W STATE ST, MT CARMEL MED CTR 43222 #305-01-2006 L2006 FP *012

RASHWAN, Ahmed Samy. 5100 W BROAD ST, DOCTORS HOSPITAL 43228 #915-04-1981 L2004 CCM *020 †20

RASMUSSEN, Ammon Garth. ■ 43221 #038-40-2008 *012

RATLIFF-SCHAUB, Karen L. 700 CHILDRENS DR, CHILDREN'S HOSPITAL 43205 #038-44-1986 L1988 PD *020 †12

RAU, Robert Carson. 3545 OLENTANGY RVR RD #124 43214 #038-41-1967 L1967 D *020 †15

RAUCH, Robert Frederick. 43220 #024-01-1945 L1952 GS *071 †85

RAUCK, Charles Riley. 793 W STATE ST 43222 #038-40-1984 L1985 AN PME *020 †05

RAULJ, Josip. 1555 BETHEL RD, COMPREHENSIVE SERVICES INC 43220 #957-01-1955 L1969 P CHP *020 †75

RAUSER, Laura. 3535 OLENTANGY RIVER RD, MED EDUCATION DEPT 43214 #038-40-2005 L2005 OBG *012

RAVEENDRAN, Rekha Priya. ■ 43215 #038-44-2007 L2007 IM *012

RAVINDRAN, Reno. 410 W 10TH AVE 43210 #495-37-2004 L2005 FP *012

RAZVI, Nighet Sultana. 2368 EASTCLEFT DR, . 43221 #016-01-1992 L1999 IM *020 †20

REA, Gary Lynn. 2050 KENNY RD, OHIO STATE SPINE CENTER 43221 #048-04-1976 L1985 NS *020 †25

REAM, Donald Louis. ■ 43235 #038-40-1946 L1946 FM *071 †18

REBER, Kristina Marie. 700 CHILDRENS DR, SECTION OF NEONATOLOGY 43205 #038-40-1991 L1992 NPM *020 †55

RECHNITZER, Donata Ann. 2939 KENNY RD STE 200 43221 #038-45-1992 L1993 FM *020 †18

RECKER, Bethany Anne. 2150 MARBLE CLF OFC PARK P 43215 #038-44-2004 L2004 FM *020 †18

REDD, Deidre Diane. 340 E TOWN ST, PHYSICAL MEDICINE 43215 #038-45-1995 L1998 PM *020 †60

REDDY, Archana Venumbaka. 456 W 10TH AVE 43210 #019-02-2000 L2001 OPH *020 †35

REDDY, K V Bhaskar. 5100 W BROAD ST, DOCTORS WEST HOSPITAL 43228 #495-62-1971 L1977 AN PMM *020 †05

REDDY, Niveditha Shankara. ■ 43210 #496-39-1997 L2004 ID *020

REDDY, Raghuram Patlola. 3820 OLENTANGY RIVER RD, OHIO GASTROENTEROLOGY 43214 #495-65-1992 L2006 GE *100 †20

REDDY, Shalini Patlolla. 111 S GRANT AVE, 3RD FL 43215 #495-70-1987 L2002 AN *020 †05

REDDY, Snigdha Thummala. 793 W STATE ST 43222 #496-21-2005 L2006 IM *012

REDDY, Venu. 6200 CLEVELAND AVE, COLUMBUS RADIOLOGY CORP 43231 #495-09-1983 L1989 PUD IM *020 †20

REDDY, Vinaya Kumar. 3525 OLENTANGY RIVER RD, STE 5360 43214 #028-03-2001 L2007 DR *020 †80

REED, Gary Lee. ■ 43232 #038-43-1978 L1980 GS *075

REES, Mitchell Allen. ■ 43206 #038-40-2008 *012

REESE, Cynthia Ann. 3400 OLENTANGY RIVER RD, STE 150 43202 #038-44-1999 L1999 IM *020 †20

REEVE, Jennifer Louise. ■ 43220 #007-02-2007 L2007 OBG *012

REHM, Robert Adrian. 500 THOMAS LN STE 3C 43214 #038-41-1954 L1956 U *020 †95

REID, Gary Craig. 500 THOMAS LN STE 3B 43214 #016-06-1977 L1988 GO GYN *020 †30

REIGEL, Martha Alison. 5969 E BROAD ST, STE 303 43213 #026-04-1981 L1988 VS GS *020 †85

REINBOLT, Raquel Elizabet. ■ 43212 #016-43-2008 *012

REINER, Charles B. 700 CHILDRENS DR, CHILDRENS HOSPITAL 43205 #041-13-1945 L1958 ATP PD *071 †55,50

REITZ, Steven Charles. 793 W STATE ST 43222 #038-43-2006 L2006 GS *012

RENNEBOHM, Robert Martin. 555 S 18TH ST 43205 #005-18-1972 L1982 RHU *020 †55

RENTEL, Victoria. 3709 N HIGH ST, STE 100 43214 #038-40-1999 L1999 FM *020 †18

RENZ, Mark Allan. ■ 43228 #038-45-2002 L2003 FP *012

RESOR, Alan Gloyd S. 1555 BETHEL RD # 101 43220 #048-04-1966 L1969 P *071 †75

RETHMAN, Douglas Ralph. 3535 OLENTANGY RIVER RD 43214 #038-43-2003 L2004 IM *020 †20

RETTER, Richard Henry. 553 E TOWN ST 43215 #056-05-1943 L1953 NS *071 †25

REYES, Alfonso Esteban. 943 WORTHINGTON WODS LP RD 43085 #649-53-1990 L1996 FM *020 †18

REYES, Luzviminda Balivia. 741 E BROAD ST 43205 #748-01-1966 L1978 P *020

REYNOLDS, Harold Thos. 5975 E BROAD ST, STE 302 43213 #055-01-1980 L1981 PM *020 †60

REYNOLDS, Rickey J. 6150 E BROAD ST, MOUNT CARMEL HEALTH PROVID 43213 #048-13-1992 L2002 N *020 †75

REYNOLDS, William. 1492 E BROAD ST # 1403 43205 #038-40-1965 L1965 ORS *020 †40

RHEAUME, Patrick Shayne. ■ 43204 #016-45-2008 *012

RHEE, Choo-Young. 1492 E BROAD ST 43205 #583-02-1964 L1978 IM HEM *020

RHOADES, Chris Allen. 745 W STATE ST, STE 550B 43222 #038-40-1990 L1992 HO *020 †20

RHOADES, Virginia Mehl. 4208 ALEXANDRIA COLONY 43215 #038-40-1988 *010

RICAURTE, Mark Douglas. 719 W TOWN ST 43222 #038-44-1986 L1988 IM *020 †20

RICCOBONO, Xavier John. ■ 43230 #035-08-1948 L1959 NR R *075 †80,28

RICH, David Howard, Jr. 515 E MAIN ST, COLUMBUS CHILDREN S HOSP 43215 #005-18-1998 L1999 PD *020 †55

RICHARDS, Ayo Lynn. ■ 43202 #025-01-2007 L2007 IM *012

RICHARDS, R Timothy. ■ 43220 #038-40-1991 L1992 IM *020 †20

RICHARDS, Stephen Ray. 4030 EASTON STA, STE 200 43219 #038-40-1979 L1979 OBG *020 †30

RICHARDSON, Debra Lynn. 320 W 10TH AVE, M210 STARLING LOVING 43210 #035-09-2001 L2006 OBG *020 †30

RICHARDSON, Jennifer A. 1211 DUBLIN RD 43215 #038-40-1998 L1999 RHU *020 †20

RICHARDSON, Kevin Andrew. 85 MCNAUGHTEN RD, STE 110 43213 #047-07-1994 L2000 TS VS *020 †85,90

RICHARDSON, Wilford Lee. ■ 43220 #038-40-2008 *012

RICHEY, Cherie Alandra. 85 MCNAUGHTEN RD STE 310 43213 #041-12-2000 L2000 OBG *020

RIDGEWAY, Joseph A, IV. 1430 S HIGH ST 43207 #038-40-1989 L1991 DR *020 †80

RIEBEL, Matthew Ryan. 941 CHATHAM LN, STE 110 43221 #038-43-1999 L1999 U *020 †95

RIEMENSCHNEIDER, H W. 4845 KNIGHTSBRIDGE BLVD, STE 200 43214 #038-40-1965 L1965 U *020 †95

RIEMER, Kristen Michelle. ■ 43204 #038-40-2008 *012

RIGSBY, William Carl. 1800 ZOLLINGER RD STE 9 43221 #038-40-1957 L1957 GYN *071 †30

RIKABI, Ali Ahmed. 1654 UPHAM DR, 630 MEANS HALL 43210 #528-01-1982 L1999 DR *020 †80

RILEY, Thomas Roberts. ■ 43204 #038-40-1960 L1960 IM END *020

RINDLER, Julie Pauline. 340 E TOWN ST, PHYSICAL MEDICINE 43215 #038-40-1987 L1989 PM *020 †60

RINGEL, Matthew David. 456 W 10TH AVE 43210 #041-14-1991 L2003 END *050 †20

RINK, Britton Delaney. 700 CHILDRENS DR, CHILDREN'S HOSP COLUMBUS 43205 #017-20-2002 L2002 MG *012

RISCILI, Brent Paul. 1654 UPHAM DR, 207 MEANS HALL 43210 #035-06-2003 L2003 PCC *012 †20

RISE, Leroy Peri. 410 W 10TH AVE, RM N1050 43210 #011-03-2004 L2004 ORS *012

RISTOW, Ryan Randall. ■ 43235 #038-43-2002 L2002 FM *020 †18

RIZER, Milisa K. 2231 N HIGH ST 43201 #038-41-1983 L1986 FM *020 †18

RO, Pamela Sue. 700 CHILDRENS DR, CHILDREN'S HOSPITAL-CARDIO 43205 #016-06-1994 L2001 PDC *020 †55

ROACH, Ewell Steve. 700 CHILDRENS DR, DIV OF CHILD NEUROLOGY ED5 43205 #047-06-1975 L2006 CHN *020 †55,75

ROBBINS, Cynthia Lynn. 700 CHILDRENS DR, SECTION OF NEONATOLOGY 43205 #038-06-2004 L2004 PD *100 †55

ROBBINS, Malcolm Lee. 1021 COUNTRY CLUB RD, STE A 43213 #023-01-1952 L1957 PD *071 †55

ROBERTS, Aaron Michael. 3705 OLENTANGY RIVER RD, MAX SPORTS INSTITUTE 43214 #654-01-2004 L2004 FSM *012 †18

ROBERTS, John Bloom. 2050 KENNY RD, STE 300 43221 #016-06-1956 L1960 ORS *071 †40

ROBERTS, William Boyd. 1336 E MAIN ST 43205 #038-45-1993 L1994 FM *020 †18

ROBERTS, William David. 410 W 10TH AVE, DEPARTMENT OF ANESTHESIA 43210 #038-40-2002 L2002 AN *100 †15

ROBERTSON, Matthew Scott. ■ 43212 #038-40-2008 *012

ROBINSON, John L. 410 W 10TH AVE, THE OHIO STATE UNIVERSITY 43210 #035-01-1961 L1963 CD IM *062 †20

ROBINSON, Julian H. 1430 S HIGH ST 43207 #047-07-1950 L1954 **IM** *071

ROBINSON, Paul Steven. ■ 43228 #038-43-2007 L2007 **EM** *012

ROBINSON, Steven Lynn. 4661 SAWMILL RD, STE 100 43220 #038-40-1988 L1992 **PS** *020 †85,65

ROBINSON-PILBEAN, Pamela. 793 W STATE ST 43222 #038-40-1985 L1990 **AN** *020 †05

ROCCO, Henry D. 2050 KENNY RD 3RD FL, OSU MED CTR DEPT ORTHO 43221 #038-40-1962 L1962 **ORS** *020 †40

ROCKWELL, Lynn Mason. ■ 43221 #047-06-2001 L2005 **CHP** *100

ROCK-WILLOUGHBY, Jayme Ly. 3535 OLENTANGY RIVER RD, RIVERSIDE METHODIST HOSP 43214 #038-75-2006, ▲ L2006 **IM** *012

RODABAUGH, Galon S. ■ 43229 #038-40-1939 L1939 **AN** *071 †05

RODWAY, Nancy V. 1492 E BROAD ST 43205 #038-40-1986 L1988 **OM** *020 †50,70

ROGERS, Alan David. 410 W 10TH AVE, 635 MEANS HALL 43210 #038-41-2002 L2003 **DR** *100 †80

ROGERS, Barbara Maher. 410 W 10TH AVE, DEPT OF ANESTHESIA 43210 #038-40-1995 L1996 **AN** *020 †05

ROGERS, David Lorenzo. 555 S 18TH ST STE 4C, PEDIATRIC OPHTHALMOLOGY AS 43205 #038-45-2002 L2007 **OPH** *100 †35

ROGERS, Nicholas Andrew. ■ 43202 #038-40-2006 L2006 **OBG** *012

ROGERS, Peter Damien. 700 CHILDRENS DR, CHILDRENS HOSP-ADOLESCENT 43205 #047-06-1970 L1974 **PD ADL** *012

ROGERS, Philip Alan. 3555 OLENTANGY RIVER RD 43214 #038-40-1973 L1973 **GYN** *071 †30

ROHANINEJAD, Mohammadreza. 410 W 10TH AVE, OHIO STATE UNIV 43210 #517-01-1999 L2007 **GS** *012

ROHL, Jacqueline Tran. 456 W 10TH AVE, STE 2B 43210 #038-44-1996 L1999 **OBG** *020 †30

ROHNER, Ralph Geo, Jr. 3600 OLENTANGY RIVR RD #C1 43214 #038-40-1964 L1964 **ORS** *020 †40

ROHYANS, Jo Ann. 4775 KNIGHTSBRIDGE BLVD, STE 207 43214 #038-40-1979 L1982 **PD** *020 †55

ROMANELLI, Vincent A. 2941 KENNY RD, STE 110 43221 #035-19-1983 L1986 **AN** *020 †05

ROMEO, Freddie P. 750 MOUNT CARMEL MALL, STE 220 43222 #038-40-1990 L1993 **P** *020 †75

ROSADO-DE-CHRISTENSON, M. 1654 UPHAM DR, 630 MEANS HALL 43210 #023-12-1980 L1982 **DR** *020

ROSE, David Michael. ■ 43207 #023-12-2006 L2006 **PD** *012

ROSE, Stewart Mc Clellan. 4830 KNIGHTSBRIDGE BLVD #A 43214 #038-40-1955 L1955 **CD IM** *071

ROSEN, Heather Lynn. ■ 43209 #104-01-2004 L2006 **FP** *012

ROSENFELD, Rachel A. 700 CHILDRENS DR, AMBULATORY PEDIATRICS CHIL 43205 #048-02-1995 L1998 **PEM** *020 †55

ROSENSTEIN, Patricia Fine. 700 CHILDRENS DR 43205 #038-45-1991 L1994 **PD** *020 †55

ROSENTHAL, Joseph Aaron. ■ 43220 #007-02-2006 L2006 **PM** *012

ROSS, Mary Elizabeth. 700 CHILDRENS DR RM WA5022, COLUMBUS CHILDRENS HOSP 43205 #035-06-1997 L2005 **PHO** *050 †55

ROSSEL, Charles Wm. 5311 CHATHAM LN 43221 #038-40-1955 L1955 **NS AM** *071 †25

ROSSI, Thomas Anthony. 340 E TOWN ST, PHYSICAL MEDICINE 43215 #038-40-1991 L1992 **PM OS** *020 †60

ROTH, Andrew Harry. ■ 43221 #038-43-2001 L2001 **AN** *100 †05

ROTHE, William S, III. 6001 E BROAD ST 43213 #038-44-1995 L1998 **EM** *020 †16

ROTHERMEL, William S, Jr. 4885 OLENTANGY RIVER RD, STE 230 43214 #038-40-1973 L1973 **GS** *020 †85

ROTT, Danielle Elana. 1670 UPHAM DR 43210 #038-40-2005 L2005 **P** *012

ROVIN, Brad Harris. 1654 UPHAM DR, NEPHROLOGY 43210 #016-11-1983 L1990 **NEP IM** *030 †20

ROWLAND, Daniel Gerard. 700 CHILDRENS DR, CHILDREN'S HOSPITAL 43205 #035-45-1987 L1993 **PD** *020 †55

ROWLAND, Dennis W. 1875 MILLIKIN RD, OHIO STATE UNIVERSITY 43210 #020-02-1965 L1971 **IM** *071

ROWLAND, Timothy Everett. 697 THOMAS LN 43214 #038-40-2004 L2004 **FM** *020 †18

ROY, Richard Arnold. 85 MCNAUGHTEN RD, STE 350 43213 #035-06-1980 L1990 **U** *020 †95

ROYLANCE, Erin R. 1670 UPHAM DR 43210 #018-75-2004, ▲ L2004 **P** *012

ROYSE, Thomas Lloyd. 4606 SAWMILL RD 43040 #038-40-1983 L1985 **AN IM** *020 †20,05

RUBERG, Robert Lionel. 410 W 10TH AVE, DOAN HALL N-809 43210 #024-01-1967 L1975 **PS GS** *040 †85,65

RUBINO, Julie Marie. 1021 COUNTRY CLUB RD 43213 #038-44-1993 L1994 **PD** *020 †55

RUEGSEGGER, Nutan Khosla. 111 S GRANT AVE STE 116, GRANT FAM PRAC RES 43215 #759-12-2001 L2002 **FM** *020 †18

RUFF, Michael Edward. 3400 OLENTANGY RIVER RD, STE 200 43202 #038-40-1979 L1980 **HS ORS** *020 †40

RUFF, Paul David. 410 W 10TH AVE 43210 #038-40-1973 L1973 **CD IM** *020 †20

RUFF, Victoria Nikolaidis. 3535 OLENTANGY RIVER RD 43214 #038-40-1978 L1980 **CCM IM** *020

RUFFIN, Richard D. ■ 43221 #047-07-1953 L1958 **U** *071

RUIZ, Oscar R. 3545 OLENTANGY RIVER RD, STE 525 43214 #429-01-1979 L1991 **GS CCS** *020 †85

RUND, Douglas Andrew. 450 W 10TH AVE, OHIO STATE UNIVERSITY HOSP 43210 #005-11-1971 L1976 **EM FM** *020 †16,18

RUNDELL, Kristen Bolton. 797 THOMAS LN 43214 #007-02-1997 L2006 **FM** *020 †18

RUPERT, Robert Dean, Jr. 1492 E BROAD ST, OSU HOSPITALS EAST 43205 #038-40-1987 L1988 **ON HEM** *020

RUPP, Germain H. 5877 CLEVELAND AVE 43231 #028-34-1968 L1969 **A PD** *020 †55,03

RUPPEL, Dennis Franklin. 2150 MARBLE CLIFF OFC PARK 43215 #038-40-1980 L1981 **FM** *040 †18

RUSIN, Jerome Allan. 700 CHILDRENS DR 43205 #010-01-1981 L1995 **PDR PD** *020 †55,80

RUSS, John Steve. 1080 BEECHER XING N, NORTHEAST OB GYN INC 43230 #038-40-1977 L1977 **OBG** *020 †30

RUSSELL, Matthew Douglas. 3535 OLENTANGY RIVER RD 43214 #038-43-2005 L2005 **IM** *012

RUSSO, John. 700 CHILDRENS DR 43205 #016-11-1998 L2004 **PG** *020

RUTECKI, Gregory Wm. 793 W STATE ST, MT CARMEL HOSPITAL WEST 43222 #016-11-1974 L1982 **IM NEP** *020 †20

RUTHERFORD, James Herbert. 285 E STATE ST STE 610 43215 #038-40-1968 L1968 **ORS** *020 †40

RUYMANN, Frederick Beeman. 700 CHILDRENS DR 43205 #005-06-1962 L1982 **PHO ON** *071 †55

RYAN, James Michael. 473 W 12TH AVE, STE 200 43210 #038-40-1979 L1985 **CD** *020 †20

RYAN, John Thomas. 1171 FAIRWAY BLVD, FAIRWAY FAMILY PHYSICIANS 43213 #038-40-1998 L2001 **FM** *020 †18

RYAN, Margaret Stang. ■ 43212 #038-40-2008 L2008 *012

RYAN, Maria U. ■ 43215 #407-19-1941 L1950 **GP** *071

RYAN, Patricia Ann. 700 CHILDRENS DR - ED650, CHILDREN'S HOSPITAL 43205 #038-41-2005 L2005 **MPD** *012

RYAN, Thomas John. 473 W 12TH AVE, STE 100 43210 #017-20-1981 L2007 **CD** *030 †20

RYAN, Valerie Amber. 1654 UPHAM DR, OHIO STATE UNIV MED CTR 43210 #048-15-2006 L2006 **OBG** *012

RYAZANSKY, Irina. 4310 CLIME RD STE B, SOUTHWESTERN INTERNAL MEDI 43228 #913-35-1983 L1997 **IM** *020 †20

RYOO, Cherie. ■ 43206 #016-11-2005 L2005 **OTO** *012

SABOL, David Andrew. 777 W STATE ST, OHIO GASTROENTEROLOGY 43222 #038-43-1998 L2004 **GE** *020 †20

SABOL, Elizabeth Ann. 1080 BEECHER XING N, NORTHEAST OB GYN INC 43230 #045-01-2000 L2004 **OBG** *020

SADAKA, Akram. 1492 E BROAD ST # 1405 43205 #875-01-1981 L1985 **FM OM** *020 †70

SADAR, Edward Stephan. ■ 43206 #038-06-1968 L1968 **NS** *071 †25

SADEQ, Adnan M.A. 1375 PERRY ST RM 5, CO OSU HOSPS-MED EDU DEPT 43201 #919-05-1992 L2000 **GS** *012

SAFAR, Aida. 410 W 10TH AVE, OSU MEDICAL CENTER 43210 #875-02-1986 L1997 **PTH HMP** *020 †50

SAGE, Harry Morton, Jr. ■ 43220 #038-40-1943 L1944 **OPH** *071 †35

SAGE, Kevin James. 1087 DENNISON AVE 43201 #018-75-2004, ▲ L2004 **AN** *012

SAGONE, Arthur L, Jr. 410 W 10TH AVE 43210 #041-12-1963 L1970 **HEM ON** *020 †20

SAHA, Lakhan Kumar. 285 E STATE ST, STE 360 43215 #160-07-1978 L1991 **NEP IM** *020 †20

SAHA, Sumita. ■ 43204 #010-02-2006 L2006 **GS** *012

SAHENK, Zarife. 700 CHILDRENS DR, RM WA3024 43205 #902-05-1972 L1978 **N** *050 †75

SAINI, Naveen Chandra. ■ 43212 #004-01-2006 L2007 **DR** *012

SAINI, Vijay Singh. 1087 DENNISON AVE 43201 #654-01-1997 L2000 **FM** *020 †18

SAKIN, Caner. 370 W 9TH AVE, 200A MEILING HALL 43210 #038-40-2006 L2006 **IM** *012

SALAMA, Meriam Salama Mou. 410 W 10TH AVE 43210 #915-02-2003 L2007 **P** *100

SALAMON, Thomas. 85 MCNAUGHTEN RD, STE 110 43213 #038-43-1994 L1997 **TS** *020 †85,90

SALAZAR, Luis Demetris. ■ 43219 #019-02-2007 L2007 **FP** *012

SALEEM, Zakaria. ■ 43230 #704-21-1996 L2006 **NEP** *012 †20

SALIM, Muhammad Faisal. 700 CHILDRENS DR, CHILDRENS HOSP 43205 #704-16-2000 L2007 **CHN** *012

SALON, Jeffrey Eric. 625 CLEVELAND AVE 43215 #017-20-1980 L1991 **CCM IM** *062 †20

SALT, William Bradley, II. 777 W STATE ST STE 400, OHIO GASTROENTEROLOGY GROU 43222 #038-40-1972 L1972 **GE IM** *020 †20

SALTZ, Joel Haskin. 333 W 10TH AVE, 3190 GRAVES HALL 43210 #036-07-1985 L2002 **PTH** *050 †50

SAMADDER, Anjana. 99 N BRICE RD, STE 100 43213 #495-02-1988 L1996 **GE** *020 †20

SAMADDER, Gautam Kumar. 99 N BRICE RD, STE 1 43213 #495-47-1984 L1995 **PUD** *020 †20

SAMODELOV, Leonid F. 5100 W BROAD ST, ANESTHESIA DOCTORS HOSP.WE 43228 #409-25-1984 L1993 **AN** *020 †05

SAMS, Jeffrey Steven. 150 TAYLOR STATION RD #290 43213 #038-40-1978 L1987 **GE IM** *020 †20

SAMUEL, Mervyn J. 5910 CLEVELAND AVE 43231 #495-27-1965 L1973 **OBG** *020 †30

SAMUEL, Milroy J. 793 W STATE ST 43222 #047-07-1997 L1998 **OBG** *020 †30

SAMUELS, Michael Andrew. 262 NEIL AVE, STE 220 43215 #024-07-1988 L1992 **RO** *020 †80

SAMUELS, Philip. 1654 UPHAM DR DEPT OBG, 5TH FL MEANS HALL 43210 #048-15-1980 L1982 **MFM OBS** *040 †30

SANCHEZ, Angelita Rodrigu. 410 W 10TH AVE 43210 #748-10-1991 L2000 **CHP** *100 †75 ‡

SANCHEZ SOTO, Carlos Enri. 3535 OLENTANGY RIVER RD 43214 #429-01-2004 L2006 **IM** *012

SANDERS, Christopher Ian. ■ 43202 #038-40-2008 *012

SANDERSON, Alan Blake. ■ 43220 #038-40-2008 *012

SANDHOLM, Patricia Hahn. ■ 43221 #035-15-2003 L2003 **PS** *012

SANEHOLTZ, William Eugene. 3535 OLENTANGY RIVER RD 43214 #038-40-1957 L1957 **AN** *071

SANGVAI, Shilpa Gangadhar. 700 CHILDRENS DR, AMBULATORY PEDIATRICS 43205 #038-45-1998 L2003 **PD** *020 †55

SANHAJI, Mounir. 1087 DENNISON AVE 43201 #655-03-1998 L2002 **FM** *100 †18

SANT, Dhanawanti. 1021 COUNTRY CLUB RD STE A 43213 #038-40-1994 L1995 **PD** *020 †55

SANTAEMMA, Philip Harry. 1144 DUBLIN RD 43215 #038-40-1988 L1989 **FM** *020 †18

SANTIAGO, Michelle Casino. ■ 43201 #016-11-2006 L2007 **AN** *012

SANTILLI, Scott Ralph. ■ 43212 #038-40-2008 *012

SANTIN, Brian Joseph. ■ 43206 #038-40-2006 L2006 **GS** *012

SANTOS, Alexia Beatriz. ■ 43205 #429-02-1998 L2002 **PDC** *100

SANTOS, Augusto Abad. 1430 S HIGH ST 43207 #748-01-1962 L1971 **AN** *072

SANTOYO-STEIN, Maria C. 1631 NW PROFESSIONAL PLZ 43220 #649-02-1963 L1976 **AN OS** *071 †05

SANYIKA, Mwawaza Mfikiri. 4480 REFUGEE RD, STE 102 43232 #038-45-1998 L2000 **FM** *020 †18

SARAN, Manish. 1087 DENNISON AVE 43201 #422-01-1998 L2000 **P** *100

SARIKAYA, Ismet. 1654 UPHAM DR 60, OHIO STATE UNIVERSITY MEDI 43210 #902-03-1990 L2003 **NM** *020 †28

SARIN, Tony B. 5969 E BROAD ST, STE 401 43213 #957-01-1967 L1975 **OBG** *020 †30

SARKAR, Atom. ■ 43206 #011-02-1998 L2006 **NS** *100

SARTAWI, Rami Tariq. ■ 43201 #038-40-2007 L2007 **TY** *012

SARWAR, Shakir S. 340 E TOWN ST, STE 8-200 43215 #704-07-1992 L2004 **HO** *020 †20

SATEREN, Stanley Gene. 5900 ROCHE DR STE 440 43229 #016-06-1969 L1973 **IM ADM** *020 †20 ‡

SATIANI, Bhagwan. 285 E STATE ST, STE 260 43215 #704-02-1971 L1977 **VS** *020 †85

SAUERS, Adelaide E. 700 CHILDRENS DR 43205 #038-06-1951 L1951 **PD** *071 †55

SAULS, Bryan Auston. 3525 OLENTANGY RIVER RD, STE 4330 43214 #055-02-2005 L2005 **IM** *012

SAUNDERS, William H. 456 W 10TH AVE, UNIV OTOLARYNGOLOGISTS INC 43210 #018-03-1943 L1954 **OTO** *071 †45

SAVAGE, Lily. ■ 43235 #038-45-1996 L1997 **IM** *020

SAVAGEAU, Andrew Carl. ■ 43202 #038-40-2008 *012

SAVEANU, Radu Vasile. 1670 UPHAM DR, STE 130 43210 #024-07-1981 L1998 **P** *030 †75

SAVEANU, Traian Ioan. ■ 43221 #781-01-1953 L1984 **GPM** *071

SAWCHYN, Gregory Ivan. ■ 43235 #038-40-2006 *012

SAWHNEY-AMAZAN, Susan. 410 W 10TH AVE, OSU HOSPITALS 43210 #495-08-1981 L1992 **AN IM** *020 †05

SAWYER, David Matthew. 793 W STATE ST, MOUNT CARMEL MEDICAL CENTE 43222 #051-04-1986 L1993 **AN PME** *020 †05

SAWYER, Margaret Sterrett. 410 W 10TH AVE, 316-A MEANS HALL 43210 #038-40-2002 L2002 **GS** *012

SAYAT, Jason G. 1315 W LANE AVE 43221 #038-40-1998 L1999 **OBG** *020 †30

SAYAT, Linbee Valencia. 456 W 10TH AVE, STE 2B 43210 #038-40-1999 L2000 **OBG** *020

SAYERS, Martin Peter. ■ 43221 #038-40-1945 L1945 **NS N** *071 †25

SAYMEH, Layth Akram. 5131 BEACON HILL RD, STE 200 43228 #875-03-1991 L2005 **GE** *020 †20

SAYRE, Michael Richard. 1654 UPHAM DR 43210 #038-41-1984 L1990 **EM** *020 †16

SCANSEN, Kimberly Anne. ■ 43228 #025-07-2003 L2003 **PEM** *012 †55

SCARBROUGH, Stephen D. 4606 SAWMILL RD 43220 #038-40-1974 L1974 **AN IM** *020 †20,05

SCARBROUGH, Timothy L. 2240 N BANK DR, UPPR 43220 #038-45-1982 L1983 **AN** *020 †05

SCHAAL, Stephen Frederick. 473 W 12TH AVE 2ND FL 43210 #038-40-1964 L1964 **CD IM** *040 †20

SCHAEFFER, Karl Ira. 5969 E BROAD ST, STE 401 43213 #041-01-1972 L1973 **OBG OS** *020 †30

SCHAFFERNOCKER, Troy A. ■ 43235 #038-40-2002 L2002 **PCC** *012 †20

SCHAFFIR, Jonathan A. 456 W 10TH AVE, STE 2B 43210 #043-01-1990 L2000 **OBG** *020 †30 ‡

SCHARRE, Douglas Wm. 1654 UPHAM DR, OHIO STATE UNIVERSITY 43210 #010-02-1983 L1993 **N** *020 †75

SCHAUB, Eric Andrew. 86 N WILSON RD 43204 #038-44-1985 L1987 **OM IM** *020 †20,70

SCHECKELHOFF, Sara Christ. ■ 43228 #038-40-2007 **EM** *012

SCHEIBE, Trenton J. 2231 N HIGH ST, RARDIN FAMILY PRAC 43201 #048-14-2002 L2006 **FP** *012

SCHELL, Michael Todd. 370 W 9TH AVE, OH STATE U COLL OF MED 43210 #038-40-2000 **GS** *012

SCHERZER, Daniel J. 700 CHILDRENS DR, SECTION OF EMERGENCY MEDIC 43205 #043-01-1989 L1994 **PD PEM** *020 †55

SCHIFF, Keith Aaron. 410 W 10TH AVE 43210 #045-01-2005 L2005 **AN** *012

SCHLESSEL, Kevin Dale. 1211 DUBLIN RD, COLUMBUS ARTHRITIS CENTER 43215 #038-43-1986 L1987 **RHU IM** *020 †20

SCHLONSKY, Joseph. 5969 E BROAD ST STE 402 43213 #038-40-1966 L1966 **ORS** *020 †40

SCHLOSS, Brian Steven. ■ 43228 #038-40-2007 **EM** *012

SCHLOSS, Charles David. 793 W STATE ST 43222 #041-02-1958 L1959 **R RO** *071 †80

SCHMELING, John Arthur. 3900 E LIVINGSTON AVE 43227 #041-12-1984 L1985 **FM** *020 †18

SCHMERLER, Betsy Lynn. 700 CHILDRENS DR, DEPT OF EMERGENCY MEDICINE 43205 #036-01-1997 L2000 **PEM** *020 †55

SCHMIDT, Catherine Ann. 6075 E BROAD ST 43213 #038-40-1992 L1993 **OBG** *071 †30

SCHMIDT, David William. 3535 OLENTANGY RIVER RD, RMH EMERGENCY DEPARTMENT 43214 #025-01-1998 L2002 **EM** *020 †16

SCHMIDT, Grant. 4830 KNIGHTSBRIDGE BLVD 43214 #028-03-1976 L1981 **REN OBG** *020 †30

SCHMIDT, Hernan Saml. 1910 CROWN PARK CT, STONEBUINER ARTHUR & ASSOC 43235 #005-12-1976 L1977 **P** *012

SCHNABEL, David Charles. 370 W 9TH AVE, OH STATE U COLL OF MED 43210 #038-40-2002 L2004 **GPM** *020 †70

SCHNEIER, Andrew Jacob. ■ 43201 #038-40-2008 *012

SCHNEIR, Steven Richard. 5965 E BROAD ST STE 230, HARDING-OHIO STATE UNIV 43213 #038-40-1982 L1983 **P** *020 †75

SCHNOSE, Christina Marie. ■ 43219 #019-02-2007 L2007 **IM** *012

SCHOECH, Michael Robert. ■ 43221 #038-41-2006 L2006 **IM** *012

SCHOEFF, Jonathan Eric. ■ 43202 #038-41-2004 L2004 **GS** *012

SCHOEN, Anne Beyer. ■ 43206 #038-40-2005 L2005 **IM** *012

SCHOTTENSTEIN, Michael S. 2700 E MAIN ST STE 206 43209 #038-40-1992 L1994 **P CHP** *020 †75

SCHREINER, Andrew David. ■ 43206 #038-40-2008 *012

SCHROER, Brian Carl. 1654 UPHAM DR, 215 MEANS HALL 43210 #011-04-2004 L2004 **MPD** *012

SCHUDA, Marian. 3535 OLENTANGY RIVER RD 43214 #038-40-1979 L1980 **IM IMG** *030 †20,16

SCHULLER, David Edward. 456 W 10TH AVE, RM 4110 43210 #038-40-1970 L1970 **OTO** *020 †45

SCHULTE, Gregory Todd. 2050 KENNY RD, 7TH FL 43221 #038-40-1991 L1992 **PME AN** *020

SCHULTZ, Norman E, Jr. 3535 OLENTANGY RIVER RD, RIVERSIDE METHODIST HOSPIT 43214 #038-45-1995 L1996 **EM** *020 †16

SCHUMACHER, Douglas Ray. 1275 OLENTANGY RIVER RD, STE 202 43212 #038-40-1990 L1992 **FM** *012

SCHUSTER, Andreas Walter. 930 BETHEL RD, OHIO SURGERY CENTER 43214 #038-40-1988 L1989 **AN** *020 †20,05

SCHWAB, Katherine Varda. ■ 43212 #025-12-2004 L2004 **OBG** *012

SCHWARTZ, David Solomon. 3341 E LIVINGSTON AVE, STE L 43227 #023-01-1966 L1974 **GS** *071 †85

SCHWARTZ, Lawrence Israel. 700 CHILDRENS DR 43205 #041-12-1995 L2005 **AN CCP** *020 †05,55

SCHWARTZ, Randall M. 700 CHILDRENS DR, DEPT OF CARDIOLOGY 43205 #041-02-2000 L2000 **CCP** *100 †55

SCHWARTZ, Sarah Boehmer. 697 THOMAS LN 43214 #038-40-2006 L2006 **FP** *012

SCHWARTZ, Wm Burnside. ■ 43221 #038-40-1948 L1948 **R DR** *071 †80

SCHWARZELL, John Richard. 1492 E BROAD ST STE 1402 43205 #038-40-1965 L1965 **GS** *020 †85

SCOTT, Mary Elizabeth. 4488 W BROAD ST 43228 #038-44-1997 L1998 **FM** *020 †18

SEAMON, Leigh. 320 W 10TH AVE, M210 STARLING LOVING, 43210 #028-78-2000, ▲ L2006 **OBG** *020

SEARCY, Gregory Dale. 5965 E BROAD ST, STE 490 43213 #038-40-1995 L1999 **OPH** *020 †35

SEASON, Edwin Herbert, III. 1492 E BROAD ST STE 1303 43205 #038-40-1971 L1971 **ORS** *020 †40

SEAVOLT, Jason Edwin. 3535 OLENTANGY RIVER RD, RIVERSIDE RADIATION ONCOLO 43214 #038-43-1997 L1998 **RO** *020 †80

SECADA-LOVIO, Orestes O. ■ 43209 #847-10-1974 **P** *074

SECK, Nisha Gala. ■ 43235 #056-05-2005 L2006 **AN** *012

SEELANDT, Charles M. 2541 RIVER OAKS DR 43228 #038-40-2001 L2001 **AN** *100 †05

SEGAL, Mark Louis. 745 W STATE ST, STE 550B 43222 #038-40-1976 L1979 **IM HO** *020 †20

SEGMILLER, William Chas. 1800 ZOLLINGER RD 43221 #041-01-1958 L1961 **P** *071

SEGUIN, John Hector. 3555 OLENTANGY RIVER RD, STE 3050 43214 #038-41-1980 L1981 **NPM** *020 †55

SEIDENSTICKER, Gregory L. 111 S GRANT AVE 43215 #038-40-2001 L2003 **EM** *020 †16

SEIDT, Richard Julius, II. 111 S GRANT AVE 43215 #038-45-2002 L2002 **FM** *020 †18

SEILER, Stephanie Joyce. ■ 43204 #038-40-2006 L2006 **IM** *012

SELMAN, Alberto Elias. 505 MEANS HALL, OSU MED CTR 43210 #231-01-1987 *100

SETTY, Naveen Chandra. 370 W 9TH AVE, OH STATE U COLL OF MED 43210 #038-40-2001 L2001 **HS** *100

SEVERYN, Steven Anthony. 2050 KENNY RD, OHIO STATE SPINE CENTER 43221 #038-40-1980 L1980 **PME AN** *020 †20

SEWARD, Shelly Marie. ■ 43228 #051-07-2004 L2004 **OBG** *012

SEYERLE, John Robert. ■ 43209 #038-40-2002 L2002 **PD** *100

SHABSIGH, Ahmad. 456 W 10TH AVE, DEPRT OF UROLOGY, 4960 CRA 43210 #875-02-1995 L2005 **U** *012

SHADCHEHR, Ali. ■ 43220 #517-01-1967 L1991 **IM GE** *071 †20

SHAFFER, Michael Wesley. ■ 43224 #038-40-2007 L2007 **FP** *012

SHAH, Ali Ahsen. 410 W 10TH AVE, DEPT IM 43210 #041-15-2007 L2007 **PM** *012

SHAH, Asha Dinesh. ■ 43235 #038-44-2005 L2005 **U** *012

SHAH, Ashish Raju. 6001 E BROAD ST 43213 #038-40-2001 L2001 **OTO** *020 †45

SHAH, Bipinchandra N. 3545 OLENTANGY RIVER RD 43214 #495-22-1967 L1982 **U** *020

SHAH, Bivik. 6499 E BROAD ST, STE 130 43213 #038-40-1994 L1995 **GS PS** *020 †65

SHAH, Kaushal J. 285 E STATE ST, STE 260 43215 #033-06-1998 L2007 **VS** *020 †85

SHAH, Ketul Kirtikumar. CREDEN2050 KENNY, CO CORPORATE 43221 #495-96-1997 L2007 **GS** *012

SHAH, Manisha Himatlal. 320 W 10TH AVE, 438A STARLING-LOVING HALL 43210 #495-76-1990 L1997 **HO IM** *020 †20

SHAH, Mrunal Shirish. 697 THOMAS LN, RIVERSIDE FAMILY PRACTICE 43214 #038-44-1997 L1998 **FM** *040 †18

SHAH, Mukesh Ratilal. 5969 E BROAD ST, STE 202 43213 #495-76-1976 L1984 **CD CCM** *020 †20 ‡

SHAH, Sonal Dhananjai. ■ 43215 #038-40-2008 *012

SHAH, Zarine Ketul. ■ 43235 #495-96-1998 *100

SHALWITZ, Robert Alan. 625 CLEVELAND AVE 43215 #035-06-1980 L1996 **PDE PD** *020 †55

SHANAAH, Arwa Y. 410 W 10TH AVE, E 310 DOAN HALL 43210 #575-01-1989 L1999 **BBK HMP** *020 †50

SHANK, Craig Francis. 793 W STATE ST, MOUNT CARMEL MEDICAL CENTE 43222 #038-43-2004 L2004 **ORS** *012

SHANKER, Pradheep Jothi. 3525 OLENTANGY RIVER RD, STE 5360 43214 #665-01-2000 L2007 **DR** *100 †80

SHANKS, William Ronald. ■ 43235 #038-44-2006 L2006 **GS** *012

SHAO, Yanfu. 410 W 10TH AVE, 416 N. DOAN 43210 #243-38-1982 L2000 **AN** *020 †05

SHAPIRO, Charles Louis. 320 W 10TH AVE, HOSP/B421 STARLING-LOVING 43210 #035-06-1984 L1998 **ON IM** *050 †20

SHAREEF, Mohammed R. 393 E TOWN ST STE 115 43215 #495-65-1978 L1982 **PUD** *020 †20

SHAREEF, Nayyar F. 393 E TOWN ST, STE 115 43215 #495-57-1982 L1994 **FM** *020 †18

SHARKIS, David Harold. 770 JASONWAY AVE STE G2, JASONWAY INTERNAL MEDI 43214 #038-40-1991 L1997 **IM** *020 †20

SHARMA, Animesh. 6001 E BROAD ST 43213 #038-44-1994 L1997 **IM** *020 †20

SHARMA, Hari M. 2000 KENNY RD 43221 #495-05-1961 L1973 **PTH** *071 †50

SHARMA, Randhir. ■ 43201 #038-45-2003 L2003 **FM** *020 †18

SHARMA, Tarang. ■ 43232 #495-45-1996 L2003 **IM** *100 †20

SHARP, David Scott. 456 W 10TH AVE, 4839 CRAMBLETT MEDICAL CLI 43210 #048-04-1999 L1999 **U** *100

SHATNAWI, Raed Ali. ■ 43205 #575-02-1996 L2003 *020

SHEARES, Reuben A, III. 423 E TOWN ST, STE 1000 43215 #048-04-1981 L1991 **CD IM** *020 †20

SHEEHAN, Mara Elisabeth. 793 W STATE ST, MT CARMEL MED CTR 43222 #154-07-1999 L2005 **IM** *012

SHEHADI, Joseph A. 393 E TOWN ST STE 110 43215 #035-45-1993 L2002 **NS** *020 †25

SHEIKH, Shahid I. 700 CHILDRENS DR, DIV OF PULMONARY MEDICINE 43205 #704-05-1984 L1999 **PDP AI** *020 †03,55

SHELL, Richard Davis. 700 CHILDRENS DR, DEPT PEDIATRIC PULMONOLOGY 43205 #038-43-1993 L1994 **PDP** *020 †55

SHELL, Stephen Dennis. 5969 E BROAD ST 43213 #038-40-1969 L1969 **IM DIA** *020 †20

SHELLHAAS, Cynthia S. 1654 UPHAM DR, ROOM 535 MEANS HALL 43210 #038-44-1988 L1989 **OBG MFM** *020 †30

SHELLMAN, Sondra Ann. 1492 E BROAD ST 43205 #038-40-1994 L1997 **EM** *020 †16

SHEN, Rulong. 410 W 10TH AVE, STE 310 43210 #243-93-1981 L2000 **PCP** *020 †50

SHENK, Allison Marie. ■ 43215 #038-40-2008 *012

SHEPHERD, Edward Geoffrey. 700 CHILDRENS DR 43205 #048-13-1999 L1999 **PD** *020 †55

SHEPHERD, Larry Mason. 1495 MORSE RD 43229 #051-04-1981 L1985 **PD** *020 †20

SHERIDAN, Brendan Patrick. 1654 UPHAM DR, 146 MEANS 43210 #038-41-2004 L2004 **EM** *020

SHERMAN, Jason Richard. ■ 43228 #038-45-2004 L2004 **PM** *012

SHERMAN, Marion Eleanor. 2200 W BROAD ST 43223 #038-06-1985 L1997 **CHP P** *020 †75

SHIDHAM, Ganesh Baburao. 1654 UPHAM DR, NEPHROLOGY 43210 #495-83-1984 L2002 **NEP** *020 †20

SHIDHAM, Shubhangi Ganesh. 793 W STATE ST, CO MT CARMEL HOSP-MED EDU 43222 #495-83-1991 L2003 **END** *020 †20

SHIELS, Wm Eugene, II. 700 CHILDRENS DR, DEPT OF RADIOLOGY 43205 #041-77-1983, ▲ L1988 **PDR DR** *020 †80

SHIM, Rose Lin. 1654 UPHAM DR, NEPHROLOGY 43210 #038-40-2001 L2001 **NEP** *100

SHISILA, David Alan. ■ 43221 #038-40-2006 L2006 **PD** *012

SHIVELY, Wyant Jos. 111 S GRANT AVE DEPT PATH 43215 #041-02-1954 L1955 **PTH** *020 †50

SHNEKER, Bassel Fawzi. 1654 UPHAM DR, DEPT OF NEUROLOGY 43210 #875-01-1994 L2002 **N** *020 †75

SHOAPS, Paul Ethan. 5969 E BROAD ST, STE 200 43213 #038-43-1998 L1999 **MPD** *020 †20,55

SHOCKLEY, Joel Alan. 866 W BROAD ST 43222 #038-40-1997 L1999 **R** *020 †80

SHOEMAKER, Lance Heston. 3545 OLENTANGY RIVER RD, STE 226 43214 #038-40-1997 L1999 **GS** *020 †85

SHOEMAKER, Larry Wayne. 1555 BETHEL RD 43220 #038-40-1965 L1965 **P** *020

SHONKWILER, Ronald Joseph, II. ■ 43085 #035-01-2008 *012

SHOOK, Scott Lewis. PO BOX 18322 43218 #038-45-1988 **P PYA** *100

SHOTT, Julie Zwiesler. 697 THOMAS LN 43214 #038-40-2005 L2005 **FP** *012

SHULTZ, John Phillip. 2999 E DUBLIN GRANVILLE RD 43231 #038-40-1958 L1958 **PD** *071 †55

SHUTTLEWORTH, Edwin C, Jr. 410 W 10TH AVE 43210 #035-03-1962 L1966 **N** *040 †75

SICKLES, Robert Trent. 3705 OLENTANGY RIVER RD, 2ND FL 43214 #038-40-1981 L1981 **FM FSM** *018 †18 ‡

SICKLE-SANTANELLO, Brenda. 285 E STATE ST, STE 300 43215 #038-40-1980 L1984 **SO GS** *020 †85

SIDES, James Allen. 51 S SOUDER AVE 43222 #038-40-1981 L1982 **ORS** *020 †40

SIDHARTA, Nathanael O. 2200 W BROAD ST 43223 #506-02-1969 L1980 **P** *030

SIKIC-KLISOVIC, Eleonora. 1670 UPHAM DR, DEPT OF PSYCHIATRY 43210 #957-01-1993 L2000 **P** *020 †75

SILAKOSKI, Kristin Lynn. 700 CHILDRENS DR, NATIONWIDE CHILDREN'S HOSP 43205 #038-43-2005 L2005 **PD** *012

SILBER, Jeff S. 3525 OLENTANGY RIVER RD, STE 5360 43214 #048-04-1992 L1998 **DR** *020 †80

SILBER, Jeffrey Lee. 3525 OLENTANGY RIVER RD, STE 5360 43214 #035-46-1984 L1986 **ID IM** *050 †20

SILVA, Ariel Chavez-Danie. 1335 DUBLIN RD STE 110 43215 #305-01-2001 L2002 **FM** *100

SIMAY, Stephan Eugen. ■ 43235 #473-02-1941 L1955 **GP** *071

SIMENSKY, Steve Geoffrey. 285 E STATE ST, STE 430 43215 #050-02-2001 L2002 **N** *100

SIMONETTI, Joseph Anthony, Jr. ■ 43201 #038-40-2008 *012

SIMPSON, Sabrina Lee. ■ 43206 #056-06-2006 L2006 **PTH** *012

SINARD, James Michael. 5969 E BROAD ST, STE 306 43213 #025-01-1986 L1992 **GS** *020 †85

SINGH, Errol O'Neil. 500 THOMAS LN STE 3C 43214 #030-05-1977 L1990 **U** *020 †95

SINGH, Giridhar. 2200 W BROAD ST, TWIN VALLEY BEHAVIORAL HEA 43223 #495-65-1985 L1997 **P** *020 †75

SINGH, Raorajeshwar. 793 W STATE ST 43222 #495-43-2004 L2005 **IM** *012

SINGHAL, Nidhi. ■ 43201 #038-40-2008 *012

SINGLA, Nina. 500 THOMAS LN, STE 3G 43214 #038-44-1994 L1996 **IM** *020 †20

SINHA, Shantanu. 423 E TOWN ST, STE 1000 43215 #496-09-1992 L2002 **CD** *020 †20

SIRAK, Howard D. ■ 43209 #038-40-1947 L1947 **TS CD** *071 †85,90

SIVAPATHAM, Thinesh. ■ 43214 #047-06-2003 L2004 **DR** *020

SIVARD, James Gordon, Jr. 3555 OLENTANGY RIVER RD, COLUMBUS SURGICAL 43214 #038-40-1978 L1978 **GS** *020 †85

SKULLY, Robert James. 111 S GRANT AVE, MEDICAL EDUCATION 43215 #038-40-1979 L1981 **FM** *020 †18

SLAGER, Richard F. ■ 43220 #038-40-1953 L1953 **ORS** *071 †40

SLATER, Theodore Arthur. 750 MOUNT CARMEL MALL, STE 300 43222 #038-45-2000 L2005 **EM** *100 †16

SLEEPER, Todd William. ■ 43230 #056-06-2008 *012

SLEESMAN, Henry Craig. 3400 OLENTANGY RIVER RD, STE 150 43202 #038-40-1974 L1976 **IM** *020 †20

SLIVINSKI, Alfred F. ■ 43220 #023-07-1947 L1953 **FM** *071 †18

SLIVKA, Andrew Paul, Jr. 1654 UPHAM DR, RM 423 43210 #038-40-1980 L1987 **N** *020 †75

SLONE, Hasel Wayne. 1654 UPHAM DR, 630 MEANS HALL 43210 #038-40-1989 L1990 **RNR** *020 †80

SLUBOWSKI, Richard Jos. ■ 43221 #693-02-1982 L1990 **EM** *020 †20

SMALL, Karin Patricia. 240 PARSONS AVE, PERINATAL PROJECT 43215 #038-06-1996 L2002 **FM** *020 †18

SMALL, Robert Harold. 410 W 10TH AVE, THE OHIO STATE UNIV HOSPIT 43210 #038-40-1992 L1993 **AN** *040 †05

SMART, Laura Ellen. ■ 43220 #020-02-2007 L2007 **IM** *012

SMEAD, William Lewis. 1654 UPHAM DR, MEANS HALL, N325 43210 #047-05-1972 L1978 **VS GS** *020 †85

SMITH, David Michael. 750 MOUNT CARMEL MALL 43222 #038-40-1974 L1975 **EM** *020 †16

SMITH, Delaney Mc Ginnis. 2200 W BROAD ST 43223 #038-40-2002 L2002 **PFP P** *100 †75

SMITH, Forrest Wayne. P.O. BOX 118, 246 N. HIGH STREET 43266 #055-01-1977 L1981 **PD** *020 †55

SMITH, Gary Alan. 700 CHILDRENS DR, CTR FOR INJURY RESEARCH 43205 #005-06-1979 L1990 **PEM EM** *050 †55,70

SMITH, James Hansen. 685 BRYDEN RD 43205 #017-20-1990 L1993 **ID IM** *020 †20

SMITH, Jason Wayne. 370 W 9TH AVE, OH STATE U COLL OF MED 43210 #038-40-2002 L2002 **CCS** *100

SMITH, Jeffrey Vass. 505 KING AVE, BATTELLE HEALTH SVCS 43201 #038-40-1984 L1987 **OM PHP** *020 †70

SMITH, Jennifer Hale. ■ 43202 #008-01-2006 L2007 **IM** *012

SMITH, Mark Allen. 750 MOUNT CARMEL MALL 43222 #038-40-1982 L1983 **EM** *020 †16

SMITH, Marykay Schwaninge. ■ 43202 #038-40-2005 *100

SMITH, Niti B. 5151 REED RD STE 105-, MIDWEST PHYSICIAN ANESTHES 43220 #038-41-2003 L2003 **AN** *020

SMITH, Paul Curtis. 6164 CLEVELAND AVE, REHABILITATION CARE GROUP 43231 #038-40-1978 L1979 **FM** *020 †16,18

SMITH, Shane Wesley. ■ 43202 #038-43-2002 L2002 **RNR** *012 †80

SMITH, Stephen Puntenney. ■ 43212 #038-40-2001 L2001 **OTO** *020 †45

SMITH, Stephen Puntenney. 85 MCNAUGHTEN RD, STE 350 43213 #038-40-1970 L1978 **U** *020 †95

SMITH, Thomas Joseph. 410 W 10TH AVE, N416 DOAN HALL 43210 #038-44-2003 L2003 **AN** *100

SMITH, Timothy Patrick. 700 CHILDRENS DR, DEPARTMENT OF ANESTHESIOLO 43205 #038-41-2002 L2002 **AN PAN** *020 †05

SMITH, Vance Labaron. ■ 43219 #038-43-2003 L2003 **GS** *012

SMITH, Wendy Meredith. ■ 43235 #038-40-2006 L2006 **OPH** *012

SMITH, Wilton Leon. ■ 43203 #047-07-1971 L1976 **GS OS** *020

SMITH-E-INCAS, Bianca L. ■ 43236 #654-01-1983 *100

SMITH E INCAS, Jaime C. 1829 E LONG ST 43203 #010-03-1951 L1954 **P N** *071

SMOYER, William Ernest. 700 CHILDRENS DR, NATIONWIDE CHILDRENS HOSP 43205 #011-03-1986 L1989 **PN** *020 †55

SMYKE, Norman Alan, Jr. 111 S GRANT AVE, GRANT ANESTHESIA ASSOC 43215 #038-40-1989 L1991 **AN IM** *020 †05

SNOOK, Derek Lee. 85 MCNAUGHTEN RD 43213 #017-20-1997 L1999 **ORS** *020 †40

SNYDER, Dane Anthony. ■ 43219 #038-43-2005 L2005 **PD** *012

SNYDER, Melissa Anne. ■ 43209 #038-45-2005 L2005 **PD** *012

SO, Brian Jin. ■ 43204 #023-01-2007 L2007 **IM** *012

SODER, Carrie Rose. 1654 UPHAM DR, FIFTH FLR MEANS HALL 43210 #038-43-2001 L2001 **OBG** *020 †30

SODHI, Ajay Paul Singh. 285 E STATE ST STE 6, EDUC DEPT 43215 #495-43-2001 L2006 **FP** *020

SOEHNER, David Francis. 2200 W BROAD ST, COLUMBUS CAMPUS 43223 #038-40-1989 L1990 **PFP** *020 †75

SOKOLOV, Howard H. 30 E BROAD ST, STE 2435 43215 #035-08-1965 L1969 **P PFP** *020 †75

SOLDANO, James Bennett. 4882 E MAIN ST, STE 200 43213 #047-06-1975 L1977 **FM** *020 †18

SOMANI, Anita Preeti. 4845 KNIGHTSBRIDGE BLVD, STE 220 43214 #038-43-1988 L1990 **OBG** *020 †30

SOMASUNDARAM, Shivkamini. 4845 KNIGHTSBRIDGE BLVD 43214 #038-40-1999 L1999 **OBG** *020 †30

SOMMER, Annemarie. 700 CHILDRENS DR 43205 #038-40-1964 L1964 **CG PD** *020 †55,19

SONDRUP, Logan Cole. ■ 43228 #049-01-2007 L2007 **EM** *012

SONG, Won-Geel. 1430 S HIGH ST 43207 #583-02-1964 L1976 **ORS PM** *020 †40

SONI, Renu. 2150 AGLER RD, CAPITAL PARK FHC 43224 #496-07-1990 L2007 **IM** *020 †20

SONI, Sandeep. 700 CHILDRENS DR, ED 546 EDUCATION BLDG 43205 #495-45-1988 L2006 **PHO** *020 †55

SOOD, Namita. 473 W 12TH AVE, 201 HEART & LUNG RES. INS. 43210 #613-02-1988 L2001 **PCC** *020 †20

SOPIRALA, Madhuri Mulam. 793 W STATE ST 43222 #495-70-1999 L2002 **ID** *100 †20

SORIANO, Fortunato M. ■ 43213 #748-08-1957 L1968 **CLP ID** *072 †50

SOTAK, Michael Patrick. ■ 43213 #005-19-1992 L1993 **EM** *020 †16

SOTOS, Juan Fernandez. 700 CHILDRENS DR RM ED421 43205 #847-08-1951 L1963 **END PD** *040 †55

SOUBA, Wiley W, Jr. 370 W 9TH AVE RM 254, MAILING HALL 43210 #048-14-1978 L2008 **GS CRS** *020 †85

SOUSSOU, David Yacoub. 111 S GRANT AVE 43215 #654-01-2004 L2005 **FP** *012

SOUTH, Christopher David. ■ 43201 #038-40-2004 L2005 **GE** *012 †20

SPAETH, Douglas Michael. 6200 E BROAD ST 43213 #038-40-1990 L1991 **EM IM** *020 †20

SPAGNA, Vincent Anthony. 370 S FRONT ST, FRANKLIN COUNTY JAIL 43215 #035-09-1974 L1978 **IM** *020 †20

SPAHN, Mitchell Wm. 5965 E BROAD ST, STE 260 43213 #017-20-1987 L1990 **OBG** *020 †30

SPAIN, Sheria Diane. ■ 43228 #020-02-2007 L2007 *012

SPARKS, Edward De Lancy. 793 W STATE ST 43222 #038-40-1964 L1964 **IM** *020 †20

SPATA, Tyler Cooley. ■ 43212 #048-02-2008 *012

SPEAS, Gaylynn Jane. 410 W 10TH AVE, DEPT OF ANESTESIA OSU MED 43210 #018-03-1978 L1987 **AN CCM** *020 †05

SPEICHER, Carl Eugene. 410 W 10TH AVE RM N-343 43210 #041-01-1958 L1977 **PTH** *071 †50

SPEIDEL, Ronald Lee. 3311 TREMONT RD, STE 101 43221 #038-40-1973 L1973 **FM** *020

SPELLACY, Kristen Marie. 700 CHILDRENS DR, COLUMBUS CHILDREN'S HOSPIT 43205 #038-40-2004 L2004 **MPD** *012

SPENCER, Charles Hiram. 700 CHILDRENS DR, SECTION OF RHEUMATOLOGY 43205 #021-05-1973 L2007 **PD RHU** *040 †55

SPENCER, Sandra Patrice. ■ 43206 #038-40-2006 L2006 **PD** *012

SPETIE, Dan Nicolae. 1654 UPHAM DR, NEPHROLOGY 43210 #781-01-1991 L1997 **NEP** *020 †20

SPICER, Kevin Bryant. 700 CHILDRENS DR, OF I 43205 #020-12-1999 L1999 **PDI** *012 †55

SPIGOS, Dimitrios G. 1654 UPHAM DR, 630 MEANS HALL 43210 #418-01-1968 L1992 **R CD** *030 †80

SPLAINGARD, Mark Louis. 700 CHILDRENS DR, DIRECTOR, SLEEP DISORDER C 43205 #016-11-1977 L2004 **PM PDP** *020 †55,60

SPRAGUE, Michael Steven. 1080 BEECHER XING N, NORTHEAST OB GYN INC 43230 #028-34-1978 L1979 **OBG** *020 †30

SPRINGER, Andrew Neil. ■ 43235 #038-40-2008 *012

SREENIVAS, Venkatachala I. ■ 43235 #495-29-1961 L2006 **GS CRS** *071 †85

SROA, Novie. ■ 43220 #038-40-2006 L2006 **D** *012

STACK, Stephen Arthur. 3341 E LIVINGSTON AVE, STE D 43227 #025-07-1995 L1999 **FM** *020 †18

STAHL, Deborah Ann. 3535 OLENTANGY RIVER RD 43214 #038-40-1988 L1992 **AN** *020 †05

STAMOOLIS, Christina Evye. ■ 43212 #038-40-2008 *012

STANKO, John, Jr. 750 MOUNT CARMEL MALL, STE 380 43222 #016-43-1986 L1997 **CD IM** *020 †20

STARK, Owen Matthew. ■ 43215 #025-01-2004 L2006 **DR** *012

STARODUB, Alexander N. 1654 UPHAM DR, 202 MEANS HALL 43210 #038-40-2003 L2003 **HO** *012 †20

STARR, Jean Ellen. 1654 UPHAM DR, MEANS HALL, N325 43210 #038-40-1989 L1994 **VS** *020 †85

STARR, Jon E. ■ 43214 #038-40-1970 L1970 **OM FM** *030

STASEK, Jerome Edward, Jr. 473 W 12TH AVE, DEPT OF INTERNAL MEDICINE 43210 #017-20-1986 L2006 **PCC IM** *020 †20

STATHULIS, Evan Dennis. 535 OFFICENTER PL, STE A 43230 #038-40-1992 L1993 **FM** *020 †18

STECHSCHULTE, Mark. 777 W STATE ST, OHIO GASTROENTEROLOGY 43222 #038-40-1988 L1991 **GE** *020

STEFANOSKI, Stevco. 410 W 10TH AVE, 207 MEANS HALL 43210 #036-05-2005 L2005 **IM** *012

STEGINSKY, Alan David. ■ 43220 #038-40-1983 L1984 **IM** *020 †20

STEIMAN, George Gerald S. 5150 E MAIN ST, STE 100 43213 #062-01-1973 L1978 **N** *020 †55,75

STEIN, George Gordon. ■ 43229 #038-40-1941 **GP** *071

STEIN, John Andrew. 6150 E BROAD ST, 2ND FL 43213 #038-40-1996 L1997 **FM** *020 †18

STEINBAUGH, Jan Thos. 5969 E BROAD ST, STE 404 43213 #038-40-1969 L1969 **GE IM** *020 †20

STEINBERG, Steven Michael. 410 W 10TH AVE, DOAN HALL N-717 43210 #038-40-1978 L1978 **GS CCS** *020 †85

STEMPEL, Laurence Eric. 3535 OLENTANGY RIVER RD 43214 #028-02-1976 L1977 **OBG** *040 †30

STENGER, Michael Robert. 700 CHILDRENS DR, SECTION OF NEONATOLOGY 43205 #020-12-2001 L2001 **NPM** *100 †55

STEPANIAN, Marshall S. 1654 UPHAM DR, DPT OF OBGYN 5TH FL 43210 #038-41-2000 L2002 **OBG** *020

STEPHENS, Amanda Lynn. ■ 43221 #055-01-2005 L2005 **PD** *012

STEPHENS, Scott Perry. ■ 43204 #038-43-2007 L2007 **ORS** *012

STEPHENS, Sheryl Lynne. 1833 PARSONS AVE, JOHN MALONY SOUTH SIDE HEA 43207 #055-02-1988 L1990 **FM GP** *012

STEPHENSEN, Sigurdur A. 931 CHATHAM LN, STE 200 43221 #062-01-1981 L1986 **NS** *020 †25

STERLING, Donna Bazzoli. 4885 OLENTANGY RIVER RD, STE 2-10 43214 #038-40-2003 L2003 **PD** *020 †55

STERN, Jordan Russell. ■ 43212 #038-40-2008 *012

STERNSTEIN, Amy Renee. 700 CHILDRENS DR, CHILDREN'S HOSPITAL 43205 #051-01-1986 L1988 **PD** *062 †55

STEVENS, Harold Craig. 1492 E BROAD ST 43205 #038-40-1989 L1992 **IM** *020 †20

STEVENS, Robert Michael. ■ 43214 #038-41-2002 L2002 **DR** *100 †80

STEVENSON, Camille Critch. ■ 43235 #049-01-2004 L2004 **OBG** *012

STEVENSON, Kristin Kay. 700 CHILDRENS DR 43205 #038-40-2003 L2003 **PD** *020 †55

STEVENSON, Kurt Brown. 410 W 10TH AVE, N-1147 DOAN HALL 43210 #049-01-1983 L2005 **ID IM** *050 †20

STEWART, David Wm. 750 MT CARMEL MALL, STE 350 43222 #038-41-1981 L1983 **U** *020 †95

STEWART, Gregory Bryan. 700 CHILDRENS DR, PEDIATRIC EMERGENCY MEDICI 43205 #038-45-2002 L2002 **PEM** *012 †55

STEWART, Suellywn. 1405 S HIGH ST, OSU FAMILY PRACTICE 43207 #665-01-2000 L2000 **FM** *020 †18 ‡

STIDHAM, Grant Jos. 410 W 10TH AVE, BOX 625 43210 #038-40-1981 *100

STIERMAN, Sarah. ■ 43202 #038-43-2007 L2007 **IM** *012

STILES, Kathleen Carole. 6096 E MAIN ST, STE 112 43213 #019-02-2000 L2000 **PD** *020 †55

STIVER, Kevin Lessard. ■ 43201 #017-20-2008 *012

ST JOHN, Roy Carl. 793 W STATE ST 43222 #038-40-1985 L1987 **PUD CCM** *020 †20

STOCK, Stewart Frederick. 340 E TOWN ST, STE 7-100 43215 #038-40-1966 L1966 **CD** *020 †20

STOCKTON, Michael Alan. 16 W LONG ST, SE MENTAL HEALTH SVCS INC 43215 #028-79-1986, ▲ L1991 **P CHP** *020 †75

STOCKUM, Alfred Emmett. 410 W 10TH AVE 43210 #038-40-1958 L1958 **R VIR** *071 †80

STOCKWELL, David G. 3545 OLENTANGY RIVER RD, STE 411 43214 #038-40-1973 L1973 **OBG** *020 †30

STONE, Linda Chapman. 370 W 9TH AVE, 155G MEILING HALL 43210 #038-40-1979 L1981 **FM** *040 †18 ‡

STONE, Robert L. 4030 HENDERSON RD, CENTRAL OH MED 43220 #023-07-1993 L1996 **IM** *020 †20

STONER, Michael James. 700 CHILDRENS DR, EMERGENCY MEDICINE 43205 #011-04-1995 L2000 **PEM** *100 †55

STOUT, Michael Thomas. 2050 KENNY RD, STE 2400 43221 #025-07-2004 L2007 **HO** *012

STRACK, Leanne K. 500 THOMAS LN, FL 2 43214 #038-75-2003, ▲ L2003 **PCC** *012 †20

STRAFFORD, Jessica Ruth. 1670 UPHAM DR, OHIO STATE UNIVERSITY 43210 #038-40-2003 L2003 **CHP** *012

STRAFFORD, Katherine E. 1654 UPHAM DR, MEANS HALL RM 539 43210 #016-06-2002 L2002 **OBG** *100

STRAKOWSKI, Jeffrey Allen. 3555 OLENTANGY RIVER RD 43214 #017-20-1990 L1991 **PM** *020 †60

STRANGE, Brandon Collins. 1670 UPHAM DR STE 130, DEPT OF PSYCHIATRY 43210 #047-07-2001 L2001 **OS** *100 †55

STRATES, Basil S. PO BOX 16529, ADRIA LAB IN 43216 #418-02-1967 **PA END** *030

STREICHER, Michael David. 3555 OLENTANGY RIVER RD, STE 2060 43214 #016-11-1979 L1991 **TS VS** *020 †85,90

STRIEGEL, Peter Guyon. 2511 OAKSTONE DR, VISITING PHYSICIANS ASSOCI 43231 #038-41-1996 L2000 **FM** *020 †18

STROH, Brian Christopher. ■ 43206 #038-40-2002 L2002 **P** *020

STUBBS, Anne Therese. 750 MOUNT CARMEL MALL, STE 300 43222 #038-40-1990 L1991 **EM** *020 †16

STUBBS, Maureen Elizabeth. 930 BETHEL RD 43214 #038-40-1989 L1993 **AN PME** *020 †05

STUKUS, David Robert. 700 CHILDRENS DR, CHILDRENS HOSPITAL 43205 #041-12-2002 L2002 **AI** *012 †55

SU, Andrew Tsu. 543 TAYLOR AVE, CHALMERS P. WYLIE VETERANS 43203 #038-06-1990 L1991 **IM** *020 †20

SUBLER-SMYKE, Mary Kay. 1021 COUNTRY CLUB RD, STE B 43213 #038-40-1989 L1991 **OBG** *071 †30

SUCHAK, Dhruti Arunkant. 285 E STATE ST STE 6, EDUC DEPT 43215 #016-42-2004 L2004 **FM** *100 †18

SUGGS, Cassandra. 3341 E LIVINGSTON AVE # D, METRO FAMILY CARE INC 43227 #038-45-1994 L1995 **FM** *020 †18

SUGUMARAN, Rajkumar Kathi. ■ 43212 #038-45-2005 L2005 **IM** *012

SUKALICH, Sara Ann. 3535 OLENTANGY RIVER RD, STRONG MEMORIAL HOSPITAL 43214 #038-41-1999 L2007 **OBG** *100 †30

SULLIVAN, Christine Roth. 3555 OLENTANGY BLVD 43214 #038-40-1982 L1990 **PS GS** *020 †65

SULLIVAN, Michael Jos. 7706 OLENTANGY RIVER RD, PLASTIC & RECONSTRUCTIVESU 43235 #038-40-1980 L1981 **FPS** *020 †45

SUMMERS, Marcia. 750 MT CARMEL MALL STE 100 43222 #038-44-1997 L2000 **OBG** *020 †30

SUN, Benjamin Chengpang. 410 W 10TH AVE, N847 DOAN HALL 43210 #035-48-1989 L2002 **TS GS** *020 †85,90

SUN, Qixin. 2511 OAKSTONE DR 43221 #243-43-1982 L1998 **IM** *020 †20

SUNDARAM, Natarajan. 6096 E MAIN, STE 105 43213 #495-04-1985 L1998 **FPG** *020 †20

SUNDARAM, Poongothai. 3100 PLAZA PROPERTIES BLVD 43219 #495-94-1994 L1998 **HO** *020 †20

SURESH, Rudrappa. 99 N BRICE RD, STE 140 43213 #495-09-1978 L1984 **IM A** *020 †20,03

SUTTON, Christopher John. 700 CHILDRENS DR 43205 #038-40-1982 L1983 **AN EM** *020 †05

SVENDSEN, Dale Phillip. 30 E BROAD ST FL 8 43215 #038-40-1967 L1967 **P** *020 †75

SWAIN, Anshuman Raja. ■ 43214 #038-45-2004 L2004 **AN** *012

SWAMY, Sudha. 2939 KENNY RD STE 101 43221 #038-40-1991 L1994 **IM** *020 †20

SWAN, Joseph Fowler. 410 W 10TH AVE, N 416 DOAN HALL, ANESTHESI 43210 #038-41-1981 L1985 **AN** *020 †05

SWANNER, Larry Dean. 150 TAYLOR STATION RD, STE 140 43213 #016-45-1983 L1988 **FM** *020 †18

SWARTZ, Nathan Denny. ■ 43228 #038-43-2007 L2007 **IM** *012

SWEENEY, Michael Cameron. 370 W 9TH AVE, OH STATE U COLL OF MED 43210 #038-40-2007 L2007 **GS** *012

SWEENEY, Thomas Jos. 810 JASONWAY AVE, STE A 43214 #038-40-1992 L1999 **IM** *020 †20

SYED, Ahsan Shemaz. 700 CHILDRENS DR, DEPT OF ANESTHESIOLOGY 43205 #704-01-1996 L2005 **AN PD** *020 †05

SZABO, Lukas. ■ #473-01-1951 L1962 **P** *072 †75

SZYKOWNY, Lee Shackelford. 5151 REED RD, STE 128C 43220 #038-40-1988 L1996 **CHP** *020 †75

TABASUM, Abida. 1375 PERRY ST 5, OSU HOSPITAL 43201 #495-51-1979 L2003 **AN** *020

TADENA-THOME, Lilian. 543 TAYLOR AVE 43203 #748-10-1973 L1981 **NEP IM** *020 †20

TAGHIZADEH, Maakan. 410 W 10TH AVE, 316-A MEANS HALL 43210 #023-01-2006 L2006 **GS** *012

TAHBOUB, Rundsarah M. 340 E TOWN ST, STE 8-550 43215 #575-01-1997 L2000 **END** *012 †18,20 ‡

TALAG, Emelita Borja. 1087 DENNISON AVE 43201 #748-08-1988 L2002 **CHP** *012

TALLO, Diane. 500 THOMAS LN, STE 3G 43214 #038-40-1974 L1974 **END IM** *020 †20

TAMAMA, Kenichi. ■ 43210 #572-33-1995 L2002 **CLP PCH** *050 †50

TAMASKAR, Vikram. 793 W STATE ST, MEDICAL CENTER 43222 #038-41-1994 L1996 **IM** *020 †20

TAMBURELLO, Ellen R. 1495 MORSE RD 43229 #038-40-1994 L1995 **PD** *020 †55

TANDON, Padma Mehrotra. 1515 E BROAD ST 43205 #495-05-1963 L1983 **P** *020

TANNER, John Barlow. ■ 43201 #038-40-2008 *012

TANO, Sheila N. 16 W LONG ST 43215 #038-43-1991 L1998 **P** *020 †75

TARIGOPULA, Leena. 3820 OLENTANGY RIVER RD, OHIO GASTROENTEROLOGY 43214 #496-35-1996 L2003 **GE** *020 †20

TARIQ, Fouzia. 3555 OLENTANGY RIVER RD, SUITE1080 43214 #704-02-1996 L2004 **IM** *020 †20

TASHIMA, David Lee. ■ 43204 #038-40-2004 L2004 **PM** *012

TATE, Larry Raymont. 700 ACKERMAN RD, STE 380 43202 #025-01-1971 L1973 **FOP ATP** *020

TAXIER, Michael. 3820 OLENTANGY RIVER RD, OHIO GASTROENTEROLOGY 43214 #035-06-1975 L1978 **GE** *020 †20

TAYAL, Neeraj Hari. 2050 KENNY RD, STE 2400 43221 #024-07-1997 L1998 **IM** *020 †20

TAYAL, Suzanne Chopin. 370 W 9TH AVE, OH STATE U COLL OF MED 43210 #038-40-1999 L2000 **IM** *100

TAYLOR, Anne. 2 EASTON OVAL, STE 545 43219 #038-40-1990 L1992 **PS** *020 †65 ‡

TAYLOR, Brian Scott. 285 E STATE ST STE 670, GRANT MED CTR 43215 #038-40-2007 L2007 **FP** *012

TAYLOR, David Charles. 6001 E BROAD ST, MT CARMEL EAST HOSP DEPT O 43213 #038-43-1994 L2003 **PTH** *020 †50

TAYLOR, Deborah Lynn. 1615 FISHINGER RD 43221 #036-01-1983 L1984 **IM** *071 †20

TAYLOR, Dennis J. 85 MCNAUGHTEN RD, STE 200 43213 #038-45-1982 L1987 **ORS** *020 †40

TAYLOR, Erica Lynne. ■ 43206 #038-45-2005 L2005 **MPD** *012

TAYLOR, Gordon Chris. ■ 43235 #028-02-1956 L1962 **DR** *071 †80,28

TAYLOR, Katharine Roxanne. ■ 43214 #048-02-2005 L2005 **PS** *012

TAYLOR, Mark Alan. ■ 43235 #038-41-2005 L2007 **FP** *012

TAYLOR, Philip H, Jr. 3545 OLENTANGY RIVER RD, STE 525 43214 #038-40-1986 **GS** *020 †85

TAYLOR, Philip Hayward. 3545 OLENTANGY RVR RD #202 43214 #041-02-1955 L1955 **GS** *020 †85

TAYLOR, Renee Suzanne. 3433 AGLER RD STE 130 43219 #041-12-1976 L1980 **PD** *020 †55

TAYLOR, Robert Moroz. 1654 UPHAM DR, 422 MEANS HALL 43210 #038-40-1985 L1989 **PLM N** *020 †75

TAYLOR, Ronald Bernard. 3535 OLENTANGY RIVER RD 43214 #021-06-1983 L1984 **EM** *020 †16

TBAKHI, Abedelghani. ■ 43235 #575-01-1986 L1998 **HMP** *100 †50

TEATER, Julie Elizabeth. ■ 43212 #038-40-2008 *012

TEICH, Steven. 555 S 18TH ST, CHILDRENS SURGICAL 43205 #035-06-1981 L1989 **PDS CCS** *020 †85

TEMIZER, Hasip. 1430 S HIGH ST 43207 #902-01-1951 L1963 **IM** *020

TENNISWOOD, Christine M. 7706 OLENTANGY RIVER RD, SULLIVAN CENTRE 43235 #028-46-1995 L1996 **FM** *020 †18

TERCERO, Francisco Manuel. 1375 PERRY ST, CO OSU HOSPS 43201 #649-13-1997 L2001 **PTH** *100

TEREBUH, Annette Katrien. 456 W 10TH AVE 43210 #038-43-1987 L1988 **OPH OS** *020 †35

TERMUHLEN, Amanda Muench. 700 CHILDRENS DR 43205 #038-40-1984 L1987 **PHO PD** *020 †55

TESKE, Douglas Wm. 700 CHILDRENS DR, CHILDRENS HOSPITAL 43205 #018-03-1971 L1975 **PD PDC** *020 †55

TESSLER, Lee Eric. 370 W 9TH AVE, OH STATE U COLL OF MED 43210 #038-40-2001 L2003 **NS** *020

TETERIS, Nick John. 1654 UPHAM DR DEPT OBG 43210 #038-40-1954 L1954 **OS OBG** *030 †30

TETIRICK, Daniel Hartman. ■ 43214 #038-40-1980 L1982 **P IM** *020 †75

THACKERAY, Jonathan David. 655 E LIVINGSTON AVE 43205 #038-43-2000 L2003 **MPD** *020 †20,55

THAI, Beth Lee. ■ 43221 #038-45-2007 **OBG** *012

THAKURIAH, Anil Chandra. ■ 43235 #495-78-1969 L1982 **IM** *020 †20

THAKURIAH, Paraja. 1515 E BROAD ST 43205 #495-78-1970 L1984 **P** *020

THALASSINOS, Arthur. 750 MOUNT CARMEL MALL 43222 #418-02-1987 L2000 **P PYG** *020 †75

THANOS, Daniel. ■ 43214 #035-15-1943 L1952 **OBG** *072 †30

THENOR, Fritz. 1515 E BROAD ST 43205 #132-02-1970 L1980 **P GP** *020 †75

THEODOROPOULOS, Georgios. 111 S GRANT AVE, CO GRANT MED CTR-MED EDU D 43215 #418-01-1992 L2000 **CRS** *020 †85,10

THIESSEN, Jessica Ruth. ■ 43212 #038-40-2008 *012

THIRUGNANAM, Mohan. ■ 43235 #038-41-2004 L2004 **IM** *100 †20

THOMA, Mark Andrew. ■ 43220 #020-02-2006 L2006 **PD** *012

THOMAN, William James. 410 W 10TH AVE, N-1021 43210 #011-03-2002 L2002 **NS** *012

THOMAS, Alicia Christine. ■ 43221 #036-01-2006 L2006 **GS** *012

THOMAS, Andrew Mc Lean. 2050 KENNY RD, STE 2400 43221 #038-40-1995 L1996 **IM** *040 †20

THOMAS, Fred B. 410 W 10TH AVE, ROOM 21 DOAN HALL 43210 #038-40-1965 L1965 **GE IM** *040 †20

THOMAS, Heather Ownby. 1631 NW PROFESSIONAL PLZ, STE 107 43220 #028-46-1992 L1996 **AN** *020 †05

THOMAS, James Peter. 1375 PERRY ST, BTL-13-6-016 43201 #056-06-1991 L2006 **ON** *020 †20

THOMAS, Kristen Leigh. ■ 43215 #038-40-2004 L2004 **ORS** *012

THOMAS, Leigh Alan. 750 MOUNT CARMEL MALL, STE 300 43222 #038-40-1975 L1976 **EM** *020 †16

THOMAS, Lovely. 285 E STATE ST STE 670, GRANT MED CTR 43215 #495-37-2004 L2006 **FP** *012

THOMAS, Marvin Harlan. 1515 E BROAD ST 43205 #018-03-1961 L1968 **RHU IM** *020 †20

THOMAS, Melvin Wilson. 4278 INDIANOLA AVE 43214 #038-40-1982 L1983 **FM** *020 †18

THOMAS, Olivia Marie. 700 CHILDRENS DR 43205 #030-06-1976 L1979 **PD** *030 †55

THOMAS, Ronald Edward. 2929 KENNY RD, STE 160 43221 #028-46-1993 L1994 **CCA** *020 †05

THOMAS, Tinu Emmanuel. ■ 43202 #012-01-2006 L2006 **AN** *012

THOMAS, Walter Alvin. 111 S GRANT AVE 43215 #010-03-1952 L1957 **GYN** *071

THOMAS, Yalaunda Michelle. 410 W 10TH AVE N717, THE OHIO STATE UNIVERSITY 43210 #036-01-2000 L2006 **TRS CCS** *020 †85

THOMPSON, Arnold Theodore. ■ 43229 #018-03-1964 L1965 **PHP FM** *020 †18

THOMPSON, Craig Richard. 4919 DIERKER RD 43220 #038-40-1989 L1990 **PD** *020 †55

THOMPSON, Daniel Lee. 4856 SAWMILL RD, PMB 307 43235 #038-40-1983 L1983 **EM IM** *075

THOMPSON, Douglas Corey. 7630 RIVERS EDGE DR, MILLHON CLINIC 43235 #038-43-1998 L1999 **IM** *020 †20

THOMPSON, Mark Edward. 3100 PLAZA PROPERTIES BLVD 43219 #038-45-1981 L1982 **ON HEM** *020 †20

THOMPSON, Robert Lee. 7630 RIVERS EDGE DR, MILLHON MEDICAL CLINIC 43235 #038-40-1968 L1968 **IM** *071 †20

THOMPSON, Rohan Anthony. 700 CHILDRENS DR, ED 435 - DEPT PULM 43205 #010-01-1998 L2006 **PDP** *020 †55 ‡

THOMPSON, Tamara Jo. 270 E TOWN ST 43215 #038-44-2000 L2004 **OBG** *020

THOMPSON, Victor Brandon. 340 E TOWN ST, PHYSICAL MEDICINE 43215 #017-20-2002 L2002 PM *020 †60

THORNE, Jonathan Gilbert. 810 JASONWAY AVE, STE B 43214 #041-01-1996 L1997 IM *020 †20

THORPE, Eric Joseph. ■ 43220 #038-40-2008 *012

THORWARD, Sul Ross Olen. 2200 W BROAD ST, COLUMBUS CAMPUS 43223 #048-13-1973 L1978 P *020 †75

THRASHER, Sandra Kay. 930 BETHEL RD 43214 #028-34-1988 L1992 AN *020 †05

THRUSH, Philip Taylor. ■ 43221 #038-40-2006 L2006 PD *012

THURMAN, Mark Wm. 85 MCNAUGHTEN RD, OHIO GASTROENTEROLOGY 43213 #008-02-1978 L1979 IM GE *020 †20

TIMAN, Christopher John. 700 CHILDRENS DR, SECTION OF NEONATOLOGY #ED 43205 #038-40-1993 L1994 NPM *020 †55

TIMBADIA, Paresh Jerambha. 2760 AIRPORT DR, STE 120 43219 #495-23-1994 L2003 PCC SME *020 †20

TINGLEY, David Alan. 700 CHILDRENS DR 43205 #048-12-1986 L1990 PAN *020 †05 ‡

TIPPLE, Trent Edward. 700 CHILDRENS DR #017-20-2000 L2000 PD *100 †55

TISHKO, D J. 5965 E BROAD ST STE 340 43213 #038-41-1983 L1986 TS *020 †85,90

TIWARI, Katherine A. 700 CHILDRENS DR, EMERGENCY MEDICINE 43205 #008-01-2000 L2003 PD *020 †55

TIWARI, Pankaj. 4830 KNIGHTSBRIDGE BLVD, SURGERY 43214 #035-19-2000 L2007 PS *100

TOLBERT, Herman Andre. 1430 S HIGH ST, 2ND FL 43207 #005-18-1974 L1976 CHP P *020 †75

TOMPKINS, Andrew Jarrett. ■ 43215 #016-43-2005 L2006 OTO *012

TONTI, Marleise. 34 N HIGH ST 43215 #038-43-1982 L1990 GPM PM *020 †70

TOOHEY, Patricia Marie. 2231 N HIGH ST 43201 #038-43-1999 L1999 MPD *020 †20,55

TOPINKA, Marcus Auke. 1087 DENNISON AVE, DOCTORS HOSPITAL 43201 #025-12-1985 L1988 EM FM *020 †18

TOPLAK, Bogdan Alexander. 6435 E BROAD ST, MT CARMEL EAST URGENT CARE 43213 #038-40-1992 L1993 FM *020 †18

TORCH, Martin Armand. 259 TAYLOR STATION RD, INC. 43213 #038-40-1961 L1961 ORS *020 †40

TORELLO, Lynne Ann. 100 W 3RD AVE, STE 200R 43201 #038-40-1984 L1985 FM OM *020 †18

TORRES, Carlos A. 1654 UPHAM DR, 146 MEARIS HALL 43210 #187-06-1988 L1996 EM *020 †16

TOSCANO, Robert Louis. 3545 OLENTANGY RIVER RD, STE 525 43214 #017-20-1991 L1996 GS *020 †85

TOURKOW, Benjamin Ahron. ■ 43209 #017-20-2004 L2007 DR *012

TRANOVICH, Mark. 543 TAYLOR AVE, CHALERS P WYLIE VETS CLC 43203 #038-40-1981 L1995 ORS *020 †40 ‡

TRAPPE, Karen Lynn. ■ 43221 #017-20-2007 L2007 OBG *012

TREECE, Timothy Allen. 4971 ARLINGTON CENTRE BLVD 43220 #038-40-1982 L1990 PS *020 †85,65

TRELL, Eugene F. 1087 DENNISON AVE, DOCTORS HOSPITAL 43201 #018-75-1962, ▲ L1963 FM *071

TRGOVAC, Tracey Leigh. 1117 W 1ST AVE 43212 #038-40-1997 L1998 MPD *020 †20,55

TRIFELOS, Nick P. ■ 43221 #038-40-1962 L1962 U HEM *071

TRIOLA, Craig Albert. ■ 43201 #038-40-2004 L2004 DR *012

TRITTMANN, Jennifer Bullo. ■ 43202 #038-40-2005 L2005 PD *012

TROTTER, Alice W. ■ 43220 #028-02-1969 L1969 IM PD *071 †20

TROTTER, Marianne Monet W. 1962 BRAEMAR DR 43220 #028-02-2001 L2001 FM *020 †18

TROYER, Sara Ann. ■ 43215 #038-40-2008 *012

TRUDEAU, Gwendolyn D C. ■ 43215 #038-40-1949 L1949 OS AN *071 †05

TRUMP, Thomas John. ■ 43220 #038-40-1974 L1974 FM ADL *012

TSAI, Bonny Mae. 700 CHILDRENS DR 43205 #038-44-2003 L2003 PD *020 †55

TSAI, Rita. ■ 43212 #016-11-2005 L2005 OBG *012

TSAI, Thomas Tung-Fang. 3805 N HIGH ST 43214 #242-09-1938 L1963 P *075

TSAO, Chang-Yong. 700 CHILDRENS DR 43205 #244-04-1977 L1984 CHN *020 †75,55

TU, Joseph Chau-Sen. ■ 43215 #018-03-2005 L2005 PM *012

TUATAY, Hulusi. ■ 43221 #902-01-1946 L1960 P *071 †75

TUCKER, Allen. 1830 E BROAD ST 43203 #038-40-1978 L1979 FM IMG *020 †18

TUGAOEN, Justin Falgui. 111 S GRANT AVE, THIRD FLOOR 43215 #038-40-1992 L1995 AN *020 †05

TUGGLE, Blayre Rebecca. 85 PHILLIPI RD 43228 #038-40-1982 L1986 IM OS *020

TULEBAEV, Samir Raisovich. 6001 E BROAD ST, MT CARMEL EAST HOSP 43213 #913-29-1989 L1998 IM *020 †20

TURNER, Jeffrey Layne. 50 MCNAUGHTEN RD, STE 200 43213 #038-45-1992 L1993 GS *020 †85

TURNER, Katherine K. 1299 OLENTANGY RIVER RD, STE B 43212 #048-13-2000 L2000 FM *020 †18

TURNER, Katja Regina. 410 W 10TH AVE, OHIO STATE UNIVERSITY MED 43210 #409-05-1994 L1998 AN *020 †05

TURNER, Robert Calvin. 51 S SOUDER AVE 43222 #038-40-1973 L1974 ORS *020 †40

TURNER, Stephen A. 3500 E LIVINGSTON AVE 43227 #038-40-1993 L1996 OBG *020 †30

TUTTLE, Elizabeth S. 2231 N HIGH ST 43201 #011-03-1978 L1979 GP *020 †20

TWEEL, Charles Tofie, Jr. 4945 OLENTANGY RIVER RD, RM A 43214 #055-01-1976 L1977 FM *020 †18

TYBERG, Shifra S. 3341 E LIVINGSTON AVE, STE D 43227 #067-01-1987 L1990 FM *020 †18

TYLER, Jaret Dean. ■ 43204 #056-06-2003 L2006 CD *012 †20

TYZNIK, John Wm. 535 OFFICENTER PL, STE A 43230 #038-41-1981 L1982 FM FSM *020 †18

TZAGOURNIS, Manuel. 456 W 10TH AVE, UNIVERSITY HOSP 43210 #038-40-1960 L1960 END IM *020 †20

TZOU, Martha S. ■ 43214 #038-40-2007 L2007 IM *012

UEBERROTH, Adam Nicholas. 931 CHATHAM LN, NEUROLOGICAL ASSOCIATES, I 43221 #038-06-2003 L2003 CN *012

UGBANA, Obiaghanwa S. 700 CHILDRENS DR, CHILDRENS HOSP AMBULAT PED 43205 #306-01-1995 L1999 PD *020 †55

UHLENBROCK, James Michael. 6001 E BROAD ST 43213 #038-40-1988 L1993 PTH *020 †50

UNGER, Michael Thomas. 16 W LONG ST, SOUTHEAST INC 43215 #035-09-1995 L1999 P *020 †75

UNNIREVI, Jayaraj. 1375 PERRY ST RM 5, CO OSU-MED EDU DEPT 43201 #495-37-1988 L2000 IM *100

UPPAL, Rohit. 370 W 9TH AVE, OH STATE U COLL OF MED 43210 #038-40-2001 L2001 FM *020 †18

URAM, Rebecca. 555 S 18TH ST RM 546, PEDIATRIC ACADEMIC ASSOCIA 43205 #038-45-1997 L2002 AI *020 †03,55

URS, Jagadisha Raje K. 700 CHILDRENS DR, CHILDREN'S HOSPITAL 43205 #495-09-1988 L2006 PD *020 †55

UTRATA, Peter John. 303 E TOWN ST, OF OHIO 43215 #038-40-1968 L1968 OPH *020 †35

VACCARELLO, Luis. 3100 PLAZA PROPERTIES BLVD 43219 #041-01-1984 L1992 OBG GO *020 †30

VACCARO, Patrick Saml. 1654 UPHAM DR N325, OSU/DIV OF VASC SURG 43210 #038-41-1975 L1976 VS *020 †85

VAGHY, Laszlo P. 1375 PERRY ST RM 5, CO OSU HOSPS-MED EDU DEPT 43201 #473-02-1994 L2000 N *100

VAIDA, Alexandru Mihai. 410 W 10TH AVE, DIV OF CARDIO SURG 43210 #781-05-1995 L2004 GS *020 †85

VAIL, Matthew Allison. 3545 OLENTANGY RIVER RD, STE 425 43214 #064-01-1976 L2000 OM *020 †20

VALDEZ, Maria Elisa. ■ 43235 #007-02-2007 L2007 *012

VALDIVIA ARENAS, Martin A. 473 W 12TH AVE, STE 201 43210 #737-05-1999 L2004 PCC *020

VALDMAN, Boris. 5969 E BROAD ST, STE 200 43213 #913-73-1989 L1995 IM *020 †20 ‡

VALENTINE, Christina J. 700 CHILDRENS DR, CHILDRENS HOSP 43205 #048-04-1999 L2002 NPM *100 †55

VALENTINE, Christopher W. 1654 UPHAM DR, N210 MEANS HALL 43210 #038-06-1998 L2001 NEP *020 †20

VALENTINE, Karl John. 6164 CLEVELAND AVE, REHABILITATION CARE GROUP, 43231 #038-40-1983 L1984 UCM *020

VALLABHANENI, Ramadevi V. 543 TAYLOR AVE 43203 #495-50-1992 L1998 IM *020 †20

VALLANGEON, Dana Sue. 1251 W BROAD ST 43222 #038-40-1996 L1997 FM *020 †18

VALLERY, Beatrice Sexton. ■ 43201 #038-40-1951 L1951 P *072

VANAJA, Loka. ■ 43229 #495-21-1994 AN *100

VANAMAN, Scott Elwin. 4605 SAWMILL RD 43220 #038-40-2000 L2000 OFA *020

VAN BUREN, Ronald Carl. 4808 N HIGH ST 43214 #038-40-1964 L1964 FM GP *020 †18

VANDERHOFF, Bruce T. 111 S GRANT AVE, MEDICAL EDUCATION 43215 #041-01-1990 L1993 FM *040 †18

VANDEUSEN, Jeffrey Bryan. 370 W 9TH AVE, OH STATE U COLL OF MED 43210 #038-40-2006 IM *012

VANEK, Cynthia Marie. 3525 OLENTANGY RIVER RD 43214 #038-43-1998 L1999 OBG *020 †30

VAN FOSSEN, Albert Wayne. 262 NEIL AVE # 370 43215 #038-40-1954 L1954 OPH *020 †35

VANGORP, Cornel Christian. 2050 KENNY RD, STE 3300 43221 #038-43-1992 L1999 ORS *020 †40

VAN HOFF, Corey Lee. 410 W 10TH AVE, N1050 DOAN HALL 43210 #055-01-2002 L2002 ORS *012

VANIK, Philip E. 700 CHILDRENS DR 43205 #038-40-1960 L1960 AN *071 †05

VAN LIGTEN, Peter Frank. 750 MOUNT CARMEL MALL, STE 300 43222 #005-06-1983 L1986 EM *050 †16

VARA, Thomas Martin. 6075 E BROAD ST, STE 2 43213 #038-40-1981 L1982 GS *020 †85

VARAKIS, Kaliope Eleffher. 1375 PERRY ST 5T, CO OSU HOSPS-MED EDU DEPT 43201 #418-03-1993 L2001 RNR *020

VARLAS, Pantelhs Pete. 697 THOMAS LN 43214 #038-44-2001 L2001 FM *020

VARMA, Ashok B. 793 W STATE ST 43222 #495-57-1973 L1981 AN *020 †05

VARMA, Hemank. ■ 43220 #495-41-1967 L1983 *020

VARMA, Jasmine. 793 W STATE ST 43222 #495-65-1999 L2004 IM *100 †20

VARMA, Nilesh Vrundachara. 793 W STATE ST 43222 #495-65-1999 L2003 IM *020 †20

VARUGHESE, Mary Jenny. 793 W STATE ST 43222 #820-02-2004 L2005 IM *012

VARVERIS, Maria Yiannaki. 810 JASONWAY AVE STE B, PHYSICIANS, INC 43214 #038-44-1998 L1999 IM *020 †20

VARY, Marshall Gordon. 3535 OLENTANGY RIVER RD 43214 #025-07-1973 L1976 CHP P *030 †75

VASIL, Katherine Elizabet. 3535 OLENTANGY RIVER RD 43214 #038-40-2006 L2006 IM *012

VASILEFF, William Kelton. ■ 43201 #038-40-2008 *012

VASILOFF, Jeffrey. 400 E CAMPUS VIEW BLVD, OHIO REHAB SVCS COMMISSION 43235 #038-40-1981 L1984 PHP IM *050 †20

VASKO, Susan Dietrich. 4971 ARLINGTON CENTRE BLVD 43220 #038-40-1986 L1987 PS *020 †65

VASQUEZ, Edelma S B. 400 E CAMPUS VIEW BLVD 43235 #132-01-1962 L1976 PD PDE *062 †55

VASQUEZ, Sergio Arturo. 370 W 9TH AVE, OH STATE U COLL OF MED 43210 #038-40-2002 PD *100

VASSY, Louis Eugene. 5969 E BROAD ST, STE 400 43213 #038-40-1967 L1967 PDS GS *020 †85

VASUDEVAN, Abu Raghavan. 1581 DODD DR, 491 MCCAMPBELL HALL 43210 #495-27-1986 L2006 END *100 †20

VASUDEVAN, Raghavan. 456 W 10TH AVE 43210 #495-66-1971 L1974 CD IM *020 †20

VAUGHAN, Geoff Clarke. 2050 KENNY RD, STE 2400 43221 #038-40-1993 L1994 IM *020 †20

VAUGHAN, Nancy Morgan. 4605 SAWMILL RD, EXCELLENCE 43220 #038-45-1994 L1995 PM PME *020 †60

VEACH, J Douglas. 4343 E LIVINGSTON AVE 43227 #038-41-1957 L1957 OBG *071 †30

VECOZOLS, Aivests Livius. ■ 43214 #407-02-1950 L1950 P *071 †75

VELLUCCI, Sean Michael. 700 CHILDRENS DR 43205 #019-02-2000 L2000 PDC *100 †55

VENKAT, Deepak. ■ 43212 #016-06-2006 L2006 IM *012

VENKATARAMAN, Rajagopalan. 745 W STATE ST, STE 520 43222 #495-16-1975 L1982 NEP *020 †20

VENNEMEYER, Michael David. 793 W STATE ST, C/O MT CARMEL HOSP-MED EDU 43222 #038-40-2002 L2002 PS *020

VENTRESCA, Elio. 3650 OLENTANGY RIVER RD, STE 302 43214 #038-40-1988 L1989 IM *020

VER MEULEN, Victor R, Jr. 553 E TOWN ST 43215 #025-01-1960 L1966 OTO *071 †45

VERMILION, Blair Dale. 1654 UPHAM DR, MEANS HALL, N325 43210 #038-40-1972 L1972 VS GS *020 †85

VERNE, G Nicholas. 395 W 12TH AVE, 288A OFFICE TOWER 43210 #035-15-1989 L2007 GE IM *020 †20

VERRILL, Andrew David. 410 W 10TH AVE 43210 #038-40-1977 L1979 DR *020 †80

VESCO, Paul Anthony. 410 W 10TH AVE, N846 DOAN HALL 43210 #020-12-1997 L2003 TS *012 †85

VETTER, John Henry. 5975 E BROAD ST, STE 302 43213 #038-45-1983 L1984 PM OS *020 †60

VIDAURRE, Jorge Alberto. 700 CHILDRENS DR, DEPT OF NEUROLOGY 43205 #341-03-1995 L2005 CHN *020

VIJAN, Stephen Roth. 3555 OLENTANGY RIVER RD, STE 4020 43214 #041-13-1982 L1989 U *020 †95

VILLALOBOS, Rafael E. 1151 BETHEL RD, STE 101 43220 #055-75-1991, ▲ L1992 PS *020

VILLALON, Roberto R. PO BOX 29449 43229 #275-01-1951 L1964 OBG *071

VILLALONA, Miguel Angel. 320 W 10TH AVE, B401 STARLING-LOVING HALL 43210 #308-02-1985 L1999 ON IM *050 †20

■ = Address Information Privacy Protected

VILLARREAL, Randy Hector. 410 W 10TH AVE 43210 #166-03-2004 L2007 **FP** *012

VINCENT, Donald J. 3535 OLENTANGY RIVER RD 43214 #038-40-1937 L1937 **IMG IM** *071 †20

VINSON, David, Jr. 2511 OAKSTONE DR 43231 #038-06-1986 L1989 **GPM** *100

VISOCAN, Phyllis. 1669 W LANE AVE 43221 #038-40-1973 L1973 **OPH** *020 †35

VITEK, Lauren Vaile. 580 N 4TH ST, STE 270 43215 #016-43-1982 L1983 **ON HEM** *050 †20

VITELLAS, Kenneth M. 1654 UPHAM DR, 630 MEANS HALL 43210 #038-40-1991 L1995 **DR** *020 †80

VODOVOTZ, Daniel Leonardo. 543 TAYLOR AVE, OUTPATIENT CLINIC 43203 #132-01-1962 L2004 **U** *020 †95

VOGEL, Thomas Timothy. 1492 E BROAD ST 43205 #010-02-1965 L1966 **GS OS** *071 †85

VOLPE, Anthony Jon. 931 CHATHAM LN, STE 101 43221 #038-40-1979 L1981 **ORS OFA** *020 †40

VONDERAU, Kara Renee. ■ 43206 #017-20-2005 L2005 **PD** *012

VONFISCHER, Nathaniel Dav. ■ 43201 #038-40-2008 *012

VON VISGER, Jon Raymond. 1654 UPHAM DR, NEPHROLOGY 43210 #023-01-1996 L2005 **NEP** *020 †20

VORBROKER, Michael Louis. 750 MOUNT CARMEL MALL 43222 #038-40-1991 L1992 **EM** *020 †16

VORONTSOVA, Natalya. 793 W STATE ST, MT CARMEL MEDICAL CENTER 43222 #913-53-1996 L2000 **IM** *020

VORYS, Nichols. 1430 S HIGH ST 43207 #041-02-1953 L1954 **OBG** *071 †30

VRACHLIOTIS, Thomas E. 450 W 10TH AVE, RHODES HALL 43210 #418-01-1988 **DR** *100 †80

WADWA, Janak. 700 CHILDRENS DR 43205 #495-49-1960 L1969 **PD** *020 †55

WAGENBRENNER, Leo T. 974 BETHEL RD 43214 #038-40-1958 L1958 **OTO** *071 †45

WAGGONER, Alexis Catherin. ■ 43212 #038-40-2008 *012

WAGGONER, Raymond W, Jr. 100 OUTERBELT ST, GESTALT ASSOCIATES, INC 43213 #025-01-1959 L1987 **CHP P** *012

WAGMAN, Phillip Gary. ■ 43201 #041-09-1984 L1998 **GP NM** *020 †28

WAGNER, Andrew Duane. ■ 43204 #038-40-2006 L2006 **EM** *012

WAHEED, Rehan. ■ 43204 #038-44-2008 *012

WAHEED, Umar. 1492 E BROAD ST, TOWER 15 43205 #704-20-1995 L2004 **NEP** *012 †20

WAHOFF, Charles Geo. 43221 #038-40-1959 L1959 **PD NEP** *020 †55

WAIKHOM, Suraj S. ■ 43235 #038-41-2003 L2003 **DR** *012

WAITE, Michael David. 3535 OLENTANGY RIVER RD 43214 #054-04-1993 L1994 **CCM EM** *020 †16

WAKELY, Paul E. 700 ACKERMAN RD, STE 380 43202 #028-34-1975 L1976 **PTH PCP** *020 †50

WALKER, Earl Alfred. 85 MCNAUGHTEN RD, STE 220 43213 #038-06-1974 L1977 **D** *020

WALKER, Jon Paul. 410 W 10TH AVE, 515 DOAN HALL 43210 #038-41-2001 L2001 **GE** *100

WALKER, Michael James. 300 W 10TH AVE 43210 #035-15-1972 L1988 **SO GS** *020 †85

WALKER, Michelle Duong. 111 S GRANT AVE, THIRD FLOOR 43215 #038-40-2001 L2001 **AN** *020 †05 ‡

WALKER, Sonya Gail. 111 S GRANT AVE 43215 #038-40-1991 L1993 **FM** *020 †18

WALL, Bruce Allison. 4885 OLENTANGY RIVER RD, CENTRAL OHIO PRIMARY CARE 43214 #038-40-1977 L1977 **RHU IM** *020 †20

WALL, Patrick Michael. 700 CHILDRENS DR 43205 #038-40-1972 L1972 **NPM PD** *020 †55

WALLACE, Rachel L. ■ 43235 #048-13-2005 L2005 **OBG** *012

WALLACE, William Arthur. 4830 KNIGHTSBRIDGE BLVD, SURGERY 43214 #039-01-1999 L2000 **PS** *100 †85

WALLEN, Elizabeth Anne. 48 E FRANKFORT ST, 48 EAST FRANKFORT ST. 43206 #038-45-1986 L1987 **AN** *020 †55

WALLENBROCK, Mark Allen. 3555 OLENTANGY RIVER RD, TOWER 3050 43214 #039-01-1979 L1992 **NPM PD** *020 †55

WALLIN, Jay M. 6075 E BROAD ST 43213 #020-12-1997 L1998 **IM** *020 †20

WALTON, Janelle Renee. ■ 43221 #041-12-2014 L2004 **OBG** *012

WALTONEN, Joshua Douglass. ■ 43214 #038-06-2001 L2006 **OTO** *020 †45

WALZ, Elizabeth Terese. 750 MOUNT CARMEL MALL #250, NEUROLOGY CTR COLUMBUS I 43222 #038-40-1989 L1991 **N** *020 †75

WALZAK, Doris Elaine. 456 W 10TH AVE, FL 3 43210 #038-06-1969 L1975 **IM OS** *020 †20

WANAMAKER, Steven Roger. 340 E TOWN ST, STE 10-100 43215 #038-43-1979 L1980 **GS CCM** *020 †85

WANG, Alice Wentsuo. ■ 43228 #025-01-2004 L2005 **DR** *012

WANG, Erica. ■ 43209 #038-44-2005 L2005 **PM** *012

WANG, Hongping. 410 W 10TH AVE 43210 #243-45-1988 L2006 **P** *012

WANG, Peter. ■ 43235 #055-01-1999 L2000 **FM** *020

WARD, Emily Kay. ■ 43206 #038-40-2006 L2006 **MPD** *012

WARD, Eric Sean. 941 CHATHAM LN, STE 110 43214 #038-40-1991 L1996 **U** *020 †95

WARD, Jenaya Judonne. ■ 43230 #016-11-2007 L2007 **OBG** *012

WARD, John Jos. 85 MCNAUGHTEN RD, OHIO GASTROENTEROLOGY 43213 #038-40-1992 L1994 **GE** *020 †20

WARD, Richard Moran. 3600 OLENTANGY ROAD 43214 #007-02-1958 L1963 **ORS** *072 †40

WARE, Kevin Vaughn. 750 MOUNT CARMEL MALL 43222 #038-43-1991 L1992 **P** *020 †75

WARE, Rebecca Ann. 5151 REED RD, STE 128C 43220 #038-43-1997 L1998 **P** *020 †75

WARMOLTS, John Russell. 1654 UPHAM DR RM 405 43210 #025-01-1959 L1975 **N** *071 †75

WARNER, Mary Louise Oman. 700 CHILDRENS DR 43205 #038-40-1955 L1955 **AN OS** *071 †05

WARREN, Patrick Stanford. ■ 43204 #051-01-2005 L2006 **DR** *012

WARRIER, Veda. 1670 UPHAM DR 43210 #495-44-1997 L2001 **P** *020 †75

WASHINGTON, William Lloyd. 2339 CLEVELAND AVE, LINDEN MED CTR 43211 #038-40-1989 L1990 **FM** *020 †18

WASIELEWSKI, Ray Carl. 500 E MAIN ST, STE 240 43215 #038-40-1986 L1992 **ORS** *020 †40

WASSERMAN, James Michael. 3535 OLENTANGY BLVD 43214 #028-34-1967 L1975 **P** *020 †75

WATERFALL, Kim W. ■ 43213 #017-20-1974 L2007 **FM** *020 †18

WATERFIELD, Catherine Ann. 3311 TREMONT RD, STE 101 43221 #038-40-1998 L1999 **FM** *020 †18

WATERMAN, George David, Jr. 700 CHILDRENS DR, PEDIATRIC EMERGENCY MEDICI 43205 #035-08-1999 L2002 **PEM** *100 †55

WATKINS, Lawrence B. 2686 CROSSROADS PLAZA DR 43219 #041-12-1978 L1981 **PD** *020 †55

WATSON, Daniel R. 3555 OLENTANGY RIVER RD, RD #2060 43214 #038-44-1983 L1984 **GS TS** *020 †90,85

WATSON, Joshua Robert. ■ 43235 #036-01-2007 L2007 **MPD** *012

WATSON, Larry Wm. 4605 SAWMILL RD 43220 #055-02-1986 L1987 **ORS OSM** *020 †40

WATSON, Wm Daugherty, II. 3555 OLENTANGY RIVER RD, STE 2060 43214 #038-40-1976 L1976 **TS** *071 †85,90

WATTANASARN, Padet. ■ 43235 #891-02-1961 L1972 **N** *020 †75

WAYNAR, Marin Beth. 1021 COUNTRY CLUB RD, STE A 43213 #038-43-2002 L2002 **PD** *100 †55

WEAVER, Mark Edwin. 1933 E DUBLN GRNVL PMB 255 43229 #038-41-1983 L1984 **GP** *020

WEBB, Bradley Thomas. ■ 43220 #038-40-2008 *012

WEBB, Jimmy Webster. 5320 E MAIN ST, STE 400 43213 #038-40-1965 L1965 **GP OS** *020 †18

WEBER, Hartmut T. ■ 43220 #407-10-1947 L1958 **GP GS** *020

WEBER, Paul August. 456 W 10TH AVE 43210 #016-06-1974 L1975 **OPH** *020 †35

WEED, Harrison Goodale. 2050 KENNY RD, STE 2400 43221 #024-05-1987 L1990 **IM ID** *020 †20

WEIGAND, John Mark. 6150 E BROAD ST STE B29, GERIATRIC PHYSICIAN ASSOCI 43213 #038-41-1989 L1990 **FM** *040 †18

WEIL, David Charles. ■ 43202 #038-40-1995 L1996 **FM** *020 †18

WEINBERG, Alan Gary. 3120 E MAIN ST 43209 #024-01-1965 L1966 **IM CD** *020 †20

WEINBERGER, Janet Marie. 4351 OLENTANGY BLVD 43214 #038-43-1993 L2004 **EM** *020 †16

WEINERMAN, Julia Ann. 543 TAYLOR AVE 43203 #016-06-1977 L1978 **PM** *020 †60 ‡

WEINSTOCK, Elizabeth Ann. 1299 OLENTANGY RIVER RD 43212 #038-40-1994 L1996 **FM** *020 †18

WEISENBERG, Alan Frank. 750 MOUNT CARMEL MALL 43222 #038-40-1973 L1973 **EM** *020 †16

WEISENBURGER, Robert A. 3555 OLENTNGY RVR RD #1070 43214 #038-40-1960 L1960 **ORS** *020 †40

WEISER, Adam Craig. 750 MT CARMEL MALL, STE 350 43222 #033-06-1995 L2002 **UP** *020 †95

WEISS, Jordan Paul. 5965 E BROAD ST, STE 230 43213 #016-11-1976 L1977 **P IM** *020 †75

WEISS, Michael Louis. 4626 SAWMILL RD 43220 #038-43-1987 L1988 **FM** *020 †18

WEISS, Raul. 473 W 12TH AVE, DHLRI, STE 200 43210 #132-05-1988 L2001 **CD** *020 †20

WELKER, Mary Jo. 2231 N HIGH ST 43201 #038-40-1976 L1977 **FM** *020 †18

WELLING, D Bradley. 456 W 10TH AVE, STE 4A 43210 #049-01-1983 L1989 **OTO** *020 †45

WELLING, Rodney Duane. ■ 43220 #025-01-2007 L2007 **TY** *012

WELLS, Mark. 340 E TOWN ST STE 7-250 43215 #065-05-1983 L1996 **PS HS** *020 †65

WELLS, Patrick R. 3525 OLENTANGY RIVER RD, STE 5320 43214 #048-14-1997 L2006 **TS** *020 †85,90

WELTY, Stephen E. 700 CHILDRENS DR 43205 #040-02-1982 L2000 **NPM PD** *020 †55

WEN, Ping. 3535 OLENTANGY RIVER RD, DEPT OF PATH RIVERSIDE MEH 43214 #243-63-1983 L1999 **PTH PCP** *020 †50

WENGER, Aaron Samuel. 1654 UPHAM DR, MEANS HALL 202 43210 #020-12-2003 L2003 **IM** *100 †20

WENZKE, David Joseph. 1654 UPHAM DR, 202 MEANS HALL 43210 #038-40-2002 L2002 **GE** *012 †20

WERMAN, Howard A. 2827 W DUBLIN GRANVILLE RD, OMNIFLIGHT 43235 #035-06-1981 L1982 **EM** *050 †16

WERNER, Jeff David. ■ 43228 #016-45-2006 L2007 **DR** *012

WERNER, Joseph Gregory. ■ 43206 #038-40-2004 L2004 **AN** *012

WESTERHEIDE, Kenneth J. 85 MCNAUGHTEN RD 43213 #038-40-1997 L2002 **OSM** *020

WESTMAN, Judith A. 370 W 9TH AVE, 155A MEILING HALL 43210 #038-40-1981 L1982 **CG PD** *040 †55,19

WEWERS, Mark Damian. 1655 UPHAM DR, N325 MEANS HALL 43210 #004-01-1976 L1986 **PUD IM** *050 †20

WEXLER, Randell Keith. 504 HAVENS CORNERS RD 43230 #038-45-1990 L1991 **FM FSM** *020 †18

WHELLER, John James. 700 CHILDRENS DR, DEPARTMENT OF CARDIOLOGY 43205 #038-40-1973 L1983 **PDC** *020 †55

WHISLER, Ronald Lloyd. 480 W 9TH AVE S2056, UNIVERSITY HOSPITALS 43210 #038-40-1968 L1968 **RHU** *020 †20

WHITACRE, Gary Lowell. 5555 SCARBOROUGH BLVD 43232 #038-40-1962 L1962 **FM OM** *020 †18

WHITAKER, Elizabeth Rose. 5072 REED RD, MEDICINE 43220 #038-44-1991 L1992 **PD** *020 †55

WHITE, Jennifer Lynn. 4885 OLENTANGY RIVER RD, STE 2-10 43214 #038-40-1986 L1987 **PD** *020 †55

WHITE, Jolanda Monique. 700 CHILDRENS DR, NATIONWIDE CHILDREN'S HOSP 43205 #041-01-1999 L2006 **PG PD** *020 †55

WHITE, Mark Anthony. 3433 AGLER RD, STE 1100 43219 #038-40-1992 L1997 **IM** *020

WHITE, Matthew James. ■ 43235 #038-44-2005 L2005 **EM** *012

WHITE, Matthew Miller. 4766 W BROAD ST 43228 #038-45-1998 L2000 **PD** *020 †55

WHITE-CHOUNG, Lisa L. 3555 OLENTANGY RIVER RD, STE 4000 43214 #038-41-2000 L2000 **APM** *020 †60

WHITEHEAD, George Frederi. ■ 43228 #038-40-2006 L2006 **OPH** *012

WHITEHOUSE, Wm Keller. ■ 43221 #038-03-1956 L1963 **U** *071 †95

WHITLATCH, Joseph Paul. 1171 FAIRWAY BLVD, FAIRWAY FAMILY PHYSICIANS 43213 #038-40-1974 L1974 **FM** *020 †18

WHITSON, Wesley Joseph. ■ 43219 #038-40-2008 *012

WIDMAN, Julie Hornback. 777 W STATE ST, STE 101 43222 #038-41-1988 L1990 **DR** *020 †80

WIET, Gregory James. 555 S 18TH ST STE 2A, CHILDREN'S SURGICAL ASSOCI 43205 #016-42-1989 L1991 **PDO OTO** *020 †45

WILBERS, Lawrence Lee. 111 S GRANT AVE 43215 #011-03-1974 L1981 **BBK PTH** *020 †50

WILKIN, Jonathan Keith. ■ 43214 #038-40-1974 L1989 **D PA** *062 †15

WILKIN, Olive Craigo. ■ 43214 #051-04-1984 L1988 **AN** *020 †05

WILLETT, Darryl Neal. 974 BETHEL RD, STE A 43214 #038-40-1991 L1992 **OTO** *020 †45

WILLIAMS, Anthony. 1492 E BROAD ST 43205 #038-40-1978 L1979 **FM** *020 †18

WILLIAMS, Gwynette M. 4885 OLENTANGY RIVER RD, 2-10 43214 #038-40-1982 L1985 **PD** *020 †55

WILLIAMS, Homer Elbert. 393 E TOWN ST, STE 229 43215 #038-40-1956 L1956 **D** *020 †15

WILLIAMS, Jamar Geo, Jr. 3433 AGLER RD, STE 1100 43219 #038-45-1988 L1990 **IM** *020

WILLIAMS, James E. 111 S GRANT AVE 43215 #038-41-1949 L1949 **U** *071 †95

WILLIAMS, Joanna Dawn. 410 W 10TH AVE 43210 #038-40-2000 L2000 **PTH** *100 †50 ‡

WILLIAMS, L Thos. ■ 43207 #041-02-1957 L1958 **OM OS** *071

WILLIAMS, Lowell L. ■ 43212 #030-40-1951 L1953 **OS OPH** *072

WILLIAMS, Oliver K, III. ■ 43235 #038-40-1970 L1970 **EM AM** *075 †18

WILLIAMS, P Tennyson. 456 W 10TH AVE RM B 43210 #038-06-1951 L1951 **FM** *071 †18

WILLIAMS, Ransome R. ■ 43235 #038-41-1952 L1952 **FM OS** *071 †18

WILLIAMS, Steven Ross. 4830 KNIGHTSBRIDGE BLVD, STE E 43214 #038-40-1981 L1983 **REN OBG** *020

WILLIAMS, Thomas E, Jr. 410 W 10TH AVE 43210 #038-40-1963 L1963 **TS** *030 †85,90

WILLIAMS, Thomas J. 3400 OLENTANGY RIVER RD, STE 150 43202 #016-06-1951 L1953 **IM** *020 †20

WILLIAMS, Vernon. 1492 E BROAD ST, STE 1302 43205 #020-02-1995 L1999 **FM** *020 †18

WILLIAMSON, Eric Michaell. ■ 43201 #038-40-2007 L2007 **TY** *012

WILLIARD, Michael B. 85 MCNAUGHTEN RD 43213 #038-40-1987 L1989 **ORS** *020 †40

WILLIARD, Thomas Buttimer. ■ 43209 #038-41-1955 L1955 **IM** *071

WILSON, Jessica Cybeleeli. ■ 43202 #012-01-2006 L2006 **N** *012

WILT, Roger Duane. 3311 TREMONT RD, STE 101 43221 #038-40-1989 L1990 **FM** *020 †18

WINANS, Patrick Conrad. 793 W STATE ST 43222 #038-40-1965 L1965 **IM** *071

WINCH, Peter Donald. 700 CHILDRENS DR 43205 #038-41-1997 L2000 **AN** *020 †05,55

WINCHELL, Joseph Sean. 370 W 9TH AVE, OH STATE U COLL OF MED 43210 #038-40-2002 L2002 **FM** *020 †18

WINDLER, Henry D. 3535 OLENTANGY RIVER RD 43214 #055-01-1982 L1986 **DR** *020 †80

WINGATE, Jamie Rene. ■ 43235 #038-40-2008 *012

WINKLEMAN, Brian James. ■ 43228 #017-20-2003 L2003 **GS** *012

WINLAND, Ronald Dean. 3400 OLENTANGY RIVER RD, STE 150 43202 #038-40-1976 L1978 **IM** *020 †20

WINNER, Marshall Wayne. ■ 43212 #038-40-2004 L2004 **IM CD** *100 †20

WINTER, Chester Caldwell. 410 W 10TH AVE 43210 #018-03-1946 L1960 **U** *071 †95

WINTERHALTER, Jason Mark. 697 THOMAS LN, RIVERSIDE FAMILY MEDICINE 43214 #038-43-2004 L2004 **FM** *020 †18

WINTERHALTER, Melissa Daw. 700 CHILDRENS DR 43205 #038-43-2004 L2004 **PD** *020 †55

WINTERS, Janine Penfield. 3595 OLENTANGY RIVER RD 43214 #038-45-1994 L1996 **FM** *020 †18 ‡

WINZENREAD, John Warren. 3311 TREMONT RD, STE 101 43221 #038-40-1982 L1984 **FM** *020 †18

WIRTZ, Dylan Jacob. ■ 43215 #038-40-2007 L2007 **IM** *012

WISE, Henry Alexander, II. 941 CHATHAM LN, STE 110 43221 #051-01-1964 L1972 **U GS** *071 †95

WISE, William E, Jr. 3545 OLENTANGY RIVER RD, STE 500 43214 #024-05-1983 L1985 **CRS** *85,10

WISPE, Jonathan Raln. 700 CHILDRENS DR, NATIONWIDE CHILDREN'S HOSP 43205 #018-03-1979 L1985 **NPM PD** *050 †55

WISSEL, Mary Ellen. 995 E BROAD ST 43205 #038-40-1980 L1982 **BBK IM** *030 †20

WITMAN, Patricia Mary. 700 CHILDRENS DR, DIV OF PEDIATRIC DERMATOLO 43205 #056-06-1994 L2006 **D** *020 †15

WOLF, Jacob Marvin. 7400 HUNTINGTON PARK DR, STE 200 43235 #016-42-1997 L1999 **FM** *020 †18

WOLFE, Heather Ann. ■ 43215 #025-01-2005 L2005 **MPD** *012

WONG, Cecelia Hsun. 3525 OLENTANGY RIVER RD, STE 4330 43214 #038-40-2001 L2001 **IM** *020 †20

WONG, Michael Tetwing. 370 W 9TH AVE, OH STATE U COLL OF MED 43210 #038-40-2002 **FM** *100

WOOD, Joel Christopher. 504 HAVENS CORNERS RD, OSU FAMILY PRACTICE GAHANN 43230 #038-40-1997 L1998 **FM** *020 †18

WOOD, Karen Lynn. 473 W 12TH AVE, 201 DAVIS HEART & LUNG RES 43210 #038-44-1996 L1997 **PCC** *020 †20

WOODARD, Donald Darell. 4337 CLEVELAND AVE, GLOBAL HEALTH CARE CENTER 43224 #038-43-1979 L1981 **FM EM** *020 †20

WOODARD, Martin Jeffery. 750 MOUNT CARMEL MALL 43222 #038-41-1988 L1990 **EM** *020 †20

WOODARD, Wiley Gray, Jr. 750 W BROAD ST 43222 #038-40-1978 L1979 **OBG** *020

WOODLIEF, Cameron Michael. 6465 E BROAD ST, STE D 43213 #036-01-1997 L2000 **IM** *020 †20

WOODROW, Virginia C. 3535 OLENTANGY RIVER RD, G/RMH, BEHAVIORAL HEALTH 43214 #038-40-1981 L1982 **P** *075 †75

WOODRUFF, Robert Theodore. 1654 UPHAM DR, MEANS HALL 4TH FLOOR 43210 #038-40-2003 L2003 **N** *012

WOODS, John Walter. 3700 CORPORATE DR, STE 200 43231 #038-40-1965 L1965 **AN** *071 †05

WOOLEY, Charles Francis. 473 W 12TH AVE, HEART LUNG INSTITUTE 43210 #035-09-1954 L1960 **CD IM** *050 †20

WOYACH, Jennifer Ann. 1654 UPHAM DR 43210 #038-40-2005 L2005 **IM** *012

WRENN, Jennifer Ann. 1021 COUNTRY CLUB RD, STE B 43213 #017-20-2000 L2000 **OBG** *020 ‡

WRIGHT, Francis Stuart. 700 CHILDRENS DR 43205 #035-45-1955 L1981 **OS PD** *020 †55,75

WRIGHT, Frank Creamer. ■ 43221 #038-40-1964 L1964 **OBG** *071 †30

WRIGHT, Kenneth James. 370 W 9TH AVE, OH STATE U COLL OF MED 43210 #038-40-2000 L2005 **GS** *020 †85

WROBLE, Randall Robt. 323 E TOWN ST, SPORTS MEDICINE GRANT 43215 #016-11-1982 L1987 **ORS OSM** *020 †40

WU, Grace Yehwie. 700 CHILDRENS DR, ED 650 A 43205 #001-02-2004 L2004 **MPD** *012

WU, Gwo-Chen. 543 TAYLOR AVE 43203 #244-04-1970 L1975 **CD** *020 †20

WU, Haifeng. 410 W 12TH AVE, 290 MEDICAL RESEARCH FACIL 43210 #243-72-1984 L2001 **PTH** *020 †50

WU, Sandra Jones. 1194 OLD HENDERSON RD, STE A 43220 #038-40-1996 L1997 **D** *020 †15

WULF, John Wm. 810 JASONWAY AVE STE B, CENTRAL OH PRIMARY CARE 43214 #038-43-1985 L1986 **IM** *020 †20

WURAPA, Raymond Kofi. 259 TAYLOR STATION RD 43213 #038-06-1995 L2001 **HS** *020 †40

WURST, Ann Marie. 921B JASONWAY AVE 43214 #038-40-1985 L1986 **OBG** *020 †30

WURSTER, Mark Winfred. 320 W 10TH AVE, OSU MEDICAL CENTER, DIVISI 43210 #043-01-1982 L2002 **IM HEM** *020 †20

WYATT, Robert Howard. 931 CHATHAM LN, STE 200 43220 #012-01-1975 L1979 **N** *020 †75

WYNBRANDT, Jonathan Harri. 1654 UPHAM DR, 202 MEANS HALL 43210 #305-01-2003 L2003 **PCC** *012 †20

WYND, Mary Ann. 1492 E BROAD ST 43205 #038-40-1985 L1986 **FM OM** *020 †18

WYNN, Timothy John. 6001 E BROAD ST, MT CARMEL EAST HOSPITAL 43213 #038-40-1984 L1985 **IM** *020 †20

WYSE, Donald Gene. 1727 BETHEL RD 43220 #038-40-1961 L1961 **FM** *071 †18

WYSOKINSKI, Robert Ralph. 1601 W BROAD ST, COLUMBUS DEVELOPMENTAL CEN 43222 #561-17-1981 L1988 **FM** *020 †18

XIA, Yun. 410 W 10TH AVE # N-416, DEPT OF ANESTHESIOLOGY 43210 #243-21-1983 L2000 **AN GE** *020

XU, Yi-Qing. 320 W 10TH AVE, B321 STARLING LOVING HALL 43210 #243-16-1988 L2001 **HO** *020 †20

YABLOK, David Owen. 410 W 10TH AVE, N-146 DOAN HALL 43210 #038-40-1985 L1988 **AN** *020 †05

YADAV, Sanjay. 5109 W BROAD ST, STE 101 43228 #495-45-1991 L2004 **HO** *020 †20

YADAV, Suresh Kumar. 1492 E BROAD ST, WEST ANNEX MODULAR UNIT 43205 #672-01-1999 L2006 **IM** *020 †20

YAFFE, Michael Eric. 4030 W HENDERSON RD 43220 #038-40-1980 L1982 **IM ADL** *020 †20

YAHNER, Michael Jos. 3535 OLENTANGY RIVER RD 43214 #048-13-1985 L1992 **EM** *020 †16

YAKHMI, Rajiv. 2415 DEEWOOD DR STE B 43229 #495-29-1992 L2000 **FM** *020

YAMARICK, Warren Kyle. 3535 OLENTANGY BLVD 43214 #038-40-1984 L1985 **EM FM** *020 †16

YAN, Weiming. ■ 43212 #038-40-2008 *012

YANG, Lin. 793 W STATE ST 43222 #243-65-1983 L2006 **IM** *012

YANG, Ming. 410 W 10TH AVE 43210 #243-46-1993 L2007 **NR** *012

YASINSKI, Michael Stephen. 1670 UPHAM DR 43210 #003-01-2007 L2007 **P** *012

YATES, Allan James. 333 W 10TH AVE, 4166 GRAVES HALL 43210 #060-01-1967 L1975 **NP** *020

YATES, Andrew Richard. 700 CHILDRENS DR 43205 #038-40-2001 L2001 **CCP** *012 †55

YAU, Nancy Yeechuen. 43219 #048-02-2006 L2006 **PD** *012

YEAGER, Nicholas Dominic. 55 S 18TH ST, DEPT OF HEMATOLOGY 43205 #038-44-1996 L1997 **PHO** *020 †55 ‡

YEARSLEY, Martha M.. 410 W 10TH AVE 43210 #264-02-1986 L2001 **PTH** *100

YEE, Lisa Diane. 300 W 10TH AVE 43210 #008-01-1986 L1996 **SO GS** *020 †85

YEEN, Wing Choy. 410 W 12TH AVE 43210 #143-03-1998 L2005 **TS** *100 †85

YEHSAKUL, David Chuenwing. ■ 43201 #038-40-2008 *012

YELDELL, Peter B. 750 MOUNT CARMEL MALL 43222 #028-46-1983 L1986 **EM** *020 †16

YEN, Jack Cheng-Chieh. 410 W 10TH AVE 43210 #305-01-2006 L2007 **P** *012

YERINGTON, Christopher L. 793 W STATE ST 43222 #038-06-1998 L1999 **AN** *020 †05

YERINGTON, Gregory Cannon. ■ 43220 #038-06-2000 L2000 **IM** *020 †05

YILMAZ, Serdar. 1654 UPHAM DR, 363 MEANS HALL 43210 #902-03-1986 L1999 *020

YIMEN, Meron. ■ 43202 #038-40-2006 L2006 **IM** *012

YIN, Chung Kill. 5969 E BROAD ST, STE 100 43213 #583-02-1970 L1979 **RO** *020 †80

YING, Alan J. 370 W 9TH AVE, OH STATE U COLL OF MED 43210 #038-40-1999 **GS** *100

YNCLINO, Vicente Cuico. ■ 43217 #748-11-1963 L1977 **AM FM** *020 †70,18

YOKUM, Michael David. ■ 43216 #038-40-1989 *075

YOO, Ho Min. 410 W 10TH AVE, 5024 UHC 43210 #583-10-1972 *100

YORK, Nowell Robert. 370 W 9TH AVE, OH STATE U COLL OF MED 43210 #038-40-2003 L2003 **FM** *020 †18

YOST, Nathan I. ■ 43209 #016-11-1977 L1996 **IM PUD** *020 †20

YOUNG, Angela Murray. ■ 43205 #038-40-2004 L2004 **PD** *100

YOUNG, Cody Mark. 5100 W BROAD ST, DEPT OF MED EDUCATION 43228 #028-79-2006, ▲ L2006 **DR** *012

YOUNG, Elizabeth M. 6100 E MAIN ST, STE 105 43213 #038-40-2003 L2007 **OBG** *020

YOUNG, Gordon Alexander. 700 CHILDRENS DR 43205 #062-01-1957 L1961 **PDP PD** *071 †55

YOUNG, James Louis, Jr. 1670 UPHAM DR 43210 #048-14-1995 L1996 **P** *020 †75

YOUNG, Jennifer Hweitan. 50 MCNAUGHTEN RD 43213 #016-06-1988 L1994 **OPH** *020 †35

YOUNG, Jeremy David. 1654 UPHAM DR, 202 MEANS HALL 43210 #025-07-2001 L2001 **ID** *100

YOUNG, Louise Chai-Yi C. 2510 SLATE RUN DR 43220 #242-16-1949 L1960 **GYN** *020

YOUNG, Steven Albert. 3525 OLENTANGY RIVER RD, STE 5360 43214 #025-01-1998 L2005 **DR** *100 †28,80

YOUNGMAN, James Douglas. 4701 OLENTANGY RIVER RD, STE 2 43214 #017-20-1974 L1974 **P** *020 †75

YU, Joseph Ps. 1654 UPHAM DR, 630 MEANS HALL 43210 #038-40-1987 L1990 **DR** *020 †80

YU, Michael Lawrence. ■ 43228 #055-01-2004 L2004 **N** *012

YUH, William T C. 1654 UPHAM DR, 630 MEANS HALL 43210 #001-02-1980 L2004 **RNR NM** *040 †80,28

YUNKER, Douglas Eugene. 2240 N BANK DR, UPPR 43220 #038-40-1982 L1986 **AN PME** *020 †05

ZADIKOFF, Cindy. 370 W 9TH AVE, OH STATE U COLL OF MED 43210 #038-40-1999 L2003 **N** *020 †75

ZAFIRIDES, Peter Panos. 5151 REED RD, STE 128C 43220 #038-40-1992 L1994 **P** *020 †75

ZAIDI, Syed Ali Nasir. 473 W 12TH AVE, STE 200 43210 #704-25-1999 L2006 **CD** *012 †55,20

ZAKMAN, Mijo. 1960 W BROAD ST 43223 #957-01-1956 L1972 **P** *020

ZAMEL, Khaled Mohamed. 700 CHILDRENS DR, DIVISION OF PEDIATRIC NEUR 43205 #915-03-1990 L2001 **CHN CN** *020 †75

ZANAGNOLO, Vanna Luisa. 2050 KENNY RD, CO OSU HOSPS-CORP CRED OFC 43221 #561-29-1985 L2003 **OBG** *020

ZANGMEISTER, Jeffrey. 3100 PLAZA PROPERTIES BLVD 43219 #038-40-1981 L1981 **ON HEM** *020 †20

ZARTMAN, Kevin Charles. ■ 43201 #038-40-2007 L2007 **ORS** *012

ZEEB, Paul. 750 MOUNT CARMEL MALL 43222 #038-45-1980 L1981 **OM EM** *020 †16,18

ZEGAR, Alsaghir Sadat. 1670 UPHAM DR, 140B NEUR 43210 #915-07-1986 **P** *100

ZELLMER, Richard Burdett. 3535 OLENTANGY BLVD 43214 #056-06-1981 L1997 **PTH** *020 †50

ZEN, Ilias. ■ 43220 #165-04-1973 L1977 **CD IM** *020 †20

ZENO, Brian Ross. 3545 OLENTANGY RIVER RD, RIVERSIDE PULMONARY 43214 #038-44-2000 L2006 **PCC** *020 †20

ZHAO, Xiaosong. 410 W 10TH AVE, OH STATE UNIV HOSP 43210 #243-52-1989 L2006 **N** *020

ZHOU, Xiaoping. 2050 KENNY RD, OHIO STATE UNIV HOSP 43221 #243-58-1986 L2006 **PTH** *012

ZIETLOW, Christopher Mark. ■ 43204 #038-40-2005 L2005 **IM** *012

ZIMMERMAN, Michelle Rae. 697 THOMAS LN 43214 #038-40-2003 L2003 **FM** *020 †18

ZIPF, William Byron. 6353 PRESIDENTIAL GTWY, STE 120 43231 #038-40-1972 L1978 **END PD** *020 †20

ZIRWAS, Matthew James. 5965 E BROAD ST, STE 290 43213 #041-12-2000 L2004 **D** *020 †15

ZOCHOWSKI, Adam Michael. 750 MT CARMEL MALL STE 200, MID OHIO SURG ASSOC INC 43222 #038-45-1998 L1999 **GS** *020 †85

ZOZ, Donald F. 1654 UPHAM DR, 202 MEANS HALL 43210 #038-40-2005 L2005 **IM** *012

ZSOLDOS, Robert Jonathan. ■ 43214 #055-01-2006 L2006 **IM** *012

ZULLIGER, John Jos. 5320 E MAIN 43213 #038-40-1977 L1980 **OTO FPS** *020 †45

ZUMBERGE, Nicholas Andrew. 700 CHILDRENS DR, CHILDREN'S RADIOLOGICAL IN 43205 #038-40-2000 L2000 **RNR** *020 †80

ZUSPAN, Frederick P. 410 W 10TH AVE, OHIO STATE UNIV 43210 #038-40-1951 L1951 **OBG** *071 †30

ZVARA, David Alexander. ■ 43220 #038-40-1985 L1986 **AN** *030 †05

ZWEIER, Jay Louis. 473 W 12TH AVE, 110G DHLRI 43210 #023-01-1981 L2003 **CD IM** *020

ZWIEBEL, Susan Christine. 2150 MARBLE CLF OFC PARK P 43215 #038-40-2003 L2003 **FM** *020 †18

COLUMBUS GROVE – PUTNAM

SANDY, John Steven. 204 E SYCAMORE ST 45830 #038-40-1974 L1975 **FM** *020 †18

CONCORD TOWNSHIP – LAKE

VLADIC, Franjo. ■ 44077 #038-40-1999 L1999 **GE** *100 †20

CONNEAUT – ASHTABULA

ABUEG, Hector Tolentino. 224 PARRISH RD 44030 #748-01-1964 L1973 **GS** *020 †85
ANDERSON, Wm Henry, Jr. ■ 44030 #036-07-1953 L1965 **GP CD** *071 †18
ANGERMAN, Douglas Robert. 167 W MAIN RD, STE F 44030 #038-40-1970 L1970 **FM** *020 †18
DORAN, William Francis. ■ 44030 #023-01-1954 L1955 **FM** *071
FRANLEY, Douglas K. 167 W MAIN RD STE F 44030 #038-06-1972 L1973 **IM** *020 †20
GALLO-GODOY, Claudio. ■ 44030 #847-08-1964 L1973 **GS VS** *071 †85
KONDRU, Nafisa Banu. 167 W MAIN RD STE D 44030 #495-11-1977 L1992 **PD** *020 †55
MERANDA, John Richard. 167 W MAIN RD, STE G 44030 #038-40-1982 L1983 **FM EM** *020 †18
NAGAPRAKASH, Kaveripatnam. 167 W MAIN RD STE D 44030 #495-09-1967 L1974 **PD** *020
QUAGLIA, Mauro. ■ 44030 #033-05-1997 L1999 **IM** *020 †20
REHMATULLAH, Nasimullah. 167 W MAIN RD, STE C 44030 #704-01-1974 L1981 **ORS** *020 †40
RICAURTE, Jorge A. PO BOX 58 44030 #319-01-1951 L1960 **IM** *071
SCHWARTZ, Robert Herman. 158 W MAIN RD 44030 #038-40-1961 L1961 **OBG** *071 †30
SINGH, Parminder. 235 PARRISH RD ■ B 44030 #495-29-1980 L1992 **IM** *020 †20
TAN, Antero Cacchero. 158 W MAIN RD 44030 #748-01-1961 L1970 **GS GP** *071
VENABLE, John E, Jr. ■ 44030 #038-40-1957 L1957 **EM FM** *071 †16,18
WEBER, Linda Elaine. 167 W MAIN RD, STE G 44030 #038-40-1985 L1988 **FM OBS** *020 †18
YOON, Moon Kyung. 224 PARRISH RD 44030 #583-08-1968 L1975 **OBG** *020

CONTINENTAL – PUTNAM

KRASKA, Joseph Paul. 102 ASH ST BOX 999 45831 #306-01-1987 L1996 **FM** *020 †18

COPLEY – SUMMIT

ABDUL AZIZ, Mohammed Rafi. ■ 44321 #704-17-1984 L2006 **CHP** *012
ADAMS, Sarah Renee. 100 HUNT CLUB DR, ■ 182 44321 #028-02-2007 L2007 **EM** *012
AL-NAJJAR, Suleiman I. ■ 44321 #575-01-1982 *100
AQUINO, Jennifer Bautista. ■ 44321 #748-02-2004 L2006 **IM** *012
ARCINUE, Maria Roxanne Ai. ■ 44321 #748-01-2003 L2007 **PD** *012
ATHOTA, Padmaja. ■ 44321 #495-57-1989 L2006 **MSR** *100 †80
AUDINO, Anthony Natalino. ■ 44321 #038-43-2006 L2006 **PD** *012
BEFUS, Steven Peter. ■ 44321 #025-07-1978 L2002 **FM** *020 †18
BEHNAWA, Walid Ahmad. 2752 GLENHAVEN AVE, APT G 44321 #305-01-2005 L2006 **FP** *012
BRAR, Inderjeet Singh. ■ 44321 #495-29-1999 L2001 **PCC** *012 †20
BRICKNER, Eugene Walter. ■ 44321 #038-06-1956 L1956 **OS** *020 †30
BRODERICK, Erin Kate. ■ 44321 #038-44-2006 L2006 **EM** *012
CATLETT, Justin David. ■ 44321 #038-44-2003 L2003 **FM** *020 †18
CHUDYK, Alison Therese. ■ 44321 #038-43-2007 L2007 **TY** *012
CLEARY, Francis A. ■ 44321 #038-40-1953 L1953 **FM** *071 †18
DAVIES, Brian Wm. ■ 44321 #017-20-1979 L1983 **PS HS** *075
DECKERT, David Wm. 4777 RIDGEWOOD RD 44321 #038-44-1988 L1989 **P** *020 †75
DI BARTOLOMEO, Andrew E. ■ 44321 #038-40-1972 L1972 **ADM** *016
EFEBERA, Yvonne Adeduni. 4623 LINDA LN 44321 #041-14-1998 L2000 **HO** *012 †20 ‡
EGHBAL, Azam Abbasi. ■ 44321 #011-03-2001 L2003 **PDR** *100 †80
ESIMAI, Ogenna Adibeli. ■ 44321 #001-02-2005 L2006 **PD** *012
FENTON, Bradford. ■ 44321 #024-05-1995 L2005 **OBG** *020 †30 ‡
FERRIS, Robert John. ■ 44321 #020-02-1942 L1943 **IM GP** *071
HEIM, Brian David. 1394 S CLEVELAND MASSLN RD 44321 #038-44-1995 L1996 **FM** *020 †18
HIREMATH, Kotreshwar C. ■ 44321 #495-35-1974 L1998 **P** *020 †75
KALTENTHALER, Albert. ■ 44321 #407-10-1953 L1959 **FOP** *062 †50
KAUR, Hanspreet. ■ 44321 #038-44-1991 L1992 **HO** *020 †50,20
LENCZEWSKI, Brian C. ■ 44321 #035-09-2002 L2007 **GS** *012
LEONARD, James David. ■ 44321 #038-45-2005 L2005 **EM** *012
LOMARDA, Maria Celeste Ba. ■ 44321 #748-02-2004 L2006 **FP** *012
LU, Jyhi James. ■ 44321 #038-40-2007 L2007 **EM** *012
MALIK, Shruti. ■ 44321 #038-44-2007 L2007 **OBG** *012
MANTON, Richard Brook. ■ 44321 #038-40-1987 **DR** *075
MARCANTHONY, Nicholas Bra. ■ 44321 #038-44-2008 *012
MARIANO, Sinukuan Canete. 4535 WESTMONT BLVD, AKRON CLINIC 44321
 #748-08-1967 L1974 **DR** *062 †80
MASE, Sharon Elizabeth. ■ 44321 #038-44-2007 L2007 **OBG** *012
NARAYANAN, Rama. ■ 44321 #495-04-1988 L2006 **IM** *012
PATINO, Maria Minamahal C. ■ 44321 #748-02-2004 L2005 **IM** *012
PATURI, Anuradha N. ■ 44321 #038-43-2003 L2004 **OPH** *012
PHAN, Vu Duynguyen. ■ 44321 #056-06-2004 L2004 **EM** *012
QUA, Debbie Anne Chiu. ■ 44321 #748-02-2005 L2007 **IM** *012
REDDY, Rahul Kutur. ■ 44321 #038-43-2003 L2004 **OPH** *012
REISBERG, Irwin Robt. ■ 44321 #017-20-1961 L1963 **GE IM** *071
ROZANSKY, Alison Joy. ■ 44321 #016-42-2003 L2003 **ORS** *012
SAAVEDRA, Carlos Angel. ■ 44321 #132-01-1962 L1978 **VS GS** *071 †85
SAXENA, Nibha. ■ 44321 #495-77-1999 L2002 **PTH** *100 †50
SCHAAF, Adam Carlton. ■ 44321 #038-40-2004 L2004 **ORS** *012
SCHIEDA, Jill Janine. ■ 44321 #038-43-2003 L2003 **IM** *100
SHAH, Manish Vipinchandra. ■ 44321 #495-76-1993 L2005 **OBG** *012
SHOTT, Robert Steven. ■ 44321 #038-40-2005 L2005 **PTH** *012
SINGH, Deepjot. ■ 44321 #495-45-1995 L1999 **HO** *020 †50,20
STEWART, Kimberly Ann. 1053 S CLEVELAND MASSLN RD 44321 #038-44-1986 L1988
 RHU *020 †20
TURNBULL, Jessica Marie. ■ 44321 #038-41-2006 L2006 **PD** *012
TURNER, Tiffany Lynn. ■ 44321 #038-44-2005 L2005 **PD** *012
WADIA, Shernaz Aspi. ■ 44321 #038-41-2007 L2007 **PD** *012
WANEK, Steven Allen. ■ 44321 #038-43-2003 L2003 **GS** *012
WHITE, Erik David. 4886 PAXTON RD 44321 #038-40-1995 L1996 **AI** *020 †03,55

CORTLAND – TRUMBULL

ABDUL-AAL, Amine Rustom. 550 TRUMBULL AVE 44410 #605-01-1986 L1995 **OBG** *020 †30
AMES, Howard Scott. 2630 ELM RD NE, BLDG C 44410 #051-04-1984 L1989 **DR** *020 †80
ASHRAF, Sheikh Mohammad. 2654 ELM RD NE 44410 #704-01-1962 L1974 **PD** *071
ASHTON, Robert Andrew. ■ 44410 #035-47-1999 L2006 **DR** *020
BOETSCH, Charles Edward. 2630 ELM RD NE, BLDG C 44410 #056-05-1990 L1999
 DR NM *020 †80,28
BUNN, William H, Jr. 2600 STATE ROUTE 5 44410 #038-06-1953 L1953 **IM CD** *071 †20
COLIADIS, Koula. 2630 ELM RD NE, BLDG C 44410 #038-44-1991 L1993 **VIR** *020 †80
CRAWFORD, Wm Lawrence. 2630 ELM RD NE, BLDG C 44410 #038-40-1970 L1970
 DR *020 †80
CUCULIC, Linda Louise. 2600 STATE ROUTE 5, BLDG D 44410 #649-14-1981 L1988
 FM *020 †18
EUCKER, Jonathan Trent. 2652 ELM RD NE 44410 #038-44-1996 L1997 **OBG** *020
FEALKO, Monika Gerda. 2652 ELM RD NE 44410 #038-44-1999 L1999 **OBG** *020 †30
FECOWYCZ, Bohdan Orest. 2630 ELM RD NE, BLDG C 44410 #033-05-1969 L1975
 R DR *071 †80
FONTANAROSA, Mary Ann. 2600 STATE ROUTE 5, BLDG D 44410 #038-43-1982 L1984
 IM *020 †20
GIBSON, Gary Randall. 2634 ELM RD NE, ELM RD MEDICAL PARK 44410 #038-06-1980 L1983
 IM *020 †20
GOULD, Paul Nathan. 2630 ELM RD NE, BLDG C 44410 #306-01-1993 L2001 **DR** *020 †80
GRONER, Thomas Robt. 2630 ELM RD NE, BLDG C 44410 #038-43-1987 L1990 **DR** *020 †80
HILDEBRAND, Carl R. ■ 44410 #038-40-1960 L1960 **OS P** *030
JOHNSON, Lynn Marie. 550 TRUMBULL AVE 44410 #038-41-2000 L2003 **PD** *020 †55
KAMINSKI, Thomas D. 2630 ELM RD NE, BLDG C 44410 #048-04-1983 L1987 **DR** *020 †80
KANTERMAN, Leonard Harvey. 2600 STATE ROUTE 5, BLDG D 44410 #035-08-1977 L1984
 IM *020 †20
KOWAL, Maria Dariatanya. 2642 STATE ROUTE 5 44410 #025-12-1996 L1999 **PD** *020 †55
LAZAROU, Spiros Alexander. ■ 44410 #023-01-1985 L1986 **PS GS** *020
LEE, Lamberto Tee. ■ 44410 #748-01-1963 L1971 **IM** *020
LOGES, Richard J, III. 2630 ELM RD NE, BLDG C 44410 #038-45-1990 L1996 **DR VIR** *020 †80
LUCERO, Marisha A. 2630 STATE ROUTE 5 44410 #748-10-1989 L1999 **OS PD** *020 †55
OLSON, Dan Neil. 2600 STATE ROUTE 5, BLDG D 44410 #038-40-1974 L1980 **IM** *020 †20
PATEL, Bipinchandra M. 170 S HIGH ST 44410 #495-01-1972 L1981 **FM** *020 †18
PULLIAM, Morris Wade. 2630 ELM RD NE BLDG C 44410 #028-02-1966 L1998 **NS LM** *020 †25
QUARLES, Ruth F. 2600 STATE ROUTE 5 44410 #047-07-1981 L1983 **FM EM** *020 †18
REDLICH, Robert Steven. 2630 ELM RD NE, BLDG C 44410 #038-43-1988 L1995
 DR RNR *020 †80
ROSTOM, Mourad Louis. 2600 STATE ROUTE 5, BLDG D 44410 #915-02-1980 L1991
 IM *020 †20
ROSTOM, Sohair K. 2600 STATE ROUTE 5, BLDG D 44410 #915-02-1985 L1993 **IM** *020 †20
SANSOTERRA, David J. 2642 STATE ROUTE 5 44410 #025-12-1996 L1999 **PD** *020 †55
SHIPMAN, Tara Ann. 2652 ELM RD NE 44410 #038-06-1995 L1997 **OBG** *020 †30
STECHER, Robert Pamler. 2588 ELM RD NE 44410 #048-16-1999 L2006 **DR** *100 †80
VLAD, John O. 2654 ELM RD NE BLDG C 44410 #038-40-1960 L1960 **DR** *020 †55
WOODRUFF, R Wayne. ■ 44410 #019-02-1963 L1967 **U** *071 †95

COSHOCTON – COSHOCTON

ALVERSON, Tammy Susan. 311 S 15TH ST 43812 #045-04-1995 L1996 **FM** *072 †18
BROWN, Stuart K. 1325 CHESTNUT ST 43812 #038-75-1994, ▲ L1995 **FM** *020
CARVER, Gary James. 406 S 15TH ST 43812 #038-43-1979 L1981 **IM IMG** *020 †20
CARVER, Susan H Magness. 507 S 16TH ST 43812 #038-43-1979 L1979 **PD** *020 †55
GIBSON, Clayton Tyler. 311 S 15TH ST, STE 206 43812 #016-06-1979 L2004 **ORS HS** *020 †40
GOSKY, Gregory James. 406 S 15TH ST 43812 #038-40-1975 L1975 **IM** *020 †20
GRAHAM, William Ralph. ■ 43812 #038-40-1957 L1957 **FM GS** *071
GWINN, Robert B. 440 BROWNS LN 43812 #018-75-1980, ▲ L1981 **FM** *020 †18
HOUMSSE, Mahmoud. 311 S 15TH ST, STE 101 43812 #875-02-1989 L1995 **ICE CD** *020 †20
JOHNSON, Robert R. 440 BROWNS LN 43812 #038-06-1951 L1951 **AN FM** *071
KUNDERT, Ernest Edgar. 311 S 15TH ST, STE 105 43812 #016-11-1966 L2001 **GS** *020 †85
MAGNESS, Alfred H. 1415 ORANGE ST, # 1 43812 #041-01-1945 L1945 **GS TRS** *071 †85
MAGNESS, Linda Joyce. 503 S 16TH ST 43812 #038-40-1973 L1973 **DR** *020 †80
MAGNESS, Thomas Book. 230 CHESTNUT ST 43812 #038-43-1981 L1981 **OPH** *020 †35
MERZWEILER, Susan Marie. 406 S 15TH ST 43812 #038-06-1998 L2001 **PD** *020 †55
MEYER, Jerold Alan. 440 BROWNS LN 43812 #038-43-1977 L1978 **FM FPG** *020 †18
MUGOSA, Mike. ■ 43812 #957-02-1987 L2005 **GS** *020 †85
PRIOR, Paul Aaron. 311 S 15TH ST, STE 102 43812 #038-40-1994 L2000 **OBG** *020 †30
SAFAR, Ammar. 1523 WALNUT ST, STE 1 43812 #875-02-1997 L1999 **IM** *020 †20
SCHLABACH, Renee Ann. 406 S 15TH ST 43812 #038-43-2000 L2000 **FM** *020 †18
SECREST, Robert Warren. 406 S 15TH ST, STE 3 43812 #038-40-1957 L1957 **FM PHP** *071
SHAH, Arvind M. 311 S 15TH ST, STE 105 43812 #495-17-1971 L1983 **GS CD** *020 †85
SISON, Francisco. 125 N 7TH ST 43812 #748-01-1963 L1975 **IM** *020
SZEMETYLO, Victor. 1523 WALNUT ST, GASTROENTEROLOGY 43812 #035-15-1987 L1991
 GE *020 †20
VELASQUEZ, David Antonio. 125 N 7TH ST 43812 #649-38-1990 L2000 **IM** *020 †20
VIROSTKO, Douglas John. 440 BROWNS LN 43812 #038-40-1990 L1991 **FM OBS** *020 †18
VOTYPKA, Raymond Jos. 311 S 15TH ST STE 202 43812 #030-06-1966 L1969 **OTO** *020 †45
WARREN, Don Garn. 406 S 15TH ST 43812 #038-40-1956 L1956 **GP** *071 †18
WOOLERY, Michael David. 440 BROWNS LN 43812 #038-40-1997 L1998 **FM** *020 †18
WRIGHT, Norman L. 440 BROWNS LN 43812 #038-06-1951 L1951 **FM GS** *020 †18
YANDAM, Gabriel J. 656 CHESTNUT ST 43812 #875-02-1978 L1996 **OBG** *020 †30

COVINGTON – MIAMI

RICE, Donald Warren. 320 LARRY ST BOX 128 45318 #038-40-1959 L1959 **GP AM** *071

CRESTLINE – CRAWFORD

LIU, Ning Chen. 291 HEISER CT 44827 #244-04-1968 L1981 **GP AN** *020
PADIVAL, Pradyumna Kumar. 293 CHAMBERS ST 44827 #495-09-1968 L1978 **IM CD** *020 †20

REID, Mendel Sebastian. 700 N COLUMBUS ST, URGENT CARE 44827 #025-12-1991 L1994 **GS** *020

CRIDERSVILLE – ALLEN

IRVING, Thomas Herbert. ■ 45806 #041-09-1961 L1962 **AN** *071 †05

CROOKSVILLE – PERRY

ALBIRINI, Abdulmawla. 712 CHINA ST, CLINIC, INC 43731 #875-01-1997 L2000 **IM IMG** *020 †20

NELSON, Neely Nicole. ■ 43731 #038-40-2005 L2005 **GS** *100

CROTON – LICKING

LUCAS, Donald B. ■ 43013 #038-40-1942 L1942 **GP** *071

WELLS, Thomas Hixson. ■ 43013 #020-02-1946 L1947 **OS** *071

CUYAHOGA FALLS – SUMMIT

ACUS, Raymond Wm, III. 437 PORTAGE TRL, FALLS ORTHO SURG 44221 #038-40-1986 L1987 **ORS** *020 †40

AGARWAL, Prahladkumar J. 1900 23RD ST 44223 #495-01-1964 L1971 **CLP PTH** *020 †50

ALI, Zulfiqar. ■ 44224 #038-44-2007 **TY** *012

ALTUGLU, Lisa. 3239 STATE RD 44223 #038-44-1995 L1996 **MPD PD** *020 †20,55

AMANAMBU, Chimezie C. 1900 23RD ST 44223 #690-04-1989 L1996 **IM** *020 †20

AYOUBI, Ahmad Siar. ■ 44221 #654-01-2004 L2005 **FP** *012

BABADE, Mosunmola O. ■ 44221 #038-44-2007 L2007 **TY** *012

BABAI, Massood-Reza. 275 GRAHAM RD STE 8 44223 #517-01-1965 L1972 **P PYG** *020 †75

BEAR, Thomas Francis. 437 PORTAGE TRL, DIV OF CRYSTAL CLINIC 44221 #038-40-1970 L1970 **ORS** *020 †40

BLACK, Ross R, II. 265 PORTAGE TRAIL EXT W, # 200 44223 #038-40-1973 L1973 **FM EM** *020 †18

BOWLING, Gerald Francis. PO BOX 1149 44223 #038-06-1957 L1957 **RHU IM** *071 †20

CERONE, Andrea Gennaro. 3239 STATE RD 44223 #010-02-2001 L2001 **FM** *020 †18

CHEKKA, Ravi Kumar. ■ 44221 #038-43-2007 **PD** *012

CHEMA, Andrew Russell. ■ 44221 #038-44-2007 L2007 **FP** *012

CHERONIS, George Gus. 275 GRAHAM RD, STE 11 44223 #038-75-1992, ▲ L1996 **DR PDR** *020

CHOKSI, Krutarth Prabodh. 939 PORTAGE TRL 44221 #495-23-1974 L2002 **P CHP** *020 †75

CHUNG, Matthew S. 1232 BUCHHOLZER BLVD 44221 #038-44-1988 L1989 **IM** *020 †20

CONLEY, Hannah Lynn. ■ 44223 #038-44-2008 *012

COOK, Mary Catherine. 210 PORTAGE TRAIL EXT W, STE 102 44223 #038-45-1990 L1991 **FM** *020 †18

COVEN, Charles Jos. 718 GRAHAM RD 44221 #038-40-1971 L1972 **FM** *020

DAHLEN, Donald Alfred. 265 PORTAGE TRAIL EXT W, # 200 44223 #026-04-1979 L1980 **FM** *020 †18

DARNELL, Kyle Austin. ■ 44221 #038-44-2007 L2007 **IM** *012

DEMBINSKI, Arthur Francis. ■ 44221 #032-01-1974 L1976 **EM IM** *020 †20

DESSENS, Peter Nicolas. 1825 PORTAGE TRL 44223 #068-01-1982 L1984 **IM** *020 †20

DE WITT, James C. ■ 44221 #010-01-1951 L1952 **OS P** *075

DILAURO, Cynthia Lynne. 739 GRAHAM RD 44221 #038-44-1989 L1990 **IM** *020 †20

DI LAURO, Rosanne Marie. 739 GRAHAM RD 44221 #038-44-1981 L1983 **IM** *020 †20

DONOFRIO, Lorena. 1900 23RD ST 44223 #038-75-2006, ▲ L2006 *012

DONTHI, Kiran Ramamurthy. 275 GRAHAM RD STE 2 44223 #495-19-1970 L1978 **OPH** *020 †35

FAZEKAS, Zsuzsanna. 1900 23RD ST 44223 #305-01-2000 L2007 **D** *020

FLOWERS, Gwendolyn Ellen. ■ 44221 #038-43-2007 L2007 **EM** *012

FLOWERS, Kerwyn L. ■ 44221 #038-75-2007, ▲ L2007 *012

FRANTZ, Susan E Clark. 1900 23RD ST 44223 #038-43-1987 L1998 **OBG** *020 †30

FRENCH, Tricia M. 2668 N HAVEN BLVD 44223 #038-44-1995 L1997 **FM** *020 †18

GARN, Michael Chas. 650 GRAHAM RD, STE 1 44221 #038-40-1986 L1986 **FM OS** *020 †18

GEIGER, Robert Stephen. 1900 23RD ST, SUMMIT PAIN SPECIALIST 44223 #038-43-1980 L1985 **AM** *020 †05,18

GOLDMAN, Benjamin. 96 GRAHAM RD, STE B 44223 #550-02-1981 L1983 **IM GPM** *020 †20 ‡

GYORGAK, Danielle M. ■ 44221 #038-43-2007 L2007 **PD** *012

HELLMAN, Martin Gary. 1900 23RD ST, FALLS EMERGENCY 44223 #041-12-1976 L1984 **EM PD** *040 †55,16

HOLAN, Keith Raymond. 3033 STATE RD 44223 #028-34-1972 L1979 **IM GE** *020 †20

HUBBARD, Dawn Renee. 265 PORTAGE TRAIL EXT W, STE 200 44223 #038-44-1995 L1996 **FM** *020 †18

IRVINE, Linda Calvert. 2107 4TH ST 44221 #038-45-1983 L1986 **IM** *020 †20

KAFOREY, Mary Jane. 1860 STATE RD, STE D 44223 #038-44-1982 L1982 **OBG** *071 †30

KANG, Suk Ho. 2680 N HAVEN BLVD STE 6 44223 #583-01-1961 L1972 **FM** *020

KARNOUPAKIS, John Angelo. 2795 FRONT ST 44221 #055-01-1964 L1967 **FM** *020 †18

KLINE, Jeffrey S. 1754 PORTAGE TRL 44221 #035-06-1976 L1978 **PD** *020 †55

KLIONS, Howard Allan. 1900 23RD ST 44223 #041-07-1984 L1989 **CCM IM** *020 †20

KNAZEK, Elizabeth Anne. ■ 44221 #038-44-2005 L2005 **ORS** *012

KRUTKY, Theodore K. 802 GRAHAM RD 44221 #561-01-1973 L1976 **IM** *020

LAIKOS, George Demetrios. 1232 BUCHHOLZER BLVD 44221 #038-41-1988 L1990 **IM** *020 †20

LASZLO, Daniel Barnabas. 1900 23RD ST 44223 #038-40-2002 L2002 **FM** *020 †18

LASZLO, Peter. 1900 23RD ST 44223 #038-40-2003 L2003 **FM** *100 †18

LEQUIER, Laurance L. ■ 44221 #060-01-1992 L1995 **CCP** *100 †55

LIGON, Kathy A. ■ 44223 #038-44-2007 L2007 **IM** *012

MACIEJEWSKI, Walter Z. 1900 23RD ST, FALLS EMERGENCY 44223 #038-45-1981 L1983 **EM** *020 †18

MADER, Carl Jos. 275 GRAHAM RD STE 9 44223 #064-01-1954 L1958 **IM OS** *071

MATLACK, Timothy Carmalt. ■ 44223 #038-45-2005 L2005 **EM** *012

MATRIANO LIM, Charles V. ■ 44221 #021-06-2001 L2001 **CCM** *012

MC FADDEN, John Harry. 3033 STATE RD 44223 #038-40-1963 L1963 **FM** *071 †18

MEHANDRU, Sonali. ■ 44221 #038-06-2007 L2007 **IM** *012

MOHAN, Chander. 275 GRAHAM RD STE 5 44223 #495-75-1978 L1993 **P PYG** *020

MONROE, Emmett P. 3033 STATE RD, STE 201 44223 #038-40-1953 L1953 **FM** *071 †18

MYER, Timothy James. 437 PORTAGE TRL 44223 #038-40-1973 L1974 **ORS** *020 †40

NAGY, Devin Lee. ■ 44221 #038-44-2006 L2006 **TY** *012

NELMAN, Kyle Ryan. ■ 44223 #038-41-2005 L2005 **ORS** *012

NEWMAN, Timothy Loren. 650 GRAHAM RD, STE 106 44221 #055-01-1975 L1976 **OM** *030

NIEMEYER, Harold Gladding. ■ 44224 #016-06-1955 L1956 **R** *072 †80

NUNTHIRAPAKORN, Thida Nit. ■ 44221 #038-44-2006 L2006 **OBG** *012

ORMOND, Alexander P, Jr. 209 PORTAGE TRAIL EXT W, STE 100 44223 #041-01-1959 L1959 **CD IM** *071

ORMOND, Alexander P, III. 355 PORTAGE TRL 44221 #038-40-1988 L1989 **OBG** *020 †30

PAKEEREE, Renga A. 275 GRAHAM RD, STE 10 44223 #919-05-1974 L1977 **P** *020 †75

PANTAZIS, Alethia Helen. ■ 44221 #038-44-2007 L2007 **TY** *012

PARIKH, Hemendra O. 275 GRAHAM RD 44223 #495-20-1967 L1976 **IM** *020 †20

PARIKH, Pratibha Hemendra. 275 GRAHAM RD, STE 3 44223 #495-96-1971 L1979 **P** *020

PAYNE, Albert E. 600 PORTAGE TRL 44221 #005-12-1977 L1980 **OBG** *020 †30 ‡

PERERA, Clifford C. 3033 STATE RD, STE 202 44223 #220-01-1968 L1974 **P** *020 †75

PETERS, Christina. ■ 44221 #038-75-2007, ▲ L2007 *012

PIERSON, Marshall J. ■ 44221 #041-13-1943 L1947 **FM A** *072 †18

PRIGOZEN, Jason Michael. ■ 44223 #038-06-2002 L2007 **PS** *012

QADRI, Muntzra Khatoon. 939 PORTAGE TRL 44221 #704-02-1962 L1982 **P** *020

RAFFERTY, Todd Allen. 1900 23RD ST 44223 #654-01-2003 L2004 **FM** *020 †18

RAJ, Sneh. 2125 FRONT ST 44221 #495-05-1958 L1981 **P N** *020 †75

RAMA-MURTHY, Donthi. 275 GRAHAM RD STE 2 44223 #495-21-1970 L1977 **GS** *020 †85

RANIOL, Marianne Paula. 96 GRAHAM RD 44223 #038-45-1983 L1986 **IM** *020 †20

REUBEN, Rufus A. 275 GRAHAM RD, STE 4 44223 #495-65-1981 L1993 **FPG** *020 †18

ROMAN, Marlena Anna. ■ 44221 #038-43-1991 L1993 **P** *020 †75

SHAH, Asad A. ■ 44223 #038-43-2005 L2005 **IM** *012

SHIN, Sung III. 1600 PORTAGE TRL 44223 #583-10-1962 L1974 **PS** *071 †65

SOUTHERN, Alison Patrice. ■ 44221 #038-43-2004 L2004 **EM** *020

STEIDL, Daniel L. 600 PORTAGE TRL 44221 #023-07-1973 L1983 **IM GP** *020 †20

VALENTE, Michael. ■ 44223 #038-75-2005, ▲ L2005 **GS** *012

VALENTE, Stephanie Ann Si. ■ 44223 #038-75-2005, ▲ L2005 **GS** *012

VILLALBA, Abdon Enrique. 2321 2ND ST, STE 114 44221 #132-04-1954 L1964 **P** *071 †75

WAKER, Andrea Elizabeth. 96 GRAHAM RD, STE B 44223 #010-03-1994 L1999 **MPD** *020

WHITTLE, Edward. ■ 44223 #065-09-1957 L1964 **IM FM** *020

WIKAS, Schield Martin. 421 GRAHAM RD, STE C 44221 #028-78-1979, ▲ L1981 **D** *020

WILBER, Amy E. ■ 44221 #038-75-2007, ▲ L2007 *012

WILLIAMS, Nicole Olivia. ■ 44221 #038-44-2007 L2007 **IM** *012

WOOLARD, Joan. ■ 44223 #028-78-1960, ▲ L1960 **AN** *071

ZEISZLER, Lee Christopher. ■ 44221 #051-04-2002 L2002 **DR** *100 †80

DALTON – WAYNE

MURRAY, Steven Duane. 129 WENGER RD N 44618 #038-44-1994 L1996 **FM** *020 †18

DANVILLE – KNOX

TIDYMAN, John Dunster, Jr. ■ 43014 #038-40-1963 L1963 **FM** *071

DAYTON – DARKE

ONADY, Gary Michael. 110 E NORTH ST, MEDICAL SERVICES BLDGING 45390 #038-45-1987 L1988 **MPD PD** *040 †20,55

DAYTON – GREENE

ABRAHAM, Charlie. 3640 COLONEL GLENN HWY, DEPT MED 45435 #875-01-2001 L2007 **IM** *012

AHMED, Sameer. PO BOX 927 45435 #496-21-2000 L2005 **IM** *012

ALI, Shoaib. PO BOX 927 45435 #306-01-2005 L2006 **IM** *012

ALMAZAN, Susan Pena. ■ 45432 #748-10-1988 L2006 **PDE** *020 †55

AMBALAVANAN, Siva. 1244 MEADOW BRIDGE DR 45434 #495-04-1985 L1998 **IM NEP** *020 †20

AMIN, Mansi Hasmukh. 3640 COLONEL GLENN HWY, AEROSPACE MEDICINE, WSU 45435 #035-75-2002, ▲ L2005 **AM IM** *020

ANTHONY, Dennis Michael. 3640 COLONEL GLENN HWY, FREDERICK A. WHITE HEALTH 45435 #038-41-2000 L2000 **MPD** *100

APPLETON, Charlotte Chase. ■ 45431 #045-04-2005 L2005 **IM** *012

ARNOLD, Rudolph Paul. 4881 SUGAR MAPLE DR 45433 #038-45-1982 L1989 **GP** *020

ARORA, Avni. 1010 WOODMAN DR 45432 #495-90-1990 L2001 **AN** *100

ARSENEAU, April Michelle. ■ 45430 #035-03-2007 L2007 **IM** *012

BADRUDDUJA, Mustafa Syed. 45431 #020-12-2003 L2003 **GS** *012

BAKER, Roger Alan. 3640 COLONEL GLENN HWY, SCHOOL OF MEDICINE 45435 #038-41-1963 L1963 **OBG** *020 †30

BALAKRISHNAN, Krish. 1010 WOODMAN DR 45432 #495-42-1963 L1975 **GS** *071 †85

BALOGH, Kimberly Mae. 4881 SUGAR MAPLE DR, 88 SGOS/SGCJ 45433 #048-13-2002 L2008 **AN** *020

BEGUM, Umera. PO BOX 927 45435 #496-27-1998 L2006 **FP** *012

BERNIE, Jan Edward. 2145 N FAIRFIELD RD 45431 #017-20-1964 L1971 **U** *020 †95

BERRY, Catherine Louise. 5030 PATTERSON PKWY, WRIGHT PATTERSON AFB 45433 #028-34-1997 L2001 **PD** *020 †55

BHATT, Amit Ashok. ■ 45430 #028-34-2006 L2006 **PD** *012

BISHOP, Jeffrey Marshall. 1320 WOODMAN DR STE 200 45432 #048-15-1984 L2001 **P** *020 †75

BIXLER, Gary Michael. ■ 45432 #038-45-2008 *012

BOWEN, Sara Davis. ■ 45431 #041-14-2005 L2005 **PD** *012

BRATSLAVSKY, Yelena Serge. PO BOX 927 45435 #913-15-1995 L2005 **FM** *012

BROWN, Susan Kremer. 4881 SUGAR MAPLE DR 45433 #038-41-1987 L1990 **PD** *020 †55

BRUNER, Karen Elizabeth. ■ 45430 #051-01-2007 L2007 **PD** *012

BURNHAM, Clyde M. 45433 #007-02-1973 L1979 **FM ADM** *071 †18

CARRION, Stephanie Lorrai. ■ 45431 #005-12-2006 L2006 **EM** *012

CATA, Ceferino Javier. 2141 N FAIRFIELD RD, DAYTON CARDIOLOGY & 45431 #038-41-1988 L1989 **CD IM** *020 †20

CHALLA, Jyothi. PO BOX 927 45435 #495-57-1996 L2004 **IM** *100 †20

CHANDLER, Fritz-Jose E. 4881 SUGAR MAPLE DR, BLDG 830 45431 #440-01-1990 L2005 **AN** *020

CHAUDHURI, Rameswar. ■ 45432 #495-32-1979 L1999 **IM** *020 †20

CHERUVELIL, Sheila T. ■ 45431 #035-19-1997 L2006 **IM** *020 †20

CHITWOOD, Mary O'Brien. 3140 DAYTON XENIA RD, STE C 45434 #038-45-1990 L1992 **PD** *020 †55

CHOI, Steve Hwan-Soo. 1010 WOODMAN DR 45432 #143-11-1999 L2001 **FM** *100

CHUN, Soon Ja. ■ 45432 #583-08-1971 L1981 **AN GP** *020

CLARK, Jerry Alan. 722 N FAIRFIELD RD 45434 #038-45-1985 L1986 **IM** *020 †20

CLARK, Larry Edward. ■ 45432 #038-40-1965 L1965 **OM** *020 †18

COLEMAN, Florence Squire. ■ 45434 #038-45-1988 L1989 **P ADP** *020 †75

CONLON, Jennifer Marie. 3140 DAYTON XENIA RD, STE C 45434 #038-40-1992 L1993 **PD** *020 †55

COUNTRYMAN, Jacqueline. 4881 SUGAR MAPLE DR, 74TH MEDICAL GROUP/SGHJ 45433 #035-03-1996 L1997 **P** *020 †75

COX, James W. ■ 45433 #048-14-2007 L2007 **IM** *012

DARKWA, Elizabeth Amorkor. 3140 DAYTON XENIA RD, STE C 45434 #412-02-1998 L2004 **PD** *020 †55

DERKSEN, James Andrew. 1343 WOODMAN DR 45432 #038-45-1985 L1986 **FM** *020 †18 ‡

DHINGRA, Rajnish Kumar. 1244 MEADOW BRIDGE DR 45434 #016-11-1995 L2001 **NEP** *020 †20

DONIGIAN, Aram Moses. 1244 MEADOW BRIDGE DR 45434 #023-12-1984 L2002 **ORS OSM** *020 †40

DUDASH, Jos Gregory, Jr. 2145 N FAIRFIELD RD, STE E 45431 #038-45-1982 L1983 **FM** *020 †18

DURNING, Steven James. 4881 SUGAR MAPLE DR, 74TH MEDICAL GROUP/SGHJ 45433 #041-12-1995 L1998 **IM** *020 †20

ELREFAI, Sara M. ■ 45431 #305-01-2005 L2005 **MPD** *012

ELRUFAY, Rawiya Ismail. PO BOX 927 45435 #848-04-2003 L2006 **IM** *012

ERRAGOLLA, Srinivas. ■ 45431 #495-21-1996 L2007 **SCI** *012 †60

FAZLI, Muhammad Anwar Sib. ■ 45435 #704-01-1996 *100

FELDMAN, Jennifer Michele. 3140 DAYTON XENIA RD, STE C 45434 #038-45-2002 L2002 **PD** *020 †55

FERNANDES, Ashley Keith. 3640 COLONEL GLENN HWY, COM HEALT 45435 #038-40-2003 L2006 **PD** *100 †55

FESTER, Eric William. 4881 SUGAR MAPLE DR, BLDG 830 45433 #023-12-1993 L1995 **ORS** *040

FRENCH, Brian Lavin. 4881 SUGAR MAPLE DR, 88TH MDOS/SGOMI 45433 #026-04-2001 L2001 **IM** *020

FROEHLICH, Janette Reid. 2322 LAKEVIEW DR, STE 2C 45431 #038-41-1998 L1999 **FM** *020 †18

GARDNER, Tasha Kynece. ■ 45430 #010-03-2006 L2006 **EM** *012

GATARIC, Gordana. 5100 SPRINGFIELD ST, STE 400 45431 #957-07-1988 L2007 **IM** *020 †20

GUTMAN, Kathleen Anne. 2322 LAKEVIEW DR, STE 300 45431 #038-45-1992 L1996 **PD** *020 †55

HACKETT, Paul Samuel, II. 2510 COMMONS BLVD, STE 200B 45431 #005-14-1999 L2006 **CRS** *020 †85

HAGGERTY, Paul Flavian. ■ 45434 #023-12-2006 L2006 **IM** *012

HALL, Matthew Stephen. ■ 45434 #038-45-2008 *012

HARDWICK, Matthew Glen. 2322 LAKEVIEW DR, STE 300 45431 #038-40-1985 L1986 **PD** *020 †55

HASAN, Rubina Tabassum. PO BOX 927 45435 #495-17-2003 L2006 **IM** *012

HERCHLINE, Marylynn. 3140 DAYTON XENIA RD, STE C 45434 #038-41-1985 L1988 **PD** *020 †55

HERNIT, Rogelio Capacio. ■ 45432 #748-01-1965 L1974 **CHP** *020

HOUGH, Gregory H. ■ 45431 #048-14-2003 L2006 **GS** *012

IBEZUE, Stella Akwuka Ogo. PO BOX 927 45435 #690-05-2005 L2006 **IM** *012

JAGANATHAN, Sudha Prasad. ■ 45431 #496-23-2004 L2005 **IM** *012

JAMELARIN, Edward Bergema. WRIGHT STATE UNIV SCH OF M, RESIDENCY/INT MED 45432 #748-02-2000 L2002 **HO** *012 †20

JASPER, Taunya Michelle. ■ 45431 #020-02-2005 L2005 **PD** *012

JOHNSON, Amy Bentley. 4881 SUGAR MAPLE DR 45433 #020-12-2000 L2000 **PD** *020 †55

JORDAN, Kimberly E. 1343 WOODMAN DR 45432 #038-45-2001 L2001 **FM** *100 †18

KAHLON, Damanjeet. PO BOX 927 45435 #495-80-2003 L2005 **IM** *012

KALPALATHIKA, Mrudula P.. ■ 45431 #166-01-2000 L2004 **FM** *100

KELLEY, Patrick Sheen. ■ 45431 #038-43-1996 L2004 **OPH** *020 †35

KELLY, Michael. ■ 45434 #539-06-1956 L1966 **PTH CLP** *071 †50

KOHNEN, Angela May. 1244 MEADOW BRIDGE DR, STE 100 45434 #038-41-1994 L1995 **FM** *020 †18

KOLES, Paul Gregory. 3640 COLONEL GLENN HWY, 125 FRED WHITE HLTH CTR 45435 #005-12-1979 L1981 **PTH PCP** *040 †50

KONCAL, Scott David. ■ 45431 #038-45-2007 L2007 **EM** *012

KREPPEL, Andrew Joseph. ■ 45431 #028-34-2003 L2003 **PD** *020 †55

LAUF, Peter Kurt Alfred. 3640 COLONEL GLENN HWY, WRIGHT STATE U SCH MED 45435 #407-05-1960 **OS** *050

LAUGHLIN, Harold J. 1244 MEADOW BRIDGE DR # 10 45434 #028-34-1952 L1953 **GP** *071

LEWIS, Aaron David. ■ 45431 #023-12-2006 L2006 **IM** *012

LEWIS, Roy J. ■ 45434 #038-41-1951 L1951 **AN** *071 †05

LYTLE, Patrick J. 2510 COMMONS BLVD, STE 200B 45431 #018-75-1988, ▲ L1995 **CD IM** *020

MADEN, Larry Gene. 4881 SUGAR MAPLE DR, 74TH MEDICAL GROUP/SGHJ 45433 #047-06-1971 L1971 **NPM PD** *071 †55

MAKKAR, Jagdish Chander. ■ 45434 #496-38-1958 L1972 **GS CRS** *071 †85

MARTIN, Donald Joseph. 3640 COLONEL GLENN HWY, DEPT OF INTERNAL MEDICINE 45435 #030-06-2006 L2006 **IM** *012

MARTIN, Wilmont Gregory. ■ 45431 #045-01-2006 L2006 **PD** *012

MC CAULEY, Kathleen M. 4881 SUGAR MAPLE DR, 74 MDOS/SGOG 45433 #041-14-1978 L1981 **OBG** *020 †30

MEISTER, Linda Marie. 3140 DAYTON XENIA RD, STE C 45434 #038-45-1985 L1986 **PD** *020 †55

MERANDA, Joseph Abraham. ■ 45431 #038-45-2008 *012

MOORE, Matthew D. 2141 N FAIRFIELD RD, STE C 45431 #055-01-1982 L1987 **FM** *020 †18

MOSALI, Deepthi. 2510 COMMONS BLVD, STE 200B 45431 #496-01-1996 L2003 **CD** *020 †20

MUENNICH, Elizabeth A L. ■ 45432 #038-45-2004 L2004 **D** *012

MUFTI, Omar Idris. PO BOX 927 45435 #704-24-2003 L2006 **IM** *012

NELSON, Morton. 3640 COLONEL GLENN HWY, WRIGHT STTE UNIV 45435 #005-17-1962 L1983 **PHP FM** *030

NEWLAND, Guy Mallery. 4881 SUGAR MAPLE DR # 830, 74TH MEDICAL GROUP/SGHJ 45433 #023-12-1982 L1991 **EM GP** *020 †16

OKOYE, Nkeiruka Eucharia. PO BOX 927 45435 #690-04-2002 L2006 **IM** *012

PALAKODETI, Ratna Kumar. 1244 MEADOW BRIDGE DR # 10 45434 #495-11-1974 L1991 **FM** *020 †18

PANTOJA, Enrique. WRIGHT STATE MED SCH/RAD 45431 #042-01-1958 L1978 **DR RO** *020 †80

PARKER, William A, Jr. 3300 KEMP RD, ALLERGY & ASTHMA ASSOCIATE 45431 #021-01-1981 L1989 **AI PD** *071 †55,03

PARMELEE, Dean Xandor. 3640 COLONEL GLENN HWY, P O BOX 927 45435 #035-45-1975 L2001 **CHP P** *030 †75

PASHA, Rizwan. ■ 45434 #038-40-1996 L1998 **EM** *020 †16

PERCIVAL, Candace Suzanne. ■ 45434 #023-12-2005 L2005 **PD** *012

PERFILIO, Adrienne Elizab. ■ 45431 #016-43-2006 L2006 **OBG** *012

PFEIFER, Moira Curley. 4881 SUGAR MAPLE DR, 74TH MEDICAL GROUP/SGHJ 45433 #023-12-1987 L1993 **P** *020 †55

QAZI, Momina. ■ 45431 #704-09-1999 L2003 **IM** *100 †20

QURAISHI, Muhammad Bilal. PO BOX 927 45435 #704-20-2004 L2006 **IM** *012

RAHE, John Michael. 3140 DAYTON XENIA RD, STE C 45434 #038-41-1989 L2002 **PD** *020 †55

RAO, Anita Balakrishna. ■ 45431 #038-44-2007 L2007 **GS** *012

REDDY, Tarak Chandramohan. PO BOX 927 45435 #496-23-2005 L2006 **IM** *012

RICH, Mark Monroe. 3640 COLONEL GLENN HWY, NCBP 45435 #028-02-1989 L2005 **N** *020 †75

ROBINOWITZ-ELINS, Hillary. ■ 45431 #654-01-2001 L2007 **OBG** *020

ROER, David Lloyd. 3140 DAYTON XENIA RD, STE C 45434 #038-45-1984 L1985 **PD** *020 †55

RUSSELL, Raymond Scott. ■ 45431 #038-45-1996 L1997 **U** *020 †95

SAHIAR, Farhad. 3640 COLONEL GLENN HWY, AEROSPACE MEDICINE 45435 #495-73-1989 L1997 **AM** *020 †70

SARANGA, Vinay Paran. PO BOX 927 45435 #759-06-2004 L2005 **P** *012

SESHADRI, Srividyalakshmi. 3640 COLONEL GLENN HWY, WRIGHT STATE UNIV 45435 #496-23-1993 L2001 **HO** *012 †20

SHAH, Anjana H. 722 N FAIRFIELD RD, FAIRFIELD RD PHYSICIANS 45434 #495-37-1985 L1993 **IM** *020 †18

SHAIKH, Azim. ■ 45431 #038-44-1995 L1996 **IM** *075 †20

SHAMIYEH, Samir Boulos. ■ 45431 #047-06-1959 L1960 **GS** *030 †85

SHARMA, Kanan. PO BOX 927, WRIGHT STATE UNIV 45435 #496-12-2002 L2005 **IM** *012

SHIDELER, Robert Mark. 3640 COLONEL GLENN HWY, WRIGHT STATE UNIV 45435 #023-12-1998 L2007 **P** *012

SHIRLEY, Grant Carlton. 3640 COLONEL GLENN HWY 45435 #012-05-1991 L2007 **GPM** *020

SIMON, Maria Cecilia Sobr. PO BOX 927 45435 #748-20-2000 L2005 **IM** *012

SINGH, Darshan. 1320 WOODMAN DR, STE 200 45432 #495-05-1971 L1999 **CHP PFP** *020 †75

SINGRI, Prasannakumarm. ■ 45434 #495-09-1967 L1972 **IM EM** *020

SINHA, Amruta Mulay. PO BOX 927 45435 #496-42-2003 L2006 **FP** *012

SMITH, Jenell Charese. ■ 45431 #038-45-2008 *012

SMITH, Milton J. USAF HOSP 45433 #028-34-1949 L1949 **PTH** *074 †50

SOIN, Amol. ■ 45431 #038-44-2002 L2002 **PME AN** *020 †55

SOSTRE, Samuel. ■ 45431 #042-01-1970 L1976 **NM IM** *020 †20,28

SPROTT, Lisa Gay. ■ 45431 #566-01-1997 L2000 **FM** *020

STARRETT, William Grant. 5100 SPRINGFIELD ST, STE 400 45431 #038-43-1997 L1999 **ID IM** *020 †20

STEWART, Alicia Danielle. ■ 45431 #038-45-2006 L2006 **PD** *012

STEWART, Heather Leigh. ■ 45433 #030-06-2005 L2005 **PD** *012

SWARTZEL, Robert Lee. ■ 45434 #038-41-1947 L1947 **DR** *071 †80

THOMAS, Marcia J. 3371 KEMP RD, GMH URGENT CARE/WORKPLUS 45431 #038-40-1976 L1977 **FM OM** *020 †18

THOMAS-JOHN, Maria. 722 N FAIRFIELD RD 45434 #038-45-2001 L2002 **RHU** *020 †20

THOTA, Naveen. PO BOX 927 45435 #495-65-2001 L2006 **IM** *012

TIMPONE, Michael Jonathan. 2145 N FAIRFIELD RD STE E 45431 #038-40-1976 L1977 **FM EM** *020 †18

TOURANGEAU, Leslie Susan. ■ 45431 #030-06-2006 L2006 **PD** *012

URQUHART, Wanda Joy. ■ 45431 #030-06-1990 L1990 **PD** *020

VAIDYA, Moushumi Shailesh. ■ 45431 #495-28-1999 L2001 **IM** *020

VAN TREASE, Lisa Renee. 1244 MEADOW BRIDGE DR, STE 100 45434 #038-40-1996 L1999 **FM** *020 †18

VENANZI, William Earl, Jr. 4881 SUGAR MAPLE DR, 74TH MEDICAL GROUP/SGHJ 45433 #023-01-1989 L1993 **RHU** *020 †20

VINSANT, Jessica Louise. ■ 45431 #038-45-2008 *012

WALSH, Pamela Mary. ■ 45431 #020-02-2005 L2005 **EM** *012

WELTON, Randon Scott. ■ 45434 #023-12-1990 L1991 **P** *020 †75

WESTERFIELD, Lindsey Mari. ■ 45431 #038-45-2008 *012

WHITE, Bryan Matthew. 4881 SUGAR MAPLE DR, INTERNAL MEDICINE CLINIC B 45433 #023-12-2002 L2002 **CD** *012 †20

WHITMER, Daniel Lee. 2145 N FAIRFIELD RD, STE E 45431 #038-41-1981 L1982 **FM OM** *020 †18

WICK, Tracy Katherine. 3140 DAYTON XENIA RD, STE C 45434 #038-45-1997 L1998 **PD** *020 †55

WYATT, Robby Wayne. ■ 45434 #038-41-2000 L2002 **P** *020 †75

YOHANNES, Theodros. 2145 N FAIRFIELD RD 45431 #035-06-1994 L1999 **U** *020 †95 ‡

YOURA, Gary Michael. 3140 DAYTON XENIA RD, STE C 45434 #025-01-1979 L1982 **PD** *020 †55

DAYTON – MONTGOMERY

ABBOUD, Patricia A. 1 CHILDRENS PLZ, DAYTON CHILDS 45404 #038-45-2000 L2000 **CCP** *020 †55 ‡

ABDEL RAZIK, Gihan Nabil. 4100 W 3RD ST, 116-M 45428 #915-04-1992 L2001 **P** *020 †75

ABOUHOSSEIN, Ahmad. 9000 N MAIN ST, STE 333 45415 #407-32-1966 L1974 **GS** *020 †95

ABROMOWITZ, Herman Irwin. 1 FRANCISCAN WAY STE 100, ELIZABETH PL W MED PLZ 45408 #038-40-1958 L1958 **FM OM** *020 †18 ‡

ABROMOWITZ, Howard B. 9000 N MAIN ST, STE 333 45415 #038-45-1982 L1983 **U** *020 †95

ACEITUNO, Federico Oscar. ■ 45420 #275-01-1941 L1971 **GP** *071

ACEITUNO, Jose Antonio. ■ 45429 #275-01-1943 L1977 **OM IMG** *071

■ = Address Information Privacy Protected

ADAM, Jeffery Stephens. 9000 N MAIN ST, STE 238 45415 #041-02-1977 L1978 **OTO** *020 †45

ADEGBILE, Gideon Sunday A. 1152 W 3RD ST 45402 #047-07-1971 L1972 **FM FPG** *020

ADEN, Darmaan Osman. ■ 45458 #104-01-2004 L2004 **IM** *020 †20

ADIB, Abdulla. 9000 N MAIN ST, STE 238 45415 #875-01-1979 L1991 **OTO** *020 †45

AFRICK, Cynthia Zane. 30 E APPLE ST # 6254, OHIO NERUOSUGICAL INSTITUT 45409 #016-43-1989 L2000 **NS GS** *020 †25 ‡

AGARWAL, Ajay. ■ 45429 #495-05-1993 L2005 **IM** *020

AGARWAL, Asha. 7405 BRANDT PIKE 45424 #495-34-1972 L1984 **IM** *020

AGARWAL, Sunita. 2218 S PATTERSON BLVD 45409 #495-20-1980 L1997 **CHP** *020

AGGARWAL, Rajendra Kumar. 1135 N GETTYSBURG AVE, NORTH DAYTON PHYSICIANS 45417 #495-03-1966 L1979 **FM** *020

AGNA, Mary J Allott. 601 S EDWIN C MOSES BLVD, DPT FP 45408 #038-41-1950 L1950 **FM GPM** *040 †18

AGRAWAL, Sangeeta. 7415 BRANDT PIKE, STE 2 45424 #495-65-1989 L2002 **GE** *020 †20

AHERN, John Kevin. 8111 TIMBERLODGE TRL 45458 #038-40-1988 L1991 **FM** *020 †18

AHLUWALIA, Gurpal Singh. 1 WYOMING ST, CO WSUMIAMI VALLEY HOSP-SU 45409 #038-45-2003 L2003 **ORS** *012

AHMAD, Ejaz. 2222 PHILADELPHIA DR, GOOD SAMARITAN HOSPITAL 45406 #704-02-1992 L2004 **HMP PTH** *020 †50

AHMAD, Shafik. 5212 BRANDT PIKE STE C 45424 #690-07-1987 L1997 **FM** *020 †18

AHMED, Nadeem Manzoor. 405 W GRAND AVE, GRANDVIEW MEDICAL CENTER 45405 #704-20-1987 L2007 **APM** *020 †05

AHMED, Syed Nayeemuddin. ■ 45458 #495-65-1971 L1984 **AN** *020

AKELLA, Radhika Rukmini. 2661 SALEM AVE, STE 220 45406 #495-98-2000 L2003 **IM** *020 †20

AKOTO, Barbara Yankson. 3300 PHILADELPHIA DR 45405 #412-01-1994 L1999 **IM** *020 †20

AKRAM, Salma. ■ 45458 #704-20-1991 L2007 **GE** *040

AKUTHOTA, Pani. 2200 PHILADELPHIA DR, STE 650 45406 #495-21-1968 L1979 **PM** *020 †60

ALDSTADT, James Douglas. 9000 N MAIN ST STE 300 45415 #038-43-1978 L1979 **FM** *020 †18

ALEJANDRINO, Sergio S. 111 W 1ST ST, ONE ELEVEN BLDG STE 550 45402 #748-07-1953 L1964 **IM CD** *020

ALEXANDER, James Lee. 349 S MAIN ST, COMMUNITY BLOOD CENTER 45402 #039-01-1989 L2003 **BBK** *030 †50

ALEXANDER, Stanley Lake. 15 IRONGATE PARK DR 45459 #038-40-1975 L1975 **GS HS** *020

ALEXINAS-MATHEWS, Erin L. 101 WYOMING ST 45409 #038-45-2002 L2002 **FM** *020 †18

ALI, Median. 6728 LOOP RD, STE 304 45459 #875-03-1994 L2001 **CCM** *020 †20

ALI, Sayed Asad. ■ 45414 #704-01-1996 L2000 **NEP** *020 †20

ALI, Syed Ahsan. 4100 W 3RD ST, VA MEDICAL CENTER (GI UNIT 45428 #704-01-1997 L2000 **GE** *100 †20

ALI, Syed Imran. 3171 RESEARCH BLVD, DEPT OF INTERNAL MEDICINE 45420 #496-27-2001 L2005 **IM** *012

ALIU, Valerie Adesuwa. ■ 45449 #308-03-2003 L2005 **IM** *012

ALLEN, Joseph Patrick. ■ 45424 #038-45-2006 L2006 **FP** *012

ALMAZAN, Anthony Jude. 725 S LUDLOW ST, MEDWORK 45402 #038-45-1997 L1999 **FM** *020 †18

AL-SAMKARI, Osama. 1121 LINDEN AVE 45410 #875-01-1972 L1977 **CD IM** *050 †20

ALTER, Sherman John. 1 CHILDRENS PLZ, THE CHILDREN'S MEDICAL CEN 45404 #038-40-1976 L1980 **PD PDI** *062 †55

AMBROSE, Martin Palmer. 9000 N MAIN ST, STE 328 45415 #025-01-1983 L1990 **PUD IM** *020 †20

AMES, Ashlee Rae. ■ 45419 #038-45-2008 *012

AMESSE, Lawrence Sheldon. 128 APPLE ST STE 3800CHE, DEPT OF OB/GYN 45409 #047-20-1985 L1998 **OBG MG** *020 †30

AMONGERO, Marcos Enrique. 3205 WOODMAN DR 45420 #010-01-1989 L1990 **OSS ORS** *020 †40

AMOS, William Thos, III. 601 S EDWIN C MOSES BLVD 45408 #038-41-1968 L1968 **PTH** *020 †50

ANDARSIO, Evangeline C. 1 WYOMING ST STE 3120 45409 #038-45-1984 L1985 **OBG FM** *020 †18,30

ANDERSON, Harry L, III. 1 WYOMING ST 7000, MIAMI VALLEY HOSP 45409 #025-01-1985 L2005 **TRS CCS** *020 †85

ANDERSON, Michael Joseph. ■ 45419 #056-05-2007 L2007 **ORS** *012

ANDREWS, Jeremias Antonio. 540 LINCOLN PARK BLVD, STE 100 45429 #264-01-1966 L1972 **R** *020 †80

ANIM, Mamle. 3535 SALEM AVE, UNIVERSITY INTERNAL MEDICI 45406 #965-01-1990 L1996 **IM** *040 †20

ANSTADT, Mark Peter. 30 E APPLE ST, STE 6252 45409 #038-45-1986 L1988 **TS** *020 †90,85

ANUSIONWU, Chike Chiazor. 1 WYOMING ST 45409 #690-04-2002 L2003 **IM** *020 †20

APESOS, James. 5441 FAR HILLS AVE 45429 #010-02-1974 L1984 **PS** *020 †65,85

APPALANENI, Vasundhara. ■ 45458 #495-50-1996 L2000 **GE** *020 †20 ‡

APPLEMAN, James Edgar, II. 1 FRANCISCAN WAY 45408 #020-12-1975 L1976 **FM** *071 †18

APPLETON, James C. ■ 45409 #020-02-1946 L1952 **AN OS** *071 †05

ARANHA, Olivia. 3120 GOVERNORS PLACE BLVD 45409 #495-96-1995 L2007 **HO** *020

ARORA, Aditya. 1362 WILD IVY WAY 45440 #041-12-1998 L1999 **EM** *020 †16

ARTHUNGAL, Sonia Sarah. 8638 TROY PIKE, STE 101 45424 #010-03-2001 L2001 **PD** *020 †55

ASHAI-KHAN, Farhat Nafisa. 1 CHILDRENS PLZ, WSU DEPT OF PEDIATRIC GAST 45404 #704-06-1980 L1990 **PD** *050 †55

ASHBAUGH, Keith Eldon. 2611 WAYNE AVE 45420 #017-20-1981 L1983 **P FM** *020 †75,18

ASKENAZI, Joseph. 9000 N MAIN ST, STE 202 45415 #550-01-1970 L1984 **CD** *020 †20

AVVA, Somasundaram. ■ 45415 #495-62-1966 L1974 **PS GS** *071 †65

AYE, Yin Yin. PO BOX 927, WRIGHT STATE UNIVERSITY 45401 #209-01-2002 L2007 **IM** *012

AZIE, Nnamdi. 30 E APPLE ST, STE 6252 45409 #690-04-1986 L2006 **TS GS** *020 †85,90

AZIZ, Tarek M. 1520 GERMANTOWN ST 45408 #915-02-1990 L2000 **P** *020 †75 ‡

AZMEH, Ramzieh. 5250 FAR HILLS AVE, STE 260 45429 #875-01-1981 L1996 **MPD** *020 †20,55

BABICKI, Maria Elzbieta. 1530 NEEDMORE RD, BEAVERCREEK HEART CENTER 45414 #759-07-1985 L1993 **CD** *071 †20

BAHR, Richard Frederick. ■ 45429 #038-41-1947 L1947 **FM GP** *071

BAINS, Loveleen. 33 W RAHN RD, STE 201 45429 #038-45-2001 L2004 **IM** *020

BAIR, Nicole Sue. ■ 45410 #038-45-2008 *012

BAKOS, Matthew Aaron. 4244 INDIAN RIPPLE RD 45440 #038-45-2003 L2003 **D** *020 †15

BALAJ, Rebecca Raack. 1 WYOMING ST, DEPT OF PATHOLOGY 45409 #038-44-1991 L1992 **PTH** *062 †50

BALL, Bruce Ryan. ■ 45419 #056-06-2004 L2004 **OBG** *012

BALQUIEDRA, Delmar Elento. ■ 45409 #748-01-1961 L1971 **TRS GS** *071

BALSTER, Gary Allen. 2218 S PATTERSON BLVD 45409 #038-41-1983 L1984 **P PYG** *075

BANE, Charles Leo. 9000 N MAIN ST, STE G-36 45415 #028-02-1988 L2000 **HO** *020 †20

BANE, Mary Everly. 5300 FAR HILLS AVE, STE 300 45429 #048-13-1990 L2001 **D** *020 †15

BANERJEE, Manibha U. 2222 PHILADELPHIA DR, NORTH DAYTON PATHOLOGISTS 45406 #495-02-1969 L1975 **PTH** *020 †50

BARBER, Dennis Dan. 1 WYOMING ST DEPT OBG 45409 #056-05-1958 L1979 **GYN OBG** *040 †30

BARCLAY, James C. 9000 N MAIN ST 45415 #038-45-1997 L1998 **P** *020 †75

BARDE, Susan Holliday. 3075 GOVERNORS PLACE BLVD, STE 110 45409 #035-06-1976 L1985 **AI PD** *020 †55,03

BARGMEYER, Kevin Robert. 30 E APPLE ST, STE 6250 45409 #038-43-2002 L2002 **FM** *020 †18

BARHAN, Sheela Madhav. 128 E APPLE ST STE 3800 45409 #021-01-1992 L1996 **OBG** *020 †30

BARKER, Robert Louis, Jr. 33 W RAHN RD STE 102 45429 #005-12-1978 L1980 **IM CCM** *020 †20

BARNES, Jacqueline Kay. ■ 45424 #038-45-2004 L2004 **EM** *012 †20

BARNES, Ladonna Jean. 1323 W 3RD ST, CHARLES DREW HEALTH CTR 45402 #038-45-1991 L1994 **MPD** *020

BARNETT, Michael David, Jr. 30 E APPLE ST, STE 2200 45409 #038-45-2000 L2000 **ORS** *100

BARNEY, Linda Marie. 1 WYOMING ST STE 7000CHE 45409 #038-45-1985 L1986 **GS CCS** *040 †85

BARROW, Michael Wesley. 40 W 4TH ST, STE 17 45402 #017-20-1984 L1987 **FM FSM** *020 †18

BASHA, Imad Shamsi. 9000 N MAIN ST, STE 222 45415 #875-01-1981 L1993 **PUD CCM** *020 †20 ‡

BASHIR, Chowdry Mujahid. ■ 45458 #704-05-1987 L1994 **IM** *020 †20

BASURAY, Biswa Nath. 4100 W 3RD ST, VA MED CTR 45428 #495-38-1962 L1984 **IM IG** *020

BATATA, Sara Naima. 627 S EDWIN C MOSES BLVD, ELIZABETH PLACE 45408 #038-40-1996 L1999 **PFP P** *071 †20

BATHINI, Ramaswamy. 9000 N MAIN ST STE 101, PREMEIR HEART ASSOC INC 45415 #495-65-1970 L1974 **CD IM** *020 †20

BAUMANN, Michael Alan. 4100 W 3RD ST 45428 #038-40-1979 L1985 **HEM ON** *020 †20

BEAN, James W. 1030 HIDDEN RIDGE LN, 6720 LOOP ROAD 45459 #004-01-1969 L1974 **OTO** *020 †45

BEAULIEU, Ronald Allan. 4100 W 3RD ST, DAYTON VAMC 11P 45428 #024-16-1983 L1990 **IM** *020 †20

BECK, Gregory John. 75 SYLVANIA DR 45440 #038-40-1984 L1985 **GE GS** *020 †20

BEERS, Kenneth Norman, Sr. ■ 45414 #041-02-1956 L1971 **AM FM** *071 †70,18

BEITZEL, Raymond Eugene. 215 E STROOP RD 45429 #038-40-1947 L1947 **IM** *071 †20

BEMBRY, James Scott. 111 HARBERT DR 45440 #038-45-1991 L1998 **OBG** *020 †30

BENBOW, Melissa Kay. ■ 45429 #038-40-2008 *012

BERNER, Susan Elaine. 2345 PHILADELPHIA DR 45406 #038-45-2001 L2001 **FPG** *100 †18

BERNIE, Bruce Jeremy. 30 W RAHN RD, STE 26 45429 #051-04-1971 L1975 **OBS** *020 †30

BERNSTEIN, Robert Alan. 1 CHILDRENS PLZ 45404 #041-09-1967 L1972 **PDA A** *071 †55,03

BERNSTEIN, Theodore W. 3533 SOUTHERN BLVD # 535 45429 #038-41-1965 L1965 **NS** *020 †25

BESSON, Michael Jay. 89 SYLVANIA DR, DAYTON EYE ASSOCIATES, INC 45440 #017-20-1976 L1976 **OPH** *020 †35

BHAT, Prashanth. 2200 KETTERING TOWER 45423 #038-41-1989 L1990 **EM** *020 †16

BHAT, Rajindra Prashad. 1323 W 3RD ST, CHARLES DREW HEALTH CENTER 45402 #495-51-1973 L1997 **IM** *020 †20

BIALOWAS, Todd Allan. ■ 45419 #038-45-2008 *012

BIBLE, Lizbeth Ann. 8662 N MAIN ST 45415 #038-45-2002 L2002 **FM** *020 †18

BICKERS, Rex G. 1 WYOMING ST 45409 #017-20-1978 L1982 **NPM OS** *020 †55

BIDWELL, John Keith. 3535 SOUTHERN BLVD, KETTERING RADIOLOGISTS, IN 45429 #038-45-1983 L1988 **DR GS** *020 †80

BIDWELL, Mark Curtis. 128 E APPLE ST, STE 3800CHE 45409 #038-45-1984 L1985 **OBG REN** *020 †30

BIENENFELD, David Gerald. 627 S EDWIN C MOSES BLVD, STE 1 45408 #038-41-1978 L1979 **P PFP** *040 †75

BINSKI, James Chester. 1989 MIAMISBURG CENTRVL RD, STE 202 45459 #016-43-1968 L1990 **ORS RHU** *020 †40

BIRDI, Amarjeet S. 627 S EDWIN C MOSES BLVD, STE 5K 45408 #495-14-1977 L1997 **P** *020 †75

BLAIR, Mark Erik. 2000 RUSSELL AVE 45420 #017-20-2000 L2000 **P** *020

BLATZ, Peter James. ■ 45406 #042-03-2005 L2006 **IM** *012

BLETHEN, Harry Samson. 6455 CHAMBERSBURG RD 45424 #051-04-1955 L1965 **GP PD** *020

BLOCKER, David Clinton. 808 E FRANKLIN ST, GATES, KITZE AND GAPINSKI, 45459 #048-13-1981 L1991 **DR NM** *020 †80

BLOOM, John Edward. 6601 CENTERVILLE BSNS PKWY 45459 #035-15-1955 L1956 **PD** *030 †55

BLOOM, Melinda A. 9000 N MAIN ST, STE 227 45415 #038-75-1999, ▲ L2000 *020

BLOOM, Naomi. 2611 WAYNE AVE, TWIN VALLEY BEHAVORIAL HLT 45420 #035-45-1990 L1993 **CHP** *020 †75

BLOOM, Robert Todd. 1 CHILDRENS PLZ, CHILDRENS MED CTR 45404 #038-40-1989 L1990 **OPH** *020 †35

BOCKOVEN, John Bradley. 1 W 2ND ST 45402 #035-20-1961 L1962 **OPH** *071 †35

BOGGS, Michael Todd. 2222 PHILADELPHIA DR 45406 #038-43-1993 L1994 **FM** *020 †18

BOHRER, Jeanne Marie. 1561 YANKEE PARK PL, CONTEMPORARY PEDS. INC. 45458 #038-45-1988 L1991 **PD ADL** *075 †55 ‡

BOLDEN, Tracie. ■ 45449 #038-45-2005 L2005 **FP** *012

BOLTON, Barrett Henry. ■ 45406 #016-06-1956 L1958 **IM HEM** *071 †20

BONANNO, Elizabeth S. 2611 WAYNE AVE, TWIN VALLEY BEHAVIORAL HEA 45420 #036-01-1989 L2000 **P** *020 †75

BONNIN, Arturo Jose. 8039 WASHINGTON VILLAGE DR, STE 100 45458 #847-11-1985 L1992 **AI** *020 †20,03

BOOTH, Branyan Ann. ■ 45429 #038-40-2004 L2006 **GS** *100

BORCHERS, Samia W. 5727 FAR HILLS AVE 45429 #038-45-1980 L1981 **D FM** *020 †15

BOUQUETT, Gaston. ■ 45449 #017-20-1961 L1965 **OPH** *075

BOWERS, Rick Thos. 180 E SPRING VALLEY RD, STE B 45458 #038-45-1988 L1989 **CHP** *020 †20

BOYCE, Casey Renee. 1 WYOMING ST 45409 #038-45-2003 L2003 **OBG** *020

BOYD-LAWHORN, Susan R. PO BOX 927, WSU HOSPS-INTERNAL MED DEP 45401 #020-02-1999 L1999 **MPD** *020

BOYLE, John Robert. 7707 PARAGON RD, STE 101 45459 #038-40-1976 L1979 **IM** *072 †20

BRAMMER, Paul Wm. 6611 CLYO RD, STE D 45459 #038-43-1980 L1984 **FM** *020 †18

BRANDT, Robt La Vern, Jr. 1 WYOMING ST 45409 #038-45-1980 L1981 **FM OS** *020 †18

BREIDENBACH, Lois M. 4861 ARROWHEAD DR 45440 #038-40-1962 L1962 **PS** *071 †65

BREMER, Dav Wm. 1201 E ALEX BELL RD 45459 #028-34-1978 L1982 **OPH EM** *020 †35
BRENNER, L Peter. 5250 FAR HILLS AVE STE 220 45429 #016-06-1962 L1967 **OBG** *071 †30
BRETZ, G William. 1563 E DOROTHY LN, STE 101 45429 #473-01-1960 L1971 **R NM** *071 †55,80,28
BREYER, Paul Ronald. 1 CHILDRENS PLZ, THE CHILDREN'S MEDICAL CEN 45404 #056-05-1989 L1995 **PDE** *020 †55
BRICKING, Keith Douglas. 1 WYOMING ST, DEPT OF EMERGENCY MEDICINE 45409 #020-12-2002 L2005 **EM** *100 †16
BRODSTON, John Anthony. 9661 PRESERVE PL 45458 #030-06-1980 L2001 **AM EM** *020 †16
BROERING, Julie Rose. 1 WYOMING ST 45409 #038-41-2003 L2003 **FM** *020 †18
BROOKS, Jordan Alan. 4100 W 3RD ST, DAYTON VA MEDICAL CENTER 45428 #041-09-1989 L1993 **N** *020 †75
BROOKS, Wilbur Ray. 1323 W 3RD ST, CHARLES DREW HEALTH CENTER 45402 #038-40-1977 L1978 **FM** *020 †18
BROWN, Dennis Mark. 2200 PHILADELPHIA DR, DR. STE.446 45406 #038-45-1983 L1984 **ORS OAR** *020 †40
BROWN, George Robt. 30 APPLE ST STE 6252 45409 #023-01-1969 L1971 **GS** *071 †85,90
BROWN, Hubert M. ■ 45409 #023-07-1953 L1958 **D** *071 †15
BROWN, Marion Francis. 1 WYOMING ST 45409 #035-46-1978 L1989 **TS GS** *071 †85,90
BROWN, Morris Lamar. 301 W 1ST ST, STE 100 45402 #047-07-1974 L1975 **FM** *020 †18
BROWN-PURYEAR, Latonya. 33 W RAHN RD, STE 201 45409 #036-01-1999 L2005 **PCC** *020 †20
BROXSON, Emmett H, Jr. 1 CHILDRENS PLZ 45404 #001-02-1979 L1988 **PHO PD** *020 †55
BRUMFIEL, Bruce Alan. 4244 INDIAN RIPPLE RD 45440 #038-40-1971 L1971 **D IM** *020 †15
BRYAN, Jonathan Alan. 405 W GRAND AVE, DEPT OF MED EDUCATION 45405 #039-79-2006, ▲ L2006 **IM** *012
BUCHWALDER, M Pelszynski. 300 COLLEGE PARK 45469 #038-40-1986 L1987 **FM** *020 †18
BUCK, Angeles Michelle. 128 E APPLE ST, WRIGHT ST UNIV SCH OF MED 45409 #020-75-2004, ▲ L2004 **OBG** *012
BUCK, Donald A. 2451 WAYNE AVE 45420 #038-41-1952 L1952 **IM** *072
BULLOCK, John David. 45429 #024-01-1968 L1974 **OPH** *020 †35
BURBA, William H. 2611 WAYNE AVE 45420 #038-41-1951 L1951 **P** *074
BURDETTE, Steven Dale. 128 E APPLE ST, CHE BUILDING 2ND FL 45409 #038-45-2000 L2000 **ID** *020 †20 ‡
BURKE, Ann E. 1 CHILDRENS PLZ 45404 #051-01-1992 L1995 **PD** *020 †55
BURKE, Brian Vincent. 30 E APPLE ST 45409 #051-01-1992 L1995 **IM** *020 †20
BURNETTE, Robert Eugene. 4237 BROOKHILL LN 45405 #024-05-1998 L2005 **EM** *020 †16
BURNS, Arthur Chas. ■ 45429 #038-41-1968 L1968 **PTH** *075 †50
BURNS, Cassandra Jean. 1 CHILDRENS PLZ, C/O CHILDRENS MED CTR-MED 45404 #023-12-2002 L2002 *020 †55
BURT, James Caird. 1 FRANCISCAN WAY 45408 #035-45-1945 L1951 **GYN OS** *075
BUSCH, Calvert Raymond. 8057 WASHINGTON VILLAGE DR, STE D 45458 #056-06-1969 L1979 **CD IM** *020 †20
BUTLER, Melissa Mei-Jung. 33 W RAHN RD, STE 201 45429 #051-07-2001 L2001 **IM** *100
BUTMAN, Abdulnaser A. 9000 N MAIN ST, STE 305 45415 #915-08-1984 L1992 **IM** *020 †20
BUTT, Shazdeh Gul. 2345 PHILADELPHIA DR 45406 #704-01-1999 L2007 **FP** *012
CAGLE, Orel H. 7345 FAR HILLS AVE 45459 #047-06-1952 L1956 **P** *071
CALKINS, Anne. 1 CHILDRENS PLZ, DEPT OF RADIOLOGY 45404 #017-20-1989 L1999 **PDR** *062 †55,80
CALLEJO, Vicente E. 4100 W 3RD ST 45428 #748-10-1964 L1985 **P GP** *020
CALVERT, Christopher Ross. ■ 45402 #038-43-2006 L2006 **EM** *012
CALVO, Alejandro R. 1 ELIZABETH PL, # 10B 45408 #015-03-1992 L1996 **HO HEM** *020 †20
CAMMERER, Richard Chas. 75 SYLVANIA DR 45440 #038-40-1968 L1968 **GE IM** *071 †20
CAMPBELL, Dudley Kiefer. 1563 E DOROTHY LN, MEDICAL RADIOLOGISTS, INC 45429 #041-13-1964 L1971 **R** *071 †80
CAMPBELL, Mark Steven. 1 WYOMING ST, MIAMI VALLEY HOSPITAL 45409 #023-12-1988 L2006 **OBG** *020 †30,18
CAMPBELL, Michael Francis. ■ 45403 #038-45-2008 *012
CAMPBELL, Tamara Miller. ■ 45426 #038-45-2005 L2005 **P** *012
CANESSA, Leonardo Mario. 1 CHILDRENS PLZ, DEPT NEPHROLOGY 45404 #737-01-1981 L1995 **PN PD** *020 †55
CAPORAL, Robert Edward. ■ 45405 #038-40-1962 L1962 **FM** *071
CAPOZZIELLO, Valerie Patr. ■ 45429 #038-45-2007 L2007 **GS** *012
CARAMAN, Elena. ■ 45403 #038-45-2008 *012
CARDIFF, Suzie Kim. ■ 45429 #020-12-2003 L2003 **CHP** *012
CARLSON, John Ellert. 405 W GRAND AVE 45405 #026-04-1987 L1995 **DR GS** *020 †80,28
CARO, Roberto A. 111 TURNER RD, CARO PEDIATRIC CENTER 45415 #042-01-1982 L1988 **PD OS** *020
CARPENTER, Michael Dean. ■ 45405 #038-41-2001 L2001 **PM** *020 †60
CARR, David Raymond. ■ 45402 #038-40-2006 L2006 **D** *012
CARROLL, Michael Rea. 1563 E DOROTHY LN STE 101 45429 #017-20-1975 L1978 **DR NR** *020 †80
CARROLL, Richard Michael. 7707 PARAGON RD, STE 106 45459 #016-43-1973 L1975 **DR** *020 †80
CASALMIR, Eduardo Caspe. 1520 S MAIN ST 45409 #748-08-1966 L1972 **PUD CCM** *071 †20
CASALMIR, Rebecca T O. ■ 45409 #748-10-1968 L1975 **PD** *020
CASCIELLO, Michael C. ■ 45409 #023-12-1997 L1998 **CD** *020 †20
CASS, William Oak. ■ 45419 #038-41-1956 L1956 **GP** *071
CASTO, Bryan Douglass. 361 W 3RD ST 45402 #055-02-1998 L2001 **FOP** *020
CATA, Ceferino Jose. 2611 WAYNE AVE 45420 #275-01-1951 L1972 **IMG PD** *071
CATALDI, Oscar Blas. 600 WAYNE AVE 45410 #132-01-1954 L1972 **P** *030
CATANZARITE, Michelle L. 2132 E 3RD ST 45409 #041-12-2003 L2003 **FM** *020 †18
CAVANAUGH, David James. 1 CHILDRENS PLZ 45404 #007-02-1969 L1970 **R NM** *071 †80,28
CHABALI, Raul. 1 CHILDRENS PLZ 45404 #038-40-1977 L1978 **PEM PD** *020 †55
CHAMBERS, Mark Jos. 4983 WALNUT WALK 45429 #038-40-1981 L1981 **AN** *020 †05
CHAMBERS, Steven Lawrence. 1520 S MAIN ST, STE 2 45409 #023-12-1982 L2006 **PUD CCM** *020 †20
CHAN, Kathran. 7707 PARAGON RD, 1 WYOMING ST 45459 #038-45-1984 L1994 **DR** *020 †80
CHANDRA, Arti. ■ 45458 #495-45-1991 L2007 **IM** *020 †20
CHANG, Kuang Shah. ■ 45403 #038-45-2008 *012
CHANGCHIEN, Eric Ming. ■ 45402 #038-45-2007 **GS** *012
CHAPMAN, Deitrice. 3140 E DOROTHY LN 45409 #055-12-1994 L1996 **FM** *020 †18
CHARNEY, David Ian. 1989 MIAMISBURG CENTRVL RD, STE 302 45459 #041-01-1984 L2000 **NEP IM** *020 †20
CHATTERJI, Atindra Nath. 8701 OLD TROY PIKE, STE 70 45424 #495-20-1966 L1983 **IM GE** *020 †20

CHEEK, Andrew Glenn. ■ 45429 #005-12-2007 L2007 **TY** *012
CHELLIS, Mary Elizabeth. 1 WYOMING ST, DEPT OF EMERGENCY MEDICINE 45409 #038-45-1992 L1993 **EM** *020 †16
CHERRY, Rebecca Therese. 6096 BRANDT PIKE 45424 #038-40-1990 L1991 **FM** *020 †18
CHERUKURI, Ravi. 7271 N MAIN ST, MEDICAL IMAGING PHYSICIANS 45415 #041-01-1998 L2004 **DR** *020 †80
CHIAFFITELLI, Oreste T. 304 TALBOTT TOWER 45402 #561-20-1952 L1963 **P** *075
CHIANG, Tsing-Yun. 4100 W 3RD ST 45428 #385-02-1959 L1991 **N OS** *071 †75 ‡
CHIRAKALWASAN, Naricha. PO BOX 927, CO WSU-INTERNAL MEDICINE D 45401 #891-01-1999 L2001 **PCC** *012
CHIU, Ronald Cabanas. 2222 PHILADELPHIA DR, DEPT OF PATHOLOGY 45406 #748-19-1999 L2006 **HMP** *020 †20
CHONG, Grace Yuncha. ■ 45459 #583-03-1958 L1977 **PM** *071
CHOUDARY, Vidya. PO BOX 927, WRIGHT STATE UNIVERSITY 45401 #495-65-2003 L2007 **IM** *012
CHRISTIAN, Jeffrey Scott. 1 CHILDRENS PLZ, CHILDREN'S MEDICAL CENTER 45404 #038-45-1985 L1993 **PDS** *020 †85
CHRISTMAN, Kenneth Danl. 2717 MSBG CNTVL RD STE 212 45459 #005-12-1973 L1981 **PS GS** *020 †65
CHRISTOFF, Nicholas Peter. 1427 BUSINESS CENTER CT 45410 #036-05-1979 L1984 **NEP IM** *020 †20
CHU, Jamie Wenwam. 1 WYOMING ST, MIAMI VALLEY HOSPITAL 45409 #038-45-2000 L2000 **P** *100 †75
CHU, Linda W. 3535 SOUTHERN BLVD 45429 #005-12-1976 L1980 **PTH PCP** *020 †50
CHUNG, K Chris. 2591 MIAMISBURG CENTRVL RD, STE 302 45459 #583-03-1970 L1981 **DR VS** *020 †80
CLARK, James R. ■ 45419 #041-77-1971, ▲ L1978 **R** *075
CLARK, William Michael. 2222 PHILADELPHIA DR 45406 #038-45-1982 L1983 **EM** *071 †16
CLONTZ, Robert Michael, II. ■ 45440 #023-12-2008 *012
COALSON, Richard Chas. ■ 45458 #039-01-1974 L1975 **EM FM** *071 †18,16
COFFIN, Julia Faucette. ■ 45419 #011-04-2008 *012
COHEN, Steven Michael. 4450 BUCKEYE LN, UNIT 332 45440 #038-41-1978 L1978 **IM** *020 †20
COLAVINCENZO, Paul R. 3535 SOUTHERN BLVD 45429 #038-40-1986 L1986 **AN** *020 †05
COLGLAZIER, Jack L. ■ 45459 #030-05-1945 L1950 **OM** *071
COLLARES, Jose Antonio A. 600 WAYNE AVE 45410 #187-11-1960 L1981 **P** *020
COLLIER, Gary Steven. 1 WYOMING ST 45409 #017-20-1975 L1975 **IM** *020 †20
COLLINS, Christopher M. 950 E ALEX BELL RD 45459 #038-41-1999 L1999 **OTO** *020 †45
COLLINS, Robert Eugene. 9985 DAYTON LEBANON PIKE 45458 #056-06-1958 L1959 **PS GS** *071
COLLISON, Jason Robert. ■ 45458 #038-40-2007 L2007 **P** *012
CONLEY, Christopher Dean. 30 W RAHN RD 45429 #038-45-1993 L1998 **DR** *020 †80
CONLEY, Gary Lee. 2451 WAYNE AVE 45420 #038-45-1991 L1992 **IM** *020 †20
CONNELLY, Patrick Joseph. 160 WYOMING ST, STE 5 45409 #020-02-1977 L1981 **PTH CLP** *020 †50
CONOVER, Paul. ■ 45409 #038-45-1987 L1993 **CRS GS** *020 †85,10
CONOVER, Steven Robt. 7707 PARAGON RD, RADIOLOGY PHYSICIANS INC 45459 #038-43-1984 L1986 **DR** *020 †80
CONVERY, Sean Robt. 6601 CENTERVILLE BSNS PKWY, STE 101 45459 #038-45-1981 L1982 **FM FSM** *020 †18
COOK, Robert M. ■ 45459 #038-45-1985 L1990 **NM** *020 †80
COOK, Thomas Michael. 9000 N MAIN ST, STE 227 45415 #033-75-1997, ▲ L1998 **FM** *020 †20
COOPER, Joan. 101 WYOMING ST 45409 #038-45-1984 L1985 **FM** *040 †18
CORCORAN, Erica Elizabeth. ■ 45410 #038-45-2008 *012
COWAN, Allison Elaine. ■ 45419 #039-01-2006 L2006 **P** *012
COX, Merrilee Imes. 1 CHILDRENS PLZ, CHILDRENS MEDICAL CTR 45404 #038-45-1998 L1999 **PD** *020 †55
CRAIG, Michael William. 1 WYOMING ST 45409 #041-02-1962 L1963 **PUD IM** *030 †20
CRAWFORD, Courtney Kathle. ■ 45459 #038-43-2008 *012
CRAWFORD, Kelly Marie. ■ 45458 #038-45-2008 *012
CRAWFORD, Mark Alan. 2773 ORCHARD RUN RD, KETTERING ANESTHESIA MGMT 45449 #005-12-1977 L1991 **AN** *020 †05
CRESPO, Jorge Maturana. 33 W RAHN RD, STE 102 45429 #176-03-1970 L1976 **IM ID** *040 †20
CRITES, Gerald E. 1 ELIZABETH PL, STE 500 45408 #038-40-1991 L1993 **IM** *020 †20
CROMARTIE, Junius E, Jr. 211 S MAIN ST, STE 600 45402 #047-07-1949 L1957 **GS GYN** *071
CROOM, Christopher Scott. 1 WYOMING ST, BERRY BLDG, GRND 45409 #041-05-1983 L1995 **MFM OCC** *020 †30
CROSBY, Lynn A. 30 E APPLE ST STE 5250, MIAMI VALLEY HOSPITAL 45409 #038-40-1983 L2000 **ORS** *020 †40
CROUCH, Jeremy Michael. ■ 45459 #054-04-2006 L2006 **OBG** *012
CROWDER, Michael William. ■ 45419 #041-15-2003 L2006 **EM** *012
CRUZ, Patrocino G. 1997 MIAMISBURG CENTRVL RD, SOUTHVIEW HOSPITAL 45459 #748-08-1966 L1977 **PTH** *020 †20
CRUZ, Rafael. 1362 E STROOP RD 45429 #847-03-1955 L1972 **U** *020 †95
CUNNINGHAM, John. ■ 45429 #038-40-1964 L1964 **GS ORS** *050 †85,90
CUSTER, Robert Mcmillion. 9985 DAYTON LEBANON PIKE 45458 #038-40-1989 L1996 **AN** *020 †05
CZACHOR, John Stanley. 128 E APPLE ST, 2ND FL WEBER EDUC BLDG 45409 #038-45-1983 L1984 **ID IM** *040 †20
DABBAS, Wassef M. 1425 E STROOP RD 45429 #875-02-1973 L1978 **IM FM** *020
DALLAL, Mohammed Mazen. 1520 S MAIN ST STE 2, CONSULTANTS, INC. 45409 #875-02-1985 L1994 **PUD CCM** *040 †20
DALSTROM, David Jens. ■ 45429 #038-40-2003 L2003 **ORS** *012
DALTON, Yvonne. 2521 FAR HILLS AVE 45419 #041-07-1962 L1965 **CHP** *020 †20
DANESHJOO, Parviz. 1 WYOMING ST STE 4110 45409 #517-01-1964 L1971 **GYN REN** *071 †30
DANIEL, Kristin Joy. ■ 45429 #005-12-2007 L2007 **OBG** *012
DANKO, William R. 332 CONGRESS PARK DR, PREMIERE HEALTH CARE SERV, 45459 #038-45-1991 L1992 **IM** *020
DANOPULO, Damianos. 3080 ACKERMAN BLVD, STE 310 45429 #902-10-1952 L1983 **CD IM** *020
DARNSTEADT, Derrick Ryan. ■ 45419 #016-06-2004 L2007 **EM** *012 ‡
DARST, Marc Alan. 1 ELIZABETH PL, STE 200 45408 #017-20-1990 L2002 **DMP** *020 †18,15
DAVIS, James Harvey, Jr. 361 W 3RD ST, MONTGOMERY COUNTY CORONER' 45402 #027-01-1970 L1970 **FM FOP** *020 †20
DAVIS, John Danl. 1 WYOMING ST 45409 #017-20-1975 L1975 **OM EM** *030 †16
DAVIS, Nicholas Daniel. ■ 45424 #038-45-2006 L2006 **FP** *012
DEARMOND, Marilyn K. 1 WYOMING ST, MIAMI VALLEY HOSP 45409 #048-14-1991 L1995 **AN** *020 †05

DE BARD, Mark Lyman. 1 FRANCISCAN WAY 45408 #038-40-1975 L1975 **EM FM** *020 †18,16
DE BARD, Richard Mark. ■ 45458 #018-75-1951, ▲ L1951 **GP** *071
DE BOLD, Conrad. ■ 45429 #028-02-1943 L1950 **OBG** *071 †30
DEENADAYALU, R Paul. 2222 PHILADELPHIA DR 45406 #495-04-1965 L1971 **PD NPM** *020 †55
DE GUZMAN, Bernadette Mon. 101 WYOMING ST, PRACTICE R 45409 #025-07-2005 L2005 **FP** *012
DE GUZMAN, Dolores D. ■ 45429 #748-01-1956 L1968 **GP FM** *071
DE GUZMAN, Josephine. PO BOX 927, CO PSYCHIATRY DEPT PO 45401 #048-16-2004 L2004 **P** *012
DE GUZMAN, Ricardo D. ■ 45429 #748-02-1955 L1967 **IM END** *071 †20
DEHNER, Gerard Alan. 6601 CENTERVILLE BSNS PKWY, STE 201 45459 #017-20-1964 L1972 **ORS** *071 †40
DE LIMA, Clarence Anthony. ■ 45405 #495-17-1964 L1977 **P N** *075 †75
DELLON, Steven Curtis. 4200 INDIAN RIPPLE RD, CONSULTANTS, PC 45440 #023-01-1987 L1990 **GE IM** *020 †20
DEMIRJIAN, Charles. 7034 CORPORATE WAY 45459 #025-07-1965 L1983 **PMM N** *071 †75
DENEN, Mickey Ellewyn. 6611 CLYO RD 45459 #038-45-1987 L1988 **IM PD** *020 †55,20
DENLINGER, David Eldon. 89 SYLVANIA DR FL 1, DAYTON EYE ASSOCIATES, INC 45440 #038-40-1979 L1981 **OPH** *020 †35 ‡
DEOL, Gurdev Singh. 2222 PHILADELPHIA DR 45406 #495-32-1955 L1972 **GS CRS** *020
DESAI, Kunal Rohitbhai. ■ 45440 #495-89-2005 L2007 **IM** *012
DESAI, Priyakant Kantilal. ■ 45440 #495-23-1966 L1973 **U** *071 †95
DEVARA, Ravi S. 550 W DAVID PKWY 45429 #495-50-1971 L1979 **PS HS** *020 †18
DEVORE, Ronald Lee. 8371 YANKEE ST 45458 #038-41-1986 L1991 **OTO HNS** *020 †45
DE WALL, Richard A. ■ 45419 #026-04-1953 L1966 **TS** *071 †85,90
DEWANI, Shabana Jaynul. PO BOX 927, DEPT OF INTERNAL MED 45401 #496-60-2005 L2006 **IM** *012
DICKERSON, Patricia A. 1299 E ALEX BELL RD 45459 #038-40-1986 L1987 **D** *020 †15
DIERUF, William James. 7076 CORPORATE WAY 45459 #028-02-1965 L1970 **OPH A** *020 †35
DILEGO, Roberta Anne. 730C VALLEY ST 45404 #038-43-1985 L1993 **PD PHP** *020 †55
DIRCKX, John Henry. ■ 45420 #056-06-1963 L1964 **GP** *020
DITZEL, Douglas Wm. 1 WYOMING ST 45409 #016-76-1983, ▲ L1983 **RO** *020 †80
DIXON, Thomas Raywood. 2451 WAYNE AVE 45420 #038-45-1997 L1998 **FM** *020 †18
DOCK, Jayson Carl. 1 WYOMING ST, STE 7000 45409 #026-04-2001 L2001 **GS** *020 †85
DOERGER, Joseph James. ■ 45419 #038-41-2005 L2005 **GS** *012
DOERGER, Phyllis T. 1 WYOMING ST 45409 #038-41-1989 L1990 **EM** *020 †16
DOERR, Mary E Minges. ■ 45409 #407-04-1952 L1957 **AN** *071
DOLAN, Kendra Leagh. ■ 45424 #041-14-2002 L2007 **EM** *020 †16
DOLE, Mukund Govind. 1 CHILDRENS PLZ, PEDIATRIC HEMATOLOGY 45404 #496-38-1985 L1997 **PHO PD** *020 †55
DONNELLY, Thomas James. 1520 S MAIN ST STE 2, CONSULTANTS, INC 45409 #038-40-1988 L1997 **PUD CCM** *020 †20
DOSHI, Bhadresh P. 6550 N MAIN ST 45415 #495-17-1982 L1991 **OBG** *020 †30
DOUGLAS, Anquenetta Latos. ■ 45459 #017-20-2006 L2006 **AN** *012
DOWDY, Yvonne Gwyneth. 5250 FAR HILLS AVE 45429 #041-01-1992 L2001 **PTH HMP** *020 †50
DOWNER, Robert Nye. 2222 PHILADELPHIA DR 45406 #021-01-1970 L1970 **OTO FPS** *075 †45
DOWNEY, Douglas Merritt. ■ 45458 #001-02-2003 L2006 **GS** *012
DOWNING, Melissa Lynn. ■ 45420 #038-45-2008 *012
DRAZNER, Dana Lynn. 1 CHILDRENS PLZ, THE CHILDREN'S MEDICAL CEN 45404 #035-46-1988 L1991 **PD** *020 †55
DREHMER, Timothy Joel. 1 ELIZABETH PL, NWG STE 500E ST CHE 2ND FL 45408 #023-12-1985 L1997 **IM RHU** *020 †20
DROLLINGER, Dale Wm. 5676 FAR HILLS AVE 45429 #038-45-1983 L1984 **OBG** *020 †30
D'SOUZA, Bernadette B. 627 S EDWIN C MOSES BLVD, STE 3G 45408 #495-73-1974 L1978 **P N** *030 †75
DUCHAK, John Michael, III. 8367 YANKEE ST, DAYTON CARDIOLOGY & 45458 #038-43-1987 L1993 **CD** *020 †20
DUENO, Otto Richard. 627 S EDWIN C MOSES BLVD, 5TH FLOOR SUITE K 45408 #042-03-1992 L1994 **P PYG** *020 †75
DUFFETT, Kate Marie. ■ 45419 #041-15-2003 L2005 **FM** *020 †18
DUKE, Henry Michael. 6210 N MAIN ST 45415 #004-01-1974 L1979 **D** *020 †15
DUKE, Janice Mosny. 627 S EDWIN C MOSES BLVD, GROUND FLOOR 45408 #038-45-1996 L1997 **OBG** *020 †30
DUNCAN, Matthew David. ■ 45458 #038-44-1998 L1999 **DR** *020 †80
DUNN, Margaret M. 30 E APPLE ST, STE 5253 45409 #041-02-1977 L1982 **GS** *030 †85
DURNING, James Patrick. 4100 W 3RD ST STE 112, DAYTON VA MEDICAL CENTER 45428 #041-14-1978 L1995 **GS AM** *020 †85
DUVALL, Beth Ellen. 6611 CLYO RD, STE A 45459 #038-45-1993 L1994 **MPD PD** *020 †55,20
DYER, Brien Wm. 601 S EDWIN C MOSES BLVD, ELIZABETH PL NW BLDG 45408 #001-02-1978 L1979 **P PFP** *030 †75
DZENIS, Verena Akermanis. ■ 45429 #594-01-1940 L1954 **PTH** *071 †50
EARLEY, Stanley A, Jr. 1 WYOMING ST 45409 #869-07-1952 L1954 **FM OS** *020
EARNEST, Ryan Eric. ■ 45424 #023-12-2007 L2007 **GS** *012
EATON, Elizabeth A. 1 WYOMING ST, MIAMI VALLEY HOSPITAL ETC 45409 #038-44-1989 L1991 **EM** *020 †16
EBERT, James Ray. 1 ELIZABETH PL, STE 500 45408 #038-41-1979 L1980 **ADL PD** *040 †55
ECKERT, Philip A. 229 E STROOP RD 45429 #038-41-1942 L1942 **PD** *071 †55
EDMONSON, Alan Lee. 35 SOUTHMOOR CIR NE 45429 #038-40-1961 L1961 **P** *071 †75
EDUAFO, Augustus K. 455 TURNER RD, RENAL PHYSICIANS INC 45415 #412-01-1986 L1997 **NEP IM** *020 †20
EDWARDS, Calvin L. 2801 FAR HILLS AVE 45419 #005-12-1949 L1965 **GS** *071 †85
EDWARDS, Kenny Bernard. ■ 45440 #038-45-2006 L2006 **ORS** *012
EDWARDS, Margaret Ann. 1 ELIZABETH PL STE 280 45408 #038-45-1992 L1997 **IM** *020
EGBERT, Lisa Bohman. 7720 PARAGON RD, PARAGON WOMEN'S CARE 45459 #038-40-1993 L1994 **OBG** *020 †30
EKEH, Akpofure P. 1 WYOMING ST, CHE SUITE 7000 45409 #690-01-1991 L2000 **GS CCS** *020 †85
ELLER, Sylvan Dean. 1 WYOMING ST, MIAMI VALLEY HOSPITAL 45409 #017-20-1967 L1968 **DR NM** *071 †80
ELLGASS, Katie Anne. ■ 45402 #017-20-2008 *012
ELLIS, Brenda Garrett. 7271 N MAIN ST, STE 2 45415 #047-07-1985 L1989 **PD** *020
ELLISON, David Michael. 2661 SALEM AVE, STE 221 45406 #038-45-2000 L2000 **IM** *020 ‡
ELLMAN, Harley Morton. 1101 RIDGEWAY RD 45419 #051-04-1961 L1964 **IM RHU** *020 †20
ELMI, Abdolali. 9000 N MAIN ST, STE 201 45415 #517-04-1970 L1982 **ORS** *020 †40
ELROD, Mike. ■ 45458 #038-75-2001, ▲ L2001 *020
ENDRIKHOVSKAYA, Liubov Y. 2345 PHILADELPHIA DR 45406 #913-15-1996 **FP** *012
ENDRIKHOVSKAYA, Liubov Yu. ■ 45415 #913-15-1996 L2007 **FP** *012
ENGLAND, Stephen Geo. 7720 PARAGON RD 45459 #048-04-1972 L1976 **OBG** *020 †30
ENSELEIT, Stephen Michael. 2480 KETTERING TOWER, EMERGENCY MEDICENE SPECIAL 45423 #038-41-2003 L2006 **EM** *020 †16
ERICKSON, Mary Jo-Ellen. 1 CHILDRENS PLZ, CHILDREN'S EMERGENCY SERVI 45404 #038-41-1996 L1997 **PEM** *020 †55
ERVIN, Michael Eugene. 626 W DAVID RD 45429 #041-13-1974 L1977 **OS EM** *030 †16
ERWIN, J William. 30 E APPLE ST, STE 6250 45409 #038-45-1993 L1994 **FM** *020 †18
ERWIN, William A. ■ 45440 #020-02-1956 L1957 **FM** *071 †18
ESTEP, Carrol Howard. 979 CONGRESS PARK DR 45459 #020-12-1973 L1975 **FM** *020 †18
EULER, Donald Steven. ■ 45406 #047-06-2005 L2006 **IM** *012
EVANS, Dale Gregory. 1 CHILDRENS PLZ 45404 #038-45-1986 L1988 **PEM PD** *020 †55
EVANS, Daniel Allen. 1 CHILDRENS PLZ, CHILDREN'S EMERGENCY SERVI 45404 #038-45-1990 L1991 **PDP** *020 †55
EVANS, James Baxter. 2600 FAR HILLS AVE, STE 6 45419 #038-40-1955 L1956 **IM** *071
EY, Elizabeth Hovda. 1 CHILDRENS PLZ, DEPT OF RADIOLOGY 45404 #021-01-1983 L1987 **PDR DR** *020 †80
FACTORA, Gabriel V. ■ 45458 #748-01-1970 L1978 **PTH** *020 †50
FALLANG, David James. 1 ELIZABETH PL 45408 #038-40-1975 L1975 **GS** *020 †85
FAN, Kaili. 33 W RAHN RD, STE 201 45429 #243-68-1986 L2005 **ID** *020 †20
FEDERINKO, Susan Porter. 2345 PHILADELPHIA DR, GOOD SAMARITAN HOSPFAM PRA 45406 #038-45-1999 L2000 **FM** *020 †18
FEHRMAN, Gary Andrew. 30 E APPLE ST # 5254 45409 #016-43-1963 L1964 **IM DIA** *071
FENBERG, William Harvey. 38 SOUTHMOOR CIR NE 45429 #038-40-1975 L1975 **FM** *020 †18
FENNIG, Julie Lynn. 1775 DELCO PARK DR, PEDIATRIC ASSOCIATES OF DA 45420 #038-43-2001 L2001 **PD** *020 †55
FENSTER, Mark Evan. 5300 FAR HILLS AVE, STE 215 45429 #051-04-1989 L1997 **DS D** *020 †15
FERRIS, Walter Cecil. 101 WYOMING ST 45409 #038-40-1977 L1977 **FM PLM** *040 †18
FESTUS-ABIBO, Laetitia Ch. 2345 PHILADELPHIA DR 45406 #690-04-1982 L2003 **FM** *100 †18
FESUS, Susan Margaret. 60 WYOMING ST 45409 #038-45-1980 L1982 **ON IM** *075
FIERROS, Melinda Gloria. ■ 45440 #048-02-2005 L2005 **P** *012
FINDLAY, Joann Clare. 1520 S MAIN ST, STE 3 45409 #023-07-1981 L1986 **END DIA** *020 †20
FINDLEY, Austin Daniel. ■ 45419 #030-06-2005 L2005 **OBG** *012
FINK, Robert Jos. 1 CHILDRENS PLZ, PULMONRY MED 45404 #038-06-1974 L1977 **PDP PD** *020 †55
FINNAN, Ryan Patrick. ■ 45429 #016-43-2005 L2005 **ORS** *012
FISHBAIN, Harold. 2222 PHILADELPHIA DR 45406 #056-05-1949 L1952 **P** *040 †75
FISHBEIN, Gary Jay. 1530 NEEDMORE RD 45414 #041-09-1987 L1993 **CD** *020 †20
FISHER, Barry Alan. 3205 WOODMAN DR 45420 #038-45-1985 L1986 **FSM** *020 †18
FISHMAN, Harold. 7415 BRANDT PIKE, STE 2 45424 #041-02-1951 L1960 **GE IM** *020 †20
FLEAGLE, Kurt Andrew. 5678 FAR HILLS AVE 45429 #038-45-1993 L1994 **IM** *020 †20
FLEISHMAN, John Andrew. 1520 S MAIN ST STE 5 45409 #038-06-1981 L1989 **OPH** *020 †35 ‡
FLORA, Daniel Blake. ■ 45458 #038-45-2008 *012
FLORES, Carmel Anne G. 211 S MAIN ST 45402 #748-01-1992 L1999 **CHP** *020 †75
FLORES, Charles Edward. ■ 45440 #033-05-2004 L2007 **PD** *012
FORBIS, Shalini G. 730C VALLEY ST 45404 #038-43-1997 L1998 **PD** *020
FORD, Curtis Rashaan. ■ 45402 #007-02-2007 L2007 **PD** *012
FOX, Justin Paul. ■ 45424 #023-12-2007 L2007 **GS** *012
FOX, Katherine Ann. ■ 45419 #038-45-2008 *012
FOX, Matthew John. 9985 DAYTON LEBANON PIKE 45458 #038-45-1992 L1995 **PS GS** *020 †65
FRANZ, John D. ■ 45414 #017-20-1953 L1958 **AN** *071 †05
FRANZ, Martha J Neal. ■ 45414 #017-20-1953 L1958 **PDP PD** *071 †55
FRASIER, Percy Lee. 1989 MIAMISBURG CENTRVL RD, STE 204 45459 #047-07-1975 L1983 **OBG** *020
FRAZIER, Jimmy L. 1 FRANCISCAN WAY 45408 #047-07-1967 L1971 **FM** *020 †18
FRENCH, James Allen, II. 1 CHILDRENS PLZ, DEPT OF HEMATOL-ONCOL 45404 #051-04-1990 L2000 **PHO PD** *020 †55
FRITZ, Rupa Rao. 75 SYLVANIA DR 45440 #495-37-1997 L2000 **GE** *020 †20
FRITZ, Thomas James. 9000 N MAIN ST 45415 #020-12-1991 L1992 **AN PME** *020 †05
FRONISTA, George Richard. 1102 WAYNE AVE 45410 #028-34-1964 L1965 **FM OM** *071 †18
FRONISTA, Harry. 6096 BRANDT PIKE 45424 #038-40-1964 L1964 **FM** *020 †18
FRONISTA-WARD, Stephanie. 6096 BRANDT PIKE 45424 #038-40-1994 L1998 **FM** *020 †18
FUJIMURA, Marty Ken. 9000 N MAIN ST STE 403 45415 #038-45-1984 L1987 **FM** *020 †18
FULCHIERO, Randall Marino. 1520 S MAIN ST, STE 2 45409 #041-02-1981 L1995 **CCM PUD** *020 †20
FUNKHOUSER, James Wm. ■ 45409 #038-40-1957 L1957 **PTH** *071 †50
GAGLIONE, Elaine Knoll. 80 E WOODBURY DR, STE B 45415 #038-40-1987 L1988 **IM** *020 †20
GALBRAITH, James Howard. 33 W RAHN RD, STE 201 45429 #038-40-1995 L2001 **ID** *020 †20
GALBRAITH, Susan Colleen. 1520 S MAIN ST, STE 3 45409 #038-40-1988 L1996 **NEP IM** *020 †20
GALLAGHER, Jessica Denise. 40 W 4TH ST, STE 17 45402 #038-40-1998 L1999 **FM** *020 †18
GAMM, Steven Robt. 725 S LUDLOW ST 45402 #038-41-1983 L1984 **OM EM** *020 †16
GANDHI, Dharmesh V. 1520 S MAIN ST STE 2 45409 #495-22-1989 L1999 **PUD CCM** *020 †20
GANDHI, Ramesh Kumar. 7415 BRANDT PIKE, STE 2 45424 #495-03-1972 L1977 **GE IM** *020 †20
GANDHI, Saroj. ■ 45459 #495-03-1974 L1979 **GP** *020
GANTI, Shyamala. 4100 W 3RD ST 45428 #495-11-1982 L1999 **IM** *020 †20
GARCIA, Feliciano Austria. 2263 SALEM AVE 45406 #748-01-1966 L1982 **PTH FM** *050
GARDIKES, Arthur. 5150 COUNTRY PL 45429 #038-40-1965 L1965 **OTO A** *071 †45
GARRETY, David Allen. 2222 PHILADELPHIA DR 45406 #038-40-1961 L1961 **FM OM** *040 †18
GARRISON, Kathryn. ■ 45424 #039-01-1999 L2007 **PD** *020 †55
GARRISON, Richard Thos. 2222 PHILADELPHIA DR, EMGY TRAUMA CENTER 45406 #038-43-1980 L1981 **EM UM** *020 †16
GATES, Gayla Darnell. ■ 45458 #038-41-2004 L2005 **FP** *012
GAYLOR, Robert Earl. 75 SYLVANIA DR 45440 #055-01-1978 L1980 **GE** *020 †20
GEBHART, Mark Edward. 3155 RESEARCH BLVD STE 105 45420 #038-45-1997 L1998 **EM** *040 †16
GENDLER, Irina Aleksandr. 2345 PHILADELPHIA DR, C/O GOOD SAM/DAYTON COMM-M 45406 #913-72-1986 L2003 **FM** *100 †18
GENOVESI, Giovanni. 6550 N MAIN ST 45415 #561-01-1956 L1968 **OBG** *020 †30
GEORGE, Gary L, Jr. 1 WYOMING ST, MIAMI VALLEY HOSPITAL 45409 #023-12-1983 L2003 **DR AM** *020 †80

■ = Address Information Privacy Protected

GERMAN, John Pierre. 540 LINCOLN PARK BLVD, STE 100 45429 #051-04-1978 L1983 DR *020 †80

GERSON, Jonathan. 9000 N MAIN ST 45415 #047-05-1985 L1986 **AN PME** *020 †05

GERSTNER, Tami Sue. 2980 RIDGE AVE 45414 #040-02-1991 L1992 **EM** *020 †16

GETACHEW, Yohannes B. 1 CHILDRENS PLZ, DEPT OF ANESTHESIOLOGY 45404 #366-01-1988 L2003 **PAN** *05

GHAHERI, Mehdi. 1 WYOMING ST DEPT RAD 45409 #517-06-1970 L1975 DR *071 †80,28

GIBBS, Paul Michael. 160 WYOMING ST, STE 5 45409 #005-06-1990 L1996 **PTH** *020 †50

GILBERT, Lawrence Alan. 4100 W 3RD ST, VA MED CTR DEPT NM 45428 #041-13-1973 L1974 **NM PTH** *071 †50,28

GILL, Aradhana. ■ 45458 #495-29-1986 L1993 **P** *020 †75

GILLIAM, Michael C. ■ 45459 #048-13-2005 L2005 IM *012

GILLIG, Paulette M. 2222 PHILADELPHIA DR, P O BOX 927 45406 #038-43-1977 L1981 **P N** *020 †75

GILLIOTTE, Benjamin John. 30 E APPLE ST, STE L-200 45409 #038-45-1984 L1988 **PM** *020 †60

GINGER, John Frederick. ■ 45458 #038-43-1979 L1982 **PD NPM** *075

GIRARD, Jon Dylan. ■ 45419 #038-41-2005 L2005 IM *012

GIRGIS, Faiza Hanna S. ■ 45405 #330-04-1957 L1974 **IM** *020 †20

GISCOMBE, Cecil S, Jr. ■ 45427 #047-07-1944 L1946 **GP** *071

GLASER, Rebecca Louise. 7740 WASHINGTON VILLAGE DR, STE 110 45459 #038-41-1983 L1984 **OS** *020 †85

GLASS, Kenneth David. 2611 WAYNE AVE, TWIN VALLEY BEHAVIORAL HEA 45420 #038-43-1978 L1979 **P** *020 †75

GLOVER, Kathleen. 128 W 1ST ST 45402 #038-45-1988 L1990 **IM** *020

GLOVER, Melanie M. 1 WYOMING ST, MIAMI VALLEY HOSPITAL; 45409 #020-12-2003 L2003 **OBG** *020

GOBRAIL, Makram Issa. 165 S EDWIN C MOSES BLVD, HEALTH CENTER 45402 #330-03-1965 L1973 **PD NPM** *020 †75

GOEL, Freesia. 4100 W 3RD ST, DEPT OF VETERANS AFFAIRS 45428 #495-37-1997 L2001 **IM** *020 †20

GOEL, Parkash. 730 S MAIN ST 45402 #495-29-1965 L1975 **IM** *020 †20

GOEL, Sunder Lal. 730 S MAIN ST 45402 #495-03-1958 L1973 **N OS** *020

GOHARI, Parviz. 30 E APPLE ST STE 5252 45409 #517-05-1967 L1976 **OBG PD** *072 †30

GOLDSTICK, Lawrence P. 1 ELIZABETH PL STE 2 45408 #025-12-1979 L1984 **N** *020 †75

GOLLAMUDI, Jayakrishna. ■ 45440 #038-44-2008 *012

GOLLAMUDI, Rama Krishna. 4100 W 3RD ST, VA MEDICAL CTR 45428 #495-50-1978 L2000 **P** *020

GOMAA, Laila I. 8120 GARNET DR, PRIME HEALTH MEDICAL SVCS 45458 #915-02-1968 L1995 **AN PME** *020

GOMEZ, Telesforo. ■ 45424 #308-01-1967 **U GS** *020

GONZALEZ-REGALADO, G. ■ 45459 #275-01-1943 L1979 **P** *020

GOODWIN, Charles Dru. 1 CHILDRENS PLZ 45404 #021-01-1968 L1977 **PDS** *020 †85

GOPALAKRISHNAN, R. ■ 45439 #495-04-1988 L1996 **IM** *020 †20

GOPALASWAMY, N. 4100 W 3RD ST # 111, VA MED CTR 45428 #495-09-1963 L1975 **GE IM** *040 †20

GOPALSWAMY, Girija. ■ 45429 #495-21-1966 L1980 **PTH** *074

GORDON, Douglas Alex. 7677 YANKEE ST, STE 110 45459 #067-06-1981 L1988 **HS** *020 †40

GORSKY, Michael Wm. 4200 INDIAN RIPPLE RD 45440 #038-41-1984 L1990 **GE IM** *020 †20

GOSHTASBY, Parviz Hiroshi. ■ 45409 #024-07-2001 L2007 **PS** *012

GOTTRON, Laura E. 1 WYOMING ST 45409 #038-45-2001 L2001 **EM** *100 †16

GOULD, William David. 4100 W 3RD ST, DEPT OF VETERANS AFFAIRS P 45428 #025-07-1977 L1993 **OM FM** *030 †70,18

GOYAL, Amit. 707 S EDWIN C MOSES BLVD 45408 #041-02-1985 L1992 **IC CD** *020 †20

GOYAL, Anuj. 9000 N MAIN ST, STE 222 45415 #038-41-1995 L1996 **PCC IM** *020 †20

GRAHAM, James Patrick. 1520 S MAIN ST STE 2, CONSULTANTS INC 45409 #030-06-1968 L1969 **PUD SME** *020 †20

GRANDHI, Susan Meera. ■ 45458 #496-20-1988 L2001 **IM** *020

GRASS, Jennifer Maria. 1 CHILDRENS PLZ, DEPT OF ANESTHESIOLOGY 45404 #038-44-1991 L1992 **AN PAN** *020 †05 ‡

GREEN, Jennifer Dawn. 9000 N MAIN ST, STE 300 45415 #038-45-2000 L2000 **FM** *020 †18 ‡

GREENE, Judy. 540 LINCOLN PARK BLVD, STE 100 45429 #038-06-1976 L1977 **R** *020 †80

GREENE, Kenneth Wilton. ■ 45402 #038-45-1995 L1996 **IM** *020 †20

GREENE, Mary Kathleen. 1 CHILDRENS PLZ, THE CHILDREN'S MEDICAL CEN 45404 #011-02-1982 L1993 **DR PDR** *020 †80

GREENE, Richard N., Jr. ■ 45410 #038-45-2008 *012

GREER, Thomas Carr. 426 PATTERSON RD 45419 #038-41-1988 L1989 **FM** *020 †18

GREGG, Michael Lester. 1 WYOMING ST, DEPT MEDICAL IMAGING 45409 #038-43-1985 L1991 DR *020 †80

GREGG, Richard Warren. 33 W RAHN RD, STE 102 45429 #025-07-1981 L1992 **IM CCM** *020 †20

GRIFFIN, Roger H. 7707 PARAGON RD, STE 101 45459 #041-12-1973 L1976 **IM RHU** *020 †20

GRIFFITH, Denise Annette. 2132 E 3RD ST 45403 #038-41-1991 L1993 **FM** *020 †18

GRIGG, David Redfield. 3535 SOUTHERN BLVD, KETTERING MEDICAL CTR 45429 #017-20-1985 L1989 **AN** *020 †05

GRIMM, Bradford Pearce. ■ 45410 #019-02-2008 *012

GROGER, Richard Kevin. 33 W RAHN RD, STE 201 45429 #038-06-1992 L2005 **ID IM** *020 †20

GROLL, Jeremy Michael. 175 THRUSTON BLVD E, CB #7570 OLD CLINIC BUILDI 45419 #025-07-1997 L2004 **OBG** *020 †30

GROSS, Howard Michael. 9000 N MAIN ST, STE G-36 45415 #038-41-1976 L1977 **ON HEM** *020 †20

GROSSMANN, Robert Tyson. 4441 FAR HILLS AVE 45429 #031-01-1992 L1998 **FM** *020 †18

GROVE, Denise Renee. 2661 SALEM AVE, STE 120 45406 #038-45-1988 L1989 **EM** *020 †16

GRUBER, Jack Sidney. 128 E APPLE ST STE 3800, CHE 45409 #038-40-1970 L1970 **GYN REN** *071 †30

GUADALUPE, Harold Wilson. 1 WYOMING ST, MIAMI VALLEY EMERG SPECIAL 45409 #038-45-1998 L2000 **MPD** *020 †55

GUIAO, Antonio Mercado. 2222 PHILADELPHIA DR 45406 #748-07-1955 L1968 **PS HS** *071

GUL, Ghazala. 7345 FAR HILLS AVE, UKCMC-GME 45459 #704-09-1994 L2005 **PD** *100

GUL, Waheed. 30 E APPLE ST, STE 6250 45409 #704-09-1992 L2006 **ID** *020 †20

GUNASEKERA, Joseph Nihal. 1530 NEEDMORE RD 45414 #220-01-1981 L1993 **CD IM** *020

GUPTA, Piush. 4200 INDIAN RIPPLE RD 45440 #495-30-1988 L2003 **GE** *020 †20

GUPTA, Raj. 117 S MAIN ST 45402 #495-03-1966 L1975 **PD** *020 †55

GUPTA, Ramesh Chander. 8111 TIMBERLODGE TRL 45458 #495-45-1972 L1975 **EM IM** *020 †20,16

GUPTA, Satyendra Chand. VET ADMIN HOSP 45428 #495-03-1960 L1972 **CD IM** *020 †20

GUPTA, Sharda. ■ 45459 #495-20-1972 L1976 **PTH** *020 †50

GURUSAMY, Soundari. PO BOX 927, WRIGHT STATE UNIVERSITY 45401 #306-01-2006 L2007 **IM** *012

GUY, Michael Stephen. ■ 45424 #038-45-2008 *012

HAAS, Marjorie Marie. 1775 DELCO PARK DR 45420 #038-41-1988 L1991 **NPM** *020 †55

HACKETT, Russell H. 1 CHILDRENS PLZ 45404 #038-40-1972 L1972 **PD EM** *020 †05

HADAWAY, Catherine Anne. ■ 45429 #038-40-1989 L1991 **P** *020 †75

HADAWAY, Scott J. 1 WYOMING ST, MIAMI VALLEY HOSP 45409 #038-40-1989 L1992 **AN** *020 †05

HAHN, Harvey Sungha. 8057 WASHINGTON VILLAGE DR, STE D 45458 #005-12-1994 L1997 **CD IM** *020 †20

HAINES, Roy Walter. 3535 SOUTHERN BLVD 45429 #005-12-1977 L1984 **AN** *020

HALE, E Ronald. ■ 45459 #035-06-1991 L1993 **RO** *020 †70

HALL, Molly J. ■ 45459 #035-20-1977 L1992 **P** *020 †75

HALLER, Sandra Schwarber. 1 WYOMING ST, MIAMI VALLEY HOSPITAL 45409 #038-41-1991 L1995 **AN** *020 †05

HAMILTON, James Christoph. ■ 45419 #038-40-2004 L2005 **EM** *100

HAMILTON, Jeffrey Lynn. 1 WYOMING ST 45409 #038-41-1990 L1992 **AN** *020 †05

HAMILTON, John Adam. 128 E APPLE ST RM 2 45409 #030-06-2006 L2006 **ORS** *012

HANLEY, Paul Francis. 600 WAYNE AVE 45410 #011-04-1997 L1998 **P** *020 †75

HANSON, Maria Pilar. 1 CHILDRENS PLZ 45404 #847-13-2001 L2004 **PD** *100

HARDMAN, Robert Paul. 300 FOREST AVE 45404 #024-01-1955 L1962 **CHN N** *020 †20

HARDY, James Thos. 405 W GRAND AVE 45405 #028-79-1980, ▲ L2002 **FM EM** *020 †18

HARI, Shailaja. ■ 45429 #495-65-1986 L2003 **N** *020 †75

HARLAN, Karen Ann. 1335 PATTERSON RD 45420 #038-43-1979 L1980 **FM** *020 †18 ‡

HARLAN, Wayarne A. 2200 PHILADELPHIA DR, STE 101 45406 #038-40-1985 L1985 **OBG** *020 †30

HARMAN, Timothy W. 4160 LITTLE YORK RD, STE 10 45414 #028-78-2001, ▲ L2001 **HS** *020

HARPER, John Michael. 1 CHILDRENS PLZ 45404 #038-40-1962 L1962 **ORS** *071 †40

HARRIS, Andre Todd, Sr. ■ 45414 #038-45-2002 L2002 **OBG** *020

HARSHBARGER, Kent Edward. 361 W 3RD ST, MONTGOMERY CO CORNERS OFF 45402 #016-45-1996 L2000 **PTH** *020 †50

HART, David Andrew. ■ 45419 #038-45-2004 L2004 **P** *012

HARTEL, Walter Charles. 89 SYLVANIA DR, DAYTON EYE ASSOCIATES INC 45440 #036-05-1979 L1984 **OPH** *020 †35 ‡

HARTSHORN, Benjamin Linde. ■ 45424 #038-45-2008 *012

HASAN, Syed Fareeduddin. 89 SYLVANIA DR, DAYTON EYE ASSOCIATES 45440 #016-42-1998 L2003 **OPH** *020

HAVERKOS, Bradley Michael. ■ 45410 #038-45-2008 *012

HAWK, Andrew Clay. 1 WYOMING ST, MIAMI VALLEY HOSP 45409 #038-45-1987 L1990 **EM** *020 †16

HAWLEY, Harrison Bradford. 1 WYOMING ST 45409 #051-04-1969 L1979 **ID IM** *071 †20

HAYES, Margaret Loretta. 2222 PHILADELPHIA DR, MEDICAL STAFF OFFICE 45406 #035-03-1965 L1970 **OBG** *071 †30

HAYNAL, Peter James S. 2773 ORCHARD RUN RD 45449 #005-12-1977 L1981 **AN** *020 †05

HECKMAN, Louis Paul. 7707 PARAGON RD, STE 101 45459 #038-40-1981 L1983 **IM** *020 †20

HEFFERNAN, Michael Paul. 1 ELIZABETH PL STE 200, DEPT OF DERMATOLOGY 45408 #025-01-1993 L1998 **D** *040 †15

HELLER, Abraham. 1400 RUNNYMEDE RD, WRIGHT STATE UNIVERSITY 45419 #024-05-1957 L1977 **P** *071 †75

HENDERSON, Thomas Werner. 3075 GOVERNORS PLACE BLVD, STE 110 45409 #025-01-1974 L1987 **RHU IM** *020 †20

HENDI, Talieh. PO BOX 927, CO INTERNAL MEDICINPO 45401 #517-08-1976 L2004 **IM** *012

HENDRICKS, Charles M. 2222 PHILADELPHIA DR, INPATIENT MENTAL HEALTH 45406 #038-45-1998 L1999 **P** *020 †75

HENRY, Susan Kay. 1 VALLEY ST, EMEGERGENCY DEPARTMENT 45404 #038-40-1985 L1987 **EM PD** *020 †55

HENSEL, James Irving. ■ 45429 #264-05-1980 L1984 **AN** *020 †05

HERBENICK, Michael Afton. 1 WYOMING ST, MIAMI VALLEY HOSPITAL 45409 #038-45-2000 L2000 **ORS** *020

HERCHLINE, Thomas Edward. 128 E APPLE ST, WEBER BLDG 2ND FL 45409 #038-41-1985 L1986 **ID IM** *020 †20

HERITAGE, Charles Kirby. 2222 PHILADELPHIA DR 45406 #036-05-1980 L1984 **NPM PD** *020 †55

HERTEL, James C. ■ 45429 #038-41-1950 L1950 **GP** *071

HERTING, Judy Lynn. 1 CHILDRENS PLZ, THE CHILDREN'S MED CTR 45404 #017-20-1986 L1987 **AN** *020 †05

HESS, Andrea Michelle. 2345 PHILADELPHIA DR, CO GOOD SAMDAYTON COMM-MED 45406 #038-45-2000 L2000 **FM** *100

HESS, Thomas Anthony. 3535 SOUTHERN BLVD 45429 #038-45-1983 L1984 **AN IM** *020 †05

HEYD, Timothy John. 7740 WASHINGTON VILLAGE DR 45459 #038-45-1990 L1992 **FM** *020 †18

HEYSE, Paul Frank. 1520 S MAIN ST STE 210 45409 #017-20-1978 L1979 **VS GS** *020 †85

HICKMANN, Martha Ann. 6210 N MAIN ST 45415 #030-06-1987 L1990 **D AI** *020 †20,15

HICKS, Ralph Andrew. 1 CHILDRENS PLZ, CHILDREN'S MEDICAL CENTER 45404 #020-02-1982 L1989 **PD OS** *020 †55

HIGGINS, Ashantice Kenyan. ■ 45405 #038-41-2007 L2007 **IM** *012

HILLMAN, Nosrat Makky. ■ 45419 #517-01-1967 L1979 **CLP PTH** *020 †50 ‡

HINMAN, Craig G. ■ 45424 #054-04-1973 L1980 **U GP** *030 †95

HIRT, Thomas Westendorf. 6520 ACRO CT, PRIMED PHYS CENTERVILLE 45459 #038-41-2001 L2001 **FM** *020 †18 ‡

HITCH, David Charles. 1 CHILDRENS PLZ, STE 2071 45404 #036-07-1966 L1988 **PDS ON** *020 †85

HITTNER, Harry R. ■ 45414 #017-20-1952 L1953 **R** *071 †80

HIXSON, Michael Murray. ■ 45409 #048-02-2007 L2007 **EM** *012

HIXSON, Paige Morgan. ■ 45409 #048-02-2007 L2007 **IM** *012

HO, Charles Chiu-Chung. 4100 W 3RD ST 45428 #649-33-1984 L1994 **PM PA** *020 †60

HOBACK, Richard Thos. 8701 TROY PIKE, KETTERING WORKERS CARE 45424 #038-40-1966 L1966 **FM** *071 †18 ‡

HOCHWALT, Jerome P. 38 SOUTHMOOR CIR 45429 #038-41-1941 **GP IM** *071

HODGE, James R. 405 W GRAND AVE 45405 #028-78-1971, ▲ L1972 **CRS** *071

HOFELDT, Mark Richard. 1 CHILDRENS PLZ 45404 #016-11-1982 L1985 **AN** *020 †05

HOFMANN, Rudolf Alois. 2300 FAR HILLS AVE 45419 #407-05-1967 L1974 **ORS OM** *020 †40

HOGARTH, Margaret Helen. ■ 45429 #038-45-1995 *100

HOLLAND, Laurence John. 3535 SOUTHERN BLVD 45429 #005-12-1977 L1981 **AN** *020 †05

HOMOLYA, Coutney Richelle. ■ 45440 #038-43-2005 L2006 **AN** *012
HOOD, Daniel Lane. 1 WYOMING ST, MIAMI VALLEY HOSPITAL 45409 #038-45-1985 L1990 **PTH** *020 †50
HORLACHER, James Kyle. 1 WYOMING ST, STE 4140 45409 #038-40-1971 L1971 **OBG** *020 †30
HORWITZ, Jeffrey Alanson. 301 W 1ST ST, STE 3A 45402 #038-41-1966 L1967 **OPH IM** *071 †35
HOTT, Katherine M. 824 E FRANKLIN ST STE B 45459 #038-41-1974 L1978 **P CHP** *020 †75
HOUSTON, Richard Warren. 7415 BRANDT PIKE, STE 2 45424 #017-20-1971 L2004 **GE IM** *020 †20
HUGHES, Philip Caldwell. 89 SYLVANIA DR 45440 #041-02-1958 L1965 **OPH** *071 †35
HUMPERT, Andrew Dale. ■ 45429 #019-02-2006 L2006 **MPD** *012
HURT, Rochelle Denise. 9775 GREENSIDE CT 45458 #051-07-1988 L1995 **DR** *020
HUSSAIN, Irshad. 8367 YANKEE ST, DAYTON CARDIOLOGY & 45458 #495-04-1984 L2000 **CD** *020 †20
HYAMS, Kenneth Barry. 30 W RAHN RD 45429 #047-06-1970 L1975 **DR** *020 †80
IMBODY, Brent Wilson. 1 WYOMING ST, BERRY PAVILLION STE 3110 45409 #038-45-1988 L1992 **OBG** *020 †30
IMBROGNO, Diane Foley. 3535 SOUTHERN BLVD 45429 #038-45-1981 L1982 **AN** *020 †05
IMBROGNO, Eugene Edward. 7187 TARRYTON RD 45459 #038-45-1981 L1982 **OM EM** *020 †16,70
INAPARTHY, Aparna. 2661 SALEM AVE, STE 220 45406 #495-21-1999 L2002 **IM** *100 †20
IOSSI, Michael Franklin. ■ 45403 #018-03-2005 L2005 **ORS** *012
IQBAL, Naveed Syed. 3171 RESEARCH BLVD, DEPT OF INTERNAL MEDICINE 45420 #104-01-2004 L2005 **IM** *012
ISKANDER, Magda Nasif. 2261 MIAMISBURG CENTRVL RD 45459 #915-02-1974 L1978 **GP DR** *020
ISLAM, Nafisa. ■ 45458 #038-40-2005 L2005 **FP** *012
ISLAM, Shaikh Mohammed B. ■ 45458 #495-39-1959 L1976 **GS EM** *071
IVERSEN, Peter Christian. 2611 WAYNE AVE, TWIN VALLEY BEHAVIORAL 45420 #038-45-2001 L2001 **P** *020
JABALLAS, Elvira Rosca. 1 ELIZABETH PL, STE 500 45408 #748-01-1961 L1972 **PD** *020 †55
JABALLAS, Rodrigo Laracas. 1 FRANCISCAN WAY 45408 #748-08-1962 L1972 **GS GP** *071
JACKSON, Cheryl Yvonne. 1 CHILDRENS PLZ, DIVISION OF NEPHROLOGY 45404 #038-41-1979 L1984 **PD** *020 †55
JACKSON, Marvin William. 2312 FAR HILLS AVE 45419 #005-14-1993 L2004 **AM** *020
JACOB, Antony T. 30 E APPLE ST, STE L200 45409 #495-44-1979 L1989 **PM** *020 †60
JACOBS, Alan Keith. 1 ELIZABETH PL, STE 210 45408 #035-47-1977 L1981 **N IM** *020 †75
JACOBS, Liesl Jade. ■ 45419 #038-45-2006 L2006 **P** *012
JACOBS, Martin Paul. 3535 S BLVD NUCLEAR MED 45429 #035-15-1981 L1983 **NM IM** *020 †20,28
JAFFE, Michael Austin. 7211 N MAIN ST, STE 1 45415 #038-40-1963 L1963 **ORS** *020 †40
JAFFERY, Ali Turab. 45414 #704-20-2002 L2004 **IM** *100
JAMES, Stanley Anthony. 2363 POLO PARK DR 45439 #005-12-2001 L2001 **IM** *100
JAN, Mohammad Abdullah. 9000 N MAIN ST, STE 202 45415 #704-09-1967 L1973 **CD IM** *020 †20
JANG, Suk Chang. 2222 PHILADELPHIA DR 45406 #583-02-1963 L1972 **PTH** *071 †50
JANZ, Timothy Geo. 1052 LITTLE SUGAR CREEK RD 45440 #038-40-1979 L1980 **CCM EM** *040 †20,16
JASPER, Robert Anthony. 2222 PHILADELPHIA DR 45406 #038-41-1979 L1979 **EM** *020 †16
JEDICK, Rocky Peterjosep. ■ 45419 #038-45-2008 *012
JENKINS, Herbert Stanley. 1222 S PATTERSON BLVD, FL 2 45402 #038-45-1989 L1991 **GS** *020 †85
JHANGIANI, Anil H. 1126 S MAIN ST 45409 #496-38-1989 L1997 **CD** *020 †20
JIANG, Kecheng. 33 W RAHN RD, STE 201 45429 #243-45-1990 L2004 **IM** *100 †20
JILANI, Shamin Zafar. 9000 N MAIN ST 45415 #704-18-1980 L1995 **ON** *020 †20
JIT, Rajkamal. 7415 BRANDT PIKE, STE 2 45424 #495-10-1991 L1996 **GE** *020 †20
JOFFE, Charles David. 1530 NEEDMORE RD, THE DAYTON HEART CENTER 45414 #038-41-1971 L1972 **IC CD** *020 †20
JOGAN, Lori Lyn. 332 CONGRESS PARK DR 45459 #038-40-1997 L2000 **EM** *020 †16
JOHN, Sherin Elizabeth. PO BOX 927, C/O WSU-INTERNAL MEDICINE 45401 #473-04-2002 L2003 **IM** *100 †20
JOHNSON, David Kinnaird. 2591 MIAMISBURG CENTRVL RD, STE 300 45459 #038-40-1981 L1982 **PM** *020 †60
JOHNSON, Dean Russell. ■ 45429 #005-12-1956 L1959 **AN** *071 †05
JOHNSON, Ewanah Dawn. 33 W RAHN RD, STE 102 45429 #005-12-1999 L1999 **IM** *020 †20
JOHNSON, George Franklin. 1735 CHAPEL ST 45404 #038-06-1947 L1947 **PDR** *071 †80
JOHNSON, Ron Michael. 30 E APPLE ST, STE 5257 45409 #038-41-1988 L1990 **PS GS** *020 †85,65
JOHNSON, Shelsea Lea. 1 CHILDRENS PLZ 45404 #038-45-2001 L2001 **PD** *100 †55
JOHNSON, Stacie Lynn. 45440 #046-01-2000 L2001 **END** *020 †20 ‡
JOHNSON, Thomas Lewis, II. 45440 #020-12-2000 L2000 **AI** *100 †55,03
JOHNSTONE, Sara Kay. ■ 45424 #026-04-2005 L2005 **OBG** *012
JOINER, Shelly Claire. 8501 TROY PIKE 45424 #010-03-1989 L1996 **OBG** *020 †30
JOLY, David Andrew. 1 WYOMING ST, DEPT OF ANESTHESIOLOGY 45409 #038-43-1999 L2004 **AN** *020 †05
JONES, Amy Keebler. 8638 TROY PIKE, STE 101 45424 #038-45-2000 L2000 **PD** *020 †55
JONES, Eduardo G. ■ 45459 #264-04-1961 L1976 **P CHP** *020 †75
JONES, Gregory Philip. 1 WYOMING ST, DEPT OF MED EDUCATION 45409 #039-79-2006, ▲ L2006 **OBG** *012
JONES, Roland Peter. ■ 45458 #011-04-2000 L2004 **N** *020 †75
JOVANOV, Aco. 9000 N MAIN ST STE 4, MAIN STREET FAMILY PRACTIC 45415 #957-04-1993 L2001 **FM** *020 †18
JUERGENS, Daniel Paul. 77 E WOODBURY DR, STE 100 45415 #038-41-1974 L1975 **OPH** *020 †35
JUSTINIANO TORO, Luis. 2222 PHILADELPHIA DR 45406 #847-10-1971 L1983 **P** *020
KADAKIA, Chaitanya S. 7111 N MAIN ST, STE 10 45415 #495-23-1976 L1982 **IM IMG** *020 †20
KAHN, Ronald Stephen. 3080 ACKERMAN BLVD STE 210 45429 #038-43-1976 L1977 **FM** *020 †18
KAKDE, Susheel Suhas. ■ 45429 #495-28-1973 L1982 **OM** *020 †16
KALNINS, Aivar Imants. 30 E APPLE ST 45409 #024-07-1959 L1967 **GS OBG** *071 †85
KAMDAR, Bharati. 7345 FAR HILLS AVE 45459 #496-07-1975 L1991 **PD** *020 †55
KAMINSKI, Douglas Paul. 9985 DAYTON LEBANON PIKE 45458 #030-06-1985 L1987 **AN EM** *020 †05
KAMMER, Jodie Marie. ■ 45409 #038-45-2007 L2008 *012
KAMRAN, Khurram. 2661 SALEM AVE, STE 220 45406 #704-09-1992 L2006 **IM** *020 †20

KANBAR, Ali Hussein. 33 W RAHN RD, STE 201 45429 #605-01-2002 L2003 **HO** *012 †20
KANDULA, Narayana V. ■ 45415 #495-11-1960 L1975 **GS IMG** *071 †85
KANDULA, Suseelamma R. 325 JACQUELYN CT 45415 #495-11-1959 L1977 **PTH OBG** *020 †50
KANG, Hye Yung. 3533 SOUTHERN BLVD, STE 3100 45429 #038-45-1991 L1993 **IM** *020
KANTHAWAR, Ashok S. 7415 BRANDT PIKE, STE 2 45424 #495-09-1988 L2002 **GE** *020 †20
KAPADIA, Shefali A.. PO BOX 927, CO WRIGHT STATE UNIV-MED E 45401 #654-01-2000 L2002 **ID** *020 †28
KAPLON, Michael Kenneth. 4100 W 3RD ST I, DEPT OF VETERAN AFFAIRS ME 45428 #047-05-1981 L2006 **HEM ON** *020 †20
KARABATAK, Ziwar. 8057 WASHINGTON VILLAGE DR, STE D 45458 #875-01-1983 L1990 **CD** *020 †20
KARDAN, Azar. 617 SHROYER RD 45419 #517-01-1972 L1979 **PD A** *020 †55
KARDAN, Javad. 4200 INDIAN RIPPLE RD 45440 #517-01-1968 L1979 **GE IM** *020 †20
KASIM, Walid Said. 30 E APPLE ST STE 3200 45409 #605-01-1981 L1994 **OBG EM** *020 †30
KASTEN, Eileen Frances. 1 CHILDRENS PLZ, THE CHILDREN'S MEDICAL CEN 45404 #017-20-1978 L1981 **PD OS** *020 †55
KATZ, Neil. 4100 W 3RD ST 45428 #051-04-1985 L1995 **NM** *020 †20,28
KAUFHOLD, Jeffrey Joseph. 7231 SHULL RD 45424 #038-41-1986 L1989 **NEP IM** *020 †20
KAUFMAN, Leesa Ann. 9000 N MAIN ST, STE 232 45415 #011-04-1998 L2007 **OBG** *020 †30
KAY, Bruce S. 1074 PATTERSON RD, DAYTON PAIN MANAGEMENT LLC 45420 #035-08-1977 L1983 **PME ORS** *020 †40
KAY, Jerald. 627 S EDWIN C MOSES BLVD, ELIZABETH PLACE, EAST MEDI 45408 #023-01-1971 L1971 **P CHP** *020 †75
KENEASTER, Kari A. ■ 45439 #038-75-2007, ▲ L2007 *012
KENNEBECK, Caroline E. 5701 FAR HILLS AVE 45429 #023-12-1994 L2005 **OBG** *020 †30
KENNEDY, Jessica Carolyn. 101 WYOMING ST, MIAMI VALLEY HOSP FP PGM 45409 #054-04-2006 L2006 **FP** *012
KERNS, Maryjo Jacobson. 1 ELIZABETH PL 45408 #038-40-2004 L2004 **D** *012
KESSLER, William Jos. 2600 FAR HILLS AVE STE 15 45419 #038-41-1978 L1982 **OPH** *020 †35
KEYES, Walter Wm. 4441 FAR HILLS AVE 45429 #056-06-1969 L1970 **FM** *020 †18
KHALID, Mohammad Atiq. 1530 NEEDMORE RD, STE 300 45414 #704-21-1986 L2002 **CD** *020 †20
KHALIFE, Ghada E. 349 S MAIN ST 45402 #605-02-1990 L2001 **PTH** *020 †50
KHALIL, Qasim. 33 W RAHN RD, STE 201 45429 #305-01-2004 L2004 **IM** *020 †20
KHALILI, Mark Hamid. ■ 45429 #654-01-1996 L2000 **FM** *020 †18 ‡
KHAN, Abdur Rehman. 2661 SALEM AVE, STE 220 45406 #704-02-1990 L2007 **IM** *100
KHAN, Aliya U. 3075 GOVERNORS PLACE BLVD 45409 #495-09-1987 L1992 **RHU AI** *020 †20,03
KHAN, Mujtaba Ali. 1126 S MAIN ST, DAYTON CARDIOLOGY & 45409 #495-21-1981 L1997 **CD** *020 †20
KHAN, Nadir. 1 CHILDRENS PLZ, CHILDRENS MEDICAL CENTER 45404 #704-09-1981 L1990 **CHN** *020 †75
KHANAM, Rasheda Akter. PO BOX 927 45401 #160-17-1997 L2007 **IM** *012
KHAVARI, Andrew Reza. ■ 45429 #038-45-2004 L2004 **P** *012
KHOUZAM, Juvy Marie T. 1 WYOMING ST, MIAMI VALLEY HOSPITAL 45409 #748-10-1993 L2000 **AN** *020
KHOUZAM, Sameh Nadim. 1530 NEEDMORE RD, STE 300 45414 #915-04-1992 L2000 **ICE** *020 †20
KIANI, M Younas. ■ 45459 #704-02-1957 L1975 **ORS HS** *071
KIBRIA, Rizwan E. 4100 W 3RD ST, GASTROENTEROLOGY DEPT 45428 #704-01-1995 L2000 **GE** *012 †20
KIDD, Sarah Jayne. ■ 45459 #038-45-2007 L2007 **OBG** *012
KIEFABER, Matthew Paul. ■ 45459 #038-40-2003 L2003 **EM** *020 †16
KIEFABER, Robert Woodhull. 8057 WASHINGTON VILLAGE DR, STE D 45458 #038-06-1974 L1985 **CD IM** *020 †20
KIETURAKIS, Jolanta M. 1 WYOMING ST, DEPT OF ANESTHESIA 45409 #759-07-1977 L1994 **AN** *020 †05
KILBURN, Jeremy Paul. ■ 45458 #028-34-2005 L2005 **IM** *012
KILIAN, Steven Douglas. 160 WYOMING ST 45409 #038-40-1976 L1977 **OBG** *020 †30
KIM, Buup Justin. 2661 SALEM AVE, STE 232 45406 #051-01-1979 L1991 **TS** *020 †85,90
KIM, Catherine Minghsia. 1 WYOMING ST 45409 #038-45-2005 L2005 **EM** *012
KIM, Seong-Bae. 5877 BATSFORD DR 45459 #583-10-1967 L1974 **AN** *020 †05
KIM, Taewoong. 6929 N MAIN ST 45415 #583-02-1967 L1975 **OBG** *020 †30
KING, Henry Lee. 5341 DUSHORE DR 45427 #010-03-1964 L1969 **ORS** *020
KIRCHER, Konrad Felix. 111 W 1ST ST STE 918, STE 918 45402 #407-16-1950 L1955 **R** *071 †80
KIRKHAM, Karen Elaine. 1 ELIZABETH PL, STE 500 45408 #038-45-1989 L1994 **IM** *020 †20
KIRKLAND, Clem Lee, Jr. 5928 SPRINGBORO PIKE 45449 #048-04-1971 L1977 **FM** *020 †18
KIRKLAND, Eugene Brent. ■ 45459 #038-06-2008 *012
KIRKLAND, Jeanne Marie. 5928 SPRINGBORO PIKE 45449 #048-13-1978 L1980 **FM** *020 †18
KIRKWOOD, David Chas. 2838 LINDEN AVE 45410 #020-12-1983 L1984 **FM** *020 †18
KIRSCHMAN, David Louis. 30 E APPLE ST, STE 5257 45409 #007-02-1996 L2002 **NS** *020
KITCHENER, Jacob Manoj. 30 E APPLE ST, STE 5254 45409 #038-44-2000 L2000 **N** *020 †75
KITTOE, David Akwainja. 2661 SALEM AVE, STE 220 45406 #412-01-1999 L2002 **IM** *100 †20
KLANKE, Lisa Weider. 1 CHILDRENS PLZ, DAYTON CHILDREN'S HOSPITAL 45404 #038-45-2005 L2005 **PD** *012
KLEIN, Alan Herbert. 2661 SALEM AVE, STE 220 45406 #038-40-1958 L1958 **IM** *071 †20
KLEIN, Richard Martin. 205 HAVER RD, UNIT 504 45419 #035-46-1960 L1970 **DR** *071 †80,28
KLEIN, Ronald Stephen. 8701 TROY PIKE, KETTERING WORKERS CARE 45424 #005-12-1982 L1985 **FM OM** *020 †70,18 ‡
KLEINER, Laurence Irwin. 1 CHILDRENS PLZ, THE CHILDRENS MEDICAL CENT 45404 #041-13-1980 L2002 **NSP** *025
KLEINHENZ, Benjamin Patri. ■ 45429 #038-41-2007 L2007 **ORS** *012
KLEINHENZ, Steven Michal. 6601 CENTERVILLE BSNS PKWY 45459 #038-45-1981 L1982 **ORS** *020 †40
KLOSTERMAN, James Jos. 9000 N MAIN ST STE 227 45415 #038-41-1988 L1996 **ORS OSM** *020 †40 ‡
KLUG, Mark Stephen. 5300 FAR HILLS AVE, STE 100 45429 #038-41-1977 L1978 **HS ORS** *020 †40
KLYKYLO, William Michael. 627 S EDWIN C MOSES BLVD, WSU DEPT OF PSYCHIATRY 45408 #025-01-1975 L1979 **CHP P** *040 †75
KNAPP, Victor Richard. 2611 WAYNE AVE, TWIN VALLEY BEHAVIORAL HLT 45420 #041-01-1982 L1996 **P PFP** *020 †75
KNOLL, Aaron Lewis. 80 E WOODBURY DR, STE B 45415 #038-40-1985 L1992 **GE IM** *020 †20
KNOLL, Herman Charles. 80 E WOODBURY DR, STE B 45415 #038-40-1955 L1955 **IM CD** *020 †20

KNOPF, Patricia Schneider. 2773 ORCHARD RUN RD, KETTERING ANESTHESIA ASSOC 45449 #038-43-1993 L1997 **AN** *020 †05
KNOWLES, James Roy. 4235 INDIAN RIPPLE RD, STAHL VISION INC 45440 #026-08-1984 L2005 **OPH** *020 †70,35
KNUDSON, Stephen Hugh. 25 E FORAKER ST 45409 #018-03-1965 L1992 **EM FM** *020 †16,18
KODE, Lakshmi. 7271 N MAIN ST, NORTH MAIN IMAGING CENTER 45415 #038-41-1988 L1989 **RNR R** *020 †80
KODURI, Jhansi Lakshmi. 9000 N MAIN ST, STE G-36 45415 #495-58-1997 L2000 **HO** *020 †20
KOHNEN, Benjamin L. ■ 45419 #038-45-2008 *012
KOKOROPOULOS, P C. 1 WYOMING ST, DEPT OF ANESTHESIOLOGY 45409 #016-11-1990 L1994 **AN** *020 †05
KOLLER, William Siegfried. 6445 FAR HILLS AVE 45459 #038-06-1942 L1942 **DR** *071
KOLODZIK, Paul W. 332 CONGRESS PARK DR 45459 #038-45-1984 L1985 **EM** *020 †16
KOLOKOLO, Dennis. 1 WYOMING ST, DEPT OF MEDICINE 45409 #690-04-1982 L2006 **IM** *020 †20
KONDAGUNTA, Gnanamba V. 3120 GOVERNORS PLACE BLVD 45409 #035-20-1998 L2007 **ON IM** *020 †20
KONSTANTAKOS, Emmanuel K. ■ 45429 #038-06-2002 L2002 **GS** *100
KOROSCIL, Thomas Michael. 1 ELIZABETH PL STE 500 45408 #023-12-1984 L2003 **END IM** *020 †20
KOTINSLEY, Benjamin Marti. ■ 45419 #038-45-2008 *012
KOUMAS, Peter Constantine. 105 SUGAR CAMP CIR STE 200 45409 #028-79-1980, ▲ L1981 **OPH** *020 ‡
KRAMER, Matthew Geo. 1 WYOMING ST, DEPT OF ANESTHESIOLOGY 45409 #023-01-1991 L1995 **AN** *020 †05
KRAMER, Samuel Nelson. 405 W GRAND AVE, DEPT OF PATHOLOGY 45405 #019-02-1969 L1977 **PTH** *020 †50
KRAVITZ, Kevin Drew. 1530 NEEDMORE RD 45414 #041-07-1989 L1996 **ICE CD** *020 †20
KREBS, Mary Elizabeth. 101 WYOMING ST 45409 #038-40-2004 L2004 **FM** *020 †18
KREMER, Christina Marie. 1 WYOMING ST, CO MIAMI VALLEY HOSP-FAMIL 45409 #038-43-2000 L2000 **FM** *100 †18
KRISHNAMURTHY, Anil B. 4100 W 3RD ST, DAYTON VA MED CLR #112 45428 #495-37-1983 L1999 **OAR** *020
KRISHNAMURTHY, Padmini. ■ 45458 #495-33-1991 L1999 **GE** *100 †20
KRZMARZICK, Thomas Robt. 1 CHILDRENS PLZ, EMERGENCY DEPT 45404 #018-03-1984 L1988 **PD** *020 †55
KUCHLEWSKI, Robert John. ■ 45420 #010-02-1969 L1973 **OPH** *071 †35
KULSHRESTHA, Pankaj. 2200 PHILADELPHIA DR, ADVANCED HEART & LUNG SURG 45406 #495-36-1982 L2006 **TS** *020 †85,90
KUMAR, Deepak. 9000 N MAIN ST, STE 326 45415 #495-03-1970 L1975 **CRS** *020 †10,85
KUMAR, Geetika. 5833 STONE LAKE DR 45429 #495-20-1984 L2003 **HO** *020 †20
KUMAR, Gogi. ■ 45429 #495-15-1999 L2005 **CHN** *020 †55,75
KUNESH, John Charles. 2601 FAR HILLS AVE 45419 #038-40-1993 L1994 **OPH** *020 †35 ‡
KUNESH, Michael Thos. 2601 FAR HILLS AVE 45419 #038-40-1986 L1987 **OPH** *020 †35 ‡
KUNESH, Sarah Lee. ■ 45458 #038-40-1993 L1996 **RHU** *020 †20
KUNESH-PART, Kristine A. 2601 FAR HILLS AVE 45419 #038-40-1982 L1983 **OPH** *020 †35 ‡
KUPPER, Thomas Edward. 9000 N MAIN ST, STE 101 45415 #038-45-1984 L1985 **CD IM** *020 †20
KURUVILLA, Mary. 1520 GERMANTOWN ST 45408 #495-31-1968 L1988 **P** *020 †75
KUTWAL, Atul. PO BOX 927, WRIGHT STATE UNIVERSITY 45401 #495-37-2005 L2007 **IM** *012
KWIAT, Glenn Alan. 111 HARBERT DR 45440 #038-41-1987 L1988 **FM** *020 †18
KWIATEK, Kim David. 2222 PHILADELPHIA DR 45406 #038-41-1977 L1978 **EM OM** *020 †18,16
KWON, Nancy Jung-Hee. 1 WYOMING ST, DEPT OF ANESTHESIOLOGY 45409 #583-08-1975 L1981 **AN** *020 †05
LANE, Jeffrey Lee. 1 WYOMING ST, DEPT OF ANESTHESIOLOGY 45409 #017-20-1995 L2006 **AN** *020 †05
LANE, Raynald Allan. 601 S EDWIN C MOSES BLVD 45408 #067-01-1961 L1969 **CD IM** *030 †20
LARSON, Julie Ann Heil. 40 W 4TH ST, STE 17 45402 #054-04-1987 L2001 **FM** *020 †18
LAUGHLIN, Richard Thos. 30 E APPLE ST STE L-2200, DEPT OF ORTHOPEDIC SURGERY 45409 #048-15-1988 L1994 **ORS** *020 †40
LAVIN, William Jeffrey. 7707 PARAGON RD, RADIOLOGY PHYSICIANS INC 45459 #036-05-1982 L1986 **DR** *020 †80
LAW, Catherine H. ■ 45419 #038-45-2008 *012
LAWHORNE, Larry Wayne. 627 S EDWIN C MOSES BLVD, DEPT OF GERIATRICS 5TH FL 45408 #051-01-1973 L2006 **FPG FM** *040 †18
LAWLESS, Matthew William. 30 E APPLE ST, STE L200 45409 #020-02-1995 L1996 **ORS OSM** *020 †40
LAWS, James Gentry. 425 W GRAND AVE, STE 2002 45405 #028-78-1970, ▲ L1971 **CD IM** *020
LE, Namchi Phan Khac. 1 WYOMING ST, EMERGENCY MEDICINE ADMIN 45409 #005-14-1995 L1997 **EM** *020 †16
LEBAMOFF, Damian Ivan. 1520 S MAIN ST, STE 210 45409 #038-45-1992 L1996 **GS** *020 †85
LEBOWITZ, Jeffrey Bart. 332 CONGRESS PARK DR, PREMIER HEALTHCARE SVCS 45459 #035-46-1989 L2003 **EM** *020 †16
LECHNER, George Wm. 2801 FAR HILLS AVE 45419 #005-12-1956 L1963 **GS VS** *071 †85
LEE, Adrienne Waiwah. ■ 45402 #038-40-2007 L2007 **PD** *012
LEE, Dong-Eun. 228 TROY ST, CONCENTRA MEDICAL CENTERS 45404 #583-01-1967 L1977 **OM GS** *020 †85
LEE, Yong-Ho. PO BOX 927, INT MED 45401 #583-01-1977 **AM** *020
LEHMAN, Lee Danl. 361 W 3RD ST 45402 #017-20-1982 L1987 **FOP PTH** *020 †50
LEIBOLD, Joseph David. 1 WYOMING ST, MIAMI VALLEY HOSP 45409 #038-45-2002 L2002 **EM** *020 †16
LEITHOLD, Joseph Scott. 4235 INDIAN RIPPLE RD, STE 210 45440 #038-45-1992 L1996 **FM** *020 †18
LELAND, John. ■ 45429 #012-05-1949 L1950 **GP** *071
LEMMON, Gary Wayne. 2222 PHILADELPHIA DR 45406 #017-20-1980 L1981 **VS GS** *020 †85
LEPAGE, John Charles. 5300 FAR HILLS AVE, STE 300 45429 #050-02-1972 L1979 **D** *020 †15
LE ROY, Gary Lewis. 2132 E 3RD ST 45403 #038-45-1988 L1989 **FM OS** *020 †18 ‡
LESCHANSKY, Edward James. ■ 45459 #028-34-1955 L1956 **GP OS** *071
LEVELLE, Jonathan Patrick. 1 WYOMING ST, NETWORK, LTD 45409 #055-01-1981 L2000 **AN** *020 †05
LEVINE, Carol Lynn. 30 E APPLE ST 45409 #038-45-1994 L1995 **IM** *071 †20
LEVITT, Stephen Barry. 9000 N MAIN ST, STE 321 45415 #649-14-1971 L1978 **D** *020
LEWIS, William J. ■ 45429 #017-20-1951 L1952 **FM** *071 †18
LIDDY, Bernard James. 2222 PHILADELPHIA DR 45406 #038-40-1964 L1964 **GP FM** *020
LIEBLEIN, Suzanne Marie. ■ 45402 #038-45-2007 L2007 **GS** *012
LIGHT, Dawn Elizabeth. 1 CHILDRENS PLZ 45404 #038-45-1982 L1985 **PDR DR** *020 †18,80
LIKKI, Santosh Reddy. 9001 N MAIN ST, STE A 45415 #495-21-1994 L2000 **CD** *012 †20
LIM, David Francis. 500 LINCOLN PARK BLVD, STE 220 45429 #005-12-1977 L1978 **IM** *020 †20,16
LIM, Kok Hoo. 2661 SALEM AVE, STE 232 45406 #624-01-1978 L1991 **TS** *020 †85,90
LIM-KONG, Maria B. 8501 TROY PIKE 45424 #748-01-1968 L1974 **OBG** *071 †30
LINDOWER, John Oliver. 3535 SOUTHERN BLVD 45429 #038-40-1955 L1955 **OS PA** *040
LINTA, James Michael. 60 WYOMING ST, STE 200 45409 #041-12-1968 L1977 **GS** *071 †85
LISTON, Richard Lee. 89 SYLVANIA DR, DAYTON EYE ASSOCIATES, INC 45440 #049-01-1989 L1994 **OPH PO** *020 †35
LITTLE, Alex G. 1 WYOMING ST, STE 7000 45409 #023-07-1974 L2003 **GS TS** *030 †85,90
LITTLEFIELD, William G. 3205 WOODMAN DR 45420 #038-40-1983 L1993 **ORS AM** *020 †40
LIU, Hong. 1 CHILDRENS PLZ 45404 #243-52-1992 L2004 **PHO** *100
LIU, Nancy Wenchin. 5678 FAR HILLS AVE 45429 #038-44-1996 L1997 **IM** *020 †20
LJUNGREN, Warren R. 111 HARBERT DR 45440 #038-41-1984 L1985 **FM** *020 †18
LLENADO-LEE, Marian A. 3533 SOUTHERN BLVD, STE 3750 45429 #748-01-1979 L1984 **ON HEM** *020
LONG, Marlene Elizabeth. 1 FRANCISCAN WAY 45408 #010-03-1963 L1967 **PS HS** *020
LONG-PRENTICE, Angela C. 3535 SALEM AVE, STE 201 45406 #038-45-1991 L1992 **FM** *020 †18
LOO, Tricia Cheping. ■ 45409 #005-12-2007 L2007 **GS** *012
LOPEZ, Glenda Joy. 7211 N MAIN ST STE 6 45415 #748-08-1979 L1984 **IM** *020 †20
LUCENTE, Julia Immaculata. 620 KLING DR 45419 #038-41-1984 L1985 **IM** *020 †20
LUGER, Richard Kevin. ■ 45419 #023-12-2007 L2007 **GS** *012
LUGO, Anthony Ferdinand. 7720 PARAGON RD, STE B 45459 #038-40-1973 L1973 **GP** *020 †18
LUNA, Lina D. 4100 W 3RD ST, DAYTON VAMC 45428 #748-07-1965 L1981 **GP OS** *020
LUNDERMAN, Jack Catlett. 1 WYOMING ST 45409 #038-45-1984 L1985 **P** *020
LUNEAU-GORDON, Colette P. 111 W 1ST ST STE 207, DUARTE MARGOLIS ASSOC 45402 #396-01-1974 L1988 **NS** *020
LUSTGARTEN, Barbara. 1034 WILMINGTON AVE 45420 #011-02-1959 L1963 **FM GP** *020
LUTTER, Donald Ray. 4200 INDIAN RIPPLE RD 45440 #038-40-1979 L1981 **GE IM** *020 †20
LUTZ, Robert J. 1 CHILDRENS PLZ 45404 #038-40-1953 L1953 **PD** *071 †55
LYNCH, John William, III. ■ 45419 #020-12-2001 L2007 **CD** *020
MABREY, Jay Donald. 1 WYOMING ST, BERRY BLD GOUND 45409 #035-20-1981 L1983 **ORS OTR** *020 †40
MAC GREGOR, Roderick H. 332 CONGRESS PARK DR, PREMIER HEALTH CARE SERVIC 45459 #064-01-1973 L1994 **FM OM** *020
MACHICAO, Carlos Niki. 2222 PHILADELPHIA DR, PATHOLOGY DEPT 45406 #176-01-1981 L1989 **PTH PCP** *020 †50
MAC NEALY, Gregory Anton. 2222 PHILADELPHIA DR 45406 #016-06-1978 L1982 **DR** *062 †80
MAGDY, Khaled R. 1520 S MAIN ST, STE 2 45409 #915-03-1980 L1999 **PUD CCM** *020 †20
MAGNOTTA, Alfred James. 627 S EDWIN C MOSES BLVD 45408 #038-41-1961 L1961 **OBG** *072 †30
MAGNUSEN, David Kenneth. 2591 MIAMISBURG CENTRVL RD, STE 300 45459 #017-20-1997 L1999 **PM** *020 †60
MAGUIRE, John Patrick. 30 E APPLE ST, STE 6258 45409 #005-12-1973 L1974 **OS GS** *020 †85
MAHAJAN, Mahendra Kumar. 9000 N MAIN ST STE 301 45415 #495-14-1971 L1979 **P CHP** *020
MAHAJAN, Sarita A. 4100 W 3RD ST, VA VETERANS MEDICAL CTR B3 45428 #495-01-1985 L2002 **P** *020 †75
MAIMON, Henry Newman. 4200 INDIAN RIPPLE RD, GASTROINTESTINAL & LIVER 45440 #038-41-1968 L1968 **GE IM** *020 ‡
MAIMON, Walter Ned. 950 E ALEX BELL RD 45459 #030-05-1979 L1981 **OTO HNS** *020 †45
MALEMPATI, Padmavathi. 321 AMHERST BND 45440 #495-50-1994 L2000 **IM** *020 †20
MALIK, Aamir Iftikhar. 9000 N MAIN ST, DAYTON LUNG & SLEEP MEDICI 45415 #704-22-1991 L2005 **PCC** *100 †20
MALIK, Ghazala S. 332 CONGRESS PARK DR, PREMIER HEALTH CARE SERVIC 45459 #704-16-1990 L1996 **IM** *020 †20
MALONE, Kathleen Ann. 1 WYOMING ST, EMERGENCY TRAUMA CENTER 45409 #038-40-1977 L1977 **GS** *020 †16
MANGANARO, Andrew Joseph. 580 LINCOLN PARK BLVD, STE 322 45429 #035-19-1972 L1981 **TS GS** *020 †85,90
MANGUBAT, Ophelia V. 2165 W CENTERVILLE RD 45459 #748-01-1961 L1975 **PD OS** *071 †55
MANSOUR, Fawzi Saad. 30 E APPLE ST, CHE BLDG 3RD FLOOR 45409 #330-01-1957 L1966 **OBG OS** *020 †30
MANTIL, Jose Chacko. KETTERING MEDICAL CTR, NUCLEAR MEDICINE/PET DEPT 45429 #649-33-1977 L1981 **NM IM** *020 †20,28
MANZ, Daniel James. 2661 SALEM AVE, STE 221 45406 #038-41-2003 L2003 **IM** *020 †20
MARABOYINA, Sudhakar. 1530 NEEDMORE RD, THE DAYTON HEALTH CENTER 45414 #495-21-1968 L1974 **CD IM** *020 †20
MARADANI, Sudama. PO BOX 927 45401 #495-11-2002 L2005 **IM** *100
MARCUS, David Roy. 1530 NEEDMORE RD, STE 300 45414 #038-40-1963 L1963 **CD IM** *071 †20
MARDIS, Donald Curtis, III. 1 WYOMING ST, MIAMI VALLEY HOSPITAL 45409 #038-43-2002 L2002 **AN** *020 †05
MARGER, Donald. 3535 SOUTHERN BLVD 45429 #036-07-1969 L1974 **RO** *071 †80
MARINELLA, Mark Alan. 33 W RAHN RD, STE 201 45429 #038-45-1993 L1996 **HO** *012 †20
MARKUS, Michael Jos. 30 E APPLE ST 45409 #038-45-1983 L1985 **IM** *040 †20
MARKUS, Timothy David. 1530 NEEDMORE RD, STE 300 45414 #038-45-1981 L1982 **CD IM** *020 †20
MARRIOTT, William R. 8111 TIMBERLODGE TRL 45458 #038-45-1991 L1992 **EM** *020 †16
MARSHALL, Don Alfredo. 9000 N MAIN ST 45415 #047-07-1967 L1968 **EM** *020
MASHBURN, Sally Ann. 3535 SOUTHERN BLVD 45429 #005-12-1981 L1984 **AN** *020 †05
MASSENGILL, Jason C. 1 WYOMING ST, CO WSUMIAMI VALLEY HOSP-OB 45409 #023-12-2003 L2003 **OBG** *020
MASSULLO, James Mario. ■ 45420 #038-44-2004 L2004 **GS** *012
MASTERS, Thomas Chrisman, II. ■ 45410 #038-45-2008 *012
MATHAI, Stephen Thos. 25 THORPE DR, CCHC-EAST 45420 #495-27-1970 L1982 **PD** *020 †55
MATHEWS, James Robt. 570 W STEWART ST 45408 #010-03-1963 L1965 **FM GP** *020
MATIJEVIC-JOZIC, Vlasta. ■ 45419 #957-01-1954 L1979 **FM** *071 †18
MATRE, William Michael. 1 CHILDRENS PLZ 45404 #038-40-1975 L1978 **PD OS** *020 †55
MATTHEWS, John Bennett. ■ 45449 #038-41-1978 L1978 **EM OS** *020
MAUGANS, Todd Allen. 1 CHILDRENS PLZ, THE CHILDREN'S MEDICAL CEN 45404 #041-13-1985 L2004 **NS OBS** *020 †18,25
MAUNG, Lay Khin. PO BOX 927, WRIGHT STATE UNIVERSITY 45401 #748-21-2001 L2007 **IM** *012
MAYS, Dewey Ordic, III. ■ 45406 #047-07-1981 L1988 **IM** *075

MAZIMBA, Sula Elvis. 33 W RAHN RD, STE 201 45429 #965-01-2002 L2002 **IM** *100 †20
MC CALIP, Benjamin L. 1 WYOMING ST 45409 #048-13-2001 L2007 **PCP** *020 †50
MCCANN, Edward Thomas, III. ■ 45410 #041-02-2006 L2006 **IM** *012
MC CARTHY, Mary Catherine. 128 E APPLE ST, 7TH FL 45409 #017-20-1977 L1990 **GS TRS** *020 †85
MC CLURE, Dennis Elliott. 8654 N MAIN ST 45415 #017-20-1978 L1988 **NS** *020 †25
MC CORKLE, Barry Scott. 2451 WAYNE AVE 45420 #038-45-1988 L1989 **IM OS** *020 †20
MC DOWELL, Patricia Ann. 5250 FAR HILLS AVE 45429 #016-11-1983 L1987 **PTH BBK** *020 †50
MC GILTON, Ronald Lee. 9000 N MAIN ST, STE 300 45415 #038-45-1998 L1999 **FM** *020 †18
MC HENRY, Eric Michael. 1525 E STROOP RD 45429 #038-45-1988 L1989 **FM** *020 †18
MC INTYRE, Sally S. 2451 WAYNE AVE 45420 #038-06-1987 L1993 **IM** *020
MC KENNA, David Stephen. 1 WYOMING ST, GROUND FLR 45409 #038-06-1992 L1993 **OBG** *020 †30
MC KENZIE, Richard A. 3535 SOUTHERN BLVD 45429 #038-45-1985 L1986 **VIR** *020 †80
MCLEAN, Jamie Sussan. 627 S EDWIN C MOSES BLVD, ELIZABETH PLACE EAST 1ST F 45408 #038-45-2003 L2003 **P** *012
MC LIN, Ronald Wm. ■ 45459 #056-06-1963 L1967 **AN** *071 †05
MCLOUGHLIN, David Edward. 2200 PHILADELPHIA DR # 301, SURGEONS INC 45406 #010-02-1989 L2004 **TS** *020 †85,90
MEADOWS, Kirk Paul. 1222 S PATTERSON BLVD, STE 120 45402 #020-02-1982 L1983 **GS TRS** *020 †85
MEAGHER, David P, Jr. 1 CHILDRENS PLZ 45404 #048-04-1973 L1974 **PDS GS** *020 †85
MEALY, Arthur Taylor. ■ 45418 #047-07-1942 L1943 **GP** *071
MEDINA, Asuncion Ver. ■ 45458 #748-02-1958 L1972 **CHN PD** *071 †55
MEEKER, Lesley Ann. 2600 FAR HILLS AVE, STE 6 45419 #038-45-2000 L2000 **FM** *020 †18
MEHMOOD, Muddassir. PO BOX 927, WRIGHT STATE UNIVERSITY 45401 #704-20-2003 L2007 **IM** *012
MEININGER, Dan Earl. 30 W RAHN RD 45429 #017-20-1957 L1963 **DR RO** *071 †80
MELASHENKO, Robert Allen. 972 W ALEX BELL RD 45459 #005-12-1978 L2008 **AN CCM** *020 †05
MELVIN, Kelli Jean. 4428 INDIAN RIPPLE RD, INDIAN RIPPLE FAMILY HEALT 45440 #038-45-2000 L2000 **FM** *020 †18 ‡
MENG, Hsien-Ming. KETTERING MEMORIAL HOSP 45429 #005-12-1958 L1965 **DMP EM** *072 †50
MERANDA, Kattie Ynez. ■ 45406 #038-45-2006 L2006 **FP** *012
MEREDITH, Jody Ann. PO BOX 927 45401 #820-02-2005 L2007 **MPD** *012
MERL, Stuart Allan. 1 ELIZABETH PL, # 10B 45408 #043-01-1978 L1987 **ON HEM** *020 †20
MESGHALI, Homayoun. 9000 N MAIN ST, STE 227 45415 #517-01-1968 L1975 **ORS** *020 †40
MESKER, David Armin. 9000 N MAIN ST, STE G-35 45415 #038-45-1988 L1989 **FM** *020 †18
METRY, Terez Rida Rizk. 2451 WAYNE AVE 45420 #915-09-1991 L1995 **IM** *020 †20
MEYER, Christopher Scott. 1222 S PATTERSON BLVD, STE 120 45402 #038-40-1990 L1992 **GS** *020 †85
MEYER, Gerald E. ■ 45429 #038-40-1952 L1952 **FM** *071 †18
MEZOFF, Adam Gary. 1 CHILDRENS PLZ 45404 #038-41-1981 L1983 **PD PG** *020 †55
MICK, Thomas Chas. 111 WEST FRIST ST STE 918 45402 #038-41-1963 L1963 **R** *071 †80
MICK, Thomas Marcus. 1563 E DOROTHY LN, STE 101 45429 #016-02-1995 L2001 **OS IM** *100 †20,75
MIGALLY, Nabil Bushra. 5212 BRANDT PIKE, STE A 45424 #038-45-1988 L1989 **IM** *020
MIHATA, Leanne Catherine. ■ 45459 #023-12-2001 L2003 **GP** *062
MIHATA, Ryan Garnerkazuo. ■ 45459 #023-12-2005 L2006 **EM** *012
MILFORD, Kimberly Ann. ■ 45440 #047-06-2007 L2007 **PD** *012
MILLARD, Jeffrey Reddert. 111 HARBERT DR 45440 #038-41-1982 L1984 **FM** *020 †18
MILLER, Deborah Elizabeth. 101 WYOMING ST, BERRY FAMILY HEALTH CENTER 45409 #038-45-1991 L1992 **FM OBS** *040 †18
MILLER, Kennon Andrew. ■ 45458 #038-45-2007 L2007 **TY** *012
MILLER, Marvin Elliott. 1 CHILDRENS PLZ, DEPT OF MEDICAL GENETICS 45404 #008-01-1973 L1992 **MG PD** *020 †55,19
MILLER, Rasa Kristen. 2345 PHILADELPHIA DR 45406 #913-96-1987 L2002 **FM** *020 †18
MILLER, Steven Abbott. 301 W 1ST ST STE 3A 45402 #024-05-1970 L1980 **OPH** *020 †35
MILLING, Cassandra Jean. 1 ELIZABETH PL STE 210, NEUROLOGY SPECIALISTS 45408 #035-46-1995 L2006 **CN** *020 †75
MINELLA, Philip Arthur. 30 E APPLE ST STE 6254 45409 #038-41-1972 L1972 **NS** *020 †25
MIRANDA, Rogelio S. 2200 PHILADELPHIA DR, STE 447 45406 #748-08-1964 L1972 **OBG** *020 †30
MIRAU, Helen Kim. 2600 FAR HILLS AVE STE 204 45419 #035-01-1988 L2002 **OBG** *020 †30 ‡
MIREMADI, Abdol-Reza. 160 WYOMING ST, LOWER LEVEL 45409 #035-01-1998 L2001 **OS** *020
MIRKIN, L David. 1 CHILDRENS PLZ 45404 #132-01-1957 L1987 **PP ATP** *020 †50
MISSICK, Benjamin James. 2345 PHILADELPHIA DR 45406 #038-45-2007 L2007 **FP** *012
MISTOVICH, Ronald Justin. ■ 45410 #038-45-2008 *012
MITCHELL, David Frederick. 2591 MIAMISBURG CENTRVL RD, STE 300 45459 #038-40-1978 L1979 **PM** *071 †60
MITCHELL, Jenny Z. 1 WYOMING ST, DEPARTMENT OF ANESTHESIA 45409 #035-19-1993 L1997 **AN** *020 †05
MOAD, John C. 7835 PARAGON RD 45459 #028-46-1987 L1999 **DMP PTH** *020 †50
MOBLEY, Henry Mc Kinley. 211 S MAIN ST, STE 600 45402 #010-03-1959 L1961 **GS** *071 †85
MOELL, Michael Anthony. 359 FOREST AVE STE 106 45405 #038-40-1989 L1991 **PD** *020 †55
MOEZZI, Ahmad. 1 WYOMING ST, BERRY PAVILLION STE 3110 45409 #517-01-1970 L1981 **OBG** *020 †30
MOEZZI, Jazbieh Mostashfi. 4100 W 3RD ST 45428 #517-01-1971 L1982 **PTH** *050 †50
MOHAMMED, Abdul Mannan Ma. PO BOX 927, WRIGHT STATE UNIVERSITY 45401 #496-27-2001 L2007 **IM** *012
MONCRIEF, Hugh. 30 E APPLE ST, STE 6254 45409 #019-02-1972 L1987 **NS** *020 †25
MONK, Susan Marie. 1 CHILDRENS PLZ, CHILDREN'S MEDICAL CENTER 45404 #041-02-1971 L1975 **PD** *020 †55
MOODY, Charles Dean. 3716 WILMINGTON PIKE, KETTERING FAMILY PRACTICE 45429 #017-20-1958 L1959 **FM** *020
MOODY, Martha Anne. 2600 FAR HILLS AVE, PRIMED PREM INTGRTD MEDL 45419 #038-41-1982 L1983 **IM** *071 †20
MOON, Dong Soo. 6728 LOOP RD STE 201 45459 #583-04-1968 L1978 **P ADM** *020 †75
MOONEY, Joseph Francis. 2308 SHROYER RD, PREMIER HLTH CARE SERV 45419 #016-06-1986 L1991 **EM IM** *020 †16
MOORE, Ashlee Elisabeth. ■ 45429 #038-45-2006 L2006 **GS** *012
MOORE, John Pease, III. 2595 NEEDMORE RD 45414 #045-04-1994 L1995 **PME** *020
MORALES, Luis Jose. 1 WYOMING ST, STE 3120 45409 #042-01-1985 L1992 **OBG** *020 †30
MORAR, Kamal. 3075 GOVERNORS PL, STE 120 45409 #422-01-1999 L2004 **VIR** *020 †80
MORITZ, Charles Roger. 369 W 1ST ST, STE 120 45402 #038-40-1956 L1956 **REN OBG** *071 †30
MORRISON, Jaime Leigh Ste. 1 CHILDRENS PLZ, DEPT OF MED EDUCATION 45404 #422-01-2006 L2006 **PD** *012
MORSE, Gregory James. ■ 45459 #028-34-1991 L1994 **NM** *020 †80,28
MOSER, Ronald Jos. 301 W 1ST ST 45402 #020-12-1975 L1980 **ORS** *071 †40
MOSSMAN, Douglas. 627 S EDWIN C MOSES BLVD, EAST MEDICAL PLAZA, 1ST FL 45408 #025-01-1981 L1982 **P PFP** *020 †75
MOTEKALLEM, Mohammad H. 1530 NEEDMORE RD STE 300 45414 #517-01-1968 L1975 **CD IM** *020 †20
MOYER, Paul David. 89 SYLVANIA DR, FL 1 45440 #038-41-1995 L1996 **OPH** *020 †35
MUELLER, Gary Arthur. 1 CHILDRENS PLZ, DIVISION OF PULMONARY MEDI 45404 #025-01-1987 L1993 **PDP PD** *020 †55
MUELLER, Michelle Jane. ■ 45414 #038-41-2006 L2006 **IM** *012
MUKKU, Sindhu Bhairavi. PO BOX 927, WRIGHT STATE UNIVERSITY 45401 #422-01-2007 L2007 **IM** *012
MULLAPUDI, Ravindra Nath. 8638 OLD TROY PIKE, STE 102 45424 #495-50-1978 L1991 **FM** *020 †18
MURIITHI, Ruth Wambui. PO BOX 927, WRIGHT STATE UNIVERSITY 45401 #577-01-2004 L2007 **IM** *012
MURPHY, Gordon Kristen. ■ 45419 #038-41-1965 L1965 **PTH FOP** *071 †50
MURPHY, James Joseph. 1520 S MAIN ST STE 2, CONSULTANTS 45409 #038-40-1979 L1981 **PUD CCM** *020 †20
MURPHY, Mary Elizabeth. ■ 45410 #038-45-2008 *012
MURPHY, Thomas Frederick. 1 CHILDRENS PLZ 45404 #008-02-1972 L1980 **PD ID** *020 †55
MUST, Burton Garwood, Jr. 111 W 1ST ST, STE 918 45402 #038-41-1963 L1963 **R** *071 †80
MUTH, Warren Frederick. 3533 SOUTHERN BLVD # 2250 45429 #010-01-1970 L1977 **GS VS** *020 †85
MUTHIAH, Venkatachlam. 1 ELIZABETH PL, STE 190 45408 #495-04-1959 L1972 **NEP IM** *071
NAGLE, James Boyd. 1 WYOMING ST 45409 #409-10-1972 L1976 **FM IMG** *020
NAGUBADI, Sandhya. PO BOX 927, CO WSU-INTERNAL MEDICINE D 45401 #495-21-1998 L2001 **IM** *020
NAHHAS, William Aziz. 1 WYOMING ST, DPT OBG 45409 #605-01-1963 L1983 **GO OBS** *020 †30 ‡
NAJWA, Tabrah. 3533 SOUTHERN BLVD, STE 4600 45429 #528-01-1964 L1973 **GYN** *020 †30
NAKFOUR, Bassam Shaker. 7720 PARAGON RD, STE A 45459 #605-01-1972 L1976 **OBG IM** *020 †30
NANAGAS, Maria T P. 730C VALLEY ST 45404 #748-02-1970 L1975 **PD** *020 †55
NANAGAS, Victor N, Jr. 1 WYOMING ST 45409 #748-02-1964 L1975 **PDS** *020 †85
NANGLE, Gerald Francis. ■ 45459 #023-01-1954 L1955 **GP** *071
NARASIMHA REDDY, Y. 3763 SALEM AVE 45406 #495-11-1960 L1972 **U GS** *020
NARAYAN, Kailash K. 2200 PHILADELPHIA DR, STE 644 45406 #495-27-1981 L2005 **NS GS** *020 †25
NARAYAN, Raj Kumar. 2200 PHILADELPHIA DR, STE 644 45406 #495-27-1976 L2002 **NS** *020 †25
NARRON, Jill Victoria. 1 CHILDRENS PLZ, DAYTON CHILDRENS CARDIO 45404 #051-01-1993 L1996 **PDC** *020 †55
NAZIR, Raja A. 2222 PHILADELPHIA DR, GOOD SAMARITAN HOSPITAL 45406 #704-01-1990 L1996 **CD** *020 †20
NEIGER, Ran. 1 WYOMING ST, PERINATAL PARTNERS 45409 #550-04-1983 L2002 **MFM OBG** *020 †30
NEKROSIUS, W Scott Damian. 5300 FAR HILLS AVE, STE 200 45429 #056-06-1971 L1978 **P CHP** *020 †75
NENONENE, Kwasi Alfred. 2457 N GETTYSBURG AVE, NENONENE FAMILY MEDICINE 45406 #038-45-1998 L2000 **FM** *020
NEWMAN, William Brian. 128 APPLE ST, STE 3800 45409 #022-75-2000, ▲ L2007 **OBG** *012 †18
NG, Wenn Jean. 3535 SOUTHERN BLVD, DEPT OF MED EDU 45429 #060-02-2004 L2005 **IM** *012
NOOR, Aliya. PO BOX 927, CO WSUINTERNAL MEDICINE DE 45409 #704-21-1995 L2000 **PCC** *100 †20
NOORDSIJ-JONES, Matthew R. PO BOX 927, PEDS PGM 45401 #056-06-2006 L2006 **MPD** *012
NOYES, Matthew Proctor. ■ 45402 #038-43-2007 L2007 **GS** *012
NWOKORO, Ugochukwu O. 1 ELIZABETH PL, STE 260 45408 #690-04-1994 L2000 **IM** *020 †20
NWUNELI, Nancy Nneka. ■ 45458 #038-45-2008 *012
O'BRIEN, Paul Edward. 2717 MIAMISBURG CENTRVL RD, STE 200 45459 #017-20-1974 L1975 **GS** *020 †85
O CONNELL, Matthew L. 979 CONGRESS PARK DR 45459 #038-45-1986 L1987 **FM** *020 †18
O'FLYNN, Jay Hardy, III. 7707 PARAGON RD, STE 101 45459 #020-12-1978 L1979 **IM** *020 †30,20
O'HARA, Jacques Mandel. 75 SYLVANIA DR 45440 #038-41-1955 L1955 **GE IM** *071 †20
OLSON, Charissa Anne. ■ 45459 #008-02-2008 *012
OMOLOJA, Abiodun Aderogba. 1 WYOMING ST, MIAMI VALLEY HOSP 45409 #690-08-1991 L1998 **PN PD** *020 †55
ONINKU, Seth A. 2222 PHILADELPHIA DR 45406 #038-45-1989 L1990 **FM** *020 †18
ORMOND, Brian Eugene. 2773 ORCHARD RUN RD, KETTERING ANESTHESIA ASSOC 45449 #038-41-1985 L1988 **AN** *020 †05
ORUGANTI, Nagaraja S. 9000 N MAIN ST, STE 405 45415 #495-65-1982 L2001 **GE** *020 †20
OSBORNE, John E. ■ 45458 #051-01-1952 L1953 **OPH OM** *071
OSMAN, Sabuhi. PO BOX 927, CO WSU-PSYCHIATRY DEPT 45401 #495-39-1990 L2002 **P** *012
OSWALT, Kristopher M. 1 WYOMING ST, CO MIAMI VALLEY HOSP-MED E 45409 #016-11-2003 L2003 **GS** *012
OTI, Ifeatu Uchenna. 2661 SALEM AVE, STE 221 45406 #690-04-2001 L2002 **NEP** *012 †20
OUELLETTE, James R. 1222 S PATTERSON BLVD, STE 220 45402 #028-78-1998, ▲ L2000 **SO GS** *020 †85
OVIDE, Pinchas Manes. 1 CHILDRENS PLZ 45404 #550-02-1980 L1983 **PD** *020 †55
OYEKANMI, Oyekunle A. ■ 45458 #690-05-1991 L2003 **GPM** *020 †20,70
OZA, Amita Ratnam. 1100 S MAIN ST, STE 203 45409 #495-01-1981 L1984 **IM** *020 †20
OZA, Ratnam Anupam. 1100 S MAIN ST 45409 #496-38-1975 L1979 **IM** *020 †20
PACHECO, Jaime. 4100 W 3RD ST 45428 #847-04-1964 L1975 **ON HEM** *071 †20
PACIA, Ellen Beltran. 9001 N MAIN ST STE A, DAYTON RESPIRATORY CENTER 45415 #035-08-1991 L2004 **PUD** *020 †20
PADDON, Kristen Jane. 1 CHILDRENS PLZ, CHILDS EMERG SERV 45404 #016-11-1989 L2000 **PEM** *020 †55

■ = Address Information Privacy Protected

PAESSUN, Rebecca J. 9000 N MAIN ST, RADIATION ONCOLOGY 45415 #038-41-1984 L1985 **RO IM** *020 †80
PALACIO, Roberto A. 9000 N MAIN ST, STE 321 45415 #042-01-1973 L1997 **D PD** *020
PALEY, Jonathan Jos. 5491 FAR HILLS AVE 45429 #038-06-1987 L1987 **OSM** *020 †40
PALEY, Joseph Basil. 1 FRANCISCAN WAY 45408 #041-09-1958 L1965 **ORS** *071 †40
PALLERLA, Swapna Reddy. 2661 SALEM AVE, STE 220 45406 #495-37-1999 L2003 **IM** *100 †20
PALMER, Bruce Melvin. ■ 45424 #023-12-2006 L2006 **GS** *012
PALMER, Eldon Gus. ■ 45424 #023-12-2006 L2006 **PD** *012
PALMER, Gary Douglas. 6720 LOOP RD 45459 #020-02-1977 L1979 **D IM** *020 †15
PALMER, Gary John. 7073 CLYO RD 45459 #038-45-1998 L1999 **IM** *020 †20
PALMER, Leo Eugene. ■ 45419 #038-41-1945 L1945 **PD A** *071 †55
PALOMINO, Daniel Arturo. 7707 PARAGON RD, STE 106 45459 #038-43-1994 L2000 **DR** *020 †80
PALOMINO, Nola P Jones. 1 WYOMING ST, MIAMI VLY HOSP/DEPT PATH 45409 #055-01-1967 L1970 **PTH** *020 †50
PAN, Yang. 1997 MIAMISBURG CENTRVL RD 45459 #243-69-1985 L2000 **AN** *020
PANDEY, Maneesha. 361 W 3RD ST, MONTGOMERY CO CORONERS OFF 45402 #495-63-1996 L2005 **FOP** *020
PANDRANGI, Hema Latha. 1530 NEEDMORE RD, STE 300 45414 #495-11-1994 L2001 **CD** *020 †20
PANGALANGAN, Darin J. 1 WYOMING ST, MIAMI VALLEY HOSPITAL ETC 45409 #038-43-1993 L1994 **EM** *020 †16
PANOSIAN, Michael Saml. ■ 45440 #035-45-1986 L1998 **OTO AM** *030 †45
PAPPENFUS, David Jos. 3535 SOUTHERN BLVD 45429 #005-12-1978 L1979 **AN IM** *020 †05
PARAND, Ali. ■ 45459 #038-41-2005 L2005 **IM** *012
PARAND, Cyrus Mohammad S. 4501 POWELL RD 45424 #517-05-1959 L1970 **PD** *020
PARILO, Miguel Antonio. 1222 S PATTERSON BLVD, STE 210 45402 #038-45-1997 L1998 **IM DIA** *020 †20
PARK, In Kyu. ■ 45458 #583-02-1950 L1974 **P** *071 †75
PARK, Yung Suh. VET ADMI MED CTR 45428 #583-01-1956 L1969 **PTH OS** *071 †50
PARKAR, Nadeem Dawood. 33 W RAHN RD 45429 #495-01-1992 L2005 **DR** *012 †20
PARKAT, Judy Xavier. 405 W GRAND AVE, GRANDVIEW HOSPITAL 45405 #495-63-1970 L1980 **PTH** *020
PARKS MYTON, Alexis Demai. 7271 N MAIN ST, STE 3 45415 #038-45-1991 L1994 **IM** *020 †20
PART, Howard Mitchell. 1 ELIZABETH PL, STE 500 45408 #038-40-1982 L1983 **IM** *030 †20
PASCOE, John Manford. 1 CHILDRENS PLZ, OHIO PEDIATRICS INC 45404 #025-01-1971 L1980 **PD PHP** *020 †55
PASHA, Jaseem. 1520 GERMANTOWN ST, DAYMONT B H C INC 45408 #704-02-1967 L1974 **P N** *020
PASHA, Nooranissa J. 1 ELIZABETH PL, RIVERVIEW HEALTH INSTITUTE 45408 #704-02-1965 L1977 **PTH BBK** *030 †50
PAST, Si Alexander. ■ 45414 #036-07-1954 L1962 **GP** *071
PATALINGHUG, Norma C. 2611 WAYNE AVE, DAYTON MENTAL HLTH CTR 45420 #748-07-1966 L1995 **P** *075
PATEL, Amita Rajesh. 627 S EDWIN C MOSES BLVD, EAST MEDICAL PLAZA 45408 #495-17-1986 L1989 **P PYG** *020 †75 ‡
PATEL, Deepak Rasikbhai. 4172 INDIAN RIPPLE RD, STE A 45440 #495-89-1991 L2001 **IM EM** *020 †20
PATEL, Kamini Pranav. 4172 INDIAN RIPPLE RD, INTERGRATED MEDICAL GROUP 45440 #495-48-1997 L2001 **IM** *020 †20
PATEL, Meenakshi. 6611 CLYO RD, STE E 45459 #496-38-1980 L1986 **IM IMG** *020 †20 ‡
PATEL, Naynesh Ramesh. 4172 INDIAN RIPPLE RD, STE A 45440 #038-45-1987 L1989 **FM OS** *020 †18
PATEL, Piyush Vinaykumar. 30 E APPLE ST STE 6250, MIAMI VALLEY HOSPITALIST G 45409 #496-41-1999 L2007 **IM** *020 †20
PATEL, Rajesh Chandubhai. 9000 N MAIN ST, STE 222 45415 #495-17-1980 L1989 **PUD IM** *020 †20
PATEL, Ranapreet Kaur. 4100 W 3RD ST 45428 #305-01-2002 L2003 **IM** *020 †20
PATEL, Shashikant Rameshb. PO BOX 927, WRIGHT STATE UNIVERSITY 45401 #495-22-2005 L2007 **IM** *012
PATEL, Smita Vinubhai. ■ 45458 #495-22-1969 L1984 **AN** *020 †05
PATEL, Vipul V. 1 CHILDRENS PLZ, CHILDREN;S MEDICAL CENTER 45404 #495-22-1987 L1995 **CCP** *020 †55
PATIL, Saraswati S. 4100 W 3RD ST, DEPT VET AFFAIRS 45428 #495-98-1973 L1983 **IM GP** *020
PATRICK, Teressa Joan. 7415 BRANDT PIKE, STE 2 45424 #038-40-1983 L1985 **GE IM** *020 †20
PATTERSON, Alonzo, III. 1152 W 3RD ST 45402 #038-41-1989 L1990 **PD** *020 †55
PATWA, Sneh. 627 E C MOSES BLVD STE D 45408 #495-20-1974 L1982 **IM OM** *030
PATWA, Vinod Kumar. 1 ELIZABETH PL, # 111 45408 #495-20-1969 L1979 **P** *020 †75
PAUL, Sunila. 2661 SALEM AVE, STE 220 45406 #496-37-2001 L2004 **IM** *020 †20
PAULDING, Katrina Kearney. 9000 N MAIN ST STE G-35, SAMARITAN NORTH HEALTH CEN 45415 #011-03-1992 L1999 **FM** *020 †18
PAULET, Juan Augusto N. 2222 PHILADELPHIA DR 45406 #132-05-1965 L1971 **OBG** *020 †30
PAULUS, Richard John. 3442 MARBLECREST CT 45440 #056-06-1963 L1964 **FM** *020 †18
PEARSALL, Carolyn P. 2222 PHILADELPHIA DR, NORTH DAYTON PATHOLOGISTS 45406 #036-01-1994 L1999 **PTH** *020 †50
PEASE, Paul J. 2222 PHILADELPHIA DR 45406 #035-01-1962 L1963 **OPH** *071 †35
PEDDANNA, Narayanaswamy. 7415 BRANDT PIKE, STE 2 45424 #495-72-1985 L1998 **IM GE** *020 †20
PEDDIREDDI, Kavita Yalla. ■ 45458 #495-11-1994 L1998 **IM** *020 †20
PEDOTO, Michael Jos. 30 E APPLE ST, STE L200 45409 #038-41-1991 L1992 **PM** *020 †60
PELFREY, Jo Yvette. 5678 FAR HILLS AVE 45429 #038-45-1985 L1986 **IM IMG** *020
PELLERITE, Matthew Micah. ■ 45402 #038-45-2008 *012
PELSTRING, Richard Jos. 5250 FAR HILLS AVE 45429 #038-41-1985 L1989 **PTH HMP** *020 †50
PELT, Alvin D. 1800 N JAMES H MCGEE BLVD 45427 #025-07-1984 L1989 **P GS** *020 †75
PEPPARD, Rory Jon. 2222 PHILADELPHIA DR 45406 #016-06-1975 L1995 **NPM** *020 †55
PERERA, Priyan Vasantha. ■ 45440 #038-45-2008 *012
PEREZ, Maureen Kennedy. 979 CONGRESS PARK DR 45459 #038-43-1987 L1988 **FM** *020 †18
PEREZ-FIGAREDO, Rafael A. 9000 N MAIN ST, STE 321 45415 #042-01-1969 L1989 **D** *020 †15
PEREZ-JORGE, Emilio V. 4100 W 3RD ST 45428 #847-08-1993 L2002 **ID** *012 †20
PETERS, Lynn Jeffreykay. 1 CHILDRENS PLZ 45404 #038-41-1989 L1991 **PD** *020 †55
PETERS, Nicolas Lee. 1 CHILDRENS PLZ, CHILDREN'S HOSPITAL MEDICA 45404 #422-01-2007 L2007 **PD** *012
PETERS, Paul Gregory. ■ 45419 #025-07-2005 L2005 **ORS** *012
PETERS, Timothy F. 9000 N MAIN ST STE 401 45415 #016-76-1997, ▲ L1999 **ORS OTR** *020
PETERSON, Wylan Cornelius. 1 WYOMING ST, MIAMI VALLEY HOSPITAL, WCH 45409 #028-46-2001 L2002 **GS** *012
PETRY, Jeffrey Wayne. 2661 SALEM AVE, STE 220 45406 #038-45-1983 L1984 **FM** *020 †18
PFAFF-AMESSE, Teresa. ■ 45419 #054-04-1987 L2007 **PTH** *040 †50
PFLUM, Barbara Ann. ■ 45419 #010-02-1971 L1972 **A PD** *071 †55,03
PHILLIPS, Michael O. 2222 PHILADELPHIA DR 45406 #038-40-1958 L1958 **GP** *071
PICKOFF, Arthur Steven. 1 CHILDRENS PLZ, CHILDREN'S MEDICAL CENTER 45404 #035-46-1975 L1998 **PD PDC** *030 †55
PLUMMER, Alicia Kay. 1 CHILDRENS PLZ, DAYTON CHILDREN'S MED CTR 45404 #017-20-2006 L2006 **PD** *012
PLUMPTON, Jessica Joyce. ■ 45404 #035-06-2001 L2001 **PDI** *020 †55
PO, William D. 30 E APPLE ST, CHE BLDG 45409 #048-02-1990 L2005 **OBG** *020 †30
POELSTRA, Raymond John. 5692 FAR HILLS AVE, STE 1 45429 #048-04-1977 L1986 **NS** *020 †25
POHL, Kenneth Paul. 5692 FAR HILLS AVE 45429 #056-06-1965 L1970 **ORS** *020 †40
POHLMAN, Ronald Bernard. 111 HARBERT DR 45440 #038-40-1982 L1983 **FM** *020 †18
POLLACK, Laura Elizabeth. ■ 45459 #407-10-1953 L1957 **OBG** *071
POOL, Janelle Lynn. 1 CHILDRENS PLZ, CHILDRENS MEDICAL CENTER 45404 #038-45-2000 L2000 **PD** *100 †55
PORTER, Talmage Newton. 979 CONGRESS PARK DR 45459 #038-41-1973 L1973 **FM** *020 †18
POSTON, Leann Theresa. 5250 FAR HILLS AVE 45419 #038-45-1990 L1993 **PD** *071 †55
POTHOULAKIS, Anthony J. 122 WYOMING ST 45409 #418-01-1984 L1993 **CD IM** *020 †20
POUAGARE, Marios Costas. 7415 BRANDT PIKE, STE 2 45424 #011-02-1988 L1992 **GE** *020 †20
POWELL, Shelli Ann. 9000 N MAIN ST, STE 401 45415 #038-44-1991 L1995 **ORS** *020 †40
PRACHA, Shamsuddin C. 30 E APPLE ST STE 6250 45409 #704-02-1990 L2000 **IM** *020 †20
PRASAD, Kavya. 1 WYOMING ST, MED SURGICAL HLTH CTR 45409 #495-72-2001 L2005 **IM** *012
PRATT, Raymond Gordon. 1126 S MAIN ST, DAYTON CARDIOLOGY & 45409 #038-43-1981 L1982 **CD IM** *020 †20
PRAYSON, Michael Jos. 30 E APPLE ST, STE 5250 45409 #038-44-1989 L1991 **OTR** *020 †40
PREMANANDAN, Joseph. 1 ELIZABETH PL 45408 #495-52-1970 L1974 **NEP** *071 †20
PRINCE, Douglas Chapman. 1 CHILDRENS PLZ 45404 #016-43-1974 L1976 **PD** *030
PROCTOR, Thomas Scott. 3535 SOUTHERN BLVD, KETTERING MEDICAL CENTER 45429 #038-45-1993 L1994 **EM** *020 †16
PULLARKAT, Annu Narayanan. ■ 45406 #495-63-2004 L2005 **IM** *012
QAZI, Mohammad Arif. 30 E APPLE ST, STE 6250 45409 #704-09-1992 L2003 **GE** *012 †20
QUADRI, Mustafa. 9000 N MAIN ST, STE 328 45415 #704-02-1980 L1988 **IM PUD** *020 †20
QUADRI, Nazneen M. 5692 FAR HILLS AVE, STE 3 45429 #704-02-1981 L1991 **PD** *020 †55
QUINLAN, Kathleen Martina. 601 S EDWIN C MOSES BLVD 45408 #539-02-1974 L1981 **P** *020 †75
QUINLIVAN, Wm Francis. ■ 45419 #041-77-1944, ▲ L1950 **NS** *072
QUINN, Timothy Patrick. 6601 CENTERVILLE BSNS PKWY 45459 #038-40-1976 L1977 **ORS OSM** *020 †40
QUINONES, Jose Dulcidio. 1 WYOMING ST, MIAMI VALLEY HOSPITAL 45409 #023-01-1964 L1972 **NM IM** *020 †20,28
QURESHI, Asma Amir. 1 WYOMING ST, 233 GRAY STREET 45409 #704-06-1995 L2006 **AN** *020 †05
RAB, Thomas Paul. ■ 45429 #038-06-1943 L1943 **GS** *071 †85
RADEMACHER, James Robert. 101 W SCHANTZ AVE 45409 #038-41-2000 L2000 **OPH** *020
RAGER COLON, Vicki Lynn. 1 WYOMING ST, STE 3120 45409 #038-45-2003 L2003 **OBG** *020
RAGHUPATHY, Chethana J. 7707 PARAGON RD, STE 101 45459 #495-09-1997 L2000 **IM** *020 †20
RAHIMI, Cyrus. 7079 TAYLORSVILLE RD 45424 #517-01-1968 L1975 **GYN** *040 †30
RAI, Ripudeep. ■ 45419 #495-03-2001 L2004 **IM** *100 †20
RAJARATNAM, Sheila. 9985 DAYTON LEBANON PIKE 45458 #412-01-1974 L1981 **AN** *020
RAJSHEKER, Radhika. PO BOX 927, WRIGHT STATE UNIVERSITY 45401 #495-57-2003 L2007 **IM** *012
RAJU, Robert N. 3120 GOVERNORS PLACE BLVD 45409 #495-33-1972 L1988 **ON HEM** *020 †20
RALSTON, Randall Ray. 3535 SOUTHERN BLVD 45429 #039-05-1982 L1988 **AN PME** *020 †05
RAMANATHAN, Ganapathy S. 1530 NEEDMORE RD, STE 300 45414 #495-80-1976 L2004 **CD IM** *020 †20
RAMOS, Carlos. 1 CHILDRENS PLZ, CO CHILDRENS MED CTR-MED E 45404 #275-04-1986 L2002 **PD** *100
RAMSY, Maged G. 1775 DELCO PARK DR 45420 #915-04-1988 L1997 **PD** *020 †55
RANA, Lolita L. 2263 SALEM AVE 45406 #748-08-1962 L1972 **OBG** *020 †30
RANDALL, Kyle Lee. ■ 45440 #038-45-2008 *012
RANDALL, William John. 948 PATTERSON RD 45419 #038-41-1988 L1989 **FM** *020 †18
RANPURA, Saroja L. 4100 W 3RD ST 45428 #495-33-1963 L1972 **AN OBG** *020 †05
RAO, Indumathi Natarajan. 33 W RAHN RD, STE 201 45429 #965-01-1988 L1998 **PTH IM** *020 †20
RAO, Pallavi Kothapalli. 33 W RAHN RD, STE 201 45429 #496-22-2000 L2002 **GE** *012 †20
RASLICH, Marc Anthony. 1 ELIZABETH PL, STE 500 45408 #056-05-1996 L2001 **PD IM** *020 †20,55
RASMUSSEN, Jennifer Terry. 1 WYOMING ST 45409 #049-01-2005 L2005 **EM** *012
RASP, Gregory Michael. 9000 N MAIN ST 45415 #016-11-1992 L1996 **RO** *020 †80
RATTAN, Shachi Nandan. 33 W RAHN RD STE 102, ACUTE CARE CONSULTANTS INC 45429 #495-43-1978 L1987 **CCM IM** *020 †20
RAU, Thomas Michael Geo. ■ 45440 #038-41-1968 L1968 **GP** *020
RAYMOND, Sven Eric. ■ 45424 #038-06-2003 L2003 **IM** *100 †20
REAGAN, Edgar Jos. ■ 45419 #028-34-1945 L1946 **OM GP** *071
REDDY, Bhimavarapu K. 1 ELIZABETH PL 45408 #495-21-1968 L1973 **AN PME** *020 †05
REDDY, C Narayan. 2200 PHILADELPHIA DR, STE 548 45406 #495-21-1968 L1979 **PUD CCM** *020 †20
REDDY, Indira B. 1 ELIZABETH PL 45408 #495-62-1970 L1974 **PD PN** *020 †55
REDDY, Sujatha Kesavarapu. 4100 W 3RD ST 45428 #495-62-1975 L1986 **AN** *020 †05
REDDY, Vasumathy R. 5903 N DIXIE DR 45414 #495-21-1970 L1978 **PD** *020 †55
REED, David Paul. 405 W GRAND AVE 45405 #028-79-2005, ▲ L2005 *100
REEVE, Fredrick Mark. 9000 N MAIN ST STE 238, 3359 KEMP ROAD SUITE 210 45415 #038-40-1993 L1999 **ORS** *020 †40
REID, Lester Abbott. ■ 45439 #023-07-1968 L1974 **IM** *030
REILING, Walter A, III. 40 W 4TH ST, STE 17 45402 #038-41-1989 L1990 **FM** *020 †18
REINHARDT, Nancy Sue T. 540 LINCOLN PARK BLVD, STE 100 45429 #005-12-1973 L1979 **R** *020 †80
REINSCH, John Martin. 3535 SOUTHERN BLVD 45429 #021-01-1977 L1981 **AN** *020 †05
REITZ, Anne Christine. 9000 N MAIN ST STE 635 45415 #038-41-1997 L2000 **FM** *020 †18

■ = Address Information Privacy Protected

RENEGADO, Leonardo L. ■ 45459 #748-11-1967 L1974 CD IM *020
RENO, Joseph Loren. ■ 45440 #038-06-2007 L2007 GS *012
RETTIG, Lloyd Wm, III. 3038 OLIVE RD 45426 #041-07-1992 L1993 OBG *020 †20
REVEAL, Danny Lee. 2300 FAR HILLS AVE 45419 #017-20-1969 L1974 ORS *020 †40
RHEE, Choong Young. 1 WYOMING ST 45409 #583-01-1965 L1975 IM IMG *020
RHEE, On-Kyung Chung. ■ 45459 #583-08-1970 L1977 GP *020
RIAZ, Asma. 33 W RAHN RD, STE 201 45429 #496-27-1991 L2003 IM *020 †20
RIAZ, Kamran. 1530 NEEDMORE RD STE 300 45414 #704-01-1987 L2002 CD NC *020 †20
RICH, John Murray. 122 WYOMING ST 45409 #036-07-1966 L1967 CD *020 †20
RICHARDSON, Warren Scott. 1 ELIZABETH PL, STE 500 45408 #010-02-1979 L2002 IM *020 †20
RIDDIFORD, T. 6255 CHAMBERSBURG RD, NORTHEAST FAMILY PRACTICE 45424 #038-45-1991 L1992 FM *020 †18
RIDDLE, Kevin Lee. 2717 MIAMISBURG CENTRVL RD, STE 211 45459 #038-45-1988 L1989 FM EM *020 †18
RINCON, Alberto W. 4100 W 3RD ST, DAYTON VA MED CTR 45428 #935-01-1962 L2002 ADP P *020 ‡
RITTER, Steven Ekberg. 5260 NEWELL CIR 45440 #017-20-1993 L2004 D *020 †15
RIVERA-AMISOLA, Maria Cec. 1 CHILDRENS PLZ, CHILD MED CTR DEVE PEDS 45404 #748-10-1991 L2004 PD *020 †55
RIVERA-PADILLA, Maritza. ■ 45424 #042-03-1987 L1993 IM *020
RIZZARDI, Roger Neil. 8701 OLD TROY PIKE, DOCTORS URGENT CARE OF NOR 45424 #165-01-1975 L1990 FM OS *020 †18
RO, Oh-Sang. 4764 FISHBURG RD 45424 #583-03-1971 L1979 GP *020
ROBBINS, Lynn Joseph. 5692 FAR HILLS AVE, STE 1 45429 #028-34-1972 L1973 NS *020 †25
ROBERT, Gayle Marie T. 1 WYOMING ST 45409 #021-05-1986 L2004 AN *020 †05
ROBERTSON, Harold D. 6441 FAR HILLS AVE # 116 45459 #035-45-1950 L1955 R *071 †80
ROBINSON, Cheryl J. 2222 PHILADELPHIA DR 45406 #038-45-1982 L1983 FM *020 †18
ROBINSON, Kelley Lynn. 332 CONGRESS PARK DR, PROFESSIONAL MEDICAL GROUP 45459 #038-41-1997 L1998 EM *020 †16
RODES, Mary Elizabeth. 4428 INDIAN RIPPLE RD 45440 #038-45-2004 L2004 FM *020 †18
RODRIGUEZ, Hilton John. 1110 WEBSTER ST 45404 #041-09-1987 L1999 CHP *020
ROELLE, Melissa Pence. 1520 S MAIN ST, STE 210 45409 #038-45-2002 L2002 GS *020
ROESCH, Erica Marie. 101 WYOMING ST, DEPARTMENT OF FAMILY PRACT 45409 #038-45-2006 L2006 FP *012
ROJJANAVAROE, Bunyium. 627 S EDWIN C MOSES BLVD, PROFESSIONAL PAVILION SUIT 45408 #891-02-1967 L1974 PS HS *020 †85,65
ROLITSKY, Chris David. 1 WYOMING ST, MIAMI VALLEY HOSPITAL 45409 #038-40-1999 L1999 PTH *020
ROLL, John Matthias. ■ 45419 #028-34-1948 L1949 OBG *071 †30
ROLL, William A. ■ 45419 #038-41-1952 L1952 U *071 †95
ROMAN, Brenda J Barth. 627 S EDWIN C MOSES BLVD, STE 1 45408 #030-05-1988 L1989 P *020 †75
ROMANOWSKI, Ami Patel. 1 CHILDRENS PLZ 45404 #055-01-2003 L2004 PD *100 †55
ROMEO, David Philip. 75 SYLVANIA DR, DIGESTIVECARE INC. 45440 #035-03-1981 L1987 GE IM *020 †20
ROMER, James Florenz. 627 S EDWIN C MSS BLVD #3G 45408 #056-06-1964 L1969 TS *071 †85,90
ROMER, Nancy Marie. 1 WYOMING ST # 3130 45409 #028-34-1982 L1984 OBG *020 †30
ROMER, William Anthony. 6611 CLYO RD 45459 #038-43-1979 L1983 FM EM *075 †18
RONALD, Patricia Mary. ■ 45415 #352-06-1961 L1970 PD *071
RONE, Jerod Matthew. 1 CHILDRENS PLZ, CHILDREN'S MEDICAL CENTER 45404 #038-45-1991 L1993 NPM *020 †55
ROSADO MORALES, Jose. ■ 45439 #649-38-2005 L2006 IM *012
ROSE, Catherine M. 1 CHILDRENS PLZ 45404 #038-40-1982 L1983 OPH *020 †20
ROSS, Suzanne E. 1 WYOMING ST 45409 #042-01-1982 L1983 IM *071
ROSSET, Jill Suzanne. 1 FRANCISCAN WAY 45408 #038-06-1981 L1990 PTH FOP *020 †50
ROSTAMI, Giti. 75 SYLVANIA DR 45440 #517-01-1984 L1992 IM GE *020 †20
ROTHSTEIN, Lawrence Brian. 1 ELIZABETH PL, DAYTON LASER SPINE CTR 45408 #038-40-1987 L1988 AN GS *020 †05
ROWIN, Mark E. 1 CHILDRENS PLZ, CHILDREN'S MEDICAL CENTER 45404 #048-14-1989 L1997 CCP *020 †55
ROWSER, Rhea Renee. 101 WYOMING ST, BERRY FAMILY HEALTH CENTER 45409 #038-41-1996 L1997 FM *020 †18
ROYALTY, Jonathan Cain. 33 W RAHN RD, STE 201 45429 #038-45-2001 L2007 IM *020 †20
ROYCE, Frederick H, Jr. 1 CHILDRENS PLZ, PEDIATRIC PULMONOLOGY 45404 #054-04-1985 L1987 PD PDP *050 †55
ROYER, Judith Anne. ■ 45426 #017-20-1989 L1990 EM *020 †16
RUBINO, Louis J, III. 30 E APPLE ST, STE 2200 45409 #010-02-1999 L2000 OSM OTR *040
RUEVE, Marie E. 2611 WAYNE AVE, TWIN VALLEY BEHAVIORAL HEA 45420 #038-45-2002 L2002 P *100 †75
RUFF, Michael Joseph. ■ 45405 #038-43-1998 L1999 FM *040 †14
RUNDELL, William Kennard. 30 E APPLE ST, STE 5253 45409 #048-12-1967 L1979 VS *020 †85
RUSSELL, Charles Edward. ■ 45437 #025-12-1982 L1984 EM *020 †16
RUTLEDGE, Tonya Rene. 2701 HOME AVE, MEDICAL DEPARTMENT MC F4-9 45417 #038-41-1986 L1988 IM OM *020
RYAN, Carol Jeanne Gaut. 1360 E STROOP RD 45429 #051-04-1972 L1975 FM *020
RYAN, Jon Patrick. 8769 N MAIN ST STE 100, DBA JON P. RYAN, MD, COMP 45415 #018-75-2000, ▲ L2000 RHU *020
RYMER, Michael Colin. ■ 45440 #055-01-2007 L2007 GS *012
RYMER, Stephen Kent. 1 WYOMING ST, MIAMI VALLEY HOSPITAL-EMER 45409 #055-01-1972 L1975 EM *020 †16
SABAGH, Tarek M. 9000 N MAIN ST 45415 #915-09-1983 L1992 ON HEM *020 †20
SABBAGH, Wissam. 2661 SALEM AVE, DAVUE BUILDING STE 221 45406 #875-01-1996 L2002 ID *012 †20
SABINO, Alan Dale. 2773 ORCHARD RUN RD, KETTERING ANESTHESIA ASSOC 45449 #005-12-2000 L2004 AN *100 †05
SACHS, Edward William, III. ■ 45459 #038-40-1968 L1968 IM *020 †20
SADIKOV, Polina. 9000 N MAIN ST, STE 300 45415 #913-01-1979 L1994 FM *020 †18
SAKLAYEN, Muhammad Golam. 4100 W 3RD ST, VA MEDICAL CENTER 45428 #160-02-1974 L1981 NEP IM *020 †20
SALEH, Mervet Kamel. 1235 E ALEX BELL RD 45459 #915-04-1973 L1984 AN PMM *020 †05
SALEH, Mohey Kamel. 30 E APPLE ST STE 6252 45409 #915-02-1975 L1987 TS VS *020 †85,90
SALEM, Mohamed Elsayed Ah. 2661 SALEM AVE, STE 220 45406 #915-03-2000 L2004 IM *020 †20
SALERNO, Francesco M. 6840 LOOP RD, CENTURY MEDICAL CLINIC 45459 #561-12-1952 L1965 U *071 †95

SALGRAM, Fnu. 2661 SALEM AVE, STE 220 45406 #704-02-1999 L2005 IM *020 †20
SALIH, Emad Ahmed Ali. 1 ELIZABETH PL, WEST MEDICAL PLAZA STE 210 45408 #915-04-1994 L2001 CN *100 †75
SALLAPUDI, Naveena. 301 W 1ST ST, STE 100 45402 #566-01-1990 L1999 IM *020 †20
SAMIEC, Tamisha Detrick. 2222 PHILADELPHIA DR 45406 #038-43-1987 L1993 NPM *020 †55
SAMUEL, Sanju Susan. 1 CHILDRENS PLZ, DEPT OF MED EDU 45404 #496-34-2000 L2005 PD *012
SANDERS, Kent David. 8111 TIMBERLODGE TRL 45458 #016-06-1980 L1983 EM IM *020 †20,16
SANDERS, Richard Douglas. 4100 W 3RD ST, 116/MENTAL HEALTH 45428 #038-45-1988 L1995 P *020 †75
SANDHIR, Sanjay. 75 SYLVANIA DR 45440 #055-01-1991 L1995 HEP GE *020 †20
SANDO, Don E. ■ 45459 #016-06-1949 L1955 IM *071 †20
SANFORD, Kathryn Anne. 1 WYOMING ST 45409 #025-12-1992 L1996 OBG *020 †30
SANGHVI, Kamlesh C. 6310 N MAIN ST, STE A 45415 #496-38-1980 L1985 OBG *020 †30
SANTA, Sheila Edna. ■ 45403 #038-45-2008 *012
SARABIA, Victor N. 627 S EDWIN C MOSES BLVD 45408 #737-01-1953 L1967 GS *071 †85
SARLAY, Robert, Jr. ■ 45440 #048-14-1999 L2005 EM *012
SARLE, Sumiko Suzue. 9000 N MAIN ST 45415 #016-11-1991 L1995 AN *020 †05
SARODIA, Bipin. 1520 S MAIN ST, STE 2 45409 #495-23-1986 L1997 PCC *020 †20
SARWAL, Deepak. 5563 FAR HILLS AVE, DEEPAK SARWAL M.D., LLC 45429 #495-36-1982 L1999 IM DIA *020 †20
SATYANARAYAN, Manjula. ■ 45458 #496-01-1989 L2004 IM *100 †20
SAULTZ, Alisha Beth. 1 WYOMING ST, MIAMI VALLEY HOSP 45409 #038-75-2006, ▲ L2006 FP *012
SAVAGE, Terri Lynne. 30 W RAHN RD, AESTHETICS 45429 #038-45-1995 L1998 HO *020
SAWH, Shailendra. 33 W RAHN RD 45429 #566-01-1990 L1999 CCM *020 †20
SAWMILLER, Carol Joanne. 3533 SOUTHERN BLVD, STE 2250 45429 #038-40-1994 L2006 GS *020 †85
SAXE, Jonathan Craig. 75 SYLVANIA DR 45440 #041-02-1984 L1988 GE IM *020 †20
SAXE, Jonathan Mark. 1 WYOMING ST, DEPT OF SURGERY/CHE 7TH FL 45409 #025-07-1985 L1998 GS TRS *020 †85
SAXEN, Richard Joseph. ■ 45419 #038-43-2004 L2007 IM *100 †20
SCHAERER, Steven L. 4441 FAR HILLS AVE 45429 #038-45-1982 L1983 FM *020 †20
SCHARF, John Robert. ■ 45459 #028-34-1962 L1965 AN *071
SCHARRER, Richard Gordon. 8501 TROY PIKE 45424 #038-41-1979 L1981 OBG *020 †30
SCHATZEL, Jason William. 9000 N MAIN ST, STE 305 45415 #038-44-1997 L1998 IM *020 †20
SCHEAR, Martin John. 1100 SALEM AVE 45406 #016-42-1977 L1977 FM FPG *020 †18
SCHIBLER, Kelly Annette. 101 WYOMING ST, BERRY FAMILY HEALTH CENTER 45409 #038-43-1990 L1991 FM *040 †18
SCHISSEL, Anna Marie. 1 WYOMING ST, DEPT OF MED EDUCATION 45409 #028-79-2006, ▲ L2006 OBG *012
SCHLONEGER, Mark Regan. 7211 N MAIN ST, STE 1 45415 #038-45-2001 L2001 FM *020 †18
SCHMID, Catherine Ann. ■ 45402 #038-45-1991 L1993 GS *020 †85
SCHMIDT, Steven Paul. 9985 DAYTON LEBANON PIKE 45458 #005-12-1988 L1999 PS *072 †85,65
SCHMITT, Elizabeth Lace. ■ 45424 #038-45-2007 L2007 P *012
SCHMITZ, Wendy Gay. 33 W RAHN RD, STE 201 45429 #005-12-1994 L1995 IM *020 †20
SCHNADER, Jeffrey Yale. 4100 W 3RD ST, DAYTON VA WRIGHT STATE U 45428 #067-01-1979 L1997 PUD IM *050 †20
SCHNEIDERMAN, Norman. 1 WYOMING ST, MIAMI VALLEY HOSPITAL 45409 #035-08-1975 L1976 EM OM *020 †16
SCHNELL, Melissa Anne. 455 TURNER RD 45415 #038-45-2000 L2000 NEP *020 †20
SCHOLL, Kent Keafauver. 1829 E 3RD ST 45403 #016-43-1954 L1954 FM GP *020 †18
SCHOULTIES, Daniel Leroy. 2222 PHILADELPHIA DR, GOOD SAMARITAN HOSPITAL 45406 #020-12-1978 L1979 FM EM *020 †18
SCHRAMM, Arthur Richard. 130 W 2ND ST, STE 960 45402 #016-11-1962 L1968 CHP P *020
SCHRIBER, Robert Alan. 130 W 2ND ST, NO 1430 45402 #038-41-1969 L1969 RHU IM *020 †20
SCHUBERT-MOELL, Kathryn A. 2200 PHILADELPHIA DR, STE 101 45406 #038-40-1986 L1988 OBG *020 †30 ‡
SCHUETZ, Lynn Teresa. 2345 PHILADELPHIA DR 45406 #038-45-2005 L2005 FP *012
SCHULTE, Jerome John, Jr. 2222 PHILADELPHIA DR, GOOD SAMARITAN HSOP 45406 #025-07-1988 L1989 P PYG *020 †75
SCHUMANN, Stephen Paul. 1222 S PATTERSON BLVD, STE 300 45402 #038-41-1985 L1994 OPH *020 †35
SCHUSTER, Barbara L N. 1 ELIZABETH PL, STE 500 45408 #035-45-1977 L1995 IM *030 †20
SCHUSTER, Benjamin. 3533 SOUTHERN BLVD, STE 355 45429 #056-05-1952 L1956 CD IM *072 †20
SCHUSTER, Richard Joel. 1 ELIZABETH PL, STE 500 45408 #038-45-1976 L1995 IM *020 †20
SCHWARTZ, Brian Peter. 8057 WASHINGTON VILLAGE DR, STE D 45458 #005-12-1989 L1991 CD *020 †20
SCHWARTZ, Paul Jeffrey. 4100 W 3RD ST, VAMC 45428 #038-41-1983 L1984 P *020 †75
SEE, Josephraymo Habitan. 30 E APPLE ST, STE 6250 45409 #038-45-2002 L2002 IM *020 †20
SEILER, James Francis. 7211 N MAIN ST, STE 1 45415 #038-40-1986 L1987 FM *020 †18
SEILER, Marie Rodriguez. 7111 N MAIN ST 45415 #038-40-1986 L1989 FM *020 †55
SEITZMAN, Howard Alan. 131 N LUDLOW ST 45402 #047-06-1981 L1988 AN *020 †05
SENI, Pietro. 3205 WOODMAN DR 45420 #264-04-1959 L1968 ORS OFA *020 †40
SEQUEIRA, Pamela B. 3535 SOUTHERN BLVD 45429 #495-37-1988 L1996 NP *020 †50
SEQUEIRA, Reginald M. 5538 PHILADELPHIA DR 45415 #496-15-1989 L1995 CD *020 †20
SHAH, Mahesh M. 1 CHILDRENS PLZ 45404 #495-48-1968 L1975 PD *020 †55
SHAH, Ranjana Nitin. ■ 45458 #495-22-1968 L1976 IMG FM *020 †20
SHAH, Tushar Nandlal. 540 LINCOLN PARK BLVD, STE 200 45429 #036-01-1994 L2005 CD *020 †20
SHAIK, Mohammed Mubbashee. 2661 SALEM AVE, STE 220 45406 #496-27-1999 L2004 IM *020 †20
SHAMMA, Hassan N. 7835 PARAGON RD 45459 #605-01-1990 L1999 PTH DMP *020 †50
SHARMA, Karuna. 332 CONGRESS PARK DR 45459 #495-85-1984 L2001 IM EM *020 †20
SHARMA, Pankaj. 33 W RAHN RD, STE 201 45429 #305-01-2002 L2002 IM *020 †20
SHARMA, Sunil Kumar. 1 WYOMING ST, CO MIAMI GALLEY HOSP-MED E 45409 #495-12-1985 L2002 GS *100
SHAW, Scott David. 2037 NEEDMORE RD 45414 #038-45-1984 L1986 IM *020 †20
SHEHADEH, Ihab Numan. 4100 W 3RD ST, GI UNIT 45428 #575-01-1993 L1999 GE *020 †20
SHENOUDA, Nadia Malek. 1 WYOMING ST, MIAMI VALLEY HOSP ANESTH 45409 #915-02-1971 L1983 AN *020
SHERIDAN, James Frederick. ■ 45419 #038-41-1960 L1960 NS *071 †25

SHIE, David Wm. 5701 FAR HILLS AVE 45429 #038-40-1975 L1977 **OBG** *020 †30
SHIE, John Mark. 1 WYOMING ST 45409 #038-40-1983 L1984 **OBG** *020 †30
SHIVELY, Franklin L, Jr. ■ 45429 #016-06-1939 L1939 **GS** *071 †85
SHOPE, Adam Leigh. 332 CONGRESS PARK DR, SPRINGFIELD/URBANA EMERGEN 45459 #038-43-2003 L2003 **EM** *020 †16
SHRIT, Mohammed Atef. 1 WYOMING ST, PATH DEPT-MIAMI VLY HOSP 45409 #875-02-1979 L1987 **PTH HMP** *020 †50
SHUSTER, David Bryan. 128 E APPLE ST, STE 2830 45409 #030-06-1985 L1990 **ORS** *100 †60
SICKLER, Donald Premier. 2222 PHILADELPHIA DR, MED DIR INTEGRATED CARE MG 45406 #005-12-1965 L1966 **NS** *030 †25
SIDDIQI, Mohammed Wajid H. 1 CHILDRENS PLZ 45404 #704-02-1963 L1977 **PD** *071 †55
SIDDIQI, Munawar. 1 ELIZABETH PL, STE 230 45408 #704-16-1986 L1999 **AN PME** *020
SIDDIQI, Sehba. 1520 GERMANTOWN ST 45408 #704-02-1968 L1981 **P** *020 †75
SIDDIQUI, Abdul Mannan. 30 E APPLE ST, STE 6250 45409 #704-16-1987 L1993 **IM** *020 †20
SIDDIQUI, Abdul R. 30 E APPLE ST, MAIMI VALLEY HOSP 45409 #704-02-1989 L1995 **IM** *020 †20
SIDDIQUI, Mehr Afroz. 4100 W 3RD ST 45428 #495-47-1962 L1980 **N** *020 †75
SIDDIQUI, Mujeeb. 2717 MIAMISBURG CENTRVL RD, STE 215 45459 #028-79-1991, ▲ L2004 **GS** *020
SIDDIQUI, Sabiha Tabassum. 2717 MIAMISBURG CENTRVL RD, STE 215 45459 #495-65-1993 L2005 **FM** *100 †18
SIMMONS, Erron Lashawnda. 2345 PHILADELPHIA DR 45406 #038-45-2004 L2005 **FP** *012
SIMON, Ryan Quinn. PO BOX 927, WRIGHT STATE UNIV MED PEDS 45401 #654-01-2005 L2005 **MPD** *012
SIMONI, Eugene Jos. 2200 PHILADELPHIA DR, STE 400 45406 #041-09-1980 L2005 **VS GS** *020 †85
SIMS, James Arthur. 3080 ACKERMAN BLVD, STE 220 45429 #038-41-1968 L1968 **A** *020
SINCLAIR, Bernice Adella. 2345 PHILADELPHIA DR 45406 #038-45-2001 L2001 **FM** *100 †18 ‡
SINENENG, Rolando S. 4200 INDIAN RIPPLE RD 45440 #748-02-1967 L1974 **GE IM** *020 †20
SINGER, Melody Noelle. 33 W RAHN RD, STE 201 45429 #038-41-1996 L1998 **IM** *020 †20
SINGH, Gurjeet. 6611 CLYO RD, STE E 45459 #495-10-1996 L2006 **IMG** *020 †20
SINGLA, Disha. PO BOX 927, WRIGHT STATE UNIVERSITY 45401 #495-29-2005 L2007 **IM** *012
SINGLA, Prem A. 1625 S ALEX RD 45449 #495-41-1961 L1972 **FM** *071 †50
SINGLA, Ramesh Kumar. 89 SYLVANIA DR, FL 1 45440 #495-29-1969 L1981 **OPH** *020 †35 ‡
SINNATHAMBY, Kitren B. 5538 PHILADELPHIA DR, ROSEWOOD BUILDING 45415 #021-06-1992 L1997 **IM** *020 †20
SINNATHAMBY, Kuddy Thamby. 5538 PHILADELPHIA DR 45415 #495-37-1961 L1970 **IM CD** *020 †20
SINNATHAMBY, Sukirtharan. 1126 S MAIN ST 45409 #038-40-1989 L1991 **CD** *020 †20
SIVA, Senthuran Thiru. PO BOX 927, WRIGHT STATE UNIVERSITY 45401 #422-01-2007 L2007 **IM** *012
SKROBOT, Barry James. 101 WYOMING ST, FAMILY HEALTH CENTER 45409 #038-40-1975 L1975 **FM** *040 †18
SLAGEL, Wylie Aaron. 4100 W 3RD ST, RM 1 E 118 45428 #020-12-1968 L1995 **OM PHP** *020 †70
SMALL, David George. ■ 45429 #005-12-1962 L1970 **GS** *071 †85 ‡
SMILE, David H. 332 CONGRESS PARK DR 45459 #038-43-1979 L1982 **EM** *020 †16
SMITH, Andrew Brewster. ■ 45419 #039-01-2006 L2006 **P** *012
SMITH, David Michael. 349 S MAIN ST, COMMUNITY BLOOD CENTER 45402 #038-45-1983 L1986 **FOP PTH** *030 †50
SMITH, Jeanette Marie. ■ 45440 #005-12-1981 L1983 **GPM** *020 †70
SMITH, Revonna J Cooper. 9985 DAYTON LEBANON PIKE 45458 #018-75-1986, ▲ L1988 **AN** *020 †05
SMITH, Richard Dewey. 9000 N MAIN ST STE 332 45415 #038-45-1984 L1985 **PD** *020 †55
SMITH, Townsend, III. 1222 S PATTERSON BLVD, DAYTON, OHIO 45402 45402 #038-40-1987 L1996 **AN** *020 †05
SMOLOWITZ, Edwin Larry. 8934 KINGSRIDGE DR, STE 102 45458 #051-04-1975 L1998 **U GS** *020 †95
SNEEDER, William H. 8701 TROY PIKE, KETTERING WORKERS CARE 45424 #023-12-1986 L2006 **GPM** *020 †70,18
SNIDER, Brad David. 1 WYOMING ST 45409 #038-40-1994 L1995 **FM** *020 †18
SOBOL, Todd Lowell. 8913 N MAIN ST, STE B 45415 #036-08-1987 L1988 **IM IMG** *020 †20
SOLOMON, Glen David. 128 E APPLE ST, WEBER CHE BLDG 2ND FL 45409 #016-01-1979 L1982 **IM PMM** *040 †20
SOMUSETTY, Pavan. PO BOX 927, PSYCHIATRY DEPT 45401 #496-23-2004 L2005 **P** *012
SONEK, Jiri David. 1 WYOMING ST, BERRY BLDG GROUND 45409 #016-02-1981 L1983 **MFM OCC** *020 †30
SONGER, Susan Kay. 80 E WOODBURY DR 45415 #038-41-1996 L1997 **P** *020 †75
SORAUF, Thomas John. 617 SHROYER RD 45419 #056-06-1967 L1971 **PD DBP** *020 †55
SORG, Timothy Bruce. 30 E APPLE ST 45409 #038-40-1978 L1985 **ID IM** *020 †20
SPERBER, Edward E. ■ 45458 #020-12-1967 L1995 **PTH NP** *071 †50
SPERRY, George Phillips. ■ 45459 #038-06-1956 L1956 **PD** *071 †55
SPIEGEL, Jerome Chas. 950 E ALEX BELL RD 45459 #038-40-1971 L1971 **OTO HNS** *020 †45
SPROWL, Matthew Lawrence. 1222 S PATTERSON BLVD 45402 #016-06-1983 L1984 **OPH EM** *020 †35
SRIVASTAVA, Monica. PO BOX 927, CO INTERNAL MEDICINPO 45401 #473-04-2002 L2004 **IM** *100 †20
SRIVASTAVA, Sangeeta. 4100 W 3RD ST, MEDICAL CENTER 45428 #495-05-1990 L1997 **PUD** *020 †20
SROUR, Jay. 1 WYOMING ST, ANESTHESIA DEPARTMENT 45409 #561-11-1987 L1999 **AN IM** *020 †05
STAHL, Brian Ray. 4235 INDIAN RIPPLE RD, STAHL VISION INC 45440 #038-40-1988 L1989 **OPH** *020 †35
STARK, James Matthew. 1 CHILDRENS PLZ, DEPT OF PEDIATRICS 45404 #038-06-1983 L1985 **PD PUD** *050 †55
STARR, Tom Reutti. 1044 S MAIN ST 45409 #016-06-1961 L1963 **IM** *020 †20
STEELE, Jack E. ■ 45459 #016-06-1950 L1957 **P GP** *071
STEFFAN, Michael Edward. 1 CHILDRENS PLZ, DAYTON CHILDS HOSP-SLEEP C 45404 #048-04-1984 L1990 **PD PDP** *020 †55
STEIN, Alvin L. 8913 N MAIN ST, STE B 45415 #020-02-1978 L1980 **IM IMG** *020 †20
STEIN, Leon. 2222 PHILADELPHIA DR 45406 #020-02-1946 L1950 **IM** *071
STEINFURTH, Lee. ■ 45458 #038-40-1968 L1968 **OTO** *071 †45
STEVENS, Michael Wayne. 3075 GOVERNORS PLACE BLVD, STE 110 45409 #038-45-1989 L1990 **RHU IM** *020 †20
STOECKICHT, Frederic Paul. ■ 45459 #561-10-1952 L1960 **OBG** *071 †30
STONE, Lisa Michele. 75 SYLVANIA DR 45440 #038-45-1995 L2001 **GE** *020 †20
STONE, Rodney Edmund. 160 WYOMING ST STE 4 45409 #030-05-1978 L1985 **END IM** *020 †20
STOUT, Robert Dale. 1 CHILDRENS PLZ, CHILDREN'S MEDICAL CENTER 45404 #017-20-1954 L1976 **PHO PD** *020 †55
STRAUGHEN, William Jos. 1028 S MAIN ST, VALLEY PATHOLOGISTS INC 45409 #041-09-1958 L1967 **PTH CLP** *071 †50
STRAWSBURG, John R. 6445 FAR HILLS AVE, # 515 45459 #038-40-1953 L1953 **IM** *071 †20
STRICKLAND, Lisa Enid. ■ 45459 #034-01-2005 L2005 **IM** *012
STULL, Virginia Elizabeth. ■ 45458 #048-02-1966 L1967 **PM OM** *071 †60
STULTZ, David Brewer. 8057 WASHINGTON VILLAGE DR, STE D 45458 #038-41-2000 L2000 **CD** *020 †20
STUTES, Shahan Ahmed. PO BOX 927, PEDS PGM 45401 #048-16-2004 L2004 **MPD** *012
SUGUMARAN, Ramasamy T. 5300 BRANDT PIKE 45424 #495-42-1973 L1978 **IM IMG** *020 †20
SULTAN, Shumaila. 321 BOX ELDER DR 45458 #038-45-2008 *012
SUMME, Alan Turpin. 332 CONGRESS PARK DR 45459 #020-12-1996 L1997 **EM** *020 †16
SUMMER, Mory. 2295 PHILADELPHIA DR 45406 #016-11-1957 L1961 **FM** *071
SUPRENANT, Ronald Mark. ■ 45458 #025-07-1982 L1998 **FM** *072 †18
SURDYK, Jerome S. ■ 45429 #016-43-1938 L1938 **CRS** *071
SURYA PRASAD, Agaram G. 4100 W 3RD ST 45428 #495-33-1963 L1974 **CD IM** *020 †20
SURYAPRASAD, Seethalakshi. 4100 W 3RD ST, VA HOSPITAL 45428 #495-33-1970 L1978 **PTH** *020 †50
SUSEC, Thomas Mario. 1 WYOMING ST, EMERGENCY DEPT 45409 #038-45-1999 L2002 **EM** *020 †16
SUTHERIN, Steven Ray. 1222 S PATTERSON BLVD, STE 120 45402 #038-45-1984 L1984 **GS** *020 †85
SWAMY, Lalitha. 4100 W 3RD ST 45428 #495-16-1953 L1970 **IM** *040 †20
SWARUP, Jyothi. 2222 PHILADELPHIA DR 45406 #496-21-1992 L2004 **NPM** *020 †55
SWEDLUND, Steven Kent. 101 WYOMING ST 45409 #016-45-1978 L1979 **FM FPG** *020 †18
SWENSON, Krista Marie. ■ 45419 #056-05-2007 L2007 **OBG** *012
SZE, Peter Chienchung. 4100 W 3RD ST, DEPT OF NUCLEAR MEDICINE 45428 #035-47-1988 L1999 **NM** *020 †20,28
SZILAGYI, Nathalie Marie. 332 CONGRESS PARK DR, PREMIER HEALTH CARE SERVIC 45459 #038-06-1997 L2004 **FM** *020 †18
SZIRTES, Balazs Gyula. 1 WYOMING ST, CO MIAMI VALLEY HOSP-MED E 45409 #473-01-1995 L2001 **GS** *100
TABATABAIAN, Djavad N. 2200 PHILADELPHIA DR, STE 544 45406 #517-06-1965 L1973 **IM CD** *020 †20
TALLUTO, Donna Marie. 1 WYOMING ST 45409 #041-02-1992 L2006 **OPH** *020 †35
TAN, Josefina So. ■ 45429 #748-01-1957 **PD HEM** *074 †55
TAN, Nina Mathanthann. 2222 PHILADELPHIA DR 45406 #038-45-1989 L1992 **FM** *020 †18
TAYLOR, Barry Edward. 1520 S MAIN ST, STE 3 45409 #017-20-1983 L1983 **IM** *020 †20
TAYLOR, John Hayes. 1 WYOMING ST 45409 #025-01-1958 L1959 **GS VS** *071 †85
TAYLOR, Rodger L M. 1 FRANCISCAN WAY 45408 #047-07-1952 L1953 **FM** *071
TCHORZ, Kathryn Mary. 1 WYOMING ST, CHE 7TH FL DEPT OF SURGERY 45409 #033-05-1994 L2006 **GS CCS** *020 †85
TEATER, Brian Scott. 979 CONGRESS PARK DR, PRIMED CONGRESS PARK 45459 #038-45-1997 L1998 **FM** *020 †18
TEEGALA, Yamini Venkata. 2345 PHILADELPHIA DR 45406 #496-34-1999 L2004 **FM** *020
TEEL, Donovan Dee, II. 30 E APPLE ST, STE 6258 45409 #005-12-2000 L2005 **GS** *020 †85
TEJTEL, Sara Kirsten. ■ 45440 #038-45-2006 L2006 **PD** *012
TELLEZ, Luis Arsenio. 1 ELIZABETH PL, ST E'S URGENT CARE 45408 #005-12-1996 L1997 **FM** *020 †18
TEN EYCK, Raymond P. 4100 W 3RD ST, DAYTON VA MED CTR 45428 #010-02-1976 L1995 **EM** *040 †16
TERMUHLEN, Paula Maureen. 1222 S PATTERSON BLVD, STE 220 45402 #028-34-1989 L2001 **GS SO** *020 †85
TEUFEL, Karolyn Mary. ■ 45419 #041-15-2003 L2005 **IM** *020 †20
THACKERMANN, Dominic Ramo. 101 WYOMING ST, MIAMI VALLEY HOSP FP PGM 45409 #038-06-2006 L2007 **FP** *012
THAKKAR, Asish Govind. PO BOX 927, WRIGHT STATE UNIVERSITY 45401 #305-01-2006 L2007 **MPD** *012
THAKORE, Gnan N. 1520 S MAIN ST STE 2, PULMONARY & CRITICAL CARE 45409 #495-22-1987 L1994 **CCM** *020 †20
THAMBIPILLAI, Thavachentha. 30 E APPLE ST, CHE BLDG 7TH FLOOR 45409 #539-05-1996 L2004 **GS** *020
THESING, Paul Francis, Jr. 3017 WILMINGTON PIKE 45429 #056-06-1961 L1962 **FM** *020 †18
THIELE, Craig Smith. 3533 SOUTHERN BLVD, STE 2100 45429 #038-45-1986 L1988 **IM** *075 †20
THOMAS, Jerry Jose. PO BOX 927, DEPT OF PSYCHIATRY 45401 #422-01-2005 L2005 **P** *012
THOMAS, John Walter. 8638 TROY PIKE 45424 #025-01-1995 L1998 **PD** *030 †55
THOMASON, Gina Marie. ■ 45440 #048-16-2005 L2005 **PD** *012
THOMPSON, Dori Robin. 41 CATHERINE ST 45402 #020-12-1998 L2000 **FM** *020 †18
THUNEY, John Michael. 4441 FAR HILLS AVE 45429 #038-40-1982 L1984 **FM** *020 †18
THURMAN, Alan R. 1222 S PATTERSON BLVD, STE 120 45402 #038-41-1986 L1995 **GS** *020 †85
TIMKO, Moriah Lynn. ■ 45419 #038-44-2008 *012
TOBAN, Raghdaa. 4100 W 3RD ST 45428 #875-01-1972 L1977 **IMG IM** *020 †20
TOBIANSKY, Joel Hilton. 1530 NEEDMORE RD, THE DAYTON HEART CENTER 45414 #836-02-1978 L1985 **CD IM** *020 †20
TOCA, Bertilia Mariella. 600 WAYNE AVE 45410 #308-07-1982 L1995 **P** *020
TODD, Timothy Lee. 600 WAYNE AVE 45410 #038-45-1997 L1999 **P** *020
TOFTE, Keith Allen. 707 S EDWIN C MOSES BLVD 45408 #038-41-1996 L1997 **EM** *020 †16
TORBECK, Terence Paul. 1 S MAIN ST 45402 #038-41-1972 L1972 **FM** *030 †18
TORNA, Alya D. 2345 PHILADELPHIA DR 45406 #913-19-1987 L2006 **FP** *012
TORRES, Mary Ellen. ■ 45410 #017-20-1989 L1991 **OBG** *020 †30
TORRES, Michele Doreen. 1 WYOMING ST, CO MIAMI VALLEY HOSP-FAMIL 45409 #038-45-2003 L2003 **FM** *100 †18
TOTH, Laszlo. 1 ELIZABETH PL STE 100, MIDWEST SURGEONS OF DAYTON 45408 #473-01-1981 L1992 **GS** *020 †85
TOUSSAINT, Gregory John. 1 CHILDRENS PLZ 45404 #051-04-1980 L1988 **PD** *020 †55
TOZBIKIAN, Carmelita M. 1 CHILDRENS PLZ 45404 #748-01-1970 L1978 **AN** *020 †05
TOZBIKIAN, Haig G. 1 CHILDRENS PLZ, CHILDREN'S MEDICAL CENTER 45404 #198-01-1972 L1978 **PAN PME** *020 †05
TRAN, Chau Quynh. ■ 45419 #051-01-2006 L2007 **PD** *012
TRAN, Elizabeth P. ■ 45440 #021-01-2003 L2003 **GS** *012
TRAN, Luan Cong. ■ 45440 #021-01-2003 L2003 **GS** *012

■ = Address Information Privacy Protected

TREADWELL, Randall Eric. ■ 45429 #048-12-1978 L1978 **FM OS** *020 †18

TREVINO, Julian John. 1 ELIZABETH PL, STE 200 45408 #038-45-1987 L1989 **D IM** *020 †20,15

TREVINO, Justin James. 2611 WAYNE AVE 45420 #038-45-1987 L1989 **P ADP** *030 †75

TRINIDAD, Salvador B. 4450 BUCKEYE LN UNIT 210 45440 #038-40-1993 L1998 **DR RNR** *020 †80

TROHA, Frank Vincent. 1520 S MAIN ST, MIAMI VALLEY PLASTIC SURGE 45409 #038-45-1984 L1984 **PS HS** *020 †65

TRULZSCH, Dietmar V. 249 GREENMOUNT BLVD 45419 #409-05-1965 L1982 **GE IM** *050 †20

TSALIKOVA, Fatima Davudov. ■ 45415 #913-15-1990 L2005 **FP** *012

TSATALIS, James T. 1 WYOMING ST, MIAMI VALLEY HOSPITAL 45409 #041-02-1989 L1995 **DR** *020 †80

TUCHFARBER, Michael J. 33 W RAHN RD, STE 201 45429 #038-41-2002 L2006 **IM** *020 †20

TULENKO, Christina Lee. 332 CONGRESS PARK DR, PREMIER HEALTH CARE SERVIC 45459 #038-40-1998 L2002 **MPD** *020 †20

TURK, Robert Peter. 1 WYOMING ST STE 7000 45409 #001-02-1960 L1979 **GS** *040 †85

TURNER, Richard Allen. 1 CHILDRENS PLZ, CHILDREN'S MEDICAL CENTER 45404 #038-45-2005 L2005 **PD** *012

TUURI, Dwight Thos. ■ 45429 #038-41-1957 L1957 **PDC** *071 †55

TWYMAN, Marlon Demarcie. 1152 W 3RD ST 45402 #038-43-1984 L1988 **FM** *020 †18

TYTKO, James Marion. 2033 E STROOP RD, GREYSTONE FAMILY CARE 45429 #038-41-1980 L1981 **FM FSM** *020 †18

UDREA, Anca Romelia. 2600 FAR HILLS AVE, STE 216 45419 #005-12-1988 L1990 **IM** *020 †20

UNGER, Frances M Horwitz. 1 CHILDRENS PLZ, CHILDRENS MEDICAL CENTER 45404 #038-06-1967 L1973 **PDR** *071 †55,80

UPTEGROVE, Russell Louis. 361 W 3RD ST 45402 #045-01-1993 L1999 **PTH** *020

UPTMOR, Robert Anthony. 8111 TIMBERLODGE TRL 45458 #016-11-1979 L1980 **EM FM** *020 †18,16

URBAN, Maria Danuta. 469 RIDGE LINE CT 45458 #041-07-1973 L1981 **PDE PD** *020 †55

URS, Niveditha. 33 W RAHN RD, STE 201 45429 #496-35-1994 L2000 **IM** *020 †20

USMAN, Ahmed. ■ 45458 #495-21-1957 L1991 **IM CD** *071

USMAN, Niaz. 75 SYLVANIA DR 45449 #495-09-1991 L1994 **GE** *020 †20

UY, Yolanda Go. 4100 W 3RD ST 45428 #748-10-1984 L2001 **IM** *020

VALASSIADES, John X. 30 E APPLE ST, STE 6257 45409 #018-03-1960 L1961 **FM** *071 †18

VALLABHANENI, Rajani Varm. 2525 PHILADELPHIA DR 45406 #496-01-1992 L2003 **FM** *100

VANDEHOEF, Scott Alan. ■ 45419 #016-43-1995 L2006 **EM** *012 †18 ‡

VAN DER HOEVEN, Ludolph H. 532 STONEHAVEN RD, KETTERING OF OH 45429 45429 #660-04-1942 L1956 **PTH OS** *071 †50

VANDERSLUIS, Joel. 1 ELIZABETH PL, 1ST FL 45408 #065-10-1989 L1992 **N** *020 †75

VASILIU, Anton C. 6611 CLYO RD, STE C 45459 #781-01-1982 L1993 **IM** *020 †20

VASILIU, Irina. ■ 45419 #038-45-2008 *012

VAVUL-ROEDIGER, Lori C. 1 CHILDRENS PLZ, DEPT OF CHILD ADVOCACY 45404 #038-45-1996 L1997 **PD** *020 †55

VELASCO, Jonathan Earl. 1520 S MAIN ST, STE 210 45409 #017-20-1992 L1996 **VS GS** *020 †85

VENKATARAYAPPA, Indresh. PO BOX 927, DEPT OF ORTHOPADIC TRAUMA 45409 #496-39-1998 L2005 *100

VENKATESH, Anju. ■ 45458 #495-72-1994 L1999 **IM** *020 †20

VENTOLINI, Gary. 627 S EDWIN C MOSES BLVD, GROUND FLOOR 45408 #561-11-1977 L1995 **OBG** *020 †30,18 ‡

VERMA, Shannon Michelle. ■ 45458 #038-40-2004 L2004 **D** *012

VERMA ANSIL, Bikram. 7415 BRANDT PIKE, STE 2 45424 #495-69-1981 L1993 **GE IM** *020 †20

VERNETTI, Nicholas John. ■ 45429 #028-03-2006 L2006 **IM** *012

VITOLS, Aivars. 1137 LYONS RD # D 45458 #028-79-1971, ▲ L1972 **ORS** *020

VOHRA, Amit. 1 CHILDRENS PLZ 45404 #495-36-1996 L2003 **CCP PD** *020 †55 ‡

VON MALUSKI, Frank Clark. 1520 S MAIN ST, ASSOCIATED SPECIALISTS OF 45409 #038-45-1984 L1988 **IM** *020 †20

VOSS, Kevin Hal. 7707 PARAGON RD, RADIOLOGY PHYSICAL INC 45459 #023-12-1983 L1997 **DR** *020 †80

WAGNER, Robert Sherwood. ■ 45419 #038-40-1973 L1973 **IM** *020 †20

WAITE, Jilian A. 2440 BRITTANY CT 45459 #038-45-1995 L1998 **IM** *020

WALKER, Ellen Maria. ■ 45419 #038-44-2005 **P** *012

WALLACE, Thomas Mark. 1 WYOMING ST, MIAMI VALLEY HOSP. PATHOLO 45409 #028-34-1986 L1991 **PTH PCP** *020 †20

WALLS, Bruce Edward. 1 WYOMING ST 45409 #038-40-1980 L1981 **EM** *020 †16

WALSH, Mark James. 75 SYLVANIA DR 45440 #010-02-1983 L1984 **GE IM** *020 †20

WALUSIMBI, Mbaga. 1 WYOMING ST, STE 7000CHE 45409 #016-11-1992 L2004 **GS** *020 †85

WALZ, Edward Jos, Jr. 1 CHILDRENS PLZ, DEPT ANESTH CMC 45404 #016-02-1985 L1994 **AN PAN** *020 †05

WAMSLEY, Donald Lane. 1 ELIZABETH PL, STE B 45408 #038-45-1987 L1989 **N** *020

WANAT, Edward R, II. 8701 TROY PIKE, KETTERING WORKERS CARE 45424 #028-78-1985, ▲ L1992 **OM** *020 †70

WANG, Chih-Kuan. 1 CHILDRENS PLZ, CO CHILDREN S HOSP-MED EDU 45404 #244-04-1995 L2003 **PD** *100 †55

WANG, Qiong. 1 WYOMING ST, ANESTHESIOLOGY SERVICE NET 45409 #243-16-1984 L2004 **AN** *005

WANI, Shobha Ravindra. 3075 GOVERNORS PLACE BLVD, STE 110 45409 #495-33-1991 L1999 **RHU** *020 †20

WARD, Philip Everett. 601 N MIAMI AVE, ST ELIZABETH MED CTR 45449 #020-12-1976 L1977 **FM** *020 †18

WARD, Stephen Dennis. 3017 WILMINGTON PIKE 45429 #038-40-1994 L1998 **OPH** *020 †35

WARE, David Matthew. ■ 45458 #305-01-2003 L2003 **GS** *012

WAREHAM, Marshall Claude. 5250 FAR HILLS AVE 45429 #005-12-1982 L1984 **OPH IM** *020 †20,35

WARWAR, Ronald Elias. 3100 GOVERNORS PLACE BLVD, STE 100 45409 #038-41-1991 L1996 **OPH** *020 †35 ‡

WASE, Abdul. 9000 N MAIN ST, STE 101 45415 #495-77-1980 L1989 **IM CD** *020 †20

WASYLYSHEN-VELASCO, Janet. 33 W RAHN RD, STE 201 45429 #005-12-1998 L2000 **MPD** *020 †55,20 ‡

WATSON, Alicia Marie. 1 WYOMING ST, DEPT OF MED EDUCATION 45409 #011-75-2006, ▲ L2006 **OBG** *012

WATT, Kevin Jerome. 2457 N GETTYSBURG AVE 45406 #038-45-1995 L1996 **OPH** *020

WATTS, Michael Allan. 30 E APPLE ST, STE L200 45409 #056-05-1993 L1997 **PM** *020 †60

WEE, Amparo M. 600 WAYNE AVE 45410 #748-08-1968 L1994 **P CHP** *020

WEINBERG, Michael Neil. 2222 PHILADELPHIA DR, GOOD SAMARITAN HOSP & HLTH 45406 #048-12-1974 L1980 **PTH PCP** *020 †50

WEINBERG, Sylvan Lee. 707 S EDWIN C MOSES BLVD 45408 #016-06-1947 L1953 **CD MDM** *040 †20

WEINSTEIN, Jeffrey W. 33 W RAHN RD, STE 201 45429 #024-07-1990 L1996 **ID** *020 †20

WEISLEDER, Pedro. 1 CHILDRENS PLZ 45404 #649-01-1985 L2007 **CHN** *020 †75

WEISMAN, Philip Albert. 2222 PHILADELPHIA DR 45406 #038-41-1945 L1952 **PS** *071 †65

WELKER, Michael Charles. 6601 CENTERVILLE BSNS PKWY 45459 #041-14-1994 L1999 **ORS** *020 †40

WELTGE, Wilfred H. ■ 45419 #028-02-1951 L1957 **GS** *071 †85

WELTY, Kenneth Adam, Jr. 1520 S MAIN ST 45409 #038-43-1978 L1980 **PS** *020

WENKER, Josef Clement. 5025 JAMESWOOD CIR 45429 #038-41-1982 L1986 **DR VIR** *020 †80

WENZKE, Frank Joseph. 707 S EDWIN C MOSES BLVD 45408 #016-06-1972 L1973 **IC IM** *020 †20

WEPRIN, Justin Ross. CO FAMILY PRACTICE, MIAMI VALLEY HOSPITAL 45409 #654-01-2007 L2007 **FP** *012

WEPRIN, Larry Wm. 4200 INDIAN RIPPLE RD 45440 #038-40-1976 L1976 **GE IM** *020 †20

WERNER, Mildred Marie. ■ 45459 #005-12-1965 L1969 **GP** *071

WERNER, Pamela Sue. 1222 S PATTERSON BLVD, STE 160 45402 #038-40-1981 L1983 **IM** *020 †20

WESKE, John Christopher. ■ 45458 #023-12-1998 L1999 **DR** *020 †80

WESTBROCK, David Anthony. 7720 PARAGON RD, STE C 45459 #038-40-1972 L1972 **END IM** *020 †20

WESTON, Christina G. 627 S EDWIN C MOSES BLVD, DEPARTMENT OF PSYCHIATRY 45408 #035-06-1994 L1995 **CHP** *020 †75

WHATLEY, Jennifer L. ■ 45440 #048-13-2005 L2005 **IM** *020

WHITAKER, John R, Jr. 1 WYOMING ST 45409 #041-01-1952 L1957 **GS** *071 †85

WHITECAR, Philip Scott. 4428 INDIAN RIPPLE RD 45440 #016-11-1983 L1987 **FM** *040 †18

WHITFIELD, Regina Rae. 1 WYOMING ST, MIAMI VALLEY HOSPITAL 45409 #016-01-2004 L2004 **OBG** *012

WHITMER, Richard Lee. ■ 45414 #038-40-1958 L1958 **GP OM** *071 †18

WHITSETT, Mark W. 2600 FAR HILLS AVE STE 309 45419 #038-41-1980 L1981 **IM OM** *062 †20

WIBOWO, Ahmad S. 1 WYOMING ST, DEPT OF PATHOLOGY 45409 #506-15-1983 L1995 **HMP PTH** *020 †50

WIEGAND, Samantha Lynn. 30 E APPLE ST 45409 #038-45-2003 L2003 **OBG** *020

WILCHER, John Scott. 7111 N MAIN ST, STE 60 45415 #038-40-1986 L1991 **GS TS** *020 †85

WILLE, Robert Christopher. 4200 INDIAN RIPPLE RD 45440 #047-05-1985 L1989 **GE** *020 †20

WILLIAMS, Melissa Anne. 1 WYOMING ST 45409 #005-12-2004 L2004 **EM** *012

WILLIAMS, Nathan Edward. 1 WYOMING ST, MIAMI VALLEY HOSP/ORTHO SU 45409 #005-12-2002 L2002 **ORS** *012

WILLIAMS, Ned Lawlor. ■ 45424 #003-75-2004, ▲ L2005 **OBG** *012

WILLIAMS, Philip C, Jr. 1520 S MAIN ST, STE 210 45409 #035-01-1973 L1980 **GS VS** *020 †85

WILLIAMS-WHITE, Suzanne K. 7345 FAR HILLS AVE 45459 #025-07-1976 L1996 **PD ADL** *020 †55

WILSON, Joseph Mc Milton. ■ 45459 #038-40-1942 L1942 **CD IM** *071 †20

WILSON, Thomas. ■ 45429 #036-07-1964 L1971 **OBG** *020 †30

WILSON, William C M. 1 WYOMING ST 45409 #041-09-1979 L1983 **GE IM** *020 †20

WITT, Coleman Boyd. ■ 45458 #020-02-1956 L1957 **FM OS** *071

WITTBERG, Kathleen Long. 9000 N MAIN ST, MAIN STREET FAMILY PRACTIC 45415 #038-41-1980 L1982 **FM** *020 †18

WOLF, David Henry. 7707 PARAGON RD, STE 106 45459 #020-02-1964 L1967 **DR** *020 †80

WOLF, John Wm. 1989 MIAMISBURG CENTRVL RD, STE 100 45459 #038-40-1970 L1970 **A PD** *020 †55,03

WOLFSON, Barbara Jane. 1 CHILDRENS PLZ 45404 #035-09-1974 L2004 **PDR** *020 †80 ‡

WOLL, Judith Esther. 349 S MAIN ST, COMMUNITY BLOOD CTR 45402 #016-02-1969 L1994 **BBK HEM** *030 †20

WONG, Raymond Choon Fatt. 1 CHILDRENS PLZ, CHILDRENS MEDICAL CENTER 45404 #624-01-1974 L1984 **PTH PP** *020 †50

WOOD, Robert Emerson. 1 WYOMING ST, STE 4140 45409 #047-05-1970 L1974 **PD PUD** *050 †55

WOOD, Virginia C. 1 WYOMING ST 45409 #041-02-1977 L1978 **CCM IM** *030 †20

WOOD, William Roberts, III. 1 WYOMING ST, STE 4140 BERRY BLDG 45409 #016-01-1996 L2000 **OBG** *020 †20

WOODE, Charmaine B. 2166 N GETTYSBURG AVE 45406 #001-02-1995 L2005 **PD** *020 †55

WOODE, Dwain E. ■ 45475 #001-02-2004 L2005 **MPD** *012

WOODS, Randy. 30 E APPLE ST, STE 5253 45409 #017-20-1991 L1993 **GS TRS** *020 †85

WORNDLE, Johan Michael. ■ 45429 #422-01-2003 L2006 **IM** *100 †20

WOZNIAK, Curtis Jay. ■ 45419 #023-12-2004 L2004 **GS** *012

WRIGHT, William Roger. 1 WYOMING ST, MIAMI VALLE HOSP 45409 #038-40-1976 L1977 **EM** *020 †16

WU, Jennifer Zonang. 9000 N MAIN ST 45415 #038-45-1999 L2000 **GS** *020 †85

WU, Jinyun. 1 ELIZABETH PL, # 280 45408 #243-16-1987 L2000 **IM** *020 †20

WUNDERLICH, Howard F. 33 W RAHN RD, STE 201 45429 #038-40-1974 L1974 **ID IM** *020 †20

WYDERSKI, Richard Jos. 1 WYOMING ST # 7TH, MIAMI VALLEY HOSPITAL 45409 #038-41-1986 L1987 **IM IMG** *040 †20

WYMYSLO, Theodore Edward. 101 WYOMING ST, MIAMI VALLEY HOSPITAL BERR 45409 #038-40-1979 L1980 **FM** *040 †20

XU, Ling. 540 LINCOLN PARK BLVD, STE 390 45429 #243-64-1983 L2006 **N CN** *020 †75

YAMAGUCHI, Steven Phillip. 332 CONGRESS PARK DR 45459 #038-41-1995 L1996 **EM** *020 †16

YANES, Basel. 1 ELIZABETH PL, # 10B 45408 #875-01-1971 L1974 **HEM ON** *020 †20

YAP, Jayson Lee. 4100 W 3RD ST, DAYTON VA MEDICAL CTR 45428 #748-02-1985 L1989 **IM NEP** *020 †20

YAVUZ, Ferit Ibrahim. 1 FRANCISCAN WAY 45408 #902-10-1946 L1968 **IM CD** *071

YAZDANBAKHSH, Nikou. 4501 POWELL RD 45424 #517-05-1966 L1975 **OBG** *020 †30

YELLIN, James Andrew. 7707 PARAGON RD, SUITE100 45459 #038-41-1983 L1987 **DR** *020 †80

YEZUITA, James P. 600 WAYNE AVE, EASTWAY BEHAVIORIAL HEALTH 45410 #048-13-1998 L2000 **P** *100 †75

YOHANNAN, Mulakkan David. 1 CHILDRENS PLZ 45404 #495-44-1974 L1993 **PD NPM** *020 †55

YORK, Robert S. ■ 45420 #021-06-2004 L2004 **GS** *012

YU, Michael Kweysen. 30 E APPLE ST STE 5258 45409 #035-19-1995 L2006 **U** *020 †95

YUNGER, Thomas Matthew, Jr. 9001 N MAIN ST, STE A 45415 #038-40-1995 L1996 **PCC SME** *020 †20

YUNUS, Azhar Mahmood. PO BOX 927, CO WSU-PSYCHIATRY DEPT 45401 #665-01-2002 L2003 **CHP** *012

ZAGURSKY, Joyce Ann. 115 W MONUMENT AVE 45402 #041-07-1981 L1983 **IM** *020

ZAIDE, Dennis Banez. 1 CHILDRENS PLZ, C/O CHILDREN S HOSP-MED ED 45404 #748-01-2001 L2003 **MPD** *020 †20

■ = Address Information Privacy Protected

ZAKKAR, Mohamed M. 9000 N MAIN ST, STE 328 45415 #875-01-1988 L1999
PUD CCM *020 †20
ZAMAN, Syed Ali. 30 E APPLE ST, STE 6252 45409 #704-25-1995 L2005 TS *020 †85,90
ZAVECKAS, Jennifer. 128 E APPLE ST, STE 3800 45409 #051-75-2007, ▲ L2007 OBG *012
ZAYUR EZZEDDINE, Dina A. 4200 INDIAN RIPPLE RD 45440 #605-01-1994 L1997 GE *020 †20
ZECHIEL, Kristy Ann. ■ 45419 #038-45-1999 L1999 FM *020 †18
ZEGARSKI, Thomas Joseph. 617 SHROYER RD 45419 #038-41-1992 L1993 PD *020 †55
ZERNZACH, Randall Curtis. 1 CHILDRENS PLZ 45404 #023-12-1995 L2004 PD *020 †55
ZHANG, Zhiming. 1 WYOMING ST, WSU-MIAMI VALLEY HOSPOBGYN 45409
#243-21-1987 L2000 OBG *020
ZHU, An. ■ 45419 #243-47-1983 L2006 PCP *020 †50
ZIMBRAN, Mary Anne W. 45440 #035-03-1960 L1962 GP *071
ZIMMERMAN, Brian D. 1 WYOMING ST, EMERGENCY ADMIN. OFFICE 45409
#028-34-1998 L2000 MPD *020 †20,55
ZRAIK, Talal R. 33 W RAHN RD, STE 201 45429 #875-01-1975 L1988 ID IM *020 †20
ZRYD, Teresa Wilkins. 2345 PHILADELPHIA DR 45406 #038-45-1995 L1996 FM *020 †18
ZWART, Hans Henk Jan. 328 YANKEE TRACE DR 45458 #660-03-1962 L1973
TS VS *020 †85,90
ZWIESLER, Mary Louise. 7211 N MAIN ST, STE 1 45415 #038-45-1986 L1988 FM *020 †18
ZYCH, Paul Randall. 3535 SOUTHERN BLVD 45429 #016-43-1981 L1982 EM *020 †16

DEFIANCE – DEFIANCE

ABOU ABDALLAH, Dany Said. 1250 RALSTON AVE 43512 #605-02-1996 L2002
PCC SME *020 †20
AHMED, Mahtab U. 1250 RALSTON AVE, STE 106 43512 #160-03-1983 L1994 FM *020 †18 ‡
ALBERTI, Rafael V. 1206 E 2ND ST 43512 #308-01-1961 L1971 OBG *071 †30
ARSHAD, Amer. 1250 RALSTON AVE, STE 202 43512 #704-20-1991 L1997 IM *020 †20
BAKER, Eileen Frances. 1404 E 2ND ST, MERCY HOSPITAL 43512 #050-02-1998 L1999
EM *020 †16
BARNETT, Robert Edward. 1250 RALSTON AVE, STE 104 43512 #038-43-1977 L1979
FM *020 †18
BERNARDO, Alipio D. 1250 RALSTON AVE 43512 #038-41-1991 L1993 PCC *020 †20
BESAW, Beth Alexander. 1250 RALSTON AVE, STE 104 43512 #038-43-1997 L1999 FM *020 †18
BEST, Angela P. 1206 E 2ND ST 43512 #038-43-1978 L1981 P *020
BOOMER, George Louis. ■ 43512 #016-06-1943 L1951 GP GS *071
BROSE, Paul Elbert. 1400 E 2ND ST, DEFIANCE CLINIC BOX 218 43512 #017-20-1960 L1968
IM CD *020 †20
BROWN, Homer Clarence. ■ 43512 #025-01-1948 L1950 GP A *071
BUSTEED, William Savage. 1400 E 2ND ST 43512 #025-01-1954 L1955 FM AN *071
CABATAN, Edgardo Orena. 306 CLINTON ST 43512 #748-08-1978 L2001 P *020 †75
DAJCZAK, Stanislaw P. 1250 RALSTON AVE, STE 102 43512 #065-06-1991 L2004
ORS *020 †40
DIAZ, Carlos Ramon. 1200 RALSTON AVE 43512 #649-01-1955 L1958 GS *020
DOYLE, Harry A, Jr. 1400 E 2ND ST 43512 #038-43-1981 L1987 FM *020 †18
DUCATT, Daniel Louis. 1901 TANGLEWOOD DR 43512 #038-41-1966 L1966 U *020
DUHAIME, Lisa Ann. 1400 E 2ND ST, DEFIANCE CLINIC 43512 #038-43-1998 L2005
HO *020 †20
EISENBERG, J P. 1400 E 2ND ST, THE DEFIANCE CLINIC 43512 #038-06-1976 L1979 DR *020
FERNANDES, Karl Shane. 1250 RALSTON AVE 43512 #038-40-1991 L1997 PCC SME *020 †20
FOLDVARY, Robert James. 1400 E 2ND ST, DEFIANCE CLINIC 43512 #038-41-1972 L1972
PD *020 †55
FOUT, Larry Roy. 1400 E 2ND ST 43512 #038-40-1959 L1959 FM AM *020 †70,18 ‡
FOX, Gary Norman. 1400 E 2ND ST, DEFIANCE CLINIC 43512 #036-07-1976 L1993
D FM *020 †18
GARDNER, Alan Martin. 1250 RALSTON AVE, STE 205 43512 #025-01-1980 L1994 AN EM *020
GASPAR, Allen Louis. 1400 E 2ND ST 43512 #038-40-1976 L1976 IM *020 †20
GRAY, Jerrold Franklin. 211 BIEDE AVE 43512 #038-43-1995 L1999 P *020 †75
HASHMI, Masud Shah. 1250 RALSTON AVE, STE 203 43512 #704-01-1971 L1979
GS *020 †85,16
HASHMI, Nighat Fatima. 1200 RALSTON AVE 43512 #704-06-1979 L2000 PTH *062 †50
HOGAN, Timothy Harvey. 1125 RALSTON AVE 43512 #065-01-1983 L1993 FM *020 †8
KARNIK, Rajmohan S. 1400 E 2ND ST, DEFIANCE CLINIC 43512 #495-21-1978 L1993
CD IM *020 †20
KHALIL, Hany Youssef Y. 1250 RALSTON AVE 43512 #915-02-1979 L1988 PUD IM *020 †20
KOSE, Robert Erik. 1250 RALSTON AVE 43512 #038-40-1977 L1978 PUD CCM *020 †20
LENHART, Francis M. 1400 E 2ND ST 43512 #038-06-1944 L1944 FM *071 †18
LENHART, Peter C. 1400 E 2ND ST 43512 #038-40-1994 L2000 IM *020 †20
MAHANY, Thomas Michael. 1250 RALSTON AVE, STE 203 43512 #051-04-1984 L2000
GS *020 †18
MERCADO, Melchor L. 1250 RALSTON AVE STE 105, DEFIANCE REGIONAL PSYCHIAT 43512
#748-11-1978 L1996 P *020 †75
MIERZWIAK, David Scott. 1206 E 2ND ST 43512 #038-43-1987 L1988 EM *020 †16
MITCHELL, John A. 1200 RALSTON AVE 43512 #020-02-1966 L1970 DR NR *020
MOLITOR, Jean Marie. 211 BIEDE AVE 43512 #038-43-1988 L1989 P *020 †75
NEWMAN, Terence Robt. 1250 RALSTON AVE 43512 #918-01-1975 L2003 AN *020 †05
OBRI, Samer Samaan. 1250 RALSTON AVE, STE 202 43512 #875-02-1992 L2001 IM *020 †20
O'DONNELL, Philip Hugh. 1490 PINEHURST DR 43512 #041-02-1988 L1992 OPH *020 †35
OKULEY, Gary Edward. 1400 E 2ND ST 43512 #038-40-1997 L1999 FM *020 †18
PALMER, Paul Edward. 1206 E 2ND ST 43512 #038-06-1954 L1954 OBG *071
PIPOLY, Daniel John. 1250 RALSTON AVE 43512 #038-41-1981 L1987 PCC IM *020 †20
POLICHERLA, Prasad N. 1400 E 2ND ST 43512 #495-70-1978 L1999 N CN *020
PRUITT, Jeffrey Allyn. 1400 E 2ND ST 43512 #038-43-1987 L1991 GS VS *020 †85
RACCIATO, John Jos. 1400 E 2ND ST, DEFIANCE CLINIC 43512 #041-13-1978 L1986
OPH *020 †35
REEVES, John Davis. 1400 E 2ND ST, DEFIANCE CLINIC 43512 #038-45-1988 L1989
IM *020 †20
REITER, Rosemary Karen. 1250 RALSTON AVE, STE 204 43512 #038-43-2000 L2003
FM *020 †18
RICHTER, William Hutton. 26427 STATE ROUTE 281, PO BOX 70 43512 #047-06-1975 L1981
FM PHP *020 †18
ROHRS, Rita Arend. 1400 E 2ND ST 43512 #038-40-1995 L1998 FM *020 †18
ROY, Vicki Lea. 1400 E 2ND ST, DEFIANCE CLNC 43512 #005-12-1997 L1998 IM *020 †20
SAAD, Michael Wahba. 1250 RALSTON AVE, STE 204 43512 #915-02-1995 L2005 FM *020 †18

SCHWEITZER, Jennifer Anne. 1250 RALSTON AVE, STE 106 43512 #038-45-1993 L1994
FM *020 †18
SHAW, John Wesley. 1400 E 2ND ST 43512 #038-41-1990 L1995 GS *020 †85
SHAW, Robert Allan. 409 JEFFERSON AVE 43512 #038-40-1963 L1963 P PYG *020 †
SHERRATT, Amanda Jane. 1250 RALSTON AVE, STE 204 43512 #038-02-1993 L2001
PD *020 †55
SMITH, Richard Grant. 1400 E 2ND ST 43512 #041-09-1975 L1986 OTO *020 †45
SOUTHWORTH, Robt Raymond. 1400 E 2ND ST, DEFIANCE CLINIC 43512 #024-07-1955 L1962
CD IM *071 †20
SUJARITCHAN, Noparat. 1206 E 2ND ST 43512 #891-02-1968 L1975 OPH *020 †35
TARTAGLIA, Louis Anthony. 1250 RALSTON AVE 43512 #561-01-1978 L1995
ADP ADM *071 †75
VAUGHN, Glen Edward. 1200 RALSTON AVE 43512 #038-40-1985 L1986 EM GP *020 †16
VELTRI, Salvatore. 1400 E 2ND ST, DEFIANCE CLINIC 43512 #025-07-1989 L1996 ON *020 †20
VEMULAPALLI, Jaganmohan R. 1400 E 2ND ST 43512 #495-70-1972 L1981 U *020 †95
WINNER, David Elliott. 1250 RALSTON AVE, STE 104 43512 #038-41-1994 L1996 FM *020 †18

DELAWARE – DELAWARE

ALBERS, Anne Robinson. 551 W CENTRAL AVE 43015 #038-40-1998 L1999 CD *020 †20
ALFARUQI, Tayma. 7651 STAGERS LOOP 43015 #038-45-1991 L1996 DR *020 †80
ALFONSO, Mark. 7651 STAGERS LOOP 43015 #038-45-1990 L1996 DR *020 †80
ALLEN, Dorothy M Stannard. ■ 43015 #056-05-1948 L1951 PD *071
ARMSTRONG, Arthur Thomas. ■ 43015 #422-01-2001 L2006 RHU *020 †20
BADERTSCHER, Victor Edwin. ■ 43015 #038-40-1963 L1963 IM GE *020 †20
BAUMERT, John Erland, Jr. 7651 STAGERS LOOP 43015 #018-03-1971 L1974
NM IM *020 †20,28
BAY, Janet Winifred. 561 W CENTRAL AVE 43015 #038-40-1973 L1979 NS *020 †25
BELCH, Richard Patrick. 561 W CENTRAL AVE, PHYSICIAN RECRUITMENT 43015
#038-45-1987 L1991 AN PME *020 †05
BHATLA, Sumit. 7651 STAGERS LOOP 43015 #038-44-2000 L2000 VIR *100 †80
BINKHORST, Johan Lucien. 561 W CENTRAL AVE 43015 #660-03-1953 L1959 GS GYN *071
BORGESS, Mary Pat. 7651 STAGERS LOOP 43015 #038-40-1976 L1977 DR OS *020 †80
BRINKMAN, Anne Marie. 550 W CENTRAL AVE 43015 #038-40-1995 L1996 FM *020 †18
BUDZIK, Ronald F, Jr. 7651 STAGERS LOOP 43015 #038-41-1990 L2001 RNR *020 †80
BUSE, Thomas Marce. 7651 STAGERS LOOP 43015 #038-41-1992 L1997 DR *020 †80
CARDWELL, Todd Nelson. 551 W CENTRAL AVE 43015 #038-40-1994 L1995 CD *020 †20
CAULKINS, Robert S, Jr. 265 W LINCOLN AVE 43015 #038-06-1953 L1953 FP *020 †20
COLEMAN, Lewis S. 561 W CENTRAL AVE 43015 #035-09-1974 L2003 AN *020 †05 ‡
CORDERO, Gretchen Grisell. 7651 STAGERS LOOP 43015 #042-03-1993 L2001 DR *020 †80
COSTA, John Joseph. 7651 STAGERS LOOP 43015 #038-40-1994 L1995 CD *020 †20
DAVIS, Thomas Maldwynne. 7651 STAGERS LOOP 43015 #038-40-1983 L1989 VIR *020 †80
DEAN, Laurian Mark. 7651 STAGERS LOOP 43015 #010-03-1989 L2000 VIR *020 †80
DE ANDRADE, Ronald, Jr. 1788 COLUMBUS PIKE 43015 #055-02-1983 L1991 NEP IM *020 †20
DOLEN, Eric Gregg. 7651 STAGERS LOOP 43015 #035-46-1993 L2002 VIR *020 †80
EVANS, Thomas Paul. 561 W CENTRAL AVE 43015 #660-06-1967 L1969 UCM GP *020 †20
FLEMING, James Brett. ■ 43015 #038-06-2005 L2007 NS *012
FRENCH, Gerald Thos. 454 W CENTRAL AVE 43015 #038-40-1979 L1979 IM EM *020 †20
FULLER, Raymond Dayre. 90 E WILLIAM ST 43015 #038-41-1991 L1991 GS *020 †85
GAJDOWSKI, Richard Jan. ■ 43015 #065-09-1984 L1994 EM *020 †16
GAMBOA, Pablo Alejandro. 7651 STAGERS LOOP 43015 #264-13-1989 L1999 DR *020 †80
GARCIA, Godofredo Igno. 561 W CENTRAL AVE, GRADY MEMORIAL HOSPITAL 43015
#748-02-1983 L2005 IM *020 †20
GIBBONS, Rebecca Galford. 7651 STAGERS LOOP 43015 #055-01-1979 L1980 DR *020 †80
GNADE, Robert. 43 NORTHWOOD DR 43015 #038-40-1980 L1981 FM *020
GRAFFEO, Kenneth Charles. 90 E WILLIAM ST 43015 #038-45-1999 L1999 GS *020 †85
HAMMETT, William Beatty. 551 W CENTRAL AVE, STE 103 43015 #038-41-1990 L1998
OBG *020 †30
HE, Gang. ■ 43015 #243-38-1982 L2007 SP *020 †50
HELD, Judith Kidd. 695 W CENTRAL AVE 43015 #038-40-1966 L1966 IM ADM *020
HERTZENDORF, Jill Connie. 561 W CENTRAL AVE, GRADY MEMORIAL HOSPITAL 43015
#125-15-1985 L1988 EM *020 †16
HESS, Mary Lee. 7651 STAGERS LOOP 43015 #038-43-1980 L1982 DR *020 †80
HICKMAN, Mark Allen. 241 PADDOCK CT 43015 #038-40-1998 L1999 FM *020 †18
HIRSCH, Steven Marc. 551 W CENTRAL AVE STE 202 43015 #038-40-1987 L1987
OTO *020 †45
HIXSON, Carolyn Sue. 6 LEXINGTON BLVD 43015 #038-40-1983 L1985 OBG *020 †30
HOANG, David. 241 PADDOCK CT 43015 #038-40-1999 L2000 ORS *020 †40
HUBBELL, Patricia Ann A. 223 E WILLIAM ST, STUDENT HEALTH CLINIC/O.W. 43015
#028-46-1975 L1979 FM *020 †18
HUBBELL, Thomas Park. 550 W CENTRAL AVE 43015 #028-46-1975 L1978 FM OBS *020 †18
JACOBS, Darick Lee. 7651 STAGERS LOOP 43015 #041-01-1996 L2005 DR VIR *020 †80
JORDAN, Kevin Otis. ■ 43015 #035-08-1997 L2004 FM *020 †16
KEMP, Susan M. 7651 STAGERS LOOP 43015 #041-13-1981 L2003 DR *020 †80
KOEHLER, Matthew. 454 W CENTRAL AVE, DELAWARE NTERNAL MEDICINE 43015
#038-43-1992 L1994 IM *020 †20
KONSTANTINIDIS, K. ■ 43015 #418-02-1980 L1985 GS *020 †85
KUHN, Mary Kinsey. 561 W CENTRAL AVE 43015 #019-02-1946 L1948 FM *071
KUNZ, Bradley Legan. 550 W CENTRAL AVE 43015 #038-41-1995 L1996 FM *020 †18
LAFFERTY, Peter Rollin. 7651 STAGERS LOOP 43015 #038-41-1991 L2000 DR *020 †80
LAUFMAN, Leslie A Rodgers. 561 W CENTRAL AVE 43015 #041-12-1972 L1976
HO IM *020 †20
LEACH, John Matthew. 7651 STAGERS LOOP 43015 #038-40-1999 L1999 DR *100 †80
LEWIS, James William. 1788 COLUMBUS PIKE 43015 #016-43-1967 L1969 NEP IM *030 †20
LIPPERT, John Allan. 7651 STAGERS LOOP 43015 #023-01-1994 L2000 VIR *020 †80
LOMBARDI, Thomas James. 7651 STAGERS LOOP 43015 #055-07-1989 L1997 DR *020 †80
LOUVAKIS, Hariklia. 551 W CENTRAL AVE, STE 103 43015 #473-01-1998 L2003 OBG *020 ‡
MAC DOWELL, Andrew Scott. 551 W CENTRAL AVE 43015 #038-40-1998 L1999
MPD *020 †20,55
MACLAUGHLIN, Lewis Harte. 7651 STAGERS LOOP 43015 #038-40-1999 L1999 DR *020 †80
MARTI, Charles Jay. ■ 43015 #026-04-1977 L1985 EM IM *020 †20,16
MC DOUGALL, Patricia Ann. ■ 43015 #038-44-1987 L1990 P *100
MC GRAIL, John Wm. 241 PADDOCK CT 43015 #056-06-1966 L1974 ORS *020 †40
MC GRAW, James Kevin. 7651 STAGERS LOOP 43015 #045-01-1991 L1997 VIR DR *020 †80

MECKLER, Gary Mitchell. 357 W CENTRAL AVE 43015 #028-02-1977 L1981 **FM** *020 †18

MILLHON, Judson Severn. 551 W CENTRAL AVE 43015 #038-40-1990 L1992 **CD** *020 †20

MOUSTOFI, Farid. ■ 43015 #038-43-2008 *012

NARDIN, David Webster. ■ 43015 #038-40-1965 L1965 **FM GP** *071 †18

OBETZ, Merry Lee. 561 W CENTRAL AVE 43015 #041-13-1967 L1972 **R NM** *071 †80

PANTANGCO, Linda Bautista. 561 W CENTRAL AVE 43015 #748-08-1967 L1975 **AN** *020

PAPPA, Karl Steven. 551 W CENTRAL AVE, STE 101 43015 #038-40-1987 L1988 **OPH** *020 †35

PARKER, George Wm. ■ 43015 #038-34-1960 L1961 **GS** *071 †85

PEMA, Peter James. 7651 STAGERS LOOP 43015 #038-40-1987 L1988 **DR IM** *020 †80

PHILLIPS, Merle Le Roy. ■ 43015 #038-40-1946 L1946 **OS** *071

PUGLIESE, Robert Allen. 250 S HENRY ST, CENTRAL OHIO MENTAL HLTH 43015 #038-40-1965 L1965 **P** *020 †75

RAIKEN, David Paul. 7651 STAGERS LOOP 43015 #023-12-1994 L2005 **DR** *020 †80

RATH, David A. 149 N SANDUSKY ST, DELAWARE COUNTY CORONERS O 43015 #654-01-1982 L1989 **IM PA** *020

RAVE, Elizabeth M. 1788 COLUMBUS PIKE 43015 #038-43-2000 L2000 **NEP IM** *020 †20

READER, Douglas William. 7651 STAGERS LOOP 43015 #038-43-1997 L1999 **DR** *020 †80

REUTER, Michael Danl. 561 W CENTRAL AVE 43015 #038-40-1972 L1972 **R NM** *020 †28,80

ROLFE, Stephen J. 561 W CENTRAL AVE 43015 #038-40-1983 L1984 **CD IM** *071

ROSENFIELD, John Alfred. 1201 US HIGHWAY 23 N, STE E 43015 #038-40-1977 L1980 **PD** *020 †55

RUDY, David R. ■ 43015 #038-40-1960 L1960 **OM FM** *072 †70,18

RUMBALSKI, David Eric. 551 W CENTRAL AVE 43015 #038-41-1996 L1997 **FM** *020 †18

RYAN, Martin Terry. ■ 43015 #038-40-1992 L1993 **P** *020 †75

SABGIR, David Andrew. 551 W CENTRAL AVE 43015 #038-43-1997 L1998 **CD** *020 †20

SAUNDERS, Christopher S. 1788 COLUMBUS PIKE 43015 #038-06-1982 L1985 **NEP IM** *020 †20

SCHIRMER, William John. 241 PADDOCK CT 43015 #023-07-1983 L1984 **AS GE** *020 †85

SCHORY, William Henry. 50 S FRANKLIN ST, REHAB WORKS INC 43015 #038-06-1966 L1966 **GP PTH** *071 †50

SCHROEDER, Kevin Lee. 1788 COLUMBUS PIKE 43015 #038-40-1997 L1998 **IM** *020 †20

SCHULER, Stephen Lee. 104 N UNION ST, STE A 43015 #038-40-1975 L1976 **PD** *020 †55

SCHULTZ, Joseph Chas. 7651 STAGERS LOOP 43015 #038-40-1973 L1977 **DR** *020 †80

SETH, Sumit Kumar. 7651 STAGERS LOOP 43015 #038-40-1998 L2000 **DR** *020 †80

SHAFFER, Phillip Byron. 7651 STAGERS LOOP 43015 #038-43-1976 L1977 **NM NR** *020 †80

SHAMIM, Ajmal. 561 W CENTRAL AVE, GRADY MEMORIAL HOSPITAL 43015 #704-16-1990 L2004 **IM** *020 †20

SHECKET, Gordon Neal. 561 W CENTRAL AVE, GRADY MEMORIAL HOSPITAL 43015 #038-06-1976 L1976 **PTH** *020 †50

SHONK, Jason Richard. 7651 STAGERS LOOP 43015 #038-06-1999 L1999 **DR** *020 †80

SIMMONS, Jason Levon. ■ 43015 #045-04-2007 **IM** *012

SINCLAIR, Daniel Scott. 7651 STAGERS LOOP 43015 #038-40-1993 L1999 **DR** *020 †80

SINGRI, Naveen. 1788 COLUMBUS PIKE 43015 #038-41-1997 L2003 **NEP** *020 †20

SMITH, David Ray, Jr. 1201 US HIGHWAY 23 N 43015 #038-40-1960 L1960 **OPH** *071 †35

SMITH, Douglas L. 244 PADDOCK CT 43015 #038-06-1951 L1951 **A D** *072 †03

SNYDER, Ann Diller. 250 S HENRY ST 43015 #038-40-1972 L1972 **P** *020 †75

SPELMAN, Jessica Eve. 551 W CENTRAL AVE STE 301 43015 #038-40-1996 L2001 **MPD** *020 †20,55

STECHSCHULTE, John Robt. 551 W CENTRAL AVE, STE 101 43015 #038-40-1980 L1985 **OPH** *020 †35

STEGER, Michael Warren. 241 PADDOCK CT, WARREN LORAINE INC 43015 #020-02-1998 L2001 **FM** *020 †18 ‡

STEIN, Moni. 7651 STAGERS LOOP 43015 #065-01-1988 L2006 **VIR DR** *020 †80

TARRANT, William Prescott. 7651 STAGERS LOOP 43015 #055-01-1996 L2001 **DR** *020 †80

TIMKO, Timothy Lee. 551 W CENTRAL AVE 43015 #038-44-1986 L1987 **CD IC** *020 †20

TOBLER, Jerry. 7651 STAGERS LOOP 43015 #008-01-1983 L2004 **DR VIR** *020 †80

TRAETOW, Wayne Danl. 561 W CENTRAL AVE 43015 #038-40-1978 L1979 **AN CCM** *020 †05

TROTTI, Girolamo Jerry. 7651 STAGERS LOOP 43015 #038-45-1994 L2000 **DR** *020 †80

UJAYLI, Alaa Abdul Salam. 551 W CENTRAL AVE 43015 #875-01-1984 L1991 **IM CD** *020 †20

VASWANI, Kuldeep K. 7651 STAGERS LOOP 43015 #035-08-1992 L1997 **DR OS** *020 †80

WARD, Charles Edward. ■ 43015 #051-04-1946 L1958 **OBG** *020

WATSON, David Donald. 561 W CENTRAL AVE 43015 #038-41-1987 L1990 **FM EM** *020 †18

WEINERMAN, Philip M. 7651 STAGERS LOOP 43015 #016-06-1977 L1978 **DR** *020 †80

WIOT, Jerome Geoffrey. 7651 STAGERS LOOP 43015 #038-41-1982 L1983 **RNR R** *020 †80

WITTY, Robert Travis. ■ 43015 #011-02-1973 L1976 **NEP IM** *071 †20

WONGSAM, Patricia E. 561 W CENTRAL AVE 43015 #566-01-1975 L1979 **PM OM** *071 †60

ZADVINSKIS, David Paul. 7651 STAGERS LOOP 43015 #025-07-1989 L1999 **DR** *020 †80

ZIENTEK, Dawn Marie. ■ 43015 #038-43-2000 L2000 **OBG** *100

ZINN, Edward Russell. ■ 43015 #038-45-1989 L1990 **FM** *020 †18

DELPHOS — ALLEN

HUX, Perry Monroe. 1800 E 5TH ST STE 1 45833 #038-43-1978 L1979 **FM ADM** *020 †18

LOPEZ, Celeste Doreen. 154 W 3RD ST 45833 #049-01-1989 L2000 **PD** *020 †55

MUHA, Michael John. 1800 E 5TH ST 45833 #038-45-1987 L1988 **ORS HS** *020 †40

SELLER, Gregory James. 1800 E 5TH ST 45833 #038-41-1978 L1979 **FM EM** *020 †18

SHEIKH, Tariq I. 1800 E 5TH ST 45833 #704-01-1986 L2000 **GE** *020 †20

DELTA — FULTON

REED, Benjamin H, Jr. 6696 US HIGHWAY 20A 43515 #020-02-1950 L1953 **GP** *071

DENNISON — TUSCARAWAS

BELMONTE, Rogel Reyes. 304 FUHR ST 44621 #748-01-1969 L1974 **FM EM** *075 †18

BHAIRAPPA, Vaijanath. 819 N 1ST ST 44621 #495-35-1970 L1999 **PD** *020 †55

BUTT, Khurram Asharaf. 819 N 1ST ST, TWIN CITY HOSP 44621 #704-01-1985 L2000 **IM** *020 †20

CLARKE, John S. 819 N 1ST ST, TWIN CITY HOSPITAL 44621 #035-03-1963 L1968 **TS** *020 †85,90

HOWLAND, Willard J. 819 N 1ST ST 44621 #019-02-1950 L1959 **R** *071 †80

KADER, Ayman Mohammad. 820 N 3RD ST 44621 #915-02-1981 L1997 **IM** *100

LEWIS, James Pearl. 819 N 1ST ST 44621 #038-40-1978 L1979 **EM** *020 †20,16

MARTINEZ, Jose Yabut, Jr. 819 N 1ST ST 44621 #748-01-1967 L1973 **GS GP** *071 †20

NAVARRO, Ignacio. 819 N 1ST ST 44621 #264-03-1958 L1967 **U GP** *071 †95

OLYMPIA, Christian Lomio. 819 N 1ST ST 44621 #038-40-1999 L2004 **IM** *100

PRETORIUS, John Jacob. 819 N 1ST ST 44621 #038-44-1988 L1991 **IM** *020 †20

SAYAT, Nila Zamora. 819 N 1ST ST 44621 #748-01-1967 L1974 **OBG** *020 †30

SHANMUGAM, Makilzhan. 819 N 1ST ST 44621 #495-04-1988 L1998 **CD** *020 †20

SILVERSTONE, Irwin Aaron. 819 N 1ST ST 44621 #869-05-1956 L1958 **R** *071 †80

SOROLLA, Maricelle Goingc. 819 N 1ST ST 44621 #748-02-1999 L2004 **IM** *020 †20

DESHLER — HENRY

ASAD, Usman Bin. 141 N KEYSER AVE 43516 #704-01-1990 L1997 **FM** *020 †18

BLOUGH, Robert J. 141 N KEYSER AVE 43516 #041-09-1952 L1953 **GP AM** *071 †18

DOVER — TUSCARAWAS

AHMED, Maaz. ■ 44622 #704-01-1987 L1999 **IM** *020 †20

AHMED, Sumayya. 335 OXFORD ST, STE C 44622 #160-02-1994 L2000 **IM** *020

AREJOLA, Thomas Reyes. 659 BOULEVARD ST, UNION HOSPITAL 44622 #748-01-1971 L1976 **PTH** *020 †50

BETKERUR, Umesh Nagappa. 204 S BELLEVUE AVE 44622 #495-23-1960 L1977 **PD** *020 †55

BHAGAT, Alok. 659 BOULEVARD ST 44622 #495-54-1975 L1982 **N OS** *020 †75

BOGDAN, Charles John. 340 OXFORD ST, STE 310 44622 #038-40-1989 L1994 **OTO** *020 †45

BRADEN, Donald Ray. 420 S REEVES AVE STE B 44622 #038-40-1971 L1971 **FM** *020 †18

BRAVO, Miguel Angel. 659 BOULEVARD ST 44622 #319-01-1971 L1985 **GS CRS** *020 †85,10

BRYAN, Joseph Edmond. 300 MEDICAL PARK DR, STE 204 44622 #026-04-1979 L1998 **IM** *020 †20

BURNHAM, John Stanley. 1716 N CROSS ST 44622 #038-40-1984 L1985 **FM IMG** *020 †18

CAMERON, Jeffrey Lee. 659 BOULEVARD ST 44622 #038-44-1986 L1987 **EM** *020 †16

CAMERON, Steffen Scott. 659 BOULEVARD ST 44622 #038-45-1991 L1994 **FM** *020 †18

CAMPANO, Mark Anthony. 659 BOULEVARD ST 44622 #038-45-1982 L1986 **AN** *020

CARINO, Fernando Jaico. 201 HOSPITAL DR, COMM MENTAL HLTH CARE 44622 #748-01-1956 L1966 **P** *071

CARPIO, Victoria T B. 204 S BELLEVUE AVE 44622 #748-01-1983 L1996 **PD** *020 †55

CHARPENTIER, Arthur O, Jr. 659 BOULEVARD ST 44622 #050-02-1976 L1977 **FM** *020 †18

CHISMAR, Steven Alex. 200 MEDICAL PARK DR, STE A2 44622 #038-44-1997 L2001 **OBG** *020 †30

CLEMENS, Daniel James. 340 OXFORD ST STE 340 44622 #038-41-1975 L1976 **OPH** *030 †35

COMELLA, Charles M. 659 BOULEVARD ST 44622 #038-06-1953 L1953 **GS** *071 †85

DACIO, Loreto Ruiz. 659 BOULEVARD ST 44622 #748-10-1964 L1972 **GS GP** *071

DAOUD, Rimon. 659 BOULEVARD ST, UNION HOSPITAL 44622 #875-01-1996 L2003 **FM** *020 †18

DESIATO, Timothy Paul. 1716 N CROSS ST 44622 #038-41-1981 L1982 **FM** *020 †18

EICHER, Donald Matthew. 300 MEDICAL PARK DR, TRICOUNTY HEMATOLOGY & 44622 #038-44-1984 L1986 **ON HEM** *020 †20

FLEAK, Michele Dawn. 400 MEDICAL PARK DR, STE 103 44622 #055-01-1999 L1999 **IM** *020 †20

FRONZAGLIA, Douglas, II. 400 MEDICAL PARK DR, STE 103 44622 #041-78-2000, ▲ L2005 **IM OMM** *020

GABRAIL, Nashat Yousif. 340 OXFORD ST, STE 110 44622 #528-02-1976 L1990 **HEM ON** *020 †20

GARREN, Kurt Charles. 659 BOULEVARD ST 44622 #038-40-1996 L1997 **OTO** *020 †45

GEDULDIG, Roy. 227 W 4TH ST 44622 #869-07-1954 L1956 **PD** *071

GIGAX, Jennifer Macke. 204 S BELLEVUE AVE 44622 #038-40-1999 L1999 **PD** *020 †55

GIGAX, Michael Ralph. 300 MEDICAL PARK DR, STE 103 44622 #038-40-1999 L2000 **U** *020 †95

HARPER, Anne Marie. 897 E IRON AVE 44622 #038-44-1985 L1987 **IM** *020 †20

HARROLD, Leslie Stuart. 659 BOULEVARD ST 44622 #041-02-1974 L1975 **PTH IM** *020 †20,50

HARTMAN, David Mark. 335 OXFORD ST, STE A 44622 #041-15-1999 L2004 **OTO** *020 †45 ‡

HELLMANN, Joseph Raymond. 340 OXFORD ST, ORTHOPAEDIC 44622 #041-14-1997 L2000 **ORS** *020 †40

HOLDER, Blair Thos. 300 MEDICAL PARK DR 44622 #025-07-1978 L1987 **GE IM** *020 †20

HOLDER, Scott Frederick. 205 HOSPITAL DR 44622 #025-01-1980 L1983 **ORS** *020 †40

HOUGLAN, James John. 123 W 3RD ST 44622 #038-40-1959 L1959 **AN GP** *071 †18

JOHNSON, Nathan Andrew. ■ 44622 #038-40-2002 L2005 **EM** *020 †16

KEYSER, Douglas Robt. 300 MEDICAL PARK DR, STARK RADIATION ONCOLOGY 44622 #038-44-1990 L1992 **RO** *020 †20,80

KLIMO, Gerald Francis. 340 OXFORD ST, ORTHOPAEDIC 44622 #038-44-1994 L1995 **ORS** *020 †40

KOLLMAN, Robin Dale. 400 MEDICAL PARK DR, STE 201 44622 #038-40-1981 L1982 **FM** *020 †18 ‡

KOSER, Eugene Richard, Jr. 320 OXFORD ST 44622 #038-40-1980 L1986 **AN** *020 †05

KUBINA, Mark Norbert. 659 BOULEVARD ST, DEPT OF EMERGENCY MEDICINE 44622 #038-44-1993 L1994 **EM** *020 †16

KUCZYNSKI, Darrin James. 205 HOSPITAL DR 44622 #038-44-1990 L1993 **ORS** *020 †40

KUEHNE, Lori Ann. 603 MONROE ST 44622 #038-45-1990 L1991 **FM** *020 †18

LEHMAN, Joel Anthony. 659 BOULEVARD ST, EMERGIMED INC 44622 #011-03-1993 L1996 **EM** *020 †16

LEINDECKER, Kristi Marie. 400 MEDICAL PARK DR, STE 201 44622 #038-45-1996 L1998 **FM** *020 †18

LEVITT, Robert Mark. 400 MEDICAL PARK DR, STE 203 44622 #041-14-1991 L1992 **GS** *020 †85

LEY, Robert Earl, III. 420 S REEVES AVE STE C 44622 #038-40-1971 L1972 **FM** *020 †18

LOHR, Stephen Allen. 340 OXFORD ST, ORTHOPAEDIC 44622 #038-41-1970 L1970 **ORS** *020 †40

LUXENBERG, Andrew M. 659 BOULEVARD ST 44622 #654-01-1986 L1992 **AN EM** *020 †20,05

MAITRA, Arup. 659 BOULEVARD ST 44622 #495-73-1982 L1993 **NEP** *020 †20

MASTIN, Donald W. ■ 44622 #038-06-1952 L1952 **AN GP** *020 †18

MAY, Maureen Alanna. 340 OXFORD ST STE 340 44622 #038-43-1982 L1986 **OPH** *020 †35

MC COMBS, Michael M. 400 MEDICAL PARK DR, STE 103 44622 #041-77-1996, ▲ L1997 **IM** *020

MC FADDEN, Paul Wesley. 319 N TUSCARAWAS AVE 44622 #038-40-1971 L1971 **FM** *020 †18

MCQUILLAN, James Edmund. 205 HOSPITAL DR 44622 #028-34-1983 L1985 **ORS** *020 †40

MEHTA, Rajesh R. 847 BOULEVARD ST 44622 #495-22-1974 L1989 **DR** *020

MILLER, Matthew Todd. 400 MEDICAL PARK DR, STE 203 44622 #038-40-1999 L2004 **VS** *020 †85

MOORE, James David. 603 MONROE ST 44622 #038-45-1990 L1991 **FM FSM** *020 †18

MYERS, Susan Marie. 204 S BELLEVUE AVE 44622 #038-43-1993 L1995 **PD** *020 †55

NWIZU, Marcel Nnadike. 200 MEDICAL PARK DR, STE B 44622 #038-45-1990 L1991 **OBG** *020 †30

OLMOS, Anita S. 204 S BELLEVUE AVE 44622 #748-01-1972 L1978 **PD** *020

ORAFU, Chinyere Glorya. 420 S JAMES ST, STE D 44622 #038-44-1998 L2000 **OBG** *020 †30

OSSAKOW, Steven Jay. 340 OXFORD ST, STE 310 44622 #038-06-1980 L1987 **OTO HNS** *020 †45

PADRO-ACEVEDO, Efrain. 659 BOULEVARD ST 44622 #649-01-1956 L1960 **OBG** *071

PENEPACKER, Andrea. 204 S BELLEVUE AVE, CENTER OF AKRON 44622 #038-41-1998 L2003 **PD** *020 †55

PENTZ, Anthony Steven. 340 OXFORD ST, ORTHOPAEDIC 44622 #038-44-1981 L1983 **ORS** *020 †40

PHILLIPS, Matthew Wayne. 340 OXFORD ST, STE 220 44622 #038-44-1983 L1985 **GS** *020 †85

PIPOLY, Stephen William. 821 ANOLA ST, STARK MEDICAL SPECIALTIES 44622 #038-43-1982 L1983 **CD IM** *020 †20

PLESHINGER, John Michael. 659 BOULEVARD ST, UNION HOSPITAL 44622 #021-05-1989 L1990 **EM** *020 †16

PRINCE, Brenda S. 659 BOULEVARD ST 44622 #028-78-1990, ▲ L1992 **EM** *020 †16

RAFIQUE, Noman Mohd. 300 MEDICAL PARK DR, TRICOUNTY HEMATOLOGY & 44622 #704-16-1989 L1999 **ON HEM** *020 †20

RAMSEY, Kent Leroy. 340 OXFORD ST, STE 310 44622 #038-40-1987 L1992 **OTO HNS** *020 †45

RANDOLPH, Walter Watson. 420 S JAMES ST, STE C 44622 #038-43-1995 L1996 **OBG** *020 †30

RICHTERMAN, Ira Edward. 340 OXFORD ST, ORTHOPAEDIC 44622 #035-46-1991 L1997 **ORS** *020 †40

SAMSON, Jose R, Jr. 899 E IRON AVE 44622 #748-01-1960 L1975 **OBG** *020

SCHNEIDER, Philip Alan. 300 MEDICAL PARK DR, STARK RADIATION ONCOLOGY 44622 #038-41-1981 L1994 **RO** *020 †50

SHAH, Daksha Satish. ■ 44622 #495-23-1969 **PD** *100

SHAH, Pratima Yogendra. 659 BOULEVARD ST 44622 #495-17-1966 L1975 **AN** *020

SHAH, Yogendra A. 1000 N WOOSTER AVE 44622 #495-23-1959 L1974 **IM ON** *020

SMITH, Darrell Richard. 340 OXFORD ST, STE 310 44622 #038-06-1993 L1998 **OTO** *020 †45

STINE, Lucille Elizabeth. 897 E IRON AVE, TUSCARAWAS COUNTY HEALTH D 44622 #038-40-1976 L1978 **OBG** *020 †30

SWOGER, William V. 400 MEDICAL PARK DR, STE 103 44622 #038-75-1992, ▲ L1993 **PUD** *020

TEATER, Thomas L. 205 HOSPITAL DR 44622 #038-40-1988 L1991 **ORS** *020 †40

THOMA, Margaret Elizabeth. 659 BOULEVARD ST 44622 #047-06-1984 L1986 **EM GS** *020 †16

TRIPATHY, Ghana Shyam. ■ 44622 #495-13-1950 L1960 **GS OM** *071

VAN EPPS, Keith Chapin. 400 MEDICAL PARK DR, STE 103 44622 #047-06-1965 L1971 **IM OS** *020

WARREN, Norman Mickey. 340 OXFORD ST 44622 #051-01-1978 L1979 **FM** *020 †18

WEBER, Gregory Margileth. 420 S REEVES AVE 44622 #038-41-1972 L1972 **FM** *020 †18

WHERLEY, Andrew Jack. 658 BOULEVARD ST 44622 #038-40-1994 L1995 **OPH** *020 †35

WHERLEY, Benjamin J. 658 BOULEVARD ST 44622 #035-06-1965 L1966 **OPH** *020 †35

ZAMUDIO, Ricardo Ray. 659 BOULEVARD ST 44622 #018-03-1989 L1990 **EM** *020 †16

ZEMIS, Joseph N. 500 MEDICAL PARK DR # 203 44622 #012-05-1990 L1991 **GS EM** *020 †85

ZETS, Jeffrey Michael. 659 BOULEVARD ST, UNION HOSP 44622 #038-44-1988 L1989 **EM** *020 †16

DOYLESTOWN – WAYNE

GILCREST, Philip Norman. 220 N PORTAGE ST 44230 #038-40-1954 L1955 **GP FM** *020

PANDREA, Kristy Kay. ■ 44230 #038-44-2001 L2001 **PD** *100

SCROGGINS, Kathleen Mary. 80 N PORTAGE ST 44230 #038-45-1985 L1996 **FM** *020 †18

SOLTIS, Melissa Carin. ■ 44230 #038-44-2005 L2005 **IM** *012

STEINER, Scott Richard. ■ 44230 #038-44-2006 L2006 **OPH** *012

WENGER, Douglas Allen. 80 N PORTAGE ST 44230 #038-06-2002 L2002 **FM** *020 †18

DRESDEN – MUSKINGUM

SHOMAN, Alfred F, Jr. 101 W DAVE LONGABERGER AVE, STE 102-B 43821 #038-40-1964 L1964 **IM** *020

DUBLIN – FRANKLIN

ABAZA, Ronney. ■ 43017 #016-06-2000 L2000 **U** *100 †95

AHMAD, Asad Hayat. ■ 43016 #704-21-1997 L2000 **HMP** *100 †50

AKUSOBA, Eucharia Chinwe. ■ 43016 #690-15-2001 L2006 **IM** *100 †20

ALMEIDA, Ryan Matthew. ■ 43017 #038-06-2003 L2007 **AN** *020

AMESUR, Nirmalchandra R. ■ 43017 #495-01-1948 L1968 **EM FM** *071 †18,16

AMSTERDAM, Peter Bernard. 6905 HOSPITAL DR, STE 240 43016 #024-01-1990 L1997 **CD** *020 †20

ANANDAJEYA, Wendy. ■ 43017 #038-44-2008 *012

ANDRITSOS, Leslie Ann. ■ 43016 #048-02-1999 L2006 **HO** *100 †20

ANNADURAI, Ramesh. ■ 43017 #038-40-2008 *012

APLING, Elden Lew. 5070 BRADENTON AVE 43017 #038-40-1976 L1977 **IM** *020 †20

ARCHER, Thomas Patrick. 6670 PERIMETER DR 43016 #038-40-1992 L1993 **CD** *020 †20

ARLIN, Scott William. 6670 PERIMETER DR, STE 200 43016 #038-40-1999 L1999 **GE** *020 †20

ATIGRE, Philip. ■ 43016 #275-01-1996 L2006 **IM** *020

ATKURI, Lakshmi Venkata N. ■ 43016 #495-27-1991 L2007 **PD** *020

AUYANG, Elizabeth Yuenmei. ■ 43016 #038-41-2006 L2006 **FP** *012

BAIG, Mirza Nusrutullah. ■ 43016 #010-03-2003 L2003 **NS** *012

BALTURSHOT, Katherine. 5361 CROSSING LN 43016 #038-40-1997 L1998 **FM** *020 †18

BARR, James J. 250 W BRIDGE ST, STE 101 43017 #429-01-1980 L1984 **FM** *020 †18

BARTHOLOMEW, Deborah A. 4053 W DUBLIN GRANVILLE RD 43017 #051-04-1983 L1998 **OBG ATP** *020 †50,30

BASHIOUM, Ashley Laurel. ■ 43016 #036-08-2007 L2007 **PD** *012

BAUMAN, Dennis Jerry. 3900 STONERIDGE LN 43017 #024-01-1966 L1974 **CD IM** *020 †20

BAYRAM, Melike. ■ 43016 #016-06-2004 L2007 **CD** *012 †20

BECKMAN, Kenneth Alan. 5155 BRADENTON AVE, STE 200 43017 #038-40-1991 L1993 **OPH** *020 †35 ‡

BEHRENS, Sarah Arnold. 5050 BLAZER MEMORIAL PKWY, STE 100 43017 #038-40-1999 L2000 **PD** *020 †55

BEKAII-SAAB, Tanios Sam. 3900 STONERIDGE LN 43017 #605-01-1996 L2002 **HO** *020 †20

BEKAL, Yeshwanth P. ■ 43017 #495-04-1962 L1997 **FM GS** *020 †16

BENNETT, Chester A, Jr. ■ 43017 #038-40-1963 L1963 **AN** *071

BENNETT, Myla Nicole. ■ 43016 #038-40-2006 L2006 **GS** *012

BERAN, Robin Francis. 6017 POST RD 43017 #038-40-1979 L1984 **OPH** *020 †35

BHARMOTA, Satya. 6089 FRANTZ RD, STE 103 43017 #495-45-1964 L1976 **GP PTH** *020

BHINDER, Arvinder Singh. ■ 43016 #495-30-1996 L2007 **HO** *012

BICHSEL, David Garver. 6670 PERIMETER DR 43016 #038-41-1981 L1987 **CD IM** *020 †20

BILON, Ann M. ■ 43016 #038-40-1991 L1994 **P** *100

BLOOM, Michael Scott. 5155 BRADENTON AVE 43017 #038-40-1992 L1993 **OPH** *020 †35

BOLEY, Jerry Joe. 6670 PERIMETER DR 43016 #023-07-1990 L1996 **CD IM** *020 †20

BOLOURIAN, Reza. ■ 43016 #035-08-2003 L2005 **GS** *100

BOYLE, Brian Joseph. 250 W BRIDGE ST, STE 101 43017 #038-40-2003 L2003 **FM** *020 †18

BOYLES, Beth Ann. 6905 PERIMETER LOOP RD 43016 #017-20-1982 L1983 **OBG** *020 †30

BOYLES, Melissa Lee. 6905 PERIMETER LOOP RD 43016 #017-20-1988 L1991 **OBG** *020 †30

BRADY, Monique Sharae. ■ 43016 #038-40-2006 L2006 **FP** *012

BRESLER, Priscilla Ann. 3900 STONERIDGE LN 43017 #035-06-1984 L1998 **IM** *020 †20

BURGIN, Michael Alan. 3900 STONERIDGE LN 43017 #038-40-1978 L1979 **IM** *020 †20

BURNSIDES, David Dean. 5070 BRADENTON AVE 43017 #038-40-1978 L1979 **IM** *020 †20

BUSH, Charles Arthur. 3900 STONERIDGE LN 43017 #038-06-1965 L1965 **CD IM** *040 †20

BYRD, John Clark. 3900 STONERIDGE LN 43017 #004-01-1991 L2001 **HO** *020 †20

CACCHIO, Stacey Lynn. ■ 43017 #038-45-2006 L2006 **OBG** *012

CARDUCCI, Joseph. 250 W BRIDGE ST, STE 101 43017 #561-17-1981 L1985 **FM** *020 †18

CARPENTER, Kenneth Neff. 6350 FRANTZ RD STE E 43017 #038-40-1964 L1965 **GP** *020

CASEY, Anthony Michael. ■ 43016 #038-41-2006 L2006 **FP** *012

CASS, Mary Beth. 5040 BRADENTON AVE, CENTRAL OHIO PRIMARY CARE 43017 #038-40-1979 L1982 **PD** *020 †55

CASTELLANO, David. 6435 POST RD, OSU EYE PHYSICIANS & SURGE 43017 #032-01-1991 L1992 **OPH** *020 †35

CATTANEO, Stephen Michael. ■ 43017 #024-07-1963 L1970 **TS** *071 †85,90

CHAEL, Thomas C. ■ 43016 #017-20-1953 L1990 *071

CHAPIN, Eva Tilsworth. 7235 SAWMILL RD 43016 #065-06-1978 L1982 **DR NR** *020 †80 ‡

CHAPMAN, Donald Craig, Jr. ■ 43017 #038-41-1977 L1978 **EM PTH** *071

CHEN, Edward. 6708 PERIMETER LOOP RD 43017 #038-40-1996 L1997 **AN** *020 †05

CHEN, Naomi Hsiang. ■ 43016 #038-40-2006 L2006 **GS** *012

CHILUKURI, Meenapratap. ■ 43016 #495-65-1997 L2006 **IM** *012 †18

CHOPIN, Anne Elizabeth. ■ 43017 #028-34-2004 L2004 **PD** *100 †55

CHOUNG, Edward Yonghoon. ■ 43016 #038-40-2006 L2006 **DR** *100 †80

CHOWDHURY, Tim Imtiaz. 7211 SAWMILL RD, STE 101 43016 #160-01-1987 L2002 **PM APM** *020 †60

COBLER, Michael Robert. 6708 PERIMETER LOOP RD 43017 #038-40-1995 L1996 **AN** *020 †05

COLLINS, Elmer Clare. ■ 43017 #038-40-1955 L1955 **OPH** *071 †35

CONWAY, Devon Scott. ■ 43016 #038-06-2005 L2006 **N** *012

COOK, Tracy Lin. 6905 PERIMETER LOOP RD, STE 110 43016 #038-40-1993 L1996 **OBG** *020 †30

CUDNIK, Michael Thomas. ■ 43017 #038-45-2002 L2002 **EM** *100 †16

CULLIVAN, Jessica Quantz. ■ 43016 #038-44-2005 L2005 **FP** *012

DALSTROM, Elizabeth Grace. 5040 BRADENTON AVE 43017 #038-40-2005 L2005 **PD** *012

D'ANGELO, Karen Debora. 6350 FRANTZ RD, STE A 43017 #038-40-1997 L1998 **OBG** *020 †30

DAVAKIS, Nicholas James. 6905 HOSPITAL DR, STE 240 43016 #038-40-1981 L1983 **CD CCM** *020 †20

DAVIS, Aaron Edward. ■ 43016 #038-40-2005 L2005 **IM** *100

DAVY, Susan. 6350 FRANTZ RD, STE A 43017 #038-40-2001 L2001 **OBG** *020 †30

DEBBADI, Rammohan Rao. ■ 43016 #495-57-1968 L1982 **EM** *020

DE BOURBON, Ernest Bitela. 5060 BRADENTON AVE STE B 43017 #018-03-1991 L1997 **EM** *020

DEBROSSE, Charles Walter. ■ 43017 #038-41-2005 L2005 **PD** *012

DEMITA, Rachel Lauren. ■ 43016 #038-43-2005 L2005 **IM** *012

DERICK, Robert J. 5155 BRADENTON AVE, STE 200 43017 #016-11-1986 L1987 **OPH** *020 †35

DORNER, Brian Kenneth. 6425 POST RD STE 102 43016 #025-01-1996 L1997 **PS** *020 †65

DUNNAN, James Bernard. 5130 BRADENTON AVE STE A 43017 #038-40-1990 L1991 **FM** *020 †18

ELLIS, Thomas James. ■ 43016 #047-05-1992 L2007 **ORS** *020 †40

ENGLUND-KAYUHA, Elsa I. ■ 43017 #038-40-2001 *100

EVANS, Cynthia Beth. 4053 W DUBLIN GRANVILLE RD 43017 #038-40-1985 L1989 **OBG** *020 †30

FAHY, Ruairi Joseph. 3900 STONERIDGE LN 43017 #539-05-1988 L1996 **PCC** *020 †20

FANNING, Thomas Stewart. 6670 PERIMETER DR 43016 #038-40-1993 L1994 **IC** *020 †20

FISHER, John Allen. 6670 PERIMETER DR 43016 #038-40-1981 L1983 **CD IM** *020 †20

FITKIN, James Glenn. 6350 FRANTZ RD, STE E 43017 #038-40-1994 L1997 **FM** *020 †18

FLEISHMAN, Bruce Lawrence. 6905 HOSPITAL DR, STE 240 43016 #016-42-1980 L1981 **CD** *020 †20

FLEMING, Alfred Joseph. ■ 43016 #038-40-2004 L2004 **OTO** *012

FLORY, John Frederick. 5155 BRADENTON AVE, STE 150 43017 #038-40-1976 L1978 **PS HS** *020 †65

FLYNN, Dennis Michael. 6760 AVERY MUIRFIELD DR, STE A 43017 #038-40-1981 L1983 **FM** *020 †18

FONKEM, Ekokobe. ■ 43016 #038-75-2007, ▲ L2007 **N** *012

FROMKES, John Jos. 3900 STONERIDGE LN, STONERIDGE ENDOSCOPY CENTE 43017 #016-43-1970 L1971 **GE IM** *020 †20

GALLAGHER, Janice Marie. 5040 BRADENTON AVE 43017 #038-40-1979 L1993 **PD** *020 †55

GALLO, Samuel Anthony. 6620 PERIMETER DR, STE 100 43016 #038-41-1994 L2002 **OPH** *020 †35

GARRISON, George Harvey. 43016 #038-06-1945 L1945 **U** *071 †95

GELLEGANI, Rolando M. ■ 43016 #748-01-1967 L1998 **FM** *020

GEMMA, Steven Marc. ■ 43017 #048-02-1988 L2006 **P** *020 †75

GERACE, Charles Anthony. ■ 43017 #038-40-1972 L1972 **GS** *071 †85

GIBBS, Randolph Douglas. ■ 43016 #016-45-2006 **GS** *012

GINOCCHI, Kathryn L. 5050 BLAZER PKWY, STE 100 43017 #038-43-1998 L1999 **PD** *020 †55

GOOD, Arnold Paul. 6905 HOSPITAL DR, STE 240 43016 #035-09-1985 L1986 **CD IM** *020 †20

GOODLIVE, Susan Lynn. ■ 43017 #055-01-1997 L1998 **IM** *020 †20

GOODRICH, Suzanne Porter. ■ 43016 #017-20-2006 L2006 IM *012
GORDISH, Deborah Ann. 3900 STONERIDGE LN 43017 #038-41-1996 L1997 IM *020 †20
GOYAL, Navin. ■ 43016 #038-41-2003 L2007 AN *020
GRABER, Harry L. 3900 STONERIDGE LN 43017 #028-34-1964 L1965 CD IM *071 †20
GREVER, Michael Rhodes. 3900 STONERIDGE LN 43017 #041-12-1971 L1978 IM *020 †20
HACHWA, Bachar. 4908 APPLECROSS DR 43017 #875-02-1992 L2002 AN *020 †05
HACKETT, Francis Kevin. 6670 PERIMETER DR 43016 #038-40-1986 L1992 CD ICE *020 †20
HACKSHAW, Dawn Monica. 7275 SAWMILL RD 43016 #038-40-1992 L1994 PD *020 †55
HARMON, Thomas Louis. 6905 PERIMETER LOOP RD, STE 110 43016 #038-40-1988 L1990 OBG *020 †30
HARRIS, Dale Alan. 5995 HATHAWAY AVE 43016 #038-40-1992 L1998 AN PME *020
HENDERSON, Randall Eugene. ■ 43017 #038-40-1986 L1986 AN *020 †20
HENNESSY, Bruce Liam. 6670 PERIMETER DR, STE 200 43016 #038-40-1999 L1999 GE *020 †20
HERSEY, Stephen J. 7275 SAWMILL RD 43016 #038-40-2000 L2003 PD *020 †55
HESTAND, Harold Edgar. 5675 VENTURE DR, URGENT CARE 43017 #038-40-1974 L1974 PD *050
HEWITT, Geri Dawn. 4053 W DUBLIN GRANVILLE RD 43017 #038-40-1990 L1994 OBG *020 †30
HICKEY, Charles Jos. 5155 BRADENTON AVE, FL 2 43017 #038-40-1979 L1979 OPH *020 †35
HICKS, Kristin Lynn. ■ 43016 #038-43-2007 L2007 P *012
HIESTAND, Daniel C. 6708 PERIMETER LOOP RD 43017 #038-40-1984 L1990 AN CCM *020 †20,05
HOEGLER, Joseph John. ■ 43016 #038-41-2002 L2007 ORS *100
HOLINGA, Andrea Jean. ■ 43017 #038-40-2006 L2006 GS *100
HOMSY, James John. 7303 COVENTRY WOODS DR, PROSCAN IMAGING GAHANNA 43017 #035-46-1994 L2000 IM *030 †20
HOOVER, Robert James. 6670 PERIMETER DR, STE 140 43016 #041-14-1989 L1995 ICE CD *020 †20
HORST, Sara Nicole. ■ 43017 #038-40-2004 L2004 IM *100 †20
HOSPEL, Thomas Gerhard. 94 N HIGH ST, STE 200 43017 #056-05-1995 L1998 FM FSM *020 †18
HROMALIK, Larry Ray. 7500 HOSPITAL DR, DUBLIN METHODIST HOSPITA 43016 #038-40-1987 L1988 OBG *020 †30
HUGHES, Leon D. 8843 LOCHERBIE CT, 8843 LOCHERBIE COURT 43017 #011-04-1980 L1982 FM *020 †18
HUSSEIN, Abdel Hakim A. 6805 AVERY MUIRFIELD RD, STE 202 43016 #915-02-1982 L1996 N *020 †75
HUSTON, Robinette Jean. 5130 BRADENTON AVE, STE A 43017 #038-40-1991 L1992 FM *020 †18
JACKSON, Atiba Diarra. ■ 43016 #038-41-2004 L2004 ORS *012
JANICKI, Todd Anthony. ■ 43017 #035-06-2003 L2007 IM *100 †20
JENKINS, Joseph Ray. ■ 43017 #011-04-2007 L2007 PTH *012
JEWELL, Gregory Michael. ■ 43017 #038-40-1980 L1981 OM *030 †70,16
JOHNSON, Scott Weyburn. 5070 BRADENTON AVE 43017 #038-40-1976 L1976 IM *020 †20
JONES, Stuart R, Jr. 6905 PERIMETER LOOP RD, STE 110 43016 #038-40-1988 L1989 OBG *020 †30
KANTOR, Robert John. 6089 FRANTZ RD STE 10 43017 #028-34-1995 L2000 OM IM *030 †70
KARANFILOV, Boris I. 5378 AVERY RD, OHIO SINUS INSTITUTE 43016 #038-40-1997 L1999 OTO *020 †45
KASHUBECK, John Ray. ■ 43016 #038-40-1992 L1993 EM *020 †16
KATZ, Gary Ivan. ■ 43016 #038-40-1961 L1961 ORS *071 †40
KENNEDY, Deborah Jane. 6905 PERIMETER LOOP RD 43016 #038-43-1978 L1983 OBG *020 †30
KIM, Carolyn Young. ■ 43017 #038-44-2008 *012
KIM, Juen. ■ 43016 #025-01-1996 L2001 AI PDA *020 †55
KIRKPATRICK, Robert Bruce. 3900 STONERIDGE LN 43017 #028-02-1974 L1985 GE IM *050 †20
KIRSCHNER, Stephen David. 6905 HOSPITAL DR, STE 240 43016 #035-09-1974 L1975 CD *020 †20
KNIPFER, John Frantz. 6708 PERIMETER LOOP RD 43017 #038-45-1997 L2002 AN *020 †05
KOCHHEISER, Max Louis. 7239 SAWMILL RD STE 111 43016 #038-40-1956 L1956 R *071 †80
KOYAWALA, Manish I. ■ 43017 #495-01-1984 L1993 AN *020 †05
KRANTZ, Carl Arnold. 6905 PERIMETER LOOP RD, STE 110 43016 #038-40-1972 L1972 OBG *020 †30
KREGER, Cynthia Gail. 3900 STONERIDGE LN 43017 #038-40-1985 L1988 IM *020 †20
KRISHNA, Rajeev. ■ 43016 #038-40-2008 *012
LARRY, John Alan. 3900 STONERIDGE LN 43017 #035-15-1989 L1990 CD IM *020 †20
LEE, Jonathon Andrew. ■ 43016 #038-40-2002 L2002 DR *020 †80
LEIMBACH, Warren H. ■ 43017 #038-40-1946 L1946 NS OS *071 †25
LENOBEL, Scott S. ■ 43016 #038-06-2007 L2007 TY *012
LEVINE, Edward Jay. 3900 STONERIDGE LN 43017 #038-40-1981 L1983 IM GE *050 †20
LI, Kewa. 5050 BLAZER PKWY, STE 101 43017 #243-76-1982 L1999 IM *020 †20 ‡
LITTS, Patricia Streicher. 8035 LUCKSTONE DR, GRANT HOSPITAL 43017 #016-42-1991 L2005 OBG *020 †30
LOAR, Michael Carl. 5110 BLAZER PKWY 43017 #001-06-1981 L1984 PD *020 †55
MACKEY, Scott Thos. 6350 FRANTZ RD, STE E 43017 #038-40-1991 L1992 FM EM *020 †18
MAHONEY, Michele. 100 N HIGH ST STE A, RIVER'S EDGE PEDIATRICS 43017 #038-45-1999 L1999 PD *020 †55
MAIN, Robert Emerson. ■ 43017 #038-40-1943 L1943 PHP GS *071
MAKADIA, Neil Nathalal. ■ 43016 #166-03-2000 L2003 FM *100
MALOON, Jerry L. ■ 43017 #038-40-1964 L1964 LM *071
MAY, Harold Edward. ■ 43016 #004-01-1947 L1952 IM OM *071
MAYADEV, Angeli Shyam. ■ 43017 #038-44-2003 L2003 PM *100
MCALEER, Amanda Michelle. ■ 43017 #038-44-2007 L2007 OBG *012
MC GOVERN, William A. ■ 43017 #023-07-1959 L1985 IM AN *020
MC HALE, James Andrew. 5155 BRADENTON AVE, STE 200 43017 #038-40-2000 L2000 OPH *020 †35
MCNEILIS, James William. ■ 43016 #038-40-2003 L2003 RHU *012 †20
MEHTA, Tejas Ashvin. 6905 HOSPITAL DR, STE 240 43016 #038-44-1998 L2000 CD IC *020 †20
METZGER, Paul St Clair. ■ 43017 #038-40-1948 L1949 IM *020
MILLER, Carole Ann. 5745 NEWBANK CIR, STE 405 43017 #038-40-1966 L1966 NS *071 †25
MILLER, Steven Neil. 6905 PERIMETER LOOP RD, STE 200 43016 #038-75-1991 ▲ L1992 *020
MISCHLER, Mary Binder. 4351 DALE DR, STE 200 43016 #056-06-1986 L1987 IM *020 †20
MOBINUDDIN, Asma. 5040 BRADENTON AVE 43017 #038-40-1992 L1995 PD *020
MOORE, Francis Euclid. ■ 43017 #038-40-1954 L1954 AN *071 †05

MOSELEY, Mark Glenn. ■ 43016 #038-40-2002 L2005 EM *040 †16
MOSLENER, Juergen Hans. PO BOX 336 43017 #407-07-1954 L1963 PTH *020 †50
MOSLENER, Rotraud Ingrid. ■ 43017 #407-07-1956 L1961 P *071
MURNANE, Michael Robert. 6670 PERIMETER DR 43016 #038-40-1981 L1982 CD IM *020 †20
NALLURI, Venkata Suseela. 4757 VISTA RIDGE DR 43017 #495-50-1985 L1997 P *020 †75
NICOL, Steven John. 3900 STONERIDGE LN 43017 #038-40-1986 L1986 ON HEM *050 †20
ODORISIO, Nathan John. 3900 STONERIDGE LN 43017 #038-40-1998 L1999 MPD *020,50,55
ORAHOOD, Richard Cushman. 425 METRO PL N, STE 300 43017 #035-01-1963 L1974 GS *071 †85
ORLANDO, Richard Gerard. 5155 BRADENTON AVE, STE 200 43017 #038-40-1979 L1980 OPH EM *020 †35
OSTARCHVIC, Jamie Michael. 6708 PERIMETER LOOP RD 43017 #038-40-2002 L2006 AN *005
OSWALD, Jennifer Marie. 5040 BRADENTON AVE, OHIO CNTR FOR PEDIATRICS 43017 #038-45-1997 L1998 PD *020 †55
PANCHAL, Purvi Champak. ■ 43016 #011-03-2001 L2007 GE *100
PARAIL, Abraham Cherian. 6905 HOSPITAL DR, STE 240 43016 #056-06-1995 L1996 CD *020 †20
PARKER, John Robert. ■ 43016 #048-15-2007 L2007 OBG *012
PATEL, Bhairavi Mukesh. ■ 43016 #038-40-2002 L2002 IM *100 †20
PATEL, Rupenkumar Rameshb. ■ 43016 #496-41-1998 L2002 IM *100 †20
PAUL, Elaine Anne. 6905 PERIMETER LOOP RD 43016 #038-40-1981 L1981 OBG *020 †30
PELFREY, John David, III. 250 W BRIDGE ST, STE 101 43017 #038-43-1987 L1989 FM *020 †18
PERRY, Jan E. 5050 BLAZER PKWY, STE 100 43017 #038-40-1989 L1990 PD *020 †55
PETERSON, Eric Vincent. ■ 43017 #038-43-1998 L1998 DR *100
PIERSON, Christopher R. ■ 43016 #025-07-1997 L2007 NP *100 †50
PLACHTA, Laura Dolores. 5050 BLAZER PKWY, STE 100 43017 #025-12-1993 L1994 PD *020 †55
POPEHARMAN, Amy Loren. 3900 STONERIDGE LN 43017 #038-40-1989 L1993 PCC *020 †20
POVOSKI, Stephen Peter. 4019 W DUBLIN GRANVILLE RD 43017 #035-15-1989 L1990 GS *020 †85
PRASAD, Vinay. ■ 43016 #496-35-1992 L2007 ATP PP *020 †50
PUGH, Manoshi Bonnie. 5040 BRADENTON AVE 43017 #038-43-2001 L2001 PD *020 †55
PUNATI, Jaya Bharati. ■ 43016 #495-65-1997 L2004 PD *100 †55
RACKE, Frederick K. ■ 43016 #038-06-1994 L1997 PTH *020 †50
RAHMANIAN, Shiva Daneshma. ■ 43017 #038-40-2003 L2007 PCC *012 †20
RAMADAN, Yaser. 5613 TAYSIDE CIR 43016 #781-01-1981 L2000 P *020
RAMASWAMY, Bhuvaneswari. 4019 W DUBLIN GRANVILLE RD 43017 #495-59-1987 L2000 IM *020 †20
RANJITSINGH, Jebamoney D. ■ 43017 #495-16-1962 L1989 IM *020 †20
REARDON, Michael Edmond. 6708 PERIMETER LOOP RD 43017 #038-40-1991 L1993 AN *020 †05
REDDY, Pallavy Gopal. 7281 SAWMILL RD, STE 100 43016 #011-02-1998 L2005 END *020 †20
REDDY, Venu. ■ 43016 #041-02-1998 L2005 RNR *020 †80
REDMAN, Charles Richard. ■ 43016 #038-40-2006 L2006 MPD *012
RIALS, Seth James. 6905 HOSPITAL DR, STE 240 43016 #016-42-1984 L1999 CD *020 †20
RICCIARDO, Jennifer R. 7275 SAWMILL RD 43016 #038-40-2002 L2005 PD *020 †55
RIKABI, Nada A. ■ 43016 #528-01-1992 L2000 FP *012 †50
RITTENBERRY, Jennifer T. 7281 SAWMILL RD STE 100 43016 #048-02-2000 L2000 END *020 †20
RODGERS, Jeffrey Alan. ■ 43016 #038-75-1998, ▲ L2000 FM *020
ROMERO, Ricardo. 5725 LISCARROLL PL 43016 #038-40-1984 L1986 UCM *020 †18
ROSS, Jeffrey R. ■ 43017 #038-40-1988 GS *020
ROTHBAUM, Howard Russell. 3900 STONERIDGE LN 43017 #038-40-2002 L2002 IM *020 †20
ROTHE, James Robt. ■ 43017 #038-40-1966 L1966 DR RO *071 †80
ROTHERMEL, Kim Gage. 5040 BRADENTON AVE 43017 #016-01-1975 L1976 PD PHO *020 †55
RUSH, Adam Allen. ■ 43016 #038-40-2007 L2007 IM *012
SAAP, Liliana Juliette. 650 SHAWAN FALLS DR, AFFILIATED DERM 43017 #011-02-2000 L2005 D DS *020 †15
SAS, Jessica Ann. ■ 43016 #038-45-2005 L2005 MPD *012
SATTAR, Munazza Mian. ■ 43016 #025-07-1997 L2007 OPH *020
SCARBOROUGH, Dwight Allen. 650 SHAWAN FALLS DR, STE 105 43017 #005-12-1979 L1980 D DS *020 †15 ‡
SCHLESINGER, Larry Seth. 3900 STONERIDGE LN 43017 #033-06-1982 L2002 AM IG *050 †20
SCHMIDT, Helmut Siegfried. 4975 BRADENTON AVE 43017 #065-01-1964 L1968 SME P *020 †75
SCHMIDT, Markus Helmut. 4975 BRADENTON AVE, OHIO SLEEP MEDICINE INSTIT 43017 #038-43-1997 L1999 SME N *020 †75
SCHMITTHENNER, Jerry E. ■ 43017 #041-01-1948 L1965 IM *071
SCHROEDER, Martin Joel. ■ 43017 #056-05-1985 L2005 AN PME *020 †05
SEARCY, William Andrew. 7275 SAWMILL RD, NORTHWEST PEDIATRICS 43016 #041-12-1988 L2000 PD *020 †55
SEDMAK, Primrose Ann. 3900 STONERIDGE LN, STONERIDGE INTERNAL MEDICI 43017 #038-40-1989 L1991 IM *020 †20
SHADEL, Robert Floyd. 6089 FRANTZ RD, STE 102 43017 #016-11-1971 L1999 OM *020 †70,18
SHANKER, Kirti R.. ■ 43017 #495-65-2001 L2007 FP *012
SHERIDAN, James J. ■ 43017 #056-06-1945 GP *020
SHERMAN, Nathaniel, III. ■ 43017 #038-45-1982 L1983 IM OS *020
SHERZAI, Emal. 6568 DELBURN CT 43017 #286-13-1993 L2001 IM *100
SIDHU, Santokh Singh. ■ 43017 #038-45-2008 *012
SIRILLA, Rachel Michelle. ■ 43016 #038-06-2001 L2001 HO *012
SMITH, Tyler Gordon. ■ 43017 #031-01-2004 L2004 ORS *012
SOMANI, Pitambar. ■ 43016 #495-34-1960 L1982 PA CD *062
SPENCE, Patrick E. 6708 PERIMETER LOOP RD 43017 #048-02-1993 L1996 AN *020 †05
STAFFORD, Patricia Ann. 5156 BLAZER PKWY, STE 120 43017 #038-41-1987 L1988 R *020 †80
STANG, John Mc Naugher. ■ 43017 #038-40-1972 L1975 IM CD *040 †20
STANKO, Robin Gerald. 5325 RESERVE DR 43017 #038-40-1980 L1981 PM OM *020 †60
STANLEY, Alison Linda. ■ 43017 #038-40-2008 *012
STECHSCHULTE, Elizabeth H. 3900 STONERIDGE LN 43017 #038-40-1988 L1991 IM *020 †20
STEWART, William John. 6708 PERIMETER LOOP RD 43017 #038-40-1980 L1981 AN *020 †05
ST JOHN, Jean Capella. 5050 BLAZER MEMORIAL PKWY, PHYSICIANS, INC. 43017 #038-40-1988 L1990 PD *020 †55
STOCK, Michael Robt. 5935 WILCOX PL STE C 43016 #038-40-1982 L1984 FM *020 †18
STURGES, Blake Zachary. 6708 PERIMETER LOOP RD 43017 #038-40-2001 L2001 AN *020 †05
STYLES, Michael Joel. 6708 PERIMETER LOOP RD 43017 #041-07-1985 L1989 AN *020 †05

SUBBARAYAN, Rishi. 5046 CLOSEBURN CT 43017 #038-44-2008 *012
SUMMERHILL, Wendy L. 6760 AVERY MUIRFIELD DR #B 43017 #019-02-1996 L1997 FM *020 †18
SURESH, Aruna Albur. 7630 SAWMILL RD, STE 100 43016 #495-72-1982 L1994 END *020
SYBERT, David Allen. 6708 PERIMETER LOOP RD 43017 #038-40-1990 L1994 AN *020 †05
THOMAS, Jamie Elizabeth. ■ 43016 #038-43-2007 PD *012
THOMPSON, Kristin E. 5050 BLAZER PKWY, STE 147 43017 #038-40-1996 L1997 PD *020 †55
TICE, Frank David, IV. 6670 PERIMETER DR 43016 #038-40-1986 L1988 CD *020 †20
TRABUE, Jeffrey Dean. 4351 DALE DR 43017 #038-40-1982 L1983 FM *020 †18
TRAN, Charles. ■ 43016 #016-76-2001, ▲ L2007 *012
TROUT, Wayne C. 4053 W DUBLIN GRANVILLE RD 43017 #041-01-1990 L1991 OBG *020 †30
TYLKA, Eleanor M. ■ 43016 #010-02-1956 L1957 PD *071 †55
TZAGOURNIS, John Paul. ■ 43017 #038-40-1999 L1999 GE *020 †20
UPTMOR, Kristin Elizabeth. ■ 43016 #038-40-2007 L2007 OBG *012
UZMANN, Michael George. ■ 43017 #038-43-2007 L2007 IM *012
VAGNIER, Susan L. 6350 FRANTZ RD, STE A 43017 #038-40-1984 L1985 OBG *020 †30
VANEGAS, Christian Yezeni. ■ 43016 #038-43-2008 *012
VAUGHAN, James Alan. ■ 43016 #038-40-1962 L1962 N *071
VIRK, Subhdeep. ■ 43016 #495-03-1995 L2007 P *100
VOET, Sherry Lynne. 5130 BRADENTON AVE, STE A 43017 #038-40-1991 L1992 FM *020 †18
WALKER, Steven Scott. 6670 PERIMETER DR 43016 #038-41-1978 L1981 CD *020 †20
WALZ, Christina Joy. ■ 43016 #038-40-2003 L2003 PM *100
WALZ, Donald Victor. ■ 43017 #018-03-1947 L1960 CLP PTH *071 †50
WEILAND, Jeffrey Earl. 3900 STONERIDGE LN 43017 #038-40-1979 L1983 IM PUD *020 †20
WELLS, James Michael. ■ 43016 #047-20-2002 L2007 ORS *100
WENZKE, Jennifer Laura. 6670 PERIMETER DR 43016 #038-40-1998 L1999 IC *020 †20
WHEELER, Brett Alan. 5005 PARKCENTER AVE, COLUMBUS SURGICAL CENTER 43017 #038-40-1990 L1997 AN *020 †05
WHEELING, George Hamilton. ■ 43016 #041-12-1961 L1962 ORS *071 †40
WHISMAN, Gregory Michael. ■ 43016 #038-40-2003 L2005 FP *012
WHITEHEAD, Robert D. 6955 HOSPITAL DR, DUBLIN URGENT CARE 43016 #055-01-1990 L1991 FM FSM *020 †18
WILKINSON, John H. ■ 43017 #041-12-1950 L1951 IM *071
WILLIAMS, David Morgan. ■ 43016 #038-40-2000 L2000 NM *020 †80,28 ‡
WILLIS, John Wm. 7251 SAWMILL RD STE 10 43016 #038-40-1971 L1971 IM *020 †20
WININGER, David Alan. 3900 STONERIDGE LN 43017 #017-20-1989 L1995 ID *020 †20
WINTER, Sarah Lynn. 5533 ASHFORD RD 43017 #026-04-1987 L1999 PD *020 †55
WOLERY, Laura Lee. 4351 DALE DR, STE 200 43017 #038-40-1977 L1979 IM *020 †20
WONGCHAOWART, Nicholas T. ■ 43016 #038-44-2001 L2001 PTH *020 †50
WU, Jeffrey Kai. ■ 43016 #005-14-2007 *012
YEATES, Scott Walden. ■ 43017 #038-40-2008 *012
ZAMANI, Tanveer. ■ 43016 #704-16-1988 L2007 GS *012
ZEPP, Charles Egbert. ■ 43017 #038-40-1958 L1958 OPH *071 †35

EAST CLEVELAND – CUYAHOGA

ABRAMOFF, Hinda R M. 13951 TERRACE RD, HURON HOSPITAL 44112 #038-75-1980, ▲ L1981 AN PME *020 †05
ADAB, Hamidreza. 13951 TERRACE RD, HURON HOSPITAL 44112 #517-01-1994 L2007 IM *012
AGBAOSI, Oluwatoyin Jimmy. ■ 44112 #690-02-2003 L2006 IM *012
AGDINAOAY, Marlene A. 13916 EUCLID AVE, FIRST FLOOR 44112 #422-01-1988 L1997 MPD *020
AHMED, Naveed Ali. 13951 TERRACE RD, STE 230 44112 #704-21-1988 L2000 GS CCS *020 †85
AL BAEER, Mohammad. 13951 TERRACE RD, HURON HOSPITAL 44112 #875-01-2002 L2007 IM *012
ANUMULA, Sharada Reddy. 13951 TERRACE RD, HURON HOSPITAL 44112 #495-21-2005 L2007 IM *012
ASIAMAH, Kofi Awuah. 13951 TERRACE RD, HURON HOSPITAL 44112 #412-01-1999 L2005 IM *012
BADGER, Victor Obodai. 13951 TERRACE RD, HURON HOSPITAL 44112 #412-01-1998 L2004 IM *012 †20
BAIRAGI, Deepak Bhai. 13951 TERRACE RD, HURON HOSPITAL 44112 #672-02-2002 L2006 IM *012
BARONIA, Priya. 13951 TERRACE RD, DEPT OF GME 44112 #496-38-2003 L2006 IM *012
BEEHARILAL, Permanandsa J. ■ 44112 #010-03-2001 L2005 IM *100
BRATEANU, Andrei Calin. 13951 TERRACE RD 44112 #781-02-1990 L1999 IM *040 †20
BROBBEY, Andrew. 13951 TERRACE RD 44112 #412-01-1998 L2001 IM *100 †20
BROWN, Delorise. 1831 FOREST HILS BLVD #105 44112 #019-02-1974 L1976 IM END *020 †20
BROWNLEE, John David. 13951 TERRACE RD, HURON HOSP-DEPT SURGERY 44112 #038-45-1992 L1998 GS CCS *020 †85
CAMPBELL, Elaine Arnold. 13951 TERRACE RD 44112 #038-06-1993 L2000 DR *020
CHANG, Young Doo. 13951 TERRACE RD, HURON HOSPITAL 44112 #583-15-2002 L2007 IM *012
CHUNG, Raphael Shing Kwan. 13951 TERRACE RD, MERIDIA HURON HOSPITAL 44112 #462-01-1964 L1988 AS GS *020 †85
CRAIG, Thomas Lewis, III. 2114 NOBLE RD # 106 44112 #038-45-1986 L1988 IM *020
CRISTESCU, George Valenti. 13951 TERRACE RD, DEPT OF GME 44112 #781-01-2005 L2006 GS *012
CRUZ PICO, Christian Xavi. 13951 TERRACE RD, HURON HOSPITAL 44112 #319-07-2003 L2007 GS *012
DHILLON, Navdeep Kaur. 13951 TERRACE RD, DEPT OF GME 44112 #496-59-2004 L2006 IM *012 †20
DONCA, Ionel Zamfir. 13951 TERRACE RD, DEPT OF GME 44112 #781-03-1996 L2006 IM *012
EGRISELASHVILI, Anna M.. 13951 TERRACE RD, DEPT OF GME 44112 #912-02-1998 L2006 IM *012
FARINAS CHOPITE, Angel Fr. 13951 TERRACE RD, DEPT OF GME 44112 #935-01-2002 L2006 GS *012
FASS, Peter H. 1975 NOBLE RD, GENERAL ELECTRIC MEDICEAL 44112 #035-08-1976 L1994 OM IM *020 †20,16
FLEMING, James E. 13930 EUCLID AVE 44112 #010-03-1962 L1967 IM *075
FRIEDMAN, Ernest Harvey. 1831 FOREST HILLS BLVD 44112 #038-40-1956 L1956 P *020 †75
GHANAMAH, Mohammed Said M. 13951 TERRACE RD, HURON ROAD 44112 #575-01-1999 L2001 GS *100

GOLUBIC, Mladen. 13951 TERRACE RD, DEPT OF GME 44112 #957-01-1983 L2006 IM *012
HATOUM, Bechara. 13951 TERRACE RD 44112 #605-02-1972 L1977 AN PME *020 †05
HORWITZ, Marc Jeffry. 13951 TERRACE RD 44112 #038-40-1964 L1964 P PYA *020 †75
JANZEN, Mark Laverne. 13951 TERRACE RD, HURON HOSPITAL CCHS 44112 #422-01-2001 L2002 GS *100 †85
JYOTULA, Kavita Sridevi. 13951 TERRACE RD, HURON HOSPITAL 44112 #495-58-2001 L2006 IM *012
KAPLAN, Mark Eduardovich. 13951 TERRACE RD, HURON HOSPITAL 44112 #913-36-1992 L2007 IM *012
KARIM, Tariq. 13916 EUCLID AVE 44112 #704-04-1986 L2000 IM *020 †20
KARJALAINEN, Nina Sofia. 13951 TERRACE RD, HURON HOSPITAL 44112 #374-02-2005 L2007 GS *012
KAZDAN, Philip. 13951 TERRACE RD 44112 #038-40-1951 L1951 OPH *071 †35
KELLICI, Adriatik. 13951 TERRACE RD, HURON HOSPITAL 44112 #120-01-1991 L2006 IM *012
KOBAIVANOVA, Nana Abram. 13951 TERRACE RD 44112 #912-02-1997 L2006 IM *020 †20
KODJOE, Gladys. 13951 TERRACE RD, DEPT OF MEDICINE 44112 #412-01-2002 L2006 IM *012
KOTTON, Bernard. 13951 TERRACE RD 44112 #836-01-1963 L1978 OTO *020
LEE, Richy Tai On. 13951 TERRACE RD, DEPT OF GME 44112 #661-02-2006 L2006 GS *012
LIU, Xuwan. 13951 TERRACE RD, HURON HOSPITAL 44112 #243-65-1990 L2007 IM *012
MANTA, Dragos Nicolae. 13951 TERRACE RD, HURON ROAD HOSP-INTERNAL M 44112 #781-01-1997 L2000 PCC *012 †20
MARSHALL, Joy Margaret. 13951 TERRACE RD 44112 #038-06-1989 L1991 FM *020 †18
MIRESCU, Andra Silvina. 13951 TERRACE RD, HURON HOSPITAL 44112 #781-05-1999 L2006 IM *012
MOHAMMADI, Afshin. 13951 TERRACE RD, HURON HOSPITAL 44112 #517-05-1996 L2007 IM *012
NORMAN, Norris Adarkwa. 13951 TERRACE RD, HURON HOSPITAL 44112 #412-01-2003 L2007 IM *012
RABIN, Erwin Reynold. 13951 TERRACE RD, MERIDIA HURON HOSPITAL 44112 #028-02-1956 L1976 PTH *071 †50
SANDHU, Kirandeep Singh. 13951 TERRACE RD, HURON HOSPITAL 44112 #913-33-2001 L2007 IM *012
SAWYER, Royden K. 13951 TERRACE RD 44112 #038-06-1943 L1944 GP *071
SESHABHATTAR, Praveen. 13951 TERRACE RD, HURON HOSPITAL 44112 #495-58-2000 L2003 IM *100
SHAH, Vipuj Amit. 13951 TERRACE RD, HURON HOSPITAL 44112 #495-17-2000 L2006 IM *012
SINTEAN, Marius Emil. ■ 44118 #781-04-1988 L2000 AN *100
SMITH, Howard Rubin. 13951 TERRACE RD 44112 #024-05-1977 L1989 RHU IG *020 †20
SULLIVAN, Benjamin H, Jr. ■ 44112 #010-01-1938 L1962 IM GE *071 †20
TAMASKAR, Ila Ranjit. 13951 TERRACE RD 44112 #495-01-2000 L2002 IM *100 †20
TORRES MIRANDA, Ernesto V. 13951 TERRACE RD, DEPT OF GME 44112 #737-01-1997 L2005 GS *100
UMEDA, Yuji. 13951 TERRACE RD, DEPT OF GME 44112 #572-44-1983 L2006 IM *012
VENKATASUBRAMANIAN, S. 13951 TERRACE RD 44112 #495-44-1988 L1995 IM *020 †20
WILLIAMS, Walter Aloysius. 13951 TERRACE RD 44112 #649-14-1976 L1981 GS *020

EAST LIBERTY – LOGAN

HARDESTY, Carolyn L.. ■ 43319 #038-06-2006 L2006 FP *012
HESS, Helena Castro. ■ 43319 #847-04-1971 *100

EAST LIVERPOOL – COLUMBIANA

ABRAHAM, F Matthew. 425 W 5TH ST, EAST LIVERPOOL CITY HOSPIT 43920 #055-01-1992 L2007 IM EM *020 †20
AMATO, Jack Carl. 16687 SAINT CLAIR AVE 43920 #038-41-1973 L1973 OBG *020 †30
AZIZ, Ghulam Rabbani. 16218 SAINT CLAIR AVE 43920 #704-21-1989 L2001 IM PCC *020 †20
BATISH, Dharam Bir. 1100 PENNSYLVANIA AVE 43920 #495-29-1964 L1977 FM EM *020
BEATTY, Richard Wayne. 48462 BELL SCHOOL RD, STE A 43920 #038-43-1991 L1994 IM *020 †20
BEATTY, Robert Walker. 517 BROADWAY ST, STE 500 43920 #038-40-1967 L1986 IM CD *020 †20
CAHALL, Clement Albert. 205 W 6TH ST 43920 #041-15-1999 L2002 IM *020 †20
CASTRO, Orlando Roa. 16687 SAINT CLAIR AVE, ORLANDO R CASTRO MD INC 43920 #748-01-1967 L1976 GS *075 †85
CINELLI, Albert Burton. 244 W 5TH ST, EYE CARE ASSOCIATES INC 43920 #010-02-1963 L1967 OPH *071
CULANCULAN-MAPA, Helouise. 142 W 5TH ST 43920 #748-01-1967 L1974 PD A *020 †55
FAZAL, Najeed. 332 W 6TH ST, VA OUT PATIENT CLINIC 43920 #308-11-1986 L1994 IM *020 †20
GRAHAM, Wm Alexander, Jr. 50519 CARROLL RD, P O BOX 2740 43920 #030-06-1967 L1973 PTH DMP *020 †50
GUJRAL, Inder J S. 425 W 5TH ST 43920 #495-05-1967 L1981 ORS *020
HUSAIN, Mumtaz J. PO BOX 2346 43920 #704-02-1987 L1995 IM *020
HUTCHINSON, David Barry. ■ 43920 #062-01-1957 L1985 *020
JACKSON, J Fraser. ■ 43920 #041-12-1944 L1950 GP IM *071 †18
JAHDI, Nasrollah. 48462 BELL SCHOOL RD 43920 #422-01-1981 L1993 GE IM *020
JUNG, Tae Hui. 16687 SAINT CLAIR AVE, STE 204 43920 #025-07-1998 L2000 FM *020 †18
KUMAR, Satish Shrivastava. 15613 PINEVIEW DR, STE B 43920 #495-47-1974 L2004 PD *020
LACH, Joseph John. 15655 STATE ROUTE 170, STE B 43920 #017-20-1975 L1980 GS *020 †85
LARACUENTE, Benjamin. 16761 SAINT CLAIR AVE, TRI-STATE PULMONARY MEDICI 43920 #042-03-1988 L2001 PUD *020 †20
LATULIPPE, Steven Edward. 425 W FIFTH ST, EAST LIVERPOOL CITY HOSPIT 43920 #021-01-1991 L2000 PTH *020 †20
LENTINI, Ross Rosario. 414 E 5TH ST 43920 #308-11-1983 L1992 EM IM *020
LIM, Paul Won. 425 W 5TH ST DEPT DR 43920 #583-02-1960 L1974 DR *020 †80
MAPA, Manolo P. 129 W 4TH ST 43920 #748-01-1967 L1974 IM *020 †20
MC LAUGHLIN, Gerard P. 16728 SAINT CLAIR AVE, GERARD MCLAUGHLIN MD INC 43920 #165-04-1963 L1978 IM P *071
MITCHELL, Bradford K. 16687 SAINT CLAIR AVE, STE 102 43920 #041-02-1987 L1997 GS *020 †85
NARANG, Shashi Rani. 16687 SAINT CLAIR AVE, STE 202 43920 #495-12-1967 L1981 PD *020 †55
NARANG, Sherry. ■ 43920 #041-15-2005 PD *012

NAVARRA, Victoria G. 425 W 5TH ST 43920 #748-01-1968 L2007 **GS GP** *020 †85

O'BRIEN, Allan Adrian Jos. 101 E 6TH ST RM 405 43920 #065-01-1955 L1966 **GP PS** *071 †85

ORLANG, Lavern Edward. 501 JEFFERSON ST 43920 #025-07-1982 L1985 **FM** *020 †18

PARULKAR, Rekha Sunil. 205 W 6TH ST 43920 #495-92-1971 L1986 **PTH GP** *075

PARULKAR, Sunil Sitaram. 205 W 6TH ST 43920 #495-17-1967 L1969 **U** *020 †95

PORIATH, Annakutty K. 231 W 7TH ST 43920 #561-09-1969 L1980 **OBG** *020

PRICE, William Anthony. 416 JACKSON ST 43920 #038-44-1983 L1984 **P** *020 †75

PULIDO, Jonathan Vincent. ■ 43920 #038-44-2008 *012

REYNOSO-SORIANO, Zoraida. 129 W 4TH ST 43920 #748-08-1989 L1994 **IM FM** *020 †20

ROBERTSON, Bryan John. 15700 STATE ROUTE 170 43920 #055-01-1997 L2005 **IC** *020 †20

ROHELA, Hira B. 130 W 4TH ST 43920 #495-96-1972 L1978 **CD IM** *020

SINGH, Mohinder Pal. 425 W 5TH ST 43920 #496-17-1996 L2000 **IM** *020 †20

SINGH, Rajinder. 15898 SAINT CLAIR AVE, RAJ MEDICAL & ASSOCIATES 43920 #495-29-1972 L1981 **IM PUD** *075

SPAHIJA, Berislav. 16687 SAINT CLAIR AVE, STE 201 43920 #957-01-1989 L1999 **N** *020 †75

SPAHIJA, Mirjana. 16687 SAINT CLAIR AVE, STE 201 43920 #957-01-1990 L2002 **PM** *020 †60

STURM, Patrick Wm. 16761 SAINT CLAIR AVE 43920 #038-41-1978 L1979 **PUD CCM** *020 †20 ‡

THOMAS, Shery. 15688 STATE ROUTE 170, THOMAS & HUSAIN MEDICAL AS 43920 #495-31-1988 L1994 **IM** *020 †20

TIU, Marilyn C. 142 W 5TH ST 43920 #748-01-1982 L1996 **PD** *020 †55

TRETOLA, Robert James. ■ 43920 #021-05-1979 L1986 **GS** *020 †85

TURNER, Kenneth W. ■ 43920 #041-02-1952 L1953 **AN GP** *071

WENTZ, Christopher Miller. 15700 STATE ROUTE 170, STE D 43920 #041-12-1998 L2005 **CD** *020 †20

WILSON, Keith Alan. 244 E 5TH ST, EYE CARE ASSOCIATES INC 43920 #038-06-1982 L1985 **OPH** *020 †35

WRIGHT, John C Young, Jr. 48462 BELL SCHOOL RD, STE C 43920 #055-01-1978 L1979 **OBG OBS** *020 †30

ZIPFEL, Terrence Edward. 15613 PINEVIEW DR, STE C 43920 #041-12-1994 L1998 **OTO** *020 †45

EAST SPARTA – STARK

NICOLETTI, Rosanna R. 10025 CLEVELAND AVENUE S 44626 #654-01-1996 L1998 **FM** *020 †18

EASTLAKE – LAKE

KHAN, Taj Amjad. 36237 WINDWARD DR 44095 #495-21-1955 L1969 **GP GS** *020

PATEL, Pragna Bharat. ■ 44095 #038-44-2005 L2005 **OBG** *012

PUSKAR, Joseph. 34230 GLEN DR 44095 #038-06-1997 L2000 **FM** *020 †18

ROSPLOCK, Kenneth George. 741 ORIOLE DR 44095 #038-41-2008 *012

EATON – PREBLE

DARROW, John David P. 550 HALLMARK DR 45320 #038-41-1959 L1959 **FM GP** *071 †18

FERGUSON, Harold A, Sr. ■ 45320 #028-79-1957, ▲ L1957 **GP** *071

GADDIPATI, Jagadeesh C. 550 HALLMARK DR, CANCER AND BLOOD DISEASE 45320 #495-50-1974 L1991 **IM** *020 †20

KOCH, Christian Edward. 550 HALLMARK DR 45320 #038-41-1997 L1998 **FM** *020 †18

MANYAM, Vani. 550 HALLMARK DR, CANCER AND BLOOD DISEASE 45320 #495-11-1979 L1996 **ON** *020 †20

PETERSON, Chas De Wayne. 200 EATON LEWISBURG RD, TRANSITIONS 45320 #018-03-1974 L1986 **NM** *020 †18,28

VOSLER, John Albert. 200 LEWISBURG RD # 208, PREBLE COUNTY MED CTR 45320 #028-79-1955, ▲ L1955 **GP** *071

VOSLER, Scott Randall. 450B WASHINGTON JACKSON RD, STE 104 45320 #028-79-1982, ▲ L1983 **GP** *020

EDGERTON – WILLIAMS

BOERGER, Victor Ladson. ■ 43517 #017-20-1943 L1948 **GP** *071

KANURI, Rajya Lakshmi. 324 W VINE ST 43517 #495-50-1993 L2001 **FM** *020 †18

ROWAN, Stanley Eugene. 324 W VINE 43517 #038-45-1982 L1983 **FM** *020 †18

EDON – WILLIAMS

VASI, Zoher Nomanbhai. 110 E INDIANA ST, EDON MEDICAL CLINIC 43518 #495-01-1971 L1980 **GP ADM** *020 ‡

ELIDA – ALLEN

PAJOR, Kalman O. ■ 45807 #407-16-1948 L1960 **PTH** *071 †50

ELKTON – COLUMBIANA

SIHA, Victor Labib. 8730 SCROGGS RD 44415 #330-02-1965 L1970 **IM NEP** *020

ELMORE – OTTAWA

DEUBNER, David Carl. 14710 W PORTAGE RVR STH RD 43416 #035-45-1971 L1992 **OM GPM** *030 †70

KIEFFER, Edward Wm. 210 JACKSON ST 43416 #038-40-1954 L1954 **FM OM** *071

MC TAGUE, Jerome Anthony. 19740 W STATE ROUTE 105 43416 #028-02-1991 L1992 **EM** *020 †16

NARRA, Bhaskara Rao. 210 JACKSON ST 43416 #495-65-1966 L1974 **GP** *020 †18

NARRA, Ravi. 210 JACKSON ST, ELMORE MEDICAL ASSOC. 43416 #038-43-1996 L1998 **IM** *020 †20

RAI, Krishna Prasad. 210 JACKSON ST, C/O ELMORE MEDICAL ASSOCIA 43416 #496-01-1987 L1995 **FM** *020 †18

ELYRIA – LORAIN

ABBOUD, Walid Afif. 1260 ABBE RD N 44035 #913-35-1998 L2000 **IM** *020 †20

ABOU HAIDAR, Antoinette S. 108 BRIAR LAKE DR 44035 #605-02-1989 L1999 **FM** *020 †18

ABRIGO, Amada E. ■ 44035 #748-01-1962 L1970 **PD** *071 †55

ABUMERI, Sana Hassan. 860 E BROAD ST 44035 #528-01-1986 L1992 **IM** *020 †20

AHMED, Iqbal. 125 E BROAD ST, NORTH COAST 44035 #495-29-1971 L1981 **GE IM** *020 †20

AHN, Byong Jik. 347 MIDWAY BLVD, STE 110 44035 #583-03-1964 L1977 **P** *020

BAKER, Vickie Ehrlich. 824 E BROAD ST 44035 #038-43-1994 L2001 **FM** *020 †18

BALDOZA, Roger L. 511 S ABBE RD, STE C 44035 #748-08-1963 L1971 **AMI IMG** *020

BARKER, Bradley Don. 1120 E BROAD ST, P O BOX 30 44035 #038-45-1988 L1989 **FM** *020 †18

BASILE, Karen Elizabeth. 1900 W RIVER RD N 44035 #038-06-1992 L1993 **PDR** *020 †80

BENIT, Meir. 661 E RIVER ST 44035 #550-01-1968 L1973 **GYN** *020

BURRELL, Joel Brion. 511 S ABBE RD, STE C 44035 #041-13-1987 L1991 **N OS** *075

CALOPE, Petrus. 412 E RIVER ST 44035 #748-01-1970 L1975 **GP IM** *020

CARANDANG, Celso M. 184 WINDBROOK CT 44035 #748-01-1957 L1969 **GS ON** *020 †85

CARROCCIO, James. 1120 E BROAD ST, P O BOX 30 44035 #038-75-1994, ▲ L1995 **FM** *020 †18

CARSON, Dennis Edward. 1120 E BROAD ST, P O BOX 30 44035 #038-45-1988 L1989 **FM** *020 †18

CHARI, Ravi Vedantum. 210 E BROAD ST 44035 #038-41-1992 L1995 **GS** *020 †85

CINQUEMANI DENGEL, Polly. 1260 ABBE RD N 44035 #005-12-1978 L1980 **IM EM** *020 †20

COHEN, Chad Reev. 1900 W RIVER RD N 44035 #038-40-1976 L1976 **DR** *020 †80

CRAMER, Jack Wm. 1120 E BROAD ST, P O BOX 30 44035 #018-75-1977, ▲ L1978 **FM** *020 †18

CULLEN, Craig Edward. 160 CLEVELAND ST 44035 #005-14-1972 L1977 **GP P** *020

DACHA, Usha Rani. 125 E BROAD ST, STE 119 44035 #495-21-1971 L1981 **NEP** *050 †20

DAKTERS, Juris George. 135 HILLCREST LN 44035 #038-06-1962 L1962 **NS** *020 †25

DAVID, Ruppert. 1900 W RIVER RD N 44035 #033-05-1974 L1978 **R NR** *072 †80

DE LA PENA, Raymundo R. 412 E RIVER ST 44035 #649-02-1953 L1956 **FM GS** *071

DENGEL, Fredrich Harold. 1900 W RIVER RD N 44035 #005-12-1978 L1980 **DR** *020 †80

DHILLON, Harmohinder S. 125 E BROAD ST, STE 202 44035 #495-29-1992 L1997 **IM** *020 †20

DHINGRA, Rahul Kumar. 125 E BROAD ST, STE 215 44035 #495-34-1975 L1986 **CD** *020 †20

DONASTORG, Rosa A. ■ 44035 #308-01-1962 L1976 **PTH** *020 †50

DOROBEK, Ann Marie. 630 E RIVER ST, EMH REGIONAL MEDICAL CENTE 44035 #038-06-1998 L2002 **FM** *020 †18

EKSTEIN, Jeffrey Michael. 1900 W RIVER RD N 44035 #024-05-1990 L1991 **EM** *020 †16

EPPLEY, Robert De Venney. ■ 44035 #041-02-1955 L1960 **P CHP** *071

ESCURO, Ruben Sales. 41201 SCHADDEN RD, STE 2 44035 #748-02-1981 L1986 **HEM ON** *020 †20

FARHAT, Naim Zreik. 125 E BROAD ST, GATES MEDICAL BUILDING STE 44035 #875-01-1980 L1985 **CD IM** *020 †20

FAWZY, Ahmed Moustafa. 1170 E BROAD ST, # 2 44035 #915-08-1980 L1999 **NEP** *020 †20

FLORO, Francisco S. 455 GRISWOLD RD 44035 #748-02-1957 L1967 **IM PUD** *071

FLORO, Norman A. 455 GRISWOLD RD 44035 #038-41-1989 L1994 **IM** *020 †20

FRANK, James Dennis. 1900 W RIVER RD N 44035 #038-43-1982 L1986 **DR** *020 †80

GHANMA, Manhal Amjad. 630 E RIVER ST 44035 #605-01-1974 L1978 **ORS OS** *020 †40

GRESSEL, Michael Gregory. 303 CHESTNUT COMMONS DR 44035 #038-41-1978 L1982 **OPH** *020 †35

GUPTA, Parshotam Chand. 860 E BROAD ST, STE 1 44035 #495-43-1973 L1978 **AN** *020 †05

HAJI, Abdul Qadir. 125 E BROAD ST, STE 305 44035 #495-51-1987 L2000 **ICE CD** *020 †20

HAMPOLE, Vagesh M. 125 E BROAD ST, STE 202 44035 #495-09-1971 L1978 **RHU IM** *020 †20

HANSFORD, Carmen K. 1170 E BROAD ST, STE 101 44035 #026-04-1981 L1985 **PD NPM** *020 †55

HEIMANN, Priscilla. 630 E RIVER ST 44035 #038-44-1987 L1992 **PTH** *020 †50

HUEY, Diane. 1260 N ABBE RD, CCF ELYRIA INTERNAL MEDICI 44035 #038-40-1975 L1988 **IM IMG** *020 †20

IYER, Sridhar K. 125 E BROAD ST, STE 119 44035 #495-53-1983 L1990 **PUD** *020 †20

JAGIELSKI, Maciej Bogdan. 125 E BROAD ST 44035 #759-04-1959 L1968 **OBG** *020 †30

KALVA, Sadasiva Reddy. 630 EAST AVE 44035 #495-57-1973 L1978 **AN** *020 †05

KANTHARAJ, Belagodu N. 41201 SCHADDEN RD, STE 2 44035 #495-09-1973 L1981 **ON IM** *020 †20

KEARNEY, Francis Michael. 1900 W RIVER RD N 44035 #041-09-1980 L1986 **DR** *020 †80

KESHOCK, Maureen. 630 EAST AVE 44035 #038-44-1989 L1993 **AN** *020 †05

KHERANI, Ismet Razak. 125 E BROAD ST, STE 202 44035 #495-17-1969 L1974 **GP** *020

KHERANI, Razak Usman. 125 E BROAD ST, STE 305 44035 #495-17-1967 L1973 **CD IM** *020 †20

KIM, Yun Hwa. 511 S ABBE RD, STE E 44035 #583-10-1962 L1975 **GP** *020

KODSY, Maher Saad. 630 EAST AVE 44035 #915-04-1985 L1997 **AN** *020 †05

KOVACH, Corie Lynn. 125 E BROAD ST, STE 218 44035 #038-44-1994 L1998 **OBG** *020 †30 ‡

KSENICH, Nicholas John. 1120 E BROAD ST, P O BOX 30 44035 #038-40-1990 L1991 **FM** *020 †18

KULASINGHAM, S Michael. 1900 W RIVER RD N 44035 #038-44-1994 L1998 **DR** *020 †80

LANGER, Michael Monroe. 125 E BROAD ST, STE 305 44035 #041-77-1997, ▲ L2005 **CD** *020 †20

LEE, Duck Kee. 2106 N RIDGE RD 44035 #583-10-1965 L1976 **GP** *020

LEE, Suk W. ■ 44035 #583-02-1962 L1972 **OBG** *071

LENDER, Joyce Ann. 630 E RIVER ST 44035 #038-06-1987 L1987 **D** *020 †15

LISI, James Edward. 125 E BROAD ST, STE 114 44035 #038-45-1989 L1991 **GE IM** *020 †20

LITAM, Patrick P. 41201 SCHADDEN RD, STE 2 44035 #748-10-1981 L1991 **HO** *020 †20

LOCKHART, Eric Richard. 1120 E BROAD ST, P O BOX 30 44035 #038-40-1987 L1988 **FM** *020 †18

LYNK, Rodney Hamilton. 1180 E BROAD ST 44035 #010-03-1971 L1980 **OPH OS** *020 †35

MARTINEZ, Eduardo P. 1900 W RIVER RD N 44035 #038-43-1978 L1979 **DR** *020 †80

MASRI, Ramiz Saleem. 125 E BROAD ST STE 218 44035 #915-04-1966 L1975 **OBG** *020 †30

MATEEGA, Arthur L B. 160 CLEVELAND ST 44035 #905-01-1989 L1997 **IM** *020 †20

MC CORMAC, John Anthony. 1900 W RIVER RD N 44035 #038-06-1999 L2004 **DR** *020 †80

MC DONALD, Douglas G. 630 E RIVER ST, EMH REGIONAL MEDICAL CENTE 44035 #038-06-1989 L1990 **EM GP** *020

MC GOWAN, Commer Kellie. 140 TAFT AVE 44035 #005-17-1962 *100
MC MILLAN, David Wm. 860 E BROAD ST, STE 1 44035 #051-04-1983 L1984 AN *020 †05
MEHTA, Govindram K. 125 E BROAD ST, STE 322 44035 #495-23-1973 L1983 OTO *020 †45
MEHTA, Hemendra J. 125 E BROAD ST STE 202 44035 #495-17-1960 L1973 IM CD *071 †20
MICLAT, Aurora T B. 1060 N ABBE RD 44035 #748-02-1970 L1975 IM *071
MIHALIK-POTOCZAK, Karen. 125 E BROAD ST STE 201 44035 #038-45-1989 L1991
    OBG *020 †30
MIKHAIL, Fayez Soliman. 125 E BROAD ST STE 101, THE GATES MEDICAL BUILDING 44035
    #915-05-1972 L1979 TS *020 †85,90
MILLER, Cathy. 1900 W RIVER RD N 44035 #021-06-1982 L1983 R NR *020 †80
MISTRY, Niraj C. 125 E BROAD ST, STE 215 44035 #495-76-1990 L1998 IM *020 †20
MOORE, Richard Allen. 507 E RIVER ST 44035 #008-01-1961 L1963 PD *071 †55
MORLEY, Wynne Allison. 303 CHESTNUT COMMONS DR 44035 #041-02-1989 L1994
    OPH *035
NADKARNI, Vivek. 1170 E BROAD ST, STE 2 44035 #041-15-2000 L2005 NEP *100 †20
NAEEM, Mohammad Akbar. 630 E RIVER ST 44035 #704-01-1963 L1972 FM *020 †18
NAIR, Sivaramakrishnan S. 125 E BROAD ST #495-01-1970 L1976 IM GE *020 †20
NELSON, Dvora Yisrael. 125 E BROAD ST, STE 219 44035 #005-02-1997 L1999 GS *020 †85
NICHOLS, William Franklin. 125 E BROAD ST 44035 #038-40-1957 L1957 GS *071 †85
NIXON, Kristi Ann. 125 E BROAD ST 44035 #038-44-1997 L2001 OBG *020
ONYENEKE, Chuka D. 160 CLEVELAND ST 44035 #305-01-1990 L1993 FM *020
O'SHAUGHNESSY, Chas David. 125 E BROAD ST STE 305, NORTH OHIO HEART CENTER,
    I 44035 #038-43-1976 L1977 IC CD *020 †20
PASCUAL, Felix Hernando. 1185 GULF RD 44035 #748-07-1956 L1963 DR *071
PATEL, Dineshchandra G. 630 EAST AVE 44035 #495-23-1971 L1976 AN *020
PATEL, Dinubhai C. ■ 44035 #495-23-1972 L1979 GE IM *071 †20
PEDRO, Abraham Olanrewaju. 1120 E BROAD ST, P O BOX 30 44035 #690-01-1982 L1999
    FM *020 †18
POTOCZAK, Douglas John. 1120 E BROAD ST, P O BOX 30 44035 #038-45-1989 L1990
    FM PD *020 †18
RAFFERTY, Thomas Dave. 125 E BROAD ST #038-06-1980 L1981 GS VS *020 †85
RAMADUGU, Ashok. 661 E RIVER ST, # C 44035 #495-09-1982 L1996 PUD CCM *020 †20
RAO, Kancherla Srinivasa. 125 E BROAD ST 44035 #495-57-1973 L1981 P *071
REFFELL, Shanna Jean. ■ 44035 #038-40-2008 *012
RIBOVICH, Martin Lee. 41201 SCHADDEN RD, COMMUNITY HEALTH PARTNERS 44035
    #038-40-1991 L1996 RO *020 †80
ROBINSON, Allison Arnold. 511 N ABBE RD STE G 44035 #038-06-1982 L1985 IM ADM *020
ROHIRA, Lalsingh P. 347 MIDWAY BLVD STE 306, MIDWAY PLAZA BUILDING 44035
    #495-01-1970 L1978 P *020
ROMERO, Lynne D. 303 CHESTNUT COMMONS DR 44035 #748-01-1975 L1983 PD *020 †55
ROY, Somnath Dandapat. 125 E BROAD ST, STE 122 44035 #495-54-1992 L1999 IM *020 †20
SABOORI, Mehran. 41201 SCHADDEN RD, THE IRELAND CANCER CENTER 44035
    #035-09-1996 L2007 RO *020 †80
SCHAEFFER, Matthew S. 10325 DEWHURST RD, OHIO MED GROUP 44035
    #038-40-2000 L2001 FM FSM *020 †18
SEO, Monica Eunjoo. 1260 N ABBE RD, CLEVELAND CLINIC 44035 #038-06-1996 L1998
    IM *020 †20
SHELDON, Donald Stafford. 630 E RIVER ST 44035 #038-41-1978 L1979 EM FM *030 †16,18
SIDLOSKI, Jay E. 41201 SCHADDEN RD, STE 2 44035 #018-75-1997, ▲ L1999 IM *020 †20
SIEW, Lieng Kong. 630 E RIVER ST 44035 #385-02-1967 L1974 OBG *020 †30
SIGALOVE, William Herman. 1100 N ABBE RD 44035 #016-42-1959 L1968 HEM IM *020
SINGH, Chandra Vir. 125 E BROAD ST, STE 119 44035 #495-41-1976 L2002 PCC *020 †20
SINGH, Deeppreet. 630 E RIVER ST 44035 #495-29-1994 L1998 IM *020 †20
STAMATIS, Bonnie. 860 E BROAD ST 44035 #038-45-1989 L1992 IM *020
STARR, Allan Floyd. 630 E RIVER ST, EMH REG MED CTR EMGY DEPT 44035
    #038-40-1975 L1975 EM *020 †85,16
STOUT, David Paul. 1900 W RIVER RD N 44035 #043-01-1987 L1991 DR *020 †80
SUESS, Steven Hermann. 630 E RIVER ST 44035 #038-43-1981 L1984 FM EM *020 †18
TABBAA, Mousab. 125 E BROAD ST, NORTH COAST 44035 #875-01-1981 L1986
    GE IM *020 †20
THOMAS, Roy Hamilton. 850 E BROAD ST, THE ELYRIA EYE CLINIC INC 44035
    #038-06-1980 L1986 OPH *020
VAN DERVORT, Robert S. 507 E RIVER ST, ELYRIA RESP PAIN CLINIC 44035
    #041-12-1946 L1957 OS AN *071 †05
VICARIO, Deborah Anne. 10325 DEWHURST RD 44035 #038-06-1997 L1998 FM *020 †18
VISWANATH, Basavarajappa. 125 E BROAD ST, STE 209 44035 #495-99-1973 L1979 FM *020 ‡
WANESS, Abdelkarim. 10325 DEWHURST RD 44035 #895-01-1986 L1993 IM *020 †20
WARNER, Keith M. 125 E BROAD ST, STE 219 44035 #020-12-1979 L1985 GS *020 †85
WEISS, Robert Alan. 303 CHESTNUT COMMONS DR, DRIVE ECC-2 44035 #028-02-1974 L1979
    PD ATP *050,55
WILDEN, Robert Thos. 860 E BROAD ST, STE 1 44035 #038-45-1985 L1987 AN *020 †05
WILLIAMS, Thomas E. 992 N ABBE RD 44035 #038-41-1955 L1955 FM PD *071 †18
WINTER, Karen Louise. 6012 FORD RD 44035 #041-07-1984 L1989 FM *020 †20
WISLER, Kevin Eugene. 125 E BROAD ST STE 302 44035 #038-41-1982 L1984 GYN *020 †30
WOISNET, Timothy James. 1900 W RIVER RD N 44035 #038-43-1984 L1985 DR *020 †80
YATES, Shane Allan. 630 EAST AVE 44035 #038-40-1994 L1996 AN *020 †05

ENGLEWOOD – MONTGOMERY

CHUNDURI, Ramamohan. 1230 UNION BLVD 45322 #495-11-1968 L1974 IM EM *020 †20
CORCORAN, Mark Eric. 211 W NATIONAL RD, STE 1 45322 #038-45-1985 L1986 FM *020 †18
DOMINGUEZ, Kathleen Marie. ■ 45322 #007-02-2004 L2004 GS *012
GREENWOOD, Jeffrey Edward. ■ 45322 #038-45-2005 L2005 EM *012
HAMILTON, Michael Edward. 5 N MAIN ST 45322 #030-06-1972 L1973 FM *020 †18
HAMMON, Jerry L. ■ 45322 #038-40-1952 L1952 GP MDM *071
HUEY, James Robt, Jr. 5 W WENGER RD STE D 45322 #020-12-1966 L1976 OBG OBS *020 †30
LONGENECKER, Douglas P. 7074 SALEM CROSSING PL 45322 #038-41-1964 L1964
    MDM FM *030 †18
LOVING, Marjorie Lynn. 20 W WENGER RD, STE 3 45322 #038-45-1993 L1994 FM *020 †20
MARGOLIS, Robert Michael. 50 HILLSIDE CT 45322 #028-34-1980 L1981 PUD CCM *020 †20
MC DOWELL, Claire. 120 W WENGER RD, NORTHWEST DAYTON PEDS 45322
    #038-45-2003 L2003 PD *020 †55
MERY, Albert M. ■ 45322 #007-02-1943 L1943 OM *071

MESKER, Dennis Allen. 211 W NATIONAL RD, STE 1 45322 #038-45-1990 L1991
    FM EM *020 †18
MULLENNIX, Dixie Rene. 20 W WENGER RD, STE 3 45322 #038-45-1999 L1999 FM *020 †18
PERRY, Travis Lamont. ■ 45322 #036-08-1999 L2007 CCS *100
WEPRIN, Stuart Alan. 20 W WENGER RD 45322 #748-40-1974 L1975 OBG *020 †30

ENON – CLARK

BAKER, Thomas Edward. ■ 45323 #038-45-2001 L2004 EM *020 †16
DAHDAH, Salim Oblen. 340 E MAIN ST, STE A 45323 #429-01-1976 L1979 CD IM *020 †20
FARLEY, Jane Diane. 240 ENON RD 45323 #038-45-1992 L1994 FM *020 †18
FAZIO, G Thos Jos. 7185 DAYTON RD 45323 #038-40-1962 L1962 FM IM *020 †18
KABIR, Md Anwarul. 340 E MAIN ST, STE A 45323 #160-06-1989 L1998 CD *100 †20
VALLS, Francisco Xavier. 340 E MAIN ST, STE A 45323 #429-02-1999 L2005 IM *020 ‡
VANDERGLAS, Joel. ■ 45323 #041-12-1960 L1961 FM *071 †18
VENKATESH, Latha. 340 E MAIN ST, STE A 45323 #496-20-1989 L1999 IM *020 †20
YANG, Han Mok. 340 E MAIN ST, STE A 45323 #583-01-1966 L1975 IM *020

EUCLID – CUYAHOGA

ARCHACKI, Stephen Raymond. 26250 EUCLID AVE, FAMILY PHYSICIANS 44132
    #038-06-1994 L1995 IM *020 †20
BARRETT, Timothy Scott. 18599 LAKE SHORE BLVD, MACDONALD COMMUNITY OB-
    GYN 44119 #016-43-1977 L1979 OBG *020 †30
BELL, Herbert S. 18901 LAKE SHORE BLVD 44119 #021-01-1953 L1960 NS *071 †25
BELLO, Victor Manuel. 99 NORTHLINE CIR, STE 101 44119 #187-01-1969 L1977 OPH *020 †35
BERTSCH, John Patrick. 26250 EUCLID AVE, STE 625 44132 #038-45-1987 L1989 FM *020 †18
BEYLINSON, Alexander Mark. 26250 EUCLID AVE, STE 415 44132 #913-29-1987 L2002
    GS *100
BORDEN, Lester Stuart. 99 NORTHLINE CIR, STE 100 44119 #035-09-1969 L1975
    ORS *020 †40
BOTTI, Robert Ernest. 25701 N LAKELAND BLVD, STE 101 44132 #041-01-1954 L1961
    CD IM *040 †20
CASTANEDA, Juanita Marzan. 27691 EUCLID AVE 44132 #748-07-1977 L1983 IM *020
CHEN, Pao-Chiu. ■ 44143 #385-03-1965 L1980 GP *071
COGAN, David Paul. 18599 LAKE SHORE BLVD 44119 #038-03-1973 L1980 IM *020 †20
COLLINGS, Matthew Ward. 26250 EUCLID AVE STE 415, VPA-CLEVELAND 44132
    #051-04-1970 L1973 IM IMG *071 †20
CRITCHFIELD, Frank H, Jr. ■ 44119 #041-12-1947 L1954 OBG *071 †30
CUMMINS, Kevin Strattan. 26300 EUCLID AVE, STE 632 44132 #038-06-1978 L1981
    IM *020 †20
CUNNINGHAM, Michael John. 18599 LAKE SHORE BLVD, UNIVERSITY HOSPITALS
    HEALT 44119 #049-01-1982 L1998 CD IM *020 †20
DALTON, Charles S, Jr. ■ 44117 #038-40-1951 L1951 AN OS *071
DI CELLO, Michael Andrew. 25100 EUCLID AVE STE 200 44117 #016-43-1968 L1969
    PM PMM *020 †60
DONCA, Mihaela. 503 E 200TH ST STE 102 44119 #781-03-1995 L2003 IM *020 †20
FANNEY, Grafton C, Jr. 26300 EUCLID AVE 44132 #028-02-1947 L1951 PD *071 †55
FORSYTHE, William Elmer. 18901 LAKE SHORE BLVD 44119 #038-06-1935 L1935 U *071 †95
FRITZ, Jason Scott. 23001 EUCLID AVE, RM 14 44117 #041-13-2003 L2005 PCC *012 †20
FULLER, Daniel Guy. 26250 EUCLID AVE STE 611 44132 #038-06-1975 L1977 PD *020 †55
FUREY, J Geo. 25701 N LAKELAND BLVD 44132 #035-01-1947 L1955 ORS *071 †40
GROSS, Gilbert L. 20690 LAKELAND BLVD, BUSINESS HEALTH CLINICS 44119
    #024-01-1949 L1952 AN *071 †05
HACKER, Vernon D. ■ 44117 #038-06-1946 L1946 GS *071 †85
HAMMETT, Rochelle Denise. 26250 EUCLID AVE, STE 415 44132 #038-06-1997 L2000 IM *020
HERNANDEZ, Juan Michael. 20050 LAKE SHORE BLVD, STE 3 44123 #026-04-1984 L1985
    PME OM *020
JACONO, Kari M. 25670 EDGECLIFF DR 44132 #038-06-2001 L2001 PD *020 †55
JEDLICKA, Lynn Marie. ■ 44117 #038-44-2004 L2004 PM *012
KHAKWANI, Nasir Khan. ■ 44117 #704-01-1974 L1980 OBG *020
KHIN, Mimi. 18901 LAKE SHORE BLVD, EUCLID HOSPITAL CCHS 44119 #209-01-1977 L1998
    AN *020 †05
KIZLIK, Julie Daub. 18901 LAKE SHORE BLVD 44119 #038-43-1992 L1994 EM *020 †16
KOSOGLOV, Anthony Thos. 99 E 189TH ST, STE 215 44119 #132-03-1984 L1989 IM *020 †20
LAUTMAN, Jeffrey Howard. 25300 EUCLID AVE 44117 #038-40-1986 L1988 NEP *020 †35
LENK, Jean Botti. 99 NORTHLINE CIR STE 200 44119 #038-06-1988 L1989 IM *020 †20
LE VINE, Mark Joel. 26300 EUCLID AVE, STE 736 44132 #023-01-1972 L1979 D *020 †15
LOCKE, Todd Wm. 24701 EUCLID AVE 44117 #041-14-1982 L1985 IM *020 †20
LOPEZ-VELEZ, Milagros. 26250 EUCLID AVE STE 415, VISITING PHYSICIANS ASSOC 44132
    #308-01-1982 L1988 END IM *020
MAJMUDAR, Himanshu D. 18901 LAKE SHORE BLVD 44119 #495-23-1972 L1979
    IM EM *020 †20
MOSENKIS, Ari. 25301 EUCLID AVE 44117 #035-46-1998 L2005 NEP *020 †20
NEUENDORF, Kathleen Adria. ■ 44117 #038-43-2006 L2006 IM *012
NIEMCZURA, Richard Thos. 99 NORTHLINE CIR 44119 #038-06-1975 L1976 GS VS *020 †85
O'NEILL, Beverly V. 99 NORTHLINE CIR, STE 235 44119 #038-40-1987 L1988
    PUD CCM *020 †20
PARRAN, Theodore Vandoren. ■ 44117 #023-07-1952 L1956 IM *020
PERETZ, Jack. 26300 EUCLID AVE, STE 312 44132 #035-15-1957 L1961 OPH *071 †35
PERSE, Jessica Ann. 18901 LAKE SHORE BLVD 44119 #038-44-1985 L1990 GS VS *020 †85
POLSTER, Sheldon Alan. 18599 LAKE SHORE BLVD, STE 200 44119 #038-06-1962 L1962
    PUD CCM *020 †20
POSK, Lori Kmiec. 18901 LAKE SHORE BLVD 44119 #025-12-1991 L1992 IM *020 †20
POST, Stanley. 26300 EUCLID AVE, STANLEY POST & ASSOCIATES 44132 #035-08-1953 L1957
    OBG *071 †30
SHEPARD, Dale Randall. ■ 44117 #038-40-2003 L2003 HO *012 †20
SIMPSON, Gregory Louis. 18599 LAKE SHORE BLVD, PEDIATRICS STE 100 44119
    #047-07-1983 L1998 PD FM *020
SLAWINSKI, Thomas P. 99 NORTHLINE CIR STE 225 44119 #759-01-1982 L1988 GS *020 †85
SPIVEY, Jason Edward. ■ 44119 #038-06-2007 L2007 P *012
SUNDARAM, Meenakshi P. 26250 EUCLID AVE, STE 415 44132 #495-01-1982 L1993 GS *020
SUNDARESH, Hurikadale P. 26250 EUCLID AVE STE 201 44132 #495-09-1969 L1976
    PD *020 †55

SURH, Chung Sun. ■ 44117 #583-06-1953 L1975 **GP** *071
SZOLOMAJER, Joseph A. 22221 SAINT CLAIR AVE 44117 #154-01-1950 L1953 **OM GPM** *072 †70
SZOLOMAJER, Wildtraut. 25701 N LAKELAND BLVD 44132 #407-20-1950 L1956 **D** *071
TAHSILDAR, Hassan I. 26250 EUCLID AVE STE 711 44132 #308-11-1985 L1992 **ON** *020 †20
TAYLOR, Clarence Leotis. 26250 EUCLID AVE STE 415, VISITING PHYSICIANS ASSOCI 44132 #047-07-1982 L1985 **IM** *020 †20 ‡
WALTZ, Robert Claude. ■ 44132 #023-01-1947 L1955 **GS CD** *071 †85
WILSON, Thomas Stuart. 18599 LAKE SHORE BLVD, UNIVERSITY HOSPITALS HEALT 44119 #035-45-1980 L1983 **CD** *020 †20
YIMEN, Mekeleya. ■ 44123 #010-01-2005 L2005 **IM** *012

FAIRBORN – GREENE

ALAPPATT, Anessa Dawn. 2180 GATEWAY DR 45324 #038-44-1996 L2000 **FM** *020 †18
ALI, Sameer Syed. ■ 45324 #038-45-2008 *012
AMBALAVANAN, Geetha. 2180 GATEWAY DR 45324 #495-94-1993 L2004 **FM** *020 †18
BANDI, Sindhura. ■ 45324 #038-45-2008 *012
BAUTISTA, Dan F. 1840 COMMERCE CENTER BLVD 45324 #748-07-1991 L1997 **FM** *020 †18
BRODERICK, Pamela Joy. ■ 45324 #039-01-2005 L2005 **P** *012
CATALDI, Oscar B, Jr. 2180 GATEWAY DR 45324 #038-45-1999 L2000 **IM** *020
CONNER, Tara Lynn. ■ 45324 #025-12-2005 L2005 **PD** *012
COX, Paul Sheridan. ■ 45324 #055-01-1995 L2002 **IM** *020 †20
DERRICKSON, Adam Kirk. ■ 45324 #005-12-2006 L2006 **IM** *012
DESAI, Manoj Ramanlal. 717 W XENIA DR 45324 #495-22-1969 L1977 **ON PD** *020 †20
DODGE, Ross William. ■ 45324 #051-04-2008 *012
EDWARDS, Howard Charles, Jr. ■ 45324 #038-45-2008 *012
FATTAHI, Pooia. ■ 45324 #038-45-2008 *012
FLOYD, Angela Maria. ■ 45324 #038-45-2007 L2007 **MPD** *012
GERSON, Nora Elizabeth. ■ 45324 #041-14-2001 L2002 **EM** *020
GIWA, Rifquat Olamide. ■ 45324 #038-45-2006 **IM** *012
GROTH, Aaron Thomas. 7790 DAYTON RD 45324 #038-40-2003 L2003 **FM** *020 †18
HALLEY, Franklin Maxwell. 600 E DAYTON YLW SPRNGS RD 45324 #019-02-1983 L1995 **P** *020 †75
HAMMOCK, Ryan. ■ 45324 #038-45-2006 L2006 **FP** *012
JAKUBOWICZ, Andrew. ■ 45324 #038-45-2008 *012
JANIK, Matthew Paul. ■ 45324 #038-45-2006 L2006 **D** *012
JEWELL, Bryan Steven. ■ 45324 #038-45-2008 *012
KELLEY, Kevin Daniel. ■ 45324 #038-45-2008 *012
LOUSTEAU, Suzanne Marie. ■ 45324 #021-05-2007 L2007 **FP** *012
MAHONEY, Christopher Ray. ■ 45324 #025-01-2008 *012
MCCONNELL, Erin Elizabeth. ■ 45324 #038-45-2006 L2006 **MPD** *012
MERVES, Matthew Henry. ■ 45324 #038-45-2008 *012
MOHLER, Stanley Ross. 3640 COL GLENN HWY, WRIGHT STATE UNIV SCHOOL M 45324 #048-02-1956 L1978 **AM PHP** *071 †70
MYERS, Michael John. 2180 GATEWAY DR 45324 #038-40-2004 L2004 **FM** *020 †18
NORMAN-COX, Cheryl. ■ 45324 #055-01-1994 L1996 **GE** *020 †20
NUGENT, Paul Fordham, Jr. ■ 45324 #035-20-1954 **AM GPM** *100 †70
O'DANIEL, Tori Lee. ■ 45324 #038-43-2006 **OBG** *012
PARIHAR, Robin. ■ 45324 #038-45-2008 *012
PATEL, Chirag Rajni. 1131 WINDSONG TRL, DEPT IM 45324 #654-01-2002 L2003 **IM** *100 †20
PAUL, Susan Denise. ■ 45324 #038-45-2008 *012
PURI, Muhammad Rehan Azhe. ■ 45324 #704-02-2000 L2006 **FM** *100
RAJSHEKER, Srilakshmi. ■ 45324 #038-43-2006 L2006 **DR** *012
RAJSHEKER, Srinivas. ■ 45324 #496-23-2003 L2005 **IM** *012
RICH, Kevin William. ■ 45324 #041-77-2007, ▲ L2007 **IM** *012
RYAN, Mark Mcgrath. ■ 45324 #038-45-2008 *012
SCHUMER, Ross Aron. ■ 45324 #041-02-2004 L2004 **ORS** *012
SIMON, Paul Menolette. ■ 45324 #748-20-2000 L2003 **IM** *020 †20
THERIOT, Laurie Marie. ■ 45324 #021-05-2006 L2006 **FP** *012
THOMAS, Charles Norman. ■ 45324 #012-01-1958 **CD IM** *071
VAFAIE, Akbar. 1854 S MAPLE AVE 45324 #517-01-1964 L1972 **PD** *071 †55
VENABLE, Walter Gregg. 2180 GATEWAY DR 45324 #038-45-1983 L1985 **FM** *072 †18
WELLS, Britton Colby. 850 E XENIA DR, STE 500 45324 #028-34-1997 L2005 **ORS** *020 †40
ZAKALUZNY, Scott Adrian. ■ 45324 #023-12-2003 L2003 **GS** *012
ZELLER, Charles Joseph. ■ 45324 #016-76-1978, ▲ L1979 **FM** *020 †18

FAIRFIELD – BUTLER

ABOU EL SAAD, Tamer Y. 2960 MACK RD, STE 206 45014 #915-03-1993 L2002 **CN** *020 †75
ADJEI, Stephen. ■ 45014 #412-01-1996 L2005 **PCC** *012 †20
ALBERS, Mary E. 3000 MACK RD 45014 #017-20-1986 L1996 **ON** *020 †20
ALCASID, Susan Alvaran. 945 DEIS DR 45014 #748-18-1983 L1999 **IM** *020 †20
ALLEE, Jeannine Marie. 5900 BOYMEL DR, PEDIATRIC ASSOCIATES OF FA 45014 #038-41-2004 L2004 **PD** *020 †55
ALQUIZOLA, Florenda M C. 3000 MACK RD 45014 #748-01-1962 L1979 **ATP CLP** *020 †50
ALTER, Kathleen Anne. 2960 MACK RD, STE 210 45014 #038-40-1983 L1984 **IM** *020 †20
AMARO, Pacifico Catabay. 526 NILLES RD 45014 #748-01-1954 L1967 **FM** *020 †18
ANDERSON, Carol Louise. 5161 PLEASANT AVE 45014 #025-07-1976 L1984 **OPH** *020
ARAND, Arthur Gerard. 2960 MACK RD, STE 203 45014 #038-41-1986 L1991 **NS** *020 †25
ARMSTRONG, Diane Lynn. 5150 SANDY LN 45014 #038-43-1985 L1988 **FM** *020 †18
ARROM, Robert F. 3000 MACK RD 45014 #264-05-1973 L1985 **OBG GS** *020 †30
BACEVICH, Bernard Bron. 3830 WOODRIDGE BLVD, STE C 45014 #038-41-1967 L1967 **ORS LM** *072 †40
BAKALI, Salim Ahmed. 5116 SANDY LN, BAKALI MEDICAL ASSOCIATES 45014 #704-02-1986 L1996 **IM** *020 †20
BARBER, Michael Jay. 3000 MACK RD 45014 #017-20-1973 L1976 **OS FM** *030 †18
BAUER, George Paul. 2960 MACK RD STE 107 45014 #038-45-1986 L1993 **NO OTO** *020 †45
BEHLER, Anthony Francis. 5150 SANDY LN 45014 #038-40-1980 L1980 **IM** *020 †20
BLANKENBURG, Robert Scott. 1251 NILLES RD, STE 8 45014 #038-45-1982 L1985 **PD** *020 †55
BRANDABUR, Joseph Hubert. 3000 MACK RD 45014 #028-34-1963 L1968 **PTH FOP** *071 †50
BREWER, Edward L, III. 5331 S GILMORE RD 45014 #021-06-1989 L1993 **AN** *020 †05
CAMPBELL, Kevin Giles. 2960 MACK RD, STE 205 45014 #038-40-1989 L1991 **U** *020 †95
CHAIT, Robert Harlan. 2960 MACK RD STE 208 45014 #038-41-1980 L1982 **OTO A** *020 †45
CHIN, Neeoo. 2814 MACK RD 45014 #038-40-1981 L1985 **REN GYN** *020 †30
CIANCHETTI, Jeffrey A. 3000 MACK RD, MERCY FAIRFIELD HOSP 45014 #038-40-1975 L1975 **EM** *030 †16
CO, Christopher See. 511 NILLES RD 45014 #748-11-1996 L2000 **PD** *020 †55
CO, Victoriano Tan. 511 NILLES RD 45014 #748-01-1962 L1971 **PD** *020 †55
COBB, Marcus Lillord. 5150 SANDY LN 45014 #038-41-1987 L1990 **IM** *020
COLANGELO, Gregory. 5150 SANDY LN 45014 #038-41-1985 L1986 **PUD IM** *020 †20
CONTI, Terrance Ross. 2832 MACK RD 45014 #038-41-1988 L1992 **IM** *020
CONTRACTOR, Zainab P. 2960 MACK RD, STE 206 45014 #704-25-1995 L2007 **CN** *020
CRANE, Edward Joseph. 3000 MACK RD 45014 #016-11-1999 L1999 **HO** *020 †20
DACIO, Loreto Escusa. 945 DEIS DR 45014 #748-10-1998 L2000 **IM** *020 †20
DAOUD, Fuheid Shakir. 3000 MACK RD, STE 100 45014 #407-10-1963 L1975 **CD IM** *020 †20
DAVID, Pacita Aurea. 6580 SOSNA DR, DIPLOMAT EXECUTIVE CENTER 45014 #055-01-1991 L1996 **P IM** *020 †75
DIMACULANGAN, Carmen V. 2990 MACK RD, FL 1 45014 #748-08-1966 L1979 **AN** *030
DOCENA, Samuel Chicano. 1244 NILLES RD 45014 #748-01-1975 L1983 **FM** *020 †18
EYNON, Lawrence Edward. 3000 MACK RD, MERCY HOSPITAL 45014 #038-41-1974 L1975 **DR NR** *020 †80
FEENEY, Douglas Edward. 2960 MACK RD, STE 205 45014 #016-02-1990 L1996 **U** *020 †95
FEIBEL, John H. 2960 MACK RD, STE 206 45014 #035-01-1967 L1982 **N PHP** *020 †75
FENTON, William Stanley. 1251 NILLES RD STE 3 45014 #038-45-1991 L1992 **FM** *020 †18
GEDDAM, Bapi Raju. 5331 S GILMORE RD, STE A 45014 #495-11-1976 L1996 **AN** *020 †05
GERLINGER, Brooks Bryson. 3000 MACK RD, STE 100 45014 #038-43-1991 L1998 **CD** *020 †20
GONZALEZ, Claudia Isabel. 2760 MACK RD 45014 #048-14-2000 **FM** *062
GOODMAN, Jerry Alan. 3050 MACK RD, STE 375 45014 #017-20-1970 L1974 **OBG** *020 †30
GOODMAN, Stanley Myron. 5900 BOYMEL DR 45014 #165-04-1957 L1959 **PD** *071
GORMAN, Robyn Michelle. ■ 45014 #038-41-2006 L2006 **PD** *012
GREENBLATT, David. 5150 SANDY LN 45014 #025-01-1977 L1978 **RHU IM** *020 †20
GREER, Ineke H. 8841 HITCHINGHAM RD 45014 #660-05-1980 *075
GREVEY, Scott Chas. 1213 NILLES RD 45014 #038-43-1989 L1990 **D** *020 †15
GUNDAVARPU, Sai Mohan. 5331 S GILMORE RD, HAMILTON ANESTHESIA ASSOCI 45014 #495-21-1986 L2001 **AN** *020 †05
HELMER, Fredric Allan. 2960 MACK RD, STE 210 45014 #017-20-1958 L1968 **NS** *071 †25
HERZIG, Edward Blaine. 5150 SANDY LN 45014 #038-41-1971 L1975 **RHU** *020 †20
HOFFMAN, Lisa Marie. 5150 SANDY LN 45014 #038-41-1994 L1995 **IM** *020 †20
HOWARD, Mark Richard. 3000 MACK RD 45014 #017-20-1983 L1985 **U GS** *020 †95
HSU, James Pei Liang. 3050 MACK RD, STE 310 45014 #385-04-1966 L1973 **ORS HS** *020 †40
IMWALLE, Donald Kolman. 3000 MACK RD 45014 #038-41-2001 L2001 **R** *020 †80
IMWALLE, Mark David. 3000 MACK RD 45014 #038-41-1969 L1969 **R NM** *020 †80,28
JUNG, Simon Changyun. 3000 MACK RD, STE 100 45014 #019-02-1989 L2000 **CD** *020 †20
KINGREY, John Frederick. ■ 45014 #028-34-2007 L2007 **IM** *012
KOBLENZER, Frances E S. 6570 SOSNA DR, STE 5 45014 #041-07-1988 L2006 **CHP PD** *020
KOEHL, Rebecca Sue. 741 WESSEL DR, FAIRFIELD MEDICAL GROUP IN 45014 #038-45-2000 L2000 **FM** *020 †18
KOSTER, Kenneth Henry. 3000 MACK RD, MERCY HOSPITAL 45014 #038-06-1982 L1985 **EM MDM** *020 †16
KRALL, Elizabeth Anne. 1866 HIGHCLIFF CT 45014 #038-43-2005 L2005 **P** *012
KRALL, William Richard. 5150 SANDY LN 45014 #038-40-1973 L1973 **PUD IM** *020 †20
LANGENDERFER, Matthew A. 2960 MACK RD, STE 101 45014 #051-01-1995 L1997 **ORS** *020 †40
LENK, Stephen Andrew. 3000 MACK RD 45014 #038-41-2001 L2001 **DR** *020 †80
LEWIS, Stephen Julian. 3000 MACK RD, STE 100 45014 #041-01-1958 L1962 **IM** *071 †20
LOUGHERY, Edward Joseph. 3000 MACK RD, STE 100 45014 #017-20-1985 L1991 **CD IM** *020 †20
LOVE, Robt Alexander, III. 3000 MACK RD 45014 #038-41-1967 L1967 **R** *020 †80
MACEJKO, Thomas Theodore. 563 WESSEL DR 45014 #038-41-1972 L1972 **OPH** *020 †35 ‡
MARTIN, Stephen Paul. 2990 MACK RD, STE 107 45014 #038-41-1988 L1990 **GE** *020 †20
MAUNTEL, William Joseph. 741 WESSEL DR 45014 #038-40-1984 L1985 **FM** *020 †18
MEIER, Christopher J. 3000 MACK RD 45014 #038-41-1977 L1978 **FM** *020 †18
MILLER, Michael Edward. 1248 NILLES RD, STE 8 45014 #035-09-1982 L1988 **P FPG** *020 †75
MOORTHY, Palanivel Ganesa. 759 WESSEL DR STE I, NEURO DIAGNOSTIC CENTER IN 45014 #495-59-1968 L1978 **N** *020 †75
MORAVEC, Joseph J. 3000 MACK RD 45014 #038-40-1973 L1973 **OTO FPS** *020 †45
MOUSA, Soha. 5150 SANDY LN 45014 #041-14-1998 L2004 **RHU** *020 †20
NAGESETTY, Girish Babu. 1251 NILLES RD STE 17, CLOCK TOWER PLACE 45014 #495-58-1972 L1982 **GS VS** *020 †85
NARASIMHAN, Bharati. 1251 NILLES RD, STE 4 45014 #495-38-1974 L1982 **FM** *020 †18
NARASIMHAN, Muthuswamy K. 2960 MACK RD STE 102 45014 #495-66-1970 L1974 **GS** *020 †85
NGUYEN, Thomas Bao. 1251 NILLES RD STE 6 45014 #041-09-1992 L1997 **IM AM** *020 †20
ORFAHLI, M Nizar. 3000 MACK RD 45014 #875-01-1978 L1991 **PUD CCM** *020 †20
PAN, Huai Chin. 2960 MACK RD STE 212 45014 #495-11-1971 L1978 **PS GS** *020 †85,65
PARANANDI, Vani. 3000 MACK RD 45014 #496-24-1996 L2002 **IM** *020 †20
PAULEY, Janice L. 5331 S GILMORE RD 45014 #038-40-1987 L1989 **AN** *020 †05
PFEIFFER, Gerald Raymond. 3000 MACK RD 45014 #038-41-1964 L1964 **AN PME** *020 †05
PHALEN, Timothy Joseph. 3000 MACK RD, RADIOLOGY DEPT 45014 #038-41-1994 L1999 **VIR** *020 †80
PORTUGAL, Jesse Anthony. 2960 MACK RD, STE 203 45014 #026-04-1987 L1990 **PM PMM** *020 †60
RAJAN, Vijay. 2960 MACK RD, STE 201 45014 #495-04-1982 L1988 **N OS** *020 †75
RAMPTON, Daryl Verne. 5331 S GILMORE RD, STE A 45014 #020-02-1987 L1996 **AN** *020 †05
REBOULET, James Dow. 3000 MACK RD 45014 #038-41-1970 L1970 **OBG** *020 †30
REGINELLI, Joel Peter. 3000 MACK RD, STE 100 45014 #038-40-1995 L2000 **CD** *020 †20
REINA, Juan Carlos. 1020 SYMMES RD 45014 #264-05-1997 L2004 **OBG** *020 †30
REYES, Eleia Joyce S. 945 DEIS DR 45014 #748-18-1988 L1996 **FM** *020 †18
RICHARDS, Arthur Isaac. 3000 MACK RD 45014 #038-41-1966 L1966 **ON HEM** *020 †20
RINGEL, Erich W. 3000 MACK RD 45014 #038-41-1949 L1949 **GP** *020
ROPER, Emmett C, Jr. 5150 SANDY LN 45014 #038-40-1991 L1992 **IM** *020 †20
ROSEN, Jeffrey. 2960 MACK RD 45014 #016-11-1988 L2004 **GS TRS** *020 †85
SAMAAN, Robert George. 3050 MACK RD STE 305 45014 #915-03-1982 L1996 **IM** *020 †20
SCHNEIDER, Marc Cohan. 3050 MACK RD, STE 310 45014 #038-06-1994 L1995 **OSM** *020 †40
SCHNEIDER, Ronald Cary. 2990 MACK RD, STE 107 45014 #025-07-1970 L1974 **GE IM** *020 †20

■ = Address Information Privacy Protected

SCHOLL, Heather Anne. ■ 45014 #038-45-2007 L2007 **GS** *012
SIMCOE, James Patrick. 741B WESSEL DR 45014 #038-41-1972 L1972 **FM** *020 †18
SIMMS, Robert Maris. 3174 MACK RD, STE 3 45014 #041-14-1988 L1990 **CHP** *020 †75
SLIVKA, Scott Laurence. 3050 MACK RD STE 200 45014 #038-41-1988 L1997 **ORS OSM** *020 †40
SOLORIA, Eduardo Moya. ■ 45014 #748-01-1955 L1968 **EM FM** *020 †16
STOTZ, Jeffrey David. 2990 MACK RD, STE 107 45014 #038-40-1998 L1999 **GE** *020 †20
SUNTAY, Glenn Jacinto. 3000 MACK RD 45014 #748-08-1983 L1986 **AN** *020 †05
SWINEHART, James Ward. 3000 MACK RD 45014 #038-40-1964 L1964 **PTH** *020 †50
TAYLOR, David Eric. 3050 MACK RD, STE 310 45014 #038-41-1989 L1994 **ORS** *020 †40
VALKER, Louis E. 6120 S GILMORE RD 45014 #030-06-1959 L1960 **D** *071
VARATHARAJAH, Malathy. 3000 MACK RD 45014 #220-04-1986 L1995 **IM** *020 †20
VASI, Rahib Nomanbhai. 3050 MACK RD, STE 305 45014 #495-01-1970 L1978 **IM GP** *020 †20
VICKERS, Lisa Lynn. 3050 MACK RD, STE 310 45014 #038-06-1991 L1992 **ORS** *020 †40
WEATHERINGTON, Mary A. 5150 SANDY LN 45014 #016-45-1992 L1994 **IM** *020 †20
WEBER, Fredrick Louis, Jr. 2740 MACK RD 45014 #035-20-1970 L1981 **GE IM** *050 †20
WEISENBERGER, Paula A F. 3000 MACK RD 45014 #038-41-1974 L1964 **PTH** *020 †20
WOLFE, James Thos. III. 3000 MACK RD, MERCY HOSPITAL FAIRFIELD L 45014 #020-02-1981 L1998 **PTH PCP** *062 †50
WOODALL, Bradford Harold. 3000 MACK RD 45014 #038-41-1984 L1985 **DR** *020 †80
YATHIRAJ, Dummi P. 311 NILLES RD, STE C 45014 #495-37-1961 L1974 **IM END** *020 †20
YOUNGPETERS, Richard W. ■ 45014 #038-41-1968 L1968 **PD** *020 †55
YU, Dale Patrick. 5184 SANDY LN 45014 #038-41-2000 L2000 **IM** *020 †20
YU, Joseph. 5184 SANDY LN 45014 #748-02-1962 L1975 **IM CD** *020

FAIRLAWN – SUMMIT

ABOAGYE, Evelyn Abena Opp. ■ 44333 #412-01-2002 L2007 **PD** *012
ALEXANDER, Joseph F, Jr. 3090 W MARKET ST STE 110 44333 #038-43-1975 L1976 **AI IM** *020 †20,03
ALLOTEY, Adorkor. ■ 44333 #412-02-2002 L2005 **PD** *012
ALSTON, Linda Lee Reed. 3085 W MARKET ST STE 102 44333 #018-03-1970 L1971 **D** *071 †15 ‡
ARMAO, Joseph Chas. 3090 W MARKET ST, THIRD FLOOR 44333 #038-41-1986 L1987 **FM** *020 †18 ‡
BERMEA, Raymond Phillip. 3624 W MARKET ST, STE 103 44333 #038-45-1986 L1987 **IM** *020 †20
BRASHEAR, Linda Gerda. 484 S MILLER RD, STE 201 44333 #038-43-1998 L2000 **IM** *020 †20
BRIGGS, Joanne Harris. 3600 W MARKET ST, STE 100 44333 #038-06-1988 L1991 **OPH** *020
BURNS, Robert Calvin. 3632 RIDGEWOOD RD 44333 #035-03-1962 L1966 **FM** *020 †18
CAJIGAS, Israel James. ■ 44333 #038-44-2005 L2005 **FP** *012
CARMICHAEL, Melisa Ann. 3428 W MARKET ST, STE 101 44333 #038-44-1993 L1994 **PD** *020 †55
CHAE, Clara Ji. ■ 44333 #038-44-2006 L2006 **OBG** *012
CHASE, Matthew Wentworth. 2640 W MARKET ST 44333 #001-02-1980 L1981 **EM** *020
CHATURVEDI, Anand Mohan. 3200 W MARKET ST STE 205 44333 #038-44-1998 L1999 **P** *020
CLARKE, John Franklin, Jr. 130 N MILLER RD 44333 #038-44-1984 L1986 **FM** *020 †18
DANESIS, Gregory G. 2651 W MARKET ST, CENTER FOR UROLOGIC HEALTH 44333 #038-44-1984 L1986 **U** *020 †20
DINICOLA, Nicholas Joseph. ■ 44333 #038-40-2004 L2004 **ORS** *012
DOMDERA, Richard James, Jr. 130 N MILLER RD 44333 #038-40-1998 L1999 **FM** *020 †18
DUGGIRALA, Umadevi. 2640 W MARKET ST, STE 203 44333 #495-58-1981 L1994 **FM** *020 †18 ‡
DUNCAN, Yolanda Regina. 71 BAKER BLVD 44333 #038-41-2000 L2000 **FM** *020 †18 ‡
ELSON, Thomas James. 3428 W MARKET ST STE 100 44333 #038-40-1984 L1985 **EM** *020 †16
FISH, Barry Jason. 3428 W MARKET ST, STE 100 44333 #038-44-1995 L1997 **OBG** *020 †30
GALM, Janis Jean. 3428 W MARKET ST, STE 101 44333 #038-06-1988 L1991 **PD** *020 †55
GELLER, Lawrence L. 2651 W MARKET ST 44333 #020-02-1987 L1987 **U** *020 †95
GOLDBERG, Marcy Diane. 2590 FALMOUTH RD 44333 #041-09-1983 L1984 **PD** *020 †55
GROESBECK, Marcie Ann. 50 N MILLER RD, FAIRLAWN FAM PRAC 44333 #038-44-1981 L1983 **FM** *020 †18
IEMMA, Joseph Thos. 71 BAKER BLVD, STE 101 44333 #305-01-1990 L1994 **IM** *020 †20
JIMENEZ-TOMADA, Connie Ru. ■ 44333 #748-02-2004 L2006 **IM** *012
JURY, David R. ■ 44333 #038-44-2008 *012
KARAPASHEV, Ljubka N. ■ 44333 #957-04-1961 L1976 **P** *020 †75
KING, Jack Dennis. 3094 W MARKET ST 44333 #038-40-1977 L1979 **PD** *020
KITSON, Patricia Ann. 605 N CLEVELAND MASSILN RD 44333 #038-43-1981 L1982 **FM** *020 †18
KROEGER, Carl Bernhardt. ■ 44333 #038-40-1954 L1954 **A IM** *071
LAPASIA, Rajiv Bipin. ■ 44333 #038-44-2000 **NS** *100
LEFKOVITZ, Norman Wayne. 60 N MILLER RD 44333 #038-40-1981 L1983 **N** *020 †75
LEFTON, Douglas Leigh. 50 N MILLER RD 44333 #038-06-1996 L1997 **FM** *020 †18
LERMER, Alexander Sascha. 3600 W MARKET ST 44333 #407-16-1950 L1958 **PTH FOP** *040 †50
LIBECCO, James Frederick. 3085 W MARKET ST, STE 102 44333 #038-44-2001 L2001 **D** *020 †15
LOUTFI, Chadi Habib. 2852 MOREWOOD RD 44333 #605-01-2001 L2001 **PCC** *012
LUECKEN, Carolee Lander. 3094 W MARKET ST, STE 105 44333 #038-06-1976 L1979 **PD** *020 †55
MABEE, Scott Watson. 3624 W MARKET ST, STE 103 44333 #038-40-1991 L1992 **IM** *020 †20
MAC INNIS, Michael V. 3094 W MARKET ST 44333 #067-01-1952 L1957 **OBG** *020 †30
MANSOUR, Maher Monir. 3200 W MARKET ST STE 205 44333 #915-02-1974 L1991 **P** *020 †75
MELI, Joseph Jesse. 3600 W MARKET ST STE 200 44333 #038-40-1973 L1974 **IM** *020 †20
MOSS, Bradford Lawrence. 2651 W MARKET ST, PHYSICIANS UROLOGY 44333 #011-02-1984 L1985 **U** *020 †95
MUSSON, Robert Arthur. 3618 W MARKET ST STE 102 44333 #038-40-1989 L1990 **OS FM** *020 †18
NAGEL, Elizabeth Marie. 3250 W MARKET ST, STE 202 44333 #017-20-1988 L1990 **CHP P** *020 †75
NOVAK, Keith Gordon. 3090 W MARKET ST 44333 #038-44-1995 L1997 **FM** *020 †18
OYAKAWA, Steven Mark. 3600 W MARKET ST, STE 200 44333 #038-45-1984 L1985 **IM** *020 †20
PANZNER, Joseph Lawrence. 3632 RIDGEWOOD RD 44333 #038-40-1976 L1977 **FM** *020 †18
PARIKH, Anil Madhukant. 70 N MILLER RD 44333 #496-38-1981 L1985 **P ADP** *020 †75 ‡

PARISI, Edward Jos. 50 N MILLER RD, FAIRLAWN FAM PRAC 44333 #038-40-1991 L1992 **FM** *020 †18 ‡
PAYTON, J Joseph. 50 N MILLER RD 44333 #041-77-1973, ▲ L1974 **FM** *020 †18
PINTA, Gary Bruce, Jr. 50 BAKER BLVD 44333 #038-44-1994 L1995 **IM** *020 †20
PLATT, Russell Lindbergh. 3094 W MARKET ST, STE 138 44333 #047-07-1960 L1964 **IM** *020
POLLEY, William Emory, Jr. 3094 W MARKET ST STE 345 44333 #038-43-1974 L1975 **IM** *020 †20
POTTER, Susan Lynn. 3428 W MARKET ST, CHILDRENS HOSPITAL PHYS 44333 #038-06-1992 L1996 **PD** *020 †55
RAYNOR, Andrew Carlton. 471 N CLEVELAND MASSILN RD 44333 #038-43-1975 L1976 **RHU IM** *020 †20
ROTH, Marta. 3094 W MARKET ST STE 136 44333 #038-06-1992 L1994 **FM** *020 †18 ‡
SABIN, Kelli Ruth. 130 N MILLER RD, OHIO FAMILY PRACTICE 44333 #038-44-1993 L1996 **FM** *020 †18
SANDEL, Allan Jay. ■ 44333 #035-03-1970 L1971 **PS** *071 †65
SAWAN, Edward A. ■ 44333 #010-02-1940 L1947 **PD** *071 †55
SCHPRECHMAN, Elliot David. 3618 W MARKET ST, STE 200 44333 #047-07-1981 L1988 **CD IM** *020 †20
SEIDEL, Robert K. 3624 W MARKET ST, STE 103 44333 #047-07-1973 L1975 **IM** *020 †20
SERENE, Michael David. 2651 W MARKET ST 44333 #055-01-1971 L1972 **U** *020 †95
SHAH, Bharat J. 63 BAKER BLVD 44333 #495-22-1978 L1984 **P** *020 †75
SHAH, Dhruv Jayantilal. 3600 W MARKET ST STE 101, SUMMIT MEDICAL PLAZA 44333 #495-76-1983 L2004 **PM** *020 †60
SHAW, Molly Kathleen. 3428 W MARKET ST, STE 101 44333 #038-45-2001 L2001 **PD** *020 †55
SINGARAJU, Anupama. 2640 W MARKET ST 44333 #496-01-2001 L2003 **FM** *100
SINHA, Tushar Kanti. 3353 STANLEY RD 44333 #495-02-1965 L1976 **IM DIA** *020
STEINBERGER, Sidney J. 2708 CRAWFIS BLVD 44333 #038-41-1980 L1985 **OTO FPS** *020 †45
STOVER, Thomas Lewis. 3428 W MARKET ST, STE 100 44333 #055-01-1973 L1974 **GYN** *020 †30
SWITZER, Michella Janel. ■ 44333 #028-78-2004, ▲ L2004 **OBG** *012
TAMBYRAJA, Samuel M. 3200 W MARKET ST, STE 111 44333 #220-02-1968 L1976 **CHP P** *040 †75
TOMADA, Jon Rupert Tumbag. ■ 44333 #748-02-2004 L2006 **IM** *012
TOREM, Moshe. 4125 MEDINA RD, STE 209 44333 #550-01-1970 L1978 **P** *020 †75
VERGHESE, Sheila. 3090 W MARKET ST 44333 #495-16-1969 L1974 **OBG** *020
WANG, Jianhua. 3090 W MARKET ST, FAIRLAWN MEDICAL OFFICES 44333 #243-16-1987 L1997 **IM** *020 †20
WEIDMAN, Amy Ruth. 3600 W MARKET ST STE 200 44333 #038-43-1987 L1988 **IM** *020 †20
WHITE, Clarence Gerald. ■ 44333 #047-07-2005 L2005 **IM** *012
YOUNG, Aundree Noretta. 3090 W MARKET ST, KAISER HEALTH FOUNDATION 44333 #025-01-1973 L1976 **PD** *020 †55
ZEBARI, Joseph F. 3634 W MARKET ST STE 102 44333 #025-07-1979 L1984 **OBG** *020 †30
ZELLING, Daniel A. 2850 W MARKET ST, OH INSTITUTE 44333 #660-03-1961 L1964 **PYA P** *020
ZINK, Jill Nicole. ■ 44333 #038-41-2006 L2006 **GS** *012

FAIRVIEW PARK – CUYAHOGA

AMIN, Sheikh Noor Ul. ■ 44126 #665-01-2007 L2007 **FP** *012
ANGLEY, Nabil Fahmy. 21800 LORAIN RD 44126 #330-02-1959 L1972 **ORS** *072 †40
BOGARD, Brent M. 20455 LORAIN RD, STE 353 44126 #048-13-1987 L1990 **GS TRS** *020 †85
CASTELE, Theodore John. ■ 44126 #038-06-1957 L1957 **R OS** *071 †80
COLETTA, John E. ■ 44126 #038-41-2002 L2002 **CD** *012 †20
COMERFORD, Thomas John. 20455 LORAIN RD, SECOND FLOOR 44126 #038-06-1970 L1977 **CD IM** *020 †20
CONFORTO, James Rocco. 21245 LORAIN RD STE LL100 44126 #038-06-1975 L1976 **OPH** *020 †35
COSTANZO, Frank Anthony. ■ 44126 #024-01-1952 L1955 **IM** *071
DAABOUL, Bisher. ■ 44126 #875-01-1993 L1996 **GE** *020 †20
DEAN, Leslie Scott, II. ■ 44126 #038-06-1955 L1955 **FM** *072
DRESING, Thomas John. 20455 LORAIN RD, SECOND FLOOR 44126 #001-02-1993 L2000 **ICE** *020 †20
FETKO, Carl Nicholas. ■ 44126 #038-40-2004 L2004 **DR** *012
GALVIN, Jeffrey Owen. 20455 LORAIN RD STE 104, WEST VALLEY MEDICAL BLDG 44126 #038-40-1990 L1991 **IM** *020 †20
GANNON, James Michael. ■ 44126 #038-43-2004 L2004 **NM** *012
GIANNIOS, Nichole. ■ 44126 #038-75-2005, ▲ L2005 **OBG** *012
HANG-FU, Lee C C. 21080 LORAIN RD 44126 #065-06-1983 L1991 **PS HS** *020 †65
HOLLE, Lois. ■ 44126 #016-42-1975 L1979 **D GP** *071 †15
ISSA, Meltiady. ■ 44126 #875-03-2004 L2007 **CLP** *012
KLAUS, Robert L, Jr. 20800 WESTGATE MALL, STE 310 44126 #041-13-1987 L1999 **OBG** *020 †30
KOTHARI, Ajeet Ramanlal. 20800 WESTGATE MALL # 206 44126 #495-23-1974 L1981 **OBG** *020 †30
KOTHARI, Purnima Ajeet. 20800 WESTGATE MALL # 206 44126 #495-22-1974 L1979 **OBG** *020 †30
KREBS, Carla Marie. 21375 LORAIN RD, FAIRVIEW EYE CTR 44126 #038-06-1990 L1994 **OPH** *020 †35
LEE, Kenneth. 20455 LORAIN RD, STE 353 44126 #038-06-1991 L1992 **GS** *020 †85
LEONOV, Andrey. ■ 44126 #036-05-2003 L2007 **PD** *020 †55
LEWIS, Craig Donald. 4132 WEST 200 14TH 44126 #025-01-2004 L2005 **OPH** *012
LIM, Hilario Aguinaldo. ■ 44126 #748-07-1962 *100
LINDERMAN, Charles Geo. 20455 LORAIN RD, STE 353 44126 #038-45-1992 L1997 **GS** *020 †85
LYONS, Sean Vincent. 20455 LORAIN RD, FL 2 44126 #038-41-1986 L1993 **IM ICE** *020 †20
MASTERSON, Kevin John. 20455 LORAIN RD, STE 102 44126 #025-01-1978 L1980 **FM** *020 †18
MEADOWS, Steven Roger. 21375 LORAIN RD, FAIRVIEW EYE CTR 44126 #038-40-2001 L2002 **OPH** *020 †35
MELLINO, Marcello. 20455 LORAIN RD, SECOND FLOOR 44126 #561-23-1974 L1977 **CD IM** *020 †20
NILGES, Thomas Charles. ■ 44126 #038-40-1962 L1962 **OTO OS** *020 †45
NUKTA, Emad M. 20455 LORAIN RD, FL 2 44126 #875-01-1981 L1985 **IM CD** *020 †20
PAULINO, Edgardo D. 22900 LORAIN RD 44126 #748-01-1960 L1974 **AN P** *020
POPESCU, Andrei. ■ 44126 #781-01-1999 L2005 **IM** *012

RANCHOFF, John Y. 20800 WESTGATE MALL # 506, WESTGATE MED ARTS CTR 44126 #035-06-1952 L1953 **D** *071 †15
RANCHOFF, Richard Edward. 20455 LORAIN RD, STE 103 44126 #038-40-1982 L1983 **D** *020 †15 ‡
RILEY, Robert Peter. ■ 44126 #028-34-1955 L1957 **IM** *071 †20
RIVERA, Ann Louise. ■ 44126 #038-06-2005 L2005 **DR** *012
SAKIEWICZ, Andrew Joseph. 20455 LORAIN RD, SECOND FLOOR 44126 #154-01-1993 L1998 **CD** *020 †20
SELTZER, Gerard. 22935 LORAIN RD 44126 #035-19-1952 L1953 **OM LM** *071 †20
SMITH, Andrew Crawford. 20455 LORAIN RD, STE 353 44126 #016-43-1998 L2000 **GS** *020 †85
TLAYGEH, Haytham Mohamed. ■ 44126 #605-01-1999 L2003 **PCC** *100 †20
VLASTARIS, Anthony Geo. 20455 LORAIN RD, SECOND FLOOR 44126 #038-06-1991 L1992 **CD** *020 †20
VLASTARIS, Philip A. ■ 44126 #418-01-1952 L1964 **IM CD** *071 †20
VLASTARIS-UNDERMAN, C A. 20455 LORAIN RD, STE 304 44126 #038-06-1992 L1993 **D** *020 †20,15
WASHNITZER, Robert Jay. ■ 44126 #010-03-1961 L1965 **IM OS** *020

FARMERSVILLE – MONTGOMERY

RATCLIFF, Lawrence Gene. 49 E CENTER ST 45325 #025-07-1975 L1976 **FM PSM** *020 †18
YOUNG, Margo Patricia. 49 E CENTER ST 45325 #038-45-1990 L1991 **IM** *020 †20

FAYETTE – FULTON

NYCE, Robert Wynne. 124 W MAIN ST 43521 #041-09-1954 L1955 **GP** *071

FAYETTEVILLE – BROWN

BATTAGLIA, Steven Anthony. 1061 BRUNSWICK DR, P O BOX 59 45118 #038-43-1987 L1992 **GS** *020 †85
CHARLES, Doris I Shields. ■ 45118 #038-41-1959 L1959 **GP** *071
NEFF, Anthony William. 19589 US 68 45118 #038-41-2000 L2000 **FM** *020 †18

FINDLAY – HANCOCK

AGRAWAL, Chiranji Lal. 1995 TIFFIN AVE STE 308 45840 #495-74-1975 L1984 **AN** *020
AGRAWAL, Prem Kishore. 1400 S MAIN ST 45840 #495-49-1963 L1981 **U** *020
AJALA, Musa A. 1717 MEDICAL BLVD STE B 45840 #781-04-1985 L2001 **NEP IM** *020 †20
ALAMMAR, Jihad Ibrahim. 1725 S MAIN ST 45840 #025-07-1996 L2001 **GS** *020 †85
ALCOTT, William Herbert. 301 W WALLACE ST, FINDLAY ORTHOPEDIC ASSOCIA 45840 #038-06-1969 L1969 **ORS** *071 †40
ALMARASTANI, Mohamad Nour. ■ 45840 #875-01-1998 L2007 **GS** *100
ARMSTRONG, Paul Forrest. 15840 MEDICAL DR S, STE A 45840 #038-40-1980 L1980 **OPH EM** *020 †35 ‡
ARNETTE, Greg Alan. 1900 S MAIN ST 45840 #038-40-1985 L1986 **EM FM** *020 †18
AYRES, Amber Marie. ■ 45840 #038-43-2006 L2006 **PD** *012
AZAR, Hassan G. 200 W PEARL ST, BLANCHARD VALLEY MEDICAL A 45840 #875-02-1984 L2004 **IM PCC** *020 †20
BAILEY, Dean Christopher. 15840 MEDICAL DR S, STE B 45840 #038-43-2004 L2004 **FM** *020 †18
BAKOS, Panagiotis E. 1900 S MAIN ST, MIDWEST PAIN TREATMENT CEN 45840 #418-02-1990 L2004 **APM AN** *020 †05
BANERJEE, Promila. 200 W PEARL ST, BLANCHARD VALLEY MED ASSOC 45840 #665-01-1997 L2004 **GE** *020 †20
BARKEY, Joseph G. ■ 45840 #017-20-1952 L1953 **FM AM** *072
BARRETT, Christine Louise. ■ 45840 #025-07-1977 L1981 **PD** *074
BASH, Harry Elden. 1920 S MAIN ST, STE G 45840 #038-06-1977 L1981 **OPH** *020
BASU, Basanti Mehta. 2515 N MAIN ST, CENTURY HEALTH 45840 #495-02-1967 L1993 **P** *020
BECK, Robert David. 1818 CHAPEL DR, BLANCHARD VALLEY 45840 #017-20-1973 L1975 **PD** *055
BEEKMAN, Jerome Frederic. 200 W PEARL ST 45840 #038-40-1975 L1975 **CD IM** *020 †20
BLAKE, Charles Richard. ■ 45840 #051-04-1956 L1957 **FM** *071 †18
BOUTS, Bruce Alan. 200 W PEARL ST 45840 #038-43-1986 L1987 **IM CCM** *020 †20
BREWSTER, Benjamin Dougla. ■ 45840 #020-12-2008 *012
BROWNING, Eric Christian. 300 W WALLACE ST, FINDLAY SURGICAL ASSOC 45840 #038-40-1979 L1985 **GS TS** *020 †85
BRUMLEY, Thomas Benj. ■ 45840 #038-40-1967 L1967 **OPH** *071 †35
BRYAN, Kathryn Ann. 1900 S MAIN ST, BLANCHARD VALLEY REG HLTH 45840 #056-06-1983 L2005 **DR** *020 †80
BUDKE, Heidi Linda. 1900 S MAIN ST 45840 #038-41-1990 L1996 **PTH HMP** *020 †50
BUTT, Taimur S. 1900 S MAIN ST, BLANCHARD VALLEY HOSPITAL 45840 #704-01-1989 L2002 **IM** *020 †20
CABOTAGE, Eduardo Venida. 1820 CHAPEL DR STE 1 45840 #748-01-1966 L1974 **IM GP** *020
CAIRNS, Michael Leo. 200 W PEARL ST 45840 #038-45-1995 L1996 **D** *020 †15
CHENEY, Daren Bradford. 1920 S MAIN ST STE E 45840 #038-43-1986 L1987 **FM** *020 †18 ‡
CHODISETTY, Subrahmanyam. 117 E WALLACE ST 45840 #495-11-1988 L2001 **CN** *020 †75
COLE, Brian Gary. 1920 S MAIN ST, STE E 45840 #038-43-1991 L1994 **FM** *020 †18
CONNER, Jennifer Lea. 1725 WESTERN AVE STE A 45840 #038-43-1994 L1995 **FM** *020 †18
COSIANO, Frank Anthony. 1725 WESTERN AVE STE A 45840 #038-40-1979 L1980 **FM** *020 †18
COSIANO, Frank Ralph. 1725 WESTERN AVE, STE A 45840 #038-40-1963 L1963 **FM OM** *071 †18
CROUSER, Kirk Darwin. 1900 S MAIN ST, HOSPITALIST DEPARTMENT 45840 #038-41-1998 L1999 **IM** *020 †20
DAVIS, Paul Thackrah. 1912 GREENDALE AVE 45840 #020-02-1983 L1986 **FM** *062 †18
DEERHAKE, Richard Henry. 301 W WALLACE ST 45840 #038-40-1971 L1971 **ORS** *071 †40
DELOS SANTOS, Edgar Ray S. 1995 TIFFIN AVE STE 30 45840 #748-22-1986 L2004 **AN** *020 ‡
DOONE, Jana Lynn. 1900 S MAIN ST, BLANCHARD VALLEY REG HLTH 45840 #038-45-1991 L1994 **PD** *020 †55
DY, Ernesto Yu. 1900 S MAIN ST, 2ND FL CDS 45840 #748-01-1970 L1979 **GS OS** *020 †85
ECHAVARRE, Irineo Plantig. 1900 S MAIN ST 45840 #748-02-1963 L1974 **TS GS** *071

EVERT, Donald Thomas. 300 W WALLACE ST, STE A1 45840 #038-40-1972 L1972 **P EM** *020 †16,75
FEIGERT, M Wesley. ■ 45840 #038-40-1946 L1946 **U** *071 †95
FOX, Mark R. 200 W PEARL ST 45840 #025-12-1993 L1996 **IM** *020
FRESHWATER, Stephen John. 1900 S MAIN ST 45840 #055-01-1984 L1985 **FM** *020 †18
GABRIEL, Josue Pereira. 301 W WALLACE ST 45840 #041-01-1991 L1997 **ORS OSS** *020 †40
GELDERMAN, Jana K. 1900 S MAIN ST, HEALTH CENTER 45840 #055-75-1995, ▲ L1999 **IM** *020 †20
GERSCHUTZ, Gregory Paul. 200 W PEARL ST 45840 #038-40-1996 L2000 **CD** *020 †20
GIDEON, James Alan. 200 W PEARL ST 45840 #038-40-1997 L1998 **RHU** *020 †20
GILBERT, Andre. 1651 N LAKE CT 45840 #187-67-1981 L1995 **U** *020 †95
GUAN, Liping. 1900 S MAIN ST 45840 #243-45-1983 L2001 **IM** *020 †20
GUNDA, Rajeswari. 2461 S MAIN ST 45840 #495-50-1976 L1988 **HO** *050 †20
HAAS, Donald Anson. ■ 45840 #038-06-1948 L1948 **IM** *071
HABIB, Farhana. 3949 N MAIN ST 45840 #704-02-1988 L1995 **OM** *020 †70
HANAWALT, Martin Earl. 1900 S MAIN ST, NEW CENTURY PEDIATRICS 45840 #038-40-1992 L1996 **PD** *072 †55
HAQ, Ihsan-Ul. 3949 N MAIN ST STE C 45840 #704-01-1979 L2002 **HO IM** *020 †20
HASSINK, George Van. 1818 CHAPEL DR STE C, BLANCHARD VALLEY OB-GYN IN 45840 #038-40-1977 L1981 **OBG** *071 †30
HATAHET, Mohamad Hazem. 1900 S MAIN ST, BLANCHARD VALLEY HEALTH SY 45840 #875-01-2002 L2006 **IM** *020 †20
HAZNECI, Sina Sami. 1900 S MAIN ST 45840 #025-07-1984 L1988 **DR** *020 †80
HEACOCK, Robert Lewis. 200 W PEARL ST, ATTN: CRYSTAL CLARK 45840 #038-40-1976 L1982 **GE IM** *020 †20
HECHT, Brian Patrick. 7595 TOWNSHIP ROAD 236, NORTHWEST OHIO ORTHOPEDIC 45840 #038-40-1993 L2001 **ORS** *020 †40
HECK, Bruce Eric. 7595 TOWNSHIP ROAD 236, NORTHWEST OHIO ORTHOPEDIC 45840 #038-44-1992 L1997 **ORS** *020 †40
HENDERSHOT, Jack G G. 15840 MEDICAL DR S, STE A 45840 #038-40-1973 L1974 **OPH** *020 †35
HIRSCHFELD, Gary Edward. 200 W PEARL ST 45840 #038-41-1974 L1978 **IM** *020
HOPKINS, William Eugene. 1725 WESTERN AVE STE A 45840 #038-43-1993 L1994 **FM** *020 †18
HUFF, Randal Eugene. 200 W PEARL ST 45840 #038-06-1990 L1991 **GE** *020 †20
JORDAN, Miguel Angel. 1900 CHAPEL DR 45840 #038-40-1986 L1987 **OBG OS** *020 †30
KLASS, Mandy Ann. 1920 S MAIN ST, STE E 45840 #038-43-2001 L2001 **FM** *020 †18
KNOR, Lisa Marie. 200 W PEARL ST 45840 #038-43-1986 L1989 **IM** *020 †20
KOEPKE, George H. 1900 S MAIN ST 45840 #038-41-1949 L1949 **PM** *071 †60
KOKOCHAROV, Stoyan Ivanov. 100 W PEARL ST 45840 #198-01-1985 L2004 **OPH** *020 †85
KOSE, William Henrik. 200 W PEARL ST 45840 #038-40-1971 L1972 **IM** *020 †20
LAI, David Yu-Shen. 1900 S MAIN ST 45840 #385-02-1965 L1971 **PTH NM** *020 †28,50
LAKSHMIPATHY, Narendranth. 1900 S MAIN ST 45840 #496-22-1989 L1997 **AN PME** *020 †05
LAMANCUSA, Joseph Carl. 207 W WALLACE ST 45840 #031-01-1986 L1988 **N** *020 †75
LEWIS, Danya Krystyna. 1900 S MAIN ST, BLANCHARD VALLEY HEALTH AS 45840 #035-03-2000 L2006 **P** *020
LI, Chaoyang. 15990 MEDICAL DR S 45840 #243-38-1985 L2003 **HO** *020 †20 ‡
LINDAMOOD, Michael Wm. 200 W PEARL ST 45840 #038-40-1971 L1971 **RHU IM** *020 †20
LINDER, Brian Jon. 539 S MAIN ST, MARATHON OIL CO 45840 #038-43-1987 L1988 **OM** *020 †70,18
LOGAN, Sean Raymond. 7595 COUNTY ROAD 236 45840 #038-45-1981 L1984 **NS GS** *020 †25
LUTZ, Stephen Thos. 1900 S MAIN ST, BLANCHARD VALLEY REGIONAL 45840 #025-01-1992 L2001 **RO** *020 †80
MAA, Tsong-Juen Shane. 300 W WALLACE ST STE A4 45840 #244-02-1972 L1981 **NS** *020
MAHLER, Herbert Adam. 1900 S MAIN ST 45840 #038-40-1956 L1956 **IM GE** *071
MALONE, Michael David. 1900 S MAIN ST, CDS SUITE 349 45840 #041-09-1991 L2004 **VS** *020 †85
MANUEL, Michael John. 1900 S MAIN ST, BLANCHARD VALLEY HOSPITAL 45840 #023-01-1996 L1999 **FM** *020 †18
MARUTHAVANAN, Ramalingam. 1900 S MAIN ST 45840 #495-61-1997 L2006 **PD** *020 †55
MC EVOY, Robert Enoch. 1725 WESTERN AVE, STE A 45840 #038-43-1979 L1980 **FM** *020 †18
MEIER, David John. 200 W PEARL ST, BLANCHARD VALLEY MEDICAL A 45840 #038-40-1998 L2005 **IC CD** *020 †20
MILLER, James Arden. 3949 N MAIN ST 45840 #038-40-1961 L1961 **GP FM** *020 †18
MORROW, Amy Elizabeth. 1900 S MAIN ST, CENTER 45840 #035-06-1999 L2002 **PD** *020 †55
MOUNT, Thomas Lyle. 1900 S MAIN ST 45840 #038-43-1986 L1987 **PD** *020 †55
NIE, Feng. 1995 TIFFIN AVE STE 308 45840 #243-21-1983 L2002 **AN** *020 †05 ‡
NIELSEN, Erik Wagner. 1110 W MAIN CROSS ST 45840 #025-07-1978 L1995 **OTO** *020 †45
NIESE, Christine Mary. 7595 TOWNSHIP ROAD 236, NORTHWEST OHIO ORTHOPEDIC 45840 #038-43-1995 L1996 **FM OS** *020 †18 ‡
ORR, Ami Janine. 1818 CHAPEL DR, BLANCHARD VALLEY PEDIATRIC 45840 #495-01-1992 L1993 **PD** *020 †55
ORR, Stephen Howard. 45840 MEDICAL DR S 45840 #038-40-1993 L1994 **OPH** *020 †35
OSBORNE, Carmela Gayle. 1733 S MAIN ST 45840 #020-12-1993 L2000 **PM** *020 †60
PAREKH, Mahendrakumar C. 763 ALDRIDGE PL 45840 #496-38-1963 L1972 **OBG** *020 †30
PARENTEAU, Gary Louis. 1900 S MAIN ST, CDS 3RD FL 3349 45840 #025-01-1986 L1996 **TS** *020 †85,90
PATEL, Subhaschandra R. 300 W WALLACE ST STE A5 45840 #495-37-1980 L1994 **PS** *020 †85
PEDLER, Kristi Lynn. 1917 S MAIN ST 45840 #025-07-2002 L2002 **OBG** *100
POHLMEYER, Ronald Arthur. 1900 S MAIN ST 45840 #038-40-1971 L1971 **HO** *071 †20
POLDER, Richard Michael. 300 W WALLACE ST, FINDLAY SURGICAL ASSOC 45840 #038-40-1984 L1987 **GS** *020 †85
PRAPROTNIK, Darja. 1900 S MAIN ST 45840 #957-03-1988 L2000 **PTH** *020 †50
PRUDEN, Youngmi. ■ 45840 #038-43-2008 *012
RABENHORST, Arthur Edward. ■ 45840 #422-01-2002 L2004 **OM** *020
RAO, Lalitha Kumari R. 1900 S MAIN ST 45840 #495-59-1978 L1982 **P CHP** *020 †75
RATNASAMY, Nathaniel A. 1816 CHAPEL DR, STE J 45840 #037-01-1989 L2002 **ID IM** *020 †20
RAY, Angela. 200 W PEARL ST 45840 #038-40-2000 L2000 **IM** *020 †20
REEDS, Ralph Edgar, Jr. 1920 S MAIN ST 45840 #018-03-1956 L1982 **D** *020
REID, Andrew James. 1110 W MAIN CROSS ST, FINDLAY EAR NOSE & THROAT 45840 #065-05-1976 L1996 **OTO** *020 †45
RICKETTS, Gregory Andrew. 200 W PEARL ST 45840 #038-40-1993 L1995 **IM** *020 †20
RITZ, Andrew Neil. 1818 CHAPEL DR STE D, BLANCHARD VALLEY PED INC 45840 #038-43-1984 L1986 **PD** *020 †55
ROBERTSON, James Richard. 1110 W MAIN CROSS ST, FINDLAY EAR NOSE & THROAT 45840 #038-40-1970 L1970 **OTO A** *020 †45

ROWER, John Marvin. 7383 TOWNSHIP ROAD 95 45840 #038-40-1972 L1972 **D** *020 †15

SAJED, Mohammad. 300 W WALLACE ST STE B- 45840 #496-27-1998 L2006 **N** *100 †75 ‡

SAVAGE, Donald Ray, Jr. 1818 CHAPEL DR, BLANCHARD VALLEY 45840 #038-40-1981 L1982 **PD** *020 †55

SCHROEDER, Leroy Lavern. 200 W PEARL ST 45840 #038-40-1971 L1971 **END IM** *020 †20

SCHULTZ, Jeffrey William. 1900 S MAIN ST, ADULT HOSPITALIST 45840 #038-44-1995 L1998 **FM** *020 †18

SCHUTZ, Robert Edward. 1641 S LAKE CT 45840 #038-43-1986 L1989 **OBG** *020 †30

SENN, Loren Edgar. ■ 45840 #038-40-1947 L1947 **GS** *072 †85

SHAH, Vipul Bhupatrai. 1900 S MAIN ST, IMAGING CONS OF FINDLAY 45840 #495-76-1984 L2004 **R RNR** *020 †80 ‡

SIA-UY, Agripina. ■ 45840 #748-08-1971 L1980 **AN** *071

SIERRA, Edward. ■ 45840 #038-43-1986 L1988 **FM** *020 †18

SKIBICKI, Richard. 1900 S MAIN ST, CENTER-FINDLAY CAMPUS 45840 #038-43-1980 L1982 **EM FM** *020 †16,18

SOLAIMAN, Abdel Raouf M S. 1725 S MAIN ST 45840 #915-03-1970 L1977 **CRS GS** *071 †10,85

SORRELLS, Jimmy Ray. 1900 S MAIN ST, DEPT OF PATHOLOGY 45840 #017-20-1976 L1989 **PTH GP** *020 †50

STITT, William. ■ 45840 #038-40-1968 L1968 **IM IMG** *071 †20

STRIGLE, Thomas Ralph. 300 W WALLACE ST, FINDLAY SURGICAL ASSOC 45840 #038-44-1986 L1988 **GS** *020 †85

STUMP, Michael Chas. 340 COLLEGE ST 45840 #038-41-1989 L1992 **FSM** *020 †18

TIDABACK, Austin J. ■ 45840 #035-03-1942 L1961 **R** *071

TONG, Alan Theodore. 1641 N LAKE CT 45840 #038-40-1971 L1971 **GYN** *020 †30

TREMAINS, Michael Robert. 1900 S MAIN ST 45840 #038-43-1997 L1998 **ORS** *020 †40

TROPF, Thomas Edward. 1900 S MAIN ST, BLANCHARD VALLEY HOSP 45840 #038-43-1986 L1987 **EM FM** *020 †18

UY, Domingo S. 1900 S MAIN ST 45840 #748-08-1967 L1972 **AN** *071 †05

VALENTZ, Thomas Michael. 1900 S MAIN ST, BLANCHARO VALLEY RHC 45840 #038-41-1996 L1997 **DR** *020 †80

WARE, David Allen. 1725 WESTERN AVE, STE A 45840 #038-40-1997 L2000 **FM** *020 †18

WATSON, Rick David. 200 W PEARL ST 45840 #038-40-1975 L1980 **PUD IM** *020 †20

WEINGATES, Joseph A, Jr. 1818 CHAPEL DR, STE C 45840 #038-40-1968 L1968 **OBG** *020 †30

WOJCIECHOWSKI, Thomas E. 1900 S MAIN ST, PEDIATRIC HOSPITALIST OF N 45840 #038-43-1994 L1995 **PD** *020 †55 ‡

YODER, Douglas Wm. 1725 S MAIN ST 45840 #038-41-1991 L1998 **CRS** *020 †85,10

ZIEGLER, Emil Christian. 1900 S MAIN ST 45840 #038-40-1971 L1971 **OBG** *020 †30

FORT JENNINGS – PUTNAM

MARKWARD, Tammy L. ■ 45844 #038-43-2008 *012

FORT RECOVERY – MERCER

ROHRER, David Michael. 807 BLUE JACKET DR, FORT RECOVERY FAMILY MEDIC 45846 #038-45-1993 L1994 **FM** *020 †18

FOSTORIA – SENECA

ANVARI-HAMEDANI, Mohammad. 324 W TIFFIN ST 44830 #517-01-1964 L1970 **OBG GP** *020 †30

ASSALY, Ragheb A. 501 VAN BUREN ST 44830 #781-03-1984 L1996 **IM** *020 †20

BEIDELSCHIES, Tim Arthur. 217 N COUNTYLINE ST 44830 #038-43-1997 L2000 **FM** *020 †18

BENNETT, Kathryn Marie. 506 VAN BUREN ST, GRAYSTONE CLINIC 44830 #063-01-1996 L1998 **FM** *020 †18

BIELEFELD, Michael John. 501 VAN BUREN ST STE 202 44830 #038-44-1989 L1994 **GS** *020 †85

BYATT, James Sydney. 501 VAN BUREN ST, STE 202 44830 #060-02-1981 L1998 **FM** *020

DAVIDSON, James Jos. 506 VAN BUREN ST 44830 #036-07-1992 L1998 **ORS** *020 †40

DAVIS, Edwin Brayton. 502 VAN BUREN ST 44830 #038-40-1966 L1966 **FM** *020 †18

DAVIS, Randolph John. 506 VAN BUREN ST, GREYSTONE CLINIC 44830 #063-01-1987 L1998 *100

ENGLE, Jewel Ann. 501 VAN BUREN ST 44830 #038-43-1991 L1995 **IM PD** *020 †55,20 ‡

ERULKAR, Solomon Eliab. 801 PARK AVE 44830 #496-38-1956 L1972 **IM CD** *020

FONDESSY, Terrence Merle. 217 N COUNTYLINE ST 44830 #038-43-1983 L1984 **FM EM** *020 †18

GARCIA, Carolyn Rivera. 801 KIRK ST, STE 3 44830 #748-07-1986 L2005 **PD** *020 †55

GOOD, Lowell Kenyon. 501 VAN BUREN ST 44830 #025-07-1956 L1957 **EM FM** *071 †18

GUNDA, Anjaneyulu. 506 VAN BUREN ST 44830 #496-01-1972 L1988 **PD** *020

HARVEY, Roy Edgar, III. 506 VAN BUREN ST 44830 #038-40-1973 L1973 **FM EM** *020 †18

KORRAPATI, Govardhana Rao. 301 PERRY ST 44830 #495-98-1974 L1981 **IM** *020 †20

LALI, Monwabisi David. 709 N VINE ST 44830 #050-02-1993 L1996 **IM** *020

LOWERY, Samuel R. 1225 N COUNTYLINE ST 44830 #041-12-1955 L1956 **AN GP** *071

PADANILAM, George Jos. 501 VAN BUREN ST 44830 #495-31-1964 L1972 **GS FM** *020 †85

SCHEIBLY, Donald Jos. 909 WASHINGTON T R 243 44830 #020-02-1983 L1986 **FM** *020 †18

THIRASILPA, Pramuan. 948 EBERSOLE BLVD 44830 #891-02-1967 L1972 **GP PD** *020 †55

FRANKFORT – ROSS

SEYFANG, Todd Leroy. ■ 45628 #038-41-1994 *100

FRANKLIN – WARREN

BEDEL, Gary Werner. 333 CONOVER DR, STE E 45005 #038-45-1990 L1991 **FM** *020 †18

BEEBE, Nathan Lewis. 333 CONOVER DR, STE E 45005 #005-12-1993 L1997 **FM** *020 †18

CHOCKALINGAM, Porselvi. ■ 45005 #495-37-2001 L2005 **HO** *012 †20

CRESPO, Dolores Luz. 333 CONOVER DR, STE E 45005 #176-03-1970 L1981 **FM PTH** *072

HOWARD, Kyle L. ■ 45005 #017-20-1988 L1992 **FM** *020 †18

MC MAHAN, Steven Dwight. 235 INDUSTRIAL DR 45005 #038-43-1997 L1999 **EM** *020 †16

MIRANDA, David Michael. 3290 VILLAGE DR 45005 #038-45-1993 L1994 **FM** *020 †18

NICOLAS, Victor Timothy. 5950 INNOVATION DR, BIDWELL SURGERY CENTER 45005 #038-41-1983 L1986 **AN** *020 †05

PAI, Dinesh Vasudev. 1 MEDICAL CENTER DR, EMERGENCY DEPT 45005 #495-99-1981 L2006 **FM** *020 †18

SOOY, Robert Earl. 3290 VILLAGE DR 45005 #649-01-1962 L1964 **FM** *071 †18

ZOLLETT, Jeffrey Sloan. 200 MEDICAL CENTER DR, STE 490 45005 #016-42-1973 L1977 **GP** *020

ZOLLETT, Scott Lawrence. 200 MEDICAL CENTER DR, STE 490 45005 #016-42-1974 L1976 **IM** *020

FRAZEYSBURG – MUSKINGUM

POIRIER, Robert Francis. 42 E 3RD ST 43822 #064-01-1997 L2000 **FM** *020 †18

FREDERICKSBURG – WAYNE

KORNHAUS, Robert Kim. ■ 44627 #038-40-1992 L1993 **FM** *020 †18

FREDERICKTOWN – KNOX

ANDREWS, Jennifer Lynn. 16361 VILLAGE PKWY 43019 #038-43-1991 L1994 **PD** *020 †55

BOWERS, Jeffery John. 16361 VILLAGE PKWY 43019 #041-02-1983 L1991 **FM FPG** *020 †18

ELDER, William Allen. 122 COLUMBUS RD 43019 #038-45-1980 L1981 **FM** *020 †18

SMITH, Matthew Bradley. 122 COLUMBUS RD 43019 #038-43-1999 L1999 **FM** *020 †18

FREEPORT – GUERNSEY

BARTUNEK, Kathleen Rickey. PO BOX 207, 110 W MAIN ST 43973 #038-40-1988 L1989 **FM** *020 †18

CIMONS, Ira Marvin. ■ 43973 #869-02-1960 L1963 **AN** *020 †05

FREMONT – SANDUSKY

ADUSUMILLI, Ravi Kumar. 715 S TAFT AVE, STE 195 43420 #495-58-1983 L1995 **CD IM** *020 †20

AHMED, Fateh. 715 S TAFT AVE 43420 #704-02-1990 L2002 **PCC** *020 †20

AREVALO, Iracema. 410 BIRCHARD AVE 43420 #737-06-1997 L2007 **PDI** *100 †55

BELCH, Richard Hughes. ■ 43420 #038-06-1948 L1948 **AN IM** *071

BERLACHER, Paul Douglas. 715 S TAFT AVE, STE 195 43420 #038-43-1976 L1981 **CD IM** *020 †20

BINGLE, James Francis. 715 S TAFT AVE, STE 195 43420 #038-40-1975 L1985 **CD IM** *020 †20

BISHARA, Nagi Amin Sadek. 715 S TAFT AVE, STE 195 43420 #915-02-1975 L1984 **CD IM** *020 †20

BOWER, Mary Frances. 1479 N RIVER RD 43420 #038-43-1996 L1997 **FM** *020 †18

BROWN, Frank Cyril, II. 1916 GLEN SPRINGS DR 43420 #038-43-2001 L2003 **FM** *020 †18

BROWN, Jennifer Lynn. 715 S TAFT AVE 43420 #038-43-2001 L2004 **IM** *020 †20

BUSH, Everett Martin. 715 S TAFT AVE, STE 195 43420 #038-40-1972 L1972 **CD IM** *020 †20

CHUDZINSKI, Abigail C. ■ 43420 #038-75-2007, ▲ L2007 *012

CHUNG, Soo Wook. 2539 HAYES AVE 43420 #583-09-1969 L1977 **PD NPM** *071 †55

COLEMAN, Gary Bernard. 605 3RD AVE, STE A 43420 #025-01-1989 L1994 **OTO HNS** *020 †45

DALAL, Karl Noshir. 715 S TAFT AVE 43420 #925-82-1996 L2004 **PD** *020 †55

DEBENEDETTI, Laura Lynn. 715 S TAFT AVE, STE 195 43420 #038-43-1998 L1999 **CD** *020 †20

DE FRANCE, David Thos. 715 S TAFT AVE 43420 #038-44-1984 L1985 **FM** *020 †18

DIERKSHEIDE, Eugene F. 715 S TAFT AVE 43420 #038-40-1957 L1957 **OBG** *071 †30

DILLER, Jonathan Ford. 2575 HAYES AVE STE 4 43420 #038-43-1979 L1980 **FM EM** *020 †18

DITTEMORE, Harold Eugene. ■ 43420 #019-02-1953 L1967 **GP** *075

EVANS, Cynthia Lynn. 715 S TAFT AVE 43420 #038-40-1979 L1980 **P** *020

FARRELL, Scott James. 528 3RD AVE 43420 #025-01-1976 L1982 **GYN** *020 †30

FARRUKH, Naghmana. 410 BIRCHARD AVE 43420 #704-16-1987 L2004 **PD** *020 †55 ‡

GEDERT, Robert James. 1908 GLEN SPRINGS DR 43420 #010-02-1956 L1956 **GS** *071

GROSSMAN, Thomas G. 528 3RD AVE BOX 1129 43420 #038-40-1974 L1974 **GYN** *071 †30

HARRISON, Kurt D. 1920 GLEN SPRINGS DR 43420 #041-78-1997, ▲ L2002 **OBG** *020

HASHIM, Muhammad. 2340 HAYES AVE 43420 #704-02-1962 L1975 **PD ADL** *020 †55

HAYNES, Heather Ann. 2265 HAYES AVE 43420 #038-45-2004 L2007 **FM** *020 †18

HIESTAND, John Jos. 2575 HAYES AVE, STE 1 43420 #038-40-1987 L1991 **IM PD** *020 †20,55

HOTTOIS, Michael David. 675 BARTSON RD, SERVICES OF SANDUSKY CTY 43420 #038-43-1988 L1996 **CHP** *020 †18

HULL, Charles Edward. 1916 GLEN SPRINGS DR 43420 #035-20-1963 L1965 **IM** *020 †20

IMM, John Paul. 410 BIRCHARD AVE 43420 #038-43-1991 L1992 **FM** *020 †18

ISSA, Mark G. 715 S TAFT AVE, STE 195 43420 #028-78-1992, ▲ L1998 **CD** *020 †20

JACKSON, Alvin Deron. 410 BIRCHARD AVE 43420 #038-40-1989 L1993 **FM** *020 †18

JACKSON, Clara Marie. 2539 HAYES AVE 43420 #038-43-2001 L2006 **MPD** *020

JACKSON, Nkenge Ayeola. 595 BARTSON RD 43420 #012-21-2000 L2000 **OBG** *020 †30

JAIN, Navin Kumar. 715 S TAFT AVE 43420 #495-45-1982 L1995 **PCC SME** *020 †20

JOG, Alaka Prakash. ■ 43420 #495-28-1970 L1990 **AN** *071 †05

JOSEPH, K Abraham. ■ 43420 #495-44-1965 L1975 **IM HEM** *071 †20

KODURI, Vinod Kumar. 715 S TAFT AVE 43420 #495-21-1973 L1983 **AN PMM** *020

LEWIS, Anita Marie. 410 BIRCHARD AVE 43420 #038-43-1990 L1994 **FM** *071

LONGABAUGH, John Peter. 715 S TAFT AVE, STE 195 43420 #041-12-1982 L2003 **CD IM** *020 †20

MAAIEH, Mohammad A. 715 S TAFT AVE, STE 195 43420 #575-01-1991 L1999 **CD** *020 †20

MARSHALL, Robert Aaron. 715 S TAFT AVE 43420 #038-40-1982 L1983 **OM FM** *020 †18

MARTINS, Maria Nisha. ■ 43420 #496-38-1998 L2006 **PD** *020 †55

MEADE, Gary Wesley. 771 BARKER RD 43420 #047-06-1971 L1972 **PTH** *062 †50

MILLER, Carroll Denman. ■ 43420 #025-07-1946 L1947 **GP OM** *071

MONAHAN, John Wm. 1900 HAYES AVE 43420 #016-11-1946 L1949 **FM** *071

MONROE, Todd Lewis. 715 S TAFT AVE, STE 195 43420 #020-12-1987 L1990 **FM** *020 †18

MOORE, Leon Hamilton. ■ 43420 #038-06-1943 L1944 **GS** *071 †85

MULLINS, Penny Lynn. 410 BIRCHARD AVE 43420 #038-40-1994 L1995 **FM** *020 †18

O'LEARY, Arthur Hugh. 675 BARTSON RD, FIRELANDS COUNSELING AND R 43420 #038-40-1983 L1984 **P** *020 †75

OSORIO, Millicent Go. 410 BIRCHARD AVE 43420 #748-01-2001 L2007 **IM** *020 †20

PADAMADAN, William Louis. 715 S TAFT AVE 43420 #495-31-1962 L1990 **CD IM** *020 †20

PETERS, Ralph William. 1908 GLEN SPRINGS DR 43420 #017-20-1993 L1998 **GS** *020 †85

PORTER, Jason Jeremy. ■ 43420 #038-43-1998 L2007 **AN** *020

QUTEISH, Veeda Omaia. 418 BIRCHARD AVE 43420 #575-01-1998 L2007 **IM** *020 †20

RANDALL, John Kelly. 605 3RD AVE 43420 #038-43-1977 L1981 **ORS** *020 †40

REED, Eldon Sherman. 2105 PINEHURST TRL, 715 SOUTH TAFT AVENUE 43420 #018-03-1964 L1990 **AN PME** *020

ROUSH, Kenneth Wayne. 715 S TAFT AVE, STE 195 43420 #038-43-1982 L1985 **CD IM** *020 †20

SANGAL, Sanjay. 715 S TAFT AVE 43420 #038-45-1987 L1988 **IM AN** *020 †05

SAYANI, Jairaj Navinchand. 1220 E STATE ST 43420 #496-26-1999 L2006 **FM** *020 †18

SCHWARTZ, John Lorain. 715 S TAFT AVE, STE 195 43420 #025-07-1978 L1983 **CD IM** *020 †20

SHARIFF, Afser. 605 3RD AVE, STE A 43420 #028-46-1997 L2003 **OTO** *020 †45

SHEEN, Youngkyu Peter. 3051 PORT CLINTON RD 43420 #583-02-1963 L1972 **U** *062 †95

SMILEY, Nasser Hussein. 715 S TAFT AVE, STE 195 43420 #038-40-1985 L1987 **CD IM** *020 †20

STIERWALT, Howard Geo. 2575 HAYES AVE STE 3 43420 #038-40-1977 L1978 **FM** *020 †18

STIERWALT, James Lee. 715 S TAFT AVE 43420 #038-45-1984 L1985 **AN** *020 †05

STOCKTON, Frederick R. 715 S TAFT AVE, STE 195 43420 #024-07-1986 L1987 **CD** *020 †20

SUFI, Naheed. 715 S TAFT AVE, MEMORIAL HOSPITAL HEALTHLI 43420 #704-18-1982 L1995 **FM** *020 †18

TAMIRISA, Praveen Kumar. 715 S TAFT AVE, STE 195 43420 #495-21-1991 L2001 **IC** *020 †20

UPAMAKA, Gopinath Rao. 715 S TAFT AVE, STE 195 43420 #495-21-1982 L1987 **CD IM** *020 †20

VALONE, Charles L, Jr. 1223 OAK HARBOR RD 43420 #041-77-1978, ▲ L1982 **GP IM** *020

VON KUSTER, Larry Carl. 715 S TAFT AVE 43420 #005-12-1977 L1982 **PTH DMP** *020 †50

WIECEK, Richard Michael. 2281 HAYES AVE 43420 #038-45-1999 L2004 **GS** *020 ‡

WONDERLY, Mary Beth. 2575 HAYES AVE STE 3 43420 #038-43-2001 L2003 **FM** *020 †18 ‡

WRIGHT, Rickey. 1823 W STATE ST 43420 #047-07-1986 L1989 **GP** *020

FRIENDSHIP – SCIOTO

SCHOETTLE, Louis M. ■ 45630 #038-40-1953 L1953 **GP** *071

GAHANNA – FRANKLIN

ALEXANDER, Michael James. 504 HAVENS CORNERS RD 43230 #038-40-1999 L1999 **FM** *020 †18

ARBONA, Fernando Luis. 4156 GUSTON PL 43230 #038-41-2001 L2001 **AN** *100 †05

BARUA, Sambit Kumar. ■ 43230 #160-02-1973 L1983 **AN** *020

BOHNERT, Christina Marie. 1110 BEECHER XING N, STE B 43230 #038-40-1999 L1999 **FM** *020 †18

BRAVERMAN, Lisa Jo. 765 N HAMILTON RD, COLUMBUS EAST INTERNAL MED 43230 #038-40-1989 L1991 **IM** *020 †20

BROWN, Lora J. 765 N HAMILTON RD STE 235 43230 #038-40-1990 L1991 **IM** *020 †20

CALLION, Raleigh S, Jr. 947 E JOHNSTOWN RD 43230 #038-40-1981 L1983 **FM** *020 †18

COLON, Fernando. 1050 BEECHER XING N, STE C 43230 #308-03-1977 L1984 **PS GS** *020 †65

CONROY, Maria Riza Blanca. 504 HAVENS CORNERS RD 43230 #748-14-1995 L2000 **FM** *020 †18

COTELL, Stephanie L. 925 N HAMILTON RD, STE 100 43230 #016-06-1993 L2001 **D** *020 †15

COX, Nadine Elizabeth. 1329 CHERRY WAY DR STE 200 43230 #038-40-1998 L1999 **FM** *020 †18

CUNNINGHAM, Jos Harry, Jr. 4625 MORSE RD, STE 200 43230 #023-01-1970 L1979 **PUD IM** *020 †20

DINEEN, Patrick Jos. 117 N HIGH ST 43230 #016-02-1976 L1979 **IM** *020 †20

DOLMAN, Mortimer. 175 W JOHNSTOWN RD 43230 #065-05-1963 L1970 **IM END** *020 †20

DONOGHUE, Brian David. ■ 43230 #016-11-2004 L2004 **EM** *020

DOYLE, Susan Kugel. 1375 CHERRY WAY DR, STE 110 43230 #038-40-1984 L1985 **OBG** *020 †30

DUTTON, Olena Mykolaivna. 4477 COLLIER DR 43230 #913-57-1994 L2004 **IM** *012 †20

EDDY, Steven Robert. ■ 43230 #038-40-2006 L2006 **ORS** *012

EDWARDS, Mohammed Farid. ■ 43230 #836-02-1966 L1974 **AN** *020 †05

GHATAK, Arnab. ■ 43230 #041-01-2001 **IM**

GREEN, Leslie Mormol. 765 N HAMILTON RD STE 255 43230 #038-45-1991 L1992 **FM** *020 †18

HANINGER, Glenn J. ■ 43230 #016-43-1949 L1955 **OBG** *071 †30

HEINMILLER, Daniel John. 470 SILVER LN 43230 #038-40-1982 L1985 **PD** *020 †55

HERRON, Joel Bain. 925 N HAMILTON RD, STE 100 43230 #045-04-1997 L2001 **D** *020 †15

HONER, Jeffrey James. ■ 43230 #038-40-2008 *012

KAHWASH, Rami. ■ 43230 #875-01-1997 L2007 **CD** *100 †20

KELLY, Brian Scott. ■ 43230 #038-40-2003 L2006 **EM** *020 †16

KERN, Richard Alan. 470 SILVER LN, GAHANNA PEDIATRICS 43230 #038-40-1982 L1985 **PD** *020 †55

LEIMBACH, Warren H, II. 1329 CHERRY WAY DR, STE 700 43230 #649-14-1980 L1988 **NS** *020 †25

LUTZ, Joseph G, Jr. 535 OFFICENTER PL, STE A 43230 #038-40-1984 L1984 **FM** *020 †18

MARQUES, Laurel Elizabeth. ■ 43230 #038-40-1995 L2005 **FM** *020 †18

MASON, Janet Rae. 504 HAVENS CORNERS RD 43230 #038-45-1995 L1996 **FM** *020 †18 ‡

MC INTOSH, Sara S Alford. ■ 43230 #038-40-1986 L1987 **P** *020 †75

MC KELVEY, Michael Todd. 925 N HAMILTON RD 43230 #038-40-2002 L2002 **D** *020 †20

MILLER, Jeffery David. 765 N HAMILTON RD, STE 255 43230 #038-40-1987 L1988 **FM** *020 †18

MORGAN-FOLLOWELL, Bethanie. ■ 43230 #020-12-2006 L2006 **PD** *012

MYERS, William Ambler. ■ 43230 #038-40-1965 L1965 **FM IMG** *071 †18

OH, Shi Han. ■ 43230 #583-02-1960 L1992 **OBG** *020 †30 ‡

OLMO, Franklin A. 98 GRANVILLE ST, OLMO FAMILY PRACTICE INC 43230 #042-02-1992 L1995 **FM** *020 †18 ‡

PARKER, Audra Justine. ■ 43230 #038-40-2004 L2004 **IM** *020 †20

PRESTON, Mark Clifford. 765 N HAMILTON RD STE 130 43230 #038-40-1984 L1985 **PS** *020 †65

SCHREIBER, Donald Merle. 1329 CHERRY WAY DR, STE 500 43230 #020-02-1974 L1994 **IM GPM** *020 †20

SCHULTIES, Daniel Robert. ■ 43230 #056-05-2002 L2002 **PD** *020 †55

SCHUMACHER, Kristina Sue. 206 W JOHNSTOWN RD, KRISTINA SCHUMACHER MD INC 43230 #038-45-1992 L1994 **FM** *020 †18

STEPHENSON, Camille. ■ 43230 #038-40-2006 L2006 **P** *012

SUBISAK, Daniel Craig. ■ 43230 #038-40-2007 L2007 **IM** *012

TAYLOR, Benjamin Craig. ■ 43230 #038-40-2005 L2005 **ORS** *012

TEAGUE, Delois. 1375 CHERRY WAY DR 43230 #038-41-1984 L1986 **OBG** *020 †30

TEAGUE, Dimitri. ■ 43230 #038-41-1984 L1986 **EM** *062

THOMPSON, Jamie Beth. ■ 43230 #038-40-2005 L2005 **PD** *012

ZAINO, John Paul. 765 N HAMILTON RD, STE 255 43230 #038-45-1996 L1997 **FM** *020 †18

ZOCHOWSKI, Nicole Marie. 1375 CHERRY WAY DR 43230 #038-45-2003 L2003 **OBG** *020

GALENA – DELAWARE

DELL, John Chas. 3879 LAKEVIEW DR, P O BOX 398 43021 #048-14-1981 L1982 **IM** *020 †20

KERSEY, Joe Stephen. ■ 43021 #038-40-1975 L1975 **AN GP** *020 †05

NELIN, Mary Ann Cook. ■ 43021 #048-13-1982 L2003 **PD** *074 †55

RAGHAVAN, Anu. ■ 43021 #028-46-2000 L2004 **P** *020 †75

WEBER, Stephen Wm. ■ 43021 #038-40-1961 L1961 **R** *020 †80

GALION – CRAWFORD

AGRAWAL, Narendra Kumar T. 815 HARDING WAY W 44833 #495-23-1972 L1979 **CD IM** *020 †20

BELARDO, Orpha T Eusebio. 269 PORTLAND WAY S 44833 #748-08-1963 L1973 **AN** *071

BROWN, Marcia Fischer. 955 BUCYRUS RD 44833 #016-11-1991 L1994 **PD** *020 †55

CHOI, Andrew An-Hong. ■ 44833 #583-09-1968 L1974 **PD** *020 †55

CHOW, Johnson Hsiangsheng. ■ 44833 #242-09-1946 L1956 **PTH NM** *071 †50

DAWSON, Robert L. 955 HOSFORD RD 44833 #041-07-1998 L2003 **ORS** *020 †40

EBNER, Theodore Frank. 269 PORTLAND WAY S 44833 #038-40-1969 L1969 **ORS** *075 †40

ECKSTEIN, Howard M. 270 PORTLAND WAY S, P O BOX 607 44833 #035-08-1991 L1998 **PD** *020 †55

EUBANK, Geoffrey Alan. 269 PORTLAND WAY S 44833 #038-40-1991 L1992 **N** *020 †75

GOUDY, James Arthur, II. 270 PORTLAND WAY S 44833 #038-40-1987 L1988 **IM** *020 †20

HANNA, John Thos. 270 PORTLAND WAY S 44833 #038-45-1986 L1987 **FM** *020 †18

HEON, David Guy. 270 PORTLAND WAY S 44833 #038-43-1991 L1995 **GS** *020 †85

HUGGINS, Tyler Kauffman. 1200 STATE ROUTE 598 44833 #038-40-1988 L1991 **OBG** *020 †30

KERBS, James Randall. 269 PORTLAND WAY S 44833 #005-12-1987 L1989 **ORS** *020 †40

MANSFIELD, Bernard M. 955 BUCYRUS RD 44833 #020-02-1947 L1949 **FM IMG** *071 †18

MANTHEY, William Chauncey. 860 HARDING WAY W 44833 #041-13-1954 L1955 **GP PHP** *071

ORIS, William R. PORTLAND WAY SOUTH 44833 #038-40-1953 L1953 **R** *071 †80

PABST, Lawrence Allen. 955 HOSFORD RD 44833 #038-40-1974 L1975 **ORS** *020 †40

PARK, Joon Man. 269 PORTLAND WAY S, DEPT OF PADROLOGY 44833 #583-01-1969 L1989 **PTH PCP** *062 †50

RONDON, Antonio. 270 PORTLAND WAY S 44833 #847-02-1957 L1966 **OBG** *071 †30

SANDER, Daryl Ray. 269 PORTLAND WAY S 44833 #038-40-1985 L1986 **GS** *020 †85

SANTIAGO, Roberto. 396 PORTLAND WAY N 44833 #042-01-1985 L1988 **GP OS** *020 †16

SEETHARAMAN, Patabi. 251 PORTLAND WAY N 44833 #203-01-1987 L1989 **OPH IM** *020 †35

TUGAOEN, Melanie Kay. 740 GROVE AVE 44833 #038-40-1990 L1991 **IM** *020

VELANDIA, Plinio E. 269 PORTLAND WAY S 44833 #264-01-1959 L1967 **OBG** *020 †30

WIDMAN, Donald Eugene. ■ 44833 #038-41-1960 L1960 **DR** *071 †80

WOOD, Mark A. 955 BUCYRUS RD 44833 #038-75-1985, ▲ L1986 **FM** *020

GALLIPOLIS – GALLIA

ABBASI, Saqib Arif. 90 JACKSON PIKE 45631 #704-20-1998 L2005 **PD** *020

ABELS, Gene Harland. 936 STATE ROUTE 160 45631 #038-40-1957 L1957 **CD IM** *020 †20

AGYEI-GYAMFI, Kwadwo. 90 JACKSON PIKE 45631 #412-01-1993 L2004 **GE** *020 †20

AL-ATAIE, Mohammad Bashar. 90 JACKSON PIKE, HOLZER CLINIC 45631 #875-01-1991 L1997 **IM** *020 †20

ALLI, Aderemi Basit. 90 JACKSON PIKE, HOLZER CLINIC 45631 #690-01-1991 L2004 **IM** *100 †20 ‡

ALONZO, Restituto H. ■ 45631 #748-01-1957 L1964 **U** *071 †95

ALQADAH, Farouq Darwish S. 90 JACKSON PIKE 45631 #875-01-1974 L1980 **IM HEM** *020 †20

ALTHAUS, David Paul. 90 JACKSON PIKE 45631 #016-11-1976 L1992 **PTH** *062 †50

AMENDT, Wayne Cleave. 90 JACKSON PIKE, HOLZER CLINIC INC 45631 #005-12-1976 L1985 **OAR OSM** *020 †40

ATKINS, Diane L. ■ 45631 #056-05-1973 L1991 **PD AN** *020 †55

BIVENS, Spencer Lee, Jr. 90 JACKSON PIKE 45631 #055-01-1964 L2001 **IM** *071

BLACK, Daniel Robt, Jr. 90 JACKSON PIKE 45631 #041-77-1985, ▲ L1989 **PM** *020 †60

BLEVINS, David Virgil. 90 JACKSON PIKE, HOLZER CLINIC INC 45631 #038-40-1993 L1994 **GS** *020 †85

BLODGETT, Thomas Peter. 995 JACKSON PIKE, STE 102 45631 #038-40-1994 L1998 **D** *020 †15

BOWERS, Glenn Wilson, Jr. ■ 45631 #047-06-1963 L1969 **PD A** *071 †55

BOZKIR, Naci Ihsan. 90 JACKSON PIKE, HOLZER CLINIC 45631 #038-41-1986 L1991 **OPH** *020 †35

BRAGA-NEWBOLD, V. 90 JACKSON PIKE, HOLZER CLINIC 45631 #919-03-1974 L1992 **OS EM** *050 †16

BRANDEBERRY, Keith Robt. ■ 45631 #038-06-1946 L1946 **OBG** *071 †30

BROY, Lance Frederick. 90 JACKSON PIKE 45631 #055-01-2001 L2007 **FM** *100 †18

BRUBAKER, Reid Clarence. 90 JACKSON PIKE, HOLZER CLINIC INC 45631 #038-40-1970 L1970 **IM** *020 †20

CALLICOTT, Rod Wesley. ■ 45631 #305-01-1998 L2007 **ATP PCP** *020 †50

CANADY, Michael Ray. 90 JACKSON PIKE, HOLZER CLINIC 45631 #036-05-1985 L1990 **GS** *020 †85

CAPPELLETTI, Danielle T. 90 JACKSON PIKE 45631 #055-02-2003 L2006 **PD** *020 †55

CASANOVA, Manuel Aguirre. 90 JACKSON PIKE, HOLZER CLINIC 45631 #748-10-1971 L1978 **R** *020 †80

CASTILLO, Santiago S, Jr. 100 JACKSON PIKE, HOLZER MED CTR LAB 45631 #748-02-1975 L1990 **PTH GP** *020 †50

CHAKSUPA, Montrie. 90 JACKSON PIKE 45631 #891-03-1968 L1975 **OBG** *020 †30

CHRISTOPHER, Mark G. 90 JACKSON PIKE 45631 #495-04-1977 L1983 **GE** *020 †20

■ = Address Information Privacy Protected

CLARK, Christopher B. 90 JACKSON PIKE 45631 #055-02-1998 L2003 **AI** *020 †20,03
CONLEY, Steven Dean. ■ 45631 #055-02-2008 *012
CRUM, Joseph Dexter. 90 JACKSON PIKE, HOLZER CLINIC INC 45631 #055-75-1993, ▲ L1994 *020
DACHOWSKI, Alice A. 90 JACKSON PIKE, HOLZER CLINIC 45631 #028-02-1981 L1985 **GS** *020 †85
DACHOWSKI, Edward Albert, Jr. 90 JACKSON PIKE, HOLZER CLINIC 45631 #041-02-1997 L1999 **P CHP** *020 †75
ECONOMIDES, Nicholas-John. 90 JACKSON PIKE 45631 #418-01-1973 L2002 **PS GS** *020 †85,65
ELLISON, John R. 90 JACKSON PIKE, HOLZER CLINIC 45631 #055-75-1983, ▲ L1984 **FM OM** *020
EL-SAYED, Osama Mohamed M. 90 JACKSON PIKE 45631 #915-03-1991 L2001 **IC** *012 †20
EVANS, David Paul. 90 JACKSON PIKE, HOLZER CLINIC 45631 #038-40-1976 L1980 **IM** *020 †20
FAHMY, Nabil Wassili. 90 JACKSON PIKE 45631 #915-02-1975 L1993 **IM END** *020 †20
FISHER, Glenn Aaron. 90 JACKSON PIKE 45631 #016-45-1991 L1998 **FM** *020 †18
GAGUCAS, Raul Jaravata. 90 JACKSON PIKE, HOLZER CLINIC PATH DEPT 45631 #748-01-1984 L1997 **PTH PCP** *020 †50
GAINES, Lyndon Blaine. 90 JACKSON PIKE, HOLZER CLINIC 45631 #038-40-1991 L1998 **OBG** *020 †30
GEORGANDELLIS, Lucas. 90 JACKSON PIKE, C/O HOLZER CLINIC 45631 #561-01-1968 L2003 **NEP CCM** *020 †20
GRANDIA, Ronn A. 90 JACKSON PIKE, HOLZER CLINIC INC 45631 #016-01-1986 L1991 **GS** *020 †85
GUTTA, Veerendra Kumar. 90 JACKSON PIKE, HOLZER CLINIC 45631 #495-21-2000 L2006 **IM** *020 †20
HAMID, Khawaja. 90 JACKSON PIKE 45631 #704-16-1991 L1996 **ON** *020 †20
HOJAT, Saied Mohammad K. 100 JACKSON PIKE, HOLZER MEDICAL CTR 45631 #517-03-1962 L1981 **R** *020 †80
HOLLINGSWORTH, J Derek. 90 JACKSON PIKE, HOLZER CLINIC INC 45631 #018-75-1998, ▲ L2000 **FM** *020 †18
JAGARLAMUDI, Annapurna. 90 JACKSON PIKE 45631 #495-11-1996 L2006 **IM** *020 †20
JONES, Nicolette Monique. 90 JACKSON PIKE, HOLZER CLINIC, INC. 45631 #038-41-1992 L1998 **U** *020 †95
KANAGALINGAM, Sri Ranjini. 90 JACKSON PIKE, ATTN STAFFING COORDINATOR 45631 #220-04-1993 L2003 **IM** *020 †20
KANDULA, Pradeep Kumar. 90 JACKSON PIKE 45631 #495-21-1981 L1997 **PD** *020 †55
KANDULA, Renuka. 90 JACKSON PIKE, HOLZER CLINIC 45631 #495-21-1985 L1998 **IM** *020 †20
KHOSLA, Subhash. 170 JACKSON PIKE, HOLZER CTR CANCER CARE 45631 #496-07-1964 L1986 **RO** *020 †80
KHOURY, Basel. 90 JACKSON PIKE, HOLZER CLINIC INC 45631 #875-01-1999 L2005 **IM** *020 †20
KIM, I H. 90 JACKSON PIKE 45631 #051-07-1981 L1984 **PD** *020 †55
KINNEY, John H, Jr. 90 JACKSON PIKE, HOLZER CLINIC 45631 #770-02-1977 L1981 **UCM EM** *020
KIRKHART, Laurel Ann. 100 JACKSON PIKE 45631 #038-41-1986 L1990 **OBG** *020 †30
KNIGHT, John Patrick. 90 JACKSON PIKE 45631 #023-01-1985 L1988 **FM** *020 †18
LEE, Kang Kuk. 90 JACKSON PIKE, C/O HOLZER CLINIC 45631 #583-06-1971 L1981 **PD ADL** *020 †55
LONG, Phillip Blaine. 90 JACKSON PIKE, HOLZER CLINIC 45631 #038-43-1990 L1992 **DR VIR** *020 †20
MAGNUSSEN, April Joyce. 90 JACKSON PIKE, HOLZER CLINIC INC 45631 #038-40-1974 L1974 **IM** *020 †20
MAVI, Santpal S. 90 JACKSON PIKE, HOLZER CLINIC INC 45631 #495-47-1979 L1999 **IM PUD** *020 †20
MEHTA, Shailen K. 90 JACKSON PIKE, HOLZER CLINIC INC 45631 #048-02-1990 L1994 **PM** *020 †60
MENDIETA, Richard. 90 JACKSON PIKE 45631 #649-14-1982 L1997 **PD** *020 †55
MEYERS, Samuel. 2216 EASTERN AVE, LOT 34 45631 #352-11-1935 L1967 **GP IMG** *071
MICKUNAS, Gregory Joseph. 90 JACKSON PIKE 45631 #038-45-1998 L1999 **FM** *020 †18
NUGGUD, Jamshed. 2500 OHIO AVE 45631 #495-01-1968 L1977 **P GP** *020 †75
ORR, James M. 90 JACKSON PIKE 45631 #035-06-1953 L1959 **PD** *071 †55
OWENS, Michael Jonathan. 90 JACKSON PIKE 45631 #038-41-1985 L1990 **IM** *020 †20
PATTERSON, Richard Gale. 325 4TH AVE 45631 #016-11-1962 L1970 **EM** *020 †30
PENNINGTON, Bruce Lester. 90 JACKSON PIKE 45631 #020-12-1986 L1990 **DR** *020 †80
RASHEED, Mehmoodur. 90 JACKSON PIKE 45631 #704-02-1991 L2003 **IM RHU** *020 †20
REAVES, Lisa H. 90 JACKSON PIKE 45631 #030-05-1997 L2000 **OPH** *020 †35
ROSENBERG, Matthew W. 90 JACKSON PIKE, HOLZER CLINIC 45631 #016-11-1984 L2003 **PS** *020 †85,65
SAJJAN, Rajendra Nagedrap. 100 JACKSON PIKE 45631 #495-21-1997 L2003 **IM** *020 †20
SATTLER, Arnold Jos. 90 JACKSON PIKE 45631 #154-07-1957 L1967 **IM** *071 †20
SHAHEEN, Rizwana. 3086 STATE ROUTE 160, WOODLAND CENTER INC 45631 #704-16-1990 L2000 **CHP** *020 †75
SHERIDAN, Edward J, III. 1456 JACKSON PIKE, STE 2 45631 #035-45-1962 L1975 **OPH** *071 †35
SHERRILL, Monique M. 90 JACKSON PIKE, HOLZER CLINIC INC. 45631 #041-09-1996 L1999 **PD** *020 †55
SICILIANO, Dean Anthony. 90 JACKSON PIKE, HOLZER CLINIC INC 45631 #038-43-1992 L1996 **DR** *020 †80
SIMPSON, Richard Bowers. 90 JACKSON PIKE, HOLZER CLINIC INC 45631 #036-05-1961 L1970 **PD** *020 †55
SKINNER, Bridget Yvonne. 90 JACKSON PIKE 45631 #038-40-1993 L1995 **OBG** *020 †30
SOLA, Antonio Garcia. 90 JACKSON PIKE, HOLZER CLINIC INC 45631 #748-01-1959 L1975 **NM DR** *020
STEPHENSON, Melanie Ann. 90 JACKSON PIKE, HOLZER CLINIC INC 45631 #055-02-1985 L1997 **IM ADM** *075
STOUT, Rodney Barry. 90 JACKSON PIKE, HOLZER CLINIC INC 45631 #028-03-1990 L1995 **END** *020
STRAFFORD, Rebecca L T. 100 JACKSON PIKE 45631 #038-40-1972 L1972 **GP FPG** *020
STRATTON, Randall Louis. 90 JACKSON PIKE 45631 #004-01-1984 L1987 **EM** *020 †16
SUBBIAH, Balusamy. 936 STATE ROUTE 160 45631 #495-16-1964 L1979 **IM PUD** *020 †20
SUD, Mohendra. 90 JACKSON PIKE, HOLZER CLINIC 45631 #495-36-1961 L1971 **IM** *071
SULLIVAN, Jon Michael. 90 JACKSON PIKE, HOLZER CLINIC PEDS 45631 #038-45-1985 L1987 **PD** *020 †55

TAYLOR, Steven Kenneth. 90 JACKSON PIKE 45631 #011-75-1999, ▲ L2004 **IM** *020
UNGERLEIDER, James Saml. 90 JACKSON PIKE 45631 #038-40-1965 L1965 **ON HEM** *071 †20
VALLEE, Gerald Eugene. 936 STATE ROUTE 160 45631 #011-03-1961 L1965 **IM PUD** *020 †20
VIALL, John Henry. 90 JACKSON PIKE 45631 #038-40-1972 L1972 **OTO** *020 †45
WALKER, Mark Alan. 90 JACKSON PIKE, HOLZER CLINIC 45631 #038-41-1976 L1982 **HEM IM** *020 †20
WATTS, William Randall. 90 JACKSON PIKE, HOLZER CLINIC INC. 45631 #051-04-1987 L1995 **AN** *020 †05
WHITELEY, Daniel Hamlin. ■ 45631 #035-15-1965 L1966 **GS** *071 †85
WICKAS, Louis John, III. 90 JACKSON PIKE, HOLZER CLINIC INC 45631 #055-01-1986 L2002 **AN** *020 †20
YODLOWSKI, Lawrence Jos. 90 JACKSON PIKE, HOLZER CLINIC 45631 #038-43-1973 L1976 **U** *020 ‡

GALLOWAY — FRANKLIN

ACACIO, Corazon Arabejo. ■ 43119 #748-01-1964 L1972 **PD** *020
ACACIO, Irineo P, Jr. ■ 43119 #748-01-1960 L1971 **OPH** *071 †35
BAIRD, Jeffrey Downes, Jr. ■ 43119 #038-41-2004 L2004 **P** *100
BEATTY, Eddie B. ■ 43119 #047-07-1971 L1988 **PHP GPM** *020
BLUM, Kristy Renee. ■ 43119 #038-43-2006 L2006 **FP** *012
BOWERSOCK, Jason David. ■ 43119 #038-45-2005 L2005 **GS** *012
CASLOW, Renee A. ■ 43119 #041-77-2007, ▲ L2007 *012
CASTILLO, Ernesto C. ■ 43119 #748-07-1961 L1978 **P** *020
DESILVA, Brad William. ■ 43119 #038-40-2003 L2003 **OTO** *012
ELMORE, Jennifer L. ■ 43119 #048-78-2006, ▲ L2007 **AN** *012
FRAZER, Kimberly Michelle. 990 GALLOWAY RD 43119 #038-40-1995 L1996 **FM** *020 †18
GORDON, Amanda Elene. ■ 43119 #038-43-2004 L2004 **IM** *100 †20
MAY, Markita Leigh. ■ 43119 #038-45-2007 L2007 *012
OWENS, Matthew Thomas. ■ 43119 #038-43-2005 L2005 **PM** *012
TIPIRNENI, Eswara Prasad. ■ 43119 #495-50-1967 L1973 **AN** *020 †05

GAMBIER — KNOX

CAPASSO, Rebecca Marie. PO BOX 1254 43022 #026-08-2006 L2007 **P** *012
CLUTTER, Steven Emerson. ■ 43022 #038-43-1991 L1994 **IM** *020 †20
HART, Paul Vincent, Jr. ■ 43022 #030-06-1976 L1977 **FM EM** *020 ‡

GARFIELD HEIGHTS — CUYAHOGA

ABDEL-DAYEM, Mamdouh M. 12000 MCCRACKEN RD STE 209 44125 #915-03-1981 L1995 **P** *020 †75
AGGARWAL, Saroj. 12000 MCCRACKEN RD, STE 215 44125 #495-19-1958 L1967 **OPH** *020 †35
ALONSO, Victoria L. 12300 MCCRACKEN RD, DEPT LAB 44125 #748-08-1969 L1977 **PTH** *020 †50
ALRED, Thayne Robt. 12300 MCCRACKEN RD 44125 #049-01-1986 L1987 **EM** *020 †16
BERNSTEIN, Leonard H. 12000 MCCRACKEN RD 44125 #038-06-1963 L1963 **U** *020 †95
BOGAR, Kevin Lee. 12000 MCCRACKEN RD, STE 550 44125 #038-45-1996 L1999 **IM** *020 †20
BORDEN, Bradford Lee. 12300 MCCRACKEN RD 44125 #038-41-1987 L1989 **EM** *020 †16
CHECK, Lynne E Zegiob. 12575 ROCKSIDE RD STE 102 44125 #038-06-1970 L1971 **IM** *020
CHERNIN, Diane. 12300 MCCRACKEN RD 44125 #038-06-1986 L1986 **OBG** *071 †30
CUTUJIAN, Boghos Hagop. 12300 MCCRACKEN RD 44125 #605-01-1956 L1961 **GS GP** *020 †85
DECRISTOFARO, Lisa. 12000 MCCRACKEN RD, STE 550 44125 #038-45-1996 L2000 **FM** *020 †18
DE LONAIS-TURNER, Anne M. PO BOX 25547 44125 #038-45-1997 L1999 **EM** *020 †16
DOMB, Jane Alice. 12300 MCCRACKEN RD, MARY MOUNT HOSPITAL 44125 #024-01-1987 L1989 **P** *020 †75
FLORES, Toribio Carrillo. 5400 TRANSPORTATION BLVD, STE 8 44125 #748-01-1973 L1980 **OTO HNS** *020 †45
GALUN, Steven Alan. 12000 MCCRACKEN RD, STE 450 44125 #038-40-1990 L1991 **OBG** *020 †30
GAREWAL, Gurdev S. 12300 MCCRACKEN RD, DEPT PATH 44125 #495-27-1963 L1970 **PTH** *020 †50,28
GROSSMAN, William F. 13201 GRANGER RD, STE 3 44125 #038-41-1990 L1994 **OBG** *020 †30
GUPTA, Arun Kumar. 12000 MCCRACKEN RD, STE 104 44125 #495-03-1981 L1990 **IM** *020 †20
GUSTAFERRO, Thomas James. 12000 MCCRACKEN RD, STE 252 44125 #038-07-1989 L1993 **OPH** *020 †35 ‡
HAMILTON, Pamela Mary. 12000 MCCRACKEN RD, STE 157 44125 #919-01-1969 L1978 **GYN** *020 †30
HRUBY, Pamela Jean. 12000 MCCRACKEN RD, STE 206 44125 #038-44-1985 L2001 **OBG** *020 †30 ‡
IANNUZZI, Phyllis Lisa. 12300 MCCRACKEN RD 44125 #035-06-1977 L1978 **RHU IM** *020 †20
IHSANULLAH, S M. 12300 MCCRACKEN RD, MARYMOUNT HOSP EMG DEPT 44125 #704-09-1968 L1973 **EM** *020 †85,90,16
JABBOUR, Jehad. 12000 MCCRACKEN RD, STE 550 44125 #875-01-1993 L2000 **IM** *020 †20
JAVIER, Conrad G. 12000 MCCRACKEN RD, STE 106 44125 #748-01-1957 L1968 **IM CD** *071
KHATRI, Saloni. ■ 44125 #495-29-1993 L2001 **IM** *020
KNOTEK, Jeanne Marie. 13201 GRANGER RD 44125 #038-40-1999 L1999 **OBG** *020 †30
KOHLER, Douglas Orin. 12000 MCCRACKEN RD, STE 550 44125 #038-40-1995 L1996 **IM** *020 †20
KONDRAY, Gregory F. 12000 MCCRACKEN RD, STE 101 44125 #473-04-1966 L1976 **U** *020 †95
KONDRAY, Ildiko T. 12000 MCCRACKEN RD, STE 101 44125 #035-06-1977 L1981 **OPH** *020 †35
LEVINE, Howard Leslie. 5555 TRANSPORTATION BLVD 44125 #016-06-1970 L1971 **OTO** *020 †45
LINDENBERG, Judah Raphael. 12000 MCCRACKEN RD, STE 107 44125 #041-15-2000 L2000 **N** *020 †75
MALINOWSKI, Mark Donald. 13201 GRANGER RD, STE 2 44125 #023-07-1996 L1997 **PD** *020 †55
MANADAN, Mathew Augustine. 12300 MCCRACKEN RD 44125 #495-52-1970 L1974 **AN CCA** *020 †05

MAROCCO, Avi Shlomo. 12000 MCCRACKEN RD, STE 550 44125 #035-46-1998 L2000 IM *020 †20

MARSHALL, Cyril Esmond. 12300 MCCRACKEN RD 44125 #495-28-1955 L1972 ORS PME *020 †40

MASTEN, James Edward. 12300 MCCRACKEN RD, MARYMOUNT HOSPITAL 44125 #038-40-1976 L1977 DR *020 †80 ‡

MATHEW, Shila Jacob. 12300 MCCRACKEN RD 44125 #495-63-1979 L1985 P *020 †75

MEDINA, Maria A Michelle. 12300 MCCRACKEN RD, STE 206 44125 #748-02-1994 L1998 PD *020 †55

MINN-JINN, Byung Hyun. 12300 MCCRACKEN RD, MARYMOUNT HOSPITAL 44125 #583-03-1964 L1972 P CHP *020

NAIR, Daksha S. 12300 MCCRACKEN RD 44125 #905-01-1969 L1977 OBG *020

NANDIGAM, Nirmala. 4901 TURNEY RD 44125 #495-57-1974 L1979 IM *020

NASSIF, Anthony C. 12300 MCCRACKEN RD 44125 #330-03-1959 L1966 GP GS *071 †85

NATHAN, Howard Steven. 12300 MCCRACKEN RD, MARYMOUNT HOSPITAL 44125 #038-43-1993 L1994 IM *020 †20

OSTENDORF, Richard James. 5595 TRANSPORTATION BLVD, STE 220 44125 #016-11-1973 L1982 OM EM *020 †16,70

PATEL, Vijaykant Ratilal. 12300 MCCRACKEN RD, MARY MOUN 44125 #495-01-1969 L1978 EM *020 †16

PEREZ, Carlos Antonio. 12000 MCCRACKEN RD STE 203 44125 #847-04-1965 L1976 IM *020 †20

RAM, Puran. ■ 44125 #495-03-2000 IM *012

RAZMI, Syed S. 12000 MCCRACKEN RD, STE 201 44125 #704-02-1989 L2004 PCC *020 †20

ROBINSON, Shawn Adam. ■ 44125 #038-45-2007 L2007 PD *012

ROSENTHAL, Edward Steven. 12000 MCCRACKEN RD, STE 453 44125 #038-40-1985 L1986 IM *020 †20

SADOWSKI, Edmund Z. 12000 MCCRACKEN RD, STE 155 44125 #759-03-1980 L1988 IM *020 †20

SALAS, Susana B. 12000 MCCRACKEN RD, MARYMOUNT MED BLDG.,ROOM 1 44125 #748-01-1967 L1976 IM *020 †20

SCHNIER, Gregory Glenn. 12000 MCCRACKEN RD STE 558 44125 #038-06-1990 L1996 VS *020 †20

SHAH, Arunika Nagindas. 9700 GARFIELD BLVD STE 103 44125 #495-22-1970 L1982 PM FM *020

SHAW, Thomas Eades. 12300 MCCRACKEN RD 44125 #038-40-1965 L1965 PS HS *020 †85,65

SHELLY, M Hickey. 12300 MCCRACKEN RD 44125 #030-06-1942 L1944 P U *071

SIDANI, Walid Ibrahim. 12300 MCCRACKEN RD 44125 #605-02-1972 L1977 U *030 †95

SINGSON-FABI, Elizabeth F. ■ 44125 #748-01-1961 L1973 OBG PTH *071

TOPALSKY, George Vojislav. 12000 MCCRACKEN RD STE 550 44125 #038-06-1987 L1988 IM IMG *020 †20

TSIVITSE, Paul Terry. 12000 MCCRACKEN RD # 201, STE 111 44125 #038-06-1987 L1989 IM PUD *020 †20

WEINER, David M. 12000 MCCRACKEN RD, STE 201 44125 #024-07-1976 L1979 PCC IM *020 †20

GARRETTSVILLE — PORTAGE

ANDREWS, Annette Louise. 1 MEMORY LN STE 200 44231 #038-40-1985 L1988 IM *020 †20

LEU, Sang Ming. 8307 WINDHAM ST 44231 #244-04-1969 L1974 FM *020 †18

GATES MILLS — CUYAHOGA

ANTONIOU, Elias. ■ 44040 #418-02-1984 L1999 DR *020 †80

BOLE, Allayne Ernst. ■ 44040 #038-06-2006 L2007 PD *012

BOLE, Aparna. ■ 44040 #025-01-2006 L2006 PD *012

BOLTUCH, Robert Lawrence. ■ 44040 #035-19-1964 L1975 DR U *020 †95,80

CURTISS, Constance. ■ 44040 #038-06-1945 L1947 IM *071 †20

DUDZINSKI, Barbara. ■ 44040 #041-09-1979 L1980 ID ON *020 †20

ESSA, Yazeed Mansi. 1039 HILLCREEK LN 44040 #038-06-1994 L1997 EM *020

HEALY, Bernadine P. ■ 44040 #024-01-1970 L1986 CD PTH *030 †20

HUSNI, Elias A. ■ 44040 #605-01-1951 L1958 VIR GS *071 †85

KASHANI, Javad H. 1894 COTTESWORTH LN 44040 #517-04-1969 L1991 CHP P *020 †75

KATZ, Sidney. ■ 44040 #038-06-1948 L1948 GPM PHP *071

LIU, David. 841 HANOVER RD 44040 #038-06-2007 L2007 P *012

MANDEL, Miriam Beth. ■ 44040 #305-01-1998 L2003 PD *020

POULOS, John Geo. 6970 NORVALE CIR W 44040 #038-40-1964 L1964 AN *040 †05

RABIN, Michael Irl. ■ 44040 #038-06-1988 L1989 GP *030

RENNER, Daniel S. ■ 44040 #025-01-1957 L1961 TS VS *071 †90,85

ROTHENBERG, Joan O. 742 KENWOOD DR 44040 #038-06-1976 L1979 EM *020 †20,16

SABIO, Morada Aquias. 6900 NORVALE CIR W 44040 #748-01-1957 L1969 AN OS *020

SUTHERLAND, Charles John. 7670 BRIGHAM RD, SIGMA ASSOCIATES 44040 #008-01-1971 L1996 ORS *020 †40

ZELCH, Margaret C Groth. 7555 OLD MILL RD 44040 #038-40-1966 L1968 OS *020 †80

GENEVA — ASHTABULA

CONGER, David Matthew. 870 W MAIN ST, MEMORIAL HOSPITAL OF GENEV 44041 #038-06-1988 L1992 AN *020 †05

DEFENSOR, Emolyn M. 810 W MAIN ST 44041 #748-02-1971 L1979 PD *020 †55

DESAI, Kishore Ramanlal. 870 W MAIN ST 44041 #495-01-1954 L1969 EM *071

DRUBLIONIS, Raimantas. 254 S BROADWAY 44041 #913-49-1994 L2005 IM *020 †20

GOEL, Amitabh P. 870 W MAIN ST, UH GENEVA MEDICAL CENTER 44041 #918-01-1989 L1998 GS CCS *020 †85

HUANG, Cheng-Nan. 810 W MAIN ST 44041 #244-04-1971 L1977 GP *020

HUSSAINI, Syed Aijaz. 810 W MAIN ST 44041 #495-65-1968 L1977 PD N *020 †55

LEANZA, Raymond Fortune. 870 W MAIN ST, MEM HOSP OF GENEVA 44041 #038-06-1974 L1975 AN GP *020 †05

MAHMOUD, Ma Elena Mangay. 254 S BROADWAY 44041 #748-08-1967 L1975 IM *071

MESHGINPOOSH, Manoochehr. 254 S BROADWAY 44041 #517-01-1961 L1968 IM CD *020 †20

MIKHAIL, Yasser Samuel. 254 S BROADWAY 44041 #915-04-1986 L1998 IM *020 †20

PERALA, Norman Reid. ■ 44041 #038-06-2004 *100

POPOVIC, John. 870 W MAIN ST 44041 #957-03-1971 L1978 GS *020

ROBSON, Bruce Hickman. ■ 44041 #035-06-1977 L1980 DR *071 †80

GENOA — OTTAWA

EGBERT, Nathan David. ■ 43430 #038-43-2008 *012

MAPES, Kenneth Leroy. ■ 43430 #038-41-1996 L1998 EM *020

MEINKE, Aaron Martin. 22614 W STATE ROUTE 51 43430 #038-40-1997 L1999 FM *020 †18

NADAUD, Mark C. 22614 W STATE ROUTE 51, GENOA MED CTR 43430 #018-75-1978, ▲ L1979 FM *020

ODEH, Neiman Toufek. 22614 W STATE ROUTE 51 43430 #018-75-1992, ▲ L1993 FM *020 †18 ‡

GEORGETOWN — BROWN

ACHE, Andrew Joe. 425 HOME ST 45121 #038-43-1982 L1983 FM *020 †18

BHASKAR, Arcot. 425 HOME ST 45121 #495-04-1973 L1983 GE IM *020 †20

CONWAY, Gene F. 425 HOME ST 45121 #038-41-1952 L1952 OS CD *062 †20

DONOHOO, Jeffrey Scott. 421 HOME ST 45121 #038-41-1981 L1982 FM *020 †18

EGAN, Peter Timothy. 4903 STATE ROUTE 125 45121 #030-05-1988 L1989 IM *020 †20

FAROOQUI, Sheema. 425 HOME ST 45121 #495-33-1970 L2001 GS PD *020 †55

GHASEMZADEH, Ali R. 5062 SR 125 45121 #305-01-1987 L2001 CD *020

HAAS, Christopher Thos. 421 HOME ST 45121 #038-40-1976 L1977 FM *020 †18

KALEEM, Muhammad Imran. 421 HOME ST 45121 #704-16-1990 L1995 IM *020 †20

KAPUR, Sandeep. 425 HOME ST 45121 #496-09-1990 L2002 PUD *020 †20

KAPUR, Sandeep Kumar. 425 HOME ST 45121 #917-21-1995 L2000 IM *100 †20 ‡

KERSCHNER, Magdalena Eva. 425 HOME ST 45121 #025-07-1987 L1998 AN *020 †05

LEE, Ji Woo. 900 MT ORAB PIKE 45121 #583-02-1972 L1991 GS VS *020 †85

MC GANN, Kevin Chas. ■ 45121 #028-34-1947 L1948 GP *071

MCHENRY, Michael Scott. 421 HOME ST 45121 #038-40-1994 L1995 FM *020 †18 ‡

MOORE, William Arthur. 425 HOME ST 45121 #038-41-1940 GS *071

OWENS, Heather Marie. 425 HOME ST 45121 #038-45-1999 L2003 FM *020 †18

POWELL, John Albert. RR 1 BOX N 45121 #038-41-1955 L1955 OBG AS *071 †30

SHAH, Dipika Jayesh. 75 BANTING DR, BROWN COUNTY COUNSELLING C 45121 #495-22-1987 L2002 P *020

STEIN, Burton Roswell. ■ 45121 #035-06-1943 L1946 CD IM *071

VALLIAPPAN, Swaminathan. 425 HOME ST 45121 #495-16-1965 L1974 ON HEM *020 †20

WILLIAMS, Todd Wallace. 421 HOME ST 45121 #038-40-1994 L1997 FM *020 †18

GERMANTOWN — MONTGOMERY

DEGROAT, Michelle Renee. ■ 45327 #038-45-2005 L2005 GS *012

PAYNE, Charles Benj. ■ 45327 #041-01-1956 L1963 IM PUD *072 †20

WATSON, Noel Jay. 1217 W MARKET ST 45327 #038-40-1971 L1971 FM *020 †18

GIBSONBURG — SANDUSKY

ADAMS, Laura Page. ■ 43431 #038-43-2008 *012

WASSIL, Megan Beth. ■ 43431 #038-43-2008 *012

GIRARD — TRUMBULL

CHUNG, Kwok-Ban. 5692 LAMPLIGHTER DR 44420 #385-03-1968 L1972 GS *020 †85

GERMAN, Norton Isaiah. ■ 44420 #035-46-1960 L1979 PTH PHP *071 †50

GUTTIKONDA, Ravi Kumar. ■ 44420 #038-40-2008 *012

KAKKASSERIL, Pratheek Sim. ■ 44420 #038-44-2005 L2005 GS *012

MARTIN, William Thos. ■ 44420 #041-12-1957 L1957 OM FM *071

MONROE, Rickie Kelvin. 5755 LOGAN ARMS DR, 5755 LOGAN ARMS 44420 #047-07-1988 L1993 AN *020 †05

POTOR, George, Jr. ■ 44420 #038-40-1957 L1959 OS GP *050

SEKMAN, Michael G. 1616 E LIBERTY ST # B 44420 #748-19-1988 L1990 PD IM *020 †55

SHAH, Kruti Munir. 121 E LIBERTY ST 44420 #495-76-1990 L2001 IM *100

SHAPIRO, Richard David. ■ 44420 #041-02-1964 L1965 OPH *071 †35

TOCHTENHAGEN, Sam Ernest. 512 N STATE ST 44420 #038-41-1955 L1955 IM OM *072 †18

ZELLER, Louis Chryst, Jr. ■ 44420 #041-09-1946 L1947 GP *071

GLANDORF — PUTNAM

PHILLIPS, Linda Ann. PO BOX 81, 601 US 224 45848 #038-40-1996 L2000 FSM *020 †18

GOSHEN — CLERMONT

LEE, Mary A. 6746 STATE ROUTE 132 45122 #748-11-1971 L1977 IM *020

MOLIN, John A. ■ 45122 #858-03-1958 L1978 DR *071

STRICKLAND, Neil Richard. ■ 45122 #017-20-1956 L1990 GYN *072

GRAFTON — LORAIN

DEAK, Andrew Justen. ■ 44044 #038-44-2004 L2007 *100

LEANO, Francisco B. 2075 AVON BELDEN RD, LORAIN CORRECTIONAL INSTIT 44044 #748-07-1953 L1967 FM GP *071 †18

LEANO, Nicandro V. 489 MAIN ST 44044 #748-01-1956 L1962 IM GP *071 †18

MANTON, J Herbert. 2500 AVON BELDEN RD, RESIDENTIAL TREATMENT UNIT 44044 #038-40-1959 L1959 P *020

OJUKWU, Mbanefo Emmanuel. 2075 AVON BELDEN RD, MEDICAL DEPT LORCI 44044 #690-04-1994 L2002 IM *020 †20

PALEKAR, Rakhee Sanjay. ■ 44044 #038-40-2002 L2002 FM *100 †18

RAVICHANDRAN, Kamaleswary. 489 MAIN ST 44044 #220-04-1987 L2000 IM *020 †20

RUSH, James Lowell. 18626 CHAMBERLAIN RD 44044 #038-40-1956 L1956 **FM** *030
SABINE, Laurie L. 489 MAIN ST 44044 #038-45-1981 L1982 **FM** *020 †18

GRANVILLE – LICKING

ADAMS, John Lawrence. ■ 43023 #035-15-1970 L1972 **PD** *071 †55
ARANT, James Hunter. 116 W BROADWAY 43023 #041-13-1984 L1985 **AN** *020 †05
BARFIELD, Jason Lee. ■ 43023 #017-20-2002 L2007 **CN** *020 †75
BARTH, Michael David. 1264 WEAVER DR, PRACTICE-GRANVILLE 43023 #038-43-1986 L1988 **FM** *020 †18
BORN, David Ervin. 2000 NEWARK GRANVILLE RD 43023 #038-41-1996 L1997 **FM** *020 †18
COLE, Linda Sue. ■ 43023 #050-02-1984 L1985 **P CHP** *020 †75
CZARNECKI, Daniel Francis. PO BOX 617, DENISON UNIVERSITY 43023 #038-40-2007 2007 *012
DESHETLER, Donald Albert. 2000 NEWARK GRANVILLE RD 43023 #038-40-1995 L1999 **FM** *020 †18
DILS, Lawrence Albert. 1264 WEAVER DR, PRACTICE-GRANVILLE 43023 #038-41-1963 L1963 **FM** *020 †18
EUBANKS, Angela Adrena. 1945 NEWARK GRANVILLE RD, WELSH HILLS FAMILY HEALTH 43023 #038-43-1993 L1994 **FM** *020 †18
FERRAND, Susan Kathryn. ■ 43023 #032-01-1982 L1987 **CD IM** *020 †20
FINLEY, Kevin Jay. 1264 WEAVER DR, PRACTICE-GRANVILLE 43023 #038-45-1997 L1999 **FM** *020 †18
GROVE, James H. ■ 43023 #038-06-1946 L1946 **R** *071 †80
HALL, Mary Beth. 2000 NEWARK GRANVILLE RD 43023 #038-40-1976 L1979 **FM** *020 †18
JONES, Randy Eugene. 3382 DEEDS RD 43023 #049-01-1999 L1999 **EM** *020 †16
KARAFFA, Frederick N. 3339 GOOSE LN, BOX 550 43023 #038-40-1963 L1963 **FM ADM** *071
KARAFFA, Tracee Laing. 1945 NEWARK GRANVILLE RD, WELSH HILLS FAMILY HEALTH 43023 #038-40-1992 L1993 **FM** *020 †18
LEWIS, Bradley Richard. ■ 43023 #038-43-2003 L2003 **AN** *020
MEYER, Jeffrey Vaughn. ■ 43023 #036-05-1999 L2005 **FOP** *100
RAKER, Robert Paul. ■ 43023 #038-40-1963 L1963 **LM OM** *071
RATTERMAN, Michael Paul. 1264 WEAVER DR 43023 #025-01-1965 L1972 **FM** *020 †18
SAND, David Jay. ■ 43023 #043-01-1982 L1994 **OTO FPS** *071 †45
SCARPITTI, Patrick Jos. 2000 NEWARK GRANVILLE RD 43023 #038-40-1980 L1980 **FM** *020 †18
SEIPEL, Andrew Carl. 1264 WEAVER DR, PRACTICE-GRANVILLE 43023 #038-43-1990 L1991 **FM** *020 †18
SINSABAUGH, Charles F. ■ 43023 #038-40-1951 L1951 **FM IM** *071 †18
SYLVESTER, Robert F, Jr. ■ 43023 #028-02-1945 L1946 **PD** *071 †55
UNDERWOOD, Jackie Lynne. 1963 NEWARK GRANVILLE RD, ERINWOOD PRIMARY CARE, INC 43023 #038-40-1979 L1982 **FM** *020 †18
WOOFTER, Melinda Joann. 1959 NEWARK GRANVILLE RD, MIDWEST DERMATOLOGY CENTRE 43023 #016-45-1991 L1998 **D** *020 †20,15 ‡
ZIVKOVICH, Anna Halley. ■ 43023 #055-01-2007 L2007 **IM** *012

GREENFIELD – HIGHLAND

ABOU-AMRO, Aref Mahmoud. 550 MIRABEAU ST 45123 #875-01-1989 L2004 **IC CD** *020 †20
ANFONE, Benjamin Arcilla. 545 SOUTH ST 45123 #748-11-1963 L1975 **FM P** *020
GHAZAL, Joseph Samir. 550 MIRABEAU ST 45123 #038-45-1994 L1996 **CD** *020 †20
HENSON, Mark Owen. 536 MIRABEAU ST 45123 #038-41-1997 L1999 **FM** *020 †18
JAMIESON, David A. 550 MIRABEAU ST 45123 #064-01-1991 L1995 **FM EM** *020
JONES, Thomas Lawson. 545 SOUTH ST 45123 #023-01-1953 L1957 **EM GP** *075
KABBANI, Samer Souheil. 550 MIRABEAU ST 45123 #605-01-1994 L1997 **IM** *020 †20
KANAYJORN-NA-AYUTHAYA, E. 1092 JEFFERSON ST 45123 #748-11-1986 L2000 **IM** *020 †20
MIZER, Richard David. 1075 N WASHINGTON ST 45123 #038-43-1983 L1985 **FM** *020 †18
MORGAN, Jeanette Marie. 536 MIRABEAU ST 45123 #038-41-1988 L1990 **FM** *020 †18
PATEL, Shashikant B. 550 MIRABEAU ST 45123 #495-23-1973 L1979 **CD IM** *020 †20
ROBERTS, David Earnest. 550 MIRABEAU ST 45123 #038-40-1972 L1972 **CD IM** *020 †20
ZENT, Kevin Benjamin. 1075 N WASHINGTON ST 45123 #020-02-2003 L2003 **FM** *020 †18

GREENVILLE – DARKE

ANDERSON, Diane Hope. 835 SWEITZER ST 45331 #055-75-1990, ▲ L1991 **DR** *020 †80
ANTONELLI, Roger Louis. 835 SWEITZER ST 45331 #038-40-1973 L1976 **DR** *020 †80
BALLEN, Jay Lee. 835 SWEITZER ST 45331 #031-01-1994 L2001 **DR** *020 †80
BANOUB, Ashraf Fayez. 835 SWEITZER ST 45331 #915-03-1989 L1996 **AN CCA** *020 †05
BERGER, Daniel Steven. 5735 MEEKER RD, STE 3 45331 #038-41-1979 L1981 **FPG** *020 †18
BLICKENSTAFF, Delbert D. PO BOX 747, 7603 CELINA RD 45331 #040-02-1956 L1959 **GP GS** *020
BOLI, Virgil R. ■ 45331 #035-01-1949 L1953 **GP OS** *071
BOWLIN, Rick David. 130 MARTZ ST, STE 3 45331 #038-45-1992 L1994 **IM** *020 †20
BROWN, Thomas Dickerson. 5735 MEEKER RD, STE 3 45331 #038-40-1987 L1988 **FM** *020 †18
CARPENTER, Richard W. 750 CHESTNUT ST, # OAKVIEW2 45331 #047-05-1962 L2005 **OS IM** *020 †20
CECCHINO, Robert Andrew. 742 SWEITZER ST, MEDICAL ARTS BUILDING 45331 #038-41-1973 L1973 **GS** *020 †85
CECH, Roxanne Michelle. 1193 WAYNE AVE 45331 #038-43-1987 L1989 **FM** *020 †18
CHONG, Henry Hyohae. 742 SWEITZER ST, STE 1 45331 #023-01-1990 L1996 **CD** *020 †20
CLARK, Michael Loren. 5735 MEEKER RD, STE 3 45331 #038-45-1990 L1991 **OBG** *020 †30
COOPERIDER, Todd J. 835 SWEITZER ST 45331 #038-43-1985 L1989 **AN** *020 †05
DIETZ, Wolfgang F. 1189 WAYNE AVE 45331 #038-43-1985 L1988 **OTO** *020 †45
DING, Yungao. 835 SWEITZER ST 45331 #243-16-1983 L2000 **R NM** *020 †80,28
DOWNING, Dawn Leeper. ■ 45331 #038-45-2005 L2005 **FM** *100
ENGLE, Joseph Harold. ■ 45331 #041-13-1956 L1982 **ORS** *071 †40
GIRMANN, Robert Anthony. 835 SWEITZER ST 45331 #038-40-1994 L1997 **EM** *020 †16
GULLIA, Emil Mario, Jr. 1185 WAYNE AVE 45331 #004-01-1971 L1972 **FM** *020 †18
HALL, Bruce Evans. 835 SWEITZER ST 45331 #023-07-1989 L1996 **R RNR** *020 †80 ‡
HART, Joy Ann. 5735 MEEKER RD 45331 #038-40-1989 L1993 **OBG** *020 †30
HAWLEY, Mary Lynne. 130 MARTZ ST, STE 1 45331 #038-43-1994 L1995 **MPD** *020 †20,55

HENSEL, Margaret S. 835 SWEITZER ST 45331 #048-13-1975 L1978 **FPG** *020 †18
JACOBS, Edward C. 114 S BROADWAY ST, KETTERING UROLOGY 45331 #005-12-1968 L1997 **PD U** *020 †95
JONES, Jason Michael. ■ 45331 #038-43-2007 L2007 **IM** *012
KANE, Maurice M. ■ 45331 #038-40-1933 **CD** *071
KATHMAN, Timothy Danl. 1185 WAYNE AVE 45331 #038-41-1981 L1982 **IM** *020 †20
KATNENI, Ranjit. 812 CENTRAL AVE 45331 #495-65-1996 L2003 **IM** *020 †20 ‡
KENSINGER, Robert Donn. 5735 MEEKER RD, STE 3 45331 #038-41-1994 L1995 **FM** *020 †18
KHAN, Mohamed Fazlulla. 130 MARTZ ST, DAYTON CARDIOLOGY & 45331 #495-37-1986 L2003 **CD** *020 †20
LEAHEY, Jerome Martin. 835 SWEITZER ST 45331 #017-20-1962 L1999 **GP PHP** *020
LONGEVIN, Scott Douglas. 835 SWEITZER ST 45331 #038-43-1986 L1987 **EM OM** *020
MAY, Robert Arthur. 835 SWEITZER ST 45331 #038-43-1982 L1987 **AN CCA** *020 †05
MC CARTNEY, Jodi Delee. 5735 MEEKER RD, STE 3 45331 #038-45-2001 L2005 **OBG** *020 †30
MENENDEZ, Carlos Klecker. 5735 MEEKER RD, STE 3 45331 #495-47-1983 L1984 **FM** *020 †18
MOBLEY, John Curtis. 5735 MEEKER RD, STE 3 45331 #020-02-1990 L1995 **GS** *020 †85
OSTERBUR, William Henry. 5735 MEEKER RD, STE 3 45331 #016-11-1981 L1982 **FM** *020 †18
PATEL, Mahendrakumar G. 1189 WAYNE AVE 45331 #495-23-1972 L1980 **FM** *020 †45
PAYNE, Theodore Kirgan. 835 SWEITZER ST 45331 #017-20-1969 L1976 **DR GP** *020 †80
PENNINGTON, Norman E. 835 SWEITZER ST 45331 #038-45-1983 L1987 **DR** *062 †80
POHLMAN, Donald Walter. 835 SWEITZER ST 45331 #038-45-1983 L1984 **FM** *020 †18
POLENAKOVIK, Hari Momir. 812 CENTRAL AVE, WAYNE HOSPITAL 45331 #957-04-1993 L1998 **ID IM** *020 †20
POLENAKOVIK, Sylvia. 835 SWEITZER ST 45331 #957-04-1994 L2000 **IM** *020 †20
PU, Le-Ping. 835 SWEITZER ST 45331 #243-40-1983 L2005 **RNR** *020 †80
RAPKIN, Jeffrey Scott. 6060 STATE ROUTE 571 45331 #056-06-1982 L1991 **OPH** *020 †35
RAWLINS, Jennifer Lynn. 5735 MEEKER RD, STE 3 45331 #038-45-1996 L2002 **FM** *020 †18
REILMAN, Randall James. 835 SWEITZER ST 45331 #038-41-1994 L1996 **DR** *020 †80
SAMBA, Krishna. 835 SWEITZER ST, WAYNE HOSPITAL 45331 #495-21-1983 L2003 **AN** *020 †05
SCRIPTURE, Kevin Thomas. 6050 STATE ROUTE 571 45331 #017-20-1994 L1998 **OPH** *020 †35
SINGH, Anjali. 835 SWEITZER ST 45331 #495-30-1992 L2003 **DR** *020 †80
SORKIN, Stuart Jeffrey. 835 SWEITZER ST 45331 #035-15-1975 L1980 **R NM** *020 †80,28
STEDJE, Kurt Gunnar. 835 SWEITZER ST 45331 #038-41-1990 L1996 **DR OS** *020 †80
STEINBRECHER, Le Roy M. 835 SWEITZER ST 45331 #041-09-1962 L1972 **GS** *071 †85
STUDEBAKER, John P. 832 CENTRAL AVE 45331 #042-01-1975 L1977 **FM** *020 †18
TREVINO, Guillermo Glen. 835 SWEITZER ST, WAYNE HOSPITAL 45331 #038-40-2002 L2002 **IM** *100 †20
TYRRELL, Robert Lee, II. 835 SWEITZER ST 45331 #038-06-1983 L1984 **DR** *020 †80
VEHRE, Beth Boyer. 5735 MEEKER RD, STE 3 45331 #025-01-1989 L1996 **FM** *020 †18
WIGNESWARAN, John Robert. 130 MARTZ ST, STE 3 45331 #024-07-1995 L2002 **NEP** *020 †20
ZELLER, Ross Maxwell. 750 CHESTNUT ST 45331 #038-40-1936 L1936 **GP OS** *071

GREENWICH – HURON

BROWN, Christopher R. 13 TILTON ST 44837 #038-40-1992 L1995 **FM** *020 †18
LEE, Joseph Charles. 65 W MAIN ST, GREENWICH FAMILY MEDICINE 44837 #422-01-1999 L2002 **FM** *020 †18

GROVE CITY – FRANKLIN

ADKINS, Eric James. 4395 GLENGOLD DR 43123 #055-01-2002 L2007 **PCC EM** *012 †20
ALDERMAN, Sara Marie. 1897 OHIO DR 43123 #016-06-2002 L2002 **OBG** *020
AUERBACH, Bruce L. 4176 KELNOR DR 43123 #041-09-1981 L1985 **CD IM** *020 †20
AXELSON, David Brian. 3148 STRINGTOWN RD 43123 #038-41-1989 L1992 **P** *020 †75
BALASUBRAMANIAN, Ammunni. ■ 43123 #495-04-1964 L1978 **R** *020
BALLENGER, Ralph Richard. 3000 MEADOW POND CT, STE 400 43123 #038-40-1966 L1966 **OBG** *020 †30
BARROWS, Holly Jean. 1897 OHIO DR 43123 #038-40-1980 L1983 **OBG** *020 †30
BAUGHMAN, Charles Dale. 6024 HOOVER RD, STE A 43123 #038-40-1988 L1989 **FM** *020 †18
BELTRAN, Ralph Jeorge. ■ 43123 #038-40-2004 L2004 **AN** *012
BENDO, Seth Edmund. ■ 43123 #038-40-2008 *012
BENNETT, Paul W. 4151 HOOVER RD 43123 #038-06-1979 L2005 **FM OS** *020 †18
BENNINGTON, Garth Allen. 2030 STRINGTOWN RD 43123 #038-40-2002 L2002 **FM** *020 †18
BLAKE, Byron. 4191 KELNOR DR, STE 300 43123 #038-40-1955 L1955 **FM** *020 †18
BOER, Annette Karen. 4079 GANTZ RD, WORKHEALTH SW 43123 #038-40-1985 L1986 **FM** *020 †18
BRANTNER, Linda Mariko. 2065 STRINGTOWN RD 43123 #010-02-1984 L1998 **PD ADL** *020 †55
BUENDIA, Francisco C. 3154 PARK ST 43123 #038-45-1993 L1994 **FM** *020 †18
CARANNA, Charles Anthony. 3000 MEADOW POND CT, STE 400 43123 #038-40-1968 L1968 **OBG** *020 †30
CARDENAS, Juan. 4079 GANTZ RD, STE B 43123 #040-02-1976 L1982 **PD** *020 †55
CARPENTER, Clarence J. ■ 43123 #038-40-1954 L1954 **FM P** *072
CHAWLA, Harmeet Singh. 1901 OHIO DR 43123 #051-04-1987 L1991 **OPH** *020 †35
CHEN, Michael Chunwei. 3989 JACKPOT RD, STE A 43123 #038-40-2003 L2003 **D** *020 †15
CLOUD, Adam Ralph. ■ 43123 #038-40-2008 **OPH** *012
COLEMAN, Thomas Walter. ■ 43123 #005-15-1981 L1986 **IM** *075
COOK, Matthew Doyle. 3636 BROADWAY 43123 #038-45-1987 L1988 **FM** *020 †18
CORLEY, Bonnie Sierra. 1897 OHIO DR 43123 #036-05-1996 L1998 **OBG** *020 †30
CRISAN, Mirela. 3000 MEADOW POND CT, STE 100 43123 #781-03-1995 L2001 **FM** *020 †18
CRUZ-RAMON, Julio C. 3989 JACKPOT RD, STE A 43123 #042-01-1987 L1992 **D PTH** *020 †50,15
DICKSON, Bradley Earl. 4079 GANTZ RD STE B 43123 #038-43-1992 L1993 **PD** *020 †55
DODD, Kathy. ■ 43123 #038-41-2006 L2006 **FP** *012
ELLIOTT, Larry Stephen. 3000 MEADOW POND CT, MT.CARMEL URGENT CARE GROV 43123 #038-40-1973 L1974 **EM** *020 †16
EVANCHAN, Jason P. ■ 43123 #038-75-2007, ▲ L2007 *012
FAHLER, Donald Alan. ■ 43123 #017-20-2007 L2007 *012
FEHSKENS, Mary Katherine. 2030 STRINGTOWN RD 43123 #033-06-1990 L1996 **FM** *020 †18
FELLER, Trista Schnickel. 6172 RICHARD ROSS RD 43123 #038-40-2001 L2001 **OBG** *020 †30
FISHER, Bryan Tole. ■ 43123 #056-05-2005 L2005 **GS** *012
FLOWERS, Stephanie Trent. 3667 MARLANE DR 43123 #038-40-1993 L1994 **FM** *020 †18

GALLANOSA, Arvin Joseph. 2065 STRINGTOWN RD 43123 #017-20-1999 L1999 **PM** *020 †60 ‡
GENTILE, Patricia Marie. 5665 HOOVER RD, BUCKEYE RANCH 43123 #017-20-1986 L1998 **P CHP** *020 †75
GODDARD, Charles Michael. 4079 GANTZ RD STE B, SOUTH WEST PEDIATRICS INC. 43123 #038-43-1992 L1995 **PD** *020 †55 ‡
GROGG, Terry Winton. 4461 BROADWAY 43123 #038-40-1988 L1989 **OBG** *020 †30
HAGERTY, Genevieve Brooks. 4461 BROADWAY 43123 #038-40-1998 L1999 **OBG** *020 †30
HALL, Clinton Ryan. ■ 43123 #011-04-2004 L2004 **GS** *012
HALL, Robert Leslie. ■ 43123 #038-40-2003 L2003 **PM** *020
HARPER, Michael Jos. 6024 HOOVER RD STE A, GROVE CITY FAMILY HEALTH 43123 #038-40-1992 L1993 **FM** *020
HATHEWAY, John Mark. 6024 HOOVER RD 43123 #038-40-1970 L1970 **ORS** *020 †40
HESSEL, Adam B. 3989 JACKPOT RD, STE A 43123 #035-19-1985 L1989 **D DMP** *020 †15
HETRICK, Jennifer Ellen. ■ 43123 #038-06-1995 L2006 **FM** *020 †18
HIRTH, Charles Scott. 4151 HOOVER RD 43123 #038-40-1981 L1981 **FM** *020 †18
HOLLISTER, Jonathan D. 2030 STRINGTOWN RD 43123 #038-45-2001 L2001 **FPG** *020 †18
HORN, John Andrew. 6024 HOOVER RD, STE A 43123 #038-40-1995 L1996 **FM** *020 †18
HORVATH, James W, Jr. ■ 43123 #038-44-2006 L2006 **PTH** *012
JAIN, Sushil. 6024 HOOVER RD, STE F 43123 #495-30-1977 L1985 **HEM ON** *020 †20 ‡
JAIN, Sushil Kumar. 6024 HOOVER RD, STE F 43123 #496-14-1989 L1994 **IM** *020 †20
JAIN, Vijay. 6024 HOOVER RD, STE F 43123 #495-30-1977 L1987 **IM** *020 †20 ‡
JANCZAK, Richard Matthew. 3154 PARK ST 43123 #038-43-1981 L1983 **FM EM** *020 †16,18
JASKOT, Robert Alan. 4461 BROADWAY 43123 #038-40-1992 L1993 **OBG** *020 †30
KARSIES, Todd Jonathan. ■ 43123 #039-01-2004 L2004 **CCP** *012 †55
KEBE, Stephen Louis. 4074 GANTZ RD 43123 #038-40-1984 L1985 **PD** *020 †55
KILMAN, James Wm. 4231 JACKSON PIKE 43123 #017-20-1960 L1966 **TS** *071 †85,90
KING, Ryan Gregory. ■ 43123 #035-01-2004 L2007 **GS** *100
KNISELY, Anne Jan-Tausch. ■ 43123 #038-06-1949 L1949 **AN OS** *071 †05
MACKLIN, Jamie R. ■ 43123 #021-01-2006 L2006 **MPD** *012
MARAR, Uma U. 2441 OLD STRINGTOWN RD, CAPITOL SLEEP MEDICINE 43123 #495-94-1987 L1996 **IM** *020 †20
MARTIN, Anthony D. 3148 BROADWAY, STE 300 43123 #308-03-1988 L1991 **P CHP** *020
MARTINEZ, Sherri Lynn. 2030 STRINGTOWN RD, GRANT FAMILY MEDICINE 43123 #038-45-2001 L2001 **FM** *020 †18
MC ILROY, Scott Allen. 2399 OLD STRINGTOWN RD 43123 #038-40-1975 L1976 **OBG** *020 †30
MORRIS, Michelle Ann. 3667 MARLANE DR 43123 #051-04-1981 L1982 **FM** *020 †18
NGUYEN, Harry P. 2030 STRINGTOWN RD 43123 #941-01-1974 L1979 **EM ADM** *020 †16
NOBLE, Edward John. 4160 BROADWAY 43123 #038-40-1958 L1958 **GP** *071
PATEL, Gayatri Harshad. ■ 43123 #038-45-2008 *012
PETERSON, Lisa Michelle. 2051 STRINGTOWN RD 43123 #038-40-1998 L1999 **FM** *020 †18
PRATT, Cedric S. ■ 43123 #048-78-2006, ▲ L2006 **OPH** *012
RADAWSKI, Jeffrey Daniel. ■ 43123 #025-12-2007 L2007 **GS** *012
RODENBERG, Richard Edward. 2030 STRINGTOWN RD 43123 #038-43-1998 L2003 **MPD ISM** *020 †20,55
ROSINSKI, Jocelyn Ann. ■ 43123 #008-02-2007 L2007 *012
RUNSER, Gregory Lewis. 6024 HOOVER RD, STE A 43123 #038-40-1989 L1990 **FM** *020 †18
SAMS, Sarah. 2030 STRINGTOWN RD, GRANT FAMILY MED 43123 #038-40-1991 L1992 **FM** *020 †18
SCHLOESSER, Bretton Lee. ■ 43123 #025-01-2004 L2004 **MPD** *012
SHANA'AH, Aroob Younis. 2030 STRINGTOWN RD 43123 #575-02-2001 **FP** *012
SIMON, Larry Allen. 3000 MEADOW POND CT, STE 400 43123 #038-40-1970 L1970 **OBG** *020 †30
SNASHALL, Jonathan Thomas. ■ 43123 #010-01-2008 *012
STERN, Phillip Jos. 3055 COLUMBUS ST 43123 #038-40-1975 L1977 **IM** *020 †20
STOKES, Julia Yen. 6024 HOOVER RD STE A, GROVE CITY FAMILY HLTH 43123 #038-40-2003 L2003 **FM** *020 †18
TARR, Erin Renee. 3667 MARLANE DR 43123 #038-41-2001 L2001 **FM** *020
TRINH, Channhu. 2030 STRINGTOWN RD, AMERICA'S URGENT CARE 43123 #016-45-1997 L2006 **FM** *020 †18 ‡
VAN DEUSEN, Loren Millard. 3636 BROADWAY 43123 #038-40-1984 L1985 **FM** *020 †18
VAZIRI, David Mohamet. 6024 HOOVER RD 43123 #055-01-1988 L1994 **ORS OFA** *072 †40
VOGEL, David Laurence. ■ 43123 #030-06-2004 L2005 **GS** *012
WALLACE, Douglas Craig. 3154 PARK ST 43123 #038-40-1982 L1983 **FM** *020 †18
WALTER, Timothy James. 2441 OLD STRINGTOWN RD, CAPITOL SLEEP MEDICINE 43123 #038-40-1994 L1999 **N** *020 †75
WASHINGTON, William James. ■ 43123 #038-41-2003 L2006 **EM** *100 †16
WENDORFF, Daniel James. 3055 COLUMBUS ST 43123 #038-40-1984 L1985 **IM** *020 †20
ZITTER, Diana Meiring. 4461 BROADWAY 43123 #038-40-1980 L1981 **OBG** *020 †30

GROVEPORT – FRANKLIN

ADOLPH, Michael David. 3965 HAMILTON SQUARE BLVD, BARIATRIC SPECIALISTS OF O 43125 #038-41-1989 L1990 **GS MDM** *020 †85
BATES, Genevieve C. 3964 HAMILTON SQUARE BLVD 43125 #038-45-1992 L1994 **IM** *020 †20
MC CARTY, Richard Norman. 495 MAIN ST 43125 #025-76-1975, ▲ L1976 **FM** *071
PRESTON, Matthew Michael. ■ 43125 #038-40-2007 L2007 **P** *012
TANZER, Steven F. 5345 HENDRON RD 43125 #028-78-1976, ▲ L1977 **FM** *020
TEDROW, Brant Wm. 6269 LITHOPOLIS RD 43125 #038-40-1964 L1964 **GP NTR** *020
VIGLIANCO, James Peter. 3964 HAMILTON SQUARE BLVD 43125 #055-02-1985 L1990 **GS** *020 †85
WISE, Greg Alan. 4100 VENTURE PL 43125 #038-41-1986 L1987 **FM** *020 †18 ‡

HAMILTON – BUTLER

AHMED, Abdul Q. 1010 CEREAL AVE, STE 301 45013 #704-04-1980 L2004 **ORS** *020
ALATORRE, Salvador. 630 EATON AVE 45013 #649-01-1951 L1959 **GP** *071
ALMQUIST, Marvin Dean. 3721 ROSSGATE CT 45013 #038-40-1993 L1995 **OBG** *020 †30
ALWIS, Sri Kantha D. 630 EATON AVE 45013 #220-01-1966 L1974 **P** *020 †75
AUGUST, Spencer Fred. ■ 45013 #038-40-1963 L1963 **U OS** *071 †95
BADEN, James Paul. 25 OFFICE PARK DR 45013 #035-20-1965 L1966 **GS** *020 †85
BALKOWIEC, Krzysztof A. 1010 CEREAL AVE STE 212 45013 #759-03-1991 L1997 **FM** *020 †18
BARICH, Louis Luke. 549 MAIN ST 45011 #041-12-1958 L1962 **D** *020
BARLOW, John Leslie Robt. ■ 45011 #917-03-1950 *072

BENSON, Donald Earl. 630 EATON AVE 45013 #038-41-1984 L1985 **IM** *020 †20
BERESH, John Erik. 3145 HAMILTON MASON RD, STE 201 45011 #038-41-2001 L2001 **PME PMM** *020
BHARGAVA, Lena. 903 NW WASHINGTON BLVD, STE A 45013 #038-44-2004 L2004 **IM** *020 †18
BIEDENBENDER, Harold L. 855 STAHLHEBER RD, # 219 45013 #038-41-1943 L1943 **OS GS** *071
BLANKENBURG, Mark Edward. 25 N F ST 45013 #038-40-1981 L1984 **PD** *020 †55
BONAR, Michael John. 630 EATON AVE 45013 #038-41-1982 L1984 **PTH** *020 †50
BONDOC, Cesario Espinosa. 1010 CEREAL AVE 45013 #748-01-1953 L1973 **OM GP** *071
BROCKMAN, James Thos. 9582 PRINCETON GLENDALE RD 45011 #038-41-1986 L1987 **FM** *020 †18
BROWN, Rodger Rawson. 100 RIVERFRONT PLZ 45011 #038-41-1971 L1971 **R** *020 †80
BROWN, Timothy Harold. 903 NW WASHINGTON BLVD, STE A 45013 #038-41-1979 L1981 **IM ID** *020 †20
BRUMBERGER, Harvey. 301 HIGH ST, STE 420 45011 #165-04-1972 L1976 **AN** *071 †05
BRYANT, David Leon. 500 MAIN ST 45013 #011-03-1967 L1969 **ORS** *020 †40
BUERK, Gerald Stephen. 630 EATON AVE, STE 1 45013 #038-40-1966 L1966 **OPH** *071 †35
BURKHARDT, Richard Peter. 315 HIGH ST 45011 #038-41-1964 L1964 **FM FOP** *071 †18
CARR, James Robt. 512 MAIN ST 45013 #038-41-1956 L1956 **U** *071 †95
CARR, Phillip Chas. 840 NW WASHINGTON BLVD # A 45013 #038-41-1982 L1982 **OBG** *020 †30
CHALASANI, Madhu. 630 EATON AVE 45013 #051-04-1998 L2001 **IM** *020 †20
CHAMBERLIN, Clyde G. 100 RIVERFRONT PLZ 45011 #038-41-1939 L1948 **OTO** *071 †45
CHOUDARY, Kavitha Aluri. 855 EATON AVE 45013 #495-21-1996 L2000 **IM** *020 †20
CIESLAK, Frederick S. ■ 45013 #035-06-1961 L1966 **AN** *071 †05
CREECH, William Wiley. ■ 45013 #020-12-1968 L1974 **AN** *071 †05
CUCINOTTA, Robert Bernard. 1010 CEREAL AVE STE 209 45013 #038-40-1984 L1989 **GE IM** *020 †20
DAVIN, Harry Maurice. 903 NW WASHINGTON BLVD, STE A 45013 #038-41-1974 L1974 **PLM IMG** *020 †20
DEITSCHEL, Charles Harold. 3721 ROSSGATE CT 45013 #016-43-1965 L1969 **PD** *071 †55
DE LA ROSA, Andres A. 100 RIVERFRONT PLZ 45011 #748-01-1957 L1978 **EM GP** *020
DESAI, Shwetal Gunvantrai. 435 PARK AVE, AJAY K MANGAL MD INC 45013 #495-89-1984 L1991 **IM** *020 †20
DIMATULAC, Conrado Ylagan. 630 EATON AVE 45013 #748-01-1948 **GS OS** *020
DOROCHOWICZ, Mikola. ■ 45013 #407-04-1951 L1960 **OBG OS** *071
DUNKLE, Chad Hewey. 903 NW WASHINGTON BLVD, STE A 45013 #038-41-1972 L1972 **FM** *020 †18
ERRANDO, Jose M. ■ 45011 #847-02-1973 L1977 **DR** *020
EVANS, John Martin. 1010 CEREAL AVE STE 100, HELATHLINE 45013 #038-41-1966 L1966 **FM OM** *071 †18 ‡
FITZPATRICK, James Edward. 25 OFFICE PARK DR 45013 #038-40-1995 L2000 **GS** *020 †85
FLETCHER, Ronald L. 3570 PLEASANT AVE 45015 #047-07-1974 L1976 **ON IM** *020
FLOYD, Henry Lewis. ■ 45011 #038-40-1945 L1945 **TS PUD** *071 †85,90
GHAZAL, Elie Robert. 630 EATON AVE, FORT HAMILTON HOSPITAL 45013 #005-12-1994 L1996 **IM** *020 †20
GOLDMAN, Philip Mark. 1199 MAIN ST 45013 #038-43-1987 L1990 **FM U** *020
GOVIL, Sumita. 3145 HAMILTON MASON RD, FL 2 45011 #496-07-1992 L2007 **FPG** *020 †18
HALE, George Carl. 3145 HAMILTON MASON RD, FL 2 45011 #047-07-1956 L1959 **IM** *020
HARTMAN, Kevin Patrick. ■ 45011 #038-41-2008 *012
HAUGER, Deborah. 1380 NW WASHINGTON BLVD, TAFT PLACE MEDICAL BUILDIN 45013 #048-13-1984 L1990 **CD IM** *020 †20
HEAR, Andrew John. 2275 MILLVILLE AVE STE A 45013 #654-01-1995 L1998 **IM** *020 †20
HINGSBERGEN, Douglas C. 25 OFFICE PARK DR 45013 #038-40-1984 L1985 **GS** *020 †85
HOFFMANN, Michael Anthony. 9582 PRINCETON GLENDALE RD, VA BUTLER CNTY HLTHCRE #B 45011 #038-41-1994 L1998 **IM** *020 †20
HOLTMAN, Helen Ann. 840 NW WASHINGTON BLVD, STE C 45013 #038-41-1991 L1993 **P** *020 †75
HUM, Rick Lee. 903 NW WASHINGTON BLVD, STE B 45013 #038-41-1979 L1991 **IM** *020 †20
JOBALIA, Nilesh B. 3145 HAMILTON MASON RD, STE 201 45011 #016-11-1990 L1991 **AN PME** *020 †05
KAKKASSERIL, Job Simon. 1010 CEREAL AVE STE 307 45013 #495-90-1972 L1979 **GS VS** *071 †85
KATZ, David Lee. 630 EATON AVE, FORT HAMILTON HOSPITAL 45013 #035-15-1968 L1975 **DR** *020 †80
KEJRIWAL, Ashok. 435 PARK AVE 45013 #495-54-1986 L1992 **IM** *020
KHANNA, Rajesh. 903 NW WASHINGTON BLVD, SUITA A 45013 #067-01-1993 L1996 **FM** *020 †20
KRIPAL, Jerry Alan. 630 EATON AVE, HOSPITAL 45013 #030-05-1991 L1992 **EM** *020 †16
KUENZIG, Paul Victor. 100 RIVERFRONT PLZ 45011 #028-34-1955 L1958 **FM** *020
KUHN, Allen Edward, Jr. 3035 HAMILTON MASON RD, STE 106 45011 #038-43-1976 L1979 **OBG** *020 †30
LANG, Evan Zhihong. 860 NW WASHINGTON BLVD, STE E 45013 #243-58-1986 L1997 **HO** *020 †20
LANG, Kathleen J Henke. 3740 ROSSGATE CT 45013 #020-12-1981 L1982 **FM** *020 †18
LEIPZIG, Jeffrey Rogers. 512 MAIN ST, ALLERGY AND ASTHMA 45013 #038-40-1991 L1998 **AI** *020 †55,03
LEYRER, Carl August. 230 N 3RD ST 45011 #041-09-1940 L1941 **GS** *071
LEYRER, Earl Thos. 230 N 3RD ST 45011 #036-05-1969 L1973 **IM PUD** *020
MAHIDA, Bhupendra Hari. 3090 MCBRIDE CT, STE B 45011 #836-02-1972 L1991 **NEP IM** *020 †20
MAMLOUK, Lotfi Fahmi. 630 EATON AVE 45013 #875-02-1995 L2001 **MPD** *020 †20,55
MANAVALAN, Pius Louis. 3090 MCBRIDE CT, STE B 45011 #495-52-1983 L2001 **NEP** *020 †20
MANITSAS, Geo Telemachus. 1380 NW WASHINGTON BLVD 45013 #035-45-1964 L1969 **CD IM** *020 †20
MAREPALLY, Rama. 3145 HAMILTON MASON RD 45011 #495-57-1995 L2004 **GE** *020 †20
MARTENS, James Patrick. ■ 45011 #038-41-2003 L2003 **ORS** *012
MARTIN, Richard Franklin. 630 EATON AVE 45013 #054-04-1968 L1974 **PTH CLP** *020 †50
MAYFIELD, Kevin Bill. 8230 BECKETT PARK DR, STE B 45011 #028-03-1982 L1990 **PS HS** *020 †85,65
MC LELLAN, Jennifer Marie. 3740 ROSSGATE CT 45013 #038-40-1997 L1998 **FM** *020 †18
MELVIN, Cyril Keith. 3145 HAMILTON MASON RD, FL 2 45011 #038-41-1980 L1982 **IM** *020
MILLER, H Chas. 1 N BROOKWOOD AVE 45013 #038-41-1974 L1974 **FM OS** *030
MILLER, Stanley Harvey. ■ 45013 #038-41-1943 L1944 **GP OS** *071
MITAL, Chetna. 1010 CEREAL AVE, STE 307 45013 #495-12-1981 L1985 **IM GP** *020 †20

■ = Address Information Privacy Protected

MUNSON, Jennifer Lynne. 3090 MCBRIDE CT STE B, SOUTHWESTERN OHIO INC 45011 #038-44-1983 L1985 **NEP IM** *020 †20

NACKHLA, G Habib. 100 RIVERFRONT PLZ 45011 #330-04-1957 L1967 **OBG** *071

NALAGATLA, Sucharitha. 2275 MILLVILLE AVE, STE A 45013 #495-70-1991 L1997 **IM** *020 †20

NATH, Geeta Amaresh. 1755 S ERIE HWY STE C 45011 #495-01-1984 L1999 **IM** *020 †20

NIEHAUS, Daniel Geo. 903 NW WASHINGTON BLVD, STE A 45013 #038-41-1972 L1972 **FM** *020 †18

OKOCHA, Patricia Ifeoma. 3145 HAMILTON MASON RD, FL 2 45011 #690-04-1990 L2000 **IM** *020 †20

OKUM, Neil Howard. 3145 HAMILTON MASON RD, STE 200 45011 #010-01-1975 L1976 **OTO** *020 †45

PATHROSE, Mini Peterson. 903 NW WASHINGTON BLVD, STE A 45013 #495-01-1994 L2000 **FM** *020 †18

PAWLOSKY, Frank X. ■ 45011 #041-12-1953 L1954 **GP OM** *071 †18

PETTIT, Kathryn Nell. ■ 45011 #001-06-2008 *012

PETTIT, Ryan Christopher. ■ 45011 #001-06-2008 *012

PIERCE, Charles H. 1 N BROOKWOOD AVE, URGENT CARE OF HAMILTON 45013 #068-01-1968 L2003 **FM PA** *071 †18

POTLURI, Jithendra C. 1380 NW WASHINGTON BLVD 45013 #496-01-1990 L1998 **IC** *012 †20

PRASAD, Chalasani S R. ■ 45011 #495-50-1969 L1973 **AN** *020

PRESSLER, John Elliott. 1710 TATUM LN, JOHN E. PRESSLER, M.D. 45013 #038-40-1973 L1978 **GS** *020 †85

QUADRI, Syed A. 1010 CEREAL AVE, STE 201 45013 #495-65-1996 L2000 **PCC** *100 †20

RAJAN, Susheela. 630 EATON AVE, THE FORT HAMILTON HOSPITAL 45013 #495-04-1994 L1999 **IM** *020 †20

RAJARATNAM, Shanthi. 3740 ROSSGATE CT, HERITAGE HEALTH ALLIANCE, 45013 #060-01-1986 L1996 **FM** *020 †18

RAMADAS, Holenarasipur S. 25 OFFICE PARK DR 45013 #495-33-1973 L1981 **GS VS** *020 †85

RAMIREZ MARTINEZ, Karla. 210 S 2ND ST 45011 #649-13-2000 L2006 **FM** *100 †18

RANDOLPH, Brady Fitz. ■ 45011 #016-06-1945 L1958 **ORS** *071 †40

RAY, Gary Lee. 1010 CEREAL AVE, STE 311 45013 #038-41-1982 L1985 **PM** *020 †60

REMOTIGUE, Tiberius E. 630 EATON AVE #548-08-1958 L1967 **CLP** *020

ROBINSON, Kent. 3145 HAMILTON MASON RD, FL 2 45011 #038-41-1983 L1985 **IM** *020 †20

ROCK, Raymond Patrick. 3145 HAMILTON MASON RD, STE 200 45011 #038-41-1982 L1983 **OTO** *020 †45

RODEN, Carl Arthur. ■ 45013 #038-41-1940 **GP** *071

ROEBUCK, Richard Ramsay. 1010 CEREAL AVE 45013 #038-41-1977 L1978 **OPH** *020 †35 ‡

ROGERS, William M, III. 123 COURT ST, BUTLER COUNTY JAIL 45011 #038-41-1985 L1986 **EM** *020 †16

SACHDEVA, Rohini Dhamija. 903 NW WASHINGTON BLVD, STE A 45013 #496-30-1999 L2003 **IM** *100 †20

SANTHANAM, Uma Maheshwari. 20 N E ST 45013 #496-28-1994 L1999 **IM** *020 †20

SARGERO, Thomas V. 1010 CEREAL AVE, STE 305 45013 #010-01-1982 L1985 **IM** *020 †20

SAVAGE, Gregory L. 903 NW WASHINGTON BLVD, STE A 45013 #038-41-1974 L1974 **FM** *020 †18

SCHUMACHER, Gunter. 601 N B ST 45013 #407-06-1958 L1969 **OM OS** *020

SCHWALLIE, Robert Bruce. 630 EATON AVE, FT HAMILTON HOSP EMGY DEPT 45013 #038-40-1980 L1980 **EM IM** *020 †16

SCOTT, James Inch, Jr. 1380 NW WASHINGTON BLVD 45013 #038-41-1961 L1961 **CD LM** *071 †20

SHUBS, Gerald Alan. 1490 UNIVERSITY BLVD 45011 #010-02-1969 L1972 **P** *020 †30,75

SIH, Ing Khoen. 630 EATON AVE 45013 #660-01-1959 L1967 **IM** *071

SOIKA, Christopher Willia. 840 NW WASHINGTON BLVD, STE A 45013 #023-12-1982 L1994 **GS** *020 †85

SOTO, Wendy Sue. 5971 GOLF CLUB LN 45011 #038-45-2002 L2002 **MPD** *020 †20

STAKIC, Josif. ■ 45011 #038-41-2008 *012

STEWART, James Antenen. 630 EATON AVE 45013 #038-41-1947 L1947 **GS** *071

STEWART, John Antenen. 6 HISTORIC CRESCENT DR 45013 #038-41-1945 L1945 **OBG** *071

TABAO, Michelle Pamplona. 3145 HAMILTON MASON RD, STE 201 45011 #748-21-1998 L2000 **PM** *020 †60

TROCHE, Milton. 840 NW WASHINGTON BLVD 45013 #042-03-1983 L1992 **OBG** *020 †30

VANCE, Miles Monroe. ■ 45013 #038-41-1957 L1957 **FM** *071 †18

VERGEL DE DIOS, Domingo S. ■ 45013 #748-01-1948 **GP OS** *074

VERHAGEN, Arie Dirk. ■ 45013 #660-02-1946 L1966 **PDS GS** *071 †85,90

WEHR, Kenneth Lewis. 1380 NW WASHINGTON BLVD 45013 #036-05-1968 L1974 **PUD IM** *020 †20

WEINTZ, John Philip. 5150 SANDY LN 45014 #038-41-2000 L2000 **IM** *020 †20

WHALEN, Chas Eldridge, Jr. 1010 CEREAL AVE 45013 #020-02-1980 L1981 **IM AN** *020 †16

WILLBRAND, Jeffrey Willia. 3145 HAMILTON MASON RD, STE 200 45011 #028-02-1974 L1975 **OTO** *020 †45

WILLKE, Thomas J. 4125 HAMILTON MIDDLETWN RD 45011 #038-41-1976 L1979 **FM FPG** *020 †18 ‡

WRIGHT, Ralph Jay, III. 630 EATON AVE 45013 #038-43-1988 L1992 **RO** *020 †80

YANG, Paul Potsang. 3570 PLEASANT AVE, LINDENWALD MEDICAL ASSOCIA 45015 #025-01-1993 L1996 **FM** *020 †18

ZANCAN, Walter Louis. 50 RIVERFRONT PLZ 45011 #010-03-1977 L1978 **ORS** *020 †40

ZAYYAT, Elie Johnny. 25 OFFICE PARK DR 45013 #605-03-1991 L1997 **VS** *020 †85

ZETTLER, Richard Louis. 3570 PLEASANT AVE 45015 #028-34-1948 L1949 **GP** *020 †18

HAMMONDSVILLE – JEFFERSON

COSTARELLA, Adam Earle. 2976 PLEASANT RIDGE RD 43930 #038-40-1975 L1975 **EM IM** *020 †20,16

HARPSTER – WYANDOT

FALK, Jessica Ann. ■ 43323 #038-40-2008 *012

HARRISON – HAMILTON

BAILEY, Joseph Michael. 10450 NEW HAVEN RD 45030 #038-41-1991 L1992 **PD** *020 †55

CHAUDHRY, Suhail Bashir. 1100 HARRISON AVE, CORPORATION OF SOUTH 45030 #704-02-1983 L2001 **IM** *020 †20

CIAMBARELLA, Ernest. 10450 NEW HAVEN RD 45030 #038-41-1974 L1976 **PD EM** *020 †55

DONATH, Rudolf. 1100 HARRISON AVE, CORPORATION OF SOUTH 45030 #038-41-1957 L1957 **IM OS** *071 †20

FINLEY, Allison Marie. ■ 45030 #038-44-2008 *012

HAAS, Paul Jos. ■ 45030 #028-34-1958 L1961 **OBG** *071 †30

HAGEDORN, Suzanne Mary. 1100 HARRISON AVE 45030 #020-02-1976 L1979 **IM** *071 †20

HARP, Sharon L. 10450 NEW HAVEN RD 45030 #038-44-1994 L1995 **PD** *072 †55

HOOPES, Terri Wallace. 1149 STONE DR, STE 1000 45030 #038-41-1988 L1990 **OBG** *020 †30

JOHNSON, Steven Donald. 1149 STONE DR, STE 1000 45030 #038-06-1994 L2000 **OBG** *020 †30

KIM, Tai-Won. 108 S STATE ST 45030 #583-01-1967 L1974 **FM** *020 †20

KONSTANTINOU, Chris. 1100 HARRISON AVE, CINCINNATUS CENTER 2ND FL 45030 #038-40-1989 L1998 **CD** *100 †20

MICHAELS, Geo Leslie, Jr. 1100 HARRISON AVE 45030 #038-06-1976 L1978 **PD PEM** *020 †55

RAJU, Uma Sagi. 1100 HARRISON AVE 45030 #038-45-1995 L2000 **FM** *020 †18

RENUSCH, Joseph Allen. 10400 NEW HAVEN RD 45030 #020-12-1986 L1989 **EM** *020 †16

RYBALSKY, Irina. 10400 NEW HAVEN RD 45030 #913-15-1976 L2000 **PD** *020 †55

SCHUERMANN, Stephen J. 1149 STONE DR, STE 1000 45030 #038-41-1996 L1997 **OBG** *020 †30

SIEFFERMAN, L Thos. ■ 45030 #038-41-1957 L1957 **GP FM** *071

SMITH, Graig William. 1149 STONE DR, STE 1000 45030 #038-43-1981 L1986 **GYN** *020 †30

STEWART, Cecily Ann. 10400 NEW HAVEN RD 45030 #035-46-1988 L1996 **EM** *020 †16

TILLER, Tracy. 10400 NEW HAVEN RD 45030 #001-02-1983 L1985 **EM PD** *020 †55

TURNER, Traci Ann. 10450 NEW HAVEN RD 45030 #038-41-2001 L2001 **IM** *020

WINCHESTER, Hana. 1100 HARRISON AVE, CORPORATION OF SOUTH 45030 #286-02-1996 L2000 **IM** *020 †20

WONG, Perry. 10450 NEW HAVEN RD 45030 #038-41-1983 L1985 **FM** *020 †18

WUEST, Richard Jon. ■ 45030 #038-40-1980 **FM** *100

HARTVILLE – STARK

BARBUSH, Thomas Jos, Jr. 855 W MAPLE ST 44632 #038-40-1986 L1987 **VIR DR** *020 †18,80

BRINE, David Richard. 855 W MAPLE ST 44632 #038-43-1992 L1998 **DR** *020 †80

CLAY-ROGERS, Shelby L. 2736 RITA ST NE 44632 #038-44-1997 L1999 **EM** *020 †18

DE GALAN, Mark Robt. 855 W MAPLE ST 44632 #011-02-1990 L1995 **R NM** *020 †80,28

KLIPEC, Martha Jean. 855 W MAPLE ST STE 110, COMMUNITY HEALTH CARE 44632 #038-44-1985 L1987 **FM** *020 †18

LOIUDICE, Jean Anne Lang. 855 W MAPLE ST STE 12, TRI COUNTY EMERGENCY MED S 44632 #016-76-1972, ▲ L1974 **IM FM** *020 †20,18

MC NULTY, Barry Chas. 855 W MAPLE ST 44632 #041-12-1991 L1997 **RNR** *020 †80

POSERIA, Harsh Vardhan. 89 WEST DR 44632 #495-20-1977 L1984 **IM** *020

REAVEN, Robert Edward. 855 W MAPLE ST 44632 #038-43-1976 L1978 **R** *020 †80

SEAGER, Jon Christian. 855 W MAPLE ST, STE 110 44632 #038-40-1999 L1999 **FM** *020 †18

SRIVASTAVA, Rashmi. 855 W MAPLE ST STE 130 44632 #495-38-1997 L2002 **IM** *020 ‡

VESY, Thomas Leverne, Jr. 855 W MAPLE ST 44632 #038-44-1996 L1998 **DR** *020 †80

VOGELGESANG, Mark Wesley. 104 EAST DR 44632 #038-40-1977 L1982 **OTO HNS** *071 †45

HEATH – LICKING

BARCELONA, Ramon L. 687 HOPEWELL DR, BLDG 2 43056 #748-20-1987 L1996 **FM** *020 †18

MARTY, Charles Jacob. 444 HEBRON RD, ARUINMERITOR 43056 #038-40-1975 L1978 **FM** *020 †18

HICKSVILLE – DEFIANCE

BLAD, Denise Elaine. 208 COLUMBUS ST 43526 #422-01-1998 L2004 **FM** *020 †18

CHESLER, Richard Glenn. 208 COLUMBUS ST 43526 #039-01-1985 L1987 **EM** *020

KELLY, Kevin James. 208 COLUMBUS ST 43526 #038-40-1976 L1977 **CD IM** *020 †20

MILLER, Laverne L. 208 COLUMBUS ST 43526 #038-40-1975 L1980 **FM FPG** *020 †18

UNDERWOOD, Daniel La Von. 208 COLUMBUS ST 43526 #038-43-1980 L1982 **FM** *020 †18

WHITE, T Eric. 208 COLUMBUS ST 43526 #017-20-1990 L1996 **CD** *020 †20

HIGHLAND HEIGHTS – CUYAHOGA

ADVANI, Anjali Sunder. ■ 44143 #036-07-1996 L2002 **HO IM** *020 †20

ARROSSI, Andrea Valeria. ■ 44143 #132-01-1995 L2002 **SP** *100 †50

BERNARD, Philip Noel. 5341 CHARLES PL 44143 #038-06-1986 L1986 **FM** *020 †18

BRZOZOWSKI, Philip Chris. 468 LASSITER DR 44143 #041-14-1980 L1986 **OBG** *020 †30

HOLZHAUER, Markus. ■ 44143 #409-10-1992 L2006 **IM** *020 †80

KASSAIE, Ali. ■ 44143 #517-01-1997 L2000 **DR** *020 †80

KENOYER, Quentin D. 27155 CHARDON RD, 334 B W LEGEND COURT 44143 #017-20-1947 L1977 **GS GP** *020 †80

KWASNIAK, Laura Annette. ■ 44143 #019-02-2008 *012

PARMAR, Rajvinder. ■ 44143 #496-59-2000 L2005 **IM** *012

PATEL, Sangita T. 850 BRAINARD RD 44143 #028-46-1992 L1993 **DR** *020 †80

RATHOD, Amee. ■ 44143 #038-06-2006 L2006 **IM** *012

RAYMOND, Chad Eric. ■ 44143 #016-76-2007, ▲ L2007 **IM** *012

HILLIARD – FRANKLIN

ACKERMAN, William Edward, IV. ■ 43026 #038-41-1999 L1999 **OBG** *100

ALBRECHT, Daniel Raymond. ■ 43026 #016-42-2006 L2006 **PM** *012

ALEXANDER, Angelice Letah. 3617 HERITAGE CLUB DR 43026 #038-41-2000 L2000 **FM** *020 †18

ALEXANDER, Bryan Scott. ■ 43026 #038-45-2007 L2007 **TY** *012

AREND, David Charles. ■ 43026 #046-01-2003 L2004 **U** *012

BACHMANN, Daniel Josef. ■ 43026 #038-06-2002 L2007 **EM** *012

BACHMANN, Gina Marie. ■ 43026 #038-06-2002 L2007 **FM** *020 †18

BALDWIN, Robert Marcus. 5123 NORWICH ST 43026 #038-40-1966 L1966 **AI PDA** *020 †55,03

BARTSCH, John Eric. ■ 43026 #038-43-2005 L2005 **PM** *012

BARUDI, Mustafa. 2432 PEARSON WAY 43026 #875-01-1979 L1987 PHO *020 †55
BATRA, Nikesh. 3645 RIDGE MILL DR 43026 #495-30-1992 L2002 AN PME *020 †05
BEHBAKHT, Ozra. 4961 CEMETERY RD 43026 #517-01-1960 L1980 PD *071
BLOCH, Daniel J. 3600 MAIN ST 43026 #043-01-1977 L1995 FM *020 †18
BOCK, Sara Marie. ■ 43026 #038-44-2007 L2007 *012
BRANNON, Robert Wm. 3750 RIDGE MILL DR 43026 #038-40-1954 L1954 OBG *075 †30
BRAWNER, Emily Jane. ■ 43026 #038-75-2002, ▲ L2002 PCC *012 †20
BREEN, Richard Jon. 3643 RIDGE MILL DR 43026 #038-40-1998 L1999 PD *020 †55
BRUCE, Jarrod Thomas. ■ 43026 #038-40-2003 L2003 MPD *100 †20
BUENDIA, Michelle S. 5510 NIKE DR 43026 #038-45-1993 L1994 PD *020 †55
BURNETT, Tyler Martin. ■ 43026 #049-01-2006 L2007 AN *012
CHAWDRY, Fatima Ijaz. ■ 43026 #038-45-2003 L2003 IM *020 †20
CHAWLA, Gurbachan Singh. ■ 43026 #495-36-1963 L1970 PD PHO *071 †55
CHIO, Eugene Gehink. ■ 43026 #017-20-2004 L2004 OTO *012
COLLINS, Amy Lee. ■ 43026 #011-04-2007 L2007 GS *012
CONLEY, Brian. ■ 43026 #031-01-2005 L2005 EM *100
CRECELIUS, Jeffrey W. 3931 BERRY LEAF LN 43026 #038-40-1987 L1988 PD *020 †55
DAVIS, John Michael. ■ 43026 #041-09-1974 L1981 P *020
DRYDEN, Emily Robinson. ■ 43026 #041-12-2006 L2006 OBG *012
EFAW, Brad Scott. 3958 LEAP RD, STE 101 43026 #038-40-1993 L1994 FM *020 †18
EMAMI, Mandana. 5677 SCIOTO DARBY RD, STE 400 43026 #517-05-1989 L2000 IM *020 †20
EZENEKE, Nneka Stella. 5968 HAMPTON CORS N 43026 #690-04-1997 L2000 IM *020 †20 ‡
FLESHMAN, Daniel Jos. 3617 HERITAGE CLUB DR 43026 #038-40-1991 L1992 FM *020 †18
FRANKLIN, Nicholas Paul. ■ 43026 #038-44-2006 L2006 AN *012
FREEMAN, Eric David. ■ 43026 #038-40-2008 *012
GAINES, Steven Thomas. 3777 TRUEMAN CT 43026 #045-01-1983 L1985 ORS GS *020 †40
GORBETT, Daniel G, Jr. ■ 43026 #038-40-2008 *012
GRAY, Teri Lynn. ■ 43026 #038-40-2008 *012
GREEN, Michael Brian. ■ 43026 #020-12-2001 L2001 PCC *012
GRIFFIN, Brian Frederic. 3655 RIDGE MILL DR 43026 #038-41-1978 L1979 EM LM *020 †16
GRIFFIN, Jason. 5621 BLUE LAGOON LN 43026 #038-75-2003, ▲ L2003 FPG IM *100 †20
HALIM-ARMANIOS, Mona Y. 4744 RIVERWOOD DR, 410 WEST 10TH AVENUE 43026 #915-04-1968 L1987 AN OS *020 †05
HALTER, Jeffrey Michael. ■ 43026 #011-02-1999 L2007 PDS *012
HALTERMAN, Timothy Eric. ■ 43026 #038-40-2005 L2005 IM *012
HAMMOND, Thomas Hale. 5850 PRIVILEGE DR 43026 #049-01-2000 L2000 OTO *020 †45
HARRIS, Thomas Leroy. ■ 43026 #050-02-2007 L2007 AN *012
HEINLEN-BELARDO, Leah. 3958 LEAP RD, STE 101 43026 #038-40-1992 L1993 FM *020 †18
HENDRICKER, Ryan Matthew. ■ 43026 #016-11-2005 L2005 OTO *012
HESTAND, Nancy Lee. 5510 NIKE DR 43026 #038-40-1974 L1974 PD *050 †55
HILL, Crystal Dawn. ■ 43026 #038-45-2006 L2006 PD *012
HIMES, Alison K. ■ 43026 #038-75-2007, ▲ L2007 *012
HOEFLINGER, Geo Richard. ■ 43026 #038-40-1946 L1946 GP *071 †18
HOWSON, Robyn Doll. ■ 43026 #038-40-2004 L2004 MPD *012
HUEFNER, Julianne. 3535 FISHINGER BLVD, STE 285 43026 #049-01-1992 L2001 IM *020 †20
HUSSEIN, Ehab. ■ 43026 #038-75-2007, ▲ L2007 *012
INGERSKI, Michael S. ■ 43026 #051-01-2003 L2004 AN *100
JEU, Joseph Marian. 3958 LEAP RD, STE 101 43026 #038-40-1980 L1981 FM *020 †18
JHAVERI, Nishit G. 5300 NIKE DR 43026 #496-38-1993 L1997 IM *020 †20
KANELLITSAS, Ioanna. 5300 NIKE DR 43026 #038-40-1995 L1999 OBG *020 †30
KANNAN, Rajesh Periaswami. ■ 43026 #495-04-1995 L2007 FOP *100 †50
KASHEER, Enaas F. 3966 BROWN PARK DR, SUITES C & D 43026 #915-04-1983 L1999 PD *020 †55
KASICK, David Phillips. ■ 43026 #038-40-2003 L2003 P *100
KATABAY, Adil Omar. 3645 RIDGE MILL DR 43026 #056-05-1997 L2002 AN *020
KAVAL, Daria Beth. ■ 43026 #038-40-2005 L2005 FP *012
KELCH, Lisa Brandstaetter. 3931 BERRY LEAF LN 43026 #038-40-1990 L1991 PD *020 †55
KELLY, Brian Robert. ■ 43026 #038-44-2007 L2007 AN *012
KING, Karen V Guss. 3712 RIDGE MILL DR 43026 #038-43-1988 L1990 OBG *020 †30
KOENIG, James Wm. ■ 43026 #038-40-1954 L1954 AN *071 †05
KOPPERUD, Andrew Jon. ■ 43026 #026-04-2005 L2005 MPD *012
KUBE, Erika Charlotte. ■ 43026 #016-42-2006 L2006 EM *012
LAMONTE, Robert Chas. 3720 RIDGE MILL DR, PEDIATRIC ASSOCIATES 43026 #038-40-1991 L1992 PD *020 †55
LANE, Edward James. 4444 DAVIDSON RD 43026 #038-40-1998 L1999 FM *020 †18
LEEMAN, Alyson Hope. 3712 RIDGE MILL DR 43026 #038-40-1989 L1990 OBG *020 †30
LEIST, Maureen Kaye. 2264 GLENCROFT DR 43026 #038-44-2002 L2002 AN *020 †05
LICHTBLAU, Steven Hilary. 3535 FISHINGER BLVD, STE 285 43026 #038-40-1967 L1967 IM END *020
LINDAUER, Jaina Rachelle. 3712 RIDGE MILL DR 43026 #038-40-1999 L2000 OBG *020 †30
LINDLEY, Kenneth Todd. ■ 43026 #038-40-2008 *012
LINGAM, Kalyan Sai. 3645 RIDGE MILL DR 43026 #038-44-2000 L2000 APM *020 †05
LUCAS, Janet Marie. 3750 RIDGE MILL DR 43026 #038-40-1977 L1978 GYN *020 †30
MADAN, Rajesh. 4531 CEMETERY RD 43026 #495-36-1993 L1997 IM *020 †20
MARTIN, Jay Ellis. 3535 FISHINGER BLVD, STE 2852 43026 #038-40-1997 L1998 IM *020 †20
MC CLURE, David Brian. 3535 FISHINGER BLVD, STE 285 43026 #038-40-1985 L1986 IM *020 †20
MC MANAMON, Thos Vincent. ■ 43026 #028-34-1954 L1956 OM LM *071 †70
MC QUILLAN, Sharon P. 3452 FAIRWAY COMMONS DR 43026 #038-40-1983 L1984 FM OS *040
MEADOWS, James Ryan. ■ 43026 #038-40-2008 *012
MEHMOOD, Syed Adil. ■ 43026 #016-42-2002 L2007 TS *012
MEHTA, Daxa B. ■ 43026 #495-22-1968 L1981 GP *020
MELON, David Ethan. ■ 43026 #033-06-2007 L2007 OTO *012
MILLER, Michael David. 3958 LEAP RD, STE 101 43026 #038-40-2002 L2002 FM *020 †18
MILLER, Vicki Lynn. 3712 RIDGE MILL DR 43026 #038-40-1993 L1999 OBG *020 †30
MOHAMED, Mohamud Sheikhah. ■ 43026 #561-31-1994 L2000 IM *020 †20 ‡
MORAN, Kenneth Ray. ■ 43026 #038-40-2004 L2004 AN *012
MURESAN, Mark Aurel. 5510 NIKE DR 43026 #038-43-1993 L1994 PD *020 †55
MURPHY, Link Robert. 3535 FISHINGER BLVD, STE 285 43026 #038-40-1980 L1980 IM OS *020 †20
NARULA, Komal. 3913 BERRY LEAF LN 43026 #025-01-1991 L1992 OBG *020 †30
NIRMALAN, Niruban. ■ 43026 #038-44-2001 GS *100
NUTHAKKI, Sushma. ■ 43026 #495-57-2001 L2004 NPM *012 †55
OKAM, Ngozi Vivien. ■ 43026 #035-06-2008 *012
ORZO, Michael Eugene. 3645 RIDGE MILL DR 43026 #038-40-1995 L1996 AN *020 †05
PAGE, Maurice-Pierre. ■ 43026 #020-12-2007 L2007 GS *012
PALMER, Bryan Seth. ■ 43026 #038-40-2008 *012
PAN, James. ■ 43026 #038-44-2007 L2007 GS *012
PANTELIS, Joseph Anthony. ■ 43026 #038-44-2004 L2004 IM *100 †20
PAREKH, Ketki Mahendra. 3617 HERITAGE CLUB DR 43026 #038-41-1997 L1998 FM *020 †18
PERCHINIAK, Nicholas Adam. ■ 43026 #041-02-2007 L2007 EM *012
PERCY, Carmella D'Incogni. ■ 43026 #003-75-2007, ▲ L2007 EM *012
PLEISTER, Adam Paul. ■ 43026 #056-06-2004 L2004 IM *100
POOL, Kathryn S. 3535 FISHINGER BLVD 43026 #048-13-1998 L2000 OBG *020 †30
QUARRIE, Ricardo Orlando. ■ 43026 #038-40-2007 L2007 GS *012
RANCITELLI, Philip Neil. 3915 BERRY LEAF LN 43026 #038-43-1999 L2000 AI *020 †55,03
RAYO, Barbara Brooks. 3720 RIDGE MILL DR 43026 #038-40-1983 L1985 PD *020 †55
REDDY, Cherkupalli V. ■ 43026 #495-21-1983 L1992 P *020 †75
REIS, Robert Drake. 3720 RIDGE MILL DR 43026 #001-02-1991 L1992 PD *020 †55
RICHTER, Juli Marie. ■ 43026 #038-40-2004 L2004 NPM *012 †55
ROCK, Jonathan Bernard. ■ 43026 #038-40-2007 L2007 PTH *012
SACOLICK, Alan Robt. 3750 RIDGE MILL DR 43026 #038-40-1984 L1985 OBG *020 †30
SCHROER, Eric Christian. 3823 TRUEMAN CT 43026 #038-40-1989 L1990 FM *020 †18
SCHULTZ, Dana Jos. 3643 RIDGE MILL DR 43026 #038-40-1984 L1987 PD *020 †55
SESHADRI, Lakshmi. 5300 NIKE DR, HILLIARD FAMILY HEALTH 43026 #038-44-1993 L1995 FM *020 †18
SKILLMAN, Thomas G. ■ 43026 #038-41-1949 L1949 IM *071 †20
SNYDER, Robert Wescott. 3931 BERRY LEAF LN 43026 #041-02-1995 L1996 PD *020 †55
STEENSEN, Robert N. 3617 HERITAGE CLUB DR 43026 #038-44-1982 L1983 ORS OSM *020 †40
SULLIVAN, Lori Ann. 3617 HERITAGE CLUB DR 43026 #038-45-1985 L1986 FM *020 †18
TEACH, Patricia Lynn. 3712 RIDGE MILL DR 43026 #038-43-1995 L1997 OBG *020 †30
TELLER, Timothy Allen. 3931 BERRY LEAF LN, HILLIARD PEDIATRICS, INC 43026 #038-41-1991 L1992 PD *020 †55
TOPOLNYCKY, Diana M. ■ 43026 #051-75-2007, ▲ OBG *012
TURNER, Leslie Paige. 3535 FISHINGER BLVD, STE 280 43026 #038-40-1993 L1995 OBG *020 †30
VARKER, Kimberly Ann. ■ 43026 #035-15-1995 L1997 GS *020 ‡
WAGNER, Diana T. 3720 RIDGE MILL DR 43026 #038-43-1991 L1992 PD *020 †55
WANG, Xiuqiong. 4800 CANTERWOOD CT 43026 #243-70-1985 L2002 IM *020 †20
WARRICK, Joann Edith. ■ 43026 #017-20-2003 L2003 GS *012
WATKINS, Nicholas Robert. 3958 LEAP RD, STE 101 43026 #038-40-1993 L1994 FM *020 †18 ‡
WESTENDORF, Sheila Kay. 5300 NIKE DR, HILLIARD FAMILY HEALTH 43026 #038-45-1992 L1995 FM *020 †18
WHEASLER, Ray Stanton, III. 5510 NIKE DR 43026 #005-06-1983 L1985 PD *020 †55
WILL, Kerry Catherine. ■ 43026 #028-46-2004 L2004 IM *020 †20
WILSON, William Murray. ■ 43026 #038-40-1959 L1959 A PDA *020
YOUNG, Courtney Renee. ■ 43026 #038-44-2005 L2005 FP *012
ZELINSKI, Daniel Paul. ■ 43026 #038-40-2005 L2005 EM *012
ZIEGLER, Rebecca Marie. ■ 43026 #026-04-2008 *012
ZULLIGER, Laurel Anne. 3823 TRUEMAN CT 43026 #038-45-1985 L1986 FM *020 †18

HILLSBORO – HIGHLAND

ASHRAF, Mohammed Ali. 1275 N HIGH ST, HIGHLAND DIST HOSP EMERGEN 45133 #305-01-1998 L1999 FM *020 †18
AYRES, David St Clair. 6320 STATE ROUTE 138 45133 #017-20-1955 L1956 FM *071 †18
BART, Gerald Norman. 102 TE MAR WAY 45133 #495-37-1964 L2007 OTO AI *020 †45 ‡
BEERY, Jeffrey Scott. 1275 N HIGH ST 45133 #038-41-1989 L1992 IM *020 †20
BERNHOFFER, Erik Thos. 9765 E PROSPECT RD, PROSPECT ROAD FAM PRACTICE 45133 #038-06-1992 L1994 FM *020 †18
CLARKE, Gregory Bennett. 1275 N HIGH ST, STE 3 45133 #017-20-1986 L1995 CD *040 †20
CUDKOWICZ, Leon. PULMONARY CLINIC HIGHLAND 45133 #352-07-1946 L1977 CD PUD *071
FORBES, Craig Wallace. 1121 NORTHVIEW DR STE A 45133 #035-48-1988 L1994 OBG *020 †30
FRY, Harry Ford. 219 W MAIN ST 45133 #041-01-1968 L1976 CD IM *071 †20
GUNDERMAN, David Jos. 104 ERIN CT 45133 #038-41-1987 L1988 FM FPG *020 †18
JONES, Jeffrey Kenneth. ■ 45133 #060-01-1990 L1995 FM *020
JUSCHKA, Dirk N. 104 ERIN CT 45133 #065-01-1981 L1985 FM AN *020
KANABAR, Sudhin Dhiraj. 1121 NORTHVIEW DR, STE 2 45133 #917-30-1990 L1999 N *020 †75
KARNES, Julie Gay. 1275 N HIGH ST 45133 #038-45-1995 L1996 FM *020 †18
MELINK, Regina L. 1275 N HIGH ST 45133 #048-13-1990 L1995 IM *020 †20
MESINA, Sophela M. 1275 N HIGH ST 45133 #748-11-1966 L1973 PD *020
MORENTZ, Paul E. 108 ERIN CT 45133 #035-01-1951 L1994 P *020 †75
NADKARNI, Seema Santosh. ■ 45133 #305-01-2002 L2005 PD *100
NAVALKAR, Sushant Ram. 1487 N HIGH ST, STE 102 45133 #305-01-1999 L2004 *100
ODLAND, Lawrence T. ■ 45133 #005-06-1952 L1969 AM *072 †70
PELBERG, Robert Alan. 1275 N HIGH ST, STE 3 45133 #016-06-1993 L2002 CD *020 †20
RANDALL, Thomas Robert. 1275 N HIGH ST 45133 #038-40-1996 L1997 FM *020 †18
ROUSH, Glenn Stephen. ■ 45133 #038-41-1978 L1989 DR *020 †80
RYU, Grace Young. 1275 N HIGH ST 45133 #038-41-1990 L1991 AI *020 †55,03
SALIDO, Monica Besana. ■ 45133 #748-09-1964 L1978 PD *020
SCHREIBMAN, Paul Herbert. 1440 N HIGH ST, COMMUNITY MED CTR 45133 #038-40-1965 L1965 IM DIA *020 †20
SHANAHAN, Catherine A. 1402 N HIGH ST 45133 #038-41-1991 L1999 FM *020 †18
SHIVANI, Ramesh Kumar. 1121 NORTHVIEW DR 45133 #704-16-1990 L2000 P PYG *020 †75
SLATER, Todd Dale. ■ 45133 #038-41-1983 L1984 OBG *020 †30
STORRS, Albert Miller. ■ 45133 #038-41-1946 L1947 GS *071 †85
STOYANOV-TODD, Radosveta. 108 ERIN CT, SCIOTO PAINT VALLEY MENTAL 45133 #198-01-1988 L2000 P CHP *020 †75
TANZER, Fred Louis. 1275 N HIGH ST, DIST HOSP 45133 #038-41-1988 L1989 IM EM *020
TERRELL, Paul William. 6000 STATE ROUTE 247 # 340 45133 #038-40-1962 L1962 AM *020
WELDER, Linda Ruth. 1404 N HIGH ST, BOX 839 45133 #041-12-1979 L1984 GS *020 †85
WETHERINGTON, Anthony P. 1487 N HIGH ST, STE 100 45133 #038-41-1996 L1997 FM *020 †18
ZANOWICK, Russell Saml. ■ 45133 #028-34-1958 L1959 GP *071
ZILE, Ronnie Allen. 1402 N HIGH ST 45133 #038-45-1988 L1989 FM *020 †18 ‡

HINCKLEY – MEDINA

EDMISON, John Michael. ■ 44233 #038-06-2002 L2002 GE *012 †20

■ = Address Information Privacy Protected

FENDRIKOVA MAHLAY, Natalia. ■ 44233 #913-05-1994 L2005 **IM** *012
FIKAR, Joseph O. ■ 44233 #286-02-1931 L1953 **GP** *071
MASON, Richard Andrew Edw. PO BOX 408 44233 #409-41-1991 L2004 **P** *012
MAZALA, Meir. 2278 STONY HILL RD 44233 #550-01-1977 L1984 **AN PME** *071 †05
REYNES, Norma B Nangit. 1945 CLOVER CIR 44233 #748-01-1965 L1972 **IM GP** *020

HOLLAND – LUCAS

AGUBOSIM, Samuel Nkem. 7960 N SHORELINE DR 43528 #038-43-1994 L1998 **APM** *020
AGUILLON, Andre Utulo. ■ 43528 #038-43-2007 L2007 **IM** *012
AGUILLON, Monina U. ■ 43528 #748-08-1969 **CHP** *062
BAIS, Sanjiv. 6855 SPRING VALLEY DR, STE 120 43528 #041-01-1988 L1994 **CRS** *020 †85,10
BENSON, Daniel Ward. 6855 SPRING VALLEY DR, STE 120 43528 #038-06-1985 L1988 **GS** *020 †85
BHATIA, Bhawna. 1106 S MCCORD RD 43528 #495-36-1969 L1975 **PD** *020 †55
BIHN, Jason William. ■ 43528 #038-43-2008 *012
BILLS, Steven William. ■ 43528 #038-43-1993 L1995 **EM** *020 †16
BLESSINGER, Brian Joseph. ■ 43528 #017-20-2007 L2007 **ORS** *012
BROERING-AMMONS, Jane A. 7429 INTERNATIONAL DR 43528 #038-43-1991 L1992 **P** *020 †75
CALAWAY, Bethany Marie. ■ 43528 #038-43-2008 *012
CAMACHO, Stephen Phillip. 6855 SPRING VALLEY DR, STE 120 43528 #038-44-1997 L2003 **FM** *040 †18
CLARK, Robert Dale. ■ 43528 #031-01-2006 L2007 **IM** *012
CRAYNE, Charles S. ■ 43528 #654-01-1984 L1992 **AN** *020
DIETZ, Suzanne Denise. ■ 43528 #038-43-2008 *012
EBY, Paul James. 7010 SPRING MEADOWS DR W, STE 101 43528 #025-07-1985 L1987 **GPM** *020 †18,70
FRIEDMAN, David Ira. 330 OAK TERRACE BLVD, WESTERN LUCAS COUNTY CLINI 43528 #649-14-1971 L1975 **FM** *020 †18
GAUGHAN, Daniel C. ■ 43528 #038-45-1992 L1993 **GP** *100
GOCIMAN, Barbu Razvan. ■ 43528 #781-01-1999 L2005 **GS** *012
GOEL, Arika. ■ 43528 #038-43-2008 *012
GRIST, Mary Elizabeth. ■ 43528 #038-43-2003 L2003 **PD** *020
HANCOCK, J Brian. 7060 SPRING MEADOWS DR W, STE D 43528 #016-01-1975 L1976 **EM IM** *020 †20,16
KONZEN, Jon Leo. ■ 43528 #065-09-1960 L1963 **OM** *072 †70
KONZEN, Marie Claudette M. ■ 43528 #065-09-1960 L1984 **PM** *071 †60
KUSHNEREIT, Aimee Marie. ■ 43528 #038-43-2008 *012
LIESER, Thomas Eugene. 7010 SPRING MEADOWS DR W, STE 101 43528 #038-43-1987 L1988 **GPM FM** *020 †70,18
LIKES, Rickland. 709 WHISPERLAKE RD 43528 #022-75-2002, ▲ L2002 **OSM** *012
LOPEZ, Nicholas Michael. 6855 SPRING VALLEY DR, SPRINGMEADOW MED BLDG #120 43528 #649-14-1972 L1977 **FM** *020 †18
MABUS, Mark Samuel. ■ 43528 #038-43-2005 L2006 **FP** *012
MATTAR, Ziad Rachid. ■ 43528 #913-06-1997 L2003 **PCC** *012 †20
NAHHAS, Ahed. 6855 SPRING VALLEY DR, STE 120 43528 #875-01-1981 L1989 **CD IM** *020 †20
RAGOTHAMAN, Anitha. ■ 43528 #038-43-2008 *012
REDDY, Srinivas P.. ■ 43528 #496-22-2005 *100
ROHRS, Jonathan Edward. 6855 SPRING VALLEY DR, STE 120 43528 #028-34-1974 L1975 **FM** *020 †18
RUEGER, Milton Jerome. ■ 43528 #025-07-1937 L1937 **CD IM** *072 †20
SHAIKH, Shahida T. 6855 SPRING VALLEY DR, STE 120 43528 #704-08-1977 L1993 **FM** *020 †18
SNARSKIS, Carolyn Elizabe. ■ 43528 #038-43-2008 *012
STERNFELD, William Chas. 6855 SPRING VALLEY DR, STE 120 43528 #035-06-1971 L1973 **GS** *020 †85
STROMFELD, Robert M. ■ 43528 #539-06-1968 L1982 **EM IM** *020
SUNDHEIMER, Rosemary E. ■ 43528 #065-05-1975 L1979 **RO IM** *071
WAGNER, Robinette. ■ 43528 #038-43-2008 *012
WASH, David Keane. ■ 43528 #025-07-1999 L2000 **FM** *020 †18
WILLIAMSON, Victoria Anne. ■ 43528 #038-43-1980 L1983 **AN FM** *075
WILSON, Michael Dean. ■ 43528 #038-43-2003 L2008 **DR** *012

HOMEWORTH – COLUMBIANA

SANOR, Teri Lee. ■ 44634 #038-44-2006 L2006 **IM** *012
WAGNER, James Lowell. PO BOX 105, 5281 ROCHESTER RD 44634 #038-41-1984 L1985 **PTH** *020 †50

HOUSTON – SHELBY

FRANK, Karen J. 3131 STATE ROUTE 47 45333 #055-75-1996, ▲ L2001 **FM** *020 †18
MARTIN, Kimberly J. 3131 STATE ROUTE 47 45333 #038-41-1995 L2001 **FM** *020 †18 ‡

HOWARD – KNOX

BOZKIR, Dogan. ■ 43028 #902-01-1950 L1971 **IM** *071
KING, Holmer W. ■ 43028 #038-06-1952 L1952 **PD** *071 †55
PAYNE, Rebecca Lynne. ■ 43028 #038-44-2008 *012
POTTS, Donald Eugene. ■ 43028 #041-02-1955 L1955 **EM OBG** *071

HUBBARD – TRUMBULL

KATZ, Bertram. ■ 44425 #016-11-1948 L1955 **GS** *071 †85
LAKSHMINARASIMHAN, R. ■ 44425 #495-33-1976 L1984 **IM** *020
MANGALAT, Dev. ■ 44425 #539-06-2003 L2003 **GS** *012
MAZZI, James A. 4503 LOGANWAY AVE 44425 #028-79-1957, ▲ L1957 **FM** *071
WALKER, Joy Lee. ■ 44425 #011-02-1967 L1969 **GP** *030

HUBER HEIGHTS – MONTGOMERY

AGARWAL, Vivek Anand. 7405 BRANDT PIKE 45424 #495-12-1974 L1983 **IM** *020 †20
BLUMBERG, Wendy. 7371 BRANDT PIKE, STE C 45424 #038-44-1998 L1999 **PD** *020 †55
CHAPPELL, Lestrita T. 8638 OLD TROY PIKE #001-02-1987 L1995 **IM** *020 †20
COLES, Joseph G. ■ 45424 #038-41-2006 L2006 **P** *012
DANGE, Sulabha R. 8701 OLD TROY PIKE, STE 102 45424 #495-28-1983 L1995 **IM** *020 †20
DEETER, Jane Anetta. ■ 45424 #051-01-1980 L1995 **N IM** *071
FRONISTA, Sylvia Eleny. 6096 BRANDT PIKE, HUBER HEIGHTS MEDICAL CENT 45424 #038-40-1992 L1994 **FM** *020 †18
HORN, Craig Alan. 8838 OLD TROY PIKE 45424 #038-45-1982 L1983 **PD** *020 †55
HUTCHISON, Laura L. 8638 OLD TROY PIKE, STE 101 45424 #038-45-1994 L1996 **PD** *020 †55
KALAHASTHY, Annadorai. 8638 OLD TROY PIKE, STE 102 45424 #495-50-1993 L1998 **IM** *020 †20
KLEIN, Lawrence W. 8701 OLD TROY PIKE, OF DAYTON, INC. - SUITE #1 45424 #028-79-1978, ▲ L1978 **NEP IM** *020
LORENZ, Kathryn Elizabeth. ■ 45424 #038-45-2006 L2006 **FP** *012
MENART, Teresa C. 6096 BRANDT PIKE 45424 #026-04-1991 L1997 **IM** *020 †20
ODENIGBO, Linda. 8838 OLD TROY PIKE 45424 #690-08-1987 L2000 **PD** *020 †55
REDDY, Anne M. 8501 OLD TROY PIKE, HUBER HEIGHTS FAMILY PRACT 45424 #038-40-1981 L1983 **FM** *020 †18
SHEPARD, Julie Schneider. 7371 BRANDT PIKE, STE C 45424 #035-01-1988 L1989 **PD** *020 †55

HUDSON – SUMMIT

AGARWAL-ANTAL, Neera P. 1325 CORPORATE DR, STE A 44236 #038-44-1992 L2000 **D DMP** *020
ALI, Syed Ijaz. 5655 HUDSON DR, STE 210 44236 #704-01-1965 L1976 **DR** *020 †80
ANDERSON, John B, Jr. ■ 44236 #035-06-1958 L1963 **IM OM** *071
ASTRINO, John Jos. 1365 CORPORATE DR, STE A 44236 #055-01-1978 L1979 **PD** *020 †55
AWENDER, Nancy Elaine. ■ 44236 #038-44-2003 L2003 **OPH** *020
BALLO, Bela Robt. 5655 HUDSON DR, STE 210 44236 #038-06-1988 L1995 **DR** *020 †80
BEDROSIAN, Emogene Lee. 5700 DARROW RD STE 106, 4M EMERGENCY SYSTEMS 44236 #005-06-1977 L2007 **EM LM** *020 †16
BELL, John Wm, II. ■ 44236 #038-40-1963 L1963 **EM OM** *020 †16
BERNSTEIN, George Murray. 5700 DARROW RD, STE 106 44236 #041-01-1975 L2000 **EM CCS** *020 †85,16
BETZ, William Bernard. 5655 HUDSON DR, STE 210 44236 #016-11-1999 L2005 **DR** *020 †80
BISSELL, Lewis F. ■ 44236 #004-01-1949 L1955 **IM EM** *071 †20
BLUM, Jonathan Eric. 5655 HUDSON DR, STE 210 44236 #023-07-1975 L1989 **DR VIR** *020 †20,80
BRENNAN, Gary Brooks. 5655 HUDSON DR, STE 210 44236 #021-01-2001 L2005 **VIR** *100 †80
BURY, Edward A, Jr. 5655 HUDSON DR, STE 210 44236 #038-44-1982 L1988 **R DR** *040 †80
CARTER, Jay Edward. 5827 FORTROSE CIR 44236 #038-44-1986 L1988 **EM** *020 †16
CASH, Shelby Joseph, III. 5778 DARROW RD, PHYSICIANS INC 44236 #038-06-1995 L2001 **IM** *020 †20
CAWTHON, Laura Ann. 5655 HUDSON DR, STE 210 44236 #025-07-1987 L1992 **DR** *020 †80
CAY, Abigail Murriel. 5655 HUDSON DR, STE 130B 44236 #748-20-2001 L2004 **FM** *020 †18
CORSINO, Anthony J. 5655 HUDSON DR, STE 210 44236 #033-75-1995, ▲ L2001 **NM** *020 †80
CRANE, Stephen S. 5655 HUDSON DR 44236 #038-40-1988 L1991 **OBG** *020 †30
CROFT, Thomas Jos. ■ 44236 #028-34-1963 L1964 **NS** *020
DALIEH, Sadi Daoud. ■ 44236 #575-01-1989 L1997 **EM AMI** *020
DANISH, Elizabeth Hager. 1365 CORPORATE DR STE A, ASSOCIATES 44236 #023-07-1974 L1979 **PD** *020 †55
DUFFY, Brendan Kieran. ■ 44236 #539-05-1997 L2003 **CD** *012 †20
DUNN, Risa Stephanie. 5655 HUDSON DR 44236 #038-40-1987 L1989 **DR** *020 †80
EL-SHAAR, Ahmad Khaled. 5655 HUDSON DR, STE 210 44236 #875-02-1973 L1979 **DR** *020 †80
EROGBOGBO, Alissa R. ■ 44236 #016-42-2004 L2004 **OBG** *012
ESSIET, Bassey Nelson. 5655 HUDSON DR, STE 210 44236 #038-43-1988 L1991 **DR** *020 †80
FAULK, Michael Wellington. 5700 DARROW RD STE 106, 4M EMERGENCY SYSTEMS 44236 #654-01-2004 L2007 **EM** *020 †16
FAUSTUS, Frank Paul. 5700 DARROW RD, STE 106 44236 #038-06-2000 L2000 **EM** *020 †16
FAYZ, Frank Mike. 5655 HUDSON DR, STE 210 44236 #005-06-1987 L1989 **DR** *020 †80
FINELLI, Daniel Albert. 5655 HUDSON DR, STE 210 44236 #038-06-1985 L1987 **DR RNR** *020 †80
FRIEDMAN, Sheldon Alan. ■ 44236 #041-02-1967 L1969 **PD** *100
GUINTO, Pedro Mendoza. ■ 44236 #748-01-1954 L1961 **AN** *020
HATJIS, Christos Geo. 5655 HUDSON DR 44236 #041-01-1975 L1988 **OBG MFM** *020 †30
HAYES, Brian Lee. 5655 HUDSON DR, STE 210 44236 #038-44-1999 L1999 **R RNR** *020 †80
HERSCHER, Elliot Stanton. 5778 DARROW RD, PEDIATRIC & ADOLESCENT 44236 #041-14-1978 L1979 **PD** *020 †55
HEWLETT, James S. ■ 44236 #020-02-1944 L1953 **ON HEM** *071 †20
HIRSH, Richard Norman. 5655 HUDSON DR, STE 210 44236 #035-09-1969 L1973 **DR NR** *020 †80
HONG, Harold Joseph. ■ 44236 #038-06-2005 **P** *012
HONG, Ki-Moon. 562 MEADOWRIDGE WAY 44236 #583-03-1972 L1979 **P** *020
HORD, Patricia Mary. 1365 CORPORATE DR, STE A 44236 #038-44-1988 L1989 **PD** *020 †55
HORNICK, David L. 5778 DARROW RD, PEDIATRIC & ADOLESCENT 44236 #041-01-1979 L1985 **PHO PD** *020 †55
ISMAIL, Saira B. 5778 DARROW RD, PHYSICIANS INC 44236 #038-44-1994 L1995 **FM** *020 †18
JEKIELEK, Susan A. 1320 CORPORATE DR STE 100, HUDSON FAM PRAC INC 44236 #048-02-1994 L1996 **FM** *020 †18
JOHNSON, Steven Lane. 1355B CORPORATE DR 44236 #038-40-1973 **PD** *020 †55
KAISER, Eric F. 72 VILLAGE WAY, STE 2B 44236 #038-40-1992 L1993 **CCA AN** *020 †05
KATZ, Sidney. ■ 44236 #038-06-1935 L1935 **AN** *071 †05
KINSELL, Lauren B. 5655 HUDSON DR, STE 210 44236 #038-43-1992 L1995 **DR** *020 †80
LADA, Robert Arne. 5655 HUDSON DR, STE 110 44236 #038-06-1993 L1995 **N** *020 †75
LAHORRA, John Michael. 5655 HUDSON DR, STE 210 44236 #038-40-1989 L1992 **DR** *020 †80,28
LAVIN, Justin Paul. 5655 HUDSON DR 44236 #041-01-1975 L1979 **MFM OS** *020 †30
LEVENTHAL, Mitchell W. 5300 DARROW RD, STE 106 44236 #039-01-1971 L1973 **EM LM** *020 †16
LICHTENBERGER, Deborah. ■ 44236 #038-45-1985 L1986 **GS** *075 †85

MAC CALLUM, Charles Lynn. 5778 DARROW RD, PHYSICIANS INC 44236 #011-02-1976 L1977 FM *020 †18
MALAJIKIAN, Krikor. 5655 HUDSON DR, STE 210 44236 #038-45-1999 L1999 DR *100 †80
MALONE, Danny Ray. 5700 DARROW RD, STE 106 44236 #010-01-1983 L2004 EM *020 †16
MARGRETT, John G. 200 LAUREL LAKE DR 44236 #065-06-1951 L1958 P *071 †75
MATA, Fernando V. ■ 44236 #132-01-1981 L1984 P *020
MC LANE, Hugh J. ■ 44236 #008-01-1946 L1950 IM CD *071 †20
MCMILLAN, Michelle Dessa. 5778 DARROW RD, PEDIATRIC & ADOLESCENT 44236 #038-06-1990 L1993 PD *020 †55
MC RAVEN, Jeffrey Walker. 5778 DARROW RD, PEDIATRIC & ADOLESCENT 44236 #038-43-1996 L1997 PD *020 †55
MESTER, Robert A. ■ 44236 #028-03-2008 *012
MODY, Malay Kunjvihari. 5655 HUDSON DR, STE 210 44236 #025-01-1994 L1999 VIR *020 †80
MORRIS, Jeffrey S. 110 W STREETSBORO ST, STE 12 44236 #038-06-01-1973 L1990 ORS HS *020
NALABOFF, Kenneth Michael. 5655 HUDSON DR, STE 210 44236 #550-02-1996 L2004 DR *020 †80
NEARY, John Philip. 571 BOSTON MILLS RD, STE 100 44236 #021-05-1992 L1993 FPS *020
PATNAIK, Asha Lata. ■ 44236 #495-73-1990 L2007 IM *020 †20
PETERSON, Eric Gregory. ■ 44236 #038-41-2007 L2007 IM *012
PHAM, Hung Hoang. 5655 HUDSON DR, STE 210 44236 #050-02-1998 L2005 DR *020 †80
PIZARRO, Araceli Torres. ■ 44236 #748-01-1957 L1968 PD IM *071
PRETORIUS, Diane L. 5655 HUDSON DR, STE 210 44236 #038-44-1988 L1991 DR *020 †80
RICHMAN, Lawrence Steven. 5655 HUDSON DR, STE 210 44236 #025-01-1970 L1977 R *020 †80
RILEY, Patrick Michael. 5655 HUDSON DR 44236 #038-41-1978 L1980 OP *071 †40
SCOTT, Tara Devi. 1305 CORPORATE DR, STE A 44236 #038-44-1992 L1997 OBG *020 †30
SHAH, Kalyani Dhruv. ■ 44236 #495-76-1983 L2004 PM *020 †60
SILBER, Angela Caldas. 5655 HUDSON DR 44236 #187-25-1992 L2000 OBG *100
SOMMER, Jennifer E. 5655 HUDSON DR, STE 210 44236 #025-76-2001, ▲ L2002 RNR *100 †80
STERBENZ, George C. ■ 44236 #033-06-1990 L2002 FOP *020 †50
SUGANO, Jonathan Riggs. 5655 HUDSON DR, STE 210 44236 #038-06-2001 L2001 NR *100 †80
TAYLOR, William Keller. 5655 HUDSON DR, STE 210 44236 #020-02-1976 L1981 DR *020 †80
THOMAS, Heather Lynn. ■ 44236 #038-44-1997 L1998 FM *020 †18
ULLMAN, Harlan Royce. 5655 HUDSON DR, STE 210 44236 #038-44-1987 L1988 DR *020 †80
VANA, August J. ■ 44236 #016-43-1949 L1959 GS GP *071
VENTIMIGLIA, Anthony J. 5655 HUDSON DR, STE 210 44236 #038-41-2001 L2001 DR *020 †80
VIBHAKAR, Shardul D. 5655 HUDSON DR, STE 210 44236 #495-17-1974 L1979 DR *020 †80
VIJAYVARGIYA, Manju. 5655 HUDSON DR, STE 210 44236 #495-20-1976 L1983 DR NM *020 †80
WEIL, Jeffrey Alan. 5655 HUDSON DR, STE 210 44236 #040-02-1995 L1997 VIR *020 †80
WHITTEMORE, Russell M. 5655 HUDSON DR, STE 210 44236 #010-02-1988 L1990 DR *020 †80
WOHLWEND, John Richard. 5655 HUDSON DR, STE 210 44236 #038-40-1994 L1996 RNR *020 †80
XIE, Xiu Yan. ■ 44236 #243-21-1989 L2005 HMP *020 †50
XU, Bo. ■ 44236 #243-47-1987 L2006 PTH *020 †50
ZHANG, Howard Hao. ■ 44236 #038-06-2000 L2006 GE *020 †20

HUNTSVILLE – LOGAN

LUDWIG, Robert Nelson. 10215 PLEASANT VIEW DR 43324 #038-40-1964 L1964 GE IM *030

HURON – ERIE

BROWNLOW, Wilfred J, Jr. 1503 CLEVELAND RD E # 24 44839 #023-01-1966 L1980 OM PHP *020 †70
CUNDIFF, Donald Lee, Jr. 300 WILLIAMS ST 44839 #038-43-1986 L1987 IM *020 †20
FEGEN, David Andrew. ■ 44839 #035-01-2006 *012
JUNG, Howard Antony. ■ 44839 #038-06-2004 U *012
KETVERTIS, Kari Michelle. 808 MAIN ST, ERIE OSTEOPATHIC ASSOCIATE 44839 #038-41-1999 L2005 FM *020 †18
MURRAY, Michael Wm. 44839 #038-43-1982 L1982 EM *020 †16
SMITH, Howard C. ■ 44839 #035-06-1953 L1958 OBG *071 †30
TASKER, Fred L. ■ 44839 #019-02-1966 L1973 OPH *071
TAYLOR, Catherine Jane. ■ 44839 #038-43-2008 *012
WILLIAMSON, Thomas Bruce. 300 WILLIAMS ST 44839 #035-45-1977 L1979 IM *020

INDEPENDENCE – CUYAHOGA

ABRAHAMS, Ruth Sharon. 4400 ROCKSIDE RD, STE 2100 44131 #065-01-1987 L1994 OBG *020 †30
ALAMIR, Amir. 6701 ROCKSIDE RD, STE 365 44131 #875-01-1987 L1995 NEP *020 †20
ALI, Saba Mubarka. ■ 44131 #038-44-2007 L2007 TY *012
ALI, Syed Saqib. ■ 44131 #038-40-2005 L2005 AN *012
ANDERSON, Susan Lynn. 5001 ROCKSIDE RD 44131 #051-04-1990 L1995 PDR *020 †20
ASSEFF, Carl Frederick. 6595 BRECKSVILLE, STE 2 44131 #038-40-1966 L1966 OPH MDM *020 †35
BASTULLI, John Anthony. 6701 ROCKSIDE RD, STE 200 44131 #038-44-1983 L1984 AN CCM *020 †05
BATUR, Pelin. 5001 ROCKSIDE RD 44131 #038-44-1998 L2000 IM *020 †20
BELHOBEK, George H. 5001 ROCKSIDE RD 44131 #020-02-1969 L1975 DR *020 †80
BHALLA, Tarun. ■ 44131 #008-02-2006 L2006 NS *012
BOJTOS, Anita A. 5001 ROCKSIDE RD, CLEVELAND CLINIC 44131 #038-40-1985 L1988 PD *020 †55
BOOSE, Eric William. 6701 ROCKSIDE RD, STE 260 44131 #038-40-1999 L2002 FM *020 †18
BOWERS, Minnie Mae. 6133 ROCKSIDE RD, STE 207 44131 #047-07-1977 L1980 P *020 †75
BURG, Carol Greenspan. 6701 ROCKSIDE RD, STE 330 44131 #035-46-1979 L1980 D *020 †15
CAHN, Howard Scott. 5001 ROCKSIDE RD 44131 #038-40-1984 L1986 DR *020 †80
CAMERON, Beverly Lehman. 5005 ROCKSIDE RD 44131 #038-06-1979 L1980 D IM *020 †15
CATANZARO, Phillip John. 6100 W CREEK RD STE 16, CLEVELAND CLINIC CANCER CT 44131 #035-20-1965 L1967 RO PTH *020 †50,80

CHAN, Vincent Chung-Yin. 5001 ROCKSIDE RD 44131 #065-01-1996 L2004 NM *020 †80,28
CHOH, Byoung Gyun. ■ 44131 #582-07-1950 L1975 P GP *071
CISAR, Claudia Chovan. 5001 ROCKSIDE RD 44131 #038-06-1983 L1985 DR IM *020 †80
COFFMAN, Byron Lewis. 6100 W CREEK RD, STE 15 44131 #038-06-1976 L1978 ON IM *020 †20
COLLIS, John Stanley. 6701 ROCKSIDE RD, STE 100 44131 #020-02-1955 L1958 NS *020 †25
COSTANTINI, Jay Kenneth. 6100 W CREEK RD, STE 35 44131 #041-01-1990 L1992 R RNR *020 †20
COWAN, Dale Harvey. 6100 W CREEK RD, STE 15 44131 #024-01-1963 L1964 ON HEM *020 †20
CROWNOVER, Brenda Powell. 5001 ROCKSIDE RD 44131 #036-07-1988 L1995 FM *020 †18
DAVIS, Charles Abraham. 5001 ROCKSIDE RD, THE CLEVELAND CLINIC 44131 #024-01-1970 L1975 PD PN *020 †55
DEEB, Ziad. 5001 ROCKSIDE RD 44131 #605-01-1969 L2001 DR RNR *020 †80
DELLAPORTAS, Sandra. 5001 ROCKSIDE RD 44131 #045-01-1991 L1994 IM *020 †20
DERGHAM, Bachar. 5001 ROCKSIDE RD 44131 #875-03-1988 L1996 HO *020 †20
DESAI, Ashokkumar J. 5001 ROCKSIDE RD 44131 #495-23-1970 L1977 R *020 †80
DESBERG, Andrea. 5001 ROCKSIDE RD 44131 #038-40-1986 L1989 DR *020 †80
DEYLING, Cynthia Louise. 5001 ROCKSIDE RD, CCF INDEPENDENCE 44131 #038-40-1984 L1985 IM *020 †20
DHILLON, Jagprit Singh. 6100 ROCKSIDE WOODS BLVD, STE 210 44131 #038-06-1994 L1996 IM *020 †20
DIARD, Lisa Elizabeth. 5005 ROCKSIDE RD 44131 #021-01-1988 L1995 PD *020 †55
EDWARDS, Tanya Iran. 5001 ROCKSIDE RD, CLEVELAND CLINIC FOUNDATIO 44131 #025-01-1987 L1988 FM *020 †55
EVANS, Peter John. 5001 ROCKSIDE RD 44131 #060-02-1987 L2001 ORS *020
FAIMAN, Matthew. 5001 ROCKSIDE RD, DEPT OF INTERNAL MEDICINE 44131 #062-01-1999 L1999 IM *020 †20
FANNING, Alicia Anne. 5001 ROCKSIDE RD 44131 #010-03-1996 L2001 GS *020 †85
FIORELLA, David John. 5001 ROCKSIDE RD 44131 #035-06-1996 L2004 RNR *020 †80
FISHER, Gretchen Lynne. 5001 ROCKSIDE RD, THE CLEVELAND CLINIC 44131 #024-01-1993 L1997 OBG *020 †30
FRANKEL, David Gordon. 5001 ROCKSIDE RD 44131 #038-41-1987 L1991 DR *020 †80
GEISINGER, Michael Adam. 5001 ROCKSIDE RD 44131 #016-43-1977 L1979 DR *020 †80
GOODWIN, Ryan Carey. 5001 ROCKSIDE RD 44131 #038-06-1998 L2000 ORS *020 †40
GRAHAM, Ruffin Judson. 5001 ROCKSIDE RD 44131 #048-15-1990 L1992 DR *020 †80
GROOFF, Paul Nicholas. 5001 ROCKSIDE RD 44131 #038-06-1993 L1995 DR *020 †80
GRUNDFEST-BRONIATOWSKI, S. 5001 ROCKSIDE RD 44131 #035-01-1973 L1978 GS CRS *020 †10,85
HANSEN, Glen Timothy. 4400 ROCKSIDE RD 44131 #038-06-2002 L2002 DR *012
HARDAWAY, Joyce C Frazier. 6701 ROCKSIDE RD, STE 200 44131 #010-03-1960 L1963 AN *005
HATEM, Stephen Frederick. 5001 ROCKSIDE RD 44131 #023-01-1989 L1995 DR *020 †80
HIRSCH, Ana L. 6701 ROCKSIDE RD, STE 330 44131 #957-01-1967 L1972 D IM *020 †15
HOLDEN, Cecilia. 5001 ROCKSIDE RD 44131 #038-41-1985 L1987 DR *020 †80
HOLDEN, David Anthony. 5001 ROCKSIDE RD 44131 #038-41-1985 L1987 PUD CCM *020 †20
HONG, Hae-Kyung. 6100 W CREEK RD 44131 #583-03-1972 L1980 RO *020 †80
HUGHES, Lisa Beth. 5001 ROCKSIDE RD 44131 #055-01-1991 L1992 DR NM *020 †20
HUNTLEY, Homer Nkrumah. 6701 ROCKSIDE RD, STE 200 44131 #025-12-1986 L1990 AN *005
INKSTER, Michelle Dawn. 5001 ROCKSIDE RD 44131 #038-06-1998 L1999 GE *020
IRISH, Craig Randall. 5001 ROCKSIDE RD 44131 #038-06-1976 L1977 DR *020 †80
IRIZARRY, Jose M. 5001 ROCKSIDE RD 44131 #042-01-1989 L1993 DR *020 †80
JANICKI, Paul Clement. 5001 ROCKSIDE RD 44131 #024-01-1971 L1974 DR *020 †80
JEFFERS, Melanie Chellman. 5001 ROCKSIDE RD 44131 #041-14-1995 L1996 DR *020 †80
JOHENNING, Paul Wm. 6701 ROCKSIDE RD, STE 100 44131 #010-02-1955 L1963 U *071 †95
JONES, Robert Wm, Jr. 5001 ROCKSIDE RD 44131 #038-43-1991 L1994 IM OS *020 †20
JOY, Susan Margaret. 5001 ROCKSIDE RD IN-10 44131 #008-02-1996 L1997 FSM FM *020 †18
KEATING, Adam P. 5001 ROCKSIDE RD 44131 #035-45-2000 L2000 PD *020 †55
KHANUJA, Ashoo. 6701 ROCKSIDE RD, STE 209 44131 #038-06-1998 L1999 GS *020 †20
KIKTA, Donald. 6701 ROCKSIDE RD, STE 340 44131 #038-40-1976 L1976 N CN *020 †75
KIM, Dong Youn. 6100 W CREEK RD, STE 15 & 16 44131 #583-04-1966 L1968 RO *020 †80
KIM, Young Hwan. 6701 ROCKSIDE RD, STE 100 44131 #583-02-1960 L1972 NS *020 †25
KRENITSKY, Gabriel H. 5005 ROCKSIDE RD, STE 360 44131 #041-14-1998 L1999 EM *020 †16
LALAK, James Edward. 5001 ROCKSIDE RD 44131 #038-40-1972 L1972 R *071 †80
LIEBERMAN, James Michael. 5001 ROCKSIDE RD 44131 #038-06-1974 L1975 DR *020 †80
MANDAT, Thomas Emil. 4400 ROCKSIDE RD, 2ND FL 44131 #038-43-1987 L1987 IM OM *071
MAZANEC, Daniel John. 5001 ROCKSIDE RD 44131 #038-06-1975 L1978 RHU IM *020 †20
MEGES, Daniel Lang. 5001 ROCKSIDE RD 44131 #016-06-1973 L1976 IM *020 †20
MEZIANE, Moulay Ahmed. 5001 ROCKSIDE RD 44131 #125-01-1979 L1987 DR *020 †80
MODEL, Alla Jacob. 5001 ROCKSIDE RD, CCF-INDEPENDENCE 44131 #913-01-1985 L2001 RHU *020 †20
MODIC, Michael Terrence. 5001 ROCKSIDE RD 44131 #038-06-1975 L1976 DR RNR *020 †80
MOSTELLER, Robert David. 5001 ROCKSIDE RD 44131 #038-40-1984 L1985 CD IM *020 †20
NG, Pamela. 5001 ROCKSIDE RD 44131 #038-06-2000 L2000 D *020 †15
PAPSIDERO, Michael Jos. 6100 OAK TREE BLVD STE 100 44131 #025-01-1977 L1982 OTO *030 †45
PETRULIS, Alice S. 5005 ROCKSIDE RD, STE 700 44131 #038-40-1975 L1976 NEP IM *020 †20
PICHA, Brad Matthew. ■ 44131 #038-06-2006 L2006 ORS *012
PICHA, George John, Jr. 5005 ROCKSIDE RD 44131 #038-06-1980 L1985 PS *020 †65
PIEN, Lily C. 5001 ROCKSIDE RD 44131 #016-06-1983 L1988 AI IM *020 †20,03
PIRAINO, David Wm. 5001 ROCKSIDE RD 44131 #038-06-1981 L1982 DR *020 †80
PODLIPSKY, Halina Mery. 6701 ROCKSIDE RD, STE 200 44131 #550-01-1977 L1985 AN *075 †25
POLSTER, Joshua Matthew. 5001 ROCKSIDE RD 44131 #038-06-1998 L2003 DR *020 †80
PRYCE, Alison Patricia. 4400 ROCKSIDE RD 44131 #038-06-1985 L1986 NR *020 †80
QUINN, Christine Agnes. 5001 ROCKSIDE RD 44131 #041-07-1971 L1972 R DR *020 †80
RADOJICIC, Cristine. 5001 ROCKSIDE RD 44131 #038-44-1995 L1997 AI PD *020 †55,03
RAHIM, Nezar. 6701 ROCKSIDE RD, STE 365 44131 #528-01-1958 L1972 IM NEP *020 †20
RECHT, Michael Paul. 5001 ROCKSIDE RD 44131 #041-01-1983 L1988 DR *020 †80
REDDY, Madhu Bandaru. 6701 ROCKSIDE RD STE 370 44131 #495-21-1974 L1979 IM IMG *020 †20
REED, John Ernest. 5001 ROCKSIDE RD 44131 #051-04-1967 L1998 DR NM *020 †80,28
RESNIK, Julius Bruce. 5001 ROCKSIDE RD 44131 #016-43-1974 L1977 IM NEP *020 †20
RICAURTE, Frank John. 5001 ROCKSIDE RD 44131 #038-43-1995 L1998 DR *020 †80

RICHMOND, Bradford James. 5001 ROCKSIDE RD 44131 #038-06-1981 L1982 **DR** *020 †80

RIM, Alice S. 5001 ROCKSIDE RD 44131 #038-43-1991 L1992 **DR** *020 †80

ROGOFF, Robert Clayton. 6701 ROCKSIDE RD, STE 200 44131 #038-40-1969 L1969 **AN** *020 †05

ROLLINS, Michael Bruce. 5001 ROCKSIDE RD 44131 #038-01-1979 L1980 **CD IM** *020 †20

ROSENBLATT, Steven M. 5001 ROCKSIDE RD 44131 #038-06-1994 L1996 **GS** *020 †85

RUGGIERI, Paul Michael. 5001 ROCKSIDE RD 44131 #033-06-1984 L1987 **RNR** *020 †80

RUTKOWSKI, Jack. 4400 ROCKSIDE RD, STE 2100 44131 #473-04-2001 L2006 **IM** *020

RUTKOWSKI, Robert John. 4400 ROCKSIDE RD, STE 2100 44131 #665-01-2003 L2003 **IM** *100

SANDS, Mark Jason. 5001 ROCKSIDE RD 44131 #016-06-1990 L1996 **VIR** *020 †80

SCHNETTLER, Lisa Elaine. ■ 44131 #038-41-2006 L2006 **PD** *012

SCHNETTLER, William Thoma. ■ 44131 #038-41-2006 L2006 **OBG** *012

SCHUTT, Alison Elizabeth. ■ 44131 #048-15-2006 L2006 **OPH** *012

SCHWEITZER, Jana Rice. 5001 ROCKSIDE RD 44131 #035-01-1985 L1990 **DR** *020 †80

SFERRA, James Jos, Jr. 5001 ROCKSIDE RD 44131 #038-43-1988 L1990 **OFA** *020 †40

SHAH, Shetal Niranjan. 5001 ROCKSIDE RD 44131 #038-43-1993 L2000 **DR** *020 †80

SHAW, Wendy Marla. 5001 ROCKSIDE RD 44131 #038-06-1977 L1982 **DR** *020 †80

SHOLITON, David Barrie. 5001 ROCKSIDE RD 44131 #038-06-1974 L1975 **OPH** *020 †35

SINGER, Anne Adair. 5001 ROCKSIDE RD 44131 #035-48-1985 L1988 **DR** *020 †80

SIVAK, Gary Evan. 6701 ROCKSIDE RD, STE 200 44131 #038-06-1980 L1988 **AN** *020 †05

SLOVER, Carol C. 5001 ROCKSIDE RD 44131 #038-06-1979 L1981 **D IM** *020 †20,15

SMITH, Jeffrey Preston. ■ 44131 #048-15-2006 L2006 **PM** *012

SOBECKS, Nancy Wysocki. 5001 ROCKSIDE RD 44131 #038-41-1993 L1995 **IM** *020 †80

SOMASUNDARAM, Meyyappan. 6701 ROCKSIDE RD, STE 100 44131 #495-04-1993 L1997 **IM** *020 †20

STEINBERG, Neil Ian. 6701 ROCKSIDE RD, STE 240 44131 #038-45-1992 L1995 **P** *020

STEVENS, Mariam. 5001 ROCKSIDE RD 1N2, DEPT of ENDCLGY CLLD CLC 44131 #028-46-1997 L2000 **END** *100 †20

SUNDARAM, Murali. 5001 ROCKSIDE RD 44131 #495-50-1968 L2004 **R** *020 †80

SUTTER, Constance Domen. 6701 ROCKSIDE RD STE 330 44131 #038-06-1985 L1989 **D IM** *020 †15

SVETS, Monica Mchenry. 5001 ROCKSIDE RD, CLEVELAND CLINIC INDEPENDE 44131 #038-45-2002 L2004 **OBG** *100

THOMAS, Joseph Michael. 6800 ROCKSIDE RD STE A, LASIK PLUS - CLEVELAND 44131 #038-06-1992 L1996 **OPH** *020 †35

TOGLIATTI, Kimberly Ann. 6571 BRECKSVILLE RD STE 2, & SPINE CENTER 44131 #038-41-1996 L1997 **IM PRS** *020 †20,60

TRAYLOR, Amelia Cleveland. 5001 ROCKSIDE RD IN20, INDEPENDENCE FAM HLTH CENT 44131 #038-41-1990 L1993 **OBG** *020 †30

VAN DYKE, Carolyn Way. 5001 ROCKSIDE RD 44131 #033-06-1976 L1978 **DR** *020 †80

VARGO, Karen Sue. 5001 ROCKSIDE RD 44131 #038-43-1987 L1999 **PD ADL** *020 †55

VENIERO, Joseph C. 5001 ROCKSIDE RD 44131 #035-46-1995 L2001 **DR** *020 †80

WANG, Weiping. 5001 ROCKSIDE RD 44131 #243-64-1983 L2003 **VIR** *020 †28,80

WARREN, Calvin E, Jr. 6060 ROCKSIDE WOODS BLVD, WELLCARE OF OH INC 44131 #010-01-1983 L1986 **IM MDM** *030 †20

WASSERMAN, Diana Ruth. 5001 ROCKSIDE RD, IN20 44131 #008-01-1977 L1980 **PD** *020 †55

WHITEMAN, Michelle L H. 5001 ROCKSIDE RD 44131 #035-03-1985 L2002 **DR RNR** *020 †80

WILLIAMS, Charles Wesley. 5001 ROCKSIDE RD 44131 #038-06-1972 L1974 **IM** *020

WILSON, Nancy J Beale. 5005 ROCKSIDE RD 44131 #023-01-1971 L1998 **PD** *020 †55

WU, Charles. 5001 ROCKSIDE RD 44131 #038-44-1992 L1993 **IM** *020 †20

YING, Chen-Ching. ■ 44131 #244-03-1959 L1978 **GP PM** *071

ZACHARY, Adrian Mark. 5001 ROCKSIDE RD 44131 #011-75-1998, ▲ L1999 **PM** *020 †60

ZUBER, Jeanne Tugaoen. 5001 ROCKSIDE RD, STE 300 44131 #038-40-1987 L1988 **IM** *020 †20

IRONTON – LAWRENCE

CANOS, Rodolfo Jalipa, Jr. 1920 S 9TH ST 45638 #748-10-1965 L1973 **GS GP** *020

CHAUDHRY, Mazhar Hussain. ■ 45638 #704-01-1966 L1972 **GP FM** *020

CRUZ-CANOS, Portia Vera. 1920 S 9TH ST 45638 #748-01-1964 L1973 **FM PTH** *020 †50,18

DAVIS, John Terrance. 1501 S 9TH ST 45638 #041-01-1967 L1975 **TS GS** *030 †85,90

DORADO, Pacifico D. 2213 S 9TH ST, BOX 60J 45638 #748-01-1964 L1972 **GS GP** *020 †85 ‡

FORD, Jason Michael. ■ 45638 #017-20-2003 **DR** *012

FORD, Jason Robert. ■ 45638 #038-41-2004 L2007 **PD** *020 †55

KADIM, Satyanarayana V. 411 CENTER ST 45638 #495-57-1972 L1981 **CD IM** *020 †20

LAMPPERT, Robert Vincent. 2111 S 7TH ST, IRONTON CARE CENTER 45638 #038-06-1960 L1960 **CD IM** *071

LARSEN, Paula Kay. 419 VERNON ST 45638 #055-02-1994 L1999 **IM** *020

LONTOC, Manolito M. 2228 S 9TH ST 45638 #748-01-1965 L1975 **GP** *020

MC COLLISTER, Randall L. 407 S 3RD ST, STE C 45638 #038-43-1981 L1982 **IM** *020 †20

MEADOWS, Rockford James. ■ 45638 #038-43-2005 **FP** *012

NG-CADLAON, Margaret L. 213 MARION PIKE 45638 #748-16-1987 L1992 **PD** *020 †55

PATIL, Rahul. 2412 S 6TH ST, LAWRENCE COUNTY MED CENTER 45638 #495-96-1988 L1995 **IM** *020 †20 ‡

PAYNE, Alva Burton. ■ 45638 #038-40-1956 L1956 **AN OM** *071

ROACH, Robert Benjamin. ■ 45638 #038-45-1993 L1998 **DR** *020 †80

SCAIFE, Aaron Lee. ■ 45638 #055-02-2003 L2005 **OBG** *012

SMITH MENSAH, William H. 1005 E RING RD 45638 #038-06-1992 L1995 **GS EM** *020 †85

TISMO, Patrio Dacuyan. 107 N 3RD ST 45638 #748-08-1953 L1971 **GS FM** *071

VIRGIN, Tony Keith. 419 VERNON ST, KDMC IRONTON BRANCH OUTREA 45638 #055-02-2000 L2001 **FM** *020

WILLIS, Kevin James. ■ 45638 #055-02-1985 L1986 **FM** *020 †18

JACKSON – JACKSON

ADESIOYE, John Adebayo. 500 BURLINGTON RD, STE 220 45640 #690-05-1992 L2007 **APM** *040 ‡

AGYEI-GYAMFI, Frances T. 607 HOLLY HILL DR 45640 #412-01-1997 L2004 **ID** *020 †20

ASH, Tonia Kay. 280 PATTONSVILLE RD, HOLZER CLINIC 45640 #038-45-1995 L1996 **FM** *020 †18

BAUTISTA, Mario Cresencio. 102 TWIN OAKS DR 45640 #748-08-1993 L2006 **PD** *020 †55

BENJAMIN, Damien M. 1000 VETERANS DR, CHILLICOTHE SURGICAL 45640 #043-01-1997 L2003 **GS** *020 †85

BERLING, Donald Leo. 1000 VETERANS DR 45640 #038-40-1960 L1960 **FM OM** *020 †18

CHARIF, Mahmoud. 500 BURLINGTON RD 45640 #875-01-1988 L1993 **HO** *012 †20

COHEN, Brian Seth. 1000 VETERANS DR 45640 #035-47-1994 L2000 **ORS** *020 †40

COLWELL, Kristin Annette. 1000 VETERANS DR 45640 #054-04-1990 L1992 **OBG** *020 †30

DAVE, Shruti Manish. 500 BURLINGTON RD, HOLZER MEDICAL CENTER-JACK 45640 #496-41-1994 L2004 **END** *020 †20

DUTTA, Nirmal Kanti. 500 BURLINGTON RD, OAK HILL SURGICAL PRACTICE 45640 #160-02-1970 L1982 **GS GP** *020 †85

FULLER, Bryan Heath. 500 BURLINGTON RD 45640 #055-02-1997 L2000 **IM** *020 †20

GEORGI, Basil A'Sad. 500 BURLINGTON RD STE 230, HOLZER MEDICAL CENTER JACK 45640 #605-01-1981 L1996 **GS** *020 †85

GREEVER, Carl Jackson. 35 VAUGHN ST 45640 #051-04-1958 L1962 **FM PHP** *020 †18

HAWKER, Gregory Patrick. 500 BURLINGTON RD 45640 #038-45-1982 L1984 **FM** *020 †18

HESS, Robert Albert. 500 BURLINGTON RD 45640 #055-02-1984 L1986 **FM** *020 †18

HYNES, Anne Marie E. 280 PATTONSVILLE RD, HOLZER CLINIC - JACKSON 45640 #063-01-1992 L1999 **FM** *020 †18

JAFFE, Karen Marie. 1000 VETERANS DR 45640 #038-45-1986 L1988 **OBG** *020 †30

KAO, Lilly, II. 14590 STATE ROUTE 93 45640 #038-44-1998 L2002 **GP PFP** *020 †75

KAPOOR, Manoj. 102 TWIN OAKS DR 45640 #495-45-1994 L2005 **PD** *020 †55

MARANZANA, Alessandro Lor. 14590 STATE ROUTE 93 45640 #422-01-2001 L2005 **PD** *020 †55

MOREHEAD, Scott Richard. 1000 VETERANS DR 45640 #038-40-1994 L1997 **OBG** *020 †30

MUNRO, Thomas Wayne. 280 PATTONSVILLE RD, JACKSON 45640 #030-05-1976 L1977 **EM** *020 †16

PAUL, Morgan Andrew. 500 BURLINGTON RD 45640 #038-43-2002 L2002 **FM** *020 †18

RASTOGI, Amit. 336 E MAIN ST 45640 #495-36-1996 L2005 **IM MG** *020 †20,19

REAVES, Jason Scott. ■ 45640 #020-12-2006 L2006 **EM** *012

ROSSI, Susan Jennifer. 280 PATTONSVILLE RD 45640 #065-06-1970 L2003 **OTO** *020 †45

SONI, Aruna. 280 PATTONSVILLE RD 45640 #495-45-1967 L1986 **IM FM** *020

TENPENNY, Teresa Renee. 336 E MAIN ST, JACKSON MEDICAL SPECIALITI 45640 #004-01-1999 L2002 **FM** *020 †18

VILLARREAL, Richard J. 1000 VETERANS DR 45640 #038-43-1992 L1994 **OBG** *020 †30

WARD, John Thos. 280 PATTONSVILLE RD 45640 #038-41-1976 L1977 **IM** *020 †20

ZIMMERLY, John Wm. 14590 STATE ROUTE 93 45640 #038-40-1960 L1960 **FM EM** *071 †18

JACKSON CENTER – SHELBY

MOHAN, Franklin S C. 602 W PIKE ST 45334 #566-01-1980 L1996 **FM** *020

JAMESTOWN – GREENE

AZMEH, Wayel. 88 SEAMAN DR 45335 #875-01-1980 L1988 **CD** *020 †20

BRUNSMAN, Thomas Lynn. 88 SEAMAN DR 45335 #038-45-1986 L1987 **FM** *020 †18

CHANDRA, Mukul. 88 SEAMAN DR 45335 #495-23-1989 L2005 **CD** *020 †20

DURKIN, Robert Martin. ■ 45335 #005-12-1998 *100

GAY, Albert G. 88 SEAMAN DR 45335 #048-13-1992 L1993 **FM** *020 †18

KENNEDY, Denise R. 88 SEAMAN DR 45335 #038-45-2002 L2002 **FM** *020 †18

KREBS, Mark Eugene. 88 SEAMAN DR 45335 #038-41-1990 L1997 **ICE CD** *020 †20

LINTON, Norman G. ■ 45335 #020-02-1944 L1945 **OS** *071

MALONE, Joseph Patrick. 88 SEAMAN DR 45335 #038-06-1975 L1976 **CD IM** *020 †20

PACENTA, James Michael. 88 SEAMAN DR 45335 #038-40-1980 L1985 **CD IM** *020 †20

SCHRECK, Stephen Chas. 88 SEAMAN DR 45335 #038-40-1978 L1980 **CD IM** *020 †20

SHARRETT, Kevin Lee. 88 SEAMAN DR 45335 #038-45-1991 L1992 **FM** *020 †18

SRIVASTAVA, Bal K. 88 SEAMAN DR 45335 #495-41-1990 L1997 **CD** *020 †20

THORNTON, Thomas Glenn. 88 SEAMAN DR 45335 #038-40-1969 L1969 **CD** *020 †20

WENZKE, Stephen C. 88 SEAMAN DR 45335 #038-40-1980 L1983 **CD IM** *020 †20

JEFFERSON – ASHTABULA

CINGIREDDI, Laxman Reddy. 234 N CHESTNUT ST, JEFFERSON HEALTH CTR 44047 #495-57-1993 L2003 **FM** *020 †18

FRANLEY, Deborah K. ■ 44047 #038-40-1973 L1973 **FM** *074 †18

PARKER, David Lorne Oscar. 234 N CHESTNUT ST 44047 #065-05-1991 L1994 **FM** *020 †18

WAID, Harlan Sample, Jr. 125 S CHESTNUT ST 44047 #038-41-1979 L1982 **FM OS** *020 †18

JEWETT – HARRISON

STARRE, Jeffrey John. ■ 43986 #038-45-1990 L1991 **FM** *020 †18

JOHNSTOWN – LICKING

KUHN, Robert H. ■ 43031 #038-41-1952 L1952 **FM OM** *071 †18

SZEKELY, Kenneth James. 151 WOODGATE DR, PRACTICE 43031 #041-02-1995 L1999 **FM** *020 †18

YOUNG, Robert Swank. ■ 43031 #038-40-1947 L1947 **FM** *071 †18

KENT – PORTAGE

ALEXANDER, Heather Anne. ■ 44240 #038-44-2007 L2007 **OBG** *012

ARORA, Nita. 5982 RHODES RD 44240 #038-40-1988 L1992 **P** *020 †75

AS-SANIE, Mohammed S. 226 FRANCES DR 44240 #875-01-1971 L1977 **OBG** *020 †30

AWADALLA, Sabry Geo. ■ 44242 #330-02-1951 L1968 **AN** *071 †05

BOZEMAN, Eleanor L Smith. ■ 44242 #047-07-1945 L1950 **IM** *071

BURKE, Edmund Chas, Jr. 5982 RHODES RD 44240 #038-44-1992 L1993 **P** *020 †75

CERRONI, Kelley T. 307 W MAIN ST, STE B 44240 #038-40-1992 L1993 **IM PD** *020 †55,20

CHASE, Joseph Edward. 401 DEVON PL, INC 44240 #016-06-1973 L1976 **FM** *020 †18

DAVIS, Tara Ann. 1951 STATE ROUTE 59, CENTER of AKRON 44240 #038-44-2001 L2001 **PD** *020 †55

DE JULIUS, Dennis Patrick. 2037 OLD FORGE RD, 2037 OLE FORGE ROAD 44240 #038-41-1993 L1994 **EM** *020 †16

■ = Address Information Privacy Protected

DUSSEL, Christopher Josep. ■ 44240 #038-44-2008 *012

FANTELLI, David Floyd. 307 W MAIN ST, STE B 44240 #038-43-2001 L2001 **IM** *020

FARMER, Mark Owen. 411 DEVON PL 44240 #038-06-1992 L1994 **AN** *020 †05

FERENCE-VALENTA, Mary J. 401 DEVON PL, INC 44240 #036-76-1996, ▲ L1997 **FM** *020 †18

FERRIS, Edward Michael. 1951 STATE ROUTE 59, STE C 44240 #038-40-1993 L1995 **OBG** *020 †30

FRAED, Cynthia Anne. ■ 44240 #030-06-1974 L2007 **OBG** *020 †30

GOSWAMI, Puja. ■ 44240 #038-44-2008 *012

HEGDE, B Vasanth Kumar. 908 S WATER ST 44240 #495-35-1965 L1972 **PD** *020 †55

HOMAFAR, Soghra. 401 DEVON PL STE 210 44240 #038-45-1993 L1995 **OBG** *020 †30

HUDAK, Mark James. DEPARTMENT OF ATHLETICS, KENT STATE UNIVERSITY 44242 #038-45-1990 L1992 **FM** *020 †18

HUDSON, Robert Danl. 411 DEVON PL 44240 #045-01-1983 L1985 **AN** *020 †05

HUTTERER, Ferenc. 275 MARTINEL DR 44240 #473-02-1953 *020

INSANA, Antonino. ■ 44240 #038-44-2007 **EM** *012

JACOBS, John C. 420 W MAIN ST 44240 #041-77-1953, ▲ L1953 *071

JANOVICK, Patrick Jos. DEWEESE STUDENT HEALTH, KENT STATE UNIVERSITY 44242 #038-40-1985 L1986 **FM** *020 †18

JASTRZEMSKI, Edward F. 408 DEVON PL, STE B 44240 #038-43-1986 L1987 **IM** *020 †20

KAY, Matthew David. 2001 STATE ROUTE 59 44240 #038-41-1986 L1987 **ORS** *020 †40

KOLB, Jason T. 4253 NEWCOMER RD 44240 #028-02-2001 L2001 **EM** *020 †16

KOPYEV, Victor Yurievich. 1949 STATE ROUTE 59, STE 102 44240 #913-06-1988 L1998 **IM OS** *020 †20

KOUSAIE, Frank M, Jr. 949 EDGEWATER CIR 44240 #030-06-1985 L1987 **AN PME** *020

KRAUZA, Matthew Lawrence. ■ 44240 #035-06-2000 L2007 **SME** *020 †20

KUDITHIPUDI, Venu. ■ 44240 #038-44-2008 *012

LUCARDIE, Nathan Robin. 307 W MAIN ST, STE B 44240 #020-02-2003 L2003 **IM** *100 †20

MC PHERSON, Selwyn-Lloyd. 1930 STATE ROUTE 59, SELSON CLINICS NEUROLOGY 44240 #566-01-1979 L1982 **N PME** *020

MEHTA, Bina. 307 W MAIN ST 44240 #038-44-1994 L1997 **PM** *020 †60

MINEO, Kevin Christian. 307 W MAIN ST, STE B 44240 #038-44-1998 L1999 **IM** *020 †20

MOHR, James D. ■ 44240 #005-11-2000 L2000 **P** *020

MYERS, Philip Francis, Jr. 1993 STATE ROUTE 59, MED CENTER ONE 44240 #038-40-1974 L1976 **FM** *020 †18

NANJUNDIAH, Parvathi. 5982 RHODES RD 44240 #495-99-1987 L2001 **P** *020

PACER, Kenneth Scott. 5982 RHODES RD, COLEMAN PROFESSIONAL SERV 44240 #038-40-1991 L1993 **P CHP** *020 †75

PADIA, Shilpa Arvind. ■ 44240 #038-44-2008 *012

PAKAN, William A. 2007 STATE ROUTE 59 44240 #038-44-1985 L1990 **ORS OSM** *020 †40

PERUMBETI, Anil. ■ 44240 #038-44-2008 *012

POSERIA, Nutan M. 408 DEVON PL, # B 44240 #495-20-1980 L1988 **IM** *020 †20

PRILUCK, Joshua Chaim. ■ 44240 #030-05-2007 L2007 **TY** *012

PRYCE, Michael Lindsey. 174 CURRIE HALL PKWY 44240 #036-05-1977 L1978 **ORS HS** *020 †16

RASALAN, Amador Pacquing. 136 N WATER ST, STE 202 44240 #748-01-1955 L1967 **GP** *020

RIGBY, Scott Paul. 307 W MAIN ST, STE B 44240 #038-40-1993 L1994 **IM** *020 †20

ROBERTSON, Rosalind S. 1951 STATE ROUTE 59 44240 #038-40-1977 L1978 **PD ADL** *020 †55

ROSENWASSER, Alan Lee. 401 DEVON PL STE 210 44240 #038-06-1984 L1985 **OBG** *020 †30

ROSENWASSER, Betsy N. ■ 44240 #038-06-1986 L1988 **EM** *020 †16

RUSSELL, John Wm. KENT STATE UNIV HLTH SVC 44240 #038-06-1954 L1954 **GP** *020

SAHNEY, Narendra. 408 DEVON PL, STE A 44240 #422-01-1998 L1999 **IM** *020 †20

SAUBER, Timothy Joseph. ■ 44240 #038-44-2007 L2007 **GS** *012

SHAH, Chirag. ■ 44240 #038-44-2007 **TY** *012

SHAKIR, Ali. 307 W MAIN ST 44240 #035-09-1999 L1999 **PM PMM** *020 †60

SMITH, Randall Howard. 1930 STATE ROUTE 59 44240 #038-40-1979 L1980 **GS** *020 †85

STUART, Scott Howard. ■ 44240 #038-44-1993 L1995 **GS** *075

TANK, Jason Clyde. ■ 44240 #038-44-2008 *012

UHALL, David Michael. 307 W MAIN ST, STE B 44240 #038-44-1989 L1990 **IM** *020 †20

WAUGH, James Jefferis. 401 DEVON PL, STE 210 44240 #836-02-1956 L1960 **IM** *071 †20

WEEKS, Brandon Daniel. ■ 44240 #038-44-2008 *012

WELLS, Kenneth Wm. 307 W MAIN ST STE B, PRIMARY CARE ASSOCIATES OF 44240 #038-40-1987 L1990 **IM** *020 †20

WELSH, Brian Charles. 5982 RHODES RD 44240 #038-43-1996 L2001 **PFP** *020 †75

YOHO, Alan Verl. ■ 44240 #051-04-1954 L1962 **U** *071 †95

ZNIDARSIC, Robin Lyn. 307 W MAIN ST, STE B 44240 #038-43-1994 L1995 **FM** *020 †18

KENTON – HARDIN

ABDULKARIM, M Saadallah. 75 WASHINGTON BLVD, STE 102 43326 #875-01-1972 L2001 **GS GP** *020 †85

BINKLEY, Wm Frederick. 921 E FRANKLIN ST 43326 #038-40-1948 L1948 **CD IM** *071

CASTRILLO, Jose A. ■ 43326 #847-08-1964 L1969 **AN** *020

COLE, Sharon Kay. 75 WASHINGTON BLVD, STE 107 43326 #038-40-1990 L1991 **ON** *020 †20

DESHMUKH, Murlidhar R. 15047 STATE ROUTE 309 43326 #495-19-1970 L1985 **IM** *020 †20

HRUSCHKA, Judith K. 60 WASHINGTON BLVD 43326 #038-40-1999 L1999 **IM** *020 †20

JOHNSON, Katherine E. 60 WASHINGTON BLVD 43326 #038-43-1991 L1995 **IM** *020 †20

KINNISON, Martin William. ■ 43326 #038-43-2002 L2002 **GS** *012

MORRIS, Larry Lee. 13532 COUNTY ROAD 195 43326 #017-20-1968 L1975 **GS** *020 †85

OATES, Larry Allen. ■ 43326 #038-40-1964 L1964 **IM MDM** *020 †12

OKPALAOKA, Osita. 921 E FRANKLIN ST 43326 #690-01-1979 L2002 **IM** *020 †20

PANSURIA, Harjibhai D. 921 E FRANKLIN ST, HARDIN MEMORIAL HOSPITAL 43326 #495-48-1971 L1998 **AN GS** *020

PANSURIA, Minaxi H. ■ 43326 #495-22-1970 L1980 **FM PTH** *020 †18

PETERSEN, Clark Edman. 921 E FRANKLIN ST 43326 #028-34-1989 L1996 **AN** *020 †05

PFEIFFER, Jay Edward. ■ 43326 #038-40-1967 L1967 **GP** *020 †18

SMITH, Leonard Karr. 900 E FRANKLIN ST 43326 #011-02-1972 L1973 **FM OBG** *020 †18

KETTERING – GREENE

DEL SORDO, Andrew Anthony. ■ 45430 #051-04-1969 L1970 **FM** *020 †18

KETTERING – MONTGOMERY

ADIB, Malak S. 540 LINCOLN PARK BLVD, STE 200 45429 #875-01-1984 L1996 **IM** *020 †20

AHMAD, Saleem. 540 LINCOLN PARK BLVD, STE 200 45429 #690-03-1980 L1989 **CD IM** *020 †20

AHSAN, Muhammad Kamran. 540 LINCOLN PARK BLVD, STE 350 45429 #704-02-1991 L2003 **IM** *020 †20

AKTURE, Nihat. 1364 E STROOP RD 45429 #902-01-1952 L1966 **IM** *072

ALAME, Diana. 3525 SOUTHERN BLVD, DEPT OF EMERGENCY MED 45429 #016-11-2007 L2007 **EM** *012

ALLISON, Nathan Kyle. 3525 SOUTHERN BLVD 45429 #047-06-2002 L2002 **EM** *020 †16

AMANN, Deborah Marie. ■ 45429 #038-45-2008 *012

AMES, Donald Wm. 3737 SOUTHERN BLVD, STE 2100 45429 #025-07-1984 L1989 **ORS** *020 †40

ANDERSON, Gary Lee. 3533 SOUTHERN BLVD, STE 2250 45429 #018-75-1986, ▲ L1988 **GS** *020

ANDERSON, Rita Marie. 3533 SOUTHERN BLVD, STE 2250 45429 #038-45-1997 L1998 **GS** *020 †85

ARUDCHENTHAN, T S. ■ 45429 #539-05-1992 L2001 **GS** *020

BACHELLER, Catherine D. 500 LINCOLN PARK BLVD, STE 220 45429 #005-12-1979 L1981 **ID IM** *040 †50,20

BAHL, Shalini. 500 LINCOLN PARK BLVD #200 45429 #025-07-1996 L1997 **D** *020 †15

BAHNER, Don Robt. ■ 45429 #065-05-1954 L1962 **GS** *071

BAIG, Khawajashahidh. 540 LINCOLN PARK BLVD, STE 200 45429 #704-01-1985 L2002 **ICE** *020 †20

BANIAS, Bruce Bland. 3075 GOVERNORS PL, STE 210 45409 #045-01-1984 L1985 **NPM OBG** *020 †30

BARDE, Christopher J. 999 BRUBAKER DR STE 1, DIGESTIVE SPECIALISTS, INC 45429 #035-06-1976 L2003 **GE IM** *020 †20

BATATA, AI. 3535 SOUTHERN BLVD 45429 #330-02-1950 L1978 **PTH CLP** *071 †50

BEDOYA, Joseangel Damian. 3525 SOUTHERN BLVD, DEPT OF EMERGENCY MED 45429 #042-01-2006 L2006 **EM** *012

BEERS, Richard Thos. 3535 SOUTHERN BLVD, OF PMR 45429 #038-45-1983 L1984 **PM IM** *020 †20,60

BENDER, Mary Ann. 3535 SOUTHERN BLVD, DEPT ROTAT 45429 #038-41-1989 L1996 **N** *100

BERNSTEIN, Jack M. 500 LINCOLN PARK BLVD, STE 220 45429 #010-02-1975 L1987 **ID IM** *020 †20

BHANDARU, Sivakrishna. ■ 45429 #495-45-2002 L2003 **IM** *020 †20

BHARIJA, Ankur. 3535 SOUTHERN BLVD, DEPT OF MED EDUCATION 45429 #495-37-2004 L2006 **IM** *012

BIEGLER, Ryan Frederick. 3535 SOUTHERN BLVD, KETTERING MED CTR 45429 #005-12-2004 L2004 **IM** *100 †20

BLUNK, Richard Carl. ■ 45439 #016-01-2003 L2003 **PD** *020 †55

BOCKHORN, Debra Ellen. 5250 FAR HILLS AVE, PRIMED PHYSICIANS 45429 #016-43-1998 L2001 **PD** *020 †55

BOCOCK, Jennifer M. 3535 SOUTHERN BLVD, MEDICAL CENT 45429 #035-15-1998 L2001 **EM** *020 †16

BORSODY, Karl John. 3533 SOUTHERN BLVD, STE 5650 45429 #038-43-1995 L2007 **TS** *020 †85,90

BOSSCHER, Brian Michael. 3535 SOUTHERN BLVD 45429 #025-12-2001 L2001 **EM** *020 †16

BOYD, Julia Ann. 3140 E DOROTHY LN 45420 #038-40-1987 L1988 **FM** *020 †18

BOYD, Stephen Douglas. 3535 SOUTHERN BLVD, KETTERING MED CTR 45429 #005-12-2005 L2005 **IM** *012

BRADY, William Edward. 3535 SOUTHERN BLVD, C/O MEDICAL EDUCATION DEPT 45429 #038-45-2006 L2006 **EM** *012

BRANDENBERG, Gregory A. 3533 SOUTHERN BLVD, STE 3000 45429 #030-05-1987 L2005 **NS** *020 †25

BRETZ, Giselle. ■ 45429 #473-01-1963 L1971 **RO** *071 †80

BROCK, Kenneth Wilson. 3535 SOUTHERN BLVD, KETTERING MEDICAL CENTER 45429 #055-01-1973 L1974 **GS** *020 †16

BROCKBANK, Aaron Spencer. ■ 45420 #010-01-2004 L2004 **GS** *012

BROWN, Harold M. 3535 SOUTHERN BLVD 45429 #041-77-1989, ▲ L1992 **FM** *020 †18

BROWN, James Edward, Jr. 3525 SOUTHERN BLVD 45429 #020-02-1991 L1994 **EM** *040 †16

BROWN, Richard Jerome. 3535 SOUTHERN BLVD 45429 #038-41-1976 L1984 **CHP NM** *020 †28,75

BRUCE, James Alan. 3533 SOUTHERN BLVD, STE 3100 45429 #005-12-1973 L1977 **AN** *020

BRYANT, James Allen. 500 LINCOLN PARK BLVD #302 45429 #005-12-1973 L1974 **PD** *020 †55

BUENAVENTURA, Ricardo M. 3490 FAR HILLS AVE, DAYTON PAIN MED . 45429 #021-01-1990 L1995 **APM AN** *020 †05 ‡

BULLMASTER, John Rollo. 3535 SOUTHERN BLVD 45429 #038-43-1979 L1981 **GS** *020 †85

BURTON, George Gateley. 3535 SOUTHERN BLVD 45429 #005-12-1961 L1983 **PUD SME** *020 †20

BURWINKEL, Thomas Henry. 3533 SOUTHERN BLVD # 4100 45429 #038-41-1986 L1987 **OBG REN** *020 †30

BYERS, Matthew William. ■ 45419 #038-40-2008 *012

BYLSMA, Glenn Wm. 3535 SOUTHERN BLVD 45429 #005-12-1954 L1963 **PTH** *071 †50

CAMACHO, Veronica Ines. 3535 SOUTHERN BLVD 45429 #176-03-2003 **IM** *100

CAMPBELL, James Phillip. 3533 SOUTHERN BLVD, STE 5650 45429 #017-20-1974 L1982 **VS OS** *020 †85,90

CHADWICK, Cathryn Lynn. ■ 45409 #020-02-2004 L2004 **GS** *012

CHAHAL, Amandeep Singh. 3535 SOUTHERN BLVD 45429 #496-39-1999 L2005 **IM** *012

CHAMI, Robert G. 580 LINCOLN PARK BLVD, STE 300 45429 #005-12-1983 L1988 **PS GS** *020 †85,65

CHILDRESS, Lorenzo, III. 3535 SOUTHERN BLVD, CO KETTERING MED CTR-MED E 45429 #038-45-2001 L2003 **IM** *020

CLARK, Max A. 2632 WOODMAN CENTER CT 45420 #028-78-1970, ▲ L1985 **OBG GO** *020 †30

COLLINS, Marcia Lynn. 3533 SOUTHERN BLVD STE 4, GYNECOLOGY SOUTH 45429 #041-07-1968 L1971 **GYN OBG** *020 †30 ‡

COLON, Roberto Jose. 3535 SOUTHERN BLVD, KETTERING MED CTR 45429 #041-14-2000 L2000 **IM** *020

COMPARIN, Leesa Irene. 540 LINCOLN PARK BLVD, STE 200 45429 #038-40-1988 L1991 **IM** *020 †20

CRESPO-BITHORN, Jorge H. 33 W RAHN RD, STE 102 45429 #847-06-1975 L1978 **OTO** *075

CULLEN, Natalie. 3525 SOUTHERN BLVD 45429 #035-03-1992 L1994 **EM** *020 †16

DALSTROM, Meghann Nelles. ■ 45429 #038-40-2004 L2004 **GS** *012

DEC, Eric Keith. 3535 SOUTHERN BLVD, KETTERING MED CTR 45429 #007-02-2003 L2006 **IM** *012

DENMARK, Scot Warren. 580 LINCOLN PARK BLVD, STE 22 45429 #038-43-1979 L1983 **TS CD** *020 †85,90

DODGE, Robin Earle. 3155 RESEARCH BLVD STE 201 45420 #060-01-1976 L1980 **AM** *040 †70
DODSON, Verne Harold. 3535 SOUTHERN BLVD 45429 #038-40-1965 L1965 **FM FPG** *020 †18
DONNELLY, Heidi. 500 LINCOLN PARK BLVD, STE 200 45429 #016-11-1990 L1997 **DS** *020 †15
DOSHI, Sagar D. 3525 SOUTHERN BLVD, DEPT OF EMERGENCY MED 45429 #038-44-2006 L2007 **EM** *012
DUNCAN, Philip John. 3120 GOVERNORS PL, PLACE BLVD. 45409 #025-01-1981 L1982 **RO** *020 †80
EARICK, Heather Alyse. 3535 SOUTHERN BLVD, KETHERING MEDICAL CENTER 45429 #003-01-1996 L1998 **IM** *075
ECKARD, Laina Jo. ■ 45409 #051-01-2006 L2006 **PD** *012
EGBERT, Bradley David. 3535 SOUTHERN BLVD 45429 #038-40-1993 L1994 **AN** *020 †05
EILERS, Mark Alan. 3525 SOUTHERN BLVD 45429 #036-05-1978 L1979 **EM** *020 †16
ELDENBURG, Larry Donald. 3535 SOUTHERN BLVD 45429 #005-12-1988 L1992 **AN** *020 †05
ELINSON, Phyllis Robin. 500 LINCOLN PARK BLVD, # 302 45429 #025-12-1985 L2001 **PD** *020 †55
FADELL, Ronald James. 3535 SOUTHERN BLVD 45429 #038-40-1985 L1986 **DR** *020 †80
FAIN, Matthew Benjamin. 3525 SOUTHERN BLVD 45429 #020-12-2001 L2001 **EM** *020 †16
FERNANDES, Laila Maria. 500 LINCOLN PARK BLVD, STE 220 45429 #495-01-2001 L2007 **ID** *100 †20
FITZMARTIN, Cheryl Ann. 500 LINCOLN PARK BLVD, STE 305 45429 #038-43-1983 L1985 **FM** *020 †18
FLATH, Laura Ann. 3535 SOUTHERN BLVD, KETTERING MED CTR 45429 #040-02-2006 L2006 **IM** *012
FLORIO, Cindy Lou. 3525 SOUTHERN BLVD, DEPT OF EMERGENCY MED 45429 #023-12-2004 L2004 **EM** *020
FRANCO, Zurisadai. 3535 SOUTHERN BLVD, KETTERING MED CTR 45429 #005-12-2005 L2005 **IM** *012
GALVIN, Stephen Matthew. 3525 SOUTHERN BLVD, DEPT OF EMERGENCY MED 45429 #011-03-1995 L2006 **EM** *012 †18
GASPAR, John Scott. 508 JUDITH DR 45429 #005-12-1982 L2005 **DR** *020 †80
GAUR, Shobhana. ■ 45429 #495-49-2002 L2005 **IM** *012
GOLDBLUM, Keith Donald. 3535 SOUTHERN BLVD 45429 #028-46-1978 L1990 **EM** *020 †16
GRALNICK, Harvey Ray. 45440 #038-41-1961 L1961 **IM PTH** *020 †20
GRAY, Lenora. 3533 SOUTHERN BLVD 45429 #041-07-1960 L1964 **N CN** *071 †75
GREENO, Richard Lee, Jr. 3535 SOUTHERN BLVD, DEPT OF EMERGENCY MEDICINE 45429 #047-20-1992 L1994 **EM** *020 †16
GRESHAM, Paul Martin. 500 LINCOLN PARK BLVD, STE 302 45429 #017-20-1975 L1977 **PD** *020 †55
GRILLIOT, Melissa Ann. ■ 45429 #038-45-2008 *012
GUZMAN, Jorge Enrique. 3535 SOUTHERN BLVD, KETTERING MED CTR 45429 #038-40-2007 L2007 **IM** *012
HACHAAMBWA, Lottie Malemb. 3535 SOUTHERN BLVD 45429 #965-01-2000 L2005 **IM** *012
HAHM, Geoffrey Kenneth. 3535 SOUTHERN BLVD 45429 #038-40-1996 L1997 **PTH** *020 †50
HAMILTON, Glenn Chas. 3525 SOUTHERN BLVD 45429 #025-01-1973 L1979 **EM IM** *020 †20,16
HAMWAY, Sammy. 3535 SOUTHERN BLVD 45429 #605-01-1969 L1975 **U** *020 †95
HARDY, John T. ■ 45420 #048-15-2004 L2004 **OBG** *012
HARRIS, Jeffrey Nathan. 3525 SOUTHERN BLVD, DEPT OF EMERGENCY MED 45429 #045-04-2005 L2005 **EM** *012
HARTSOCK, Jennifer Kather. ■ 45429 #038-45-2008 *012
HERITAGE, Rita W. 5250 FAR HILLS AVE 45429 #055-01-1980 L1984 **PD** *020 †55
HESS, Lawrence H. ■ 45429 #005-12-1964 L1967 **FM** *071
HO, Rosa. ■ 45440 #748-08-1967 L1976 **AN** *020
HOCHWALT, John Jerome. 38 SOUTHMOOR CIR NE 45429 #038-40-1971 L1972 **FM** *020 †18
HOFFMAN, Jeffrey Keith. 580 LINCOLN PARK BLVD, STE 322 45429 #025-01-1973 L1981 **TS CD** *071 †85,90
HOUSE, Stephen Terry. 3535 SOUTHERN BLVD 45429 #017-20-1971 L1972 **FM OS** *030 †18 ‡
HUDSON, Ava Deon. ■ 45429 #019-02-2005 L2005 **MPD** *012
HUGHES, Edward N. 2632 WOODMAN CENTER CT, FIRST DAYTON CANCER CARE 45420 #023-07-1982 L1994 **RO** *020 †80,55
HUMPHREY, Isaac Paul. ■ 45440 #016-43-2005 L2005 **IM** *012
INANKUR, Aysha Emily. 3535 SOUTHERN BLVD, KETTERING MED CTR 45429 #005-12-2006 L2006 **IM** *012
JARNOT, Thomas Frederick. 3155 RESEARCH BLVD, WRIGHT STATE UNIVERSITY DI 45420 #012-01-2003 L2007 **GPM** *012 †18
JERKINS, James Hamilton. 3535 SOUTHERN BLVD, KETTERING MED CTR 45429 #005-12-2007 L2007 **IM** *012
JOHNSON, Kevin Walker. ■ 45440 #041-02-1999 L1999 **PD** *020 †55
JOHNSTON, Renate A. 3525 SOUTHERN BLVD DEPT EM 45429 #038-45-1990 L1991 **EM** *020 †16
JORDAN, Carlos Alberto. 3535 SOUTHERN BLVD 45429 #176-04-2002 L2007 **IM** *012
JUMP, John Chas. 3535 SOUTHERN BLVD 45429 #038-40-1975 L1976 **PM GP** *020 †60
KALVAKOTA, Saraswathi. 500 LINCOLN PARK BLVD 45429 #495-21-1972 L1981 **IM PD** *020 †55,20
KENDELL, Steven Frederick. 738 TREASURY DR 45429 #038-45-1996 L2005 **P** *020
KENNEBECK, Gregory Allen. ■ 45419 #023-12-1996 L2005 **EM** *012 †18
KIHM, John Matthew. 3535 SOUTHERN BLVD, KETTERING MEDICAL CENTER 45429 #038-45-1985 L1986 **FM** *020 †18
KIM, Paul Sangik. 540 LINCOLN PARK BLVD, STE 390 45429 #051-01-1985 L1997 **END IM** *020 †20
KIMBLE, Emily Ann. 3533 SOUTHERN BLVD, STE 4600 45429 #038-44-2003 L2007 **OBG** *020
KIME, S Wesley, Jr. 3535 SOUTHERN BLVD 45429 #005-12-1953 L1975 **PTH IM** *071 †20,50
KNIGHT, Shirlann Denise. 3535 SOUTHERN BLVD, MEDICAL STAFF OFFICE 45429 #038-45-1985 L2003 **P** *020 †75
KOEHLER, Lawrence Richard. 3604 WILMINGTON PIKE 45429 #038-41-1960 L1960 **FM OM** *020 †18
KOMOROWSKI, Susan Marie. 3533 SOUTHERN BLVD STE 460 45429 #038-45-1986 L1988 **OBG** *020 †30
KONG, Roberto M. 3533 SOUTHERN BLVD, MIAMI VALLEY HOSPITAL 45429 #748-08-1985 L1996 **AN** *020 †05
LAMBERT, Christopher Ned. 3535 SOUTHERN BLVD, CO KETTERING MED CTR-MED E 45429 #055-02-2001 L2007 **EM** *020 †16
LANEVE, Samuel A. 500 LINCOLN PARK BLVD 45429 #010-02-1951 L1955 **IM END** *020 †20
LAVELLE, Joseph Walters. 3120 GOVERNORS PLACE BLVD 45409 #038-75-1997, ▲ L1998 **HO** *020
LEARY, Maryellen. 3535 SOUTHERN BLVD 45429 #038-45-1990 L1992 **OBG** *020 †30

LEE, Victor Wong. 3533 SOUTHERN BLVD, STE 3750 45429 #748-01-1979 L1989 **IM IMG** *020 †20
LEHRER, Douglas Sidney. 3533 SOUTHERN BLVD, STE 5200 45429 #038-41-1987 L1988 **P PFP** *050 †75
LIESNER, Cathy Elaine. 3533 SOUTHERN BLVD STE 4 45429 #038-41-1983 L1985 **OBG** *020 †30
LIN, Katherine Sue. 3535 SOUTHERN BLVD 45429 #016-11-1996 L1998 **OBG** *020 †30
LOESCH, Ronald Erwin. 1956 E WHIPP RD 45440 #038-40-1967 L1967 **GYN** *071 †30
LOPEZ, Alberto Jose. ■ 45429 #042-02-2006 L2006 **GS** *012
MAINORD, Matthew Elliott. 3535 SOUTHERN BLVD 45429 #422-01-2006 L2007 **IM** *012
MALCOLM, Thomas Glenn. 3604 WILMINGTON PIKE 45429 #038-45-1980 L1982 **FM** *020 †18
MARSHALL, William John. 3525 SOUTHERN BLVD 45429 #023-01-1958 L1964 **CD IM** *071 †20
MARTINEZ, Alfredo Luis. ■ 45429 #275-01-1947 L1977 **GP P** *020
MAUER, John Edwin. 540 LINCOLN PARK BLVD, STE 200 45429 #005-12-1986 L1987 **IM** *020 †20
MAURO, Joseph Michael. 3525 SOUTHERN BLVD, DEPT OF EMERGENCY MED 45429 #038-43-2006 L2007 **EM** *012
MCCLUSKEY-ERSKINE, Kelly. ■ 45440 #038-45-2006 L2006 **OBG** *012
MC CULLOUGH, Wm M, Jr. 1956 E WHIPP RD, OAK CREEK OB/GYN 45440 #038-40-1982 L1983 **OBG** *020 †30
MC DONALD, Stephen Devitt. 3535 SOUTHERN BLVD, KETTERING MED CTR 45429 #005-12-1973 L1990 **END IM** *040 †20
MCFARLAND, Shawn Michael. ■ 45419 #038-45-2007 L2007 **PD** *012
MERLE, Thomas Joseph. 580 LINCOLN PARK BLVD, STE 322 45429 #038-40-1982 L1987 **TS VS** *020 †85,90
MIECZKOWSKI, Lawrence E. 580 LINCOLN PARK BLVD 45429 #038-41-1982 L1985 **IM GPM** *020 †20
MILLER, Daniel Barton. 3535 SOUTHERN BLVD 45429 #016-42-1976 L1977 **U** *020 †95
MILLER, Debra Ann. 3535 SOUTHERN BLVD 45429 #038-45-1986 L1987 **OBG** *020 †30
MODGIL, Parminder. 540 LINCOLN PARK BLVD, PRIMED PHYSICIANS 45429 #495-29-1988 L1998 **IM** *020 †20
MONSON, Benjamin. ■ 45429 #023-12-2004 L2004 **GS** *012
MORENO VILLAMIZAR, Zaira. ■ 45429 #935-04-2000 L2004 **OBG** *012
MORRISON, Roderick George. 3535 SOUTHERN BLVD, DEPT OF EMERGENCY MED 45429 #422-01-2005 L2006 **EM** *012
MOUSSA, Tarek Mohamed. 3535 SOUTHERN BLVD 45429 #915-03-1997 L2003 **IM** *100 †20
MUEHLBERGER, Patrick M. 3535 SOUTHERN BLVD, KETTERING MEMORIAL HOSPITA 45429 #023-12-2000 L2000 **EM** *020
NELSON, Jill Clarissa. ■ 45429 #038-45-2008 *012
NEWAZ, Selim. 3604 WILMINGTON PIKE 45429 #160-01-1982 L1994 **IM** *020 †20
NICHOLSON, Gary Lewis. 3120 GOVERNORS PLACE BLVD 45409 #020-12-1971 L1972 **ON IM** *071 †20
NIELSON, Jeffery Leigh. ■ 45429 #017-20-2000 L2000 **DR** *020 †80
NOLTING, Laura Angela. ■ 45429 #038-45-2007 L2007 **EM** *012
NOVICK, David Miles. 999 BRUBAKER DR STE 1, DIGESTIVE SPECIALISTS INC 45429 #035-08-1974 L1991 **GE IM** *020 †20
O'BRYAN, Meghan Colleen. ■ 45420 #048-12-2005 L2005 **GS** *012
OPSAHL, Paul Jonathan. 3535 SOUTHERN BLVD 45429 #038-41-1981 L1982 **FM** *020 †18
PALILEO, Lauro G. ■ 45429 #748-02-1944 L1986 **PTH GP** *071 †50
PALOMAR, Juan Manuel. 10 SOUTHMOOR CIR NW 45429 #847-11-1971 L1979 **U UP** *071 †95
PAULICK, Joshua Alan. ■ 45420 #038-41-2007 L2007 **GS** *012
PAVLINA, Peter Michael. 3533 SOUTHERN BLVD, STE 5650 45429 #017-20-1982 L1989 **CD TS** *020 †85,90
PERCY, Thomas. 3533 SOUTHERN BLVD STE 4 45429 #495-31-1970 L1974 **PS HS** *020 †85,65 ‡
PETERSON, Gary Ragner. 3604 WILMINGTON PIKE 45429 #041-02-1967 L1969 **FM** *020 †18
PETTY, John J, Jr. 3535 SOUTHERN BLVD 45429 #038-40-1975 L1975 **PM** *020 †60
PHUNGRASAMEE, Vichit. 3131 SAL DIXIE, STE 535 45429 #891-01-1966 L1972 **AN** *071
PICKENS, Cynthia Lorraine. 4316 BURCHDALE ST, CYNTHIA L. PICKENS, M.D. 45440 #038-45-1990 L1992 **FM** *020 †18
PIPIK, Mary Catherine. 1775 DELCO PARK DR, OHIO PEDIATRICS INC 45420 #038-45-1987 L1990 **PD** *020 †55
POOK, Nancy Anne. 3535 SOUTHERN BLVD, DEPT OF EMERGENCY MEDICINE 45429 #035-15-1992 L1993 **EM** *020 †16
PORTER, Dale Orville. 3535 SOUTHERN BLVD 45429 #030-05-1946 L1958 **TS CD** *071 †85,90
PRUTZMAN, Cherish Joy. 3535 SOUTHERN BLVD 45429 #665-01-2003 L2003 **IM** *100
PURYEAR, Jerome, Jr. 3535 SOUTHERN BLVD, DEPT OF RADIOLOGY 45429 #055-02-1997 L2005 **VIR** *020 †80
QARQSAH, Ahmad J. ■ 45440 #575-01-1984 L1994 **GE** *100 †20
RAMIREZ, Francisco Jeroni. ■ 45429 #042-01-2004 L2004 **EM** *020
REDDY, M Niranjan. 540 LINCOLN PARK BLVD, STE 200 45429 #496-28-1993 L1996 **CD** *020 †20
REDDY, Sunita. 3533 SOUTHERN BLVD, STE 4600 45429 #495-57-1990 L1996 **OBG** *020 †30
REHANI, Bhavya. 3535 SOUTHERN BLVD 45429 #495-37-2004 L2007 **TY** *012
REYNOLDS, Douglas Ernest. 3525 SOUTHERN BLVD 45429 #038-43-2002 L2002 **EM** *100 †16
RICHARDSON, Candie Michel. 3535 SOUTHERN BLVD, CO KETTERING MED CTR-MED E 45429 #047-20-2002 L2003 **EM** *020
RIGANO, William Chas. 500 LINCOLN PARK BLVD 45429 #038-43-1985 L1986 **PS FPS** *020 †65
ROBBE, Steven Lawrence. 1525 E STROOP RD 45429 #038-45-1986 L1987 **FM** *020 †18
ROBERTS, Nicholas Brian. ■ 45429 #038-45-2007 L2007 **GS** *012
ROMER, Mark Danl. 1382 E STROOP RD 45429 #038-41-1986 L1987 **ON HEM** *020 †20
ROSE, Bernard Jos. 3017 WILMINGTON PIKE 45429 #038-40-1984 L1985 **FM** *020 †18
ROSE, Karl Gerard. 3017 WILMINGTON PIKE, BEAVERTOWN CLINIC 45429 #038-40-1988 L1989 **FM** *020 †18
ROSE, Norman Louis. ■ 45419 #028-34-1955 L1956 **FM GP** *071
ROSEN, Ira A. 121 SNOW HILL AVE 45429 #561-17-1980 **CHP IM** *072
RUBIN, Aaron Mills. ■ 45429 #023-12-2004 L2005 *100
RUFFNER, James David. 3535 SOUTHERN BLVD 45429 #020-02-1956 L1957 **FM OM** *020
RUSSELL, Aimee George. 3535 SOUTHERN BLVD, KMC-RADIATION ONCOLOGY 45429 #026-04-2000 L2005 **RO** *020 †80
RUSSELL, Raymond Grant. 787 STANBRIDGE DR 45429 #847-06-1971 L1973 **IM PUD** *020
RYAN, Joseph Lee. 3535 SOUTHERN BLVD, KETTERING MED CTR 45429 #017-20-2007 L2007 **TY** *012
SABIERS, James Harry. 1382 E STROOP RD 45429 #038-06-1988 L1989 **HO IM** *020 †20
SAUNDERS, David Allen. ■ 45429 #005-12-2006 L2006 **IM** *012
SCHLICHER, Nathaniel Ryan. 3525 SOUTHERN BLVD, DEPT OF EMERGENCY MED 45429 #054-04-2006 L2006 **EM** *012

■ = Address Information Privacy Protected

SCHLONEGER, Melisssa Anne. ■ 45409 #038-45-2003 L2003 **EM** *020
SCHMIDT, Mark Dwayne. 3535 SOUTHERN BLVD 45429 #038-06-1986 L1986 **FM** *020 †18
SCHWARTZ, Lyndetta P. 3535 SOUTHERN BLVD, DEPT OF INTERNAL MED 45429 #005-12-1982 L1989 **IM IMG** *040 †20
SENSIBA, Paul Richard. ■ 45429 #038-40-2004 L2004 **ORS** *012
SEYMOUR, David Scott. 3535 SOUTHERN BLVD 45429 #038-45-1985 L1989 **PM OS** *020 †60
SHAH, Ketan Sharad. 3120 GOVERNORS PLACE BLVD 45409 #495-28-1982 L1991 **HO IM** *020 †20
SHERK, William Mc Kay. 3535 SOUTHERN BLVD 45429 #038-41-1957 L1957 **OBG** *071 †30
SHETH, Manish Rasiklal. 3533 SOUTHERN BLVD # 3750, MARIAN A LLENADO-LEE INC 45429 #496-41-1993 L2004 **HO IM** *020 †20
SIMMONS, Joel Rahman. 3120 GOVERNORS PLACE BLVD 45409 #038-44-2002 L2002 **RO** *020
SINGH, Baldev. 3535 SOUTHERN BLVD 45429 #825-01-1974 **CD** *020
SMITH, Robert Endres. 500 LINCOLN PARK BLVD #305, DAYTON CHEST MEDICINE INC 45429 #025-01-1979 L1984 **PUD CCM** *020 †20
SMITH, Robert Thos. 3535 SOUTHERN BLVD 45429 #005-12-1981 L1983 **IM** *020 †20
SOSA, Ismael T. 3535 SOUTHERN BLVD, KETTERING MED CTR 45429 #048-13-2007 L2007 **IM** *012
SPRINGER, Brian Lee. 3525 SOUTHERN BLVD 45429 #048-12-1998 L2000 **EM** *020 †16
STALTER, William Theodore. 2345 W STROOP RD 45439 #038-40-1967 L1967 **OBG** *020 †30
STAN, Thomas Calvin. 3484 FAR HILLS AVE, FAR HILLS SURGICAL CENTER 45429 #004-01-1985 L1986 **AN PME** *020 †05
STOIK, Vaida Maciute. 540 LINCOLN PARK BLVD #390, VAIDA MACIUTE STOLK MD 45429 #913-96-1995 L2004 **IM RHU** *020 †20
SUCIU, Anca. 3535 SOUTHERN BLVD #781-03-2001 L2005 **IM** *012
SWAMY, Venkatasubbiah K. ■ 45429 #495-09-1952 L1968 **IM** *020
SYED, Mubin Isaac. 3075 GOVERNORS PLACE BLVD, DAYTON INTL RADIOLOGISTS 45409 #024-05-1989 L1996 **VIR RNR** *020 †80
TABESH, Enayatollah. 5250 FAR HILLS AVE 45429 #517-01-1956 L1969 **CD IM** *071 †20
TAHA, Jamal M. 3533 SOUTHERN BLVD, STE 3000 45429 #605-01-1984 L1996 **NS** *020 †25
TAYLOR, Victoria Susanne. 5250 FAR HILLS AVE, PRI MED PHYSICIANS 45429 #017-20-1983 L1983 **PD** *020 †55
TELLER, Douglas Wm. 3535 SOUTHERN BLVD, KETTERING MED CTR 45429 #005-12-1981 L1983 **IM ADM** *020 †20
TEMPLETON, Gilbert Walter. 540 LINCOLN PARK BLVD, STE 200 45429 #041-13-1967 L1977 **CD** *071 †20
THAKORE, Jigna Narendra. 999 BRUBAKER DR, STE 1 45429 #759-06-2001 L2001 **GE** *020
THOMAS, Edward Robert, Jr. 3535 SOUTHERN BLVD 45429 #038-41-1962 L1962 **OPH** *020 †35
THOMAS, Lora Denise. 3535 SOUTHERN BLVD, KETTERING MED CTR 45429 #038-43-2000 L2000 **ID** *100 †20
TIBBITS, David Lyle. 3535 SOUTHERN BLVD, DEPARTMENT OF ANESTHESIOLO 45429 #038-40-1996 L1997 **AN** *020 †05
TOGLIATTI, Tamara C. 540 LINCOLN PARK BLVD, STE 200 45429 #048-14-1997 L1999 **IM** *020 †20
TOMLINSON, Terry Lynn. ■ 45429 #023-12-1984 L1993 **DR** *020 †80
TURNER, Louis Emil. 3535 SOUTHERN BLVD 45429 #005-12-1955 L1963 **AN** *071 †05
VARGAS, Matthias Jonathan. 3535 SOUTHERN BLVD 45429 #030-06-1980 L1994 **EM** *020 †16
VERMA, Vishal. 3535 SOUTHERN BLVD, KETTERING MED CTR 45429 #028-02-2007 L2007 **TY** *012
VEVERIS, Ieva. 42 E RAHN RD, STE 107 45429 #407-02-1951 L1961 **P** *020
VILLARREAL, Fernando A. 3080 ACKERMAN BLVD STE 200 45429 #010-01-1973 L1974 **FM** *020 †18
VUKIN, David R. 3535 SOUTHERN BLVD 45429 #038-40-1975 L1976 **AN** *020 †05
WALKER, Matthew Anthony. 3535 SOUTHERN BLVD 45429 #038-41-2004 L2007 **EM** *100
WANG-CHENG, Rebekah May. 3535 SOUTHERN BLVD, KETTERING MED CTR QUAL DEP 45429 #005-12-1979 L2007 **IM** *030 †20
WARGACKI, Ronald Stephen. 3533 SOUTHERN BLVD, STE 3100 45429 #055-01-1987 L2002 **AN** *020 †05
WELSH, John Duncan. 3535 SOUTHERN BLVD 45429 #038-40-1956 L1956 **FM** *071
WHITE, Phillip Allen. 3533 SOUTHERN BLVD 45429 #048-04-1992 L1999 **N** *020 †75
WIGHTMAN, John Matthew. 3525 SOUTHERN BLVD, DEPT OF EMERG MED 45429 #028-03-1988 L1991 **EM LM** *020 †16
WILLIAMS, Beverly Ann. 3525 SOUTHERN BLVD 45429 #038-40-2001 L2001 **EM** *020 †16
WISE, Gregory Rommel. 3535 SOUTHERN BLVD, KETTERING MED CTR 45429 #005-12-1973 L1997 **IM IMG** *030 †20
WONG, Kintung. ■ 45440 #041-01-1989 L1995 **NM** *100 †80,28
YANES, Burhan. 1382 E STROOP RD 45429 #875-01-1981 L1991 **ON** *020 †20

KIDRON — WAYNE

DUNSTER, Patrick Cameron. PO BOX 117, 4139 SOMMERS RD 44636 #038-40-1986 L1988 **EM** *020

KILLBUCK — HOLMES

DIX, John Harlan. 33600 CR132 44637 #038-06-1945 L1945 **AI IM** *071 †20,03
LANDON, Marion Matouk. ■ 44637 #035-03-1960 L1961 **OS** *071

KINGSTON — ROSS

THURSTON, Charles Jenkins. ■ 45644 #038-43-1978 L1979 **GP** *020 †16

KINSMAN — TRUMBULL

BEDLION, Jeffrey. 8511 MAIN ST 44428 #038-44-1995 L1996 **IM** *020 †20
BERRY, Thomas Patrick. ■ 44428 #041-09-1944 L1945 **GP GS** *071
JOHNSON, Lynne Marie. 8511 MAIN ST, KINSMAN HEALTH CENTER 44428 #038-40-2000 L2000 **PD** *020 †55
VARGA, Sabrina Kelly. 8511 MAIN ST 44428 #038-43-1996 L1997 **FM** *020 †18

KIRTLAND — LAKE

BARTOLO-BASQUINEZ, Aida M. ■ 44094 #748-07-1965 L1974 **OBG** *071 †30
CAHILL, John Jos. ■ 44094 #050-02-1954 L1959 **EM** *071 †30
CUNNINGHAM, Carol A. ■ 44094 #035-19-1984 L1987 **OPH** *020 †35
WEATHERHEAD, Virginia N A. ■ 44094 #021-01-1950 L1959 **IM** *071

LA RUE — MARION

BAKER, Penny Dawniel. ■ 43332 #038-40-2005 L2005 **FP** *012
BHARMOTA, Harjit Singh. 12 S HIGH ST 43332 #495-03-1960 L1975 **GP GS** *075

LAFAYETTE — ALLEN

REYNOLDS, Michael Dayne. ■ 45854 #023-07-1965 L1994 **RHU IM** *071 †20

LAGRANGE — LORAIN

OJUKWU, Ifeoma Ada Chinwe. ■ 44050 #690-04-1996 L2004 **IM** *100 †20
PIERRE, Daniel John. ■ 44050 #038-06-2007 L2007 **IM** *012

LAKE MILTON — MAHONING

ESCOBAR, Martin. 17674 MAHONING AVE 44429 #305-01-1998 L1999 **IM** *020

LAKEMORE — SUMMIT

WILLETT, Matthew Christia. ■ 44250 #038-44-2006 L2006 **OPH** *012

LAKESIDE MARBLEHEAD — OTTAWA

KRANER, James Clem. ■ 43440 #038-40-1956 L1956 **CD IM** *071

LAKEWOOD — CUYAHOGA

ABDEL-RAZEQ, Hikmat N. 44107 #575-01-1988 L1993 **HO** *020 †20
ADAMS, Ellis Wentworth. ■ 44107 #036-07-1941 L1948 **PD** *071 †55
ADAMS, Henry Geo. 14519 DETROIT AVE 44107 #030-05-1980 L1990 **DR OS** *020 †80 ‡
AKHTAR, Nila Joyce. ■ 44107 #016-45-2003 L2004 **DR** *012
AL-DHAHIR, Wafa M. 14519 DETROIT AVE, LAKEWOOD HOSP 44107 #584-01-1987 L1997 **PTH PP** *020 †50
ALFES, John Conrad. 14600 DETROIT AVE 44107 #025-07-1986 L1987 **IM PD** *020 †55,20
AL MALKI, Mhd Monzr. 12900 LAKE AVE, APT 1027 44107 #875-01-2003 L2005 **IM** *012
AMA-MC GUINNESS, Perlita. 15000 MADISON AVE 44107 #748-01-1975 L1983 **IM** *020 †20
AMMAJI, Narra. 14600 DETROIT AVE 44107 #495-50-1970 L1978 **IM** *020 †20
ANTON, Hany Sobhy Youssef. 14601 DETROIT AVE, STE 490 44107 #915-02-1992 L1997 **NEP** *020 †20
ASSAAD, Joe Emile. ■ 44107 #038-06-2004 L2004 **DR** *012
BADAL, Daniel Walter. ■ 44107 #038-06-1937 L1937 **P PYA** *071 †75
BAKDASH, Suzanne. ■ 44107 #875-01-1999 L2007 **BBK** *100 †50
BAUTISTA, Jan Rey. 16215 MADISON AVE 44107 #023-07-1998 L2000 **IM** *020 †20
BAYLON, Juanito E. 14519 DETROIT AVE 44107 #748-10-1961 L1969 **AN** *071
BEREDO, Cipriano S, Jr. 14519 DETROIT AVE 44107 #748-08-1966 L1973 **IM** *020 †20
BHALLA, Anita. 15000 MADISON AVE 44107 #496-07-1989 L2000 **ID** *020 †20
BINDRA, Sanjit S. 14601 DETROIT AVE, STE 595 44107 #495-28-1995 L2007 **END** *020 †20
BORSELLINO, Sam Richard. 14601 DETROIT AVE, STE 330 44107 #038-40-1999 L1999 **NS** *020
BRUNO, Romeo B. 14519 DETROIT AVE 44107 #748-01-1963 L1980 **GS** *020
BUSTAMI, Bassem. 14519 DETROIT AVE 44107 #605-01-1984 L1993 **CD** *020 †20
CARANDANG, Rosemelinda T. 14519 DETROIT AVE DEPT MED 44107 #748-01-1963 L1974 **IM GP** *071
CASH, Adam Daniel. ■ 44107 #038-06-2006 L2006 **PS** *012
CECH, Dennis Dominic. 14701 DETROIT AVE, STE 730 44107 #021-05-1978 L1979 **AI IM** *020 †20,03
CHAPMAN, Kenneth Wilmott. 14601 DETROIT AVE STE 640 44107 #038-06-1963 L1963 **ORS** *020 †40
CHAVEZ, Altagracia M. 14601 DETROIT AVE, LAKEWOOD PROFESSIONAL BUIL 44107 #035-19-1977 L1987 **TS GS** *020 †90,85
CHEN, George C. 14519 DETROIT AVE 44107 #748-08-1966 L1973 **IM** *020
CHEN, Siu S L. ■ 44107 #748-08-1967 L1978 **AN** *074
CHOPRA, Anish. 12900 LAKE AVE 44107 #495-03-2001 L2005 **IM** *012
CHRISTIAN, Stefanie S. 1450 BELLE AVE STE 310, LAKEWOOD OBSTETRICST GYN 44107 #038-06-1987 L1987 **OBG** *020 †30
CIEMINS, Vilnis Andris. 14519 DETROIT AVE 44107 #038-06-1960 L1960 **N** *020 †75
CLAUSEN, Christoph Claus. ■ 44107 #649-10-1991 **NPM** *100
CLIFFEL, Thomas Patrick. 14200 MADISON AVE 44107 #038-40-1967 L1967 **OPH** *020 †35
COHEN, Truvy Isabel. ■ 44107 #264-18-1991 L2001 **IMG** *100 †20
COLACARRO, Robert Thos. 16215 MADISON AVE 44107 #038-40-1974 L1974 **IM** *020 †20
COTTLE, Edward Chas. 14600 DETROIT AVE, STE 1495 44107 #008-01-1971 L1978 **PTH** *020 †50
COVERDALE, Philip Jos. 14600 DETROIT AVE, STE 1495 LAKEWOOD CENTER N 44107 #038-06-1982 L1983 **EM** *020 †16
CRANDALL, Stephen Andrew. ■ 44107 #054-04-2004 L2005 **EM** *012
CRANDELL, James R. 14601 DETROIT AVE, STE 460 44107 #038-44-1983 L1990 **CD IM** *020 †20
CRAWFORD, Thomas Leo. 12535 EDGEWATER DR 44107 #028-34-1955 L1957 **IM** *071
CUNNINGHAM, Carol Anita. 14600 DETROIT AVE 44107 #038-41-1986 L1987 **EM** *020 †16
DARWICHE, Hussein Fadl. ■ 44107 #025-07-2005 L2006 **ORS** *012
DASO, Amy Arszman. 14601 DETROIT AVE, STE 670 44107 #038-06-2000 L2000 **PD** *020 †55 ‡

DEFILIPPO SZUCS, Melinda. ■ 44107 #038-75-2007, ▲ L2007 *012

DE LA ROCA, Rogelio R. 15644 MADISON AVE 44107 #748-08-1962 L1972 **IM** *020

DHINGRA, Upma. 14701 DETROIT AVE STE 3 44107 #495-03-1976 L1988 **P** *020 †75

DIAMANTIS, Nicholas. 14701 DETROIT AVE, STE 450 44107 #038-06-1994 L1995 **CS** *020

DICK, Arthur Peter. 14601 DETROIT AVE STE 480 44107 #065-06-1977 L1984 **N UM** *020 †75

DIXON, Morris S, Jr. 14519 DETROIT AVE 44107 #035-45-1951 L1954 **PD** *030 †55

D'SILVA, Nelson John. 14601 DETROIT AVE, STE 360 44107 #496-15-1978 L1992 **FM** *020 †18

DUBSKY, Jonathan Adam. 14926 ESTHER AVE 44107 #038-41-2000 L2000 **AN** *020 †05

DUHIGG, William J. ■ 44107 #041-02-1952 L1953 **N** *071

EDMINSTER, Joel David. ■ 44107 #038-06-2005 L2005 **EM** *012

EKMAN, Kristen Annika. 1450 BELLE AVE, STE 310 44107 #035-03-1999 L1999 **OBG** *020 †30

EL-GAZZAR, Mourad Mazhar. 15000 MADISON AVE 44107 #915-02-1972 L1989 **IM** *020

ELSAID ELGOUHARI, Hesham. ■ 44107 #915-06-1997 L2006 **ID** *100

EROSSY, Peter J. 14701 DETROIT AVE, LAKEWOOD CENTER NORTH 44107 #396-30-1982 L1984 **IM** *020 †20

ESMAILI, Ali. ■ 44107 #023-01-2003 **IM** *100 †20

ESMAILI, Ali. ■ 44107 #005-06-2005 L2006 **DR** *012

EVANS, Virginia Ann. ■ 44107 #038-06-1975 L1977 **EM** *030 †16

FAN, Zhen. ■ 44107 #038-41-2002 L2002 **GS** *100 †85

FARRELL, Charles John. 14601 DETROIT AVE 44107 #030-06-1963 L1965 **VS GS** *071 †85

FAYEN, William John. 14601 DETROIT AVE STE 610 44107 #038-06-1947 L1947 **IM NM** *020 †20,28

FEGEN, J Peter. 14701 DETROIT AVE, STE 720 44107 #035-20-1963 L1964 **U** *071 †95

FOTINOS, Komninos Stauros. 11801 CLIFTON BLVD 44107 #418-01-1979 L1988 **IM** *020

FRANKO, Andrew Paul. 14601 DETROIT AVE 44107 #038-41-1987 L1990 **FM** *020 †18

FRAZEE, Troy Austin. 14701 DETROIT AVE, STE 450 44107 #038-06-2000 L2000 **PS** *020 ‡

FRIRES, Richard Francis. 14600 DETROIT AVE, STE 1495 44107 #016-01-1977 L1983 **EM FM** *020 †16,18

GARVEN, Charles John. 14601 DETROIT AVE, STE 260 44107 #038-06-1987 L1987 **FM** *020 †18

GITIFOROOZ, Habibeh Mohd. 1450 BELLE AVE, STE 310 44107 #916-01-1992 L2000 **OBG** *020 †30

GOLDSCHMIDT, Matthew J. 14701 DETROIT AVE, STE 450 44107 #008-02-1999 L2003 **CS CFS** *020

GOVANI, Nitin Shantilal. 13535 DETROIT AVE STE 1 44107 #495-22-1991 L2000 **IM** *020 †20

GREENE, Richard Anthony. ■ 44107 #051-07-1998 L2006 **PTH** *100

HARDAWAY, Tiffany Jean. ■ 44107 #025-07-2005 L2007 **AN** *012

HASSAN, Syed Ommar. ■ 44107 #704-26-1999 L2006 **FP** *012

HASTINGS, Otis Mark. 14519 DETROIT AVE, LAKEWOOD HOSP EMERG DEPT 44107 #033-05-1975 L1989 **EM PE** *020 †16

HIGUERA RUEDA, Carlos Alb. ■ 44107 #264-04-1999 L2004 **ORS** *012

HOHN, Brooke Erin. 14600 DETROIT AVE, STE 103 44107 #038-45-2002 L2002 **FM** *020 †18

HUFFMAN, William L. 14701 DETROIT AVE STE 720 44107 #038-06-1943 L1944 **U** *071 †95

JASSANI, Kadhim Jawad. ■ 44107 #528-01-1958 L1966 **PTH HEM** *072 †50

JETTE, Norman Timothy. 2077 MORRISON AVE 44107 #008-01-1971 L1977 **CHP P** *020 †05,75

KALASH, Mohamad Saleh. 15644 MADISON AVE, STE 101 44107 #875-01-1979 L1991 **IM** *020 †20

KAMBHAMPATI, Venkatesh. ■ 44107 #038-40-2006 L2006 **EM** *012

KAPUR, Rahi. ■ 44107 #038-06-2004 L2004 **EM** *100

KAYLOR, William Mickey. ■ 44107 #038-06-1947 L1947 **U** *071 †95

KEBEDE, Zelalem Wodajo. ■ 44107 #286-13-1992 L2003 **PD** *074 †55

KHADDAM, Mohammad Hani F. 15644 MADISON AVE, STE 202 44107 #875-01-1972 L1979 **TS VS** *020 †85,90

KHURI, Munther. 14601 DETROIT AVE, STE 400 44107 #875-03-1992 L1998 **IM** *020 †20

KILANI, Ahmad Mazhar. 15644 MADISON AVE STE 104, PREMIER PHYSICIANS CENTERS 44107 #875-01-1991 L1998 **IM** *020 †20

KILROY, Terence Edward. 14701 DETROIT AVE, STE 650 44107 #038-41-1979 L1981 **PUD CCM** *020 †20

KOSTER, Charles K. 16400 HILLIARD RD 44107 #028-34-1954 L1963 **OPH** *020 †35

KRAFT, Mary Alyce. 13535 DETROIT AVE, PIERSON OFFICE BLDG 44107 #056-06-1948 L1949 **IM** *020

KREINBRINK, Katherine Den. ■ 44107 #038-45-2005 L2005 **OBG** *012

KUMAR, Vikramjeet. 14601 DETROIT AVE STE 540, DIABETES & ENDOCRINOLOGY C 44107 #495-54-1994 L2007 **END** *020 †20

LABBAD, Jakleen Mary. ■ 44107 #038-43-2006 L2007 **FP** *012

LAMBERT, Claude B. 14600 DETROIT AVE # 10 44107 #067-06-1971 *100

LANDEN, F Gifford. ■ 44107 #038-06-1988 *100

LARKIN, Kathleen Susan. ■ 44107 #038-40-2006 L2006 **OBG** *012

LASHUTKA, Matthew Kenneth. 14519 DETROIT AVE 44107 #038-40-1999 L1999 **EM** *020 †16

LEE, Chiu-Ho. 14519 DETROIT AVE 44107 #572-12-1969 L1973 **PTH** *062 †50

LIN, Selina Jiahwa. ■ 44107 #011-02-1999 L2006 **OPH** *020 †35

LINKE, Thomas Frank. 14601 DETROIT AVE 44107 #038-06-1955 L1955 **ORS** *071 †40

LOOS, Bryan Donald. 14600 DETROIT AVE, STE 103 44107 #038-41-1990 L1991 **FM** *020 †18

MAGGIO, Lindsay. ■ 44107 #033-06-2008 *012

MALM, Lawrence Hawes. 14519 DETROIT AVE 44107 #024-07-1962 L1963 **IM** *071

MARISCALCO, Michael Willi. ■ 44107 #038-45-2007 L2007 **ORS** *012

MARKAKIS, Aristotelis Geo. 11801 CLIFTON BLVD 44107 #418-01-1951 L1961 **GS** *072

MASON, Kerri L. 14519 DETROIT AVE 44107 #030-05-1999 L1999 **EM** *020

MASON, Travis Jaya. ■ 44107 #024-07-2004 L2004 **GS** *012

MENDOZA, Cesar M. 14519 DETROIT AVE, RADIOLOGY DEPARTMENT 44107 #748-01-1968 L1980 **DR** *020

MESSICK, Craig A. 1272 W CLIFTON BLVD 44107 #048-14-2005 L2005 **GS** *012

MIKOL, Sharon Jean. 1450 BELLE AVE, APT 300 44107 #038-40-1982 L1984 **OBG** *020 †30 ‡

MILLER, Edward Douglas. 1450 BELLE AVE 44107 #036-07-1981 L1988 **OBG PHP** *020 †30

MISNY, Thomas Jos. 14519 DETROIT AVE 44107 #038-06-1979 L1981 **GS** *071 †85

MOHAMED, Mohamed Wasef. ■ 44107 #575-02-1997 L2007 **NPM** *012 †10

MOONEY, Mary Alyce. ■ 44107 #038-40-1979 L1985 **PTH** *020 †50

MOYER, Eric Douglas. ■ 44107 #012-05-2006 L2007 **FP** *012

MUHAMMAD, Nader Husam. 2118 ELDRED AVE 44107 #038-44-2000 L2000 **AN** *020 †05

MUNIAK, Ruthanne Marie. 16251 MADISON AVE 44107 #041-07-1967 L1968 **PD** *020 †55

MURRAY, Trevor Guy. ■ 44107 #038-06-2004 L2004 **ORS** *012

NADER, Simone. 14601 DETROIT AVE, STE 460 44107 #187-21-1988 L2000 **CD** *020 †20

NEMEH, Issam. 14519 DETROIT AVE 44107 #759-12-1980 L1989 **OS GS** *020

NEMR, Gasan. 15000 MADISON AVE, PREMIER PHYSICIANS CENTERS 44107 #305-01-2000 L2000 **GS** *020

NG, Alan S. ■ 44107 #038-06-2003 L2003 **PMM** *012

NGUYEN, Tony Kim. ■ 44107 #010-01-2004 L2006 **ORS** *012

O'BRIEN, Vincent John. 14601 DETROIT AVE STE 450 44107 #038-40-1972 L1972 **ON HEM** *020 †20

OPASKAR, Frank Alan. 14600 DETROIT AVE 44107 #025-01-1970 L1972 **PD** *020 †55

PASALIS, John Gust. 14701 DETROIT AVE, UROLOGY ASSOCS W INC 44107 #016-06-1965 L1966 **U** *071 †95

PATEL, Kevin. ■ 44107 #917-03-2002 L2004 **IM** *100 †20

PATEL, Kishor Parbhubhai. 15644 MADISON AVE 44107 #495-05-1976 L1990 **IM** *020 †20

PATHAK, Shridhar. ■ 44107 #495-19-1956 L1971 **ORS** *020

PEARCE, Harry Bartholomew. 14519 DETROIT AVE 44107 #038-40-1973 L1973 **EM** *020 †16

PEARSE, Steven Craig. 14601 DETROIT AVE, STE 350 44107 #007-02-1974 L1981 **VS GS** *020 †85

PIDGEON, John S. ■ 44107 #035-15-2003 L2003 **CN** *012

POPOVICH, William Francis. ■ 44107 #305-01-2004 L2004 **IM** *020 †20

POSLUSZNY, Joseph Anthony. ■ 44107 #036-01-2006 L2006 **GS** *012

PRESSWALA, Nuruddin J. 15600 MADISON AVE 44107 #495-01-1973 L1978 **GP** *020

PRINGPUANGKEO, T. 15644 MADISON AVE STE 202 44107 #891-02-1962 L1971 **TS** *071 †85,90

PUDVAN, William Roy. ■ 44107 #038-06-1954 L1954 **R** *020 †80

RAMACHANDRAN, Umarani. 14601 DETROIT AVE STE 395 44107 #495-94-1992 L2000 **PD** *020 †55

RAMOS, Domingo S. 13535 DETROIT AVE 44107 #748-01-1965 L1974 **FM EM** *020

RAO, Bharati. 14519 DETROIT AVE 44107 #495-11-1964 L1974 **PD EM** *020 †55

REPENNING, Dennis Benjami. 2143 WASCANA AVE 44107 #422-01-2001 L2001 **MPD** *020 †55,20

REYES, Rebecca T Robancho. 14701 DETROIT AVE, STE 740 44107 #748-08-1966 L1974 **GP** *020

RIEBEL, William John. 14601 DETROIT AVE, STE 570 44107 #016-11-1978 L1979 **ID IM** *020 †20

ROBBINS, Rosemary Gordon. 14601 DETROIT AVE, STE 250 44107 #038-06-1994 L1997 **OBG** *020 †55

ROJAS, Carole Angela. 14601 DETROIT AVE, STE 400 44107 #025-01-1996 L1998 **IM** *020 †20

RUDINSKY, Kari Anne. ■ 44107 #038-45-2007 L2007 **OBG** *012

SABLE, James Timothy. ■ 44107 #038-44-2005 L2005 **AN** *012

SAND, Steven Edward. ■ 44107 #038-06-2008 *012

SANDOVAL, Flory Marquez. 15700 MADISON AVE 44107 #748-01-1955 L1964 **IM OS** *071

SCHAPIRO, Juergen Leo. ■ 44107 #154-02-1951 L1955 **R NM** *071 †80

SELLARS, Walter S. 14519 DETROIT AVE 44107 #064-01-1941 L1948 **IM** *071

SESHAN, Rajinikanth. 14519 DETROIT AVE, LAKEWOOD HOSPITAL 44107 #496-28-1997 L2003 **NEP** *012 †20

SHEN, Shujane. 14519 DETROIT AVE 44107 #038-06-1990 L1993 **DR** *020 †80

SHIE, Marvin Dacosta, III. 15644 MADISON AVE 44107 #038-40-1972 L1972 **GS** *020 †85

SKOCH, Mary K Gardner. 14601 DETROIT AVE, STE 670 44107 #038-06-1987 L1989 **PD** *020 †20

SNYDER, Jennifer Lea. 14600 DETROIT AVE, STE 103 44107 #038-45-1997 L1999 **FM** *020 †18

SOMANI, Ally. ■ 44107 #065-01-2002 L2004 **D** *012

SOMANI, Najwa. ■ 44107 #065-01-2000 L2005 **D** *100 †15

SPIESS, Jeffrey Lewis. 14601 DETROIT AVE 44107 #038-43-1980 L1982 **PLM ON** *020 †20

STATESIR, Richard Allen. 14701 DETROIT AVE STE 280 44107 #041-09-1982 L1986 **OPH GP** *020 †35

STAUB, Frank J. ■ 44107 #035-15-1952 L1954 **AN** *071 †05

ST CLAIR, Selvon Francisc. ■ 44107 #035-19-2004 L2004 **ORS** *012

STEWART, John Jay. 14701 DETROIT AVE 44107 #025-01-1945 L1951 **D** *071 †15

SUNTALA, Christopher Ray. 14701 DETROIT AVE, STE 475 44107 #024-05-1981 L1984 **IM** *020 †20

SYM-LIPSKY, Joanna. ■ 44107 #407-05-1950 L1957 **PTH FOP** *071 †50

TABORA, Hippocrates P. 14519 DETROIT AVE 44107 #748-08-1967 L1974 **GP** *020

TEBA, Luis. ■ 44107 #847-03-1974 L1980 **IM CCM** *020 †18,20

THAI, Hue Chan. ■ 44107 #054-04-2008 *012

THOMAS, Biju. ■ 44107 #495-28-1996 L2003 **PD** *012

THOMAS, Kristina Valerie. ■ 44107 #041-15-2004 L2004 **OPH** *012

TOMSIK, Philip Edward. 16110 DETROIT AVE 44107 #038-45-1998 L1999 **FM** *020 †18

TOTH, Margaret Maria. ■ 44107 #008-01-1991 L1994 **IM** *020 †20

TRUNZO, Joseph Angelo. ■ 44107 #038-45-2005 L2005 **GS** *012

TSAO, Lawrence. ■ 44107 #035-08-2001 L2007 **HMP** *100 †50

TSCHEINER, Melissa Ann. ■ 44107 #038-43-2004 L2004 **EM** *012

VARTORELLA, Georganne. 14805 DETROIT AVE, STE 400 44107 #010-02-1982 L1986 **IM PTH** *020 †20

VENIZELOS, Alexander Paul. ■ 44107 #038-45-2007 L2007 **IM** *012

VERNON, Joan. 14519 DETROIT AVE, LAKEWOOD HOSPITAL 44107 #038-43-2000 L2000 **EM** *020

WAGAMON, Kyle L. ■ 44107 #038-06-2002 L2002 **D DMP** *020 †15

WALBORN, A Mary. 16215 MADISON AVE 44107 #025-12-1977 L1979 **IM** *020 †20

WANG, Ingrid Yinwen. 16215 MADISON AVE 44107 #035-45-2000 L2000 **IM** *020 †20

WEHBE, Charles Rafic. ■ 44107 #038-06-2006 L2006 **DR** *012

WELLINGTON, Joseph A. ■ 44107 #038-06-2004 *100

WEST, Michael. 14601 DETROIT AVE STE 33, LAKEWOOD HOSPITAL PROFESSI 44107 #062-01-1973 L1994 **NS** *020

WILLIAMS, Ryan Sherard. ■ 44107 #025-12-2000 L2000 **CRS** *100 †85

WOO, Henry Heesang. 14601 DETROIT AVE, STE 330 44107 #035-19-1995 L2002 **NS** *020

WOOD, David Newton. 14601 DETROIT AVE STE 540 44107 #038-06-1947 L1947 **IM** *071

YADERA, Mary Elizabeth. ■ 44107 #041-02-2007 L2007 **FP** *012

YALAMANCHILI, Chaethana. ■ 44107 #048-15-2005 L2005 **EM** *012

YU, Ling. 15644 MADISON AVE 44107 #244-02-1962 L1977 **PD** *020 †55

YUN, Romy Djuhiee. ■ 44107 #038-06-2007 L2007 **IM** *012

ZACHARY, John Donald. ■ 44107 #016-02-1967 L1968 **ORS** *071 †40

ZEIN, Nazih. 14601 DETROIT AVE STE 590 44107 #875-01-1972 L1977 **RHU IM** *020 †20

ZHANG, Janet Jie. ■ 44107 #038-43-2007 L2007 **OBG** *012

ZIMNICKYJ, Eugene A. 12700 LAKE AVE APT 2006, WINTON PLACE 44107 #913-31-1941 L1961 **AN** *071

LANCASTER – FAIRFIELD

ABIDIN, Johnny. 135 N EWING ST STE 305 43130 #005-12-1992 L1994 **IM** *020 †20

ABROMOWITZ, Leslie Mira. 1592 GRANVILLE PIKE 43130 #038-45-1987 L1988 **CHP P** *020 †75

AEBI, Mark Ellis. 1800 GRANVILLE PIKE 43130 #038-40-1988 L1989 **FM** *020 †18

ALLEY, Sarah Jo. 1781 COUNTRY SIDE DR 43130 #038-40-1992 L1993 **FM** *020 †18

AMSTUTZ, Hubert Menno. ■ 43130 #038-40-1934 L1934 **OTO OPH** *071 †45

AYERS, Jeffrey Maynard. 216 TRACE DR 43130 #018-75-1972, ▲ L1974 **FM** *020

BAKER, Scott Robt. 1955 LANCASTER NEWRK RD NE 43130 #038-40-1987 L1989 **FM** *020 †18

BANKS, Mark Andrew. 422 N COLUMBUS ST 43130 #038-45-1995 L1996 **PM OS** *020 †60

BARRETT, James Lloyd. 112 N EWING ST 43130 #038-41-1967 L1967 **D** *020 †15

BATTEN, William Henrichs. 1500 E MAIN ST 43130 #055-01-1982 L1987 **U** *020 †95

BAUER, Peter Kazeryu. 401 N EWING ST, FAIRFIELD MEDICAL CENTER 43130 #654-01-1999 L1999 **PTH** *062 †50

BERNARD, Philip James. ■ 43130 #038-40-1962 L1962 **P** *020

BLAHA, Rene Vladislav. 3484 CINCINNAT ZNSVL RD NE, ROAD, NE 43130 #409-16-1973 L1979 **FM** *020 †18

BOULGER, Creagh Turner. ■ 43130 #038-45-2008 *012

BOWMAN, Kevin Karl. 1201 RIVER VALLEY BLVD 43130 #038-40-1988 L1989 **EM** *020 †16

BRATTON, Judith Lynn. 401 N EWING ST 43130 #038-40-1986 L1988 **ID** *020 †20

BROWN, David Gregory. 121 W 6TH AVE 43130 #038-43-1973 L1975 **PUD IM** *020 †20

BROWN, Judith Lynn. 1981 GRANVILLE PIKE 43130 #055-01-1992 L2000 **IM PD** *062 †55,20

CANTER, Hall G, Jr. 401 N EWING ST 43130 #010-02-1982 L1984 **FM** *020 †18

CASTELLON, Roberto Javier. 2405 N COLUMBUS ST, STE 230 43130 #011-03-1996 L2001 **OTO** *020 †45

CHANG, Yeong Koon. 401 N EWING ST 43130 #583-04-1966 L1973 **AN** *020 †05

CHASE, Daniel Warren. 2405 N COLUMBUS ST, STE 230 43130 #011-02-1986 L1988 **OTO** *020 †45

CONLEY, David Lee. 2401 N COLUMBUS ST 43130 #038-40-1990 L1994 **AN** *020 †05

COOK, Charles Harker. ■ 43130 #038-40-1968 L1968 **GS TRS** *071 †85

CORNER, Christopher J. 1334 SHERIDAN DR, STE 2 43130 #001-02-1988 L1991 **P CHP** *020

COX, Steven David. 1566 MONMOUTH DR, STE 101 43130 #038-40-1979 L1984 **GS** *020 †85

CRAWFORD, David Beatty. 401 N EWING ST 43130 #918-01-1965 L1998 **DR** *020 †80

CUSTER, Timothy John. 2405 N COLUMBUS ST, STE 250 43130 #038-40-1996 L1998 **GS** *020 †85

DARNELL, Mark Thos. 401 N EWING ST 43130 #055-01-1987 L1988 **EM** *020 †16

DE COSTE, Michele. ■ 43130 #041-07-1977 L1978 **IM** *020 †16

DE WALT, John D. 214 HARMON AVE 43130 #028-79-1977, ▲ L1978 **VS** *020

DOMINGUEZ, Robert Javier. 1201 RIVER VALLEY BLVD 43130 #308-03-1981 L1985 **FM EM** *020 †18

DOSS, Lawrence L. 2865 WHEELING RD NE 43130 #004-01-1973 L1998 **GP FPG** *020 †80

DOUGLASS, Michelle Aretta. 2401 N COLUMBUS ST 43130 #038-45-1994 L1995 **AN** *020 †05

DUNBAR, David Joe. 1500 E MAIN ST, MEDICAL ASSOC LANCASTER 43130 #038-40-1978 L1981 **IM** *020 †20

DYE, Jayne Hardy Wunsch. ■ 43130 #048-02-1959 L1982 **PD** *071

ELDADAH, Mazen Khalid. 401 N EWING ST 43130 #915-07-1977 L1995 **N** *020

ENLOW, Susan Alice. 401 N EWING ST 43130 #038-45-1988 L1992 **DR** *020 †80

ENTSUAH, Laurence Kobina. 111 HARMON AVE 43130 #409-24-1991 L2003 **GE** *020 †20 ‡

FERMO-ULLOM, Rosalie P. 401 N EWING ST 43130 #748-01-1986 L1998 **AN** *020 †05 ‡

FROMAN, Sarah Lynn. 135 N EWING ST STE 201 43130 #038-06-1991 L1992 **OBG** *020 †30 ‡

FYIE, Mathew Cameron. 2401 N COLUMBUS ST 43130 #025-07-1993 L1997 **AN** *020 †05

GIBSON, Jennifer Dawn. 1548 SHERIDAN DR, STE 200 43130 #036-01-1995 L1996 **MPD PD** *020 †20,55

GINTY, Joseph Michael. 1800 GRANVILLE PIKE 43130 #038-40-1990 L1991 **FM** *020 †18

GOGATE, Shashikala Anand. 401 N EWING ST, FAIRFIELD MEDICAL CENTER 43130 #495-20-1962 L1972 **PTH** *020 †50

GOKHALE, Anil Sudhir. 2405 N COLUMBUS ST, STE 270 43130 #041-12-1996 L2000 **OTO** *020 †45

GONELA, Renuka. 1550 SHERIDAN DR, STE B 43130 #495-04-1969 L1996 **MPD** *020

GORENSTEIN, Aryeh. 2405 N COLUMBUS ST, STE 270 43130 #062-01-1973 L1982 **OTO** *020 †45

GRAHAM, Michelle L. 1781 COUNTRY SIDE DR 43130 #038-43-1997 L1999 **FM** *020 †18

HARRIS, Martin H, II. 1550 SHERIDAN DR, STE 102 43130 #030-06-1976 L1986 **PD** *020 †55

HARTLE, Richard Eugene. ■ 43130 #038-40-1958 L1958 **FM** *071 †18

HASL, David Michael. 2405 N COLUMBUS ST, STE 250 43130 #038-45-1992 L1996 **GS** *020 †85

HAZLIP, John Russell. 401 N EWING ST 43130 #038-40-1982 L1985 **FM EM** *020 †18

HENDRICKSON, Brett Willia. ■ 43130 #038-06-2006 **PTH** *012

HENSLEY, Michele Mekyung. 1550 SHERIDAN DR STE 102, PED ASSOCS OF LANCASTER 43130 #038-40-1998 L1999 **PD** *020 †55

HOLLINGSWORTH, Gretchen E. 2401 N COLUMBUS ST 43130 #038-40-1988 L1997 **AN** *020 †05

HOLLINGSWORTH, Keith Alan. 2405 N COLUMBUS ST, STE 120 43130 #038-40-1988 L1997 **ORS** *020 †40

HOOD, Henry Harding. 1750 GRANVILLE PIKE 43130 #041-02-1966 L1967 **ORS** *020 †40

HOUSSEIN, Assem. 2405 N COLUMBUS ST, STE 130 43130 #781-01-1986 L1993 **END** *020 †20

HUMES, Katherine Alicia. ■ 43130 #005-19-1992 L1995 **FM** *020 †18

JOHNSON, Scott Owen. 2405 N COLUMBUS ST, STE 250 43130 #038-40-1992 L1993 **GS** *020 †85

KASSUR, Danuta Ana. 135 NORTH ST, STE 305 43130 #759-03-1982 L1992 **IM** *020 †20

KEY, James Edward. 1550 SHERIDAN DR STE 202 43130 #017-20-1966 L1969 **FM** *020 †18

KIM, Yong Won. 799 WAGNER DR SW 43130 #583-01-1972 L1992 **OBG** *020 †30

KIRKPATRICK, Jos Francis. 1500 E MAIN ST 43130 #010-02-1958 L1964 **OPH** *071 †35

KOLLI, Srinivas. 1500 E MAIN ST 43130 #001-02-1988 L1995 **GE IM** *020 †20

KOLLI, Susmitha P. 1500 E MAIN ST 43130 #016-02-1993 L1995 **OPH** *020 †35

KOOP, Darryl Glen. ■ 43130 #062-01-1989 L1996 *020 †70

KOSIER, Marilyn Kay. 1520 SHERIDAN DR 43130 #038-40-1980 L1988 **OPH IM** *020 †35

KRAKER, Jack L. ■ 43130 #038-40-1952 L1952 **GP** *071

LAKATOS, Ronald. 2405 N COLUMBUS ST, OHIO SPINE CENTER INC 43130 #041-09-1984 L1994 **ORS OTR** *020 †40

LANDER, Laura Ellen. 1548 SHERIDAN DR, STE 200 43130 #038-40-1998 L1999 **MPD** *020 †20,55

LAUS, Agnes M. 1781 COUNTRY SIDE DR 43130 #748-02-1984 L1996 **PD** *020 †55

LE SAR, James Frederick. 1550 SHERIDAN DR, STE 202 43130 #041-09-1977 L1981 **EM IM** *020 †20

LEVE, Brian Edward. 135 N EWING ST, STE 206 43130 #038-45-1996 L2003 **OBG** *020 †30

LEWIS, Bradley Johnathan. 1147 E MAIN ST 43130 #038-40-1986 L1987 **FM** *020 †18

LICHTEN, Jason Brett. 135 N EWING ST, STE 202 43130 #041-02-1998 L2003 **PS** *020 †65

LIFER, David Charles. 135 N EWING ST, STE 201 43130 #038-40-1962 L1962 **GYN OBG** *071 †30

LLOYD, John Edward. 2405 N COLUMBUS ST STE 200, ARBORVIEW FAM MED 43130 #038-40-1977 L1977 **FM** *020 †18

LOWREY, Charles Edward. 2405 N COLUMBUS ST STE 220 43130 #038-40-1982 L1984 **ORS OM** *020 †40

MANNELLA, Joseph Julian. 401 N EWING ST, FAIRFIELD MEDICAL CENTER 43130 #041-13-1993 L1997 **AN** *020 †05

MASONE, Robert John. 401 N EWING ST 43130 #035-46-1982 L1987 **PME AN** *020 †05

MATHEWSON, Roger Connell. 401 N EWING ST, FAIRFIELD MED CTR PATH DEP 43130 #031-01-1989 L1990 **PTH HMP** *020 †50

MC ANALLEN, Curtis M. 1201 RIVER VALLEY BLVD 43130 #055-02-1990 L1991 **EM** *020 †18

MCGOWAN, Cynthia M. ■ 43130 #038-75-2006, ▲ L2006 *012

MENOSKY, Martin Edward. 1781 COUNTRY SIDE DR 43130 #038-45-1995 L1996 **FM** *020 †18

MERK, James Albert. 1587 GRANVILLE PIKE 43130 #028-34-1956 L1959 **FM** *020 †18

MESZAROS, Frank James. 135 N EWING ST 43130 #038-41-1992 L1993 **PM** *020 †60

MURRY, Andrew R. 1253 E MAIN ST 43130 #038-40-1993 L1994 **ID IM** *020 †20

NATARAJ, H. 2405 N COLUMBUS ST, STE 260 43130 #495-33-1982 L1995 **AI IM** *020 †20,03

NICKISON, Christopher S. 135 N EWING ST, STE 305 43130 #038-44-1994 L1996 **IM** *020 †20

NICODEMUS, Darell Elroyce. ■ 43130 #038-40-1958 L1958 **GP** *020

NOLAN, Bernard. 401 N EWING ST 43130 #539-03-1967 L1977 **ORS** *020 †40

NORBERTO, Jose J. 618 PLEASANTVILLE RD, STE 202 43130 #308-01-1988 L2000 **TS** *020 †90,85

NUSBAUM, Jonathan Wilford. 135 N EWING ST STE 205, PAVILION 43130 #038-40-1967 L1967 **GS** *020 †85

OPPENHEIMER, Stuart. 131 N EWING ST 43130 #038-40-1966 L1966 **P** *020 †75

ORICOLI, Brian Jon. 2405 N COLUMBUS ST, OHIO PHYSICIAL MEDICINE & 43130 #035-08-1998 L1999 **PM** *020 †60

OSGOOD, Ronald Darcy. 1241 RIVER VALLEY BLVD 43130 #035-06-1973 L1978 **DR** *020 †80

OTT, Stephanie Jo. 618 PLEASANTVILLE RD, STE 201 43130 #034-01-2001 L2005 **RHU IM** *020

PABST, Jeffrey C. 401 N EWING ST, FAIRFIELD MEDICAL CENTER 43130 #038-43-1988 L1991 **AN** *020 †05

PANDYA, Pradeep. 131 N EWING ST STE A 43130 #495-20-1970 L1979 **U GS** *020 †95

PARKER, James Morgan. 401 N EWING ST 43130 #038-40-1966 L1966 **N** *030 †75

PATEL, Nalin A. 2401 N COLUMBUS ST 43130 #495-48-1965 L1976 **AN** *020 †05

PATEL, Prafulla Nalin. 401 N EWING ST 43130 #495-48-1968 L1981 **OPH** *020

PAYNE, Edwin Robt. ■ 43130 #038-41-1968 L1968 **R** *071 †80

PEARLMAN, Jonathan Henry. 2405 N COLUMBUS ST, OHIO PHYSICIAL MEDICINE & 43130 #045-01-1986 L1991 **PM** *020 †60

POPE, Douglas Allen. 1548 SHERIDAN DR, STE 200 43130 #038-40-1993 L1994 **MPD** *020 †55,20

PRIANO, Steven Vincent. 2405 N COLUMBUS ST STE 120, OHIO ORTHO CTR 43130 #041-09-1996 L2001 **OSM** *020 †40 ‡

PRUITT, Charles Lee. 1532 WINDMERE CT 43130 #020-02-1981 L1982 **FM** *020 †18,16

QUAMME, Bradley Donavon. ■ 43130 #043-01-1984 L1987 **AN** *020

RAMACHANDRA, Rajagopal. 1550 SHERIDAN DR STE 100, LANCASTER CEBOC 43130 #495-33-1973 L1999 **IM** *020 †20

RANKIN, Michael Jos. 401 N EWING ST, FAIRFIELD EMERGENCY PHYSIC 43130 #038-43-1989 L1991 **EM FM** *020

RAYA, Neelkant. 1203 RIVER VALLEY BLVD, STE A 43130 #495-04-1986 L1995 **IM** *020 †20

REDDY, C Guru. 1973 E MAIN ST 43130 #495-33-1974 L1978 **CD IM** *020 †20

RHODES, Robin L. 1550 SHERIDAN DR, STE 102 43130 #051-07-1979 L1986 **PD** *020 †55

ROBERTSON, David James. 135 N EWING ST STE 304 43130 #056-06-1998 L2000 **GS** *020 †85

ROBERTSON, Jean. 1550 SHERIDAN DR STE 102, PEDIATRIC ASSOC OF LANCAST 43130 #056-06-1998 L1999 **PD** *020 †55

ROCHE, Jerome Jos, Jr. 401 N EWING ST 43130 #038-06-1970 L1985 **ON HEM** *020 †20

ROMAKER, Ralph Richard. 1800 GRANVILLE PIKE 43130 #038-40-1974 L1974 **FM** *020 †18

ROSS, Steven Edward. 401 N EWING ST 43130 #038-40-1992 L1994 **GP OM** *020 †70

SANTINO, Laurel Jozwiak. 135 N EWING ST, STE 201 43130 #038-40-1994 L1998 **OBG** *020 †30 ‡

SCHWENDEMAN, Harold John. 2651 MARIETTA RD NE 43130 #038-41-1954 L1954 **GP** *071

SCOGGIN, David Matthew. 2405 N COLUMBUS ST STE 200 43130 #038-40-1986 L1987 **FM** *020 †18 ‡

SHEHATA, Mahmoud. 1592 GRANVILLE PIKE 43130 #915-02-1979 L1994 **P** *020 †75

SHEIDLER, David Hall. 1500 E MAIN ST 43130 #038-40-1959 L1959 **GS** *071 †85

SHURILLA, Elaine Marie. 1147 E MAIN ST 43130 #038-40-1988 L1990 **IM** *020 †20

SIELSKI, Richard Brian. 2405 N COLUMBUS ST, STE 200 43130 #038-44-1985 L1986 **FM** *020 †18

SINGH, Kanwaljit. 401 N EWING ST, INC 43130 #495-43-1986 L1992 **HO** *020 †20

SMIDEBUSH, Gerald Charles. 1241 RIVER VALLEY BLVD, FAIRFIELD DIAGNOSTIC IMAGI 43130 #038-41-1989 L1993 **DR** *020 †80

SMITH, Sheridan. 624 E MAIN ST 43130 #016-42-1983 L1987 **P** *020 †75

SNIDER, Gordon Bright. ■ 43130 #038-40-1954 L1954 **IM** *062 †20

SOLOMON, Paul Edward. 2401 N COLUMBUS ST 43130 #038-40-1992 L1993 **AN** *020 †05

SPROUSE, Robert Johnson. 1800 GRANVILLE PIKE 43130 #038-40-1978 L1981 **FM** *020 †18

SRIVATSA, Preeti J. 123 N EWING ST, MCFARLAND CLINIC 43130 #495-21-1990 L2007 **OBG** *020 †30

STANDEFORD, Thomas Lowell. 401 N EWING ST, FEPI 43130 #038-40-1980 L1981 **EM FM** *020 †18,16

STERGIOU, Angeline. 131 N EWING ST STE C 43130 #038-43-1988 L1992 **P** *020 †75

STROMINGER, Richard David. 121 N EWING ST 43130 #038-40-1976 L1980 **PD** *020 †55

THOMPSON, Shelly Lynn. 135 N EWING ST, STE 205 43130 #038-40-1991 L1993 **OBG** *020 †30

TREECE, Matthew Warren. ■ 43130 #038-41-2003 L2003 **AN** *020

TZAGOURNIS, Adam Charles. 2405 N COLUMBUS ST, STE 260 43130 #038-40-1993 L1994 **GE** *020 †20

USILTON, Richard Eric. 401 N EWING ST 43130 #040-02-1978 L1981 **DR** *020 †80

VAJEN, Thomas Robt. 282 SELLS RD, FAIRHOPE HOSPICE 43130 #038-40-1973 L1981 **EM FM** *020 †16,18

VARNEY, Leroy Brian. 2682 KULL RD 43130 #038-40-2000 L2000 **FM** *020 †18 ‡

VOTO, Stephen Jos. 2405 N COLUMBUS ST, STE 120 43130 #038-40-1984 L1985 **ORS OSM** *020 †40

VRABEL, Gregory Louis. 401 N EWING ST 43130 #038-06-1992 L1996 **AN** *020 †05

WAGNER, Renee Allison. 2401 N COLUMBUS ST 43130 #038-44-1985 L1986 **AN** *020 †05

WALTER, John A. 2405 N COLUMBUS ST, OHIO PHYSICIAL MEDICINE & 43130 #038-75-2000, ▲ L2000 **PM** *020 †60

WARD, Bonita Shelby. 401 N EWING ST 43130 #038-40-1994 L2003 **PTH** *020

WEAVER, John Milton. 401 N EWING ST 43130 #038-43-1999 L2002 **AN** *020 †05 ‡

■ = Address Information Privacy Protected

WELSH, Richard Anthony. 401 N EWING ST 43130 #038-40-1947 L1947 **R** *071 †80
WHETSTONE, Anna M Stahly. 401 N EWING ST 43130 #038-40-1950 L1950 **FM OS** *071 †18
WHETSTONE, James Walter. 401 N EWING ST 43130 #038-40-1987 L1988 **FM** *020 †18
WILLIAMS, John Farrell. 1981 GRANVILLE PIKE 43130 #016-11-1975 L1979 **EM** *020 †40
WOO, Benedict C. 2405 N COLUMBUS ST, OHIO PHYSICIAL MEDICINE & 43130 #041-12-1996 L2000 **PM** *020 †60
YENCHAR, Jeffrey Keith. 135 N EWING ST, STE 304 43130 #025-07-1993 L1999 **GS** *020 †85

LEAVITTSBURG – TRUMBULL

ISTANBOULI, Fayez. ■ 44430 #915-03-1983 L1991 **IM** *020 †20

LEBANON – WARREN

ARMITAGE, Jeffrey Neville. 100 ARROW SPRINGS BLVD, STE 2700 45036 #038-40-1980 L1980 **IM** *020 †20
AUTRY, Stephen Tilden. 100 ARROW SPRINGS BLVD 45036 #039-01-1973 L1978 **ORS** *020 †40
BELL, Jonathan William. 100 ARROW SPRINGS BLVD 45036 #024-05-1981 L1992 **ORS** *020 †40
BURICHIN, Judith J. 1000 COLUMBUS AVE, HILLTOP OB & GYN INC 45036 #038-45-1993 L1994 **OBG** *020 †30
CACERES, Mauricio H. 100 ARROW SPRINGS BLVD, STE 2800 45036 #264-04-1984 L1992 **FM** *020 †18
COOK, Cynthia Marie. 986 BELVEDERE DR 45036 #038-45-1998 L2000 **PD** *020 †55
CROAKE-ULEMAN, Tricia Kay. 272 COUNTRYSIDE DR, DESERT VALLEY PRIMARY CARE 45036 #038-45-1998 L1999 **FM** *020 †18
DAVIS, Jack Chris. 1000 COLUMBUS AVE, HILLTOP OB & GYN INC 45036 #038-40-1982 L1989 **OBG** *020 †30
DULAN, Michael Benjamin. 1000 COLUMBUS AVE, DULAN & MOORE DULAN FAMILY 45036 #038-40-1994 L1996 **FM** *020 †18
DYSART, Richard Rufus. ■ 45036 #038-40-1954 L1954 **AN** *071 †05
EVANS, Robert Lee. 986 BELVEDERE DR 45036 #038-41-1988 L1989 **PD** *020 †55
FESSLER, Gordon Steven. 100 ARROW SPRINGS BLVD 45036 #017-20-1969 L1973 **GE IM** *020 †20
GOLDFARB, Steven Joel. 100 ARROW SPRINGS BLVD 45036 #016-11-1990 L1993 **ORS** *020 †40
GRENDEL, Steven Howard. 100 ARROW SPRINGS BLVD, STE 2700 45036 #038-41-1974 L1976 **IM** *020 †20
HAGEMAN, Charles Lawrence. 1000 COLUMBUS AVE, HILLTOP OB & GYN INC 45036 #038-41-1982 L1984 **OBG** *020 †30
HALL, Tiffany N. 1000 COLUMBUS AVE 45036 #038-45-1996 L1997 **OBG** *020 †30
HAYES, Gary Phillip. 1004 OREGONIA RD 45036 #020-12-1968 L1969 **FM OS** *020 †18
HILKOWITZ, Heather Pfeffe. 1000 COLUMBUS AVE, HILLTOP OB & GYN INC 45036 #038-45-2000 L2004 **OBG** *020 †30
HORSLEY, Charles David. 767 COLUMBUS AVE 45036 #038-41-1982 L1983 **FM** *020 †18
KOLES, Terren Burgess. 416 S EAST ST, HEALTH DISTRICT 45036 #005-12-1979 L1984 **GP** *020
KOLLMAN, Paul Vincent. 100 ARROW SPRINGS BLVD, STE 2700 45036 #038-41-1965 L1965 **IM** *020 †20
KOSARAJU, Madhumathi. 17 N MECHANIC ST 45036 #495-50-1993 L2004 **IM** *020 †20
LA CROIX, James Matthew. 110 S BROADWAY ST 45036 #025-07-1998 L1999 **FM** *020 †18
MC CLELLAN, William Alton. 45036 #038-06-1943 L1944 **OM** *071 †70
MC CONNELL, Timothy Brian. 100 ARROW SPRINGS BLVD 45036 #051-04-1997 L2001 **ORS** *020 †40
MC WEENEY, James Michael. 1618 DEERFIELD RD, PROFESSIONAL CENTER 2 45036 #041-02-1981 L1984 **FM EM** *020 †16
MEZCUA-FULLANA, Sergio L. 100 ARROW SPRINGS BLVD 45036 #308-03-1987 L1994 **IM OM** *020 †20
MOORE, Rosalind. 1000 COLUMBUS AVE 45036 #038-40-1994 L1995 **FM** *020 †18
PENCE, Robert Carey. 513 SILVERWOOD FARMS DR 45036 #038-45-2001 L2001 **EM GP** *020 †16
PHELAN-ADAMS, Anne L. 718 MCBURNEY DR, CONSULTATIVE MED SERV 45036 #051-01-1981 L1995 **FM OS** *020 †18
ROMANOWSKI, James Richard. ■ 45036 #055-01-2003 L2003 **ORS** *012
SCHARF, Michael Chas. 100 ARROW SPRINGS BLVD, STE 2700 45036 #038-45-1992 L1994 **IM** *020 †20
SHAW, Kevin John. 100 ARROW SPRINGS BLVD 45036 #033-06-1995 L1998 **ORS** *020 †40
SIEBEN, Candice Marie. 100 ARROW SPRINGS BLVD, STE 2800 45036 #038-45-1997 L1998 **FM** *020 †18
SKINNER, Cheryl Ann. 670 N BROADWAY ST 45036 #038-41-1981 L1982 **ON HEM** *020 †20
SPEARS, Bruce Tyler. 1240 THORNY RIDGE TRL 45036 #020-02-1987 L1990 **EM** *020 †16
TURCHIN, Natalie. 100 ARROW SPRINGS BLVD, STE 2700 45036 #913-89-1974 L1996 **IM** *020 †20
VAN HARLINGEN, George W. ■ 45036 #038-40-1950 L1950 **GP** *071
WILLIAMS, Jarrod Michael. ■ 45036 #038-41-2006 **EM** *012
WRIGHT, Lance Paul. 17 N MECHANIC ST 45036 #038-45-1984 L1985 **FM** *075

LEETONIA – COLUMBIANA

ANGELO, Debra Gail. ■ 44431 #661-03-2006 L2007 **IM** *012

LEWIS CENTER – DELAWARE

BENSON, Don Michael, Jr. ■ 43035 #038-44-1999 L2003 **IM** *100 †20
CATERINO, Jeffrey Michael. ■ 43035 #041-14-1999 L2004 **OS** *020 †20,16
CHRISTOPHER, James Wm. 3023 E POWELL RD, LEWIS CENTER 43035 #025-07-1972 L1973 **CHP P** *020
DAVID, Patricia Helena. 8917 S OLD STATE RD, STE 124 43035 #038-40-1992 L1999 **GPM** *020 †70
DILLAHUNT, Paul Huston. ■ 43035 #038-40-1942 L1942 **FM** *071
GRANATA, Jaymes D. ■ 43035 #031-01-2006 L2006 **ORS** *012
HARRINGTON, Ryan Benedict. ■ 43035 #019-02-1960 L1961 **N IM** *071 †75
HOBE, Harold Richard. ■ 43035 #041-12-1965 L1971 **IM** *071 †20

HUDAK, John P. ■ 43035 #028-34-1949 L1955 **ORS** *020
MARTTER, Danielle Goodyea. ■ 43035 #038-40-2005 L2005 **OBG** *012
MINNICH, Lisa Ann. 2977 LAURA PL 43035 #038-40-1992 L1993 **NPM** *020 †55
MURRAY, Laszlo, Jr. ■ 43035 #473-01-1974 L1979 **OBG** *020
NEMALI, Sreedevi. ■ 43035 #495-70-1975 L1983 **IM** *020 †20
PADAMADAN, William David. 171 GREEN MEADOWS DR S 43035 #495-44-1966 L1972 **CD GP** *071 †20
PARIKH, Samir Vasant. ■ 43035 #038-41-2006 L2006 **IM** *012
RAMEY, Amy Katherine. ■ 43035 #038-40-2001 L2001 **EM** *020 †16
RAMEY, Curtis Woodrow. 1801 ROYAL OAK DR, 1801 ROYAL OAK DRIVE 43035 #038-40-1976 L1976 **FM** *020 †18
ROBISON, Robert Nelson. ■ 43035 #023-01-1977 L1978 **FM** *030 †18
SUVAG, Seda. ■ 43035 #038-43-2007 L2007 **IM** *012
WRIGHT, Chadwick Lewis. ■ 43035 #038-40-2006 L2006 **DR** *012

LEXINGTON – RICHLAND

CLYMER, David Dietz. 250 CEDARWOOD DR 44904 #038-40-1959 L1959 **FM** *020 †18

LIBERTY TOWNSHIP – BUTLER

BLANKENSHIP, Kelly. ■ 45044 #038-75-2004, ▲ L2004 **CHP** *012
BONAR, Kimberly Ann. 6770 CINCINNATI DAYTON RD, STE 100 45044 #038-44-1990 L1991 **OBG** *020 †30
BOWMAN, Jeffrey Glenn. ■ 45011 #038-40-1995 L1997 **EM** *020
BRENNER, Amy Gail. 6770 CINCINNATI DAYTON RD, STE 100 45044 #038-43-1996 L2000 **OBG** *020 †30
GANAPATHYSUBRAMONYAM, Shan. ■ 45044 #495-16-1997 L2005 **RNR** *100
GARCIA-RIVERA, Roberto S. ■ 45011 #275-01-1951 L1969 **FM** *071
GOLDBERG, Jaron Stuart. ■ 45011 #038-06-2002 L2005 **EM** *020 †16
GORANTLA, Venkatesan R. ■ 45011 #495-94-1978 L1991 **PD NPM** *020 †55
HELSINGER, Brenda Kay. ■ 45011 #038-41-2002 L2002 **OPH** *012
JOHNSON, Larry Gene. 6770 CINCINNATI DAYTON RD, STE 100 45044 #038-41-1988 L1989 **OBG** *020 †30
KNOX, Thomas Jos. 6456 CEDAR HILL DR 45011 #038-45-1983 L1984 **AN** *020 †05
LAM, Philip C. 7117 DUTCHLAND PKWY 45044 #038-44-1991 L1992 **EM** *020 †16
LEASURE, William Brooks. ■ 45044 #012-05-2007 L2007 **P** *012
LEE, Julia H. 6770 CINCINNATI DAYTON RD, STE 100 45044 #048-14-1992 L1996 **OBG** *020 †30
MARTIN, Bradley Tuck. 7117 DUTCHLAND PKWY 45044 #038-41-1969 L1969 **EM IM** *020 †20,16
NARENDRAN, Mamata Vivek. 6770 CINCINNATI DAYTON RD, STE 100 45044 #495-96-1991 L2000 **OBG** *020 †30
NIEMER, Alvin Henry. ■ 45011 #020-02-1965 L1969 **D** *071 †15
OPPENHEIMER, Allison Joan. ■ 45011 #038-41-2002 L2002 **EM** *020
OWENS, Robert Gregory. 6770 CINCINNATI DAYTON RD, STE 112 45044 #021-06-1990 L1996 **OBG** *020 †30
PACKARD, Lori Jenine. 6770 CINCINNATI DAYTON RD, STE 100 45044 #038-41-2002 L2002 **OBG** *020
ROBERTSON, Alvin Michael. ■ 45044 #020-02-2000 L2000 **IM** *020 †20
SHRAKE, Robert Guy. ■ 45044 #038-45-1984 L1986 **PD EM** *020 †55
SILVER, Eric Kenneth. 6770 CINCINNATI DAYTON RD, STE 100 45044 #917-07-1973 L1979 **OBG** *020 †30
SPLETZER, Karen Andrea. ■ 45044 #038-40-1987 L1991 **AN** *020 †05
STRAUBING, Stephen Alan. 6770 CINCINNATI DAYTON RD, STE 100 45044 #030-06-1976 L1977 **OBG** *020 †30
SWAYZE, Colleen Fretz. 6770 CINCINNATI DAYTON RD, STE 100 45044 #047-05-1995 L1997 **OBG** *020 †30
VU, Davis Dinh. ■ 45011 #038-41-2002 L2006 **FSM** *020 †18

LIMA – ALLEN

ABDELBAKI, Zoheir Ahmad. 770 W HIGH ST, STE 370 45801 #605-01-1996 L2002 **CD** *020 †20
ADEWUMI, Waheed Adewale. 825 W MARKET ST, STE 301 45805 #690-02-1989 L2003 **IM** *020 †20
AGBAJE, Ismailu O. 830 W HIGH ST, STE 370 45801 #056-06-1999 L2004 **PM** *020 †60
AGGARWAL, Manu Bala. ■ 45806 #055-01-2003 L2007 **FM** *100 †18
AGOSTO, Madeline. 730 W MARKET ST 45801 #042-03-1991 L1995 **FM** *020 †18
AKERS, Matthew Martin. 830 W HIGH ST, STE 201 45801 #038-45-1995 L1997 **PS** *020 †85,65
ALBERTSON, John D. ■ 45805 #038-40-1951 L1951 **GP** *071
ALLISON, Thomas Dent. ■ 45804 #024-01-1943 L1950 **R** *071 †80
ALMUDALLAL, Ali Saib. 770 W HIGH ST, STE 360 45801 #528-01-1991 L1999 **N** *020
AMBALAVANAN, Suria N. 770 W HIGH ST, STE 480 45801 #495-61-1978 L2007 **OTO HNS** *020 †45
AMBEKAR, Anjali A. 5011 BROOKHILL LN, ATHENS CANCER CENTER 45807 #495-28-1967 L1985 **RO FPG** *020
AMER, Magid Hashim. 803 W MARKET ST, GERAD CENTER FOR CANCER TR 45805 #915-02-1963 L2001 **ON IM** *020 †20
AMIN, Ashwin V. 1001 BELLEFONTAINE AVE 45804 #495-23-1966 L1978 **GS EM** *020 †85
AMIN, Shama Ashwinbhai. 1001 BELLEFONTAINE AVE 45804 #495-22-1971 L1978 **PD PDE** *020 †55
ANIGBOGU, Joseph M. 1001 BELLEFONTAINE AVE 45804 #690-04-1989 L2001 **PUD** *020 †20
ANIGBOGU, Nkoli Tania. ■ 45805 #690-07-1994 L2001 **IM** *020 †20 ‡
ANOUTI, Ahmad A. 770 W HIGH ST 45801 #605-01-1990 L2008 **N** *020 †75
ATKINS, Anthony Dewayne. 441 E 8TH ST 45804 #038-40-1999 L2000 **FM** *020
AZEEZ, Kemi L. 920 W MARKET ST, STE 210 45805 #690-01-1982 L1992 **IM** *020 †20
BAGENSTOSE, James Ellis. 801 MEDICAL DR, STE B 45804 #038-41-1972 L1972 **ORS** *020 †40
BAJWA, Rajbir Singh. 830 W HIGH ST, STE 102 45801 #025-07-1993 L1995 **PD** *020 †55
BAKER, James Edward. ■ 45805 #038-40-1955 L1955 **GP EM** *071
BAKER, Robert Love. ■ 45805 #041-12-1948 L1949 **NS** *071 †25
BAKER, Robert Love, II. 1005 BELLEFONTAINE AVE, STE 350 45804 #028-78-1980, ▲ L1981 **NS** *020
BALDAUF, Frank Michael. 1003 BELLEFONTAINE AVE, STE 125 45804 #038-40-1973 L1973 **FM** *020 †18

BALSINK, Edward Benj. 730 W MARKET ST, ST RITA'S MEDICAL CENTER 45801 #038-41-1984 L1986 **GPM** *020

BALUSU, Pratap. 750 W HIGH ST, STE 250 45801 #496-01-1988 L1997 **IM** *020

BALUSU, Subba Rao. ■ 45807 #495-11-1950 L1980 **PM** *071 †60

BANSAL, Narendra Kumar. 770 W HIGH ST, STE 350 45801 #495-12-1967 L1975 **U** *020 †95

BEERY, Walter Clark. ■ 45805 #008-01-1939 L1941 **GS GP** *071

BEIL, Herbert John. 1001 BELLEFONTAINE AVE 45804 #407-16-1958 L1961 **OPH** *071

BELL, Ronald Paterson. 1103 BANK ONE TOWER 45801 #038-40-1959 L1959 **AN** *071 †05

BERAKI, Solomon Mehari. 830 W HIGH ST, STE 255 45801 #366-03-1991 L2006 **ID** *020

BIGGS, Robert Douglas. 855 W MARKET ST, STE A 45805 #025-01-1955 L1959 **OPH** *071 †35

BOULTER, Jeffrey Neil. 730 W MARKET ST 45801 #038-45-1983 L1984 **EM FM** *020 †18

BOWLUS, James Theodore. 610 E KIRACOFE AVE 45807 #038-40-1973 L1973 **FM** *020 †18

BRADLEY, Alan Belmont. 1220 E ELM ST, STE 204 45804 #038-40-1978 L1978 **OBG** *020 †30

BRIGGS, Lloyd Clark, Jr. 801 MEDICAL DR, STE A 45804 #021-01-1992 L1998 **ORS** *020 †40

BRUNELLE, Charles Wm. 770 W HIGH ST, STE 450 45801 #035-08-1973 L1978 **GE** *020 †20

BRYANT, Glenn Allen, III. 750 W HIGH ST, STE 150 45801 #038-41-1994 L1995 **NEP** *020 †20

BUCH, Hector Anthony, Jr. 750 W HIGH ST, STE 250 45801 #847-12-1976 L1979 **IM CD** *020 †20

BUSH, Ronald Gene. 770 W HIGH ST, STE 420 45801 #017-20-1971 L1983 **TS GS** *020 †85,90

CAPONE, Richard R. 939 W MARKET ST 45805 #035-15-1970 L1977 **GE IM** *020 †20

CARDER, Lynnea Terese. ■ 45805 #038-43-1997 L1999 **P** *020 †75

CARGILL, James David. 750 W HIGH ST, STE 150 45801 #048-13-1982 L1996 **NEP IM** *020 †20

CHANAMOLU, Sreenivasa Rao. 1001 BELLEFONTAINE AVE 45804 #495-50-1994 L2006 **PCC** *100 †20

CHANG, Fred Fei Shung. 730 W MARKET ST, ST RITA'S MEDICAL CENTER 45801 #385-02-1967 L1978 **DR** *071 †80

CHUNG, Maurice Kai Y. 310 S CABLE RD 45805 #024-07-1985 L1989 **OBG U** *020 †30 ‡

COLLINS, Donald Dean. 1303 BELLEFONTAINE AVE 45804 #038-40-1980 L1981 **FM ADM** *020 †18

CONGER, Clyde Wm. ■ 45805 #038-40-1956 L1956 **AN** *071 †05

CONLEY, James Edward. 750 W HIGH ST 45801 #038-40-1987 L1988 **PTH** *020 †18,50

CONNAUGHTON, Patrick A. ■ 45805 #028-34-1951 L1952 **IM RHU** *071 †20

COOLEY, David Alan. 830 W HIGH ST, STE 204 45801 #038-40-1982 L1983 **NS** *020 †25

COX, Marcus Felix. 1003 BELLEFONTAINE AVE, STE 150 45804 #036-01-1995 L2000 **GS** *020 †85

CRAIG, Michael Thos. 1005 BELLEFONTAINE AVE, STE 140 45804 #017-20-1986 L1993 **OPH** *020 †35

CURRY, Robert Irwin. 658 W MARKET ST 45801 #038-40-1957 L1957 **FM** *020

DALTON, Randall Elliott. 770 W HIGH ST, STE 480 45801 #028-02-1976 L2003 **OTO EM** *020 †45

DAMSCHRODER, Richard Lee. 830 W HIGH ST, STE 304 45801 #038-40-1974 L1974 **OBG** *020 †30

DANIEL, Arthur P. ■ 45805 #028-34-1943 L1948 **GP** *071

DANIK, Francis John. 1103 BANK ONE TOWER, ANESTHESIA ASSOC OF LIMA 45801 #028-02-1981 L1994 **AN** *020 †20,05

DASARI, Grace Rajakumari. 730 W MARKET ST 45801 #495-50-1986 L2004 **PM** *020 †60 ‡

DECANIO, Rogelio. 1001 BELLEFONTAINE AVE 45804 #935-01-1967 L1992 **PTH PCP** *020 †50

DEMOSTHENE, Antoine Yvan. 830 W HIGH ST, BOX 27 45801 #440-01-1967 L1980 **P** *020

DE NISCO, Anthony John. 1001 BELLEFONTAINE AVE 45804 #035-01-1973 L1979 **OPH** *071 †35

DUNCAN-SAMPSON, Tilly E. 415 W MARKET ST, STE A 45801 #412-01-1985 L1999 **PD** *020 †55

ELLIS, Wilfred J G. 329 N WEST ST 45801 #028-02-1982 L1990 **ID IM** *020

EVANS, Jack Lee James. 1001 BELLEFONTAINE AVE 45804 #016-42-1978 L1979 **EM** *020 †16

FALER, Richard Lee. 750 W HIGH ST, STE 150 45801 #038-40-1970 L1970 **NEP IM** *020 †20

FISHER, Eric Bruce. 658 W MARKET ST STE 201 45801 #038-40-1973 L1973 **IM** *020 †20

FOTOUHI, Farzin. 1005 BELLEFONTAINE AVE, STE 230 45804 #024-07-1991 L1999 **GS** *020 †85,90

FOX, Stephen Paul. 750 W HIGH ST, STE 210 45801 #017-20-1993 L2002 **OPH** *020 †35

FUMICH, Frank Edward. 801 MEDICAL DR, STE A 45804 #055-02-1999 L2005 **ORS** *020 †40

GARNES, Carol Olinda. ■ 45806 #010-03-1971 L1972 **PD A** *020

GAYNIER, Christine Renee. 2875 W ELM ST 45805 #038-43-2001 L2003 **FM** *020 †18

GERAD, Henry. 803 W MARKET ST, STE 200 45805 #035-47-1977 L1985 **ON IM** *020 †20

GERHARD, Albrecht K. 1303 BELLEFONTAINE AVE, LIMA CBOC 45804 #028-34-1979 L1992 **IM** *020 †20

GIDEON, Anne Michele. 750 W HIGH ST 45801 #025-01-1982 L1986 **PTH** *020 †50

GLANCE, Jennifer. 310 S CABLE RD, ALLIANCE FOR WOMEN'S HEALT 45805 #025-76-1998, ▲ L2006 **OBG** *020

GODWIN, Jeffrey Eugene. 1001 BELLEFONTAINE AVE 45804 #038-41-1985 L1986 **PUD CCM** *020 †20

GREENE, Henry Rex. 825 W MARKET ST 45805 #005-15-1969 L2006 **ON HEM** *030 †20

GRIFFITH, Kirk Matthew. 750 W HIGH ST STE 400 45801 #051-01-1984 L1989 **PTH FOP** *020 †50

HAMAN, Steven Paul. 801 MEDICAL DR, STE A 45804 #038-43-2000 L2000 **OTR ORS** *020 ‡

HANNA, Adel Gobran. 770 W HIGH ST STE 490, ALPHA & OMEGA HEALING ARTS 45801 #038-45-1993 L1998 **FM** *020 †18

HANNA, Salim W. 1220 E ELM ST, STE 210 45804 #875-02-1988 L1996 **FM** *020 †18

HANNA, William Robt. ■ 45805 #038-40-1955 L1955 **ORS** *071 †40

HASAN, Abul Q. 3200 N WEST ST, OAKWOOD CORRECT FAC 45801 #160-02-1979 L1997 **P** *020 †75

HEAPHY, Michael Riley. 1005 BELLEFONTAINE AVE, STE 225 45804 #038-40-1973 L1977 **D DS** *020 †15

HERMAN, George Allen. 730 W MARKET ST 45801 #038-45-1984 L1986 **FM** *020 †18

HIXENBAUGH, Todd Jonathan. 830 W HIGH ST, STE 207 45801 #020-02-1983 L1984 **GS** *020 †85

HOBAYAN, Vivian Maria P. 750 W HIGH ST, STE 260 45801 #748-01-1986 L1999 **RHU** *020 †20

HOLLADAY, Robert Lawrence. ■ 45805 #038-40-1958 L1958 **FM OM** *071

HOLMES, Michael Dale. 730 W MARKET ST 45801 #038-40-1973 L1973 **PTH** *071 †50

HORSTMAN, Anna Mae. 730 W MARKET ST 45801 #038-43-1981 L1983 **FM** *020 †18

HOVEST, Amy Sue. ■ 45805 #038-43-2004 L2004 **FM** *100 †18

HUANG, Charles. 121 W HIGH ST, FL 5 45801 #035-01-1989 L1991 **ORS OSM** *020 †40

HUBBELL, John D. 700 BANK ONE TOWER 45801 #038-40-1952 L1952 **AN** *071

HUBBELL, Susan Lee. 658 W MARKET ST STE 106 45801 #038-40-1976 L1977 **PM PRS** *020 †60

HUGHES, John Gregory. 730 W MARKET ST, DEPT OF EMERGENCY MEDICINE 45801 #038-41-1988 L1989 **IM** *020 †20

HUMPHREY, Michael Raymond. 730 W MARKET ST 45801 #038-40-1987 L1988 **IM** *020 †20

HYACINTHE, Gerard Serge. 2338 N WEST ST, ALLEN CORRECTIONAL INSTITU 45801 #440-01-1977 L1998 **P** *020

IGNARSKI, Todd Edward. 750 W HIGH ST STE 390 45801 #038-41-1996 L1999 **FM EM** *020 †18

IMAM, Syed Mohammad A. 750 W HIGH ST STE 250, PHYSICIANS, INC. 45801 #704-02-1992 L2002 **IM** *020 †20

IMLER, David Lee. 1005 BELLEFONTAINE AVE 45804 #016-76-1977, ▲ L1982 **NEP IM** *072

INGALLS, Connie Sue. 1220 E ELM ST, STE 150 45804 #038-43-1994 L1997 **FM** *020

IOANNIDIS, Christos B. 1220 E ELM ST, STE 203 45804 #418-01-1964 L1975 **N HS** *020

JEAN-PAUL, Marie Judith. ■ 45806 #056-06-1999 L2005 **NM** *020

JIMENEZ-MEDINA, Evelyn E. ■ 45802 #035-03-1984 L1995 **PM** *030 †60 ‡

KAHN, James Lee. 830 W HIGH ST, OB GYN SPECIALISTS OF 45801 #038-40-1974 L1976 **OBG** *020

KAMEPALLI, Ravi Kumar. 830 W HIGH ST STE 255 45801 #495-50-1995 L2003 **ID** *020 †20 ‡

KAREL, Douglas Barry. 658 W MARKET ST, STE 208 45801 #165-03-1985 L1996 **N** *020

KHALIL, Abbas Mahmoud. 825 W MARKET ST, STE 203 45805 #915-09-1976 L1998 **HEM** *020 †20

KIDD, Charles Russell. 730 W MARKET ST 45801 #038-40-1954 L1954 **FM GP** *071

KILLOUGH, Kevin Russell. 730 W MARKET ST, LIMA RADIOLOGICAL ASSOC 45801 #027-01-1995 L2005 **NS** *020 †80

KIM, Bak Chul. 1103 BANK ONE TOWER 45801 #583-03-1969 L1976 **AN** *020

KIM, David K. 830 W HIGH ST STE 302 45801 #035-45-1988 L1999 **OSS** *020 †40

KIM, Jung Hyeon. 799 S MAIN ST 45804 #583-02-1965 L1976 **P** *020

KINDIG, Marilyn Joy. 1005 BELLEFONTAINE AVE, STE 175 45804 #018-75-1994, ▲ L1996 **OBG** *020

KIRSCHNER, Eric Steven. 730 W MARKET ST, INTENSIVE CARE UNIT 4D 45801 #038-44-1981 L1984 **PUD CCM** *020 †20

KLIMA, Brian Todd. ■ 45806 #038-45-2005 L2005 **PD** *012

KOTTAPALLI, Venkata S. 375 N EASTOWN RD 45807 #495-50-1990 L2000 **GE HEP** *020 †20

KRENDL, Karri Lou. 2875 W ELM ST, FAMILY PHYSICIANS OF LINA, 45805 #038-40-1984 L1984 **FM OBS** *020 †18

KRISHNA, Alok. ■ 45805 #496-01-1993 L2000 **FM** *020 †18

KRISHNA, Vasanthi. 2727 SAINT JOHNS RD, STE C 45804 #496-01-1993 L2000 **CN** *020 †75 ‡

KUCHIPUDI, Sarat Babu. 750 W HIGH ST, STE 300 45801 #495-57-1975 L1998 **PUD IM** *020 †20

KUHLMAN, Kurt. 730 W MARKET ST 45801 #038-75-1992, ▲ L1993 **PM** *020 †60

KUHNS, John Robt. 770 W HIGH ST, STE 210 45801 #041-09-1971 L1977 **CD IM** *020 †20

LAX, Frederick. 770 W HIGH ST, STE 390 45801 #041-09-1975 L1994 **NS** *020 †25

LEAHY, William John. 825 S CABLE RD STE A 45805 #038-40-1996 L1998 **FM** *020 †18

LEIFER, Mark Howard. 2793 SHAWNEE RD 45806 #023-07-1977 L1988 **GE IM** *020 †20

LIGGETT, John Saml, Jr. 730 W MARKET ST, NEW CENTURY PEDIATRICS 45801 #041-02-1976 L1990 **PD PDP** *020 †55

LIGHT, William Oliver. 1001 BELLEFONTAINE AVE 45804 #025-01-1966 L1972 **D** *020 †15

LIN, Cheng-Te. 1617 LEIST AVE 45805 #385-02-1950 L1973 **NS** *071 ‡

LIN, Thomas Chai-I. 967 BELLEFONTAINE AVE, STE 202 45804 #244-01-1970 L1978 **N** *071 †75

MADAN, Ravi D. 825 W MARKET ST, STE 260 45805 #495-29-1980 L1999 **HO IM** *020 †20

MAGEE, Ronald Ray. 1003 BELLEFONTAINE AVE, STE 150 45804 #028-02-1988 L2004 **VS** *020 †85

MAHMOUD, Shaban Elsayed A. 750 W HIGH ST, STE 250 45801 #041-13-1994 L1998 **IM** *020 †20

MAK, Kin-Yee. 825 W MARKET ST 45805 #385-02-1959 L1969 **IM PUD** *071

MALCOLM, Elsa Kuo. 750 W HIGH ST 45801 #051-01-1996 L2001 **PTH** *020 †50

MALHOTRA, Praveen Kumar. 525 N EASTOWN RD 45807 #495-45-1969 L1978 **DR** *020 †80

MARTIN, Benjamin James. 770 W HIGH ST, UROLOGY ASSOCIATES OF OHIO 45801 #038-40-1999 L2004 **U** *020 †95

MARTIN, Jay Weldon. 2195 ALLENTOWN RD 45805 #038-43-1977 L1978 **GP** *020 †16

MARTINEZ, Guillermo. ■ 45805 #275-01-1954 L1969 **GP** *071

MATHIESON, Mark Eugene. 1920 ALLENTOWN RD 45805 #045-04-1994 L1999 **PS** *020 †85,65

MATOUK, Khalid Rashid. 2338 NORTHWEST ST, ATTN MENTAL HEALTH 45801 #154-07-1967 L1978 **P** *071

MC DONALD, Mark G. 801 MEDICAL DR, ORTHOPAEDIC INST OF ORTHO 45804 #038-40-1991 L1995 **ORS** *020 †40

MC NAMARA, Bonnie Lynn. 1003 BELLEFONTAINE AVE, STE 125 PROF OFC BLDG III 45804 #038-40-1990 L1991 **FM** *020 †18 ‡

MC NEAL, Sheilla D. 830 W HIGH ST, STE 102 45801 #038-41-1996 L1999 **PD** *020 †55

MEDINA, Rhonda Jean. 310 S CABLE RD 45805 #025-07-1996 L2000 **OBG** *020 †30

MIGALLY, Magdy Bushra. 1820 C ST 45804 #056-05-1978 L1979 **D A** *020 †15

MILLS, Alicia Ellen. 441 E 8TH ST 45804 #038-45-2004 L2007 **PD** *020 †55

MISHR, Suman Kumar. 830 W HIGH ST, STE 380 45801 #495-05-1962 L1977 **END IM** *020 ‡

MONROE, Melvin. 939 W MARKET ST, MED-CARE CLNC 45805 #041-13-1962 L1983 **GP PTH** *020 †50

MOON, Robert Wm. 1103 BANK ONE TOWER 45801 #041-12-1983 L1986 **AN** *020 †05

MORRIS, Susan. 1003 BELLEFONTAINE AVE, STE 125 PROF OFC BLDG III 45804 #048-13-1982 L1996 **FM** *020 †18

MOSER, Norman O. 750 W HIGH ST, STE 150 45801 #028-79-1990, ▲ L1991 **NEP** *020

MUELLER, Mark Thomas. 1220 E ELM ST, STE 210 45804 #038-43-1998 L1999 **FM** *020 †18

MYERS, Maryann Margaret. 830 W HIGH ST, STE 150 45801 #038-40-1987 L1989 **PM** *020 †60

NALLU, Ram Chandra Reddy. 1220 E ELM ST, STE 220 45804 #495-65-1975 L1999 **PD** *020 †55 ‡

NEIDHARDT, David James. 915 W MARKET ST 45805 #038-43-1986 L1987 **FM** *020 †18

NELSON, Nicole A. 730 W MARKET ST, DEPT RAD 45801 #038-41-2000 L2005 **DR RNR** *020 †80

NOBLE, William E. 730 W MARKET ST 45801 #038-40-1951 L1951 **FM OM** *071

NOCKOWITZ, Richard Adam. 1800 ALLENTOWN RD, STE A 45805 #035-46-1993 L1997 **P** *020 †75

NOORI, Mostafa. 730 W MARKET ST 45801 #517-01-1962 L1972 **R** *071

OH, William Young-Bae. 1003 BELLEFONTAINE AVE, STE 100 45804 #005-12-1973 L2001 **ORS HS** *020 †40 ‡

OJO, Oluremi Adebola. 830 W HIGH ST STE 370 45801 #690-01-1988 L2003 **IM** *020 †20

OLT, Sarah Leslie. 750 W HIGH ST, STE 220 45801 #038-40-1992 L1998 **GS** *020 †85

OMITOWOJU, Olayinka O. 920 W MARKET ST, STE 210 45805 #690-01-1986 L1995 **IM** *020 †20

ONAMUSI, Babatunde Taiwo. 1875 S DIXIE HWY 45804 #690-01-1988 L2001 **GPM** *020 †20,70

O'NEILL, James Anthony. 801 MEDICAL DR 45804 #016-02-1982 L1984 **ORS** *020 †40

OVERMIER, James B. 1001 BELLEFONTAINE AVE 45804 #038-40-1948 L1948 **FM** *072

PAI, Ashwin Ananth. ■ 45805 #016-06-2003 *100

PAI, Ramanath Padmanabha. 1220 E ELM ST STE 206 45804 #495-37-1964 L1977 **GS VS** *071 †85.

PAI, Shobha R. 1001 BELLEFONTAINE AVE 45804 #495-09-1971 L1977 **PTH** *020 †50.

PAJKA, John Thos. 855 W MARKET ST, STE A 45805 #038-40-1986 L1987 **OPH** *020 †35.

PARKER, Tammy Agnes. 1001 BELLEFONTAINE AVE 45804 #056-06-1996 L1999 **EM** *020 †16.

PARRANTO, Gregory B. 441 E 8TH ST 45804 #026-04-2002 L2002 **FM** *020 †18.

PARSA, Prabhakar. 1103 BANK ONE TOWER, ANESTHESIA ASSOCIATES OF L 45801 #495-57-1982 L1999 **AN** *020 †05.

PATHADAN, Paul Antony. 1001 BELLEFONTAINE AVE, L M HOSITAL, RADIOLOGY DEP 45804 #025-07-1992 L1999 **DR** *020 †80,28.

PATICK, Kenneth Edwin. ■ 45805 #003-01-1980 L1999 **AN** *020 †05.

PATRICIO, Manuel Florent. 730 W MARKET ST 45801 #748-08-1987 L1995 **FM EM** *020 †18.

PAUFF, James Michael. ■ 45801 #038-40-2008 *012.

PERONA, Philip Stephen. 635 W SPRING ST 45801 #004-01-1980 L1985 **CD IM** *020 †20.

PIERSON, Dennis James. 1220 E ELM ST STE 240 45804 #038-40-1979 L1979 **FM FPG** *020 †18.

PIRTLE, Sarah Leah. 967 BELLEFONTAINE AVE 45804 #020-12-1984 L1985 **PD** *020 †55.

POHL, Ronald L. 1005 BELLEFONTAINE AVE, STE 230 45804 #038-45-1985 L1986 **TS VS** *020 †85,90.

PORTER, Eric James. 730 W MARKET ST 45801 #038-06-1980 L1988 **AN** *020 †05.

POTURALSKI, Gary Allen. 730 W MARKET ST 45801 #038-43-1981 L1984 **FM FPG** *020 †18.

PUDUPAKKAM, Ramachandra K. 528 W MARKET ST, STE 120 45801 #495-09-1964 L1973 **PD AI** *020 †03,55.

PUTTHOFF, Dara Elizabeth. 1001 BELLEFONTAINE AVE 45804 #020-12-1988 L1989 **END PDE** *020 †55,20.

QUAZI, Abdul Mabud. 1001 BELLEFONTAINE AVE 45804 #160-05-1966 L1988 **GS** *020 †16.

RAHMAN, Abdul W. 730 W MARKET ST, ST. RITA'S MEDICAL CENTER 45801 #160-02-1988 L2002 **IM** *020 †20.

RAJJOUB, M Hassan. 770 W HIGH ST, STE 370 45801 #875-03-1991 L2002 **IC** *020 †20.

RAMENENI, Anuradha. 2508 DOGWOOD DR 45805 #495-21-1991 L1998 **IM** *020 †20.

RASEKHY, Bahman. ■ 45805 #517-01-1959 L1983 **IM IMG** *072.

RAZA, Qamar. 730 W MARKET ST, ST RITA'S MEDICAL CENTER 45801 #704-16-1989 L1996 **IM** *020 †20.

REDDY, Panathur S G. 967 BELLEFONTAINE AVE 45804 #495-33-1969 L1978 **PD** *020 †55.

REED, Harold Paul. 1103 BANK ONE TOWER 45801 #038-40-1985 L1988 **AN GP** *020 †05.

REED, Peter Weber. 1001 BELLEFONTAINE AVE, DPT RAD 45804 #051-01-1955 L1965 **R** *071 †80.

RHEE, Michelle Sangmin. ■ 45805 #005-11-2006 L2008 **FP** *012.

RHEE, Young Wung. 915 W MARKET ST, STE D 45804 #583-02-1962 L1977 **P CHP** *020 †75.

RINESMITH, Scott Evan. ■ 45805 #038-41-2001 L2001 **GE** *020 †20.

RINTO, Erin Elaine. 730 W MARKET ST, ST RITAS MED CTR EMGY 45801 #038-44-2003 L2003 **EM** *020.

RODRIGUEZ, Jose Rafael. ■ 45805 #042-01-1999 L2008 **TS** *020 †85 ‡.

ROGERS, Derrick Thomas. 730 W MARKET ST, ATTN CREDENTIALING DEPT 45801 #017-20-1999 L2004 **OTO** *020 †45.

ROHDES, Fred David. 2635 ADGATE RD 45805 #017-20-1958 L1959 **END IM** *071 †20.

ROMERO, Vicente W. 730 W MARKET ST, ST RITA'S HOSP MEDICAL CEN 45801 #319-03-1981 L1993 **NPM** *020.

ROSENBERG, Seth. 730 W MARKET ST, ST. RITA'S MEDICAL CENTER 45801 #028-34-1985 L1987 **MPD PD** *020 †55.

ROVNER, Marc Stuart. 1001 BELLEFONTAINE AVE 45804 #041-07-1987 L1989 **PCC IM** *020 †20.

ROY, Subrata. 529 S ELIZABETH ST 45804 #913-92-1979 L2000 **ADP** *020.

RUEDISUELI, Glennard S. 3200 N WEST ST 45801 #024-07-1974 L1974 **P CHP** *020 †55.

RYAN, Charles Richard. 830 W HIGH ST, OB GYN SPECIALISTS OF 45801 #038-40-1974 L1974 **OBG** *020 †30.

SALINAS, Julio E. 730 W MARKET ST 45801 #737-05-1967 L1975 **NS** *020 †25.

SANKO, William Andrew. 801 MEDICAL DR, STE A 45804 #038-43-1987 L1992 **OSM ORS** *020 †40.

SCHERGER, William Elmer. 830 W HIGH ST, OB GYN SPECIALISTS OF 45801 #038-40-1982 L1984 **OBG FM** *020 †18,30 ‡.

SCHNEIDER, Michael Jos. 1103 BANK ONE TOWER, ANESTHESIA ASSOC OF LIMA I 45801 #016-02-1983 L1986 **AN** *020 †05.

SCHNIEGENBERG, Gary M. 801 MEDICAL DR, STE A 45804 #038-43-1978 L1979 **ORS OP** *020 †40.

SCHROEDER, Kelly Ann. 750 W HIGH ST, STE 250 45801 #038-41-1999 L1999 **IM** *020 †20.

SCHUMM, Herbert A. 730 W MARKET ST 45801 #038-45-1986 L1987 **FM** *030 †18 ‡.

SEO, Youn Seok. 1001 BELLEFONTAINE AVE 45804 #583-02-1968 L1977 **OTO** *020 †45.

SHAFIQ, Mussarat. ■ 45805 #704-16-1987 L2008 **PD** *020 †55.

SHAHEEN, Adel Mohammed. 770 W HIGH ST, STE 370 45801 #915-02-1979 L1988 **IM CD** *020 †20.

SHANK, M. 715 W NORTH ST 45801 #038-40-1986 L1988 **END DIA** *020 †20.

SHANKLAND, Wesley Earl. 1155 BIBLE RD, FORD MOTOR COMPANY 45801 #038-40-1957 L1957 **FM OM** *020 †20.

SHANMUGAM, Sasikala T. 920 W MARKET ST, STE 210 45805 #495-16-1994 L2000 **IM** *020 †20.

SHEEHAN, Michael Thos. 730 W MARKET ST 45801 #038-43-1988 L1989 **GS VS** *020 †85.

SICRE, Candida Amelia G. 3200 N WEST ST, OAKWOOD CORRECTIONAL FACIL 45801 #275-01-1960 L1968 **P** *071.

SIFUENTES, Jorge Luis. 1001 BELLEFONTAINE AVE 45804 #056-05-1986 L1987 **AN CCA** *020.

SLABY, James Alan. 658 W MARKET STE 208, WCOARS, INC 45801 #038-43-1986 L1992 **PS** *020 †85.

SMITH, Karen Sue. 1005 BELLEFONTAINE AVE, STE 245 45804 #025-12-1997 L1998 *020 †55.

SOLOMON, Howard John. 770 W HIGH ST, STE 450 45801 #041-09-1984 L1993 **GE IM** *020 †20.

SOO, Dixie Lee Boney. 1001 BELLEFONTAINE AVE 45804 #038-06-1959 L1964 **N** *020 †75.

SREENAN, Joseph James. 750 W HIGH ST 45801 #038-43-1991 L1995 **PTH** *020 †50.

STALLKAMP, Eric Todd. 2875 W ELM ST 45805 #038-40-1996 L1997 **FM** *020 †18.

STALLKAMP, Scott Craig. 830 W HIGH ST, OB GYN SPECIALISTS OF 45801 #038-40-1995 L1997 **OBG** *020 †30.

STALLKAMP, Todd Craig. 830 W HIGH ST, OB GYN SPECIALISTS OF 45801 #038-40-1964 L1964 **OBG** *071.

STALLKAMP, Vanessa L. 830 W HIGH ST, OB GYN SPECIALISTS OF 45801 #035-06-1993 L1995 **OBG** *020 †30.

STANLEY, Kenneth Emerson. 1220 E ELM ST, STE 101 45804 #019-02-1987 L1989 **U** *020 †95.

STECHSCHULTE, Clarence J. 830 W HIGH ST STE 102 45801 #028-34-1955 L1956 **PD** *071 †55.

STEINER, David Braun. ■ 45805 #038-40-1965 L1965 **ORS** *071 †40.

STERN, Robert James. 1001 BELLEFONTAINE AVE 45804 #038-40-1956 L1956 **GS** *071 †85.

STIENECKER, Roger Scott. 830 W HIGH ST, STE 255 45801 #038-40-1989 L1994 **ID IM** *020 †20.

STORER, Ben F. 2238 N WEST ST, ALLEN CORRECTIONAL INST 45801 #056-06-1947 L1950 **P** *071.

TABORA, Emmanuel Juane. 4732 WENATCHIE TRL, 1001 BELLEFONTAINE AVE. 45805 #748-10-1967 L1974 **EM GS** *020.

TALWAR, Raman. 770 W HIGH ST, STE 200 45801 #495-69-1980 L1991 **GS VS** *020.

TATAD, Magdalino M. 730 W MARKET ST 45801 #748-11-1982 L2002 **PD** *020.

TAYLOR, Russell John. 770 W HIGH ST, STE 350 45801 #035-09-1973 L1980 **U** *020 †95.

TERUEL, Roque E, Jr. 825 W MARKET ST 45805 #748-01-1965 L1971 **U** *020 †95.

THOMPSON, Charles Lynn. 1001 BELLEFONTAINE AVE 45804 #038-40-1973 L1974 **FM** *030 †18.

THUKKANI, Thiru Gnanam. 1005 BELLEFONTAINE AVE, STE 230 45804 #495-16-1962 L1997 **TS GS** *071 †85,90.

TOTH, David Bradley. 1001 BELLEFONTAINE AVE, LIMA MEMORIAL HOSP 45804 #065-06-1978 L1996 **FM** *020.

TRAN, Duc Duy. 525 N EASTOWN RD 45807 #049-01-1989 L1995 **RNR** *020 †80.

TREMOULIS, Edward Lewis. 915 W MARKET ST 45805 #038-40-1984 L1985 **FM** *020 †18.

TRIPURANENI, Ashok Kumar. 525 N EASTOWN RD, THE AMERICAN COMMUNITY CAN 45807 #495-65-1982 L1999 **HO IM** *020 †20.

TUCKER, William Ellis. 730 W MARKET ST, EMERGENCY DEPT-ST RITAS MC 45801 #035-09-1985 L1991 **EM IM** *020 †16.

TUNGPALAN-GRONDOLSKY, Lori. 200 W 1ST ST, 1103 BANK ONE BLG 45804 #014-01-2000 L2004 **AN** *100 †05 ‡.

UGWANYI, Ebere Maxwell. 1005 BELLEFONTAINE AVE, STE 340 45804 #690-01-1985 L1997 **CD IM** *020 †20.

UKIWE, Jonah O. 750 W HIGH ST, STE 150 45801 #306-01-1988 L1993 **NEP** *020 †20.

VAN ATTA, Glen Benj, Jr. 770 W HIGH ST, STE 290 45801 #010-01-1975 L1976 **ORS** *020.

WALDRON, Laura Jean B. 525 N EASTOWN RD, LIMA MEMORIAL MEDICAL PARK 45807 #023-01-1974 L1985 **FM** *020 †18.

WANGLER, Mark Adrian. 121 W HIGH ST, 1103 CHASE BANK TOWER 45801 #038-40-1981 L1982 **AN PME** *020 †05.

WATTS, Robert Albert. 140 E SPRING ST 45801 #010-03-1957 L1960 **GP IM** *071.

WEHRI, Carl Sylvester. 730 W MARKET ST 45801 #038-40-1976 L1976 **FM** *020 †18.

WEI, Victor Mark. 799 S MAIN ST, C/O FAMILY RESOURCES CTRS 45804 #051-04-1989 L1994 **CHP** *020 †75 ‡.

WEIS, Thomas Thedieck. PO BOX 1665 45802 #010-02-1962 L1964 **PD** *071 †55.

WHEELER, Robert Alan. 750 W HIGH ST STE 250 45801 #048-16-1988 L1991 **IM** *020 †20.

WIESER, Michael Jay. 801 MEDICAL DR, STE A 45804 #038-41-1983 L1985 **ORS** *020 †40.

WINERMAN, Mark Alan. 830 W HIGH ST STE 102 45801 #017-20-1978 L1981 **PD** *020 †55.

WOLERY, James Scott. 770 W HIGH ST STE 210 45801 #038-40-1980 L1981 **CD IM** *020 †20.

WOLERY, Walter Wayne. 730 W MARKET ST 45801 #038-40-1955 L1955 **GP** *071.

WRIGHT, Gene E. 1001 BELLEFONTAINE AVE 45804 #038-40-1953 L1953 **FM** *071 †18.

XU, Yihe. 1103 BANK ONE TOWER 45801 #243-45-1983 L2000 **AN** *020 †05.

YOUNG, Lawrence Linden. 825 W MARKET ST 45805 #010-01-1962 L1968 **OPH** *071 †35.

ZELENAK, Mary Elizabeth. 730 W MARKET ST, ST RITAS MED CTR 45801 #041-09-1977 L2001 **EM UM** *020 †16.

ZHANG, Hong. 525 N EASTOWN RD, MEDICAL CANCER INSTITUTE 45807 #243-29-1982 L2000 **RO** *020 †80.

ZHOU, Anthony Tong Gao. 1103 BANK ONE TOWER 45801 #243-45-1982 L2001 **AN** *020 †05.

ZIMMERMAN, Rena Beth. 803 W MARKET ST, ALLISON RADIATION ONCOLOGY 45805 #038-44-1983 L1986 **RO** *020 †80.

LISBON – COLUMBIANA

BARNES, Elizabeth Stewart. 7880 LINCOLE PL, COLUMBIANA COUNTY 44432 #051-01-1985 L2000 **FM** *020 †18.

BHAT, Banarikammaje N. 330 N MARKET ST, STE B, P.O. BOX 369 44432 #495-09-1971 L1977 **PD** *020 †55 ‡.

BUJDOSO, Laszlo J. ■ 44432 #473-04-1951 L1964 **GS** *071.

FRESHLEY, Barbara Dale. 7880 LINCOLE PL, HEALTHY FOCUS FAM PRACTICE 44432 #038-44-1986 L1988 **FM** *020 †18.

GETZINGER, Karl Eugene. 356 E LINCOLN WAY 44432 #038-43-1979 L1980 **FM** *020 †18.

MANDRY, David L. ■ 44432 #041-13-1951 L1952 **GP** *071.

RYHAL, Maria Lynn. 356 E LINCOLN WAY 44432 #038-44-1987 L1989 **FM** *020 †18.

VELEZ CALDERON, Eduardo. 356 E LINCOLN WAY 44432 #264-04-1997 L2005 **PCC** *020 †20.

LITTLE HOCKING – WASHINGTON

ATKINSON, Billie Martin. 45 S BRUCE ST 45742 #055-01-1965 L1989 **GS EM** *071 †85.

LODI – MEDINA

ACKLEY, Kevin Ray. 225 ELYRIA ST 44254 #038-40-1993 L1994 **EM** *020 †16.

BALDI, Rachel Amy. 221 ELYRIA ST, STE 104 44254 #038-43-1996 L1997 **IM** *020 †20.

BURKEY, Jeffrey Allen. 402 HIGHLAND DR 44254 #038-43-1997 L1998 **FM** *020 †18.

DICHOSO, Graciano B. 402 HIGHLAND DR 44254 #038-08-1961 L1971 **IM GP** *020 ‡.

DOVICO, Vincent. 225 ELYRIA ST 44254 #038-40-1967 L1968 **GS GP** *020 †85.

GRABLE, Bennis E. ■ 44254 #038-40-1951 L1951 **GS** *071 †85.

LISHNEVSKI, Alexia. 402 HIGHLAND DR 44254 #473-03-2002 L2003 **FM** *100 †18.

LOGAN – HOCKING

ANZALONE, Scott Joseph. 751 STATE ROUTE 664 N # D 43138 #038-43-1995 L1998 **FM** *020 †18.

BONTRAGER, Roy Roman. 751 STATE ROUTE 664 N 43138 #038-40-1966 L1966 **FM OS** *020 †18.

CARR, Douglas Ballard. 1383 W HUNTER ST 43138 #038-40-1992 L1995 **FM** *020 †18.

CUMMIN, David Lawrence. 751 STATE ROUTE 664 N 43138 #038-40-1994 L1995 **FM** *020 †18.

GAY, Alfonso Young. 601 STATE ROUTE 664 N 43138 #748-01-1960 L1972 **VS GS** *071 †85.

HAQUE, Max Mahfuzul. 31480 CHIEFTAIN DR, APT A 43138 #495-18-1974 L1996 **P PYG** *020 ‡
HSIEH, Karl Su. 819 STATE RTE 664 N, HOCKING VALLEY MED 43138 #028-02-1976 L1978 **OBG PTH** *020 †50,30
KAYALI, Bashar. 31480 CHIEFTAIN DR 43138 #875-01-1975 L1989 **PD PDI** *020 †55
KENNEDY, James V. ■ 43138 #035-01-1946 L1953 **IM OS** *071
KUDLAPUR, Shivaprakash T. 1383 W HUNTER ST 43138 #495-09-1989 L1993 **IM** *020 †20
LABRADOR, Rosario M. 31480 CHIEFTAIN DR, APT C 43138 #748-02-1964 L1973 **PD NPM** *020 †55
LABRADOR, Rowan D. 14848 BRADFORD DR 43138 #748-02-1964 L1973 **GS** *071
LUBBERS, Judith R. 601 STATE ROUTE 664 N, COMMUNITY HOSPITAL 43138 #038-40-1985 L1987 **FM** *020 †18
MENON, Jaykumar. 1383 W HUNTER ST 43138 #496-18-1989 L2002 **IM** *020 †20
NEFF, Robert Jos. 751 STATE RTE 664 N UNIT C 43138 #048-12-1979 L1980 **FM** *020 †18
RALPH, Georg T. 678 SUMMIT DR 43138 #038-41-1971 L1971 **EM** *020 †16
RIVERA, Edgardo Hechanova. 601 STATE ROUTE 664 N, HOCKING VLY COMM HOSP 43138 #748-09-1967 L1997 **PD FM** *020 †55
SCARMACK, Mark John. 31480 CHIEFTAIN DR, HOCKING VALLEY MEDICAL 43138 #041-12-1995 L1996 **PD** *020 †55
SCISM, Loretta Jane. ■ 43138 #016-45-2004 L2007 **FM** *020 †18
SUSSMAN, Clyde G. ■ 43138 #017-20-1942 L1949 **OTO OPH** *071
TORNWALL, Michael S. 819 STATE RTE 664 N, HOCKING VALLEY MEDICAL 43138 #048-02-1987 L1994 **GS EM** *020 †85
VILLEGAS, Mario Carlos. 601 STATE ROUTE 664 N 43138 #005-06-1982 L1984 **EM** *020

LONDON – MADISON

ANDERSON, George P, Jr. ■ 43140 #025-01-1951 L1955 **IM** *071
ANKENMAN, Ralph Larue. 210 N MAIN ST, MADISON COUNTY HOSPITAL 43140 #038-41-1959 L1959 **P** *020
ARIKAWA, Brawley. 214 ELM ST 43140 #572-12-1952 L1960 **FM** *071
BEISLER, Anthony John, IV. 214 ELM ST 43140 #038-40-1997 L2004 **GS** *020 †85
CHAN, Yiuchung. 210 N MAIN ST 43140 #038-40-1995 L1996 **P** *020 †75
CHITKARA, Vinay Kumar. 136 E HIGH ST 43140 #496-04-1981 L1991 **CD** *020 †20,55
COATE, Mark Allen. 214 ELM ST 43140 #038-40-1981 L1982 **GS VS** *020 †85
DUFF, David Lawrence. 210 N MAIN ST, MADISON COUNTY HOSP 43140 #038-40-1997 L2000 **EM OBS** *020 †18
ELKINS, Blake Elgin. ■ 43140 #021-06-2008 *012
GAINER, Sarah Marie. ■ 43140 #038-41-2006 **GS** *012
GEIB, Martha Ellen. 55 PARK AVE STE 240, LONDON PEDIATRICS, INC 43140 #038-40-1991 L1998 **PD** *020 †55
HAY, Charles Terrill. 214 ELM ST 43140 #038-40-1957 L1957 **GP** *020
JOHN, Calvin Peter. 210 N MAIN ST 43140 #038-45-2000 L2000 **FM** *100 †18
KAEHR, James Winston. 214 ELM ST, MADISON MEDICAL CENTER 43140 #038-40-1995 L2000 **AM** *020 †18
KHAN, Saleem. 214 ELM ST 43140 #704-09-1971 L1988 **NEP** *020 †20
KIM, Hong. 214 ELM ST 43140 #583-01-1968 L1977 **OBG** *020 †30
KIM, Soo Ja. 214 ELM ST 43140 #583-01-1968 L1977 **PD** *020 †55
LOCKE, William Call. ■ 43140 #018-75-1955, ▲ L1955 **GP** *071
MARKUS, Helge. 115 E HIGH ST 43140 #038-41-1977 L1978 **FM GP** *020
OSBORN, Crystl C. 210 N MAIN ST 43140 #011-02-1988 L1992 **P** *020 †75
PARK, Han Young. 210 N MAIN ST, MADISON COUTY HOSPITAL 43140 #583-02-1964 L1993 **AN** *020
POWELL, Jennifer. 306 LAFAYETTE ST 43140 #038-43-2001 L2001 **OBG** *020 †30
RICHARDSON, Steven Grant. 306 LAFAYETTE ST 43140 #038-40-1990 L1992 **FM** *020 †18
ROBERTS, Matthew Michael. ■ 43140 #038-45-2007 L2007 **EM** *012
SELVARAJAH, Ramalingam. 194 ELM ST, SAI FAMILY PRACTICE 43140 #495-16-1979 L1998 **FM** *020 †18
STARR, John Clark. 15 S MAIN ST 43140 #038-40-1960 L1960 **GP PHP** *020
TALLINI, Camille Elizabet. ■ 43140 #021-06-2007 L2007 **PTH** *012
TURNER, Michael Shane. 214 ELM ST 43140 #038-43-1988 L1989 **FM** *020 †18
VILLANUEVA, Angel. 214 ELM ST 43140 #748-01-1969 L1977 **IM** *020

LORAIN – LORAIN

ABBUD, Rita. 1800 LIVINGSTON AVE, STE 101 44052 #605-01-1988 L1992 **ID IM** *020 †20
ABDEL MALAK, Osama Anis. 4804 LEAVITT RD, COMPREHENSIVE PAIN CARE CE 44053 #915-02-1983 L1998 **APM** *020 †05
AHMED, Ismail S. 3600 KOLBE RD, STE 127 44053 #704-02-1976 L1991 **CD IM** *020 †20
ALAMIR, Samer. 6140 S BROADWAY 44053 #875-01-1992 L1997 **P** *020 †75
ALI, Faizi Haq. 3700 KOLBE RD 44053 #704-05-1996 L2001 **HMP** *020 †50 ‡
AMIRI, Mohammed Ali. A3700 KOLBE RD 44053 #869-04-1958 L1966 **IM PHP** *071 †20
ANDERSON, Marvin Moore. ■ 44053 #047-07-1952 L1953 **AN** *071
ANDRASKO, James John. 3600 KOLBE RD STE 106 44053 #038-40-1978 L1979 **GS** *020 †85
ARANEZ, Jose Tibayan, Jr. 3700 KOLBE RD, COMMUNITY HEALTH PARTNERS 44053 #748-10-1985 L1999 **OBG** *020 †30
ARORA, Paresh. 1720 COOPER FOSTER PK RD W 44053 #038-06-1991 L1992 **DR** *020 †80
ARORA, Piara Lal. 3600 KOLBE RD, STE 15 44053 #495-03-1962 L1978 **IMG PUD** *020 †20
ARTHUR-MENSAH, Theophilus. 3700 KOLBE RD 44053 #412-01-1976 L1995 **P** *020 †75
ASUNCION, Liwanag. 1515 KANSAS AVE, LIWANAG ASUNCION MD INC 44052 #748-08-1964 L1972 **IM NEP** *020 †20
AYCINENA, Patricio R. 3600 KOLBE RD STE 105 44053 #429-01-1976 L1983 **END IM** *020 †20
BANKO, Bradley Thorpe. 205 W 20TH ST, VA OUTPATIENT CLNC 44052 #016-11-1997 L1998 **FM** *020 †18 ‡
BARILE, Angelo Michael. 5700 COOPER FOSTR PRK RD W 44053 #654-01-2003 L2003 **IM** *100 †20
BARTULICA, Paul Branko. 205 W 21ST ST 44052 #957-01-1977 L1982 **OBG** *020
BAUMGARD, Marc Allan. 3700 KOLBE RD, COMMUNITY HEALTH PARTNERS 44053 #055-01-1994 L1995 **EM** *020 †16
BELIZAIRE, Harold Dunbar. 205 W 20TH ST 44052 #566-01-1972 L1977 **OBG** *071 †30
BERENGER, Philippe Gerard. 5700 COOPER FOSTR PRK RD W, CLEVELAND CLINIC LORAIN 44053 #396-20-1983 L1985 **PME OM** *020 †20
BITAR, Jihad Chafik. 3700 KOLBE RD 44053 #847-05-1975 L1988 **OBG** *071
BLANFORD, Donald Francis. 3700 KOLBE RD, COMMUNITY HEALTH PARTNERS 44053 #016-02-1968 L1975 **MDM ORS** *030 †40

BOAKYE, Julius Kwame. 6125 S BROADWAY 44053 #412-01-1979 L1991 **AN** *020 †05
BOYE-DOE, Alexander H. 5040 OBERLIN AVE 44053 #412-01-1970 L1980 **OBG** *020
BRAWNER, Maria Cynthia V. 3600 KOLBE RD, STE 120 44053 #748-02-1973 L1995 **PD** *020 †55
BUKOWSKI, Martin Jos. ■ 44052 #041-01-1955 L1982 **PD** *071 †55
BURKE, Shelley Annette. 3700 KOLBE RD, COMMUNITY HOSP 44053 #025-07-1998 L2000 **P** *020 †75
CANCINO, Francisco P. ■ 44052 #748-01-1956 **AN** *020
CARANDANG, Edwin C. ■ 44055 #748-01-1989 L1992 **FM** *020
CELERIO, Briccio A. 5700 COOPER FOSTR PRK RD W 44053 #748-07-1965 L1977 **AN** *020
CHANG, James Chun. 205 W 20TH ST 44052 #583-01-1937 L2000 **GP** *071
CHAPPLE, Craig Jos. 3700 KOLBE RD 44053 #056-06-1969 L1971 **FM** *020 †18
CHERUKURI, Subbarao V. 4654 OBERLIN AVE STE 1, SV CHERUKURI MD INC 44053 #495-11-1965 L1976 **U UP** *020 †95
CHRISMER, Lynn C, Jr. 5700 COOPER FOSTR PRK RD W, PARK ROAD 44053 #038-40-1975 L1978 **IM IMG** *020 †20
CHRISTIAN, Lorraine. 6140 S BROADWAY, NORD CENTER 44053 #038-20-1975 L1977 **P R** *020 †75
CLOSE, Alba Ortega. 1800 LIVINGSTON AVE, PEDIATRIC CLINIC 44052 #038-40-1996 L1999 **PD** *040 †55
COLEMAN, James Regis, III. 6125 S BROADWAY 44053 #038-44-1998 L2002 **AN** *020 †05 ‡
CROTSER, Conleth Marie. 1800 LIVINGSTON AVE, LORIAN COUNTY HEALTH & DEN 44052 #038-43-1981 L1991 **PD** *020 †55
CRUZ, Teresita Del Carmen. A3700 KOLBE RD 44053 #748-01-1961 L1972 **PD** *071
DIOKNO, Victoria. 5700 COOPER FOSTR PRK RD W, CLEVELAND CLINIC - LORAIN 44053 #748-02-1996 L2000 **AI** *020 †20
EDMUNDS, Robert T. 1807 E 28TH ST 44055 #035-01-1951 L1984 **OM** *020 †85
EL DALATI, Haysam. 3600 KOLBE RD STE 108, LORAIN CARDIAC SURG 44053 #917-02-1977 L2000 **TS** *020 †85,90
ENGSTROM, Conley Walter. 6100 S BROADWAY, STE 101 44053 #025-07-1976 L1978 **D** *020 †15
EREN, Ibrahim Naci. 1130 TOWER BLVD, STE B 44052 #902-10-1951 L1965 **FM** *071
EREN, Itri Arif. 1130 TOWER BLVD # B 44052 #038-41-1981 L1984 **IMG** *020 †20
EREN, Mustafa Kazim. 1130 TOWER BLVD STE B 44052 #038-41-1980 L1982 **PUD IM** *020 †20
ESCH, Peter Allan. 5700 COOPER FOSTR PRK RD W 44053 #038-06-1974 L1977 **IM IMG** *020 †20
ETZKORN, Peter Anthony. ■ 44052 #028-34-1944 L1947 **IM** *071
FAGAN, Kathleen Marie. 1800 LIVINGSTON AVE, COMMUNITY HEALTH PARTNERS 44052 #038-06-1978 L1984 **OM IM** *020 †70
FANOUS, Mourad Helmy. 205 W 20TH ST, VA CLINIC 44052 #915-04-1978 L1983 **IM IMG** *020 †20
FERBER, William Leonard. 221 W 8TH ST 44052 #038-06-1978 L1981 **DR** *020 †80
FERENCZY, Stephen Joseph. 5700 COOPER FOSTER PK RD W, LORAIN HEALTH CENTER 44053 #038-40-1995 L1998 **IM** *020 †20
FETERIK, Kristian. 5700 COOPER FOSTR PRK RD W, DEPT. OF INTERNAL MEDICINE 44053 #286-06-2000 L2001 **IM** *020
FINLEY, Lori Beth. 5700 COOPER FOSTR PRK RD W 44053 #038-45-2004 L2004 **PD** *020 †55
FLASK, Vaishali A. 5700 COOPER FOSTR PRK RD W 44053 #038-06-1997 L1999 **PD** *020 †55
FLINT, Eric Chas. 221 W 8TH ST 44052 #038-40-1984 L1985 **DR RNR** *020 †80
FROILAN, Jorge T. 4751 OBERLIN AVE 44053 #748-01-1955 L1965 **OTO** *072 †45
FUSILERO, Victorino M. 4287 OBERLIN AVE STE C, LORAIN MEDICAL ARTS BLDG 44053 #748-01-1965 L1971 **PS** *020 †65
GEORGE, Joseph William, Jr. ■ 44053 #038-43-2002 L2007 **ORS** *100
GETACHEW, Samuel. 2152 REID AVE 44052 #366-01-1983 L1990 **PD** *020 †55
GONZALEZ, Domingo. 1511 LINCOLN BLVD 44055 #132-01-1964 L1973 **NS N** *020 †25
GUAY, Marc Eric. 3600 KOLBE RD, STE 227 44053 #016-43-1990 L1993 **OTO** *020 †45
HARRINGTON, John Jos. ■ 44052 #024-01-1954 L1957 **AN** *071 †05
HARROFF, Peter Edward. 221 W 21ST ST, STE 8 44053 #038-40-1977 L1981 **GYN** *020 †30
HAZEN, Paul Gregory. 6100 S BROADWAY, STE 101 44053 #025-01-1973 L1974 **D DS** *020 †15
HUERTA, Enrique. 6140 S BROADWAY 44053 #649-01-1963 L1974 **P CHP** *020 †75 ‡
HUH, Jung. ■ 44053 #583-01-1961 L1971 **ORS** *071 †40
JARMOSZUK, Irene. 3600 KOLBE RD, STE 206 44053 #033-05-1977 L1994 **AI PD** *020 †55,03
JARMOSZUK, Nicholas. 3600 KOLBE RD, COMMUNITY HEALTH PARTNERS 44053 #041-02-1972 L1979 **GE** *020 †20
JEET, Anant. 3600 KOLBE RD, STE 203 44053 #495-45-1993 L2002 **END** *020 †20
JOYCE, David Blaine. 3600 KOLBE RD, STE 127 44053 #038-41-1982 L1986 **CD IM** *020 †20
JUREK, Ilona Elizabeth. 3600 KOLBE RD STE 203 44053 #038-43-1990 L1991 **FM** *020 †18 ‡
KERRO, Robert. 6125 S BROADWAY 44053 #038-44-2001 L2001 **AN** *020 †05 ‡
KOLCZUN, Michael C. 5700 COOPER FOSTR PRK RD W 44053 #021-05-1968 L1968 **ORS** *072 †40
KOLTA, Ragaie Zaki. 1503 LINCOLN BLVD 44055 #915-04-1960 L1976 **AN** *020 †05
KOOBA, Eino. 3600 KOLBE RD, STE 227 44053 #869-07-1953 L1961 **IM OM** *071
KORINEK, Josef. 3885 OBERLIN AVE 44053 #286-02-1966 L1987 **GE IM** *020
LEE, Won Ho. 3700 KOLBE RD 44053 #583-02-1959 L1971 **PTH PCP** *020 †50
LEHOCZ, Donald Denis. ■ 44052 #065-09-1953 L1958 **GP** *071
LENHART, Richard Kenneth. 221 W 8TH ST 44052 #038-41-1970 L1970 **DR** *020 †80
LEONE, Doris Maria. 6125 S BROADWAY 44053 #038-43-1983 L1985 **AN** *020 †05
MACCHI, Mario Antonio. 221 W 8TH ST 44052 #132-02-1961 L1970 **DR NM** *071
MAKADIA, Ashok P. 3600 KOLBE RD, STE 109 44053 #495-22-1988 L2000 **PUD** *020 †20
MANICKAM, Sundara Kannan. 1130 TOWER BLVD STE B 44052 #496-23-1991 L1998 **IM** *020 †20
MARFORI, Norberto Reyes. 4287 OBERLIN AVE 44053 #748-02-1964 L1973 **PS GS** *020 †65
MARTIN, Thomas Richard. ■ 44053 #038-40-1967 L1967 **R NM** *071 †80,28
MASSOUH-KHABAZ, Rafik. 3700 KOLBE RD 44053 #875-01-1991 L1997 **IM** *020 †20
MC CALLISTER, Scott H. 3700 KOLBE RD 44053 #016-09-1986 L1997 **CD IM** *020 †20
MC NAMEE, Brian Francis. 5373 OBERLIN AVE, OBERLIN AVE MED CTR 44053 #028-34-1971 L1972 **R NR** *075 †80
MESSERLY, Margaret M. 6140 S BROADWAY 44053 #038-43-1992 L1995 **P** *020 †75
MICLAT, Romeo Sapuriada. 3700 KOLBE RD 44053 #748-02-1970 L1975 **NEP IM** *020 †20
MILLER, David Gerard. 6100 S BROADWAY, RETINA ASSOCIATES OF 44053 #038-41-1993 L1998 **OPH** *020 †35
MOHAN, Geetha. 3600 KOLBE RD STE 127, NORTH OHIO HEART CENTER, I 44053 #495-31-1985 L1992 **CD** *020 †20
MORA, Romulo Jesoro. 4287 OBERLIN AVE 44053 #748-01-1961 L1973 **IM NM** *071
MORSCHER, Katrina M. 6125 S BROADWAY, ANESTHESIA ASSOC OF NO OH 44053 #051-04-1995 L1997 **AN** *020

MURRY, Paul Jos. 1800 LIVINGSTON AVE 44052 #038-43-1989 L1993 **ID** *020 †20
NASR, Christian Elias. 5700 COOPER FOSTR PRK RD W, PARK ROAD 44053 #605-02-1988 L1998 **END** *020 †20
NEMETH, Victor Anthony. 3600 KOLBE RD STE 100 44053 #017-20-1977 L1983 **ORS** *020 †40
NEPOMUCENO, Oscar F. 4270 E LAKE RD 44054 #748-01-1961 L1972 **IM** *071 †20
NOVAK, Michael Andrew. 6100 S BROADWAY, RETINA ASSOCIATES OF 44053 #038-06-1977 L1983 **OPH** *035
OCAMPO, Teresita Salapare. 1720 COOPER FOSTR PRK RD W, STE B 44053 #748-01-1963 L1974 **R GP** *050 †80
OZBARDAKCI, George. 5700 COOPER FOSTR PRK RD W 44053 #902-10-1973 L1980 **OTO** *020 †45
PAIGE, Beverly Joan. 3600 KOLBE RD, STE 106 44053 #038-06-1984 L1984 **GS CCS** *020 †85
PANCHAGNULA, Sastry S. 3600 KOLBE RD, STE 109 44053 #495-62-1976 L1996 **PUD IM** *020 †20
PARAS, Carolyn Modesta A. 6140 S BROADWAY, NORD CENTER 44053 #748-10-1992 L2000 **P** *020
PATEL, Achala A. 6140 S BROADWAY 44053 #495-23-1981 L1987 **P** *020
PATEL, Chandralekha P. 221 W 8TH ST 44052 #495-55-1972 L1980 **RO** *020
PATEL, Paresh A. 3700 KOLBE RD 44053 #495-23-1968 L1976 **GS** *085
PATTERSON, James Blake. 4995 ONEIL BLVD 44055 #016-43-1957 L1957 **FM** *071 †18
PENDERGAST, Scott David. 6100 S BROADWAY, RETINA ASSOCIATES OF 44053 #024-05-1991 L1997 **OPH OS** *020 †35 ‡
PUCCINELLI, Samuel. 5700 COOPER FOSTR PRK RD W 44053 #041-09-1975 L1980 **CD IM** *020 †20
QASEM, Khaled Ali. 3700 KOLBE RD 44053 #539-06-1960 L1975 **EM** *020 †20
QUAN, Walter W, Sr. ■ 44053 #242-21-1947 L1960 **GS** *071
QUERUBIN, Renato P. 3700 KOLBE RD 44053 #748-10-1967 L1989 **OTO FPS** *020
RADEFELD, Denis A. 3600 KOLBE RD # NO-205 44053 #038-06-1944 L1944 **GS** *071 †85
RAZACK, Abdul. 3600 KOLBE RD STE 221 44053 #495-80-1980 L1992 **GE IM** *020 †20
REDDY, Sathya Pelleti. 5700 COOPER FOSTR PRK RD W 44053 #495-65-1995 L2000 **RNR** *020 †20
REYES, Jovita. 1515 KANSAS AVE 44052 #748-08-1964 L1972 **ON IM** *020 †20
ROMAN-TAYLOR, Gloria A. 6125 S BROADWAY 44053 #042-03-1988 L1990 **AN** *020
SABO, Frank Michael, Jr. 3600 KOLBE RD STE 100 44053 #025-07-1992 L1997 **ORS** *020 †40
SAINI, Dilbagh S. 6140 S BROADWAY 44053 #495-15-1980 L1994 **P** *020
SALKA, Mohamad Ghassan. 3600 KOLBE RD STE 223 44053 #915-04-1970 L1976 **CD IM** *020 †20
SANDOVAL, Victor M. 3600 KOLBE RD STE 11 44053 #319-01-1969 L1978 **PD OS** *020 †55
SCHAEFFER, John Wm. 3600 KOLBE RD, STE 120 44053 #038-40-1971 L1971 **CD IM** *020 †20
SECRIST, John G. 5700 COOPER FOSTR PRK RD W 44053 #035-06-1970 L1977 **D** *020 †15
SEO, Jwa-Il James. 4560 OBERLIN AVE 44053 #583-02-1965 L1972 **PD PHO** *020 †55
SEO, Okja Lee. ■ 44053 #583-03-1968 L1986 **GP** *071
SERHAL, Dina Ibrahim. 5700 COOPER FOSTR PRK RD W, PARK ROAD 44053 #605-01-1995 L2000 **IM** *020 †20
SERNA, Alfred. 5700 COOPER FOSTR PRK RD W 44053 #023-07-1988 L1995 **OSM** *020 †40
SERTICH, Mario Miguel. 1511 LINCOLN BLVD 44055 #035-09-1976 L1981 **NS GS** *020 †25
SESE, Norman T. 6155 PARK SQUARE DR, STE 6 44053 #748-10-1989 L1997 **N** *020 †75
SFEIR, Sami A. ■ 44053 #605-02-1954 L1966 **ORS** *071 †40
SHAH, Bharat C. 4804 LEAVITT RD 44053 #495-22-1980 L1989 **PME IM** *020 †20
SHAPIRO, David Borden. 5800 COOPER FOSTR PRK RD W, PARK ROAD 44053 #038-06-1986 L1992 **HS ORS** *020 †40
SHARBEK, Mohammad Fathi. 3600 KOLBE RD STE 103 44053 #915-03-1972 L1979 **OBG GS** *020 †30
SHELDON, Warren N. 221 W 8TH ST 44052 #026-04-1950 L1955 **DR NM** *071
SHOR, Steven John. 3700 KOLBE RD 44053 #041-09-1989 L1990 **EM** *020 †16
SINGLE, Daniel John, Jr. 5700 COOPER FOSTR PRK RD W 44053 #038-41-1998 L2000 **OTO** *020 †40
SIVANANDAM, Eswari A. 3700 KOLBE RD 44053 #495-66-1968 L1976 **PTH GP** *020 †50
SOLIS, Juan Salvador. ■ 44053 #748-01-1992 L2000 **IM IMG** *020 †20
SUICO, Edward Mortola. 6125 S BROADWAY, WEST SUITE 44053 #748-11-1972 L1981 **AN IM** *020
SUICO, Sharleen Anne. ■ 44053 #038-43-2005 L2005 **PM** *012
SUN, Yun-Lai. 5295 OBERLIN AVE 44053 #244-02-1973 L1976 **GP** *020 †50
TICICH, Stephan Michael. 221 W 8TH ST 44052 #038-40-1957 L1957 **DR R** *071 †80
TREUHAFT, Paul Steven. 5800 COOPER FOSTER PK RD W 44053 #016-02-1968 L1993 **ORS OS** *020 †40
TROTT, Martin S. 3600 KOLBE RD, STE 227 44053 #035-45-1989 L1990 **OTO** *020 †45
TSUI, Pang. 6125 S BROADWAY, WEST SUITE 44053 #038-06-1998 L2000 **AN** *020 †05 ‡
TURNER, Kevin Leo. 3600 KOLBE RD, STE 120 44053 #021-01-1993 L1994 **PD** *020 †55
VARGAS, Fremio Alberto. 221 W 21ST ST STE 5, COMMUNITY HLTH PARTNERS 44052 #308-01-1969 L1976 **GS** *020
VENABLE, Phillip A. 6125 S BROADWAY 44053 #038-43-1994 L2001 **AN** *020 †05 ‡
VILLAMIN-CELERIO, Rosario. 3700 KOLBE RD 44053 #748-01-1965 L1974 **GP** *020
WARE, Rebecca Ann. 5700 COOPER FOSTR PRK RD W 44053 #038-41-2000 L2004 **IM** *020 †20
WENDSCHUH, Philip D. 3600 KOLBE RD, STE 127 44053 #038-06-1985 L1986 **CD IM** *020 †20
WILKE, Richard M. ■ 44053 #038-06-1943 L1943 **OBG** *071 †30
YALAMANCHILI, Anuradha. 205 W 20TH ST, VA OUTPATIENT CLC 44052 #495-50-1991 L1996 **IM** *020
YU, Masao Siang-Siu. 5340 OBERLIN AVE 44053 #244-04-1968 L1977 **FM A** *020
YUZON, Florencio. 3885 OBERLIN AVE 44053 #748-01-1964 L1972 **IM GE** *020 †20
ZEGARRA, Hernando. 6100 S BROADWAY, RETINA ASSOCIATES OF 44053 #737-06-1968 L1976 **OPH** *020 †35
ZOLLI, Alexander Francis. 2173 N RIDGE RD E, STE A 44055 #561-01-1977 L1986 **TS** *020 †85

LOUDONVILLE — ASHLAND

KAYE, William Howard. ■ 44842 #038-40-1964 L1964 **OTO** *071 †45
KUTTOTHARA, Abraham C. ■ 44842 #869-07-1967 L1974 **GS ON** *072
TOMCHAK, David John. 546 N UNION ST, AMERICAN HEALTH NTWK OF OH 44842 #038-44-1988 L1990 **FM** *020 †18

LOUISVILLE — STARK

CHUGHTAI, Samina Alderete. 1012 W MAIN ST 44641 #654-01-2001 L2002 **PD** *020

CHUGHTAI, Zenaida A. 1012 W MAIN ST 44641 #748-10-1967 L1973 **PD** *020
GALANG, Lamberto Trinidad. 1010 W MAIN ST 44641 #748-01-1971 L1976 **FM** *020
HIRST, Robert R. ■ 44641 #038-06-1946 L1946 **IM GP** *071
LAGO, William Jos. 1302 W MAIN ST 44641 #038-44-1991 L1993 **FM** *020 †18
PANSINO, Terrence Lee. 1909 WILLIAMSBURG WAY NE 44641 #038-40-1983 L1986 **IM** *020 †20
PROSSER, Elizabeth A. 1909 WILLIAMSBURG WAY NE 44641 #038-40-1983 L1986 **IM IMG** *020 †20
TABB, Catharine Jane. 1303 CALIFORNIA AVE 44641 #038-43-1977 L1978 **FM** *020 †18

LOVELAND — CLERMONT

AHMAD, Salman. 11899 SHENANDOAH TRCE 45140 #704-01-1991 L1999 **IM** *020 †20
ATAYA, Samir Mhd. Kher. 3594 SPRINGLAKE CIR 45140 #875-01-1998 L2003 **PCC** *020 †20
BLANCHARD, Dennis Allen. ■ 45140 #033-05-1967 L1968 **GS** *020 †85
BLITZER, Helene P. 10572 LOVELAND MADEIRA RD 45140 #008-01-1973 L1982 **PD** *020 †55
BOSLEY, Jacob Raymond. ■ 45140 #038-06-2006 L2006 **ORS** *012
BUNCH, Paul Timothy. ■ 45140 #038-41-2008 *012
BUNDY, Kevin Michael. 1507 STATE ROUTE 28 45140 #038-45-1997 L1998 **FM** *020 †18
CANNON, Michael Thomas. ■ 45140 #038-41-2006 L2006 **P** *012
CHO, Kenneth S I. ■ 45140 #583-03-1968 L1975 **AN** *075
COFFEY, David Cyrus. 1507 STATE ROUTE 28 45140 #038-45-1989 L1992 **FM** *020 †18
CONDORODIS, Christopher J. ■ 45140 #038-41-2005 L2005 **OBG** *012
DANKO, Michael Donald. ■ 45140 #038-40-2008 *012
DAVLIN, Erin Cathleen. 1507 STATE ROUTE 28, GOSHEN FAMILY PRACTICE 45140 #038-06-1985 L1985 **FM** *075 †18
DEPERIO, Marie Antoinette. 1161 RED BIRD RD 45140 #010-02-2002 L2005 **ID** *012 †20
DOUGHMAN-BUCKLEY, R. ■ 45140 #047-07-1989 L1991 **P** *020
FORTMAN, James Kenneth. ■ 45140 #038-41-2006 L2006 **AN** *012
FRANKOWSKI, Deborah Lynne. 10675A LOVELAND MADEIRA RD, HEALTH FIRST PHYSICIANS, L 45140 #038-40-1995 L1996 **FM** *020 †18
FREMONT, Susan Lezan. 10675A LOVELAND MADEIRA RD, HEALTH FIRST PHYSICIANS,LL 45140 #038-45-1996 L1997 **FM** *020 †18
GARVIN, Rachel Ellen. ■ 45140 #038-21-2006 L2006 **EM** *012
GILBERT, David Grant. ■ 45140 #016-06-1971 L1972 **EM PD** *020 †55,16
GO-LIN, Carmen. 1608 STATE ROUTE 28 45140 #748-01-1969 L1974 **FM PD** *020 †55
GONZALES, Yury R. ■ 45140 #737-01-1990 L1995 **IM** *020 †20
JOHNSON, Aleda Nash. 411 W LOVELAND AVE, STE 102 45140 #038-41-2000 L2001 **FM** *020 †18
KARAM-CHANDANI, Hema K. ■ 45140 #038-44-2007 *012
KNIPP, Michael John. ■ 45140 #017-20-2006 L2007 **DR** *012
LANKIN, Daniel L. 126 S LEBANON RD, LOVELAND OHIO LIFE SQUAD 45140 #038-41-1976 L1976 **EM** *020 †16
LE VAN, James H, Jr. ■ 45140 #041-01-1960 L1962 **ORS OAR** *071 †40
LONG, Nathan Wayne. ■ 45140 #038-44-2002 L2002 **EM** *020 †16
LONG, Sara Elizabeth. ■ 45140 #046-01-2000 L2000 **GS** *020 †85
MOORE, Douglas Lee. ■ 45140 #038-40-1996 L1997 **FM** *020 †18
MOORMAN, Debra Lynn. ■ 45140 #023-12-1984 L1986 **AM** *030 †70
MORMAN, Richard Thos. 10675A LOVELAND MADEIRA RD, HEALTH FIRST PHYSICIANS 45140 #038-41-1988 L1995 **FM** *020 †18
NGUYEN, Trang Hong. ■ 45140 #021-06-1993 L2002 **GPM** *100 †18
NOBLE, Gregory Leisle. 10675A LOVELAND MADEIRA RD 45140 #038-41-2001 L2001 **FM** *020 †18
NOORY, Mahboob U. 411 W LOVELAND AVE, STE 202 45140 #118-01-1979 L1991 **FM** *020 †18
OPRESCU, Nicolae-Catalin. 10146 ELMFIELD DR 45140 #781-01-1997 L2006 **PCC** *012 †20
ORABELLA, Martha Mahler. ■ 45140 #038-41-2008 *012
PANCHOLY, Apurva Bipin. ■ 45140 #011-02-1996 L2004 **OBG** *020 †30
PATER, Luke Edmond. ■ 45140 #038-41-2006 L2006 **RO** *012
SAGRI, Samina Ghafoor. 1507 STATE ROUTE 28 45140 #704-20-1997 L2006 **FM** *020 †18
SPRINGER, Ellen Smearsoll. 10404 GROG RUN RD, CHILDREN'S HOSPITAL MEDICA 45140 #038-40-1995 L1996 **PD** *020 †55
STAMATAKOS, Maria Mary. ■ 45140 #038-41-2003 L2003 **CPP** *012 †55
STEINBAUGH, Linda Anne. ■ 45140 #038-41-2008 *012
TODARO, Thomas Gerard. ■ 45140 #035-08-1981 L1983 **CD IM** *050 †20
WALL, David Michael. ■ 45140 #038-43-2006 L2006 **OBG** *012
WEBER, Richard Jos. ■ 45140 #028-34-1947 L1948 **FM** *072 †18
WIEBRACHT, Emily Louise. ■ 45140 #038-41-2008 *012
WILSON, Chester. ■ 45140 #038-40-1961 L1961 **N P** *071
WOLIVER, Edward. ■ 45140 #038-41-1940 **GS GYN** *071 †85

LOWELL — WASHINGTON

KRONBERG, Jon Karl. 838 ARNOLD RD 45744 #038-41-2008 *012

LOWELLVILLE — MAHONING

SLAVEN, Stacy Marie. ■ 44436 #038-44-2005 L2005 **IM** *012

LOWER SALEM — WASHINGTON

TATRO, Michael Todd. 1100 E FORK RD 45745 #305-01-2000 L2000 **EM** *020 †16

LUCASVILLE — SCIOTO

LEE, William B. ■ 45648 #583-02-1963 L1973 **GP FPG** *071
LYON, Walter. ■ 45648 #038-40-1961 L1961 **OM** *071 †70

LUDLOW FALLS — MIAMI

HORMAN, Elmer C. ■ 45339 #028-78-1962, ▲ L1962 **FM AM** *071

■ = Address Information Privacy Protected

LYNCHBURG – HIGHLAND

MONTANEZ, Emma Pabualan. 8900 STATE ROUTE 134, LYNCHBURG MEDICAL CTR 45142 #748-11-1991 L2002 **ID** *020 †20

LYNDHURST – CUYAHOGA

AGARWAL, Indu Tara. 1950 RICHMOND RD TR56 44124 #038-40-2000 L2000 **DR** *020 †80
ANSARI, Monireh Joo. 29001 CEDAR RD, STE 518 44124 #517-05-1966 L1976 **OBG** *071 †30
BLATNIK, Jeffrey Alan. ■ 44124 #038-06-2007 L2007 **GS** *012
BOGOLIN, Barbara. ■ 44124 #038-44-2004 L2004 **OBG** *012
BOU SERHAL, Chadi Elias. ■ 44124 #605-01-2002 L2005 **PCC** *012 †20
BRINBERG, Don Edward. 29001 CEDAR RD, STE 110 44124 #024-01-1982 L1987 **GE IM** *020 †20
BROWN, John Arthur. 1950 RICHMOND RD, CCF REGIONAL RADIOLOGY 44124 #038-40-1976 L1977 **DR** *020 †80
CASSELBERRY, Ronald Blane. 5555 MAYFIELD RD 44124 #038-40-1985 L1986 **PMM AN** *020
COHEN, Phill Irwin. 29001 CEDAR RD, STE 430 44124 #048-04-1958 L1959 **P PYG** *020
FITZGERALD, John James. 29017 CEDAR RD, ZEEBA AMBULATORY SURGERY C 44124 #038-44-1983 L1985 **AN** *020 †05
GOLER, George G. 29001 CEDAR RD, STE 650 44124 #038-06-1943 L1943 **OBG** *071 †30
GREEN, Rodney Allan. 29001 CEDAR RD STE 307 44124 #836-01-1979 L1983 **PS HS** *020 †65
HOLZ, Gwynne Gala. 1950 RICHMOND RD, TR56 44124 #025-01-1987 L1990 **DR** *020 †80
JONES, Philbert Paul, III. 5150 THREE VILLAGE DR 44124 #038-41-1974 L1974 **HS PS** *020
KHAMBATTA, Parvez B. 5035 MAYFIELD RD, STE 201 44124 #496-38-1966 L1973 **GE IM** *020 †20
KIM, Vladlen. 5187 MAYFIELD RD 44124 #913-29-1993 L1997 **IM** *020 †20
KLEIN, Milton David. 29001 CEDAR RD, STE 430 44124 #038-40-1956 L1956 **GP** *020
LANIER, Karah Maher. 1950 RICHMOND RD, REGIONAL RADIOLOGY TR-56, 44124 #036-08-2001 L2008 **RNR** *012 †20
LEVIN, Erwin. 29001 CEDAR RD, STE 650 BRANARD MED BLDG 44124 #020-02-1944 L1947 **GE IM** *071 †20
LORIG, Ronald Joe. 1950 RICHMOND RD, TR56 44124 #038-06-1982 L1985 **DR** *020 †80
MAKIEJUS, Raymond Victor. ■ 44124 #017-20-1992 L2001 **GS** *020
MEASE, Elizabeth W. 4955 COUNTRYSIDE RD 44124 #024-07-1982 L1985 **IM** *020 †20,70
MORROW, Jay Stuart. 29001 CEDAR RD, STE 203 44124 #041-14-1976 L1993 **END IM** *020 †20
MUNIR, Sayf Riyadh. ■ 44124 #038-06-2008 *012
NARAYAN, Ajita. ■ 44124 #496-15-1995 L2006 **HO** *012 †20
PATEL, Bhupendra P. 1950 RICHMOND RD - 56, CLEVELAND CLINIC REGION RA 44124 #495-37-1970 L1978 **DR R** *020 †80
PATHOMVANICH, Damkerng. ■ 44124 #891-02-1970 L1977 **GS ORS** *100 †85
PATMOMVANICH, Pachnee. ■ 44124 #891-02-1970 L1977 **IM** *020 †20
PRADA, Daniela Iulia. 5195 MAYFIELD RD, # 105 44124 #781-04-1986 L2001 **IM** *020 †20
REED, Deborah Ann. 29001 CEDAR RD, STE 303 44124 #041-07-1983 L1989 **PYG** *020 †75
SHARMA, Sadhana. 5187 MAYFIELD RD 44124 #495-49-1997 L2006 **FM** *100 †18
SHEPARDSON, Laura Beth. 1950 RICHMOND RD, CLEVELAND CLINIC REGIONAL 44124 #038-06-2002 L2002 **DR** *100 †80
SOLTANIAN, Hooman Ted. 29017 CEDAR RD 44124 #409-16-1993 L2006 **PS HS** *020 †65
STEPNICK, David Wm. 29001 CEDAR RD, STE 203 44124 #041-12-1984 L1986 **FPS HNS** *020 †45
STONER, Kristen Renee. ■ 44124 #038-06-2006 L2006 **PD** *012
VARYANI, Sandhia. ■ 44124 #038-44-1999 L1999 **OBG** *020 †30
VISHNY, Miriam Liza. 29001 CEDAR RD, STE 110 44124 #048-13-1986 L1990 **GE IM** *020 †20
ZFAZ, Jennifer. ■ 44124 #010-02-2001 L2001 **IM** *100

MACEDONIA – SUMMIT

BALAKUMAR, Krishnaswamy. ■ 44056 #495-16-1966 L1979 **P** *020
KLABBATZ, Leslie Dale. ■ 44056 #041-07-1992 L1995 **GS EM** *020
PATEL, Brijal Thakor. ■ 44056 #038-41-2007 **EM** *012
ROXAS, Cesar E. ■ 44056 #748-01-1958 **PTH** *100
SINGH, Maninder. ■ 44056 #038-43-2008 *012
WHEELER, Jenna Joy. ■ 44056 #038-45-2008 *012

MADEIRA – HAMILTON

BAKER, Ryan Jon. ■ 45243 #038-41-2007 L2007 **PD** *012
BERNARDON, Michael D. 7829 LAUREL AVE 45243 #038-41-1998 L2001 **FM** *020 †18
CASTELLANOS, Andrew John. ■ 45243 #010-03-2004 L2007 **IM** *012
SMAIL, Jennifer Margaret. ■ 45243 #001-02-2003 L2003 **ORS** *012
WEINBERG, Nolan Louis. 7825 LAUREL AVE 45243 #026-04-1974 L1977 **IM IMG** *020 †20

MADISON – LAKE

CHAPMAN, Joseph Dudley. 1424 HUBBARD RD 44057 #005-17-1962 L1975 **GYN P** *071 †75
HAYEK, Fathallah. 6270 N RIDGE RD 44057 #875-02-1977 L1986 **EM** *020
HENG, Julia Ann. 6270 N RIDGE RD 44057 #038-06-1990 L1993 **FM** *020 †18
JENNINGS, Matthew Scott. 6270 N RIDGE RD 44057 #038-06-1999 L1999 **PD** *020 †55
KESSLER, Joseph John, Jr. 6270 N RIDGE RD 44057 #038-40-1996 L1997 **FM** *020 †18
LANDIS, James Alexander. 6270 N RIDGE RD 44057 #038-43-1993 L2000 **PM** *020
MALLICK, Geronima A. ■ 44057 #748-02-1960 L1972 **OBG** *071
MANOHAR, Chenguttai J. 701 N LAKE ST 44057 #495-04-1983 L1998 **IM** *020 †20
MIKHAIL, Josephine R. 701 N LAKE ST 44057 #915-09-1992 L1998 **IM** *020 †20
POIRIER, Virginia C. 2999 MCMACKIN RD 44057 #041-02-1968 L1995 **RNR DR** *020 †80
VELOSO, Hazel Marie Galon. 428 N LAKE ST 44057 #748-02-1995 L1998 **GE** *020 †20

MAINEVILLE – WARREN

CARTER, Krista E. 45039 #038-43-2000 L2000 **PD** *100 †55
FRANK, Robert Emmet. 5571 OAK VIEW DR 45039 #038-40-1972 L1972 **OS IM** *062 †20

KERMAN, David M. ■ 45039 #038-41-1952 L1952 **GP** *071
MAST, Kelley Jean. ■ 45039 #038-44-2005 L2005 **PD** *012
MEHRTENS, Jason Michael. ■ 45039 #016-45-2000 L2007 **ADL** *012 †18 ‡
ROGERS, Glenn Alvin. 87 E US 22-3, STE 200 45039 #038-41-1998 L1999 **FM** *020 †18
ROSS, David Mc Collough, II. ■ 45039 #004-01-2003 L2003 **DR** *012
SALZER, Richard B. 8355 ISLAND LN 45039 #038-41-1950 L1950 **OBG** *020 †30
SCHOETTINGER, Ted Jos. 87 E US 22 AND 3 STE 400 45039 #038-41-1991 L1992 **FM** *020 †18
SNYDER, Jonathan Robert. ■ 45039 #038-41-2007 L2007 **GS** *012
SORGER, James. ■ 45039 #035-09-1963 L1964 **PD** *071
VASHAKMADZE, Tamar. ■ 45039 #913-23-1994 L2006 **FP** *012
WACKSMAN, Jeff. ■ 45039 #038-41-1970 L1970 **PD U** *020 †95
WALKER, Gloria. 3116 STATE ROUTE 22 3 # O 45039 #038-40-1976 L1977 **FM** *020 †18
WEECH, Alexander A, Jr. ■ 45039 #035-01-1959 L1963 **P PYA** *020 †75

MALVERN – CARROLL

STASIAK, Joni. PO BOX 548, 635 LOCUST ST 44644 #038-44-1992 L1994 **FM** *020 †18

MANCHESTER – ADAMS

DETTMER, Cornelia M. 33 E 2ND ST 45144 #038-41-1957 L1957 **GP** *071 †80
NAYAK, Dinesh U. 28 E 2ND ST 45144 #495-09-1979 L1994 **FM** *020 †18

MANSFIELD – RICHLAND

ACHAREKAR, Arun Laxman. ■ 44906 #495-28-1967 L1984 **EM PD** *020 †16
ADAIR, Charles Valloyd. ■ 44907 #038-06-1947 L1947 **IM** *071 †20
ADKINS, Edward Eugene. 2007 W 4TH ST 44906 #016-43-1974 L1983 **FM** *020 †18
AGUADO, Enrique. 335 GLESSNER AVE 44903 #847-02-1951 L1964 **PTH CLP** *020 †50
ALTON, Mary E. 680 PARK AVE W, MID OHIO HEART CLINIC 44906 #038-40-1986 L1987 **CD** *020 †20
AMALFITANO, Michael Louis. 680 PARK AVE W 44906 #041-77-1985, ▲ L1991 **CD** *020
ANDREWS, Dana Harold. 370 CLINE AVE 44907 #038-40-1991 L1994 **IM** *020 †20
ATHMARAM, P K. 661 PARK AVE E 44905 #495-33-1977 L1985 **IM** *020
BACON, James Phillip. 680 PARK AVE W 44906 #038-40-1982 L1984 **CD IM** *040 †20
BADDOUR, Blanche D. 335 GLESSNER AVE 44903 #330-02-1962 L1979 **GP** *020
BADDOUR, Raymond Jos. 605 W TRIMBLE RD, STE B 44906 #038-40-1990 L2000 **N** *020
BAKENHASTER, Kathy H. 2007 W 4TH ST 44906 #038-40-1985 L1985 **FM** *020 †18
BALLINGER, William Scott. 770 BALGREEN DR, STE 203 44906 #038-40-1981 L1981 **IM** *020 †20
BALLITCH, Harold A, II. 1991 PARK AVE W, ADVANCED EYE CARE CENTER I 44906 #025-12-1987 L1992 **OPH PS** *020 †35
BANKO, Stephen. 600 W 3RD ST 44906 #041-13-1960 L1961 **PD** *071 †55
BARKETT, Robert Edward. 341 CLINE AVE 44907 #041-02-1960 L1961 **IM** *071 †20
BARKETT, Robt Edward, Jr. 341 CLINE AVE 44907 #041-02-1990 L1991 **IM** *020 †20
BAUMANN, Marlene Julie. ■ 44903 #038-43-2004 L2004 **DR** *012
BEARD, Julie Christine. 680 PARK AVE W STE 204 44906 #038-40-1997 L1998 **FM** *020 †18 ‡
BECKER, Melissa Sizemore. 661 PARK AVE E 44905 #017-20-1996 L2001 **FM OBS** *020 †18 ‡
BEDDARD, Donald Norwood. 480 GLESSNER AVE 44903 #038-40-1961 L1961 **IM** *071 †20
BEHESHTI ALE-AGHA, Firooz. 335 GLESSNER AVE, MEDCENTRL HLTH SYSTEM DEPT 44903 #517-01-1962 L1984 **PTH** *071 †50
BEHI, Fereidoun. 480 GLESSNER AVE 44903 #517-01-1967 L1975 **CD IM** *020
BELLAMKONDA, Ramesh. 335 GLESSNER AVE 44903 #495-36-1975 L1984 **GE IM** *071 †20
BELT, Richard Bryson. ■ 44907 #040-02-1954 L1957 **GP** *071
BERGESE, Jorge Juan. 370 CLINE AVE 44907 #132-02-1968 L1975 **PS** *020 †65 ‡
BHAT, Padmanabha B. 275 CLINE AVE 44907 #495-09-1966 L1973 **GS** *020
BOCKA, Joseph John. 335 GLESSNER AVE 44903 #033-05-1985 L1994 **EM** *020 †16
BOLDON, Douglas Phillip. 370 CLINE AVE 44907 #038-40-1968 L1968 **A** *020 †55,03
BORKAR, Chandrashek J. 335 GLESSNER AVE 44905 #495-01-1972 L1980 **AN** *020
BOSSART, Barbara Ann. ■ 44903 #035-20-1976 L2001 **GS** *85
BROWN, David Alan. 770 BALGREEN DR, STE 107 44906 #005-19-1985 L1992 **TS** *020 †85,90
BROWN, Elizabeth Ann. 770 BALGREEN DR, STE 107 44906 #038-40-1990 L1992 **PCC** *020 †20
BUEHRER, Paul Chas. 1987 W 4TH ST, RADIOLOGY ASSOCIATES OF 44906 #038-41-1975 L1978 **DR** *020 †80
BURGESS, John Howard. 335 GLESSNER AVE 44903 #026-08-1979 L1990 **PTH** *020 †50
BURNS, John Alexander. 466 S TRIMBLE RD, OPHTHALMIC SURG AND CONS 44906 #038-40-1964 L1964 **OPH** *020 †18
BURNS, Robert David. 770 BALGREEN DR, STE 101 44906 #038-40-1978 L1981 **PD** *020 †55
CALENDINE, Philip Edward. 335 GLESSNER AVE, RADIOLOGY ASSOCIATES OF 44903 #038-45-1997 L1998 **DR** *020 †80
CAPALDO, Guy. 500 S TRIMBLE RD 44906 #038-43-1978 L1980 **OBG** *020 †30
CHALASANI, Aruna Kumari. ■ 44907 #495-57-1968 L1979 **PTH ORS** *020 †50
CHAN, David L. 2050 W 4TH ST 44906 #244-04-1974 L1979 **GP P** *020
CHANG, Paul Andrew. 2981 W 4TH ST 44906 #011-02-1996 L2000 **MPD** *020 †20,55
CHENG, Lawrence Mason. 335 GLESSNER AVE, RADIOLOGY ASSOCIATES OF 44903 #010-01-1988 L2001 **DR** *020 †80
CHOPKO, Bohdan Wolodymyr. 39 WOOD ST, MID OHIO NEUROSURGICAL CAR 44903 #038-44-1993 L2000 **NS** *020 †25
CLARK, John Jacques. ■ 44903 #038-40-1937 L1937 **GP OS** *071
CLEMENTS, James Francis. 271 CLINE AVE 44907 #038-40-1966 L1966 **FM A** *071
COLLIER, Leonard Jos. 35 PARK ST N, CENTRAL OHIO 44902 #917-20-1961 L1987 **GYN** *071 †30
COURSON, Jeffery Paul. 680 PARK AVE W, STARK MEDICAL SPECIALISTS 44906 #038-75-1996, ▲ L1998 **ICE** *020
CRALL, Frederick V, Jr. 680 PARK AVE W 44906 #038-41-1977 L1982 **CD** *020 †20
CRASKE, W Don, III. 370 CLINE AVE 44907 #016-76-1980, ▲ L1986 **VS OS** *020
CROGHAN, Thomas Henry. 500 S TRIMBLE RD 44906 #038-40-1965 L1965 **OBG** *020 †30
CURRY, James D. ■ 44904 #038-06-1949 L1949 **R** *071 †80
DAWES, Michael D. 600 W 3RD ST 44906 #566-01-1985 L1995 **FM** *020 †18
DEES, Marvin F. ■ 44907 #012-05-1949 L1951 **IM CD** *071
DENTON, Robert Allen. 391 GLESSNER AVE 44903 #038-41-1979 L1980 **PUD CCM** *020 †20

DESAI, Kishorkumar K. 335 GLESSNER AVE 44903 #495-28-1972 L1982 **NM** *071 †80
DESAI, Vasanti K. 799 LEXINGTON AVE 44907 #495-22-1971 L1982 **AN** *071
DESAI, Yogesh K. 146 MARION AVE 44903 #495-48-1978 L1992 **P** *020
DETRICH, Daniel Earl. 215 WOOD ST, RICHLAND SURGICAL 44903 #038-41-1985 L1986 **GS** *020 †85
DORSEY, Cynthia Ann. 295 GLESSNER AVE, FL 4 44903 #016-02-1987 L1997 **END IM** *020 †20
DOSHI, Ashish Nikhil. 1515 OAK RUN CT 44906 #036-07-2008 *012
DOSHI, Nikhil. 799 LEXINGTON AVE, ANESTHESIA ASSOC OF MANSFI 44907 #495-48-1973 L1984 **AN** *020
DRAKE, Robert Lance. 680 PARK AVE W 44906 #038-75-1997, ▲ L1998 **FM** *020
EATON, Gregory. 680 PARK AVE W 44906 #038-40-1986 L1991 **CD** *020 †20
EXTEN, Robert E. 475 LEXINGTON AVE 44907 #038-40-1975 L1975 **IM HO** *020 †20
FAHMY, Andrew. 680 PARK AVE W 44906 #038-44-1989 L1991 **CD** *020 †20
FAHMY, Anthony Nabil. 215 WOOD ST, RICHLAND SURGICAL 44903 #038-44-1983 L1998 **GS** *020 †85
FAHMY, Nabil Gabra. ■ 44907 #330-01-1951 L1963 **AN** *071 †05
FAIN, Erin Beirne. 770 BALGREEN DR, STE 101 44906 #056-05-1988 L1992 **PD** *020 †55
FAIN, Jonathan Simon. 335 GLESSNER AVE, ASSOCIATED PATH LABS INC 44903 #056-05-1987 L1992 **PTH** *020 †50
FEICHTNER, Larry Richard. 500 S TRIMBLE RD 44906 #038-40-1967 L1967 **OBG** *071 †30
FERNANDEZ, Felipe Nery. 82 STURGES AVE 44902 #429-01-1958 L1975 **P** *071 †75
FERRINI, Victor Frank. 215 WOOD ST, RICHLAND SURGICAL 44903 #038-40-1996 L2000 **GS** *020 †85
FINLAYSON, George D. 335 GLESSNER AVE 44903 #038-06-1953 L1953 **IM** *071
FLINN, Celia Jane. 770 BALGREEN DR, SUTE 101 44906 #038-06-1976 L1977 **PD PDC** *020 †55
FRANTZ, Gary James. 248 BLYMYER AVE 44903 #038-06-1978 L1979 **FM** *020 †18
FREEMAN, Gary Stuart. 335 GLESSNER AVE 44903 #028-34-1967 L1968 **AN** *020 †05
GARBADAWALA, Mustafa S. 465 HOME RD N, INTERNAL MEDICINE ASSOC OF 44906 #038-43-1996 L1997 **IM** *020 †20
GARDILCIC, Stjepan. 675 BALLY ROW 44906 #957-01-1977 L1991 **U** *020
GARDNER, Raymond John. 248 BLYMYER AVE 44903 #038-40-1979 L1981 **FM** *020 †18
GIBSON, Lawrence Lee. 536 S TRIMBLE RD, MANSFIELD ORTHOPEDIC SURGE 44906 #041-12-1966 L1973 **ORS** *020 †40
GOLBUS, Ronald Jan. 215 WOOD ST 44903 #016-11-1969 L1976 **GS** *071 †85
GRANSON, Alfred, Jr. 70 MADISON RD 44905 #308-03-1986 L1997 **IM** *020
GRIMES, Eric Russell. 558 S TRIMBLE RD, ENT/HNS OF N.E. OHIO, INC. 44906 #038-06-2000 L2005 **OTO** *020 †45
GRUND, Bruce Mark. 248 BLYMYER AVE 44903 #051-04-1982 L1989 **FM** *020 †18
GUNZENHAEUSER, Michael D. 500 S TRIMBLE RD 44906 #038-40-1974 L1977 **OBG** *020 †30
GUTH, Joseph Jay. 536 S TRIMBLE RD 44906 #038-40-1988 L1993 **ORS** *020 †40
HAAR, Jay D. 605 S TRIMBLE RD, STE D 44906 #583-04-1966 L1978 **P** *020
HALDAR, Kali S. 270 PARK AVE W 44902 #495-32-1955 L1972 **GS PCS** *020
HEINS, Gregory C. 680 PARK AVE W, MID OHIO HEART CLC INC 44906 #028-78-1996, ▲ L2003 **CD IM** *020
HILL, Kevin Francis. 1987 W 4TH ST, MANSFIELD 44906 #035-03-1989 L1999 **DR** *020 †80
HOPE, George Malcolm. 335 GLESSNER AVE 44903 #919-05-1971 L1975 **EM PD** *020 †55,16
HOUSTON, William Robt. ■ 44906 #038-06-1948 L1948 **OPH** *020 †35
HUGHES, John Kelly. 341 CLINE AVE 44907 #038-43-1994 L1995 **IM** *020 †20
HURLEY, Jerome E. 555 LEXINGTON AVE 44907 #035-06-1953 L1959 **IM PHP** *020
JACKSON, James Bruce. ■ 44907 #038-40-1956 L1956 **GS OM** *071 †85
JOHNSTONE, Daniel Mackie. ■ 44904 #803-09-1950 L1965 **P** *071
JOSHI, Satish Sadashiv. 660 SCOTT DR, CRAWFORD COUNTY ANESTHESIO 44906 #495-21-1983 L1997 **AN** *020 †05
JUHASZ, Tamas Y. 799 LEXINGTON AVE 44907 #473-04-1990 L2001 **AN PME** *020 †05
KAMADANA, Mohan Rao. 661 S TRIMBLE RD, KIDNEY ASSOCIATES, INC. 44906 #495-50-1971 L1978 **NEP IM** *020 †20
KANNAPIRAN, Kandhasamy. 339 CLINE AVE 44907 #495-42-1968 L1983 **IM** *020
KANNAPIRAN, Madhu. ■ 44906 #038-40-2005 L2005 **IM** *012
KAUFMAN, Sam. 335 GLESSNER AVE 44903 #010-01-1966 L1968 **PLM** *020
KAYE, Joel Edmund. 146 MARION AVE 44903 #038-40-1960 L1960 **R NM** *071 †80,28
KEITH, Fraser Mc Lennan. 770 BALGREEN DR, STE 107 44906 #065-05-1976 L2004 **TS** *020 †90,85
KOH, Kyee Young. 335 GLESSNER AVE 44903 #583-02-1971 L1979 **RO** *020 †80
LAI, Mei-Chiew. 335 GLESSNER AVE 44903 #244-03-1973 L1985 **PM LM** *020 †60
LANGACHER, Karl T. ■ 44904 #024-01-1936 L1937 **GP OM** *071
LEE, Andrew John. 2981 W 4TH ST 44906 #048-13-1991 L1995 **IM PD** *020 †55,20
LENEHAN, Stephen Paul. 1221 S TRIMBLE RD, STE C3 44907 #038-40-1982 L1983 **CD IM** *020 †20
LIGMAN, Paul Jos. 1030 CRICKET LN 44906 #030-06-1990 L1994 **AN** *020 †05
LITAO, Achilles Espino. 2003 W 4TH ST, ONTARIO CHILDREN'S HEALTH 44906 #748-10-1992 L2005 **PD PSM** *020 †55
LIU, Jackson. 661 S TRIMBLE RD, KIDNEY ASSOC INC 44906 #038-44-2000 L2006 **NEP IM** *020
LOESCH, George Walter. ■ 44903 #038-40-1956 L1956 **GYN** *071 †30
LOMEO, Mark David. 466 S TRIMBLE RD 44906 #038-06-1990 L1993 **OPH** *020 †35 ‡
LONG, G David. 2007 W 4TH ST 44906 #063-01-1980 L1983 **FM** *020 †18
LUNA, Teodoro Arellano. 1750 W 4TH ST, MEDCENTRAL WORKABLE 44906 #748-01-1959 L1983 **OM PD** *020
LUNDEEN, James E, Sr. 1 MARION AVE, STE 113 44903 #016-42-1983 L1985 **OM LM** *020
MAC FARLANE, Charles E. 1121 LEXINGTON AVE 44907 #132-01-1961 L1972 **GYN** *071 †30
MALHOTRA, Ravindra Kumar. 1070 CRICKET LN 44906 #495-47-1980 L1995 **IM GE** *020 †20
MARTIN, Bruce Allen. 630 LEXINGTON AVE 44907 #038-43-1985 L1986 **IM PD** *030
MASSIE, David Walter. 824 PARK AVE W 44906 #041-13-1982 L1983 **P** *020 †75
MASSIE, Walter Arthur. 824 PARK AVE W 44906 #041-13-1948 L1954 **P N** *071 †75
MATHAN, Sukumar. 339 CLINE AVE 44907 #495-04-1984 L1997 **IM** *020 †20
MAXWELL, Robert Joseph. 215 WOOD ST, RICHLAND SURGICAL 44903 #041-13-1990 L1995 **GS** *020 †85
MC CARTHER, David Douglas. 600 W 3RD ST 44906 #038-40-1988 L1992 **FM** *020 †18
MC GEE, Scott William. 371 CLINE AVE, OHIO CANCER SPECIALISTS 44907 #038-40-2000 L2000 **HO** *020 †20
MCLEAN, Shoghi Mihdi. 335 GLESSNER AVE 44903 #308-04-1995 L2000 **IM** *020 †20
MC MILLAN, Edroy Lorenzo. 500 S TRIMBLE RD 44906 #005-12-1987 L1991 **OBG** *020 †30
MIDKIFF, Anthony Jos. 7721 STEAM CORNERS RD, ATTN SAFETY OFFICE 44904 #038-44-1991 L1992 **EM** *020 †16
MILLER, William Joseph. 370 CLINE AVE 44907 #045-01-1987 L1996 **VIR** *020 †80
MONEME, Victor Udemba. 2003 W 4TH ST 44906 #690-01-1972 L1979 **PD PHO** *020 †55
MOONEY, James Harold. 1456 PARK AVE W 44906 #038-06-1994 L1996 **IM** *020 †20
MORALES-RAMOS, Teresita. 335 GLESSNER AVE 44903 #042-03-1981 L2002 **EM GS** *020 †16
MORITZ, Deborah Lynne. 335 GLESSNER AVE 44903 #048-14-1984 L1987 **D DS** *020 †15
MORKEL, Kevin E. ■ 44907 #649-14-1982 *074
MUNTHER, Antoine Saiid. 215 WOOD ST, RICHLAND SURGICAL 44903 #605-01-1972 L1993 **GS ON** *020 †85
MYERS, Stephan Ray. 770 BALGREEN DR, STE 209 44906 #038-41-1980 L1983 **GS** *020 †85
NADOLSON, Karen Sue. 741 SCHOLL RD 44907 #038-40-1991 L1994 **IM** *020 †20
NANI, Carlos Cesar. 370 CLINE AVE 44907 #132-02-1970 L1985 **PS HS** *020 †65 ‡
NGUYEN, Dung. 335 GLESSNER AVE 44903 #032-01-1989 L2007 **RO** *020 †80
NIRMALNATH, John S. 295 GLESSNER AVE 44903 #495-04-1979 L1994 **IM** *020 †20
NITZSCHE, David Dale. 799 LEXINGTON AVE 44907 #038-41-1985 L1988 **AN** *020
NOVY, Angela Mae. 295 GLESSNER AVE, FL 4 44903 #038-40-1997 L2003 **END** *020 †20
OPREMCAK, E Mitchel. 466 S TRIMBLE RD 44906 #038-40-1981 L1982 **OPH IG** *020 †35
ORTEGA-CARR, Debora Ann. 370 CLINE AVE 44907 #038-40-1987 L1994 **AI** *020 †20,03
PALACIOS, Jaime Jesus. ■ 44907 #264-03-1956 L1968 **D PTH** *071
PARKINSON, John Wm. 799 LEXINGTON AVE 44907 #051-07-1984 L1985 **AN** *020 †05
PATEL, Chandravadan P. 741 SCHOLL RD 44907 #495-01-1975 L1985 **P GP** *020
PATEL, Chaturbhai B. 458 GLESSNER AVE 44903 #495-22-1972 L1980 **PUD IM** *020 †20
PATEL, Mital Shirish. 335 GLESSNER AVE, HOSPITALISTS MANAGMENT GR 44903 #496-38-2001 L2006 **IM** *020 †20
PAUL, Anil E. 120 STURGES AVE, NORTH CENTRAL OHIO CLINIC, 44903 #495-99-1994 L1999 **IM** *020 †20
PAWAR, Ravindra. 661 S TRIMBLE RD 44906 #495-20-1985 L1992 **NEP** *020 †20
PAWAR, Rehka. 1456 PARK AVE W, STE N 44906 #496-01-1986 L1993 **NEP** *020 †20
PENHOS, J C. 635 S TRIMBLE RD 44906 #010-01-1973 L1989 **GS** *020 †85
PERVEZ, Rashid. 800 PARK AVE W, STE 103 44906 #704-02-1982 L2000 **P** *020
PHILLIPS, Charles Bernard. ■ 44907 #005-12-1955 L1956 **GP** *071
PRUETT, Allison Marie. 500 S TRIMBLE RD 44906 #038-43-1998 L1999 **OBG** *020 †30
QUICK, Carl Merwyn. ■ 44906 #038-40-1943 L1944 **OPH** *071 †45
QUICK, Leonard Dennis. 466 S TRIMBLE RD 44906 #038-41-1980 L1980 **OPH** *020 †35
RAJAN, Semur Perumal G. 275 CLINE AVE 44907 #495-16-1962 L1971 **GS TRS** *020 †85
RAJARAM, Venkatakrishnan. 1456 PARK AVE W, 1456 VA CLINIC 44906 #496-23-1993 L2000 **IM** *020 †20
RAMAN, Palani K. 408 GLESSNER AVE 44903 #495-16-1977 L1982 **GE IM** *020 †20
RANCHOD, Nagin. 517 PARK AVE E, MADISON URGENT CARE CENTER 44905 #869-04-1959 L1964 **IM** *071
REDDING, Mark Mccleery. 600 W 3RD ST 44906 #038-45-1988 L1997 **PD** *020 †55
REDDING, Sarah B. 741 SCHOLL RD 44907 #038-45-1988 L1997 **GPM** *020 †70 ‡
REED-DEDEHAYIR, Barbara A. 177 PARK AVE W 44902 #038-40-1949 L1949 **IM OS** *071
REHMAR, Alan Jay. 466 S TRIMBLE RD 44906 #038-40-1985 L1986 **OPH** *020 †35
RICHARDSON, James Edward. 370 CLINE AVE STE C6 44907 #036-01-1981 L1982 **IM** *020 †20
RICHARDSON, V Diana. 2003 W 4TH ST 44906 #038-06-1981 L1982 **PD PHP** *020 †55
ROEMER, Peter Timothy. 120 STURGES AVE 44903 #038-40-1974 L1974 **FM** *020 †18
ROHIRA, Bhagwanti L. 2001 W 4TH ST, # A 44906 #495-01-1973 L1983 **N** *020
ROSMARIN, Phillip Carl. 295 GLESSNER AVE 44903 #038-40-1981 L1989 **IM** *020 †20
RYCKMAN, Stewart Douglas. 335 GLESSNER AVE 44903 #038-40-1977 L1981 **OBG** *071 †30
SAMPATH, Govindarajan. 1456 PARK AVE W, LOUIS STOKES CLEVELAND VAM 44906 #495-33-1975 L1996 **IM** *020 †75
SANSAIT, Nicomedes M. 741 SCHOLL RD 44907 #748-07-1988 L1999 **CHP P** *020
SCHAMADAN, William Evan. ■ 44907 #038-40-1956 L1956 **OS OBG** *071 †30
SCHOUTKO, Walter Wm. 770 BALGREEN DR, STE 207 44906 #038-40-1991 L1993 **OBG** *020 †30
SCHUMER, Douglas James. 240 W COOK RD 44907 #038-43-1987 L1994 **OPH** *020 †35
SECREST, James Lloyd. ■ 44906 #035-45-1948 L1954 **D** *071
SELSER, Richard E, Jr. 466 S TRIMBLE RD, OHIO EYE ASSOCIATES 44906 #021-05-1981 L2006 **OPH** *020 †35
SETHI, Sushil Mitter. 1221 S TRIMBLE RD, STE B1 44907 #495-29-1962 L1991 **TS GS** *020 †85,90,70
SHAKER, Chandra R. 120 STURGES AVE 44903 #495-09-1970 L1978 **PD GP** *020 †55
SHAW, Charles Henry, Jr. 370 CLINE AVE 44907 #038-40-1978 L1981 **PD** *020 †55
SHETH, Piyush N. 215 WOOD ST, RICHLAND SURGICAL 44903 #016-43-1990 L1996 **GS** *020 †85
SHOOK, Charles David. ■ 44907 #038-41-1965 L1965 **VS** *071 †85,90
SIDDIQUI, Siraj Ahmed. 2666 LEXINGTON AVE 44904 #495-65-1980 L1993 **IM** *020
SRINGERI, Vijeth R. 275 CLINE AVE 44907 #495-09-1990 L1999 **IM** *020 †20
STADNICK, David Storer. 536 S TRIMBLE RD, MANSFIELD ORTH SURGEONS IN 44906 #033-05-1981 L1984 **RHU IM** *020 †20
STOCKINGER, Fred Stanley. 770 BALGREEN DR STE 209, OSU CARDIO SURG 44906 #017-20-1966 L1997 **TS** *020 †85,90
STONE, Thomas Robt. ■ 44906 #030-05-1990 L1997 **OM** *020 †70
STRUBLE, Robert Allen. 1221 S TRIMBLE RD 44907 #038-40-1966 L1966 **A** *020 †55,03
SUBICH, David Chas. 120 STURGES AVE 44903 #038-43-1982 L1983 **IM** *020
SURESH, Pammal. 1221 S TRIMBLE RD, STE B2 44907 #495-04-1977 L1988 **CD IC** *020 †20 ‡
SWARN, Frances Irma. 741 SCHOLL RD 44907 #055-02-1996 L2000 **P** *020
TADDEO, Ronald Michael. 370 CLINE AVE, STE B3 44907 #016-43-1997 L1998 **IM** *020 †20 ‡
THAI, Khanh Hoang. 335 GLESSNER AVE 44903 #038-40-1996 L1998 **EM** *020 †16
THOMPSON, Lawrence C. ■ 44907 #038-40-1948 L1949 **PD** *071 †55
TICORAS, Christ John. 770 BALGREEN DR, STE 201 44906 #038-45-1991 L1992 **D** *020 †15
TIMPERMAN, Albert Leo. 295 GLESSNER AVE 44903 #016-43-1963 L1964 **NS** *020 †25
TOGLIATTI, Theodore J. 812 PARK AVE E 44905 #038-41-1997 L2004 **PMM PM** *020 †20,60
TOME, Julie A. 799 LEXINGTON AVE 44907 #038-44-1983 L1998 **AN PD** *020 †05 ‡
TOWARD, Brett Edward. 2007 W 4TH ST 44906 #038-44-1996 L1998 **FM** *020 †18
TURKSON, Emmanuel Ofosu. 68 STURGES AVE 44902 #409-10-1966 L1984 **IM** *075
VADADA, Padmini Veera. 555 LEXINGTON AVE, MORCHD 44907 #495-11-1976 L1999 **FM** *020 †18
VADADA, Suresh C. 661 S TRIMBLE RD 44906 #495-11-1975 L1998 **NEP** *020 †20
VAIDYA, Prity Sunil. 295 GLESSNER AVE, THIRD FLOOR 44903 #495-01-1983 L1989 **ID IM** *020 †20
VAIDYA, Sunilkumar J. 335 GLESSNER AVE 44903 #495-22-1980 L1990 **PUD IM** *020 †20
VIAU, Michael Roger. 536 S TRIMBLE RD 44906 #025-07-1979 L1984 **ORS** *020 †40
VIETTI, Michael John. 558 S TRIMBLE RD 44906 #038-41-1994 L1995 **OTO** *020 †45
VIGESAA, Greg S. 680 PARK AVE W 44906 #025-12-1982 L1988 **CD IM** *020
VISWANATHAN, Srividya. 1456 PARK AVE W, VA CLINIC 44906 #496-23-1996 L2000 **IM** *020 †20
VOCAL, Rodolfo Suria. 556 LEXINGTON AVE 44907 #748-07-1957 L1964 **P** *071

■ = Address Information Privacy Protected

VOEGELE, Albert H Robt. 335 GLESSNER AVE 44903 #041-01-1940 L1947 **IM** *071 †20
WAGENHALS, Karen Sue. ■ 44904 #038-40-1976 L1977 **PTH** *020 †50
WESTON, Terry Lee. 335 GLESSNER AVE 44903 #038-40-1975 L1975 **FM** *020 †18
WHITE, Linda Lee. 913 BOWMAN ST 44903 #047-20-1984 L1987 **IM** *020
WIECHER, Frederick Jos. 466 OLD MILL RUN RD 44906 #038-40-1968 L1968 **U** *020 †95
WIGGIN, James Walker. 335 GLESSNER AVE 44903 #024-01-1958 L1963 **GS** *071 †85
WILEY, Robert F, Jr. 370 CLINE AVE 44907 #047-05-1966 L1971 **TS VS** *020
WILSON, Arthur Hunter. 500 S TRIMBLE RD 44906 #055-02-1984 L1988 **OBG** *020 †30
WOOD, Timothy Clifton. 480 GLESSNER AVE 44903 #038-40-1986 L1998 **D** *020 †18,15
YOUNG, Charles Gladden. 370 CLINE AVE 44907 #038-40-1957 L1957 **IM** *071 †20

MANTUA — PORTAGE

GROSSBERG, Richard Ivan. 9772 DIAGONAL RD, HATTIE LARLHAM FOUNDATION 44255 #041-09-1993 L1999 **PD** *020 †55
SAFKO, Lonna Louise. ■ 44255 #038-44-2008 *012

MAPLE HEIGHTS — CUYAHOGA

GOLOB, Joseph Frank. ■ 44137 #041-12-2004 L2004 **GS** *012
HOCHMAN, Todd Scott. 20676 SOUTHGATE PARK BLVD, STE 100 44137 #038-43-2000 L2000 **MPD** *020
POLAND, John Jack. ■ 44137 #407-10-1951 L1958 **OS P** *075
SIDHU, Surinder Singh. 5183 LEE RD 44137 #496-13-1979 L1999 *020
ZECHEL, Marc Andre. 20508 SOUTHGATE PARK BLVD, NORTH COAST DENTAL 44137 #038-06-2005 L2005 **GS** *100

MARBLEHEAD — OTTAWA

ZGRABIK, Scott Donald. 3914 S MEMORIAL SHOREWY DR 43440 #038-43-1985 L1988 **EM** *020 †16

MARENGO — MORROW

FERRARO, James Wm. ■ 43334 #038-40-1967 L1967 **PS FPS** *071 †85,65

MARIA STEIN — MERCER

SCHWIETERMAN, Donald Jos. 8381 STATE ROUTE 119, D J SCHWIETERMAN MD INC 45860 #038-41-1958 L1958 **FM** *071 †18
SCHWIETERMAN, James Thos. 8381 STATE ROUTE 119 45860 #038-41-1988 L1990 **FM** *020 †18
SCHWIETERMAN, Thomas D. 8381 STATE ROUTE 119 45860 #038-41-1993 L1995 **FM** *020 †18

MARIETTA — WASHINGTON

ABALOS, Jose Marzan. 611 2ND ST 45750 #748-10-1969 L1988 **AN PME** *020
AHMED, Rashid. PO BOX 284 45750 #704-02-1966 L1975 **DR** *020 †80
ANDERSON, Roger Dale. 400 MATTHEW ST 45750 #422-01-1983 L1992 **IM ID** *020 †20
BOKER, Steven Mark. 401 MATTHEW ST, MARIETTA IMAGING, INC 45750 #010-02-1986 L1996 **DR R** *020 †80
BOSO, Edwin Brian. 611 2ND ST 45750 #055-01-1986 L1996 **AN** *020 †05
BROCKETT, Michael Kim. 400 MATTHEW ST, STE 220 45750 #038-43-1977 L1979 **FM** *020 †18
BURKE, Paul Webber, Jr. 324 PIKE ST 45750 #024-07-1977 L1986 **GS** *075 †85
BUTLER, Andrew Kimmins. ■ 45750 #016-01-1942 L1956 **DR** *071 †80
BYLER, Debra Lynn. 401 MATTHEW ST 45750 #039-05-1984 L1994 **N PD** *020 †75,55
BYLER, Tony L. 701 HILDRETH LN 45750 #041-12-1988 L1993 **P OS** *020 †75
CAIN, Richard Edward. 210 S 7TH ST 45750 #055-02-1988 L1998 **EM** *020 †18
CARDENAS, Ignacio. 611 2ND ST 45750 #055-02-1988 L1996 **OS** *020 †05
CARLSON, Judy Ann. 401 MATTHEW ST 45750 #005-12-1981 L2006 **PD** *020 †55
CASES, Jane Alano. 701 HILDRETH LN 45750 #748-01-1993 L2005 **END** *020 †20
CASTO, David Roger. 802 WAYNE ST, STE 204 45750 #038-41-1983 L1984 **IM** *020 †20
CAWLEY, Kelli Ann. 401 MATTHEW ST 45750 #038-40-1992 L1994 **HO** *020 †20
CLARE, Timothy Peter. 800 PIKE ST, STE 3 45750 #041-02-1982 L1985 **FM** *020 †18
CLARK, Richard Don. 802 WAYNE ST 45750 #038-40-1987 L1991 **FM** *020 †18
COOPER, Joseph David. 400 MATTHEW STE 100 45750 #041-09-1983 L1987 **OPH** *020 †35
COOPER, Warren Lindley. 410 2ND ST 45750 #055-01-1981 L1985 **OBG** *020
CRUIKSHANK, Dwight P, III. ■ 45750 #023-01-1941 L1941 **OBG** *071
DEHMLOW, Curtis Lew. 400 MATTHEW ST 45750 #016-11-1966 L1972 **IM** *020
DE JOSEF, Aniano Beltran. 401 MATTHEW ST DEPT PATH 45750 #748-01-1967 L1976 **PTH** *020 †50
DENNIS, Lloyd David. 800 PIKE ST, STE 3 45750 #038-41-1982 L1984 **FM** *020 †18
DICKERSON, Susan Ellen. 401 MATTHEW ST, ANESTHESIA DEPARTMENT 45750 #045-01-1981 L1998 **AN** *020 †05
EGLI, Charles Theodore. ■ 45750 #016-11-1963 L1985 **EM** *071 †85
ERDELYI, Bob-Paul. 400 MATTHEW ST 45750 #198-01-1995 L1999 **IM** *020 †20
FLEMING, Donald Eugene. ■ 45750 #051-04-1952 L1954 **GP** *071
GALANG, Leandro Pingol. 324 PIKE ST 45750 #748-01-1965 L2005 **FM GS** *020 †18
GALUPO, Maria Paula. 410 2ND ST 45750 #038-40-1997 L1999 **OBG** *020 †30
GIRO, Eva Katarzyna. 400 MATTHEW ST 45750 #759-03-1993 L1999 **IM** *020
GROSEL, John Michael. 401 MATTHEW ST 45750 #038-40-1992 L1994 **DR** *020 †80
GROSEL, William Cornelius. 401 MATTHEW ST 45750 #038-40-1980 L1984 **DR** *020
GRZONKA, Robert Louis. 400 MATTHEW ST, STE 303 45750 #016-06-1985 L2005 **U** *020 †95
GUTIERREZ, Gilberto D. ■ 45750 #682-01-1956 L1967 **GP GS** *020
HAMIRANI, Mirza Tajuddin. 1019 PIKE ST, GAMBRO HEALTHCARE 45750 #704-02-1990 L2002 **NEP** *020 †20
HARRIS, Deborah G. 1106 COLEGATE DR 45750 #038-75-1998, ▲ 2001 **GS** *020
HAWKINS, Larry Todd. 701 HILDRETH LN 45750 #038-43-1995 L1996 **P** *020 †75
HEFLIN, Robert E, II. 611 2ND ST 45750 #055-01-1984 L1996 **AN** *020 †05

HERSHEY, Richard Hutton. 401 MATTHEW ST 45750 #041-01-1971 L1973 **GS** *020 †85
HILL, David Peter. 701 HILDRETH LN 45750 #036-07-1969 L1974 **P** *020 †75
HILLE, Richard R. 401 MATTHEW ST 45750 #038-40-1951 L1951 **GP** *071
HOY, James Elwyn. 401 MATTHEW ST 45750 #038-41-1959 L1959 **OPH** *071 †35
HUNKELE, Eric Carl. 802 WAYNE ST, STE 204 45750 #055-01-1995 L2002 **FM** *020 †18
HUNKELE, Kimberly Dawn. 802 WAYNE ST, STE 204 45750 #055-01-1995 L2002 **IM P** *020 †20
IMAM, Mona A. 400 MATTHEW ST, STE 101 45750 #849-01-1986 L1997 **AI** *020 †03,55
JACOBY, William Dair. 400 MATTHEW ST STE 212, SUITE 212 45750 #038-41-1967 L1967 **PD** *071 †55
JOHNSON, David Grant. 401 MATTHEW ST, MARIETTA MEMORIAL HOSPITAL 45750 #055-01-1975 L1988 **EM IM** *071 †16
JONES, Brenda Fay. 210 N 7TH ST, STE 200 45750 #036-01-1980 L1987 **OPH** *020 †35
KANE, Matthew Donald. 401 MATTHEW ST 45750 #012-01-1990 L1996 **DR** *020 †80
KLUGE, Glenn Herman. 1106 COLEGATE DR 45750 #011-02-1979 L1988 **IM** *020 †20
KRUPADEV, Hitnebagilu L. 408 3RD ST 45750 #495-33-1972 L1978 **IM IMG** *020 †20
KUO, Che-Fu. 400 MATTHEW ST STE 201 45750 #244-01-1980 L1998 **IM** *020 †20
LACEY, David Wm. 800 PIKE ST STE 3 45750 #038-40-1986 L1994 **PM SCI** *020 †60
LEE, Francis Yew-Wei. 400 MATTHEW ST, STE 305 45750 #825-01-1984 L1997 **PCC SME** *020 †20
LEE, John Chong. 401 MATTHEW ST 45750 #038-41-1985 L1986 **AN CCA** *020 †05
LEOPOLD, Kenneth Joe. 800 PIKE ST, STE 3 45750 #038-43-1977 L1978 **FM** *020 †18
LOUDEN, Malcolm B, Jr. 401 MATTHEW ST 45750 #055-01-1976 L1980 **N SME** *020 †75
MACATOL, Fortunato R. 401 MATTHEW ST DEPT PATH 45750 #748-11-1967 L1973 **PTH** *020 †50
MACATOL, Matthew Jonathan. ■ 45750 #038-44-2003 L2004 **PTH** *020
MAYO, Joseph Raymond. 400 MATTHEW ST STE 302 45750 #038-40-1983 L1983 **CD** *020 †20
MC ELROY, James Allen. 400 MATTHEW ST 45750 #038-40-1996 L1997 **GS** *020 †85
MEDARAMETLA, Hanumantharao. 401 MATTHEW ST, ANESTHESIA 45750 #495-57-1971 L1987 **AN** *020
MINARD, Alexander D. 400 MATTHEW ST 45750 #038-41-1999 L1999 **PM** *020 †60
MOREHEAD, Michael A. 401 MATTHEW ST 45750 #055-01-1970 L1974 **N SME** *020 †75
MYERS, Todd Richard. 410 2ND ST 45750 #055-01-1995 L1999 **OBG** *020 †30
NAYAK, Naresh Kumar. 611 2ND ST 45750 #065-06-1985 L1991 **ORS OTR** *020 †40
NESE, Sevket Turgut. ■ 45750 #902-01-1954 L1970 **AN** *020
NICKERSON, Irving A. 401 MATTHEW ST 45750 #038-40-1953 L1953 **EM OS** *071
NILL, Michael Robt. 400 MATTHEW ST, STE 401 45750 #041-12-1991 L1993 **GS** *020 †85
PANTELIDIS, Peter George. 400 MATTHEW ST, STE 209 45750 #055-01-2000 L2000 **APM** *020 †05
PARMER, Shane Scott. 400 MATTHEW ST, ST. 340 45750 #051-07-1998 L2006 **VS** *100 †85
PATEY, Jeffrey A. 401 MATTHEW ST 45750 #011-04-1990 L1991 **EM** *020 †16
PETTY, Gary Joe. 800 PIKE ST, STE 3 45750 #055-02-1992 L1999 **FM** *020 †18
PRACHUN, Paul. 401 MATTHEW ST 45750 #065-01-1971 L1992 **DR NM** *020 †20
RINGS, Sudhakar. 401 MATTHEW ST, MARIETTA MEMORIAL HOSPITAL 45750 #496-24-1994 L2002 **FM** *020 †18
ROSE, William Chandler. 401 MATTHEW ST, DEPT EM 45750 #038-44-1990 L1997 **EM** *020 †16
SCILEPPI, Edward Myron. 1106 COLEGATE DR 45750 #035-08-1961 L1973 **GYN** *071 †30
SESHACHARY, Paravasthu. 401 MATTHEW ST, MARIETTA MEM HOSP 45750 #495-53-1970 L1980 **CD IM** *020 †20
SMITH, Macy Curtis, Jr. 400 MATTHEW ST 45750 #001-02-2001 L2004 **ICE** *012 †20
SOLE, Leonard Scott. 401 MATTHEW ST 45750 #055-02-1994 L1998 **N** *020 †75
STEIGER, Charles A. 400 MATTHEW ST STE 303 45750 #056-05-1993 L1999 **U** *020 †95
TIPTON, Jon Paul. ■ 45750 #038-40-1960 L1960 **A PUD** *071
TOKODI, George, Jr. 4800 STATE ROUTE 60 45750 #055-75-1980, ▲ L1981 **ORS** *020
USMAN, Ahsan. 400 MATTHEW ST 45750 #704-01-1999 L2003 **IM** *020 †20
WHALIN, Brian Geoffrey. 324 PIKE ST 45750 #016-45-1978 L1978 **EM OM** *020
WHITACRE, Mary Lois. ■ 45750 #038-40-1956 L1956 **PHP GP** *071
WIEFERICH, James Roger. 800 PIKE ST, STE 3 45750 #023-01-1983 L1990 **FM** *020 †18
WILLIAMS, Rodney Richard. 410 2ND ST 45750 #055-01-1973 L1984 **OBG** *071 †30
WIRTZ, David Leonard. 400 MATTHEW ST 45750 #038-40-1975 L1975 **M** *020 †20
YOAK, Matthew Brian. 400 MATTHEW ST, STE 203 45750 #055-02-1995 L2004 **PS** *020 †85,65

MARION — MARION

AHMAD, Mushtaq. 1021 HARDING MEMORIAL PKWY, CHEST MEDICINE 43302 #704-09-1983 L2006 **PCC** *020 †20
ANDROW, David Paul. 1000 MCKINLEY PARK DR, MARION GENERAL HOSPITAL 43302 #038-43-1988 L1990 **EM** *020
ARORA, Chander Mohan. 1728 MARION WALDO RD 43302 #495-45-1982 L1987 **IM** *020
ASFAW, Teferi. ■ 43302 #605-01-1967 L1978 **EM** *020
ASHWORTH, Jeanne Ellen. 1150 CRESCENT HEIGHTS RD 43302 #038-41-1991 L1999 **RO** *020 †80
AWASTY, Vivek Ranjan. 980 S PROSPECT ST, # 2 43302 #495-73-1985 L1993 **IM** *020 †20
BAILEY, David Groves. 990 S PROSPECT ST STE 1 43302 #025-01-1971 L1983 **OTO HNS** *020 †45
BELL, Gregory Allen. 1036 MT VERNON AVE 43302 #038-40-1985 L1985 **FM** *020 †18
BRIGHTMAN, Rebecca Paige. 1000 MCKINLEY PARK DR 43302 #024-05-1984 L1985 **NS** *020 †25
BUCK, Edward Geo, Jr. 1000 MCKINLEY PARK DR 43302 #023-07-1963 L1984 **U GS** *020 †95
CAETON, Anthony John. 1000 MCKINLEY PARK DR, MARION GENERAL HOSP 43302 #020-12-1980 L1999 **NPM PD** *020 †55
CAMPBELL, Bradley David. 1073 HARDING MEMORIAL PKWY 43302 #038-40-1991 L1997 **OBG** *020 †30
CHAUDHRY, Arshad Nazir. ■ 43302 #704-01-1973 L1982 **HEM IM** *020 †20
COLLIER, William Rucker. 1000 MCKINLEY PARK DR 43302 #038-43-2000 L2001 **FM** *020 †18
CONCEPCION, Raymundo L. 1040 DELAWARE AVE 43302 #748-07-1953 L1964 **U** *020
CULLER, Paul Ridge. 1000 MCKINLEY PARK DR 43302 #038-40-1989 L1990 **FM** *020 †18
DAVIS, Mark Eugene. 1069 DELAWARE AVE 43302 #038-45-1989 L1990 **FM EM** *040 †18
DAVY, Edwin Gilbert. 1000 MCKINLEY PARK DR, MARION GENERAL HOSPITAL 43302 #038-40-1969 L1969 **DR** *071 †80
DE LOS REYES, Bayani B. 1000 MCKINLEY PARK DR 43302 #748-08-1968 L1981 **AN** *020
DEL ROSARIO, Luciano P. 1073 HARDING MEMORIAL PKWY 43302 #748-08-1966 L1973 **PD** *020 †55
DESAI, Bipin M. 1125 ELLEN KAY DR STE D 43302 #965-01-1981 L1989 **P** *020 †75
DIXON, Kathy Diane. 1069 DELAWARE AVE STE 202 43302 #038-45-1988 L1990 **FM** *020 †18

■ = Address Information Privacy Protected

EBOH, Noel Nse, II. ■ 43302 #038-43-2003 L2008 *100

FOULK, David Wm. 1140 INDEPENDENCE AVE 43302 #038-40-1980 L1980 **OBG** *020 †30

FRIEDLEY, Walter Jonathan. 1040 DELAWARE AVE, SMITH CLINIC 43302 #422-01-1997 L1999 **PD** *020 †55

GARNER, Timothy Francis. 1069 DELAWARE AVE, STE 205 43302 #020-12-1982 L1984 **FM DIA** *020 †18

GILLIAM, Dorsey Lee. 1125 ELLEN KAY DR, STE E 43302 #038-40-1962 L1962 **OM FM** *062

GOLDER, Philip M. ■ 43302 #038-41-1977 L1979 **PTH** *071 †50

HART, Dale Evans. MC KINLEY PARK DR 43302 #038-06-1944 1944 **GS IM** *071 †85

HECKENDORN, Ted Allan. MC KINLEY PARK DR 43302 #038-40-1980 L1983 **PTH** *071 †50

HEINZMANN, Henry Geo. 1040 DELAWARE AVE, F.C. SMITH CLINIC 43302 #033-05-1971 L1978 **PUD IM** *071 †20

HERING, James Stephen. ■ 43302 #038-40-1965 L1965 **TS GS** *071 †90,85

HETRICK, Ernest Wm. 666 VIRGINIA AVE 43302 #038-41-1967 L1967 **R** *071 †80

JAFRI, Iram. 1167 INDEPENDENCE AVE 43302 #704-25-1992 L2000 **PD** *020 †55

JERNEJCIC, Randy Michael. 1000 MCKINLEY PARK DR, DEPT OF EMERGENCY MEDICAL 43302 #038-40-1997 L1999 **FM EM** *020 †18

JOSHI, Raj Kumar. 1728 MARION WALDO RD 43302 #495-45-1981 L1999 **IM** *020 †20

KANNAN, Kevin Robert. 1050 DELAWARE AVE, SMITH CLINIC 43302 #495-17-1974 L1981 **CD IM** *020

KAPCAR, Albert Danl. ■ 43302 #041-02-1944 L1950 **U** *071 †95

KARAKULA, Thulasi. 1000 MCKINLEY PARK DR, MARION GENERAL HOSPITAL 43302 #495-62-1999 L2005 **IM** *020 †20

KEELER, William Henry. ■ 43302 #035-09-1948 L1975 **GP GPM** *071 †70

KELLER, John Jeffrey. 1040 DELAWARE AVE, SMITH CLINIC 43302 #038-41-1998 L1999 **CD** *020 †20

KELLUM, Jesse Blake, Jr. 1728 MARION WALDO RD, STE B 43302 #027-01-1980 L1984 **N** *020 †75

KELNER, Paul Evan. 1000 MCKINLEY PARK DR 43302 #038-40-1989 L1991 **FM** *020 †18

KHAN, Muhammad Ibrahim A. 1199 DELAWARE AVE 43302 #704-16-1991 L2004 **IM** *020 †20

KIRKHAM, Steven Michael. 1462 MARION WALDO RD 43302 #038-40-1991 L1992 **OPH** *020 †35

KIRKHAM, William Howard. 1050 DELAWARE AVE 43302 #038-41-1959 L1959 **PTH** *071 †50

KNOX, David Wayne. 125 EXECUTIVE DR STE 200 43302 #038-40-1967 L1967 **D** *020 †18,15

KUNDRA, Hena. 1040 DELAWARE AVE, SMITH CLINIC 43302 #496-17-1991 L1999 **IM** *020 †20

LANDEFELD, Ronald Alfred. ■ 43302 #038-40-1973 L1974 **IM** *075

LEMASTER, Roy Neal. ■ 43302 #038-40-2007 L2007 **FP** *012

LENZO, Victor Geo. 1040 DELAWARE AVE 43302 #038-40-1958 L1958 **FM PD** *020 †18

LEVITSKY, Lance. 1462 MARION WALDO RD 43302 #038-40-1971 L1971 **OPH** *020 †35

LIM, Shun Ping. 1199 DELAWARE AVE STE 1 43302 #143-08-1970 L1983 **CD CCM** *020 †20

LIU, Ching-Shau. 940 MARION WILLIMSPRT RD E 43302 #244-03-1962 L1978 **GP** *020

LUI, Chuck Hing. 413 EXECUTIVE DR 43302 #243-64-1961 L1979 **AN** *020

LUNZ, Steven Richard. 1150 CRESCENT HEIGHTS RD 43302 #038-41-1985 L1986 **IM** *020 †20

MATURU, Amita Venkata. ■ 43302 #038-40-2007 **IM** *012

MAY, Albert Nast. 1040 DELAWARE AVE 43302 #041-09-1959 L1965 **PD PDA** *071 †55

MC GLEW, James Ambrose. MC KINLEY PARK DR 43302 #028-34-1944 L1950 **CD IM** *071

MILLS, Richard Ward, Jr. 43301 #016-06-1942 L1950 **IM** *071 †20

MITCHELL, Betty Margaret. 1040 DELAWARE AVE, SMITH CLINIC 43302 #025-12-1997 L1998 **GPM** *020

MOODLEY, Jaybalan R. 960 S PROSPECT ST, MARION WOMEN'S HEALTH CENT 43302 #038-40-1991 L1994 **OBG** *020 †30

MORTERA, Antonio Narciso. 1051 HARDING MEMORIAL PKWY 43302 #748-02-1952 L1968 **U** *071 †95

NOWACKI, Bernard Harold. 1043 HARDING MEMORIAL PKWY 43302 #025-07-1977 L1982 **ORS OSM** *020 †40

O'BRIEN, Gregory M. ■ 43302 #063-01-1979 L1983 **GP** *020

PONNUSAMY, Narayanan. 300 EXECUTIVE DR 43302 #495-42-1969 L1978 **GS** *071 †85

PUA, Jaime M. 1000 MCKINLEY PARK DR 43302 #748-07-1967 L1973 **AN** *020

PUA, Tricia Lee. ■ 43302 #038-40-2006 L2006 **PTH** *012

PUREWAL, Tarlok Singh. 1130 INDEPENDENCE AVE 43302 #495-08-1967 L1972 **IM** *020 †20

PUREWAL-REIER, Preena. 1069 DELAWARE AVE, STE 205A 43302 #055-02-1995 L1998 **IM** *020 †20

RAJKOTWALA, Khozema M. 990 S PROSPECT ST, STE 2 43302 #495-01-1987 L1994 **IM** *020 †20

RAVI, Srinivas Prasad. 300 EXECUTIVE DR, MARION INDEPENDENT PHYSICI 43302 #495-50-1986 L2006 **GS** *020 †85

REDDY, Sudesh Sandadi. 402 S STATE ST, STE A 43302 #495-21-1982 L1986 **IM** *020 †20

REDDY, Yeshwant Patlolla. 1167 INDEPENDENCE AVE 43302 #495-21-1982 L2001 **PM PME** *020 †60

REIER, Allan Robert. 1050 DELAWARE AVE, MARION REGIONAL IMAGING 43302 #041-02-1997 L1999 **VIR R** *020

REVILLA, Leon Salvador. ■ 43302 #649-02-1953 L1961 **ORS GS** *071

RIEGO, Filmore Alteros. 1462 MARION WALDO RD, MARION EYE CENTER 43302 #748-10-1972 L1978 **OPH** *020 †35

SABAG-TISCARENO, Assad. 1040 DELAWARE AVE, ENT DEP 43302 #649-01-1971 L1979 **OTO** *020 †20

SANIDAD, Benjamin R, Jr. 1050 DELAWARE AVE 43302 #748-07-1970 L1975 **AN** *020

SCHULER, James Alan. 1140 INDEPENDENCE AVE 43302 #016-43-1948 L1953 **OBG** *071

SCHULER, Peter Jos. 300 EXECUTIVE DR 43302 #038-40-1990 L1995 **GS** *020 †85

SCHULER, Suzanne Suarez. 205 W CENTER ST STE 200, CENTER STREET COMM CLINIC 43302 #038-40-1991 L1994 **IM** *020 †20

SCHULER, Walter Richard. ■ 43302 #016-41-1956 L1960 **OBG GP** *071

SEGARRA, Juan Bautista. 1040 DELAWARE AVE, THE FREDERICK C SMITH CLIN 43302 #847-08-1974 L1984 **ORS** *020

SHAH, Mayank K. 1051 HARDING MEMORIAL PKWY, STE A 43302 #495-23-1982 L1992 **CD IM** *020 †20

SHAH, Niranjan T. MCKINLEY PK DR MARION HOSP 43302 #496-38-1970 L1979 **PTH** *020 †50

SHEIKH, Shahryar A. ■ 43302 #704-01-1969 L1976 **IM** *020 †20

SIDDIQUI, Saud Ikram. 1199 DELAWARE AVE STE 10, MARION PAIN CLINIC 43302 #704-02-1990 L2002 **APM** *020 †20

SINGH, Parminder Bob. ■ 43302 #422-01-1997 L2001 **IM** *020 †20

SINGH, Punjab. 1199 DELAWARE AVE, STE 102 43302 #495-03-1961 L1987 **IM** *071 †20

SITTERLEY, Brooks Hummell. MCKINLEY PK DR MARION HOSP 43302 #025-01-1961 L1966 **R RO** *071 †60

SOLIE, Carol Marie. 1000 MCKINLEY PARK DR 43302 #038-41-1981 L1982 **OBG** *020 †30

SPARE, Joseph Timothy. 1125 ELLEN KAY DR, STE B 43302 #020-02-1972 L1973 **P** *020 †75

STALLWORTH, William Alvin. 1167 INDEPENDENCE AVE, STE 100 43302 #016-11-1976 L1989 **U IM** *020 †95

STEVENS, Deanna Jende. 1462 MARION WALDO RD 43302 #038-40-1999 L2000 **OBG** *020 †35

STORER, Timothy Jon. 1040 DELAWARE AVE 43302 #038-41-1997 L2001 **D** *020 †15 ‡

SUTHERLAND, Stephen R. 250 EXECUTIVE DR, STE D 43302 #050-02-1981 L1986 **N CN** *020 †75

TULLOSS, James Richard. 1069 DELAWARE AVE, STE 101 43302 #001-02-1984 L1991 **ORS PM** *020 †20

WINANS, Bradford Alan. 1040 DELAWARE AVE, MARION REGIONAL IMAGING 43302 #041-07-1993 L1999 **DR** *062 †80

WINEGARNER, Frederick G. 1063 HARDING MEMORIAL PKWY 43302 #038-40-1961 L1961 **GS VS** *020 †85

WOROBIEC, Michael Walter. ■ 43302 #038-40-1995 L1997 **IM** *020

MARSHALLVILLE – WAYNE

UNDERWOOD, Melissa Horst. ■ 44645 #038-44-2005 L2005 **EM** *012

MARTINS FERRY – BELMONT

AGCAOILI, Demetrio Jose. 92 N 4TH ST, STE 26 43935 #748-01-1984 L2003 **ID** *020 †20

ALMARIO, Vicente P, Jr. 90 N 4TH ST 43935 #748-01-1972 L1977 **R** *020 †80

ARAKAWA, Patrick Katzuo. 90 N 4TH ST 43935 #649-02-1961 L1966 **GP** *020

BATRA, Devender K. 92 N 4TH ST 43935 #495-55-1979 L1994 **CD** *020 †20

CAPITO, Joseph Carl. 90 N 4TH ST 43935 #055-02-1986 L1993 **DR GS** *020 †80

CHAUDHRY, Sanjay. 92 N 4TH ST, STE 11 43935 #041-07-1987 L1991 **GE** *020 †20

COOK, Fred Wm, Jr. 90 N 4TH ST 43935 #041-09-1944 L1946 **FM GP** *071

DARIO, Nepomuceno Z, Jr. 92 N 4TH ST, EORH MED COMPLEX STE 4 43935 #748-07-1965 L1975 **IM** *020 †20

DEL POZO, Jesus Fresno. 90 N 4TH ST 43935 #847-04-1958 L1970 **PTH** *062 †50

GAINER, Kenneth Matthew. 222 N 5TH ST 43935 #055-01-1997 L2004 **OPH** *020

GLASS, Richard Salvatore. 222 N 5TH ST 43935 #023-01-1966 L1977 **ORS** *020 †40

HAMMOND, Mary Theresa. 222 N 5TH ST, STE 101 43935 #055-01-1989 L1999 **PD** *020 †55

HECETA, Estherbelle A. EAST OH REGIONAL HOSP 43935 #748-10-1961 L1974 **AN** *071 †05

JAO, Monina Martinez. 92 N 4TH ST, C/O DR. MARIO MEJIA 43935 #748-15-1988 L1997 **IM** *020 †20

JONES, Walter Wm. 90 N 4TH ST 43935 #035-06-1969 L1981 **OPH OS** *020 †35 ‡

KALLA, Abdullah M. 90 N 4TH ST 43935 #654-01-1987 L2000 **AN** *020

KAPPEL, David Alan. 222 N 5TH ST, STE 202 43935 #055-01-1969 L1982 **PS HS** *020 †85,65

KENAMOND, Mark C. 90 N 4TH ST 43935 #055-01-1984 L1989 **DR GS** *020 †80

LAVAPIES, Felipe V. 90 N 4TH ST 43935 #748-01-1953 L1966 **FM** *071 †18

LAVAPIES, Nermin Demirbag. ■ 43935 #902-10-1956 L1968 **FM** *071 †18

LAWSON, John Michael. 92 N 4TH ST STE 3 43935 #055-01-1976 L1977 **OBG** *020 †30

LUNA, Ignacio Hoelzl, Jr. 92 N 4TH ST, E.O.R.H. OFFICE BUILDING 43935 #748-01-1964 L1975 **U** *020

MEJIA, Mario Cordova. 92 N 4TH ST, STE 18 43935 #748-08-1970 L1976 **IM GP** *020 †20

MELIA, Jose Ma Avia. BUILDING MARTINS FERRY 43935 #847-06-1963 L1974 **ORS** *071 †40

MICHALSKI, John Alexander. 90 N 4TH ST, MICHALSKI ORTHOPEDIC CENTE 43935 #041-02-1985 L2000 **ORS OSM** *020 †40

NAUM, George Phillip, Jr. 222 N 5TH ST, STE 102 43935 #055-01-1963 L1970 **R GP** *020 ‡

NOGA, Gerald Wayne. 75 N 4TH ST 43935 #010-01-1966 L1986 **OM GP** *075 †70 ‡

PATRIZI, James D, Jr. 90 N 4TH ST 43935 #016-42-1993 L2000 **DR** *020 †80

PORTER, Charles Vernon. 92 N 4TH ST, STE 3 43935 #055-01-1968 L1976 **OBG** *020 †30

RAHBAR, Ahmad. 92 N 4TH ST, STE 17 43935 #025-01-1969 L1981 **TS CD** *020 †85,90

RAIMONDE, Romeo A. 92 N 4TH ST 43935 #038-40-1951 L1951 **GP** *071

ROMANO, Judith Theresa. 222 N 5TH ST, STE 101 43935 #055-01-1987 L1999 **PD** *020 †55

ROMANO, Thomas James. 205 N 5TH ST 43935 #035-19-1977 L1982 **RHU IM** *020 †20 ‡

RYNCARZ, Richard Eugene. 92 N 4TH ST, STE 7 43935 #055-02-1995 L2000 **PUD** *020 †20

SAKLA, Samy. 92 N 4TH ST 43935 #915-04-1979 L1990 **PME AN** *020

SELLA, Gabriel Eugen. 92 N 4TH ST, BUILDING E.O.R.H. 43935 #561-14-1977 L1984 **FM PM** *020 ‡

SHOPE, James Russell. 92 N 4TH ST, STE A 43935 #041-09-1987 L1990 **PS** *020 †65

THEAKER, Lee Parks. 90 N 4TH ST, EAST OHIO REGIONAL HOSPITA 43935 #038-45-1993 L1994 **AN** *020 †05

TRACY, Charles Alan. 222 N 5TH ST, STE 202 43935 #055-01-1985 L1987 **HS** *020 †65

WETZEL, Robert James. 92 N 4TH ST, STE 11 43935 #041-09-1989 L1998 **OBG** *071 †30

MARYSVILLE – UNION

ALAIN, Nikola. 610 S PLUM ST 43040 #875-02-1977 L1984 **PD** *020 †55

AMPARO, Demosthenes C. 16501 SQUARE DR 43040 #748-01-1964 L1972 **GS** *020

APPLEGATE, David Terrence. 1044 COLUMBUS AVE 43040 #038-40-1988 L1989 **FM OBS** *020 †18

APPLEGATE, Mary S. 1044 COLUMBUS AVE 43040 #038-40-1987 L1988 **PD IM** *020 †20,55

BADENHOP, Daniel Leroy. 358 DAMASCUS RD 43040 #038-40-1988 L1989 **FM** *020 †18

BOX, Judyth H. 19300 RAYMOND RD 43040 #143-08-1972 L1974 **P** *020 †75

BRINKER, Debra Lynn. 500 LONDON AVE, OHC 43040 #038-43-1982 L1983 **EM OM** *020 †16

BRYAN, Bradley Alan. 498 LONDON AVE STE B 43040 #038-40-1987 L1988 **GS** *020 †85

EVANS, John Robt. 500 LONDON AVE, UNION COUNTY 43040 #038-40-1959 L1959 **IM CD** *071

FAY, Michael Lynn. 19900 STATE ROUTE 739, HEALTH PARTNERS 43040 #038-45-1985 L1987 **FM** *020 †18

FIORINI, William David. 14210 SCOTTSLAWN ROAD, SCOTTS MEDICAL SERVICES 43041 #038-41-1976 L1981 **FM** *020 †20

GAO-HICKMAN, Xiaomei. 500 LONDON AVE 43040 #243-48-1992 L2002 **N** *020 †75

GARBER, Philip Lewis. 500 LONDON AVE, MEM HOSP OF UNION COUNTY 43040 #038-45-1990 L1996 **FM** *020 †18

GORDON, Chrisanne. 500 LONDON AVE, MEMORIAL HOSPITAL OF UNION 43040 #038-40-1977 L1978 **PM OM** *020 †60

GRAHAM, Timothy Patrick. 19900 STATE ROUTE 739 43040 #038-40-1999 L1999 **FM** *020 †18

GUPTA, Abha Rani. 500 LONDON AVE 43040 #495-08-1987 L2005 **RHU** *020 †20

HASTINGS, Marcy Lynn. 500 LONDON AVE, ATTN EMERGENCY DEPT 43040 #038-45-1998 L2000 **EM** *020 †16

■ = Address Information Privacy Protected

HAZELBAKER, Matthew T. 150 MOREY DR 43040 #038-40-1995 L1997 **OBG** *020 †30
HENZEL, Kevin Patrick. 660 LONDON AVE, STE A 43040 #038-40-2001 L2001 **IM** *020 †20
HERZOG, Delia Rabby. 388 DAMASCUS RD 43040 #038-40-1992 L1993 **FM** *020 †18
HIGHBERGER, William A. 500 LONDON AVE 43040 #045-01-1987 L1988 **AN** *020 †05
HURL, Rodney Beck. 500 LONDON AVE 43040 #041-13-1955 L1955 **FM** *071 †18
JOHNSON, Susanna E. 118 MOREY DR 43040 #038-44-1999 L1999 **FM** *020 †18
KIRKBY, Cheryl Kaye. 1140 CHARLES LN 43040 #041-14-1998 L2001 **PD** *020 †55
KRUMM, Lisa H. 1140 CHARLES LN 43040 #038-45-1995 L1999 **PD** *020 †55
LADU, Keith Alan. 1140 CHARLES LN 43040 #016-76-1992, ▲ L1993 **ORS** *020
LEESS, Fred R. 498 LONDON AVE, STE G 43040 #041-12-1983 L2003 **OTO FPS** *020 †45
LEWIS, David K, II. 500 LONDON AVE 43040 #038-40-1988 L1991 **EM** *020 †20
LEWIS, George William. ■ 43040 #038-40-1962 L1962 **OBG OS** *071 †30
LINSCOTT, John Richard. 225 STOCKSDALE DR 43040 #038-40-1958 L1958 **FM** *020 †18
LINSCOTT, Joseph C. 500 LONDON AVE 43040 #028-78-1994, ▲ L1995 **FM** *020 †18
MAGORIEN, Douglas M. 660 LONDON AVE 43040 #038-40-1991 L1993 **CD** *020 †20
MC FARLANE, Brian Arthur. 19900 STATE ROUTE 739, HEALTHPARTNERS 43040 #065-01-1974 L1996 **FM** *020 †18
MC LEMORE, William Estes. 500 LONDON AVE 43040 #041-02-1980 L1982 **DR** *020 †80
MOORE, Jeffrey Eugene. 388 DAMASCUS RD 43040 #038-40-1985 L1986 **FM** *020 †18
MORRAN, Stacy Lynn. 114 SCOTT FARMS BLVD 43040 #038-40-1998 L1999 **PD** *020 †55
MORRISON, Jennifer Anne. 114 MOREY DR 43040 #028-34-1998 L1999 **OPH** *020 †35
MORRISON, Karen Margaret. 14210 SCOTTSLAWN RD 43041 #038-40-1992 L1993 **FM OM** *020 †18
MOSHER, Constance Aleeta. 1479 COLLINS AVE, OHIO REFORMATORY FOR WOMEN 43040 #017-20-1978 L1995 **FM** *020 †18
MUNIYAPPA, Prasanna Kumar. 660 LONDON AVE, LONDON AVENUE SPECIALITY C 43040 #038-44-1995 L1997 **IM** *020 †20
MURRAY, Scott Alan. 660 LONDON AVE 43040 #025-07-1992 L1993 **PM** *020 †60
NIEMI, Neil Andrew. 150 MOREY DR 43040 #038-40-2002 L2002 **OBG** *020
PATEL, Smitha. 498 LONDON AVE, STE A 43040 #038-44-1998 L2003 **CHP** *020 †75
REED, Donald Eric. 660 LONDON AVE 43040 #038-44-1988 L1992 **GS** *020 †85
SAMPSEL, James Wm. 211 STOCKSDALE DR 43040 #038-04-1946 L1946 **GS** *071 †85
SEIFFERTH, Brian Scott. 500 LONDON AVE, UNION COUNTY MEMORIAL HOSP 43040 #038-40-1994 L1995 **EM** *020 †16
SORG, Laura Leigh. ■ 43040 #038-40-2007 L2007 **FP** *012
STEVENS, Keisha Consuella. ■ 43040 #036-07-2001 L2003 **IM** *020 †20
VILLANUEVA, Esberdado S. ■ 43040 #748-01-1965 L1975 **FM GYN** *020 †18
WALLENBROCK, Angela Bell. 715 S PLUM ST 43040 #045-01-1973 L1983 **P CHP** *030 †75
WARREN, Connie Jo. 681 LONDON AVE 43040 #038-45-1985 L1987 **FM** *020 †18
WILSON, Deborah Lynn. 498 LONDON AVE STE C 43040 #003-01-1995 L1997 **FM** *020 †18

MASON – WARREN

ABDEL-AZIZ, Mohamed A. 4276 MACKENZIE CT, EASTERN STATE HOSPITAL 45040 #915-04-1991 L2001 **P** *020
ADLER, John Dean. 608 READING RD, STE A 45040 #017-20-1979 L1983 **GYN** *020 †30
AICHHOLZ, David Dravis. 7450 S MASON MONTGOMERY RD, UNIT 202 45040 #038-41-1990 L1991 **OBG** *020 †30
ANSARI, Saba Azher. 6442 CEDAR CREEK CT 45040 #026-04-1999 L2000 **FPG** *020 †20
BAIN, Michael Andrew. 8355 SNIDER RD, DEERFIELD TWP FIRE DEPARTM 45040 #038-41-1986 L1987 **EM** *020 †16
BAKER, Jeffrey Thos. 9311 S MASON MONTGOMERY RD, STE 102 45040 #051-07-1981 L1982 **IM** *020 †20
BALSKE, Ana Maria. 8700 S MASON MONTGOMERY RD, SBA #2143 45040 #014-01-1989 L2000 **IM** *020 †20
BARREAU, Carla Cecilia. 9600 CHILDREN DR, SUBURBAN PEDIATRIC ASSOC, 45040 #308-03-1986 L2000 **PD** *020 †55
BAWA, Parul K. 7450 S MASON MONTGOMERY RD, UNIT 206 45040 #023-07-1994 L2002 **PD** *020 †55
BEARY, John F, III. 8700 S MASON MONTGOMERY RD, PROCTOR & GAMBLE PHARM 45040 #024-01-1973 L1997 **RHU IM** *050 †20
BEATTY, Wm Coombs, II. 4770 DUKE DR STE 196 45040 #020-02-1971 L1983 **P PYA** *020 †18,75
BEHM, Patrick Lee. ■ 45040 #038-43-2007 L2007 **AN** *012
BRAMSON, Marsha Lynn. 770 READING RD STE A 45040 #041-01-1977 L1978 **IM OS** *020 †20
BRANE, Suja Merlin. 9311 S MASON MONTGOMERY RD, STE 102 45040 #038-41-2001 L2001 **FM** *020 †18
CERVANTES, Victorio M. ■ 45040 #748-07-1959 **GP** *100
CHARNAS, Terry. 4964 VILLAGE GREEN DR 45040 #038-06-1988 L1989 **EM** *020 †16
CHAUDHRY, Meher Riffat. ■ 45040 #038-44-2006 L2006 **EM** *012
CHINES, Arkadi C. 8700 S MASON MONTGOMERY RD, PHARMACEUTICALS 45040 #913-96-1976 L1996 **END** *020
CHOKSHI, Sonali. 9311 S MASON MONTGOMERY RD, STE 113 45040 #016-43-1995 L2004 **IM** *020 †20
CHU, Guoxiang. ■ 45040 #243-78-1986 L2005 **IM** *012
CHUNN, Michael Andrew. 6860 TYLERSVILLE RD, STE 12 45040 #004-01-1998 L1999 **FM** *020 †18
CLEVELAND, Craig Purcell. 846 READING RD 45040 #038-41-1981 L1982 **IM OM** *020
COTTON, Robin Thos. 9560 CHILDREN DR 45040 #917-03-1965 L1972 **PDO HNS** *020 †45
CRAWFORD, Camille Renee. 5386 COX SMITH RD, STE A 45040 #047-07-1979 L1985 **PD** *020 †55
CUSICK, Brian Chas. 7423 S MASON MONTGOMERY RD 45040 #038-41-1985 L1997 **OTO** *020 †45
DAVID, Eric L. ■ 45040 #748-02-1956 L1975 **ORS** *071
DAWODU, Adetokunbo. ■ 45040 #690-01-1999 L2005 **PDE** *012 †55
DEARWORTH, David F. 4268 SPRING FIELD LN 45040 #038-41-1993 L1994 **IM** *020 †20
DOSCHER, John Charles. 4834 SOCIALVILLE FOSTER RD 45040 #020-02-1983 L1985 **PD** *020 †55
DUMONT, Christina Marie. 9600 CHILDREN DR 45040 #038-41-1998 L1999 **PD** *020 †55
EID, Samia Ishak. 9311 S MASON MONTGOMERY RD, STE 102 45040 #915-03-1972 L1984 **FM ADL** *020 †18
ESCHENBACHER, William Lee. 7423 S MASON MONTGOMERY RD 45040 #048-12-1978 L2004 **IM PUD** *020 †20
FARLEY, Chad William. ■ 45040 #003-01-2007 L2007 **NS** *012

FITZGERALD, Kevin Robert. 608 READING RD, STE A 45040 #017-20-1983 L1987 **OBG** *020 †30
FLANAGAN, Robert Reese. 608 READING RD, STE A 45040 #035-09-1975 L1977 **GYN** *020 †30
FORTUNA, Gerald Richard. ■ 45040 #045-04-1999 L2005 **GS** *012
FORTUNA, Sarah Odaniel. ■ 45040 #045-04-2000 L2002 **FM** *020 †18
FU, Eric Chengyu. ■ 45040 #038-40-2008 *012
FU, Juian-Juian Liu. 4834 SOCIALVILLE FOSTER RD, STE 20 45040 #038-41-1986 L1987 **D** *020 †15
GEERING, Timothy John. 9311 S MASON MONTGOMERY RD, STE 102 45040 #035-06-1982 L1985 **IM** *020 †20
GENNANTONIO, Margretta E. 5467 CEDAR VILLAGE DR 45040 #038-45-1996 L1997 **IM IMG** *020 †20
GLUNTZ, William A, III. 9311 S MASON MONTGOMERY RD, STE 102 45040 #038-41-1988 L1990 **FM** *020 †18
GOODLANDER, Deborah A N. 7450 S MASON MONTGOMERY RD, UNIT 103 45040 #038-41-1972 L1972 **PD** *020 †20
GRUBB, Shannon Leigh. 4201 AERO DR, DEERFIELD FAMILY PRACTICE 45040 #038-41-1987 L1988 **FM** *020 †18
GUION, Matthew James. ■ 45040 #038-41-1998 **IM** *100
HARRIS, Joseph Cabel. 9378 S MASON MONTGOMERY RD, STE 416 45040 #020-02-1979 L1985 **EM FM** *020 †18,16
HARRISON, Jennifer. 771 READING RD 45040 #048-14-1991 L1992 **SCI PM** *020 †20,60
HAYNER, Jay Matthew. 7423 S MASON MONTGOMERY RD 45040 #055-02-1991 L1994 **IM** *020 †20
HENDERSON, Clyde Edward. 7450 S MASON MONTGOMERY RD, ORTHOPAEDIC DIAGNOSTIC 45040 #038-41-1977 L1978 **ORS HS** *020 †40
HOFFMAN, Brian Dennis. 608 READING RD, STE C 45040 #020-12-1993 L1994 **FM** *020 †18
HORN, James Matthew. ■ 45040 #038-40-2000 L2000 **EM** *020 †20
HOVERMALE, Amy Karen. 9311 S MASON MONTGOMERY RD, STE 102 45040 #038-41-1993 L1994 **IM** *020 †20
HUERTA, Christopher L. ■ 45040 #028-02-1981 L1982 **EM** *020 †16
JACKSON, Bradley Scott. 5386 COX SMITH RD, # A 45040 #038-45-1988 L1990 **PD** *020 †55
JAVAHERI, Shahrokh. 4780 SOCIALVILLE FOSTER RD 45040 #517-05-1971 L1983 **PUD IM** *050 †20
JOHNSON, Danielle Janyne. 4075 OLD WESTERN ROW RD, LINDNER CENTER OF HOPE 45040 #041-15-2004 L2004 **P** *012
JOST, Linda Ann. 7450 S MASON MONTGOMERY RD, UNIT 206 45040 #030-05-1977 L1982 **PD** *020 †55
KABALIN, Cynthia Ann S. ■ 45040 #051-04-1989 L2002 **AI PD** *020 †55
KARAS, Bill James. 9311 S MASON MONTGOMERY RD, STE 103 45040 #038-41-1974 L1976 **IM** *020 †20
KASTEN, Bernard Louis, Jr. 4690 PARKWAY DR 45040 #038-40-1971 L1971 **CLP PTH** *020 †50
KAULFERS, Anne-Marie Dore. ■ 45040 #021-05-2003 L2004 **PDE** *012 †55
KAUR, Harpinder. ■ 45040 #495-29-1991 L2000 **AI** *100
KAY-DEVORE, Cynthia. ■ 45040 #038-41-1983 L1986 **OBG** *020 †30
KELLOGG, Ellen Ann. 7450 S MASON MONTGOMERY RD, UNIT 206 45040 #055-01-1985 L1988 **PD** *020 †55
KNIGHT, William Allen, IV. ■ 45040 #038-41-2003 L2003 **EM** *100
KONERU, Srilakshmi. 7423 S MASON MONTGOMERY RD 45040 #495-50-1996 L2000 **RHU** *020
KORN, Paul. 4834 SOCIALVILLE FOSTER RD, STE 50 45040 #035-08-1988 L1990 **PD** *020 †55
KOVAR, Joyce Marie. ■ 45040 #030-06-1999 L2007 **PTH** *012
KRZESKI, Robert. 7423 S MASON MONTGOMERY RD 45040 #759-03-1986 L1995 **PD** *020 †55
KUDALKAR, Deepa Prasad. ■ 45040 #496-38-1996 L2007 **RHU** *012
KUDALKAR, Prasad Ramakant. ■ 45040 #496-38-1993 L2000 **HO** *020 †20
KULICK, Roy Matthew. 8700 S MASON MONTGOMERY RD, MAILBOX 505 45040 #041-01-1981 L1991 **PD EM** *020 †55
LABELLA, Gennaro Dino. 7423 S MASON MONTGOMERY RD 45040 #665-01-2000 L2001 **GS** *100 †85
LADINSKY, Morissa Jean. 7423 S MASON MONTGOMERY RD, GROUP HEALTH ASSOCIATES 45040 #048-04-1990 L1999 **PD** *020 †55
LANG, Faye Young. 7451 S MASON MONTGOMERY RD 45040 #243-58-1986 L1999 **IM** *020 †20
LEE, Kenneth H. 7915 DEER CROSSING DR 45040 #024-05-1998 L2006 **PDO** *020
LEHENBAUER, Martin Paul. 608 READING RD, STE C 45040 #038-41-1981 L1984 **FM** *020 †18
LIMOUZE, Susan Cooper. 7450 S MASON MONTGOMERY RD, UNIT 103 45040 #035-09-1975 L1979 **PD PHO** *020 †55
LINKER, Timothy James. 6860 TYLERSVILLE RD, STE 12 45040 #038-45-1998 L1999 **FM FSM** *020 †18
LOEWENSTINE, Harold V. 9311 S MASON MONTGOMERY RD 45040 #038-43-1987 L1988 **IM** *020 †20
LORENZO, Conrado Cuna. ■ 45040 #748-02-1991 L1997 **HO** *100 †20
MADDALI, Annapurna J. 9311 S MASON MONTGOMERY RD, STE 113 45040 #495-62-1984 L1996 **FM** *020 †20
MALINOWSKI, Barry Chas. 4361 IRWIN SIMPSON RD 45040 #050-02-1977 L1978 **PD** *020 †55
MANGELS, David Gregory. 9311 S MASON MONTGOMERY RD, STE 111 45040 #038-43-1988 L1989 **GE IM** *020 †20
MCKIERNAN, Christopher Ja. 9311 S MASON MONTGOMERY RD, STE 102 45040 #038-41-2004 L2004 **IM** *020 †20
MEIER, Edward John. 5378D COX SMITH RD 45040 #020-12-1998 L2002 **OPH** *020 †35
MENDELSOHN, Jon Edward. 5175 BOWEN DR, ADVANCED COSMETIC SURGERY 45040 #035-15-1992 L1997 **OTO FPS** *020 †45
MILLER, Kim Lauren. 770 READING RD 45040 #024-16-1989 L2001 **IM** *020 †20
MITCHELL, Dyatra B. 4834 SOCIALVILLE FOSTER RD, STE 10 45040 #038-45-1995 L1998 **IM** *020 †20
MORRIS, Beth Conway. 6961 CINTAS BLVD 45040 #038-45-1985 L1990 **IM EM** *020
MOSS, Fred Robt. 5740 GATEWAY, STE 101 45040 #016-06-1988 L1990 **P CHP** *020 †75
MOSTOWY, Weislaw M. ■ 45040 #422-01-1988 L1998 **IM** *020 †16
MUCCIO, James David. 846 READING RD 45040 #051-01-1995 L2000 **ORS** *020 †40
MUNIR, Muhammad Ahmed. 6576 ROSEWOOD LN, DEPT OF ANESTHESIA 45040 #704-01-1994 L2005 **APM** *100 †05
MUSLU, Halim Ozgur. ■ 45040 #902-10-1996 L2007 **IM** *020 †20
NEACK, Lawrence Emery. 770 READING RD, STE A 45040 #020-02-1982 L1985 **IM HEM** *020
NICKELL, Garvin Benjamin. 9311 S MASON MONTGOMERY RD, STE 111 45040 #038-45-1993 L1996 **IM** *020 †20
NORDLUND, James J. 7423 S MASON MONTGOMERY RD 45040 #026-04-1965 L1983 **D** *020 †20,15

NWANKWO, Ngozi Perpetua. 5738 TRAILSIDE CT 45040 #690-04-1993 L2004 **IM** *100 †20

OKANO, David Ryusuke. ■ 45040 #572-83-1988 L2006 **PMM** *012

O'MALLEY, Kathryn Ellen. 608 READING RD STE D, MUDDY CREEK PEDIATRICS 45040 #038-43-1982 L1985 **PD** *020 †55

ONG RIVERA, Jo Ann Dee. 9311 S MASON MONTGOMERY RD, STE 102 45040 #748-01-1990 L1994 **IM** *020 †20

OWENS, Richard Farrel. ■ 45040 #038-41-2004 L2004 **ORS** *012

PATEL, Samir Bhogilal. 9311 S MASON MONTGOMERY RD, STE 104 45040 #038-41-1998 L2000 **D DMP** *020 †15

PATEL, Sanjiv Pradip. 4780 SOCIALVILLE FOSTER RD 45040 #038-44-1996 L1997 **SME PCC** *020 †20

PETTY, Sharon Rene. 6353 TARTON FIELDS LN, P O BOX 778 45040 #035-48-1986 L2000 **FM** *050 †18

PICHARDO, Betsy. 608 READING RD, STE C 45040 #308-04-1998 L2003 **FM** *100 †18

PLEATMAN, Stephen Ira. 9600 CHILDREN DR, BLDG B 45040 #038-41-1980 L1981 **PD** *020 †55 ‡

RANKIN, Denise Marie. 3611 SOCIALVILLE FOSTER RD 45040 #028-02-1992 L1994 **FM** *020 †05

REHMAN, Muhammad I. 8700 S MASON MONTGOMERY RD, MAIL BOX 2121/MS 2165 45040 #704-21-1988 L1997 **RHU PA** *050 †20

REIDY, Andrew Michael. ■ 45040 #035-75-2006, ▲ L2006 **EM** *012

REITER, Gerald Robt. ■ 45040 #038-41-1967 L1967 **D GP** *071 †15

RIGNEY, Susan Joan. 6831 ROSS LN 45040 #038-41-1992 L1995 **AN** *020 †05

RINGEL, Jennifer Friedman. 9600 CHILDREN DR, DEPT OF PEDIATRICS 45040 #038-06-1998 L1999 **PD** *020 †55

ROESCH, Thomas Anthony. 5386 COX SMITH RD, STE A 45040 #038-40-1982 L1994 **PD** *020 †55

ROSEVEAR, Mary Ann. 4222 MACKENZIE CT 45040 #049-01-1989 L1993 **AN** *020 †05

ROSS, Clara Sue. ■ 45040 #038-41-1985 L1987 **OM LM** *062 †70

SADHASIVAM, Senthil Kumar. ■ 45040 #495-66-1993 L2004 **PAN** *100 †05 ‡

SAINI, Anita B. 7423 S MASON MONTGOMERY RD 45040 #495-28-1996 L2000 **IM** *020 †20

SANDROCK, Balzer Conrad. 3611 SOCIALVILLE FOSTER RD 45040 #021-05-1986 L1990 **PD PHO** *020 †55

SCHERTZINGER, Howard, Jr. 7451 S MASON MONTGOMERY RD, STE C 45040 #038-40-1988 L1993 **IM PD** *020 †55,20

SCHNEIDER, Ronna. 9600 CHILDREN DR 45040 #038-41-1997 L1998 **PD** *020 †55

SEKAR, Jayasri. 7450 S MASON MONTGOMERY RD, UNIT 206 45040 #495-04-1981 L1991 **PD** *020 †55

SHELTON, Rachel Lea. ■ 45040 #020-02-2003 L2003 **GS** *012

SHELTON, Tommy Warren. ■ 45040 #020-12-2002 L2003 **GS** *012

SHOCKLEY, Thomas Edward. 7450 S MASON MONTGOMERY RD, ORTHOPAEDIC DIAGNOSTIC 45040 #047-07-1986 L1992 **ORS GS** *020 †40

SINGERMAN, Joel Alan. 7450 S MASON MONTGOMERY RD, UNIT 103 45040 #038-41-1981 L1983 **PD** *020 †55

SMITH, Kellie Kay. 770 READING RD, STE A 45040 #038-45-1990 L1993 **IM** *020 †20

SOLIMAN, Abdelrhman A. ■ 45040 #308-11-1985 L2004 **ADP** *020 †75

SPATZ, Jeffrey David. 5784 GLENBROOK CT 45040 #038-40-2000 L2002 **EM** *020 †16

STALEY, Ronna L. 9600 CHILDREN DR, SUBURBAN PEDIATRIC ASSOCS 45040 #038-41-1980 L1982 **PD ADL** *020 †55

STAMBOUGH, Jeffery Lynn. 7450 S MASON MONTGOMERY RD, ORTHOPAEDIC DIAGNOSTIC 45040 #055-01-1980 L1986 **OSS ORS** *020 †40

STEGMAN, Susan Saker. 770 READING RD, STE A 45040 #038-41-1990 L1991 **IM** *020 †20

STERN, Errol John. 7450 S MASON MONTGOMERY RD, ORTHOPAEDIC DIAGNOSTIC 45040 #038-41-1972 L1972 **ORS** *020 †40

STOUT, Ronald Wayne. 8700 S MASON MONTGOMERY RD 45040 #005-12-1986 L1997 **FM OM** *020 †70,18

SUNA, Robyn Herdman. 7451 S MASON MONTGOMERY RD, STE C 45040 #038-06-1983 L1983 **IM** *020 †20

TAN, Ronnie. 4201 AERO DR, DOCTORS URGENT CARE OFFICE 45040 #748-01-1989 L1995 **IM EM** *020 †20

TANDOC, Ulysses Martinez. ■ 45040 #038-43-1984 L1986 **AN IM** *020 †20,05

TARSHIS, Alan Mehr. 7423 S MASON MONTGOMERY RD 45040 #064-01-1976 L1983 **GE IM** *020 †16

TAYLOR, Harold Herman, Jr. 5224 KINGS MILLS RD, STE 224 45040 #048-14-1986 L2001 **EM** *020 †16

TELLEZ, Patrick Anthony. 4690 PARKWAY DR 45040 #026-04-1978 L1995 **AI PD** *030 †55,03

TENNIE, Jay Michael. ■ 45040 #038-41-1995 L1998 **EM** *020 †16

THOMAS, Renate Wachter. 7423 S MASON MONTGOMERY RD, GROUP HEALTH ASSOCIATES 45040 #038-45-1991 L1993 **IM** *071 †20 ‡

TRUONG, Thanh Tri. 5126 BUTLER WARREN RD, 5126 BUTLER WARREN ROAD 45040 #016-01-1992 L1997 **PD** *020 †55

UNDERINER, Angeli. 4834 SOCIALVILLE FOSTER RD, LANDEN LAKE PEDS 45040 #038-41-1999 L1999 **PD** *020 †55

VANDIVIER, Robin H. 6263 EDGEWATER 45040 #038-41-1995 L2002 **IM** *100 †20

WALLACE, Robert Patrick. 9600 CHILDREN DR, SUBURBAN PED ASSOCS 45040 #041-15-1999 L2002 **PD** *020 †55

WANG, Xiang. ■ 45040 #243-03-1996 L2005 **IM** *012

WEISBROT, Albert Jos. 7451 S MASON MONTGOMERY RD, STE C 45040 #038-41-1975 L1975 **FM** *020 †18

WEXELBLATT, Scott Louis. 3611 SOCIALVILLE FOSTER RD 45040 #050-02-1996 L1997 **PD** *020 †55

WHITE, John E, Jr. 608 READING RD, STE A 45040 #020-12-1984 L1988 **OBG** *020 †30

YACYSHYN, Bruce Rudolf. 8700 S MASON MONTGOMERY RD, BOX 2165 45040 #060-01-1982 L2001 **GE IM** *050 †20

ZIMMERLY, Kira Ann. 7423 S MASON MONTGOMERY RD 45040 #038-06-2004 L2004 **PD** *020 †55

MASSILLON – STARK

AITI, Mohammed Yasser. 344 GAIL AVE NE STE 3 44646 #875-01-1978 L1982 **CD IM** *020 †20

BALSA, Venkat. 3000 ERIE ST S, BEHAVIORAL HEALTHCAR 44646 #495-98-1977 L1994 **P** *020 †75

BANEZ, Nestor Virata. 830 AMHERST RD NE, NESTOR V BANEZ MD INC 44646 #748-01-1958 L1969 **CD IM** *071

BARAT, Michael. 830 AMHERST RD NE 44646 #550-03-1980 L1984 **OTO GS** *020 †45

BELARDO, Diane S. 6722A WALES AVE NW, NORTHWEST 44646 #038-44-1993 L1994 **PD** *020 †55

BELARDO, Lito June. 6724 WALES AVE NW, MASSILLON FAMILY PRACTICE 44646 #038-44-1993 L1995 **FM** *020 †18

BREYFOGLE, Ernest Edwin. 875 8TH ST NE 44646 #038-40-1941 L1941 **R** *072 †80

BRIONES, Florante Liganor. 2500 WALES AVE NW, STE A 44646 #748-08-1966 L1972 **IM** *020

BUSH, Craig Michael. ■ 44646 #023-12-2004 L2005 **IM** *020

CASABAR, Lucila Corpus. ■ 44646 #748-02-1954 L1974 **AN** *071

CHAMBERS, Catherine Brown. 2500 WALES AVE NW, STE A 44646 #038-44-1994 L1995 **IM** *020 †20

CHEPYALA, Vishnu Vardhan. ■ 44646 #496-49-2002 L2006 **IM** *012

CHOW, Christopher Shaopao. 2500 WALES AVE NW, STE A 44646 #039-05-1990 L1991 **IM** *020 †20

CLARK, Debra Lynn. 5166 SHERLIN AVE NW 44646 #038-40-1988 L1991 **FM** *020 †18

CONLAN, Tim Kiernan. 2606 WALES AVE NW 44646 #038-40-1989 L1998 **ORS** *020 †40

CONRAD, Carl Gregory. 400 AUSTIN AVE NW 44646 #654-01-1985 L2004 **AN PME** *040 †05

COSS, Harold Steven. 2037 WALES RD NE 44646 #038-06-1989 L1991 **AM** *020 †40

COTIAUX, Gertrude P. 830 AMHERST RD NE STE 104 44646 #038-44-1993 L1994 **FM** *020 †18

DANG, Son N. 2606 WALES AVE NW, STE 200 44646 #308-03-1987 L1996 **FM** *020 †18

DANG, Thang Ngoc. 2606 WALES AVE NW, MASSILLON FAMILY CARE 44646 #308-03-1997 L2002 **FM** *020 †18

DE SANCTIS, Alfred L. 845 8TH ST NE 44646 #023-07-1951 L1956 **GS** *071

DRAKE, Timothy Edward. 875 8TH ST NE 44646 #025-07-1975 L1977 **OBG** *020 †30

DRUMMOND-RAY, Pamela D. 2606 WALES AVE NW, STE 300 44646 #038-44-1997 L2000 **GYN OS** *020 †30

DUFFEY, Jeffery Allen. 830 AMHERST RD NE 44646 #038-40-1975 L1975 **FM** *020 †18

DULIK, Jeffrey S. 2606 WALES AVE NW 44646 #038-75-1995, ▲ L1997 **ORS** *020

ERGUN, Hulusi. 400 AUSTIN AVE NW 44646 #902-05-1974 L1980 **R** *020 †80

FABELLA, Luisa G. ■ 44646 #748-01-1964 L1972 **AN** *020

FACTORA, Vicarthur Ranara. PO BOX 540 44648 #748-07-1970 **PHP P** *074

FOUST, Patricia A. ■ 44646 #038-06-1951 L1951 **AN** *071 †05

GARBADAWALA, Shabbir T. 400 AUSTIN AVE NW 44646 #495-23-1967 L1977 **PTH** *020 †50

GREGORY, Shirley W. ■ 44646 #010-03-1951 L1953 **FM PHP** *030

GRESSER, Michael Louis. ■ 44646 #056-05-1967 L1978 **FM PME** *071

HASSANI, Dhya M A. ■ 44646 #528-01-1960 L1974 **FM PD** *071 †55

HILL, James Lee, Jr. ■ 44646 #038-44-2008 *012

HUMBLE, Lewis Alain. 323 MARION AVE NW, STARK MEDICAL SPECIALTIES 44646 #038-44-1994 L1996 **IM** *020 †20

JOHNSON, Gene Aidan. ■ 44646 #038-06-2005 L2005 **OPH** *012

JOHNSON, Michael Lee. ■ 44646 #038-41-2001 L2007 **IM** *020

KAMEL, Mouhamed Kamal. 812 AMHERST RD NE 44646 #875-01-1972 L1975 **IM CD** *020

KAZLAUSKAS, Rita Regina. 6722 WALES AVE NW, STE A 44646 #038-43-1988 L1991 **PD** *020 †55

KIM, Hyung Kun. 3000 ERIE ST S, MASSILLON PSYCHIATRIC CENT 44646 #583-03-1953 L1976 **GP** *071

KIM, Joseph Jaikon. 3000 ERIE ST S 44646 #583-10-1966 L1983 **GP** *020

KOBE, Margaret Frieda. 2037 WALES RD NE, STE 130 44646 #038-40-1985 L1987 **ID PDI** *020,55

KOFOL, Warren Henry. 2815 AARONWOOD AVE NE 44646 #038-43-1980 L1981 **GS** *020 †85

KOTHARI, Rajnikant R. 4051 LINCOLN WAY E 44646 #495-20-1969 L1979 **P** *020 †75

KOTHARI, Saroj R. 4051 LINCOLN WAY E 44646 #495-48-1970 L1979 **FM** *020

KOTNIK, Tracy Ann. 2859 AARONWOOD AVE NE, # 3 44646 #038-45-1990 L1991 **FM PHP** *020 †18

KRISHNAMURTHI, Ramesh. 830 AMHERST RD NE, STE 201 44646 #654-01-2001 L2002 **IM** *020 †20

LABABIDI, Mouhamed Rahis. 875 8TH ST NE 44646 #875-02-1973 L1980 **U** *020 †95

LACH, Joseph Robt. 2037 WALES RD NE STE 130 44646 #038-40-1985 L1986 **IM GE** *020 †20

LAFFERTY, Mark Williams. 2815 AARONWOOD AVE NE, STARK CTY SURGEONS 44646 #038-06-1984 L1988 **GS VS** *020 †85

LAIPPLY, Erica Lee. ■ 44646 #038-44-2007 L2007 **GS** *012

LANG, Jessica Lee Falvo. 6724 WALES AVE NW 44646 #038-45-1997 L1999 **FM** *020 †18

LEBRUN, Lisette Johanna. ■ 44646 #038-40-1991 L1994 **PD** *020 †55

LIMARDO, Ricardo. ■ 44646 #308-01-1964 L1972 **IM GE** *071 †20

LOYOLA, Tito Andrew. 6200 DREXEL ST NW 44646 #748-10-1963 L1976 **EM OM** *020 †20

MALIK, Razia Saeed. ■ 44646 #704-06-1966 **CHP** *020

MARASIGAN, Dionisio C. 2400 WALES AVE NW 44646 #748-01-1958 L1969 **PD** *020 †55

MARKEL, Michael Lawrence. 323 MARION AVE NW, STARK MEDICAL SPECIALTIES 44646 #038-40-1981 L1990 **ICE CD** *020 †20

MASDEN, Robin Joy. 8206 TRAPHAGEN ST NW, STE A 44646 #051-07-1983 L1987 **PD** *020 †55

MC CLAIN, Brian Wayne. 2823 AARONWOOD AVE NE 44646 #038-43-1993 L1994 **IM** *020 †20

MCDANIEL, Kevin Jay. ■ 44646 #038-44-2005 L2005 **FP** *012

MC FEELY, Patrick Daniel. 2500 WALES AVE NW, MEDCORP OF STARK COUNTY IN 44646 #038-43-1982 L1984 **IM** *020 †20

MENDIOLA, Amanda. ■ 44646 #038-44-2007 L2007 **GS** *012

NAGPAUL, Gurbilash Kaur. 430 LAKE AVE NE 44646 #495-08-1967 L1977 **RO** *020 †80

NANNAPANENI, Indira. 2606 WALES AVE NW 44646 #495-11-1989 L2000 **OBG** *020 †30

NAVARRO, Kathryn. 6722 WALES AVE NW, STE A 44646 #035-09-2001 L2004 **PD** *020 †55

PAQUELET, Charles John. 875 8TH ST NE 44646 #038-40-1959 L1959 **ORS** *071 †40

PARRISH, Jill Lynn. 6724 WALES AVE NW, MASSILLON FAMILY PRACTICE 44646 #038-44-2003 L2003 **FM** *020 †18

PERKOWSKI, Vincent Edward. 3300 BAILEY ST NW, STE 102 44646 #038-75-1993, ▲ L1995 **EM** *020

PERRENOUD, Jeannine Marie. 400 AUSTIN AVE NW, DRS HOSP STARK CITY 44646 #028-78-2001, ▲ L2001 **GS** *020

PERRY, John Wesley. 323 MARION AVE NW, STE 104 44646 #035-06-1989 L1998 **TS** *020 †85,90

POGORELEC, Jill E. ■ 44646 #028-79-2006, ▲ **FP** *012

POSEDEL, Miroslav. 111 TREMONT AVE SW, WESTCARE 44647 #286-02-1956 L1963 **P** *071 †75

RAMACHANDRAN, Vidhya. ■ 44646 #495-59-1999 L2006 **PD** *100

RAO, Aruna. 830 AMHERST RD NE, STE 205 44646 #654-01-2001 L2001 **IM** *100

RAUCHENSTEIN, Alyce T. ■ 44646 #038-44-1985 L1986 **OM EM** *020

RAUCHENSTEIN, John Norman. 7452 FULTON DR NW 44646 #038-44-1983 L1987 **DR NM** *020 †80

RIVERA-WEISS, Michael. 400 AUSTIN AVE NW 44646 #042-02-1985 L1991 **AN PME** *020

SAHGAL, Lokendra Bahadur. 845 8TH ST NE STE 3 44646 #495-57-1966 L1980 **FM EM** *020 †18

SCHEUFLER, Steven Grant. 6724 WALES AVE NW, MASSILLON FAMILY PRACTICE 44646 #038-44-1990 L1993 **FM** *020 †18

SCHIRACK, Frank John. 400 AUSTIN AVE NW 44646 #038-06-1948 L1948 **AN EM** *071 †05

SICARD, Guillermo. 875 8TH ST NE 44646 #308-01-1960 L1969 **D DMP** *020 †15

SIMMONS, Brian Elijah. 830 AMHERST RD NE, STE 202 44646 #056-05-1980 L1991 **CD IM** *050 †20

SIMMONS, Xiomara A. 3000 ERIE ST S, HEARTLAND BEHAVIOR HLTHCAR 44646 #682-01-1978 L1997 **P** *020 †75

SIVARAM, Krishnan. 3000 ERIE ST S, HEARTLAND BEHAVIORAL HEALT 44646 #495-42-1979 L1997 **P** *020

SLAGA, Delia Marasigan. 2400 WALES AVE NW 44646 #748-01-1966 L1975 **PD GP** *020 †55

STEINECK, Brady Scott. ■ 44646 #038-44-2008 *012

SURMITIS, Joseph Michael. 323 MARION AVE NW, STARK MEDICAL SPECIALTIES 44646 #038-44-1984 L1985 **CD IM** *020 †20

TELESZ, Walter Joseph. 2815 AARONWOOD AVE NE 44646 #041-12-1965 L1966 **GS** *071 †85

THALLURI, Ranga R. 400 AUSTIN AVE NW 44646 #495-58-1981 L1991 **P** *020

THOMSON, Steven Dean. 3000 ERIE ST S, HEARTLAND BEHAVIORAL HEALT 44646 #038-44-1981 L1983 **P PFP** *020 †75

UMAR, Ahmet Feridun. PO BOX 540 44648 #902-03-1947 L1969 *020

VASARHELYI, Farkas Janos. 400 AUSTIN AVE NW, AFFINITY MEDICAL CENTER-AN 44646 #473-01-1995 L2000 **AN** *020 †05

VELLANKI, Roy P. 3000 ERIE ST S 44646 #496-24-1992 L1995 **P** *020 †75

VIOLET, James T. 2606 WALES AVE NW 44646 #028-78-1971, ▲ L1973 **ORS OSM** *020

WALLSH, Eugene. ■ 44646 #035-19-1961 L1990 **TS** *020 †85,90

WASDAHL, Dan Alexander. ■ 44646 #037-01-1987 L1993 **PTH** *020 †50

WEBER, Erin. 6722 WALES AVE NW, STE A 44646 #038-41-2002 L2002 **PD** *020

WERSTLER, Maureen Frances. ■ 44646 #038-40-1991 L1993 **FM** *020 †18

WESTERBECK, John Chas. 2037 WALES RD NE, STE 130 44646 #038-44-1985 L1986 **IM** *020 †20

WILLIAMS, Scott Downing. 323 MARION AVE NW, STARK MEDICAL SPECIALTIES 44646 #038-44-1998 L1999 **IM** *020 †20

YOUNG, Maria Siobhanne. ■ 44646 #021-01-2000 L2007 **IM** *020 †20

MASURY – TRUMBULL

STRASSBURG, Alex B. 8055 ADDISON RD, ORANGE VILLAGE NURSING HOM 44438 #056-05-1997 L2001 **IM** *020 †20

MAUMEE – LUCAS

ABAZA, Fadia Mahjoub. 650 BEAVER CREEK CIR, STE 130 43537 #875-01-1969 L1976 **PD** *020 †55

ALMASRI, Mohamad. 5901 MONCLOVA RD, ST LUKES HEART CTR 43537 #875-01-1988 L1998 **AN CCA** *020 †05

ANDONIAN, James J. 5901 MONCLOVA RD, OCCUPATIONAL HEALTH SERVIC 43537 #025-07-1976 L2005 **OM GPM** *071 †70

AOUTHMANY, Moustafa M. 5901 MONCLOVA RD 43537 #875-01-1975 L1993 **PD NPM** *020 †55

ARCHAMBEAU, Lurley John. 3600 BRIARFIELD BLVD, STE 3 43537 #038-43-1972 L1973 **P ADP** *020 †75

ASHTON, Philip Floyd. 5901 MONCLOVA RD 43537 #038-43-1985 L1987 **IM** *020 †20

AZEEZ, Nasser. 6005 MONCLOVA RD 43537 #496-20-1998 L2005 **FP** *012

BAIBAK, Laurence Matthew. 1360 ARROWHEAD DR 43537 #038-43-1985 L1990 **PS GS** *020 †65

BALOG, Anna Ruth. ■ 43537 #038-43-2008 *012

BAUTISTA, Armando B. 5901 MONCLOVA RD 43537 #748-01-1961 L1972 **PTH** *071 †50

BENSON, Aaron Gabriel. 6005 MONCLOVA RD, STE 320 43537 #025-01-1999 L2004 **OTO** *020 †45

BERNBLUM, Eva. 120 W DUDLEY ST 43537 #561-11-1973 L1977 **FM** *020 †18

BERNBLUM, Neriel. 120 W DUDLEY ST 43537 #561-11-1972 L1975 **FM** *020 †18

BHATTI, Saad Ahmad. 5901 MONCLOVA RD, INTERNAL MEDICINE HOSPITAL 43537 #704-01-1999 L2005 **CCM CCM** *012 †20

BOLDYS, Susan Elaine. 5901 MONCLOVA RD, ST LUKES HOSPITAL 43537 #025-07-1979 L1980 **PTH GP** *020 †50

BOYCE, Vanessa. 3355 BRIARFIELD BLVD STE E 43537 #038-43-1996 L1997 **FM** *020 †18

BRAR, Gagandeep. 5901 MONCLOVA RD 43537 #495-43-1992 L2005 **NPM** *020 †55

BUCHER, Kyle Fitzgerald. ■ 43537 #038-43-2000 L2000 **IM** *020

CHAUDHARY, Haleem Nasim. ■ 43537 #038-41-2000 L2000 **ORS** *100

CHAUDHURI, Bina. ■ 43537 #495-38-1971 L1987 **PTH** *020 †50

CHAUDHURI, Prabir Kumar. 3600 BRIARFIELD BLVD 43537 #495-38-1970 L1986 **GS GS** *020 †85

CHEN, Kenneth. ■ 43537 #038-43-2008 *012

CLARK, Rebecca Campbell. 660 BEAVER CREEK CIR, STE 100 43537 #038-43-1999 L2000 **FM OS** *020 †18

CLIMO, Randy L. 1690 WOODLANDS DR, STE 1207 / P O BOX 1207 43537 #305-01-1985 L1989 **FM OS** *020 †18

COLELLA, Joseph Anthony. 5705 MONCLOVA RD STE 20 43537 #038-40-1974 L1976 **TS** *020 †85

CONFER-SEELEY, Kim L. 660 BEAVER CREEK CIR, STE 200 43537 #038-43-1992 L1993 **OBG** *020 †30

CORBETT, Thomas Henry. 5901 MONCLOVA RD, DEPT OF SURGERY 43537 #025-01-1963 L1978 **AN OM** *020 †05,70

COX, Elizabeth Hazard. 302 W HARRISON ST 43537 #038-43-2001 L2001 **P** *100 ‡

COX, Stephen Andrew. 302 W HARRISON ST, STEPHEN COX 43537 #038-43-2000 L2000 **P** *020 †75 ‡

COX, Thomas Philip. 660 BEAVER CREEK CIR 43537 #038-43-1997 L1998 **FM MDM** *020 †18

CROCI, John Michael. 5705 MONCLOVA RD, FORT MIAMI MEDICAL CENTER 43537 #038-43-1972 L1973 **FM** *020 †18

CULLEN, Bernard J. ■ 43537 #539-01-1942 L1955 **PD** *071 †55

DABOUL, Nizar. 6450 WHEATSTONE CT, FALLEN TIMBERS INTERNAL ME 43537 #875-01-1991 L1997 **IM** *020 †20

DALAGIANNIS, Athanasios. 1360 ARROWHEAD DR, ARROW HEAD PLASTIC SURGEON 43537 #038-45-1994 L1997 **PS GS** *020 †75

DAVIDSON, Joel Russell. ■ 43537 #038-43-2008 *012

DAY, Carolyn Kirchmaier. ■ 43537 #038-43-2008 *012

DE LUCIA, Jennifer Fallon. 5901 MONCLOVA RD 43537 #038-43-1994 L1996 **PD** *020 †55

DE LUCIA, John Dennis. 5901 MONCLOVA RD, SOUTHWEST ANESTHESIA SERVI 43537 #038-43-1994 L1996 **AN** *020

DERAN, Barry Peter. 5705 MONCLOVA RD, STE 204 43537 #038-43-1986 L1987 **CD IM** *020 †20

DETRICK, Jonathan Marion. 5757 MONCLOVA RD STE 14 43537 #038-40-1979 L1979 **GYN** *020 †30

DETRICK, Marion F, Jr. 5757 MONCLOVA RD, DETRICK & DETRICK INC 43537 #038-40-1947 L1947 **GYN** *071 †30

DONEFF, Donald Anton. 660 BEAVER CREEK CIR, STE 110 43537 #017-20-1961 L1964 **FM** *071 †18

DOOD, Steven Bradford. 5901 MONCLOVA RD 43537 #038-43-1993 L1994 **FM** *020 †18

DOUGLASS, Thomas Garrett. 1725 TIMBER LINE RD 43537 #012-05-1962 L1962 **ADM IM** *071

DOUMET, Mahdi N. 2425 DETROIT AVE 43537 #875-01-1985 L1994 **IM** *020

DUCKETT, Timothy George. 999 ILLINOIS AVE, NORTHWEST SURGICAL 43537 #038-43-1989 L1990 **GS** *020 †85 ‡

DULL, Scott Thos. 5901 MONCLOVA RD 43537 #017-20-1988 L1996 **NS GS** *020 †25

ECKLES, Warren Delos, Jr. ■ 43537 #038-43-1984 **GPM CD** *030

EDJE, Louito Catherina. 5705 MONCLOVA RD 43537 #025-01-1995 L1997 **FM** *020 †18 ‡

EICH, Regina Suzanne. 520 W SOPHIA ST 43537 #038-45-1999 L2000 **PD** *020 †55

EREL, Sharon Perkins. 427 W DUSSEL DR, STE 104 43537 #902-10-1968 L1973 **IM** *020

ERICKSEN, Steven Thomas. ■ 43537 #005-15-2006 L2006 **ORS** *012

EVANS, Darrell Kennedy, Jr. 999 ILLINOIS AVE, NORTHWEST SURGICAL 43537 #003-01-1975 L1980 **GS** *020 †85 ‡

EWRY, James Anthony. 660 BEAVER CREEK CIR, STE 110 43537 #038-43-1985 L1986 **FM** *030 †18

FATINIKUN, Olatunde O. 1645 INDIAN WOOD CIR, COMPREHENSIVE BEHAVIORAL H 43537 #690-02-1980 L2004 **CHP** *020 †75

FOWLER, Elizabeth Stella. 5901 MONCLOVA RD, SOUTHWEST ANESTHESIA INC 43537 #063-01-1985 L1999 **AN** *020 †05

FRISCH, Nicholas Carl. ■ 43537 #038-43-2008 *012

GALLAGHER, Thomas Wm. 570 LONGBOW DR 43537 #038-43-1976 L1977 **EM IM** *020 †16

GERKE, Paul Wells. 5901 MONCLOVA RD 43537 #055-01-1975 L1977 **EM** *020 †16

GOH, Chit-Guan. 660 BEAVER CREEK CIR, STE 100 43537 #385-03-1968 L1974 **PD** *020 †55

GOMEZ, Carlos Eduardo. ■ 43537 #264-18-1991 L2005 **OTR** *100

GORMAN, James Francis. 5705 MONCLOVA RD, STE 205 43537 #056-06-1961 L1966 **VS GS** *020 †85

GUINNESS, Michael L. 5901 MONCLOVA RD, ST LUKES HOSP 43537 #065-01-1977 L1980 **EM OM** *020 †16

HAI, Shaikh Abdul. 3956 MAGNOLIA CIR 43537 #704-25-1991 L2002 **GS CCS** *020 †85

HASLEY, John Hoeffler. ■ 43537 #010-02-1963 L1971 **U** *071 †95

HAZIMAH, Youssef. 2425 DETROIT AVE 43537 #915-03-1982 L1985 **IM** *020 †20

HODEL, Paul Erhard. ■ 43537 #016-06-1961 L1984 **AN** *071 †05

HOEFLINGER, Michael John. 5705 MONCLOVA RD, WEST SIDE ORTHOPEDIC 43537 #038-41-1987 L1991 **ORS** *020 †40

HOUSTON, Thomas Michael. 5755 MONCLOVA RD, WEST SIDE ORTHOPEDIC 43537 #028-02-1975 L1979 **ORS** *020 †40

HUTTNER, James Jacob. 520 W SOPHIA ST 43537 #038-43-1981 L1984 **PD** *020 †55

IAGULLI, Nicholas Dominic. ■ 43537 #038-40-2005 L2005 **ORS** *012

JAIN, Arihant. CO FAMILY PRACTICE, UTST LUKE'S HOSPITAL 43537 #495-43-2005 L2007 **FP** *012

JINDAL, Jay Richard. 6005 MONCLOVA RD, STE 320 43537 #038-06-1990 L1996 **OTO** *020 †45

JINDAL, Valentina. 5901 MONCLOVA RD, ST. LUKES HOSPITAL 43537 #038-06-1990 L1996 **EM** *020 †16

KANAMA-ZAHER, Enas. 5705 MONCLOVA RD 43537 #875-02-1995 L2000 **FM** *020 †18

KANG, Su-Pa. ■ 43537 #583-06-1965 L1972 **GE IM** *071

KANIOS, Chris Mary. 660 BEAVER CREEK CIR, STE 200 43537 #038-43-1984 L1988 **OBG** *020 †30

KANWAL, Neeraj Kumar. 1901 INDIAN WOOD CIR 43537 #041-02-1980 L1983 **IM OS** *030 †20

KARNITIS, Sue A. 660 BEAVER CREEK CIR, STE 100 43537 #038-40-1987 L1991 **PD** *020 †55

KELLY, Kristopher James. ■ 43537 #038-44-2002 L2002 **OPH** *020 †35

KELLY, Victoria Calvina. ■ 43537 #038-44-2002 L2002 **P** *020 †75

KESLER, Carl Jefferson. 1360 ARROWHEAD DR 43537 #038-43-1985 L1990 **GS** *020 †85,65

KINKAID, Kristen Ann. ■ 43537 #038-43-2008 *012

KOLLARITS, Carol Ann Roth. 3509 BRIARFIELD BLVD, EYE INSTITUTE OF NWO 43537 #038-40-1970 L1970 **OPH** *020 †35

KOTCHKOSKI, William Derek. ■ 43537 #038-43-2008 *012

KOTHARI, Deven Suresh. ■ 43537 #038-40-2004 L2004 **AN** *012

LEE, Scott Robert. 5705 MONCLOVA RD 43537 #038-06-1998 L2000 **FM** *020 †18

LEININGER, Anita L. 5901 MONCLOVA RD, NW OHIO CTR BREAST CARE 43537 #025-07-1993 L2001 **GS** *020 †85

LEMON-CRAWFORD, Mary Beth. 5901 MONCLOVA RD 43537 #038-40-1992 L1993 **EM** *020 †16

LINDEMAN, Brian Michael. ■ 43537 #038-43-2005 L2006 **FP** *012

MAGOUN, Sarah Jane. 520 W SOPHIA ST 43537 #007-02-1997 L2000 **PD** *020 †55

MASON, Renee Elaine. 660 BEAVER CREEK CIR 43537 #038-43-1991 L1992 **OBG** *020 †30

MATANI, Aruna Surendra. 1661 HOLLAND RD, STE 400 43537 #495-01-1967 L1972 **PD PHP** *071 †55

MATTEVI, Patricia Ann. ■ 43537 #038-43-1992 L1994 **EM** *020 †16

MATTISON, Lalaine Marie. 1661 HOLLAND RD, PULMONARY & CRITICAL CARE 43537 #748-11-1969 L1991 **PCC SME** *020 †20

MATTISON, Timothy James. 5757 MONCLOVA RD, STE 15 43537 #748-11-1988 L1996 **IM** *020 †20

MCGEE, Lisa Anne. ■ 43537 #038-43-2008 *012

MEDAGLIA, Antoinette L. 660 BEAVER CREEK CIR, STE 100 43537 #038-43-1990 L1993 **PD** *020 †55

MEDEL, Marietta J. ■ 43537 #748-10-1975 L2000 **CN** *100

MIAN, Alec. 5901 MONCLOVA RD 43537 #913-04-1976 L1982 **ATP CLP** *020 †50

MIKHAIL, Ramzy Naguib. ■ 43537 #330-04-1957 L1970 **CRS** *071 †85,10

MILLER, Brian Keith. 5705 MONCLOVA RD 43537 #038-40-1988 L1989 **FM** *020 †18

MOHAMMADIONE, Dayna F. 660 BEAVER CRK, STE 200 43537 #020-12-1982 L1987 **OBG** *020 †30

■ = Address Information Privacy Protected

MORRIS, Robert Kandelin. 5757 MONCLOVA RD, STE 17 43537 #025-07-1982 L1987
GS *020 †85

MUKHERJEE, Asish. 5705 MONCLOVA RD, STE 203 43537 #495-02-1981 L1997
CRS GS *020 †10,85

NELSON, Richard John. 6005 MONCLOVA RD, STE 320 43537 #025-01-1983 L1991
OTO *020 †45

NEUHOFF, Ronica Ann. 660 BEAVER CREEK CIR, STE 200 43537 #025-12-1993 L1994
OBG *020 †30

NEWTON, Susan Louise. ■ 43537 #038-43-1986 L1987 **EM** *020 †16

NIELSEN, Jay Walter. 1900 INDIAN WOOD CIR, STE 100 43537 #038-43-1975 L1977
FM OS *020 †18

OATIS, Paul Francis. ■ 43537 #038-43-1990 L1993 **IM** *020 †20

OKIN, Cynthia Rachel. 660 BEAVER CREEK CIR, STE 200 43537 #038-43-1996 L2000
OBG *020 †30

OSTROWSKI, Emily Ann. 660 BEAVER CREEK CIR, STE 110 43537 #038-43-2002 L2002
FM *020 †18

OWEIS, Thomas Daniel. 999 ILLINOIS AVE, NORTHWEST SURGICAL 43537 #025-07-1992 L1997
GS *020 †85 ‡

PAAT, Antonio Belmonte. 235 W WAYNE ST 43537 #748-01-1955 L1967 **FM GS** *071 †18

PAAT, Richard Allen. 5901 MONCLOVA RD 43537 #038-43-1986 L1987 **IM** *020 †20

PALMA GIL, Aquiles P. 5757 MONCLOVA RD STE 19 43537 #748-01-1963 L1972 **AN** *071

PARODI, Jose E. 1574 HENTHORNE DR, STE C 43537 #924-01-1984 L1998 **GS** *020 †85

PERRING, Paul David. ■ 43537 #038-43-2006 L2006 **GS** *012

POPE, Sarah Georgina D. 5757 MONCLOVA RD, STE 31 43537 #065-09-1964 L1990
R OS *071 †80

PRIBIS, Erica. ■ 43537 #016-43-2000 L2000 **EM** *020

PROVENZANO, Joel David. ■ 43537 #038-43-2008 *012

RAMIREZ, Hector R. 5757 MONCLOVA RD 43537 #429-01-1966 L1975 **OS** *071

RASOR, Travis Edward. 5705 MONCLOVA RD 43537 #038-75-2000, ▲ L2000 **FM** *020

RECKER, Anthony Louis. ■ 43537 #038-43-2003 *100

RENCH, Michael Jerome. 5757 MONCLOVA RD STE 29 43537 #017-20-1964 L1965
PS HS *071 †65

REZVAN, Azadeh. ■ 43537 #038-43-2008 *012

RHEE, Ann. 660 BEAVER CREEK CIR, STE 200 43537 #033-05-1996 L2000 **OBG** *020 †30

RITTER, Howard Lester, Jr. 5805 MONCLOVA RD, NORTHWEST OHIO ONCOLOGY CL 43537
#038-43-1974 L1991 **ON HEM** *020 †20

ROHS, Michael Henry, Jr. ■ 43537 #038-43-2008 *012

RUCH, Anne Towey. 660 BEAVER CREEK CIR, STE 200 43537 #038-43-1988 L1989
OBG *020 †30

RUST, John Lebeau, Jr. 5901 MONCLOVA RD, ST. LUKES HOSPITAL 43537 #025-12-1990 L1998
AN PME *020 †05

SALPIETRO, Benjamin J, Jr. 5755 MONCLOVA RD, WEST SIDE ORTHOPEDIC 43537
#038-43-1989 L1991 **ORS** *020 †40

SALVI, Ashok R. 6005 MONCLOVA RD, STE 220 43537 #495-28-1971 L1995 **AN PME** *020 †05

SAMSEY, Kathleen Michelle. ■ 43537 #012-05-2004 L2006 **EM** *020

SAVAGE, Brian John. 5757 MONCLOVA RD, STE 11 43537 #038-43-1996 L2001 **NEP** *020 †20

SCHAFER, Patrick. 5901 MONCLOVA RD, SOUTHWEST ANESTHESIA SERV 43537
#038-43-1992 L1996 **AN** *020 †05

SCHOLLER, Beverly Jean. 660 BEAVER CREEK CIR, STE 100 43537 #038-40-1985 L1988
PD *020 †55

SCHWEICKERT, Adam Joseph. ■ 43537 #038-43-2007 **PD** *012

SCHWISOW, Allen Gene. 5600 MONCLOVA RD 43537 #038-40-1978 L1979 **IM** *020 †20

SETH, Satish Kumar. ■ 43537 #010-03-1970 L1976 **EM GP** *071 †20,16,18 ‡

SHAH, Rama Parikh. 5705 MONCLOVA RD STE 203 43537 #495-22-1970 L1977 **AN** *020

SHAH, Ranchhodbhai S. 5705 MONCLOVA RD 43537 #495-23-1969 L1973 **CRS GS** *100 †85,10

SHAHZAD, Khawaja. 1645 INDIAN WOOD CIR, STE 202 43537 #704-02-1992 L2004
CHP *020 †75

SHARMA, Ajeet L. 6005 MONCLOVA RD, STE 360 43537 #495-41-1973 L1999 **CD** *020 †20

SHERIDAN, Victoria Louise. ■ 43537 #038-43-2008 L2008 *012

SHORT, Scott Randall. 920 ILLINOIS AVE, MAUMEE STAMPING PLANT 43537
#038-43-1999 L1999 **FM** *020 †18

SHRESTHA, Niranjan. ■ 43537 #672-03-2002 L2005 **FP** *012

SIM, Isabel Y. 1661 HOLLAND RD, STE 200 43537 #748-01-1965 L1975 **OBG** *020

SMALE, Robin Lynn. 660 BEAVER CREEK CIR, STE 200 43537 #038-43-1992 L1995
OBG *020 †30

SONTCHI, Shari Joyce. 660 BEAVER CREEK CIR, STE 100 43537 #038-43-1989 L1992
PD *020 †55

SPAYDE, Amber Lyn. ■ 43537 #038-43-2008 *012

STIERWALT, Robert Jos, Jr. 5901 MONCLOVA RD 43537 #038-43-1980 L1981 **IM EM** *020 †20

TANCOUS, Emily Elizabeth. ■ 43537 #038-43-2008 *012

TE, Minda Ng. 5901 MONCLOVA RD 43537 #748-10-1981 L1991 **PD NPM** *020 †55

TIPTON, Warren Sheldon. 5901 MONCLOVA RD 43537 #038-43-1973 L1975 **EM FM** *020 †16

TORRES, Sesinando R. 5901 MONCLOVA RD, ST LUKES HOSPITAL 43537 #748-01-1969 L1974
IM EM *020

TRIVEDI, Vivek. 6005 MONCLOVA RD, STE 220 43537 #913-89-1984 L1996 **AN** *020 †05

TUMKUR, Shivaprakas Manju. ■ 43537 #038-43-2007 L2007 **TY** *012

WEBB, William Donald. 1015 CONANT ST, MAUMEE URGENT MEDICAL CARE 43537
#038-40-1965 L1965 **EM** *072

WEBSTER, John Blair. ■ 43537 #038-06-1959 L1959 **OM IM** *020 †70

WEHRMEISTER, John Richard. 5757 MONCLOVA RD, STE 4 43537 #038-43-1981 L1982
IM *020 †20

WEIDAW, Clark D. 5655 MONCLOVA RD 43537 #038-43-1972 L1973 **OPH** *020 †35

WHITE, Beth Ann. 999 ILLINOIS AVE, NORTHWEST SURGICAL 43537 #041-12-1988 L1993
GS *020 †85

WOODS, Daniel Patrick. ■ 43537 #038-43-2008 *012

XANTHAKOS, Ursula F. 5901 MONCLOVA RD 43537 #407-33-1966 L1970 **PD** *020 †55

YANIK, Michael Allen. 1360 ARROWHEAD DR 43537 #038-34-1974 L1979 **PS CCS** *020 †85,65

ZACIEWSKI, Thomas Gerard. ■ 43537 #038-43-2007 L2007 **U** *012

MAYFIELD – CUYAHOGA

JHALA, Varsha M. ■ 44143 #495-48-1972 L1980 **AN** *020 †05

SAHLANI, Kamal. 6555 WILSON MILLS RD, STE 103D 44143 #759-01-1980 L1987
IM GP *020 †20

MAYFIELD HEIGHTS – CUYAHOGA

AGARWAL, Rajesh. 6780 MAYFIELD RD, STE 425 44124 #495-45-1995 L1997 **IM** *020 †20

ALVAREZ, Benito A. 6770 MAYFIELD RD, STE 336 44124 #270-02-1988 L1993
OBG IM *020 †20,30

ANSCHUETZ, Robert H. 6770 MAYFIELD RD # 441 44124 #028-02-1976 L1977 **ORS** *020 †40

ANTON, George E. 6801 MAYFIELD RD STE 146, HILLCREST MEDICAL BLDG 2 44124
#010-03-1978 L1983 **VS GS** *020 †85

BAJAJ, Harpreet Singh. ■ 44124 #495-45-2001 L2007 **IM** *100 †20

BLANK, Mary Griswold. 6803 MAYFIELD RD STE 305, HILLCREST OBGYN ASSOCIATES 44124
#038-06-1986 L1986 **OBG** *020 †30

BUTLER, Harold Edward. 6780 MAYFIELD RD, DEPT OF RADIOLOGY 44124
#038-06-1975 L1976 **R** *020 †80

CALIBAG, Liwanag Morando. 6780 MAYFIELD RD, MERIDIA HILLCREST HOSPITAL 44124
#748-01-1973 L1988 **AN** *020 †20

CHAPPELOW, Aimee Virginia. ■ 44124 #016-06-2005 L2006 **OPH** *012

CORN, Robert Curtis. 5885 LANDERBROOK DR, STE 150 44124 #041-09-1975 L1976
ORS HS *020 †40

DANVIRIYASUP, Kowit. ■ 44124 #891-04-1971 L1979 **NEP** *020 †20

DELOOZE, Dawn Elizabeth. ■ 44124 #038-40-2005 L2005 **PD** *012

DEUTCH, Steven Jeff. 6780 MAYFIELD RD, HILLCREST HOSPITAL 44124 #038-40-1984 L1989
DR *020 †80

DEWS, Teresa Elaine. 6803 MAYFIELD RD, STE 200 44124 #038-06-1988 L1991
AN PME *020 †05

DIPIERRO, Jacqueline M. ■ 44124 #038-44-1990 L1995 **PS** *020 †65

DORSKY, John. 6770 MAYFIELD RD STE 348 44124 #035-20-1981 L1986 **GS** *020 †85

DRAPER-STEPANOVICH, Karen. 6770 MAYFIELD RD, STE 348 44124 #025-12-1993 L2006
GS *020 †85

EDWARDS, Thomas Craig. 6770 MAYFIELD RD STE 220, C.C.F. CHILD HOSP/HILLCRST 44124
#028-03-1984 L2006 **PDC** *020 †55

EIDLIN, Natalia. ■ 44124 #913-06-1987 L2001 **DR** *020 †80

FEIGHAN, Elizabeth B. 5850 LANDERBROOK DR, STE 210 44124 #038-06-1990 L1991
PD *020 †55

FROIMSON, Avrum Isaiah. 6770 MAYFIELD RD, STE 336 44124 #021-01-1955 L1958
ORS HS *020 †40

FUMICH, Robert Mark. 6803 MAYFIELD RD STE 314, THE HILLCREST MED BLDG #1 44124
#038-40-1974 L1975 **ORS OS** *020 †40

GAINER, Danielle Michelle. ■ 44124 #038-45-2007 L2007 **P** *012

GERBLICH, Adi A. 6770 MAYFIELD RD 44124 #550-02-1972 L1975 **PUD CCM** *020 †20

GLASS, Ian Scott. 6780 MAYFIELD RD, # ADMIN 44124 #038-06-1977 L1980 **IM** *020 †20

GOTTESMAN, David Lawrence. 6770 MAYFIELD RD, STE 424 44124 #035-19-1975 L1978
IM GE *020 †20

GRADY, Martin Vincent. 6780 MAYFIELD RD, MERIDIA HILLCREST HOSPITAL 44124
#038-06-1984 L1984 **AN IM** *020 †05

GUSTAFERRO, Cynthia A. 6770 MAYFIELD RD # 443, HILLCREST MEDICAL OFFICE B 44124
#046-01-1987 L1993 **ID IM** *040 †20

HADRO, Jennifer. 6780 MAYFIELD RD, HILLCREST RADIOLOGY ASSOCI 44124
#041-02-1994 L2005 **DR** *020 †80

HANNA, Michael A. 6770 MAYFIELD RD STE 333 44124 #875-01-1964 L1971 **CD IM** *020 †20

HAUER, Christopher A. 6780 MAYFIELD RD, DEPT OF PATHOLOGY 44124 #038-06-1980 L1985
PD *020 †50

HISSA, Edwin Alex, Jr. 6770 MAYFIELD RD STE 443 44124 #038-41-1981 L1982 **ORS** *020 †40

HUTT, David Mark. 6770 MAYFIELD RD # 421 44124 #038-06-1979 L1985 **IM ID** *020 †20

HU-WHITTEMORE, Eva. 1280 SOM CENTER RD, STE 234 44124 #035-15-1983 L1988 **N** *020

JACOBS, David Saml. 6780 MAYFIELD RD, MERIDIA HILLCREST HOSP 44124
#035-46-1986 L1991 **DR RNR** *020 †80

JOHNSON, Kristin M. ■ 44124 #038-75-2003, ▲ L2004 **NMN** *012

JOHNSON, Valerie Anne. 5850 LANDERBROOK DR 44124 #038-43-2003 L2006 **IM** *100 †20

KAHN, Leonard Aaron. 6780 MAYFIELD RD, RADIOLOGY DEPARTMENT 44124
#836-01-1984 L1991 **DR** *020 †80

KASSOUF, Amy Hehr. 5850 LANDERBROOK DR, DRIVE. #304 44124 #038-06-1992 L1993
D *020 †15

KAVOUKSORIAN, Cynthia Ann. 6770 MAYFIELD RD STE 430 44124 #041-01-1977 L1983
PS HS *071 †65 ‡

KESSLER, Fred Bruce. 6770 MAYFIELD RD, RM 424 44124 #010-01-1975 L1983 **GE** *020 †20

KRALIK, Rita Marie. ■ 44124 #038-06-1980 L1984 **IM** *075

KRANTZ, Mark Allen. 6780 MAYFIELD RD, DEPARTMENT OF ANESTHESIA 44124
#038-41-1985 L1989 **AN** *020 †05

KRISHNA, Sangeeta. 6770 MAYFIELD RD, # 220 44124 #496-07-1989 L2007 **PD** *020 †55

KRISHNAN, Ravi Venkata. 6803 MAYFIELD RD 44124 #495-16-1988 L1994 **IM** *020 †20

KURLANDER, Donald Jay. 5252 MAYFIELD RD, STE 302 44124 #038-40-1957 L1957
GE IM *071 †20

KUROSAKA, Masahiro. ■ 44124 #572-30-1977 **OS** *050

LAFFAY, Dennis Lee. 6780 MAYFIELD RD 44124 #025-01-1973 L1974 **PTH HMP** *020 †50

LALLI, Anthony Frederick. 6780 MAYFIELD RD 44124 #016-02-1954 L1954 **R** *020 †80

LEVINE, Louis Hyman. 6780 MAYFIELD RD 44124 #038-40-1968 L1969 **PTH** *020 †50

LEVINSON, Michael Maurice. 6780 MAYFIELD RD, HILLCREST HOSPITAL 44124
#035-47-2000 L2006 **EM** *020 †16

LIBERTIN, Mark. 6803 MAYFIELD RD, STE 305 44124 #038-44-1985 L1987 **OBG** *020 †30

LIU, Patty Tzeng. ■ 44124 #038-43-2008 *012

MALICK, Omar. ■ 44124 #704-20-1992 L2002 **IM** *020

MARINO, John Anthony. 6770 MAYFIELD RD # 443 44124 #041-13-1979 L1981 **IM** *020 †20

MARKOWITZ, Martin Alan. 6770 MAYFIELD RD STE 326 44124 #016-42-1965 L1966
OPH *020 †35

MATHAVAN, Viney Kumar. ■ 44124 #496-17-1995 L2003 **GS** *012

MC GREW, Thomas Lee. 6803 MAYFIELD RD, STE 305 44124 #020-02-1978 L1981
OBG *020 †30

MEDEN, Glenn Jos. 6770 MAYFIELD RD, STE 305 44124 #038-40-1979 L1981
PUD CCM *020 †20

MILLER, Susan. 6780 MAYFIELD RD 44124 #038-40-1987 L1990 **DR IM** *020 †80

MURTHY, Prabha Srinivasa. 6770 MAYFIELD RD 44124 #495-09-1965 L1971 **PTH** *020 †50

MUSTAFA, Hossameldin Imam. ■ 44124 #848-03-2002 L2007 **IM** *100 †20

NOWAK, Catherine Joyce. 6770 MAYFIELD RD, STE 200 44124 #038-06-1983 L1988
GYN *071 †30

NUNEZ, Carlos. 6780 MAYFIELD RD, HILLCREST HOSP 44124 #847-05-1972 L1979
ATP PCP *020 †50

OBERFELD, Sheldon M. 6770 MAYFIELD RD, # 326 44124 #048-04-1986 L1988 **OPH** *020 †35
OKWUONE, Celestine O. ■ 44124 #690-06-1996 L2003 **AN** *100 †05 ‡
OLBRYCH, Thomas Geo. 6770 MAYFIELD RD, STE 323 44124 #038-40-1981 L1982 **PUD CCM** *020 †20
PESICK, Shelly Debbie. 6770 MAYFIELD RD, STE 310 44124 #025-01-1986 L1987 **PD** *020 †55
PHILIPSON, Elliot Harris. 6770 MAYFIELD RD, STE 336 44124 #561-17-1975 L1980 **OBG MFM** *020 †30
PORTER, Susan Elizabeth. 6780 MAYFIELD RD 44124 #041-02-1999 L1999 **PTH** *020 †50
PRATA, James Michael. 6780 MAYFIELD RD, HILLCREST HOSPITAL 44124 #041-02-1983 L1986 **AN** *05
PRIMAK, Lara Kristina. ■ 44124 #035-45-1994 L1999 **CCP** *020 †55
RAJU, Rajeeva Ratna. 6780 MAYFIELD RD 44124 #495-47-1980 L2000 **PCP** *020 †50
RAO, Shakuntala Dinkar. 6770 MAYFIELD RD, STE 236 44124 #495-37-1975 L1983 **PD** *020 †20
REICHSTEIN, Benj James. 6770 MAYFIELD RD STE 421 44124 #016-42-1976 L1989 **GS** *020 †85
RICH, Justin Thomas. 5850 LANDERBROOK DR, STE 200 44124 #038-40-2003 L2003 **PD** *020 †55
RIZZO, Anthony. 6801 MAYFIELD RD, STE 146 44124 #041-13-1990 L2000 **VS** *020 †85
ROBINSON, Gina Myisha. 6770 MAYFIELD RD STE 310 44124 #010-03-1995 L1997 **PD** *020 †55
ROCKEY, Daniel Karl. 6780 MAYFIELD RD, DEPT OF RADIOLOGY 44124 #038-43-1985 L1986 **R** *020 †80
ROSS, Elisa Krapf. 6770 MAYFIELD RD STE 336, CLEVELAND CLINIC FOUNDATIO 44124 #025-01-1986 L1988 **OBG** *020 †30
ROSS, Ronald Jay. 6780 MAYFIELD RD DEPT RAD 44124 #035-46-1960 L1961 **R** *071 †80
RUPP, Dennis John. ■ 44143 #038-41-1980 L1988 **CD IM** *020 †20
SANTOSCOY, Thomas Gerald. 6770 MAYFIELD RD, # 400 44124 #019-02-1976 L1977 **CHP** *020 †85,90
SARAIYA, Jayshree R. 6780 MAYFIELD RD 44124 #495-76-1982 L1997 **IM** *020 †20
SCHAFFER-POLAKOF, Paula. 6770 MAYFIELD RD STE 249 44124 #038-06-1984 L1986 **OBG** *020 †30
SCHINABECK, Matthew K. 6770 MAYFIELD RD # 443, ID CONSULTANTS 44124 #038-06-1997 L1999 **ID** *020 †20
SCHNEIDER, Kurt Wesley. 6803 MAYFIELD RD RM 4, HILLCREST MEDICAL BUILDING 44124 #038-43-1999 L1999 **U** *020 †95
SCIVITTARO, Vincenzo. 6001 LANDERHAVEN DR, STE D 44124 #561-21-1988 L1995 **IM** *100
SHIN, Yee Victor. 6770 MAYFIELD RD STE 338 44124 #495-79-1974 L1981 **OPH** *020 †35
SIEGEL, M Barry. 6770 MAYFIELD RD, STE 225 44124 #038-41-1966 L1966 **NEP IM** *040 †20
STANESCU, Gabriel Lupu. 5850 LANDERBROOK DR, STE 105 44124 #781-01-1982 L1995 **IM** *075 †20
STOCKFISH, Jeffrey Howard. 6770 MAYFIELD RD, # 300 44124 #038-40-1985 L1985 **OPH** *020 †35
STOLL, Colleen Marie. ■ 44124 #036-05-1990 L1994 **PD** *100
TAUB, Steven Jeffrey. 6803 MAYFIELD RD STE 510 44124 #035-08-1976 L1980 **D** *020 †15
TOMA, Ihab Yehia Saad. 6780 MAYFIELD RD 44124 #915-04-1983 L2000 **AN** *020 †05
TOWER, Marcus Earl. 6770 MAYFIELD RD, STE 225 44124 #017-20-1977 L1981 **OBG** *020 †30
UTECH, Kathleen. 5850 LANDERBROOK DR, STE 210 44124 #035-03-1996 L1999 **PD** *020 †55
VENNA, Ranga Prabhakar. 6503 MARSOL RD # 267, UNIVERSITY HOSPITALS 44124 #495-49-1979 L2000 **AN** *020 †05
VERMONT, Carmen. 6780 MAYFIELD RD, DEPT OF RADIATION ONCOLOGY 44124 #781-02-1988 L2003 **RO** *020 †80
VILLABONA, Claudia Patric. 5850 LANDERBROOK DR, STE 100 44124 #264-12-1987 L2000 **IM** *020
VOGT, Clifford John, Jr. 6801 MAYFIELD RD, STE 336 44124 #038-06-1965 L1965 **PS** *020 †85,65
VYROUBAL, Vlasta. ■ 44124 #957-01-1954 L1963 **P** *072 †75
WAGENBERG, Scott Alan. 6770 MAYFIELD RD, STE 326 44124 #025-01-1995 L2000 **OPH** *020 †35
WAGGONER, David Michael. 6803 MAYFIELD RD STE 500, HILLCREST MED OFC BLDG 1 44124 #036-07-1969 L1970 **IM** *030 †20
WAITE, Donna Jeanette. 6770 MAYFIELD RD, STE 400 44124 #024-16-1979 L1986 **TS** *020 †85,90
WEINLAND, Robert Logan. HILLCREST HOSPITAL 44124 #017-20-1977 L1985 **EM** *020 †16
WOLF, Jason M. 6770 MAYFIELD RD STE 424 44124 #048-12-1997 L2000 **GE** *020 †20
WOLOVITZ, Brian Mark. 5850 LANDERBROOK DR, STE 100 44124 #836-01-1989 L1997 **IM** *020 †20
WULFFHART, Jeffrey Ivor. ■ 44124 #836-01-1986 **IM** *020
YANG, Peter. 6770 MAYFIELD RD, STE 424 44124 #023-07-1977 L1983 **GE IM** *020 †20
ZAAS, Robert David. 6803 MAYFIELD RD STE 314 44124 #016-02-1957 L1959 **ORS** *020 †40
ZAKHARY, Emad Monid A. 6801 MAYFIELD RD, BLDG 2 44124 #915-02-1984 L2000 **VS** *100 †85

MC ARTHUR – VINTON

WALTER, Stacey Lynn. 31891 STATE ROUTE 93 45651 #041-12-2004 L2007 **FM** *020 †18
YADAV, Biplav. 31891 STATE ROUTE 93 45651 #672-01-1994 L2006 **FM** *020 †18

MC COMB – HANCOCK

DOONE, James Owen, Jr. 271 S PARK DR, MCCOMB FAMILY PRACTICE 45858 #038-45-1991 L1993 **FM** *020 †18

MC CONNELSVILLE – MORGAN

HENTHORN, Raymond Bruce. 155 E MAIN ST, RM 135 43756 #055-01-1980 L1982 **GP LM** *075 †16 ‡
MURRELL, Barbara Gay. 4279 N STATE ROUTE 376 NW 43756 #038-40-1978 L1980 **FM** *020 †18

MC DONALD – TRUMBULL

VUKOVIC, Adam Alexander. ■ 44437 #038-41-2008 *012

MEDINA – MEDINA

ABELLERA, Manuel C. 750 E WASHINGTON ST, STE D4 44256 #748-01-1969 L1974 **GP GS** *020
ALEXANDER, Susan Louise. 3591 RESERVE COMMONS DR, STE 100 44256 #065-06-1978 L1987 **PD EM** *020 †18,55,16
AL-SHAHED, Abdallah M. A.. 3645 MEDINA RD 44256 #875-02-1999 L2002 **IM** *020 †20
ARCENEAUX, Susan Marie. 805 E WASHINGTON ST, STE 100 44256 #032-01-1988 L1992 **PM PME** *020 †60
AUSTRIACO, Alfredo Reyes. 970 E WASHINGTON ST STE 3 44256 #748-08-1965 L1972 **IM CD** *020
BASHOUR, Fadi Nicola. 3985 MEDINA RD, STE 120 44256 #875-01-1987 L1993 **GE** *020 †20
BERNACCHIA, Dean Hugo. ■ 44256 #038-40-1961 L1961 **U** *071 †95
BHATT, Mukesh C. 970 E WASHINGTON ST, STE 4D 44256 #495-17-1980 L1989 **HEM ON** *020 †20
BICA, Thomas Dennis. 970 E WASHINGTON ST STE 6C 44256 #016-43-1974 L1976 **GS** *020 †85
BLACKBURN, Joseph Bruce. 1075 S COURT 44256 #035-06-1992 L1999 **FM** *020 †18
BODNAR, Myron Eugene. 970 E WASHINGTON ST, STE 201 44256 #038-06-1982 L1983 **OPH** *020 †35
BROWN, Allison Jeanne. ■ 44256 #038-43-2005 L2006 *100
BROWN, Eric Lawrence. 1000 E WASHINGTON ST, ATTN MEDICAL STAFF OFFICE 44256 #038-41-1996 L1997 **EM IM** *020 †16
CASTELE, Robert John. 970 E WASHINGTON ST # 104 44256 #038-06-1978 L1979 **PUD IM** *020 †20
CHEN, Keshiau. 970 E WASHINGTON ST, STE 6C 44256 #385-02-1958 L1971 **GS R** *071 †85
CHI, Thomas S K. 1000 E WASHINGTON ST 44256 #035-19-1989 L1994 **OPH** *020 †35
CHOI, Keun Lyol. ■ 44256 #583-06-1960 L1974 **AN FM** *071
CULLEN, Stephen Boyd. 970 E WASHINGTON ST, STE 4B 44256 #038-06-1999 L1999 **FM** *020 †18
DENTON, Alice Moorhead. 3617 RESERVE COMMONS DR, IM ASSOC INC 44256 #038-43-1994 L1995 **IM** *020 †20
DESAI, Dhanlaxmi. 1000 E WASHINGTON ST 44256 #495-21-1978 L1999 **PP** *100
DRENTH, Douglas Mitchell. 1000 E WASHINGTON ST 44256 #041-02-1997 L1999 **EM** *020 †16
DULLE, Erika Kathleen. 1000 E WASHINGTON ST, ATTN EMERGENCY DEPARTMENT 44256 #038-41-1998 L2000 **EM** *020 †16
EBNER, Kristen Angela. 970 E WASHINGTON ST STE 6C 44256 #038-41-1996 L2001 **GS** *020 †85
EBNER, Thomas Gharet. 970 E WASHINGTON ST # 102 44256 #038-40-1969 L1969 **ORS** *020 †40
ENRIQUEZ, Anya Szeglin. 5783 WOOSTER PIKE, TRILLIUM CREEK 44256 #008-01-2003 L2003 **D** *020 †15
FALL, Douglas Lawrence. 4015 MEDINA RD, STE 50 44256 #019-02-1996 L1997 **PD** *020 †55
FARNHAM, Edward Lynn. ■ 44256 #038-40-1958 L1958 **GS** *071 †85
FOOTE, Meghan J. 970 E WASHINGTON ST, MEDINA OB/GYN ASSOCIATES 44256 #028-78-2003, ▲ L2003 **OBG** *020
FUNK, Jonathan Roy. 970 E WASHINGTON ST, STE 5F 44256 #038-06-1990 L1991 **OBG** *020 †30
FUNK, Walter Ray. 970 E WASHINGTON ST, STE 5F 44256 #038-06-1957 L1957 **GS GP** *071
GAICH, Steven Alexander. 970 E WASHINGTON ST, STE 6B 44256 #038-44-1995 L1996 **OBG** *020 †30
GEORGE, Walter Lloyd, Jr. 1000 E WASHINGTON ST 44256 #038-06-1975 L1979 **R** *020 †80
GOYAL, Yatish. 970 E WASHINGTON ST, STE 204 44256 #496-14-1992 L1998 **IM** *020 †20
GRIFFITHS, Maria M. 970 E WASHINGTON ST, STE 203 44256 #038-44-1990 L1994 **AN PME** *020 †05
GROSS, Richard Martin. ■ 44258 #005-02-1956 L1963 **R** *071 †80
HAWKINS, Edward Francis. 1000 E WASHINGTON ST, MEDINA GENERAL HOSPITAL 44256 #056-06-1983 L1986 **FM** *020 †18
HOLLOWAY, William H. ■ 44256 #041-12-1949 L1950 **P** *030 †75
HULL, Thomas Patrick. 3591 RESERVE COMMONS DR, THE RETINA GROUP OF 44256 #036-05-1994 L1995 **OPH** *072 †35
HUMMEL, Karen Marie. 4015 MEDINA RD 44256 #038-44-1995 L1996 **MPD PD** *020 †20,55
JACKSON, Glenna Smith. 970 E WASHINGTON ST, STE 3 44256 #038-44-1989 L1990 **FM** *020 †18
JAIN, Shail. 1000 E WASHINGTON ST, PATHOLOGY DEPT MEDINA GEN 44256 #495-15-1976 L1984 **PTH** *020 †50
JAIN, Than Mal. 970 E WASHINGTON ST, STE 2E 44256 #495-15-1974 L1981 **CD IM** *020 †20
JAYASWAL, Bijay Kumar. 3457 MEDINA RD 44256 #495-15-1963 L1978 **CD IM** *020 †20
JEDACEK, Natalie Patricia. 3591 RESERVE COMMONS DR, STE 100 44256 #038-41-1995 L1996 **PD** *020 †55
JENISON, Eric Lee. 970 E WASHINGTON ST, GYN ONCOLOGISTS OF NE 44256 #038-43-1974 L1975 **GO OBG** *020 †30 ‡
KALUCIS, John Yani. 750 E WASHINGTON ST 44256 #902-01-1955 L1968 **OTO** *071
KARIM, Mohammad Shaukat. 3645 MEDINA RD 44256 #495-15-1976 L2002 **IM** *020 †20
KASE, Jeffrey Allan. 970 E WASHINGTON ST, STE 4B 44256 #038-40-1973 L1978 **FM** *020 †18
KENNEDY, Tamika Jai. ■ 44256 #038-40-2006 L2006 **PD** *012
KHANDELWAL, Shobha. 970 E WASHINGTON ST, STE 2F 44256 #495-15-1977 L1987 **IM** *020 †20
KILLIAN, Patrick Michael. 5779 WOOSTER PIKE, TRILLIUM CREEK DERM 44256 #038-40-1999 L1999 **D DS** *020 †15
KRANZ, Kristin Marie. 970 E WASHINGTON ST, STE 3 44256 #038-41-1992 L1997 **FM** *020 †18
KUEHN, John Lampert. ■ 44256 #038-40-1957 L1957 **P N** *071 †17
KWAK, Myung Sook. 696 E WASHINGTON ST 44256 #583-08-1973 L1977 **P** *020 †75
LAMKIN, Jeffrey Charles. 3591 RESERVE COMMONS DR, THE RETINA GROUP OF 44256 #025-01-1987 L1992 **OPH** *020 †35
LAZOR, Thomas Adam. ■ 44256 #038-40-1978 L1978 **FM** *071 †18
LEONARD, Raymond Patrick. ■ 44256 #055-01-2005 L2005 **PD** *012
LEVINE, David Alexander. 1000 E WASHINGTON ST, EMERGENCY DEPT 44256 #048-13-1998 L1999 **EM** *020 †16
LEWTON, Zachary Richard. 3985 MEDINA RD, STE 200 44256 #035-45-1999 L2004 **N** *020 †75
LIAUBA, Rimas Albinas. 3575 RESERVE COMMONS DR, STE 150 44256 #038-41-1970 L1970 **OTO** *020
LIN, I-Huei. 970 E WASHINGTON ST, STE 303 44256 #385-04-1966 L1976 **PD GP** *020 †55
LONG, John Warren. ■ 44256 #019-02-1970 L1971 **TS CD** *020 †85,90
MADRILEJOS, Tomas A. 738 E SMITH RD 44256 #748-01-1966 L1978 **GP** *020
MANDEVILLE, Richard Chas. ■ 44256 #028-34-1954 L1958 **OS** *071

MAST, Harold Linn. 3583 RESERVE COMMONS DR 44256 #038-40-1970 L1970 **OPH** *071 †35
MAYER, Daniel Jay. 4067 N JEFFERSON ST 44256 #041-01-1973 L1986 **OPH** *020 †35
MC COMSEY, Kevin William. 970 E WASHINGTON ST, STE 5F 44256 #038-06-1995 L1996 **OBG** *020 †30
MC CORMICK, Kenelm F. 797 N COURT ST 44256 #038-45-1988 L1989 **FM PLM** *020 †18
MC KELVEY, Erin Jeanine. 970 E WASHINGTON ST, STE 5F 44256 #038-06-1996 L1997 **OBG** *020 †30
MEMBERG, Stacey Jean. 4015 MEDINA RD, STE 50 44256 #038-06-1997 L1999 **PD** *020 †55
MENDPARA, Suresh D. 970 E WASHINGTON ST, STE 4D 44256 #495-89-1994 L2000 **HO** *020 †20
MILJKOVIC, Susan M. 970 E WASHINGTON ST STE 6C 44256 #038-40-1998 L2000 **GS** *020 †85
MITRA, Kunal. 3575 RESERVE COMMONS DR, STE 150 44256 #495-02-1968 L1985 **IM** *020 †20
MOHR, Mary Elizabeth. ■ 44256 #038-40-1960 L1960 **R** *071 †80
MOK, Yue Pang. 970 E WASHINGTON ST, STE 203 44256 #244-02-1973 L1975 **AN PME** *020 †05
MONHEIM, K M. 3617 RESERVE COMMONS DR 44256 #038-44-1981 L1982 **IM** *020 †20
MORAN, Mark F. ■ 44256 #130-01-2002 L2007 **IM** *100 †20
MUSGRAVE, Mark Matthew. 4015 MEDINA RD STE 90 44256 #038-40-1994 L1995 **ORS** *020 †40
MYERS, David Brown. 3985 MEDINA RD, STE 120 44256 #038-40-1986 L1988 **GE** *020 †20
MYERS, Martha Lee. 4015 MEDINA RD, STE 44 44256 #038-44-1990 L1992 **PD** *020 †55
NAPLES, Patrick Jos. 4018 MEDINA RD, STE C 44256 #038-44-1982 L1985 **OBG** *020 †30
NOREIKA, Joseph Casimir. 3609 MEDINA RD 44256 #041-02-1976 L1983 **OPH** *020 †35
O'CONNOR, Mary Kathleen. 970 E WASHINGTON ST, PEDIATRIC EMERGENCY DEPART 44256 #038-06-1995 L1997 **PD** *020 †55
OMELSKY, Paul Theodore. 3076A REMSEN RD 44256 #038-40-1968 L1968 **CHP** *020 †75
PAP, Steven Michael. 970 E WASHINGTON ST, STE 6B 44256 #038-40-1977 L1978 **OBG** *071 †30
PEIFFER, Geraldine M. ■ 44256 #016-43-1949 L1950 **AN** *071 †05
QUERESHY, Faisal A. 3591 RESERVE COMNS DR #300 44256 #038-06-1997 L1999 **OMF CS** *020
RAMANAVARAPU, Sampath K. 970 E WASHINGTON ST, STE 2E 44256 #495-58-1974 L1992 **CD** *020 †20
REEVES, Julie Ann. 3637 MEDINA RD, STE 70 44256 #036-08-1995 L1999 **FM** *020 †18
RICE, Brenda L. 801 E WASHINGTON ST, STE 200 44256 #038-44-1990 L1992 **OBG** *020 †30
RINGEL, Jozef. 1000 E WASHINGTON ST 44256 #759-01-1936 L1955 **GP** *071
ROACH-ARMAO, Laurel. 4015 MEDINA RD, STE 50 44256 #038-45-1990 L1993 **PD** *020 †55
ROBERTSON, William Denny. 970 E WASHINGTON ST, STE 301 44256 #038-40-1968 L1968 **FM** *071 †18
ROSE, Richard F. 970 E WASHINGTON ST 44256 #024-05-1973 L1977 **ORS** *020 †40
ROSE, Warren Wm. 970 E WASHINGTON ST 44256 #038-06-1986 L1987 **GS** *020 †85
RUF, Walter Richard. ■ 44256 #016-11-1964 L1966 **GS TRS** *020 †85
SCHEINBERG, Schayel. 1000 E WASHINGTON ST 44256 #047-06-1938 L1965 **GS OM** *071 †85
SELESHI, Ermias. 246 NORTHLAND ST STE 200A 44256 #366-01-1976 L1982 **P N** *020 †75
SHARMA, Bipin. 3985 MEDINA RD, STE 120 44256 #495-78-1976 L1989 **GE IM** *020 †20
SHARMA, Hem. 3076 REMSEN RD # A 44256 #495-41-1966 L1976 **P** *020 †75
SHEWBRIDGE, Richard Kevin. 4087 MEDINA RD, STE 400 44256 #025-07-1988 L1996 **END IM** *020 †20
SLABY, Denis Jos. 970 E WASHINGTON ST # 403 44256 #038-43-1977 L1978 **U** *020 †95
SONNIE, Clifford Michael. 3985 MEDINA RD STE 250 44256 #038-41-1981 L1983 **OS** *020 †16
SPEELMAN, Mark Clarence. 970 E WASHINGTON ST, STE 4B 44256 #038-40-1973 L1973 **FM** *020 †18
SPRINGER, Donald Ladd. 200 GRANGER RD, UNIT 93 44256 #028-34-1963 L1964 **GE IM** *071
STANFORD, Mark Warner. 1000 E WASHINGTON ST 44256 #039-01-2002 L2002 **EM** *100 †16
STEED, James Warren. ■ 44256 #038-45-1984 L1985 **IM** *020
STUART, Annmarie. 970 E WASHINGTON ST, STE 5A 44256 #038-45-1999 L2002 **FM** *020 †18
SURSO, John Michael. 970 E WASHINGTON ST, STE 3 44256 #038-40-1977 L1977 **FM EM** *020 †18 ‡
SUTANDAR, Gunadi. 600 E SMITH RD 44256 #506-01-1960 L1974 **GP** *071
SYED, Qarab H. 3457 MEDINA RD 44256 #704-25-1991 L2004 **CD IM** *020 †20
SZIRAKY, Patrick Earl. 970 E WASHINGTON ST 44256 #038-44-1988 L1990 **ORS** *020 †40
TAN, Alfredo Mercado. 3995 MEDINA RD, STE 250 44256 #748-01-1956 L1962 **GP** *020 †18
TERRY, Francine Marie. 5501 BEACH RD 44256 #035-15-1988 L1989 **FM OM** *020 †18
TOROK, Helen. 1000 E WASHINGTON ST 44256 #038-40-1973 L1974 **D** *020 †15
TOROK, Leonard Jos. ■ 44256 #038-40-1973 L1974 **ORS** *020 †40
TROCIO, Rogaciano L. ■ 44256 #748-09-1967 L1981 **GP EM** *020
TSAI, Thomas Jay. 3591 RESERVE COMMONS DR, THE RETINA GROUP OF 44256 #038-41-1979 L1979 **OPH** *020 †35
VAN TILBURG, Charles P. ■ 44256 #038-41-1965 L1965 **PD GP** *040 †55
VROBEL, Matthew David. ■ 44256 #038-40-2004 L2007 **EM** *100
WALLACE, John W. 1000 E WASHINGTON ST 44256 #023-01-1960 L1980 **AN** *020
WARMAN, Dhiraj. 970 E WASHINGTON ST 44256 #038-43-1993 L1994 **CD IM** *020 †20
WEEKS, Douglas Clark. 3985 MEDINA RD, BALANCE OF LIFE CLINIC 44256 #056-05-1974 L1979 **EM** *020 †16
WILDER, Christine. ■ 44256 #038-06-1977 L1979 **CHP P** *075
ZEIGER, Todd Michael. 1000 E WASHINGTON ST 44256 #017-20-1992 L1993 **FM** *020 †18

MEDWAY – CLARK

WALLACE, Donald Kiblinger. ■ 45341 #038-06-1965 L1972 **PHP** *030 †70

MENTOR – LAKE

AHLUWALIA, Jaspal Singh. ■ 44060 #038-40-2006 L2008 **GPM** *012
ALDANA, Luis Francisco. ■ 44060 #264-04-1962 L1970 **EM** *020
ARNETT, Heather Elizabeth. 7200 CENTER ST 44060 #001-02-1999 L1999 **PD** *020 †55
ASCHA, Ahmad. 9500 MENTOR AVE 44060 #875-01-1979 L1985 **GE IM** *020 †20
BANIEWICZ, John Jos. 9485 MENTOR AVE, STE 210 44060 #038-44-1988 L1989 **IM** *020 †20
BARANAUSKAS, Michael V. 9485 MENTOR AVE, STE 210 44060 #038-43-1995 L1996 **IM** *020 †20
BARBOZA, L E. ■ 44060 #737-01-1967 L1977 **EM GS** *071
BASHIAN, John. 6965 CENTER ST 44060 #902-01-1951 L1957 **GS FM** *071
BAUD, Eric Bret. 9485 MENTOR AVE, STE 102 44060 #038-06-1992 L1993 **D** *020 †15

BAUM, Stephen Alexander. 9485 MENTOR AVE, STE 210 44060 #041-14-1979 L1986 **IMG IM** *020 †20
BELL, Gordon K. ■ 44060 #065-09-1953 L1958 **GS OS** *071 †85
BELLER, Nancy Ogden. 9485 MENTOR AVE 44060 #038-40-1986 L1988 **IM** *020 †20
BERGMAN, Mark D. 9485 MENTOR AVE, STE 3 44060 #048-13-1994 L2007 **HO** *020 †20
BLANCHARD, Janet M. 9500 MENTOR AVE 44060 #041-09-1976 L1977 **PS** *075 †65 ‡
BOLD, E Luke. 9500 MENTOR AVE STE 200 44060 #038-06-1989 L1990 **OTO** *020 †45
BREWER, Janice Elizabeth. 9500 MENTOR AVE STE 200, LAKE OBSTETRICS AND GYNECO 44060 #038-40-1993 L1996 **OBG** *020 †30
BROWN, Roberta Elise. 8300 TYLER BLVD STE 300 44060 #025-07-1987 L1992 **FM** *020 †18
BROWNING, Gale Marie. 8005 HART RD, GALE M BROWNING, MD INC 44060 #038-43-1989 L1990 **PM** *020 †60
BULLARD, Jeffrey Wm. 9485 MENTOR AVE, STE 210 44060 #038-40-1969 L1969 **HEM IM** *020 †20
BURTCH, Brian. 8300 TYLER BLVD, STE 102 44060 #038-43-2002 L2002 **END IM** *020 †20
CANO-ALLEN, Emilia A. 6965 CENTER ST 44060 #748-01-1952 L1961 **OM FM** *071
CHEN, Foo-Shon. ■ 44060 #385-04-1967 L1973 **EM** *071 †16
CHIN, Min-Choong. ■ 44060 #825-01-1960 L1973 **DR IM** *071 †80
CIFRA-BEAN, Laura Ann. 9485 MENTOR AVE 44060 #038-06-1992 L1996 **PD** *020 †55
CIUFO, Russell Anthony. 9000 MENTOR AVE, UNIVERSITY MEDNET 44060 #005-19-1986 L1990 **PUD IM** *020
COCHRAN, Bertram Hughes. 8224 MENTOR AVE, STE 104 44060 #038-40-1960 L1960 **IM CD** *020
COLIZOLI, Lucia. 7060 WAYSIDE DR 44060 #038-06-1976 L1980 **P** *020 †75
COMBS, Steven Paul. 9500 MENTOR AVE, STE 210 44060 #018-03-1970 L1979 **ORS OSM** *020 †40
COOPER, Danielle D. 9500 MENTOR AVE, STE 100 44060 #038-44-2000 L2000 **FM** *020 †18 ‡
CURRAN, Robert Morgan. 8224 MENTOR AVE 44060 #038-40-1961 L1961 **ALI IM** *020
DAVIS, Barbara Loeb. 9485 MENTOR AVE STE 101, LAKE MEDICAL CAMPUS 44060 #041-07-1977 L1979 **PD NPM** *020 †55
DE OREO, Peter Butler. 9000 MENTOR AVE, STE 105 44060 #038-06-1972 L1974 **NEP IM** *020 †20
DOUGLAS, Elizabeth Anne. ■ 44060 #025-12-2006 L2006 **PTH** *012
DOYLE, Timothy P. 9500 MENTOR AVE, STE 360 44060 #016-14-1979 L1980 **CD** *020 †20
DYKEMAN, Susan Marie. 9000 MENTOR AVE 44060 #038-06-1989 L1990 **PD** *020 †55
EIPPERT, Gregory Alan. 9485 MENTOR AVE, OPHTHALMIC PHYSICIAN 44060 #038-43-1992 L1993 **OPH** *020 †35
EISWERTH, Thomas F, Jr. 9485 MENTOR AVE, STE 210 44060 #038-41-1992 L1993 **IM** *020 †20
ERTEL, Joy Bibbee. 9000 MENTOR AVE STE 100, UNIV PREMIER PEDIATRICIANS 44060 #038-06-1986 L1987 **PD** *020 †55
ESPINOSA, Maria Teresita. 9485 MENTOR AVE, STE 3 44060 #748-01-1983 L1992 **ON HEM** *020 †20
FARUKHI, Shermeen Taj. 9485 MENTOR AVE 44060 #038-06-2000 L2006 **IM IMG** *020 †20
FELDMAN, David Borden. 7350 PALISADES PKWY 44060 #038-40-1981 L1985 **P PYG** *020 †75
FERRON, John Patrick. 9500 MENTOR AVE STE 300 44060 #016-42-1979 L1981 **AS VS** *020 †85
FRIEDENBERG, Keith Alan. 9485 MENTOR AVE, STE 105 44060 #005-14-1988 L1994 **GE IM** *020 †20
GADDAMANUGU, Madhavi. ■ 44060 #496-24-1997 L2006 **IM** *020 †20
GALLAGHER, Marilee L. 9000 MENTOR AVE STE 100, UNIV PREMIER PEDS 44060 #038-06-1977 L1980 **PD** *020 †55
GAUGLER, Michael David. 9500 MENTOR AVE STE 200 44060 #038-41-1996 L2001 **OTO** *020 †45
GEORGE, Elizebath Palayur. 9000 MENTOR AVE, MENTOR URGENT CARE 44060 #495-44-1993 L2000 **FM** *020 †18
GIBBS, James Elliotte. 6990 LINDSAY DR, STE 3 44060 #023-07-1979 L1979 **FM IMG** *020 †18
GOLISH, Joseph A, Jr. 7676 REYNOLDS RD 44060 #038-40-1973 L1975 **PUD IM** *020 †20
GUERRIERI, James Paul, Jr. 9500 MENTOR AVE, STE 220 44060 #038-43-1987 L1995 **OBG** *020 †30
GUTMAN, David. 8224 MENTOR AVE, STE 132 44060 #038-06-2001 L2001 **IM** *020
GUYTON, Kevin Harold. ■ 44060 #025-07-1992 L2000 **FM** *100
HACKETT, Martha Ellen. 8300 TYLER BLVD STE 300 44060 #038-06-1979 L1979 **FM** *020 †18 ‡
HINNES, Robert Lucas. 9000 MENTOR AVE, STE 205 44060 #038-06-1972 L1974 **OBG** *020 †30
IQBAL, Rukhsana. ■ 44060 #038-44-2004 L2004 **FPP** *012
IRVIN, Robert A. 8224 MENTOR AVE 44060 #038-06-1946 L1946 **PD** *071 †55
JEVNIKAR, Frank William. 9500 MENTOR AVE, STE 370 44060 #038-43-1997 L1998 **U** *020 †95
JUDGE, Constance Marie. 7200 CENTER ST, STE 200 44060 #038-06-1992 L1994 **PDC** *020 †55
JUNEJA-MUCCI, Joti R. ■ 44060 #038-44-2007 L2007 **AN** *012
KEUM, Matthew Minseok. 9485 MENTOR AVE, STE 115 44060 #035-09-1992 L2000 **PM** *020 †60
KNEILE, Jeffrey Richard. ■ 44060 #038-41-2002 L2002 **PTH** *100 †50
KOBY, Elizabeth Victoria. 8224 MENTOR AVE 44060 #038-41-1980 L1980 **P CHP** *020 †75
KOMAR, Mark Kenneth. 9500 MENTOR AVE, STE 100 44060 #038-06-1979 L1980 **FM EM** *020 †18 ‡
KOUSA, Haitham Jos. 9485 MENTOR AVE, STE 104 44060 #875-01-1984 L1990 **IM** *020 †20
KRUG, William Vincent. 9485 MENTOR AVE, STE 102 44060 #041-13-1976 L1978 **D** *020
KUCERA, Richard Alan. 9500 MENTOR AVE, STE 100 44060 #038-40-1982 L1983 **FM** *020 †18
KUSHNIR, Yael. 9485 MENTOR AVE, OPHTHALMIC PHYSICIAN 44060 #550-02-1983 L1992 **OPH** *020 †35
KUTSIKOVICH, Gary Robert. 8224 MENTOR AVE, STE 126 44060 #038-41-2000 L2000 **N** *020 †75
LEE, Howard Hahn. 9485 MENTOR AVE STE 115 44060 #038-40-1987 L1991 **PM GP** *020 †60
LEININGER, John Thos. 9000 MENTOR AVE, UNIVERSITY UROLOGISTS OF C 44060 #038-41-1969 L1969 **U RO** *020 †95
LELE, Anju Shreeniwas. 9000 MENTOR AVE STE 105, UNIVERSITY HOSPITALS MEDIC 44060 #495-34-1993 L1999 **IM** *020 †20
LELE, Shreeniwas. 9000 MENTOR AVE, STE 105 44060 #495-34-1989 L1998 **IM** *020 †20
LEMASTER, Elizabeth. 9000 MENTOR AVE 44060 #038-44-1999 L1999 **FM OS** *020 †18
LESTER, Diane Marie. 9485 MENTOR AVE 44060 #038-43-1997 L1999 **PD** *020 †55
LOUBE, Julian M. 7441 CENTER ST 44060 #010-01-1972 L1973 **FM EM** *020
LUCKER, John Donald. 9485 MENTOR AVE 44060 #035-45-1957 L1959 **PD** *020 †55
MAC DOUGALL, Monica K. 9500 MENTOR AVE, STE 240 44060 #010-01-1975 L1976 **P** *020 †30,75
MAHNA, Satish Kumar. 7750 REYNOLDS RD, OCCHEALTH CONCEPTS 44060 #495-55-1977 L1986 **GP OM** *020 †70

MAJESKI, Lisa Jean. 9000 MENTOR AVE, UNIVERSITY MEDNET 44060 #038-06-1994 L1995 DR *020

MARTIN, Lawrence. 9000 MENTOR AVE 44060 #011-03-1969 L1976 **PUD CCM** *020 †20

MC NAUGHTON, Marc Joseph. 9500 MENTOR AVE, STE 100 44060 #038-06-1998 L2000 **FM** *020 †18

MILLER, James Robt. 6990 LINDSAY DR 44060 #050-02-1986 L1988 **PS** *020 †85,65

MIOTTO, Paul Victor. 7956 TYLER BLVD 44060 #035-06-1988 L1991 **FM FSM** *020 †18

MUNI, Anthony John. ■ 44060 #038-40-2005 L2005 **IM** *012

MURAD, Mohamed Hatem N. 9000 MENTOR AVE, UNIVERSITY MEDNET 44060 #915-04-1980 L1995 **N** *020 †75

NAHRA, Mitchell Elias. 9500 MENTOR AVE, STE 210 44060 #038-06-1987 L1987 **ORS HS** *020 †40

NEHRER, Jonathan Mark. 8445 MUNSON RD 44060 #035-46-1985 L1988 **P CHP** *020 †75

NELSON, Scott Mc Leod. 9500 MENTOR AVE, STE 200 44060 #038-41-1974 L1984 **OTO** *020 †45

NEMUNAITIS, John Geo, Jr. 9000 MENTOR AVE 44060 #038-06-1961 L1961 **PM** *030 †60,20

NISHIYAMA, Fumie Jill. 8300 TYLER BLVD, STE 102 44060 #038-06-1998 L2000 **END** *020 †20

NOALL, Carol Lynn. 9000 MENTOR AVE, STE 205 44060 #038-40-1993 L1996 **FM** *020 †18

PARRIS, David Chas. 9000 MENTOR AVE, STE 105 44060 #165-07-1979 L1994 **IM** *020 †20

PARSONS, Eric Matthew. 9500 MENTOR AVE, STE 210 44060 #038-40-2001 L2007 **OSM** *020

PHI, Ka Kee P. ■ 44060 #748-08-1967 L1976 **AN** *020

PILLAY, Roopa Rani. 9000 MENTOR AVE, UNIVERSITY MEDNET 44060 #495-31-1978 L1980 **IM** *020 †55

PLATZ, Michelle Marie. 9000 MENTOR AVE STE 101, UPCP MENTOR URGENT CARE 44060 #038-44-2000 L2000 **FM** *020 †18

POPOVSKY, Jennifer Levin. 9485 MENTOR AVE, STE 102 44060 #041-13-1995 L1999 **D** *020 †15

POSNER, Ronald Edgar. 9485 MENTOR AVE, OPHTHALMIC PHYSICIAN 44060 #038-06-1963 L1963 **OPH** *020 †35

PRITCHARD, Timothy James. 9500 MENTOR AVE, STE 300 44060 #024-01-1981 L1982 **CRS GS** *020 †85,10

PUGH, David Bentley. 9000 MENTOR AVE 44060 #025-07-1977 L1983 **OPH** *020 †35

PUNJABI, Eshwar B. 9000 MENTOR AVE 44060 #495-17-1970 L1979 **GE IM** *020 †20

QUINN, Patrick Alfred. 9500 MENTOR AVE STE 220 44060 #038-40-1980 L1983 **OBG** *020 †30 ‡

RAHMAN, Mahboob. 7156 BUNKER CV 44060 #495-21-1988 L1993 **NEP IM** *020 †20

REEF, James Saml. 9000 MENTOR AVE, UNIVERSITY MEDNET 44060 #041-02-1958 L1966 **R RO** *020

RIAD, Kamal Soddi. 9500 MENTOR AVE, STE 360 44060 #915-02-1989 L2001 **CD** *071 †20

RIFFLE, Gregory Clell. 9485 MENTOR AVE, OPHTHALMIC PHYSICIAN 44060 #038-06-1978 L1978 **OPH** *020 †35

ROBIE, Richard Robt. ■ 44060 #041-12-1956 L1965 **GYN** *071 †30

ROBINSON, Clifford Grant. ■ 44060 #038-06-2004 L2004 **RO** *012

ROSACE, John C, Jr. 9000 MENTOR AVE STE 100 44060 #038-44-1988 L1993 **PD** *020 †55

ROTER, Elisabeth Sharon D. 9000 MENTOR AVE, UPCP 44060 #038-06-1995 L2000 **RHU** *020 †20

SABET-SHARGHI, Farid. 7350 PALISADES PKWY 44060 #017-20-1987 L1988 **P** *020 †75

SAGE, Sherilyn Ann. 9000 MENTOR AVE, UNIVERSITY OB/GYN ASSOCIAT 44060 #016-42-1989 L1993 **OBG** *020 †20

SALOMONE, Raymond J, Jr. 9500 MENTOR AVE, STE 330 44060 #038-06-1984 L1985 **PCC SME** *020 †20

SCHUTTE, Norbert Paul. 7750 REYNOLDS RD STE 100 44060 #038-44-1985 L1986 **OM GP** *020 †70

SENFT, James Alan. 9000 MENTOR AVE, STE 105 44060 #038-40-1992 L1996 **IM** *020 †20

SHAO, Haining. 6013 SEA PINES DR 44060 #243-03-1987 L2000 **P** *100

SHULGA, Irina. 7350 PALISADES PKWY 44060 #913-09-1978 L2000 **ADP** *020

SIMINOVITCH, Jeffrey M P. 9500 MENTOR AVE STE 370 44060 #067-01-1974 L1980 **U EM** *020 †95

SMITH, Ethelee Ray. ■ 44060 #028-02-1956 L1961 **PME PMM** *071 †05

STEPHANS, Kevin Lee. ■ 44060 #038-06-2004 L2004 **RO** *012

TAYLOR, Jay Michael. 9500 MENTOR AVE, STE 100 44060 #038-40-1982 L1983 **FM** *020 †18

THIEL, Jack Patrick. ■ 44060 #038-06-1940 L1940 **GS GP** *071

TROTTER, Kirsten Marion. 9485 MENTOR AVE, STE 102 44060 #051-04-1986 L1990 **D** *020 †15

TURBETT, Elizabeth Ann. 9500 MENTOR AVE, STE 100 44060 #038-40-1986 L1989 **FM** *020 †18

TURBETT, James Anthony. 9500 MENTOR AVE, STE 100 44060 #038-40-1986 L1989 **FM** *020 †18

USIS, Eriks Andris. 7200 CENTER ST, STE 200 44060 #038-06-1997 L1998 **PD** *020 †55

VANEK, Paul Frank, Jr. 9485 MENTOR AVE, STE 100 44060 #035-45-1989 L1996 **PS HS** *020 †85,65 ‡

VITO, Kenneth Jos. 9500 MENTOR AVE, STE 200 44060 #041-01-1991 L1996 **OTO** *020 †45

WALDBAUM, Basil Saml. 8300 TYLER BLVD, STE 300 44060 #775-01-1971 L1979 **FM** *020 †18

WARD, Lisa Marie. 9485 MENTOR AVE, OPHTHALMIC PHYSICIAN 44060 #038-41-1984 L1990 **OPH** *020 †35

WEISS, Daniel. 8300 TYLER BLVD STE 102 44060 #048-12-1979 L1986 **IM END** *020 †20

WEST, Joyce Arlene. 10270 HOOSE RD # 9 44060 #038-06-1966 L1966 **PTH** *020 †50

WIESELTHIER, Janet Sue. 9485 MENTOR AVE, STE 102 44060 #035-08-1985 L1996 **D DMP** *020 †20,15

WILSON, Lawrence Henry. 9500 MENTOR AVE, STE 100 44060 #035-06-1979 L1981 **FM** *020 †18

WOLKOFF, Lawrence Herman. 9500 MENTOR AVE, STE 370 44060 #038-06-1983 L1983 **U** *020 †95

YAKKUNDI, Prakash K. 9485 MENTOR AVE, STE 202 44060 #495-35-1972 L1978 **IM** *020 †20

YAMINI SHARIF, Bahman. 8334 MENTOR AVE, STE 103 44060 #517-05-1975 L1982 **P** *020 †75

YANG, Youapa Susan. 7956 TYLER BLVD 44060 #026-04-2002 L2007 **FM** *020 †18

ZAIM, Mohammad Tarif. 9485 MENTOR AVE, STE 102 44060 #875-01-1977 L1985 **DMP PTH** *020 †50

MENTOR ON THE LAKE – LAKE

CASTROVINCI, Anthony John. 7915 MUNSON RD STE 4 44060 #017-20-1968 L1968 **D** *020 †15

MAMLOUK, Mohamed Bashar. 7915 MUNSON RD STE 3 44060 #875-01-1971 L1975 **IM CD** *020 †20

METAMORA – FULTON

EVANOFF, John Christ, Jr. 1990 COUNTY ROAD U 43540 #038-43-1987 L1990 **FM** *040 †18

HARDIN-EVANOFF, Kelly J. 1990 COUNTY ROAD U 43540 #038-43-1989 L1990 **FM PD** *020 †18

KOELSCH, Emily Mika. ■ 43540 #038-43-2005 **PD** *012

MIAMISBURG – MONTGOMERY

AJLOUNI, Sayyah. 527 E CENTRAL AVE 45342 #875-01-1983 L1996 **IM CD** *020 †20

ALBRECHT, Joseph Merrill. ■ 45342 #038-40-1958 L1958 **FM** *071 †18

AROCHO, Michael Albert. ■ 45342 #023-12-2005 L2005 **EM** *012

ASHCRAFT, William B. 1012 E CENTRAL AVE 45342 #038-44-1984 L1985 **FM** *020 †18

BAJILLAN, Hendren Akram. ■ 45342 #528-06-2003 L2007 **IM** *012

BAKER, Jon. ■ 45342 #038-75-2006, ▲ L2006 **FP** *012

BASHE, Winslow J, Jr. ■ 45342 #016-43-1945 L1957 **GPM PD** *071 †55

CLINE, Allen Lee. 2115 LEITER RD, KETTERING FACULTY 45342 #024-01-1961 L1962 **IM END** *072 †20

DAGROSA, Richard Louis, Jr. ■ 45342 #041-15-2003 L2006 **EM** *020 †16

DERUSSY, Peter Kirk. 2115 LEITER RD, SYCAMORE PRIMARY CARE CENT 45342 #011-04-1997 L1999 **IM** *020 †20

DSOUZA, Pamela Pritisagar. ■ 45342 #005-12-2007 L2007 **TY** *012

DUTRO, John Arthur. 415 BYERS RD STE 500 45342 #038-45-1982 L1983 **GS CCS** *020 †85

EICHTEN, David Estia. ■ 45342 #028-78-2007, ▲ L2007 *012

EZIKE, Agnes Chinwe. ■ 45342 #690-01-1999 L2004 **IM** *020 †20

FARHANGI, Vida. 2130 LEITER RD STE 207 45342 #517-08-1989 L2000 **IM DIA** *020 †20

FASANO, Frank Jos, Jr. 2130 LEITER RD, STE 110 45342 #028-34-1983 L1988 **ORS** *020 †40

FOLEY, Gretchen Nicole. ■ 45342 #038-44-2006 L2006 **P** *012

FRAMBACH, Gwyn E. ■ 45342 #038-75-2007, ▲ L2007 *012

FRESHWATER, Lara Kathrine. ■ 45342 #038-41-2008 *012

GEBHART, Clifford E. ■ 45342 #038-06-1951 L1951 **GP** *071

GLEICK, Jeffrey Blake. 415 BYERS RD, STE 300 45342 #020-12-1993 L1994 **FM** *020 †18

GUPTA, Suresh. 8210 SPRINGBORO PIKE, MIAMI VALLEY URGENT CARE 45342 #496-05-1977 L1993 **APM AN** *020 †20

HANDEL, Franklin. 2150 LEITER RD, SCHUSTER CARDIOLOGY 45342 #041-01-1976 L1982 **CD** *020 †20

HARDACRE, Suzanne Shirley. ■ 45342 #038-40-2004 L2005 **FP** *012

HECK, Thomas Anthony. 415 BYERS RD, STE 500 45342 #010-02-1978 L1983 **GS** *020 †85

HEIDARI, Zahra. 1012 E CENTRAL AVE 45342 #517-05-1996 L2000 **FM** *020 †18

HOWARD, James Jos, Jr. 2150 LEITER RD 45342 #038-41-1979 L1979 **EM** *020 †16

HUGHES, Randall Stanford. ■ 45342 #038-45-1995 *100

HUSSAIN, Sarah. 415 BYERS RD STE 300 45342 #496-27-1991 L2000 **FM** *020 †18

HYMON, Bruce Gregory. 2150 LEITER RD, SCHUSTER CARDIOLOGY 45342 #038-41-1972 L1974 **CD IM** *020 †20

IBERICO, Mariano Martin. 2150 LEITER RD, PULMONARY MEDICINE OF 45342 #737-01-1983 L1989 **PUD CCM** *020 †20

JONES, Joy Katherine. ■ 45342 #020-02-2004 L2004 **P** *012

KANOMATA, Thomas Isao. 4000 MIAMISBURG CENTRVL RD, STE 104 45342 #005-12-1990 L1991 **IM** *020 †20

KAVTSCHITSCH, Joseph. ■ 45342 #407-16-1952 L1962 **P CHP** *030

KELLER, Michael Wesley. 4000 MIAMISBURG CENTRVL RD 45342 #038-45-1981 L1985 **GS** *020 †85

KHOSLA, Raman. 4000 MIAMISBURG CENTRVL RD, STE 207 45342 #495-45-1994 L1996 **IM** *020 †20

LEFKEN, Edward Bernard. ■ 45342 #038-41-1947 L1947 **N IM** *071 †20

LEWIS, Peter M. 2150 LEITER RD, SCHUSTER CARDIOLOGY 45342 #035-75-1985, ▲ L1989 **IM** *020 †20

LUTHAS, Vernon C. ■ 45342 #005-12-1953 L1958 **AN** *071

MAKOLA, Diklar. ■ 45342 #775-01-1985 L2001 **IM** *040

MC KELLAR, Daniel Patrick. 415 BYERS RD, STE 500 45342 #016-43-1987 L1988 **GS** *020 †85

MEHTA, Rajeev. 415 BYERS RD, STE 100 45342 #495-05-1974 L1990 **GE IM** *020 †20

MEZU, Patrick Uche. 2150 LEITER RD, PULMONARY MEDICINE OF 45342 #690-01-1992 L1999 **IM** *020 †20

MHISH, Hassan. 527 E CENTRAL AVE 45342 #875-01-1991 L1997 **CD IM** *020 †20

MILLER, Jaime Dawn. ■ 45342 #038-45-2008 *012

NATHAN, Milton Fred. 2150 LEITER RD, SCHUSTER CARDIOLOGY 45342 #038-41-1972 L1976 **CD IM** *020 †20

PAGE, David Sheridan. 415 BYERS RD, STE 300 45342 #038-45-1986 L1987 **FM** *020 †18

PAULS, Gary Lee. 4000 MIAMISBURG CENTRVL RD, STE 100 45342 #005-12-1988 L2003 **CD** *020 †20

POK-TODD, Soriya Varaman. ■ 45342 #017-20-2005 L2005 **EM** *012

RAZI, Salman S. 2150 LEITER RD, PULMONARY MEDICINE OF 45342 #048-16-1997 L2005 **PCC** *020 ‡

REILING, Walter Anthony. 415 BYERS RD, STE 500 45342 #024-01-1965 L1969 **GS** *020 †85

RUBIO, Felipe A. 2150 LEITER RD, PULMONARY MEDICINE OF 45342 #847-04-1976 L1983 **PUD IM** *020 †20

SANSONE, Randy Alan. 2115 LEITER RD 45342 #038-40-1978 L1978 **P** *030 †75 ‡

SANTILLAN, Edgar R. 2150 LEITER RD, PULMONARY MEDICINE OF 45342 #176-03-1992 L1998 **IM** *020 †20

SAWYER, Robert John. 2115 LEITER RD, SYCAMORE PRIMARY CARE CENT 45342 #038-40-1993 L1996 **IM** *020 †20

SCHUMACHER, David Lyle. 2115 LEITER RD STE 100, KETTERING BARIATRICS 45342 #038-40-1987 L1996 **GS** *020 †85

SEALS, Steven Roger. ■ 45342 #038-40-1967 L1967 **OM GP** *020 †55,70

SENI, Ivo Giampiero. 2150 LEITER RD, PULMONARY MEDICINE OF 45342 #264-02-1987 L1997 **IM** *020 †20

SHAH, Hemant Mahendra. 2150 LEITER RD, PULMONARY MEDICINE OF 45342 #496-38-1985 L1993 **PUD CCM** *020 †20 ‡

SHRADER, John Alan. 2115 LEITER RD 45342 #005-12-1979 L1981 **IM** *020 †20

SIMMAN, Richard. 2130 LEITER RD, STE 205 45342 #165-07-1991 L2004 **GS** *020 †65

SPRIGGS, Raymond Geo. 2130 LEITER RD STE 110 45342 #041-14-1972 L1974 **ORS** *020 †40

THAKKER, Nitesh Ramesh. ■ 45342 #496-44-1999 L2005 **IM** *012

THOMAS, Ayesha Ayene. ■ 45342 #010-03-2006 L2006 **GS** *012

TRIVEDI, Mehul Shammi. 2115 LEITER RD, STE 100 45342 #033-06-1992 L2006 **GS** *020 †85

WAGSHUL, Fred. 445 BYERS RD, ASTHMA & RESPIRATORY CTR 45342 #308-03-1980 L1986 **IM PUD** *020

WILLIS, Donna L. ■ 45342 #005-12-1977 L1980 **IM OS** *062

■ = Address Information Privacy Protected

ZAKI, Nancy Ramzi. 415 BYERS RD, STE 300 45342 #915-02-1990 L2000 **FM** *020 †18

MIDDLE BASS – OTTAWA

HERMAN, Robert John. GENERAL DELIVERY 43446 #038-41-1945 L1945 **IMG FM** *071

MIDDLEBURG – LOGAN

VENTENILLA, Doroteo Olba. ■ 43336 #748-07-1967 **OS** *075

MIDDLEBURG HEIGHTS – CUYAHOGA

AUBREY, Richard W. 18697 BAGLEY RD 44130 #038-41-1951 L1951 **PTH** *071 †50
AUGUSTIN, Paul Ralph. ■ 44130 #440-01-1995 L2005 **FP** *012
BOLOGNA, John Felix, Jr. 18697 BAGLEY RD 44130 #038-44-1988 L1991 **AN** *020 †05
BUTT, Shahid Hussain. 18820 BAGLEY RD STE 104 44130 #704-01-1971 L1979 **OBG** *020
CALUYA, Claro Valdez, Jr. 7155 PEARL RD # 30242 44130 #748-01-1960 L1977 **GS GP** *020
ELIAS, Husam Gaafar. 6950 W 130TH ST, SEARS DENTAL 44130 #038-06-2007 L2007 **GS** *012
GERARDO, Hortencia R F. ■ 44130 #748-01-1954 L1967 **IM P** *020
GLIGA, Lucius Leonida. 7225 OLD OAK BLVD, STE B315 44130 #781-03-1975 L1985 **GS** *020 †85
OWEN, James Mathew. ■ 44130 #654-01-1988 L1999 **OBG** *020 †30
PLECHA, Fred Rudolph. 7255 OLD OAK MEDICAL PAVLN, STE 108 44130 #038-06-1960 L1960 **VS** *071 †85
RODRIGUEZ-FONSECA, Juan M. 7215 OLD OAK BLVD STE 3102 44130 #264-01-1961 L1972 **ORS** *071 †40
SHIN, Charles Cheul Ya. 7215 OLD OAK BLVD, STE A416 44130 #583-04-1966 L1975 **ORS** *020 †40
THOMAS, Stephanie W. 18660 BAGLEY RD, MIDDLEBURG HTS MED ART BLD 44130 #038-40-1980 L1982 **OPH** *020 †35
WALKER, Cheryl Ann. ■ 44130 #003-75-2005, ▲ L2005 **AN** *012
WILLIAMS, Brian James. 18697 BAGLEY RD, DEPT. OF ANESTHESIOLOGY 44130 #056-06-1995 L2001 **AN** *020 †05
YAP, Sisenando O. 18820 BAGLEY RD STE 3 44130 #748-01-1965 L1972 **GS** *071

MIDDLEFIELD – GEAUGA

DECIPEDA, Reynaldo M. PO BOX 112, 16030 E HIGH ST 44062 #748-02-1958 L1968 **IM** *071
FLORIANO, Jon Joseph. 15561 W HIGH ST 44062 #038-06-1994 L1997 **FM** *020 †18
FRANKLIN, Peter Scott. 15389 KINSMAN RD 44062 #038-06-1973 L1974 **FM** *020 †18
SABRANSKY, Richard. 15976 E HIGH ST 44062 #016-42-1953 L1956 **PM GP** *020
WILLIAMS-REID, Jennifer. PO BOX 368, 28 EVANS MIDDLEFIELD MED 44062 #038-44-1999 L1999 **FM** *020 †18

MIDDLETOWN – BUTLER

ALAPPATT, Chacko Jose. 1515 S BREIEL BLVD, OF SOUTHWEST OHIO 45044 #038-44-1996 L2000 **IM** *020 †20
ALBERS, Henry Wm. 3005 SHERMAN AVE, STE A 45044 #038-40-1992 L1998 **ORS** *020 †40
ALBERT, Michael Chas. 3005 SHERMAN AVE, STE A 45044 #038-45-1983 L1984 **OP** *020 †40
ALSHAMI, Emad. 1060B SUMMITT SQ 45042 #875-01-1991 L2004 **PYG P** *020 †75
AMMENTORP, Peter Ancher. 105 MCKNIGHT DR 45044 #297-01-1953 L1955 **OS IM** *071 †20
ANDREW, William John. 103 MCKNIGHT DR STE A 45044 #038-41-1991 L1992 **OBG** *020 †30
AVERA, Leah Marie. 1042 SUMMITT SQ, GENERATIONS FAMILY MEDICIN 45042 #038-41-1997 L1998 **FM** *020 †18
BARNES, John W. PO BOX 427 45042 #016-06-1952 L1954 **GS VS** *071 †85
BARRORD, John Francis. 1055 SUMMITT SQ 45042 #038-41-1982 L1986 **OTO** *020 †45
BERNAL, Jorge. 500 S BREIEL BLVD 45044 #264-05-1963 L1986 **OBG** *071
BRADY, Sheila Kathleen. 105 MCKNIGHT DR, MATERNAL-CHILD HEALTH CLIN 45044 #038-41-1993 L1996 **PD** *020 †55
BRIONES, Tristan St Elena. 102 MCKNIGHT DR, MIDDLETOWN CANCER CENTER 45044 #748-07-1966 L1987 **RO GP** *020 ‡
BROWN, Gary Chas. 200 N BREIEL BLVD, MIDDLETOWN CARDIOVASCULAR 45042 #038-45-1986 L1992 **CD** *020 †20
BUCHERT, Charles Howard. ■ 45042 #038-41-1943 L1943 **PD** *071 †55
BUELL, Tamara Isabel. ■ 45044 #038-40-1995 L1996 **FM** *020 †18
BURGHARD, Kelly Lynn. 200 N BREIEL BLVD 45042 #038-45-2000 L2000 **IM** *020 †20 ‡
BURING, Robert Earl. 105 MCKNIGHT DR 45044 #020-12-1982 L1983 **OM EM** *020
CAMPBELL, James Wilford. ■ 45042 #055-01-1968 L1977 **OBG** *071 †30
DANOSI, Steve Francis. 105 MCKNIGHT DR 45044 #025-07-1979 L1992 **IM** *020 †16
DIETZ, Richard Arthur. ■ 45044 #016-06-1956 L1962 **OBG** *071 †30
DUNCAN, Paul Ervin. 1060B SUMMITT SQ 45042 #038-45-1996 L1997 **FM** *020 †18
EINSELEN SMALL, Diana J. 331 N BREIEL BLVD 45042 #038-43-1981 L1983 **PD PDA** *020 †55
FENNEL, Craig Eugene. 505 VINCENT CT 45042 #046-01-1980 L1985 **GS** *020 †85
FERNANDEZ, Adelaida. 500 S BREIEL BLVD 45044 #038-41-1986 L1989 **P** *020 †75
FLOERING, David Andrew. 105 MCKNIGHT DR, DEPT PATHOLOGY 45044 #038-40-1972 L1972 **PTH PCH** *020 †50
FOSTER, Robert Edward. 4701 CENTRAL AVE 45044 #025-01-1988 L1992 **OPH** *020 †35
FRAZER, Mark Eugene. 1010 SUMMITT SQ 45042 #038-41-1982 L1983 **FM** *020 †18
FREELAND, Judith Ann. 1659 S BREIEL BLVD 45044 #038-45-1987 L1989 **CHP P** *020 †75
FURLONG, Thomas Edward. 74 N BREIEL BLVD 45042 #038-40-1972 L1972 **FM** *020 †18
GAEKE, Mary Ellen B. 82 N BREIEL BLVD 45042 #016-02-1975 L1980 **ON IM** *020 †20
GAEKE, Richard Francis. 42 N BREIEL BLVD 45042 #016-02-1973 L1974 **GE IM** *020 †20
GAKER, Douglas Luke. 112 S MAIN ST 45044 #051-01-1985 L1989 **U** *095
GAKER, Louis B. 112 S MAIN ST 45044 #038-41-1951 L1951 **U** *071 †95
GERBER, Gregory Douglas. 255 N BREIEL BLVD, MID-VALLEY GASTRO ASSOC. 45042 #038-40-1979 L1980 **GE** *020 †20
GLICKFIELD, William Scott. 105 MCKNIGHT DR 45044 #017-20-1979 L1982 **FM ORS** *020 †18
GRAY, Jacqueline Jenkins. 331 N BREIEL BLVD, 331 N BREIEL BLVD 45042 #021-06-1997 L1999 **PD** *020 †55

GRUNDY, David Anthony. 105 MCKNIGHT DR 45044 #038-41-1998 L1999 **EM** *020
GUPTA, Sandeep. 231 N BREIEL BLVD, STE 200 45042 #495-69-1985 L1997 **CD IM** *020 †20
HACKER, Daryl. 255 N BREIEL BLVD 45042 #038-41-1984 L1985 **GE IM** *020 †20
HARPER, Jahannah Beth. ■ 45044 #038-45-2008 *012
HERRMANN, Eugene David. 1055 SUMMIT SQ 45042 #038-40-1974 L1974 **OTO HNS** *020 †45
HUFFMAN, Stephen A. 105 MCKNIGHT DR 45044 #038-43-1992 L1993 **FM EM** *020 †18
HURLBURT, Omer C, III. 3913 ROOSEVELT BLVD 45044 #038-41-1990 L1994 **FM CCM** *020 †18
HURLBURT, Omer Chas. 3913 ROOSEVELT BLVD 45044 #038-41-1961 L1961 **FM** *071 †18
JARRETT, Jeffrey Allen. 105 MCKNIGHT DR 45044 #017-20-1981 L1984 **FM** *020 †18
JENNEWINE, Paul Russell. 200 N BREIEL BLVD 45042 #038-43-1995 L1997 **IM** *020 †20
JOHNSON, Craig Whitaker. 134 N BREIEL BLVD 45042 #045-01-1979 L1983 **PD ID** *020
KAH, Ralph Edward. ■ 45042 #038-40-1959 L1959 **GYN END** *071 †30
KESEG, David Paul. 105 MCKNIGHT DR 45044 #038-40-1978 L1979 **EM** *020 †16
KHAN, Shazia. 930 9TH AVE, BUTLER COUNTY COMMUNITY HE 45044 #704-01-1999 L2004 **FM** *020 †18
KOMER, James Michael. 331 N BREIEL BLVD 45042 #038-40-1987 L1990 **PD** *020 †55
LEHNER, James Timothy. 3005 SHERMAN AVE, STE A 45044 #038-40-1973 L1973 **ORS** *020 †40
LEON, Alberto Antonio. 105 MCKNIGHT DR 45044 #038-40-1980 L1981 **EM IM** *020
LINDER, Lawrence Harold. 701 N UNIVERSITY BLVD, LINDER SURGICAL ASSOC INC 45042 #016-06-1956 L1969 **GS** *071 †85
LYMAN, John Leslie. 105 MCKNIGHT DR 45044 #038-45-1980 L1981 **EM** *020 †16
MALCOLM, Albert Staebler. 235 N BREIEL BLVD, ATTN BRENDA 45042 #038-40-1986 L1987 **ON HEM** *020 †20
MALCOLM, Russell L, Jr. ■ 45042 #017-20-1960 L1964 **PTH** *071 †50
MALLOY, Kevin Gerard. 930 9TH AVE 45044 #051-04-1980 L1981 **FM** *020 †18
MANN, Dennis Michael. 105 MCKNIGHT DR 45044 #665-01-1999 L2003 **EM** *020 †16
MAX, Marvin Edgar. 105 MCKNIGHT DR 45044 #036-01-1961 L1962 **FM** *071
MIKUTIS, Jeffrey Louis. 3005 SHERMAN AVE, STE A 45044 #022-75-1983, ▲ L1992 **FM** *020
MILLER, Daniel Matthew. 4701 CENTRAL AVE 45044 #038-40-2000 L2000 **OPH** *020 †35
MILLER, David Chas. 1064 SUMMITT SQ 45042 #017-20-1986 L1987 **U** *020 †95
MILLER, John Michael. 3005 SHERMAN AVE, STE A 45044 #038-40-1990 L1994 **TS CD** *020 †85,90
MITCHELL, Percy David, Jr. 1045 SUMMITT SQ 45042 #010-03-1968 L1973 **CHP P** *020 †75
MOORE, Stephen Robt. 1040 SUMMITT SQ 45042 #649-30-1984 L1987 **PUD IM** *020 †20
MUNICK, Leo Harold. 105 MCKNIGHT DR 45044 #024-07-1960 L1965 **PS** *071 †65
MURDOCK, Kenneth Edwin. 105 MCKNIGHT DR 45044 #035-09-1968 L1979 **RO ON** *071 †80 ‡
NISBET, Dick Marvel. 1000 1ST AVE 45044 #016-06-1947 L1947 **OPH** *071 †45
OCHES, Eric Ronald. 331 N BREIEL BLVD 45042 #038-40-1964 L1964 **PD** *020 †55
ONADY, Alice. 1659 S BREIEL BLVD 45044 #038-45-1988 L1997 **P** *020 †75
ONGKIKO, Carlos M, Jr. 210 S BREIEL BLVD 45044 #748-02-1964 L1971 **NS N** *020 †25
PALEY, Kevin Jos. 105 MCKNIGHT DR 45044 #038-41-1990 L1995 **OSM** *020 †40
PATE, Kenton Allen. 331 N BREIEL BLVD 45042 #017-20-1979 L1981 **PD** *020 †55
PATTERSON, Elizabeth J W. 200 N BREIEL BLVD 45042 #020-12-1968 L1970 **FM PHP** *062 †18
PLEDGER, Stephen Roy. 1044 SUMMITT SQ 45042 #017-20-1970 L1971 **ORS OSS** *020 †40
RAY, Marvin Lee. 200 N BREIEL BLVD, MIDDLETOWN MEDICAL GROUP 45042 #051-04-1991 L1998 **IM** *020 †20
REDDIVARI, Ajay. 38 N BREIEL BLVD 45042 #495-58-1981 L1990 **CD** *020 †20
RICHMOND, Aimee M. ■ 45044 #041-07-1948 L1950 **FM** *071 †18
RIDGE, Jennifer Mylius. 210 N BREIEL BLVD 45042 #038-40-1989 L1990 **D** *020 †15 ‡
RIOLO, Stephanie Ann. 1131 CENTRAL AVE, STE M 45044 #025-12-1993 L2006 **CHP P** *020 †55,75
RITAN, John Leif. 105 MCKNIGHT DR 45044 #039-01-1957 L1972 **DR NR** *071 †80
ROBERTSON, Barry Alan. 105 MCKNIGHT DR 45044 #020-02-1975 L1976 **IM IMG** *020 †20
ROEHLL, Walter Henry, Jr. 1006 N UNIVERSITY BLVD 45042 #038-41-1955 L1955 **IM GP** *020 †20
RUSH, Martin. 4950 LEFFERSON RD BX 44912, MARTIN RUSH MD 45044 #038-41-1953 L1953 **P** *020 ‡
RUSTERHOLZ, Joyce E. ■ 45044 #020-02-1980 L1990 **OBG** *020 †30
RUTAN, John Michael, Jr. 1801 CRAWFORD ST, AK HEALTH SERVICES 45043 #038-45-1990 L1991 **OM** *020
RYAN, John Jos. 74 N BREIEL BLVD 45042 #017-20-1979 L1982 **FM** *020 †18
SCHAUBLIN, Greg Alan. 105 MCKNIGHT DR, STE A 45044 #038-43-2001 L2001 **N** *020 †75
SCOTT, William Thos. 200 N BREIEL BLVD 45042 #038-41-1959 L1959 **IM GE** *071 †20
SHARMA, Kuldip. 255 N BREIEL BLVD 45042 #495-85-1977 L1990 **GE** *020 †20
SIEWNY, Gregory W. 103 MCKNIGHT DR, STE A 45044 #038-40-1982 L1983 **OBG** *020 †30 ‡
SKIMMING, Louis Homer, II. ■ 45044 #038-40-1957 L1957 **IM** *071 †20
SMITH, George D. 105 MCKNIGHT DR 45044 #038-41-1953 L1953 **GP** *071
SMITH, Kirk Ellis. 2403 CENTRAL AVE 45044 #038-75-1987, ▲ L1988 **FM** *020 †18
SNIDER, Robb Mc Kerron. 105 MCKNIGHT DR, MEDICAL PAVILION, SUITE A 45044 #038-41-1993 L2002 **N** *020 †75
STEEL, Barbara Lee. ■ 45042 #005-14-1987 L1995 **PTH** *020 †50
STEINER, Malcolm Lorie. 200 N BREIEL BLVD 45042 #028-03-1981 L1983 **END** *020 †20
STEWART, James Franklin. 3 ALAMEDA CIR 45042 #038-41-1956 L1956 **U** *071 †95
STRAIT, Kevin Christopher. 1010 SUMMITT SQ, SUMMIT FAMILY PHYSICIANS I 45042 #038-40-1978 L1981 **FM** *020 †18
STRAUS, Tom Frederick. 4701 CENTRAL AVE 45044 #038-41-1977 L1981 **OPH** *020 †35
SZAWALUK, John Jos. 231 N BREIEL BLVD, STE 200 45042 #010-02-1990 L2003 **CD IM** *020 †20
TABRAH, Farouk Abdul J. 38 N BREIEL BLVD 45042 #528-01-1964 L1973 **CD IM** *020 †20
TALBOT, George Theodore, III. 20 S BREIEL BLVD, SOUTHWEST OHIO OB/GYN 45044 #038-41-1993 L1997 **OBG** *020 †30
TALKERS, Ralph Henry. 105 MCKNIGHT DR 45044 #038-40-1980 L1981 **EM** *020 †16
TASSET, Jerry Jos. 105 MCKNIGHT DR 45044 #038-41-1987 L1990 **EM OM** *030 †16
VARNEY, John H, Jr. ■ 45042 #025-01-1950 L1951 **AN** *071 †05
VERNON, Matthew J. 74 N BREIEL BLVD 45042 #048-12-2001 L2004 **FM** *020 †18 ‡
VRINDAVANAM, Nandagopal S. 235 N BREIEL BLVD, SIGNAL POINT HEMATOLOGY/ON 45042 #495-42-1989 L2001 **HO** *020
VUONG, Phuong Hoang. 182 N BREIEL BLVD 45042 #941-01-1978 L1988 **PUD CCM** *020 †20
WADHWA, Subodh Kumar. 1049 SUMMITT SQ 45042 #495-03-1974 L1981 **N** *020 †75
WAGERS, Brian Eugene. ■ 45044 #038-41-2006 L2006 **PD** *012
WALSH, Martin John. 1064 SUMMITT SQ 45042 #038-43-1991 L1997 **U** *020 †95
WARD, James Michael. 105 MCKNIGHT DR 45044 #038-40-1973 L1975 **EM** *020 †16
WATSON, Clyde Stewart. ■ 45042 #028-03-1974 L1975 **EM FM** *020 †18,16
WHITLATCH, Stephen P. 105 MCKNIGHT DR, MIDDLETOWN REGIONAL-PATH 45044 #038-43-1978 L1979 **PTH** *020 †50

■ = Address Information Privacy Protected

WILLIAMS, Mark Eugene. 105 MCKNIGHT DR 45044 #038-41-1992 L1993 **FM** *020 †18
WISE, Marc Steven. 105 MCKNIGHT DR 45044 #038-43-2003 L2003 **EM** *020 †16
WOODWARD, Paul M, Jr. ■ 45044 #038-41-1951 L1951 **OPH** *071 †35
WOURMS, Timothy Nicholas. 1010 SUMMIT SQ 45042 #038-45-1995 L1997 **FM** *020 †18

MILAN — ERIE

BARNEY, Daniel Brett. 2114 STATE ROUTE 113 E 44846 #035-45-2003 L2007 **AN** *020
CRUZ, Jaime Benjamin. 2114 STATE ROUTE 113 E, ZZZ ANESTHESIA INC 44846 #264-01-1994 L2000 **AN** *020 †05
DORMAN, Sharon Lee. 2108 STATE ROUTE 113 E 44846 #022-75-1992, ▲ L1994 **OBG FM** *020 ‡
DRAEGER, John Carl. ■ 44846 #020-02-1974 L1980 **P** *020 †75
JOHNSON, Suzanne M. 2114 STATE ROUTE 113 E 44846 #064-01-1988 L1995 **FM** *020
KELLER, Todd Alan. 2114 STATE ROUTE 113 E 44846 #021-01-1997 L2001 **AN** *020
WYSE, Susie Mae. 2012 MASON RD E 44846 #038-43-1984 L1985 **EM** *020 †16

MILFORD — CLERMONT

AGANON, Efren C. 400 TECHNE CENTER DR, STE 402 45150 #748-02-1985 L1999 **NPM PD** *020 †55
AMATYA, Sudha Shrestha. 1083 STATE ROUTE 28 STE A 45150 #704-02-1984 L2006 **PD** *020 †55
BAUMAN, Anya Carrel. 5400 DUPONT CIR, SUITE A 45150 #039-01-1995 L1998 **PD** *020 †55
CAPURRO, John Robt. 201 OLD BANK RD, STE 103 45150 #654-01-1982 L1989 **FM** *020 †18
CHARLEVILLE, Roger P. 5827 HAPPY HOLLOW RD, STE 210 45150 #038-41-1968 L1968 **DR** *020 †80
CHICK, Ernest W. ■ 45150 #036-07-1953 L1963 **OS GPM** *071
CHICK, Jon Blair. 400 TECHNE CENTER DR, STE 401 45150 #020-12-1982 L1985 **FM** *020 †18
DAVISON, Rita R. 703 STATE ROUTE 28, STE B 45150 #038-40-1991 L1992 **PD** *020 †55
DECKER, Carl Larry. 935 STATE ROUTE 28 45150 #038-41-1966 L1966 **EM OS** *030 †16
DE LAND, Christina Jean. 400 TECHNE CENTER DR, SOUTHERN OHIO HEALTH SERVI 45150 #038-44-2000 L2000 **FM** *020 †18
DE SILVA, Bernard. 79 POWHATTON DR 45150 #220-01-1965 L1972 **P OS** *072
EIPPERT, Jill Pendleton. ■ 45150 #038-44-1989 L1990 **EM** *020 †16
EWING, Reginald Stansmore. 1105 SPRINGRIDGE CT 45150 #035-45-1997 L2003 **ADL** *020 †55
FERMANN, Gretchen Marie. 5718 SIGNAL HILL CT, STE A 45150 #038-41-1992 L1996 **OBG** *020 †30
FESENMEIER, Michael F. 5718 SIGNAL HILL CT, STE A 45150 #001-06-2001 L2001 **OBG** *020 †30
FIXLER, Robert Marc. 231 MAIN ST 45150 #038-41-1984 L1985 **D** *020 †20,15
FLEMING, Christopher M. 5718 SIGNAL HILL CT, STE A 45150 #038-40-1989 L1990 **OBG** *020 †30
GREENE, James Edward. 5861 CINEMA DR 45150 #038-43-1981 L1988 **FM** *030 †18
GRISCHY, Robert Charles. 5861 CINEMA DR 45150 #048-12-1985 L1986 **IM** *020 †20
GRYNIUK, Marta. 400 TECHNE CENTER DR, HEALTH SERVICES 45150 #759-07-1983 L1997 **IM** *020 †20
HARPER, David Jay. 935 STATE ROUTE 28 45150 #038-41-1987 L1989 **FM UCM** *020 †18
HEATON, Jeffery Paul. 905 MAIN ST 45150 #017-20-2000 L2000 **PD** *020 †55
HOBLER, Kirtland Edward. ■ 45150 #035-15-1962 L1968 **GS** *072 †85
HOLLIDAY, Michael Blair. 5400 DUPONT CIR, STE A 45150 #038-41-1997 L1998 **FM** *020 †18
JANI, Mudra Kujadkumar. 935 STATE ROUTE 28, DOCTORS URGENT CARE OFFICE 45150 #012-05-2003 L2006 **FM** *020 †18
JONES, Everett Linn. 732 LILA AVE 45150 #038-40-1955 L1955 **D** *020 †15
KORDIS, Steven Michael. 1648 SQUIRES WOOD CT, HARRISON MEMORIAL HOSPITAL 45150 #038-41-1981 L1982 **CD IM** *020
KOSTUR, Alexandra Mary. 905 MAIN ST, ESD PEDIATRIC GROUP 45150 #016-43-2000 L2000 **PD** *020 †55
LEQUES, Alzira Bermudez. ■ 45150 #055-01-2006 L2006 **OBG** *012
LIN, Kau-Shan. 1110 MAIN ST 45150 #385-04-1966 L1974 **GP PDC** *020 †55
LONG, Rebekah Ruth. 400 TECHNECENTER RD # 402, NETWORK (DBA) EASTGATE PED 45150 #038-41-1997 L2000 **PD** *020 †55
MC KINIVAN, C Elizabeth. 5400 DUPONT CIR, STE A 45150 #020-12-1970 L1973 **PD PDC** *020 †55
MC NEELY, Bonnie La Belle. ■ 45150 #038-41-1956 L1956 **IM OM** *020
MURTHY, Kode. 732 LILA AVE 45150 #495-11-1964 L1972 **P GP** *020 †75
ORTIZ, Xavier Guillermo. 5718 SIGNAL HILL CT, STE A 45150 #025-12-1991 L1992 **OBG** *020 †30
PACK, George Thos, Jr. ■ 45150 #038-40-1946 L1946 **GP** *071
PASTOR-ITURRICHA, Silva E. 5861 CINEMA DR 45150 #025-07-1988 L1990 **IM** *020 †20
PATEL, Ketan Kakalbhai. 201 OLD BANK RD, STE 100 45150 #495-76-1989 L1998 **IM** *020 †20
PATRIDGE, Barbara J. 400 TECHNE CENTER DR, HEALTH SERVICES 45150 #046-01-1981 L1985 **OBG** *020 †30
PEDIGO, Ann. 400 TECHNE CENTER DR, STE 402 45150 #020-02-1984 L1986 **FM EM** *020 †20
PETKOV, Sophia Borisova. 75 POWHATTON DR, # 75 45150 #198-01-1955 L1974 **GP** *020
RAKEL, Donald Paul. 905 MAIN ST, ESD PEDIATRIC GRP 45150 #038-41-1975 L1976 **PD ADL** *020
RANDOLPH, David Chas. 5724 SIGNAL HILL CT 45150 #038-40-1975 L1975 **OM** *020 †70
SAN NICOLAS, Nicanor P. 5400 DUPONT CIR, STE A 45150 #748-10-1991 L2001 **PD** *020 †55
SCHULER, John Kenneth. ■ 45150 #038-41-1975 L1975 **ORS** *020 †40
SHELDON, Laura Beckman. ■ 45150 #016-06-2002 *100
SHETH, Sheela Eric. 5861 CINEMA DR 45150 #495-17-1988 L1993 **FM** *020 †18
SPER, John Ronald. 905 MAIN ST 45150 #038-41-1960 L1960 **PD OS** *071 †55
STARKS, Keith Scott. ■ 45150 #017-20-1978 L1983 **ORS** *071 †40
STRICKLAND, Michael D. 703 STATE ROUTE 28, COMPREHENSIVE HEALTHCARE O 45150 #048-13-1990 L1991 **OS** *020 †20
THISTLETHWAITE, Wm Frank. 703 STATE ROUTE 28, STE B 45150 #047-05-1974 L1975 **PD** *020 †55
TOCHIP, Eusebio Tan. 1083 STATE ROUTE 28 STE A 45150 #748-11-1972 L1978 **PD** *020 †55
TUMBUSCH, Theresa Marie. 5861 CINEMA DR 45150 #038-41-1997 L2000 **IM** *020 †20
UY, John Sy. 1083 STATE ROUTE 28 STE A 45150 #748-11-1981 L1992 **PD** *020 †55
VERBOSKY, Laurie Anne. 935 STATE ROUTE 28, DOCTORS URGENT CARE 45150 #038-43-1994 L2002 **FPG** *020

WANG, Stanley Chia-Chi. 738 LILA AVE 45150 #244-03-1961 L1974 **FM** *071 †18
WATKINS, George J. 147 CLEVELAND AVE 45150 #038-41-1951 L1951 **GP** *072
WEISS, Helen Louise. 5400 DUPONT CIR, STE A 45150 #654-01-1997 L2000 **FM** *020 †18
ZABRECKY, Anna. 5718 SIGNAL HILL CT, STE A 45150 #038-41-1985 L1986 **OBG** *020 †30

MILFORD CENTER — UNION

PLA, Maria E R. 14199 MAPLE RIDGE RD 43045 #048-02-1984 L1985 **PM GP** *020 †60

MILLBURY — WOOD

SEDLMEIER, Adrienne J. 3601 AYERS RD 43447 #038-43-1996 L1997 **FM** *020 †18
SWARTZ, Jeffery Douglas. 3601 AYERS RD 43447 #038-43-1980 L1982 **FM FSM** *020 †18
TOFLINSKI, Andrea Lee. ■ 43447 #038-43-2005 L2005 **EM** *012

MILLERSBURG — HOLMES

ANTHONY, Robert James. 981 WOOSTER RD 44654 #056-06-1980 L1983 **AN** *020 †05
ARORA, Deepak. 1261 WOOSTER RD, STE 200 44654 #495-69-1973 L1985 **OBG** *020 †30
BARR, Laura E. 151 PARKVIEW DR 44654 #038-41-1998 L2000 **FM** *020 †18
BOYD, Stan Carter. 981 WOOSTER RD 44654 #038-40-1981 L1982 **EM FM** *020 †18,16
BRINGELSEN, Karen A. 1261 WOOSTER RD 44654 #033-06-1981 L1991 **PHO PD** *020 †55
BROWN, Scott Francis. 151 PARKVIEW DR 44654 #038-41-1990 L1991 **FM** *020 †18
CONWAY, Collin James. ■ 44654 #038-44-2008 *012
DELONG, Gregory Allen. 1261 WOOSTER RD, STE 200 44654 #035-09-1997 L2001 **OBG** *020 †30
DORNAN, Kurtis Charles. 981 WOOSTER RD 44654 #038-43-2004 L2004 **FM OBS** *020 †18
DUGAN, William Vernon. ■ 44654 #038-41-1958 L1958 **AN** *020 †05
DUTCHER, Titus Lynn. 981 WOOSTER RD 44654 #038-45-1987 L1988 **FM** *020 †18
HADDAD, Haitham I. 1261 WOOSTER RD, STE 210 44654 #875-01-1987 L1992 **IM** *020 †55
HART, Charles H. 151 PARKVIEW DR 44654 #038-41-1952 L1952 **FM AN** *071 †12
HART, Robert Anderson. 151 PARKVIEW DR 44654 #038-40-1985 L1986 **FM OBS** *020 †18
JAROCH, Mark Thos. 1261 WOOSTER RD 44654 #056-06-1981 L1987 **GS** *020 †85
JARVIS, Amy Marie. 981 WOOSTER RD, POMERENE HOSPITAL 44654 #038-40-2001 L2002 **GS** *020 †85
JOHNSON, Todd Lewis. 1261 WOOSTER RD, STE 200 44654 #017-20-1990 L1991 **CD** *020 †20
KASSIR, Mohamad Said. 1261 WOOSTER RD, STE 200 44654 #875-02-1980 L1991 **CD IM** *020 †20
LATOUF, Butros. 1261 WOOSTER RD STE 230 44654 #875-01-1987 L1993 **IM** *020 †20
MC FADDEN, Dwight Julius, III. 931 WOOSTER RD, HOLMES COUNTY DEPT OF HLTH 44654 #036-07-1998 L2003 **FM** *030 †18
MIEDEL, Hannah Elaine. 931 WOOSTER RD, HOLMES COUNTY HEALTH DEPT 44654 #041-13-2001 L2007 **IM** *020 †20
MILLER, Leon. 1261 WOOSTER RD, STE 215 44654 #036-07-1983 L1989 **GS** *020
MILLER, Rodney Alan. 1261 WOOSTER RD, STE 120 44654 #038-43-1992 L1993 **ORS** *020 †40
MILLER, Roy. 5797 TOWNSHIP ROAD 353 44654 #038-41-1973 L1974 **FM** *020 †18
OMRAN, Yasser. 1261 WOOSTER RD STE 230 44654 #875-01-1984 L1992 **IM ID** *020 †20
PRASNAL, Frank Louis, Jr. 981 WOOSTER RD, EMERGENCY DEPARTMENT 44654 #033-05-1981 L1988 **EM IM** *020 †20
RADWAN, Karam. 1261 WOOSTER RD STE 230 44654 #875-01-1997 L2003 **CHP** *020 †75
ROTH, Paul Edward. 981 WOOSTER RD 44654 #016-06-1957 L1958 **GP** *071
ROZUK, Claudia Maria. 1665 COUNTY ROAD 150 44654 #005-12-1978 L1981 **DR** *020 †80
SHALOWITZ, Robert Jeffrey. 1261 WOOSTER RD, STE 200 44654 #023-01-1976 L1980 **OBG** *020 †30
SHELCHKOV, Dmitry A. 981 WOOSTER RD, POMERENE HOSP 44654 #913-17-1983 L2001 **AN** *020 †05 ‡
STUTZMAN, Maurice Wm. 981 WOOSTER RD 44654 #038-40-1981 L1983 **FM** *020 †18
TAWIL, Camille. 1261 WOOSTER RD STE 23, MILLESBURG CLINIC 44654 #875-01-1997 L2003 **IM** *020 †20 ‡
VACCARIELLO, John Anthony. 151 PARKVIEW DR, HOLMES FAMILY PRACTICE CTR 44654 #038-43-1993 L1994 **FM** *020 †18
WEAVER, Wayne M. 981 WOOSTER RD 44654 #051-01-1971 L1989 **FM** *020

MILLERSPORT — FAIRFIELD

WHETSTONE, Paul M. 12135 LANCASTER NWRK RD NE, WHETSTONE MEDICAL CLINIC 43046 #038-40-1953 L1953 **FM** *071

MINERVA — STARK

AHMED, Ashraf Ibrahim. 625 N MARKET ST, PREMIER HEALTH ASSOCIATES 44657 #915-02-1991 L1999 **IM** *020 †20
BARR, Edward Nelson. 1028 E LINCOLNWAY 44657 #038-40-1981 L1983 **FM** *020 †18
FLEISHER, Perry Lee. 1168 ALLIANCE RD NW 44657 #035-03-1978 L1984 **CD** *020 †20
HINES, Robert H. 625 N MARKET ST, MINERVA CLINIC INC 44657 #010-01-1949 L1950 **PD GP** *071
LARSON, Raminder Kaur. ■ 44657 #018-75-1997, ▲ L2005 **DR** *020
MANUS, Roslyn Abalos. 200 CAROLYN CT 44657 #748-01-1994 L2000 **IM** *020 †20
RODOCOY, Pamela Anne. 1168 ALLIANCE RD NW 44657 #038-06-1997 L1999 **IM** *020 †20
WEIR, Samuel Lloyd. ■ 44657 #038-40-1935 L1935 **OS** *071
WILLIAMS, Diana R. 200 CAROLYN CT 44657 #038-40-1998 L2000 **FM** *100

MINFORD — SCIOTO

HAMM, Cynthia Gems. 8792 STATE ROUTE 335 45653 #038-40-2001 L2001 **FM** *020 †18
HENDRIX, Amy. ■ 45653 #038-75-2007, ▲ **OBG** *012

MINGO JUNCTION — JEFFERSON

BALZANO, John Frank. 110 VALLEY RD 43938 #041-07-1996 L2000 **DR** *020 †80

MINSTER – AUGLAIZE

BALLAS, Karen A. 11531 STATE ROUTE 66 45865 #038-40-1993 L1994 **FM** *020 †18
BALLAS, Michael Thomas. 11531 STATE ROUTE 66 45865 #038-40-1993 L1994 **FM FSM** *020 †18
GILL, Robert Patrick. 4 EAGLE DR 45865 #038-43-1976 L1977 **FM PUD** *020 †18
KAISER, Lisa M. ■ 45865 #036-07-2008 *012
PRENGER, Kristine Louise. ■ 45865 #038-40-1987 L1997 **FM** *020 †18

MOGADORE – PORTAGE

BIEDENBACH, Rachel Alice. 754 S CLEVELAND AVE, STE 100 44260 #038-43-2000 L2000 **OPH** *020 †35
CAIN, Brian Richard. 754 S CLEVELAND AVE # 300 44260 #038-44-1988 L1991 **FM** *020 †18
MC CLUSKEY, Dennis Connor. 754 S CLEVELAND AVE, STE 300 44260 #001-02-1976 L1977 **FM EM** *020 †18
POLLOCK, James Harold. ■ 44260 #038-40-1942 L1942 **FM** *071

MONCLOVA – LUCAS

NICHOLSON, Harry Edward. ■ 43542 #038-41-1961 L1961 **FM GP** *071
PACIO, Christina Ignacio. 8450 SNAPDRAGON LN 43542 #038-06-1999 L2004 **OPH** *020
RODEWALD, Katherine Jane. ■ 43542 #038-43-2008 *012

MONROE – BUTLER

BERRIMAN, Katherine Anne. 20 OVERBROOK DR STE C 45050 #068-01-1983 L1990 **FM** *020 †18
BURGHARD, Joe Dean. 20 OVERBROOK DR, STE C 45050 #038-45-2000 L2000 **FM** *020 †18 ‡
CRAWFORD, William John. ■ 45050 #041-12-1956 L1964 **OPH** *071 †35
GUPTA, Chandan. 20 OVERBROOK DR, STE C 45050 #495-85-1990 L1997 **FM** *020 †18
KERSH, Joann Heck. ■ 45050 #038-41-1962 L1962 **GP GYN** *030
SINHA, Prabhat K. ■ 45050 #016-76-2000, ▲ L2004 **SME** *012 †20
SWANSON, Maurice Gene. 20 OVERBROOK DR, STE C 45050 #016-45-1988 L1991 **FM** *020 †18
VAN VALKENBURG, Dyrk A. 20 OVERBROOK DR, STE C 45050 #048-14-1982 L1985 **FM** *020 †18

MONTGOMERY – HAMILTON

CLEMENT, John Francis. 10506 MONTGOMERY RD, STE 407 45242 #038-40-1975 L1978 **FM** *020 †18
LIM, Foongyen. ■ 45242 #045-01-1997 L2006 **PDS** *100 †85
MEHLMAN, Ned. 10496 MONTGOMERY RD, STE 104 45242 #067-01-1975 L1978 **CD IM** *020 †20

MONTPELIER – WILLIAMS

BERNARDI, Diane M. 935 E SNYDER AVE 43543 #033-05-1981 L1995 **D IM** *020 †20,15
HALLETT, Peggy Lynn. 935 E SNYDER AVE 43543 #038-43-1997 L1999 **FM** *020 †18
PARK, Kevin Lee. 935 E SNYDER AVE 43543 #038-43-1986 L1987 **FM** *020 †18
SEAMAN, Glen Thomas. 935 E SNYDER AVE 43543 #305-01-2000 L2000 **FM** *020 †18

MONTVILLE – GEAUGA

PREHAL, Julius S. ■ 44064 #473-03-1944 L1962 **OBG** *071

MORAINE – MONTGOMERY

BARBERA, Raymond Thos, Jr. 3180 KETTERING BLVD 45439 #010-02-1979 L2005 **AN AM** *020 †05
BEHERA, Vikram. ■ 45439 #495-36-2000 L2007 **IM** *020 †20
BORGEMENKE, David Earl. 3180 KETTERING BLVD 45439 #038-41-1989 L1990 **AN** *020 †05,55 ‡
CHAVEZ, Annette Marie. 2501 S DIXIE DR, CARILLON FAMILY PRACTICE 45409 #038-40-1985 L1987 **FM** *020 †18
CHUNG, Kirk Patrick. 5350 LAMME RD, KETTERING HOSPITAL YOUTH S 45439 #005-12-1994 L2005 **CHP** *020
ERONDU, Amaechi Iheanyi. 3180 KETTERING BLVD 45439 #690-05-1989 L2004 **AN** *020 †05
FELLER, H Allan. 4700 SPRINGBORO PIKE 45439 #038-41-1960 L1960 **NEP IM** *071 †20
FITZ, Stephanie C. 3095 KETTERING BLVD, SOUTH COMM BEHAVIORAL HLTH 45439 #017-20-1988 L1991 **P** *020 †75
FOLEY, Anthony Ernest. 2360 W DOROTHY LN, STE 101 45439 #038-40-1973 L1973 **FM** *040 †18
GUIRNALDA, Leonardo M. 3077 KETTERING BLVD, VISITING PHYSICIANS ASSOCI 45439 #748-10-1968 L1973 **FM GP** *020 †18
GUPTA, Rakesh Kumar. 4700 SPRINGBORO PIKE, RENAL PHYSICIANS INC 45439 #496-03-1977 L1989 **NEP IM** *020 †20
HIGHTOWER, Carla Renee. 3180 KETTERING BLVD 45439 #016-06-1987 L2004 **AN** *020 †05
HINES, Dale Ray. 3131 S DIXIE DR, DAYTON ONCOLOGY HEMATLGY 45439 #016-06-1957 L1958 **HEM ON** *071 †20
JASON, Lisa Wright. 3180 KETTERING BLVD 45439 #038-41-1988 L1992 **AN CCM** *020 †05
JENKINS, Alfred Percyvelt. 3180 KETTERING BLVD 45439 #051-04-1981 L1984 **AN** *020
KAHKONEN, Martti Ellis. 2023 SPRINGBORO W, KETTERING WORKERS CARE 45439 #005-12-1983 L1985 **OM** *020
KAZ, Steven Jonathan. 3077 KETTERING BLVD # 319, VISITING PHYS ASSOC DAYTON 45439 #038-40-1981 L1983 **FM EM** *062 †18
KELLEY, Horace Aubrey. ■ 45439 #649-38-1988 **FM** *100

LONGO, Edward Chas, III. 3095 KETTERING BLVD, SO COMM BEHVRL HLTHCARE 45439 #038-41-1985 L1986 **P ADM** *020 †75
MATHIAS, Maria Bernadette. 3095 KETTERING BLVD 45439 #038-41-1995 L1997 **P** *020 †75
MHASKAR, Nilesh Suresh. 4700 SPRINGBORO PIKE 45439 #005-06-1997 L2007 **NEP** *020 †20
MOBLEY, Evelyn M Harris. 3900 SPRINGBORO PIKE 45439 #047-07-1960 L1961 **OM IM** *071
NANDY, Parimal Kumar. 3180 KETTERING BLVD 45439 #495-13-1970 L1982 **AN** *071 †05
OH, Danny Siew-Leng. 3180 KETTERING BLVD 45439 #005-12-1974 L1977 **PS** *020 †18,65
PHILLIPS, Vincent Craig. 3180 KETTERING BLVD 45439 #036-01-1991 L1995 **AN** *020 †05
PRADA, German V. 3131 S DIXIE DR, STE 108 45439 #132-01-1963 L1976 **P** *071
RAMAGOPALA REDDY, Avutu. 3180 KETTERING BLVD 45439 #495-50-1966 L1973 **AN PUD** *020
RAO, Vijayakumar P. 3180 KETTERING BLVD 45439 #495-65-1984 L1999 **AN** *020 †05
REDDY, Nuvvuru C. 3180 KETTERING BLVD 45439 #495-62-1971 L1975 **AN** *020 †05
SEILER, Francis Jos. 3131 S DIXIE DR, STE 535 45439 #028-34-1957 L1958 **AN** *071
SHAHID, Abdul Qudoos. 3180 KETTERING BLVD 45439 #308-13-1998 L2004 **AN** *020 †05
SHERK, Derek W. 3077 KETTERING BLVD, STE 319 45439 #038-45-1998 L1999 **FM** *020 †18
SIMON, Daniel. 4700 SPRINGBORO PIKE 45439 #020-12-1972 L1983 **NEP IM** *071 †20
STEDJE, Susan Erwin. 2501 S DIXIE DR, CARILLON FAMILY PRACTICE 45409 #038-41-1986 L1987 **FM** *020 †18
TECSON, Teofilo T, Jr. 3180 KETTERING BLVD 45439 #748-07-1964 L1972 **AN** *020
TRACEWELL, Wendy Suzanne. 3095 KETTERING BLVD 45439 #038-45-1993 L1996 **CHP** *020
TREVINO, Joe J. 3131 S DIXIE DR, STE 108 45439 #649-01-1957 L1962 **P PFP** *020
WALDMAN, Adam Blake. 3180 KETTERING BLVD 45439 #025-01-1994 L1998 **AN** *020 †05
WIDO, Thomas Michael. 2217 ARBOR BLVD 45439 #038-43-1991 L1992 **EM** *020 †16

MORELAND HILLS – CUYAHOGA

ABDEL-HAMID, Ossama. ■ 44022 #915-04-1977 **OTO** *100
BAKOS, Edward Robt. ■ 44022 #017-20-1956 L1970 **P N** *071 †75
BODAS, Alina. ■ 44022 #038-06-2004 L2004 **AN** *012
BODAS, Prasad Vinayak. ■ 44022 #038-06-2004 L2004 **PD** *020
CAUFIELD, Jeffrey Hale. ■ 44022 #038-06-1977 L1978 **EM IM** *020 †16
DI, Xiao. 212 MEADOWOOD LN 44022 #243-64-1983 L2003 **NS NSP** *020
GILLINOV, Sheldon Jerry. 220 BASSWOOD LN 44022 #038-40-1960 L1960 **OBG** *020 †30
GOTA, Carmen Eugenia. ■ 44022 #781-03-1989 L2002 **RHU** *020 †20
JULKA, Neeraj. ■ 44022 #495-29-1975 L1979 **FM GP** *071
RICHMAN, Benjamin David. 245 MEADOWOOD LN 44022 #028-34-1967 L1974 **ORS OSM** *020 †40
SCHWARTZ, Marcy Lynn. ■ 44022 #047-05-1989 L2006 **PDC** *020 †55
SUGERMAN, David Lawrence. ■ 44022 #021-01-1987 L1991 **EM** *020 †16
TAM, Rose Chun Wah. ■ 44022 #035-08-1973 L1981 **D** *020 †15
TIRGAN, Nima. ■ 44022 #038-43-2006 L2006 **IM** *012
WALKER, Judith J. 4005 SOM CENTER RD 44022 #038-06-1982 L1983 **D** *020 †15
YOON, Hyon Jun. ■ 44022 #583-03-1964 L1979 **AN** *020 †05

MORROW – WARREN

BATHORI, Maria K. ■ 45152 #473-03-1964 L1976 **FM GP** *071
BHATT, Sanat R. 519 W PIKE ST 45152 #495-75-1970 L1977 **IM** *020 †20
HAHN, Penny Leue. 158 E PIKE ST 45152 #038-45-1989 L1991 **GP** *020
HOLTZCLAW, Reid Dawson. ■ 45152 #023-12-1996 L1997 **IM** *020 †20
HOLTZCLAW, Suezane Lee. ■ 45152 #023-12-1996 L1997 **GPM** *020 †70
MC GLINN, Joan F. ■ 45152 #041-07-1973 L1974 **EM** *020
ROHRER, Richard Glenn. ■ 45152 #038-40-1955 L1955 **AN OS** *020

MOSCOW – CLERMONT

MILLER, William Richard. ■ 45153 #038-41-1961 L1961 **GP** *071

MOUNT GILEAD – MORROW

BACHELDER, Brian Leroy. 642 W MARION RD 43338 #038-41-1981 L1983 **FM** *020 †18
BELARDO, Angelito Velando. 7326 STATE ROUTE 19 # 2708 43338 #748-08-1965 L1972 **GS** *071
FREUNDLICH, Thomas Edward. 900 MEADOW DR STE A 43338 #038-43-1989 L1990 **FM** *020 †18
GALBRAITH, John Grant. 6519 US HWY 42 43338 #065-01-1984 L1997 **FM** *020 †18
GHAZI, Mohiuddin. 900 MEADOW DR, STE B 43338 #704-02-1988 L1993 **IM** *020 †20
HANSEN, Eric Albert. 651 W MARION RD, EMERGENCY DEPARTMENT 43338 #023-07-1996 L1997 **FM** *020 †18
HINTZ, Matthew Allan. 712 BAKER ST 43338 #038-40-2001 L2001 **FM** *020 †18
JAMMU, Baljeet Kaur. 950 MEADOW DR 43338 #495-98-1996 L2000 **CHP** *020 †75
JONES, Jeffrey Vincent. 950 MEADOW DR 43338 #038-45-1995 L1997 **P** *020 †75
KUMAR, Praveer. 245 NEAL AVE, STE C 43338 #495-45-1992 L1998 **IM** *020 †20
LEE, James M. ■ 43338 #038-45-2006 L2006 **PD** *012
MCRAE, Melissa K. 6519 US HWY 42, STE 2 43338 #038-75-1998, ▲ L1999 **FM** *020 †18
MEFTAH, Parviz. 651 W MARION RD 43338 #396-04-1974 L1979 **GS GP** *020
SCANDINARO, David Wm. 950 MEADOW DR 43338 #041-14-1981 L1991 **CHP P** *020 †75
SIMPSON, Larry Walker. 950 MEADOW DR 43338 #038-40-1969 L1969 **CHP P** *020 †75
STRONG, Deborah Jane. 7326 STATE ROUTE 19 # 1911 43338 #038-40-1969 L1969 **EM** *030

MOUNT HEALTHY – HAMILTON

BRODERICK, Joseph D. 1380 COMPTON RD 45231 #028-34-1953 L1956 **IM** *071
LONGSHORE, Richard D. 7620 PERRY ST 45231 #020-02-1967 L1968 **FM** *071 †18
RUSSELL, Lillette Yvonne. 1380 COMPTON RD 45231 #047-07-1980 L1994 **FM** *020 †18

MOUNT ORAB – BROWN

BRICKING, Todd R. 111 VANDAMENT WAY, MT. ORAB URGENT MEDICAL CA 45154 #020-12-1995 L1996 **EM** *020 †16

■ = Address Information Privacy Protected

KISSEL, Julia Marilyn. 111 VANDAMENT WAY 45154 #038-41-1996 L1997 FM *020 †18
LEEDS, F Stuart. 111 VANDAMENT WAY 45154 #038-06-1995 L1998 FM *075 †18
MC KINLEY, Chas Timothy. 111 VANDAMENT WAY, MT ORAB REGL FAM HLTH CARE 45154 #038-41-1983 L1984 FM *020 †18
RICHEY, Valerie Lynne. 109 S HIGH ST 45154 #038-40-1995 L1996 FM *020 †18
SKLENA, Paul James. 614 S HIGH ST 45154 #016-02-1995 L1999 MPD *020 †20,55

MOUNT PLEASANT – JEFFERSON

PELTZ, Carrie Marie. ■ 43939 #038-44-2006 L2006 IM *012

MOUNT STERLING – MADISON

WONG, Leung-Bun. 27 N LONDON ST 43143 #385-03-1967 L1975 GPM FOP *020

MOUNT VERNON – KNOX

AMICON, Robert Francis. 11660 UPPER GILCHRIST RD, KNOX COUNTY HEALTH DEPARTM 43050 #038-40-1958 L1958 FM CD *071
ARNOLD, Misty Elaine. 1330 COSHOCTON AVE 43050 #038-40-1994 L1995 EM *020 †16
BAZZOLI, Allan Scott. 300 W VINE ST 43050 #038-41-1980 L1980 PM *020 †60
BELL, Charles Raymond. 1320 COSHOCTON AVE STE F 43050 #047-07-1982 L2005 PD ADL *020 ‡
BLACKBURN, Edward Dowe. 1330 COSHOCTON AVE 43050 #038-40-1973 L1973 FM *020
BRAXTON, Brian Eric. 1330 COSHOCTON AVE 43050 #038-45-1994 L2001 EM *012 †18
BRECKENRIDGE, Mary Beth. 1451 YAUGER RD 43050 #038-40-1992 L1993 CD *020 †20
BUDDIE, Mark Alan. ■ 43050 #038-40-1993 L1994 FM FPG *020
BUTLER, Richard Markland. 1558 COSHOCTON AVE 43050 #017-20-1968 L1997 DR *020 †80
CARHART, James Milton. 1330 COSHOCTON AVE 43050 #016-06-1952 L1956 IM CD *071 †20
CARROLL, Frederick C. 1661 VENTURE DR, STE A 43050 #038-40-1999 L1999 IM *020 †20
CHO, Myung Ja. 1330 COSHOCTON AVE 43050 #583-08-1965 L1974 CLP PTH *020 †50
CRESPO-SANTOS, Jose A. 1558 COSHOCTON AVE, # 138 43050 #042-02-1995 L1998 OBG *020
CUSH, Gregory Jos. 1451 YAUGER RD STE 2B 43050 #038-45-1990 L1996 OSM *020 †40
DEBAETS, Debbra-Lynne. 1451 YAUGER RD 43050 #038-40-1973 L1973 CD IM *020 †20
DICKEY, Morris W. ■ 43050 #017-20-1952 L1966 GS EM *071 †85
DOOLITTLE, Kenneth H, II. 1330 COSHOCTON AVE 43050 #038-40-1985 L1986 ORS *020 †40
DRAEGER, Steven Chas. 1330 COSHOCTON AVE 43050 #038-40-1979 L1979 FM *020 †18
DYCK, David Matthew. 11 WOODLAKE TRL, STE A 43050 #305-01-2002 L2002 FM *020 †18
ELLIOTT, James Lee. 501 N MAIN ST, APT 1 43050 #038-41-1981 L1982 IMG *020 †20
FAIRCHILD, Alan Kent. 1320 COSHOCTON AVE 43050 #038-40-1965 L1965 OBG *020 †30
FLADEN, Robert Stanley. ■ 43050 #038-40-1955 L1956 IM *071
FORMAN, Patricia Reilley. 8402 BLACKJACK ROAD EXT 43050 #038-40-1978 L1980 P *020 †75
GANGADHARAM, Yamuna. ■ 43050 #495-65-1980 L2003 IM *020 †20
GEORGE, Barry Scott. 1451 YAUGER RD 43050 #038-40-1979 L1980 CD IM *062 †20
HILL, Stephen Alan. 1330 COSHOCTON AVE 43050 #048-12-1976 L1976 N OS *020 †75
HUSTON, John Theodore. 1451 YAUGER RD 43050 #038-40-1961 L1961 IM *020 †20
JANTSCH, William Martin. 1330 COSHOCTON AVE 43050 #008-02-1978 L1979 EM IM *020 †20,16
JONES, Malcolm Justice. ■ 43050 #020-02-1964 L1965 GP EM *071
KARCIC, Arsad. 1451 YAUGER RD 43050 #957-01-1994 L2003 CD IM *020 †20
KASSERMAN, David. 307 VERNEDALE DR 43050 #038-44-1986 L1986 GS *020 †85
KENT, Blanca P Smith. ■ 43050 #187-03-1951 L1958 PDS *071 †85
KNOTT, Julie Veronica. 1330 COSHOCTON AVE 43050 #038-41-1996 L1999 GS *020 †18
KOONTZ, Warren Neil. 8402 BLACKJACK ROAD EXT 43050 #038-40-1947 L1947 GP IM *071
KOSO, Sylvi Kyllikki. 1355 YAUGER RD 43050 #038-06-1980 L1981 OPH *020 †35
KRISHNA, Samavedam Ananta. 1320 COSHOCTON AVE STE C 43050 #496-09-1991 L1996 IM *020 †20
KYRIAKEDES, Christ Geo. 1330 COSHOCTON AVE 43050 #028-79-1988, ▲ L1989 EM *040
LAIRD, Emerson Lee. 11660 UPPER GILCHRIST RD 43050 #038-40-1962 L1962 IM *020
MANGRU, Bala. ■ 43050 #649-02-1955 L1961 P *020
MAYR, William Thomas. 1330 COSHOCTON AVE 43050 #038-40-1998 L2003 N CN *020 †75
MC CANN, David Jay. 1330 COSHOCTON AVE 43050 #038-43-1987 L1988 FM EM *020 †18
MC CANN, James Richard. ■ 43050 #038-40-1962 L1962 GP OBG *071
MC DOWELL, Lauren E. 1330 COSHOCTON AVE 43050 #041-02-1995 L2006 GS *020 †85
MC KINLEY, Thomas Dean. 1451 YAUGER RD, STE 1F 43050 #038-41-1993 L1996 IM *020 †20
MILLER, Albert S. 1330 COSHOCTON AVE 43050 #038-41-1983 L1983 FM GPM *020 †18
MOHLER, Christopher M. 1330 COSHOCTON AVE 43050 #038-43-2001 L2001 EM *020 †16
MURCKO, Lawrence Geo. 1451 YAUGER RD 43050 #036-05-1977 L1978 CD *020 †20
MURNEN, Amy Denise. 1451 YAUGER RD, STE 1E 43050 #038-43-1994 L1995 FM *020 †18
NELSON, James Hissom, III. 1451 YAUGER RD, STE 2E 43050 #035-08-1971 L1974 U AM *020 †95
NEUENSCHWANDER, James F. 1330 COSHOCTON AVE 43050 #038-06-1995 L1998 FM EM *020 †16
NIMETH, Brent Chas. 1220 YAUGER RD 43050 #038-43-1988 L1989 FM EM *020 †18
NUSSBAUM, Joseph Howard. 1320 COSHOCTON AVE 43050 #038-40-1966 L1966 OBG *020 †30
ORRACA-TETTEH, Kingsley A. 1575 YAUGER RD 43050 #412-01-1976 L1990 DR RNR *020 †80
PALANIAPPAN, Jawahar. 7 WOODLAKE TRL STE A 43050 #495-04-1975 L1980 CD IM *020 †20
PALEY, Daniel Seth. 1684 VENTURE DR, STE D 43050 #038-40-1993 L2000 GS *020 †85
PAMULAPATI, Ramanadha Rao. 812 COSHOCTON AVE 43050 #495-50-1964 L1978 U *020 †95
PATEL, Shailesh C. 812 COSHOCTON AVE BOX 926 43050 #495-22-1971 L1979 IM *020 †20
PERLE, William S. 1330 COSHOCTON AVE 43050 #913-23-1945 L1960 GP *072
PETERS, Marilynn Joanne. 8402 BLACKJACK ROAD EXT 43050 #038-40-1988 L1993 CHP P *020 †75
PLOCKI, Leonard Keith. 1330 COSHOCTON AVE 43050 #041-12-1977 L1990 PTH ORS *020 †50
POMPUTIUS, Wm Francis, Jr. 12200 UPPER FREDERCKTWN RD 43050 #041-12-1960 L1977 FM *020 †50
POOLE, Joseph Ralph. 1250 VERNONVIEW DR, MVDC 43050 #005-12-1958 L1959 FM *020
POSADA, Hernando. 126 E VINE ST 43050 #264-01-1954 L1974 FM PD *020

RAJ, James L. 119 E CHESTNUT ST 43050 #495-16-1971 L1982 OTO *020
RASA, Gangaram. ■ 43050 #495-65-1981 L2002 CD *020 †20
REED, Larry Carl. 307 VERNEDALE DR 43050 #038-43-1981 L1983 FM *020 †18
REEDER, Deborah Johnson. 1355 YAUGER RD 43050 #038-41-1990 L1991 OPH *072 †35
RISKO, James Howard. 307 VERNEDALE DR 43050 #041-13-1966 L1973 GS *020 †85
RODSTROM, Robert Edward. 1451 YAUGER RD, STE 1F 43050 #025-07-1970 L1973 IM IMG *020 †20
ROMERO, Jesus Silan. 784 SOUTHRIDGE DR 43050 #748-08-1965 L1972 AN GS *071
ROSS, Patrick, Jr. 7 WOODLAKE TRL, STE A 43050 #028-34-1983 L1991 TS *020 †85,90
SCHERMER, Tracy Warren. 1330 COSHOCTON AVE 43050 #038-40-1979 L1979 ADL EM *020
SCHWARTZ, Judy Ellen. 1330 COSHOCTON AVE, KNOX COMMUNITY HOSP 43050 #018-03-1971 L1972 OS CD *030 †85,90
SHERMAN, Roger Howard. 1355 YAUGER RD 43050 #038-40-1968 L1968 OPH *020 †35
SIRAK, John Howard. 7 WOODLAKE TRL, STE A 43050 #038-06-1991 L1995 TS *020 †85
SMITH, Robert Elton. ■ 43050 #041-01-1948 L1949 FM FPG *071 †18
SPENCER, Jeffrey Clark. 507 WOOSTER RD 43050 #023-07-1974 L1977 IM *020 †20
SRIVASTAVA, Tribeni N. 7 WOODLAKE TRL, STE A 43050 #495-49-1961 L1971 CD IM *040 †20
STILSON, Rebecca A. 1451 YAUGER RD, STE 2D 43050 #038-40-1988 L1996 OBG *020 †30
STOLFI, Joseph Edwin. 1330 COSHOCTON AVE 43050 #021-05-1969 L1975 N *020 †75
STURMI, James Edward, III. 1320 COSHOCTON AVE, STE E 43050 #038-43-1989 L1990 FM FSM *020 †18
SULLIVAN, Michael Patrick. 1451 YAUGER RD, STE 2D 43050 #047-06-1990 L1996 OBG *020 †30
TALUKDER, Kamal R. 1451 YAUGER RD STE 1D 43050 #160-07-1980 L1996 PD *020
TAN, Gubert L. 1330 COSHOCTON AVE 43050 #748-01-1988 L1998 N *020 †75
THOMAS, Myron Earl. 1330 COSHOCTON AVE 43050 #038-40-1963 L1963 IM *071
TORRES-SANTIAGO, Roxanna. 1320 COSHOCTON AVE 43050 #042-02-1998 L2004 OBG *020
URBAN, Jacquelyn Diann. 1320 COSHOCTON AVE 43050 #038-06-1982 L1983 GS *020 †20
VAN FOSSEN, Douglas Bruce. 1451 YAUGER RD 43050 #038-40-1980 L1981 CD IC *020 †20
VICTORIOSO, Rebecca. 12200 UPPER FREDERCKTWN RD 43050 #748-10-1973 L1987 OBG *071
WANKEN, James John. 307 VERNEDALE DR 43050 #018-03-1966 L1967 ORS *071 †40
WESTERHEIDE, Robert Lee. 306 E HIGH ST, WESTERHEIDE SURGERY & ONCO 43050 #028-34-1960 L1960 GS ON *071
WILLIAMS, Craig Edward. 8402 BLACKJACK ROAD EXT 43050 #038-40-1977 L1981 P CHP *040 †75
ZUBERI, Mussaret A. 1330 COSHOCTON AVE 43050 #704-02-1981 L1992 IM *020 †20

MUNROE FALLS – SUMMIT

AZEM, May. 43 S MAIN ST, AKRON GEN ARTH & RHEUM ASC 44262 #875-01-1998 L2000 RHU *020
BANYASZ, Michael James. ■ 44262 #038-43-2006 L2006 EM *012
DAS VARMA, Ranendra Lal. 444 N MAIN ST 44262 #495-15-1958 L1967 CD IM *071 †20
ELLIS, William Geo, Jr. ■ 44262 #051-04-1961 L1962 AN *071 †05
GLUECKERT, Michael John. ■ 44262 #038-45-2007 L2007 EM *012
GUNKELMAN, Samantha Megan. ■ 44262 #038-44-2006 L2006 PD *012
HENAULT, Charles Leon. 527 S MAIN ST 44262 #038-40-1955 L1955 FM AM *071 †18
KHAITAN, Alka. ■ 44262 #038-06-2003 L2003 PDI *012 †55
KOLACZEWSKI, Gayleen P. 265 N MAIN ST STE 17 44262 #038-40-1981 L1983 IM GE *020 †20
MORRIS, Ray Danl, II. 43 S MAIN ST, # 2 44262 #010-01-1976 L1978 RHU IM *020 †20

NAPOLEON – HENRY

BARUA, Aruna. 11600 STATE ROUTE 424 43545 #160-02-1994 L2003 IM *020 †20
BIDWELL, Kip Alan. 11644 STATE ROUTE 424 #101 43545 #038-43-1990 L1997 FM *020 †18
BROWN, Thos Hartwell, Jr. ■ 43545 #047-05-1945 L1946 ORS *071 †40
CHIU, Simon S. 600 FREEDOM DR 43545 #065-01-1985 L1994 P *020 †75
DE MICHIEI, Mark E. 11644 STATE ROUTE 424 #101 43545 #038-40-1984 L1985 FM *020 †18 ‡
ELLIOTT, Laura Lynn. 11600 STATE ROUTE 424 43545 #011-02-1992 L2005 OBG *020 †30
ERWIN, Kermit Ray. 407 INDEPENDENCE DR 43545 #038-45-1987 L1999 OBG *020 †30
FLORA, Romeo Santos. ■ 43545 #748-01-1957 L1970 OBG GP *071
FOY, Robyn Ann. 589 E RIVERVIEW AVE 43545 #038-43-1999 L1999 CHP *020 †75
GREGO, Gary Alan. 1426 N SCOTT ST, NAPOLEON CLINIC 43545 #025-07-1989 L1990 FM *020 †18
KNIPE, Clarice Lynn. 589 E RIVERVIEW AVE 43545 #038-43-1985 L1986 P *020
KNIPE, Stephen Michael. 11600 STATE ROUTE 424 43545 #038-43-1988 L1990 FM *020 †18 ‡
KOH, Beom Seong. ■ 43545 #583-12-1989 IM *100
LOSEY, Thomas Alan. 1426 N SCOTT ST, NAPOLEON CLINIC 43545 #038-43-1996 L1998 FM *020 †18
MANAHAN, Raymond James. 11600 STATE ROUTE 424 43545 #025-07-1954 L1955 GP OM *071
MC MASTER, Anna Marie. 11644 STATE HWY 424, STE 101 43545 #038-43-1998 L1999 FM *020 †18
SEAL, Morris Leslie. 11644 STATE HWY 424, STE 104 43545 #038-45-1986 L1987 FM OM *020 †20
SKOSKIEWICZ, Marek J. 11644 STATE ROUTE 424, STE 102 43545 #759-03-1963 L1993 GS *020 †85
SOMOZA, Edmundo Avila. ■ 43545 #748-02-1971 L1983 R *020 †80
SOMOZA, Justine Joyb. ■ 43545 #038-44-2006 OBG *012
STOUGH, Wilson J. 515 AVON PL 43545 #038-40-1955 L1955 GP ID *020

NASHPORT – MUSKINGUM

BURRIER, Gail Warren. ■ 43830 #038-40-1956 L1956 FM IMG *071 †18
SAFKO, Joseph Steven. ■ 43830 #028-34-1960 L1967 R NM *071 †80,28

NAVARRE – STARK

ANDREADIS, Athena Ann. ■ 44662 #654-01-2007 L2007 IM *012
ANGERMAN, Robert Harold. ■ 44662 #016-43-1943 L1943 FM *071

KOVAC, Magdalena. 24 CECIL ST NE 44662 #286-03-1957 L1976 **GP** *020
VINCENT, Roger. 7532 SHEPLER CHURCH AVE SW 44662 #016-76-1964, ▲ L1964 **AN** *071

NEGLEY – COLUMBIANA

WACASER, Lawrence Keyes. PO BOX 390 44441 #016-11-1962 L1986 **NS** *020

NELSONVILLE – ATHENS

ALVAREZ-FLORES, Norma. 1950 MOUNT SAINT MARYS DR 45764 #748-01-1964 L1973 **FM IM** *071 ‡
AYUB, Hafiz Muhammed. 1950 MOUNT SAINT MARYS DR 45764 #704-04-1988 L1997 **IM** *020 †20
CLOTHIER, Maureen Ann. 1950 MOUNT SAINT MARYS DR 45764 #018-75-1984, ▲ L2003 **IM** *020
FAERBER, George Oswald. 1950 MOUNT SAINT MARYS DR 45764 #041-77-1961, ▲ L1967 **NM R** *071 †28
FLORES, Reuben C. 1950 MOUNT SAINT MARYS DR, DOC HOSP OF NELSONVLE-ER 45764 #748-01-1964 L1972 **GP GS** *020 †18
RANDOLPH, Michele K. 1950 MOUNT SAINT MARYS DR 45764 #025-07-1970 L1993 **PTH** *020 †50
ROSENBERG, William Aaron. 1950 MOUNT SAINT MARYS DR, DOCTORS HOSPITAL NELSONVIL 45764 #030-05-2001 L2005 **FSM** *100 †18

NEW ALBANY – FRANKLIN

AL-SAIF, Osama Habib. ■ 43054 #797-03-1994 L2005 **GS SO** *100 †85
ARORA, Amol. ■ 43054 #038-44-2003 L2003 **OBG** *020
ASAD, Farhana. ■ 43054 #704-02-1986 L2007 **IM** *020 †20
BAGENSTOSE, Cheryl Ackley. ■ 43054 #038-41-1999 L2002 **PD** *020 †55
BALCHICK, Robert John. ■ 43054 #038-40-1981 L1982 **U** *071 †95
BALIGA, Ragavendra R. ■ 43054 #495-52-1984 L2004 **CD** *020
BANDARU, Himabindu. ■ 43054 #495-62-2000 L2002 **IM** *020 †20
BARNETT, Daniel Jeremy. ■ 43054 #038-40-1999 **IM** *100
BEARD, David Andrew. 7277 SMITHS MILL RD, STE 250 43054 #038-40-1997 L1998 **IM** *020 †20
BEREND, Keith Robert. 7727 SMITHS MILL RD, STE 200 43054 #036-07-1997 L2002 **ORS** *020 †40
BERRY, Kevin Robt. 7277 SMITHS MILL RD, STE 250 43054 #038-45-1981 L1983 **IM** *020 †20
BIHONEGN, Hellen Yigzaw. ■ 43054 #366-03-1991 L2007 **IM** *100 †20
BOLTON, Mark James. 5195 HAMPSTED VLG CNTR WAY, STE 256 43054 #055-12-1994 L1995 **FM EM** *020 †18
BOYSEL, Steven Chas. 55 N HIGH ST 43054 #038-45-1990 L1991 **FM** *020 †18
CALLAND, Jon Wm. 7190 ASHCOMBE DR 43054 #038-40-1992 L1993 **AN** *020 †05
CANDLER, Eric Michael. 8741 SWISHER CREEK XING 43054 #038-40-1981 L1984 **AN** *020 †05
CARSON, Courtney Rae. ■ 43054 #038-43-2007 L2007 **PD** *012
CAVENDER, Richard Keith. 68 N HIGH ST, BLDG A 43054 #055-01-1992 L1994 **EM** *020 †16
COPPEL, Lewis Wm, Jr. 6525 W CAMPUS OVAL, STE 150 43054 #038-06-1975 L1976 **UCM EM** *020 †16
DAGES, Wendy Kathleen. ■ 43054 #038-40-1997 L1999 **PD** *100 †55
DIENHART, Peter W Maria. ■ 43054 #041-13-2000 L2007 **GE** *020 †20
EHRENBERG, Hugh Michael. ■ 43054 #033-05-1996 L2000 **OBG** *020 †30 ‡
GERKIN, Seth Eric. 7277 SMITHS MILL RD, STE 250 43054 #038-40-1995 L1996 **IM** *020 †20
GREWAL, Indira D. ■ 43054 #038-44-1990 **PTH** *100
GRUENTHER, Raymond Carl. 55 N HIGH ST, NEW ALBANY FAMILY HLTH 43054 #051-04-1975 L1989 **FM** *020 †18
HATFIELD, Mark C. 6520 W CAMPUS OVAL, CENTRAL OHIO SURGICAL INST 43054 #038-43-1988 L1996 **AN** *020 †05
ITEN, George J. ■ 43054 #023-01-1951 L1953 **GP IM** *071
KECK, Robert Jos. ■ 43054 #038-40-1970 L1971 **PD** *071
KELLER, Jamie Lynn. 4040 BAUGHMAN GRANT 43054 #048-04-1986 L2006 **AN** *020 †05
KHAN, Ayesha Saliha. ■ 43054 #025-07-2005 L2005 **EM** *012
KING, Jeffrey C. 7627 LAMBTON PARK RD, MATERNAL-FETAL MEDICINE 43054 #016-01-1975 L1995 **OBG MFM** *062 †30 ‡
KNEPEL, Sheri Anne. ■ 43054 #038-40-2003 L2005 **EM** *020 †16
KRASNIEWSKI, Jeffrey Alex. 153 W MAIN ST 43054 #038-40-2001 L2004 **PD** *020 †55
LECHIARA, Steven Scott. 7333 SMITHS MILL RD 43054 #038-44-1988 L1993 **AN** *020 †05
LEWIS, Donald Lloyd. 85 E MAIN ST, NORTHWEST EYE SURGEONS 43054 #038-40-1961 L1961 **OPH** *020 †35
LITTLE, Larry John. 240 MARKET ST, STE A 43054 #030-05-1977 L1982 **D** *020 †15
LOMBARDI, Adolph V, Jr. 7727 SMITHS MILL RD, STE 200 43054 #041-13-1981 L1986 **ORS** *020 †40 ‡
MADDOCKS-CHRISTIANSON, Kam. ■ 43054 #046-01-2005 L2005 **IM** *012
MATRE, Jeffrey John. 153 W MAIN ST 43054 #038-40-1994 L1995 **EM** *020 †16
MC RURY, Jonna Marie. 7585 N GOODRICH SQ 43054 #038-41-1988 L1993 **PD** *040 †55
MILKS, Jeffrey Wm. 153 W MAIN ST, STE 100 43054 #038-40-1978 L1981 **FM FPG** *020 †18
MOHAN, Vijendra Singh. 7277 SMITHS MILL RD, STE 250 43054 #038-44-1990 L1992 **IM** *020 †20
NARCELLES, Nestor Millan. 7333 SMITHS MILL RD, NEW ALBANY ORTHOPEDIC ANES 43054 #038-40-1994 L1996 **AN** *020 †05
NOWINSKI, Robert John. 7277 SMITHS MILL RD, STE 300 43054 #038-75-1996, ▲ L1998 **ORS** *020
ORTIZ, Anahi Mercedes. ■ 43054 #035-08-1983 L1992 **PD** *020 †55
OTIS, Scott Michael. 7277 SMITHS MILL RD, STE 300 43054 #038-40-1996 L1997 **PM** *020 †60
PAUL, William Teachnor. ■ 43054 #041-13-1955 L1956 **FM** *071 †18
RIZK, Sam Magdi. 1300 WINDTREE CT 43054 #038-06-1990 L1991 **APM** *020 †05
ROGERS, Ann M Lehman. 153 W MAIN ST 43054 #038-40-1970 L1971 **PD NPM** *020 †55
ROGERS, James Tyler. 153 W MAIN ST 43054 #038-40-1997 L1999 **PD** *020 †55
ROGERS, Nicholas Alan. 85 E MAIN ST, NORTHWEST EYE SURGEONS 43054 #038-40-2002 L2002 **OPH** *020 †35
ROSENBERG, Gerald M. 7727 SMITHS MILL RD, STE 200 43054 #038-40-1979 L1980 **ORS** *020 †40

RUTHERFORD, K. ■ 43054 #038-40-1987 L1988 **IM** *020 †20
SAHA, Sharmeela. ■ 43054 #038-41-2008 *012
SCHIAVONE, Dana Marie. ■ 43054 #038-40-2004 L2004 **PS** *012
SHIN, Jung Hae. ■ 43054 #583-08-1971 L1982 **PTH** *071
SHOLITON, Charles Alan. ■ 43054 #038-40-1976 L1977 **EM** *020
SIEGEL, Randall Scott. 7277 SMITHS MILL RD, STE 250 43054 #038-40-1990 L1992 **IM** *020 †20
SLAYBAUGH, Randall Scott. 7277 SMITHS MILL RD, STE 250 43054 #038-43-1995 L1996 **VM IM** *020 †20
SMUCKER, Jerry D. 7277 SMITHS MILL RD, STE 250 43054 #038-40-1983 L1987 **IM PA** *020 †20
STANLEY, David Earl. 55 N HIGH ST 43054 #038-45-1985 L1987 **FM** *020 †18
STUTZMAN, Desmond. 7277 SMITHS MILL RD, STE 300 43054 #038-75-1995, ▲ L1997 **ORS** *020
SUBBARAYUDU, Koppera. ■ 43054 #495-62-1970 L1983 **IM NEP** *020 †20
SWEENEY, Patricia. ■ 43054 #038-40-1982 L1982 **IM GP** *075
SYBERT, Daryl R. 7277 SMITHS MILL RD, STE 300 43054 #038-75-1986, ▲ L1986 **OSS ORS** *020
SZABO, Martha A. 18 WIVELISCOMBE, GRANT ANESTHESIA SERVICES 43054 #038-43-1990 L1993 **APM** *020 †05
TEREBUH, Victor Derk. 7333 SMITHS MILL RD, NEW ALBANY ORTHOPEDIC ANES 43054 #038-40-1995 L2000 **AN** *020 †05
WEDDINGTON, Wilburn H. ■ 43054 #010-03-1948 L1956 **FM** *071 †18
WELTNER, Daniel Eugene. 4111 BREMO RECESS 43054 #038-40-1960 L1960 **FM** *020 †18
WHITAKER, Todd Edwin. 85 E MAIN ST, NORTHWEST EYE SURGEONS 43054 #038-40-1996 L1997 **OPH** *020 †35
WILLARD, Mark Allen. 7277 SMITHS MILL RD, STE 250 43054 #016-45-1998 L2001 **IM** *020 †20
WITTENSOLDNER, Kimberle A. ■ 43054 #038-40-1999 L2000 **IM** *020
WOODS, Stephen Thomas. 7277 SMITHS MILL RD, STE 300 43054 #023-01-1999 L2000 **PM PMM** *020 †60
YU, Emily J. 7277 SMITHS MILL RD, STE 300 43054 #038-40-1993 L1997 **PM** *020 †60
ZAKI, Joseph. ■ 43054 #038-40-1998 L1999 **AN** *020 †05

NEW BOSTON – SCIOTO

HANZEL, David Brewster. 206 VINE ST 45662 #036-05-1972 L1973 **GP** *020
PHILLIPS, Ralph Louis. 4140 GALLIA ST 45662 #038-40-1942 L1942 **GP OS** *075
SUDHAKARAN, Emmanuel. ■ 45662 #495-70-1973 L1979 **CD IM** *020 †20

NEW BREMEN – AUGLAIZE

BOWLING, John Francis. 03920 SOUTHLAND RD, SOUTHLAND FAMILY MEDICINE 45869 #028-34-1960 L1961 **FM** *020
HEAP, James Russell. 44 S WASHINGTON ST 45869 #003-01-1975 L1994 **OM EM** *030 †18 ‡
HOLZER, Franklin. ■ 45869 #869-07-1967 L1989 **OTO HNS** *071 †45
KAKARLA, Rajendra Prasad. 03920 SOUTHLAND RD 45869 #495-58-1982 L1991 **IM** *020 †20
LUEDEKE, James David. 03920 SOUTHLAND RD, PO BOX 127 45869 #038-43-1981 L1983 **FM** *020 †18 ‡
YEH, Eric Minghui. 149 SAINT CLAIR PL 45869 #016-06-1995 L2002 **OBG** *020 †30

NEW CARLISLE – CLARK

DEVATHA, Ashok P. 432 N MAIN ST 45344 #496-22-1989 L1997 **FM** *020 †18 ‡
GALLARDO, Estella Maria. 201 E LAKE AVE 45344 #038-40-1988 L1989 **FM** *020 †18
VISHNUPAD, Kalpana K. 1701 ADDISON NEW CARLSL RD 45344 #495-35-1983 L1998 **P** *020 †75

NEW CONCORD – MUSKINGUM

DAOU, Aline Georges. 1 E MAIN ST, STE 200A 43762 #605-01-1999 L2006 **FM** *020 †18
KEARFOTT, Kitrina Lou. 1 E MAIN ST, STE 2 43762 #055-02-1986 L1989 **FM** *020 †18
MARSH, Howard John. 1 E MAIN ST, STE 200B 43762 #038-06-1966 L1966 **FM** *020
OVERHOLSER, Wm Huntley. 1 E MAIN ST, STE 100A 43762 #038-40-1971 L1971 **FM** *020 †18
SMITH, Melissa Nicole. 163 STORMONT ST, MUSKINGUM COLLEGE 43762 #038-06-2007 L2007 **PD** *012
SPRAGG, Carl Edward. 71 W MAIN ST 43762 #038-40-1955 L1955 **FM OS** *071 †18

NEW HOLLAND – PICKAWAY

CHEN, Chuan-Feng. ■ 43145 #385-02-1963 L1979 **OTO** *075

NEW LEBANON – MONTGOMERY

BINGHAM, Dennis Al, Jr. 550 W MAIN ST 45345 #038-45-1992 L1994 **IM** *020 †20
CHUNG, Jin Baik. 220 E MAIN ST, SAMARITAN FAMILY CARE 45345 #583-10-1968 L1978 **FM GS** *020 †18
THIELE, Melanie Green. ■ 45345 #038-45-1988 L1990 **PD** *074

NEW LEXINGTON – PERRY

CRAPES, Susan Ellen. 409 LINCOLN PARK DR 43764 #038-40-1975 L1976 **FM** *020 †18
MC CREERY, Jerry David. 409 LINCOLN PARK DR 43764 #038-40-1983 L1984 **FM OBS** *020 †18
REICHLEY, Anthony Emmett. 1625 AIRPORT RD, BOX 596 43764 #038-45-1992 L1995 **FM** *020 †18

NEW LONDON – HURON

ERLENBACH, Harold Donald. 43 S MAIN ST 44851 #038-06-1956 L1956 **IM** *071

■ = Address Information Privacy Protected

HARWOOD, Jeffrey Allen. 187 W MAIN ST 44851 #038-43-1986 L1987 **FM OM** *020 †18
PAI DHUNGAT, Avadhut Camu. ■ 44851 #495-01-1967 L1977 **PD** *020

NEW MADISON – DARKE

IDRIS, Syed Ali Shan. ■ 45346 #704-20-1997 L2005 **MPD** *020 †20

NEW MIDDLETOWN – MAHONING

GUGLIOTTI, Matthew Guy. ■ 44442 #038-45-2007 L2007 **FP** *012
MATHEW, Ajith. ■ 44442 #422-01-2004 L2004 **NPM** *012

NEW PARIS – PREBLE

AHN, Jeung Woo. 206 CEDAR SPRINGS RD 45347 #583-09-1968 L1977 **FM** *020

NEW PHILADELPHIA – TUSCARAWAS

BOWERS, Larry Herbert. 617 WABASH AVE NW 44663 #038-40-1968 L1968 **OTO** *020 †45
BRAVO, Daniel. 134 2ND ST SW 44663 #319-01-1964 L1971 **GS** *071 †85
CHARETTE, Dennis Joseph. 155 MCDONALD DR NW 44663 #055-02-1999 L2001 **FM** *020 †18
DOUGHTEN, Philip T. ■ 44663 #038-06-1941 L1946 **FPG** *071
OZA, Bharat H. 656 S BROADWAY ST 44663 #495-23-1967 L1977 **IM** *020
PACKOVICH, Milan John. 306 W HIGH AVE 44663 #016-02-1961 L1963 **IM OM** *020
PINELLI, Jose Luciano. ■ 44663 #132-04-1969 L1969 **GS** *071
ROBINSON, Donald David. 1260 MONROE ST NW STE 15H, NEW PHILADELPHIA VA. CLINI 44663 #654-01-1981 L1992 **IM** *020 †20
SHAH, Hasmukh Himatlal. 119 2ND ST NE 44663 #495-20-1966 L1973 **FM** *020
VARRATI, Nicholas Vincent. 306 W HIGH AVE 44663 #038-40-1983 L1984 **OM PMM** *020 †18
ZELLER, James F. ■ 44663 #035-06-1952 L1957 **GS** *071

NEW RICHMOND – CLERMONT

EHA, James Anthony. ■ 45157 #038-40-1961 L1961 **D** *071
JONES, John Paul, Jr. ■ 45157 #048-12-1957 L1957 **GP PHP** *071
KENDLER, Ady. ■ 45157 #016-02-1992 L2003 **NP** *020 †50
KOO, David G. 1050 OLD US 52, NEW RICHMOND FAMILY PRACTI 45157 #038-41-1996 L1999 **FM** *020 †18
REYNOLDS, Ronald Davison. 1050 OLD US HIGHWAY 52 45157 #025-01-1984 L1985 **FM** *020 †18

NEW WASHINGTON – CRAWFORD

BARTH, L James. 120 W MAIN ST, BOX 207 44854 #038-40-1958 L1958 **GP** *071
KENNY, Daniel Patrick. 740 BUCYRUS ST 44854 #038-40-1958 L1958 **FM** *071 †18
KHAVARI, Fereshte. 120 W MAIN ST, NEW WASHINGTON MEDICAL PRA 44854 #038-45-1997 L1998 **FM** *020 †18
NIESET, Brad Allen. 202 W MANSFIELD ST, NEW WASHINGTON MEDICAL CEN 44854 #422-01-1999 L1999 **FM** *020 †18

NEWARK – LICKING

ABAD, John Philamer Vila. 843 N 21ST ST STE 103 43055 #748-10-2000 L2003 **FM** *020 †18
ABDELMESSIH, Hanaa. 1865 TAMARACK RD 43055 #050-02-1989 L1992 **PD** *020 †55
ABDELMESSIH, Mourad. 1916 TAMARACK RD 43055 #915-04-1983 L1996 **N** *020
ABDULLA, Hani Mohammad. 399 E MAIN ST 43055 #539-06-1981 L1986 **NEP IM** *020 †20
ANDERSON, John Peyton, Jr. 1320 W MAIN ST 43055 #004-01-1965 L1972 **GP** *020 †50
BALTISBERGER, Richard A. 1865 TAMARACK RD, CORP. 43055 #037-01-1995 L1996 **PD** *020 †55
BAUN, Robert Russell. 1865 TAMARACK RD 43055 #038-44-1994 L1995 **PD** *020 †55
BAY, William Howard. 1320 W MAIN ST 43055 #038-40-1971 L1971 **IM NEP** *020 †20
BORDERS, Phillip Lloyd. 200 MESSIMER DR 43055 #038-44-1991 L1993 **P** *020 †75
BULAS, Mieczyslaw A. PO BOX 948 43058 #407-10-1955 L1961 **DR NM** *071
BURGHARDT, Michael Bruce. 1320 W MAIN ST 43055 #028-34-1964 L1992 **PD** *020
CAIRNS, Craig Blake. 1320 W MAIN ST, LICKING MEMORIAL HOSP 43055 #038-40-1974 L1974 **MDM OM** *030 †70,18
CHERDRON, Darryl Robt. 1320 W MAIN ST 43055 #038-40-1974 L1974 **PTH** *020 †50
CHERUKURI, Subbarao. 2112 CHERRY VALLEY RD 43055 #495-11-1966 L1974 **R** *020 †80
CHITTURI, Punyavathi. 1320 W MAIN ST 43055 #495-50-1980 L1994 **AN** *020 †05
CHITTURI, Srihari. 1320 W MAIN ST, ATTN ANESTHESIA DEPARTMENT 43055 #495-58-1978 L1992 **AN** *020 †05
CHOE, Eunkoo. 2000 TAMARACK RD 43055 #583-02-1963 L1971 **AN** *020 †05
DAVIDOFF, Elliot. 1371 W MAIN ST 43055 #035-09-1971 L1977 **OPH** *020 †35
DAWSON, Bruce. ■ 43055 #038-40-1974 L1974 **FM** *075
DOMENICO, Don Ross. ■ 43055 #016-43-1981 L1988 **PTH HEM** *020 †50
DULL, Pamela Ann. 399 E MAIN ST 43055 #038-40-1984 L1985 **FM** *020 †18
EHRSAM, Gerald Robt. 120 MCMILLEN DR, MEDICINE 43055 #038-40-1973 L1973 **IM** *020 †20
FALKENHAIN, Michael E. 1320 W MAIN ST 43055 #028-34-1988 L1992 **NEP** *020 †20
FARGHALY, Samar Ali. 1320 W MAIN ST 43055 #915-03-1994 L2000 **IM** *100 †20
FILIPOW, Wesley. 1320 W MAIN ST 43055 #038-40-1974 L1974 **FM** *020
FONDRIEST, Joseph Earl. 2112 CHERRY VALLEY RD 43055 #038-41-1989 L1994 **DR** *020 †80
GALVAN, Juan Rene. 2000 TAMARACK RD 43055 #275-01-1960 L1968 **AN** *071
GATENS, Timothy Robt. 1320 W MAIN ST 43055 #028-46-1978 L1979 **PM** *020 †60
GITTENS, Shelley Maria. 1865 TAMARACK RD 43055 #038-45-1995 L1999 **PD** *020 †55
GOLDENBERG, Ilya G.. ■ 43055 #913-01-1996 L2000 **IM** *020 †20
GONZALES, Leonardo P. 36 MCMILLEN DR 43055 #748-02-1971 L1985 **OBG FM** *075
GOODYEAR, Michael D, II. 1970 TAMARACK RD 43055 #038-02-1994 L2000 **GS** *020 †85
GOVIER, Ann Verlene. ■ 43055 #030-05-1979 L1984 **AN** *020 †05
GRAUER, John Gerhard. 15 MESSIMER DR 43055 #016-01-1985 L1986 **OBG** *020 †30

GREATHOUSE, Talya R. 150 MCMILLEN DR, LICKING MEMORIAL FAM PRACT 43055 #038-40-1996 L1997 **FM** *020 †18
HALL, Thomas Joe. 1865 TAMARACK RD 43055 #038-40-1976 L1979 **EM OM** *071 †16
HELDMAN, Debra Ann. 1320 W MAIN ST 43055 #038-40-1982 L1987 **CD** *020 †20
HOLT, Mark Allen. 1272 W MAIN ST BLDG 2, NEWARK ORTHOPEDICS 43055 #038-41-1987 L1988 **ORS OSM** *020 †40
HOOK, Henry Lynn. ■ 43055 #038-40-1948 L1948 **PUD CD** *071 †20
HUNTER, Roberta J. 1320 W MAIN ST, GASTROENTERLOGY DEPARTMENT 43055 #025-01-1991 L2005 **GE** *020 †20
JACKSON, David Moore. 1980 TAMARACK RD 43055 #038-40-1980 L1982 **ORS** *020 †40
JEFFRIES, James M, III. 1272 W MAIN ST, BLDG 2 43055 #033-05-1983 L2007 **PS** *020 †65
JONES, Donald Gordon. 36 MCMILLEN DR 43055 #047-06-1956 L1962 **GYN** *071 †30
JONES, Jacqueline Johnson. 1320 W MAIN ST 43055 #011-03-1978 L1984 **ON HEM** *020
JUAN, Alex Duyongco. 1970 TAMARACK RD 43055 #748-11-1975 L1983 **GS TS** *020
KAMPS, Robert Richard. 1320 W MAIN ST 43055 #038-40-1973 L1976 **IM** *020 †20
KASSUR, Michal Maciej. 200 MESSIMER DR 43055 #759-03-1982 L1992 **P** *020 †75
KASTENS, Kipp Verling. 65 MESSIMER DR 43055 #038-40-1973 L1973 **CHP** *020 †75
KELCH, Harold Eugene. ■ 43055 #028-02-1956 L1957 **GYN OBS** *071 †30
KILLION, Jennifer Dawn. 1920 TAMARACK RD 43055 #038-44-2001 L2001 **PD** *020 †55
KIM, Yoon Seong. 2112 CHERRY VALLEY RD 43055 #583-02-1969 L1978 **R** *062 †80
KNOBELOCH, William Edwin. 1920 TAMARACK RD 43055 #038-40-1998 L1999 **PD** *020 †55
KRET, Bassam. 1320 W MAIN ST, LICKING MEMORIAL HOSPITAL 43055 #875-01-1986 L2002 **IM** *020 †20
LAW, Mark Stephen. 1371 W MAIN ST, CENTER FOR SIGHT 43055 #051-04-1987 L1992 **OPH IM** *020 †35
LEE, Chang Sup. 1272 W MAIN ST 43055 #583-02-1958 L1973 **GS** *071 †85
LEE, Owen. 2112 CHERRY VALLEY RD 43055 #023-01-1979 L1984 **DR NM** *020 †80
LEMAY, Diane Marie. 399 E MAIN ST, PRACTICE 43055 #038-45-1988 L1989 **PD** *020 †55
LEMMON, Todd Fraser. 15 MESSIMER DR, LICKING MEMORIAL WOMEN'S H 43055 #038-41-1988 L1991 **OBG** *020 †30
LEWIS, Donald John. 1902 TAMARACK RD 43055 #010-02-1986 L1996 **U** *020 †95
LEYMASTER, Kirsten Ruth. 1960 TAMARACK RD STE D, MCDONALD PEDIATRICS 43055 #038-41-1999 L1999 **PD** *020 †55
LINKE, Kaye Ann. 1320 W MAIN ST, LICKING MEMORIAL HOSPITAL 43055 #038-40-1984 L1986 **ON IM** *020 †20
LONG, Robert Wilson. ■ 43055 #056-06-1961 L1973 **PTH OS** *020 †50
MC BRIDE, Donald W. 2112 CHERRY VALLEY RD 43055 #039-01-1983 L1987 **DR** *020 †80
MC DONALD, Donna Jean. 1960 TAMARACK RD # D 43055 #020-12-1982 L1985 **PD** *020 †55
MILLS, Turner Thos. 150 MCMILLEN DR 43055 #038-40-1959 L1959 **FM** *071
MILTON, Alana Christen. 1320 W MAIN ST 43055 #018-03-2002 L2002 **PD** *020 †55
MITCHELL, Mark Aloysius. 120 MCMILLEN DR, MEDICINE 43055 #038-40-1973 L1976 **IM GP** *020 †20
MONTALTO, Paul N. 1272 W MAIN ST # 2 43055 #038-40-1950 L1950 **FM GYN** *072
MORRIS, Angela Marie. 270 GOOSEPOND RD, ANMED HEALTH-FAMILY PRACTI 43055 #045-01-2004 L2007 **FM** *020 †20
MORRIS, William J. 1320 W MAIN ST 43055 #038-40-1984 L1986 **GE IM** *020 †20
ONG, Lucena Lim. 843 N 21ST ST, STE 105 43055 #748-11-1972 L1989 **GP PD** *020
PACHT, Eric Reed. 1272 W MAIN ST, BLDG 2 43055 #056-05-1980 L1981 **PUD CCM** *020 †20
PARK, Seung Hah. 2000 TAMARACK RD 43055 #583-01-1973 L1983 **AN** *020 †05
PARKER, John Jos. ■ 43055 #038-40-1987 L1992 **EM** *020 †16
PARKER, Kenneth Carroll. 88 MCMILLEN DR 43055 #038-41-2001 L2006 **OTO** *020 †45
PASLEY, Larry Norman. 1272 W MAIN ST STE 3 43055 #038-40-1976 L1978 **GS VS** *020 †85
PATEL, Shantilal H. 2000 TAMARACK RD 43055 #495-22-1971 L1984 **AN** *020
PETRYK, Thomas Kelley. 1930 TAMARACK RD 43055 #038-45-1989 L1990 **FM** *020 †18
PFAU, Brad Timothy. 1920 TAMARACK RD 43055 #038-40-1991 L1992 **PD** *020 †55
PLUMMER, Raymond Guy. ■ 43058 #038-40-1935 L1935 **GP AN** *071
PROUTY, Richard Ross. 1272 W MAIN ST # 5 43055 #038-40-1964 L1964 **OTO** *020 †45
QUIMJIAN, John D. 1980 TAMARACK RD 43055 #038-41-1981 L1982 **ORS** *020 †40
RASHEED, Husain A. 1032 BUCKEYE AVE 43055 #495-77-1997 L2004 **HO** *020 †20
REDDY, Sudhathi Chennuru. 1032 BUCKEYE AVE 43055 #496-35-1997 L2000 **HO** *020 †20 ‡
REDMOND, Paul Chas. 200 MESSIMER DR 43055 #035-01-1965 L1967 **GS** *020 †85
REED, Nicholas Eugene. 15 MESSIMER DR 43055 #038-40-1965 L1965 **OBG OS** *020 †30
RINGLE, Kurt Anthony. 1912 TAMARACK RD 43055 #038-40-1981 L1981 **FM** *020 †18
SAVOLAINE, Edward Russell. 2112 CHERRY VALLEY RD 43055 #038-41-1962 L1962 **DR RNR** *020 †80
SCHULTZ, Randolph Oliver. 1930 TAMARACK RD, ALLIANCE PRIMARY CARE 43055 #038-41-1993 L1994 **FM** *020 †18
SCOTT, M Jane. 1320 W MAIN ST, HOSPITAL 43055 #038-41-1981 L1991 **EM** *020 †16
SEIN OHN, Karen E. 1272 W MAIN ST, BLDG 2 43055 #566-01-1985 L2002 **GE** *020 †20
SHAHINFAR, Shahin. 1651 W MAIN ST, BLOOMBERG EYE CTR 43055 #016-11-1990 L1995 **OPH** *020 †35
SIMON, Richard Eugene. 1272 W MAIN ST, PRACTICE-MOUNDBUILDERS 43055 #038-40-1975 L1975 **FM** *020 †20
SONEK, Mojmir Geo. ■ 43055 #286-04-1952 L1982 **GYN** *020
SPIRIDONIDIS, Charalampos. 1032 BUCKEYE AVE 43055 #418-02-1978 L1984 **HEM ON** *020 †20
STARINCHAK, Edward Jos. 1320 W MAIN ST 43055 #038-40-1963 L1963 **OTO HNS** *020 †45
STEVENSON, Matt Curtis. 65 MESSIMER DR 43055 #038-40-1995 L1996 **P** *020 †75
SUBLER, David Edward. 1320 W MAIN ST, LICKING MEMORIAL HOSPITAL 43055 #038-40-1987 L1993 **GE** *020 †20
SUTLIFF, Gary Dean. 1930 TAMARACK RD 43055 #038-43-1995 L1996 **FM** *020 †18
SWEDA, Susan Gail. 1272 W MAIN ST, N/A 43055 #038-43-1980 L1989 **AN** *020 †05
SZEKELY, Keith Joseph. 1272 W MAIN ST BLDG 5, PRACTICE 43055 #041-02-1995 L1999 **FM** *020 †18
TANNERU, Padmaja Rao. 42 MESSIMER DR 43055 #496-31-2000 L2006 **IM** *020 †20
TEWOLDEMEDHIN, Hintsa A. 42 MESSIMER DR, PRIMIER HEALTH INC 43055 #366-01-1988 L2002 **IM** *020 †20
THORNE, Cecil Michael. 1320 W MAIN ST 43055 #407-32-1957 L1965 **PTH** *071 †50
TIMSON, Katrina Marie. 399 E MAIN ST 43055 #055-02-1988 L1989 **FM** *020 †18
TORCHIA, Mary Jean. 1320 W MAIN ST 43055 #038-43-1984 L2007 **AN** *020 †05
TREFELNER, Eric Chas. 1320 W MAIN ST 43055 #016-11-1985 L2002 **DR RNR** *020 †80
VARGAS, Rene Corvera. ■ 43055 #748-01-1962 L1984 **GS GP** *075
VENKATARAMAN, Vijaya. 1320 W MAIN ST 43055 #496-09-1992 L2006 **IM NEP** *020 †20
VERDE, Katrina Kay. 150 MCMILLEN DR 43055 #038-45-1998 L2004 **FM** *020 †18
WAGGONER, Carl David. 2269 CHERRY VALLEY RD SE 43055 #017-20-1975 L1979 **FM PLM** *020 †18

WALKER, David M. 1930 TAMARACK RD, MEDICAL AND SURGICAL ASSOC 43055 #023-12-1991 L1992 **P PFP** *020 †75

WALLIS, Barrett Jeffrey. 1320 W MAIN ST, GASTROENTEROLOGY 43055 #035-20-1979 L2006 **GE HEP** *020 †20

WALTHER, John W, Jr. 399 E MAIN ST, FAMILY MEDICAL CENTER 43055 #041-13-1967 L1968 **FM GP** *020 ‡

WEE, Hang Sing Sui. 1320 W MAIN ST 43055 #748-10-1970 L1979 **CD IM** *020

WESTERHEIDE, Edward Lee. 1980 TAMARACK RD 43055 #038-40-1993 L1998 **ORS** *020 †40

WHISMAN, Pattye Ayn. 150 MCMILLEN DR 43055 #038-40-1975 L1975 **FM** *020

WHITNEY, Richard Nason. 200 MESSIMER DR, SHEPHERD HILL 43055 #048-12-1978 L2001 **ADM PMM** *020 †16 ‡

WILMER, William Arnold. 1320 W MAIN ST 43055 #038-43-1988 L1990 **NEP** *050 †20

WOOD, Thom Doddridge. 1320 W MAIN ST, LICKING MEMORIAL HOSPITAL 43055 #038-40-1975 L1975 **EM** *020 †16

YABLONSKI, Maureen Yvonne. 30 MESSIMER DR, MOUNDVIEW OBSTETRICS & 43055 #035-15-1986 L1990 **OBG** *020 †30

YAKHMI, Bhupinder. 65 MESSIMER DR 43055 #495-01-1950 L1980 **P GS** *020

NEWBURY – GEAUGA

MARTINEZ, Ana F. 12171 KINSMAN RD 44065 #042-01-1984 L1996 **P** *020 †75

WILLIAMS, David John. ■ 44065 #038-40-2007 L2007 **P** *012

NEWCOMERSTOWN – TUSCARAWAS

AGRICOLA, Waldemar R. 232 CROSS ST 43832 #038-06-1938 L1938 **FM** *071

BURRIER, David Jeffrey. 60881 COUNTY ROAD 9 43832 #038-40-1994 L1995 **FM** *020 †18

NEWTON FALLS – TRUMBULL

PATEL, Nitin Kanubhai. 1978 MILTON BLVD 44444 #495-23-1983 L1989 **IM** *020 †20

RAFII, Mostafa. 340 RIDGE RD 44444 #517-01-1963 L1973 **IM** *071

YAP, Pedro T. 1978 MILTON BLVD 44444 #748-01-1962 L1971 **GS GP** *071

NILES – TRUMBULL

ALLOUSH, Nabil. 1252 YOUNGSTOWN WARREN RD 44446 #875-02-1975 L1982 **CD** *020 †20

BORTS, Frederick T. ■ 44446 #010-02-1975 L1980 **R** *020 †80

CILETTI, Michael Thos. 425 ROBBINS AVE 44446 #038-44-1989 L1991 **FM** *020 †18

CORDOVA, Joseph Ronald. 1254 YOUNGSTOWN WARREN RD, STE A 44446 #422-01-1995 L1997 **FM** *020 †18

FERRARA, Melissa Valantin. 918 YOUNGSTOWN WARREN RD, STE C 44446 #038-44-2002 L2002 **PD** *020 †55

GEORGE, Pradeesh Mathew. ■ 44446 #018-75-2007, ▲ L2007 *012

LAZARO, Benigno P, Jr. 1254 YOUNGSTOWN WARREN RD, # 3A 44446 #748-01-1987 L1995 **FM** *020 †18

MONTALVO-LEFEBRE, Luis. ■ 44446 #275-01-1953 L1965 **OS** *020

SHETH, Yogesh Ochhavlal. 940 ROBBINS AVE 44446 #495-37-1963 L1972 **IM** *020

TING, Manuel Tan. 624 VIENNA AVE 44446 #748-01-1962 L1969 **IM** *020

WILLIAMS, Mary Beth. 327 VIENNA AVE STE 1 44446 #038-40-1980 L1980 **IM** *075

YOCUM, Teresa Ann. 918 YOUNGSTOWN WARREN RD, STE C 44446 #038-44-2002 L2002 **PD** *020 †55

NORTH BALTIMORE – WOOD

OLSON, Oscar Carl. 209 BRIAR HILL RD, STE B 45872 #062-01-1968 L1995 **FM** *020

ROBERTS, William H. ■ 45872 #038-06-1951 L1951 **FM** *071 †18

ROBERTS, Wm Henry, III. 328 N MAIN ST 45872 #038-40-1978 L1982 **PTH** *020 †50

NORTH BEND – HAMILTON

BIEHL, Gary Richard. ■ 45052 #038-45-1980 L1981 **FM OS** *020 †18

CASSIDY, Marc Andrew. ■ 45052 #038-41-2003 L2003 **AN** *020

MEYERS, Jessica Leigh. ■ 45052 #038-45-2008 *012

MORELLI, Jeanine M. ■ 45052 #035-15-1987 L1994 **FM** *020 †18

NORTH CANTON – STARK

ADAMICK, Christine Marie. 6525 MARKET AVE N, STE 100 44721 #025-07-1995 L2002 **D** *020 †15

AGUJIOBI, Obinna Eugene. ■ 44720 #690-04-2000 L2007 **IM** *012

AHMAD, Arsal. 6651 FRANK AVE NW 44720 #033-05-2002 L2006 **PM** *020 †60

ANDERSON, Stanley R. 6877 WALES AVE NW 44720 #038-41-1986 L1987 **FM OM** *020 †18

ANDREA, John. ■ 44720 #016-06-1952 L1952 **PD** *071 †55

ARNOLD, Ryan Wells. ■ 44720 #040-02-2004 L2005 **DR** *012

BARTOS, Paul. 4860 FRANK RD NW 44720 #041-02-1979 L1980 **FM IMG** *020 †18

BARTRAM, Chester E, Jr. 6046 WHIPPLE AVE NW 44720 #038-40-1969 L1969 **IM ID** *020 †20

BHATT, Sharad Hariprasad. 907 S MAIN ST, P O BOX 2367 44720 #495-98-1980 L1990 **P** *020 †75

BILLUPS, Timothy F. ■ 44720 #038-43-1992 L1993 **EM** *020 †16

BOTSCHNER, Andrew Walter. 1360 S MAIN ST 44720 #038-06-1959 L1959 **OBG** *020 †30

BOUTROS, Nihad M. 5590 LAUBY RD, STE 2 44720 #875-01-1989 L1993 **PCC** *020 †20

BRUNO, Joanna Moore. 6046 WHIPPLE AVE NW 44720 #038-43-2002 L2002 **IM** *020

BUSSAN, Reita Ruth Meyer. ■ 44709 #039-01-1949 L1955 **OBG** *071

CANDAGE, Raymond Lester. ■ 44720 #038-43-2004 L2004 **GS** *012

CARUSO, Carrie Lee. ■ 44720 #038-44-2007 L2007 **IM** *012

CONNELLY, Steven Eugene. 6046 WHIPPLE AVE NW 44720 #038-40-1982 L1985 **IM** *020 †20

CONSTANTINIDI, Emil R. ■ 44720 #781-03-1954 L1974 **P IM** *020

DEPUE, Kent Andrew. ■ 44720 #038-45-2005 L2005 **PD** *012

DI GIACOMO, Peter E. 6555 FRANK AVE NW 44720 #038-75-1990, ▲ L1991 **OBG** *020 †30

DJURIC, Vladimir. 6651 FRANK AVE NW 44720 #038-43-1990 L1991 **PM** *020 †60

FAYEN, William Thos. 6046 WHIPPLE AVE NW 44720 #038-06-1977 L1978 **IM** *020 †20

FORD, Lisa Marie. ■ 44720 #011-03-1990 L2006 **NPM** *020 †55

FRANGOS, Michelle Fran. ■ 44709 #038-40-2003 L2003 **EM** *020

GADE-PULIDO, Karen. 6651 FRANK AVE NW 44720 #036-07-1992 L1996 **PM** *072 †60

GIBBENS, Gregory Ray. ■ 44720 #023-01-1977 L1978 **FM** *020 †18

GONZAGA, Josefa. ■ 44720 #748-02-1934 *071

GRAY, Gregory Mark. 6407 FRANK AVE NW 44720 #038-40-1974 L1975 **OPH** *020 †35

GREENFIELD, Antje L. 8040 CLEVELAND AVE NW, UNIT 200 44720 #408-30-1994 L2000 **DR** *020 †80

HABAN, Gregory Alan. 4860 FRANK RD NW 44720 #038-43-1975 L1976 **FM** *020 †18

HAKE, Susan R B. 6512 WHIPPLE AVE NW 44720 #038-44-1992 L1993 **FM** *020 †18

HANDWORK, Lawrence W. 6046 WHIPPLE AVE NW, NORTH CANTON MED FOUNDATIO 44720 #038-44-1986 L1988 **PD PSM** *020 †55

HAUPT, Kathy Marie. 6512 WHIPPLE AVE NW 44720 #038-44-1997 L1998 **FM** *020 †18

HAWKINS, Wade Scott. 4860 FRANK RD NW 44720 #038-44-1991 L1992 **FM PTH** *020 †50,18

HOFMANN, Lawrence Vincent. 6046 WHIPPLE AVE NW 44720 #041-02-1968 L1978 **PD** *020 †55

HUMPHREY, John Brooks, Jr. 6046 WHIPPLE AVE NW 44720 #041-02-1968 L1976 **IM** *020 †20

JENRETTE, Marilyn Spragg. 133 WILBUR DR NE 44720 #038-40-1980 L1983 **FM** *020 †18 ‡

JOHNSON, Clifford Gary. 6046 WHIPPLE AVE NW 44720 #035-46-1981 L1984 **IM** *020 †20

KELTY, Richard Harry. ■ 44720 #025-01-1943 L1944 **IM** *071 †20

KEPPLE, Richard Newton. 7300 WHIPPLE AVE NW, STE 1 44720 #020-02-1974 L1975 **FM** *020 †20

KNOCH, Matthew Fitzgerald. ■ 44720 #038-40-2006 L2006 **IM** *012

KNOTEK, Nicole Anne. 6046 WHIPPLE AVE NW 44720 #038-44-2005 L2005 **PD** *012

KOLP, Joseph W. ■ 44709 #028-34-1946 L1947 **IM** *071

KUNZE, Peter Gerhard. 5080 AULTMAN RD 44720 #038-06-2000 L2001 **AN** *100

LAFONT, Gerardo. 907 S MAIN ST 44720 #847-04-1958 L1970 **P CHP** *071

LANZINGER, William David. ■ 44720 #038-44-2004 L2004 **GS** *012

LAUFER, Peter. 6046 WHIPPLE AVE NW 44720 #847-01-1974 L1984 **AI PDA** *020 †55,03

LIAO, Shaw-Meei. ■ 44720 #244-05-1971 L1976 **FM** *020

LICAUSE, Matthew John. 6512 WHIPPLE AVE NW 44720 #038-44-1985 L1987 **FM** *020 †18

MAKI, David Robt. 6046 WHIPPLE AVE NW 44720 #030-06-1960 L2007 **PD** *055

MALACAMAN, Edgardo Altura. 4900 FRANK RD NW 44720 #748-01-1967 L1972 **PD** *020 †55

MALIK, Farzana. ■ 44720 #704-02-1995 L2005 **IM** *012

MALLAMACI, David John. 6877 WALES AVE NW, JACKSON FAMILY PRACTICE 44720 #038-44-1997 L1998 **FM** *020 †18

MARCINKOSKI, Beth Ann. 6046 WHIPPLE AVE NW 44720 #038-44-1986 L1987 **PD** *020 †55

MARINO, Joseph Francis. 7300 WHIPPLE AVE NW STE 1, KUHNLEIN & MARTIN INC 44720 #041-01-1978 L1990 **IM OM** *020 †20

MARKLE, Cheryl May. 6046 WHIPPLE AVE NW, N CANTON MEDICAL FOUNDATIO 44720 #038-45-1992 L1994 **PD** *020 †55

MARSHALL, Howard E. 4860 FRANK RD NW 44720 #038-40-1976 L1976 **FM** *020 †18

MARTIN, Paul Christopher. 7300 WHIPPLE AVE NW, STE 1 44720 #005-19-1981 L1984 **FM OM** *020 †70,18

MASON, Grant Albert, Jr. 6046 WHIPPLE AVE NW 44720 #038-06-1965 L1965 **IM GE** *020 †20

MATHEWS, Daniel C. ■ 44720 #051-04-2006 L2007 **DR** *012

MAYHEW, Richard Franklin. ■ 44720 #038-06-1975 L1980 **GE IM** *020 †20

MC CARREN, Stephen Thos. ■ 44720 #038-44-1991 L1992 **AN** *020 †05

MCCARTER, John Douglas. ■ 44720 #038-40-2007 L2007 **OBG** *012

METZGER, Howard Martin. 6512 WHIPPLE AVE NW 44720 #041-09-1987 L1994 **FM** *020 †18

MIRANDE, Melanie Ethell. 6525 MARKET AVE N, STE 100 44721 #038-06-1994 L1997 **FM** *020 †18

NAROUZE, Samer Nabil. 7616 PEACHMONT AVE NW 44720 #915-04-1989 L2000 **APM** *020 †20

NELSON, David William. 6407 FRANK AVE NW 44720 #012-05-1987 L1992 **OPH FPS** *020 †35

NICOLETTI, Francesco G. 101 E MAPLE ST, THE HOOVER COMPANY 44720 #561-15-1966 L1971 **FM** *020 †18

NORCH, Elena K. 6447 FRANK AVE NW 44720 #654-01-1998 L2000 **IM** *020 †20

OBERLY, Julie Lynn. 1401 S MAIN ST, STE 101 44720 #038-44-1998 L1999 **IM** *020 †20

PANTELAS, Gust Geo. 6512 WHIPPLE AVE NW 44720 #038-44-1986 L1987 **FM** *020 †18

PAULINO, Corazon. ■ 44720 #748-01-1962 L1972 **OS** *074

PELLEGRINO, Mark Julius. 6651 FRANK AVE NW 44720 #038-40-1984 L1985 **PM** *020 †60

PERLMAN, Meade Andrew. 6046 WHIPPLE AVE NW 44720 #038-06-1974 L1977 **IM IMG** *020 †20

POWERS, Patricia Lizabeth. 6461 FRANK AVE NW 44720 #030-05-1984 L1988 **D** *020 †15

PRATT, Hugh M. 6046 WHIPPLE AVE NW 44720 #035-45-1950 L1960 **IM CD** *071 †20

PUSZ, Max Daniel. 7455 BENTLER AVE NE 44721 #038-44-2007 *012

RANK, Douglas Richard. 6046 WHIPPLE AVE NW, NORTH CANTON MEDICAL FOUND 44720 #005-11-1996 L1999 **IM** *020 †20

RENNECKER, Lynette Marie. 6046 WHIPPLE AVE NW, NORTH CANTON MEDICAL FDTN 44720 #038-44-1994 L1995 **IM** *020 †20

REYNOLDS, Thomas Lehman. 6513 FRANK AVE NW, CHILD & ADOL PSY 44720 #038-06-1990 L2004 **CHP ADP** *020 †75

RICCIARDI, Erin Nicole. ■ 44720 #038-44-2008 *012

RO, Jae Seon. 1606 PORTAGE ST NW, STARK MED AUCUPUNCTURE CLC 44720 #583-02-1966 L1975 **AN OS** *020

RODRIGUEZ, Daniel W. 6046 WHIPPLE AVE NW 44720 #649-30-1991 L1997 **IM** *020 †20

ROMERO, Jorge Raul. 6555 FRANK AVE NW 44720 #042-01-1987 L1992 **OBG** *020 †30

RONNING, Lawrence M, II. 6046 WHIPPLE AVE NW 44720 #055-01-1976 L1978 **OPH** *020 †35

ROSE, Mark Norman. ■ 44720 #025-01-1981 L1986 **LM GS** *020

ROWLEY, Gilbert Richards. 6046 WHIPPLE AVE NW, THE NORTH CANTON MED FOUND 44720 #038-40-1986 L1987 **IM** *020 †20

RUTTIG, Nathaniel Jacob. ■ 44720 #038-44-2000 L2007 **OPH** *012

SARADA, Dasu. ■ 44720 #495-50-1959 L1979 **PTH** *100 †50

SAWYER, Jenny Kay. 4860 FRANK RD NW 44720 #038-44-1996 L1997 **FM** *020 †18

SCHUMAKER, David Lee. 6046 WHIPPLE AVE NW 44720 #038-40-1974 L1975 **IM** *020 †20

SCHUSTER, John Soame. 6046 WHIPPLE AVE NW 44720 #038-06-1968 L1968 **IM** *020

SEIBERT, Dalson Henry. 4860 FRANK RD NW, FAMILY PHYSICIANS INC 44720 #038-43-2005 L2005 *012

SEIBERT, Megan Louise. 4860 FRANK RD NW, FAMILY PHYSICIANS INC 44720 #038-43-2005 L2005 **FP** *012

SETH, Kimberly Jo. 1580 YORKSHIRE TRCE SE 44709 #038-43-1999 L1999 **FM** *020 †18

SHEMORY, Thomas Allan. 4860 FRANK RD NW 44720 #038-43-1982 L1983 **FM** *020 †18

■ = Address Information Privacy Protected

SHEPARD, Mark Jos. 6100 WHIPPLE AVE NW, STE 180 44720 #028-02-1989 L1995 OSM ORS *020 †40

SHIRALI, Charulata S. 4900 FRANK RD NW, CANTON REHABILITATION CLIN 44720 #495-28-1961 L1972 PM N *020 †60

SHIRALI, Sudheer Ramdas. 4900 FRANK RD NW 44720 #495-28-1960 L1962 PD PDE *020 †55

SIMS, Andrea Nicole. ■ 44720 #038-44-2008 *012

SLIMAN, Robert James. 6046 WHIPPLE AVE NW 44720 #038-06-1983 L1985 IM *020 †20

SMITH, Hannelore. 6046 WHIPPLE AVE NW 44720 #154-07-1969 L1979 PD *020 †55

SPANGLER, Theodore Lynn. ■ 44720 #038-41-2002 L2002 EM *100 †16

STAUS, Mary Ellen. 6046 WHIPPLE AVE NW 44720 #030-06-1980 L1983 D *020 †15

THIRUPPATHI, Damothara. 4900 FRANK RD NW 44720 #495-16-1965 L1974 PD EM *020 †55

TOBIAS, Thurman Edward. 6046 WHIPPLE AVE NW 44720 #035-45-1963 L1968 R *020 †80

WARBURTON, Ralph Thos. 6046 WHIPPLE AVE NW 44720 #038-06-1933 L1933 IM *071 †20

WATTERSON, Reich Leis, Jr. 44709 #038-06-1952 L1952 PD PM *071 †55

WEAVER, Steven Michael. 6046 WHIPPLE AVE NW 44720 #038-44-1990 L1991 IM *020 †20

WERNER, Gary Lee. 6046 WHIPPLE AVE NW 44720 #041-12-1971 L1978 GS *020 †85

WHITTIER, Frederick C, Jr. 6046 WHIPPLE AVE NW 44720 #016-43-1965 L1986 NEP IM *020 †20 ‡

WYMYSLO, Edmund Louis, Jr. 4860 FRANK RD NW 44720 #038-43-1988 L1989 FM *020 †18

ZADINSKY, Leo Walter. ■ 44720 #041-09-1948 L1949 GP OM *071

NORTH JACKSON — MAHONING

OSBORNE, Jay Richard. PO BOX 487, 10850 MAHONING AVE 44451 #038-44-1988 L1989 FM *020 †18

REESEY, Walter Clare. 439 S SALEM WARREN RD, NORTH JACKSON 44451 #038-41-1957 L1957 FM PD *020

NORTH LIMA — MAHONING

DONATO, Dylia E. ■ 44452 #308-01-1986 L1990 PD *020

MC GRATH, Sean Thomas. ■ 44452 #038-44-2003 L2003 PM *020

MURPHY, Leslie A. 11993 SOUTH AVE 44452 #038-44-1999 L1999 FM *020 †18

NORTH OLMSTED — CUYAHOGA

ABAZA, Hadeel. ■ 44070 #038-43-2001 L2006 ORS *020

BAKER, Abdul Abu. ■ 44070 #038-45-2007 L2007 FP *012

BELARDO, Michelle J. 24700 LORAIN RD, STE 302 44070 #038-44-1993 L1995 OBG *020 †30

BLAZEK, Matthew C. 24700 LORAIN RD, STE 302 44070 #038-40-1980 L1983 FM *020 †18

BLOOD, William. 26777 LORAIN RD, STE 600 44070 #038-06-1993 L1995 GS *020

BOEHM, Gregory Xavier. 26777 LORAIN RD STE 716 44070 #038-41-1976 L1977 P CHP *020 †75

BROOKS, Lizabeth Ann. 24700 LORAIN RD, STE 304 44070 #016-11-1998 L2002 OBG *020

BUNDE, Donald Wm. 24700 LORAIN RD, STE 304 44070 #038-40-1955 L1955 OBG *071 †30

CAMACHO, Mauricio. 24700 LORAIN RD 44070 #264-04-1962 L1972 OBG *020

CARNS, Megan Frances. ■ 44070 #038-43-2008 *012

CHARLTON, Edgar Lee. 186 VISTA CIR, EDGAR L CHARLTON MD 44070 #038-40-1978 L1981 *020

CRAVEN, Paul Wm. 4859 DOVER CENTER RD STE 7 44070 #038-40-1980 L1981 OPH *020 †35

DIRANDO, Jesse Mark. 5690 GREAT NORTHERN BLVD A 44070 #038-43-1988 L1989 EM *020 †16

EL-DAHB, Ashraf Heshmat F. 24700 LORAIN RD 44070 #915-02-1975 L1988 OBG *020 †30

FERNBACH, John. 24700 LORAIN RD, STE 304 44070 #957-01-1967 L1974 OBG *020 †30

FITCH, Ernestine Louise. 4859 DOVER CENTER RD # 10 44070 #036-01-1981 L1983 FM *020 †18

GLASENAPP, Michael Patric. 6679 BRETTON RIDGE DR 44070 #038-41-2008 *012

GRAUEL, George Linus. ■ 44070 #038-40-1968 L1968 R *020

GREENE, Giesele Mona. 25000 COUNTRY CLUB BLVD, STE 255A 44070 #010-03-1978 L1980 IM *020 †20

GUADIZ, Isabelita E. 24700 LORAIN RD, STE 104 44070 #748-01-1974 L1980 PD *020 †55

HOUSTON, Sarah Nicole. ■ 44070 #038-45-2007 *012

JHAVERI, Nalini Ramesh. 24700 LORAIN RD, STE 304 44070 #495-01-1961 L1970 OBG *020 †30

JHAVERI, Stasia. 24700 LORAIN RD, STE 304 44070 #038-40-1994 L1997 OBG *020 †30

KAFILMOUT, Khalid. 28067 FORESTWOOD PKWY 44070 #528-01-1961 L1976 IM *020

KLEIN, Mary Ruth. 25761 LORAIN RD, FL 2 44070 #038-43-1995 L1996 FM *020 †18

KOSMIDIS, Alexander P. 4519 WESTVIEW DR 44070 #038-06-2007 L2007 TY *012

KUNAM, Srinivasa Reddy. ■ 44070 #495-11-1999 L2003 IM *020 †20

KURTZ, Erin Lynne. ■ 44070 #028-78-2007, ▲ L2007 *012

LIEBL, Max Edward. ■ 44070 #056-06-2005 L2005 GS *012

LITTMAN, Heidi Joy. 24700 LORAIN RD, STE 201 44070 #038-06-1992 L1993 PD *020 †55

LUCAS, Jennifer Lynn. ■ 44070 #038-40-2005 D *012

MEHLE, Mark Emil. 25761 LORAIN RD, 3RD FL 44070 #038-44-1987 L1991 OTO HNS *020 †45

MOGHAL, Alinawaz K. 28895 LORAIN RD STE 200, CLEVELAND THERAPY CTR 44070 #704-02-1956 L1969 GP GS *020 †85

NEMETH, Attila Stephen, Jr. ■ 44070 #038-43-2005 L2005 IM *012

PEARCE, Anjali Doll. ■ 44070 #038-06-2005 L2005 MPD *012

PELINI, Susan Ewers. 24700 LORAIN RD 44070 #024-05-1980 L1983 IM *020 †20

RAMBASEK, Todd Edward. 25761 LORAIN RD, 3RD FL 44070 #038-06-1998 L2000 IM *020 †20,03

RAO, Akhilesh. 24700 LORAIN RD STE 207, WEST SIDE INTERNAL MEDICIN 44070 #496-35-2000 L2001 IM *020

RAUSCHKOLB, Elizabeth W. 26777 LORAIN RD STE 508 44070 #038-06-1957 L1957 D *020 †15

ROZAKIS, George Wm. 25730 LORAIN RD 44070 #035-20-1982 L1987 OPH *020 †35

ROZIN, Debra Ann. 24700 LORAIN RD STE 207 44070 #038-06-1990 L1991 IM *020 †20

SCHWEID, Jonathan Edward. ■ 44070 #038-43-2004 L2004 GS *012

SHARROTTA, Joseph V. ■ 44070 #028-02-1950 L1951 CD IM *071 †20

SHETH, Baiju Priyavadan. ■ 44070 #665-02-2001 L2005 AN *012 †12

THAKKER, Dilipkumar M. ■ 44070 #495-22-1981 L1991 IM *020 †20

THOMPSON, Robert Henry. ■ 44070 #038-06-1939 L1939 EM GS *020

TURELL, Mary Elizabeth. 24741 COUNTRY CLUB BLVD, # 330 44070 #008-01-2006 L2007 OPH *012

VERIKIS, Kalliniki D. 24700 LORAIN RD 44070 #418-01-1982 L1988 OBG *020 †30

WILBUR, Margaret Gerling. 24700 LORAIN RD 44070 #038-06-1980 L1982 IM *020 †20

NORTH RIDGEVILLE — LORAIN

ATASSI, Firas Souheil. 34500 CENTER RIDGE RD 44039 #875-01-1971 L1976 GS *020

BROBBEY, Victoria Nyanko. ■ 44039 #038-06-2006 L2006 IM *012

CAMERON, Derrick Leon. 39000 CENTER RIDGE RD 44039 #048-12-1995 L2005 OM FM *020 †18,70

DALENCOUR, Chantal I. 34960 CENTER RIDGE RD 44039 #016-11-1990 L1998 PD PDC *020 †55

FARES, Wassim H. 37140 BOLTON DR 44039 #605-01-2000 L2001 IM *020

FEYS, Jean Omer. ■ 44039 #165-04-1954 L1957 P *071

HITI, Frank Matthew. 6180 EMERALD ST 44039 #038-41-1988 L1990 FM *020 †18

JAGETIA, Mona K. 34960 CENTER RIDGE RD 44039 #038-44-1995 L1997 PD *020

KAYANJA, Mark Makumbi. ■ 44039 #905-01-1991 ORS *012

MURTHY, Siva R. 33917 DONNA AVE 44039 #048-13-1981 L1984 HEM ON *020 †20

PALMA, Gabriella. 34960 CENTER RIDGE RD 44039 #422-01-1990 L2000 FM *020 †18

RAFFERTY, George Anthony. ■ 44039 #035-06-1982 L1984 P *075

RECKO, Craig Joseph. ■ 44039 #038-43-2006 L2006 FP *012

RESETAR, Amy. ■ 44039 #038-75-2007, ▲ L2007 *012

SCHULTZ, Kathleen Ann. 39000 CENTER RIDGE RD 44039 #038-44-1991 L1992 OM EM *020 †16

WEBER, Charles Arthur. 34100 CENTER RIDGE RD, STE 107 44039 #055-01-1985 L1988 PD *020 †55

NORTH ROYALTON — CUYAHOGA

AL-AFYOUNI, Motasem M. ■ 44133 #613-02-1988 L2005 IM *012

AWADALLAH, Nida Sami. ■ 44133 #038-44-2007 L2007 FP *012

BARNES, Bella Gracia C. ■ 44133 #748-08-1957 PD *071

BARNES, Felino Villaverde. ■ 44133 #748-01-1951 L1969 PD *071 †55

CHEEMA, Amandeep K. ■ 44133 #038-43-2004 L2004 PD *020 †55

CHEEMA, Navneet Kaur. ■ 44133 #016-06-2008 *012

DEJAK, Irene Louise. 14200 RIDGE RD 44133 #038-06-2000 L2003 IM *020 †20

DRAVID, Sheela Narayan. ■ 44133 #495-34-1967 L1984 FM EM *020

FIKAR, Catherine Julia. 12289 RIDGE RD 44133 #038-44-1986 L1990 GS *020

FRANTZ, Martin Jos. 12744 STATE RD 44133 #038-06-1991 L1992 FM *020 †18

FRANTZ, Matthew J. 12744 STATE RD 44133 #038-75-1983, ▲ L1984 FM *020

HANNA, Nancy N. ■ 44133 #038-40-2007 L2007 TY *012

KAYA, Muhlis Yekta. ■ 44133 #902-01-1956 L1967 OBG *071 †30

KILARU, Jyothsna. ■ 44133 #495-50-1973 L1980 IM *020

KILARU, Silpa Deepa. ■ 44133 #038-40-2006 L2006 IM *012

KUCHARSKI, Leonard Jos. ■ 44133 #056-06-1956 L1957 OBG *071

LEIBY, Grant A, Jr. ■ 44133 #038-06-1950 L1950 GS OM *071 †85

LIVENGOOD, Teodora A. ■ 44133 #038-75-2007, ▲ FP *012

MARSH, Theodore Francis. ■ 44133 #016-43-1957 L1958 IM *071

NAZIR, Noreen Tehniyat. ■ 44133 #038-44-2008 *012

NEKL, Kenneth Evan. 14200 RIDGE RD 44133 #038-40-1988 L1989 END IM *020 †20

PANNU, Kulbir Singh. 8523 RIDGE RD 44133 #495-03-1978 L1983 IM NEP *020 †20

PARAS, Francisco F A, Jr. ■ 44133 #748-02-1989 L1994 PTH *012

PARAS, Wilfredo M. 8501 OAKWOOD LN 44133 #748-08-1965 L1972 IM *020

POLA, Suresh. ■ 44133 #038-06-2006 IM *012

RAMAMURTHY, Conjeevaran G. ■ 44133 #495-04-1955 L1976 P OBS *020

RANGANATHAN, C. 18301 BUCCANEER DR, SPY GLASS HILL 44133 #495-16-1970 L1975 IM END *020 †20

ROBLE, Arlene Grace. ■ 44133 #422-01-2000 L2001 PD *020 †55

RODRIGUEZ, Orlando E. 8523 RIDGE RD 44133 #042-03-1980 L1989 IM NEP *020 †20

SREEKUMAR, Beena. 14200 RIDGE RD 44133 #495-63-1991 L2005 IM *020 †20

SUCHOCKI, Elizabeth Ann. ■ 44133 #038-40-2008 *012

SUTARIA, Hansa Vinod. ■ 44133 #561-17-1955 L1959 EM *071

TOOR, Hafeez Mohammad. 11205 BRISTOL CT 44133 #704-01-1969 L1985 R *062 †80

VALENTE, Benedetto. ■ 44133 #025-01-1966 L1975 ORS *020 †40

WEIKER, Garron Gordon. ■ 44133 #038-75-2007, ▲ L2007 *012

WURST, Jennifer Lynn. 12744 STATE RD 44133 #038-06-2000 L2000 FM *100 †18

NORTHFIELD — SUMMIT

AGLIAM, Aquilio Corpuz. 10333 NORTHFIELD RD UNIT D 44067 #748-08-1970 L1983 GS *020

BLUMETTI, Brooke L. ■ 44067 #038-75-2007, ▲ L2007 *012

DANIACHEW, Anthony E. ■ 44067 #038-06-1998 L2000 FOP *012

DANIAL, Azmy T. 1756 SAGAMORE RD, CARE SYS, NORTHFIELD CAMPU 44067 #915-02-1966 L1996 P *020

FARIVAR, Michel Farhad. 1756 SAGAMORE RD, INST., E SYSTEM, BOX 305 44067 #165-01-1993 L2000 P *020 †75

HODGSON, Jessica Rae. ■ 44067 #038-44-2007 L2007 PD *012

KAPALCZYNSKI, Przemyslaw. 1756 SAGAMORE RD, HEALTH CARE FORENSIC DEPT 44067 #038-06-1999 L2000 P *020

KHAISHGI, Assadulla Khan. 1756 SAGAMORE RD, RM 107B 44067 #704-25-1997 L2001 IM *020

NWAJEI, Emmanuel E. 1756 SAGAMORE RD, NORTHCOAST BEHAVIORAL HEAL 44067 #690-04-1980 L1994 P *020 †75

PARK, Yong Jai. 1756 SAGAMORE RD, OHIO DEPT OF MENTAL HLTH 44067 #583-03-1962 L1980 GP PHP *071

SALES, Julio Luna. 1756 SAGAMORE RD, CARE SYSTEM 44067 #748-07-1971 L1990 P GP *020

SIVIK, Mary Teresa. 885 W AURORA RD, STE 3 44067 #038-40-1990 L1996 D *020 †20,15

SMITH, Douglas Alan. 1756 SAGAMORE RD 44067 #023-01-1993 L1998 PFP P *020 †75 ‡

STANKOWSKI, Joy Ellen. 1756 SAGAMORE RD, CARE 44067 #041-14-1997 L2002 P PFP *020 †75

ST CLAIR, Peggy-Jeanne. 115 W AURORA RD 44067 #041-07-1953 L1955 OBG *020 †30

TRIVEDI, Daksha Hemant. 1756 SAGAMORE RD, NORTHCOAST BEHAVIORAL HEAL 44067 #495-76-1975 L1986 P *020 †75

■ = Address Information Privacy Protected

NORTHWOOD – WOOD

GARDYZA, Stephanie Marie. ■ 43619 #038-43-2008 *012
JOHNSON, Peter Carl. 4400 WOODVILLE RD, STE B 43619 #038-43-1990 L1993 **OBG** *020 †30

NORTON – SUMMIT

BRUN, Miguel. ■ 44203 #176-01-1966 L1981 **OBG** *071
COEN, Sophia Papantoniou. 4111 CLEVELAND MASSILLN RD 44203 #418-01-1952 L1962 **OBG** *071
FISHER, Donald Lee. 1309 NORTON AVE, # 150 44203 #038-40-1987 L1988 **ORS OSM** *020 †40
KATSAROS, Peter Niketas. 3300 GREENWICH RD, STE 8 44203 #038-43-1990 L1993 **IM** *020 †20
LITTLEJOHN, Robert. ■ 44203 #035-09-1957 L1960 **FM PHP** *071
LUKATS, Paul G. ■ 44203 #023-01-1943 L1947 **OS GS** *071 †85
MARTIN, Joseph Edward. 3300 GREENWICH RD, STE 8 44203 #038-45-2001 L2001 **MPD** *020
MUIR, Garth James. ■ 44203 #010-01-2006 L2007 **TY** *012
SCHROEDER, Lisa Marie. 3172 CREEKSIDE DR 44203 #038-44-2000 L2000 **FM** *020 †18
SEALS, David Edward. 3282 WADSWORTH RD 44203 #035-03-1996 L2006 **OBG** *020 †30
STOKES, Joseph D, Jr. 1193 NORTON AVE, STE A 44203 #020-12-1984 L1987 **FM** *020 †18

NORWALK – HURON

AL-JADDA, Souheil M. 34 EXECUTIVE DR 44857 #875-01-1971 L1975 **GS GP** *020 †85
ALLEN, Kerry Michael. 278 BENEDICT AVE, STE 300 44857 #034-01-1983 L1985 **OPH GP** *020 †35
BALGUDE, Amit Pandurang. ■ 44857 #038-06-2004 L2004 **DR** *012
BIGLER, Mark Andrew. 85 BENEDICT AVE, STE 101 44857 #038-40-1994 L1999 **FM** *020 †18 ‡
CAMARDESE, Nino M. ■ 44857 #038-40-1953 L1953 **GP FM** *071
CENTA, Joseph Emil. 34 EXECUTIVE DR 44857 #038-40-1996 L2002 **GS VS** *020 †85
CHMIELEWSKI, Wendy Ann. 282 BENEDICT AVE, STE B 44857 #038-43-1996 L1997 **PD** *020 †55
CORNELIO, Celerino B, Jr. ■ 44857 #748-07-1956 L1968 **AN** *071
CORNELL, William Beard. 272 BENEDICT AVE, FISHER TITUS MED CTR 44857 #027-01-1986 L1986 **PTH** *062 †50
CROSBY, Peter Douglas A. 44 EXECUTIVE DR, NORWALK FAMILY PRACTICE IN 44857 #064-01-1993 L1995 *020 †18
DIONNE, Jeanette A. 54 EXECUTIVE DR, STE A 44857 #064-01-1994 L1997 **FM** *020 †18
DIONNE, Matthew Louis. 54 EXECUTIVE DR, STE A 44857 #064-01-1995 L1997 **FM** *020 †18
DUBHASHI, Sunil Narayan. 26 EXECUTIVE DR 44857 #495-17-1966 L1974 **OBG** *020
ENGELER, George Phillip. 272 BENEDICT AVE 44857 #017-20-1991 L1995 **RO** *020 †80
GARIN-VARGAS, Pura G. 38 EXECUTIVE DR 44857 #748-01-1957 L1969 **AN FM** *020 †05
GECSI, Kimberly Sauchak. 278 BENEDICT AVE, STE 500 44857 #038-06-2002 L2006 **OBG** *020
GHAZOUL, Teresa Helen. 278 BENEDICT AVE, STE 450 44857 #038-43-1985 L1988 **PS** *020 †85,65 ‡
GIBSON, Stephanie Frances. 54 EXECUTIVE DR, STE A 44857 #038-40-1999 L1999 **FM** *020 †18
GOTTFRIED, James Allen. 257 BENEDICT AVE 44857 #038-40-1975 L1975 **FM** *020 †18
GUTOWICZ, Matthew F, Jr. 272 BENEDICT AVE, FISHER TITUS MEDICAL CENTE 44857 #041-77-1972, ▲ L1977 **DR NM** *020 †28,80
HADLEY, Larry Lee. 175 SHADY LANE DR 44857 #025-01-1963 L1964 **IM** *071
HOOTON, Archie Burton. 272 BENEDICT AVE, FISHER TITUS MEMORIAL HOSP 44857 #869-04-1963 L1980 **P** *071
HUSAIN, Syed Zakir. 272 BENEDICT AVE 44857 #704-02-1981 L1986 **EM** *020 †16
JUNGBLUT, Melanie E. 282 BENEDICT AVE STE B 44857 #048-14-1988 L1991 **PD** *020
KASTEN, James Douglas. 278 BENEDICT AVE, STE 500 44857 #038-40-1982 L1982 **OBG** *020 †30
LYNCH, Timothy R. 280 BENEDICT AVE, MED PARK 4 44857 #038-75-2000, ▲ L2000 **ORS** *020
MAHMOUD, Walied Mohamed R. 272 BENEDICT AVE 44857 #915-04-1999 L2002 **EM** *020
MARK, James David. 272 BENEDICT AVE 44857 #038-44-1995 L1998 **EM** *020 †16
MAY, Ralph Norman Manfred. 44 EXECUTIVE DR, NORWALK FAMILY PRACTICE IN 44857 #038-43-1989 L1990 **FM** *020 †18
MC LONEY, Earl Robt. 66 NORWOOD AVE, GAYMONT NURSING CENTER 44857 #038-41-1956 L1956 **FM** *071
MINIER, Jayne Ann. 278 BENEDICT AVE, STE 800 44857 #025-07-1984 L1993 **GS** *020 †85
MURPHY, Brian Richard. 272 BENEDICT AVE 44857 #025-07-1986 L1992 **HEM ON** *020 †20
MURRAY, Michael Jos. 272 BENEDICT AVE, FISHER TITUS MEDICAL CENTE 44857 #038-41-1984 L1986 **IM** *020 †20
OBENAUF, Carl Dean. 278 BENEDICT AVE, STE 300 44857 #038-40-1974 L1978 **OPH** *020 †35
OWENS, William Francis. ■ 44857 #649-01-1959 L1963 **OS** *071
RAZA, Ahmad. ■ 44857 #704-04-2000 L2007 **IM** *020 †20
REDDY, Kattangur P. 272 BENEDICT AVE 44857 #495-57-1967 L1985 **AN** *020
RENUART, Donald James. 272 BENEDICT AVE 44857 #038-43-1993 L1994 **EM** *020 †16
RICE, Robert Wm. 34 EXECUTIVE DR 44857 #064-01-1974 L1981 **U** *020
SAID, Farid H. 34 EXECUTIVE DR, FARID SAID MD #ACS 44857 #847-06-1968 L1974 **GS GP** *020 †85
SCHMIDT, Eric Robt. 278 BENEDICT AVE, STE 800 44857 #025-07-1985 L1993 **GS** *020 †85
SWANSON, Thomas Harold. 1 E MAIN ST 44857 #025-07-1986 L1993 **N** *020 †75
THOMAS, Timothy John. 272 BENEDICT AVE 44857 #038-43-1977 L1978 **EM** *030 †16
TRIPPE, Glenn John. 282 BENEDICT AVE STE B 44857 #038-43-1976 L1979 **PD OTO** *020 †55
WACKENHEIM, Harold Wm. 272 BENEDICT AVE 44857 #067-01-1954 L1955 **GP** *071
WNEK, Paul Richard. 282 BENEDICT AVE STE B, NEW BEGINNINGS PEDIATRICS 44857 #038-43-1992 L1995 **PD** *020 †55
ZADEH, Barry Jon. 282 BENEDICT AVE STE A, ENDOVASCULAR THERAPIES INC 44857 #035-03-1980 L2006 **TS** *020 †90,85

NORWOOD – HAMILTON

ALBERS, Frank John. 4623 WESLEY AVE, STE N 45212 #038-41-1984 L1996 **NEP IM** *020 †20
BEERMAN, Stephen Patrick. 4600 WESLEY AVE 45212 #038-41-1992 L1995 **IM** *020 †20
CONNERS, Kristin Kelly. 4411 MONTGOMERY RD STE 200, BETHESDA FAMILY PRACTICE 45212 #038-41-2005 L2005 **FP** *012

FIXLER, Don Sheldon. 4411 MONTGOMERY RD, STE 201 45212 #038-41-1983 L1990 **FM** *020 †18
HILL, Maxwell C. ■ 45212 #038-41-2008 *012
JAMES, Shama Pazhachira. 4600 WESLEY AVE 45212 #038-44-2003 L2003 **FM** *020 †18
LAI, Hsiao Ling. ■ 45212 #011-03-2001 L2005 **PN** *012 †20,55
MANZLER, Alan Duane. 4600 WESLEY AVE, STE B 45212 #035-01-1963 L1965 **NEP IM** *071 †20
MONTOPOLI, Michael A. 45212 #038-44-1986 L1989 **OM PHP** *030 †70
RICHIE, Lucas Bryan. ■ 45212 #038-41-2008 *012
RISSOVER, Howard E. 5235 MONTGOMERY RD 45212 #038-41-1952 L1952 **FM** *071

NOVELTY – GEAUGA

ALTEMUS, Richard Bruce. ■ 44072 #035-03-1969 L1972 **EM PD** *020
DI BLASIO, Joseph Anthony. 8315 BELLE VERNON DR, RUSSELL TOWNSHIP 44072 #561-17-1980 L1983 **GS** *020 †85
DU BOIS, Pamela Suzanne. ■ 44072 #038-06-1980 **PD** *020
HOLMES, Denise Ophelia. ■ 44072 #038-06-1980 L1988 **ORS** *020 †40
KOROSEC, Marian. ■ 44072 #038-40-1983 L1986 **PCC IM** *020 †20
MAY, Charles S. ■ 44072 #005-11-1977 L1999 **FM EM** *020 †16,18
NELSON, Aaron Scott. ■ 44072 #038-43-2001 L2003 **DR** *100
SPRECHER, Dorothy Sanford. 8398 KINSMAN RD, CTR FOR HOPE AND HEALING 44072 #012-01-1987 L1990 **FM** *020 †18
ZEIT, Paul Rudolph. ■ 44072 #038-06-1943 L1943 **GYN** *071 †30

OAK HARBOR – OTTAWA

BLUNT, Chad Michael. 11697 W STATE ROUTE 163 43449 #038-45-1998 L1999 **FM** *020 †18
CALLAHAN, Sean Patrick. 11697 W STATE ROUTE 163, RW MINICK MEDICAL CENTER 43449 #038-43-1995 L1998 **FM** *020 †18
MINICK, Robert Walton. 9849 W STATE ROUTE 163 43449 #038-06-1948 L1948 **GP** *020
RAGOTHAMAN, Krishna M. 128 N LOCUST ST 43449 #495-37-1978 L1995 **FM** *020 †18
REEVES, Robert Schneider. ■ 43449 #067-01-1954 L1954 **PTH** *071 †50
SHEMENSKI, Ronald Stanley. ■ 43449 #047-06-1975 L1976 **FM** *020 †18

OAK HILL – JACKSON

COOK, John Merton. 350 CHARLOTTE AVE 45656 #038-06-1940 L1940 **GP GE** *071 †85

OAKWOOD – PAULDING

KREIT, Rim Naim. 109 S 1ST ST 45873 #875-02-1995 L2001 **FM** *020 †18

OAKWOOD VILLAGE – CUYAHOGA

SCHOENBERGER, Joseph A. 7690 FIRST PL, BLDG D 44146 #028-34-1989 L1991 **VIR** *020 †80

OBERLIN – LORAIN

ALDOORI, Dhia Y. ■ 44074 #528-01-1979 L1995 **IM** *020 †20
APPLETON, Judith Linn. 200 W LORAIN ST 44074 #035-45-1967 L1977 **FM** *020 †18
BEJ, Mark Danl. 224 W LORAIN ST STE C 44074 #041-14-1987 L1992 **N IM** *020
CHANDURKAR, Alaknanda. 224 W LORAIN ST 44074 #495-20-1967 L1984 **PD** *020
CHUANG, Mann Mann. 395 EDGEMEER PL 44074 #244-02-1970 L1975 **A PD** *020 †55,03
CHUANG, Wuu Shung. 224 W LORAIN ST, STE A 44074 #244-02-1970 L1975 **IM** *020 †20
ESSEL, Emmanuel K. 224 W LORAIN ST 44074 #412-01-1976 L1993 **OBG** *020 †30
FOX, James Philip. 224 W LORAIN ST 44074 #038-40-1972 L1976 **OBG EM** *020
GRAY, Ted Alan. 224 W LORAIN ST 44074 #035-45-1959 L1960 **OBG** *071 †30
GREIFFENHAGEN, Wolf W. ■ 44074 #407-21-1955 L1964 **GS ORS** *071
HOFMAN, Feite Foeke. 224 W LORAIN ST, AMC PHYSICIANS, INC. 44074 #660-03-1956 L1962 **IM GE** *071 †20
HUDGENS, Edward D. ■ 44074 #021-01-1952 L1954 **P OM** *071
JENKINS, Eric Dean. 319 W LORAIN ST 44074 #038-06-1999 L2000 **FM** *100 †18
JUNGSCHAFFER, Helmut J. 224 W LORAIN ST STE E 44074 #409-05-1986 L1990 **PD PPR** *020 †55
LUCIANO, Joseph Romualdo. 224 W LORAIN ST, OBERLIN CLINIC 44074 #025-01-1969 L1974 **PD OS** *071 †55
MASON, Delbert Dean. 224 W LORAIN ST, THE OBERLIN CLINIC INC 44074 #038-06-1961 L1961 **PD** *071 †55
MATTHEWS, Charles D, Jr. ■ 44074 #035-06-1955 L1956 **P** *071 †75
MATUS, Paul Michael. 90 FAIRWAY DR, 90 FAIRWAY DR 44074 #038-41-1976 L1977 **FM EM** *020 †18
MC CORKLE, Hugh F. ■ 44074 #038-06-1951 L1951 **PTH** *071 †50
MC KIBBEN, W Jeanne. 94 S OBERLIN RD 44074 #025-12-1976 L1977 **IM IMG** *071 †20
MC LAUGHLIN, Beth Louise. ■ 44074 #041-12-2000 L2001 **FM** *071 †18
MIHU, Basil Vasile. ■ 44074 #561-17-1958 L1962 **P IMG** *020
MILLER, William Weaver. ■ 44074 #041-01-1958 L1967 **PDC PD** *071 †55
NEWMAN, Georgia Lynne. 224 W LORAIN ST, STE A 44074 #024-01-1971 L1974 **IM ON** *020 †20
OLMSTED, Levona Williams. ■ 44074 #039-01-1951 L1974 **RO OS** *071 †80
OZKAZANC, Ismet B. 224 W LORAIN ST, STE B 44074 #902-05-1979 L1997 **IM** *020 †20
PATEL, Mahendrakumar R. 224 W LORAIN ST, MED ARTS BLDG STE B 44074 #495-22-1959 L1971 **ORS** *071 †40
POPA, Carmen. 200 W LORAIN ST 44074 #781-02-1995 L2000 **IM** *020 †20
RAY, Richard. 60 S PLEASANT ST STE B 44074 #038-44-1989 L1994 **AN** *020 †05
ROLLINS, Ronald Allen. 224 W LORAIN ST, THE OBERLIN CLINIC INC 44074 #036-05-1961 L1970 **GYN** *071 †30
ROTER, Eric Paul. 200 W LORAIN ST 44074 #038-06-1994 L1997 **EM** *020 †16
SHARMA, Vasanti N K. 200 W LORAIN ST 44074 #495-28-1961 L1971 **PTH** *020 †50

SLOCUM, Harold Elwyn. 319 W LORAIN ST, PHYSICIANS IN FAMILY PRACT 44074 #035-15-1971 L1990 **FM FPG** *071 †18
TOMBLIN, Cristal Denise. 247 W LORAIN ST, STE A 44074 #038-45-2000 L2001 **FM** *020 †18
VAN DYKE, Don P. 224 W LORAIN ST 44074 #038-06-1952 L1952 **OPH** *071 †35
WALKER, Barry Quentin. ■ 44074 #038-06-1956 L1956 **DR** *071 †80
WEBSTER, Joan Beth. ■ 44074 #041-01-1981 L1988 **PD** *020 †55
WINANS, Carl W. 224 W LORAIN ST 44074 #028-79-1960, ▲ L1960 **GP** *071
WU, Tson-Kuang. 200 W LORAIN ST 44074 #385-02-1968 L1975 **R NM** *020 †80
YOUNG, Keith R. ■ 44074 #041-02-1951 L1952 **IM** *071 †20

OHIO CITY – VAN WERT

WILLIAMS, Conrad Rex. ■ 45874 #020-02-1957 L1957 **P** *071

OLD FORT – SENECA

EDGAR, Philip Allen. 8153 MAIN ST 44861 #064-01-1990 L1995 **GP** *020
HIESTAND, E Crede. 8153 MAIN 44861 #038-40-1955 L1955 **FM** *072 †18

OLMSTED FALLS – CUYAHOGA

BEST, Amy Rachelle. ■ 44138 #038-41-2007 **P** *012
CIPOLLETTI, Christine. 9828 TUTTLE RD 44138 #038-06-1999 L1999 **OBG** *020
DIULUS, Lewis. ■ 44138 #024-05-2002 L2002 **GS** *020 †85
GREENWALD, Chas Mortimer. ■ 44138 #045-03-1948 L1954 **R** *071 †80
HAHNEL, Germaine Rita. 26376 JOHN RD, RENAISSANCE RETIREMENT COM 44138 #038-41-1957 L1957 **FM FPG** *071 †18
HILTON, Emmett Walters. ■ 44138 #038-06-1960 L1960 **CHP** *020
KELLY, James Thos, Jr. 26908 COOK RD 44138 #038-40-1987 L1988 **FM** *020 †18
KOTHARI, Samir Thakorlal. ■ 44138 #038-06-1998 **IM** *030
LOZANO, Enrique Alfredo. ■ 44138 #649-03-1950 L1959 **FM EM** *071
LOZANO, Maria De La Luz. 8871 HOLLY CANE 44138 #038-06-1979 L1981 **EM FM** *020 †18,16
LUDWIG, David Carl. 7856 BROOKSIDE DR 44138 #038-40-1991 L1993 **FM** *020 †18
REINEKS, Edmund Zigurds. ■ 44138 #038-06-2005 L2005 **PTH** *012
SHEMISA, Othman Aly. 26908 COOK RD 44138 #056-05-1977 L1986 **FM OBG** *020 †18
VELEZ-HOLVINO, Oscar D. 26908 COOK RD 44138 #042-03-1980 L1988 **FM PTH** *020 †18
WOJNAR, Walter James. 26908 COOK RD 44138 #038-06-1997 L1998 **FM** *020 †18

OREGON – LUCAS

ABAZA, Mohamed Bassam. 3156 DUSTIN RD, STE 203 43616 #915-03-1964 L1975 **PD** *020 †55
ABAZA, Wahida M. 3156 DUSTIN RD, STE 203 43616 #016-11-2001 L2004 **PD** *100 †55
ABDUL-AZIZ, Tammam. 2801 BAY PARK DR, DEPT OF SURG 43616 #875-01-1986 L2003 **AN** *020
ADAPPA, Vijay M. 1050 ISAAC STREETS DR, STE 137 43616 #495-37-1971 L1980 **OTO** *020 †45
AFOLABI, Akinfemi Samson. 2702 NAVARRE AVE STE 201 43616 #690-05-1988 L2001 **NEP IM** *020 †20
AFRIDI, Mohammad Farooq. 2751 BAY PARK DR, STE 100 43616 #704-09-1972 L1981 **VS** *020 †85
AFTAB, Suhail. 2600 NAVARRE AVE, FL 6 43616 #704-16-1990 L2003 **AN PMM** *020
AHMAD, Farid Aref. 2702 NAVARRE AVE 43616 #875-02-1992 L1999 **N** *100
AHMAD, Farid Uddin. 2702 NAVARRE AVE 43616 #704-16-1989 L2003 **GE** *020 †20
AL-KHALILI, Adnan R. 2600 NAVARRE AVE 43616 #575-01-1990 L2008 **ON** *020 †20
AMONETTE, Melissa Kay. ■ 43616 #038-43-2006 L2006 **EM** *012
ASSENMACHER, Dennis Roy. 1050 ISAAC STREETS DR #122, ASSENMACHER ORTHOPEDICS IN 43616 #025-01-1969 L1976 **ORS** *020 †40
ASSENMACHER, Joseph A. 1050 ISAAC STREETS DR, STE 122 43616 #038-41-1995 L2000 **ORS OSM** *020 †40
ASSI, Zakaria Ismail. 2801 BAY PARK DR 43616 #605-01-1994 L2002 **DR IM** *020 †20,80
BAMBRICK, Thomas Gilbert. 2600 NAVARRE AVE 43616 #038-43-1975 L1977 **IM PD** *020 †20
BARROW, Danielle Michelle. 2751 BAY PARK DR, STE 302 43616 #038-43-2002 L2002 **OBG** *020
BARTON, John Mathew. 2600 NAVARRE AVE 43616 #038-43-1977 L1978 **EM OM** *030 †16
BEEKS, David Allen. 2702 NAVARRE AVE, STE 102 43616 #049-01-1995 L2007 **ORS OSS** *020 †40
BERNARDO, Manuel Sarreal. PO BOX 167879 43616 #748-01-1963 L1972 **IM** *020
BERUTI, I Beruti. 2739 NAVARRE AVE STE 304 43616 #915-03-1969 L1975 **OBG** *020 †30
BLOCH, Ted. 715 S COY RD 43616 #017-20-1982 L2006 **PTH BBK** *020 †50 ‡
BOMMANA, Venu Gopala Redd. 3841 NAVARRE AVE 43616 #495-21-2000 L2007 **IM** *100
BRUE, James Dominic. 2600 NAVARRE AVE 43616 #038-40-1982 L1983 **OM FM** *020 †70,18
BUCK, Leonard Jos. 1050 ISAAC STREETS DR #116 43616 #038-43-1978 L1979 **ORS OSM** *020 †40
BUCK, Lindy Allison. 3207 NAVARRE AVE 43616 #038-43-2000 L2001 **FM** *020
BURKE, Charles Saunders. 2600 NAVARRE AVE 43616 #011-04-1979 L1989 **P** *020 †75
BURNS, J Bradley. 3113 DUSTIN RD, X RAY ASSOCIATES AT 43616 #038-43-1992 L1997 **DR** *020 †80
BURTON, Glen Mark. 2751 BAY PARK DR, STE 206 43616 #038-43-1974 L1975 **HO IM** *020 †20
BYRNE, Paul Adam. 2600 NAVARRE AVE 43616 #028-34-1957 L1990 **PD NPM** *020 †55
CASEY, Lisa Marie H. 2702 NAVARRE AVE, STE 206 43616 #038-75-1997, ▲ L1998 **FM** *040
CELIK, Ayse Gulsen. 1050 ISAAC STREETS DR, STE 140 43616 #902-10-1966 L1975 **PD** *020
CHABLANI, Lachman V. 2600 NAVARRE AVE, ST. CHARLES HOSPITAL 43616 #496-38-1962 L1971 **PTH** *020 †50
CHAKRAVARTY, Rahul. 2600 NAVARRE AVE, FL 6 43616 #038-43-2003 L2003 **AN** *100
CHAUDHARY, Riaz Nasim. 3841 NAVARRE AVE 43616 #704-01-1969 L1975 **IM** *020 †20
CHO, Dong Ki. 3458 NAVARRE AVE, RADIOLOGICAL ASSOC INC 43616 #583-01-1963 L1970 **R** *071
COLLACO, Joseph Frederick. 2600 NAVARRE AVE, ST CHARLES HOSPITAL 43616 #496-38-1971 L1975 **EM GP** *020 †16
COLLACO, Josephine. 1050 ISAAC STREETS DR, STE 104 43616 #038-43-1971 L1975 **GP** *020 †18

CONRAD, Edward Jos. 2702 NAVARRE AVE, STE 206 43616 #038-40-1954 L1954 **FM** *071
COOK, Charles Wm. 2600 NAVARRE AVE 43616 #038-43-1984 L1988 **PD IM** *020 †55
CREDICO, John Dominic. 2702 NAVARRE AVE STE 301 43616 #019-02-1978 L1986 **OBG** *020 †30
CUEVAS, Maria Luisa S. 1050 ISSAC STS ST # NO-104 43616 #748-08-1971 L1977 **GP** *020
DARR, Mahmood Riaz. 3841 NAVARRE AVE, OREGON CLINIC INC 43616 #704-01-1990 L1996 **IM IMG** *020 †20
DEVLIN, Michael Francis. 2801 BAY PARK DR 43616 #041-12-1980 L1998 **AN CCM** *020 †05
D'SOUZA, John Leonard. 3113 DUSTIN RD, X RAY ASSOCIATES INC AT 43616 #035-06-1994 L2001 **RNR** *020 †80
DUDENHOEFER, Brian Daniel. 2740 NAVARRE AVE 43616 #041-02-2000 L2005 **OPH** *020 †35
ELDRIDGE, Stephen Albert. 3113 DUSTIN RD, X RAY ASSOCIATES INC AT 43616 #065-09-1984 L1991 **DR VIR** *020 †80
FERNANDES, Shaila Patel. 715 S COY RD 43616 #038-40-1992 L2000 **PTH** *020 †50
FERNANDES, Sydney Oswald. 1050 ISAAC STREETS DR, STE 110 43616 #495-17-1967 L1972 **IM** *020 †20,18
FLOCKENHAUS, Peter. 2600 NAVARRE AVE 43616 #407-15-1955 L1960 **GP** *071
GAD, Mohammad Adel. 1050 ISAAC STREETS DR, STE 143 43616 #063-01-1987 L2001 **IM** *020 †28,20
GILL, Kaleem Ullah. 2751 BAY PARK DR, STE 303 43616 #704-04-1999 L2003 **FM** *020 †18
GILL, Sukhwinder S. 2600 NAVARRE AVE, FL 6 43616 #495-03-1974 L1994 **AN** *020 †05
GUPTA, Manish Raj. 1050 ISAAC STREETS DR #136 43616 #654-01-1997 L1999 **PS HS** *020 †85,65
GUVENDI, Mustafa. 3521 NAVARRE AVE 43616 #902-10-1964 L1983 **GS** *020 †85
HAGEMAN, John Herbert. 2751 BAY PARK DR, STE 100 43616 #008-01-1962 L1984 **VS GS** *020 †85
HAMIDI, Ramin Edward. 3232 NAVARRE AVE, OREGON URGENT CARE 43616 #028-78-2000, ▲ L2001 **RNR** *012
HASAN, Syed Zaheer. 2600 NAVARRE AVE 43616 #704-15-1980 L1987 **N CHN** *020 †55
HICKEY, Timothy Michael. 1050 ISAAC STREETS DR #134 43616 #038-43-2001 L2001 **N** *020
HODDINOTT, Mark Bennett. 715 S COY RD 43616 #028-34-1983 L1997 **PTH** *062 †50
HUSAIN, Ishrat. 3521 NAVARRE AVE 43616 #704-09-1969 L1983 **GS** *020 †85
HUSS, Robert Jos. 2702 NAVARRE AVE, STE 205 43616 #038-41-1964 L1964 **OPH** *071 †35
HUSSAIN, Sayed Amjad. 2600 NAVARRE AVE, # MEZININE 43616 #704-09-1962 L1974 **TS CD** *020 †85,90
IRONS, Michelle Marie. 2600 NAVARRE AVE 43616 #038-43-1992 L1994 **PD** *020 †55
JAMES, William Geo, Jr. 2752 BAY PARK DR, STE 209 43616 #025-07-1981 L1984 **AN PME** *005
JONES, Thomas Patrick. 3113 DUSTIN RD, X RAY ASSOCIATES INC AT 43616 #025-07-1997 L2003 **DR** *020 †80
KAHLE, Charles Thos. 2600 NAVARRE AVE 43616 #038-40-1968 L1968 **GP** *020
KAKISSIS, Soterios John. 3458 NAVARRE AVE 43616 #418-01-1960 L1975 **R** *071 †80
KAMAU, John Ngugi. 2702 NAVARRE AVE, NAVARRE FAMILY MEDICINE AS 43616 #577-01-1992 L2004 **FM** *100 †18
KATRAGADDA, Bindu. 2600 NAVARRE AVE 43616 #495-50-1989 L1998 **IM** *020 †20
KHAN, Shakil. 2751 BAY PARK DR 43616 #704-02-1974 L1980 **PUD IM** *020 †20
KHAZAN, Uri. 2737 NAVARRE AVE, STE 204 43616 #038-43-1985 L1989 **ID IM** *020
KOOP, Richard Henry. 2702 NAVARRE AVE, STE 205 43616 #056-06-1964 L1970 **OPH** *020 †35
KUMAR, Surendra. 3929 NAVARRE AVE 43616 #495-24-1972 L1977 **FM EM** *020 †18 ‡
KUMARAN, Thurai Yogaraj. 3841 NAVARRE AVE, OREGON CLINIC INC. 43616 #495-42-1989 L1998 **IM** *020 †20
LABHSETWAR, Snehalata A. 1050 ISAAC STREETS DR, STE 131 43616 #495-28-1962 L1991 **OBG** *020 †30
LAKKIMSETTI, Vasu Nagaraj. ■ 43616 #495-65-2001 L2005 **FP** *012
LEMIEUX, Bernard Joseph. 3113 DUSTIN RD, STE A 43616 #016-43-1969 L1973 **R NM** *071 †80
LI, Guang Hue. 2600 NAVARRE AVE, 6TH FL 43616 #243-38-1982 L2002 **AN** *020 †05 ‡
LI, Qingjun. 2600 NAVARRE AVE, FL 6 43616 #243-41-1983 L2003 **AN** *020 †05
LINARES, Claudio Esteban. 2735 NAVARRE AVE, STE 101 43616 #308-03-1982 L1993 **OBG GP** *020 †30
LOEFFLER, Richard Melvin. 1050 ISAAC STREETS DR 43616 #016-43-1958 L1959 **ORS** *071 †40
LORTON, Michael Darrell. 2600 NAVARRE AVE 43616 #038-40-1982 L1982 **CD IM** *020 †20
LUKETIC, Karl Jos. 2702 NAVARRE AVE 43616 #038-44-1991 L1992 **OPH** *020 †35
MADRAZO, Manuel V. 2600 NAVARRE AVE, ST CHARLES HOSPITAL 43616 #748-08-1971 L1981 **EM** *020 †16
MAHAJAN, Kewal Krishan. 3841 NAVARRE AVE 43616 #495-29-1971 L1978 **IM IMG** *020 †20
MARTIN, William G. 2740 NAVARRE AVE 43616 #023-01-1977 L1981 **OPH** *020 †35
MASON, Lynn Tiara. 2600 NAVARRE AVE 43616 #038-45-1995 L1996 **EM** *020 †16
MATHENY, Amanda Marie. 2751 BAY PARK DR, STE 202 43616 #038-43-2001 L2001 **GS** *020 †85
MC NAMARA, Mary Phillis. 2815 DUSTIN RD, STE C 43616 #038-40-1981 L1982 **ID IM** *020 †20
MEHTA, Gunvant Bhimjibhai. 3113 DUSTIN RD, X RAY ASSOCIATES INC AT 43616 #495-17-1969 L1977 **R** *071 †80
MILLIE, Annette Rose. 5517 CORDUROY RD 43616 #038-43-1992 L1994 **FM** *020 †18 ‡
MIRAMONTES, David Alan. 2600 NAVARRE AVE, ST CHARLES MERCY HOSP EMGY 43616 #038-43-1996 L1997 **EM** *020 †16
MISTRY, Arvindkumar H. 2600 NAVARRE AVE, FL 6 43616 #495-76-1970 L1985 **AN** *020 †05
MORSE, Bradley John. 2702 NAVARRE AVE STE 102, MAUMEE BAY ORTHOPEDICS INC 43616 #038-43-1989 L1991 **ORS** *020 †40
MOTIWALE, Minakshi S. 3232 NAVARRE AVE, MERCY URGENT CARE 43616 #495-20-1977 L1996 **IM** *075
MUHAMMAD, Ruqiyya Tufail. 3163 NAVARRE AVE #704-05-2001 L2004 **FM** *100 †18
NAIDU, Pangulur Sudhakar. 2702 NAVARRE AVE 43616 #495-70-1977 L1986 **GE IM** *020 †20
NOPKHUN, Vijit. 1050 ISAAC ST STE 1, STE 106 43616 #891-02-1968 L1974 **OBG** *020 †30
O'MARA, Kevin Thos. 2600 NAVARRE AVE, EMERGENCY CENTER 43616 #038-43-1999 L2002 **EM ESM** *020 †16
PENG, Lu. 2600 NAVARRE AVE, FL 6 43616 #243-76-1982 L1999 **AN** *020 †05 ‡
PERRAS, Albert Derald. 2600 NAVARRE AVE 43616 #028-03-1959 L1960 **GP AN** *071
PUNSALAN, Legaspi Maylad. ■ 43616 #748-01-1962 L1971 **AN GP** *071
PUREWAL, Sukhjit Singh. 2600 NAVARRE AVE 43616 #495-03-1966 L1973 **ORS LM** *062 †40
RAFEEQ, Mohammed R. 1050 ISAAC STREETS DR #128 43616 #495-65-1973 L1982 **A PD** *020 †55,03
RATRA, Champa K. 2600 NAVARRE AVE, FL 6 43616 #495-05-1962 L1976 **AN PME** *020
RAVINDRAN, Anand. 2751 BAY PARK DR 43616 #495-31-1995 L2000 **NEP** *020 †20
REARDON, Mark Edward. 2600 NAVARRE AVE 43616 #038-43-1986 L1987 **FM** *020 †18

RIZA, Erol D. 3465 NAVARRE AVE 43616 #902-03-1970 L1976 **OBG** *020 †30
ROBINSON, Tara Stipe. 4330 NAVARRE AVE, STE 103 43616 #038-43-1997 L2000 **FM** *020 †18
ROSHONG-DENK, Stacie Lynn. 715 S COY RD 43616 #038-43-2001 L2001 **PTH** *100 †50
SEFFERNICK, Cynthia Kay. 2751 BAY PARK DR, STE 302 43616 #038-43-1993 L1997
  OBG *020 †30
SHEKUT, Steven Edward. 3113 DUSTIN RD, X RAY ASSOCIATES INC AT 43616
  #038-43-1997 L2003 *020 †80
SIEBENALER, Jack Gilbert. 3232 NAVARRE AVE 43616 #038-43-1985 L1986 **FM EM** *020 †18
SIGLER, Kristi Renee. 2815 DUSTIN RD, STE C 43616 #038-43-1997 L2000 **FM** *020 †18 ‡
SIM, Lily Naguit. 3156 DUSTIN RD, STE 100 43616 #748-08-1960 L1972 **PD** *071 †55
STOCKARD, Herbert Eugene. 2702 NAVARRE AVE STE 201, NAVARRE MEDICAL PLAZA 43616
  #038-43-1973 L1975 **NEP IM** *071
SUNGURLU, Mehmet Akif. 2737 NAVARRE AVE STE 204 43616 #902-04-1981 L1990 **IM** *020
SURIYAPA, Chinda. 1050 ISAAC STREETS DR, STE 104 43616 #891-02-1963 L1972
  GS EM *020 †85
SUTTON, Stephen Paul. 1050 ISAAC STREETS DR #126 43616 #025-01-1978 L1979 **U** *020 †95
SZCZESNIAK, David Martin. 3113 DUSTIN RD, X RAY ASSOCIATES INC AT 43616
  #036-05-1995 L2000 **RNR** *020 †80
SZYMANSKI, David Eugene. 2600 NAVARRE AVE 43616 #038-40-1991 L1993 **N** *020
TAMIRISA, Kiran Chary. 2600 NAVARRE AVE, BLDG 3 43616 #495-50-1974 L1980
  AN PME *020 †05
TAMIRISA, Mithilesh K. 2600 NAVARRE AVE, ST. CHARLES MERCY HOSP 43616
  #495-11-1979 L1984 **PME** *020 †20
TAYLOR, Henry Joe, III. 3207 NAVARRE AVE 43616 #038-43-1992 L1993 **FM** *020 †18
THAMBUSWAMY, Ayyaswamy. 1050 ISAAC STREETS DR 43616 #495-04-1957 L1972
  GS GP *071 †85
THOMPSON, Joseph Bankole. 2702 NAVARRE AVE, MERCY HEALTH PARTNERS 43616
  #025-01-1997 L2006 **FM** *020 †18
THUSAY, Manish Mahadeo. 2751 BAY PARK DR 43616 #495-28-1991 L2003 **GS** *020 †85
URRUTIA, Jose Guillermo. 2801 BAY PARK DR 43616 #341-01-1973 L1979 **NPM PD** *020 †55
VEGA, Patricia M. 3458 NAVARRE AVE 43616 #025-07-1983 L1984 **FM** *020 †18
VILELA, Oswaldo E. 2737 NAVARRE AVE, STE 203 43616 #737-01-1971 L1980 **OBG** *020 †30
VONDEREMBSE, Sandra Sue. ■ 43616 #038-43-1990 L1991 **P** *020
WEXLER, Wendy Ilene. 2600 NAVARRE AVE 43616 #038-43-1992 L1995 **IM PD** *020 †20,55
YEASTING, Joel Alexander. 3028 NAVARRE AVE, OCCUPATIONAL CARE CONSULTA 43616
  #038-43-1994 L1995 **OM** *020 †16
YOAKIM, Kamal Nader Tadro. ■ 43616 #915-02-2000 L2006 **FP** *012
YOUNG, Bradford Andrew. 2741 NAVARRE AVE, STE 401 43616 #038-41-1993 L1996
  FM *020 †18
YOUNG, Edward Geo. 2741 NAVARRE AVE STE 401 43616 #566-01-1956 L1978 **FM** *020
YUAN, Joses Kai Hsin. 2751 BAY PARK DR, STE 303 43616 #583-09-1956 L1971
  FM EM *020 †18
YUCE, Metin. 2600 NAVARRE AVE 43616 #902-01-1956 L1968 **IM** *020
YUSAFZAI, Nilofer Faqir. 2600 NAVARRE AVE 43616 #704-09-1977 L1981 **EM** *020 †18,16
ZAVELA, Norman Ginther. 2600 NAVARRE AVE, FL 6 43616 #025-07-1991 L1995
  AN OS *020 †05

OREGONIA – WARREN

DES MARAIS, John Richard. 6442 FLINT TRAILS 45054 #038-41-1986 L1987 **FM** *020 †18

ORIENT – PICKAWAY

ADAMS, John Martin. PO BOX 209 43146 #056-05-1969 L1970 **P** *020 †75
JOHNSON, Amy Brook Guingr. ■ 43146 #038-40-2007 L2007 **FP** *012
MADERIA, Leah Marie. 9085 SOUTHERN ST, STE B 43146 #038-44-2003 L2007 **OBG** *020
WARD, Alan Newton. 9085 SOUTHERN ST 43146 #038-45-1987 L1990 **IM** *020

ORRVILLE – WAYNE

BAVIS, James Robert, Jr. 830 S MAIN ST, STE 5 44667 #038-06-1999 L2003 **N SME** *020 †75
BEAM, William Clifford. 832 S MAIN ST 44667 #038-06-1945 L1945 **GP AM** *071
COX, William Michael. 832 S MAIN ST 44667 #036-08-1987 L1991 **AN** *020
HUTSON, Robert Hiram, III. 830 S MAIN ST 44667 #038-43-1978 L1979 **FM** *020 †18
LAING, Amelia Efua. 830 S MAIN ST, STE 6 44667 #412-01-1987 L1997 **OBG** *020 †30
LEHMAN, Brent Lamar. 832 S MAIN ST 44667 #038-45-1995 L1999 **FM** *020 †18
LYNCH, Daniel Edward. 832 S MAIN ST, STARK MEDICAL SPECIALTIES 44667
  #025-07-1992 L1999 **AN PME** *020 †05
MARQUEZ, Hector. 832 S MAIN ST, DUNLAP MEMORIAL HOSPITAL 44667 #042-03-1986 L2007
  AN *020
MOTTA ROMERO, Jorge E. 830 S MAIN ST, STE 7&8 44667 #264-01-1961 L1973 **GS** *020
NAUMOFF, Andrew Jerome. 830 S MAIN ST 44667 #038-43-1979 L1981 **FM** *020 †18
SANDER, Larry Dean. 830 S MAIN ST 44667 #038-06-1974 L1977 **FM** *020 †18
WANG, Linda Marie. 830 S MAIN ST, SUITES 7 & 8 44667 #023-12-1988 L2000 **GS** *020 †85
WEEMAN, Ben K. 832 S MAIN ST 44667 #038-45-1993 L1995 **AN** *020 †05

OSTRANDER – DELAWARE

URBAN, Kenneth Michael. 8080 MILLS RD 43061 #038-40-1963 L1963 **IM** *020

OTTAWA – PUTNAM

BANSAL, Surinder Kumar. 144 N WALNUT ST 45875 #495-69-1968 L1974 **U** *020
EIDEN, Jeffrey Scott. 1740 N PERRY ST, STE A 45875 #038-40-1997 L1998 **FM** *020 †18
EIDEN, Leah. 1740 N PERRY ST, STE A 45875 #038-40-1997 L1998 **FM** *020 †18
KLASS, Katelyn Ann. 144 SPRING ST 45875 #038-41-2008 *012

OTTAWA HILLS – LUCAS

ABOWD, Thomas Vincent. ■ 43606 #025-01-1963 L1970 **CD IM** *071

ASSAD, Refat Mohammed. ■ 43606 #875-03-1994 *100
CIRALSKY, Jessica Blair. ■ 43615 #023-07-2004 L2005 **OPH** *012
DITMYER, Paul James. ■ 43615 #038-41-1956 L1956 **AN** *071 †05
FINKEL, Robert Ian. ■ 43615 #008-01-1965 L1973 **RHU** *071 †20
FULCHER, Eric David. ■ 43606 #020-02-2005 L2005 **EM** *012
GOHARA, Sabry Fawzy. ■ 43606 #330-02-1964 L1972 **TS** *020 †85,90
GOSLING, Robert J. ■ 43606 #025-01-1946 L1961 **PM** *071 †60
HAMMERLING, Lee Wm. 4339 BROOKSIDE RD 43615 #016-02-1980 L1983 **AN** *020 †05
HARRISON, Charles Henry. ■ 43606 #010-03-1959 L1965 **EM IM** *071
HURST, Loren Marie. ■ 43615 #038-43-2008 *012
JHUNJHUNWALA, Jagadish S. ■ 43606 #495-19-1963 L1972 **U** *071 †95
JOHNSON, Nicholas Kahlert. ■ 43606 #026-04-2006 L2006 **U** *012
KUEBBELER, Philip Lambert. ■ 43606 #025-01-1963 L1966 **GYN** *071 †30
KUNNATHUR, Vidhya Anand. ■ 43606 #038-44-2008 *012
KURCZYNSKI, Thaddeus W. ■ 43606 #038-06-1970 L1976 **CG CHN** *020 †75,19
NAEEM, Nauman. ■ 43606 #308-13-1997 L2000 **PCC** *012
OCKULY, John J. ■ 43606 #020-02-1951 L1957 **U OS** *071
O'CONNOR, Deirdre Mary. ■ 43615 #539-06-1956 L1960 **GP PHP** *020
OFORI, Abena Obenewa. 2528 CHALLEDON CT 43615 #028-02-2002 L2006 **D** *100 †15
POHLMAN, Carol Lee. ■ 43606 #038-40-1967 L1967 **IM** *075
ROSENBERG, Veronica Melan. ■ 43615 #038-40-2003 L2004 **IM** *100
RUPPERT, Elizabeth S. 3314 PELHAM RD 43606 #038-40-1961 L1961 **PD** *072 †55
SILVERMAN, Henry R, III. 3751 SULPHUR SPG 43606 #038-40-1976 L1980 **CD IM** *020 †20
THAKUR, Subhash. ■ 43606 #495-36-1999 L2006 **VS** *012

OXFORD – BUTLER

ADAM, David Roscoe. 5141 MORNING SUN RD 45056 #038-40-1983 L1984 **OPH** *020 †35
BERNIE, Howard Lee. 10 N LOCUST ST, STE C 45056 #051-04-1975 L1978 **GE IM** *020
BERSCHBACK, John Christop. ■ 45056 #025-07-2007 **ORS** *012
BIRKLE, Matthew Elliott. 421 S CAMPUS AVE 45056 #038-45-1994 L1995 **EM PHL** *020 †16
BROWNE, Wm Alexander, IV. MIAMI UNIV STUD HLTH SERV 45056 #041-02-1961 L1962
  ADL GP *020
BRUDZINSKI, Erika Diane. 10 N LOCUST ST, STE D 45056 #016-45-2001 L2005 **IMG** *020
BRUNCKHORST, Rolf F, Jr. 146 STONE CREEK DR 45056 #005-14-1981 L1987
  CRS GS *020 †85
BUCHER, Rick James. 5237 MORNING SUN RD 45056 #038-41-1982 L1985 **FM** *020 †18
BUERK, Kenneth Melvin. ■ 45056 #028-02-1968 L1971 **OPH** *071 †35
CALKINS, Gregory Paul. 222 RYAN DR 45056 #025-01-1978 L1979 **EM** *020 †16
CANGEMI, Paul Jos. 10 N LOCUST ST, STE 1B 45056 #010-02-1972 L1973 **ORS** *020 †40
COTTLE, Margaret. ■ 45056 #061-01-1978 L1979 **GP** *020
DAILEY, Stephen Wayne, Jr. 10 N LOCUST ST, STE 100 45056 #038-40-1989 L1990
  EM *020 †16
EMMERT, Molly Ann. 12 W CHURCH ST 45056 #038-41-1995 L1999 **MPD** *020 †20,55
EVANS, Hillary A. 110 N POPLAR ST, MCCULLOUGH HYDE MEMORIAL H 45056
  #038-41-1992 L1997 **DR** *020 †80
FISCHBACH, Cliffton M. 110 N POPLAR ST 45056 #020-02-1937 L1962 **GP PHP** *071
FITZPATRIC, Mary Michele. 110 N POPLAR ST, MCCULLOUGH-HYDE MEMORIAL H 45056
  #038-41-2002 L2002 **DR** *020 †80
GARNETT, Gregory Lee. 421 S CAMPUS AVE 45056 #056-05-1973 L1991 **FM** *020
GOLDEY, James Alan. 110 N POPLAR ST 45056 #038-41-1960 L1960 **EM OS** *071
GRAY, Bruce Carson. 110 N POPLAR ST, MCCULLOUGH HYDE MEM HOSP 45056
  #561-11-1984 L2003 **CCA** *020
HAGERMAN, Dwain D. ■ 45056 #024-01-1950 L1989 **OS** *071
HARLAN, John Trumbull. 10 N LOCUST ST 45056 #038-06-1987 L1989 **OBG** *020 †30
HAWKINS, Sarah Jo. 10 N LOCUST ST 45056 #038-41-2003 L2003 **OBG** *020
HOKE, Jason Andrew. 10 N LOCUST ST, STE D 45056 #038-44-1998 L1999 **FM** *020 †18
HOKE, Jennifer Lee. ■ 45056 #038-45-2002 L2002 **P** *012
HORN, Steven Robt. 110 N POPLAR ST, MCCULLOUGH HYDE MEM HOSP 45056
  #038-41-1978 L1983 **EM** *020 †18,16
HUGHES, Thos Michael, Jr. 421 S CAMPUS AVE 45056 #038-40-1970 L1970 **FM OS** *020 †18
KNOEDLER, Mary Margaret. 110 N POPLAR ST 45056 #026-04-1983 L1987 **DR** *020 †80
LOGEMAN, William Jos. 5141 MORNING SUN RD, OXFORD PEDIATRICS & ADOLES 45056
  #038-41-1979 L1981 **PD** *020 †30
LUTMER, Jeffrey Edward. ■ 45056 #038-43-2006 L2006 **PD** *012
MILLER, Antonina. ■ 45056 #407-16-1949 **D** *071
MOEBIUS, Mary Catherine. 110 N POPLAR ST 45056 #038-41-1980 L1981 **DR** *020 †80
MORRIS, Nathaniel Lee. 10 N LOCUST ST STE D, INDIAN CREEK FAMILY HEALTH 45056
  #021-06-1997 L1999 **FM** *020 †18
NAGY, Szilvia. ■ 45056 #038-41-2006 **OBG** *012
PALECHEK, Carl Richard. 10 N LOCUST ST STE 1B 45056 #038-40-1962 L1962 **ORS** *071 †40
PAULS, John Jeffrey. 421 S CAMPUS AVE 45056 #038-40-1989 L1999 **GP** *020
PORTER, Stephen Randall. 12 W CHURCH ST, OXFORD INTERNAL MEDICINE / 45056
  #055-02-1994 L1995 **IM** *020
PRINCELL, Roger Holman. 5225 MORNING SUN RD STE C 45056 #026-04-1960 L1963 **FM** *020
RICHARDSON, Deborah Jean. 421 S CAMPUS AVE, STUDENT HEALTH SERVICE 45056
  #038-45-1987 L1990 **OS** *020 †18
SIMPSON, Patricia Carol. 421 S CAMPUS AVE 45056 #041-12-1969 L1970 **GP** *071
SMITH, Michael John. ■ 45056 #016-11-1999 L2000 **EM** *020 †16
SVIRBELY, John Richard. 110 N POPLAR ST 45056 #023-01-1977 L1978 **PTH MM** *020 †50
WIESENMAYER, E C. 5225 MORNING SUN RD, STE A 45056 #038-40-1968 L1968
  OBG *020 †30
WILKINSON, Scott J, II. 111 E WITHROW ST 45056 #023-07-1959 L1963 **PD** *072 †55
YANKOW, Paul Kenneth. MIAMI UNIV STU HLTH SER 45056 #038-41-1968 L1968 **OS** *020

PAINESVILLE – LAKE

ALKOTOB, Mohammad Luay. 124 LIBERTY ST 44077 #875-01-1996 L2000 **CD** *020 †20
ARO, Edgardo Reyes. 40 W ERIE ST 44077 #748-01-1967 L1976 **AN** *075
BANNA, Ahmad. 124 LIBERTY ST RM B 44077 #875-02-1974 L1980 **IM CD** *020 †20
BARCELO, Mark Jeffery. 89 E HIGH ST 44077 #038-06-1987 L1988 **PTH PCP** *020 †50
BRINGARDNER, Albert M. ■ 44077 #038-40-1953 L1953 **GYN** *071 †30
BROWNLEE, Rosemary R. 89 E HIGH ST, STE 2 44077 #038-45-1992 L1995 **OBG** *020 †30

COLOPY, Robert Wm. 89 E HIGH ST 44077 #028-34-1947 L1948 **GYN** *072 †30
CRESS, William Eric. 8350 TEWKSBURY LN 44077 #025-07-1980 L1983 **AN** *020 †05
DAMIAN, Armando B, Jr. 50 NORMANDY DR, STE 4 44077 #748-08-1967 L1974 **GS** *020 †85
DOMADIA, Mansukhlal J. 89 E HIGH ST, STE 7 44077 #495-28-1956 L1975 **GS GP** *071
DUCHON, Method Anthony. 89 E HIGH ST, STE 2 44077 #016-43-1974 L1976 **OBG** *071 †30
ESPINOSA, Roger G. 124 LIBERTY ST RM B 44077 #748-11-1979 L1986 **CD IM** *020 †20
FARRINGTON, David Linwood. 40 W ERIE ST 44077 #024-07-1956 L1961 **AN OS** *020 †05
FELDSTEIN, Marvin Allen. 10 E WASHINGTON ST 44077 #023-01-1957 L1963 **IM END** *020
FERNANDES, M Martin. 50 NORMANDY DR 44077 #496-15-1971 L1979 **IM** *020
FLETCHER, William E. ■ 44077 #038-06-1949 L1949 **GS GP** *071 †85
FRIEDMAN, Howard Alan. 7 W JACKSON ST 44077 #038-06-1987 L1987 **IM** *020 †20
GOUD, Gundumalla Sathaiah. 7529 FREDLE DR 44077 #495-21-1974 L1979 **IM IMG** *020 †20
GRASSIE, Karen Renee. 50 NORMANDY DR, STE 4 44077 #038-43-1997 L1998 **GS** *020 †85
HANAHAN, Paul Canning. 150 MENTOR AVE 44077 #038-06-1976 L1976 **OM GP** *020
JOHNSON, Brian Kendall. ■ 44077 #019-02-2000 L2001 **AN** *020 †05 ‡
JONES, Paul Linden. 89 E HIGH ST, STE 2 44077 #038-40-1989 L1996 **OBG** *020 †30
JORDAN, Christine Ann. 10 E WASHINGTON ST 44077 #041-07-1977 L1983 **AN CCA** *020 †05
JOYCE, Tina. 7879 AUBURN RD 44077 #038-75-2003, ▲ L2003 **FM** *100
KEEP, David James. 89 E HIGH ST 44077 #038-06-1992 L1993 **PTH** *020 †50
KOSIK, Edward S. ■ 44077 #038-75-2003, ▲ L2003 **AN** *012
KUERBITZ, Carolyn Hanisko. 7 W JACKSON ST 44077 #025-07-1984 L1995 **IM** *020 †20
LAGMAN, Dennis Velasquez. 10 E WASHINGTON ST, LAKE E HOSP 44077 #748-01-1991 L1998 **IM** *020 †20
LETTERIO, John James. ■ 44077 #038-40-1987 L2007 **PD** *020 †55
LO CRICCHIO, John. 10 E WASHINGTON ST 44077 #038-40-1959 L1959 **D A** *071 †50
LUEBBERS, Ellen L. 89 E HIGH ST 44077 #028-46-1986 L1988 **PTH** *020 †50
MAC DOUGALL, Robert Lewis. 89 E HIGH ST STE 3 44077 #010-03-1975 L1976 **IM AI** *020 †20
MAHER, Joseph J. 30 S PARK PL 44077 #010-02-1945 L1958 **OTO A** *072 †45
MEHANDRU, Prem L. 10 E WASHINGTON ST, LAKE EAST HOSP 44077 #496-07-1977 L1989 **PD NPM** *020 †55
PATEL, Sunil Shashikant. ■ 44077 #033-05-2001 L2007 **GE** *020
PATEL, Tarulata M. 50 NORMANDY DR, STE 3 44077 #495-01-1969 L1972 **PTH** *020 †50
PAUL, John Harsha. 50 NORMANDY DR STE 1 44077 #495-09-1960 L1972 **ORS** *020
PISZEL, Bruce Anthony. 470 BACON RD 44077 #305-01-1999 L2003 **P** *020
POPOVEC, Bobbi. 40 W ERIE ST, STE 201 44077 #038-44-1983 L1985 **AN** *020 †05
RIZZO, Salvatore Geo. 10 E WASHINGTON ST 44077 #038-06-1959 L1959 **FM GP** *020
RONKE, Roy Edward, Jr. ■ 44077 #008-01-1961 L1962 **AN** *071 †05
SCHOEN, Joanne Agnes. ■ 44077 #065-09-1965 L1966 **OBG** *071 †30
SHIN, Carl Kwaangsik. 126 S SAINT CLAIR ST 44077 #038-40-1978 L1979 **OPH** *020 †35 ‡
SKRINSKA, Joseph. 10 E WASHINGTON ST 44077 #616-01-1940 L1952 **FM GP** *071
SMITH, Lynn Alderson. 150 MENTOR AVE 44077 #038-06-1966 L1966 **FM OBG** *020
SPITTLER, Quentin James. 89 E HIGH ST, STE 2 44077 #038-40-1963 L1963 **OBG** *071 †30
TANI, Marie. 7535 FREDLE DR 44077 #038-06-1989 L1991 **N** *020 †75
TOMASZEWSKA, Maria S. 10 E WASHINGTON ST, LAKE HOSPITAL SYSTEM 44077 #759-01-1980 L1996 **NPM** *020 †55
VELOTTA, Jennifer Anne. ■ 44077 #038-43-2007 L2007 **OBG** *012
VILLENO, Norma T. 89 E HIGH ST, STE 7 44077 #748-08-1967 L1973 **GE IM** *020
WALKER, James Howard. 7551 FREDLE DR 44077 #028-34-1991 L1997 **ORS** *020 †40
WARD, Boushra. 124 LIBERTY ST # A 44077 #875-02-1974 L1981 **PD** *020 †55
WEAVER, Michael Grafton. 89 E HIGH ST 44077 #038-06-1987 L1988 **PTH PCP** *020 †50
WEINBERGER, Leonard Mark. 7535 FREDLE DR 44077 #025-01-1988 L1990 **N** *020 †75
ZART, David James. ■ 44077 #038-06-1996 **ORS** *100

PANDORA – PUTNAM

HOUSTON, David Duane. 5560 STATE ROUTE 12 W #299 45877 #038-43-1979 L1980 **FM** *020 †18
LUGIBIHL, Oliver Noah. PO BOX 299, 5560 STATE ROUTE 12 W 45877 #038-06-1957 L1957 **FM OS** *071
MC CULLOUGH, Steven K. 5560 STATE ROUTE 12 W #299 45877 #016-76-1979, ▲ L1981 **FM NPM** *020 †18
WOODRUFF, David Lee. 5560 STATE ROUTE 12 W #299 45877 #038-45-1987 L1988 **FM** *020 †18

PARIS – STARK

DONALDSON, Edward E. ■ 44669 #038-06-1951 L1951 **PD** *071 †55

PARMA – CUYAHOGA

ALVI, Sohail Imran. ■ 44134 #045-04-2002 L2005 **IM** *020 †20
ARAKAKI, Felix. ■ 44130 #737-01-1964 L1972 **IM CD** *071
BAUTISTA, Angelina S. 7007 POWERS BLVD 44129 #748-01-1969 L1981 **PTH** *020 †50
BEST, Garnett Skeete. 12301 SNOW RD 44130 #407-10-1966 L1971 **OBG** *020
BHAIJI, Alok. 5500 RIDGE RD, STE 133 44129 #038-43-1993 L1994 **IM** *020 †20
BHAIJI, Khushal C. 5500 RIDGE RD, STE 133 44129 #495-20-1963 L1972 **IM CD** *020
BIDARI, Timmappa P. 6820 RIDGE RD, STE 204 44129 #495-35-1966 L1974 **ON HEM** *020 †20
BINSTOCK, Mark A. 12301 SNOW RD, KAISER PARMA MED CTR 44130 #016-06-1983 L1994 **OBG** *020 †30
BOHENICK, Carrie Ann. 6681 RIDGE RD STE 205 44129 #041-15-2002 L2002 **PD** *020 †55
BOUMITRI, Mirna Georges. ■ 44134 #038-43-2005 L2005 **IM** *012
BRINKIS, Edmund Z. 12301 SNOW RD, KAISER PERMANENTE 44130 #305-09-1994 L2002 **OAR** *020 †40
BROOKS, Robert E. 6789 RIDGE RD, STE 103 44129 #010-02-1951 L1952 **CD IM** *071 †20
BROWN, Trudi Jo. 6707 POWERS BLVD STE 100 44129 #055-01-1990 L1995 **GS** *020 †85
BUI, Don Thanh. ■ 44134 #038-44-2006 L2006 **GS** *012
BURKE, Michelle Lynne. ■ 44129 #038-43-2006 L2006 **PD** *012
BUTLER, Diane Arlene. 6681 RIDGE RD STE 205, PARMA PEDIATRICS INC 44129 #038-40-1978 L1979 **PD** *020 †55
CANDAPPA, Sivakamavalli. 7007 POWERS BLVD, PARMA COMMUNITY HOSP PAT D 44129 #495-42-1961 L1983 **OS** *071
CARLIN, Leo Y. 3400 CHEVR BLVD-0098 44130 #748-02-1957 L1973 **OM** *071 †85

CHANG, Keuck. 6789 RIDGE RD STE 203 44129 #583-02-1970 L1977 **IM** *020 †20
CHEHADE, Nabil C. 12301 SNOW RD, KAISER PERMANENTE MEDICAL 44130 #038-43-1992 L1998 **U** *020 †95
CHENG, Stephen L. 12302 SNOW RD 44130 #067-01-1987 L1996 **OAR** *020 †40
COSERIU, Michael Vasile. 6115 POWERS BLVD STE 300 44129 #038-43-1978 L1981 **OPH** *020 †35
CROWE, William Edward. 6681 RIDGE RD, STE 204 44129 #028-34-1972 L1975 **PM RHU** *020 †20
CUTARELLI, Renato. 6681 RIDGE RD, STE 404 44129 #561-17-1954 L1962 **CD** *020 †20
DAHMAN, Ayman. 6789 RIDGE RD, STE 201 44129 #875-01-1986 L1989 **OBG** *020 †30
DA MERT, Gary Jay. 12301 SNOW RD 44130 #056-06-1972 L1984 **IM ID** *020 †20
DE LA FUENTE, Nelson L. 7007 POWERS BLVD, PARMA COMMUNITY GENERAL HO 44129 #748-01-1968 L1975 **AN** *020
DE LA IGLESIA, Raul A. ■ 44134 #132-01-1955 L1970 **PM DR** *072
DIETRICH, Marie Clare. 12301 SNOW RD, PARMA MEDICAL CENTER 44130 #033-05-1984 L1985 **PDI PD** *020 †55
DOBRINICH, Robert J. 12301 SNOW RD 44130 #038-45-1982 L1987 **ID IM** *020 †20
DOBROWSKI, John Michael. 6707 POWERS BLVD STE 202 44129 #028-34-1979 L1987 **OTO FPS** *020 †20
DSOUZA, Carol Ann. 12301 SNOW RD 44130 #495-52-1981 L1988 **IM** *020 †20
DUARTE, Alfredo E. 6789 RIDGE RD 44129 #264-01-1953 L1967 **GS GP** *071
DURVE, Mohan Jagannath. 6681 RIDGE RD, STE 305 44129 #496-38-1971 L1977 **AI PD** *020 †55,03
ELGUDIN, Larissa. 12301 SNOW RD 44130 #913-66-1988 L2000 **CHP P** *020 †75
ESMURDOC, Rafael G. ■ 44130 #308-01-1960 L1979 **GP OS** *020
FALKO, John Jos. 6681 RIDGE RD 44129 #038-40-1966 L1966 **OBG** *020
FARES, Maan A. 12301 SNOW RD, KAISER PERMANENTE 44130 #875-01-1990 L1995 **CD** *020 †20
FERGUSON, Elizabeth Ann. 8669 ROYALVIEW DR 44129 #038-06-1994 L1996 **EM** *020 †16
FRANK, Kay Ellen Burdette. 12301 SNOW RD, KAISER PERMANENTE MEDICAL 44130 #041-02-1969 L1970 **OPH** *020 †35
FU, Shih-Ching Keith. 12301 SNOW RD 44130 #244-02-1972 L1978 **IM ON** *020 †20
GAL, Thomas A. 12301 SNOW RD 44130 #473-01-1975 L1980 **IM** *020
GEMBUS, Daniel Walter. 7007 POWERS BLVD, PARMA COMMUNITY HOSPITAL 44129 #038-40-1986 L1989 **AN GS** *020 †05
GEORGE, Stephany Ann. 6115 POWERS BLVD, STE 306 44129 #038-06-1994 L1995 **OBG** *020 †30
GIGLIOTTI, Philip Louis. 6789 RIDGE RD, STE 105 44129 #038-06-1979 L1980 **IM** *020
GITTINGER, Richard Allen. 6115 POWERS BLVD STE 100, SOUTHWEST ORTHOPAEDICS INC 44129 #038-06-1984 L1985 **ORS** *020 †40
GORDON, Ronald. 7007 POWERS BLVD, PARMA COMM GENERAL HOSP 44129 #005-06-1984 L1995 **EM** *020 †16
GRIESER, Kathleen Sue. 12301 SNOW RD 44130 #038-43-1976 L1979 **IM** *020 †20
GURANGO, Emilie Marion E. 6681 RIDGE RD, STE 200 44129 #748-01-1969 L1973 **GP AN** *020
HAAS, Peter Francis. 7007 POWERS BLVD 44129 #035-48-1999 L2003 **EM** *020 †16
HAHN, William Kenneth, Jr. 6681 RIDGE RD, STE 206 44129 #038-43-1991 L1993 **OBG** *020 †30
HENIG, Israel. 6789 RIDGE RD, STE 209 44129 #550-02-1978 L1982 **OBG REN** *020 †30
HO, Donghai Viet. ■ 44129 #020-02-2008 *012
HSU, Shih Mou. 12301 SNOW RD 44130 #244-04-1971 L1977 **CD IM** *020
HU, Benjamin Van. 6688 RIDGE RD STE 1200 44129 #038-06-1983 L1988 **OPH** *020
HUDOCK, Paul Anthony. 6681 RIDGE RD, STE 411 44129 #038-06-1989 L1992 **OBG** *020 †30
ISLA, Edward Charles. 7007 POWERS BLVD 44129 #038-45-1995 L2000 **IM** *020 †20 ‡
JUGUILON, Augusto C. 6800 RIDGE RD 44129 #748-01-1970 L1974 **N OS** *020 †75
KAHL, Joseph Leo. 12301 SNOW RD 44130 #016-43-1974 L1976 **P** *020 †75
KARGIOTIS, Minnie H. 7007 POWERS BLVD 44129 #737-01-1956 L1980 **IM RHU** *071
KICZEK, Christopher Paul. 5400 CHEVROLET BLVD, MEDICAL CENTER 44130 #654-01-1984 L1989 **IM** *071
KIM, Hong Yong. ■ 44134 #583-01-1960 L1979 **GP** *020
KLATTE, Paul Anthony. 7007 POWERS BLVD, DEPT RAD 44129 #038-40-1982 L1986 **DR** *020 †80
KLOS, Alexander Adrian. 5903 STATE RD 44134 #407-23-1949 L1956 **IM** *072
KMIECK, John Albert. ■ 44129 #028-34-1947 L1949 **U** *071 †95
KOZIY, Rostyslav. 7007 POWERS BLVD, PARMA COMM GENERAL HOSP 44129 #913-89-1988 L2006 **AN** *020 †05
LIANG, James Tsung Hwa. 5500 RIDGE RD STE 220 44129 #244-04-1971 L1976 **PD AI** *020 †55
LIBECCO, Julia Ann. 6707 POWERS BLVD, STE 203 44129 #038-44-2000 L2000 **PD** *020 †55
LONGVILLE, Susan Marie. 7007 POWERS BLVD, PARMA COMM GEN 44129 #038-44-1982 L1983 **EM** *020 †16
MALATY, Ramez Albert. ■ 44130 #038-43-2005 L2005 **DR** *012
MANDEL, Armand. 6681 RIDGE RD, STE 409 44129 #038-06-1951 L1951 **IM CD** *071 †20
MANUEL, Frederico Mopera. ■ 44134 #748-01-1958 L1973 **IM CD** *020
MASTROIANNI, Anthony. 6525 POWERS BLVD 44129 #038-06-1992 L1993 **RO LM** *020 †80
MAZANEC, Orie Albert. ■ 44130 #038-06-1944 L1944 **GP OM** *071 †85
MAZKALNINS, Elga M. 6681 RIDGE RD 44129 #407-24-1951 L1958 **P CHP** *071
MC BRIDE, Maureen Rita. 12301 SNOW RD 44130 #038-06-1987 L1989 **OPH** *020 †35
NAEEM, Shabbir Ahmad. ■ 44129 #704-01-1967 L1973 **DR NM** *020 †80
NAM, Kwan Woo. 12301 SNOW RD, KAISER PERMANENTE MEDICAL 44130 #583-03-1971 L1979 **R** *020 †80
NAPORA, Taras Eugene. 7007 POWERS BLVD, PARMA COMM GEN HOSP 44129 #038-44-2000 L2000 **EM** *020 †16
NOWAK, Michael Mark. 12301 SNOW RD, CLEVELAND HTS MEDICAL CENT 44130 #038-06-1982 L1984 **GS** *020 †85
ONG, Romeo Siy. 5500 RIDGE RD STE 236 44129 #748-01-1973 L1978 **OTO A** *020 †45
OSWALD, Gregory Louis. 7007 POWERS BLVD, PARMA COMM GEN HOSP 44129 #038-43-1998 L1999 **EM** *020 †16
OWENS, Bernard James. 12301 SNOW RD, DEPT OF SURGERY OPM6 44130 #035-08-1972 L1998 **VS GS** *020 †85
PAAT, Erdulfo Paz. 6681 RIDGE RD STE 302 44129 #748-08-1966 L1972 **IM** *020
PAGANO, Samuel Wm. 7007 POWERS BLVD 44129 #010-01-1974 L1982 **EM FM** *020 †18,16
PAJKA, Stanley Francis. 5500 RIDGE RD, STE 102 44129 #038-40-1991 L1992 **OPH** *020 †30
PAKRASHI, Brojesh. 6688 RIDGE RD STE 1420 44129 #495-02-1958 L1979 **CD IM** *020
PALAZIJ, Rodion. 6688 RIDGE RD, PARMATOWN MED BLDG SOUTH 44129 #065-01-1966 L1968 **D** *072
PATEL, Ankita Bharat. ■ 44129 #038-44-2006 **PD** *012

■ = Address Information Privacy Protected

PIMENTEL, Renato Reyes. 2560 NELSON BLVD 44134 #748-08-1967 L1974 **AN** *020
POIS, Allen Jos. 12301 SNOW RD 44130 #024-07-1957 L1989 **TS** *071 †85,90
PUPILLO, Giovanni Alberto. 5580 STATE RD 44134 #561-17-1965 L1976 **IM CD** *072
PUSNIK, Alan John. 12301 SNOW RD 44130 #041-09-1972 L1977 **PD IM** *020 †55
RAVEENDRAN, P. 12301 SNOW RD 44130 #495-31-1969 L1979 **OTO** *020 †45
RAYKOV, Paul Anthony. 12301 SNOW RD, KAISER HOSPITAL 44130 #025-07-1980 L1996 **EM IM** *020 †20,16
RENNER, Patrick A. 6707 POWERS BLVD, STE 100 44129 #038-41-1988 L1994 **GS** *020 †85
RHEE, Sang Bong. 6789 RIDGE RD, WOMEN & WELLNESS 44129 #583-02-1953 L1964 **OBG** *071 †30
SADASIVAN, P. 12301 SNOW RD 44130 #495-31-1969 L1975 **NEP IM** *020 †20
SAGHAFI, Dariush. 6681 RIDGE RD, STE 407 44129 #649-14-1988 L1996 **N** *020
SAGHAFI, Mohammed Mehdi. 6681 RIDGE RD STE 407 44129 #517-06-1959 L1970 **GS GYN** *020
SALEH, Ali Jawad. 7007 POWERS BLVD 44129 #654-01-2000 L2000 **IM** *100 †20 ‡
SARACCO, Sonia Maria. 12301 SNOW RD 44130 #023-01-1983 L1988 **PTH PCP** *020 †50
SCHEFFT, Paul A. 12301 SNOW RD 44130 #028-34-1975 L1981 **U** *071 †95
SCHNELL, Frederick R. 5500 RIDGE RD 44129 #038-06-1947 L1947 **IM** *071 †20
SCHNELL, Stephen James. 5831 RIDGE RD 44129 #038-06-1984 L1987 **IM** *020 †20
SEAWARD, Percival Doug. 12301 SNOW RD 44130 #836-01-1954 L1981 **GS** *020
SHAGAWAT, Barbara Ann. 12301 SNOW RD, KAISER PERMANENTE 44130 #035-06-1992 L1994 **OBG** *020 †30
SHIPCHANDLER, Laurie O'Ma. 6681 RIDGE RD STE 205 44129 #017-20-2003 L2003 **PD** *020 †55
SO, Rosa Rosales. 5500 RIDGE RD, STE 213 44129 #748-01-1966 L1978 **P** *020
SONG, Yong Jae. 6731 RIDGE RD 44129 #583-02-1969 L1976 **IM** *020 †20
STAHL, Robert Ray. 6474 STATE RD UNIT 5 44134 #023-01-1948 L1950 **IM** *071 †20
STEINETZ, Caroline Grace. 7007 POWERS BLVD 44129 #038-44-1986 L1990 **PTH PCP** *020 †50
STEPHENS, Robert Paul. 5500 RIDGE RD STE 237 44129 #035-45-1993 L1995 **PD** *020 †55
STERN, Lawrence Gene. 6731 RIDGE RD, STE 301 44129 #035-45-1973 L1978 **NS** *020
SULLIVAN, Peter Daly. 7007 POWERS BLVD, PARMA HOSPITAL 44129 #038-40-1985 L1986 **EM** *020 †16
SUTARIA, Vinod Manilal. 12301 SNOW RD, KAISER PERMANENTE 44130 #495-22-1961 L1975 **IM HEM** *020 †20
TAGLIABUE, James Robt. 12301 SNOW RD, DEPT OF RADIOLOGY 44130 #033-05-1984 L1989 **DR** *020 †80
TOETZ, Colleen Elizabeth. 5707 ELY VISTA DR 44129 #038-41-2008 *012
TOLEDO, Juan Antonio. 12301 SNOW RD 44130 #847-04-1972 L1981 **N** *020 †75
TOLENTINO, Hermelino V. ■ 44134 #748-01-1962 L1973 **AN** *020
TOMASCHEK, Laszlo S. 6390 PEARL RD 44130 #035-06-1976 L1980 **OPH** *020 †35
TSOU, Pon Lion. 44129 #654-01-2004 L2005 **P** *012
TUGAOEN, Domingo T. ■ 44134 #748-01-1956 L1975 **EM** *071 †16
UJLA, Dilip Khushmanlal. 7441 W RIDGEWOOD DR, STE 255 44129 #495-17-1970 L1979 **EM FM** *020
ULVI, Bashir M. 6325 YORK RD, STE 304 44130 #704-01-1963 L1971 **PS** *020 †85,65
UNGIER, Mirfee Klein. 6820 RIDGE RD, STE 102 44129 #038-06-1980 L1980 **OPH** *020 †35
VARGA, Ildiko. ■ 44129 #473-01-1968 L1987 **GP** *071
VOGELGESANG, Ryan James. 5500 RIDGE RD STE 237 44129 #038-06-1995 L1997 **PD** *020 †55
WOLANIN, Andre Felix. 6115 POWERS BLVD, STE 100 44129 #038-44-1990 L1994 **ORS** *020 †40
WOLFSON, Donn A. 6707 POWERS BLVD STE 104 44129 #043-01-1976 L1979 **PUD CCM** *020 †20
YANG, David Cheng-I. 12301 SNOW RD 44130 #244-04-1978 L1993 **IM** *020 †20
ZONFA, Charles Anthony. 12301 SNOW RD 44130 #038-44-1993 L1996 **OBG** *020 †30

PARMA HEIGHTS – CUYAHOGA

ABERNETHY, Rachel Webber. 12301 SNOW RD 44130 #038-06-1966 L1966 **IM NEP** *020 †20
DVORAK, Kenneth James. 6363 YORK RD, STE 101 44130 #038-06-1976 L1977 **OTO ORS** *075 †45
GASKIN, Gregory Bernard. ■ 44130 #025-07-2004 L2005 **AN** *012
GO, Corazon L. 6363 YORK RD, STE 103 44130 #748-11-1971 L1977 **PD** *020 †55
GO, Jaime Luz. 6315 PEARL RD 44130 #748-08-1973 L1982 **FM GP** *020
JAMHOUR, Joseph Asad. 6363 YORK RD, STE 103 44130 #605-01-1976 L1978 **PD** *020 †55
KENNEDY, Philip Aiken, III. 6420 YORK RD 44130 #038-06-1977 L1980 **FM** *020 †18
NORBY, Alicia Marie. ■ 44130 #037-01-2006 L2006 **IM** *012
QURESHI, Amer S. ■ 44130 #704-01-1986 L2000 **FPG** *020 †20
STEWART, Ralph Edward. 12301 SNOW RD 44130 #016-06-1986 L1991 **OPH** *020 †35

PATASKALA – LICKING

ATWOOD, Jeannie M. 8200 HAZELTON ETNA RD SW 43062 #038-43-1987 L1989 **OBG** *020 †30
CLEMENTE, Marc Gennaro. 3698 ALWARD RD SW 43062 #038-44-1981 L1982 **P** *020 †75
DECKER, Emily Anne. 1 HEALTHY PL, PEDIATRICS-PATASKALA 43062 #038-40-2002 L2002 **PD** *020 †55
FOURAS, Alexios G. ■ 43062 #418-01-1959 L1964 **PTH** *030 †50
GUTRIDGE, Jennifer K. 8200 HAZELTON ETNA RD SW, STE 100 43062 #038-45-1998 L1999 **FM** *020 ‡
PAAL, Miklos. ■ 43062 #473-03-1932 L1953 **PUD AN** *071
REZAI, Mostafa. 127 PEBBLE CREEK DR 43062 #517-01-1959 L1971 **FM GS** *020
ROBERTSON, Williette M. ■ 43062 #038-45-1995 L1997 **IM** *020 †20
SCHWARTZ, Norman Allan. 621 BROAD ST SW 43062 #038-40-1987 L1988 **FM** *020 †18
SHAFFER, Colleen. 1 HEALTHY PL, STE 101 43062 #038-41-1994 L2001 **FM** *020 †18
WILSON, Shannon Elizabeth. ■ 43062 #038-43-2006 **OBG** *012
WODARCYK, Michael Andrew. 8200 HAZELTON ETNA RD SW, STE 200 43062 #038-43-1985 L1990 **U** *020 †95

PAULDING – PAULDING

BAZALI, Walter. 11558 STATE ROUTE 111 45879 #154-02-1951 L1958 **GP IM** *071

BOWER, Meagan Bridget. 1030 W WAYNE ST 45879 #038-43-1995 L1996 **IM** *020
DOBBINS, Richard Lawrence. 1035 W WAYNE ST 45879 #038-41-1959 L1959 **EM AN** *020 †18
DOZIER, James Crosby. 1035 W WAYNE ST 45879 #038-41-1985 L1985 **NS** *020 †25
HALACHANOVA, Virginia. 1032 W WAYNE ST 45879 #286-06-1996 L1999 **IM** *020
LANGENKAMP, Paul Henry. 11558 STATE ROUTE 111 45879 #038-41-1985 L1988 **FM** *020 †18
MILLER, William Max. ■ 45879 #038-41-1970 L1973 **FM** *020
MUNZ, Michael. 1035 W WAYNE ST 45879 #067-01-1987 L1999 **NS** *020 †25
RAFIQ, Kamran. 1035 W WAYNE ST, PAULDING COUNTY HOSPITAL 45879 #704-01-1989 L1999 **IM** *020 †20
SNYDER, Don Kimsey. 1030 W WAYNE ST 45879 #016-06-1958 L1959 **GP AN** *071
SPANGLER, Wendell James. 1032 W WAYNE ST, PCH PHYSICIAN SERVICES 45879 #038-43-1999 L2000 **FM** *020 †18 ‡
SPENCER, Becky Jo. 11558 STATE ROUTE 111 45879 #038-45-1998 L1999 **MPD** *020 †20
STRAWTER, Wm Hamilton. 1035 W WAYNE ST 45879 #012-05-1974 L2005 **GS VS** *020 †85

PEEBLES – ADAMS

AINA, Olayinka Olusola. 154 ELLIOTT AVE 45660 #690-01-1984 L1992 **IM** *020

PEMBERVILLE – WOOD

EULBERG, Le Roy Jos. 135 E FRONT ST 43450 #038-40-1957 L1957 **GP** *071
PIERCE, John Edward. 20311 PEMBERVILLE RD 43450 #038-45-1987 L1988 **FM** *020 †18
WEISENBURGER, Jeanne F. ■ 43450 #038-43-1985 L1986 **FM** *071 †18

PENINSULA – SUMMIT

FRANCIS, Michael Arthur. 4341 RIVERVIEW RD LOT 6 44264 #047-07-1968 L1973 **ON GS** *020 †85
MYER, Daniel Mackenzie. ■ 44264 #038-40-2006 L2006 **ORS** *012
POOL, Loren Richard. 4557 QUICK RD 44264 #038-06-1977 L1978 **EM FM** *020 †18

PEPPER PIKE – CUYAHOGA

ALI, Sawsan. 18 HUNTING HOLLOW DR 44124 #875-03-1989 L1997 **FM** *020 †18
BRZOZOWSKI, Paul Mark. 31200 PINETREE RD 44124 #041-09-1991 L1992 **AN** *020 †05
CESAR, Cynthia A Taylor. ■ 44124 #041-07-1975 L1979 **AN** *071 †05
CESAR, Joseph Andre. ■ 44124 #869-04-1967 L1975 **GP P** *020
CHEPLA, Kyle James. 31200 PINETREE RD 44124 #038-40-2007 L2007 **PS** *012
CHO, Kathleen Y. ■ 44124 #038-40-2000 L2004 **AN** *025
CLEVELAND, Wm Bingham, III. 31200 PINETREE RD 44124 #748-01-1980 L1983 **AN** *020 †05
DECATES, Andre M. 31200 PINETREE RD 44124 #038-06-1996 L1997 **AN** *020
DONOHUE, James Francis. 31200 PINETREE RD 44124 #025-01-1990 L1994 **AN** *020 †05
ESSELSTYN, Caldwell B, Jr. ■ 44124 #038-06-1961 L1961 **GPM** *071 †85
FELDKIRCHER, Mary Colleen. 31200 PINETREE RD 44124 #038-06-1987 L1987 **AN** *020 †05
FIGUEROA, Priscilla I. ■ 44124 #035-20-1985 L2005 **PTH IM** *020 †50
FISHMAN, Julius. ■ 44124 #038-06-1950 L1950 **IMG** *071 †20
GEHAMY, Robert Anton. ■ 44124 #875-01-1964 L1973 **EM CRS** *020 †10,16
HAGOPIAN, John Richard. 31200 PINETREE RD 44124 #038-43-1997 L2002 **AN** *020 †05
HALMOS, Balazs. ■ 44124 #473-01-1992 L2004 **IM HO** *020 †20
HERMAN, Donald Kenneth. ■ 44124 #038-40-1960 L1960 **OBG** *071 †30
HOSLER, Jun-Ja Chung. 31200 PINETREE RD 44124 #583-06-1965 L1972 **AN** *020
JACKSON, Cheryl Yvette. 28160 RED RAVEN RD 44124 #038-40-2004 L2004 **OBG** *012
JOYCE, David Michael. ■ 44124 #038-06-2007 L2007 **ORS** *012
KAO, Patricia Fungyu. ■ 44124 #038-06-2001 L2001 **NEP** *100
KATZMAN, Richard Allen. ■ 44124 #016-02-1955 L1956 **IM CD** *071 †20
KIM, De-Sung. 31200 PINETREE RD 44124 #583-06-1970 L1980 **AN** *020
KIRSH, Susan Riga. ■ 44124 #038-43-1992 L1993 **IM** *030 †20
KOBLENTZ, Leslie Margolis. ■ 44124 #038-06-2000 L2000 **P** *020 †75 ‡
KOFMAN, Esther. ■ 44124 #913-70-1971 L1977 **PD EM** *020 †55
LEE, Young Jai. 31200 PINETREE RD 44124 #583-04-1966 L1974 **AN** *020
LEEDY, Jason Eugene. ■ 44124 #038-06-2000 L2004 **PS** *020 †65
LEVIN, Howard Stanley. ■ 44124 #023-01-1958 L1970 **ATP** *071 †50
LEVINE, Ari Daniel. ■ 44124 #038-41-2007 L2007 **ORS** *012
LIDSKY, Isadore. ■ 44124 #065-01-1951 L1956 **GS VS** *071 †85
LUCAS, Melvin A. 8 LOUIS DR 44124 #038-41-1949 L1949 **AN PME** *071 †05
MANIAR, Smita Dilip. 31200 PINETREE RD 44124 #496-38-1963 L1975 **AN** *020
MARTIN, Ruth D Swimmer. 28351 CAMBRIDGE LN 44124 #035-08-1971 L1976 **P** *020 †75
MARTIN, Scott Frederick. ■ 44124 #038-06-2006 L2006 **P** *012
MARTIN, Sonya L. ■ 44124 #035-19-2008 *012
MC HENRY, Martin C. ■ 44124 #038-41-1957 L1957 **ID** *072 †20
MEDINA, Federico Santos. ■ 44124 #038-02-1960 L1970 **AN** *020
MENTARI, Asikin. ■ 44124 #506-01-1968 L1975 **PM PMM** *071 †60
MIR-MADJLESSI, Seid H. ■ 44124 #561-17-1965 L1984 **IM** *020 †20
MORRISON, Stuart C. 3150 NORTHWOOD DR 44124 #352-06-1970 L1980 **R** *020 †80
NEEDLMAN, Robert David. ■ 44124 #008-01-1985 L1993 **PD** *050 †55
ORRINGER, Daniel Avram. ■ 44124 #038-40-2004 L2006 **NS** *012
PALEY, Michael Jay. 2844 KERSDALE RD 44124 #038-06-1990 L1992 **DR** *020 †80
ROHRER, Max Leslie. ■ 44124 #035-45-1947 L1949 **PD** *071 †55
ROYAK, Boris. 30799 PINETREE RD # 308 44124 #038-06-1999 L2002 **P** *020 †75
SALOVON, Gary Alan. 31200 PINETREE RD 44124 #038-43-1994 L1999 **AN** *020 †05
SANDHU, Gurneet Singh. ■ 44124 #038-40-2006 L2006 **GS** *012
SCERBO, John Jos. 31200 PINETREE RD 44124 #038-43-1988 L1991 **AN** *020 †20,05
SCHUBERT, Karen Speck. ■ 44124 #023-12-1983 L1990 **GP** *020
SEGEL, Alvin Sanford. ■ 44124 #038-40-1954 L1954 **R** *071 †80
SETHI, Neil. ■ 44124 #038-41-2001 *100
SMITH, Charles Elliot. 2660 HICKORY LN 44124 #067-03-1983 L1988 **AN** *020 †05
STUBBS, Cailin Marie. 31200 PINETREE RD 44124 #038-40-1992 L1996 **AN** *020 †05
SUBRAMANYAN, Smitha. ■ 44124 #041-01-1993 L2000 **ON** *020 †20
TUASON, Mauro Serrano. ■ 44124 #748-01-1957 L1966 **AN** *020
VARGHAI, Nayyer H. ■ 44124 #517-01-1990 L2000 **FM** *020 †18

WHITAKER, Donnah W. 31200 PINETREE RD 44124 #055-02-1984 L1986 **AN** *020 †05

WOLF, Nancy Gail. ■ 44124 #024-01-1990 L1997 **PTH** *020 †50,19

YOSOWITZ, Gerald Marvin. ■ 44124 #038-40-1964 L1964 **ORS** *020 †40

PERRYSBURG – WOOD

ALCOVER, Ingrid. ■ 43551 #308-02-1977 L1982 **IM EM** *071

ALKHATEEB, Mohammed. 1103 VILLAGE SQUARE DR, STE 202 43551 #875-02-1990 L1998 **CD** *020 †20

BADIK, Bryan James. 1601 BRIGHAM DR, STE 250 43551 #038-43-2003 2003 **FM** *020 †18

BENNETT, Cecilia V. 26890 THOMPSON RD 43551 #748-02-1955 L1967 **FM OS** *071 †50,18

BERTKA, Vicki M. 30000 E RIVER RD, HOSPICE OF NORTHWEST OHIO 43551 #038-43-1982 L1984 **FM PLM** *020 †18

BHATIA, Raj Kumar. 11201 SANDUSKY ST STE 101 43551 #495-45-1967 L1974 **CD IM** *020 †20

BHODA, Raja Sekhar Reddy. ■ 43551 #495-21-1996 L2005 **FP** *012

BIALECKI-HAASE, Dee Ann. 1601 BRIGHAM DR, STE 250 43551 #038-41-1993 L1994 **FM** *020 †18

BIHN, Cheryl Ann. 28442 E RIVER RD 43551 #038-43-1993 L2001 **PM** *020 †60

BIHN, Gerald Thos, II. 1103 VILLAGE SQUARE DR, STE 205 43551 #038-43-1987 L1989 **PM** *071 †60

BIRCH, Dorrin Marie. 27068 OAKMEAD DR, OAKMEAD COMMONS 43551 #038-43-1982 L1983 **GP OS** *071

BISWAS, Haridas. 11201 SANDUSKY ST, STE 101 43551 #160-02-1972 L1980 **CD IM** *020 †20

BLOMQUIST, Thomas Morgan. ■ 43551 #038-43-2008 *012

BOAG, Charles Brixner. ■ 43551 #003-75-2004, ▲ L2004 **OBG** *012

BRIDGES, Teresa Pamala. ■ 43551 #017-20-1983 L1985 **EM** *020 †16

BROWN, Marian Louise. ■ 43551 #038-43-1991 L1994 **CHP** *020

BUEHLER, Jamie Angela. ■ 43551 #038-43-2008 *012

CAMERON, Donald Ian. 27121 OAKMEAD DR, STE B 43551 #566-01-1975 L1982 **CHN OS** *062 †55,75

CANNELLA, Jonathan David. ■ 43551 #038-43-2008 *012

CARROLL, Nancy Belle. 975 COMMERCE DR 43551 #038-43-1982 L1984 **CHP P** *020 †75

CASSAVAR, Daniel Kent. 1601 BRIGHAM DR, STE 120 43551 #038-43-1989 L1993 **CD** *020 †20

CLARK, Stephen Eric. 351 E BOUNDARY ST 43551 #038-40-1991 L1992 **OPH** *020 †35

COARD-MITCHELL, Hope T. 900 W SOUTH BOUNDARY ST #6 43551 #038-43-1994 L1998 **D** *020 †15

CROTTE, Fernando. ■ 43551 #649-01-1953 L1966 **GS** *071

DE FRANCO, Vincent James. ■ 43552 #028-34-1954 L1955 **OS** *072

DOMINI, Leslie Joseph. 702 COMMERCE DR, STE 160 43551 #038-43-1972 L1973 **FM** *020 †18

DONAWA, Robert Marc. 702 COMMERCE DR, STE 160 43551 #038-41-1996 L1998 **FM** *020 †18

DUNCAN, Brannon Charles. ■ 43551 #045-01-2005 L2005 **EM** *012

DVORAK, Jon Robt. 1601 BRIGHAM DR, STE 200 43551 #038-43-1983 L1985 **PD** *020 †55

EVANS, Jason Lynn. 1601 BRIGHAM DR, STE 250 43551 #028-02-1997 L1998 **FM** *020 †18 ‡

GBUR, Charles Jos, Jr. 1601 BRIGHAM DR, STE 120 43551 #038-40-1987 L1987 **CD VM** *020 †20

GERKEN, Andrew Spencer. ■ 43551 #038-40-2000 L2003 **FSM** *020 †18

GOERTZEN, Eugene Wilbert. ■ 43551 #038-02-1964 L1982 **PS HNS** *071 †45

GRIESEMER, Mark V. ■ 43551 #028-78-2007, ▲ L2007 **EM** *012

GUNDABOLU, Bhaskar. ■ 43551 #495-50-2000 L2006 **END** *100 †20

HANDYSIDE, Edward Randolp. ■ 43551 #130-01-2007 L2007 **FP** *012

HASHMI, Raza. 1103 VILLAGE SQUARE DR, STE 202 43551 #704-21-1981 L2003 **CD** *020 †20

HERTZFELD, Robert James. 10246 FORD RD 43551 #038-40-1968 L1968 **AN** *020 †05

HOST, Eleanor J. 28442 E RIVER RD, STE 204 43551 #038-44-1992 L1993 **FM** *020 †18

HUDSON, Jeffrey Scott. 230 W 7TH ST 43551 #038-43-2005 L2008 **OBG** *012

HUENEFELD, Suzette Lynn. 27511 HOLIDAY LN, # 101 43551 #038-43-1993 L1994 **FM** *020 †18

ISKERSKY, Victor. ■ 43551 #913-05-1943 L1954 **FM** *018

ISLAM, Mahjabeen. 900 W S BOUNDARY ST # 1B, PERRY TOWNE SQUARE 43551 #704-02-1981 L1986 **FM** *020 †18

JENKINS, Tasha Yvette. 28754 OREGON RD # C3 43551 #038-45-1998 L2000 **FM** *020

JOHNSON, Gregory Gene. 1021 SANDUSKY ST, STE C 43551 #038-40-1979 L1982 **OBG** *020 †30

KABOUR, Ameer. 1103 VILLAGE SQUARE DR, STE 202 43551 #875-01-1984 L1996 **CD IM** *020 †20

KALE, Lawrence. 26550 CATAWBA DR, P O BOX 791 43551 #038-43-1992 L1994 **OM IM** *020 †70

KANAAN, Tarif. 1103 VILLAGE SQUARE DR, STE 202 43551 #875-02-1988 L2000 **IC CD** *020 †20

KAZOR, Kelley Marie. ■ 43551 #038-43-2003 *100

KELLEY, Bernard Joseph. ■ 43551 #045-01-2002 L2006 **AN** *012

KENNEDY, Carol A. 1601 BRIGHAM DR STE 200, PERRYSBURG PEDIATRICS 43551 #038-43-1986 L1988 **PD** *020 †55

KHALED, Mounir Khaled. ■ 43551 #781-02-1993 L2004 **IM** *020 †20

KHAN, Farrukh Ahmed. 1601 BRIGHAM DR, STE 120 43551 #704-16-1987 L2004 **FM** *020 †20

KINDERVATER, Karen Ann. 975 COMMERCE DR 43551 #038-43-1980 L1985 **CHP P** *020

LLOYD, Janice S. ■ 43551 #038-41-1979 L1980 **OM GPM** *030 †18,70

LORTON, Christy Ann. 900 W S BOUNDARY ST, BLDG 6 43551 #038-40-1982 L1983 **D** *020 †15

LUKE, Crystal J. 28442 E RIVER RD, STE 204 43551 #496-29-1992 L1997 **FM** *020 †18

MANN, James Eugene. ■ 43552 #038-40-1960 L1960 **GP** *075

MATHEW, Rajesh. ■ 43551 #496-23-2004 L2006 **IM** *012

MATYAS, Florence B. 1021 SANDUSKY ST STE 43551 #038-43-1994 L1996 **FM** *020 †18

MC CULLOUGH, Lynne C S. ■ 43551 #038-40-1966 L1966 **AN** *071 †05

MC GREEVEY, John F, Jr. 30000 E RIVER RD, HOSPICE OF NORTHWEST OHIO 43551 #038-43-1978 L1981 **IMG IM** *040 †20

MC NAMARA, Patrick Kelly. 28442 E RIVER RD, STE 102 43551 #038-40-1984 L1989 **IM ADM** *071 †20

MEIER, John David. 1601 BRIGHAM DR, STE 250 43551 #038-45-1985 L1987 **FM** *062 †18

MEREDITH, Todd Aaron. 1021 SANDUSKY ST STE C 43551 #038-43-1999 L1999 **IC** *020

MILLER, Cameron Kennedy. ■ 43551 #038-43-2008 *012

MINGUILLAN, Javier. 28442 E RIVER RD, STE 101 43551 #847-13-1982 L2001 **GE** *020 †20

MULROW, Patrick J. ■ 43551 #035-20-1951 L1975 **IM END** *071 †20

NEISWANDER, Michael Allen. 28442 E RIVER RD, STE 100 43551 #038-43-1996 L1998 **FM** *020 †18

NGUYEN, Tuan Thanh. ■ 43551 #166-01-2006 L2006 **FP** *012

O CONNOR, Mark Francis. 1103 VILLAGE SQUARE DR, STE 202 43551 #025-01-1986 L1997 **CD IM** *020 †20

ORLOP, Stanley J. 1103 VILLAGE SQ, STE 100 43551 #038-75-1997, ▲ L2000 **IM** *020

O'TOOLE, Michael. ■ 43551 #539-02-1955 L1963 **FM** *071 †19

PAPPULA, Jyothi Sri. ■ 43551 #496-24-1993 L2007 **FM** *020 †18

PARK, Danny Sanghun. ■ 43551 #038-43-2006 L2006 **TY** *012

PATIBANDLA, Anita. ■ 43551 #038-43-2003 L2007 **OBG** *020

PAUL, Marsha D. 30000 E RIVER RD, HOSPICE OF NW OHIO 43551 #038-43-1995 L1997 **IM** *020 †20

RANK, John B. #016-06-1948 L1954 **OS GS** *071 †85

RETHOLTZ, Joel S. 1103 VILLAGE SQUAR DR #100 43551 #016-76-1974, ▲ L1976 **IM** *020

ROSHE, Joseph. ■ 43551 #016-42-1953 L1960 **TS** *071 †85,90

ROYAL, Stacey Yvette. 1090 W S BOUNDARY ST # 200, CENTER, INC 43551 #038-43-1998 L2001 **FM** *020 ‡

RUGGIERO, Gayle A. ■ 43551 #038-43-2004 L2006 **P** *012

SALEH, Jamal Mohamad. ■ 43552 #038-43-2003 L2003 *100

SCHNEIDER, Joseph Donald. 26281 SEMINARY RD 43551 #038-43-1972 L1973 **FM** *020 †18

SHELDON, Charles Silsby. 1103 VILLAGE SQUARE DR, STE 100 43551 #016-76-1980, ▲ L1984 **IM** *020

SKIVER, Stephen Allen. 28350 KENSINGTON LN, STE 200 43551 #038-43-1974 L1977 **IM** *020 †20

SMITH, Brian. ■ 43551 #038-43-2003 L2003 **GS** *012

SMITH, Charles Loren. 351 E BOUNDARY ST 43551 #025-01-1966 L1970 **OPH** *071 †35

SMOLEN, Katheryn Marie. 580 CRAIG DR STE 8, PMB 182 43551 #038-43-1995 L1998 **IM** *020 †20

STONER, Judith Anne. 14951 STONEHAVEN DR 43551 #038-43-1979 L1981 **IM** *020

SYED, Tauseef G. 900 W SOUTH BOUNDARY ST, BLDG 5B 43551 #704-06-1983 L1996 **RHU** *020 †20

TAYLOR, Frank Willis. 351 E BOUNDARY ST 43551 #038-40-1947 L1947 **OPH** *071 †35

THOMFORD, Neil Roger. 25010 W RIVER RD 43551 #026-04-1955 L1965 **GS** *040 †85

TSAI, Cynthia Hsiehchi. ■ 43551 #011-03-1986 L1991 **IM** *020

TURK, Kenneth Andrew. 1601 BRIGHAM DR, STE 200 43551 #038-43-1997 L2000 **PD** *020 †55

WALKER, Paul Roger. 14848 ROACHTON RD 43551 #038-43-1991 L1992 **EM** *020 †16

WASIK, Donald Theophil. ■ 43551 #025-07-1976 L1982 **PD** *020 †55

WEBB-SMITH, Frances E. 28442 E RIVER RD, STE 111 43551 #038-45-1992 L1996 **OBG** *020

WEEBER-MORSE, Carmen M. 1601 BRIGHAM DR STE 200, C/O PERRYSBURG PEDIATRICS 43551 #038-43-1993 L1996 **PD** *020 †55

WELCH, Thomas Gerald. 1103 VILLAGE SQUARE DR, STE 202 43551 #016-43-1968 L1971 **CD IM** *020 ‡

WELTER, Patricia Ann. 842 W SOUTH BOUNDARY ST 43551 #038-43-1985 L1986 **OPH OS** *020 †35 ‡

WILLIAMS, Daniel Geo. 28442 E RIVER RD, STE 100 43551 #038-41-1982 L1983 **FM** *020 †18

WING, Steven Clayton. ■ 43551 #041-02-2001 L2004 **EM** *020 †16

WIREBAUGH, Jeffrey Frank. 702 COMMERCE DR, STE 160 43551 #038-43-1982 L1984 **FM EM** *020 †18

WOOD, Bobbijean Ellen. ■ 43551 #038-43-1997 L1998 **EM** *020 †16

WOOD, Robert Francis. ■ 43551 #038-43-1997 L1998 **EM** *020 †16

YAP, Antonio Cuenco. ■ 43552 #748-07-1962 L1971 **PD** *071

YARAMADA, Hemalatha. ■ 43551 #495-65-1999 L2007 **FP** *012

ZAVELL, Beth Ann. 900 W SOUTH BOUNDARY ST, BLDG 6 43551 #038-43-1990 L1994 **D** *020 †15

ZHURAKOVSKI, Galina D. 27072 CARRONADE DR, BRONX PSYCHIATRIC SERVICES 43551 #913-04-1975 L1986 **P** *020 †75 ‡

ZIMMERMAN, Robert Alan. 580 CRAIG DR STE 8, PMB 182 43551 #038-43-1986 L1988 **IM PD** *020

PICKERINGTON – FAIRFIELD

ARMEN, Todd Andrew. ■ 43147 #038-40-2003 L2003 **AN** *020

ARTHURS, Barrington Linds. ■ 43147 #038-40-2004 L2006 **AN** *012

AWAN, Zafar Ahmad. 127 PICKERINGTON RIDG DR D 43147 #704-15-1984 L2006 **IM** *100 †20

BEECROFT, Matthew John. ■ 43147 #038-06-2004 L2004 **EM** *012

BIALECKI, Phillip I. ■ 43147 #038-06-1993 L1994 **EM** *020 †16

BLESCH, William R. ■ 43147 #038-40-1950 L1950 **FM GP** *071

BURNS, Shari Lyn. 1310 HILL RD N, PEDIATRIC ASSOC 43147 #016-06-1997 L2000 **PD** *020 †55

BURNS SERRANO, Lisa A. 11299 STONECREEK DR, PICKERINGTON FAMILY PRACTI 43147 #019-02-1991 L1992 **FM** *020 †18

CALDWELL, Willa L. ■ 43147 #010-03-1951 L1954 **FM** *020

CALE, Brent Alan. ■ 43147 #038-40-1996 L1997 **FM FSM** *020 †18

CAYCE, Kenneth Odin. 1797 HILL RD N, STE 100 43147 #130-01-1999 L2001 **FM FSM** *020 †18

CHEN, Bernadette. ■ 43147 #038-44-2001 L2007 **NPM** *100 †55

COOKE, Robert S. 12941 STONECREEK DR, UNIT A 43147 #021-01-1990 L1999 **AN** *020 †05

CRAIG, Janice Lee. 437 HILL RD N 43147 #038-45-1981 L1987 **CHP P** *020 †75

ESCHBACH, Jeffrey Chas. ■ 43147 #041-02-1989 L1990 **FM** *020 †18

GLAVAN, Bogomir John. ■ 43147 #038-40-1973 L1973 **EM FM** *020 †16,05

HARPER, Jannifer Drake. 13233 WATERTON DR 43147 #038-06-1981 L1983 **IM** *020 †20

HERPOLSHEIMER, Bradley C. 475 HILL RD N, HILL ROAD FAMILY PRACTICE 43147 #025-12-1997 L1997 **FM** *020 †18

JENKINS, Catherine M. 1310 HILL RD N, PEDIATRIC ASSOCIATES 43147 #047-06-1989 L1990 **PD** *020 †55

JENKINS, Connie Sue. 38 N CENTER ST 43147 #038-41-1992 L1995 **P** *020 †75

KAGEORGE, David Allen. 641 HILL RD N STE A, PICKERINGTON FAMILY PRAC 43147 #038-44-1981 L1983 **FM** *020 †18

KASHIF, Waqar Uddin. ■ 43147 #704-02-1996 L2000 **PCC** *100 †20

KRISHNASAMY, Venkatesh Pe. ■ 43147 #038-44-2007 L2007 **GS** *012

LONG, William Walter. 1310 HILL RD N 43147 #055-01-1988 L1989 **PD** *020 †55

LOTT, Brian Michael. 488 COLONY PARK DR 43147 #038-44-1990 L1991 **FM** *040 †18

MAYER, David Chas. ■ 43147 #028-34-1964 L1965 **IM CD** *020

MBAH, May Uzoamaka. ■ 43147 #690-12-1997 L2001 **IM** *100 †20

MILLER, Regan Frank. ■ 43147 #038-40-2004 L2004 **N** *012

MOGIL, George David. ■ 43147 #038-06-1948 L1948 **PD** *071 †55

NEHUS, Edward Jerome. ■ 43147 #038-43-2006 L2006 **PD** *012

NICHOLS, Gina Michelle. 38 E COLUMBUS ST 43147 #038-44-2002 L2003 **FM** *020 †18

OUTSEN, Shad. ■ 43147 #049-01-2005 L2005 **PD** *012

■ = Address Information Privacy Protected

POLAND, Michael Patrick. 475 HILL RD N, HILL ROAD FAMILY PRACTICE 43147 #038-40-1991 L1992 **FM** *020 †18

SEARS, Rob Edward. 641 HILL RD N, STE A 43147 #038-40-1999 L2000 **FM** *020 †18

SEESE, Robert Thomas. ■ 43147 #038-40-2002 L2002 **PDI** *100

SERRANO, Eric Rafael. 475 HILL RD N 43147 #019-02-1991 L1992 **FM** *020 †18

SHAW, Joel Lewis. 1797 HILL RD N, STE 100 43147 #038-43-1999 L2007 **FSM** *100 †18

SLANE, Audry Louise. ■ 43147 #001-02-2005 L2005 **EM** *012

STEVENS, Nicholas Steve. 1310 HILL RD N, % PEDIATRIC ASSOCIATES 43147 #038-40-1997 L1998 **PD** *020 †55

THOMPSON, Steven Jermaine. 13848 VIOLET MEADOWS AVE 43147 #038-43-2000 L2004 **EM** *020 †16

TYSON, H Scott. 1310 HILL RD N 43147 #041-14-1996 L1997 **PD** *020 †55

WINNARD, Alissa Vira. 9781 CAMELOT ST 43147 #038-40-2001 L2001 **ID** *020

ZIMMERMAN, Lois Ruth. ■ 43147 #038-40-1955 L1955 **FM OBG** *071 †18

ZUSPAN, Mark Frederick. 11299 STONECREEK DR, STE B 43147 #038-40-1983 L1985 **OBG** *020

PIKETON – PIKE

FARINET, Catherine L. 100 INDIAN RIDGE DR, PIKETON PROFESSIONAL CTR 45661 #038-41-1998 L1999 **MPD** *020

MARQUEZ, Marcial I. 585 S WEST ST 45661 #748-10-1963 L1972 **GP** *071

PROTS, Robert Allan. ■ 45661 #038-06-1962 L1963 **OS** *020 †85

SCHLIE, Daniel Edwin. 7777 US HIGHWAY 23, PIKETON FAMILY HEALTH CENT 45661 #038-41-1972 L1972 **GP** *020

SMITH, Justin Wayne. ■ 45661 #038-41-2007 L2007 **IM** *012

PIQUA – MIAMI

BALTA, Naim A. 145 N SUNSET DR 45356 #902-01-1952 L1963 **GYN** *071 †30

BEHDAD, Mehdy. 821 NICKLIN AVE, STE 207 45356 #517-01-1964 L1972 **PD PDC** *020 †55

BROWN, Thomas Danl. 1219 RECKER RD 45356 #038-40-1966 L1967 **RO** *020 †80

CHEN, Yang Guu. 821 NICKLIN AVE 45356 #385-04-1967 L1978 **PD GP** *020 †55

GALLAGHER, John W. ■ 45356 #041-09-1951 L1955 **AN GP** *071

GARIETY, Charles Eugene. 624 PARK AVE 45356 #038-34-1954 L1955 **GS** *071 †85

GROVE, Christopher Allen. 200 KIENLE DR 45356 #001-02-1996 L1997 **GS** *020 †85

HATHAWAY, Karen Lynn. 280 LOONEY RD STE 101, THE PEDIATRIC GROUP 45356 #035-09-1987 L2003 **PD** *020 †55

HOANG, Choon Gill. 821 NICKLIN AVE 45356 #583-06-1965 L1973 **GYN** *020 †30

LANDES, Robert Chas. 9159 N COUNTY ROAD 25A 45356 #038-40-1980 L1981 **FM** *020 †18

LORENZ, Gretchen Marie. 9159 N COUNTY ROAD 25A 45356 #038-45-2004 L2004 **FM** *020 †18

LOWRY, Lyle Stewart. 200 KIENLE DR 45356 #038-40-1991 L1993 **GS VS** *020 †85

LUNA, Donald Philip. 230 W HIGH ST 45356 #048-13-1978 L1979 **FM** *020 †18

MADIREDDY, Naga Prasuna. 821 NICKLIN AVE 45356 #495-50-1997 L2000 **IM** *020 †20 ‡

MANIS, Ronal Doyle, Jr. 1752 W HIGH ST 45356 #038-40-1979 L1979 **ID IM** *020 †20

NICKOL, Rowan Reece. 200 KIENLE DR 45356 #038-41-1979 L1982 **GS AS** *020 †85

PONFERRADA, Virgilio A. 9163 N COUNTY ROAD 25A, UPPER MIAMI VALLEY UROLOGY 45356 #748-01-1969 L1974 **U** *020

SAUNDERS, Edmund Leon. ■ 45356 #024-05-1947 L1956 **R** *071

SHAH, Alka Mayank. 821 NICKLIN AVE 45356 #495-48-1971 L1975 **IM** *020

TAYLOR, Daniel Stark. 200 KIENLE DR 45356 #038-41-1994 L1995 **GS** *020 †85

TRAVIS, Thomas M. 601 W HIGH ST 45356 #038-45-1980 L1981 **FM GS** *071

PITSBURG – DARKE

HEISE, Jesse L. 200 N JEFFERSON ST 45358 #038-41-1952 L1952 **FM** *071 †18

PLAIN CITY – MADISON

ANDRAS, Robert Louis. 9611 PLN CTY GSVL RD NE 43064 #038-40-1974 L1974 **EM** *020 †16

CORSE, Kenneth J, II. 43064 #035-15-1983 L2008 **IM** *012

FRIESEN, John. 10030 SMITH CALHOUN RD 43064 #062-01-1995 L1997 **FM** *020 †18

MAXWELL, Maria Therese. 240 W MAIN ST 43064 #038-40-1989 L1990 **FM** *020 †18

RUEGER, William John. ■ 43064 #038-41-1916 L1956 **PD** *071 †55

SNYDER, Gary Edward. 7399 PLAN CTY GRGSVL RD NE 43064 #017-20-1982 L1990 **PD** *020 †55

PLYMOUTH – RICHLAND

OANIA, Maximo Aranda. 1956 ST RTE 224 44865 #748-07-1956 L1965 **GP OBG** *071

POLAND – MAHONING

BLACK, Michael Lane. 6615 CLINGAN RD, STE A 44514 #038-40-1994 L1995 **FM** *020 †18

BURKERT, Thomas Scott. 205 S MAIN ST 44514 #038-44-1993 L1995 **IM** *020 †20

BURLEY, Michael William. 715 E WESTERN RESERVE RD 44514 #024-16-1988 L1996 **CD** *020 †20

CIARALLO, Robert L. 1320 BOARDMAN POLAND RD, ASPEN DENTAL 44514 #041-12-1991 L1993 **OS** *020

ENGLE, Michael Thomas. 822 E WESTERN RESERVE RD 44514 #038-44-2000 L2000 **PM** *020 †60

EVAN, Michael Bogan. 6615 CLINGAN RD, STE A 44514 #038-45-1985 L1986 **FM** *020 †18

FREDETTE, Paul Bryan. ■ 44514 #005-12-2004 L2005 **GS** *012

HURT, Sonia R. 6404 TARA DR 44514 #308-03-1986 L1999 **PD** *020 †55

JAYARAM, Archana. ■ 44514 #496-39-2002 L2003 **NPM** *012 †55

LEONELLI, James Edward. 1040 S COMMONS PL 44514 #038-45-1981 L1982 **OBG OCC** *020 †30

MATEO, Francisco Alberto. 89 N MAIN ST 44514 #308-02-1982 L1996 **PUD IM** *020 †20

MC CLUSKY, Robert C. 3294 STONES THROW AVE 44514 #038-40-1972 L1972 **OBG** *020 †30

MC GOWEN, Charles Hammond. 205 S MAIN ST 44514 #038-40-1961 L1961 **IM END** *020 †20

MIKOLICH, John Ronald. 38 AUDUBON RD, ASSOCIATES 44514 #038-40-1974 L1974 **CD** *020 †20

MOONDA, Afreen Husain. ■ 44514 #038-44-2004 L2005 **PTH** *012

MOONDA, Faroq Dada. ■ 44514 #041-15-2000 L2005 **AN** *020 †05

MOSER, Robert John. 6400 OLDE STONE XING 44514 #038-44-2002 L2002 **IM** *100

NOBLE, Robert Cutler. ■ 44514 #036-07-1964 L2004 **ID IM** *071 †20

O'BRIEN, Michael Joseph, Jr. 6615 CLINGAN RD, STE A 44514 #038-44-1999 L1999 **FM** *020 †18

PERNI, Uma Chapa. 7067 TIFFANY BLVD, STE 220 44514 #041-02-1996 L2005 **OBG** *020 †30

PERRY, Alicia Bridget. ■ 44514 #038-44-2008 *012

PETROLLA, Amber Angela. ■ 44514 #038-44-2005 L2005 **PTH** *012

PROIA, Nicholas Gerard. 89 N MAIN ST 44514 #561-04-1984 L1986 **PUD CCM** *020 †20

RAI, Hardeep Singh. ■ 44514 #913-65-2000 L2007 **IM** *012

SCOCCIA, Vincent F. 590 E WESTERN RESERVE RD 44514 #018-75-1993, ▲ L1994 **IM EM** *020

SPIRTOS, Theodore. ■ 44514 #038-41-1980 L1980 **EM** *020 †16

YOSSEF, Sayed Mohamed. 3304 STONES THROW AVE 44514 #915-04-1979 L1987 **GE GS** *020 †20

YURICH, Joseph F. ■ 44514 #038-44-2004 L2004 **GS** *012

ZUBIL, John R. ■ 44514 #561-01-1973 L1978 **EM IM** *020 †16

POMEROY – MEIGS

CORONEL, Marcel Quizon. 88 E MEMORIAL DR 45769 #748-01-1952 L1966 **FM** *071 †18

MANSFIELD, Wilma Ann. 88 E MEMORIAL DR, HOLZER MEIGS CLNC 45769 #038-40-1976 L1976 **FM** *020 †18

RIDGWAY, John H. ■ 45769 #005-15-1962 L1975 *071

SIMON, Mel P. 113 E MEMORIAL DR 45769 #748-01-1959 L1968 **U AM** *072 †95

WITHERELL, James E, Jr. 88 E MEMORIAL DR, HOLZER MEIGS CLINIC 45769 #038-40-1974 L1979 **FM** *020 †18

PORT CLINTON – OTTAWA

AFFAN, Aban A. 615 FULTON ST 43452 #915-04-1982 L1999 **AN** *020 †05

AKINS, Kenneth Lee. ■ 43452 #038-40-1961 L1961 **GP** *072

BODIE, David Andrew. 621 FULTON ST 43452 #038-43-2001 L2001 **FM** *020 †18

BRIEDE, Jennifer Lynn. 621 FULTON ST 43452 #038-41-2001 L2004 **FM** *020 †18 ‡

BUDD, Neilma Jane. ■ 43452 #917-24-1959 L1980 **PTH** *071 †50

BUONO, Dennis J. 2861 E HARBOR RD, OTTAWA MEDICAL CLINCIL 43452 #011-75-2000, ▲ L2005 **FM** *020 †18

CADIGAN, Daniel G. 2861 E HARBOR RD 43452 #063-01-1992 L1995 **FM UCM** *020

CHARNOCK, Edward Lester. ■ 43452 #038-40-1967 L1967 **EM** *062 †55,16

COON, William Thos. 600 E 6TH ST 43452 #038-40-1959 L1959 **GP** *071

COVER, Barry Reed. 621 FULTON ST 43452 #038-40-1970 L1970 **IM GE** *071 †20

CRISOLOGO, Guillermo V. 620 JEFFERSON ST 43452 #748-10-1962 L1970 **GS GP** *020

CROUCH, David Edward. 621 FULTON ST 43452 #038-40-1970 L1970 **GP** *071 ‡

FELBER, Dietrich Werner. 615 FULTON ST 43452 #407-21-1951 L1958 **ORS** *071

HESS, Robert Mc Donald. ■ 43452 #038-40-1957 L1957 **NS** *030 †25

KLAEGE, Karen Louise. 621 FULTON ST 43452 #038-40-2004 L2004 **FM** *020 †18

LE, Quang Kim. 615 FULTON ST 43452 #038-43-1997 L1998 **IM** *020 †20

LEDUC, Marc Andre. 2861 EAST HARBOR RD 43452 #025-07-1989 L1992 **FM** *020 †18

MAGILL, George Thos. 615 FULTON ST 43452 #038-43-1985 L1986 **EM** *020 †16

MCLEAN, James Alexander. 621 FULTON ST 43452 #064-01-1983 L1995 **GP** *020

PERNG, Susan Suchi. 1250 FULTON ST 43452 #038-40-1997 L1998 **FM** *020 †18

QUE, Leonardo Tan. 602 E 6TH ST STE D 43452 #748-11-1977 L1984 **CD IM** *020 †20

QUE, Virgie Uy. 602 E 6TH ST, STE B 43452 #748-11-1977 L1986 **IM** *020 †20

RITTER, Frank K. 615 FULTON ST 43452 #028-34-1952 L1953 **AN GP** *020

ROWE, Thomas Daniel. 1250 FULTON ST 43452 #038-40-1999 L2000 **FM** *020 †18

SHINDE, Sharadchandra G. 130 JEFFERSON ST APT 3A 43452 #495-01-1960 L1978 **OBG** *071 †30

SOLZE, Dale Austin. 615 FULTON ST 43452 #038-40-1967 L1967 **OPH** *020 †35

STRANATHAN, Christopher A. 602 E 6TH ST, STE C 43452 #038-44-1988 L1990 **IM** *020 †20

TEFERRA, Samuel. 600 E 6TH ST, STE B 43452 #366-01-1985 L1996 **FM** *020 †18

TIRUMALASETTY, Kuberan. 615 FULTON ST 43452 #495-50-1965 L1992 **R** *020 †80

VANDEN BERG, Peter Martin. 600 E 6TH ST, STE A 43452 #025-07-1981 L2000 **GS VS** *020 †85

WOODSON, Riley Donald. ■ 43452 #019-02-1956 L1968 **TS CD** *071 †85,90

PORTSMOUTH – SCIOTO

ADAMS, Darren. 1611 27TH ST STE 302 45662 #038-75-2002, ▲ L2002 **OBG OMM** *020

AILES-FRICK, Angela Kae. 2001 SCIOTO TRL, STE 100 45662 #038-45-1995 L1996 **FM** *020 †18

ALI, Arshad. 2001 SCIOTO TRL, STE 1B 45662 #704-20-1984 L2007 **CD IC** *020 †20

AL-NAKEEB, Sadiq Jafar. 1805 27TH ST, SOMC ADMINISTRATION OFFICE 45662 #528-01-1995 L2001 **PCC** *020 †20

ANGELOS, William J. 1805 27TH ST 45662 #035-03-1988 L1997 **EM** *020 †16

ARRICK, Ronald Eugene. 1611 27TH ST, STE 103 45662 #038-40-1976 L1978 **IM PD** *020 †20

AVILES, Christopher W. 23030 STATE ROUTE 73 45663 #038-45-2003 L2006 **FM** *020 †18

BANALAGAY, Ernesto Espe. 1711 27TH ST, BLDGK 45662 #748-01-1981 L1998 **NEP IM** *020 †20

BATES, Philip Dean. 1735 27TH ST, STE 103 45662 #038-40-1985 L1999 **GS** *020 †85

BAWAZER, Abbas. 2669 SHERMAN RD 45662 #915-04-1967 L1975 **P EM** *020

BENITEZ, Luis F. 1805 27TH ST, SOUTHERN OHIO MEDICAL CENT 45662 #042-01-1990 L2001 **AN** *020

BETTS, Ronelle Luanne. 1805 27TH ST, SOMC 45662 #396-24-1990 L1994 **EM** *020

BEUTNER, Hans Rudolf. ■ 45662 #407-10-1047 L1957 **AN** *071

BONZO, Suzann Marie. 1611 27TH ST BLDG J, STE 101 45662 #038-43-1978 L1979 **IM** *020

BUENTE, William Louis. 1805 27TH ST 45662 #038-41-1975 L1976 **DR** *020 †80

CAMPBELL, Doyle Edward. ■ 45662 #038-40-1964 L1964 **OPH** *075

CARIAS, Katherine Deborah. 715 5TH ST 45662 #308-02-1988 L1996 **AI** *020 †03,20

CHABOUDY, Louis R. ■ 45662 #038-41-1944 L1944 **GYN OS** *071 †30

CHANG, Lifen Lien. 1121 KINNEYS LN, SOMC CANCER CENTER 45662 #017-20-1991 L1995 **RO** *020 †80

CHRISTOPHER, Samuel G V. 1805 27TH ST 45662 #495-42-1967 L1979 N *020
CORBLY-MARTIN, Mary Lynne. ■ 45662 #038-41-1991 L1992 PD *020 †55
COREY-ARNETT, Carolyn M. 1735 27TH ST, STE 202 45662 #038-75-1993, ▲ L1994 OBG *020
DAEHLER, William E. ■ 45662 #025-01-1952 L1954 AN FM *071 †18
DARNELL, Zane Ashley. 2001 SCIOTO TRL STE 20, CUMBERLAND CARDIOLOGY, PSC 45662 #038-44-1995 L2001 CD *020 †20
DEEB, Wasim Elias. 1735 27TH ST, STE B06 45662 #875-01-1994 L2003 END IM *020 †20
DITRAGLIA, John Francis. 717 5TH ST 45662 #033-05-1978 L1982 PD *020 †55
DRIEDGER, Harry John. 1870 COLES BLVD, STE A 45662 #065-06-1974 L1979 CD *020 †20
EGEL, James Wm. 1648 11TH ST, JMC DIALYSIS UNIT 45662 #041-02-1978 L1984 NEP IM *020
EPLING, Christopher P. 2001 SCIOTO TRL STE 20, CUMBERLAND CARDIOLOGY, PSC 45662 #055-75-1997, ▲ L2003 IC *020
ESHAM, William Thurn. 1611 27TH ST, BLDG J 45662 #020-02-1970 L1974 U *020 †95
GHANEM, Ammar. 1735 27TH ST STE 108 45662 #875-01-1994 L2004 PUD SME *020 †20
GILBERT, John Chas. 1611 27TH ST, BLDG J 45662 #038-75-1989, ▲ L1991 IM *071
GILL, Roy Alon. 1735 27TH ST, STE B06 45662 #041-07-1987 L2007 FM *030 †18 ‡
GINDIN, R Arthur. ■ 45662 #051-04-1959 L1982 NS *071 †25
GOHMANN, Joseph Theodore. ■ 45662 #020-02-1943 L1951 PTH *071 †50
GOLLAMUDI, Murthy V L. 1735 27TH ST, STE 108 45662 #495-04-1992 L2000 IM PCC *020 †20
GUZMAN, Mina Lourdes T. 1805 27TH ST 45662 #748-10-1992 L1997 AN *020
HAIDER, Shabbir. ■ 45662 #704-04-1961 L1975 GS TS *020
HANSING, Jerald Dahl. ■ 45662 #008-01-1978 L1982 DR NR *020 †80
HASELL, Louise Cantey. 2001 SCIOTO TRL STE 100, PORTSMOUTH MEDICAL SPECIAL 45662 #045-01-1983 L1996 IM PUD *020 †20
HILL, Chalonda Katrice. 1248 KINNEYS LN 45662 #047-07-2002 L2006 IM *100 †20,70
HOBBS, Donna L. 901 WASHINGTON ST, SHAWNEE MENTAL HEALTH CENT 45662 #017-20-1974 L1995 P *020
HORTON, Heather Louise. 1735 27TH ST, BLDNG C STE 207 45662 #041-07-1989 L2006 CD IC *020 †20
HUGENBERG, Janet M B. ■ 45662 #038-41-1946 L1946 OS *075
INOSHITA, Tsuyoshi. 916 11TH ST 45662 #572-01-1975 L1987 ON *020 †50,20
JABLONSKI, Jeffrey James. 1805 27TH ST 45662 #038-43-1979 L1980 FM *020 †18
JACOBS, Norman Martin. 1805 27TH ST, P O BOX 1502 45662 #041-13-1978 L1984 DR *020 †80
JOHNSON, George Vaughn. 1805 27TH ST, P O BOX 1473 45662 #038-40-1966 L1966 R *020 †80
JOSEY, Willie Leroy. 1805 27TH ST, SOUTHERN OHIO MEDICAL CENT 45662 #045-01-1977 L1987 FM IM *020
KAAKAJI, Hazem. 1870 COLES BLVD 45662 #875-02-1997 L2006 IM *100 †20
KANG, Hong Sik. 1825 OAKLAND AVE STE C, MERCY MEDICAL PLAZA 45662 #583-03-1960 L1979 P EM *020
KHOURY, Thomas L. 1711 27TH ST, STE 306 45662 #605-01-1982 L1993 GS VS *020 †85
KING, Gretzel Cecilia. 1805 27TH ST, SOUTHERN OHIO MEDICAL CENT 45662 #176-03-1993 L2001 IM *020 †20
KIO, Ebenezer Abumere. 1121 KINNEYS LN 45662 #690-06-1995 L2004 HO *100 †20
KNOX, Robert James. 1603 11TH ST 45662 #038-40-1996 L2000 OPH *020 ‡
KSEIBI, Samer Abdul-Wahab. 1735 27TH ST, BLDG C 45662 #875-01-1993 L2001 PUD *020 †20
LICHTENSTEIN, Sonja Marie. 1805 27TH ST 45662 #035-15-1996 L2002 GS *020 †85
LILLY, John Francis, II. 724 8TH ST 45662 #038-41-1979 L1993 GS ORS *075
LIU, Kou Sin. 1805 27TH ST 45662 #244-04-1968 L1976 AN *071
LIVINGSTON, David Elmo. ■ 45662 #035-45-1955 L1956 GS *071 †85
LOGAN, Scott Donovan. 1805 27TH ST, SINC RADIOLOGY DEPT 45662 #038-45-1995 L2000 DR *020 †80
MAC DONALD, Eric Paul. 1805 27TH ST 45662 #038-41-1983 L1996 AN IM *020 †20,05
MALAYA, Ramon O. ■ 45662 #748-01-1965 L1972 IM *020 †20
MALHOTRA, Amir Singh. 717 5TH ST 45662 #495-30-1970 L1977 N *020 †75
MALHOTRA, Gurdeep Kaur. 3283 CHATEAU DR 45662 #495-45-1971 L1983 RO *020
MARCHYN, Duane James. 1735 27TH ST, STE 308 45662 #035-03-1978 L1983 ORS OSM *020 †40
MARKS-AUSTIN, Kathy Ann. 1735 27TH ST, BLDG C 45662 #041-13-1989 L1998 PCC *020 †20
MARTIN, Michael Edward. 1735 27TH ST, BLDG C 45662 #038-41-1991 L1992 IM *020 †20
MARTIN, Michael J, Jr. 1723 27TH ST 45662 #038-44-1995 L1996 FM *020 †18
MILLER, Spencer W. 1610 28TH ST, # 216 45662 #018-03-1934 L1952 R *071 †80
MULLINS, James Ray. 1611 27TH ST, STE 104 45662 #005-02-1978 L1980 FM *020
MURPHY, Rick David. 1405 11TH ST 45662 #038-43-1980 L1982 PD *020 †55
NASSEF, Ashraf S. 717 5TH ST 45662 #915-02-1983 L1998 N *020
NOVOSELAC, Amory Vedran. 1121 KINNEYS LN, SOMC CANCER CTR 45662 #957-01-1996 L2004 HO *020 †20
NOWAK, Kristie Day. 1805 27TH ST, UNIVERSITY PHYSICIANS AND 45662 #010-02-1995 L2007 IM *020 †20
ONODERA, Takaaki. 1805 27TH ST 45662 #572-20-1995 L2004 EM *020 †16
PADEN, Vabian Lewitt. 1805 27TH ST 45662 #010-03-1985 L1996 PM *020 †60
PARIKH, Indravadan. 621 BROADWAY ST, VA CLINIC CBOC 45662 #495-23-1965 L1975 IM GP *020 †20
PATEL, Jitendra Kumar. 723 8TH ST 45662 #495-79-1981 L1995 FM *020 †18
PATEL, Prakash Bhupendra. 1121 KINNEYS LN 45662 #495-76-1977 L1986 RO IM *020 †80
PAULUS, Richard Eberhardt. 2001 SCIOTO TRL STE 2, CUMBERLAND CARDIOLOGY, PSC 45662 #050-02-1973 L1994 CD *020 †20
PAZ-BANALAGAY, Mary F. 1112 GALLIA ST 45662 #748-01-1981 L1998 PD *020 †55
PETTEY, James. 1611 27TH ST, FULTON BUILDING, STE 304 45662 #020-12-1983 L1984 ORS *020 †18,40
PETTIT, George Patrick. 1729 27TH ST, GEORGE P PETTIT MD INC 45662 #038-40-1969 L1969 OBG *020 †30 ‡
PHILLIPS, Roger Matthew. ■ 45662 #038-75-2007, ▲ L2007 *012
RINI, Jerome Martin. 1725 27TH ST 45662 #038-40-1948 L1948 GS *072 †85
RISHEH, Jihad. 1805 27TH ST, SOUTH OHIO MEDICAL CENTER 45662 #875-01-1994 L2003 AN PAN *020 †05
SAAB, Elie Michel. 1735 27TH ST, STE 108 45662 #308-11-1985 L1994 PCC SME *020 †20
SAMUEL, Reena Pattasseril. 1727 27TH ST BLDG H, STE 202 45662 #495-80-1990 L1998 NEP IM *020
SCARPINATO, Vincent M. 1735 27TH ST, WALLER BUILDING, STE 102 45662 #035-09-1987 L2007 GS EM *020 †85
SCHOETTLE, Rebecca Joan. 1735 27TH ST, STE 201 45662 #038-06-1982 L1982 PD CCM *020 †55

SCHWAMBURGER, Matthew S. ■ 45662 #038-41-2003 L2003 AN *020
SHIVAPRASAD, Hullukunte B. 1870 COLES BLVD 45662 #495-33-1972 L1980 CD IM *020 †20
SKITARELIC, Kathryn F. 1431 OFFNERE ST 45662 #023-01-1969 L1969 PTH *020 †50
SMITH, Thomas Robt. 1805 27TH ST 45662 #017-20-1980 L1992 AN *020 †05
SONG, Yong Duck. 1611 27TH ST, BLDG J 45662 #583-02-1963 L1973 OBG *020 †30
SOTO, Hector Villacorta. 1010 24TH ST 45662 #748-01-1964 L1973 ORS *020 †40
SPEARS, George Newton. 1610 28TH ST APT 3G29 45662 #038-06-1942 L1942 GS OM *071 †85
STEWART, Kendall Leuomon. 1725 27TH ST, BLDG C 45662 #012-01-1976 L1981 P *030 †75 ‡
TEMPONERAS, John S. 1004 24TH ST 45662 #561-17-1962 L1971 GYN *020 †30
TOOMBS, Miller F. ■ 45662 #038-40-1950 L1950 FM OS *020
TRINIDAD, Gerardo Dumlao. 1735 27TH ST STE 107, BLDG C 45662 #041-09-1993 L1998 ORS OSM *020 †40
TURNER, Ronald Ross. 1248 KINNEYS LN 45662 #016-11-1969 L1974 ORS *075 †40
VARIATH, Joju T. 901 WASHINGTON ST 45662 #495-50-1988 L1998 P *020 †75
VELURY, Sriharsha. 2001 SCIOTO TRL, STE 1B 45662 #495-65-1982 L1997 CD *020 †20
WALKER, David Scott. 723 8TH ST 45662 #020-12-1994 L1996 FM *020 †18
WALKER, John Arthur. ■ 45662 #038-41-1963 L1963 U *071 †95
WELSH, Terrence Bourke. 1611 27TH ST # J-202 45662 #038-41-1986 L1990 PM *020 †60
WHEELER, Wayne B. 1248 KINNEYS LN 45662 #016-11-1980 L1982 EM OM *020 †16,70
WHITE, George Franklin. ■ 45662 #051-04-1967 L1972 OTO *071 †45
WILLIAMS, Jeffery Wilbert. 1805 27TH ST, DEPT PM & R INPATIENT 45662 #305-01-2000 L2005 PM *020 †60
WONG, Charles Chu-Li. 1735 27TH ST, STE 307 45662 #748-10-1984 L1992 GE *020 †20
WOODARD, Christopher M. 5611 GALLIA ST 45662 #038-45-1999 L1999 FM *020 †18
ZAYNEH, Ibrahim Michael. 2127 25TH ST 45662 #875-03-1983 L2002 D IM *020 †20

POWELL – DELAWARE

ADELI, Anahita. ■ 43065 #038-40-2007 L2007 IM *012
ARBONA, Guillermo A. 10567 SAWMILL PKWY 43065 #038-41-1998 L2004 *020 †80
ARBONA, Guillermo Luis. 10567 SAWMILL PKWY 43065 #042-01-1976 L1977 DR *020 †80
AYOUB, Edmund, Jr. ■ 43065 #038-45-2005 L2005 FP *012
BELL, David Clarence. 10244 SAWMILL RD 43065 #038-40-1981 L1984 OBG *020 †30
BENTLY, Philip Edgar. ■ 43065 #038-41-1959 L1959 OPH *071 †35
BHATT, Vina Vasudev. ■ 43065 #306-01-2002 FM *100
BIBLER, William Bradford. 10567 SAWMILL PKWY, RADIOLOGY INC 43065 #038-41-1989 L1990 RNR *020 †80
BLOOMBERG, Ross Calvin. ■ 43065 #038-40-2004 L2004 OPH *012
BOUNIF, Farid. ■ 43065 #125-01-1989 L2000 IM *100 †20
BRACK, Mitchell Andrew. 10567 SAWMILL PKWY, RADIOLOGY INC 43065 #038-40-1987 L1992 DR *020 †80
BRAHOS, George James. ■ 43065 #028-02-1972 L1980 TS GS *071 †85,90
BRANDEMIHL, Adam Scott. ■ 43065 #038-40-2002 L2002 P *020
BREZNY, Steven F. 10330 SAWMILL PKWY 43065 #038-45-1999 L2000 FM *020 †18 ‡
BRYAN, Donald Keith. 10330 SAWMILL PKWY, STE 600 43065 #038-41-1967 L1967 OBG *020 †30 ‡
BUBASH, Lori Ann. ■ 43065 #026-04-1997 L2007 RNR *020 †80
CARDUCCI, Ernest Sante. 10567 SAWMILL PKWY 43065 #038-40-1974 L1975 DR *020 †80
CARNEY, Glenn Patrick. 90 VILLAGE POINTE DR 43065 #041-12-1988 L1993 R NM *020 †80,28
CAVALIERE, Robert. ■ 43065 #035-09-1999 L2005 IM *020 †75
CELY, Rafael A. 10567 SAWMILL PKWY 43065 #847-06-1970 L1978 DR *030 †80
CHAMBERS, Linda F. ■ 43065 #005-02-1979 L1991 BBK PTH *020 †50
CHEVALIER, Laurie Mizer. ■ 43065 #038-40-2001 L2001 IM *020 †20
CHIOCCA, Ennio Antonio. ■ 43065 #048-14-1988 L2004 NS *020 †25
CHO, Seong-Koo. 10567 SAWMILL PKWY STE 100 43065 #583-02-1965 L1971 DR *020 †80
CHO, Young Kap. 10567 SAWMILL PKWY, RADIOLOGY INC 43065 #583-02-1970 L2000 RO *020 †80
CLOUTIER, Chas Theodore. ■ 43065 #024-05-1965 L1982 GS TRS *071 †85
CONRAD, Patricia Dale. 240 N LIBERTY ST, STE T 43065 #038-40-1992 L2001 PD PHO *020 †55
COPELAND, Christopher M. 10244 SAWMILL PKWY 43065 #038-40-1978 L1982 OBG *020 †30
CROUSER, Sangeeta Jhaveri. 10330 SAWMILL PKWY, STE 600 43065 #038-41-1990 L1993 OBG *020 †30
CULL, Kimberly Jo. 95 S LIBERTY ST 43065 #038-40-1991 L1992 OBG *020 †30
CYGNOR, Ronald Jos. ■ 43065 #038-40-1961 L1961 IM *020 †20
DONEPUDI, Sirisha. ■ 43065 #495-65-1998 L2007 END *012 †20
DOWELL, Glenn Coe, Jr. ■ 43065 #038-40-1949 L1949 AN *071 †05
DRIESEN, Jerome Edward. ■ 43065 #035-06-1962 L1992 ADP ADM *020
DUNBAR, John David. 3466 TIMBERSIDE DR D2 43065 #038-40-1955 L1955 R PDA *020 †80
EDGAR, Rick Lloyd. ■ 43065 #038-40-2005 L2005 NS *012
FAHRBACH, Karl C. 10567 SAWMILL PKWY, STE 100 43065 #016-06-2001 L2007 DR *100 †80
FAHRIG, Charles Matthew. ■ 43065 #038-40-1985 L1988 IM *020 †20
FOX, Thomas Thurman. 90 VILLAGE POINTE DR 43065 #038-40-1971 L1971 DR NM *020 †28
FRANKS, Michael Robert. 35 CLAIREDAN DR, POWELL PEDIATRIC CARE, LLC 43065 #038-40-2000 L2003 PD *020 †55 ‡
FRANZ, Joseph Carl. 18 GRACE DR, VILLAGE MEDICAL OFFICE 43065 #055-01-1978 L1989 FM *020 †18
FREY, Edward Eugene. 10567 SAWMILL PKWY, RADIOLOGY INC 43065 #041-13-1980 L1987 DR *020 †80
GALLOWAY, Robert Wayne. 10567 SAWMILL PKWY, STE 100 43065 #055-02-1999 L2000 DR *100 †80
GARDNER, Kathryn Gladys. 10567 SAWMILL PKWY, STE 100 43065 #038-06-1987 L1987 DR PDR *020 †80
GONELA, Satish. ■ 43065 #496-34-2004 L2006 IM *012
GOODMAN, Lauren Frances. ■ 43065 #038-40-2005 L2005 IM *012
HAAS, Steven Douglas. 90 VILLAGE POINTE DR 43065 #038-40-1981 L1981 DR *020 †80
HENDERSON, David Edward. 4141 NORTHHAMPTON DR, STE 103 43065 #038-40-1974 L1974 PD *020 †55
HERMAN, Leigh Jay. 10567 SAWMILL PKWY, RADIOLOGY INC 43065 #038-40-1980 L1983 DR EM *020 †80
HOUTS, Christopher Brian. 35 CLAIREDAN DR 43065 #038-40-1986 L1987 PD *020 †55
HUCEK, Peter David. 4141 NORTHHAMPTON DR # 100 43065 #038-41-1989 L1990 FM *020 †18

IRSIK, Ronald Dean. 10567 SAWMILL PKWY, RADIOLOGY INC 43065 #019-02-1983 L1989
   VIR RNR *020 †80
ISKANDER, Hany Maurice. 10619 PEMBROOKE PL 43065 #915-06-1984 L1998 **AN** *020 †05
JACK, Melinda Kristine. ■ 43065 #038-41-2004 L2004 **GS** *012
JENKINS, William Andrew. ■ 43065 #038-41-2004 L2004 **EM** *020
JUNG, Stephen Shukwon. 10567 SAWMILL PKWY, RADIOLOGY, INC. 43065 #038-40-1990 L1993
   VIR *020 †80
KENNEY, Kristen Whitney. ■ 43065 #038-40-2002 L2002 **FM** *100 †18
KHANNA, Sanjeev. ■ 43065 #038-44-1998 L2001 **VIR** *100 †80
KIM, Julia Minjung. ■ 43065 #038-41-2001 L2001 **PD** *020 †55
KORTHALS, Theodore Harry. ■ 43065 #660-03-1950 L1965 **GP PUD** *071 †18
LEON, Raul. ■ 43065 #737-06-1993 L2001 **PCP** *100 †50
LIN, Tom Kuoyuan. ■ 43065 #038-45-2001 L2004 **PD** *100 †55
LINGAM, Deepa Channaiah. ■ 43065 #038-45-2003 L2003 **D** *020 †15
LLOYD, Thomas Vincent, III. 10567 SAWMILL PKWY 43065 #041-02-1966 L1971
   DR PDR *020 †80
LOTHES, Eric Williams. 27 CLAIREDAN DR 43065 #038-43-1986 L1987 **OPH** *071 †35 ‡
MC GHEE, Robert Brown, Jr. 10567 SAWMILL PKWY, RADIOLOGY INC . 43065
   #038-40-1983 L1986 **R N** *020 †80
MEDICHERLA, Lakshmi Uday. ■ 43065 #495-21-1980 L2003 **P** *020
MELILLO, Jason Victor. 10244 SAWMILL PKWY 43065 #038-40-1997 L1998 **OBG** *020 †30
MILLER, Robert Louis. 10567 SAWMILL PKWY, RADIOLOGY INC 43065 #038-40-1992 L1995
   DR *020 †80
MILLS, Craig Stephen. 10567 SAWMILL PKWY 43065 #847-09-1978 L1980 **DR** *020 †80
MOID, Farah Yasin. ■ 43065 #704-01-1985 L2005 **PTH HMP** *020 †50
MORRISON, Mary C. 10567 SAWMILL PKWY, STE 100 43065 #036-07-1983 L2002
   DR R *020 †80
MURTHY, Mysore S N. ■ 43065 #495-09-1951 L1963 **PTH** *071 †50
NAHAR, Shamsun. 3973 DORSET CT 43065 #160-02-1993 L2003 **P** *020
NAHMAN, Beverly Johnson. 10567 SAWMILL PKWY, RADIOLOGY INC 43065
   #038-43-1979 L1983 **R DR** *020 †80
NAYYAR, Sunil. ■ 43065 #665-01-2005 L2006 **FP** *012
NEAL, David Evan. 10567 SAWMILL PKWY, RADIOLOGY INC 43065 #038-43-1988 L1994
   DR *020 †80
NOVAK, John Christopher. ■ 43065 #038-40-2004 L2004 **N** *012
NTUKIDEM, Nseobong I. ■ 43065 #690-10-1992 L2006 **HO** *012 †20
OEHLER, Mary Catherine. 10567 SAWMILL PKWY, RADIOLOGY INC 43065 #038-40-1988 L1991
   RNR *020 †80
ORSINELLI, August Michael. 10567 SAWMILL PKWY, ADVOCATE/RADIOLOGY INC 43065
   #038-40-1995 L2000 **DR** *020 †80
OSTHAUS, Laura Elizabeth. 35 CLAIREDAN DR, POWELL PEDIATRIC CARE 43065
   #025-01-1995 L2002 **PD** *020 †55
OTTAVIANO, Joseph A. 264 S LIBERTY ST 43065 #055-02-1987 L1988 **FM** *020 †18
PAUL, David John. 10567 SAWMILL PKWY, RADIOLOGY INC 43065 #038-40-1963 L1963
   R *040 †80
PAUL, Robert J, Jr. 10567 SAWMILL PKWY 43065 #038-44-1984 L1985 **DR NR** *020 †80
PERDZOCK, David Alfons. 10330 SAWMILL PKWY 43065 #038-40-1975 L1975
   AN AM *020 †30,05
PLACE, Andrew Zachary. 10330 SAWMILL PKWY 43065 #038-40-1998 L1999 **FM** †18
PROBST, Stephen Frank. 10567 SAWMILL PKWY, RADIOLOGY INC 43065 #038-40-1968 L1968
   DR *020 †80
RESTUCCIO, Anthony Paul. 10330 SAWMILL PKWY, STE 30 43065 #038-40-1988 L1989
   FM *020 †18
RIVELLO, Louis John. 10567 SAWMILL PKWY, RADIOLOGY INC 43065 #038-44-1983 L1985
   RO *020 †80
ROBINSON, Roger Alan. ■ 43065 #038-40-1965 L1965 **R** *071 †80
ROBITAILLE, Patricia Anne. 10330 SAWMILL PKWY, STE 300 43065 #026-04-1989 L1992
   EM *020 †16
SAHAI, Vivek. ■ 43065 #038-44-2005 L2005 **ORS** *012
SAMAD, Isa Abdus. ■ 43065 #495-15-1947 L1964 **P ADP** *071 †75
SCHOETTMER, John Thos. ■ 43065 #038-40-1991 L1992 **FM** *020 †18
SCHROEDER, Richard A. ■ 43065 #038-40-1950 L1950 **OBG** *071
SHEPHERD, Kimberly Sue. 10330 SAWMILL PKWY, STE 600 43065 #048-13-1999 L1999
   OBG *020 †30
SHIPP, Michele P L. ■ 43065 #440-01-1975 L1998 **FM** *100
SIMON, Donald Craig. 90 VILLAGE POINTE DR 43065 #038-40-1981 L1982 **R NR** *020 †80
SMITH, Barton Taylor. ■ 43065 #030-05-1948 L1955 **OBG** *071 †30
SMULLEN, Timothy Lawrence. 10567 SAWMILL PKWY 43065 #038-40-2000 L2000
   VIR *020 †80
SPETIE, Lacramioara. ■ 43065 #781-01-1991 L1997 **CHP** *020 †75
SUAREZ, Adrian Adolfo. ■ 43065 #270-01-1995 L2007 **PCP** *100 †50
TANDON, Amit. ■ 43065 #038-41-2003 L2003 **IM** *020
TEMPLE, Michael William. 4141 NORTHHAMPTON DR 43065 #038-40-1996 L1997 **PD** *020 †55
THIEL, Eric James. ■ 43065 #038-43-2004 L2004 **ORS** *012
TRIPATHI, Veena Rajkishor. ■ 43065 #038-40-2008 *012
TURNER, Carson Robert. ■ 43065 #020-02-2003 L2006 **CD** *012 †20
URS, Latha. ■ 43065 #495-72-1988 L2006 **PP** *012 †80
VAN AMAN, Michael Elwin. 10567 SAWMILL PKWY, RADIOLOGY INC 43065
   #038-40-1971 L1971 **R** *020 †80
WAGNER, Matthew Mansfield. 10567 SAWMILL PKWY, RADIOLOGY INC 43065
   #038-40-1996 L2002 **DR** *020 †80
WANG, Chien Yi. 10567 SAWMILL PKWY, RADIOLOGY INC 43065 #187-11-1971 L1985
   DR *020 †80,28
WHITE, Daniel Jo. 10567 SAWMILL PKWY, RADIOLOGY INC 43065 #038-40-1986 L1991
   DR IM *020 †80
WIDMAN, Douglas Wm. 10567 SAWMILL PKWY, RADIOLOG INC 43065 #038-41-1988 L1999
   RO *020 †80
WOODS, Joseph Wilbur. ■ 43065 #038-40-1966 L1966 **OBG** *020 †30
YU, Jenny Ying. ■ 43065 #038-40-2003 L2003 **IM** *100
ZENG, Ming. 10567 SAWMILL PKWY 43065 #243-95-1986 L2002 **RO** *020 †80
ZHAO, Weiqiang. ■ 43065 #243-76-1982 L2007 **PTH** *100
ZUCKER, Ivan L. 9980 BREWSTER LN, STE 100 43065 #041-13-1989 L1997 **NM** *020 †80,28

PROCTORVILLE – LAWRENCE

BATISTE, C Steven. 98 STATE ST 45669 #055-02-1987 L1990 **FM** *020 †18

BOLANO, Luis E. 5897 STATE ROUTE 7, THREE GABLES SURGERY CENTE 45669
   #048-04-1986 L2001 **ORS HS** *020 †40 ‡
BROWNING, Shannon Lea. ■ 45669 #055-02-2004 **MPD** *012
CHOWDHURY, A K M Mehdi H. 43 TOWNSHIP ROAD 1525, PIKEVILLE METHODIST
   HOSPIT 45669 #160-02-1979 L2007 **IM EM** *020 †20
CLAPP, Lawrence Edward. ■ 45669 #038-40-1988 L1990 **N** *020 †75
DAVIS, Glenn Scott. 98 STATE ST 45669 #055-01-1995 L1997 **IM** *020 †20
GABRIEL, Michael H. ■ 45669 #055-02-2006 **AN** *012
IMLAY, Glen Paqying. 98 STATE ST 45669 #028-03-1998 L2002 **PM PMM** *020 †60
KUMARI, Vinita. ■ 45669 #495-54-1996 **IM** *020
MAHMOOD, Taslima. ■ 45669 #160-06-1990 L2007 **IM** *020 †20
ROA, R Arturo. 96 TOWNSHIP ROAD 369 # 101 45669 #025-01-1985 L2000 **OTO NO** *020 †45
WHEATON, Jennifer C. ■ 45669 #028-78-2003, ▲ L2007 **END** *012 †20
YAQUB, Abid. ■ 45669 #704-01-1995 L2005 **END** *100 †20
YAQUB, Sobia. ■ 45669 #704-06-1998 **IM** *012

PROSPECT – MARION

PIACENTINI, Mark John. 102 W WATER ST 43342 #038-40-1984 L1987 **FM OBG** *020 †18

PUT IN BAY – OTTAWA

BIRMINGHAM, William Edgar. 177 E. TRIMOTOR DRIVE 43456 #041-09-1945 L1949
   DR RO *071 †80

QUAKER CITY – GUERNSEY

CHILDS, Wesley Alan. ■ 43773 #048-02-1942 L1961 **GS** *071 †85

RAVENNA – PORTAGE

ABBASS, Abdul Hay A F. 6693 N CHESTNUT ST 44266 #875-01-1960 L1989 **OTO** *071 †45
ABBASS, Fadi. 6693 N CHESTNUT ST, STE 215 44266 #038-06-1997 L2000 **OTO** *020 †45
ABBASS, Hassan. 6693 N CHESTNUT ST, STE 215 44266 #038-06-1993 L1995
   OTO FPS *020 †45
ADAMS, Brian Keith. 6847 N CHESTNUT ST 44266 #038-40-1994 L1995 **EM** *020 †16
AHMAD, S. 6847 N CHESTNUT ST, STE 10 44266 #495-70-1971 L1994 **RO** *020 †80
AL-MADANI, Mohamed Majed. 6693 N CHESTNUT ST 44266 #875-02-1974 L1979 **OBG** *071
ARNOLD, Robert Brower. 6847 N CHESTNUT ST 44266 #038-41-1958 L1958
   PTH FOP *071 †50
ARORA, Anand. 6847 N CHESTNUT ST 44266 #495-12-1962 L1973 **PTH** *020 †50
BLANDFORD, Sherri. 6847 N CHESTNUT ST 44266 #038-44-1995 L1998 **FM** *020 †18
BOWLING, Agnes Victoria. 6847 N CHESTNUT ST, ROBINSON MEMORIAL HOSPITAL 44266
   #038-40-1980 L1983 **CCM IM** *020 †20
BRINKER, William Robrock. 250 S CHESTNUT ST 44266 #038-06-1958 L1958 **OPH** *071 †35
CASTALDI, Louis Vincent. 6847 N CHESTNUT ST # 200 44266 #038-41-1957 L1957 **GP** *071
CHEN, Peter Fu-Ming. 3973 LOOMIS PKWY 44266 #385-03-1968 L1972 **GS** *020 †85
DARGO, Jonathan James. ■ 44266 #038-44-2008 *012
DEAN, Steven Junior. 3973 LOOMIS PKWY 44266 #038-40-1974 L1974 **IM** *020 †20
DEORAS, Mita Satish. ■ 44266 #038-44-2008 *012
EBERLEIN, Robert Michael. 6847 N CHESTNUT ST 44266 #038-06-1988 L1992 **EM** *020 †16
EGDELL, Robert Wray. 6847 N CHESTNUT ST # 300 44266 #041-02-1969 L1975 **OBG** *020 †30
FOOTE, Carol Lynn. 6847 N CHESTNUT ST 44266 #038-44-1982 L1985 **OBG** *020 †30
FROMM, Mitchel Lee. 6847 N CHESTNUT ST, STE 10 44266 #041-01-1972 L1986
   RO PD *020 †55,80
GHUMRAWI, Badr Khalil. 6693 N CHESTNUT ST, STE 268 44266 #605-01-1971 L1974
   TS GS *020 †85,90
GUSZ, John Robt. 3973 LOOMIS PKWY, STE A 44266 #033-06-1984 L1996 **GS** *020 †85
HAUCH, James Francis. 6847 N CHESTNUT ST 44266 #056-05-1977 L1978 **GS EM** *020 †85
HAVER, Dennis Wm. 6547 N CHESTNUT ST, ROBINSON MEMORIAL HOSPITAL 44266
   #038-41-1987 L1990 **EM** *020 †16
HOSNY, Ihab Ahmed. 6847 N CHESTNUT ST, ROBINSON MEMORIAL HOSPITAL 44266
   #915-04-1979 L1990 **PTH PP** *020 †50
JAHNKE, Michelle Alyce. 6693 N CHESTNUT ST, 125 A&B 44266 #038-06-1996 L1997
   D *020 †15
JAKUBOWYCZ, Alex. 6847 N CHESTNUT ST 44266 #038-06-1999 L2002 **EM** *020 †16
JESIONEK, Paul Chester. 6847 N CHESTNUT ST 44266 #038-06-1989 L1991
   EM IM *020 †20,16
KAISER, Heather. 6847 N CHESTNUT ST, STE 10 44266 #038-45-1999 L1999 **RO** *020 †80
KELLEY, Frank Michael. 3973 LOOMIS PKWY 44266 #038-40-1994 L1995 **IM** *020 †20
KEMERER, Cheryl Lynn. 6847 N CHESTNUT ST, (RHA) 44266 #041-09-1997 L1999 **PD** *020 †55
KHAN, Zia-Ur-Rahman. 3957 LOOMIS PKWY, STE 101 44266 #704-01-1970 L1979
   OTO HNS *020 †45
KLICH, Bryan Joseph. 6847 N CHESTNUT ST 44266 #038-41-2001 L2001 **EM** *020 †16
KWON, Okap. 964 E MAIN ST 44266 #583-04-1971 L1977 **IM** *072
LEFOER, Dominic Salvador. 6847 N CHESTNUT ST 44266 #038-44-1993 L1994 **FM** *020 †18
L'HOMMEDIEU, Roger H, Jr. 4857 HARDING AVE 44266 #038-43-1979 L1980 **EM** *020 †16
MAKENS, Neal Richard. 6847 N CHESTNUT ST 44266 #028-34-1969 L1988 **PTH** *071 †50
MARCIAL, Rogelio G. ■ 44266 #748-01-1952 L1960 **FM P** *020 †18
MASTROMATTEO, Michael F. 6847 N CHESTNUT ST 44266 #038-40-1968 L1968 **GS OS** *071
MINOTT, Howard Basil. 3963 LOOMIS PKWY 44266 #035-09-1979 L1982 **U** *020 †95
MONTEMAYOR, Pedro B, Jr. 6847 N CHESTNUT ST # 200 44266 #748-07-1956 L1963 **GP** *071
NELSON, Richard Lowry. 6847 N CHESTNUT ST 44266 #038-44-1992 L1997 **PCP** *020 †50
NEMES, John. 6847 N CHESTNUT ST 44266 #781-03-1978 L1989 **IM** *020 †20
NETHING, Joshua Blaine. ■ 44266 #038-44-2008 *012
PALMSTROM, David S. ■ 44266 #051-04-1949 L1953 **OS FM** *071 †18
PANZETER, Edward Scott. 3973 LOOMIS PKWY STE B 44266 #038-40-1996 L1999 **GS** *020 †85
PELLEGRINO, Karen Smith. 6847 N CHESTNUT ST 44266 #038-43-2003 L2006 **EM** *020 †16
PENG, James Chung. 6847 N CHESTNUT ST 44266 #244-05-1972 L1980 **GP** *020
RAFECAS, Jose C. 6847 N CHESTNUT ST, STE 330 44266 #035-08-1981 L1987 **N SME** *020 †75
RAJAMOHAN, V. 6847 N CHESTNUT ST 44266 #495-16-1965 L1972 **GS GP** *020

RAMALINGAM, Ashok. 6847 N CHESTNUT ST, STE 10 44266 #038-44-1999 L1999 **RO** *020 †80

RAUX, William A, III. 6847 N CHESTNUT ST # 200 44266 #018-75-1983, ▲ L1984 **FM** *020 †18

REID, John David. 6847 N CHESTNUT ST 44266 #671-01-1946 L1966 **PTH** *071 †50

RICHMOND, Maryann. 6751 N CHESTNUT ST, RAVENNA VA OUTPATIENT CLIN 44266 #038-41-1998 L2000 **IM** *020 †20

ROY, Robert E. 246 S CHESTNUT ST 44266 #038-06-1949 L1949 **IM** *071 †20

SABLE, Jennifer Rebecca. 6847 N CHESTNUT ST, ST.STE 200 44266 #038-43-2000 L2000 **IM** *020

SARAMPOTE, Rolando V. PO BOX 687 44266 #748-10-1967 L1974 **FM** *075 †18

SCHRICKEL, Tyson Thomas. ■ 44266 #038-44-2006 L2006 **ORS** *012

SVEDA, Stephen James. 6847 N CHESTNUT ST 44266 #038-40-1966 L1966 **ORS** *075

VINCENT, Richard L. 6847 N CHESTNUT ST 44266 #038-44-1983 L1984 **EM** *020 †16

WOJTASIK, Lynn Ann. 3973 LOOMIS PKWY, STE B 44266 #038-45-1999 L1999 **GS** *020 †85

YOHO, Emma Jane Smith. 6693 N CHESTNUT ST, NORTH CHESTNUT MEDICAL ART 44266 #051-04-1954 L1958 **D OS** *071 †15

YUH, Jen-Nan. 3973 LOOMIS PKWY STE B 44266 #244-04-1975 L1981 **CRS GS** *020 †10,85

ZHAO, John Y. ■ 44266 #243-78-1983 L1999 **U** *020 †95

RAYLAND – JEFFERSON

MURRAY, Phillip John. 10686 STATE ROUTE 150 43943 #836-02-1968 L1987 **FM PHP** *020 †18

READING – HAMILTON

DENNIS, Robert Charles. 9400 READING RD, READING FAM PRACT 45215 #038-41-1997 L1998 **FM** *020 †18 ‡

MONTEMAYOR-RIVERA, Mary A. 9400 READING RD, READING FAMILY PRACTICE 45215 #748-01-1988 L1997 **FM** *020 †18

NOLAN, John Jeremiah, Jr. 9400 READING RD STE 2 45215 #038-41-1992 L1993 **FM** *020 †18

REPUBLIC – SENECA

DIEHL, Clarence E, Jr. 210 WASHINGTON 44867 #041-12-1950 L1951 **FM OS** *071 †18

REYNOLDSBURG – FRANKLIN

BANSAL, Girraj Kishore. 6490 E MAIN ST, STE D 43068 #038-40-1982 L1983 **IM** *020 †20

BENADUM, Timothy Scott. 8901 CORAL CANYON CIR 43068 #038-40-1984 L1991 **EM FM** *020 †18

CANTOR, Ronald Earl. ■ 43068 #038-40-1968 L1968 **OM MDM** *030

CHANG, Edith. 6895 E MAIN ST 43068 #038-40-1993 L1994 **FM** *020 †18 ‡

COVEL, Bonita B. 6702 E MAIN ST 43068 #038-40-1975 L1977 **FM** *020 ‡

DICOCCO, Jennifer Marie. ■ 43068 #038-41-2006 L2006 **GS** *012

DORADO, James Roderick. 6421 E MAIN ST, PHYSICIANS, INC 43068 #038-45-1993 L1994 **MPD** *020 †20,55

GREENE, Philip Sheldon. 1418 BRICE RD 43068 #062-01-1970 L1970 **GE** *062 †20

GRULKOWSKI, Mary Sigrid. 6895 E MAIN ST 43068 #038-44-1986 L1987 **FM** *020 †18

HALPIN, Thomas Jos. ■ 43068 #038-41-1967 L1967 **GPM** *071 †70

HAWTHORNE, T L. 7730 SLATE RIDGE BLVD, FAIRFIELD COUNTY HEALTH DE 43068 #038-40-1982 L1982 **FM OS** *020

KOHL, Jack Harvey. 7323 E MAIN ST 43068 #065-01-1982 L2006 **P** *020 †75

KUMAR, Manoj. ■ 43068 #495-90-1993 *100

LOCSEY, Geza. ■ 43068 #042-01-1968 L1968 **GP** *020

MC MULLEN, Timothy R. 6488 E MAIN ST, PHYSICIANS, INC 43068 #038-40-1987 L1988 **FM** *020 †18

MILLER, Jennifer Lynn. ■ 43068 #017-20-2006 L2006 **PD** *012

MOORE, James Richard. 6421 E MAIN ST 43068 #038-40-1982 L1983 **IM** *020 †20

OSER, Beryl Macy, Jr. 6702 E MAIN ST 43068 #038-40-1973 L1974 **FM** *020 †18

PANTANGCO, Irineo P, Jr. 6415 E LIVINGSTON AVE 43068 #748-10-1967 L1975 **OTO** *020 †45

PEGUES, Ramona Marie. ■ 43068 #038-40-1989 *100

RENNEKER, Nancy Jean. 2040 BRICE RD STE 100A, INDEPENDENT MEDICAL EVAL 43068 #038-41-1985 L1986 **PM IM** *020 †60

SAMLOWSKI, Werner Ernst. 1653 BRICE RD 43068 #407-23-1951 L1955 **FM GE** *071 †18

SMITH, Andrew Chas. 6421 E MAIN ST, 6421 E MAIN STREET 43068 #038-41-1978 L1979 **IM** *020 †20

SULLIVAN, Miller J, Jr. 6421 E MAIN ST 43068 #045-04-1987 L1988 **PD** *020 †55

WEBSTER, Joseph Curley. ■ 43068 #010-03-1974 L1985 **P GP** *020

WEISENBERGER, Gregory E. 7657 E MAIN ST 43068 #038-40-1979 L1980 **IM** *020 †20

WOLF, Robert F. 6488 E MAIN ST, PHYSICIANS, INC 43068 #065-06-1991 L1996 **FM** *020 †18 ‡

WORLEY, Fred Watson. 7657 E MAIN ST 43068 #038-40-1970 L1970 **IM GP** *020 †20

RICHFIELD – SUMMIT

DI LAURO, Sharon Lynne. ■ 44286 #038-44-1984 L1985 **P** *012

DUBCHUK, Vladimir. ■ 44286 #913-89-1986 L1999 **GS** *020 †85

MOURAD, Samir Youssef. 3871 BROADVIEW RD 44286 #330-02-1957 L1971 **P** *020 †75

PELAGALLI, James Arthur. ■ 44286 #016-43-1955 L1959 **GS** *071 †85

SCHWEIKERT, John Robt. ■ 44286 #047-05-1964 L1964 **END** *030 †20

SHIN, Soo Yong. ■ 44286 #583-02-1954 L1978 **P GP** *020

STUDEBAKER, Mark Edwin. 4059 KINROSS LAKES PKWY 44286 #017-20-1983 L1984 **IM NTR** *030 †20

RICHMOND HEIGHTS – CUYAHOGA

ASGERI, Mehrdad. 27100 CHARDON RD, RICHMOND HOSPITAL 44143 #517-03-1992 L2003 **IM** *020 †20

BOROS, William Michael. ■ 44143 #038-43-2004 L2004 **IM** *020

BRZOZOWSKI, Leonard Luke. 27100 CHARDON RD 44143 #041-09-1987 L1992 **GS** *020 †85

CARRINGTON, Victoria Lynn. ■ 44143 #038-06-1995 L1997 **P** *020

EISENGART, Seth W. 27100 CHARDON RD, UNIVERSITY COMMUNITY SURGE 44143 #016-42-1970 L1979 **PS GS** *020 †65,85

GALICIA, David Edward. ■ 44143 #056-06-1965 L1971 **P** *020

GLAUDE, Larry Eugene. 27100 CHARDON RD 44143 #038-06-1979 L1983 **IM** *020 †20

GRANDON, Deepa Maria. ■ 44143 #495-37-2000 L2008 **IM** *020 †20

GRUBER, Amelia B. ■ 44143 #041-13-1955 L1957 **IM SCI** *020 †20

HO, Chester Ho-Kai. ■ 44143 #917-03-1992 L2000 **SCI** *020 †60

IBIKUNLE, Olorunshola Ala. ■ 44143 #913-15-1996 L2004 **GS** *012

KEMP, Janet Lee. 4893 HIGHLAND PLACE CT 44143 #038-44-2003 L2006 **CHP** *012

LEU, Roberta Mingyi. ■ 44143 #051-01-2004 L2004 **SME** *012

MAGNUS, Patrick Craig. 27100 CHARDON RD, RICHMOND HEIGHTS HOSPITAL 44143 #566-01-1999 L2006 **IM** *020 †20

MUSKARA, Tarik Orhan. ■ 44143 #902-01-1948 L1961 **AS GS** *071

OKUTAN, Abdullah Muzaffer. ■ 44143 #902-01-1943 L1962 **PUD** *071

TRIMBLE, George Layton. ■ 44143 #038-44-2007 L2007 **FP** *012

RICHWOOD – UNION

HOLCOMB, Charles Wm. ■ 43344 #051-04-1946 L1951 **GP** *071

KAPRALY, Pamela E. 5 S CLINTON ST 43344 #038-40-1989 L1990 **FM** *020 †18

RIO GRANDE – GALLIA

PANDYA, Jyotsna R. ■ 45674 #495-22-1943 L1972 **P N** *071

RIPLEY – BROWN

ADAMS, Gretchen May. ■ 45167 #041-07-1998 L2006 **FM** *020 †18

ALLEY, Consuela R. 9 MAIN ST, RIVERVIEW PRIMARY CARE 45167 #020-02-1995 L2000 **FM** *020 †18

ARRIOLA, Maria Rowena S. 14 N 2ND ST 45167 #748-11-1981 L1992 **IM** *020 †20

BENTSON, William H. 14 N 2ND ST 45167 #016-11-1977 L1980 **PD** *020 †55

CENEDELLA, Amy Kathleen. 14 N 2ND ST 45167 #051-04-2001 L2001 **MPD** *020 †20,55

DERINGER, Kimberly Gaye. 14 N 2ND ST 45167 #038-45-2003 L2003 **MPD** *020 †20,55

RITTMAN – WAYNE

CHITTUM, John Raymond. ■ 44270 #036-07-1953 L1954 **GP OM** *071

CORBACIOGLU, Cahit. ■ 44270 #902-03-1951 L1958 **IM** *071

GASSER, Ryan Mitchel. ■ 44270 #038-40-2007 L2007 **ORS** *012

GHOUBRIAL, Sam Nabil. 25 S MAIN ST 44270 #038-43-1993 L1994 **IM** *020 †20

GUNNING, Richard Henry. 25 S MAIN ST 44270 #056-06-1988 L1992 **FM** *020 †18

PETRILLA, Eugene Francis. 223 N MAIN ST, MEDICAL CENTER OF RITTMAN 44270 #041-77-1985, ▲ L1986 **FM** *020 †18

WIDMER, Darrell Leroy. 25 S MAIN ST STE B 44270 #038-44-1995 L1996 **FM** *020 †18

ROCK CREEK – ASHTABULA

BARON, John Carl Mapili. 3330 S MAIN ST 44084 #748-02-1992 L2000 **PUD CCM** *020 †20

CHELIDZE, Teah A. 3330 S MAIN ST, ROCK CREEK HEALTH CENTER 44084 #912-02-1997 L2000 **IM** *100 †20

MOHSENI, Razieh. 3330 S MAIN ST, ROCK CREEK HEALTH CENTER 44084 #561-06-1991 L1998 **IM** *020 †20

ROCKBRIDGE – HOCKING

GUDA, Harry Eugene. 2444 DUNLAT RD 43149 #038-40-1962 L1962 **P** *071 †75

ROCKFORD – MERCER

SELL, Jerry Dwight. 506 S MAIN ST 45882 #038-40-1976 L1976 **FM** *020 †18

ROCKY RIVER – CUYAHOGA

AHMAD, Munawar. ■ 44116 #704-09-1961 L1971 **OPH** *071

AIRALDI, Julio Cesar. 20525 CENTER RIDGE RD # 40 44116 #726-01-1962 L1970 **IM CD** *020

ARMSTRONG, James Remagen. ■ 44116 #038-06-1956 L1956 **OPH** *071 †35

BECK, Glenn Paul. ■ 44116 #038-40-1963 L1963 **AN** *071

BIDROS, Dani Sirop. ■ 44116 #021-05-2004 L2006 **NS** *012

BRAUN, Raymond F. ■ 44116 #038-06-1949 L1949 **OM** *071

BRENNAN, John Francis. ■ 44116 #028-34-1943 L1946 **IM** *071

CHAMBERLAIN, Wendy Ann. ■ 44116 #048-12-2005 L2005 **PTH** *012

CHANDURKAR, Sudhakar N. 21851 CENTER RIDGE RD, STE 109 44116 #495-19-1962 L1978 **CD IM** *020 †20

COALE, Robert Milton. ■ 44116 #023-01-2005 L2005 **ORS** *012

DALE, Diana Ann. 20220 CENTER RIDGE RD, STE 3 44116 #025-07-1975 L1995 *020

DE LONG, Erika Venta. 20325 CENTER RIDGE RD #410 44116 #154-07-1957 L1961 **P** *020 †75

DEL VALLE, Paul G. ■ 44116 #033-06-2005 L2005 **AN** *012

DENKO, J Joanne Decker. ■ 44116 #023-07-1951 L1960 **P OS** *050

DEO, Datinder Bir Singh. 19133 HILLIARD BLVD 44116 #496-43-1999 L2007 **NEP** *020 †20

DRIVER, Maier Milton. ■ 44116 #035-06-1946 L1949 **GS** *071 †85

DSOUZA, Maria Sujata. ■ 44116 #017-20-2006 L2006 **OPH** *012

FUMICH, Paul M. ■ 44116 #028-34-1950 L1956 **IM PUD** *071

GARG, Ankur. ■ 44116 #495-09-1954 L1971 **GE IM** *020

GAZELLE, Harry. 19000 LAKE RD, THE WESTLAKE / SUITE 123 44116 #330-03-1953 L1960 **R** *020 †80

GOWDA, Budiyappa E. ■ 44116 #495-09-1954 L1971 **GE IM** *020

HEBSUR, Shrinivas. ■ 44116 #038-40-2007 L2007 **IM** *012

HENDERSHOT, Edward L. 21851 CENTER RIDGE RD 44116 #038-40-1952 L1952 **OTO** *071 †45
HOXHA, Alma. ■ 44116 #120-01-2001 L2004 **AN** *012
INGAL, Marcial Santos. ■ 44116 #748-09-1967 **GP** *074
JIMENEZ, Bienvenido Reyes. 21851 CENTER RIDGE RD, STE 109 44116 #748-01-1953 L1961 **IM CD** *020
KANDERIAN, Anne Sami. ■ 44116 #041-14-2001 L2001 **IM** *020
KAYES, Julie Davis. 20006 DETROIT RD, STE 101 44116 #038-41-2000 L2000 **FM** *020 †18
KHAN, Mehwish Khurram. ■ 44116 #704-01-2002 L2006 **IM** *020
KIRK, Robert Chapman. 3591 ELDORADO DR 44116 #038-06-1942 L1942 **OPH** *071 †35
KLEIN, Jonathan Robt. 2639 WOOSTER RD 44116 #038-06-1988 L1990 **EM** *020 †16
KLEIN, Louis David. 20220 CENTER RIDGE RD 44116 #025-07-1977 L1978 **PYG P** *020 †75
LALWANI, Vidya C. 21851 CENTER RIDGE RD 44116 #495-17-1962 L1970 **IM P** *020
LYDON, Joseph Francis. ■ 44116 #041-13-1947 L1956 **GS VS** *071 †85
MC KENNA, Carl Myron. ■ 44116 #036-05-1958 L1959 **GS** *071 †85
MIRALDI, Virginia Anne. ■ 44116 #038-06-2007 L2007 **IM** *012
MULLIGAN, James Edwin. ■ 44116 #038-06-1955 L1955 **IM** *071
PATEL, Shilen Narendra. ■ 44116 #422-01-2004 L2007 **HO** *012 †20
POPOVICH, Nicholas R. 20575 CENTER RIDGE RD, STE 500 44116 #038-06-1957 L1957 **PD OS** *071 †55
ROBINSON, Harold Danell. 2639 WOOSTER RD, LAKELAND EMERGENCY ASSOC 44116 #038-06-1999 L1999 **EM** *020 †16
ROWBOTTOM, Rosetta Geraci. 2639 WOOSTER RD, LAKELAND EMERGENCY ASSC 44116 #038-41-1987 L1988 **IM EM** *020 †20
SALAPARE, Christmas V. 20006 DETROIT RD, STE 101 44116 #748-01-1970 L1978 **GP** *071
SANDERS, John Harrold. ■ 44116 #025-01-1941 L1949 **GYN OBG** *071 †30
SCHADE, Andrew Edward. ■ 44116 #038-06-2005 L2005 **PTH** *012
SCHOECK, Ronald Jos A. ■ 44116 #028-34-1958 L1961 **R OS** *071 †80
SEKEL, Susan Diane. ■ 44116 #051-04-2006 L2006 **GS** *012
SHARMA, Rajesh. 20525 CENTER RIDGE RD, RSTE 220 44116 #495-20-1990 L1996 **IM** *020 †20
STOTZ, Lori G. 19460 BATTERSEA BLVD 44116 #038-40-1998 L2000 **FM** *020 †18
STRANG, Marilee. ■ 44116 #056-06-1983 L1993 **CHP** *020
STRAUBS, Victor. ■ 44116 #594-01-1944 L1954 **FM** *071 †18
STRUNETS, Anton Vladimiro. ■ 44116 #913-12-1997 L2003 *100
SURESH, Keelapandal R. 21851 CENTER RIDGE RD, STE 309 44116 #495-53-1979 L1989 **NEP IM** *020 †20
UTZ, Christopher Joseph. ■ 44116 #038-06-2007 L2007 **ORS** *012
WATTS, Richard W. ■ 44116 #038-06-1946 L1950 **CD IM** *071 †20
WENDT, David Matthew. 19324 DETROIT RD 44116 #038-40-1999 L1999 **FM** *020 †18
WHITCOMB, John G. ■ 44116 #038-41-1951 L1951 **GS PDS** *071 †85
ZAHRA, Muhammed Hassan. 20220 CENTER RIDGE RD, STE 120 44116 #875-01-1980 L1984 **CD IM** *020 †20

ROOTSTOWN — PORTAGE

ADIHETTY, Nishan Dharshan. 4209 STATE ROUTE 44 44272 #220-01-2003 L2005 **P** *012
CLANCY, Christopher Lee. ■ 44272 #038-44-2008 *012
COSTA, Anthony Jos. 4209 STATE ROUTE 44, NE UNIV COLLEGE OF MED 44272 #038-40-1973 L1976 **FM FPG** *040 †18
GERGIS, Sherry Labib. 4209 STATE ROUTE 44 44272 #305-01-2007 L2007 **P** *012
KINNEY, Amanda Kristine. ■ 44272 #038-44-2008 *012
MISJA, Charles M. 4209 STATE ROUTE 44 44272 #305-01-2007 L2007 **P** *012
MOON, Jonah Ralph. ■ 44272 #038-44-2008 *012
NORA, Lois Margaret. 4209 STATE ROUTE 44, NORTHEASTERN OH UNIV 44272 #016-01-1979 L2003 **OS N** *020 †75
PATEL, Chiraag S. 4209 STATE ROUTE 44, NORTHEASTERN OH UNIVS COLL 44272 #038-44-2005 L2005 **IM** *012
PAVLIDAKEY, Peter George. ■ 44272 #038-44-2008 *012
PENN, Mark Anthony. 4209 STATE ROUTE 44 44272 #038-43-1977 L1978 **FM** *020 †18
PRASANA, Prasanth M. 4209 STATE ROUTE 44 BOX 95, NORTHEASTERN OH UNIVS COLL 44272 #038-44-2005 L2005 **DR** *012
SHEMISA, Kamal Othman. ■ 44272 #038-44-2008 *012
THOMAS, Tiffany Christine. ■ 44272 #038-44-2004 L2004 **P** *012 †55

ROSEVILLE — MUSKINGUM

BUTTERFIELD, Jack D, Jr. 167 S MAIN ST 43777 #036-05-1979 L1980 **FM** *020 †18

ROSSFORD — WOOD

FOX, Jill Marquart. 1200 DIXIE HWY 43460 #038-43-1991 L1992 **CHP** *020 †75
HASAN, Irshad I. 930 DIXIE HWY 43460 #704-20-1988 L1994 **FM** *020 †18
MARSHALL, Donald B. 1265 DIXIE HWY 43460 #016-76-1972, ▲ L1974 **FM OS** *071
MARSHALL, Rebecca Suzanne. 1265 DIXIE HWY 43460 #016-76-2003, ▲ L2003 **FM** *020 †18
SCHMIDT, Robert Allen. 930 DIXIE HWY 43460 #038-43-1972 L1973 **FM P** *020
THAKUR, Binod K. 1265 DIXIE HWY 43460 #495-15-1979 L1995 **PD AI** *020 †03,55
TUFAIL, Mohammad. ■ 43460 #704-09-1995 L2005 **CHP** *020
WOODS, George Richard. 513 SUPERIOR ST 43460 #025-01-1964 L1965 **OBG** *071 †30

RUSHVILLE — FAIRFIELD

SHEETS, Jerome R. ■ 43150 #038-06-1949 L1949 **GP DIA** *071

RUSSELL — GEAUGA

RACHITSKAYA, Aleksandra V. ■ 44072 #038-06-2008 *012

RUSSELLS POINT — LOGAN

ABRAMS, Jeffrey Alan. ■ 43348 #038-40-1971 L1971 **FM** *020 †18

ESCOBEDO, Leo Aranas. 208 LINCOLN BLVD 43348 #748-01-1967 L1974 **GP** *020 †18

SABINA — CLINTON

HAYES, Ruth Anna. 88 N HOWARD ST 45169 #038-41-1965 L1965 **GS** *020 †85
LEVERICH, Joy Dawn. 12459 STATE RT 22 AND 3 45169 #049-01-1988 L1994 **GS** *020 †85

SAGAMORE HILLS — SUMMIT

BOSTELMAN, Mark Alan. 493 ALLIANCE DR, DEPT ANESTHESIOLOGY 44067 #038-44-1992 L1993 **AN** *020 †05
BROGLIO, Michelle Anne. 8557 DEEP COVE DR 44067 #038-06-2000 L2000 **PD** *020 †55
HEGDE, Nikita. ■ 44067 #496-39-2002 L2002 **RHU** *020 †20
MORRISSEY, Kelly Ann. ■ 44067 #038-06-2008 *012
POSCH, James John. 863 W AURORA RD, BLDG 1 44067 #056-06-1955 L1956 **PD** *071 †55
RAGUCCI, Bartholomew Danl. 842 GREENGATE OVAL 44067 #038-40-1957 L1957 **D** *071 †15

SAINT BERNARD — HAMILTON

SINGER, Jonathan Israel. 110 WASHINGTON AVE, CITY OF ST BERNARD COM OF 45217 #038-41-1972 L1972 **PD EM** *020 †55
TAFT, William Biggins. ■ 45217 #028-02-2005 L2005 **CPP** *012

SAINT CLAIRSVILLE — BELMONT

ALLEN, Kenneth Jean. 52160 NATIONAL RD E, THE HEALTH PLAN 43950 #041-13-1958 L2003 **FM FPG** *071 †18 ‡
ANDRONIC, Maura. 68353 BANNOCK RD 43950 #781-01-1989 L2000 **P** *020 †75
BAE, William Harvey. ■ 43950 #583-09-1964 L1979 **EM** *071
BARRETT, Edgar Leicester. 51339 NATIONAL RD E 43950 #352-08-1953 L1970 **ORS** *071 †40
BILAL, Bassam. 51342 NATIONAL RD 43950 #875-02-1991 L1999 **IM** *020 †20
CHAR, Kalpana Vedavyasa. 46380 COUNTRY LAKE DR 43950 #036-01-1992 L2000 **IM** *020 †20
CHIA, Imelda Caparas. 51342 NATIONAL RD 43950 #748-07-1977 L1986 **IM NEP** *020 †20
CHOKKAVELU, Viswanathan. 100 N SUGAR ST 43950 #495-04-1970 L1975 **ID IM** *020 †20
CHREST, Robert B. ■ 43950 #055-75-2007 *012
CODDINGTON, R Dean. ■ 43950 #035-45-1951 L1967 **CHP P** *071
CURTIS, Rodney Lee. 51370 NATIONAL RD E 43950 #055-01-1986 L1992 **U** *020
DE FILIPPO, John L, Jr. 69568 CRESCENT RD 43950 #038-06-1989 L1990 **DR** *020 †80
DELA CRUZ, Renato Falgui. 51342 NATIONAL RD STE J 43950 #748-01-1976 L1990 **IM** *020
DE LA CRUZ, Reynaldo A. 51342 NATIONAL RD E, STE J 43950 #748-01-1976 L1996 **IM** *020
GOSWAMI, Naba. 109 PLAZA DR, # A1 43950 #495-78-1974 L1995 **IM CD** *020
GUPTA, Shashi Bala. 51339 NATIONAL RD, BELMONT COMMUNITY HOSPITAK 43950 #495-30-1974 L1999 **IM** *020 †20
KANT, Ravi. 67670 TRACO DR, FOX RUN HOSPITAL 43950 #495-08-1982 L1993 **P CHP** *020 †75
LANCIONE, Sarah M. 106 PLAZA DR 43950 #495-78-1973 L1984 **OBG** *020
LEE, Charles Virtue. ■ 43950 #038-40-1943 L1943 **GP OBG** *071
MANALAC, Fernando Jacinto. 68353 BANNOCK RD 43950 #748-01-1963 L1965 **P** *072
MEHTA, Rajesh M. 68377 STEWART DR, STE 202 43950 #495-48-1978 L1992 **IM** *020 †20
MORENO, Maria R Lim. 50375 HEMINGWAY DR 43950 #748-19-1988 L1999 **P** *020 †75
MOUHLAS, Gus John. 111 N MARIETTA ST 43950 #418-01-1968 L1974 **GYN** *020 †30
MUSOLIN, Lisa Michelle. ■ 43950 #055-75-2003, ▲ L2003 **FM** *100
ORTIZ, German V. 51339 NATIONAL RD E 43950 #649-01-1951 L1958 **IM CD** *071
PETERSEN, J Michael. 109 PLAZA DR 43950 #055-01-1982 L2000 **GS** *020 †85
RAYMOND, Bruce A. 52160 NATIONAL RD E 43950 #038-02-1949 L1999 **TS** *030 †85,90
REYES, Samson D, Jr. 51710 NATIONAL RD E, SAMSON D REYES MD INC 43950 #748-01-1966 L1974 **GS GP** *075
RICHEY, Drake. ■ 43950 #010-01-1959 L1962 **R OS** *071 †80
SATHAPPAN, Kasiraja. 157 E LAWN AVE 43950 #495-04-1985 L1994 **P CHP** *030
SHACKELFORD, Howard Lee, Jr. 109 PLAZA DR 43950 #055-01-1976 L1978 **TS CD** *020 †85,90
SINGH, Gurmeet. 106 PLAZA DR 43950 #495-45-1982 L1990 **N** *020 †75,55
SINGH, Paramjit. PO BOX 420, SUITE 461455 43950 #495-03-1985 L1993 **PUD IM** *020 †20
SUKYS, Nancy. 107 PLAZA DR STE D 43950 #055-01-1991 L1996 **FM** *020 †18
TROUTEN, Jasmine Tugaoen. 51339 NATIONAL RD E 43950 #038-40-1991 L1992 **IM** *020 †20
UZOKWE, Festus Ikechukwu. 68353 BANNOCK RD 43950 #690-12-1989 L2004 **P CHP** *020 †75
WANG, Hsinn-Hong. 51339 NATIONAL RD E 43950 #385-02-1967 L1975 **PD NPM** *020 †55
WILSON, Mark Joseph. 135 E MAIN ST STE D 43950 #055-01-1997 L2002 **PD** *020 †55
WINSCH, John Jos. 103 PLAZA DR, STE A 43950 #038-40-1971 L1971 **FM AM** *020 †18

SAINT HENRY — MERCER

KLEINHENZ, Heather Ann. ■ 45883 #038-45-2004 L2004 **FM** *100 †18

SAINT MARYS — AUGLAIZE

ANNAM, Seeta Ramaiah. 200 SAINT CLAIR AVE 45885 #495-50-1971 L1979 **AN** *020 †05
ATALLA, Emad S. 200 SAINT CLAIR AVE, JTDM HOSPITAL 45885 #915-02-1987 L1996 **AN** *020 †05
ATILLO, Nicanor A, Jr. 200 SAINT CLAIR AVE 45885 #748-01-1955 L1975 **PTH** *071 †50
BACHMAN, Katherine Marie. 200 SAINT CLAIR AVE 45885 #038-06-1997 L2000 **OBG** *020 †30
BEHAL, Ashni Kumar. 200 SAINT CLAIR AVE 45885 #917-02-1974 L1979 **DR** *020 †80
BOUTROS, Dina. 1165 S KNOXVILLE AVE, STE F 45885 #915-02-1987 L1997 **N** *020 †75
BUHARIWALLA, Reeshad R. 1300 GREENVILLE RD, SAINT MARY FAMILY PRAC 45885 #064-01-1986 L1995 *020
CHALASANI, Padmaja. 1300 GREENVILLE RD 45885 #495-58-1990 L1998 **IM** *020 †20
DAVIS, David Lee. 1002 S KNOXVILLE AVE 45885 #056-05-1971 L1979 **ORS OAR** *020 †40
DAVIS, Keevin Rene. 1005 S KNOXVILLE AVE 45885 #038-43-1978 L1981 **OBG** *020 †30
DOZIER, Thomas C. 112 COURT ST 45885 #018-75-1949, ▲ L1953 **FM** *071

FORNADEL, Brian John. 200 SAINT CLAIR AVE 45885 #038-40-1996 L1997 FM *020 †18
GAERKE, Cynthia Marie. 1040 HAGER ST, ADULT MEDICINE AND PEDIATR 45885 #038-45-1994 L1998 MPD *020
JELINGER, Eric Victor. 200 SAINT CLAIR AVE 45885 #038-43-1985 L1991 DR *020 †
KUCK, Cheryl Ruth. 1010 HAGER ST 45885 #038-45-1992 L1995 PD *020 †55
MANSFIELD, William P. 200 SAINT CLAIR AVE 45885 #012-21-1987 L2001 DR *020 †80
MISSON, Joseph Raymond. 1002 S KNOXVILLE AVE 45885 #038-43-2000 L2006 ORS *020
PAGUIRIGAN, Alfredo A. 1132 HAGER ST 45885 #748-02-1964 L1970 IM GE *020
PATEL, Samir Mahesh. 1002 S KNOXVILLE AVE 45885 #055-01-1999 L2005 HS *020 †40
PATTERSON, James John. 1002 S KNOXVILLE AVE 45885 #038-41-1995 L1999 ORS *020 †40
PLAZA, Ruben German. 1005 S KNOXVILLE AVE 45885 #176-01-1970 L1978 OBG GP *020 †30 ‡
QUINTER, Paul Lawrence. 1165 S KNOXVILLE AVE 45885 #038-40-1973 L1973 GS *020 †85
RAJSHEKER, Kollipara. 200 SAINT CLAIR AVE 45885 #495-65-1973 L1980 AN *020 †05
RAVIPATI, Seetaram. 200 SAINT CLAIR AVE 45885 #495-50-1970 L1981 DR OS *020 †20
STEGALL, Victor John. 200 SAINT CLAIR AVE 45885 #047-06-1969 L1970 FM *020 †18
TORRES-CORDERO, Juan V. 200 SAINT CLAIR AVE 45885 #042-02-1988 L2001 OM GPM *030 †70
WHITE, Jeffrey Allan. 200 SAINT CLAIR AVE, JOINT TOWNSHIP DISTRICT ME 45885 #064-01-1984 L2001 GP *020

SAINT PARIS – CHAMPAIGN

SHAFER, Alan D. ■ 43072 #035-20-1949 L1955 PDS *071 †85

SALEM – COLUMBIANA

AEY, Susan. 564 E 2ND ST, SALEM INTERNAL MED. ASSOC. 44460 #038-40-1993 L1998 IM *020 †20
AMIN, Naseem A. 1076 E STATE ST 44460 #024-05-2001 L2004 PD *100 †55
APICELLA, Frank Vincent. 1995 E STATE ST 44460 #028-34-1958 L1965 R NM *071 †80
APICELLA, Peter Lee. 2094 E STATE ST 44460 #028-02-1990 L1992 DR *020 †80
APICELLA, Salvatore Carl. 2094 E STATE ST 44460 #010-02-1962 L1966 R NM *020 †80
BANNING, Richard Leon. 1995 E STATE ST 44460 #038-40-1973 L1973 FM *020 †18
BENNETT, Lisa Ann. 1995 E STATE ST, SALEM COMMUNITY HOSPITAL 44460 #038-44-1993 L2001 EM *020 †16
BERNAT, John Raymond. 1070 E STATE ST 44460 #038-44-1996 L2000 D *020 †15
BRINE, Bart John. 1059 E STATE ST 44460 #038-43-1991 L1995 OPH *020 †85
BUDDE, Oscar Eduardo. 1995 E STATE ST 44460 #132-02-1959 L1971 PTH *071 †50
CIBULA, Peter R. ■ 44460 #038-06-1952 L1952 IM CD *071
CITINO, Anna Maria. 1995 E STATE ST 44460 #038-40-1987 L1990 IM *020 †20
DAWSON, John Mac. 1995 E STATE ST 44460 #028-79-1981, ▲ L1989 EM OBS *020 †18
DEMAS, William Fitzgerald. 2020 E STATE ST, STE A 44460 #035-08-1981 L1986 RO *020 †80
DOTY, Angela Ann. 2094 E STATE ST, STE B 44460 #038-44-1991 L1997 OBG *020 †30
DRAKE, Pamela Dawn. ■ 44460 #038-43-1982 L1993 P *075 †75
ECONOMOUS, Dean Vasilios. 2370 SOUTHEAST BLVD, FAMILY PRACTICE CENTER OF 44460 #038-45-1994 L1996 FM *020 †18
EVANS, Howard David. 1995 E STATE ST 44460 #041-01-1962 L1964 OBG *071 †30
FAWCETT, Richard Lee. 2370 SOUTHEAST BLVD, FAMILY PRACTICE CENTER OF 44460 #038-06-1974 L1975 FM *020 †18
FRANCISCO, Benj Silvestre. ■ 44460 #748-07-1912 L1964 GP *072
FREDRICKSON, Lauren Stull. 1995 E STATE ST 44460 #048-15-1987 L1991 EM GS *020 †16
GARDNER, James Gregory. 2370 SOUTHEAST BLVD, FAMILY PRACTICE CENTER OF 44460 #038-40-1978 L1979 FM *020 †18
GUERRIERE-KOVACH, Pamela. 1070 E STATE ST 44460 #038-44-1996 L1998 DMP *020 †50
HACKSTEDDE, Anita Angela. 1995 E STATE ST, BEEGHLY MEDICAL PARK 44460 #038-40-1994 L1998 MPD *020 †20,55
ITIKALA, Sreenivas Rao. 1995 E STATE ST 44460 #495-21-1963 L1972 IM CD *020
JULIUS, Marcus John. 1995 E STATE ST 44460 #038-44-1994 L1999 DR *020
KERPSACK, Joseph T. 2094 E STATE ST, STE B 44460 #038-45-1994 L1998 OBG *020 †30
KIMBOROWICZ, Mark Thos. 1995 E STATE ST, EMERG DEPT SALEM COMM HSP 44460 #038-40-1980 L1982 EM *020
KOLOZSI, William Zoltan. 2020 E STATE ST, STE H 44460 #020-02-1976 L1980 GE *020
LATORRE, Humberto A. 2376 SOUTHEAST BLVD 44460 #319-01-1961 L1972 END PD *020 †55
LEE, Fu Nen. 2376 SOUTHEAST BLVD 44460 #244-02-1970 L1973 OBG *030
LUNNE, Denis R. 564 E 2ND ST 44460 #038-44-1988 L1990 IM *020 †20
MACABOBBY, Danielle R. 1076 E STATE ST 44460 #038-44-2002 L2002 PD *020 †55
MADISON, John Robt. 2094 E STATE ST 44460 #038-40-1960 L1960 GS HNS *020 †85
MADISON, Michael Edward. 2094 E STATE ST, STE D 44460 #038-44-1994 L1996 GS *020 †85
MASRY, Mohammed. 2380 SOUTHEAST BLVD, STE C 44460 #875-01-1969 L1974 GS *020 †85
MC NAIR-TOLIVER, Karla. 2020 E STATE ST 44460 #038-44-1995 L1998 PD *020
MILLIGAN, James R. 166 VINE 44460 #041-02-1950 L1951 GP *071
MOHAN, Kiran. 2020 E STATE ST 44460 #495-74-1971 L1995 IM PD *020
MUELLER, Eugene Alexander. ■ 44460 #023-01-1954 L1962 GS *071 †85
ORTIZ, Madeleine Ana. 1076 E STATE ST, 44460 #308-03-1981 L1990 PD *020 †55
PAUMIER, John Cletus. 2376 SOUTHEAST BLVD 44460 #038-44-1988 L1989 ORS *020 †40
PEDERZOLLI, Andrew Carl. 1059 E STATE ST 44460 #038-41-1978 L1979 OPH *020 †85 ‡
PENIX, Laurie Ann. 2020 E STATE ST, STE C 44460 #038-44-1986 L1998 PD *020 †55
PERRICO, Ralph. 1995 E STATE ST 44460 #038-44-1996 L1997 DR *020 †80
POTLURI, Chinna Babu. 1995 E STATE ST 44460 #495-58-1968 L1974 EM *020 †50,16
PRITCHARD, Leonard S. 1995 E STATE ST 44460 #041-12-1952 L1954 FM PD *020
ROBERTSON, Steven Peter. 2364 SOUTHEAST BLVD 44460 #038-06-1996 L2000 MPD *020 †20,55
ROUSSEAU, William Roberts. 1995 E STATE ST 44460 #038-41-1963 L1963 AN *071 †05
SANKOVIC, Danny E. 1515 E STATE ST 44460 #038-44-1987 L1994 GS GE *020 †85
SEVILLA, Michael J. 2370 SOUTHEAST BLVD, FAM PRACT CTR OF SALEM 44460 #038-44-1998 L2000 FM *020 †18
SHANNON, Patrick Lee. 1070 E STATE ST 44460 #038-44-1995 L1999 D *020 †15
SHIMEK, Jocelyn Florendo. 2380 SOUTHEAST BLVD, STE B 44460 #018-75-1978, ▲ L1981 IM *020 †20
SHIVERS, Richard Mark. 1000 W STATE ST 44460 #038-44-1992 L1993 FM *020 †18
SIMON, Lee Thos. 2222 OAK ST 44460 #038-40-1978 L1979 ORS *020 †40
SOTO, Sonia Milagros. 1076 E STATE ST 44460 #042-03-1995 L1999 PD *020 †55

TORTI, Dardo Sergio. 2360 SOUTHEAST BLVD 44460 #132-02-1960 L1970 PD *020
WEAVER, Joshua Aaron. ■ 44460 #038-44-2005 L2005 PTH *012

SALINEVILLE – COLUMBIANA

KEYLOR, Hubert Karl. 103 W MAIN ST, SALINEVILLE FAM CARE CTR 43945 #038-40-1961 L1961 EM GP *074

SANDUSKY – ERIE

AGRAWAL, Satendra Kumar. 1221 HAYES AVE 44870 #495-41-1962 L1971 TS *071
AHLUWALIA, Charanjit S. 3006 CAMPBELL ST, MEDICAL SERVICES, INC. 44870 #495-03-1970 L1985 CD IM *020
AHLUWALIA, Shavinder Kaur. 3006 CAMPBELL ST 44870 #495-29-1973 L1985 GP PD *020
AIYAPPASAMY, Sidhaiyan. 1221 HAYES AVE, STE K 44870 #495-16-1974 L1978 PUD IM *020
AL-TURK, Issam Ahmad. 208 E PERKINS AVE #847-01-1977 L1998 FM *020
AVENDANO, Christopher E. 2800 HAYES AVE BLDG G 44870 #038-40-1993 L1995 PCC *020 †20
BABIUCH, Michael C. 1101 DECATUR ST, DEPT OF EMERGENCY MEDICINE 44870 #038-43-1979 L1981 EM *020 †16
BARTHOLOMEW, Robt Eugene. 1218 CLEVELAND RD 44870 #016-06-1954 L1970 PD *071 †55
BEERMAN, Martin Howard. 1116 DECATUR ST 44870 #038-40-1978 L1979 GE IM *020 †20
BLANK, Michael Scott. 1101 DECATUR ST, FIRELANDS REGIONAL MEDICAL 44870 #422-01-2000 L2005 ID *020 †20
BODIE, John Francis. 3116 STONEWOOD DR 44870 #038-40-1963 L1963 R *071 †80
BRAUN, Dale Earl. 703 TYLER ST, STE 350 44870 #038-45-1982 L1985 NS *020 †25
BRAUN, Marcia Elizabeth. ■ 44870 #038-45-2005 L2005 FP *012
BRAUSCH, Charles Cole. 1200 PROSPECT, STE 302 44870 #038-06-1957 L1957 N *020 †75
BRINDLE, Fred Andrew. 3006 CAMPBELL ST, STE 2 44870 #055-01-1968 L1985 NS *020 †25
BUEHRER, Jeffrey Lynn. 703 TYLER ST STE 351, N.O.V.S.A., L.L.C. 44870 #025-01-1986 L1996 VS *020 †85
BUMAGINA, Nataliya. 1012 E PERKINS AVE, PEDIATRIC ASSOC SANDUSKY 44870 #913-18-1991 L2004 PD *020 †55
CAMPBELL, Scott Michael. 1101 DECATUR ST, DEPT OF EMERGENCY MEDICINE 44870 #038-43-1989 L1990 EM *020 †16
CARROLL, Robert Gerard. 1101 DECATUR ST 44870 #041-12-1968 L1969 NM AN *020 †28
CHABAN, Kamal. 2800 HAYES AVE BLDG G 44870 #875-02-1986 L1992 PUD CCM *020 †20
CHANDRAN, Mohan S. 1200 PROSPECT ST 44870 #496-16-1980 L1992 N NM *020 †20
CHINTALAPALLI, Ananda R G. PO BOX 838 44871 #495-33-1967 L1973 AN *020
COOK, Gregory Paul. 2800 HAYES AVE, BLDG D 44870 #038-43-1990 L1991 U *020 †95
COOK, John Paul. 703 TYLER ST, SANDUSKY OB-GYN INC 44870 #041-13-1962 L1965 GYN *020 †30
COOPER, Marsha Diane. 2819 HAYES AVE STE 6 44870 #041-09-1978 L1982 IM CD *020 †20
CULLATH, Sathishkumar Har. 3006 CAMPBELL ST, NORTH CENTRAL OHIO MED SER 44870 #496-21-2000 L2006 IM *020 †20
DABBS, Charles King. 1617 W BOGART RD 44870 #021-01-1984 L1990 OPH OS *020 †35
DARWICH, Maamun Darwich. 1101 DECATUR ST 44870 #847-01-1995 L2002 GS *020
DE RISO, Anthony J, II. 1200 PROSPECT ST, STE 103 44870 #028-34-1984 L1992 CD GS *020 †85,90
DRURY, John Walter. 2015 E PERKINS AVE 44870 #038-40-1971 L1972 OPH *020 †35
DUTKO, Karen Elsie. 1218 CLEVELAND RD 44870 #035-15-1981 L1985 PD *020 †55
DUTKO, Stephen John. 1218 CLEVELAND RD, SANDUSKY PEDIATRICIANS 44870 #038-40-1980 L1980 PD *020 †55
ELASHI, Essam Bashir. 2819 HAYES AVE 44870 #915-06-1981 L1997 NEP IM *020 †20
EVERHART, Clarence E, Jr. ■ 44870 #010-01-1952 L1953 PTH *071 †50
FLEMING, Thomas E. 2819 HAYES AVE STE 3 44870 #038-06-1994 L1996 D DS *020 †15
GALLAGHER, James Patrick. 149 E WATER ST 44870 #038-43-1979 L1981 IM *020 †20
GASPAR-YOO, Vicenta C. 703 TYLER ST, STE 350 44870 #748-10-1989 L2000 PM *020 †60
GOULD, Jennifer W. 2819 HAYES AVE, STE 3 44870 #038-06-1994 L1995 D *020 †15
GRAYSON, David John, Jr. 1031 PIERCE ST STE A, FIRELANDS CORPORATE HLTH 44870 #038-45-1982 L1983 FM OM *020 †18
HAKIM, Jonathan I. 2800 HAYES AVE BLDG D 44870 #038-41-1997 L2000 U *100
HERRON, Timothy. 1200 PROSPECT ST 44870 #038-06-1984 L1984 N *020 †75
HILL, Robert Lewis. 2800 HAYES AVE BLDG B 44870 #038-41-1997 L1998 IM *020 †20
HOFFMAN, Harry Lowell. ■ 44870 #038-06-1947 L1947 GS CRS *071 †85
HOLLADAY, Catherine A. 1717 E PERKINS AVE 44870 #039-79-1990, ▲ L1993 P *020
HONG, Young Kyu. 1101 DECATUR ST 44870 #583-13-1978 L1984 DR *020 †80
HUANG, Eugene Hsu. 417 QUARRY LAKES DR 44870 #048-04-2002 L2006 RO *020
IBRAHIM, Hassan Mohamad. 703 TYLER ST STE 250, NORTH OHIO HEART CENTER, I 44870 #875-03-1980 L1995 CD IM *020 †20
INGLIS, William D. 1200 SYCAMORE LINE, STEIN HOSPICE SERVICE, INC 44870 #041-02-1957 L1958 IM PLM *020 †20
ISPHORDING, Thomas E, Jr. 1218 CLEVELAND RD, SANDUSKY PEDIATRICIANS 44870 #038-41-1986 L1987 PD *020 †55
JUNG, Byung Ha. 1101 DECATUR ST 44870 #583-04-1970 L1980 AN *020
KARAMCHANDANI, Jagdish H. 540 BUCHANAN ST 44870 #308-11-1985 L2002 PM *020 †60
KELLER, Richard Ralph. 3103 CAMPBELL ST 44870 #038-41-1982 L1983 FM *020 †18
KELLIS, Augustine John. 2600 HAYES AVE 44870 #038-06-1989 L1990 OPH *020 †35
KESARIA, Ashwinkumar C. 1200 PROSPECT ST, STE 102 44870 #577-01-1974 L1982 DR NM *020 †80
KESARIA, Gopi Ashwin. ■ 44870 #038-44-2008 *012
KEYS, Kemmes. ■ 44870 #038-45-1983 L1983 IM *020 †20
KHAN-HUDSON, Alia. 1313 W BOGART RD 44870 #704-06-1996 L2004 IMG *020 †20
KHOSLA, Narinder Nath. 1006 GRANT ST 44870 #495-29-1967 L1980 PME AN *020
KIM, Gwang Ooh. 2819 HAYES AVE, STE 1 44870 #583-01-1969 L1977 NEP IM *020 †20
KRAUSS, Willy. 2020 HAYES AVE, STE 101 44870 #550-01-1965 L1985 P PYG *020 †75
KUMAR, Vimal Shiv. 2800 HAYES AVE, TREATMENT CENTER BLDG A 44870 #038-43-1986 L1989 IM *020 †05
LAVENDER, Clinton F. 1912 HAYES AVE 44870 #038-06-1946 L1949 PD *071 †55
LEAKE, Jonathan Frank. 3004 HAYES AVE, NOMS OB/GYN, INC 44870 #038-41-1984 L1991 OBG GO *020 †30
LEBRON, Juan F. 1617 W BOGART RD 44870 #042-01-1994 L2000 OPH *020 †35
LEE, Han Jun. 1617 W BOGART RD STE 5 44870 #583-06-1970 L1978 P CHP *020

LEE, John Yong. ■ 44870 #583-02-1958 L1976 **R NM** *071 †28,80
LENHART, Donald White. 1221 HAYES AVE 44870 #038-06-1970 L1976 **GS GP** *020 †85
LEONARDY, Nicholas John. 1617 W BOGART RD 44870 #036-07-1984 L1991 **OPH** *020 †35
LIN, Ih-Foo. 1221 HAYES AVE STE A 44870 #385-01-1967 L1984 **P** *020 †75
LOEFFLER, Donald Ferner. 703 TYLER ST, STE 102 44870 #038-06-1954 L1954 **RO R** *071 †80
LYSTER, Michael J. 703 TYLER ST STE 250, NORTH OHIO HEART CENTER, I 44870
    #028-78-1987, ▲ L1994 **CD IM** *020 †20
MACFARLANE, Noble T. ■ 44870 #051-01-1953 L1956 **PD** *071 †55
MC CORMACK, Lawrence R. 1410 MILAN RD 44870 #038-40-1972 L1972 **GE IM** *020 †20
MC GUINN, William Patrick. 703 TYLER ST STE 250, NORTH OHIO HEART CENTER, I 44870
    #038-43-1984 L1985 **CD IM** *020 †20
MCMILLION, Charyse M. ■ 44870 #038-75-2007, ▲ L2007 *012
MICHIENZI, Francesco. 3406 HAYES AVE 44870 #561-17-1951 L1961 **TS GS** *020 †85,90
MINOTTI, Anthony Jos. 1200 PROSPECT ST, STE 102 44870 #038-45-1991 L1992 **DR** *020 †80
MITCHEL, Bradley William. 1101 DECATUR ST 44870 #038-40-2001 L2001 *020 †05 ‡
MONTAGINO, Neil J. 703 TYLER ST 44870 #038-44-1967, ▲ L1967 **AN CCM** *071
MORRIS, David Neil. 1019 PIERCE ST 44870 #038-44-1986 L1990 **IM PD** *020 †20,55
ORGEL, Ira Kalmin. 1617 W BOGART RD 44870 #041-09-1984 L1991 **OPH** *020 †35
OSINOWO, Latifat Oluwatoy. 3416 COLUMBUS AVE, SANDUSKY OUTPATIENT CLINIC 44870
    #690-01-1987 L2004 **CHP** *100 †75
PALLAPOTHU, Sukeshini R. 1221 HAYES AVE STE GS 44870 #495-21-1967 L1983 **PM** *072
PARNELL, Christopher E. 1912 HAYES AVE 44870 #005-76-2001, ▲ L2007 **PM** *020 †60
PARSCHAUER, Kenneth E. 2600 HAYES AVE 44870 #041-77-1980, ▲ L1981 **OPH** *020
PASTERAK, George Elmer. ■ 44870 #038-06-1944 L1944 **P** *020 †75
PATEL, Shailen R. 1200 PROSPECT ST, STE 103 44870 #919-01-1988 L2006 **TS** *020 †85,90
PESIN, Samuel Richard. 1617 W BOGART RD 44870 #008-01-1985 L1991 **OPH** *020 †35
PFAHL, Stannard Baird, Jr. 703 TYLER ST, STE 120 44870 #041-12-1959 L1960
    OPH OS *071 †35
POLUBINSKY, Laurie Jo. 1221 HAYES AVE, STE J 44870 #012-01-1997 L2007 **P** *020 †75
PRINTY, Brian Jos. 3004 HAYES AVE 44870 #038-41-1991 L1993 **OBG** *020 †30
PRITHVIRAJ, Panju. 703 TYLER ST, STE 200 44870 #495-04-1975 L1985 **ON HEM** *020
REDDY, Sreenivas A. 1101 DECATUR ST 44870 #495-57-1970 L1978 **AN** *020
ROTHERMEL, Harold C. ■ 44870 #038-41-1952 L1952 **P PYG** *071
SAMSA, Nathan P. ■ 44870 #038-75-2007, ▲ L2007 *012
SAUERS, James Byron. 1801 E PERKINS AVE 44870 #038-40-1958 L1958 **PDA AI** *040 †55
SAWICKI, Robert Stephen. 4308 TIMBER LAKE LN 44870 #016-43-1967 L1970 **R** *071 †80
SCHILD, Harris Slavin. 1200 PROSPECT ST, STE 120 44870 #038-40-1990 L1994 **OPH** *020 †35
SCHILL, John Edward. 1101 DECATUR ST, DEPT OF EMERGENCY MEDICINE 44870
    #038-41-1996 L1997 **EM** *020 †16
SCHLICHT, Edward Vincent. 3416 COLUMBUS AVE 44870 #038-40-1956 L1956 **GP** *020
SCHMIEDL, Mark David. 1101 DECATUR ST, DEPT OF EMERGENCY MEDICINE 44870
    #038-41-1983 L1986 **EM** *020 †16
SCHNITZER, David Brian. 1617 W BOGART RD 44870 #023-01-1988 L1994 **OPH** *020 †35
SHEEHAN, Karen Elizabeth. 1111 HAYES AVE 44870 #038-44-1991 L1992 **DR** *020 †20
SIDDIQUI, Khalid Rasheed. 417 QUARRY LAKES DR 44870 #160-01-1970 L1982 **RO** *020 †80
SMITH, Claudet Caroline. 703 TYLER ST, STE 200 44870 #038-40-1997 L2000 **IM** *020 †20
SMITH, John Allen. 1101 DECATUR ST, DEPT OF EMERGENCY MEDICINE 44870
    #038-43-1986 L1987 **EM** *020 †16
SNEDDEN, Harold E. ■ 44870 #038-41-1941 L1948 **ORS** *071 †40
STEVENSON, Rosalind L. 188 MARINA POINT DR 44870 #067-01-1973 L1981 **AN** *020 †05
SUH, James H. ■ 44870 #043-01-2005 L2007 **PTH** *012
SUH, Kyungim Park. ■ 44870 #583-08-1973 L1983 **PTH** *020 †50
SWAIN, John Michael. 1101 DECATUR ST 44870 #038-40-2002 L2002 **AN** *020 †05
SWAYNGIM, Dowzell M, Jr. 703 TYLER ST STE 251 44870 #036-05-1974 L1977 **VS OS** *020 †85
TABESH, Ahmad. ■ 44870 #517-01-1962 L1962 **OTO GS** *100
VACCA, Kimberly Ann. 1218 CLEVELAND RD, SANDUSKY PEDIATRICIANS 44870
    #038-41-1995 L1996 **PD** *020 †55
VARGAS, Albert Victorio. 703 TYLER ST STE 150 44870 #038-40-1990 L2001 **GS** *020 †85
VERMEEREN, Jack Albert. ■ 44870 #067-01-1945 L1964 **GYN OBS** *071 †30
WATERS, Patrick Raul. 2800 HAYES AVE, EXECUTIVE UROLOGY BLGD D 44870
    #056-06-1992 L1996 **U** *020 †95
WERTENBERGER, George F. 4618 PINEWOOD DR 44870 #038-06-1946 L1946 **PTH** *071 †50
WISEMAN, Terry Eugene. 1218 CLEVELAND RD, SANDUSKY PEDIATRICIANS 44870
    #038-40-1989 L1990 **PD** *020 †55
WYSOR, James Johnston. 3103 CAMPBELL ST 44870 #038-41-1981 L1982 **FM** *020 †18
YOO, Bo Hyun. 703 TYLER ST STE 350 44870 #041-09-1992 L1999 **NS** *020 †25
YOUNG, Don J. 703 TYLER ST, STE 250 44870 #012-05-1964 L1965 **CD IM** *020 †20

SARDINIA – BROWN

HANNAH, Charles W. MAPLE AV, SARDINIA MEDICAL CENTER 45171 #017-20-1953 L1958
    GP *072
SPACCARELLI, John Francis. 7109 BACHMAN RD 45171 #038-41-1974 L1977
    FM FPG *020 †18

SCIOTOVILLE – SCIOTO

NEWMAN, Robert Eugene. 5611 GALLIA ST, SOMC SCIOTOVILLE FAMILY PR 45662
    #038-45-1997 L1998 **FM** *020 †18

SEAMAN – ADAMS

ALBERS, Frank J, Jr. 218 STERN RD 45679 #038-40-1981 L1985 **OBG** *020 †30
BASA, Jose Lugay. 17907 STATE ROUTE 247 45679 #748-11-1965 L1974 **GS** *071
BENINTENDI, Robert S. 218 STERN RD 45679 #035-08-1958 L1961 **OBG GS** *020 †30
BEST, Larry Warren. 230 MEDICAL CENTER DR 45679 #038-41-1963 L1963 **FM** *020 †18
ENGEL, Peter James. 230 MEDICAL CENTER DR 45679 #035-19-1971 L1973 **CD IM** *030 †20
HAJJAR, Martin Michel. 17862 STATE ROUTE 247, NORTHERN ADAMS MEDICAL CEN 45679
    #875-02-1988 L1994 **FM** *020 †18
MENON, Santosh G. 230 MEDICAL CENTER DR 45679 #495-80-1988 L2000 **CD** *020 †20
SCHNEIDER, John Frank. 230 MEDICAL CENTER DR 45679 #024-05-1976 L1980
    CD IM *020 †20

SWEDBERG, Phillip L. 218 STERN RD, SOUTHERN OHIO HLTH SRVS 45679
    #037-01-1999 L1999 **IM** *020 †20

SEBRING – MAHONING

DAVIES, George H. 800 44672 #030-05-1950 L1954 **IMG GP** *020
DIB, Jean Dib. 116 S 15TH ST, PREMIER HEALTH ASSOCIATES 44672 #875-01-1990 L1999
    IM *020 †20
EL MOBASHER, Gamal G. 116 S 15TH ST, PREMIER HEALTH ASSOCIATES 44672
    #915-04-1990 L1998 **IM** *020 †20
GETTY, Paul Allen. ■ 44672 #025-01-1957 L1965 **EM GS** *020 †85
HIRST, Timothy Lee. 345 N 15TH ST 44672 #038-06-1973 L1974 **GP** *020
MARTSOLF, John. ■ 44672 #041-02-1944 L1944 **GS** *071 †85

SEVEN HILLS – CUYAHOGA

AZIZ, Hany F. 7571 PLEASANT RUN DR 44131 #915-04-1979 L1993 **NPM PD** *020 †55
DEOGRACIAS, Cornelio B. ■ 44131 #748-01-1954 L1962 **GS GP** *020
EXCONDE, Teodorico Gemil. 949 BITTERSWEET DR 44131 #748-08-1960 L1972 **GS GP** *020
FALCONI, Teresita L. ■ 44131 #748-07-1964 L1977 **GP P** *020
HERMOSURA, Bernardo B. 6723 DONNA RAE DR 44131 #748-02-1960 L1973 **GS GP** *071
ING, Julita T. ■ 44131 #748-01-1958 L1968 **AN** *020
JUGUILON, Felicitas D. 6000 LOMBARDO CTR 44131 #748-01-1969 L1979 **GP** *020
LENGU, Irma Jorgji. ■ 44131 #038-06-2005 L2005 **U** *012
MOYSAENKO, John. ■ 44131 #913-04-1939 L1956 **GS GP** *072
PALADIN, Arnold Peter, Jr. ■ 44131 #035-15-1970 L1975 **PD** *020 †55
PARAISO-DEOGRACIAS, T. ■ 44131 #748-01-1954 L1963 **AN** *071 †05
RUSYN, George. ■ 44131 #407-16-1961 L1964 **NEP** *020
SEBALLOS, Raul Hernandez. ■ 44131 #748-08-1962 L1977 **FM PD** *071
SHAH, Nirav Jitendra. ■ 44131 #038-40-1998 L2001 **AN** *012
TAMAYO, Anna-Lynn Santiag. ■ 44131 #748-29-2001 L2005 **P** *012
VASSILAKIS, George B. 855 SIMICH DR 44131 #418-01-1951 L1963 **U** *071

SEVILLE – MEDINA

HOUGLAN, Todd David. 9044 CENTER ST 44273 #038-45-1997 L2000 **FM** *020 †18
WOLF, Arthur Frederick. ■ 44273 #038-41-1943 L1943 **GP** *071

SHADYSIDE – BELMONT

ANTALIS, Angelo John. 3801 LINCOLN AVE 43947 #038-06-1943 L1943 **GP OM** *071

SHAKER HEIGHTS – CUYAHOGA

ABBOTT, Derek Wesley. ■ 44122 #047-05-2000 L2000 **PTH** *020 †50
ABOUHASSAN, William. ■ 44122 #038-45-2004 L2004 **GS** *100
ADIBE, Chiagozie Adaobi. ■ 44120 #012-22-2005 L2005 **IM** *012
ALLEN, Christopher Lee. ■ 44120 #517-24-1994 L2003 **CN** *100
AMINAI-MASHHADI, Shahram. ■ 44120 #020-02-2004 L2005 **DR** *012
ANANTHAKRISHNAN, Lakshmi. ■ 44120 #020-02-2000 L2007 **GS** *020 †85
ANANTHAKRISHNAN, Preya. ■ 44122 #020-02-1989 L2004 **AN** *020 †05
ANDERSON, Eileen Perry. ■ 44122 #038-06-2006 L2006 **IM** *012
ASNES, Andrea Gottsegen. 3261 BRAEMAR RD 44120 #035-47-1998 L2003 **PD** *020 †55
AWAIS, Mazen. ■ 44122 #038-06-2006 L2006 **IM** *012
BABB-TARBOX, Velma Michel. ■ 44122 #048-15-2005 **D** *012
BAILLOT, Richard. 18405 NEWELL RD 44122 #067-02-1975 L1982 **TS** *020
BARANOWSKI, Bryan James. ■ 44122 #047-05-2001 L2004 **ICE** *012
BENDEZU, Rafael Angel. ■ 44122 #737-01-1964 L1976 **IM END** *020 †20
BENIS-FRIEDMAN, Robin. 23700 SHELBURNE RD 44122 #038-06-1985 L1988 **NPM** *020 †55
BERGER, Bruce Edward. 20901 CLAYTHORNE RD 44122 #035-15-1978 L1987 **NEP** *020 †20
BISHKO, Frederic Carl. ■ 44122 #038-41-1965 L1965 **RHU IM** *071 †20
BOHL, Jennifer Rebecca. ■ 44122 #038-06-2002 L2002 **OPH** *020 †35
BONDER, David Neumann. ■ 44122 #649-01-1975 L1981 **PTH** *020
BOYD, Arthur Bernette, Jr. ■ 44122 #047-07-1978 **GS** *075
BREWIN, Anne M. ■ 44122 #048-02-1983 L1987 **P PA** *071 †75
BRIGHTON, Brian Kenneth. ■ 44122 #024-05-2002 L2002 **ORS** *012
BRODY, Robert. 3461 WARRENSVILL CNTR RD R 44122 #025-01-1974 L1975 **D** *020 †15
BROWN, Douglas Delafield. ■ 44122 #352-04-1952 L1955 **P N** *071 †75
BRYSON, Heidi Ann. ■ 44122 #025-12-2006 L2006 **PD** *012
BRYSON, Thomas Coffman. ■ 44122 #025-12-2006 L2006 **DR** *012
BURG, Richard W E. ■ 44122 #026-04-2002 L2007 **ORS** *100
BURKHARDT, John David, Jr. 2529 WARWICK RD 44120 #020-02-1996 L2002 **ICE** *020 †20
BUSTAMANTE, Sergio Elias. ■ 44120 #264-10-1995 L2003 **AN** *012
CHA, Walter Sun. ■ 44122 #041-09-1996 L2006 **GS** *020 †85
CHAVINSON, Melvin Jay. 21169 CLAYTHORNE RD 44122 #016-02-1964 L1969
    CHP P *020 †55,75
CHELLAPPA, Shyamala. ■ 44122 #495-66-1972 L1980 **PD** *020
CHENG, Hsuehyu Wesley. ■ 44120 #030-06-2006 L2006 **ORS** *012
CHIU, Louisa W. ■ 44120 #048-12-2005 L2005 **GS** *012
CHRENKA, Paul. ■ 44122 #038-06-1939 L1946 **DR R** *071 †80
CHUIDIAN, Francis S. ■ 44120 #748-01-1984 L1993 **PCC IM** *020 †20
COULTER, Amy Hyojung. ■ 44120 #038-06-2005 L2005 **GS** *012
COWAP, Charles Richardson. ■ 44118 #038-06-1999 L1999 **FM** *020
COWDREY, Charles Richard. ■ 44122 #038-06-1963 L1963 **PTH OS** *071 †50
COWETT, Richard M. 3024 CHADBOURNE RD 44120 #038-41-1968 L1968 **PD NPM** *020 †55
CUBBERLEY, Peter Travis. ■ 44122 #038-06-1961 L1961 **IM** *071
CURRIE, Philip James. ■ 44122 #143-08-1977 L1986 **CD** *020 †20
DAVEIGA, Edward C. ■ 44122 #016-43-2003 L2007 **IM** *100
DEANE, Daniel Anthony. 16100 PARKLAND DR, CLEVELAND CLINIC FOUNDATIO 44120
    #021-05-1980 L2005 **PD** *020 †55

DEOREO, Elizabeth H. ■ 44122 #038-06-2004 P *012

DOLINER, Stuart Jeff. ■ 44120 #011-04-1982 L1984 AN CCM *020 †05

DOWLING, Alexander S, Jr. 22300 S WOODLAND RD 44122 #035-45-1955 L1959 PYA P *020 †75

EDELSTEIN, Josef. ■ 44120 #275-01-1954 L1963 CD *071

ELLNER, Rebecca Diane. ■ 44122 #038-06-1999 L1999 P *100

EPPES, Robert Bennett. ■ 44122 #041-01-1962 L1966 D IM *071 †15

ESCOBEDO, Joel. ■ 44122 #025-01-2007 L2007 OBG *012

FEGHALI, Nassif Toufic. ■ 44122 #605-01-1985 L1991 CD *100 †20

FILBY, Steven James. ■ 44120 #021-05-2001 L2007 IC *012

FLORANDA, Eric Estayan. ■ 44120 #748-02-2001 L2007 NMN *012

FONSECA, Carmen Maria. 3199 FALMOUTH RD 44122 #042-02-1987 L1991 OS IM *020 †20

FOXMAN, David. ■ 44122 #038-40-1954 L1954 DR *071 †80

FRIEDMAN, Aaron Douglas. ■ 44122 #035-01-2002 L2002 OTO *012

FRODYMA, Susan Eppes. 22001 FAIRMOUNT BLVD, BELLEFAIRE JCB 44118 #038-06-2000 L2001 CHP *100

FURMAN, Robert Ayres. 19910 MALVERN RD 44122 #035-01-1947 L1949 PYA *020 †55

GALLAGHER, Patrick Jos. 3710 WINCHELL RD 44122 #038-06-1979 L1980 EM *020 †16

GILFILLAN, Carol Anne. ■ 44122 #056-05-1977 L1982 PD *020 †55

GLAUSER, Sarah Rebecca. ■ 44122 #038-43-2008 *012

GOLDMAN, Zyama. 20600 CHAGRIN BLVD STE 620 44122 #913-69-1970 L1991 *020

GOLDSTON, Norman Ward. ■ 44120 #038-06-1954 L1954 END IM *071 †20

GOLDSTONE, Murray Austin. 2882 DRUMMOND RD, MURRAY A GOLDSTONE MD INC 44120 #024-01-1958 L1960 PYA P *071 †75

GONUGUNTA, Vivekananda. ■ 44122 #495-62-1989 L2002 NS *012

GRIGGS, Robert C. ■ 44120 #024-01-1949 L1956 HEM IM *071 †20

GULANI, Vikas. ■ 44122 #016-11-2000 L2006 DR *100 †80

GUNZLER, Julie Richards. ■ 44122 #035-45-2004 L2004 PD *020 †55

GUNZLER, Steven Alexander. ■ 44122 #035-45-2000 L2007 N *020 †75

GUY, Dennis James. ■ 44120 #038-40-2003 L2006 EM *020 †16

HAHN, Ryan. ■ 44122 #041-77-2004, ▲ L2007 CCP *012 †55

HAMIK, Anne. ■ 44122 #039-01-1999 L2006 CD *100 †20

HANSEN, Jennifer Kiyoko. ■ 44122 #049-01-2007 L2007 AN *012

HARDMAN, Angela Latson. ■ 44120 #038-40-2004 L2004 PDE *012 †55

HARSHMAN, Kenneth Vincent. 3461 WARRENSVILL CNTR RD R 44122 #038-40-1955 L1955 IM GE *071 †20

HAWKINS, Matthew Thos. ■ 44122 #010-01-1977 L1998 EM IM *020 †20,16

HENRICKSON, Robert Gene. ■ 44122 #051-04-1974 L1977 P *075 †20

HESS, Karl Weldon. ■ 44122 #024-07-1961 L1966 PD *072 †55

HISE, Amy G. ■ 44122 #010-01-1996 L1997 IM *020 †20

HONG, Michael Seungwoo. ■ 44122 #033-06-2002 L2002 CD *012 †20

HORSBURGH, Karl William. 2563 KENDALL RD 44120 #143-02-1985 L2001 FM *020 †18 ‡

HUBBELL, Stacey Lynn. ■ 44122 #038-06-2007 *012

HUBERT, Katherine Cheney. ■ 44122 #028-34-2004 L2004 GS *100

HUFFMAN, Ryan Patrick. ■ 44122 #010-01-2004 L2004 AN *012

HUMMER, Gregory James. ■ 44122 #038-40-1978 L1978 EM *020 †16

IMERMAN, Kenneth William. ■ 44122 #010-01-2005 L2005 N *012

ISMAIL-BEIGI, Faramarz. ■ 44122 #023-07-1966 L1993 IM *040 †20

JAFFE, Jack W. ■ 44122 #035-46-1960 L1961 U OS *071 †95

JANICKI, Anna J. ■ 44120 #759-03-1973 L1980 P *075

JATKAR, Suhas V. ■ 44122 #495-01-1967 L1979 *020

JEPPSON, Peter Clegg. ■ 44122 #028-34-2006 L2006 OBG *012

JO, Greta Susan. ■ 44120 #048-02-2008 *012

JOHNSON, Freedom. ■ 44120 #005-19-2003 L2004 OTO *012

JOHNSON, John J. ■ 44120 #010-03-1950 L1956 FM IM *071

JOHNSON, Lucileia Teixeir. ■ 44120 #187-14-1991 L2001 ID *100 †20

JONES, G Alexander. ■ 44122 #038-40-2001 L2005 NS *012

JONES, Jessica Leeching. ■ 44120 #030-06-2006 L2006 IM *012

JONES, L Morris. ■ 44120 #047-07-1957 L1958 FM GP *071

JONES, Tiffany Sheree. ■ 44122 #025-07-2007 L2007 P *012

JORDAN, James William. ■ 44122 #045-01-2004 L2004 N *012

KELLEY, Joseph F. ■ 44122 #038-06-1953 L1953 AI IM *071 †03

KELLY, Harold Broadway. ■ 44120 #010-03-1946 L1955 GYN *020 †30

KHANDHAR, Paras Bharat. ■ 44122 #030-06-2005 L2005 MPD *012

KHASNIS, Atul Ashok. ■ 44122 #496-38-1998 L2007 RHU *012 †20

KIM, Yong Jin. ■ 44118 #583-12-1973 L1978 AN *020

KIRILCUK, Natalie Nina. ■ 44122 #005-11-2005 L2006 GS *012

KLAUSNER, David Abba. ■ 44122 #038-40-1961 L1961 OBG *071 †30

KOLKIN, Alla. 3461 WARRENSVILLE CENTR RD, STE 207 44122 #913-69-1980 L1999 PD *020 †55

KRUMMEN, Kaylyn Gresh. 15700 VAN AKEN BLVD 44120 #048-04-2005 L2005 AN *012

LEE, David S. ■ 44120 #048-12-2005 L2005 *100

LEVITZKY, Benjamin Evan. ■ 44120 #041-13-2002 L2006 GE *012 †20

LIKLY, Beverly Ann. ■ 44122 #010-02-1954 L1958 PD IM *071 †55

LIN, Roger Chin. ■ 44122 #038-06-2008 *012

LOCKE, Susan Carol. ■ 44122 #035-20-1985 L1987 P *020 †20,75

MADATHIL, Ronson Joseph. ■ 44120 #041-12-2006 L2006 GS *012

MAHMOOD, Syed Kashif. ■ 44120 #496-57-2004 L2005 IM *012

MAHONEY, Timothy Hugh. ■ 44122 #033-05-2002 L2005 CD *012 †20

MAILER, Karen. 16500 PARKLAND DR, REAR 44120 #038-06-1996 L2004 FM *020 †18

MAJORS, Kristin Elaine. ■ 44122 #020-02-2007 L2007 GS *012

MANKARIOUS, Sabri Maksoud. ■ 44122 #915-04-1985 L1999 AN *020

MARINSPIOTTA, Alejandro. ■ 44122 #041-01-2005 L2005 NS *012

MARTIN, Joseph Popel. ■ 44120 #010-03-1944 L1949 OBG *071 †30

MATTHEWS, Norman Eakes. 3535 LEE RD, CLEVELAND SURGI-CENTER,INC 44122 #024-01-1958 L1966 GYN *071 †30

MC DONNELL, Jonelle S. 22900 SHELBURNE RD 44122 #038-43-1987 L1989 D *020 †20,15

MC FADDEN, Edward R, Jr. ■ 44122 #041-12-1963 L1984 PUD GP *050 †20

MERCHANT, Rashid Nuruddin. 24940 SHAKER BLVD 44122 #495-27-1961 L1971 GS *020 †85

MICHAEL, Michael Assad. 3461 WARRENSVILLE CENTR RD, STE 105 44122 #038-40-1962 L1962 PD PDA *071 †55

MILLER, Holly Dara. 3605 WARRENSVILLE CENTR RD, MSC 9223 44122 #035-46-1987 L2000 IM *020

MOISE, Mireille Astrid. ■ 44122 #041-01-2000 L2006 VS *012 †85

MUNERA, Lucille. ■ 44120 #308-03-1984 L1993 IM *020

MURPHY, Douglas Scott. ■ 44120 #038-06-1995 L1996 IM SCI *020 †20

NAGEL, Sean Jeremy. ■ 44122 #010-02-2003 L2003 NS *012

NAGENDRA, Shweta. ■ 44122 #010-12-2003 L2003 IM *100 †20

NAMBOODIRI, Sally. 3461 WARRENSVILLE CENTR RD, STE 306 44122 #038-43-1989 L1992 IM *040 †20

NEARY, Mary Geraldine. ■ 44122 #539-02-1994 *100

NEWMAN, Robert I. ■ 44122 #038-06-1951 L1951 IM *020 †20

NICKLES-FADER, Amanda. ■ 44122 #051-04-2002 L2004 OBG *100

NODINE, Elizabeth Stewart. ■ 44118 #056-05-1996 L2005 FM *020 †18

NWAONU, Jane Ngozi. ■ 44122 #690-04-1998 L2006 RHU *012 †20

OCKNER, Stephen Allan. ■ 44122 #041-01-1955 L1975 IM NEP *071 †20

OLORUNRINU, Kikelomo. ■ 44120 #008-01-2007 L2007 *012

PADAREV, Halina M. 3461 WARRENSVILLE CENTR RD, STE 207 44122 #759-01-1963 L1985 PD *020

PARCHMAN, Andrew James. ■ 44122 #038-41-2007 L2007 IM *012

PARKER, Karen Elaine. ■ 44120 #038-06-2006 L2006 IM *012

PATJANASOONTORN, Boonsong. ■ 44120 #891-05-1983 PUD IM *100

PIRACHA, Fyza Ubaid. ■ 44122 #704-25-2001 L2006 PD *020

PLUCINSKY, John Jos. ■ 44122 #041-12-2003 L2006 IM HO *071 †20

PONITZ, Keith Lawrence. 3461 WARRENSVILL CNTR RD R 44122 #016-42-1989 L1993 PD *020 †55

PROWELLER, Aaron. ■ 44122 #035-45-1998 L2007 CD *100 †20

RAMASWAMY, Anuradha. ■ 44122 #495-37-2000 L2005 IM *020

RANASINGHE, Elizabeth S P. 16500 CHAGRIN BLVD 44120 #220-01-1981 L1991 IM FM *020 †18

RAYMOND, Alexa Rousseau. ■ 44122 #041-02-1999 L2006 FM *020 †18

RAZAVI, Susan. ■ 44122 #038-45-2004 L2004 IM *020 †20

RAZZAK, Najma A. 23439 WIMBLEDON RD 44122 #704-02-1989 L2004 ID *020 †20

REICHSTEIN, Ari Reubencut. ■ 44122 #038-06-2007 GS *012

REINE, Tanyanika Phillips. ■ 44122 #035-45-1998 L2007 ON *100 †20

RICKARD, John. ■ 44122 #010-02-2004 L2007 IM *100 †20

RITTER, James Michael. ■ 44122 #917-09-1974 L1982 PA IM *050 †20

RIXEY, Melinda Zuber. ■ 44122 #001-06-2006 L2007 DR *012

ROBERTO, Daniel Paul. ■ 44122 #016-43-1941 L1941 GP *020

ROWE, Jennifer Jordi. ■ 44122 #035-03-2001 L2007 PTH *100 †50

RUIZRODRIGUEZ, Ernesto. ■ 44120 #042-03-2008 *012

SCHARDT, Susan Marie. ■ 44122 #038-40-2003 L2006 EM *020 †16

SCHIKOWSKI, Carl Blaine. ■ 44122 #038-41-1983 L1984 EM *020 †16

SCHWEITZER, Gillian Vera. 3280 KENMORE RD 44122 #035-46-1994 L2000 P *020

SEGAL, David Grant. ■ 44120 #836-01-1993 L2000 PDE *100 †55

SERNA, Derek Steven. ■ 44122 #056-06-2005 L2005 IM *012

SHAFII, Alexis Edward. ■ 44120 #011-04-2002 L2007 TS *012

SHANKER, Jaymie Anne. 19202 LOMOND BLVD 44122 #038-06-1993 L1995 P *020 †75

SHAPIRO, Manuel Abraham. ■ 44122 #038-06-1928 L2008 AP *071 †35

SHEFFLER, Lynne Ruth. 23649 STANFORD RD 44122 #038-43-1990 L1990 PM *020 †60

SHERMAN, Bruce Wm. 3175 BELVOIR BLVD 44122 #035-19-1984 L1987 IM PCC *020 †20

SHUCK, Linda Wayne. ■ 44122 #034-01-1974 L1981 PS *074 †65 ‡

SHUCKETT, Rhonda. ■ 44122 #062-01-1978 L1987 IM *100

SIDDIQUI, Sameena Khan. ■ 44122 #496-27-1995 L2007 CN *012

SIMMONS, Matthew Neil. ■ 44122 #005-11-2003 L2003 U *012

SINGH, Rishi Paul. ■ 44122 #024-05-2001 L2005 OPH *100 †35

SINGH, Simran Kaur. ■ 44122 #024-05-2000 L2005 IM *020 †20

SKALAK, Anthony Francis. ■ 44122 #038-06-2003 L2003 ORS *012

SKIRBALL, David Vincent. 3461 WARRENSVILL CNTR RD R 44122 #038-06-1976 L1977 PUD IM *020

SMUCKER, Jon Benjamin. ■ 44122 #017-20-2004 L2004 ORS *012

SOS, Melissa Ann. ■ 44122 #042-02-2002 L2006 AN *020

STEINHAUSER, Sarah Kather. ■ 44122 #041-12-2007 L2007 PD *012

STOUT, Philip Lewis. ■ 44122 #019-02-1974 L1978 EM *020 †20,16

STRASBURG, Eric Raymond. ■ 44122 #836-01-1955 L1978 OBG *071 †30

SUBHAN, Abdul. ■ 44122 #704-02-1996 L2006 P *012

SYDOW, Gregg Peter. ■ 44120 #016-45-2007 L2007 IM *012

TABENKIN, Hava. 3597 INGLESIDE RD 44122 #550-02-1977 L1990 *020

TAN, Joanna A. 2575 KEMPER RD # A3 44120 #060-02-2005 L2005 IM *100

TAN, Paul John. ■ 44122 #011-02-1999 L1999 AN *012

TANG, Aaron Lonhin. ■ 44122 #028-34-2007 L2007 IM *012

TAVILL, Frederick. ■ 44122 #917-08-1949 L1976 GPM OS *030 †70

TEGTMEYER, Peter James. ■ 44122 #028-34-1960 L1969 OS *050 †50

TEMPLETON, Jesse Ellis. ■ 44120 #018-03-2003 L2003 ORS *012

TIRONA OBIAS, Sharon Lynn. ■ 44122 #051-07-2005 L2005 PD *012

TIU, Ramon Velasquez. 12700 FAIRHILL RD 44120 #748-01-2000 L2003 HO *012 †20

TRAN, Lily Hoang. ■ 44122 #035-45-2005 L2005 CHN *012

TRIOZZI, Pierre Lorenzo. ■ 44122 #038-40-1980 L1986 HO IM *020 †20

TUTTLE, John B. ■ 44122 #049-01-2006 L2007 D *012

UMAR, Nadia Kamel. ■ 44122 #051-04-2006 L2006 IM *012

VALDES, Ximena Lopez. ■ 44122 #231-01-1971 L2006 PD PDC *020 †55

VILLA FORTE, Alexandra S. ■ 44122 #187-09-1993 L1999 RHU *100 †20

VINCENT, Lisa Poovan. ■ 44120 #894-01-2002 L2007 CCP *012

VOGEL, Jon Douglas. ■ 44122 #041-09-1997 L1999 CRS *020 †85,10

WADHWA, Anish. ■ 44122 #038-41-2005 L2005 IM *012

WAGNER, Gretchen A Bieber. ■ 44120 #041-01-1948 L1976 PM *071

WALDBAUM, Naomi Zipporah. ■ 44122 #836-02-1965 L1983 PM *062 †60

WALSH, Nancy Mychalak. ■ 44122 #012-22-2007 L2007 OBG *012

WASSON, Sanjeev. ■ 44120 #495-45-1995 L2006 ICE *012 †20 ‡

WATTS, Katherine Elizabet. ■ 44122 #004-01-2007 L2007 *012

WEIGHT, Christopher John. ■ 44122 #049-01-2004 L2004 U *012

WEINSTEIN, Cheryl Ermann. 18600 S WOODLAND RD 44122 #023-07-1972 L1974 IM IMG *040 †20

WEISS, James Albert. ■ 44122 #005-14-1965 L2002 PMM AN *071 †05

WENTZ, William Budd. ■ 44118 #038-06-1958 L1958 ON GYN *071 †30

WHITTEN, Ira. ■ 44120 #041-02-2008 *012

WHITTIER, Faith Melanie. ■ 44122 #038-06-1994 L1996 OBG *020 †30

WOLPAW, Adam James. ■ 44120 #035-01-2008 *012

WONG, Vincent Kwokwai. ■ 44122 #038-02-2006 L2007 DR *012

WOODS, Cynthia A. ■ 44122 #025-01-2005 L2005 AN *012

WYATT, Christopher Ryan. ■ 44120 #038-06-2006 L2006 **EM** *012
YOUNGS, David Dalmer. ■ 44122 #025-01-1962 L1988 **OBG P** *071 †75,30
YOUNG-TAN, Alison Michell. ■ 44122 #011-02-1999 L2000 **MPD** *020 †20
ZIMBWA, Peter. ■ 44122 #775-01-1992 L2005 **IM** *100

SHARON CENTER – MEDINA

HOYNES, Sean Danl. 5133 RIDGE RD, SHARON FAMILY PHYSICIANS 44274 #038-40-1992 L1994
   FM *020 †18
MONE, Tyra Lynn. 5133 RIDGE RD, SHARON FAMILY PHYSICIANS 44274 #038-41-1992 L1993
   FM *020 †18

SHARONVILLE – HAMILTON

BAYLESS, David Robt. 11258 LEBANON RD 45241 #038-41-1955 L1955 **PD** *071 †55
KOBET, Christopher Andrew. ■ 45241 #038-41-2006 L2006 **N** *012
PALASANI, Indupriya. ■ 45241 #495-50-1997 L2008 **RHU** *100

SHEFFIELD VILLAGE – LORAIN

BAK, Malgorzata Anna. 5334 MEADOW LANE CT 44035 #759-10-1985 L2004 **FM** *020 †18
BARTEK, Francis Andrew. 5319 HOAG DR, STE 210 44035 #023-01-1970 L1973 **OBG** *020 †30
FARROW, Tracy Ann. 5054 WATERFORD DR 44035 #038-43-1993 L1997 **OBG** *020 †30
GAYOMALI, Nestor Generala. 5311 MEADOW LANE CT, STE 3 44035 #748-08-1981 L1998
   IM NEP *020 †20
GIRGIS, Joseph Abdel M. 5334 MEADOW LANE CT 44035 #915-02-1991 L1998 **IM** *020 †20 ‡
HAAS, Christopher Adam. 5319 HOAG DR 44035 #038-06-1993 L1994 **U** *020 †95
JOHNS, Nathaniel William. 5255 N ABBE RD STE 1, APPLEWOOD CTRS INC 44035
   #243-69-1984 L2002 **CHP** *020
LACERNA, Rogener Burgos. 5319 MEADOW LANE CT, NORTH COLLEGE MEADOWS 44035
   #748-01-1972 L1984 **GP** *020
MAHER, Judith Anne. 5320 HOAG DR, STE B 44035 #035-48-1976 L1983 **N PM** *020 †75
MAYS, Judith A Wicklund. 5334 MEADOW LANE CT, SUPERIOR MEDICAL CARE INC 44035
   #038-43-1973 L1990 **IM** *020 †20
MOYA, Digna Rilcopiro. 5334 MEADOW LANE CT 44035 #748-10-1991 L1996 **FM** *020 †18
MOYA, Rummel T. 5334 MEADOW LANE CT 44035 #748-10-1991 L1996 **IM** *020 †20
ORNELLA, Gregory Allen. 5371 RESERVE WAY, STE E 44054 #038-40-1984 L1986
   OM GPM *030 †70
PRITI, Nair. 5319 HOAG DR, STE 260 44035 #038-44-1993 L1997 **PM** *020 †60
PUROHIT, Umakant T. 5319 HOAG DR 44035 #495-22-1961 L1978 **ORS** *020 †40
RAMSEY, Teresa Nicole. 5334 MEADOW LANE CT 44035 #038-43-2000 L2004 **PD** *020 ‡
REYNOLDS, Jordan Paul. ■ 44054 #038-44-2004 L2004 **PTH** *012
RIDGEL, Jason Dain. 5323 MEADOW LANE CT, STE A 44035 #055-07-1998 L2000 **FM** *020 †18
SENG, Michael L. 5320 HOAG DR, STE A 44035 #038-44-1983 L1985 **P IM** *020 †20,75
SPIRNAK, J Patrick. 5319 HOAG DR, STE 240 44035 #012-05-1977 L1978 **U** *020 †95
SPIRNAK, Joseph Patrick. 5319 HOAG DR, STE 130 44035 #038-06-1989 L1997 **DR** *020 †80
TRZECIAK, Victor John. 5334 MEADOW LANE CT 44035 #038-44-1984 L1985 **IM** *020 †20
WARREN, Robert C. 5077 WATERFORD DR, STE 305 44035 #024-05-1986 L1995 **GS** *020 †85
WELLS, Jessica B. 5307 RESERVE WAY 44054 #038-45-1999 L2004 **IM** *020 †20
WYNN, Mary Elizabeth. 5334 MEADOW LANE CT 44035 #056-05-1987 L1990 **FM** *020 †18
ZANOTTI, Robert Michael. 5001 TRANSPORTATION DR, CENTER FOR ORTHOPEDICS 44054
   #041-01-1991 L1997 **ORS** *020 †40
ZAWORSKI, Daniel C. 5255 N ABBE RD 44035 #010-01-1967 L1968 **PLM IM** *020 †20

SHELBY – RICHLAND

BECKETT, John Henry. 20 MORRIS RD 44875 #016-42-1987 L1997 **EM** *020 †16
BIHL, Adam Joel. 24 E WHITNEY AVE, STE 1 44875 #038-40-1997 L1998 **FM** *020 †18
CHAWLA, Ajay. 110 AUBURN AVE, AJAY CHAWLA, MD 44875 #496-09-1994 L2001
   IMG *020 †20
CHIZEVER, Gary Edward. 31 E MAIN ST, STE 3 44875 #041-02-1993 L2002 **GS** *020 †85
CLARK, Richard Lloyd. ■ 44875 #065-06-1964 L1983 **GS TRS** *071
DAS, Saurabh B. 31 E MAIN ST, STE 2 44875 #041-13-1994 L2000 **HO IM** *020 †20
DEMERS, Marion C. 24 E WHITNEY AVE, STE 1 44875 #038-45-1996 L1997 **FM** *020 †18
DEWALD, Donald Lee. 31 E MAIN ST, STE 2 44875 #038-06-1975 L1976 **ON IM** *020 †20
DOWDS, Edward Grant. ■ 44875 #038-06-1956 L1956 **GP OBG** *071 †18
GUIMARAES, Omar Frederick. 24 MORRIS RD STE 3 44875 #026-04-1987 L1995 **OBG** *020 †30
JOHNSON, Roy Jos, Jr. 39 S GAMBLE ST 44875 #038-40-1961 L1961 **FM GP** *071
KIM, Chin Kyll. 20 MORRIS RD 44875 #583-04-1961 L1972 **GP** *071 †30
LEW, Keun Sun. 20 MORRIS RD, SHELBY MEMORIAL HOSP 44875 #583-10-1964 L1970 **R** *020
MC HUGH, John Francis. 110 AUBURN AVE 44875 #038-40-1958 L1958 **FM** *071 †18
MILAMBILING, Ligaya C. 31 E MAIN ST, STE 1 44875 #748-01-1971 L1994 **FM** *020
PHILPOTT, Stephanie Lynn. 24 MORRIS RD, STE 1 44875 #063-01-1993 L1995
   GP OBG *020 †18
SATAYATHUM, Pradist. 20 MORRIS RD 44875 #891-01-1955 L1965 **ORS** *071 †40
SINHA, Sudhir Kumar. 24 E WHITNEY AVE 44875 #495-54-1980 L1990 **IM** *020 †20
SMITH, John Orr. 20 MORRIS RD 44875 #038-40-1955 L1955 **GP** *071
TONGSON, Virgilio Millado. 31 E MAIN ST 44875 #748-01-1977 L1986 **GS** *074 †85
VILLAO, Alfredo Najito. 100 W MAIN ST, STE 2 44875 #748-08-1963 L1970 **GS GP** *020 †85
WANG, Melinda. 24 E WHITNEY AVE, STE 1 44875 #055-01-1997 L2004 **FM** *020 †18
YOUSE, Bradley David. 24 MORRIS RD STE 2, RICHLAND ORTHOPEDIC SURG, 44875
   #041-13-1989 L1994 **OSM** *020 †40

SHILOH – RICHLAND

DOMINGO, Evillo Manuel. 21 W MAIN ST 44878 #748-08-1981 L1998 **FM** *020 †18

SHREVE – WAYNE

DAILEY, Janet G. 126 W MCCONKEY ST 44676 #038-40-1978 L1979 **FM** *020 †18

SIDNEY – SHELBY

BAHNG, Chang Hwan. 915 MICHIGAN ST 45365 #583-03-1965 L1977 **R** *020 †80
BAUMANN, Timothy Gale. 915 MICHIGAN ST 45365 #056-06-1963 L1964 **OM** *020
BERGMAN, Gregory Alan. 915 MICHIGAN ST 45365 #038-45-1981 L1982 **FM OBG** *020 †18
BLATCHLY, Stephen W, Jr. 300 3RD AVE 45365 #035-15-1978 L1979 **FM FPG** *020 †18 ‡
BOHINC, Rudy Joe. 915 MICHIGAN ST, WILSON MEMORIAL HOSPITAL 45365
   #748-19-1985 L1988 **IM** *020
BOSTICK, Eric Von. 915 MICHIGAN ST 45365 #038-41-1980 L1983 **DR** *020 †80
BRANDEWIE, Elizabeth V. 915 MICHIGAN ST, WILSON MEMORIAL HOSPITAL 45365
   #038-06-1998 L2000 **OBG** *020 †30
BUDDHADEV, Ashok G. 915 MICHIGAN ST, YAGER PROF BLDG 2ND FL 45365
   #495-76-1984 L1994 **OBG** *020 †30
CHURCH, Thomas Wm. 915 MICHIGAN ST 45365 #056-05-1981 L1983 **DR VIR** *020 †80
COOK, Andrew Peter. 915 MICHIGAN ST 45365 #038-45-1987 L1989 **DR** *020 †80
GHODASARA, Chandulal D. 915 MICHIGAN ST, MICHIGAN MEDICAL BLDG. A 45365
   #495-48-1973 L1993 **PD** *020
HALDEMAN, Mark Tuxford. 1081 FAIRINGTON DR 45365 #038-45-1990 L1999 **FM** *020 †18
HALE, Roger Allen. 915 MICHIGAN ST 45365 #038-06-1978 L1982 **OPH** *071 †35
HAUSSMAN, Frederick R, III. 915 MICHIGAN ST 45365 #038-45-1984 L1985 **EM** *020 †18
HAWLEY, Aimee Lauer. 915 MICHIGAN ST 45365 #023-12-1985 L2001 **DR** *020 †80
HILTY, Timothy Mark. 915 MICHIGAN ST 45365 #038-45-2000 L2000 **FM** *020
JANOUSEK, Joel Edward. 915 W MICHIGAN ST, WILSON MEMORIAL HOSPITAL 45365
   #030-05-1975 L1979 **DR** *071 †80
JUSTICE, Stephen Eric. 1205 FAIRINGTON DR 45365 #038-45-1997 L1998 **FM** *020 †18 ‡
KOCH, H Bruce. 915 W MICHIGAN ST, WILSON MEMORIAL HOSPITAL 45365
   #036-08-1988 L1989 **EM** *020
LI, Ching Po. ■ 45365 #049-01-1954 L1958 **R** *071 †80
MCCARTHY, Robert Lewis. 915 MICHIGAN ST, INTERNAL MEDICINE GROUP 45365
   #038-43-1990 L1993 **IM** *020
MC CUTCHAN, Patricia L. 915 MICHIGAN ST 45365 #038-43-1994 L1996 **DR** *020
MC DEVITT, Robert J, Jr. 915 W MICHIGAN ST, WILSON MEMORIAL HOSPITAL 45365
   #038-41-1983 L1988 **GS** *020 †85
MC DONALD, Andrew David. 915 MICHIGAN ST, WILSON MEDICAL BUILDING 45365
   #016-45-1991 L1995 **GS CCS** *020 †20
MESTEMAKER, Jerome Frank. ■ 45365 #056-06-1968 L1969 **GP** *071
MILLER, Marcus. 915 MICHIGAN ST, OCCUPATIONAL MEDICINE 45365 #025-01-1964 L1966
   FM OM *020
MILLER, Robert John. 322 2ND AVE 45365 #030-06-1973 L1975 **FM EM** *020
MONTANA, Enrique Conanan. 915 MICHIGAN ST, WILSON MEDICAL BUILDING 45365
   #748-01-1969 L1977 **GS GP** *020 †85
NELSON, Trudy Joyce. 430 4TH AVE 45365 #004-01-1979 L1990 **PD ADL** *075
NEWMAN, Donald Eric. 915 W MICHIGAN ST, WILSON MEMORIAL HOSPITAL 45365
   #039-05-1983 L1985 **EM** *020 †18
OBEID, Remon. 1103 FAIRINGTON DR, SERVICES 45365 #875-03-1986 L2000 **IM CD** *020 †20
OREM, Randall Corey. 1103 FAIRINGTON DR 45365 #028-78-1984, ▲ L1985 **CD IM** *020 †20
PALTE-KNAPKE, Mary Jane. 915 MICHIGAN ST 45365 #038-40-1991 L1992 **EM** *020 †16
POSTLEWAITE, Jennifer J. 915 MICHIGAN ST, WILSON MEMORIAL HOSPITAL 45365
   #038-43-1996 L1997 **FM** *020 †18
PRASHANTH KUMAR, T. 1025 FAIR RD 45365 #495-04-1986 L1996 **END IM** *072 †20
PUNUKOLLU, Pavan Kumar. 915 MICHIGAN ST 45365 #024-07-1992 L1998 **VIR** *020 †80
RAO, Patrick Michael. 915 MICHIGAN ST 45365 #025-01-1991 L2004 **DR** *020 †80
REYES, Florencio Leonardo. 430 4TH AVE 45365 #748-01-1964 L1972 **IM GE** *020 †20
RHEE, M David. 838 W NORTH ST 45365 #583-04-1965 L1973 **OBG** *020 †30
ROGERS, Nakiisa Johnson. 915 MICHIGAN ST 45365 #017-20-2000 L2005 **DR** *020 †80
SCHMIDT, Louis Andre, II. ■ 45365 #038-40-1960 L1960 **AN** *030 †05
SCHULTE, Valerie Lynn. 915 MICHIGAN ST, WILSON MEMORIAL HOSPITAL 45365 #038-75-1997,
   ▲ L1998 **OBG** *020
SHOENFELT, Jennifer Lynn. ■ 45365 #038-45-2003 L2003 **CHP** *012
SIKORSKI, John Paul, III. 915 MICHIGAN ST 45365 #016-06-1974 L1979 **AN CCM** *020 †05
SIMPSON, Frederick R. 1081 FAIRINGTON DR 45365 #038-41-1996 L1997 **FM** *020 †18
TAN, Tom Xiao Lin. 915 MICHIGAN ST 45365 #243-64-1985 L1996 **DR** *020 †80,28 ‡
THAKKER, Suresh P. 915 MICHIGAN ST, YAGER MEDICAL BLDG 45365 #308-11-1986 L1993
   PD *020 †55
THORPE, Paul S. 915 W MICHIGAN ST, WILSON MEMORIAL HOSPITAL 45365
   #049-01-1981 L1989 **PTH** *020 †50
TOPALOV, Miguel. 915 MICHIGAN ST 45365 #132-01-1974 L1982 **IM** *020
TRAMONTANA, Raul E. 915 MICHIGAN ST 45365 #737-01-1957 L1967 **GP** *071 †85
VYAS, Darshan Kirit. 915 MICHIGAN ST STE 301 45365 #025-01-1993 L1998 **OTO** *020 †45
WANG, George Zhongshan. 915 MICHIGAN ST, WILSON MEMORIAL HOSPITAL 45365
   #243-16-1985 L2002 **IM** *020 †20
WELSH, Randall Louis. 915 MICHIGAN ST 45365 #038-41-1979 L1980 **OTO** *020 †45
WILDING, John Jos, Jr. 915 MICHIGAN ST 45365 #028-79-1982, ▲ L1983 **OPH** *020
YOUNG, Mark Edward. 322 2ND AVE 45365 #033-05-1997 L2003 **FM** *020 †18

SILVER LAKE – SUMMIT

ADKINS, Kate Wierdsma. ■ 44224 #045-01-2002 L2003 **OBG** *012
ALLISON, Henry Willard. ■ 44224 #038-40-1942 L1942 **IM OS** *020 †20
BEESON, Michael Scott. 3025 SILVER LAKE BLVD 44224 #038-40-1982 L1983 **EM** *020 †16
BURGESS, Everett Carl, Jr. ■ 44224 #038-06-1969 L1977 **END IM** *071 †20
HOBENSACK, John D. ■ 44224 #038-06-1951 L1951 **PD** *071 †55
JONES, Marc Franklin. 1202 GRAHAM RD 44224 #008-01-1998 L2002 **OPH** *020 †35
LOHMAN, Lawrence Edward. 1202 GRAHAM RD 44224 #038-40-1976 L1976 **OPH OS** *020 †35
MOSTELLER, Robert Edward. ■ 44224 #016-76-1960, ▲ L1960 **P CHP** *071 †75
NELSON, Martha Jane Dixon. 1100 GRAHAM ROAD CIR 44224 #041-12-1956 L1958 **PHP** *071
SCHWARZ, Harold M. ■ 44224 #028-34-1950 L1951 **FM** *072 †18

SOLON – CUYAHOGA

ALDANA, Zenaida Higoy. ■ 44139 #748-01-1963 L1973 **IM** *020
AL-MUDALLAL, Riadh. 34501 AURORA RD, STE 306 44139 #528-01-1976 L1986
   GE IM *020 †20

BAILAS, Nicholas J. 33610 WELLINGFORD CT 44139 #418-01-1954 L1971 **TS CD** *071 †85,90

BALLESTEROS, Samson. 33001 SOLON RD, STE 112 44139 #014-01-1984 L1986 **IM EM** *020 †20

BENISH, Janet Lorraine. 33001 SOLON RD 44139 #025-01-1979 L1994 **PD** *020 †55

BERNAT, Viera. 32901 STATION ST 44139 #286-03-1967 L1983 **PD EM** *020

BEVINS, Charles Lee. ■ 44139 #023-01-1983 L1997 **PD MG** *050 †55,19

BHAVNANI, Sangeeta. 30680 BAINBRIDGE RD, PHYSICIAN STAFFING, INC 44139 #495-17-1988 L1997 **IM** *075 †20

BLOOMFIELD, Michael M. 29800 BAINBRIDGE RD, SOLON 44139 #038-06-1981 L1983 **OBG** *020 †50

BROWN, Katherine Conway. 29800 BAINBRIDGE RD 44139 #038-45-1994 L1996 **PD** *020 †55

BROWN, Marvin Jos. 34501 AURORA RD 44139 #869-07-1954 L1958 **OBG** *071 †30

BRUCK, William E. ■ 44139 #028-34-1950 L1951 **GS TS** *071 †85

CARPENTER, Elizabeth Ross. 33001 SOLON RD STE 115, SUBURBAN PEDIATRICS 44139 #038-06-1996 L2000 **PD** *020 †55

CARTELLONE, Chris. 34501 AURORA RD, STE 104 44139 #038-06-1985 L1986 **IM** *020 †20

CASSADY, Charles Louis. ■ 44139 #038-40-1961 L1961 **OTO** *071 †45

CATALANO, James Wm. ■ 44139 #038-44-1991 L1993 **GS** *020

CATANZARO, Peter Michael. 33001 SOLON RD 44139 #038-06-1997 L2000 **PD** *020 †55

CHADALAVADA, Rajagopal. 29350 MILES RD 44139 #495-37-1993 L2004 **GE** *012 †20 ‡

CHEN, Longwen. ■ 44139 #243-47-1992 L2005 **PTH** *100 †50

CLUBB, Bryce Steven. 31105 BAINBRIDGE RD 44139 #143-03-1969 L1979 **R** *020 †80

COOPER, Cathy Lynne. 29800 BAINBRIDGE RD, CLEVELAND CLINIC SOLON-1-M 44139 #038-40-1989 L1992 **IM** *020 †20

DANNAN, Emad Eddin. ■ 44139 #875-01-1987 **GS** *100

DESAI, Rajul. 29800 BAINBRIDGE RD, RHEUMATOLOGY / S040 44139 #495-23-1994 L2005 **RHU** *020 †20

DE SANTIS, Lisa. 29800 BAINBRIDGE RD 44139 #038-06-1995 L1996 **FM** *020 †18

DIMAYUGA, Cesar De Leon. ■ 44139 #748-02-1989 **OMO** *100

ELKHAIRI, Fadel Shukri. ■ 44139 #038-43-2005 L2005 **U** *012

EL-MALLAWANY, Jung Jin. 34501 AURORA RD STE 101 44139 #583-08-1972 L1978 **P** *020 †75

ERGUN, Zekiye. ■ 44139 #902-03-1953 L1968 **AN** *071

FARNER, Gordon Noble. 33001 SOLON RD, STE 210 44139 #030-05-1948 L1952 **ORS** *071 †40

FELDMAN, Bruce Jay. 6200 SOM CENTER RD STE A24 44139 #016-04-1977 L1978 **GP GS** *020 †85

FORBES, Olwen Evans. ■ 44139 #041-77-1942, ▲ *071

FORD, Donald Brooks. 29800 BAINBRIDGE RD, FAMILY MEDICINE/SO 10 44139 #038-06-1997 L1998 **FM** *020 †18

FREEDMAN, Wendy Jane. 30680 BAINBRIDGE RD 44139 #038-44-1984 L1993 **OBG GS** *020 †30

FRIEDMAN, Arnold B. 34501 AURORA RD, STE 206 44139 #038-40-1953 L1953 **PD** *071 †55

FRIEDMAN, Deborah Beth. 33001 SOLON RD 44139 #038-06-1989 L1990 **PD** *020 †55

FULLER, Keith Allen. 29800 BAINBRIDGE RD 44139 #038-44-1987 L1988 **IM ISM** *020 †20

GORAYA, Shazia Tanvir. 29800 BAINBRIDGE RD 44139 #704-20-1989 L1997 **IM** *020 †20

GORE, Julia Inetta. ■ 44139 #038-06-1998 L2005 **GE** *100 †20

GRIFFIN, Chas Sidney, Jr. 34501 AURORA RD STE 206 44139 #051-04-1974 L1977 **PD** *020 †55

GROPPE, Carl Wm, Jr. 30680 BAINBRIDGE RD 44139 #041-12-1960 L1970 **ON HEM** *071 †20

GUO, Wei. ■ 44139 #038-06-2008 *012

GUTJAHR, Charmaine Dora. ■ 44139 #038-43-2000 L2000 **MPD** *100 †20,55

HAYDEN, Jeera. 33001 SOLON RD, STE 203 44139 #917-28-1967 L1989 **FM** *020

HERMAN, Michael L. ■ 44139 #038-44-1986 L1987 **AN CCA** *075

HERTZ, Andrew Roy. 33001 SOLON RD 44139 #038-06-1992 L1993 **PD** *020 †55

HOPKINS, Kevin Dale. 29800 BAINBRIDGE RD, CLEVELAND CLINIC-SOLON 44139 #038-45-2002 L2002 **FM** *020 †18

HUML, Anne Marie. ■ 44139 #038-44-2006 L2006 **IM** *012

HURST, Charles Benson. 33001 SOLON RD STE 112 44139 #038-40-1964 L1964 **GS EM** *020 †85

IGBOELI, Prosper I. 6221 N HUNTINGTON DR 44139 #035-15-1977 L1980 **OBG** *020 †30 ‡

IHEME, Uchenna Gordon. 7150 WITCH HAZEL LN # 101, LEVERS MEDICAL ASSOC LLC 44139 #690-02-1985 L1998 **IM** *020 †20

IMRIE, Elizabeth Ruth. 29800 BAINBRIDGE RD 44139 #918-01-1964 L1980 **PD ADL** *020

JOHNSON, Nancy Kurfess. ■ 44139 #038-06-1954 L1954 **GYN** *020 †30

KATZ, Robert Lawrence. 29800 BAINBRIDGE RD 44139 #038-06-1963 L1963 **OTO PDO** *020 †45

KHALIL, Shereif N. 30390 STILLWATER LN, SHEREIF KHALIL MD 44139 #038-40-1988 L1990 **DR VIR** *020 †80

KHATAMI, Sayed Saeid. ■ 44139 #517-13-1993 L2001 **GE** *012

KIM, Richard Dongsuk. ■ 44139 #005-02-2006 L2006 **IM** *012

KLETTER, Ian A. 30680 BAINBRIDGE RD 44139 #033-05-1977 L2000 **CCS TRS** *020 †85

KOROBKOVA, Irina. 37000 FOX RUN DR 44139 #913-36-1995 L2004 **P** *012

KOSMIDES, Robert Wm. 33001 SOLON RD, STE 112 44139 #051-07-1989 L1990 **N** *020

KOTTAPALLI, Manjula Subra. 7500 STOCKWOOD DR 44139 #495-21-1995 L1999 **CHP** *020 †75

KRATCHE, Richard Paul. 29800 BAINBRIDGE RD, CLEVELAND CLINIC SOLON 44139 #038-40-1987 L1990 **FM** *020 †18

KUZAS, Adolfas. ■ 44139 #407-04-1949 L1955 **OBG** *071 †30

LAH, Harry K. ■ 44139 #583-04-1971 L1979 **R** *020 †80

LAMPE, John Bernard. 29800 BAINBRIDGE RD 44139 #038-06-1977 L1980 **PD** *020 †55

LIPTON, Mark Alan. 29800 BAINBRIDGE RD, CLEVELAND CLNC SOLON 44139 #038-06-1972 L1974 **IM** *020 †20

LORENZ, Lyn Hollis. 33001 SOLON RD 44139 #035-45-1996 L1997 **PD** *020 †55

LUCZEK, Stephen F. ■ 44139 #165-04-1962 L1966 **OBG** *071 †30

LUDIN, Adir. ■ 44139 #935-01-1987 L1998 **RO** *020 †80

MANOLACHE, Petrica. ■ 44139 #781-03-1985 L1999 **IM** *020 †20

MARTINEZ, Camilo B. ■ 44139 #748-02-1960 L1969 **AN** *020 †05

MAZANSKY, Hillel. 34055 SOLON RD 44139 #836-03-1966 L1978 **FM** *072 †18

MC KNIGHT, Timothy James. 36680 BAINBRIDGE RD, COMMUNITY HOSPITALISTS 44139 #024-07-1989 L1998 **PD PEM** *020

MILLSTONE, Heidi Lee. ■ 44139 #005-02-1991 L1994 **IM** *020 †20

MOAYERI, Mohammad Ali. 33001 SOLON RD STE 212 44139 #517-05-1974 L1980 **RHU** *040 †20

MOHAMMED, Tan-Lucien. ■ 44139 #047-07-1997 L2004 **DR** *020 †80

MUEHRCKE, Robert Carl, Jr. 30455 SOLON RD 44139 #016-01-1979 L1980 **ORS EM** *020

MYLES, Jonathan Louis. ■ 44139 #038-43-1983 L1987 **PTH CD** *020 †50

NANDIGAM, Sreelatha. 34430 SEMINOLE WAY 44139 #495-50-1992 L2000 **AN** *020 †05

NEIDES, Daniel Marc. 29800 BAINBRIDGE RD, CLEVELAND CLINIC - SOLON 44139 #038-40-1992 L1993 **FM** *020 †18

NELSON, Nan E. 6200 SOM CENTER RD, STE D20 44139 #048-13-1989 L1991 **CHP P** *020 †75

NGANGANA, Jerome M W. 5109 STANSBURY DR 44139 #042-01-1969 L1998 **TS GS** *020 †85

OAS, John Gilbert. 30455 SOLON RD, OHIO HEAD & NECK INST LLC 44139 #048-02-1986 L1998 **NO N** *020 †75

OWUSU, Osei-Tutu. ■ 44139 #412-02-1984 L2005 **HO** *100 †20

PALEY, Richard Gary. ■ 44139 #038-40-1964 L1964 **OTO** *071

PARKER-DEULEY, Paula J. 33001 SOLON RD STE 202 44139 #038-41-1989 L1992 **IM** *020 †20

PATEL, Shetal Natu. ■ 44139 #023-07-2003 L2006 **EM** *100 †16

POMERANETS, Svetlana B. 29800 BAINBRIDGE RD, CLEVELAND CLINIC FOUNDATIO 44139 #913-03-1994 L1999 **PD** *020 †55

RAGHAVENDRA, Pratibha P. ■ 44139 #496-39-1990 L2000 **IM** *020 †20

REED, Vicki Rae. 29800 BAINBRIDGE RD 44139 #038-45-1997 L1998 **OBG** *020 †30

REYES, Felino P, Jr. ■ 44139 #748-01-1954 L1969 **AN OBG** *071

RICH, Todd Howard. 29800 BAINBRIDGE RD, SOLON FAMILY PRACTICE CENT 44139 #025-07-1973 L1975 **IM** *020 †20

ROHWEDER, Thomas Chas. 33001 SOLON RD, SUBURBAN PEDIATRICS INC 44139 #025-01-1959 L1964 **PD** *071 †55

ROSEN, Mike Joshua. ■ 44139 #005-06-1997 L2000 **GS** *100 †85

ROSENBAUM, Harvey Milton. 29800 BAINBRIDGE RD, CLEVELAND CLINIC-SOLON 44139 #041-12-1961 L1965 **IM END** *020 †20

ROSIAN, Rochelle. 29800 BAINBRIDGE RD, CLEVELAND CLINIC SOLON 44139 #038-44-1990 L1995 **RHU IM** *020 †20

RUBINSTEIN RIVITZ, Thais. ■ 44139 #187-04-1995 L2005 **PD** *075 †55

RYU, Daniel Young. 33001 SOLON RD, STE 220 44139 #038-41-1993 L1994 **AN** *020 †70

SAFFOLD, Scott Harris. 34055 SOLON RD 44139 #047-07-1994 L1996 **OTO** *020 †45

SALON, Joel Marc. 34501 AURORA RD STE 301 44139 #017-02-1982 L1982 **OMF** *020

SANAD, Mohamed A. 30680 BAINBRIDGE RD 44139 #915-09-1986 L1999 **HOS IM** *020 †20

SARAC-LEONARD, Suzana. 33001 SOLON RD, STE 202 44139 #957-08-1988 L1995 **IM** *020 †20

SHAW, Stephen Thomas. 30680 BAINBRIDGE RD, COMMUNITY HOSPS 44139 #016-02-1997 L2002 **HOS** *020 †20

SHERMAN, Donald J. 30455 SOLON RD, SOLON OCCUP MED CTR 44139 #041-09-1959 L1987 **OM MDM** *072 †70

SILBERMAN, Seth Jon. 34055 SOLON RD STE 108 44139 #038-40-1987 L1994 **OTO** *020 †45

SINGER, Eric Chas. ■ 44139 #056-05-1985 L1992 **PD** *020 †55

SNELSON, Marc Edward. 34501 AURORA RD, STE 205 44139 #038-44-1989 L1991 **OBG** *020 †30

SORIN, Steven Barry. 33001 SOLON RD STE 217 44139 #016-06-1974 L1976 **RHU IM** *020 †20 ‡

SPERDUTO, Andrea Rita. 29800 BAINBRIDGE RD 44139 #033-05-1985 L1992 **PD** *020 †55

SRINIVAS, Shyam Mohan. ■ 44139 #005-15-2001 L2006 **NM** *100

STEIN, Richard Lawrence. 33001 SOLON RD, STE 202 44139 #038-06-1982 L1983 **RHU IM** *020 †20

STEMPOWSKI, Melanie D. 5837 BRIARWOOD LN 44139 #038-40-1990 L1995 **PD** *020 †55

STRASBURG, Jessica Marie. 29800 BAINBRIDGE RD 44139 #038-40-1998 L1999 **FM** *020 †18

SULLIVAN, Daniel Michael. 29800 BAINBRIDGE RD 44139 #035-09-1982 L2006 **IM IMG** *020 †12

TERMAN, Stuart Marc. 32901 STATION ST STE 103, COLONY SQUARE BLDG 44139 #056-06-1974 L1976 **OPH** *020 †35

THOMAS, Aju. ■ 44139 #495-31-1998 L2007 **DR** *020 †28,80

THORNTON, John Daryl. ■ 44139 #028-02-1995 L2005 **PCC PUD** *050 †20

TURNER, Frederick D. ■ 44139 #005-06-1950 L1950 **GS** *071 †85

UMAPATHY, Priyadharshini. ■ 44139 #220-01-1991 L2000 **IM** *020 †20

VIBHAKAR, Neha Shardul. ■ 44139 #038-45-2007 **IM** *012

WAMSLEY, Richard Chas. 33001 SOLON RD 44139 #041-02-1961 L1962 **PD** *020 †55

WEISBLAT, Joel David. 29800 BAINBRIDGE RD 44139 #038-06-1990 L1993 **IM** *020 †20

WILBUR, Carly Wieder. 33001 SOLON RD 44139 #035-46-2000 L2000 **PD** *020 †55

YAN, Maohe. ■ 44139 #243-39-1983 L2002 **PD** *100 †55

ZENG, Deli. ■ 44139 #243-45-1987 *100

ZHOU, Lan. ■ 44139 #243-16-1991 L2005 **PTH** *020 †50

SOMERSET – PERRY

DUNMYER, Shelly Lin. 116 W MAIN ST, STE 159 43783 #038-40-1997 L1998 **FM** *020 †18

GILLESPIE, Harold Arthur. 313 NORTH DR 43783 #038-44-2000 L2000 **FM** *020 †18

VAN METER, Jeffrey Paul. 116 W MAIN ST, STE 159 43783 #038-40-1994 L1995 **FM** *020 †18

SOUTH BLOOMFIELD – PICKAWAY

ANSEL, Gary Martin. 5034 N WALNUT ST 43103 #038-40-1986 L1987 **CD IC** *020 †20

BOTTI, Charles Francis. 5034 N WALNUT ST 43103 #035-03-1986 L1990 **CD IC** *020 †20

CHAPEKIS, Anthony T. 5034 N WALNUT ST 43103 #025-01-1983 L1989 **CD IC** *020 †20

KANDER, Nathan Howard. 5034 N WALNUT ST 43103 #025-07-1983 L1990 **CD IC** *020 †20

PURVIS, Jerry G, Jr. 5034 N WALNUT ST 43103 #012-01-1992 L1997 **VS GS** *020 †85

TUGAOEN, John Falgui. 5034 N WALNUT ST 43103 #038-40-1987 L1988 **CD IC** *020 †20

SOUTH CHARLESTON – CLARK

FIPPIN, William Clinton. 8943 WILDLANE DR, RR 1 45368 #038-40-1955 L1955 **IMG** *071

SOUTH EUCLID – CUYAHOGA

ABOUHASSAN, Soozan Souad. ■ 44121 #038-45-2004 L2004 **AN** *012

ADEPITAN, Olayinka Omolar. 4102 PRINCETON BLVD 44121 #690-02-1992 L2000 **AN** *020 †05

ANDERSON, Philip Alden. 1611 S GREEN RD STE 260, UNIV SUBURBAN HEALTH CENTE 44121 #038-06-1978 L1981 **IM IMG** *020

BAUM, David Latimer. ■ 44121 #038-41-2004 L2004 **PG** *012 †55

BHAVNAGRI, Sharukh Jamshi. ■ 44121 #038-06-2005 L2005 **DR** *012

BRENKUSOVA, Katarina. ■ 44121 #036-05-2003 L2004 **IM** *100 †20

■ = Address Information Privacy Protected

BROOKS, Emma Rose. ■ 44121 #035-47-2005 L2006 **FP** *012
BUCCHIERI, Elizabeth Z. 2054 S GREEN RD 44121 #035-01-1992 L2000 **PD** *020 †55
BURNS, Rebecca Lynn. ■ 44121 #038-06-2006 L2006 **IM** *012
CIRINO, Robert Allan. 1611 S GREEN RD STE 260 44121 #038-06-1990 L1991 **IM** *020 †20
CLEM, Bill Dean. 1611 S GREEN RD 44121 #017-20-1954 L1960 **PD** *071 †55
CLEMENS, Norman Andrew. 1611 S GREEN RD, STE 301 44121 #024-01-1959 L1961 **P PYA** *020 †75
COCHRAN, Jennifer V. 1611 S GREEN RD STE 35 44121 #050-02-1994 L1996 **PD** *020 †55
CURRIE, Thos Lauchlin, Jr. ■ 44121 #051-04-1969 L1969 **IM** *071
DE JOSEPH, Debra Ann. 1611 S GREEN RD 44121 #038-06-1991 L1992 **IM** *020 †20
EISENGART, Jonathan Aaron. 1611 S GREEN RD, STE 306B 44121 #038-40-2000 L2000 **OPH** *100 †35
FAGAN, Howard Edward. 1611 S GREEN RD, CLEVELAND PHYSICIANS INC 44121 #038-06-1956 L1956 **IM** *071
FERNANDO, I Cletus M. ■ 44121 #220-01-1969 L1978 **OBG** *020 †30
FINKELSTEIN, Denise Lynn. 1611 S GREEN RD 44121 #038-06-1990 L1991 **IM** *020 †20
FORNEY, Michael Carl. ■ 44121 #038-06-2006 L2006 **DR** *012
FREEDMAN, Joshua. ■ 44121 #036-07-2004 L2004 **PDP** *012 †55
GOSHE, Jeffrey Michael. ■ 44121 #038-06-2006 L2006 **OPH** *012
HABER, Robert Seth. 14077 CEDAR RD 44121 #038-03-1986 L1992 **D PD** *020 †15,55
HAERR, Mary Frances. 1611 S GREEN RD STE 204 44121 #048-12-1985 L1989 **GYN** *020 †30
HALL, Shawn Michael. ■ 44121 #028-79-2003, ▲ L2004 **AN** *020
HAMILTON, Cecelia Lynn. 1611 S GREEN RD, STE 146 44121 #038-40-1988 L1991 **D** *020 †15
HANTUS, Stephen Timothy. ■ 44121 #012-01-2003 L2004 **CN** *012
HOOVER, Danielle Marie. ■ 44121 #016-42-2004 L2007 **IM** *020 †20
JUNGLAS, Donald Wilbert. 1611 S GREEN RD, STE 160 44121 #038-06-1959 L1959 **IM** *020 †20
JUNGLAS, Philip Donald. 1611 S GREEN RD, STE 160 44121 #038-06-1991 L1992 **IM** *020 †20
KATES, Georgianna Perara. 1611 S GREEN RD 44121 #010-03-1994 L1996 **IM** *020
KING, Thomas J. 1611 S GREEN RD 44121 #038-40-1983 L1985 **IM** *020 †20
KLEIN, David Elias. 1611 S GREEN RD STE 106 44121 #038-06-1957 L1957 **U** *071 †95
KOEHLER, Michael Kernan. 1611 S GREEN RD, STE 160 44121 #038-06-1990 L1992 **GE** *020 †20
LAFFERTY, Frederic Wood. 1611 S GREEN RD STE 147 44121 #024-01-1956 L1959 **IM END** *020 †20
LAMPING, Kathleen Anne. 1611 S GREEN RD STE 144 44121 #038-41-1978 L1980 **OPH** *020 †35
LAUX, Douglas Earl. ■ 44121 #028-03-2005 L2005 **IM** *012
LESLIE, James Thos. 1611 S GREEN RD, UNIV SUBURBAN HLTH CTR 44121 #038-41-1987 L1990 **PD** *020 †55
LEVY, Yael. ■ 44121 #550-01-1977 L1988 *100
LIN, Haiyee. 1611 S GREEN RD, WRIGHT SURGERY CTR 44121 #385-02-1971 **AN** *071 †05
LINDAN, Rosemary Jackson. ■ 44121 #352-07-1944 L1972 **ID OS** *071
MANN, Donald Chas. 1611 S GREEN RD 44121 #017-20-1968 L1973 **N CHN** *020 †75
MILLER, Paul Edmund. 4639 MCFARLAND RD 44121 #038-43-1980 L1981 **CD IM** *020 †20
MINGER, Jill Elizabeth. ■ 44121 #038-06-2007 L2007 **OBG** *012
MITCHELL, Arnold Michael. 1611 S GREEN RD STE 306B, CLEVELAND EYE SPECIALIST 44121 #038-40-1957 L1957 **OPH** *020 †35
MITCHELL, David Jos. 1611 S GREEN RD STE 306B, CLEVELAND EYE SPECIALIST 44121 #038-06-1983 L1985 **OPH** *020 †35
MORGAN, Janet Denese. 1611 S GREEN RD 44121 #038-06-1989 L1990 **IM** *020 †20
MORGENSTERN-CLARREN, H S. 1611 S GREEN RD 44121 #026-04-1975 L1978 **IM** *020 †20
NAMROW, Alexander Harold. 1611 S GREEN RD 44121 #023-01-1998 L1999 **PD** *020 †55
OBOKHARE, Iziokhai Daniel. ■ 44121 #010-03-2006 L2006 **GS** *012
PLOTKIN, Franklin H. 1611 S GREEN RD 44121 #035-08-1952 L1954 **IM** *020 †20
POPHAL, Mark David. 1611 S GREEN RD, STE 306B 44121 #038-41-1988 L1990 **OPH** *020 †35
RAPHAELY, Susan Dea. 1611 S GREEN RD STE 124, UNIV SUBURBAN ANESTHIOLO 44121 #045-01-1991 L1993 **AN** *020 †05
REISMAN, Allen Tony. 1611 S GREEN RD 44121 #016-42-1993 L1996 **OTO** *020 †45
RENSTON, Jeffrey Paul. 1611 S GREEN RD, STE 203 UNIV SUB HLTH CTR 44121 #038-06-1986 L1987 **PUD CCM** *020 †20
ROSENBAUM, Michael Aaric. ■ 44121 #038-06-2005 L2005 **GS** *012
ROULET, Norman Lawrence. 1611 S GREEN RD, UNIV SUBURBAN HEALTH CTR 44121 #041-01-1958 L1959 **P PYA** *020 †75
RUDOLPH, Stephen Alan. 1611 S GREEN RD 44121 #038-06-1988 L1989 **IM** *020 †20
RUFF, Robert Louis. 4026 PRINCETON BLVD 44121 #054-04-1976 L1984 **N SCI** *040 †75
SAFAVI, Roknedin. 1611 S GREEN RD STE 209 44121 #517-05-1977 L1980 **P PYA** *020 †75
SCIPPA-PLAZA, Miguel. ■ 44121 #319-04-1985 **NPM** *100
SHEAHAN, Michael Geo. 1611 S GREEN RD 44121 #038-06-1969 L1969 **RHU IM** *071 †20
SOLIVAS-MALUYAO, Jennifer. 1801 BEACONWOOD AVE 44121 #748-02-1999 L2004 **IM** *020 †20
STEINER, William W, II. 1611 S GREEN RD, STE 260 44121 #011-02-1986 L1988 **IM** *020 †20
STEWART, Daniel Brian. 1611 S GREEN RD STE 146 44121 #005-11-2002 L2007 **D** *020 †15
SUMMERS, Jessica Ida. ■ 44121 #041-15-2005 L2005 **GS** *012
THOMPSON, Robert Denman. 1611 S GREEN RD, STE 200 44121 #035-01-1962 L1964 **IM NEP** *071 †20
TOMM, Richard. 1611 S GREEN RD STE 213 44121 #038-06-1995 L1996 **IM** *020 †20
TUROCZI, Steve. 1611 S GREEN RD 44121 #038-06-1997 L1999 **IM** *020 †20
VRABEL, Matthew Mark. ■ 44121 #038-06-2005 L2005 **P** *012
WITT, Ann Marie Hawn. 2054 S GREEN RD 44121 #038-06-1995 L1998 **FM** *020 †18
WOODHOUSE, Justin Gary. 1611 S GREEN RD, STE 146 44121 #018-03-2001 L2001 **D** *020 †15

SOUTH POINT — LAWRENCE

CHEN, Yan. ■ 45680 #243-33-1985 L2007 **PCP** *100
FIORET, Philip William. 384 COUNTY ROAD 120 S, BURLINGTON FAMILY CARE CEN 45680 #065-01-1981 L1998 **FM OM** *020 †18
KITCHEN, James Christophe. ■ 45680 #055-02-2008 *012
MERKEL, Steven Jerome. 55 TOWNSHIP ROAD 508 E, SOUTH POINT MEDICAL CENTER 45680 #038-41-1984 L1985 **FM** *020 †18

SOUTH VIENNA — CLARK

KHAN, Shahida Aziz. PO BOX 219, 8490 E NATIONAL RD 45369 #704-09-1972 L1990 **PD** *050

SPENCER — MEDINA

BOWEN, Kim Dial. 13277 OLD MILL RD 44275 #038-43-1987 L1990 **EM** *020 †16
LECH, Ronald Frederick. ■ 44275 #048-13-1983 L1985 **CD** *071 †20

SPENCERVILLE — ALLEN

KUCHIPUDI, Vijaya Lakshmi. 401 N BROADWAY ST 45887 #495-50-1976 L1998 **FM** *020 †18
MACK, Donald Owen. 107 N CANAL ST 45887 #038-40-1984 L1985 **FM FPG** *030 †18
NIEMEYER, Eric Morgan. ■ 45887 #038-41-2006 L2006 **FP** *012
RINGWALD, Ronald Alan. 107 N CANAL ST 45887 #038-43-1993 L1994 **FM** *020 †18
WRIGHT, William T. 610 SUNSET DR 45887 #041-09-1951 L1952 **FM** *071

SPRING VALLEY — GREENE

HOYLE, Joseph Chad. ■ 45370 #038-40-2003 L2003 **N** *012
OZOUDE, Kingsley. ■ 45370 #016-11-1996 L2002 **RNR** *020 †80
SVETIC, Antonela. ■ 45370 #957-01-1986 L1998 **N** *020 †75

SPRINGBORO — WARREN

ABBOTT, Kent Davis. ■ 45066 #049-01-1996 L1998 **DR** *020 †80
AFAZ, Sadia Farhana. ■ 45066 #160-04-1994 L2002 **IM** *020 †20
AGGARWAL, Nalini. 8 SYCAMORE CREEK DR 45066 #038-44-1997 L1998 **PD** *020 †55 ‡
AGRAWAL, Alok. 360 W CENTRAL AVE 45066 #495-49-1987 L1999 **NEP** *020 †20
ALBRIGHT, Scott. ■ 45066 #038-45-2003 L2003 **FSM** *020 †18
ALTMAN, Arthur Alan. 758 W CENTRAL AVE 45066 #038-40-1978 L1979 **OBG** *020 †30
ANAND, Sanjeev. ■ 45066 #495-69-1980 L1985 **NEP IM** *020
AVERY, Kurt Balmer. 360 W CENTRAL AVE, SURE CARE MED CNTR 45066 #038-45-1991 L1992 **FM** *020 †18
BALL, Connie S. 84 N MAIN ST 45066 #038-45-1992 L1994 **IM** *020
BARI, Khurram. ■ 45066 #704-01-2001 L2007 **IM** *012
BEBO, Daniel Jason. ■ 45066 #038-45-2006 L2006 **IM** *012
BLAIR, Frederic Ward. 243 W CENTRAL AVE 45066 #038-41-1986 L1997 **FM** *020 †16
BROMBERG, Adam Michael. ■ 45066 #665-01-2005 L2005 **EM** *012
CHALFIE, Craig Evan. 76 REMICK BLVD 45066 #038-41-1998 L2000 **FM** *020 †55
CONFORTI, Daniel Michael. 243 W CENTRAL AVE 45066 #055-01-1976 L1977 **PD** *020 †55
CUNNINGHAM, Frank Eugene, Jr. 78 N MAIN ST 45066 #038-45-1999 L2000 **FM** *020 †18
DACANAY, Anna Carmencita. ■ 45066 #748-10-1992 L2000 **SCI** *020 †60
DEY, Malay K. 75 ELEANOR DR 45066 #496-08-1983 L2000 **GE** *020 †20
DOEBELE, James Francis. ■ 45066 #016-11-1985 L2006 **AN PAN** *020 †05
DRITZ, Jay Harris. ■ 45066 #028-02-2001 L2007 **NPM** *020
DUFFEY, Michael Craig. ■ 45066 #038-45-2002 L2002 **D** *012 †55
EBERHART, Gregory Mark. 76 REMICK BLVD, CORNERSTONE PEDS 45066 #038-45-2006 L2006 **IM** *012
ESSELSTEIN, Brian Andrew. 8 SYCAMORE CREEK DR, AN 45066 #038-45-1986 L1988 **PD** *020 †55
FREDERICKSON, Renee Alta. 10 REMICK BLVD 45066 #016-06-1999 L2005 **OBG** *020 †30
FRILOT, Michele Charise. ■ 45066 #035-03-2004 L2007 **ADL** *012 †55
GENRICH, Toby John. ■ 45066 #041-15-2004 L2004 **OBG** *012
GOLSHAN, Kazem. 360 W CENTRAL AVE, SPRINGBORO OFFICE 45066 #517-05-1966 L1979 **OTO PS** *071 †45
GRAU, Susan Beth. 5 SYCAMORE CREEK DR, STE A 45066 #038-43-1996 L1998 **FM** *020 †18
GRIJALVA, Galo A. 90 REMICK BLVD 45066 #055-01-1992 L2003 **GS** *020 †85
HAMMOND, Jerry Dale. 5 SYCAMORE CREEK DR, SPRINGBORO FAMILY HEALTH C 45066 #038-40-1959 L1959 **FM** *071 †18
HAROVER, Richard Lee, Jr. ■ 45066 #038-41-1995 L1997 **EM** *020 †18,16
HAWKINS, Robert A. 360 W CENTRAL AVE 45066 #007-02-1977 L1979 **RHU IM** *020 †20
HAYDEN, Kerry David. 280 HICKORY HILLS DR 45066 #038-40-1976 L1978 **EM OM** *020 †16
HICKS, Todd Leander. ■ 45066 #035-20-2001 L2001 **PS** *012
HOFFMAN, Jay Gregory. 360 W CENTRAL AVE, SURECARE MEDICAL CENTER 45066 #038-45-1986 L1988 **IM** *020 †20
HUTCHISON, Charles Lynn. 8 SYCAMORE CREEK DR 45066 #041-12-1992 L1996 **PD** *020 †55
JASPER, Nicholas Robert. ■ 45066 #017-20-2007 L2007 **TY** *012
JORDAN, Alexandra J. ■ 45066 #016-11-2003 L2003 **IM** *020 †20
KANISTROS, Peter Mike. 170 LAKESIDE DR 45066 #038-45-1993 L1997 **NM** *020 †80
KEJRIWAL, Raj Kumar. ■ 45066 #495-24-1971 L2000 *100
KHERA, Samira Yasmin. 5 SYCAMORE CREEK DR 45066 #010-02-1997 L2007 **GS** *020 †85
KHOSLA, Kimberly Cook. 8 SYCAMORE CREEK DR 45066 #038-45-1996 L1997 **PD** *020 †55
KING, Kristi Ann. ■ 45066 #025-12-2005 L2007 **FP** *012
LARREATEGUI, Alberto G. ■ 45066 #025-01-1959 L1963 **GPM GS** *072 †85
LITTLE, Robert Alan. 10 REMICK BLVD 45066 #038-40-1990 L1998 **OBG** *020 †30
LOCHNER, John Jos, III. 360 W CENTRAL AVE 45066 #028-34-1980 L1986 **ORS** *020 †40
MAENPA, Ryan Robert. ■ 45066 #038-41-2002 L2002 **PM** *020 †60
MANAHAN, Jill C. 5 SYCAMORE CREEK DR, STE A 45066 #038-75-2001, ▲ L2001 **FM** *020 †18
MANOCHA, Vivekanand. 52 REMICK BLVD 45066 #422-01-2001 L2001 **PM APM** *020 †60
MARTINEZ, Enrique. ■ 45066 #264-02-1956 L1965 **ORS** *040 †40
MASON-ZIED, Dena E. 243 W CENTRAL AVE 45066 #038-75-2000, ▲ L2000 **FM** *020 †18
MAURO, Tara Codee. ■ 45066 #020-75-2004, ▲ L2004 **P** *012
MILLS, Carrie Elizabethf. ■ 45066 #038-45-2007 L2007 **EM** *012
NAQVI, Afia Idris. 57 CROCKETT DR 45066 #704-22-1991 L2001 **IM** *020 †20
PICKETT, Jason Raine. ■ 45066 #051-07-2005 L2005 **EM** *012
PILATI, Louis Eugene. ■ 45066 #038-45-1993 L1995 **UM EM** *020 †16
ROSENBAUM, Benjamin Paul. ■ 45066 #047-05-2008 *012
ROTH, Jill Elizabeth. ■ 45066 #022-75-2005, ▲ L2005 **OBG** *012
SCHOFIELD, Kira. 90 REMICK BLVD 45066 #041-12-1987 L1994 **GS** *020 †85
SCROGGS, William Andrew, III. ■ 45066 #001-06-2007 L2007 **GS** *012
SHAATH, Rami Mohammed. ■ 45066 #155-01-1998 L2002 **IM** *020 †20
SLAUGHENHAUPT, James F. 243 W CENTRAL AVE 45066 #018-75-1996, ▲ L1997 *020
SMITH, Kathleen Patriciab. 243 W CENTRAL AVE 45066 #038-41-2004 L2004 **PD** *020 †55
STARRETT, Karen Elizabeth. 76 REMICK BLVD, CORNERSTONE PEDIATRCIS 45066 #038-43-1997 L1999 **PD** *020 †55

UNGERLEIDER, Beverly A T. 8 SYCAMORE CREEK DR 45066 #038-40-1965 L1965 **PD** *020 †55
WASCAK, Kimberly. ■ 45066 #038-45-2002 L2004 **EM** *020 †16
WURZELBACHER, Alan Edward. ■ 45066 #038-40-2007 **IM** *012
ZAKI, Safwat K. 243 W CENTRAL AVE 45066 #915-04-1980 L1994 **U** *020 †95

SPRINGDALE – HAMILTON

KRESS, Timothy Scott. 290 NORTHLAND BLVD 45246 #038-41-1989 L1990 **OBG** *020 †30
OTENG, Kwabena Owusu. 360 GLENSPRINGS DR, DOCTORS URGENT CARE OFFICE 45246 #305-01-1999 L2000 **FM** *020 ‡

SPRINGFIELD – CLARK

ABBOTT, Sally Ann. 2701 MOOREFIELD RD 45502 #051-04-1966 L1967 **FM** *020 †18 ‡
ABDURRAHMAN, Lubabatu. 2624 LEXINGTON AVE 45505 #690-03-1985 L1992 **PDC** *020 †55
ABRAHAM, Kamel Sobhi. ■ 45502 #915-02-1975 L1987 **AN ORS** *020 †05
ABRAHAM, Phoebe Alice. ■ 45502 #038-45-2007 L2007 **GS** *012
ADRIATICO, Claude Lacaya. 2685 E HIGH ST, SPRINGFIELD SURGERY CENTER 45505 #748-11-1984 L2001 **AN** *020 †05
AGUDU, Eyra Adjoa. 2624 LEXINGTON AVE 45505 #041-14-1994 L1998 **OBG** *020 †30 ‡
AHMED, Ashfaq Taj. 1174 E HOME RD, STE N 45503 #038-44-1996 L1997 **CD IM** *020 †20
AHMED, Imtiaz. 2131 N LIMESTONE ST, STE 1 45503 #495-21-1982 L1991 **IM** *020 †20
AHMED, Khairatuddin. 1 E PLEASANT ST 45506 #495-57-1966 L1974 **IM** *020
AHMED, Mohammed S. 1174 E HOME RD 45503 #495-65-1979 L1996 **CD IM** *020 †20
AHMED, Najeeb. 1174 E HOME RD 45503 #305-01-1998 L2000 **CD** *100 †20
AHMED, Tajuddin. 1174 E HOME RD 45503 #495-57-1967 L1972 **CD** *020 †20
AKHTER, S M Faiq. 1911 E HIGH ST 45505 #704-02-1988 L1999 **CD** *020 †20
AMOS, Crystal F. 2555 CREEKWOOD CT, COMMUNITY URGENT CARE CENT 45504 #038-45-1991 L1992 **FM** *020 †18
ANDARSIO, Carlos Orestes. ■ 45501 #275-01-1955 L1962 **CRS** *071
ANDORFER, Paul Edward. 1220 E HOME RD 45503 #017-20-1967 L1973 **PME** *020
ANNAMRAJU, Ananth. 1345 N FOUNTAIN BLVD 45504 #038-44-1994 L1995 **U GS** *020 †95
BANKS, Jana R. 1343 N FOUNTAIN BLVD, EMERGENCY DEPARTMENT 45504 #038-40-1991 L1992 **EM** *020 †16
BARNES, Audra Suzanne. ■ 45503 #038-45-2008 *012
BASHIR, Shahid. 2615 E HIGH ST, STE 1350 45505 #704-02-1987 L1996 **PCC IM** *020 †20
BASHOVER, David Wm. 2615 E HIGH ST 45505 #017-20-1979 L1980 **EM PD** *020 †55,16
BATIE, Rodney E. 1835 E HIGH ST 45505 #005-76-1986, ▲ L1991 **OBG** *020
BAVER, Robin Sue. 6125 URBANA RD, NAVISTAR 45502 #047-05-1986 L1988 **OM GP** *020 †70
BECKER, Albert Eugene. 30 W MCCREIGHT AVE STE 110 45504 #038-40-1972 L1972 **ORS** *020 †40
BEERS, Kenneth N, Jr. ■ 45503 #038-45-1984 L1985 **FM** *020 †18
BELTRAN, Francisco Victor. 1343 N FOUNTAIN BLVD, MERCY MEDICAL CENTER 45504 #748-10-2000 L2006 *020
BERLEY, Harry Mercedes. 2615 E HIGH ST 45505 #016-06-1944 L1944 **FM** *071 †18
BERTRAM, Martin Fredrick. 4960 MIDDLE URBANA RD 45503 #016-43-1990 L1994 **PM PMM** *020 †60
BIANCHI, James E, III. 2615 E HIGH ST 45505 #038-43-1994 L1995 **EM** *020 †16
BOARD, Thos Mc Kinney, Jr. 580 W EVA CIR 45504 #020-02-1963 L1970 **U** *020 †95
BOEHMER, Laura B. 280 RED COACH DR 45503 #038-45-2001 L2001 **FM** *020 †18
BOOR, Keith Allan. 211 NORTHPARKE DR 45503 #038-45-1981 L1983 **IM** *020 †20
BOSTON, George Michael. 1343 N FOUNTAIN BLVD, DEPT OF ANESTHESIA 45504 #038-45-2002 L2002 **AN** *020
BREDEMEYER, Hans Gunter. ■ 45504 #407-12-1954 L1965 **OPH** *071
BRINLEY, Jerald L. 1343 N FOUNTAIN BLVD 45504 #020-02-1969 L1981 **R** *071 †80
BROWN, Robert Lewis. 2615 E HIGH ST, COMMUNITY HOSPITAL 45505 #038-40-1969 L1969 **OM** *062
BUCKLEW-WILDER, Pamela. 2100 EMMANUEL WAY, STE D 45502 #038-45-1982 L1991 **GS VS** *020 †85
BURKS, Steven C. 363 S BURNETT RD 45505 #038-40-1988 L1990 **IM** *020 †20
BURMAWALA, Sameer. 1174 E HOME RD 45503 #305-01-1999 L2000 **ID** *100 †20
BUTT, Shehla M. 2555 CREEKWOOD CT, COMMUNITY URGENT CARE INC. 45504 #704-06-1969 L1983 **PTH FM** *020
CARDLIN, Kenneth Michael. 2501 E HIGH ST, COMMUNITY MERCY OCCUPATION 45505 #051-04-1983 L1994 **OM FM** *020 †70,18
CARROLL, Trent Jos. 2254 OLYMPIC ST 45503 #038-41-1983 L1987 **OPH** *020 †35
CHADHA, Amrit Lal. 1240 E MAIN ST 45503 #495-03-1964 L1974 **N** *020 †75
CHITKARA, Vijay Kumar. 218 N PARKE DR STE B 45503 #496-09-1978 L1988 **PD ADL** *020 †55
CHU, Paul P. 2615 E HIGH ST 45505 #005-12-1984 L1986 **AN** *020 †05
COCHRAN, Geo Alfred, Jr. ■ 45503 #016-11-1964 L1970 **GS VS** *071 †85
COLE, Kerry Y Patterson. ■ 45503 #038-40-1983 L1987 **DR** *020
COOK, Martin J. 2430 SAINT PARIS PIKE, UNIT 11 45504 #016-01-1941 L1948 **OPH** *071 †35
COOPER, Amanda S. ■ 45504 #038-44-1992 L2007 **DR** *020 †80
COOPER, Raymond Nelson. 2624 LEXINGTON AVE 45505 #017-20-1963 L1968 **PD** *071 †55
CROMWELL, James Lynn. 2121 E HIGH ST 45505 #017-20-1968 L1974 **GYN** *020 †30 ‡
DANIELS, Jennifer Marie. 30 W MCCREIGHT AVE, STE 208 45504 #038-41-1999 L1999 **GS** *020 †85
DARR, Richard Bruce. 444 W HARDING RD, STE A 45504 #034-01-1970 L1991 **IM IMG** *020 †20,16
DATA, Richard Eric. 2615 E HIGH ST 45505 #038-41-1978 L1988 **PTH HMP** *020 †50
DAYKIN, Lawrence Eric. 2624 LEXINGTON AVE, PEDIATRIC ASSOCIATES OF 45505 #038-40-2000 L2000 **PD** *020 †55
DEAN, Jacob Thomas. 1343 N FOUNTAIN BLVD 45504 #038-41-2000 L2000 **FM** *020 †18
DEBOO, Noshir Erach. 1822 N LIMESTONE ST 45503 #495-23-1970 L1975 **ORS** *020 †40
DE LONG, Lisa Marie. 1821 E HIGH ST 45505 #038-43-1991 L1992 **OBG** *020 †30
DEMETER, Joseph Gerard. 30 W MCCREIGHT AVE, STE 208 45504 #038-41-1987 L1992 **GS VS** *020 †85
DOBSON, John Wm. 2330 E HIGH ST 45505 #038-40-1979 L1984 **ORS** *020 †40
DUDNEY, Jerald Steven. 2121 E HIGH ST 45505 #047-05-1977 L1994 **IM** *020 †20
DUFFEE, James Harvey. 651 S LIMESTONE ST 45505 #048-13-1979 L1990 **PD CHP** *020 †55,75
DUNAWAY, Thomas E. 38 S BURNETT RD 45505 #038-40-1978 L1978 **OBG** *020 †30
DU VALL, Michael Brent. 1343 N FOUNTAIN BLVD 45504 #038-41-1975 L1980 **OTO** *020 †45
ERHARDT, Peter Anton. ■ 45504 #028-34-1973 L1977 **EM IM** *020
ERICKSEN, Thomas Wm. 1835 E HIGH ST 45505 #016-11-1977 L1990 **IM** *020 †20
ESPINOSA, Eric A. 1345 N FOUNTAIN BLVD 45504 #048-13-2000 L2000 **U** *020 †95
ESSIG, John Robt. ■ 45505 #038-40-1955 L1955 **AN** *071 †05
FARNLACHER, Nancy Marie. 1343 N FOUNTAIN BLVD, MERCY MEDICAL CENTER 45504 #038-43-1994 L1997 **EM** *020 †16
FARRALL, John Reese. 2608 E HIGH ST 45505 #036-05-1965 L1967 **ORS** *020
FEAGINS, Stephen Ray. 247 S BURNETT RD STE 2 45505 #047-06-1995 L1996 **IM** *020 †20
FIFER, George Lee. ■ 45502 #051-04-1956 L1959 **OM** *071
FISCHBACH, Howard P, III. 2614 E HIGH ST 45505 #038-41-1971 L1971 **AN GS** *020 †05
FISEROVA, Jana Anna. ■ 45502 #286-02-1958 L1974 **PD** *020
FISH, Larry Alan. 2330 E HIGH ST, GREATER OHIO EYE SURGEONS, 45505 #038-40-1985 L1992 **OPH** *020 †35
FRENCH, Dale Eugene. 30 W MCCREIGHT AVE, STE 104 45504 #038-41-1965 L1965 **FM OS** *071
FREYHOF, J Matthew. 5379 DAYTON RD 45502 #038-43-2003 L2003 **EM** *020 †16
FURAY, Richard Ward. 2100 EMMANUEL WAY, STE D 45502 #038-43-1982 L1987 **GS** *020 †85
GABBARD, Alan Lanier. 247 S BURNETT RD 45505 #041-07-1976 L1977 **GE IM** *020 †20
GALLUCH, David Brian. 30 W MCCREIGHT AVE 45504 #038-43-2000 L2005 **OSM** *020
GARG, Tarsem Chand. 1929 E HIGH ST 45505 #495-29-1966 L1975 **ORS HS** *020 †40
GARRINGER, William Arthur. 2655 W NATIONAL RD 45504 #038-40-1976 L1976 **FPG FM** *020 †18
GIBFRIED, James Paul. 1086 MOUND ST 45505 #038-40-1972 L1972 **P** *020 †75
GILLEN, John Bernard. 435 S BURNETT RD 45505 #038-41-1988 L1993 **OTO HNS** *020 †45
GIRGIS, Sami Bishara. 2615 E HIGH ST, COMMUNITY HOSPITAL OF 45505 #330-04-1957 L1974 **PUD IM** *071
GORDON, Richard Edgar, Jr. 2701 MOOREFIELD RD 45502 #038-43-1980 L1982 **FM OS** *020 †18
GOYAL, Lalit Kishore. 2615 E HIGH ST 45505 #495-74-1982 L1996 **EM FM** *020 †16
GRIMSON, Misti Marita. 651 S LIMESTONE ST 45505 #038-45-2000 L2000 **FM** *020 †18
GROVES, Mary Jo. 1343 N FOUNTAIN BLVD 45504 #038-40-1980 L1981 **FM** *020 †18
GUERRIERO, David Joseph. 2615 E HIGH ST 45505 #038-41-1997 L1999 **EM** *020
HADI, Syed Abdul. ■ 45503 #495-21-1963 L1974 **PTH ATP** *075
HALEEM, Syed Abdul. 202 S BELMONT AVE 45505 #495-21-1956 L1974 **U** *071
HASKELL, Gerald Clayton. 2615 E HIGH ST 45505 #010-03-1945 L1946 **IM** *071
HAZEL, Joe Michael. 1671 N LIMESTONE ST 45503 #020-12-1965 L1967 **D** *020 †15
HEINRICH, Guenter E. 1671 N LIMESTONE ST 45503 #016-02-1938 L1941 **GP** *071
HICKERSON, Timothy Wm. 444 W HARDING RD 45504 #038-41-1986 L1987 **IM** *020 †20
HOLT, Gilbert Anthony, Jr. 2624 LEXINGTON AVE, SPRINGFIELD MEDICAL & SURG 45505 #067-01-1969 L1984 **AI IM** *020 †20,03
HORTON, George Robt. 202 S BELMONT AVE 45505 #017-20-1942 L1952 **U** *071 †95
IMAMURA, Yoichi Charley. 2624 LEXINGTON AVE, STE 330 45505 #005-12-1993 L1996 **IM** *020 †20
JACKSON, Angela Ruth. 1821 E HIGH ST 45505 #025-12-2000 L2004 **OBG** *020
JAWADI, M Husain. 30 W MCCREIGHT AVE STE 111 45504 #495-21-1971 L1997 **DIA IM** *040 †20
JOHNSON, Donald Bruce. 30 W MCCREIGHT AVE, STE 209 45504 #016-11-1971 L1990 **GYN EM** *020 †30
JONES, Helen May. 2701 MOOREFIELD RD 45502 #010-02-1956 L1978 **FM** *071 †18
KALNINS, Guntis. ■ 45504 #038-44-1985 L1986 **DR** *020
KALWEIT, Wilhelm Harald. 1343 N FOUNTAIN BLVD 45504 #050-02-1981 L1987 **CD IM** *020 †20
KATAI, Freddy M. 1343 N FOUNTAIN BLVD 45504 #917-18-1986 L2002 **DR VIR** *020 †80
KEARFOTT, Jeffrey Lynn. 20 S BURNETT RD 45505 #038-45-1986 L1987 **OPH** *020 †35
KENCANA, Filix. 148 W NORTH ST 45504 #409-21-1994 L2006 **HO** *020 †20
KENNINGTON, Rohn Tysen. 2615 E HIGH ST 45505 #004-01-1979 L1980 **EM FM** *020 †16,18
KHAN, Aamir. 444 W HARDING RD 45504 #704-09-1982 L1996 **IM** *020 †20
KHAN, Adnan Atta. 1117 E HOME RD 45503 #704-01-2000 L2004 **IM** *020
KHANNA, Ravi Chandra. 148 W NORTH ST 45504 #495-03-1972 L1977 **IM** *020 †20
KNEISLEY, Robert Edward. 247 S BURNETT RD STE 210 45505 #038-40-1977 L1978 **FM** *020 †18
KNUDSON, Gregory Steven. 1345 N FOUNTAIN BLVD 45504 #016-11-1986 L1992 **U** *020 †95
KOJA, Abed. 2200 N LIMESTONE ST, STE 100 45503 #875-02-1973 L2006 **NS** *020 †25
KORAYM, Ashraf. 1911 E HIGH ST, CHAMPAIGN COUNTIES 45505 #422-01-1998 L2005 **ICE** *100 †20
KRAFT, Emily Claire. ■ 45504 #038-45-2008 *012
KURIAN, Pius. 247 S BURNETT RD, STE 100 45505 #495-63-1986 L1993 **NEP IM** *020 †20
LAGMAN, Mary Grace Singia. 2615 E HIGH ST, COMMUNITY HOSPITAL 45505 #748-02-2001 L2006 *020 †20
LAU, Gary John. 2330 E HIGH ST 45505 #010-02-1978 L1984 **OPH** *020 †35
LAWRENCE, David Long. ■ 45504 #020-02-1962 L1971 **R** *071 †80
LAWRENCE, Walter Robt. ■ 45503 #038-41-1959 L1959 **GS OM** *071 †85
LEAHY, William Michael. 2624 LEXINGTON AVE, PEDIATRIC ASSOCIATES OF 45505 #038-40-1967 L1967 **PD** *020 †55
LEE, Ki Hwan. 421 S BURNETT RD 45505 #583-10-1964 L1976 **OBG** *071
LEMMING, Robert Matthew. 2615 E HIGH ST 45505 #038-45-1992 L1997 **DR** *020 †80
LITTLE, John Zebulon. 2615 E HIGH ST 45505 #036-01-1967 L1975 **GS** *071 †85
LOTHE, Meenal S. 1117 E HOME RD 45503 #496-38-1999 L2003 **IM** *020 †20
MAC LEAN, Bruce Foster. ■ 45503 #038-41-1964 L1964 **DR NM** *071 †80
MACY, Joel David. 3250 MIDDLE URBANA RD 45502 #038-43-1999 L1999 **FM** *020 †18
MANCY, Emmanuel Gus. 2624 LEXINGTON AVE, PEDIATRIC ASSOCIATES OF 45505 #038-40-1968 L1968 **PD** *020
MARDOVIN, Vlada. 1345 N FOUNTAIN BLVD 45504 #038-45-1994 L1995 **U** *020 †95
MARSH, Elizabeth. 2624 LEXINGTON AVE, SPRINGFIELD HEALTH CARE 45505 #025-01-1976 L1980 **IM** *020 †20
MARTINEZ, Augusto Lloren. 444 W HARDING RD 45504 #748-01-1975 L1991 **CRS** *020 †10,85
MAST, Duane Lee. 120 N FOUNTAIN AVE, CLARK COUNTY JAIL 45502 #038-45-1985 L1986 **FM** *020 †18
MC CULLOCH, Rudolph P. ■ 45502 #036-07-1941 L1948 **CD IM** *071
MC FANN, Lori Beth. 1200 E HOME RD, STE B 45503 #038-45-1995 L1998 **FM** *020 †18
MC KEE, Kathryn Goleman. 1101 E HIGH ST, MCKINLEY HALL 45505 #038-40-1980 L1981 **FM** *020 †18
MC KEE, Michael Steven. 247 S BURNETT RD STE 210 45505 #038-45-1981 L1982 **FM** *020 †18
MC LEMORE, Robert A. ■ 45503 #041-02-1944 L1950 **GS** *071 †85
MC SURDY, Donald James. ■ 45504 #038-41-1958 L1958 **AN** *071

■ = Address Information Privacy Protected

MESSER, William Dean. 30 W MCCREIGHT AVE STE 20 45504 #038-45-1992 L1994 FM *020 †18

MILLER, E Sue. ■ 45504 #038-40-1954 L1954 GP *071

MIRZA, Mohammad R. 1416 W 1ST ST 45504 #704-09-1967 L1989 CD IM *020 †20

MISICK, Lofton Nathaniel. 1343 N FOUNTAIN BLVD 45504 #028-02-1988 L1997 TS *020 †85,90

MOHAMMED, Akber. 1911 E HIGH ST 45505 #495-21-1981 L1994 CD *020 †20

MONJOT, David Geo. 30 W MCCREIGHT AVE, STE 100 45504 #038-41-1976 L1977 PUD IM *020 †20

MORGENSTERN, Steven Joel. 444 W HARDING RD, STE F 45504 #038-40-1984 L1989 NEP IM *020 †20

MORMAN, Joseph Michael. 247 S BURNETT RD STE 210 45505 #038-41-1990 L1991 FM *020 †18

MORRISON, Ann Kerr. 1086 MOUND ST 45505 #056-05-1985 L1989 P *020 †75

MORTON, Timothy Allen. 2615 E HIGH ST 45505 #056-06-1993 L1996 EM *020 †16

MUIR, Peter J. 3250 MIDDLE URBANA RD 45502 #046-03-1988 L1989 FM *020 †18

MUKERJEE, Kumar. 25 W HARDING RD 45504 #495-08-1965 L1973 GE IM *020 †20

NARCELLES, Marvin Millan. 2105 E HIGH ST 45505 #038-40-1995 L1997 IM *020 †20

NATHAN, Annette R. 2615 E HIGH ST, COMMUNITY HOSPITAL 45505 #035-03-1984 L1993 EM GS *016 ‡

NEDELMAN, Richard Martin. 30 W MCCREIGHT AVE, SPRINGFIELD, INC. 45504 #038-41-1987 L1990 GS *020 †20

NEDELMAN, Stanley Howard. ■ 45503 #038-41-1956 L1956 R *071 †80

NERAVETLA, Surender Reddy. 1343 N FOUNTAIN BLVD 45504 #495-21-1974 L1981 TS VS *020 †90,85

NESSELROADE, Daniel Wayne. 1821 E HIGH ST 45505 #038-43-1995 L1997 OBG *020 †30

NKADI, Chukwuemeke Oscar. 1416 W 1ST ST 45504 #016-11-1990 L1992 GD *020 †20

NORMAN, Robin Anderson. 1835 MIRACLE MILE 45503 #017-20-1991 L2004 P CHP *020 †75

OEHLERS, Stephen Joseph. 2105 E HIGH ST, STE 1 45505 #041-12-2000 L2004 IM *020 †20 ‡

OSTERHOLT, Shawn Steven. 1108 VESTER AVE, OB-GYN LTD 45503 #038-44-1997 L1999 OBG *020 †30

PANAYIDES, Marios Petron. 30 W MCCREIGHT AVE 45504 #028-34-1969 L1971 GS CD *020 †85

PARK, Young Rewng. 1343 N FOUNTAIN BLVD, SPRINGFIELD REGIONAL MEDIC 45504 #583-04-1971 L1977 AN *020 †20

PARSONS, Charles David. 202 S BELMONT AVE 45505 #017-20-1974 L1979 U *020 †95

PATEL, Vipul Kanaiyalal. 2624 LEXINGTON AVE, SPRINGFIELD HEALTH CARE 45505 #495-23-1997 L2000 IM *020 †20

PATRICK, Michael Dennis. 2624 LEXINGTON AVE, PEDIATRIC ASSOCIATES OF 45505 #038-40-1994 L1995 PD *020 †55

PAVLATOS, Nicholas B. ■ 45504 #038-41-1943 L1943 GP IM *071

PEDRAZA, Miguel Angel. ■ 45503 #264-01-1956 L1964 CLP *071 †50

PHELPS, Susan J. PO BOX 1822 45505 #025-07-1987 L1995 DR *020 †80

POMPUTIUS, James Michael. 1221 E COUNTY LINE RD 45502 #041-12-1967 L1970 P *020 †75

POTDAR, Ganesh Ghanashyam. ■ 45503 #496-38-1960 L1981 RO *020 †80

POTDAR, Malati Ganesh. 2100 E HIGH ST STE 110 45505 #495-35-1964 L1981 OBG *020 †20

POTTS, Richard Dale. 247 S BURNETT RD, STE 220 45505 #038-41-1962 L1962 FM ADM *020 †18

PRATTIPATI, Aruna Kumari. 2615 E HIGH ST 45505 #495-58-1996 L2000 IM *020 †20

PURAM, Jyothi. 2624 LEXINGTON AVE, STE 340 45505 #495-04-1982 L1993 IM *020 †20

RAHIMUDDIN, Mohammad. ■ 45502 #495-21-1957 L1967 IM *020 †20

RAK, Thomas Paul. 218 N PARKE DR STE A 45503 #038-43-1988 L1995 PS *020 †85,65

RALSTON, Michael Alan. 2624 LEXINGTON AVE 45505 #038-40-1985 L1985 PDC PD *020 †55

RAMAKRISHNAIAH, Vidya Bij. 651 S LIMESTONE ST, THE ROCKING HORSE CENTER 45505 #496-34-2002 L2006 PG *100

RANGANATHAN, V. 3152 EL CAMINO DR 45503 #495-57-1980 L1998 N *020 †75

RANGINWALA, Moin Ahmed. 2029 E HIGH ST, STE 101 45505 #704-02-1980 L1986 CCM PUD *020 †20

RANGINWALA, Mujeeb. 2029 E HIGH ST, STE 102 45505 #704-02-1989 L1993 PYG *020 †20

RAO, Mythri R. 1343 N FOUNTAIN BLVD, MERCY MEDICAL CENTER 45504 #495-09-1997 L2003 IM *020 †20

RAUF, Abdur. 30 W MCCREIGHT AVE STE 205 45504 #704-01-1979 L1988 IM GE *020 †20

ROBERTO, Janet Hammond. 3250 MIDDLE URBANA RD 45502 #038-45-1985 L1986 FM *020 †18

ROBERTO, Mark S. 3250 MIDDLE URBANA RD 45502 #038-41-1980 L1981 FM *020 †18

RODNEY, Denise Patrice. 2057 S LIMESTONE ST 45505 #010-03-1996 L1997 FM *020 †18

ROGERS, Olsen Jordan, Jr. 2624 LEXINGTON AVE STE 300, PEDIATRIC ASSOCIATES OF 45505 #033-06-1989 L1992 PD *020 †55

ROHRER, James Frank. 2242 OLYMPIC ST 45503 #030-06-1972 L1989 D OS *020 †15

ROSS, Joseph Eugene. 2624 LEXINGTON AVE 45505 #038-41-1963 L1963 PDC PD *020 †55

RYU, David Tai Hyung. 30 W MCCREIGHT AVE, STE 209 45504 #583-13-1975 L1984 OTO FPS *020 †45

SAGAR, Satyavolu Subhadra. 1911 E HIGH ST 45505 #495-11-1975 L1982 CD *050 †20

SAINI, Narinder Kumar. 14 E MAIN ST, STE 205 45502 #495-29-1972 L1981 IM *020

SANDERS, Howard Earl. ■ 45503 #023-07-1944 L1947 IM *071

SANTOS, Ferdinand B. 4350 BALLENTINE PIKE 45503 #748-11-1980 L1997 AN *020

SARIHAN, Behzat. 1200 E HOME RD, NORTHSIDE URGENT CARE CTR 45503 #902-01-1953 L1967 EM OM *071

SCOTT, Robert James. 2624 LEXINGTON AVE, SPRINGFIELD HEALTH CARE 45505 #035-45-1970 L1975 IM IMG *020 †20

SHAH, Chirag Ashvin. 211 N PARKE DR 45503 #654-01-1997 L1999 IM *020 †20

SHAHZAD, Rustum Ali. 512 S BURNETT RD, SPRINGFIELD CBOC 45505 #704-02-1990 L2001 IMG *020 †20

SHELL, Jerry Keith. 2254 OLYMPIC ST 45503 #017-20-1972 L1980 OPH *020 †35

SHIDLER, Merrill Joe. 2615 E HIGH ST, THE COMMUNITY HOSPITAL 45505 #005-12-1970 L1984 FM AN *030 †18

SICKEL, George Wm. 1343 N FOUNTAIN BLVD #1380 45504 #041-13-1954 L1963 PTH *020 †50

SIDDIQI, Sajjad-Ul-Haq. 2131 N LIMESTONE ST 45503 #704-02-1963 L1972 IM *071 †20

SINGH, Daljeet. 148 W NORTH ST 45504 #495-36-1974 L1980 ON HEM *020 †20

SIRAJ, Urmee. 1010 S LIMESTONE ST 45505 #160-02-1996 L2000 GE *012 †20

SIRAJ, Yaser. 1416 W 1ST ST 45504 #704-25-1995 L2002 CD *100 †20

SMITH, David Dawson. ■ 45503 #051-04-1954 L1955 GYN *071 †30

SMITH, Joseph Matthew. 1200 E HOME RD STE B 45503 #038-41-1995 L1997 FM *072 †18

SMITH, Mark Alan. 1345 N FOUNTAIN BLVD 45504 #038-43-1980 L1982 P *020 †20

SMITH, Ronald Morton, Jr. 435 S BURNETT RD 45505 #017-20-1998 L2003 OTO *020 †45

SMITH, Wm Orlando, Jr. 2100 EMMANUEL WAY, STE C 45502 #039-01-1957 L1974 NS *020 †25

SOUTHWORTH, Patricia Ann. 821 N LIMESTONE ST, DR SOUTHWORTH'S CLINIC 45503 #041-07-1976 L1991 IM OM *020

SPIELDOCH, Risa Lynn. 247 S BURNETT RD, STE 210 45505 #019-02-1993 L1996 FM *020 †18

SPIER, Ronald B. 247 S BURNETT RD 45505 #010-01-1975 L1980 GS *020 †85

SPOHN, William Anthony. 651 S LIMESTONE ST 45505 #041-02-1975 L1982 PD *020 †55

STATON, Harvey Thos. 435 S BURNETT RD 45505 #038-40-1966 L1966 OTO A *071 †45

SUBLETT, Toni Denise. 1343 N FOUNTAIN BLVD 45504 #036-07-1994 L1998 IM *020

SULLIVAN, Dennis Patrick. 30 W MCCREIGHT AVE, STE-103 45504 #038-40-1974 L1974 N *020 †75

SUTTER, John Robt. 3250 MIDDLE URBANA RD 45502 #038-40-1991 L1994 FM *020 †18

SWARUP, Anu B. 1117 E HOME RD 45503 #495-37-1996 L2000 IM *020 †20

TAPOGNA, Richard H. ■ 45503 #016-43-1950 L1957 OS ORS *071 †40

THANAMAYOORAN, Siva. 1010 S LIMESTONE ST, OICC PRIMARY CARE 45505 #690-04-1991 L1998 IM *020 †20

THOMPSON, Ian Martin. 30 W MCCREIGHT AVE STE 106, MEDICINE INSTITUTE LLC 45504 #025-07-1999 L2004 ORS *020 †40

TO, Nha Thuc. 1345 N FOUNTAIN BLVD 45504 #038-45-1987 L1988 IM *020 †20

TOWNSEND, Charles James. 1030 N FOUNTAIN AVE 45504 #051-04-1953 L1954 IM *071

UMERANI, Ajaz. 2121 E HIGH ST 45505 #704-02-1989 L1996 IM *071

VARGHESE, George. 247 S BURNETT RD 45505 #495-31-1974 L1983 NEP IM *020

VELLANKI, Umamaheswara R. 1835 MIRACLE MILE 45503 #495-58-1979 L1992 CHP *020 †75

VEMANA, Siva Ramaiah. 30 W MCCREIGHT AVE STE 101 45504 #495-50-1971 L1976 IM *020

VICTOR, Sandra J. 148 W NORTH ST, CLARK RADIATION ONCOLOGY 45504 #038-44-1994 L1999 RO R *020 †80

WAGNER, Peter William. 30 W MCCREIGHT AVE STE 208 45504 #038-41-1973 L1978 GS *020 †20

WATSON, Stephen David. 2816 W 1ST ST 45504 #038-45-1983 L1992 EM *020 †05

WEBER, Erwin John. 2615 E HIGH ST 45505 #041-09-1973 L1978 EM *020 †16

WILLIAMS, Marvin H, Jr. 2615 E HIGH ST 45505 #038-45-1984 L1984 EM FM *020 †18

WILLIAMS, Thomas Jackie. 2555 CREEKWOOD CT 45504 #038-40-1962 L1962 EM OM *020

WILLIAMSON, William B. 2440 E HIGH ST 45505 #038-41-1952 L1952 FM PD *071

WILSON, Libby Jo. 280 RED COACH DR 45503 #038-45-2001 L2001 FM *020 †18

WIN, Arthur Hla. 411 W HARDING RD 45504 #209-01-1980 L1993 IM *020 †20

WITTSTEIN, Peter Brian. 2254 OLYMPIC ST 45503 #008-02-1978 L1995 OPH *020 †35

YAKHMI, Damanjit Kaur. 1505 N LIMESTONE ST 45503 #495-29-1960 L1972 P *020 †75

YAKHMI, Devinder. 1505 N LIMESTONE ST 45503 #495-20-1959 L1972 P *020 †75

YOUSUF, Abdul Kader. ■ 45503 #495-65-1962 L1973 EM *020

ZAINEY, David Anthony. 2624 LEXINGTON AVE, PEDIATRIC ASSOCIATES OF 45505 #038-45-1983 L1987 PD *020 †55

STEUBENVILLE – JEFFERSON

AGGARWAL, Kamlesh Kumar. 4000 JOHNSON RD, KRISHAN K AGGARWAL MD INC 43952 #495-45-1969 L1980 IM HEM *075 †20

AGRESTA, Ronald Ceasar. 2315 SUNSET BLVD STE B 43952 #038-40-1965 L1965 OPH GP *020 †35

AL KAED, Amjad Muti. 1 ROSS PARK BLVD # 106 43952 #875-01-1987 L1996 PD *020 †55

ALKHADDO, Jamil Bawerjan. 401 MARKET ST STE 1000, RIVERSIDE MEDICAL OF OHIO 43952 #875-02-2002 L2005 IM *100 †20

AMIN, Kumar Bipin. 1 ROSS PARK BLVD, STE G-03 43952 #048-12-1990 L1996 ORS OSM *020 †40

AYALA, Fernando Lusterio. 1524 SUNSET BLVD 43952 #748-01-1962 L1971 U *020 †95

BRIGHT, Nancy Hafer. 380 SUMMIT AVE 43952 #041-07-1954 L1962 P *071 †55

CABOTAJE, Liberato G. 380 SUMMIT AVE 43952 #748-02-1968 L1973 PTH HMP *020 †50 ‡

CHATTHA, Amrik Singh. 3150 JOHNSON RD STE C 43952 #495-29-1960 L1974 N CHN *020 †75

CHINAKARN, Lattee W. 1524 SUNSET BLVD 43952 #891-01-1971 L1983 PD *020 †55

CHINAKARN, Narong. 1 ROSS PARK BLVD STE 201 43952 #891-02-1970 L1975 OBG *020 †30

CHING, Santiago Ong. 1 ROSS PARK BLVD, STE 203 43952 #748-01-1964 L1971 GE IM *020 †20

CHOPRA, Ravinder. 4000 JOHNSON RD, 20 W EMERGENCY ROOM 43952 #495-45-1974 L1985 EM *020 †16

CLARK, Jeffrey Randall. 2720 SUNSET BLVD, STEUBEN RAD ASSOCS, INC 43952 #038-45-1993 L1998 DR *020 †80

COLFLESH, Matthew Aaron. 380 SUMMIT AVE 43952 #055-02-2000 L2003 IM *020 †20 ‡

COLUMBUS, John Thos. 4000 JOHNSON RD, TRINITY MEDICAL CENTER - W 43952 #023-12-1987 L1994 GP EM *020

CULP, Jane Ann. 1 ROSS PARK BLVD, OHIO VALLEY HOSPITAL 43952 #038-43-1986 L1990 IM PD *020

CUTONE, Tina M. 4100 JOHNSON RD, STE 100 43952 #055-01-1995 L1999 OBG *020 †30

DEOL, Prabhjot Singh. 3150 JOHNSON RD, STE C 43952 #496-14-1979 L1999 P *020 †75

DI BIASE, Paul A, Jr. 2315 SUNSET BLVD 43952 #041-12-1993 L1998 OTO *020 †45

DOSHI, Himanshu M. 380 SUMMIT AVE 43952 #496-38-1983 L1993 PTH *020 †50

EDWARDS, Robert Harry. 114 BRADY CIR E 43952 #038-45-1988 L1989 OBG *020 ‡

ELIZAGA, Teodora B. 1524 SUNSET BLVD 43952 #748-08-1964 L1974 GYN *020

FIGEL, John N. 1805 SINCLAIR AVE 43953 #038-44-1986 L1988 FM *020 †18

GARCIA, Diosdado A. 1 ROSS PARK BLVD 43952 #748-02-1962 L1977 NEP CCM *020 †20

GILMAN, Rachel S. 4100 JOHNSON RD, STE 100 43952 #041-13-1996 L2003 OBG *020 †18,30

GIOIA, Vincent Mark. 2230 SUNSET BLVD STE 1, VALLEY EYE CARE, INC. 43952 #055-01-1986 L1990 OPH *020 †35

HAVERLAND, Harry W. ■ 43953 #038-40-1953 L1953 PTH *071 †50

HOLMAN, John Edward. 1 ROSS PARK BLVD, ROSS PARK PROFESSIONAL CTR 43952 #055-01-1965 L1969 OBG *071 †30

HOSSEINI, Leila Donna. 1 ROSS PARK BLVD, STE G1 43952 #041-12-1996 L2003 FM *020 †18

JESICK, Gretchen Ann. 4000 JOHNSON RD 43952 #041-12-1997 L2001 AN *020 †05

JOSE, Gumercindo R. ■ 43952 #748-08-1966 L1973 GS GP *020

KANE, Patrick Leonard. 3204 JOHNSON RD 43952 #041-12-1986 L1994 IM *020 †20

KATSAROS, Constantine V. 705 N 4TH ST 43952 #418-01-1964 L1971 IM CD *020 †20

KNOB, Randolph Edward. 1 ROSS PARK BLVD, STE G-3 43952 #035-08-1973 L2007 GS *020 †85

KOH, Jae Myung. ST JOHN HOSP, DEPT RAD 43952 #583-04-1964 L1975 DR *020 †80

KRAMER, Kenneth. 380 SUMMIT AVE 43952 #041-12-1978 L1979 PTH BBK *020 †50

KURUC, Stephen Gabriel. 114 BRADY CIR E 43952 #038-40-1973 L1973 IM *020

LUCCI, John Alan. 380 SUMMIT AVE STE 1, TRINITY MEDICAL CENTER EAS 43952 #055-01-1992 L1996 AN *020 †05

MACEDONIA, Dominic A, Jr. 523 N 4TH ST 43952 #038-40-1968 L1968 **TS VS** *020 †85,90
MAGGE, Sathish L. 401 MARKET ST, STE 200 43952 #495-09-1982 L1996 **CD** *020 †20
MALIK, Sudhir. 4100 JOHNSON RD STE 103 43952 #495-45-1984 L1989 **N SME** *020 †55,75
MARSH, James Milton. 43952 #028-34-1956 L1960 **HEM IM** *071
MASTROS, Nicholas Paul. 2315 SUNSET BLVD 43952 #038-40-1990 L1995 **OTO** *020 †45
MASTROS, Paul Nicholas. 705 N 4TH ST, PAUL N MASTROS MD INC 43952 #010-02-1960 L1960 **CD** *071 †20
MATADAR, Akbar G. 4032 ARGONNE AVE 43952 #495-01-1969 L1976 **OTO HNS** *020 †45
MC BRIDE, Gary John. 380 SUMMIT AVE, TRINITY HEALTH SYSTEM 43952 #649-14-1972 L1977 **EM** *020
MCCOY, Robert Matthew. 380 SUMMIT AVE, TRINITY MEDICAL CENTER 43952 #038-45-1990 L1995 **PTH** *020 †50
MELHEM, Ali Mohammad. 380 SUMMIT AVE, TOWER 2 43952 #605-01-1996 L2000 **P** *020 †75
METCALF, John Wm, Jr. 110 BRAYBARTON BLVD 43952 #023-01-1953 L1954 **GYN** *020 †30
METZGER, Clyde Chas. 4100 JOHNSON RD, STE 201 43952 #041-01-1960 L1969 **CD IM** *020 †20
MIKITA, William Brezuch. 380 SUMMIT AVE 43952 #020-02-1944 L1952 **ORS** *072 †40
MILIC, Milorad M. 2230 SUNSET BLVD, STE 1 43952 #957-02-1957 L1966 **OPH** *020 †35 ‡
MORISETTY, Satyasagar. 401 MARKET ST, STE 200 43952 #495-65-1983 L1991 **PUD IM** *020 †20
MUPAS, Rogelio S. 1 ROSS PARK BLVD 43952 #748-08-1965 L1972 **OBG** *020 †30
MURTY, Indubala M. 401 MARKET ST, STE 1000 43952 #495-62-1976 L1988 **IM** *020
MURTY, Ramana M. 401 MARKET ST, STE 200 43952 #495-11-1973 L1980 **CD IM** *020 †20
NASSAR, Soha C A. 1 ROSS PARK BLVD, 380 SUMMIT AVENUE SUITE G1 43952 #875-01-1987 L1994 **PD** *020 †20
NICOL, Philip Dunbar. 141 BRADY CIR W 43952 #065-01-1981 L1998 **IM CD** *020 †20
PATEL, Narendra Kumar. 4000 JOHNSON RD, DEPT OF ANESTHESIOLOGY 43952 #919-05-1974 L1981 **AN** *020
PRASAD, Siripurapu R. 200 LURAY DR 43953 #495-19-1972 L1978 **IM GP** *020 †20
PRIORE, Robert Michael. ■ 43952 #024-05-1957 L1980 **GYN** *071 †30
RAHMAN, Mohammad Pervaiz. 3204 JOHNSON RD, UPCI 43952 #704-02-1985 L2000 **ON** *020 †20
RAYABHARI, Ananth. 1 ROSS PARK BLVD, STE 106 43952 #495-65-2001 L2003 **PD** *020 †55
REA, Ralph Mario. ■ 43952 #561-21-1950 L1956 **GP** *071
REDDY, Jayapal L. 1 ROSS PARK BLVD, # 105 43952 #495-70-1980 L1999 **GS** *020
REDDY, Vardhan Jonnala. 4000 JOHNSON RD 43952 #495-50-1985 L2001 **TS VIR** *020 †90,85
RIVERA, Fernando T, Jr. 380 SUMMIT AVE 43952 #748-01-1953 L1964 **PD** *071
RODRIGUEZ, Robt Maldonado. 820 N 4TH ST, STE 2 43952 #649-02-1985 L1989 **IM** *020
ROIG, George M. 380 SUMMIT AVE STE 10, TRINITY MEDICAL CENTER EAS 43952 #847-01-1966 L1974 **AN** *071
ROIG, Santiago Leis. 4000 JOHNSON RD, C/O TRINITY MED CTR 43952 #308-03-1984 L1988 **FM EM** *020 †18
ROSARIO, Patrick G. 4000 JOHNSON RD, STE 100 43952 #495-73-1984 L1998 **TS** *020 †85,90
ROSENBLUM, Lee Allen. 114 BRADY CIR E 43952 #038-41-1955 L1955 IM *071 †20
SANCHEZ, David S. 4220 SUNSET BLVD 43952 #748-01-1955 L1972 **IM PD** *071
SANCHEZ, Edgar H. 401 MARKET ST STE 601 43952 #319-01-1976 L1993 **PUD** *020 †20
SCHMULEVICH, Rafael L. 4100 JOHNSON RD, STE 207 43952 #132-06-1983 L1991 **CD** *020 †20
SCURTI, Anthony Vincent. 401 MARKET ST, STE 1100 43952 #649-03-1966 L1968 **GP FM** *020
SELLITTI, Tony Patsy, Jr. 2315 SUNSET BLVD, STE B 43952 #605-01-1990 L1994 **OPH** *020 †35
SHAFFER, Frances Jane. 380 SUMMIT AVE 43952 #005-02-1943 L1949 **IM** *020
SHAH, Atul P. 380 SUMMIT AVE 43952 #495-22-1981 L1994 **IM** *020 †20
SHAH, Krishnajivan C. 4000 JOHNSON RD, TRINITY MEDICAL CTR WEST 43952 #495-76-1978 L1984 **DR CD** *020 †80
SHOSHI, Shaban A. 4100 JOHNSON RD STE 200, THE MEDICAL PAVILION AT TR 43952 #957-09-1985 L1997 **IM** *020 †20
SINGH, Satbir. 1524 SUNSET BLVD, STE A 43952 #055-02-1994 L2001 **GS** *020 †95
SMITH, Roy Eugene. 1 ROSS PARK BLVD 43952 #038-40-1973 L1973 **IM HEM** *020 †20
SOHN, Chong-Sook Lee. 380 SUMMIT AVE 43952 #583-08-1966 L1972 **PTH DMP** *030 †50
SOLOMON, Robert Chas. 4000 JOHNSON RD, TRINITY HEALTH SYSTEM 43952 #041-12-1982 L1990 **EM** *020 †16
SRIVASTAVA, Prem Shankar. 4000 JOHNSON RD, DEPARTMENT OF RADIOLOGY 43952 #038-43-1995 L2001 **DR** *020
SUNSERI, Francis Albert. 340 S HOLLYWOOD BLVD 43952 #038-40-1963 L1963 **FM ADM** *020 †18
SUWAID, Wijdan Dib. 1 ROSS PARK BLVD, TRINITY HEALTH SYSTEM 43952 #875-01-1994 L2006 **FM** *020 †18
TEREZIS, Nick Louis. 141 BRADY CIR W 43952 #041-12-1956 L1963 **GS TS** *071 †85
TERMANINI, Basel. 1805 SINCLAIR AVE 43953 #875-02-1983 L1997 **GE** *020 †20
THAKUR, Navin Shankar. 401 MARKET ST 43952 #495-36-1978 L1999 **TS** *020 †85,90
TIBALDI, Nicholas Anthony. 4000 JOHNSON RD, TRINITY W MEDICAL CENTER 43952 #038-06-1992 L1993 **GE IM** *020 †20
VALUSKA, James William. 4000 JOHNSON RD 43952 #035-01-1962 L1967 **ORS** *071 †40
VALUSKA, James William, Jr. 2990 JOHNSON RD 43952 #038-40-1995 L2000 **GS** *020 †85
VARGAS, Alfred Perez. ■ 43952 #038-40-2005 **IM** *012
VARGAS, Belen Perez. TRINTY MEDICAL CTR 43952 #748-01-1965 L1975 **R** *020 †80
VAUGHAN, W Hunter. 4000 JOHNSON RD, TRINITY MED CTR W 43952 #036-01-1966 L1972 **DR** *020 †80
VEATCH, Ronald Irving. 4000 JOHNSON RD, TRINITY HEALTH SYSTEM 43952 #028-03-1969 L1973 **R NM** *020 †80,28
VITVITSKY, Eugene V. 3150 JOHNSON RD, STE 108 43952 #913-06-1984 L2003 **TS** *020 †85,90
WALTHER, Thomas Robt. 4000 JOHNSON RD 43952 #041-13-1988 L1989 **AN** *020 †16,05
YOO, Heung Joon. ■ 43953 #583-03-1965 L1974 **DR** *020 †80

STOUT – SCIOTO

WITTUM, Roger Lee. 127 RIVERVIEW CT 45684 #005-12-1973 L1986 **CD** *020 †20

STOUTSVILLE – FAIRFIELD

PERKINS, Paul Copeland. ■ 43154 #038-45-1980 L1982 **EM GS** *020

STOW – SUMMIT

ARREDONDO, Mark Douglas. ■ 44224 #038-44-2007 L2007 **IM** *012
BARDEN, Christopher John. ■ 44224 #038-45-2007 L2007 **EM** *012
BASTOLLA, Joseph John. 3869 DARROW RD, STE 209 44224 #561-01-1963 L1967 **FM** *071
BETITA, Julian Paras, Jr. ■ 44224 #748-01-1962 L1974 **GS EM** *020
BILLINGS, Nathaniel Proch. ■ 44224 #038-44-2007 L2007 **EM** *012
CHASE, Joseph Matthew. 4465 DARROW RD 44224 #038-44-2003 L2003 **FM** *020 †18
CORNICI, Paul George. ■ 44224 #038-43-2005 L2005 **EM** *012
DEVENY, Sandra Lopina. 3913 DARROW RD, STE 100 44224 #038-43-1986 L1987 **EM** *020 †16
DILISIO, Matthew Francis. ■ 44224 #028-34-2008 *012
DOUGHERTY, Caroline D H. 3925 DARROW RD, STE 105 44224 #038-06-1989 L1990 **PD ADL** *020 †55
ERICKSON, Dean Wm. 3913 DARROW RD, STE 100 44224 #026-04-1978 L1991 **OM EM** *020 †20,70
FENDER, Trace Isaiah. ■ 44224 #038-44-2008 *012
FLANAGAN, Kirby James. 3913 DARROW RD, STE 100 44224 #030-06-1969 L1994 **OM EM** *020 †18,70
GIBBONS, Paul. 4465 DARROW RD 44224 #038-43-1989 L1991 **IM PD** *020 †55,20
HAWES, Ronald Gene. 1100 GRAHAM ROAD CIR, SUMMIT COUNTY HEALTH DEPT 44224 #038-43-1979 L1980 **MDM OM** *030 †18
HAYNES, Aaron Daniel. ■ 44224 #046-01-2007 L2007 **IM** *012
HOLMER, Michelle Annette. 2971 GRAHAM RD 44224 #038-06-1996 L1996 **FM** *020 †18
HOWELL, Bonnie Jean. 4466 DARROW RD STE 12 44224 #038-44-1986 L1987 **OBG GS** *020 †30
JANOLO, Oliver Labrador. 3913 DARROW RD, STE 100 44224 #748-21-2002 L2004 **FM** *020 †18
JOHNS, John Chas. 5071 TRICIA RAE LN 44224 #016-43-1961 L1964 **DIA IM** *071
JOSHI, Shalini. ■ 44224 #495-30-1997 L2002 **IM** *012
KOHLER, Lisa Jo. ■ 44224 #038-43-1993 L1998 **FOP** *020 †50
LEB, Robert Bruce. 3913 DARROW RD 44224 #038-40-1987 L1990 **ORS** *020 †40
MAGGIO, Michael John. 4466 DARROW RD 44224 #038-43-1983 L1984 **IM** *020 †20
MAGOLINE, Michael Robert. 4465 DARROW RD 44224 #038-06-1993 L1996 **OSM** *020 †40
MAINZER, Ernest B. ■ 44224 #869-01-1936 L1939 **IM** *071
MANN, Rubeal Singh. ■ 44224 #038-45-2007 L2007 **IM** *012
MARCHETTI, Pennie R. 3917 DARROW RD 44224 #038-45-1988 L1992 **FM** *020 †18
MARSHALL, Michele Coates. 3925 DARROW RD, STE 105 44224 #038-45-1990 L1993 **PD** *020 †55
MITCHELL, Joyce M. 3913 DARROW RD, STE 100 44224 #010-02-1976 L1992 **EM IM** *020 †20,16
MOHRMAN, Lisa Rae. ■ 44224 #028-03-2007 L2007 **GS** *012
NORR, Sigmund Carl. 3913 DARROW RD, STE 100 44224 #011-02-1980 L1981 **PD FM** *020 †55
OSHILAJA, Olaronke. ■ 44224 #038-44-2007 L2007 **PTH** *012
PARENTE, John Joseph. 3913 DARROW RD, STE 100 44224 #038-75-2004, ▲ L2004 **EM** *020
PASSALAQUA, Anthony M. 4161 BRIDGEWATER PKWY 44224 #035-19-1970 L1981 **NM R** *020 †80,28
PETNO, Vincent. ■ 44224 #045-01-1968 L1975 **CD IM** *071 †20
PLOWGIAN, Craig Alan. ■ 44224 #038-44-2007 L2007 **PD** *012
POMIDOR, William Jos. ■ 44224 #038-44-1986 **OS** *072
QUERY, Margaret Anne. 4465 DARROW RD 44224 #036-08-1997 L2002 **PD** *020 †55
RAO, Vinod Balakrishna. ■ 44224 #038-44-2008 *012
RUCKER, Christopher Louis. ■ 44224 #038-43-2004 L2004 **MPD** *012
SALEEM, Tariq. 4466 DARROW RD 44224 #704-01-1971 L1978 **IM CD** *020 †20
SOLAN, George Miley. ■ 44224 #051-04-1955 L1970 **P** *020
SORBORO, John Michael. 3251 W CHASE CIR 44224 #038-43-1990 L1991 **P** *020 †75
SPITTLER, Robert Paul. 4465 DARROW RD 44224 #038-40-1982 L1983 **FM** *020 †18
STOVSKY, Erica. ■ 44224 #038-44-2007 L2007 **IM** *012
SUAREZ, Jennifer Marie. ■ 44224 #038-43-2004 L2004 **OBG** *012
TAY, Edward Chorying. ■ 44224 #038-41-2005 L2005 **N** *012
TOSINO, Jon Eric. 4472 DARROW RD 44224 #038-43-1987 L1989 **FM** *020 †18
TREBBE-HAAS, Susan E. ■ 44224 #016-11-1980 L1997 **P** *020
UMBACH, Rebecca Ruth. ■ 44224 #023-01-1979 L1980 **PD** *071 †55
YURKEWYCZ-TARAS, C. 3869 DARROW RD STE 209 44224 #038-45-1988 L1989 **FM** *020 †18

STRASBURG – TUSCARAWAS

DONAHUE, Thomas Michael. ■ 44680 #038-40-2007 L2007 **GS** *012

STREETSBORO – PORTAGE

AHMED, Azfar. ■ 44241 #654-01-2005 L2005 **FP** *012
BAILEY, James Michael. 9424 STATE ROUTE 14 44241 #038-44-1994 L1995 **FM** *020 †18
BARATIAN, Marcus Aram. 9480 ROSEMONT DR, STE 200 44241 #025-07-1996 L1999 **PD** *020 †55
BROWN, Todd Alexander. 9150 MARKET SQUARE DR, STE 201 44241 #038-41-1992 L1994 **PAN** *020 †18,05
CUSTODIO, Ramon J. 9088 SUPERIOR AVE, STE 105 44241 #748-01-1949 L1963 **FM** *071
FOSS, John Chas. 9480 ROSEMONT DR, STE 100 44241 #025-01-1986 L1988 **FM** *020 †18
GILCREST, Harry Roger. ■ 44241 #038-02-1962 L1975 **OPH** *071 †35
HABO, Khalid A.. ■ 44241 #915-02-1990 L2005 **PD** *020 †55
HARSHBARGER-KELLY, Martha. 9150 MARKET SQUARE DR, STE 201 44241 #038-06-1996 L1999 **MPD** *020 †55,20
KARA, Mahmud Mustafa. 9305 MARKET SQUARE DR, # B 44241 #613-02-1991 L2001 **IM** *020
LANG, Sarah E Slater. 9150 MARKET SQUARE DR, STE 203 44241 #038-41-2000 L2000 **FM** *020 †18
LEONARD, John David, Jr. 9480 ROSEMONT DR STE 200, PORTAGE PEDIATRICS 44241 #038-44-1993 L1997 **PD** *020 †55
REED, Amy Jo. 9480 ROSEMONT DR, STE 100 44241 #038-44-1995 L1997 **FM** *020 †18
RUPP, Kenneth Francis. 9279 STATE ROUTE 14 44241 #030-06-1957 L1957 **FM PHP** *071
SMITH, Scott Brian. 9150 MARKET SQUARE DR, STE 201 44241 #038-40-1984 L1984 **IM** *020 †20
STULL, Sheridan L. ■ 44241 #038-44-2008 *012

■ = Address Information Privacy Protected

VO, Luong Van. 9424 STATE ROUTE 14, STREETSBORO MED CENTER ONE 44241 #942-01-1971 L1992 **GP FM** *020

STRONGSVILLE – CUYAHOGA

ALAPATI, Sampath K. 12426 STEEPLECHASE LN, (THE CROSSING) 44149 #496-30-1991 L1999 **DR** *020

ALESSIO, Reno Louis, II. 11351 PEARL RD, STE 201 44136 #038-43-2000 L2000 **OPH** *020 †35

ALI, Mir Yousuf. 16761 SOUTHPARK CTR 44136 #495-33-1994 L1997 **HO** *020 †20

ALLSHOUSE, Lisa Catherine. 16000 PEARL RD, STE 309 44136 #038-43-1998 L2002 **MPD** *020 †18

ANDREANO, Judith Michelle. 10800 PEARL RD STE B5 44136 #038-40-1985 L1986 **D IM** *020 †15

AREVALO, Mila. ■ 44149 #748-08-1967 L1976 **P** *071

ASHER, Damyanti Girish. ■ 44136 #495-22-1970 L1980 **PTH HS** *020

BAINS, Sonia Noreen. ■ 44136 #704-25-1999 L2006 **AI** *012

BAUER, Sally E Gasser. 12130 THE BLF 44136 #038-06-1972 L1976 **EM FM** *071 †16

BELTRAN, Maria Rita. 20417 DONEGAL LN 44149 #038-45-1987 L2006 **DR** *020 †80,28

BICANOVSKY, Lesley K. ■ 44149 #041-78-1999, ▲ L2004 **OBG** *020 ‡

BOCANEGRA, Jose Arturo, Jr. 19640 W 130TH ST 44136 #038-40-2001 L2001 **FM** *020 †18

BRAUSTON, Bruce Barry. ■ 44136 #038-06-2004 L2004 **OPH** *071 †35

BROWN, Vance Meredith. 16761 SOUTHPARK CTR 44136 #008-01-1985 L1999 **EM** *020 †20,18

CULLISON, Brian Matthew. 10309 STAMFORD CT 44136 #005-02-1999 L2000 **EM** *020 †16

DATTA, Gautam. 14206 BRIDLE TRL 44136 #495-43-2002 L2003 **P** *100

DAVIS, Nicholas Wm R. 16761 SOUTHPARK CTR 44136 #917-09-1986 L1992 **FM** *020 †18

DEBROSSE, Suzanne Denise. ■ 44136 #038-06-2004 L2004 **CHN** *012

DEL RIO PEREZ, Anaibelith. ■ 44149 #038-06-2006 L2006 **PTH** *012

DEMASTES, Cathy. 16761 SOUTHPARK CTR 44136 #038-44-1996 L1998 **FM** *020

DEVANS, Richard Alan. 16761 S PARK CTR, FAMILY MEDICINE/ST10 44136 #038-40-1980 L1981 **FM** *020 †18

DONG, Julie Ann. 16000 PEARL RD, STE 309 44136 #024-05-1991 L1995 **D** *020 †15

DREHER, Nicholas John. 17406 ROYALTON RD, KAISER PERMANENTE 44136 #038-41-1986 L1990 **MPD PD** *020 †20,55

FALCONI, Genevive Rita C. 16761 SOUTHPARK CTR, CLEVELAND CLINIC STRONGSVI 44136 #748-01-1991 L2000 **PHO** *020 †55

FLEMING, Dallas John. 17406 ROYALTON RD, KAISER PERMANTE MED CENTER 44136 #038-06-1993 L1995 **IM** *020 †20

GEORGE, Robert A. 12222 WINDCLIFF RD, STE 1 44136 #038-06-1951 L1951 **IM OM** *071 †20

GOLONKA, Gregory Gerard. 18181 PEARL RD 44136 #038-40-1993 L1996 **PD** *020 †55

GONZALES, Mila Galang. 18181 PEARL RD, STE A206 44136 #748-01-1970 L1975 **GP** *020

GRAHAM, Eugenia R Mc Peek. 16761 S PARK CTR, STRONGSVILLE FAM HLTH CENT 44136 #051-04-1996 L1997 **MPD** *020 †20,55

GUBANICH, Paul Joseph. 16761 S PARK CTR, AND SURGICAL CENTER 44136 #038-40-2001 L2001 **ISM IM** *020

HAGEN, Elizabeth Allis. 18181 PEARL RD 44136 #056-06-1997 L1999 **PD** *020 †55

HARHAY, Jeff Stanley. 16761 SOUTHPARK CTR 44136 #038-43-2001 L2001 **IM** *100

HINCH, Bryan Thomas. 16000 PEARL RD, STE 309 44136 #038-43-1998 L1999 **MPD** *020 †20,55

HINES, John David. 16761 SOUTHPARK CTR 44136 #036-05-1959 L1968 **HEM ON** *020 †20

JEWELL, John Kernan. 16761 S PARK CTR, CLEVELAND CLINIC FOUNDATIO 44136 #010-02-1998 L2000 **IM** *020 †20

JIMENEZ, Reynaldo Octavo. ■ 44149 #748-01-1954 L1973 **AN** *071

KAUFMAN, Elizabeth Suits. 16000 PEARL RD, STE 309 44136 #024-01-1985 L1991 **ICE CD** *020 †20

KEARNS, Barbara P. 16761 S PARK CTR 44136 #539-03-1993 L1997 **MPD** *020 †20,55

KHATRI, Lakshmi J. 16761 SOUTHPARK CTR 44136 #038-44-2001 L2001 **IM** *100

KNECHTGES, David Scott. 16761 SOUTHPARK CTR, / FT40 44136 #038-40-1987 L1990 **IM** *020 †20

KRAUS, Kimberly Ann. 18181 PEARL RD STE B206 44136 #038-43-1995 L1996 **OBG** *020 †30

KRCIK, Jennifer Lynn. 16761 S PARK CTR 44136 #016-01-1996 L1999 **PD** *020

KURTZ, Lisa H. 13550 FALLING WATER RD, STE 101 44136 #422-01-1996 L2004 **N** *020

LALAK, Irene Christine. 16761 S PARK CTR, CLEVELAND CLINIC FOUNDATIO 44136 #038-06-1988 L1990 **D** *020 †20,15

LEVINE, Adam A. 16000 PEARL RD, STE 309 44136 #035-48-1995 L1998 **MPD** *020 †20,55

LIM, Chong. ■ 44149 #583-04-1965 L1973 **IM CCM** *020 †20

LOVINA, Zenaida Ramos. 21529 MONTCLARE BLVD, STRONGSVILLE 44149 #748-08-1972 L1981 **AN** *020

LUCAS, Walter R. 17075 PEARL RD 44136 #748-01-1972 L1979 **PD** *020 †55

MANSOUR, David Joel. 16000 PEARL RD, STE 309 44136 #025-12-1994 L1995 **MPD PD** *020 †20,55

MARDINI, Houssam Eddin. 14191 PEPPERCREEK DR 44136 #875-01-1992 L2001 **IM** *020 †20

MISTRY, Darshan Bhupendra. 17406 ROYALTON RD 44136 #495-22-1984 L1992 **IM** *020 †20

MOLANO, F Castro. ■ 44136 #748-02-1944 L1960 **GP EM** *071

MORONA, Roberto V. ■ 44136 #748-10-1964 L1974 **FM GP** *020

MURPHY, Mary Anne. 16000 PEARL RD, STE 15 44136 #028-02-1982 L1985 **PD** *020 †55

NILSSON, Jack. 19612 W 130TH ST 44136 #038-44-1983 L1986 **FM** *071 †18

O'NEILL, Johanna Red. 18181 PEARL RD STE B206 44136 #038-41-1995 L1997 **OBG** *020 †30

PAUL, Bobby Walia. 10850 PEARL RD STE D2 44136 #495-03-1986 L1992 **IM** *020 †20

PERZY, Holly Beth. 16000 PEARL RD, STE 309 44136 #038-06-1989 L1990 **MPD** *020 †20,55

PRASADINI, Kudithipudi N. 17514 PIONEERS CREEK CIR, P O BOX 36305 44136 #495-50-1974 L1982 **AN** *020

RIACHI, Naji J. ■ 44149 #605-01-1986 L1992 **N** *020 †75

RICHTER, Kelly Ann. 16761 SOUTHPARK CTR, DEPT OF ORTHOPAEDICS 44136 #017-20-1995 L2003 **MPD** *020 †20,55

RIEDEL, Kathryn Ann. ■ 44149 #001-02-1987 L2004 **IM** *020 †20

SAGE, Joseph Louis. 16000 PEARL RD, STE 309 44136 #016-02-2001 L2001 **MPD** *020 †20,55

SEBALLOS, Raymond M. 10633 PEARL RD, STE 2 44136 #038-41-1990 L1991 **PS** *020 †85,65

SEDA-OLMO, Alex Jose. ■ 44136 #042-03-2003 L2007 **IM** *020 †20

SEE, Pedro Y. PO BOX 360589 44136 #748-10-1962 L1973 **N** *071

SINGH, Katherine Ann. ■ 44136 #038-41-2004 L2004 **OBG** *012

SMITH, Keisha Monique. 16761 SOUTHPARK CTR 44136 #005-18-1997 L2000 **OBG** *020

SMOLAK, Michael James. 16761 SOUTHPARK CTR, STRONGSVILL FAM HTLH & SUR 44136 #038-45-1999 L1999 **FM** *020 †18

STOKES, Womack Chas. 16761 SOUTHPARK CTR 44136 #005-02-1989 L1993 **OBG** *020 †30

STONE, David Daniel. 19640 W 130TH ST, IDEAL HEALTH OF STRONGSVIL 44136 #038-40-2001 L2001 **FM** *020 †18

SUBRAMANIAN, Ahila. ■ 44136 #038-41-2007 L2007 **MPD** *012

TAM, Dominic Wai Ho. 16000 PEARL RD 44136 #035-08-1975 L1979 **D** *020 †15

THAKKAR, Snehal Govind. ■ 44136 #038-45-2000 L2000 **HO** *020

THANKAPPAN, Baburaj. ■ 44136 #495-31-1994 L2007 **CN** *012

TIEN, Matthew Hua. 16761 S PARK CTR, AND SURGERY CENTER 44136 #038-06-1999 L2005 **PD** *020 †55

VINCENT, Joseph Palackal. 16761 S PARK CTR, CLEVELAND CLINIC 44136 #496-32-1995 L2003 **AN** *012

VISCOMI, Jeffrey. 10633 PEARL RD, DOCERE PHYSICIANS 44136 #038-45-1993 L1994 **FM** *020 †18

WATERS, Judith Kuczek. 18181 PEARL RD, STE A104 44136 #038-06-1991 L1994 **FM** *020 †18

WATSON, Anita. ■ 44149 #038-40-1986 L1989 **PD** *020

WEAKLEY, Frank Louis. ■ 44149 #041-01-1955 L1962 **CRS OS** *071 †10

WERTMAN, James Michael. 17406 ROYALTON RD 44136 #055-01-1975 L1995 **PD** *020 †55

WILLIAMS, Bridget Lovery. 16761 SOUTHPARK CTR, CCF STRONGSVILLE FAMILY HE 44136 #025-12-2001 L2001 **FM** *020 †18

WITTEN, Eileen Kirsten. ■ 44149 #056-06-2006 L2006 **OBG** *012

YAMAT, Catherine R. 16761 S PARK CTR, CLEVELAND CLINIC - ST 20 44136 #748-01-1989 L2000 **AN** *020 ‡

YAMAT, Roderick Angeles. 16761 SOUTHPARK CTR, CENTER ST-20 44136 #654-01-1991 L2001 **AN** *020 ‡

ZELIS, Brian David. 18181 PEARL RD, STE A104 44136 #038-44-1997 L2000 **FM** *020 †18

ZELIS, Cynthia. 18181 PEARL RD, STE A-104 44136 #038-44-1996 L1997 **FM** *020 †18

STRUTHERS – MAHONING

PETRUNAK, Amy Marie. ■ 44471 #038-44-1993 L1995 **PD** *020 †55

SUGAR GROVE – FAIRFIELD

BROWN, Harold Tway. ■ 43155 #038-40-1954 L1954 **P** *072

SUGARCREEK – TUSCARAWAS

GERBER, Robert Lee. ■ 44681 #038-40-1965 L1965 **GP** *071

GHARPURE, Varsha P. 605 DUTCH VALLEY DR NE 44681 #496-38-1989 L2002 **PD CCP** *020 †55

MILLER, Kevin Jason. ■ 44681 #038-44-2004 L2007 **EM** *020

PETERSON, John A. ■ 44681 #528-01-1945 L1959 **PUD FM** *020

SCHULTZ, William J. 126 S BROADWAY ST 44681 #048-14-1984 L1987 **FM** *075 †18

TEAGUE, Phillip Chas. 126 1/2 N BROADWAY ST 44681 #038-44-1985 L1989 **FM OBS** *020 †18

SUNBURY – DELAWARE

ARNOLD, L Eugene. ■ 43074 #038-40-1963 L1963 **CHP P** *071 †75

BUKER, Wallace Robt. ■ 43074 #005-14-1970 L1971 **OS** *020

CHRISMAN, Scot Tatlock. ■ 43074 #020-02-1971 L1973 **P** *020

FRAZIER, Alice A. 100 TIPPETT CT, STE 101 43074 #038-43-1973 L1974 **FM** *071 †18

HUM, Hillman H. 44 KINTNER PKWY, STE B 43074 #654-01-1991 L1997 **IM GP** *020 †20

PATEL, Trupti Kumbhojkar. 100 TIPPETT CT, STE 101 43074 #759-12-2002 L2002 **FM** *020 †18

WITTIG, James Gibson. 100 TIPPETT CT, STE 101 43074 #041-15-2000 L2000 **FM** *020 †18

SWANTON – FULTON

COCKLEY, Mark. 1 TURTLE CREEK CIR STE F 43558 #038-41-1997 L1998 **MPD** *020 †20,55

FAY, Lorraine Marie. 22 TURTLE CREEK CIR, OAK VALLEY PRIMARY CARE 43558 #038-43-1980 L1983 **PD** *020 †55

HAUPRICHT, Bradley Jon, Jr. ■ 43558 #038-43-2008 **PD** *012

MANN, Elizabeth Joy. ■ 43558 #038-45-1983 L1986 **PD** *074 †55

MITCHEM-WALTER, Christina. 1 TURTLE CREEK CIR, STE F 43558 #038-43-1999 L1999 **MPD** *020

MOUGINIS, Tamyra Lee. 7225 S FULTON LUCAS RD, MEDICAL COLLEGE OF OHIO 43558 #038-06-1988 L1989 **IM** *020 †20,05

SYCAMORE – WYANDOT

CISAR, Norman Scott. 103 N PENNINGTON ST, SYCAMORE MEDICAL ASSOCIATE 44882 #038-43-1980 L1983 **FM** *020 †18

SMITH, Donald Phillip. 103 N PENNINGTON ST 44882 #038-41-1958 L1958 **FM** *020 †18

SMITH, Franklin M. ■ 44882 #038-40-1932 L1932 **GP** *071

SYLVANIA – LUCAS

ABDELKHALEK, Mohamed E. ■ 43560 #042-01-2000 L2007 **IM** *020

ABRAHAM, Rebecca Puthusse. 5300 HARROUN RD, DEPT FM 43560 #495-37-1999 L2005 **FP** *012

AHMAD, Usman. ■ 43560 #038-43-2007 L2007 **IM** *012

AJARADDER, Vidya R.. 5300 HARROUN RD 43560 #496-37-1998 L2003 **FM** *020 †18

ANAND, Vanathi. 5300 HARROUN RD, FLOWER HOSP 43560 #496-32-2000 L2004 **FM** *100

ANDERSON, Michael Luther. 5465 MAIN ST, THE RIVER CENTRE CLINIC 43560 #026-04-1979 L2006 **P** *020 †50

ANTYPAS, Elias Joseph. ■ 43560 #038-43-2008 *012

AOUTHMANY, Ahmad. ■ 43560 #038-43-2008 *012

APPLEBAUM, Michael Singer. 7640 SYLVANIA AVE, WEST TOLEDO INTERNAL 43560 #038-43-1978 L1980 **IM** *020

AVAKIAN, Saro. 5300 HARROUN RD 43560 #517-11-1997 L2003 **FM** *020 †18

AXONOVITZ, Robert Geo. 7640 SYLVANIA AVE, WEST TOLEDO INTERNAL 43560 #038-43-1980 L1983 **IM** *020 †20
BABU, Seilesh Chodavarapu. 5200 HARROUN RD 43560 #038-44-1997 L2005 **NO** *020 †45
BAEHREN, David Frederick. 5200 HARROUN RD 43560 #038-43-1986 L1987 **EM** *020 †16
BANKOLE-JONES, Louis Samu. 5300 HARROUN RD, FLOWER HOSP 43560 #823-01-1996 L2004 **FM** *100
BANOUB, Rita Wissa. ■ 43560 #915-03-1988 L1999 **PAN** *020 †05
BECTON, William Walton. 5200 HARROUN RD 43560 #047-06-1991 L1992 **OS** *020 †05
BEER, Karl Jos. 6444 MONROE ST STE A 43560 #017-20-1982 L1986 **ORS** *020 †40
BELL, Paul Luther. ■ 43560 #038-41-1941 L1941 **PUD** *071
BERDY, David Michael. 7640 SYLVANIA AVE, STE K 43560 #038-43-1998 L1999 **FM** *020 †18
BLOOD, Jeffrey Patrick. ■ 43560 #048-78-2000, ▲ L2000 *020
BOGGUS, Van Buell, Jr. 6444 MONROE ST, STE A 43560 #007-02-1977 L1982 **ORS** *020 †40
BRADLEY, Brian Scott. 5200 HARROUN RD 43560 #025-01-1984 L1993 **NPM PD** *020 †55
BURKHART, Craig Garrett. 5600 MONROE ST, STE 106 43560 #038-43-1975 L1978 **D** *020 †15
CHAN, Edwin. 5300 HARROUN RD 43560 #654-01-2005 L2006 **FP** *012
CHINTA, Shashi. 5300 HARROUN RD 43560 #495-72-2001 L2006 **FP** *012
CHOPRA, Pavan. ■ 43560 #016-01-1999 L2002 **NEP** *100 †20
CHURCH, Sue Sneeringer. 5600 MONROE ST, STE 104 43560 #038-40-1961 L1961 **IM OS** *071
CULBERSON, John Lloyd. 5300 HARROUN RD STE 201 43560 #038-41-1962 L1962 **FM AM** *071 †18
DARDIR, Noha Sami Hussein. 5300 HARROUN RD 43560 #915-03-2000 L2005 **FP** *012
DELATORE, Luca Richard. 5200 HARROUN RD 43560 #038-43-2001 L2003 **EM** *020 †16
DELUGA, Karl Steven. 5200 HARROUN RD 43560 #017-20-1979 L1993 **NPM PD** *020 †55
DIETHELM, James Martin. 7640 SYLVANIA AVE STE E 43560 #028-34-1947 L1948 **FM** *071 †18
DODD, Joseph Thos. 5800 MONROE ST, BLDG G 43560 #048-12-1982 L1989 **GS** *020 †85
DURKIN, Margaret Rose. 5300 HARROUN RD # 201, HARROUN ROAD FAMILY PHYSI 43560 #033-06-1985 L1995 **ID IM** *020 †20
DURRANI, Khalida. 7640 SYLVANIA AVE, STE E 43560 #704-09-1991 L2000 **FM** *020 †18
FELIX, Charles George. 5151 MAIN ST 43560 #495-31-1977 L2001 **FM** *020 †18 ‡
FERNANDO, Shaneli A. ■ 43560 #016-11-2001 L2006 **RO** *100 †80
FINE, Mark David. 7640 SYLVANIA AVE, WEST TOLEDO INTERNAL 43560 #020-02-1973 L1975 **IM** *020 †20
FISHER, Phillip Herschel. 7640 SYLVANIA AVE, STE K 43560 #038-43-1977 L1978 **FM** *020 †18
FURLONG, Judith Anne. 5300 HARROUN RD 43560 #038-43-1984 L1985 **FM** *075 †18
GARLO, Alma Lydia. 5200 HARROUN RD STE 119 43560 #038-45-1983 L1987 **OBG** *020 †30
GEORGE, Saramma. 5200 HARROUN RD, CO FLOWER HOSP-MED EDU DEP 43560 #495-31-1997 L2002 **FPG** *100 †18
GIBBS, Terry M. 5200 HARROUN RD 43560 #018-75-1983, ▲ L1986 **OBG** *020 †30
GORSUCH, George Edward. ■ 43560 #038-41-1954 L1954 **CD IM** *071 †20
GRIFFITH, Joan Reed. ■ 43560 #038-41-1978 L1986 **PD ADL** *020 †55
GUL, Afaq Alam. ■ 43560 #308-13-2003 L2007 **FP** *012
GUNER, Mikhail. ■ 43560 #913-01-1955 L1983 **N** *020
GUTIERREZ, Maria A. 6116 DURBIN RD 43560 #715-01-1964 L1981 **AN** *071 †05
HANDLER, Harvey Lewis. 5300 HARROUN RD STE 226 43560 #017-20-1969 L1969 **D** *020 †15
HARTWIG, Robert Henry. 6444 MONROE ST, STE A 43560 #025-01-1974 L1980 **HS ORS** *020 †40
HEFZY, Hebah Mohamedsami. ■ 43560 #038-44-2005 L2005 **N** *012
HEFZY, Muhammad Sheriff. ■ 43560 #038-43-2008 *012
HELM, Eric Robert. ■ 43560 #038-43-2008 *012
HERCHER, Rhonda Lea. 5151 MAIN ST, STE C 43560 #038-43-1992 L1996 **MPD** *020 †20
HILTNER, Laura Elizabeth. ■ 43560 #038-43-2008 *012
HOLUP, Jeanne Marie. 6832 CONVENT BLVD, NONE 43560 #038-40-1992 L2000 **P** *020 †75
HOPPS, Carin Vera. 7640 SYLVANIA AVE, STE L 43560 #047-05-1995 L2000 **U** *020 †95
HUMENIUK, Harry Michael. 4935 HARROUN RD 43560 #038-43-1986 L1991 **D OS** *020 †15
HUTTNER, Jeanine S. 5200 HARROUN RD 43560 #038-40-1979 L1983 **FM FPG** *040 †18
ISMAIL, Shurouk. ■ 43560 #038-43-2005 L2005 **PD** *012
JAIN, Mohit. 5300 HARROUN RD 43560 #495-26-1998 L2005 **FP** *012
JAUREGUI, Connie Lee. 5200 HARROUN RD 43560 #038-43-1991 L1994 **IM** *071
JENKINS, Oliver Haskel. 5200 HARROUN RD 43560 #041-13-1989 L2000 **OTO GS** *020 †45
JOSH, Sanjiv. 5300 HARROUN RD 43560 #495-08-1995 L2001 **FM** *020
KALRA, Sunita Bala. 5300 HARROUN RD, FLOWER HOSP 43560 #661-03-2003 L2005 **FP** *012
KATRAPATI, Prashanth Simh. ■ 43560 #038-43-2007 L2007 **IM** *012
KAVANAGH, Lloyd Richard. ■ 43560 #016-43-1959 L1960 **GYN** *071 †30
KHAN, Rana M. ■ 43560 #308-03-1982 L1998 **CHP P** *020
KHAN, Waqar Ahmad. ■ 43560 #704-09-1990 L2007 **HMP** *020 †50
KIM, Casey Kwon. 5300 HARROUN RD 43560 #166-01-2002 L2003 **FM** *020 †18
KLEIN, Linda Marie. 7640 SYLVANIA AVE, STE K 43560 #038-41-1982 L1983 **FM** *020 †18
KRISHNAN, Venkatesan. 5200 HARROUN RD 43560 #495-09-1966 L1978 **NPM** *020 †55
KRISTOF, Kraig Alan. ■ 43560 #038-43-2003 L2003 **ORS** *012
LA POINTE, Diane Doris. 5200 HARROUN RD 43560 #038-43-1980 L1982 **EM** *020 †16
LATEEF, Humaira K. 5300 HARROUN RD 43560 #704-05-1995 L2005 **FP** *012
LOWDEN, Roland Gilbert. 5246 SPRING CREEK LN 43560 #038-41-1967 L1967 **CHP PTH** *020 †50
LOWRY, Brooke Marie. ■ 43560 #038-43-1999 L2000 **MPD IM** *100
MADIGAN, Howard Stone. ■ 43560 #010-02-1945 L1964 **OS** *071 †85
MASCARENHAS, Sheryl Felic. ■ 43560 #038-45-2008 *012
MASONGSONG, Martina Barte. 5300 HARROUN RD, FAMILY PHYSICIANS ASSOCIAT 43560 #748-15-1986 L1999 **FM** *020 †18
MEHTA, Krunal. ■ 43560 #495-23-2001 L2007 **FP** *012
MEHTA, Mukulika. 5300 HARROUN RD 43560 #496-42-1999 L2006 **FP** *012
METZGER, James Bruce. 5200 HARROUN RD 43560 #023-07-1977 L1982 **ID IM** *020 †20
MEYER, William J. ■ 43560 #028-34-1952 L1953 **OBG** *071 †30
MITCH, Paul Steve. 6465 MONROE ST STE 203 43560 #038-40-1971 L1971 **P** *020 †75 ‡
MOHAN, Vedagiri. 5200 HARROUN RD 43560 #495-04-1974 L1985 **NPM PD** *020 †55
NADOUR, Jalaa Munzer. ■ 43560 #875-02-1995 L2002 **IM** *100 †20
NANDA, Sucheta. 5200 HARROUN RD 43560 #496-07-1978 L2000 **AN** *020 †05
NENSEL, Richard Emil. 7248 FOREST BROOK DR 43560 #056-06-1968 L1969 **AM PTH** *074 †50
NICHOLAS-BUBLICK, Selena. ■ 43560 #038-43-2005 L2005 **N** *012
NIMEH, Diana. ■ 43560 #875-01-1980 L1998 **PTH** *020 †50
NIRDLINGER, Edwin L, II. 5300 HARROUN RD STE 21 43560 #016-11-1974 L1983 **GS** *020 †85
NIRDLINGER, Mary Ann S. 5300 HARROUN RD, STE 202 43560 #016-11-1975 L1983 **AN** *071 †05
OBILLO, Kristin Marianne. ■ 43560 #748-10-2000 L2007 **FP** *012
OCKULY, Joan Marie. 5066 BRENDEN WAY 43560 #038-43-1989 L1990 **EM** *020 †16
OLSEN, Margaret Mary. 4424 VICKSBURG DR, STE N 43560 #056-05-1975 L1982 **PDS GS** *020 †85
PAPADIMOS, Thomas John. 7162 COPPERWOOD LN, 7162 COPPERWOOD LANE 43560 #038-43-1978 L1979 **CCA GP** *020 †70,05
PARNGS, Tong Glen. 5200 HARROUN RD, CO FLOWER HOSP-MED EDU DEP 43560 #306-01-2001 L2004 *020
PATEL, Deepak Shashikant. 5300 HARROUN RD 43560 #473-04-2002 L2006 **FM FSM** *020 †18
PICARD, Jonathan C. ■ 43560 #021-05-2002 L2002 **U** *012
PINEDA, Joy Hechanova. 5300 HARROUN RD 43560 #748-19-1994 L2005 **FP** *012
PINSKY, Sonja V Stahl. 5600 MONROE ST STE 204A 43560 #041-07-1958 L1959 **P PTH** *020 †50,75
PIPOLY, George Michael. ■ 43560 #038-40-1973 L1973 **ON HEM** *020 †20
POLA, Parijatha. ■ 43560 #654-01-2000 L2001 **IM** *100
PRASAD, Anil S.. ■ 43560 #496-34-2001 L2003 **GP** *020
RAY, Suranjan. ■ 43560 #495-02-1956 L1981 **ORS** *071
REMLEY, Stuart K. 5200 HARROUN RD 43560 #041-02-1953 L1967 **END OM** *071
RISNER, Robert James. ■ 43560 #038-43-1983 L1984 **OBG** *020 †30
ROCCHI, Ranieri. 5855 MONROE ST 43560 #561-15-1959 L1964 **FM** *020
ROH, Chung Ok. ■ 43560 #583-03-1958 L1972 **AN** *071
ROMANOFF, Bennett Sanford. 5300 HARROUN RD STE 112 43560 #038-40-1974 L1974 **OPH** *020 †35 ‡
ROSEN, Gerald Phillip. 5200 HARROUN RD 43560 #065-01-1959 L1992 **OTO** *020 †45
ROST, Elmer Chas. ■ 43560 #016-43-1947 L1948 **OBG** *071 †30
RUBIN, Allan Maier. 5300 HARROUN RD 43560 #065-01-1979 L1987 **OTO HNS** *020 †45
RUSIN, Joseph J. 5750 ALEXIS RD, SYLVANIA ORTHOPEDS & REHAB 43560 #016-42-1984 L1989 **ORS** *020 †40
SAINI, Sunita Kaur. 5300 HARROUN RD 43560 #038-43-2000 L2000 **PD** *100 †55 ‡
SAJID, Naoshiba Aziz. 5300 HARROUN RD, FLOWER HOSP 43560 #496-27-1999 L2006 **FP** *012
SALEM, Omar Sine. 4848 N HOLLAND SYLVANIA RD 43560 #038-40-1978 L1984 **D DMP** *020 †15
SANTOS, Maria Camille Vel. 5300 HARROUN RD 43560 #748-08-2000 L2004 **FM** *020 †18
SARIKONDA, Kesari Babu. 5200 HARROUN RD 43560 #495-65-1988 L1996 **ICE CD** *020 †20
SARROUJ, Bassam Jabra. 4610 DOVEWOOD LN, PULMONARY AND CRITICAL CAR 43560 #875-01-1983 L2003 **CCM** *020 †20
SATISH, Malini. 5200 HARROUN RD 43560 #495-70-1974 L1980 **NPM PD** *020 †55 ‡
SAYRE, Joe Wm. 5300 HARROUN RD 43560 #038-40-1981 L1984 **CRS** *020 †10,85
SBROCCHI, Richard Dean. 7640 SYLVANIA AVE STE N 43560 #038-43-1978 L1985 **VS** *020 †85
SCHMIDT, Lindsay Bergman. ■ 43560 #056-06-2005 L2005 **PTH** *012
SCHMIDT, Michael Scott. ■ 43560 #056-06-2004 L2004 **GS** *012
SCHMIDT, Robert Wm. 5200 HARROUN RD 43560 #038-40-1954 L1954 **PTH PCP** *071 †50
SCHOONMAKER, Judith Ann. 7640 SYLVANIA AVE, WEST TOLEDO INTERNAL 43560 #038-43-1984 L1987 **IM** *020 †20
SEVILLA, Ramon Martin. ■ 43560 #038-43-2008 *012
SFERRA, Joseph J. 5800 MONROE ST # G 43560 #038-40-1986 L1991 **GS** *020 †85
SHAH, Sanjay Surendra. 5800 MONROE ST, BLDG A 43560 #041-14-1992 L1999 **PM** *020 †60
SHERMAN, Christopher A. 5200 HARROUN RD 43560 #025-12-1997 L1999 **FM** *020 †18
SHERMIS, Robin Barry. 5200 HARROUN RD 43560 #038-06-1986 L1986 **DR** *020 †80
SHIPLE, Frederick Jos. 6444 MONROE ST, STE A 43560 #016-06-1971 L1976 **ORS** *071 †40
SICILIANO, Katherine Mari. ■ 43560 #016-43-2008 *012
SICKELS, Malcolm James. 5300 HARROUN RD 43560 #025-01-2001 L2001 **FM** *020
SIDO, Gregor, Jr. 5200 HARROUN RD 43560 #028-34-1946 L1949 **FM** *071
SIGMAN, Timothy Hall. 5800 MONROE ST, BLDG A 43560 #025-12-1988 L1992 **PM IM** *020 †60
SINGH, Amanpreet. 5300 HARROUN RD 43560 #308-13-2002 L2006 **FP** *012
SNODGRASS, Bethanne. 5300 HARROUN RD 43560 #041-14-1979 L1984 **PS** *020 †65
SNYDER, Harry Leming. 5660 MONROE ST 43560 #025-01-1955 L1956 **FM AN** *071
SOOD, Rama. 5300 HARROUN RD 43560 #495-51-1969 L1975 **PD** *020 †55
SOOD, Satish Kumar. 5300 HARROUN RD STE 114 43560 #495-21-1970 L1976 **U** *075 †95
STEIN, Howard Mark. 5200 HARROUN RD 43560 #041-09-1986 L1996 **PDC** *020 †55
STEINER, Gerry Andrew. 5200 HARROUN RD 43560 #038-41-1979 L1980 **FM FPG** *030 †18
STENGLE, John Bernard. 5800 MONROE ST, BLDG G 43560 #038-40-1990 L1995 **GS** *020 †85
STRIPH, Karen Beth. 5300 HARROUN RD STE 304 43560 #041-12-1984 L1989 **FM** *071 †18
SULLIVAN, Daniel Jos. 5660 MONROE ST, STE 4 43560 #010-02-1982 L1992 **ORS OSS** *020 †40
SUMAWAY, Cherubin Shaheed. 5300 HARROUN RD, FLOWER HOSP 43560 #748-21-2001 L2006 **FP** *012
SUN, Kwoh Cheng. ■ 43560 #242-45-1944 L1969 **OS GP** *075
SUNDERMEYER, John F. ■ 43560 #056-06-1953 L1954 **CD IM** *071 †20
SZABO, Linda Sue. 7640 SYLVANIA AVE, STE D 43560 #038-43-1988 L1991 **IM** *020 †20
TANNER, Daniel G. 5200 HARROUN RD 43560 #038-40-1951 L1951 **GE IM** *071
TENNETI, Lakshmi V S. ■ 43560 #495-58-2001 L2007 **IM** *020 †20
THAKUR, Shantanu Kumar. ■ 43560 #038-40-2008 *012
TONKS, Shari Mae. 7640 SYLVANIA AVE, STE K 43560 #025-07-1991 L1994 **FM FSM** *020 †18
TOUMA, Yara. ■ 43560 #038-43-2006 L2006 **DR** *012
TSANG, Albert Weijeich. ■ 43560 #025-07-2004 L2004 **GS** *012
UDDARAJU, Maithry. ■ 43560 #661-02-2005 L2007 **FP** *012
UNDERHILL, Warren Earl. ■ 43560 #067-01-1957 L1958 **AN** *071 †05
VALADE, John Wm. 7640 SYLVANIA AVE, STE D 43560 #038-43-1989 L1991 **IM** *020 †20
VANNUYEN, Jackie. 5300 HARROUN RD STE 226, FLOWER HOSP MED OFFICE BLD 43560 #038-43-1999 L2005 **OBG** *020 †30
VELYCHKO, Inna Volodymyri. ■ 43560 #913-57-2000 L2007 **FP** *012
WANG-ODESKY, Nana Hui. ■ 43560 #243-64-1983 **IM** *100
WHITE, Patrick. 5800 MONROE ST, BLDG G 43560 #056-06-1975 L1980 **GS** *020 †85
WILLIAMS, Stephanie Lynn. ■ 43560 #038-43-2008 *012
WINDER, John Andrew. 5860 ALEXIS RD, STE B 43560 #055-01-1971 L1978 **A PDA** *050 †55,03
WOLFE, Ann Marie. 7640 SYLVANIA AVE, WEST TOLEDO INTERNAL 43560 #038-43-1997 L2000 **IM** *020 †20
YIM, Yoon Myung. 5800 MONROE ST 43560 #583-02-1968 L1975 **PM PMM** *020 †60
YOUNGEN, Robert Eugene. 5200 HARROUN RD 43560 #008-01-1957 L1965 **U** *071 †95
ZONA, J Christian. 5200 HARROUN RD 43560 #045-01-1985 L1986 **FM PD** *040 †18 ‡

SYLVANIA TOWNSHIP - LUCAS

SHAIKH, Bahu Sultan. 4235 SECOR RD 43623 #704-02-1968 L1981 **IM HO** *020 †20

■ = Address Information Privacy Protected

TALLMADGE – SUMMIT

AMLANI, Anita Kishan. 65 COMMUNITY RD, STE C 44278 #025-12-1999 L1999 **FM** *020 †18
BACHTEL, Jeffrey Dale. 182 EAST AVE 44278 #038-44-1981 L1982 **FM** *020 †18
BARTON, Fred Delano. 99 NORTHWEST AVENUE, A 44278 #038-06-1965 L1965 **P N** *071 †75
BERNATH, Otto Nicolaus. 33 NORTH AVE, STE 103 44278 #473-01-1956 L1962 **FM** *071 †18
BRODERICK, Meredith J. ■ 44278 #038-40-2003 L2003 **N** *020
BROOKS, Steven. ■ 44278 #038-44-2004 L2004 **EM** *012
CROMBIE, Bradley Hall. 65 COMMUNITY RD, STE C 44278 #038-40-1994 L1995 **IM** *020 †20
DORMAN, Regina Markovna. 65 COMMUNITY RD, STE C 44278 #913-11-1987 L1996 **FM** *020 †18
GORSUCH, Steven Matthew. 121 NORTHWEST AVE 44278 #038-44-1997 L1998 **OBG** *020 †30
GULMI, Robert Wallace. 143 NORTHWEST AVE, STE 102 44278 #038-34-1968 L1969 **PD OS** *071 †55
HAMMONDS-CUTLIP, Pamela J. ■ 44278 #038-43-2003 L2003 **EM** *020
HOFF, David Lee. 65 COMMUNITY RD, STE D 44278 #038-40-1968 L1968 **FM IM** *030 †18
HUTZLER, John Nelson. 121 NORTHWEST AVE 44278 #055-01-1970 L1971 **OBG** *020 †30
JADALLAH, Ahmad Khaled. 121 NORTHWEST AVE 44278 #038-40-1993 L1995 **OBG** *020 †30
JIAMBOI, Gina Marie. ■ 44278 #038-44-2008 *012
KEDIA, Anurag W. 33 NORTH AVE, STE 103 44278 #495-37-1997 L2000 **FM** *020 †18
MAJMUNDAR, Neil Devendra. ■ 44278 #038-44-2006 **GS** *012
MEYER, Mark. 65 COMMUNITY RD, STE C 44278 #038-41-1983 L1984 **FM** *020 †18
MEYER, Sue Ellen. 65 COMMUNITY RD, STE C 44278 #038-41-1983 L1985 **FM** *020 †18
PARKE, William Royden. 33 NORTH AVE, STE 103 44278 #017-20-1983 L1983 **FM** *020 †18
PRIEBE, Carrie Susanne. 143 NORTHWEST AVE, BLDG D 44278 #038-44-1998 L1999 **PD** *020 †18
REED, William T, III. 182 EAST AVE 44278 #041-12-1978 L1979 **IM IMG** *020 †20
RICH, Craig Louis. ■ 44278 #308-03-1986 L1992 **IM** *020
ROUSH, William Raymond. ■ 44278 #010-01-1966 L1967 **IM** *071 †16
SCHOENFELD, Andrew Jason. ■ 44278 #038-44-2003 L2003 **ORS** *012
SELLERS, Bradley Randall. 33 NORTH AVE, STE 103 44278 #038-44-1999 L1999 **FM** *020 †18
TAGGART, Christopher Euge.. ■ 44278 #038-44-2007 L2007 **FP** *012
TURNEY, Eric James. ■ 44278 #038-44-2006 L2006 **GS** *012
WALLACE, Charles William. 33 NORTH AVE, STE 103 44278 #038-43-1999 L1999 **FM** *020 †18
WILLIAMS, Bruce. ■ 44278 #038-75-2005, ▲ L2005 **OBG** *012

TERRACE PARK – HAMILTON

LOWRY, Peter H. ■ 45174 #038-41-1985 L1990 **OS LM** *062
MOULTON, James A L. ■ 45174 #038-06-1946 L1946 **N P** *071
WANG, Lawrence P. 614 WOOSTER PIKE, STE 7 45174 #038-06-1998 L2001 **IM** *020 †20

THE PLAINS – ATHENS

MAC MILLAN, James Edmund. ■ 45780 #038-41-1946 L1946 **GP** *071 †75

TIFFIN – SENECA

AGARWAL, Meera. 485 W MARKET ST 44883 #495-41-1978 L1982 **AN** *020 †05
AHMAD, Munir. ■ 44883 #690-01-1983 L1994 **IM RO** *020 †20,80
AKERS, Mark Justin. ■ 44883 #038-45-1998 L1999 **IM** *020 †20
ALPAY, Ilhan. 485 W MARKET ST 44883 #902-03-1957 L1964 **IM** *020
AMIN, Dipakkumar P. 486 W PERRY ST 44883 #495-23-1980 L1992 **FM** *020 †18
ANDUJAR SCHEKER, Jose. 500 W MARKET ST, # A 44883 #308-13-1994 L2003 **GS** *020 †85,10
ANTHONY, James Michael. 485 W MARKET ST 44883 #038-41-1979 L1980 **OM FM** *020 †18
BASU, Asish Kumar. 455 W MARKET ST 44883 #495-02-1965 L1993 *020
BERCKMUELLER, David E. 470 W MARKET ST 44883 #017-20-1965 L1972 **OPH** *071 †35
BISHOP, Stephanie Artner. 485 W MARKET ST, OCCUPATIONAL HLTH SERVICES 44883 #038-41-1987 L1988 **FM** *020 †18
BOSSE, James F. 662 MIAMI ST 44883 #038-75-1990, ▲ L1991 **FM FPG** *020 †18
CEPEDA PEETERS, Jorge. 485 W MARKET ST 44883 #264-04-1967 L1976 **DR PD** *020 †80
CHRISTIAN, Samuel Jos. 478 W MARKET ST 44883 #010-03-1984 L1991 **GS** *020 †85
COPELAND, Steven C. 672 MIAMI ST 44883 #016-02-1999 L2005 **OSM** *100 †40
CORDERO-MURILLO, Abner. 143 S MONROE ST 44883 #649-14-1983 L1994 **OBG** *020
DALAL, Bankimchandra H. 433 W MARKET ST 44883 #496-15-1975 L1982 **GE IM** *020 †20
DESAI, Ajitkumar M. 485 W MARKET ST 44883 #495-23-1967 L1976 **U** *020 †95
FELTON, James Michael. 486 W PERRY ST 44883 #038-40-1977 L1977 **IM** *020 †20
GANESAN, Mahamuni. 23 W PERRY ST, P O BOX 550 44883 #495-16-1964 L1972 **IM** *020 †16
GARLAPATI, Krishnaiah. 455 W MARKET ST 44883 #495-62-1975 L1979 **IM** *020
GASE, Andrew James. 437 W MARKET ST 44883 #038-40-1985 L1986 **FM** *020 †18
HAVENS, Philip Eugene. 672 MIAMI ST 44883 #038-43-1981 L1986 **ORS** *020 †40
HEDGES, Wesley Warner. 1344 W SENECA AVE, PERSONAL TOUCH DELIVERIES 44883 #038-06-1985 L1986 **OBG** *020 †30 ‡
INNIS, Eliz Jane Cowgill. 76 ASHWOOD DR 44883 #016-06-1947 L1948 **P** *020
JASTY, Rama. 485 W MARKET ST 44883 #496-05-1987 L1996 **PHO** *020 †55
JOHAR, Bikram Singh. 65 SAINT FRANCIS AVE, SENECA COUNTY DIALYSIS 44883 #495-43-1989 L1998 **NEP IM** *020 †20
KAKARALA, Prasad Choudary. 485 W MARKET ST 44883 #495-58-1969 L1978 **PD FM** *020 †55
KOTHARI, Kusum Suresh. 485 W MARKET ST 44883 #495-01-1975 L1983 **PTH** *020
KOTHARI, Prashant S. 485 W MARKET ST 44883 #495-48-1971 L1979 **AN GS** *020
LIM, Virgilia Aliganga. ■ 44883 #748-11-1966 L1972 **IM** *020
LUPICA, Anthony Santo. ■ 44883 #028-34-1957 L1957 **GP** *071
MC MATH, Jeffery Alan. 672 MIAMI ST, STE B 44883 #038-41-1989 L1994 **ORS** *020 †40
MOORJANI, Romena Indur. 455 W MARKET ST 44883 #748-10-1988 L1995 **PD** *020 †55
MUNOZ, Guillermo Julian. ■ 44883 #275-01-1951 L1959 **R OS** *071 †80
PIATZ, Michael Anthony. 485 W MARKET ST, TIFFIN MERCY HOSPITAL 44883 #046-01-1998 L1999 **EM** *020
RAABE, Thomas Michael. 672 MIAMI ST, STE B 44883 #038-40-1973 L1973 **ORS** *020 †40
RAO, Kommula Chiranjeevi. 485 W MARKET ST 44883 #495-11-1971 L1982 **DR NR** *020 †80
RAO, Vidya Kommula. ■ 44883 #038-44-2005 L2005 **AN** *012
RINDANI, Arun Bhaskerrao. 65 SAINT FRANCIS AVE 44883 #496-38-1955 L1987 **ORS** *020 †40
SALEM, Mohamed S. 350 W MARKET ST 44883 #915-04-1978 L1994 **GS** *020 †85

SEARS, Christopher David. 81 ASHWOOD DR 44883 #038-45-2002 L2002 **IM** *020 †20
SHANABROOK, Donald Warren. 1344 W SENECA AVE 44883 #038-40-1958 L1958 **OBG** *071 †30
SONI, Renu. 485 W MARKET ST 44883 #496-07-1981 L1993 **ON HO** *020
THEKDI, Dinesh Chhotalal. 485 W MARKET ST 44883 #495-22-1969 L1977 **CD IM** *020 †20
THEKDI, Sonal Dinesh. ■ 44883 #038-40-2003 L2003 **AN** *012
TOGRUL, Hamit Yilmaz. ■ 44883 #902-03-1953 **IM** *075
VELA, John Frank. 71 SAINT FRANCIS AVE 44883 #038-43-1974 L1975 **FM FSM** *020 †18
VELA, Rudolph Jesse. 3101 W US HIGHWAY 224, STE A 44883 #038-40-1984 L1986 **FM OS** *020 †18 ‡
YOUNG, Merris Townsend. 3101 W US HIGHWAY 224 44883 #017-20-1985 L1988 **OM IM** *020 †20
YOUNG, Wade Earle. 60 ASHWOOD DR 44883 #016-06-1983 L1984 **OPH OS** *020 †35

TIPP CITY – MIAMI

ABBOUD, Fayez Dimitri S. 450 N HYATT ST, DIGESTIVE SPECIALTY CARE 45371 #915-04-1980 L1989 **GE IM** *020 †20
ANKOLKAR, Sameer Munirudd. 450 N HYATT ST 45371 #496-52-1997 L2002 **FM** *020 †18
BARRE, Peter Stephen. 450 N HYATT ST 45371 #025-12-1978 L1982 **HS ORS** *020 †40
BERRETTONI, Beth Anne. 450 N HYATT ST 45371 #038-06-1986 L1986 **ORS** *020 †40
CARRIGAN, Thomas Warren. 450 N HYATT ST, DIGESTIVE SPECIALTY CARE 45371 #038-45-1983 L1986 **GE IM** *075 †20
DANIS, Christopher J. 450 N HYATT ST 45371 #038-45-1982 L1984 **HS PS** *020 †65
FORSTER, Richard W. 25 S TIPPECANOE DR 45371 #067-01-1980 L1988 **ORS** *020 †40
FROST, James Burl. 450 N HYATT ST, STE 302 45371 #005-12-1970 L1977 **DR** *020 †80
GOOTZEIT, Brian Jeremy. 450 N HYATT ST, DIGESTIVE SPECIALTY CARE 45371 #035-48-1998 L2004 **GE** *020 †20
HARJU, Aaron Christopher. 450 N HYATT ST, STE 202 45371 #038-41-1999 L1999 **FM** *020 †18
HORVATH, Kevin Allan. 1483 W MAIN ST 45371 #038-43-1982 L1985 **PD** *020 †55
HOSKINS, Jeffrey Scott. 25 S TIPPECANOE DR 45371 #028-03-1999 L2005 **ORS** *012
KIM, Gene. 25 S TIPPECANOE DR 45371 #016-06-1992 L1998 **ORS HS** *020 †40
KULKARNI, Anupama Sunil. 450 N HYATT ST 45371 #038-45-1994 L1995 **FM** *020 †18
MILLER, Nessa Evelyn. ■ 45371 #038-45-2008 *012
MORLIDGE, Elihu Root, Jr. 450 N HYATT ST STE 202 45371 #038-41-1960 L1960 **FPG** *071
NASH, Deborah Jane. 423 W MAIN ST 45371 #038-40-1978 L1979 **FM** *020 †18
NITZ, Paul Anthony. 25 S TIPPECANOE DR 45371 #017-20-1980 L1990 **ORS OSM** *020 †40
PAN, Cheng Tsing. 227 S GARBER DR 45371 #495-11-1975 L1987 **P** *020 †75
PETERS, John Christopher. 450 N HYATT ST, STE 204 45371 #038-45-1985 L1986 **FM** *020 †18
PRICE, Robert J B. 450 N HYATT ST, STE 204 45371 #038-41-1958 L1958 **GP** *071
PUTHOFF, Michael Scott. 450 N HYATT ST, STE 202 45371 #038-40-1998 L1999 **FM** *020 †18
PYLES, Robert O. 450 N HYATT ST STE 202 45371 #020-02-1966 L1967 **FM PD** *071
TAMBRINI, Alex Anthony. 450 N HYATT ST 45371 #016-01-1996 L2001 **FM** *020 †18

TOLEDO – LUCAS

ABBAS, Jihad T. 3065 ARLINGTON AVE, DEPT OF SURGERY 43614 #605-01-1992 L2000 **VS** *020 †85
ABBAS, Saima. 3000 ARLINGTON AVE 43614 #704-06-1997 L2005 **IM** *012
ABBAS, Shan-E-. CO GME-RM 320-MUL, UNIVERSITY OF TOLEDO 43614 #704-02-2005 L2007 **N** *012
ABBATI, Frank. 4303 TALMADGE RD STE 104 43623 #561-17-1956 L1967 **CD IM** *020 †20
ABBOUD, Jeffrey. ■ 43615 #065-09-1987 L1992 **PS** *020 †65
ABDULLAH, Asif. 2213 CHERRY ST 43608 #306-01-2005 L2006 **DR** *012
ABIDI, Syed Mansoor Mehdi. 2222 CHERRY ST, NEPHROLGY ASSOC STE 1700 43608 #704-02-1988 L2002 **NEP** *020 †20
ABOUL-SAOUD, Ammar. 2213 CHERRY ST, ST VINCENTS HOSP MED CTR 43608 #875-01-1996 **FM** *100
ABRAHAM, Ajit Oommen. 3045 ARLINGTON AVE, MULFORD LI 43614 #495-31-1999 L2003 **IM** *100
ABRAHAM, Sherin Koshy. 3439 GRANITE CIR 43617 #016-43-1990 L1997 **GE** *020 †20
ABRAMSON, Eli Carl. ■ 43617 #038-40-1954 L1954 **IM CD** *071 †20
ABROU, Ayad Edward. 4126 N HOLLAND SYLVANIA RD, STE 200 43623 #025-07-2001 L2006 **D** *020 †15
ABUHANTTASH, Khaled M N. 3000 ARLINGTON AVE, UNIVERSITY OF TOLEDO 43614 #560-01-2004 L2007 **IM** *012
ABU MALOUH, Abdel Kareem. 3000 ARLINGTON AVE 43614 #575-02-2005 L2007 **IM** *012
ABUMERI, Imad. 3065 ARLINGTON AVE, DIV OF NEUROSURGERY 43614 #655-01-1987 L1999 **NS** *020 †25
ABUSAMIEH, Mohammed A. 3922 WOODLEY RD, STE 200 43606 #575-02-1993 L2003 **RHU** *020 †20
ACHINGER, Debra Sue. 4841 MONROE ST, STE 103 43623 #019-02-1992 L2002 **DR** *020 †80
ADAMS, Christopher Steven. ■ 43614 #038-43-2007 L2007 **IM** *012
ADAMS-FERGUSON, Karen M. 4895 MONROE ST STE 203 43623 #038-40-1983 L1985 **OBG** *020 †30
ADAS, Mohammad A. 2213 CHERRY ST 43608 #561-17-1978 L1987 **IM PTH** *020 †20
ADIL, Jahangir. 2200 JEFFERSON AVE, MERCY FAMILY MEDICINE 43604 #704-01-1990 L2000 **FM** *020 †18
ADKINS, Jennifer Lynne. 2213 CHERRY ST, ST VINCENT MERCY CHILDREN' 43608 #038-40-1999 L1999 **PD** *020 †55
ADLER, Kenneth Harold. 4159 N HOLLAND SYLVANIA RD 43623 #038-43-1972 L1976 **P CHP** *020
AGEE, Marilyn. 5965 RENAISSANCE PL, STE 3 43623 #038-43-1988 L1989 **FM OBS** *020 †18 ‡
AGKO, Mouchammed. 3045 ARLINGTON AVE, CO GME- RM 330 - 43614 #902-07-2000 L2005 **GS** *100
AGRAWAL, Ramkumar. 2142 N COVE BLVD 43606 #495-20-1965 L1973 **NEP IM** *071 †20
AGUILLON, Lodovico S. 1850 EASTGATE RD STE B 43614 #748-08-1969 L1974 **IM** *020
AGWANI, Sufian Mohammad Y. ■ 43615 #704-02-1996 L2007 **CHP** *012
AHMAD, Munir. 2450 N REYNOLDS RD 43615 #704-09-1969 L1974 **PD EM** *020
AHMED, Ageel. ■ 43614 #704-02-1986 L2004 **PTH** *020
AHMED, Mohammed M. 3120 GLENDALE AVE 43614 #704-20-1990 L2006 **IM** *020 †20
AHMED, Mohammed Y. 2409 CHERRY ST, MOB #303 43608 #495-21-1962 L1971 **GS TRS** *020
AHMED, Shaheda Begum. 3000 ARLINGTON AVE 43614 #495-65-1966 L1972 **PTH PCP** *020 †50

AHMED, Suraiya Jabeen. 2020 STARR AVE, FAMILY MEDICAL CENTER 43605 #495-77-1972 L1994 **FM** *020 †18 ‡
AHRENS, Jodee Elizabeth. 5800 PARK CENTER CT, STE A 43615 #038-43-1987 L1990 **IM** *020 †20
AKPANUDO, Sutoidem Moses. 3000 ARLINGTON AVE 43614 #690-12-1997 L2006 **IM** *012
AKPUNONU, Basil Emeka. 3120 GLENDALE AVE, MS 1186 43614 #010-03-1982 L1984 **IM** *020 †20
ALAM, Shadia Mansoor. ■ 43617 #038-41-2005 L2005 **PTH** *012
ALANIS TREVINO, Fidencio. 1500 N SUPERIOR ST STE 303, 1500 N SUPERIOR ST #303 43604 #649-02-1964 L1972 **PD** *020
AL-ASTAL, Amro Yassin. 3000 ARLINGTON AVE, CO MCOT-INTERNAL MEDICINE 43614 #409-21-1994 L2000 **PCC** *100 †20
AL-AYOUBI, Aroub. 3830 WOODLEY RD, STE C 43606 #875-01-1987 L1995 **PD** *020 †55
AL-BAGHDADI, Mohamad Wiss. 3000 ARLINGTON AVE, UNIVERSITY OF TOLEDO MEDIC 43614 #875-01-1998 L2001 **PCC** *012
AL-BAWAB, Osama A. 5800 PARK CENTER CT, STE C 43615 #575-02-1991 L2005 **CD IM** *020 †20
ALHABIAN, Oula. 7140 PORT SYLVANIA DR, STE 300 43617 #875-01-1990 L1997 **FM** *020 †18
AL-HARTHY, Abdullah. 3065 ARLINGTON AVE 2, CO MCOT-ORTHO SURGERY DEPT 43614 #919-05-1989 L2000 **GS** *020
ALI, Imran I. 3000 ARLINGTON AVE MS 1195, UNIV OF TOLEDO COLL OF MED 43614 #704-25-1989 L1996 **N** *040 †75
ALI, Nasir. 4235 SECOR RD 43623 #704-01-1962 L1971 **PUD IM** *020 †20
ALISHAHIE, Mohammad Javad. ■ 43614 #517-01-1971 **CHP P** *100
AL-KHATIB, Yasser. 2121 HUGHES DR STE 750, CHILDREN HEART CENTER 43606 #875-02-1982 L2001 **PDC** *020 †55
ALLISON, David Coulter. 3000 ARLINGTON AVE 43614 #025-01-1967 L1992 **OS AN** *020 †85
ALMAROOF, Babatunde Hamed. ■ 43614 #690-02-2000 L2005 **GS** *012
AL-NIMRI, Nizar Ghazi. 3000 ARLINGTON AVE 43614 #575-01-2001 L2006 **IM** *012
ALO, Abed El-Mannan. 3909 WOODLEY RD, STE 800 43606 #875-02-1974 L1982 **CRS GS** *020 †10,85
ALOSH, Humam. 320-MUL3045 ARLING, CO GME-RM 43614 #875-01-2006 L2007 **PD** *012
ALSABBAGH, Nina Tahseen. 2109 HUGHES DR STE 920, CONRAD JOBST TOWER 43606 #575-01-1988 L1999 **NEP** *020 †20
ALSAKA, Mhd Adnan. 3000 ARLINGTON AVE 43614 #875-01-1999 L2003 **IM** *100 †20
AL-SAYED, Samarah Hassan. 2150 W CENTRAL AVE, CENTER FOR HEALTH SERVICES 43606 #875-02-1987 L1996 **PD** *020 †55
ALVI, Saud Ahmed. 2213 CHERRY ST, DEPT OF MED EDU 43608 #704-05-1990 L2006 **IM** *012
AMER, Hammad Mohamed. ■ 43615 #016-42-2004 L2004 **GS** *012
AMRO, Osama Abdallah Abde. 3000 ARLINGTON AVE 43614 #575-01-2003 L2006 **OBG** *012
ANDERS, John Paul. 4126 N HOLLAND SYLVANIA RD, STE 200 43623 #038-40-1968 L1968 **D** *020 †15
ANDERS, Timothy Joseph. 4126 N HOLLAND SYLVANIA RD, STE 200 43623 #038-43-1996 L2002 **D** *020 †15
ANDERSEN, Thomas Jeffrey. 3439 SOUTHPOINT RD 43615 #038-43-1988 L1990 **AN** *020 †05
ANDERSON, Tyler Brian. ■ 43614 #038-43-2008 *012
ANDRABI, Imran Amjad. 2213 CHERRY ST, FIRST FLR EDUCATION BLDG 43608 #704-01-1990 L1995 **FM** *020 †18
ANDRESEN, Matthew Carl. ■ 43614 #038-43-2008 *012
ANDREWS, Stephen James. 3120 GLENDALE AVE, UNIVERSITY OF TOLEDO MEDIC 43614 #038-06-1985 L1988 **OBG GO** *020 †30
ANTIPORDA, Celso M. 2409 CHERRY ST, STE 305 43608 #748-02-1979 L1991 **AN** *020 †05
ANTONYRAJAH, Bernadette C. 3000 ARLINGTON AVE 43614 #539-06-2004 L2005 **PD** *012
AOUAD, Arlette T. 2222 CHERRY ST, STE 1400 43608 #605-02-1991 L2001 **ID** *020 †20
APOSTOLAKIS, James Louis. 4841 MONROE ST 43623 #025-01-1962 L1968 **R** *071 †80
ARAR, Habeeb Hussein. 3000 ARLINGTON AVE 43614 #528-03-1990 L2006 **P** *012
ARIAS, Fernando. 2142 N COVE BLVD, FL 3D 43606 #264-01-1958 L1998 **MFM OBG** *075 †30 ‡
ARISS, Steven M. 4235 SECOR RD 43623 #605-02-1973 L1979 **U OS** *020
ARMAH, Freda Amanyiwah. 3000 ARLINGTON AVE 43614 #412-01-2001 L2005 **AN** *012
ARMSTRONG, Anthony Jos. 4853 MONROE ST 43623 #038-45-1985 L1989 **OBG** *020 †30
ARMSTRONG, Carl Lawrence. 4853 MONROE ST 43623 #047-07-1952 L1959 **OBG** *071 †30
ARQUETTE, Nancy Ann. 3840 WOODLEY RD, STE B 43606 #038-45-2003 L2007 **OBG** *020
ARROUK, Rami. 3000 ARLINGTON AVE 43614 #875-01-2005 L2007 **PD** *012
ARTIS, Kimberly Anne. 2213 FRANKLIN AVE 43620 #038-43-1980 L1983 **PD** *020 †55
ASAD, Younis Ahmad. ■ 43623 #409-10-1968 L1976 **PD FM** *071
ASCHER, Joel David. ■ 43606 #038-43-2008 *012
ASHRAF, Nadia Fatima. ■ 43617 #038-43-2004 L2004 **EM** *020
ATALLAH, Joseph Noshi. 3000 ARLINGTON AVE 43614 #915-07-1987 L2007 **APM** *020 †05
AUBERLE, James A. 4235 SECOR RD, THE TOLEDO CLNC 43623 #035-08-1985 L1989 **CN N** *020 †75
AUH, Sun Mi Yun. 1500 N SUPERIOR ST, STE 310 43604 #583-08-1967 L1975 **PD GP** *020 †18
AVASTHI, Salil. 3045 ARLINGTON AVE, DEPT OF GME 43614 #495-29-2005 L2006 *100
AVRAM, Raluca. 3000 ARLINGTON AVE, MEDICAL COLLEGE OF OHIO 43614 #781-01-2000 L2003 **IM** *100 †20
AYALA, Giovanni Francesco. ■ 43614 #561-02-1957 L1982 **N** *020
AZZOUNI, Faris Sabri. 3045 ARLINGTON AVE, CO MCOT-GRAD MED EDU DEPT 43614 #575-01-2000 L2003 **GS** *012
BADAWI, Caroline Hanna. ■ 43614 #305-01-2005 L2005 **OBG** *012
BAIBAK, George John. 2213 CHERRY ST 43608 #025-01-1955 L1956 **PS HS** *071 †65
BAIG, Mirza Moazzamali. 2000 REGENCY CT, STE 201 43623 #038-43-2001 L2001 **U** *100
BAJPAI, Manju. 3045 ARLINGTON AVE M, CO MCOT-MED EDU DEPT RM 33 43614 #495-54-1977 L2001 **CHP** *020
BAKER, Donald Allen. 3000 ARLINGTON AVE 43614 #038-43-1976 L1977 **ORS** *071
BALAA, Anas. 3045 ARLINGTON AVE M, CO MCOT-INTERNAL MEDICINE 43614 #875-01-1999 L2003 **PCC** *012 †20
BALDWIN, Mary Margaret. 3020 N MCCORD RD 43615 #038-43-1986 L1991 **FM FPG** *020 †18
BALDWIN, Tanya Riley. 2127 JEFFERSON AVE 43604 #038-43-1998 L2000 **FM** *020
BALKANY, Louis. 1614 S BYRNE RD, STE FF 43614 #025-01-1969 L1971 **VS** *020 †85
BANERJEE, Jashoman. 3000 ARLINGTON AVE 43614 #495-39-1998 L2006 **OBG** *012
BANERJEE, Sanjay. 2109 HUGHES DR, STE 860 43606 #495-30-1985 L2002 **CHP** *020 †75
BANERJEE, Sanjoy. 2109 HUGHES DR, STE 860 43606 #495-53-1988 L2006 **PG** *020 †55
BANERJEE, Sunita. 2213 CHERRY ST, ST.VINCENT MERCY MEDICAL C 43608 #495-21-1995 L2006 **IM** *020 †20
BANOUB, Mounir F. 2409 CHERRY ST, ST STE305 43608 #915-03-1985 L1995 **AN PAN** *020 †05
BARAK, Rakesh. 3000 ARLINGTON AVE, MEDICAL UNIVERSITY OF OH 43614 #495-69-2001 L2005 **DR** *012
BARGNESI, David Scott. ■ 43612 #038-41-2004 L2004 **U** *012
BARLEKAMP, Harold Curtiss. 4411 N HOLLAND SYLVANIA RD, STE 102 43623 #038-44-1986 L1988 **FM** *020 †18
BARMAN, Pooran Chand. 3922 WOODLEY RD, STE 201 43606 #495-41-1963 L1971 **CD IM** *071
BARMANN, Mary Louise. 3020 N MCCORD RD 43615 #038-43-1985 L1986 **FM** *020 †18
BARNES, David Paul. ■ 43613 #038-44-2007 L2007 **FP** *012
BARNETT, Jayson Wayne. 2914 S REPUBLIC BLVD 43615 #305-01-1986 L1992 **AN** *020 †05
BARONE, Frank Emidio. 2000 REGENCY CT, STE 204 43623 #038-43-1980 L1983 **PS** *020 †65
BARRETT, Michael J. 2409 CHERRY ST, STE 305 43608 #056-06-1981 L1992 **AN PME** *020 †05
BARSHEL, Brenda Anne. 2142 N COVE BLVD, STE 5NORTH 43606 #038-43-1989 L1990 **PD** *020 †55
BASHIR, Mwaffak. 5045 DOUGLAS RD 43613 #875-02-1990 L1996 **PD** *020 †55
BASISTA, Michael Hubert. 3439 GRANITE CIR 43617 #041-02-1984 L1985 **GE IM** *020 †20
BASSETT, James S, Jr. 2445 N REYNOLDS RD 43615 #038-43-1990 L1991 **APM** *020 †05
BASTANINEJAD, Bijan. 2142 N COVE BLVD, STE 5NORTH 43606 #422-01-2002 L2006 **PD** *020 †55
BATES, Christopher A. 415 N MICHIGAN ST 43604 #038-43-1982 L1984 **IM** *020 †20
BATES, George N. ■ 43614 #067-01-1942 L1944 **OM** *071 †85
BAUGH, Evelyn Frances. 1 AURORA L GONZALEZ DR, NEIGHBORHOOD HEALTH ASSN 43609 #025-07-1962 L1975 **PD** *040 †55
BEAUMONT, Jos Edward, Jr. 2222 CHERRY ST STE 1700 43608 #038-40-1969 L1969 **NEP IM** *071 †20
BECHTEL, Louisa Ruth. ■ 43606 #038-43-2008 *012
BECKER, Aaron Blake. 3045 ARLINGTON AVE, CO GME - RM 330 43614 #020-12-2004 L2004 **U** *012
BEEBE, Hugh Grenville. 2109 HUGHES DR, STE 400 43606 #035-45-1964 L1991 **VS** *050 †85
BEGEMAN, Garett Alan. ■ 43614 #038-43-2004 L2004 **DR** *012
BEHAM, Richard Albert. 3140 W CENTRAL AVE 43606 #038-43-1986 L1987 **END IM** *020 †55,20
BEHNIAY, Hassan. ■ 43609 #038-43-2006 L2006 **IM** *012
BEHNIAYE, Hossein. ■ 43609 #038-43-2007 L2007 **FP** *012
BEHRLE, Kevin Michael. 4235 SECOR RD, THE TOLEDO CLINIC 43623 #038-43-1982 L1986 **GE IM** *020 †20
BEIRISE, Sarah Rebecca. 2150 W CENTRAL AVE 43606 #056-06-2002 L2002 **FM** *020 †18
BEISSER, Cynthia Smith. 2595 ARLINGTON AVE, LUCAS CO CORONERS OFFICE 43614 #047-06-1986 L1991 **FOP** *020 †50
BELOW, Angela Ann. 3400 MEIJER DR, PEDIATRI CARE ASSOC 43617 #038-43-1999 L2000 **PD** *020 †55
BENDIXEN, Charles Dennis. ■ 43606 #018-03-1966 L1967 **OM** *020 †70
BENNETT, David Chas. ■ 43609 #038-43-1988 L1998 **IM** *020
BERLACHER, Franz J. 1000 REGENCY CT, HEART SPECIALISTS OF NW OH 43623 #016-02-1951 L1957 **CD IM** *071 †20
BERNSDORFF, Kurt Randall. 3439 GRANITE CIR 43617 #038-43-1990 L1996 **GE** *020 †20
BERNSTEIN, Jonathan M. 3000 REGENCY CT, STE 100 43623 #065-01-1987 L1993 **OPH** *020 †35
BERTKA, Kenneth Robert. 2200 JEFFERSON AVE, FAM PRAC RESIDENCY PROGRAM 43604 #038-41-1983 L1984 **FM OS** *030 †18
BHAGAT, Indira. 2142 N COVE BLVD, STE 5NORTH 43606 #496-17-1992 L2003 **PD** *020 †55
BHANDARI, Vinod Kumar. 544 E WOODRUFF AVE 43604 #495-08-1977 L1991 **CHP** *020
BHANDARU, Lakshman Rao. 2230 W LASKEY RD 43613 #495-65-1972 L1980 **END IM** *020 †20
BHANDARU, Suvarna. 2230 W LASKEY RD 43613 #495-50-1973 L1980 **PD** *020 †55
BHAT, Ramachandra J. 3404 W SYLVANIA AVE, ST.ANNE MERCY HOSPITAL 43623 #495-35-1973 L1978 **AN** *020 †05
BHAT, Zeenat Yousuf. 3045 ARLINGTON AVE 43614 #495-51-2001 L2005 *100
BHATT, Shashi Bhushan. 3000 ARLINGTON AVE, MEDICAL COLLEGE OF OHIO 43614 #495-45-1982 L1996 **CCA** *020 †05
BHOOPAL, Kiran. ■ 43615 #654-01-2004 L2006 **AN** *012
BHUMBRA, Nasreen. 2222 CHERRY ST 43608 #495-14-1972 L1982 **ID PD** *040 †55
BHUMBRA, Raspal Singh. 3454 OAK ALLEY CT, STE 101 43606 #495-14-1971 L1981 **N IM** *020 †75
BILLINGS, Thomas Arthur. 3922 WOODLEY RD, STE 100 43606 #038-41-1982 L1984 **FM** *020 †18
BINKLEY, Robert F. ■ 43623 #028-34-1952 L1953 **AN OS** *071 †05
BISHOP, Kent Edward. 3740 W SYLVANIA AVE, STE 103 43623 #038-43-1989 L1990 **OBG** *020 †30
BITTAR, Samih. 3000 ARLINGTON AVE, DEPT OF MEDICINE MS 1186 43614 #875-02-1994 L2004 **IM** *020 †20
BIYANI, Ashok. 3065 ARLINGTON AVE, MS 1094 43614 #496-03-1982 L2000 **OSS ORS** *020 †40
BLACK, Howard Adam. 2914 S REPUBLIC BLVD 43615 #045-01-1984 L1985 **AN** *020 †05
BLACK, Marianne L Marzen. 3000 ARLINGTON AVE 43614 #038-43-1990 L1992 **PD** *020 †55
BLACK, Sanford Lee. 4235 SECOR RD 43623 #038-43-1975 L1977 **AN** *020 †05
BLAKE, Brian James. ■ 43604 #038-40-2004 L2004 **ORS** *012
BOBBEY, Adam John. ■ 43614 #038-43-2008 *012
BOBO, Robert Carl. 2109 HUGHES DR, STE 860 43606 #030-06-1968 L1970 **GE** *020 †55
BODE, Ernest Geo, Jr. 2150 W CENTRAL AVE 43606 #038-43-1986 L1990 **IM PD** *020 †20
BODI, Shirley Marie. 2051 W CENTRAL AVE 43606 #038-43-1992 L1993 **FM** *040 †18
BODINE, Kristen Lee. 7140 PORT SYLVANIA DR, STE 300 43617 #038-43-1996 L1997 **FSM** *020 †18
BOEHM, Kathryn Elaine. 3454 OAK ALLEY CT, STE 210 43606 #038-43-1986 L1988 **PD ADL** *020 †55
BOHMAN, Keith Daniel. ■ 43615 #038-43-2006 L2006 **PTH** *012
BOHMAN, Summer Lee. ■ 43615 #038-43-2006 L2006 **PTH** *012
BOLLINENI, Aruna. 3000 ARLINGTON AVE 43614 #496-24-2004 L2007 **N** *012
BOLOVAN, Daniel Thos. ■ 43615 #038-41-1958 L1958 **R** *071 †80,28
BOOTH, Robert Lee, Jr. 3000 ARLINGTON AVE, MED UNIV OF OHIO PATHOLOGY 43614 #038-43-1985 L1986 **PTH HMP** *062 †50
BORIEUX, Marcyriane. 3045 ARLINGTON AVE, CO GME- RM 330 - 43614 #038-43-2003 L2004 **PD** *020
BORRILLO, Donato Joseph. 2150 W CENTRAL AVE 43606 #035-06-1990 L1991 **AM** *020 †70
BORST, Marilyn Jane. 3065 ARLINGTON AVE, DARLING HALL ROOM 2134 43614 #017-20-1990 L2004 **CCS CRS** *040 †85
BOSIO, Raul Martin. 320-MUL3045 ARLING, CO GME-RM 43614 #132-02-1997 L2007 **GS** *012
BOSS, Devin N. 2213 CHERRY ST 43608 #003-75-2006, ▲ L2006 **EM** *012
BOUCOURAS, Marios C. ■ 43623 #418-01-1944 L1962 **ORS** *071
BOUREY, Raymond Earle. 4041 W SYLVANIA AVE # 202, REG CTR FOR SLEEP MEDICINE 43623 #016-45-1982 L1994 **SME IM** *020 †20

■ = Address Information Privacy Protected

BOUTROS, Mounir. 5951 RENAISSANCE PL, STE C 43623 #875-01-1986 L1991 **D P** *020 †75,15
BOVINO, Jerald A. 1000 REGENCY CT, STE 212 43623 #035-06-1971 L1979 **OPH** *071 †35
BOWEN, Robert Tilton. 3000 ARLINGTON AVE 43614 #305-01-2005 L2006 **IM** *100
BOWLUS, Thomas P. 2020 STARR AVE 43605 #025-01-1951 L1952 **FM** *071
BOYLE, Emmett T, Jr. 3500 EXECUTIVE PKWY, GENITO-URINARY SURGEONS 43606 #038-43-1984 L1992 **U** *020 †95
BRACE, Cathi Ann. 3120 GLENDALE AVE STE 130, MEDICAL UNIVERSITY OF OHIO 43614 #038-43-2003 L2003 **PD** *100 †55
BRADFORD, Mark A. ■ 43609 #038-43-2008 *012
BRADY, Brenda Marie. 525 HAMILTON ST, STE 101A 43604 #038-43-1991 L1994 **P** *020 †75
BRAIDA, Anthony Louis. 3000 ARLINGTON AVE 43614 #038-43-1988 L1992 **AN** *020 †05
BRAR, Balhinder S. 2222 CHERRY ST, STE 1700 43608 #495-08-1988 L2004 **NEP** *020 †20
BRAUN, Theodore Mark. 2000 REGENCY CT, STE 100 43623 #038-06-1975 L1975 **GS** *020 †85
BRENNER, James Robt. 2914 S REPUBLIC BLVD 43615 #038-43-1985 L1985 **AN** *020 †05
BRENNER, Richard Alfred. 2142 N COVE BLVD 43606 #038-40-1959 L1959 **AN** *071 †05
BRICKMAN, Kristopher Ray. 3000 ARLINGTON AVE, MED COLLEGE OF OHIO HOSP 43614 #038-45-1983 L1984 **EM ESM** *030 †16
BRIEL, Mark Alan. 4853 MONROE ST, STE 3 43623 #047-05-1980 L1984 **OBG** *020 †30
BRIGHT, Justin Lee. 2213 CHERRY ST 43608 #654-01-2007 L2007 **EM** *012
BRINKER, Ray Allen. 3000 ARLINGTON AVE, DEPT OF RADIOLOGY 43614 #018-03-1957 L1985 **R RNR** *071 †80
BRITTON, Andrew James. 2222 CHERRY ST, ST VINCENT MED CTR/HOSP 43608 #038-40-1982 L1986 **PTH** *020 †50
BRODBECK, Suzanne Frances. 930 S DETROIT AVE, NORTHCOAST BEHAVIORAL HEAL 43614 #038-43-2000 L2000 **P** *020 †75
BROOKFIELD, Ernest Gordon. 3000 ARLINGTON AVE 43614 #025-01-1955 L1958 **PD PDC** *071 †55
BRUCH, Steven Walter. 2142 N COVE BLVD 43606 #016-11-1987 L2002 **GS** *020 †85
BRUENING, Frank Raymond. 3740 W SYLVANIA AVE, STE 500 43623 #038-40-1969 L1970 **OBG** *020 †30
BRUGGEMANN, Wm Gerhard. 2150 W CENTRAL AVE, WOMEN'S CLINIC 43606 #038-40-1959 L1959 **OBG** *020 †30
BRUHL, Steven Richard. 3000 ARLINGTON AVE 43614 #038-43-2005 L2005 **IM** *012
BRUNNER, John Edward. 3140 W CENTRAL AVE 43606 #028-34-1980 L1981 **DIA END** *020 †20
BRUNNER, John F. 2238 JEFFERSON AVE, ALLDREN EOCC 43604 #028-34-1953 L1958 **ILI END** *071 †20
BRUNOT, Eddy Severe. 158 DARTMOUTH DR 43614 #440-01-1992 L2000 **P** *100 †75
BRYM, Anthony W. 5810 SOUTHWYCK BLVD, NES 43614 #759-03-1969 L1976 **GS** *020 †16
BUDINSKY, Robert Patrick. ■ 43615 #038-43-2008 *012
BUEHLER, Mark Alan, II. ■ 43614 #038-43-2008 *012
BUENCAMINO, Alice Jane C. 1622 SPIELBUSCH AVE, LUCAS COUNTY CORRECTIONS C 43604 #748-10-1984 L1991 **IM** *020
BUERK, Aaron August. 2121 HUGHES DR, STE 980 43606 #010-02-1998 L1999 **ORS** *020 †40
BUGANSKI, Raymond Richard. 2121 HUGHES DR, MARY ELLEN K PIZZA MD 43606 #028-34-1957 L1958 **PD** *071 †55
BUI, Ann Huynh. ■ 43614 #038-43-2008 *012
BURCHFIELD, John Clarence. 4235 SECOR RD 43623 #038-40-1965 L1965 **AN** *020 †05
BURKET, Mark Wm. 3000 ARLINGTON AVE, RM 1192 43614 #038-40-1979 L1981 **CD** *020 †20
BURLEN, Laura Lile. 1015 GARDEN LAKE PKWY 43614 #038-43-2001 L2003 **FM** *020 †18 ‡
BURLINGAME, Alan Lee, II. 2121 HUGHES DR, STE 300 43606 #038-45-1992 L1994 **PD** *020 †55
BUTLER, Candilee. 2000 REGENCY CT, STE 100 43623 #038-43-1982 L1987 **GS** *020 †85
BUTT, Sonia Taimur. 2200 JEFFERSON AVE, MERCY HEALTH PARTNERS FP R 43604 #704-20-1993 L2002 **FM** *100 †18
BUTTO, Fouad. 2121 HUGHES DR, STE 750 43606 #550-02-1978 L1990 **PD PDC** *020 †55
CABRERA-RAFANAN, Claudia. 3045 ARLINGTON AVE, MULFORD LI 43614 #748-11-1993 L1999 **AN** *100
CALDERON, Eduardo F. ■ 43615 #231-03-1958 L1974 **N** *071 †75
CALDERON, Eduardo Tomas. 3949 SUNFOREST CT, TOLEDO NEUROLOGICAL 43623 #038-40-1986 L1991 **N OS** *020 †75
CALDERON, Marlene Sayoc. 3000 ARLINGTON AVE 43614 #036-01-1994 L2004 **PS** *020 †65
CAMERON, Donald K. ■ 43617 #038-40-1949 L1949 **GP** *071
CAMPBELL, Donald Bruce. 2109 HUGHES DR 43606 #038-40-1967 L1968 **GS** *071
CAMPBELL, Earl Wm, Jr. 3120 GLENDALE AVE, RM 0012 RUPPERT HEALTH CEN 43614 #035-45-1962 L1965 **HEM IM** *040 †20
CANTOR, Cathy Lynn. 2865 N REYNOLDS RD, STE 130 43615 #001-06-2001 L2001 **FSM** *100 †55
CARLSON, Glenn Harold. 4235 SECOR RD 43623 #038-41-1981 L1987 **HS ORS** *020 †40
CARLSON, Kathleen Sue. 2142 N COVE BLVD 43606 #038-41-1981 L1987 **NPM** *020 †55
CARONE, Heather Lyn. 2213 CHERRY ST 43608 #038-43-2001 L2005 **EM** *100 †16
CARRIGAN, Catherine G. 4411 N HOLLAND SYLVANIA RD, STE 201 43623 #038-43-2001 L2002 **FM** *020 †18 ‡
CARROLL, Jennifer Lee. 3840 WOODLEY RD STE B 43606 #038-43-1997 L2000 **OBG** *020 †30
CARSON, Stephanie Elaine. ■ 43620 #038-43-2008 *012
CARVALHO, Henrique L F. 3438 GRANITE CIR 43617 #187-11-1968 L1979 **PS HS** *020 †65
CASABIANCA, Andrew Bruno. 3000 ARLINGTON AVE, DEPT OF ANESTHLGY RM 2195 43614 #038-43-1988 L1992 **AN** *020 †05
CASEY, Stephanie Nicole. ■ 43615 #038-43-2008 *012
CASON, Frederick D. 3065 ARLINGTON AVE, DEPT OF SURGERY 43614 #028-34-1978 L2005 **GS TRS** *020 †85
CASTILLO, Arturo. 313 JEFFERSON AVE 43604 #649-01-1956 L1962 **FM** *071 †18
CASTILLO, Michael Brian. ■ 43615 #019-02-2005 **GS** *012
CASTILLO SANG, Mario Augu. 3000 ARLINGTON AVE 43614 #649-52-2004 L2005 **GS** *012
CEDARGREN, Amy Marie. 3400 MEIJER DR, PEDIATRICARE ASSOCIATES 43617 #038-43-1991 L1996 **PD** *020 †55
CELIK, Ziya. 4235 SECOR RD 43623 #902-10-1966 L1975 **GS** *020 †85
CERILLI, Gregory James. 2109 HUGHES DR, STE 220 43606 #041-02-1993 L1995 **GS** *020 †85
CERVANTES, David R, III. 2658 W LASKEY RD 43613 #038-41-1991 L1995 **DR** *020 †80
CHAHAL, Bhupinder Singh. 6800 W CENTRAL AVE STE D3 43617 #495-29-1976 L1983 **P** *020
CHAHAL, Mangeet Kaur. ■ 43615 #038-43-2005 L2005 **IM** *012
CHAKRAVARTY, Jyoti M. 3140 W CENTRAL AVE 43606 #495-45-1967 L1977 **IM END** *020 †20
CHAKRAVARTY, Supriya. 4235 SECOR RD 43623 #495-45-1968 L1977 **CD IM** *020 †20
CHAND, Kishan. 3045 ARLINGTON AVE, DEPT OF GME 43614 #704-08-2001 L2005 **FP** *012
CHANG, James Ching Hwa. 1500 N SUPERIOR ST STE 004, JC PAIN CLINIC 43604 #244-04-1973 L1981 **AN** *020
CHAPPELL, Barbara Anne. 2142 N COVE BLVD, TOLEDO CHILDREN'S HOSPITAL 43606 #030-05-1985 L1997 **NPM PD** *020 †55
CHAUDHARY, Rekha Tripathi. 3000 ARLINGTON AVE, MS 1186 43614 #038-44-1998 L1999 **ON** *020 †20
CHEN, Shaoxiong. 3000 ARLINGTON AVE, UNIV OF TOLEDO 43614 #243-52-1987 L2005 **PTH** *012
CHETHANA, Mukkamalla Umam. 2213 CHERRY ST 43608 #495-62-2003 **TY** *012
CHILOFLISCHI, Laura. 320-MUL3045 ARLING, CO GME-RM 43614 #781-05-2000 L2007 **OBG** *012
CHINYADZA, Tanyanyiwa Web. 2222 CHERRY ST, STE 1400 43608 #422-01-2001 L2006 **ID** *020
CHIRICOLO, Antonio. PO BOX 10008 43699 #305-01-2007 L2007 **AN** *012
CHITKARA, Nishant. 3000 ARLINGTON AVE 43614 #495-36-2004 **PTH** *012
CHRISTNER, Jennifer Gold. 3000 ARLINGTON AVE, DEPT OF PEDIATRICS 43614 #038-43-1995 L1998 **PD** *020 †55
CHUTANI, Surendra Kumar. ■ 43614 #495-74-1976 L2006 **IM** *012
CIFUENTES, Douglas I. 2409 CHERRY ST, STE 302 43608 #022-75-1995, ▲ L1999 **IM** *020
CINTRON, Emma Lisette. 3000 ARLINGTON AVE 43614 #042-01-1973 L1981 **P CHP** *075
CLARK, Bruce Kendall. ■ 43606 #025-01-1956 L1957 **GP P** *071
CLARK, Leo Jos Patrick. 2222 CHERRY ST, STE M200 43608 #010-01-1970 L1976 **NS** *020 †25 ‡
CLARK, Mary Williams. 1565 S BYRNE RD, STE 100 43614 #008-01-1967 L1997 **OP OS** *020 †40
CLARK, Michael Lawrence. ■ 43620 #038-40-1974 L1976 **AN** *020 †05
CLARK, Paul Michael. 2213 CHERRY ST # 303 43608 #033-05-1968 L1976 **VS** *020 †85
CLAY HUFFORD, Susan D. 2121 HUGHES DR STE 300 43606 #038-41-1984 L1988 **PD** *020 †55
CLEMENS, Adam Jacob. ■ 43614 #038-43-2008 *012
COCHRAN, Carson P. 2213 CHERRY ST 43608 #038-40-1956 L1956 **PD** *030 †55
COLLIER, Annette Kay. 3909 WOODLEY RD 43606 #038-43-1987 L1989 **IM** *020 †20
COLLINS, Gary Thos. 3922 WOODLEY RD, STE 100 43606 #038-40-1980 L1980 **PD** *020 †55
COLTURI, Thomas Joseph. 3439 GRANITE CIR 43617 #038-43-1978 L1989 **GE** *075 †20
COLVILLE, Craig Wm. 2865 N REYNOLDS RD STE 250 43615 #017-20-1983 L1990 **PS** *020 †85,65
COLYER, William Randall, Jr. 3000 ARLINGTON AVE, MEDICAL COLLEGE OF OHIO 43614 #038-43-1996 L2000 **CD IC** *020 †20
COMEROTA, Anthony James. 2109 HUGHES DR STE 400, JOBST VASCULAR CENTER 43606 #041-13-1974 L1978 **VS GS** *020 †85
COMPEAN, Jose Ricardo. 2213 CHERRY ST 43608 #130-01-2005 L2005 **FP** *012
CONLAN, Barry Owen. 3020 N MCCORD RD 43615 #038-43-1987 L1989 **FM** *020 †18
CONWAY, Anita Golberg. 2213 CHERRY ST, ST. VINCENT MERCY MEDICAL 43608 #038-43-2005 L2005 **EM** *012
COOK-KHAZAN, Karen Lynn. 3333 GLENDALE AVE, VETERANS ADMINISTRATION OU 43614 #038-43-1986 L1989 **IM** *020
COOMBS, Robert Jack. 3000 ARLINGTON AVE, MED COLLEGE OF OHIO 43614 #038-43-1977 L1978 **R** *020 †80
COOPER, Christopher John. 3000 ARLINGTON AVE, MEDICAL COLLEGE OF OHIO 43614 #038-41-1988 L1994 **CD** *020 †20
COOPER, Jeffrey Scott. 2213 CHERRY ST 43608 #030-05-1987 L1993 **EM** *020 †16
COOPER, Simone Selena. 3045 ARLINGTON AVE, CO GME- RM 330 - 43614 #305-01-2004 L2005 **AN** *012
COX, Donald L. 3000 REGENCY CT, STE 105 43623 #030-06-1951 L1952 **AN** *071
COX, Donnie Lee. 3435 KENWOOD BLVD 43606 #039-01-1995 L2000 **DR** *020 †80
CRANMER, Linus Reed. 2142 N COVE BLVD 43606 #025-01-1944 L1951 **OTO** *071 †45
CRESCENZO, Donald Gerard. 2109 HUGHES DR, STE 720 43606 #010-02-1988 L2000 **TS** *020 †85,90
CRIDER, Ernest Ford. 2142 N COVE BLVD 43606 #020-02-1946 L1950 **AN** *071 †05
CRILE, Jason Donald. ■ 43615 #038-43-2008 *012
CROCKETT, Roy E. ■ 43623 #038-40-1951 L1951 **FM** *071
CROTTE, Fernando. 3900 SUNFOREST CT, STE 229 43623 #038-43-1980 L1983 **IM IMG** *020 †20
CROTTY, Michael James, III. ■ 43609 #038-43-2008 *012
CUATICO, Agnes Tan. 2150 W CENTRAL AVE, FL 3 43606 #748-10-1974 L1986 **EM GP** *020
CULLEN, Marc Lemay. 2121 HUGHES DR STE 620, CHILDRENS SURGICAL SRVC OF 43606 #043-01-1978 L2004 **PDS** *020 †85
CULLER, Amy Sue. 4841 MONROE ST, STE 103 43623 #038-43-1995 L1997 **DR OS** *020 †80
CUMMINGS, Tracy Suzanne. 3120 GLENDALE AVE - RUPP, ADULT PSYCHIATRY- RM 0079 43614 #038-43-2005 L2007 **P** *012
DABOUL, Isam. 2616 GRAY FOX CURV 43617 #875-01-1989 L2001 **GE** *020 †20
D'AGOSTINO, Rosemary. 3740 W SYLVANIA AVE, STE 250 43623 #038-43-1987 L1989 **PD** *020 †55
DAIBER, Robert Raymond. 2526 N REYNOLDS RD # 1 43615 #038-43-1991 L1992 **FM** *020 †18
D AMATO, Luigi Orlando, Jr. 3740 W SYLVANIA AVE # 103 43623 #038-43-1976 L1977 **OBG** *020 †30
DAMER, Brent Michael. 2213 CHERRY ST 43608 #018-75-2003, ▲ L2003 **ORS** *012
DANIELS, Kettlie Joseph. ■ 43609 #038-43-1987 L1988 **P** *020 †75
DASANI, Haridas Madhavji. 1500 N SUPERIOR ST, STE 310 43604 #495-23-1971 L1976 **GP** *020
DASANI, Suresh Madhavji. 2755 SHORELAND AVE 43611 #495-23-1981 L1986 **FM** *020 †18
DAVENPORT, Charles Wm. MED COLLEGE OH CS 10008 43699 #025-01-1961 L1976 **CHP P** *040 †75
DAVID, Christopher Kent. ■ 43606 #038-43-2006 L2006 **EM** *012
DAVIDSON, Benjamin Harris. ■ 43609 #038-43-2008 *012
DE BEUKELAER, Martin M. 2222 CHERRY ST STE 2300, MERCY CHILDRENS HOSPITAL 43608 #165-01-1965 L1980 **PN PD** *020 †55
DE CARVALHO, Carlos A. 4895 MONROE ST, STE 102 43623 #187-06-1972 L1980 **N** *020 †75
DEETER, David Perry. 1455 W ALEXIS RD 43612 #038-40-1977 L1999 **OM AM** *030 †70
DE FRONZO, Nicholas Romeo. ■ 43614 #561-01-1959 L1964 **GP** *071
DE LAMATER, Paul Virden. 3140 W CENTRAL AVE 43606 #038-40-1969 L1969 **PDE PD** *020 †55
DELAPP, Dennis Kearney. 4041 W SYLVANIA AVE, STE 100 43623 #019-02-1986 L1987 **FM** *040 †18
DE MIGUEL, Mariano H. 4235 SECOR RD 43623 #132-01-1982 L1999 **IM NEP** *020 †20
DERICK, Dale Edwin. 2150 W CENTRAL AVE 43606 #025-01-1971 L1980 **OBG** *071 †30
DE ROSA, Robert Thos. 3740 W SYLVANIA AVE, STE 103 43623 #038-43-1986 L1987 **OBG** *020 †30
DE SAINT VICTOR, Paul R. 2213 CHERRY ST, EMERGENCY DEPARTMENT CONSU 43608 #065-09-1971 L1979 **EM** *040 †16
DESSNER, Daniel Adam. ■ 43614 #038-41-1988 L1993 **DR** *020 †80

DEV, Santosh. 3922 WOODLEY RD, STE 100 43606 #495-65-1969 L1978 **PD** *020 †55
DEVARAHALLY, Sharada Shre. ■ 43608 #495-09-2001 L2003 **NPM** *012 †55
DIDIO, Arthur Silva. 1920 PARKWOOD AVE 43604 #038-41-1990 L1992 **ORS** *020
DIEROLF, Sandra Lillian. ■ 43614 #003-01-1994 L1997 **EM** *020 †16
DIETHELM, James David. 2213 CHERRY ST 43608 #038-41-1978 L1978 **FM FSM** *020 †18
DILLON, Thomas Kearns. 6591 W CENTRAL AVE, STE 105 43617 #010-02-1962 L1962 **D** *020 †15
DI SALLE, Robert Stephen. 4841 MONROE ST, STE 103 43623 #038-43-1994 L1997 **VIR** *020 †80
DISTLER, Michael Kenneth. ■ 43614 #038-43-2008 *012
DIZON, Maria Felicitas Me. ■ 43604 #748-10-1992 L2005 **FP** *012
DO, Cuong Quoc. 2142 N COVE BLVD, EMERGENCY CENTER 43606 #016-42-1997 L1999 **EM GS** *020 †16
DOBELBOWER, Ralph R, Jr. 3000 ARLINGTON AVE 43614 #041-02-1967 L1979 **RO ON** *071 †80
DOERFLER, Richard Bruce. ■ 43623 #016-43-1975 L1976 **DR OS** *071 †80
DOERMANN, Edward Leo. 4235 SECOR RD, SUITE 1 43623 #038-41-1943 L1950 **GS** *071 †85
DOLLMAN, Allison Lucille. ■ 43614 #038-43-2006 L2006 **FP** *012
DONABEDIAN, Haig. 3120 GLENDALE AVE 43614 #008-01-1975 L1982 **IM** *040 †20
DOONER, John James. 2409 CHERRY ST, STE 305 43608 #019-02-1979 L1986 **AN** *05
DORONILA, Querico D. ■ 43614 #748-01-1954 L1967 **CHP** *071
DOSICK, Steven Martin. 2109 HUGHES DR, STE 550 43606 #016-11-1969 L1974 **VS** *020 †85
DOUKIDES, Panagiotis T. 4027 N HOLLAND SYLVANIA RD 43623 #418-02-1976 L1981 **P** *020 †75
DOUMET, Bouchra S. 2127 JEFFERSON AVE 43604 #875-01-1990 L2000 **FM** *020 †18
DOYLE, Malcolm Thomas. 7111 W CENTRAL AVE 43617 #038-43-1994 L1999 **DR** *020 †80
DRAHEIM, Jerry W. 3900 SUNFOREST CT 43623 #041-01-1953 L1958 **OPH** *071 †35
DRAPER, David Edward. 2222 CHERRY ST, PEDIATRIC CARDIOLOGY; ST. 43608 #060-01-1981 L2005 **PDC** *020 †55
D'SOUZA, Deborah Lynne. 3120 GLENDALE AVE 43614 #035-06-1994 L2002 **OBG** *020 †30
DUCKETT, Sara Jane. ■ 43609 #038-43-2006 L2006 **GS** *012
DUGGAN, Joan Marie. 3120 GLENDALE AVE, THE UNIVERSITY OF TOLEDO-H 43614 #038-43-1989 L1992 **ID IM** *020 †20
DUNOSKI, Stefen F. ■ 43623 #957-02-1966 L1976 **OS** *020
DURHAM, Samuel J. 3065 ARLINGTON AVE, SURGEONS OF NW OHIO INC 43614 #024-01-1983 L1993 **TS** *020 †85,90
DUTY, Joseph Edward, Jr. 2200 JEFFERSON AVE, FL 4 43604 #038-40-1964 L1964 **AN** *071
DZIAD, Peter Michael. 2109 HUGHES DR, STE 220 43606 #038-43-1982 L1985 **GS** *020 †85
EARLY, Martha Evelyn. 1946 N 13TH ST, STE 301 43604 #038-40-1966 L1966 **PTH** *020 †50 ‡
EBRAHEIM, Nabil Anwar. 3065 ARLINGTON AVE, DEPT OF ORTHO SURG UNIV OF 43614 #915-02-1975 L1985 **ORS OTR** *020 †40
ECONOMIDES, Vassilis C. 3000 ARLINGTON AVE, MED COLL OF OHIO MEDICINE 43614 #409-05-1991 L1999 **CD** *100 †20
EGGLESTON, Wm Duffney. 2142 N COVE BLVD 43606 #038-40-1956 L1956 **RO R** *071 †80
EHLINGER, Thomas Michael. ■ 43604 #010-02-1984 L2007 **OBG** *020 †30
EISNER, Arlynne Mildred. ■ 43610 #003-01-2003 L2007 **FP** *012
ELANGO, Subha. 3045 ARLINGTON AVE, DEPT OF GME 43614 #495-65-1999 L2006 **FP** *012
EL BROLOSY, Basem Mohamed. 117 MAIN ST, PHYSICIAN 43605 #915-03-1991 L2005 **FP** *012
ELKAMBERGY, Hussam Mohame. 2213 CHERRY ST, DEPT OF INTERNAL MED 43608 #286-12-1999 L2006 **IM** *012
ELKHATIB, Mounir B. 4129 N HOLLAND SYLVANIA RD 43623 #330-04-1969 L1973 **IM** *020 †20
ELLIOT, Ian Scott. 4235 SECOR RD 43623 #023-01-1978 L1979 **END** *020 †20
ELLIS, Christine Diane. 4411 N HOLLAND SYLVANIA RD, STE 102 43623 #038-43-1981 L1982 **FM IM** *020 †18
ELMER, Lawrence Wm. 3000 ARLINGTON AVE MS 1195, DEPT OF NEUROLOGY 43614 #011-03-1987 L1998 **N** *020 †75
ELROD, Walter Lee. 2142 N COVE BLVD, THE TOLEDO HOSPITAL 43606 #016-11-1997 L1998 **EM** *020 †16
ELSAMALOTY, Haitham M. 3000 ARLINGTON AVE, MEDICAL COLLEGE OF OHIO 43614 #915-03-1987 L1997 **NM R** *020 †80,28
EL SAYYAD, Mohammad Mahmo. 3045 ARLINGTON AVE, DEPT OF GME 43614 #605-01-2002 L2006 **FP** *012
EL-SHAFIE, Mohamed. 2142 N COVE BLVD 43606 #330-04-1957 L1975 **PDS** *071 †85
ELTAHAWY, Ehab Ahmed T. 3045 ARLINGTON AVE, CO GME- RM 330 - 43614 #915-04-1994 L2004 **IC** *012 †20
EL-TAJI, Amal Mahamad H. 3401 GLENDALE AVE STE 212 43614 #875-01-1972 L1978 **OBG** *020 †30
ELTAKI, Ahmed Mohamed. 2409 CHERRY ST, STE 305 43608 #915-03-1975 L1991 **AN** *020 †05
EMCH, Kelly Marie. 3740 W SYLVANIA AVE, STE 100 43623 #038-40-1989 L1990 **FM** *020 †18
EMMERT, Gregor K, Sr. 3500 EXECUTIVE PKWY 43606 #038-40-1963 L1963 **U** *071 †95
EMMERT, Gregor Kreul, Jr. 3500 EXECUTIVE PKWY 43606 #038-40-1988 L1994 **UP U** *020 †95
ENGOREN, Milo Crotona. 2409 CHERRY ST, STE 305 43608 #050-02-1982 L1983 **AN CCM** *020 †20,05
ERICKSON, Grant Bryan. ■ 43615 #005-12-2003 L2003 **GS** *012
ERIKSEN, David Edwin. 3715 AIRPORT HWY STE C 43615 #038-40-1965 L1965 **OPH** *020 †35
ERULKAR, Ruth Solomon. 3454 OAK ALLEY CT, STE 108 43606 #495-28-1965 L1983 **CHP P** *020
ERVIN, David Christopher. 1830 LYNBROOK DR 43614 #038-44-1999 L1999 **ORS** *020
EUDELA, Segunda Suson. 635 N ERIE ST 43604 #748-09-1966 L1976 **PTH GP** *020
FACEY, William Kermit. 3740 W SYLVANIA AVE, STE 100 43623 #025-07-1976 L1977 **FM** *020 †18
FADELL, Michael Frederick. 2658 W LASKEY RD, FL 2 43613 #038-43-1972 L1976 **R** *020 †80
FADELL, Michael Frederick. 3000 REGENCY CT, STE 105 43623 #038-43-2003 L2004 **DR** *012
FAHED, Samir. ■ 43617 #875-01-1997 L2006 **AN** *012
FAIRCHILD, Darlene. 6800 W CENTRAL AVE, STE K 43617 #035-06-1985 L1990 **FM** *020 †18
FALK, Derik Michael. ■ 43606 #038-43-2008 *012
FANELLY, Lawrence J. 2800 W CENTRAL AVE 43606 #018-75-1981, ▲ L1982 **PTH** *020 †50
FARBER, Stephen Jay. 4235 SECOR RD 43623 #035-08-1968 L1976 **RHU IM** *020 †20
FARJO, Qais Anastas. 2865 N REYNOLDS RD, STE 170 43615 #025-01-1995 L2004 **OPH** *020 †35
FAROOQ, Amjad. ■ 43614 #704-09-1982 L1999 **FM** *020 †18 ‡
FAROOQ, Shabana. 2127 JEFFERSON AVE 43604 #704-09-1981 L1999 **FM** *020 †18
FAROOQI, Ruby. 2127 JEFFERSON AVE, CO MERCY HLTH PARTNERS FAM 43604 #495-51-1995 L2000 **FM** *020 †18
FARRELL, Steven James. 3065 ARLINGTON AVE 43614 #038-43-1992 L1996 **PM** *020 †60

FATH, John Jos. 3000 ARLINGTON AVE, UNIV OF TOLEDO MED CTR 43614 #036-07-1979 L2005 **TRS GS** *020 †85
FATIMA, Huma. 3045 ARLINGTON AVE, C/O MCOT-MED EDU DEPT RM 3 43614 #704-20-1997 L2002 **PCP** *100 †50
FAYEZ, Fady Shawky. PO BOX 10008 43699 #915-04-2001 **IM** *100
FAZILI, Amna. 3000 ARLINGTON AVE 43614 #495-51-1969 **R** *100
FAZZARI, Theodore Ernest. ■ 43614 #561-01-1975 L1977 **OS** *100
FEDERMAN, Douglas Jay. 3000 ARLINGTON AVE, MAIL STOP #1186 43614 #038-43-1988 L1991 **IM** *020 †20
FEDERMAN, Susan M. 3909 WOODLEY RD, STE 500 43606 #038-43-1988 L1989 **FM** *020 †18
FELL, Richard Arthur. 4235 SECOR RD, TOLEDO CLINIC 43623 #016-43-1973 L1979 **CD IM** *020 †20
FELLER, Gretchen Delene. 3000 ARLINGTON AVE, GENERAL SURGERY DEPT 43614 #038-43-1994 L1997 **GS** *020 †85
FENG, Yongqing. 3000 ARLINGTON AVE 43614 #243-95-1985 L2004 **IM** *020 †20
FENTON, Paul John. 2865 N REYNOLDS RD, STE 160 43615 #038-43-1988 L1991 **ORS OSM** *020 †40
FERGUSON-RAYPORT, Shirley. 1565 S BYRNE RD 43614 #035-15-1947 L1969 **N P** *072 †75
FERRARA, Gina Isabella. 3000 ARLINGTON AVE, DEPARTMENT OF PSYCHIATRY, 43614 #038-43-2002 L2002 **P** *012
FIELD, Jean Krumrine. ■ 43606 #025-01-1940 L1946 **OS** *071
FIGY, Rex N. 3020 N MCCORD RD 43615 #038-43-1991 L1992 **FM** *020 †18
FILATOFF, Gregory. 3000 ARLINGTON AVE, DEPT. OF ANESTHESIOLOGY 43614 #038-43-2002 L2002 **AN** *100 †05
FILIPIAK, Charles Louis. 3355 GLENDALE AVE, # 125 43614 #038-43-1988 L1995 **GE** *020 †20
FINE, Burril Brook. ■ 43617 #067-02-1954 L1958 **CD IM** *071
FINKEN, Randall Lee. 3909 WOODLEY RD, STE 500 43606 #038-40-1963 L1963 **FM** *020 †18
FIORE, Michael Angelo. 3840 WOODLEY RD, STE B 43606 #561-17-1956 L1958 **OBG** *071 †30
FITZGERALD, Sarah Elizabe. ■ 43606 #038-41-2005 L2005 **PD** *012
FLICKINGER, Allen Lane. 2109 HUGHES DR STE 920 43606 #038-43-1988 L1989 **NEP IM** *020 †20
FOETISCH, Christopher A. 4235 SECOR RD 43623 #038-43-1994 L1996 **ORS OSM** *040
FOLLEY, Andrew Geo, Jr. 3740 W SYLVANIA AVE, STE 103 43623 #038-43-1980 L1983 **OBG** *020 †30
FORD, Jeffrey. 5843 RYEWYCK DR 43614 #038-43-2001 L2001 **EM** *020 †16
FOSTER, Scott Alan. 3065 ARLINGTON AVE, HEALTH SCIEN 43614 #038-43-2005 L2005 **ORS** *012
FRANCIS, Todd Paul. 7140 PORT SYLVANIA DR, STE 300 43617 #010-02-2001 2004 **FM FSM** *020 †18
FRANZBLAU, David Robt. 3425 EXECUTIVE PKWY 43606 #025-12-1980 L1992 **P** *020 †75
FREDRICK, Robert Scott. 2051 W CENTRAL AVE 43606 #025-12-1986 L1987 **FM** *040 †18
FREEMAN, Steven Dale. 7140 PORT SYLVANIA DR, STE 300 43617 #038-43-1990 L1992 **FM** *020 †18
FRENCH, Linda M. 3000 ARLINGTON AVE, STE M RUPPERT CTR 43614 #231-04-1988 L2007 **FM** *040 †18
FREY, Theresa Marie. ■ 43617 #038-43-2008 *012
FRIES, James C. ■ 43606 #041-12-1950 L1951 **GP** *071
FROGAMENI, Anthony D, III. 2865 N REYNOLDS RD STE 160 43615 #038-43-1985 L1989 **ORS OSM** *020 †40
FRUGH, Ahmed. 1530 N SUPERIOR ST, RM 4802 43604 #902-01-1952 L1961 **N** *071
FUNKE, Barbara Mary. 525 HAMILTON ST, STE 101A 43604 #038-43-1985 L1986 **P** *020 †75
FURICCHIA, James Vincent. 1500 N SUPERIOR ST, STE 302 43604 #025-07-1989 L1993 **OPH** *020 †35
FYNES, Evan Michael. ■ 43606 #038-43-2008 *012
GABEL, Christopher M. ■ 43606 #038-43-2007 L2007 **TY** *012
GADOMSKI, Amy Kathleen. ■ 43606 #038-43-2008 *012
GALE, Steven S. 2109 HUGHES DR STE 550 43606 #035-01-1974 L1982 **VS** *020 †85
GALLAGHER, Mark Dennis. 5800 PARK CENTER CT, STE A 43615 #038-43-1984 L1985 **IM** *020 †05
GALLUP, William Pessefall. 2914 S REPUBLIC BLVD 43615 #038-43-1987 L1990 **AN** *020 †05
GARD, Elloise Carol. 1565 S BYRNE RD 43614 #038-40-1985 L1988 **IM** *020 †20
GARLAND, Joseph M. 3540 SECOR RD STE 309 43606 #008-01-1952 L1953 **P** *071
GARRITANO, Nina Marie. 2865 N REYNOLDS RD 43615 #038-43-1992 L1994 **AN** *020 †05
GARVIN, Edward John. 2213 CHERRY ST 43608 #016-43-1961 L1968 **OPH** *071 †35
GATTO-WEIS, Cara. 3000 ARLINGTON AVE 43614 #033-06-1994 L2003 **PTH PCP** *020 †50
GEHLING, Daniel J. ■ 43613 #056-06-2003 L2003 **ORS** *012
GEHLOT, Upender. 3045 ARLINGTON AVE, DEPT OF GME 43614 #495-72-2004 L2006 **P** *012
GEHRING, Richard F. 3909 WOODLEY RD, STE 500 43606 #038-40-1956 L1956 **FM** *071
GEMMILL, W David. 2222 CHERRY ST, STE 1650 43608 #038-40-1959 L1959 **PD OS** *071 †55
GENNARI, Kristen Elizabet. ■ 43614 #038-43-2005 L2005 **FP** *012
GENTCHEV, Lynda Irene. 3045 ARLINGTON AVE, C/O MCOT=MED EDU DEPT RM 3 43614 #198-02-1998 L2002 **PTH** *100
GEORGIADIS, Gregory Minas. 2121 HUGHES DR, STE 310 43606 #017-20-1984 L1989 **ORS OTR** *020 †40
GERACIOTI, Thomas Dino. 2121 HUGHES DR, MC INTOSH TOWER 43606 #010-02-1959 L1961 **NEP IM** *020 †20
GERARD, Gary. 1000 REGENCY CT, STE 208 43623 #041-09-1975 L1990 **N** *020 †75
GERKEN, Sarah Ann. ■ 43623 #038-43-2006 L2006 **FM** *012
GERKEN, Thomas Wm. 3000 ARLINGTON AVE 43614 #038-43-1985 L1986 **AN** *020 †05
GERSTENMAIER-LARA, Luis R. 2238 JEFFERSON AVE 43604 #649-01-1967 L1973 **END** *020
GHAI, Vikas. 3000 ARLINGTON AVE 43614 #495-98-2000 L2004 **FM** *100
GHERMAY, Timnit. 2200 JEFFERSON AVE, CO ST VINCENT MERCY-MED ED 43604 #025-01-2003 L2003 **DR** *012
GILL, Satwant K. 544 E WOODRUFF AVE, UNISON BEHAVIOR HEALTH GRO 43604 #495-03-1974 L1996 **P** *020
GILLESPIE, Carmella Mary. 5555 AIRPORT HWY, EYE INSTITUTE OF NWN OH 43615 #038-43-1977 L1981 **OPH** *074 †35
GIPSON, Frederick Vance. 4027 N HOLLAND SYLVANIA RD 43623 #041-09-1946 L1947 **FM** *071 †18
GIRGIS, Sonia Fahmy Kamel. 2142 N COVE BLVD 43606 #915-04-1984 L1999 **PM** *020 †60
GLAD, Robert Michael. 2142 N COVE BLVD 43606 #041-02-1963 L1964 **IM** *030 †20
GLADDEN, Jamie Lynne. 3120 GLENDALE AVE, DEPT OF PSYCHIATRY 43614 #038-40-1997 L1999 **P OBG** *012 †30
GLADIEUX, Gary Francis. ■ 43614 #038-43-1985 L1988 **PD** *075 †55
GLASSBERG, Gerald Bruce. 2658 W LASKEY RD, STE A 43613 #035-08-1974 L1979 **R DR** *020 †80

■ = Address Information Privacy Protected

GLASSNER, Amy Lynn. 3130 CENTRAL PARK W STE B, CENTRAL PARK PEDIATRICS 43617 #038-43-2001 L2001 **PD** *020 †55

GLOWACKI, David Mark. 2658 W LASKEY RD, CONSULTING RADIOLOGISTS CO 43613 #041-07-1988 L1994 **DR** *020 †80 ‡

GOETZ, Kenneth Michael. 1 OWENS CORNING PKWY, OWENS CORNING 43659 #035-09-1983 L1996 **OM IM** *030 †20,70

GOHARA, Amira Faltaous. 1565 S BYRNE RD 43614 #330-02-1964 L1972 **CLP PTH** *020 †50

GOKULA, Ramanamurthy. 3000 ARLINGTON AVE, RUPPERT HEALTH CENTER, SUI 43614 #496-24-1993 L2007 **FM FPG** *020 †18 ‡

GOLD, Jeffrey Philip. 3000 ARLINGTON AVE 43614 #035-20-1978 L2005 **TS GS** *020 †85,90

GOLDBERGER, Edward. 3922 WOODLEY RD, STE 200 43606 #038-43-1986 L1991 **RHU IM** *020 †20

GOLDBLATT, Peter Jerome. 3000 ARLINGTON AVE 43614 #038-06-1959 L1959 **PTH OS** *030 †50

GOLIVER, Christopher A. 2213 CHERRY ST 43608 #038-43-2000 L2000 **EM** *020 †16

GOMBASH, Mary Jane. 4571 WESTBOURNE RD, SUBSTANCE ABUSE SERVICES, 43623 #038-40-1980 L1982 **EM ADM** *020 †16

GOMEZ, Michael Sazon. ■ 43613 #038-43-2003 L2003 **U** *012

GONZALEZ, Antonio Rafael. 2142 N COVE BLVD 3RD FL, CTR WOMENS HEALTH 43606 #308-03-1981 L1993 **MFM OBG** *020 †30

GOODENDAY, Lucy Sherman. 3000 ARLINGTON AVE, RM 1192, MAIL STOP 1118 43614 #035-09-1963 L1978 **CD** *020 †20

GOODIN, Thomas Leadis. 2620 PEMBERTON DR 43606 #010-03-1978 L1991 **OBG** *020 †30

GORDON, Michael Alan. 3922 WOODLEY RD, STE 200 43606 #030-06-1977 L1982 **RHU IM** *020 †20

GORDON, Steven Edward. 2658 W LASKEY RD, FL 2 43613 #038-41-1969 L1969 **DR NM** *020 †80

GORDON, Tess Maria. 3000 ARLINGTON AVE 43614 #038-43-2000 L2000 **OBG** *020 †30 ‡

GOSMAN, James Howard. 2222 CHERRY ST, STE 1400 43608 #025-01-1970 L1975 **ORS** *020 †40

GOTTLIEB, Marvin Emanuel. 544 E WOODRUFF AVE, UNISON BEHAVIORAL HLTH GRP 43604 #038-06-1961 L1961 **P** *071 †75

GOTTWALD, Lorie Danielle. 3120 GLENDALE AVE, RUPPERT HEALTH CENTER 43614 #038-43-1990 L1996 **D IM** *020 †15

GOUDA, Jan Jack. 3065 ARLINGTON AVE, DEPT OF NEUROLOGICAL SURGE 43614 #915-05-1982 L1997 **NS PMM** *020

GOYAL, Amar Nath. 7053 W CENTRAL AVE, FOR PAIN MANAGEMENT 43617 #495-20-1993 L2005 **AN PMM** *020 †05

GOYAL, Rajan. 3000 ARLINGTON AVE #495-03-2004 L2005 **IM** *012

GOYAL, Rashmi. 4816 FOREST HILL DR 43623 #038-43-1994 L1996 **IM** *020 †20

GRAMLING, Jeffrey Arthur. 2865 N REYNOLDS RD 43615 #038-43-1987 L1991 **AN** *020 †05

GRANT, Jeffrey M. ■ 43609 #064-01-1983 L1988 **EM** *020 †16

GRAY, Joseph Wm, III. 313 JEFFERSON AVE 43604 #047-07-1963 L1969 **PD** *020 †55

GREENFIELD, Lazar J, Jr. 1565 S BYRNE RD 43614 #051-01-1989 L1999 **N** *050 †75

GRETSINGER, Mark David. 3439 GRANITE CIR 43617 #038-45-1983 L1985 **GE IM** *020 †20

GRIGG, Rhonda Cobb. 2213 CHERRY ST, MEDICAL STAFFING SERVICES 43608 #039-05-1988 L1990 **PD** *020 †55

GROSS, Susan Ann. 3020 N MCCORD RD 43615 #038-43-1992 L1994 **IM** *020 †20

GROSS, Thomas Henry. 3020 N MCCORD RD STE 100 43615 #038-43-1985 L1988 **IM PD** *020 †20

GROSSMAN, David Lee. 4640 W ALEXIS RD 43623 #038-43-1974 L1975 **IM ID** *020 †20

GRUBB, Blair Paul. 3000 ARLINGTON AVE, MEDICAL UNIVERSITY OF OHIO 43614 #308-03-1981 L1988 **CD IM** *020 †20

GRUM, Daniel Frank. 3000 ARLINGTON AVE, MAILSTOP 1137 ANES 43614 #016-06-1973 L1974 **AN CCA** *020 †05

GUERRA, Jose. ■ 43615 #649-02-1940 L1955 **AN** *071

GUNDAPPA, Anand Nyathappa. 3045 ARLINGTON AVE, CO MCOT-GRAD MED EDU DEPT 43614 #495-72-1987 L2003 **N** *100

GUNTSCH, Deborah Ann. 3740 W SYLVANIA AVE, STE 100 43623 #038-45-1985 L1986 **FM** *020 †18

GUPTA, Kul Bhushan. 4447 TALMADGE RD, STE C 43643 #495-08-1975 L1978 **P** *020 †75

GUPTA, Usha. 2213 CHERRY ST, ST VINCENT MERCY MEDICAL C 43608 #495-69-1973 L1984 **NPM PD** *020

GUPTA, Varun. PO BOX 10008 43699 #495-36-2004 **GS** *012

GUPTA, Vineet Kumar. 2213 CHERRY ST, 6TH FL 43608 #038-43-1998 L2000 **CCP** *020 †55

GUSTINE, Patrick Andrew. 3900 SUNFOREST CT STE 136 43623 #025-01-1995 L2000 **DR RNR** *020 †20

HABASH, Nadim Rizeq. 5555 AIRPORT HWY, STE 110 43615 #528-01-1971 L1992 **OPH** *020 †35

HACKER, Timothy B. 4640 W ALEXIS RD 43623 #038-40-1974 L1974 **IM** *020 †20

HADDAD, Nader Muner. ■ 43614 #575-02-2003 L2005 **OBG** *012

HAFEEZ, Faizan. 3020 N MCCORD RD, STE 203 43615 #704-02-1989 L1999 **N IM** *020 †75

HAGELBERG, Richard S. 2109 HUGHES DR, STE 220 43606 #025-01-1979 L2007 **CCS** *020 †85

HAIDAR, Hani. 3830 WOODLEY RD, STE C 43606 #875-01-1987 L1993 **PD** *020 †55

HAJJA, Waddah Khalil. 2051 W CENTRAL AVE, DEPT OF MED EDUCATION 43606 #305-01-2005 L2006 *100

HALEY, Susan Carol. 525 HAMILTON ST, STE 101A 43604 #038-43-1983 L1985 **P PYG** *020 †75

HALL, Tadrell Andre. 117 MAIN ST 43605 #038-45-1995 L1997 **FM** *075

HALUSZKA, Harry Stephen. ■ 43611 #038-40-1973 L1973 **EM** *075 †16

HAMAD, Adiba. 2142 N COVE BLVD, STE 5NORTH 43606 #875-01-1988 L1998 **PD** *020 †55

HAMAKER, Sara Ashley. ■ 43614 #038-43-2007 L2007 **D** *012

HAMEED, Muhammad Khurram. 3000 ARLINGTON AVE, UNIVERSITY OF TOLEDO 43614 #704-01-2004 L2004 **IM** *012

HAMMERSLEY, Jeffrey Ross. 3000 ARLINGTON AVE, PULM/CCM AND SLEEP MED UNI 43614 #025-07-1976 L1994 **PCC SME** *020 †20

HAMMOND, Bruce L. 3137 W CENTRAL AVE, PMB 8950 43606 #038-40-1978 L1982 **DR NM** *020 †80

HANSON, Daniel J. ■ 43623 #026-04-1953 L1954 **PTH** *071 †50

HARPER, David Allen. 2150 W CENTRAL AVE 43606 #038-43-1989 L1991 **OBG** *020 †30

HARRIS-MARTORANA, Melissa. ■ 43623 #038-43-2004 L2006 *020

HARTLEY, Julie Ann. 930 S DETROIT AVE, 930 SOUTH DETROIT 43614 #024-07-1991 L1996 **P** *020 †75 ‡

HARTLEY-DYMARKOWSKI, Brend. 2121 HUGHES DR STE 300 43606 #038-43-1991 L1992 **PD** *020 †55

HARTUNG, Walter H, Jr. 2800 W CENTRAL AVE 43606 #016-43-1944 L1945 **PTH** *071 †50

HARWANI, Ashok N. ■ 43623 #495-19-1983 L1995 **EM IM** *020 †20,16

HASAN, Samina Z. 6800 W CENTRAL AVE, STE K1 43617 #704-04-1980 L1991 **FM** *020 †18

HASELHUHN, Gregory Dean. 2000 REGENCY CT, STE 200 43623 #025-01-1989 L1995 **U** *020 †95

HASHMI, Fatima. 3045 ARLINGTON AVE, CO MCOT-GRAD MED EDU DEPT 43614 #704-06-1986 L2003 **PTH** *100

HASSAN, Ali Mohamad. 3000 ARLINGTON AVE, DEPT ANESTHESIOLOGY 43614 #875-01-1978 L2000 **AN** *020 †20

HASSAN, Rifat. 3000 ARLINGTON AVE, UNIVERSITY OF TOLEDO 43614 #495-51-2000 L2007 **IM** *012

HASSELBACH, Nina Nayantar. 3404 W SYLVANIA AVE, ST. ANNE MERCY HOSPITAL 43623 #016-01-1990 L1994 **AN** *020 †05

HAWKINS, Terrence Earl. 1000 REGENCY CT STE 100, ASSOCIATED EYE CARE 43623 #028-79-1968, ▲ L1970 **OPH** *020

HAY, Michael Robt. 4841 MONROE ST STE 101 43623 #025-07-1971 L1978 **R NM** *020 †80

HAYS, James Russell. 3500 EXECUTIVE PKWY 43606 #038-43-1983 L1986 **AN** *020 †05

HAZELRIGG, Robert Le Roy. 4235 SECOR RD, SUTIE 1 43623 #016-11-1968 L1976 **NP** *071 †75

HEALY, Michael Alan. 2222 CHERRY ST, STE M200 43608 #025-12-1983 L1990 **NS NSP** *020 †25

HEGDE, Krathik K. 2213 CHERRY ST 43608 #496-22-2002 L2007 **TY** *012

HEIL, Sharon Ann. 3400 MEIJER DR, PEDIATRICARE ASSOCIATES 43617 #038-43-1990 L1993 **PD** *020 †55

HEINZ, Dorothy C V. ■ 43620 #025-01-1932 L1933 **P** *075

HENDRICKS, Virginia Konz. ■ 43604 #016-11-1950 L1957 **OS** *071

HENNESSY, James Robt. 2222 CHERRY ST STE 2800, PEDIATRIC CARDIOLOGIST 43608 #038-41-1971 L1979 **PDC PD** *020 †55

HERMAN, Todd Christopher. ■ 43614 #038-43-2008 *012

HICKEY, Donald Kevin. 2051 W CENTRAL AVE, WW KNIGHT FAMILY PRACTICE 43606 #038-40-1979 L1980 **FM** *020 †18

HICKEY, Jennifer M. ■ 43609 #038-43-2008 *012

HIGGINS, Amahl Jonathan. 3000 ARLINGTON AVE 43614 #566-01-2002 L2006 **GS** *012

HILL, Crystal Renee. 2409 CHERRY ST, STE 305 43608 #038-43-2001 L2005 **AN** *020

HILL, Nathan Aaron. PO BOX 140066 43614 #038-43-1999 L1999 **PM** *020 †60

HILL, Olivia Noelle. ■ 43614 #038-43-2008 *012

HILLARD, Bruce L. 3922 WOODLEY RD, STE 100 43606 #038-43-1984 L1991 **FM** *020 †18

HILLARD, Mark Douglas. 4041 W SYLVANIA AVE, STE 100 43623 #038-40-1977 L1983 **FM** *040 †18

HNATIUK, Mark. 3829 WOODLEY RD, BLDG B 43606 #025-07-1999 L2005 **OTO** *020 †45

HO, Edmund Ping. 4841 MONROE ST 43623 #028-34-1971 L1977 **RO** *020 †80

HO-A-LIM, Frederick G. 4759 VIOLET RD 43623 #047-07-1983 L1987 **FM IM** *020

HOEFLINGER, Brian F. 4235 SECOR RD, TOLEDO CLINIC INC 43623 #038-43-1993 L1999 **NS** *020 †25

HOEFLINGER, Cynthia B. 3170 W CENTRAL AVE, BUSINESS OFFICE 43606 #038-43-1992 L1999 **PTH** *020 †50

HOFFMAN, Daniel Jos. 7140 PORT SYLVANIA DR, STE 250 43617 #038-41-1991 L1993 **FM OBS** *020 †18

HOFFMAN, Elizabeth Ann. 3909 WOODLEY RD, STE 300 43606 #038-43-1992 L1995 **IM** *020 †20

HOFMANN, James Patrick. 3000 ARLINGTON AVE 43614 #038-43-1984 L1986 **AN GS** *020 †05

HOLDSHIP, Matthew Keith. 1850 EASTGATE RD, STE A 43614 #041-15-2000 L2004 *020

HOLZ, Stephanie Peggy. ■ 43613 #038-43-2004 L2004 **DR** *012

HONG, Ock Lan. 525 HAMILTON ST, STE 101A 43604 #583-08-1973 L1978 **P CHP** *020 †75

HOOKER, Michael. 2213 CHERRY ST 43608 #038-75-1999, ▲ L1999 *020

HOPPLE, Craig Theron. 4640 W ALEXIS RD 43623 #038-43-1975 L1976 **IM EM** *020 †20

HOPPLE, Theron Lingard. ■ 43617 #016-02-1942 L1948 **NS** *071 †25

HORN, Lawrence James. 3065 ARLINGTON AVE, DOWLING HALL 43614 #016-06-1978 L1992 **PM** *030 †60

HORNER, James Michael. 2222 CHERRY ST STE 2300 43608 #025-01-1973 L1979 **PDE PD** *020 †55

HOROWITZ, Phillip Louis. 4129 HOLLAND SYLVANI RD #G 43623 #035-19-1955 L1961 **IM CD** *071 †20

HORRIGAN, Terrence John. 3000 ARLINGTON AVE 43614 #016-11-1971 L1987 **OBG** *040 †30

HORTON, Frank Oscar, III. 2109 HUGHES DR STE 760, CONRAD JOBST TOWER 43606 #038-43-1973 L1974 **PUD OSM** *020 †20

HOTEIT, Wissam Khalil. 3045 ARLINGTON AVE 43614 #913-35-1999 L2005 **P** *012

HOUCK, Mary Hellthaler. 3103 EXECUTIVE PKWY, STE 404 43606 #025-01-1960 L1962 **AN** *071

HOWARD, John Malone. 3065 ARLINGTON AVE, MEDICAL UNIV OF OHIO 43614 #041-01-1944 L1944 **GS TS** *071 †85,90

HOWARD, Russell Van Buren. 2121 HUGHES DR, SUSAN CLAY-HUFFORD MD 43606 #025-01-1955 L1960 **PD** *071 †55

HOWE, Murray Albert. 4841 MONROE ST STE 103 43623 #025-01-1986 L1991 **DR** *062 †80

HU, Shimin. PO BOX 10008 43699 #243-47-1993 L2007 **PTH** *012

HUANG, Canhui. 3045 ARLINGTON AVE, CO MCOT-GRAD MED EDU DEPT 43614 #243-74-1984 L2005 **GE** *012 †20

HUDSON, Tymesia. ■ 43614 #045-01-2001 L2001 **OBG** *020

HUFFMAN, Cheryl Ilene. 3000 ARLINGTON AVE 43614 #038-43-1998 L2000 **PD** *020 †55

HUFFORD, David R, Jr. 2142 N COVE BLVD 43606 #038-43-1982 L1985 **PD PUD** *020 †55

HUGUS, Jeffrey Stephen. ■ 43606 #038-43-1999 L2001 **EM** *020 †16

HUNTER, David Wm. 3425 EXECUTIVE PKWY, STE 107 43606 #041-13-1965 L1973 **AI IM** *020 †20,03

HUNYADI, James Wm. 2121 HUGHES DR STE 920 43606 #019-02-1980 L1983 **PS** *020 †65

HUSAIN, Adeel. ■ 43614 #038-43-2008 *012

HUSAIN, Arshad A. 1155 E ALEXIS RD, ALEX INDUS MEDICAL CTR 43612 #704-02-1987 L1994 **IM** *020 †20

HUSAIN, Azfar. PO BOX 10008, MED COL OF OH PSYCH 43699 #704-02-1989 **P** *100

HUSSEIN, Ahmed Abdellatie. ■ 43623 #915-02-1998 L2007 **IFP** *012

HUSSEIN, Fadhil Abbas. 3404 W SYLVANIA AVE 43623 #038-45-1991 L1993 **CD** *020 †20

HUSTED, Timothy Matlack. 4235 SECOR RD 43623 #051-01-1986 L1991 **GS** *020 †85

HYMEL, Gregory Paul. 2213 CHERRY ST 43608 #021-05-1993 L1994 **EM** *020 †16

HYSELL, Diane Charlene. 123 22ND ST 43604 #038-43-1990 L1993 **CHP P** *020 †75

IBRAHIM, Mohamed Youssri. 3065 ARLINGTON AVE, MEDICAL UNIVERSITY OF OHIO 43614 #915-03-1980 L2006 *100

IMAM, Syed Amjad. 3045 ARLINGTON AVE, CO MCOT-GRAD MED EDU DEPT 43614 #704-16-1990 L2003 **CHP** *100

INDURTI, Sreekanth V. 930 S DETROIT AVE 43614 #495-11-1978 L2000 **P** *020

IRANI, Farzan Hosang. 2213 CHERRY ST, DEPT OF INTERNAL MED 43608 #496-44-2001 L2007 **IM** *012

IRLAM, John Harland. ■ 43614 #016-76-2007, ▲ L2007 PTH *012

IRVIN, Sara Rebecca. 2051 W CENTRAL AVE 43606 #038-44-2004 L2004 FM *020 †18

ISAACSON, Jules Jos. 4235 SECOR RD 43623 #038-41-1966 L1966 D *020

IWUAGWU, Cletus Uzogo. 3355 GLENDALE AVE, GERIATRY & GERONTOLOGY DE 43614 #308-03-1988 L1999 IMG IM *020 †20

IZSAK, Eugene. 2142 N COVE BLVD, EMERGENCY CENTER 43606 #017-20-1977 L1980 PD EM *020 †55

JAARA, Ziad. 2150 W CENTRAL AVE, CENTER FOR HEALTH SERVICES 43606 #875-02-1987 L1992 PD *020 †55

JABALY, Georges Tawfik. 4405 N HOLLAND SYLVANIA RD 43623 #875-02-1986 L1999 FM *020 †18 ‡

JABATI, Sallu Mohamed. 7053 W CENTRAL AVE 43617 #305-01-2000 L2003 IM *100 †20

JACOB, Moshir Khalil. 4235 SECOR RD 43623 #915-04-1988 L1998 *020

JACOBS, George David. 3000 REGENCY CT, STE 105 43623 #038-43-1973 L1977 DR *020 †80

JACOBS, Lloyd Alan. 3045 ARLINGTON AVE, MEDICAL COLLEGE OF OHIO 43614 #023-07-1969 L2004 VS *030 †85

JAFRY, Amna A. 2213 CHERRY 43608 #704-01-1975 L1990 PD EM *020

JAHN, David Wm. 525 HAMILTON ST, STE 101A 43604 #038-43-1991 L1992 P *020 †75

JAMAL, Raheel. 2409 CHERRY ST, STE 204 43608 #704-16-1989 L2003 PCC *020 †20

JAMES, A David B. 3020 N MCCORD RD 43615 #038-43-1989 L1992 IM PD *020 †20,55

JAMIE, Sharon Saheb. 2213 CHERRY ST 43608 #104-01-2004 L2007 FP *012

JAMWAL, Neena. 2801 W BANCROFT ST, UNIV OF TOLEDO 43606 #496-17-1994 L2007 N *012

JANJUA, Ahmed Jamal. PO BOX 10008 43699 #704-20-1991 L2007 P *012

JANOWICZ, Michael John. 4235 SECOR RD 43623 #025-01-1988 L1993 OPH *020 †35

JAUREGUI-PEREDO, Luis E. 2222 CHERRY ST, STE 1400 43608 #025-07-1972 L1977 ID IM *020 †20

JINDAL, Steve Kumar. 4841 MONROE ST, TOLEDO RADIOLOGICAL ASSOC, 43623 #038-41-1994 L2000 DR *020 †80

JOE, Roger Gee. 2142 N COVE BLVD 43606 #104-01-2007 L2007 FP *012

JOHN, Jijan. 2200 JEFFERSON AVE, DEPT OF FAMILY PRACTICE 43604 #495-49-1994 L2006 FP *012

JOHNSON, David Melvin. 2213 CHERRY ST 43608 #051-07-1990 L1991 EM *040 †16

JOHNSON, Harold Albert. 4841 MONROE ST STE 103, TOLEDO RADIATION ONCOLOGY 43623 #036-01-1997 L2002 RO *020 †80

JOHNSON, Houston, Jr. 4447 TALMADGE RD, STE D 43623 #024-01-1975 L1992 GS SO *020 †85

JOHNSON, Jamie L. ■ 43613 #025-07-2006 L2006 EM *012

JOHNSON, Larry Wayne. 1015 GARDEN LAKE PKWY, DEPARTMENT OF FAMILY MEDIC 43614 #056-05-1967 L1979 FM *030 †18

JONES, Angela Renee. 3840 WOODLEY RD 43606 #038-43-2001 L2001 OBG *020

JONES, Hudson V. 620 W BANCROFT ST 43620 #047-07-1978 L1981 IM *020

JONES, Ralph M. 2142 N COVE BLVD 43606 #047-06-1952 L1954 FM *020 †18

JOSEPH, Attaya Elizabeth. ■ 43614 #038-43-1998 L2007 IM *020 †20

JOSHI, Mandar Mukund. 2213 CHERRY ST, STE 400 43608 #025-01-2000 L2006 OPH *100 †35

JOSHI, Prachi. ■ 43615 #495-16-2003 L2007 FP *012

JOYE, Steven Martin. 2213 CHERRY ST 43608 #005-77-2005, ▲ L2005 EM *012

JUDGE, Lisa S. 2213 CHERRY ST, DIVISION OF NEONATOLOGY 43608 #018-03-1991 L1997 NPM *020 †55

JUDIS, Jeffrey Marc. 3740 W SYLVANIA AVE, STE 103 43623 #038-40-1991 L1992 OBG *020 †30

JUENG, Wei Sun. 2865 N REYNOLDS RD 43615 #038-40-1991 L1995 AN *020

JURADO CARRIZO, Javier An. 3000 ARLINGTON AVE 43614 #270-02-2000 L2005 CD *012

KABBANI, Mouhamad Samer. 2409 CHERRY ST, STE 100 43608 #875-01-1991 L2007 IM *020 †20

KAHN, Gary Randolph. 4041 W SYLVANIA AVE 43623 #038-43-1979 L1984 OBG *075

KAJI, Yasuhiko. 1544 S BYRNE RD 43614 #572-58-1958 L1972 GYN *071 †30

KALB, Robert Lee. 3900 SUNFOREST CT, STE 119 43623 #038-40-1976 L1977 ORS *020 †18,40

KANE, John Timothy. 3065 ARLINGTON AVE, DEPT OF PHYSICAL MED & REH 43614 #038-40-1974 L1975 PM OS *020 †60

KANJWAL, Mohammed Yousuf. 3000 ARLINGTON AVE, RM 1192 43614 #495-51-1983 L2000 CD *020 †20

KANJWAL, Mohd Shaffi. 3000 ARLINGTON AVE 43614 #495-51-2003 L2005 IM *012

KAPLISH, Neeraj. 3045 ARLINGTON AVE, C/O MCOT-GRAD MED EDU DEPT 43614 #495-47-2001 L2002 CN *100

KAPPUS, Richard Geo. 7140 PORT SYLVANIA DR, STE 200 43617 #028-34-1954 L1955 PD *072 †55

KARAFFA, Camille Alexis. 2200 JEFFERSON AVE 43604 #038-40-1980 L1985 ID IM *020 †20

KARAMALI, Adil M. 5800 PARK CENTER CT, STE C 43615 #654-01-1986 L1996 CD *020 †20

KARNITIS, Vitauts Jos. 2142 N COVE BLVD, THE TOLEDO HOSPITAL FERTIL 43606 #038-40-1987 L1992 OBG *020 †30

KAROL, Kathleen Kaye. 2865 N REYNOLDS RD, STE 170 43615 #038-43-1981 L1985 OPH *020 †35

KARP, Robert Alan. 930 S DETROIT AVE, NORTHCOAST BEHAVIORAL HEAL 43614 #016-42-1982 L1990 P PFP *020 †75

KARR, Samuel L. ■ 43623 #041-13-1952 L1960 CD *071 †20

KARUNAKARAN, Siva. 3000 ARLINGTON AVE RM 4143, MCOT HOSPSINTERNAL MED DEP 43614 #422-01-1995 L2000 NEP *100 †20

KASMANI, Rahil Mohamed. 2213 CHERRY ST, DEPT OF INTERNAL MED 43608 #495-83-1994 L2007 IM *012

KASPER, Gregory Charles. 2213 CHERRY ST, STE 303 43608 #038-41-1994 L1997 VS *020 †85

KASUNIC, Timothy Charles. 4235 SECOR RD, TOLEDO CLINIC 43623 #025-07-2000 L2006 HO *072

KATCHKA, David M. 2142 N COVE BLVD 43606 #025-01-1939 L1942 AN *071

KATKO, Jeffery Danl. 3404 W SYLVANIA AVE, ST ANNE MERCY HOSPITAL 43623 #038-41-1992 L1995 EM *020 †16

KATRAGADDA, Srinivas. 2222 CHERRY ST, STE 1400 43608 #495-50-1987 L1998 PCC SME *020 †20

KATRAPATI, Sarma V. 3900 SUNFOREST CT STE 114, ADULT PRIMARY CARE 43623 #495-27-1994 L2000 IM *020 †20

KATZ, Laura Alyce. 4235 SECOR RD, DEPT OF OB/GYN 43623 #025-07-1996 L1997 OBG *020 †30

KAUFMAN, Allan Stephen. 4841 MONROE ST, STE 103 43623 #023-01-1974 L1978 DR *020 †80

KAUR, Harinder. PO BOX 10008 43699 #495-43-1996 L2007 P *012

KAURA, Neil Vinny. ■ 43615 #030-05-2007 L2007 GS *012

KAW, Dinkar. 2213 CHERRY ST 43608 #495-51-1981 L1999 NEP IM *040 †20

KAZIMIRKO, Nicolay N. 3404 W SYLVANIA AVE, ST. ANNE MERCY HOSPITAL 43623 #913-86-1981 L2002 AN *020

KAZMI, Alamdar H. 930 S DETROIT AVE, CARE SYSTEM 43614 #704-15-1985 L1999 CHP *020 †75

KEIGLEY, Blaine Alan. 4841 MONROE ST STE 103 43623 #041-01-1983 L1988 DR *020 †80

KEISER, Vincent James. 4841 MONROE ST STE 10, HARVEST SQUARE 43623 #038-40-1996 L2000 DR *020 †80

KENYON, Jack M. 2142 N COVE BLVD 43606 #065-01-1939 L1949 P *071 †75

KERN, Elizabeth. ■ 43606 #038-44-2005 PD *012

KESSLER, Nancy Ann. 3020 N MCCORD RD, STE 100 43615 #038-43-1996 L1997 MPD *020 †20,55

KHADKE, Neelam Pralhad Vi. 3000 ARLINGTON AVE 43614 #496-36-2003 L2006 PD *012

KHAMOUSIA, Nidaa O.. 3045 ARLINGTON AVE, C/O MCOT-MED EDU DEPT RM 3 43614 #875-01-1991 L2002 IM *100 †20

KHAN, Abid Hussain. 3065 ARLINGTON AVE, MEDICAL COLLEGE OF OHIO 43614 #495-57-1968 L1982 GS *020 †85

KHAN, Ali. 2200 JEFFERSON AVE, MERCY FAMILY PRACTICE 43604 #704-21-1996 L2001 FM *020 †18

KHAN, Gulnaz. 2213 CHERRY ST 43608 #690-08-1997 L2001 FM *100 †18

KHAN, Kashif Abdullah. 3000 ARLINGTON AVE, UNIV OF TOLEDO 43614 #704-16-1994 L2006 CHP *012

KHAN, Naveed Abas. 3000 ARLINGTON AVE 43614 #495-51-2005 L2006 IM *012

KHAN, Wakil. 1614 S BYRNE RD STE P, BEVERLY HILLS MEDICAL CENT 43614 #704-09-1969 L1977 P GP *020 †75

KHERALLAH, M Nizar. 2222 CHERRY ST STE 2900 43608 #875-01-1990 L1997 PDP *020 †55

KHOURI, Samer Jean. 3000 ARLINGTON AVE, RM 1192 43614 #875-01-1992 L1999 CD *020 †20

KHURSHID, Nauman. ■ 43614 #704-15-2002 L2004 OBG *012

KIECHEL, Stephen F. 4235 SECOR RD 43623 #051-01-1971 L1977 ORS *020 †40

KIM, Wun Jung. 3130 GLENDALE AVE 43614 #583-02-1975 L1982 CHP P *020 †75

KIMMEL, Sanford Richard. 3120 GLENDALE AVE, FAMILY MEDICINE CLINIC 43614 #038-40-1974 L1974 FM PD *020 †55,18

KIMMELMAN, Jerome. 1565 S BYRNE RD, STE 100 43614 #038-40-1948 L1949 D *071 †15

KING, Randall Wm. 2213 CHERRY ST 43608 #038-43-1981 L1982 EM *040 †16

KINI, Vishwas Manjunath. ■ 43615 #495-35-2000 L2007 FP *012

KIRKHOPE, Thomas Geo. ■ 43614 #056-06-1963 L1964 OBG *071 †30

KIRSNER, Allan Bernard. 4235 SECOR RD 43623 #038-41-1962 L1962 RHU *020 †20

KITCHEN, Brenda Joyce. 2222 CHERRY ST STE 2800, DEPT OF PEDIATRIC HEM/ONC 43608 #028-02-1988 L1990 PHO *050 †55

KIZAUR, Jessica. 2142 N COVE BLVD, HOSPITAL EMERGENCY DEPT 43606 #020-02-1996 L1997 EM *020 †16

KLEIN, Charles Mosher. 4841 MONROE ST, TOLEDO RADIOLOGY ASSOC INC 43623 #038-06-1958 L1958 DR *071 †80

KLEIN, Michael David. 2121 HUGHES DR, STE 620 43606 #038-06-1971 L2004 PDS CCM *020 †85

KLEIN, Peter Frederick. 3909 WOODLEY RD, STE 800 43606 #038-43-1995 L2001 CRS *020 †85,10

KLEINBERG, Martha V. 3454 OAK ALLEY CT, STE 102 43606 #035-08-1969 L1974 PD PDC *020 †55

KLEINBERG, Warren M. 2213 FRANKLIN AVE, FAMILY CARE PEDIATRICS 43620 #035-08-1968 L1974 PD PHP *020 †55

KLESHINSKI, James Francis. 3120 GLENDALE AVE 43614 #038-43-1996 L1998 IM *020 †20

KLEVER, Robert Grant, Jr. ■ 43614 #038-41-2008 *012

KNAPINSKI, Gregory Jerome. 3045 ARLINGTON AVE, C/O MCOT-MED EDU DEPT RM 3 43614 #038-43-2002 L2002 AN *100

KNIEP, Joel Nelsen. ■ 43614 #038-43-2008 *012

KNISELY, Robert R. ■ 43605 #038-41-1946 L1947 GP OS *020

KNOTTS, Frank Barry. 2409 CHERRY ST, MOB 303 43608 #005-14-1975 L1990 TRS GS *020 †85

KOBERLEIN, George C. ■ 43614 #038-43-2008 *012

KODALI, Ravi Prakash. 3000 REGENCY CT, STE 105 43623 #025-01-1993 L2003 DR *020 †80

KODUMAGULLA, Mrinalini Su. 2213 CHERRY ST 43608 #495-70-1992 L2005 FP *012

KOFFEL, Kevin Kelly. 3439 GRANITE CIR 43617 #038-43-1978 L1981 GE IM *020 †20

KOFFMAN, Boyd Moreau. 3000 ARLINGTON AVE, MAIL STOP 1195 #010-01-1990 L1998 N *020 †75

KOLI, Rajeshree Moreshwar. 320-MUL3045 ARLING, CO GME-RM 43614 #495-96-1993 L2007 OBG *012

KONERU, Bhavani. 2150 W CENTRAL AVE 43606 #017-20-1986 L1996 IM *020 †20

KONESWARAN, Suresh Aravin. ■ 43614 #495-37-2001 L2006 CD *012 †20

KOSINSKI, Daniel Jos. 3120 GLENDALE AVE, DIVISION OF CARDIOLOGY, RM 43614 #038-43-1988 L1992 IM *020 †20

KOSTRZEWSKI, Krzysztof A. 3020 N MCCORD RD, STE 201A 43615 #759-03-1974 L1996 FM *020 †18

KOSTRZEWSKI, Maria I. 544 E WOODRUFF AVE 43604 #759-03-1974 L1999 P *020 †75

KOTA, Sanjeev Sundaram. 320-MUL3045 ARLING, CO GME-RM 43614 #496-22-2005 L2007 PD *012

KOTLAREVSKY, Alexander An. 2213 CHERRY 43608 #913-10-1997 L2005 FP *012.

KOUBA, David Jonathan. 4235 SECOR RD, HENRY FORD HEALTH SYSTEM 43623 #041-02-2000 L2007 D *020 †15

KOZY, David William. 2213 CHERRY ST STE 400 43608 #038-40-1978 L1982 OPH OS *020 †35

KRIAUCIUNAS, Juozas. ■ 43607 #616-01-1939 L1953 GP *071

KRILL, Larry Wadsworth. 2142 N COVE BLVD 43606 #038-43-1990 L1991 IM *020 †20

KRISTEN, Erich Erwin. ■ 43615 #407-16-1955 L1960 FM *071

KROL, David Matthew. 3120 GLENDALE AVE, STE 1600 43614 #008-01-1996 L1997 PD *020 †55

KROPP, Kenneth Alan. 2222 CHERRY ST STE 1800, PEDIATRIC UROLOGY 43608 #016-06-1961 L1971 U UP *020 †95

KRUSE, Roger John. 2865 N REYNOLDS RD, STE 130 43615 #038-41-1978 L1979 FM FSM *020 †18

KSSEIRY, Iyad. ■ 43614 #875-01-1992 L2000 END *020 †20

KUCWAY, Roger Terrence. 4841 MONROE ST, STE 103 43623 #025-07-1997 L2007 RO *020 †80

KUECK, Angela Suzanne. 3120 GLENDALE AVE, MEDICAL UNIVERSITY OF OHIO 43614 #010-02-1999 L2005 OBG *020

KUMAR, Bijender. 2213 CHERRY ST, DEPT OF INTERNAL MED 43608 #495-69-2000 L2007 IM *012

KUTAISH, Nadeem. 3170 W CENTRAL AVE, BUSINESS OFFICE 43606 #875-01-1973 L1992 PTH OS *020 †50

KUTNIK, Shawn Michael. ■ 43614 #035-09-2006 L2006 ORS *012

KWYER, Thomas Anthony. 2865 N REYNOLDS RD, STE 260 43615 #025-01-1975 L1988 OTO *020 †45

LA FORREST, Barbara Jean. 525 HAMILTON ST, STE 101A 43604 #038-43-1985 L1986 P PYG *020 †75

LAMMERS, Anne H. ■ 43606 #030-06-1952 L1963 CHP *071 †75

LANCZ, Colleen D. 3000 ARLINGTON AVE 43614 #038-43-1989 L1992 AN *020 †05

LANGENBURG, Scott Edward. 2121 HUGHES DR, STE 620 43606 #025-01-1990 L2003 PDS *020 †85

LANGLOIS, Melanie. 3120 GLENDALE AVE, MEDICAL COLLEGE OF OHIO 43614 #067-03-1998 L2003 *020

LANKA, Kiranmayee. 3045 ARLINGTON AVE, DEPT OF GME 43614 #495-21-2003 L2006 IM *012

LASEK, Konrad John. ■ 43606 #869-07-1959 L1962 GP *071

LATHAM, Jill Ann. 2200 JEFFERSON AVE 43604 #038-43-1982 L1983 EM *020 †16

LAU, Man-Yiu Peter. 2275 COLLINGWOOD BLVD 43620 #748-01-1963 L1975 HEM IM *030 †20

LAUNGANI, Bina Rajesh. 5965 RENAISSANCE PL, STE 3 43623 #495-83-1994 L2002 FM *020 †18

LA VALLEY, Antoinette L. 2658 W LASKEY RD 43613 #038-40-1984 L1985 DR RNR *020 †80

LAWRENCE, Edmund Pond. 2222 CHERRY ST, STE M200 # 2 43608 #047-05-1972 L1978 NS *020 †25

LE, Tho Duc. ■ 43615 #038-43-2008 *012

LECSO, Phillip Andrew. CS 10008 43699 #038-43-1982 L1983 IM *020 †20

LEDRICK, David James. 2213 CHERRY ST, DEPT OF EMERGENCY MEDICINE 43608 #041-07-1993 L1995 EM *020 †16

LEE, Augustine Changdae. ■ 43614 #038-43-2008 *012

LEE, Dochil. ■ 43614 #583-05-1944 AN CD *040

LEE, Effie Mae. ■ 43606 #038-43-1993 PD *100

LEE, Hungchih. 3218 SECOR RD, OLEDO PAIN RELIEF CENTERS 43606 #422-01-1993 L2000 APM *020

LEE, Jason Tse-Shan. ■ 43623 #654-01-2005 L2007 FP *012

LEE, Jennifer Helen. ■ 43614 #038-43-2008 *012

LE GOLVAN, Dennis Paul. 3404 W SYLVANIA AVE 43623 #025-01-1969 L1976 PTH PCP *020 †50

LEHMANN, Sarah Elizabeth. ■ 43615 #038-43-2008 *012

LELLI, Jos Lawrence, Jr. 2121 HUGHES DR, STE 620 43606 #025-12-1986 L1995 PDS *020 †85

LEMBACH, Mark Louis. ■ 43609 #038-43-2008 *012

LEMPERT, Kenneth David. 2109 HUGHES DR, STE 920 43606 #036-01-1976 L1986 NEP IM *020 †20

LENKAY, Mary Anne. 3120 GLENDALE AVE 43614 #016-43-1956 L1956 P PYG *020

LENTINI, Jennifer Ann. ■ 43617 #045-01-2005 L2005 CHP *012

LENZ, William Julius. 930 S DETROIT AVE, TOLEDO MENTAL HEALTH CTR 43614 #038-40-1970 L1970 P *071 †75

LEOPOLDT, Gerd. ■ 43606 #286-02-1945 L1956 P *071 †75

LEPKOWSKI, Philip Michael. 4235 SECOR RD 43623 #038-41-1983 L1984 FM IMG *020 †18

LESTER, Jason Bryant. 2213 CHERRY ST 43608 #305-01-2006 L2006 EM *012

LETCHER, John Raymond. 2940 N MCCORD RD, NORTHWEST OHIO CARDIOLOGY 43615 #041-09-1985 L1991 CD IM *020 †20

LEVINE, Amy P. 4841 MONROE ST, STE 103 43623 #038-43-2000 L2000 DR *100 †80

LEVINE, Jason William. 3000 ARLINGTON AVE 43614 #038-43-2000 L2000 ORS *100

LEVISON, Lauri B. 4411 N HOLLAND SYLVANIA RD, STE 201 43623 #038-43-1995 L1996 FM *020 †18

LEWIS, Christopher K. ■ 43606 #003-75-2005, ▲ L2005 AN *012

LEWIS, Jeffrey Ray. 2051 W CENTRAL AVE 43606 #038-43-1980 L1985 FM *040 †18

LEWIS, Jeromy Robert. 2213 CHERRY ST 43608 #038-43-2005 L2005 EM *012

LEWIS, Terrence Jos. 2658 W LASKEY RD, CONSULTING RADIOLOGISTS CO 43613 #038-06-1991 L1992 DR *020 †80

LI, Xin. CO GME-RM 320-MUL, UNIVERSITY OF TOLEDO 43614 #243-72-1986 L2007 PTH *012

LIANG, Liang. 3000 ARLINGTON AVE 43614 #243-16-1990 L2005 IM *012

LINDBLOOM, Kristopher L. ■ 43613 #028-78-2004, ▲ L2004 *100

LINDSTROM, David August. 2142 N COVE BLVD, PRO MEDICA AIR 43606 #025-12-1980 L1981 EM CCM *020 †16

LIU, Dennis Bernard. 745 WASHINGTON ST, # 503 43604 #016-06-1998 L2000 U *020 †95

LODGE, Kevin Paul. 2865 N REYNOLDS RD 43615 #038-44-1983 L1987 AN *020 †05

LOFTY, Ibrahim Hesham. 3045 ARLINGTON AVE, MULFORD LI 43614 #915-02-1992 L2001 AN *100

LOGUE, Francis M. 1838 PARKWOOD AVE, STE 100B 43604 #005-17-1962 GP *071

LOH, Terence Terng-Yun. 2658 W LASKEY RD 43613 #017-20-1977 L1981 VIR DR *020 †80

LONGWORTH, John Colby. PO BOX 327 43697 #270-01-1981 L1992 FM *020 †18

LOOMUS, Mark Geoffrey. 3949 SUNFOREST AVE, TOLEDO NEUROLOGICAL 43623 #025-07-1984 L1990 N IM *020 †20,75

LU, Heyi. 3000 ARLINGTON AVE, UNIVERSITY OF TOLEDO 43614 #243-13-1992 L2007 IM *012

LUGHMANI, Naeem Ahmad. 4428 SECOR RD STE A, TOLEDO CLINIC, INC 43623 #704-24-1989 L1991 SME PUD *020

LUTTON, Robert G. 3030 W SYLVANIA AVE 43613 #041-12-1949 L1961 U *071

LYNN, Amy A A. 3170 W CENTRAL AVE 1ST FL, CONSULTANTS IN LAB MED 43606 #025-01-1992 L2001 ATP DMP *020 †50

LYNN, Christopher Kenneth. 3000 ARLINGTON AVE, DEPARTMENT OF MEDICINE 43614 #038-43-1983 L1985 IM *040 †20

MA, Marcus. 2142 N COVE BLVD, THE TOLEDO HOSP EMERGENCY 43606 #025-01-1994 L1998 EM *020 †16

MACIEJEWSKI, Jacob Norman. ■ 43613 #038-43-2006 L2006 PD *012

MACK, Harry Cameron. 4235 SECOR RD, TOLEDO CLINIC 43623 #038-40-1955 L1955 IM *071

MACK, Michael Stephen. 4235 SECOR RD 43623 #038-40-1973 L1974 OBG *071 †30 ‡

MADOFF, Leonard Harvey. 2222 CHERRY ST 43608 #035-15-1976 L1980 PTH PCP *020 †50

MAGSI, Zafar Masood. 2121 HUGHES DR, STE 630 43606 #704-08-1992 L2004 NEP *020 †20

MAH, Chong Gi. 4841 MONROE ST, TOLEDO RADIOLOGICAL ASSOCI 43623 #583-01-1963 L1972 R *020 †20

MAHAJAN, Ajay. 2150 W CENTRAL AVE 43606 #495-51-1973 L1981 FM PTH *020 †20

MAHAJAN, Vijay Kumar. 2222 CHERRY ST, STE 1400 43608 #495-69-1966 L1978 PUD CCM *020 †20

MAHBOOB, Mohammad. 4235 SECOR RD, TOLEDO CLINIC INC 43623 #704-02-1970 L1975 PUD IM *020 †20

MAHMOOD, Shahid. 5012 TALMADGE RD 43623 #704-21-1983 L1993 BBK *020 †50

MALHOTRA, Deepak Kumar. 3120 GLENDALE AVE, RICHARD RUPPERT HEALTH CEN 43614 #038-06-1985 L1987 IM *020 †20

MALIK, Ajay. 3000 ARLINGTON AVE 43614 #495-29-1986 L1999 AN *020 †05

MALLORY, David Glenn. 3740 W SYLVANIA AVE, STE 100 43623 #038-45-1983 L1984 FM *020 †18

MALONEY, James Driscoll. 3000 ARLINGTON AVE 43614 #041-13-1966 L1981 CD IM *020 †20

MALUDY, Jeffrey C. 4417 N HOLLAND SYLVANIA RD, STE 301 43623 #038-43-1978 L1983 CD IM *020 †20

MALY, George Thomas. 3949 SUNFOREST CT, STE 201 43623 #305-01-1999 L2000 CD *020 †20

MANCINI, Arthur A. 4235 SECOR RD 43623 #025-01-1966 L1973 U *071 †95

MANICKAVASAGAM, Ezhilarasi. 320-MUL3045 ARLING, CO GME-RM 43614 #496-69-2004 L2007 PD *012

MANION, Sheila S. 3000 REGENCY CT 43623 #038-43-1981 L1985 DR *020 †80

MANN, Joseph. 1614 S BYRNE RD STE J 43614 #407-15-1954 L1960 P *071

MANNING, Peter Geo. ■ 43607 #917-30-1971 L1979 EM OS *020 †16

MANOUCHERI, Elmira. ■ 43606 #038-43-2008 *012

MANSOUR, Nasr Atieh. 3125 DOUGLAS RD 43606 #165-01-1964 L1966 PD *071

MARCO, Alan P. 3000 ARLINGTON AVE 43614 #023-07-1986 L1997 AN MDM *040 †05

MARCO, Catherine Mikat. 2213 CHERRY ST 43608 #023-07-1986 L1992 EM *020 †16

MARDOLKAR, Sanjay S. 2213 FRANKLIN AVE, 3RD FL 43620 #495-98-1984 L1999 PD *020 †55

MARESKA, John Chas. 2213 CHERRY ST, APT 304 43608 #016-06-1969 L1975 N *020 †75

MARINA, Vamsee Priya. 2213 CHERRY ST, DEPT OF MED EDU 43608 #495-50-2003 L2006 IM *012

MARKAKIS, George Aristotl. ■ 43606 #038-43-2007 L2007 TY *012

MARKOWICZ, Allen Lee. 4129 N HOLLAND SYLVANIA RD, NORTHWEST OHIO MEDICINE 43623 #038-40-1971 L1971 IM *020 †20 ‡

MARTIN, Kevin Alan. 3404 W SYLVANIA AVE, ST. ANNE MERCY HOSPITAL ER 43623 #038-43-1997 L1999 EM *020 †16

MARTIN, Tamara Norman. 4841 MONROE ST STE 103 43623 #025-07-1992 L1997 DR *020 †80

MARTINEZ, Bernard D. 2213 CHERRY ST, STE 305 43608 #132-06-1970 L1976 VS GS *085 †20

MASHALKAR, Vishwas J. 2109 HUGHES DR, STE 640 43606 #496-30-1991 L2000 CHP *020 †75

MASOOD, Azhar. 2127 JEFFERSON AVE 43604 #704-01-1995 L1999 FM *100

MASOOD, Naghmana. 2127 JEFFERSON AVE 43604 #704-01-1990 L1997 FM *020 †18

MASOOLTONDKAR, Farzaneh. ■ 43617 #166-01-2002 L2003 UCM *100

MATHER, Gordon Michael. 3909 WOODLEY RD STE 600 43606 #025-01-1963 L1969 IM *071 †20

MATOS, Stanley Anthony. 2865 N REYNOLDS RD 43615 #038-43-1993 L2002 AN *020 †05

MATTES, Fred Howard. 3036 W SYLVANIA AVE 43613 #035-09-1974 L1980 R *071 †80

MATTIN, Michael David. 2142 N COVE BLVD 43606 #038-43-1998 L1999 EM *020 †16

MATUS, Coral Delight. 2051 W CENTRAL AVE 43606 #038-40-1995 L1996 FM *020 †18

MAYHEW, Harry Eugene. 1015 GARDEN LAKE PKWY 43614 #025-01-1958 L1976 FM *071 †18

MCABEE, Olga Leonidovna. 3000 ARLINGTON AVE 43614 #913-12-1985 L2005 N *012

MC ALEAR, Thomas Gerard. 3909 WOODLEY RD, STE 300 43606 #038-43-1988 L1989 IM *020 †20

MC BRIDE, John David. 3830 WOODLEY RD, STE C 43606 #038-41-1994 L1997 PD *020 †55

MC CORMICK, Diane Alane. 6011 RENAISSANCE PL 43623 #038-43-1984 L1987 EM *020 †16

MC CORMICK, Patrick Wm. 2222 CHERRY ST, STE 200 43608 #038-41-1984 L1990 NS SCI *020 †25 ‡

MC CORMICK, Randall P. 2409 CHERRY ST, STE 207 43608 #035-47-1977 L1980 IM *020 †20

MC DONNELL, Christopher F. 5620 SOUTHWYCK BLVD, ANESTHESIA SERVICES 43614 #539-05-1963 L1966 AN OS *071

MC GINNIS, Ronald Anthony. 3120 GLENDALE AVE 43614 #038-43-1977 L1979 P *020 †18,75

MCHUGH, Patrick Ryan. ■ 43606 #038-43-2008 *012

MC PHEE, Michael D. 7140 PORT SYLVANIA DR, STE 420 43617 #035-15-1990 L1992 GS *020 †85

MC QUILLAN, Anne Conklin. 3170 W CENTRAL AVE, BUSINESS OFFICE 43606 #025-01-1985 L1990 PTH *020 †50

MCVICKER, Brooke Renee. ■ 43614 #038-43-2008 *012

MEADE, Heather Monique. ■ 43614 #038-43-2004 L2004 PD *020 †55

MEDHKOUR, Azedine. 3000 ARLINGTN AVE #SURGERY, MAIL STOP 1088 43614 #125-01-1977 L2000 GS *020 †20

MEER, Shahnawaz. 3000 ARLINGTON AVE 43614 #704-02-1992 L2006 P *012

MEHELAS, Thomas James. 3335 MEIJER DR 43617 #038-43-1978 L1982 OPH OS *020 †35

MEHTA, Anil. 4235 SECOR RD 43623 #496-04-1980 L1994 IM NEP *030 †20

MEHTA, Sonia. ■ 43614 #495-29-2003 L2005 OBG *012

MENDOZA, Leonardo C. 4352 W SYLVANIA AVE STE L 43623 #649-02-1965 L1970 IM *020 †20

MERRELL, David Marx. 2865 N REYNOLDS RD, STE 260 43615 #028-02-1971 L1979 OTO *020 †45

MERRICK, Hollis W, III. 3065 ARLINGTON AVE, MEDICAL COLLEGE OF OHIO 43614 #067-01-1964 L1977 GS *020 †85

MEYER, Indrek. ■ 43614 #038-43-2008 *012

MICHAELIS, Thomas Wm. 1160 W SYLVANIA AVE 43612 #038-40-1970 L1970 OBG *020 †30

MIEDLER, Leo J. 3900 SUNFOREST CT 43623 #025-07-1951 L1968 D OM *071 †15

MIKKILINENI, Hima. 3045 ARLINGTON AVE, CO MCOT-GRAD MED EDU DEPT 43614 #496-24-1999 L2003 CD *012 †20

MILLER, Allan. 2000 REGENCY CT STE 100 43623 #028-78-1961, ▲ L1961 PRO *020

MILLER, Lillian Gay. 3740 W SYLVANIA AVE, STE 103 43623 #038-40-1991 L1992 OBG *020 †20

MILLER, Marian Christine. ■ 43607 #038-43-2008 *012

MILLER, Roger Allen. 2121 HUGHES DR, STE 850 43606 #018-03-1966 L1974 CD IM *071 †20

MILLS, Robert Wm. 3400 MEIJER DR, PEDIATRICARE ASSOCIATES 43617 #038-43-1987 L1988 PD *020 †55

MIOCINOVIC, Ranko. ■ 43609 #038-43-2002 L2003 U *012

MIR, Farhaan Rowshan. ■ 43615 #038-43-2008 *012

MISTRY, Jimmy. 4428 SECOR RD 43623 #495-01-1957 L1970 OBG *020 †30

MISTRY, Yogesh Shankar. 43699 #654-01-2000 MPD *100

MOGHAL, Nadeem Nawaz. 7053 W CENTRAL AVE, TOLEDO PAIN SERVICES 43617 #759-06-2000 L2003 APM *020 †05

MOHAMED, Iman E. 3000 ARLINGTON AVE MS 1186, DEPARTMENT OF MEDICINE 43614 #584-01-1985 L1999 ON IM *020 †20

MOHAMMAD, Shaden Fawzi. 3000 ARLINGTON AVE, MEDICAL COLLEGE OF OHIO 43614 #038-43-2004 L2004 DR *012

MOHAN, Geetali. 2213 CHERRY ST, DEPT OF INTERNAL MED 43608 #496-07-2005 L2006 IM *012

MONTESINOS, Efrain. 1565 S BYRNE RD, STE 100 43614 #737-01-1963 L1976 GS TS *071

MOORE, Brian William. ■ 43608 #038-43-2008 *012

MOORJANI, Zubeida G. 3404 W SYLVANIA AVE, SAINT ANNE MERCY HOSPITAL 43623 #495-01-1960 L1972 AN GP *020

MOORMAN, Gary L. 2942 SHORELAND AVE, ST. VINCENT MERCY MED. CTR 43611 #028-79-1980, ▲ L1981 EM FM *040 †16

MORAN, Joseph P, Jr. ■ 43614 #038-06-1943 L1943 **GS** *071 †85
MORONT, Michael Geo. 2109 HUGHES DR STE 720 43606 #010-02-1984 L1993 **TS** *020 †85,90
MORSE, Willis Michael. 3909 WOODLEY RD, STE 500 43606 #038-43-1991 L1994 **FM** *020 †18
MOTLEY, Darlene Mary. ■ 43617 #041-12-1995 **PM** *075
MOUSSA, Sara Afif. ■ 43613 #038-43-2005 L2005 **PD** *012
MOWAT, Rex Bradford. 4235 SECOR RD, TOLEDO CLINIC, INC 43623 #025-07-1985 L1992 **ON HEM** *020 †20
MOYNIHAN, Vivian Frances. 3120 GLENDALE AVE STE 1520, DEPT OF OB/GYN RUPPERT HLT 43614 #038-40-1980 L1981 **GYN OBS** *020 †30 ‡
MUBASHIR, Eisha. 3120 GLENDALE AVE, RHC - RM 12 43614 #704-20-1993 L2006 **RHU** *100
MUGASHE, Frederick L. 2700 MONROE ST, STE F 43606 #913-15-1967 L1978 **GP** *075
MUGAWISH, Suhair. 4235 SECOR RD 43623 #875-01-1990 L2006 **PCC** *020 †20
MUJEEB, Sheikh Abdul. 3045 ARLINGTON AVE, MED UNIV OF OHIO 43614 #495-51-1998 L2006 *100
MUKUNDAN, Deepa. 2222 CHERRY ST, ST VINCENTS MERCY CHILD 43608 #495-59-1987 L1999 **PDI** *100 †55
MUNK, Richard L. 2121 HUGHES DR STE 980, HARRIS MC INTOSH TOWER 43606 #035-06-1971 L1984 **OP ORS** *020 †40
MUNOZ, Jose Armando. ■ 43623 #649-02-1955 L1967 **AN** *071
MURPHY, Ian Deighton. PO BOX 12177 43612 #067-01-1960 L1961 **GP OS** *020
MURPHY, John Michael. 2142 N COVE BLVD, FERTILITY CENTER OF NORTHW 43606 #041-13-1989 L1993 **REN** *020 †30
MURTAGH, Daniel Sullivan. 3500 EXECUTIVE PKWY 43606 #038-43-1978 L1983 **U** *020 †95
MURTAGH, Jennifer Joan. 3830 WOODLEY RD STE C 43606 #038-43-1987 L1988 **PD** *020 †55
MUSA, Mahmoud Nimir. ■ 43617 #056-06-1979 L1996 **P GP** *075 †75
MUSHKBAR, Saudia. 3000 ARLINGTON AVE 43614 #704-02-2000 L2005 **FP** *012
MUSTAPHA, Abdul A. 1565 S BYRNE RD 43614 #062-01-1992 L2000 **HS** *020 †40
MUTGI, Anand B. 3120 GLENDALE AVE, RHC 0012 43614 #495-33-1976 L1988 **IM** *020 †20
MYCHALISKA, George Boris. 2222 CHERRY ST, STE 1800 43608 #005-02-1991 L2006 **PDS** *020 †85
MYERS, Richard Emanuel. 3000 REGENCY CT, STE 105 43623 #038-06-1958 L1958 **R NM** *071 †80
NABOR, Asuncion G. ■ 43615 #748-01-1956 L1983 **P** *020
NADAUD, Jonathan Andrew. 4841 MONROE ST STE 103, TOLEDO RADIOLOGICAL ASSOC. 43623 #038-44-1996 L2002 **DR** *020 †80
NADAUD, Joshua Peter. ■ 43614 #028-34-2004 L2004 **ORS** *012
NADDAF, Housam. 4235 SECOR RD 43623 #038-43-1996 L1998 **FM** *020 †18
NADERER, Marc Anthony. 2051 W CENTRAL AVE 43606 #038-43-2005 L2005 **FP** *012
NADIG, Malini Visalam. 2222 CHERRY ST, STE M200 43608 #016-02-1998 L2007 **NS** *100
NADOUR, Alaa Munzer. 3000 ARLINGTON AVE 43614 #875-02-1994 L2003 **IM** *100 †20
NAGEL, Michael Andrew. 4235 SECOR RD, TOLEDO CLINIC INC 43623 #035-08-1983 L1996 **CHN CN** *020 †75,55
NAQVI, Syed Anwar H. 2222 CHERRY ST, STE 1400 43608 #704-20-1989 L2001 **ID** *020 †20
NARAHARISETTY, Kalpana. 2213 CHERRY ST, DEPT OF INTERNAL MED 43608 #495-50-2004 L2007 **IM** *012
NARANG, Supriya. 3000 ARLINGTON AVE, CO MCOT-PSYCHIATRY DEPT 43614 #496-04-1996 L2000 **P** *020 †75
NASR, Esfandiar. 2051 W CENTRAL AVE, TOLEDO HOSPITAL FAMILY PRA 43606 #305-01-2003 L2003 **FM** *020 †18
NATIVIDAD, Recto Orate. 635 N ERIE ST 43604 #748-08-1959 L1972 **FM GP** *071
NAVARRE, Robert Jos, Jr. 3500 EXECUTIVE PKWY 43606 #038-43-1978 L1983 **U** *020 †95
NAZZAL, Maisa Ali. 3000 ARLINGTON AVE 43614 #575-02-2000 L2006 **IM** *012
NAZZAL, Munier Mohamed S. 3065 ARLINGTON AVE, DOWLING HALL 43614 #584-01-1983 L1999 **VS GS** *020 †85
NAZZAL, Mustafa Darwish. PO BOX 10008 43699 #915-04-2001 L2007 **GS** *012
NELSON, Lois Anne. 2222 CHERRY ST, STE 2300 43608 #016-02-1973 L1980 **AI IG** *040 †55,03
NEMBHARD, Jacqueline J. ■ 43614 #038-43-1999 **FOP** *100
NEVILLE, Robert G. 2865 N REYNOLDS RD, STE 170 43615 #025-12-1979 L1980 **OPH** *020 †35
NEWBURN, Andrew Dwight. ■ 43614 #038-43-2008 *012
NEWTON, John J. 905 NEBRASKA AVE, CORDELIA MARTIN HEALTH CTR 43607 #016-43-1952 L1952 **FM** *071 †18
NGUYEN, Thinh Phu. ■ 43614 #011-02-2005 L2005 **OBG** *012
NICHOLAS, Kirsten. ■ 43614 #038-43-2008 *012
NICHOLSON, Jonathon K. 2213 CHERRY ST, ST VINCENT MERCY MEDICAL C 43608 #038-43-1998 L1999 **MPD** *020
NIGROVIC, Vladimir. 3000 ARLINGTON AVE, DEPT ANESTH MED CLG OF OH 43614 #407-10-1962 L1979 **AN** *071 †05
NIMMAGADDA, Prasad V S. 1565 S BYRNE RD, STE 100 43614 #495-50-1985 L1994 **AN** *020 †05
NIMR, Soad A Mohamed. 1565 S BYRNE RD, STE 100 43614 #915-03-1969 L1974 **AN** *020 †05
NONOY, Teodoro B, Jr. 4235 SECOR RD, TOLEDO CLINIC INC 43623 #748-07-1960 L1974 **AN** *071
NORTH, James Linus. 3909 WOODLEY RD, STE 500 43606 #038-45-1986 L1987 **FM** *020 †18
NORWOOD, Andrea Maia. 2222 CHERRY ST, MOB 2 STE 1100 43608 #025-07-1997 L2001 **PD** *020 †55 ‡
NOVAK, William G. 7111 W CENTRAL AVE 43617 #035-06-1975 L1976 **DR PDR** *020 †80
NOVAKOVIC, Rachel Lamb. 2213 CHERRY ST 43608 #025-07-1987 L1996 **GS TRS** *020 †85 ‡
NOWICKI, Philip Daniel. 3045 ARLINGTON AVE, CO GME- RM 330 - 43614 #016-43-2004 L2004 **ORS** *012
NUCKLOS, Ruby Nell. 3120 GLENDALE AVE RM 12, MEDICAL COLLEGE OF OHIO 43614 #038-43-1980 L1984 **IM** *020 †20
OATIS, Pamela Jane. 2213 FRANKLIN AVE 43620 #038-43-1980 L1986 **PD** *020 †55
OFORI-AKYEAH, Jason. 2865 N REYNOLDS RD 43615 #412-01-1972 L1981 **OPH GS** *020 †35 ‡
OGNEN, Leo. 5705 DORR ST 43615 #957-02-1979 L1995 **FM** *020
O'GRADY, Thomas John. 4235 SECOR RD, THE TOLEDO CLINIC 43623 #035-20-1958 L1965 **TS** *071 †85,90
O'HARA, David Vance. 2213 CHERRY ST 43608 #038-43-2001 L2001 **EM** *020 †16
OKOLI, Kelechi Chima. 2213 CHERRY ST, DEPT OF INTERNAL MED 43608 #690-04-1999 L2006 **IM** *012
OKORO, Bonaventure C. 5542 AIRPORT HWY 43615 #781-03-1984 L1996 **IM** *020 †20
OLSON, Dan Emil. 3000 ARLINGTON AVE, P O BOX 10008 43614 #007-02-1973 L1993 **PUD IM** *020 †20
OLSZEWSKI, Colleen Marie. 2142 N COVE BLVD 43606 #038-43-1995 L1997 **PD MPD** *020 †20,55
OMORI, Michael Shige. 2213 CHERRY ST 43608 #038-43-1980 L1982 **EM** *020 †16
ONYEWUCHE, Vivian Nnenna. 2213 CHERRY ST 43608 #690-04-1996 L2005 **AN** *012
ORQVIST, Aaron Matthew. 2213 CHERRY ST 43608 #038-43-2003 L2006 **EM** *100 †16
ORR, Kathryn Elizabeth. ■ 43614 #038-43-2008 *012
OSINOWO, Thomas Olaide. 930 S DETROIT AVE 43614 #690-01-1987 L2003 **P PFP** *020 †75
OSOWIK, Rosemarie Ohliger. 2100 W ALEXIS RD, NORTHERN LIGHTS MEDICAL CE 43613 #038-43-1987 L1989 **FM** *020 †18
OSSE, Evan. 3000 ARLINGTON AVE 43614 #875-01-2000 L2004 **IM** *100
OSWANSKI, Michael Francis. 2109 HUGHES DR, STE 220 43606 #038-43-1975 L1980 **GS** *020 †85
OTT, Thomas Edward. 3232 CENTRAL PARK W, STE B 43617 #038-41-1991 L1994 **FM** *020 †18
OWEIS, Shadi Ed. 3000 ARLINGTON AVE, U.M.C 43614 #875-01-1995 L2004 **NEP** *012 †20
PACHA DHARMA, Jeevarathnam. 3000 ARLINGTON AVE 43614 #495-59-2003 L2005 **PD** *012
PADANILAM, Denise Ann. 7140 PORT SYLVANIA DR, STE 200 43617 #016-06-1992 L1995 **PD** *020 †55
PADANILAM, Thomas Geo. 2865 N REYNOLDS RD, TOLEDO ORTHOPAEDIC SURGEON 43615 #038-43-1991 L1997 **ORS OFA** *040 †40
PADDA, Harsant Singh. 4235 SECOR RD 43623 #495-73-1976 L1989 **GE IM** *075 †20
PADDA, Roshinder. 4235 SECOR RD 43623 #495-43-1975 L1989 **OBG** *020 †30
PAI, Ajith Kalsank. 2409 CHERRY ST, STE 305 43608 #495-37-1974 L1978 **AN PME** *020 †05
PAK, Daniel. ■ 43614 #038-43-1994 **P** *100
PALMA GIL, Teresita N C. 313 JEFFERSON AVE, MILDRED BAYER CLINIC 43604 #748-08-1965 L1972 **GP** *020
PALMER, Robert Michael. 4235 SECOR RD, DEPT OF GENERAL SURGERY 43623 #038-43-2002 L2007 **GS** *020 †85
PALUSZNY, Maria Janina D. 3000 ARLINGTON AVE, CHILD PSYCHIATRY CS-10008 43614 #025-01-1962 L1986 **CHP P** *020 †75
PANDEY, Rahul Gopal. ■ 43614 #495-23-1999 L2007 **IM** *012
PANDYA, Utpal Harivallabh. ■ 43615 #025-07-1998 L2005 **IC** *100 †20
PANSKY, Ben. 2809 MANCHESTER BLVD 43606 #035-09-1968 L1970 **PTH N** *040
PAOLINI, David J. 2109 HUGHES DR STE 400 43606 #041-13-1999 L2006 **VS** *012 †85
PAPPAS, Michael Demetrios. 4405 N HOLLAND SYLVANIA RD, STE 1202 43623 #654-01-1988 L1994 **CCP** *020 †55
PAPPAS, S John D. 3000 ARLINGTON AVE, UNIVERSITY OF TOLEDO MEDIC 43614 #654-01-1986 L1992 **IM** *020
PAPPAS, Thomas Mitcho. 2940 N MCCORD RD, NORTHWEST OHIO CARDIOLOGY 43615 #038-44-1990 L1991 **IM** *020 †20
PAREDES, Julieta M L. MED COLL TOLEDO ASSC ANES 43699 #748-11-1968 **AN** *100
PAREDES, Rolando Inting. 2409 CHERRY ST, ASSOCD ANESTHESIOLOGISTS 43608 #748-01-1967 L1979 **AN** *071
PAREKH, Hasmukh C. PO BOX 10008, DEPT PSYCH 43699 #496-38-1961 **P** *100
PARIKH, Parag Ushakant. 2845 TRACEWOOD DR 43617 #025-07-1986 L1990 **DR** *020 †80
PARKER, David Alan. 7111 W CENTRAL AVE 43617 #025-07-1979 L1989 **DR NR** *020 †80
PARKINS, Sue Major. 2213 CHERRY ST 43608 #038-43-1976 L1977 **OM EM** *020 †16
PARVEZ, Yasmin. 3333 GLENDALE AVE, DEPARTMENT OF VETERANS AFF 43614 #704-04-1982 L1999 **FM** *020 †18
PASCH, Bruce Arthur. 2109 HUGHES DR, JOBST TOWER , STE 640 43606 #038-40-1976 L1978 **PD** *020 †55
PATEL, Arun. 3900 SUNFOREST CT, STE 212 43623 #803-05-1963 L1979 **ORS** *020 †40
PATEL, Ashalata. 2213 FRANKLIN AVE 43620 #917-28-1966 L1979 **PD PHO** *020 †55
PATEL, Bharatkumar Dahyab. ■ 43615 #495-23-2002 L2006 **N** *012
PATEL, Jaylata Madhusudan. 4334 SECOR RD 43623 #495-22-1972 L1985 **P CHP** *020 †75
PATEL, Jigneshkumar Kesha. ■ 43604 #495-89-2000 L2006 **IM** *012
PATEL, Kalpesh. ■ 43614 #038-43-2007 *012
PATEL, Madhusudan. 723 PHILLIPS AVE 43612 #495-01-1972 L1984 **FM** *020 †18
PATEL, Pravinbhai Z. ■ 43614 #495-23-1966 **FM** *100
PATEL, Shamit Pravin. ■ 43614 #038-43-1998 L2002 **MPD** *020 †55,20
PATEL, Yogeshkumar. 2658 W LASKEY RD, STE A 43613 #495-22-1974 L1990 **DR NM** *020 †28,80
PATRICK, James Richard. 2595 ARLINGTON AVE, LUCAS COUNTY CORONERS OFC 43614 #008-01-1956 L1969 **FOP ATP** *030 †55,50
PATTABIRAMAN IYER, C. 3000 ARLINGTON AVE, DEPT ANESTH 43614 #495-66-1977 L1999 **AN** *020 †05
PAYNE, Hosea. 2213 CHERRY ST 43608 #025-07-1963 L1967 **U** *020 †95
PAYNE, Nicole Ylonne. ■ 43614 #038-43-2003 L2003 **PM** *012
PELLIONI, Mary Mc Carthy. 1600 N SUPERIOR ST 43604 #038-43-1991 L1996 **IM** *020 †20
PENAMON, Wanda Amelia. ■ 43612 #021-05-1990 L1993 **OS** *020
PEOPLES, Richard Bailey. ■ 43617 #041-02-1954 L1958 **ORS** *020 †40
PEREZ, Diego E A. ■ 43609 #275-01-1956 **P** *071
PEREZ, Vincent Leo. 2658 W LASKEY RD 43613 #014-01-1988 L1994 **DR NM** *020 †80,28
PERLMUTTER, David Monis. ■ 43617 #038-43-1977 L1978 **AN** *020 †05
PERON, Salvador Eloy, Jr. 3436 GRANITE CIR 43617 #025-01-1982 L1987 **U** *020
PETERS, Cecelia C Selvey. 313 JEFFERSON AVE 43604 #010-03-1967 L1973 **PD** *020
PETERSON, Duane Gordon. 2450 N REYNOLDS RD 43615 #038-41-1961 L1961 **GP** *020
PETROU, Peter Geo. 2020 STARR AVE 43605 #418-01-1955 L1961 **FM PHP** *020
PHIBBS, Garth D. 2109 HUGHES DR STE 820 43606 #065-06-1973 L1981 **GO GYN** *020 †30 ‡
PHILLIPS, Edwin Robt. 1565 S BYRNE RD 43614 #056-05-1970 L1981 **ATP OS** *071 †50
PHINNEY, Richard Clifton. ■ 43606 #038-43-2006 L2006 **IM** *012
PIGOTT, John Arthur. 2109 HUGHES DR 43606 #028-34-1959 L1960 **PD** *071 †55
PIGOTT, John Patrick. 2109 HUGHES DR STE 450 43606 #038-43-1984 L1985 **VS** *020 †85
PIKE, Edward John. 2213 CHERRY ST 43608 #041-12-1960 L1960 **ADL OS** *071 †55
PILLAI, Anitha. 3045 ARLINGTON AVE, CO MCOT-GRAD MED EDU DEPT 43614 #496-20-2000 L2002 **IM** *100 †20
PINSKY, Stanley Theodore. 3000 ARLINGTON AVE, DEPT OF RADIOLOGY-MCO 43614 #038-40-1955 L1955 **R NM** *071 †80,28
PIRZADA, Noor Ali. 3000 ARLINGTON AVE MS 1195, UNIVERSITY OF TOLEDO MEDIC 43614 #495-51-1980 L1996 **N** *020 †75
PIRZADA, Yasmin Drabu. 4235 SECOR RD, THE TOLEDO CLINIC 43623 #495-51-1980 L2000 **ID** *100
PISANI, Sheilnin. 2100 W ALEXIS RD 43613 #038-40-1993 L1998 **MPD** *020 †20,55
PITRODA, Mukesh V. 3000 ARLINGTON AVE, DEPARTMENT OF ANESTHESIOLO 43614 #495-22-1984 L1997 **AN** *020
PIZZA, Eric Anthony. 3500 EXECUTIVE PKWY, GENITO-URINARY SURGEONS, I 43606 #038-43-1982 L1988 **U** *020 †95
PLEWA, Michael Casimir. 2213 CHERRY ST 43608 #025-01-1985 L1993 **EM** *020 †16
PLUMMER, Cassandra Denise. 2051 W CENTRAL AVE, PRACTICE RE 43606 #104-01-2006 L2007 **FP** *012

PLUNDO, Terri Lynn. 3922 WOODLEY RD, STE 101 43606 #018-75-1992, ▲ L1993 *020

POHLOD-MILLER, Susan Ann. ■ 43623 #007-02-1996 L2000 **OBG** *020 †30

POLAMREDDY, R. 3829 WOODLEY RD, STE 1 43606 #495-62-1973 L1978 **PD** *020 †55

PONDER, Terry Brent. 3170 W CENTRAL AVE, CONSULTANTSIN LABORATORY M 43606 #028-03-1985 L2005 **PTH** *020 †18,50

PONTASCH, Erich Roderick. 3404 W SYLVANIA AVE, ST ANNE MERCY HOSPITAL 43623 #038-43-1983 L1984 **EM** *020 †16

PONTASCH, Martin J. 6511 W CENTRAL AVE 43617 #038-44-1988 L1989 **EM** *020 †16

POPOVICH, Harvey Andrew. 2213 CHERRY ST, STE 203 43608 #038-43-1975 L1976 **OM FM** *020 †70,18

PRABHAKAR, Krishna. 2051 W CENTRAL AVE, TOLEDO HOSPITAL FAMILY PRA 43606 #104-01-2002 L2003 **FM** *020 †18

PRASHER, Anuj. 3065 ARLINGTON AVE, HEALTH SCIEN 43614 #025-07-2006 L2006 **ORS** *012

PRICE, Charles I. 7111 W CENTRAL AVE 43617 #041-01-1986 L1991 **DR** *020 †80

PRICE, Joy Ann. 525 HAMILTON ST, STE 101A 43604 #038-43-1985 L1986 **P PYG** *020 †75

PRINCE, Gregory M. 3170 W CENTRAL AVE, BUSINESS OFFICE 43606 #016-01-1988 L1996 **PTH** *020 †50

PRINZ, Deborah Marie. ■ 43614 #038-43-2008 *012

PROCTOR, Amanda Lerae. ■ 43614 #038-43-2008 *012

PROVENZANO, Joseph A. 5916 CRESTHAVEN LN, APT 510 43614 #016-11-1943 L1947 **PDC** *072

PRZYNOSCH, Stephen L. 3909 WOODLEY RD, STE 500 43606 #035-06-1999 L1999 **FM** *020 †18

PURANDARE, Aditi Vinayak. ■ 43614 #011-02-2005 L2006 **IM** *012

QAYUM, Erum Naz. 1015 GARDEN LAKE PKWY, MEDICAL COLLEGE OF OHIO 43614 #704-18-1995 L2001 **FM** *100 †18

QUINN, Eileen Ann. 2222 CHERRY ST 43608 #025-01-1983 L1988 **PD** *020 †55

QUINN, Timothy James. 4841 MONROE ST, TOLEDO RADIOLOGICAL ASSOC, 43623 #016-01-1994 L1999 **DR** *020 †80

QUINONEZ, Shane. ■ 43615 #025-01-2008 *012

QURAISHY, Nur Jehan. 3510 EXECUTIVE PKWY 43606 #704-02-1974 L1983 **BBK PTH** *062 †50

RABENOLD, Jason D. 2801 W BANCROFT ST, DEPT ORS 43606 #035-15-2003 L2003 **ORS** *012

RACHWAL, William Jos. 2109 HUGHES DR, STE 720 43606 #025-07-1990 L1998 **TS** *020 †85,90

RADECKI, Daniel J. 4303 TALMADGE RD 43623 #028-34-1949 L1954 **GS END** *020 †85

RADUEGE, Kevin Michael. 2409 CHERRY ST, MEDICAL OFFICE BUILDING, S 43608 #038-43-2001 L2001 **AN** *040 †05

RAE, Robert Sean. 7140 PORT SYLVANIA DR, STE 420 43617 #539-03-2002 L2006 **MPD** *020 †55,20

RAFANAN, Albert L. 2222 CHERRY ST, STE 1400 43608 #748-02-1992 L1998 **PCC** *020 †20

RAFFOUL, Khalil Albert. 1000 REGENCY CT STE 100 43623 #025-01-1991 L1996 **OPH** *020 †35

RAGAN, Luke Matthew. 2865 N REYNOLDS RD, STE 160 43615 #038-43-1998 L1999 **FSM** *020 †18

RAGOTHAMAN, Nagaveni. 525 HAMILTON ST, STE 101A 43604 #495-94-1979 L1994 **P** *020

RAIMONDE, Anthony Jay. 2409 CHERRY ST STE 303 43608 #038-40-1985 L1989 **GS CCS** *020 †85

RAIS, Alina Rahel. 3000 ARLINGTON AVE, MEDICAL COLLEGE OF OHIO 43614 #781-01-1984 L2000 **P** *020 †75

RAIS, Theodor Bernard. 3130 GLENDALE AVE 43614 #781-01-1982 L1999 **CHP** *020 †75

RAJA, Naureen Shamsher. 3000 ARLINGTON AVE 43614 #038-43-2007 L2007 **IM** *012

RAKOLTA, George Gabriel. 2213 CHERRY ST 43608 #025-01-1962 L1974 **ORS HS** *071 †40

RALLS, Matthew William. ■ 43615 #038-43-2008 *012

RAMASAMY, Arun Kumar. 3000 ARLINGTON AVE 43614 #495-16-2001 L2006 **GS** *100

RAMASWAMI, Ganesh. 2109 HUGHES DR, CONRAD JOBST TOWER - 4TH F 43606 #495-32-1984 L2006 **VS** *012 †85

RAMIREZ, Ixsy Abigail. 2222 CHERRY ST, STE 1100 43608 #305-01-2006 L2006 **PD** *012

RAMIREZ, Mark Allan Ng. 3045 ARLINGTON AVE, CO GME- RM 330 - 43614 #748-01-2000 L2004 **N** *012

RAMPERSAD, Avind Darryl. 3000 ARLINGTON AVE 43614 #539-06-2003 L2006 **PD** *012

RAMSEY-WILLIAMS, Vicki A. 3120 GLENDALE AVE, RHC 1450 43614 #038-43-1999 L1999 **N CN** *020 †75

RAO, Sudhir Gondy. 7255 CROSSLEIGH CT STE 1 43617 #495-50-1988 L1995 **AI** *020 †55,20,03

RAPPORT, Daniel John. 3120 GLENDALE AVE, UNIV OF TOLEDO CLG OF MED 43614 #038-45-1985 L1987 **P** *020 †75

RASHID, Michael George. 3500 EXECUTIVE PKWY 43606 #025-07-1996 L2002 **U** *020 †95

RASHID, Shaukat. 2121 HUGHES DR STE 630, ASSOC INC 43606 #704-20-1989 L2005 **NEP** *020 †20

RASHID, Sumia. 3045 ARLINGTON AVE M, CO MCOT-GRAD MED EDU DEPT 43614 #495-51-1999 L2000 **NEP** *012

RATNAM, Shobha. 3000 ARLINGTON AVE 43614 #038-43-1999 L1999 **NEP** *020 †20

RAVIN, Louis C. 3000 REGENCY CT, THE EYE CENTER OF TOLEDO 43623 #025-07-1937 L1938 **OPH** *071 †35

READ, Elizabeth Meyer. 3840 WOODLEY RD, STE B 43606 #038-43-1988 L1992 **OBG** *020 †30

REAMES, David Robt. 1600 N SUPERIOR ST 43604 #025-01-1983 L1984 **FM** *020 †18

REDDY, Prashanth Kundur. 3000 ARLINGTON AVE 43614 #496-01-2002 L2005 **IM** *012

REDDY, Sahaja Sri. 3454 OAK ALLEY CT, STE 209 43606 #495-62-1986 L2003 **P** *020 †75

REDDY, Sapna T. 4235 SECOR RD 43623 #495-21-1989 L1998 **GE** *020 †20

REECE, Tiffani Lynn. ■ 43614 #038-43-2008 *012

REES, Michael Alan. 3065 ARLINGTON AVE, MEDICAL COLLEGE OF OHIO UR 43614 #025-01-1991 L1999 **U** *020 †95

REGA, Paul Patrick. ■ 43615 #561-17-1975 L1979 **EM** *040 †16

REGUEYRA, Francisco I. 2200 JEFFERSON AVE 43604 #275-01-1960 L1967 **GS** *071

REHMAN, Syed M Maseehur. 2213 CHERRY ST 43608 #704-02-1983 L1996 **PD AI** *020 †55,03

REHMAN, Tabinda O. 1565 S BYRNE RD 43614 #704-02-1990 L1998 **CHP** *020

REILLY, Peter Joseph. 4841 MONROE ST 43623 #038-40-1978 L1981 **GE** *020 †20

REINER, Louis Michael. 3909 WOODLEY RD, STE 300 43606 #038-43-1988 L1989 **IM** *020 †20

REITER, Robert Cole. 2142 N COVE BLVD # 950, PRO MED HLTH SYS 43606 #048-04-1981 L2001 **OBG** *020 †30

REJENT, Marian M. 2213 CHERRY ST 43608 #056-06-1946 L1947 **PD PHP** *072 †55

REN, Daan. 3045 ARLINGTON AVE, DEPT OF GME 43614 #243-16-1995 L2006 **FP** *012

RETHOLTZ, Michael. ■ 43617 #038-75-2003, ▲ L2003 *020

RETTIG, Adam Jarett. 2213 CHERRY ST, ST. VINCENT MERCY MEDICAL 43608 #038-43-2003 L2003 **EM** *020 †18

RHEE, Chi Sun Yoo. ■ 43623 #583-06-1964 L1973 **OBG** *071 †30

RIAZ, Hamid. 2200 JEFFERSON AVE 43604 #704-15-1979 L1998 **FM** *040 †18 ‡

RICE, Christopher Ashley. ■ 43609 #038-43-2008 *012

RICE, Susan Growney. 419 N REYNOLDS RD, EXCEL MEDICAL GROUP LLC 43615 #038-43-1990 L1994 **PM OM** *020 †60

RICKER, Victor John. 3922 WOODLEY RD, STE 100 43606 #038-43-1976 L1987 **FM** *020 †18

RICKS, Michael James. ■ 43615 #038-43-1978 **FM** *075

RIESE, Amy Elizabeth. ■ 43613 #056-06-2004 L2004 **P** *012

RIESEN, Matthew Christoph. ■ 43614 #038-43-2007 L2007 **FP** *012

RIETHMILLER, Michael K. 2213 CHERRY ST, ST VINCENT MEDICAL CENTER 43608 #025-01-1973 L1978 **FM OM** *040 †70,18

RIMARACHIN, Julio Anibal. 3045 ARLINGTON AVE, CO MCOT-GRAD MED EDU DEPT 43614 #737-01-1984 L2007 **OBG** *020

RIORDAN, Christopher J. 2213 CHERRY ST, SURGEONS OF NW OHIO INC 43608 #008-02-1989 L1997 **TS** *020 †18

RIYAZ, Najmun. 3045 ARLINGTON AVE, CO MCOT-GRAD MED EDU DEPT 43614 #495-51-1997 L2002 **P** *020 †75

RIZK, Tallat Mahrous. 3045 ARLINGTON AVE, UNIVERSITY MEDICAL CENTER 43614 #915-02-1989 L2000 **PM** *020 †60

ROBERTS, James C. 3949 SUNFOREST CT 43623 #038-40-1955 L1955 **AI OS** *071 †55,03

ROBERTS, James C, Jr. 3110 W CENTRAL AVE, STE B 43606 #038-43-1981 L1982 **CD IM** *020 †20

ROBERTS, James Mortimer. 5415 MONROE ST, STE 4 43623 #025-01-1963 L1968 **OPH** *071

ROBY, James Gerard. 2150 W CENTRAL AVE 43606 #038-43-1980 L1987 **FM OM** *020 †18

ROCA, Pedro. 2213 CHERRY ST, ST VINCENT MERCY MEDICAL C 43608 #042-01-1992 L2006 **OBG** *020 †30

RODGERS-OHLAU, Melissa Ma. ■ 43620 #038-43-2008 *012

RODRIGUEZ-WINTER, Duane A. 1 STRANAHAN SQ STE 414, FMLY SRVC OF NW OHIO 43604 #041-01-1982 L1983 **P FM** *020 †18,75

ROGALSKI, Francis Jos. 3400 MEIJER DR, PEDIATRICARE ASSOCIATES 43617 #038-43-1986 L1987 **PD** *020 †55

ROJESKI, Maria Theresa. 3120 GLENDALE AVE, DEPT OF INTERNAL MED RM 00 43614 #038-41-1980 L2000 **END IM** *020 †20

ROLF-ANDERSEN, Joann M. 3740 W SYLVANIA AVE, STE 103 43623 #038-43-1988 L1990 **OBG** *020 †30

ROONEY, Thomas Alan. 3000 ARLINGTON AVE, DEPARTMENT OF ANESTHESIA 43614 #038-06-1986 L1986 **AN** *020 †05

ROSENTHAL, J Gregory. 2213 CHERRY ST 43608 #028-02-1984 L1989 **OPH** *020 †35

ROSOL, Stanley J. 2200 JEFFERSON AVE, FL 4 43604 #028-79-1972, ▲ L1977 **GS UM** *020 †05

ROSS, David Russell. ■ 43615 #025-12-2007 L2007 **ORS** *012

ROSS, Johnathon Saml. 2213 CHERRY ST 43608 #038-43-1975 L1980 **IM PHP** *020 †20

ROSS, Scott F. ■ 43613 #025-07-2006 L2006 **FP** *012

ROTH, Matt Daniel. 2051 W CENTRAL AVE 43606 #038-40-2004 L2004 **FSM** *012 †18

ROTH, Victor S. 1455 W ALEXIS RD, MEDICAL BAY A-7, ROOM 125 43612 #038-41-1975 L1988 **OM FM** *030 †18,70

ROWAN, Charles Edward. 3454 OAK ALLEY CT, STE 308 43606 #017-20-1959 L1965 **IM OS** *020

ROYEN, Peter Mark. 2658 W LASKEY RD 43613 #024-07-1968 L1974 **DR** *020 †80

RUBENSTEIN, Forrest Scot. 2213 CHERRY ST # 309ACC 43608 #001-06-1984 L2001 **TS** *020 †85,90

RUDDOCK, Martin Dennis. 328 22ND ST 43604 #028-02-1977 L1978 **OBG** *020

RUHLEN, Michael Eugene. 2142 N COVE BLVD, TOLEDO CHILDREN'S HOSPITAL 43606 #038-41-1980 L1984 **PD HOS** *030 †20

RUIZ, Jamey Juan. 3000 ARLINGTON AVE 43614 #038-43-2000 L2000 **PCC** *020

RUPPERT, Richard Dale. 3000 ARLINGTON AVE 43614 #038-40-1961 L1961 **IM** *072 †20

RUSIA, Anirudh. 3000 ARLINGTON AVE 43614 #496-49-2002 L2005 **IM** *012

RUSS, John Albert, III. 3000 ARLINGTON AVE, MED COLLEGE OF OHIO HOSP 43614 #038-43-1980 L1981 **EM** *020 †16

RUSSELL, Todd Eugene. 2109 HUGHES DR, STE 450 43606 #038-45-1992 L1998 **VS** *020 †85

RUSZKIEWICZ, Edward D. 4841 MONROE ST 43623 #028-34-1972 L1973 **GE IM** *071 †20

RUTTER, Matthew Edward. 3000 ARLINGTON AVE, UNIVERSITY OF TOLEDO MEDIC 43614 #038-43-1997 L2002 **U** *020 †35

SADDEMI, Stephen Ross. 2865 N REYNOLDS RD, STE 160 43615 #038-43-1982 L1987 **ORS OSM** *020 †40

SAFADI, Ghassan Salah. 4126 N HOLLAND SYLVANIA RD, STE 130 43623 #575-01-1987 L1991 **AI PD** *020 †03,55

SAFERIN, Eric Nathan. ■ 43617 #038-43-2008 *012

SAIKUMAR, Jagannath Herem. 3000 ARLINGTON AVE, UNIVERSITY OF TOLEDO 43614 #496-21-2001 L2007 **IM** *012

SALEM, Mazin Sine. 5800 PARK CENTER CT, STE A 43615 #038-43-1991 L1994 **IM** *020 †20

SALVI, Usha Ashok. 1425 STARR AVE, UNISON B H G 43605 #495-01-1973 L1998 **P** *020 †75

SALZMAN, Robert Jan. 3715 AIRPORT HWY 43615 #517-05-1976 L1983 **PD NPM** *020

SAN ANTONIO, Mary Jane Ta. 2200 JEFFERSON AVE, ST VINCENT MERCY MED CTR 43604 #748-08-1993 L2004 **FM** *020 †18

SANDER, James Edward. 4235 SECOR RD, TOLEDO CLINIC 43623 #016-06-1971 L1985 **CHN N** *020 †55,75

SANDOVAL-GONZALES, Nidia. ■ 43615 #935-01-1969 L1977 **PD** *020 †55

SANTACROCE, Dino. ■ 43643 #038-43-2005 L2005 **U** *012

SANTA RITA, Samuel Dayag. 4235 SECOR RD, SUTIE 1 43623 #748-07-1955 L1962 **AN PHP** *071

SARAIYA, Purvi Rajiv. 4235 SECOR RD 43623 #495-22-1993 L2001 **CN** *100

SARDELIS, Thomas Nicholas. 4841 MONROE ST, TOLEDO RADIOLOGICAL ASSOCI 43623 #025-01-1974 L1981 **R DR** *071 †80

SCANLON, Clayton Greer. ■ 43615 #038-43-2008 *012

SCHAEFER, Paul Leland. 1015 GARDEN LAKE PKWY 43614 #038-43-2004 L2006 **FM** *100 †18

SCHAEUFELE, John Thos. 2222 CHERRY ST 43608 #038-43-1986 L1989 **PD** *030 †55

SCHAFER, Richard Lewis. ■ 43615 #041-01-1948 L1955 **HEM ON** *071 †04

SCHAFER, William P. 3900 SUNFOREST CT, STE 220 43623 #016-06-1983 L1992 **CD IC** *020 †20

SCHEER, David Karl. 3909 WOODLEY RD, STE 600 43606 #038-40-1943 L1944 **IM CD** *020 †20

SCHLIEVERT, Randall Scott. 3120 GLENDALE AVE # 1300, DEPT OF PEDIATRICS 43614 #038-43-1998 L2000 **PD** *020 †55

SCHMITT, Dorrie J Louth. 3909 WOODLEY RD, STE 100 43606 #038-43-1986 L1988 **IM** *020

SCHOECK, Daniel Jos. 2865 N REYNOLDS RD 43615 #038-43-1988 L1992 **AN** *020 †05

SCHREIBER, James Gus. ■ 43606 #048-12-1968 L1998 **P** *020

SCHROEDER, Homer Fred. 2200 JEFFERSON AVE 43604 #028-34-1946 L1947 **OBG** *071 †30

SCHWANN, Thomas A. 2213 CHERRY ST, SURGEONS OF NW OHIO INC 43608 #035-01-1986 L1994 **TS** *020 †85,90

SCHWARTZ, Richard Allen. 3020 N MCCORD RD 43615 #038-43-1974 L1986 **FM OS** *020 †85,18

SCOVELL, William Martin. 3922 WOODLEY RD, STE 100 43606 #038-43-1998 L2001 PD *020 †55

SEBASTIAN, Matthew V. 1946 N 13TH ST STE 48, CONSULTING RADIOLOGISTS CO 43604 #422-01-1999 L1999 DR *020 †80

SEHGAL, Karn Vir. 2900 CARSKADDON AVE 43606 #495-43-1971 L1974 IM SCI *020 †20,60

SEHGAL, Siddharth. 3000 ARLINGTON AVE 43614 #495-28-2004 L2007 N *012

SEIWERT, Andrew James. 2109 HUGHES DR, STE 450 43606 #016-11-1986 L1997 VS GS *020 †85

SELMAN, Steven Howard. 3065 ARLINGTON AVE, MED CLGE OF OHIO-UROLOGY 43614 #038-06-1974 L1976 U *020 †85,95

SEMINERIO, Jennifer Lea. ■ 43615 #038-43-2008 L2008 *012

SEO, Kenneth Kw. 4841 MONROE ST, TOLEDO RADIOLOGICAL ASSOCI 43623 #583-02-1968 L1979 DR *020 †50

SEPAHBODI, Teymour. 2213 CHERRY ST 43608 #517-01-1971 L1981 CHP P *020

SERAFINI, Ruggero. 3000 ARLINGTON AVE 43614 #561-23-2001 L2004 N *012

SERVOSS, Michael Moore. 2865 N REYNOLDS RD 43615 #038-43-1986 L1990 AN *020 †05

SETHI, Namrata. 3045 ARLINGTON AVE, DEPTOF GME 43614 #495-16-2003 L2006 *100

SETOODEH, Farhad. 5620 SOUTHWYCK BLVD 43614 #517-01-1971 L1980 PTH HMP *062 †50

SEVILLA, Ramon Z. 2000 REGENCY CT STE 200 43623 #748-01-1960 L1975 TS CD *020

SHAFFER, Crystal Lee. 2865 N REYNOLDS RD, STE 140 43615 #038-45-2004 L2004 FSM *012 †18

SHAFIQ, Qaiser. 3045 ARLINGTON AVE, DEPT OF GME 43614 #704-21-2002 L2006 PM *012

SHAH, Aamir Sayeed. 2213 CHERRY ST, SURGEONS OF NW OHIO INC 43608 #024-05-1991 L2001 TS *020 †85,90

SHAH, Ajay Ramesh. 1946 N 13TH ST 43604 #025-12-1986 L1991 PTH *020 †50

SHAH, Divyaprabha V. 2505 WIMBLEDON PARK 43617 #495-01-1966 L1978 PD OS *020 †55

SHAH, Gaurang Surendra. 2213 CHERRY ST 43608 #496-38-1996 L2006 IM *012

SHAH, Madhukar Dharamdas. 4235 SECOR RD 43623 #495-01-1966 L1977 AN PME *020 †05

SHAH, Rubina. 2658 W LASKEY RD STE A 43613 #495-51-1982 L2000 DR *020 †80

SHAH, Shirish Manilal. 2213 CHERRY ST 43608 #495-01-1972 L1979 OBG *020

SHAHID, Agha. 525 HAMILTON ST, STE 101A 43604 #704-02-1972 L1978 P PYG *020 †75

SHAHID, Nauman. 3000 ARLINGTON AVE 43614 #704-01-2004 L2006 IM *012

SHAIKH, Khurrum Ali. 3000 ARLINGTON AVE 43614 #704-02-1995 L1999 IM *020 †20

SHAMY, Tara. 3830 WOODLEY RD, STE C 43606 #038-43-2004 L2004 PD *020 †55

SHANAHAN, Robert E. 2121 HUGHES DR 43606 #025-01-1958 L1981 PS HS *071 †85,65

SHAPIRO, Joseph Isaac. 3000 ARLINGTON AVE, RHC, 0012 43614 #033-05-1980 L1997 IM *020 †20

SHAPIRO, Ronald Saml. 3404 W SYLVANIA AVE 43623 #038-40-1965 L1965 PMM NEP *020

SHAPIRO, Susan P. 3170 W CENTRAL AVE, BUSINESS OFFICE 43606 #036-07-1976 L1980 PTH BBK *020 †50

SHARMA, Om P. 2142 N COVE BLVD 43606 #495-22-1964 L1973 GS TRS *020 †85

SHARMA, Rajni Bala. 2142 N COVE BLVD 43606 #495-03-1964 L1974 OBG *020 †30

SHARMA, Suman Ramgopal. 3000 ARLINGTON AVE 43614 #495-96-2001 L2006 PD *012

SHASTRI, Ravi Kaushikkuma. ■ 43609 #038-43-2008 *012

SHEA, Eduardo Velasco. 1500 N SUPERIOR ST, STE 2B 43604 #748-01-1957 L1972 IM GE *020

SHELLEY, Ellen Dorinda. 3000 ARLINGTON AVE 43614 #028-03-1966 L1983 D *071 †15

SHELLEY, Walter Brown. 3120 GLENDALE AVE, MED COLL OH-DERM 43614 #026-04-1943 L1983 D *071 †15

SHEON, Robert Philip. 4235 SECOR RD, SUTIE 1 43623 #028-34-1958 L1959 RHU *071 †20

SHERIDAN, Pamela Louise. 3000 ARLINGTON AVE 43614 #016-11-1987 L1987 N *020 †75

SHERMAN, Thomas George. 3900 SUNFOREST CT 43623 #038-43-1972 L1973 P *020 †75

SHERMETA, Dennis Wm. ■ 43606 #025-01-1965 L1994 PDS PD *020 †85

SHETTY, Akshatha. 544 E WOODRUFF AVE, UNISON BEHAVIORAL HEALTH G 43604 #495-98-1998 L2002 P *020

SHIDYAK, Amjad. 3000 ARLINGTON AVE, UNIVERSITY OF TOLEDO 43614 #875-02-1992 L2007 IM *012

SHUER, Bernard Benj. 2402 DENSMORE DR 43606 #038-40-1943 L1943 N NS *071

SHULTZ, Kelley Heller. 2222 CHERRY ST, STE 1100 43608 #036-05-1986 L1987 PD *020 †55

SHURTZ, Cherilyn Marie. 3000 ARLINGTON AVE 43614 #422-01-2004 L2004 PD *020

SHUSHUNOV, Sergey. 2213 CHERRY ST 43608 #913-69-1977 L1990 PD CCM *020 †55

SIDDIQ, Sajid. ■ 43606 #704-02-1989 P *100

SIDDIQI, Tariq A. 2200 JEFFERSON AVE 43604 #704-01-1976 L1997 FM *020 †18

SIDDIQUI, Fouzia. 3045 ARLINGTON AVE, CO GME- RM 330 - 43614 #704-02-1996 L2006 N *012

SIDERS, Richard Wayne. 2658 W LASKEY RD, FL 2 43613 #025-07-1969 L1973 VIR R *020 †80

SIH, Victoria. 5215 MONROE ST STE 3 43623 #748-07-1966 L1995 GP OS *071 ‡

SIM, Abraham Y. 3915 SUNFOREST CT 43623 #748-08-1961 L1972 OPH *020 †35

SIMON, Richard Shereef. 2127 JEFFERSON AVE 43604 #038-43-1990 L1992 FM *100

SINGER, Natalie Ann. ■ 43614 #038-43-2007 L2007 U *012

SINGH, Ajay Pal. PO BOX 10008 43699 #495-43-1997 L2007 P *012

SINGH, Birjitender. ■ 43604 #495-29-1990 L2002 IM *020

SINGH, Surendra P. 2142 N COVE BLVD, CONSULTANTS IN LAB MEDICIN 43606 #495-23-1984 L1990 PTH *020 †20

SINGH, Tanvir Singh. ■ 43615 #496-17-1996 L2003 P *100

SINHA, Asok Kumar. 3404 W SYLVANIA AVE 43623 #495-02-1967 L1982 EM *020 †16

SIPE, Eilynn Kim. 3909 WOODLEY RD, STE 800 43606 #038-44-1997 L1999 CRS *020 †85,10

SISON, Carmencita. 43605 #748-01-1969 PD *020

SKEEL, Roland Thor. 3000 ARLINGTON AVE, DEPARTMENT OF MEDICINE 43614 #038-41-1964 L1969 ON *030 †20

SKIBICKI, Cheri Diller. 4411 N HOLLAND SYLVANIA RD, STE 201 43623 #038-43-1981 L1982 FM *020 †18

SKIE, Martin Chas. 3000 ARLINGTON AVE 43614 #038-43-1989 L1992 HS *020 †40

SLAM, Kristine Danielle. 3000 ARLINGTON AVE, UNIVERSITY OF TOLEDO 43614 #038-43-2003 L2003 GS *012

SLEE, Gregory Robt. 3439 GRANITE CIR 43617 #038-43-1978 L1981 GE ID *020 †20

SMAILI, Sleiman Khalil. 3045 ARLINGTON AVE, DEPT OF GME 43614 #198-01-1997 L2006 OBG *012

SMALLWOOD, Thomas Edward. 1614 S BYRNE RD, STE B 43614 #038-06-1991 L1994 IM *020 †20

SMITH, Ann Jean. 3740 W SYLVANIA AVE, STE 500 43623 #038-43-1982 L1985 OBG *020 †30

SMITH, Asher O. 3065 ARLINGTON AVE, U. T. DEPARTMENT OF ORTHOP 43614 #017-20-2005 L2005 ORS *012

SMITH, Christine Renee. 3000 ARLINGTON AVE, EMERGENCY DEPARTMENT 43614 #038-45-1995 L1996 EM *020 †16

SMITH, David F. 3060 W SYLVANIA AVE 43613 #024-07-1990 L1993 IM *020 †20

SMITH, Lisa Lynn. 4805 SUDER AVE, STE A 43611 #038-43-1994 L1996 FM *020 †18

SMITH, Mary Kay. 3120 GLENDALE AVE, THE UNIVERSITY OF TOLEDO-P 43614 #038-43-1991 L1995 P *020

SMITH, Mary Russell. 3000 ARLINGTON AVE 43614 #065-09-1966 L1978 HEM ON *020

SMUKLER, Abigail Russell. 4235 SECOR RD, TOLEDO CLINIC 43623 #035-48-1997 L2005 RHU *020 †55,20

SMYTHE, Peter Stanley. 3170 W CENTRAL AVE, BUSINESS OFFICE 43606 #025-01-1983 L1988 ATP CLP *040 †50

SODEMAN, Thomas Christian. 3120 GLENDALE AVE STE 0012 43614 #038-43-1995 L2005 HEP GE *020 †20

SODEMAN, Wm Anthony, Jr. 2213 CHERRY ST 43608 #041-01-1960 L1973 GE LM *040 †20

SOLAIMAN, Deana Shaikh. 3000 ARLINGTON AVE R, MCOT HOSPSINTERNAL MED DEP 43614 #038-43-2000 L2000 IM *020 †20

SOLAIMAN, Souhaila Shaikh. 525 HAMILTON ST, STE 101A 43604 #915-03-1969 L1977 P PTH *020 †50

SOLOMON, Susan Jill. 4411 N HOLLAND SYLVANIA RD, STE 201 43623 #024-07-1986 L1989 FM *020 †18

SPELAR, Marc Jonathan. ■ 43614 #038-43-2008 *012

SPETKA, Lawrence M. 4235 SECOR RD, TOLEDO CLINIC 43623 #038-43-1976 L1990 NS *020 †25

STACEY-ERWIN, Karen J. 3404 W SYLVANIA AVE, EMERGENCY ROOM 43623 #038-40-1996 L1997 EM UCM *020 †18 ‡

STADLER, Nancy Jane. 3909 WOODLEY RD, STE 500 43606 #038-43-1995 L1996 FM *020 †18

STAHL, Ryan Howard. 2213 CHERRY ST 43608 #016-42-2001 L2001 EM *020 †16

STARK, Gerald. 2213 CHERRY ST 43608 #028-34-1948 L1954 GS *071 †85

STARK, Michael Edward. 2000 REGENCY CT 43623 #038-43-1977 L1978 GS *020 †85

STATSEVYCH, Volodymyr. ■ 43614 #038-43-2007 L2007 TY *012

STECK, Ann Marie. ■ 43606 #038-43-2006 L2006 FP *012

STEIN, Dagmar T. 2142 N COVE BLVD, STE 5 43606 #041-14-1990 L1996 PHO *020 †55

STELNICKI, Bethany Marie. ■ 43606 #038-43-2007 L2007 TY *012

STEVENS, Joseph R. 2213 CHERRY ST 43608 #028-34-1950 L1955 GS IM *071

STIFF, Philip Cecil. 3949 SUNFOREST CT, STE 204 43623 #016-43-1973 L1978 IM *020 †20

STOCKMANN, Paul Terrence. 2121 HUGHES DR, STE 620 43606 #028-03-1983 L2003 PDS *020 †85

STOCKSLAGER, Viki Lynn. 2213 FRANKLIN AVE, PEDIATRICS AT ST.VINCENT F 43620 #038-45-1985 L1989 IM PD *020

STOLER, Stanley Howard. 2213 CHERRY ST, OCCUPATIONAL HEALTH SERVIC 43608 #649-14-1971 L1975 DR OM *020

STOLL, Stephen Frederick. 4841 MONROE ST, STE 103 43623 #016-45-2000 L2006 DR *020 †80

STOREY, Anyse J. 1614 S BYRNE RD STE GG 43614 #038-06-1983 L1985 U *020

STOTZ, Walter Erhard. 5800 PARK CENTER CT, STE A 43615 #025-01-1983 L1986 IM *020 †20

STRAUB, Robert Francis. 4235 SECOR RD 43623 #038-43-1986 L1993 GE *020 †20

STRAUB, Thomas Paul. 2213 CHERRY ST 43608 #056-06-1962 L1968 OBG *020 †30

STRAUS, Barbara. 3715 AIRPORT HWY, AIRPORT HIGHWAY PEDIATRICS 43615 #308-03-1980 L1988 PD *020 †55

STRICKLEN, Valarie N. 3120 GLENDALE AVE STE 1600, RUPPERT HEALTH CTR 43614 #038-43-2001 L2001 PD *020

STRIPH, Gerald Glenn. 2865 N REYNOLDS RD, STE 160 43615 #025-07-1984 L1989 OPH OS *020 †35 ‡

STROBEL, Stephen Lewis. 2213 CHERRY ST, ST VINCENT MERCY MEDICAL C 43608 #038-40-1981 L1985 PTH PCH *020 †50

STROTHER, Robert B. ■ 43614 #020-02-1940 L1954 GS *071 †85

STRUNK, Crawford J. 2142 N COVE BLVD, STE 5 43606 #035-15-2000 L2003 PHO *020 †55

SU, Na. 3333 GLENDALE AVE, OUTPATIENT CLINIC 43614 #243-38-1982 L2002 FM *020 †18

SUAREZ, William A. 2222 CHERRY ST STE 2800 43608 #043-01-1991 L1994 PDC *020 †55

SUBHANI, Nida. 3000 ARLINGTON AVE 43614 #704-16-2002 L2005 IM *012

SULISZ, Cheryl Ann. 1455 W ALEXIS RD, MEDICAL DEPARTMENT 43612 #025-12-1987 L2004 GP OM *020 †70

SUNDARARAGHAVAN, Sree K. 1565 S BYRNE RD 43614 #495-16-1991 L1999 PDC *020 †55

SUNDERJI, Shiraz. 2142 N COVE BLVD 3RD FL, CENTER FOR WOMEN HEALTH 43606 #905-01-1972 L2001 MFM OBG *020 †30

SUNDHEIMER, Alan Bruce. 3909 WOODLEY RD, STE 600 43606 #025-01-1975 L1976 IM HO *050 †20

SUTARIA, Rachana Pankajku. 330-MUL3045 ARLING, CO GME-RM 43614 #495-23-1999 L2006 OBG *012

SUTHERLAND, Gerald W. 2865 N REYNOLDS RD, STE 160 43615 #065-01-1958 L1964 ORS *071 †40

SUTTER, Noah Andrew. ■ 43614 #038-43-2006 L2006 PD *012

SVALA, Kathleen Marie. ■ 43606 #038-43-2008 *012

SWEDAN, Majed Hazza. 3401 GLENDALE AVE, STE 212 43614 #875-01-1960 L1967 GYN *071 †30

SYED, Ibrahim Naveed. 7111 W CENTRAL AVE 43617 #016-02-1996 L2001 DR *020 †80

TAGANAS, Marianne Rachell. 2200 JEFFERSON AVE, DEPT OF FAMILY PRACTICE 43604 #748-10-1994 L2006 FP *012

TAJI, Jamil Hakam. 3000 ARLINGTON AVE 43614 #473-02-2002 L2005 IM *012

TAKI, Hassan. 3454 OAK ALLEY CT, STE 214 43606 #038-43-01-1980 L1996 ALI PD *020 †55,03

TALBUT, Dorrence Coney. ■ 43623 #038-40-1955 L1955 PD *072 †55

TALEB, Mohammed Mahmoud. 3000 ARLINGTON AVE 43614 #605-04-2003 L2006 IM *012

TALEB, Nada. ■ 43617 #875-01-1990 L2001 ID *100 †20

TALLA, Rekha. 2213 CHERRY ST 43608 #495-21-1999 L2005 FP *012

TALMAGE, Lance Allen. 2150 W CENTRAL AVE 43606 #025-01-1964 L1964 OBG *020 †30 ‡

TAMBURRINO, Marijo B. 3120 GLENDALE AVE, MAIL STOP 1193 43614 #038-43-1977 L1979 P *030 †75

TAMIRISA, Kamala Priya. 2940 N MCCORD RD 43615 #495-14-1995 L2005 ICE *020 †20

TANG, Jianlin. 3065 ARLINGTON AVE, DEPT OF SURGERY 43614 #243-44-1982 L2004 GS *012

TANSEY, John James. 2213 CHERRY ST 43608 #025-01-1944 L1949 PD *071

TAPPER, Richard Ivan. 3500 EXECUTIVE PKWY 43606 #038-40-1967 L1967 U *020 †95

TARABISHI, M Ridwan Mehdi. 2222 CHERRY ST, STREET 2300 43608 #875-01-1990 L1996 PN *100 †55

TASNEEM, Tehmina. 2213 CHERRY ST 43608 #496-27-2003 L2005 FP *012

TAUB, David Andrew. 3500 EXECUTIVE PKWY, UNIVERSITY OF MICHIGAN 43606 #025-07-2000 L2007 U *020 †

TAUSIF, Farzana N. 2150 W CENTRAL AVE 43606 #704-02-1984 L1995 FM *020 †18 ‡

TAYEB, Zeeshan K. 3065 ARLINGTON AVE 43614 #038-45-2004 L2004 PM *012

TAYLOR, Kevin Wells. 2117 TANGLEWOOD DR 43614 #038-43-1992 L1995 GP *020

■ = Address Information Privacy Protected

TAYLOR, Lorree. 3740 W SYLVANIA AVE, STE 100 43623 #038-44-1982 L1983 **FM OS** *020 †18

TAYLOR, Ward Melborne. ■ 43623 #025-01-1957 L1971 **GS** *071 †85

TAYLOR, Wesley Kirt. ■ 43609 #025-12-2006 L2006 **GS** *100

TEMESY-ARMOS, Peter N. 3000 ARLINGTON AVE, MEDICAL COLLEGE OF OHIO 43614 #038-40-1971 L1971 **CD ICE** *040 †20

TENNYSON, Gregory Edward. 3120 GLENDALE AVE 43614 #025-12-1981 L2000 **IM OS** *050 †20

THAKUR, Sachin. 2213 CHERRY ST 43608 #495-53-1993 L2003 **NPM** *020 †55

THAXTON, Lora Lee. 3915 SUNFOREST CT 43623 #055-01-1995 L1996 **PM** *020 †60

THIYAGARAJAN, Thanigaiarsu. 2213 CHERRY ST, DEPT OF INTERNAL MED 43608 #495-16-1998 L2007 **IM** *012

THOMAS, Gregory Michael. 3130 W CENTRAL AVE 43606 #016-11-1971 L1982 **PM PMM** *020

THOMBRE, Melanie S. 2142 N COVE BLVD 43606 #016-11-1979 L1982 **CHP P** *020 †75

THOMPSON, Ana Marie. 4126 N HOLLAND SYLVANIA RD, STE 200 43623 #048-02-1997 L2002 **D** *020 †15

THOMPSON, Patricia M. 2150 W CENTRAL AVE, CENTER FOR HEALTH SVCS 43606 #038-43-1985 L1986 **IM** *020 †20

THUMA, Lynette Marie. 2142 N COVE BLVD 43606 #305-01-2005 L2005 **FP** *012

TIETJEN, Gretchen E. 3000 ARLINGTON AVE, DEPT OF NEUROLOGY, MS 1195 43614 #025-01-1984 L1996 **N IM** *020 †75

TINKEL, Jodi Lee. 3000 ARLINGTON AVE, RM 1192 43614 #038-43-2000 L2000 **CD** *020 †20

TITA, James Anthony. 2222 CHERRY ST, STE 1400 43608 #016-76-1980, ▲ L1982 **IM PCC** *020 †20

TO, Philip. 142 VAN BUREN AVE 43605 #038-41-2008 *012

TODD, Melissa Jane. 135 YALE DR, 135 YALE DRIVE 43614 #038-43-2002 L2002 **EM** *012 †18

TOLEK, Cuneyd Ali. 5151 MONROE ST, STE 200 43623 #038-45-1981 L1982 **FM OM** *020 †18

TOMA, Vincent Sabah. 3829 WOODLEY RD, BLDG B 43606 #025-07-2000 L2005 **OTO A** *020 †45

TOMC, Jerome Wm. ■ 43614 #056-06-1967 L1973 **N** *020

TORCHIA, Richard Thomas. 2865 N REYNOLDS RD, STE 170 43615 #028-34-1961 L1962 **OPH** *071 †35

TORE, Joseph Anthony. ■ 43614 #038-43-1999 L2000 **AN** *100

TORSEKAR, Kiron Sumitra. 3949 SUNFOREST CT, TWIN OAKS # 203 43623 #495-01-1972 L1978 **PD** *020 †55

TORSEKAR, Pratap Govind. 4334 SECOR RD, HARBOR BEHAVIORAL HEALTHCA 43623 #495-01-1973 L1978 **P** *020 †75

TOSINO, Claro Torbela. 2200 JEFFERSON AVE, FL 4 43604 #748-01-1956 L1968 **AN** *071

TRAIN, Polly Fleet. 3045 ARLINGTON AVE, CO GME- RM 330 - 43614 #654-01-2003 L2004 **OBG** *012

TRAVIS, Charles Bartlett. 1015 GARDEN LAKE PKWY, MEDICAL COLLEGE OF OHIO 43614 #561-01-1971 L1978 **FM ADM** *071 †18

TRAVIS, Ryan Jeffrey. 3000 ARLINGTON AVE, UT DEPT. OF PSYCHIATRY 43614 #038-43-2004 L2004 **P** *012

TREUHAFT, William Hahn. 3922 WOODLEY RD, STE 200 43606 #038-06-1975 L1978 **RHU IM** *020 †20

TRIVEDI, Rekha R. 3900 SUNFOREST CT, STE 215 43623 #495-22-1971 L1983 **PM** *020 †60

TRUE, Roger Alan. 2142 N COVE BLVD 43606 #017-20-1978 L1981 **FM** *020 †18

TUCKER, Mark Harrison. 313 JEFFERSON AVE, NEIGHBORHOOD HEALTH ASSN. 43604 #025-01-1974 L2001 **PD** *030 †55

TULLIS, David Harrison. 3740 W SYLVANIA AVE, STE 500 43623 #038-40-1967 L1967 **OBG** *020 †30

TURKMANI, Mustapha. 930 S DETROIT AVE 43614 #561-17-1980 L1992 **P** *020

TURLEY, Kenneth Rheim. 3000 ARLINGTON AVE, DEPT. OF ANESTHESIOLOGY 43614 #038-43-2004 L2005 **AN** *012

TWADDLE, Michael Alan. ■ 43614 #038-43-1995 L1995 **FM** *100

UCHE, John Obinna. 3000 ARLINGTON AVE # 2240, MS 1179 DPT OF FMLY MDCNE 43614 #690-04-1986 L2005 **FM** *100 †18

UMAPATHI, Pramila Masur. 5810 SOUTHWYCK BLVD # 205, NATIONAL EMERGENCY SERVICE 43614 #495-04-1971 L1982 **EM FM** *020

UTHAMARAJAN, Saigeetha. 3045 ARLINGTON AVE, C/O MCOT-GRAD MED EDU DEPT 43614 #496-32-2000 L2002 **FM** *100 †18

UTIGER, Cheryl Ann. 2142 N COVE BLVD 43606 #025-01-1988 L1994 **HMP** *020 †50

VALIJAN, Sevak. ■ 43614 #038-43-2008 *012

VALKO, Tim Robt. 3130 EXECUTIVE PKWY, FL 8 43606 #038-43-1987 L1989 **CHP P** *020 †75

VAN DER VEER, John R. 2109 HUGHES DR, STE 900 43606 #067-01-1951 L1958 **P CHP** *071 †75

VARMA, Ritu. 3000 ARLINGTON AVE 43614 #496-07-1998 L2007 **AN** *012

VARSHNEY, Prashant. 2213 CHERRY ST 43608 #495-77-1998 L2007 **TY** *012

VARSHNEY, Shalini. 3045 ARLINGTON AVE, CO MCOT-GRAD MED EDU DEPT 43614 #495-77-1992 L2003 **OBG** *012

VAUTHY, Pierre Alain. 2121 HUGHES DR, STE HMT 640 43606 #035-09-1972 L1974 **CCP PDP** *020 †55

VELASCO, Manuel Eduardo. 3000 ARLINGTON AVE 43614 #132-02-1967 L1978 **NP ATP** *020 †50

VEMURU, Lakshmi Gali. 2142 N COVE BLVD, DEPT OF ER MED CHLDRN HOSP 43606 #495-62-1990 L2002 **PD PEM** *020 †55

VENK-VENCKUNAS, George. 3140 SECOR RD STE 809, MIDWEST INSTITUTE 43606 #407-16-1948 L1960 **P IM** *072

VERGARA, Cawilie G. 2409 CHERRY ST 43608 #748-08-1969 L1974 **AN** *071

VERGARA, Rita Diaz. ■ 43623 #748-08-1966 L1994 **FM** *020

VETTETH, Sandeep. 3045 ARLINGTON AVE 43614 #495-31-2004 L2005 *100

VIANZON, Edna Santos. 3740 W SYLVANIA AVE, STE 250 43623 #748-02-1992 L2004 **PD** *020 †55 ‡

VICENTE, Armando M. 3900 SUNFOREST CT, STE 2 43623 #770-03-1960 L1967 **VS CD** *020 †85

VICENTE, David C. 3900 SUNFOREST CT, STE 2 43623 #038-43-1993 L2000 **VS** *020 †85

VIDOVICH, Rick Allen. 4235 SECOR RD 43623 #005-15-1984 L1989 **AN** *020 †05

VIJENDRA, Divya Goutam. 905 NEBRASKA AVE, CORDELIA MARTIN HEALTH CEN 43607 #496-39-1997 L2004 **IM IMG** *020 †20

VO, Phung Ngoc. 3000 REGENCY CT STE 201 43623 #038-40-1984 L1989 **OBG** *020

VOGEL, Donald Wm. 3740 W SYLVANIA AVE 43623 #038-45-1990 L1992 **FM** *020 †18

VYAS, Parimal Ramniklal. 3900 SUNFOREST CT STE 223 43623 #495-23-1978 L1986 **U** *020 †95

WADHWANI, Nisha. 2200 JEFFERSON AVE, CO MERCY HLTH PRTNRS-MED E 43604 #495-26-1999 L2001 **FSM** *100 †18

WAGNER, Steven Michael. 4841 MONROE ST 43623 #038-40-1973 L1974 **GE IM** *020 †20

WAHL, Jeffrey Wm. 3130 GLENDALE AVE, KOBACKER CTR MED COLLEGE O 43614 #025-01-1979 L1986 **CHP** *040 †75

WAHLQUIST, Marc. 3045 ARLINGTON AVE M, CO MCOT-MED EDU DEPT RM 33 43614 #016-11-2002 L2002 **ORS** *100

WAINSTEIN, Mark Alan. 3500 EXECUTIVE PKWY, GENITO URINARY SURGEONS 43606 #024-07-1990 L1997 **U** *020 †95

WAINSTEIN, Mayer Louis. 3500 EXECUTIVE PKWY 43606 #038-40-1965 L1965 **U** *020 †95

WAINZ, Ronald John. 2109 HUGHES DR STE 760 43606 #028-02-1984 L1989 **PUD CCM** *020 †20

WAJSKOL, Aron. 1565 S BYRNE RD, STE 100 43614 #913-01-1955 L1974 **AN** *071 †05

WALDEN, Robert E. 1565 S BYRNE RD, STE 100 43614 #047-07-1945 L1969 **P** *071 †75

WALKER, James Michael. 2109 HUGHES DR, JOBST TOWER, STE 640 43606 #654-01-1996 L1999 **PD** *020 †15

WALSH, Francis Michael. 3170 W CENTRAL AVE 43606 #056-06-1971 L1989 **CLP PTH** *030 †50

WALTERS, John Brandon. 2051 W CENTRAL AVE 43606 #038-43-2005 L2005 **FP** *012

WANG, Haojie. ■ 43614 #243-16-1997 L2005 **IM** *012

WANG, Hui. 3045 ARLINGTON AVE, C/O MCOT-GRAD MED EDU DEPT 43614 #243-46-1987 L2002 **ON** *100 †20

WARE, Theodore John. 2409 CHERRY ST STE 207 43608 #038-43-1982 L1984 **IM** *020 †20

WASHING, Douglas James. ■ 43614 #038-40-1998 L2001 **PCP** *020 †50

WASSEF, Andrew Jonathan. 3065 ARLINGTON AVE, HEALTH SCIEN 43614 #010-03-2007 L2007 **ORS** *012

WATKINS, Traci Nicole. 3909 WOODLEY RD, STE 500 43606 #038-40-1996 L1998 **FM** *020 †18

WEATHERS, Donald Gregory. 3949 SUNFOREST CT, STE 202 43623 #025-12-1973 L1979 **GP** *020 †30

WEBB, James Hugh. 4543 GOLF CREEK DR 43623 #038-41-1945 L1945 **NS OS** *071 †25

WEBER, Klaus Wolfgang. 2213 CHERRY ST 43608 #407-10-1964 L1994 **R** *020 †80

WEBER, Steven John. ■ 43615 #003-75-2007, ▲ L2007 *012

WEIHER, Junell Carol. ■ 43614 #038-43-2008 *012

WELDY, David Lee. 3000 ARLINGTON AVE, MS 1205 43614 #038-43-1983 L1985 **FM FSM** *020 †18

WELLS, John Spencer. ■ 43614 #038-43-2008 *012

WELLS, Kimberly Elizabeth. 2213 CHERRY ST 43608 #038-75-2005, ▲ L2005 **EM** *012

WELT, Daniel Andrew. 5742 PARK CENTER CT 43615 #038-43-1996 L1998 **FM** *020 †18

WELT, Ionel. 5742 PARK CENTER CT 43615 #550-02-1968 L1978 **PD FM** *020 †55

WENTZ, Mark Allen. 6800 W CENTRAL AVE STE K 43617 #038-45-1983 L1985 **FM** *020 †18

WENTZ, Sabrina Christine. ■ 43615 #038-43-2004 **GS** *100

WENZKE, Robert Edmund. 4640 W ALEXIS RD 43623 #038-40-1975 L1977 **IM** *020 †20

WESTERINK, Maria Anna J. 3120 GLENDALE AVE, UNIVERSITY OF TOLEDO MEDIC 43614 #660-02-1978 L1993 **ID IM** *050 †20

WESTHOVEN, Joseph B. ■ 43613 #016-43-1943 L1943 **U** *071 †95

WETZEL, Matthew Scott. ■ 43609 #038-43-2008 *012

WHALEN, Daniel Ray. ■ 43609 #038-43-2008 *012

WHALEN, Ralph Charles. 2109 HUGHES DR, STE 450 43606 #038-43-1972 L1973 **VS** *020 †85

WHITE, Peter. 1565 S BYRNE RD 43614 #041-01-1955 L1969 **IM HEM** *071 †20

WILKS, Kate J. ■ 43614 #038-43-2008 *012

WILLEY, James Campbell. 3000 ARLINGTON AVE, DEPT OF MED/PULMONARY DIVI 43614 #038-43-1978 L1994 **IM PUD** *020 †20

WILLIAMS, Brett Brunner. ■ 43614 #038-43-2008 *012

WILLIAMS, Julie Ann. 3000 ARLINGTON AVE, M/S 1186 43614 #038-43-1999 L1999 **IM** *020 †20

WILLIAMS, Kristi Skeel. 3000 ARLINGTON AVE 43614 #038-43-1990 L1991 **P** *020 †75

WILLIAMS, Thomas J. 3409 N HOLLAND SYLVANIA RD, WILLIAMS MEDICAL CENTER 43615 #028-79-1955, ▲ L1955 **FM** *071

WILLIS, William Henry. 3829 WOODLEY RD, BLDG B 43606 #016-11-1965 L1970 **OTO A** *071 †45

WILSON, John Mcfarland. ■ 43606 #020-12-2006 L2006 **U** *012

WILSON, Keith David. 4841 MONROE ST, HARVEST SQUARE TRA 43623 #038-40-1969 L1969 **DR** *020 †80

WILSON, Laura Elizabeth. 3020 N MCCORD RD, STE 100 43615 #038-43-1997 L2000 **PD** *020 †55

WILSON, Peter Jerome. 2914 S REPUBLIC BLVD 43615 #038-40-1982 L1983 **AN** *020 †05

WIN, Thomas Tun. 2658 W LASKEY RD 43613 #038-06-1990 L1991 **DR NM** *020 †80

WINKLE, Daniel Andrew, Jr. ■ 43614 #038-43-2008 *012

WINSLOW, Marguerite. ■ 43613 #038-43-2005 L2005 **FP** *012

WINSLOW, William Andrew. 3020 STARR AVE 43605 #025-11-1955 L1956 **GP** *071

WIRICK, John William. ■ 43614 #038-41-2002 *100

WISELEY, Richard Jos. 3425 EXECUTIVE PKWY, STE 235 43606 #038-41-1961 L1961 **AI PUD** *020 †20,03

WISINGER, Barney Mac. 2121 HUGHES DR, STE 820 43606 #004-01-1954 L1960 **PUD IM** *020 †20

WOLDENBERG, Lee Steven. 3000 ARLINGTON AVE, DEPT OF RADIOLOGY 43614 #038-06-1967 L1967 **DR** *020 †80

WOLFRAM, Roy Wayne. 2213 CHERRY ST 43608 #041-13-1977 L1998 **EM PD** *020 †55,16

WOODSON, Donna Ailport. 3000 ARLINGTON AVE, DEPT OF FAMILY MEDICINE 43614 #038-43-1972 L1973 **FM** *020 †18 ‡

WORTHINGTON, Richard D. 2213 CHERRY ST 43608 #016-11-1989 L1991 **EM** *020 †16

WRIGHT, Jonathan Dean. 2000 REGENCY CT, STE 100 43623 #038-40-1982 L1983 **GS** *020 †85

WRIGHT, Lori Creadon. 7140 PORT SYLVANIA DR, STE 300 43617 #038-43-1991 L1994 **FM** *020 †18

WROBLEWSKI, Mary Elizabet. 3120 GLENDALE AVE, STE 1300 43614 #038-43-2005 L2005 **PD** *012

WRONKOWICZ, Shannon Marie. 2213 CHERRY ST 43608 #038-43-2004 L2004 **PD** *020 †55

WU, Liang. 3000 ARLINGTON AVE, UNIVERSITY OF TOLEDO 43614 #243-46-1997 L2007 **IM** *012

XANTHAKOS, Dimitrios. 2142 N COVE BLVD 43606 #418-01-1961 L1970 **GS SO** *071 †85

YAQOOB, Aneela. 3120 GLENDALE AVE, OHIO AT 43614 #704-01-1988 L2006 **ID** *012 †20

YASSINE, Khaled Ahmad. 3020 N MCCORD RD, STE 201A 43615 #198-02-1990 L2001 **N** *020 †75

YAZJI, Ghiath Abdallah. 4235 SECOR RD 43623 #875-01-1982 L1996 **CD IM** *020 †20

YECHOOR, Siva Ramakrishna. 544 E WOODRUFF AVE 43604 #495-73-1983 L1996 **P** *020 †75

YEE, Eleanore. 3000 ARLINGTON AVE 43614 #422-01-2007 L2007 **AN** *012

YOBBAGY, Jonathan Jos. 4841 MONROE ST 43623 #038-40-1981 L1983 **DR IM** *020,80

YODER, John Robt. 4841 MONROE ST 43623 #035-45-1954 L1957 **R** *071 †80

YOON, Young S. 3000 ARLINGTON AVE, DEPT OF MEDICINE 43614 #132-01-1983 L2000 **PUD** *020 †20

YOUNG, James Edward, III. 3000 ARLINGTON AVE 43614 #025-12-1991 L1999 **EM** *020 †16

YOUNG, Mark Everett. 1020 VARLAND AVE, NAVARRE PARK FAM HEALTH CE 43605 #038-43-1984 L1988 **FM** *020 †18

YOUNG, Monica Jeanne. 3900 SUNFOREST CT, STE 227 43623 #038-43-1984 L1987 **FM** *020 †18

YOUNG, Robert L. ■ 43614 #038-75-2007, ▲ L2007 **EM** *012

YOUSAFZAI, Aamir Nadeem. 2213 CHERRY ST 43608 #704-09-2002 L2007 **FP** *012

YOUSUF, Naveed. ■ 43617 #704-09-1969 L1987 **OTO** *020 †45

ZACHARIAS, Anoar. 2213 CHERRY ST STE 309, ST VINCENT HOSP & MED CTR 43608 #187-08-1962 L1974 **TS** *071 †85,90

ZAFAR, Karim Nawaz. 1850 EASTGATE RD 43614 #704-02-1970 L1974 **IM EM** *020

ZAFAR, Saleem Shahzad. ■ 43617 #038-43-2001 L2002 **U** *012

ZAHER, Aiman. 3000 ARLINGTON AVE 43614 #875-01-1984 L1996 **PTH PCP** *020 †50

ZAKELJ, Mary Jane. 3740 W SYLVANIA AVE, STE 250 43623 #038-43-1981 L1984 **PD PSM** *020 †55

ZAKERIGHOZANI, Ahmad. 4235 SECOR RD 43623 #035-46-1988 L1995 **NS** *020 †25

ZAMBRANO, Nestor P. 313 JEFFERSON AVE, CORDELIA MARTIN HEALTH CEN 43604 #748-08-1966 L1973 **GP EM** *020

ZAMBRANO, Severino P. 1500 N SUPERIOR ST 43604 #748-01-1965 L1970 **GP** *020

ZANGARA, Peter Paul. 3949 SUNFOREST CT, TOLEDO NEUROLOGICAL 43623 #033-05-1977 L1981 **N OS** *020 †75

ZAVELL, John Francis. 2865 N REYNOLDS RD STE 250 43615 #025-01-1985 L1987 **PS** *020 †85,65

ZEIDNER, Steven R. 4841 MONROE ST 43623 #020-02-1969 L1975 **RO R** *020 †80

ZEILER, Alean Joyce. 2213 FRANKLIN AVE 43620 #038-43-1974 L1975 **PD** *020 †55

ZEISS, Jacob. 3000 ARLINGTON AVE 43614 #038-43-1974 L1975 **R** *020 †80

ZEITOUNI, Nader Moufid. 2142 N COVE BLVD, EMERGENCY ROOM 43606 #605-01-1997 L2000 **PCC** *012 †20

ZELENOCK, Gerald Bruce. 3000 ARLINGTON AVE, MS 1095 DEPT OF SURGERY 43614 #025-01-1973 L2007 **VS GS** *030 †35

ZHENG, Zhe. 3045 ARLINGTON AVE, DEPT OF GME 43614 #243-46-1993 L2006 **IM** *012

ZIMMERMAN, Janis Edith. 1500 N SUPERIOR ST, COMMUNITY HEALTH NORTH 43604 #038-43-1993 L1995 **FM** *020 †18

ZIMMERMAN, Willis Walter. ■ 43614 #028-79-1958, ▲ L1959 **GP** *071

ZOGRAFIDES, Peter George. 4235 SECOR RD 43623 #038-43-1994 L1995 **U** *020 †95

ZORICK, Frank John. ■ 43617 #023-01-1967 L1976 **SME P** *074 †75

ZOUBI, Najeeb Fawwaz. 2222 CHERRY ST, STE 2300 43608 #575-01-1992 L2007 **PD** *020 †55

ZRULL, Joel Peter. 3130 GLENDALE AVE 43614 #025-01-1957 L1973 **P CHP** *040 †75

ZUCKER, David Bruce. 2865 N REYNOLDS RD 43615 #035-46-1989 L1999 **AN** *020 †05

TORONTO — JEFFERSON

FOJAS, Augusto Para. 1878 FRANKLIN ST 43964 #748-01-1966 L1972 **IM GP** *020

KELLERMIER, Harry Clayton. ■ 43964 #038-44-2001 L2001 **NP** *012 †50

LOPEZ, Francisco Dulay. 1878 FRANKLIN ST 43964 #748-01-1974 L1986 **IM EM** *020

STROVILAS, Crist G. 812 N 4TH ST 43964 #038-40-1959 L1959 **FM** *020

TRENTON — BUTLER

GERMANN, William Julian. ■ 45067 #023-12-1982 L2007 **FM** *020 †18

SCHULZ, Andrew Paul. 841 W STATE ST 45067 #038-40-1998 L1999 **FM** *020 †18

SOLAR, Ronald John. ■ 45067 #038-41-1965 L1965 **PD** *071 †55

TROTWOOD — MONTGOMERY

BANERJEE, Partha. ■ 45426 #495-02-1968 L1974 **IM END** *020 †20

BETHEL-MURRAY, Kimberly F. 38 OLIVE RD, TROTWOOD PHYSICIAN CENTER 45427 #038-45-1987 L1989 **IM** *020

CORNEY, Isaac. 3038 OLIVE RD 45426 #038-45-1988 L1991 **FM** *020 †18

DICKENS, Duane Patton. 3038 OLIVE RD, TROTWOOD PHYSICIAN CENTER 45426 #010-03-1988 L1991 **FM** *020 †18

THOMAS, Mark Hunter. 2580 SHILOH SPRINGS RD, STE B 45426 #038-40-1982 L1985 **FM ADM** *020 †18

TROY — MIAMI

BARTNICK, David A. 998 S DORSET RD, UPPER VALLEY PROFESSION CO 45373 #046-01-1981 L1996 **FM** *020 †18

BELLAS, Richard Clifford. 420 S MARKET ST, RICHARD C BELLAS 45373 #004-01-1971 L1978 **R AM** *020 †80

BONANNO, Vincent Anthony. 998 S DORSET RD STE 301 45373 #036-01-1989 L2001 **IM** *020 †20

BROST, Bruce Bailey. 50 TROY TOWN RD, STE B 45373 #030-05-1968 L1970 **OS** *075

BROWN, Evelyn S W. 3006 N DIXIE HWY, STE 106 45373 #028-02-1976 L1989 **N** *020 †75

BUERK, Bruce Mcvey. 1861 TOWNE PARK DR, STE C 45373 #038-40-1998 L2004 **OPH OS** *020 †35

CARROLL, C Patrick. 1861 TOWNE PARK DR, STE C 45373 #038-40-1975 L1975 **OPH** *020 †35

CASTALDO, William. 3006 N DIXIE HWY, STE 102 45373 #561-15-1981 L1993 **PUD** *020 †20

CAUGHEY, Curtis Lee. 3130 N DIXIE HWY, UPPER VALLEY MEDICAL CENTE 45373 #005-02-1979 L1980 **EM** *020 †16

CHOUCAIR, Michelle M. 3006 N COUNTY ROAD 25A 45373 #605-01-1990 L2001 **D** *020 †15

CHRISTOPHER, Charles Robt. ■ 45373 #038-40-1973 L1973 **OBG OS** *020 †30

CORTEZ, Rosalindo T. 61 S STANFIELD RD 45373 #748-07-1967 L1973 **OBG GP** *020

CROWLEY, Stephen Fuller. 3150 MAGNOLIA DR 45373 #051-01-1963 L1994 **R DR** *020 †80

CULLIS, Cass Miller. 3006 N COUNTY ROAD 25A, STE 104 45373 #038-40-1976 L1977 **CD IM** *020 †20

CZAJKA, William. 3006 N COUNTY ROAD 25A, STE 104 45373 #038-41-1980 L1982 **CD** *020 †20

DELCAMP, Don Douglas. 76 TROY TOWN DR 45373 #038-40-1982 L1983 **ORS** *020 †40

DIAZ, Christopher David. 1430 W MAIN ST 45373 #038-43-2003 L2003 **GP** *020

DILWORTH, Daniel John. 3130 N DIXIE HWY, STE 203 45373 #038-43-1995 L1997 **OBG** *020 †30

DURITSCH, Stephen Wm. 998 S DORSET RD, STE 104 45373 #038-41-1988 L1991 **PM** *020 †60

ELLENBOGEN, Enrique. 700 S STANFIELD RD STE B 45373 #737-06-1968 L1975 **OPH** *020

ERDAHL, Kendall Jay. 700 S STANFIELD RD 45373 #038-45-2004 L2004 **FM** *020 †18

EVERT, Barbara Harbor. 3130 N DIXIE HWY 45373 #038-43-1978 L1980 **FM** *020 †18

FERNANDES, Shruti Shivpur. 700 S STANFIELD RD, UPPER VALLEY FAMILY CARE 45373 #038-40-2003 L2006 **FM** *020 †18

FORNAL, Robert Earl. 3130 N DIXIE HWY 45373 #051-01-1976 L1978 **P FM** *020 †75,18

FOSS, Harold G. 61 S STANFIELD RD 45373 #016-43-1951 L1961 **GYN** *071 †30

FRANTZ, Richard Wm. 3130 N DIXIE HWY, UPPER VALLEY MEDICAL CENTE 45373 #045-04-1992 L1993 **EM** *020 †16

GOODENOUGH, Roger R, Jr. 998 S DORSET RD, STE 301 45373 #030-05-1968 L1969 **GP** *020

GOULD, Lawrence Allen. 3130 N DIXIE HWY 45373 #038-06-1965 L1965 **OBG** *020 †30 ‡

GOULD, Todd Jeffery. 180 S STANFIELD RD 45373 #056-05-1992 L1996 **OPH** *020 †35

GRENKO, Ronald Trent. ■ 45373 #038-41-1985 L1985 **ATP** *020 †50

HALL, Phillip Keith. 45 S STANFIELD RD 45373 #051-04-1991 L1996 **DS D** *020 †15

HAQ, Naveed Ul. 3130 N COUNTY ROAD 25A, # 101 45373 #704-01-1994 L2002 **NEP IM** *020 †20

HESS, B Mark. 1300 N DIXIE HWY, HEALTH PARTNERS FREE CLINI 45373 #038-06-1966 L1966 **IM PLM** *071 †20

HILL, Barbara Ann. 31 S STANFIELD RD STE 202 45373 #038-45-1992 L1994 **IM** *020 †20

HILLMAN, Thomas Michael. 550 SUMMIT AVE, STE 101 45373 #038-41-1971 L1979 **TS VS** *074 †85,90

HOAK, Carl Graham. 1208 N DORSET RD 45373 #019-02-1946 L1955 **PTH** *071 †50

HOOVER, James B. 998 S DORSET RD STE 104 45373 #038-41-1980 L1982 **PM** *020 †60

HUSSAIN, Belayet. 3130 N COUNTY ROAD 25A, # 205 45373 #160-01-1972 L1989 **U** *020 †95

IKRAMUDDIN, Ilyas. 3130 N COUNTY ROAD 25A, # 109 45373 #028-78-1995, ▲ L1997 **GE IM** *020

JAMES, Trenton Leon. ■ 45373 #038-45-1999 L2002 **P** *100

KAEBNICK, Warren Walter. ■ 45373 #041-12-1955 L1956 **GS** *071 †85

KITCHENER, Rabindra. 3006 N DIXIE HWY, STE 106 45373 #495-27-1973 L1979 **N** *020

KNUPP, Keith A. 998 S DORSET RD, MIAMI COUNTY SURGEONS 45373 #055-01-1984 L1985 **GS** *020 †85

KROUSGRILL, Lois A. 3006 N DIXIE HWY, STE 106 45373 #038-45-1996 L1998 **CHN** *020 †75

KULKARNI, Rajeev. 3130 N DIXIE HWY, STE 107 45373 #496-38-1985 L2002 **HO** *020 †25

LEE, Suk Wan. 998 S DORSET RD, STE 206 45373 #583-01-1967 L1974 **IM CD** *020 †20

LE FEVRE, Larry Edward. 31 S STANFIELD RD 45373 #038-40-1973 L1973 **IM EM** *020 †20

LIN, Tzy-Shan. 3130 N DIXIE HWY, UPPER VALLEY MED CTR 45373 #385-02-1959 L1971 **PTH NM** *071 †50,28

MALARKEY, Robert Francis. 76 TROY TOWN DR 45373 #020-12-1985 L1986 **ORS** *020 †40

MARTINEK, Ann Marie. 1861 TOWNE PARK DR, STE C 45373 #025-01-1991 L1996 **OPH OS** *020 †35

MAURER, Joseph Leo. 1031 DELLWOOD DR 45373 #038-41-2008 *012

MEYER, Stacy Lynn. ■ 45373 #038-45-2006 L2006 **PD** *012

NGUYEN, Thong Duc. 441 MEADOWOOD DR, DAYTON 4100 45373 #941-01-1970 L1983 **DR GP** *020

NICKRAS, Judith Ann G. 530 CRESCENT DR 45373 #038-40-1973 L1973 **IM** *020 †20

NICKRAS, Thomas John. 530 CRESCENT DR 45373 #038-40-1973 L1974 **IM** *020 †20

NIKTASH, Mohammedreza. 998 S DORSET RD STE 301 45373 #539-05-1990 L1993 **FM** *020 †18

NIMS, Peter Edward. 3130 N COUNTY ROAD 25A 45373 #038-40-1964 L1964 **P ADM** *020

NORDQUIST, Bruce Oliver. 2372 CASSTOWN SIDNEY RD 45373 #025-01-1972 L1973 **GP** *020

NUTHAKKI, Mohan Rao. 3130 N COUNTY ROAD 25A 45373 #495-57-1970 L1990 **ON HEM** *020 †20

OCAMPO, Victoria Guardian. 61 S STANFIELD RD 45373 #748-10-1966 L1974 **OBG** *020 †30

PATTUGALAN, Norma Iringan. 1405 STONYCREEK RD 45373 #748-10-1966 L1974 **PD** *020 †55

PEREYMA, Constantine. ■ 45373 #407-04-1950 L1955 **GS EM** *071 †85

PEREZ, Ramon Benito. 1405 STONYCREEK RD 45373 #275-01-1952 L1962 **PD** *071 †55

PETERS, Matthew E. 31 S STANFIELD RD, STE 304 45373 #038-45-1983 L1985 **FM** *020 †18

PHILLIPS, Chandler Allen. 3130 N DIXIE HWY 45373 #005-06-1969 L1973 **AM EM** *050 ‡

RAHMAN, Shakil Shafqatur. 3130 N DIXIE HWY, UPPER VALLEY MEDICAL CENTE 45373 #661-01-1998 L2005 **OS** *020 ‡

RAJAB, Al-Mouthanna Slima. ■ 45373 #875-02-1989 L2000 **AN** *020

RAJAB, Ebaa Sliman. ■ 45373 #913-15-1992 L2000 **AN** *020 †05

RAO, Kodem Sambasiva. 31 S STANFIELD RD STE 206 45373 #495-11-1958 L1980 **TS VS** *020 †85,90

RASHID, Taj A. 3006 N COUNTY ROAD 25A, STE 101 45373 #160-03-1982 L1994 **IM** *020 †20

RAVAL, Yagnesh Rameshwar. 3130 N DIXIE HWY 45373 #495-23-1971 L1976 **DR OS** *020 †80

REBAR, Michael J. 3130 N DIXIE HWY STE 105, MIDWEST MEDICAL SERVICES 45373 #041-77-1998, ▲ L1999 **IM** *020 †20

REINHOLD, Robert Vancourt. 180 S STANFIELD RD 45373 #038-41-1978 L1980 **PD** *020 †55

RODGERS, Gregory Keith. 3130 N DIXIE HWY, DEPT EM 45373 #020-12-2001 L2001 **EM** *100 †16

SATTU, Padmaja. 3006 N DIXIE HWY, STE 101 45373 #496-01-1998 L2001 **IM** *020

SETZKORN, Ronald Karl. 3130 N DIXIE HWY, UPPER VALLEY CANCER CENTER 45373 #041-02-1982 L2000 **RO** *020 †80

SHAH, Pari M. ■ 45373 #043-01-2004 L2007 **IM** *100 †20

SOBOL, Warren Michael. 1861 TOWNE PARK DR, STE C 45373 #036-07-1984 L1985 **OPH GS** *020 †35

SPAGNOLA, Nicholas R. 998 S DORSET RD, STE 207 45373 #038-40-1977 L1977 **FM** *020 †18

SPENCER, David M. 550 SUMMIT AVE 45373 #038-41-1946 L1948 **OTO A** *072

SUTANDI, Reza Harlan. 31 S STANFIELD RD STE 301 45373 #038-44-1996 L2000 **OBG** *020 †30

THOMAS, Easaw. ■ 45373 #495-31-1972 L1979 **AN** *020

TORDILLA, Felino Padilla. 3130 N DIXIE HWY, UPPER VALLEY MEDICAL CENTE 45373 #748-01-1967 L1975 **EM** *020 †16

VAGLIENTI, Patrick A. 3130 N DIXIE HWY, UPPER VALLEY MEDICAL CENTE 45373 #038-40-1997 L2000 **EM** *020 †16

VYAS, Pradip Mahendrabhai. 65 S STANFIELD RD 45373 #495-76-1981 L1987 **IM** *020 †20

WEBER, Paul Wm. 1174 S RIDGE AVE 45373 #028-34-1990 L1996 **PD** *020 †55

YACOUB, Georges S. 3006 N COUNTY ROAD 25A 45373 #605-02-1989 L2001 **PUD** *020 †20

YALAVARTHI, Jyothsna. 3006 N COUNTY ROAD 25A, STE 101 45373 #495-50-1997 L2000 **IM** *020 †20

YEO, Joon Koo. 57 ROBINHOOD LN 45373 #583-02-1970 L1978 **NEP IM** *020 †20

ZARRABY, Mansur. 3006 N COUNTY ROAD 25 #101 45373 #517-01-1964 L1971 **IM PUD** *020 †20

TUSCARAWAS — TUSCARAWAS

DONEHUE, William Chas. PO BOX 329 44682 #020-12-1975 L1975 **GP AM** *075

KOLLMAN, Dale Ralph. ■ 44682 #025-01-1956 L1967 **FM EM** *071 †18

TWINSBURG – SUMMIT

AHMED, Azzam N. 10820 RAVENNA RD, STONE CREEK COMMONS 44087 #915-03-1971 L1977 **OBG** *020 †30
CARRILLO, Peter. 10828 RAVENNA RD 44087 #038-44-1991 L1994 **GS TRS** *075
CAYABYAB, Consuelo G. 2839 MYRICK LN 44087 #748-01-1955 L1968 **IM EM** *020
COTES, Enrique Eduardo. 2451 EDISON BLVD, QUEST DIAGNOSTICS INC 44087 #308-01-1980 L1991 **PTH PCP** *020 †50
KAWALEK, Wayne Keith. 2000 E AURORA RD, DAIMLER CHRYSLER 44087 #035-08-1980 L1981 **EM OM** *030 †16
KOCKA, John Edward. 2676 E AURORA RD, STE 102 44087 #038-43-2000 L2000 **FM** *020 †18
LE, Tram Bao. ■ 44087 #305-01-1999 L2004 **FM** *100 †18
LEU, Melanie Lynne. 2365 EDISON BLVD 44087 #038-06-1996 L1997 **FM** *020 †18
LITTMAN, William Kenneth. ■ 44087 #038-06-1957 L1957 **DR** *020 †80
MARK, Myra J. 8920 CANYON FALLS BLVD 44087 #038-44-1997 L1998 **FM** *020 †18
MASTERSON, Kimberly Ann. 8054 DARROW RD, STE 3 44087 #038-06-1996 L1998 **PD** *020 †55
MESSEMER, Jane E. 8054 DARROW RD, STE 3 44087 #017-20-1992 L2006 **PD** *020 †55
NEDELKOFF, Jeko Mladenoff. ■ 44087 #407-20-1951 L1955 **P EM** *071
PAIDHUNGAT, Ashwin A. 2365 EDISON BLVD, STE 100 44087 #038-44-1997 L1999 **FM** *020 †18
PERLMUTTER, Mark Steven. 8819 COMMONS BLVD, STE 100 44087 #038-06-1972 L1974 **IM END** *020 †20
PRISTOU, Walter. 10568 RAVENNA RD STE 11 44087 #005-17-1962 L1975 *100
PROCOP, Gary Wayne. ■ 44087 #055-02-1992 L1998 **PTH** *020 †50
REED, Nevada Ann W. 8054 DARROW RD, SUITES 5&6 44087 #028-02-1997 L2003 **CHN** *020 †75 ‡
SAMONTE, Armando Flores. ■ 44087 #748-01-1962 L1975 **AN** *071
SARAIYA, Rajeshkumar N. 10812 RAVENNA RD, SARAIYA MEDICAL CENTER 44087 #495-23-1982 L1997 **IM** *020 †20
SHAH, Susan Renee. 8054 DARROW RD, STE 3 44087 #021-01-1992 L1993 **PD** *020 †55
SYCZ, Enhew. 2000 E AURORA RD, C/O CHRYSLER CORP, MED DEP 44087 #038-41-1949 L1950 **OM DR** *072
WALTON, Jennifer Rose. ■ 44087 #038-44-2006 L2006 **PD** *012

UHRICHSVILLE – TUSCARAWAS

DUROSE, Galen George, Jr. 932 EASTPORT AVE 44683 #038-41-1997 L1999 **FM** *020 †18
KAGAOAN, Edgardo Rubio. PO BOX 32 44683 #748-01-1964 L1971 **OBG** *020
MC KNIGHT, Timothy Alan. 932 EASTPORT AVE 44683 #038-40-1997 L1998 **FM** *020 †18

UNIONTOWN – STARK

BURKET, David Glenn. 3838 MASSILLON RD, STE 370 44685 #041-02-1972 L1973 **OPH** *020 †35
CALVIN, Bryce Eugene. ■ 44685 #038-44-2002 L2004 **IM** *020 †20
CANNATTI, James Anthony. 3838 MASSILLON RD, STE 370 44685 #038-44-1988 L1989 **OPH** *020 †35
CARP, Steven Scott. 4031 MASSILLON RD, # A 44685 #025-07-1987 L1997 **PS** *020 †85,65
CARRABINE, Timothy John. 3838 MASSILLON RD STE 360, OAK CLINIC 44685 #030-06-1985 L1988 **IM** *020
CHENOWITH, Irene Maude. 1700 BOETTLER RD, STE 200 44685 #038-43-1980 L1983 **IM IMG** *020 †20
CHO, M Jeannette. 1587 BOETTLER RD STE 102 44685 #038-44-1992 L1993 **IM** *020 †20
DANNEMILLER, Lisa Ann. 11932 KING CHURCH AVE NW 44685 #038-40-1992 L1994 **IM** *020 †20
DASH, Anita. 3838 MASSILLON RD, STE 370 44685 #038-44-1992 L1998 **OPH** *020 †35 ‡
DAVIES, Sidney Ifor. ■ 44685 #946-01-1950 L1961 **PTH** *071 †50
ELLISON, Richard Robt. 3838 MASSILLON RD, STE 370 44685 #038-06-1984 L1987 **OPH** *020 †35
ELYADERANI, Deborah Reed. 1700 BOETTLER RD, STE 250 44685 #030-06-1992 L1999 **N** *020
FRANCIS, Mary Kathleen. ■ 44685 #038-44-2006 L2006 **EM** *012
GSELLMAN, Robert Michael. 4444 ARLINGTON RD 44685 #038-40-1977 L1977 **FM OS** *020 †18
HATHERILL, Michele Leigh. 1587 BOETTLER RD, STE 104 44685 #038-44-1982 L1987 **ORS** *020 †40
HOJAT, Rod A. ■ 44685 #042-03-2007 L2007 **OBG** *012
HOLLOWAY, Benjamin Joseph. 4444 ARLINGTON RD 44685 #038-41-2002 L2002 **MPD** *020,50,55
IKEJIANI, Boniface N. ■ 44685 #017-20-1994 L1996 **OBG** *020 †30
JAMES, Andrew Emerson. ■ 44685 #028-79-2007, ▲ L2007 **PD** *012
KANTARAS, Anthony Thomas. 1587 BOETTLER RD, STE 104 44685 #038-44-1995 L2000 **ORS** *020 †40
KIRVEN, Melissa S. 1700 BOETTLER RD, STE 225 44685 #038-44-1996 L1997 **OBG** *020 †30
LANG, David Paul. ■ 44685 #038-44-2005 L2005 **IM** *012
LEESON, Mark Christopher. 1587 BOETTLER RD, STE 104 44685 #055-01-1978 L1979 **ORS** *050 †40
LENZ, Paul Joseph. 1700 BOETTLER RD, STE 100 44685 #038-41-1994 L1995 **FM** *020 †18
LIPPITT, Steven B. 1587 BOETTLER RD, STE 104 44685 #055-01-1984 L1992 **ORS GS** *020 †40
MAMONIS, Alexsandra M. 1700 BOETTLER RD, STE 125 44685 #038-44-1993 L1996 **IM** *020 †20
MANALAC, Tyrone Christoph. ■ 44685 #748-02-2004 L2005 **IM** *012
MC INTOSH, G Andrew. 3705 MASSILLON RD 44685 #038-44-1991 L1992 **FM** *020 †18
OLIVETI, John Francis. 1790 TOWN PARK BLVD, STE I 44685 #055-01-1988 L1989 **PD PDP** *020 †55
PINKOWSKI, John Louis. 1587 BOETTLER RD, STE 104 44685 #038-44-1985 L1986 *020
QADIR, Riffat Hanif. 3838 MASSILLON RD STE 380A 44685 #020-02-1986 L1995 **OTO GS** *020 †45
ROMIG, Jeffrey Brian. 4016 MASSILLON RD, # C 44685 #038-43-1994 L1995 **END NTR** *020
SALTIS, Lawrence Michael. 1700 BOETTLER RD, STE 250 44685 #038-40-1971 L1971 **N** *020 †75

SANCHEZ, Kimberly Ellen. ■ 44685 #038-44-2007 L2007 **TY** *012
SHEPPARD, Christopher A. 3838 MASSILLON RD, STE 360 44685 #038-44-1982 L1984 **N IM** *020 †20,75
SMITH, Michael Jos. 1587 BOETTLER RD, STE 104 44685 #026-04-1986 L1987 **OSS ORS** *020 †40
STEURER, Paul Anthony, Jr. 1587 BOETTLER RD, STE 104 44685 #038-40-1971 L1971 **ORS** *020 †40
STRACHAN, Thomas Lee. 1700 BOETTLER RD, STE 250 44685 #038-40-1973 L1974 **N** *020 †75
TOLENTINO-BELEN, Mariquita. ■ 44685 #748-02-2004 L2007 **FP** *012
VALORE, Milania Maria. 1700 BOETTLER RD, STE 125 44685 #038-43-1994 L1996 **IM** *020 †20
VRABEC, Gregory Alan. 1587 BOETTLER RD, STE 104 44685 #060-01-1982 L1984 **ORS** *020 †40
WAGES, Duane Willard. 4444 ARLINGTON RD 44685 #041-14-1979 L1980 **FM EM** *020 †18
YOUNG, Amanda Irene. ■ 44685 #038-45-2008 *012
ZAIDI, Syed Furgan. ■ 44685 #035-47-2001 L2007 **VIR** *100 †80

UNIVERSITY HEIGHTS – CUYAHOGA

ABU SHAHIN, Fadi. ■ 44118 #875-01-1999 L2006 **OBG** *100
AKHTAR, Mateen. ■ 44118 #005-18-2003 L2006 **CD** *012 †20
ALBRIGHT, Matthew Brian. ■ 44118 #001-02-2005 L2005 **OPH** *012
ALLEN, Rachel. ■ 44118 #028-79-2007, ▲ L2007 *012
ALVES, Carlos Moura. 13940 CEDAR RD 44118 #048-12-2002 L2005 **CD** *012 †20
ARFONS, Lisa Marie. ■ 44118 #038-06-2003 L2003 **HO** *012 †20
AUSTIN, Bethany Anne. ■ 44118 #050-02-2003 L2006 **CD** *012 †20
AZELIS, Anthony. ■ 44118 #616-01-1942 L1954 **GP GS** *071
BENNETT, Andrew, III. ■ 44118 #038-06-2001 L2006 **RNR** *100 †80
BHATT, Amit. ■ 44118 #894-01-2003 L2005 **IM** *012
BLOOMFIELD, Michael Rober. ■ 44118 #016-06-2006 L2006 **ORS** *012
BLUM, Eric Benson. ■ 44118 #023-01-2002 L2005 **GE** *012 †20
BOLEK, Tina Monique. ■ 44118 #038-43-2003 L2003 **DR** *012
CANNON, Jamie Marie. 20700 N PARK BLVD # 9999 44118 #041-02-2007 L2007 **OBG** *012 †85
CATENACCI, Michelle. ■ 44118 #025-07-2005 L2005 **OBG** *012
CAYAYAN, Ninfa Diesca. ■ 44118 #748-08-1965 L1979 **FM** *020
CHHATRIWALLA, Adnan K. ■ 44118 #038-06-2001 L2004 **IC** *012
CHIPMAN, Gregory Carl. ■ 44118 #049-01-2002 L2002 **HO** *012 †20
COVIELLO, James Jos. ■ 44118 #028-34-1955 L1957 **CD IM** *071 †20
CYDULKA, Samuel. ■ 44118 #407-16-1953 L1957 **IM IMG** *071
DHAR, Sorabh. 14165 WASHINGTON BLVD 44118 #035-06-2000 L2004 **ID** *020 †20,55
EADS, Jennifer Rachel. ■ 44118 #024-07-2005 L2005 **IM** *012
FROLICH, Harold. ■ 44118 #038-41-1977 L1992 **IM** *020 †20
GARCIA, Jerald Mark. ■ 44118 #026-04-2005 L2005 **AN** *012
GEORGE, John Edward, III. ■ 44118 #038-06-2001 L2001 **AN** *012
HARTMAN, Douglas Joseph. ■ 44118 #038-41-2004 L2004 **PTH** *012
HARWARD, Bradley James. ■ 44118 #038-45-2005 L2005 **PTH** *012
HAUCK, Eugene Murphy. ■ 44118 #030-05-2007 L2007 **GS** *012
HAYNIE, Robert Lee. 2403 TRAYMORE RD, STE 330 44118 #038-06-1978 L1978 **IM** *040 †20
HERSHKOVITZ, Avital Levy. ■ 44118 #550-04-1987 **IMG** *100
HISSONG, John Gilmary. ■ 44118 #041-01-2000 *100
HORWITZ, Edward James. ■ 44118 #038-06-2004 L2004 **NEP** *012 †20
HUNTER, Grant Kirton. ■ 44118 #051-01-2007 L2007 **RO** *012
JOFFE, Simona Maria. ■ 44118 #056-05-2006 L2006 **AN** *012
KAHLENBERG, Joanne Michel. ■ 44118 #038-06-2006 L2006 **IM** *012
KAMINSKI, Beth Anne. ■ 44118 #038-06-2002 L2006 **PDE** *012 †55
KELLEMS, Matthew David. ■ 44118 #038-41-2004 L2004 **AN** *012
KLEIN, John Brian. ■ 44118 #051-01-2005 L2005 **U** *012
LEE, Ho Hyung. ■ 44118 #005-14-2003 L2003 **ORS** *012
LEE, Joyce Kerri. ■ 44118 #045-04-2005 L2005 **N** *012
LEVY, Matthew Nathan. ■ 44118 #038-06-1945 L1945 **OS** *050
MALEC, Chris Paul. ■ 44118 #041-12-2006 L2006 **AN** *012
MANZ, Ryan Michael. ■ 44118 #056-05-2006 L2006 **OTO** *012
MARKOWSKI, Kevin. 2174 WARRENSVILLE CENTR RD 44118 #038-44-1993 L1994 **EM** *020 †16
MAYO, Angelina Q L. 2174 WARRENSVILLE CENTR RD 44118 #748-08-1968 L1991 **GP AN** *020
MCCULLOUGH, Devin P. ■ 44118 #038-75-2007, ▲ L2007 **AN** *012
MEDALION, Benjamin. ■ 44118 #550-03-1990 *100
MORRISON, Amy Heather. ■ 44118 #010-01-2006 L2006 **FP** *012
MORROW-WHITE, Cheryl L. 2226 WARRENSVILL CNTR RD R, UNIVERSITY HEIGHTS 44118 #038-06-1981 L1984 **PD** *020 †55
MURPHY, Erin Sennett. ■ 44118 #038-06-2005 L2005 **RO** *012
PATEL, Shamil Surendra. ■ 44118 #038-06-2006 L2007 **OPH** *012
PRYKHODKO, Mykola Oleksey. ■ 44118 #913-05-1988 L2007 **OTO** *012
RAE, Kathryn Watson. ■ 44118 #035-06-2007 L2007 **OBG** *012
RAMIREZ, Regina E. ■ 44118 #038-45-2007 L2007 **FP** *012
RAMSEY, Rory Robert. ■ 44118 #918-01-1997 L2000 **SME** *012 †20
REHANY, Uri. ■ 44118 #550-01-1970 L1981 **OPH** *020 †35
REMY, Kenneth Eugene. ■ 44118 #041-02-2004 L2004 **MPD** *012
REZNIKOVA-STEINWAY, Svetla. ■ 44118 #003-01-2006 L2006 **EM** *012
RICHARDSON, Amy Catharine. ■ 44118 #051-01-1980 L1991 **PD** *020 †55
ROSE, Yocheved. ■ 44118 #035-19-2005 **EM** *012
RUNDO, Jessica Vensel. ■ 44118 #038-43-2004 L2004 **N** *012
SANGREE, Jill Allison. 2226 WARRENSVILLE CENTR RD 44118 #038-40-2000 L2000 **PD** *020 †55 ‡
SCHWARTZ, Rama. ■ 44118 #550-01-1995 L1999 **PD** *020 †55
SENGUPTA, Jay. ■ 44118 #048-15-2004 L2007 **IM** *100 †20
SHIVAKUMAR, Deepti Annapu. ■ 44118 #495-99-2002 L2004 **FM** *020 †18
SMITH, Matthew Vernon. ■ 44118 #051-04-2002 L2002 **ORS** *012
SMITH, Robert Paul. 2520 MILTON RD, 2520 MILTON ROAD 44118 #048-15-1985 L1986 **EM** *020 †16
SOLOMON, Jeffrey David. ■ 44118 #038-06-2005 L2006 **MPD** *012
STEINWAY, Matthew Lee. ■ 44118 #003-01-2005 L2005 **U** *012
TANCHULING, Rebecca B. 3852 MEADOWBROOK BLVD 44118 #748-02-1990 L1994 **PD** *020 †55
TAUB, Ira Barry. ■ 44118 #035-46-2007 L2007 **PD** *012
TILLUCKDHARRY, Lisa Omate. ■ 44118 #566-01-1999 L2006 **PCC** *012 †20

TILLUCKDHARRY, Nicole Ved. ■ 44118 #539-06-2003 L2004 **IM END** *100 †20
TSAO, Juna. 2174 WARRENSVILL CNTR RD R, MEDGROUP 44118 #005-12-1996 L2000 **FM** *020 †18
TURELL, Marni. ■ 44118 #035-06-2004 L2004 **PD** *020 †55
VASSILOPIULOS, Dimitrios. ■ 44118 #418-01-1990 L1997 **RHU** *100 †20
WAHBA, Yacoub David. ■ 44118 #915-04-1957 L1978 **AN OPH** *071 †35
WEINERMAN, David J. ■ 44118 #038-40-2007 L2007 **IM** *012
WILKINS, Catherine Angley. ■ 44118 #038-06-2005 L2005 **OBG** *012
WOOD, Erica Michelle. ■ 44118 #143-02-1989 L1999 **BBK HO** *100
XIA, Zongqi. ■ 44118 #038-06-2005 L2005 **IM** *100
YE, Peggy. ■ 44118 #038-06-2008 *012
ZACK, Brian Harris. ■ 44118 #010-01-2006 L2006 **PD** *012
ZEKAS, John Carlson. 44118 #028-34-1991 L1993 **AN** *020
ZOCHOWSKI, Christopher Ge. ■ 44118 #038-41-2005 L2005 **PS** *012

UPPER ARLINGTON – FRANKLIN

ARCE-LARA, Carlos Eduardo. ■ 43220 #270-02-1999 L2005 **HO** *100
BLISSENBACH, Kenneth Wm. 1985 W HENDERSON RD, # 300 43220 #038-40-1970 L1970 **P EM** *020 †75
CLEM, Kelley Lee. 4605 SAWMILL RD 43220 #038-40-2002 L2002 **FSM** *020 †18
CORPUS, Manuel Velasco. 2424 WENBURY RD 43220 #748-08-1957 L1973 **IM AM** *071
COYLE, Christen Marie. 3440 RIVERSIDE DR 43221 #038-40-2004 L2004 **FM** *020 †18
DAMME-SORONEN, Jessie L. ■ 43221 #016-06-2001 **OBG** *020
EDWARDS, Peter H, Jr. 4605 SAWMILL RD 43220 #038-40-1988 L1994 **OSM** *020 †40
FITZ, William Robt. 4605 SAWMILL RD 43220 #038-40-1986 L1987 **PM** *020 †60
GARLING, David John. 2470 DORSET RD, DEPT OF VEETERAN AFFAIRS 43221 #038-43-1982 L1991 **OM** *012
HAGHIGHAT, Peyman. ■ 43221 #422-01-2003 L2006 **HO** *012 †20
HAMILTON, Edwin B. ■ 43221 #038-40-1952 L1952 **FM** *071 †85
HANNA, Atef Nagib. ■ 43220 #915-04-1978 L2001 **PTH** *012
HARROLD, Melissa Jordan. 1975 GUILFORD RD, ARLINGTON PRIMARY CARE 43221 #038-40-2001 L2001 **MPD** *020 †20,05
HECK, Robert Todd. 4971 ARLINGTON CENTRE BLVD 43220 #038-43-1995 L1997 **PS** *020
MASON, James Franklin. 3311 TREMONT RD, NORTHWEST FAMILY PHYS INC 43221 #038-40-1956 L1956 **FM** *071 †18
MC SHANE, Michael Anthony. 4605 SAWMILL RD 43220 #038-44-1983 L1984 **ORS** *020 †40
MELARAGNO, Paul Gerard. 4605 SAWMILL RD 43220 #038-40-1992 L1993 **ORS OAR** *020 †40
MIELY, William Richard. 4605 SAWMILL RD 43220 #038-43-1982 L1983 **ORS OSS** *020 †40
MILETI, Joseph. 4605 SAWMILL RD 43220 #038-40-1996 L1998 **OAR** *020
O'BRIEN, Gregory Francis. ■ 43221 #038-40-1969 L1974 **OTO HNS** *020 †45
O'LEARY, John Francis. 4605 SAWMILL RD 43220 #038-40-1980 L1980 **ORS** *020 †40
PLOCHARCZYK, Elizabeth Fr. ■ 43220 #038-40-2008 *012
POKABLA, Christopher Mark. ■ 43212 #038-44-2003 L2003 **ORS** *012
RETZKE, Jason Douglas. ■ 43221 #038-40-2006 L2006 **OBG** *012
RICE, Charles Douglas, Jr. ■ 43221 #020-12-2008 *012
RIEPENHOFF, John P. ■ 43221 #010-02-1945 L1946 **PD** *071 †55
ROAN, Jessica Marie. ■ 43221 #038-40-2006 L2006 **PD** *012
ROBIE, David Brooks. 4605 SAWMILL RD 43220 #020-02-1981 L1982 **ORS** *020 †40
SATOSKAR, Anjali Abhay. ■ 43221 #496-42-1996 L2007 **PTH** *100 †50
TRIFFON, Mark James. 2631 ABINGTON RD 43221 #038-40-1986 L1988 **ORS OSM** *020
TWEHUES, Andrew Robert. ■ 43212 #020-12-2005 L2005 **IM** *012
UNVERFERTH, Kurt Louis. 2631 ABINGTON RD 43221 #038-40-1994 L2001 **ORS** *020 †40
UNVERFERTH, Louis John. 4605 SAWMILL RD 43220 #038-40-1966 L1966 **ORS OSM** *020 †40
VANSTEYN, Scott Jeffrey. 4605 SAWMILL RD 43220 #036-07-1990 L1992 **OSM** *020 †40
WAKELIN, John Keene, III. 4971 ARLINGTON CENTRE BLVD 43220 #038-40-2000 L2000 **PS** *020 †65
WARD, Linda Ann. ■ 43221 #038-43-1988 L1991 **IM** *020 †20
WOLFE, Claire V Rendar. 4605 SAWMILL RD 43220 #038-40-1968 L1968 **PM OS** *020 †60
WOLFE, John Sohn, II. 4605 SAWMILL RD 43220 #038-40-1968 L1968 **ORS** *020 †40

UPPER SANDUSKY – WYANDOT

ATTAR, Talal Tafankaji. 885 N SANDUSKY AVE 43351 #875-02-1992 L1997 **IC** *020 †20
BARKER, Bruce Alan. 885 N SANDUSKY AVE 43351 #038-40-1997 L2004 **PM** *020 †18
BARRETT, Robert Laurence. 885 N SANDUSKY AVE, RADIOLOGY DEPT 43351 #025-07-1978 L1981 **DR OS** *020 †80
BAZZOLI, James M. 885 N SANDUSKY AVE 43351 #561-01-1970 L1976 **OBG** *020
BRINKER, Sheri Louise. 885 N SANDUSKY AVE 43351 #038-43-1996 L2005 **DR** *020
BROWNE, Joseph James. 777 N SANDUSKY AVE 43351 #038-40-1959 L1959 **GYN** *020
BUKHARI, Syed Azim. 885 N SANDUSKY AVE 43351 #704-01-1970 L1970 **PD PDC** *020 †55
BURTON, Gary Dean. 885 N SANDUSKY AVE 43351 #038-40-1984 L1985 **OPH** *035
CHA, Ae Seon. 777 N SANDUSKY AVE 43351 #038-44-1998 L2000 **OBG** *030
CHA, Chong Sun. 885 N SANDUSKY AVE 43351 #583-06-1966 L1977 **GP EM** *020
CHAUDRY, Naseer Ahmed. 885 N SANDUSKY AVE 43351 #704-01-1970 L1981 **NEP IM** *020 †20
CHOY, Young Chul. 885 N SANDUSKY AVE, RADIOLOGY DEPT 43351 #583-02-1971 L1984 **DR NM** *020 †28,80
COLLAZO, Antonio E. 885 N SANDUSKY AVE 43351 #042-01-1985 L1991 **OTO** *020 †45
CONCEPCION, Roberto S. 885 N SANDUSKY AVE 43351 #748-08-1979 L1983 **GS U** *020 †95
CROWELL, Robert Raymond. 885 N SANDUSKY AVE 43351 #017-20-1979 L1979 **OSS** *020 †40
EBOH, Noel Nse. 885 N SANDUSKY AVE 43351 #847-11-1972 L1979 **NS N** *012
FITKIN, David Lee. 885 N SANDUSKY AVE 43351 #038-43-1984 L1990 **U** *020
FRANK, Edgar. 885 N SANDUSKY AVE 43351 #042-01-1979 L2004 **OTO** *020 †45
GANDHI, Ashok D. 885 N SANDUSKY AVE 43351 #495-48-1979 L1991 **AI PD** *020 †55,03
GARVIN, J Chas. 885 N SANDUSKY AVE 43351 #005-06-1977 L1978 **OPH MDM** *020 †35
GETACHEW, Eskender. 885 N SANDUSKY AVE 43351 #038-43-1999 L2000 **N** *100 †75
GIFEISMAN, Mark. 885 N SANDUSKY AVE 43351 #422-01-1998 L2003 **CCA** *020 †05
HANEY, Kevin Mark. 885 N SANDUSKY AVE 43351 #038-40-2001 L2001 **FM** *020 †18
HARRIS, Keri Sue. 885 N SANDUSKY AVE, WYANDOT MEMORIAL HOSPITAL 43351 #038-40-2002 L2002 **MPD** *020 †20,55
HAYES, Michael James. 885 N SANDUSKY AVE 43351 #025-12-1980 L1983 **IM RHU** *020 †20
HUSAIN, Khurshid Nazim. 885 N SANDUSKY AVE 43351 #495-49-1967 L1976 **FM IM** *020 †18

IDREES, Ghulam. 885 N SANDUSKY AVE 43351 #704-09-1982 L1999 **IM** *020
ISKANDER, Samir Sabah. 885 N SANDUSKY AVE 43351 #915-05-1984 L2005 **PM** *020
JANCHAR, Leonard Jos L. 885 N SANDUSKY AVE 43351 #038-06-1971 L1971 **PD PSM** *075
KIM, Seong Il. 885 N SANDUSKY AVE 43351 #583-01-1981 L1989 **ON HEM** *020 †20
KREMER, Gerald Lee. 885 N SANDUSKY AVE 43351 #038-40-1987 L1988 **FM** *020 †18
LASSITER, James Earl. 885 N SANDUSKY AVE 43351 #045-01-1990 L1991 **OBG** *020
LEE, Andy Chian. 885 N SANDUSKY AVE 43351 #038-43-1988 L1989 **FM** *020 †18
LEE, Steven. 885 N SANDUSKY AVE 43351 #038-06-2001 L2001 **PD** *020 †55
MADIA, Dalsukh Amritlal. 885 N SANDUSKY AVE 43351 #495-48-1972 L1978 **AN** *020 †05
MADIA, Ila Dalsukh. 885 N SANDUSKY AVE 43351 #495-17-1971 L1978 **AN** *020
MAHAFFEY, William Butler. ■ 43351 #038-40-1962 L1962 **GPM OS** *071 †05
MATURU, Prasad S. 885 N SANDUSKY AVE 43351 #495-09-1976 L1986 **GE IM** *020 †20
MAUR, Philip Robt. 885 N SANDUSKY AVE 43351 #038-41-1975 L1977 **PD EM** *020 †55,16
MC DONOUGH, John William. 885 N SANDUSKY AVE 43351 #025-07-1997 L2002 **GS** *020 †85
MILLER, Donald Mitchell. 885 N SANDUSKY AVE 43351 #038-43-1974 L1975 **DR** *020 †80
MOORE, Cindy M. 885 N SANDUSKY AVE 43351 #045-01-1997 L2001 **IC** *100 †20
MORALES, Byron B. 885 N SANDUSKY AVE 43351 #319-01-1981 L1994 **FM** *020 †20
NAQVI, Syed Anser Ali. 885 N SANDUSKY AVE, DEPT OF EMERGENCY MEDICINE 43351 #704-01-1987 L2002 **EM** *020 †20
NATHAN, Meera R. 885 N SANDUSKY AVE 43351 #496-21-1989 L2006 **PCC** *020 †20
NIVAR-ARISTY, Rafael A. 885 N SANDUSKY AVE 43351 #308-03-1979 L1989 **PTH** *020 †50
OKUGBENI, Jude Ogho. ■ 43351 #047-07-1994 L1996 **MPD PD** *020 †20
PARK, Kyle Kyu. 107 HOUPT DR 43351 #583-01-1968 L1974 **GP PTH** *020 †50
PATEL, Suryaprakash D. 885 N SANDUSKY AVE 43351 #495-17-1967 L1974 **AN** *020
PROK, Aleksey A. 885 N SANDUSKY AVE 43351 #913-11-1987 L1999 **APM** *020 †05 ‡
PROVANZANA, Kathleen M. 885 N SANDUSKY AVE 43351 #038-40-1995 L1996 **FM** *020 †20
RAMA, Bhola Nath. 885 N SANDUSKY AVE 43351 #495-54-1980 L1994 **CD** *020 †20
RHODES, Herschel A. 777 N SANDUSKY AVE 43351 #038-40-1953 L1953 **FM** *071
RIZZO, Joseph John. 885 N SANDUSKY AVE 43351 #561-01-1973 L1984 **GYN** *020
ROSARIO, Antonio. 885 N SANDUSKY AVE 43351 #033-05-1980 L1990 **ORS** *020 †40
RUIZ FLOREZ, Danl Enrique. 885 N SANDUSKY AVE 43351 #264-01-1967 L1975 **ID IM** *020 †20
SAVAGE, Brent Michael. 885 N SANDUSKY AVE 43351 #038-44-1998 L1999 **GS** *020
SBERNA, Joseph Gerard. 885 N SANDUSKY AVE, WYANDOTE MEM HOSP 43351 #038-41-1976 L1976 **OBG** *020 †30
SHAH, Hiten Girishkumar. 885 N SANDUSKY AVE 43351 #305-01-2000 L2006 **PUD** *020 †20
SMITH, David Ronald. 885 N SANDUSKY AVE 43351 #038-40-1988 L1990 **OPH IM** *020 †35
SMITH, Pamela Spencer. ■ 43351 #038-41-1984 L1985 **PD** *055
SOLACOFF, Konstantine K. 777 N SANDUSKY AVE 43351 #038-40-1956 L1956 **GP AN** *020
TAYLOR, Diana Lee. 885 N SANDUSKY AVE 43351 #038-40-1991 L1992 **FM** *020 †18
THOMPSON, Craig Smith. 885 N SANDUSKY AVE 43351 #038-43-1979 L1982 **IM RHU** *020 †20
THORNTON, Thomas C. 224 W JOHNSON ST 43351 #016-43-1975 L1981 **FM PHP** *020 †18
VALE, Jose L. 885 N SANDUSKY AVE 43351 #042-01-1987 L1992 **GS** *020 †85
VOEGELE, Francis Albert. 885 N SANDUSKY AVE 43351 #038-40-1989 L1990 **FM** *020 †18
VORA, Sanjay Krishnakant. 885 N SANDUSKY AVE 43351 #495-89-1988 L1994 **IM** *020 †20

URBANA – CHAMPAIGN

AHMED, Aijaz. ■ 43078 #495-65-1979 L1990 **IM HEM** *020 †20
CHACKO, Paul. 970 STATE ROUTE 54 43078 #495-27-1999 L2006 **IM** *020 †20
CRANKSHAW, John Daniel. 900 SCIOTO ST, STE 7 43078 #038-40-2001 L2005 **MPD** *020 †20,55
DAUGHERTY, Elillian J. 904 SCIOTO ST 43078 #048-14-1987 L1996 **PTH PCP** *020 †50
FLORA, John Harrison. 904 SCIOTO ST 43078 #038-40-1963 L1963 **GS** *071 †85
GOODRICH, James Thos. 904 SCIOTO ST 43078 #025-07-1970 L2001 **OM OBG** *020 †70
GROGAN, Terrence Francis. 904 SCIOTO ST 43078 #038-41-1961 L1969 **FM** *020 †20
KHAN, Mohammed Shamsuddin. 900 E COURT ST 43078 #495-21-1982 L1989 **CD IM** *020 †20
KOH, Jae Joong. 904 SCIOTO ST 43078 #583-06-1969 L1977 **GP EM** *020
MARSH, Richard Alan. 904 SCIOTO ST 43078 #025-01-1976 L1980 **PTH** *020 †50
METZ, Joseph Michael. 900 SCIOTO ST, STE 7 43078 #038-40-2000 L2000 **FM** *020
NILAVAR, Sundar V. ■ 43078 #495-72-1970 L1976 **DR NR** *020 †80
PARAMESWARAN, Lakshmy. 904 SCIOTO ST 43078 #495-80-1996 L2005 **PCP** *020 †50
PAVLATOS, Thales Nicholas. 601 SCIOTO ST 43078 #038-40-1980 L1985 **AN IM** *020 †20,05 ‡
PAXTON, Barry Lee. 900 SCIOTO ST 43078 #041-12-1971 L1972 **IM IMG** *020 †20
POLSLEY, John Steven. 900 SCIOTO ST, STE 7 43078 #038-40-1976 L1977 **FM** *020 †18
POND, John Kent. ■ 43078 #038-40-1954 L1954 **FM** *071 †18
RANDOLPH, John Robert. 904 SCIOTO ST 43078 #038-40-1996 L1998 **FM** *020 †18
RICHARDS, Joshua F. 848 SCIOTO ST 43078 #038-45-1984 L1985 **FM** *020 †18
RICHARDS, Theodore Edwin. 848 SCIOTO ST 43078 #038-40-1954 L1954 **FM** *072 †18
SMITH, Valerie. 900 SCIOTO ST STE 3 43078 #038-45-2001 L2001 **FM** *020 †18
STEWART, Robert Vail. 904 SCIOTO ST 43078 #038-43-1976 L1978 **PTH FOP** *020 †50
ULLAH, Ahsan. 904 SCIOTO ST 43078 #913-89-1991 L1999 **NEP** *012 †20
WEBER, Kim Eugene. 601 SCIOTO ST 43078 #038-45-1986 L1988 **AN PME** *020 †05

VALLEY CITY – MEDINA

GRABENSTETTER, Neil F. 6605 CENTER RD 44280 #038-06-1978 L1980 **FM FPG** *020 †18
GRABENSTETTER, Paul James. ■ 44280 #038-06-2005 L2005 **PTH** *012

VALLEY VIEW – CUYAHOGA

BRUSTEIN, Daniel Joshua. 8555 SWEET VALLEY DR, MEDSOURCE ONE 44125 #038-06-1987 L1987 **OM IM** *020 †20
GREENWOOD, Murray Andrew. 8555 SWEET VALLEY DR, MEDSOURCE ONE 44125 #065-01-1988 L2000 **PM** *012 †70
SINGER, Scott Evan. 8555 SWEET VALLEY DR 44125 #038-40-1989 L1990 **OM OSM** *020 †70

VAN WERT – VAN WERT

ADAMS, Rebecca. 1178 PROFESSIONAL DR 45891 #038-45-2002 L2002 **FM** *020 †18
ADAMS, Robert Clark. 1178 PROFESSIONAL DR 45891 #038-40-1976 L1976 **FM** *020 †18

AL-FAWAKHIRI, Muhammed Ra. ■ 45891 #875-01-1995 L2001 **IM** *020
BAMDAD, Ahmad. 140 FOX RD 45891 #396-36-1976 L1986 **CD CCM** *020 †20
BATTULA, Venkateswara R. 140 FOX RD 45891 #495-50-1990 L2002 **CD** *020 †20
BRADRICK, R Duane. 1250 S WASHINGTON ST 45891 #038-40-1957 L1957 **AN EM** *071
CAMPBELL, Brian Scott. 1250 S WASHINGTON ST 45891 #038-41-1995 L1996 **EM** *020
CHOO, Michael Chulho. 1250 S WASHINGTON ST 45891 #024-05-1987 L1988 **EM** *020 †16
CONTE, Thomas E. 140 FOX RD, STE 401 45891 #016-42-1984 L1996 **TS GS** *020 †85
COX, Jack Horton. 1250 S WASHINGTON ST 45891 #038-40-1952 L1952 **FM** *020 †18
CULLER, Fredrick Ira. 2 WILDWOOD DRIVE 45891 #038-40-1960 L1960 **AN** *020
DAUGHERTY, H Sayler. 140 FOX RD 45891 #036-05-1968 L1975 **OTO** *020 †45
EASLEY, Jeffrey Arnold. 140 FOX RD, STE 201 45891 #017-20-1987 L1988 **FM** *020 †18
HAMDI, Bashar. 140 FOX RD, STE 301 45891 #875-01-1973 L1978 **GS** *020 †85
HANLEY, Peter Christopher. 1250 S WASHINGTON ST 45891 #917-09-1978 L1990
CD IM *020 †20
HANSON, Craig Eugene. 140 FOX RD, STE 102 45891 #025-12-1991 L1995 **OBG** *020 †30
HAZEN, Mark Saml. 1250 S WASHINGTON ST, VAN WERT COUNTY HOSPITAL 45891
#038-44-1984 L1985 **CD IM** *020 †20
HOUG, Adam Jacob. 1178 PROFESSIONAL DR 45891 #038-45-2000 L2000 **FM** *020 †18 ‡
JARVIS, Scott Wm. 140 FOX RD STE 209 45891 #038-43-1991 L1992 **IM** *020 †20 ‡
JOHNSON, Terrence Lea. 1178 PROFESSIONAL DR 45891 #038-43-1973 L1975 **FM** *020 †18
JONES, Jacob Burl. 1178 PROFESSIONAL DR 45891 #038-45-2003 L2003 **FM** *020 †18
KAISER, Adam Ridge. 140 FOX RD, STE 307 45891 #025-01-1998 L2005 **OTO** *020 †45
KALOGEROU, Paul Anthony. 1052 S WASHINGTON ST 45891 #004-01-1987 L1989
IM GP *020
KLOPFENSTEIN, Lee Alan. 1250 S WASHINGTON ST 45891 #038-40-1987 L1988 **FM** *020 †18
KNERR, Joel David. 1250 S WASHINGTON ST 45891 #038-40-1982 L1982 **FM** *020 †18
LAUTZENHEISER, Nancy E G. ■ 45891 #038-41-1940 L1949 **PHP GPM** *071
MILLER, Matthew Wayne. 140 FOX RD, STE 201 45891 #025-07-1995 L2000 **FM** *020 †18
NEIDICH, Robert Lester. 140 FOX RD, STE 105 1/2 45891 #038-41-1989 L1995 **GE IM** *020 †20
NIEMAN, James Michael. 1180 PROFESSIONAL DR 45891 #038-43-1994 L1999 **ORS** *020 †40
PERCHALSKI, John Edwin. 1178 PROFESSIONAL DR 45891 #011-03-1967 L1995
FM IM *020 †18
RAMANI, Krishnan. 1250 S WASHINGTON ST 45891 #495-04-1992 L2003 **CD** *020 †20
RIVERON, Ricardo. 1250 S WASHINGTON ST 45891 #016-42-1983 L1986 **EM** *020
SANDS, Dennis Edward. 140 FOX RD, STE 102 45891 #038-41-1995 L2005 **OBG** *020 †30
SCHEIDT, Robert Basil. 1001 MAPLEWOOD DR, STE T 45891 #016-06-1960 L1962 **GS** *020 †85
SCHROEDER, Stephen Blaine. 1250 S WASHINGTON ST, VAN WERT COUNTY HOSPITAL 45891
#017-20-1967 L1969 **NS OS** *071 †25
SMITH, Harold Carlton. 1250 S WASHINGTON ST 45891 #038-40-1955 L1955 **FM PHP** *072 †18
SUNDARAM, Appukuttan. 1250 S WASHINGTON ST 45891 #495-16-1963 L1986
OTO FPS *020 †45
SWINT, Robert Edwin. 1250 S WASHINGTON ST 45891 #016-43-1970 L1979 **CD IM** *020 †20
THOMAS, Adam Craig. 140 FOX RD, NORTHEAST INDIANA UROLOGY 45891
#017-20-1999 L2007 **U** *020 †95
WAGNER, Theodore Thomas. 140 FOX RD, NORTHEAST INDIANA UROLOGY 45891
#038-40-1994 L1996 **U** *020 †95
WRAY, Jocelyn M. 140 FOX RD, PHYSICAL MC VANWERT STE303 45891 #038-43-1994 L2000
PM *020 †60

VANDALIA – MONTGOMERY

BRODERICK, George Thomas. 1 E NATIONAL RD 45377 #038-45-1983 L1991 **CD IM** *020 †20
COUCH, Mark Allan. 1 E NATIONAL RD 45377 #038-45-1983 L1985 **FM** *020 †18
DAUFEL, Pamela Marie. 55 ELVA CT 45377 #038-40-1991 L1992 **FM** *020 †18
DEWAN, Gopi A. ■ 45377 #496-07-1950 L1972 **IMG FM** *071 †18
DUNAWAY, Daniel Jos. 55 ELVA CT 45377 #038-45-1990 L1991 **ORS** *020 †40
GIBSON, Merle Eugene. 254 JAMES BOHANAN DR 45377 #028-34-1962 L1963 **OM GP** *020
GRICE, Patricia Ann. 1 E NATIONAL RD 45377 #038-45-1986 L1988 **FM** *020 †18
GUY, Stephen Russell. 900 S DIXIE DR 45377 #038-40-1981 L1982 **OBG** *020 †30
HALUSCHAK, John James. 55 ELVA CT 45377 #005-12-1987 L1988 **ON HO** *020
JESSEN, Huascar E. 1 W NATIONAL RD 45377 #737-01-1965 L1972 **IM CD** *020 †20
JOHNS, Jacob M. ■ 45377 #495-63-1970 L1993 **AN** *020
JONES, Marilyn. 1 W NATIONAL RD 45377 #047-07-1996 L1997 **FM** *020 †18
KEY, David Walter. 55 ELVA CT, DAYTON INC 45377 #020-12-1986 L1991 **U** *020 †95
LEASE, Gene Alan. 55 ELVA CT 45377 #038-43-1989 L1990 **FM** *020 †18 ‡
LITSCHER, Lawrence John. 55 ELVA CT, DAYTON INC 45377 #018-03-1976 L1986 **U** *020 †95
MONSOUR, Mark Allen. 55 ELVA CT, DAYTON INC 45377 #020-02-1993 L1999 **U** *020 †95
PERILMAN, David Mark. 55 ELVA CT 45377 #055-01-1979 L1980 **FM** *020 †18
PROPHATER, Robert Charles, Jr. 55 ELVA CT 45377 #038-40-1974 L1974 **FM** *020 †18 ‡
ROBINSON, Chester Kelley. 55 ELVA CT 45377 #038-40-1970 L1970 **FM PD** *020 †18
SMITH, Cynthia Rhee. 55 ELVA CT 45377 #038-41-1978 L1980 **FM OM** *020 †18
SMITH, James Thos. 55 ELVA CT 45377 #038-41-1965 L1965 **FM** *071 †18
SUNTAY, Wilfredo Jacinto. 113 W NATIONAL RD 45377 #038-40-1987 L1990 **DR** *020 †80
VANDERBURGH, David F. 113 W NATIONAL RD 45377 #023-12-1985 L2000 **DR EM** *020 †80
WELTY, Kenneth Adam. 55 ELVA CT 45377 #028-34-1945 L1946 **P CHP** *071
WILCHER, James E. 107 KENBROOK DR 45377 #038-75-1989, ▲ L1990 **FM** *020
WILSON, Everett E. 18 ELVA CT, # 4 45377 #028-78-1947, ▲ L1949 **OPH** *071

VENEDOCIA – VAN WERT

MORRIS, Warren C, Jr. ■ 45894 #038-41-1982 L1984 **IM** *020

VERMILION – ERIE

ADAMS, Charles Gordon. 1607 STATE RD STE 6 44089 #035-06-1962 L1963 **FM** *020
CHOHAN, Muhammad Ramzan. 4685 LIBERTY AVE 44089 #704-01-1965 L1976 **IM GP** *020
DOYLE, Evelyn Lorraine. 4608 COMPASS ROSE, UNIT 24 44089 #041-07-1977 L2004
ORS *020 †40
ERNST, David Carl. 12817 W LAKE RD, E.R. DOC, INC. 44089 #038-43-1989 L1990 **EM** *062
MEYER, Stephen Edward. 1607 STATE RD, STE 6 44089 #038-41-1975 L1978 **FM** *020 †18
MOC, Rudy Geo. ■ 44089 #038-41-1958 L1958 **IM IMG** *071 †20
SEYMOUR, Donald Edmund. ■ 44089 #038-06-1955 L1955 **IM** *071 †20

VERSAILLES – DARKE

BOWLIN, Julia Anne. 10484 KLEY RD, STE A 45380 #038-45-1993 L1994 **FM** *020 †18 ‡
ELSHOFF, Daniel Jay. 471 MARKER RD, UPPER VALLEY PROFESSIONAL 45380
#038-45-1994 L1995 **FM** *020 †18
HARSHBARGER, Kenneth Gene. 10484 KLEY RD STE B, FAMILY HEALTH SERVICES OF 45380
#038-40-1996 L1997 **FM** *020 †18
KLAMAR, Anne Eiting. 60 VISTA DR 45380 #038-40-1990 L1991 **FM** *030 †18
KLAMAR, Robert Christian. 471 MARKER RD 45380 #038-40-1990 L1991 **FM** *020 †18
PLATT, Charles Wm. 552 S WEST ST 45380 #038-41-1964 L1964 **GP A** *071

VIENNA – TRUMBULL

DONAHEY, Sue Ann. 3976 KING GRAVES RD, UNIT 11 44473 #041-12-1979 L1982 **IM** *020 †20

WADSWORTH – MEDINA

ALDANA, Marcial Morales. 195 WADSWORTH RD 44281 #748-01-1964 L1979 **AN** *020
ARAGON, Lynn D. ■ 44281 #041-12-1960 L1985 **GP EM** *071
BAGE, Michael David. 195 WADSWORTH RD 44281 #038-41-1995 L1996 **CD** *020 †20
BAUMAN, William Bernard. 195 WADSWORTH RD 44281 #038-41-1972 L1972 **CD IM** *020 †20
BELLANTE, Anita Marie. 195 WADSWORTH RD 44281 #038-44-2000 L2000 **OBG** *020
BENZION, Sabrina. 165 SMOKERISE DR 44281 #016-42-2001 L2005 **PD** *020 †55
BERKOVITZ, Kenneth Eugene. 195 WADSWORTH RD 44281 #047-05-1985 L1991
CD IM *020 †20
BERREY, Teresa Renee. 165 SMOKERISE DR 44281 #038-44-1989 L1991 **PD** *020 †55
BIANCO, Michael Anthony. 185 WADSWORTH RD STE F 44281 #038-40-1973 L1973
IM *020 †20
BISKO, Stephanie P. ■ 44281 #010-01-1983 L1984 **AN** *100
BLAIR, Kimberly Ann. 1225 HIGH ST, WADSWORTH PEDIATRICS 44281 #038-43-1998 L1999
PD *020 †55
BURELLI, Roland. 195 WADSWORTH RD 44281 #561-17-1951 L1957 **FM OBG** *020
CHAFFEE, Roger Blake. 195 WADSWORTH RD 44281 #038-40-1984 L1986 **CD** *020 †20
COEN, Barbara Lynne. 185 WADSWORTH RD STE J 44281 #038-43-1994 L1998 **OBG** *020 †30
COLEMAN, Michele Lynn. 251 LEATHERMAN RD 44281 #038-44-1995 L1996 **FM** *020 †18
COLEMAN, Timothy Edison. 251 LEATHERMAN RD 44281 #038-44-1996 L1998 **FM** *020 †18
CRAWFORD, Robert Scott. 251 LEATHERMAN RD 44281 #038-43-1989 L1992 **FM** *020 †18
CUTLER, David Alan. 195 WADSWORTH RD 44281 #012-05-1988 L1996 **CD** *020 †20
DEBEVEC, Cynthia Diane. ■ 44281 #038-06-1992 L2003 **GYN** *020 †30
DE MUND, Marjorie. 195 WADSWORTH RD, STE 301 44281 #038-40-1984 L1985 **OBG** *020 †30
DEORAS, Jyoti Satish. 180 HIGH ST 44281 #495-01-1974 L1982 **PD** *020 †55
DERANEK, Lisa Marie. ■ 44281 #038-40-1989 L1990 **EM** *020 †20,16
DESMAN, Reynold Paul. ■ 44281 #016-43-1941 L1941 **FM** *071
DONELAN, Brian John. 195 WADSWORTH RD 44281 #038-40-1990 L1993 **CD** *020 †20
FANNIN, Stephen Wayne. 195 WADSWORTH RD 44281 #038-44-1988 L1989 **CD** *020 †20
FINNERAN, Matthew Patrick. 251 LEATHERMAN RD 44281 #038-41-1983 L1984
FM FPG *020 †18 ‡
GOMEZ, Jose Alejandro. ■ 44281 #264-04-1991 L2000 **PTH** *020 †50
HAYEK, Emil R. 195 WADSWORTH RD 44281 #023-07-1995 L1999 **CD IM** *020 †20
HEUPLER, Stephen Matthew. 195 WADSWORTH RD 44281 #038-40-1991 L1997 **CD** *020 †20
HLIVKO, Jonathan Thomas. ■ 44281 #051-04-2007 L2007 **IM** *012
HORWITZ, Louis Albert. 195 WADSWORTH RD, WADSWORTH HOSP EMERGENCY D 44281
#025-01-1979 L1983 **EM** *020 †16
HUGHES, Michael Morrison. 195 WADSWORTH RD 44281 #045-01-1983 L1986 **CD IM** *020 †20
KALAPODIS, Chris. 185 WADSWORTH RD, WADSWORTH-RITTMAN HEALT SY 44281
#038-44-1996 L2000 **EM** *020 †16
KARAS, David Roman. 165 SMOKERISE DR 44281 #038-43-2000 L2000 **PD** *020 †55 ‡
KESSLER, Richard Thomas. 195 WADSWORTH RD, WADSWORTH- RITTMAN HOSPITA 44281
#038-40-1993 L1994 **EM** *020 †16
KEYSER, Philip Harwood. 195 WADSWORTH RD 44281 #038-40-1979 L1981 **CD** *020 †20
KITSON, Richard Ray. ■ 44281 #038-43-1982 L1984 **FM** *020 †18
KLAUTKY, Stephen Albert. 195 WADSWORTH RD 44281 #055-01-1999 L2006 **CD** *020 †20
KLEINMAN, Robert Leslie. 185 WADSWORTH RD STE B 44281 #038-40-1978 L1983
ORS *020 †40
KONTAK, Jeffery Reynold. 323 HIGH ST, WADSWORTH-RITTMAN FAM PRAC 44281
#038-41-1986 L1987 **FM** *020 †18
LANG, Jeffrey Brian. 251 LEATHERMAN RD 44281 #016-06-1976 L1977 **IM IMG** *020 †20
LASSALETTA, Margarita M. 185 WADSWORTH RD, STE 2E 44281 #036-08-1992 L1994
FM *020 †18
LEHNER, Patricia Pierko. ■ 44281 #038-44-1986 *074
LISHNEVSKI, Michael. 195 WADSWORTH RD 44281 #561-17-1978 L1984 **IMG IM** *020
MC MILLEN, Todd Randall. 1225 HIGH ST 44281 #038-44-1999 L1999 **PD** *020 †55
NAFZIGER, Myrl Andrew. ■ 44281 #016-06-1954 L1955 **PD** *071 †55
NEWTON, Daniel Joseph. 195 WADSWORTH RD 44281 #016-43-1996 L2003 **IC** *020 †20
NICOLOZAKES, Alexandros W. 195 WADSWORTH RD 44281 #038-40-1989 L1991
CD IM *020 †20
NIEDERMAIER, Otfried N W. 195 WADSWORTH RD 44281 #409-04-1985 L1990 **CD** *020 †20
OEHLENSCHLAGER, William F. 195 WADSWORTH RD 44281 #045-01-1993 L1994 **PD** *020 †55
OFORI, Cyril S. 195 WADSWORTH RD 44281 #412-01-1987 L1995 **CD** *020 †20
PELINI, Michael Anthony. 195 WADSWORTH RD 44281 #038-44-1987 L2000 **CD IM** *020 †20
PIFER, Randolph Lee. PO BOX 1012 44282 #055-01-1966 L1971 **PD** *020 †55
PROCHNOW, George J, Jr. ■ 44281 #016-06-1951 L1955 **P** *071
REDLE, Joseph Danl. 195 WADSWORTH RD 44281 #038-45-1991 L1997 **CD** *020 †20
RESTIVO, Joseph Michael. 195 WADSWORTH RD 44281 #038-43-1997 L2001 **CD** *020 †20
REYNOLDS, Julie Ann. 1225 HIGH ST 44281 #038-43-1996 L1999 **PD** *020 †55
RINALDI, Joseph. 195 WADSWORTH RD 44281 #038-40-1996 L1997 **CD** *020 †20
RUBIN, David N. 195 WADSWORTH RD 44281 #011-04-1991 L1994 **CD** *020 †20
SANYURAH, Saad Afif. 185 WADSWORTH RD STE H 44281 #605-01-1984 L1989
AI PD *020 †55,03
SCOTT, David Lee. 195 WADSWORTH RD 44281 #038-44-1993 L1994 **CD** *020 †16
SILVER, Kevin H. 195 WADSWORTH RD 44281 #035-01-1986 L1998 **CD IM** *020 †20
SLEIK, Khaled M. 195 WADSWORTH RD 44281 #613-02-1991 L2004 *020 †20
SMITH, Jason Kane. 195 WADSWORTH RD 44281 #038-40-1995 L1997 **ICE** *020 †20

■ = Address Information Privacy Protected

SPOLJARIC, Lawrence Jos. 251 LEATHERMAN RD 44281 #038-40-1973 L1973 **IM** *020
TOBIAS, Stephen Leslie. 195 WADSWORTH RD 44281 #836-01-1978 L1991 **IM** *020 †20
TRAYNOR, Leora Angeline. 5021 RIDGE RD 44281 #025-01-1963 L1964 **A PDA** *020 †55,03
TSAI, Albert Roger. 195 WADSWORTH RD 44281 #021-01-1977 L1977 **CD CCM** *020 †20

WAITE HILL – LAKE

SATO, Sam Isamu. ■ 44094 #007-02-1946 L1951 **D** *071 †15

WAKEMAN – HURON

CANFIELD, Christina Ann. 24 HYDE ST, STE A 44889 #038-01-1990 L1991 **FM** *020 †18
JENKINS, Clive Andrew. ■ 44889 #024-05-1977 L1979 **EM** *020 †16

WALBRIDGE – WOOD

MATHEWS, Anicia Zambrano. 114 N MAIN ST 43465 #748-07-1953 L1961 **FM GP** *020
RAGLOW, Paul John. ■ 43465 #016-43-1959 L1959 **R** *071 †80
SZEPIELA, Ryan Michael. ■ 43465 #038-43-2006 L2006 **PM** *012

WALNUT CREEK – HOLMES

MILLER, Jon Eric. ■ 44687 #038-43-1997 L2000 **FM** *020 †18

WALNUT HILLS – HAMILTON

JONES, Sanford Logan, Jr. 1501 MADISON RD, GREATER CINCINNATI BEHAVIO 45206 #020-12-1984 L1991 **P** *020 †75
SKALE, Tracey Goodman. 1501 MADISON RD, GREATER CINICNNATI BEHAVIO 45206 #038-41-1989 L1991 **P** *020 †75

WAPAKONETA – AUGLAIZE

CHALASANI, Venkata K. 812 REDSKIN TRL 45895 #495-99-1993 L1998 **IM** *020 †20
CRUZ, Juan J. 509 COUNTY ROAD 25A 45895 #748-01-1964 L1966 **GP AN** *071
CUMMINS, Barbara Jill. 807 GLYNWOOD RD 45895 #017-20-1963 L1964 **FM** *020 †18
FACTORA, Myrna M. 711 GIBBS AVE 45895 #748-01-1970 L1981 **CLP FM** *030
FREYTAG, Thomas Robt. 1251 LINCOLN HWY BOX 2018 45895 #038-40-1978 L1979 **FM** *020 †18
HERMAN, Parmie Andaloro. 1007 W AUGLAIZE ST 45895 #038-45-1984 L1986 **FM PLM** *020 †18
HORMAN, Deron Lee. ■ 45895 #038-43-1993 L1994 **FM** *020 †18
JACKMAN, Paul Donald. 711 GIBBS AVE 45895 #063-01-1991 L1996 *100
JOSE, Mathew M. 310 PERRY ST 45895 #495-37-1989 L1997 **FM** *020 †18
MILLS, Kyle Finnian. ■ 45895 #038-45-1992 L1993 **EM FM** *020
STIENECKER, Charles Denny. 820 GLYNWOOD RD 45895 #038-40-1962 L1962 **GP** *071

WARREN – TRUMBULL

AHMED, Nafees. 8747 SQUIRES LN NE 44484 #704-02-1959 L1978 **FM** *030
AHMED, Nazir. 1350 E MARKET ST 44483 #704-02-1961 L1972 **IM** *020 †20
AIAD-TOSS, Albert Shockry. 667 EASTLAND AVE SE 44484 #915-04-1990 L1996 **IM** *020 †20
AKPOM, Cyril Amechi. 408 DANA ST NE, STA #14B 44483 #919-01-1963 L1990 **OM GPM** *071 †70
ALAM, Ramamurthy N. 1910 E MARKET ST 44483 #495-50-1964 L1977 **IM** *020 †20
ALAPPATT, Jose L. 1350 E MARKET ST 44483 #495-31-1961 L1976 **P IM** *020 †75
ALTAWIL, Badi. 4439 MAHONING AVE NW STE A 44483 #875-01-1989 L1997 **IM** *020 †20
AMIRTHALINGAM, Kowriah N. 156 ELM RD NE 44483 #495-16-1973 L1983 **PUD CCM** *020 †20
ANDERSON, Deborah Lynn. 8720 E MARKET ST STE 1C 44484 #038-43-1981 L1984 **PD** *020 †55
ANGNARDO, Eduardo Tan. 130 TOWSON DR NW 44483 #748-01-1961 L1971 **PD IM** *071 †55
ANSTADT, David La Rue. 2512 E MARKET ST, STE B 44483 #041-13-1975 L1977 **IM OM** *020 †20
AWADALLAH, Bahaa Azmy. 3843 E MARKET ST, STE 112 44484 #915-03-1986 L1999 **IM** *020 †20
AWAIDA, Amy Beth. 1745 NILES CORTLAND RD NE, STE 5 44484 #035-08-2000 L2007 **HO** *020 †20
BAJI, Sudhir G. 1700 E MARKET ST 44483 #495-21-1965 L1976 **U GS** *020 †95
BAKY, Emad Shawky. 627 EASTLAND AVE SE, WOMENS CARE CTR 44484 #915-04-1980 L1999 **OBG** *020 †30
BALLESTER, Pedro Antonio. 1405 E MARKET ST 44483 #042-01-1981 L1989 **FM AN** *020 †05,18
BARTON, Nichole V. ■ 44484 #003-75-2007, ▲ L2007 *012
BASCIANO, Rocco J. 1460 TOD AVE NW 44485 #016-43-1979 L1981 **IM IMG** *020 †20
BAUTISTA-BUSTAMANTE, O. 1350 E MARKET ST 44483 #748-01-1962 L1977 **IM** *020
BEHARI, Vijay Bans. 1700 E MARKET ST STE 101 44484 #495-45-1966 L1971 **CD IM** *020 †20
BENNETT, Robert Campbell. 1350 E MARKET ST 44483 #038-43-1988 L1993 **PTH** *020 †50
BERENHOLZ, Leonard Paul. 3893 E MARKET ST, WARREN OFFICE 44484 #041-09-1983 L1998 **OTO** *020 †45
BHATTI, Masud-Ur-Rehman. 1745 NILES CORTLAND RD NE, STE 5 44484 #704-02-1965 L1973 **ON HEM** *020 †20
BLASS, Leonard P. 1350 E MARKET ST 44483 #016-11-1979 L1980 **ID IM** *020 †20
BRENNAN, Ronald Patrick. 667 EASTLAND AVE SE, ST. JOSEPH'S HOSPITAL 44484 #041-09-1984 L1986 **DR** *020 †80 ‡
BRODELL, James David. 2614 E MARKET ST 44483 #038-06-1978 L1982 **ORS** *020 †40
BRODELL, Linda Prichard. 2660 E MARKET ST 44483 #035-45-1981 L1985 **OPH** *020 †35
BRODELL, Robert Thos. 2660 E MARKET ST 44483 #035-45-1979 L1985 **D DMP** *020 †15 ‡
BROWN, John Harold. 3921 E MARKET ST 44484 #041-02-1974 L1988 **PS GS** *020 †85,65

BRYS, David Alan. 1806 E MARKET ST, BRYS ORTHOPEDICS 44483 #038-40-1982 L1988 **ORS OSM** *062 †40
BURNS, Joseph E. 1806 E MARKET ST 44483 #038-06-1946 L1946 **ORS** *071 †40
BUSTAMANTE, Divino U. 1350 E MARKET ST 44483 #748-08-1959 L1976 **IM** *071
BUTCHER, Suzanne Amelia R. TRUMBULL MEM HOSP 44482 #036-07-1965 L1967 **PTH** *020 †50
BUTLER, Edward Thos, Jr. 8747 SQUIRES LN NE, HILLSIDE REHABILITATION HO 44484 #035-09-1967 L1971 **PM** *020 †60
CAIRNS, Jean Anne. 1651 E MARKET ST 44483 #038-44-1998 L2000 **OBG** *020 †30
CASTILLEJO, Raymundo A. 1934 NILES CORTLAND RD NE 44484 #748-11-1972 L1990 **AN** *020 †05
CHAVES, Fernando G. 1421 E MARKET ST, PULMONARY MED 44483 #308-03-1981 L1986 **PUD IM** *020 †20
CHUIRAZZI, Christopher C. 9375 E MARKET ST, STE 1 44484 #038-40-1993 L1994 **IM** *020 †20
CONEY, Joseph Michael. 3919 E MARKET ST, RETINA ASSOCIATES OF 44484 #016-43-1999 L2000 **OPH** *100 †35
CORNICELLI, Samuel F, Jr. ■ 44485 #038-44-1986 L1991 **ORS** *020
CROSBY, Lori Ann. 1745 NILES CORTLAND RD NE, STE 5 44484 #038-45-1998 L2000 **HO** *020 †20
CUESTA, Julio Enrique. ■ 44484 #275-01-1956 L1964 **GP OS** *071
D'AMICO, Lawrence M, Jr. 8601 E MARKET ST 44484 #038-45-1989 L1994 **GS** *020 †85
DANGARAN, Artemio Juario. 1350 E MARKET ST 44483 #748-01-1963 L1970 **IM** *071
DAYAL, Bimleshwar. 1934 NILES CORTLAND RD NE 44484 #495-15-1974 L1982 **NPM** *020 †55,05
DEAN, Rosanna Deborah. 7116 TOD AVE SW 44481 #038-45-2000 L2000 **FM** *020 †18
DEMACOPOULOS, Nicola D. 1950 NILES CORTLAND RD NE, STE 7 44484 #038-44-1989 L1992 **IM** *020 †20
DESAI, Cecil F. 1988 PARKMAN RD NW 44485 #495-22-1974 L1979 **PD** *020 †55
DE SALVO, Anthony Ross. 1842 E MARKET ST 44483 #038-44-1995 L1996 **OBG** *020 †30
ERZURUM, Sergul Ayse. 199 NILES CORTLAND RD SE, EYE CARE ASSOCIATES INC 44484 #038-44-1988 L1989 **OPH** *020 †35
FACCINI, Kathryn Lorraine. 667 EASTLAND AVE SE, CANCER CARE CTR 44484 #048-15-1987 L2000 **IM** *020 †20
FAOUR, Mahmoud Ali. ■ 44483 #605-02-1963 L1985 **GS** *075
FARMER, Tonia Lorraine. 3893 E MARKET ST 44484 #051-04-1996 L2001 **OTO** *020 †45
FREDERICKA, David N. 1753 E MARKET ST, APT 1 44483 #016-43-1974 L1976 **CD IM** *020 †20
GAMAD, Romulo Robledo, Jr. 667 EASTLAND AVE SE 44484 #748-08-1963 L1974 **IM** *075
GANTA, Vishnu V. ■ 44484 #306-01-2005 L2007 **PTH** *012
GASKINS, Christopher Alan. 1350 E MARKET ST, TRUMBULL MEMORIAL HOSPITAL 44483 #038-41-1993 L1994 **EM** *020 †16
GERMANIUK, Humphrey Don. 1863 E MARKET ST 44483 #561-20-1984 L1987 **FOP PTH** *020 †50
GONZALEZ-CASTRO, Antonio. 8098 E MARKET ST 44484 #847-13-1974 L1981 **N** *020 †75
GOODWIN, Fareedah Z. 8700 E MARKET ST STE 4 44484 #038-44-2002 L2002 **FM** *020 †18
GOROSPE, Alfredo Reyes. 1400 TOD AVE NW DEPT PTH 44485 #748-02-1963 L1970 **PTH** *020 †50
GRACILLA, Ranulfo V. 1350 E MARKET ST 44483 #748-01-1953 L1964 **ORS** *071 †40
GRIMA, John Anthony. ■ 44483 #028-34-1943 L1948 **GS** *071 †85
GURDAK, Robert George. 1350 E MARKET ST 44483 #028-34-1982 L1987 **PTH PCP** *020 †50
GURSKY, Andrei. 1350 E MARKET ST, TRUMBULL MEMORIAL HOSP FOR 44483 #422-01-1998 L1999 **GS** *100 †85
GURUMURTHY, K. 8720 E MARKET ST, HUNTERS SQUARE PLAZA 44484 #495-66-1974 L1983 **PD PN** *020 †55
GUTTIKONDA, Prasad B. 1192 NORTH RD NE, DBA: WILLIAM BECKETT & ASS 44483 #495-57-1972 L1982 **P** *020 ‡
HABIB, Shawki Nagib. 611 EASTLAND AVE SE 44484 #330-02-1964 L1975 **CD** *020 †20
HADDAD, Ayham Yousef. 628 NILES CORTLAND RD SE, STE 103 44483 #875-02-1990 L2000 **IM** *020 ‡
HART, Rick Anthony. 213 PERKINSWOOD 44483 #038-45-1985 L1987 **GP** *020
HASHMI, Yasmeen Ferzana. 667 EASTLAND AVE SE 44484 #704-01-1971 L1985 **GP PTH** *020
HAUN, James Charles. 311 NILES CORTLAND RD NE 44484 #038-44-1993 L1994 **FM** *020 †18
HECKER, Engelbert. ■ 44484 #407-25-1951 L1959 **R** *071 †80
HELMS, Amy Elizabeth. ■ 44484 #023-12-2007 L2007 **IM** *012
HELMS, Stephen Ellsworth. 735 NILES CORTLAND RD SE, WARREN DERM & ALLERGY 44484 #038-40-1973 L1974 **D** *020 †15
HELWIG, Robert Gerard. 2660 E MARKET ST, BRODELL MEDICAL, INC 44483 #038-43-1984 L1987 **OPH IM** *020 †35,20
HENNON, Shaun Adrian. 1934 NILES CORTLAND RD NE 44484 #041-07-1985 L1987 **AN** *020 †05
HILL, Philip Edward. ■ 44484 #016-11-1963 L1989 **CD IM** *071 †20
HOUT, Wahoub M. 611 EASTLAND AVE SE 44484 #605-01-1983 L1988 **CD** *020 †20
JAMES, Thomas Emrys, Jr. 1350 E MARKET ST, TRUMBULL MEMORIAL HOSP 44483 #038-40-1970 L1970 **IM** *030 †20
JONES, Kenneth Earl. 1552 NORTH RD SE, STE 101 44484 #038-40-1994 L1998 **ORS** *020 †40 ‡
JONES, Michael Anthony. 1552 NORTH RD SE STE 101 44484 #041-77-2001, ▲ L2006 **ORS** *020
JONES, Thomas Benj, Jr. 1552 NORTH RD SE, STE 101 44484 #041-13-1987 L1991 **ORS** *020 †40 ‡
KALIA, Judith. 247 HOMEWOOD AVE SE 44483 #917-18-1972 L1994 **OBG** *020 †30
KALLMAN, Kathy Marie. 1350 E MARKET ST, TRUMBULL MEMORIAL HOSPITAL 44483 #038-44-1995 L1998 **EM** *020 †16
KAVANAGH, Joseph Edward T. 2660 SOUTH ST SE 44483 #539-05-1966 L1971 **P** *020
KELOTRA, Bharat. 1700 E MARKET ST, STE 114 44483 #495-20-1966 L1974 **GS** *020 †85
KESHAVA REDDY, Gundarpi H. ■ 44484 #495-09-1965 L1973 **NS** *020 †25
KHAN, Mujahid Husain. 1244 E MARKET ST 44483 #704-02-1962 L1978 **IM** *020 †20
KHANUJA, Kartar Singh. 1700 E MARKET ST 44483 #495-20-1962 L1975 **GE IM** *020
KHANUJA, Ranjit Kaur. 8052 E MARKET ST 44484 #495-01-1967 L1978 **IM PTH** *020
KHATERPAUL, Subhash. 735 NILES CORTLAND RD SE, STE 2 44484 #495-76-1976 L1995 **IM** *020 †20
KHAVARI, Mohammad Reza. 1227 E MARKET ST 44483 #517-01-1960 L1968 **OBG** *075 †30
KHAVARI, Parisa. 1227 E MARKET ST 44483 #038-40-1989 L1993 **OBG** *020 †30
KHOURY, Ronald. 8790 E MARKET ST, STE 100 44484 #561-06-1970 L1989 **GS** *020 †85
KIM, Chang Hun. 1934 NILES CORTLAND RD NE 44484 #583-01-1970 L1980 **AN** *020 †05
KIM, Hyo Hwan. 1552 NORTH RD SE 44484 #583-01-1982 L1988 **PM PME** *020 †60
KIM, Jin K. ■ 44484 #583-08-1981 L1986 **P** *020
KISTLER, Cara Ruth. ■ 44481 #038-43-2005 L2005 **IM** *012

KNIGHT, Chris Allan. 1745 NILES CORTLAND RD NE, STE 5 44484 #038-40-1979 L1980 ON HEM *020 †20

KO, Nam Kyu. 1507 E MARKET ST 44483 #583-02-1968 L1982 U *020 †95

KONDOLIOS, James Harry. 2625 E MARKET ST, KONDOLIOS & ASSOICATES INC 44483 #038-06-1995 L1997 IM *020 †20

KONDOLIOS, Pete Elias. 321 NILES CORTLAND RD NE 44484 #038-44-1990 L1991 PD *020 †55

KONDOLIOS, Zenovia. 321 NILES CORTLAND RD NE 44484 #038-06-1998 L2000 PD *020

KOSTRABA, Andrew John. ■ 44483 #038-40-2001 L2001 MPD *100 †20,55

KRISHNARAO, Desai Gopala. 735 NILES CORTLAND RD SE, ALLERGY 44484 #495-70-1974 L1980 AI IM *020 †20,03

KRISHNARAO, Indira. 735 NILES CORTLAND RD SE, ALLERGY 44484 #495-17-1977 L1983 D *020 †15

KUMAR, Ashok G. 8052 E MARKET ST 44484 #495-31-1962 L1972 IM *020 †20

KURUP, Siva Prasad. 1350 E MARKET ST 44483 #495-41-1963 L1973 P *020 †75

KURZ, Frederick Gottlieb. 1934 NILES CORTLAND RD NE 44484 #038-43-1985 L1986 AN *020 †05

KWATRA, Kapil. 9375 E MARKET ST STE 2, MEDICAL ASSOC OF WARREN, I 44484 #495-85-1980 L1995 IM *020 †20

LABIB, Atef Sobhi. 611 EASTLAND AVE SE 44484 #915-02-1970 L1980 CD IM *020 †20

LAINEZ-LOZADA, Cesar. 1234 E MARKET ST 44483 #737-01-1955 L1969 IM CD *071

LANEY, Lee Clark. 1622 E MARKET ST, THE GASTOR CLINIC & ENDOSC 44483 #047-07-1977 L1983 GE IM *050

LA POLLA, James Jos. 8588 E MARKET ST 44484 #036-07-1961 L1962 PD *030 †55

LA TORRE, L Donald, Jr. 1934 NILES CORTLAND RD NE 44484 #025-07-1988 L1997 AN PME *020 †05

LEE, Young Keun. 627 EASTLAND AVE SE, WOMENS CARE CTR STE 301 44484 #583-03-1968 L1976 OBG *071

LIELBRIEDIS, George Lind. 1543 E MARKET ST 44483 #407-02-1951 L1958 P CHP *071

LIMPEROS, Nicholas Anthon. ■ 44483 #038-44-2006 L2006 GS *012

LIPPY, William Henry. 3893 E MARKET ST, WARREN OTOLOGIC GROUP INC 44484 #038-40-1954 L1954 OTO NO †45

LOGAN, Joseph L. 1350 E MARKET ST 44483 #010-03-1951 L1952 GP *071

LYNCH, William Stafford. 735 NILES CORTLAND RD SE, ALLERGY 44484 #010-01-1970 L1973 D *020 †15

MAGGIDO, Holly Josephine. 983 NILES CORTLAND RD SE 44484 #038-43-1989 L1993 N *020 †75

MAHJOUB, Mazen. 9375 E MARKET ST, STE 3 44484 #875-02-1986 L1997 CD *020 †20

MANGALJI, Zulfikar S. 1244 E MARKET ST 44484 #905-01-1972 L1978 IM *020 †20

MARSH, David George, Jr. ■ 44484 #038-44-2006 ORS *012

MARTUCCIO, James Vincent. 302 NILES CORTLAND RD NE 44484 #038-44-1987 L1988 OPH *020 †35

MASTERS, William Edward. 5000 E MARKET ST, STE 18 44484 #041-09-1957 L1958 AN *071 †05

MATHIAS, Charles Wilfred. 1350 E MARKET ST 44483 #038-06-1940 L1940 OS NTR *071

MC CHESNEY, Jason Paul. 3893 E MARKET ST, NORTHMAR CENTER II 44484 #038-06-1997 L2002 OTO *020 †45 ‡

MC CLAIN, Jeffrey Richard. ■ 44484 #041-12-1997 L1999 GS *020

MC GUIRE, Thaddeus David. 2760 PARKMAN RD NW 44485 #038-40-1956 L1956 GP *071

MC MANNIS, Michael Glen. 1934 NILES CORTLAND RD NE 44484 #016-11-2000 L2004 AN *020 †05

MEHRABI, Yousef. 2512 E MARKET ST 44483 #517-06-1968 L1978 PD HEM *050 †55

MEHTA, Paresh Girdharlal. 2390 PARKMAN RD NW, PARKMAN ROAD MED ASSOC 44485 #496-38-1983 L1992 OBG *020 †30

MEMULA, Narayana Goud. 1353 E MARKET ST, IRELAND CANCER CTR 44483 #495-21-1974 L2005 RO GP *020 †80

MERKIN, Bruce Jeffrey. ■ 44484 #410-02-1982 L2004 IM *075 †20

MIKHAIL, Heba Louis. 3843 E MARKET ST, STE 112 44484 #915-04-1993 L2000 IM *020 †20

MIKULA, Justin Paul. 1615 N RIVER RD NE, STE 1 44484 #038-06-2002 L2002 IM *020 †20

MILLER, Madeline Darlene. 1934 NILES CORTLAND RD NE 44484 #047-06-1978 L1984 AN PD *020 †55,05

MITROO, Neeta. 1934 NILES CORTLAND RD NE 44484 #496-07-1964 L1979 AN *020 †05

MOHAPATRA, Basanta Kumar. 1934 NILES CORTLAND RD NE 44484 #495-13-1990 L2000 CCA *020 †05

MOKGETHI, Sonia Botlhale. 1934 NILES CORTLAND RD NE 44484 #008-02-1996 L2005 AN *020 †05

MONDARY, Natalie. 1651 E MARKET ST 44483 #038-44-1997 L1998 OBG *020 †30

MOSKOWITZ, Jesse Brit. ■ 44484 #473-01-2001 L2002 GS *012

MUSSER, Guy R. 1350 E MARKET ST 44483 #041-02-1953 L1958 OBG *020

NADDOUR, Fadi. 1353 E MARKET ST, HEART AND VASCULAR CLINIC 44483 #875-01-1991 L2001 IC CD *020 †20

NAFFAH, Farid. 9225 E MARKET ST 44484 #035-46-1982 L1988 GE IM *020 †20

NAGHIBI-SHAIBANI, Parvin. 1032 E MARKET ST 44483 #517-05-1965 L1985 PD *020 †55

NATH, Sarita Sharha. 1934 NILES CORTLAND RD NE 44484 #495-49-1977 L1984 AN *020

NEUMAN, Thomas Raymond. 349 NILES CORTLAND RD NE 44484 #025-07-1988 L1996 OTO *020 †45

NEWMAN, Nigel Kevin. 3921 E MARKET ST, FL 2CD 44484 #041-12-1967 L1967 OPH OS *071 ‡

NIMMAGADDA, Haranadha B. ■ 44484 #495-58-1964 L1979 OPH GP *020 †35

NISSEN, Rolf-Guenther. 920 PERKINSWOOD BLVD SE 44484 #407-15-1953 L1960 IM OM *071

NORCHI, Charles Howard. ■ 44484 #539-11-1956 L1959 AN OS *071

O'BRIEN, Garrett. 546 WASHINGTON ST SW 44483 #011-02-1968 L1974 N *020

OCHOA, Fabio. 5000 E MARKET ST, STE 18 44484 #264-05-1964 L1972 IM RHU *020

OLOWOYEYE, John Olubunmi. ■ 44484 #690-01-1972 L1990 CD IM *020 †20

OWEN, William Spurlock. ■ 44483 #012-05-1954 L1968 N *071 †25

PADUBIDRI, Arvind Narayan. 1924 E MARKET ST 44483 #495-72-1982 L1999 PS HS *020 †65

PAI-DHUNGAT, Asheesh A. 1930 NILES CORTLAND RD NE 44484 #496-15-1994 L1999 FM *020 †18

PARRIS, Herbert Arthur. 8747 SQUIRES LN NE, HILLSIDE REHAB. HOSPITAL 44484 #010-03-1968 L1974 PM RHU *020 †60

PATCHEN, Patrick Nelson. 8601 E MARKET ST 44484 #041-02-1989 L1994 GS *020 †85

PATEL, Harish Keshavlal. 1704 NORTH RD SE, STE B 44484 #495-22-1976 L2004 P *020 †75

PATEL, Jagdish Hariprasad. 1455 PARKMAN RD NW 44485 #495-96-1971 L1978 GP *020

PATEL, Usha. ■ 44484 #495-23-1973 P *075

PENCE, Robert Edward. ■ 44484 #041-01-1954 L1963 PTH HEM *071 †50

PERNI, Veeraiah C. 1934 NILES CORTLAND RD NE 44484 #495-50-1970 L1978 AN PME *020 †05

PERSON, Donald Lewis. 1934 NILES CORTLAND RD NE 44484 #036-01-1981 L1982 AN *020 †05

PETTENATI, Angela Marie. 1350 E MARKET ST 44484 #038-44-2000 L2001 PD *020 †55 ‡

PHEN, Lovsho. 8747 SQUIRES LN NE 44484 #495-20-1976 L1987 IM *020

PHIPPS, William. ■ 44484 #038-44-2000 L2000 CCS *020

PILGER, Lawrence Geo. 667 EASTLAND AVE SE 44484 #038-41-1963 L1963 IM *020 †20

POLLIS, Steven A. 2760 PARKMAN RD NW 44485 #038-40-1956 L1956 GP *071

PRINCE, Benjamin Thomas. ■ 44481 #038-43-2008 *012

RAGHEB, Essam Shafik. 5901 MAHONING AVE NW 44483 #915-04-1979 L1985 IM *020 †20

RAGHEB, Nevine Tawfik. 5901 MAHONING AVE NW 44483 #915-02-1987 L2000 IM *020 †20

RAMMOHAN, Muthuramalingam. 1700 E MARKET ST STE 108 44483 #495-66-1968 L1976 IM END *020 †20

RAO, Sudhakar V. 1821 E MARKET ST 44483 #495-65-1963 L1979 PDC PD *020 †55

RASHID, Mohammad. 1451 E MARKET ST 44483 #704-09-1972 L1988 GS *020 †85

RAYMUNDO, Emmanuel Le Duc. ■ 44483 #748-01-1964 L1971 IM *075

REEVES, William Geo. 1745 NILES CORTLAND RD NE, STE 5 44484 #035-15-1978 L1984 ON HEM *020 †20

RICOTTI, Carlos Alberto. 1373 E MARKET ST 44483 #132-02-1972 L1977 GE *020 †20

ROBERTS, Michael Keith. 1400 TOD AVE NW 44483 #038-44-1999 L2000 FM *020 †18

ROUWEYHA, Marwan Riad. ■ 44484 #605-02-1962 L1977 ORS *071

RUSSELL, Theodore Albert. ■ 44484 #038-06-1956 L1956 U OS *071 †95

SAADI, Elias Tufic. 3921 E MARKET ST, OHIO HEART INSTITUTE INC 44484 #010-02-1957 L1957 CD *071 †20

SALIB, Louis Girgis. 1934 NILES CORTLAND RD NE 44484 #915-02-1974 L1990 AN PME *020 †05

SARGIOUS, Ehab L. 2000 E MARKET ST 44483 #915-04-1986 L1998 P *020 †75

SARGIOUS, Nabila Lamey. 2000 E MARKET ST 44483 #915-04-1983 L2001 P *020

SARKOS, Lewis Peter. 2400 NILES CORTLAND RD SE 44484 #028-34-1958 L1964 OTO *071 †45

SAUNDERS, Marc S. 627 EASTLAND AVE SE, STE 302 44484 #035-75-1987, ▲ L1993 GS *020 †85

SCHAFFER, Robert Irwin. ■ 44484 #025-01-1967 L1975 OTO GS *071 †45

SCHNUR, Kathryn Cook. 1350 E MARKET ST 44483 #032-01-1978 L1984 GS *020 †85

SCHURING, Arnold Garth. 3893 E MARKET ST, WARREN OFFICE 44484 #025-01-1961 L1962 OTO NO *071 †45

SHAH, Vijaykumar S. ■ 44484 #495-23-1989 L1998 IM *020 †20

SHEIK, Zafar Ahamedshah. 3921 E MARKET ST, SECOND FLOOR 44484 #038-43-1996 L2001 OPH *020 †35

SHENOY, Ashok Narayan. 1934 NILES CORTLAND RD NE 44484 #495-37-1978 L2004 AN *020 †05

SHESHADRI, Haruvu N. 8747 SQUIRES LN NE, DEPT OF RADIOLOGY 44484 #495-21-1963 L1973 R *062 †80

SHETH, Ramona. 2760 PARKMAN RD NW 44485 #038-41-1999 L1999 IM *020 †20

SHETH, Sanjay Yogesh. 2760 PARKMAN RD NW 44485 #654-01-2002 L2002 IM *020 †20

SHILEY, Janet Lee. 983 NILES CORTLAND RD SE 44484 #038-44-1987 L1990 GS *020 †85 ‡

SHIN, Han Soo. 667 EASTLAND AVE SE 44484 #583-02-1959 L1971 R *020 †80

SINGERMAN, Lawrence Jay. 3919 E MARKET ST, RETINA ASSOCIATES OF 44484 #025-07-1969 L1970 OPH *020 †35

SINOFF, Clive Leonard. 8740 E MARKET ST STE 2 44484 #836-01-1973 L1993 PMM IM *020

SNITZER, Michael Thos. 735 NILES CORTLAND RD SE 44484 #038-44-1991 L1993 IM *020

SOBOSLAY, Theodore W. 1863 E MARKET ST 44483 #407-02-1958 L1964 IM LM *020

SORRELL, Meredith Earl. 1650 BONNIE BRAE AVE NE 44483 #038-41-1954 L1954 PD *071 †55

STARR, Philip A, III. 611 EASTLAND AVE SE, STE C 44484 #038-75-1995, ▲ L2001 FM *040

STERLE, Oscar Francisco. 321 NILES CORTLAND RD NE 44484 #132-01-1963 L1972 ORS *020 †40

STRICKLAND, Sylvia Louise. ■ 44485 #038-40-1969 L1970 OS PD *071 †55

SUDHEENDRA, R. 4100 YOUNGSTOWN RD SE 44484 #495-09-1965 L1976 TS CD *020 †85

SUDIMACK, James Michael. 1350 E MARKET ST, ATTN: EMERGENCY DEPARTMENT 44483 #038-40-1984 L1986 EM *020 †16

SULLIVAN, Esther E. 438 N PARK AVE 44481 #035-06-1943 L1946 GP OS *071

TANDRA, Brahmaiah. 8577 E MARKET ST 44484 #495-14-1973 L1993 P CHP *020 †75

TARESHAWTY, Eugene F, Jr. 1745 NILES CORTLAND RD NE, STE 5 44484 #308-03-1987 L1989 IM PLM *020 †20

TAYLOR, Robert Wade. ■ 44484 #036-07-1957 L1966 NS *071 †25

THOMPSON, Helen Mary. 8747 SQUIRES LN NE 44484 #025-01-1941 L1943 IM IMG *071

TORREM, Isaac. 1534 E MARKET ST 44483 #550-01-1974 L1980 OPH IM *020 †35 ‡

TORRES, Emilita F. 1700 E MARKET ST 44483 #748-01-1968 L1979 OBG *020

TRUONG, Thong Gia. 461 NILES CORTLAND RD SE 44484 #306-01-1997 L2000 IM *020 †20

UNALAN, Ferruh. 2697 YOUNGSTOWN RD SE 44484 #902-10-1950 L1966 IM *075

URAM, Marc H. 1934 NILES CORTLAND RD NE 44484 #041-09-1975 L1984 AN *020 †05

VANCE, John David. 1350 E MARKET ST 44483 #038-06-1981 L1984 IM *020 †20

VARGO, Frank Paul. 2400 PARKMAN RD NW 44485 #038-40-1955 L1955 IM PD *020

VENETTA, Columbus Mario. 2239 E MARKET ST 44483 #038-40-1955 L1955 GS *071 †85

VILLAREAL, Domingo P. 667 EASTLAND AVE SE 44484 #748-08-1957 L1967 AN *071

VINCI, Giovanna Khoury. 8790 E MARKET ST, STE 300 44484 #561-06-1976 L1989 CHP PD *020

VISWANATHAN, Pushpa A. 8720 E MARKET ST, PEDIATRIC CARE ASSOC INC 44484 #495-31-1995 L2001 PDE *012 †55

WASSIL, John George, III. ■ 44481 #041-12-1994 L2000 PM *020 †60

WEITZEL, Richard Leonard. 2219 E MARKET ST 44483 #041-14-1981 L1986 CD IM *075 †20

WINDOM, Reginald Odester. ■ 44485 #008-01-1986 L1990 PTH IM *020

WOODRUFF, Robert W, Jr. 627 EASTLAND AVE SE # 302 44484 #034-01-1993 L1998 GS *020 †20

WU, Haw-Chyr. 1353 E MARKET ST 44483 #385-01-1966 L1971 P *075 †75

YANTES, Edmond Kiefer. ■ 44484 #041-02-1942 L1943 IM *071

YARLAGADDA, Srinivasa C. 611 EASTLAND AVE SE 44484 #496-24-1991 L2000 CD *020 †20

YOUNG, Amy Rice. 8720 E MARKET ST 44484 #038-40-1985 L1987 PD *020 †55

YOUSSEF, Adel I M. 1622 E MARKET ST 44483 #915-02-1977 L1989 GE PTH *020 †20

YOUSSEF, Mona Abdel-Halim. 1954 ELM RD NE 44483 #915-04-1986 L2001 CD *020 †20

YUMANG, Servillano Yamat. 8098 E MARKET ST 44484 #748-01-1955 L1967 GS AS *020 ‡

ZAKOV, Zvetan Nikolov. 3919 E MARKET ST, RETINA ASSOCIATES OF 44484 #035-01-1970 L1973 OPH OS *020 †35

ZARRINMAKAN, Mehrdad. 8952 E MARKET ST 44484 #917-02-1991 L2000 TS *020 †85,90

WARRENSVILLE HEIGHTS – CUYAHOGA

BROOKS, Barry Howard. 20050 HARVARD AVE, STE 107 44122 #024-01-1976 L1977 IM OS *020

BROWN, Leon A, Jr. 20000 HARVARD AVE 44122 #035-08-1968 L1976 PTH *020 †50
ERKINS, Johnny Mack. 20050 HARVARD AVE, STE 300 44122 #038-06-1976 L1977 OBG *020 †30
GLINER, Boris. 4200 WARRNSVL CNTR RD #430 44122 #913-82-1977 L1986 IM *020 †20
KILGORE, Sony Pamela. 20000 HARVARD AVE 44122 #025-01-1997 L1999 HMP *020 †50
MAHONEY, Stephen A, III. 20050 HARVARD AVE, STE 207 44122 #024-07-1958 L1959 U LM *030 †95
UNGER, Jeffrey Scott. 20000 HARVARD AVE, SOUTHSIDE RADIOLOGY ASSOC, 44122 #024-07-1987 L1991 DR *020 †80

WARSAW – COSHOCTON

BAIG, Mohammad Arif. 221 RAILROAD ST, WARSAW MEDICAL CLINIC 43844 #704-01-1985 L1998 IM *020
HAMZA, Mohamed H. 221 RAILROAD ST 43844 #875-02-1989 L1996 IM *020 †20

WASHINGTON COURT HOUSE – FAYETTE

AL-YAMOUR, Adil Younis. 4 COMMERCIAL AVE 43160 #902-10-1962 L1982 GS GP *020
ANDERSON, Robert U. 43160 #017-20-1952 L1954 GP *072
CARVER, Joseph Claude. ■ 43160 #649-14-1981 L1991 OBG *020
CHAN, Kevin K W. 2 COMMERCIAL AVE 43160 #385-02-1965 L1973 PD *071 †55
HAJJAR, Victor. 1430 COLUMBUS AVE, STE 320 43160 #875-01-1999 L2001 IM *020
HALLIDAY, Penelope Ann. 403 E MARKET ST 43160 #038-40-1979 L1981 FM *020 †18
HANCOCK, Thomas John. ■ 43160 #038-06-1943 L1944 GS *071 †85
HEINY, Robert Alvin. 1430 COLUMBUS AVE, HOSPITAL 43160 #038-40-1955 L1955 FM *071 †18
HODGES, Mark William. 1450 COLUMBUS AVE, STE 201 43160 #038-40-1998 L1999 IM *020 †20
HORNICK, Anthony Michael. 1165 STORYBROOK DR 43160 #019-02-1978 L1993 GS *020 †85
HUNG, Cheng-Haw. 1450 COLUMBUS AVE, STE 105 43160 #385-02-1963 L1971 IM *020 †20
KLAMET, Frank X. 1450 COLUMBUS AVE, STE 106 43160 #038-06-1995 L1996 FM OBS *020 †18
LETTVIN, Daniel Stuart. 1300 E PAINT ST 43160 #016-11-1986 L1988 P *020 †75
LEVY, Susan Joy. 1300 E PAINT ST 43160 #038-41-1980 L1980 CHP P *020 †75
LORENTE, Abdiel. 1450 COLUMBUS AVE, STE 104 43160 #041-13-1967 L1976 GS VS *071 †85
PALUSIAK, Maritza. 1430 COLUMBUS AVE 43160 #264-04-1974 L2002 GE IM *020 †20
RANPURA, Lalit G. 1430 COLUMBUS AVE 43160 #495-48-1965 L1973 AN *020
RENO, Dale Edward. 1005 E TEMPLE ST 43160 #038-40-1978 L1983 FM *020 †18
ROSADO, David Alejandro. 207 GLENN AVE 43160 #042-01-1984 L1992 OBG *020
ROSZMANN, Marvin Henry. ■ 43160 #038-40-1941 L1941 GP AN *071
SHAW, Mary Louise. 1430 COLUMBUS AVE 43160 #038-40-1981 L1983 FM *020 †18
STEVENSON, William Cage. 1450 COLUMBUS AVE, STE 106 43160 #038-40-1981 L1981 GS *020 †85
YAMOUR, Beverly J D. 4 COMMERCIAL AVE 43160 #020-02-1971 L1982 CD IM *020 †18,20

WASHINGTON TOWNSHIP – MONTGOMERY

ACKNER, Stephanie Elise. ■ 45459 #038-45-2002 L2002 P *020

WATERVILLE – LUCAS

BAZELEY, Stephen Poll. 900 WATERVILLE MONCLOVA RD, STE A 43566 #038-43-1974 L1976 FM *020 †18
BRUSS, Andrea Kathryn. 900 WATERVILLE MONCLOVA RD 43566 #038-41-2004 L2004 FM *020 †18
BRUSS, Mark Richard. 900 WATERVILLE MONCLOVA RD, STE A 43566 #038-43-1974 L1975 FM *020 †18 ‡
BRUSS, Patrick Mark. ■ 43566 #038-41-2007 L2007 EM *012
DUCK, Marymargar Rose. 1121 WESTRIDGE DR 43566 #038-41-2008 *012
FAZEKAS, Renate Katrin. 139 SOUTH ST 43566 #407-20-1960 L1971 FOP OBG *100 †50
GOVEIA, Crystal Rose. 900 WATERVILLE MONCLOVA RD, STE A 43566 #496-38-1969 L1975 FM PD *040 †55,18
GRAFF, Russell Jay. ■ 43566 #038-43-1996 L1997 FM *020 †18
PODINS, Ojars. ■ 43566 #594-01-1936 L1955 FM *071
RIGAL, R Danl. ■ 43566 #038-40-1956 L1956 PTH PCP *071 †50
SIDERS, Rebecca Lynn. 900 WATERVILLE MONCLOVA RD 43566 #038-75-2001, ▲ L2001 *020
SIDO, Robert Leroy. 900 WATERVILLE MONCLOVA RD, STE A 43566 #038-40-1963 L1963 FM GP *071 †18
WAGNER, Ryan Scott. ■ 43566 #038-43-2008 *012

WAUSEON – FULTON

ARVILLE, John E, Jr. 725 S SHOOP AVE 43567 #748-01-1965 L1977 DR *020 †80
BARBER, Ted Edward. 725 S SHOOP AVE 43567 #038-43-1980 L1989 N EM *020
BOURN, Jana Lyn. ■ 43567 #038-45-2004 L2004 FM *020 †18
DAVID, Charles. 725 S SHOOP AVE, FULTON COUNTY HEALTH CENTE 43567 #748-08-1981 L1988 EM IM *020 †18
DAVIS, Richard Lee. 137 S FULTON ST 43567 #038-40-1960 L1960 GP *071
ELLIOTT, Francis E. 43567 #038-06-1944 L1944 OBG GP *071
FREDERICK, Scott Alan. 447 N SHOOP AVE 43567 #038-43-2001 L2001 IM *020
GALANI, Jayantilal Devshi. 447 N SHOOP AVE 43567 #495-48-1970 L1977 IM *020
GRIESER, Richard Jon. 495 S SHOOP AVE 43567 #038-41-1983 L1984 FM *020 †18
HAGERMAN, Kimberly Loann. 128 DEPOT ST 43567 #038-43-1998 L1999 FM *020 †18 ‡
ISSA, Ramon Antony. 725 S SHOOP AVE, WAUSEON FAMILY PRACTICE 43567 #005-12-2001 L2001 FM *020 †18
KAHALEH, M Bashar. 725 S SHOOP AVE 43567 #875-01-1972 L1975 RHU IM *020 †20
KAMP, Kenton James. 725 S SHOOP AVE 43567 #065-06-1992 L1994 FM *020 †18
KATTAR, Rajendra Rao. 734 S SHOOP AVE 43567 #056-06-1990 L1998 CD *020 †20
MANGEN, Mary Jane. 725 S SHOOP AVE 5TH FL, FULTON CNTY HLTH CTR 43567 #038-43-1988 L1989 P CHP *020 †75

MC CLARREN, Rebecca Sloan. 495 S SHOOP AVE 43567 #038-40-1980 L1983 FM *020 †18
MC KERNAN, Daniel John. 735 S SHOOP AVE, WEST SIDE ORTHOPEDIC 43567 #051-01-1986 L1995 OSM *020 †40 ‡
MIQUIABAS, Estela T. 725 S SHOOP AVE 43567 #748-01-1970 L1974 PTH *071 †50
MORGAN, Alexander Eugene. 725 S SHOOP AVE, FULTON COUNTY HEALTH CENTE 43567 #041-15-2002 L2006 OPH *100
NEUBERGER, Sally Vogel. ■ 43567 #038-06-1977 IM *100
SCHECHT, Howard Morris. 725 S SHOOP AVE 43567 #038-43-1990 L1992 N *020 †75
SENGUPTA, Dipak Kumar. 725 S SHOOP AVE, P O BOX 506 43567 #495-32-1959 L1974 GS *071 †85
SPIELES, Christopher Jos. 735 S SHOOP AVE, WEST SIDE ORTHOPEDIC 43567 #038-41-1992 L1996 ORS *020 †40
URIBES, Anthony Gilbert. 128 DEPOT ST 43567 #038-40-2000 L2000 FM *020 †18 ‡
VANDER MEER, Peter Jos. 725 S SHOOP AVE 43567 #025-01-1979 L1984 OTO *020 †45
WEIGAND, Truman F, Jr. 725 S SHOOP AVE, 1ST FL 43567 #056-05-1985 L1986 GS *020 †85
WILLIAMS, George Russell, III. 725 S SHOOP AVE, FULTON COUNTY HEALTH CENTE 43567 #038-43-1988 L1992 P *020 †75

WAVERLY – PIKE

ALI, Mohammad Tariq S. 227 VALLEY VIEW DR 45690 #704-09-1989 L1999 PD *020 †55
ALLEN, Jennifer Sue. 12340 STATE ROUTE 104, STE 200 45690 #038-40-1977 L1980 PD *020 †55
BANKS, Brenda L. 850 W EMMITT AVE, STE 5 45690 #047-07-1981 L2001 CD *020
BENUTTO, Jose R. 411 E EMMITT AVE 45690 #649-02-1948 L1964 GP *071
BRADLEY, William Allan. ■ 45690 #041-13-1957 L1958 OS FM *020 †18
DAUPHIN-BECKFORD, M. 194 E EMMITT AVE 45690 #010-03-1993 L2000 PD *020 †55
DE LA PENA, Noli Bibiano. 330 E NORTH ST 45690 #748-09-1962 L1975 GS GP *020 †85
FORTNEY, John L, III. 12340 STATE ROUTE 104, STE 200 45690 #038-40-1979 L1981 PD *020 †55
GRAHAM, Gary Files. 12340 STATE ROUTE 104, STE 200 45690 #051-01-1996 L2002 FM *020 †18
GRIGSBY, Timothy Ryann. 100 DAWN LN 45690 #005-12-1995 L1996 IM *020
HAMBRICK, Claude Seth. ■ 45690 #038-40-1952 L1952 FM *071 †18
HANEL, John H. ■ 45690 #041-01-1950 L1951 FM *071 †18
HELZ, Mary Stradley Krise. ■ 45690 #041-12-1945 L1968 IMG FM *071
HWANG, Janie. ■ 45690 #242-16-1948 L1956 AN *072
HWANG, Thomas Chao-Hun. ■ 45690 #242-09-1943 L1956 R *071 †80
HYZIAK, Boguslawa. 12340 STATE ROUTE 104, STE 200 45690 #759-01-1981 L1989 PD *020 †55
JANE-WIT, Kantima. 12340 STATE ROUTE 104, STE 200 45690 #891-03-1971 L1977 PD *020 †55
KESSLER, David Robert. 100 DAWN LN STE 4, PIKE PROF BLDG 45690 #005-12-1994 L1997 FM *020 †18
KITTAKA, Harry Takaji, Jr. 12340 STATE ROUTE 104, STE 200 45690 #031-01-1996 L1999 FM *020 †18 ‡
KULCSAR, Francis Eugene. ■ 45690 #473-04-1925 L1958 N P *071 †75
LACH, Ralph Dennis. 12340 STATE ROUTE 104 45690 #038-40-1959 L1960 CD IM *071 †20
LEE, Frederick Byoungkul. 12340 STATE ROUTE 104 45690 #028-34-1998 L2004 GS *020 †40
LUCKEYDOO, Amy Kathleen. 12340 STATE ROUTE 104, STE 200 45690 #051-04-1997 L2004 PD OS *020 †55
MC KAIN, Christine. 100 DAWN LN, PIKE COMM HOSP 45690 #038-41-1992 L1996 EM *020 †16
MONG, Alan Thos. 12340 STATE ROUTE 104 45690 #038-40-1985 L1997 GS *020 †85
MORALEJA, Estelito A. 227 VALLEY VIEW DR 45690 #748-10-1963 L1971 FM EM *071 †18
MOSALEM, Ahmed Mohamed Y. 227 VALLEY VIEW DR 45690 #915-03-1993 L2007 IM *020 †20
PACHECO, Alexander A. 118 E 2ND ST REAR 45690 #649-01-1955 L1969 GP *020
PARCINSKI, Henry Jos, Jr. 100 DAWN LN 45690 #028-78-1970, ▲ L1970 ORS HS *020
PARIKH, Naresh Kalidas. 231 W EMMITT AVE 45690 #495-01-1957 L1971 OPH *071 †35
PATEL, Chetan P. 12340 STATE ROUTE 104 45690 #495-89-1990 L1996 CD IM *020 †20
RADFORD, John Richard. 12340 STATE ROUTE 104, STE 200 45690 #038-45-1989 L1990 PD *020 †55
ROACH, Jane Ann. 12340 STATE ROUTE 104, STE 200 45690 #038-43-1976 L1979 PHO *071 †55
ROBERTS, Philip. 227 VALLEY VIEW DR 45690 #038-75-2004, ▲ L2004 FM *100
RODDY, David Eugene. 100 DAWN LN STE 4, PIKE PROF BLDG 45690 #005-12-1984 L1985 IM *020 †20
SEVER, Heather Morgan. 12340 STATE ROUTE 104, STE 200 45690 #018-75-2002, ▲ L2002 PD *020 †55
TYREE, Robert Fenton. 621 E 5TH ST 45690 #011-02-1989 L1993 FM *020 †18 ‡
WILKINSON, Kenneth Arthur. 207 SAINT ANNS LN, WAVERLY MEDICAL PRACTICE 45690 #005-12-1960 L1961 GP *020

WAYNE – WOOD

EVANS, John Christopher. ■ 43466 #025-07-2003 L2003 CD *012 †20

WAYNESBURG – STARK

BROPHY, Robert Paul. 8320 WAYNESBURG DR SE 44688 #038-44-1989 L1990 FM *020 †18
WURST, Teresa Lynn. 8320 WAYNESBURG DR SE, WAYNESBURG FAMILY PRACTICE 44688 #038-44-1993 L1996 FM *020 †18 ‡

WAYNESFIELD – AUGLAIZE

NIELSEN, David Walter. 24545 FAIRMOUNT RD 45896 #038-41-1944 L1944 FM AM *071
TRAN, Kha Huynh. 529 N WESTMINSTER ST 45896 #305-01-2001 L2001 FM *020 †18

WAYNESVILLE – WARREN

ALLGEYER, Deanna Marie. 4353 E STATE ROUTE 73 45068 #038-45-2003 L2003 FM *030 †18

ARNO, Robert Allen. ■ 45068 #055-01-1992 L1996 **AN** *020 †05
DORNON, Lester. 4353 E STATE ROUTE 73 45068 #016-06-1986 L1989 **FM** *020 †18
GLENN, William E, II. ■ 45068 #038-40-1993 L1995 **AN** *020 †05
HAREWOOD, Sandra Kay. 4353 E STATE ROUTE 73 45068 #038-40-1977 L1980 **IM** *040
MORGAN, Darin Kip. ■ 45068 #027-01-1998 L1999 **MSR** *020 †80
PALMER, Alyson Lucille. ■ 45068 #005-12-1956 L1966 **EM GP** *071
RICHARDS, Emily Jo. ■ 45068 #038-45-2007 L2007 **IM** *012
ROSENGARTEN, Audrey Renee. ■ 45068 #038-40-2008 *012
WOLF, Leslie Rae. ■ 45068 #019-02-1986 L1988 **EM** *075 †16

WELLINGTON – LORAIN

KONGTHONG, Jang. 508 DICKSON ST, STE 4 44090 #891-02-1968 L1974 **FM** *020 †18

WELLSVILLE – COLUMBIANA

AVELLANA, Francisco D. 420 BROADWAY AVE 43968 #748-01-1959 L1969 **GS GE** *020
LAUVA, Janis. 1262 HILLCREST RD 43968 #407-24-1949 L1955 **FM** *071

WEST ALEXANDRIA – PREBLE

BLAND, Carol Louise. 60 W DAYTON ST, TWIN VLY FAMILY PRACTICE 45381
#038-06-1996 L1997 **FM** *020 †18
FRENCH, Ginny Marie. ■ 45381 #038-45-2007 *012
WOLF, Raymond D. 1 MARTY LN 45381 #033-75-1986, ▲ L1987 **PHL** *020

WEST CARROLLTON – MONTGOMERY

AGARWAL, Anil Kumar. 1625 S ALEX RD 45449 #495-14-1975 L1988 **FM** *020 †18
GARBER, Stanley Lee. 5649 MARINA DR 45449 #038-41-1959 L1959 **FM** *020 †30
JOHNSTON, Martha Anne. 1625 S ALEX RD 45449 #038-45-1982 L1984 **EM GP** *020 †16
KAPUR, Suneil. ■ 45449 #065-06-1997 L1999 **IM** *020 †20
KHANZADA, Zakir Jalal. 1625 S ALEX RD, STE 100 45449 #704-08-1992 L2007 **ID IM** *020 †20
OSMAN, Hassan Elsir. 7 KENNYWOOD LN 45449 #848-01-1996 L2000 **IM** *020 †20
PARMAR, Jagdish P. ■ 45449 #495-76-1989 L1996 **IM** *100

WEST CHESTER – BUTLER

ABAS, Salomon. ■ 45069 #660-01-1955 L1963 **R NM** *071 †80,28
ABDULLAH, Anthony Jasseim. 7985 COX RD 45069 #038-43-2002 L2002 **EM** *020 †16
AHMAD, Masood. 6464 TYLERSVILLE RD 45069 #704-15-1983 L1988 **PDA AI** *020 †55,03
AHMAD, Syed Arif. 7700 UNIVERSITY CT, STE 0558 45069 #023-01-1992 L2001 **GS** *020 †85
AKBIK, Hammam Hadi. 7759 UNIVERSITY DR, STE C 45069 #875-02-1988 L1998 **AN** *020 †05
ALLEN, Flordeliza. 6511 W CHESTER RD, STE A 45069 #748-01-1982 L1991 **FM** *020 †18
ASGHAR, Ferhan Ali. 7700 UNIVERSITY CT, STE 2800 45069 #048-04-1999 L2005 **ORS** *020
BAIRD, Micah William. ■ 45069 #038-45-2004 L2004 **PPM** *012
BISHOP, Mary Anastasia. 5900 W CHESTER RD 45069 #038-41-2001 L2001 **FM** *020 †18
BLANCHARD, Paul Lewis. 7665 MONARCH CT STE 101, WEST CHESTER MED GRP 45069
#012-01-1992 L2001 **IM AM** *071 †20
BONSALL, Dean John. 7700 UNIVERSITY CT 45069 #041-14-1994 L2005 **PO** *020 †35
BRENEMAN, John Chas. 7710 UNIVERSITY CT 45069 #018-03-1981 L1985 **RO** *020 †80
BRINN, Steven Robt. 7097 LIBERTY CENTRE DR 45069 #038-41-1976 L1977 **PD** *020 †55
BROOKS, Sally L. 9050 CENTRE POINTE DR, STE 400 45069 #055-02-1988 L1989
IMG IM *030 †20
BROWN, Richard William. 8806 CINCINNATI DAYTON RD 45069 #038-43-1996 L1999 **P** *050
BUTLER, Daniel Andrew. 7798 UNIVERSITY CT, STE B 45069 #017-20-1989 L1994
GS VS *020 †85
CADENA, Rhonda Sue. ■ 45069 #016-45-2005 L2005 **EM** *012
CARPENTER, Jeremy Daniel. ■ 45069 #038-41-2007 L2007 **P** *012
CATALANOTTO, Thomas James. 7795 UNIVERSITY CT, PEDIATRIC ASSOCIATES OF 45069
#016-43-1971 L1976 **PD** *020 †55
CAUDELL, Richard William. 7750 UNIVERSITY CT 45069 #045-01-1993 L1998 **APM** *020 †05
CAVITT, Jennifer Lee. 7700 UNIVERSITY CT, STE 3500 45069 #019-02-1997 L2001 **N** *020 †75
CHAUDHRY, Kern Khalid. ■ 45069 #104-01-2005 L2007 **IM** *012
CHECROUN, Anthony J. 7798 UNIVERSITY CT 45069 #017-20-1992 L1998 **ORS** *020 †40 ‡
CHIRUMAMILLA, Seshendra. 5066 HUNTINGTON CIR 45069 #496-01-1998 L2005 **AN** *020 †05
COBB, Gary Arthur. 7798 UNIVERSITY CT, STE B 45069 #038-40-1984 L1985 **GS VS** *020 †85
DASARI, Sarita. ■ 45069 #495-35-1991 L1996 **IM** *020 †20
DASSO, Edwin J. 8108 EAGLE RIDGE DR 45069 #048-12-1983 L1991 **AN** *020 †05 ‡
DELSIGNORE, Madhavi G. 8752 UNION CENTRE BLVD, PEDIATRIC CARE INC 45069
#038-44-1995 L1996 **PD** *020 †55
DESAI, Shaili Jaykumar. ■ 45069 #038-44-2006 L2006 **IM** *012
DIATTE, Christopher John. 4870 WUNNENBERG WAY 45069 #039-05-1989 L1990 **FM** *020 †18
D'IMPERIO, John Salvatore. 8806 CINCINNATI DAYTON RD, BRIDGEPOINTE
PSYCHOLOGICAL 45069 #033-05-1996 L2000 **CHP** *020
DINE, Mark S. 8752 UNION CENTRE BLVD, PEDIATRIC CARE INC 45069 #038-41-1950 L1950
PD A *020 †55
DONOVAN, James F, Jr. 7700 UNIVERSITY CT, STE 0558 45069 #016-06-1978 L2003
U GS *020 †85,95
DROHAN, Edward Pierce. 7665 MONARCH CT, STE 101 45069 #649-14-1972 L1975 **IM** *020
DRUMMOND, Arnold Everett. 7665 MONARCH CT STE 101 45069 #055-02-1989 L1990
IM *020 †20
FAIRBANKS, Joseph Philip. 7593 TYLERS PLACE BLVD, STE 121 45069 #010-02-1948 L1950
FM OM *071
FERNANDEZ, Otilia. 7097 LIBERTY CENTRE DR 45069 #038-41-1984 L1987 **PD** *020 †55
FERRARA, Edward Vincent. 7665 MONARCH CT STE 101 45069 #035-15-1964 L1970 **IM** *020
FICKER, David Michael. 7700 UNIVERSITY CT, STE 3500 45069 #038-41-1992 L1997
N CN *020 †75
FISCHER, David Richard. 7700 UNIVERSITY CT, STE 0558 45069 #038-41-1996 L1997
GS *020 †85

FREEMAN, Lawrence Chas. 7593 TYLERS PLACE BLVD 45069 #038-41-1970 L1970
OBG *071 †30
FRIEDBERG, Daniel Lee. 8752 UNION CENTRE BLVD, PEDIATRIC CARE INC 45069
#038-41-1961 L1965 **PD** *020 †55
GANGL, Paul Michael. 4900 WUNNENBERG WAY 45069 #038-06-1983 L1984 **ORS** *020 †40
GARG, Dinesh. ■ 45069 #035-08-1992 L1992 **NS** *050
GLENCHUR, Jane B. ■ 45069 #020-02-1983 L1988 **D DMP** *020 †15
GOLNIK, Karl Clifford. 7700 UNIVERSITY CT 45069 #023-07-1986 L1994 **OPH** *020 †35
GONZALEZ-LOCKHART, Ida. ■ 45069 #649-14-1978 L1996 **PD** *020
GORDON, Christopher B. 7700 UNIVERSITY CT, STE 0558 45069 #025-01-1989 L2002
PS *020 †65
GRAHAM, Camille Cecile. 7777 UNIVERSITY DR 45069 #038-41-1977 L1980 **PD ADL** *020 †55
GREEN, Lisa Lynn. 7777 UNIVERSITY DR 45069 #038-41-1986 L1989 **PD** *020 †55
GROTE, Paul Frederick. 7320 KINGSGATE WAY STE A 45069 #038-41-1979 L1982 **FM** *020 †18
HAN, Hauw T. 7593 TYLERS PLACE BLVD 45069 #028-34-1984 L1992 **GS PS** *020 †85,65
HANS, Sandra Lee. 7589 TYLERS PLACE BLVD 45069 #038-40-1991 L1992 **FM** *020 †18
HARKNESS, Cameron Blair. 7700 UNIVERSITY CT 45069 #011-04-1996 L2003 **GO** *020 †30
HARRIS, John Jos. 7345 KINGSGATE WAY, URGENT CARE OF WESTCHESTER 45069
#047-06-1970 L1974 **OS OM** *020
HASKELL, Jennifer Sharon. 7795 UNIVERSITY CT, PEDIATRIC ASSOCIATES OF 45069
#047-05-2002 L2002 **PD** *020 †55
HAVLIN, Kathleen Anne. 7700 UNIVERSITY CT, STE 2700 45069 #016-06-1982 L2007
ON IM *020 †20
HEIDT, Robert Saml, Jr. 8737 UNION CENTRE BLVD 45069 #038-41-1976 L1977 **ORS** *020 †40
HEIN, Patrick Stanley. 8752 UNION CENTRE BLVD, PEDIATRIC CARE INC 45069
#038-40-1997 L1998 **PD** *020 †55
HESS, Lori Kaye. 9050 CENTRE POINTE DR, STE 400 45069 #038-44-1991 L1993 **FM** *020 †18
HILL, Jennifer M. 7665 MONARCH CT, STE 101 45069 #038-45-1998 L2000 **IM** *020
HILL, Robert John. 4900 WUNNENBERG WAY 45069 #041-77-1987, ▲ L1994 **ORS** *020
HOM, David B. 7700 UNIVERSITY CT, STE 39 45069 #005-14-1982 L2007 **FPS OTO** *020 †45
HORAK, Holli Ann. 7700 UNIVERSITY CT, STE 3500 45069 #038-40-1994 L1995 **CN** *020 †75
HOWELL, Laura Kathryn. ■ 45069 #017-20-2005 L2005 **PD** *012
HURFORD, William Edward. 7750 UNIVERSITY CT 45069 #041-01-1981 L2003 **AN** *020 †05
JANELLE, Jean Gaston. 7795 UNIVERSITY CT, PEDIATRIC ASSOCIATES OF 45069
#024-05-1969 L1972 **PD PDA** *020 †55
JAWEED, Abdul Kadir S. ■ 45069 #495-21-1963 L1971 **GS** *020
JAWEED, Bilquis Sultana. ■ 45069 #495-21-1962 L1975 **GP** *020
JUNG, Everette Leroy. 6134 HOLLY HILL LN 45069 #028-02-1955 L1961 **ORS** *071 †40
KABITHE, David Wanjohi. 7798 UNIVERSITY CT, STE B 45069 #020-02-1997 L2000 **GS** *020 †85
KALETA, Michele Denise. 7795 UNIVERSITY CT, PEDIATRIC ASSOCIATES OF 45069
#038-41-1993 L1996 **PD** *020 †55
KANTER, Daniel Stuart. 7700 UNIVERSITY CT, STE 3500 45069 #038-06-1987 L1987
N NS *020 †75
KENTER, Keith. 7700 UNIVERSITY CT, STE 2800 45069 #028-03-1990 L2002 **ORS** *040 †40
KERN, Roberta M. ■ 45069 #038-40-2006 L2006 **FP** *012
KHALID, Jawaria. ■ 45069 #704-01-2000 L2002 **FM** *020 †18 ‡
KHALIL, Ahmed Khalil Moha. 7755 UNIVERSITY CT 45069 #915-02-1993 L2000 *020 †05
KHAN, Muhammad Ali. 8336 MEETING ST, APT 109 45069 #704-02-2000 L2007 **PMM** *012
KHOSLA, Siddarth M. 7700 UNIVERSITY CT, STE 39 45069 #036-05-1991 L2001 **OTO** *020 †45
KIEFHABER, Ray Eugene. 7700 UNIVERSITY CT 45069 #038-41-1954 L1954 **ORS** *020 †40
KISSELA, Brett Mancos. 7700 UNIVERSITY CT, STE 3500 45069 #028-02-1995 L1999
N *020 †75
KITCHENS, Gerald Taylor. 7750 UNIVERSITY CT 45069 #017-20-1998 L2004 **AN** *020 †05
KITZMILLER, William John. 7700 UNIVERSITY CT, STE 0558 45069 #036-07-1983 L1983
PS *020 †65,85
KLEINDORFER, Dawn Olson. 7700 UNIVERSITY CT, STE 3500 45069 #028-02-1997 L2001
N *020 †75
KOMROKJI, Rami S. 7700 UNIVERSITY CT, STE 2700 45069 #875-01-1996 L1999 **HO** *020 †20
KRUG, Stewart. 7700 UNIVERSITY CT 45069 #035-09-1972 L1975 **OPH** *020 †35
LANGWORTHY, William Dwain. 7798 UNIVERSITY CT 45069 #038-41-1961 L1961 **ORS** *020 †40
LEE, Kyu Dal. ■ 45069 #583-02-1968 L1978 **R** *020 †80
LEE, Timmy. ■ 45069 #021-06-2001 L2007 **NEP** *100
LERER, Robert Jan. 7795 UNIVERSITY CT, PEDIATRIC ASSOCIATES OF 45069
#023-07-1970 L1973 **PD PHP** *020 †55
LEWIS, Margie A. 7700 UNIVERSITY CT, STE 2700 45069 #025-07-1998 L2000 **HO OS** *020 †20
LICHTER, Timothy Joseph. 5900 W CHESTER RD 45069 #046-01-1986 L1989 **FM** *020 †18
LISCO, Steven Jay. 7750 UNIVERSITY CT 45069 #016-43-1988 L2004 **AN CCA** *020 †05,20
LUCHT, Stephen Russell. 9050 CENTRE POINTE DR, STE 400 45069 #005-12-1981 L1983
IM *030 †20
LUTTS, Mina. 8859 BROOKSIDE AVE, STE 101 45069 #020-12-1995 L1997 **FM** *020 †18
MAGONE, Jerry Brian. 7798 UNIVERSITY CT 45069 #041-12-1982 L1983 **ORS** *020 †40
MAKKAD, Benu. 7750 UNIVERSITY CT 45069 #495-47-1996 L2000 **AN** *020 †05
MALIK, Khurram Murad. ■ 45069 #704-04-1998 **OBG** *100
MANNIX, Lisa Kaye. 7908 CINCINNATI DAYTON RD, STE J 45069 #038-41-1992 L1996
N *020 †75
MARROCCO, Peter Anthony. 7665 MONARCH CT, STE 101 45069 #024-05-1964 L1970
IM *020 †20
MATHIEU, Luckson Noe. ■ 45069 #047-07-2006 L2006 **IM** *012
MAUPIN, Emily J. ■ 45069 #038-75-2007, ▲ L2007 *012
MEHTA, Apurva C. 7700 UNIVERSITY CT, STE 2000 45069 #496-38-1991 L2002 **HO** *020 †20
MITCHELL, Lina. 7593 TYLERS PL, STE 121 45069 #913-96-1987 L2000 **END** *020 †20
MOCH, Abigail Terese. ■ 45069 #026-04-2007 L2007 **EM** *012
MODAWAL, Arvind. 7700 UNIVERSITY CT # 3100, UNIV FMLY PHYS UNIV POINTE 45069
#495-77-1980 L1996 **FM FPG** *020 †18
MOEBIUS, Arthur James. 7665 MONARCH CT, STE 104 45069 #038-41-1985 L1988
PD *020 †55
MOSLEY, Francine Robinson. 7345 KINGSGATE WAY 45069 #020-12-2001 L2001 **FM** *020 †18
MURTHY, Srilakshmi. 7700 UNIVERSITY CT, STE 3100 45069 #495-01-1993 L1999 **FM** *020 †18
NA, Yu-Chun. ■ 45069 #638-01-1937 **GP** *071
NAJEED, Syed Ashfaq H. 7798 UNIVERSITY CT 45069 #496-01-1992 L2002 **CD** *020 †20
NAMDE, Madjimbaye Charles. ■ 45069 #036-07-2007 L2007 **EM** *012
NELSON, Lindsey Allan. 7750 UNIVERSITY CT 45069 #026-04-1998 L2000 **AN** *020 †05
NORTHUP, Christopher Joe. ■ 45069 #055-01-1998 L2004 **GS** *020 †85
NUSSBAUM, Michael Scot. 7700 UNIVERSITY CT, STE 0558 45069 #041-01-1981 L1985
GS CCS *020 †85
O'BRIEN, Teresa Mary. ■ 45069 #038-43-2007 L2007 **FP** *012

O'BRIEN, Thomas M. 45069 #035-45-2001 L2001 **CD** *012 †20
OELRICH, Dennis Mark. 7665 MONARCH CT, STE 107 45069 #038-41-1980 L1981 **D IM** *020 †20,15
OERTHER, Monica C. 7795 UNIVERSITY CT, PEDIATRIC ASSOCIATES OF 45069 #016-06-1997 L2000 **PD** *020 †55
OLEKSOWICZ, Leslie Ann. 7700 UNIVERSITY CT, STE 2700 45069 #024-07-1982 L2003 **ON IM** *020 †20
O'NEILL, Kelly Patrick. 7593 TYLERS PLACE BLVD, STE 107 45069 #034-01-1985 L1991 **OPH** *035
ORCUTT, Marsha Jo M. 7700 UNIVERSITY CT 45069 #035-15-1976 L1979 **R IM** *020 †80
OSBORNE, Bradley James. 9075 CENTRE POINTE DR, STE 160 45069 #038-43-1990 L1995 **GS VS** *020 †20
OSHER, Robert Henry. 7700 UNIVERSITY CT 45069 #035-45-1976 L1981 **OPH PS** *020 †35
PATIL, Yash Jagdish. 7700 UNIVERSITY CT, STE 39 45069 #047-05-1996 L2006 **OTO HNS** *020 †45
PECK, Allan Lawrence. 8859 BROOKSIDE AVE, STE 101 45069 #038-41-1988 L1993 **GE IM** *020 †20
PECK, Lauren A. 7097 LIBERTY CENTRE DR 45069 #016-02-1990 L1993 **PD** *020 †55
PHENOW, Kenneth Jos. ■ 45069 #056-06-1992 L1994 **FM** *020 †18
PIERRE, Rachelle Bernice. ■ 45069 #024-01-2006 L2006 **EM** *012
POST, Lee Henry. 7908 CINCINNATI DAYTON RD, STE 45069 #038-41-1981 L1982 **IM** *074
RAHE, Jeffrey Kenneth. 7665 MONARCH CT, STE 101 45069 #038-43-1989 L1991 **OBG** *020 †30
RAMACHANDRAN, R. 7795 UNIVERSITY CT, PEDIATRIC ASSOCIATES OF 45069 #495-16-1986 L1994 **PD** *020 †55
RAMASAHAYAM, Manju. ■ 45069 #495-21-2001 L2006 **IM** *100 †20
RAMOS, Victor Ladrillo. ■ 45069 #748-07-1953 L1967 **FM** *020 †85
REDMOND, Kevin Patrick. 7710 UNIVERSITY CT 45069 #038-41-1982 L1983 **RO GP** *020 †80
RICHARDSON, Jade Lindsey. ■ 45069 #011-04-2005 L2005 **OBG** *012
RICHARDSON, Marc Allen. 7795 UNIVERSITY CT, PEDIATRIC ASSOCIATES OF 45069 #038-41-1995 L1996 **PD** *020 †55
RITCHEY, Dasen Ronald. 7798 UNIVERSITY CT, STE B 45069 #030-05-2000 L2000 **GS** *020 †85
ROEBUCK, Kim Lavenelle. ■ 45069 #005-02-1982 L1984 **P** *020 †75
ROMAN, Robert Jos. 7798 UNIVERSITY CT 45069 #038-41-1990 L1995 **ORS** *020 †40
ROSS, Diana L. 7665 MONARCH CT, STE 101 45069 #038-06-1972 L1979 **CHN PD** *020 †55,75
SAFA, Malek Mohamad. 7700 UNIVERSITY CT, STE 2000 45069 #605-01-1995 L1998 **HO** *020 †20
SAMAHA, Frederick James. 7700 UNIVERSITY CT, STE 3500 45069 #024-07-1959 L1977 **N** *071 †75
SAMY, Ravi N. 7700 UNIVERSITY CT, STE 39 45069 #036-07-1995 L2005 **OTO** *020 †45
SANDS, Joshua Jonathan. 7700 UNIVERSITY CT 45069 #030-06-1982 L1983 **OPH** *020 †35
SCHMIDT, James Edward. 7798 UNIVERSITY CT 45069 #038-41-1983 L1984 **CD IM** *020 †20
SEIDEN, Allen Mark. 7700 UNIVERSITY CT, STE 39 45069 #033-05-1980 L1984 **OTO** *040 †45
SHAREEF, Shahin Rashid. 7665 MONARCH CT, STE 105 45069 #038-45-1995 L1997 **PD** *020 †55
SIEGRIST, Carl Wm. 7700 UNIVERSITY CT, STE 2000 45069 #038-41-1964 L1964 **HEM** *020 †20
SINGH, Manoj Kumar. 7700 UNIVERSITY CT, STE 3100 45069 #063-01-1991 L1995 **FM** *020 †18 ‡
STALEY, Barry Edward. 7589 TYLERS PLACE BLVD, WETHERINGTON FAM MED 45069 #038-41-1980 L1981 **FM** *020 †18
STARNES, Sandra Lynne. 7700 UNIVERSITY CT, STE 0558 45069 #016-11-1995 L2005 **TS** *100 †85,90
STEPHENS, Robert Jos, Jr. 7700 UNIVERSITY CT, STE C 45069 #038-41-1979 L1980 **OBG** *020 †30
STEWARD, David L, Jr. 7700 UNIVERSITY CT, STE 39 45069 #038-41-1994 L1996 **OTO** *020 †45
STOCKHOLM, Bethany Joel. ■ 45069 #035-03-2004 L2004 **P** *012
SULENTIC, Jon Eric. 7798 UNIVERSITY CT 45069 #025-76-1999, ▲ L2003 **FSM FM** *020 †18
SUN, Gordon H. ■ 45069 #041-12-2006 L2006 **OTO** *012
SZAFLARSKI, Jerzy Pawel. 7700 UNIVERSITY CT, STE 3500 45069 #759-16-1991 L1999 **N CN** *020 †75
TADEPALLI, Gayathri D. ■ 45069 #495-65-1981 L1998 **CHP** *020 †75
TEW, John Mc Lellan, Jr. 7700 UNIVERSITY CT, STE 3400 45069 #036-05-1961 L1969 **NS** *020 †25
THOMAS, Joseph David. 4900 WUNNENBERG WAY 45069 #038-41-1985 L1986 **ORS GS** *020 †40
TRUE, Mark Scott. 7798 UNIVERSITY CT 45069 #038-41-1988 L1993 **ORS** *020 †40
VARADARAJAN, Shruti. ■ 45069 #038-41-2006 **FP** *012
VOVAN, Houston Alexandra. ■ 45069 #665-01-2006 L2006 **IM** *012
WALTERS, Daniel Hugh. 8859 BROOKSIDE AVE, STE 101 45069 #038-41-1985 L1985 **FM P** *020 †18
WANDER, Arden Hale. 7700 UNIVERSITY CT 45069 #038-41-1967 L1967 **OPH** *020 †35
WARE, Thomas Racke. 7106 KENDAL LN 45069 #038-41-1990 L1991 **AN PME** *020 †05
WEATHERINGTON, Vincent W. 7795 UNIVERSITY CT, PEDIATRIC ASSOCIATES OF 45069 #016-45-1991 L1994 **PD** *020 †55
WEBB, Warren Steven. 7795 UNIVERSITY CT, PEDIATRIC ASSOCIATES OF 45069 #020-12-1974 L1983 **PD** *020 †55
WEHRMEYER, Joel Thomas. 7777 UNIVERSITY DR 45069 #038-45-2000 L2003 **PD** *020 †55
WEIH, Jack E. ■ 45069 #016-43-1943 L1945 **OPH** *071 †35
WHITE, Jennifer Nicole. ■ 45069 #025-01-2005 L2005 **FP** *012
WICHMANN, Gerhard Krause. ■ 45069 #407-02-1970 **D** *050
WILLIAMS, Daniel B. 7700 UNIVERSITY CT, STE 3000 45069 #028-46-1985 L2002 **OPH** *020 †30
WILSON, Keith Michael. 7700 UNIVERSITY CT, STE 39 45069 #035-20-1986 L1991 **OTO** *020 †45
WIWI, Dennis Jerome. 8899 BROOKSIDE AVE STE 101 45069 #017-20-1978 L1982 **OBG** *020 †30 ‡
WOCHNER, Raymond Dean. 9050 CENTRE POINTE DR, STE 400 45069 #028-02-1960 L1983 **IM MDM** *062 †20
WOO, Daniel. 7700 UNIVERSITY CT, STE 3500 45069 #038-41-1994 L1996 **N** *020 †75
YANG, Michael Brian. 7700 UNIVERSITY CT 45069 #024-01-1993 L2002 **OPH PO** *020 †35
YEH, Hwa-Shain. 7700 UNIVERSITY CT, STE 3400 45069 #385-03-1967 L1980 **NS N** *040 †25
ZIMMER, Lee Alexander. 7700 UNIVERSITY CT, STE 39 45069 #023-01-1999 L2005 **OTO** *020 †45

WEST JEFFERSON — MADISON

CHATTERJEE, Madhumita. 35 S TWIN ST 43162 #038-45-1993 L2005 **FM** *020 †18

HURT, J Richard. 35 S TWIN ST 43162 #038-40-1957 L1957 **FM OM** *020
LIN, Chau-Chi. 82 W MAIN ST 43162 #244-01-1962 L1976 **GP** *020
SCHAEFER, Stephanie M. 121 E MAIN ST 43162 #011-04-1997 L1999 **D** *012 †20
VENNEKOTTER, Kathleen S. 487 W MAIN ST, DARBY FAMILY PRACTICE, INC 43162 #038-40-1998 L1999 **FM** *020 †18
WELLER, Samuel David. 35 S TWIN ST 43162 #038-40-1998 L2000 **FM** *020 †18

WEST LAFAYETTE – COSHOCTON

ASHRAF, Muhammad. 600 E MAIN ST 43845 #704-05-1980 L2002 **IM** *020 †20
DUMITRESCU, Ovidiu C. 600 E MAIN ST 43845 #781-01-1991 L1999 **IM** *020 †20

WEST LIBERTY – LOGAN

ARORA, Harpreet Singh. 4879 US HIGHWAY 68 S 43357 #661-02-2002 L2003 **FM** *100 †18
ARORA, Shefali. 4879 US HIGHWAY 68 S 43357 #661-02-2003 L2004 **FM** *100 †18
GRIFFITH, Linda Jean. PO BOX 817, 1521 N DETROIT ST 43357 #033-05-1981 L1999 **P FM** *020 †18,75
JOHNSON, Ryan Douglas. 4879 US HIGHWAY 68 S 43357 #019-02-1999 L2006 **FM** *020 †18
KAUFFMAN, Roger J. 4879 US HIGHWAY 68 S, OAKHILL MEDICAL 43357 #051-04-1977 L1979 **FM** *020 †18
KAUFFMAN, Ryan Dale Buche. 4879 US HIGHWAY 68 S, OAKHILL MEDICAL 43357 #038-40-2003 L2003 **FM** *020 †18
KRATZ, Charles Vernon. 4879 US HIGHWAY 68 S, OAKHILL MEDICAL 43357 #041-13-1993 L1996 **FM** *020 †18
LONGENECKER, Randall Lee. 4879 US HIGHWAY 68 S, OAKHILL MEDICAL 43357 #041-01-1979 L1982 **FM** *040 †18
LUTHMAN, Scott Andrew. 9718 TOWNSHIP RD, STE 166 43357 #038-40-1997 L1999 **PD** *020 †18
MCCAULEY, Leesa Damar. ■ 43357 #017-20-2006 L2006 **FP** *012
MILLER, Kenneth Chas. 4879 US HIGHWAY 68 S, OAKHILL MEDICAL 43357 #038-40-1985 L1986 **FM** *020 †18

WEST MILTON – MIAMI

FAZE, Kenneth James. ■ 45383 #038-40-1959 L1959 **GP EM** *071
GINN, William Norman. 751 S MIAMI ST, MILTON-UNION MEDICAL CENTE 45383 #038-40-1981 L1981 **FM FSM** *020 †18
GOODWYN, Erik Dennis. ■ 45383 #038-41-2005 L2005 **P** *012

WEST POINT – COLUMBIANA

GARN, Russell. PO BOX 458, 13293 STATE ROUTE 45 44492 #038-44-1997 L1999 **IM** *020 †20

WEST PORTSMOUTH – SCIOTO

DUNCAN, James H. 22442 STATE ROUTE 73, JAMES H DUNCAN DO INC 45663 #028-79-1976, ▲ L1977 **FM FPG** *020
ORTIZ, Lilliam Ivette. 23030 STATE ROUTE 73 45663 #008-02-1988 L1991 **PD** *062 †55

WEST SALEM – WAYNE

BETT, Bari Joan. ■ 44287 #038-06-1985 L1987 **FM** *020 †18

WEST UNION – ADAMS

ASHLEY, Bruce Marion. 210 N WILSON DR 45693 #020-02-1971 L1973 **EM GP** *020 †16
CHASE, Stewart Patrick. 210 N WILSON DR 45693 #038-40-1964 L1964 **DR** *040 †80
DUNKIN-BLANTON, Susan E. 211 N WILSON DR 45693 #038-41-1982 L1984 **FM** *020 †18
HABLITZEL, William E. 113 E MULBERRY ST 45693 #038-43-1986 L1987 **IM** *020 †20
JOHNSON, Charles Murray. 210 N WILSON DR 45693 #010-03-1969 L1974 **EM NS** *020
LIM, Timple Wee. 107 N WILSON DR 45693 #748-08-1961 L1976 **GP** *071
MATHIAS, Dale L, Jr. 333 GATEWOOD DR 45693 #038-41-1980 L1982 **FM EM** *020 †18,16
SHUKLA, Amul. 210 N WILSON DR 45693 #495-23-1977 L1981 **IM** *020 †20
SHUPERT, Angela Marie. 126 N CROSS ST 45693 #038-41-2000 L2003 **FM** *100 †18
SHUPERT, John Heath. 126 N CROSS ST, CEDAR VLY MED ASSOC INC 45693 #038-41-1999 L1999 **IM** *020 †18
STEVENS, Francis Leonard. ■ 45693 #038-41-1956 L1956 **FM** *071
WICKREMASINGHE, Felix A. 150 CHESTNUT RIDGE RD 45693 #495-45-1981 L1994 **FM** *075 †18

WESTERVILLE – DELAWARE

AMIRI, Rannie Basim. 570 POLARIS PKWY STE 250 43082 #038-41-1996 L1997 **IM** *020 †20
ARBONA, Heidi Darnell. 444 N CLEVELAND AVE 43082 #038-41-1998 L2003 **OBG** *020 †30
AWALE, Omar Mohamud. 4780 SAINT MEDAN DR 43082 #561-11-1996 L2002 **FM** *020
BADDOUR, A Alfred. ■ 43082 #330-02-1954 L1967 **U** *071 †95
BARBER, Terry Philip. 433 N CLEVELAND AVE, HEALTH CARE CENTER 43082 #038-41-1980 L1981 **PD** *020 †55
BEAN, Cybil Michele. 433 N CLEVELAND AVE 43082 #038-43-1999 L1999 **OPH** *020 †35
BECKER, Louis. ■ 43082 #038-41-1957 L1957 **GP** *020
BIERNAT, Brian Paul. 428 COUNTY LINE RD W 43082 #030-05-1993 L1997 **DS D** *020 †15
BLOCKER, Denise Lynne. 110 POLARIS PKWY STE 250 43082 #038-43-1991 L1992 **MPD** *020 †55,20
BREMER, Don L. 433 N CLEVELAND AVE 43082 #028-34-1975 L1977 **PO** *020 †35
BRIONES, Jennifer J. 444 N CLEVELAND AVE 43082 #748-10-2000 L2003 **FM** *020 †18
BROOKS, Jonathan Benj. 5415 STILLWATER AVE 43082 #041-07-1985 L1986 **EM** *020 †16
BUCHANAN, Timothy Kerr. 101 COMMERCE PARK DR 43082 #038-40-1987 L1988 **FM** *020 †18

CARLISLE, David Charles. 428 COUNTY LINE RD W, CENTER FOR SURGICAL DERMAT 43082 #055-01-2001 L2003 **D** *020
CHANNAIAH, Nanda. 428 COUNTY LINE RD W 43082 #038-75-2003, ▲ L2003 **D** *020
CHIORAN, George M. 450 ALKYRE RUN, STE 100 43082 #017-20-1989 L1993 **OPH** *020 †35
DAIRO, Omolara Yewande. 444 N CLEVELAND AVE, STE 210 43082 #690-01-1990 L2000 **PD** *020 †55
DEMAS, Christopher Lou. 109 COMMERCE PARK DR 43082 #038-40-1978 L1978 **FM FPG** *020 †18
DONOVAN, Joseph Wm. 300 POLARIS PKWY, STE 110 43082 #035-45-1986 L1990 **AN** *020 †05
ESGUERRA, Deogracias, Jr. ■ 43082 #748-01-1954 L1971 **GS** *020
FELIBERTY-SEPULVEDA, M. ■ 43082 #042-01-1964 L1988 **CD IM** *071
FOJAS, Ferdinand Saplala. ■ 43082 #038-43-1993 L2000 **AN** *020
FUCHS, Richard Jos. 5361 CLUB DR, RADIOLOGY INC 43082 #038-40-1979 L1984 **DR** *020 †80
GANDHI, Bela Mulraj. ■ 43082 #038-44-2001 L2001 **CHP** *020 †75
GIRVIN, James Reeder. 470 OLDE WORTHINGTON RD, STE 200 43082 #038-40-1988 L1990 **P** *020 †75
GOLDEN, Richard Philip. 433 N CLEVELAND AVE 43082 #038-40-2000 L2004 **OPH** *020 †35
GOSSARD, Laurie E. 484 COUNTY LINE RD W, STE 200 43082 #038-41-1992 L1997 **IM** *020 †20
HELVEY, William C. 410 ASHFORD DR 43082 #038-40-1978 L1978 **EM** *020 †16
HERWIG, Theodor Frederick. 101 COMMERCE PARK DR 43082 #038-40-1958 L1958 **FM** *020 †18
HINZMAN, Gary Wade. 350 WORTHINGTON RD 43082 #041-12-1966 L1967 **OS DR** *030 †80,28
HUGHES, Jeannine Marie. 444 N CLEVELAND AVE 43082 #038-45-1994 L1995 **FM** *020 †18
ISABELLE, Frank Edward. 155 COMMERCE PARK DR, STE 1 43082 #038-40-1966 L1966 **OBG** *020 †30
JOHNSON, Owen Elwood. 9200 WORTHINGTON RD 43082 #038-40-1965 L1965 **IM** *071
KRUECK, Katherine Jane. ■ 43082 #048-12-1999 L2000 **PD** *020 †55
KRUPKO, John Burkey. 484 COUNTY LINE RD W, STE 200 43082 #038-40-1972 L1972 **IM END** *020 †20
LISKO, Bradley Alex. 110 POLARIS PKWY, STE 250 43082 #038-40-1991 L1992 **IM PD** *020 †55,20
LYSANDER, Vimalesh. ■ 43082 #495-04-1983 L1991 **IM** *020
MARQUARDT, April. ■ 43082 #038-40-2003 L2003 **RHU** *012 †20
MARQUARDT, David John. ■ 43082 #028-34-2001 L2001 **CCP** *012 †55
MARSICK, Christine N. 470 OLDE WORTHINGTON RD, STE 250 43082 #016-11-2000 L2002 **GS** *020
MCGREGOR, Mary Lou. 433 N CLEVELAND AVE 43082 #038-44-1985 L1986 **PO** *020 †35
MOULTON, Dana Michelle. 484 COUNTY LINE RD W, STE 230 43082 #038-41-2001 L2004 **OBG** *020
MURNANE, Alan James. 444 N CLEVELAND AVE, WESTOR OB/GYN 43082 #038-41-1987 L1988 **OBG** *020 †30
NILAND, Marylynn. 507 EXECUTIVE CAMPUS DR, STE 160 43082 #038-40-1997 L1998 **PEM** *020 †55
PANGALANGAN-MOLER, Amy M. ■ 43082 #038-43-1993 L1999 **DR** *020
PORTS, Michael Robt. 450 ALKYRE RUN, STE 380 43082 #038-40-1975 L1975 **IM** *020 †20
PRITCHETT, C. 7385 STATE ROUTE 3, UNIT 117 43082 #654-01-1988 L1995 **FM** *020
RANALLI, Mark Anthony. ■ 43082 #016-02-1989 L1999 **PHO** *020 †55
RANGI, Baljit Singh. 85 COMMERCE PARK DR 43082 #038-40-1993 L1994 **FM** *020 †18
RICHARD, Neil Edward. 444 N CLEVELAND AVE, STE 200 43082 #038-40-1993 L1994 **FM** *020 †18
RICHARDSON, Steven Lane. 9200 WORTHINGTON RD 43082 #019-02-1980 L1982 **PHP GP** *030 †70
ROGERS, Gary Leigh. 433 N CLEVELAND AVE 43082 #038-40-1968 L1968 **PO** *020 †35
RYZENMAN, John Martin. 387 COUNTY LINE RD W, STE 115 43082 #038-41-1999 L1999 **NO** *020 †45
SHANAHAN, Tracey Colleen. ■ 43082 #035-06-2000 L2000 **PD** *100
SIEGLE, Ronald Jay. 428 COUNTY LINE RD W 43082 #035-15-1979 L1984 **D DS** *020 †15
SILVER, Jennifer Ann. ■ 43082 #038-40-2004 L2004 **FM** *020 †18
SIMON, Phillip N. 110 POLARIS PKWY, STE 250 43082 #038-45-2001 L2001 **MPD** *020 †55,20
SIVIER, Robert Alan. 5507 WILLOW BEND CT 43082 #028-02-1985 L1993 **FM EM** *020 †18
SLAYMAN, Terry Scott. 444 N CLEVELAND AVE 43082 #016-01-1984 L1985 **FM** *020 †18
SNAPP, Meredith. ■ 43082 #038-40-2008 *012
SO'BRIEN VANPUTTEN, Juliet. 444 N CLEVELAND AVE, STE 1 43082 #038-40-2000 L2000 **FM PHP** *030 †18 ‡
SOLEIMANI, P K. ■ 43082 #517-01-1963 L1971 **RO DR** *020 †80
SOTOS, John Phillip. 444 N CLEVELAND AVE, STE 210 43082 #038-40-1987 L1989 **PD** *020 †55
SPIESS, Catherine O. 484 COUNTY LINE RD W, STE 200 43082 #038-43-1998 L2003 **IM** *020 †20
SPITTLER, Genevieve Marie. 444 N CLEVELAND AVE, STE 1 43082 #038-40-1987 L1988 **EM** *020 †16
STARK, Maureen. 115 COMMERCE PARK DR, STE A 43082 #038-40-1973 L1973 **P** *020 †75
SUH, Steven Hwan. 450 ALKYRE RUN, STE 100 43082 #038-40-1994 L2000 **OPH** *020 †35
TANSKY, Katrina Suzanne. 507 EXECUTIVE CAMPUS DR, STE 160 43082 #038-43-2000 L2000 **PD** *020 †55
THOMAS, John Wm. 450 ALKYRE RUN, STE 200 43082 #028-34-1964 L1975 **TS VS** *020 †85,90
THOMAS, Tammi Taurica. ■ 43082 #038-40-2008 *012
TUCAY, Rodney Fernandez. ■ 43082 #748-10-1973 L1994 **PTH** *071
WAIZMANN, Maria T. 444 N CLEVELAND AVE, STE 1 43082 #038-45-1998 L1999 **FM** *020 †18
WILSON, Ian James. 484 COUNTY LINE RD W, STE 200 43082 #919-05-1977 L1980 **IM** *020 †20
WISLER, Jonathan Robert. ■ 43082 #038-41-2008 *012
YALCH, Peter Andrew. 85 COMMERCE PARK DR 43082 #038-40-1997 L1998 **FM** *020 †18
YU, Edward Eden Romero. ■ 43082 #748-01-1965 L1970 **DR NR** *071
YU, Imelda L. ■ 43082 #748-08-1965 L1972 **AN** *071

WESTERVILLE – FRANKLIN

AMATO, Joseph Ferrara. 500 S CLEVELAND AVE 43081 #038-40-1985 L1985 **OBG** *020 †30
AMICO, Jacqueline M. 3382 PARIS BLVD 43081 #038-45-1988 L1989 **IM** *020 †20
AMOS, Alan Edgar. ■ 43081 #038-40-1977 L1978 *020
ANDERSON, Timothy Wayne. 631 COPELAND MILL RD, STE A 43081 #038-40-1998 L1999 **ID** *020 †20
AURAND, Robert Luther. 631 COPELAND MILL RD, PHYSICIANS, INC SUITE A 43081 #038-40-1983 L1984 **IM** *020 †20
BACH, Joseph Thomas. 500 S CLEVELAND AVE 43081 #038-40-1990 L1995 **PTH** *020 †50
BALAGOPAL, Ashwin. ■ 43081 #035-47-2000 L2004 **ID** *012
BALDOCK, William Edgar. 595 COPELAND MILL RD 43081 #041-02-1945 L1951 **PD** *071 †55
BALTURSHOT, Gregory W. 955 EASTWIND DR 43081 #038-40-1997 L1998 **NS** *020
BASTON, Robert Kirk. ■ 43081 #045-01-1994 L2000 **BBK** *020 †50
BEED, Elaine Alfreda. 660 COOPER RD STE 600 43081 #016-06-1977 L1981 **ON HO** *020 †20
BEGET, Nathan Roy. ■ 43081 #005-12-2005 L2005 **AN** *012
BENEDICT, Stephanie Lee. 495 COOPER RD, STE 309 43081 #038-44-1997 L1998 **FM** *020 †18
BERNACKI, Walter Lang. 495 COOPER RD, STE 414 43081 #038-40-1995 L1996 **PS** *020 †65
BIGLER, Lane Richard. ■ 43081 #028-34-1989 L1993 **D DMP** *020 †15
BLUE, Michael Sherman. 575 COPELAND MILL RD, STE 1D 43081 #038-40-1979 L1980 **FM** *020 †16
BOFILL, Lora Libo-On. 495 COOPER RD STE 309, MOUNT CARMEL FAMILY PRACTI 43081 #748-01-2000 L2004 **FM** *020 †18
BONASSO, Christian Louis. 955 EASTWIND DR 43081 #038-41-1995 L1997 **NS** *020 †25
BRAUN, Chad Matthew. 495 COOPER RD, STE 309 43081 #038-41-1996 L1997 **FM** *020 †18
BRIGGS, Jeffrey Allen. 495 COOPER RD STE 420, ASSOC IN CTRL OHIO OB/GYN 43081 #038-40-1978 L1979 **OBG** *020 †30
BROWN, Diane Cheryl. ■ 43081 #038-41-1981 L1988 **OBG** *020 †30
BRYANT, David Albert. 500 S CLEVELAND AVE 43081 #038-44-1991 L1996 **PTH** *020 †50
CALLOWAY, Geo Franklin, Jr. 495 COOPER RD STE 415 43081 #038-40-1975 L1975 **OPH OS** *020 †35
CANNELL, Christopher D. 70 S CLEVELAND AVE, ORTHONEURO 43081 #038-45-1984 L1985 **PM** *020 †60
CARROLL, Patrick Douglas. ■ 43081 #056-06-2004 L2004 **NPM** *012 †55
CARTER, Michael F. 500 S CLEVELAND AVE, CENTRAL OHIO ANESTHESIA IN 43081 #055-01-1985 L2005 **AN PME** *020 †05
CEBUL, Dennis Ray. 495 COOPER RD, STE 420 43081 #038-40-1973 L1973 **OBG** *020 †30
CHO, Nami Lee. 555 W SCHROCK RD STE 110 43081 #048-02-1995 L1997 **IM** *020 †20
CHOBAN, Stephen Jos. 500 S CLEVELAND AVE 43081 #038-06-1983 L1991 **ORS** *020 †40
CHOPRA, Sandeep. 495 COOPER RD, STE 211 43081 #495-28-1988 L1995 **CD** *020 †20
COSTELLO, Julie Lee. 495 COOPER RD, INC 43081 #038-40-1982 L1985 **PUD CCM** *020 †20
COULING, Sidney Lawrence. 595 COPELAND MILL RD 43081 #038-40-1980 L1985 **PD** *020 †55
DADMEHR, Nahid. 555 W SCHROCK RD, STE 140 43081 #517-01-1979 L1990 **N P** *020 †75
DAVANZO, Mark Edward. 477 COOPER RD, STE 440 43081 #038-40-1980 L1985 **GS** *020 †85
DAVIES, Heather Elizabeth. 595 COPELAND MILL RD # 2A, MID-OHIO PEDIATRICS & ADOL 43081 #041-14-2002 L2002 **PD** *020 †55
DAVIS, William Wiant. ■ 43081 #047-05-1937 L1953 **OM PD** *071 †55
DAWDY, W David. 801 EASTWIND DR, 801 EASTWIND DRIVE 43081 #016-11-1966 L1967 **PD OS** *020 †55
DEMARIA, Jess Jos. 660 COOPER RD, STE 400 43081 #038-40-1985 L1987 **D IM** *020 †15
DIAZ, Donna Tait. 495 COOPER RD, STE 400 43081 #041-14-1986 L1989 **OBG** *020 †30
DICKSON, Matthew David. 575 COPELAND MILL RD, STE 1D 43081 #038-41-2001 L2004 **EM** *020 †16
DOHN, Anita Lynn. ■ 43081 #038-41-1980 L1982 **FM** *040 †18
DOHN, Michael Nelson. ■ 43081 #038-41-1979 L1980 **IM PUD** *030 †20
DORINSKY, Paul Michael. ■ 43081 #038-40-1978 L1980 **PUD CCM** *020 †20
DUFFEY, Timothy Patrick. 70 S CLEVELAND AVE 43081 #016-76-1982, ▲ L1983 **ORS OSM** *020
EMERICK, Jane Louise. 615 COPELAND MILL RD, STE 2D 43081 #038-43-1984 L1986 **ID IM** *020 †20
FINN, James Wallace. 660 COOPER RD, STE 400 43081 #038-40-1969 L1969 **D** *020 †15
FOSSELMAN, Douglas Dale. 555 W SCHROCK RD STE 110, MEDWEST II COMPLEX 43081 #038-40-1982 L1983 **IM** *020 †20
FREEMAN, William Nash. 74 N STATE ST 43081 #038-41-1961 L1961 **GP** *020
FULTON, Mark Andrew. 955 EASTWIND DR 43081 #049-01-1992 L1997 **NS** *020 †25
GAYTON, Samuel Ellsworth. ■ 43081 #038-45-1989 L1990 **FM** *020
GEWIRTZ, Robert Judah. 955 EASTWIND DR 43081 #038-41-1990 L2000 **NS** *020 †25
GHILONI, Bryan Wm. 500 S CLEVELAND AVE 43081 #038-45-1990 L1991 **FM FSM** *020 †18
GIRARDI, Gerald John. 477 COOPER RD, STE 150 43081 #038-40-1980 L1981 **OBG** *020 †30
GOLD, Alan Jack. ■ 43081 #005-06-1967 L1976 **PD** *050 †55
GOLDSMITH, Mark Edward. ■ 43081 #038-41-1970 L1975 **P** *020 †80
GOODWIN, Rose A. 500 S CLEVELAND AVE 43081 #055-02-1982 L1986 **PTH** *020 †50
GRANT, Iain Lachlan. 477 COOPER RD, STE 180 43081 #671-01-1984 L1998 **OTO** *020 †45
GREEN, Lawrence Perry. ■ 43081 #035-01-1958 L1967 **P** *071
GREIWE, Cathy Anne. 477 COOPER RD, STE 200 43081 #038-40-1995 L1996 **FM** *020 †18
GRISCHOW, Bryan Thomas. 477 COOPER RD, STE 440 43081 #038-75-1994, ▲ L1999 **GS** *020
GRODNER, Herbert Allen. 158 WETHERBY LN 43081 #038-40-1967 L1967 **PUD IM** *020 †20
GUTTMAN, Todd Gerard. ■ 43081 #038-40-1985 L1988 **EM** *020 †16
HAINES, Jennifer Ann. 3382 PARIS BLVD 43081 #038-40-2001 L2004 **IM** *020
HALL, Linda Jeanne. ■ 43081 #008-01-1978 L1987 **IM** *020 †20
HALL, Orin Lamont. 660 COOPER RD, STE 800 43081 #048-14-1998 L2000 *020
HAMELBERG, Kim Scott. 495 COOPER RD 43081 #038-40-1977 L1988 **GS** *020 †85
HAMMAR, Eileen Kay. 291 W SCHROCK RD 43081 #041-07-1982 L2002 **FM FPG** *020 †18
HAN, Linda Kyungwon. 495 COOPER RD STE 225 43081 #017-20-1986 L1988 **GS** *020 †85
HARNISH, Wesley James. 550 S CLEVELAND AVE, STE E 43081 #038-40-1984 L1986 **OPH N** *020 †35
HART, Albert Jos, Jr. 901 EASTWIND DR 43081 #038-40-1966 L1966 **OBG** *020 †30
HASTEDT, Randall Coleman. 500 S CLEVELAND AVE 43081 #038-40-1974 L1974 **PTH** *020 †50
HEFFELFINGER, John W. ■ 43081 #038-40-1950 L1950 **FM OS** *071 †18
HEIGHTON, Douglas Alan. 477 COOPER RD, STE 200 43081 #038-45-1998 L1999 **FM** *020 †18
HERRINGTON, Ryan Douglass. 60 WESTERVIEW DR 43081 #051-01-1995 L1999 **GPM** *020 †70
HIGBY, Nicholas Steven. ■ 43081 #038-40-2005 L2005 **PD** *012
HILL, David Brian. 575 COPELAND MILL RD, STE 1D 43081 #005-19-1997 L2002 **FM** *020 †18
HNILICA, Mark A. 955 EASTWIND DR, CENTRAL OHIO NEUROLOGICAL 43081 #048-04-1991 L2003 **NS** *020 †25
HOLZAEPFEL, Christopher D. 568 S CLEVELAND AVE, STE F 43081 #038-40-1980 L1981 **ORS** *020 †40
HOLZHAUSER, Ruth Ann. 5050 PINE CREEK DR STE B 43081 #038-40-1976 L1980 **PD PHP** *020
HOUSER, Robert George. 495 COOPER RD, STE 217 43081 #038-40-1962 L1962 **PS HS** *071 †85,65
HOUSER, Robert Scott. 495 COOPER RD, STE 217 43081 #038-75-1997, ▲ L1998 **PS** *020 †65
HUBBELL, Michael Preston. ■ 43081 #016-01-2007 L2007 **OTO** *012
HUH, Johnny Joon. 631 COPELAND MILL RD STE A, PHYSICINAS INC 43081 #038-44-1995 L1998 **ID** *020 †20

■ = Address Information Privacy Protected

HUMPHREYS, Eric Martin. 500 S CLEVELAND AVE, COA,INC. ST ANNS HOSPITAL 43081 #055-01-1980 L1991 **AN IM** *020 †20,05
IBRAHIM-NOMA, Mayriza Edm. ■ 43081 #748-32-2001 *100
JACOB, Elizabeth Mary. 595 COPELAND MILL RD, STE 2A 43081 #041-14-1994 L1995 **PD** *020 †55
JAFRI, Fatima. ■ 43081 #704-02-1999 L2007 **IM** *100 †20
JAFRI, Nayyer H. 500 S CLEVELAND AVE 43081 #704-16-1990 L1998 **ATP PCP** *020 †50
JASTI, Indira. ■ 43081 #495-50-1993 L1997 **IM** *075 †20
JENKINS, Todd Alan. 495 COOPER RD, STE 400 43081 #001-02-1994 L1999 **OBG** *020 †30
JEPSEN, Stephen Jos. 477 COOPER RD 43081 #016-43-1980 L1993 **VS** *020 †85
JOPLING, Michael Wayne. 500 S CLEVELAND AVE 43081 #055-01-1980 L1990 **AN** *020 †05
KANG, Dong Hui. 495 COOPER RD STE 220 43081 #038-43-1993 L1996 **IM** *020 †20
KELLER, Richard David. ■ 43081 #038-43-2008 *012
KELLY, Timothy. 477 COOPER RD, STE 440 43081 #038-40-1977 L1979 **GS** *020 †85
KENNEDY, Merle Leslie, Jr. 164 WETHERBY LN 43081 #038-40-1980 L1982 **ORS EM** *020 †40
KIEHM, Kelly Jiyong. 955 EASTWIND DR 43081 #017-20-1999 L2000 **NS** *100 ‡
KINCAID, Richard Matthew. 1223 THREE FORKS DR S, PHYAMERICA PHYSICIAN SERVI 43081 #038-40-1980 L1981 **EM OS** *020 †16
KLINGER, Robert Jos. 677 COOPER RD 43081 #038-40-1973 L1973 **PD** *020 †55
KLUMP, Richard. 495 COOPER RD, STE 320 43081 #038-43-1985 L1987 **U** *020 †95
KOVAL, Ann Renee. 291 W SCHROCK RD 43081 #038-40-1987 L1989 **IM** *020 †20
KUGAJEVSKY, Krista O. 575 COPELAND MILL RD, STE 1D 43081 #023-07-1998 L2002 **EM** *020 †16
LADSON-WOFFORD, Stephanie. 495 COOPER RD STE 425, NEPHROLOGY 43081 #038-40-1987 L1989 **NEP GP** *020 †20
LANG, Eric Andrew. 500 S CLEVELAND AVE 43081 #046-01-1989 L1996 **PCP** *020 †50
LEYMASTER, Michael J. 495 COOPER RD STE 325, WESTERVILLE PEDIATRIC SPEC 43081 #038-41-1998 L1999 **IM** *020 †55
LIN, Rosina Piebou. 235 W SCHROCK RD 43081 #041-02-1990 L1993 **D** *020 †15
LINDNER, Steve Edward. 595 COPELAND MILL RD 43081 #038-40-1981 L1984 **PD** *020 †55
LINDSEY, Mark Alan. 495 COOPER RD 43081 #038-40-1991 L1992 **GS** *020 †10,85
LONGSTRETH, Ryan Wesley. 575 COPELAND MILL RD, STE 1D 43081 #038-44-2000 L2003 **EM** *020 †16
LOUIS, David Leonard. 568 S CLEVELAND AVE, STE F 43081 #038-40-1964 L1964 **ORS** *020 †40
MALIK, Noman Ilai. 500 S CLEVELAND AVE 43081 #704-01-1966 L1974 **PTH** *062 †50
MASSICK, Douglas Damien. 477 COOPER RD, STE 180 43081 #056-06-1997 L1998 **OTO** *020
MATHEWS, Jack Lamar. 555 W SCHROCK RD 43081 #038-40-1978 L1979 **FM** *020 †18
MAYER, Gina Kristine. 631 COPELAND MILL RD, STE A 43081 #038-40-2000 L2000 **IM** *020 †20
MC DOWELL, Gladstone, II. 955 EASTWIND DR, STE B 43081 #048-13-1982 L1983 **AN** *020
MC HUGH, Mary P. 500 S CLEVELAND AVE 43081 #038-41-1989 L2002 **PTH** *020 †50
MIRVIS, Bruce Robt. 495 COOPER RD STE 325 43081 #012-01-1973 L1976 **PD** *020 †55
MOAZAMPOUR, Winnie M. 495 COOPER RD STE 230 43081 #038-43-1999 L1999 **FM** *020 †18
MOBIN-UDDIN, Saeeda. 495 COOPER RD STE 414 43081 #704-06-1960 L1975 **OBG** *071
MONETT, Robert Alan. ■ 43081 #038-41-1974 L1977 **FM** *020 †18
MONGKOLLUGSANA, Jackrit. 154 W SCHROCK RD, STE B 43081 #038-44-1992 *100
MOORE, Stephen Frederick. 500 S CLEVELAND AVE 43081 #038-40-1976 L1976 **PTH** *020 †50
MOSSER, Joy Lynn. 660 COOPER RD, SUITE400 43081 #038-44-1993 L1996 **D** *020 †15
MUDD, Mary Elizabeth. 660 COOPER RD STE 800 43081 #038-40-1983 L1984 **FM OBS** *020 †18
NASH, Jennifer Lynn. 660 COOPER RD, STE 400 43081 #038-40-1997 L2000 **D** *020 †15
NELTNER, Carolyn Scott. 955 EASTWIND DR 43081 #016-42-1993 L1999 **NS GS** *020 †25
NIEMANN, Theodore Hollis. 500 S CLEVELAND AVE 43081 #016-45-1988 L1994 **PCP** *020 †50
NIMS, Thomas Andrew. ■ 43081 #038-40-1966 L1966 **SO** *071 †85
OGDEN, John Russell. 955 EASTWIND DR 43081 #003-01-2001 L2001 **NS** *020
OLSON, Lyle Terrance. 659J PARK MEADOW RD, STE 220 43081 #038-40-1994 L1995 **IM** *020 †20
ORWICK, Elizabeth Ann. 495 COOPER RD, STE 400 43081 #038-40-1996 L1997 **OBG** *020 †30
PAGEDAR, Ujwala. ■ 43081 #495-49-1999 L2004 **IM** *020
PANDYA, Jyoti Bhushan. 500 S CLEVELAND AVE, DEPT OF ANESTHESIOLOGY 43081 #495-36-1978 L1984 **AN PME** *020 †05
PANDYA, Urmil Bhadrayu. 1330 PANNELLY PL 43081 #038-44-2002 L2002 **GS** *100 †85
PANGALANGAN, Augusto L. ■ 43081 #748-08-1957 L1967 **GP** *020
PAPPAS, Tom E. 74 N STATE ST 43081 #038-41-1961 L1961 **GP** *071
PARASKOS, John Patrick. 495 COOPER RD, STE 400 43081 #048-12-1987 L1987 **OBG** *020 †30
PARNES, Marc Louis. 904 EASTWIND DR 43081 #038-44-1981 L1982 **OBG** *020 †30
PARSONS, Susan Elizabeth. 737 ENTERPRISE DR, STE 2 43081 #038-40-1996 L1997 **FM** *020 †18 ‡
PATEL, Neeral Subhash. ■ 43081 #028-34-2005 L2005 **IM** *012
PATEL, Taralkumar H. 495 COOPER RD, STE 314 43081 #495-23-1989 L1998 **HO** *020 †20
PELLEGRINI, Arthur Edward. 495 COOPER RD, STE 306 43081 #041-12-1970 L1987 **D DMP** *020 †50,15
PETRELLA, Richard Anthony. 595 COPELAND MILL RD, STE 2A 43081 #038-40-1977 L1977 **PD** *020 †55
PIIRA, Thomas Alan. 500 S CLEVELAND AVE 43081 #025-07-1974 L1993 **PTH HMP** *020 †50
POLEN, Geoffrey Marc. 500 S CLEVELAND AVE 43081 #055-02-1996 L1998 **IM** *020
POWELL, David Michael. 477 COOPER RD, STE 180 43081 #051-01-1994 L1995 **FPS OTO** *020 †45
PRALL, Dawn Michelle. 575 COPELAND MILL RD, STE 1D 43081 #038-40-2000 L2000 **EM** *020 †16
PRENGER, Scott Alan. 631 COPELAND MILL RD, STE A 43081 #038-41-1997 L1998 **IM** *020 †20
PUSHKIN, Natalia. 631 COPELAND MILL RD, STE A 43081 #913-06-1983 L1994 **IM** *020 †20
PYLAEVA, Olga Valerjevna. 500 S CLEVELAND AVE 43081 #913-36-1987 L2001 **IM** *020
QADOOM, Mahmoud Mohammad. 477 COOPER RD, STE 203 43081 #575-01-1992 L2006 **PCC** *020 †20
QUINN, Thomas Edward. 555 W SCHROCK RD STE A 43081 #038-40-1979 L1980 **FM** *020 †18
RAJAH, Vasanthy. 291 W SCHROCK RD 43081 #220-02-1984 L1994 **IM** *020 †20
RALSTON, David Ray. 495 COOPER RD, STE 125 43081 #038-40-1990 L1991 **PCC** *020 †20
RANGI, Inderpreet Kaur. 477 COOPER RD STE 200, INDERPREET KAUR RANGI MD 43081 #495-29-2001 L2002 **FM** *100 †18
RAO, Lingam Panduranga. 1245 S SUNBURY RD, STE 201 43081 #495-50-1968 L1979 **PME AN** *020 †05
RAYMOND, Clifford Wm. 904 EASTWIND DR 43081 #038-40-1973 L1973 **OBG** *020 †30
ROBYN, Jamie Ann. ■ 43081 #038-40-1994 L1998 **IM** *020 †20
ROGERS, Kathleen Marie. 615 COPELAND MILL RD, STE 1E 43081 #038-40-1984 L1988 **D** *020 †15
ROLDAN-ROLDAN, Arnaldo. ■ 43081 #042-01-1955 L1961 **GP** *075 †18
ROSS, Jessica A. 52 WESTERVILLE SQ # 144 43081 #024-05-1976 L1986 **CD IM** *020
RUEDRICH, David Allen. 495 COOPER RD, STE 400 43081 #038-40-1982 L1984 **MFM OBG** *020 †30
RUPERT, Linda Schulski. 428 COUNTY LINE RD - WES 43081 #038-40-1990 L1992 **D** *020 †15
RUSSINOVICH, Nicholas A. ■ 43081 #847-10-1971 L1972 **DR** *020 †80
SAID, Bahadar. 495 COOPER RD, STE 312 43081 #704-09-1988 L2005 **IM** *020 †20
SAI-SUDHAKAR, Chittoor B. 7895 LEDBURY CT 43081 #495-16-1982 L2002 **TS** *020 †85,90
SCHUMACHER, Melinda L. 500 S CLEVELAND AVE 43081 #038-45-1982 L1987 **PTH MM** *020 †50
SCHWARZ, Paul Benj. ■ 43081 #539-02-1955 L1968 **AN** *071
SEAVOLT, Maralyn Barton. 660 COOPER RD, STE 400 43081 #038-43-1997 L1998 **D** *020 †15
SEEDER, Lewis. 568 S CLEVELAND AVE, STE B 43081 #016-11-1970 L1971 **PM OM** *020 †16,60
SELINE, Peter Carl. 428 COUNTY LINE RD - WES 43081 #026-08-1992 L2000 **DS D** *020 †15
SEN, Anindya Kumar. 631 COPELAND MILL RD 43081 #038-40-2000 L2000 **IM** *020 †20 ‡
SHEETS, Eileen Hewitt. 595 COPELAND MILL RD 43081 #038-40-1987 L1988 **PD** *020 †55
SHEIKH, Farrukh Sayyar. 500 S CLEVELAND AVE 43081 #704-01-1959 L1975 **PTH CLP** *020 †50
SHENIGO, Mary Ann. ■ 43081 #038-40-1992 L1993 **FM** *020 †18
SHUBERT, Phillip Jos. 500 S CLEVELAND AVE 43081 #038-40-1985 L1986 **OBG** *020 †30
SINAI HEDE, Rajiv. 495 COOPER RD, STE 211 43081 #496-15-1985 L2002 **CD** *020 †20
SMITH, Keith Ronald. 575 COPELAND MILL RD, STE 1D 43081 #010-01-1988 L1989 **EM** *020 †16 ‡
SODER, Bradley Steven. 428 COUNTY LINE RD 43081 #038-43-2002 L2006 **D** *020 †15
SPIESS, Adam Christopher. 477 COOPER RD, STE 180 43081 #038-43-1998 L2003 **OTO** *020 †45
SREEDEVI, Sunkireddy. 501 W SCHROCK RD, STE 103 43081 #495-62-1995 L2003 **NEP** *020 †20
STARKEY, Roy Wm. ■ 43081 #038-40-1954 L1954 **PM** *020 †60
STIFF, Michael Gerard. 495 COOPER RD, STE 330 43081 #038-40-1982 L1983 **GE** *020 †20
STOCK, Kimberly Anne. 3382 PARIS BLVD 43081 #024-05-1997 L1998 **IM** *020 †20
TAKATS, Jenifer Marie. 575 COPELAND MILL RD STE 1 43081 #038-40-1987 L1991 **P** *020 †75
TAYLOR, Charles W, III. 495 COOPER RD 43081 #038-06-1983 L1988 **CRS GS** *020 †85,10
TETERIS, John Nicholas. 495 COOPER RD, STE 400 43081 #038-40-1988 L1990 **OBG** *020 †30
TOBIN, Evan Jos. 477 COOPER RD, STE 180 43081 #048-12-1992 L1994 **OTO** *020 †45
TRELA-FULOP, Kathleen J. 595 COPELAND MILL RD 43081 #038-40-1995 L1996 **PD** *020 †55
TUTTLE, Steven Eugene. 885 EASTWIND DR 43081 #011-03-1978 L1979 **PTH** *020 †50
USELMAN, James Henry. 955 EASTWIND DR 43081 #041-12-1986 L1988 **NS** *020 †25
VAUGHN, Hilary Leigh. 500 S CLEVELAND AVE, ST ANN'S HOSPITAL 43081 #038-41-1996 L1997 **DR** *020 †20
VAUGHN, John Anthony. 575 COPELAND MILL RD # 1D 43081 #038-40-1997 L1998 **FM** *020 †18
VER MEULEN, John Hendrik. ■ 43081 #660-04-1955 L1963 **P** *072
VILLAVECER, Hermenegildo. 100 S STATE ST 43081 #748-08-1962 L1971 **GP IM** *071
VINCENT, Gilford Stephan. 477 COOPER RD 43081 #025-07-1979 L1987 **VS GS** *020 †85
VITULLO, John Frank. ■ 43081 #038-45-2007 L2007 **FP** *012
WALUZAK, Michael Douglas. 555 W SCHROCK RD STE 110 43081 #025-12-1978 L1982 **IM EM** *020 †16,20
WEINSTOCK, Michael B. 575 COPELAND MILL RD, STE 1D 43081 #038-40-1991 L1992 **FM** *020 †18
WEISE, Kenneth Barker. ■ 43081 #035-08-1969 L1970 **GS** *071 †85
WHITLATCH, Joseph P, Sr. 495 COOPER RD, STE 212 43081 #010-02-1948 L1949 **FM** *071
WILCOX, Joseph Felton. 164 WETHERBY LN, NORTHEAST ORTHOPEDICS, INC 43081 #016-02-1995 L2000 **OSM** *020 †40
WILKIN, Nathaniel Kevin. 660 COOPER RD, STE 400 43081 #038-40-2001 L2006 **D** *100 †15
WINKLE, M Phillip. 500 S CLEVELAND AVE, ST ANNS HOSPINIC FOUNDATIO 43081 #038-45-1988 L1990 **AN** *020 †05
WODARCYK, Kathleen Marie. 495 COOPER RD STE 325 43081 #038-43-1985 L1988 **PD** *020 †55
WURMBRAND, Joan Ellen. 291 W SCHROCK RD 43081 #051-04-1979 L1980 **FM** *020 †18
XIE, Edward E. ■ 43081 #038-40-2005 L2006 **FP** *012
YASHON, David. 955 EASTWIND DR 43081 #016-11-1960 L1966 **NS** *020 †25
YAW, Michelle Emelia. 495 COOPER RD, STE 325 43081 #017-20-1995 L1997 **PD** *020 †55
YODER, Frank Wallace. 29 W COLLEGE AVE 43081 #017-20-1972 L1973 **D** *020 †15
ZAIDI, Syed Khurram Abbas. ■ 43081 #704-02-1999 L2007 **IM IMG** *100 †20
ZAINO, Robert Paul. 500 S CLEVELAND AVE 43081 #038-40-1987 L1988 **FM** *020 †18
ZARRABY, Roya. 631 COPELAND MILL RD, PHYSICIANS, INC. 43081 #038-45-1995 L1996 **IM** *020 †20
ZERICK, William Robert. 955 EASTWIND DR 43081 #055-01-1988 L1992 **NS** *020 †25
ZIMMERMAN, Robert Edward. 555 W SCHROCK RD, STE A 43081 #038-40-1987 L1988 **FM** *020 †18
ZYNIEWICZ, Kelley Joann. 660 COOPER RD, STE 400 43081 #025-12-1985 L1991 **D** *020 †15

WESTFIELD CENTER – MEDINA

WINTER, Robert Hudson. 8849 CONCORD DRIVE, WELTFIELD CENTER 44251 #036-07-1964 L1970 **R** *071 †80

WESTLAKE – CUYAHOGA

AL-HADDAD, Safaa Fiak. 30033 CLEMENS RD 44145 #528-01-1988 L1997 **IM** *020 †20
ALKAYED, Khaldoun Jamal. ■ 44145 #575-01-2001 L2007 **PHO** *012 †55
AL-LAHHAM, Bassel. ■ 44145 #875-01-1999 L2003 **IM** *020 †20
ALLAN, Daniel. 30033 CLEMENS RD 44145 #038-06-1997 L2000 **FM** *020 †18
AL-MUBARAK, Nadim A. 29101 HEALTH CAMPUS DR, BLDG 2 44145 #154-07-1987 L2002 **CD** *071 †20
ANDREWS, George Naguib. ■ 44145 #915-02-1997 L2002 **AN** *012
ASHWATH, Ravi Chandra. ■ 44145 #495-09-1994 L2004 **PDC** *100 †55
ASSAF, Richard R. 1991 CROCKER RD, STE 310 44145 #038-41-1990 L1993 **D** *020 †15
BABAKI, Abbas. ■ 44145 #517-03-1973 L1981 **IM** *020
BACEVICE, Anthony E, Jr. 2001 CROCKER RD, STE 520 44145 #038-06-1981 L1982 **OBG MFM** *020 †30

7654

■ = Address Information Privacy Protected

BAGAI, Rakesh Kumar. 1481 BARCLAY BLVD 44145 #038-41-2008 *012

BAHNTGE, Michael F. 25200 CENTER RIDGE RD, STE 2100 44145 #035-08-1979 L1983
IM *020 †20,75

BAIG, Mirza I. 25200 CENTER RIDGE RD, STE 1400 44145 #495-65-1982 L1990 **PM** *020 †20,60

BALDADO, Florante Anfone. 29099 HEALTH CAMPS DR #320 44145 #748-01-1965 L1972
FM *020

BAMBAKIDIS, Peter. 25200 CENTER RIDGE RD, STE 2100 44145 #038-06-1984 L1989
N CN *020 †75

BARDENSTEIN, David Sander. 950 CLAGUE RD, BLDG B 44145 #025-01-1979 L1990
OPH EM *020 †35

BARSOUM, Wael Kamal. 30033 CLEMENS RD 44145 #038-40-1995 L1997 **ORS** *020 †40

BARTON, Frederick Jos. 960 CLAGUE RD, IRELAND CANCER CENTER 44145
#038-06-1989 L1990 **RO** *020 †80

BEDI, Harprit Singh. ■ 44145 #035-03-2003 L2003 **DR** *012

BEKENY, James Ronald. 850 COLUMBIA RD STE 202 44145 #038-06-1977 L1982
VS GS *020 †85

BELKIN, Julie Kest. 950 CLAGUE RD, BLDG B 44145 #038-43-1989 L1990 **OPH** *020 †35

BELL, David Murray. 24723 DETROIT RD, ORTHOPAEDIC ASSOCIATES 44145
#038-06-1955 L1955 **ORS** *071 †40

BELLE, Natalie Jane. ■ 44145 #010-03-2002 L2004 **GS** *100

BENNET, John B, II. 850 COLUMBIA RD, STE 101 44145 #035-03-1985 L1988 **PD** *020 †55

BENNHOFF, David Frederick. 805 COLUMBIA RD, STE 111 44145 #017-20-1962 L1969
OTO HNS *020 †45

BERKOWITZ, Robert Jon. 2211 CROCKER RD 44145 #050-02-1999 L1999 **ORS** *020 †40

BIGGINS, John. ■ 44145 #539-06-1952 L1960 **AN** *071 †05

BLADES, Edmond William. 850 COLUMBIA RD, NORTH SHORE 44145 #035-01-1982 L1984
GE *050 †20

BOLLA, Ravisankar R. 25200 CENTER RIDGE RD, STE 1100 44145 #495-50-1980 L1990
CD IM *020 †20

BOULANGER, Scott Charles. 960 CLAGUE RD, STE 1600 44145 #038-40-1995 L2006
PDS *020 †85

BOURNIGAL, Lionel Jose. ■ 44145 #308-01-1957 L1963 **IM RHU** *071 †20

BUCZEK, Marek Antoni. 960 CLAGUE RD, STE 3120 44145 #759-15-1984 L1999 **N** *020 †75

BURKEY, Brent William. 30033 CLEMENS RD, WL10 44145 #041-15-2001 L2001 **HOS IM** *020 ‡

BUZON, Moises Lozada. ■ 44145 #748-08-1961 L1970 **AN** *071

CABAL, Eustaquio V, Jr. 29099 HEALTH CAMPUS DR 44145 #748-07-1965 L1972
OBG GPM *020 †30

CALIWARA-DAMIAN, C. ■ 44145 #748-08-1966 L1974 **IM** *071

CAMPBELL, Colleen Mcgee. ■ 44145 #038-06-2004 L2004 **PD** *100 †55

CARAVELLA, Philip Joseph. 30033 CLEMENS RD, THE CLEVELAND CLINIC 44145
#028-34-1970 L1977 **FM** *020 †18

CAREY, Fachtna. 29000 CENTER RIDGE RD, RADIOLOGY DEPT 44145 #539-02-1974 L1986
DR FM *020 †80

CARRUTHERS, Amy B. 960 CLAGUE RD, PRACTICES INC 44145 #038-40-1992 L1996
PD *020 †55

CASSERLY, Caroline Mary. 30033 CLEMENS RD 44145 #038-06-1992 L1994 **CD** *020 †20

CASTLE, Lon Wayne. 30033 CLEMENS RD, CLEVELAND CLINCI WESTLAKE 44145
#041-13-1965 L1973 **CD** *020 †20

CHADWICK, Neal Carl. 805 COLUMBIA RD, STE 101 44145 #041-02-1974 L1979
PUD IM *020 †20

CHERIYAN, Anita. 25200 CENTER RIDGE RD, STE 3200 44145 #495-27-1975 L1985
GE *020 †20

CHIKUNGUWO, Silas Mbasera. ■ 44145 #010-03-2000 L2006 **GS** *020 ‡

CHRISTIAN, Jeffrey Schupp. 29325 HEALTH CAMPUS DR, STE 1 44145 #038-06-1987 L1987
OBG *020 †30

CHWALS, Walter Jakob. 960 CLAGUE RD, STE 1600 44145 #759-01-1980 L2002 **PDS** *020 †85

COLUMBRO, Marcia Lee. 960 CLAGUE RD, PRACTICES INC 44145 #038-40-1986 L1988
PD *020 †55

COMISKEY, Mariana Georget. ■ 44145 #781-03-1995 L2007 **N** *100

CONNOLLY, Suzanne Denise. 805 COLUMBIA RD, STE 102 44145 #038-43-2002 L2002
PD *100 †55

CONWAY, Jessica Louise. 30033 CLEMENS RD 44145 #038-43-2001 L2001 **FM** *020 †18

CORPUS, James Thomas. 25200 CENTER RIDGE RD, STE 3500 44145 #011-03-1993 L1996
FM GS *020 †85,18

COSSLER, Nancy Jo. 960 CLAGUE RD, STE 2410 44145 #038-44-1983 L1989 **OBG** *040 †30

CULLEY, Carl Albert, Jr. 30033 CLEMENS RD 44145 #038-40-1974 L1974 **IM** *020 †20

DAS, Jagannath. 29099 HEALTH CAMPUS DR, STE 170 44145 #495-02-1960 L1977
OBG *020 †30

DASARI, Lakshmi Narayana. 25200 CENTER RIDGE RD, STE 2300 44145 #495-62-1972 L1977
IM *020 †20

DAUM, Wayne John Gattas. 30033 CLEMENS RD 44145 #028-34-1971 L1980 **ORS** *020 †40

DAVILA, Roberto, Jr. 29099 HEALTH CAMPUS DR, STE 120 44145 #042-03-1980 L1985
IM NEP *020

DAW, Hamed. 30033 CLEMENS RD 44145 #165-01-1988 L1999 **HO** *020 †20

DAYARATNA, Sandra Dilani. 960 CLAGUE RD, STE 2410 44145 #033-06-1996 L2006
OBG *020 †30

DESHPANDE, Krishna. ■ 44145 #495-56-1967 L1977 **GS** *020 †85

DIAZ, Romeo M. 25101 DETROIT RD 44145 #748-01-1967 L1976 **GS ON** *020 †85

DIPALI, Aravind Lingo. 29099 HEALTH CAMPUS DR #32 44145 #495-35-1973 L1978
PD *020 †55

DIWAN, Renuka. 29101 HEALTH CAMPUS DR, BLDG 2 44145 #495-01-1982 L1984
DS D *020 †15

DOBRE, Mirela Aurora. ■ 44145 #781-04-1997 **IM** *012

DOLEH, Mohamad Khader. ■ 44145 #038-06-2003 L2003 **IM** *100 †20

EDEL, Thomas Bernard. 30033 CLEMENS RD 44145 #025-07-1984 L1989 **ICE CD** *020 †20

EISMON, Jennifer Lynn. ■ 44145 #038-43-2004 L2004 **AN** *012

ELTOMEY, Mohamed Abd E. ■ 44145 #915-02-1964 L1975 **P FM** *020 †75,18

EVANS, Stephen Bir. ■ 44145 #038-45-1980 L1981 **EM FM** *020 †16,18

EVANS, Stephen Bir, Jr. 26908 DETROIT RD 44145 #038-45-1996 L1999 **HS GS** *020

EYRE, John Chas. 960 CLAGUE RD STE 3201 44145 #038-40-1989 L1995 **IM** *020 †20

FINE, Edward David. 30033 CLEMENS RD 44145 #038-06-1990 L1991 **OTO** *020 †45

FOX, Kermit William. ■ 44145 #048-12-2005 L2006 **PM** *012

FRACKELTON, James Pierson. 24700 CENTER RIDGE RD 44145 #038-06-1954 L1954
CD GPM *020

FRANCZEK, Vincent Jos. 850 COLUMBIA RD 44145 #038-43-1989 L1994 **AN IM** *020 †20,05

FREEDMAN, Paul Steven. ■ 44145 #038-41-1986 L1989 **ORS** *020

FREEMAN, Richard Boyd. 30033 CLEMENS RD, ATT RICHARD FREEMAN(WL30) 44145
#038-06-1975 L1979 **HNS OTO** *020 †45

FRIEDELL, Richard Alan. 24803 DETROIT RD # D-1 44145 #038-06-1971 L1971 **P CHP** *020 †75

FROST, Frederick Sheehan. 30033 CLEMENS RD 44145 #016-06-1983 L1988 **PM** *020 †60

GALETARI, Lucia C. 29101 HEALTH CAMPUS DR, BLDG 2 44145 #781-04-1987 L1994
IM *020 †20

GANNON, Patricia Ann. 30033 CLEMENS RD, CLINIC FOUNDATION 44145 #038-43-1990 L1992
IM *020 †20

GARCIA, Alma J. ■ 44145 #038-75-2006, ▲ L2006 **PM** *012

GARCIA, Maximo Cueto, Jr. 30143 SAINT IVES, STE 6 44145 #748-08-1964 L1978 **TS IM** *020

GARCIA, Ronald Steven D. 25200 CENTER RIDGE RD, STE 3300 44145 #748-08-1983 L1987
IM *020 †20

GARCIA, Serafin C, Jr. 26314 CENTER RIDGE RD, STE 1 44145 #748-08-1965 L1972
IM CD *020

GARG, Savita. 26955 KENLEY CT 44145 #038-06-1996 L1999 **FM** *020 †18

GARNER, Andrew Seyfarth. 960 CLAGUE RD, PRACTICES INC 44145 #038-06-1997 L2000
PD *020 †55

GERACE, John Parker. 29257 CENTER RIDGE RD 44145 #038-41-1990 L1991 **FM** *020 †18

GIOITTA, Nunzio Anthony. 29000 CENTER RIDGE RD 44145 #869-05-1959 L1960 **OTO OS** *075

GIPSON, Mark Joel. 26908 DETROIT RD, STE 200 44145 #048-13-1980 L1985 **PD** *020 †55

GORDILLO, Manuel E. 30400 DETROIT RD, STE 301 44145 #737-01-1958 L1966 **P** *020 †75

GOSAIN, Sudhir. 25101 DETROIT RD 44145 #496-09-1980 L1994 **PUD** *020 †20

GREENBERG, Mary Kay. 960 CLAGUE RD, PRACTICES INC 44145 #038-40-1992 L1994
PD *020 †55

GREENWALT, Peter H. 850 COLUMBIA RD, NORTH SHORE 44145 #038-06-1970 L1975
GE IM *020 †20

GROSS-SAWICKA, Ewa M. 2236 INDIANPATH DR 44145 #759-07-1981 L1997 **IM** *020 †20

GUIRGUIS, Amir Fouad. 902 WESTPOINT PKWY, STE 320 44145 #915-04-1981 L1998
IM *020 †20

GUPTA, Ajay Kumar. 29101 HEALTH CAMPUS DR, STE 340 44145 #038-41-1999 L2004
OPH *020 †35 ‡

GUTIERREZ, James Francis. 30033 CLEMENS RD 44145 #038-06-1990 L1994 **IM** *020 †20

HAAS, Leonard Thos. 2001 CROCKER RD, STE 650 44145 #028-34-1971 L1972 **GYN** *020 †30

HADDAD, Basem Ghanem. 25200 CENTER RIDGE RD, STE 3400 44145 #875-01-1993 L1999
CCM *020

HAGHIGHI, Daryush. 29099 HEALTH CAMPUS DR, STE 270 44145 #517-04-1956 L1965 **CD** *071

HALADAY, Robert. ■ 44145 #035-48-1999 L2006 **IM RHU** *020 †20

HAMMAD, Azzam. ■ 44145 #875-03-1988 L1994 **PTH** *020 †50

HANNA, Amgad Hanna Nashid. ■ 44145 #915-04-1998 L2005 **AN** *012

HARRIS, Craig Kurt. 850 COLUMBIA RD, NORTH SHORE 44145 #038-40-1976 L1976
GE IM *020 †20

HASAN, Kamrul. 26633 DETROIT RD 44145 #704-02-1972 L1978 **OBG** *020 †30

HATTAB, Helen Gergis. 29133 HEALTH CAMPUS DR 44145 #528-03-1976 L1990 **P** *020 †20

HAZEN, Gale. 27337 PINEVIEW DR 44145 #016-01-1973 L1978 **NS** *020 †25

HENSON, Jennifer Trang. 25651 DETROIT RD, STE 304 44145 #038-40-1998 L2007
FM *020 †18

HEVENER, Kara Suzanne. ■ 44145 #038-43-2004 L2005 **GS** *012

HILL, Regina. 29325 HEALTH CAMPUS DR 44145 #038-44-1990 L1992 **OBG** *020 †30

HOGAN, Patrick W. ■ 44145 #003-75-2003, ▲ L2003 **PMM** *012

HONG, Chong Yeal. ■ 44145 #583-02-1965 L1974 **GS** *020

HRITZ, Michael George. 24723 DETROIT RD, ORTHOPAEDIC ASSOCIATES INC 44145
#038-06-1975 L1976 **ORS** *020 †40

HULYALKAR, Atul R. 29325 HEALTH CAMPUS DR # 3 44145 #050-02-1985 L1993
CD *020,05

HUSSAIN, Azmat. 29099 HEALTH CAMPUS DR, BLDG 3 44145 #704-01-1981 L1995
CD IM *020 †20

IBRAHIM, Emil Kaldas. 25125 DETROIT RD, STE 140 44145 #915-02-1971 L1995 **P** *020

IBRAHIM, Lamia. ■ 44145 #915-04-1995 L2004 **SME** *012

IRISH, Keith Randall. ■ 44145 #016-11-1946 L1957 **R NM** *071 †80,28

ISARADISAIKUL, Voravit. ■ 44145 #891-01-1969 L1976 **OBG** *020 †30

ISSA, Khaled. 850 COLUMBIA RD, NORTH SHORE 44145 #875-02-1983 L1989 **GE IM** *020 †20

JACKOSKY, Catherine Ivy. 24600 CENTER RIDGE RD #225 44145 #048-14-1991 L1998
CHP *075

JARJOURA, Pascal Milad. 29325 HEALTH CAMPUS DR 44145 #605-02-1998 L2002 **OBG** *100

JAZWA, Jeff. 1947 SAVANNAH PKWY 44145 #038-06-1982 L1983 **AN** *020 †20

JESSE, Joan Marie. 850 COLUMBIA RD, STE 330 44145 #038-06-1987 L1987 **OBG** *020 †30

JOHNSON, Charles David. ■ 44145 #048-43-1998 L2007 **PD** *020 †55

JOHNSON, Karen Schwenk. ■ 44145 #016-43-2001 L2007 **DR** *020 †80

JUDGE, John Robt. ■ 44145 #038-40-1961 L1961 **LM IM** *072 †50

JURAK, Stephen Stanley. 2001 CROCKER RD, STE 600 44145 #025-07-1978 L1980
PD *020 †20

JURDI, Raja Anis. ■ 44145 #605-01-1980 L1993 **DR** *020 †80

KADHIM, Hayder Mohammad. 850 COLUMBIA RD, STE 120 44145 #528-01-1979 L2003
N *020 †75

KANDULA, Padmaja Naga. ■ 44145 #038-44-1999 L1999 **N** *020 †75

KASICK, James Michael. 29099 HEALTH CAMPUS DR, STE 330 44145 #038-40-1973 L1977
D OS *020 †18,15

KAUH, Jae Joon. 2620 WYNDGATE CT 44145 #583-01-1950 L1976 **GP** *020

KENNEDY, Daniel William. ■ 44145 #030-06-2005 L2006 **DR** *012

KHERANI, Kausar Salim. 805 COLUMBIA RD STE 115 44145 #495-17-1974 L1980 **PD** *020 †55

KILROY, Edward G. 800 BRICK MILL RUN 44145 #028-34-1950 L1951 **TS** *071 †85,90

KIM, Danny Yuntae. ■ 44145 #005-19-2004 L2005 **OPH** *012

KIM, Hoonki. ■ 44145 #583-13-1984 L2005 **FP** *012

KIRPEKAR, Sona S. 960 CLAGUE RD, STE 3201 44145 #024-05-1995 L1996 **IM** *020 †20

KISH, Louis Stephen, II. 29101 HEALTH CAMPUS DR # 4 44145 #038-06-1979 L1980 **D** *020 †15

KISS, Attilla. 29000 CENTER RIDGE RD, ST JOHN WESTSHORE HOSPITAL 44145
#038-44-2000 L2003 **EM** *020 †16

KNAPP, Joseph Maynard. 30033 CLEMENS RD 44145 #028-34-1994 L1997 **IM** *020 †20

KOMITAU, Jason Jon. 30033 CLEMENS RD, CLEVELAND CLINIC WESTLAKE 44145
#038-43-2002 L2002 **FM** *020 †18

KONANAHALLI, Basavaraj P. ■ 44145 #495-22-1959 L1968 **IM CD** *071

KONSTAN, Robert Michael. 29000 CENTER RIDGE RD 44145 #038-40-1987 L1990 **R** *020 †80

KONTAK, James Arthur. 29101 HEALTH CAMPUS DR, UROLOGY PARTNERS INC 44145
#038-43-1999 L2005 **U** *020 †95

KOO, Peter J. ■ 44145 #583-04-1965 L1974 **OBG** *020 †30

KOSHY, Premila. 29000 CENTER RIDGE RD, MEDICAL STAFF SERVICES 44145 #495-31-1974 L1994 **IM** *020

KREBS, John Anthony. 30033 CLEMENS RD 44145 #038-40-1968 L1968 **D** *020 †15

KREBS, John Keith. 2211 CROCKER RD 44145 #020-12-1988 L1994 **ORS** *020 †40

KUNDU, Neilendu. ■ 44145 #038-44-2008 *012

KUNDU, Sunanda. 29000 CENTER RIDGE RD 44145 #495-39-1971 L1981 **GP** *020

KUTINA, Charles Bruce. 25200 CENTER RIDGE RD, STE 1200 44145 #038-43-1977 L1979 **OPH** *020 †35

KWON, J Helen. 29101 HEALTH CAMPUS DR, STE 240 44145 #583-04-1966 L1971 **PD** *020 †55

LAGWINSKI, Nikolaj Paul. ■ 44145 #038-44-2004 L2004 **PTH** *012

LAPLANTE, Mary. 850 COLUMBIA RD, STE 330 44145 #038-40-1990 L1991 **OBG** *020 †30

LASCH, Susan Jean. 960 CLAGUE RD, STE 2410 44145 #038-06-2001 L2001 **OBG** *020 †30

LAVERY, Ian Calder. 30033 CLEMENS RD 44145 #143-05-1967 L1977 **CRS** *020 †10

LAVERY, Mary Ann. 27059 CENTER RIDGE RD 44145 #038-40-1977 L1977 **OPH** *020 †35

LEE, Michael Hyukwon. ■ 44145 #035-19-2000 L2005 **GE** *012 †20

LEE, Saebom. ■ 44145 #038-40-2005 L2005 **AN** *012

LEICHT, George Peter. 805 COLUMBIA RD, OB-GYN WEST INC 44145 #016-43-1952 L1952 **OBG** *072 †30

LEISINGER, Kevin Jeffrey. ■ 44145 #038-43-2006 L2006 **FP** *012

LEVY, David Alan. 29000 CENTER RIDGE RD 44145 #016-42-1989 L1990 **U** *020 †95

LEVY, Edward Albert. 850 COLUMBIA RD STE 103 44145 #038-41-1986 L1992 **PS GS** *020 †85,65

LEWIN, Walter O. ■ 44145 #010-01-1944 L1947 **GS CRS** *072 †85

LIM, Tracy Agnes. 805 COLUMBIA RD STE 102, FUTURE GENERATION PED 44145 #038-43-1994 L1996 **PD** *020 †55

LIN, Thomas C. ■ 44145 #244-02-1961 L1976 **N EM** *020

LLERENA, Amelia Veronica. 29099 HEALTH CAMPUS DR, STE 290 44145 #748-02-1961 L1981 **IM** *020

LOCKHART, Curtis Major. 29101 HEALTH CAMPUS DR, STE 155 44145 #038-06-1981 L1991 **VS GS** *020 †85

LONSDALE, Derrick. 24700 CENTER RIDGE RD 44145 #352-07-1948 L1962 **P** *020 †55

LUCAS, Robert Bradley. 960 CLAGUE RD, STE 1100 44145 #038-43-1991 L1994 **OBG** *020 †30

LY, Uyen. ■ 44145 #048-78-2006, ▲ L2006 **PTH** *012

MABINI, Theodore R. ■ 44145 #748-01-1952 L1967 **PTH GP** *020

MACHEN, Sevella Karen. 29000 CENTER RIDGE RD 44145 #016-11-1995 L1998 **PTH** *020 †50

MAC INTYRE, Stephen S. 30033 CLEMENS RD, CLEVELAND CLINIC WESTLAKE 44145 #038-06-1976 L1981 **IM** *071 †20

MAHAJAN, Sangeeta Tina. 960 CLAGUE RD, STE 2410 44145 #038-40-1998 L2005 **OBG** *020 †30

MAHALAHA, Saroj. 850 COLUMBIA RD, STE 330 44145 #495-49-1970 L1977 **OBG** *020 †30

MANDEL, Irwin Michael. 24723 DETROIT RD, 24723 DETROIT ROAD 44145 #038-06-1996 L1997 **ORS OSM** *020 †40

MANSNERUS, Roger Alan. 850 COLUMBIA RD, STE 105 44145 #016-06-1970 L1980 **IM** *020 †20

MANZON, Judith Directo. 30033 CLEMENS RD, WL40 44145 #038-40-2002 L2002 **IM** *100 †20

MARSH, Lisa Anne. 30033 CLEMENS RD, CLEVELAND CLINIC WESTLAKE 44145 #038-44-1998 L1999 **FM** *020 †18

MASSOUH, Marwan. 29101 HEALTH CAMPUS DR, STE 260 44145 #875-01-1982 L1987 **IM** *020 †20

MATHAI, Susan Philip. ■ 44145 #496-32-1997 L2005 **IM** *020 †20

MATHEW, George K. 29099 HEALTH CAMPUS DR, STE 230 44145 #495-31-1975 L1980 **GP IM** *020

MC CAFFERTY, Francis, Sr. 31314 CENTER RIDGE RD 44145 #028-34-1959 L1961 **P OS** *020 †75

MCCONOUGHEY, David Anthon. ■ 44145 #016-76-2007, ▲ L2007 *012

MC CORMICK, Robt Richard. ■ 44145 #038-40-1955 L1955 **OS** *030

MCINTYRE, Alice Gong. ■ 44145 #038-43-2001 L2001 **MPD** *020 †55

MC NAMEE, Lawrence Jos. 1648 CANTERBURY RD 44145 #028-34-1966 L1973 **R** *020 †80

MC NUTT, Robert A. 26908 DETROIT RD, STE 200 44145 #039-01-1976 L1993 **RHU IM** *020 †20

MERVART, Michael Jaroslav. 30033 CLEMENS RD 44145 #063-01-1979 L1987 **NS** *020

MERVART, Miloslava Ann. 850 COLUMBIA RD, STE 330 44145 #035-19-1979 L1987 **OBG** *020 †30

MLADENOV, Patricia. ■ 44145 #665-02-2005 L2006 **IM** *100

MOHR, Rose M. 29101 HEALTH CAMPUS DR, STE 230 44145 #041-07-1972 L1973 **OTO** *020 †45

MOINUDDIN, Doug S. 28360 CENTER RIDGE RD 44145 #038-41-1994 L2002 *100

MOLINA, Alberto. 29325 HEALTH CAMPUS DR # 3 44145 #264-04-1956 L1968 **IM ADM** *071

MORSE, Reid Morton. 29101 HEALTH CAMPUS DR, UROLOGY PARTNERS INC 44145 #038-06-1984 L1985 **U** *020 †95

MOURANY, Adnan. 29099 HEALTH CAMPUS DR, STE 250 44145 #875-01-1978 L1982 **OTO** *020 †45

MULLIGAN, Kathleen Anne. 1991 CROCKER RD STE 310 44145 #038-06-1992 L1993 **D IM** *020 †15

NADER, Jose Alfredo. ■ 44145 #917-09-1976 L1979 **PDC IM** *020 †20

NAYAK, Sagarika. 29099 HEALTH CAMPUS DR, NORTH COAST NEURO INC #390 44145 #038-45-1986 L1991 **N** *020 †75

NEBESH-JATSYSHYN, C. 30400 DETROIT RD, STE 404 44145 #038-43-1995 L1998 **CHP P** *020 †75

NEILSEN, Susan A. 850 COLUMBIA RD 44145 #038-43-1991 L1993 **FM** *020 †18

NELSON, Rebecca Ann. 29325 HEALTH CAMPUS DR, STE 1 44145 #025-01-1993 L1999 **OBG** *020 †30

NERI-NIXON, Maria S. 850 COLUMBIA RD, STE 120 44145 #748-10-1983 L2002 **IM** *020 †20

NEWTON, Erin Vale. 30033 CLEMENS RD 44145 #038-06-1997 L1998 **HO** *020 †20

NOVESKE, F Gregory. 29101 HEALTH CAMPUS DR, STE 293 44145 #038-40-1974 L1974 **P CHP** *020 †75 ‡

O'MALLEY, James Richard. ■ 44145 #028-34-1947 L1948 **GS PDS** *071 †85

ORR, Robert Douglas. 30033 CLEMENS RD 44145 #065-01-1989 L2003 *020 †40

O'TOOLE, John Michael. 1751 FARRS GARDEN PATH, SAINT VINCENT MEDICAL BUIL 44145 #038-41-1989 L1994 **GS** *020 †85

PALAPARTY, Poornanand. ■ 44145 #495-65-1974 L1978 **IM ON** *020 †20

PANG, Tet Hyun. ■ 44145 #242-50-1948 L1961 **GS TS** *020

PARRAS, George Peter. 29101 HEALTH CAMPS DR #440 44145 #038-40-1984 L1990 **FPS OTO** *020 †45

PARTAL, George. 29325 HEALTH CAMPUS DR, STE #3 OHIO MED GROUP 44145 #781-02-1970 L1993 **IM** *020 †20

PASUNURI, Ramya S. 29000 CENTER RIDGE RD, MEDICAL STAFF OFFICE 44145 #913-89-1994 L1999 **IM** *020 †20

PATEL, Rajnikant Manibhai. 1636 BALMORAL WAY 44145 #495-22-1976 L1983 **GS** *020 †85

PATTERSON, Ryan William. ■ 44145 #005-15-2005 L2005 **ORS** *012

PAVLUK, Charles Harry. 960 CLAGUE RD, STE 3260 44145 #010-01-1977 L1978 **IM** *020 †20

PECKHAM, Roger Sanford. 29101 HEALTH CAMPUS DR, BLDG 2 44145 #056-05-1976 L1983 **END IM** *020 †20

PELAEZ-ANDRES, Leticia E. ■ 44145 #748-01-1962 L1977 **IM CD** *020

PERSAUD, Harry. 29099 HEALTH CAMPUS DR, STE 110 44145 #917-14-1983 L1987 **IM** *020 †20

PERSAUD, Roberta Bender. 29099 HEALTH CAMPUS DR, STE 110 44145 #038-45-1984 L1987 **ID IM** *020 †20

PIETZ, Jeffery Thos. ■ 44145 #028-34-1978 L1989 **NPM PD** *020 †55

PILLAY, Balakrishna Gopal. 25200 CENTER RIDGE RD, STE 3300 44145 #495-31-1966 L1976 **IM** *020

PLASA, Enkelejda. 25200 CENTER RIDGE RD, STE 2600 44145 #120-01-1997 L2001 **IM** *020

PRESCOTT, Jon Stephen. 28812 WEYBRIDGE DR 44145 #043-01-1990 L1991 **RO** *020 †80

PRESSLER, Richard W. 30033 CLEMENS RD, CLEVELAND FOUNDATION 44145 #038-43-1977 L1980 **FM** *020 †18

QUIRINO, Gregorio Pineda. 29000 CENTER RIDGE RD, ST JOHN-WEST SHORE HOSPITA 44145 #748-10-1973 L1981 **GS** *050

RADIGAN, Patricia E. 26908 DETROIT RD STE 200 44145 #035-08-1979 L1982 **IM** *020 †20

RAID, Adnan. 25200 CENTER RIDGE RD, STE 2600 44145 #409-07-1980 L1996 **GE** *020 †20

RAJ, Joyesh. 850 COLUMBIA RD 44145 #038-41-1997 L2000 **PS** *020 †65

RAK, Max. ■ 44145 #154-01-1952 L1960 **GP** *071

RAMANA, Chigurupati V. 29000 CENTER RIDGE RD 44145 #038-06-1989 L1991 **DR VIR** *020

RAMIREZ, Luis F. 24803 DETROIT RD # D-1 44145 #264-05-1967 L1976 **P** *030 †75

RANDT, George Alvin S. 26908 DETROIT RD 44145 #038-06-1967 L1967 **IM** *072 †20

RASIWALA, Saifuddin S. ■ 44145 #495-01-1961 L1968 **AN** *071 †05

RASLAN, Fares. 25200 CENTER RIDGE RD, THIRD FLOOR 44145 #875-01-1983 L1994 **AN EM** *020 †05

RAVICHANDRAN, R. 29325 HEALTH CAMPUS DR 44145 #220-04-1987 L1995 **IM** *020 †20

REDDY, Satti Sethu-Kumar. 2472 SILVERIDGE TRL 44145 #063-01-1980 L1995 **IM END** *020 †20 ‡

REED, Steven Thomas. ■ 44145 #038-44-2004 L2004 **DR** *012

REESE, Christopher Simon. 29101 HEALTH CAMPUS DR, UROLOGY PARTNERS INC 44145 #038-43-1989 L1995 **U** *020 †95

REVOLINSKY, Mary Clare. 29325 HEALTH CAMPUS DR, STE 2 44145 #038-43-1990 L1991 **FM** *020 †18

REYNOLDS, Robert Walk. 30033 CLEMENS RD, CLEVELAND CLINIC FOUNDATIO 44145 #007-02-1959 L1966 **CD IM** *020 †20

RICE, Sheila Mary. 30033 CLEMENS RD 44145 #038-43-1997 L1999 **IM** *020 †20

RIMMERMAN, Curtis Mark. 30033 CLEMENS RD, CLEVELAND CLNC WESTLAKE 44145 #038-06-1987 L1993 **CD IM** *020 †20

ROSS, Joseph John. 29101 HEALTH CAMPUS DR, STE 380 44145 #038-06-1984 L1985 **OPH PS** *020 †35

SABHARWAL, Josephine L. 29133 HEALTH CAMPUS DR 44145 #495-18-1990 L2000 **ADP** *100

SALAZAR, Alexander Carlos. ■ 44145 #016-11-2005 L2005 **AN** *012

SALIBA, Walid Ibrahim. 30033 CLEMENS RD 44145 #605-01-1988 L1998 **ICE IM** *020 †20

SAMANICH, David Edward. 2001 CROCKER RD STE 650 44145 #038-43-1988 L1992 **OBG** *020 †30

SAYED, Hosam A. 31537 DEER RUN LN 44145 #875-02-1984 L1992 **PCC IM** *020 †20

SAYED, M Eiad. 29101 HEALTH CAMPUS DR, STE 270 44145 #875-02-1988 L1994 **IM** *020 †20

SCARCELLA, James Vincent. 850 COLUMBIA RD STE 300 44145 #041-02-1958 L1964 **PS** *020 †65

SEHGAL, Bindu Reddi. 29325 HEALTH CAMPUS DR 44145 #495-50-1990 L1996 **FM** *020 †18

SEIKEL, George R, III. 25200 CENTER RIDGE RD, STE 3200 44145 #038-40-1992 L1993 **FM** *020 †18

SEITZ, Roy Edward. 29000 CENTER RIDGE RD, ST JOHN WEST SHORE HOSPITA 44145 #038-41-1978 L1980 **EM FM** *020 †16,18

SEKHON, Baldev Singh. 29099 HEALTH CAMPUS DR, STE 380 44145 #495-43-1980 L1987 **TS** *020 †85,90

SEXTON, Donna Jean. 960 CLAGUE RD, STE 3201 44145 #038-40-1987 L1989 **RHU IM** *020 †20

SHEEHAN, John Patrick. 25101 DETROIT RD, STE 440 44145 #539-03-1976 L1983 **END IM** *020 †20

SHIE, Marvin Da Costa, Jr. ■ 44145 #038-06-1944 L1945 **GYN** *071

SHRISHRIMAL, Kumarpal Cha. ■ 44145 #495-28-2003 L2007 **IM** *100

SIMMONS, Edwina Elaine. 29325 HEALTH CAMPUS DR 44145 #008-01-1984 L1987 **OBG** *020 †30

SIMPSON, Lynn Marie. 850 COLUMBIA RD, STE 330 44145 #038-40-1992 L1995 **OBG** *020 †30

SOLYMOS, Kornelia C. 29325 HEALTH CAMPUS DR, STE 1 44145 #038-45-1990 L1991 **FM** *020 †18

SOUTHWORTH, Elizabeth Ann. 30033 CLEMENS RD 44145 #038-06-1993 L1995 **IM** *020 †20

SPRINGER, Michael Don. 850 COLUMBIA RD, NORTH SHORE 44145 #018-03-1976 L1978 **GE IM** *020 †20

STANFIELD, William Burton. 2211 CROCKER RD 44145 #038-40-1992 L1994 **ORS** *020 †40

STERN, Robert Martin. 29101 HEALTH CAMPS DR #340 44145 #035-06-1982 L1986 **OPH** *020 †35

STOCKMASTER, Kimberly Jo. ■ 44145 #038-45-2006 L2006 **OBG** *012

STROH, Eileen Frances. 30033 CLEMENS RD 44145 #038-45-1994 L1997 **IM** *020 †20

SYED, Ikram B. 29099 HEALTH CAMPUS DR, STE 130 # 3 44145 #495-39-1968 L1979 **PUD IM** *020 †20

TAN, Annie R. ■ 44145 #748-01-1992 L2008 **IM** *020 †20

TANPHAICHITR, Artthapol. 26908 DETROIT RD STE 103, ASSOCIATES IN DERMATOLOGY 44145 #038-44-1998 L1999 **D** *020 †15

TEMES, Roy Thos. 30033 CLEMENS RD 44145 #023-07-1984 L1999 **GS** *020 †85,90

THA, Khin Z. 960 CLAGUE RD, STE 3280 44145 #209-01-1979 L1996 **FM** *020 †18

THOMAS, Agnes Kelanthara. 26908 DETROIT RD, STE 200 44145 #038-43-1987 L1993 **FM** *020 †18

THOMAS, John Maron. 25651 DETROIT RD STE 304 44145 #038-40-1983 L1984 **FM** *020 †18

THOMAS, Sapna. 960 CLAGUE RD, STE 2300 44145 #028-46-1998 L2000 **GE** *020 †20

TRILLIS, Floyd, Jr. 29099 HEALTH CAMPUS DR, STE 225 44145 #050-02-1981 L1983 **GS** *020 †85

VASAVADA, Prasankumar J. 25200 CENTER RIDGE RD, STE 2600 44145 #495-01-1961 L1973 **IM NM** *020,28

VATEV, Virginia Renee. 960 CLAGUE RD STE 3201 44145 #038-45-1988 L1991 **IM** *020 †20

VENIZELOS, Paul C. 805 COLUMBIA RD 44145 #038-40-1975 L1975 **PUD IM** *020 †20

WAGHRAY, Nisheet. ■ 44145 #038-43-2004 L2004 **IM** *100 †20
WAGHRAY, Satesh Kumar. 25651 DETROIT RD, STE 304 44145 #495-65-1966 L1979 **FM OS** *020 †18
WALLACE, Robert James. ■ 44145 #038-40-1954 L1954 **AN** *071
WANG, James Jingbo. 25200 CENTER RIDGE RD, STE 3300 44145 #243-95-1983 L1999 **IM** *020 †20
WASSERBAUER, Thomas John. 29099 HEALTH CAMPUS DR, STE 180 44145 #038-06-1968 L1968 **PD** *020 †55
WEIL, Stacie. 960 CLAGUE RD, STE 2410 44145 #016-11-1987 L2005 **OBG REN** *020 †30
WILLINS, Colette Renee. 29325 HEALTH CAMPUS DR, STE 1 44145 #038-40-1993 L1994 **FM** *020 †18 ‡
WIRTZ, John Victor. 25651 DETROIT RD, STE 304 44145 #038-43-1992 L1993 **FM** *020 †18
WLADECKI, Mark Jos. 805 COLUMBIA RD STE 111, E.N.T. GROUP OF CLEVELAND 44145 #038-41-1985 L1990 **OTO HNS** *020 †45
WOJTANOWSKI, Michael H. 2237 CROCKER RD STE 140 44145 #023-01-1974 L1975 **PS** *020 †65
WOOD, James Wallace. 805 COLUMBIA RD 44145 #016-06-1963 L1967 **OTO HNS** *071 †45
YANNARAS, Niki Maria. ■ 44145 #038-43-2007 L2007 **DR** *012
YASUMOTO, Eric Kiyoshi. ■ 44145 #024-07-1998 L2003 **DR** *100 †80
ZAKARI, Adel M. ■ 44145 #915-04-1995 L2002 **PMM** *012
ZANOTTI, Daniel James. 2211 CROCKER RD 44145 #041-14-1997 L2003 **OSM** *020 †40
ZANOTTI, Kristine Marie. 960 CLAGUE RD, STE 2410 44145 #008-01-1993 L2000 **GO** *020 †30
ZARIF, Linda A. ■ 44145 #605-01-1989 L1997 **NEP** *020 †20
ZEVALLOS, Carlos E. 29099 HEALTH CAMPS DR #350 44145 #737-06-1967 L1975 **IM RHU** *020 †20
ZUCHOWSKI, Sara. 29133 HEALTH CAMPUS DR 44145 #038-43-1995 L2000 **P** *020 †75

WHEELERSBURG — SCIOTO

BAILONY, Fadi. 8046 OHIO RIVER RD 45694 #875-02-1996 L2001 **IM** *020 †20
CHANG, Charles C. ■ 45694 #583-10-1966 L1975 **FM P** *020 †18
CLARK, Curtis Ray. ■ 45694 #665-01-2001 L2006 **AN** *100
ESHAM, George E. 536 BULWER ST 45694 #020-02-1975 L1982 **IM** *020 †20
KALO, Mohammad Mouhib. 351 DUIS ST 45694 #875-01-1994 L2000 **IM** *020 †20
MC GLONE, Timothy Craig. 8770 OHIO RIVER RD 45694 #038-44-1994 L1997 **FM** *020 †18
ROMANELLO, Marcus Gregory. ■ 45694 #038-41-2003 L2003 **EM** *020
SCHOONOVER, Jean Ann. 11826 GALLIA PIKE RD, STE A 45694 #021-01-1998 L2004 **IM** *020 †20
SEE, Ashley M. ■ 45694 #038-75-2007, ▲ L2007 *012
SOKAN, Babatunde Olusegun. 8930 OHIO RIVER RD, WHEELERSBURG FAMILY CARE C 45694 #690-08-1989 L2002 **FM** *020 †18
TEMPONERAS, Margy. 418 CENTER ST, MARGY TEMPONERAS, MD 45694 #038-43-1992 L1997 **FM** *020 †18
TURJOMAN, A John. 536 BULWER ST 45694 #024-07-1996 L2003 **PD** *020 †55
YOUNG, Wayne Everett. GALLIA AND BULWER 45694 #036-01-1981 L1982 **FM** *020

WHIPPLE — WASHINGTON

KNOCH, Lana Rachelle. ■ 45788 #038-41-2007 L2007 **OBG** *012

WHITEHALL — FRANKLIN

LEE, Robert Thomas. 1021 COUNTRY CLUB RD STE A, PEDIATRIC ASSOCS 43213 #038-40-1993 L1994 **PD** *020 †55

WHITEHOUSE — LUCAS

EVERLY, Bradley Paul. ■ 43571 #038-43-2008 *012
FITZPATRICK, Michael L. 10550 WATERVILLE ST, VIL OF WHITHUSE IS AGV ENT 43571 #038-43-1984 L1985 **EM FM** *020 †18

WICKLIFFE — LAKE

COLLINS, Virginia Mary. ■ 44092 #028-46-1988 *075
GEORGE, Antony Minor. 28080 CHARDON RD, STE 204 44092 #038-43-1984 L1992 **GPM** *020 †70
KANE, Anthony Michael. 28478 YESHIVA LANE 44092 #041-02-1985 L1987 **OTO GS** *020
KLETECKA, Maria Delcarmen. ■ 44092 #034-01-2006 L2006 **PTH** *012
MUENSTER, George. 29640 EUCLID AVE 44092 #028-79-1962, ▲ L1963 **CRS FM** *071
O'CONNELL, Daniel Michael. 2775 BISHOP RD, STE A 44092 #038-40-2006 L2006 **MPD** *012

WILLARD — HURON

BACK, Billy. 218 S MYRTLE AVE 44890 #038-43-1999 L1999 **IM** *020 †20
BROWN, Vicki Jean. 315 CRESTWOOD DR, UNIT 1 44890 #038-40-1992 L1995 **FM** *020 †18
CLINGMAN, Stephen Richard. 315 CRESTWOOD DR, FAMILY HEALTH PARTNERS 44890 #038-41-1994 L2006 **FM** *020 †18
DIMITROV, Veselin D. 110 E HOWARD ST 44890 #198-03-1990 L1999 **FM** *020 †18
EMERY, John Victor. ■ 44890 #038-40-1947 L1947 **GP** *071
GATZ, Alan Christopher. 110 E HOWARD ST 44890 #038-40-1982 L1983 **FM EM** *020 †18
KHAN, Shahzad Mahmood. 1509 S CONWELL AVE 44890 #704-21-1988 L2003 **HO** *020 †20
KOTHARI, Punita Prashant. 110 E HOWARD ST 44890 #495-48-1971 L1979 **PTH** *020 †50
PAIK, Woo Hyun. 110 E HOWARD ST 44890 #583-10-1974 L1983 **OBG** *020 †30
PRACK, Amelia M Schrag. 315 CRESTWOOD DR, UNIT 1 44890 #038-40-1981 L1982 **FM** *020 †18
PRACK, Eric Gregory. 315 CRESTWOOD DR 1 44890 #038-40-1981 L1982 **FM** *020 †18
RANA, Jatinder Singh. 1510 S CONWELL AVE 44890 #495-69-1984 L1999 **P** *020 †20
ROSSO, James Edwin. 218 S MYRTLE AVE 44890 #038-43-1985 L1986 **IM PD** *020 †20,55
ROSSO, John E. 218 S MYRTLE AVE 44890 #038-40-1960 L1960 **FM** *071
SALIM, Ali. 110 E HOWARD ST 44890 #704-01-1993 L2000 **EM P** *020

SECOR, Robert William. 218 S MYRTLE AVE 44890 #038-45-1987 L1988 **FM** *020 †18 ‡
SHIM, Seong-Sool. 1510 S CONWELL AVE 44890 #583-15-1980 L1994 **P** *020 †75
STANBERY, David Lee. 388 E HOWARD ST 44890 #041-13-1976 L1982 **GS** *020 †85
STECYK, Orest. 110 E HOWARD ST 44890 #038-40-1980 L1981 **FM EM** *020 †18
VARGAS, Andres Iroma, Jr. ■ 44890 #748-01-1957 L1970 **U** *071 †95
VERHOFF, Nancy Lynn. 218 S MYRTLE AVE, WILLARD MEDICAL CENTER, IN 44890 #038-43-2000 L2000 **FM** *020 †18

WILLIAMSBURG — CLERMONT

JOHNSTON, Jeremy Michael. ■ 45176 #038-41-2008 *012
MEHTA, Jyoti. 1001 W MAIN ST 45176 #495-17-1980 L1985 **IMG** *020 †20
SHAH, Babulul Keshorchand. 1001 W MAIN ST 45176 #495-17-1947 L1968 **FM TRS** *071
STUCKERT, Jeffery Arthur. ■ 45176 #038-41-1981 L1982 **GS EM** *020 †16

WILLOUGHBY — LAKE

ACHARYA, Satya S. 5105 SOM CENTER RD 44094 #496-33-1994 L1999 **IM** *020 †20
ADUSUMILLI, Vijay. 36000 EUCLID AVE 44094 #010-03-1998 L2002 **EM** *020 †16
AFNAN-BADREE, Jalaloddin. 7586 EAGLE RD 44094 #517-05-1961 L1968 **OTO HNS** *071 †45
AKHRASS, Rami. 36100 EUCLID AVE STE 280 44094 #875-01-1987 L1993 **TS GS** *020 †85,90
ALLEN, Marc Kevin. 36000 EUCLID AVE 44094 #038-45-1982 L1983 **EM** *020 †16
ANSTANDIG, Jack. 34900 CHARDON RD, STE 201 44094 #041-12-1984 L1985 **N** *020 †75
ATASSI, Mohamed A. 36100 EUCLID AVE STE 120 44094 #875-01-1962 L1974 **CD IM** *020 †20
AUSTRIA, Alfred John, Jr. 36000 EUCLID AVE 44094 #038-43-1991 L1995 **EM** *020 †16
AZEM, Jamal Mouayad. 36100 EUCLID AVE, STE 330A 44094 #875-01-1981 L1989 **NEP IM** *020 †20
AZEM, Khalil. 36100 EUCLID AVE STE 350 44094 #875-01-1965 L1986 **OTO PS** *020 †45
BAILEY, Laura Marie. 36100 EUCLID AVE, STE 240 44094 #038-40-1990 L1991 **IM** *020 †20
BALIN, Jeanine. ■ 44095 #869-05-1953 L1960 **PD PHP** *071
BARLEY, Leonard V. 35900 EUCLID AVE 44094 #048-13-1973 L2006 **P** *020 †75
BENJAMIN, Jaye E. 36060 EUCLID AVE, STE 202 44094 #038-41-1978 L1982 **D** *020 †15
BINDER, Michael Peter. 36100 EUCLID AVE, STE 290 44094 #038-40-1978 L1983 **PS HS** *020 †65
BIRNBAUM, Gary I. 35040 CHARDON RD STE G200 44094 #035-19-1957 L1982 **GP IM** *020 †16
BLATT, David Robt. 2785 SOM CENTER RD 44094 #038-41-1988 L1999 **NS** *020 †25
BOES, Cynthia Ruth. 35040 CHARDON RD, PRIMEHEALTH WOMENS HEALTH 44094 #038-40-1992 L1998 **OBG** *020 †30
BROWN-YOUNG, Diane E. 2570 SOM CENTER RD, THE CLEVELAND CLINIC 44094 #038-06-1991 L1992 **OBG** *020 †30
BUCCHIERI, John Stephen. 36060 EUCLID AVE STE 104 44094 #035-01-1993 L2000 **ORS GS** *020 †40
BYERS, Keith Edward. 35040 CHARDON RD STE G200 44094 #038-40-1976 L1976 **IM** *020 †20
CECYS, Alfons. ■ 44094 #616-01-1935 L1953 **IM** *071
CEPULIS, Algimantas L. ■ 44094 #407-05-1953 L1957 **GS** *071 †85
CHAPNICK, Ronald. 36000 EUCLID AVE 44094 #035-19-1955 L1959 **PTH** *071 †50
CHIANG, M H Phillip. 36001 EUCLID AVE STE B4 44094 #244-04-1971 L1975 **EM FM** *020 †16
CLINGER, Wendy J. 35040 CHARDON RD, PRIMEHEALTH WOMENS HEALTH 44094 #038-40-1991 L1995 **OBG** *020 †30
CLOUGH, Mary M Lorentz. 5105 SOM CENTER RD 44094 #010-01-1965 L1970 **PD** *020 †55
COLBURN, Nora Elizabeth. ■ 44094 #038-06-2007 L2007 **IM** *012
CONVERY, Patrick Geo. 36060 EUCLID AVE STE 203, LAKE WEST PHYSICIAN PAVILI 44094 #036-05-1979 L1985 **ORS** *020 †40
CORNETTE, Victoria E. 2570 SOM CENTER RD 44094 #051-04-1993 L1995 **MPD** *020 †20,55
CORNICELLI, Diane Marie. 36001 EUCLID AVE 44094 #038-43-1983 L1988 **IM RHU** *020 †20
CUA, Warren Go. 36000 EUCLID AVE, LAKE COUNTY MEM HOSP W 44094 #748-01-1964 L1974 **EM** *020 †16
CUDNIK, Daniel Boles. 36100 EUCLID AVE, STE 290 44094 #056-06-1968 L1977 **PS HS** *020 †85,65
DAHER, Anthony Ferris. 36000 EUCLID AVE, LAKEWEST HOSP-EMERGENCYDEP 44094 #038-06-1997 L2000 **EM** *020 †16
DANAN, Naser A. 4212 STATE ROUTE 306, STE 304 44094 #875-01-1985 L1992 **PD PHO** *020 †55
DAVIS, Keith Lynn. 38429 LAKE SHORE BLVD 44094 #038-43-1984 L1985 **FM** *020 †18
DAVIS, Lisa Ann. 36100 EUCLID AVE, STE 490 44094 #038-06-1990 L1993 **PS** *020 †65
DEMANGONE, David Anthony. 6025 COMMERCE CIR, STE 2 44094 #041-12-1991 L1996 **AN** *020 †05
DE MARCO, J Edward. ■ 44094 #038-40-1956 L1956 **ORS** *071 †40
DINGA, Marc James. 4212 STATE ROUTE 306, STE 110 44094 #026-04-1978 L1979 **PUD IM** *020 †20
DOLGAN, Dennis Anthony. 36000 EUCLID AVE 44094 #038-44-1983 L1984 **EM** *020 †16
DRUZINA, Irene Lesica. 2570 SOM CENTER RD, INTERNAL MEDICINE/WH10 44094 #038-45-1991 L1993 **IM** *020 †20 ‡
EAPEN, Georgina. ■ 44094 #495-27-1958 L1974 **PD** *020
ECKHAUSER, Christine T H. 36470 BILTMORE PL, UNIT3 44094 #035-08-1977 L1982 **DR PDR** *020
EDEN, Diane Holly. 35000 CHARDON RD, STE 210 44094 #038-43-1985 L1986 **P** *020 †75
EPPRIGHT, Thomas David. 35900 EUCLID AVE, UHHS LAURELWOOD HOSP 44094 #028-03-1986 L1999 **P CHP** *020 †75
FARUKHI, Fahhad Imtiaz. 44094 #038-06-2006 L2006 **IM** *100
FARUKHI, Shahzad Rahim. ■ 44094 #038-41-2006 *012
FEINGOLD, Mark Henry. 5105 SOM CENTER RD 44094 #028-02-1963 L1966 **PD** *030 †55
FIKE, William Richard. 2570 SOM CENTER RD, CLEVELAND CLINIC FOUNDATIO 44094 #041-09-1969 L1991 **IM** *072 †20
FITZGERALD, Kim Saul. 5105 SOM CENTER RD 44094 #035-08-1979 L1984 **U** *020 †95
FOLEY, Terrence Geo. 36100 EUCLID AVE 44094 #038-06-1986 L1987 **RHU IM** *020 †20
FRYXELL, Eric Ellis. 2570 SOM CENTER RD, ATTN:MEDICAL STAFF OFFICE 44094 #038-06-1993 L2000 **FM** *020 †20
FUENTES, Freddie Florante. 2570 SOM CENTER RD 44094 #748-01-1991 L1995 **IM** *020 †20
GARLISI, Andrew Peter. 36000 EUCLID AVE 44094 #038-43-1978 L1996 **EM** *020 †20,16
GENKIN, Igor. 36000 EUCLID AVE 44094 #913-36-1990 L1998 **HO IM** *020 †20
GLORIOSO, Efren Merto. 36000 EUCLID AVE 44094 #748-01-1962 L1973 **EM GP** *020
GOLDBERG, Mark Chas. 36001 EUCLID AVE STE B6, VASCULAR SOLUTIONS 44094 #016-01-1984 L2004 **GS** *020 †85

GOLDBERG, Philip. 38429 LAKE SHORE BLVD 44094 #154-07-1954 L1959 **IM** *071 †20

GORDON, Timothy L. 34950 CHARDON RD, STE 104 44094 #038-06-1986 L1986 **ORS** *020 †40

GOSSELIN, Robert Edmond. 36001 EUCLID AVE STE C2, WILLO MEDICAL BLDG 44094 #035-45-1947 L1957 **OS** *072

GRANIERI, Janice Angela. 2550 SOM CENTER RD 44094 #038-06-1987 L1990 **RHU IM** *020 †20

GREEN, Armin Jay. 2570 SOM CENTER RD 44094 #038-06-1969 L1970 **ON HEM** *020

GREENFIELD, Aric Wm. 2570 SOM CENTER RD 44094 #038-43-1981 L1984 **IM** *050 †20

GREENWALD, Rose Mary. 2570 SOM CENTER RD 44094 #038-06-1990 L1993 **IM** *020 †20

GUTIERREZ, Cynthia Liza. 2570 SOM CENTER RD 44094 #035-19-1994 L1997 **IM** *020 †20

HAAS, Gwen. 5105 SOM CENTER RD 44094 #065-10-1984 L1989 **FM** *020 †18

HACKETT, Michael Harry. 2570 SOM CENTER RD, CCF WILLOUGHBY HILLS FHC 44094 #038-06-1979 L1979 **FM** *020 †18

HAN, Sung Soo. 38429 LAKE SHORE BLVD, ERIESIDE MEDICAL GROUP, IN 44094 #583-02-1963 L1971 **IM GE** *020 †20

HANNA, Lisa Grace. 2570 SOM CENTER RD 44094 #038-43-1998 L1999 **MPD** *020 †20,55

HAULER, Rita Keefer. 5105 SOM CENTER RD 44094 #038-40-1970 L1970 **D** *020 †15

HO, Winston. 38429 LAKE SHORE BLVD, ERIESIDE MEDICAL GROUP, IN 44094 #209-01-1982 L1993 **IM** *020 †20

HRITZ, Ann Jo. 2570 SOM CENTER RD 44094 #035-01-1978 L1986 **IM** *020 †20

HUGHES, Lawrence Michael. 2570 SOM CENTER RD 44094 #038-06-1994 L1996 **IM** *020 †20

IAFELICE, John Philip. 2570 SOM CENTER RD, WILLOUGHBY HILLS 44094 #038-06-1982 L1984 **OBG** *020 †30

ITANI, Abdul Latif. 2785 SOM CENTER RD, N.E. OHIO NEUROSURGICAL AS 44094 #605-01-1968 L1979 **NS** *020 †25

JACKSON, Jo Ann. 2570 SOM CENTER RD, CLEVELAND CLC 44094 #016-43-1984 L1987 **ADL PD** *020 †20,55

JACOBSON, Bruce Robt. 36000 EUCLID AVE 44094 #038-06-1981 L1982 **OPH** *020 †35

JACOBSON, Neil Alan. 34940 RIDGE RD, DIGESTIVE HEALTH INC 44094 #038-40-1977 L1980 **GE** *020 †20

JASANI, Kundanbala. ■ 44094 #495-23-1977 **AN** *071

JOSEPH, Dawn R. 5105 SOM CENTER RD, KAISER WILLOUGHBY MEDICAL 44094 #038-06-1991 L1997 **GE IM** *020 †20

JULIAN, Christine Joan. 2570 SOM CENTER RD 44094 #023-07-1985 L1988 **IM** *062 †20

KALAKUNTLA, Vikram Rao. 36060 EUCLID AVE STE 107 44094 #495-16-1996 L2005 **VS** *020 †85

KAMMER, Gary Michael. 36100 EUCLID AVE STE 170, ARTHRITIS ASSOC INC 44094 #038-40-1970 L1970 **RHU IG** *020 †20

KANNENSOHN, Jon David. 2570 SOM CENTER RD 44094 #038-40-1997 L2000 **PD** *020 †55

KAPLAN, Gary Brian. 36001 EUCLID AVE STE C6 44094 #035-15-1982 L1987 **PUD CCM** *020 †20

KEZELE, Gregory Paul. 36060 EUCLID AVE, STE 107 44094 #038-45-1987 L1988 **VM FM** *020 †18

KHAN, Asif Iqbal. 2980 LAMPLIGHT LN 44094 #422-01-1997 L2007 **AI** *020 †20

KHOURY, Allan Thos. 5105 SOM CENTER RD 44094 #011-02-1980 L1983 **IM** *030 †20

KIRK, Sonia Ann. 36000 EUCLID AVE 44094 #051-01-1982 L1985 **EM IM** *020 †20

KIRSCH, Michael. 34940 RIDGE RD, DIGESTIVE HEALTH INC 44094 #035-19-1985 L1988 **GE IM** *020 †20

KOELLIKER, Joseph W, Jr. 36100 EUCLID AVE 44094 #038-06-1952 L1952 **FM** *071

KOELSCH, Rachel Anne. 2550 SOM CENTER RD WH20, CLEVELAND CLINIC 44094 #038-43-1999 L2003 **AI** *020 †55,20,03

KOMINSKY, Suzanne B Engel. 2570 SOM CENTER RD 44094 #041-14-1985 L1996 **IM** *030 †20

KORAH, Joey Matthew. 36100 EUCLID AVE 44094 #048-14-2003 L2003 **PD** *020

KOTAK, Sandeep Veljibhai. 36100 EUCLID AVE, STE 240 44094 #495-23-1992 L1996 **IM** *020 †20

KRASNYANSKY, Inna. 36001 EUCLID AVE STE C17 44094 #913-07-1982 L1999 **IM** *020 †20

KRUDY, Adrian Geo. 2785 SOM CENTER RD, EASTSIDE IMAGING CENTER 44094 #025-01-1971 L1973 **DR** *020 †80

LANE, James Scott. 5105 SOM CENTER RD 44094 #047-05-1987 L1989 **OPH** *020 †35 ‡

LANTNER, I L. 38429 LAKE SHORE BLVD, ERIESIDE MED GROUP, INC 44094 #407-07-1952 L1955 **PD** *071 †55

LAVIK, Paul Sophus. ■ 44094 #038-06-1959 L1959 **RO ON** *071 †80

LEVINE, Frederic Jay. 36001 EUCLID AVE, STE C2 44094 #038-06-1983 L1990 **U** *020 †95

LEVINSOHN, Morris Wolf. 4212 STATE ROUTE 306, STE 204 44094 #836-02-1962 L1972 **CHN N** *020

LEVITAN, Nathan. 36000 EUCLID AVE 44094 #024-07-1980 L1991 **ON HEM** *020 †20

LOHREY, Ralph C. ■ 44094 #038-06-1943 L1943 **PD** *071 †55

LOVELAND, James Paul. 34940 RIDGE RD, DIGESTIVE HEALTH INC 44094 #038-06-1971 L1972 **GE IM** *020

MAGRO, Robert Jos. 36000 EUCLID AVE, STE B16 44094 #035-06-1988 L1991 **PD** *020 †55

MALAMENT, Izold. 36001 EUCLID AVE 44094 #913-06-1969 L1983 **U** *020

MALIK, Simee I. 36001 EUCLID AVE STE B16 44094 #051-04-1996 L1999 **PD** *020 †55

MANDEL, Martin Lee. 36100 EUCLID AVE, LAKE WEST MEDICAL CENTER-S 44094 #038-40-1972 L1972 **END DIA** *020 †20

MANDELIK, James Andrew. 38429 LAKE SHORE BLVD 44094 #038-40-1988 L1991 **AI PD** *020 †55

MARKEY, Richard Bennett. 35900 EUCLID AVE 44094 #038-06-1958 L1958 **P CHP** *075

MASCARO, John Robt. 4230 STATE ROUTE 306 # 350 44094 #038-06-1992 L1994 **FPS** *020

MC CAIN, French Howell. ■ 44094 #028-02-1942 L1942 **IM** *071 †20

MC GEE, Eileen Schelorke. 38879 MENTOR AVE STE C 44094 #035-19-1978 L1980 **P CHP** *020 †55,75

MC KENZIE, Margaret L. 2570 SOM CENTER RD, WILLOUGHBY HILLS 44094 #028-02-1988 L1990 **OBG** *020 †30

MIKHAIL, Emad A. 34900 CHARDON RD STE 107, GREAT LAKES PAIN MANAGEMEN 44094 #915-02-1984 L1998 **APM** *020 †05

MOLINAR, Alddo Antonio. ■ 44094 #048-12-2005 L2006 **AN** *012

MOODLEY, Manikum. ■ 44094 #836-05-1974 L2004 *100

MORLEDGE, Thomas Jos. 2570 SOM CENTER RD, CLEVELAND CLINIC FOUNDATIO 44094 #038-06-1986 L1986 **IM PD** *020 †20,55

MOSCHKOVICH, Moises. 36001 EUCLID AVE STE B4 44094 #132-01-1948 L1971 **FM** *071 †18

MOSSAD, Dalia Mounir. 2570 SOM CENTER RD 44094 #915-02-1996 L2000 *020 †20

MULCAHY, Robert Thos. 36100 EUCLID AVE STE 240 44094 #038-43-1982 L1983 **IM** *020 †20

NICHOLS, Theodore John. 36100 EUCLID AVE, STE 240 44094 #038-06-1979 L1980 **IM** *030 †20

NICKODEM, Robert Jos, Jr. 36100 EUCLID AVE 44094 #010-02-1980 L1985 **ORS** *020 †40

OROSZ, Linda S. 35010 CHARDON RD, STE 205 44094 #038-43-1991 L1994 **PD** *020 †55

ORRACA-TETTEH, Sophia. 5105 SOM CENTER RD 44094 #412-01-1976 L1990 **PD OS** *020 †55

PASQUALONE, Sarah Norment. 35040 CHARDON RD, PRIMEHEALTH WOMENS HEALTH 44094 #038-06-1992 L1994 **OBG** *020 †30

PAZIRANDEH, Mahmood. 36100 EUCLID AVE 44094 #517-01-1958 L1968 **RHU IM** *020 †20

PERLA, Bernard David. 36100 EUCLID AVE STE 450 44094 #038-41-1990 L1992 **PO OPH** *020 †35

PERSE, Elmer John. 36001 EUCLID AVE STE B3 44094 #016-06-1971 L1973 **GS** *030 †85

PESEK, Todd Jeffrey. ■ 44096 #038-40-2004 L2006 *100

PETRAIUOLO, William James. 36060 EUCLID AVE, STE 204 44094 #050-02-1986 L1991 **GS** *020 †85

PIGNOLET, Wesley J. 36100 EUCLID AVE, STE 450 44094 #038-40-1949 L1949 **OPH** *071 †35

PORTER, Lawrence Martin. 36000 EUCLID AVE 44094 #038-06-1982 L1983 **IM** *020 †20

PORTER, Victoria Lyn. 2550 SOM CENTER RD STE 380, CLEVELAND CLNC-N BLDG 44094 #038-06-1997 L2000 **IM** *020 †20

POSNER, Gary Allen. 5105 SOM CENTER RD, CLEVELAND HEIGHTS MED CTR 44094 #025-01-1979 L2002 **FM** *020 †18

PURISIMA, Mary Grace V. 5105 SOM CENTER RD 44094 #748-10-1989 L1995 **IM** *020 †20

QUADERI, Mahboob A. 5105 SOM CENTER RD 44094 #160-02-1980 L1996 **IM** *020 †20

RAY, Michael. 35900 EUCLID AVE, LAURELWOOD HOSPITAL 44094 #913-65-1993 L2000 **P** *020 †75

REIGLE, Melissa D. 36001 EUCLID AVE, STE C2 44094 #038-06-1992 L1997 **U GS** *020 †95

REZAEE, Mohammad Hasan. 38429 LAKE SHORE BLVD 44094 #517-05-1961 L1971 **OBG** *071

ROBINSON, Jo Ann. 2570 SOM CENTER RD, CLEVELAND CLINIC 44094 #038-06-1992 L1995 **PD** *020 †55

ROBINSON, Joi Michelle. 36001 EUCLID AVE, C-7 44094 #001-02-1997 L2001 **OBG** *020 †30

ROLLINS, David L. 36100 EUCLID AVE, STE 280 44094 #016-42-1976 L1989 **VS GS** *020 †85

ROOD, Richard Paul. 34940 RIDGE RD, DIGESTIVE HEALTH INC 44094 #038-45-1982 L1983 **GE IM** *020 †20

RORICK, Mark Benj. 35040 CHARDON RD, STE 110 44094 #038-06-1985 L1986 **N** *020 †75

ROWANE, Barbara. 4212 STATE ROUTE 306, STE 304 44094 #038-40-1992 L1994 **PD** *020 †55

RUBIN, Sheila Nancy. 2570 SOM CENTER RD 44094 #038-43-1996 L2007 **N** *020 †75

RUCH, Theresa O'Connor D. 2785 SOM CENTER RD 44094 #038-06-1979 L1981 **NS** *020 †25

SABER, Suzan Arafeh. 2570 SOM CENTER RD WH10, THE CLEVELAND CLINIC FOUND 44094 #605-01-2000 L2002 **IM** *020 †20

SALTZMAN, Martin Irwin. 5105 SOM CENTER RD 44094 #038-06-1967 L1967 **IM** *071 †20

SAMSA, John A. 36100 EUCLID AVE, STE 120 44094 #038-75-1988, ▲ L1989 **CD IM** *020 †20

SCHIBLER, Kurt Ryan. 36001 EUCLID AVE, STE C2 44094 #038-41-1984 L2001 **NPM PD** *020 †55

SCHULZ, Doris Frauke. 2570 SOM CENTER RD 44094 #407-07-1958 L1962 **PD** *071 †55

SCHWAB, William Stix, III. 5105 SOM CENTER RD 44094 #028-02-1990 L2001 **IM** *020 †20

SCHWARTZ, Steven Michael. 36100 EUCLID AVE STE 270 44094 #038-40-1988 L1994 **GE IM** *020 †20

SHAH, Sambhav. 36000 EUCLID AVE, LAKE EMERGENCY SERVICES, I 44094 #038-06-1999 L2002 **EM** *020 †16

SHETH, Neha Naresh. 4212 STATE ROUTE 306 44094 #035-06-2000 L2000 **PD** *020 †55 ‡

SILVERBLATT, James H. 35010 CHARDON RD, STE 101 44094 #016-42-1984 L1985 **IM** *030 †20

SLESH, Marvin. 36000 EUCLID AVE 44094 #038-40-1962 L1962 **GS VS** *020 †85

SLOTTA, Christine Marie. 35040 CHARDON RD, PRIMEHEALTH WOMENS HEALTH 44094 #038-43-1997 L1999 **OBG** *020 †30

SMITH, Andre Leo. 5105 SOM CENTER RD 44094 #035-01-1982 L1994 **IM** *020 †20

SMITH, Jude Thos. 5105 SOM CENTER RD 44094 #024-05-1972 L1986 **ORS RHU** *020 †40

SPECH HOLDERBAUM, M. 36100 EUCLID AVE, STE 240 44094 #038-44-1986 L1989 **IM** *020 †20

STANTON-HICKS, Ursula. 2570 SOM CENTER RD, WILLOUGHBY HILLS 44094 #409-25-1987 L1998 **D** *020

STEFANSSON, Thorarinn. ■ 44094 #484-01-1966 L1974 **IM GE** *071 †20

STONE, Sidney J, Jr. 12 PUBLIC SQ, # 100 44094 #038-40-1956 L1956 **ORS GS** *020 †85,40

SUMEGO, Marianne J. 2570 SOM CENTER RD, CLEVELAND CLINIC FOUNDATIO 44094 #038-45-1992 L1993 **MPD** *020 †20,55

SUMMERS, Sanford. 35900 EUCLID AVE 44094 #038-06-1959 L1959 **P PYG** *072

SUNSHINE, Joshua Jay. 35040 CHARDON RD, STE 110 44094 #035-46-1991 L1992 **N** *020 †75

SVETE, Thomas Jos. 34950 CHARDON RD STE 202 44094 #038-44-1988 L1990 **P** *020 †75

TADDEO, Ronald Joseph. 36100 EUCLID AVE 44094 #041-12-1962 L1964 **PS HS** *071 †65

TAKACY, Florence. 38027 EUCLID AVE 44094 #041-07-1945 L1947 **FM OS** *071

TCHEN, Peter Chou-Yuen. 35900 EUCLID AVE 44094 #242-22-1949 L1961 **P** *072

TELL, Damilya L. 35000 CHARDON RD STE 210 44094 #913-15-1994 L2000 **P** *020 †75

TESSMAN, Patrick A. 35040 CHARDON RD, STE 110 44094 #038-06-2001 L2001 **CN** *020 †75

THOMAS, Mary Alice Howe. ■ 44094 #041-09-1947 L1948 **IM** *071 †20

TURC, Marinela L. 36001 EUCLID AVE # B11, STE B11 44094 #781-04-1987 L1999 **IM** *020 †20

URBAN, Monica Mary. 5105 SOM CENTER RD 44094 #759-03-1984 L1986 **ID IM** *020 †20

URSO, May Jewel G. 36000 EUCLID AVE 44094 #011-02-1962 L1971 **R OS** *071 †80

VENTO, J Michael. 34600 CHARDON RD, UNIT 7 44094 #038-40-1984 L1985 **ORS** *020 †40

VINOGRADSKY, Borislav V. 36100 EUCLID AVE STE 330B 44094 #913-64-1986 L1999 **GS TRS** *020 †85

VITO, Liese Kasparek. 35040 CHARDON RD STE 205, PRIMEHEALTH WOMENS HEALTH 44094 #041-01-1991 L1993 **OBG** *020 †30

WARREN, Mark Jay. 35900 EUCLID AVE 44094 #023-07-1979 L1991 **P** *020 †75

WHITE, Gail M. 5105 SOM CENTER RD 44094 #038-06-1996 L1997 **IM CCM** *020 †20

WHITEHOUSE, Robert Jos. 36001 EUCLID AVE, STE B15 44094 #056-05-1974 L1984 **FPG** *020 †18

WINCHELL, Murray Gerald. ■ 44094 #038-40-1958 L1958 **GP** *071

YADMARK, Nitaya. 5105 SOM CENTER RD 44094 #891-01-1965 L1974 **EM** *020

ZART, Jane Marie. 35040 CHARDON RD, PRIMEHEALTH WOMENS HEALTH 44094 #038-40-1992 L1993 **OBG** *020 †30

ZOU, Linuo Lenore. ■ 44094 #060-01-1997 L2006 **FM** *100

WILLOWICK - LAKE

DORADO, Gapin P. 30498 LAKESHORE BLVD 44095 #748-01-1957 L1968 **GP FM** *071

GOZDANOVIC, Jon Allen. ■ 44095 #038-45-2007 L2007 **ORS** *012

HERMAN, Robert Geo. 30498 LAKESHORE BLVD 44095 #038-41-1983 L1984 **FM** *020 †18

TEKNIPP, William James. 32313 VINE ST 44095 #038-40-1955 L1955 **OPH** *071 †35

■ = Address Information Privacy Protected

WILMINGTON – CLINTON

ADAMS, Gayle W. 138 SPRINGBIRD CT 45177 #051-04-1986 L1991 **FM IM** *075 †18

AL-ABDULLA, Sally Abdul-S. 825 W LOCUST ST, DEPT OF MED EDUCATION 45177 #820-02-2006 L2006 **FP** *012

BACH, Son M. 825 W LOCUST ST, CLINTON MEMORIAL HOSP 45177 #665-02-2006 **FP** *012

BAIN, Jennifer Eileen. 825 W LOCUST ST, MEMORIAL HOSPITAL 45177 #038-40-1996 L1998 **FM** *020 †18

BATH, Edwin F. 222 W MAIN ST 45177 #020-02-1966 L1969 **FM** *020 †18

BAYOMI, Ahmed Saber. 825 W LOCUST ST, CLINTON MEMORIAL HOSP 45177 #915-03-2002 L2006 **FP** *012

BENDER, Aaron Lee. 610 W MAIN ST 45177 #038-41-1994 L1995 **EM** *020 †16

BOYD, Foster J. 643 W MAIN ST 45177 #038-41-1944 L1944 **GS** *071 †85

BRAUNLIN, Daniel Edward. 610 W MAIN ST 45177 #038-41-1978 L1978 **PM** *020 †60

BUCHANAN, Emily L Behrman. 150 CAPE MAY DR, # 134B 45177 #038-41-1941 **OS** *071

BYARS, Chad Frederick. 610 W MAIN ST 45177 #021-01-1997 L1998 **EM** *020 †16

CHEN, Chia-Hung Joe. 596 W MAIN ST, EYE SERVICES 45177 #038-43-1997 L1999 **OPH** *020

CHOO, Joseph Kwangho. 630 W MAIN ST, STE 101 45177 #008-01-1993 L2001 **IM** *020 †20

CHOW, Theodore. 630 W MAIN ST, STE 101 45177 #023-07-1993 L2000 **ICE IM** *020

COHEN, David Stephen. 2107 ROMBACH AVE 45177 #035-15-1996 L1997 **EM** *020 †16

COMPTON, Rick. 630 W MAIN ST STE 102 45177 #038-40-1983 L1985 **ORS** *020 †40

COMTE, Thomas Eugene. ■ 45177 #665-02-2001 L2004 **FM** *020

CONTI, Richard L. 610 W MAIN ST, CLINTON MEMORIAL HOSPITAL 45177 #016-11-1980 L1989 **DR** *020 †80

DENLEY, Eric Carney. ■ 45177 #016-42-2005 L2006 **FM** *100

DOOLEY, Ruth Ann. 1150 W LOCUST ST, STE 300 45177 #041-02-1988 L1994 **PD** *020 †55

EVANS, Kelly L. 825 W LOCUST ST, CLINTON MEMORIAL HOSPITAL 45177 #305-01-2006 L2007 **FP** *012

FAULEY, Kathryn Jean. 630 W MAIN ST, STE 300 45177 #038-43-1989 L1991 **OBG** *020

GABBARD, Tina Marie. 1184 W LOCUST ST, WILMINGTON MEDICAL ASSOCIA 45177 #038-45-1985 L1986 **FM OBS** *020 †18

GAILLIOT, Christopher R. 891 W LOCUST ST 45177 #051-01-1992 L1994 **IM** *020 †20

GARFUNKEL, Felix. 610 W MAIN ST 45177 #319-01-1957 L1961 **R NM** *072 †80,28

GICK, Janet Faye. 825 W LOCUST ST 45177 #038-40-1975 L1976 **FM EM** *020 †18

GONZALEZ-SAENZ, Hilda B. 825 W LOCUST ST, CO CLINTON MEM HOSP - MED 45177 #048-02-2000 L2001 **FM** *020 †18

GOODWIN, Roy Delmore. 630 W MAIN ST 45177 #020-02-1947 L1948 **OBG** *072

HAJJAR, Elias F. 610 W MAIN ST 45177 #875-02-1989 L2000 **FM HEM** *020

HAMILTON, Maxine R Keiter. 610 W MAIN ST 45177 #038-41-1949 L1949 **OS GP** *071

HANNAH, Rancie Wayne. 825 W LOCUST ST 45177 #020-02-1998 L1999 **FM** *020 †18

HAVEY, James Patrick. 610 W MAIN ST, DEPT OF RADIOLOGY 45177 #018-03-1982 L1986 **DR NM** *020 †80

HEIN, Stephen Robt. 3039 STATE ROUTE 73 W 45177 #038-40-1981 L1982 **OPH** *071 †35

HENRY, Christine Ellen. 891 W LOCUST ST 45177 #038-41-1980 L1981 **IM** *020 †20

HOLDERMAN, Dennis Russel. 825 W LOCUST ST 45177 #038-41-2000 L2000 **FM** *020 †18

HOLLON, John Thomas. 222 W MAIN ST 45177 #038-40-1975 L1975 **IM** *020 †20

HOLTEN, Terry Kerr. 111 S NELSON AVE STE 1 45177 #038-41-1983 L1983 **PD** *030 †55

HORN, Connie Sue. 807 W MAIN ST, CLINTON ANES ASSOC 45177 #038-40-1978 L1984 **AN** *020

HUNTER, Lorenzo. ■ 45177 #305-01-1990 L2000 **FM** *100

INWOOD, Mary Louise. 1150 W LOCUST ST 45177 #038-41-1986 L1989 **IM** *020 †20

ITTICHERIA, Achamma Sonia. 610 W MAIN ST, DEPT OF MED EDU 45177 #306-01-2002 L2005 **FP** *012

JAGANNATHAN, Vikram. 825 W LOCUST ST, CLINTON MEMORIAL HOSPITAL 45177 #496-23-2003 **FM** *100

JHA, Leena. 825 W LOCUST ST, CLINTON MEMORIAL HOSPITAL 45177 #495-75-2001 L2005 **IM** *012

KERR, Abraham A. 757 W MAIN ST 45177 #330-02-1954 L1971 **U** *071 †95

KIM, Yong-Jin. 630 W MAIN ST, STE 305 45177 #583-02-1957 L1970 **OBG** *071 †30

KIRLIN, David Lee. 630 W MAIN ST, STE 304 45177 #038-41-1971 L1971 **ON HEM** *020 †20

KLEATHER, Chris Scott. 825 W LOCUST ST, CLINTON MEMORIAL HOSPITAL 45177 #104-01-2006 L2007 **FP** *012

KLOSTERMEIER, Timothy T. 610 W MAIN ST, CLINTON MEM HOSP 45177 #038-41-1993 L1995 **DR NM** *020 †80

KONG, James Allen. 630 W MAIN ST, STE 101 45177 #036-07-1998 L2005 **CD** *020 †20

LIMING, John Douglas. 610 W MAIN ST, SLEEP CARE 45177 #038-40-1990 L1991 **PCC** *020 †20

LING, Stella. 31 FARQUHAR AVE, REGIONAL CANCER CENTER 45177 #005-18-1973 L1978 **RO PD** *020 †55,80

LIU, Alan Sanhoun. 1184 W LOCUST ST 45177 #005-18-1990 *100

LIU, Allen Kweiloon. 825 W LOCUST ST 45177 #038-41-2003 L2003 **FM** *020 †18

LOVELL, Dana S. 630 W MAIN ST STE 307 45177 #017-20-1994 L1995 **OBG** *020 †30

MAKKAR, Pushpa Lata. 610 W MAIN ST, CLINTON MEMORIAL HOSPITAL 45177 #496-07-1961 L1972 **PTH** *020 †50

MANSER, Jeffrey David. 1150 W LOCUST ST, STE 300 45177 #038-45-1985 L1987 **PD** *020 †55

MERLING, John Wm. 1184 W LOCUST ST, WILMINGTON MEIDCAL ASSOCIA 45177 #038-41-1987 L1988 **FM** *020 †18 ‡

MERLING, Mary A Haneberg. 1150 W LOCUST ST, STE 300 45177 #038-41-1987 L1990 **PD** *020 †55

MITCHELL, Martin West. ■ 45177 #038-41-1991 L1993 **DR** *020 †80

MOLLOY, Mark. 610 W MAIN ST 45177 #028-34-1984 L1994 **GS** *020 †85

MUHAMMEDKARIM, Fouzia Ban. 825 W LOCUST ST, CLINTON MEMORIAL HOSP 45177 #704-02-1996 L2006 **FP** *012

NEVILLE, Thomas Michael. 1150 W LOCUST ST 45177 #038-40-1975 L1980 **FM FPG** *020 †18

NEWMAN, Michael David. 1665 W MAIN ST 45177 #038-41-1981 L1990 **GS** *020 †85

OMORUYI, Osawaru Jude. 875 W LOCUST ST 45177 #690-01-1998 L2005 **FM** *100 †18

ONDULICK, Brian W. 586 W MAIN ST, WILMINGTON SURGICAL 45177 #041-77-1999, ▲ L1999 *020

ONUSKO, Edward Mark. 825 W LOCUST ST 45177 #038-06-1981 L1983 **FM** *020 †18

PATEL, Matthew Naren. 610 W MAIN ST 45177 #038-40-1993 L1995 **EM** *020 †16

PATEL, Rajiv R. 630 W MAIN ST, STE 307 45177 #038-44-1993 L1999 **OBG** *020 †30 ‡

PAWAR, Narendrasing M. ■ 45177 #495-01-1976 L1999 **FM** *020

PELNICK, Cory Levi. 953 S SOUTH ST 45177 #035-15-1994 L1998 **P** *020

PESANTE, Maisha Laila. 825 W LOCUST ST, CLINTON MEMORIAL HOSPITAL 45177 #038-41-2005 L2005 **FP** *012

PIRNAT, Timothy Jay. 110 FAIRWAY DR, STE 1 45177 #038-45-1986 L1990 **PM** *020 †60

RACKLEY, Angela Yvette. 630 W MAIN ST, STE 207 45177 #038-41-2002 L2002 **CN N** *020

RANZ, Mary Boyd. ■ 45177 #038-41-1947 L1947 **PHP** *071

RASHID, Bina Abdul. 825 W LOCUST ST 45177 #104-01-2004 L2007 **FP** *012

REILEY, Eddie Don. 120 FAIRWAY DR, STE C 45177 #038-40-1979 L1979 **GS** *020 †85

REVAN, Vidyashankar Banga. 110 FAIRWAY DR STE 2 45177 #495-33-1988 L2002 **AI** *020 †20,03

SAHAY, Rashmi Darbari. 610 W MAIN ST, CLINTON MEM HOSP 45177 #495-49-1991 **FM** *100

SALARY, Cheryl Yvonne. ■ 45177 #025-07-2002 L2007 **CHP** *100

SALARY, Montell Dupree. 825 W LOCUST ST, CLINTON MEMORIAL HOSP 45177 #038-40-2002 L2007 **FP** *012

SANCHEZ, Joseph David. ■ 45177 #017-20-1980 L1986 **EM OM** *020 †16

SATCHWELL, Jeffrey Alan. 1150 W LOCUST ST 45177 #038-02-1988 L1990 **IM** *020 †20

SCHIRMER, Timothy Patrick. 586 W MAIN ST, WILMINGTON SURGICAL ASSOC, 45177 #038-40-1994 L1999 **GS** *020 †85

SCHULTE, Heather Mae. 610 W MAIN ST 45177 #026-08-1988 L1989 **P** *020 †75

SEAMAN, Ronald Gilbert. 610 W MAIN ST 45177 #038-43-1989 L1990 **EM** *020 †16

SIMMONS, Scott Patrick. ■ 45177 #104-01-2003 L2005 **FP** *012

STALEY, Bruce Edmund. 891 W LOCUST ST 45177 #038-41-1980 L1981 **IM CD** *020

STANFORTH, Shelley Ann. 1184 W LOCUST ST, WILMINGTON MEDICAL ASSOC 45177 #038-41-1992 L1993 **FM** *020 †18

SWICK, Shawn Michael. 222 W MAIN ST 45177 #038-43-2003 L2003 **FM** *020 †18

TIMPERMAN, Walter W, Jr. 610 W MAIN ST 45177 #038-40-1986 L1995 **PTH** *020 †50

VARGAS, Charlene. ■ 45177 #748-08-1996 L2004 **PD** *020 †55

VEASEY, Gilbert Dean, Sr. 825 W LOCUST ST 45177 #104-01-2007 L2007 **FP** *012

VENKATESH, Mangala K. 594 W MAIN ST, CLINTON NEUROLOGICAL SVCS 45177 #495-27-1977 L1981 **N** *020 †75

WANTZ, Anita Johnson. 1184 W LOCUST ST 45177 #038-45-1985 L1986 **FM** *020 †18

WARD, Patrick John. 630 W MAIN ST, STE 304 45177 #038-40-1997 L1998 **HO** *020 †20

WATHEN, Ronald Larry. 1675 ALEX DR 45177 #048-12-1968 L2000 **IM NEP** *030 †20

WHITTENBURG, Elissa. 610 W MAIN ST, CLINTON MEMORIAL HOSPITAL 45177 #038-41-1996 L1998 **MPD** *020,55

ZIEMNIK, Lisa Susan. 1184 W LOCUST ST, WILMINGTON MEDICAL ASSOCIA 45177 #038-41-2003 L2003 **PD** *020 †55

WINCHESTER – ADAMS

CAMPBELL, Tyler Joseph. ■ 45697 #038-45-2002 L2002 **FM** *020 †18

WINDSOR – ASHTABULA

HAVRE, Dale Chas. ■■ 44099 #038-06-1961 L1961 **OPH** *071 †35

WINTERSVILLE – JEFFERSON

AL-SHABAB, Wadie. 107 MAIN ST, TRINITY PEDIATRIC CARE CEN 43953 #875-01-1990 L1996 **PD** *020 †55

ASUNCION, Otilia J. 200 LURAY DR 43953 #748-02-1964 L1973 **IM CD** *020

BEDI, Maninder Singh. 100 WELDAY AVE, UNIVERSITYOF PITTSBURGH 43953 #495-11-1996 **ICE** *100 †20

BHANDARI, Ranjan Parkash. 100 WELDAY AVE, STE E 43953 #495-90-1980 L1991 **ON** *020 †20

CAGATA, Artemio Napigkit. ■ 43953 #748-09-1960 *100

DESAI, Himanshu Parmanand. 200 LURAY DR 43953 #917-08-1985 L1994 **GE IM** *020 †20

EDDY, Stephen Derrick. 200 LURAY DR 43953 #055-01-2001 L2002 **PSM** *020 †55 ‡

LUCERO, Vicente Siatong. OPAL BLVD AL 43952 #748-01-1951 **GS** *100

MERCADO, Milagros Lantin. ■ 43953 #748-07-1966 L1977 **FM GP** *071

WRIGHT, Ivan Douglas. ■ 43953 #143-06-1975 L1978 **EM** *020 †18

WOODSFIELD – MONROE

GUPTA, Rajnish K. 37984 AIRPORT RD BOX 658, MONROE FAMILY HLTH CTR 43793 #496-09-1985 L1995 **FM** *020 †20

PIATT, Donald Roy. 154 S MAIN ST 43793 #038-40-1964 L1964 **FM** *071 †18

SNYDER, Geoffrey David. 97 E COURT ST 43793 #023-12-1992 L1995 **GP LM** *020

WILLIAMSON, Ronnie Hank. 108 S MAIN ST 43793 #055-75-2002, ▲ L2002 **FM** *100

WOODVILLE – SANDUSKY

BROCKE, Michael Robt. ■ 43469 #038-40-1969 L1969 **AN** *071

NELSONBROWN, Wendy Gale. 104 E MAIN ST 43469 #038-43-1997 L1999 **PD** *020 †55

SANDER, Duane Lynn. 1100 W MAIN ST 43469 #038-43-1982 L1983 **FM** *020 †18

WOOSTER – WAYNE

ALLSHOUSE, Herbert Edward. ■ 44691 #038-06-1961 L1966 **GP** *071

ANGERMAN, Dale Chas. 1740 CLEVELAND RD, CLEVELAND CLINIC WOOSTER 44691 #038-40-1975 L1975 **FM** *020 †18

ARMOGIDA, Sheila A. 721 E MILLTOWN RD, CLEVELAND CLINIC WOOSTER 44691 #038-40-1998 L1999 **AI** *020 †20

ARORA, Urmil. 1736 BEALL AVE 44691 #496-07-1968 L1975 **GYN** *020 †30

BAAB, Robert Orr. 1761 BEALL AVE, WOOSTER COMM HOSP 44691 #038-40-1957 L1957 **AN OBS** *020

BARAN, Gregory Wayne. 721 E MILLTOWN RD 44691 #038-06-1977 L1979 **DR NM** *020 †80

BARE, Wayne Allen. 1740 CLEVELAND RD 44691 #038-40-1970 L1970 **OBG** *020 †30

BAY, James Hugh. 128 E MILLTOWN RD STE 102 44691 #038-45-1981 L1982 **FM** *020 †18

BEAM, Brian Bruce. 1740 CLEVELAND RD, CLEVELAND CLINIC-WOOSTER 44691 #038-06-1976 L1988 **FM** *020 †18

BEEHARRY, Tariq. 1761 BEALL AVE 44691 #308-13-2001 L2006 **IM** *020 †20

BELLOW, Philip. 1739 CLEVELAND RD 44691 #021-05-1979 L1992 **OBG** *020 †30

BENEKOS, Emily Louise. 1761 BEALL AVE 44691 #003-01-1992 L1997 **OBG** *020 †30

BERKE, Jay Paul. 2200 BENDEN DR, STE 4 44691 #016-11-1971 L1977 **N** *020 †75

BONEZZI, Dana Louise. 546 WINTER ST, STE 200 44691 #038-44-1996 L1997 **IM** *020 †20

BOSNAK, Jerry N. ■ 44691 #041-12-1952 L1957 **OBG** *071 †30

BOYE, Harold Odartei. 1761 BEALL AVE 44691 #412-01-2001 L2006 **IM** *020 †20

BROWN, Charles Alton. 1739 CLEVELAND RD 44691 #038-40-1970 L1970 **OBG** *020 †30

BUTTERBAUGH, William Thos. ■ 44691 #038-06-1961 L1961 **P** *072 †75

CANFIELD, Teresa Pauling. 1740 CLEVELAND RD, THE WOOSTER CLINIC 44691 #038-43-1995 L1997 **OBG** *020 †30

CEBUL, Frank. 1740 CLEVELAND RD 44691 #038-45-1981 L1982 **FM** *020 †18

CEBUL, Frank Anton, Jr. 1740 CLEVELAND RD 44691 #038-06-1946 L1946 **GS OS** *071 †85

CEBUL, Robert Douglas. 546 WINTER ST STE 210 44691 #047-05-1984 L1990 **GS** *020 †85

CLAPAROLS, Joseph Manuel. ■ 44691 #847-01-1961 L1968 **ATP CLP** *071 †50

CLARKE, Callisia Nathelee. 1189 BEALL AVE, BOX C-1338 44691 #038-41-2006 L2006 **GS** *012

CORDOVA-FERRER, Getsy. 526 WILLIAMSBURG CT, STE 5 44691 #042-01-1955 L1961 **AN** *020

CROWLEY, Paul Jos, Jr. 128 E MILLTOWN RD STE 201 44691 #018-03-1981 L1988 **U UP** *020 †95

DE HORTA, Eric. ■ 44691 #308-03-1985 L1993 **AN** *020 †05

ELDERBROCK, Mark Danl. 1740 CLEVELAND RD 44691 #038-40-1986 L1987 **FM FSM** *020 †18

FENZL, Thomas Carl. 3519 FRIENDSVILLE RD 44691 #021-01-1978 L1983 **OPH** *020 †35 ‡

FINNERAN, Mark Thos. ■ 44691 #038-40-1988 L1990 **OM OS** *020

GALLO, Ugo Ernesto. 1761 BEALL AVE 44691 #038-41-1986 L1987 **EM** *020 †16

GEHO, Hans Christopher. 146 S BEVER ST 44691 #038-06-1995 L1997 **IM** *020

GEHO, Walter Blair. ■ 44691 #038-06-1966 L1966 **PA** *050

GESLER, James Wendell. 3727 FRIENDSVILLE RD, UNIT 2 44691 #038-06-1976 L1977 **ORS** *020 †40

GRAVES, Thomas Murrell. ■ 44691 #041-01-1962 L1964 **IM** *071 †20

GUTTMAN, Richard Theodore. 1740 CLEVELAND RD 44691 #016-11-1992 L2002 **GS** *020 †85

HALLEY, Gregory Lee. ■ 44691 #005-12-1981 *100

HANNAN, Jodi Lynn. 1740 CLEVELAND RD, CLEVELAND CLNC WOOSTER 44691 #038-40-1999 L1999 **FM** *020 †18

HANNAN, Scott Andrew. 1740 CLEVELAND RD, CLEVELAND CLNC WOOSTER 44691 #038-40-1999 L1999 **FM** *020 †18

HEINTZ, James Jos. ■ 44691 #038-06-1984 L1985 **ORS** *020 †40

HELMUTH, Dennis Osborn. 128 E MILLTOWN RD, GEN PSYCH STE 202 44691 #038-06-1985 L1986 **P ADP** *020 †75

HELMUTH, Kathryn Osborn. 1761 BEALL AVE 44691 #038-06-1982 L1983 **PD** *020 †55

HESSLER, James Robt. 1749 CLEVELAND RD 44691 #038-06-1980 L1983 **OTO** *020 †45

HIGH, Luther W. ■ 44691 #038-40-1934 L1934 **FM GS** *071

HUFF, Albert B. ■ 44691 #036-07-1950 L1952 **GP AN** *071

HUNYADI, Steve, Jr. 721 E MILLTOWN RD 44691 #038-06-1993 L2000 **OTO** *020 †45

JABOUR, Vincent F. 128 E MILLTOWN RD 44691 #422-01-1988 L1995 **GE** *020 †20

JACKSON, Thomas Wm. ■ 44691 #041-01-1944 L1951 **AN** *071 †05

JENTES, Paul K. ■ 44691 #038-40-1943 L1943 **GP** *071

JOLLIFF, Amy Stocker. 128 E MILLTOWN RD, STE 105 44691 #038-40-1988 L1989 **FM** *020 †18

KANCHERLA, Anand. 1761 BEALL AVE 44691 #048-14-1993 L1997 **AN** *020 †05 ‡

KATZ, William. 128 E MILLTOWN RD, STE 101 MILLTOWN PROFESSIO 44691 #051-01-1961 L1969 **TS** *071 †85

KEARNEY, Walter H. 1740 CLEVELAND RD, WOOSTER CLINIC 44691 #041-01-1966 L1967 **GS** *071 †85

KIM, Young Chul. 1761 BEALL AVE 44691 #583-04-1967 L1981 **DR NM** *020 †80,28

KIRCHNER, Loren Michael. 1761 BEALL AVE 44691 #038-44-1999 L1999 **IM** *020 †20

KRILL, Carl Emil, Jr. 1761 BEALL AVE 44691 #041-01-1959 L1961 **PHO ON** *020 †55

KUFFNER, George H. 1740 CLEVELAND RD, CLEVELAND CLC WOOSTER 44691 #023-07-1975 L1976 **D IM** *020 †20,15 ‡

KWOK, Taichi. 128 E MILLTOWN RD, STE 205 44691 #038-06-1996 L1998 **FPG** *020 †18

LANG, Kyle Shane. 1740 CLEVELAND RD, CLEVELAND CLINIC- WOOSTER 44691 #038-44-2002 L2002 **FM** *020 †18

LEE, Daesung. 721 E MILLTOWN RD, CLEVELAND CLNC WOOSTER 44691 #035-48-1997 L2004 **RO** *020 †80

LEE, Ting Yang. ■ 44691 #244-01-1963 L1977 **PTH** *071

LE VERE, Robert Wesley. ■ 44691 #038-40-1955 L1955 **AN** *020 †05

LOGEE, Mary Jo. 3727 FRIENDSVILLE RD, UNIT 2 44691 #038-45-1989 L1990 **OS GPM** *020

LOGEE, Owen Williamson. 3727 FRIENDSVILLE RD, UNIT 2 44691 #038-40-1970 L1970 **ORS** *020 †40

LOUDENSLAGER, John E. 1761 BEALL AVE 44691 #038-40-1955 L1955 **GP** *071

LUCAS, Lisa Marie. 1189 BEALL AVE, BOC C-2149 44691 #038-06-2007 *012

LUN, Lapman. 721 E MILLTOWN RD, CLEVELAND CLINIC WOOSTER 44691 #038-40-1989 L1996 **HO** *020 †20

MALEK, Nabil Shehata Rizk. 1761 BEALL AVE 44691 #330-04-1961 L1970 **AN** *020

MALGIERI, John Jos. 721 E MILLTOWN RD, CLEVELAND CLINIC WOOSTER 44691 #035-20-1973 L1976 **U GS** *020 †85,95

MARTYN, Janine Rochelle. 721 E MILLTOWN RD 44691 #038-45-1988 L1990 **DR** *020 †80

MASIH, Arun E. 1761 BEALL AVE 44691 #018-75-1992, ▲ L1997 **PTH** *020 †50

MASON, Raymond Gregory. 128 E MILLTOWN RD 44691 #038-06-1997 L2000 **FM** *020 †18

MATHUR, Arun K. 1749 CLEVELAND RD 44691 #495-45-1967 L1973 **OTO A** *020 †45

MATHUR, Kevin Kumar. 1749 CLEVELAND RD 44691 #038-43-1998 L2003 **OTO** *020 †45

MAXWELL, Richard A. 1740 CLEVELAND RD 44691 #038-40-1972 L1972 **PD** *020 †55

MIEDEL, Anson Thomas. ■ 44691 #041-02-2001 L2007 **OPH** *020 †35

MILLER, John Keith. 128 E MILLTOWN RD 44691 #038-41-1977 L1980 **FM** *020 †18

MITRI, Osama. 128 E MILLTOWN RD, STE 101 44691 #875-01-1994 L1999 **IM** *020 †20

MOLNAR, Donald Steven. 1740 CLEVELAND RD, WOOSTER CLINIC,CLEVELAND C 44691 #038-44-1998 L2000 **IM** *020 †20

MOODISPAW, Paul Franklin. 546 WINTER ST STE 110, NORTHEAST OHIO CARDIOVASCU 44691 #038-40-1989 L1992 **CD IM** *020 †20

MOON, Doksu. 721 E MILLTOWN RD 44691 #038-40-1996 L2000 **DR RNR** *020 †80

MOON, Eunice Kim. 721 E MILLTOWN RD 44691 #041-07-1995 L1999 **VIR DR** *020 †80

MORRIS, Matthew Grant. 1761 BEALL AVE, APOGEE PHYSICIANS 44691 #038-43-1995 L1996 **FM** *020 †18

MORRIS, Tiffany. 128 E MILLTOWN RD, STE 105 44691 #038-43-1995 L1996 **FM** *020 †18

MOYER, Roger Clinton. 1761 BEALL AVE 44691 #038-41-1957 L1957 **PD** *071 †55

MURPHY, James White. 1740 CLEVELAND RD 44691 #016-01-1977 L1978 **GE IM** *020 †20

NELSON, Tina Marie. 3477 COMMERCE PKWY, STE A 44691 #038-40-1998 L1999 **FM** *020 †18

NGUYEN, Son Hoai. 1761 BEALL AVE 44691 #038-45-1993 L1994 **AN** *020 †05

PARKER, Craig Philip. 1761 BEALL AVE, WAYNE COUNTY RADIOLOGY 44691 #038-40-1983 L1984 **DR FM** *071 †80

PATEL, Minaldevi Dinubhai. 1761 BEALL AVE 44691 #496-07-1975 L1981 **PTH** *020 †50

PEABODY, Daniel Putnam, III. 721 E MILLTOWN RD 44691 #038-45-1993 L1994 **GS** *020 †85

PERKINS, Jeffrey Walter. 3519 FRIENDSVILLE RD 44691 #016-43-1993 L1996 **OPH** *020 †35

PLAYL, Timothy Mark. 1740 CLEVELAND RD, THE CLEVELAND CLINIC-WOOST 44691 #028-03-1985 L1992 **PD** *020 †55

PRATT, Joel Fuller. ■ 44691 #038-40-1946 L1946 **GP OS** *071

QUESTEL, James Theodore. 1761 BEALL AVE 44691 #038-40-1954 L1954 **LM GP** *020

RAMBHATLA, Rajyalakshmi. 1740 CLEVELAND RD 44691 #495-48-1992 L1997 **PD** *020 †55

RANNEY, Christopher Behr. 128 E MILLTOWN RD STE 105, MILLTOWN FAMILY PHYSICIANS 44691 #051-07-2000 L2006 **FM OSM** *020 †18

REDDY, Chandrasekhara R. 2285 BENDEN DR 44691 #495-62-1964 L1979 **P** *020 †75

REDDY, Nukala Ranadheer. 2285 BENDEN DR 44691 #495-57-1970 L1978 **P GP** *020 †75

REYNOLDS, David B. 1740 CLEVELAND RD 44691 #038-40-1977 L1978 **IM IMG** *020 †20

RICHARD, Thomas Chas. 1740 CLEVELAND RD 44691 #038-40-1969 L1969 **IM PUD** *020 †20

RUSSELL, Rebecca Lynn. 1739 CLEVELAND RD 44691 #038-44-2001 L2001 **OBG** *020 †30

SANFORD, Peter Danl. 721 E MILLTOWN RD 44691 #016-42-1980 L1985 **ORS FM** *020 †40

SCHAEFFER, Jill A. 1740 CLEVELAND RD, CLEVELAND CLINIC WOOSTER 44691 #038-43-1995 L2001 **IM** *020 †20

SCHMIDT, Dana Christine. 1740 CLEVELAND RD, THE CLEVELAND CLINIC WOOST 44691 #041-09-1994 L1997 **PD** *020 †55

SCHULER, Michael Alan. 1740 CLEVELAND RD 44691 #038-40-1975 L1993 **IM PUD** *020 †20

SEIDER, Michael J. 2376 BENDEN DR, CANCER TREATMENT CTR PARTN 44691 #048-14-1983 L1987 **RO** *020 †80

SHAFER, Kenneth Earl. 721 E MILLTOWN RD, CLEVELAND CLINIC WOOSTER 44691 #028-34-1979 L1999 **CD IM** *020 †20

SHEWMON, David A M. 721 E MILLTOWN RD, CLEVELAND CLINIC 44691 #016-11-1981 L1993 **END IM** *020 †20

SHRINER, Anne Marie. 1761 BEALL AVE 44691 #038-44-1995 L1997 **OBG** *020 †30

SIBILIA, Robert Vincent. 128 E MILLTOWN RD STE 206 44691 #016-43-1989 L1995 **PUD** *020 †55,20

SIBILIA, Sharon Rose. 1740 CLEVELAND RD 44691 #016-43-1988 L1995 **PD** *020 †55

SKELLY, William James, III. 3727 FRIENDSVILLE RD # 2, MEDICINE CENTER 44691 #038-06-1985 L1987 **ORS** *020 †40

SLAGLE, Harry Richard. 343 W MILLTOWN RD 44691 #041-09-1961 L1967 **GYN** *071 †30

SMITH, Eric Arthur. 128 E MILLTOWN RD, STE 105 44691 #024-16-1999 L2007 **FM** *020 †18

SMITH, William Thos. 1740 CLEVELAND RD 44691 #036-07-1970 L1973 **FM** *020 †18

STALLINGS, Lawrence M. 2326A EAGLE PASS 44691 #038-06-1977 L1983 **HO HEM** *020 †20

ST AMAND, Renault. 1761 BEALL AVE 44691 #440-01-1957 L1970 **PTH** *020 †50

STARTZMAN, Viola Virginia. ■ 44691 #038-06-1945 L1945 **GP PD** *071 †55

STEINER, Gerald Wesley. 1761 BEALL AVE 44691 #038-40-1967 L1967 **OBG** *020 †30

STERN, Larry Albert. 2200 BENDEN DR 44691 #038-40-1982 L1987 **GS VS** *020 †85

STEWART, David Scott. 1740 CLEVELAND RD 44691 #038-41-1981 L1983 **OBG** *020 †30

STRONG, John Headley. 1740 CLEVELAND RD, THE CLEVELAND CLNC WOOSTER 44691 #055-01-1994 L1997 **PD** *020 †55

STUMP, Daniel Eric. 1535 WILLOUGHBY DR 44691 #038-40-1969 L1969 **DR** *071 †80

SWOPE, David Kent. 2285 BENDEN DR 44691 #038-40-1986 L1987 **P** *020 †75

TALAMPAS, Liza Dacio. 1740 CLEVELAND RD 44691 #038-40-1995 L1998 **IM** *020 †20

THOMAS, John Warner. 3519 FRIENDSVILLE RD 44691 #038-06-1974 L1975 **OPH** *020 †35

TIZZANO, Anthony Paul. 1740 CLEVELAND RD 44691 #038-40-1988 L1989 **OBG** *020 †30

VELASQUEZ, Victor Dominic. 1761 BEALL AVE 44691 #748-01-1987 L2001 **IM** *020 †20

VELLANKI, Padma L. 3727 FRIENDSVILLE RD, THE ARTHRITIS CLINIC LLC 44691 #495-50-1988 L1995 **RHU IM** *020 †20

WATKINS, Richard J. ■ 44691 #041-01-1953 L1955 **ORS** *072 †40

WEEMAN, John Michael. 1761 BEALL AVE 44691 #038-40-1989 L1990 **OBG** *020 †30

WERNER, Bennett Evan. 1740 CLEVELAND RD, WOOSTER CLINIC, LLC 44691 #023-01-1977 L1980 **CD IM** *020 †20

WILLIAMS, Perry. 2201 BENDEN DR 44691 #654-01-1985 L1992 **FM** *030 †18 ‡

WRIGHT, Jeff Todd. ■ 44691 #038-44-1994 L1995 **EM** *020 †16

ZARKO, Rebecca Marie. 2285 BENDEN DR 44691 #038-44-1999 L1999 **CHP** *020 †75

ZINK, Harry Albert. 3519 FRIENDSVILLE RD 44691 #041-01-1971 L1976 **OPH** *020 †35

WORTHINGTON – FRANKLIN

ABBOTT, Cynthia A. ■ 43085 #020-02-1993 L1996 **D** *020 †15

ACKERMAN, G Adolph. ■ 43085 #038-40-1954 L1954 **OS** *071

BECKLEY, Steven Anthony. ■ 43085 #038-41-2006 L2006 **AN** *012

BERMAN, Brandon Ira. 6565 WORTHINGTON GALENA RD, STE B205 43085 #038-43-1997 L1998 **FM** *020 †18

BOWE, Deborah Mitchell. 91 E SELBY BLVD 43085 #038-45-1983 L1988 **IM PUD** *050 †20

CASTOR, Terrance Alan. 6565 WORTHINGTON GALENA RD, STE B105 43085 #038-06-1973 L1974 **IM** *020 †20 ‡

CATON, Anthony Ruthven. 6565 WORTHINGTON GALENA RD, STE B206 43085 #025-07-1999 L2005 **FM** *020 †18

CHANDLER, Jason Claud. ■ 43085 #047-06-2003 L2007 **HO** *012

CHONG, Gabriel Tsingtzong. 1129 HICKORY GROVE CT 43085 #036-07-2006 L2006 **OPH** *012

DANGLER, Laurie Ann. 6565 WORTHINGTON GALENA RD, STE B206 43085 #038-40-1996 L1997 **FM** *020 †18

DELLINGER, Mark Adam. ■ 43085 #038-43-1997 L1998 **IM** *020 †20

DENNIS, Linda Jean. 55 W LINCOLN AVE 43085 #017-20-1987 L1991 **AN** *020 †05

DI LAURO, Marie Nancy. 47 E WILSON BRIDGE RD 43085 #038-40-1978 L1978 **D OS** *020 †18

GAHMAN, James Worthy. ■ 43085 #038-40-1962 L1962 *062 †18

GARAS, Souhair Adeeb. 1035 PROPRIETORS RD, CENTRAL OHIO COUNSELING 43085 #915-05-1970 L1983 **P** *030

GHOSH, Mimi Ananya. 445 E DUBLIN GRANVILLE RD 43085 #065-05-1994 L1996 **FM** *020 †18

GILBERT, Ivan Saml. 100 W OLD WILSON BRIDGE RD 43085 #038-40-1945 L1945 **MDM FPG** *071

GROEN, David Keith. 81 E WILSON BRIDGE RD 43085 #065-05-1994 L1996 **FM FSM** *020 †18

HARDING, Herndon Price. 445 E GRANVILLE RD 43085 #005-12-1957 L1958 **P PYG** *071 †75

HAWK, Thomas Jennings. ■ 43085 #038-40-1960 L1960 **NS** *071 †25

HIRSH, Connie Kessler. 1035 PROPRIETORS RD 43085 #035-46-1984 L2004 **P** *020 †75

HODGES, Willis Holland. ■ 43085 #036-07-1945 L1948 **GP** *071

HUNDZIAK, Marcel. 445 E DUBLIN GRANVILLE RD 43085 #407-23-1952 L1962 **CHP P** *072

HUNTER, Jeffrey. 445 E DUBLIN GRANVILLE RD 43085 #038-75-1994, ▲ L1995 **FM OMM** *020 †18 ‡

7660

■ = Address Information Privacy Protected

JHA, Rakesh. ■ 43085 #025-01-1998 L2004 **DR** *100 †80

JOHNSON, Heidi. 660 HIGH ST, STE 202 43085 #038-43-1999 L2003 **P** *020 †75 ‡

KADIEV, Steven. ■ 43085 #836-01-1997 L2004 **PCC** *012 †20

KODURI, Atchuthamba. ■ 43085 #495-11-1973 L1984 **GP PD** *020 †05

KOFFLER, Elizabeth N. 1298 ABBEYHILL DR 43085 #038-43-2001 L2001 **OBG** *020 †30

LALONDE, Joseph Gerard. 1035 PROPRIETORS RD 43085 #016-06-1972 L1973 **P** *020 †75

LAWHON, William Thomas. ■ 43085 #038-40-2007 L2007 **IM** *012

LEE, L Edgar. 1033 HIGH ST 45, HOME 43085 #051-01-1956 L1985 **P MDM** *072 †75

LOY, Nancy Jane. 81 E WILSON BRIDGE RD 43085 #038-41-1983 L1987 **FM** *020 †18

MACRAE, Erin Renee. ■ 43085 #038-06-2005 L2007 **IM** *012

MARTIN, Stanley Ian. ■ 43085 #047-06-2000 L2006 **ID** *100 †20

MATSON, James E. ■ 43085 #038-40-1950 L1950 **AN** *071 †05

MC CAUGHAN, Joyce Ann S. 445 E DUBLIN GRANVILLE RD 43085 #041-07-1960 L1968 **P** *071

MEARA, Joseph Fisher. ■ 43085 #038-41-1960 L1960 **PTH** *071 †50

MICHALAK, Dale Andrew. 874 PROPRIETORS RD 43085 #038-40-1989 L1990 **FM** *020 †18

MINTER, Richard Eugene. 6649 N HIGH ST, STE LL6 43085 #016-02-1974 L1981 **P** *020 †75

MOWBRAY, Erin Elizabeth. 319 LOVEMAN AVE 43085 #020-02-2002 L2002 **MPD** *020 †20

NANDA, Paul Kalra. 445 E DUBLIN GRANVILLE RD 43085 #654-01-2003 L2004 **FM** *100 †18

NOVENA, Anthony Michael. 6565 WORTHINGTON GALENA RD, STE B105 43085 #038-40-1984 L1985 **IM** *040 †20

PFAHLER, Larry Lee. 6827 N HIGH ST STE 121 43085 #038-40-1969 L1969 **P GS** *020

PHILLIPS, John Anthony. ■ 43085 #056-06-2004 L2007 **CD** *012 †20

PRESCOTT, David Hires. 81 E WILSON BRIDGE RD 43085 #038-45-1981 L1982 **FM** *020 †18

RANKEY, David Scott. ■ 43085 #038-41-2007 L2007 **EM** *012

RASCO, Francine. 933 HIGH ST STE 240 43085 #038-40-1975 L1980 **P** *020 †75

REVKO, Lindsay Baird. ■ 43085 #003-75-2007, ▲ L2007 **FP** *012

ROSE, Melissa June. ■ 43085 #041-77-2001, ▲ L2005 **PHO** *012 †55

ROZMIAREK, Andrew James. ■ 43085 #041-12-2003 L2007 **AN** *012

SCHUEN, Wendy Diane. 955 PROPRIETORS RD STE B 43085 #038-40-1988 L1990 **D** *020 †15

SCHWARTZ, Harold. ■ 43085 #028-79-1951, ▲ L1980 *071

SHOEMAKER, Abigail Jo. 874 PROPRIETORS RD 43085 #038-40-1997 L2000 **FM** *020 †18

SIDDIQI, Bushra. 445 E DUBLIN GRANVILLE RD 43085 #704-06-1992 L2000 **FM** *020 †18

SIMMONS, Richard Elsworth. 933 HIGH ST STE 220 43085 #038-06-1958 L1958 **PO** *020 †35 ‡

STEGEMILLER, Robert Earl. ■ 43085 #038-41-1965 L1965 **AN** *071

STROEBEL, Frank Wm. ■ 43085 #038-40-1958 L1958 **PD** *071 †55

SUDIMACK, Joseph. ■ 43085 #038-40-1956 L1956 **OM** *071 †70

TAHBOUB, Majed Abdul M. 81 E WILSON BRIDGE RD 43085 #915-03-1968 L1979 **PS HS** *020 †85

UNK, Elizabeth Sauter. 6565 WORTHINGTON GALENA RD, STE B206 43085 #038-40-2000 L2000 **FM** *020 †18

WETTERAUER, Damon E. ■ 43085 #038-40-1943 L1943 **A PUD** *071

WHITE, Jeffrey Eugene. 81 E WILSON BRIDGE RD 43085 #038-43-1997 L1999 **FM** *020 †18

WHITE, Laura Mae. ■ 43085 #038-40-2004 L2004 **PS** *012

WILLIAMS, Glenn Robert, Jr. 6565 WORTHINGTON GALENA RD, STE B206 43085 #038-40-1998 L1999 **FM** *020 †18

WINKLER, Lenaann. ■ 43085 #038-45-2008 *012

WOOD, Catherine Louise. ■ 43085 #036-07-1981 **IG** *100

YAZVAC, Linda Stokely. 6711 MARKWOOD ST, YAZVAC & ASSOCIATES LLC 43085 #055-01-1979 L1990 **IM** *030 †20

WRIGHT PATTERSON AIR FORCE BASE – GREENE

ABUERREISH, Sameh Ghaleb. 4881 SUGAR MAPLE DR, BLDG 830 45433 #575-01-1994 L2008 **IM** *020 †20

ANDERSON, Brett Kirk. 4881 SUGAR MAPLE DR 45433 #041-15-2001 L2005 **AN** *020 †05

ASHER, Guy Chadwick, Jr. 4881 SUGAR MAPLE DR, BLDG 830 45433 #017-20-1997 L1999 **NEP** *020 †20

BALLARD, Timothy Dean. 2950 P ST, AFIT, HQ AFIT.CIM 45433 #023-12-1992 L2006 **FM** *020 †18

BAUER, Kristen Marie. 4881 SUGAR MAPLE DR, BLDG 830 45433 #041-15-1999 L2000 **ID** *100 †20

BAYNES, Brantly Webster. 4881 SUGAR MAPLE DR, 88TH MDG/SGH 45433 #023-12-1988 L1993 **PD** *030 †55

BEAN, Ethan Alan. 4881 SUGAR MAPLE DR, BLDG 830 45433 #045-01-1999 L2004 **P** *020

BELL, Jason Scott. 4881 SUGAR MAPLE DR, ORTHO SURG SGCO 45433 #005-15-1999 L2000 **ORS** *020 †40

BOWEN, Michael David. 4881 SUGAR MAPLE DR, 88TH MDOS/SGOHE 45433 #041-14-2003 L2003 **P** *020

BROWN, Christopher M. 4881 SUGAR MAPLE DR, 88TH MEDICAL GRP/SGOMI-A 45433 #020-12-2001 L2001 **IM** *020

BROWN, James W. 4881 SUGAR MAPLE DR, 88 MDG/SGHJ, BLDG 830 45433 #011-02-1973 L1974 **NM EM** *020 †35,28

BRUUN, John Steven. 4881 SUGAR MAPLE DR, 88 SGOS/SGCQ 45433 #023-12-2000 L2006 **GS** *100 †85

BUCKINGHAM, Heidi. 4881 SUGAR MAPLE DR 45433 #048-13-1998 L2006 **END** *020 †20

BUTCHKO, Gary Jon. 5030 PATTERSON PKWY, PED CLINIC BLDG 219 45433 #038-40-1996 L1997 **PDC** *020 †55

COX, Ronald Lee. 4881 SUGAR MAPLE DR, BLDG 830 45433 #019-02-1994 L1995 **ALI** *020 †20,03

EICHER, Tracy Jeanne. 4881 SUGAR MAPLE DR, BLDG 830 45433 #019-02-2001 L2006 **N** *020 †75

ERCHINGER, Thomas Andrew. 4331 SUGAR MAPLE DR, 88 SGOS/SGC 45433 #023-12-1988 L1990 **CRS GS** *020 †10,85

GLADISH, Sheri Lyn. 4881 SUGAR MAPLE DR 45433 #047-07-1996 L1997 **EM** *020 †16

GRAHAM, James Adam. 4881 SUGAR MAPLE DR, 88 MDE/MDOS-SEOMP 45433 #045-01-1998 L2005 **PCC** *020 †20

GUYE, Mary Lydon. 4881 SUGAR MAPLE DR, 88 SGOS/SGCQ 45433 #023-12-1997 L2006 **GS** *020 ‡

HAACK, Gregory James. 4881 SUGAR MAPLE DR, 88 MDOS/SGOMI 45433 #038-41-2000 L2000 **IM A** *020 †20 ‡

HAAK, James Cameron. 45433 #005-12-1979 L1980 **DR** *020 †80

HALSEY, Eric Stuart. 4881 SUGAR MAPLE DR, 88TH MDOS/SGOMB 45433 #019-02-1999 L2000 **IM ID** *020 †20

HERMES, Eric Dietrich. 4881 SUGAR MAPLE DR, 88TH MEDICAL GROUP/SGHJ 45433 #011-04-2000 L2001 *020

HERRINGTON, Sandra Jean. 4881 SUGAR MAPLE DR, DEPT. OF RADIATION ONCOLOG 45433 #019-02-1990 L2005 **RO** *020 †80

HICK, Eric James. 4881 SUGAR MAPL DR #PATHGY, 885G05/SGCXU 45433 #016-76-1999, ▲ L2008 **U** *020 †95

HIGH, Eric Andrew. 4881 SUGAR MAPLE DR, 88 M.D.G. 45433 #016-45-2002 L2007 **AN** *020 †05

HOOPES, David John. 4881 SUGAR MAPLE DR, 88MDOS ISGOMR 45433 #023-12-2002 L2004 **RO** *020

HUIZENGA, James Edward. 4881 SUGAR MAPLE DR, 88TH MEICAL GROUP/SGHJ 45433 #025-01-2000 L2000 **EM** *020 †16

HURLEY, Leo Danl. 4881 SUGAR MAPLE DR, 88 MDG/SGCXE BLDG 830 45433 #023-12-1988 L2006 **OPH** *020 †35

KAPELLEN, Phyllis Jean. 4881 SUGAR MAPLE DR, BLDG 830 45433 #003-01-1999 L2005 **DR** *020 †80

KLIMO, Paul, Jr. 4881 SUGAR MAPLE DR, 88TH MEDICAL GROUP SGOS/SG 45433 #056-06-1999 L2006 **NS** *100

LOUIS, David Jonathan. 4881 SUGAR MAPLE DR, 88TH MEDICAL GROUP/SGHJ, B 45433 #038-40-1990 L1990 **OM AM** *030 †70,18

LOWRY, Thomas R. 4881 SUGAR MAPLE DR, 88 SGOS/SGCXL 45433 #048-15-1997 L2005 **OTO** *020 †45

LYAKER, Michael Ray. 4881 SUGAR MAPLE DR, DEPT OF ANESTH MED CTR 45433 #047-05-2001 L2005 **AN** *020 †05

LYONS, Keegan Michael. 2950 P ST, HQ AFIT/CIM 45433 #038-43-1998 L1999 **PTH** *012 †70

MACPHERSON, Glen Douglas. 2950 P ST, AFIT WPAFB 45433 #028-02-2001 L2008 **GPM** *020 †70

MASSET-BROWN, Judith M. 5030 PATTERSON PKWY 45433 #020-02-1994 L1995 **PD** *020

MATHESON, Virginia Grace. 4881 SUGAR MAPLE DR, ATTN CREDENTIAL OFFICE 45433 #025-01-2000 L2000 **CHP** *020 †75 ‡

MATHEWS, Karen Michelle. 4225 LOGISTICS AVE RMN209, HQ AFMC/SGOC 45433 #028-02-1985 L1988 **FM** *030 †18 ‡

MCKAY, Matthew J. 4881 SUGAR MAPLE DR, WPAFB MEDICAL CENTER 45433 #016-45-2001 L2006 **EM** *020 †10

MC PHERSON, Oliver Lamont. 4881 SUGAR MAPLE DR, BLDG 830 45433 #051-07-1999 L2003 **P** *020 †75

MICHAELSON, Peter Gregg. 4881 SUGAR MAPLE DR, 88 SGOS / SGCXL 45433 #023-12-2001 L2006 **OTO** *020

MILLER, C. Brock. 4881 SUGAR MAPLE DR, 74TH MEDICAL GRP 45433 #016-43-2005 L2005 **IM** *012

MITCHELL, John Patrick. 4881 SUGAR MAPLE DR, 88TH MDG/SGHJ 45433 #041-13-1984 L1987 **PUD CCM** *030 †20

MURDOCK, Cabot Stratford. 4881 SUGAR MAPLE DR, 88TH MEDICAL GROUP 45433 #023-12-1996 L2005 **GS** *020 †85

NELSON, Erik Jon. 4881 SUGAR MAPLE DR, 88 MDG SGHJ 45433 #023-12-1992 L2007 **AN** *020 †05

OBERLIN, John Michael. 4881 SUGAR MAPLE DR, 88 MDOS/SGOCP 45433 #028-03-2003 L2005 **PD** *020 †55

PAONESSA, Damian John. 4881 SUGAR MAPLE DR, 74 MEDICAL GROUP/SGHJ 45433 #010-02-1991 L2006 **OBG** *020 †30

PATTON-EVANS, Anja Alther. 4881 SUGAR MAPLE DR, 88 MDG/88 MDOS/GROUP 45433 #023-12-1991 L1995 **PUD CCM** *020 †20

PEELLE, Michael Whitney. 4881 SUGAR MAPLE DR, SGOS/SGCO 45433 #028-02-2000 L2006 **ORS** *100

QUENNEVILLE, Daniel Jason. 4881 SUGAR MAPLE DR, 88TH MED GRP/SGQX BLDG 830 45433 #023-12-1986 L2002 **DR EM** *020 †80

RICE, Michael David. 4881 SUGAR MAPLE DR, BLDG 830 45433 #025-07-1998 L1998 **GE** *020

RICK, James Robert. 4881 SUGAR MAPLE DR, 88TH MEDICAL GROUP/SGHJ 45433 #023-12-1993 L2005 **PG** *100 †55

RUSS, Brian Wm. 4881 SUGAR MAPLE DR 45433 #038-43-1987 L1989 **D** *020 †18,15

SANSONE, Lori A. 4881 SUGAR MAPLE DR, 88TH MDOS / SGOPC 45433 #038-40-1982 L1983 **FM** *020 †18

SHORT, Rebecca Wambaugh. 88 MDOS/SGOMD, 4881 SUGAR MAPLE DR 45433 #020-02-1999 L2000 **D** *020 †15

STUART, Rory Patrick. 88 SGOS/SGCQ 45433 #023-12-2007 L2007 **GS** *012

TABATCHNICK, Larry. 4881 SUGAR MAPLE DR, 88TH DENTAL SQD. 45433 #048-13-1996 L1998 **GS** *020

TAYLOR, Jon Carl. 4881 SUGAR MAPLE DR, 88TH MEDICAL GROUP/SGHJ 45433 #038-41-1996 L2001 **EM** *020 †16

TUPER, Gale Timothy, Jr. 2950 P ST, AFIT-WPAFB 45433 #047-05-1998 L2000 **OTO** *012

WAHL, Elmer Francis. 4881 SUGAR MAPLE DR, 88 MDOS / SGOPC 45433 #038-41-1971 L1975 **FM FPG** *020 †18

WALCHNER, Andreas Max. AIR FORCE HSP ALLERGY CLNC 45433 #028-02-1967 L1967 **AI PD** *071 †55,03

WIEGAND, Robb Jay. 4881 SUGAR MAPLE DR, 74TH AMDS SGPF 45433 #038-43-2003 L2004 **EM** *012

WILLIAMS, Denise Ruth. 4881 SUGAR MAPLE DR, 88MDOS/SGOPC 45433 #051-04-1991 L1997 **FM** *020 †18

WILSON, Delano Donald. 4881 SUGAR MAPLE DR, BLDG 830 45433 #056-06-1986 L1988 **DR** *020 †80

WILSON, Douglas Drew. 4881 SUGAR MAPLE DR, 88TH MDOS/SAOPC 45433 #010-01-1973 L1978 **FM** *020 †18

WOOD, Charles Paige. 4881 SUGAR MAPLE DR, 88TH MDOS/SGOMI 45433 #023-12-1996 L2006 **IM** *020 †20

WOOD, Roger Allen. ■ 45433 #023-12-1999 L2000 **HO** *020 †20

WRIGHT, Joshua Leigh. 4881 SUGAR MAPLE DR, BLDG 830 45433 #056-06-1999 L2003 **EM** *020 †16

WYOMING – HAMILTON

KIM, Christopher. ■ 45215 #038-41-2008 *012

KINLAW, Leah Marie. ■ 45215 #041-14-2008 *012

MALIT, Bonita Dale. ■ 45215 #011-03-1978 L1993 **FM PHP** *071 †70,18

RAMIREZ, Bryant Rafael. ■ 45215 #038-45-2006 L2006 **N** *012

SCHAPERA, Cecil Herbert. ■ 45215 #836-02-1958 L1965 **FM** *071 †18

WOODSIDE, Frank C. ■ 45215 #038-41-1973 L1973 **LM** *075

WRIGHT, Asalet Mennan O. ■ 45231 #902-01-1954 **OBG** *074

WOODARD, Wayne Chas. 50 N PROGRESS DR 45385 #028-34-1980 L1988 **ORS** *020 †40

XENIA – GREENE

AHMAD, Ibrahim. 215 S ALLISON AVE, ROBERT T MORRISON MD & ASS 45385 #875-03-1992 L2000 **NEP** *020 †20
ALKHAWAGA, Esam Hamed. 452 W MARKET ST 45385 #915-07-1986 L2006 **P** *020 †75
APPLIN, Shirelle. 1141 N MONROE DR 45385 #038-41-1997 L1999 **FM** *020 †18
ARNOLD, Scott Joseph. 1141 N MONROE DR 45385 #038-45-1994 L1999 **SP** *020 †50
ARUNTHARI, Cheerasak. 1141 N MONROE DR 45385 #891-01-1970 L1974 **EM** *020
BAILEY, Linda Ellen. 244 WILSON DR 45385 #038-40-1982 L1982 **GS CRS** *020 †85
BLACHLY-FLANAGAN, Theresa. 452 W MARKET ST 45385 #038-45-1995 L2000 **CHP** *020 †75
BOETTLER, Mark Arden. 1237 N MONROE DR 45385 #038-41-1986 L1988 **IM** *020 †20 ‡
BROWN, David Le. 1141 N MONROE DR 45385 #038-41-1984 L1989 **R** *020 †80
BRUMFIELD, Daniel Howard. 1141 N MONROE DR 45385 #038-45-1992 L1993 **FM** *020 †18
BUTT, Waseem. 1141 N MONROE DR, GREENE MEMORIAL HOSPITAL 45385 #704-01-1996 L2006 **IM** *020 †20
BYERS, Richard Henry, Jr. 1157 N MONROE DR, MEDICAL SERVICE ASSOC 45385 #038-40-1978 L1978 **FM FPG** *020 †18
CARTER, David Wm. 1141 N MONROE DR 45385 #038-45-1984 L1985 **EM** *020 †16
COLLINS, James Robt. PO BOX 113 45385 #038-06-1937 L1937 **OBG** *071 †30
COLLINS, Mark Stephen. 1141 N MONROE DR 45385 #023-12-1983 L1993 **IM** *020 †20
CRAWFORD, Robert Ian. 452 W MARKET ST 45385 #025-01-1956 L1985 **P GP** *071
CRAWFORD, Steven Warren. 1157 N MONROE DR, STE 220 45385 #038-41-1993 L1994 **OBG** *030
CUDKOWICZ, Margaret R. ■ 45385 #917-20-1953 L1976 **FM** *020
DAY, Shandra Rose. ■ 45385 #038-45-2005 L2005 **IM** *012
DEUTSCH, David Hampton. 244 WILSON DR 45385 #039-01-1986 L1987 **GS** *020 †85
DILLAPLAIN, Robert Paul. 25 S ALLISON AVE, WOMEN'S HEALTH SERVS INC 45385 #048-04-1973 L1982 **OBG** *020 †30
DIXON, Charles Steven. ■ 45385 #038-45-1984 L1985 **EM** *020 †16
GENTILE, Julie Patrice. 452 W MARKET ST 45385 #038-45-1996 L1997 **P** *020 †75
GOOD, Michael Wayne. 1141 N MONROE DR 45385 #038-45-2003 L2003 **EM** *020
HASSEL, Rebecca Mae. ■ 45385 #038-45-2004 L2006 **GS** *012
HEDRICK, Jason Thomas. ■ 45385 #005-12-2005 L2005 **GS** *012
HEDRICK, Sarah Marie. ■ 45385 #005-12-2005 L2005 **IM** *012
HENDERSON, Richard A, III. ■ 45385 #036-07-1969 L1997 **OM AM** *020 †70
HENDRICKSON, Robert Duane. 50 N PROGRESS DR 45385 #038-40-1945 L1945 **FM ORS** *071
HERNANDEZ, Isagani T. 98 PARK ST 45385 #038-45-1972 L1972 **IM MD** *020 †20
HESZ, Nancy Jean. 1659 W 2ND ST 45385 #016-11-1979 L1994 **PD CHP** *020 †55
HOGAN, Penny Sue. 1162 N MONROE DR 45385 #038-40-1995 L1996 **FM FSM** *020 †18
HOUSEKNECHT, Valerie E. 452 W MARKET ST 45385 #038-45-2001 L2005 **P** *020 †75
JIMENEZ-PAGES, Lazaro O. 1157 N MONROE DR, STE 210 45385 #847-06-1980 L1995 **FM** *020 †18
KATHULA, Satheesh Kumar. 1141 N MONROE DR 45385 #496-24-1994 L1998 **HO** *020 †20
KELLY, Richard Franklin. 1237 N MONROE ST 45385 #038-41-1947 L1947 **FM** *072 †18
KEMPER, Robert James. ■ 45385 #036-05-1961 L1964 **AN** *071 †05
KHURMA, Santosh. 50 N PROGRESS DR 45385 #495-14-1972 L1981 **IM IMG** *020 †20
KHURMA, Sukhdev Hari. 101 S ORANGE ST, HOMETOWN URGENT CARE 45385 #495-43-1974 L1978 **IM** *020 †20
KIM, David Dohoon. ■ 45385 #005-06-2002 L2002 **OBG** *020 †30
KOEHLER, John Erwin. ■ 45385 #038-40-1960 L1960 **GP** *075
MADISON, Christopher K. 244 WILSON DR 45385 #038-45-2000 L2000 **GS** *020
MARSHALL, Lisa Ann. 1114 N MONROE DR 45385 #038-40-1994 L1995 **PD** *020 †55
MILLS, Justin Gerard. 1141 N MONROE DR, GREENE MEMORIAL HOSPITAL 45385 #038-45-1983 L1994 **RO** *020
MORRISON, Robert T. 215 S ALLISON AVE 45385 #035-03-1985 L1994 **NEP IM** *020 †20
MUHTADIE, Sami Faez. 1197 W 2ND ST 45385 #062-01-1974 L1995 **PD** *020 †55
OWENS, Tiffany Jane. ■ 45385 #038-45-2006 L2006 **PD** *012
PACHOLKA, Roger Wm. ■ 45385 #038-45-1985 L1986 **EM** *020 †16
PAGES, Helena Duque. 50 N PROGRESS DR 45385 #264-11-1978 L1992 **FM** *020 †18 ‡
PALMER, Alan Arthur. 1141 N MONROE DR 45385 #038-41-1971 L1971 **GS** *071 †85
PATEL, Rajendrabhai A. 382 N DETROIT ST 45385 #495-23-1970 L1976 **PUD IM** *020 †20
PATIL, Somashekhar S. 1160 N MONROE DR 45385 #495-37-1963 L1972 **IM PUD** *020 †20
PEH, Khang Hong. 1141 N MONROE DR 45385 #244-03-1968 L1975 **OBG** *075
PLOTKIN, Karl Julius. 1141 N MONROE DR 45385 #030-06-1978 L1982 **DR** *020 †80
PORTER, Carl Douglas. 1157 N MONROE DR 45385 #038-40-1989 L1993 **PM IMG** *020 †60
PRINCESA, Gerardo S. ■ 45385 #748-08-1991 L2007 **AN** *100
RADCLIFFE, James Danl. 244 WILSON DR 45385 #038-40-1979 L1980 **GS** *020 †85
RAHMAN, Mahmood. 442 N DETROIT ST 45385 #704-15-1983 L1994 **P** *020
ROJAS, Luisa Alfonso. ■ 45385 #275-01-1961 L1978 **OS** *075
SALISBURY, Alvin B, Jr. 1141 N MONROE DR 45385 #038-40-1949 L1949 **GP OS** *071
SARMINA, Ignacio. 390 N DETROIT ST 45385 #038-43-1982 L1983 **U** *020 †95
SCHMITT, Eugene John. ■ 45385 #028-34-1948 L1950 **IMG** *071
SCIBETTA, Richard Chas. ■ 45385 #038-06-1955 L1955 **P** *071
SHAMSI, Shamim Ahmad. 1141 N MONROE DR 45385 #704-02-1963 L1970 **PTH** *071 †50
STOCKWELL, Frederick D. 50 N PROGRESS DR 45385 #008-01-1972 L1979 **FM** *020 †18
SUTTON, Joseph E, Jr. 1141 N MONROE DR 45385 #010-03-1962 L1988 **DR NM** *020
TAYLOR, Ronald Stuart. 426 N DETROIT ST 45385 #004-01-1973 L1975 **FM** *020 †18
TRIPLETT, Thaddene O. 1659 W 2ND ST 45385 #038-45-1991 L1993 **PD** *020 †55
VALIDO, Constantino L. 1197 W 2ND ST 45385 #748-01-1951 L1968 **PD PDC** *071 †55
VERNIER, Paul Chas. 1141 N MONROE DR 45385 #038-40-1943 L1943 **GP** *071
VITALITI, Constance Jean. ■ 45385 #041-07-1979 L1981 **AN** *075
VITALITI, John Carmen. ■ 45385 #041-07-1979 L2005 **AN IM** *071 †05,20
WAIKHOM, J Singh. 124 OFFICE PARK DR 45385 #495-24-1964 L1974 **OPH** *020 †35 ‡
WAIKHOM, Sanahanbi Devi. 124 OFFICE PARK DR 45385 #495-18-1967 L1974 **EM OM** *020 †16
WALTERS, Charles Lee. 755 VINE ST STE 200 45385 #021-05-1970 L1977 **P N** *020 †75 ‡
WARD, Deborah Elizabeth. 1141 N MONROE DR, GREENE MEMORIAL HOSP 45385 #038-40-1981 L1985 **PTH** *020 †50
WARNER, Rodney D. 50 N PROGRESS DR 45385 #041-01-1949 L1952 **FM** *020
WILLIAMS, Scott Elizabeth. 50 N PROGRESS DR, THE CTR FOR NUTRITION 45385 #038-45-2003 L2003 **IM NTR** *020 †20
WOLFF, John L. 244 WILSON DR 45385 #008-01-1952 L1955 **GS** *071 †85

YELLOW SPRINGS – GREENE

AGNA, James W. ■ 45387 #038-41-1949 L1949 **IM** *071 †20
BELL, Amanda Lynn. 1001 XENIA AVE, UNIVERSITY FAMILY HEALTH C 45387 #038-45-1997 L1998 **FM** *020 †18
BINDER, Stephen Bruce. 1001 XENIA AVE 45387 #051-01-1985 L1987 **FM** *020 †18
BLACKBURN, Jeffery Beil. 1001 XENIA AVE, CENTER-WRIGHT STATE UNIV 45387 #017-20-1967 L1970 **FM** *020 †18
BONDURANT, Teresa M. ■ 45387 #047-07-1996 **IM** *100
BUDZAK, Mary Louise. 1001 XENIA AVE, YELLOW SPRINGS FAMILY HLTH 45387 #016-11-1981 L1982 **FM** *020 †18
CHIANG, Meicheng. ■ 45387 #038-40-2004 L2004 **P** *012
CLASEN, Mark Edward. 1001 XENIA AVE 45387 #027-01-1979 L1982 **FM** *020 †18
DONNELLY, John Francis. 1001 XENIA AVE, YELLOW SPRINGS FAM HEALTH 45387 #048-14-1985 L1997 **FM** *040 †18
HALE, Pamela Candace. ■ 45387 #649-35-1980 L1995 **P** *020
HAWKINS, Jennifer Renee. 1001 XENIA AVE 45387 #038-45-2005 L2005 **FP** *012
HOLMAN, Lainie Kathleen. ■ 45387 #038-43-2002 L2002 **FM** *100 †55
HYDE, Carl Dudley. ■ 45387 #038-06-1952 L1952 **FM** *071 †18
HYDE, David Estlow. 1425 XENIA AVE 45387 #308-03-1981 L1987 **FM EM** *020 ‡
JOHN, P George. 1001 XENIA AVE 45387 #495-29-1962 L1998 **FM PD** *040 †55,18
KHAVARI, Sarah Grace. 1001 XENIA AVE 45387 #038-45-2005 L2005 **FP** *012
LITTLE, David Roy. 1001 XENIA AVE 45387 #038-44-1987 L1988 **FM** *040 †18
OLSEN, Cynthia G. 1001 XENIA AVE 45387 #038-45-1985 L1986 **FM FPG** *020 †18
RHODE, Jennifer Morris. ■ 45387 #001-02-1991 L2006 **OBG** *020 †30 ‡
STRINGER, Sarah Jane. ■ 45387 #023-12-2006 L2007 **P** *012
VAN AUSDAL, Carol M. ■ 45387 #038-40-1973 L1973 **PD** *020 †55
VAN AUSDAL, Paul Francis. 1425 XENIA AVE 45387 #038-40-1973 L1973 **FM** *020 †18
WATSON, Keith Anthony. 100 KAHOE LN 45387 #045-01-1978 L1979 **OBG** *020 †30
WEBB, Paul Paine. ■ 45387 #051-01-1946 L1963 **NTR AM** *071
WINEBURGH, George Lewis. ■ 45387 #035-20-1970 L1994 **DR** *020 †80 ‡

YOUNGSTOWN – MAHONING

ABDEL MONEIM MOHAMED HASHE, . 465 GYPSY LN 44504 #915-04-2001 L2004 **IM** *100 †20
ABDU, Rashid A. 1044 BELMONT AVE, ST ELIZABETH HEALTH CENTER 44504 #010-01-1960 L1965 **GS** *071 †85
ABOUJAOUDE, Salim Semaan. 500 GYPSY LN, STE 304 44504 #605-01-1985 L1993 **PUD CCM** *020 †20
ADAMOPOULOU, Chrysavgi. 500 GYPSY LN, DEPT OF MED EDU 44504 #418-01-2003 L2006 **IM** *100
AEY, John Patrick. 1075 W WESTERN RESERVE RD, EYE CARE ASSOCIATES INC 44514 #038-40-1993 L1998 **OPH** *020 †35
AGGARWAL, Ashok Kumar. 726 WICK AVE 44505 #495-29-1979 L1983 **OBG** *020 †30
AGNEW, Scott Manning. 901 TRAILWOOD DR 44512 #038-45-1983 L1985 **FM** *020 †18
AGUOLU, Obianuju Geneviev. 500 GYPSY LN, DEPT OF MED EDUCATION 44504 #690-15-2004 L2006 **PD** *012
AHMED, Ghazanfar. 1044 BELMONT AVE 44504 #654-01-2003 L2003 **FM** *020 †18
AHMED, Iram Fatima. 1044 BELMONT AVE, AMBULATORY CARE CENTER 44504 #654-01-2001 L2001 **FM** *020 †18
ALBAALBAKI, Fysal. 500 GYPSY LN, CARE SYSTEM/FO 44504 #875-01-2000 L2004 **IM** *012
ALBINI, Salo. ■ 44505 #781-02-1934 L1955 **PUD IM** *020
ALDIAB, Muna. 500 GYPSY LN, 2ND FLOOR RRC 44504 #875-01-2004 L2007 **IM** *012
ALEXANDER, Louis Peter. 64 REDFERN DR 44505 #030-06-1963 L1966 **OBG** *030 †30
AL HASAN, Muthanna. 500 GYPSY LN, DEPT OF MED EDU 44504 #875-01-2001 L2006 **IM** *012
AL-HAWWAS, Malek. ■ 44504 #915-02-1999 L2005 **IM** *012
ALKHATIB, Hassan. 345 OAK HILL AVE, WESTERN RESERVE CARE SYS 44502 #875-01-1993 L2006 **IM** *012
ALLEN, Robert James, Jr. 1044 BELMONT AVE, HEALTH CENTER 44504 #008-02-2007 L2007 **TY** *012
AL-SAIEG, Nawar. ■ 44504 #875-03-1997 L2004 **IM** *020 †20
AL-TAIEB, Khaled Mohammed. 345 OAK HILL AVE, WESTERN RESERVE CARE SYS 44502 #915-02-2000 L2006 **IM** *012
ALTIER, John K. 64 REDFERN DR 44505 #016-43-1962 L1963 **IM ON** *020
ALTMAN, George Lawrence. ■ 44505 #016-11-1945 L1952 **R** *071 †80
AL ZOBY, Muneer M. Basher. ■ 44504 #875-02-1999 L2007 **IM** *012
AMBROSE, Joseph Anthony. 64 REDFERN DR 44505 #038-06-1997 L1998 **GS** *020 †85
AMIT, Abraham Rami. 500 GYPSY LN, TOD CHILDREN' HOSPITAL 44504 #550-03-1973 L1997 **CHN N** *020 †75
ANGELO, Robert Nicholas. 2031 BELMONT AVE, YOUNGSTOWN 44505 #038-44-1991 L1992 **IM** *020 †20
ANGTUACO, Ernesto V. 25 N CANFIELD NILES RD, CRESTWOOD X-RAY CENTER 44515 #748-01-1972 L1975 **DR NR** *020 †80
ANSARI, Larry Shareef. ■ 44512 #025-12-2003 L2003 **GS** *012
ARIZA, Cesar Augusto. 4970 BELMONT AVE 44505 #308-01-1960 L1974 **P N** *020
ARIZA, Guaroa D. 7 BELGRADE ST 44505 #308-01-1966 L1974 **OS** *020
ATANASOFF, Nicholas A. 64 REDFERN DR 44505 #028-78-2000, ▲ L2000 **P** *020 ‡
ATHWAL, Amardeep Singh. ■ 44514 #654-01-2005 L2007 **FP** *012
AUBEL, Steven. 250 DEBARTOLO PL, BLDG B 44512 #025-07-1984 L1985 **DR** *020 †80
AWAD, Maher Fayez. 1044 BELMONT AVE, C/O ST ELIZ HLTH CTR-MED E 44504 #915-01-1998 L1998 **IM** *020 †20
AWAD, Mounir. 755 BOARDMAN CANFIELD RD, STE A1 44512 #605-02-1976 L1981 **GS** *020 †85
AWADALLA, Maged Ibrahim. 725 BOARDMAN CANFIELD RD U 44512 #915-02-1981 L1994 **IM** *020 †20
AYASS, Mouhab F. 500 GYPSY LN 44504 #875-01-1985 L1992 **PD PHO** *020 †55
AZARVAN, Asad. 250 DEBARTOLO PL, BLDG B 44512 #517-03-1971 L1981 **R** *020 †80
AZIZ, Osama Naguib. 500 GYPSY LN, CO WRCS - MED EDU DEPT 44504 #915-04-1997 L2001 **CCM** *100
BABYAK, John W. 500 GYPSY LN 44504 #025-01-1982 L1988 **OTO** *020 †45
BAILEY, Rebecca S. 960 WINDHAM CT STE 1 44512 #036-05-1979 L1982 **PUD CCM** *020 †20 ‡
BAILEY, Ronald Allen. 1044 BELMONT AVE 44504 #020-02-1971 L1972 **R NM** *020 †80

BAILEY, Thomas Andrew. 25 N CANFIELD NILES RD, STE 100 44515 #038-44-1999 L1999 **IM** *020 †20
BAL, Harjinder Singh. 1044 BELMONT AVE, DEPT IM 44504 #495-03-1998 L2003 **IM** *100
BAL, Surjit Kaur. 8302 SOUTHERN BLVD 44512 #495-03-1967 L1973 **PTH** *020 †50
BAL, Tejinder Singh. 550 PARMALEE AVE, SUTIE #210 44510 #495-03-1966 L1973 **IM CCM** *020 †20
BALLAS, Steven Lee. 250 DEBARTOLO PL, STE 2750 44512 #038-40-1981 L1982 **CD** *020 †20
BALLO, Bela Frank. 500 GYPSY LN 44504 #035-06-1964 L1965 **R** *020 †80
BARILLARE, Shannon Marie. ■ 44505 #038-43-2005 L2005 **FP** *012
BARMADA, Bicher. 500 GYPSY LN, STE 101 44504 #605-02-1968 L2002 **TS** *020 †85,90
BARR, Richard Gary. 25 N CANFIELD NILES RD, YOUNGSTOWN ASSOCIATES IN 44515 #038-06-1985 L1986 **DR** *020 †80
BASA, Ramon Roland Isidro. ■ 44515 #748-10-2002 L2006 **IM** *012
BATH, Harneet Singh. ■ 44504 #495-03-2004 L2005 **IM** *012
BECKER, John Robt, Jr. 550 PARMALEE AVE, STE 200 44510 #038-43-1989 L1990 **N** *020 †75
BELDING, Robert C. ■ 44512 #025-07-1973 L2002 **PTH OS** *050 †50
BERNAT, Donald R. 3040 BELMONT AVE 44505 #030-06-1950 L1951 **GP GS** *075
BERNSTINE, Richard Lee. ST ELIZABETH HOSP MED CTR 44504 #041-02-1948 L1976 **OBG OS** *071 †30
BETHUY, Joseph Alphonse. 3622 BELMONT AVE STE 13& 44505 #025-07-1975 L1984 **PD** *020 †55
BETTS, Walter Lee. ■ 44504 #047-07-1971 L1974 **IM PHP** *071
BHATTACHARJEE, Pradip. 500 GYPSY LN, WESTERN RESERVE CARE SYSTE 44504 #654-01-1998 L1999 **PTH** *020 †50
BITONTE, Anthony Gary. 1044 BELMONT AVE 44504 #038-40-1973 L1973 **U** *020 †95
BITONTE, Dianne Marlo. 500 GYPSY LN 44504 #038-44-1981 L1982 **EM** *020
BLEACHER, John Henry O. 500 GYPSY LN, TOD CHILDRENS HOSPITAL 44504 #041-13-1959 L1967 **PDS OS** *071 †85
BLOOMBERG, Louis. 3020 BELMONT AVE, BELMONT EYE CLINIC 44505 #038-40-1943 L1943 **OPH** *071 †35
BOGEN, Gregg Loren. 1450 S CANFIELD NILES RD, UNITD 44515 #038-44-1989 L1996 **GS SO** *020 †85
BOGYI, Antonia Maria. 2031 BELMONT AVE 44505 #025-01-1986 L1995 **P** *020 †75
BOKESCH, Paula Marie. 160 S BEVERLY AVE 44515 #036-05-1978 L1995 **AN** *020 †05
BOKHARI, Shahid Jon. 345 OAK HILL AVE 44502 #422-01-2005 L2005 **PTH** *012
BONIFACE, Raymond Sesti. 721 BOARDMAN POLAND RD, STE 202 44512 #561-01-1952 L1954 **P** *020
BONIFACE, Thomas Sesti. 835 MCKAY CT STE 100 44512 #038-44-1983 L1984 **ORS** *020 †40
BOULIS, Gust. 2921 GLENWOOD AVE 44511 #041-02-1957 L1958 **IM** *071
BOUTROS, Rafik Helmy. 602 PARMALEE AVE, STE 110 44510 #915-02-1970 L1988 **AN** *020 †05
BRANT, Arthur M. 1044 BELMONT AVE, AMBULATORY CARE CENTER 44504 #023-07-1989 L1995 **OPH** *020 †35
BROCKER, Brian Patrick. 1616 COVINGTON ST 44510 #038-43-1985 L1994 **NS** *020 †25
BROCKER, Robert J. 1616 COVINGTON ST 44510 #041-12-1952 L1961 **NS N** *071
BROWN, David B. 3622 BELMONT AVE STE 18 44505 #038-40-1951 L1951 **GE IM** *071 †20
BROWN, Robert Allan. ■ 44512 #035-06-1946 L1951 **IM** *071
BRUCE, Nadine Cecile. 1044 BELMONT AVE, ST. ELIZABETH HLTH CTR 44504 #016-11-1970 L1994 **IM IMG** *040 †20 ‡
BRUCOLI, B Patrick. 500 GYPSY LN 44504 #038-40-1959 L1959 **PD** *071 †55
BUCKLEY, John Jos. 1044 BELMONT AVE, STE C 44504 #038-40-1959 L1959 **GYN** *020 †30
BUCKLEY, John Jos, Jr. 935 TRAILWOOD DR STE C 44512 #038-41-1981 L1982 **PS** *020 †65
BULSECO, Jose Leones. ■ 44505 #748-01-1959 L1968 **GP GS** *071
BURICK, Wayne Patrick. 250 DEBARTOLO PL, BLDG B 44512 #038-41-1968 L1968 **R** *020 †80
BUTCHER, Gene Allen. 500 GYPSY LN, MED EDC PROF OFC BLDG 44504 #036-07-1965 L1966 **OS IM** *030 †20
BUTTERWORTH, Jane Rogers. 345 OAK HILL AVE 44502 #020-02-1974 L1983 **PM** *075
BUXMAN, Richard A. 1044 BELMONT AVE, ST ELIZABETH HEALTH CTR 44504 #018-75-1979, ▲ L1985 **EM** *020 †16
BUZZACCO, Dominic Michael. ■ 44512 #038-44-2008 *012
CALDERON, Javier E. 540 PARMALEE AVE, STE 610 44510 #737-06-1989 L2000 **IM ID** *020 †20
CALIMLIM, Jefferson N. 2240 HUBBARD RD, 07517-089 44505 #748-02-1970 L1978 **OTO** *020
CAMPBELL, Tom Edward. 8302 SOUTHERN BLVD 44512 #041-02-1974 L1975 **DMP ATP** *030 †50
CANACCI, Anastasia Marie. ■ 44511 #038-40-2003 L2004 **PTH** *012
CANDA, Tinah Loie Obenza. 345 OAK HILL AVE, WESTERN RESERVE CARE SYS 44502 #748-19-2004 L2005 **IM** *012
CANNON, Carrie Maykowski. 1044 BELMONT AVE, ST ELIZABETH HEALTH CENTER 44504 #038-40-1998 L2000 **NPM** *020 †55
CARBONELL, Fernando. 755 BOARDMAN CANFIELD RD 44512 #264-04-1958 L1967 **HNS OS** *072 †85
CARDONE, John Christopher. 500 GYPSY LN, STE 101 44504 #041-02-1986 L2005 **TS** *020 †85,90
CARTER, Kimbroe John. 1044 BELMONT AVE 44504 #021-01-1977 L1983 **PTH IM** *050 †50
CASTA, Dexter Runa. 500 GYPSY LN, 2ND FLOOR RRC 44504 #748-01-2003 L2007 **IM** *012
CATALINE, Philip Robert. ■ 44511 #038-44-2008 *012
CAVAROCCHI, Nicholas Chas. 540 PARMALEE AVE, STE 510 44510 #041-13-1978 L2003 **TS TTS** *020 †85,90
CESTONE, Patrick B, Jr. 250 DEBARTOLO PL, BLDG B 44512 #028-34-1995 **DR** *071 †80
CHANDRA, Shekara Setty M. ■ 44505 #495-33-1963 L1995 **U GS** *020
CHASE, Daniel Mark. 345 OAK HILL AVE, DEPT NORTHSIDE MED CTR 44502 #016-11-2004 L2004 **GS** *012
CHAUDHARY, Ganesh. 500 GYPSY LN, 2ND FLOOR RRC 44504 #672-01-2003 L2007 **IM** *012
CHAUDHRY, Mohammad Sohail. 500 GYPSY LN, CO WRCS-MED EDU DEPT 44504 #704-22-1998 L2001 **CD** *012 †20
CHEN, Charles Chihming. 7330 SOUTHERN BLVD, STE 6 44512 #038-44-1989 L1991 **IM** *020 †20
CHEN, Fred Shinglih. 500 GYPSY LN, (FORUM HEALTH) 44504 #016-11-1990 L1994 **PM** *020 †60
CHENG, Vicky Ong. 500 GYPSY LN, DEPT OF MED EDU 44504 #748-01-2003 L2006 **IM** *012
CHENTOW, Geoffrey Leslie. 64 REDFERN DR 44505 #869-05-1973 L1977 **IM** *020 †20
CHEVLEN, Eric Mark. 1044 BELMONT AVE 44504 #038-40-1974 L1976 **HO PMM** *020 †20
CHEVLEN, Harold. ■ 44504 #026-04-1949 L1949 **FM** *071
CHOI, Kyu Bo. ■ 44505 #583-10-1967 L1978 **CD IM** *020 †20
CHUA, Nanette Siopongco. ■ 44505 #748-10-2004 L2007 **IM** *012
CLEARY, William James. ■ 44505 #035-09-1957 L1957 **IM** *071 †20
COLLA, Ippolito. 800 INDIANOLA WOODSIDE RD 44512 #561-12-1967 *075
COLLINS, Robert Leon. 1044 BELMONT AVE 44504 #047-06-1976 L1986 **REN GYN** *020 †30
CONTI, John S. 25 N CANFIELD NILES RD 44515 #165-04-1967 L1971 **IM** *020
COOL-LLORENS, Dianna Mari. 345 OAK HILL AVE, WESTERN RESERVE CARE SYS 44502 #847-22-1998 L2001 **PTH** *100
COOPER, Linda June. 1044 BELMONT AVE 44504 #030-05-1976 L1994 **PD NPM** *075 †55
CORFIAS, Mike George. 7525 CALIFORNIA AVE 44512 #038-44-1993 L1994 **AN PME** *020 †05
COSSETTE, Rene. ■ 44514 #067-03-1951 L1959 **EM OS** *071
COSTIC, Donald Joseph. ■ 44504 #038-44-2007 L2007 **IM** *012
COUNTO, Vidya Jagdish. 1053 BELMONT AVE 44504 #496-15-2001 L2004 **FM** *020 †18
COWENS, Kenneth Gerad. 1350 5TH AVE, STE 320 44504 #047-07-1985 L1986 **IM PD** *020
CROPP, Alan Jay. 1044 BELMONT AVE, 4TH FL 44504 #038-40-1979 L1981 **PUD CCM** *020 †20
CRUZ, Alan Lardizabal. 500 GYPSY LN, CO WRCS-MED EDU DEPT 44504 #748-21-1999 L2002 **FM** *020 †18
CUTRONA, Anthony F, Jr. 540 PARMALEE AVE, STE 610 44510 #847-10-1984 L1987 **ID IM** *020 †20
DADOUCH, Hachem. 6505 MARKET ST, BLDG B BEEGHLY MEDICAL PAR 44512 #875-01-1989 L1994 **IM EM** *020 †20
DALLIS, Demetrios John. 1044 BELMONT AVE 44504 #038-40-1959 L1959 **GS** *071 †85
D'AMATO, Fredric Raymond. 11 FEDERAL PLAZA CENTRAL, STE 510 44503 #038-41-1948 L1948 **OPH** *071 †35
DANG, Huy Ngoc. 1044 BELMONT AVE, ST ELIZ HLTH CTR 44504 #308-03-1998 L2003 **IM** *020
D'APOLITO, James Phillip. 4316 BELMONT AVE 44505 #038-44-1988 L1991 **PD** *020 †55
DASU, Madhavarao Seshu. 500 GYPSY LN 44504 #495-50-1969 L1978 **AN** *020
DAVIDOW, Sidney L. 3030 BELMONT AVE 44505 #025-01-1935 L1939 **PD PDA** *072 †55
DAVIS, David Michael. 64 REDFERN DR 44505 #038-40-1995 L1999 **FM** *020 †18
DAWOOD, Murtaza Yousuf. 500 GYPSY LN, DEPT OF SURGERY 44504 #665-01-2002 L2002 **GS** *012
DAWSO, Sharon. 500 GYPSY LN, FAMILY PRACTICE CTR 44504 #063-01-1999 L2002 **FM** *040 †18
DE, Sumit Kumar. ■ 44504 #025-01-2004 L2007 **GS** *012
DE CICCO, Gabriel E. ■ 44512 #041-02-1936 L1937 **FM OS** *071
DE GIDIO, Anthony James. ■ 44509 #005-17-1962 L1975 **GP** *075
DEGRAEFF, Pieter. YOUNGSTOWN HOSP, DEPT MED 44502 #660-02-1975 **IM** *100
DELATORE, Jason Richard. 540 PARMALEE AVE, STE 410 44510 #038-40-1996 L2003 **VS** *020 †85
DEL MASTRO, John Alan. 500 GYPSY LN, WESTERN RESERVE CARE SYSTE 44504 #041-13-1997 L1999 **FOP** *020
DE MARTINO, Julianne. 935 TRAILWOOD DR, STE A 44512 #038-44-1996 L1997 **OBG** *020 †30
DENT, Monilla Monet. ■ 44502 #038-44-2008 *012
DE OLAZO, Aura Theresa Bo. 500 GYPSY LN, 2ND FLOOR RRC 44504 #748-01-2004 L2007 **IM** *012
DERAMO, Anthony Thomas. 5701 MARKET ST 44512 #011-02-1962 L1963 **AI IM** *020 †03
DEVINE, Michael Jos. 20 OHLTOWN RD 44515 #038-40-1986 L1989 **IM** *020 †20
DE VITO, Peter Michael. 7600 SOUTHERN BLVD, STE 2 44512 #038-44-1991 L1993 **GS** *020 †85
DEWAR, James Craik, Jr. 500 GYPSY LN 44504 #041-12-1986 L1992 **FM** *040 †18
DEWAR, Stephanie B. 500 GYPSY LN, TOD CHILDRENS HOSP 44504 #041-12-1986 L1990 **PD** *020 †55
DHINGRA, Jagmeet Singh. 500 GYPSY LN, DEPT OF MED EDU 44504 #495-43-2004 L2006 **IM** *012
DHITAL, Dixa Neupane. ■ 44504 #672-02-2002 L2007 **IM** *012
DIAZ, Karla Patricia. ■ 44514 #038-44-2008 *012
DO, Nghia Hieu. 1044 BELMONT AVE, CO ST ELIZ HLTH SYS-MED ED 44504 #305-01-1999 L2002 **IM** *020
DODGSON, Wilfred Burnell. 500 GYPSY LN 44504 #041-13-1954 L1955 **PD NPM** *040 †55
DORION, Heath Allen. 1044 BELMONT AVE, DEPT OF SURGERY 44504 #038-44-1997 L1999 **GS TRS** *040 †85
DUFFETT, Raymond Scott. 1335 BELMONT AVE 44504 #038-41-1982 L1982 **ORS OSM** *020 †40 ‡
DUGGAL, Abhijit. 500 GYPSY LN, WESTERN RESERVE CARE SYS 44504 #495-03-2002 L2003 **IM** *020 †20
DUNCH, David John. 250 DEBARTOLO PL STE 1640 44512 #041-09-1978 L1985 **CRS** *020 †10,85
DUNHAM, Carl Michael. 1044 BELMONT AVE, TRAUMA CRITICAL CRE SVCS 44504 #047-06-1974 L1994 **GS** *050 †85
DUNLEA, Frederick Wm. ■ 44511 #010-02-1956 L1957 **FM** *071 †18
DWINNELLS, Ronald. 726 WICK AVE, OHIO NORTH EAST HEALTH SYS 44505 #020-12-1983 L1986 **PD** *030 †55
DZIADZKA, Annelies Ruth. 1044 BELMONT AVE 44504 #409-12-1950 L1958 **AN** *071 †05
EBIE, Earl Richard. 345 OAK HILL AVE 44502 #038-41-1959 L1959 **IM** *071
ELAMIN, Fathalrahman Abda. 345 OAK HILL AVE, WESTERN RESERVE CARE SYS 44502 #848-01-1985 L2004 **PD** *020
EL-DABH, Rashad. 1044 BELMONT AVE 44504 #915-02-1977 L1987 **RO** *020 †80
ELGUIZAOUI, Ashraf Ehsan. 7330 SOUTHERN BLVD, STE 6 44512 #915-04-1974 L1999 **IM** *020
EL HAYEK, Mounir. 64 REDFERN DR 44505 #165-01-1981 L1985 **IM** *020 †20
EL-HAYEK, Salim Camille. 515 N MERIDIAN RD 44509 #396-03-1975 L1982 **GS OM** *020 †85
ENGLAND, Ronald Melvin. ■ 44505 #065-09-1977 L1985 **GP** *020
ENYEART, James Jos. 1044 BELMONT AVE 44504 #038-43-1977 L1979 **FM** *020 †18
ESPER, Richard Thomas, Jr. 250 DEBARTOLO PL, STE 2750 44512 #041-13-1997 L2005 **CD** *020 †20
ESPINO, Esmeralda C. 32 GOLDIE RD 44505 #748-01-1963 L1988 **FM FPG** *020 †18
EVAN, Stephen John. 3292 STONES THROW AVE 44514 #038-40-1992 L1994 **GS** *020 †85
FACEMYER, Gregory John. 5121 MAHONING AVE 44515 #038-44-1996 L1997 **FM** *020 †18
FADELL, Carrie Oklota. 727 E WESTERN RESERVE RD, PEDIATRIC ASSOCIATES OF 44514 #038-44-2002 L2002 **PD** *020
FARRIS, Joseph Jerome. 615 CHURCHILL HUBBARD RD, BELMONT PINES HOSP 44505 #038-40-2001 L2006 **CHP P** *020 †75
FATTEH, Shokat M. 8302 SOUTHERN BLVD 44512 #495-23-1975 L1983 **PTH DMP** *020 †50
FEDYNA, Dinah Marie. 1044 BELMONT AVE 44504 #038-44-1982 L1983 **FM** *040 †18
FINLEY-BELGRAD, Elizabeth. 1044 BELMONT AVE, ST ELIZABETH HEALTH CENTER 44504 #016-06-1987 L1995 **CHP** *020 †75
FIRDAUS, Tahir. 550 PARMALEE AVE, STE 410 44510 #495-51-1966 L1976 **GS** *020 †85,90
FISHER, Robert Ross. ■ 44514 #024-05-1948 L1950 **FM IM** *071
FIUTOWSKI, Leszek Jerzy. 1044 BELMONT AVE 44504 #060-01-1977 L2007 **CD IM** *020 †20
FLOREA, Anca Veturia. 345 OAK HILL AVE, WESTERN RESERVE CARE SYS 44502 #781-03-1997 L2004 **PTH** *012

■ = Address Information Privacy Protected

FRANCE, Anthony Lstuart. 64 REDFERN DR 44505 #020-12-1994 L1996 **EM PE** *020 †16,55
FRANCO, Alejandro A. 540 PARMALEE AVE, STE 510 44510 #737-01-1969 L1979 **TS GS** *020
FRANGOPOULOS, Michael A. 821 MCCARTNEY RD 44505 #038-40-1981 L1982 **FM** *020 †18
FRANK, Steven Eugene. 500 GYPSY LN 44504 #038-45-1986 L1988 **EM** *020 †16
FRISCH, Lawrence Edward. 50 WESTCHESTER DR, MAHONING CTY DISTRICT BOAR 44515 #024-01-1971 L2001 **FM ADL** *020 †55,70
FULTON, Jeffrey A. 540 PARMALEE AVE, STE 510 44510 #041-77-1991, ▲ L2007 **TS** *020 †85,90
FULTON, Stephen Maxey. ■ 44505 #040-02-1981 L1982 **AN** *020
GANTT, Nancy Lynn. 1044 BELMONT AVE, ST ELIZABETH HEALTH CENTER 44504 #016-02-1983 L1989 **GS** *040 †85
GENER, Melissa Ann. ■ 44511 #038-44-2007 L2007 **PTH** *012
GENTILE, Richard Danl. 6505 MARKET ST, STE A103 44512 #038-41-1982 L1982 **FPS OTO** *020 †45
GEORDAN, A Wm. 60 N CANFIELD NILES RD, STE 700 44515 #016-43-1949 L1953 **U** *030 †95
GEORGESCU, Victor Andrei. 1011 BOARDMAN CANFIELD RD, DBA DOCTORS PAIN CLINIC 44512 #781-01-1986 L2001 **AN** *020 †05
GEORGOPOULOS, Geo Adrian. BEL PARK PROFESSIONAL BLDG 44504 #418-01-1972 L1980 **TS** *075 †85,90
GESTOSANI, Antonio T. 602 PARMALEE AVE, STE 110 44510 #748-08-1969 L1979 **AN** *020
GHANI, Abdul. 4308 BELMONT AVE 44505 #704-02-1964 L1976 **GS** *020 †85
GIANETTI, John Paul. 20 OHLTOWN RD 44515 #038-44-1988 L1989 **IM** *020 †20
GIBBONS, Michael Thomas. 1053 BELMONT AVE 44504 #305-01-2005 L2006 **FP** *012
GILLETTE, Robert Dumn. 1053 BELMONT AVE, FMLY HLTH CTR ST ELIZABETH 44504 #038-41-1956 L1956 **FM** *071 †18
GILLILAND, Robert Lee. 64 REDFERN DR 44505 #051-04-1960 L1966 **N** *071 †75
GOJAR, Muhammad Aamir. ■ 44505 #704-08-1992 **IM** *100
GORDON, Brian Stewart. 64 REDFERN DR 44505 #495-37-1973 L1978 **IM OM** *020
GRAJO, Galterius. 510 GYPSY LN 44504 #748-01-1970 L1978 **DR PDR** *020 †80
GRAZIANO, Joseph Anthony. 250 DEBARTOLO PL, STE 2750 44512 #038-40-1992 L1993 **CD** *020 †20
GREESON, Clay Bryson. ■ 44504 #019-02-2007 L2007 **GS** *012
GREGG, Lester O, Jr. ■ 44505 #041-09-1942 L1951 **OTO** *071 †45
GREGORI, Joseph Sylvester. ■ 44505 #055-01-1965 L1969 **IM GE** *071 ‡
GREIFENSTEIN, Elaine M. 64 REDFERN DR 44505 #038-44-1988 L1991 **RHU IM** *020 †20
GRUBER, Brian Scott. 1044 BELMONT AVE, DEPT OF TRAUMA/CRITICAL 44504 #038-44-1998 L1999 **CCS GS** *020 †85
GUNDELLY, Praveen Kumar. ■ 44504 #495-21-2000 L2005 **IM** *012
GUNDUZ, Metin. 500 GYPSY LN BOX 240, CENTER DEPT OF EMERGENCY M 44504 #902-04-1974 L1990 **EM GS** *020 †85,16
GUPTA, Reema Taneja. 1300 BOARDMAN CANFIELD RD 44512 #495-43-1994 L1997 **IM** *020 †20
HADDAD, Ibrahim Jamil. 8560 SOUTH AVE STE 3 44514 #875-01-1981 L1991 **PD GE** *020 †55
HAFIZ, Abdul. YOUNGSTOWN HOSP SOUTH XRAY 44501 #704-03-1956 L1971 **DR OS** *020
HAGGERTY, Michael P. PO BOX 1790, 1044 BELMONT AVE 44501 #038-44-1990 L1996 **OBG** *020 †30
HALLEY, Jeffrey Craig. 250 DEBARTOLO PL, STE 2750 44512 #038-06-1989 L1990 **CD IM** *020 †20
HANDEL, Daniel Wm. 7430 SOUTHERN BLVD 44512 #028-34-1969 L1970 **D** *071 †15 ‡
HANDLER-MATASAR, Sheryl R. 500 GYPSY LN 44504 #035-01-1999 L1999 **OP** *020 †40
HANNA, Sherif Ismail. 3020 BELMONT AVE 44505 #038-43-1989 L1990 **OPH** *020 †35
HARICHAND, Usha Bedharay. 1044 BELMONT AVE, MEDICAL CENTRE 44504 #495-04-1969 L1975 **PD** *020 †55
HARIKRISHNAN, Sundaram. 3622 BELMONT AVE, STE 1 44505 #495-53-1974 L1981 **AN** *020 †05
HARO, Patricia Anne Yabut. ■ 44504 #748-16-2001 L2007 **IM** *012
HASHMI, Zubair Ali. 500 GYPSY LN 44504 #305-01-2003 L2003 **GS** *012
HASSARD, Alexander Danl. ■ 44512 #065-09-1973 L1984 **OTO** *075
HAYEK, Benj Michael, Jr. 2111 BELMONT AVE, STE 1 44505 #165-07-1977 L1979 **IM** *020 †20
HAYES, Louise A Yelding. 901 TRAILWOOD DR 44512 #020-02-1975 L1985 **PD** *020
HAZELBAKER, Norma Jean. 4531 BELMONT AVE 44505 #038-40-1967 L1967 **PD** *020 †55
HEAPS, Kenneth Paul. PO BOX 1790, 1044 BELMONT AVE 44501 #041-02-1966 L1967 **MDM PD** *030 †55
HEATON, Bren Andrew. 500 GYPSY LN, DEPT OF MED EDUCATION 44504 #305-01-2006 L2006 **GS** *012
HELWIG, William Joseph. 1075 W WESTERN RESERVE RD, EYE CARE ASSOCIATES INC 44514 #038-43-1984 L1987 **OPH** *020 †20,35
HENN, Lucas Webster. ■ 44504 #038-44-2004 L2004 **GS** *012
HILL, Rodney Earl. 1350 5TH AVE, STE 324 44504 #051-07-1989 L1997 **OBG** *020 †30
HINDI, Ammar M. 1044 BELMONT AVE, HEALTH CENTER 44504 #038-44-2007 L2007 **TY** *012
HIXSON, Clayton Allan. ■ 44512 #010-01-1961 L1965 **R NM** *071 †80,28
HOLDEN, Henry. 345 OAK HILL AVE 44502 #047-07-1948 L1956 **IM** *071
HOLMES, Jonathan William. ■ 44514 #038-40-2005 L2007 **GS** *012
HOSSEINIPOUR, Ahmad. ■ 44511 #748-09-1987 L1994 **IM** *075
HOUSTON, Robert Ross. 905 SAHARA TRL 44514 #041-02-1942 L1943 **GP** *030
HRITZO, Robert John. 3072 DECAMP RD 44511 #028-34-1957 L1958 **GS** *071 †85
HUANG, Pang Hsiung. 540 PARMALEE AVE # NO-210 44510 #244-04-1970 L1975 **OBG** *020 †30
HUNT, Robert Edward. 715 E WESTERN RESERVE RD 44514 #033-06-1985 L1991 **CD** *020 †20
HUNTER, Stephanie L. ■ 44511 #038-44-2008 *012
HUNTER, Timothy John. 500 GYPSY LN 44504 #043-01-1989 L1997 **TS** *020 †85,90
HUSAIN, Sadiq Syed. 1001 BELMONT AVE, OHIO HEART INSTITUTE 44504 #704-02-1959 L1971 **CD IM** *020 †20
HUSSAIN, Altaf. PO BOX 2163 44504 #704-01-1954 L1971 **OS** *075
HUSSAIN, Muhammad. ■ 44511 #704-02-1990 L1998 **RHU IM** *020 †20
HUSSEIN, Karim. 715 E WESTERN RESERVE RD 44514 #875-01-1984 L2005 **CD** *020 †20
HUTCHINSON, Amy. 1044 BELMONT AVE 44504 #038-44-1988 L1990 **CCA** *020 †05
HWANG, Hyon Sang. 1044 BELMONT AVE 44504 #583-02-1961 L1971 **AN** *071 †05
IDOIDZE, Nino. 345 OAK HILL AVE, WESTERN RESERVE CARE SYS 44502 #912-02-2003 L2005 **IM** *012
IQBAL, Khalid. 727 E WESTERN RESERVE RD, PEDIATRIC ASSOCIATES OF 44514 #704-01-1972 L1979 **PD** *020 †55
IQBAL, Riffat Perveen. 727 E WESTERN RESERVE RD, PEDIATRIC ASSOCIATES OF 44514 #704-06-1970 L1985 **PD PTH** *020
JACKSON, David Baxter. 1044 BELMONT AVE, SEHMC EMERGENCY MEDICINE 44504 #039-01-1986 L1990 **EM** *020 †16
JACOBS, Doris Julie. 500 GYPSY LN, FAMILY PRACTICE CTR NORTH 44504 #005-02-1978 L1987 **FM** *040 †18
JACQUES, Louis James. 3300 STONES THROW AVE 44514 #038-40-1967 L1967 **DR** *020 †80
JADALLAH, Yazan Khaled. 1044 BELMONT AVE, ST ELIZABETH HEALTH CENTER 44504 #038-43-1998 L2001 **EM** *020 †16
JAFFER, Adil Nazim. 4308 BELMONT AVE 44505 #759-12-2001 L2002 **FM** *020 †18
JAFFER, Nazim A. 4308 BELMONT AVE 44505 #539-06-1969 L1972 **IM** *020 †20
JAKUBEK, John Russell. 1044 BELMONT AVE 44504 #038-40-1982 L1983 **AN** *020 †05
JAYARAM, Aruna. 500 GYPSY LN, 2ND FLOOR RRC 44504 #495-94-2004 L2007 **IM** *012
JOHNSON, Evan Dean. 500 GYPSY LN, DEPT OF MED EDU 44504 #654-01-2005 L2005 **GS** *100
JOHNSON, William Roy. 407 BELMONT AVE 44502 #041-09-1961 L1962 **IM** *071 †20
JOSE, Joseph. 345 OAK HILL AVE 44502 #661-02-2002 L2003 **MPD** *100 †20
JULIUS, Carmen Jos. 8302 SOUTHERN BLVD 44512 #038-44-1987 L1992 **PTH BBK** *020 †50
KACHMER, Michael Andrew. 8170 SOUTH AVE, STE 1 44512 #028-34-1956 L1956 **P** *020 †75
KAHI, Hassan. ■ 44505 #875-01-2003 L2007 **IM** *012
KANN, P Elizabeth. ■ 44512 #035-03-1994 L2003 **OM PHP** *020 †70
KAPON, Michelle. ■ 44509 #665-01-2006 L2007 *012
KARTAN, Ritha. 500 GYPSY LN 44504 #495-50-1988 L1995 **CCM** *020 †20
KATKHUDA, Ragheed. 345 OAK HILL AVE 44502 #875-02-2002 L2005 **PD** *012
KATO, Julius Albert. 715 E WESTERN RESERVE RD, DIAGNOSTIC CARDIOLOGY ASSO 44514 #025-76-1999, ▲ L2005 **CD IM** *100
KAVIC, Michael Stephen. 1044 BELMONT AVE, ST ELIZABETH HLTH CTR 44504 #047-07-1966 L1969 **GS** *040 †85
KAZA, Koteswara Rao. 104 JAVIT CT 44515 #495-58-1965 L1978 **P** *020 †75
KELLY, James Raymond, Jr. ■ 44512 #041-01-1946 L1947 **GS** *071 †85
KESSLER, Edward. ST ELIZABETHS HOSP MED CTR 44505 #028-34-1946 L1963 **NEP IM** *040 †20
KHALIL, Moh'D Bilal. 345 OAK HILL AVE 44502 #575-01-2005 L2006 **IM** *100
KHANNA, Hira Lal. 1280 BOARDMAN CANFIELD RD 44512 #495-12-1955 L1974 **NS** *020 †25
KHATTAB, Mazen. 500 GYPSY LN, CO WRCS-MED EDU DEPT 44504 #875-01-1998 L2002 **HO** *012 †20
KHAWLI, Oscar Fouad. 1044 BELMONT AVE, ST ELIZABETH HOSP MED CTR 44504 #605-01-1980 L1987 **MFM OBG** *020 †30
KHVATSKY, Dmitry M. 500 GYPSY LN 44504 #305-01-2004 L2004 **MPD** *012
KIM, Jung Min. 45 MCCLURG RD 44512 #583-13-1981 L1990 **IM** *062 †20
KLAHR, Betty Jane. 4308 BELMONT AVE, PED ASSOC OF YOUNGSTOWN 44505 #016-11-1958 L1967 **PD ADL** *071
KLEKOT, Erin Lynn. 997 BOARDMAN CANFIELD RD 44512 #016-43-1996 L2004 **P** *020 †75
KLEMPAY, Christine Sue. 8302 SOUTHERN BLVD 44512 #038-44-1993 L1994 **PCP** *020 †50
KLODELL, Carl Benj. 10 DUTTON DR 44502 #041-12-1958 L1961 **OPH** *071 †35
KLOSTERMAN, Thomas Jos. 500 GYPSY LN, FORUM HEALTH FAMILY PRACTI 44504 #016-02-1971 L1985 **FM** *020 †18
KLOUB, Oxana Anatolivna. 500 GYPSY LN, NORTHSIDE HOSPITALPATHOLOG 44504 #913-13-1986 L1999 **NP** *100 †50
KO, Chi-Sown. 3132 BELMONT AVE 44505 #385-03-1968 L1973 **D** *020 †15
KOCAB, Frank James. ST ELIZABETH HOSP 44505 #028-34-1957 L1959 **PTH** *040 †50
KOHLI, Chander Mohan. 540 PARMALEE AVE, STE 310 44510 #495-36-1962 L1972 **NS N** *020 †25
KOLLIPARA, Roop K. 540 PARMALEE AVE STE 410 44510 #495-45-1975 L1978 **AI IM** *020 †20,03
KOLLIPARA, Venkata S. 540 PARMALEE AVE # NO410 44510 #495-50-1975 L1981 **VS GS** *020 †85
KONGMUANG, Aran. 345 OAK HILL AVE 44502 #891-03-1969 L1975 **EM** *020 †16
KOULIANOS, Anthony Peter. 815 SOUTHWESTERN RUN 44514 #038-44-1993 L1997 **OBG** *020 †30
KOVAL, John Michael, Jr. 6505 MARKET ST, STE 205 44512 #038-43-1980 L1982 **IM** *020 †20
KRAFFT, Rudolph Michael. 1053 BELMONT AVE, FAMILY HLTH CTR 44504 #041-02-1978 L1984 **FM EM** *040 †18
KRAVEC, Cynthia A. 1044 BELMONT AVE 44504 #038-44-2001 L2001 **IM** *020
KRAVEC, James Francis. 1044 BELMONT AVE, DEPT OF INTERNAL MED 44504 #038-44-2002 L2002 **IM** *040 †20
KRISHNAN, Rani P. 250 DEBARTOLO PL, BLDG B 44512 #495-44-1976 L1983 **DR** *020 †80
KRUDY, Adrian Geo. 500 GYPSY LN 44504 #407-20-1950 L1954 **R** *071 †80
KRUTILIN, Sergei George. 1044 BELMONT AVE, CO ST ELIZ HLTH CTR-MED ED 44504 #198-01-1971 L2000 **OBG** *100
KUPPLER, Keith Herman. 250 DEBARTOLO PL, STE 2750 44512 #038-40-1979 L1980 **CD IM** *020 †20
LAGOUTARIS, Demetrios E. 837 BOARDMAN CANFIELD RD 44512 #418-01-1962 L1978 **P** *071
LARMAND, Catherine Ceceli. 726 WICK AVE 44505 #041-15-2004 L2004 **PD** *020 †55
LARPPANICHPOONPHOL, P. 1044 BELMONT AVE, ATTN: DIANE 44504 #891-02-1997 L1999 **ID** *100 †20
LAUFMAN, Daniel Loren. 250 DEBARTOLO PL, BLDG B 44512 #016-11-1981 L1984 **DR** *020 †80
LAURIDSEN, Deborah Ilona. 345 OAK HILL AVE, WESTERN RESERVE CARE SYS 44502 #305-01-2003 L2003 **FM** *020 †18
LEBOVITZ, Daniel Jay. 500 GYPSY LN, TOD CHILDREN'S HOSPITAL 44504 #036-07-1986 L1991 **PD CCP** *020 †55
LEE, Chong Min. 1044 BELMONT AVE 44504 #583-02-1963 L1976 **AN** *071 †05
LEE, Dong Sung. 1044 BELMONT AVE 44504 #583-02-1957 L1971 **AN** *071 †05 ‡
LEE, Jae Joo. 250 DEBARTOLO PL, BLDG B 44512 #583-09-1964 L1972 **R NM** *071 †80,28
LEE, Joohee. ■ 44504 #583-19-2000 L2006 **IM** *012
LEE, Tac Zhun. 8110 MARKET ST 44512 #037-01-1998 L2004 **OPH** *020 †35
LEE, William Scott. 500 GYPSY LN, DEPT OF MED EDU 44504 #661-02-2006 L2006 **GS** *012
LENHART, Milton John. 20 OHLTOWN RD 44515 #038-40-1957 L1989 **OBG** *071 †30
LEPORE, Vincent Donald. ■ 44505 #561-17-1957 L1959 **OBG** *071 †30
LEVY, David H. 1044 BELMONT AVE, ST ELIZABETH HOSPITAL 44504 #017-20-1934 L1935 **FM** *071
LEYKO, Raymond Julius. 500 GYPSY LN, NORTHSIDE MEDICAL CENTER 44504 #665-01-1998 L1999 **FM** *020 †18
LI, Wei V. 8302 SOUTHERN BLVD 44512 #243-03-1987 L1998 **PTH** *020 †50
LIM, Bee Min. 16 COLONIAL DR 44505 #825-01-1976 L1979 **CRS** *020 †10,85
LIM, Chiao Yee. 345 OAK HILL AVE 44502 #624-04-2005 L2006 **PD** *100
LIMBERT, Dean James. ■ 44512 #016-06-1961 L1966 **U** *071 †95
LIMBU, Indra Prakash. 540 PARMALEE AVE STE 610, DISEASES ASSOCIATES 44510 #672-01-1997 L2001 **ID** *020 †20
LIPARTIA, Marine. 345 OAK HILL AVE, WESTERN RESERVE CARE SYS 44502 #912-02-2003 L2005 **IM** *012

7664

■ = Address Information Privacy Protected

LLOYD, Kenneth Merle. 8060 MARKET ST 44512 #025-01-1959 L1961 **D IM** *020 †15
LOCKWARD, Maximo B. 3528 CANFIELD RD 44511 #035-06-1991 L1996 **P** *020
LOONG, Wai-Nai. YOUNGSTOWN HOSP, DEPT SURG 44501 #385-02-1970 **GS** *100
LOSSEV, Victor Borissov. 64 REDFERN DR 44505 #198-01-1999 L2005 **IM** *012
LU, David Chung. 2031 BELMONT AVE, YOUNGSTOWN VA OPC 44505 #748-22-1985 L1990 **IM** *020 †20
LUKE, Ciby Babukunju. 345 OAK HILL AVE, WESTERN RESERVE CARE SYS 44502 #759-06-2004 L2005 **FP** *012
LUKOSE, Alina. 500 GYPSY LN 44504 #894-01-2002 L2004 **FM** *100 †18
LUTTON, Suzanne R. 715 E WESTERN RESERVE RD 44514 #025-07-1990 L1995 **CD** *020 †20
LUZAR, Michael James. 500 GYPSY LN, REGIONAL REFERRAL CENTER 44504 #038-40-1973 L1973 **RHU** *020 †20
LYRAS, Louis Sozon. 7600 SOUTHERN BLVD, STE 1 44512 #038-40-1978 L1978 **GS** *020 †85
MAAROUF, Ahmad Bassam. 500 GYPSY LN 44504 #875-01-1999 L2002 **NEP** *012 †20
MACABOBBY, Thomas Donald. 1044 BELMONT AVE 44504 #038-44-2002 L2002 **FM** *020 †18
MAHAR, Paul James, Jr. 7087 WEST BLVD STE 3 44512 #038-40-1965 L1965 **OPH** *020 †35
MAHAR-MATTHEWS, Maureen M. 7087 WEST BLVD, STE 3 SQ 3 44512 #038-44-1990 L1992 **OPH** *020 †35
MAIDEN, Phillip Glen. 310 CHURCHILL HUBBARD RD 44505 #047-20-1985 L1992 **CHP P** *020 †75
MALIK, Nadeem N. 8302 SOUTHERN BLVD 44512 #704-16-1983 L1993 **PTH** *020 †50
MANGALAT, Sheetal Niranja. 500 GYPSY LN, TOD PEDIATRICS CLINIC 44504 #539-06-2003 L2003 **PD** *100 †55
MANU, None. 500 GYPSY LN, 2ND FLOOR RRC 44504 #495-69-2004 L2007 **IM** *012
MARINA, Richard Jerome. 918 TRAILWOOD DR STE 1 44512 #016-11-1979 L1982 **GE IM** *020 †20
MARMAGKIOLIS, Konstantinos. 345 OAK HILL AVE, WESTERN RESERVE CARE SYS 44502 #418-02-2001 L2004 **IM** *100 †20
MARTINY, Stephen Edward. 1044 BELMONT AVE, DEPT OF MED EDU 44504 #858-04-2003 L2006 **FP** *012
MARX, Robert Jos. 5198 SAMPSON DR 44505 #028-79-1987, ▲ L1993 **GS** *020
MATHAI, Shyla Rachel. 345 OAK HILL AVE, WESTERN RESERVE CARE SYS 44502 #665-01-2006 L2006 **FP** *012
MATTEUCCI, Gerald Anthony. 1044 BELMONT AVE 44504 #561-01-1983 L1988 **AN PME** *020
MAWALDI, Ahmad Maher. 1044 BELMONT AVE, CO ST ELIZ HLTH CTR-MED ED 44504 #875-02-1992 L2002 **IM** *100
MAXFIELD, John Fowler. 1044 BELMONT AVE, EMERGENCY DEPARTMENT 44504 #032-01-1978 L1991 **EM OM** *020 †20,16
MC ABEE, Kimberly Lynn. 6505 MARKET ST, BEEGHLY EMERGENCY 44512 #038-44-1991 L1993 **IM** *020 †20
MC CONNELL, Robert B. ■ 44511 #028-02-1946 L1951 **U** *071 †95
MC DANIEL, Gregory Alan. 3332 ESTATES CIR 44511 #035-06-1995 L1996 **MPD** *020 †20
MCINTYRE, Mary Joanna. 25 N CANFIELD NILES RD, STE 160 44515 #038-44-2000 L2000 **PD** *020 †55
MC NEAL, Elmore R. ■ 44515 #038-06-1941 L1941 **OM IM** *071 †20
MC PHERSON, Paul Douglas. 1350 5TH AVE STE 106 44504 #041-15-2002 L2002 **PD** *100
MEADE, Patrick Godfrey. 1044 BELMONT AVE 44504 #038-41-1999 L2000 **FM** *020 †18
MEHLE, Anthony Lawrence. 960 WINDHAM CT, STE 2 44512 #038-44-1986 L1989 **D** *020 †15 ‡
MEHTA, Jeet Ram. 16 COLONIAL DR 44505 #495-45-1967 L1973 **CRS** *020 †10,85
MELNICK, John Chas. ■ 44511 #038-06-1955 L1955 **R NM** *071 †80,28
MEMO, Richard Allen. 602 PARMALEE AVE STE 300 44510 #028-34-1971 L1975 **U GP** *020 †95
MENDELSOHN, Geoffrey. 8302 SOUTHERN BLVD 44512 #836-01-1972 L1983 **PTH** *020 †50
MENDOZA, Salustiano F. 345 OAK HILL AVE 44502 #748-10-1963 L1971 **OBG** *020
MENIRU, Godwin Ikechukwu. 726 WICK AVE 44505 #690-04-1984 L1999 **OBG REN** *020 †30
MERSOL, Joseph. 1044 BELMONT AVE 44504 #028-34-1958 L1960 **FM IMG** *071 †18
MICHAELS, Richard Allen. 970 WINDHAM CT, STE 3 44512 #048-15-1985 L1987 **GS** *020
MIGHT, James Edward. 20 OHLTOWN RD, STE 2 44515 #023-01-1953 L1958 **IM** *071
MIKOLICH, Lynn Marie. 1044 BELMONT AVE 44504 #038-40-1974 L1974 **PM** *020 †60
MILADORE, Michael James. 1335 BELMONT AVE 44504 #038-44-1982 L1987 **ORS** *020 †40
MILLER, Daniel Anthony. 500 GYPSY LN, DEPT OF MED EDU 44504 #306-01-2005 L2006 **FP** *012
MILLER, Edward Jay, Jr. 6505 MARKET ST, STE 205 44512 #038-44-1994 L1995 **IM** *020 †20
MILLER, John Kevin. ■ 44505 #020-12-2004 L2004 **GS** *012
MILLER, Lynn. 1044 BELMONT AVE, CO ST ELIZ HLTH CTR-MED ED 44504 #243-72-1993 L2000 **IM** *100
MILOSEVIC, Igor. 1044 BELMONT AVE 44504 #305-01-2006 L2006 **GS** *012
MIRASOL, Arturo Pedregosa. 500 GYPSY LN 44504 #748-08-1968 L1976 **EM GS** *020
MISTRY, Prashant Navnit. 345 OAK HILL AVE, WESTERN RESERVE CARE SYS 44502 #759-12-2004 L2005 **FP** *012
MITCHELL, Edmund M. 819 MCKAY CT, STE 101 44512 #041-02-1990 L1998 **FM** *020 †18
MOAMMAR, Ousama. 345 OAK HILL AVE, WESTERN RESERVE CARE SYS 44502 #473-03-2000 L2004 **IM** *020 †20
MOCK, Theron C, Jr. ■ 44504 #038-06-1980 L1980 **GS** *020 †85
MODIC, Barbara Marie. 25 N CANFIELD NILES RD, STE 110 44515 #957-03-1982 L1987 **IM** *020 †20
MOHAMMAD AL KHASAWNEH, Eih. 345 OAK HILL AVE 44502 #575-02-2002 **PD** *100
MOORE, James Paul. 550 PARMALEE AVE STE 300 44510 #065-05-1972 L1983 **TS** *020 †85,90
MORELLI, Louis John. ■ 44511 #038-40-1970 L1970 **GP** *020
MORLEY, Brian Gerald. 500 GYPSY LN 44504 #051-07-1995 L2002 **PDR** *020
MOSKALIK, William. 64 REDFERN DR 44505 #056-06-1961 L1964 **OBG** *020 †30
MOTOLENICH, Peter Michael. 1044 BELMONT AVE 44504 #038-06-2001 L2002 **AN** *020 †05
MOZAYEN, Mohammad. 500 GYPSY LN, DEPT OF MED EDU 44504 #875-01-2005 L2006 **IM** *012
MUEHLENBEIN, Stephen J. 250 DEBARTOLO PL, BLDG B 44512 #030-06-1995 L1996 **DR** *020 †80
MULLIS, Ronald Faison, Jr. 602 PARMALEE AVE, STE 110 44510 #036-08-1986 L1990 **AN** *020 †05
MUTHUKRISHNAN, Gayathri. 345 OAK HILL AVE, WESTERN RESERVE CARE SYS 44502 #496-21-2002 L2006 **IM** *012
NAEEM, Yasir Abbas. 500 GYPSY LN, FORUM HEALTH 44504 #704-26-2000 L2001 **MPD** *100 †20
NAGPAUL, Amarjeet Singh. 755 BOARDMAN CANFIELD RD, STE 1 44512 #495-20-1964 L1977 **N** *020 †75
NAIDU, Latasha. 1044 BELMONT AVE, CO ST ELIZABETH HLTH CTR-M 44504 #665-01-2002 L2003 **ID** *012 †20
NALLAPANENI, Sudhir Kumar. 550 PARMALEE AVE, STE 100 44510 #495-50-1997 L2001 **IM** *020 †20
NALLURI, Anil Choudary. 5500 MARKET ST, STE 128 44512 #495-50-1971 L1977 **P** *020 †75
NALLURI, Babitha. 7067 TIFFANY BLVD, STE 220 44514 #496-37-1997 L2000 **OBG** *020 ‡
NARASIMHAN, Srividya. 500 GYPSY LN, DEPT OF MED EDU 44504 #495-37-2001 L2005 **FP** *012
NARAYAN, Satish D. 2980 BELMONT AVE, STE 2 44505 #495-33-1991 L1999 **P** *020 †75
NASH, David Bruce. 1995 E STATE ST, SALEM COMMUNITY HOSPITAL 44512 #035-15-1977 L1979 **PTH EM** *020 †50,16
NATH, Ravinder. 1280 BOARDMAN CANFIELD RD 44512 #495-05-1970 L1978 **IM** *020 †20
NATIVIDAD, Nora S. 500 GYPSY LN 44504 #748-10-1964 L1973 **PTH OS** *071 †50
NEGRETE, Hilmer Octavio. 807 SOUTHWESTERN RUN 44514 #737-01-1984 L2005 **NEP IM** *020 †20
NELSON, Kathie Ann. 602 PARMALEE AVE 44510 #038-44-1994 L1995 **IM** *020 †20
NEMOU, Khalil. 500 GYPSY LN, 2ND FLOOR RRC 44504 #875-01-2002 L2007 **IM** *012
NGUYEN, Huong Thi. 540 PARMALEE AVE STE 610 44510 #654-01-1996 L1999 **ID IM** *020 †20
NGUYEN, Thanh Quoc. 345 OAK HILL AVE 44502 #305-01-2002 L2002 **PD** *100
NICOLOFF, Nicola Blagoy. 715 E WESTERN RESERVE RD 44514 #038-40-1974 L1975 **CD IM** *020 †20
NIGOS, Janice. ■ 44505 #748-10-2004 L2007 **IM** *012
NIRAULA, Rajendra Prasad. 345 OAK HILL AVE 44502 #672-01-2000 L2004 **IM** *020 †20
NSEIR, Bacel. 500 GYPSY LN 44504 #875-03-2001 L2004 **MPD ID** *012
OBENG, Michael Kwame. 8423 MARKET ST STE 205, ST ELIZABETH PHYSICIAN SER 44512 #048-02-2001 L2006 **PS** *020
O'CONNOR, Kevin Peter. ■ 44515 #422-01-2001 L2005 **FM** *100
OH, Kong Tatt. 500 GYPSY LN 44504 #825-01-1969 L1978 **OPH** *020 †35
OHIAERI, Benjamin Nnamdi. ST ELIZABETH HOSP, DEPT OB/GYN 44505 #690-02-1973 L1977 **OBG** *100 †30
OMAR, Moanis Mohamed E A. 345 OAK HILL AVE 44502 #584-01-2004 L2006 **IM** *012
OSMAN, Houssam Galal-Eldi. GYPSY L, CO MEDICAL EDUCATIO500 44501 #848-01-2005 L2007 **GS** *012
PAGANO, Paul Joseph. 6505 MARKET ST, STE 311 44512 #038-40-1995 L2001 **ORS OSS** *020 †40
PALADINO, Walter Paul. 540 PARMALEE AVE, STE 200 44510 #035-46-1977 L1997 **CD** *020 †20
PALMER, Gilbert Arthur. 1044 BELMONT AVE 44504 #038-44-1999 L1999 **EM** *020 †18
PANDYA, Hasit Pradyumn. 1340 BELMONT AVE, STE 2300 44504 #495-22-1989 L2005 **NEP** *020 †20
PANICKER, Jyoti. 500 GYPSY LN, TOD CHILDRENS HOSP 44504 #495-45-1994 L2005 **PHO** *020 †55
PANTELAKIS, James N. 6615 CLINGAN RD, STE A 44514 #038-44-1995 L1996 **ORS** *020 †40
PAPPAS, Nicholas Anthony. 345 OAK HILL AVE 44502 #038-41-1966 L1966 **IM** *020 †20
PASS, Lawrence M. 345 OAK HILL AVE 44502 #016-42-1962 L1969 **HEM HO** *071 †20
PATEL, Brimal Babubhai. 500 GYPSY LN, DEPT OF MED EDU 44504 #305-01-2005 L2006 **FP** *012
PATEL, Ketankumar A. 500 GYPSY LN, NORTHSIDE MED CTRLAB MEDIC 44504 #495-23-1990 L1999 **PCP** *100 †50
PATEL, Manishkumar Kanubh. ■ 44504 #496-41-1998 L2006 **GS** *012
PATEL, Ruperl Chandrakant. ■ 44504 #305-01-2005 L2007 **FP** *012
PATEL, Shonak Bipin. 345 OAK HILL AVE 44502 #305-01-2006 L2006 **GS** *012
PEACHMAN, Frederick Alvin. 602 PARMALEE AVE, STE 110 44510 #035-03-1977 L1983 **AN** *020 †05
PEARLSTEIN, Richard P. 7227 GLENWOOD AVE, FIFTH AVE OTOLARYNGOLOGIST 44512 #038-41-1992 L1993 **OTO** *020 †45
PERJESSY, Eugene. 8584 MARKET ST 44512 #781-05-1959 **IM** *100
PERNI, Sriram Choudary. 1044 BELMONT AVE, ST ELIZABETH HEALTH CTR 44504 #038-44-1998 L2005 **MFM OBG** *020 †30
PERNI, Swarajya Lakshmi. 500 GYPSY LN, 3RD FL 44504 #495-50-1974 L1982 **DR** *020 †80
PERRY, Earnest. 1320 BELMONT AVE STE 2, EARNEST PERRY MD 44504 #047-07-1964 L1965 **GS OS** *020 †85
PERRY, Jordan. ■ 44512 #496-42-2002 L2007 **FP** *012
PERZ, Gerhard Louis. 500 GYPSY LN, TOD CHILDRENS HOSPITAL 44504 #035-03-1988 L1993 **PEM PD** *020 †55
PESA, Felix Anthony. 540 PARMALEE AVE, STE 610 44510 #038-40-1962 L1962 **VS** *020 †85
PICHETTE, Charles E, Jr. 1044 BELMONT AVE 44504 #035-15-1938 L1946 **U** *071
PICHETTE, David Earle. 755 BOARDMAN CANFIELD RD, STE B2 44512 #028-34-1971 L1973 **U** *020 †95
POLITI, Jacques. 3040 BELMONT AVE 44505 #803-02-1960 L1964 **PD AI** *020 †55,03
POLITIS, Ioannis John. 960 WINDHAM CT, STE 1 44512 #418-01-1970 L1979 **PUD IM** *020 †20
POTESTA, Eugene L, Jr. 7227 GLENWOOD AVE, FIFTH AVENUE OTOLARYNGOLOG 44512 #038-44-1984 L1990 **OTO HNS** *020 †45
PRASAD, Karipineni R. 611 BELMONT AVE 44502 #495-58-1967 L1977 **P** *020 †75
PRASAD, Kolli Mohan. 345 OAK HILL AVE 44502 #495-50-1972 L1978 **R RO** *075
PRUITT, Fred Roderic. 550 PARMALEE AVE 44510 #047-07-1967 L1973 **GP OS** *020
PUET, Terry Albert. 540 PARMALEE AVE STE 31 44510 #041-12-1980 L1981 **FM PM** *020 †18
PUGH, George B. 10 DUTTON DR 44502 #035-20-1951 L1952 **OPH** *071 †35
QADRI, Alam Mian. 64 REDFERN DR 44505 #704-02-1962 L1973 **PTH BBK** *020 †50
QUEEN, Herbert Louis. ■ 44512 #038-40-1958 L1958 **EM GP** *071
QUIRK, William Martin, III. 1044 BELMONT AVE, DEPT OF OB/GYN 44504 #038-44-1989 L1992 **OBG** *040 †30
RABINOWITZ, Asher Zeev. 3020 BELMONT AVE 44505 #550-01-1968 L1975 **OPH** *020 †35
RACHEDI, Martha Pia. 6505 MARKET ST, BLDG B BEEGHLY MEDICAL PAR 44512 #027-01-1991 L1992 **IM** *020 †20
RAHEJA, Mita. 3622 BELMONT AVE, STE 11 44505 #495-01-1984 L1993 **CD IM** *020 †20
RAIS, Neilsson. 501 GYPSY LN, STE 107 44504 #820-02-2001 L2002 **PD** *040 †55
RANGANATHA, Vijayalakshmi. 345 OAK HILL AVE 44502 #495-35-1999 L2003 **PD** *100
RANSOM, Kenneth Joe. 1044 BELMONT AVE, ST. ELIZABETH HEALTH CENTE 44504 #019-02-1974 L2002 **TRS EM** *020 †85
RAVI, Bhargava. 550 PARMALEE AVE STE 100 44510 #495-58-1981 L1988 **IM GS** *020 †20
RAVI, Vijaya Lakshmi. 2031 BELMONT AVE, YOUNGSTOWN VA CLINIC 44505 #495-58-1982 L1990 **IM** *020 †20
REDDY, Swathy Seelam. 500 GYPSY LN 44504 #665-01-2001 L2004 **IM** *012
REED, David Geo. 7087 WEST BLVD 44512 #038-41-1963 L1963 **OTO HNS** *020 †45
REGAILA, Adel Hassan. 1044 BELMONT AVE, ST ELIZABETH HOSPITAL 44504 #915-04-1992 L2004 **IM** *100
REGULE, David William. 1044 BELMONT AVE, ST ELIZABETHS HOSPITAL 44504 #038-44-2003 L2003 **RHU** *012 †20
RHODES, Ronald Allen. 64 REDFERN DR 44505 #038-44-1988 L1990 **GS** *020 †85
RICCHIUTI, Daniel Joseph. 602 PARMALEE AVE 44510 #038-44-2000 L2000 **U** *020 †95

■ = Address Information Privacy Protected

RICCHIUTI, Vincent S. 7355 CALIFORNIA AVE, STE 4 44512 #028-34-1996 L1997 **U** *020 †95
RICCIARDI, Santuccio. 7067 TIFFANY BLVD, STE 250 44514 #038-44-1988 L1989 **IM** *020 †20
RICH, David. 2959 CANFIELD RD, STE 8-9 44511 #038-44-1988 L1989 **FM** *020 †18
RICH, Paul Angelo. 5170 BELMONT AVE 44505 #038-43-1995 L1999 **FM** *020 †18
RICH, Robert Raymond. 7355 CALIFORNIA AVE, STE 4 44512 #028-34-1966 L1967 **U** *020 †95
RICHARDS, Richard Stephen. ■ 44512 #041-12-1960 L1960 **AN** *072 †05
ROBBINS, Steven Doyce. 1044 BELMONT AVE, PARK AVE BLDG 1ST FL 44504 #004-01-1996 L1997 **IM** *020 †20
ROBERTS, Angela Leung. 726 WICK AVE 44505 #038-44-1999 L1999 **FM** *020 †18
RODRIGUEZ, Sergio. 1044 BELMONT AVE, CO ST ELIZABETH HLTH CTR-M 44504 #132-09-1991 L2003 **HSO** *012 †85
ROSSI, Elena Marie. 1044 BELMONT AVE, ST ELIZABETH HEALTH CENTER 44504 #038-41-1982 L1982 **NPM PD** *020 †55
ROTHENBERG, Ralph Joel. 500 GYPSY LN, REGIONAL REFERRAL CENTER 44504 #025-12-1977 L1980 **RHU IM** *020 †20
ROTHSCHILD, Bruce M. 5500 MARKET ST 44512 #033-05-1973 L1986 **RHU IG** *020 †20
ROUSH, Gregory Robt. 8302 SOUTHERN BLVD 44512 #038-44-1988 L1990 **PTH** *020 †50
RUBINO, Nino Carlo. 6615 CLINGAN RD, STE C 44514 #038-45-2003 L2003 **FM** *020 †18
RUIZ, Juan Alberto. 725 BOARDMAN CANFIELD RD, STE O 44512 #308-01-1957 L1965 **IM CD** *071
SAALOUKE, Michael G. 500 GYPSY LN, CIRCULATORY CENTER INC 44504 #875-01-1969 L1987 **PDC PD** *020 †55
SAFFAF, Yaman. 500 GYPSY LN, CARE SYSTEM/FO 44504 #875-01-2002 L2005 **MPD** *012
SAINT-JULIEN, Jacques S. 548 GYPSY LN 44505 #440-01-1969 L1977 **OBG** *020 †30
SAKER, Souheir Hassan. 345 OAK HILL AVE 44502 #875-01-1991 L2005 **PD** *012
SALCEDO, Danilo Antonio. 1044 BELMONT AVE 44504 #308-01-1958 L1966 **AN** *071
SALCEDO, Stephen Lee. 755 BOARDMAN CANFLD RD #P2 44512 #748-01-1978 L1988 **D DMP** *020
SALEH, Ayman A. 500 GYPSY LN, 500 GYPSY LANE 44504 #875-02-1987 L1996 **PD PHO** *020 †55
SAMBANDHAM, Ragu R. 1044 BELMONT AVE 44504 #495-04-1971 L1975 **N IM** *020 †75,18
SANCHEZ-PARODI, Milton. 1975 E WESTERN RESERVE RD 44514 #847-03-1984 L1989 **FM** *020 †18
SANDHU, Mandip S. 970 WINDHAM CT, STE 6A 44512 #495-08-1977 L1994 **P** *020 †75
SARAC, Erdal S. 64 REDFERN DR 44505 #902-10-1986 L1994 **NEP IM** *020 †20
SARANTOPOULOS, C A. ■ 44512 #418-01-1956 L1967 **ORS** *071 †40
SAVICH, Susan Rose. ■ 44512 #038-43-1991 L1994 **PD** *020 †55
SCAVINA, Michael Liguore. 250 DEBARTOLO PL, STE 2750 44512 #038-40-1987 L1989 **CD** *020 †20
SCHAFFERT, Eric Paul. 345 OAK HILL AVE, WESTERN RESERVE CARE SYS 44502 #665-01-2006 L2006 **FP** *012
SCHAUB, Carl Ralph. 1044 BELMONT AVE 44504 #038-40-1981 L1982 **PTH HMP** *020 †50
SCHEETZ, Kevin Lawrence. 8302 SOUTHERN BLVD 44512 #038-44-1989 L1994 **HMP** *020 †50
SCHMETTERER, Lawrence Ira. 550 PARMALEE AVE, STE 300 44510 #016-11-1982 L1992 **VS** *020 †85,90
SCHOR, Harriet Felice. 397 CHURCHILL HUBBARD RD 44505 #017-20-1990 L1991 **FM** *020 †18
SCOTT, Ronald Stephen. 2151 RUSH BLVD 44507 #016-43-1977 L1981 **FM** *040 †18
SE GALL, Gary Kent. 8302 SOUTHERN BLVD 44512 #048-04-1982 L1992 **PTH** *020 †50
SELIM, Suzan Lewis. 901 TRAILWOOD DR 44512 #915-02-1978 L1988 **IM** *020 †20
SENTONGO, Colin. 345 OAK HILL AVE, WESTERN RESERVE CARE SYS 44502 #308-13-2003 L2004 **FM** *100
SEVACHKO, Gerald Stephen. 500 GYPSY LN 44504 #038-41-1968 L1968 **OPH** *020 †35
SEVILLA, Escarlito Uminga. 5437 MAHONING AVE STE 23 44515 #748-01-1965 L1973 **OTO A** *020 †45
SHAER, James A. 1044 BELMONT AVE 44504 #041-02-1993 L2005 **ORS** *020 †40
SHAH, Munir Pravinchandra. 527 N MERIDIAN RD 44509 #495-22-1990 L1997 **ID** *020 †20
SHAIKH, Omer S. 727 E WESTERN RESERVE RD, PEDIATRIC ASSOCIATES OF 44514 #704-02-1991 L1998 **PD** *020 †55
SHANFELD, Robin Lisa. 8302 SOUTHERN BLVD 44512 #038-40-1993 L1996 **PTH** *020 †50
SHARMA, Sharad Kumar. 345 OAK HILL AVE 44502 #672-01-2002 L2005 **IM** *012
SHATTAHI, Elias. 345 OAK HILL AVE, WESTERN RESERVE CARE SYSTE 44502 #875-01-2004 L2005 **IM** *012
SHEAKOSKI, Steven Leon. 1044 BELMONT AVE 44504 #561-12-1984 L1987 **AN GS** *020 †05
SHINA, James Francis, Jr. 1450 S CANFIELD NILES RD 44515 #038-44-2003 L2003 **IM ISM** *020 †20
SHRESTHA, Anil. PO BOX 1790 44501 #704-04-2003 L2006 **IM** *012
SHRESTHA, Anu. 500 GYPSY LN, 2ND FLOOR RRC 44504 #672-01-2003 L2007 **IM** *012
SIAL, Zia Ahmed. 500 GYPSY LN, FAMILY PRACTICE CENTER 44504 #759-01-2003 L2003 **FM** *100 †18
SIDDIQUE, Mohammad Tariq. 500 GYPSY LN, CO WRCS -MEDICAL EDUCATION 44504 #308-11-1997 L2001 **N** *012 †20
SIEGAL, Joel David. 540 PARMALEE AVE, STE 310 44510 #041-01-1992 L1998 **NS** *020 †25
SINGH, Digvijay. 550 PARMALEE AVE STE 210, BETTER BREATHING CENTER LL 44510 #496-17-1986 L1992 **PUD CCM** *020 †20
SINGH, Parduman. 126 YORK AVE 44512 #495-03-1970 L1982 **N** *071 †75
SINGH, Tejdeep. 3132 BELMONT AVE STE D 44505 #495-29-1979 L1985 **IM** *020 †20
SINGH, Tulika. 500 GYPSY LN, DEPT OF MED EDU 44504 #495-37-2000 L2005 **IM** *012
SINSHEIMER, Robert Jay. 500 GYPSY LN, OFFICE OF MEDICAL AFFAIRS 44504 #038-41-1975 L1976 **OS FM** *030 †18
SIONG, Shevyll Arvie Siy. 345 OAK HILL AVE 44502 #748-01-2002 L2005 **IM** *012
SIRIPONG, Pannee. 6505 MARKET ST, CENTER FOR BREAST HEALTH 44512 #891-04-1969 L1977 **R** *020 †80
SKAROTE, Patrick. 815 SOUTHWESTERN RUN 44514 #038-44-1994 L1998 **OBG** *020 †30
SLABOCHOVA, Bohumila. ■ 44503 #286-02-1966 L1974 **FM EM** *075
SMAROFF, Gregory George. 500 GYPSY LN, MED EDUCATION BLDS STE 101 44504 #422-01-1998 L2000 **TS** *100 †85,90
SMITH, Arthur. 1044 BELMONT AVE 44504 #038-44-2002 L2002 **EM** *012 †18
SMITH, Grace Lee. 8423 MARKET ST, BLDG C 44512 #025-01-1986 L1989 **PDC** *020 †55
SOLANKI, Padmanand Y. 560 GYPSY LN 44505 #495-97-1987 L1996 **IM** *020 †20
SOLIMAN, Sherif. 1340 BELMONT AVE, STE 2300 44504 #025-07-2000 L2005 **PFP** *100 †75
SPALDING, Janice Moore. 1053 BELMONT AVE 44504 #038-44-1987 L1988 **FM** *020 †18
SPARKS, Dorothy Ann. 500 GYPSY LN, STE 200 44504 #661-02-2006 L2006 **GS** *012
SPHABMIXAY, Thavalinh Mar. 500 GYPSY LN, DEPT OF MED EDU 44504 #305-01-2004 L2005 **FP** *012
SPIRTOS, Manuel Michael. 7355 CALIFORNIA AVE 44512 #038-44-1986 L1988 **PD** *020 †55
SPRATT, Robert Gray. 231 E MIDLOTHIAN BLVD 44507 #561-01-1977 L1983 **IM** *020
STARR, Vivian Iaderosa. 819 MCCARTNEY RD 44505 #018-75-1997, ▲ L1998 **IMG** *020
STEFEK, Paul. 715 E WESTERN RESERVE RD 44514 #035-09-1981 L1988 **IM** *020 †20
STEIN, Marsha J. 500 GYPSY LN, DEPT OF RADIOLOGY 44504 #011-02-1984 L1992 **PD** *020 †80
STILLE, James Russell. 904 SAHARA TRL 44514 #038-43-1992 L1993 **U** *020 †95
STOVER, Jeffrey Thos. 1044 BELMONT AVE, ST ELIZABETH HOSP MED CTR 44504 #039-05-1988 L1993 **GS** *020
STOWELL, Steven Douglas. 1044 BELMONT AVE, ST. ELIZABETH HEALTH CENTE 44504 #041-07-1992 L2006 **DR** *020 †80
SULLIVAN, Brian Stuart. 2980 BELMONT AVE 44505 #038-41-1982 L1986 **P** *020
SURAPANANI, Siva Prasad. 1044 BELMONT AVE, CO ST ELIZ. HLTH CTR-MED E 44504 #495-37-1999 L2003 **IM** *100 †20
SVENSON, Eric Wolfgang. 1044 BELMONT AVE, ST ELIZABETH CANCER CENTER 44504 #011-03-1975 L1986 **RO** *020 †80 ‡
TALLAM, Janardan Rao. ST ELIZABETH HOSP MED CTR, C/O EMERGENCY DEPT 44501 #495-70-1968 L1985 **EM GS** *020 †85,16
TAMBOT, Hennie Giabros. 1044 BELMONT AVE, DEPT OF MED EDU 44504 #748-01-2003 L2006 **IM** *012
TAMULONIS, Donald Jos, Jr. 1340 BELMONT AVE STE 2200 44504 #038-43-1978 L1979 **N IM** *020 †75,20
TANASE, Anca. 345 OAK HILL AVE, WESTERN RESERVE CARE SYS 44502 #781-01-2004 L2005 **IM** *012
TANASE, Armand Bogdan. 345 OAK HILL AVE, WESTERN RESERVE CARE SYS 44502 #781-01-2004 L2005 **IM** *012
TAYLOR, Monica. 500 GYPSY LN, TOD CHILDRENS HOSPITAL 44504 #041-13-2000 L2000 **PD** *020 †55 ‡
TAYLOR, Monica Joy. 510 GYPSY LN, STE 107 44504 #038-41-1998 L1999 **P** *020
THAKKAR, Kavita Piyush. 6505 MARKET ST 44512 #496-38-2002 L2006 **PD** *012
THOMAS, David J. 4308 BELMONT AVE 44505 #041-77-2000, ▲ L2000 **GS** *020 †85 ‡
THOMPSON, Adiatu A. 345 OAK HILL AVE, SOUTHSIDE MED CTR-YHA INC 44502 #913-22-1976 **PD** *100
TIAN, Qingsheng. 1044 BELMONT AVE 44504 #243-54-1984 L2000 **ATP PCP** *020 †50
TIBERIO, Frank C. ■ 44511 #038-06-1958 L1958 **CD IM** *071
TIMKO, Thomas Richard. 500 GYPSY LN 44504 #038-44-1987 L1988 **IM** *020 †20
TIZORA, Sibonokuhle Mhlop. 345 OAK HILL AVE 44502 #775-01-2003 L2006 **PD** *012
TOFIL, Scott Bryan. 602 PARMALEE AVE, STE 400 44510 #038-40-1994 L1996 **IM** *020 †20
TOLIVER, James E, Jr. 2111 BELMONT AVE, STE 3 44505 #051-07-1989 L1991 **IM** *020
TOM, Yuel Dick. 500 GYPSY LN, NORTHSIDE MED CTR-PATHOLGY 44504 #003-01-1975 L1980 **PTH HMP** *030 †50
TOMAS, Myreen Evangelista. ■ 44505 #748-01-2004 L2007 **IM** *012
TOROK, William Robt. 1107 MANSELL DR 44505 #038-40-1960 L1960 **R** *071 †80
TRACHTMAN, William Mark. 1044 BELMONT AVE, CREDENTIALING COORDINATOR 44504 #041-02-1989 L1998 **PM** *020 †60
TUNALI MADENCI, Lerzan. 1044 BELMONT AVE, DEPT OF MED EDU 44504 #902-07-1992 L2006 **IM** *012
TUNRU-DINH, Vonny W.. ■ 44512 #506-23-2001 L2005 **PTH** *012
TURNER, Gary Wayne. 1044 BELMONT AVE, DEPT OF MEDICAL EDUCATION 44504 #104-01-2005 L2006 **FP** *012
TURNER, John J. 500 GYPSY LN, MED ED BLDG 44504 #024-01-1952 L1957 **TS VS** *071 †85
UMAR, Saleem Akbar. 345 OAK HILL AVE 44502 #759-12-2003 L2003 **PCP** *012
VANEK, Vincent Wayne. 500 GYPSY LN 44504 #017-20-1982 L1987 **GS** *020 †85
VENGLARCIK, John S, III. 500 GYPSY LN, TOD CHILDRENS HOSP 44504 #038-40-1977 L1983 **ID PD** *020 †55
VEREBELYI, Melinda. 500 GYPSY LN, CO WRCS-MED EDU DEPT 44504 #473-03-2001 L2004 *100
VESCERA, Giorgio James. 500 GYPSY LN, TOD'S CHILDREN'S HOSPITAL 44504 #038-44-2001 L2001 **PD** *020 †55
VILLAPLANA, Luis E. 823 SOUTHWESTERN RUN 44514 #042-02-1986 L1988 **IM** *020 †20
VOIT, Jerry Stanley. 500 GYPSY LN 44504 #759-06-2004 L2005 **FP** *012
VOLOVAR, Chad Lawrence. 1570 S CANFIELD NILES RD, PRIMA HEALTH CARE 44515 #038-44-1999 L1999 **FM** *020 †18
WALIA, Harneet Kaur. ■ 44504 #496-59-2004 L2006 **FP** *012
WALKER, Edward Chas. 1044 BELMONT AVE 44504 #038-43-1976 L1977 **DR** *075 †80
WALL, Michal Sarah. 345 OAK HILL AVE 44502 #550-03-2002 L2004 **IM** *012
WANG, Hai-Shiuh. 1075 W WESTERN RESERVE RD, EYE CARE ASSOCIATES INC 44514 #385-02-1968 L1976 **OPH** *020 †35
WANG, Jingtian. 500 GYPSY LN, 2ND FLOOR RRC 44504 #243-44-1994 L2007 **IM** *012
WARAICH, Kanwaljit Kaur. 500 GYPSY LN, DEPARTMENT OF 44504 #495-03-2002 L2005 **IM** *012
WATSON, Jenny Lynn. 1044 BELMONT AVE, DEPT OF MED EDU 44504 #665-02-2005 L2005 **IM** *012
WEGNER, Kurt J. 500 GYPSY LN, TOD CHILDREN'S HOSPITAL 44504 #035-06-1952 L1956 **PD CG** *071 †18,55,19
WEINBERG, Adon S. 4247 BELMONT AVE 44505 #028-79-1978, ▲ L1981 **FM** *020
WEISS, Alan. 602 PARMALEE AVE, STE 110 44510 #011-04-1984 L1986 **AN PME** *020 †05
WEISS, Lisa Noble. 500 GYPSY LN, FAMILY PRACTICE CTR 44504 #020-12-1999 L2002 **FM** *040 †18 ‡
WESTON, English, III. 219 W BOARDMAN ST 44503 #010-03-1976 L1981 **IM** *020
WETZEL, Robert Harvey, Jr. 900 TRAILWOOD DR 44512 #011-03-1976 L1977 **IM** *020 †20
WHITE, Howard I. 64 REDFERN DR 44505 #016-06-1978 L1982 **EM IM** *020 †20,16
WHITTAKER, Arthur Vance. 250 DEBARTOLO PL, STE 2750 44512 #023-01-1954 L1955 **CD** *071
WIENEKE, Karl Fredric. 500 GYPSY LN BOX 240, MEDICAL EDUCATION BLDG 44504 #010-02-1958 L1968 **GS OS** *071 †85
WILKINS, Charles Edward. 1044 BELMONT AVE, ST ELIZABETH HEALTH CENTER 44504 #038-41-1975 L1976 **IMG IM** *030 †20
WILLIAMS, Mark David. 1044 BELMONT AVE, ST ELIZABETH HEALTH CENTER 44504 #005-06-1985 L2008 **GS CCS** *020 †85
WOLFF, Zachary Lewis. ■ 44514 #038-43-2006 L2007 **TY** *012
WOOD, Arthur Paul. 64 REDFERN DR 44505 #041-14-1981 L1996 **OTO** *020 †45
WOODS, Larry Aaron. 1044 BELMONT AVE 44504 #018-75-1974, ▲ L1976 **CD CCM** *050 †20
WOODS, Susan. 20 OHLTOWN RD 44515 #024-07-1991 L1994 **D** *020 †15
WYSZYNSKI, Richard Eugene. 1075 W WESTERN RESERVE RD, EYE CARE ASSOCIATES INC 44514 #038-06-1985 L1986 **OPH** *020 †35
YACONO, Sarah L. YOUNGSTOWN HOSP ASSOC RAD 44501 #561-17-1962 L1969 **DR R** *071 †80

■ = Address Information Privacy Protected

YAKUBOV, Lyn Ellen. 3155 CANFIELD RD, EYE CARE ASSOCIATES INC 44511 #038-44-1986 L1987 **OPH** *020 †35
YAP PANDURO, Jose Isidro. 540 PARMALEE AVE, STE 300 44510 #737-01-1966 L1972 **TS VS** *020 †85,90
YARAB, Ronald M, Jr. 822 E WESTERN RESERVE RD 44514 #045-04-1989 L1991 **PM** *020 †60
YARMY, Milton Marvin. ■ 44504 #025-07-1937 L1937 **IM** *071 †20
YOON, Pyongsoo. 500 GYPSY LN 44504 #051-04-1987 L1997 **TS** *020 †85,90
YORK, John Clement. 7655 MARKET ST STE 2500, CORNING CLINICAL LABORATOR 44512 #016-43-1974 L1982 **PTH** *030 †50
YOUNG, Elisabeth H. 1044 BELMONT AVE DEPT MED, ST ELIZABETH HLTH CTR 44504 #038-44-1985 L1987 **RHU IM** *040 †20
YOUNG, Gary Allen. 715 E WESTERN RESERVE RD 44514 #038-43-1980 L1981 **CD** *020 †20
YOUSSEF, Sameh I. 20 OHLTOWN RD 44515 #915-02-1986 L1996 **IM** *020 †20
YU, Inski Howard E. Quan. 1044 BELMONT AVE, ST ELIZABETH HEALTH CENTER 44504 #748-01-2001 L2004 **IM** *012
ZAFIRIDES, Panos P. 7655 MARKET ST 44512 #418-02-1958 L1975 **R** *020
ZAGHLOUL, Nibal. 500 GYPSY LN, PEDIATRIC HEMATOLOGY ONCOL 44504 #605-01-1997 L2005 **PHO** *020 †55
ZAKY, Wafik Tharwat. 345 OAK HILL AVE 44502 #915-02-2000 L2005 **PD** *012
ZERVOS, Skevos Michael. 6640 MARKET ST 44512 #418-01-1958 L1961 **GP D** *071
ZHANG, Hui. 1044 BELMONT AVE, DEPT OF MED EDU 44504 #243-39-1985 L2006 **IM** *012
ZIRAN, Bruce Harris. 1044 BELMONT AVE, ST ELIZABETH HEALTH CTR 44504 #038-06-1988 L1989 **ORS** *020 †40

ZANESFIELD – LOGAN

TETIRICK, Jack E. ■ 43360 #024-01-1951 L1956 **GS** *071 †85

ZANESVILLE – MUSKINGUM

ADAMS, John Quincy, Jr. ■ 43701 #038-06-1945 L1945 **GP OS** *020
AEPLI, Robert Otto. 945 BETHESDA DR, STE 130 43701 #041-12-1971 L1978 **OBG** *020 †30
AILES, Daniel Jos. 950 BETHESDA DR, BLDG 5 43701 #038-40-1980 L1990 **FM** *020 †18
ALAHAKOON, Oshana Vidyama. 800 FOREST AVE, RM 2201 43701 #220-01-2000 L2004 **IM** *100
ALAHAKOON, Prabhu Tharind. 800 FOREST AVE, RM 2201 43701 #220-01-2000 L2004 **IM** *100
ALBIRINI, Abdulhay. 751 FOREST AVE, STE 301 43701 #875-01-1989 L1994 **CD IM** *020 †20
ALLEN, Bradley Ronald. 2951 MAPLE AVE 43701 #038-41-1995 L1998 **EM** *020 †16
ALLEN, William Dean. 2854 BELL ST, ORTHOPEDIC ASSOCIATES OF 43701 #038-40-1986 L1988 **ORS** *020 †40
ASTORIAN, Donald Geo. 945 BETHESDA DR, STE 200B 43701 #024-05-1983 L1993 **GS** *020 †05
AUSTEN, Jeffrey L. 950 BETHESDA DR 43701 #038-43-1990 L1991 **NEP IM** *020 †20
BACKUS, Shane Keith. 838 MARKET ST, RADIOLOGY ASSOCIATES OF 43701 #055-01-1998 L2003 **DR** *020 †80
BAILEY, Gordon Alfred. 950 BETHESDA DR 43701 #047-07-1972 L1974 **EM FM** *075
BALOGH, Robert John. 975 BETHESDA DR, OHIO PSYCHIATRIC 43701 #038-40-1980 L1981 **SME P** *020 †75
BHANJA, Utpal Kumar. 751 FOREST AVE STE 201 43701 #495-32-1982 L1994 **ON HEM** *020 †20
BLISSENBACH, David Allen. 2951 MAPLE AVE 43701 #038-45-1982 L1983 **IM** *020 †20
BLOME, Dexter Wm. 930 BETHESDA DR, BLG 4 43701 #021-06-1980 L1991 **PS OTO** *020 †45,65
BODY, Lowell Harrison, II. 2854 BELL ST 43701 #038-40-1970 L1970 **ORS** *071 †40
BOOTH, Edmond Jasper. ■ 43701 #038-40-1941 L1942 **U** *071
BOOTH, Edward Jos. 2110 MAPLE AVE 43701 #038-40-1969 L1969 **U GS** *071 †95
BOOTH, Jack Branyon. 2945 MAPLE AVE 43701 #038-40-1973 L1973 **OTO** *020 †45
BOYSE, Dale Richard. 3450 S RIVER RD 43701 #025-07-1964 L1970 **RO DR** *071 †80
BRANDITZ, Fred Kim. 1210 ASHLAND AVE 43701 #041-09-1981 L1987 **PUD IM** *020 †20
BRANTLEY, Keith Wm. 751 FOREST AVE STE 301, SOUTHEASTERN OHIO, INC 43701 #038-40-1985 L1992 **CD IM** *020 †20
BRAUTIGAN, Brad Everett. 2854 BELL ST, ORTHOPEDIC ASSOCIATES OF 43701 #055-01-1994 L1995 **OSM** *020 †40
BRUNE, Dominic B. ■ 43701 #038-40-1961 L1961 **GP** *071
BURK, Jane Marie. 3287 MAPLE AVE 43701 #038-40-1982 L1983 **DR** *020 †80
CAFFARATTI, John Darius. 751 FOREST AVE STE 301, SOUTHEASTERN OHIO, INC 43701 #040-02-1974 L1992 **CD** *020 †20
CAMMA, Albert John. 751 FOREST AVE, STE 200 43701 #038-06-1967 L1967 **NS N** *020 †25
CAMPBELL, Jessica B. 1246 ASHLAND AVE, STE 101 43701 #023-07-1978 L1988 **VS GS** *020 †85
CAMPBELL, Terence Dean. 2916 VANGADER DR, SURGICAL ASSOC OF ZANESVIL 43701 #023-01-1980 L1988 **GS VS** *020 †85
CARR, Wm Clifford, Jr. 800 FOREST AVE, GOOD SAMARITAN HOSPITAL 43701 #016-01-1992 L2007 **IM** *020 †20
CATON, James W. 1246 ASHLAND AVE, STE 203 43701 #028-79-1953, ▲ L1953 **FM AM** *071
CERNEY, Charles Iams. ■ 43701 #030-05-1948 L1955 **IM PM** *071 †20
CHERNICK, Andrew Robt. 1246 ASHLAND AVE, GASTROENTEROLOGY 43701 #035-09-1987 L1993 **GE** *020 †20
CHORICH, Louis Jos, III. 2935 MAPLE AVE 43701 #038-40-1992 L1994 **OPH** *020 †35
COOKE, Coleene Gweneth. 838 MARKET ST, DUBUQUE RADIOLOGICAL ASSOC 43701 #051-07-1978 L1979 **DR R** *020 †80
DANIELS, William Kenneth. 945 BETHESDA DR STE B, ZANESVILLE ANESTHESIA PHYS 43701 #020-12-2000 L2004 **AN** *020 †05
DE CENSO, Diane Marie. 945 BETHESDA DR 43701 #038-41-1983 L1993 **IM** *020 †20
DEIGNAN, Jos Michael, Jr. 945 BETHESDA DR, STE 220 43701 #035-20-1963 L1990 **TS CD** *071 †85,90
DE LEON, Craig Warren. 945 BETHESDA DR, STE 200B 43701 #051-04-1994 L1999 **AN** *020
DEMBSKI, David Michael. 950 BETHESDA DR, BLDG 5 43701 #036-05-1990 L2007 **NEP** *020 †20
DHILLON, Gurmeet Singh. 3287 MAPLE AVE 43701 #065-06-1988 L2004 **R** *020 †80
DIEHL, Thomas Hubert. 2916 VANGADER DR 43701 #038-40-1980 L1982 **GS** *020 †85
DONOHO, Robert Smith. ■ 43701 #023-07-1954 L1958 **GS** *071
DOWNING, Jeffrey Duane. 945 BETHESDA DR STE 140 43701 #038-41-1983 L1985 **OBG** *020 †30
ELADOUMIKDACHI, Firas Gha. 2916 VANGADER DR 43701 #605-01-1998 L2006 **GS** *020
ELSTON, Amanda Storm. 1210 ASHLAND AVE 43701 #041-02-1979 L1982 **IM** *020 †20
ELSTON, Jan Eric. 2916 VANGADER DR 43701 #041-02-1979 L1983 **GS** *020 †85
ELWOOD, Lori J Wolpa. 2951 MAPLE AVE 43701 #030-05-1980 L2000 **HEM PTH** *020 †20,50
ENGDAHL, Dwight E. 2854 BELL ST, ORTHOPEDIC ASSOCIATES OF 43701 #038-41-1983 L1992 **ORS** *020 †40
ESSIG, Richard Henry. 830 BETHESDA DR, DOCTORS PARK BLDG 1 43701 #038-40-1975 L1975 **OBG** *020 †30
EVERMAN, Kelly Reid. 2935 MAPLE AVE, OPHTHALMIC SURGEONS & 43701 #020-02-1997 L2003 **OPH** *020 †35
FINKBEINER, Andrew Alex. 3287 MAPLE AVE 43701 #004-01-1999 L2006 **DR** *062 †80
FISHER, Joel Irwin. 2951 MAPLE AVE 43701 #038-40-1973 L1974 **EM** *020 †16
FORRESTAL, Thomas Patrick. 930 BETHESDA DR, BLDG IV 43701 #056-06-1958 L1970 **PTH** *020 †50
FRUEH, Andrea Katrin. 945 BETHESDA DR, STE 340 43701 #038-43-1999 L2003 **PD PSM** *020 †55
GAUDIO, Frank Eugene. 2951 MAPLE AVE 43701 #024-01-1983 L1986 **OS** *020 †16
GIFFORD, Gordon Earl. 1805 MAPLE AVE 43701 #038-40-1948 L1948 **D** *071 †15
GIRSH, Sidney. ■ 43701 #041-02-1959 L1970 **PTH CLP** *071 †50
GOODARZI, Bijan Jos. 975 BETHESDA DR 43701 #055-02-1983 L1985 **OBG** *020 †30
GRAFFEO, William Clifford. 2951 MAPLE AVE 43701 #035-09-1979 L1980 **EM** *020 †16
GRANT, William Nelson. 3777 JAMES CT 43701 #016-42-1979 L2001 **ID AI** *020
GREENSPAN, Jack. 838 MARKET ST, RADIOLOGY ASSOCIATES OF 43701 #025-12-1980 L1982 **DR R** *020 †80
GUPTA, Rajiv. 945 BETHESDA DR, STE 340 43701 #495-14-1986 L1998 **PD** *020 †55
HANNA, Said Fouad. 945 BETHESDA DR, STE 250 43701 #605-02-1968 L1978 **GS VS** *020 †85
HARRISON, Charles Simeon. ■ 43701 #023-01-1965 L1967 **GS** *071 †85
HARVEY, Ronald Ray. 1210 ASHLAND AVE 43701 #038-40-1978 L1981 **FM** *020 †18 ‡
HENZES, Mark Jos. 2951 MAPLE AVE 43701 #654-01-1981 L1993 **GP** *020
HERNANDEZ, Raul Alberto. 751 FOREST AVE, STE 402 43701 #038-40-1989 L1990 **NEP IM** *020 †20
KAKA, Zehra Salim. 800 FOREST AVE 43701 #496-38-1980 L1983 **RO** *020 †80
KALIS, Perry Michael. 129 N MAYSVILLE AVE 43701 #055-01-1971 L1975 **IM ID** *020 †20
KELLEY, James Russell. 2951 MAPLE AVE 43701 #007-02-1988 L2000 **IM** *020 †20
KELSO, Gregory Lynn. 860 BETHESDA DR 43701 #038-41-1999 L2003 **FM** *020 †18
KHOURY, Samar. 751 FOREST AVE, STE 301 43701 #875-01-1988 L1996 **CD** *020 †20
KIM, Susie Hyun. 3287 MAPLE AVE 43701 #025-07-1996 L2001 **DR** *062 †80
KIMBERLY, Steven Howard. 2854 BELL ST, ORTHOPEDIC ASSOCIATES OF 43701 #038-40-1990 L1995 **ORS** *020 †40
KLEIN, David Lynn. 2800 MAPLE AVE 43701 #038-40-1973 L1976 **OM IM** *020 †20,70
KNELL, Myron Floyd, Jr. 945 BETHESDA DR, STE 300 43701 #055-01-1972 L1976 **IM** *020 †20
KNIERIM, David Stevens. 751 FOREST AVE, STE 200 43701 #005-12-1978 L1990 **NS NSP** *020 †25
KNIGHT, Paul Raymond. 960 BETHESDA DR, STE 260 43701 #038-40-1972 L1972 **IM PUD** *020 †20
KROHN, Melvin R. ■ 43701 #035-06-1952 L1956 **ORS** *071 †40
KUKURA, David Thos. 800 FOREST AVE 43701 #028-34-1970 L1974 **FM EM** *020 †55
LACERDA, Juan Ruperto. ■ 43702 #275-01-1953 L1965 **GS GP** *071
LA NOUETTE, Gregory Wm. 2110 MAPLE AVE 43701 #038-41-1981 L1982 **U** *020 †95
LAUREN, David M. 945 BETHESDA DR, STE 240 43701 #038-75-1991, ▲ L1992 **FM** *020 †18 ‡
LAYNE, Andrew Ennis. 2854 BELL ST, ORTHOPEDIC ASSOCIATES OF 43701 #038-41-1996 L1997 **ORS** *020 †40
LEPI, John Michael. 945 BETHESDA DR STE 120 43701 #038-40-1990 L1991 **OBG** *020 †30
LEWIS, Hudnall Johnson. ■ 43701 #051-04-1963 L1964 **AN** *071
LITTLE, Raymond Roger. 800 FOREST AVE 43701 #023-01-1968 L1990 **PTH** *020 †50
LOMBARDI, Vincent Anthony. 3287 MAPLE AVE 43701 #016-43-1989 L2005 **DR** *020 †80
LONG, Roland Vance. 2951 MAPLE AVE 43701 #016-45-1978 L1980 **EM** *020 †16
LUFT, Brian William. 2315 MAPLE AVE 43701 #654-01-1997 L1999 **IM** *020 †20
MACKALL, James I. 2110 MAPLE AVE 43701 #041-02-1960 L1965 **U** *071 †95
MADSON, Derald Lee, Jr. 3964 FRAZEYSBURG RD, STE A 43701 #056-06-1987 L1990 **VS VIR** *020 †85
MALIK, Abdus Salam. 1246 ASHLAND AVE, CARDIO ASSOCS ZANESVILLE 43701 #704-02-1982 L1993 **NEP** *062 †20
MAULSBY, Gilbert Hawkins. 3287 MAPLE AVE 43701 #012-01-1996 L2000 **DR** *020 †80
MELICK, Ann Elizabeth. 2935 MAPLE AVE 43701 #038-40-1991 L1995 **OPH** *020 †35
MELICK, Nelson. 2951 MAPLE AVE 43701 #038-40-1959 L1959 **AN** *071 †05
MELLON, Richard Lee. 838 MARKET ST, RADIOLOGY ASSOCIATES OF 43701 #005-15-1974 L1984 **DR PD** *020 †55,80
MERWIN, Bruce Alan. 800 FOREST AVE, GOOD SAMARITAN MEDICAL CEN 43701 #038-40-1984 L1985 **RO** *020
METRY, Michael Najeeb. 800 FOREST AVE 43701 #016-42-1986 L1992 **CCM** *020 †20
MILLER, Kevin Chas. 751 FOREST AVE 43701 #041-14-1982 L1988 **PD** *020 †55
MILLER, Maurice Monroe. 3287 MAPLE AVE 43701 #023-01-1990 L2000 **DR** *020 †80
MILLS, Laurel Susan. 2845 BELL ST 43701 #038-06-1993 L1995 **P** *100
MINNING, Carl A, Jr. 2935 MAPLE AVE 43701 #038-40-1979 L1980 **OPH** *020 †35
MINNIS, Stephen Allen. 751 FOREST AVE 43701 #038-45-1985 L1987 **PD** *020 †55
MONATH, James Robt. 751 FOREST AVE STE 303 43701 #041-02-1989 L1997 **U** *020 †95
MOORE, Jerry Wayne. 751 FOREST AVE STE 301, SOUTHEASTERN OHIO,IN POB 3 43701 #020-12-1974 L1979 **CD IM** *020 †20
MOORE, Stephany Kay. 1246 ASHLAND AVE, STE 107 43701 #038-40-1995 L2002 **CD** *020 †20
MUCHNOK, Charles. 838 MARKET ST, RADIOLOGY ASSOCIATES OF 43701 #041-14-1992 L1996 **DR** *020 †80
MYERS, Douglas Alan. 4063 N POINTE DR, STE B 43701 #038-40-1984 L1985 **FM** *020 †18 ‡
NADEAU, Gary Joseph. 800 FOREST AVE 43701 #065-01-1987 L2000 **EM** *020
NEGRON-SOTO, Jose Manuel. 3287 MAPLE AVE 43701 #025-01-1993 L2006 **RNR R** *062 †80
NEWSOM, Eric Lloyd. 2951 MAPLE AVE 43701 #038-44-1993 L1994 **FM** *020 †18
OBENOUR, Sterling W. ■ 43701 #035-20-1952 L1953 **GS** *071 †85
OLMSTED, Adam Kenneth. 3287 MAPLE AVE 43701 #012-01-1997 L2003 **DR** *020 †80
OSBORN, Chester Woodward. 1776 LONGHILL DR 43701 #010-01-1967 L1976 **TS** *071 †85,90
PARRETT, David Bruce. 1210 ASHLAND AVE 43701 #038-43-1994 L1996 **IM** *020 †20
PAVLIK, Alice Marie. 945 BETHESDA DR, STE 110 43701 #038-40-1979 L1982 **OBG** *020 †30
PEPERA, Michael Edward. 2951 MAPLE AVE 43701 #038-40-2003 L2006 **EM** *100
PHAM, Quynhanh Hoangthi. 2916 VANGADER DR 43701 #038-44-1998 L1999 **GS** *020 †85
PHELPS-MAXWELL, Juliette. 840 BETHESDA DR, VA PRIMARY CARE 43701 #409-21-1972 L1996 **IM** *020 †20

■ = Address Information Privacy Protected

POOL, Duane Phillip. 751 FOREST AVE, STE 301 43701 #038-45-1989 L1990 **CD** *020 †20

PORTER, Larry Joe. 2854 BELL ST 43701 #038-40-1964 L1964 **ORS** *071 †40

POWELSON, Myron H. 1246 ASHLAND AVE STE 104 43701 #020-02-1949 L1954
GS GP *071 †85

POWERS, Gerald Tyrone. 3287 MAPLE AVE 43701 #025-01-1978 L1982 **DR** *020 †80

RAMARIAH, Uma Devi R. 3814 JAMES CT 43701 #496-39-1993 L2005 **PD** *100 †55

RAY, John Walker. 2945 MAPLE AVE 43701 #038-40-1960 L1960 **OTO A** *071 †45

REHAN, Arshad. 751 FOREST AVE, STE 301 43701 #704-09-1994 L2006 **IC** *020 †20

REILLY, Kim Marie. 751 FOREST AVE, STE 401 43701 #047-05-1995 L2000 **PD** *020 †55

RENNER, William Robt. 3287 MAPLE AVE 43701 #038-40-1976 L1976 **R** *020 †20,80

REPUYAN, Othello R. 3814 JAMES CT 43701 #748-01-1968 L1977 **PD** *020 †55

RHEE, Jung Moo. 2951 MAPLE AVE 43701 #583-04-1970 L1978 **AN GP** *020 †55

ROJEWSKI, Thomas Edward. 2945 MAPLE AVE 43701 #038-40-1976 L1978 **OTO** *020 †45

RUGGLES, Thomas Newton. 945 BETHESDA DR STE 200B 43701 #038-06-1967 L1967
AN *071 †05

RUSS, Edmond V, III. 838 MARKET ST, RADIOLOGY ASSOCIATES OF 43701 #038-43-1997 L2003
DR *020 †80

SANDLUND, Kristofer G. 2951 MAPLE AVE 43701 #038-40-1981 L1983 **FM** *020 †18

SARAP, Nick Anthony. 2951 MAPLE AVE 43701 #038-06-1967 L1967 **GS** *071 †85

SAUNDERS, Karl Curtis. 2854 BELL ST 43701 #038-40-1976 L1977 **ORS MDM** *020 †40

SCHEERER, Daniel Bernard. 1210 ASHLAND AVE 43701 #017-20-1979 L1982 **IM** *020 †20

SCHOWENGERDT, Carl Gordon. 1246 ASHLAND AVE 43701 #018-03-1960 L1962
TS CD *020 †85,90

SCHOWINSKY, John Lawrence. 751 FOREST AVE, STE 401 43701 #047-06-1972 L1975
PD *020 †55

SCHUSTER, Michael Robt. 2951 MAPLE AVE 43701 #038-40-1983 L1985 **EM** *030 †16

SENOR, Brett. 800 FOREST AVE 43701 #038-43-1992 L1994 **MPD** *020 †55,20

SHADE, William Allen, Jr. 945 BETHESDA DR, STE 300 43701 #038-40-1988 L1990 **IM** *020 †20

SHAHABI, Mohammad Ali. 2927 BELL ST 43701 #517-01-1957 L1968 **PM** *071

SHANER, John Edward. 945 BETHESDA DR, STE 300 43701 #038-40-1981 L1983 **IM** *020 †20

SHANNON, Michael Bruce. 1246 ASHLAND AVE 43701 #038-43-1974 L1985 **NS OS** *020 †25 ‡

SHEYN, Irena. 800 FOREST AVE 43701 #913-89-1980 L1999 **PCP** *020 †50

SHORT, Philip Eugene. 1210 ASHLAND AVE 43701 #038-40-1984 L1987 **IM** *020 †20

SIEFERT, W L Gregory. 716 ADAIR AVE, ALLIED HEALTH PAVILLION 43701 #038-40-1979 L1979
AN PMM *020 †05

SMITH, Darell Jene. 2845 BELL ST 43701 #038-40-1957 L1957 **P** *071 †75

SOMPLE, Michael Jay. 751 FOREST AVE, STE 400 43701 #041-12-1975 L1981 **N** *020 †75

SRIKANTIAH, Roopa S.. 751 FOREST AVE, STE 201 43701 #665-01-2000 L2000 **HO** *020 †20

STEINBERGER, John Walker. 838 MARKET ST BOX 231 43701 #038-40-1971 L1971
DR OS *020 †80

SWAN, Linda Toivonen. ■ 43701 #038-40-1986 L1988 **OBG** *020 †30

TABATOWSKI, Katherine. 2951 MAPLE AVE 43701 #025-07-1982 L1992 **PTH** *020 †50

TEMPERLEY, Shelly Jean. 2935 MAPLE AVE 43701 #025-07-1987 L1991 **OPH** *020 †35

THOMPSON, Robert Jorden. 945 BETHESDA DR, STE 230 43701 #041-12-1972 L1976
N *020 †75

TIBERIO, Gerald John. 751 FOREST AVE, STE 401 43701 #028-34-1974 L1977 **PD** *020 †55

TOWNING, Larry D. 3515 CLIFFHANGER WAY 43701 #038-44-1993 *100

TROUT, Mark Anthony. 870 ORCHARD HILL RD 43701 #038-40-1983 L1984 **FM** *020 †18

TUCK, Richard Harrison. 751 FOREST AVE, STE 401 43701 #035-20-1972 L1978 **PD** *020 †55

ULRICH, Stephen C. 3620 COURT DR STE K 43701 #016-45-1977 L1978 **FM EM** *020 †18

VAN GILDER, John Elman. 751 FOREST AVE, STE 301 43701 #055-01-1970 L1976
CD IM *020 †20

WALLIS, William Robert C. 838 MARKET ST, RADIOLOGY ASSOCIATES OF 43701 #038-75-1988,
▲ L1989 **R** *020

WHITACRE, Vicki A. 205 N 7TH ST, ZANESVILLE MUSKINGUM CO HL 43701
#038-40-1971 L1971 **PD GP** *020

WIELKIEWICZ, Walter James. 2945 MAPLE AVE 43701 #038-41-1984 L1985
FM FSM *020 †18 ‡

WURZBACH, Douglas William. 838 MARKET ST, RADIOLOGY ASSOCIATES OF 43701
#038-41-2001 L2001 **R** *020 †80

YOUNG, Bobby D. ■ 43701 #038-40-1953 L1953 **GP OBG** *072

YOUNG, Eugene Loo. 1246 ASHLAND AVE, GASTROENTEROLOGY 43701 #038-44-1989 L1990
GE *020 †20

YUSUFZAI, Hashim Mohammad. 2951 MAPLE AVE 43701 #118-01-1961 L1986 **FM** *020 †18

ZANGMEISTER, David Carl. 840 BETHESDA DR BLDG 3A, VA ZANESVILLE COMMUNITY
BA 43701 #038-40-1982 L1983 **FM** *020 †18

ZIMMERER, Michael Melvin. 1210 ASHLAND AVE 43701 #038-43-1977 L1978 **FM** *020 †18

ZIMMERMAN, John Scott. 2951 MAPLE AVE 43701 #038-41-1981 L1982 **EM** *020 †16

ADA – PONTOTOC

ADAIR, John Ralph. 1001 N COUNTRY CLUB RD, CHICKASAW NATION HEALTH SY 74820
#039-01-1954 L1954 **IM PUD** *071

ALCINI, John Jos. 430 N MONTE VISTA ST, VALLEY VIEW REGIONAL HOSPI 74820
#025-07-1967 L2006 **R** *020 †80

ALMASRI, Abdel R M A. 520 ARLINGTON ST 74820 #915-02-1978 L1995 **END IM** *020

ALVAREZ, Jose R. 1414 ARLINGTON ST STE 1300 74820 #042-01-1983 L2006 **GS OTO** *020

BAKER, William Joseph. 430 N MONTE VISTA ST, DEPT OF ANESTHESIA 74820
#039-01-1995 L1996 **AN** *020 †05

BARRETT, William Laurence. 520 N MONTE VISTA ST 74820 #036-01-1994 L2003 **GS** *020 †85

BAYNE, Everett Edward. 1000 ROLLING HILLS LN 74820 #039-01-1984 L1985 **P** *020

BERGER, E Stanley. ■ 74820 #039-01-1944 L1946 **IM GE** *071

BERGER, Sally Jane. 1001 N COUNTRY CLUB RD, CARL ALBERT INDIAN HEALTH 74820
#039-01-1989 L1990 **IMG** *020

BLACK, Robert Michael. 1001 N COUNTRY CLUB RD 74820 #005-15-1968 L1995
ORS HS *020 †40

CALDWELL, Troy Tinsley. 1001 N COUNTRY CLUB RD, CHICKASAW NATION HEALTH SY 74820
#039-01-2001 L2005 **AN** *020 †05

CARLIN, James Albert, Jr. 1001 N COUNTRY CLUB RD 74820 #048-02-1964 L1972
DR FPS *072

CARPENTER, Stephen Lewis. 1023 ARLINGTON ST STE B 74820 #039-01-1977 L1978
FM *020 †18,70

CARTMELL, Gerald Frank. 421 N MONTE VISTA ST, PATHOLOGY ASSOCIATES INC 74820
#039-01-1981 L1986 **PTH** *062 †50 ‡

CARTMELL, Larry Wayne. 430 N MONTE VISTA ST 74820 #039-01-1964 L1964 **PTH** *020 †50 ‡

CHARBONEAU, Roger John. 520 N MONTE VISTA ST, STE B 74820 #039-79-1998, ▲ L2003
ORS *020

CHATFIELD, Robert Bruce. ■ 74820 #039-01-1962 L1962 **DR NR** *071 †80

CHOE, Don Sik. 1001 N COUNTRY CLUB RD, FACILITY 74820 #583-11-1975 L1981 **AN** *020

CHON, Ah Ja Kim. 1001 N COUNTRY CLUB RD 74820 #583-08-1964 L1987
FM PTH *020 †50,18

COLEMAN, Boyce Rickner. 216 LAKE DR 74820 #004-01-1968 L1970 **AN GP** *020 †05

COOPER, Tina Marie. 1007 N COUNTRY CLUB RD 74820 #039-01-1995 L1996 **FM** *020 †18

CVETNIC, William Geo. ■ 74820 #041-12-1981 L1984 **NPM** *020 †55

DAVIES, Donald Wesley. 430 N MONTE VISTA ST, VALLEY VIEW HOSP 74820
#039-01-1992 L1998 **DR** *020 †80

DAVIS, Mitchell Ryan. 1001 N COUNTRY CLUB RD, CARL ALBERT INDIAN HOSPITA 74820
#024-05-1995 L1998 **FM** *020 †18

DEEN, Gordon Holmes. 1414 ARLINGTON ST 74820 #021-01-1961 L1968 **U** *071 †95

DEESE, E Frank. ■ 74820 #012-05-1945 L1973 **GP** *071

DENNIS, Bruce Wayne. 902 ARLINGTON CTR, PMB224 74820 #039-01-1992 L1993 **IM** *020 †20

DENSON, Kent D. 1001 N COUNTRY CLUB RD, CHICKASAW NATION HEALTH SY 74820
#039-01-2002 L2004 **GS** *100

DIACON, Glen Edward, Jr. 1414 ARLINGTON ST 74820 #039-01-1986 L1987 **U** *020

DOTY, Roy Jos. 1110 N MISSISSIPPI AVE 74820 #039-01-1958 L1958 **AN** *071

FALSARELLA, John Keith. 2901 ARLINGTON ST 74820 #039-01-1975 L1976 **FM OM** *020 †18

FILLMORE, Steven Louis. 1150 N HILLS SHOPPING CTR 74820 #039-01-1982 L1983
IM *020 †20

GADDY, Jasmine Reanna. 1001 N COUNTRY CLUB RD 74820 #041-13-2003 L2007 **IM** *100 †20

GILBERT, Jerald Milton. 1007 N COUNTRY CLUB RD, PRACTICE CENTER 74820
#039-01-1975 L1976 **HS AS** *020

GILLIAM, Mary Ann Engel. ■ 74821 #039-01-1968 L1969 **PD GP** *071

GLASGOW, James Alden. 325 N MONTE VISTA ST 74820 #039-01-1977 L1978 **GS** *020 †85

HARRIS, Curtis Edward. 1001 N COUNTRY CLUB RD 74820 #054-04-1973 L1977
END IM *020 †20 ‡

HOOD, Jeff Michael. 430 N MONTE VISTA ST, VALLEY VIEW REGIONAL HOSP 74820
#039-01-1995 L1996 **AN** *020 †05

HUNSAKER, Michael Robt. 1414 ARLINGTON ST 74820 #048-04-1963 L1970 **CD** *071 †20 ‡

IORGA, Stefan. 1001 N COUNTRY CLUB RD # R, C/O CAIHT 74820 #028-34-1990 L2004
PD *020 †55

IVAN, Thomas Steven. 530 N MONTE VISTA ST STE A 74820 #039-79-2002, ▲ L2003 *020

JENKINS, Arthur Wells. 1001 N COUNTRY CLUB RD, FACILITY 74820 #041-12-1970 L1999
OBG *071 †30

JOHNSTON, Thomas Reed. 625 N MONTE VISTA ST 74820 #047-06-1970 L1978 **IM** *071 †20

KLEPPER, Charlyce Ann. 430 N MONTE VISTA ST 74820 #039-01-1963 L1963 **EM PD** *071

KRAGH, Gero Spencer. 1201 ARLINGTON ST, STE A 74820 #035-15-1970 L2005 **N** *020 †75

LYTLE, Glenn Herbert. 1001 N COUNTRY CLUB RD, CARL ALBERT INDIAN HEALTH 74820
#035-45-1974 L1987 **GS AS** *020 †85

MASON, Michael Ray. 1007 N COUNTRY CLUB RD 74820 #039-01-1984 L1985 **FM** *020 †18

MASON, Patrick Lee. 1001 N COUNTRY CLUB RD 74820 #039-01-1984 L1985 **PD** *020 †55

MC CLAIN, Richard Benson. 1001 N COUNTRY CLUB RD, CHICHASAW NATION HEALTH
SY 74820 #039-01-1992 L1994 **OBG** *020 †30

MEDCALF, Timothy Wayne. 1146 N HILLS CENTRE 74820 #039-01-1986 L1987 **CD** *020 †20

MEYER, Christopher Mark. 530 N MONTE VISTA ST 74820 #039-01-1995 L1998 **FM** *020 †18

MOLINA, Daniel. 1001 N COUNTRY CLUB RD 74820 #023-12-2004 L2007 **FM** *020 †18

MORGAN, Jerry Steve. 625 N MONTE VISTA ST 74820 #039-01-1972 L1973 **IM** *020 †20

MORTON, Robert Oliver. 1000 ROLLING HILLS LN, ROLLING HILLS HOSPITAL 74820
#039-01-1972 L1975 **ADP** *020 †20

MOTA, Fabio Horacio. 1001 N COUNTRY CLUB RD 74820 #847-04-1969 L2005
IM RHU *020 †20

NOBLET, William Chester. 430 N MONTE VISTA ST 74820 #039-01-1966 L1966 **ON IM** *020

NOLLEY, Ronald E, Jr. 430 N MONTE VISTA ST 74820 #041-13-1990 L1997 **DR** *020 †80

NORRED, Troy Ray. 430 N MONTE VISTA ST 74820 #039-01-1995 L1997 **CD** *020 †20

O'GRADY, Stephen L. 1001 N COUNTRY CLUB RD, CHICKASAW NATION HEALTH SY 74820
#048-15-1988 L1991 **PD** *020 †55

PADDACK, Gary Lee. 301 N MONTE VISTA ST 74820 #048-14-1977 L1980 **IM** *020 †20

PAJARIT, Eliezer Rivera. 1001 N COUNTRY CLUB RD 74820 #748-09-1974 L1984 **EM FM** *020 ‡

PETTETT, Jack. 1005 ARLINGTON ST 74820 #039-01-1967 L1968 **OBG** *071 †30

PRATT, Kimball Nelson. 520 N MONTE VISTA ST STE C 74820 #017-20-1989 L2008 **NS** *020 †20

QUINLAN, James Thomas. 301 S BROADWAY AVE 74820 #018-03-1981 L1986 **OPH** *020 †35

QUINTERO, Humberto G. 1001 N COUNTRY CLUB RD, CHICKASAW NATION HEALTH SY 74820
#649-18-1982 L2005 **PD** *020 †55

RAMADAN, Tawfik Za'Al. 1214 ARLINGTON ST 74820 #915-02-1961 L1977 **PD NPM** *020 †55

READ, Robert Frank. ■ 74820 #020-02-1963 L1964 **DR** *071 †80

ROBIE, Geo Fielding, Jr. 3101 ARLINGTON ST, STE A 74820 #048-02-1974 L1983
OBG PD *020 †55,30

SIEGLE, John C, Jr. 807 N MONTE VISTA ST 74820 #041-02-1981 L1990 **OBG** *020 †30 ‡

STAFFORD, Michael R. 430 N MONTE VISTA ST 74820 #039-79-1983, ▲ L1984 **EM FM** *020

STEVENS, Andrew Levi. 1001 N COUNTRY CLUB RD, CARL ALBERT INDIAN HOSPITA 74820
#037-01-2000 L2007 **GS** *020

TAUPMANN, Ralf Eric. 1001 N COUNTRY CLUB RD 74820 #048-02-1968 L1972 **DR** *020 †80

TAYLOR, James Lucas. ■ 74820 #012-01-2005 L2005 **IM** *012

TAYLOR, Neill Oliver. 1001 N COUNTRY CLUB RD, CHICKASAW NATION HEALTH SY 74820
#012-01-1976 L2006 **OBG** *020 †30

TROSKA, Joseph Louis. 430 N MONTE VISTA ST 74820 #030-06-1967 L1970 **IM** *020 †20

TULEY, Barbara K. 307 N MONTE VISTA ST 74820 #028-46-1987 L1990 **IM** *020 †20

VAN HORN, Bruce Mc Millan. 430 N MONTE VISTA ST 74820 #039-01-1965 L1965
PTH *020 †50 ‡

VEST, Charles Richard. 1901 ARLINGTON ST 74820 #028-34-1974 L1975 **OTO** *020 †45

WADDELL, Robert Luther. PO BOX 1660 74821 #048-13-1974 L1997 **GS** *020 †85

WALLACE, Jimmy Byron. 1414 ARLINGTON ST, STE 1700 74820 #039-01-1964 L1964
OBG *020 †30 ‡

WEESNER, Ruth Ann. 1414 ARLINGTON ST, ADA PED CLNC STE 2400 74820
#039-05-1986 L1987 **PD** *020 †55

WEST, David Parker. 1001 N COUNTRY CLUB RD, CARL ALBERT INDIAN HOSPITA 74820
#039-01-1965 L1965 **FM** *020 †18

WHITING, Charles Everett. 902 ARLINGTON CTR # 198 74820 #005-12-1994 L2001
OBG *020 †30

WHITING, Faye Joanne. 1001 N COUNTRY CLUB RD, WOMEN'S CLINIC 74820
#005-12-1990 L2008 **OBG** *020 †30

WHITING, Kristen Claire. 902 ARLINGTON CTR 74820 #005-12-1994 L2001 **GPM** *020 †70

WIGHT, James Francis. 2901 ARLINGTON ST 74820 #039-01-1969 L1970 **FM** *020 †18

WILSON, Connie M. 430 N MONTE VISTA ST 74820 #039-79-1995, ▲ L1996 **EM** *020

YATES, Ladny Jerad. 430 N MONTE VISTA ST 74820 #039-01-1998 L2001 **AN** *020 †05

AFTON – DELAWARE

HOWARD, Donald Richard. ■ 74331 #028-03-1960 L1968 **DR RO** *071 †80

ALTUS – JACKSON

ANDERSON, Jerome Lyman. 201 S PARK LN 73521 #039-01-1979 L1980 **CD IM** *020 †20

ANDREWS, Angelia Gay. 201 S PARK LN 73521 #039-01-1995 L1997 **FM** *020 †18

BAHR, Micah Jeddy. 3301 PEACOCK LN, ATTN CREDENTIAL OFFICE 73521
#023-12-2005 L2006 **GS** *100

BALLARD, Noble Lee. 1015 E BROADWAY ST, NOBLE BALLARD MEDICAL CLIN 73521
#039-01-1964 L1964 **FM A** *020 †18

CARTER, Charles C. 1015 E BROADWAY ST, STE 102 73521 #308-11-1991 L1994
FM EM *020 †18 ‡

DAWOD, Abdallah Salah. 3000 N MAIN ST, THE MAIN ST FAMILY PRACTIC 73521
#665-01-2001 L2005 **FM** *020 †18

FLOYD, Ira Lenorris. 304 S PARK LN 73521 #011-03-1979 L2003 **ORS** *020

GALLAGHER, John Ryan. ■ 73521 #039-01-2001 L2002 **ORS** *020

GLASGOW, John Chas. 304 S PARK LN, STE B 73521 #039-01-1975 L1976 **GS** *020

HOLLOWAY, William Cody. 1200 E TAMARACK RD, JACKSON COUNTY MEMORIAL HO 73521
#039-01-2002 L2003 **P** *020 ‡

HORTON, Natalie Lynn. PO BOX 895 73522 #064-01-1990 L1994 **FM** *020 †18

HULLENDER, Martin R, Jr. 304 S PARK LN 73521 #039-01-1965 L1965 **ORS** *020 †40

KATSERES, Richard Albert. 304 S PARK LN, STE B 73521 #033-05-1988 L1996 **GS VS** *020 †85

LEVERETT, Joe Lynn. 201 S PARK LN 73521 #039-01-1982 L1983 **IM IMG** *020

LIU, Wen Cho. JACKSON COUNTY MEM HOSP 73521 #385-01-1960 L1978 **PTH FM** *071 †50,18

MATARBAZI ALMONAJED, Moham. ■ 73521 #875-01-2002 L2007 **PD** *020 †55

MIHANNI, Ashraf Ramsis. 201 S PARK LN, ALTUS MEDICAL CLINIC 73521 #915-04-1979 L1988
IM *020 †20

PEREZ, Willard O. 201 S PARK LN 73521 #748-08-1984 L2005 **IM ID** *020

RAY, Cooper Duane. 1200 E PECAN ST 73521 #028-02-1954 L1955 **FM** *071 †18

RIVERA, Julia. 1200 E PECAN ST, JACKSON COUNTY MEMORIAL HO 73521
#042-01-1993 L2001 **OBG** *020 †30 ‡

ROBERTS, Alfred Edwin. 1200 E PECAN ST 73521 #067-01-1983 L1993 *020

ROE, Charles Francis. 201 S PARK LN 73521 #803-01-1955 L1984 **GS** *075 †85

ROOT, John Chinnick. 3000 N MAIN ST 73521 #061-01-1994 L1997 **FM** *020 †18

SAYAGO, Francisco J, Jr. 1721 N MAIN ST 73521 #132-02-1997 L2001 **AN** *020

SHEETS, Randall Ernest. 201 S PARK LN 73521 #048-12-1981 L1984 **FM** *020 †18

SHURLEY, Tom Henry. 304 S PARK LN 73521 #039-01-1974 L1975 **ORS GP** *020 †40

SYNOVITZ, Carolyn Kay. ■ 73521 #039-01-1996 L2007 **EM** *020 †16

THOMPSON, A Michelle A. 201 S PARK LN 73521 #036-08-1996 L1999 **MPD** *020 †20,55

VILLAZON, Juan R. 1015 E BROADWAY ST, STE 104 73521 #176-01-1969 L1991 **N P** *020

WOMACK, James Lee. ■ 73521 #039-01-2006 L2006 **ORS** *012

ZAKHARY, Mounir Geo. 304 S PARK LN, STE B 73521 #915-04-1979 L1987 **U** *020 †95

ALTUS AIR FORCE BASE – JACKSON

HINGSON, Stephen Vaughn. 301 N 1ST ST, 97 MDG/SGH 73523 #023-12-1993 L1995 **GPM** *012

RIDER, Melinda Lee. 301 N 1ST ST, 97 MEDICAL GROUP 73523 #038-45-2000 L2000
FM *020 †18 ‡

WASHBURN, John Leonard, Jr. 301 N 1ST ST, ALTUS AFB OK 73523 #027-01-2001 L2003
FM *020 †18

ALVA – WOODS

MEYER, Bruce Lynn. 1856 E FLYNN ST, BILL JOHNSON CORRECTION 73717
#039-01-1987 L1988 **FM** *020 †18

PINEGAR, Gregory Glase. 921 OKLAHOMA BLVD 73717 #039-01-1990 L1991 **FM** *020

RATHGEBER, Mark Edwin. 604 CHOCTAW ST, NORTHWEST CTR FOR BEHAV HL 73717
#039-01-1986 L1987 **P** *020 †75

■ = Address Information Privacy Protected

SELF, Philip Mark. 410 4TH ST, STE G 73717 #039-01-1983 L1984 **IM** *020 †20

ANADARKO – CADDO

ADAMS, Marcus Webb. PO BOX 828 73005 #039-01-1959 L1960 **PD** *071 †55
BIRD PICO, Carmen B. 404 SE 11TH ST 73005 #042-01-1982 L1993 **IM** *030
FLYNN, John Wayne. 406 SE 11TH ST 73005 #039-01-1981 L1983 **GP EM** *020
FREED, James Edwin. 1002 E CENTRAL BLVD 73005 #039-01-1970 L1971 **PD** *020 †55
KEMLER, Stanley Marshal. 115 NE OLD TOWN DRIVE 73005 #050-02-1946 L1955 **P** *020
MALDONADO, Juan Antonio. 404 SE 11TH ST 73005 #042-01-1982 L1993 **IM** *020 †20
PREUNINGER, Billy Darren. ■ 73005 #039-01-2006 **OBG** *012

ANTLERS – PUSHMATAHA

ELLIS, Edwin French. 603 NE 2ND ST, ROWLAND ELLIS FLATT 74523 #039-01-1967 L1967 **FM PD** *020 †55
FLATT, G Wayne. 603 NE 2ND ST, ROWLAND ELLIS FLATT 74523 #039-79-1985, ▲ L1986 **FM** *020
LEADER, Beth L. 510 E MAIN ST 74523 #039-79-1988, ▲ L1989 **FM** *020
ROWLAND, Herbert. 510 E MAIN ST 74523 #039-01-1964 L1964 **GP** *020

APACHE – CADDO

PANMAI, Kraingsak. ■ 73006 #891-01-1972 L1975 **GP** *075

ARCADIA – OKLAHOMA

BOKE, Brandon Benjamin. ■ 73007 #046-01-2001 L2007 **EM** *020 †16
DAVIS, John Lee, III. ■ 73007 #001-02-1958 L1973 **A OTO** *071 †45 ‡

ARDMORE – CARTER

ABU-ESHEH, Baha-Aldeen A. 1219 K ST NW STE A 73401 #575-01-1999 L2003 **CN** *020 †75
ACHANTA, Venkata Lakshmi. 1011 14TH AVE NW 73401 #495-11-1999 L2006 **IM** *020 †20
ALASAD, Bashar Samir. 1101 12TH AVE NW 73401 #528-01-1985 L2001 **ON** *020 †20
ANDES, Eugene Benton. PO BOX 1273 73402 #041-01-1968 L1994 **EM OM** *020 †16
BARBER, Ronald Dewayne. 1011 14TH AVE NW, EMERGENCY DEPT 73401 #039-01-1984 L1985 **EM** *020 ‡
BASA-ENRIQUEZ, Florencia. ■ 73402 #748-01-1956 L1981 **PD** *020
BECKER, John Donald. 1011 14TH AVE NW 73401 #041-13-1972 L1975 **OBG** *020 †30
BLACK, Charles D. 3689 KINGS RD 73401 #039-79-1991, ▲ L1992 **FM** *020
BURSON, Anna Thompson. 720 GRAND AVE 73401 #021-06-1997 L2000 **FM** *020 †18
BURTON, Vaud A, III. 1012 14TH AVE NW 73401 #039-01-1968 L1969 **AN** *020 †05
CARLSON, George Wallace. 1221 G ST NW 73401 #005-12-1962 L1963 **ORS** *071 †40
CARLSON, James Wendal. 2002 12TH AVE NW STE B, OF SOUTHERN OKLAHOMA 73401 #005-12-1963 L1972 **ORS OS** *071 †40
CARNAHAN, Michael Wayne. 1104 WALNUT DR 73401 #039-01-1986 L1989 **FM** *020 †18
CHAPMAN, James Andrew. 1023 15TH AVE NW 73401 #039-01-1971 L1972 **DR NM** *020 †80,28 ‡
CLIFTON, Percy Lynn. ■ 73402 #649-14-1972 L1985 **GP** *020
COSGROVE, Ann Marie. 2007 N COMMERCE ST STE 200 73401 #005-02-1979 L1984 **GS** *020
CUMMING, Jeffrey Clayton. 2002 12TH AVE NW STE B 73401 #305-01-1999 L2002 **ORS** *020 †40
DE LIMA, Antonio C Lins. 1518 MEADOW LN NW5 73401 #187-30-1969 L1991 **U** *020 †95
DEMPEWOLF, Scott Allen. 2002 12TH AVE NW, STE D 73401 #039-01-1991 L1997 **OTO AI** *020 †45
DORROH, Frederick A. 2002 12TH AVE NW STE E 73401 #020-12-1985 L2007 **GS** *020 †85
DOUTHIT, Bruce E. 207 C ST NW, THE ARTHRITIS CLINIC 73401 #048-14-1984 L1990 **ORS OSM** *020 †40
ELLIS, Bobbie Joe. 921 14TH AVE NW 73401 #019-02-1977 L2007 **IM IMG** *020 †20
EVARD, Raymond Michel. 1119 WALNUT DR STE 3 73401 #005-12-1965 L1976 **OTO A** *071 †45
FERNANDES, Neville Oscar. 1012 14TH AVE NW 73401 #048-02-2000 L2005 **AN** *020 †05 ‡
FRANK, Lisa Lorraine. 1011 14TH AVE NW, MERCY MEMORIAL HEALTH 73401 #007-02-2000 L2005 **EM FM** *020 †18
FUENTES, Gwen Canarias. 919 15TH AVE NW 73401 #748-10-1975 L1981 **PD** *020 †55
GALOOB, Harry David. 818 16TH AVE NW 73401 #039-01-1970 L1971 **CS OS** *020 †45 ‡
GARRIDO, Miguel Camacho. 1104 WALNUT DR, FAMILY HEALTH CENTER 73401 #308-01-1980 L1993 **PD** *020 †55
GAUTHIER, Wilfred S, Jr. 921 14TH AVE NW 73401 #019-02-1965 L1966 **GS OM** *020 †85
GILMORE, Bruce Stewart. 1015 S COMMERCE ST, DEPARTMENT OF VETERAN AFFA 73401 #041-02-1982 L1984 **IM** *020 †20
GILMORE, Laura Shannon. 1203 W BROADWAY ST 73401 #039-01-2002 L2006 **OPH** *020
GORES, David Scott. 1012 14TH AVE NW 73401 #039-01-1980 L1981 **AN** *020
GREISMAN, Richard Alan. 2002 12TH AVE NW STE B, BONE & JOINT CLINIC 73401 #003-01-1990 L1996 **ORS** *020 †40 ‡
GURROLA, Alexander Peter. 1505 N COMMERCE ST, STE 204 73401 #048-15-1987 L1988 **GE IM** *020 †20
HAMBLIN, David Warren. 7657 BROCK RD 73401 #039-01-1972 L1973 **U MDM** *030
HAMILL, Joe Ray. 207 C ST NW, CROSS TIMBERS HOSPICE 73401 #039-01-1973 L1974 **IM PLM** *020 †20 ‡
HARRIS, Daniel C. 2002 12TH AVE NW STE E 73401 #048-12-1998 L2003 **GS** *020 †85
HENRY, Hayden Downs. 915 10TH AVE NW 73401 #039-01-1990 L1991 **U** *020
HOWARD, Derek G. 1023 15TH AVE NW 73401 #048-78-1996, ▲ L1997 **DR** *020 †80
JOSEPH, George K. 1505 N COMMERCE ST, OKLAHOMA CARDIOVASCULAR 73401 #495-44-1990 L2005 **ICE** *020 †20
KHAN, Abdul N. 1402 BROOKVIEW DR 73401 #704-22-1983 L1998 **NEP IM** *020 †20
LANDIS, Derek James. 921 14TH AVE NW 73401 #011-02-2004 L2007 **PD** *020
LEE, Antonio C. 1011 14TH AVE NW 73401 #748-11-1972 L1979 **IM** *020 †20 ‡
LEE, Richard Yuanchien. 1023 15TH AVE NW, C/O RADIOLOGY ARDMORE 73401 #048-12-1982 L2008 **DR VIR** *020 †80

LONG, Larry Lee. 1107 WALNUT DR 73401 #039-01-1963 L1963 **GS** *072
MARCELO, Zoilo Venturina. 1015 S COMMERCE ST, OKLAHOMA VETERANS CENTER 73401 #748-01-1965 L1977 **GP P** *071 ‡
MC ARTHUR, Lloyd Glenn. ■ 73401 #039-01-1957 L1957 **RHU IM** *071
MC CARTY, Michael Kent. 1012 14TH AVE NW 73401 #039-01-1991 L1992 **AN** *020 †05
MC CAULEY, Michael Geo. 2410 N COMMERCE ST 73401 #048-15-1976 L1981 **D IM** *020 †20,15
MILLER, David Keith. 1010 14TH AVE NW 73401 #005-12-1977 L2004 **GPM NTR** *020
MILLER, James Vance. PO BOX 1549 73402 #039-01-1962 L1962 **GP OM** *071
MITCHELL, Craig Robt. 1011 14TH AVE NW, EMERGENCY DEPARTMENT 73401 #016-06-1990 L2005 **IM** *020 †20
MULHOLLAN, Thomas J. 1011 14TH AVE NW, MERCY MEMORIAL HOSPITAL 73401 #048-13-1986 L1991 **PTH** *020 †50
MUNDLE, Gerald S K. 1015 S COMMERCE ST, ARDMORE VETERAN'S CENTER 73401 #495-24-1959 L1992 **FM** *020
MUPPIDI, Madhavi Reddy. 1101 12TH AVE NW, STE 100 73401 #495-21-1993 L2001 **IM PM** *020 †60
NEDLEY, Neil Allen. 1010 14TH AVE NW DEPT MED 73401 #005-12-1986 L1989 **IM GE** *020 †20
OLIVER, Francis Hugh. 2401 N COMMERCE ST 73401 #055-01-1987 L1993 **IM CD** *020 †20
PAPIN, Thomas Allen. 1012 14TH AVE NW 73401 #038-43-1979 L2005 **PUD OS** *020 †20
PARKER, Mary R. 2002 12TH AVE NW STE E 73401 #048-14-1989 L2000 **OBG** *020 †30
PARKER, William J. 2002 12TH AVE NW, STE E 73401 #048-14-1989 L2000 **GS VS** *020 †85
REDDY, Proddutur Vittal. 925 15TH AVE NW 73401 #495-65-1972 L1977 **CD IM** *020
REED, Kevin Haskell. 921 14TH AVE NW 73401 #048-02-1977 L1980 **IM CCM** *020 †20
ROBERTS, Courtney Rome. 1012 14TH AVE NW 73401 #039-01-2002 L2006 **AN** *100 †05 ‡
ROSE, David Dean. 1025 15TH AVE NW 73401 #039-01-1959 L1959 **IM IMG** *020 †20
ROTHER, Jeffrey Alan. 1221 G ST NW 73401 #039-01-1990 L1991 **GP PD** *020 †20,55
RUIZ, Veronica Guadalupe. 1221 G ST NW 73401 #048-02-2000 L2005 **FM** *020 †18 ‡
SABANGAN, Joel Somera. 1514 MEADOW LN 73401 #748-09-1984 L1999 **PUD SME** *020 †20
SHELTON, Kevin James. 812 12TH AVE NW, SHELTON HEALTHCARE ASSOCIA 73401 #039-01-1999 L2000 **FM** *020 †18
SHERRY, Dean M. 2408 N COMMERCE ST 73401 #021-05-1989 L1994 **OPH** *020 †35
SHOCKEY, Brian Michael. 2419 CHICKASAW BLVD 73401 #005-12-1986 L1992 **IM** *020 †20
SHOCKEY, Leonard D. ■ 73401 #005-12-1961 L1962 **FM GS** *071 †18
SMOTHERMAN, Jason Todd. 915 10TH AVE NW 73401 #039-01-1991 L1992 **U** *020 †95
SOFOLA, Bolaji Sanyaolu. 915 10TH AVE NW 73401 #039-01-1991 L1992 **U** *020 †95
SOUTHWARD, Lauren Brooks. 1107 WALNUT DR, SOUTHWARD FAMILY MEDICINE 73401 #039-01-2000 L2001 **FM** *020 †18
SPARKS, Tom Chas, Jr. ■ 73401 #048-12-1945 L1953 **GS** *071 †85
SPENCER, Gregory M. 921 14TH AVE NW 73401 #039-01-1983 L1984 **IM** *020 †20
STINE, Earle John. 1011 14TH AVE NW 73401 #025-07-1958 L1978 **DR NR** *062 †80
SUNGA, Ruben Labrador, Jr. 921 14TH AVE NW STE B, PERMIAN PROMPT CARE MEDICA 73401 #748-13-1987 L2007 **CD** *020 †20
THAYER, Loyd Elliott. 2007 N COMMERCE ST STE 200 73401 #005-02-1977 L1984 **GS TRS** *020
TROOP, Joel Keith. 2002 12TH AVE NW, STE B 73401 #048-12-1982 L1988 **ORS OAR** *020 †40
TROOP, Robert Cecil. 2002 12TH AVE NW, STE B 73401 #047-06-1962 L1970 **RHU IM** *071
VAZQUEZ, Hiram Francisco. ■ 73401 #275-01-1952 L1971 **GP PD** *074
VAZQUEZ, Josefina. ■ 73401 #275-01-1952 L1971 **GP** *074
VELASQUEZ, Toribio C, Jr. 921 14TH AVE NW 73401 #748-13-1989 L2006 **IM** *020 †20
WARD, Kimber A. 1011 14TH AVE NW, EMERGENCY DEPARTMENT 73401 #020-02-1968 L2004 **EM GS** *020 †10,85
WRIGHT, William Dale. 1505 N COMMERCE ST, OKLAHOMA CARDIOVASCULAR 73401 #039-01-1988 L1989 **CD** *020 †20
ZHANG, Wei. 1011 14TH AVE NW 73401 #243-67-1982 L2006 **IM** *020 †20

ATOKA – ATOKA

RIPPEE, Don L. 1510 S VIRGINIA AVE 74525 #028-79-1976, ▲ L1977 **GP** *020
RUMBAUGH, Bruce W. 1501 S VIRGINIA AVE 74525 #039-01-1976 L1977 **IM** *020

BARNSDALL – OSAGE

WOODS, William Michael. 112 N 5TH ST 74002 #039-01-1984 L1985 **FM** *040 †18

BARTLESVILLE – WASHINGTON

AMARATUNGE, Harshinie Cha. ■ 74006 #048-02-2005 L2008 **IM** *012
BACHMAN, Greg Randall. 3500 E FRANK PHILLIPS BLVD 74006 #019-02-1983 L2000 **AN** *020 †05
BAKER, Ben Fowler. 3400 E FRANK PHILLIPS BLVD, MEDICAL PARK CTR STE 202 74006 #039-01-1979 L1980 **OPH** *020 †35
BAKER, Vicki Cooper. 224 SE DEBELL AVE 74006 #039-01-1985 L1986 **ON HEM** *020 †20
BARBER, Bradford Dillman. 3500 E FRANK PHILLIPS BLVD, DEPT OF ANESTHESIOLOGY 74006 #039-01-1996 L2000 **AN** *020 †05
BLAYLOCK, Sharron Denise. 226 SE DEBELL AVE 74006 #047-06-1996 L2006 **IM PMM** *020 †20
BROWN, Samuel Dean. 226 SE DEBELL AVE, STE B 74006 #045-01-1977 L1990 **RHU** *020 †20
BRYNGELSON, Jay Leigh. 222 SE DEBELL AVE 74006 #021-01-1975 L1976 **ORS** *020 †40
BUMPUS, Helen Wohlgemuth. 3450 E FRANK PHILLIPS BLVD 74006 #019-02-1978 L1979 **PD** *020 †55
BUMPUS, Michael Leroy. 3450 E FRANK PHILLIPS BLVD, GEMINI MEDICAL GROUP 74006 #039-01-1979 L1981 **FM** *020 †18
CALHOON, Harold Wayne. 500 E 5TH ST 74003 #039-01-1958 L1958 **U** *071 †95
CARTER, William J. 3450 E FRANK PHILLIPS BLVD 74006 #048-02-1970 L1977 **FM** *071 †18
CARVER, James Michael. 3500 E FRANK PHILLIPS BLVD, JANE PHILLIPS MEDICAL CENT 74006 #034-01-1988 L1989 **FM** *020 †18
CAYASSO, Richard Antonio. ■ 74006 #649-14-2002 L2008 **FP** *012
COCHRAN, Scott Douglas. 3550 E FRANK PHILLIPS BLVD 74006 #039-01-1985 L1990 **ORS OSM** *020 †40
COLEMAN, Ronald Lee. 3500 E FRANK PHILLIPS BLVD, DEPARTMENT OF ANESTHESIOLO 74006 #047-06-1969 L1970 **AN** *020 †05

COLLINS, Michael Ray. 3400 E FRANK PHILLIPS BLVD, STE 400 74006 #039-05-1986 L1990 **OBG** *020 †30

CONKLING, Kristin Diane. 700 CASTLE RD 74006 #039-01-1995 L1996 **PD** *020 †55 ‡

COTNER, Roger Jeffrey. 3500 E FRANK PHILLIPS BLVD, DEPT ER MED JANE PHILLIPS 74006 #028-78-2002, ▲ L2003 **EM** *020 ‡

CRAIG, Kyle D. 3400 E FRANK PHLPS BLVD #6 74006 #048-14-2002 L2007 **FM OBS** *020 †18

CRAWLEY, Holly Beth. 226 SE DEBELL AVE BLDG A 74006 #039-01-1996 L1997 **EM** *020 †16

DE FEHR, Stanley P. 3400 E FRANK PHILLIPS BLVD 74006 #039-01-1976 L1977 **CD IM** *020 †20

DOUGHERTY, William Henry. ■ 74006 #039-01-1954 L1954 **PD** *071

DOYLE, Linda Woolbright. 3400 E FRANK PHILLIPS BLVD, STE 302 74006 #039-01-1985 L1986 **PD** *020 †55

FU, Eric Jennteu. 3400 E FRANK PHILLIPS BLVD, STE 301 74006 #005-14-1991 L1998 **GS VS** *020 †85

GLEATON, Harriet E. 3400 TUXEDO BLVD, STE G 74006 #041-13-1962 L1971 **AN** *071 †05

GRISHAM, Jeffrey Wm. 3615 SE KENTUCKY ST 74006 #039-01-1984 L1985 **OPH IM** *020 †35

GRISHAM, Richard S C. 3615 SE KENTUCKY ST 74006 #039-01-1958 L1958 **OPH** *020 †35

HARRIS, Raymond Martin. 3400 E FRANK PHLPS #302, PEDIATRICS OF BARTLESVILLE 74006 #004-01-1973 L1974 **PD** *020 †55

HATCHETT, John Webster. 3400 E FRANK PHILLIPS BLVD, STE 700 74006 #039-01-1977 L1982 **GS** *020 †85

HAY, Ronald La Vern. 3500 E FRANK PHILLIPS BLVD 74006 #019-02-1973 L1976 **FM EM** *020 †18

HILL, Tamara Lyn. 501 SE FRANK PHILLIPS BLVD, REG DERM STE 202 74003 #036-08-1989 L1990 **D** *020 †15

HOLLAND, Charles Dale. 205 SE HOWARD AVE 74006 #039-01-1954 L1955 **OTO AI** *020 †45

HOLLAND, Charles Dale, Jr. 205 SE HOWARD AVE 74006 #039-01-1985 L1986 **OTO** *020 †45

HOUTMAN, Daniel Jay. 224 SE DEBELL AVE 74006 #039-01-1968 L1968 **IM ON** *071 †20

JARRELL, Jerry Brad. 3500 E FRANK PHILLIPS BLVD 74006 #039-01-1979 L1980 **IM** *020 †20

JOHANNESEN, Terry Lee. 3975 SILVER LAKE RD 74006 #048-12-1983 L1986 **EM FM** *020 †18

KAPLAN, Robert Earle. ■ 74003 #005-15-1965 L1977 **AN** *071

KATHURIA, Pranay. 3500 STATE ST 74006 #495-45-1988 L1997 **IM** *075 †20

KIRKPATRICK, Stephen A. 3400 E FRANK PHILLIPS BLVD, STE 700 74006 #039-01-1982 L1983 **GE IM** *020 †20

KRAUSE, Maurice Donald. 3500 E FRANK PHILLIPS BLVD, DEPT OF RAD/ONC 74006 #017-20-1968 L1988 **RO** *020 †80

LAJARA-NANSON, Walter A. ■ 74006 #308-13-1991 L2007 **N P** *020 †75

LAWRENCE, Forrest C. ■ 74006 #028-02-1943 L1947 **GP GS** *071

LEATHERMAN, John C. ■ 74006 #422-01-1983 L1991 **FM** *020 †18

LE BLANC, Joseph Vincent. ■ 74006 #028-02-1956 L1974 **IM OM** *071 †20,70

LOCKARD, Vernon M. 3500 E FRANK PHILLIPS BLVD 74006 #007-02-1945 L1952 **R** *072 †80

LONEY, William Robt Ray. 3500 E FRANK PHILLIPS BLVD 74006 #026-04-1955 L1959 **D** *071 †15

LYNN, Bernard Anthony. 3615 SE KENTUCKY ST 74006 #039-01-1956 L1956 **OPH** *071 †35

MARKEL, Larry Gene. 500 E 5TH ST 74003 #019-02-1964 L1973 **U** *071 †95 ‡

MC FARLAND, James R. 3500 E FRANK PHILLIPS BLVD 74006 #039-01-1953 L1953 **OBG** *071 †30

MC QUILLEN, Paul W, Jr. 3400 E FRANK PHILLIPS BLVD, MEDICAL PARK CENTER 74006 #039-01-1977 L1978 **PD** *020 †55

MILLER, David Dow. 3400 E FRANK PHILLIPS BLVD, STE 403 74006 #039-01-1979 L1980 **OBG** *020 †55

MORELAND, Harris Jay. 3400 E FRANK PHILLIPS BLVD, STE 300 74006 #048-02-1966 L1974 **GS CD** *020 †85

MORENAS, Mario Ross. 3500 E FRANK PHILLIPS BLVD, DEPT OF ANESTHESIOLOGY 74006 #055-02-1995 L2000 **AN PME** *020 †05

MORGAN, Louis S. ■ 74006 #039-01-1948 L1948 **GP P** *071

MYERS, Mark Alan. 3400 E FRANK PHILLIPS BLVD, STE 601 74006 #039-01-1986 L1991 **PUD IM** *020 †20

OLIVER, Robert Dan. 226 SE DEBELL AVE 74006 #039-01-1972 L1973 **OBG** *020 †30

PAINTER, Carl Franklin. 4140 SE ADAMS RD, STE 102 74006 #019-02-1995 L2000 **ORS** *020 †40

PARSONS, William Chas. ■ 74003 #039-01-1984 L1985 **OM FM** *020 †18

PEARMAN, Michael H. 204 PEPPER GRASS CT 74006 #055-01-1981 L1993 **AN PME** *020 †05

PEASTER, Michael Leon. 500 E 5TH ST 74003 #056-06-1986 L2003 **U** *020 †95

PRIBIL, Gerald Frank. 3450 E FRANK PHILLIPS BLVD 74006 #039-01-1978 L1979 **FM** *020 †18 ‡

PRINGOS, Andrew A. ■ 74006 #051-01-1940 L1940 **IM** *071

REDDING, Todd Scott. 3450 E FRANK PHILLIPS BLVD 74006 #048-12-1991 L1995 **FM** *020 †18

REED, Gerald G. 1812 HILLCREST DR 74003 #039-79-1994, ▲ L1995 **IM** *020

REHMETULLAH, Mehedi Sulta. 226 SE DEBELL AVE BLDG A, BUILDING A 74006 #704-16-1994 L2007 **IMG** *100 †12 ‡

REINHARD, Sheri Lynn. 3400 E FRANK PHILLIPS BLVD 74006 #016-42-1980 L1983 **FM** *020 †18

ROBERTSON, Mark Alan. 205 SE HOWARD AVE 74006 #039-01-1991 L1997 **OTO** *020 †45

RUMPH, David R, Jr. 3500 E FRANK PHILLIPS BLVD 74006 #039-01-1983 L1986 **OBG OS** *020 †30 ‡

SAMMER, Michael Dallas. 4160 SE ADAMS RD 74006 #019-02-1974 L1980 **IM** *020 †20

SHERROCK, Elizabeth Haley. 4540 SE ADAMS RD 74006 #048-12-1992 L1995 **FM** *020 †18

SMITH, William Dale. 222 SE DEBELL AVE 74006 #039-01-1967 L1967 **ORS** *020 †40

SMITHSON, John R, Jr. 3550 E FRANK PHILLIPS BLVD 74006 #039-01-1976 L1977 **NS** *020 †25

STEWART, Kyle Andrew. ■ 74006 #039-01-2007 L2007 **PD** *012

STEWART, Kyle Leslie. 3400 E FRANK PHILLIPS BLVD, STE 402 74006 #016-11-1977 L1978 **P PMM** *020 †75

STOREY, Jennifer A. 3500 E FRANK PHILLIPS BLVD, DEPT OF ANESTHESIOLOGY 74006 #039-79-1993, ▲ L1999 **AN** *020 †05

SUBUH, Anton Agus. 226 SE DEBELL AVE STE B, JANE PHILLIPS SPECIALTY PH 74006 #506-23-1999 L2007 **ADP** *020 †75

TAYLOR, James Robert. 3500 E FRANK PHILLIPS BLVD 74006 #039-01-1962 L1963 **GP GS** *071 †18

THOMACHAN, Betcy. 3500 STATE ST 74006 #495-44-1995 L2002 **NEP** *020 †20

TINKER, William Patrick. 3400 E FRANK PHILLIPS BLVD, MEDICAL PK CTT #502 74006 #048-12-1978 L1983 **CD IM** *020 †20

VACLAW, Michael Ryan. 4150 SE ADAMS RD, PRIMARY CARE ASSOCIATES 74006 #039-01-1994 L1995 **FM** *020 †18

VAN DOREN, Bryan A. 3470 E FRANK PHILLIPS BLVD, JANE PHILLIPS CANCER CTR 74006 #019-02-1987 L1990 **HO IM** *020 †20

VASUDEVAN, Gopikrishnan. 3400 E FRANK PHILLIPS BLVD, STE 703 74006 #019-02-1987 L1997 **GE IM** *020 †20

VINYARD, Vernie Lee. ■ 74006 #039-01-1954 L1954 **GP GS** *075

WEARE, Mary Elizabeth. 300 S WYANDOTTE AVE 74003 #040-02-1973 L1981 **P** *020 †75 ‡

WENDELL, Claudia Ximena. 4150 SE ADAMS RD 74006 #264-09-2000 L2005 **FM** *020 †18

WEST, Matthew Lee. 3450 E FRANK PHILLIPS BLVD, STE 400 74006 #039-01-1999 L2001 **FM** *100 †18

WILLIAMS, Curtis Scott. 224 SE DEBELL AVE 74006 #039-01-1967 L1967 **AI** *020 †55,03

YOUNG, James Walker. 224 SE DEBELL AVE, GEMINI MEDICAL GROUP INC. 74006 #039-01-1964 L1964 **IM GE** *020 †20

ZEB, Jahan Qamar. 3400 E FRANK PHILLIPS BLVD 74006 #308-11-1997 L2006 **IC** *100 †20

ZEB, Marta H. ■ 74003 #308-11-1997 L2001 **PD** *020 †55

ZEIDERS, James Wilson. 222 SE DEBELL AVE 74006 #039-01-1960 L1960 **ORS** *020

BEAVER — BEAVER

GIROUARD, Gail Patricia. ■ 73932 #030-06-1994 L2006 **FM** *020 †18

OSEGBUE, Chinwe F. PO BOX 640, 623 AVENUE C 73932 #047-07-1978 L1979 **FM** *020

BETHANY — OKLAHOMA

ANDREW, D Ellene. ■ 73008 #039-01-1990 L1993 **OBG** *020 †30

BANKHEAD, Roy Warren. 2349 N THOMPKINS AVE 73008 #039-01-1996 L1997 **U** *020 †95

BAUTISTA-GUTIERREZ, Ana M. 7530 NW 23RD ST 73008 #748-01-1979 L1985 **P CHP** *020 †75

BRANNAN, Darin Kent. 6770 NW 39TH EXPY 73008 #039-01-1992 L1993 **PD OS** *020 †55

BRANT, Douglas Wayne. 6801 NW 39TH EXPY 73008 #039-01-1969 L1969 **FM GS** *020 †18

BROOME, Joseph Clifton. 7530 NW 23RD ST 73008 #039-01-2002 L2003 **FM** *020 †18

BROWN, Steven Dean. 7530 NW 23RD ST 73008 #039-01-1981 L1982 **IM** *020 †20

DEASON, Dean Allen. ■ 73008 #039-01-1994 L1995 **FM** *075

DO, Thang Cao. 7530 NW 23RD ST 73008 #039-01-1997 L2001 **P** *020 †75

ERWIN, Jefferson D, Jr. 6820 NW 23RD ST 73008 #039-01-1981 L1986 **FM OBG** *075

FISHER, David Earl. 7530 NW 23RD ST 73008 #039-01-1975 L1976 **EM FM** *020 †16 ‡

GILBERT, David Nelson. 7900 NW 39TH ST 73008 #039-01-2005 L2007 **IM** *012

GILBERT, James Melvin. 7530 NW 23RD ST 73008 #039-01-1970 L1971 **P** *020 †75

GILBERT, Leon N. 7916 NW 23RD ST, GILBERT MEDICAL CENTER 73008 #048-12-1950 L1953 **FM GP** *071

HAYHURST, Dru Warner. 2701 N ROCKWELL AVE 73008 #039-01-1996 L1997 **FM** *020 †18

HENRY, Millard Lafayette. 6824 NW 23RD ST, SOONER PAIN MANAGEMENT 73008 #039-01-1991 L1992 **AN** *020

HILLE, Marc Robt. 6800 NW 39TH EXPY 73008 #039-01-1980 L1981 **CHN PD** *020 †55

JUDD, Kimberly Lynn. ■ 73008 #039-01-2006 L2006 **PD** *012

MANTELL, Kristin Brooke. ■ 73008 #039-01-2007 L2007 **AN** *012

MASSAD, Paul Eugene. 5825 TULAKES AVE 73008 #039-01-1964 L1964 **R** *071 †80

MC COY, Wade Thomas. 7530 NW 23RD ST 73008 #039-01-1994 L1996 **FM** *020 †18

MORRIS, Jennifer Michelle. 7530 NW 23RD ST B 73008 #039-01-1999 L1999 **P** *020 †75

PARKHURST, Joseph D. 2349 N THOMPKINS AVE 73008 #039-01-1976 L1977 **U** *020 †95 ‡

POWERS, Joseph Dudley. 6801 NW 39TH EXPY 73008 #048-02-1962 L1963 **FM** *071 †18

RIGGS, Debra Ann. 2701 N ROCKWELL AVE 73008 #039-01-1979 L1980 **FM** *020 †18

ROTHWELL, David Thomas. 7530 NW 23RD ST, 7530 NW 23 STREET 73008 #039-01-1997 L2000 **FM** *020 †18

ROTHWELL, Paul David. 7530 NW 23RD ST 73008 #039-01-1974 L1975 **FM** *020 †18

SABINE, Jeffery Lawrence. 2701 N ROCKWELL AVE 73008 #048-02-1983 L1989 **FM** *020 †18

SCHMIDT, Helen Hughes. ■ 73008 #039-01-1948 L1948 **DR** *071

SHEEHAN, Timothy Charles. 6824 NW 23RD ST 73008 #917-04-1979 L1992 **FM IM** *020

SPENCE, William Dean. 7530 NW 23RD ST 73008 #039-01-1978 L1979 **FM** *020 †18

THOMAS, Joel Richard. 6612 NW 42ND ST, SNU BOX 2325 73008 #039-01-2006 L2006 **NS** *012

WEITZEL, Marc Anson. 6801 NW 39TH EXPY, OKLAHOMA CARDIOVASCULAR 73008 #030-05-1992 L1998 **IC CD** *020 †20

WRIGHT, Edward A. 6770 NW 39TH EXPY 73008 #048-13-1988 L2003 **PD** *020 †55,60

WYATT, Willie Glen. 2701 N ROCKWELL AVE 73008 #039-01-1968 L1968 **FM** *020 †18

ZEPEDA, Russell Wayne. ■ 73008 #048-15-1985 L1986 **N** *020

BIXBY — TULSA

BAKER, Gary Edwin. ■ 74008 #028-02-1968 L1972 **PD** *020 †55

BARTLETT, Norman Lukken. ■ 74008 #028-03-1962 L1966 **R CD** *072 †80

BROWN, Eric Jason. ■ 74008 #039-01-2007 L2007 **IM** *012

DEVINE, J C. PO BOX 10 74008 #039-01-1953 L1953 **AN OS** *071 †05

FESLER, Amy Marie. ■ 74008 #039-01-2008 L2008 **FM** *012

FULTON, Maithili Raman. 16206 S LEWIS AVE, LIFE FAMILY MEDICINE, INC. 74008 #039-05-1990 L1991 **FM** *020 †18

KING, Lance Carlton. 11911 S MEMORIAL DR 74008 #039-01-1980 L1983 **FM** *020 †18

MILLS, Andrew Carlton. 11911 S MEMORIAL DR 74008 #039-01-2001 L2004 **FM** *020 †18

MUMEY, John Fraiser. ■ 74008 #004-01-1977 L1980 **FM** *075

REVELIS, Heather Howard. ■ 74008 #039-01-1996 L1998 **P** *020

RUMLEY, Wayna Joan. ■ 74008 #039-01-1982 L2005 **EM** *020

BLACKWELL — KAY

BECKER, Donald Eugene. ■ 74631 #019-02-1954 L1955 **GP FPG** *071

BRIGGS, Paul Andrew. 1005 W DOOLIN AVE 74631 #039-01-1996 L1997 **FM** *020 †18

CHAPARALA, Sukumar. 115 W BRIDGE AVE, OSLER CLINIC 74631 #495-65-1974 L1980 **IM OS** *020

GHORMLEY, Luther Wayne. 115 W BRIDGE AVE 74631 #047-06-1947 L1950 **GS ORS** *071 †85

HAGUE, Samuel Lyle. 1009 W FERGUSON AVE 74631 #039-01-2001 L2002 **FM** *020 †18

MORGAN, Robert Fuller. 706 S 13TH ST # C 74631 #039-01-1953 L1953 **FM** *071

SHUART, Jeffrey Robt. 1009 W FERGUSON AVE, STE B 74631 #039-01-1992 L1993 **FM** *020 †18

BLANCHARD — MCCLAIN

BAIRD, Tiffany Renee. ■ 73010 #039-01-2005 L2006 **PD** *012

STRATTON, Kelly Lynn. ■ 73010 #039-01-2007 **GS** *012
WINCHESTER, Mark David. 1019 N COUNCIL AVE, STE 1 73010 #039-01-1989 L1990 **FM** *020

BOISE CITY – CIMARRON

HART, Dillis Leroy. ■ 73933 #039-01-1964 L1964 **GS TS** *075 †85
WHEELER, Jasper L, Jr. 100 S ELLIS ST 73933 #039-01-1952 L1952 **GP** *020
WHEELER, Paul Edward. ■ 73933 #039-01-1990 L1991 **FM** *075

BRISTOW – CREEK

CHAPMAN, Frank Deuel. 117 W 5TH AVE 74010 #039-01-1961 L1961 **FM** *071 †18
JONES, William Edgar, Jr. 74010 #004-01-1943 L1947 **GP** *071 †20
LOWERY, Bradley Duane. 700 W 7TH AVE, STE 6 74010 #039-01-1988 L1989 **FM** *020 †18

BROKEN ARROW – TULSA

AGBEIBOR, Victor Harry. ■ 74012 #913-65-1995 L1999 **GS** *012 †18
AL HAMWY, Mazen. ■ 74011 #875-01-1995 L2004 **CD** *100 †20
ALPRIN, Clifford N. ■ 74012 #048-13-2006 L2007 **FP** *012
ANDERSON-BROWN, Margaret. 2950 S ELM PL STE 120 74012 #048-16-1985 L1999 **PD** *020 †55
ANKLESARIA, Gaurangi M. 817 S ELM PL STE 104 74012 #495-22-1974 L1982 **FM GP** *020
ASHRAF, Muhammad. ■ 74012 #704-04-1971 *100
AUGUST, Sylvia Elena. 2950 S ELM PL 74012 #737-09-1988 L1996 **PD** *020 †55
BEEBE, James Harold. ■ 74011 #306-01-2005 L2007 **FP** *012
BHARANI, Suresh Aildas. 3300 S ASPEN AVE STE B 74012 #495-23-1976 L1981 **PD** *020 †55
BILBRUCK, Laura Beth. 1129 S ASPEN AVE 74012 #039-01-1996 L1997 **IM** *020
BLANCHARD, Werlein A. 2003 S ELM PL # A, SPRINGER CLINIC, INC. 74012 #039-01-1991 L1992 **IM** *075
BONNELL, Margaret E. ■ 74012 #039-01-1969 L1972 **GP** *074
BOYLS, Kathleen A. 2617 S ELM PL 74012 #039-05-1989 L1991 **PD** *020 †55
CAMERON, Jennifer Rene. 2617 S ELM PL 74012 #039-01-2003 L2005 **FM** *020 †18
CHOW, Christopher Yanchi. 1551 N 9TH ST 74012 #036-08-1997 L1998 **FM** *020 †18
CLEMENTS, Marchel Word. 2950 S ELM PL, STE 460 74012 #018-75-1990, ▲ L1991 **ORS** *020
DEAN, Terry Lynn. ■ 74012 #039-05-1984 L1991 **GP** *020
DES PREZ, Karen Carlson. 2617 S ELM PL 74012 #047-05-1982 L1998 **PD** *020 †55
EYE, Rita Ellen. ■ 74011 #028-03-2006 L2007 **OBG** *012
FRIEZE, Harold Wm. ■ 74012 #039-01-1954 L1954 **AN GP** *071
GARRETSON, Forrest Dorsey. 2403 S GARDENIA AVE 74012 #041-12-1957 L1973 **ON HEM** *071 †20
GERNER, Alvin L. ■ 74012 #018-75-1955, ▲ L1960 **GP** *071
GLICK, Dick L. 2950 S ELM PL STE 325 74012 #028-03-1972 L1973 **OBG** *020 ‡
GREER, Stephen Lester. 817 S ELM PL 74012 #039-01-1986 L1990 **P N** *020 †75
GUY, Ronald M. 2950 S ELM PL 74012 #048-16-1986 L1996 **OTO HNS** *020 †45
HAMRA, Mark Steven. 817 S ELM PL STE 107 74012 #039-05-1989 L1991 **AI** *020
HARRINGTON, Anne Maureen. 2950 S ELM PL 74012 #039-01-1985 L1986 **PD** *020 †55
HAWKINS-ALPRIN, Lindsey M. ■ 74012 #048-13-2006 L2007 **PD** *012
HESSE, Jeffrey Michael. 4512 W MEMPHIS ST 74012 #039-01-2001 L2002 **DR** *020 †80
HILL, Riley Mark. 2950 S ELM PL 74012 #039-01-1982 L1985 **IM** *020
HOLTE, Douglas Wm. 817 S ELM PL STE A 74012 #026-04-1984 L1985 **FM** *020 †18 ‡
HUTTON, Kimberly Kay. 1551 N 9TH ST 74012 #019-02-1996 L1999 **FM** *020 †18
KEENAN, James Donald. 3000 S ELM PL 74012 #019-02-1963 L1972 **ORS** *071 †40
KHALIDI, Hafiz Imran Ahme. ■ 74012 #704-02-1995 L2005 **IM** *020
KIM, Tchang Man. 4032 S UMBRELLA AVE 74012 #583-01-1963 L1974 **DR NM** *071 †80
LANDIS, Lesley Vaughn. ■ 74012 #039-01-2007 L2007 **GS** *012
LE, Lam Thuy. ■ 74012 #039-01-2004 L2005 **IM** *020
LEE, Sung Ae. ■ 74011 #583-01-1963 L1974 **RO** *071 †80
MAST, William Ray. ■ 74011 #041-01-1966 L1985 **OTO** *071 †45 ‡
MC BRYDE, Gary Arland. 2950 S ELM PL 74012 #004-01-1976 L1977 **IM** *020
MCGHEE, Jonathan Edward. ■ 74012 #047-07-2007 L2007 **FP** *012
MC ILMOYLE, Gaellan. ■ 74012 #065-01-1968 L1975 **P DR** *020 †28,80,75
MC RAE, Duncan L. 611 S ELM PL 74012 #036-01-1972 L1991 **IM ON** *020 †20
MILLER, David William. 2035 W HOUSTON ST 74012 #033-06-1993 L1998 **EM** *020 †16
MITTAPALLI, Mohan Rao. 2001 S ELM PL, STE C 74012 #495-11-1961 L1976 **TS CD** *071 †85,90
MITTAPALLI, Parvati. 2001 S ELM PL 74012 #495-11-1965 L1976 **OBG** *020
MORGAN, M Melissa. 1621 S EUCALYPTUS AVE, STE 202 74012 #021-06-1990 L1997 **D** *020 †15
MOSBY, Angela Yvonne. 2617 S ELM PL 74012 #004-01-1998 L2001 **FM** *020 †18
NEWHOUSE, Cashel P. ■ 74012 #048-12-2005 L2007 **PD** *012
NGUYEN, Lieuko. ■ 74012 #422-01-2006 L2006 **PD** *012
O'BRIEN, Susan Margaret. 2950 S ELM PL 74012 #039-01-1978 L1979 **PD** *020 †55
O'BRIEN, William Browning. 1129 S ASPEN AVE 74012 #039-01-1996 L1997 **IM** *020
PARKER, Stephen Mark. 2950 S ELM PL 74012 #004-01-1976 L1977 **IM** *020 †20
PASHA, Azhar Shakeel. ■ 74012 #665-01-2005 L2006 **FP** *012
PETERSON, Paul David. 2950 S ELM PL STE 460 74012 #026-04-1980 L1991 **ORS** *020 †40
PETTINGELL, Timothy G. 1621 S EUCALYPTUS AVE, STE 204 74012 #021-06-1994 L1998 **PM** *020 †60
PFANSTIEL, Carl E, Jr. 1220 N ELM PL 74012 #020-02-1967 L1980 **PD** *020 †55
PIERCE, Aaron Matthew. ■ 74011 #039-79-2004, ▲ L2005 **P** *012
POPLIN, Lenard Austin. 2950 S ELM PL, STE 260 74012 #039-01-1962 L1963 **IM** *020 †20
POWER, Jeannette Carolina. ■ 74012 #270-02-2003 L2007 **IM** *012
RAO, Sreelatha Kasuganti. ■ 74012 #496-34-2002 L2005 **MPD** *020 †20
RAU, Roberta Anne. 2950 S ELM PL 74012 #039-01-1998 L1999 **FM** *020 †18
SHAW, Denise Degner. 2950 S ELM PL 74012 #039-01-1990 L1991 **OBG** *020 †30 ‡
SILAS, Geeta R. 2617 S ELM PL 74012 #495-27-1980 L1985 **PD** *020 †55
SMITH, Robert Gene. PO BOX 16, STE 2602 74013 #028-02-1959 L1964 **LM OM** *072
STANTON, Marilyn Karyl. ■ 74012 #048-12-1982 L1986 **N** *074 †75
STRATTON, Harold L, Jr. 308 E HUNTSVILLE ST 74011 #048-12-1982 L1992 **AN** *020 †20,05
STRATTON, Harold Lee. ■ 74011 #028-02-1955 L1963 **AN** *071 †05
VASQUEZ, Ranilo Legaspi. 2950 S ELM PL, STE 260 74012 #748-14-1986 L2003 **IM** *020 †20

VON MULLER, Sarah B. 1615 S EUCALYPTUS AVE, STE 103 74012 #039-01-1991 L1993 **GE** *020 †20
WARD, James Perry. 2950 S ELM PL 74012 #039-01-1982 L1983 **PD** *020 †55
WATTS, Garrett Edward. 2950 S ELM PL, STE 415 74012 #039-01-1982 L1990 **HS ORS** *020 †40
WHEELER, Stanley Dale. ■ 74012 #005-12-1947 L1947 **GP** *071
WHITE, David Alan. ■ 74012 #011-02-1988 L1996 **IM** *020 †20
WHITLEY, Mark E. 2608 W KENOSHA ST, STE 240 74012 #048-02-1985 L1994 **DR** *020 †80 ‡
WILKINS, William Edward. 3000 S ELM PL 74012 #019-02-1995 L2003 **MPD** *020 †20,55

BROKEN ARROW – WAGONER

BLAKE, Brian Eugene. ■ 74014 #039-01-1998 L1999 **IM** *020
HOLLEMAN, James F, III. ■ 74014 #048-12-1994 L2007 **IM** *020 †20
MARGIOTTA, Mark Richard. ■ 74014 #050-02-1957 L1962 **IM** *071 †20
MCELROY, Margaret Harring. ■ 74014 #048-78-2006, ▲ **OBG** *100
THOMPSON, Shannon P. ■ 74014 #048-02-1994 L1995 **FM** *075

BROKEN BOW – MCCURTAIN

OGLESBEE, John Robt. 410 S PARK DR, GOOD HONEST MEDICINE 74728 #039-01-1968 L1969 **FM EM** *020 †18 ‡
PROANO, Luis A. 627 S PARK DR 74728 #319-01-1980 L1993 **IM** *020 †20
TODD, James Franklin. ■ 74728 #039-01-1965 L1965 **GS GP** *072

BUFFALO – HARPER

SUTHERS, Neal Kent. HWY 64 N, HUDSON-SUTHERS CLINIC 73834 #039-01-1970 L1971 **FM** *020

CACHE – COMANCHE

FINDLAY, Kathleen Elaine. ■ 73527 #019-02-2004 L2005 **FM** *020 †18
KLASSEN, Walter Ray. ■ 73527 #661-03-2002 L2006 **FP** *012

CADDO – ATOKA

HOYT, Jerry Lee. ■ 74729 #004-01-1957 **CD IM** *072

CARNEGIE – CADDO

HILL, Ronald Loewen. 102 W ASH ST, RONALD L HILL MD INC 73015 #005-06-1977 L1978 **GP OBS** *020

CATOOSA – ROGERS

ALDRICH, Ashley Noel. 5232 N STATE HIGHWAY 167, UNIVERSITY OF OKLAHOMA 74015 #039-01-2004 L2005 **FM** *020
GOURD, Johnson Clint, Jr. 5232 N HIGHWAY 167 74015 #046-01-2002 L2003 **FM** *020
TREECE, Thomas Randall. PO BOX 50 74015 #048-12-1961 L1964 **GE IM** *075 †20

CHANDLER – LINCOLN

MILEHAM, Jack C. 10TH & STEELE, MILEHAM MEDICAL CLINIC 74834 #039-01-1946 L1947 **FM** *020
REITER, Steven Jos. 114 N HIGHWAY 18 74834 #018-03-1981 L1989 **CD IM** *020 †20 ‡
SEBASTIAN, Veronique. 112 MCKINLEY AVE 74834 #495-52-1991 L1998 **P** *020 †75
SEELIG, Darrell Arnold. ■ 74834 #039-01-1953 L1953 **GP** *071

CHECOTAH – MCINTOSH

SNEED, Norma Lee. 615 S BROADWAY ST 74426 #039-01-1960 L1960 **FM A** *071 †18

CHEYENNE – ROGER MILLS

BAKER, Mary R. 100 E. BUSTER 73628 #055-01-1963 L1971 **AN** *071 †05
BUSTER, Frank K. 501 S L L MALES AVE 73628 #048-12-1949 L1950 **GP** *071
YARBROUGH, Ardry Lance. ■ 73628 #039-01-1997 L2002 **FM** *100

CHICKASHA – GRADY

BELLER, Jack Juan. 2100 W IOWA AVE 73018 #039-01-1970 L1971 **ORS LM** *020 †40 ‡
BLEDSOE, Joe Thos. ■ 73018 #039-01-1959 L1959 **IM CD** *071 †20
BOWEN, Leonard Michael. 2222 W IOWA AVE 73018 #045-01-1975 L1978 **ON HEM** *020 †20
COE, Thomas Hood. 2220 W IOWA AVE 73018 #039-01-1971 L1972 **EM** *020 †16
COPPEDGE, Mitchell Dean. 2220 W IOWA AVE 73018 #048-15-1994 L1995 **FM** *020 †18
CROWELL, Bill Bruce. 2220 W IOWA AVE 73018 #039-01-1964 L1964 **PTH ADM** *020 †50 ‡
DAVOLI, Michael James. 2100 W IOWA AVE 73018 #033-05-1977 L2003 **ORS** *071 †40
DELZER, Donald John. 2220 W IOWA AVE 73018 #034-01-1972 L1974 **DR NM** *071 †80,28
DEVER, Nancy Winfield. 2220 W IOWA AVE 73018 #025-01-1973 L1977 **OBG** *020 ‡
DOBBS, Michael Edward. 2100 W IOWA AVE 73018 #048-02-1975 L2006 **OBG GP** *020 †30
ESCOBAR, Marian Pilar. 2220 W IOWA AVE 73018 #039-01-1976 L1977 **PD** *020 †55
GANICK, Ralph G. 2222 W IOWA AVE 73018 #024-05-1967 L1978 **ON HEM** *040 †20
GEARHART, John Rathmann. 2222 W IOWA AVE 73018 #028-03-1974 L1982 **OPH** *020 †35 ‡
GONZALEZ, Xavier Lopez. 2100 W IOWA AVE, ATTN: TERESA HILL 73018 #649-14-1974 L1977 **PD** *020 †55

■ = Address Information Privacy Protected

HAMILTON, Kaleb Michael. 2100 W IOWA AVE, GRADY MEMORIAL HOSPITAL 73018 #039-01-2000 L2003 **FM** *020 †18

HARR, Virginia Louise. 2222 W IOWA AVE 73018 #028-03-1978 L1984 **GS VS** *020 †85 ‡

HARRISON, William Smith. ■ 73018 #039-01-1953 L1953 **IM A** *071 ‡

HASLAM, Donald Frank. 2220 W IOWA AVE 73018 #039-01-1980 L1981 **EM** *020 †55 ‡

HESS, Don Richard. 2100 W IOWA AVE, DBA: FIVE OAKS MEDICAL GRO 73018 #039-01-1972 L1973 **FM** *020 †18 ‡

HOOPER, John Robert. 2220 W IOWA AVE 73018 #010-02-1992 L1993 **AN** *020 †05

JENKINS, Randall Lee. 2100 W IOWA AVE, DBA: FIVE OAKS MEDICAL GRO 73018 #039-01-1977 L1980 **IM** *020 †20 ‡

JOHNSON, Linda Mae. 2222 W IOWA AVE 73018 #039-01-1968 L1969 **GS** *020 †85 ‡

KNOPP, Kathleen Margaret. 2100 W IOWA AVE 73018 #048-13-1989 L2006 **OBG** *020 †30

KUMAR, Bommasamudram Ashw. 2100 W IOWA AVE 73018 #495-21-1993 L2006 *100

LANGMACHER, Miles C. 2100 W IOWA AVE 73018 #010-02-1998 L1999 **IM** *020

LAU, Gideon To Hong. 2220 W IOWA AVE, GRADY MEMORIAL HOSPITAL 73018 #039-01-1975 L1976 **AN** *020 ‡

LESHER, Robert Chas. 2222 W IOWA AVE, SOUTHERN PLAINS MED CTR, P 73018 #041-09-1959 L1995 **ORS** *071 †40

LOH, Paul Baitsin. PO BOX 1069, SOUTHERN PLAINS MEDICAL CE 73023 #748-01-1955 L1972 **TS CD** *071

MALUF, Karen Cody. 2222 W IOWA AVE, SOUTHERN PLAINS MEDICAL CT 73018 #039-01-1997 L1998 **IM** *020 †20 ‡

MC DONIEL, James Wm. ■ 73018 #039-01-1956 L1956 **FM** *071 †18

MILTON, James Earl. PO BOX 1343, 1001N 18 73023 #039-01-1965 L1965 **DR** *020 †80

MOORE, Trudy Jane. 2222 W IOWA AVE, RADIOLOGY DEPT 73018 #004-01-1980 L1987 **R** *020 †80

ORR, Ervin Ronald. 2222 W IOWA AVE, SOUTHERN PLAINS MEDICAL CE 73018 #039-01-1962 L1962 **PD** *020 †55 ‡

PRESLEY, John Edward. 2100 W IOWA AVE 73018 #048-12-1974 L2006 **GS** *020 †85

RAMIREZ, Anthony Hector. 2220 W IOWA AVE, GRADY MEMORIAL HOSPITAL 73018 #047-06-2002 L2005 **EM** *020

SINGELMANN, Erica Edwards. ■ 73018 #028-46-2003 L2007 **OBG** *020

STEHR, Danny Lee. 2222 W IOWA AVE, SOUTHERN PLNS MEDICAL CLIN 73018 #039-01-1962 L1962 **IM** *071

STORMS, Bruce Leon. 2220 W IOWA AVE, EMERGENCY MEDICINE 73018 #039-01-1974 L1975 **EM ESM** *020 †16

SU, Chun Kuang. 2222 W IOWA AVE 73018 #385-02-1958 L1972 **IM GE** *071 †20

THOMPSON, Ian St George. 2222 W IOWA AVE, SOUTHERN PLAINS MEDICAL CE 73018 #039-01-1993 L2000 **FM** *020

TURNER, Ryan Ray. 2220 W IOWA AVE, FIVE OAKS MEDICAL GROUP 73018 #039-01-2001 L2003 **FM** *020 †18

VAIDYA, Kumudini M. 2222 W IOWA AVE 73018 #495-28-1964 L1979 **PM** *072 †60

VAIDYA, Makarand M. 2222 W IOWA AVE 73018 #495-28-1960 L1979 **AN** *072

VALUCK, Jonathan Eric. 2201 W IOWA AVE, OKLAHOMA CARDIOVASCULAR 73018 #028-03-1988 L1991 **CD IC** *020 †20

WINSLOW, James E, Jr. 2222 W IOWA AVE 73018 #047-06-1959 L1967 **ORS** *071 †40 ‡

CHOCTAW – OKLAHOMA

CARPENTER, Cary Lee. 15803 NE 23RD ST, CHOCTAW FAMILY MEDICINE 73020 #039-01-1991 L1992 **FM** *020 †18

FAILS, Robert Brian. ■ 73020 #039-01-2004 L2005 **DR** *012

FULLER, Lionel H. ■ 73020 #048-02-1959 L1960 **ORS** *071 †40

LINQUIST, Lisa Ellen. 15679 NE 23RD ST, SAINTS FAMILY HEALTH CENTE 73020 #030-05-2000 L2002 **FM** *020 †18

MOAZAM, Mustafa Mohammed. ■ 73020 #496-27-2000 L2006 **PHO** *012

PHILPOTT, William H. ■ 73020 #005-12-1951 L1975 **P A** *071

PRISE, James Gordon. 15679 NE 23RD ST 73020 #062-01-1979 L1995 **FM** *020

ROBINSON, Michael Lynn. ■ 73020 #039-01-2008 *012

STAFFORD, Bruce Alan. 15809 NE 23RD ST 73020 #039-79-2000, ▲ L2001 **FM** *020 †18

TERRY, Michael Hayden. 15809 NE 23RD ST 73020 #039-01-1977 L1978 **EM GP** *020

CLAREMORE – ROGERS

ABBASI, Kamran Ahmed. 1202 N MUSKOGEE PL 74017 #654-01-2000 L2003 **IM** *020 †20 ‡

ANDINO, Raul Rene. ■ 74017 #308-03-1985 L2005 *100

ANGLES, Alberto. 101 S MOORE AVE 74017 #737-01-1957 L1974 **GS GE** *020 †85

ARTHUR, Basil Cuthbert. CLAREMORE INDIAN HOSPITAL 74017 #005-12-1952 L1954 **TS CD** *020 †85,90

BAEHLER, Elizabeth Ann. 101 S MOORE AVE, CLAREMURE INDIAN HOSPITAL 74017 #010-01-1980 L1981 **OBG** *020 †30

BARNES, William Whitley, III. 525 E BLUE STARR DR 74017 #028-02-1973 L1975 **PD EM** *020 †55

BARRETTE, Gregoire. 1222 N FLORENCE AVE, STE D 74017 #065-09-1969 L1994 **OBG** *020 †30

BELINSKI, R Jeffrey. 101 S MOORE AVE, CLAREMORE INDIAN HOSPITAL 74017 #039-01-1990 L1991 **AN** *020

BETHEA, Ralph Chambers. ■ 74017 #023-07-1944 L1978 **OBG** *071 †30

BLUNT, Linda Kay. 213 E PATTI PAGE BLVD 74017 #039-01-1998 L2000 **FM** *020 †18 ‡

BOBEK, Donald Wayne. 101 S MOORE AVE 74017 #039-01-1955 L1955 **GS EM** *020 †85

BOWER, Timothy Roy. 202 W BLUE STARR DR 74017 #034-01-1984 L1992 **VS CCS** *020 †85

BOYLES, Gerald Dexter. 15380 S 4210 RD, NORTHEAST OKLAHOMA ANESTHE 74017 #004-01-1975 L1995 **AN** *020 †05

BROTHERTON, Lawrence Clay, III. 1501 N FLORENCE AVE, STE 250 74017 #019-02-1999 L2005 **GS** *020 †85

CALCOTE, Julia Irvine. 101 S MOORE AVE, CLAREMORE INDIAN HOSP 74017 #048-13-1997 L1998 **FM** *020 †18 ‡

CARON, Charles Edward. 527 E BLUE STARR DR, INTERNAL MEDICINE ASSOCIAT 74017 #561-01-1985 L1994 **CD** *020 †20

CHA, Bong Hwoe. 3001 W BLUE STARR DR, OKLAHOMA VETERANS CENTER 74017 #583-02-1957 L1991 **PM IMG** *071

DEAN, Robert Wm. 1222 N FLORENCE AVE, STE C 74017 #039-01-1955 L1955 **OBG** *020 †30

DURICK, William Jos. 1415 N MUSKOGEE PL 74017 #019-02-1964 L1966 **IM** *072

EBERLEY, Breece Michael. 1501 N FLORENCE PL, STE 201 74017 #039-01-1998 L1999 **IM** *020 †20

EGLESTON, Steven Andrew. 1408 N FLORENCE AVE 74017 #039-01-2000 L2001 **FM** *020 †18

ENGLES, Eric David. 1202 N MUSKOGEE PL 74017 #039-01-1983 L1984 **AN PD** *020 †05

FAUBION, Michelle Collene. 1501 N FLORENCE AVE, STE 300 74017 #019-02-2000 L2005 **OBG** *020 †30

FERNANDEZ, Fernando A. 101 S MOORE AVE 74017 #042-03-1985 L1995 **PD** *020

FORTNER, Gary Dee. 1408 N FLORENCE AVE 74017 #005-12-1976 L1980 **FM** *020 †18

FRANKLIN, Helen Lucinda. 3100 MEDICAL PKWY, STE 100 74017 #039-01-1992 L1993 **FM** *020 †18

FULLER, Cynthia Jean. 525 E BLUE STARR DR 74017 #039-01-1990 L1991 **PD** *020 †55

GATENO, Joseph. 2503 WESTWOOD DR 74017 #649-01-1950 L1976 **OBG** *020

GONZALEZ-MALAVE, Jose M. ■ 74017 #308-03-1978 L1980 **IM** *020

HARDAGE, Steven Rex. 504 E BLUE STARR DR 74017 #039-01-2000 L2001 **FSM** *020 †18

HECK, David Margrave. 1501 N FLORENCE AVE # 201, CLAREMORE INTERNAL MEDICIN 74017 #019-02-1973 L1976 **IM** *020 †20

HORTON, Samuel Le Barre. 1904 W 4TH ST S, CLAREMIRE INDIAN HOSPITAL 74017 #020-02-1979 L2001 **TRS GS** *020 †85

HRDLICKA, Larry Joe. 1220 N FLORENCE AVE 74017 #039-01-1962 L1962 **GS** *071 †85

HRDLICKA, Larry Kyle. 1220 N FLORENCE AVE 74017 #039-79-1994, ▲ L1999 **VS GS** *020

HUGHES, Calvin Thos, Jr. 74019 #024-01-1953 L1958 **OPH** *071 †35

JOHNSTON, Matthew Dee. 1501 N FLORENCE AVE STE 1 74017 #048-04-1996 L1997 **FM** *020 †18

KORGAN, Dwight Julius. 1408 N FLORENCE AVE 74017 #005-12-1975 L1977 **FM** *020 †18

LAU, Abel Lee. 3100 MEDICAL PKWY, STE 100 74017 #012-01-1988 L1989 **FM** *020 †18

LEGARRETA-LOPEZ, Juan F. 101 S MOORE AVE, CLAREMORE INDIAN HOSPITAL 74017 #308-03-1980 L1984 **FM PME** *020

LOPEZ-LEBRON, Roberto. 101 S MOORE AVE 74017 #649-14-1986 L1990 **AN** *020

MARTINEZ-FIGUEROA, Jose H. ■ 74017 #308-02-1989 L1991 **IM** *020

MC ILROY, Jeffrey Kent. 2990 N SIOUX AVE 74017 #039-01-1987 L1988 **P** *020 †75

MC KENZIE, Jerry Dean. ■ 74019 #004-01-1967 L1968 **EM** *071

MEDINA, Stephen Carlos. 1501 N FLORENCE AVE # 201 74017 #048-02-1986 L1997 **IM GE** *020 †20

MORGAN, William Burton. 125 W BLUE STARR DR 74017 #039-01-1978 L1979 **AN** *020 †18,05

MOURNING, Dennis Earl. 1501 N FLORENCE PL, STE 201 74017 #019-02-1973 L1976 **IM** *071 †20

NICHOLSON, Barney M. ■ 74017 #045-04-1990 L1992 **GS** *020 †85

NODINE, Seth David. 1501 N FLORENCE AVE, STE 101 74017 #039-01-2003 L2004 **FM** *020 †18

PARKER, Robert Chas. 509 E BLUE STARR DR 74017 #039-01-1992 L1996 **OPH** *020 †35

PROCK, Roger D. 101 S MOORE AVE 74017 #023-12-1984 L1985 **IM** *020 †20

RAMOS-FAST, Jeannette. 101 S MOORE AVE 74017 #308-01-1983 L1986 **GP** *020

REINECKE, David Moore. 1715 N LYNN RIGGS BLVD, # 1 74017 #021-01-1981 L1986 **OPH** *020 †35

ROSA, Nellie. 101 S MOORE AVE, CLAREMORE INDIAN HOSP 74017 #042-03-1985 L1993 **PD** *020

SCHWARZ, David Gerard. 1202 N MUSKOGEE PL 74017 #040-02-1970 L1978 **DR** *020 †80 ‡

SMITH, William Ogg. 1501 N FLORENCE AVE # 201, CLAREMORE INTERNAL MEDICIN 74017 #039-01-1974 L1979 **IM DIA** *020 †20

SUMMERS, John Howard. 1501 N FLORENCE AVE STE 2 74017 #039-01-1995 L1996 **CD** *020 †20

SWEETEN, Robert L, Jr. 127 W BLUE STARR DR 74017 #039-01-1979 L1980 **FM IM** *020 †20

TECHATHUVANAN, Suphong. 101 S MOORE AVE 74017 #891-02-1969 L1978 **GS EM** *020

THOMPSON, Gerald Eugene. 101 S MOORE AVE 74017 #024-05-1971 L1973 **OBG** *020

TINGLEAF, Clark Jiro. 201 W BLUE STARR DR 74017 #048-13-1995 L2003 **U** *020 †95

TROTTMAN, Jennifer Erica. 1220 N FLORENCE AVE 74017 #035-15-1990 L1999 **HEM** *020 †20

VANNARTH, Sumathy. 101 S MOORE AVE 74017 #495-04-1962 L1977 **GYN OBS** *020 †30 ‡

WORKMAN, Russell. 3100 MEDICAL PKWY, STE 100 74017 #048-13-1990 L1993 **FM EM** *020 †18

YOUNG, Larry Ivan. 1220 N FLORENCE AVE 74017 #039-01-1963 L1963 **GS** *071 †85

CLEVELAND – PAWNEE

COLE, Christopher L. 1390 W CHEROKEE ST 74020 #039-79-1993, ▲ L1994 **FM** *020

LIOU, Wei-Ming. 1400 W PAWNEE ST 74020 #244-06-1971 L1974 **GP GS** *071

RICHARDSON, Wm Waddle, Jr. ■ 74020 #035-01-1970 **IM OS** *100

TODD, Thomas Randall. 201 W DELAWARE ST 74020 #039-01-1997 L1998 **IM** *020

CLINTON – CUSTER

CASHERO, Thomas Eugene. 90 N 30TH ST STE 3, BOX 1720 73601 #025-01-1972 L1989 **GS** *020 †85

CHEN, Ching-Yi. 2513 MANOR WAY 73601 #244-06-1971 L1979 **OBG** *020

COKER, Joe Edward. 100 N 30TH ST 73601 #039-01-1967 L1979 **U** *020 †95

CRAIG, Teresa Gayle. 100 N 30TH ST 73601 #039-01-1985 L1986 **RO IM** *020 †80

EGAN, Kenneth Melville. ■ 73601 #041-14-1981 L1983 **PD** *020 †55

FEY, Vic. 90 N 30TH ST STE 1 73601 #039-01-1984 L1985 **FM** *020 †18

GARCIA, Dolly Ramiu. 10321 N 2274 RD, EXIT 69 73601 #308-02-1988 L2000 **GP** *020

HAMLIN, John. 100 N 30TH ST, INTEGRIS CLINTON REGIONAL 73601 #001-02-1991 L1992 **R NM** *020 †28,80

HAYS, Gary Gordon. 540 S 30TH ST 73601 #039-01-1960 L1961 **GS FM** *071 †85

KASSABIAN, Keith John. 100 N 30TH ST 73601 #051-04-1981 L1988 **CD IM** *020 †20

KNAPP, Stacey. 90 N 30TH ST, STE 5 73601 #039-79-2001, ▲ L2002 **FM** *020 †20

KOLKER, Christopher Trent. ■ 73601 #039-01-1996 L1997 **FM OS** *020 †18 ‡

KOURT, Kevin Brent. 533 S 30TH ST STE B 73601 #039-01-1998 L1999 **IM** *020 †20

LOPEZ, Pedro Juan. 10321 N 2274 RD, 2501 NE HIGHWAY 66 73601 #042-02-1991 L1994 **IM GP** *020 ‡

MANN, Mark Blaine. 90 N 30TH ST STE 4, FAMILY PRACTICE CLINIC 73601 #039-01-1997 L1998 **FM** *020 †18

MC KENZIE, Ernest John. 100 N 30TH ST, RADIOLOGY DEPARTMENT 73601 #063-01-1974 L1995 **DR** *020 †80

MEJIAS OCASIO, James. 10321 N 2274 RD, CLINTON INDIAN HOSPITAL 73601 #042-04-1992 L1997 **PD** *020

PRESTON, R M. 100 N 30TH ST 73601 #039-01-1955 L1956 **ORS** *020 †40

RODRIGUEZ, Ramon O. 10321 N 2274 RD, USPHS CLINTON INDIAN HOSPI 73601 #308-04-1980 L2002 **GP EM** *020
SIMON, Ralph. ■ 73601 #039-01-1944 L1945 **GP GS** *071
SWAMI, Sharad S. 533 S 30TH ST STE A 73601 #495-76-1980 L1993 **IM** *020 †20
TISDAL, James H. ■ 73601 #039-01-1945 L1946 **OS** *071
TRONCOSO, Carlos A. 90 N 30TH ST, STE 6 73601 #132-03-1957 L1973 **CRS GS** *020 †10,85
VILLANUEVA, Arsenio O, Jr. PO BOX 1209, OKLAHOMA VETERANS CTR 73601 #748-11-1967 L1979 *071
WENDT, Randall James. 100 N 30TH ST 73601 #048-13-1976 L2006 **OBG** *020 †30 ‡

COALGATE — COAL

AFAQ, Azhar. 108 W OHIO AVE, HELTON RURAL HEALTH CLINIC 74538 #704-25-1994 L2000 **IM** *020 †20
KING, John David. PO BOX 429 74538 #048-04-1947 L1947 **GP OBG** *071

COLLINSVILLE — TULSA

ANDREWS, Wesley Alan. 1205 W MAIN ST 74021 #039-01-1994 L1995 **FM** *020 †18
COLPITT, Debra Sue. 1025 W MAIN ST 74021 #039-01-1982 L1983 **FM** *020 †18
MALOY, Cynthia Ann. 112 S 11TH ST 74021 #039-01-1989 L1990 **FM** *020 †18
O'HAYRE, Patrick B, II. ■ 74021 #005-77-2007, ▲ *012

COMANCHE — STEPHENS

WOOD, James Otha, Jr. 303 N HIGHWAY 81, CHISHOLM TRL MED CLNC 73529 #047-06-1963 L1964 **FM OBG** *020 †18

COOKSON — CHEROKEE

FINNEY, Jackie Larence. ■ 74427 #039-01-1968 L1970 **PS GS** *020 †85

CORDELL — WASHITA

SUDERMAN, Emery Lowell. ■ 73632 #028-78-1961, ▲ L1962 **GP** *071
TSAI, Chiu Shang. 1209 N GLENN ENGLISH ST 73632 #244-06-1970 L1977 **GP** *020

COWETA — WAGONER

AXELSSON, Boerje Axel Uno. 30011 E STATE HIGHWAY 51 74429 #858-03-1970 L1981 **FM** *020 †18
HLADKY, Frank, Jr. 21589 E 151ST ST S 74429 #039-01-1946 L1946 **P** *040 †75

CUSHING — PAYNE

BABB, Michael James. 1030 E CHERRY ST 74023 #039-01-1982 L1983 **FM** *020 †18 ‡
BABB, Tamie S. 1025 E 2ND ST 74023 #039-01-1995 L1996 **OBG** *020 †30 ‡
CARDENAS, Alfonso Adrian. ■ 74023 #270-01-1975 L1984 **OBG** *071
DES PREZ, Roger Dalhouse. 1027 E CHERRY ST 74023 #047-05-1982 L1998 **CD PD** *020 †55,20
GONZAGA, Mars Baldoza. 1027 E CHERRY ST 74023 #748-07-1961 L1976 **GS GP** *020 ‡
HIBBARD, Andrea Brooke. 1119 E 8TH ST 74023 #039-01-2005 L2007 **OBG** *012
JEWELL, Ross Lyman. ■ 74023 #019-02-1956 **GP GS** *071
KIMMEL, Michelle Dawn. 1023 E CHERRY ST STE A 74023 #039-01-1990 L1991 **FM** *020 †18
MAREBURGER, Steven Ross. 1027 E CHERRY ST 74023 #039-01-1988 L1994 **FM** *071 †18
MORRIS, King Erwin, Jr. 1025 E 2ND ST 74023 #005-18-1991 L1997 **U** *020
OGUNDIPE, Akinola O. 1027 E CHERRY ST 74023 #690-01-1981 L1992 **IM HO** *020 †20
POINTER, Glena Dru. 1027 E CHERRY ST 74023 #048-15-2001 L2003 **GS** *020 †85
PYLES, Tracy Lynn. 1030 E CHERRY ST 74023 #039-01-1985 L1986 **FM** *020 †18
REDDY, Anil Kumar. 1027 E CHERRY ST 74023 #495-65-1988 L2000 **PM** *020 †60
REINECKE, David Linn. 1030 E CHERRY ST 74023 #039-01-1977 L1978 **IM GP** *020 †20
SONNENSCHEIN, Robert Carl. 1027 E CHERRY ST 74023 #016-01-1978 L1981 **CD IM** *020 †20
TUPPER, Joel Scott. 1025 E 2ND ST 74023 #039-01-1989 L1990 **ORS OP** *020 †40
TURNER, Scott Parkhurst. 1030 E CHERRY ST 74023 #039-01-2000 L2004 **MPD** *020 †20,55
WIPFLI, Jeffrey Alan. 1027 E CHERRY ST 74023 #039-01-1996 L2000 **OPH** *020 †35

DAVIS — MURRAY

HORANZY, Robert Raymond. 107 S 3RD ST 73030 #036-08-1995 L1997 **FM EM** *020

DEL CITY — OKLAHOMA

BARNES, Elizabeth Gaynell. ■ 73115 #039-01-2008 *012
CHOE, Wu-Jung. 1221 S SUNNYLANE RD 73115 #039-01-1984 L1985 **IM** *020
CHOE, Yung-Hye. 1221 S SUNNYLANE RD 73115 #039-01-1991 L1994 **FM** *020 †18
FIORAZO, Val Joseph. 4330 SE 29TH ST STE 3018, CENTER/OCCUCARE CORP. 73115 #051-01-1989 L1996 **OM FM** *020 †18
LA FON, William F. ■ 73115 #039-01-1937 L1938 **GP** *071
LAWLER, Kim Park. ■ 73115 #016-11-1978 L1979 **MDM GP** *062
LONG, John Steven, Jr. ■ 73115 #039-01-2008 *012
PAGE, James Edward. ■ 73115 #043-01-2007 L2007 **FP** *012
ROBiNSON, Anna. 2820 LINDA LN 73115 #038-43-2007 L2007 **EM** *012
SCEARS, Meghan Elizabeth. ■ 73115 #039-01-2008 *012

DEWEY — WASHINGTON

SMITHSON, John Richard. 802 N WYANDOTTE AVE 74029 #039-01-1955 L1955 **GP** *020 †18

DRUMRIGHT — CREEK

DHIMMAR, Dahyabhai Bhag. 116 S SKINNER AVE 74030 #495-23-1970 L1978 **FM GS** *020
DIMMITT, Sandra Kay. 601 S CREEK AVE 74030 #039-01-1977 L1978 **GP PTH** *020 †50
HICKMAN, Linda Marie. 500 LOU ALLARD DR 74030 #039-01-1994 L1995 **IM** *020 †20

DUNCAN — STEPHENS

ALBERTSON, Richard M. 2120 W ELK AVE, RM 6 73533 #048-15-1997 L1998 **GS VS** *020 †85
BUNTLEY, David Wayne. 2601 W ELK AVE 73533 #047-06-1971 L1973 **U** *020 †95
CHRISTIE, Byron H. 2701 WILDWOOD PL 73533 #048-04-1992 L2004 **DR** *020 †80
CLARK, Robert Mel. 2120 W ELK AVE 73533 #039-01-1978 L1979 **CD IM** *020 †20
COX, Demetra Graham. 1324 N HARVILLE RD 73533 #039-01-1996 L1997 **FM** *020 †18
CROW, Thomas Ray. 1606 W JONES AVE 73533 #039-01-1987 L1988 **FM** *020 †18
DICKERSON, Charles Wayne. 1601 BROOKWOOD AVE 73533 #039-01-1982 L1984 **FM** *020 †18
EDWARDS, William Louis. 2515 W ELK AVE 73533 #039-01-1964 L1964 **FM** *020 †18 ‡
EISER, Thomas John. 2815 W ELK AVE 73533 #028-02-1971 L1979 **ORS GP** *020 †40 ‡
ELLIS, Richard A. 1407 N WHISENANT DR 73533 #039-01-1945 L1946 **GP** *071
FRANK, Alexander Fredrick. 1407 N WHISENANT DR 73533 #035-15-1996 L2001 **FM** *020 †18
GILBRETH, Judy Marie. 1330 N HARVILLE RD, GILBRETH FAMILY MEDICINE 73533 #039-01-1991 L1994 **FM OBG** *020 †18
GILES, Danny W. 2815 W ELK AVE 73533 #048-02-1995 L1996 **ORS** *020 †40
GREGSTON, Jay Lance. 2004 N HIGHWAY 81, STE E 73533 #039-01-1996 L1997 **EM** *020 †16
HERNDON, Christopher M. 2515 W ELK AVE 73533 #039-01-1976 L1978 **FM** *020 †18
HERNDON, Robert Eugene. 2515 W ELK AVE, DUNCAN MEDICAL ASSOC 73533 #039-01-1948 L1948 **PD A** *071 †55 ‡
HOKETT, Jamie Lyn. 1324 N HARVILLE RD, DUNCAN FAMILY PHYSICIAN 73533 #039-01-2002 L2003 **FM** *020 †18
HUGHES, Dennis Foulkes. 2120 W ELK AVE, RM 3 73533 #060-02-1973 L1992 **IM** *020
IVORY, Mathew Jennings. 1324 N HARVILLE RD 73533 #039-01-1996 L1997 **FM** *020 †18
JONES, James Stewart. 2120 W ELK AVE RM 6 73533 #039-01-1964 L1964 **GS OBG** *071 †18,85
JONES, Jeffrey Clyde. 2515 W ELK AVE 73533 #048-12-1976 L1978 **FM** *020 †18 ‡
MC GOURAN, Francis J, III. 1334 N HARVILLE RD 73533 #039-01-1988 L1990 **FM** *020 †18
MILLER, Douglas Che. 73533 #039-01-2002 L2004 **GS** *020 †85
MITRO, Joseph C. 1312 N HARVILLE RD, 1312 HARVILLE RD 73533 #048-14-2000 L2001 **OBG** *020
MORALES, Oscar, Jr. 1509 BROOKWOOD AVE STE B 73533 #019-02-1992 L1998 **IM** *020 †20
MOYER, Philip Wesley. 2120 W ELK AVE RM 4 73533 #056-06-2000 L2001 **GS** *020 †85
MULLINS, Brenda Kris. 2120 W ELK AVE 73533 #039-01-1991 L1994 **CD** *020 †20
NELSON, Christopher Brett. ■ 73533 #048-16-2006 **DR** *012
NORMAN, Cynthia A B. 1315 JACKIE RD 73533 #048-15-1975 L1976 **FM** *020 ‡
PINKERTON, James Craig. 1407 N WHISENANT DR, DUNCAN REGIONAL HOSPITAL 73533 #039-01-1995 L1996 **EM** *020 †16
RAIZEN, Polly G F. ■ 73533 #035-19-1953 L1982 **P** *074 †75 ‡
STEPHENSON, David V. 2203 N HIGHWAY 81 73533 #030-05-1958 L1986 **GS TRS** *071 †85
STEWART, William Thos. 1324 N HARVILLE RD 73533 #039-01-1975 L1978 **FM** *020 †18
WATERS, Preston Andreas. 2515 W ELK AVE 73533 #048-04-1997 L2000 **FM** *020 †18
WATERS, Sallie Jane. 2515 W ELK AVE 73533 #048-04-1997 L2003 **FM** *020 †18
WEEDN, Robert James. 111 N 10TH ST 73533 #039-01-1967 L1967 **GS TS** *020 †85,90
YOUNG, John Russell. ■ 73533 #051-04-1969 L1990 **OBG** *071 †30

DURANT — BRYAN

ARABOLU, Bala Krishna V. 1202 N 16TH AVE DEPT PD 74701 #495-21-1972 L1978 **PD** *020 †55
BONILLA, Mario Antonio. 1901 W UNIVERSITY BLVD 74701 #341-01-1971 L1979 **CD IM** *020 †20
BUTT, Shyla Imdad. 720 BRYAN DR, STE A 74701 #704-01-1995 L2004 **IM** *020 †20
CASTRO, Dan. 1800 W UNIVERSITY BLVD, MED CENTER OF SOUTHEASTERN 74701 #396-06-1980 L2005 **HNS GS** *020 †45
CHAVERN, Hugh Edward. 1001 W MAIN ST, MENTAL HEALTH SVCS SOUTHER 74701 #041-12-1948 L1988 **P OS** *062 †75
CONWAY, Stafford Austin. 1804 CHUCKWA DR 74701 #654-01-2001 L2007 **N** *020
CUESTA, Braulio M. 1400 BRYAN DR, STE 301 74701 #847-02-1975 L1981 **OBG** *020
DAVAULT, Randall Jason. 1800 W UNIVERSITY BLVD, OUHSC - DEPT OF SURGERY 74701 #039-01-2003 L2005 **GS** *012
ENGLES, Phyllis M Pyrum. 1600 N WASHINGTON AVE 74701 #039-01-1968 L1969 **GP** *071
ENGLES, Robert Everet. 1400 BRYAN DR STE 201 74701 #039-01-1954 L1954 **GS GP** *071
GOTTLIEB, Morris B C. 1800 W UNIVERSITY BLVD, MEDICAL CENTER OF SE OKLAH 74701 #023-07-1998 L2004 **OTO** *020
HAMID, Abdool Rohoman. 1727 CHUCKWA DR STE 200, A. R. HAMID PEDIATRIC CLIN 74701 #422-01-1982 L2005 **PD** *020 †55
HEDBERG, Peter Schuyler. 1400 BRYAN DR STE 203 74701 #003-01-1989 L1997 **GS VS** *020 †85
JAISWAL, Deepak S. 702 BRYAN DR STE 100 74701 #495-76-1979 L1993 **IM** *020
JANDZISZAK, Karina. 1610 W UNIVERSITY BLVD 74701 #759-10-1986 L1998 **PDE** *020 †55
KHETPAL, Sangeeta. 1400 BRYAN DR, STE 208 74701 #704-16-1994 L2004 **IM** *020 †20
KHETPAL, Vivek. 1400 BRYAN DR, STE 208 74701 #704-16-1988 L1997 **CD** *020 †20
LACEY, Glen Warren. ■ 74701 #062-01-1988 L1994 **DR** *020 †80
MALONE, Donald Walter. 1705 N WASHINGTON AVE, STE C 74701 #048-02-1978 L2003 **ORS** *020
ORTLIP, Stephen Allison. 1800 W UNIVERSITY BLVD 74701 #026-04-1977 L1997 **U** *020 †95
PHAM-HILL, Tram B. 1400 BRYAN DR, STE 205 74701 #048-02-2002 L2004 **IM** *020
RICHARDSON, William Polk. 1723 N WASHINGTON AVE 74701 #048-04-1969 L2003 **GS VS** *020 †85
SABORIO, Jorge. 1705 N WASHINGTON AVE 74701 #682-01-1970 L1993 **U** *075 †95
SHAH, Ali Aksar. 1400 BRYAN DR 74701 #308-11-1990 L2003 **IM** *020 †20
STURCH, Christopher Lee. 1800 W UNIVERSITY BLVD 74701 #039-01-1993 L1994 **FM** *020 †18 ‡
SUREDDI, Koteswara Rao. 1400 BRYAN DR 74701 #495-11-1962 L1978 **FM OTO** *020
SUREDDI, Seetha Devi. 1400 BRYAN DR 74701 #495-50-1969 L1978 **OBG** *020 †30
TAYLOR, Christine M. 1400 BRYAN DR, STE 200 74701 #035-01-1997 L2005 **OBG** *020 †30

■ = Address Information Privacy Protected

TUCKER, Grace Book. 1901 W UNIVERSITY BLVD, TEXOMA CARE 74701 #036-05-1974 L1996 END IM *020 †20

WILLIAMS, Dennis T. 1800 W UNIVERSITY BLVD, MEDICAL STAFF SERVICES 74701 #048-04-1996 L2004 AN *020

WILLIE, Glen Robert. 411 WESTSIDE DR, DURANT DIALYSIS CENTER 74701 #026-04-1976 L2001 NEP IM *020 †20

EDMOND – OKLAHOMA

ABDEL BARY, Mona Abdel M. ■ 73034 #915-04-1980 L2003 *100

ABU-FADEL, Mazen Salim. 4117 FRISCO BRIDGE BLVD 73034 #605-01-1999 L2002 IC *100 †20 ‡

AHLUWALIA, Atul. 17109 WALES GREEN AVE 73012 #039-79-2004, ▲ L2005 AN *012

AHLUWALIA-KUMAR, Ana. 4525 OLDE VILLAGE CIR 73013 #894-01-2000 L2004 FM *020

ALAMIAN, Seyed M. ■ 73012 #308-11-1987 L2001 PUD CCM *020 †20

ALDAMA, Stephanie H. ■ 73003 #048-14-1977 L1978 D *071 †15

ALLEN, Terry Lee. 1809 CONRIDGE DR 73034 #039-01-1989 L1990 AN *020 †05

ARAKI, Motoo. ■ 73034 #572-09-1998 L2005 U *100

ARCHBALD, Emily Gail. ■ 73013 #039-01-2007 L2007 IM *012

AYRES, Sarah Elizabeth. 105 S BRYANT AVE STE 306 73034 #048-12-1965 L1969 FM *020 †18

BARR, Stephen Michael. ■ 73034 #039-01-2006 L2006 FP *012

BARSALOUX, Andrew Fennell. ■ 73083 #039-01-1997 L1998 IM *020 †20

BAX, Ami Beth. ■ 73013 #039-01-2006 L2007 PD *012

BAYCH, Lisa Marie. ■ 73013 #039-01-2007 L2007 FP *012

BEHRMANN, David Aaron. ■ 73013 #039-01-2008 *012

BELL, Cardin Harris. ■ 73013 #010-01-2006 L2006 U *012

BELL, Patrick Arthur. 105 S BRYANT AVE STE 310 73034 #039-01-1982 L1985 GS *020 †18,85

BERG, Stephanie Marie. 105 S BRYANT AVE STE 210, UNIV OF OK 73034 #039-01-2001 L2003 IM *020 †20

BHASIN, Deepak. ■ 73013 #495-14-1980 L1984 GP *075

BISSON, Roger U. 13501 TAHOE DR 73013 #023-12-1982 L1984 AM GPM *062 †70

BOGIE, Charles Paul, III. 1005 MEDICAL PARK BLVD, DEAN MCGEE EYE INSTITUTE 73013 #039-01-1997 L1998 OPH *020 †35

BOLT, Michael Stephen. ■ 73003 #019-02-1983 L1984 OPH *020 †35

BONDURANT, William Laban. 1700 RENAISSANCE BLVD 73013 #039-01-1993 L1994 FM *020 †18

BOONE, John Luther. ■ 73003 #039-01-2008 *012

BOSTROM, Jake Paul. ■ 73013 #047-06-2005 L2006 OPH *012

BOWLAN, Timothy Mark. ■ 73025 #039-01-1984 L1988 P *020 †75

BRADFORD, Reagan Howard. ■ 73013 #039-01-1961 L1961 OS IM *071

BRALY, Brett Alan. ■ 73003 #039-01-2008 L2008 *012

BRENNAN, Cynthia M. 820 W DANFORTH RD, B-30 73003 #030-06-1982 L1983 FM *020 †18

BRITTON, Bradley Don. 14701 N SANTA FE AVE 73013 #039-01-1987 L1991 OPH *020 †35

BUETHE, David Donald. ■ 73013 #011-04-2006 L2006 U *012

CAFARO, Brian Patrick. ■ 73013 #654-01-2005 L2006 FP *012

CALDWELL, Cuyler Eastes. ■ 73013 #039-01-2008 *012

CAMPBELL, Jesse Ray. 1575 N SANTA FE AVE 73003 #039-01-1996 L1997 MPD *020 †20,55

CARL, Roy Barton. ■ 73013 #039-01-1955 L1955 NS *071 †25

CARSON, Craig Weldon. 1701 RENAISSANCE BLVD, STE 110 73013 #049-01-1985 L1991 RHU IM *020 †20

CARTER, Mirela Dujmovic. ■ 73013 #039-01-2005 L2007 FP *012

CARTER, Steven Nereus. ■ 73003 #039-01-2006 L2007 GS *012

CASSADY, Charles P. ■ 73012 #048-02-2006 L2007 AN *012

CAVE, Rodney Kent. ■ 73034 #028-03-1981 L1990 DR *020 †80

CHAPMAN, Randell Barkley. ■ 73013 #039-01-1983 L1984 FM EM *020 †18 ‡

CHESLER, David J. ■ 73013 #038-40-1953 L1958 AN *071 †05

CHOPRA, Sandeep. ■ 73012 #035-15-1998 L2002 CD *020 †20

CLAFLIN, James Robt. 120 N BRYANT AVE, STE A4 73034 #039-01-1971 L1972 AI PDA *020 †55,03

CLINKENBEARD, Daniel C. 400 N BRYANT AVE, MCBRIDE CLINIC, INC 73034 #039-01-1996 L1997 FSM *020 †18

CLOWERS, Brian Edward. ■ 73013 #039-01-2005 L2006 ORS *012

COLE, Jeremy. 105 S BRYANT AVE STE 20 73034 #035-06-1973 L2003 PUD *020 †20

CONFER, Michael Edwin. ■ 73013 #039-01-2007 L2007 PD *012

CONNER, Stephen Bruce. 1701 RENAISSANCE BLVD, STE 100 73013 #039-01-1974 L1975 ORS *020 †40

CONRAD, Vicki Joyce. 1616 S BOULEVARD ST 73013 #039-01-1981 L1983 GP *020

COOK, Victoria Elena. 1700 RENAISSANCE BLVD 73013 #039-01-1995 L1996 PD *071

CROOKS, James D. 902 S BRYANT AVE, DIAGNOSTIC RADIOLOGY 73034 #039-01-1976 L1977 DR *020 †80

DAFFER, Ernest Robert. ■ 73013 #039-01-1962 L1962 GS *071

DARTER, Amy L Liebl. 609 S KELLY AVE STE J1 73003 #039-01-1997 L1998 AI IM *020 †20,03

DASHARATHY, Gayathri. 2805 S BRYANT AVE STE A, GM MEDICAL CONSULTANTS INC 73034 #495-33-1983 L1986 PYG N *020 †75

DAVE, Chandresh S. 705 BRIDGEVIEW PL 73043 #495-23-1992 L2000 OS P *020 †20

DAVENPORT, Jeffrey Craig. 105 S BRYANT AVE, STE 301 73034 #039-01-2003 L2006 FM *020 †18

DAVIS, Franklin Cleo. 1208 W 15TH ST, WESTBROOK FAMILY 73013 #039-01-1978 L1981 FM FPG *020 †18

DAVIS, Sarah Jane. ■ 73012 #028-34-2008 *012

DAVIS, Thomas Wayne. 1301 SLEEPY HOLLOW RD 73034 #039-01-1974 L1975 ADM *020 †18

DE PERSIO, Sara Anne Reed. ■ 73025 #047-06-1965 L1968 PHP OBG *071 †70

DICKINSON, Gary Peter. 1616 S KELLY AVE, THE PHYSICIANS GROUP 73013 #039-01-1980 L1981 FM *020 †18

DIMICK, Susan Miller. 3317 E MEMORIAL RD, STE 103 73013 #039-01-1984 L1985 IM *020 †20

DITTMEYER, Kale Dean. ■ 73013 #039-01-2008 *012

DOWE, Tisha. ■ 73034 #039-01-1985 L1986 PHP OBG *100 †70 ‡

DOWLING, Jason Michael. ■ 73013 #051-01-2005 L2006 GS *100

DRAELOS, Matthew Theodore. 200 N BRYANT AVE, STE 100 73034 #034-01-1985 L1986 END DIA *020

DRAIN, Ray Antoine. 105 S BRYANT AVE STE 203 73034 #039-01-1975 L1976 FM *020 †18 ‡

DUHON, Lisa Dawn. ■ 73034 #039-01-2008 *012

DUNN, Bruce Cullom. 2701 COLTRANE PL, CONSULTANTS PC 73034 #048-13-1975 L1980 PTH *020 †50

DWYER, Matthew Michael. ■ 73013 #048-14-2004 L2007 ORS *012

EASLEY, John Alan. ■ 73012 #039-01-1984 L1985 IM *071 †20

EDGMON, Kimberly Brooke. 1575 N SANTA FE AVE 73003 #039-01-2002 L2005 PD *020 †55

EDMONDS, William Bentley. 400 N BRYANT AVE 73034 #039-01-1997 L1998 ORS *020 †40

ELIMIAN, Andrew A. ■ 73034 #690-08-1985 L2005 OBG *020 †20,30

EVANS, Craig Randall. 1208 W 15TH ST, WESTBROOK FAMILY 73013 #039-01-1978 L1981 FM *020 †18

EVANS, John Patrick. ■ 73013 #039-01-1963 L1963 ORS *071 †40

FERRELL, Charles William. 3021 KELSEY DR 73013 #039-01-2005 L2006 FP *012

FICHTENAU, Joanna F. ■ 73034 #039-01-1997 N *100

FIRESTONE, Brian Keith. ■ 73034 #039-01-2008 *012

FISH, Jon Ross. ■ 73013 #039-01-2003 L2005 DR *012

FISHER, Ross Lane. 1 S BRYANT AVE 73034 #039-01-1985 L1986 IM *020 †20 ‡

FLOYD, Philip Andre. 16909 BRADBURY CIR, PHILIP FLOYD MD, PC 73012 #039-01-1994 L1999 GS *020 †85

FOZDAR, Julie Ann. ■ 73034 #039-01-2006 L2006 FM *100

FRANKLIN, Joseph Wilhelm. 321 TULLAHOMA DR 73034 #032-01-1992 L1995 EM PD *020 †16

FRANZ, F Perry. ■ 73003 #039-01-1983 L1984 PS HNS *075 †65

FREDRICK, Lori Ann. ■ 73025 #039-01-2004 L2006 DR *012

FRITZ, Christian Freihoff. ■ 73013 #154-07-1988 L1996 CD *020

GALLARDO, Graciela Cristi. ■ 73034 #132-01-1991 L2006 FP *012

GARDNER, John Howard. ■ 73003 #039-01-1959 L1959 DR NM *071 †80

GARLOW, Timothy James. ■ 73013 #039-01-2008 *012

GARRISON, Stuart Earle. ■ 73034 #054-04-1967 L2005 R *071 †80

GARRISON, Virginia F L. ■ 73034 #054-04-1967 L2005 R *071 †80 ‡

GELNAR, Charles Max. 105 S BRYANT AVE, STE 101 73034 #039-01-1966 L1970 GS *020 †85

GHABACHE, Bassam Sarkis. ■ 73003 #605-02-2001 L2007 ON *100 †20

GHANI, Mohammad Khaled J. 105 S BRYANT AVE, OKLAHOMA CARDIOVASCULAR 73034 #704-22-1984 L2002 IC *100 †20

GHEEN, Delmar Lee, Jr. 2000 E 15TH ST, STE 150C 73034 #038-40-1961 L1965 PD *071 †55

GHULOOM, Adel Ebrahim. ■ 73013 #155-01-1993 L2005 CCM *020 †20

GIERMAN, Joshua Lee. ■ 73003 #021-05-2004 L2005 GS *012

GILCHRIST, John Mark. 501 E 15TH ST, STE 300A 73013 #039-01-1986 L1987 OTO *020 †45

GLASS, Michael Lee. 3815 S BOULEVARD ST 73013 #039-01-1977 L1978 OBG *020 †30

GOLIGHTLY, Jeffrey Paul. 1900 DUXSFORD CT, J P G EMERGENCY SERVICES P 73034 #039-01-1998 L2001 EM *020 †16

GOURLEY, Robert Dean. 920 S BRYANT AVE, STE 100 73034 #048-02-1975 L1976 OPH *020 †35

GRAHAM, David L. 609 S KELLY AVE STE E2 73003 #005-11-1977 L1998 DS PS *020 †15

GRODE, Tim L. 105 S BRYANT AVE, STE 204A 73034 #039-01-1978 L1979 PUD IM *020 †20

GROZEA, Petre Nicolae. ■ 73034 #781-01-1949 L1974 ON HEM *072

GUNDA, Divya. ■ 73013 #039-01-2008 *012

GUTHERY, Brandon Kyle. ■ 73013 #039-01-2005 L2007 PTH *012

HACKNEY, John Louis. 100 N UNIVERSITY DR, UNIV OF CENTER OK 73034 #039-01-1961 L1961 FM *020 †18

HAMILTON, Tamela Jayne. ■ 73034 #039-01-1991 L1992 OM *020 †70

HAMPTON, Diana E. 1005 MEDICAL PARK BLVD 73013 #048-02-1994 L1996 OPH *020 †35

HANLON, Kathleen. ■ 73034 #028-02-1986 PD *020 †55

HAQ, Seema. ■ 73013 #704-02-1995 L2005 END *012 †20

HARKESS, John Rudman. 729 S BOULEVARD ST, INFECTIOUS DISEASE PHYSICI 73034 #012-01-1982 L1986 ID IM *020 †20

HARMS, Robin Lee. 13917 LOST CREEK DR 73013 #039-01-1993 L1994 AN *020 †05

HARVEY, Ben Jacob. ■ 73013 #048-15-2007 L2008 IM *012

HARVEY, Zane Douglas. ■ 73013 #012-22-2003 L2006 FM *100 †18

HATCH, Richard Thos. 120 N BRYANT AVE, STE A4 73034 #028-34-1986 L1997 AI PD *020 †55,03

HAYNES, Douglas Wendell. 1501 E 19TH ST, CANYON PARK MEDICAL GROUP 73013 #039-01-1998 L2001 FM *020 †18 ‡

HENNAN, Kimberly Michelle. ■ 73003 #048-02-2005 L2006 OBG *012

HENRY, Emilie Dawn. ■ 73013 #039-01-2001 L2002 CCP *100 †55

HERBERMAN, Howard Bennett. 902 S BRYANT AVE, DIAGNOSTIC RADIOLOGY 73034 #048-15-1993 L1998 DR *020 †80 ‡

HILDENBRAND, John Christi. ■ 73013 #021-05-2004 L2005 ORS *012

HILL, Gary C. 105 S BRYANT AVE, STE 108 73034 #039-01-1976 L1977 PS *020 †45

HILL, Riley Ambrose. 3120 E 2ND ST 73034 #039-01-1954 L1955 P *075

HOGGARD, Adreanne Marie. ■ 73003 #039-01-2008 *012

HOGUE, Michael Andrew. 920 S BRYANT AVE, STE 100 73034 #010-01-2000 L2004 OPH *020 †35

HOLMBOE, Mary Caroline. 2701 COLTRANE PL, CONSULTANTS PC 73034 #039-01-1993 L1994 PTH *020 †50

HOOVER, Geoffrey Wayne. 122 N BRYANT AVE, STE 1 73034 #039-01-1998 L1999 FM *020 †18

HOPKINS, Lauren Cathleen. ■ 73013 #028-78-2007, ▲ FP *012

HORN, Amanda Anne. ■ 73013 #039-01-2008 *012

HOROWITZ, Mitchell Barry. 105 S BRYANT AVE, STE 309 73034 #039-01-1979 L1980 CD *020 †20

HORST, Stanley Alan. 105 S BRYANT AVE STE 100 73034 #039-01-1979 L1980 CD *020 †20

HOTZ, Colleen Brigid. ■ 73013 #028-03-2006 L2007 PD *012

HOUCK, John Roland, Jr. 2820 N KELLY AVE STE 200, OU PHYSICIANS AT EDMOND 73003 #005-11-1977 L1990 OTO A *020 †45

HOWELL, Clifford Eric. 101 N CROSSTIMBER TRL 73034 #048-02-1986 L1987 TS VS *020 †85,90

HU, Xiaohong. ■ 73013 #243-52-1989 L2006 P *012

HUANG, Shijun. ■ 73013 #243-46-1990 L2007 *100

HULSON, Terrill D. 1208 W 15TH ST, WESTBROOK FAMILY 73013 #039-01-1976 L1977 FM *020 †18

IKEGUCHI, Alexandra P. 1227 E 9TH ST 73034 #035-01-1992 L2002 HO *020 †20

INGRAM, Russell Dean. ■ 73003 #039-01-2008 *012

JAMES, David Martin. 1208 W 15TH ST, WESTBROOK FAMILY 73013 #039-01-1978 L1979 FM *020 †18

JAMISON, Joseph A. 1700 RENAISSANCE BLVD 73013 #048-16-1993 L1994 FM *020 †18

JAY, Dathan Duane. 523 S SANTA FE AVE 73003 #039-01-2003 L2004 FM *012

JAYNE, David Kevin. 124 N BRYANT AVE, STE B 73034 #039-01-1988 L1989 FM EM *020 †18

JENKINS, Carlos Randall. 124 N BRYANT AVE, BLDG C 73034 #039-01-1974 L1975 EM *020 †16

JETT, Elizabeth Ann. ■ 73013 #039-01-1999 L2005 DR *100 †80

JOHN, Michael David. 620 W 15TH ST 73013 #020-02-1977 L1985 D *020 †15
JOHNSON, James Michael. 416 W 15TH ST, STE 400A 73013 #039-01-1983 L1984 GP OM *072 ‡
JONES, Mary M. 902 S BRYANT AVE 73034 #039-01-1976 L1977 DR *020 †80
JONES, Timothy Brian. 2820 N KELLY AVE STE 20, COFFEE CREEK MEDICAL CLINI 73003 #039-01-1985 L1986 FM *020 †18
JUDD, Dustin Ian. ■ 73013 #005-06-2007 L2007 ORS *012
KAMRA, Rita Kiron. ■ 73003 #064-01-1992 L1997 FM *072 †18
KARIM, Rehan Mehboob. ■ 73003 #704-25-1999 L2007 ICE *012 †20
KELLER, Roman Hystad. ■ 73013 #028-78-2004, ▲ L2006 DR *012
KHALILI, Mohammad Fazel. 105 S BRYANT AVE, STE 202 73034 #781-04-1992 L2004 IM *020 †20
KHALILI, Viorica. 105 S BRYANT AVE STE 20 73034 #781-04-1995 L2004 NEP *020 †20
KHAN, Ismet Ahmed. ■ 73012 #160-01-1985 L1997 P *100
KHAN, Khalid A. 105 S BRYANT AVE, STE 210 73034 #704-02-1987 L1996 APM *020 †75
KHAN, Mohammad Faisal. ■ 73013 #495-99-1992 L2006 RHU *012
KHAVARI, Shawn Akhtar. ■ 73012 #039-01-2005 L2006 P *012
KIM, Hyung Ju. ■ 73003 #039-01-2008 *012
KING, Robert W, Jr. ■ 73013 #039-01-1971 L1972 NEP IM *030 †20
KIRKPATRICK, Richard Alan. 14125 GLEN OAKS PL 73013 #039-01-2001 L2002 ORS *020
KNOLES, Curtis Lee. ■ 73003 #039-01-2006 L2006 PD *012
KOCHIE, Paul Jonathan. 73034 #056-06-1973 L1994 PTH NP *020 †50
KOESTER, Glenn. 3863 S BOULEVARD ST, STE 200 73013 #048-13-1989 L1994 D *020 †15
KOJOURI, Kiarash. ■ 73034 #517-01-1991 L2003 HO *100 †20
KONG, Jin. ■ 73013 #243-39-1982 IM *020 †20
KRISHNAIENGAR, Suparna Ru. ■ 73034 #495-09-1994 L2005 N *100
KRISHNAN, Preethi. ■ 73003 #039-01-2004 L2008 FM *020
KROUS, Timothy Fredrick. 2820 N KELLY AVE STE 100, VILLAGE CENTER PEDIATRICS 73003 #039-01-1998 L1999 PD *020 †55
LAMASCUS, Alice Mankin. ■ 73013 #039-01-2008 *012
LANIER, Lane T. ■ 73013 #048-13-2005 L2007 PD *012
LEGAKO, Ronal Dee. 1501 E 19TH ST 73013 #039-01-1966 L1966 FM *020 †18 ‡
LEVINE, Amanda Karen. 3815 S BOULEVARD ST 73013 #039-01-2001 L2005 OBG *020 †30
LEVY, Brian P. 200 N BRYANT AVE 73034 #039-01-1981 L1982 IM *020 †20
LEWIS, Richard Edwin. ■ 73034 #026-04-1943 L1943 OM PHP *071
LEWIS, Thomas R. ■ 73003 #048-16-2004 L2005 ORS *012
L'HEUREUX, E Alexander. 1405 NW 150TH ST 73013 #048-02-1991 L1997 OSS ORS *020 †40
LIMBAUGH, Manuel Carl. 1700 RENAISSANCE BLVD 73013 #048-13-1986 L1987 FM *020 †18
LIVINGSTON, John Patrick. 400 N BRYANT AVE, STE 400 73034 #039-01-1974 L1975 ORS OSS *020 †40
LOFGREN, Kathryn J. 46 E 15TH ST, ACCESS MEDICAL 73013 #040-02-1996 L2007 FM *020 †18
LORENZO-RIVERO, Shauna. 1050 E 2ND ST, # 222 73034 #028-02-1999 L2005 CRS GS *020 †85,10
LOWRY, Benjamin Paul. ■ 73003 #039-01-2006 AN *012
LYNN, Mark Reed. 105 S BRYANT AVE STE 304, MARK R LYNN MD 73034 #039-01-1983 L1984 FM *020 †05,18
MACARAEG, Emmanuel Najera. 1800 RENAISSANCE BLVD, 1ST FL 73013 #748-01-1969 L1982 AN PD *020 †55
MACKEY, Bruce Alan. 841 S KELLY AVE, STE 110 73003 #039-01-1984 L1987 PMM *020 †18
MADDEN, George Wesley. ■ 73013 #039-01-2008 *012
MAGNESS, Ashley Anne. 2601 KELLEY POINTE PKWY, LLC 73013 #039-01-1998 L1999 DR OS *020 †80
MARTIN, John Christopher. 105 S BRYANT AVE STE 300 73034 #019-02-1978 L1979 FM *020 †18
MASCHINO, Tammy Renee. 2820 N KELLY AVE STE 100 73003 #039-01-1998 L1999 PD *020 †55
MATTHIESEN, Chance Lee. ■ 73013 #039-01-2007 L2007 IM *012
MATZELL, Amy Briana. ■ 73013 #039-01-2001 L2002 DR *020
MC ALLISTER, Natalie Broo. ■ 73003 #039-01-2007 L2007 IM *012
MC CARLEY, Ben P. ■ 73003 #036-07-1952 L1955 PD *071 †55
MC DONOUGH, Kelly Neaves. 2601 KELLEY POINTE PKWY, LLC 73013 #039-01-1994 L1995 DR *020 †80
MCELMEEL, Scott Lee. ■ 73012 #003-01-2008 *012
MC KEAN, Joseph Dewey, Jr. ■ 73013 #039-01-1967 L1968 EM GP *071
MEFFORD, Brent Alan. ■ 73013 #039-01-2004 L2007 EM *100
MICHEL, Leslie Bae. 105 S BRYANT AVE, STE 210 73034 #051-04-2002 L2003 IM *020 †20
MICHEL, Ross George. ■ 73013 #051-04-2002 L2003 PCC *012
MIHALSKY, Stephen Wm. 105 S BRYANT AVE STE 40 73034 #041-02-1986 L1993 HS *020 †85
MILFORT, Marie Carlie. ■ 73012 #021-01-2004 *100
MILLS, James Berry. 3431 S BOULEVARD ST, STE 106 73013 #030-06-1959 L1961 OPH *020 †35
MILLS, William Douglas. ■ 73013 #039-01-1977 L1978 GP AM *020 †70
MITCHELL, Barry James. 1616 S KELLY AVE, THE PHYSICIANS' GROUP 73013 #039-01-1985 L1986 FM *020 †18
MITCHELL, Debra Sue. 2601 KELLEY POINTE PKWY, STE 101 73013 #039-01-1982 L1984 DR *020 †80
MOORE, Michael Bartholome. ■ 73013 #019-02-2006 L2007 OBG *012
MORGAN, Jared Keith. ■ 73012 #039-01-2006 L2007 DR *012
MORGAN, Peter Robt. 200 N BRYANT AVE 73034 #039-01-1981 L1982 IM IMG *020 †20
MORGAN, Wm Gregory, III. 105 S BRYANT AVE, STE 103 73034 #047-05-1971 L1974 OS *020 †16
MOSALLAEI-BENJAMIN, M M. ■ 73013 #039-01-2001 L2002 HO *012 †20
MUIR, Traske Mcneil. ■ 73013 #051-01-2004 L2006 ORS *012
MUNDIS, Gregory Michael. ■ 73013 #028-03-2003 L2005 ORS *012
MUNGUL, Lise M. ■ 73034 #041-02-1979 L1993 IM IMG *062 †20
MUSSER, Kathleen M. ■ 73012 #041-07-1972 L1989 OS GS *071 †85
MYERS, Gary Dean. 1 S BRYANT AVE 73034 #039-01-1980 L1981 GS VS *020 †85
NAGARATHINAM, Rajeswari. ■ 73013 #495-94-1997 L2007 PTH *012
NAGY, Ildiko. ■ 73012 #473-01-1987 L2003 PTH *020 †50
NAIK, Kamlesh Hasmukh. 3414 S BROADWAY 73013 #068-01-1989 L1998 R *020 †80
NANDAKUMAR, Suma. ■ 73013 #048-15-2004 L2006 PD *100 †55
NELSON, Daniel Richard. ■ 73013 #046-01-2007 L2007 ORS *012
NELSON, Ryan Lee. ■ 73013 #028-78-2007, ▲ *012
NESSELRODE, Robert Lynn. ■ 73034 #038-44-2005 L2006 AN *012

NICKESON, Erica Lee. ■ 73003 #030-05-2006 L2007 OBG *012
NIX, Donald Wayne. 902 S BRYANT AVE 73034 #039-01-1986 L1987 DR *020 †80
NORTHCUTT, Barry Lynn. 105 S BRYANT AVE STE 410, MEDICINE P.C. INC. 73034 #039-01-1992 L1993 ORS *020 †40
NORWOOD, O'Tar Tretreau. ■ 73012 #004-01-1957 L1961 D *071 †15
O'KEEFFE, John Brendan. ■ 73025 #539-02-1972 L1978 GP *020
OLAY, Michael P. 1700 RENAISSANCE BLVD 73013 #048-02-1994 L1995 FM *020 †18
OLAY, Sabrina R. 1700 RENAISSANCE BLVD 73013 #048-02-1994 L1995 PD *020 †55
ONESON, Ruth Hannon. 2701 COLTRANE PL, CONSULTANTS PC 73034 #023-01-1983 L1988 PTH PCP *020 †50
OPOKU, Michael. 16317 VALLEJO PL 73013 #412-02-1996 L2004 IM HOS *020
PALMER, Blake Wiley. 13906 CROSSING WAY E 73013 #039-01-2005 L2007 GS *100
PANCHAL, Jayesh Ishwar. 1 S BRYANT AVE 73034 #495-01-1982 L2002 PS *012
PAYNE, Joshua Rush. ■ 73013 #039-01-2008 *012
PEARCE, Henry Johnson. 1600 MEDICAL CENTER DR 73034 #039-01-1964 L1964 VS GS *020 †85
PEARCE, Jeffrey Newton. 2609 SWEETBRIAR, STE 105 73034 #039-01-1989 L1990 AN *020 †05
PETERSON, Dale Howard. 1050 N 2ND ST, # 242 73034 #026-04-1972 L1973 FM *071 †18
PHAM, Tuyet Ngoc. ■ 73012 #048-13-1996 L2006 PD *100
PILLOW, Bradley Wayne. ■ 73013 #048-12-2008 *012
PING, Russell David. ■ 73003 #039-01-2003 PD *100
PIRUMYAN, Georgi. ■ 73013 #913-38-1997 L2007 PTH *012
POARCH, John Ellis. ■ 73003 #039-01-1964 L1964 P *071 †75
POKHAREL, Dipesh. ■ 73013 #039-01-2004 L2005 CD *012 †20
POOLER, Jason Clifford. ■ 73012 #047-06-2004 L2006 GS *100
POWITZKY, Rosser Kennedy. ■ 73013 #048-15-2007 L2007 OTO *012
PRATER, Scott Douglass. ■ 73034 #039-01-2007 DR *012
PRATT, Marsha Carol. ■ 73013 #039-01-1978 L1979 DR *074
PROUGH, Amie Elizabeth. 1700 RENAISSANCE BLVD 73013 #039-01-2004 L2005 PD *020 †55
QURESHI, Saleem Mon. ■ 73013 #166-02-2002 L2007 IM *100 †20
RAHHAL, Lindbergh John. 516 E OAK RL 73025 #039-01-1953 L1953 R *071 †80
RAJU, Ryan Palivela. ■ 73013 #048-15-2005 L2007 OTO *012
REAVES, Ricky Lee. 2701 COLTRANE PL, CONSULTANTS PC 73034 #048-02-1979 L1988 PTH AM *020 †50
REDWINE, Susan Thornton. 1575 N SANTA FE AVE 73003 #048-13-2000 L2001 PD *020 †55
REIF, Michael Edward. ■ 73013 #028-02-1968 L1969 GS *071 †85
RIDDLE, Douglas Ryan. 3560 S BOULEVARD ST 73013 #039-01-2004 L2005 FM *020 †18
RINGROSE, Robert Edward. 1 S BRYANT AVE 73034 #039-01-1963 L1964 GE IM *020 †20
ROBERTS, Suzanne Frances. ■ 73034 #039-01-1998 L2002 EM *030
ROCKLER, Barry Michael. 2701 COLTRANE PL, CONSULTANTS PC 73034 #026-04-1976 L1981 PTH *020 †50
ROY, Johnny Bernard. 105 S BRYANT AVE, OKLAHOMA CARDIOVASCULAR 73034 #528-01-1962 L1971 U *020 †95
RUDOLPH, Andrew Henry. ■ 73003 #025-01-1966 L1967 D DS *071 †15
SALEEMI, Mudassir M. ■ 73013 #704-21-1996 L2006 FM *020 †18
SAREMIAN, Jinous. ■ 73034 #517-03-1993 L2006 PTH *012
SARTIN, Michael Allen. 3126 S BOULEVARD ST, # 306 73013 #039-01-1970 L1971 RO *020 †80 ‡
SAWYERR, Olaseinde. ■ 73013 #010-02-1970 L1976 GS VS *071 †85 ‡
SCHADER, Brandon Wayne. ■ 73013 #039-01-2000 L2004 P *020 ‡
SCHAEFER, Jeanne Marie. 1700 RENAISSANCE BLVD 73013 #048-02-1993 L1994 PD *020 †55
SCHICK, Gary Don. 400 N BRYANT AVE 73013 #039-01-1995 L2000 PM IM *020 †20,60
SCHLINKE, Shawn Clinton. 1575 N SANTA FE AVE 73003 #039-01-1990 L1991 IM *020 †20
SCHLINKE, Stephen Dennis. 1700 RENAISSANCE BLVD 73013 #039-01-1988 L1989 OBG *020 †20
SCHMITT, Allyson Doiron. ■ 73034 #047-06-2005 L2006 OPH *012
SCOTT, Brooke D. 105 S BRYANT AVE, OKLAHOMA CARDIOVASCULAR 73034 #039-01-1985 L1986 CD IM *020 †20
SEBASTIAN, Cherian. ■ 73034 #495-44-1985 L1996 *020
SEDWICK, Whitney Claire. ■ 73013 #039-01-2008 *012
SESTAK, Andrea Lynn. ■ 73013 #048-12-1998 L2002 PD *020 †55
SHAH, Mahendra Saralal. ■ 73012 #495-23-1969 L1987 U *074 †95
SHELDON, Carol V. 2601 KELLEY POINTE PKWY, LLC 73013 #007-02-1979 L1980 DR *020 †80
SHETH, Nigam Pankaj. ■ 73012 #039-01-2008 *012
SHIRK, Amy Leanne. ■ 73034 #028-02-2001 L2007 PE *020 †16
SHISSLER, G Edward. ■ 73034 #051-01-1959 L1962 PD *071 †55
SHOCKLEY, Blake Edward. ■ 73013 #039-01-2006 L2006 ORS *012
SIGLER, Scott C. 2020 E 15TH ST STE B, SIGLER AND SMART EYE ASSOC 73013 #048-13-1990 L1996 OPH *020 †35
SILER, Timothy David. 1501 E 19TH ST 73013 #039-01-1975 L1976 FM *020 †18
SIMMONS, Merl Wayne. 1575 N SANTA FE AVE 73003 #048-02-1978 L1979 PD *020 †55
SIMONSON, James Robert. ■ 73013 #001-02-2004 L2005 GS *100
SIMPSON, Ricky Jerel. 1 S BRYANT AVE 73034 #039-01-1978 L1979 AN *020 †05
SINGHAL, Karunesh. ■ 73003 #495-34-1978 L2002 FM *020 †18
SINGHAL, Pooja. ■ 73003 #039-01-2008 *012
SMEDLUND, Stephen Eric. 910 S BRYANT AVE 73034 #039-01-1980 L1981 N *020
SMITH, Joel Nicholas. ■ 73013 #004-01-2006 L2007 ORS *012
SMITH, William Edmonson. 1700 RENAISSANCE BLVD 73013 #039-01-1986 L1987 FM GE *020 †18
SNOW, Jay Michael. ■ 73013 #028-03-2005 L2007 GS *012
SOFINOWSKI, Troy Michael. ■ 73003 #023-01-2007 L2007 GS *012
SPATZ, Tony William. ■ 73003 #039-01-2008 *012
SPENCER, Jack David. ■ 73013 #039-01-1954 L1954 ORS *071 †40
STANTON, Brian Andrew. 516 HERITAGE BLVD 73025 #035-08-1982 L2000 AN *020 †05
STOLLER, James Nathaniel. ■ 73013 #039-01-2004 L2005 GS *012
STOUT, Darrel Lee. 1575 N SANTA FE AVE, MERCY HEALTH EDMOND SANTA 73003 #039-01-1983 L1984 FM *020 †18
SUMNER, Hatton Wm. 2701 COLTRANE PL, CONSULTANTS PC 73034 #028-02-1970 L1981 ATP *020 †50
SUTTON, Katie Rebecca. ■ 73034 #019-02-2006 L2006 OBG *012
SWISHER, Karen Kay. ■ 73013 #039-01-2004 L2005 IM *020 †20
TALLERICO, Daniel Louis. 3863 S BOULEVARD ST, STE 100 73013 #048-13-1974 L1975 OBG *020 †30
TARBOX, Daniel Layne. ■ 73013 #048-12-2003 L2004 DR *012
TCHERNIAK, Grigory. ■ 73034 #913-39-1985 L2004 AN *020 †05

TE, Charles Carvajal. ■ 73013 #039-01-2007 L2007 **IM** *012
TEDESCO, Dustin Shaun. ■ 73012 #039-01-2007 L2007 **IM** *012
THAKAR, Ishita G. 705 BRIDGEVIEW PL 73003 #495-45-1995 L1999 **IMG** *020 †20
THOMPSON, Jeffrey Michael. 820 W 15TH ST 73013 #024-07-1983 L2004 **GP EM** *020 †18
THOMPSON LANZA, Alicia D. ■ 73013 #028-03-1995 L2007 **CHP P** *020
THROWER, Michael Alan. ■ 73025 #039-01-2007 L2007 **IM** *012
THURGOOD, Michael Craig. ■ 73013 #054-04-2005 L2007 **DR** *012
TISDAL, Victor C, III. 13803 CROSSING WAY W 73013 #039-01-1968 L1968 **DR** *020 †80 ‡
TORTORICI, Glen Joseph. ■ 73025 #039-01-1999 **IM** *100
TRAMMELL, John Raymond. 23201 N BRIARWOOD DR ED 73025 #039-01-1959 L1959 **GP GS** *071
TRAN, Joseph Hung. ■ 73003 #038-43-2001 L2004 **FM** *020 †18
TROTTER, Lanny F. ■ 73013 #039-01-1962 L1963 **OBG OS** *072
TRUONG, Camtu Do Nguyen. ■ 73013 #039-01-2003 L2005 **SP** *012
TRYGGESTAD, Jeanie Beatri. 305 ABILENE AVE 73003 #039-01-2005 L2007 **PD** *012
TUBB, Daniel Wm. 1 S BRYANT AVE 73034 #039-01-1967 L1968 **GS** *020 †85
TUCKER, Sherri Angela. 1616 S KELLY AVE, THE PHYSICIANS GROUP 73013 #039-01-1986 L1987 **FM** *020 †18
TURNER, James Sterling. 301 S BOULEVARD ST 73034 #039-01-1963 L1963 **GP** *071
UNDERHILL, Floyd Keith. 1501 E 19TH ST 73013 #039-01-1982 L1983 **FM** *020 †18
VALENTINE, Nathan Isaac. ■ 73003 #039-01-2004 L2007 **FM** *020
VANLANDINGHAM, William Br. ■ 73013 #039-01-2008 *012
VERONNEAU, Bettina Gisela. 1575 N SANTA FE AVE 73003 #062-01-1983 L1991 **GP** *020
VERONNEAU, Stephen Jean. ■ 73034 #062-01-1983 L1987 **AM** *050 †70
WALKER, Timothy Andrew. ■ 73013 #039-01-1971 L1973 **PS GS** *071 †85,65
WALTON, Gregory Franklyn. 1800 RENAISSANCE BLVD, # 200 73013 #039-01-1989 L1997 **GS** *020 †85
WATTS, Jeff Lynn. 1705 RENAISSANCE BLVD, STE 135 73013 #039-01-1994 L2000 **DR** *020 †80
WAYNE, Ivan. 105 S BRYANT AVE, STE 210 73034 #018-03-1996 L2002 **OTO** *020 †45
WEBB, Shannon Lanae. ■ 73013 #048-16-2002 **PD** *100
WEBSTER, Nicholas Leigh. ■ 73034 #047-06-1985 L2006 **FM** *020 †70
WEDDLE, Chas Calvin, Jr. 1015 WATERWOOD PKWY # G-1 73034 #039-01-1978 L1979 **AN** *020
WHORTON, Joshua Dan. ■ 73003 #039-01-2004 L2006 **IM** *012 †20
WILD, Jennifer Lyn. ■ 73034 #039-01-2001 **IM** *100
WILLIAMS, David Kent. 3608 JIM ROBISON DR 73034 #305-01-1998 L2002 **AN** *020
WILLIAMS, Michael Orval. 105 S BRYANT AVE 73034 #028-02-1974 L1975 **ORS** *020 †40
WILLIAMS, Noel Robt. 1705 RENAISSANCE BLVD 73013 #038-40-1990 L1991 **OBG** *020 †30
WILSON, Sherrita Cotton. 2701 COLTRANE PL, CONSULTANTS PC 73034 #005-18-1991 L1996 **PTH** *020 †50
WOIWODE, Daniel Jerome. 1501 E 19TH ST 73013 #016-11-1966 L1970 **FM** *020 †18 ‡
WOLFF, James Daniel. ■ 73013 #048-04-2002 L2004 **DR** *012
WONG, Kenneth M. 1705 RENAISSANCE BLVD 73013 #048-15-1988 L1994 **CD IM** *020 †20
WOOD, Ryan Christopher. ■ 73013 #104-01-2007 L2007 **FP** *012
YACOUB, Inas Zaki. ■ 73003 #915-04-1980 L2004 **FOP** *050
YURDAKUL, Metin Mete. ■ 73013 #902-03-1961 L1971 **GP** *020
ZAIDI, Wasiq Ali. 717 FOX BEND TRL 73034 #704-04-1989 L2000 **P** *020 †75
ZAKHAROV, Vladislav Yurye. 73013 #913-32-1988 L2006 **PTH** *012
ZANTOUT, Imad A. ■ 73013 #605-01-1973 L1974 **GE IM** *071
ZHAO, Lichao. ■ 73013 #243-58-1991 L2006 **PTH** *012
ZHENG, Xiangyang. 2600 CENTURY DR 73013 #243-58-1986 L2006 **AN** *020 †05

EL RENO — CANADIAN

BUENDIA, Imelda B. 1631A E US HIGHWAY 66, EL RENO INDIAN HEALTH CLIN 73036 #748-02-1969 L1977 **FM** *020 †18
BULLEN, John Alfred. ■ 73036 #039-01-1972 L1973 **P** *071 †75
CASTRO-GUZMAN, Robt Saul. 1631A E US HIGHWAY 66, EL RENO IHS CLINIC 73036 #308-03-1980 L1983 **GP GPM** *020
DRAVID, Gangadhar K. 927 S COUNTRY CLUB RD 73036 #495-28-1961 L1977 **GS GP** *040 †85
KHASTGIR, Anupa. 1629B E US HIGHWAY 66, EL RENO REGIONAL DIALYSIS 73036 #495-45-1988 L1992 **NEP** *020 †20
LABAHN, Jacob Keenon. ■ 73036 #039-01-2004 L2006 **FM** *100 †18
MALCHER, Barbara Maria. ■ 73036 #759-01-1974 L1992 **FM P** *020 †18
MEHLE, Margaret A. 2001 PARKVIEW DR 73036 #026-04-1975 L1976 **GP** *020
REGE, Vidya Bhagwant. 927 S COUNTRY CLUB RD 73036 #495-19-1965 L1977 **OPH** *020
REUTER, Frederick Blake. 12031 RENO W 73036 #039-01-2005 L2006 **AN** *012
STRONG, Clinton Riley, III. 1515 W WADE ST 73036 #039-01-1971 L1972 **FM** *020 †18
SULLIVAN, Jesse Geo. 2001 PARKVIEW DR 73036 #039-01-1978 L1979 **GP EM** *020
SULLIVAN, Michael Dean. 2001 PARKVIEW DR 73036 #039-01-1982 L1983 **FM** *020

ELGIN — COMANCHE

JOYCE, Daniel Justin. ■ 73538 #041-77-2003, ▲ L2005 **FM** *020 †18
SANTANA, Wendis A. ■ 73538 #041-77-2004, ▲ L2007 **FM** *020

ELK CITY — BECKHAM

AHN, Duk Heh. 3080 W 3RD ST 73644 #583-08-1969 L1982 **P** *020
AHN, Yoo Chul. 1800 W 1ST ST 73644 #583-10-1967 L1978 **ORS** *020 †40 ‡
ALFARO, Maria Victoria Ri. 1705 W 2ND ST 73644 #748-21-1993 L2005 **IM** *020 †20
ANEJA, Pravin C. 1800 W 1ST ST STE 101, MARSHFIELD CLINIC 73644 #495-45-1975 L2004 **GE IM** *020
ANWAR, Sarfaraz. 2406 BELL AVE 73644 #704-02-1990 L1996 **IM EM** *020 †20 ‡
BAKER, Loren V, Jr. ■ 73648 #039-01-1955 L1955 **GP GS** *072
BANK, David Wm. 3080 W 3RD ST 73644 #039-01-1971 L1972 **FM** *020 †18
COFFEY, J Clifton. 1900 W 2ND STREET, STE C 73644 #039-01-1995 L1998 **FM OBS** *020 †18
COLVERT, James R, Jr. 125 FAIRWAY DR 73644 #039-01-1976 L1977 **IM EM** *020 †20
DRESSLER, Joe Bill. 1705 W 2ND ST 73644 #039-01-1989 L1990 **FOP** *020
FEATHERSTON, William M. 1925 W 3RD ST 73644 #047-06-1945 L1949 **A GPM** *020 †55,03
FIRTH, Paul Lynn. 503 W COUNTRY CLUB BLVD 73644 #039-01-1995 L1996 **PD** *020 †55
FRIESEN, Dennis Jay. 303 W 5TH ST 73644 #039-01-1974 L1975 **FM** *030 †18

GRAHAM, Treva Jo. 1705 W 2ND ST 73644 #039-01-1999 L2000 **FM** *020 †18
HEINE, Ralph Richard. ■ 73644 #016-06-1948 L1953 **GP ORS** *071
HENDERSON, Robert Mark. 1705 W 2ND ST 73644 #039-01-1984 L1989 **EM AN** *020
HORRILLENO, Henry Tamayo. 1800 W 1ST ST, STE 108 73644 #748-01-1972 L2007 **GS** *020 †85
JOHNSON, James Lyndon. 1705 W 2ND ST, GREAT PLAINS REGIONAL MED 73644 #038-40-1977 L2002 **EM FM** *020 †18
KEITH, Robert Carlton, Jr. 1901 W 3RD ST STE B, HIGH PLIANS OB GYN INC 73644 #039-01-1978 L1982 **OBG EM** *020 †30 ‡
KROMPECHER, Camilla M. 1800 W 1ST ST 73644 #473-04-1973 L1986 **FM** *020 †18
KROMPECHER, Stephen J. 1705 W 2ND ST 73644 #473-04-1973 L1986 **PTH** *020
MASK, Dennis Ray. 1710 W 3RD ST STE 101, CITY 73644 #039-01-1969 L1969 **NEP IM** *071
MASSOUMI, Kamran Mohajer. 1710 W 3RD ST, INC 73644 #028-34-1998 L2003 **OPH** *020
MAY, Andre R. 1710 W 3RD ST STE 101, PREMIER INTERNAL MEDICINE 73644 #047-07-1983 L2007 **IM PD** *020 †20,55
MORGAN, Brian Dale. 1710 W 3RD ST, INC 73644 #039-01-1994 L1995 **OPH** *020 †35
PAN, Cheng-Hsiung. 1710 W 3RD ST, STE 102 73644 #244-02-1972 L2005 **OTO HNS** *020 †45
PERKINS, John Robt. 601 W 3RD ST 73644 #039-01-1974 L1975 **FM FPG** *020 †18
PHELPS, Craig A. 1710 W 3RD ST STE 103B, OKLAHOMA CITY CLINIC-ELK C 73644 #019-02-1975 L1976 **FM** *020 †18
RADER, Michael David. 1121 W 3RD ST 73644 #039-01-1990 L1994 **D** *020 †15
STRIBLING, Fred S, III. ■ 73648 #011-04-1993 L2002 **P** *020
TRISSELL, Kathryn Ann. 1705 W 2ND ST 73644 #039-01-1984 L1985 **IM** *020 †20
TWIDALE, Nicholas. 1701 W AVENUE A 73644 #143-11-1981 L1990 **CD IM** *020
VILAR-JENSEN, Hetlevia R. 1710 W 3RD ST SU 73644 #715-01-1988 L2004 **FM** *020 †18
WHU, Maybelle S. 1705 W 2ND ST 73644 #016-11-1983 L2007 **FM PHL** *020 †18

ENID — GARFIELD

ABERNETHY, Edward A, III. 330 S 5TH ST, STE 201 73701 #039-01-1971 L1972 **GS VS** *071 †85
ANTHONY, Bobby Doyce. 330 S 5TH ST 73701 #039-01-1966 L1966 **ORS** *071 †40
BARNARD, David Robert. 527 GOTT RD, VANCE AIR FORCE BASE 73705 #028-02-1993 L1996 **FM** *020 †18
BARNS, Edward Leslie. 3201 N VAN BUREN ST # 500 73703 #019-02-1988 L1989 **OTO** *020 †45
BARTOLOZZI, John Joseph. 1218 W WILLOW RD STE A 73703 #016-45-1988 L2000 **CD** *020
BERGNER, Michelle Renee. 601 W OWEN K GARRIOTT RD 73701 #048-15-2000 L2004 **OBG** *020 †30 ‡
BLAKEBURN, Robert V. 620 S MADISON ST, STE 209 73701 #039-01-1987 L1990 **FM** *020 †18
BLANKENSHIP, Jerry Ben. 305 S 5TH ST 73701 #039-01-1962 L1962 **U** *071 †95
BRECKENRIDGE, Robert Jos. 405 E CHEROKEE AVE 73701 #048-78-1974, ▲ L1977 **IM** *020
BROWN, Douglas Kip. 314 E OWEN K GARRIOTT RD 73701 #017-20-1972 L1979 **CD IM** *020 †20
BRYANT PITTS, Willienell. 2600 E WILLOW RD 73701 #012-01-1983 L1992 **PD GP** *020 †55
CAMP, Roy Earl. ■ 73703 #039-01-1966 L1966 **ORS** *071 †40
CANNON, Charles Lawrence. 1133 W WILLOW RD 73703 #039-01-1989 L1990 **IM GE** *020 †20
CHATTERJI, Robi Paul. 3201 N VAN BUREN ST # 400 73703 #039-01-1993 L1994 **FM** *020 †18 ‡
CHENG, Paul Powen. 1220 W WILLOW RD STE C 73703 #039-01-1993 L1994 **AN** *020 †05
CHRYSANT, George Steven. 620 S MADISON ST, STE 203 73701 #039-01-1997 L2004 **IC** *020 †20
COLVERT, James Robert, III. 615 E OKLAHOMA AVE, STE 200 73701 #039-01-1998 L1999 **U** *020 †95
DANDRIDGE, Wm Shelton. 5801 N OAKWOOD RD, E 130 73703 #004-01-1939 L1954 **ORS** *071
DAVIS, Elaine M Neill. ■ 73703 #039-01-1962 L1962 **GYN** *071 †30
DILLING, Jerome M, Jr. 1133 W WILLOW RD 73703 #039-01-1968 L1969 **OTO** *020 †45
DUKE, Meredith Colleen. ■ 73703 #039-01-2008 *012
ERBA, Paul Stephen. 305 S 5TH ST 73701 #041-09-1984 L1988 **RO** *020
FELDMAN, Michael Lloyd. 1415 W WYNONA AVE, 2216 S. VAN BUREN 73703 #039-01-1984 L1986 **P** *020 †75
FERGUSON, James David. 615 E OKLAHOMA AVE STE 207 73701 #039-01-2002 L2003 **OBG** *020
FIKE, Edgar Allen, IV. 1133 W WILLOW RD 73703 #019-02-1993 L1998 **ORS OSM** *020 †40
FRANTZ, Kurt Smith. 615 E OKLAHOMA AVE, STE 203 73701 #028-02-1974 L1976 **FM FPG** *020 †18
GANESAN, Guruswami. 620 S MADISON STE 203, HEARTLAND CARDIOVASCULAR C 73701 #495-33-1961 L1972 **CD IM** *020
GOERING, Mark Bradley. 720 W MAINE AVE STE C 73701 #019-02-1983 L1989 **DR** *020 †80
GUNIGANTI, Uma Maheswari. 330 S 5TH ST STE 200, ENID HEART CENTER PC 73701 #495-21-1990 L2002 **CD** *020 †20
HAI, Hamid Harry Abdul. 620 S MADISON ST, STE 202 73701 #495-15-1967 L2007 **CD IM** *020 †20
HEATON, Gary Dean. 2600 E WILLOW RD, ENID STATE SCHOOL 73701 #030-05-1975 L1982 **FM** *071 †18
HENSLEY, John Allison. ■ 73703 #039-01-1996 L1997 **EM** *020 †18
HOFFMAN, Robert Chas. 615 E OKLAHOMA AVE, STE 200 73701 #039-01-1965 L1965 **U** *071 †95
HOFFSOMMER, Jeffrey G. 1121 BRIAR RIDGE RD 73703 #039-01-1987 L1990 **EM FM** *020 †18
HROMAS, Richard Leroy. 1805 W OWEN K GARRIOTT RD 73703 #039-01-1978 L1979 **FM** *020 †18
HUGHES, Dean Wesley, II. 305 S 5TH ST 73701 #039-01-1996 L1997 **DR** *020
HUGUET DEXEUS, Francisco. 825 E OWEN K GARRIOTT RD 73701 #847-12-1974 L1994 **ON IM** *020 †20
ILETO, Zaida Akang. ■ 73701 #748-01-1955 L1980 **GP** *020
JARMAN, Joe Bob. 330 S 5TH ST 73701 #039-01-1961 L1961 **ORS** *071 †40
JUTTING, John Richard, Jr. 620 S MADISON ST STE 304, ENID FAMILY MED CLINIC 73701 #422-01-2006 L2006 **FM** *100
KAH, Peter Joseph. 527 GOTT RD, VANCE AFB 73705 #020-02-1999 L2003 **FM** *020 †18
KARNS, Donald Clark. 402 S OAKWOOD RD STE B 73703 #039-01-1960 L1960 **FM** *071 †18
KELLER, David Edward. 330 S 5TH ST STE 507, 330 SOUTH FIFTH ST STE 501 73701 #004-01-1999 L2000 **ORS** *020 †18
KNAPIK, Joseph Robt. 310 S 4TH ST 73701 #039-01-1983 L1984 **N PM** *020 †75
KOENEN, Howard Peter, Jr. 620 S MADISON ST STE 304, ENID FAMILY PRACTICE 73701 #005-18-1988 L2005 **FM** *020

KRUSKA, Jarrett Daniel. 615 E OKLAHOMA AVE, STE 202 73701 #039-01-2000 L2001 **U** *020 †95

LAWRENCE, Charles A. 1133 W WILLOW RD 73703 #039-01-1976 L1977 **OPH** *020 †35

LAWRENCE, Charles Anthony. 73703 #039-01-2004 L2004 **DR** *012

LEAP, Paul A. 330 S 5TH ST 73701 #039-01-1960 L1963 **PTH** *020 †50

LONG, Fred M. ■ 73703 #039-01-1951 L1951 **DR** *071 †80

LOSTETTER, Adrienne L. ■ 73703 #048-15-1996 L2002 **PD** *020 †55 ‡

MALHOTRA, Chander Kamal. 620 S MADISON ST STE 204 73701 #495-05-1973 L1983 **CD** *020 †20

MALHOTRA, Suman. 620 S MADISON ST 2ND FL 73701 #495-51-1978 L1984 **PD** *020

MARSHALL, Vaughn Giles. 1204 W WILLOW RD, STE F 73703 #039-01-1974 L1975 **NR DR** *020 †80

MATLI, Monte Jantzen. 626 DEER RUN 73703 #048-15-1991 L1994 **AN PMM** *020 †05

MATOUSEK, David. 330 S 5TH ST, STE 202 73701 #039-01-1979 L1980 **FM** *020 †18

MATSON, Lisa Scheyer. 1204 W WILLOW RD STE B 73703 #039-01-1999 L2003 **P** *020

MC CAFFERTY, John C. ■ 73705 #023-12-1983 L1984 **GS AM** *030 †85

MCFADDEN, Dennis Stephen. 615 E OKLAHOMA AVE STE 203, ENID WOMENS HEALTHCARE ASS 73701 #039-79-2003, ▲ L2007 *020

MC INTYRE, Dennis Keith. 615 E OKLAHOMA AVE STE 208 73701 #039-01-1978 L1979 **IM** *020 †20

MC INTYRE, John Aubrey. 330 S 5TH ST 73701 #039-01-1943 L1945 **IM** *071

MILLER, David Robt. 720 W MAINE AVE STE C, SUITE C 73701 #007-02-1985 L1996 **DR** *020 †80

MILLER, John Stanley. 615 E OKLAHOMA AVE 73701 #047-05-1960 L1967 **OPH** *071 †35

MITCHELL, Dan. 615 E OKLAHOMA AVE STE 204 73701 #039-01-1958 L1958 **R NM** *072 †80

MOSELEY, Jack Ellis, Jr. 2600 E WILLOW RD, NORCE 73701 #023-07-1982 L1997 **FM MPD** *020

MUELLER, Glenn R. 6309 W PURDUE AVE 73703 #048-15-1993 L1999 **AN** *020 †05

MUELLER, Lynda L. 330 S 5TH ST, STE 202 73701 #654-01-1993 L1995 **FM** *020 †18

NAGUIB, Tarek Hosny. 120 W OWEN K GARRIOTT RD 73701 #915-02-1981 L1990 **NEP ID** *020 †20

NGUYEN, Trung B. 401 S 3RD ST 73701 #048-15-1988 L1995 **APM** *020 †20

OATHOUT, Daniel E. 620 S MADISON ST, STE 301 73701 #016-11-1973 L1981 **GYN** *020 †30

OATMAN, Mark Adam. 527 GOTT RD, 71ST MEDICAL GROUP/SGQ 73705 #039-01-2000 L2008 **FM** *100 ‡

O'QUIN, Michael James. 3201 N VAN BUREN ST, STE 300 73703 #039-01-1987 L1988 **PD** *020 †55 ‡

ORTEGA, Sandra Elaine. 3524 W PURDUE AVE 73703 #039-01-1982 L1983 **AN** *020

PANDEY, Meenu. 620 S MADISON ST STE 304, ENID FAMILY MED CLINIC 73701 #965-01-2002 L2006 **FP** *012

PARKER, David Donald. 316 W OWEN K GARRIOTT RD, WOMENS HEALTH & WELLNESS 73701 #039-01-1966 L1966 **OBG** *020 †30

PATZKOWSKY, Lawrence W. R600 S MONROE ST 73701 #039-01-1950 L1950 **FM AM** *071 †18

PENDLETON, Bruce Dwayne. 102 S VAN BUREN ST 73703 #039-01-1980 L1981 **NS** *020 †25

PETERSEN, Kristy Michele. 620 S MADISON ST, STE 209 73701 #039-01-1994 L1995 **FM** *020 †18 ‡

PHILLIPS, Steven Lynn. 1220 W WILLOW RD, INC 73703 #039-79-1979, ▲ L1980 **AN** *020 †05

POLLARD, Barry Lynn. 102 S VAN BUREN ST 73703 #039-01-1977 L1978 **NS EM** *020 †25

PONTIOUS, James Michael. 620 S MADISON ST STE 304 73701 #039-01-1979 L1980 **FM** *040 †18 ‡

PONTIOUS, Myrna Kirk. 302 W MAPLE AVE, LIFE EMERGENCY MEDICAL SVC 73701 #039-01-1983 L1984 **EM FM** *020 †18 ‡

PRICE, William Franklin. 527 GOTT RD, BLDG 810 73705 #039-01-1991 L1992 **FM** *020 †18 ‡

PROVINE, John Edward. 409 E CHEROKEE AVE 73701 #048-04-1972 L1975 **PD** *071 †55

RABOLD, Roger Alan. ■ 73703 #026-04-1966 L1970 **DR NR** *071

RAJENDRA, Krishna. ■ 73703 #422-01-2004 L2007 **OBG** *012

RAMSEYER, Lorenz Theodore. 720 W MAINE AVE 73701 #039-01-1989 L1990 **DR** *020 †80 ‡

RAO, Sanku Surender. 330 S 5TH ST STE 403 73701 #495-21-1970 L1979 **GE** *020 †20

REDDY, Adhikari Mohan. 620 S MADISON ST STE 101 73701 #495-70-1968 L1981 **N** *020 †75

REILLY, Martin Todd. 401 E OKLAHOMA AVE, STE A 73701 #048-78-1999, ▲ L2003 *020

REITZ, Craig Lee. 1220 W WILLOW RD STE A 73703 #039-01-1979 L1980 **ON IM** *020 †20

REITZ, Rolfe Dean. 310 S 4TH ST 73701 #039-01-1981 L1982 **N** *020 †75

RICKMAN, Michael Zane. 427 E CHEROKEE AVE 73701 #039-01-1973 L1976 **IM** *020 ‡

RIVERS, Richard Allen. 620 S MADISON ST, STE 209 73701 #039-01-1986 L1987 **FM** *020 †18

ROBERTS, Clarence R. 620 S MADISON ST 73701 #039-01-1956 L1956 **FM ADM** *071 †85

ROBINSON, Earl M. ■ 73703 #039-01-1943 L1945 **GS** *071

ROGERS, James R. 615 E OKLAHOMA AVE 73701 #039-01-1983 L1984 **OPH** *020 †18,35

ROHINI, Sanku. 330 S 5TH ST STE 301 73701 #495-65-1969 L1979 **PD** *020 †55

RONCK, John W. 305 S 5TH ST, EMERGENCY CONSULTANT INCOR 73701 #039-01-1976 L1977 **FM** *020 †18

RUMPH, D Ross. ■ 73703 #048-02-1958 L1985 **OBG** *071 †30 ‡

RUSSELL, David Stanton. ■ 73703 #039-01-1963 L1963 **R GPM** *071 †80 ‡

SAULS, Fielding Clark. 330 S 5TH ST, STE 104 73701 #021-05-1977 L2001 **TS CCS** *020 †85,90

SCHIFFERDECKER, Branislav. 427 E CHEROKEE AVE, OKLAHOMA CARDIOVASCULAR 73701 #286-03-1995 L2006 **IC** *100 †20

SELBY, David Moore. 3 ROLLING OAKS DR 73703 #039-01-1961 L1968 **GS** *071 †85

SHAPIRO, Bryan Eliot. 1220 W WILLOW RD, INC 73703 #041-13-1985 L2005 **AN PME** *020 †05

SHELTON, Garrett Glenn. 620 S MADISON ST, STE 209 73701 #039-01-1999 L2000 **FM** *020 †18

SHEPHERD, David James, Jr. 1133 W WILLOW RD 73703 #039-01-1975 L1980 **IM** *020 †20

SHIELDS, Charles Robt. 330 S 5TH ST STE 305 73701 #039-01-1980 L2001 **PM PMM** *020 †60

SHORT, Margo Renee. 620 S MADISON ST, STE 304 73701 #039-01-2003 L2004 **FM** *100 †18

SHRECK, Ronald W. 915 E OWEN K GARRIOTT RD 73701 #039-01-1976 L1977 **GS** *020

SHUTTEE, Robert D. ■ 73703 #039-01-1944 L1946 **PD** *071 †55

SILVERS, Heather M. ■ 73703 #039-01-2003 L2004 **GS** *020

SIMON, William Hale. 3201 N VAN BUREN ST, STE 300 73703 #039-01-1954 L1954 **PD OS** *020 †55

SMITH, William Robt. 427 E CHEROKEE AVE 73701 #039-01-1956 L1956 **IM** *071 †20

SNODGRASS, Joe Edward. 2609 N VAN BUREN ST 73703 #028-46-1990 L1995 **PTH** *020 †50

SNYDER, H Thos. 330 S 5TH ST, STE 202 73701 #039-01-1983 L1984 **FM** *020 †18

SPENCER, Elizabeth Ruth. 620 S MADISON ST STE 304, ENID FAMILY MED CLINIC 73701 #104-01-2006 L2006 **FP** *012

STAERKEL, Richard Eldo. 1133 W WILLOW RD 73703 #039-01-1977 L1978 **OBG** *020 †30

STAFFORD, Joseph Wm. ■ 73703 #039-01-1954 L1954 **GP FM** *071

STAINSBY, Donald L. ■ 73703 #040-02-1946 L1953 **NS** *020 †25

STEVENS, Amanda Layne. ■ 73703 #039-01-2006 *012

SWENTON, Joseph Robt. 305 S 5TH ST 73701 #019-02-1978 L1979 **EM** *020

SWITZER, Eve Hsing. 3201 N VAN BUREN ST, STE 300 73703 #034-01-1994 L1997 **PD** *020 †55 ‡

SWITZER, Seth Harold. 3201 N VAN BUREN ST, STE 400 73703 #034-01-1994 L1997 **FM** *020 †18

TAYLOR, Daryl Christy. ■ 73703 #005-12-1973 L1975 **P** *075

TESKE, Timothy W. 1133 W WILLOW RD 73703 #039-79-1997, ▲ L2002 **ORS** *020

TOBIN, James Vincent. 527 GOTT RD, 71ST MDG/SGQ, VANCE AFB 73705 #020-02-1975 L1976 **OBG GP** *020 †30

VANHOOSER, Alicia Fowlkes. 600 S MONROE ST 73701 #039-01-1987 L1988 **DR** *020 †80

VANHOOSER, David Wade. 620 S MADISON ST STE 1 73701 #039-01-1982 L1983 **TS VS** *020 †85,90

VANHOOSER, Jonathan Ross. 600 S MONROE ST 73701 #039-01-1987 L1988 **DR VIR** *020 †80

WALKER, Dennis Lynn. ■ 73703 #039-01-1978 L1979 **FM** *071 †18

WALSH, John Henry. 720 W MAINE AVE, STE C 73701 #041-09-1960 L1968 **R** *071 †80

WAMPLER-ROGERS, Cindy Ann. 102 S VAN BUREN ST 73703 #039-01-1985 L1987 **OM** *020

WASHBURN, Daniel D. 615 E OKLAHOMA AVE STE 208 73701 #039-01-1976 L1977 **IM END** *020 †20

WATTS, Kenneth Leroy. 330 S 5TH ST STE 401 73701 #037-01-2002 L2007 **GS** *100 †85

WEAVER, David L, Jr. 601 W OWEN K GARRIOTT RD 73701 #021-01-1985 L2002 **OBG** *020

WHINERY, Barbara S. 620 S MADISON ST, STE 209 73701 #039-01-1985 L1986 **FM** *020 †18

WHITE, Leroy Calvin. 620 S MADISON ST STE 304, ENID FAMILY MED 73701 #041-13-1981 L2006 **FP** *012

WHITENECK, Robert Wray. 1133 W WILLOW RD 73703 #039-01-1979 L1984 **ORS** *020 †40

WHITSON, Brian David. 3201 N VAN BUREN ST # 400 73703 #039-01-1989 L1995 **PUD CCM** *020 †20

WORRELL, James Patrick. 1133 W WILLOW RD 73703 #039-01-1984 L1996 **PS** *020 †85,65

WORTHEN, Rodney L, II. 615 E OKLAHOMA AVE STE 202, ENID UROLOGY ASSOCIATION 73701 #039-01-1980 L1982 **U** *020 †95

ZUECH, David Ernest. 1133 W WILLOW RD 73703 #039-01-1993 L1995 **OPH** *020 †35

EUFAULA – MCINTOSH

BEETS, Billy Conn, Jr. 800 W FORREST AVE, MUSCOGEE (CREEK) NATION HE 74432 #039-01-1997 L1999 **FP** *012

CHESNUT, Dan Edwin. ■ 74432 #039-01-1963 L1963 **OM** *020

CO, Henry G. 111 OAK ST, STE 510 74432 #748-02-1985 L1995 **IM CCM** *020 †20 ‡

FARROW, Robert Edgar. 218 N MAIN ST 74432 #004-01-1978 L1981 **FM** *020 †18

HESSE, Robert S. 800 W FORREST AVE 74432 #019-02-1969 L1974 **GP PTH** *020 †50

LEE, William Kenneth. 1 HOSPITAL DR, EUFAULA LAKE VIEW HOSPITAL 74432 #583-15-1979 L1981 **GS** *020

MASSEY, John Barry. RR 4 BOX 943 74432 #039-01-1954 L1954 **P** *020 †75

YAR, Mohammad Samie. 17 HOSPITAL DR 74432 #118-01-1966 L1979 **GS GP** *020

FAIRFAX – OSAGE

HELMBRIGHT, Jeannie Marie. 212 N MAIN ST 74637 #039-01-1997 L1999 **P** *020

HENNING, Guy Eugene. ■ 74637 #004-01-1962 L1966 **FM EM** *071 †18 ‡

FAIRVIEW – MAJOR

ALI, Solomon. 523 E STATE RD, FAIRVIEW FAMILY CLINIC 73737 #566-01-1985 L1999 **FM** *020

BENTON, Jami Luann. 523 E STATE RD 73737 #654-01-2004 L2007 **FP** *012

CROWE, Frank Patrick. 519 E STATE RD 73737 #039-01-1970 L1971 **FM** *020

HARRIS, Johnnie P. 519 E STATE RD 73737 #028-78-1963, ▲ L1965 **FM** *020

PRICE, John Stephen. 523 E STATE RD 73737 #039-01-1987 L1988 **FM** *020 †18

FINLEY – PUSHMATAHA

DE BOLT, Merlan Edward. ■ 74543 #018-03-1948 L1953 **PYA P** *071 †75

FORT SILL – COMANCHE

AKAKA, Elizabeth Gk. ■ 73503 #014-01-1998 L1998 **IM** *020

BEAUCHAMP, Jeremy Todd. ■ 73503 #023-12-2000 L2001 **FM** *020 †18

BRADLEY, Melville Douglas. ■ 73503 #042-03-1995 L1997 **FM** *020

CARDONA, Robert Andrew. 4301 NW MOW WAY RD, ATTN: CREDENTIAL OFFICE 73503 #005-12-1997 L1999 **P** *020

CHO, Moo Haeng. ■ 73503 #583-10-1968 L1975 **PTH** *020 †50

DARON, Andrew M. ■ 73503 #517-03-1962 L1989 **DR** *071 ‡

DEGAZON, Alexander Franci. 4301 NW MOW WAY RD, REYNOLDS ARMY COMMUNITY HO 73503 #649-35-1993 L2002 **FM** *020 †18 ‡

DRAKE, Susan Kathleen. 4301 NW MOW WAY RD, REYNOLDS ARMY HOSPITAL 73503 #030-06-1993 L2005 **IM** *020 †20

DYKES, Thomas Edward. 4301 NW MOW WAY RD, ATTN: MCUA-QSD 73503 #023-12-1996 L1997 **U** *020 †95

GIBSON, Brent Randall. 4301 NW MOW WAY RD, MCUA-QSD 73503 #012-01-2001 L2002 **OM** *020 †18

GLADWELL, Brian Lane. 4301 NW MOW WAY RD, MCUA-QSD 73503 #023-12-2000 L2002 **FM** *100 †18

GUERREIRO, John Palma. 4301 NW MOW WAY RD, MCUA-QSD 73503 #025-12-2000 L2001 **FM** *100 †18

HEIRIGS, Ralph Allen. 4300 THOMAS RD, REYNOLDS ARMY COMMUNITY HO 73503 #019-02-1981 L1993 **OBG** *020 †30

HORNSBY, Robert Lee. 4301 NW MOW WAY RD, ATTN: MCUA-QSD 73503 #038-44-2002 L2003 **FM** *020 †18

KODAMA, Catherine Lee. 4301 NW MOW WAY RD, MCUA-QSD 73503 #035-19-1998 L2006 **OBG** *020

KOOPMAN, Christian L. 4301 NW MOW WAY RD, REYNOLDS ARMY COMMUNITY HO 73503 #028-78-1997, ▲ L2002 **DR** *012 †16

LEBEAU, Daren Donald. 4301 NW MOW WAY RD, REYNOLDS ARMY COMMUNITY HO 73503 #047-07-1996 L1999 **N** *020 ‡

LITWACK, Lewis Jay. ■ 73503 #270-02-2000 L2006 **FM EM** *020 †18

LODHIA, Kanchan Lal. 3009 NW WILSON ST, MCUA-OM 73503 #030-05-1969 L2001 **AN** *020 †05

LOVINS, Bruce Len. 4301 NW MOW WAY RD, FORT SILL-REYNOLDS ARMY HO 73503 #023-12-1994 L1995 **FM** *030 †18

MARIANO, Rodrigo Alba. 4301 NW MOW WAY RD, MCUA-PI 73503 #748-01-1981 L1998 **IM** *020 †20

MAROKUS, Roy Sheldon. ■ 73503 #035-08-1975 L1978 **EM OM** *020 †55,70

MONDRAGON, Donald Gene. 4301 NW MOW WAY RD, REYNOLDS ARMY COMM HOSP 73503 #039-05-1985 L1987 **IM** *020 †20

MORALES, Samantha Cecilia. ■ 73503 #035-15-1998 L2000 **PD** *100

MUNITZ, Elaine Marie. 4301 NW MOW WAY RD, FORT SILL OK ATTN MCUA-PI 73503 #023-12-1991 L2001 **FM** *020 †18

NEUENSCHWANDER, Mark. 4301 NW MOW WAY RD, REYNOLDS ARMY COMM. HOSPIT 73503 #047-06-1975 L1980 **GS FM** *030 †18,85

QUINN, David Michael. 4301 NW MOW WAY RD, MCUA-QSD 73503 #004-01-1997 L2003 **PTH** *020 †50

SHEEHAN, James Joseph, Jr. 4301 NW MOW WAY RD, MCUA-QSD 73503 #025-12-1994 L1996 **GPM** *030 †70

WERNER, Wolfgang Klaus. ARMY HOSP DIAG RAD 73503 #154-07-1964 L1971 **DR OBG** *020 †30,80

FORT SUPPLY – WOODWARD

HERD, Patrick Scott. PO BOX 1, NW CTR FOR BEHAVIORAL HLTH 73841 #039-01-1991 L1992 **P** *020

KUEKES, E David. PO BOX 1, 1 MILE EAST HIGHWAY 270 73841 #039-01-1988 L2000 **CHP** *020

MARQUEZ, Jose Raneses. WESTERN STATE HOSPITAL 73841 #748-01-1955 L1979 **IM PUD** *020

PHAM, Cuong Chan. PO BOX 61, 1 WILLIAM KEY BLVD 73841 #941-01-1979 L2004 **GP PTH** *020 †50

SAMBAJON, Emilia Tolibas. PO BOX 1, 1 MILE EAST HWY 270 73841 #748-07-1965 L1978 **P** *020

FOYIL – ROGERS

BRAZEAL, Steve Dale. PO BOX 500 74031 #039-01-1992 L1994 **FM GP** *020

FREDERICK – TILLMAN

ABU EL-SHAR, Addi Sameh. 319 E JOSEPHINE AVE 73542 #575-02-1992 L1997 **IM** *020 †20

AL-IMAM, Istabrak. 319 E JOSEPHINE AVE 73542 #528-01-1972 L1992 **GS FM** *020

DU TOIT, Francois J. 319 E JOSEPHINE AVE, TILLMANN HOSP 73542 #836-04-1985 L2007 **FM** *020 †18

NEMRI, Kamil Suleiman. 1115 N 14TH ST 73542 #781-02-1983 L2003 **FM** *020 †18 ‡

SULTAN, Maha. 319 E JOSEPHINE AVE, MEDICAL CLINIC BOX 177 73542 #875-01-1980 L1993 **GP OBS** *020

GLENPOOL – TULSA

GILMORE, Robert David. ■ 74033 #021-01-1954 L1977 **FM** *071 †18

PLINSKY, Michael Duane. ■ 74033 #004-01-2008 *012

GORE – SEQUOYAH

BLISS, Bryce Owen. RR 1, BOX 211-S 74435 #039-01-1957 L1957 **PTH DMP** *071 †50

GRANDFIELD – TILLMAN

HORTON, Joe C. 203 W 2ND ST, FAMILY MEDICAL CLINICS 73546 #039-01-1952 L1952 **FM GP** *071 †85

GRANITE – GREER

KULKARNI, Shyamkant S. PO BOX 514, OKLAHOMA STATE REFORMA 73547 #495-28-1960 L1987 **IM GP** *072

GROVE – DELAWARE

ALGEO, Thomas F. 1310 S MAIN ST, INTEGRIS GROVE HOSPITAL 74344 #039-01-1981 L1982 **FM** *020 †18

ANDERSON, Shawn Michael. 900 E 13TH ST, STE 102 74344 #305-01-2000 L2002 **FM** *020 †18

BECHTOL, Zachary Townsend. 601 E 13TH ST STE H 74344 #039-01-1995 L1997 **FM OBS** *020 †18

BECK, James Stephen. 1639 PINE DR, BUFFALO SHORES 74344 #028-03-1966 L1990 **GP** *020

BLAND, Francis Rollin. 700 S MAIN ST, ST JOHNS MEDICAL GROUP 74344 #005-12-1968 L1969 **FM** *020

BLOCK, Lawrence Allen. ■ 74344 #020-12-1969 L1972 **PD** *071

BOPP, Jon Ronald. ■ 74344 #028-03-1967 L1993 **GYN** *071 †30

CALLICOAT, Paul E, Jr. 900 E 13TH ST STE 200, P O BOX 450968 74344 #036-08-1985 L1992 **CD IM** *020 †20

CHOUTEAU, Charles Jos. 601 E 13TH ST, FAMILY CARE SPECIALIST INC 74344 #039-01-1978 L1979 **FM** *020 †18 ‡

COTNER, Mark. 900 E 13TH ST, STE 103 74344 #039-01-1978 L1983 **GS SO** *020 †85

COX, Douglas Gene. 1310 S MAIN ST 74344 #039-01-1978 L1979 **FM** *020 †18,16

CROSBY, Tom Royce. 900 E 13TH ST, STE 100 74344 #039-01-1984 L1985 **FM** *020 †18

DEAKINS, Dennis Eugene. ■ 74344 #039-01-1975 L1976 **AM OM** *030 †70

FOSTER, Michael Allen. 1310 S MAIN ST 74344 #039-01-1984 L2000 **DR** *020 †80

HOPPER, Robert W. 601 S BROADWAY ST 74344 #025-12-1985 L1987 **PD FM** *020 †55

NICKLAS, Thomas Orville. 1310 S MAIN ST 74344 #039-01-1962 L1962 **OPH** *020 †35

OFFERMANN, Gail Lynn. 1310 S MAIN ST, INTEGRIS GROVE GEN HOSP 74344 #039-01-1982 L1987 **FM** *020 †18

OHLSTROM, Douglas Allen. 900 E 13TH ST, STE 102 74344 #019-02-1980 L1994 **GS** *020 †85

PUMMILL, Daniel A. 1310 S MAIN ST 74344 #039-01-1979 L1980 **FM** *020 †18

RIGGS, Thomas Earl. 900 E 13TH ST, STE 101 74344 #028-02-1967 L1969 **IM PUD** *020 †20

RUTTER, James Dull, IV. 900 E 13TH ST, STE 101 74344 #019-02-1996 L2000 **MPD** *020 †20,55

SMITH, Urby Duane. 700 S MAIN ST 74344 #005-12-1968 L1980 **FM** *020

SNIPES, James Jefferson. 1103 E 13TH ST STE A, HEART CARE & SURGICAL ASSO 74344 #004-01-1968 L1969 **IM** *020

SYNAR, Phil Harry. 2087 EVANS DR 74344 #021-01-1976 L1977 **FM EM** *020 †18

TIDWELL, Richard Harvey. 1310 S MAIN ST 74344 #039-01-1991 L1993 **FM** *020 †18

TIEMANN, J Henry. 1310 S MAIN ST, GROVE GENERAL HOSPITAL 74344 #048-02-1994 L2006 **FM EM** *020 †18

TOLLER, Kevin Keith. 1101 E 13TH ST 74344 #019-02-1994 L1999 **OPH** *020 †35

ZARINTASH, Renee Jean. 900 E 13TH ST, STE 104 74344 #039-01-1999 L2002 **FM** *020 †18 ‡

GUTHRIE – LOGAN

ACKERLEY, Stephen Michael. 200 S ACADEMY RD 73044 #039-01-1995 L2001 **ORS** *020 †40

ANDREWS, Mason Brennan. 1600 S PINE ST, OU MEDICAL CENTER 73044 #039-01-2005 L2006 **NS** *012

BAILEY, Albert Stanley. ■ 73044 #039-01-1955 L1955 **FM** *071 †18

BHAKTA, Arvindkumar. 200 S ACADEMY RD 73044 #965-01-1974 L1978 **IM GP** *020 ‡

BURTON, Robert Allen. ■ 73044 #039-01-1978 L1979 **IM** *020 †20

CASH, James David. 200 S ACADEMY RD 73044 #039-01-1983 L1989 **ORS** *020 †40

CONRAD, Gary D. 5301 SUN VALLEY DR 73044 #039-01-1977 L1978 **EM** *020

DAVIS, Patricia Ingrid. ■ 73044 #039-01-1991 L1992 **FM** *020 †18

ELLIOTT, Michael Stephen. 205 S ACADEMY RD, MEDICINE AND PEDIATRICS 73044 #039-01-1995 L1996 **MPD** *020 †20,55

FOX, Jeff Aaron. 200 S ACADEMY RD 73044 #019-02-1996 L2002 **ORS** *020 †40

HAWKINS, Bryan Jos. 200 S ACADEMY RD 73044 #021-01-1983 L1993 **ORS** *020 †40

HAWKINS, Donnie Loyd. 200 S ACADEMY RD 73044 #048-14-1975 L1980 **ORS** *020 †40

HICKS, David Reese. 200 S ACADEMY RD 73044 #021-01-1977 L1982 **ORS** *020 †40

HOWARD, Brian C. 200 S ACADEMY RD 73044 #039-01-1981 L1982 **ORS** *020 †40

INHOFE, Perry D, II. 200 S ACADEMY RD 73044 #028-02-1988 L1989 **ORS** *020 †40

KRAUSSE, Tima Suzanne. ■ 73044 #039-01-2008 *012

KREHBIEL, Todd Anthony. 205 S ACADEMY RD, MEDICINE AND PEDIATRICS 73044 #039-01-1992 L1993 **MPD** *020 †20,55

MOORE, Lloyd B, Jr. ■ 73044 #041-13-1984 L1993 **EM** *020 †16

MORRIS, Jeffrey R. 200 S ACADEMY RD 73044 #055-75-1985, ▲ L1986 **ORS** *020

NONWEILER, David Edward. 200 S ACADEMY RD 73044 #021-01-1986 L1992 **ORS** *020 †40 ‡

ORME, Laurie Anne. 205 S ACADEMY RD, MEDICINE AND PEDIATRICS 73044 #039-01-1998 L1999 **MPD** *020

PEARCE, Melanie Rachelle. ■ 73044 #028-78-2005, ▲ L2006 **DR** *012

POLLOCK, Ira Oriel. 12801 POLLOCK DR 73044 #028-02-1944 L1945 **GS ON** *072 †85

RITTENHOUSE, Lee Curtis. 116 N BROAD ST 73044 #039-01-1978 L1979 *020

ROBERTSON, Robert Clio. 200 S ACADEMY RD 73044 #039-01-2067 L1974 **ORS** *020 †40

STACY, Teresa Marie. ■ 73044 #039-01-1965 L1965 **PDR R** *071

TANNER, Michael Wm. 200 S ACADEMY RD 73044 #028-34-1978 L1983 **ORS OSM** *020 †40

VERAGIWALA, Jignesh Jayes. 324 N 19TH ST 73044 #305-01-2002 L2005 **FM** *020

WONG, David Kristian. 200 S ACADEMY RD 73044 #039-01-1986 L1987 **HS ORS** *020 †40

GUYMON – TEXAS

ANDERSEN, Steen Borup. 350 NE 12TH ST 73942 #061-01-1972 L1997 **FM** *020

BAUTISTA, Martin D. 350 NE 12TH ST 73942 #748-02-1989 L1996 **GE IM** *020 †20

BOTEZ, Maria Iuliana. ■ 73942 #781-01-1995 L2005 **IM** *020 †20

CABRERA, Agustin. 1301 N MAIN ST, AMARILLO HEART GROUP 73942 #042-02-1990 L1999 **CD** *020 †20

DARROW, Bruce Alvin. 1753 N ROOSEVELT ST 73942 #039-01-1969 L1970 **OBG GP** *020 †30

DIETRICH, Bailey L. RR 2 73942 #039-01-1953 L1953 **FM** *072

GILLES, Jeffrey Alan. 1754 N ROOSEVELT ST, STE 300 73942 #037-01-1978 L2007 **OSM ORS** *020 †40

HENSLEY, Michael Clarke. 1753 N ROOSEVELT ST, STE 200 73942 #039-01-1998 L2002 **OBG** *020

HOUSEAL, Matthew Philip. 520 MEDICAL DR, MEMORIAL HOSPITAL 73942 #025-01-1981 L2002 **EM P** *020 †16,75

LIM, Jeffrey J. 410 NE 12TH ST 73942 #748-02-1989 L1993 **IM CCM** *020 †20 ‡

MC MURRY, Russell K. 123 MEDICAL DR 73942 #028-78-1974, ▲ L1975 **GP** *020

PRACHT, Robert L. 123 MEDICAL DR 73942 #028-78-1956, ▲ L1959 **FM** *020

REED, Paul M. 1309 N EAST ST, P O BOX 1827 73942 #039-79-1995, ▲ L1996 **FM** *020 †18

RODRIGUEZ, Miguel Luis. 350 NE 12TH ST, SPECIALTY CLINICS OF ST AN 73942 #034-01-1988 L2006 **IM** *020 †20

RODRIGUEZ, Orson Pabustan. 350 NE 12TH ST, SPECIALTY CLINICS OF ST AN 73942 #748-01-1998 L2005 **FM** *020 †18

STONE, James Robert. 301 1/2 NORTHRIDGE CIR, GUYMON SURGICAL CONSULTANT 73942 #025-01-1996 L1996 **PTH** *020 †50

TAN, Sylvia R. 350 NE 12TH ST 73942 #748-02-1989 L1996 **PUD IM** *020 †20

TE, Debbie Carvajal. 520 MEDICAL DR 73942 #748-11-1977 L1989 **PD PDE** *020 †55

TE, Hianto. 1221 N MAY ST 73942 #748-11-1977 L1989 **GS FM** *020 †85

UDDIN, Muhammad Moin. 520 MEDICAL DR, MEMORIAL HOSPITAL OF TEXAS 73942 #160-02-1998 L2007 **PD** *020 †55

WILLIAMS, Robert Allan. 520 MEDICAL DR, DEPARTMENT OF RADIOLOGY 73942 #039-01-1998 L2004 **DR** *020 †80

HARRAH – OKLAHOMA

BULLOCK, Peter Paul, Jr. ■ 73045 #039-01-2007 L2007 **FP** *012

■ = Address Information Privacy Protected

GUINN, Shelbi Renee. ■ 73045 #039-01-2008 *012

HARTSHORNE – PITTSBURG

TROW, Thomas Edward. 118 PARK 74547 #039-01-1973 L1974 **FM** *020 †18

HASKELL – MUSKOGEE

RUCKER, Ralph Weller. 26217 E 191ST ST S 74436 #016-06-1967 L1969 **NPM PDP** *071 †55

HEALDTON – CARTER

HABJ-BIK, Ynal. 918 S 8TH ST 73438 #875-01-1979 L1998 **IM** *020 †20
VEINTIMILLA, James. 11 N 4TH ST 73438 #319-01-1956 L1986 **OBG** *075

HENNESSEY – KINGFISHER

MATOUSEK, Sarah Beth. ■ 73742 #039-01-2008 *012

HENRYETTA – OKMULGEE

HORWELL, Sonya Banja. ■ 74437 #039-01-2008 *012
PARKHURST, Wesley E, Jr. 617 W TRUDGEON ST 74437 #037-01-1978 L1981 **GP** *020
SWINNEY, Audie Granville. 180 S DEWEY BARTLETT 74437 #039-01-1982 L1985 **FM** *020 †18
WARDEN, Jeffrey David. ■ 74437 #039-01-2007 **EM** *012

HINTON – CADDO

INGRAM, Marshall Hubbard. PO BOX 490 73047 #039-01-1958 L1958 **FM CD** *020 †18

HOBART – KIOWA

BRIDWELL, Malcolm Edward. 700 N HILL ST 73651 #039-01-1964 L1964 **FM GS** *020
KRIEGER, Michael Doyle. 401 W FOREST LN 73651 #039-01-1980 L1981 **GP** *020
LEWELLEN-JACKSON, Samantha. 429 W ELM ST 73651 #039-01-1995 L1996 **FM** *020 †18 ‡
METCALF, Robert Paul. 429 W ELM ST, 413 WEST FOREST LANE 73651 #039-01-1964 L1964 **DR NM** *020
MOORE, Craig B. 125 N BROADWAY AVE 73651 #039-01-1976 L1978 **FM GE** *020 †18 ‡
THOMAS, Frank Adkins. 407 W FOREST LN, KIOWA COUNTY HOSPITAL 73651 #011-03-1972 L1997 **GS** *020 †85

HOLDENVILLE – HUGHES

CRAMBLET, Denny H. ■ 74848 #028-34-1945 L1949 **GP** *071
HUCKS, Preston Derl. 100 MCDOUGAL DR, HGH RURAL HEALTH CLINIC 74848 #039-01-1995 L1996 **IM** *020
LUNDBLAD, Wilfred M. ■ 74848 #026-04-1948 L1948 **IM P** *071
MC DOUGAL, Royce Carmack. 304 COUNTRY CLUB DR 74848 #039-01-1955 L1955 **GP** *071
SCOGGIN, Rikki Justice. 100 MCDOUGAL DR 74848 #039-01-1997 L2000 **FM** *020 †18

HOLLIS – HARMON

CHANDRA, Usha. 502 E CHESTNUT ST, HARMON MEDICAL CLINIC 73550 #495-45-1966 L1982 **FM** *020
NORMAN, E Wade. 502 E CHESTNUT ST, HARMON MEDICAL CLINIC 73550 #039-01-1963 L1963 **FM GP** *071
SCHAFER, Richard Wright. 509 E CHESTNUT ST 73550 #039-79-1993, ▲ L1994 **FM** *020

HUGO – CHOCTAW

BAGGETT, Lynn Dean. 1405 E KIRK ST, STE B 74743 #654-01-1982 L1983 **PD GP** *075
DORIA, Alberto. 1405 E KIRK ST 74743 #028-34-1964 L1987 **GP EM** *020
HILLSHAFER, David H. 1405 E KIRK ST 74743 #039-01-1981 L1983 **IM P** *020
LA CROIX, Julius A, Jr. 1405 E KIRK ST 74743 #039-01-1950 L1950 **GP OBG** *071
MARTIN, Susan H. 74743 #010-02-1984 L1982 **GP** *020
PABILONA, Jose Lim. 1405 E KIRK ST # A 74743 #748-08-1967 L1985 **GYN GP** *020
PAINE, Johnny R. 1201 E JACKSON ST, HUGO MEDICAL CLINIC 74743 #028-78-1983, ▲ L2001 **FM FPG** *020
PARDUE, Victoria Elaine. 1201 E JACKSON ST, HUGO MEDICAL CLINIC 74743 #039-79-1988, ▲ L1990 **GP FPG** *020
QUEJA, George P. 1201 E JACKSON ST, HUGO MEDICAL CLINIC 74743 #748-08-1973 L1983 **GS** *020
ROWLAND, Teddy Ray. 1201 E JACKSON ST, HUGO MEDICAL CLINIC 74743 #039-01-1983 L1984 **FM** *020 †18
VARAHA NARASIMHA MURTY, G. 1201 E JACKSON ST, HUGO MEDICAL CLINIC 74743 #495-11-1974 L1982 **FM** *020 ‡

HYDRO – CADDO

BULLER, Ralph Leland. 584 BROADWAY 73048 #039-01-1956 L1956 **FM** *072 †18
STUTZMAN, Brenda. 579 N BROADWAY AVE 73048 #039-79-1992, ▲ L1993 **FM** *020 †18

IDABEL – MCCURTAIN

BAGLEY, Preston Albert. 1301 E LINCOLN RD, MC CURTAIN MEM HOSP 74745 #039-01-1968 L1968 **DR NR** *020 †80

BRADLEY-LEBOEUF, Mary. 1307 LYNN LN 74745 #007-02-1991 L2001 **PD** *020 †55
CASEY, Rick Ewell. 1425 E LINCOLN RD, STE B4 74745 #048-02-1976 L1987 **OBG** *020 †30
GOMEZ, Jose J, Jr. ■ 74745 #048-13-1995 L2007 **FM** *020 †18
GREGORY, Jarrett Gordon. 1301 E LINCOLN RD 74745 #036-05-1970 L1982 **DR NR** *062 †80
GRIGORY, Scott Martin. 902 W LINCOLN RD 74745 #026-04-2003 L2006 **PD** *020
HALE, Arthur Eugene. ■ 74745 #039-01-1950 L1950 **GP** *071
HERRON, William. 124 SE AVE N 74745 #039-79-1980, ▲ L1981 **FM** *020
JOHNSON, Gilbert Eugene. RR 2, BOX 422 74745 #010-03-1966 L1995 **FM** *020
MIGLIACCIO, John H. 827 E LINCOLN RD, MCCURTAIN COUNTY EMERG MED 74745 #039-01-1979 L1980 **OBG EM** *020
VALENTINE, Mark W. 1425 E LINCOLN RD 74745 #021-01-1983 L1988 **GS** *020 †85
WHITE, Philip Hayden. 1425 E LINCOLN RD, STE B2 74745 #024-07-1971 L1979 **OPH OS** *020 †35
WONG, David Tsung-Ming. PO BOX 1224 74745 #385-01-1960 L1983 **U** *020 †95
WOODRUFF, Nancy Keim. 1301 E LINCOLN RD 74745 #033-05-1987 L1992 **GP** *020
WURZBURG, Donald Davis. 1301 E LINCOLN RD 74745 #005-19-1993 L2002 **CD** *020 †20

JAY – DELAWARE

MEASE, Darrell Robt. 659 S 14TH ST 74346 #039-01-1988 L1989 **FM** *020 †18

JENKS – TULSA

EARLS, Eva Kristina. PO BOX 1033 74037 #039-01-1992 L1993 **FM** *020
HLAVACEK, Matthew R. 74037 #028-46-2003 L2007 **OMF** *020
HOLDEN, Everett N. 74037 #048-04-1951 L1953 **GS GP** *020
JOHNSON, Erin Michelle. 74037 #039-01-2003 L2006 **EM** *020 †16
KOLJACK, Kathleen Ann. 701 E MAIN ST 74037 #039-01-1984 L1985 **PD** *020 †55
LEBECK, Martin Barry. 12323 14TH ST, MARTIN BARRY LEBECK MD 74037 #016-11-1942 L1985 **TS GS** *071 †85,90
LEE, Lawrence Frank. 74037 #056-06-2006 L2007 **FP** *012
MEANS, Melody Dawn. ■ 74037 #039-01-2004 L2005 **MPD** *012
OLSON, Clinton Burdette. ■ 74037 #056-05-2007 L2007 **FP** *012
OSTLER, Leslie Ann. ■ 74037 #049-01-2006 L2006 **OBG** *012
POTTER, Timothy Alan. ■ 74037 #035-03-2006 L2008 **FP** *012
ROMAN, Vincent Thos. 2605 W MAIN ST 74037 #041-02-1977 L1984 **FM** *020 †18
THANKACHAN, Justin Plamth. ■ 74037 #039-01-2005 L2008 **IM** *012
WAKEFIELD, Brent Alan. 615 E MAIN ST 74037 #039-01-2002 L2003 **FM** *020 †18
WALLACE, Adam Joseph. ■ 74037 #039-01-2008 *012
WINTER, Timothy Wendell. ■ 74037 #005-76-2007, ▲ *012

JONES – OKLAHOMA

ELLIS, David Paul. 15000 N DOUGLAS BLVD, OKLAHOMA PAIN MANAGEMENT C 73049 #039-01-1981 L1986 **AN PME** *020 †05
FERNANDEZ, Rodolfo S. ■ 73049 #748-23-1987 L1997 **DR GS** *020 †20
FLUX, Marinus. PO BOX 1030, 110 E ATLANTA ST 73049 #047-06-1960 L1961 **PUD PD** *020

KETCHUM – MAYES

HILLE, Charles D. ■ 74349 #048-04-1950 L1950 **GP** *020

KINGFISHER – KINGFISHER

ARTHURS, Stephen Ross. 322 W BOWMAN AVE 73750 #039-01-1974 L1979 **FM** *020 †18
BUSWELL, Arthur W. ■ 73750 #039-01-1952 L1952 **GP AM** *071
GERBER, James Stephen. 500 S 9TH ST 73750 #039-01-1977 L1978 **FM PHP** *020
HOLSTED, Carroll Eugene. 322 W BOWMAN AVE 73750 #039-01-1966 L1966 **FM** *071 †18
KESTER, Branson Ray. ■ 73750 #039-01-2006 L2008 **MPD** *012
KRABLIN, James Brett. 401 W BOWMAN AVE 73750 #039-01-1999 L2000 **IM** *020 †20
MATSON, Robbie Lee. 322 W BOWMAN AVE 73750 #039-01-1993 L1994 **FM** *020 †18 ‡
MC INTYRE, Ray V. 500 S 9TH ST 73750 #039-01-1951 L1951 **FM** *071 †18
PATEL, Atul. 322 W BOWMAN AVE 73750 #305-01-1996 L1998 **CD** *020 †20
STOUGH, Thomas Ross. 500 S 9TH ST 73750 #039-01-1968 L1969 **GP** *020

KINGSTON – MARSHALL

PERRY, John Milton, Jr. ■ 73439 #039-01-1946 L1948 **GP** *071

KONAWA – SEMINOLE

CARPENTER, Jo Ann. 527 W 3RD ST, MEDICAL 74849 #039-01-1977 L1978 **FM** *020 †18
DYE, David Bryan. 527 W 3RD ST, MEDICAL 74849 #039-01-1987 L1988 **FM** *020 †18
FAGHIHNIA, Ardeshir. 527 W 3RD ST, CENTRAL OKLAHOMA FAMILY ME 74849 #517-01-1982 L2006 **IM** *020
HOWARD, Jack Barton. 527 W 3RD ST, MEDICAL 74849 #039-01-1964 L1965 **ORS AM** *020 †40
ROUSH, Dwayne Lewis. 527 W 3RD ST 74849 #039-01-1995 L1996 **PD** *020
SAEED, Umar. 527 W 3RD ST, CENTRAL OKLAHOMA FAM MED 74849 #704-21-2000 L2006 **FM** *020 †18
SNELL, Jay Joshua. ■ 74849 #039-01-2008 *012
STOKES, Martin Luther. 527 W 3RD ST, MEDICAL 74849 #039-01-1968 L1969 **FPG** *071
VOGT, Milton Wayne. 641 S BROADWAY ST 74849 #039-01-1956 L1956 **GP P** *020

LANGSTON – LOGAN

SANFORD, Johnson Wilburne. LANGSTON UNIV. MEDICAL CL. 73050 #010-03-1956 L1961 **GP GS** *071

■ = Address Information Privacy Protected

LAWTON – COMANCHE

ABRAHAM, Bobby. 3201 W GORE BLVD, COMANCHE COUNTY MEMORIAL H 73505 #495-65-1983 L2002 IM *020 †20

AGTE, Suhas Damodar. 5108 W GORE BLVD 73505 #495-28-1978 L2003 IM NEP *020 †20

AGUILAR, Kinde Elizabeth. 102 NW 31ST ST 73505 #039-01-2002 L2007 OBG *020

ALLGOOD, Richard J. 110 NW 31ST ST 73505 #039-01-1964 L1964 TS GS *020 †85,90

ARMENDARIZ, Francis Peter. 1602 SW 82ND ST 73505 #649-02-1996 L2001 P *020

ATKINSON, William John. 605 W GORE BLVD STE 1, ATKINSON PROFESSIONAL BLDG 73501 #056-06-1958 L1967 GS *020

AXELSEN, Nils Kenneth. 110 NW 31ST ST, FL 2 73505 #048-04-1981 L2004 ORS *020 †40

AYCOCK, Alan Everett. 5402 SW LEE BLVD 73505 #039-01-1970 L1971 OTO *020 †45

AYCOCK, Byron W. 1002 W GORE BLVD 73501 #039-01-1940 L1941 OPH OTO *071 †45

AZIKIWE, Nwachukwu Abi. PO BOX 3520 73502 #035-46-1972 L2000 IM *100 †20

BALDWIN, Donald Martin. 110 NW 31ST ST, FL 2 73505 #023-01-1969 L1976 ORS *020 †40

BALOGH, Robert Cornell. 3401 W GORE BLVD, COMANCHE HOSPITILIST GRP 73505 #012-05-1995 L2006 IM *020 †20

BANOWSKY, Lynn H W. ■ 73505 #021-01-1962 L1972 U *071 †95

BARTANEN, Wendy Susan. 673 KETCH CREEK DR 73507 #026-08-1991 L1997 FM *020 †18

BEHM, David Wm. 5602 SW LEE BLVD, SOUTHWESTERN MEDICAL CENTE 73505 #016-76-1982, ▲ L1988 EM *020 †16

BELLINO, Rosemary. 4202 SW LEE BLVD, BLDG A 73505 #035-15-1971 L1981 IM *020 †20

BHARGAVA, Ajay. 4302 SW LEE BLVD 73505 #495-73-1974 L1985 GE IM *020 †20

BHARGAVA, Shireen A. 4702 SW LEE BLVD 73505 #495-22-1973 L1985 OBG ON *020 †20

BIRDWELL, Brian Gillam. 1930 NW FERRIS AVE, STE 2 73507 #039-01-1981 L1982 IM UM *020 †20

BIRDWELL, Daryl Eugene. 4417 W GORE BLVD STE 2 73505 #039-01-1974 L1975 FM *020 †18

BOATSMAN, Richard Justin. 5602 SW LEE BLVD 73505 #039-01-1970 L1972 PTH *020 †50 ‡

BORREGO ACOSTA, Jose Mari. 1202 NW ARLINGTON AVE 73507 #132-01-1991 L2007 FP *012

BOYER, Jenny Lee. 602 SW 38TH ST, JIM TACIAFERRO CMHC 73505 #039-01-1997 L1999 P *020 †75

BRITTINGHAM, Richard Thos. 3201 W GORE BLVD, STE 304 73505 #039-01-1990 L1991 IM *020 †20

BROWN, Renee C. 3811 W GORE BLVD 73505 #047-07-1988 P *020

BURKI, Masooda M. 1602 SW 82ND ST, WABASH VALLEY HOSPITAL & 73505 #704-21-1983 L1998 CHP P *020 †75

CABALLERO, Renato Manuel. 3201 W GORE BLVD STE 301 73505 #308-07-1982 L1988 FM *020 †18

CACCIOPPOLI, Giuseppe. 602 SW 38TH ST 73505 #561-16-1980 L1991 CHP P *020 ‡

CAGLE, Ronald Edward. 3201 W GORE BLVD STE 100 73505 #039-01-1958 L1958 PD *071 †55

CAMPBELL, Richard Lee. 1002 SW 52ND ST 73505 #039-01-1984 L1986 FM *020 †18

CARNS, Edwin H J. 8607 SE FLOWER MOUND RD, LAWTON CORRECTIONAL FACILI 73501 #054-04-1975 L1978 FM EM *020 †18,16

CARPENTER, Charles E. 3401 W GORE BLVD, MEDICAL STAFF OFFICE 73505 #048-12-1987 L2002 EM *020 †16

CARTER, John Nereus. 110 NW 31ST ST 73505 #021-01-1976 L1983 GS VS *020 †85

CASTANON-RIOS, Luz O. 1515 NE LAWRIE TATUM RD, LAWTON INDIAN HOSPITAL 73507 #042-02-1993 L1995 FM *020 †20

CASTILLO, Sergio H. 1602 SW 82ND ST, SOUTHWESTERN BEHAVIORAL HL 73505 #649-33-1988 L2002 P *020 †75

CHADEK, Richard F, Jr. 1202 NW ARLINGTON AVE 73507 #030-05-1994 L2000 P *020 †18

CHAPPABITTY, Edwin, Jr. 73507 #007-02-1980 L1982 FM *020

CHARLES, Ronald Alan. 3401 W GORE BLVD 73505 #048-04-1990 L2006 EM *030 †16

CHATWIN, David Matthew. ■ 73507 #049-01-2003 L2004 AN *020

CHISHOLM, Robert Miles. 605 W GORE BLVD STE 6 73501 #039-01-1996 L2001 FM *020

CIBES-SILVA, Maristela. 901 SW GOODYEAR BLVD, GOODYEAR FAMILY MED CTR 73505 #308-04-1983 L1995 IM *020 †20

COLLADO, Jose Francisco. 901 SW GOODYEAR BLVD 73505 #308-06-1986 L1997 FM *020 †18

COMPLETO, John Drake. 73507 #041-09-1996 L1998 GPM *100 †70

COOPER, George Benton. 3401 W GORE BLVD 73505 #039-01-1972 L1973 EM *020

COOPER, Michael Andrew. 73505 #038-41-1998 L2005 FM *020 †18

COUCH, Jim Carrol. 1515 NE LAWRIE TATUM RD 73507 #039-01-1962 L1962 FM *020 †18

COX, John A, Jr. 4417 W GORE BLVD STE 5 73505 #039-01-1982 L1985 IM PUD *020 †20

CRAIG, Mark Stephen. ■ 73505 #023-12-2004 L2004 PD *020 †55

CRIMMINS, Christopher Ray. 3201 W GORE BLVD, STE 201 73505 #039-01-1998 L2004 U *020 †95

CRISWELL, Dan Franklin. 1202 NW ARLINGTON AVE 73507 #039-01-1977 L1979 FM *040 †18

DAVE, Deena. 4202 S WHEEBLVD, STE C 73505 #495-48-1977 L1984 FM OBS *020 †18

DAVENPORT, James Allen. 2716 W GORE BLVD, STE E 73505 #047-06-1969 L1977 DR *020 †80

DAVIES, William Spalding. 1302 NW LAKE AVE 73507 #039-01-1966 L1966 P *020

DAVIS, Wiley Gene. 3801 NW CACHE RD STE 44, CHRISTIAN FAMILY COUNSELIN 73505 #039-01-1978 L1979 P *020

DAY, Ralph Wm. 1515 NE LAWRIE TATUM RD 73507 #039-01-1970 L1971 OBG FM *020 †30

DE LA PAZ, Fe Reyes. 1515 NE LAWRIE TATUM RD 73507 #748-01-1959 L1979 OBG GP *071

DELAROSA, Manuel Jose. 20 NW 67TH ST STE E 73505 #264-04-1982 L1999 EM *020 †16

DIX, Robert Allen. 5602 SW LEE BLVD 73505 #039-01-1967 L1968 PTH *071 †50

DONNELLY, Allen Morgan. ■ 73505 #048-04-1964 L1964 DR GP *071 †80

DOUGLAS, Oxana Vladimirov. ■ 73505 #759-18-2006 L2007 FP *012

DRAGOSLJVICH, Mittie M. 3401 W GORE BLVD 73505 #041-09-1984 L1990 RO *020 †80

DREWRY, Robert Hill. 500 MONTGOMERY SQ STE 305 73501 #039-01-1959 L1959 IM *020 †20

DUGUID, Dale Frank. 3401 W GORE BLVD 73505 #068-01-1981 L1992 FM FPG *020 †18

DUNCAN, Johnny Dean. 3401 W GORE BLVD, COMACHE COUNTY MEMORIAL HO 73505 #039-79-1992, ▲ L1993 NS *020

DUUS, Erlan Caryle. 5604 SW LEE BLVD STE 310 73505 #018-03-1970 L1987 PS OTO *020 †45,65

ELZIND, Nabila Hassan. 4411 W GORE BLVD, STE B4 73505 #915-06-1980 L1998 N IM *020 †75

ERICKSON, Heidi C. 1515 NE LAWRIE TATUM RD, LAWTON INDIAN HOSPITAL 73507 #023-12-1996 L2006 CHP PD *020 †55,75

EVANS, Kenneth L. 4427 W GORE BLVD 73505 #039-01-1967 L1967 FM *040 †18

FAKORY, Usama Marko. ■ 73505 #915-02-1992 L2008 FM *020 †18

FALK, Lee Hymanson. 602 SW 38TH ST 73505 #035-19-1948 L1991 P PYA *071 †75

FANG, John P. 3201 W GORE BLVD 73505 #047-05-2001 L2006 OPH *020

FAWAZ, Rhody F. 3201 W GORE BLVD, STE 101 73505 #605-01-1994 L1996 GE *020 †20

FOGLE, Mark Warren. 6401 SW LEE BLVD, INTERNAL MEDICINE CLINIC 73505 #048-04-1981 L1982 IM GE *020 †20

FRISCHE, Eric Ernst. 110 NW 31ST ST 2ND FL 73505 #035-01-1969 L1977 ORS *020 †40

GARRETT, Donald Hugh. 5404 SW LEE BLVD, GREAT PLAIN SURG CLNC 73505 #039-01-1968 L1968 GS VS *071 †85,90

GIACOMAN, Raul L. 602 SW 38TH ST 73505 #649-02-1960 L1979 GP *020 †18

GIBBONS, Janice Lynn. 11 NW SHADOW LAKE RD 73505 #045-04-1996 L2002 PD *020 †55

GORDON, Krista Jeanette. 5366 NW CACHE RD, STE 6 73505 #039-01-1998 L1999 FM *020 †18

GOSE, Robert Claude. 5604 SW LEE BLVD STE 200 73505 #028-03-1974 L1979 U *020 †95

GRAHAM, Eric Sean. ■ 73505 #748-10-2000 L2007 FP *012

GRANADA, Steve Anthony. ■ 73507 #039-01-1995 L1998 IM *020 †20

GRANTHAM, R Nathan. 3401 W GORE BLVD 3RD FL 73505 #039-01-1970 L1971 TS CD *020 †85,90

GRAVES, F Burton. ■ 73505 #024-07-1947 L1982 FM PD *075

GRAYBILL, Charles Shelly. ■ 73505 #039-01-1943 L1944 ORS RHU *072 †40

GREGORATTI, Guillermo J. ■ 73506 #132-01-1967 L1981 P PFP *071

HALIM, Magdi. ■ 73501 #396-06-1954 L1965 GS TRS *020 †85

HAMILTON, Mark Johnson. ■ 73507 #039-01-2006 FP *012

HANNA, Sameh William K. ■ 73505 #915-02-1986 L2007 AN *020 *05

HARPER, Howard Dale. 5116 W GORE BLVD STE 1, SOUTHWEST IMAGING CENTER, 73505 #039-01-1993 L1994 DR *020 †80

HAY, Robert Fraser. 3201 W GORE BLVD STE 301, COMANCHE COUNTY MEMORIAL H 73505 #065-06-1972 L1978 FM OS *020 †18

HAYS, David Wayne. 5110 W GORE BLVD STE 1, LAWTON DIALYSIS INC 73505 #039-01-1980 L1981 NEP IM *020 †20

HENSLEY, Ross Chas. 4417 W GORE BLVD STE 7 73505 #039-01-1972 L1973 D *020 †15 ‡

HENSON, Edwin R, III. 3201 W GORE BLVD 73505 #051-07-1988 L1989 PD *020 †55

HILLIS, Robert Ray. 102 NW 31ST ST 73505 #039-01-1959 L1959 OBG *020 †30

HILTON, Amy Beth R. 3401 W GORE BLVD, COMANCHE CO.MEMORIAL HOSPI 73505 #043-01-1988 L1998 AN *020 †20

HINMAN, Robert Chas. ■ 73505 #016-02-1961 L1993 N IM *075 †75

HOO, Chin Shin. 1515 NE LAWRIE TATUM RD 73507 #243-16-1959 L1980 DR *020 †80

HOOVER, Penny L. 412 SW SUMMIT AVE 73505 #026-04-1988 L1996 FM *020 †18 ‡

HORTON, Dan Dee. 4417 W GORE BLVD STE 6 73505 #039-01-1973 L1974 FM *020 †18

HUNTER, Elissa Jean. 110 NW 31ST ST 73505 #068-01-1977 L2001 GS *020 †85

HWANG, Sung Hyun. 3400 W GORE BLVD, COMANCHE COUNTY MEMORIAL H 73505 #654-01-2001 L2006 AN *100

HYDE, Glen Dewayne. 2716 W GORE BLVD, STE E 73505 #039-01-1997 L1998 IM *020 †20

IFEZUE, Dolores Ngozi. 1515 NE LAWRIE TATUM RD, US PUBLIC HEALTH SVC 73507 #690-02-1991 L2005 PD *020 †55

IGWE, Daniel. 5604 SW LEE BLVD STE 210, CENTER FOR SURGICAL TREATM 73505 #422-01-1987 L2007 GS *020 †85

IHSAAN, Michael. 1515 NE LAWRIE TATUM RD, LAWTON INDIAN HOSPITAL 73507 #030-06-1989 L2005 GYN OBS *020

IKEDIONWU, Freedom K. 1819 W GORE BLVD 73501 #690-08-1985 L1994 NEP *020 †20

ISMAIL, Sherif Sayed. 2716 W GORE BLVD STE E 73505 #915-04-1993 L2002 FM *020 †18

JOHNSON, Linda Diann. 2502 W GORE BLVD 73505 #048-02-1988 L1994 PD *020 †55

JOHNSON, Richard Eric. 3401 W GORE BLVD, COMANCHE COUNTY MEMORIAL H 73505 #043-01-1988 L1998 AN *020 †05

JOHNSON, Wayne Anthony. 904 SW 38TH ST 73505 #047-07-1991 L1994 ORS *020 †40

JOINER, Laura Rihl. ■ 73505 #012-01-2000 L2003 OBG *020 †30

JOLLY, William P. 3401 W GORE BLVD 73505 #025-01-1949 L1956 IM *071 †20

JONES, Martin Kelly. 1002 SW 52ND ST 73505 #039-01-1983 L1984 OBG *020 †30 ‡

JONES, Robert Edward. 3201 W GORE BLVD STE 202, COMANCHE COUNTY MEMORIAL H 73505 #065-10-1972 L1977 FM *020 †20

JOSEPH, James William. 6943 NW EISENHOWER DR 73505 #041-02-1997 L2001 FM *020 †18

JOSLIN, Gregory. 102 NW 31ST ST, GREAT PLAINS GYN & OB 73505 #028-02-1994 L2000 OBG *020 †30

JOYCE, Alina Juzwowicz. ■ 73505 #759-11-1981 L1999 PTH *020 †50

JURKOWICZ, Abel Marcos. 1602 SW 82ND ST STE E 73505 #132-01-1967 L2007 CHP P *020 †75

KADIVAR, Aryan Parker. 4427 W GORE BLVD 73505 #305-01-2001 L2005 FM *100 †18

KANG, Dae Oh. 1515 NE LAWRIE TATUM RD, LAWTON INDIAN HOSPITAL 73507 #583-10-1966 L1989 AN GS *020

KARO, Jason Edward. ■ 73505 #051-01-2002 L2004 OPH *020 †35

KAZA, Naga Pushpa L. 602 SW 38TH ST, JIM TALIAFERRO COMMUNITY M 73505 #495-11-1964 L1996 P *020

KERN, Robert Louis. 102 NW 31ST ST, GREAT PLAINS GYN & OB 73505 #035-09-1979 L1997 OBG *020 †30

KING, Robert Wayne. 19939 STATE HIGHWAY 49, P O BOX 61 73507 #039-01-1974 L1975 AN EM *020

LANE, Richard Thos. 3401 W GORE BLVD, FL 3 73505 #048-15-1984 L1990 ICE CD *020 †20

LECKMAN, Thomas Jay. 505 NW SHERIDAN RD, STE C 73505 #041-12-1971 L1976 IM *020 ‡

LEGAKO, Edward Anthony. 3201 W GORE BLVD, STE 100 73505 #039-01-1978 L1979 PD *020 †55

LENNON, Carol Ann. 102 NW 31ST ST, STE 200 73505 #008-02-1992 L2000 OBG MFM *020 †30

LEPP, Janice Marie. 102 NW 31ST ST, GREAT PLAINS GYN & OB 73505 #068-01-1977 L1995 OBG *020 †30

LESLIE, Samuel B, Jr. ■ 73507 #039-01-1942 L1943 OPH *071 †35

LEWIS, Elizabeth G. 2701 SW CORNELL AVE 73505 #039-01-1982 L1983 PD *020 †55

LOGIE, Brad. ■ 73507 #011-03-2004 *100

LOPEZ, Martin James, Jr. 5602 SW LEE BLVD 73505 #039-01-1988 L1989 AN PME *020 *05

LOVE, Robert Milton. 6401 SW LEE BLVD 73505 #039-01-1974 L1975 IM EM *020 †20

LOVE, Vernon Michael. 1301 NW 40TH ST 73505 #048-13-1998 L2005 FM *020 †18

MALLING, Heidi Lynne. 1202 NW ARLINGTON AVE, SW OK FAMILY MEDICINE RESI 73505 #026-04-1994 L2008 FM *020 †18

MAURY, David. 5604 SW LEE BLVD STE 245 73505 #041-13-1979 L1982 FM *020 †18

MC ALLISTER, Julieta. LAWRIE TATUM RD 73507 #748-07-1964 L1989 FM *100

MC GATH, John Hamilton. 4920 SW LEE BLVD 73505 #030-06-1979 L1992 OTO *020 †45

MC GINNIS, Michael C. 4704 NW MOTIF MANOR BLVD, STE 7 73505 #031-01-1990 L1995 ATP PCP *020 †50

MEANS, Diane M. 3401 W GORE BLVD, ATTN: MEDICAL STAFF OFFICE 73505 #039-01-1999 L1999 EM *020 †16

MEANS, Kelly Dean. 110 NW 31ST ST 73505 #039-01-1992 L1994 GS *020 †85

MEEK, Melton P. ■ 73505 #047-06-1945 L1954 PD *071 †55

MICHENER, Frank Rosback. 3201 W GORE BLVD, STE 201 73505 #039-01-1960 L1960 U *071 †95
MICHENER, Scott Lewis. 3201 W GORE BLVD STE 201 73505 #039-01-1990 L1996 U *020 †95
MILLER, Jeffrey L. ■ 73507 #048-13-1997 L2006 FP *012
MILLNAMOW, Gregory Alan. PO BOX 6220 73506 #039-01-1995 L1997 DR *020
MITHLO, Maria Mercedes. 4411 W GORE BLVD, ANADARKO INDIAN HEALTH CEN 73505 #847-05-1982 L1999 GP *020
MOHANDAS, Kalpana. ■ 73507 #496-24-1988 L1997 FM *100
MONTAGUE, Burt Chesley. 5604 SW LEE BLVD STE 357 73505 #039-01-1965 L1965 OBG *020 †30
MONTAZERI, Morteza N. 910 NW 38TH ST 73505 #517-04-1966 L1981 OBG *020 †30 ‡
MORTENSEN, Charles Eric. 3401 W GORE BLVD, COMANCHE COUNTY MEMORIAL H 73505 #012-05-1978 L1999 AN *020 †05
MORTON, Gregory K. 412 SW SUMMIT AVE 73501 #035-06-1975 L1983 GYN GP *020
MUNSON, Anne Alice. 4202 SW LEE BLVD, BLDG A 73505 #045-04-1988 L2001 DR *012 †20
MURARI, Pamela J. ■ 73505 #495-04-1964 L1990 PTH *020 †50
MURARI, Timeri Mahinder. 3401 W GORE BLVD, BOX 129 73505 #495-04-1965 L1980 ORS PM *020 †40
NAVARRO, John Matthew. 3401 W GORE BLVD, COMANCHE COUNTY HOSPITAL 73505 #030-05-1993 L2003 AN *020 †05
NAZ, Shehla. 1202 NW ARLINGTON AVE 73507 #704-15-1996 L2006 FM *020 †18
NDEKWE, Henry Norbert O. 2308 NE VILLAGE DR # 2 73507 #016-11-1994 L1999 APM *020
NEUENSCHWANDER, Elizabeth. ■ 73505 #047-06-1974 L1980 OBS FM *040 †30,18
NEWBY, Edgar Lee, Jr. ■ 73507 #039-01-1984 L1985 FM *020 †18
NEWPORT, Kathryn Sue. 6801 NW GRAYSONS MNTN DR D 73505 #039-01-1987 L1988 AN *020 †05 ‡
NIMEH, Nadim Fouad. 5002 SW LEE BLVD 73505 #605-01-1975 L1982 HEM ON *020 †20
NOLD, William Lorence. 1515 NE LAWRIE TATUM RD, USPHS IHS LAWTON INDIAN HO 73507 #016-43-1957 L1959 IM *020
OFORI-KWAKYE, Stephen K. 3201 W GORE BLVD, STE 303 73505 #008-01-1979 L2000 NS N *020 †25
OLIVEROS, Danilo. ■ 73501 #748-08-1965 L1976 GP *020
ORME, Anthony Lloyd. 513 NW HILLIARY RD STE C, 602 SE WALLOCK 73507 #030-06-1978 L1979 OM EM *020
ORR, Linda Sue Goodin. ■ 73505 #039-01-1969 L1969 N CHN *071 †75
ORTIZ-CRUZ, Desiree. 2701 SW A AVE 73505 #042-01-1983 L2003 N *020 †75
PAGNANELLI, David Michael. 5604 SW LEE BLVD STE 35 73505 #010-01-1976 L2004 NS *020 †25
PARIKH, Vrajesh M. 3106 NW ARLINGTON AVE 73505 #495-22-1971 L1981 CD IM *020 †20
PASCOE, Handel Franklyn. 3401 W GORE BLVD, COMANCHE COUNTY MEMORIAL H 73505 #047-07-1987 L1999 AN *020 †05
PASCUAL, Vianmar G. 1515 NE LAWRIE TATUM RD 73507 #748-10-1966 L1972 GS EM *020
PASZKOWIAK, Jaroslaw Krzy. 4411 W GORE BLVD 73505 #759-10-1993 L2005 FM *100 †18
PATEL, Prabhudas Khodidas. 2716 W GORE BLVD 73505 #495-75-1967 L1977 GS GP *020 †85
PEREZ-CRUET, Jorge. ■ 73505 #042-01-1957 L1994 P PA *020 †75
PERRY, Patricia Anne. 1515 NE LAWRIE TATUM RD, LAWTON INDIAN HOSPITAL 73507 #001-02-1981 L2007 PD *020 †55
PILAR, Jaime B. 1515 NE LAWRIE TATUM RD, USPHS INDIAN HOSP 73507 #748-08-1970 L1975 GS VS *020
PONTIKES, Leon. 110 NW 31ST ST 73505 #068-01-1986 L2001 GS *020 †85
POOLAW, Bryce Monroe. 1515 NE LAWRIE TATUM RD, LAWTON INDIAN HOSPITAL 73507 #032-01-1976 L1977 FM *020 †18
PYUN, Jin Chul. ■ 73505 #050-02-2001 L2001 EM *020 †16
QUINONES-NAZARIO, Gabriel. 4202 SW LEE BLVD 73505 #649-14-1996 L2007 ID IM *020 †20
RAFFI, Zareena. 602 SW 38TH ST, JIM TALIAFERRO COMMUNITY M 73505 #495-59-1986 L2002 P *020 †75
RAMIREZ, Cecilio R. ■ 73501 #308-03-1983 L1990 GP *020
RAMOS, Michael. 3811 W GORE BLVD STE 1 73505 #007-02-1981 L1989 FM *020 †18
RAO, Imran Akram. ■ 73505 #704-01-1991 L2004 IM *020 †20
RARICK, Joseph Francis. 3811 W GORE BLVD, STE 6 73505 #039-01-1977 L1978 PD *020
REDDY, Punaepalli S. 3401 W GORE BLVD, COMANCHE COUNTY MEMORIAL H 73505 #495-70-1989 L2003 AN *020 †05
REIMER, J Paul. 4417 W GORE BLVD STE 1 73505 #039-01-1957 L1957 R *020 †55,80
REINA, Luis Andres. 2701 SW A AVE 73505 #847-06-1980 L2003 N *020 †75
REYES-VILLANUEVA, Angel M. 73507 #042-01-2001 ORS *020
RIVERA, Maria D. 4008 NW CACHE RD, BEBECITOS CHILDRENS CLINIC 73505 #308-06-1986 L2000 PD *020
ROBIN, Manal L. 5002 SW LEE BLVD 73505 #915-04-1989 L2001 HO *020 †20
ROMAN, Maritza. ■ 73505 #042-03-1983 L1988 PD FM *020
ROMERO, Fernando L. 602 SW 38TH ST DEPT CHP 73505 #649-01-1956 L1975 P CHP *071
ROSENFELD, Michael Lewis. 5602 SW LEE BLVD 73505 #035-09-1962 L1979 IM IMG *020
ROSS, J Shane. 1320 NW HOMESTEAD DR STE H 73505 #048-14-1993 L1997 PM *020 †60
ROUNDTREE, Joe Mark. 4208 SW LEE BLVD 73505 #039-01-1978 L1979 D GP *020 †15
RYAN, Dianna Elizabeth. ■ 73505 #030-06-1988 L1997 GP *020
SALIBA, Bassam Shafic. 3106 NW ARLINGTON AVE 73505 #605-03-1990 L2000 CD IC *020 †20
SANNER, Marty Kell. 4202 SW LEE BLVD, BLDG A 73505 #039-01-1992 L1993 IM *020 †20
SAWYER, Michael Anthony. 110 NW 31ST ST 73505 #033-06-1985 L2004 GS *071 †85
SCHUTZ, George Frank. 3401 W GORE BLVD, COMANCHE COUNTY MEMORIAL H 73505 #039-01-1988 L2003 DR *020 †80
SCROGGINS, Kurt Robt. 1320 NW HOMESTEAD DR, STE E 73505 #039-01-1974 L1975 IM GE *020 †20
SHEA, Elena S. ■ 73507 #048-15-1992 L2007 FP *012
SIDDIQUI, Asma Ahmed. ■ 73505 #704-16-1996 L2004 IM *020
SIEGMANN, Renee Marie. ■ 73505 #023-12-1998 L1999 D *020 †15
SMALL, Tina Christine. 3401 W GORE BLVD, DEPT PHYSICAL MEDICINE 73505 #665-01-1999 L2004 PM *020
SMITH, Richard Brent. 4411 W GORE BLVD STE B5 73505 #039-01-1980 L1983 FM *020 †18
SNELL, Joy Ann. 5108 W GORE BLVD STE 1 73505 #004-01-1990 L1995 PTH *020 †50
SNELL, Stephen Ware. 5402 SW LEE BLVD 73505 #004-01-1990 L1995 OTO *020 †45
SODAM, Bali Reddy. 6401 SW LEE BLVD 73505 #495-70-1993 L2005 NEP *020 †20
SOLITARIO, Edna C. 3201 W GORE BLVD STE 100, 3201 W GORE BLVD STE 100 73505 #748-10-1979 L1996 PD PDE *020 †55
SONI, Jyotish C. 3401 W GORE BLVD, MEMORIAL HOSP 73505 #495-22-1973 L1995 AN CCA *020 †05
SORENSON, Charles Lamont. 5602 SW LEE BLVD 73505 #028-34-1986 L1987 EM *020

STILLICK, Wayne Edward. 3201 W GORE BLVD, STE 100 73505 #039-01-1999 L2000 PD *020 †55
STOCKARD, Rex E. 4417 W GORE BLVD 73505 #039-01-1965 L1965 IM CD *020 †20
STRICKLAND, George M. 3811 W GORE BLVD STE 10, COMANCHE COUNTY MEMORIAL H 73505 #028-34-1995 L2001 P *020 †75
SUPERIOR, Michael John. ■ 73505 #010-02-2005 L2008 GS *020
SWEENEY, Robert Francis. 3106 NW ARLINGTON AVE, HEART & VASCULAR CTR 73505 #422-01-1987 L1994 CD IM *020 †20
TAYLOR, Ross Maitland. 5602 SW LEE BLVD 73505 #062-01-1969 L1982 GE NTR *020 †20
TRACHTE, Aaron L. 3401 W GORE BLVD 73505 #018-03-1996 L1997 TS VS *020 †85,90
TRAN, Khanh Van. 910 NW 38TH ST STE B 73505 #840-01-1966 L1980 N NS *020 †75
TRAN, Phuong My Le. 4202 SW LEE BLVD, BLDG A 73505 #941-01-1966 L1983 P *020 †75
TYBURSKI, Claudia J. 102 NW 31ST ST, STE 200 73505 #030-06-1984 L1992 OBG *020 †30
TYBURSKI, Robert Edward. 20 NW 67TH ST STE E, LAWTON URGENT CARE ASSOCIA 73505 #030-06-1984 L1987 EM IM *020 †16
VAL, Michelle Susan. ■ 73505 #041-13-2004 L2006 FM *100 †18
VASSILEVA, Ivanka Avramov. 5610 SW LEE BLVD 73505 #198-01-1986 L2004 FM *020 †18
VELURY, Padmashree. 4202 SW LEE BLVD BLDG A 73505 #495-11-1991 L2006 FM *020 †18
WARN, Ann Acers. 3201 W GORE BLVD 73505 #019-02-1990 L1991 OPH *020 †35
WEBB, Orville Lynn. 1301 NW 67TH ST 73505 #028-03-1968 L1969 FM *071 †18
WEEDN, Alan James. 102 NW 31ST ST 73505 #039-01-1975 L1979 OBG *020 †30 ‡
WHITESIDE, James H. 3401 W GORE BLVD, COMANCHE COUNTY MEMORIAL H 73505 #048-16-2001 L2005 N *020
WILLIAMS, James Robt. ■ 73505 #039-01-1973 L1974 FM *020 ‡
WOODSON, Ronald Glen. 3106 NW ARLINGTON AVE, THE HEART AND VASCULAR CTR 73505 #039-01-1977 L1978 CD IM *020 †20
WRIGHT, Timothy Francis. 110 NW 31ST ST, FL 2 73505 #019-02-1988 L1997 ORS *020 †40
YOUNG, Joseph James. 4214 SW LEE BLVD 73505 #039-01-1980 L1981 OPH *020 †35 ‡
ZIEGLER, James Christian. 3401 W GORE BLVD, DEPT OF RADIATION ONCOLOGY 73505 #041-07-1983 L1993 RO *020 †80
ZWEIG, Jeffrey Lawrence. 4411 W GORE BLVD STE B1 73505 #005-02-1973 L2006 OBG GP *020 †30

LEFLORE – LE FLORE

MINGS, Harold Harvey. ■ 74942 #039-01-1957 L1957 GS FM *071 †85

LEXINGTON – CLEVELAND

ROLLINS, John G. ■ 73051 #039-01-1950 L1950 FM OS *071 †18

LINDSAY – GARVIN

BOECKMAN, Matthew Jared. ■ 73052 #039-01-2008 *012

LUTHER – OKLAHOMA

VANDERLINDE, Megan Daniel. PO BOX 246 73054 #665-02-2007 L2007 IM *012
VOIGHT, Krystal Marie. ■ 73054 #039-01-2007 L2007 MPD *012

MACOMB – POTTAWATOMIE

GERMANN, Antonio Michael. ■ 74852 #005-19-2008 *012

MADILL – MARSHALL

AHEARN, Pamela E. 3 HOSPITAL DR, TEXOMACARE 73446 #039-01-1995 L1996 FM *020 †18 ‡
CHAMBERS, Shannon Goodwin. 3 HOSPITAL DR 73446 #039-01-1995 L1998 FM *020 †18
POTTER, Joe Lynn. 3 HOSPITAL DR 73446 #039-01-1975 L1976 IM *020 †20

MANGUM – GREER

CALEY, David Lewis, Jr. 114 S LOUIS TITTLE AVE 73554 #039-01-1984 L1985 FM *020 †18
HALLABA, Moheb Abdel S. 1 WICKERSHAM ST 73554 #330-03-1954 L1981 FM VS *020 †85
HOLLENBACK, Byron C. RR 2 73554 #035-03-1949 L1961 R *071 †80
KINGERY, Phillip N. 114 S LOUIS TITTLE AVE 73554 #039-01-1966 L1966 FM AN *020
LESTER, Jeffry Stephen. ■ 73554 #039-01-1975 L1976 FM OS *020
TRUONG, Hanh N. 200 N LOUIS TITTLE AVE, MEDICAL & SURGICAL CLNC 73554 #941-01-1971 L1982 FM EM *020
TRUONG, Thach Cao. 1606 N LOUIS TITTLE AVE 73554 #941-01-1967 L1979 FM *071 †18

MANNSVILLE – JOHNSTON

DE ROSE, Sonja Del. ■ 73447 #005-12-1989 L1990 FM PHP *074 †18

MARIETTA – LOVE

HUTCHINS, Stephen Irving. 301 WANDA ST 73448 #039-05-1986 L1987 FM *020 †18 ‡
POWELL, Larry Dean. 300 WANDA ST, CLINIC 73448 #021-06-1982 L2003 GP *020 ‡
SMITH, Virgil Dan. 301 WANDA ST, DOCTORS CLINIC LOVECOUNTYH 73448 #039-01-1934 L1973 IM CD *071

MARLOW – STEPHENS

GREGSTON, Jack L. ■ 73055 #039-01-1945 L1946 GP EM *071
KING, Kent Thos. 501 N 4TH ST 73055 #039-01-1986 L1987 FM *020 †18

■ = Address Information Privacy Protected

SABEDRA, Miguel R. 501 N 4TH ST 73055 #026-04-1987 L1990 **FM** *020 †18

MCALESTER – PITTSBURG

ADAMS, Robert Michael. 2 E CLARK BASS BLVD, STE 203 74501 #039-01-1966 L1971 **U** *071 †95

AVERITT, Susan M. 1401 E VAN BUREN AVE, WARREN CLINIC - MCALESTER 74501 #004-01-1996 L2003 **PD** *020 †55

BELLAMY, Murlyn Dean. 1 E CLARK BASS BLVD 74501 #048-02-1960 L1969 **PTH** *071 †50

BENSON, Robert Alan. 2 E CLARK BASS BLVD # 301 74501 #021-01-1984 L2003 **CD IM** *020 †20

BERLIN, Howard Scott. 1401 E VAN BUREN AVE, STE 908 74501 #035-47-1981 L2000 **OPH** *035

BLANCHARD, William Grant. 1401 E VAN BUREN AVE # 908 74501 #039-01-1955 L1955 **GS** *071 †85

BOWDEN, Richard Tad. 1401 E VAN BUREN AVE, STE 908 74501 #039-01-1991 L1992 **P** *020 †75

BOYER, Michael Frank. 4 E CLARK BASS BLVD, STE 205 74501 #030-05-1975 L1982 **AN GP** *020 †05

BRIDGES, Delta Walker, Jr. 1401 E VAN BUREN AVE, BOX 908 74501 #039-01-1963 L1963 **PD** *071

BROADWAY, Eric Stark. 1101 E MONROE AVE 74501 #039-01-1988 L1989 **P** *020 †75

CARLSON, Simon P. 1 E CLARK BASS BLVD 74501 #048-12-2000 L2006 **DR** *020 †80

CASE, Robert Geo. 1401 E VAN BUREN AVE 74501 #039-01-1966 L1966 **OPH** *071 †35

CHACKO, Geophilips. 3 E CLARK BASS BLVD STE 1 74501 #010-03-1998 L2003 **IM** *020 †20

CHIN, Paul Y. ■ 74501 #422-01-1997 L2002 **IM** *020

COTTON, John Bert. 1401 E VAN BUREN AVE, STE 908 74501 #004-01-1967 L1970 **FM** *020 †18

CRISS, Marcia Ann. 3 E CLARK BASS BLVD STE 2 74501 #041-09-1996 L2006 **OBG** *020 †30

CURTIS, Karen Lynne. 1401 E VAN BUREN AVE, STE 908 74501 #025-07-1995 L2006 **FM** *020 †18

DAKIL, Samuel E. ■ 74501 #039-01-1950 L1950 **OTO** *071

DEJECACION, Celso Austria. 11TH & MONROE 579 CAMHC 74501 #748-01-1956 L1986 **P GP** *071

DELA ROSA, Arturo B. PO BOX 97, WEST & STONE WALL STREETS 74502 #748-09-1965 L1980 **P** *071

DIXON, Raymond Willis. ■ 74501 #047-06-1971 L1992 **GS** *020 †85

DMELLO, Anita. 4 E CLARK BASS BLVD, STE 204 74501 #048-12-1991 L2004 **IM** *020 †20

DOYLE, David Lee. 1401 E VAN BUREN AVE, STE 908 74501 #048-04-1980 L1983 **OBG** *020 †30

DOYLE, Jonathan Andrew. ■ 74501 #039-01-2006 L2007 **P** *012

DOYLE, Lonnie Dwain. 1401 E VAN BUREN AVE, STE 908 74501 #048-04-1978 L1982 **OBG** *020 †30

DUNAGIN, James Love, Jr. 220 N 6TH ST 74501 #039-01-1971 L1972 **OPH** *020 †35

FEIGAL, Cheryl Lee. 5571 E CREEK ST, CHERYL FEIGAL, M.D. 74501 #048-02-1976 L1978 **P** *071 †75

FLANTROY, Kesha Major. 3 E CLARK BASS BLVD STE 2 74501 #012-21-2003 L2007 **OBG** *020

GAHRING, Stanley Ross. 4 E CLARK BASS BLVD STE 2 74501 #039-01-1975 L2005 **U** *020 †95

GALIS, Smaranda Andreia. 2 E CLARK BASS BLVD, STE 305 74501 #781-03-1989 L2001 **N** *020 †75

GANNON, Patrick Russel. 1401 E VAN BUREN AVE, STE 908 74501 #028-02-1993 L1998 **ORS** *020 †40

GOLLA, James Allen. 1401 E VAN BUREN AVE 74501 #026-08-1980 L1985 **GE IM** *020 †20

GUPTON, William Edwin, III. 1401 E VAN BUREN AVE, STE 908 74501 #047-06-1975 L1979 **FM** *020 †18

HARDY, Stacy Renae. 1401 E VAN BUREN AVE, STE 908 74501 #048-13-1986 L1989 **IM** *020 †20

HAYES, John M. 1401 E VAN BUREN AVE, STE 908 74501 #048-15-1989 L1995 **GS** *020 †85

HILL, John Morrie. 513 E CHOCTAW AVE 74501 #039-01-1958 L1958 **PTH PD** *071 †55,50

HOLLAND, Charles K, Jr. 1401 E VAN BUREN AVE # 908 74501 #047-05-1945 L1951 **IM** *071 †20

JACKSON, Robert Kern. 1401 E VAN BUREN AVE, STE 908 74501 #039-01-1972 L1973 **IM** *020 †20

JAMES, Melton B. 5571 E CREEK ST 74501 #048-02-1978 L1979 **DR** *020 †80

JUDGE, Ricky L. 1 E CLARK BASS BLVD 74501 #048-02-1983 L1990 **PTH** *020 †50

KHORASANCHIAN, Abdolkarim. 1101 E WADE WATTS AVE 74501 #517-03-1971 L1979 **CD IM** *020 †20

KIM, Sundra S. 1401 E VAN BUREN AVE, STE 908 74501 #005-02-1979 L2004 **IM IMG** *020 †20

KURVINK, Kim Lawrence. 1401 E VAN BUREN AVE, STE 908 74501 #046-01-1977 L1978 **FM** *020 †18 ‡

LEWIS, Larry Don. 1401 E VAN BUREN AVE, STE 908 74501 #039-01-1980 L1985 **FM** *020 †18

MARSH, John Henry. ■ 74501 #039-01-1963 L1963 **FM PTH** *071

MC ALESTER, Norman Wesley. SECOND & WASHINGTON, MED ARTS BLDG., STE 102 74501 #039-01-1996 L1997 **FM** *020 †18

MC CAULEY, Jon Michael. 4 E CLARK BASS BLVD # 203 74501 #039-01-1988 L1989 **NEP IM** *020 †20

MC CLINTOCK, Joseph M. 1029 E WASHINGTON AVE 74501 #048-15-1989 L1995 **U** *020 †95

METCALFE, Elliott James. ■ 74501 #039-01-1994 L2008 **IM** *020 †20

MILLER, Kenneth Richard. 1401 E VAN BUREN AVE, STE 908 74501 #039-01-1967 L1967 **IM** *020 †20

MILTON, Leroy Marvin. 1401 E VAN BUREN AVE, STE 908 74501 #039-01-1959 L1960 **IM CD** *020

MINGS, Wm Woodrow, Jr. ■ 74502 #028-34-1976 L2007 **P** *020 †75

MOUSSA, Ali Houssayn. 901 N STRONG BLVD, CANCER CARE ASSOCIATES 74501 #605-01-1994 L1999 **ON** *020 †20

O'BRIEN, Bruce Edward. 4 E CLARK BASS BLVD, STE 202 74501 #039-01-1979 L1980 **DR** *020

PIKLER, George Maurice. 901 N STRONG BLVD, CANCER CARE ASSOCIATES 74501 #319-01-1968 L1978 **ON HEM** *071 ‡

RAUNIKAR, John Erik. 1101 E WASHINGTON AVE 74501 #039-01-1990 L1991 **IM** *020 †20

RIDDEL, Stephen James. 1401 E VAN BUREN AVE 74501 #019-02-1985 L1989 **OBG** *020

SCHATZMAN, Ronald C, Jr. 1401 E VAN BUREN AVE, BOX 908 74501 #038-41-1963 L1998 **ORS** *071 †40

SEHGAL, Mark. 1401 E VAN BUREN AVE, STE 908 74501 #025-07-1994 L2006 **OTO** *020 †45

SHULLER, Donald Herbert. 4 E CLARK BASS BLVD, STE 202 74501 #048-02-1963 L1971 **R** *020 †80

SHULLER, Thurman. 1401 E VAN BUREN AVE # 908 74501 #004-01-1939 L1948 **PD** *071 †55

SMITH, James Randolph. 4 E CLARK BASS BLVD 74501 #422-01-1984 L2006 **AN** *020 †05

TARABISHI, Mohamed Hisham. ■ 74501 #915-03-1967 L1979 **OTO PS** *071 †45

THOMAS, Paul Stephen. 1401 E VAN BUREN AVE, STE 908 74501 #048-15-1981 L1982 **PD A** *020 †55

TRENTHAM, Reginald Bennet. 1401 E VAN BUREN AVE, STE 908 74501 #035-08-1970 L1974 **GS VS** *020 †85

WASHBURN, Phillip Earl. ■ 74501 #039-01-1966 L1966 **GP OM** *020

WILLIAMS, Kenneth Oladipo. PO BOX 579, 1101 E MONROE 74502 #690-01-1989 L2000 **P** *020 †75

WILSON, Jody M. 1401 E VAN BUREN AVE, STE 908 74501 #048-14-1997 L2006 **PD** *020 †55

WILSON, Winter. ■ 74501 #037-01-2008 *012

WYANT, Kathy L. 4 E CLARK BASS BLVD, STE 202 74501 #039-01-1981 L1982 **DR** *020

ZELLMER, Johnny Alvin. 1 E CLARK BASS BLVD 74501 #039-01-1996 L1997 **FM** *020 †18

MCLOUD – POTTAWATOMIE

COVINGTON, Charles Thos. 29501 KICKAPOO RD, MABEL BASSETT CORRECTIONAL 74851 #005-15-1965 L1969 **GP** *020

HANIGAR, Kimberly K. 107 S MAIN ST 74851 #019-02-1993 L1994 **FM** *020 †18

LUCIO, Linda. 29501 KICKAPOO RD 74851 #003-01-1991 L1992 **IM** *020 †20

MC CANN, Beryl Royce. ■ 74851 #039-01-1956 L1956 **FM** *071 †18

WYNN, Jeremy Don. ■ 74851 #039-01-2008 *012

MEAD – BRYAN

GOOD, Tina Denise. 1496 S TEXOMA RD 73449 #039-01-1992 L1995 **IM** *020 †20

HUSEN, Luverne Alfred. ■ 73449 #039-01-1963 L1963 **FM IM** *075

MIAMI – OTTAWA

ANTHONY, Scott Bryan. ■ 74354 #028-02-1974 L1998 **ORS OS** *071 †40

BELFORD, Guy Patrick. 200 2ND AVE SW 74354 #039-05-1984 L1985 **FM EM** *020 †18

CARNAHAN, Don Alan. 310 2ND AVE SW 74354 #004-01-1994 L1995 **PD** *020

COSBY, Glenn W. ■ 74354 #039-01-1943 L1945 **FM GYN** *071 †18

DONEY, Jack Richard. 310 2ND AVE SW STE 201 74354 #054-04-1976 L1978 **OBG GP** *020

ELKINGTON, Mark Wayne. 130 A ST SW, WILLOW CREST HOSPITAL 74354 #049-01-1991 L1998 **CHP** *020 †75

FUHRMEISTER, Paul Konrad. ■ 74355 #008-02-1984 L2003 **FM** *071 †18

GROTHEER, Martin Herman. 10 S TREATY RD, BOX 1328 74354 #019-02-1972 L1973 **FM** *020

HUSSAIN, Muzaffar. PO BOX 1203, ORTHO SURGERY CLN 74355 #704-21-1986 L2003 **OSS** *020

LIN, Su Su. ■ 74354 #209-01-1994 L2005 **IM** *020 †20

MADER, Elaine Mary. 200 2ND AVE SW 74354 #019-02-1983 L1989 **FM EM** *020 †18

MANGELS, Kyle Joe. 30 B ST SW 74354 #039-01-1996 L2002 **NS** *020

MOORE, James Davis. PO BOX 1498 74355 #039-01-1961 L1961 **GP** *071

OSBORN, James Mark. 310 2ND AVE SW, STE 104B 74354 #039-01-1984 L1987 **FM** *020 †18 ‡

OSBORN, John Clark. 200 2ND AVE SW 74354 #039-01-1983 L1986 **FM** *020 †18

OSBORN, Thomas Matthew. ■ 74354 #039-01-1990 L1994 **AN** *020 †05

RAY, Fred Allen. 10 S TREATY RD 74354 #019-02-1970 L1971 **FM** *020

SMITH, William Kenneth. 109 1ST AVE NE 74354 #048-12-1968 L1974 **DR** *020 †80

STEPHENS, Bradford Jay. 310 2ND AVE SW STE 101 74354 #039-01-1992 L1993 **IM** *020 †20

STEWART, Jeff N. 310 2ND AVE SW 74354 #039-01-1989 L1994 **GS** *020 †85

STOUT, Patrick Earl. 310 2ND AVE SW STE 1 74354 #048-45-1991 L1996 **U** *020

SWAN, Bryan Edward. 310 2ND AVE SW, STE 203 74354 #039-01-1990 L1991 **OBG** *020 †18,30

WILLKOM, Jean M. 310 2ND AVE SW 74354 #748-01-1961 L1972 **DR NM** *020 †80,28

WITCRAFT, Chauncey B. 310 2ND AVE SW STE 105 74354 #039-01-1980 L1981 **OPH PD** *020 †35 ‡

ZIN, Thant. 310 2ND AVE SW 74354 #209-03-1987 L1999 **IM** *020 †20

MIDWEST CITY – OKLAHOMA

AHMED, Mohammed N. 8121 NATIONAL AVE, STE 300 73110 #704-08-1991 L1999 **CD** *020 †20

AMIN, Muhammad. 2801 PARKLAWN DR, STE 301 73110 #704-04-1977 L1986 **PUD SME** *020 †20

ANDERSON, Joel Williiam. 2829 PARKLAWN DR, EMERGENCY DEPARTMENT 73110 #039-01-1986 L1987 **EM IM** *020

AREVALOS, Anthony R. 1001 S DOUGLAS BLVD 73130 #039-01-1981 L1985 **IM** *020 †20

ARNOLD, James Kerley. ■ 73110 #039-01-1956 L1956 **R** *071

BARNETT, Franklin Dewees. 11516 E SURREY LN 73110 #019-02-1961 L1967 **OBG** *071 †30

BARRY, Christopher John. 238 N MIDWEST BLVD, STE 201 73110 #016-43-1998 L2005 **NS** *100

BERNHARDT, Karis. 2801 PARKLAWN DR, STE 101 73110 #039-01-1991 L1992 **IM** *020 †20

BERNHARDT, Keith Irion. 2801 PARKLAWN DR STE 101 73110 #039-01-1962 L1962 **GP** *071 †18

BERNHARDT, William Gene. 2801 PARKLAWN DR, STE 101 73110 #039-01-1958 L1958 **FM GS** *020 †18

BLICK-NOLAN, Anita R. 1001 S DOUGLAS BLVD, CENTRAL OKLAHOMA MEDICAL G 73130 #039-01-1988 L1989 **PD** *020 †55

BOZARTH, Christopher. 230 N MIDWEST BLVD 73110 #039-01-1994 L1995 **RO** *020 †80 ‡

BUCHINGER, James Brant. 1800 S DOUGLAS BLVD 73130 #422-01-2003 L2005 **OBG** *020

CAMPBELL, Ann Elaine. 2825 PARKLAWN DR 73110 #028-46-1977 L1984 **IM** *020 †20

CHESLER, Donald Bruce. 801 N AIR DEPOT BLVD 73110 #039-01-1984 L1985 **P** *020 †75 ‡

CHOHAN, Asim Jafar. 8121 NATIONAL AVE STE 30 73110 #704-01-1987 L1992 **CD IM** *020 †20

CLEMONS, John Powers. 2825 PARKLAWN DR 73110 #039-01-1982 L1983 **EM** *020 †16

COLLIER, Sara Ann. ■ 73110 #039-01-2008 *012

CROSS, Cory Damon. 2612 MURRAY DR 73110 #039-01-2005 L2007 **IM** *012

CROSS, Michael Connor. ■ 73110 #039-01-2007 L2007 **IM** *012

DAWSON, David W. 351 N AIR DEPOT BLVD, STE BB 73110 #010-03-1981 L1991 **FM** *020 †18

DEAN, Seana Hudson. 600 NATIONAL AVE 73110 #039-01-1996 L1997 **PD** *020 †55

DEGNER, Alfred C. 2825 PARKLAWN DR 73110 #039-01-1985 L1986 **DR PDR** *020 †80

DENG, Zeming. 2801 PARKLAWN DR STE 101 73110 #243-09-1987 L2002 **FM** *020 †18

DICKEY, Robert Allan. 2801 PARKLAWN DR STE 101 73110 #039-01-1967 L1968 **FM IMG** *020 †18

DODD, Maryellen Leann. 801 N AIR DEPOT BLVD, PSYCHIATRIC ASSOCIATES, IN 73110 #039-01-2001 L2005 **P** *100 †75

DOMBEK, Stanley Jos, Jr. 2801 PARKLAWN DR, STE 204 73110 #039-01-1967 L1967 **TS** *071 †85,90

DONER, Richard Earl. 6908 E RENO AVE 73110 #039-01-1963 L1963 **FM** *020 †18

DONNELL, Dan Duffy. 2825 PARKLAWN DR, MIDWEST MED CTR 73110 #039-01-1978 L1981 **EM** *020 †18,16

FALCON, Oscar, Jr. 2825 PARKLAWN DR 73110 #039-01-1992 L1993 **VIR** *020 †80

FUNCHES-WILLIAMS, Terri L. 6908 E RENO AVE STE 10, HERITAGE PARK MEDICAL CENT 73110 #039-01-1991 L1992 **IM** *020

GADDE, Laxminarayana Rao. ■ 73110 #495-21-2001 L2006 **IM** *100 †20

GOVETT, Gregg Stanley. 2828 PARKLAWN DR 73110 #048-15-1985 L1995 **OTO A** *020 †45

GUERRA, Rico Anthony. 238 N MIDWEST BLVD 73110 #016-11-2002 L2004 **AN** *100 †05

HASHMI, Fayyaz Haider. 238 N MIDWEST BLVD, STE 201 73110 #704-01-1974 L2002 **TS CD** *020 †85,90

HAYHURST, Joseph Warner. 2825 PARKLAWN DR 73110 #039-01-1968 L1969 **PS HS** *020 †65

HINKLE, Royce Albert. 1032 S DOUGLAS BLVD 73130 #039-01-1963 L1964 **GP GS** *020

HOWELL, Taysha L. 2825 PARKLAWN DR, MIDWEST WOUND CARE 73110 #039-01-1993 L1994 **EM** *020 †16

ISENBERG, Jeffrey Scott. 2801 PARKLAWN DR # 203, STE 203 73110 #021-01-1986 L1995 **PS HS** *075

ISHMAEL, Richard Glendon. 230 N MIDWEST BLVD 73110 #566-01-1974 L1981 **ON PD** *050 †55

ISON, Lee Andrew. 2817 PARKLAWN DR 73110 #039-01-1962 L1963 **GS** *020

JACKSON, Dorothy L. 6908 E RENO AVE, HERITAGE PARK MEDICAL CENT 73110 #023-12-1987 L2002 **FM** *020 †18

JARMAN, Robert Neil. 2825 PARKLAWN DR, P O BOX 1088 73110 #039-01-1989 L1991 **DR** *020 †80

JOHN, Alex. ■ 73110 #496-19-2000 L2006 **PTH** *012

JOHN, Elcy Mathai. 1001 S DOUGLAS BLVD, STE 300 73130 #048-13-1999 L2006 **OBG** *020 †30

JORDAN, Christopher. 1201 S DOUGLAS BLVD 73110 #016-43-1973 L2000 **ORS** *020 †40

KALCICH, Michael Von. 2825 PARKLAWN DR, MIDWEST REGIONAL MEDICAL C 73110 #039-01-1993 L1994 **EM** *020 †16

KAY, Felix Ross. 6520 E RENO AVE 73110 #039-01-1959 L1960 **FM GS** *020

KHAN, Matheen K. 8121 NATIONAL AVE, STE 401 73110 #495-53-1975 L1981 **PTH** *020 †50

KING, Joseph Walter, III. 1001 S DOUGLAS BLVD, STE 300 73130 #047-07-1981 L2003 **OBG** *040 †30

KLIEWER, Todd Michael. 230 N MIDWEST BLVD 73110 #039-01-1994 L1995 **HO** *020 †20

KUNKEL, James Albert. ■ 73130 #039-01-1959 L1959 **OPH** *071 †35

LEE, James Kevin. 2801 S DOUGLAS BLVD, MIDWEST REGIONAL MEDICAL C 73130 #039-01-1992 L1998 **PM OS** *020 †60

LIMES, Barney Joe. 1201 S DOUGLAS BLVD, STE 49 73130 #039-01-1955 L1955 **U** *020 †95

LOWERY, Jim Dale. 801 N AIR DEPOT BLVD 73110 #039-01-1974 L1974 **P** *020 †75

MAHMOOD, Tariq. 2828 GLENHAVEN DR 73110 #495-29-1979 L1991 **HEM ON** *020 †20

MARTIN, Zachary. 2825 PARKLAWN DR 73110 #039-01-1982 L1983 **EM** *020 †18

MAYS, James E, III. 1201 S DOUGLAS BLVD 73130 #039-01-1984 L1985 **OS** *020 †95

MAYS, James Ernest. 8121 NATIONAL AVE, STE 306 73110 #047-06-1956 L1960 **PD PHP** *071 †55

MC COWN, Phillip Lee. 2817 PARKLAWN DR 73110 #039-01-1971 L1972 **ORS** *020 †40

MCGUIRE, William Edwin. 2825 PARKLAWN DR, MIDWEST REG MED CTR 73110 #039-01-1968 L1968 **DR** *020 †80 ‡

MC KINNIS, Gregory Hunt. 2801 PARKLAWN DR, STE 201 73110 #023-12-1992 L1994 **PCC** *020 †20

MEHTA, Sulabha. 600 NATIONAL AVE 73110 #495-37-1968 L1980 **PD** *020 †55

MEYER, Jeffrey Paul. 238 N MIDWEST BLVD 73110 #039-01-1999 L2003 **APM** *020 †05 ‡

MILLER, Kevin Wayne. 8121 NATIONAL AVE STE 300 73110 #039-01-1993 L1994 **CD** *020 †20

MILLER, Paul Richard. 9020 E RENO AVE, STE 100 73130 #039-01-1982 L1983 **ORS** *020 †40

MIRJANICH, John Kevin. 2825 PARKLAWN DR, MIDWEST REGIONAL HOSPITAL 73110 #039-01-1983 L1984 **AN** *020

MORGAN, Patrick Maurice. 8121 NATIONAL AVE, STE 402 73110 #039-01-1973 L1975 **IM** *020 †20

NGUYENLEHIEU, B-S. ■ 73130 #941-01-1964 L1976 **FM PHP** *075 †18

OLBERT, Mark Don. 2825 PARKLAWN DR 73110 #039-01-1985 L1986 **DR IM** *020 †20,80

ORUC, Nafi Mehmet. ■ 73110 #902-01-1962 L1972 **PTH CLP** *100

OTISI, Lillian Chinyere. 777 N AIR DEPOT BLVD # 22 73110 #305-01-2007 L2007 **IM** *012

PADGHAM, Michael David. 2825 PARKLAWN DR 73110 #039-01-1990 L1991 **EM** *020 †16

PARKISON, Reid Edward. 1001 S DOUGLAS BLVD 73130 #039-01-1974 L1975 **FM** *020

PATEL, Dipakkumar S. 238 N MIDWEST BLVD STE 20 73110 #495-48-1975 L2005 **AN** *040 †05

PETRO, Michael Curtis. 8121 NATIONAL AVE, STE 305 73110 #017-20-1998 L2004 **GS** *020 †85

PRATT, Wallace Roy. 1205 S AIR DEPOT BLVD, # 291 73110 #003-01-1975 L1994 **AI** *020 †55,03

RAHHAL, John Mark. 801 N AIR DEPOT BLVD 73110 #039-01-1986 L1987 **P** *020 †75

RICHARDS, Troy Albert. 230 N MIDWEST BLVD, ATTN: NANETTE HAAG 73110 #021-01-1996 L2004 **RO** *020 †80

ROBERTSON, Scott Courtney. 9060 HARMONY DR, STE E 73130 #018-03-1992 L1998 **NS** *020 †25

ROBINSON, R Randall. 8121 NATIONAL AVE, STE 407 73110 #039-01-1976 L1977 **OPH** *020 †35

ROY, Renee M. 10002 SE 15TH ST 73130 #067-01-1984 L1994 **FM** *020 †18

RUIDERA, Emilio Rubio. 8121 NATIONAL AVE STE 309 73110 #748-08-1979 L1995 **PTH** *020 †50

SEATON, Brian Joseph. 2825 PARKLAWN DR, MIDWEST REGIONAL MEDICAL C 73110 #039-01-1995 L1995 **EM** *020 †16

SHAKIR, Afshan. 412 S AIR DEPOT BLVD, STE A 73110 #495-04-1989 L1992 **PD** *020 †55

SHAKIR, Arif Ali. 412 S AIR DEPOT BLVD 73110 #495-04-1982 L1987 **CD IM** *020 †20

SHAKIR, Sadiq Ali. 1714 S MIDWEST BLVD 73110 #495-16-1980 L1983 **IM** *020 †20

SOTER, Elaine. 2825 PARKLAWN DR 73110 #039-01-1978 L1979 **UME OS** *020 †16

SUBRAMANIAN, Vasantha. ■ 73110 #495-42-1964 **AN** *100

SUTTER, Steven Harold. 8121 NATIONAL AVE STE 210 73110 #005-06-1985 L1992 **D** *020 †15

TARDIBONO, George. 351 N AIR DEPOT BLVD # BB 73110 #028-34-1993 L1994 **IM** *072 †20

THOMAS, Rupert Rockwell. 351 N AIR DEPOT BLVD, STE DD 73110 #047-07-1976 L1980 **OBG OBS** *020

TU, Quang Minh. 2801 PARKLAWN DR, STE 207 73110 #039-01-1988 L1995 **PS** *020 †65

VARLEY, Thomas. ■ 73110 #748-01-1972 L1989 **IM** *020

WALSH, John David. 2825 PARKLAWN DR 73110 #032-01-1998 L2002 **EM** *020 †16

WANG, Clark Gang. ■ 73140 #243-38-1981 **GS** *100

WILBER, Don Lane. 600 NATIONAL AVE 73110 #039-01-1978 L1979 **PD** *020 †55

ZEWDIE, Wudeneh. 1201 S DOUGLAS BLVD, STE K 73130 #366-01-1997 L2005 **NEP** *020 †20

MOORE – CLEVELAND

ADESINA, Oreofeoluw Oluwa. ■ 73160 #039-01-2008 *012

BATEMAN, Gustin Don. ■ 73160 #039-01-2006 L2007 **AN** *012

BORRSON, Beverly Aileen. ■ 73170 #039-01-2005 L2006 **OBG** *012

CAMP, Carl D. 320 N SERVICE RD 73160 #039-01-1962 L1962 **FM** *071 †18

DELEON, David. ■ 73160 #048-13-2006 L2006 **FP** *012

DELEON, Stephanie Dawn. ■ 73160 #048-13-2006 L2007 **PD** *012

DOUGLAS, Chad Allen. ■ 73160 #039-01-2007 L2007 **IM** *012

FANNING, Janet Lois. 400 N EASTERN AVE 73160 #019-02-1982 L1991 **FM** *020 †18 ‡

FANNING, Kyle Wyatt. 400 N EASTERN AVE 73160 #019-02-1982 L1991 **FM** *020 †18

FETT, Wilma Jean. 400 N EASTERN AVE, FAMILY CARE-MOORE 73160 #046-01-1986 L1989 **P** *012 †20

HAMILTON, Stephen Anthony. 520 S TELEPHONE RD, STE 207 73160 #039-01-1991 L1992 **HO** *020 †20

HARMON, Betty Leora. 700 S TELEPHONE RD # 300 73160 #039-01-1989 L1991 **PD** *020 †55

HOFFMAN, Lisa Christine. ■ 73160 #039-01-2006 **PD** *012

HSIEH, Misty Dawn. 700 S TELEPHONE RD, STE 100 73160 #039-01-2000 L2002 **FM** *020 †18 ‡

JACKS, Cheava Lynn. ■ 73160 #039-01-2007 L2007 **FP** *012

KEEN, Laura Michelle. ■ 73160 #039-01-2008 *012

KESINGER, Adrienne Norris. ■ 73160 #039-01-2007 L2007 **MPD** *012

KING, Robert Ryan. ■ 73160 #039-01-2008 *012

KOCH, Jamie Christopher. ■ 73160 #039-01-2008 *012

LE, Alain Irving. ■ 73160 #036-05-2007 L2007 **AN** *012

LE, Vu. ■ 73160 #104-01-2006 L2006 **IM** *012

LEEMASTER, Jay Elton. 520 S TELEPHONE RD, STE 101 73160 #039-01-1980 L1981 **OPH** *020 †35

MENDROS, Harry G. 2100 N BROADWAY ST 73160 #418-01-1969 L1977 **P OS** *020

MILES, Rodney James. 520 S TELEPHONE RD, STE 110 73160 #039-01-1981 L1982 **GP** *020

MIRCHIA, Sanjay A. ■ 73160 #039-01-2008 *012

MOTE, W Robt. ■ 73160 #039-01-1958 L1959 **OM** *071 †70

NELLER, Eric James. 504 PINEWOOD DR 73160 #039-01-2005 L2006 **AN** *012

NOORI, Darius. 1267 S EASTERN AVE 73160 #306-01-1998 L2004 **P** *020 ‡

PANTER, Benjamin Isaac. ■ 73160 #039-01-2007 L2007 **ORS** *012

QUY, Tyson Dinh. ■ 73170 #305-01-2007 L2007 **FP** *012

RUDRARAJU, Madhavi. ■ 73160 #495-11-2001 L2005 **GE** *012 †20

SEITSINGER, David W. 320 N SERVICE RD 73160 #039-79-1996, ▲ L1997 **FM** *020

SWENSON, Richard T. 700 S TELEPHONE RD, MOORE MEDICAL CENTER EMERG 73160 #039-01-1982 L1983 **EM** *040 †16

SYLVESTER, Carl Louis. 520 S TELEPHONE RD STE 101 73160 #039-01-1996 L2003 **OPH** *020 †35

WILSON, William Chas. 400 N EASTERN AVE 73160 #048-02-1968 L1991 **FM** *020

WORKMAN, Meredith Christi. ■ 73160 #038-44-2006 L2007 **GS** *012

MULDROW – SEQUOYAH

CHISUM-PRICE, Amanda Gaye. ■ 74948 #026-04-2002 L2002 **GS** *012

RICHARDSON, Morris A. PO BOX 1995 74948 #028-34-1960 L1965 **GP** *071

MUSKOGEE – MUSKOGEE

AGGARWAL, Vijay Kumar. 1011 HONOR HEIGHTS DR 74401 #495-36-1972 L1978 **NM IM** *020 †28

ALEXANDER, Robert Lin, Jr. HONOR HEIGHTS, MUSKOGEE VAMC 74401 #039-01-1961 L1961 **GS** *071 †85

AMIGO, Therese Maria B. 350 S 40TH ST, CARDIOLOGY CLINIC OF MUSKO 74401 #748-11-1989 L1999 **PD** *020 †55

ARYA, Satyendra. 300 ROCKEFELLER DR, MUSKOGEE REGIONAL MEDICAL 74401 #495-36-1990 L1998 **DR** *020 †80

ATWELL, Dwayne Henry. 251 S 37TH ST 74401 #039-01-1978 L1989 **OTO HNS** *020 †45

BAIRD, Deborah Noble. 3101 CHANDLER RD STE 101 74403 #041-09-1966 L1978 **PD CHP** *020 †55

BAKER, James Harold. 350 S 40TH ST 74401 #039-01-1982 L1984 **IM** *020 ‡

BERNHARD, Margaret Buford. 74403 #039-01-1974 L2002 **FM** *020 †16

BLAKE, George. 384 S 33RD ST 74401 #035-09-1965 L1992 **P** *075

BOLENE, Jim Andrew. 300 ROCKEFELLER DR, DEPT RADIOLOGY 74401 #039-01-1984 L1985 **R** *020 †80

BOX, Murff Wm, II. 3520 CHANDLER RD 74403 #021-01-1970 L1990 **IM** *020 †20

BOYD, Edgar Morris, Jr. 101 ROCKEFELLER DR, STE 203 74401 #047-06-1987 L1993 **OTO HNS** *020 †45

BRENNEMAN, A Russell. 2800 W BROADWAY ST 74401 #008-01-1958 L1978 **D IM** *030 †20,15

BRESTEL, Craige Montane. 3401 W BROADWAY ST, MUSKOGEE WOMEN CLINIC 74401 #055-02-1986 L1996 **OBG** *020 †30

BROWN, Raymond Scott. 350 S 40TH ST 74401 #047-07-1990 L2006 **NEP IM** *020

BROWNELL, Robert Boucher. ■ 74403 #048-12-1957 L1961 **OTO** *071 †45

CAMPBELL, Doyle Ray. 350 S 40TH ST 74401 #011-02-1970 L2003 **IM** *020 †20

CHAMBERLAIN, Wm Patrick. 3701 W BROADWAY ST 74401 #016-11-1961 L1973 **PTH** *071 †50

CHANDRASEKHAR, Polepalle. 3720 W BROADWAY ST 74401 #308-11-1985 L1992 **GE IM** *020 †20

CHEONG, Joel S. 350 S 40TH ST, CCOM MEDICAL GROUP 74401 #748-08-1989 L1999 **IM** *020 †20

CHILDS, Sabrina. 1805 N YORK ST, STE E 74403 #010-03-1994 L1996 **FM** *020 †18

CIBULA, Lawrence M, Jr. 300 ROCKEFELLER DR 74401 #038-40-1968 L1979 **RO PLM** *020 †80

COBURN, Thomas Allen. 3330 W OKMULGEE ST, ASSOC LLC 74401 #039-01-1983 L1984 **FM OS** *020

■ = Address Information Privacy Protected

COUCH, Ellis Phillip. 103 N 37TH ST 74401 #048-04-1968 L1978 **LM** *071 †40 ‡
COX, Alfred Taylor. 1011 HONOR HEIGHTS DR 74401 #041-13-1965 L1983 **FM EM** *020
CRAIG, Kenneth Burton. 300 ROCKEFELLER DR 74401 #039-01-1958 L1959 **GP GS** *020
CRITCHFIELD, Carl Fred. 300 ROCKEFELLER DR 74401 #007-02-1969 L1976 **DR** *020 †80
DAFTARY, Sudhir Ramniklal. 300 ROCKEFELLER DR, MUSKOGEE REGIONAL MEDICAL 74401 #495-48-1973 L2003 **AN** *020
DANIEL, Marjorie Y. ■ 74403 #748-07-1966 L1980 **AN** *074
DANIELS, Jewell Lee, Jr. 101 ROCKEFELLER DR 74401 #010-03-1975 L2003 **U** *020 †95
DANISA, Kola. 1011 HONOR HEIGHTS DR, DEPT OF VA MEDICAL CENTER 74401 #690-02-1968 L1976 **IM PTH** *020 †20
DANSBY, Jason Don. 3330 W OKMULGEE ST, ASSOC LLC 74401 #039-01-1999 L2002 **FM** *020 †18
DAUGHERTY, Jamie Suzette. 1001 S 41ST ST E, THREE RIVERS HEALTH CENTER 74403 #039-01-2003 L2005 **FM** *100 †18
DIAZ, Rigoberto. ■ 74403 #649-03-1951 **GP** *071
DUBBS, William Franklin. 1011 HONOR HEIGHTS DR 74401 #030-05-1975 L1990 **GS** *030 †85
EDDE, Robert Richard. ■ 74403 #039-01-1971 L1972 **AN** *020 †05
ELGIN, Donald M. 3520 CHANDLER RD 74403 #039-01-1976 L1978 **FM** *020 †18
ELLISON, Carl. 1805 N YORK ST, STE E 74403 #035-06-1970 L1987 **PD** *030 †55
ERDMANN, Paul Martin. ■ 74403 #039-01-1982 L1983 **P** *072 †75
EVANS, Gary Gene. 300 ROCKEFELLER DR 74401 #039-01-1963 L1965 **DR** *071 †80
FERNAN, Maximo L, Jr. 615 S 32ND ST 74401 #748-11-1983 L1996 **IM PUD** *020 †20
FITE, Fulton Williams. ■ 74403 #051-01-1958 L1977 **OTO** *071 †45
FORD, Lori Janine. 384 S 33RD ST, STE B 74401 #037-01-1989 L1995 **GE IM** *020 †20
FREIE, John Thos. 4708 HOWARD ST, VAMC MUSKOGEE 74401 #035-09-1964 L1970 **U** *020 †95
FULLENWIDER, Charles G. 333 S 38TH ST 74401 #028-02-1943 L1948 **OPH** *071 †35
FULLENWIDER, Chas Berry. 333 S 38TH ST STE F 74401 #039-01-1978 L1979 **NS** *020 †25
GEPHARDT, Maurice C. 300 ROCKEFELLER DR 74401 #039-01-1943 L1944 **IM** *071 †20
GIBBS, Robert Harrison. 1011 HONOR HEIGHTS DR, VA MED CTR OFC CHIEF STAFF 74401 #036-07-1959 L1973 **IM END** *020 †20
GRAYSON, Susan Lois. 1011 HONOR HEIGHTS DR 74401 #039-01-1985 L1986 **P** *020 †75
GREGORY, Jay Allen. 333 S 38TH ST STE D 74401 #039-01-1976 L1982 **GS TS** *020 †85 ‡
GRICE, Paul Frederick. ■ 74401 #016-11-1947 L1976 **GS HS** *071 †85
GROOMS, Guy Eric. 209 S 36TH ST, MUSKOGEE BONE & JOINT 74401 #016-42-1989 L1997 **ORS** *020 †40
HAMILTON, Mary F. 1120 ILLINOIS ST 74403 #004-01-1938 L1957 **P** *071
HAMMOND, Michael Wayne. 3501 W BROADWAY ST 74401 #039-01-1984 L1985 **FM** *020 †18
HARALSON, Ivie Peyton, Jr. ■ 74403 #047-06-1964 L1972 **U** *071 †95
HARRIS, Victoria Gayle. 1011 HONOR HEIGHTS DR, VA MEDICAL CENTER 74401 #039-01-1979 L1980 **IM IMG** *020 †20
HENDERSON, James Lamar. 333 S 38TH ST, STE E 74401 #039-01-1972 L1981 **U** *020 †95
HIGGINBOTHAM, Robert Lee. ■ 74403 #004-01-1981 L1989 **P** *020 †75
HODGE, Tommy Gordon. 4421 W OKMULGEE ST # 361 74401 #039-01-1960 L1960 **IM** *020
HOFFMAN, Edward Stewart. 3401 W BROADWAY ST 74401 #023-01-1965 L1984 **OBG** *071 †30
HOLDER, Timothy Wayne. 3330 W OKMULGEE ST, MATERNAL/FAMILY PRAC ASSOC 74401 #048-14-1987 L1996 **FM PLM** *020 †18
HONEA, Robert Arnold. 300 ROCKEFELLER DR 74401 #039-01-1956 L1957 **AN** *071
HONEA, Thomas Jean. ■ 74401 #039-01-1960 L1960 **AN** *072
HUMPHREY, Diego Sebastian. 1011 HONOR HEIGHTS DR 74401 #422-01-1984 L1996 **CD** *020 †20
JACKSON-LOCKYER, Margo. 300 ROCKEFELLER DR, MUSKOGEE REGIONAL MEDICAL 74401 #005-12-1998 L2005 **FM** *020 †18
JAMES, Joseph M. 300 ROCKEFELLER DR 74401 #041-12-1952 L1957 **IM** *071
JAVVAJI, Nagamanohar. 333 S 38TH ST STE A, SUITE A 74401 #495-21-1982 L1993 **IM** *020 †20
JOEL, Juanito Rono. 350 S 40TH ST 74401 #748-01-1979 L2006 **FM FPG** *020 †18
JOHNSTON, Diane Dale. 2822 IRVING ST, DEPT OF VETERANS AFFAIRS 74403 #039-01-1979 L1980 **FM PTH** *020 †18
JOSLIN, Gale Leslie. 3501 W BROADWAY ST 74401 #039-01-1991 L1992 **DR** *020 †80
JOSLIN, Petrina. 350 S 40TH ST 74401 #039-01-1991 L1992 **RHU** *020 †20
JUMEAN, Hani. 3206 W OKMULGEE ST, STE C, MUSKOGEE CANCER CLN 74401 #605-01-1967 L1992 **ON HEM** *020 †20
KENNEDY, Joseph C. 1011 HONOR HEIGHTS DR, BEHAVIORAL MEDICINE SERVIC 74401 #039-01-2003 L2007 **P** *020
KENNEDY, Mary S Basolo. ■ 74403 #028-02-1972 L1974 **D PD** *020 †15
KENT, Ann L Kiel. 1011 HONOR HEIGHTS DR 74401 #018-03-1953 L1958 **IM** *071 †20
KENT, Bartis Milton. ■ 74401 #048-04-1948 L1957 **IM** *071 †20
KIM, Soon. 350 S 40TH ST 74401 #583-11-1986 L2006 **ID** *020 †20
KINCADE, Thomas Allen. 1001 S 41ST ST E 74403 #039-01-1997 L1998 **PD** *020 †55
KLAASSEN, Katherine Lynn. 1011 HONOR HEIGHTS DR, MAIL CODE #122 74401 #019-02-1989 L1993 **P** *020 †75
KODURI, Madhusudan. 1011 HONOR HEIGHTS DR, MUSKOGEE VA MEDICAL CENTER 74401 #495-21-1984 L1993 **P PYA** *020 †75
KOHLI, Satish. 3340 W OKMULGEE ST 74401 #495-36-1978 L1987 **CD IM** *020 †20
KRAMER, Gary Michael. 209 S 36TH ST 74401 #016-01-1985 L2002 **ORS** *071
KRISHNAMURTHI, Manjula. 1011 HONOR HEIGHTS DR 74401 #495-04-1978 L1989 **HO** *020 †20
KRISHNAMURTHY, Choodamani. HONOR HEIGHTS DR 74401 #495-38-1958 L1980 **PTH** *071 †50
KUYKENDALL, Kennon L. 333 S 38TH ST STE A 74401 #039-01-1976 L1977 **IM** *020 †20
KYGER, David Louis. 3332 W OKMULGEE ST 74401 #028-02-1967 L1970 **IM** *020 †20
KYROLLOS, Adel George H. 350 S 40TH ST, CCOM MEDICAL GROUP, INC. 74401 #915-04-1984 L1999 **IM** *020 †20
LADD, George H. ■ 74403 #039-01-1960 L1960 **R** *071 †80
LAMOREUX, Nancy C. 1011 HONOR HEIGHTS DR 74401 #004-01-1984 L1985 **IM** *020 †20
LAW, Maggie Sweelan-Win. 1011 HONOR HEIGHTS DR, 1011,HONOR HEIGHTS DR 74401 #209-01-1981 L1996 **IM** *020 †20
LEE, Sang Gang. 615 S 32ND ST 74401 #583-02-1979 L1987 **PUD IM** *020
LESTER, Charles Alan. 101 ROCKEFELLER DR 74401 #039-01-1989 L1990 **P** *020 †75
LESTER, David James. 333 S 38TH ST STE A 74401 #039-01-1977 L1978 **IM** *020 †20
LEWIS, Marvin Owen. 1011 HONOR HEIGHTS DR 74401 #041-02-1946 L1968 **GS GE** *072 †85
LUTTON, Charles W. 333 S 38TH ST STE H 74401 #048-13-1988 L1993 **N PM** *020
MAHAN, Frank L. 300 ROCKEFELLER DR 74401 #039-01-1953 L1953 **AN** *072 †05
MANES, Janet L. 1011 HONOR HEIGHTS DR 74401 #039-79-1998, ▲ L1999 **IMG** *020 †20
MASK, Neal Allen. 1011 HONOR HEIGHTS DR 74401 #016-06-1976 L1981 **PUD CCM** *020 †20
MATTE, Paul Jos, Jr. ■ 74403 #005-06-1952 L1952 **IM LM** *071 †18
MATTHEWS, Virgil Dale, Jr. 530 S 34TH ST, MUSKOGEE COUNTY HEALTH DEP 74401 #047-06-1945 L1948 **GP** *072
MC ALISTER, John Edwards. ■ 74403 #039-01-1961 L1961 **P** *071
MC CANCE-LOWE, Jeannie M. 826 E BROADWAY ST 74403 #031-01-1983 L1989 **P** *020
MC GOWAN, Patrick Francis. 350 S 40TH ST 74401 #539-05-1975 L1988 **VS** *020 †85
MC INTOSH, Brad Anthony. 3330 W OKMULGEE ST, ASSOC LLC 74401 #039-01-1998 L1999 **FM** *020 †18 ‡
MC KINNE, Richard Alan. 344 S 38TH ST 74401 #039-01-1964 L1965 **OTO** *020
MOORE, Joseph Patrick. 341 S 33RD ST 74401 #039-01-1981 L1982 **ON HEM** *020 †20
MORGAN, Charles Thos. 300 ROCKEFELLER DR 74401 #039-01-1956 L1956 **FM** *071
MORONEY, Edward Francis. 1011 HONOR HEIGHTS DR, MUSKOGEE V.A. MEDICAL CENT 74401 #028-34-1961 L1966 **IM** *020 †20
MURPHY, Daniel Patrick. 300 ROCKEFELLER DR 74401 #039-01-1989 L1990 **RO** *020 †80
NELSON, Don Gaylord. 1011 HONOR HEIGHTS DR 74401 #016-11-1965 L1973 **IM PUD** *071 †20
NICHOLSON, Richard Waldo. 211 S 36TH ST, STE B 74401 #024-01-1948 L1975 **PUD AN** *071 †05 ‡
OBSEQUIO, Romeo. 350 S 40TH ST 74401 #748-29-1987 L2000 **IM** *020 †20
OGHAFUA, Gregson Orobosa. 350 S 40TH ST 74401 #010-03-1984 L2006 **CD IM** *020 †20
OLAFSSON, Snorri. 1011 HONOR HEIGHTS DR 74401 #484-01-1959 L1975 **PUD IM** *075 †20
OLSHEN, Andrew Russell. 333 S 36TH ST 74401 #033-06-1994 L2003 **PM** *020 †60
ONG, Samuel Wisco. 350 S 40TH ST 74401 #748-01-1990 L1999 **CD** *020 †20 ‡
ONG, Yee Se Choa. 350 S 40TH ST 74401 #748-01-1972 L1979 **CD IM** *020 †20
PACE, Scott Emory. 3369 W BROADWAY ST 74401 #048-12-1987 L1992 **NEP IM** *020
PARMAR, Jitendra Ravji. 1011 HONOR HEIGHTS DR 74401 #577-01-1978 L1985 **GE IM** *020 †20
POLLARD, Janet Helen. ■ 74403 #039-01-2008 *012
POWELL, David Ray. 3401 W BROADWAY ST 74401 #047-07-1981 L1986 **OBG** *020 †30
PRICE, Landon Dewey. 1011 HONOR HEIGHTS DR, BLUE TEAM 74401 #030-06-1978 L1981 **FM** *020 †18
RANDALL, Harvey Paul. 3701 W BROADWAY ST 74401 #048-02-1961 L1968 **PTH CLP** *071 †50
RAYMER, Doug Myrle. 1011 HONOR HEIGHTS DR, VA MED CTR 74401 #055-01-1991 L1992 **FM EM** *020 †18
REUTLINGER, Richard A. 200 S 37TH ST 74401 #048-13-1991 L1992 **GS** *020 †85
RILEY, Michael David. 300 ROCKEFELLER DR 74401 #039-01-1990 L1991 **IM** *020
ROBBINS, Wellington G. 1011 HONOR HEIGHTS DR, VAMC 74401 #004-01-1970 L1974 **IM** *020 †20 ‡
ROBERTS, Ifor J W. 3520 CHANDLER RD 74403 #803-03-1966 L1993 **GS OS** *075
ROBISON, Clarence, Jr. 3300 CHANDLER RD STE 105, FIRSTCARE MEDICAL CLINIC 74403 #039-01-1948 L1948 **CCS DS** *071 †85
ROBISON, Timothy Dwight. 200 S 37TH ST 74401 #039-01-1981 L1982 **GS VS** *020 †85
ROGERS, C David. 1011 HONOR HEIGHTS DR, JACK C. MONTGOMERY VAMC 74401 #039-79-1989, ▲ L1990 **FM** *020 †18
ROTH, Russell Blanchard. 3401 W BROADWAY ST 74401 #025-07-1969 L1975 **OBG** *020 †30
RUEFER, Fred Michael. 209 S 36TH ST, MUSKOGEE BONE & JOINT 74401 #018-03-1972 L1980 **ORS** *020 †40
SANGAL, Ajay Kumar. 384 S 33RD ST STE B 74401 #495-41-1977 L1990 **GE IM** *020 †20
SANGAL, Shalini. 384 S 33RD ST, STE B 74401 #495-41-1982 L1990 **P** *020
SAXON, John Harold, III. ■ 74403 #039-01-1981 L1982 **AN** *072
SCHOEPPEL, Stephen Mark. 300 ROCKEFELLER DR 74401 #039-01-1982 L1983 **AN** *020
SMALLEY, Kent Ragan. 300 ROCKEFELLER DR 74401 #039-01-1991 L1994 **N PMM** *030
SOPER, Michael Lynn. 300 ROCKEFELLER DR 74401 #039-01-1977 L1978 **OPH** *020 †35
STEELBERG, Schuyler T. 1001 S 41ST ST E 74403 #019-02-1996 L1999 **FM** *030 †18
TAWAKLNA, Mohamad Talat. 333 S 38TH ST STE B 74401 #875-01-1977 L1996 **PUD IM** *020 †20
THEIN, Tin Maung. 350 S 40TH ST 74401 #209-02-1981 L1996 **IM** *020 †20
TULL, Frank. 209 S 36TH ST 74401 #028-02-1955 L1972 **ORS** *071 †40
TURLINGTON, James Thos. 3336 W OKMULGEE ST 74401 #048-04-1970 L1981 **U AM** *020 †95
VARSIREDDY, Ravi Kumar. 341 S 33RD ST 74401 #495-57-1982 L1999 **HO** *020 †20
WADE, Kevin Francis. 3505 W BROADWAY ST, WADE PEDIATRICS 74401 #039-01-1991 L1992 **PD** *020
WATSON, David Farl. 300 ROCKEFELLER DR 74401 #036-07-1955 L1961 **PD** *071 †55
WATTY, Hubert H. 202 N 37TH ST, AGAPE FAMILY PRACTICE 74401 #012-21-1995 L2004 **FM** *020 †18
WAYMAN, James David. 3401 W BROADWAY ST 74401 #039-01-1975 L1977 **OBG** *020 †30
WEAVER, Jack Eugene. 209 S 36TH ST, MUSKOGEE BONE & JOINT 74401 #039-01-1993 L1996 **FM** *020 †18 ‡
WEIZENBERG, Abraham. ■ 74401 #038-40-1973 L2003 **IM CD** *071 †20
WHALEN, Michael Howard. 1011 HONOR HEIGHTS DR, VA MEDICAL CENTER 74401 #039-01-1962 L1962 **IM** *071 †20
WHATLEY, Jerry David. 3101 CHANDLER RD, STE 101 74403 #654-01-1992 L1995 **PD** *020
WILKINSON, D I. 3101 CHANDLER RD, STE 101 74403 #021-01-1962 L1966 **PD PDA** *020 †55 ‡
WILLIAMS, James M. 1011 HONOR HEIGHTS DR, VA MEDICAL CENTER 74401 #035-03-1989 L1992 **EM** *020 †16
WILSON, David Stanton. 1601 W OKMULGEE ST 74401 #019-02-1984 L1985 **GS IM** *020 †20,85
WINN, Berry Ellis. 300 ROCKEFELLER DR 74401 #039-01-1989 L1990 **GS** *020
WONG-SICK-HONG, Jackson. 350 S 40TH ST 74401 #165-04-1982 L1994 **CD IM** *020 †20
WOOD, Charles Douglas. 1011 HONOR HEIGHTS DR 74401 #067-01-1970 L1982 **GS CRS** *020 †10,85
WRIGHT, James C, Jr. 1011 HONOR HEIGHTS DR 74401 #048-02-1950 L1984 **CD IM** *020 †20
YARROZU, Anandavardhan. 1011 HONOR HEIGHTS DR 74401 #495-50-1971 L1982 **AN** *020
YEABOWER, John, Jr. 3502 W BROADWAY ST 74401 #039-01-1983 L1987 **DR** *020 †80
ZOLLINGER, Wm Kerr, Jr. 1011 HONOR HEIGHTS DR, MUSKOGEE VETERANS HOSPITAL 74401 #041-12-1967 L1976 **OTO HNS** *020 †45

MUSTANG – CANADIAN

AMUNDSEN, Gerald Arthur. 206 N MUSTANG MALL TER, MUSTANG FAMILY PHYSICIANS 73064 #039-01-1996 L1997 **FM** *020 †18
COLANGELO, Eugene John. ■ 73064 #038-40-1958 L1987 **AM PTH** *020
COSBY, Donna Raye. 500 PARK PL 73064 #039-01-1985 L1986 **PD** *020 †55
DENNIS, Gregory Jerome. 501 N MUSTANG RD 73064 #028-34-1980 L1986 **RHU IG** *020 †20

■ = Address Information Privacy Protected

FORSYTHE, John Thos. ■ 73064 #047-06-1960 L1961 **BBK NM** *071

FRAZIER, Judith A. 250 S CASTLE ROCK LN 73064 #039-01-1999 L2000 **FM** *020 †18

HERREN, Cherie Lynette. ■ 73064 #039-01-2006 L2006 **PD** *012

HOPE, John Malcolm. 207 N TRADE CENTER TER, PLLC 73064 #041-13-1975 L2006
OPH LM *020 †35

KEARNS, Harry James. ■ 73064 #039-01-1957 L1966 **R NM** *071 †80

KYRIAKOPOULOS, Adrian A. ■ 73064 #418-01-1947 L1971 **PA IM** *071

LEWIS, Sara Renee. ■ 73064 #048-15-2007 L2007 **PD** *012

MAHMOOD, Hamid. 1100 N MUSTANG RD 73064 #704-24-1987 L2003 **IM** *020 †20

MILLER, Jeffrey Allen. ■ 73064 #039-01-2006 L2007 **AN** *012

RADER, Robert William. 501 N MUSTANG RD 73064 #039-01-1998 L1999 **FM** *040 †18

RODGERS, Janet Elaine. 136 W STATE HIGHWAY 152 #A 73064 #039-01-1975 L1976 **EM** *071

SCHOOLER, Gary Robert. ■ 73064 #039-01-2008 *012

SHAVER, Jeffrey Thos. 207 N TRADE CENTER TER, PLLC 73064 #039-01-1988 L1989
OPH *020 †35

WOLF, Thomas Chas, Jr. 207 N TRADE CENTER TER, PLLC 73064 #039-01-1980 L1981
OPH *020 †35

NEWCASTLE – MCCLAIN

EASTHAM, Edmund John. 4 BRIDGE PARK 73065 #917-04-1969 **PD** *050

GIBSON, Breeanna Daniela. ■ 73065 #039-01-2008 *012

MOSLANDER, Terry Vance. ■ 73065 #039-01-2004 L2007 **EM** *020

POPE, Wesley Edward. 300 BY PASS RD 73065 #039-01-1989 L1990 **FM** *020 †18

SCHOELEN, Steve L. 300 BY PASS RD, TRI CITY FAM PHYSICIANS 73065 #039-01-1990 L1991
FM *020 †18

NEWKIRK – KAY

GREGORY, Mark Eugene. 11 DIAMOND BLVD, GREGORY FAMILY MEDICAL CEN 74647
#039-01-1987 L1988 **EM** *020 †18

NICHOLS HILLS – OKLAHOMA

CONFER, Stephen David. ■ 73116 #039-01-2004 L2006 **U** *012

DIGGES, Nicholas Edward. ■ 73120 #036-05-2000 L2005 **OTO** *100 †45

GOETZINGER, Billy Richard. ■ 73116 #039-01-1956 L1956 **AN** *071 †05

HAHN, Devon. ■ 73116 #039-01-1992 L1993 **PD** *040 †15

HALL, William Harvey. 1710 HUNTINGTON AVE 73116 #023-07-1960 L1972 **GE IM** *071 ‡

KIMBALL, Gale R. ■ 73116 #039-01-1951 L1951 **GP** *071

LEHR, Cristie Lynn. ■ 73116 #039-01-1993 L1995 **DR** *020 †80

LONG, Wendell M. ■ 73116 #028-02-1962 L1967 **U** *071

LOWE, Julie L. ■ 73116 #048-13-1999 L2005 **D** *100 †15

MAGILL, Victoria L. 6442 AVONDALE DR, LASERLIGHT SKIN CLINIC 73116 #039-01-1996 L1997
FM *020 †18

MESSENBAUGH, Jos Fife, III. 1621 QUEENSTOWN RD, NICHOLS HILLS 73116
#039-01-1958 L1958 **ORS** *071 †40

PARKE, David Wilkin, III. ■ 73120 #048-04-2007 L2007 **IM** *012

RHOADES, Everett Ronald. ■ 73120 #039-01-1956 L1956 **PHP ID** *030 †20

SMALL, Robert G. ■ 73120 #008-01-1951 L1964 **OPH GS** *071 †85,35

SUKMAN, Robert. ■ 73116 #048-02-1946 L1953 **RO** *071 †80

TONKIN, Jeremy Brian. ■ 73120 #028-46-2003 L2004 **U** *012

TRAUB, Sidney P. ■ 73116 #065-01-1948 L1972 **DR R** *071

WARD, Clark Anderson. 1504 W WILSHIRE BLVD 73116 #021-01-1978 L1988 **DR** *020 †80

WAUGH, Ashlee M. ■ 73116 #039-01-2004 L2008 **IM** *100

WEBB, Laura Jean. ■ 73120 #039-01-2004 L2006 **P** *012

WILSON, Keely Dawn. ■ 73116 #010-01-2006 L2007 **FM** *020

NOBLE – CLEVELAND

HARALSON, Harold H, II. PO BOX 519, 408 N MAIN ST 73068 #039-01-1980 L1981
GP EM *020 †16 ‡

NORMAN – CLEVELAND

ADAMS, Jared Michael. ■ 73069 #039-01-2008 *012

ADAMS, Mark Hawkins. 901 N PORTER AVE 73071 #039-01-1983 L1984 **IMG IM** *020

ADERHOLD, Herndon C. ■ 73072 #305-01-1983 L1986 **P** *020

ALEXANDER, Catherine. ■ 73072 #039-01-1953 L1954 **IMG GP** *071

ALLEN, Karen Suzanne. ■ 73069 #039-01-2007 L2007 **IM** *012

ALVIS, James Michael. 724 24TH AVE NW, STE 210 73069 #001-06-1988 L1994
NS OSS *020 †25

ANDERSON, Carol Kay. 500 E ROBINSON ST, STE 2400 73071 #039-79-1990, ▲ L1991
OBG *020

ANWAR, Muhammad. 500 E ROBINSON ST STE 900, C/O DR M SARWAR 73071
#704-01-1978 L1986 **CD IM** *020 †20

ARDOIN, Stanley Paul. 900 E MAIN ST, GRIFFIN MEMORIAL 73071 #039-01-1990 L1991
P *020 †75

ARORA, Satish Kumar. 1125 N PORTER AVE, STE 301 73071 #495-69-1988 L1998 **GE** *020 †20

ATKINSON, Dean Alan. 950 N PORTER AVE, STE 101 73071 #039-01-1988 L1989 **AI** *020 †20,03

AWAN, Abila Farah. 900 E MAIN ST, BLDG 52 73071 #306-01-2000 L2003 **P** *020 †75 ‡

AYERS, Norman Paul. 3400 W TECUMSEH RD, STE 300 73072 #039-01-1999 L2002
CD IC *020 †20

AZIZ, Bushra. PO BOX 151 73070 #704-16-1998 L2006 **P** *012

BAGWELL, Kenneth Hugh. 415 W GRAY ST 73069 #039-01-1957 L1957 **AN GS** *020 †05

BAKER, William Leroy. ■ 73072 #039-01-1960 L1960 **P** *071

BALLARD, Lydia Jeffcoat. 950 N PORTER AVE 73071 #039-01-1992 L1993 **IM** *020 †20

BALSAMO-HOFFMAN, Doris L. 4112 DRAWBRIDGE LN, P O BOX 722788 73072
#039-01-1995 L1997 **FM** *020 †20

BANNET, Jacob. 909 ALAMEDA ST, CTRL OK COMM MHC 73071 #869-02-1973 L1994
P PYG *020 †75

BARRY, George Newton, Jr. 718 N PORTER AVE, STE 102 73071 #039-01-1965 L1965
DR NM *071 †80

BELKNAP, Harold R, Jr. 950 N PORTER AVE, STE 300 73071 #021-01-1960 L1967 **IM** *020 †20 ‡

BETHEL, Shelba Jean. 809 N FINDLAY AVE STE 100 73071 #039-01-1965 L1965
GYN OBG *020 †30 ‡

BETHEL-MULLIGAN, Lesa J. 809 N FINDLAY AVE, # 100 73071 #039-01-1991 L1992
OBG *020 †30

BIRD, Philip Cavett. 1125 N PORTER AVE, STE 301 73071 #039-01-1971 L1973 **GE IM** *020 †20

BLACK, Andrew William. 1125 N PORTER AVE, STE 301 73071 #032-01-1996 L2006
GE *020 †20

BLUE, Mary Fons. ■ 73072 #039-01-1992 L1993 **PD** *020 †55

BOBB, David William. 825 E ROBINSON ST, MEDICINE CENTER-NORMAN PC 73071
#039-01-1996 L2001 **ORS** *020 †40

BOEHM, Theodore Alan. 1124 N PORTER AVE 73071 #039-01-2003 L2004 **FSM** *020 †18

BOHN, Shelley Ann. 700 24TH AVE NW 73069 #039-01-1981 L1983 **PD** *020 †55

BOND, James Lee. 1124 N PORTER AVE, OK UNIV HEALTH SCIENCES CE 73071
#039-01-2000 L2001 **OSM** *100

BOREN, Nathan Altus, Jr. 15702 E STATE HIGHWAY 9 73026 #039-01-1996 L1997
UCM FM *020 †18

BOYD, Aaron Lee. 500 E ROBINSON ST STE 1, THE LUNG CENTER, INC 73071
#039-01-1992 L1993 **PCC** *020 †20

BOZALIS, John Russell. 950 N PORTER AVE, STE 101 73071 #039-01-1965 L1965
A IM *020 †20,03

BROWN JACKSON, Kimberly M. ■ 73071 #039-01-2008 *012

BYNUM, Chester Lee. 1125 N PORTER AVE, STE 104 73071 #039-01-1957 L1957 **R** *020 †80

CARLSON, Richard Allan. 500 E ROBINSON ST 73071 #038-41-1970 L1974 **PD** *071 ‡

CATER, Ester Balatan. 900 E MAIN ST, GRIFFIN MEMORIAL 73071 #748-01-1956 L1985
P GP *020

CATER, Nilo T. ■ 73072 #748-01-1957 L1976 **GP** *075

CHACE, John Burton. 500 E ROBINSON ST, STE 2300 73071 #030-05-1992 L2005 **GS** *020 †85

CHAMBERS, Richard Gerald. 501 ALAMEDA ST, STE B 73071 #048-02-1964 L1971
PTH *072 †50

CHANES, Raul Emir. ■ 73026 #132-01-1955 L1970 **ON IM** *071

CHIOCO, Carmen Warren. 19200 GUILDFORD CRT 73072 #748-01-1962 L1981 **P** *071

CHRISTIANSEN, John R. 500 E ROBINSON ST, STE 1700 73071 #039-01-1967 L1967
PUD IM *020 †20

CLAYTON, Charles E. 901 N PORTER AVE 73071 #039-01-1976 L1977 **AN FM** *020 †05

CLEMENS, David Paul. 950 N PORTER AVE 73071 #039-01-1977 L1978 **FM** *020 †18

COBB, James Price. ■ 73072 #039-01-1973 L1974 **OTO** *071 †45

COFFEY, Kenneth Paul. 3400 W TECUMSEH RD, STE 104 73072 #039-01-1975 L1976
DR *020 †80 ‡

CONNALLY, Tom Shi. 500 E ROBINSON ST, STE 2300 73071 #048-12-1998 L2003 **GS** *020 †85

CONNERY, Lisa Blankenship. 1010 24TH AVE NW 73069 #039-01-1988 L1989 **FM** *020 †18

CONNERY, Stephen Edward. 950 N PORTER AVE, STE 102 73071 #039-01-1986 L1987
FM *020 †18

COOK, Shon W. ■ 73072 #038-41-1998 L2004 **NS** *020

COOPER, Frank Harry. ■ 73072 #039-01-1958 L1958 **U** *071 †95

COWPERTHWAITE, Robyn Lyn. 320 12TH AVE NE, OKLAHOMA YOUTH CENTER 73071
#039-01-1997 L2006 **CHP** *020 †75

COX, Alana Palomar. ■ 73072 #041-02-2005 L2005 **P** *012

CROOK, Jeffrey Allen. 3400 W TECUMSEH RD, STE 300 73072 #039-01-1985 L1986
CD IM *020 †20

CROSS, Braden Riehl. 805 E ROBINSON ST, PHYSICIANS SURGICAL CENTER 73071
#039-01-1975 L1976 **AN** *020

CUKA, Gabriel Matthew. 900 E MAIN ST BOX 151 73071 #030-05-1996 L1997 **P** *020

CURRY, Nancy A. 620 ELM AVE RM 201 73069 #039-01-1982 L1985 **P** *020

DAGG, Kathy Kernek. 701 E ROBINSON ST, ASSOCIATES-NORMAN OFFICE 73071
#039-01-1982 L1983 **ON HEM** *020 †20

DAKIL, Samuel Edward. 500 E ROBINSON ST, STE 1300 73071 #039-01-1982 L1983 **U** *020 †95

DANESH, Ali B. 718 N PORTER AVE, STE 102 73071 #517-06-1965 L1975 **P** *020

DAUTENHAHN, Justine Coyle. 901 N PORTER AVE 73071 #039-01-1980 L1981 **DR** *020 †80

DAVIS, Audie White. ■ 73071 #001-02-1957 L1962 **AM ADM** *030 †70

DEEBA, Reshma. 900 E MAIN ST, GRIFFIN MEMORIAL HOSPITAL 73071 #704-02-1987 L2006
FM *020

DEHADRAI, Gautam. 300 36TH AVE SW 73072 #495-73-1991 L2006 **VIR** *020 †80

DELAGARZA, Scott Martin. ■ 73071 #016-11-2000 L2002 **ORS** *020

DIEZMO, Rafael Fermo. 909 ALAMEDA ST BOX 400, CENTRAL OK COMM MH CTR 73071
#748-01-1958 L1985 **P GP** *071

DILLE, John Robt. ■ 73069 #041-12-1956 L1972 **OS AM** *072 †70

DOW, Robert Wm. 950 N PORTER AVE STE 300, NORMAN CLINIC 73071 #039-01-1976 L1990
N *020 †75

DUKES, Charles Huston. 900 E MAIN ST, BLDG 40 73071 #305-01-2003 L2005 **P** *020

DUNCAN, David Keith. 2413 PALMER CIR 73069 #039-01-1990 L1991 **D** *020 †15

DUNCAN, James Edward. 1125 N PORTER AVE STE 300 73071 #039-01-1978 L1979
N EM *020 †75

DURICA, Sherri Sutton. 701 E ROBINSON ST, ASSOCIATES-NORMAN OFFICE 73071
#048-16-1986 L1988 **IM HEM** *020 †20

EAGLE, Rebecca Worrell. 901 N PORTER AVE 73071 #039-01-1986 L1992 **PUD CCM** *020 †20

EDGE, Christopher A. 500 E ROBINSON ST STE 300, DEPT FAM PRAC 73071 #039-79-1985,
▲ L1986 **FM** *020

EDGE, Jodie Lee. 500 E ROBINSON ST STE 600 73071 #039-01-1955 L1955 **P** *071

ENNAMURI, Kumar B. 1818 W LINDSEY ST STE C 73069 #495-70-1991 L1997 **IM** *020 †20

FARIS, Kevin Jay. 901 N PORTER AVE 73071 #039-01-1982 L1988 **IM** *020 †20

FAZILI, Tasaduq Nazir. 901 N PORTER AVE, BOX 1308 73071 #495-51-1994 L2007 **ID** *020 †20

FELICIANO, Rebecca Acosta. 4709 SUNDANCE CT 73072 #748-10-1973 L1985 **P** *020

FERMO, John Victor. 900 E MAIN ST, GRIFFIN MEMORIAL HOSPITAL 73071 #748-10-2003 L2007
P *012

FIELDS, James Edwin. 500 E ROBINSON ST STE 2600 73071 #039-01-1979 L1980 **PD** *020 †55

FIELDS, Justin Elliot. ■ 73072 #048-02-2007 L2007 **MPD** *012

FINCHER, Mark Lynn. ■ 73072 #039-01-1983 L1984 **ORS** *020

FOLMSBEE, Glenn A. ■ 73069 #035-09-1952 L1958 **IM OS** *074

FORSHEE, Judy Ann. 900 E MAIN ST, GRIFFIN MEMORIAL 73071 #039-01-1998 L1999
GP *020 †75

FOX, Eileen Marie. 500 E ROBINSON ST STE 2600 73071 #048-02-1979 L1980 **PD** *020 †55 ‡

GIDEON, Rose Catherine. 1125 N PORTER AVE, STE 100 73071 #039-01-1973 L1974
DR *071 †80

GILLUM, Paul Stevens. 2413 PALMER CIR 73069 #039-01-1991 L1992 **D DMP** *020 †15
GOLDBERG, Andrew Stephen. 500 E ROBINSON ST STE 1 73071 #008-02-1986 L2004 **PUD** *020 †20
GREENHAW, Anderson Frank. 1818 W LINDSEY ST, BLDG C 73069 #039-01-2004 L2005 **AN** *012
GRIMES-COCHRAN, Gloria L. ■ 73072 #036-07-1949 L1952 **PD OS** *071 †55
GUTIERREZ, Nicasio S, Jr. 909 ALAMEDA ST, CENTRAL OKLAHOMA MENTAL HE 73071 #748-01-1979 L1984 **P** *020 †75
HADDOCK, John P. 231 E GRAY ST 73069 #047-06-1937 L1939 **GP GYN** *071
HAGGLUND, Howard Edward. 1818 W LINDSEY ST STE C100, HAGGLUND CLINIC 73069 #030-05-1965 L1970 **GP** *020
HAN, Suk J. 900 E MAIN ST, GRIFFIN MEMORIAL 73071 #583-06-1972 L1979 **P** *020
HANCOCK, Rita Malvaso. 1020 24TH AVE NW STE 100, OKLAHOMA ORTHO INST 73069 #035-06-1994 L1998 **PM PME** *020 †60
HARRIS, William Paul. 825 E ROBINSON ST, NORMAN PHYSICIANS GROUP 73071 #039-01-1980 L1981 **ORS OSS** *020 †40
HARTMAN, Richard Raymond. 3800 STONELEIGH PL, CENTER 73072 #004-01-1995 L1996 **P** *020 †75
HASBROOK, Vivian G. 900 E MAIN ST, BLDG 52 73071 #039-01-1993 L1994 **P** *020
HAWS, Laura Marie. ■ 73071 #039-01-2007 L2007 **PD** *012
HAYS, Katherine. ■ 73069 #039-01-2003 L2004 **CD** *012 †20
HEAD, Haskell Lee. 900 E MAIN ST, GRIFFIN MEMORIAL 73071 #039-01-1972 L1973 **P FM** *020 †75
HENNING, Jos Regnald, II. 501 ALAMEDA ST, STE B 73071 #019-02-1961 L1968 **PTH** *071 †50
HERNANDEZ, Hospicio Sunga. ■ 73072 #748-07-1960 L1982 **GP** *020
HIGGINS, John Richard. ■ 73071 #039-01-1971 L1972 **IM END** *030 †20
HILL, Edwin Eugene. ■ 73072 #039-01-1992 L1993 **P** *020 †75
HILL, John Billy. ■ 73072 #039-79-1999, ▲ L2000 **AN** *020 †05
HOLBROOK, Robert Michael. 1125 N PORTER AVE, STE 206 73071 #039-01-2000 L2001 **GE** *020 †20
HOLLOWAY, Joel Ellis. 2500 MCGEE DR, STE 148 73072 #039-01-1970 L1971 **D** *020 †15 ‡
HOLLOWAY, Willis, Jr. 900 E MAIN ST 73071 #039-01-1984 L1985 **CHP P** *020 †75
HOOD, Archie Newton D, Jr. ■ 73071 #048-02-1957 L1981 **P** *071
HOOK, Carl Truman. 900 N PORTER AVE, STE 209 73071 #039-01-1970 L1971 **OTO SME** *030 †45
HOOS, Marcia Lee. ■ 73071 #039-01-2003 L2006 **EM** *100 †16
HOSSEINI-MOJALAL, Jalal. ■ 73071 #517-08-1977 *100
HOUGH, Scott Matthews. ■ 73072 #039-01-2003 L2005 **EM** *020
HOUNG, Vivian Shaoing. 620 ELM AVE 73069 #036-05-1994 L2000 **FM** *020 †18
HOUSTON, Angela Chevelle. 900 E MAIN ST BOX 151 73071 #039-01-1997 L1999 **P** *020 †75
HOZAIR, Syed Mohammed. 900 E MAIN ST, GRIFFIN MEMORIAL HOSPITAL 73071 #704-02-1984 L2004 **P** *100
HUDDLESTON, Rodney Lynn. ■ 73072 #021-01-1980 L2006 **IM** *020 †20
HUGHES, Dale Ray. 901 N PORTER AVE 73071 #039-01-1962 L1962 **GS VS** *071 †85
HUNT, Laura Tryphena. ■ 73071 #039-01-2007 L2007 **PD** *012
HUSAIN, Farhat. 950 N PORTER AVE 73071 #704-02-1973 L1991 **N OS** *020 †75
INGELS, George Wm. 901 N PORTER AVE 73071 #039-01-1961 L1961 **RO PTH** *071 †50
INGELS, Stephen Clark. 901 N PORTER AVE 73071 #028-02-1992 L1997 **PTH** *020 †50
INGMIRE, Thomas Eugene. 901 N PORTER AVE, NORMAN HOSPITAL 73071 #039-01-1990 L1991 **EM** *020 †16
IRWIN, Julia Jane. 820 WALL ST 73069 #039-01-1995 L1997 **P** *020 †75 ‡
ISHAQ, Muhammad. ■ 73071 #704-05-1995 L2007 **P** *012
JACKSON, Donna Sexton. 808 WALL ST 73069 #039-01-1991 L1992 **PD** *020 †55
JACOB, Reena. ■ 73072 #495-31-1999 L2006 *100
JACOB, Roy George. ■ 73072 #495-31-1999 L2007 **IM** *012
JAMES, Andrea. ■ 73071 #495-37-1996 L2004 **P** *012
JARMAN, Yana. 900 E MAIN ST, BLDG 52 73071 #039-79-2003, ▲ L2004 **CHP** *012
JARVIS, Nicole Teresa. 1407 N PORTER AVE 73071 #039-01-1999 L2003 **OBG** *020 †30
JIMERSON, Steven Dee. 1407 N PORTER AVE 73071 #039-01-1971 L1972 **OBG** *020 †30
JONES, Philip Lee, Jr. 500 E ROBINSON ST, STE 1300 73071 #039-01-1987 L1988 **U** *020 †95
JUERS, John Alan. ■ 73072 #041-12-1966 L1973 **PUD IM** *075 †20
KARDOKUS, Merl Evan. 901 N PORTER AVE 73071 #039-01-2000 L2001 **DR** *020 †80
KARUMANCHI, Dinesh Kumar. 900 E MAIN ST, GRIFFIN MEM HOSP 73071 #495-50-1994 L2003 **P** *020
KEARNS, Lauri Jones. 320 12TH AVE NE, OKLAHOMA YOUTH CENTER 73071 #020-02-1987 L1991 **CHP** *020 †75
KHALID, Mansoor. ■ 73069 #704-09-2003 L2007 **IM** *012
KHAN, Rabiya Masood. ■ 73072 #039-01-2007 *012
KOO, Sang-Wahn. PO BOX 720900 73070 #583-01-1988 L2007 **P** *012
KRODEL, John Michael. 950 N PORTER AVE 73071 #039-01-1991 L1992 **IM** *020 †20
KUHLS, Thomas Louis. 808 WALL ST 73069 #035-06-1981 L1987 **PD ID** *020 †55
KUNAMNENI, Sudhakara Rao. 900 N PORTER AVE STE 208A, PEDIATRIX MEDICAL GRUOP OF 73071 #495-70-1978 L1990 **NPM PD** *020 †55
KURKJIAN, Theodorus Jonat. ■ 73069 #048-12-2007 **PS** *012
LACKEY, Charles Lee. 1125 N PORTER AVE STE 206 73071 #039-01-1978 L1979 **GE IM** *020 †20
LANCASTER, Taylor F. ■ 73069 #039-01-2003 L2004 **DR** *012
LANDAAL, Barbara Jane D. 901 N PORTER AVE 73071 #030-05-1986 L1994 **DR** *020 †80
LASHBROOK, Daphne Lynn. 500 E ROBINSON ST STE 2400 73071 #039-01-1999 L2003 **OBG** *020 †30
LAVON, Rosalie Anderson. 310 W ROBINSON ST 73069 #039-01-1964 L1964 **IM CD** *020
LAWRENCE, Carol Biggs. ■ 73072 #039-01-1987 L1988 **PD** *074 †55
LAWRENCE, Mason Clawdell. 1818 W LINDSEY ST BLDG C 73069 #039-01-1990 L1991 **AN** *020 †05
LEE, Kyung Za Choi. PO BOX 1668, OKLA VETERANS CENTER 73070 #583-09-1968 L1985 *020
LEONARD, Jason Edward. 415 W GRAY ST 73069 #039-01-1996 L1997 **AN** *020 †05
LEONARD, Joseph Edward. 600 N PORTER AVE 73071 #039-01-1967 L1967 **OTO HNS** *020 †45
LEWIS, Kathleen Elizabeth. 1300 MCGEE DR STE 100 73072 #039-01-1980 L1981 **GP OM** *020 ‡
L'HOMMEDIEU, Jeffrey W. 3400 W TECUMSEH RD, NORMAN URGENT CARE CENTER 73072 #039-01-1995 L1996 **FM** *020 †18
LIN, Zuorong. ■ 73072 #243-70-1990 L2007 **P** *012
LINDSEY, Stephen Guy. 950 N PORTER AVE, STE 200 73071 #039-01-1979 L1982 **FM** *020 †18
LLAN DE ROSOS, Osvaldo R. 1553 N PORTER AVE 73071 #132-01-1973 L1978 **NEP IM** *020 †20
LOBB, Quentin Daniel. 1818 W LINDSEY ST BLDG C 73069 #039-01-2004 L2005 **AN** *012
LOPEZ, Sylvia. 900 N PORTER AVE, STE 208A 73071 #048-12-1981 L1987 **NPM PD** *071 †55
LOVE, James Edward. 900 N PORTER AVE STE 310 73071 #039-01-1985 L1986 **IM** *020 †20
LYNN, Clyde Arthur. ■ 73072 #039-01-1958 L1958 **AM OM** *071 †70
MALAHY, Martin Daniel. 901 N PORTER AVE 73071 #039-01-1993 L1994 **PTH** *020 †50
MALL, Gagan Deep. 900 E MAIN ST, GRIFFIN MEMORIAL HOSP 73071 #495-29-1995 L2003 **P GP** *020 †75
MANATT, Christopher Scott. 500 E ROBINSON ST STE 1300, NORMAN UROLOGY ASSOCIATES 73071 #048-13-2002 L2004 **U** *020
MAQBOOL, Farooq. 15702 E STATE HIGHWAY 9, ABSENTEE SHAWNEE TRIBAL CL 73026 #495-51-1985 L1993 **IM** *020 †20 ‡
MARCELO, Charito Quiambao. 320 12TH AVE NE 73071 #748-07-1964 L1977 **P** *020
MARTINEZ, Mars Surbano. 901 N PORTER AVE, EMERGENCY DEPARTMENT 73071 #748-02-1979 L1982 **EM** *020 †18
MAUDUDI, Tazeen. ■ 73069 #704-16-1987 L2007 **P** *012
MC CARTER, John Wm. 900 N PORTER AVE 73071 #039-01-1977 L1978 **IM** *072
MC CLOY, Robert Burt. 901 N PORTER AVE 73071 #039-01-1967 L1967 **EM CD** *071 †16
MC CULLOUGH, Gerald Wm. 900 N PORTER AVE, STE 107 73071 #039-01-1954 L1954 **GS** *020 †85
MC CURDY, James R. 500 E ROBINSON ST STE 2300, NORMAN SURGICAL ASSOCIATES 73071 #039-01-1969 L1970 **TS GS** *020 †85,90
MC DORMAN, Wesley Steven. ■ 73072 #039-01-1997 *100
MC GOVERN, Jos Dunn, Jr. 3750 W MAIN ST, RM 138 73072 #039-01-1953 L1953 **OS** *071 †40
MC MILLAN, William Black. ■ 73072 #041-12-1972 L1974 **IM OS** *030 †20
MC NEIL, Thomas L. 4108 NAILON DR 73072 #048-16-1988 L1990 **P CHP** *020
MERIDETH, Lawren Alycea. 900 E MAIN ST, BLDG 52 73071 #039-01-2001 L2002 **P** *020
MERRILL, Thomas Henry. 950 N PORTER AVE 73071 #039-01-1982 L1983 **IM** *020 †20
MILLER, Griffith Champion. 630 24TH AVE SW 73069 #039-01-1961 L1962 **FM** *020
MILLIGAN, Michael J. 808 WALL ST, NORMAN PEDIATRIC ASSOC. 73069 #039-79-1998, ▲ L1999 **PD** *020 †55
MITROO, Serena. ■ 73071 #039-01-2007 L2007 **IM** *012
MOORE, Jeremy Adam. 900 N PORTER AVE STE 209, UNIVERSITY OF KANSAS MED C 73071 #039-01-2002 L2007 **OTO** *020
MORRIS, Clayton Douglas. 900 E MAIN ST, BLDG 52 73071 #039-01-2004 L2006 **P** *012
MOSES, Mark Robert. 3400 W TECUMSEH RD, STE 104 73072 #039-01-1998 L2003 **ORS** *020 †40
MULLINS, Jennifer Beth. ■ 73072 #039-01-2004 L2006 **PD** *100 †55
MULLINS, Michael Leon. ■ 73072 #039-01-1987 L1988 **AN** *020 †05
MULLINS, Roy Curtis, III. 901 N PORTER AVE, NORMAN REGIONAL HOSPITAL 73071 #048-12-1980 L2008 **PUD CCM** *020 †20
MURPHY, Terrence E. 900 E MAIN ST 73071 #039-01-1983 L1984 **P** *075
NAEL, Raha. ■ 73071 #039-01-2004 L2005 **IM** *020
NAGUMALLI, Sridevi. ■ 73072 #495-58-1982 L2006 **CHP** *012
NARULA, Rajesh K. 149 12TH AVE SE, NORMAN REGIONAL DIALYSIS C 73071 #495-49-1985 L1999 **NEP** *020 †20
NAWAZ, Mudassir. ■ 73071 #704-02-1993 L2006 **IM** *020 †20
NEES, Jeff Paul. 3400 W TECUMSEH RD, STE 305 73072 #039-01-1991 L1992 **NS** *020 †25
NGHIEM, Huc Xuan. ■ 73071 #941-01-1959 L1979 **GP** *071
NGUYEN, Phuc Kim. ■ 73072 #039-01-2008 *012
NICKOLLS, Charles Leslie. 620 ELM AVE 73069 #039-01-1955 L1957 **P GP** *072
OLLAR-SHOEMAKE, Leslie J. 500 E ROBINSON ST STE 240 73071 #039-79-1993, ▲ L1994 **OBG** *020
OOMMEN, Reena. ■ 73072 #039-01-2006 **FM** *100
OVERHULSER, Patricia I. 950 N PORTER AVE, STE 101 73071 #048-13-1986 L1991 **AI** *020 †55,03
OZINGA, Lynne Valerie. 1125 N PORTER AVE, STE 104 73071 #039-01-1991 L1992 **DR RNR** *020 †80
PARIKH, Chintan A. 1125 N PORTER AVE, STE 301 73071 #495-76-1990 L1999 **GE** *020 †20 ‡
PARKER, Russell Bruce. 1407 N PORTER AVE 73071 #048-02-1981 L1985 **OBG** *020 †30
PARVEZ, Saleh Mohammed. PO BOX 151, 900 E MAIN ST 73070 #160-04-1992 L2004 **P** *020
PASKOWSKI, Christopher A. 600 N PORTER AVE 73071 #039-01-1996 L2001 **OTO** *020 †45
PEDDIREDDY, Rupa. 900 E MAIN ST 73071 #496-01-1996 L2008 **P** *012
PHAM, David Nguyen. ■ 73071 #654-01-2006 L2007 **FP** *012
PHUNG, Can Dinh. 1776 E ROBINSON ST 73071 #941-01-1973 L1985 **GP EM** *020
PINEDA, Honorata P. 1829 CEDAR HILL RD 73072 #748-07-1964 L1983 **P** *020
PIRTLE, John Kindrick. 31959 WESTERN AVE 73072 #039-01-1965 L1965 **PCC IM** *020 †20
PLUSQUELLEC, Paul L, Jr. 950 N PORTER AVE 73071 #021-06-1992 L1995 **IM** *020 †20
POIRIER, William Thos. ■ 73072 #041-09-1971 L1978 **OTO A** *020 †45
PORTER, David Ashley. 1407 N PORTER AVE 73071 #039-01-1978 L1982 **OBG** *020 †30 ‡
POWELL, Joshua Trent. 816 24TH AVE NW 73069 #039-01-2001 L2005 **OPH** *020 †35
PRABHU, Santosh Thos. 700 24TH AVE NW 73069 #495-52-1979 L1983 **CD IM** *020 †20
PROCTOR, Scott Michael. 1818 W LINDSEY ST, BLDG C 73069 #039-01-2001 L2002 **AN** *020
PULLING, Susan Lee. 900 N PORTER AVE, STE 210 73071 #039-01-1984 L1985 **OPH** *020 †35
QUIAMBAO, Benjamin Yambao. ■ 73071 #748-21-2000 L2005 **P** *012
QUIAMBAO, Venancio R, Jr. ■ 73070 #748-07-1956 L1967 **U** *071 †95
QUIVER, Donald Murray. ■ 73071 #039-01-1993 L1996 **P** *020
RABLE, Denise Lynn. 500 E ROBINSON ST, ST 2300 73071 #039-01-1990 L1991 **GS** *020 †85
RAINS, Kelsey Elizabeth. ■ 73072 #039-01-2008 *012
RAIZEN, John Frank. 320 12TH AVE NE 73071 #039-01-1994 L1995 **CHP** *020 †75
RAMAKRISHNAN, Lakshmin. 3400 W TECUMSEH RD, STE 200 73072 #495-59-1993 L1999 **IMG IM** *020 †20
RATLIFF, Gary Don. 900 N PORTER AVE STE 310 73071 #039-01-1980 L1981 **IM** *020 †20
RATLIFF, Hansel Lavern. 700 24TH AVE NW 73069 #039-01-1962 L1962 **FM** *020 †18
RAZOOK, Joel Christopher. 1215 CROSSROADS BLVD, STE 200 73072 #039-01-1995 L1996 **OPH** *020 †35
REDDY, Rajkumar Padira. 900 N PORTER AVE STE 208A 73071 #495-57-1979 L1992 **PD NPM** *020 †55
REID, Laurance S, Jr. ■ 73072 #041-01-1970 L1999 **P** *072 †75
REMY, Bruce K. ■ 73072 #039-01-1976 L1983 **IM** *020
RESNEDER, John Ray. 900 N PORTER AVE STE 110 73071 #039-01-1978 L1979 **OBG** *020 †30
RICE, Craig Edward. 620 ELM AVE 73019 #039-01-1987 L1988 **FM** *020 †18
RIDDLE, Joe Dixon. 900 N PORTER AVE 73071 #039-01-1973 L1974 **IM** *020 †20
RIPPERGER, Joseph Michael. 900 N PORTER AVE STE 200 73071 #039-01-1989 L1990 **P** *020 †75
ROBERTS, Victor Alan. 3221 RIVERWALK DR, VIC ROBERTS P.C. 73072 #039-01-1996 L1997 **FM** *020 †18
ROBERTSON, John Anthony. 700 24TH AVE NW, INTEGRIS PROHEALTH NORMAN 73069 #039-01-1997 L2006 **FM** *020 †18

■ = Address Information Privacy Protected

7687

ROBERTSON, Madeline Jane. ■ 73072 #041-01-1996 *100
ROBINSON, Brian Lloyd. 900 N PORTER AVE, STE 310 73071 #039-01-1988 L1989 **IM** *071 †20
RUNKLE, R Layton. 600 N PORTER AVE 73071 #039-01-1966 L1966 **OTO PS** *071 †45
SALIM, Muhammad. 900 N PORTER AVE STE 1800, DISEASES 73071 #704-01-1986 L1994 **CD** *020 †20
SALOMON, Gregory. 901 N PORTER AVE 73071 #016-11-1992 L1998 **DR VIR** *020 †80
SAMBAJON, Galileo A. PO BOX 1637 73019 #748-07-1964 L1980 **P** *020
SANDHU, Peeran Ditta. ■ 73071 #759-06-2004 L2007 **IM** *012
SAN PEDRO, Sergio Basilio. 901 N PORTER AVE 73071 #649-01-1968 L1974 **CD IM** *020
SARALE, Delia Cristina. 1553 N PORTER AVE 73071 #132-01-1973 L1979 **PDE CG** *071 †55,19
SARWAR, Muhammad. 500 E ROBINSON ST 73071 #704-01-1972 L1980 **CD** *020 †20
SCHMIDT, Robert Danl. 500 E ROBINSON ST, STE 1450 73071 #035-08-1988 L1993 **GE HEP** *020 †20
SCHULTZ, Steven Clyde, Jr. 3400 W TECUMSEH RD, STE 104 73072 #039-01-1998 L2004 **ORS** *020 †40
SEAY, James Wm. 501 ALAMEDA ST 73071 #004-01-1968 L1974 **PTH** *020
SELLERS, Gail Marcellia. ■ 73072 #039-01-1988 L1989 **P** *020
SELLERS, Michael David. 950 N PORTER AVE 73071 #039-01-1988 L1989 **CD** *020 †20
SERQUINA, Florida Javier. 900 E MAIN ST 73071 #748-07-1953 L1982 **GP** *020
SHADID, Ernest Geo. 3280 MARSHALL AVE 73072 #039-01-1955 L1956 **P** *040 †75
SHADID, Gregory Ernest. 3280 MARSHALL AVE 73072 #039-01-1993 L1998 **P** *020 †75
SHAH, Parind Suryakant. PO BOX 151 73070 #495-89-1989 L2006 **P** *012
SHAHSAVARI, Mehran. 900 N PORTER AVE, STE 206 73071 #517-01-1991 L2000 **IM** *020 †20
SHEAD, William L. 901 N PORTER AVE, P O BOX 1308 73071 #021-01-1949 L1953 **CD IM** *071
SHELTON, George Allen, Jr. 901 N PORTER AVE, EMERGENCY DEPARTMENT 73071 #039-01-1975 L1976 **EM** *020
SHONGO-HIANGO, Hilaire. 900 E MAIN ST 73071 #266-03-1993 L2006 **P** *012
SIECK, Christian Cummins. 901 N PORTER AVE 73071 #039-01-1995 L1996 **FM** *020 †18
SILMAN, James B. 901 N PORTER AVE, NORMAN REGIONAL HOSPITAL 73071 #048-04-1951 L1961 **IM OM** *071 ‡
SIMMERING, James Virgil. 1300 MCGEE DR 73072 #039-01-1955 L1955 **GP ADM** *020
SMITH, Sheryl Mc Niven. ■ 73072 #039-01-2004 L2006 **ORS** *012
SMITH, Steven Earl. 620 ELM AVE 73069 #039-01-1993 L1994 **FSM** *020 †18
SMITH, Twyla Jean. 2500 MCGEE DR STE 149 73072 #039-01-1983 L1984 **P** *020 †75
STACY, Tadgy Del Hodges. 808 WALL ST 73069 #039-01-1995 L1996 **PD** *020 †55 ‡
STITES, Ronald Paul. 901 N PORTER AVE 73071 #039-01-1974 L1975 **IM** *020 †20
SULLIVAN, John Patrick. 805 E ROBINSON ST 73071 #039-01-1983 L1984 **AN** *020 †05
SULLIVAN, Robert R. 500 E ROBINSON ST 73071 #039-01-1955 L1955 **D** *071
SUNDARARAJAN, Vijaya. ■ 73072 #039-01-1989 L1994 **GPM IM** *020 †20
SWANSON, Terrell John. ■ 73071 #039-01-2007 L2007 **PD** *012
TAM, Weyton Wingho. 3700 36TH AVE NW, MCBRIDE CLINIC 73072 #039-01-1989 L1995 **DR** *020 †80
TANKERSLEY, William Earl. 900 E MAIN ST, BLDG 52 73071 #039-01-2004 L2006 **P** *012
TAYLOR, Cynthia Leigh. 1237 ALAMEDA ST, FAMILY MED ASSOCS 73071 #047-06-1992 L1999 **FM** *020 †18
THOMPSON, Eric Justin. 901 N PORTER AVE 73071 #039-01-1996 L1997 **PTH** *020 †50
THURSTON, Thomas Watson. 900 N PORTER AVE STE 108 73071 #039-01-1957 L1957 **PD** *020 †55
TIPPIE, Martin Alan. 620 ELM AVE 73069 #039-01-1971 L1972 **FM** *020 †18
TRAN, Cristina My. 2201 MCKOWN DR, STE 1 73072 #019-02-1999 L2000 **OPH** *020 †35
URICE, Thomas Duke. 2413 PALMER CIR 73069 #039-01-1978 L1981 **D** *020 †15
VERMA, Ajay K. 900 N PORTER AVE, STE 208A 73071 #495-45-1982 L1999 **NPM PD** *020 †55
VIDAURRI, Lytorre Denise. ■ 73072 #016-01-2005 **AN** *012
VIERA, Vivian. 500 E ROBINSON ST 3 73071 #042-02-1985 L1993 **FM** *020 †18
VILLANO, Michael Lee. 900 N PORTER AVE, STE 106 73071 #048-13-1991 L2005 **CD IM** *020 †20
VOGEL, R Brad. 825 E ROBINSON ST, OSC-NORMAN, P.C. 73071 #028-79-1995, ▲ L1996 **ORS HS** *020
VOTO, Joe Don. 1818 W LINDSEY ST, BLDG C 73069 #039-01-1998 L1999 **AN** *020 †05 ‡
WAKEFIELD, Natalie Marie. ■ 73072 #039-01-2008 *012
WALL, James Sidney. 901 N PORTER AVE 73071 #039-01-1966 L1966 **FM** *020 †18
WALTNER, Jeffrey Michael. ■ 73071 #048-12-1965 L1972 **ORS** *071 †40
WATERMAN, Lisa R Hoke. 500 E ROBINSON ST STE 2400 73071 #039-79-1996, ▲ L1997 *020
WAUTERS, Brent Louis. 3770 W ROBINSON ST STE 116, BROOKHAVEN CLINIC 73072 #039-01-1979 L1980 **EM GP** *020 †16
WEBBER, Chadwick Lee. 901 N PORTER AVE 73071 #039-01-2000 L2001 **DR** *020 †80
WEBER, Maril Joy. 701 E ROBINSON ST, ASSOCIATES-NORMAN OFFICE 73071 #003-01-1979 L1980 **ON HEM** *020 †20
WEDEL, Richard James. 901 N PORTER AVE 73071 #039-01-1998 L2003 **DR** *020 †80
WHITE, Stephanie Allison. ■ 73072 #039-01-2006 L2007 **OBG** *012
WHITESELL, Clifton Louis. 500 E ROBINSON ST, STE 1300 73071 #039-01-1980 L1981 **U** *020 †95
WIESNER, Elise Rose. 900 N PORTER AVE, STE 310 73071 #039-01-1991 L1992 **IM** *020 †20
WIGGS, William G. 448 36TH AVE NW, STE 101 73072 #039-01-1983 L1984 **N** *020 †75
WILSON, Pamela L. ■ 73026 #028-79-1994, ▲ L1995 **DR** *020 †80
WILSON, Victor Thos. 700 WALL ST 73069 #039-05-1984 L1990 **PD A** *020 †55
WISE, Kimberly Marie. 2201 MCKOWN DR, STE 1 73072 #039-01-1993 L1994 **OPH** *020 †35
WITT, Janice Hunter. 901 N PORTER AVE 73071 #039-01-1982 L1989 **RO** *075 †80
WOLLMANN, Eric A. 1125 N PORTER AVE STE 100, P O BOX 1387 73071 #319-01-1973 L1977 **DR** *020 †80
WONG, Stephen Kwun. 5001 LYON RD 73072 #039-01-2005 L2005 **DR** *012
WOODWARD, Harold Jackson. 2201 MCKOWN DR, STE 1 73072 #039-01-1967 L1967 **OPH** *071 †35
YEAMAN, Brian Allen. 950 N PORTER AVE STE 200 73071 #039-01-2002 L2003 **FM** *020 †18
YOHE, Ruth E Mc Chesney. ■ 73069 #041-07-1954 L1957 **PDA A** *071 †55,03
YOUNG, Glenna Kaye. 901 N PORTER AVE 73071 #039-01-1980 L1981 **DR** *020 †80
YOUSIF, Raed Hikmet. 900 E MAIN ST, GRIFFIN MEMORIAL HOSP 73071 #528-01-1992 L2006 **P** *012
ZIELINSKI, Richard F. 900 E MAIN ST, GRIFFIN MEMORIAL HOSPITAL 73071 #041-13-1983 L1994 **P** *020 †18

NOWATA – NOWATA

BURGE, Terry Eugene. 712 E OSAGE AVE, NOWATA FAMILY MEDICINE 74048 #028-03-1962 L1981 **FM** *071 †18

CAUGHELL, David Sean. 712 E OSAGE AVE 74048 #039-05-1985 L1986 **FM** *020 †18
FLORA, Homer N. PO BOX 629, 401 S LOCUST 74048 #028-78-1953, ▲ L1959 **GP** *071

OKEENE – BLAINE

ATENDIDO, Amadeo G. 124 S 6TH ST, OKEENE MEDICAL CLINIC INC 73763 #748-01-1957 L1981 **GS** *020
DOTTER, Billy Dale. 124 S 6TH ST 73763 #039-01-1959 L1959 **FM GS** *071 †18

OKEMAH – OKFUSKEE

ANDERSON, Zachariah J. 309 N 14TH ST, HOSPITAL 74859 #037-01-1999 L2002 **FM** *020
BEE, Lee Peter. 309 N 14TH ST 74859 #003-75-2004, ▲ L2005 **IM** *100
KRUEGER, John Timothy. 309 N 14TH ST, CREEK NATION COMMUNITY HOS 74859 #039-01-2000 L2006 **FM** *020 †18
MILLER, Bonnie J Gibson. 201 N 14TH ST 74859 #039-01-1959 L1961 **FM** *020 †18
MILLER, Noel Eugene. 201 N 14TH ST 74859 #039-01-1959 L1959 **FM** *020 †18

OKLAHOMA CITY – CLEVELAND

AYERS, Karyn Marie. ■ 73170 #023-12-1999 L2007 **FM OM** *020 †18
BARNES, Jennifer Carol. ■ 73170 #039-01-2007 **PD** *012
BROWN, Donald Chas. 1600 SW 119TH ST 73170 #039-01-1978 L1979 **OBG OS** *020 †30
BUI, Phiyen Nguyen. ■ 73170 #039-01-2008 *012
CHAWLA, Jaspal Singh. 2413 SW 111TH ST 73170 #495-08-1970 L1977 **IM NEP** *020 †20
CHEN, Theresa Xuan. ■ 73170 #039-01-2007 L2007 **IM** *020 †80
CLARK, Robert Kenneth. 11401 S WESTERN AVE 73170 #025-01-1971 L1982 **OBG** *020 †30
COTTON, Charles Adam. ■ 73170 #039-01-2006 L2007 **AN** *012
DANG, Hoang Huy. 12549 CRICK HOLLOW CT 73170 #039-01-2005 L2008 **IM** *012
DIXON, Robert Wendell. ■ 73170 #039-01-1944 L1946 **OM** *071
DOWDELL, Roy Wesley. ■ 73170 #039-01-1963 L1963 **GP GPM** *071
EGAS, Carlos Adrian. 2117 RIVERWALK DR, RIVERWALK SURGICAL SERVICE 73160 #319-01-1991 L2006 **GS** *020 †85
GONZALEZ, Vincent. 12201 LORIEN WAY, MORNINGSTAR EMERGENCY PHYS 73170 #024-05-1988 L1989 **EM** *020 †16
GUGLIELMO, Eric Scott. ■ 73170 #031-01-2005 L2006 **OPH** *012
HANNA, Rami Kamal-Matta. ■ 73170 #605-03-2000 L2007 **PCC** *012 †20
HINZ, Wesley Dean. 700 S TELEPHONE RD # 100, NORMAN REGIONAL HEALTH SYS 73160 #039-01-1978 L1979 **FM OM** *020 †18 ‡
HOUSTON, Michael Shawn. ■ 73170 #039-01-2004 L2006 **FM** *100
JOHNSON, Audra Kay. 700 S TELEPHONE RD # 100, NORMAN REGIONAL HEALTH SYS 73160 #039-01-2002 L2003 **FM** *020 †18
KIM, Donald Hyungjoon. 2815 SW 119TH ST 73170 #306-01-1997 L2000 **IM PME** *020 †20
LANNEAU, Grainger Steele. ■ 73170 #012-01-1994 L2005 **OBG** *020 †30
LEE, Daniel Chae. 1035 SW 19TH ST, STE B 73160 #039-01-1995 L2002 **IM** *020
LONG, Jonathon Ray. ■ 73170 #039-01-2007 L2007 **FP** *012
LOOFBOURROW, Patricia C. ■ 73160 #016-01-1990 L1991 **FM** *062 †18
MANEVITZ, Rebecca Leah. 700 S TELEPHONE RD 73160 #039-01-1981 L1982 **IM** *020 †20
MASTERS, Harold Arnold. ■ 73170 #039-01-1956 L1958 **FM GPM** *071
MAULDIN, Howard Paul. ■ 73170 #039-01-1953 L1953 **FM** *071 †18
MCEVOY, Jennifer Rae. ■ 73160 #005-15-2006 L2006 **GS** *012
NGUYEN, Long Thanh. ■ 73170 #039-01-1995 L1997 **IM** *020 †20
O'BRIEN, Kevin Lee. 2625 SW 119TH ST, STE A 73170 #039-01-1998 L1999 **FM** *020 †18
PATEL, Amit Manu. ■ 73170 #039-01-2008 *012
PATEL, Jigar Hemant. ■ 73160 #104-01-2006 L2006 **IM** *012
PERRY, Jamie Frances. ■ 73170 #021-05-2006 L2006 **IM** *100
PREJEANT, Kristi C. ■ 73160 #021-06-2003 L2005 **GS** *012
REYNA, Tania Alejandra. ■ 73160 #649-54-1998 L2007 **N** *012
ROBERTS, Michael William. ■ 73170 #039-01-2007 L2007 **GS** *012
ROBLEY, Frederick A, III. 10706 WOODRIDDEN 73170 #039-01-1979 L1980 **EM OM** *020 †16
SANTANGELO, Kathy Lee. 12508 SHIRE LN 73170 #041-09-1985 L1990 **TS GS** *020 †85,90
SELMON-MARSHALL, Angela L. 2117 RIVERWALK DR, MEDEX PLUS 73160 #039-01-1988 L1990 **EM** *020 ‡
SHAKIR, Faiz Ahmed. ■ 73170 #039-01-2006 L2008 **IM** *012
STIDHAM, Anna Irene. ■ 73170 #039-01-2003 L2005 **DR** *012
STIDHAM, Shane Edward. 13005 ANDUIN AVE, SHANE E STIDHAM, MD, PLLC 73170 #039-01-2002 L2003 **AN** *020 †05
STRICKLAND, Luther Jearl. ■ 73165 #039-01-1961 L1961 **GP** *071
TREACY, Bryan Jos. 2117 RIVERWALK DR 73160 #039-03-1986 L2004 **OBG REN** *020 †30
WELSH, Jack Daryl. ■ 73170 #030-05-1954 L1959 **GE IM** *071 †20

OKLAHOMA CITY – OKLAHOMA

ABATIELL, Andrew John. ■ 73118 #039-01-2008 *012
ABBAS, Syed Ameer. 4221 S WESTERN AVE, STE 4000 73109 #704-01-1982 L1998 **CD** *020 †20
ABBOTT, Craig Leon. 3500 S WESTERN AVE 73109 #039-01-1990 L1991 **D DMP** *015
ABDULLAH, Sakher Abdullah. 920 SL YOUNG BLVD # WP2040 73104 #875-01-1996 L2006 **HO** *020 †20
ABEDIN, Moeen. 825 NE 10TH ST, STE 2500 73104 #048-12-1998 L2007 **ICE** *020 †20
ABELL, Robert David. 608 NW 9TH ST, STE 1000 73102 #039-05-1984 L1999 **FM** *020 †18
ABER, Penny. 7801 N ROBINSON AVE BLDG J 73116 #039-01-1993 L1994 **FM** *030 †18
ABEYEWARDENE, Lankike N. 9204 N MAY AVE 73120 #220-01-1980 L1993 **AN** *020 †05
ABID, Farida. 711 SL YOUNG BLVD, STE 215 73104 #704-02-1989 L2006 **CHN** *100
ABLAH, Rochelle Eva. 1000 N LEE AVE 73102 #039-01-1988 L1989 **FM** *020 †18 ‡
ABRAMSON, Wendy Brynn. 750 NE 13TH ST STE 200, DEPT OF ANESTHESIA 73104 #041-02-2000 L2004 **AN** *020 †05
ACKER, Robin Eugene. 1200 EVERETT DR, EVERETT TOWER, ROOM 1606 73104 #039-01-1982 L1983 **DR** *040 †80
ADAIR, Alana Elaine. 4140 W MEMORIAL RD, STE 413 73120 #039-01-1979 L1980 **PD** *020 †55
ADAMS, Donald Eugene. 6205 N SANTA FE AVE, STE 200 73118 #005-12-1997 L2002 **PM** *020 †60

■ = Address Information Privacy Protected

ADAMS, Gerald Stephen. PO BOX 18256 73154 #063-01-1980 **IM** *020
ADAMS, Jana Lee. 5622 N PORTLAND AVE, STE 200 73112 #039-01-1994 L1998 **PD** *020 †55
ADAMSON, Philip Bentley. 4050 W MEMORIAL RD, OKLAHOMA CARDIOVASCULAR 73120 #039-01-1991 L1992 **CD** *020 †20
ADDISON, Paul Davis. 4300 W MEMORIAL RD 73120 #048-04-1983 L1990 **PTH** *075 †50
ADHAM, Mehdi N. 4401 S WESTERN AVE 73109 #010-03-1977 L1982 **PS HS** *020 †85,65 ‡
ADLER, Jill Elizabeth. 940 NE 13TH ST, 3000MRI 73104 #039-01-1985 L1987 **PD** *071 †55
ADLER, Stephen Neil. 4140 W MEMORIAL RD STE 208 73120 #056-06-1973 L1978 **PUD IM** *020 †20
ADOWEI, Franklin Oyinke. ■ 73147 #690-01-1984 L2003 **P** *100
AGUDELO HIGUITA, Nelson I. 608 NW 9TH ST, STE 1000 73104 #451-01-2004 L2006 **IM** *012
AHMAD, Iftikhar. 608 NW 9TH ST STE 4000 73102 #495-51-1973 L1978 **CD IM** *020 †20
AHMAD, Jihad Nasir. 4913 W RENO AVE 73127 #005-02-1975 L1977 **PD** *020
AHMAD, Saeed. 4221 S WESTERN AVE, STE 2010 73109 #704-04-1971 L1983 **CD IM** *020 †20
AHMAD, Salima. 608 NW 9TH ST STE 4000, CARDIAC IMAGING CENTER INC 73102 #495-51-1978 L1983 **NM** *020 †28
AHMAD, Vaqar. 1111 N LEE AVE 3RD FL, SUITE 334 73103 #704-02-1991 L2002 **END** *020
AHMAD, Waqar. 940 STANTON L YOUNG BLVD 73104 #704-21-2000 L2007 **IM** *012
AHMAD, Wazir Saleem. 1211 N SHARTEL AVE, STE 606 73103 #039-01-1978 L1979 **PD** *020 †55
AHMAD, Zahid Bashir. 825 NE 10TH ST, STE 4500 73104 #704-01-1985 L1995 **NEP** *020 †20
AHMED, Imran. 940 STANTON L YOUNG BLVD 73104 #704-01-2000 **FM** *012
AHMED, Maqbool. 711 STANTON L YOUNG BLVD 73104 #704-02-1994 L2007 **N** *012
AHMED, Shaista. ■ 73116 #704-18-1992 L1997 **IM** *020 †20
AHMED, Tanveer. WP 1310, 920 S L YOUNG BLVD, 73190 #704-20-1989 L1994 **PCC** *020 †55,20
ALBERS, Donald D. 700 NE 13TH ST 73104 #016-06-1943 L1950 **U** *071 †95
ALBIEK, Hamed. 3330 NW 56TH ST FL 400, THE PEDIATRIC GROUP, PLLC 73112 #875-02-1990 L1993 **PD** *020 †55
AL-BOTROS, Adonis Simon. 4400 N LINCOLN BLVD 73105 #875-01-1989 L2000 **P** *020 †75
ALBRACHT, William Raymond. ■ 73112 #048-12-1964 L1973 **R** *071 †80
ALBRECHT, Roxie Mae. 920 STANTON L YOUNG BLVD, RM 2140WP 73104 #018-03-1984 L2001 **GS** *020 †85
ALDRICH, Ryan Kyle. 3500 NW 56TH ST STE 100 73112 #039-01-2005 L2006 **FP** *012
ALGAN, Ozer. 825 NE 10TH ST, DEPT OF RADIATION ONCOLOGY 73104 #056-05-1992 L2007 **RO** *020
ALGAN, Sheila M. 920 STANTON L YOUNG BLVD, RM WP1380 73104 #056-05-1991 L2007 **OSM** *020 †40
ALHAJ, George Samer A. 1044 SW 44TH ST, FL 6 73109 #875-03-1993 L2002 **AN** *020 †05
ALI, Fazal Akbar. 940 STANTON L YOUNG BLVD, UNIV OF OK COLL OF MED 73104 #704-21-1999 L2006 **NEP** *012 †20
ALI, Munawar. 921 NE 13TH ST, SURGERY SEEMILE 73104 #704-21-1997 L2005 **HS** *100
ALI, Riyaz M. ■ 73190 #039-01-2007 L2007 **TY** *012
ALI, Tauseef. 920 SL YOUNG BLVD, WP 1360 73104 #704-01-2001 L2006 **GE** *012 †20
AL-KALI, Aref. 920 SL YOUNG BLVD, WP 2040 73104 #875-01-2000 L2006 **HO** *012 †20
AL-KHOURI, Haisam. 105 SE 45TH ST 73129 #875-02-1980 L1993 **P** *020
ALLEE, Mark Richard. 825 NE 10TH ST, STE 4500 73104 #039-01-1993 L1994 **IM** *020 †20
ALLEMAN, Anthony Michael. 1200 EVERETT DR 1NP606, OUHSC RADIOLOGY 73104 #021-05-1991 L2000 **DR** *100 †45,80
ALLEN, David Randel. 608 NW 9TH ST STE 6 73102 #039-01-1986 L1987 **PUD CCM** *020 †20
ALLEN, Helen Christine. 1200 EVERETT DR, RM 8N8305 73104 #039-01-1998 L1999 **PD** *020 †55
ALLEN, James Ross. 920 STANTON L YOUNG BLVD 73104 #065-01-1961 L1974 **P CHP** *020 †75
ALLEN, Pamela Sue. 619 NE 13TH ST 73104 #005-12-1996 L1999 **D** *020 †20,15
ALLEN, Russell Floyd. 5300 N MERIDIAN AVE STE 2 73112 #039-01-1963 L1963 **GP P** *071
AL-NAIMI, Suhail Fakhry S. 1604 NE 8TH ST 73117 #528-01-1971 **P** *100
AL QUTSHAN, Dhyia Ibrahim. 940 STANTON L YOUNG BLVD 73104 #575-01-2002 L2007 **PD** *012
ALTSHULER, Geoffrey P. 920 STANTON L YOUNG BLVD 73104 #143-03-1964 L1976 **PP PD** *020 †50
ALTSHULER, Laurence H. 2520 NW EXPRESSWAY 73112 #039-01-1976 L1977 **IM PMM** *020 †20
ALWARD, Erin Kimberly. 920 SL YOUNG BLVD, WP 2410 73104 #039-01-2004 L2005 **OBG** *012
ALY, Aly Salah-Eldin. 3366 NW EXPRESSWAY, STE 730 73112 #915-04-1995 L2003 **P** *012
AMAYEM, Ahmed A. 1145 W I 240 SERVICE RD, STE I100 73139 #915-03-1982 L1994 **PMM PME** *020 †05 ‡
AMBRUSTER, Scott Harrison. 3300 NW EXPRESSWAY RM 100 73112 #048-13-2004 L2005 **DR** *012
AMIL, Azhar. 2225 SW 59TH ST, THE HEART CLINIC 73119 #704-01-1974 L1980 **CD** *020
AMIN, Rajendra J. 1044 SW 44TH ST, FL 6 73109 #495-23-1972 L1977 **AN PME** *020
ANDERSON, Gary B. 3301 NW 50TH ST 73112 #038-40-1989 L1996 **OSM ORS** *020 †40
ANDERSON, John David. 921 NE 13TH ST 73104 #026-04-1963 L1968 **IM EM** *020
ANDERSON, John Willis. 3301 NW 50TH ST 73112 #039-01-1989 L2001 **ORS OP** *020 †40
ANDERSON, Lanny Gordon. 3435 NW 56TH ST 73112 #039-01-1961 L1961 **TS GS** *072 †85,90
ANDERSON, Michael Terry. 1201 N DOUGLAS BLVD, MIDWEST MEDICAL GROUP 73130 #039-01-1975 L1976 **FM** *020 †18
ANDERSON, Robert Eugene. 608 SL YOUNG, DEAN A MCGEE EYE INST 73104 #048-04-1975 L1996 **OS DIA** *050
ANDRADE, Jose Dario. ■ 73159 #319-03-1982 **PTH** *020
ANDRADE, Stephen A. 14101 PARKWAY COMMONS DR 73134 #034-01-1980 L1981 **AN** *020
ANDREWS, M Dewayne. 940 STANTON L YOUNG BLVD, # 357 73104 #039-01-1970 L1971 **IM IMG** *030 †20
ANDREZIK, Joseph Albert. 4401 S WESTERN AVE 73109 #039-01-1987 L1988 **DR VIR** *020 †80
ANDRUS, John Christopher. 5100 N BROOKLINE AVE, FL 900 73112 #039-01-1979 L1980 **P OS** *020 †75 ‡
ANG, Grace Asuncion T. 800 RESEARCH PKWY 73104 #748-01-1980 L1995 **PTH** *020 †55
ANWAR, Muhammad Saleem. 940 STANTON L YOUNG BLVD, DEPT NEUR 73104 #704-02-1997 **N** *100
ANZALDUA, Alejandro S.. ■ 73118 #665-01-2007 L2007 **FP** *012
APODACA-WERNER, Carla. 13321 N MERIDIAN AVE, STE 406 73120 #034-01-1978 L1979 **FM PD** *020 †18
APPLEWHITE, Jerry Michael. ■ 73107 #039-01-1984 *020
AQUI, Eileen Gladys. 920 SL YOUNG BLVD, DEPARTMENT OF PSYCHIATRY 73104 #649-38-1988 L2007 **P** *020 †75
ARAUJO, Lorenzo. 921 NW 13TH ST, VA MEDICAL CTR 73106 #308-01-1977 L2004 **P PYG** *020

ARCE, Agapito, Jr. ■ 73112 #748-01-1959 L1982 **GS** *020
ARCHER, Ann Gray. 825 NE 10TH ST # 3500, OU BREAST INSTITUTE 73104 #036-01-1983 L2004 **R** *020 †80
ARCHER, James Stephen. 1211 N SHARTEL AVE, STE 300 73103 #039-01-1980 L1981 **U** *020 †55
ARDIS, Janita M. 3817 NW EXPRESSWAY 73112 #917-04-1974 L1984 **P** *020 †75
ARMITAGE, John Brooks. 1001 N LINCOLN BLVD 73104 #036-07-1992 L1996 **BBK** *020 †50
ARMOR, Jess Franklin. 4401 S MCAULEY BLVD STE 375 73120 #039-01-1999 L2002 **HO** *020 †20
ARMSTRONG, Edward Raymond. 5501 N PORTLAND AVE 73112 #039-01-1989 L1990 **IM** *020 †20
ARNOLD, Charles David. 1200 EVERETT DR 1NP606 73104 #048-02-1979 L1985 **NM** *020 †20,28
ARNOLD, Robt Carlton, Jr. 3433 NW 56TH ST, STE 820 73112 #039-01-1965 L1965 **GS** *071 †85
ARONSON, Willard. 920 STANTON L YOUNG BLVD 73104 #041-01-1954 L1967 **PTH** *071 †50
ARSHAD, Ahmed Bilal. 711 STANTON L YOUNG BLVD, OF MED 73104 #704-01-2004 L2007 **IM** *012
ARTHUR, R Eugene. 9600 BROADWAY EXT 73114 #038-40-1968 L1978 **RHU IM** *020 †20
ARUNACHALAM, Annapoorani. 940 STANTON L YOUNG BLVD 73104 #495-66-1998 L2007 **PD** *012
ASBURY, Jeffrey Michael. ■ 73112 #039-01-1998 L1999 **CD** *020 †20
ASIF, Shahida. ■ 73134 #704-04-1996 L2008 **IM** *020 †20
ASKINS, Dale C. 4401 S WESTERN AVE 73109 #028-79-1979, ▲ L1983 **EM** *020
AUGELLI, Jennifer Ann. 940 NE 13TH ST 73104 #039-01-2002 L2003 **NPM** *012 †55
AUSTERMAN, David B. 3300 NW EXPRESSWAY 73112 #039-01-2000 L2004 **AN** *020 †05
AVILA-RIVERA, Anibal. 1121 SW 44TH ST 73109 #308-03-1980 L1994 **GP** *020 †20
AWAB, Ahmed. 920 SL YOUNG BLVD, WP 1130 73104 #704-01-2001 L2006 **PCC** *012 †20
AXTELL, Jerry Leigh. ■ 73132 #039-01-1978 L1979 **FM** *020 †20
AXTON, Jon Clayton. 5300 N GRAND BLVD 73112 #039-01-1973 L1974 **U** *020 †95
AYEE, Kyawt Kyawt. 921 NE 13TH ST, VAMC - DEPT OF GERIATRIC M 73104 #209-01-1988 L2006 **IMG** *020 †20
AZARIAN, Maureen Hieronym. ■ 73109 #039-01-2008 *012
AZEEM, Fazilat. 920 STANTON L YOUNG BLVD, WP3440 73104 #495-19-1981 L2002 **P** *020 ‡
AZIZ, Tarman. PO BOX 18256 73154 #422-01-1998 **IM** *020
BABER, Zaheer Ud-Din. 8121 NATIONAL AVE, STE 300 73110 #704-04-1971 L1978 **CD IM** *020 †20
BADDOUR, Hazem Mohammad. 3300 NW EXPRESSWAY, OK TRANSPLANTATION INST 73112 #915-03-1989 L1994 *020
BADER, Rami. ■ 73102 #875-01-1979 L2007 **PAN** *100
BADER, Teddy Fritz. 3300 NW EXPRESSWAY 73112 #028-02-1980 L2002 **GE IM** *020 †20
BAG, Remzi. 3300 NW EXPRESSWAY, 100-3445 73112 #902-22-1988 L2007 **IM PCC** *020 †28,20
BAHR, Carman Bloedow. 901 NE 13TH ST, OKLAHOMA CITY VA MED CTR 73104 #038-40-1956 L1961 **IM END** *071 †20
BAHU, Najwa Adma. 4140 W MEMORIAL RD STE 421 73120 #654-01-1994 L1997 **PCC** *020 †20
BAILEY, David M. 721 NW 6TH ST # A 73102 #039-01-1981 L1982 **IM IMG** *020 †20
BAINS, Ashish Pal Singh. ■ 73112 #495-45-2003 L2007 **PTH** *012
BAIR, Jack Martin. 4401 S WESTERN AVE 73109 #019-02-1982 L1983 **EM** *020 †16
BAJAJ, Paramjit Singh. 6205 N SANTA FE AVE 73118 #495-29-1961 L1973 **PS HS** *020 †65 ‡
BAKER, Dustin Riley. 7221 W HEFNER RD, FAITH FAMILY CARE 73162 #039-01-2004 L2005 **FM** *020 †18
BAKER, James Mark. 5350 S WESTERN AVE STE 419 73109 #039-01-1986 L1987 **AN** *020 †05
BAKER, Jennifer Ann. 940 NE 13TH ST RM 2308, THE CHILDREN'S HOSP OF OKL 73104 #039-01-2003 L2005 **PD** *020 †16
BAKER, Mary Zoe. 825 NE 10TH ST 73104 #039-01-1982 L1983 **END IM** *040 †20
BAKER, R Stanley. 3300 NW EXPRESSWAY 73112 #039-01-1981 L1983 **OTO NO** *020 †45
BAKER, Sherri Sue. 940 NE 13TH ST 73104 #039-01-1995 L2001 **PDC** *020 †20
BAKER, Sterling Sheldon. 14000 N PORTLAND AVE, STE 101 73134 #035-03-1974 L1975 **OPH** *020 †35 ‡
BAKSHI, Nasir Ahmed. 920 STANTON L YOUNG BLVD 73104 #495-51-1993 L2005 **HMP** *020 †50
BALDWIN, John Timothy. 4401 S WESTERN AVE 73109 #039-01-1969 L1970 **ADM EM** *020 †16
BALUJA, Pankaj. 920 SL YOUNG BLVD, WILLIAMS PAVILION SUITE 11 73104 #496-26-2001 L2005 **NEP** *012
BAMGBOLA, Fatai O. 940 NE 13TH ST 1B1306 73104 #690-08-1986 L2003 **PN** *020 †55
BANE, Barbara Linda. 920 STANTON L YOUNG BLVD 73104 #025-07-1982 L1989 **PTH** *020 †50
BANOWETZ, John Mike. 4120 W MEMORIAL RD, STE 218 73120 #039-01-1973 L1974 **N** *020 †75
BAO, Bui Quang. 2524 N MILITARY AVE # 109 73106 #941-01-1967 L1979 **FM** *071 †18
BARCLAY, Kerri Kathleen. 3400 NORTHWEST EXPY BLDG C, STE 815 73112 #001-02-1995 L1998 **PD** *020 †55
BARKI, May Li. 4140 W MEMORIAL RD, CENTER FOR WOMENS HEALTH 73120 #039-01-1977 L1978 **OBG** *020 †30 ‡
BARNARD, Christian N. BAPTIST MED CTR 73112 #836-02-1953 **CD** *075
BARNES, Daniel P. 11000 HEFNER POINTE DR 73120 #039-01-1983 L1984 **U** *020 †95
BARNES, Heather Dianne. 3500 NW 56TH ST STE 1 73112 #039-01-2005 L2006 **FP** *020 †18
BARNES, Shelby Dee. 11000 HEFNER POINTE DR 73120 #039-01-1954 L1956 **U** *020 †95
BARNES, Steven Brent. 4401 S WESTERN AVE 73109 #039-01-1993 L1994 **EM** *020 †16
BARNES, William Franklin. 4200 S DOUGLAS AVE, STE 200 73109 #048-02-1973 L1974 **U** *020 †95
BARNEY, Jack Alroy. 400 NW 13TH ST 73103 #039-01-1956 L1956 **GS** *020 †85
BARRETO, Angelique. 3705 W MEMORIAL RD, STE 601 73134 #495-04-1991 L2001 **FM FPG** *020 †18
BARRETT, James Richard. 1000 N LINCOLN BLVD 73104 #023-07-1987 L1991 **FM FSM** *020 †18
BARRETT, Jon Valentine. 940 STANTON L YOUNG BLVD 73104 #028-79-2004, ▲ L2005 **AN** *012
BARTON, Carrie Ann. 26 SW 104TH ST, MORNINGSTAR EMERGENCY PHYS 73139 #039-01-1994 L2004 **EM** *020 †16
BARUSYA, Caroline. 608 NW 9TH ST STE 1000, ST ANTHONY HOSPITAL 73102 #166-06-2006 L2008 *012
BARVE, Archana P. 5701 N PORTLAND AVE 73112 #539-06-1990 L1998 **PM** *020 †60
BASS, Stephen A. ■ 73102 #021-06-2004 L2005 **IM** *100
BASS, William Scott. 12925 CARRIE CT, WILLIAM SCOTT BASS MD 73120 #021-01-1965 L1966 **P FM** *062 †18
BATTISTE, Aldo A, Jr. 4401 S WESTERN AVE 73109 #030-06-1986 L1987 **DR** *020 †80
BAUER, Christopher Eric. 920 STANTON L YOUNG BLVD, WP 3010 73104 #028-34-2004 L2007 **CD** *012 †20

BAUMAN, Mary Ann. 3400 NW EXPRESSWAY, STE 500 73112 #025-07-1978 L1989 IM *020 †20
BAYAN, Nami. 6101 W RENO AVE 73127 #517-01-1995 L2004 IM *020 †20
BAYLESS, James Douglas. 5501 N PORTLAND AVE 73112 #039-01-1992 L1993 AN *020
BAYLESS, Robin Tanner. 11200 N PORTLAND AVE 73120 #039-01-1986 L1987 AN *020 †05
BAYLOR, Dustin Lee. 608 NW 9TH ST STE 11 73102 #039-01-2005 L2006 FP *012
BEALL, Douglas Preston. 6201 N SANTA FE AVE 73118 #010-02-1993 L1994 DR *020 †80
BEAM, Chester Wray. 2224 NW 50TH ST, STE 276W 73112 #039-01-1975 L1976 R *020 †80 ‡
BEARD, R Lacy. 900 NE 10TH ST, OU FAMILY MEDICAL CLINIC 73104 #039-01-2004 L2006 FM *020 †18
BEARD, Reba Ann. 1001 S DOUGLAS BLVD 73130 #021-06-1980 L1982 PD *020 †55
BEASLEY, Robert Harlin. 3625 NW 56TH ST, SERV, FIVE CORPORATE PLAZA 73112 #039-01-1972 L1973 CHP P *020 †75
BEAVERS, James Clyde. ■ 73142 #039-01-1955 L1955 GYN *071 †30
BEAVERS, John Eric. 10021 S WESTERN AVE 73139 #039-01-1986 L1993 PD *020
BECK, Laoma Yanire Lee. ■ 73106 #039-01-2008 *012
BECK, Lisa Steincamp. 921 NE 13TH ST 73104 #039-01-1986 L1987 N IM *020
BECKERLEY, Robert James. 3433 NW 56TH ST, STE 580 73112 #056-06-1976 L1978 IM *020 †20
BECKETT, Louise. 1111 N LEE AVE STE 400, IPS RESEARCH COMPANY 73103 #005-19-1987 L1993 P *020 †75
BECKMAN, Karen June. 825 NE 10TH ST, STE 2500 73104 #016-06-1980 L1990 CD IM *020 †20
BEKKEM, Anupama. 921 NE 13TH ST, VA MEDICAL CENTER 73104 #495-62-1997 L2002 IM *020 †20
BELARDO, John P. 11308 N PENNSYLVANIA AVE 73120 #033-05-1987 L1992 OPH FPS *020 †35
BELL, Bruce Gene. 4200 S MAY AVE, STE D 73119 #039-01-1963 L1964 IM *020
BELL, John Mark. 701 NE 10TH ST 73104 #039-01-1987 L1988 OPH *020 †35
BELL, Walter Willis. 3435 NW 56TH ST STE 700 73112 #039-01-1981 L1982 GS *020 †85 ‡
BELLER, Rick Dionne. 4300 W MEMORIAL RD 73120 #039-01-1972 L1973 ORS *020 †40
BENDER, Jeffrey Stuart. 920 STANTON L YOUNG BLVD, WP 2140 73104 #023-01-1978 L2001 GS EM *020 †85
BENJAMIN, Ashley Bezaleel. 921 NE 13TH ST, OKLAHOMA CITY VAMC 73104 #019-02-1993 L1999 P *020 †75
BENNETT, Sevim. 921 NE 13TH ST 73104 #902-07-1987 L1998 CHP *020 †75
BERNARD, Marie Antonia. 825 NE 10TH ST, STE 4500 73104 #041-01-1976 L1990 IM *020 †20
BERNHARDT, Samuel Chas. 6521 S WESTERN AVE 73139 #039-01-1960 L1960 GP *020
BERRY, Donnie G. 940 NE 13TH ST 73104 #048-15-2000 L2001 PD *020 ‡
BERRY, Jeffrey Gene. 1111 N LEE AVE, STE 236 73103 #039-01-1995 L1996 AN *020
BERRYHILL, Wayne Edward. UNIV OF OKLAHOMA, BOX 26901 WP 1290 73190 #026-04-1996 L2003 OTO PDO *020 †45
BESON, Brent Allen. 4221 S WESTERN AVE, STE 5000 73109 #039-01-1999 L2004 N *020 †75
BEST, Timothy J. 920 SL YOUNG BLVD, # 4SP220 73104 #065-06-1988 L1996 *020
BETHEA, Chas Fuller, Jr. 3433 NW 56TH ST, STE 400 73112 #039-01-1971 L1972 CD IM *020 †20
BEVERS, William Stanley. 10021 S WESTERN AVE 73139 #039-01-1986 L1987 FM *020 †18
BEVILLE, Lee Walker, III. ■ 73116 #308-03-1980 L1981 DR CTR *020 †80
BHAKTARAM, Vivek J. 8121 NATIONAL AVE, MIDWEST CITY CARDIOLOGY 73110 #495-37-1984 L1994 CD IM *020 †20
BHANDARKAR, Vidya Nagesh. ■ 73104 #495-01-1999 L2006 PD *012
BHANDARY, Amar N. 7100 N CLASSEN BLVD STE 10 73116 #495-73-1984 L1996 P *020 †75
BHARUCHA, Kersi J. 711 SL YOUNG BLVD STE 209, DEPARTMENT OF NEUROLOGY 73104 #495-53-1981 L1995 N OS *020 †75
BHATIA, Surindar Kumar. 608 NW 9TH ST, STE 4000 73102 #495-03-1961 L1971 CD IM *020 †20
BHATT, Nilaksha. 1111 N LEE AVE STE 343 73103 #048-13-1992 L1993 AN *020 †05
BHOPLAY, Suneela Vinay. 1211 N SHARTEL AVE STE 1 73103 #495-28-1975 L1992 PD *020
BHOPLAY, Vinay Govind. 1211 N SHARTEL AVE STE 100 73103 #495-45-1978 L1986 OBG *020 †30
BHUPATHIRAJU, Rajeswarara. 4400 N LINCOLN BLVD 73105 #495-11-1978 L1993 P *020
BICKET, Paul Chas. 4200 W MEMORIAL RD, STE 703 73120 #039-01-1977 L1978 AN *020 †05
BIELECKI, Dennis Karl. ■ 73102 #759-01-1982 L2008 NM *012
BIGGERS, Ryan Marshall. 1212 S DOUGLAS BLVD, LLC 73130 #039-01-2002 L2004 FM *020 †18
BIGGS, Daniel Alan. 920 STANTON L YOUNG BLVD 73104 #039-01-1982 L1983 AN *020 †05
BILBAO, Jubel Jhun Sullan. 1916 HERITAGE PARK DR # 25 73120 #305-01-2007 L2007 FP *012
BISHOP, Nancy Giger. 11200 N PORTLAND AVE 73120 #023-12-1990 L1993 OBG *020 †30
BISSELL, David. 200 S QUADRUM DR, CONCENTRA MEDICAL CENTER 73108 #016-02-1963 L1997 OM PD *020 †55
BISSON, Albert Jos. 4120 W MEMORIAL RD 73120 #039-01-1989 L1991 PM *020 †60
BISWAS, Kavitha. 4601 SW 3RD ST 73128 #496-23-2003 L2008 *100
BIZZELL, Juliana. ■ 73135 #028-78-2007, ▲ *012
BLACK, Cheryl Phillips. 5401 N PORTLAND AVE, STE 310 73112 #039-01-1986 L1987 END IM *020 †20
BLACKETT, Piers Rupert. 940 NE 13TH ST 73104 #836-02-1967 L1975 PD END *020 †55
BLACKSHAW, David Glenn. 5501 N PORTLAND AVE 73112 #039-01-1987 L1988 EM *020
BLAKEY, Gregory Lee. 920 STANTON L YOUNG BLVD 73104 #048-12-1997 L1998 PTH *100 †50
BLALOCK, Deborah S. 608 NW 9TH ST, STE 6110 73102 #039-01-1988 L1989 GE IM *020 †20
BLALOCK, James Mattison. 608 NW 9TH ST STE 6110 73102 #039-01-1978 L1979 PUD IM *020 †20
BLANCHARD, Allison Adele. 713 NW 48TH ST 73118 #039-01-1985 L1990 EM *020
BLANTON-GREEN, Gloria N. 921 NE 13TH ST 73104 #047-07-1949 L1981 P *071 †75
BLASCHKE, John A. 1111 N DEWEY AVE 73103 #039-01-1950 L1950 RHU IM *071 ‡
BLASCHKE, Jon Word. 608 NW 9TH ST STE 4 73102 #039-01-1971 L1978 RHU *020 †20
BLEVINS, Steve M. 825 NE 10TH ST, STE 4500 73104 #048-04-1989 L1992 IM *020 †20
BLOCK, Mary Frances B. 4140 W MEMORIAL RD, STE 500 73120 #020-12-1971 L1972 OBG NPM *071 †30
BLOMGREN, James Kaye. 605 SW 102ND ST, LINCOLN FAMILY MED GROUP P 73139 #039-01-1979 L1980 FM *020 †18 ‡
BLOUGH, Joseph Arden. 5501 N PORTLAND AVE 73112 #039-01-1994 L1995 FM *020 †18
BOATMAN, Karl K. 3525 NW 56TH ST, STE 100C 73112 #039-01-1952 L1952 GS SO *071 †85
BOCAR, Nelson Dasillo. 4200 W MEMORIAL RD, STE 703 73120 #748-10-1967 L1979 AN *020
BOCK, Alan Stuart. 5401 N PORTLAND AVE # 220 73112 #048-02-1984 L1985 IM *020 †20
BOCK, Dana Jean. 3300 NW EXPRESSWAY 73112 #039-01-1989 L1990 AN *020 †05
BODENHAMER, Robert Mark. 4050 W MEMORIAL RD, OKLAHOMA CARDIOVASCULAR 73120 #039-01-1979 L1980 TS *020 †85,90
BODINE, Charles D. 5501 N PORTLAND AVE 73112 #039-01-1943 L1944 OBG CD *071 †30 ‡
BOE, Justin Joel. HEALTH SCIENC, UNIV OF OKLAHOMA 73190 #018-03-2003 L2007 DR *012 †55
BOGARDUS, Carl Robt, Jr. 825 NE 10TH ST 73104 #020-02-1959 L1964 RO NM *030 †80,28
BOGER, James R. 2200 N CLASSEN BLVD # 1504 73106 #048-02-1994 L2007 CHP *012
BOGGS, Brian Robt. 4140 W MEMORIAL RD 73120 #039-01-1981 L1982 GS *020 †90,85
BOGGS, David Stewart. 3400 NW EXPRESSWAY, STE 105 73112 #039-01-1989 L1993 PUD CCM *020 †20
BOGIE, Amanda L. 940 NE 13TH ST 73104 #039-01-1994 L1995 PD *020 †55
BOGIE, Gemini Jill. 3500 NW 56TH ST 73112 #039-01-1996 L1997 OPH *020
BOGLE, Misty Marie. ■ 73128 #039-01-2008 *012
BOHN, Tim Gerard. 8241 S WALKER AVE, STE 100 73139 #039-01-1977 L1978 FM *020 †18
BOLES, Gerald Wm. 1111 N LEE AVE, STE 254 73103 #039-01-1957 L1957 RO R *071 †80
BOND, Gary Dean. 3366 NW EXPRESSWAY, KIDNEY SPECIALISTS OF 73112 #039-01-1988 L1989 NEP *020 †20
BONNER, Matthew Ray. 4401 S WESTERN AVE 73109 #039-01-2002 L2005 EM *020
BOOKMAN, Larry A. 8121 NATIONAL AVE, STE 303 73110 #039-01-1977 L1978 GE IM *020 †20
BOOMER, Jeffrey Allen. 608 SL YOUNG BLVD 73104 #019-02-2001 L2002 OPH *100 †35
BOOTH, Keley John. 5350 S WESTERN AVE, STE 419 73109 #039-01-2002 L2004 AN *020 †05
BOOTHE, Richard Lee, II. 608 NW 9TH ST, STE 1000 73102 #039-01-1978 L1989 FM *030 †18
BORDEN, Robert Clayton. ■ 73112 #027-01-2005 L2006 OTO *012
BORISSOVA, Irina V. 940 NE 13TH ST STE 4B4200, CHILDREN'S HOSPITAL 73104 #913-06-1978 L2004 PAN *020 †05
BORSKY, Bart Jonathan. 4400 WILL ROGERS PKWY, STE 105 73108 #051-04-1987 L1992 AN *020 †05
BOSE, Prithviraj. ■ 73112 #495-02-2002 L2007 HO *012 †20
BOTTOMLEY, Richard Harold. 4301 S WESTERN AVE, CANCER CARE ASSOCIATES 73109 #039-01-1958 L1958 ON HEM *030 †20
BOTTOMLEY, Sylvia Stakle. 921 NE 13TH ST, HEMATOLOGY - ONCOLOGY 111J 73104 #039-01-1958 L1958 HO IM *050 †20
BOUCHER, Jeremy Michael. 4400 WILL ROGERS PKWY, OKLAHOMA UNIVERSITY HSC 73108 #039-01-2003 L2004 AN *020
BOULWARE, Paul C. ■ 73134 #028-46-2002 L2004 DR *100
BOUVETTE, Christopher M. 4120 W MEMORIAL RD STE 1 73120 #020-02-1991 L1997 PM CN *020 †60
BOUVETTE, Kimberly. 4120 W MEMORIAL RD 73120 #020-02-1991 L1997 PM *020 †60
BOVA, Abby Rose. 11100 HEFNER POINTE DR, OU MEDICAL CENTER 73120 #039-01-2001 L2002 HO *020
BOWERS, Betty Ann. 4400 WILL ROGERS PKWY, STE 105 73108 #026-04-1976 L1981 AN *072 †05
BOWERS, Fred Allen. 1111 N LEE AVE, STE 343 73103 #012-01-1987 L1992 AN *020
BOWERS, John Douglas. 4625 S WESTERN AVE 73109 #048-12-1991 L1995 DR *020 †80
BOWLWARE, Karen Leah. 940 NE 13TH ST, RM 1B1306 73104 #039-01-1997 L1998 PDI *020 †55
BOYCE, David Melvin. 608 NW 9TH ST STE 1000 73102 #305-01-2006 L2007 FP *012
BRADEN, Barbara A Foster. 921 NE 13TH ST 73104 #039-01-1957 L1957 IM N *020
BRADEN, Donald Kent. 700 NE 13TH ST 73104 #039-01-1957 L1957 NS *071 †25
BRADFORD, Cynthia A. 608 STANTON L YOUNG BLVD, DEAN MCGEE EYE INSTITUTE 73104 #048-02-1983 L1984 OPH *020 †35 ‡
BRADFORD, Reagan H, Jr. 608 STANTON L YOUNG BLVD, DEAN A MCGEE EYE INSTITUTE 73104 #039-01-1980 L1981 OS *020 †35
BRADFORD, Wm Conrad, Jr. 825 NE 10TH ST 73104 #039-01-1977 L1978 DR *020 †80
BRADLEY, Nathan Edward. 3301 NW 50TH ST 73112 #039-01-1970 L1971 ORS OSS *071 †40
BRAND, James Lee. 700 NE 13TH ST 73104 #039-01-1984 L1985 FM *020 †18
BRANDT, Edward Newman, Jr. 801 NE 13TH ST 73104 #039-01-1960 L1960 PHP MDM *071 ‡
BRANNON, Dale Martin. 1200 EVERETT DR 73104 #039-01-2001 L2003 NM *020 †28
BRATZLER, Dale Wayne. 14000 QUAIL SPRINGS PKWY, STE 400 73134 #028-78-1981, ▲ L1982 IM *030
BRAWNER, James Travis. 920 STANTON L YOUNG BLVD 73104 #028-03-2004 L2005 OTO *012
BREKKE, Charles Ellis. 4300 MCAULEY BLVD 73120 #048-02-1986 L1987 DR *020 †80 ‡
BRENNER, Phillip Colin. ■ 73156 #143-07-1982 L1994 *020
BRESSIE, Jerry Lee. 3400 NW EXPRESSWAY, STE 700 73112 #039-01-1958 L1958 CD IM *071 †20
BREWER, Kathryn Lynn. 5701 N PORTLAND AVE 73112 #039-01-1990 L1992 IM *020 †20
BRIGHT, Amanda Marie. ■ 73104 #039-01-2008 *012
BRINDLEY, Jerry Dean. 5501 N PORTLAND AVE 73112 #039-01-1978 L1979 EM *020 †16
BRINKER, David Bruce. 5600 N PORTLAND AVE 73112 #038-41-1966 L1968 OPH *020 †35
BRINKWORTH, James Michael. 1000 N LEE AVE, ST ANTHONY HOSPITAL 73102 #039-01-1978 L1979 PTH *020 †50 ‡
BRITT, Matthew Jos. 3400 NW EXPRESSWAY, PULMONARY SPECIALISTS 73112 #039-01-1985 L1986 PUD GS *020 †20
BROADY-SYMES, Belinda G. 8121 NATIONAL AVE 73110 #039-01-1989 L1991 OBG *020 †30
BRONZE, Michael Stuart. P.O. BOX 26901, 920 S L YOUNG BLVD, RM WP 73190 #047-06-1982 L2000 ID IM *050 †20
BROOKS, Clifton Rowland. ■ 73120 #056-05-1946 L1952 OM AM *030 †55
BROOKS, Daniel Richard. 940 STANTON L YOUNG BLVD, DEPT OPH 73104 #050-02-2006 L2007 OPH *012
BROOKS, Jay Paul. 920 STANTON L YOUNG BLVD 73104 #047-06-1981 L2003 BBK *020 †50
BROU, Juan Adolfo. 5300 N GRAND BLVD STE 205 73112 #737-06-1982 L1990 PS GS *020 †65
BROWN, Aline C. 3400 NW EXPRESSWAY STE 410 73112 #039-01-1981 L1982 ID IM *020 †20
BROWN, Brent Reiff. 825 NE 10TH ST, STE 2500 73104 #039-01-1984 L1985 IM PUD *020 †20
BROWN, Curtis Lynn. 3300 NW EXPRESSWAY 73112 #039-01-1987 L1988 FM *020 †18
BROWN, David R. 3301 NW 50TH ST 73112 #039-01-1949 L1949 ORS *071 †40
BROWN, David Randolph. 11013 HEFNER POINTE DR 73120 #039-01-1984 L1985 OPH PO *020 †35
BROWN, Gary Alan. 4400 WILL ROGERS PKWY #105 73108 #039-01-1974 L1975 AN *071
BROWN, John Marion. 5300 N MERIDIAN AVE, STE 5 73112 #047-06-1945 L1949 GP GS *071
BROWN, Michael Scott. 4120 W MEMORIAL RD 73120 #048-04-1994 L1998 PM *020 †60
BROWN, Michelle Renee. 1800 S DOUGLAS BLVD 73130 #039-01-2003 L2007 OBG *020
BROWN, Phillip Benton. 4400 WILL ROGERS PKWY, STE 105 73108 #039-01-2003 L2004 AN *020
BROWN, Robert Chas. 3433 NW 56TH ST STE 400 73112 #024-07-1955 L1960 IM ON *020 †20
BROWN, Ryan David. 940 NE 13TH ST 73104 #039-01-2001 L2002 PD *020 †55
BROWN PACHECO, Carmen. 14300 N MAY AVE # 3 73134 #042-03-1984 L2004 FM PHP *020 †18

■ = Address Information Privacy Protected

BRUMBAUGH, Peter Flory. 3000 UNITED FOUNDERS BLVD, STE 234 73112 #003-01-1977 L1981 **PTH** *020 †50
BRUNE, Adriana Monica. 940 NE 13TH ST 73104 #132-05-1987 L2004 **D** *012 †55
BRUSH, Ruth Govier. 4300 W MEMORIAL RD 73120 #030-05-1983 L1990 **DR** *062 †80
BRYAN, Philip Clay. 4200 W MEMORIAL RD # 1010 73120 #039-01-1969 L1969 **GS** *071 †85
BRYANT, Charles Austin. 3366 NORTHWEST EXPY, STE 520 73112 #048-12-1972 L1998 **MDM PD** *030 †55
BRYANT, Charles Eugene. 3705 NW 63RD ST 73116 #039-01-1978 L1979 **ORS** *020 †40
BRYANT, Cheryl Lynne. 940 NE 13TH ST 2B2305 73104 #039-01-1995 L1996 **PD** *020 †55
BRYANT, Thomas Roy. 1800 S DOUGLAS BLVD 73130 #039-01-1972 L1973 **OBG** *020 †30
BUCKLEY, Dustan Pierce. 4140 W MEMORIAL RD STE 303 73120 #039-01-1992 L1993 **IM** *020 †20
BUENDIA, Arsenio G. 3435 NW 56TH ST # *404 73112 #748-02-1969 L1977 **FM EM** *020 †18
BUFFINGTON, Billy Joe. 36 W MEMORIAL RD 73114 #039-01-1985 L1986 **EM OM** *020
BUKHARI, Nasreen. 921 NE 13TH ST, VETERANS AFFAIRS MEDICAL C 73104 #495-51-1987 L1996 **IM** *020 †20
BUMPUS, John Wm. 4545 N LINCOLN BLVD # 124 73105 #048-04-1956 L1960 **FM OBG** *071 †18
BURGER, Sarah. 537 NW 42ND ST 73118 #039-01-2005 L2006 *100
BURMAN, Mark Lewis. 1000 N LINCOLN BLVD # 200, OKLAHOMA ORTHOPEDICS 73104 #067-01-1992 L1998 **ORS** *020
BURNER, Steven Allen. 5201 W MEMORIAL RD 73142 #039-01-1978 L1979 **FM** *020 †18
BURROUGHS, Lyle Wendell. ■ 73120 #028-02-1948 L1961 **PDA PD** *071 †55,03
BURWELL, Robert Chad. 940 STANTON L YOUNG BLVD 73104 #048-78-2004, ▲ L2005 **AN** *012
BUSH, John D. 4625 S WESTERN AVE 73109 #039-01-1960 L1960 **R** *071 †80
CABALLERO, Michelle R. 920 STANTON L YOUNG BLVD 73104 #048-14-1999 L2004 **PAN** *020 †05
CABALLERO, Renato Manuel, III. ■ 73103 #039-01-2008 *012
CAGLE, Stephen Keith. 4120 W MEMORIAL RD 73120 #039-01-1975 L1976 **NS** *020 †25
CAIL, Melinda Jane. 1919 E MEMORIAL RD 73131 #039-01-2000 L2001 **FM** *020 †18 ‡
CAIN, Joan Parkhurst. 940 NE 13TH ST, RM 3B3308 73104 #039-01-1986 L1987 **PD PHO** *040 †55
CALDWELL, Ashley Christin. ■ 73104 #039-01-2006 L2007 **ORS** *012
CALDWELL, Conrad C. 4300 W MEMORIAL RD, EMER ROOM 73120 #039-01-1999 L2002 **EM** *020 †16
CALENZANI, David German. 4200 W MEMORIAL RD, STE 804 73120 #737-01-1981 L1984 **P CHP** *020
CALHOON, Scott W. 210 PARK AVE STE 282 73102 #039-01-1976 L1977 **GS** *020 †85
CALIFANO, John Anthony. ■ 73190 #039-01-2006 L2007 **U** *012
CAMPBELL, David A. ■ 73162 #001-02-1951 L1976 **GP** *071
CAMPBELL, Gregory Rex. 3330 NW 56TH ST, PRIMARY CARE PARTNERS OF 73112 #039-01-1981 L1982 **DR** *062 †80 ‡
CAMPBELL, Shelia Busch. 4400 WILL ROGERS PKWY, STE 105 73108 #039-01-1981 L1982 **AN** *020 †05
CANFIELD, Vikki Ann. 4205 MCAULEY BLVD, STE 375 73120 #054-04-1980 L1992 **ON HEM** *020 †20
CANFIELD, William Monroe. 800 RESEARCH PKWY 73104 #054-04-1982 L1993 **HO IM** *050 †20
CANNON, Jay Paul. 3435 NW 56TH ST STE 210 73112 #039-01-1970 L1971 **GS** *020 †85
CANTOR, Amy Gabrielle. ■ 73103 #048-13-2007 L2007 **IM** *012
CAPERTON, Kevin Standley. ■ 73135 #048-15-2006 L2007 **ORS** *012
CAPERTON, Kimberly Krista. ■ 73135 #048-15-2006 L2007 **OTO** *012
CAPRA, Joseph Donald. 825 NE 13TH ST 73104 #050-02-1963 L1998 **IM** *050
CAREY, John Christopher. 4221 S WESTERN AVE 73109 #039-01-1980 L1981 **GS IM** *020 †85
CAREY, John Merwin. ■ 73142 #024-01-1945 L1954 **CD TS** *071 †85,90
CAREY, Joshua Paul. 920 STANTON L YOUNG BLVD 73104 #019-02-1999 L2004 **GS** *020 †85
CARL, Michael James. 3048 SW 89TH ST 73159 #017-20-1991 L1995 **PM PME** *020 †60
CARLILE, Paul Vore, Jr. 825 NE 10TH ST, STE 2500 73104 #028-02-1976 L1979 **PUD IM** *020 †20
CARMAN, Jacob Cyrus. 940 STANTON L YOUNG BLVD 73104 #003-75-2005, ▲ L2006 **AN** *012
CARMICHAEL, Danl Herbert. 3400 NW EXPRESSWAY, STE 400 73112 #035-01-1970 L1977 **GS** *071 †85
CARPENTER, Dean Robt. 13301 N MERIDIAN AVE STE A, BLDG 300 73120 #007-02-1974 L1985 **OBG** *020 †30
CARPENTER, Robert Le Roy. ■ 73116 #019-02-1956 L1966 **IM OM** *020
CARSON, Martiece J. 11212 N MAY AVE 73120 #039-01-1984 L1985 **N** *020
CARTER, Bradley Dean. 3366 NORTHWEST EXPY 73112 #039-01-1995 L2000 **NEP IM** *020 †20
CARTER, Donald Robt. 920 SL YOUNG BLVD, DEPT OF SURGERY, ROOM 2140 73104 #039-01-1960 L1960 **GS** *071 †85
CARTER, Merle Dean. 3400 NW EXPRESSWAY, STE 410 73112 #039-01-1959 L1959 **IM ID** *072 †20
CASPER, Gary David. 10021 S WESTERN AVE 73139 #039-01-1972 L1977 **ORS** *020 †40
CASPER, Pete D. PO BOX 15568 73155 #039-01-1946 L1947 **FM** *071
CASSIDY, Francis P, Jr. 1000 N LEE AVE 73102 #041-12-1979 L1991 **R DR** *020 †80
CASTELLON INESTROZA, Ricar. 608 NW 9TH ST STE 1000, ST ANTHONY HOSPITAL 73102 #451-01-2003 L2006 **FM** *020 †18
CATES, Aaron Byron. 3300 NW EXPRESSWAY 73112 #039-01-1999 L2000 **AN** *020 †05 ‡
CATES, Kathryne King. ■ 73107 #039-01-2006 L2007 **AN** *012
CATES, Max Gaylen. 220 SW 89TH ST, STE A 73139 #039-01-1977 L1978 **FM** *020 †18
CATHEY, Charles Wesley. ■ 73156 #039-01-1953 L1953 **CD IM** *071 †20
CATHEY, Timothy Mark. 1000 NE 10TH ST, OKLAHOMA STAE HLTH TRAUMA 73117 #039-01-1991 L1996 **OBG** *030 †30
CAUTHEN, Brett Balfour. 415 SW 59TH ST 73109 #048-02-1997 L2006 **FM** *020 †18
CHACKO, George Nalamvelil. 5401 N PORTLAND AVE, STE 330 73112 #495-08-1975 L1990 **NM** *020 †28
CHADWELL, Donald Ray. 5801 W BRITTON RD STE J 73132 #649-14-1980 L1988 **PM** *020 †60
CHAFFIN, John Stephen. 3433 NW 56TH ST, BLDG B 73112 #039-01-1975 L1976 **TS TTS** *020 †85,90
CHAKRABARTY, Shouvik. 825 NE 10TH ST, STE 4500 73104 #039-01-1999 L2002 **IM** *020
CHAKRABURTTY, Amal. 5100 N BROOKLINE AVE 73112 #495-32-1981 L1993 **P IM** *020 †75
CHALMERS, Laura Jane. 940 NE 13TH ST 73104 #654-01-2000 L2002 **END** *012 †20,55
CHAMBERS, Louis Mc Millan. 4300 W MEMORIAL RD 73120 #039-01-1986 L1987 **PTH GS** *020 †50
CHAMBERS, Susan Louise. 11200 N PORTLAND AVE, FL 2 73120 #039-01-1982 L1983 **OBG** *020 †30
CHANDRASEKARAN, Suresh. 8121 NATIONAL AVE, MIDWEST CITY CARDIOLOGY 73110 #495-42-1990 L1997 **CD** *020 †20
CHANDRASEKHARAN, Nalina. 940 STANTON L YOUNG BLVD 73104 #495-42-2000 L2007 **PD** *012
CHANSOLME, David Henri. 4221 S WESTERN AVE, STE 5050 73109 #039-01-1997 L2004 **ID** *020 †20
CHAPPELL, Scott Allen. 5501 N PORTLAND AVE 73112 #039-01-2002 L2005 **EM** *020 †16
CHARANIA, Roseleen Sadrud. 920 STANTON L YOUNG BLVD, FELLOW - DEPARTMENT OF HEM 73104 #496-15-2002 L2007 **HO** *012 †20
CHARD, Stanley Ray. 8121 NATIONAL AVE 73110 #030-05-1965 L1972 **OBG** *020 †30
CHAUDHARY, Shuchi. 500 CENTRAL PARK DR # 12 73105 #496-07-2006 L2007 **P** *012
CHAUDHRY, Shabbir Ahmed. 5611 MOSTELLER DR 73112 #905-01-1972 L1977 **IM** *020 †20 ‡
CHAUDHRY, Taimur Latif. ■ 73190 #035-48-2002 L2002 **OBG** *012
CHAUHAN, Smit Sureshkumar. ■ 73105 #495-76-2005 L2007 **P** *012
CHAVARRIA, Veronica J.. 940 STANTON L YOUNG BLVD 73104 #715-01-2000 L2008 **PD** *012
CHAVEZ-BUENO, Susana. ■ 73112 #649-01-1997 L2000 **PDI** *020 †55
CHAVEZ DE PAZ VILLANUEVA, . P.O. BOX 26901 73190 #737-01-1998 L2006 *100
CHBEIR, Elie Abdo. 940 STANTON L YOUNG BLVD 73104 #605-02-2002 L2005 **PCC** *012 †20
CHEATHAM, James Eugene. 3435 NW 56TH ST 73112 #039-01-1973 L1977 **TS EM** *020 †85,90
CHEDIAK, Charles. 3037 NW 63RD ST STE 100W 73116 #275-01-1954 L1975 **P PYA** *071 †75
CHEEMA, Zahid Farooq. 825 NE 10TH ST, STE 4500 73104 #704-21-1992 L1996 **N CN** *020 †75
CHEN, Gene Wei. 608 STANTON L YOUNG BLVD, DEAN MCGEE EYE INSTITUTE 73104 #056-06-2004 L2006 **OPH** *012
CHEN, Ting-Kon. 1111 N LEE AVE 73103 #048-02-1991 L1992 **AN** *020 †05
CHENG, Paul Chee C. 920 STANTON L YOUNG BLVD 73104 #825-01-1986 **AN** *020
CHERNYAK, Yevgeny. 825 NE 10TH ST, STE 4500 73104 #913-69-1980 L1995 **AN** *020 †05
CHERRY, Mohamad Ali. P O BOX 26901, 921 S L YOUNG BLVD, WP 114 73190 #605-03-2001 L2006 **IM** *020 †20
CHESNUT, John Kent. ■ 73103 #039-01-1959 L1960 **DR** *072 †80
CHESSER, Tatiana Volkova. 940 STANTON L YOUNG BLVD 73104 #913-06-1992 L2006 **FP** *012
CHETTY, Pramod Kumar. 750 NE 13TH ST OAC-200 73104 #495-27-1980 L1984 **AN** *020 †05
CHICOO, Jose Sideco. 3545 NW 58TH ST, STE 220 73112 #748-10-1963 L1981 **P** *020
CHITTURI, Shalini. ■ 73134 #495-50-1999 L2006 **FM** *100 †18
CHODOSH, James. 608 STANTON L YOUNG BLVD 73104 #048-04-1988 L1995 **OPH** *050 †35
CHOI, Chai Suck. 901 N STONEWALL AVE 73117 #583-08-1966 L1983 **FOP** *062 †50
CHOI, David Jae-Myung. 900 NE 10TH ST 73104 #048-02-2004 L2006 **FM** *020 †18
CHOPRA, Karen. 1111 N LEE AVE STE 334 73103 #496-21-1998 L2002 **IM** *020 †20
CHRISTENSEN, Robert Jay. ■ 73150 #039-01-2006 L2007 **AN** *012
CHRYSANT, Catherine S. 5850 W WILSHIRE BLVD 73132 #418-01-1970 L1979 **PTH** *020
CHRYSANT, Steven G. 5850 W WILSHIRE BLVD 73132 #418-01-1959 L1973 **CD IM** *020 †20
CIARIMBOLI, Betsy Ann. 13820 WIRELESS WAY 73134 #024-05-1999 L2006 **CHP** *100
CLAFLIN, Dale Gene. ■ 73112 #039-01-1967 L1996 **AM** *020 †70
CLAPP, Janae Michelle. 4401 S WESTERN AVE 73109 #039-01-1995 L2002 **HO** *020 †20
CLAPP, Todd David. 4221 S WESTERN AVE # 3030, SOUTHWEST FAMILY MEDICINE 73109 #039-01-1995 L2002 **MPD PD** *020 †20,55
CLARAVALL, Leonardo H. 219 S SOONER RD 73110 #748-01-1962 L1974 **GS GPM** *020
CLARK, Douglas Lloyd. 1011 N DEWEY AVE STE 101, ST ANTHONY RADIATION ONCOL 73102 #054-04-1988 L2008 **RO** *020 †80
CLARK, Keith Fredrick. 608 NW 9TH ST, STE 5100 73102 #025-01-1978 L1983 **OTO** *020 †45
CLARK, Rachel Elizabeth. 3300 NW EXPRESSWAY, INTEGRIS BAPTIST MED CTR 73112 #039-01-1998 L1998 **EM** *020 †16
CLAY, Richard A. 415 NW 11TH ST 73103 #039-01-1943 L1945 **OPH** *071 †35
CLEAVER, William Raymond. ■ 73112 #039-01-1958 L1958 **FM** *071
CLEMENS, Ted, Jr. ■ 73118 #039-01-1952 L1952 **ON IM** *071 †20
CLEMENSON, Neal David. 3500 NW 56TH ST STE 100 73112 #017-20-1979 L1990 **FM** *030 †18
CLEMENTS, Melissa K. 6301 WATERFORD BLVD # 100 73118 #049-01-1981 L1984 **D** *020 †15
CLEVENGER, Johanna. ■ 73152 #048-12-1963 L1999 **P** *030 †75
CLICK, Russell Craig. ■ 73118 #039-01-2005 L2006 **FP** *012
CO, Edward Chua. 3300 NW EXPRESSWAY 73112 #748-01-1980 L1990 **NPM PD** *020 †55
COBB, Ester Elaine. ■ 73103 #039-01-2007 L2007 **FP** *012
CODDING, Christine Ellen. 1211 N SHARTEL AVE, STE 700 73103 #039-01-1986 L1987 **RHU** *020 †20
COFER, Amanda M. 920 STANTON L YOUNG BLVD, WP 24 73104 #048-78-2004, ▲ L2005 **OBG** *012
COFFMAN, David Lewis. 3500 NW 56TH ST STE 105, OPENSIDED MRI 73112 #039-01-1983 L1984 **RNR** *020 †80
COHEN, Donald Elliot. 8125 S WALKER AVE, PRIMARY CARE PARTNERS OF 73139 #035-47-1980 L1981 **FM LM** *020 †18
COLE, Jennifer Lyn. ■ 73116 #039-01-2007 L2007 **AN** *012
COLEMAN, Brian Rickner. 900 NE 10TH ST, FAMILY MEDICINE CENTER 73104 #039-01-1997 L1998 **FSM** *020 †18
COLEMAN, Laura Elizabeth. ■ 73115 #039-01-2004 L2006 **MPD** *012
COLEMAN, Patrick B. ■ 73102 #539-02-1965 L2005 **AN FM** *020
COLEMAN, William O. 3435 NW 56TH ST, STE 211 73112 #039-01-1947 L1948 **GS** *062 †85
COLES, D Glen. 11000 HEFNER POINTE DR 73120 #016-11-1987 L1988 **U GS** *020 †95
COLLAZO, William Anthony. 608 NW 9TH ST, STE 4106 73102 #048-04-1981 L1991 **IC IM** *020 †20
COLLINS, Roger Barrett. 3330 NW 56TH ST, STE 206 73112 #047-06-1967 L1973 **DR NM** *071 †80 ‡
COMP, Philip Cinnamon. 825 NE 10TH ST, STE 4500 73104 #054-04-1971 L1974 **IM HEM** *030 †20,03
CONIGLIONE, Thos Christy. 3300 NW EXPRESSWAY 73112 #051-04-1967 L1972 **IM ISM** *020 †20
CONLEY, Arthur Hobart, III. 10001 S WESTERN AVE, STE 101 73139 #048-04-1990 L2000 **OSS ORS** *020 †40
CONNORS, Sean Patrick. ■ 73118 #063-01-1992 L1998 **CD** *100
CONRADY, Rickie Allan. 13321 N MERIDIAN AVE, STE 408 73120 #039-01-1981 L1984 **FM FPG** *020 †18
CONWAY, Jim H, Jr. 6205 N SANTA FE AVE 73118 #039-01-1983 L1989 **ORS** *020 †40
COOK, Kathryn Lindsey. 940 NE 13TH ST 3N340, THE CHILDREN'S HOSPITAL OF 73104 #039-01-2004 L2006 **PD** *100 †55
COOK, Melvin Dean, Jr. 1201 S DOUGLAS BLVD, MIDWEST MEDICAL GROUP 73130 #039-01-1990 L1991 **FM** *020 †18 ‡
COOK, Timothy Hale. 3433 NW 56TH ST STE 580, VITAL IN PATIENT SERVICES 73112 #047-06-1977 L1999 **IM CD** *020 †20

■ = Address Information Privacy Protected

COOK, William Wesley. 3366 NW EXPRESSWAY STE 660 73112 #039-01-1972 L1973 PUD CCM *020 †20

COOKE, Richard Ellis. 5100 N BROOKLINE AVE 73112 #039-01-1982 L1983 DR *020 †80

COOKE, Robert Northington. 3435 NW 56TH ST STE 410 73112 #039-01-1980 L1981 GS *020 †85

COOPER, Drew Kevin. 3801 N CLASSEN BLVD, STE 100 73118 #039-01-1995 L1996 FM *020 †18

COPELAND, Kenneth Claud. 940 NE 13TH ST, RM 2B-2426 73104 #048-04-1973 L1999 PDE PD *020 †55

COPELAND, Terry Nizo. 721 NW 6TH ST, 2ND FL 73102 #039-01-1985 L1986 IM *020

CORDER, Clinton N. 1211 N SHARTEL AVE 73103 #028-02-1971 L1980 PA IM *050

CORLEY, Stanley Dean. 5201 W MEMORIAL RD 73142 #039-01-1978 L1979 FM EM *020 †18

CORMAN, Maurice Ernest. 900 NE 10TH ST, DEPT OF FAMILY MEDICINE 73104 #039-01-2003 L2005 FM *020

CORN, Ayumi Ide. 3000 UNITED FOUNDERS BLVD, STE 234 73112 #039-01-1994 L1995 HMP *020 †50

CORN, Carolyn Ruth. 3400 NW EXPRESSWAY, OKLAHOMA CARDIOVASCULAR 73112 #039-01-1977 L1985 CD *020 †20

CORN, Todd Douglas. 3433 NW 56TH ST, VITAL IN PATIENT SERVICES 73112 #039-01-1997 L2005 IM *020

CORNELISON, Raymond Louis. 825 NE 10TH ST, STE 4500 73104 #039-01-1968 L1968 D DMP *020 †15

CORNELIUS, George Robt. 4215 N CLASSEN BLVD 73118 #039-01-1957 L1957 OPH *071 †35

CORSTVET, Lisa Margaret. 4200 W MEMORIAL RD, STE 703 73120 #039-01-1987 L1988 AN *020 †05

COSSAART, Nicole Rene. ■ 73118 #019-02-1998 L2004 PCC *100

COUCH, James Russell, Jr. 711 SL YOUNG BLVD 73104 #048-04-1965 L1992 N IM *040 †75

COUPENS, Steven Donald. 6205 N SANTA FE AVE, STE 200 73118 #030-05-1986 L1987 ORS GS *020 †40

COWLEY, Benj Dollar, Jr. 920 SL YOUNG BLVD, WP2250 73104 #048-04-1981 L2001 NEP EM *020 †20

COX, J Gregory. 4140 W MEMORIAL RD STE 408 73120 #039-01-1977 L1981 OBG *020 †30 ‡

COX, Louis Howard Andres. 5401 N PORTLAND AVE, STE 220 73112 #021-01-1985 L1986 IM PM *020 †20

CRAIG, Latasha B. 1000 N LINCOLN BLVD, STE 300 73104 #048-02-1998 L2006 REN *020

CRAIG, Nancy Ryan. 3300 NW EXPRESSWAY 73112 #039-01-1949 L1949 AN EM *071 †05

CRAIN, Russell Dean. 5501 N PORTLAND AVE 73112 #039-01-1982 L1983 OPH *020 †35

CRAMER, Ralph, Jr. 3300 NW EXPRESSWAY 73112 #039-01-1964 L1964 R *071 †80

CRANE, David Lynn. 1111 N LEE AVE, STE 400 73103 #039-01-1974 L1975 AN *020 †05

CRANMER, Kerry Wayne. 3545 NW 58TH ST, STE 750 73112 #039-01-1975 L1976 FPG PLM *020 ‡

CRAVEN, Pamela C. 5401 N PORTLAND AVE, OKLAHOMA CARDIOVASCULAR 73112 #039-01-1990 L1991 CD *020 †20

CRAWFORD, Kenneth Lee. 4200 W MEMORIAL RD STE 405 73120 #019-02-1983 L1989 GS CCS *020 †85

CRAWFORD, Michael Kenneth. 13321 N MERIDIAN AVE, STE 210 73120 #039-01-1983 L1984 IM *020 †20

CRAWFORD, Steven Alan. 900 NE 10TH ST, OU PHYSICIANS FAM MED CTR 73104 #016-11-1979 L1982 FM *040 †18

CRESPO, Manuel O. 3433 NW 56TH ST, STE 580 73112 #028-78-1988, ▲ L1993 FM OS *020 †18

CRITTENDEN, Mickey Eugene. 1919 E MEMORIAL RD 73131 #039-01-1973 L1977 PD *020 †55

CRITTENDEN BYERS, Cathryn. 940 NE 13TH ST STE 3N3409, CHILDREN'S HOSPITAL OF OKL 73104 #039-01-2003 L2004 PD *100 †55 ‡

CROOK, Richard Harold. 3233 NW 63RD ST, ACCIDENT CARE AND TREATENT 73116 #039-01-1973 L1974 EM *020 †16

CROSBY, Warren Melville. 825 NE 10TH ST, STE 4500 73104 #019-02-1957 L1962 GYN OBG *072 †30 ‡

CROUSE, Elisa Anne. 825 NE 10TH ST, STE 3300 73104 #028-02-1989 L1997 OBG NTR *020 †30

CRUTCHER, James Michael. 1000 NE 10TH ST RM 305 73117 #039-01-1980 L1981 GPM AM *030 †70

CRUZAN, Jeffrey Brent. 6601 W HEFNER RD 73162 #039-01-1985 L1986 FM *020 †18

CUCCIO, Anne Elizabeth. 920 STANTON L YOUNG BLVD 73104 #051-04-1991 L1994 CHP *020 †75

CUENCA AGUIRRE, Abigail L. 3300 NW EXPRESSWAY 73112 #319-03-1988 L1996 *020

CULKIN, Daniel J. 920 SL YOUNG BLVD, # WP3150 73104 #030-06-1979 L1994 U OS *020 †95

CUNNINGHAM, Jay D. 4200 W MEMORIAL RD, STE 703 73120 #039-79-1987, ▲ L1988 AN *020 †05

CURRY, Geo Alexander, II. 1200 EVERETT DR, UH-R INP606 73104 #055-01-1972 L1999 DR N *071 †75

CVITANIC, Oliver Anthony. 9901 S PENNSYLVANIA AVE, SOUTHWEST OKLAHOMA MRI 73159 #041-01-1987 L1988 DR *020 †80

CZERWINSKI, Anthony Wm. 4221 S WESTERN AVE, STE 2040 73109 #028-34-1959 L1960 NEP IM *020 †20

DACE, De Jean Lea. ■ 73116 #039-01-2000 L2001 DR *020

DACHAUER, John. 701 NE 10TH ST 73104 #056-06-1980 L1985 OBG *020 †30

DAHER, Nadim Nadim. ■ 73120 #605-03-2001 L2006 PCC *012 †20

DAHLGREN, Ryan Michael. ■ 73142 #039-01-2006 L2007 DR *012

DAHR, A S. 3366 NW EXPRESSWAY, STE 680 73112 #875-01-1962 L1972 CD IM *020

DAHR, Sami S. 3366 NORTHWEST EXPY 73112 #039-01-1999 L2000 OPH *020 †35 ‡

DALBIR, Dinesh Kumar. 5721 NW 132ND ST 73142 #913-32-1991 L2002 IM *020 ‡

DALTON, William Edward. 3301 NW 63RD ST 73116 #051-04-1962 L1971 PS GS *020 †85,65

DALY, Timothy Shaun. 940 NE 13TH ST 73104 #039-01-2001 L2002 CD *012 †20

DANG, Hung Huy. 920 SL YOUNG BLVD 73104 #039-01-2003 L2004 OTO *012

DANG, Tay Nhu. 921 NE 13TH ST 73104 #840-01-1963 L1982 FM *074 †18

DANG, Van Thuy. 920 SL YOUNG BLVD, WP 1130 73104 #039-01-2003 L2004 ID *012 †20

DANIEL, Edna. 1000 N LEE AVE 73104 #495-08-1970 L1991 AN *020

DANIEL, Howard Grady. 825 NE 10TH ST, STE 4500 73104 #012-05-1968 L1974 R *020 †80

DANIELS, Bruce Alan. 4221 S WESTERN AVE # 4045 73109 #039-01-1975 L1976 IM CD *020 †20

DANNAWAY, Douglas Charles. 1200 EVERETT DR, 7TH FL 73104 #004-01-1998 L2003 PD NPM *020 †55

DARBE, Shantharam. 4601 N CLASSEN BLVD 73118 #495-58-1974 L1987 P *020

DARROW HOPKINS, Sharon M. 750 NE 13TH ST, STE 200 OAC BLDG 73104 #039-79-2007, ▲ AN *012

DASARI, Tarun Watson. 940 STANTON L YOUNG BLVD 73104 #495-21-2002 L2007 IM *012

DAUTENHAHN, Dale Edwin. 4400 WILL ROGERS PKWY #105 73108 #039-01-1987 L1988 AN PME *020 †05

DAUTENHAHN, David Lee. 1111 N LEE AVE, STE 236 73103 #039-01-1980 L1981 AN *020 †05

DAVENPORT, Stephen Roy. 3301 NW 50TH ST 73112 #008-01-1980 L1998 ORS GS *020 †40

DAVIDSON, Deborah Ellen. ■ 73118 #039-01-1982 *020

DAVIDSON, Harold Dean. 3366 NW EXPRESSWAY, STE 140 73112 #039-01-1962 L1962 R OS *071 †80

DAVIS, Charlyce Erin. ■ 73120 #047-07-2004 L2006 IM *020 †20

DAVIS, Chris Myron. 3433 NW 56TH ST STE 760 73112 #039-01-1986 L1999 CRS *020 †85,10

DAVIS, Craig Matthew. 4805 S WESTERN AVE 73109 #039-01-1991 L2003 OS PTH *020 †50

DAVIS, Elisa Anne. ■ 73118 #039-01-2006 L2006 MPD *012

DAVIS, Jonathan Lockwood. 4221 S WESTERN AVE, STE 3010 73109 #028-34-1970 L1984 DIA END *020 †20

DAVIS, Kelly Van. 711 SL YOUNG BLVD, STE 501 73104 #039-01-2003 L2005 IM *020

DAVIS, Lawrence Wm. 3433 NW 56TH ST, STE 600 73112 #039-01-1975 L1976 N *020 †75

DAVIS, Nathan John. ■ 73162 #039-01-2008 #012

DAWKINS, Mark Alan. 13174 N MACARTHUR BLVD 73142 #039-01-1994 L1995 D *020 †15

DAWSON, George B. 8121 NATIONAL AVE 73110 #056-06-1988 L1992 AN *020 †05

DAWSON, Nancy L Martens. 4805 S WESTERN AVE 73109 #028-46-1973 L1974 D *020 †15 ‡

DAWSON, Richard Beach. 4805 S WESTERN AVE 73109 #005-02-1965 L1973 OTO A *072 †45 ‡

DAYOUB, Hayan. ■ 73103 #875-01-1996 L2007 NS *012

DEARBORN, Shirley Ella. 3300 NW EXPRESSWAY 73112 #041-01-1977 L1980 MDM PD *030 †55 ‡

DE ARMENDI, Alberto J. 750 NE 13TH ST, STE 200 73104 #011-02-1978 L2006 PAN PME *012

DECAMP, Nicole. 6201 N SANTA FE AVE, STE 2015 73118 #048-13-1995 L1996 D DS *020 †15

DECK, Lawrence Vivian, III. 13321 N MERIDIAN AVE, STE 400A 73120 #039-01-1986 L1987 IM *020 †20

DECKERT, Gordon Harmon. 920 STANTON L YOUNG BLVD, 3RD FL 73104 #016-06-1955 L1962 P PHP *071 †75

DEDEKE, Amy Beth. ■ 73116 #039-01-2004 L2006 RHU *012 †20

DEDEKE, Eric Matthew. 6601 W HEFNER RD 73162 #039-01-1998 L2005 FM *020 †18

DELAFIELD, Frederick. 4200 W MEMORIAL RD 73120 #011-04-1980 L1981 RHU IM *020 †20

DELHOTAL, Charles E. ■ 73120 #039-01-1947 L1948 PDA PD *071 †55 ‡

DENNIS, Leland Wayne. 6613 N MERIDIAN AVE 73116 #039-01-1989 L1990 P *020

DERNAIKA, Tarek Ahmad Adn. 825 NE 10TH ST, STE 2500 73104 #605-03-2000 L2004 PCC *100 †20

DE SALVO, James Wood. ■ 73107 #005-11-1977 OBG END *074

DESCHAMPS-BRALY, Jordan C. ■ 73102 #039-01-2005 L2006 GS *012

DESHPANDE, Swapna Nishika. 920 STANTON L YOUNG BLVD, OU G. RAINEY PAVILION 73190 #495-19-2002 L2007 CHP *012

DE VORE, James Kilgore. 3200 W WILSHIRE BLVD 73116 #039-01-1947 L1948 IM GE *071 †20

DEWBERRY, Glenn P, Jr. 5201 W MEMORIAL RD 73142 #039-01-1976 L1977 FM *020 †18

DIAS DA SILVA, Leanne Rac. 73119 #039-01-2007 L2007 IM *012

DICKERSON, Ray Duncan. 9500 BROADWAY EXT 73114 #039-01-1997 L1998 AN *020 †05

DIEHL, Mark Allen. 4221 S WESTERN AVE, STE 3030 73109 #039-01-1981 L1982 FM *020 †18

DIESSELHORST, Matthew Mic. ■ 73112 #039-01-2007 L2007 ORS *012

DIGOY, German Paul. 825 NE 10TH ST, STE 4500 73104 #035-20-1999 L2005 OTO *020 †45

DIMAS, Christos. 2716 SW 44TH ST 73119 #418-01-1970 L1979 IM *020 †20

DIMSKI, Robert Conrad. 1212 S DOUGLAS BLVD, LLC 73130 #048-13-1983 L1984 IM *020 †18

DIMSON, Otobia Gifty. 5005 N PENNSYLVANIA AVE, STE 105 73112 #056-06-1999 L2005 D *020 †15

DITTO, Steven Wayne. 1117 S DOUGLAS BLVD 73130 #039-01-1994 L2002 FM *020 †18

DIXSON, James D. 4401 W MEMORIAL RD STE 141 73134 #039-01-1970 L1971 IM *030 †20

DOAK, Bascom Parks. 1044 SW 44TH ST, STE 620 73109 #039-01-1973 L1974 GP FPG *071

DOAN, Christopher Jon. ■ 73117 #039-01-2008 *012

DOCKENDORF, Justin Graham. 2825 PARKLAWN DR 73110 #422-01-2003 L2005 FM *020

DODD, Sharon Murphy. 1000 N LEE AVE 73102 #039-01-1981 L1982 R *020 †80

DOEDEN, Andrea. 11200 N PORTLAND AVE 73120 #026-04-1993 L1994 OBG *020 †30

DOERNER, Phillip G, Jr. 1111 N LEE AVE, STE 236 73103 #039-01-1983 L1984 AN *020 †05

DOH, Lucius Seokhwan. 5300 N GRAND BLVD 73112 #005-19-2002 L2007 RO *020

DOMEK, David B. 3366 NW EXPRESSWAY, STE 330 73112 #048-02-1985 L1986 END PD *020 †19,55

DONAT, Paul Edward. 11000 HEFNER POINTE DR 73120 #039-01-1962 L1962 U NEP *020 †95

DONOVAN, Ben Oniell. ■ 73118 #003-01-2002 L2005 UP *012

DOOLEY, Colleen Mary N. 3330 NW 56TH ST FL 400, THE PEDIATRIC GROUP, PLLC 73112 #026-04-1974 L1986 PD *020 †30

DOOLEY, William Chesnut. 825 NE 10TH ST, OKLAHOMA HEALTH 73104 #047-05-1982 L2001 SO GS *020 †85

DOSSER, John Roy. 3617 NW 58TH ST STE 200 73112 #039-01-1979 L1980 OBG *020 †30

DOTTER, Richard Gene. 1211 N SHARTEL AVE, MEDICAL NEUROLOGISTS INC 73103 #039-01-1959 L1959 N IM *071 †75

DOUGHARTY, Kent Wayne. 921 NE 13TH ST, 111AC 73104 #039-01-1984 L1985 FM *020 †18

DOUGHERTY, Raymond Jos. ■ 73118 #039-01-1947 L1948 PUD IM *071 †20

DOWELL, Matthew S. 608 NW 9TH ST STE 1000 73102 #039-79-1997, ▲ L1998 FM *020 †18

DRABU, Benazir. 1200 EVERETT DR, 7TH FL N PAVILLION 73104 #495-51-1986 L2003 PD *020

DRAKE, John Whitfield. 3433 NW 56TH ST, STE 800 73112 #028-02-1956 L1959 END *020 †20

DREVETS, Douglas Allen. 921 NE 13TH ST 73104 #019-02-1984 L1998 ID IM *050 †20

DREW, Christie L. ■ 73142 #048-12-2007 L2007 FP *012

DROOBY, S A Dean. 4140 MEMORIAL RD, STE 602 73120 #143-06-1980 L1981 IM *020 †20

DROZDZIAK, Ewa. 825 NE 10TH ST, STE 4500 73104 #759-06-1994 L2005 RHU *020 †20

D'SOUZA, Sharon Lisa. ■ 73118 #039-01-2004 L2005 DR *012

DU, Tuan Quoc. 3300 NW EXPRESSWAY, RADIOLOGY GRADUATE MED EDU 73112 #039-01-2000 L2002 DR *020 †80

DUBOIS, Gary Dean. 1117 S DOUGLAS BLVD 73130 #039-01-1979 L1980 IM NEP *020 †20

DUBOIS, Peggy Lee Culver. 1117 S DOUGLAS BLVD 73130 #039-01-1979 L1980 FM OBG *020 †18

DUCKETT, Jim Glendon. ■ 73162 #039-01-1955 L1955 PS *071

DUMIGAN, Ronald Matthew. 1110 N LEE AVE, NEW CENTURY ORTHOPEDICS AN 73103 #021-06-1999 L2007 OSM *020 †40

DUMIGAN, Shelly Hayes. ■ 73120 #039-01-2000 L2007 AN *020 †05

DUNCAN, Michael Robt. 4200 W MEMORIAL RD STE 703, AFFFILIATED ANESTHESIOLOGI 73120 #039-01-1989 L1990 AN *020 †05

■ = Address Information Privacy Protected

DUNLAP, Marianne E. 940 NE 13TH ST RM 2B2305, SECT OF COMM PEDIATRICS 73104 #039-01-1997 L1998 **PD** *020 †55

DUNN, Charles Jackson. 236 NW 62ND ST, IMAGING 73118 #016-45-1987 L1988 **DR** *020 †80

DUTTA, Sakuntala S. ■ 73142 #495-50-1965 L1980 **RO** *030

DYER, James Russell, II. 920 STANTON L YOUNG BLVD 73104 #033-06-1998 L2005 **AN** *020,05

DYER, Robert Kent. 3400 NW 56TH ST 73112 #036-05-1986 L1991 **OTO** *020 †45

EARLEY, James Ryan. 4200 W MEMORIAL RD, STE 703 73120 #039-01-2003 L2007 **AN** *020

EARP, Ancel, Jr. ■ 73118 #039-01-1947 L1948 **GS** *071 †85

EATON, Bobby Gene. 921 NE 13TH ST, DEPT OF RADIOLOGICAL SCIEN 73104 #039-01-1960 L1960 **R** *020 †80

EBERT, Andrew Benjamin. 920 STANTON L YONG BLVD #W, OUHSC, DPT OF ORTHOPEDIC S 73104 #048-16-2003 L2004 **ORS** *012

ECKMAN, Charles Eric. 1211 N SHARTEL AVE, STE 700 73103 #056-06-1978 L1979 **DR PDR** *020 †80

EDIL, Barish Halil. 940 STANTON L YOUNG BLVD 73104 #056-05-2000 L2001 **GS** *100

EDMONDS, Paul Bryan. 1800 S DOUGLAS BLVD 73130 #039-01-1961 L1961 **OBG NTR** *020 †30

EDSTROM, Steven Michael. 3300 NW EXPRESSWAY 73112 #039-01-1994 L1998 **AN** *020 †05

EDWARDS, Dearborn. 921 NE 13TH ST, VAMC (11G) 73104 #056-05-1977 L2003 **IM IMG** *020 †20 ‡

EDWARDS, Roberta Miller. 5505 N BROOKLINE AVE, BOX 12245 73112 #041-07-1962 L1965 **IM LM** *020 ‡

EDWARDS, Susan Marie. 1200 EVERETT DR RM 160, DEPT OF RADIOLOGY 73104 #007-02-1977 L1987 **DR** *062 †80

EFFRON, Alan Michael. 825 NE 10TH ST, STE 4500 73104 #047-06-1966 L1976 **DR NR** *020 †80

EICHNER, Edward Randolph. 825 NE 10TH ST 73104 #023-07-1963 L1977 **HEM IM** *071 †20

EKUNDAYO, Oluwakemi Eniol. ■ 73118 #690-01-1999 **IM** *020 ‡

EL-AMM, Jose-Marie Albert. 3300 NW EXPRESSWAY, 4160 JOHN R. 73112 #605-01-1997 L2008 **NEP** *020 †20

ELDER, Michael Drew. 4327 W MEMORIAL RD 73134 #039-01-1982 L1983 **AN** *020 †05

ELDRIDGE, Timothy Jason. 1211 N SHARTEL AVE STE 200 73103 #010-02-1989 L2001 **GS** *020 †85

ELFRINK, Nathan Donald. ■ 73118 #039-01-2006 L2006 **DR** *012

ELFRINK, Stacie Nicole. ■ 73118 #039-01-2005 L2006 **OBG** *012

EL-KEDDISSI, Jean Ibrahim. 825 NE 10TH ST, STE 2500 73104 #605-02-1993 L1997 **PCC** *020 †20

EL-KHOURY, Chaouki Kamal. 711 SL YOUNG STE 209, OUHSC 73104 #605-01-2000 L2003 **PD** *100

EL KHOURY, Christian Anto. 940 STANTON L YOUNG BLVD 73104 #605-02-2002 L2005 **HO** *012 †20

ELKINS, Charles Craig. 3433 NW 56TH ST, STE 670 73112 #039-01-1988 L1998 **TS** *020 †85,90

ELKINS, Ronald C. 920 STANTON L YOUNG BLVD, WP 2230 73104 #039-01-1962 L1962 **TS GS** *071 †85,90

ELLIOTT, Earl Sanders. 3400 NORTHWEST EXPY, STE 500 73112 #039-01-1973 L1974 **IM** *020 †20

ELLIS, Jeri Lynn. 1016 SW 44TH ST 73109 #005-14-1989 L1997 **OM GP** *020

ELLIS, John Wesley. 5100 N BROOKLINE AVE, STE 465 73112 #039-01-1968 L1969 **LM OM** *020 †18 ‡

ELLIS, Robert S. 750 NE 13TH ST, 3RD FL 73104 #016-06-1951 L1952 **A IM** *072 †20,03

ELMAJIAN, Donald Alan. 1000 N LINCOLN BLVD, STE 360 73104 #005-06-1988 L1996 **U** *020 †95

ELSEBAI, Aly Mohamed. 3366 NW EXPRESSWAY, STE 730 73112 #915-04-1980 L1996 **NEP IM** *020 †20

ELWOOD, Robin James. 6205 N SANTA FE AVE 73118 #539-03-1975 L1987 **AN PME** *020 †05 ‡

ELYA, Marwan Kamil. 920 STANTON L YOUNG BLVD, BLVD, WP1310 73104 #605-03-2001 L2005 **PCC** *012 †20

EMMONS, Steven Ware. 750 NE 13TH ST, STE OAC # 200 73104 #039-01-1988 L1994 **AN** *020

ENGELBRECHT, Valerie Ann. 11200 N PORTLAND AVE, FL 2 73120 #048-15-1989 L1990 **OBG** *020 †30

ENGLES, Chas Franklin, Jr. 4120 W MEMORIAL RD STE 208 73120 #039-01-1979 L1980 **NS** *020 †25

ENGLES, Christopher Dirk. ■ 73118 #039-01-2008 *012

ENGLES, Craig Lawson. 4221 S WESTERN AVE, STE 4035 73109 #039-01-1983 L1984 **FM** *020 †18

ENGLES, Loretta Graham. 4401 S WESTERN AVE 73109 #039-01-1951 L1951 **GP** *071

ENGLISH, Brett Charles. 940 STANTON L YOUNG BLVD 73104 #005-76-2005, ▲ L2006 **AN** *012

ENIS, John Anthony. ■ 73120 #039-01-2007 **TY** *012

EPSTEIN, Robert Bernard. 1200 EVERETT DR 73104 #016-11-1959 L1981 **ON HEM** *040 †20

ERBAR, Gerald F. 920 STANTON L YOUNG BLVD 73104 #039-01-1977 L1978 **AN** *072

ERNST, Kimberly Dawn. 1200 EVERETT DR, 7TH FL NORTH PAVILION 73104 #039-01-1997 L2003 **NPM PD** *020 †55 ‡

ERROR, Marc Edward. ■ 73120 #039-01-2008 *012

ERTL, William John J. 825 NE 10TH ST 73104 #011-02-1992 L2002 **ORS** *020 †40

ESCOBEDO, Marilyn B. 940 NE 13TH ST 73104 #028-02-1970 L2001 **NPM** *050 †55

ESPARZA, Edward. 2610 NW EXPRESSWAY 73112 #039-01-1959 L1960 **GP GS** *071

ESPARZA, Natalie Ann. 11000 HEFNER POINTE DR 73120 #039-01-1994 L2001 **U** *020 †95

ESTELL, Laura Beth. ■ 73159 #039-01-2005 L2007 **PD** *012

ESTEP, Randel D. 1110 N LEE AVE 73103 #039-79-1997, ▲ L1998 **OM** *020

ETHRIDGE, John Kendall, Jr. 920 STANTON L YOUNG BLVD, OUH OB & GYN 73104 #047-06-2005 L2007 **OBG** *012

ETLING, Roger L. 921 NE 13TH ST 73104 #039-01-1976 L1977 **IM** *020

EULBERG, Mark W. 3233 NW 63RD ST 73116 #039-01-1977 L1978 **GP** *020

EUSTAQUIO, Marcia Elaine. ■ 73118 #016-42-2006 L2007 **OTO** *012

EVANS, David Lowell. ■ 73107 #039-01-2004 L2006 **DR** *012

EVERETT, Royice Bert. 3366 NW EXPRESSWAY STE 600 73112 #039-01-1972 L1973 **OBG REN** *020 †30

EXAIRE-RODRIGUEZ, Jose Em. 825 NE 10TH ST, STE 2500 73104 #649-01-1997 L2007 *100

FAGIUOLI, Stefano. 3300 NW EXPRESSWAY, OK TRANSPLANT INST 73112 #561-11-1986 L1994 **GE** *020

FAIN, Harold Hubbard, Jr. 921 NE 13TH ST, VA MED CTR 73104 #048-02-1980 L1987 **FM GPM** *020 †70,18

FAKHARI, Farnaz D. ■ 73102 #039-01-2008 *012

FALK, Richard G, Jr. 3366 NW EXPRESSWAY, STE 140 73112 #039-01-1984 L1984 **DR** *020 †80

FANKHOUSER-CONN, Sue Ann. ■ 73118 #039-01-1971 L1973 **P FM** *071

FARHOOD, Lisa Marie. 5401 N PORTLAND AVE, STE 220 73112 #039-01-1995 L1996 **IM** *020 †20

FARHOOD, Vincent Michael. 3366 NW EXPRESSWAY, STE 140 73112 #039-01-1995 L1996 **DR** *020 †80

FARMER, Katherine Marie. 920 SL YOUNG BLVD, WP 2410 73104 #039-01-2004 L2005 **OBG** *012

FAROOQ, Saif Ullah. 940 STANTON L YOUNG BLVD 73104 #704-21-2000 L2008 **IM** *012

FARRIS, Bradley K. 921 NE 13TH ST 73104 #039-01-1980 L1981 **OPH** *040 †35

FARRIS, John J. 3625 NW 56TH ST, 5 CORPORATE PLAZA 73112 #025-12-1985 L1988 **IM** *030

FARUQUE, Hashib Deen. 4404 N LINCOLN BLVD 73105 #160-02-1984 L2001 **P** *020

FAUMUINA, Robin Beverly. ■ 73135 #305-01-2005 L2006 **FP** *012

FAZILI, Javid. 825 SL YOUNG BLVD, WP 1360 73104 #495-51-1987 L2001 **GE IM** *020 †20

FELIX-VALDES, Victor M. ■ 73101 #847-05-1966 L1993 **OBG** *020

FELTON, Fred, Jr. ■ 73102 #038-40-1978 L1982 **DR** *020

FENG, Qi. ■ 73127 #243-47-1977 **DR** *100

FENG, Yan. 921 NE 13TH ST, MENTAL HEALTH DEPT 73104 #243-47-1989 L2002 **P CHP** *020

FERGESON, Mark Ashley. 940 NE 13TH ST RM 1306-1B, GENERAL PEDIATRICS 73104 #039-01-1997 L1998 **PD** *040 †55

FERGUSON, Michael Leo. 1111 N LEE AVE STE 236 73103 #039-01-1980 L1981 **AN** *020 †05

FERNANDES, Alroy Henry. 608 NW 9TH ST, STE 1000 73102 #496-25-1999 L2004 **FP** *012

FIEGEL, Thurma Jo. 1103 NW 40TH ST 73118 #039-01-1976 L1977 **IM** *030

FILLER, Janice A. 3330 NW 56TH ST FL 400, THE PEDIATRIC GROUP PLLC 73112 #039-01-1981 L1982 **PD IG** *020 †55

FILLEY, Warren Vernon. 13321 N MERIDIAN AVE, STE 100 73120 #019-02-1976 L1977 **AI IM** *020 †20,03

FINE, Yvonne Scaily. ■ 73131 #039-01-1971 L1972 **IM** *020 †20

FINLEY, Gravelly E. 1000 N LEE AVE 73102 #047-07-1935 L1937 **FM OS** *071

FINN, Thomas C, Jr. ■ 73120 #039-01-1953 L1953 **AI** *071 †55,03

FIRDAUS, Muhammad. 825 NE 13TH ST 73104 #704-02-1994 L1998 **IMG** *020 †20

FISCHER, Trevan Dale. ■ 73105 #039-01-2008 *012

FISHER, Mark Andrew. 3435 NW 56TH ST, STE 506 73112 #041-13-1987 L1995 **N** *020 †75

FISHER, Robert Darryl. ■ 73120 #039-01-1964 L1964 **TS** *071 †85,90 ‡

FITCH, Jane C K. 750 NE 13TH ST, OAC200 73104 #048-14-1988 L2001 **AN** *040 †05

FITO, Dennis Allen Minas. 1000 N LEE AVE 73102 #748-02-2000 L2006 **FP** *012

FITZWATER, Amanda K. 3300 NW EXPRESSWAY, GRADUATE MEDICAL EDUCATION 73112 #019-02-2000 L2002 **DR** *020 †80

FIXLEY, Mark Steven. 4050 W MEMORIAL RD, 3RD FL STE B 73120 #019-02-1972 L1980 **PUD CCM** *020 †20

FLEISCHMAN, Mark Hugo. 3366 NW EXPRESSWAY, STE 720 73112 #030-06-2000 L2001 **D DS** *020 †15

FLEMING, Jim Chas. 4401 S WESTERN AVE 73109 #018-03-1982 L1983 **DR** *075 †80

FLESHER, David A. 3301 NW 50TH ST 73112 #039-01-1962 L1962 **ORS** *020 †40

FLESHER, David John. 3301 NW 50TH ST ORTHO 73112 #039-01-1985 L1991 **ORS OSM** *020 †40

FLESHER, Thomas H, III. 3301 NW 50TH ST 73112 #039-01-1977 L1981 **OSM ORS** *020 †40

FLOYD, Jeffrey Denton. 1919 E MEMORIAL RD 73131 #055-01-1996 L2003 **FM FSM** *020 †18

FOERSTER, David Wm. 6305 WATERFORD BLVD, STE 115 73118 #039-01-1958 L1958 **PS** *020 †65

FOLGER, Charles Douglas. 825 NE 10TH ST, STE 4500 73104 #039-01-1974 L1975 **IM** *030 †20

FOLGER, Teresa Ann. 11101 HEFNER POINTE DR, STE 204 73120 #039-01-1983 L1984 **OBG** *030 †30

FONG, Daniel Nelson. ■ 73112 #039-01-2007 L2007 **OBG** *012

FOOTE, Andrew Lee. ■ 73107 #039-01-2005 L2006 **P** *012

FOOTE, Elizabeth Ann. ■ 73112 #039-01-2005 L2006 **P** *012

FORREST, William J. 13321 N MERIDIAN AVE 73120 #039-01-1955 L1955 **PS** *071 †65

FORS, William J, Jr. 3433 NW 56TH ST 73112 #025-01-1963 L1972 **CD** *020

FORSBERG, Jean Elizabeth. 1001 N LINCOLN BLVD, OKLA BLOOD INSTITUTE 73104 #031-01-1993 L1994 **PTH BBK** *020 †50

FORSYTHE, Roy Louis. 4300 W MEMORIAL RD 73120 #011-03-1971 L1973 **PS** *071 †65

FORTMANN, Theodore Henry. 5501 NW EXPRESSWAY 73112 #039-01-1965 L1966 **GP OS** *020

FOSHEE, Jeri Beth. 11300 N PENNSYLVN AVE #110 73120 #039-01-2005 L2006 **D** *012

FOSHEE, Stacey Lyn. 608 NW 9TH ST STE 6 73102 #019-02-1989 L1991 **CCM IM** *020 †20

FOSTER, Darlene Kay. 3330 NW 56TH ST, STE 604 73112 #039-01-1992 L1993 **IM** *071 †20

FOSTER, Dennis Earl. 3130 SW 89TH ST, STE 100 73159 #039-01-1980 L1981 **ORS OSM** *020 †40 ‡

FOWLER, Joey Dale. 11101 HEFNER POINTE DR, STE 105 73120 #039-01-1998 L2001 **FM** *020 †18

FOX, Audralan Gayle. ■ 73135 #654-01-2006 L2006 **FP** *012

FOX, Pamela Ereckson. 920 STANTON L YOUNG BLVD 73104 #048-14-1988 L2001 **AN** *020 †05

FRAIJ, Omar B. ■ 73116 #039-01-2008 *012

FRALEY, Thomas Haskell. 1211 N SHARTEL AVE STE 900 73103 #039-01-1959 L1959 **GYN** *020

FRANCEL, Paul Christopher. 3048 SW 89TH ST 73159 #016-02-1989 L1996 **NS** *020 †25

FRANCIS, Kristin Kay. ■ 73118 #039-01-2003 L2004 **HO** *012 †20

FRANCO, Arie. 940 NE 13TH ST RM L834, DEPT OF RADIOLOGICAL SCIEN 73104 #396-04-1975 L2006 **PDR** *020 †28,80

FRANKLIN, Rachel M. 900 NE 10TH ST, OUHSC 73104 #039-01-1997 L1998 **FM** *020 †18 ‡

FRANSEN, Stephen Ralph. 608 STANTON L YOUNG BLVD 73104 #062-01-1985 L1986 **OPH** *020 †35

FRANTZ, Robert Ray, Jr. 4401 S WESTERN AVE 73109 #039-01-1996 L1997 **EM** *020 †16

FRAZIER, Joel Louis. 1044 SW 44TH ST, FL 6 73109 #016-02-1985 L2005 **ORS HS** *020 †40

FREEDE, Charles Louis. 3435 NW 56TH ST, STE 412 73112 #039-01-1945 L1946 **PD** *071 †55

FREEMAN, Chas Churchill. 4221 S WESTERN AVE, STE 401 73109 #039-01-1969 L1969 **CD IM** *020 †20

FREEMAN, Jana Allison. 13313 N MERIDIAN AVE, STE C 73120 #039-01-1994 L1995 **PD** *020 †55

FRENCH, Kyle Bradley. 3500 NW 56TH ST STE 100, RESIDENCY PROGRAM 73112 #039-01-2006 L2007 **FP** *012

FREUND, Joseph Norman. 3233 NW 63RD ST 73116 #039-01-1969 L1969 **OTR AN** *020 †05

FREY, Bret Newton. 3705 NW 63RD ST 73116 #039-01-1993 L1994 **ORS** *020 †40

FRIEDMAN, Emily D. 3433 NW 56TH ST, STE 610 73112 #010-02-1981 L1992 **NS OSS** *020 †25

FRIEDMAN, Eric Scott. 4120 W MEMORIAL RD 73120 #039-01-1988 L1989 **NS** *020 †25

FRIMBERGER, Dominic Chris. 920 STANTON L YOUNG BLVD, STE W.P. 3150 73104 #409-20-1997 L2004 **UP** *020

FROST, Andrew F. 5350 S WESTERN AVE STE 419 73109 #048-02-1983 L1984 **AN** *020 †05 ‡

FROW, Mary Apple. ■ 73112 #039-01-1980 L1982 **FM** *071 †18

FRYE, Lee Prentice, Jr. 1140 SW 44TH ST 73109 #039-01-1978 L1979 **OBG EM** *020 †30
FULLER, Bennett E. 4200 W MEMORIAL RD STE 703 73120 #039-01-1986 L1987 **AN** *020 †05
FULLER, Falon Dee. 14101 PARKWAY COMMONS DR 73134 #039-01-1984 L1985 **AN** *020 †05
FULLER, Guy Wesley. ■ 73120 #039-01-1955 L1955 **OBG** *071 †30
FULLER, John Alan. 4200 W MEMORIAL RD, STE 410 73120 #039-01-1982 L1983 **GYN** *020 †30
FUNDERBURK, Charles H, Jr. 9600 BROADWAY EXT 73114 #036-01-1985 L1991 **ORS HS** *020 †40
FUNG, Kar-Ming Armin. 920 STANTON L YOUNG BLVD 73104 #244-04-1988 L2002 **SP NP** *020 †50
FUNNELL, James Dean. 4200 W MEMORIAL RD STE 201 73120 #039-01-1960 L1960 **GYN OS** *072 †30
FURMAN, Eric Bertram. 920 STANTON L YOUNG BLVD 73104 #836-01-1958 L2000 **PAN MDM** *020 †05
GAFFAR, Mubina. 921 NE 13TH ST, VA MEDICAL CENTER(III A-C) 73104 #704-25-1992 L1998 **IM** *020 †20
GAFFNEY, Patrick Michael. 825 NE 13TH ST 73104 #026-04-1991 L2008 **HO** *020 †20
GALATI, Vincenzo. 920 STANTON L YOUNG BLVD, WP 3150 73104 #028-79-2004, ▲ L2005 **U** *012
GANDHI, Darshan Gautam. 920 STANTON L YOUNG BLVD, HEALTH SCIENC 73104 #495-76-2003 L2007 **HO** *012 †20
GANDHI, Shyama Darshan. ■ 73112 #495-23-2006 L2007 **FP** *012
GANESAN, Devaki. 4401 S WESTERN AVE 73109 #495-09-1962 L1978 **OM NM** *020 †28
GANNAWAY, Jay Keith. 3433 NW 56TH ST, STE 950 73112 #039-01-1979 L1980 **ORS HS** *020 †40
GANTA, Raghuvender. 750 NE 13TH ST, STE 200 73104 #495-65-1974 L1992 **AN** *020 †05
GARCIA, Carlos Andres. 619 NE 13TH ST, DEPT DERM OUHSC 73104 #649-13-1985 L2000 **D DS** *020
GARCIA-MORAL, Carlos A. 10914 HEFNER POINTE DR, STE 200 73120 #132-01-1961 L1975 **HS ORS** *020 †40 ‡
GARDINER, Gena Mathews. 3435 NW 56TH ST, STE 900 73112 #039-01-1986 L1989 **FM** *020 †18
GARG, Ankur. ■ 73112 #495-17-2001 L2007 **N** *012
GARG, Sindhu. 940 STANTON L YOUNG BLVD 73104 #496-03-2003 L2006 **IM** *012
GARNER, Matthew Thomas. ■ 73106 #039-01-2008 *012
GARRELTS, Rebecca Mae. ■ 73117 #039-01-2008 *012
GARRISON, George Bolar. ■ 73116 #039-01-1956 L1956 **AN** *072
GARRISON, Patrick Michael. 940 NE 13TH ST RM 2308, DEPARTMENT OF PEDIATRICS 73104 #039-01-2004 L2005 **MPD** *012
GARTON, Theresa Suzanne. 920 STANTN L YNG #3539, OUHSC DEPT OF PSY 73104 #039-01-1982 L1983 **P** *020 †75
GARZA, Jennifer J. PO BOX 26307, DEPARTMENT OF PEDIATRIC SU 73126 #048-02-1998 L2005 **GS** *100
GASBARRA, Dianne B. 4200 W MEMORIAL RD, STE 708 73120 #039-01-1981 L1982 **IM PUD** *020 †20
GAUTAM, Archana. 825 NE 10TH ST, STE 2500 73104 #495-49-1996 L2002 **CD** *100 †20
GAUTHIER, Stephen Cole. 3301 NW 63RD ST 73116 #039-01-1998 L1999 **PS** *020 †85,65
GAVINO, Alde Carlo Patdu. ■ 73134 #748-02-2001 L2006 **PTH** *012
GAWEY, Bradley Jos. 3300 NW EXPRESSWAY 73112 #021-05-1989 L1993 **AN** *020 †05
GAWEY, Elizabeth Parro. 3435 NW 56TH ST, STE 500 73112 #021-05-1989 L1993 **D** *020 †15
GAZZANIGA, Catherine A. 825 NE 10TH ST, STE 3300 73104 #005-15-1991 L1998 **OBG** *020 †30
GEIS, Heather Kaye. 1625 GREENBRIAR PL, STE 300 73159 #039-01-1985 L1986 **P** *020 †75
GEISTER, Brian Vincent. 3366 NORTHWEST EXPY 73112 #039-01-1982 L1983 **ON IM** *020 †20
GELCZER, Robert Kent. 3330 NW 56TH ST, STE 206 73112 #035-01-1992 L1998 **DR** *020 †80
GEORGE, James Noel. 801 NE 13TH ST, RM CHB-358 73104 #038-40-1962 L1990 **HEM IM** *050 †20
GEORGE, Philip. 711 SL YOUNG BLVD, STE 215 73104 #495-08-1980 **N** *100
GERMAN, Robert Augustine. 1110 N LEE AVE 73103 #045-01-1995 L1996 **ORS** *020 †40
GERMANY, Brett Alan. 4300 W MEMORIAL RD, EMERGENCY DEPARTMENT 73120 #039-01-1998 L2001 **EM** *020 †16
GERMANY, Robin Elizabeth. 825 NE 10TH ST, STE 2500 73104 #039-01-1998 L2001 **CD** *020 †20
GESSOUROUN, Morris R. 940 NE 13TH ST 73104 #023-01-1981 L1990 **CCP PD** *020 †55
GEURKINK, John Walter. 940 NE 13TH ST, DEPT OF RADIOLOGICAL SERVI 73104 #039-01-1966 L1966 **DR** *071 †80
GEYER, James Robt. ■ 73162 #016-06-1954 L1962 **U** *071 †95
GHIAS, Muhammad. ■ 73116 #704-21-1999 L2005 **IM** *020
GIBSON, Donna Fenton. 2501 CUMMINGS DR 73107 #039-01-1966 L1966 **P PHP** *020
GIBSON, Terrie Moseley. 3433 NW 56TH ST STE 400, PLAZA MEDICAL GROUP 73112 #021-06-1995 L2003 **CD** *020 †20
GILCHER, Ronald Otto. 1001 N LINCOLN BLVD 73104 #041-02-1963 L1979 **BBK HEM** *030 †20 ‡
GILL, Harpaul Singh. 711 SL YOUNG STE 215 73104 #166-02-2002 L2006 **N** *100
GILLAN, Muhammad Monem. 1211 N SHARTEL AVE, STE 700 73103 #704-21-1988 L1999 **RHU IM** *020 †20
GILLERAN, John Bernard. ■ 73123 #035-15-1961 L1967 **AN** *071
GILLESPIE, Campbell M, III. 5350 S WESTERN AVE STE 419 73109 #048-15-1985 L1992 **AN** *020 †05
GILLIAM, John Sherman. 4300 W MEMORIAL RD, EMERGENCY DEPT 73120 #039-05-1986 L1987 **EM FM** *020 †18 ‡
GILLIES, Elizabeth M. 920 STANTON L YOUNG BLVD, RM 451 73104 #748-01-1979 L1992 **PTH** *062 †50
GILLILAND, Donald Carroll. 3434 NW 56TH ST 73112 #039-01-1960 L1960 **OPH** *020 †35
GILLILAND, Sandra Jean. 500 SW 44TH ST 73109 #039-01-2004 L2005 **PD** *020 †55
GILMOUR, Julia Lynn. 825 NE 10TH ST, STE 3300 73104 #039-01-1994 L1995 **OBG** *020 †30
GILSON, Mayo Dean. 5501 N PORTLAND AVE 73112 #039-01-1967 L1967 **OBG END** *030 †30 ‡
GIN, Andrew C. 608 NW 9TH ST 73102 #039-01-1976 L1977 **N** *020
GISMONDI, Pedro Abimael. 5729 NW 132ND ST 73142 #012-01-1971 L1974 **RHU IM** *020
GLASGOW, Erin Kathleen. 3400 NW EXPRESSWAY, STE 500 73112 #039-01-1995 L2000 **IM** *020 †20 ‡
GLASS, Neil M. 4320 MCAULEY BLVD 73120 #039-01-1974 L1974 **OS** *020
GLEAVES, Todd Russell. 9809 CASA LINDA 73139 #039-01-2005 L2006 **AN** *012
GLOMSET, John Larson, III. ■ 73120 #039-01-2007 **ORS** *012
GO, Patrice Uy. 2809 NW 117TH ST 73120 #748-02-1983 L1995 **IM GP** *020 †20
GOAD, William Cleveland. 5701 N PORTLAND AVE 73112 #039-01-1984 L1985 **RO** *020 †80
GODDARD, Michael W. 1025 STRAKA TER, OK COMMUNITY HLTH 73139 #039-01-1975 L1976 **FM EM** *020
GODLEWSKI, Christopher Ad. 920 STANTON L YOUNG BLVD, OUHSC - ORTHOPEDICS 73104 #048-02-2004 L2006 **ORS** *012
GOETZINGER, Layne Evan. 1000 N LINCOLN BLVD 73104 #039-01-1987 L1988 **OPH** *020 †35
GOFF, Darren Walter. 4140 W MEMORIAL RD 73120 #049-01-1996 L1997 **OBG** *020 †30
GOFTON, Jeffery Jason. 901 N STONEWALL AVE 73117 #422-01-1996 L1998 **FOP** *062 †50
GOLD, Karen Pearce. 825 NE 10TH ST, STE 4500 73104 #039-01-1994 L1995 **OBG** *020 †30
GOLD, Michael Alan. 920 SL YOUNG BLVD, DEPT OB/GYN WP 2470 73104 #041-02-1992 L1996 **GO OBG** *020 †30
GONCE, Mike Edward. 3333 NW 63RD ST, STE 210 73116 #039-01-1989 L1990 **PS** *020 †85,65
GONZALEZ, Juan G. 4300 W MEMORIAL RD 73120 #649-02-1979 L1990 **PTH HMP** *020 †50 ‡
GONZALEZ, Robin Kay. 608 NW 9TH ST STE 1 73102 #039-01-2001 L2002 **FPG** *040
GOODMAN, Jean Ricci. 1200 EVERETT DR, DEPT OF OB/GYN - EVERETT T 73104 #010-02-1983 L2005 **MFM OBS** *020 †30
GOODRICH, Michael Earle. 4140 W MEMORIAL RD, STE 601 73120 #039-01-1975 L1976 **N** *020
GOODWIN, James E. 4401 W MEMORIAL RD, STE 141 73134 #048-12-1982 L1990 **IM** *020 †20
GORDON, David Lee. 711 STANTON L YOUNG BLVD, STE 215 73104 #011-02-1985 L2007 **N** *020 †75
GORDON, Robert Marion. 4200 W MEMORIAL RD, STE 805 73120 #039-01-1985 L1987 **PUD SME** *020 †20
GORMAN, Melissa Ann. 920 STANTON L YOUNG BLVD, - WP-1380 73104 #021-01-2004 L2006 **ORS** *012
GORMLEY, Andrew Kohlmaier. 1200 EVERETT DR, RM 8305 73104 #039-01-1997 L1998 **PD** *020 †55
GORMLEY, James Dreis. 13321 N MERIDIAN AVE, STE 200 73120 #039-01-1966 L1966 **PD** *071 †55
GORNICHEC, Russell S. 3433 NW 56TH ST 73112 #048-12-1994 L2000 **GS** *020 †85
GORTON, Michael Gene. 5622 N PORTLAND AVE, STE 200 73112 #039-01-1984 L1985 **PD NPM** *020 †55
GOSMANOV, Niyaz. 921 NE 13TH ST, OKLAHOMA CITY VA MEDICAL C 73104 #913-03-1994 L2004 **END** *020 †20
GOSMANOVA, Albina Khamidu. 920 SL YOUNG BLVD, WP 1345 73104 #913-03-1995 L2004 **END** *100 †20
GOTTIPATI, Ranjana. 940 STANTON L YOUNG BLVD 73104 #496-20-1994 L2008 **PTH** *100
GOTTIPATI, Venugopal. 940 NE 13TH ST 73104 #496-20-1992 L2005 **NPM** *020
GRANDLE, Gary Bruce. 5622 N PORTLAND AVE # 102 73112 #005-06-1970 L1993 **FM FPG** *020 †18
GRANT, Gregory Gordon. ■ 73132 #039-01-2006 L2007 **FP** *012
GRANT, Katherine Louise. ■ 73104 #028-34-2005 L2007 **PD** *012
GRAU, Renee Hamel. 619 NE 13TH ST 73104 #039-01-2002 L2003 **D** *020 †15
GRAY, Barry Anthony. WP 1310, 920 STANTON L YOUNG BLVD. 73190 #035-45-1970 L1974 **PUD AS** *020
GRAY, Courtney Von. 3300 NW EXPRESSWAY, ATTN: 100-3475 73112 #039-01-2001 L2004 **EM** *020 †16
GREEN, Phillip Edward. 1000 N LEE AVE 73102 #039-01-1956 L1956 **P** *071 †75
GREENFIELD, Ronald Alan. 920 SL YOUNG BLVD, W P 1160 73104 #035-15-1977 L1982 **IM ID** *040 †20
GREENHAW, Elizabeth K. 13321 N MERIDIAN AVE 73120 #039-01-2004 L2005 **PD** *100
GREENHAW, Erin Elizabeth. ■ 73142 #039-01-2008 *012
GREENWAY, Roy Mack. 920 SL YOUNG BLVD, WP 2140 73104 #039-01-2004 L2005 **GS** *012
GREGORY, David Max. 3435 NW 56TH ST STE 314 73112 #039-01-1965 L1966 **GE IM** *020
GREGORY, Joseph Edward. 6102 NW 63RD ST 73132 #025-07-1958 L1983 **GS OS** *020 †85
GREGORY, Seth Michael. ■ 73120 #039-01-2005 L2007 **IM** *012
GREYSON, Richard C. 1110 N CLASSEN BLVD 73106 #039-01-1974 L1975 **IM** *020
GRIEME, Bryan Russell. 1000 N LEE AVE 73102 #016-11-1983 L2006 **VIR** *020 †80
GRIFFIN, Carl Patrick. 4301 NW 63RD ST, STE 201 73116 #039-01-1988 L1989 **FM** *020 †18
GRIFFITH, Carvason Emery. 3330 NW 56TH ST STE 618 73112 #010-03-1973 L1977 **OBG** *020 †30 ‡
GRIGG, Terry Lynn. ■ 73118 #039-01-2008 *012
GRIGGS, Johnny Ray. 3300 NW EXPRESSWAY 73112 #048-12-1982 L1991 **PD** *020 †55
GRIGGS, Thomas Sigurd. 4625 S WESTERN AVE, RADIOLOGY CONSULTANTS 73109 #048-12-1994 L1995 **VIR** *020 †80
GRILLO, Joseph. 1044 SW 44TH ST FL 6 73109 #649-14-1977 L1979 **GS ORS** *020
GRIM, James Stewart. 921 NE 13TH ST, VETERANS HOSP 73104 #041-02-1964 L1969 **AN** *020 †05
GRIM, Stephanie Ann. ■ 73107 #039-01-2002 L2005 **PD** *100 †55
GRIZZLE, John Dale, II. 8325 NW EXPRESSWAY 73162 #654-01-1995 L1997 **FM** *020 †18
GROSS, Naina Lynn. 1000 N LINCOLN BLVD 73104 #048-04-1999 L2006 **NS** *020
GROSSMAN, Michael Robt. 3400 NW EXPRESSWAY, STE 420 73112 #010-03-1968 L1975 **GE IM** *020 †20
GROSS WINE, Jo Ann. ■ 73120 #041-07-1966 L1971 **PD** *071 †55 ‡
GRUEL, Curtis Robt. 3433 NW 56TH ST, STE 950 73112 #023-07-1977 L1978 **ORS** *020 †40
GRUEL, John B. 3433 NW 56TH ST 73112 #039-01-1979 L1980 **ORS OSM** *071 †40
GRUNOW, John Edward. 940 NE 13TH ST 73104 #048-12-1975 L1976 **GE PD** *020 †55
GUDE, Modhi. 6001 NW 120TH CT STE 6 73162 #495-11-1968 L1981 **END IM** *020 †20 ‡
GUESS, Scott Michael. 608 SL YOUNG BLVD 73104 #038-43-2004 L2005 **OPH** *012
GUILD, Ralph Timothy. 825 NE 10TH ST, STE 4500 73104 #039-01-1974 L1975 **GE NTR** *040 †20
GULLEDGE, Justin Anthony. ■ 73162 #039-01-2007 L2007 **AN** *012
GUMERLOCK, Mary Katherine. 1000 N LINCOLN BLVD 73104 #005-15-1977 L1990 **NS** *020 †25
GUNDA, Lakshma Reddy. 5100 N BROOKLINE AVE, FL 900 73112 #495-21-1979 L2002 **P** *020
GUPTA, Raghav. 940 STANTON L YOUNG BLVD 73104 #495-22-2005 L2006 **IM** *012
GUPTA, Roopali. ■ 73106 #495-22-2005 L2007 **FP** *012
GURAKAR, Ahmet Omur. 3300 NW EXPRESSWAY, NAZIH ZUHDI TRANSPLANT 73112 #902-07-1983 L1993 **IM GE** *020 †20
GURLEY, Fionnuala Mairead. 3433 NW 56TH ST, STE 400 73112 #039-01-1999 L2007 **CD** *020 †20
HAAG, Matthew James. 2801 NW 23RD ST, DEACONESS FAMILY CLINIC 73107 #039-01-2000 L2001 **FM** *020 †18
HAAS, Gilbert Geo, Jr. 1000 N LINCOLN BLVD # 300, CTR FOR REPRODUCTVE HLTH 73104 #048-04-1973 L1984 **REN GYN** *020 †30 ‡
HABERMAN, Jo Ann Darlene. 6307 WATERFORD BLVD, STE 100 73118 #041-13-1959 L1970 **R DR** *020
HABIB, Ashraf Shohdy. 3300 NW EXPRESSWAY, 5TH FL 73112 #915-02-1989 L1996 **IM** *020 †20
HABIB, Hanya Abadir. 4301 NW 63RD ST, STE 110 73116 #915-02-1989 L1998 **AN** *020 †05

■ = Address Information Privacy Protected

HABIB, Muhammad Adnan. 900 NE 10TH ST 73104 #704-02-2002 L2007 **FP** *012

HADI, Ghassan M.. 940 STANTON L YOUNG BLVD 73104 #528-04-1995 **IM** *100

HAGER, Julie Anne. 4200 W MEMORIAL RD STE 201 73120 #039-01-1998 L2002 **OBG** *020 †30

HAHN, Jisun. ■ 73117 #039-01-2008 *012

HAHN, Michael Ralph. 4120 W MEMORIAL RD 73120 #039-01-1992 L1993 **NS** *020 †25

HAIVALA, Darin Ray. 608 SL YOUNG BLVD, DEAN MCGEE EYE INSTITUTE 73104 #046-01-1998 L1999 **OPH** *020 †35

HAKEL, Susan Jane. 1024 NW 47TH ST, STE B 73118 #039-01-1993 L1974 **FM** *020 †18

HALE, Brent Oliver, Jr. 26 SW 104TH ST, MORNINGSTAR EMGY PHYS 73139 #024-01-1996 L1997 **EM** *020 †16

HALE, Ronal Dean. 4221 S WESTERN AVE, STE 4030 73109 #048-02-1973 L1985 **ORS** *020

HALE, William. 14100 PARKWAY COMMONS DR, STE 202 73134 #039-01-1993 L1994 **ORS** *020 †40

HALE, William John. 14100 PARKWAY COMMONS DR, STE 202 73134 #039-01-1963 L1963 **OS GP** *020 †18

HALES, Nathan Wayne. P O BOX 26901, 920 S L YOUNG BLVD, WP 12 73190 #048-14-2003 L2004 **OTO** *012

HALKO, Greg Edward. 3301 NW 50TH ST 73112 #039-01-1999 L2005 **HS** *020

HALL, David Ryan. ■ 73118 #039-01-2008 *012

HALL, Margaret Anne. 10900 HEFNER POINTE DR, STE 505 73120 #039-01-1993 L1994 **OBG** *020 †30

HALL, Terry G. 3300 NW EXPRESSWAY 73112 #039-01-1981 L1982 **FM** *020 †18

HALLUM, Glen Dale. 1211 N SHARTEL AVE, STE 700 73103 #039-01-1960 L1960 **R** *071 †80

HALVERSTADT, Donald Bruce. 711 STANTON L YOUNG BLVD, STE 707 73104 #024-01-1960 L1967 **U OS** *020 †95

HAM, Kathleen Elizabeth. ■ 73107 #039-01-2004 L2006 **PD** *100 †55

HAMADEH, Fahed M. ■ 73102 #875-03-1990 L2008 **IM** *020 †20

HAMAKER, Allen James. 5701 N PORTLAND AVE, STE 210 73112 #025-07-1990 L1998 **IM** *020 †20

HAMED, Isam Ahmad. ■ 73120 #605-01-1969 L1975 **IM** *020

HAMEED, Akhtar. 608 NW 9TH ST STE 5010 73102 #704-01-1970 L1979 **OBG** *020 †30

HAMILTON, Clark. ■ 73111 #010-03-1974 L1996 **PD** *020

HAMILTON, John Baxter. 73120 #039-01-1973 L1974 **OBG** *071 †30

HAMILTON, Murray Owen. 3330 NW 56TH ST STE 206, RADIOLOGY ASSOCIATES INC 73112 #039-01-1996 L1997 **DR** *020 †80

HAMMARSTEN, James Eric. 921 NE 13TH ST, AMBULATORY CARE 73104 #039-01-1973 L1988 **IM** *020 †20

HAMPTON, James Wilburn. 11100 HEFNER POINTE DR, LAKE HEFNER CANCER CTR 73120 #039-01-1956 L1956 **IM HEM** *020 ‡

HANAN, Russell Leon. 400 NW 13TH ST 73103 #039-01-1973 L1974 **GS OS** *020

HANCOCK, Samuel Brandon. ■ 73122 #039-01-2008 *012

HANDLEY, Robert A, Jr. 4625 S WESTERN AVE, RADIOLOGY CONSULTANTS, INC 73109 #048-02-1998 L2006 **VIR** *020 †80

HANFI, Azfar Nafees Alam. 711 STANTON L YOUNG BLVD, BLVD/STE 215 73104 #704-02-2001 L2004 **N** *100

HANSEN, Karl Richard. 1000 N LINCOLN BLVD, STE 300 73104 #039-01-1997 L1998 **REN OBG** *020 †30

HANSEN, Lori E. 11011 HEFNER POINTE DR 73120 #039-01-1979 L1981 **PS OTO** *020 †45

HAQUE, Fatema Parveen. 4400 N LINCOLN BLVD 73105 #160-04-1995 L2002 **P** *020

HARAGSIM, Lukas. 920 SL YOUNG BLVD, RM WP2 73104 #286-02-1988 L1998 **IM** *020 †20

HARDT, Joan. 6424 N WESTERN AVE, REJUVENA CLINIC 73116 #039-01-1996 L1999 **EM OS** *020

HARDZOG-BRITT, Carla J. 4140 W MEMORIAL RD, STE 413 73120 #039-01-1987 L1988 **PD** *020 †55

HARGIS, Joseph Steven. 4300 W MEMORIAL RD, LABORATORY MERCY HLTH CTR 73120 #039-01-1972 L1977 **PTH** *071 †50

HARGROVE, Kevin Wayne. 10914 HEFNER POINTE DR, STE 200 73120 #039-01-1987 L1988 **ORS OSM** *020 †40

HARLEY, John Barker. 825 NE 10TH ST, OKLA MED RESCH FNDT 73104 #041-01-1975 L1982 **RHU IM** *050 †20,03

HARLINE, Corbin D. 750 NE 13TH ST, STE 200 OAC BLDG 73104 #005-76-2007, ▲ **AN** *012

HARMON, Susan Marie. 5401 N PORTLAND AVE, STE 220 73112 #039-01-1985 L1986 **IM** *071 †20

HAROLDS, Jay A. 3366 NW EXPRESSWAY, STE 140 73112 #035-06-1971 L1980 **R NM** *020 †80,28 ‡

HARP, Eric Gregory. P O BOX 26901 BMSB 465, 940 STANTON L YOUNG BLVD 73190 #039-79-2004, ▲ **PTH** *012

HARPER, Kenneth Eugene. 4401 S WESTERN AVE 73109 #021-05-1976 L1977 **DR** *020 †80

HARPER, Richard Fred. 1211 N SHARTEL AVE STE 908, PHYSICIANS AND SURGEONS BL 73103 #039-01-1956 L1956 **OM GP** *071

HARRIS, Charles David, Jr. 4401 W MEMORIAL RD, ABIDE INSURANCE AGENCY INC 73134 #039-01-1980 L1982 **IM** *030

HARRIS, Gary Walter. 608 STANTON L YOUNG BLVD 73104 #039-01-1968 L1968 **OPH** *071 †35

HARRIS, Lauranne. 5701 N PORTLAND AVE # 201 73112 #039-01-1987 L1988 **OBG** *020 †30

HARRISON, Marc Allen. ■ 73142 #422-01-2005 L2007 **PTH** *020

HARRISON, Warren R, II. 3116 QUAIL CREEK RD 73120 #011-03-1979 L1982 **P** *020 †75

HARRISON, Wilbur Richard. 5501 N PORTLAND AVE 73112 #039-01-1973 L1974 **EM GP** *071

HARROZ, Joseph. 5300 N MERIDIAN AVE 73112 #039-01-1956 L1956 **OBG** *071 †30 ‡

HART, Jason Keith. 8325 NW EXPRESSWAY, MERCY HEALTH NW EXPRESSWAY 73162 #654-01-2003 L2006 **FM** *012

HARTSUCK, James Malcolm. 1044 SW 44TH ST, STE 520 73109 #024-01-1962 L1967 **TS VS** *071 †85,90

HARTY, Richard F. 825 NE 10TH ST 73104 #010-02-1968 L1992 **GE** *020

HARVEY, Chas Monroe, Jr. ■ 73112 #048-02-1947 L1954 **IM** *071 †20

HARVEY, James Danl. 921 NE 13TH ST, USVA HOSP 73104 #048-02-1960 L1966 **IM IMG** *020 †20

HARVEY, John R. 4050 W MEMORIAL RD 73120 #039-01-1981 L1982 **CD IM** *020 †20

HARVEY, Mark Neil. 4050 W MEMORIAL RD, THIRD FLOOR 73120 #039-01-1988 L1998 **CD IM** *020 †20

HARVEY, Wm Gipson, Jr. 4510 NW 39TH ST 73122 #039-01-1953 L1953 **FM** *020 †18

HASAN, Muhammad Khalid. ■ 73114 #704-21-1990 L2003 **GE** *012 †20

HASAN, Muhammad Yousuf. 940 NE 13TH ST 73104 #704-02-1990 L2000 **CCP PD** *020 †55 ‡

HASDEMIR, Can. ■ 73120 #902-04-1992 L1995 **CD** *020 †20

HASKELL, Bradley George. ■ 73159 #039-01-2004 L2001 **AN** *020 †05

HASKINS, John Talley. 14000 N PORTLAND AVE 73134 #039-01-1978 L1979 **AN** *020

HASLAM, Craig Alan. ■ 73120 #039-01-2005 **P** *012

HASLAM, Michael Lee. 4625 S WESTERN AVE 73109 #039-01-2000 L2005 **DR** *020 †80 ‡

HASSOUN, Basel M. 4200 W MEMORIAL RD, STE 501 73120 #584-01-1987 L1992 **U** *020 †95 ‡

HAST, Laurie Jill. 3330 NW 56TH ST, STE 206 73112 #016-02-1988 L1995 **DR** *020 †80

HATHAWAY, Linda Jewell. 825 NE 10TH ST 73104 #055-02-1987 L2003 **RO GP** *020

HAUNSCHILD, Chas Dennis. 13321 N MERIDIAN AVE, STE 100 73120 #039-01-1961 L1961 **A** *020 †55,03

HAUSER, Michael Tim. 4050 W MEMORIAL RD, OKLAHOMA CARDIOVASCULAR 73120 #039-01-1986 L1987 **CD** *020 †20

HAWK, William D. 4200 W MEMORIAL RD, STE 907 73120 #039-01-1981 L1982 **AN** *020 †05

HAWKINS, Angela Michele. ■ 73106 #039-01-2007 L2007 **OBG** *012

HAWKINS, Beau Michael. ■ 73118 #039-01-2004 L2005 **IM** *012 †20

HAWLEY, William Dean. 4300 W MEMORIAL RD 73120 #039-01-1964 L1964 **HO TS** *020 †85,90 ‡

HAYES, Christopher Dickso. 3500 NW 56TH ST STE 100, GREAT PLAINS FAMILY PRACTI 73112 #039-01-2005 L2006 **FP** *012

HAYES, Hulon Taylor. 73112 #003-01-2006 L2006 **P** *012

HAYES, Mandy Lynn. ■ 73106 #039-01-2007 L2007 **FP** *012

HEARST, Tamara Evans. 921 NE 13TH ST, MENTAL HEALTH SERVICE 73104 #039-01-2001 L2002 **P** *020

HEATH, William Donnell. 5701 N PORTLAND AVE # 105, DEACONESS MEDICAL OFFICE 73112 #039-01-1956 L1956 **OPH** *071 †85

HEIGLE, Richard Bruce. 3300 NW EXPRESSWAY 73112 #039-01-1990 L1991 **EM** *020 †16

HEIMBACH, Stephen Wayne. 1200 EVERETT DR 73104 #039-01-1993 L1994 **AN** *040 †05

HEIN, Robert Alan. 4140 W MEMORIAL RD, STE 621 73120 #039-01-1983 L1984 **PS GS** *020 †65,85

HEINLEN, Jonathan Edward. ■ 73105 #039-01-2007 L2007 **GS** *012

HEINLEN, Latisha Dawn. ■ 73105 #039-01-2008 *012

HELLER, Wallace Albert. ■ 73120 #306-01-1996 L2002 **P** *020

HELLMAN, Arthur Allan. 8121 NATIONAL AVE, STE 310 73110 #021-01-1978 L1997 **TS** *071 †85

HELTON, Rodney Alan. 3300 NW EXPRESSWAY 73112 #039-01-1992 L1993 **AN** *020 †05

HELTON, Sharla. 11200 N PORTLAND AVE, FL 2 73120 #039-01-1992 L1993 **OBG** *020 †30

HEMRIC, Ned D, Jr. 3435 NW 56TH ST 73112 #051-07-1984 L1998 **GS** *020 †85

HENDERSON, Clifford Lenny. 73120 #039-01-2008 *012

HENDRIX, James Lawrence. 4625 S WESTERN AVE 73109 #039-01-1986 L1987 **DR** *020 †80

HENGLEIN, William G, Jr. 750 NE 13TH ST STE 200 73104 #048-13-2000 L2001 **AN** *020 †05

HENNEBRY, Thomas Anthony. 920 STANTON L YOUNG BLVD, CARDIOLOGY, WP3010 73104 #539-04-1994 L2002 **IC CD** *020 †20

HENNESSEE, John Paul, Jr. 10101 S PENNSYLVANIA AVE, STE A 73159 #039-01-1992 L1993 **P** *020 †75

HENRICKSON, Michael. 940 NE 13TH ST 73104 #041-02-1984 L2005 **PPR PD** *072 †55

HENSLEY, Autumn Lynn. ■ 73112 #039-01-2008 *012

HENSLEY, Kent Curtis. 6516 N OLIE AVE, STE E 73116 #039-01-1973 L1974 **IM OM** *020 †20

HENTHORN, Randall W. 920 STANTON L YOUNG BLVD 73104 #039-01-1976 L1977 **PME AN** *020 †05

HENTHORN, Sharon K. 520 N MERIDIAN AVE 73107 #039-01-1976 L1978 **PME** *071 †18

HENZIE, Gregory Mark. 13301 N MERIDIAN AVE, SW OKLAHOMA MRI #600-A 73120 #005-06-1991 L2000 **DR** *020 †80

HERLIHY, Richard E. 4140 W MEMORIAL RD 73120 #039-01-1979 L1980 **U** *020 †95

HERMAN, Terence Spencer. 825 NE 10TH ST STE 1430, RADIATION ONCOLOGY 73104 #008-02-1972 L2006 **RO** *020 †20,80

HERMANCE, Terry Charles. ■ 73142 #039-01-2004 L2007 **EM** *012

HERNDON, Michael Wayne. 4545 N LINCOLN BLVD, OKLAHOMA HEALTH CARE AUTHO 73105 #039-79-1983, ▲ L1984 **FM** *030

HERRIN, Randall Edward. ■ 73142 #039-01-2003 L2005 **EM** *020

HESS, Richard Jacob. 1111 N DEWEY AVE, MCBRIDE CLINIC INC 73103 #041-13-1963 L1971 **RHU IM** *071 †20

HESTER, Casey Nicole. 940 NE 13TH ST RM 2B2305, CHILDREN'S HOSP. OF OKLAHO 73104 #039-01-1999 L2000 **PD** *020 †55

HESTER, Ralph Bernard, III. 3500 NW 56TH ST 73112 #039-01-1990 L1991 **OPH** *020 †35

HEWETT, Tommy Lloyd. 3000 UNITED FOUNDERS BLVD, STE 234 73112 #039-01-1971 L1972 **PTH HEM** *030 †50

HICKS, Melvin C, Jr. 700 NE 13TH ST 73104 #039-01-1949 L1949 **R** *071 †80

HIEKE, Kenneth Alan. 10914 HEFNER POINT DR #200 73120 #017-20-1978 L1989 **HS GS** *020 †85 ‡

HIGGINS, Heath Dane. 4400 WILL ROGERS PKWY, STE 105 73108 #039-01-2001 L2002 **AN** *020 †05

HIGGINS, Jason Albert. 920 SL YOUNG BLVD, WP 1380 73104 #021-06-2001 L2002 **OSM** *020

HILDEBRAND, Peter Lloyd. 1000 N LINCOLN BLVD 73104 #062-01-1981 L1990 **OPH** *020 †35

HILL, A Dodge, Jr. 3300 NW EXPRESSWAY 73112 #039-01-1966 L1966 **AN** *020 †05

HILL, Caton Leigh. ■ 73103 #039-01-2008 *012

HILL, James Avon. 12028 N MAY AVE 73120 #039-01-1963 L1964 **FM GS** *071 †18

HILL, Terry J. 4401 S WESTERN AVE 73109 #039-79-1992, ▲ L1993 **EM** *020

HILL, Timothy John. 12005 N VIRGINIA AVE 73120 #039-01-1979 L1980 **EM GP** *020 †16

HILL, William Elliott. ■ 73118 #041-01-1948 L1981 **OM** *071 †85

HILLER, Jay Scott. 825 NE 10TH ST, STE 4500 73104 #048-13-1993 L1999 **NM** *020 †28,80

HINES, Peggy Jaeger. 940 NE 13TH ST # 3B700, OUHSC DEPT PEDS 73104 #030-06-1984 L1985 **PD** *074 †55

HINES, Robert Frazer. 6205 N SANTA FE AVE # 200 73118 #048-13-1982 L1983 **ORS** *020 †40

HIRSCH, Jeffrey Gene. 120 N ROBINSON AVE, STE 153W 73102 #039-01-1975 L1976 **FM PTH** *020

HISEY, Brent Neal. 14100 PARKWAY COMMONS DR 73134 #039-01-1982 L1983 **NS** *020 †25

HITT, Daron Cecil. 1001 S DOUGLAS BLVD 73130 #039-01-1995 L1996 **PS** *020 †85

HIXSON, Janice K Tims. 4913 W RENO AVE, OKLAHOMA CITY INDIAN CLINI 73127 #039-01-1994 L1996 **PD** *020 †55

HODGDEN, Jeffrey Dean. 6201 N SANTA FE AVE, STE 2010 73118 #039-01-1993 L1994 **FM** *020 †18 ‡

HOELSCHER, Andrew M. 4001 NW EXPRESSWAY, FASTER CARE 73116 #048-13-1992 L1993 **EM** *020 †16

HOFMANN, Vernon Clifford. 8121 NATIONAL AVE 73110 #286-09-1964 L1984 **AN PME** *020

HOGAN, David E. 26 SW 104TH ST, MORNINGSTAR EMERGENCY PHYS 73139 #028-79-1984, ▲ L1992 **EM** *020 †16

HOLDEN, David Lee. 1110 N LEE AVE, MCBRIDE CLINIC 73103 #048-14-1978 L1984 **ORS** *020 †40

HOLLEN, Charles Warren. 5501 N PORTLAND AVE 73112 #039-01-1985 L1986 **HO IM** *020 †20

HOLLIMAN, John Howard. 501 E I 44 SERVICE RD 73105 #039-01-1975 L1976 **PTH** *040 †50

HOLLINGSWORTH, Alan Berch. 4300 MCAULEY BLVD 73120 #039-01-1975 L1976 **GS ATP** *020 †85

HOLLOMAN, Erin Lynne. 14000 N PORTLAND AVE, STE 101 73134 #039-01-2000 L2004 OPH *100 †35

HOLMAN, Derrick Lane. ■ 73117 #039-01-2008 *012

HOLMQUIST, Sonya Jean. 3000 UNITED FOUNDERS BLVD, STE 234 73112 #056-05-1986 L1988 PTH PCP *020 †50

HOLSAETER, Svein Matti. 1211 N SHARTEL AVE, STE 300 73103 #409-19-1983 L1993 GS *020 †85

HOLTER, Jennifer Lin. 825 NE 10TH ST, STE 4500 73104 #039-01-1999 L2000 HO *020 †20

HOLY, Vladimir. 1000 N LEE AVE 73102 #286-03-1979 L1997 FM GS *020 †18 ‡

HOMSEY, Anna Leigh. ■ 73103 #039-01-2008 *012

HOOD, J Wm. 1211 N SHARTEL AVE 73103 #039-01-1957 L1957 GE IM *071 †20

HOOD, William Edgar. ■ 73120 #039-01-1955 L1955 GYN *071 †30

HOOVER, Lance M. 5350 S WESTERN AVE, STE 419 73109 #048-13-1992 L1993 AN *020 †05

HOPE, Ellen E. 1000 N LEE AVE 73102 #039-01-1979 L1980 N *020 †75

HOPE, Ronald Richmond. 1110 N CLASSEN BLVD # 202 73106 #143-02-1966 L1978 CD IM *020

HOPKINS, Stephen Akira. 900 NE 10TH STREET 73190 #039-01-2005 L2006 FP *012

HOPPER, Stephen Bruce. 3625 N CLASSEN BLVD 73118 #039-01-1983 L1984 P *020 †75

HORANI, Mohammed Samir. 1111 N LEE AVE, STE 343 73103 #875-01-1972 L1975 AN *020 †05

HORN, Patrick Henry. ■ 73120 #039-01-2008 *012

HORST, Trenton Ferrell. 4221 S WESTERN AVE, STE 4000 73109 #039-79-1999, ▲ L2000 GE *012

HORSTMANSHOF, Douglas A. 3433 NW 56TH ST, STE 400 73112 #016-06-1996 L2005 CD *020

HORTON, Donald Dee. 14100 PARKWAY COMMONS DR 73134 #039-01-1983 L1984 NS *020 †25

HORTON, Tyler Joanna. ■ 73114 #039-01-2008 *012

HOUCHEN, Courtney Wayne. 920 SL YOUNG BLVD, WP 1360 73104 #041-13-1990 L2006 GE *020 †20

HOUGH, Jack Van Doren. 3300 NW EXPRESSWAY 73112 #039-01-1943 L1946 OTO *071 †45

HOUK, Larry Wayne. 3330 NW 56TH ST, FL 300 73112 #047-06-1993 L1994 OBG *020 †30

HOUK, Paul Cullison. 4050 W MEMORIAL RD, OKLAHOMA CARDIOVASCULAR 73120 #039-01-1959 L1959 CD IM *020

HOWARD, Rory Lance. 4400 WILL ROGERS PKWY 73108 #305-01-2003 L2005 AN *020

HOWARD, Thos Craddock, III. 9600 BROADWAY EXT 73114 #021-01-1974 L1975 ORS HS *030 †40

HOWARD, Van Hayes. ■ 73118 #039-01-1955 L1955 GS GYN *071

HSU, Chi Wan. 2809 NW 31ST ST 73112 #243-73-1960 L1980 GS *020

HSU, Monica Szeyin. 73142 #039-01-2007 OBG *012

HUA, Marcia Kay. ■ 73162 #039-01-1998 FM *100

HUANG, Yi. 3300 NW EXPRESSWAY, NAZIH ZUHDI TRANSPLANT INS 73112 #243-52-1990 L2000 TTS AS *062

HUARD, David Robert. 825 NE 10TH ST, STE 4500 73104 #054-04-1994 L1998 DR *020 †80

HUBANKS, John Mikel. ■ 73102 #039-01-2008 L2008 *012

HUBBARD, William Andrew. 4300 W MEMORIAL RD 73120 #039-01-1968 L1969 OPH *020 †35

HUDSON, Jane Karen. 3400 NORTHWEST EXPY 73112 #039-01-1994 L1995 ID *020 †20

HUDSON, Robert Jordan. 800 RESEARCH PKWY, STE 100 73104 #004-01-1964 L1970 PD OS *030 †30

HUFF, Deborah Lorraine. 11200 N PORTLAND AVE, FL 2 73120 #039-01-1984 L1985 OBG *020 †30

HUFF, John E. 3400 NW EXPRESSWAY, STE 105 73112 #039-01-1981 L1982 IM PUD *020 †20

HUGHES, Jeremy N. ■ 73120 #039-01-2008 *012

HUGHES, Richard Lee. 13420 N PENNSYLVANIA AVE 73120 #039-01-1954 L1954 GP OS *020

HUGHES, Sonja Johnson. 3330 NW 56TH ST, FL 300 73112 #047-07-1995 L2001 OBG *020 †30

HUGHES, William Lyon. 4205 MCAULEY BLVD, CANCER CARE ASSOCIATES 73120 #039-01-1957 L1957 ON HEM *071 †20

HULSEY, Gregory Hagen. 4400 WILL ROGERS PKWY, STE 105 73108 #039-01-2001 L2002 AN *020

HUME, Christopher Shane. 4401 S WESTERN AVE 73109 #039-79-2003, ▲ L2004 *020

HUMMEL, J Chris. 4205 MCAULEY BLVD, STE 401 73120 #039-01-1993 L1995 OPH *020 †35

HUMMEL, Robert Archie. 4205 MCAULEY BLVD 73120 #020-02-1960 L1969 OPH *071 †35

HUMPHREY, Mary Pridgen. 921 NE 13TH ST, DEPT OF VETERANS AFFAIRS M 73104 #048-04-1997 L2006 RHU IM *050 †20

HUNNEWELL, Jennie Oliver. 12330 SAINT ANDREWS DR 73120 #012-01-1992 L1997 OPH *020 †35

HUNTER, John R. 3433 NW 56TH ST 73112 #035-06-1971 L1981 ORS *020 †40

HUNTER, Paul David. 608 NW 9TH ST, STE 5100 73102 #020-12-1976 L1977 OTO FPS *020 †45

HUSAIN, Sanam. 73112 #704-20-2000 L2008 PTH *020

HUSSAIN, Abid. C/O ROBIN J ELWOOD MD, DEPT ANESTHESIOLOGY 73152 #919-03-1983 L1994 AN *020

HUSSEIN, Khader Khalid. 3300 NW EXPRESSWAY 73112 #605-01-1967 L1974 ON HEM *020 †20

HUYCKE, Edward James. ■ 73120 #019-02-1953 L1998 IM NM *071 †28,20

HUYCKE, Mark Martin. 921 NE 13TH ST 73104 #019-02-1982 L1983 ID IM *050 †20

HYDE, Homer Clark. 4140 W MEMORIAL RD 73120 #039-01-1966 L1967 U *020 †95

HYND, Robert Fryer. 9600 BROADWAY EXT 73114 #025-07-1977 L1986 RHU *020 †20

IDACHABA, Ojoru Andrea. 946 NE 13TH ST RM 3409-N, CHILDREN'S HOSPITAL 73104 #690-01-2000 L2005 PD *100 †55

IMES, Norman Kerr, Jr. 3555 NW 58TH ST, STE 800 73112 #039-01-1970 L1971 PUD IM *020 †20

IMRAN, Farida. 1000 N LEE AVE 73102 #704-04-1991 L2006 FM *100

INGELS, Marianne. 3300 NW EXPRESSWAY 73112 #028-02-1994 L2000 EM *020 †16

IRICANIN, Tomislav. 921 NE 13TH ST 116 73104 #957-02-1960 L1983 P *071

IRWIN, Derek Austin. 3000 UNITED FOUNDERS BLVD, STE 234 73112 #039-01-1995 L1996 PTH *020 †50

IRWIN, Megan Langdon. ■ 73105 #030-05-2007 L2007 OBG *012

JABBOUR, Nicolas. 3300 NW EXPRESSWAY 100-34, NAZI ZUHDI TRANSPLANT INST 73112 #165-01-1984 L2006 GS *020 †85

JACKMAN, Warren Maurice. 1200 EVERETT DR 6E103, CARDIAC ARRHYTHMIA RESEARC 73104 #011-03-1976 L1981 CD *050 †20

JACKSON, Allene B. 900 NE 10TH ST, OU FAMILY MEDICINE CENTER 73104 #026-04-1973 L1983 FM *020 †18

JACKSON, Anthony Dwayne. 1140 SW 44TH ST 73109 #039-01-1993 L1997 OBG *020 †30

JACKSON, David Wayne. 1000 N LINCOLN BLVD 73104 #034-01-1997 L2002 OPH *020 †35

JACKSON, Ingrid B. 5720 W MEMORIAL RD 73142 #039-01-1985 L1986 FM *020 †18

JACKSON, Jimmie Keith. 1211 N SHARTEL AVE, STE 300 73103 #039-01-1965 L1965 GS *020 †18,85

JACKSON, Michael Ray. 2901 N CLASSEN BLVD, STE 100 73106 #019-02-1993 L1996 FM *030 †18

JACKSON, Rhett Lawrence. 825 NE 10TH ST, STE 4500 73104 #039-01-1989 L1990 IM *020 †20

JACOBS, Bobby Reed. 6424 N PORTLAND AVE 73116 #039-01-1989 L1990 IM *020 †20

JACOBS, Shelly Venters. ■ 73111 #039-01-1990 L1992 GP *071

JACOCKS, Mac Alexander. 920 SL YOUNG RM WP2140, OUHSC-DEPARTMENT OF SURGER 73104 #039-01-1977 L1978 VS GS *020 †85

JAMAL, Jawaid A. 3366 NORTHWEST EXPY 73112 #704-02-1991 L2005 IM *020 †20

JAMES, Judith Ann. 825 NE 10TH ST, STE 4500 73104 #039-01-1994 L1996 RHU *020 †20

JAMES, Oscar Dean. ■ 73101 #047-07-1999 L2006 HO *020 †20

JANBAY, Nasser. 4301 S WESTERN AVE, CANCER CARE ASSOCIATES 73109 #875-01-1984 L2006 HO *020 †20

JANBEY, Ehsan Mahmoud. 920 STANTON L YONG BLVD 20, OUHSC-INTERNAL MEDICINE DE 73104 #875-01-1991 L2000 PCC *020 †20

JANSEN, Jeremiah Aaron. 3300 NW EXPRESSWAY 73112 #030-05-2006 L2007 DR *012

JANSSEN, Thomas P. 1111 N DEWEY AVE, BONE & JOINT HOSPITAL 73103 #039-01-1979 L1980 ORS FM *020 †18,40

JANZEN, Ronald James. 4200 W MEMORIAL RD STE 212 73120 #036-05-1973 L1975 GE IM *071 †20

JARRELL, Howard Ray, III. 3000 UNITED FOUNDERS BLVD, STE 221 73112 #039-01-1977 L1978 N PMM *020 †75

JARVIS, James Nelson. 940 NE 13TH ST 2B2415, OUHSC MEDICAL CENTER 73104 #050-02-1979 L1998 PPR PD *050 †55

JAVED, Muhammad Zafar. 921 NE 13TH ST 11-9, OUHSC/VAMC DEPT OF GERIATR 73104 #704-02-1986 L2000 IM *020 †20

JAY, George Robert. 1110 N LEE AVE 73103 #039-01-1962 L1962 ORS *020 †40

JAYNE, E Howard. 701 NE 10TH ST, OKLAHOMA CITY CLINIC 73104 #039-01-1957 L1958 R *072 †80

JAZZAR, Ahmad Sayaf. 4200 W MEMORIAL RD STE 501 73120 #875-02-1987 L1993 GE IM *020 †20

JENKINS, Harvey C, Jr. 8603 S WESTERN AVE 73139 #036-07-1994 L2000 ORS *020

JENNINGS, George H. 5501 N PORTLAND AVE 73112 #039-01-1952 L1952 OBG *071 †30

JETT, Mason Peck. 3330 NW 56TH ST 73112 #023-07-1973 L1975 GS *020 †85

JOHN, Andrew C. 1140 NW 63RD ST STE 403 73116 #035-45-1977 L1978 OM *062 †16

JOHN, Jijo. ■ 73135 #495-11-1996 L2004 PCC *012 †20

JOHNSON, Bradley Jay. ■ 73132 #039-01-2006 L2006 IM *012

JOHNSON, Brian Douglas. 6700 S MACARTHUR BLVD, CAMI , RM 308 73169 #038-40-1986 L1989 FM *062 †18

JOHNSON, Darlene Guin. 9220 S PENNSYLVANIA AVE, STE B 73159 #048-15-1980 L1988 FM *020 ‡

JOHNSON, David Andrew. 3500 NW 56TH ST STE 100 73112 #039-01-2006 L2007 FP *012

JOHNSON, Donna A. 8100 S WALKER AVE STE 2 73139 #038-40-1987 L1993 PD *020 †55

JOHNSON, Gary Alan. P.O. BOX 26901 WP2470, DEPT OF OB/GYN 73190 #019-02-1986 L1993 GO OBG *020 †30

JOHNSON, James Calvin. 6205 N SANTA FE AVE 73118 #039-01-1984 L1985 ORS *020 †40

JOHNSON, Jeremy Jon. ■ 73135 #039-01-2005 *020

JOHNSON, Kurt Norman. ■ 73112 #039-01-1999 L2001 *020

JOHNSON, Mark Copeland. 4300 W MEMORIAL RD 73120 #039-01-1974 L1975 IM MDM *030 †20

JOHNSON, Marla Marie. 13313 N MERIDIAN AVE, STE D3 73120 #039-01-1999 *100

JOHNSON, Paul Davis. 1200 EVERETT DR 73104 #039-01-1983 L1984 OM ADM *020 †18

JOHNSON, Scott Howard. 1111 N LEE AVE, STE 236 73103 #039-01-1996 L2000 AN *020

JOHNSTON, Gregory Wayne. 4200 W MEMORIAL RD, STE 703 73120 #048-02-1981 L1982 AN EM *020 †05,16

JOHNSTON, James M, III. 1110 N CLASSEN BLVD # 300 73106 #039-01-1970 L1971 IM END *020 †20

JOHNSTON, Jay Carter. 4200 W MEMORIAL RD STE 101 73120 #039-01-1966 L1966 OPH *020 †35

JOLLY, Valerie Nicole. 616 NW 52ND ST 73118 #039-01-2005 L2007 GS *012

JONES, Daniel Joseph. 8100 S WALKER AVE, SW ORTHO SPEC 73139 #054-04-1995 L2001 ORS *020

JONES, Edward Duane. 5701 N PORTLAND AVE # 105 73112 #039-01-1991 L1992 OPH *020 †35

JONES, Heather Dawn. 920 STANTON L YOUNG BLVD, WP 2410 73104 #039-01-2002 L2003 OBG *020

JONES, John Frederick. 5100 N BROOKLINE AVE, STE 700 73112 #041-01-1970 L1978 AN PMM *020 †05 ‡

JONES, Johnny H, Jr. 5600 N PORTLAND AVE 73112 #039-01-1967 L1968 OPH *020 †35

JONES, Johnny Lester. ■ 73120 #039-01-1978 L1979 EM PUD *020

JONES, Justin Michael. 6305 WATERFORD BLVD # 115 73118 #039-01-2001 L2002 PS *020 †65

JONES, Kellie Renee. 1122 NE 13TH ST, BLDG ORI 236 73117 #039-01-1997 L1998 PCC *020 †55,20

JONES, Kelly Elizabeth. 825 NE 10TH ST, STE 2500 73104 #039-01-2001 L2002 R *020 †80

JONES, Richard Francis. ■ 73127 #003-01-1975 L1978 OM *071 †70

JONES, Sam P. 8301 S WALKER AVE, STE 101 73139 #021-06-1999 L2002 *020

JONES, Samuel Nathan Levi. 3000 UNITED FOUNDERS BLVD, STE 234 73112 #020-12-1989 L1994 PTH *020 †50

JONES, William D. 707 NW 13TH ST 73103 #043-01-1992 L1994 OM PHP *020

JOSEPH, Pushpa. 4205 MCAULEY BLVD STE 4 73120 #495-44-1990 L2005 AN PTH *020 †05

JUDKIEWICZ, Aron Moses. 236 NW 62ND ST, IMAGING 73118 #005-06-1988 L2000 R *020 †80

JUENGEL, Randal Carl. 4401 S WESTERN AVE, PATHOLOGY 73109 #039-05-1987 L1991 PTH *020 †50 ‡

KACZMAREK, Lawrence Kent. 10101 S PENNSYLVANIA AVE, STE A 73159 #030-05-1977 L1979 P *020

KAHIRIMBANYI, Peresi Kama. 608 NW 9TH ST STE 1000 73102 #166-06-2006 L2008 *012

KAKISH, William Randall. 4200 W MEMORIAL RD, STE 901 73120 #039-01-1988 L1989 GE *020 †20 ‡

KALLENBERGER, David Alan. 3433 NW 56TH ST STE 210 73112 #039-01-1975 L1976 OBG *020 †30

KALRA, Praveen. 920 STANTON L YONG BLVD 25, OU HEALTH SCIENCE CENTER 73104 #495-41-1993 L2005 AN *020

KALYANAM, Nalini. 940 STANTON L YOUNG BLVD 73104 #495-21-2003 L2006 PD *012

KALYANARAMAN, Venkata. 921 STANTON L YONG BLVD, DEPT OF ENDOCRINLGY WP1345 73104 #495-59-1992 L1997 END *012 †20

■ = Address Information Privacy Protected

KAMALI, Ali Asghar. 1044 SW 44TH ST STE 620 73109 #517-01-1982 L1997 *020

KAMATH, Radhakrishna M. 1044 SW 44TH ST, STE 620 73109 #496-38-1966 L1976 ORS *071 †40

KAMMERLOCHER, Paul Alan. 9600 BROADWAY EXT 73114 #039-01-1989 L1990 OFA *020 †40 ‡

KAMUGISHA, Laura. 1000 N LEE AVE, ST ANTHONY HOSP 73102 #905-02-2001 L2007 FP *012

KANA'A, Mohamed Farouk. 13301 N MERIDIAN AVE, STE 501 73120 #875-01-1972 L1975 ON IM *020 †20

KANALY, Paul Jos. 3433 NW 56TH ST, STE 670 73112 #039-01-1974 L1975 TS VS *020 †85,90

KANEASTER, Shannon Kyle. 940 NE 13TH ST 73104 #021-01-2002 L2003 OTO *100 †55

KAPLAN, Douglas Warren. 4120 W MEMORIAL RD, STE 204 73120 #016-42-1988 L1994 N *020 †75

KAPUR, Manuj. 608 STANTON L YOUNG BLVD 73104 #048-16-2003 L2007 OPH *100

KARAM, Naji E. 608 NW 9TH ST STE 6 73102 #605-01-1991 L1996 CD *020 †20

KARASEK, David James. 1111 N LEE AVE, STE 334 73103 #039-01-1975 L1976 IM PM *020 †20

KARIM, Jana Turner. ■ 73120 #028-46-1986 L1987 OBG *071 †30

KASTENS, Donald J. 921 NE 13TH ST 73104 #039-01-1981 L1982 GE IM *020 †20

KATARI, Vikram. 1200 EVERETT DR 6E-103, CARI INSTITUTE 73104 #495-50-1997 L2006 ICE CD *100 †20

KAUFMAN, Chris. 920 STANTON L YOUNG BLVD, WP 2250 73104 #039-01-1967 L1970 NEP IM *040 †20

KAUL, Kalpna. 1601 SW 89TH ST, STE D300 73159 #495-51-1965 L1978 PD *020 †55

KEEFER, Mike J. 4205 MCAULEY BLVD STE 3 73120 #039-01-1981 L1982 ON HEM *020 †20

KEENAN, John Paul. 4545 N LINCOLN BLVD, STE 124 73105 #056-06-1968 L1998 IM OPH *030 †35

KEENER, Ross Stanford. 4205 MCAULEY BLVD STE 46 73120 #039-01-1997 L2002 GE *020 †20

KEIM, Robert John. ■ 73131 #005-06-1961 L1975 NO *071 †45

KELAMIS, Joseph Alexander. ■ 73104 #039-01-2008 L012

KELLER, Daniel Floyd. 1111 N LEE AVE STE 100 73103 #028-02-1958 L1964 CLP ATP *072 †50

KELLEY, Sean Francis. 9204 N MAY AVE 73120 #039-01-1986 L1987 AN *020 †05

KELLY, J Michael. 3301 NW 63RD ST 73116 #025-01-1969 L1970 FM OS *020 †18

KELLY, John Michael. 3301 NW 63RD ST 73116 #039-01-1963 L1975 PS *020 †85,65

KELLY, Kevin. 4221 S WESTERN AVE 73109 #016-11-1998 L2004 NS GS *020

KELLY, Stephen Blake. 13908 QUAILBROOK DR 73134 #039-01-1998 L1999 FM *020 †18

KEM, David Chas. 927 NE 13TH ST, VAMC ROOM 3E-108 73104 #035-01-1963 L1975 END IM *030 †20

KENNEDY, Diana L. 4205 MCAULEY BLVD, STE 420 73120 #039-01-1981 L1982 END IM *020 †20

KENNEDYE, James Raymond. 4401 S WESTERN AVE 73109 #039-01-1998 L2002 EM *020

KERN, Wm Frederick, III. 920 STANTON L YOUNG BLVD 73104 #035-08-1979 L1993 PTH IM *020 †20,50

KERNS, Christopher L. 4050 W MEMORIAL RD, OKLAHOMA CARDIOVASCULAR 73120 #039-01-1979 L1980 CD IC *020 †20 ‡

KESSERWANE, Radwane Abdul. 921 NE 13TH ST, VA MEDICAL CENTER 73104 #605-03-1992 L2003 CD *012

KESSLER, Holly Sue. 940 NE 13TH ST 73104 #016-06-1997 L2005 PD *020 †55

KEY, Andrea Lynn. 4140 W MEMORIAL RD, STE 413 73120 #039-01-1985 L1986 PD *020 †55

KHAFIF, Avraham Hefetz. 920 STANTON L YOUNG BLVD, OUHSC- DEPT OF OTOLARYNGOL 73104 #550-02-1989 *020

KHAIMI, Mahmoud Ahmad. 608 STANTON L YOUNG BLVD, HENRY FORD HOSPITAL 73104 #025-07-2002 L2006 OPH *020

KHALIFA, Mahmoud A. 2915 UNITED FOUNDERS BLVD 73112 #915-04-1978 L1991 ATP *020 †50

KHAN, Agha Khurshid U Z. 4221 S WESTERN AVE, OKLAHOMA CARDIOVASCULAR 73109 #704-01-1982 L2006 CD IM *020 †20

KHAN, Azhar Ullah. 3366 NW EXPRESSWAY, BLDG D 73112 #704-05-1982 L1996 IM PCC *020 †20

KHAN, Shahnawaz Ahmed. 900 NE 10TH ST 73104 #305-01-2001 L2004 FM *020 †18

KHAN, Tehseen. 711 SL YOUNG BLVD STE 215 73104 #495-51-1989 L2002 CN N *020 †75

KHANNA, Sudhir Kumar. 3366 NW EXPRESSWAY, KIDNEY SPECIALISTS OF 73112 #495-12-1977 L1992 NEP IM *020 †20

KHANNA, Veena. 940 NE 13TH ST 73104 #495-12-1977 L1992 PD *020 †55

KHASTGIR, Terrance. 3433 NW 56TH ST, STE 400 73112 #495-45-1982 L1992 CD *020 †20

KHICHI, Mahmood Hussain. 3300 NW EXPRESSWAY 73112 #704-02-1990 L1993 CCP *020 †55

KHOURY, Gregory Chas. 3240 W BRITTON RD STE 102 73120 #048-13-1980 L1981 P GP *020 †75

KIDON, Mona I. ■ 73162 #550-03-1987 L1993 PD *020 †55

KIEHN, Michael Edwin. 3301 NW 50TH ST 73112 #039-01-1997 L2003 OSM *020 †40 ‡

KILE, Amber Marie. ■ 73135 #048-15-2007 L2007 OTO *012

KILGORE, Brandon Heath. P O BOX 26901, 920 S L YOUNG BLVD, WP 214 73190 #035-45-2003 L2005 GS *012

KILLEBREW, Larry K. 12316 N MAY AVE, # 145 73120 #039-01-1969 L1969 DR *062 †20

KINASEWITZ, Gary Theodore. 825 NE 10TH ST, STE 2500 73104 #025-07-1973 L1988 PUD CCM *050 †20

KINCHELOE, Lawrence Reed. 3400 NW EXPRESSWAY, STE 500 73112 #039-01-1983 L1987 OBG *020 †30

KINDLEY, Karen A. 4200 W MEMORIAL RD STE 901 73120 #048-02-1988 L1989 GE *020 †20

KING, Jeanne Ann Freeman. 711 STANTON L YOUNG BLVD, STE 215 73104 #039-01-1978 L1979 N *020 †75 ‡

KING, Robert W, Sr. ■ 73116 #039-01-1950 L1950 OPH *071 †35

KINGSLEY, Ronald Mark. 608 STANTON L YOUNG BLVD 73104 #010-02-1975 L1983 OPH OS *020 †35

KINSINGER, John Wm. 11912 OLD MILL RD 73131 #039-01-1988 L1989 AN *020 †05

KIPGEN, Wynter Williams. 12324 SAINT ANDREWS DR 73120 #039-01-1992 L1993 END *020 †20

KIPPERMAN, Robert Michael. 4050 W MEMORIAL RD 73120 #305-01-1981 L1995 CD *020 †20

KIRCHHOFF, Kerri Jennelle. 3433 NW 56TH ST, STE C10 73112 #028-46-1993 L1994 DR *020 †80

KIRK, James L, Jr. 4300 W MEMORIAL RD 73120 #039-01-1982 L1983 ID IM *020 †20

KIRKPATRICK, Angelia C. 825 NE 10TH ST, STE 2500 73104 #039-01-2000 L2002 IM *020 †20

KISTLER, Damion L. 4300 W MEMORIAL RD, MERCY HEALTH CTR-LAB 73104 #051-04-1977 L1982 PTH *020 †50

KLAASSEN, Perry Arvin. 3815 N SANTA FE AVE # 122 73118 #019-02-1966 L1973 GPM GP *030 †70 ‡

KLOER, Hans-Ulrich B. 825 NE 13TH ST 73104 #407-23-1968 L1980 OS GE *050

KNEELAND, Ned Camden. 4812 N MILLER AVE 73112 #039-01-2002 L2006 AN *020

KNIFE CHIEF, Sarah Cortne. ■ 73112 #039-01-2005 L2007 ORS *012

KNOTTS, Christopher Dale. ■ 73135 #034-01-2007 L2007 PS *012

KNUDTSON, Eric James. 825 NE 10TH ST, STE 4500 73104 #019-02-1996 L2003 OBG *020 †30

KNUTSON, Nickey Glenn. 8100 S WALKER AVE, STE 230 73139 #039-01-1974 L1975 GE ID *020

KNUTSON, Zakary Adam. 920 SL YOUNG BLVD, WP 1380 73104 #039-01-2005 L2006 ORS *012

KOCHEVAR, Andrew James. 3300 NW EXPRESSWAY STE 70, OU HAND SURGERY, PHYSICIAN 73112 #039-01-2002 L2007 HSO *012

KOHLI, Vivek. 3300 NW EXPRESSWAY, DEPARTMENT 100-3443 73112 #495-36-1987 L2006 GS *020

KOONTZ, John Allen. 10021 S WESTERN AVE 73139 #649-14-1984 L1988 FM *020 †18

KOPKE, Richard Dana. 3400 NW 56TH ST 73112 #054-04-1981 L2004 NO HNS *020 †45

KORBER, David Eugene. 5320 N PORTLAND AVE, KORBER, DAVID E MD 73112 #019-02-1993 L1997 OPH *020 †35

KORNEGAY, Chase Ryan. ■ 73107 #039-01-2005 L2006 AN *012

KOSTIUK, Stefan Andre. ■ 73120 #039-01-1980 L1981 FPG FM *075 †16,18

KOWALSKI, Anthony Marion. 3601 N CLASSEN BLVD STE 10 73118 #056-06-1956 L1975 P PYA *020 †75

KOWALSKI, Mark F. 4140 W MEMORIAL RD, STE 308 73120 #039-01-1981 L1982 ORS OSM *020 †40

KRAFT, David Irving. 825 NE 10TH ST, STE 4500 73104 #035-09-1942 L1956 CD IM *071 †20

KRAUSE, Steven Gregory. 4140 W MEMORIAL RD, STE 413 73120 #039-01-1977 L1978 PD *020 †55

KRAVITZ, Herbert Melvin. 3300 NW EXPRESSWAY 73112 #035-09-1955 L1961 PS *071 †65 ‡

KREMPL, Greg Allen. 825 NE 10TH ST, STE 4500 73104 #039-01-1992 L1995 OTO HNS *020 †45

KRISHNA, Ravu Murali. 5100 N BROOKLINE AVE FL 90 73112 #495-11-1971 L1976 P *020 †75 ‡

KRISHNAN, Sowmya. 940 NE 13TH ST # 2B 73104 #495-45-1996 L2004 PDE *012 †55

KRODEL, Julie Ann. 940 NE 13TH ST RM 1B1307, CHILDREN'S HOSPITAL 73104 #039-01-1998 L1999 PD *040 †55

KROPP, Bradley Peter. 920 STANTON L YOUNG BLVD, STE WP3150 73104 #038-43-1988 L1996 U *020 †95

KUHN, John Richard. 1024 SW 44TH ST 73109 #019-02-1980 L1981 OTO *020 †45

KULVATUNYOU, Narong. 920 SL YOUNG BLVD SURG DPT 73194 #001-02-1994 L2005 TRS CCS *020 †85

KUMAR, Francis C. 920 STANTON L YOUNG BLVD 73104 #495-58-1980 L1984 AN CD *020

KUMAR, Rajesh. 700 NE 13TH ST 73104 #039-01-2000 L2002 IM *020 †20

KUMAR, Satish. 825 NE 10TH ST, STE 4300 73104 #495-27-1978 L1985 IM NEP *020 †20

KUNDI, Samiullah Khan. ■ 73114 #704-01-2002 L2007 N *012

KURDGELASHVILI, George. 921 NE 13TH ST 111C 73104 #913-23-1996 L2002 ID *100 †20

KURELLA, Ravinder Reddy. 921 NE 13TH ST, VA MEDICAL CENTER 73104 #496-27-1993 L2003 IM *020

KURKJIAN, Carla D. 921 STANTON L YOUNG BLVD, WP2040 73104 #039-01-2001 L2002 HO *020

KURKJIAN, Hrair Toros. 4200 W MEMORIAL RD, STE 713 73120 #605-01-1970 L1975 U *020 †95

KUTNER, Michael Stewart. 3300 NW EXPRESSWAY 73112 #021-01-1994 L1998 AN *020 †05

KWAN, Chun Lim. 1111 N LEE AVE, STE 236 73103 #039-01-1993 L1994 AN *020 †05

KYLES, Michael Kederick. 1111 N LEE AVE, STE 334 73103 #051-04-1975 L2004 ORS OSS *020 †40

LAFLEUR, Laci Ann. ■ 73118 #021-05-2004 L2005 D *012

LAGOS, Jorge Coloma. 2620 NW EXPRESSWAY, STE C 73112 #231-01-1958 L1969 CHN *020 †55

LALANI, Neelofar. ■ 73112 #704-08-1988 P *100

LAM, David Wong. ■ 73120 #039-01-2007 L2007 IM *012

LAM, Kristin Marie. ■ 73120 #039-01-2007 L2007 PD *012

LAMPLEY, Vicki Therese. 825 NE 10TH ST, STE 4500 73104 #039-01-1990 L1991 IMG IM *020 †20

LAMPRICH, Bradley Keith. ■ 73118 #039-01-2007 L2007 IM *012

LANCASTER, Andrew Darien. 920 SL YOUNG BLVD, WP 1345 73104 #039-01-2003 L2005 END *012 †20

LANDRUM, Lisa Michelle. WP 2410, 920 STANTON L YOUNG 73190 #039-01-2002 L2003 OBG *100

LANTIER, Steven Jude. 1111 N DEWEY AVE 73103 #021-05-1986 L1992 AN *020 †05

LAQUER, Ulric J. ■ 73132 #051-04-1949 L1951 FM *071 †18

LARSON, Gary L. 4401 S WESTERN AVE 73109 #039-01-1981 L1982 RO *020 †80

LASES, Juan. 3535 NW 58TH ST, STE 23 73112 #649-01-1970 L1976 PD *020

LASITER, Nathan David. 4400 WILL ROGERS PKWY, STE 105 73108 #039-01-2002 L2003 AN *020 †05

LAST, Alfred. 3435 NW 56TH ST, STE 906 73112 #021-01-1962 L1966 D DMP *020 †15

LATIF, Faisal. 940 STANTON L YOUNG BLVD 73104 #704-01-2000 L2005 CD *012 †20

LAU, Mark Timothy. 3300 NW EXPRESSWAY, 5TH FL 73112 #041-02-1989 L1994 AN *020 †05 ‡

LAU, Yuk Kai. 825 NE 10TH ST, STE 4500 73104 #041-01-1971 L1990 NEP IM *020 †20

LAUGHLIN, Lycurgus Orrin. 4200 W MEMORIAL RD, MERCY TOWER, SUITE 805 73120 #039-01-1959 L1959 IM NEP *071

LAW, George Stanford. 230 N MIDWEST BLVD 73110 #047-05-1990 L2004 U GS *020 †95

LAWLER, Frank H. 900 NE 10TH ST, OUHSC-DEPT OF FAMILY MEDIC 73104 #005-12-1981 L1989 FM *020 †18

LAWRENCE, Forrest C, II. 12318 SAINT ANDREWS DR 73120 #039-01-1980 L1981 OPH *020 †35

LAWTON, Sherman Bruce. 3433 NW 56TH ST STE 600 73112 #039-01-1968 L1969 N *020 †75

LAYTON-BOWLBY, L. 73106 #039-01-1976 L1977 P PTH *020 †50

LAZARO, Svetlana Claraval. 900 NE 10TH ST, OU FAMILY MEDICINE CLINIC 73104 #039-01-2005 L2007 FP *012

LAZZARA, Ralph. 800 NE 13TH ST, DEPT MEDICINE OKLA UNIV 73104 #021-01-1959 L1978 CD IM *050 †20

LAZZARA, Ralph Scott. 825 NE 10TH ST, STE 2500 73104 #025-07-1994 L1996 IM *020 †20

LE, Paul Quoc. 1111 N LEE AVE, STE 343 73103 #039-01-1996 L1997 AN *020 †05

LE, Tuan Alex. 2825 NW 23RD ST 73107 #039-01-1997 L1998 EM *020

LEBLANC, Helen Denise. 6201 N SANTA FE AVE, STE 2020 73118 #021-05-1986 L1987 FM *020 †18

LEDOUX, Joy Lynn. 10908 N WESTERN AVE 73114 #039-01-1991 L1992 IM PD *020 †55

LEE, Jwu Hsiung. ■ 73142 #244-02-1967 L1974 IM GE *071 †20

LEE, Kong Wing. 1119 NW 25TH ST 73106 #039-01-2002 L2003 FM *020 †18

LEE, Shawn Keith. 4140 W MEMORIAL RD, STE 208 73120 #039-01-1995 L1996 PCC *020 †20

LEE, Stephen Paul. 1000 N LEE AVE 73102 #039-01-1982 L1983 **DR** *020 †80

LEE, Steven Yong Ming. 3366 NW EXPRESSWAY, STE 140 73112 #039-01-1969 L1989 **CRS GS** *071 †10,85

LEECH, Richard Wiley. U OF OK HLTH SCI CTR 73190 #054-04-1961 L1985 **PTH** *071 †50 ‡

LEES, Jason Spence. WP 2140, 920 STANTON L YOUNG BLVD 73190 #039-01-1998 L1999 **GS TRS** *040 †85

LEES, Julie Ann. 940 NE 13TH ST # 1306, OUHSC GENERAL PEDIATRICS 73104 #039-01-2000 L2001 **PD** *020 †55

LEGG-JACK, Tamunosisi Eli. 921 NE 13TH ST, AMBULATORY CARE DEPARTMENT 73104 #690-12-1986 L2003 **IM** *020 †20

LEHMAN, Thomas Paul. 825 NE 10TH ST, STE 1300 73104 #039-01-1996 L1997 **HS** *020 †40

LEHR, Robert Blaine. 5701 N PORTLAND AVE # 310 73112 #039-01-1990 L1991 **D** *020 †15

LEI, William D. 8325 NW EXPRESSWAY 73162 #048-02-1995 L1996 **FM** *020 †18

LEITCH, Steven Michael. 4401 S WESTERN AVE STE 20 73109 #028-46-1986 L2002 **IM** *020 †20

LENAERTS, Marc Eugene. 711 STANTON L YONG BLVD #2, STE 215 73104 #165-03-1989 L1999 **N** *020 †75

LENSGRAF, S Jay. 2816 NW 57TH ST STE 104 73112 #039-01-1985 L1986 **P** *020 †75

LEONARD, Joe Carl. 940 NE 13TH ST 73104 #039-01-1966 L1966 **PDR NM** *071 †80,28 ‡

LEONARD, Robert Estel, II. 608 STANTON L YOUNG BLVD 73104 #039-01-1992 L2000 **OPH** *020 †35 ‡

LEPINSKE, Paul James. ■ 73156 #305-01-1997 **APM** *020

LERA, Thomas Alfred, Jr. 940 NE 13TH ST 73104 #048-02-1981 L1983 **PD PEM** *075

LESTER, Boyd Kenneth. 4027 N CLASSEN BLVD 73118 #039-01-1954 L1963 **P** *020

LETTON, Robert Warren, Jr. 1200 EVERETT DR, STE 2320 73104 #020-12-1990 L1997 **PDS** *020 †85

LEUSZLER, Richard W. 4200 W MEMORIAL RD, STE 606 73120 #039-01-1977 L1978 **OTO OS** *020 †45 ‡

LEVERIDGE, Charles A. 4140 W MEMORIAL RD, STE 413 73120 #039-01-1980 L1981 **PD** *020 †55

LEVIN, David Chas. 825 NE 10TH ST, STE 2500 73104 #038-06-1970 L1975 **PUD IM** *040 †20

LEVINE, Norman Steven. 1211 N SHARTEL AVE, STE 905 73103 #024-01-1966 L1977 **PS HS** *020 †85,65

LEVINE, Stephen Jacob. ■ 73190 #007-02-1975 L1977 **BBK** *030 †50

LEVY, Aimee Dawn. 920 STANTON L YOUNG BLVD.,, OUHSC-SURGERY WILLIAMS PAV 73190 #039-01-2005 L2007 **GS** *012

LEWIS, Jami Kristina. 940 NE 13TH ST RM 3N-3409, CHILDREN'S HOSPITAL OF OKL 73104 #039-01-2004 L2005 **NPM** *012 †55

LEWIS, Jonkeeta Alice. 1919 E MEMORIAL RD, MERCY HEALTH EDMOND MEMORI 73131 #039-01-2002 L2006 **FM** *100 †18

LEWIS, Kori Marie. 5720 W MEMORIAL RD 73142 #039-01-2003 L2004 **FM** *020 †18

LI, Shi-Feng. 3300 NW EXPRESSWAY 73112 #242-17-1984 L1996 **TTS GS** *020

LI, Yanhua. 5100 N BROOKLINE AVE, FL 900 73112 #243-21-1990 L2003 **P CHP** *020 †75 ‡

LIGHTFOOT, Stanley A. 921 NE 13TH ST 73104 #048-12-1963 L1992 **PCP ATP** *040 †50

LIM, Jonea. 940 STANTON L YOUNG BLVD 73104 #748-01-2002 L2007 **IM** *012

LIND, Stuart E. 920 STANTON L YOUNG BLVD, WP-2020 73104 #035-19-1976 L2001 **BBK** *100 †20

LINDEN, David E. 1608 NW EXPRESSWAY, LINDEN & ASSOCIATES, PC 73118 #039-01-1982 L1983 **P PYG** *020 †20

LINDENAU, Melissa Andrews. 1200 EVERETT DR, 10 FL EAST/CHEIF RES OFF 73104 #039-01-2004 L2006 **PD** *020 †55

LINDLEY, Todd Edward. 4050 W MEMORIAL RD, OKLAHOMA CARDIOVASCULAR 73120 #039-01-1995 L1997 **CD** *020 †20

LINDSEY, Ethan David. 5100 N BROOKLINE AVE, FL 900 73112 #039-01-1987 L1988 **CHP P** *020 †75

LINDSEY, Phillip Harris. 36 W MEMORIAL RD STE C3, CONCENTRA MEDICAL CENTER 73114 #039-01-1980 L1981 **OM EM** *020 ‡

LIPE, Clark Charlesworth. 1211 N SHARTEL AVE, STE 700 73103 #039-01-1966 L1967 **DR** *020 †80

LIPE, Mark Gregory. 4300 W MEMORIAL RD 73120 #039-01-1987 L1988 **EM** *020 †18

LIPRIE, Jon Christopher. 6957 NW EXPRESSWAY, STE 301 73132 #021-06-1991 L1992 **IM** *020 †20

LISLE, Achilles C, Jr. 4120 W MEMORIAL RD, STE 300 73120 #039-01-1943 L1945 **NS** *072 †25

LITCHFIELD, Lonnie W. 1907 N BROADWAY AVE STE A 73103 #039-01-1994 L1995 **AN** *020 †05

LITTLE, James Hoyt. 1240 SW 44TH ST 73109 #039-01-1962 L1962 **OPH** *071

LITTLE, Jesse Saml. ■ 73157 #039-01-1959 L1959 **R** *071 †80

LITTLE, Jesse Saml, Jr. 11000 HEFNER POINTE DR 73120 #028-02-1987 L1995 **U** *020 †95

LITTLE, Katherine Sue. 3366 NW EXPRESSWAY, STE 380 73112 #039-01-1984 L1985 **PUD CCM** *020 †20

LITTLE, Kendall Jay. 26 SW 104TH ST 73139 #039-01-2000 L2003 **EM** *020 †16 ‡

LIU, Cheng Zheng. 920 STANTON L YOUNG BLVD 73104 #243-65-1982 L2001 *020 †50

LJUNGGREN, Chandra Kay. ■ 73112 #030-05-2007 L2007 **OBG** *012

LO, Patrick Punchuk. 1506 S AGNEW AVE 73108 #039-79-1982, ▲ L1983 **FM** *020

LOCK, Thomas Morrison. 825 NE 10TH ST, STE 4500 73104 #056-05-1979 L2003 **PD** *020 †55

LOCKWOOD, Deborah Jane. 825 NE 10TH ST, STE 2500 73104 #917-01-1987 L2002 **CD ICE** *020

LOCKWOOD, Wayne Babcock. 3433 NW 56TH ST 73112 #041-01-1954 L1962 **ORS** *072 †40

LOEFFLER, Christine Lee. 800 N.E. 13TH STREET, OUHSC-DEPT RADIOLOGY 73190 #039-01-1986 L1987 **DR** *020 †80

LOEMKER, Vickie Lou. 900 NE 10TH ST, DEPARTMENT OF FAMILY MEDIC 73104 #034-01-1984 L1987 **FM** *020 †18

LOFGREN, Marty Marlon. 1801 N BROADWAY AVE 73103 #018-03-1996 L2007 **FM** *020 †18

LONG, David Allan, II. 5501 N PORTLAND AVE 73112 #039-01-1996 L1997 **EM** *020 †16

LONG, Lyda Louise. ■ 73113 #039-01-1964 L1964 **GP N** *062

LOPER, Fred Lewis. ■ 73107 #039-01-1978 L1979 **FM** *071

LORENZ, Landon Bernhardt. ■ 73118 #039-01-2004 L2005 **OBG** *012

LOVE, Benjamin Preston. 3000 UNITED FOUNDERS BLVD, STE 234 73112 #048-12-1970 L1976 **PTH HMP** *050 †50

LOVE, Tim Rodney. 11101 HEFNER POINTE DR, STE 104 73120 #039-01-1983 L1984 **PS GS** *020 †85,65

LOVELACE, Brian Eugene. P O BOX 26901, 921 S L YOUNG BLVD, WP 138 73190 #039-01-2003 L2004 **ORS** *012

LOVELESS, Trinity Michele. ■ 73116 #039-01-2007 L2007 **PD** *012

LOW, Warren Glenn. 1110 N LEE AVE, MCBRIDE CLINIC INC 73104 #048-12-1974 L1975 **ORS** *020 †40

LOWE, James Benj, III. 4200 W MEMORIAL RD, STE 1010 73120 #039-01-1992 L1998 **PS HS** *020 †85,65

LOYD, Joshua M. 608 NW 9TH ST STE 1000, ST ANTHONY FAMILY PRACTICE 73102 #048-12-2005 L2006 **FP** *012

LOYD, Ryan A. ■ 73106 #048-12-2005 L2006 **FP** *012

LOZANO, Pedro Miguel. 825 NE 10TH ST, STE 4500 73104 #264-18-1994 L2004 **CD** *020 †20

LU, You. 3000 UNITED FOUNDERS BLVD, STE 234 73112 #243-47-1987 L2002 **PTH PCP** *020 †50

LUCAS, Scott K. 4050 W MEMORIAL RD, OKLAHOMA CARDIOVASCULAR 73120 #039-01-1976 L1977 **TS** *020 †85,90

LUDWIG, Kristi Lou. 825 NE 10TH ST, STE 4500 73104 #039-01-1997 L1998 **MPD** *020 †55

LUNN, Charles Lunn, Jr. 701 NE 10TH ST, OKLAHOMA CITY CLINIC 73104 #039-01-1987 L1988 **FM** *020 †18

LUO, Jinhe. 921 NE 13TH ST, AMBULATORY CARE-VAMC 73104 #243-40-1983 L2006 **IM** *020 †20

LUONG, Phung Kim. 2224 NW 50TH ST, STE 276W 73112 #039-01-1988 L1989 **R FM** *020 †80,18 ‡

LYBRAND, Fred Ewing. 3433 NW 56TH ST, STE400 73112 #048-12-1977 L1982 **CD IM** *020 †20

LYNN, Thomas Neil. 3300 NW EXPRESSWAY 73112 #039-01-1955 L1955 **GPM CD** *071 †20,70

LYONS, Timothy James. 920 SL YOUNG BLVD, WP 1345 73104 #918-01-1977 L2002 **IM** *020

MACHADO, Linda Joy. 825 NE 10TH ST, STE 4500 73104 #654-01-1995 L1997 **IM ID** *020 †20

MACKIE, Laura L. 11200 N PORTLAND AVE, FL 2 73120 #039-01-1978 L1979 **OBG** *020 †30 ‡

MADAMANGALAM, Abhinava. 920 STANTON L YOUNG BLVD, DEPT OF ANES WP 2530 73104 #495-99-1985 L2000 **AN** *020 †05

MADHOUN, Mohammad Farouq. 940 STANTON L YOUNG BLVD 73104 #575-02-2003 L2007 **IM** *012

MADOUX, Lamarr William. ■ 73146 #039-01-1995 **P** *020

MAGNESS, Steven Michael. 4140 W MEMORIAL RD 73120 #039-01-1996 L1997 **GS VS** *020 †85

MAGRINI-GREYSON, Marlene. 4300 W MEMORIAL RD 73120 #039-01-1981 L1982 **PTH** *020 †50 ‡

MAGUIRE, Philip J. 1124 NW 50TH ST 73118 #039-01-1960 L1960 **GYN GP** *071 †30

MAHMUD, Syed Nayer. ■ 73135 #704-16-1990 L1997 **NEP** *020 †20

MAIDT, Michael Lindsay. 701 NE 10TH ST 73104 #039-01-2003 L2006 **FM** *020 †18

MAIER, Edwin Robt. ■ 73114 #019-02-1943 L1957 **ORS** *071 †40

MAKEL, Mathew Thomas. ■ 73135 #039-01-2006 L2007 **DR** *012

MAKIL, Elizabeth Susan. ■ 73150 #039-01-2008 L2012 *

MAKIPOUR, Jahanyar John. ■ 73106 #039-01-2007 L2007 **GS** *012

MALATINSZKY, George. 921 NE 13TH ST, MEDICAL CENTER-AMBULATORY 73104 #473-01-1984 L2000 **IM** *020 †20

MALES, James Lowell. 5401 N PORTLAND AVE, STE 310 73112 #039-01-1966 L1966 **END IM** *020 †20

MALHOTRA, Rajesh. 220 SW 89TH ST, STE A 73139 #496-09-1991 L1999 **NEP IM** *020 †20 ‡

MALIK, Sanober. 940 STANTON L YOUNG BLVD 73104 #704-01-2001 L2007 **IM** *012

MALLORY, David Barrett. 1240 SW 44TH ST 73109 #025-01-1968 L1975 **OPH** *020 †35

MALPANI, Ravi Kumar. 1044 SW 44TH ST STE 410 73109 #495-21-1973 L1980 **PUD IM** *020 †20

MALPANI, Vijayalakshmi. 3330 NW 56TH ST FL 400, THE PEDIATRIC GROUP, PLLC 73112 #495-21-1973 L1980 **PD** *020 †55

MANDANAS, Romeo Ang. 3366 NW EXPRESSWAY, STE 200 73112 #748-11-1983 L1993 **HO HEM** *020 †20 ‡

MANION, Carl Virgil. 10852 SUNNYMEADE PL 73120 #007-02-1965 L1977 **IM PA** *020 ‡

MANNEL, Robert S. 825 NE 10TH ST, STE 5200 73104 #048-02-1982 L1989 **GO OBG** *040 †30

MANSOUR, Lilah Salah. ■ 73118 #021-06-2003 L2006 **GE** *020 †20

MANTOR, Philip Cameron. 1200 EVERETT DR, STE 2320 73104 #048-02-1986 L1987 **PDS** *020 †85

MAPSTONE, Timothy Boyd. 1000 N LINCOLN BLVD # 400, DEPT OF NEUROLOGICAL SURGE 73104 #038-06-1977 L2005 **NS** *020 †25

MAQBOOL, Feroz. 825 NE 10TH ST, STE 4500 73104 #495-51-1986 L1999 **VIR** *020 †80

MARCY, Emily Patricia. 940 NE 13TH ST RM 3, OKLAHOMA UNIVERSITY HSC 73104 #039-01-2003 L2005 **PD** *100 †55

MARGO, Bradley Johnson. 920 SL YOUNG BLVD, WP 1380 73104 #039-01-2003 L2004 **ORS** *012

MARGO, Marvin Kenneth. ■ 73114 #039-01-1948 L1948 **ORS** *071 †40

MARIL, William David. ■ 73120 #039-01-1940 L1941 **GS OM** *071

MARINIS, Spyridon Ioannis. 920 STANTON L YOUNG BLVD, OUHSC 73104 #418-01-1993 L2005 **OBG OS** *020 †30

MARION, Brad Alan. 608 NW 9TH ST STE 3110 73102 #016-11-1977 L1979 **PUD AN** *020 †20

MARKLAND, Loy D Bridal. 825 NE 10TH ST, STE 4500 73104 #039-01-1960 L1960 **PD** *020

MARKLAND, Ralph John. ■ 73104 #039-01-1995 L1996 **PTH** *100

MARKS, John Wm. ■ 73120 #039-01-1954 L1954 **FM** *071

MARSH, Donald Wayne. 4901 W RENO AVE, STE 500 73127 #039-01-1958 L1958 **OM OPH** *071 †70

MARSHALL, Jack E, Jr. 3601 NW 138TH STE 200 73134 #039-01-1984 L1985 **AN PME** *020 †05 ‡

MARTIN, Hal David. 6205 N SANTA FE AVE 73118 #039-79-1986, ▲ L1990 **ORS** *020

MARTIN, Joseph L. 5300 N GRAND BLVD, STE 102 73112 #028-02-1954 L1959 **AN** *071 †05

MARTIN, Mary Wade. 608 NW 9TH ST, STE 4210 73102 #016-11-1991 L2003 **OBG** *020 †30

MARTIN, Michael David. 1000 N LINCOLN BLVD # 400, DEPARTMENT OF NEUROSURGERY 73104 #039-01-2001 L2002 **NS** *012

MARTINEZ, Marte A. ■ 73118 #048-12-2007 L2007 **AN** *012

MARTIN-MARSHALL, Candaca. 940 NE 13TH ST, OK CHILDRENS MEMORIAL HOSP 73104 #039-01-1985 L1986 **PG** *020 †55

MARUENDA, Javier. ■ 73120 #737-06-1988 L1999 **END** *100 †20

MASOOD, Faraz. ■ 73120 #704-16-2000 L2007 **FP** *012

MASSAD, Gary Lloyd. 2821 NW 50TH ST 73112 #039-01-1975 L1976 **LM OM** *071

MASSEY, Amber Rochelle. ■ 73112 #027-01-2005 L2007 **IM** *012

MASSION, Walter H. ■ 73190 #407-02-1951 **AN OS** *071

MASTERS, Barbara. 3101 CASTLEROCK RD UNIT 83 73184 #039-01-1990 L1991 **CHP** *020 †75

MATHEKE, Edward Yoshio. 9405 SW 32ND ST, OCCUPATIONAL HLTH DIVISIO 73179 #038-43-1978 L1983 **EM** *020 †16

MATHEW, Migy Kurian. 825 NE 10TH ST, STE 4500 73104 #654-01-1996 L1999 **FM FPG** *020 †18

MATHEW, Sunil Thomas. ■ 73142 #422-01-1999 L2006 **CD** *012 †20

MATHIAS, Jerome. 8121 NATIONAL AVE, MIDWEST CITY CARDIOLOGY 73110 #495-09-1976 L1981 **CD IM** *020 †20

■ = Address Information Privacy Protected

MATON, Paul Nicholas. 3366 NORTHWEST EXPY 73112 #917-25-1971 L1990 **GE IM** *020 †20 ‡
MATOOK, George Mark. 8121 NATIONAL AVE 73110 #024-07-1988 L1994 **ORS** *020 †40
MATTHEWS, Rex Roland. 8220 S PENNSYLVANIA AVE 73159 #039-01-1965 L1965 **PD A** *020
MAULDIN, Grant K. 5350 S WESTERN AVE STE 419 73109 #649-14-1980 L1981 **AN** *020 †05
MAULTSBY, Dwayne Alan. 920 SL YOUNG BLVD, WP 2530 73104 #041-15-2002 L2005 **AN** *020
MAUPIN, William Chas. 4200 W MEMORIAL RD 73120 #039-01-1991 L1992 **AN** *020 †05
MAVIS, Alisha Michelle. ■ 73179 #039-01-2008 *012
MAXWELL, Donald P, Jr. 12318 SAINT ANDREWS DR 73120 #039-01-1982 L2000 **OPH OS** *020 †35 ‡
MAXWELL, Scott Winn. 4200 W MEMORIAL RD, STE 703 73120 #039-01-1987 L1988 **AN IM** *020 †05
MAY, June C. ■ 73116 #039-01-1961 L1961 **R IM** *071
MAZLOUM, Assaad Edward. 940 STANTON L YOUNG BLVD 73104 #605-01-1998 **IM** *100
MC ADAMS, Devin Glen. 4140 W MEMORIAL RD, CENTER FOR WOMENS HEALTH 73120 #039-01-1995 L1999 **OBG** *020 †30
MC AFEE, William Mitchell. 8125 S WALKER AVE, PRIMARY CARE PARTNERS OF 73139 #039-01-1982 L1983 **FM IMG** *020 †18
MC ARTHUR, Robert Lynn. 1110 N LEE AVE 73103 #039-01-1984 L1985 **RHU** *020 †20
MC BRIDE, Matthew Anthony. 5701 N PORTLAND AVE, STE 305 73112 #038-43-1988 L1996 **IM** *020 †20
MCCAFFREE, Donald R. 825 NE 10TH ST, STE 2500 73104 #039-01-1969 L1969 **IM PCC** *030 †20
MCCAFFREE, Mary Anne W. 940 NE 13TH ST 73104 #039-01-1971 L1972 **PD NPM** *020 †55
MC CALEB, Morgan Jon. 750 NE 13TH ST, STE 200 73104 #048-14-1995 L2003 **APM** *020 †05
MC CALL, William W. ■ 73116 #021-01-1945 **OS GP** *071
MC CAMPBELL, Stanley R. 1211 N SHARTEL AVE, STE 1005 73103 #047-05-1952 L1957 **CD IM** *071
MC CAULEY, Michael Paul. ■ 73162 #039-01-1977 L1978 **AN** *020 †05
MC CLELLAN, Betty Jane. 940 SL YOUNG BLVD, # 451 73104 #004-01-1957 L1964 **ATP PCP** *071 †50
MC CLOY-YOUNG, Laura Beth. ■ 73151 #039-01-1998 L1999 **DR** *020 †80
MCCOLLOM, Brendon. 1000 N LEE AVE, ST ANTHONY FAMILY MED RESI 73102 #028-78-2004, ▲ L2005 **FM** *100 †18
MC COLLOM, Vance Edmond. 4300 W MEMORIAL RD, MERCY HLTH CTR-RADIOLOGY 73120 #039-01-1990 L1991 **VIR R** *020 †80
MC CONATHY, Robert Mason. 1111 N LEE AVE STE 236 73103 #039-01-2004 L2006 **AN** *012
MC COY, Angela Michele. 4625 S WESTERN AVE 73109 #039-01-1999 L2000 **DR** *020 †80
MC COY, Justin L. 920 SL YOUNG BLVD, WP 1290 73104 #004-01-2004 L2005 **DR** *012
MC CREIGHT, Wm Geo, Jr. 12005 N VIRGINIA AVE 73120 #039-01-1973 L1974 **EM OM** *020 †16
MC CURDY, Joel Brent. 12316 N MAY AVE, PMB 274 73120 #039-01-1981 L1982 **IM** *020
MCDANIEL, David Preston. ■ 73105 #039-01-2008 *012
MC DANIEL, Tanner Eugene. 1201 S DOUGLAS BLVD, MIDWEST MEDICAL GROUP 73130 #039-01-1999 L2000 **FM** *020 †18
MC DONNOLD, George F. ■ 73120 #039-01-1952 L1952 **GS OS** *071
MCENTEE, Jennifer Jo. ■ 73105 #039-01-2008 *012
MC EVER, Rodger Paul. 825 NE 13TH ST, OKLAHOMA MEDICAL 73104 #016-02-1974 L1987 **HEM ON** *050 †20
MC FARLAND, Keith Allan. 4200 W MEMORIAL RD, STE 703 73120 #039-01-1981 L1982 **AN EM** *020 †16,05 ‡
MC GANN, Gary Dean. 600 NATIONAL AVE 73110 #039-01-1973 L1978 **PD** *020 †55
MC GEE, Michael. 3300 NW EXPRESSWAY 73112 #039-01-1975 L1980 **OTO NO** *020 †45
MC GINNIS, Donald Wray. 9600 BROADWAY EXT 73114 #039-01-1990 L1991 **ORS OSM** *020 †40
MC GINNIS, Michael Dewitt. 4200 W MEMORIAL RD STE 703 73120 #039-01-1988 L1991 **AN** *020 †18,05
MC GLOHON, Dwight Mershon. 5501 N PORTLAND AVE, EMERG DEPT DEACONESS HOSP 73112 #039-01-1981 L1982 **EM** *020
MC GOWAN, Thomas Raymond. 801 NE 13TH ST 73104 #012-05-1943 L1948 **PHP GPM** *040
MC GUINN, Laura Joan. 1100 NE 13TH ST 73117 #048-02-1992 L2004 **PD PM** *020 †55
MC INNIS, Alice Elizabeth. ■ 73112 #039-01-1977 L1978 **OBG** *071
MC INNIS, Dalton Blue. ■ 73159 #039-01-1971 L1972 **IM FM** *020 †20,16,18
MC KEE, Patrick Allen. 825 NE 10TH ST, STE 4500 73104 #039-01-1962 L1962 **IM** *030 †20
MC KNIGHT, Patricia Ann. 1900 NW EXPRESSWAY, STE 506 73118 #039-01-1974 L1975 **P CHP** *020 †75 ‡
MC LANAHAN, Bonnie Braden. 940 NE 13TH ST 73104 #039-01-1985 L1986 **DR N** *020
MC LAUGHLIN, Peter F. 5501 N PORTLAND AVE 73112 #039-01-1997 L2000 **EM** *020 †16
MCLAURIN, Colby Garrett. ■ 73106 #048-13-2006 L2007 **OTO** *012
MCLAURIN, Emily Y. 608 NW 9TH ST STE 110, ST. ANTHONY FAMILY MEDICIN 73102 #048-13-2006 L2007 **FP** *012
MC LEMORE, Erin E. 3433 NW 56TH ST STE 950, DEACONESS ORTHOPAEDIC PHYS 73112 #048-12-1991 L1992 **OSM** *020 †40
MC LENDON, Irwin Chester. 11300 QUAIL CREEK RD, VILLA #12 73120 #012-01-1955 L1958 **GP AM** *071
MC LEOD, Wallace B, III. 2216 N MARTIN LTHR KNG AVE 73111 #039-01-1979 L1985 **FM** *020 †18
MCMAHAN, Michael Zann. 3500 NW 56TH ST STE 100, GREAT PLAINS FAMILY MEDICA 73112 #039-01-2005 L2006 **FP** *012
MC MASTER, Audrey Jeanne. 6608 N WESTERN AVE # 626 73116 #039-01-1964 L1964 **OBG** *040 †30
MC MEEKIN, Donald Scott. P.O. BOX 26901, 920 STANTON L YOUNG, WP247 73190 #016-43-1990 L1998 **OBG GO** *020 †30
MCMEEN, Victoria Markivna. 940 NE 13TH ST RM 3409-N, CHILDRENS HOSPITAL OF OKLA 73104 #913-05-1997 L2004 **AI** *012 †55
MC MILLAN, Euan Murray. 4200 W MEMORIAL RD STE 503 73120 #919-03-1975 L1980 **D DMP** *020 †15
MC MINN, Johnny Russell, Jr. 3366 NW EXPRESSWAY STE 200 73112 #039-01-1997 L2000 **HO** *020 †20
MC MULLEN, Kevin M. 1000 SW 44TH ST, STE 300 73109 #048-16-1986 L1991 **GS VS** *020 †85
MCMURPHY, Linda Kay. ■ 73118 #039-01-2007 L2007 **IM** *012
MC NALL-KNAPP, Rene Young. 940 NE 13TH ST 73104 #047-06-1994 L2001 **PHO** *020 †55
MCNAMARA, Kevin Mahan. ■ 73118 #039-01-2008 *012
MC NEELY, Dennis Reed. 3433 NW 56TH ST STE 820 73112 #039-01-1979 L1985 **GS** *020 †85
MCNEIL, Jennifer Jeanne. 3433 NW 56TH ST STE 760 73112 #023-12-1989 L2002 **CRS** *020 †10,85
MC WILLIAMS, Chas A, III. 4200 W MEMORIAL RD # 1007 73120 #039-01-1977 L1978 **U** *020 †95
MC WILLIAMS, David J. ■ 73112 #039-01-1991 L1992 **IM** *020 ‡
MC WILLIAMS, Josh Eric. 5501 N PORTLAND AVE 73112 #048-13-1999 L2003 **EM** *020 †16
MEDBERY, Clinton Amos, III. 1011 N DEWEY AVE, FRANK C LOVE CANCER INST 73102 #045-01-1976 L1989 **RO ON** *020 †20,80
MEDINA, Jesus Edilberto. 920 STANTON L YOUNG BLVD, RM WP1290 73104 #737-05-1974 L1984 **HNS OTO** *020 †45
MEEK, Brian Melton. 7100 S I 35 SERVICE RD, STE 7 73149 #039-01-1984 L1985 **FM** *020 †18
MEHDI, Nighat Fatima. 940 NE 13TH ST 73104 #704-06-1985 L2002 **PDP** *020 †55
MEHTA, Kautilya A. 608 NW 9TH ST STE 5204 73102 #496-38-1967 L1980 **VS GS** *020 †85
MEIRING, Marcia Elizabeth. 1111 N LEE AVE STE 400 73103 #039-01-1995 L2000 **CHP P** *020
MEIRING, Nicolaas Lingen. 4200 W MEMORIAL RD, STE 606 73120 #039-01-1965 L1965 **OTO HNS** *071 †45
MEITES, Herbert Lewis. 3433 NW 56TH ST, STE 910 73112 #038-41-1970 L1977 **GS** *020 †85
MELENDEZ, David. 4140 W MEMORIAL RD, CENTER FOR WOMENS HEALTH 73120 #042-01-1985 L1995 **OBG** *020 †30
MELLOW, Mark Harris. 3366 NW EXPRESSWAY, STE 650 73112 #035-09-1968 L1983 **GE IM** *020 †20
MERCADO-PUMAREJO, Miguel. 10021 S WESTERN AVE 73139 #847-08-1976 L1994 **FM** *020 †18
MERCER, Robert D. ■ 73120 #039-01-1951 L1951 **AN** *071 †05
MERCHANT, Adam. 3330 NW 56TH ST, STE 208 73112 #495-01-1970 L1979 **FOP** *020 †50
MERKEY, Michael Lynn. 3433 NW 56TH ST STE 970 73112 #039-01-1981 L1982 **N** *020 †75
MERRILL, Joan Tenenbaum. 825 NE 13TH ST, OK MEDICAL RES FNDT 73104 #035-20-1985 L2001 **RHU IM** *050 †20
MERRITT, Joe Paul. 5300 N GRAND BLVD STE 302 73112 #028-02-1971 L1985 **OBG** *020 †30
MESIYA, Sikander Aba Ali. 8121 NATIONAL AVE, STE 303 73110 #704-02-1992 L1997 **GE IM** *020 †20
META, Gentian. 6303 WATERFORD BLVD STE 2 73118 #120-01-1997 L2006 **AN** *020 †05
METCALF, Danny Joe. 12324 SAINT ANDREWS DR 73120 #039-01-1966 L1966 **OS** *020
METCALF, Jack Edd. 4140 W MEMORIAL RD, STE 116 73120 #039-01-1971 L1972 **NO** *020 †45
METCALF, James Preston. 4115 N CLASSEN BLVD 73118 #039-01-1971 L1973 **OM** *020
METCALF, Jordan Patrick. P.O.BOX 26901, RM.3SP.400, 920 STANTON L. YOUNG BLVD 73190 #030-05-1984 L1994 **PUD** *020 †20
METCALF, Sara Kathleen. 619 NE 13TH ST 73104 #039-01-2004 L2005 **D** *012
METCALFKELLY, Jamie Ann. 10701 N ROCKWELL AVE, ACCESS MEDICAL CENTER 73162 #024-07-1997 L2005 **FM** *020
METZ, Joseph Allan. 4200 W MEMORIAL RD STE 802 73120 #048-12-1971 L1972 **IM** *020 †20
MEYER, William Henry. 940 NE 13TH ST 73104 #041-02-1974 L1997 **PHO** *050 †55
MICHAEL, Medhat Samy Fana. ■ 73142 #915-02-1982 L2004 **FM** *020 †18
MIKAWA, Kevin Dean. 4120 W MEMORIAL RD, STE 218 73120 #011-03-1998 L2002 **N** *020 †75
MILES, Fanning C, Jr. ■ 73120 #012-05-1953 L1955 **FM** *071
MILES, James Clayton, Jr. 1111 N LEE AVE STE 236 73103 #039-01-1990 L1991 **AN** *020 †05
MILES, Laura Sarfatis. 2828 W COUNTRY CLUB DR 73116 #039-01-1991 L1992 **OPH** *020 †35 ‡
MILES, Mark Grady. 4300 W MEMORIAL RD 73120 #012-01-1986 L1993 **IM** *020 †20
MILES, Pamela Settle. 920 SL YOUNG BLVD 73104 #012-01-1986 L1990 **OBG** *020 †30
MILES, Robert Watson. 1111 N LEE AVE, STE 236 73103 #039-01-1972 L1973 **AN** *020
MILLER, Gregory Jon. 5501 N PORTLAND AVE 73112 #039-01-1995 L1996 **AN** *020 †05
MILLER, Jess E. 1000 N LEE AVE 73102 #039-01-1947 L1954 **U** *071 †95
MILLER, Peteryne Duah. 920 SL YOUNG BLVD, WILLIAMS PAVILION #3470 73104 #610-01-1989 L2003 **P** *020
MILLER, Rea Sage. ■ 73107 #028-46-2003 L2005 **DR** *012
MILLER, Romney Kip. ■ 73102 #021-05-2004 L2005 **DR** *012
MILLER, William Jess. 5501 N PORTLAND AVE 73112 #039-01-1980 L1981 **U TTS** *020 †95
MILLS, Gerald Patrick. 3330 NW 56TH ST, STE 500 73112 #065-09-1981 L1995 **FM** *020 †18 ‡
MILLS-MALONEY, Diana D. ■ 73151 #039-01-1976 L1977 **EM OM** *020 †16
MIN, Kyung Whan. 3000 UNITED FOUNDERS BLVD, STE 234 73112 #583-02-1962 L1987 **PTH** *020 †50
MINER, Philip Barton, Jr. 825 NE 10TH ST 73104 #007-02-1971 L1996 **GE IM** *020 †20
MIR, Sylvia. 2224 NW 50TH ST, STE 276W 73112 #048-02-1978 L1979 **DR** *020 †80
MIRABILE, Charles, Jr. 4140 W MEMORIAL RD STE 321 73120 #035-06-1992 L1998 **MFM OBG** *020 †30
MIRANDA, Amalia Maria. 3435 NW 56TH ST, STE 1010 73112 #847-02-1978 L1987 **OPH** *020
MITCHELL, Lynn V. 4545 N LINCOLN BLVD # 124 73105 #039-01-1984 L1985 **OM FM** *030 †70,18
MITCHELL, Scott Anthony. 3601 NW 138TH ST, STE 200 73134 #039-79-1988, ▲ L1989 **AN** *020 †05
MITCHELL, William Allen. 4404 N LINCOLN BLVD 73105 #021-06-1990 L1991 **P** *020
MIYAKE, Alan A. 1245 N STONEWALL AVE, DEPT OF ORAL & MAXILOFACI 73117 #048-14-1994 L2001 **GS** *020
MOAD, Jeremy Brandon. ■ 73103 #039-01-2007 L2007 **IM** *012
MODI, Jignesh Mahendrakum. DEPT OF RAD SCIENCES, UNIV OF OKLAHOMA HEALTH SC 73190 #495-76-2001 L2007 **VIR** *012
MODY, Ankur Devagna. 921 NE 13TH ST, ST 111AC 73104 #495-23-1998 L2004 **IM** *020
MOERY, Samantha Colou. 940 STANTON L YOUNG BLVD 73104 #039-79-2004, ▲ L2005 **FM** *020 †18
MOHAMMAD, Aamir. 3433 NW 56TH ST, STE 560 73112 #704-02-1991 L2006 **IM** *020 †20
MOHAMMAD, Shirin N. 4221 S WESTERN AVE, STE 3010 73109 #704-16-1984 L2000 **IM** *020 †20
MOHAMMED, Sameer Abdul. 4404 N LINCOLN BLVD 73105 #496-27-1997 L2005 **P** *100
MOHAN, Sowmya S. 940 NE 13TH ST RM 3N3409, OKLAHOMA UNIVERSITY HSC 73104 #820-02-2002 L2005 **NPM** *012
MOHR, John Anthony. 5121 NE 50TH ST 73121 #039-01-1964 L1964 **IMG IM** *040 ‡
MOLD, James Wm. 900 NE 10TH ST, DEPT OF FAMILY MEDICINE 73104 #036-07-1974 L1984 **FM FPG** *050 †18
MONKS, George Washington. 3366 NW EXPRESSWAY, STE 720 73112 #039-01-1999 L2000 **D** *020 †15
MONNET, Julien Chas. 3301 NW 50TH ST 73112 #039-01-1956 L1956 **ORS** *071 †40
MONTERO, J A. 4205 MCAULEY BLVD STE 300 73120 #030-06-1963 L1967 **P PFP** *020 †75 ‡
MOORAD, Amal E. 4221 S WESTERN AVE, STE 3010 73109 #039-01-1975 L1976 **IM** *040 †20
MOORE, Charles Alexander. 4167 DOVE TREE LANE 73132 #917-07-1976 L1983 **AN** *020
MOORE, Gary Medford. ■ 73111 #039-01-1968 L1969 **P** *020
MOORE, Kathleen Nadine. P O BOX 26901, WP2410 73190 #054-04-2000 L2004 **OBG** *020
MOORE, Mac Edward. ■ 73112 #021-06-2003 L2005 **ORS** *012
MOORE, Robert Kevin. 3330 NW 56TH ST FL 400 73112 #039-01-1986 L1987 **PD ADL** *020 †55

■ = Address Information Privacy Protected

MOORE, Samuel T. ■ 73114 #039-01-1938 L1939 ORS *071 †40
MORAN, Willard Brown, Jr. 940 NE 13TH ST, 3000MRI 73104 #039-01-1961 L1962 OTO PDO *071 †45
MOREAU, Annie. ■ 73103 #039-01-2006 L2007 OPH *012
MORELLI, John Nicholas. ■ 73118 #039-01-2008 *012
MOREMAN, Dena Mae. 5501 N PORTLAND AVE 73112 #039-01-1996 L1997 IM *020
MORGAN, Charles Henry. 4221 S WESTERN AVE, STE 5000 73109 #039-01-1972 L1973 N *020 †75
MORGAN, Daniel Lawrence. 920 SL YOUNG, BLVD, WP-2140 73104 #039-01-2001 L2002 GS *012
MORGAN, Michael Earl. 4221 S WESTERN AVE # 3030 73109 #048-13-1987 L1990 FM *020 †18
MORGAN, Rebecca Kathleen. 608 STANTON L YOUNG BLVD 73104 #048-13-1984 L1990 OPH *020 †35
MORGAN, Richard Randall. 6201 N SANTA FE AVE 73118 #039-01-1986 L1987 IM *020 †20
MORGAN, Robert J. ■ 73107 #039-01-1944 L1945 D *071 †15
MORGAN-VANDERLICK, Karen. 750 NE 13TH ST STE 200, DEPT OF ANESTHESIOLOGY 73104 #021-06-2003 L2007 PMM *012
MORRIS, Michael Patrick. 3300 NW EXPRESSWAY, ZUHDI TRANSPLANT INSTITUTE 73112 #039-01-1983 L1984 GE PD *020 †55
MORRIS, William Neil, Jr. 2129 SW 59TH ST, DBA ST MICHAEL HOSP 73119 #039-01-1971 L1972 PTH *020 †50
MORRISON, Astrid E. 1011 N DEWEY AVE, FRANK C LOVE CANCER INST 73102 #039-01-1991 L1996 RO *020 †80
MOSCA, Philip. 4200 S DOUGLAS AVE STE 300 73109 #039-01-1976 L1977 U *020 †95
MOSES, James Ethan. ■ 73102 #021-01-2007 L2007 FP *012
MOXLEY, Katherine Marie. 920 SL YOUNG BLVD, DEPARTMENT OF OB/GYN 73104 #039-01-2004 L2005 OBG *012
MUCHMORE, John Stephen. 3366 NW EXPRESSWAY, STE 500 73112 #039-01-1975 L1976 END IM *020 †10
MUELLER, Roger Allan. 4505 MEMORIAL CIR 73142 #048-04-1968 L1971 ORS *020 †40
MUELLER, Steven Alfred. 1111 N LEE AVE, STE 236 73103 #039-01-1980 L1981 AN *020 †05
MUENZLER, William Stanley. 4215 N CLASSEN BLVD 73118 #039-01-1960 L1960 OPH *020 †35
MUKKAMALLA, Harichandana. 940 STANTON L YOUNG BLVD 73104 #495-62-2004 L2006 IM *012
MULHOLLAND, Timothy Lloyd. 825 NE 10TH ST, STE 4500 73104 #018-03-1997 L2003 U *020 †95
MULVIHILL, John Jos. 940 NE 13TH ST, OU MED CTR-CHILDRENS ROOM 73104 #054-04-1969 L1998 CG PD *020 †55,19
MUNEERAH, Aayshah. 1025 STRAKA TER 73139 #916-01-2001 L2006 FM *020 †18
MUNNEKE, John Albert. 36 W MEMORIAL RD, STE C3 73114 #039-01-1976 L1977 OM FM *072
MUQTADIR, Mohammad Abdul. P O BOX 29601, 920 S L YOUNG BLVD, 3RD FL 73190 #495-65-1952 L1971 DR *020 †80
MURPHY, Clifton C. 608 NW 9TH ST, STE 3206 73102 #039-01-1988 L1989 IM *072
MURRAY, Christina M. 920 SL YOUNG BLVD, WP 3010 73104 #039-01-2001 L2002 CD *012
MURRAY, Don P. 3435 NW 56TH ST, STE 206 73112 #039-01-1976 L1977 GE IM *020 †20
MUSE, Gene Lester. 4200 W MEMORIAL RD, STE 1001 73120 #039-01-1980 L1981 ORS OSM *020 †40
MUSEL, Andrea Lynn. ■ 73118 #026-04-2006 L2007 D *012
MUSTAFA, Bisher Oscar. P.O. BOX 26901, 920 S L YOUNG AVE 73190 #575-02-1996 L2000 IM *020 †20
MYERS, Lynn Le Roy. 1407 N ROBINSON AVE 73103 #039-01-1959 L1959 PTH IM *071 †50
MYERS, Melissa Lynn. 921 NE 13TH ST, VAMC 111C 73104 #028-03-2000 L2003 ID *100
MYERS, Tashanna Keisha. 920 SL YOUNG BLVD, WP 2410 73104 #041-13-2002 L2006 OBG *100
NACKOS, Jeffrey Stevens. 3300 NORTHWEST EXPY, DEPT RAD 73112 #049-01-2006 L2007 DR *012
NAEL, Siavash. 4720 S WESTERN AVE 73109 #517-05-1972 L1978 P PMM *020 †75
NAGLE, Nancy Nesbitt. 3366 NORTHWEST EXPY # 660 73112 #039-01-1995 L1996 PCC *020 †20
NAGODE, Cory Dale. 3300 NW EXPRESSWAY 73112 #039-01-1984 L1985 FM *020 †18
NAHAR, Ruby. 825 NE 10TH ST, STE 2300 73104 #496-49-2001 L2005 IM *100 †20
NAIDU, Sachidanandan. 119 N ROBINSON AVE STE 160 73102 #836-05-1989 L2000 FM *020 †18 ‡
NAIFEH, Monique Mange. 940 NE 13TH ST RM 2B2305, DEPARTMENT OF PEDIATRICS 73104 #039-01-2001 L2002 PD *020 †55
NALAGAN, Edwin C. 3300 NW EXPRESSWAY 73112 #748-01-1966 L1977 AN CD *020
NALAGAN, Juan Carlos. 3300 NW EXPRESSWAY 73112 #039-01-1996 L1997 EM *020 †16
NALL, Monica Kristin. ■ 73129 #039-01-2008 *012
NANDA, Sumeeta Malhotra. 3435 NW 56TH ST, STE 404 73112 #025-01-1992 L1994 OBG *020 †30
NANDA, Sumit. 3366 NW EXPRESSWAY, BLDG D 73112 #036-07-1987 L1993 OPH IM *020 †35
NANDYAL, Rajagopal R. 1200 EVERETT DR 7TH FL, SOUTHEASTERN NEONATOLOGY 73104 #495-11-1971 L1977 NPM PD *020 †55 ‡
NARAYANA PAI, Mangalore. 3330 NW 56TH ST, STE 208 73112 #495-37-1975 L1993 P PYG *020 †75
NASR, Faysal L. 4200 W MEMORIAL RD, STE 401 73120 #605-01-1971 L1978 FM *020 †18 ‡
NASSAR, Waddah. 7221 W HEFNER RD, FAITH FAMILY PHYSICIANS 73162 #875-01-1979 L1991 FM *020 †18 ‡
NAWAR, Ola Mohamad. 1200 EVERETT DR 73104 #915-03-1981 L1998 P *020 †75
NAYLOR, Bruce Addis. 4013 NW EXPRESSWAY, STE 675 73112 #039-01-1964 L1964 IM PUD *020 †20
NAZIR, Saadia Cheema. 3525 NW 56TH ST, STE 100 73112 #704-01-1987 L1992 HO *020 †20
NEGITA, Masataka. 3300 NW EXPRESSWAY 73112 #572-58-1986 L1996 *020
NEGUSSE, Johnny A. 2825 TEALWOOD DR 73120 #038-44-2007 *012
NEGUSSE, Selamawit. 608 NW 9TH ST 73102 #305-01-2006 L2006 FM *100
NEHLS, Marilyn Kay. 3613 NW 56TH ST, STE 150 73112 #039-01-1983 L1984 NPM PD *020 †20
NELSON, David P. 3300 NORTHWEST EXPY, ATTN: 100-3445 73112 #016-06-1977 L1994 PUD OS *020 †20
NELSON, Jennifer Kathryn. 11200 N PORTLAND AVE, FL 2 73120 #039-01-1985 L1986 OBG *020 †30
NELSON, Ricky Joe. 12101 N MACARTHUR BLVD # 1 73162 #001-02-1984 L1994 GS VS *075
NEUMANN, David Anthony. 4140 W MEMORIAL RD, STE 207 73120 #039-01-1968 L1969 GE IM *020 †20
NEWMAN, Apple. 4401 S WESTERN AVE, PATHOLOGY 73109 #039-01-1998 L2000 PTH *020
NEWTON, Scott Douglas. 4200 COLETTA DR 73120 #039-01-1980 L1981 FM *020 †18

NGHIEM, Hung Xuan. 4601 N CLASSEN BLVD 73118 #941-01-1975 L1982 IM *020
NGUYEN, Andy C. 5501 N PORTLAND AVE 73112 #016-43-1993 L2000 AN *020 †05
NGUYEN, Baolien Thi. 4200 S DOUGLAS AVE, STE 225 73109 #030-05-1987 L1996 GS *020 †85
NGUYEN, Baolong. 608 NW 9TH ST, STE 2200 73102 #030-05-1996 L2003 GE *020 †20
NGUYEN, Cuong Tan. ■ 73118 #941-02-1974 *100
NGUYEN, Dan Luong. 825 NE 10TH ST, STE 4500 73104 #941-01-1973 L1980 DR *040 †80
NGUYEN, Kiet Anh. 900 NE 10TH ST, UNIV OF OKLAHOMA HEALTH SC 73104 #039-01-1999 L2001 FM *020 †18
NGUYEN, Son Hoanh. 4201 S WESTERN AVE 73109 #039-01-2000 L2001 GE *020
NGUYEN, Thuong Van. 1908 NW 23RD ST 73106 #840-01-1966 L1984 GP *020
NGUYEN, Thuy Thithanh. 1044 SW 44TH ST STE 410 73109 #039-01-1995 L1997 IM *020 ‡
NGUYEN, Thy Khanhnhat. 1011 N DEWEY AVE 73102 #039-01-1999 L2000 HO *100 †20
NGUYEN, Yendung Thi. 120 N ROBINSON AVE, STE 153W 73102 #039-01-2000 L2002 FM *020 †18
NICOLESCU, Teodora O. 920 STANTON L YOUNG BLVD, DEPT OF ANES-OU MED CTR 73104 #781-01-1987 L1999 AN *020 †05
NIDA, Brooke Allison. 940 NE 13TH ST, RM 3N3409 73104 #039-01-2005 L2007 PD *012
NIDA, Jerry Raymond. 1000 NE 13TH ST 73117 #039-01-1960 L1960 PD *071 †55
NIDHIRY, Deepa Emmanuel. ■ 73134 #495-63-1998 L2007 N *100
NIGHTINGALE, Lydia Dawn. 920 SL YOUNG BLVD, WP 2410 73104 #039-01-2004 L2005 OBG *012
NIHIRA, Mikio Albert. 920 SL YOUNG BLVD, WP 2430 73104 #005-14-1994 L2006 OBG *020 †30
NIMRI, Caramella Fuad. ■ 73120 #575-01-1991 L1999 PTH *100 †50
NING, Tak-Ling Diana. PO BOX 26901 OKLAHOMA UNIV, CARDIOVASCULAR SEC ROOM 47 73190 #243-21-1962 L1980 P PTH *020
NISBET, Robert Baxter. 800 NE 15TH ST # 426 73104 #048-12-1963 L1973 P ADP *020 †30,75
NISHINO, Ha Thanh. 73142 #039-01-2004 PTH *012
NITSCHKE, Ruprecht. 940 NE 13TH ST, CHILDREN'S MEMORIAL HOSPIT 73104 #407-19-1957 L1972 PHO OS *020 †55
NIX, Thomas Edward. 1111 N LEE AVE, 249 PASTEUR MED BLDG 73103 #016-06-1952 L1958 D *071 †15
NIZAMI, Imran. 3300 NW EXPRESSWAY, ZUHDI TRANSPLANT INSTITUTE 73112 #704-02-1987 L2001 CCM PUD *020 †20
NOKES, Timothy A. P O B 26901 DEPT MED 73190 #039-79-2007, ▲ IM *012
NORDHUES, Elaine Kay. 5701 N PORTLAND AVE, DEPT OF RADIATION THERAPY 73112 #039-01-1993 L1994 RO *020 †80
NORIEGA, Jorge F. 1111 N DEWEY AVE 73103 #737-06-1971 L1975 AN *020
NORMAN, Derek Lee. 920 STANTON L YOUNG BLVD, WP 3010 73104 #039-01-2001 L2004 IC *012
NORTH, Justin Christopher. ■ 73107 #039-01-2003 L2005 DR *012
NORTHEY, Dan Raymond. 3366 NW EXPRESSWAY, STE 400 73112 #039-01-1974 L1975 GE IM *020 †20
NUVEEN, Erik J. 2100 NW 63RD ST 73116 #038-06-2001 L2003 CS *020
NWOKOLO, Okey. 1111 N LEE AVE STE 534 73103 #690-04-1980 L1995 PD *020 †55
OAKES, Francis Donald. ■ 73142 #048-04-1956 L1965 AN *071
OCHOA, Maria Jose. 3000 UNITED FOUNDERS BLVD, STE 234 73112 #847-17-1979 L1983 ATP OS *020 †50
O'DELL, Carol Kahnert. 4300 MCAULEY BLVD 73120 #039-01-1984 L1986 DR *020 †80
O'DELL, Richard Hal, II. 3366 NW EXPRESSWAY, STE 140 73112 #019-02-1990 L1991 DR *020 †80
ODENHEIMER, Germaine L. 825 NE 10TH ST, STE 4500 73104 #021-06-1980 L2001 N IMG *020 †75
ODOR, James Michael. 14100 PARKWAY COMMONS DR, STE 200 73134 #039-01-1983 L1989 OSS *020 †40
O'DOWD, Gerard Jos. 840 RESEARCH PKWY, RM 421 DEPT OF PATHOLOGY 73104 #010-02-1977 L1990 PTH OS *020 †10
OEHLERT, Wm Herbert, Jr. 14000 QUAIL SPRINGS PKWY, STE 400 73134 #028-02-1967 L1972 IM CD *030 †20
OGUEJIOFOR, Ikechukwu Kin. ■ 73120 #038-43-2004 L2006 U *012
O'HARE, Ciaran Michael. 825 NE 10TH ST, STE 4500 73104 #539-04-1985 L1993 GS *020 †85
OLEINICK, Samuel Reuben. 825 NE 10TH ST, STE 4500 73104 #025-01-1955 L1972 IM IG *071 †20,03
OLIVA, Mario Christopher. ■ 73106 #422-01-2006 L2006 P *012
OLIVER, Cari Dawn. 900 NE 10TH ST 73104 #039-01-2004 L2006 FM *020 †18
OLSON, Jay Lindsey. 2200 N CLASSEN BLVD STE 1 73106 #039-01-1984 L1985 AN PAN *020 †05
ONARECKER, Cheyn Damon. 608 NW 9TH ST, STE 1000 73102 #039-05-1985 L1991 FM *020 †18
O'NEAL, Kevin Shane. 940 STANTON L YOUNG BLVD, UNIV OK COLL OF MED 73104 #039-79-2006, ▲ L2007 IM *012
O'NEIL, Kathleen M. 825 NE 10TH ST, STE 4500 73104 #024-07-1978 L2003 PPR PD *050 †55,03
OOMMEN, Kalarickal Jos. 711 SL YOUNG ST, DEPT OF NEUROLOGY/ROOM PPB 73104 #495-31-1974 L1977 N CN *020 †75
OPENA, Jayne Lora Lagutan. 608 NW 9TH ST STE 1000 73102 #748-01-2004 L2007 FP *012
ORCUTT, Paul D. 4300 W MEMORIAL RD, MERCY HEALTH CENTER EMER D 73120 #039-01-1976 L1977 EM *020 †16 ‡
ORGILL, Richard Dean. 3435 NW 56TH ST STE 711 73112 #039-01-2001 L2006 OTO *020 †45
ORME, Bryan Ashley. 4200 W MEMORIAL RD, STE 703 73120 #039-01-2003 L2004 AN *020
ORWIG, Steven Rhea. VET ADMIN MED CTR NO 11 C 73190 #048-13-1979 L1981 IM *030 †20
OSBORNE, Peyton Edward. 321 N HARVEY AVE, P O BOX 321 73102 #039-01-1972 L1973 OM OS *020 †70
OSHEL, Katherine Michelle. ■ 73118 #039-01-2006 L2006 IM *012
OSWAL, Alok. ■ 73116 #495-47-2000 L2006 IM *012
OUTLAW, Robert J. 5100 N BROOKLINE AVE FL 90 73112 #045-01-1951 L1963 P *071 †75
OVERHOLT, Edward D. 940 NE 13TH ST 3B3316, THE CHILDRENS HOSPITAL 73104 #039-01-1979 L1980 PDC PD *020 †55
OVERLEASE, James Robert. 608 STANTON L YOUNG BLVD, DEAN MCGEE EYE INSTITUTE 73104 #048-14-2003 L2007 OPH *020
OWEN, John Albert. 3433 NW 56TH ST, STEC10 73112 #039-01-1985 L1986 DR *020 †80
OWEN, John Roy. 3366 NW EXPRESSWAY, STE 140 73112 #039-01-1958 L1958 R *071 †80 ‡
OWEN, Larry Scott. 5401 N PORTLAND AVE, STE 220 73104 #039-01-1985 L1986 IM *020 †20
OWENS, Holly Annette. ■ 73104 #422-01-2006 L2006 PD *012
OWENS, Kerry Colleen. 3806 N BARR AVE STE 229, MORNINGSTAR DIALYSIS CENTE 73122 #039-01-1995 L1997 NEP *020 †20

■ = Address Information Privacy Protected

OWENS, Lloyd A. ■ 73112 #035-03-1950 L1955 **D** *071 †15
OWENS, Tomas P, Jr. 3500 NW 56TH ST STE 100 73112 #715-01-1986 L1989 **FM** *040 †18 ‡
OZA, Sameer Ashwinkumar. 825 NE 10TH ST, STE 4500 73104 #495-23-1996 L2003 **ICE** *020 †20
OZCAN, Mehmet Sertac. 750 NE 13TH ST, OAC 200 73104 #902-07-1996 L2004 **AN** *020 †05
OZER, Howard, Jr. 920 STANTON L YOUNG BLVD, WP 2080 73104 #008-01-1975 L2000 **IG ON** *050 †20
PADEN, Mark Alexander. 920 STANTON L YOUNG BLVD, RM WP1380 73104 #039-01-2002 L2004 **ORS** *020 †20
PADGETT, Jeanette. 4140 W MEMORIAL RD STE 502 73120 #039-01-1982 L1983 **PS GS** *020 †65
PADMANABHAN, Rajiv. ■ 73112 #496-39-2000 L2007 **N** *012
PAGE, Jay Blain. 920 STANTON L YOUNG BLVD 73104 #038-43-2003 L2005 **U** *012
PAGE, Ricky Lee. 8315 S WALKER AVE 73139 #039-01-1990 L1991 **IM** *020
PAHL, Joerg Johannes. 13301 N MERIDIAN AVE, PAHL BRAIN ASSOCIATES 73120 #836-04-1971 L1990 **P** *072
PAINTER, Kelly Anne. 26 SW 104TH ST, MORNINGSTAR EMERGENCY PHYS 73139 #012-05-2000 L2006 **EM** *020 †16
PAINTON, Ronald Phillip. 5401 N PORTLAND AVE, STE 310 73112 #039-01-1972 L1973 **END IM** *020 †20
PALADUGU, Rajendra Prasad. 920 STANTON L YOUNG BLVD 73104 #496-24-1997 L2004 **P** *020
PALIOTTA, Marco Alberto. 920 STANTON L YOUNG BLVD, UNIVERSITY OF OKLAHOMA - H 73104 #561-17-1991 L2007 **PCS VS** *020 †85,90
PALMER, Philip Ronald. 3500 NW 56TH ST, STE 100 73112 #039-01-1992 L1993 **FM FSM** *020 †18
PALMER, Susan E. 940 NE 13TH ST B2418, OUHSC /OU CHILDRENS PHYSIC 73104 #055-01-1987 L2003 **CG CMG** *040 †55,19
PANT, Shubham. 920 SL YOUNG, BLVD., WP1130 73104 #495-45-2001 L2004 **HO** *012 †20
PAPPAS, Nicholas John. 11000 HEFNER POINTE DR 73120 #018-03-1981 L1988 **U** *020 †95
PARACHA, Mohammad I. 2801 PARKLAWN 73104 #704-25-1990 L2000 **PCC** *020 †20
PARDEE, Jeffrey P. 1006 SW 104TH ST 73139 #039-01-1975 L1976 **OM** *020
PARDO, Gabriel. 4120 W MEMORIAL RD STE 103 73120 #264-19-1986 L1998 **N OPH** *020 †75
PAREKH, Mukesh. 5622 N PORTLAND AVE, STE 240 73112 #495-17-1977 L1984 **OBG** *020 †30 ‡
PARHAM, David Marion. ■ 73117 #047-06-1976 L2007 **PTH PP** *020 †50
PARIKH, Shrilekha C. 8125 S WALKER AVE 73139 #495-76-1991 L1999 **IM** *020 †20
PARKE, David Wilkin, II. 608 STANTON L YOUNG BLVD 73104 #048-04-1977 L1992 **OPH** *030 †35
PARKE, Julie Thorne. 711 SL YOUNG BLVD 73104 #048-04-1977 L1992 **CHN CN** *020 †55,75
PARKER, Dennis Matthew. 3366 NW EXPRESSWAY, STE 660 73112 #035-20-1977 L1982 **PUD IM** *020 †20
PARKER, Garlanda Lea. 13321 N MERIDIAN AVE # 200, ALL IS WELL PEDS PLL 73120 #039-01-1986 L1987 **PD** *020
PARKER, Gregory Alan. 5501 N PORTLAND AVE 73112 #039-01-1983 L1984 **ON HEM** *020 †20
PARRINGTON, Ann. 13313 N MERIDIAN AVE, STE C 73120 #039-01-1998 L1999 **PD** *020
PARRISH, Jack Walker. 73120 #039-01-1953 L1953 **OM** *072 †18
PARRISH, Pamela Prentice. ■ 73118 #039-01-1944 L1945 **P IM** *071
PARRY, William Lockhart. 1200 EVERETT DR 73104 #035-45-1947 L1962 **U GP** *020 †95
PARTIN, Michael Lynn. 4050 W MEMORIAL RD, OKLAHOMA CARDIOVASCULAR 73120 #039-01-2001 L2002 **IC** *012
PASCALE, Mark Stephen. 9600 BROADWAY EXT 73114 #011-03-1981 L1987 **OSM OAR** *020 †40
PASQUE, Charles B. 825 NE 10TH ST 73104 #039-01-1989 L1990 **ORS OSM** *020 †40 ‡
PASTUSZKO, Peter. 825 NE 10TH ST, STE 2500 73104 #041-01-1995 L2004 **TS** *020 †85,90
PATE, James Brett. 920 SL YOUNG BLVD # 2530, OKLAHOMA UNIVERISTY HSC 73104 #039-01-2001 L2003 **AN** *020 †05
PATEL, Anil Dinu. 1000 N LINCOLN BLVD 73104 #068-01-1992 L2003 **OPH** *020 †35 ‡
PATEL, Hemant Punambhai. 920 STANTON L YOUNG BLVD 73104 #495-22-1977 L1994 **P** *020 †75
PATEL, Nareshkumar G. 6112 NW 63RD ST 73132 #495-76-1974 L1984 **OBG** *020
PATEL, Nilam Prakash. ■ 73128 #496-41-1993 L2004 **P** *100
PATEL, Rahul Kanaiyalal. 608 SL YOUNG BLVD, OU COLLEGE OF MED OPHTHALM 73104 #038-44-1999 L2006 **OPH** *020
PATEL, Shiv Shashi. ■ 73102 #038-44-2007 L2007 **U** *012
PATEL, Sunilbhai Amrutlal. ■ 73132 #495-89-1999 L2005 **HO** *012 †20
PATTERSON, Conway Dowell. 608 NW 9TH ST STE 3206 73102 #004-01-1956 L1964 **PUD IM** *020 †20
PAULGER, Nancy Schupbach. 1625 GREENBRIAR PL STE 700 73159 #039-01-1980 L1981 **FM** *020 †18
PAWAR, Sanyukta Sanjay. 5401 N PORTLAND AVE, STE 220 73112 #495-28-1992 L1996 **IM** *020 †20
PAYNE, Irina Edvardovna. 825 NE 10TH ST, STE 4500 73104 #913-06-2001 L2003 **FM** *020 †18
PAYNE, Matthew Ryan. 1200 EVERETT DR 10TH, OU CHILDREN'S HOSPITAL 73104 #039-01-2005 L2007 **MPD** *012
PAYNE, Ralph Edward, Jr. 3301 NW 50TH ST 73112 #039-01-1956 L1956 **ORS** *071 †40
PEDERSON, James Arthur. 825 NE 10TH ST, STE 4500 73104 #026-04-1964 L1967 **NEP IM** *071 †20
PEDULLA, Dominic Marion. 3366 NW EXPRESSWAY, BLDG D 73112 #035-09-1986 L1991 **CD IM** *020 †20
PELOFSKY, Stanley. 4120 W MEMORIAL RD 73120 #039-01-1966 L1966 **NS GS** *020 †25
PENA, Lindsay Jane. ■ 73121 #039-01-2006 L2007 **GS** *012
PENAROZA, Shyla Michelle. ■ 73120 #014-01-2006 L2007 **DR** *012
PENDERGRAFT, L Olen, Jr. 1111 N LEE AVE STE 343 73103 #039-01-1964 L1964 **AN** *020 †05
PENG, Xiao-Cong. 840 RESEARCH PKWY 73104 #243-03-1982 L1999 **PTH** *020 †50
PENNINGTON, Larry Ray. 920 STANTON L YOUNG BLVD, DEPT OF SURGERY 73104 #039-01-1975 L1986 **GS TTS** *020 †85
PENNINGTON, Nancy R. 4300 W MEMORIAL RD 73120 #039-01-1986 L1987 **DR** *020 †80
PEREZ, Mary Carmen. 411 NW 11TH ST 73103 #935-01-1973 L1982 **PD** *020 †65
PERKINS, Barry Grant. 4221 S WESTERN AVE, STE 4000 73109 #048-14-1996 L2002 **GE** *020 †20
PERKINS, William J. 3300 NW EXPRESSWAY 73112 #039-01-1977 L1978 **AN** *020 †05
PERRY, Bryan Frank. 4050 W MEMORIAL RD, FL 3 73120 #039-01-1997 L1998 **CD** *020 †20
PERRY, Francis Lee. 231 NW 14TH ST 73103 #050-02-1957 L1966 **OBG AM** *071 †30
PERRY, John Philip. 3100 SW 39TH ST, BOX 12224 73119 #039-01-1989 L1990 **IM EM** *020
PERRY, Robert Jordan. ■ 73132 #039-01-2007 *012

PETERS, Casey Lynn. 900 NE 10TH ST, OU FAMILY MEDICINE 73104 #039-01-2005 L2007 **FP** *012
PETHE, Kalpana. 940 NE 13TH ST RM 1B1306, CHILDREN'S HOSPITAL OF OKL 73104 #496-02-1992 L2004 **PD** *020 †55
PEYTON, Marvin Dale. 825 NE 10TH ST, STE 2500 73104 #039-01-1971 1972 **TS** *020 †85,90
PEYTON, Marvin Lane. ■ 73118 #039-01-2004 L2006 **P** *012
PFEFFERBAUM, Betty. 920 STANTON L YOUNG BLVD 73104 #005-02-1972 L1989 **CHP P** *020 †75
PFENNING, Melissa Lynn. ■ 73118 #039-01-2004 L2006 **DR** *012
PHAM, Anthony Twan. 940 STANTON L YOUNG BLVD, DEPT PYSC 73104 #039-01-1996 L2004 **P** *100
PHAM, Quang Van. 921 NE 13TH ST, VAMC 111AC 73104 #942-01-1978 L1993 **IM** *020 †20
PHAM, Tan Nhat. 920 STANTON L YOUNG BLVD, WP 1345 73104 #039-01-2000 L2003 **END IM** *100
PHAM, Thuan Vu. 9100 N MAY AVE, MERCY HEALTH NORTH MAY 73120 #039-01-2001 L2002 **FM** *020 †18
PHILIP, Neena Susan. 3433 NW 56TH ST, PLAZA MEDICAL GROUP, PC 73112 #495-63-1984 L1998 **IM** *020 †20
PHILLIPS, Rod Morris, Jr. 1111 N LEE AVE, STE 236 73103 #039-01-1988 L1989 **AN** *020 †05
PHILLIPS, William Geo. 2224 NW 50TH ST, STE 276W 73112 #025-01-1970 L1973 **R** *020 †80
PHILPOTT, Jessica Ruth. 920 STANTON L YOUNG BLVD 73104 #038-40-2001 L2006 **GE** *012 ‡
PICKARD, Darrell James. 8121 NATIONAL AVE 73110 #039-01-1989 L1993 **OPH** *020 †35
PICKENS, James A. 3300 NW EXPRESSWAY, 4TH FLR NEONATOLOGY OFC 73112 #048-14-1986 L1987 **PD NPM** *020 †55
PICKETT, Roger Lee. 4400 WILL ROGERS PKWY, STE 105 73108 #007-02-1958 L1964 **AN P** *071
PICKRELL, Lori Lynn. 5701 N PORTLAND AVE, STE 325 73112 #039-01-1999 L2003 **IM** *020 †20
PIERCEFIELD, Dayne D. 4401 W MEMORIAL RD, STE 141 73134 #011-03-1990 L2007 **IM** *040 †20
PIERCEFIELD, Emily W. ■ 73151 #036-01-1991 L1993 **EM** *020 †16
PIERCY, Kathryn Marie. ■ 73127 #039-01-2008 *012
PILLOW, Ensa Katherine. 608 SL YOUNG BLVD, DEAN MCGEE EYE INSTITUTE 73104 #039-01-2002 L2003 **OPH** *020
PILLOW, Jonathan Martin. 4200 W MEMORIAL RD, STE 606 73120 #039-01-2002 L2004 **OTO** *020
PINEDA, Jose Luis. 3300 NW EXPRESSWAY 73112 #042-01-1976 L1977 **NPM** *020 †55
PINZON, Pablo Antonio. 1601 SW 89TH ST STE D100 73159 #649-14-1969 L1975 **GYN** *020 †30
PITHA, Jan Vaclav. VET ADMIN HOSP LAB SER 73104 #286-02-1959 L1973 **ATP** *040 †50
PITTMAN, John Roane. 11220 N ROCKWELL AVE 73162 #039-01-1980 L1981 **FM OS** *020 †18
PITTS, Herman Craig. 5401 N PORTLAND AVE # 260 73112 #039-01-1962 L1962 **OTO** *020 †45
PITTS, Jean Ann Dorsey. 4300 W MEMORIAL RD 73120 #039-01-1971 L1973 **CD IM** *071
PO, Sunny S. 1200 EVERETT DR # TUH-6E 73104 #244-02-1986 L2000 **CD** *020 †20
POGEMILLER, Mark Iverson. 73102 #028-03-2004 L2004 **PD** *020 †55
POK, Visal. ■ 73106 #039-01-2004 L2006 **FM** *020 †18
POLLACK, Michael Andrew. 236 NW 62ND ST, IMAGING 73118 #024-01-1986 L1992 **DR** *020 †80
PONNIAH, Umakumaran P. 940 NE 13TH ST 3B3316, DEPT OF PEDIATRIC CARDIOLO 73104 #495-35-1986 L2005 **PD** *020 †55
POOLE, Edward Chas. 840 RESEARCH PKWY 73104 #019-02-1988 L1994 **PTH** *062 †50
PORRAS, Jeffrey Ariel. 1025 STRAKA TER 73139 #682-01-1994 L2003 **FM** *020 †18
PORTER, Harriette C. 940 NE 13TH ST 2B2305 73104 #021-01-1972 L2000 **PD OS** *040 †55
PORTER, Kimberly Kay. 921 NE 13TH ST, VA MEDICAL CENTER 73104 #016-45-1994 L1998 **IMG** *020 †20
PORTER, Marilyn Gregory. 3434 NW 56TH ST 73112 #039-01-1956 L1956 **PG** *020 †55
PORTERFIELD, Garland N. 3727 NW 63RD ST, STE 200 73116 #048-02-1974 L1975 **PS OS** *020 †85,65 ‡
POSSELT, Earlene Lavone. 3433 NW 56TH ST 73112 #039-01-1980 L1981 **IM** *020 †20
POSTIER, Russell Glen. P.O. BOX 26901, 920 S L YOUNG BLVD, RM WP2 73190 #039-01-1975 L1981 **GS** *020 †85
POTTS, Kent Hardie. 4050 W MEMORIAL RD, 3RD FL 73120 #039-01-1965 L1965 **CD IM** *071 †20
POWELL, Ronald G, II. 5350 S WESTERN AVE, STE 419 73109 #039-01-1984 L1985 **AN** *020 †05
POYNOR, Tom Christian. 924 NW 58TH ST, CHESAPEAKE HEALTH CENTER 73118 #039-01-1997 L2000 **IM** *020 †20
PRABHU, Kiran. 4300 W MEMORIAL RD, MERCY RADIATION ONCOLOGY 73120 #496-38-1986 L1988 **RO** *020 †80
PRABHU, Sandeep Gajanan. ■ 73107 #495-01-1992 L2008 *100
PRABHU, Vijay N. 4200 W MEMORIAL RD, STE 901 73120 #495-52-1985 L1994 **GE** *020 †20
PRASAD, Niraj. 608 NW 9TH ST STE 4000 73102 #495-27-1985 L1999 **IC CD** *020 †20
PRASAD, Rakesh. 3330 NW 56TH ST, STE 208 73112 #495-75-1992 L1996 **IM** *020 †20
PRASAD, Sujata. 3330 NW 56TH ST, STE 208 73112 #495-75-1992 L2001 **IM** *020 †20
PRATER, Larry Michael. 1110 N CLASSEN BLVD, STE 318 73106 #039-01-1970 L1972 **P** *020 ‡
PRATT, Angela Kristina. 2524 NW 25TH ST 73107 #039-01-2005 L2007 **FP** *012
PRATT, John Brandon. ■ 73118 #048-04-1972 L1972 **PTH** *100
PRATT, Thomas Covington. 4400 WILL ROGERS PKWY, STE 105 73108 #039-01-1977 L1978 **AN** *020 †05
PRESCOTT, Stephen Michael. 825 NE 13TH ST, OK MEDICAL RESEARCH FOUNDA 73104 #048-04-1973 L2006 **IM** *050 †20
PREUSS, Donald Gordon. 700 NE 13TH ST 73104 #016-06-1961 L1964 **IM** *020 †20
PRICE, Richard B. 3330 NW 56TH ST 73112 #039-01-1951 L1951 **R NM** *071 †80,28
PRICE, Sanford Allen. 3233 NW 63RD ST, STE 104 73116 #039-01-1983 L1985 **FM** *020 †18 ‡
PRIEST, Kenneth D. 4400 WILL ROGERS PKWY, STE 105 73108 #048-16-1991 L1995 **AN** *020 †05
PRODAN, Calin Joan G. 711 SL YOUNG BLVD, PPOB STE 215 73104 #781-03-1995 L1999 **N** *020 †75
PRUITT, Jeffery Randall. 711 STANTON L YOUNG BLVD, PROB 524 73104 #039-01-2003 L2005 **IM** *020 †20
PRUTHI, Ravindar Kumar. 4400 WILL ROGERS PKWY, STE 105 73108 #495-73-1974 L1993 **AN** *020 †05
PRYTKOV, Alexei Mikhailov. 1025 STRAKA TER 73139 #913-15-1995 L2005 **FM** *020 †18
PUCKETT, Timothy Andrew. 940 NE 13TH ST 73104 #039-01-1991 L1992 **ORS** *020 †40
PUCKETT, Tony Gene. 825 NE 10TH ST, STE 3300 73104 #039-01-1962 L1967 **GYN GP** *020 †30
PUFFINBARGER, Nikola K. 940 NE 13TH ST 73104 #039-01-1991 L1992 **PDS** *020 †85
PUFFINBARGER, William Ray. 1200 EVERETT DR, STE 2320 73104 #039-01-1991 L1992 **ORS** *020 †40

■ = Address Information Privacy Protected

PUGSLEY, William Silvey. ■ 73120 #039-01-1945 L1946 **IM** *071
PUIGGARI, Marcelo Julian. 4120 W MEMORIAL RD, STE 218 73120 #132-01-1957 L1970 **N** *071 †75
PUJARI, Gangadhar M. 2801 PARKLAWN DR, STE 305 73110 #495-37-1965 L1981 **GS** *020
PUJARI, Shiva Geetha. 921 NE 13TH ST, VA MEDICAL CTR 73104 #495-33-1970 L1994 **P** *020
PULS, Jane E. 701 NE 10TH ST, OKLAHOMA CITY CLINIC 73104 #039-01-1984 L1985 **PD** *040 †55
PURCARIN, Gabriela. ■ 73112 #781-01-2004 L2006 **N** *012
PURDIE, Roderick Neil. 4400 N LINCOLN BLVD 73105 #039-01-1993 L1994 **P** *020
QAYYUM, Qaisar J. 3545 NW 58TH ST 73112 #704-08-1986 L2000 **IM** *020 †20
QUBAIAH, Osama Mohammad. ■ 73134 #575-02-1998 L2006 **HO** *100 †20
QUEVEDO, Arthur Robt. 1211 N SHARTEL AVE 73103 #067-01-1963 **OPH OS** *020 †35
QUICK, Gary. 1200 EVERETT DR 73104 #041-12-1972 L1993 **EM IMG** *020 †16
QUINN, Roger Dale. 825 NE 10TH ST, STE 4500 73104 #016-11-1959 L1965 **GYN** *071 †30
QUIROZ, Lieschen Haydee. 920 SL YOUNG, WP2410 73104 #005-06-2001 L2005 **OBG** *020
RABADI, Meherez H. 921 NE 13TH ST, 127 73104 #704-02-1981 L2000 **N** *020 †75
RACZKOWSKI, Carl Andrew. 3435 NW 56TH ST, STE 206 73112 #039-01-1990 L1991 **GE** *020 †20
RADER, David Wayne. 4200 W MEMORIAL RD STE 508 73120 #039-01-1985 L1988 **IM** *020 †20
RADER, Lloyd Edwin, III. 4200 W MEMORIAL RD STE 703, AFFILIATED ANESTHESIOLOGIS 73120 #039-01-1981 L1985 **AN U** *020 †95,05
RAFIQ, Khawar. 921 NE 13TH ST, AMBULATORY CARE MEDICINE (73104 #704-04-1977 L1993 **IM** *020 †20
RAFIQUE, Muhammad Babur. 750 NE 13TH ST, STE 200 73104 #704-05-1995 L2004 **PAN** *020 †05 ‡
RAHE, Gary Wayne. 1011 N DEWEY AVE, FRANK C LOVE CANCER INST 73102 #039-01-1965 L1965 **ON HEM** *020 †20
RAHHAL, Don K. 4140 W MEMORIAL RD, CENTER FOR WOMENS HEALTH 73120 #039-01-1971 L1974 **OBG** *020 †30
RAHHAL, Ryan Fouad. 1000 N LINCOLN BLVD # 400, COLLEGE OF MEDICINE 73104 #039-01-2004 L2006 **NS** *012
RAINBOLT, Leslie J. 619 NE 13TH ST 73104 #039-01-1994 L1995 **D** *020
RAMAKRISHNAN, K. 900 NE 10TH ST, OUHSC-DEPT OF FAMILY MEDIC 73104 #495-53-1976 L1993 **FM** *020 †18
RAMAKRISHNAN, Usha. 921 NE 13TH ST, VA MEDICAL CENTER 73104 #495-42-1981 L1993 **AN** *020 †05
RAMARAPU, Srikiran. ■ 73117 #495-65-1991 L2007 *100
RAMER, Linda Kaye. 1625 GREENBRIAR PL STE 300 73159 #039-01-1986 L1987 **CHP** *030 †75
RAMGOPAL, Vadakepat. 3400 NW EXPRESSWAY, STE 410 73112 #495-59-1969 L1977 **IM ID** *020 †20
RAMIREZ, Cesar Augusto. 921 NE 13TH ST, V.A. MEDICAL CENTER (111A- 73104 #737-06-1994 L1999 **IM** *020 †20
RAMJI, Faridali Gulamali. 940 NE 13TH ST RM 1G834, DEPT OF RADIOLOGICAL SCIEN 73104 #062-01-1986 L1999 **DR** *020 †80
RANA, Atiya Kashif. 900 NE 10TH ST, OU FAMILY MEDICINE 73104 #704-01-1995 L2008 **FP** *012
RANDHAWA, Surinder K. 3555 NW 58TH ST, STE 800 73112 #495-47-1973 L1994 **P** *020
RANDOLPH, John Douglas. 4050 W MEMORIAL RD, DR JOHN RANDOLPH 73120 #039-01-1981 L1982 **TS GS** *020 †85,90
RANGANATHAN, Dwaraka. 5104 N FRANCIS AVE STE C 73118 #495-66-1974 **NEP** *020
RANKIN, Laura Ann Isaacs. 3366 NORTHWEST EXPY 73112 #018-03-1973 L1980 **IM NEP** *020 †20
RANKIN, Robert Allyn. 3366 NW EXPRESSWAY, STE 400 73112 #018-03-1973 L1980 **GE IM** *020 †20
RAO, K Vasantha. 5900 MOSTELLER DR, STE 116 73112 #495-21-1967 L1994 **PTH** *020 †50
RAO, Vaidy Sham. 920 STANTON L YOUNG BLVD 73104 #495-21-1960 L1973 **AN CCA** *020 †05
RAPACZ, John Paul. 1212 S DOUGLAS BLVD, LLC 73130 #039-01-1986 L1987 **FM** *020 †18
RATHBUN, Suman. 920 STANTON L YOUNG BLVD, WP3010 73104 #048-13-1994 L1995 **IM** *020 †20
RATHI, Shradha. ■ 73105 #496-04-2002 L2006 **IM** *012
RAWLS, Paula Jean. 920 STANTON L YOUNG BLVD 73104 #039-01-1986 L1987 **AN** *020 †05 ‡
RAYAN, Ghazi M. 3366 NW EXPRESSWAY, STE 700 73112 #915-03-1973 L1981 **ORS PS** *020 †40
RAZOOK, Jerry Dan. 825 NE 10TH ST, STE 4500 73104 #039-01-1962 L1962 **PDC PD** *020 †55
REAMES, Jeffrey Gene. 3300 NW EXPRESSWAY 73112 #039-01-1989 L1990 **EM** *020 †16
REDDING, Cynthia Spring. 3435 NW 56TH ST STE 211 73112 #039-01-1987 L1988 **NEP IM** *020 †20
REDING, Anthony Chas. ■ 73120 #039-01-1965 L1971 **P** *020
REED, Henry Shane. 920 STANTON L YOUNG BLVD, WP2250-NEPHROLOGY 73104 #019-02-2003 L2006 **NEP** *012 †20
REED, Jeffrey Leon. 4200 W MEMORIAL RD, STE 703 73120 #039-01-1990 L1991 **AN** *020 †05
REEVES, James Edward. 4205 MCAULEY BLVD, STE 375 73120 #012-01-1981 L1992 **ON HEM** *020 †20
REEVES, Walter Paul. 11205 N MAY AVE STE A 73120 #039-01-1948 L1955 **P** *020
REFAT ABDELAZIZ, Ahmed Mo. ■ 73112 #915-14-2000 L2008 **P** *012
REGIER, Todd Stephen. 2224 NW 50TH ST, STE 276W 73112 #039-01-1999 L2000 **NM** *020 †80,28
REICHLIN, Morris. 825 NE 13TH ST, OKLA MED RESEARCH FOUNDATI 73104 #028-02-1959 L1981 **IM RHU** *050
REID, Jeff Scott. 940 STANTON L YOUNG BLVD, UNIV OF OK COLL OF MED 73104 #039-79-2006, ▲ L2007 **AN** *012
REID, Monica Suzan. 825 NE 10TH ST, STE 3300 73104 #039-01-2002 L2003 **OBG** *020
REILLY, Kathryn Elizabeth. 900 NE 10TH ST, DEPART OF FAMILY MEDICINE 73104 #024-16-1979 L1986 **FM** *040 †18
REINER, William Geo. 920 STANTON L YOUNG BLVD 73104 #005-15-1974 L2003 **CHP U** *050 †95,75
REINHARDT, Herbert Paul. ■ 73162 #004-01-1957 L1963 **IM CD** *071 †20
REISIG, Karen Sue. 13313 N MERIDIAN AVE, STE A3 73120 #039-01-1972 L1973 **OBG** *020 †30
REMONDINO, Robert Louis. 4120 W MEMORIAL RD, STE 300 73120 #039-01-1980 L1981 **NS** *020 †25
RENFROE, Jerry Delano. 3435 NW 56TH ST STE 711 73112 #030-05-1964 L1967 **OTO HNS** *020 †45
RENOUARD, Robert Spencer. 3330 NW 56TH ST 73112 #036-05-1994 L1996 **U** *020 †95
RESHEF, Eli. 3433 NW 56TH ST STE 210B 73112 #048-04-1984 L1990 **REN GYN** *020 †30
RESLER, Donald Ray. ■ 73112 #039-01-1960 L1960 **OTO** *071 †45
RESSLER, Gina Lyn. 700 NE 13TH ST, COLUMBIA PRESBYTERIAN HOSP 73104 #039-01-1994 L1997 **EM** *071 †16
RESSLER, Larry Lee. 4510 NW 39TH ST 73122 #030-06-1989 L1990 **EM** *020 †16
RETTIG, Philip James. 940 NE 13TH ST 73104 #024-01-1972 L1979 **ID ADL** *040 †55
REYES DE LA ROCHA, S R. 3366 NW EXPRESSWAY, BLDG D 73112 #308-02-1973 L1978 **PUD PD** *020 †55
REYNOLDS, Bill J. ■ 73135 #039-01-1949 L1950 **GP** *072
REYNOLDS, Dwight Wells. 825 NE 10TH ST, STE 2500 73104 #039-01-1974 L1980 **CD IM** *030 †20
REYNOLDS, Joe Bills. 4720 S WESTERN AVE 73109 #039-01-1962 L1962 **PS GYN** *075 †30
REYNOLDS, Robert Edward. 13301 N MERIDIAN AVE, BLDG 500 73120 #039-01-1996 L1997 **HO** *020 †20
REYNOLDS, William Emery. 4120 W MEMORIAL RD, STE 208 73120 #039-01-1981 L1982 **NS** *020 †25
REZAEI, Abolghasem Mark. 940 STANTON L YOUNG BLVD, DEPT OF FAMILY PRACTICE 73104 #561-14-1995 L2005 **FM** *100 †18
RHOADES, Edd Darrel. 1000 NE 10TH ST, OSDH/FAMILY HEALTH SVCS 73117 #039-01-1972 L1973 **PD PHP** *030 †55
RHODES, Cara Lynne. 3500 NW 56TH ST, MEDICINE P 73112 #047-06-2005 L2007 **FP** *012
RHODES, Stephen Bodford. 5350 S WESTERN AVE STE 419 73109 #039-01-1982 L1983 **AN** *020 †05
RIANTHAVORN, Pornpimol. 940 NE 13TH ST 73104 #891-01-1996 L2005 **PN** *020 †55
RIBEIRO, Annelise Natasha. ■ 73134 #919-05-2003 L2007 **PD** *012
RICE, Edwin Earl. 1111 N DEWEY AVE 73103 #048-04-1964 L1965 **ORS** *071 †40
RICH, Brian Keith. 2200 N CLASSEN BLVD, STE 1802 73106 #166-01-2001 L2006 **FSM** *020
RICHARD, James Marshall. 11013 HEFNER POINTE DR, CHILDREN'S EYE CARE, PLLC 73120 #039-01-1974 L1975 **OPH PO** *020 †35
RICHARDS, Steven Vance. 4200 W MEMORIAL RD, STE 606 73120 #039-01-1998 L2003 **OTO HNS** *020 †45
RICHARDSON, Alvie C. 825 NE 10TH, SUITE 3200 73190 #031-01-1999 L2007 **OBG** *020 †30 ‡
RICKEY, Orville Lee. 5501 N PORTLAND AVE 73112 #039-01-1958 L1958 **GS** *020 †85
RICKS, James R. 10443 N MAY AVE # 601 73120 #039-01-1938 L1939 **RHU IM** *071
RIGGALL, Jack Lee. ■ 73112 #007-02-1947 L1954 **GE IM** *071
RIGGS, Gary Dean. 9100 N MAY AVE 73120 #039-01-1997 L1998 **IM** *020
RIGGS, Michael Olen. 5401 N PORTLAND AVE, STE 250 73112 #039-01-1983 L1984 **GS VS** *020 †85
RIGUAL, Jose R. 1211 N SHARTEL AVE STE 405 73103 #039-01-1950 L1950 **OTO PS** *071 †45
RIHA, Pavel. 608 NW 9TH ST, STE 2106 73102 #409-19-1982 L1995 **ICE CD** *020 †20
RINDLER, Roy James. ■ 73162 #039-01-2007 L2007 **IM** *012
RIVERA, Angel D. 36 W MEMORIAL RD STE C3 73114 #308-04-1983 L1995 **GP** *020
RIZVI, Syed Mohammad I H. 920 NE 13TH ST 73104 #704-02-1990 L2003 **GE** *100 †20
ROBBINS, Galen P. 3433 NW 56TH ST, STE 400 73112 #016-06-1950 L1959 **CD** *071 †20
ROBERTS, David Neil. 920 SL YOUNG BLVD, WP 1360 73104 #039-01-2003 L2006 **GE** *012 †20
ROBERTS, Dennis Lee. 4221 S WESTERN AVE, STE 3030 73109 #305-01-1985 L1991 **FM** *020 †18
ROBERTS, Gary G. 2533 NW GRAND BLVD 73116 #020-02-1966 L1973 **R** *020 †80
ROBERTS, Pamela Rose. ■ 73131 #048-13-1987 L2006 **CCM CCS** *020 †20
ROBERTS, Richard H. 2224 NW 50TH ST, STE 276W 73112 #039-01-1976 L1977 **DR** *020 †80
ROBERTSON, Amanda Lyn. PO BOX 721637 73172 #039-01-2006 L2008 **FP** *012
ROBIDEAUX, Vance Ike. 4200 W MEMORIAL RD, STE 703 73120 #048-12-1971 L1977 **AN** *020 †05 ‡
ROBINSON, Darryl Dermot. 10021 S WESTERN AVE 73139 #051-04-1995 L2001 **PM** *020 †60
ROBINSON, Michael Fred. 3300 NW EXPRESSWAY 73112 #039-01-1978 L1979 **AN** *020
ROCHE, Lisa. ■ 73104 #039-79-2004, ▲ L2007 **DR** *012
RODONAIA, Grigoriy Tsotne. 900 NE 10TH ST 73104 #422-01-2004 L2004 **FM** *100
RODRIGUEZ, Juan Mariano. ■ 73142 #847-04-1976 L1984 **NEP** *050
ROGERS, David Gerald. 4300 W MEMORIAL RD 73120 #039-01-1962 L1962 **R** *071 †80
ROGERS, David Lincoln. 351 N AIR DEPOT BLVD 73110 #004-01-1976 L1996 **FM** *020 †18
ROGERS, John Richard. 4401 S WESTERN AVE, PATHOLOGY 73109 #025-01-1968 L1979 **PTH** *020 †50
ROGERS, Kenneth Alfred. 3435 NW 56TH ST, STE 711 73112 #039-01-1961 L1962 **OTO HNS** *020 †45
ROOMS, Laura Marie. 940 NE 13TH ST 73104 #039-01-1997 L1998 **PHO** *020 †55
ROOT, Paula Rose. 3401 NW 63RD ST, BLUELINCS HMO 73116 #039-01-1987 L1988 **OM FM** *030 †70,18
ROSACKER, James August. 3130 SW 89TH ST, STE 100 73159 #039-01-1973 L1974 **ORS** *020 †40
ROSALES, Stephen Ray. 900 NE 10TH ST 73104 #048-02-2005 L2007 **FP** *012
ROSE, Raymond Leslie. 608 NW 9TH ST, STE 4004 73102 #020-02-1957 L1967 **CD** *071 †20
ROSE, Sharon Lee Anderson. 1211 N SHARTEL AVE, STE 700 73103 #048-12-1967 L1971 **NM DR** *071 †80,28
ROSE, Traci Elizabeth. ■ 73118 #039-01-1992 *100
ROSENBERG, Emily. 921 NE 13TH ST 73104 #039-01-1984 L1985 **P** *020 †75 ‡
ROSS, Dean Lance. 3330 NW 56TH ST, STE 500 73112 #039-01-1996 L1997 **FM** *020 †18
ROSS, Elliott Danl. 825 NE 10TH ST, STE 4500 73104 #024-05-1968 L1996 **N** *050 †75
ROSS, John Paul. 1211 N SHARTEL AVE, STE 300 73103 #039-01-1981 L1982 **U** *020 †95
ROSS, Karen Michelle. 825 NE 10TH ST STE 4300 73104 #039-01-1999 L2001 **IMG** *020 †20
ROSSAVIK, Claudia L. 801 NW 23RD ST, CLINICA GUADALUPANA 73106 #649-14-1980 L1990 **IM** *020
ROSSAVIK, Ivar Kristian. 801 NW 23RD ST, (CLINICA GUADALUPANA) 73106 #693-01-1962 L1986 **GYN OBS** *071
ROSWELL, Robert Homer. 940 STANTON L YOUNG BLVD, BMSB 357 73104 #039-01-1975 L1976 **IM** *020 †20
ROTH, Christopher Charles. 920 STANTON L YOUNG BLVD, WD 3150 73104 #021-06-2002 L2007 **UP** *012
ROUGAS, Samuel Tom. ■ 73121 #035-01-2006 **IM** *012
ROUGAS, Stacie Elizabeth. 940 NE 13TH ST 73104 #039-01-1999 L2000 **MPD** *020 †20,55
ROUSSEAU, Arthur Wm. 4205 MCAULEY BLVD STE 480 73120 #039-01-1978 L1982 **P** *020 †75
ROWLAN, Alan Ray. 3400 NW EXPRESSWAY, STE 812 73112 #039-01-1996 L1997 **GS** *020 †85
ROWLETT, Bart Michael. ■ 73151 #039-01-2002 L2003 **DR** *020 †80
ROY, Lawrence Jos. 1111 N LEE AVE STE 236 73103 #039-01-1983 L1984 **AN** *020 †05
ROYALL, James Allen. 940 NE 13TH ST 73104 #048-12-1981 L1997 **PD PUD** *020 †55
ROYSE, Robert Dayton. 4400 WILL ROGERS PKWY #105 73108 #039-01-1958 L1958 **AN** *020
ROYTMAN, Mark. 4200 W MEMORIAL RD, STE 406 73120 #913-97-1970 L1984 **D** *020 †15
RUBENSTEIN, Carl Jos. 4050 W MEMORIAL RD, OKLAHOMA CARDIOVASCULAR 73120 #036-07-1964 L1972 **CD IM** *020
RUFF, Theodore Allen. 8121 NATIONAL AVE, STE 305 73110 #047-05-1990 L1998 **GS** *020 †85

■ = Address Information Privacy Protected

RUFFIN, Joseph Bernard. 400 NW 16TH ST 73103 #016-43-1953 L1962 **P OM** *020 †70,75
RUFFIN, Richard Anthony. 3300 NW EXPRESSWAY 73112 #039-01-1985 L1991 **ORS** *020 †40
RUIDERA, Grace Mata. 8121 NATIONAL AVE, STE 309 73110 #748-08-1979 L1995
　IM NEP *020 †20
RUSSELL, Keith W. 4404 N LINCOLN BLVD 73105 #039-79-1978, ▲ L1979 **FM AM** *075
RUSSELL, Thomas Ryan. 701 NE 10TH ST 73104 #039-01-1965 L1965 **CD IM** *020
RUTLEDGE, Bob Jack. 4140 W MEMORIAL RD, STE 300 73120 #039-01-1948 L1948
　NS *071 †25
RYAN, Matthew Michael. ■ 73116 #305-01-2003 L2006 **N** *012
RYAN, Robert Spranger. 608 NW 9TH ST STE 2100 73102 #016-45-1978 L1986 **OBG** *020 †30
SAADAH, Hanna Abdallah. 4205 MCAULEY BLVD STE 400 73120 #605-01-1971 L1974
　IM ID *020 †20
SACHDEV, Arun Kumar. 4200 W MEMORIAL RD 73120 #039-01-1998 L1999 **GE** *020 †20
SACHDEV, Ruchi Goel. 3000 UNITED FOUNDERS BLVD, STE 234 73112 #496-07-1997 L2001
　PTH *020 †50
SACKET, Steven Kyle. 11101 HEFNER POINTE DR, STE 105 73120 #039-01-2003 L2004
　FM *020 †18
SADBERRY, John Riley. 1000 N LEE AVE 73102 #039-01-1974 L1975 **IM GE** *020
SAEED, Musarat. 4913 W RENO AVE, OK CITY INDIAN CLNC 73127 #704-04-1973 L1988
　IM *020 †20
SAFAVI-ABBASI, Sam. 1000 N LINCOLN BLVD # 400 73104 #409-07-2002 L2007 **NS** *012
SAHA, Amitabh Pratim. 4200 W MEMORIAL RD 73120 #035-06-1995 L2001
　CRS GS *020 †85,10
SAIDI, Johnaqa. 9220 S PENNSYLVANIA AVE 73159 #118-02-1974 L1995 **FM** *020 †18
SALAMY, Stephen Geo. 2224 NW 50TH ST, STE 276W 73112 #039-01-1985 L1986
　DR FM *020 †18,80 ‡
SALEEM, Mariam. 940 STANTON L YOUNG BLVD 73104 #704-24-2001 L2006 **PD** *012
SALEEMI, Muzaffar Mueen. 9100 N MAY AVE 73120 #704-21-1995 L2008 **FM** *020 †18 ‡
SALINAS, Robert C. 825 NE 10TH ST, STE 4500 73104 #654-01-1995 L1997 **FM** *020 †18
SALMERON, John M. 4400 WILL ROGERS PKWY, STE 105 73108 #847-03-1954 L1963
　AN OS *071 †05
SALVAGGIO, Michelle Renee. 1122 NE 13TH ST, BLDG ORI 236 73117 #039-01-1998 L1999
　ID *020 †20
SAMANT, Priya Prabhakar. 1919 E MEMORIAL RD 73131 #495-96-1989 L1993
　MPD PD *020 †55,20
SAMARA, En Shea. ■ 73118 #039-01-2003 L2004 **U** *012
SAMARA, Esber Nabeeh S. 3433 NW 56TH ST, STE 910 73112 #039-01-1968 L1969
　U TTS *020 †95
SANBAR, Shafeek Sandy. 1505 N ROCKWELL AVE 73127 #605-01-1960 L1969 **CD LM** *020
SANDS, Abel J. ■ 73134 #039-01-1946 L1947 **OS GP** *072
SANGER, Fenton Monroney. 3433 NW 56TH ST STE 210 73112 #039-01-1967 L1967
　OBG OBS *020 †30
SAN JOAQUIN, Venusto H. 940 NE 13TH ST RM 2B2416, CHILDREN'S HOSPITAL OF OK 73104
　#748-08-1964 L1976 **PDI PD** *040 †55
SANTORO CALDERON, Jose E. 920 STANTON L YOUNG BLVD 73104 #319-04-1991 L2002
　PAN *020 †05 ‡
SANTOS, Perry Mitchell. 3435 NW 56TH ST 73112 #005-18-1984 L1997 **OTO HNS** *020 †45
SARFRAZ, Nazish. 940 STANTON L YOUNG BLVD 73104 #704-06-1973 L2002 **P** *020
SARKISIAN, Steven Robert. 608 STANTON L YOUNG BLVD 73104 #041-02-1999 L2006
　OPH OS *020 †35 ‡
SASTE, Vaishali Vishal. 920 SL YOUNG BLVD, WP 2040 73104 #495-96-1999 L2004
　HO *012 †20
SATER, Joe Ervin. ■ 73103 #039-01-1982 *100
SATZLER, Nancy Stark. 3366 NORTHWEST EXPY # 280, BLDG D 73112 #039-01-1988 L1990
　IM *020 †20 ‡
SAUCEDO, Jorge Felix. 825 NE 10TH ST, STE 2500 73104 #649-01-1989 L2002 **CD IM** *020
SAUCEDO, Scott. ■ 73104 #011-02-2007 L2007 **N** *012
SAUNDERS, Kristi Van Nost. 825 NE 10TH ST, STE 3300 73104 #005-15-1989 L1999
　OBG *040 †30
SAWALHA, Amr Hakam. 921 NE 13TH ST 73104 #575-02-1998 L2002 **RHU** *020 †20
SAWAN, Kamal T. 920 STANTON L YOUNG BLVD 73104 #539-06-1992 L2003 **PS** *020 †65 ‡
SAWH, Ravindranath N. 825 NE 10TH ST, STE 4500 73104 #566-01-1988 L2002 **PCP** *020 †50
SAXENA, Kapil. 940 NE 13TH ST 3B3308 73104 #039-02-1991 L2004 **PD PHO** *020 †55
SAXTON, David L. 1110 N LEE AVE, CINCINNATI SPORTS MEDICINE 73103 #039-01-2001 L2002
　ORS *020
SAYA, Shoaib Haroon. 4201 W MEMORIAL RD # 102 73134 #704-02-1993 L2003 **CD** *012 †20
SCHECHTER, Eliot. 825 NE 10TH ST, STE 2500 73104 #035-08-1958 L1974 **CD AM** *020 †20
SCHEID, Dewey Chas. 825 NE 10TH ST, STE 3300 73104 #039-01-1988 L1995 **FM** *020 †18
SCHEIHING, William Chas. ■ 73134 #048-04-1957 L1957 **GYN OS** *071 †30
SCHIMANDLE, Jeff Howard. 2149 SW 59TH ST, STE 201 73119 #033-06-1984 L1994
　OSS ORS *075 †14
SCHLESINGER, R G. 3000 UNITED FOUNDERS BLVD, STE 234 73112 #028-34-1970 L1977
　CCP BBK *030 †50
SCHMECKPEPER, Georgene M. 1507 N ROCKWELL AVE 73127 #039-01-1972 L1973 **FM** *071
SCHMIDT, Arthur E. 3300 NW EXPRESSWAY 73112 #028-02-1946 L1953 **IM CD** *071 †20
SCHMIDT, James Henry. 825 NE 10TH ST 73104 #039-01-1973 L1974 **IM** *062 †20
SCHNABEL, James Jos. 4401 S WESTERN AVE, PATHOLOGY 73109 #021-05-1984 L1990
　PTH PCH *020 †50
SCHNEBEL, Brock Emil. 9600 BROADWAY EXT 73114 #039-01-1981 L1982 **ORS OSM** *020 †40
SCHNITZ, Sidney Edward. 5701 N PORTLAND AVE, STE 210 73112 #016-11-1953 L1956
　PD *071 †55
SCHNITZ, William Martin. 5701 N PORTLAND AVE, STE 210 73112 #039-01-1987 L1988
　RHU IM *020 †20
SCHOEFFLER, Michael Earl. 4050 W MEMORIAL RD, OKLAHOMA CARDIOVASCULAR 73120
　#039-01-1996 L1997 **IC** *020 †20
SCHOENDIENST, Steven P. ■ 73112 #048-13-1990 L1991 **HO** *075 †20
SCHOENHALS, Glenn Wm. 4140 W MEMORIAL RD STE 300 73120 #039-01-1972 L1973
　NS GS *071 †25
SCHREINER, Darrel E. 3300 N MARTIN LTHR KNG AVE, KING AVE 73111 #130-01-1990 L1998
　P *020
SCHUELER, William Benson. 1000 N LINCOLN BLVD, STE 400 73104 #016-01-2004 L2006
　NS *012
SCHULTZ, Andrew David. ■ 73120 #028-03-2005 L2007 **GS** *100
SCHULTZ, Daniel Chris. 825 NE 10TH ST, STE 3300 73104 #039-01-1999 L2000 **OBG** *020 †30
SCHULTZ, Wayne Henry. ■ 73120 #028-02-1954 L1958 **R NM** *071 †80,28
SCHWARTZ, Jonathan R L. 4200 S DOUGLAS AVE STE 313 73109 #039-01-1979 L1980
　PUD IM *020 †20

SCHWARTZ, Michael Jacob. 4334 NW EXPRESSWAY, STE 270 73116 #039-01-1975 L1976
　FM PMM *020
SCHWENDEMAN, Steven A. 6500 S MACARTHUR BLVD, OCCUPATIONAL HLTH AAM-700 73169
　#026-04-1978 L1996 **OM AM** *020 †70
SCHWIEBERT, L Peter. 825 NE 10TH ST, STE 4500 73104 #016-02-1974 L1987 **FM** *020 †18
SCHWOB, Valerie Sue H. ■ 73134 #028-02-1981 L1995 **PTH** *071 †50
SCIMECA, William Hannon. 3801 NW 63RD ST, STE 106 73116 #039-01-1979 L1980
　P CHP *020 †75
SCOFIELD, Robert Hal. 825 NE 10TH ST, STE 4500 73104 #048-12-1984 L1985
　END IM *020 †20
SCOTT, Denise Campbell. 3330 NW 56TH ST, FL 400 73112 #048-02-1987 L1988 **PDE** *020 †55
SCOTT, Mark H. 11013 HEFNER POINTE DR, CHILDREN'S EYE CARE, PLLC 73120
　#048-02-1987 L1988 **OPH** *020 †35
SEAMAN, Jeff Scott. WP 3440, 920 STANTON L YOUNG BLVD 73190 #030-06-1995 L2004
　P *020 †75
SEBASTIAN, Anthony. 3300 NW EXPRESSWAY 73112 #495-52-1981 L2003 **TTS AS** *020
SECH, Candice Kay. ■ 73134 #025-07-2002 L2007 **CD** *012 †20
SEELY, J Rodman. 940 NE 13TH ST RM B2418, DEPARTMENT OF PEDIATRICS 73104
　#049-01-1952 L1963 **CG PDE** *020 †55
SEGUIN, John Edward. 1919 E MEMORIAL RD 73131 #065-09-1968 L1994 **FM** *020 †18 ‡
SEIBOLD, Leonard Keith. ■ 73120 #039-01-2007 L2007 **IM** *012
SEIKEL, Michael R. 3433 NW 56TH ST STE 210 73112 #039-01-1976 L1977 **OBG** *020 †30
SEKAR, Krishnamurthy C. 1200 EVERETT DR, ETNP 7504 73104 #495-04-1976 L1983
　NPM PD *020 †55
SELBY, George Basil. 825 NE 10TH ST STE 5200, OU PHYSICIANS-CADE CANCER 73104
　#039-01-1980 L1981 **ON HEM** *020 †20
SELF, Kristi Goodwin. 721 NW 6TH ST 73102 #039-01-1988 L1992 **PM** *020 †60
SERADGE, Houshang. 1044 SW 44TH ST, FL 6 73109 #517-01-1972 L1979 **HS ORS** *020 †40
SERBOUSEK, Leann C. 4200 W MEMORIAL RD STE 901 73120 #030-05-1985 L1986
　GE IM *020 †20 ‡
SERES, Donna Mideke. 11200 N PORTLAND AVE, FL 2 73120 #039-01-2001 L2002
　OBG *020 †30
SERES, Kenneth Andrew. 940 STANTON L YOUNG BLVD 73104 #039-01-2001 L2002 **GE** *012
SESHACHAR, Abhaya R M. 920 STANTON L YOUNG BLVD 73104 #495-52-1992 L2000
　PAN AN *020 †05
SEXAUER, Charles Louis. 940 NE 13TH ST 73104 #028-34-1968 L1975 **PHO** *020 †55
SEYWERD, Katerine Adelhei. ■ 73142 #539-04-2004 L2006 **IM** *100
SEZGINSOY, Banu. 921 NE 13TH ST, VAMC 11G 73104 #902-09-1993 L2003 **IMG** *020 †20
SFERRA, Thomas Jos. 940 NE 13TH ST RM 2B2307, PED GASTROENTEROLOGY 73104
　#038-44-1986 L2006 **PG** *050 †55
SHADEED, Edward A. 5900 MOSTELLER DR, STE 3 73112 #039-01-1995 L2001 **ORS** *020 †40
SHADID, Christopher A. 3300 NW EXPRESSWAY 73112 #039-01-2000 L2002 **AN** *020
SHADID, Derek Jason. 13820 WIRELESS WAY 73134 #039-01-1999 L2005 **GS** *020 †65
SHADID, Edward A. 13904 QUAILBROOK DR 73134 #039-01-1960 L1960 **PS** *020 †65 ‡
SHADID, Naebeal L. 5501 N PORTLAND AVE 73112 #039-01-1967 L1967 **GP** *071
SHADID, Nicole Elyselili. ■ 73118 #039-01-2006 L2007 **P** *012
SHADID, Ralph Oscar. 425 NW 42ND ST 73118 #039-01-1980 L1981 **IM IMG** *020 †20
SHAFIK, Mark Saleh. 2825 PARKLAWN DR 73110 #305-01-2005 L2007 **FP** *012
SHAH, Muddasir Ahmad. 921 NE 13TH ST, VAMC 73104 #495-51-1994 L2003 **IMG** *020 †20
SHAH, Neel. ■ 73116 #306-01-2004 L2007 **FP** *012
SHAH, Purnima Mahendra. 920 STANTON L YOUNG BLVD 73104 #495-22-1974 L1987
　AN *062 †05 ‡
SHAH, Shujahat Hussain. 4050 W MEMORIAL RD 3RD, 920 STANTON L YOUNG 73120
　#305-01-1998 L2001 **IC** *020 †20
SHAH, Vatsala Niranjan. 721 NW 6TH ST 73102 #495-01-1976 L1994 **IM** *020 †20
SHAHEEN, Safir U. 5300 N INDEPENDENCE AVE, STE 280 73112 #704-04-1981 L2002
　IM EM *020
SHAKIR, Amathul A. 1435 N ROCKWELL AVE 73127 #495-04-1976 L1980 **AN** *020
SHAKIR, Basheer Ahmed. ■ 73118 #039-01-2008 *012
SHAKIR, Mahmood Ali. 1435 N ROCKWELL AVE 73127 #495-04-1973 L1980 **CD IM** *020 †20
SHANBOUR, Kamal Anthony. 4140 W MEMORIAL RD, STE 215 73120 #039-01-1988 L1989
　OBG *020 †30
SHANE SMITH, Rebecca Pres. ■ 73117 #039-01-2007 **PTH** *012
SHARP, Adam Doyle. ■ 73135 #039-01-2008 L2008 *012
SHAVER, Robert Paul. 608 STANTON L YOUNG BLVD 73104 #039-01-1961 L1961
　OPH PTH *071 †35
SHAVNEY, Teresa Marie. 3435 NW 56TH ST, STE 211 73112 #039-01-1979 L1980 **GS** *020 †85 ‡
SHAW, Marie Louise. 921 NE 13TH ST 73104 #048-12-1945 L1979 **PTH** *071 †50
SHAW, Tanna Marie. 6613 N MERIDIAN AVE 73112 #039-01-1997 L1998 **IM** *020 †20
SHELDON, Roger Eugene. 1200 EVERETT DR, 7TH FL 73104 #016-06-1968 L1979
　PD NPM *040 †55
SHELTON, Fatima De N A P. 825 NE 10TH ST, STE 4500 73104 #187-12-1987 L1997 **N** *020 †75
SHELTON, Jeffrey Wayne. 10701 N ROCKWELL AVE, ACCESS MEDICAL CENTER 73162
　#004-01-2004 L2006 **NM** *012
SHEPHERD, David Wade. 920 STANTON L YOUNG BLVD, WP-2140 73104 #039-01-2004 L2006
　GS *012
SHEPHERD, Virgil Jerry. 3535 NW 58TH ST, STE 120 73112 #039-01-1958 L1958 **OPH** *071 †35
SHETH, Avani Pankaj. 3300 NW EXPRESSWAY 73112 #495-76-1975 L1984 **AN PME** *020 †05 ‡
SHETTY, Satheesh Kumar S. 5350 S WESTERN AVE STE 419 73109 #496-01-1980 L1994
　AN *020 †05
SHIFRIN, Richard G. 3101 CASTLEROCK RD, VILLA 103 73120 #016-11-1950 L1955
　AN *071 †05 ‡
SHIPLEY, Bret Edward. 3300 NW EXPRESSWAY 73112 #039-01-1997 L1998 **AN** *020 †05 ‡
SHIPLEY, Winston D, II. 4120 W MEMORIAL RD, STE 218 73120 #039-01-1984 L1985
　N *020 †75
SHIRES, Ernestine Carol. 9801 N KELLEY AVE, SOCIAL SECURITY STATE OF O 73131
　#039-01-1988 L1989 **GS IM** *020 †85
SHIRLEY, Larry Dee. 3300 NW EXPRESSWAY 73112 #048-04-1973 L1989 **AN** *020 †18,05
SHOBEIRI, Seyed Abbas. 825 NE 10TH ST, STE 3400 73104 #024-07-1994 L2002 **OBG** *020 †30
SHOLER, Chris Martin. 4334 NW EXPRESSWAY, STE 201 73116 #034-01-1977 L1978
　NEP IM *020 †20
SHOOK, Marcus Boyd. 921 NE 13TH ST, VAMC 111A/C 73104 #010-01-1959 L1960 **IM** *030 †20
SHRAGO, Stan Simon. 3000 UNITED FOUNDERS BLVD, STE 234 73112 #039-01-1971 L1972
　PTH *020 †50
SHROPSHIRE, Deborah Lynn. 940 NE 13TH ST 1B1306, CHILDREN'S HOSP OF
　OKLAHOM 73104 #039-01-1997 L1998 **PD** *020 †55

■ = Address Information Privacy Protected

SHUJATH, Ali Khan. 8121 NATIONAL AVE 73110 #495-61-1971 L1981 **IM GE** *020 †20

SHUKRY, Mohanad. 920 STANTON L YOUNG BLVD 73104 #875-01-1997 L2004 **AN** *100 †05

SHULTES, Margo. 1200 NE 13TH ST, OKLAHOMA DEPARTMENT OF MEN 73117 #039-01-2000 L2001 **P** *020

SHULTZ, Amy Lynn. 1110 N LEE AVE 73103 #039-01-2001 L2002 **RHU** *020 †20

SIATKOWSKI, Raymond M. 608 STANTON L YOUNG BLVD 73104 #041-02-1987 L1999 **OPH PO** *020 †35

SIATOWSKI, Rhea L. 608 STANTON L YOUNG BLVD 73104 #035-01-1994 L1999 **OPH** *020 †35

SIDOROV, Evgeny Vadimovic. 940 STANTON L YOUNG BLVD 73104 #913-81-1997 L2006 **N** *012

SIGLER, Kala Haiduk. 3330 NW 56TH ST FL 400, THE PEDIATRIC GROUP, PLLC 73112 #048-13-1989 L1996 **PD** *020 †55

SIGMON, Jason Brandt. 3435 NW 56TH ST, STE 303 73112 #039-01-1997 L2002 **OTO** *020

SILVA, Rafael E. 5101 CLASSEN CIR # 502 73118 #275-01-1944 L1974 **GP PUD** *072

SILVER, Dennis Allen. 900 NE 10TH ST 73104 #306-01-2005 L2008 **FP** *012

SILVERSTEIN, Paul. 3301 NW 63RD ST 73116 #041-01-1964 L1974 **PS GS** *020 †85,65 ‡

SIMON, Stuart B. 1200 EVERETT DR 73104 #016-11-1948 L1967 **CHP OBG** *040

SIMS, Larhonda Kay. 3330 NW 56TH ST, PRIMARY CARE PARTNERS OF 73112 #004-01-1997 L2000 **FM** *020 †18

SINCOFF, Eric Harrison. 1000 N LINCOLN BLVD 73104 #033-06-1999 L2006 **NS** *020

SINDHWANI, Puneet. 920 STANTON L YOUNG BLVD, WP3150 73104 #495-29-1989 L2005 **U TTS** *020 †95

SINGH, Indira. 1601 SW 89TH ST STE D200 73159 #496-07-1970 L1982 **PD** *020 †55 ‡

SINGH, Ram Akbal. 10001 S WESTERN AVE, STE 200 73139 #495-14-1965 L1977 **GYN** *020 †30

SINGLETON, Harry Fields. 1211 N SHARTEL AVE STE 801 73103 #039-01-1946 L1948 **IM CD** *020 †20

SIRAJUDDIN, Riaz Ahmed. 10413 GREENBRIAR PKWY 73159 #017-20-1995 L2002 **CD** *020 †20

SIVARAM, Chittur A. 825 NE 10TH ST, STE 2500 73104 #495-44-1970 L1993 **CD IM** *020 †20

SKARKY, Steve Bryan. 5929 N MAY AVE STE 501, PARADIGM RESEARCH PROFESSI 73112 #039-01-2003 L2005 **P** *020

SKINNER, Sean Christopher. ■ 73102 #305-01-1999 L2006 **PDS** *012

SKOYLES, Julian Roberts. PO BOX 53188, DEPT ANES 73152 #917-07-1984 L1994 *020

SKUTA, Gregory L. 608 STANTON L YOUNG BLVD 73104 #016-11-1981 L1992 **OPH** *020 †35 ‡

SLATER, Leonard N. 711 STANTN L YNG BLVD #430, INFECTIOUS DISEASES INST 73104 #035-19-1977 L1983 **ID IM** *040 †20

SLATER, Stanley Lloyd. ■ 73118 #035-19-1945 L1949 **IM END** *071 †20

SLATEV, Patrick Wayne. 4200 W MEMORIAL RD, STE 703 73120 #039-01-2003 L2007 **AN** *020

SLOBODOV, Gennady. 825 NE 10TH ST STE 5400, OUPB UROLOGY 73104 #039-01-2000 L2001 **U** *020 †95

SMILEY, Constance Ann. 9100 N MAY AVE, MERCY HEALTH -NORTH MAY 73120 #039-01-1985 L1986 **FM** *020 †18

SMITH, Chad Michael. 920 STANTON L YONG BLVD 24 73104 #039-01-2006 L2007 **OBG** *012

SMITH, Danny Wayne. 3435 NW 56TH ST, STE 206 73112 #039-01-1983 L1984 **GE IM** *020 †20

SMITH, David William. 3300 NW EXPRESSWAY, ATTENTION 100-3475 73112 #039-01-1994 L2000 **EM** *020 †16 ‡

SMITH, E Michael. 920 STANTON L YOUNG BLVD, # WP3536 73104 #039-01-1984 L1985 **P** *020

SMITH, Floyd Lee. 4200 W MEMORIAL RD, STE 703 73120 #039-01-1986 L1987 **AN PME** *020 †05

SMITH, George Keith. 9500 BROADWAY EXT 73114 #039-01-1986 L1990 **AN** *020 †05

SMITH, Jacqueline Jean. 750 NE 13TH ST 73104 #039-01-1982 L1983 **AN** *020 †05

SMITH, James Wayne. 1001 N LINCOLN BLVD 73104 #048-14-1978 L1988 **BBK CLP** *030 †50

SMITH, Jeffrey Jos. 3613 NW 56TH ST STE 140 73112 #026-08-1976 L1977 **GO GYN** *020 †55

SMITH, Jeffrey Jos. 3613 NW 56TH ST STE 140 73112 #030-05-1976 L1983 **GO GYN** *020 †30

SMITH, John Richard. ■ 73120 #039-01-1957 L1957 **P** *071 †75

SMITH, Kenneth R. 900 NE 10TH ST, OUHSC-DEPT OF FAMILY MEDIC 73104 #048-04-1989 L1992 **FM** *020 †18

SMITH, Kimberly Sara. 4505 MEMORIAL CIR 73142 #048-12-1991 L1992 **ORS** *020 †40

SMITH, Marcus John. ■ 73120 #039-01-2007 L2007 **IM** *012

SMITH, Michael Shawn. 5100 N BROOKLINE AVE, STE 500 73112 #048-04-1988 L1993 **PM** *020 †60

SMITH, Miranda Elisabeth. ■ 73142 #039-01-2006 L2007 **D** *012

SMITH, Raymond Orval, Jr. 921 NE 13TH ST, VA HOSPITAL 73104 #039-01-1963 L1963 **HNS OTO** *071 †45 ‡

SMITH, Richard Vertrees. 4120 W MEMORIAL RD, STE 205 73120 #039-01-1966 L1966 **NS** *030 †25

SMITH, Robert Marchand. 4200 W MEMORIAL RD 73120 #039-01-1961 L1961 **CD IM** *071 †20

SMITH, Stewart Curry. 4221 S WESTERN AVE 73109 #039-01-1984 L1985 **NS** *020 †25

SMITH, William O. 921 NE 13TH ST 73104 #024-01-1949 L1956 **IM NEP** *072 †20

SNOWDEN, Georgianne M. 3366 NW EXPRESSWAY, STE 140 73112 #039-01-1987 L1988 **DR RNR** *020 †80

SNYDER, David Deal. 5401 N PORTLAND AVE # 260 73112 #010-01-1956 L1958 **GS TS** *020 †85,90

SOBRINO, Marco Antonio. 12400 ANDREWS DRIVE 73120 #649-13-1996 L2007 **GS CS** *020 †85

SOFOLA, Samuel Adeniyi. ■ 73111 #010-03-1958 L1991 **OS** *075

SONTHEIMER, Clayton John. ■ 73120 #048-12-2008 *012

SONTHEIMER, Richard D. 619 NE 13TH ST, UNIV OF OK HEALTH SCIENCE 73104 #048-12-1972 L2005 **D IM** *020 †20,15

SOUTHMAYD, Leroy, III. 5555 N GRAND BLVD STE 100 73112 #051-07-1982 L1990 **NEP IM** *030 †20

SPALDING, James Curtis. ■ 73154 #047-05-1945 L1965 **P** *071

SPARKMAN, Jeffrey Myles. 3300 NW EXPRESSWAY, DEPT OF EMERGENCY MEDICINE 73112 #041-02-1999 L2007 **EM** *020 †16

SPARLING, Crystal Nava. ■ 73112 #039-01-2007 L2007 **PD** *012

SPARLING, David Patrick. ■ 73112 #039-01-2008 *012

SPARLING, Jeffrey Michael. 920 SL YOUNG BLVD, WP 3010 73104 #039-01-2002 L2003 **CD** *012 †20

SPEEGLE, David Burton. ■ 73162 #039-01-2006 L2006 **FP** *012

SPEER, Joe Bob. 4400 N LINCOLN BLVD 73105 #039-01-1990 L1991 **P** *020 †75

SPEIDEL, Silvia L. 608 SL YOUNG 73104 #048-04-2001 L2002 **OPH** *100

SPENCER, A Morie. 940 NE 13TH ST 73104 #039-01-1990 L1991 **IM PD** *020 †55

SPERRAZZA, Charles S. 940 NE 13TH ST 3B3316, OKLAHOMA UNIVERSITY HEALTH 73104 #033-05-1991 L2006 **PDC PD** *020 †55

SPIELMAN, Stephen Mark. 4050 W MEMORIAL RD, OKLAHOMA CARDIOVASCULAR 73120 #019-02-1976 L1980 **CD IM** *020 †20

SPLINTER, Garth Leavitt. 900 NE 10TH ST, STE 4500 73104 #039-01-1984 L1985 **FM** *030 †18

SQUIRES, John Michael. 1111 N LEE AVE STE 236 73103 #039-01-1980 L2002 **AN** *020 †05

SQUIRES, Ronald Andrew. 920 SL YOUNG BLVD, RM WP2140 73104 #028-46-1987 L1988 **GS TTS** *020 †85

SRINIVASAN, Nandakumar. ■ 73118 #495-66-2000 L2006 **IM** *012

SROUJI, Elias Salim. 940 NE 13TH ST, 3000MRI 73104 #605-01-1944 L1976 **PD** *071 †55

SROUJI, Nabil Elias. 3435 NW 56TH ST, STE 808 73112 #039-01-1989 L1990 **OPH** *020 †35

STAATS, David Owen. 825 NE 10TH ST, STE 4300 73104 #016-02-1976 L2003 **IM IMG** *040 †20

STAFFORD, John Howard. ■ 73162 #039-01-2004 L2004 **IM** *100

STAMMER, James Leslie. 5501 N PORTLAND AVE 73112 #033-05-1970 L1977 **GE IM** *071 †20

STANDERWICK, Andrew Bertr. SCI CT, UNIV OF OKLAHOMA HEALTH 73190 #048-12-2007 L2007 **GS** *012

STANFIELD, C Blake. 11220 N ROCKWELL AVE 73162 #039-01-1997 L2004 **IM** *020 †18

STANFIELD, Matthew R. 3501 NW 63RD ST STE 500 73116 #017-20-1999 L2001 **NS** *100

STANFORD, Richard Emil. 3435 NW 56TH ST, STE 800 73112 #306-01-1985 L1986 **PD** *020 †55

STANLEY, John Robt, III. 4140 W MEMORIAL RD STE 321, PERINATAL CENTER OF OKLAHO 73120 #039-01-1987 L1994 **MFM** *020 †30

STANSBERRY, Richard D. 4301 NW 63RD ST STE 205 73116 #010-01-1958 L1959 **OBG** *020

STANTON, Bruce Clifton. ■ 73109 #039-01-1972 L1973 **P** *020 †75

STARKEY, Brad Alan. 11200 N PORTLAND AVE 73120 #039-01-1994 L1995 **AN** *020 †05

STAUDT, Leslie. 825 NE 10TH ST, STE 4500 73104 #048-14-1985 L1993 **RHU IM** *040 †20

STAVRAKIS, Stavros. 940 STANTON L YOUNG BLVD 73104 #418-01-2003 L2007 **IM** *012

STAYTON, Lorry Cae. 1200 EVERETT DR, 7TH FLOOR NORTH PAVILION 73104 #039-01-1998 L1999 **NPM** *100 †55

STECKLOW, John Edward. 3613 NW 56TH ST STE 320 73112 #039-01-1996 L1997 **PD** *020 †55

STEELE, Marilyn Irene. 940 NE 13TH ST 73104 #048-02-1981 L1983 **PD GE** *050 †55

STEELMAN, Gerald Michael. 13301 N MERIDIAN AVE # 400 73120 #039-01-1973 L1974 **NTR FM** *020 †18

STEPHENS, George Kellogg. 940 NE 13TH ST 73104 #039-01-1984 L1985 **PD** *020 †55 ‡

STEPHENSON, Jack M. 1111 N LEE AVE, STE 100 73103 #039-01-1957 L1957 **CLP PTH** *071 †50

STEPP, Robert Gene. 11101 HEFNER POINTE DR, STE 105 73120 #039-01-1992 L1995 **FM** *020 †18

STEURY, Samuel Wayne. ■ 73107 #039-01-2008 *012

STEVENSON, Michael Edward. ■ 73112 #019-02-1999 L2000 **DR** *020 †80

STEVES, Charles Robt. 4505 MEMORIAL CIR 73142 #039-01-1973 L1974 **ORS OSM** *020 †40

STEWARD, Rodney Dwight. 3300 NW EXPRESSWAY 73112 #039-01-1957 L1957 **AM AN** *071

STEWART, Camisa Jean. 6228 CYPRESS GRV 73162 #039-01-1992 L1993 **P** *012

STEWART, James Benton, Jr. 3705 W MEMORIAL RD, STE 105 73134 #039-01-1978 L1990 **D FM** *020 †15,18

STEWART, William Warren. ■ 73120 #039-01-2007 L2007 **ORS** *012

STOKES, Kenneth Ray. 1000 N LEE AVE 73102 #028-34-1979 L1994 **DR VIR** *020 †80

STOKESBERRY, David S. 3366 NORTHWEST EXPY 73112 #039-01-1994 L1996 **GE** *020 †20

STONE, Dana Gail. 11200 N PORTLAND AVE, LAKESIDE WOMEN'S HOSPITAL 73120 #039-01-1991 L1992 **OBG** *020 †30

STONE, Donald U. 1200 EVERETT DR 73104 #048-12-2000 L2002 **OPH** *020 †35

STOUGH, Daniel Ross. 14100 PARKWAY COMMONS DR 73134 #039-01-1964 L1964 **NS** *020 †25

STOUGH, Rebecca Goen. 4300 MCAULEY BLVD 73120 #039-01-1975 L1976 **DR OS** *020 †80 ‡

STOUT, Billy Herman. 5501 N PORTLAND AVE 73112 #039-01-1964 L1964 **GS ADM** *020 †85

STOWELL, Donald E. 920 STANTON L YOUNG BLVD 73104 #039-01-1982 L1999 **TS** *012 †05,85

STRAHAN, Mark William. 920 STANTON L YOUNG BLVD, WP 2534 73104 #305-01-1999 L2002 **APM** *100 †05 ‡

STRATEMEIER, Phillip Hans. 2224 NW 50TH ST, STE 276W 73112 #019-02-1972 L1979 **DR RNR** *020 †80

STREAM, Lawrence. 4200 W MEMORIAL RD, STE 907 73120 #039-01-1949 L1949 **AN** *071 †05

STREAM, Millicent Marrs. ■ 73120 #039-01-1950 L1950 **OS** *071

STREBEL, Gary Franklin. 4200 W MEMORIAL RD, STE 201 73120 #039-01-1965 L1965 **OBG** *020 †30

STREBEL, Jennifer Leigh. 920 STANTN L YNG BLVD WP24 73104 #039-01-2005 L2006 **OBG** *012

STRUCK, Bryan David. 825 NE 10TH ST, STE 4500 73104 #048-14-1995 L2000 **IMG** *020 †20

STUEMKY, John Howard. 940 NE 13TH ST, CHILDREN'S HOSP OF OKLAHOM 73104 #039-01-1967 L1967 **PD PEM** *040 †55

STULL, Dana D. 3135 NW 63RD ST 73116 #041-07-1987 L1996 **P** *020 †75

STULL, Terrence Lee. 940 NE 13TH ST, RM 2B300 73104 #001-02-1976 L1994 **ID PD** *030 †55

STULTS, Harry Babcock. 13301 N MERIDIAN AVE # 300, BALANCE CONTROL 73120 #038-06-1956 L1975 **FM ADL** *071

SULE, Aditi Jagdish. 940 STANTON L YOUNG BLVD 73104 #496-20-2003 L2006 **PD** *012

SULLIVAN, J Andy. 940 NE 13TH ST, CHO-MR2000D 73104 #028-02-1969 L1976 **ORS** *020 †40

SULLIVAN, Mark Stover. 3366 NW EXPRESSWAY, STE 720 73112 #039-01-1966 L1966 **D DMP** *020 †15

SUMERFIELD, Jeannette B. ■ 73107 #035-45-1932 **P CHP** *071

SURDELL, Daniel Lee, Jr. 940 STANTON L YOUNG BLVD 73104 #030-05-2000 L2001 **NS** *020

SUTHERS, Sara Elizabeth. 4221 S WESTERN AVE 73109 #039-01-1999 L2000 **GS** *020 ‡

SUTOR, Ronald James. 3433 NW 56TH ST, STE 400 73112 #154-07-1986 L1993 **IC** *020 †20

SWARTZ, Courtney L. 940 NE 13TH ST, RM 3409 - N 73104 #039-79-2007, ▲ **PD** *012

SWICORD, Robert Luther. 900 NE 10TH ST, STE 2400 73104 #012-01-1988 L1999 **GPM** *020 †70

SWYGERT, Trina Diann. 6201 N SANTA FE AVE, STE 2020 73118 #004-01-1992 L1993 **IM** *020 †20

SYLVESTER, Deena Alli. 4205 MCAULEY BLVD STE 401, HUMMEL EYE ASSOCIATES 73120 #039-01-1996 L2001 **OPH** *020 †35

SYZEK, Elizabeth Joan. 825 NE 10TH ST STE 1430, DEPARTMENT OF RADIATION ON 73104 #038-40-1985 L1986 **RO** *020 †80

SZAFRANSKI, Jan Stanislaw. PO BOX 53188 73152 #917-12-1985 L1992 **AN** *020 †05

TAACA, Perry Thos. 3801 N CLASSEN BLVD, STE 100 73118 #039-01-1970 L1971 **FM** *020 †18

TAFISH, Islam Mohamed. 711 STANTON L YOUNG BLVD, BLVD/STE 215 73104 #915-06-1999 L2006 **N** *012

TAHIRKHELI, Naeem Khan. 4221 S WESTERN AVE, OKLAHOMA CARDIOVASCULAR 73109 #704-21-1988 L1995 **CD IM** *020 †20

TAIRA, James Wm. 1211 N SHARTEL AVE, STE 202 73103 #056-06-1983 L1990 **DMP D** *020 †50

TALBERT, Beverly J. 4200 W MEMORIAL RD, STE 610 73120 #048-02-1985 L1986 **GS** *020 †85

TALBERT, Michael Lauren. 940 SL YOUNG BLVD, RM 451 73104 #005-14-1984 L2002 **PTH** *020 †50

TAN, Soh Ping. 700 NE 13TH ST 73104 #055-01-1991 L1992 **FM** *020 †18

■ = Address Information Privacy Protected

TAN-CO, Sally Q. 1110 N CLASSEN BLVD # 204 73106 #748-01-1980 L1996 **IM** *020 †20

TARAU, Marius Calin. ■ 73120 #781-03-1995 L2007 **FOP** *012

TARAZI, Fadi. 1000 N LINCOLN BLVD # 200, OKLAHOMA ORTHOPEDICS, INC. 73104 #067-01-1991 L1998 **ORS** *100

TARGOFF, Ira N. 825 NE 10TH ST, STE 4500 73104 #035-46-1975 L1981 **RHU IM** *040 †20

TARIQ, Farhan Ahmed. 733 NE 14TH ST, APT 15 73104 #704-01-2001 L2006 **N** *012

TARPAY, Martha M. 4200 W MEMORIAL RD, STE 206 73120 #473-01-1965 L1974 **A PD** *020 †55,03

TATE, Harry Brackenridge. 700 NE 13TH ST 73104 #039-01-1963 L1963 **NS** *071 †25

TAWK, Maroun Michel. 825 NE 10TH ST, STE 2500 73104 #605-02-1996 L1999 **PCC** *020 †20

TAYLOR, Andrea Michele. 6601 W HEFNER RD, INTEGRIS FAMILY CARE NORTH 73162 #051-01-2004 L2007 **FM** *020 †18

TAYLOR, Bruce John. 619 NE 13TH ST 73104 #671-01-1980 L1987 **D** *020

TAYLOR, Charles Dewitt. 4409 N CLASSEN BLVD 73118 #039-01-1968 L1969 **GP GPM** *020

TAYLOR, Fletcher B, Jr. 825 NE 13TH ST 73104 #065-02-1956 L1975 **HEM PTH** *050

TAYLOR, Fletcher Brandon. 825 NE 13TH ST, OKLAHOMA MEDICAL RESEARCH 73104 #039-01-1986 L1988 **P** *020 †75

TAYLOR, Geoffrey Layne. 5501 N PORTLAND AVE 73112 #039-01-2001 L2005 **AN** *020 †05

TAYLOR, John R. 5701 N PORTLAND AVE, STE B102 73112 #039-01-1987 L1988 **RO** *020 †80

TAYLOR, Lisa Danelehart. 4514 MEMORIAL CIR, STE B 73142 #039-01-1990 L1991 **GS** *020 †85,65

TAYLOR, Michael David. 921 NE 13TH ST, RM 7F-110 73104 #001-06-1989 L1996 **AN** *020 †05 ‡

TAYLOR, Morgan Lucas. ■ 73139 #039-01-2008 *012

TAYLOR-ALBERT, Elizabeth. 4200 W MEMORIAL RD, STE 812 73120 #036-07-1987 L1988 **RHU IM** *020 †20

TEAGUE, David Carlton. 825 NE 10TH ST 73104 #048-12-1988 L1989 **ORS OTR** *020 †40

TENNERY, Paul Lawrence. 1919 E MEMORIAL RD, MERCY HEALTH EDMOND 73131 #039-01-1995 L1997 **FM** *020 †18

TERRAZAS, Nadine A. ■ 73118 #048-13-2007 L2007 **PD** *012

TERRELL, Mendy Renee. ■ 73120 #305-01-2007 L2007 **FP** *012

TFAYLI, Arafat Hussein. 920 SL YOUNG BLVD, STE WP2040 73104 #605-01-1995 L2002 **ON** *020 †20

THACKARA, Candis Michelle. 940 STANTON L YOUNG BLVD 73104 #422-01-2004 L2006 **GS** *020

THADANI, Dorothy Ann. 826 NW 11TH ST 73106 #917-26-1969 L1980 **GE IM** *071 †20

THADANI, Udho. 920 SL YOUNG, DEPT CARDIOLOGY 73104 #495-36-1964 L1980 **CD IM** *040

THANOU, Aikaterini. ■ 73112 #418-01-2003 L2006 *100

THAYER, James Frank. 11101 HEFNER POINTE DR, STE 105 73120 #039-01-1978 L1979 **EM** *020 †18

THOMAS, Jibi. 12912 BETH CT 73120 #048-16-2000 L2002 **DR** *020 †80

THOMAS, Johnny Andrew. 1420 NW 32ND ST 73118 #039-01-2005 L2006 **AN** *012

THOMAS, Ralph Cullen. 4140 W MEMORIAL RD 73120 #019-02-1972 L1981 **GS LM** *020 †85

THOMAS, Robert Ty. 708 NE 15TH ST 73104 #039-01-2005 L2005 **PM** *012

THOMPSON, Bruce Doyle, Sr. 4510 NW 39TH ST 73122 #039-01-1989 L2006 **IM FM** *020

THOMPSON, Chad Glenn. ■ 73114 #048-15-2005 L2006 **DR** *012

THOMPSON, Christopher Law. ■ 73104 #039-01-2006 L2008 **IM** *012

THOMPSON, David Leslie. 3366 NW EXPRESSWAY, KIDNEY SPECIALISTS OF 73112 #039-79-1997, ▲ L2002 **CCM** *020 †20

THOMPSON, J Spencer. 825 NE 10TH ST STE 143, OU HEALTH SCIENCE CTR 73104 #049-01-1989 L2006 **RO** *020 †80

THOMPSON, Julie Michelle. 4200 W MEMORIAL RD, STE 703 73120 #039-01-2002 L2005 **AN** *020 †05

THOMPSON, Kenneth Geo. 3300 NW EXPRESSWAY 73112 #035-09-1966 L1972 **OBG** *071 †30

THOMPSON, Robert B. 8121 NATIONAL AVE 73112 #039-01-1972 L1973 **ORS** *020 †40

THOMPSON, Roger Allen. 608 NW 9TH ST, STE 3000 73102 #039-01-1988 L1989 **PD** *020

THOMPSON, Saunders James. ■ 73111 #010-03-1953 L1955 **GP** *071

THOMPSON-MATHEW, Miriam E. 900 NE 10TH ST 73104 #039-01-2005 L2007 **FP** *012

THURMAN, William Gentry. 6608 N WESTERN AVE, APT 609 73116 #067-01-1954 L1954 **PD PHO** *071 †55

TIBBS, Robert Eugene, Jr. 4120 W MEMORIAL RD STE 300 73120 #001-02-1993 L2001 **NS** *020 †20

TIENABESO, Sopukro Wenike. 921 NE 13TH ST, VA MEDICAL CENTER 73104 #690-02-1984 L2005 **IM** *020 †20

TIERNEY, William Mckeever. 825 NE 10TH ST RM 2300 73104 #008-01-1990 L1997 **GE** *040 †20

TILAK, Monala Dharmaraj V. 920 STANTON L YOUNG BLVD 73104 #495-16-1984 L2000 **AN** *020 †05

TILLINGHAST, Jon Dalton. 921 NE 23RD ST 73105 #039-01-1965 L1965 **PHP** *030 †70

TINKER, Renee Ann. ■ 73112 #039-01-1984 *075

TINTERA, Nicole Lorraine. ■ 73112 #039-01-2008 *012

TIPTON, David Brent. 5100 N BROOKLINE AVE, STE 530 73112 #039-01-1988 L1993 **PM OS** *020 †60

TJAUW, Tjhi Wen. 3366 NW EXPRESSWAY, STE 140 73112 #041-02-1993 L2006 **RNR** *020 †80

TKACH, Stephen. 1110 N LEE AVE 73103 #019-02-1960 L1964 **ORS** *071 †40

TKACH, Thomas Kelly. 9600 BROADWAY EXT 73114 #039-01-1989 L1990 **ORS OAR** *020 †40

TLUCEK, Paul Stanley. ■ 73114 #039-01-2007 L2007 **IM** *012

TOAL, Kyle Wilson. 1044 SW 44TH ST 73109 #039-01-1980 L1981 **TS PD** *020 †85,90

TOALSON, Thomas Wade. 608 NW 9TH ST STE 1100 73102 #039-01-1987 L1990 **FM** *040 †18

TOBIAS, Robert David. 13420 N PENN AVE, FIRSTMED URGENT CARE 73120 #038-40-1983 L2002 **FM OM** *020 †18

TODD, Robert Arnold, Jr. 3500 NW 56TH ST STE 100, GREAT PLAINS FAMILY PRACTI 73112 #039-01-2004 L2006 **FM** *020

TOLBERT, Bernadine. 3625 NW 56TH ST, INDIAN HEALTH SERVICE 73112 #010-03-1978 L1979 **DIA IM** *030 †20

TOLLETT, Charles A, Sr. 700 NE 13TH ST 73104 #041-13-1952 L1957 **GS** *071 †85

TOMA, Aleda Ann. 3525 NW 56TH ST 73112 #039-01-1984 L1985 **HEM ON** *020 †20

TOMA, Gigi Jim. 608 NW 9TH ST, STE 6200 73102 #039-01-1987 L1988 **IM** *020 †20

TOMPKINS, John Fulton. 921 NE 13TH ST 73104 #039-01-1981 L1982 **ORS** *020 †40

TOMPKINS, S Fulton. 3435 NW 56TH ST 73112 #028-02-1942 L1950 **ORS** *071 †40

TORTORICI, Troy Anthony. 3300 NW EXPRESSWAY 73112 #039-01-1993 L1995 **AN** *020 †05

TOTH, Stephanie Jayne. 900 NE 10TH ST 73104 #039-01-2006 L2007 **FP** *012

TOTORO, James Amedio. 4205 MCAULEY BLVD, STE 615 73120 #039-01-1975 L1976 **GS VS** *020 †85

TOWNSEND, Timothy Doyle. 940 NE 13TH ST, RM 3N3409 73104 #039-01-2004 L2006 **MPD** *012

TRAN, Tony Huu. ■ 73118 #039-01-2008 *012

TRAUTMAN, Richard Philip. 920 STANTON L YOUNG BLVD 73104 #039-01-1971 L1972 **P ADP** *040 †75

TRAVIS, Stephen R. 940 STANTON L YOUNG BLVD 73104 #048-13-1996 L1997 **MPD** *020 †20,55

TRAXLER, Walter Thos. 921 NE 13TH ST, MENTAL HLTH SERVICES 73104 #027-01-1976 L1982 **P** *020

TRAYNOR, Matthew Preston. 608 STANTON L YOUNG BLVD, DEAN MCGEE EYE INSTITUTE 73104 #051-01-2004 L2005 **OPH** *012

TRIBBEY, Michael Alpheus. 4120 W MEMORIAL RD, STE 218 73120 #039-01-1977 L1978 **N CN** *020 †75

TRIGLER, Lucas. 608 STANTON L YOUNG BLVD, DEAN A MCGEE EYE INSTITUTE 73104 #010-01-1998 L2000 **OPH PO** *020 †35

TROTTER, Timothy Howard. 920 STANTON L YOUNG BLVD 73104 #039-01-1985 L1986 **TS GS** *020 †35

TROY, Jerry Robt. 7100 N CLASSEN BLVD 73116 #039-01-1969 L1970 **OM FM** *071 †18 ‡

TRUELS, William Paul. 5701 N PORTLAND AVE, STE 120 73112 #016-11-1973 L1974 **GS** *020 †85

TRUITT, Linda Jo. 3435 NW 56TH ST, STE 404 73112 #039-01-1990 L1991 **OBG** *020 †30

TRUONG, Hung Kim. 940 STANTON L YOUNG BLVD 73104 #039-79-2005, ▲ L2006 **IM** *012

TRUONG, Terrence Thao. 3500 NW 56TH ST, STE 100 73112 #048-14-1988 L1989 **FM** *020 †18

TU, Duc Minh. 1111 N LEE AVE, STE 235 73103 #039-01-1988 L1990 **FM** *020 †18 ‡

TUCKER, Phebe Mary. 920 STANTON L YOUNG BLVD 73104 #039-01-1985 L1986 **P** *040 †75

TUFAIL, Humayun. 940 STANTON L YOUNG BLVD 73104 #704-01-1994 L2007 **IM** *012

TUGGLE, David Wayne. 1200 EVERETT DR, STE 2320 73104 #048-12-1979 L1985 **PDS CCM** *020 †85

TUNELL, William Patrick. 920 STANTON L YOUNG BLVD, 3RD FL 73104 #035-20-1959 L1976 **PDS** *071 †85,90

TUNNELL, Ira Earl. ■ 73142 #048-02-1967 L1967 **P** *020

TURMAN, Martin Allan. 940 NE 13TH ST 73104 #007-02-1985 L2001 **PD PN** *020 †55

TUTT, Donald Lee. 4401 S WESTERN AVE 73109 #039-01-1965 L1966 **AN FM** *020

TWITCHELL, Annette. 1025 STRAKA TER 73139 #028-02-1973 L1974 **FM** *071 †18

TYNDALL, Robert J. 3400 NORTHWEST EXPY # 312, BLDG C 73112 #039-01-1985 L1993 **N** *020 †75

UNSELL, Robert Stanley. 6205 N SANTA FE AVE, STE 200 73118 #005-12-1976 L1995 **HS ORS** *100

VACCARO, Mark Clayton. 4401 S WESTERN AVE 73109 #023-01-1977 L1997 **DR** *020 †80

VAD, Bal Gangadhar. 3801 NW 63RD ST, STE 160 73116 #495-28-1965 L1982 **P FM** *020

VAD, Lata B. 3801 NW 63RD ST 73116 #495-45-1972 L1982 **P** *020

VANNATTA, Jerry Burr. 825 NE 10TH ST, STE 4500 73104 #039-01-1975 L1976 **IM** *020 †20

VARGAS, Jorge Alberto R M. ■ 73122 #275-01-1943 L1974 **P** *071

VARGHESE, Sally. 6613 N MERIDIAN AVE 73116 #495-33-1974 L1979 **CHP P** *020 †75

VASA, Usha Rohitkumar. 840 RESEARCH PKWY, LAB CORP 73104 #495-23-1970 L1994 **PTH PCP** *020 †50

VASAMREDDY, Chandrasekhar. 920 STANTON L YOUNG BLVD, WP 3010 73104 #495-70-1995 L2005 **CD** *012 †20

VAUGHAN, Virginia Lynn. 11200 N PORTLAND AVE, FL 2 73120 #039-01-1985 L1986 **OBG** *020 †30 ‡

VAVRICKA, Timothy Alan. 3174 NW EXPRESSWAY 73112 #039-01-2005 L2006 **GS** *012

VENKATARAMAN, Pankaja S. P O BOX 26901, NEONATOLOGY SECTION 73190 #495-53-1973 L1982 **NPM PD** *062 †55

VENKATARAMAN, Tirunelveli. 1110 N CLASSEN BLVD # 200 73106 #495-04-1970 L1982 **NEP IM** *020 †20

VERBRUGGHE, Dirk Bart. 940 NE 13TH ST STE 3409N, OU CHILDREN'S HOSPITAL 73104 #041-15-2004 L2006 **PD** *100 †55

VICTORIA, Maria Elizabeth. ■ 73120 #012-21-2006 L2007 **FP** *012

VIDAILLET, Humberto J. 940 NE 13TH ST RM 2B 73104 #275-01-1952 L1971 **PD** *020 †55

VIJ, Vikas. 3366 NW EXPRESSWAY, STE 140 73112 #039-01-1999 L2006 **RNR** *020 †80

VINCENT, Michael Don. 4140 W MEMORIAL RD, STE 413 73120 #039-01-1981 L1982 **PD** *020 †55

VINEKAR, Shreekumar S. 920 STANTON L YOUNG BLVD 73104 #495-01-1966 L1974 **P CHP** *020 †75

VIOLETT, Theodore Willis. 1000 N LEE AVE 73102 #039-01-1956 L1956 **PTH BBK** *071 †50 ‡

VISOR, Ricky Lynn. 4140 W MEMORIAL RD, STE 115 73120 #039-01-1989 L1998 **OTO** *020 †45

VODA, Jan. 14613 N KELLY AVE, ARCTIC EDGE 73103 #286-02-1968 L1983 **CD IM** *020 †20

VOGEL, Thomas Edward. 1016 SW 44TH ST, STE 500 73109 #039-01-1965 L1965 **GS FM** *071

VORSE, Hal Benton. 8315 S WALKER AVE, OKLAHOMA CITY CLINIC-SOUTH 73139 #039-01-1968 L1968 **PD ADL** *071 †55

VOSKUHL, Gene Wayne. 1200 EVERETT DR RM 6, 3513 NW 69TH 73104 #039-01-1993 L1994 **ID** *020 †20

VOSS-ALVAREZ, Barbara L. 11000 HEFNER POINTE DR 73120 #039-01-1984 L1985 **U** *020 †95

VOTH, Douglas Wade. POB 26901, 1110 N STONEWALL AVE 73190 #019-02-1959 L1973 **IM ID** *030 †20

VU, David De. 701 NE 10TH ST 73104 #039-01-1996 L1997 **FM** *020 †18

VU, Dzi Van. 921 NE 13TH ST STE 11C, VAMC 73104 #840-01-1969 L1984 **IM** *020 †20

VUONG, Andrew. 2825 PARKLAWN DR 73110 #422-01-2004 L2006 **FM** *020 †20

VYAS, Avinash Chandra. 8121 NATIONAL AVE 73110 #495-20-1969 L1977 **IM** *020 †20

WAGGAMAN, Suzanne. 6060 W BRITTON RD # D 73132 #654-01-1995 *100

WAGNER, Andrew Frederick. 825 NE 10TH ST, STE 3300 73104 #056-05-1999 L2005 **OBG MG** *020 †19,30

WAGNON, Marion Carol. 1201 S DOUGLAS BLVD, MIDWEST MEDICAL GROUP 73130 #039-01-1960 L1961 **FM GS** *020 †18

WAINGANKAR, Gauri S. 4400 WILL ROGERS PKWY 73108 #496-38-1974 L1981 **AN** *020 †05

WAJSBORT, Richard. 2925 UNITED FOUNDERS BLVD 73112 #561-19-1984 L1995 **PTH** *075

WALFORD, Andrew J. 940 NE 13TH ST, 4 BIELSTEIN ROOM 138 73104 #917-05-1974 L1988 **AN PAN** *020 †05

WALIA, Jo Jud. 4200 W MEMORIAL RD, STE 907 73120 #352-01-1970 L1981 **AN** *071 †05

WALKER, Gary Van. 5501 N PORTLAND AVE 73112 #039-01-1984 L1985 **FM** *020

WALKER, Joan Leslie. 825 NE 10TH ST 73104 #005-14-1982 L1990 **GO OBG** *050 †30

WALL, James Frank. 5701 N PORTLAND AVE, STE 220 73112 #039-01-1983 L1984 **OBG** *020 †30 ‡

WALL, Raymond Louie. 8600 S PENN AVE 73159 #039-01-1984 L1985 **FM** *020 †20

WALLIS, Clinton Graves. 3366 NW EXPRESSWAY, STE 400 73112 #654-01-1998 L1998 **GE** *020 †20

WALRAVEN, James Edward. 5701 N PORTLAND AVE # 120, 7600 NW 23RD ST 73112 #039-01-1965 L1965 **IM OS** *020

WALTER, Max Gregory. 825 NE 10TH ST, STE 4500 73104 #007-02-1961 L1963 **DR** *020 †80
WALTERS, Roland A, III. 5701 N PORTLAND AVE # 101 73112 #039-01-1968 L1968 **OPH** *020 †35 ‡
WANG, Shirley Y. 825 NE 13TH ST, MAILBOX 54 73104 #019-02-2003 L2006 **RHU** *012
WANG, Shu-Ming. 9100 N MAY AVE 73120 #054-04-1988 L2008 **FM** *020 †18
WANI, Lubna Bashir. 920 SL YOUNG BLVD, WP 3010 73104 #495-51-1998 L2007 **IM** *020 †20
WARD, Deanna L. 608 NW 9TH ST STE 1 73102 #048-14-2006 L2007 **FP** *012
WARD, Harper Ryan. ■ 73112 #039-01-2007 L2007 **AN** *012
WARD, Kent Edward. 940 NE 13TH ST, PEDIATRIC CARDIOLOGY SECTI 73190 #048-02-1979 L1980 **PDC PD** *020 †55
WARDEN, Douglas W. ■ 73162 #048-16-2006 L2007 **PTH** *012
WARDEN, Julie G. ■ 73162 #048-16-2006 L2007 **AN** *012
WARDEN, Michelle Lacroix. 3300 NW EXPRESSWAY 73112 #004-01-2000 L2001 **DR** *020 †80
WARE, Michelle. 3140 W BRITTON RD, STE B 73120 #039-01-1992 L1993 **CHP P** *020
WARNER, Ernest Gregor. 3433 NW 56TH ST, STE 970 73112 #016-11-1955 L1960 **N PM** *020 †20
WARREN, Jill Stewart. 940 NE 13TH ST 73104 #055-01-1992 L1993 **PD** *040 †55
WASEMILLER, Wayne Lee. 4120 W MEMORIAL RD, STE 218 73120 #039-01-1975 L1976 **N EM** *075
WASEMILLER-SMITH, Lisa J. 5501 N PORTLAND AVE 73112 #039-01-1980 L1981 **OBG** *020 †30
WASHBURN, Tonya Cress. 721 NW 6TH ST STE 201 73102 #039-01-1988 L1992 **PM** *020 †60
WATERS, Dan Neal. 4401 S WESTERN AVE 73109 #039-01-1983 L1984 **FM** *020 †18
WATTS, Deana Shackelford. 608 STANTON L YOUNG BLVD 73104 #039-01-1994 L2000 **OPH** *020 †35
WAUGH, Walter Scott. 900 NE 10TH ST 73104 #039-01-2004 L2007 **FSM** *012 †18
WAYMAN, Misty Lynn. 4140 W MEMORIAL RD, CENTER FOR WOMENS HEALTH 73120 #039-01-2000 L2004 **OBG** *020 ‡
WEBB, Kent Harris. 1000 SW 44TH ST, STE 100 73109 #039-01-1983 L1984 **GS VS** *020 †85
WEBB, Kevin Robert. ■ 73134 #039-01-2008 #012
WEBB, Teddy Eugene. 5201 W MEMORIAL RD 73142 #039-01-1977 L1978 **FM** *020 †18
WEBB, Tyler Alan. ■ 73120 #039-01-2008 *012
WEBER, Fred W. 3033 NW 63RD ST STE 208E 73116 #039-01-1951 L1951 **P** *020 †75
WEESE, Joshua Michael. ■ 73135 #039-01-2007 L2007 **IM** *012
WEIGAND, Dennis Allen. 619 NE 13TH ST 73104 #039-01-1963 L1963 **D DMP** *040 †15
WEIR, Kurtis Don. 1240 SW 44TH ST 73109 #039-01-1992 L1993 **OPH** *020 †35
WEISSMAN, Mark. 4200 S DOUGLAS AVE, SOUTH COMMUNITY MEDICAL CE 73109 #035-09-1974 L1985 **CD IM** *020 †20
WELBORN, Toney Lee. 900 NE 10TH ST 73104 #039-01-2000 L2001 **FM** *020 †18 ‡
WELCH, Martin Henry. 825 NE 10TH ST, STE 2500 73104 #056-05-1961 L1968 **PCC IM** *040 †20
WELCH, Richard Walter. 3366 NW EXPRESSWAY, STE 400 73112 #016-11-1968 L1981 **GE IM** *071 †20
WELLS, James Howard. 750 NE 13TH ST, FL 3 73104 #025-01-1963 L1972 **A IM** *020 †03,20 ‡
WELLS, William J. 1200 EVERETT DR, FLOOR, NEONATOLOGY 73104 #048-02-1995 L2004 **MPD** *020 †20,55
WENDELKEN, James Robt. 1211 N SHARTEL AVE, STE 300 73103 #039-01-1972 L1973 **U** *020 †95
WENZL, James Emmett. 825 NE 10TH ST, STE 4500 73104 #030-06-1959 L1967 **NEP PD** *020 †55
WEST, Eileen Chisholm. 825 NE 10TH ST STE 2300, OU PHYSICIANS/OU HEALTH CE 73104 #008-02-1998 L2002 **IM** *020 †20
WEST, Eric Alan. 4221 S WESTERN AVE # 3030 73109 #039-01-1995 L1996 **MPD** *020
WHEELER, Samuel Arthur. 8600 S PENNSYLVANIA AVE, INTEGRIS FAMILY CARE 73159 #039-01-1970 L1971 **FM** *020 †18
WHELAN, Sean Micheal. ■ 73116 #039-01-2007 L2007 **P** *012
WHITCOMB, Walter H. 921 NE 13TH ST 73104 #039-01-1953 L1953 **PM IMG** *071 †28
WHITE, Benjamin Thomas. 1000 N LINCOLN BLVD, STE 300 73104 #023-07-1994 L2000 **NS** *020 †25
WHITE, Christopher. 920 SL YOUNG BLVD, WP 1380 73104 #039-01-1998 L2006 **ORS** *020 †40
WHITE, James Porter. 3366 NW EXPRESSWAY, STE 500 73112 #039-01-1978 L1979 **IM OS** *030 †20
WHITE, Kevin Lyle. 5501 N PORTLAND AVE 73112 #039-01-2000 L2004 **EM** *020 †16
WHITE, Robert, Jr. 3330 NW 56TH ST, PRIMARY CARE PARTNERS OF 73112 #004-01-1982 L1991 **IM** *020 †20
WHITE, Traci Lynne. 125 NW 15TH ST 73103 #039-01-2004 L2004 **AN** *012
WHITSETT, Thomas Leroy. 920 SL YOUNG BLVD, RM WP3010 73104 #039-01-1962 L1962 **VM IM** *020 †20
WHITTINGTON, Kenneth Wm. 5501 N PORTLAND AVE 73112 #039-01-1968 L1968 **FM** *030 †18
WICKERSHAM, Elizabeth A. 13301 N MERIDIAN AVE, STE 702 73120 #039-01-1996 L1997 **FM** *020 †18 ‡
WIENECKE, Gretchen Miller. 750 NE 13TH ST STE 200, DEPARTMENT OF ANESTHESIOLO 73104 #039-01-1990 L1997 **APM** *020 †05
WIENECKE, Robert Jerome. 4120 W MEMORIAL RD 73120 #039-01-1998 L1999 **NS** *020 †25
WILD, Robert Allen. 920 SL YOUNG, RM 2410WP 73104 #028-03-1971 L1988 **REN GYN** *020 †30
WILES, Leslie Howard. 6625 NW 119TH ST 73162 #016-11-1976 L1977 **EM** *020 †16
WILEY, Clarence L. 1211 N SHARTEL AVE, STE 407 73103 #043-01-1977 L1981 **D DS** *020 †15
WILKES, Byron Nicholas. 608 STANTON L YOUNG BLVD 73104 #004-01-2006 L2007 **OPH** *012
WILKS, Jonathan David. 4140 W MEMORIAL RD, STE 208 73120 #039-01-1995 L1999 **IM** *020 †20
WILKS, Karen Eyler. 4140 W MEMORIAL RD STE 5 73120 #039-01-1995 L1999 **OBG** *020 †30
WILLEITNER, Andrea S. 1200 EVERETT DR 73104 #409-33-1993 L2007 **PD** *100 †55
WILLIAMS, Curtis Brian. 3433 NW 56TH ST, STE 800 73104 #039-01-1998 L1999 **IM** *020 †20
WILLIAMS, Cyndi Nicole. ■ 73105 #039-01-2008 *012
WILLIAMS, David Collier. 920 SL YOUNG BLVD, NEPHROLOGY / WP2250 73104 #039-01-2001 L2002 **NEP** *020
WILLIAMS, Elizabeth Anne. 4400 WILL ROGERS PKWY, STE 105 73108 #039-01-1988 L1989 **AN** *020 †05
WILLIAMS, Elwood F. 4140 W MEMORIAL RD, STE 421 73120 #039-01-1984 L1990 **PUD IM** *020 †20
WILLIAMS, John Michael. 3400 NORTHWEST EXPY 73112 #039-01-1992 L1993 **CD** *020 †20
WILLIAMS, Julie Deanna. 3816 N MERIDIAN, STE 113 73112 #039-01-1996 L1997 **P** *020
WILLIAMS, Kenneth Dixon. 1200 EVERETT DR 10TH, CHILDREN'S HOSPITAL 73104 #039-01-2005 L2007 **MPD** *012
WILLIAMS, Lance Dean. 4401 S WESTERN AVE 73109 #039-01-1996 L1997 **EM** *020 †16
WILLIAMS, Olatunji W. 940 NE 13TH ST, CHO 3409 73104 #048-02-1999 L2000 **PDP** *100 †55

WILLIAMS, Philip Dwight. 10812 LAKESIDE DR 73104 #039-01-1998 L2004 **IM** *020 †20
WILLIAMS, Wesley Mark. 600 NATIONAL AVE 73110 #039-01-1997 L2000 **FM** *020 †18
WILLIAMSON, Clinton Ross. ■ 73162 #012-05-2005 L2006 **DR** *012
WILLIAMSON, Paul. 3330 NW 56TH ST, STE 500 73112 #019-02-1974 L2002 **FM** *020 †18
WILLIS, Jon Thos. 3300 NW EXPRESSWAY 73112 #039-01-1965 L1965 **AN** *020
WILLIS, Larry Grant. 3555 NW 58TH ST, STE 800 73112 #039-01-1974 L1975 **RHU IM** *020 †20
WILSON, Brent Curtiss. 5501 N PORTLAND AVE 73112 #005-12-1989 L1990 **EM** *020 †16
WILSON, David Scott. 921 NE 13TH ST, VA MEDICAL CENTER 73104 #016-01-1999 L2002 **IM** *020 †20
WILSON, Don Allen. 940 NE 13TH ST 73104 #039-01-1967 L1967 **RNR PDR** *020 †20 ‡
WILSON, Frank Fredrick. 702 NE 37TH ST 73105 #010-03-1961 L1965 **OBG** *071 †30
WILSON, Gary Waine. 7101 NW EXPWY STE 335, CLEAR SIGHT CENTER 73132 #039-01-1968 L1975 **OPH** *035
WILSON, Ian George. PO BOX 53188, DEPT ANES 73152 #919-02-1979 L1990 **AN** *020
WILSON, Jacquelyn L G. 3300 NW EXPRESSWAY 73112 #010-03-1962 L1966 **PD** *071 †55
WILSON, Lorraine Theresa. 4140 W MEMORIAL RD, STE 518 73120 #039-01-1978 L1979 **NEP IM** *020 †20
WILSON, Ralph Courtney. 1000 N LEE AVE 73102 #021-01-1954 L1966 **R** *071 †80
WILSON, Richard Lynn. 8121 NATIONAL AVE 73110 #039-01-1979 L1984 **GS** *020 †85
WILSON, Robert G. 2224 NW 50TH ST STE 276W, SMS 73112 #001-02-1961 L1965 **R NM** *071 †80,28 ‡
WILSON, Robert Lyon. 4201 S WESTERN AVE 73109 #039-01-1980 L1981 **GE IM** *020 †20
WILSON, Vivian Laverne. 700 NW 24TH ST, INTEGRIS PRO HEALTH PHYSIC 73103 #007-02-1977 L1978 **FM** *020 †18
WIMBLY, Timothy. ■ 73136 #038-45-1985 L1993 **GS** *020
WINFREE, Kersey Lee. 1111 N LEE AVE 73103 #039-01-1985 L1986 **IM** *030 †20
WINN, Peter Arkell-Scott. 900 NE 10TH ST 73104 #067-01-1978 L1984 **FM FPG** *020 †18
WINNETT, Albert R. PO BOX 15598 73155 #065-05-1967 L1985 *075
WINSLOW, Clinton Alan. 4300 S SHIELDS BLVD 73129 #039-01-1983 L1984 **FM** *020 ‡
WINTERS, Michael David. 3435 NW 56TH ST, STE 206 73112 #039-01-1990 L1991 **GE** *020 ‡
WINZENREAD, Michael Leo. 4200 W MEMORIAL RD, STE 310 73120 #039-01-1975 L1978 **FM** *020 †18
WIRSING, Robyn Joanne. 608 NW 9TH ST STE 1000, ST ANTHONY HOSP 73102 #104-01-2007 L2007 **FP** *012
WISDOM, Peggy Jean. 721 STANTON L YOUNG BLVD, STE 211 73190 #039-01-1972 L1973 **N** *020 †75
WISE, James Berry. 3435 NW 56TH ST, STE 1010 73112 #023-07-1961 L1965 **OPH** *020 †35 ‡
WLODAVER, Anne Godart. 1200 EVERETT DR, 7TH FLOOR, N PAVILION 73104 #165-07-1976 L1984 **NPM PD** *020 †55
WLODAVER, Clifford Grover. 3400 NW EXPRESSWAY, STE 410 73112 #035-20-1976 L1982 **ID IM** *020 †20
WOLF, Stephen Paul. 120 N ROBINSON AVE, STE 153W 73102 #039-01-1988 L1991 **IM IMG** *020 †20
WOLRAICH, Mark Lee. 1100 NE 13TH ST, THE CHILD STUDY CTR 73117 #035-15-1970 L2001 **PD** *040 †55
WOMACK, Charles Erwin. 5252 N MERIDIAN AVE, STE 105 73112 #039-01-1973 L1974 **FM** *020
WOMBLE, Joe Russell. 711 STANTON L YOUNG BLVD, INTERNAL MEDICINE CLINIC 73104 #048-15-2006 L2007 **IM** *012
WONG, Carson. 920 STANTON L YOUNG BLVD, DEPT UROLOGY WP3150 73104 #065-06-1995 L2003 **U** *040 †95
WOOD, Kevin Lee. 4120 W MEMORIAL RD STE 206, NEUROSCIENCE INSTITUTE 73120 #039-01-1988 L1989 **N** *020 †75
WOOD, Mark Wayne. 3400 NW 56TH ST 73112 #039-01-1988 L1990 **NO** *020 †45
WOODALL, Martin A. 1635 NW 38TH ST 73118 #047-06-1960 L1980 **PD PDC** *071 †55
WOODS, Bronwyn Leigh. 3400 NW EXPRESSWAY STE 500, INTEGRIS FAMILY MEDICINE C 73112 #001-06-2000 L2003 **FM** *020 †18
WOODSON, Alexa. 3433 NW 56TH ST 73112 #039-01-1992 L1997 **FM** *020 †18
WOODSON, Benjamin Warren. ■ 73116 #027-01-2005 L2007 **GS** *100
WOODSON, Mark Robt. 3433 NW 56TH ST STE 580 73112 #039-01-1992 L1995 **FM** *020 †18
WOODWARD, Neil W, Jr. 4200 W MEMORIAL RD STE 909 73120 #039-01-1956 L1956 **CRS GS** *020 †85
WORCESTER, Gary Lee. 3433 NW 56TH ST STE 400, PLAZA MEDICAL GROUP, P.C. 73112 #039-01-1974 L1975 **CD IM** *020 †20
WORLEY, James W. 940 NE 13TH ST 73104 #039-01-1960 L1960 **PD** *071 †55
WRIGHT, Harlan Inaki. 3300 NW EXPRESSWAY, NZIT 73112 #935-01-1981 L1993 **HEP GE** *020
WRIGHT, Michael Hill. 3115 SW 89TH ST 73159 #043-01-1988 L1998 **ORS OSS** *020 †40
WRIGHT, Paul Eric. 608 NW 9TH ST STE 1000, FAM PRAC RESIDENCY 73102 #023-12-1985 L1995 **FM AM** *020 †18
WRIGHT, Phillip Jay. 3433 NW 56TH ST STE 630 73112 #039-01-1961 L1961 **RHU HEM** *075 †20
WRIGHT, Ronald Eugene. 1228 SW 44TH ST 73109 #039-01-1969 L1969 **OTO** *020 †45
WYATT, Eric Lee. 3400 NW EXPRESSWAY, STE 440 73112 #039-01-1994 L1995 **D** *020 †15
WYNN, Donny. ■ 73104 #039-01-2006 L2006 **IM** *012
YACOUB, Emad Rafla. 14900 N PENNSYLVANIA AVE, APT 1637 73134 #915-04-1978 *071
YAFFE, Angela Kay. ■ 73139 #039-01-2008 *012
YANG, Jian Tao. 940 SL YOUNG BLVD RM 451, OU HEALTH SCIENCES CENTER 73104 #243-65-1982 L2002 **PTH** *040 †50
YANG, John Chieh. 1921 NW 23RD ST 73106 #039-01-1979 L1980 **FM** *020 †18
YASIN, Muhammad. 4221 S WESTERN AVE # 2010, SOUTHWEST CARDIOLOGY ASSOC 73109 #704-04-1971 L1978 **CD IM** *020 †20
YASSER, Sadia. 711 STANTON L YOUNG BLVD, BLVD/STE 215 73104 #704-09-1997 L2006 **N** *012
YASUDA, Paul Steven. 3300 NW EXPRESSWAY 73112 #034-01-1989 L1990 **AN** *020 †05
YATES, Carlan Kent. 9600 BROADWAY EXT 73114 #039-01-1981 L1982 **ORS** *020 †40
YATES, Gaylan Dean. 14101 PARKWAY COMMONS DR 73134 #039-01-1984 L1985 **AN PME** *020 †05
YATES, Leo Everett. 4401 S WESTERN AVE 73109 #047-06-1961 L1962 **FM** *071
YEICH, Stephen Major. 4200 W MEMORIAL RD, STE 703 73120 #034-01-1976 L1987 **AN** *020 †05 ‡
YEN, Ervin Stone. 1111 N LEE AVE, STE 236 73103 #039-01-1981 L1982 **AN** *020 ‡
YERRA, Vanama. 921 NE 13TH ST # 136A1 73104 #495-11-1995 L2003 **IMG** *020
YOCUM, Harold Amos. 920 STANTON L YOUNG BLVD, STE WP-1380 73104 #041-02-1968 L1998 **HS ORS** *020 †40 ‡
YONAHARA, Maria Sachiko. 900 NE 10TH ST 73104 #422-01-2004 L2006 **FM** *020
YONG, Ye. 3300 NW EXPRESSWAY 73112 #243-52-1983 L1996 **TTS** *020

■ = Address Information Privacy Protected

YOUKHANA, Kellee. 3330 NW 56TH ST STE 3 73112 #039-01-1995 L1996 **MPD** *020 †20,55

YOUNG, Colin Henry. PO BOX 53188 73152 #919-03-1981 L1989 *100

YOUNG, Kathryn Shroyer. 3400 NW EXPRESSWAY STE 830 73112 #039-01-1985 L1986 **PD** *020 †55

YOUNG, Marianne Misciagna. 1000 N LEE AVE, SAINT ANTHONY HOSPITAL 73102 #023-12-1983 L1991 **RO** *020 †80

YOUNG, Mary Janice. ■ 73105 #039-01-1987 L2007 **P** *012

YOUNG, R B, II. 7378 S WALKER AVE, FAMILYCHOICE CLINICS 73139 #039-01-1991 L1992 **FM** *020

YOUSUF, Khalid Mohammed. ■ 73112 #021-05-2006 L2007 **ORS** *012

YUTHAS, John Sigfred. 5501 N PORTLAND AVE 73112 #039-01-1990 L1993 **EM** *074 †16

ZACHARIAS, Soni Jose. 920 SL YOUNG BLVD, WP 1130 73104 #495-63-1999 L2006 **IM** *100 †20

ZACKER, Stephen Paul. 5100 N BROOKLINE AVE, STE 790 73112 #039-01-1993 L1997 **AN** *020 †05

ZAHOOR, Abid. 940 STANTON L YOUNG BLVD 73104 #704-21-1997 L2005 **P** *020

ZANOWIAK, Zachary Daniel. 4400 WILL ROGERS PKWY, STE 105 73108 #039-01-2002 L2003 **AN** *020 †05

ZAZA, Ali Samir. 4200 W MEMORIAL RD, STE 303 73120 #875-01-1978 L1999 **GS CCS** *020 †85

ZAZA, Isam. ■ 73142 #875-01-1987 L1998 **PTH** *020

ZEAVIN, Spencer Tracy. ■ 73132 #010-02-1987 L1989 **IM** *020

ZEIDERS, Gregory James. 6205 N SANTA FE AVE 73118 #039-79-1999, ▲ L2005 *020

ZELLER, Sarah Ann. ■ 73103 #026-04-2004 L2006 **D** *012

ZHANG, Roy R. 825 NE 10TH ST, STE 4500 73104 #243-47-1987 L2004 **PTH** *020 †50

ZHONG, Min. ■ 73103 #243-45-1988 L2007 **P** *012

ZIA, Ayesha Noor. 940 STANTON L YOUNG BLVD 73104 #704-01-2003 L2006 **PD** *100

ZSCHIESCHE, Opal M Bohall. 215 DEAN A MCGEE AVE, STE 350 FED OCCPTNL CLINIC 73102 #035-15-1963 L1965 **IM OM** *020

ZUBIALDE, John Pierre. 825 NE 10TH ST, STE 4500 73104 #034-01-1984 L1987 **FM** *020 †18

ZUERKER, Joe Carroll. 4200 W MEMORIAL RD, DISEASES INC 73120 #048-15-1981 L1982 **GE IM** *020 †20

ZUHDI, Mohamed Nazih. 3300 NW EXPRESSWAY 73112 #605-01-1950 L1959 **TS CD** *071 †85,90

ZUNA, Rosemary Elizabeth. 940 SL YOUNG BLVD 73104 #041-02-1972 L1996 **ATP** *040 †50

OKMULGEE – OKMULGEE

AJANAKU, Olakunle David. 1101 S BELMONT AVE, STE 104 74447 #690-02-1982 L1993 **IM PME** *020 †20

ALEXANDER, Thos Crawford. 1212 S BELMONT AVE 74447 #039-01-1963 L1963 **IM** *020

BAUMANN, Walter Eugene. 1214 S BELMONT AVE 74447 #030-05-1973 L1974 **U** *020 †95 ‡

GAGE, Kimberly Rochelle. 1401 MORRIS DR 74447 #039-01-1995 L1996 **EM** *020 †16

GARIS, John Arthur. 1101 S BELMONT AVE STE 102 74447 #039-01-1963 L1963 **GP** *020

GILLILAND, Stephen Reed. 1401 MORRIS DR 74447 #039-01-1975 L1976 **EM HOS** *020

KHAN, Jahangir. 1201 S BELMONT AVE, STE 104 74447 #704-15-1983 L1993 **FM** *020 †18

MALATI, Adel Ramzi M. 1201 S BELMONT AVE, STE 101 74447 #915-04-1980 L1994 **IM** *020 †20

MALATI, Hani Ramzi M. 1101 S BELMONT AVE, STE 101 74447 #915-04-1973 L1984 **OTO A** *020 ‡

MILLER, Raymond Delbert N. 211 N GRAND AVE 74447 #039-01-1945 L1946 **IM PHP** *072

MINTON, Larry Allen. 1101 S BELMONT AVE 74447 #025-07-1991 L1998 **OBG EM** *020

OSBORN, Edward Wendell. 1101 S BELMONT AVE, OKMULGEE PEDIATRICS 74447 #039-01-1973 L1976 **PD** *020 †55

PAUL, Naila. 1101 S BELMONT AVE, OKMULGEE PEDIATRICS 74447 #704-09-1984 L2002 **PD** *020 †55

PENNINGTON, Dennis Geo. 1201 S BELMONT AVE 74447 #039-01-1965 L1965 **DR** *020 †80

PETERS, Dale W. 400 W 6TH ST, CREOKS MENTAL HEALTH SERVI 74447 #019-02-1945 L1956 **P GPM** *071 †75

ROBINSON, Martha Milner. 114 N GRAND AVE, STE 508 74447 #023-07-1985 L1994 **D PD** *020 †55,15

SANDLIN, Michael Ethan. 1201 S BELMONT AVE STE 207 74447 #039-01-1968 L1968 **GS** *020 †85 ‡

TOLIVER, O Graham. 1401 MORRIS DR 74447 #028-02-1974 L1975 **PYG** *020 †75

YEUNG LAI WAH, Ah Fan. 1401 MORRIS DR 74447 #919-05-1977 L1984 **CD** *020 †20

OWASSO – TULSA

ARMSTRONG, Kris. 13600 E 86TH ST N, STE 400 74055 #039-01-1981 L1982 **FM GP** *020

BARNES, Sharon Sodano. 13600 E 86TH ST N, STE 400 74055 #039-01-1996 L1997 **FM** *020 †18

BENNETT, Marjorie Ann. 13600 E 86TH ST N, STE 100 74055 #048-02-1981 L1982 **IM** *020 †20

BLESCH, Lauri. 10512 N 110TH EAST AVE, STE 300 74055 #048-13-1987 L1991 **PD** *020 †55

COOK, Paul Alan. 10512 N 110TH EAST AVE, STE 100 74055 #048-15-1989 L2006 **OBG** *020 †30

DE SANDRE, Frank A, Jr. ■ 74055 #039-01-1990 L1991 **AN** *020 †05

FARRELL, Loretta A. 13600 E 86TH ST N, STE 100 74055 #035-45-1992 L1993 **FM** *020 †18

GIFFORD, Christopher G. 13600 E 86TH ST N, STE 400 74055 #030-06-1967 L1976 **A PD** *020 †55,03 ‡

GOROSPE, Luis Ventura. 10502 N 110TH EAST AVE, STE 310 74055 #748-07-1966 L1974 **GS GP** *020 †85

GREEN, Russell John. 10512 N 110TH EAST AVE, STE 220 74055 #048-14-1974 L1991 **OM FM** *030 †18,70

HOPKINS, Ashley Dawn. ■ 74055 #039-01-2008 *012

HORTON, Theresa Lynn. 10512 N 110TH EAST AVE, STE 300 74055 #039-01-1991 L1994 **PD** *020 †55

KHETIA, Premal Arvind. 10512 N 110TH EAST AVE, STE 240 74055 #025-01-1988 L2003 **OTO FPS** *020

KLOTZ, Christopher Robt. 13600 E 86TH ST N, STE 400 74055 #039-01-1992 L1993 **FM** *020 †18

KOENIG, Joseph Harold. 13600 E 86TH ST N, STE 400 74055 #055-01-1991 L1992 **FM** *020 †18

MANN, Michael Dell. 10502 N 110TH EAST AVE, STE 305 74055 #023-12-1989 L2005 **GS** *020 †85

MARSH, Bryan Vannuel. 13616 E 103RD ST N, ST A 74055 #039-01-1994 L1995 **FM** *020 †18

MICKLE-BELL, Laurie. 10512 N 110TH EAST AVE, STE 300 74055 #039-01-1989 L1990 **PD** *020 †55

MURR, Charles David. 8751 N 117TH EAST AVE, URGENT CARE OF GREEN COUNT 74055 #048-04-2002 L2005 **FM** *100 †18

NIOCE, Paul Anthony. ■ 74055 #019-02-2007 L2007 **IM** *012

PETRAY, Jacqueline Marie. 13600 E 86TH ST N, STE 100 74055 #004-01-1986 L1987 **IM** *020

QUEZADA REAL, Ricardo Man. ■ 74055 #649-03-2005 L2007 **IM** *012

RUBINO, Beverly Joyce. ■ 74055 #048-02-1986 L1997 **PTH** *075

SHELTON, Bryan Park. 12451 E 100TH ST N, ST JOHN OWASSO HOSPITAL 74055 #039-01-1989 L1990 **AN** *020 †18

SIMMONS, Terrill Hugh. 12455 E 100TH ST N 74055 #039-01-1969 L1970 **ORS** *020 †40

SLAYDEN, Geoffrey Carl. 14904 E 90TH PL N 74055 #039-01-2003 L2004 **GS** *012

TRUETT, Casey. 13600 E 86TH ST N, STE 100 74055 #039-01-1969 L1969 **FM LM** *020 †18 ‡

VU, Michael Huynh. 13600 E 86TH ST N, STE 100 74055 #039-01-1994 L1995 **FM** *020 †18

WATERS, Edwin Carey, IV. 13600 E 86TH ST N, OMNI OWASSO 74055 #028-03-1998 L2007 **FM** *020 †18

WINGO, James Brendan. 12455 E 100TH ST N, STE 120 74055 #034-01-1991 L1992 **IM PD** *020 †55,20

PARK HILL – CHEROKEE

WOOLLEY, Eric Brady. 26771 S 524 RD 74451 #039-01-2002 L2006 **EM** *100 †16

PAULS VALLEY – GARVIN

ATKINSON, Schales Lukie. 3210 S CHICKASAW ST 73075 #021-01-1961 L1969 **OBG GYN** *020 †30

AVERION, Newton Avenido. 3210 S CHICKASAW ST 73075 #748-01-1958 L1974 **GP** *020

FARRACH, Hussem Alex. 100 VALLEY DR 73075 #649-14-1977 L2004 **FM EM** *020 †18

GIDEON, William P. RR 1, SOUTHERN OKLAHOMA RESOURCE 73075 #039-01-1969 L1969 **OBG PM** *020 †30

HEINEMAN, Laurence Arnold. 100 VALLEY DR, PAULS VALLEY GENERAL HOSPI 73075 #028-03-1962 L2001 **GP** *020 †18

HICKS, Tammy K. 200 MELVILLE DR 73075 #039-79-1998, ▲ L2001 **FM** *020 †18

HOWARD, Charles N, Jr. 415 W GUY AVE 73075 #039-01-1976 L1977 **FM** *020 ‡

JONES, Charles Kim. 1200 S WALNUT ST 73075 #028-02-1981 L1984 **FM D** *020 †18

KAO, Jack Gaung-Shi. RR 1 BOX 44, VALLEY SORC 73075 #244-06-1972 L1986 **PD FPG** *020

KOPTA, Joseph Antony. RR 3 BOX 23B 73075 #039-01-1962 L1962 **ORS** *072 †40

LINDSEY, James Harvey. ■ 73075 #016-06-1959 L1964 **GS** *071 †85 ‡

LOPER, Jeanie Marie. ■ 73075 #305-01-2005 L2007 **FP** *012

MEINDERS, Don Wesley. 200 MELVILLE DR 73075 #039-01-1965 L1965 **GP** *020

PADUA, Yolanda Sarabia. 3210 S CHICKASAW ST, SOUTHERN OKLAHOMA RESOURCE 73075 #748-07-1963 L1980 **P** *020

SPENCE, Ray E. ■ 73075 #039-01-1946 L1947 *071

WESTCOTT, Robert Michael. ■ 73075 #039-01-1993 L1994 **FM** *020 †18

PAWHUSKA – OSAGE

ARROWSMITH, Laura Lee. 1101 E 15TH ST 74056 #028-78-1977, ▲ L1978 **R** *020

CHESBRO, Robert Franklin. 715 GRANDVIEW AVE 74056 #032-01-1980 L1980 **FM** *020

COLDWELL, Douglas Michael. 1101 E 15TH ST 74056 #048-02-1980 L2007 **R ON** *020 †80

GEHRINGER, Edward J. INDIAN HLTH CTR 74056 #041-13-1966 L1967 **PD GP** *071

JORDAN, Michael Lee. 701 LEAHY AVE 74056 #039-01-1964 L1964 **FM** *071 †18

PRIEST, James Robt. 701 LEAHY AVE, PAWHUSKA MEDICAL CLINIC 74056 #039-01-1964 L1964 **FM** *020 ‡

PRIEST, Michael Vernon. 701 LEAHY AVE, PAWHUSKA MEDICAL CLINIC 74056 #039-79-1990, ▲ L1991 **FM** *020 †18 ‡

ROBERTS, Kent Thayne. 1101 E 15TH ST 74056 #048-02-1977 L1991 **DR RNR** *020 †80

WONG, Jen Hsun. 1101 E 15TH ST 74056 #016-43-1990 L1996 **DR** *020 †80

PAWNEE – PAWNEE

BAKER, Carl E. 1201 HERITAGE CIR, PAWNEE INDIAN HEALTH CENTE 74058 #030-05-1975 L1976 **AM IM** *020 †20

EVANS, Gene Harold. 535 6TH ST 74058 #019-02-1993 L2000 **FM** *020 †18 ‡

GUMBS, Jaime Enrique. 1201 HERITAGE CIR 74058 #308-01-1975 L1978 **FM GP** *020

PERKINS – PAYNE

DUBE, Philippe Abel. ■ 74059 #065-09-1972 L1994 *075

UMAKUMARAN, Geetha. 501 E HIGHWAY 33, PERKINS FAMILY CLINIC 74059 #495-44-1991 L2005 **FM** *020 †18

PERRY – NOBLE

AVILA, Estrella Zurbano. 503 N 14TH ST STE D 73077 #748-01-1962 L1992 **IM** *071

AVILA, Patricio C. 503 N 14TH ST 73077 #748-08-1962 L1991 **GS GP** *071

BAIRD, Blake Allen. 505 N 14TH ST 73077 #039-01-1986 L1987 **FM** *020 †18

BROWN, Arthur M, Jr. 501 N 14TH ST 73077 #039-01-1945 L1946 **FM GS** *071

EK, Jonathan R. 501 N 14TH ST 73077 #016-45-2001 L2004 **FM** *100

HARTWIG, Michael Dean. 505 N 14TH ST 73077 #039-01-1986 L1987 **FM** *020 †18

MARTIN, Charles Edward. 1103 BIRCH ST 73077 #039-01-1948 L1948 **FPG** *072

PICHER – OTTAWA

CHUBB, Richard Marshall. 103 S CONNELL AVE 74360 #016-06-1954 L1982 **GP PHP** *071 †70

PIEDMONT – CANADIAN

COKER, Charles Franklin. ■ 73078 #039-01-1965 L1965 **AN** *071

■ = Address Information Privacy Protected

ROGERS, Gloria D Akin. ■ 73078 #039-01-1961 L1962 **GP PD** *074

PONCA CITY – KAY

ADAMS, Karen Schick. 421 E HARTFORD AVE 74601 #028-02-1984 L1985 **FM** *020 †18
AGHA, Ahmad Saleh. 415 FAIRVIEW AVE, STE 100 74601 #915-04-1971 L1978 **PD** *020 †55
BORING, Terrence Hugh. 119 PATTON DR 74601 #048-04-1971 L1978 **ORS** *020 †40
CARTER, Thomas Muegge. 404 FAIRVIEW AVE STE 21 74601 #039-01-1966 L1966 **OPH** *020 †35
COLDIRON, Jo. 400 FAIRVIEW AVE STE 50 74601 #039-01-1983 L1984 **AN** *020
COOK, William Zachariah. ■ 74601 #039-01-1955 L1955 **GP** *020
COYNER, John Ligon. 308 FAIRVIEW AVE 74601 #051-04-1959 L1972 **R** *020 †80 ‡
DAVIS, Paul K. 400 FAIRVIEW AVE, STE 20 74601 #039-01-1975 L1976 **FM EM** *020 †18
DE LA PAZ, Bienvenido E. 200 WHITE EAGLE DR, WHITE EAGLE INDIAN HEALTH 74601 #748-07-1962 L1977 **GP EM** *020 †18
DE LA PAZ, Carmelina Cruz. ■ 74604 #748-01-1963 L1977 **FM** *020 †18
EBBESSON, Berno S E. 400 E CENTRAL AVE STE 505A, PONCA CITY SURGICAL CLINIC 74601 #019-02-1970 L1974 **GS** *071 †85 ‡
EDMONDS, Mark Bradley. 1900 N 14TH ST, PONCA CITY MEDICAL CENTER 74601 #039-01-1987 L1991 **AN PME** *020 †05
ELLIFRIT, William O. ■ 74601 #039-01-1959 L1960 **GP** *071
GARLAND, Jackie D W. ■ 74601 #007-02-1984 L1985 **FM** *020 †18
GILBERT, Timothy Berry. 121 PATTON DR 74601 #039-01-1982 L1983 **PYG** *062 †85
GLASSCOCK, Thomas Curran. 300 FAIRVIEW AVE 74601 #016-01-1942 L1946 **FM** *071
GRAHAM, William John. ■ 74604 #039-01-1971 L1972 **RO** *071 †80 ‡
GRAY, Patrick Wallace. 400 FAIRVIEW AVE, STE 17 74601 #039-01-1982 L1985 **IM** *020 †20
HAGOOD, Paul Guy. 1908 N 14TH ST STE 201 74601 #028-34-1988 L1994 **U** *020 †95
HAMILTON, William C. 425 FAIRVIEW AVE STE 3 74601 #039-01-1972 L1973 **CHP P** *020 †75 ‡
HARRIS, Caleb H. 121 PATTON DR 74601 #048-16-1996 L2003 **GS** *020 †85
HILL, C Thomas, Jr. 74602 #047-06-1952 L1954 **R NM** *071 †80,28 ‡
HILL, Jan Russell. 1715 N 5TH ST 74601 #039-01-1984 L1994 **FM** *020 †18
HOLDEN, John Webb. ■ 74601 #039-01-1998 L1999 **MPD** *020 †20
HOWARD, William Robt, II. 400 FAIRVIEW AVE 74601 #019-02-1971 L1975 **OTO HNS** *020 †45
HOWE, Elliott H, Jr. 620 W GRAND AVE, BBRIDGEWAY 74601 #039-01-1982 L1983 **FM** *075 †18
JOHNSON, Donald Alan. ■ 74604 #016-43-1956 L1979 **PTH** *071 †50
KNIGHT, Phillip Jos. 400 FAIRVIEW AVE 74601 #007-02-1976 L1979 **GP** *020
KREGER, Ron Michael. 419 FAIRVIEW AVE, STE 1 74601 #039-01-1971 L1972 **OBG** *020 †30
LEY, Paul Francis. 1717 N 4TH ST, STE 102 74601 #039-01-1975 L1976 **OBG** *020 †30
MC INTYRE, Robt Freemont. 1900 N 14TH ST, PONCA CITY MEDICAL CENTER 74601 #018-03-1978 L2005 **P** *020
MOYER, Gary Paul. 2413 ROBIN RD, 2413 ROBIN ROAD 74604 #019-02-1972 L1975 **EM IM** *020 †20
NORTHCUTT, Jeff Edward. 1908 N 14TH ST, STE 206 74601 #039-01-2001 L2002 **OBG** *020 †30
PALMER, Corley Mark. 300 FAIRVIEW AVE, STE 1 74601 #039-01-1974 L1981 **IM** *020 †20
PICKENS, Sunday June. ■ 74602 #023-01-1979 L1981 **P** *030 †75
POLAND, Pamela J. 4040 FAIRVIEW AVE STE 18, PONCA CITY EYE CLINIC 74601 #047-06-1987 L1991 **OPH** *020 †35
SCHERLAG, Michael Ara. 400 FAIRVIEW AVE, OKLAHOMA CARDIOVASCULAR 74601 #039-01-1994 L1997 **CD** *020 †20
SCHOLZ, Harley Joe. 20700 EAGLE NEST 74601 #039-01-1965 L1965 **FM** *020 †18
SCOVILL, Edward James. ■ 74601 #039-01-1984 L1985 **OM FM** *030 †18
SPARKS, David Michael. 415 FAIRVIEW AVE, STE 201 74601 #039-01-2000 L2001 **ORS** *020
SULLIVAN, Michael Jon. 400 FAIRVIEW AVE, STE 19 74601 #039-01-1972 L1974 **IM** *020 †20
THOMASON, S Jane Moseley. 417 FAIRVIEW AVE 74601 #004-01-1971 L1975 **PD** *071 †55
VAIDYA, Alzira Francisca. 400 FAIRVIEW AVE STE 10 74601 #496-38-1973 L1987 **P CHP** *020 †75
VAIDYA, Shrikrishna V. 400 FAIRVIEW AVE, STE 10 74601 #495-28-1974 L1987 **N** *020
VAIDYA, Vijay Shrikrishna. ■ 74604 #024-07-2005 L2007 **IM** *012
VEAL, Dona C. 1902 N 14TH ST 74601 #048-02-1984 L1985 **FM** *020 †18
WALKER, Michael Stephen. 415 FAIRVIEW AVE, STE 100 74601 #039-01-1990 L1991 **PD** *020 †55
WHITE, Ronald Hugh. 400 FAIRVIEW AVE, OKLAHOMA CARDIOVASCULAR 74601 #039-01-1963 L1964 **CD IM** *020
WINSLOW, Phillip Hudson. 123 PATTON DR 74601 #041-02-1965 L1971 **U NEP** *020 †95

PORTER – WAGONER

MC INTOSH, Julie Renee. ■ 74454 #039-01-1997 L1998 **FM** *020 †18

POTEAU – LE FLORE

BRUTON, James Lewis. 1200 CENTRAL ST, POTEAU DIALYSIS CENTER 74953 #004-01-1985 L2000 **N IM** *020 †20
COOK, Charles David. 1507 S MCKENNA ST, SE OK AHEC 74953 #039-01-1973 L1974 **FM** *071 †18
FOSTER, Kenneth Washie. 604 DEWEY AVE, PO BOX 1041 74953 #005-11-1978 L1986 **P** *020
HAMPTON, Robert Lee. 1323 DEWEY AVE 74953 #048-12-1958 L1970 **GS** *071 †85
JOHNS, Michael Jay. ■ 74953 #039-01-1979 L1980 **GS** *020 †85
RABIDEAU, Dana Prescott. 1200 CENTRAL ST, POTEAU DIALYSIS CENTER 74953 #016-06-1972 L1984 **NEP IM** *020 †20
SANEMAN, Paul Philip. ■ 74953 #023-01-1963 L1969 **OBG** *071 †30
SPEAR, Jeffrey Moncrieff. 34001 BERRYFROST LN 74953 #023-07-1979 L1984 **FM EM** *020 †18
WILLIS, William Alan. 204 WALL ST 74953 #039-01-1978 L1979 **GP** *020
WINTERS, Richard Bruce. 1323 DEWEY AVE 74953 #039-01-1980 L1981 **IM IMG** *020 †20
WINTERS, Richard Lee. 204 WALL ST 74953 #039-01-1953 L1953 **FM** *071 †18

PRAGUE – LINCOLN

LENZ, Anthony Louis. RR 3 BOX 245, 1501 N BLUE BELL RD 74864 #039-01-1970 L1971 **GP OBG** *071

ROSE, Miriam Sharon. ■ 74864 #040-02-2005 L2005 **P** *100

PROCTOR – ADAIR

STEVENSON-PABLO, Leticea. ■ 74457 #054-04-1993 L1999 **FM** *020 †18

PRYOR – MAYES

ABDEL-GAWAD, Khalid Saad. 562 S ELLIOTT ST 74361 #915-04-1989 L1997 **IM** *020 †20
BATTLES, Paul E. 562 S ELLIOTT ST, ELLIOTT MED PLZ 74361 #039-79-1980, ▲ L1981 **FM** *020
COLLIER, Lora Michelle. 129 N KENTUCKY ST 74361 #039-01-1999 L2000 **FM** *020 †18
COLLIER, Mitchell James. 129 N KENTUCKY ST 74361 #039-01-2001 L2002 **FM OBS** *020
COLLINS, Donald Dee. 3 REDDEN 74361 #039-01-1959 L1959 **OS** *071 †18
COONFIELD, James Wallace. 231 E GRAHAM AVE, CTR 74361 #019-02-1978 L1991 **FM** *020 †18
DILL, Steven Leroy. 109 N FAIRLAND ST STE 109 74361 #039-01-1991 L1992 **FM** *020 †18
JOY, Kelley J. 109 N FAIRLAND ST, STE 105 74361 #039-79-1998, ▲ L2002 **FM** *020
KNEPPER, Richard Thos. 120 N BAILEY ST 74361 #038-40-1964 L1972 **R** *020 †80
MARTIN, Richard Eugene. 122 N BAILEY ST 74361 #039-01-1970 L1974 **IM** *020 †20
NUNLEY, Omer Raymond, Jr. 133 N FAIRLAND ST 74361 #047-06-1967 L1972 **GS GP** *020 †85
ROY, Jess Thomas. 111 N BAILEY ST, INTEGRIS MAYES COUNTY MED 74361 #039-79-2001, ▲ L2002 **FM** *020 †18
SARFATIS, Peter. 109 N FAIRLAND ST, STE 108 74361 #869-04-1962 L1969 **GS** *020 †85
SUHAIL, Mohammad Shuaib. 562 S ELLIOTT ST 74361 #704-04-1988 L1997 **PD** *020 †55
SWAN, William Russell. ■ 74361 #039-01-1969 L1973 **GP** *020
TRINDLE, Margaret Potter. ■ 74361 #041-01-1950 L1981 **PD FM** *071
WATERS, David Bruce. 129 N KENTUCKY ST 74361 #025-01-1966 L1972 **DR** *020 †80
WILLIAMS, Pat. ■ 74361 #048-12-1954 L1962 **FM** *071 †18

PURCELL – MCCLAIN

FERGUSON, Don Keith. 1500 N GREEN AVE, PURCELL MUNIICPAL HOSPITAL 73080 #051-07-1996 L2007 **FM** *020 †18
JOACHIMS, Brian Vaughn. 1438 HARDCASTLE BLVD, PURCELL INDIAN HEALTH CLIN 73080 #019-02-1993 L2000 **FM** *020 †18
LEE, Edward Allen. 1500 N GREEN AVE 73080 #039-01-1977 L1978 **FM** *020
LYNCH, Heather Rene. 1401 N 4TH AVE STE 106 73080 #039-01-1995 L1998 **FM** *020 †18
MC COLLEY, Robin Michelle. 1500 N 4TH AVE 73080 #025-07-1992 L1994 **FM** *020 †16
MC CURDY, Wm Claude, III. 1500 N GREEN AVE 73080 #039-01-1964 L1964 **GS** *071 †85
SCHMIDT, Ricky Ron. 1500 N GREEN AVE 73080 #039-01-1984 L1985 **FM** *020 †18

RAMONA – WASHINGTON

ALLEN-CULLINS, Melinda Ro. ■ 74061 #019-02-2005 L2006 **FP** *012

ROLAND – SEQUOYAH

MITCHELL, Bob Gunter. PO BOX 859 74954 #039-01-1956 L1956 **GP OS** *030

SALINA – MAYES

GRAY, Brett Mcneil. 900 N OWEN WALTERS BLVD, AMO SALINA COMMUNITY CLINI 74365 #039-01-1994 L1995 **FM** *020 †18 ‡
GRIM, Gloria Ann. 900 N OWEN WALTERS BLVD 74365 #039-01-1993 L1994 **FM** *030 †18 ‡
HUFFMAN, Margaret Jane. 900 N OWEN WALTERS BLVD, AMO SALINA COMM CLINIC 74365 #039-01-1996 L1997 **PD** *020
UNDERWOOD, Michael R. 900 N OWEN WALTERS BLVD 74365 #039-01-1994 L1995 **FM** *020 †18

SALLISAW – SEQUOYAH

CORLEY, Bert Nelson. 104 S OAK ST, BOX 808 74955 #039-01-1962 L1963 **FM** *020 ‡
COVINGTON, Christopher G. 213 E REDWOOD AVE 74955 #039-01-1980 L1986 **NS** *020 †25
DE MOSS, Harold Leroy. 301 J T STITES BLVD, REDBIRD SMITH HEALTH CENTE 74955 #039-01-1978 L1999 **FM** *020 †18
ELLIOTT, Charles Caleb. RR 2 BOX 301A4 74955 #039-01-1962 L1962 **DR** *020 †80
GAEDE, Steven Eugene. 213 E REDWOOD AVE 74955 #039-01-1979 L1980 **NS** *020 †25
ORTIZ, Lisa Dianne. 301 J T STITES BLVD, REDBIRD SMITH HLTH CTR 74955 #025-07-2004 L2007 **IM** *100 †20
WILDE, James Oscar. PO BOX 505, 213 E REDWOOD 74955 #305-01-2000 L2004 **FM** *100 †18 ‡
WOOD, William Edmison. 409 E REDWOOD AVE 74955 #067-01-1970 L1997 **FM** *020

SAND SPRINGS – TULSA

ADORNATO, Sam Gregory. ■ 74063 #038-40-1959 L2003 **OTO** *071 †45
BROWN, Jack Howard, Jr. 401 E BROADWAY CT STE A 74063 #039-05-1988 L1989 **FM** *020 †18
BURGHART, Francine J. 796 E CHARLES PAGE BLVD 74063 #039-01-1987 L1990 **IM** *020 †20
COGGINS, Curtis Michael. 402 W MORROW RD, 100 74063 #039-01-1983 L1984 **GP** *020
ENGLESTEAD, Brady Gene. 3963 S HIGHWAY 97, # 113 74063 #031-01-1993 L1993 **PD** *020 †55
GOLJAN, Edward F. ■ 74063 #041-13-1968 L1981 **PTH** *020 †50
GREWAL, Harleen Kaur. 402 W MORROW RD, STE 100 74063 #495-03-1975 L1981 **IM** *020 †20
GREWAL, Shivrajpal Singh. 402 W MORROW RD, STE 100 74063 #495-03-1973 L1981 **IM** *020 †20
HANAN, Stanley Scott. 117 N MAIN ST 74063 #034-01-1976 L1977 **FM OBG** *020
JONES, Phillip W. 796 E CHARLES PAGE BLVD 74063 #048-16-1983 L1983 **GS** *020 †85

■ = Address Information Privacy Protected

LOBSINGER, Michael Robert. ■ 74063 #019-02-2008 *012
MC CLINTOCK, Lynn Ann. 402 W MORROW RD, STE 100 74063 #039-01-1987 L1988 FM *020 †18 ‡
MC CONNELL, Wendy Barnes. 796 E CHARLES PAGE BLVD 74063 #051-07-1976 L1981 PD *020 †55
WIEGMAN, David Eugene. 796 E CHARLES PAGE BLVD 74063 #048-02-2003 L2004 FM *020 †18

SAPULPA – CREEK

BUMGARDNER, Joyce Louise. 15 E DEWEY AVE 74066 #039-01-1980 L1981 GP EM *020
CALE, Walter, Jr. ■ 74066 #004-01-1946 L1948 FM *071
COCHRAN, Paul Chesley. 1004 E BRYAN AVE 74066 #039-01-1978 L1979 P *020 †18,16
FOX, Twilah A. 1004 E BRYAN AVE 74066 #039-01-1965 L1965 P FM *071
FUCCI, John Conville. 1004 E BRYAN AVE, ST JOHNS SAPULPA 74066 #038-41-1980 L1994 GE *020
GEBETSBERGER, Charles Jos. 1021 E BRYAN AVE 74066 #039-01-1957 L1957 FM *020
HO, Tony Hung Quan. 1004 E BRYAN AVE 74066 #869-05-1975 L1978 FM *020 †18
HUSAIN, Altaf. 1004 E BRYAN AVE 74066 #495-34-1969 L1981 DR *020
JOHNSON, Donald Franklin. 1004 E BRYAN AVE 74066 #039-01-1965 L1965 FM PTH *020 †50 ‡
JONES, Gina Renee. 838 N MOCCASIN ST 74066 #030-05-1995 L2000 FM *020 †18
KINNEY, Roger Lee. 1004 E BRYAN AVE, 2ND FL 74066 #039-01-1966 L1966 FM EM *020
KRISHNAMURTHI, S. 1004 E BRYAN AVE 74066 #495-04-1973 L1983 CD IM *020 †20
LARSON, Dana Howard. 1004 E BRYAN AVE 74066 #039-05-1985 L1989 EM *020 †16
MILOSAVLJEVIC, Emil B. 1305 E TAFT ST 74066 #957-02-1969 L1978 ORS *020
RAMSEY, Terroll Gene. 1004 E BRYAN AVE 74066 #019-02-1974 L1977 FM *020 †18
RUSSELL, James. 308 S MAIN ST 74066 #039-01-1981 L1982 GP EM *020
WARD, Michael Steven. 1004 E BRYAN AVE 74066 #039-01-1975 L1976 FM *020 ‡
WHITE, Robert Glenn. 1004 E BRYAN AVE 74066 #039-01-1956 L1956 IM GP *071
WILSON, Roger Dale. 1021 E BRYAN AVE, OMNI MEDICAL GROUP, INC 74066 #039-01-1996 L1998 IM *020
ZUMWALT, Gerald Catlin. 1004 E BRYAN AVE 74066 #039-01-1956 L1956 FM *020

SAVANNA – PITTSBURG

WALDEN, Thomas Paul. ■ 74565 #036-01-1989 *100

SAYRE – BECKHAM

BEHELAK, Youssef. PO BOX 88 73662 #065-09-1980 L1996 *020
HUBANKS, John Mark. 1415 WATTS ST 73662 #039-01-1980 L1983 FM *020 †18
WHINERY, Kenneth Eugene. RR 4 BOX 131, 1505 WATTS 73662 #039-01-1955 L1955 FM *020 †18

SEILING – DEWEY

DUFFY, Kenneth Mark. PO BOX 838, NE HIGHWAY 60 73663 #039-01-1979 L1980 FM *020 †18 ‡
LESLIE, Porter Bass. U S HWY 60 N E 73663 #649-14-1972 L1975 GP EM *020

SEMINOLE – SEMINOLE

AVERY, Thomas Andrew. 403 TIMMONS ST 74868 #039-01-1972 L1973 GP EM *075
FEUERBORN, Stephen A. 2401 W WRANGLER BLVD 74868 #039-01-1987 L1990 FM *020 †18
WOOD, Julian Deal. 606 W EVANS AVE 74868 #004-01-1944 L1947 FPG *071

SHATTUCK – ELLIS

BERENDS, Jennifer Lynn. 905 S MAIN ST, NEWMAN PHYSICIANS GROUP 73858 #039-79-2004, ▲ L2007 FM *020
BERRY, Richard Phillip. 905 S MAIN ST 73858 #039-01-1992 L1993 FM *020 †18
DERSCH, Danna Kay. 905 S MAIN ST 73858 #039-01-2002 L2006 FM *100 †18
FLAHERTY, Michael Wm. 905 S MAIN ST 73858 #039-01-1980 L1983 FM *020 †18 ‡
FREDERICK, Gary Anthony. 905 S MAIN ST 73858 #021-05-1980 L1986 FM *020 †18 ‡
MILLER, Barbara Lynn. 905 S MAIN ST 73858 #039-01-1999 L2000 FM *020 †18
PENTECOST, Richard Levi. 905 S MAIN ST, NEWMAN MEMORIAL HOSPITAL 73858 #048-02-1956 L1964 ORS *071 †40

SHAWNEE – POTTAWATOMIE

ALSUP, Cynthia Ann. 2801 SARATOGA ST, CLINIC 74804 #039-01-1987 L1988 OBG *020 †30
ANDERSON, Gaynell Marie. 1902 GORDON COOPER DR, STE 105 74801 #039-01-1996 L1999 FM *020 †16
ARGENTO, Angelo. 2801 SARATOGA ST, CLINIC 74804 #422-01-1996 L2005 IM *020 †20
BALAN, T A. 2801 SARATOGA ST 74804 #496-38-1963 L1971 ORS *071 †40
BANKS, Stephen Lynn. 2801 SARATOGA ST, CLINIC 74804 #039-01-1988 L1989 IM *020 †20
BLACKSTONE, Harlan James. ■ 74801 #039-01-1979 L1980 FM *071 †16
BLAIR, Gregory Lee. 2801 SARATOGA ST, CLINIC 74804 #039-01-1993 L1995 IM *020 †20 ‡
BUTCHER, Michael Wayne. 2801 SARATOGA ST, CLINIC 74804 #039-01-1982 L1983 IM *020 †20
BUTCHER, Orby Lee. ■ 74804 #039-01-1955 L1955 GP GS *071
CANNATA, Saml Raymond Jos. ■ 74804 #048-02-1955 L1955 GP OS *071
CHAINAKUL, Pachneerat S. 1902 GORDON COOPER DR #106 74801 #891-01-1970 L1980 PD *020 †55
CHAINAKUL, Wit. 1902 GORDON COOPER DR 74801 #891-01-1970 L1980 GS GP *020
CHAPMAN, William Arturo. 2801 SARATOGA ST, CLINIC 74804 #264-04-1978 L1985 PD PDI *020 †55 ‡
COMBS, Leon Doyle. ■ 74804 #039-01-1944 L1946 GP GS *071 †18

CONAWAY, Keith Alan. 3700 N KICKAPOO AVE, STE 124 74804 #039-01-1993 L1994 FM *020 †18 ‡
DAVIS, Francis A. 1414 N KENNEDY AVE, DOCTORS BUILDING 74801 #019-02-1950 L1951 FM OBG *071
DAVIS, Merle Leslie. 2801 SARATOGA ST, CLINIC 74804 #039-01-1973 L1974 IM *020
DEHUFF, Michael Alan. 1102 W MACARTHUR ST, UNITY HOSPITAL NORTH 74804 #039-01-1988 L1989 AN *020 †05
DORSETT, Tschantre Eujean. ■ 74801 #039-01-2008 *012
EVANS, Robert Douglass. 1102 W MACARTHUR ST 74804 #039-01-1990 L1991 AN *020
FIEBER, Mary Caroline. 1900 S GORDON COOPER DR 74801 #030-05-1983 L2004 PTH PCP *020 †50
GHAZNAVI, Jahangir H. 101 N UNION AVE 74801 #160-06-1979 L1991 P *020
GIBSON, Eldon Van. ■ 74804 #039-01-1965 L1965 IM *071 †20 ‡
GREGORY, Amy Andrews. 1900 S GORDON COOPER DR 74801 #035-19-1995 L1999 OPH *020 †35
GUNDERSON, Robert J. 1533 N HARRISON ST 74804 #039-79-1991, ▲ L1992 ORS OTR *020
GUPTA, Shikha. ■ 74801 #496-04-1978 L1983 *020
GUPTA, Sudhir K. 3700 N KICKAPOO AVE, STE 132 74804 #495-45-1978 L1986 CD IM *020 †20
HADDAD, Phillip Anthony. 2801 SARATOGA ST, CLINIC 74804 #039-01-1989 L1990 PCC *020
HADDAD, Walid John. 2801 SARATOGA ST, CLINIC 74804 #055-01-1991 L1998 CD *020 †20
HADLEY, David L. 23 E 9TH ST, STE 327 74801 #048-13-1993 L1994 FM *020 †18
HANKS, Norman Ned. 1902 S GORDON COOPER DR 74801 #039-01-1963 L1964 GS *071
HANSON, Glen Ray. 2801 SARATOGA ST, CLINIC 74804 #039-01-1989 L1994 GS *020 †85
HAYES, John Randall. 2801 SARATOGA ST 74804 #012-05-1946 L1951 IM GP *071
HOLLAND, David L, Jr. 2801 SARATOGA ST, CLINIC 74804 #019-02-1984 L1990 IM *020 †20
HOLTER, Jeremy Patrick. 2801 SARATOGA ST, CLINIC 74804 #039-01-2002 L2003 MPD *020 †20
HOWARD, Frank Huston. 2801 SARATOGA ST 74804 #039-01-1956 L1956 GS *071 †85
JENNINGS, Paul. 2801 SARATOGA ST, CLINIC 74804 #039-01-2001 L2003 OBG *020
JONES, Richard Edwin. 2801 SARATOGA ST, 1413 BRADLEY 74804 #030-05-1973 L1977 OBG *020 †30 ‡
KATCHER, Debra Raff. 2801 SARATOGA ST, CLINIC 74804 #039-01-1989 L1990 PD *020 †55
KIENZLE, John Albert. 1900 S GORDON COOPER DR 74801 #039-01-1958 L1958 GP GS *071
KOONS, Kelli Denise. 2801 SARATOGA ST, CLINIC 74804 #039-01-2000 L2001 MPD *020 †20,55
LYNCH, James Edward. 1102 W MACARTHUR ST, STUDENT HEALTH CENTER AT U 74804 #039-01-1993 L1994 FM *020 †18
MACE, Don A. 2801 SARATOGA ST 74804 #039-01-1972 L1973 IM *071
MANSOUR, Badie Saad. 1102 W MACARTHUR ST 74804 #915-02-1969 L1975 AN PME *020 †05
MATTER, Billy Joe. 2508 N HARRISON ST, SHAWNEE DIALYSIS CTR 74804 #039-01-1959 L1959 NEP IM *071
MCALISTER, Deborah Sue. 2801 SARATOGA ST, CLINIC 74804 #039-01-2001 L2002 ORS *020
MC BRIDE, David Le Marr. 1102 W MACARTHUR ST 74804 #039-01-1956 L1956 PTH *071 †50
MC CLUNE, Grant Lee. 2801 SARATOGA ST, CLINIC 74804 #018-03-1992 L2004 GS *020 †85
MC KENNA, Jos Cornelius. 1414 N KENNEDY AVE, STE 105 74801 #039-01-1979 L1980 OM EM *020 †16
MOHAN, Ramesh Kumar. 2801 SARATOGA ST, CLINIC 74804 #495-01-1967 L1972 PD *020 †55
NEVREKAR, Lila Venkatesh. 1902 S GORDON COOPER DR 74801 #495-28-1965 L1974 OBG *071 †30
NIAZI, Tariq B M. 3700 N KICKAPOO AVE 74804 #704-09-1978 L2004 ORS OTR *020
OBHRAI, Kanwal Kaur. 2801 SARATOGA ST, CLINIC 74804 #039-07-1970 L1974 PD *020 †55
PROPES, Brett Matthew. 3700 N KICKAPOO AVE # 124 74804 #654-01-2001 L2003 FM *020
RAMASUBBAMMA, Kaliki. WESTGATE CIR 74801 #495-11-1961 *100
REDING, Eric Lane. 2801 SARATOGA ST, CLINIC 74804 #004-01-1997 L1998 D *020 †15
ROBINSON, John Albert. 501 E MACARTHUR ST, ROBINSON EYE INSTITUTE 74804 #019-02-1975 L1976 OPH *020 †35
ROSE, Karen Annette. 2801 SARATOGA ST, SHAWNEE MEDICAL CENTER CLI 74804 #039-01-1999 L2000 PD *020 †55
SHETTY, Shashindra P. 2801 SARATOGA ST, CLINIC 74804 #496-38-1970 L1977 IM END *020 †20
SHI, Augustin Henry. 2801 SARATOGA ST 74804 #039-01-1973 L1974 IM GP *020 †20
SPARKMAN, Darin Craig. 2801 SARATOGA ST, CLINIC 74804 #039-01-1990 L1994 OBG *020 †30
SPURLOCK, Cory Stephen. 2307 S GORDON COOPER DR 74801 #039-01-2002 L2003 FM *020 †18
STEPHENS, Adam Vail. 2801 SARATOGA ST, CLINIC 74804 #039-01-2004 L2005 FM *020 †18
STEWART, Robert Scott. 1902 GORDON COOPER DR, STE 105 74801 #039-01-1995 L1998 FM *020 †18 ‡
STOW, Glenn Charles. 2304 N HARRISON ST 74804 #004-01-1997 L1998 FM EM *020 †18 ‡
SUMMERS, Craig St John. 2801 SARATOGA ST 74804 #039-01-1983 L2007 OTO A *020 †45
THOMAS, Edward Kent. 1102 W MACARTHUR ST 74804 #039-01-1973 L1979 EM *020
TROTTER, Stephen Eugene. 2801 SARATOGA ST, CLINIC 74804 #039-01-1978 L1982 OBG GYN *020 †30 ‡
VANZANDT, Bryan Lee. 500 W UNIVERSITY ST, BOX # 61608 74804 #039-01-2007 *012
WAINGANKAR, Nikhil. ■ 74804 #039-01-2008 *012
WAINGANKAR, Shrinivas. 2801 SARATOGA ST, CLINIC 74804 #495-97-1970 L1981 ORS *020 †40
WALSH, Christine Chouteau. 2307 S GORDON COOPER DR, CITIZEN POTAWATOMI HLTH SE 74801 #032-01-1999 L2004 IM *020 †20
WIENS, Michael Brent. 2801 SARATOGA ST, CLINIC 74804 #019-02-1991 L1996 GS *020 †85
WISDOM, Cranfill Karl. 2801 SARATOGA ST 74804 #039-01-1955 L1955 R NM *071 †80,28

SKIATOOK – OSAGE

GREEN, John Christopher. ■ 74070 #039-01-2008 *012
PROPP, Albert Geo. ■ 74070 #062-01-1959 L1979 GP *020

SNYDER – KIOWA

LYONS, Brian Joseph. 819 E ST, DBA JCMH FAMILY CLINIC 73566 #064-01-1989 L1994 FM *020

■ = Address Information Privacy Protected

SOPER – CHOCTAW

MC MURTRY, Mildred Louise. HC 71 BOX 205A 74759 #041-07-1962 L1974 GP *071

SPENCER – OKLAHOMA

SEKAR, Vimala. 2601 SPENCER RD 73084 #495-04-1975 L1983 CHP P *040 †75

STIGLER – HASKELL

HUSSAIN, Ahmer. 907 W MAIN ST, HUSSAIN'S FAMILY PRACTICE 74462 #704-25-1991 L1994 IM *020 †20
KHAN, Faisal Hamad. ■ 74462 #704-25-1996 L2005 GS *020 †85
MC CURRY, Mark Wm. 503 NW H ST 74462 #039-01-1983 L1984 FM *020 †18
MITCHELL, Christopher Mat. 2204 E MAIN ST, CHOCTAW NATION HLTH-STIGLE 74462 #654-01-2001 L2003 FM *020 †18
WASI, Faisal. 905 NW 5TH ST, STIGLER MEDICAL CLINIC 74462 #704-25-1996 L2004 CCM *020 †20

STILLWATER – PAYNE

ATKINSON, Thomas Barcley. 610 S WALNUT ST 74074 #021-06-1999 L2000 FM *020 †18
BAKER, Randal Scott. 1301 W 6TH AVE, STE 105 74074 #039-01-2000 L2001 GS *020 †85 ‡
BIERNAT, Elizabeth Jolant. 1323 W 6TH AVE, STILLWATER MEDICAL CTR 74074 #759-03-1980 L1996 AN *020 †05
BREEDLOVE, Robert Allan. 1604 W 8TH AVE 74074 #039-01-1974 L1975 D *020 †15 ‡
BROWN, Terry Neal. 1815 W 6TH AVE 74074 #039-01-1980 L1981 IM *020 †20
BULLARD, Susan Polly. 1815 W 6TH AVE 74074 #039-01-1981 L1982 PD *020 †55
BULLEN, James David. 1301 W 6TH AVE, STE 202 74074 #039-01-1981 L1982 DR *020 †80
CARLEY, James Wm. 1815 W 6TH AVE 74074 #047-06-1971 L1972 FM FPG *020 †18
CASSIDY, Danny James. 1323 W 6TH AVE, ER DEPT 74074 #039-01-1973 L1974 EM GP *020
CLARKE, Mary Sullivan. 1815 W 6TH AVE 74074 #039-01-1996 L1996 FM *020 †18
COLE, Edwin Keith. 801 S WALNUT ST 74074 #038-40-1990 L2000 GS *020 †85
COOPER, Donald L. 1202 W FARM RD, OSU HOSP & CLINIC 74078 #019-02-1953 L1960 FSM *020 ‡
CORKRAN, Susan Moore. 1606 W 7TH AVE 74074 #039-01-1987 L1988 P IM *020
COUCH, Cary Wm. 320 N PERKINS RD 74075 #039-01-1969 L1969 ORS *020 †40
CRAVEN, Thomas. 511 WINDSOR DR 74074 #036-01-1958 L1958 ORS *071 †40
CRAWLEY, Donald Eugene. 809 S WALNUT ST 74074 #039-01-1979 L1984 OTO HNS *020 †45
CUMMINGS, Steven Wayne. 709 S WESTERN RD 74074 #039-01-2002 L2004 IM *020 †20
CURTIS, Jane Louise. 1202 W FARM RD, OSU HEALTH SERVICES 74078 #048-13-1986 L1989 FM EM *020 †18
DANCER, Alison Faith L. 1301 W 6TH AVE STE 210 74074 #039-01-1990 L1991 P CHP *020 †75
DANCER, Jack T. 1301 W 6TH AVE 74074 #010-01-1961 L1962 GS GE *020 †85
DANIELS, Rebecca Jo. 406 E HALL OF FAME AVE 74075 #039-01-1993 L2002 FM *020 †18
DARBY, Richard Glenn. 1323 W 6TH AVE, STILLWATER MED CTR 74074 #039-01-1981 L1982 AN *020
DAVIDSON, Jerry Kent. ■ 74074 #039-01-1993 L1994 FM PME *071 †18
DRUMMOND, Jonathan Edward. 420 S KNOBLOCK ST 74074 #039-01-1992 L1993 OPH *020 †35
EARNEST, Sam Luper. 1815 W 6TH AVE 74074 #039-01-1971 L1972 IM GE *020
EBERT, Mark Oren. 5200 W 6TH AVE, STILLWATER WOMENS CLINIC 74074 #039-01-1981 L1982 GYN *020 †30
EMDE, Gilbert Edward. 821 S WALNUT ST 74074 #039-01-1982 L1985 IM *020 †20
ENGLISH, Dianne R. 1815 W 6TH AVE 74074 #048-02-1999 L2002 FM *020 †18
ERCUM-KRASINSKI, Baiba. 320 STUDENT UN, OSU UNIV COUNSELING SVCS 74078 #759-03-1976 L1990 P *020 †75
GAMBILL, Alice F. ■ 74075 #039-01-1949 L1949 GPM AN *071
GOLDSWORTHY, Sheila Diane. 5200 W 6TH AVE, STILLWATER WOMENS CLINIC 74074 #039-01-1997 L1998 OBG *020 †30
GREEN, Darren Todd. 1815 W 6TH AVE 74074 #039-01-1992 L1993 IM *020 †20
GRUBGELD, Lester Edward. ■ 74074 #016-11-1955 L1956 IM *071
HAGAN, Arthur Darrell. 1301 W 6TH AVE STE 110 74074 #018-03-1959 L1984 CD *020
HALL, Robin Lee. ■ 74074 #039-01-2002 L2003 AN *020
HALL, Ronald Ross. ■ 74074 #039-01-1964 L1964 PTH *071 †50
HALL, Thomas Carl. 1301 W 6TH AVE STE 108 74074 #039-01-2002 L2003 D *020 †15
HANSEN, Thomas Lowell. ■ 74075 #039-01-1966 L1966 IM GP *071
HARDER, Robert Jack. 5200 W 6TH AVE, STILLWATER WOMENS CLINIC 74074 #039-01-1992 L1996 OBG *020 †30
HAYES, Inge. 1323 W 6TH AVE, STILLWATER MEDICAL CENTER 74074 #409-33-1970 L1989 AN *020
HENRY, Glen Allen. 1411 W 7TH AVE, STE 202 74074 #039-01-1996 L1997 OBG *020 †30
HILL, Daniel Philip. 1815 W 6TH AVE 74074 #039-01-1997 L1998 FM *020 †18
HORNER, Charles Raymond. 1301 W 6TH AVE STE 202, HOT SPRINGS RADIOLOGY SERV 74074 #004-01-1994 L1995 DR *020 †80
HOYT, Eugene Maynard. 1815 W 6TH AVE 74074 #012-05-1976 L1999 IM LM *020
IVEN, Val Gene. 170 ATHLETICS CENTER 74078 #039-01-1989 L1990 FM FSM *020 †18
JACO, John William. ■ 74074 #048-14-2007 *012
JAMESON, Bretton Howard. 511 WINDSOR DR, ORTHOOKLAHOMA 74074 #039-01-1998 L1999 ORS *020 †40
JENKINS, Woody Gene. 1815 W 6TH AVE 74074 #039-01-1990 L1991 IM *020 †20
JENNINGS, Richard Thos. 2108 COUNTRY SIDE DR 74074 #039-01-1974 L1975 OBG AM *040 †30,70
JOHNSON, Charles Ronald. 1323 W 6TH AVE, # 2408 74074 #016-02-1953 L1975 AN *071 †05
JOHNSON, Jon Mark. 608 S HESTER ST 74074 #039-01-1984 L1985 IM *020 †20
KARNS, Thomas Alan. 1411 W 7TH AVE STE 202, STILLWATER WOMENS CLINIC 74074 #039-01-1980 L1981 OBG *020 †30
KELLY, Michael Thos. 1202 W FARM RD, OSU UNIVERSITY HEALTH SERV 74078 #039-01-1979 L1980 FM *020 †18
KINDELL, Gary R. 406 E HALL OF FAME AVE, STE 100 74075 #039-01-1983 L1986 FM *020 †18
KUMAR, Gaurav. ■ 74074 #495-05-1995 L2006 IM *020 †20
LAUVETZ, Robert Jos. 816 S PINE ST 74074 #030-05-1967 L1974 U *020 †95

LAUVETZ, Robert Wm. 816 S PINE ST 74074 #036-07-1991 L1997 U *020 †95 ‡
LIM, Melchor. 1509 W 8TH AVE, CARDIOLOGY STILLWATER 74074 #748-01-1976 L1985 CD IM *020 †20
MARTIN, Scott David. 1815 W 6TH AVE 74074 #039-01-1998 L1999 PD *020
MARTIN, Stephen Roger. 707 S WESTERN RD 74074 #039-01-1981 L1982 OPH *020 †35
MC ALLISTER, Kathleen M. 601 S WASHINGTON ST 74074 #048-12-1991 L1996 IM *020 †20
MILLER, Elnora G. ■ 74074 #039-01-1946 L1947 GP *071
MOYER, Michele Jonette. 1815 W 6TH AVE 74074 #039-01-1992 L1993 IM *020
MUELLER, Mark Robt. 1323 W 6TH AVE, STILLWATER EMERGENCY 74074 #028-03-1983 L1985 EM FM *020 †18
MUNSON, Mark Ellis. 320 N PERKINS RD 74075 #039-01-1979 L1980 ORS *020 †40
NEWBERRY, Robert Carroll. 1301 W 6TH AVE, STE 103 74074 #039-01-1969 L1970 PTH *020 †50
NIEMAN, Cathy E. 821 S WALNUT ST 74074 #039-01-1996 L1997 IM *020
OLSON, Charles William, Jr. 1323 W 6TH AVE, STILLWATER EMERGENCY 74074 #039-01-1993 L1994 FM *020 †18 ‡
OLTMANNS, Kevin Lynn. 1815 W 6TH AVE 74074 #039-01-1987 L1988 IM *020 †20
PAYTON, Brittany Starr. ■ 74074 #004-01-2008 *012
PHILLIPS, Robert Haskell. 1323 W 6TH AVE 74074 #039-01-1969 L1970 GS *071 †85
PINSKI, Mary Sue. ■ 74074 #039-01-1981 L1982 FM *071 †18
PUCKETT, Chris Allan. 600 S ADAMS ST, STILLWATER CANCER CTR 74074 #039-01-1986 L1987 ON HEM *020 †20
RICHARDSON, Jesse Floyd. 809 S WALNUT ST 74074 #039-01-1958 L1958 ORS *071 †40
ROACH, Marshall Scott. 1323 W 6TH AVE, STILLWATER EMERGENCY 74074 #039-01-1979 L1980 EM *020 †16
ROBERTS, Lynn Bernard. 1323 W 6TH AVE 74074 #048-04-1960 L1961 GS *072 †85
RUSSELL, Phillip Grant. 1301 W 6TH AVE, STE 202 74074 #039-01-1978 L1979 DR *020 †80
SAKSANEN, Seppo Juhani. 1411 W 7TH AVE, STE 103 74074 #374-01-1963 L1986 DR RNR *071 †80
SANDERS, Ronald Ray. 1202 W FARM RD 74078 #039-01-1960 L1968 OS PD *020
SAPP, Aaron Virgil. 1202 W FARM RD 74078 #039-01-2000 L2003 FM *020 †18
SCOTT, Jeffery Dale. 1815 W 6TH AVE, WARREN CLINIC 74074 #039-01-1988 L1989 GE *020
SHOEMAKE, Stuart Wayne. 1323 W 6TH AVE, STILLWATER EMERGENCY 74074 #039-01-1995 L1996 FM *020 †18
SKORODIN, Morton Sumner. 1411 W 7TH AVE, STE 101 74074 #016-06-1967 L1974 PUD IM *020 †20
SMALLEY, Tim Kent. 1323 W 6TH AVE 74074 #039-01-1964 L1964 IM GE *020
SMITH, Gene Reuben. 416 S KNOBLOCK ST 74074 #039-01-1970 L1971 OPH *071 †35
SMITH, Kelsey Jo. 610 S WALNUT ST, STILLWATER FAMILY CARE 74074 #039-01-2003 L2005 FM *100 †18
SMITHTON, Colbi M. 610 S WALNUT ST 74074 #039-79-1999, ▲ L2000 PD *020 †55
SMITHTON, Corby W. 610 S WALNUT ST 74074 #039-79-1999, ▲ L2000 FM *020 †18
STRANGE, Michael W. 1202 W FARM RD 74078 #039-01-1976 L1979 IM IMG *020 †20
STUBBS, Lenny Dwayne. 1301 W 6TH AVE, OKLAHOMA CARDIOVASCULAR 74074 #039-01-1998 L1999 VS *020 †85
STUBBS, Scott Nicholas. 511 WINDSOR DR, ORTHOOKLAHOMA 74074 #039-01-1997 L1998 ORS *020 †40
SUBLETT, Dwight Talburt. 1815 W 6TH AVE 74074 #039-01-1980 L1981 PD *020 †55
SWAFFORD, Thomas Arlin. 1301 W 6TH AVE STE 106 74074 #038-40-1982 L1992 GE IM *020 †20
TAGUCHI, Yasuto. 1301 W 6TH AVE, STE 204 74074 #572-32-1991 L2004 OBG *020 †30 ‡
VIJAY, Sunayana. ■ 74074 #495-55-2001 L2006 IM *100
WAGNER, Terry Lynn. 2202 W UNIVERSITY AVE, AVENUE 74074 #039-01-1977 L1978 PD *020 †18
WALTERMIRE, James Abraham. 1301 W 6TH AVE, STE 202 74074 #039-01-1966 L1970 R *071 †80
WEBB, Malinda Overton. 1815 W 6TH AVE 74074 #039-01-1987 L1996 PD *020 †55
WILLIAMS, John David. 608 S HESTER ST 74074 #039-01-1980 L1981 IM *020
WILLIAMS, Sidney D, Jr. 801 S WASHINGTON ST 74074 #039-01-1971 L1972 IM PME *020 ‡
WILLIS, Randall Jay. 801 S WALNUT ST 74074 #039-01-1979 L1980 U *020 †95
WILLIS, Victoria Renee. 801 S WALNUT ST 74074 #039-01-1979 L1980 GS *020 †85
WILSEY, Carla A Evans. 1815 W 6TH AVE 74074 #039-01-1974 L1975 PD *020 †55
WILSEY, Douglas Neal. 1323 W 6TH AVE, STILLWATER EMERGENCY 74074 #039-01-1973 L1974 EM FM *020 †18
WINGO, Sylvia J. 2608 S AUGUST ST, C/O JAMES CARLEY 74074 #039-01-1990 L1991 PD *020 †55
WRIGHT, Robert Clinton. 1823 W 6TH AVE 74074 #012-01-1976 L1977 PD *020 †55
WULLER, Thomas Geo. 511 WINDSOR DR, ORTHOOKLAHOMA, PC 74074 #039-01-1992 L1997 ORS *020 †40

STILWELL – ADAIR

BENTLEY, Nicholas J. 1401 W LOCUST ST, STE 102 74960 #039-79-1983, ▲ L1984 GP *020
CHICHESTER, Carolyn June. RR 6 BOX 840, WILMA P. MANKILLER HEALTH 74960 #039-01-1978 L1980 R *020 †80
DULOWSKI, Wojciech Lech. 1401 W LOCUST ST STE 102, PHYSICIAN'S CLINIC 74960 #759-06-1982 L1998 FM OTR *020 †18 ‡
FERRIS, John Anthony. 1401 W LOCUST ST, MEMORIAL HOSPITAL 74960 #039-01-1979 L1980 FM *020
GREEN, Burdge Freeman. 1401 W LOCUST ST, STE 102 74960 #065-06-1947 L1950 GS GP *071
GURKAN, Nihat Ilksen. 1401 W LOCUST ST, STE 102 74960 #902-10-1993 L2008 ORS OAR *020
JENKINS, Jeffery Lee. 1401 W LOCUST ST, MEMORIAL HOSPITAL 74960 #039-01-1996 L1997 FM P *020 †18,75
KEETER, Larry Phil. 1401 W LOCUST ST, # 102 74960 #039-01-1978 L1979 FM *020
MARTIN, Dennis Lee. 912 W CEDAR ST 74960 #039-01-1975 L1978 FM GS *020
MATTHEWS, Janet C. 1401 W LOCUST ST # 102 74960 #039-79-2000, ▲ L2001 OBG *020
MURIEL, Migdalia. RR 6 BOX 840, WILMA P. MANKILLER HEALTH 74960 #042-03-1981 L1996 PD *020 †20
SANTOS, Magdalena Cruz. 1401 W LOCUST ST, STE 102 74960 #748-07-1981 L1999 ID *020 †20
TAYLOR, Jimmie Wayne. 735 W LOCUST ST 74960 #039-01-1973 L1974 GP *020

■ = Address Information Privacy Protected

STONEWALL – PONTOTOC

EDIGER, William Michael. 22312 COUNTY ROAD 3 DR 74871 #019-02-1981 L1982
AM EM *020 †16

STROUD – LINCOLN

DARVIN, Kenneth Ted. 2306 W HIGHWAY 66 74079 #039-01-1996 L1997 FM *020 †18
DARVIN, Teodoro A. 74079 #748-08-1965 L1982 GP GS *020
LE CRONE, Buddy Lynn. RR 2 BOX 247 74079 #039-01-1971 L1972 FM *020 †18
MARKERT, George Conrad. PO BOX 300 74079 #039-01-1960 L1960 FM *020 †18
MEE, Debra Kay. RR 2 BOX 247 74079 #039-01-1987 L1988 P *020 †75

STUART – HUGHES

CHAPMAN, Calvin Chandler. 8564 HIGHWAY 270 74570 #035-45-1959 L1997
EM AM *020 †70,16

SULPHUR – MURRAY

HOUSE, Franklin Richard. RR 1 BOX 4001, LIFESTYLE CENTER OF AMERIC 73086
#005-12-1962 L1963 GP *071
PEREZ, Oscar Bonifacio. 200 FAIRLANE AVE 73086 #275-01-1953 L1976 GP *020
PINAROC, Ambrosio Fabian. 1714 W BROADWAY AVE 73086 #748-07-1963 L1977 FM *071
SEALE, Stuart Allan. RR 1 BOX 4001, GODDARD YOUTH CAMP ROAD 73086
#005-12-1979 L2004 FM *020 †18 ‡
SHERARD, Teresa Lynn. 309 E 2ND ST 73086 #005-12-1999 L2002 IM *020
TATOM, John Henry. 1113 W BROADWAY AVE 73086 #039-01-1958 L1958 FM *020 †85
WILLIAMS, Randal Alan. 220 W VINITA AVE 73086 #039-01-1997 L1998 FM *020 †18

TAFT – MUSKOGEE

GETTYS, Paula Belle. PO BOX 315, 400 OAK 74463 #039-01-1982 L1986 GPM FM *020 †70,18

TAHLEQUAH – CHEROKEE

AHMAD, Yahya Mahmoud. 1294 E DOWNING ST, STE 3N4 74464 #561-17-1978 L2003
PD *020 †55
ARNAUD, Guillermo Winston. 100 S BLISS AVE, WW HASTINGS INDIAN HOSP 74464
#023-01-1982 L1983 GS *020 †85
BALLEW, Jason Jasper. ■ 74464 #039-01-2003 L2006 EM *020 †16
BALUH, Hope Marie. 100 S BLISS AVE 74464 #016-45-1983 L1988 GS *020 †85
BOBB, Brian Shawn. 1203 E ROSS BYP STE A 74464 #048-13-2001 L2004 FM *020 †18
BRAVO, Francisco E. 302 E DOWNING ST 74464 #048-16-1990 L1995 GS *020
COHLMIA, Geo Shaker, Jr. 2028 MAHANEY AVE, FL 2 74464 #019-02-1975 L1984
TS CD *020 †85,90
CRAIG, Glenn John. 1325 E BOONE ST, STE 101 74464 #038-43-1991 L1992 IM *020 †20
DE PAULA, Carl J. ■ 74464 #035-06-1969 L1970 ORS *020 †40
EDWARDS, Coy Joe. 1500 E DOWNING ST, TAHLEQUAH MEDICAL 74464 #039-01-1974 L1977
FM *020 ‡
FARRIS, Brenda Lee. ■ 74464 #025-12-1985 L1988 IM *020
FARRIS, Valerie Lee. 100 S BLISS AVE, HASTINGS INDIAN MEDICAL CE 74464
#046-01-1998 L2003 IM *020
GAHN, David Richard. 100 S BLISS AVE 74464 #023-12-1998 L2002 OBG *020 †30
GARRETT, Rose Lee Hoa. ■ 74464 #748-10-1973 L1986 R *020
GILMORE, Owen Buck. 100 S BLISS AVE 74464 #007-02-1982 L2000 FM *020 †18
GREEN, Lawrence Chas. 1325 E BOONE ST, STE 203 74464 #039-01-1969 L1970 FM *020
HAYDEN, Virgil Lloyd. 5207 JEANETTE LN 74464 #004-01-1969 L1998 OBG *020 †30
JAMES-SCHMIDT, Sharon R. 100 S BLISS AVE, W.W. HASTINGS INDIAN HOSPI 74464
#024-05-1992 L1996 AN *020 †05
JENNINGS, Deborah Sue. 1400 E DOWNING ST 74464 #039-01-1986 L1987 P *020 †75
JEWELL, Peggy Hassell. 1400 HENSLEY DR, BILL WILLIS COMMUNITY MENT 74464
#039-01-1983 L1986 P *020 †75
KENNEDY, Elaine. 100 S BLISS AVE, W W HASTING INDIAN HOSPITA 74464 #047-05-1974 L1976
PD *020 †55
KOEHN, Kenneth Leroy. ■ 74464 #039-01-1961 L1961 FM GP *071 †18
LEWIS, James Andrew. 100 S BLISS AVE, W W HASTINGS HOSPITAL 74464
#039-01-1972 L1973 PD *020 †55
LOFTIN, Teresa Diane. 1323 W KEETOOWAH ST 74464 #019-02-1996 L2002 FM *020 †18
LOWE-ROACHE, Nanetta. ■ 74464 #036-01-1981 L1987 GS *020
MALABRIGO, Joel Acopio. INDIAN HOSP 74464 #748-07-1963 L1995 GS *030
MATHIS, Jennifer Lynn. 1400 E DOWNING ST 74464 #039-01-2003 L2007 FM *020 †18
MAY, Marie Delores. 1400 HENSLEY DR, CHICKASAW NATION HEALTH SY 74464
#037-01-1991 L1992 CHP *020
MC CALIP, Shawna Kay. 100 S BLISS AVE 74464 #039-01-1996 L1997 FM *020 †18
MC KINNON, Leah Jane. 2028 MAHANEY AVE, FL 2 74464 #004-01-1985 L1999
TS VS *020 †85,90
MEADE, Peter Chas. 100 S BLISS AVE, DEPARTMENT OF SURGERY 74464 #035-03-1980 L1984
GS *020 †85
MILLER, Anna Lee. 100 S BLISS AVE, W.W. HASTINGS HOSPITAL 74464 #023-12-1994 L2000
IM *020 †20
MILLS, Stanley David. 100 S BLISS AVE 74464 #018-03-1958 L1959 GS GP *020 †85
MINOR, Danny Lee. 1500 E DOWNING ST, TAHLEQUAH MEDICAL 74464 #039-01-1971 L1972
GS FM *020
MORALES, Angel Javier. 100 S BLISS AVE, HASTINGS INDIAN MED CTR 74464
#042-03-1984 L1993 PD *020
MURPHREE, James Wallace. 1400 E DOWNING ST 74464 #039-01-1947 L1948
DR NM *071 †80,28
NORTHUM, Charles S. 22216 STICK ROSS MTN RD 74464 #004-01-1962 L1997 AN *020 †05
O'BRIEN, Patrick Michael. 100 S BLISS AVE, HASTING INDIAN HOSPITAL 74464
#010-02-1983 L1994 EM *020 †16

PABLO, Daniel Lawrence. 100 S BLISS AVE, W W HASTINGS HOSPITAL 74464
#054-04-1994 L2000 GS *020
PALERMO, Vincent Gerald. ■ 74464 #028-34-1958 L1989 PTH FM *062 †50
PATTON, Stephen Michael. 100 S BLISS AVE, NATIONAL BEHAVIORAL HEALTH 74464
#039-01-1991 L1992 P *020
PEREZ, Dante. 100 S BLISS AVE, W W HASTINGS HOSPITAL 74464 #308-01-1986 L1996
PD *020
POINTER, Edwin Lowell. 1500 E DOWNING ST, STE 110 74464 #039-01-1956 L1956 R *071 †80
PRADIEU, Charles. 100 S BLISS AVE, HASTINGS INDIAN MEDICAL CE 74464
#305-01-1983 L2003 NEP *020
RASHID, Haroon. ■ 74464 #704-21-1991 L2000 IM EM *020 †20
REAVILL, Richard Blendon. ■ 74465 #026-04-1978 L1987 OS *020
ROGERS, Jena Sue. 1201 E ROSS BYP 74464 #048-13-1994 L1995 IM *020 †20
SERATT, James Mark. 1400 E DOWNING ST 74464 #039-01-1985 L1986 FM *020 †18
SIDDIQUE, Naveed. 1506 E SHAWNEE CIR 74464 #704-20-1985 L1992 PD *020 †55 ‡
SOTO, Sylvia. 100 S BLISS AVE 74464 #308-01-1986 L1990 GP *020
STEVENSON, Louis G. 100 S BLISS AVE, WW HASTING INDIAN HOSP 74464
#048-13-1989 L2002 IM *020
STEVENSON, Robin Lindell. 1325 E BOONE ST 74464 #012-01-1975 L1979 OBG EM *020 †30
STUCKY, Don E. 100 S BLISS AVE, DEPT OF FAMILY PRACTICE 74464 #030-05-1975 L1982
FM *020 †18
SUMNER, Larry Dean. 1500 E DOWNING ST, TAHLEQUAH MEDICAL 74464 #039-01-1983 L1984
FM EM *020 †18
TAYLOR, Douglas H. 1201 W 4TH ST # 735 74464 #040-02-1942 L1943 FM OS *020
TROUSDALE, William E. 100 S BLISS AVE, W. W. HASTINGS INDIAN HOSP 74464
#039-01-1974 L1975 OBG *020 †30
WARD, Louis Emmerson, Jr. 100 S BLISS AVE 74464 #067-01-1971 L1972 IM HOS *020 †20
WILSON, Jeffrey Scot. 1607 S MUSKOGEE AVE 74464 #039-05-1990 L1991 PD *075 †55
WINE, Charles Jos. 100 S BLISS AVE 74464 #038-40-1966 L1971 OTO HNS *071 †45 ‡
WOITTE, Greggory Jon. 100 S BLISS AVE, DEPARTMENT OF OB/GYN 74464
#023-12-1993 L2003 OBG *020 †30
YANDELL, Seth David. ■ 74464 #048-02-2004 L2007 IM *020 †20
YOUNG, Douglas Lynn. 1387 W 4TH ST 74464 #019-02-1971 L2000 IM IMG *020 †20

TALIHINA – LATIMER

BONIN, Thomas Charles. 1 CHOCTAW WAY 74571 #023-12-1993 L1999 FM *020 †18
EWAIDA, Nader Helmy Salib. ■ 74571 #915-04-1999 L2006 IM *100 †20
GARDNER, Marie Cole. 1 CHOCTAW WAY, CHOCTAW NATION HEALTH SERV 74571
#025-12-1986 L2007 PD *020 †55
GOODMAN, Floyd Keith. 1 CHOCTAW WAY, CHOCTAW NATION HEALTH CENT 74571
#039-01-1979 L2004 OBG *020 †30
HO, Dung Trung. RR 2 BOX 1425 74571 #941-01-1950 L1980 *020
HODGE, Rona Elsberth. 1 CHOCTAW WAY 74571 #036-01-1985 L2003 GS *020 †85
HOWARD, James Thos. 1 CHOCTAW WAY, CHOCTAN NATION HEALTH CARE 74571
#024-01-1975 L1994 CHP P *020 ‡
IVANICS, Paul. PO BOX 1168, OKLA VETRANS CTR 74571 #473-01-1944 L1977 OS *075
JUMELLE, Antoine Jean M. 1 CHOCTAW WAY 74571 #396-24-1975 L1990 GS *020 †85
LEWIS, Amelia Celeste. 1 CHOCTAW WAY, CHOCTAW NATION HLTH CARE 74571
#035-08-1961 L1962 FM EM *020
MATTHEWS, Marcia Kay. 1 CHOCTAW WAY, CHOCTAW NATION HOSP 74571
#039-01-1994 L1995 FM *020 †18
MIKHAEL, Atef Fouaad-Fahm. ■ 74571 #915-03-1995 L2007 IM *020 †20 ‡
ODUNUKWE, Chukwuka J. 1 CHOCTAW WAY 74571 #690-04-1985 L2003 GS *020 †85
PE BENITO, Charissa L. 1 CHOCTAW WAY, CHOCTAW NATION HEALTH SERV 74571
#748-02-1995 L2004 PD *100 †55
PHAM, Truong Quang. RR 2 BOX 1168, TALIHINA VETERANS CENTER 74571
#941-01-1976 L1982 GP *020
RHODES, Jerry Lee. 1 CHOCTAW WAY 74571 #039-01-1970 L1971 IM CD *020 †20
ROHDE, Melinda Sue. 1 CHOCTAW WAY 74571 #039-01-1995 L1998 PD *020 †55
ROWLAND, Harold T. RR 2 74571 #028-34-1953 L1980 GP DIA *071 †50
SHORT, Christa Nicole. ■ 74571 #039-01-2008 *012
SHORT, James Edward. ■ 74571 #034-01-1980 L1985 OBG REN *071 †30 ‡
VAN TUYL, Charles Don. 1 CHOCTAW WAY, CHOCTAW NATION HEALTH CARE 74571
#039-01-1987 L1988 P *020 †75
WORK, Gary Edward. 1 CHOCTAW WAY, EMERGENCY DEPARTMENT 74571
#039-01-1982 L1987 EM *020
ZHAO, Dong. 1 CHOCTAW WAY 74571 #243-72-1988 L2003 IM *020 †20

THOMAS – CUSTER

MOOSE, Robert Ronald. ■ 73669 #039-01-1961 L1961 GP *020

TINKER AIR FORCE BASE – OKLAHOMA

BERRYMAN, Jessica Lee. 5700 ARNOLD ST, 72D MEDICAL GROUP 73145 #025-12-2005 L2007
FM *020
BOND, Dennis Franklin, II. 5700 ARNOLD ST, 72ND MEDICAL GROUP/SGHQ 73145
#023-12-1999 L2006 ORS *100 †40
CHAWLA, Harperminder. 5700 ARNOLD ST, 72 MEDICAL GROUP 73145 #495-45-1973 L1978
PD *020 †55
DILLARD, Della Ellis. 5700 ARNOLD ST, 72D MEDICALGROUP/SGHQ 73145
#020-02-1992 L1993 FM *020 †18
FINCH, Corey Deon. 5700 ARNOLD ST, 72D MEDICAL GROUP 73145 #010-03-2005 L2007
GS *020
GEARY, Jay Alan. 5700 ARNOLD ST, 72D MEDICAL GROUP 73145 #039-01-2002 L2003
FM *020 †18
GOFORTH, Tom F. USAF HSOP AFLC 73145 #039-01-1978 L1979 FM *020 †18
HOOKS, Edmond Lee. 5700 ARNOLD ST 73145 #028-34-1976 L1985 IM *020
JACKSON, Michael W. 5700 ARNOLD ST, 72D MEDICAL GROUP/SGHQ 73145
#048-04-2001 L2002 FM *020 †18
KATKOVSKY, Leonid. 5700 ARNOLD ST, 72 MDG 73145 #913-32-1985 L1994 GPM *020 †70

■ = Address Information Privacy Protected

KING, Edward Thos. 5700 ARNOLD ST, 72 MEDICAL GROUP 73145 #039-01-1975 L1982 OM *020 †70

PACKARD, Craig Stevens. 5700 ARNOLD ST, 72 MEDICAL GROUP 73145 #023-12-1989 L1992 OM *030 †18,70

SHETH, Pankaj Dwarkadas. 5700 ARNOLD ST, 72D MEDICAL GROUP/SGHQ; 73145 #495-22-1971 L1983 OM *020 ‡

SIMONSON-FRAZIER, Stacey. 5700 ARNOLD ST, 72 MED GRP/SGHQ 73145 #016-43-1992 L1994 PD *030 †55

VAN SYOC, Daniel Lee. 5700 ARNOLD ST, 72D MEDICAL GROUP/SGHQ 73145 #018-03-1980 L1988 FM *020 †18,70

VU, Danny Xuan. 5700 ARNOLD ST, 72D MEDICAL GROUP/SGHQ 73145 #032-01-1993 L1995 FM *020

WAGNER, Jason Michael. 5700 ARNOLD ST BLDG 5801, 72ND MEDICAL GROUP/SGAR 73145 #028-03-2000 L2005 DR *020 †80

WAINNER, Kenneth Fred, Jr. 5700 ARNOLD ST, 72ND MDG/SGOL 73145 #039-01-1969 L1969 FM AM *020 †18

WEBB, Gerald Matthew. 5700 ARNOLD ST, ATTN: CREDENTIAL OFC 73145 #010-01-2001 L2002 FM *020

YOKELL, Richard Allan. 5700 ARNOLD ST, 72 MEDICAL GROUP 73145 #038-40-1994 L1995 P *020 †75

TISHOMINGO – JOHNSTON

ADLAON, Wellie Paypa. 1040 S BYRD ST 73460 #748-11-1989 L1999 IM *020 †20

BELL, Eugene S. 1101 S BYRD ST 73460 #039-01-1952 L1952 FM PHP *071 †18

PATZKOWSKY, Paul Dean. 705 W MAIN ST 73460 #039-01-1960 L1960 GP GS *020

VINSON, Billy Michael. ■ 73460 #024-01-1978 L1979 IM GS *075

WEBB, Floyd Edmond. 1000 E MAIN ST 73460 #039-01-1957 L1958 FM GS *020 †18 ‡

TONKAWA – KAY

WALCHER, Ronald Ray. 600 E GRAND AVE, RON WALCHER MD 74653 #039-01-1978 L1979 GP *020 ‡

TULSA – CREEK

PHILLIPS, Chad A. ■ 74131 #048-12-2001 L2004 EM *020 †16

THOMPSON, Lewis Wm. ■ 74131 #036-05-1960 L1982 PS HS *071 †65

TULSA – TULSA

ABADIE SOLE, Montserrat. 1111 S SAINT LOUIS AVE 74120 #451-01-2003 L2007 FP *012

ABBOTT, Eddie Mack. 2121 S COLUMBIA AVE # 501 74114 #039-01-1977 L1978 OBG *071 †30

ABDALLAH, Al-Ola Abdelfat. ■ 74104 #575-01-2005 L2007 IM *012

ABDELAZIZ, Hala M. 8988 S SHERIDAN RD, STE L 74133 #915-04-1984 L2000 PTH *020 †50

ABOUHOULI, Hassan. ■ 74104 #305-01-2004 L2007 IM *020

ABRAMOVITZ, Joel Nathan. 1919 S WHEELING AVE # 504, NEUROSURGICAL INSTITUTE 74104 #041-12-1976 L2006 NS *020 †25

ABSHERE, Chris Wayne. 3218 S 79TH EAST AVE, STE 200 74145 #039-01-1998 L2001 FM *020 †18

ABU-KHDEIR, Maha Nazmi Ah. 4502 E 41ST ST, UNIVERSITY OF OKLAHOMA COM 74135 #575-01-2005 L2007 PD *012

ACKER, Matthew Ronald. 7600 S LEWIS AVE 74136 #041-02-1995 L1996 FM *020 †18

ADAMS, Craig Vorpe. 1145 S UTICA AVE STE 903 74104 #010-02-1986 L2002 TS VS *020 †85,90

ADELSON, David Michael. 1705 E 19TH ST, STE 502 74104 #012-05-1985 L1989 D *020 †15

ADELSON, Stephen Jay. 1245 S UTICA AVE 74104 #041-09-1959 L1964 PD *020 †55

AFROZE, Anees Fatima. 2808 S SHERIDAN RD 74129 #496-27-2000 L2006 IM *012

AFZAL, Muhammad. ■ 74145 #704-01-2001 L2006 FP *012

AGARWAL, Pallavi. 2815 S SHERIDAN RD, ADULT MEDICINE CLINIC 74129 #496-59-2001 L2006 IM *020 †20

AGGARWAL, Vishal. 4502 E 41ST ST 74135 #495-30-1996 L2003 IMG *020 †20

AGUSTIN, Valentina. ■ 74133 #305-01-2006 L2007 FP *012

AIKMAN, Robert Howard. 2325 S HARVARD AVE, STE 108 74114 #067-01-1966 L1985 OBG *020

AJMERA, Haresh Kantilal. 2325 S HARVARD AVE, STE 301 74114 #496-38-1969 L1975 GE IM *020 †20

AKERS, David L. 1802 E 19TH ST STE 400, ST JOHN ANESTHESIA SERVICE 74104 #039-01-1981 L1982 AN *020 †05

AKINTOLA, Olutoyin Enitan. 1717 E 67TH PL 74136 #690-01-2001 L2007 FP *012

AKINTOLA, Olutoyin Enitan. 7600 S LEWIS AVE, IN HIS IMAGE INC 74136 #690-01-2001 FP *012

ALBOM, Jerrold Raphael. ■ 74135 #035-46-1974 L1981 DR *020 †80

ALDERMAN, Jeffrey Scott. 2815 S SHERIDAN RD, OU PHYSICIANS - INTERNAL M 74129 #010-01-1996 L2000 IM *020 †20

ALDRIDGE, John Loring. 6839 S CANTON AVE, ANESTHESIOLOGISTS INC 74136 #048-02-1974 L1977 AN *020 †05

ALETTY, Varashree. 9322 E 41ST ST, TOPC, VETERANS ADMINISTRAT 74145 #495-09-1985 L1999 IM *020 †20

ALEXANDER, Jeff. 6565 S YALE AVE, STE 503 74136 #030-05-1977 L1978 D *020 †15 ‡

ALFONSO, Silvie Louis. 6600 S YALE AVE, STE 1500 74136 #041-01-1957 L1972 FM OM *071

ALFREY, Anthony Wayne. 802 S JACKSON AVE, STE 135 74127 #039-01-1995 L1996 PTH *050

ALFREY, Laurie Ann. 2815 S SHERIDAN RD, OU PHYSICIANS PEDS CLINIC 74129 #039-01-1995 L1996 PD *040 †55

ALGEE, John Alfred. 3606 N CINCINNATI AVE 74106 #010-03-1960 L1995 IMG IM *071

ALI, Lamiaa Hassan. 4502 E 41ST ST, DEPT OF PEDS 74135 #915-04-1992 L2007 PD *040 †55

ALI, Syed Mujtaba. 6161 S YALE AVE 74136 #704-04-2000 L2007 IM *020 †20

ALLEN, Arielle Marie. 1145 S UTICA AVE STE 600, OU-TULSA - DEPT OF GYNECOL 74104 #039-79-2005, ▲ L2006 OBG *012

ALLEN, Tate Brandon. 4111 S DARLINGTON AVE, RADIOLOGY CONSULTANTS OF 74135 #039-01-1994 L1999 NM *020 †80,28

ALLISON, Mark Edward. 6160 S YALE AVE, 3RD FL 74136 #039-01-1980 L1981 OPH *020 †35

ALLRED, Howard Wm, Jr. 1919 S WHEELING AVE, STE 710 74104 #039-01-1971 L1973 CRS GS *020

AL-NABHAN, Moutaz. 1145 S UTICA AVE 74104 #875-02-2001 L2005 IM *020 †20

AMES, Scott Edward Evans. 6839 S CANTON AVE, ANESTHESIOLOGISTS INC 74136 #039-01-1979 L1980 AN *020 †05 ‡

ANAGNOST, Steven C. 1809 E 13TH ST, THE ORTHOPAEDIC CENTER 74104 #047-06-1993 L1999 ORS *020 †40

ANDERSON, Charles C, Jr. ■ 74133 #039-01-1980 L1981 DR *020 †80

ANDERSON, Craig A. 1120 S UTICA AVE, NEWBORN SPECIALISTS OF 74104 #028-79-1988, ▲ L1993 NPM PD *020 †55

ANDERSON, Jack Katsumi. 1717A S UTICA AVE 74104 #039-01-2002 L2005 EM *100

ANDERSON, Lloyd Tillman. 9330 E 41ST ST, WORKMED/ MEC EAST 74145 #039-01-1970 L1971 EM OM *020 †16

ANDERSON, Lynn Arnaud. 1725 E 19TH ST, STE 201 74104 #021-01-1983 L1994 D *020 †15

ANDERSON, Robert Leland. ■ 74114 #019-02-1942 L1948 CD TS *071 †85,90

ANDERSON, Steffan Gregory. 4502 E 41ST ST, DEPARTMENT OF SURGERY 74135 #019-02-2005 L2006 GS *012

ANGELIDIS, Prodromos Mike. 6161 S YALE AVE 74136 #039-01-2004 L2006 IM *020 †20

ANKLESARIA, Manek Edalji. 2325 S HARVARD AVE, STE 307 74114 #495-22-1970 L1982 OPH *020 †35

ANTHONY, Jonathan Martin. 1120 S UTICA AVE, TULSA-HILLCREST ANESTH PHY 74104 #039-01-1980 L1988 OBG AN *020 †20

ANYASIKE, Michael Kelechi. 7600 S LEWIS AVE 74136 #913-29-1996 L2006 FM *020 †18

APRIL, Paul Arthur. 6465 S YALE AVE 74136 #035-19-1955 L1961 IM RHU *020 †20

ARAN, Peter Patrick. 6565 S YALE AVE STE 1200, GASTROENTEROLOGY SPECIALIS 74136 #018-03-1981 L1990 GE *020 †20

ARCHUAL, Andrew Michael. ■ 74105 #041-02-2008 *012

ARQUISOLA, Maria Stella L. 1705 E 19TH ST STE 304 74104 #748-09-1992 L2000 P *020 †75

ARRENDELL, Eugene H. ■ 74136 #039-01-1943 L1946 GP *071

ARROYO, Michael Robert. 4502 E 41ST ST, TULSA DEPARTMENT OF SURGER 74135 #016-11-2004 L2005 GS *012

ASAHINA, Shoichi. ■ 74136 #016-01-1941 L1943 DR *071

ASHCRAFT, Thomas L. 2325 S HARVARD AVE STE 305 74114 #004-01-1953 L1960 PME AN *020

ASHING, Bonnie J. 9322 E 41ST ST 74145 #039-01-1981 L1984 IM *020 †20

ASHLEY, John R. 6160 S YALE AVE, 3RD FL 74136 #039-01-1981 L1982 D EM *020 †15

ASHLEY, Robert Edward. ■ 74136 #039-01-1955 L1955 P *071 †75

ASKEY, Carole Jean. ■ 74135 #041-12-1959 L1961 GP *075

ASPENSON, Donald Erik. 1265 S UTICA AVE, STE 300 74104 #039-01-1993 L2004 END *020 †20

ATHERTON, Justin Thomas. 1725 E 19TH ST STE 800 74104 #039-01-1995 L1996 GS *020 †85

ATTIATALLA, Milad Helmy H. 7600 S LEWIS AVE 74136 #915-04-1987 L2006 FM *100 †18

AUERBACH, Eric Glen. 9228 S MINGO RD STE 200, OKLAHOMA HEART INSTITUTE 74133 #011-02-1995 L2003 CD *020 †20

AXNESS, Mark E. 10109 E 79TH ST 74133 #005-02-1982 L2004 AN PME *020 †05

AYITEY, Rosemary Naa Ntee. 7600 S LEWIS AVE, IN HIS IMAGE FP RESIDENCY 74136 #412-01-1994 L2003 FM *020 †18

AZADI, Kavon Charles. ■ 74126 #039-01-2007 L2007 IM *012

BABB, Ray Claude, Jr. 6465 S YALE AVE STE 605 74136 #039-01-1977 L1978 OBG *020 †30 ‡

BACCHUS, Amy Claire. 6585 S YALE AVE, STE 1200 74136 #048-02-1998 L2005 PCC *020 †20

BAGWELL, John Wayne. 6839 S CANTON AVE 74136 #039-01-1979 L1980 AN *071

BAHAMADI, Swaleh Ali Swal. 2815 S SHERIDAN RD, ADULT MEDICINE CLIIC 74129 #577-01-2002 L2006 HO *012 †20

BAILEY, Byron Louis. ■ 74136 #039-01-1947 L1948 IM END *071

BAILEY, James Kent. 6585 S YALE AVE, STE 115 74136 #039-01-1975 L1976 IM *020 †20

BAILEY, William Patrick. 6839 S CANTON AVE, ANESTHESIOLOGISTS INC 74136 #039-01-1986 L1987 AN *020 †05 ‡

BAKER, Barbara A. 6160 S YALE AVE, SPRINGER CLINIC, INC 74136 #016-11-1977 L1983 IM DIA *020 †20

BAKER, Jonathan Chas. 9659 RIVERSIDE PKWY, RIVERSIDE PEDIATRICS 74137 #039-01-1984 L1985 PD *020 †20

BALDWIN, Jonathan Martin. 8803 S 101ST EAST AVE, STE 145 74133 #039-01-1999 L2000 OBG *020 †30

BALDWIN, Lisa Marie. ■ 74105 #039-01-2004 L2005 IM *100 †20

BALES, Robert Daniel. 4444 S HARVARD AVE, STE 300 74135 #039-01-2003 L2007 OPH *020

BALYEAT, Ray Morton. 2000 S WHEELING AVE, STE 400 74104 #039-01-1983 L1984 OPH *020 †35

BANNER, William, Jr. 6161 S YALE AVE 74136 #047-06-1976 L1994 PD PA *020 †55

BANNER, William Perry. 6161 S YALE AVE, PEDIATRIC INTENSIVE CARE U 74136 #024-01-1978 L1985 GS *020 †85

BARBEE, Richard Franklin. 1923 S UTICA AVE 74104 #039-01-1957 L1957 R NM *071 †80,28

BARBERA, Porter E. ■ 74114 #047-07-1946 L1946 GP *071

BARE, Jane Elizabeth. 10505 E 91ST ST, STE 150 74133 #019-02-1988 L1994 CD IM *020 †20

BARNES, John Renner. 6839 S CANTON AVE, ASSOC ANESTHLKGSTS INC 74136 #039-01-2000 L2004 AN *020 †05

BARRANCO, Vincent Paul. 2121 E 21ST ST 74114 #027-01-1962 L1966 D DMP *071 †15

BARRETT, Penni Alyce. 4111 S DARLINGTON AVE, RADIOLOGY CONSULTANTS OF 74135 #016-45-1986 L1991 DR *020 †80

BARTLETT, John Michael. 1623 S UTICA AVE 74104 #165-01-1979 L1982 EM OM *020 †16

BARTOLONI, Ann Elizabeth. 1923 S UTICA AVE, PHYSICIANS 74104 #039-01-1984 L1985 AN *020 †20,05

BARTON, Bruce Allen. 1725 E 19TH ST STE 200 74104 #039-01-1987 L1991 PUD CCM *020

BARTON, Clyde Wheeler. 6600 S YALE AVE STE 750 74136 #039-01-1958 L1958 OBG *071 †30

BARTON, Kami Lynne. 6465 S YALE AVE STE 704, WARREN CLINIC INTERNAL MED 74136 #011-03-1989 L1992 IM *020 †20

BARTON, Roger Phillip. 6161 S YALE AVE 74136 #039-01-1990 L1991 CCP *020 †55

BASS, Haskell Harris, Jr. 1725 E 19TH ST 74104 #021-01-1955 L1973 CRS GS *071 †85,10

BAUMGARTNER, Rowena G. 6565 S YALE AVE, STE 704 74136 #048-13-1996 L1999 PD *020 †55 ‡

BAXTER, Carolyn J. 4502 E 41ST ST, THE UNIVERSITY OF OKLAHOMA 74135 #039-01-1999 L2000 P *020 †75

BAXTER, Michael A.. 4502 E 41ST ST 74135 #039-79-2005, ▲ L2006 PD *012

BAZIH, Jaafar Mohamed. 4802 S 109TH EAST AVE 74146 #915-04-1973 L1978 ORS *020 †40

BEAMAN, Jason Walter. 4502 E 41ST ST, FAMILY PRACTICE 74135 #039-79-2007, ▲ FPP *012

BEARDEN, James Harold. 6161 S YALE AVE 74136 #048-12-1961 L1970 GE IM *071 †20

BEASLEY, Todd C. 1923 S UTICA AVE, PHYSICIANS 74104 #039-79-1999, ▲ L2002 **AN** *020 †05
BECERRA, Israel. 1111 S SAINT LOUIS AVE 74120 #048-02-2004 L2006 **FM** *100 †18
BECK, James Peter. 6585 S YALE AVE STE 500 74136 #041-01-1967 L1974 **ORS GP** *020 †40
BECKETT, Ayslin Marie. 9616 S MEMORIAL DR # 330 74133 #305-01-2006 L2008 **FP** *012
BEECHER, Brett Alan. ■ 74105 #039-01-2007 L2007 **GS** *012
BEESON, Deborah Jan. 1923 S UTICA AVE 74104 #039-01-1980 L1985 **IM** *074 †20
BEESON, James Harold. 1145 S UTICA AVE, STE 460 74104 #016-02-1976 L1983 **OBG MFM** *040 †30
BELL, Heather Linette. 4502 E 41ST ST 74135 #039-79-2004, ▲ L2005 **ID** *012
BENDER, Doyle D. 6161 S YALE AVE 74136 #037-01-1990 L1991 **EM** *020 †16
BENEAR, John Benj, II. 2421 E 26TH ST 74114 #039-01-1979 L1980 **HEM ON** *071 †20
BENEDICT, Jerrold Lee. 1541 N SHERIDAN RD 74115 #039-01-1987 L1990 **FM** *020 †18
BENNER, Benjamin Gean. 6767A S YALE AVE 74136 #048-04-1973 L1978 **NS** *020 †25
BENNETT, Bruce Wayne. 8115 S MEMORIAL DR, OMNI SOUTH TULSA 74133 #021-05-1985 L1986 **FM** *020 †18
BENNETT, Howard Allen. ■ 74133 #018-03-1943 L1948 **AN** *071 †05
BERENJI, Kambeez. 9228 S MINGO RD, STE 200 74133 #517-01-1991 L2006 **IM CD** *100 †20
BERGMAN, Donald Raymond. 6465 S YALE AVE 74136 #039-01-1962 L1962 **TS OS** *072 †85,90
BERKENBILE, Glen L. 1923 S UTICA AVE 74104 #039-01-1946 L1949 **FM GS** *071 †85
BERMUDEZ, Ovidio Bernabe. 6655 S YALE AVE 74136 #308-03-1985 L2005 **ADL PD** *020 †55
BERNARD, Jean. 1809 E 13TH ST, THE ORTHOPAEDIC CENTER 74104 #605-02-1989 L2001 **PM PME** *020 †60
BERNIER, Ralph D. ■ 74137 #039-01-1976 L1988 **ADM PMM** *030 †50
BERRY, Charles Miles. 1265 S UTICA AVE, STE 105 74104 #039-01-1977 L1984 **TS** *020 †85,90
BERRY, Christopher Edward. 7600 S LEWIS AVE 74136 #048-12-2004 L2005 **FM** *100 †18
BEVILACQUA, Paul Anthony. 1923 S UTICA AVE, PHYSICIANS 74104 #039-01-1989 L1990 **AN** *020 †05 ‡
BHAKTA, Bhadresh L. 8556 E 101ST ST STE A 74133 #047-20-1994 L2000 **APM AN** *020 †05
BHANDARI, Kusum. 1124 S SAINT LOUIS AVE, STE 61 74120 #495-30-1982 L2002 **NEP** *020 †20
BHANDARI, Rajesh. 5018 E 68TH ST, STE 100 74136 #496-03-1986 L2002 **IM** *020 †20
BIALAS, Megan Bernadette. ■ 74136 #016-11-1984 L2007 **IM GP** *020 †20
BIBY, Lloyd David. 6839 S CANTON AVE, ANESTHESIOLOGISTS INC 74136 #039-01-1987 L1992 **AN** *020 †05
BICKELL, William H. 1623 S UTICA AVE 74104 #010-02-1980 L1985 **EM** *050 †16
BIGGS, Janet E. 2000 S WHEELING AVE, STE 510 74104 #039-01-1996 L1997 **NEP IM** *020 †20
BIGGS, Jason Paul. 4500 S GARNETT RD STE 9 74146 #039-01-1997 L2002 **AN** *020 †05
BIGLER, Jeffrey L. 6565 S YALE AVE, STE 1200 74136 #039-01-1997 L1998 **GE** *020 †20
BILLINGS, Anthony Chas. 1851 E 71ST ST 74136 #040-02-1966 L1973 **NS** *071 †25 ‡
BINSTOCK, Marcel. 3121 S GARY CT 74105 #041-12-1963 L1971 **OPH** *020 †35
BIRCH, J Randolph. ■ 74114 #041-01-1962 L1969 **U** *071
BISCHOFF, James F. 6475 S YALE AVE STE 301, EASTERN OK ORTHOPEDIC CENT 74136 #048-04-1983 L1988 **ORS** *020 †40
BLACK, Jeff. 1717A S UTICA AVE 74104 #039-01-1987 L1988 **FM** *020 †18
BLACKMON, Darnell Eric. 1809 E 13TH ST, THE ORTHOPAEDIC CENTER 74104 #047-07-1996 L2002 **ORS** *020 †40
BLACKSTOCK, Melanie R. 6465 S YALE AVE, STE 815 74136 #039-01-1987 L1991 **OBG** *020 †30
BLAKE, Christine Faith. 2000 S WHEELING AVE # 800 74104 #030-05-1991 L1992 **OBG MFM** *020 †30
BLANKENSHIP, Matt Morey. 2815 S SHERIDAN RD 74129 #039-01-2001 L2002 **GE** *020
BLANKENSHIP, Robert Calvi. 1919 S WHEELING AVE # 606, CVT SURGERY INC 74104 #021-01-1973 L1980 **TS** *020 †85,90
BLAUW, Charles G. ■ 74133 #019-02-1944 L1947 **GP** *071
BLEDSOE, Drusilla Lorene. ■ 74137 #048-13-1996 **PD** *100
BLESSING, William Douglas. 6160 S YALE AVE, SPRINGER CLINIC 74136 #025-01-1968 L1975 **GS** *020 †85
BLISS, Sarah Ann. 4502 E 41ST ST, OU PSYCHIATRIC CLINIC 74135 #039-01-2005 L2006 **P** *012
BLISS, Theron Joseph. 4502 E 41ST ST, FAMILY PRACTICE 74135 #039-79-2007, ▲ **FP** *012
BLOCK, Jerome Edward. 6048 S SHERIDAN RD # B 74145 #033-05-1964 L2002 **IM UCM** *020 †20
BLOCK, Robert Walter. 4502 E 41ST ST, SCHUSTERMAN CENTER 74135 #041-01-1969 L1975 **PD ADL** *020 †55 ‡
BLOOM, Rebecca Abigail. ■ 74136 #039-01-2000 L2007 **EM** *020 †16
BLOOMBERG, Kenneth Wm. ■ 74135 #048-12-1960 **OPH OS** *020
BLUM, Jobst Gebhard. 6839 S CANTON AVE, ANESTHESIOLOGISTS INC 74136 #048-12-1976 L1982 **AN** *020 †05 ‡
BLUMENTHAL, Harvey Jay. 8110 S YALE AVE 74137 #028-03-1966 L1972 **N** *071 †75
BOATWRIGHT, Michele S. 1923 S UTICA AVE, PHYSICIANS 74104 #021-06-1991 L1996 **AN** *020 †05
BOATWRIGHT, Roger Wayne. ■ 74133 #019-02-2002 L2005 **OBG** *012
BOCK, Brian John. 1923 S UTICA AVE 74104 #030-06-1995 L2000 **PTH** *020 †50
BODEN, Ronald Conrad. ■ 74133 #010-02-1959 L1971 **OBG** *071 †30
BOEDEKER, Daniel James. 6767 S YALE AVE STE A, NEUROSURGERY SPECIALISTS 74136 #039-01-2000 L2006 **NS** *020
BOKAL, Amy. 2408 E 81ST ST 74137 #016-11-1998 L2003 **DR** *020 †80
BOLAND, Karen Lynn. 1120 S UTICA AVE 74104 #019-02-1989 L1990 **AN** *020 †30
BOLDING, Pat Sinclair. 6600 S YALE AVE, STE 700 74136 #004-01-1982 L1983 **FM** *020 †18
BOLZ, Angela. 4502 E 41ST ST, FAMILY PRACTICE 74135 #039-79-2006, ▲ L2007 **IM** *012
BOOMER, Walter Mark. 6585 S YALE AVE, STE 1200 74136 #039-01-1989 L1990 **CCM** *020 †20
BOONE, Bradford Lee. 6475 S YALE AVE STE 301 74136 #039-01-1985 L1991 **ORS OSM** *020 †40
BOONE, Ralph Tyler. 6475 S YALE AVE STE 301, EASTERN OK ORTHOPEDIC CENT 74136 #039-01-1988 L1994 **ORS** *020 †40 ‡
BOONE, Reece Richard, Jr. 3701 N CINCINNATI AVE 74106 #051-04-1945 L1956 **GS GP** *071
BOTTOMLEY, Robert Gary. 7170 S BRADEN AVE STE 185 74136 #039-01-1962 L1969 **IM** *020
BOUCHER, Colleen Rae. 2512 E 21ST ST 74114 #039-01-1983 L1984 **P IM** *072 †75
BOURDEAU, James Edward. 6465 S YALE AVE, NEPHROLOGY SPECIALISTS OF 74136 #016-06-1974 L1990 **NEP IM** *020 †20
BOWEN, William Jarvis. ■ 74136 #039-01-1989 L1990 **EM** *020 †16
BOWERFIND, Jane Strong. 1532 E 20TH ST 74120 #038-06-1991 L2004 **CHP** *020
BOWLER, Larry Donnelll. 603 E PINE ST 74106 #019-02-1978 L1981 **IM** *020 †20
BOWLER, Ulysses Simpson. 1521 N YUKON AVE 74127 #019-02-1978 L1981 **IM** *020
BOWLING, April Shea. 4444 E 41ST ST, SCHUSTERMAN CLINIC 74135 #039-01-1999 L2000 **PD** *020 †55
BOXELL, Chris Michael. 9001 S 101ST EAST AVE, STE 190 74133 #039-01-1980 L1993 **NS** *020 †25
BOYD, George Bryant. 6565 S YALE AVE STE 1003 74136 #039-01-1970 L1971 **FM** *020 †18
BRANDENBURG, Mark Andrew. 6161 S YALE AVE 74136 #039-01-1992 L1993 **EM** *020 †16
BRAVERMAN, Irvin B. 6161 S YALE AVE 74136 #030-05-1949 L1957 **PD PDC** *071 †55
BREGMAN, Richard Marvin. 6585 S YALE AVE, STE 628 74136 #030-05-1975 L1980 **SMI PUD** *020 †20
BREIPOHL, Gary Walter. 8801 S 101ST EAST AVE 74133 #019-02-1983 L1988 **AN** *020 †05
BRESLOFF, Tobie. 1265 S UTICA AVE STE 300, OKLAHAMA HEART INSTITUTE 74104 #025-07-1979 L1984 **END** *020
BRETT, Rebecca Jeanne. 7600 S LEWIS AVE 74136 #028-34-1995 L1996 **FM** *020 †18
BREWER, David Louis. 10505 E 91ST ST, STE 150 74133 #039-01-1966 L1966 **CD** *020 †20
BREWER, Jonathan Keith. 7600 S LEWIS AVE 74136 #039-01-1995 L1998 **FM OBG** *072 †18
BRICKNER, Theodore James. 6161 S YALE AVE, 5TH FL PICU 74136 #028-02-1958 L1968 **RO** *071 †80
BRIGGEMAN, Andrew R. 8803 S 101ST EAST AVE, STE 300 74133 #048-78-1999, ▲ L2003 **PM** *020 †60
BRIGGS, William Kent. 6565 S YALE AVE, STE 1200 74136 #039-01-1990 L1991 **GE** *020 †20
BRILL, Melvyn Leon. 8086 S YALE AVE BOX 118 74136 #039-01-1961 L1961 **IM CD** *071 †20
BRISTER, Zeb Linston, Jr. 1145 S UTICA AVE STE 162 74104 #039-01-1973 L1974 **OPH** *020 †35
BRITT, Mark Paul. 8803 S 101ST EAST AVE, STE 395 74133 #039-01-1985 L1988 **PUD** *020 †20
BROCKMAN, Todd Alan. 2000 S WHEELING AVE, STE 403 74104 #048-14-1982 L1986 **OPH** *020 †35 ‡
BROOKBY, Bruce Kimball. 1923 S UTICA AVE 74104 #028-03-1972 L1973 **PTH** *071 †50
BROOKOVER, Wesley Todd. 6160 S YALE AVE, STE 640 74136 #039-01-1987 L1992 **U** *020 †95
BROTHERS, Duane E. 1145 S UTICA AVE, STE 1105 74104 #004-01-1951 L1959 **AN GP** *071 †05
BROUGHAN, Thomas A. 1725 E 19TH ST, SPECIALIST 74104 #038-41-1979 L1997 **GS AS** *020 †85
BROWN, Daniel Andrian. 4502 E 41ST ST, FAMILY PRACTICE 74135 #039-79-2007, ▲ **FP** *012
BROWN, Douglas R. 1705 E 19TH ST STE 503 74104 #048-15-1995 L1998 **IM** *020 †20
BROWN, Kathryn Corinne. 1727 S UTICA AVE 74104 #028-02-1997 L2007 **AI** *020 †20,03
BROWN, Leonard H. 6913 S CANTON AVE 74136 #039-01-1945 L1948 **PS** *071 †85,65
BROWN, Matthew Eric. ■ 74112 #028-78-2007, ▲ *012
BROWN, Ronald David. 2815 S SHERIDAN RD, ADULT MEDICINE CLINIC 74129 #166-02-2002 L2005 **OS IM** *100
BROWN, Spencer H, Jr. 6585 S YALE AVE, CARDIAC SURGERY OF TULSA 74136 #039-01-1967 L1967 **TS** *071 †85,90
BROWNE, Christopher A. 6475 S YALE AVE STE 301, EASTERN OK ORTHOPEDIC CENT 74136 #019-02-1995 L2001 **ORS** *020 †40
BROWNING, David, Jr. 1725 E 19TH ST STE 702 74104 #048-04-1961 L1968 **IM NEP** *020 †20
BROWNLEE, Albert Walter. 5020 E 68TH ST 74136 #016-02-1961 L1962 **PDA PD** *071 †55
BROWNLEE, Stephen Michael. 8803 S 101ST EAST AVE, STE 110 74133 #039-01-1981 L1986 **OTO** *020 †45
BROWNSON, Richmond Jay. 6565 S YALE AVE 74136 #039-01-1964 L1966 **OTO HNS** *071 †45
BRUCE, Robert R. 6465 S YALE AVE STE 704 74136 #039-01-1976 L1978 **U** *020 †95 ‡
BRUMFIELD, Thomas J. 1044 N SHERIDAN RD 74115 #004-01-1951 L1951 **FM GP** *072
BRUNS, Stephen Don. 1725 E 19TH ST, STE 800 74104 #039-01-1997 L1998 **GS TRS** *020 †85
BRUTON, Bob Lee. 6161 S YALE AVE 74136 #039-01-1965 L1965 **FM IMG** *020 †18 ‡
BRYAN, John Dearing. 7171 S YALE AVE, STE 102 74136 #004-01-1974 L1978 **OPH** *020 †35
BRYDEN, Leslie Ann. ■ 74114 #041-02-2008 *012
BUCHOLTZ, Michelle. 1111 S SAINT LOUIS AVE 74120 #039-79-2005, ▲ L2006 **FP** *012
BUDETTI, Peter Paul. 4502 E 41ST ST, ROOM 1G08 SCHUSTERMAN CTR 74135 #035-01-1970 L1971 **PD LM** *062 †55
BULLOCK, Kaitlin Anne. ■ 74114 #039-01-2008 *012
BUNDREN, John Clark. 1145 S UTICA AVE, STE 460 74104 #039-01-1978 L1982 **OBG** *020 †30 ‡
BURDINE, Virginia D. 2738 E 51ST ST STE 290 74105 #039-01-1997 L2002 **HMP PTH** *020 †50
BURGER, David Maurice. 1418 E 17TH PL 74120 #028-34-2004 L2005 *100
BURGOS, Peter Arthur. 7600 S LEWIS AVE, FAMILY MEDICAL CARE 74136 #019-02-1991 L2000 **FM** *020 †18
BURKE, Shaye. 4502 E 41ST ST, FAMILY PRACTICE 74135 #039-79-2006, ▲ L2007 **IM** *012
BURLESON, William David. 6104 S FULTON AVE 74136 #039-01-1986 L1998 **RO** *020 †80
BURNETT, William Clair. 1923 E 21ST ST 74114 #039-01-1973 L1974 **CD IM** *020 †20
BURNS, Dixon N. ■ 74136 #047-05-1945 L1952 **GYN** *071 †30
BURNS, Patricia Gayle. 1007 S PEORIA AVE 74120 #039-01-1993 L1994 **PD MPD** *020 †20,55
BURST-SINGER, Kelley A. 6565 S YALE AVE, STE 312 74136 #039-01-1994 L1996 **IM** *020 †20
BUTCHER, Jennifer Lynn. 4502 E 41ST ST, ADULT MEDICINE CLINIC 74135 #039-01-2005 L2007 **IM** *012
BUTCHER, Thomas Mc Neal. 1923 S UTICA AVE, PHYSICIANS 74104 #039-01-1982 L1983 **AN** *020 †05
BUTLER, Phillip Michael. 6585 S YALE AVE, STE 1200 74136 #028-03-1977 L1979 **PUD IM** *020 †20
CADDELL, Joan L. 8181 S LEWIS AVE 74137 #041-01-1953 L1989 **OS PD** *050 †55
CAIN, Stephen Richard. 1611 S UTICA AVE # 253 74104 #004-01-1996 L2000 **AN** *020 †05
CALDWELL, George B, Jr. 1623 S UTICA AVE 74104 #039-01-1979 L1980 **OM EM** *020 †70,16
CALDWELL, Kammie Maria. 9521 RIVERSIDE PKWY, # 235 74137 #032-01-2001 L2004 **IM** *020
CALDWELL, Tim Symmes. 4111 S DARLINGTON AVE, RADIOLOGY CONSULTANTS OF 74135 #038-41-1961 L1969 **R** *071 †80 ‡
CALES, Robert J. ■ 74136 #021-01-1948 L1976 **OM TS** *071 †85,90
CALHOUN, Dan Earl. 6964 S 69TH EAST AVE 74133 #048-02-1978 L1979 **IM** *020 †20
CALLEGARI, Paul Robert. 6585 S YALE AVE STE 1050 74136 #065-01-1983 L1996 **PS HS** *020 †65
CALVERT, Jon Channing. 2424 E 21ST ST, STE 340 74114 #048-04-1968 L1982 **OBG FM** *020 †18,30 ‡
CALVERT, Joshua Tobin. 1705 E 19TH ST STE 30 74104 #039-01-2001 L2007 **IM** *020
CALVERT, Lynette L J. 4502 E 41ST ST 74135 #048-04-1972 L1982 **PD** *020 †55
CALVERT, Stephen Timothy. 1919 S WHEELING AVE, STE 200 74104 #039-01-2001 L2002 **MPD** *020 †20,55
CALVIN, Manuel J. 6160 S YALE AVE, SPRINGER CLINIC, INC 74136 #042-01-1984 L1989 **IM RHU** *020 †20
CAMCIOGLU, Belgin. ■ 74107 #654-01-2003 L2007 **IM** *012
CAMERON, Craig Steven. 1265 S UTICA AVE, STE 300 74104 #019-02-2000 L2007 **CD** *020 †20 ‡
CAMPBELL, Craig Henry. ■ 74135 #671-01-1972 L1982 **FM** *020

■ = Address Information Privacy Protected

CAMPBELL, John Gooch. 1924 S UTICA AVE, STE 1212 74104 #039-01-1966 L1966 OTO HNS *071 †45

CAMPBELL, Stephen Bill. 6839 S CANTON AVE 74136 #039-01-1968 L1968 AN *072 †05 ‡

CAMPBELL, William Robt. 5018 E 68TH STE 200 74136 #039-01-1978 L1979 OBG *020 †30

CANNON, Chad Michael. ■ 74104 #039-01-2008 *012

CAPEHART, Mark Allan. 6475 S YALE AVE STE 301, EASTERN OK ORTHO CTR 74136 #039-01-1971 L1972 ORS *020 †40

CAPEHART, Robert Joe. 1866 E 15TH ST 74104 #039-01-1965 L1965 CRS FM *071 †10 ‡

CAPEHART, Samuel Alfred. ■ 74137 #039-01-1948 L1948 GP *020

CAPEHART, Shelley Lynn. 1705 E 19TH ST STE 705 74104 #048-12-1999 L2006 CRS *100 †85,10

CAREY, Terence Leonard. 7125 S BRADEN AVE 74136 #836-01-1973 L1984 AI PDP *020 †55,03

CARLSON, Kathleen. 7614 E 91ST ST, STE 100 74133 #028-46-1975 L1978 OBG *020 †30

CARLSON, Paul S. 1923 S UTICA AVE, PHYSICIANS 74104 #039-01-1991 L1993 AN *05

CARMENT, John Maxwell. 4502 E 41ST ST, DETP OF INT MED GERI SECT 74135 #039-01-2002 L2007 IMG IM *040 †20

CARRICO, Bruce. 3534 E 51ST ST 74135 #005-12-1979 L1982 EM FM *020 †18,16

CARSTENS, George John, II. 4111 S DARLINGTON AVE # 7 74135 #048-13-1985 L1997 R *020 †80

CARSTENS, Mary Christine. 4111 S DARLINGTON AVE, RADIOLOGY CONSULTANTS OF 74135 #048-13-1986 L1997 PDR PD *020 †80,55

CARTER, Kimberly Dawn. 1145 S UTICA AVE 74104 #028-78-2005, ▲ L2006 OBG *012

CARTWRIGHT, Allison Lynn. ■ 74133 #039-01-2008 *012

CASNER, Steven J. 1923 S UTICA AVE 74104 #048-12-1990 L1996 PTH *020 †50

CASSIDY, John Michael. 10505 E 91ST ST, STE 150 74133 #055-02-1987 L1993 CD *020 †20

CATTANEO, John Ernest. 1919 S WHEELING AVE # 707 74104 #019-02-1991 L1995 N *020 †75

CAVANAGH, Lamont Edward. 1111 S SAINT LOUIS AVE, OU PHYSICIANS FAMILY MEDIC 74120 #039-01-1992 L1993 FSM *020 †18

CAVITT, Alisa Michelle. ■ 74128 #039-01-2006 GS *012

CEA, Claudia Evelyn. 9001 S 101ST EAST AVE 74133 #019-02-1998 L2005 FM *020 †18

CEESAY, Karamba Jalamang. 6161 S YALE AVE 74136 #047-06-2000 L2003 IM *020 †20

CHADD, Graham Douglas. 1120 S UTICA AVE 74104 #775-01-1977 L1991 AN *020 †05

CHAIN, Vicki Sue. 4111 S DARLINGTON AVE # 7 74135 #028-78-1992, ▲ L2001 DR *020

CHALKIN, Brian A. 8801 S 101ST EAST AVE 74133 #035-75-1998, ▲ L1999 ORS *020

CHAN, Linda. 7600 S LEWIS AVE 74136 #917-12-2000 L2005 FM *100 †18

CHANCE, Robert L. 1923 S UTICA AVE, PHYSICIANS 74104 #028-78-1991, ▲ L1995 PM *020 †60

CHANCELLOR, Jon Drake. 6839 S CANTON AVE, ANESTHESIOLOGISTS INC 74136 #048-02-1974 L1977 AN *020 †05 ‡

CHANDWANEY, Rajesh. 1265 S UTICA AVE STE 300, OKLAHOMA HEART INSTITUTE 74104 #016-11-1996 L2003 IC *020 †20

CHANEY, Tamara. 2738 E 51ST ST STE 290, TULSA MEDICAL LABORATORY 74105 #019-02-1992 L1997 PTH *020 †50

CHANG, Ming-Kao. ■ 74129 #244-01-1978 L1988 IM *075

CHASER, Brad. ■ 74104 #039-01-2008 *012

CHEATHAM, Kimberly Ann. 1145 S UTICA AVE, STE 460 74104 #039-01-1996 L2000 OBG *020 †30

CHEKOFSKY, Kenneth Martin. 6475 S YALE AVE, STE 202 74136 #035-47-1976 L2001 HS ORS *020 †40

CHELF, John C. 6655 S YALE AVE 74136 #039-01-1977 L1981 P OS *020 †75

CHEN, Diana Marie. 1919 S WHEELING AVE 74104 #038-43-1988 L1989 IM *020 †20

CHERNG, Wen-Shean. 1923 S UTICA AVE RM 729, ST JOHN'S MEDICAL CENTER 74104 #244-01-1974 L1987 NPM *020 †55

CHESHER, Tessa. 2808 S SHERIDAN RD, DEPT OF PSYCHIATRY 74129 #039-79-2005, ▲ L2006 P *012

CHILDS, Clinton R. ■ 74133 #048-02-1994 L1995 FM *020 †18

CHOH, Jeffery Taehwan. 10109 E 79TH STE, SOUTHWESTERN REGIONAL MEDI 74133 #038-40-1991 L2007 VIR *020

CHOI, Chisoo. 201 S GARNETT RD, BROOKHAVEN HOSPITAL 74128 #016-01-1983 L1986 IM *020 †20

CHOO, Yew Cheong. 3020 S HARVARD AVE STE C 74114 #825-01-1972 L1984 GO GYN *020 †30

CHOW, Stephen. 4502 E 41ST ST 74135 #661-02-2002 L2005 IM *100 †20

CHRISTIAN, Mary Margaret. 8177 S HARVARD AVE STE 627 74137 #032-01-1994 L2002 D *020 †15

CHRISTY, Angela D. 2325 S HARVARD AVE, STE 108 74114 #039-79-1998, ▲ L1999 OBG *020 †30

CLANCY, Gerard Patrick. 4502 E 41ST ST, STE 2B30 74135 #018-03-1988 L2002 P *030 †75

CLARK, John Montford, Jr. 6585 S YALE AVE STE 1020 74136 #048-02-1962 L1969 PS *071 †85,65

CLARK, Sandra Hewitt. 6565 S YALE AVE, STE 410 74136 #001-02-1995 L2002 PTH *020 †50

CLARK, William Charles, Jr. 4802 S 109TH EAST AVE 74146 #039-01-2001 L2006 ORS *020

CLEAVER, Edgar Milton. 1923 S UTICA AVE 74104 #030-05-1954 L1979 P FM *020

CLENDENIN, Michael Beale. 2000 S WHEELING AVE, STE 900 74104 #021-01-1975 L1981 HS ORS *020 †40

CLINE, Whitney. 4502 E 41ST ST 74135 #039-79-2005, ▲ L2006 PD *012

CLINGAN, Frank Add. 1923 S UTICA AVE, # 223 74104 #039-01-1956 L1956 GS *071 †85

CLINGAN, Rodney L. 1705 E 19TH ST STE 705 74104 #048-15-1998 L1999 CRS *020 †85,10

CLOUSER, Michael Edwin. 4111 S DARLINGTON AVE, RADIOLOGY CONSULTANTS OF 74135 #039-01-1975 L1977 DR *020 †80

COATES, John Albert. 6600 S YALE AVE STE 1315 74136 #039-01-1955 L1955 NS *071

COBB, Carolyn Louise. 3218 S 79TH EAST AVE 74145 #048-02-1979 L1980 EM IM *020 †16 ‡

COBB, Charles Roger. 4870 S LEWIS AVE, STE 190 74105 #039-01-1977 L1978 P CHP *020 †75

COBBLE, Stephanie. 2325 S HARVARD AVE, STE 108 74114 #039-01-1998 L1999 FM *020 †18

COCHRAN, J Walter. 1923 S UTICA AVE 74104 #004-01-1957 L1966 PTH *020 †50

COCHRAN, Julie Ann. 1923 S UTICA AVE 74104 #019-02-1978 L1979 FM EM *020 †18,16

COFFEY, Clinton Maurice. ■ 74105 #039-01-1958 L1958 D *071 †15

COFFEY, Robert John. 6565 S YALE AVE STE 704 74136 #039-01-1974 L1998 PD *020 †55

COHEN, Alicia M. 2000 S WHEELING AVE 74104 #048-15-1986 L1987 IM *020 †20

COHEN, Randolph D. 2000 S WHEELING AVE 74104 #039-01-1981 L1983 CD IM *020 †20

COLDWELL, James Geo. 1120 S UTICA AVE 74104 #039-01-1955 L1955 PD OS *020 †55

COLE, Christopher Robert. 6465 S YALE AVE, STE 900 74136 #055-01-1992 L1995 ICE *020

COLE, Don Hagler. 1722 S BOSTON AVE 74119 #041-13-1954 L1955 P *071

COLE, Joe Chas. 7171 S YALE AVE 74136 #039-01-1966 L1966 OPH PO *020

COLE, Michael Keith. 3010 S HARVARD AVE 74114 #048-78-1978, ▲ L2002 DR *020 †80

COMAN, James Allen, Jr. 6465 S YALE AVE STE 202, HEART RHYTHM INSTITUTE OF 74136 #001-02-1989 L1996 CD *020 †20

COMBS, David Lyle. 9001 S 101ST EAST AVE, STE 350 74133 #039-01-1990 L1991 FM *020 †18

COMPTON, Avery Paul. 6465 S YALE AVE STE 507 74136 #039-01-1957 L1957 R NM *071

CONDRIN, William Russell. 4715 S YALE AVE 74136 #028-34-1962 L1973 DR *071 †80

CONFER, David Jay. 6585 S YALE AVE, STE 640 74136 #039-01-1971 L1972 U GP *020 †95

CONKLING, Brandon A. ■ 74137 #039-79-1996, ▲ L2006 GE *020 †20

CONNOR, Gregory Sinclair. 6585 S YALE AVE STE 620 74136 #039-01-1984 L1992 N CN *020 †75

CONNORS, James Curtis. 6839 S CANTON AVE, ANESTHESIOLOGISTS INC 74136 #030-05-1974 L1978 AN *020 †05

COOK, John Michael. 6465 S YALE AVE, STE 811 74136 #039-01-1990 L1991 IM *020 †20

COOK, William Craig. 9001 S 101ST EAST AVE, STE 230 74133 #039-01-1984 L1987 IM *020 †20

COOK, William Jason. 10901 E 48TH STE 74146 #039-01-1995 L2000 U *020 †95

COON, Kelly Jo. 6161 S YALE AVE LE, WARREN CLINIC, INC 74136 #305-01-2002 L2006 IM *020 †20

COON, Robert Morris. 6839 S CANTON AVE, ANESTHESIOLOGISTS INC 74136 #048-12-1994 L1998 AN *020 †05

COOPER, James Keith. 1923 S UTICA AVE 74104 #039-01-1995 L1997 DR *012 †18

COOPER, Matthew Marc. 6151 S YALE AVE STE 301 74136 #035-19-1983 L2008 TS VS *020 †85,90

COOPER, William Isaac. ■ 74137 #010-01-1977 L1986 OBG *075 †30

CORREA, Juan Francisco. ■ 74136 #649-01-1950 L1970 AN *071 †05

CORSON, Craig Steven. 2808 S SHERIDAN RD, DEPT OF FAMILY MEDICINE 74129 #104-01-2005 L2006 FP *012

COSSMAN, Robert Lynn. 2000 S WHEELING AVE, STE 1000 74104 #028-03-1970 L1977 IM HEM *020

COTTRILL, Eric Lee. 6565 S YALE AVE, STE 1200 74136 #039-01-1980 L1981 GE *020

COUTANT, William Richard. ■ 74137 #019-02-1944 L1959 P CHP *072

COVINGTON, Terrell, Jr. 1980 UTICA SQ, STE 110 74114 #028-02-1943 L1950 IM *071

COX, Grant Richards. 2000 S WHEELING AVE # 800, WILLIAMS MEDICAL PLAZA 74104 #039-01-1996 L1997 OBG *020 †30

COX, Jon Pat. 1919 S WHEELING AVE, STE 404 74104 #048-02-1993 L1994 IM *020

COX, Shannon Gregory. ■ 74105 #039-01-2008 *012

COYLE, John F, II. 1923 E 21ST ST 74114 #019-02-1973 L1978 CD *020 †20

CRAIG, David Marshall. 6585 S YALE AVE STE 102, WILLIAM MEDICAL BLDG 74104 #048-02-1984 L1990 PS GS *020 †65

CRASS, David Paul. 1723 S BOSTON AVE 74119 #039-01-1976 L1977 P *020

CRAVEN, Perri Anne. 6161 S YALE AVE # 4 74136 #039-01-1989 L1995 PM *020 †60

CRAVEN, Thos Gilbert, Jr. 6585 S YALE AVE STE 200, CENTRAL STATES ORTHOPEDIC 74136 #039-01-1989 L1995 ORS *020 †40

CRAVENS, Jere Davies. 6465 S YALE AVE STE 414 74136 #028-02-1968 L1973 PD *020 †55 ‡

CRAWFORD, Andrew S. 1725 E 19TH ST, STE 600 74104 #039-79-1996, ▲ L1997 GE *020

CRAWFORD, Debra A. 2815 S SHERIDAN RD 74129 #039-79-2005, ▲ L2006 OBG *012

CRAWFORD, Kristoffer Lee. ■ 74132 #048-16-2008 L2008 *012

CREMER, Mark Alan. 4111 S DARLINGTON AVE, RADIOLOGY CONSULTANTS OF 74135 #039-01-1979 L1983 DR *020 †80

CRIBBS, Heather D. 1111 S SAINT LOUIS AVE, FAMILY PRACTICE 74120 #039-79-2005, ▲ L2006 FP *012

CRITCHFIELD, Kyla Lussier. ■ 74133 #039-01-2007 L2007 P *012

CROUCH, John Raymond. 7600 S LEWIS AVE 74136 #028-02-1967 L1978 FM *020 †18

CROWSON, Arthur Neil. 1923 S UTICA AVE 74104 #062-01-1980 L1998 ATP *020 †50

CRUMLEY, M Ruth. 7306 S LEWIS AVE, FAMILY MEDICAL CARE 74136 #039-01-1986 L1992 GP *072

CRUTCHER, James Edward. 4502 E 41ST ST 74135 #033-05-1972 L1995 FM *040 †18

CUADRA-RODRIGUEZ, Julio C. 3233 E 31ST ST, STE 103 74105 #682-01-1971 L1979 NPM PD *020

CULP, James R. ■ 74136 #039-01-1975 L1976 EM OM *020 †16

CUNNINGHAM, Charles Alvin. ■ 74133 #039-01-2006 L2007 OBG *012

CUNNINGHAM, Joseph Robt. 1215 S BOULDER AVE, BCBS OF OK 74119 #004-01-1984 L1985 OBG *020 †30

CURVA, Leoncio Gaite. 1620 E 12TH ST, TULSA PSYCHIATRIC CENTER 74120 #748-07-1954 L1978 P *030

CUZALINA, Lawrence Angelo. 7316 E 91ST ST, TULSA SURGICAL ARTS 74133 #001-02-1995 L1998 CS PS *020

DAHSHAN, Ahmed. 4502 E 41ST ST, STE 2A21 74135 #584-01-1986 L1998 GE PG *020 †55

DAILY, Patricia A. 5018 E 68TH ST, STE 200 74104 #048-13-1982 L1983 OBG *020 †30

DALEY, Patrick Jos. 1589 E 19TH ST 74120 #039-01-1978 L1979 PD *020 †55

DANG, Jimmy Ba. ■ 74112 #028-78-2007, ▲ *012

DANNEMILLER, Linda Lou. ■ 74124 #038-40-2007 L2007 FP *012

DARESHANI, Maak Attiya. 1611 S UTICA AVE, STE 414 74104 #704-25-1991 L1998 IM ID *020 †20

DAUTENHAHN, Paul Dee. ■ 74145 #039-01-1984 L1985 PD FM *020 †18

DAVE, Atulkumar N. 10109 E 79TH 74133 #495-48-1981 L1999 HO *020 †20

DAVEY, Joseph P. 4802 S 109TH EAST AVE 74146 #048-16-1992 L1999 ORS *020 †40

DAVIS, Cedric Emden. 4502 E 41ST ST, UNIVERSITY OF OK COM-TULSA 74135 #104-01-2005 L2007 FP *012

DAVIS, Dana Kristine. 6160 S YALE AVE 74136 #039-01-1997 L1998 MPD *020 †20,55

DAVIS, Gary Randolph. 130 N GREENWOOD AVE, STE M 74120 #032-01-1977 L1984 FM *020 †18

DAVIS-JACKSON, Rachel M. 1120 S UTICA AVE, NEWBORN SPECIALISTS OF 74104 #021-05-1994 L2007 NPM *020 †55

DAWSON, Mark S. 8414 E 101ST ST 74133 #019-02-1974 L1985 IM ID *020 †20

DAY, Geoffrey Allen. 744 W 9TH ST 74127 #039-01-1988 L1989 DR *020 †80

DAY, James Steven. 1923 S UTICA AVE, PHYSICIANS 74104 #039-01-1981 L1982 AN *020 †05

DEAN, James Wm. 8110 S YALE AVE 74137 #039-01-1992 L1996 N *020 †75

DEARDORFF, Max Allard. 3218 S 79TH EAST AVE, WARREN CLINIC 74145 #039-01-1959 L1959 GYN *020 †30

DEATON, Rebecca Ellen. 1120 S UTICA AVE, STE G100 74104 #039-01-1979 L1980 OBG *020 †30

DECKER, Gary Lee. 1809 E 13TH ST 74104 #019-02-1982 L1983 GS *020 †85

DE JESUS, Edith Mercedes. ■ 74134 #042-03-1984 L1993 IM *071

DEL CASTILLO, F B, III. 1145 S UTICA AVE, STE 262 74104 #748-02-1994 L2002 PD *020 †55

DE LEON, Antonio C, Jr. 1923 S UTICA AVE, ST JOHN CARDIOVASCULAR INS 74104 #748-02-1956 L1981 CD IM *071 †20

DELIA, Steven William. 4502 E 41ST ST # 2F, COLL MEDICINE-TU 74135 #019-02-2002 L2003 FPP *020

DE MARCO, Frank Robt. 4500 S GARNETT RD, STE 840 74146 #654-01-1983 L1984 EM PD *020 †55

DENNEHY, Daniel C. 1923 S UTICA AVE 74104 #039-01-1976 L1980 DR *071 †80

DENNEHY, Timothy Hardin. ■ 74105 #039-01-1960 L1961 OBG *071 †30

DENNIS, Brent Dewayne. 6600 S YALE AVE, STE 600 74136 #048-12-1995 L1998 IM *020 †20

DENSLOW, Gary T. 6161 S YALE AVE 74136 #020-12-1971 L1977 OPH PO *020 †35 ‡

DERINGTON, Gayle. 8115 S MEMORIAL DR 74133 #048-13-1985 L1986 FM *020 †18

DESILVA, Nirupama Karkarl. 1145 S UTICA AVE, STE 600 74104 #035-03-1999 L2005 OBG *040 †30

DETWILER, Karl Norman. 6767A S YALE AVE 74136 #039-01-1983 L1989 NS *020 †25

DEVOE, Yinyin Josephine L. 1111 S SAINT LOUIS AVE, OU FAMILY MEDICINE 74120 #918-01-1993 L2007 FP *012

DICKENS, Eugene Otto. 1809 E 13TH ST, STE 400 74104 #039-01-1998 L1999 GS *020 †85

DICKENS, Heidi Herron. ■ 74105 #039-01-1998 L2000 IM *020

DIEKER, William Eugene. 1919 S WHEELING AVE, STE 200 74104 #039-01-1967 L1967 IM CD *020

DIEP, Tuana Dinh. 9322 E 41ST ST 74145 #039-01-1993 L1994 IM *020 †20

DIESTEL, Eckhart. 4500 S GARNETT RD, STE 300 74146 #165-02-1986 L2001 CD *020 †20

DIETZ, Melissa Johnson. ■ 74136 #004-01-2005 L2006 OBG *012

DIGGDON, Philip David. 6160 S YALE AVE 74136 #016-06-1958 L1964 U *071 †95

DILGER, Joseph T. ■ 74114 #028-34-1952 L1953 GS CRS *071 †85

DIMENT, Dean Henry. 3210 E 21ST ST 74114 #039-01-1960 L1960 OBG GYN *071

DIXON, Jeffrey David. 1120 S UTICA AVE, HILLCREST MEDICAL CENTER 74104 #028-02-1989 L1990 EM *020 †16

DIXON, Richard Elliott. 1725 E 19TH ST STE 400 74104 #048-04-1969 L1974 GYN *071 †30

DO, Kim Thi. 7600 S LEWIS AVE 74136 #842-01-2001 L2007 FP *012

DOBRATZ, Stephen Chas. 2000 S WHEELING AVE, WILLIAMS MEDICAL PLAZA 74104 #051-07-1990 L1996 CD *020 †20

DODSON, Thomas Anthony. 6802 S OLYMPIA AVE, STE 200 74132 #039-01-1970 L1971 OTO FPS *020 †45

DOE, James Yao. 1111 S SAINT LOUIS AVE 74120 #412-02-1997 L2007 FP *012

DOLAN, Charles Terrence. 1923 S UTICA AVE 74104 #030-06-1962 L1980 MDM PTH *030 †50

DONNELLY, Andrew D. 1111 S SAINT LOUIS AVE, OU PHYSICIANS FAMILY MEDIC 74120 #048-13-1998 L1998 FM *020 †18

DONNELLY, Jennifer H. 2000 S WHEELING AVE # 800, WILLIAMS MEDICAL PLAZA 74104 #048-13-1998 L1999 OBG *020 †30

DONOVAN, Gerard Kevin. 4502 E 41ST ST, DEPT PED- OU CLG OF MED 74135 #039-01-1974 L1975 PG OS *020 †55 ‡

DORAN, Charles Kendrick. 2121 E 21ST ST, BOX 52588 74114 #039-01-1963 L1963 D *071

DORSEY, Kip Weston. ■ 74136 #039-01-2007 L2007 GS *012

DOSS, Richard Allen. 1717 S UTICA AVE, STE 204 74104 #004-01-1972 L1973 IM *020 †20

DOSSER, Glenn Pete. 6465 S YALE AVE STE 522, WARREN PROF BLDG 74136 #039-01-1969 L1970 D *020 †15

DOYLE, Nora Mary. 1145 S UTICA AVE STE 600, DEPARTMENT OF OBSTETRICS & 74104 #021-01-1994 L2008 OBG *020 †30

DRULAK, Karen M. ■ 74114 #062-01-1980 L1998 DR *020 †80

D'SOUZA, Liphard Oswald. 1427 E 8TH ST, DHS-DDSD 74120 #495-09-1971 L1986 PD CHN *020 †55,75

DUBOIS, Jon. 4302 S PEORIA AVE STE A 74105 #021-01-2004 L2006 FM *100

DUBRIWNY, Michael Dmytro. 6655 S YALE AVE 74136 #025-07-1969 L1977 P *020 †20

DUDNEY, William Henry. 1231 S OSWEGO AVE 74112 #023-01-1961 L1973 EM *020 †18,16

DUDNEY, William Powell. 1923 S UTICA AVE, PHYSICIANS 74104 #039-01-1989 L1990 AN *020 †05

DUFFNER, David Walters. 6160 S YALE AVE, SPRINGER CLINIC, INC 74136 #039-01-1979 L1984 ORS OSS *020 †40

DUFFY, F Daniel. ■ 74135 #041-13-1968 L1969 IM IMG *030 †20

DUIGNAN, Brian William. 7600 S LEWIS AVE 74136 #025-07-2002 L2003 FM *100 †18

DUININCK, Mitchell W. 7600 S LEWIS AVE, FAMILY MEDICAL CARE OF TUL 74136 #039-05-1985 L1986 FM *020 †18

DUKES, Kevin Michael. 4802 S 109TH EAST AVE, TULSA BONE AND JOINT ASSOC 74146 #039-01-1989 L1995 OSM *020 †40

DULLYE, Kimberlie Kaye. 1120 S UTICA AVE, TULSA-HILLCREST ANESTHES P 74104 #039-01-1992 L1993 AN *020 †05

DUNAWAY, Todd Burke. 1919 S WHEELING AVE, STE 707 74104 #039-01-1998 L2003 N *020 †75

DUNCAN, David Collier. 5505 E 51ST STE 100 74135 #011-02-1979 L1980 FM PM *020 †18

DUNCAN, Kenneth Craig. 5555 E 71ST ST STE 6105 74136 #039-01-1955 L1955 N IM *071

DUNITZ, Norman L. 4802 S 109TH EAST AVE 74146 #018-03-1953 L1958 ORS OAR *020 †40

DUNITZ, Scott Jeffrey. 4415 S HARVARD AVE, STE 100 74135 #039-01-1983 L1988 ORS *020 †40 ‡

DUNLAP, Everett Richard. 2408 E 81ST ST, STE 100 74137 #004-01-1965 L1966 GS *071

DUSA, Adrian Cristian. 6151 S YALE AVE STE 400, CARDIOLOGY OF TULSA 74136 #781-05-1993 L2007 ICE *020

EAKIN, David Vincent. 3032 S TRENTON AVE 74114 #039-01-1965 L1965 R LM *071 †80

EAKIN, David Vincent, II. 1408 S DENVER AVE 74119 #039-01-2000 L2001 P *020 †75

EASLEY, James Lawrence. 1923 S UTICA AVE, PHYSICIANS 74104 #048-12-1971 L1977 AN *020 †05

EBERT, R H, II. 4502 E 41ST ST 74135 #004-01-2000 L2004 PYG *012

ECHEVARRIA, Jose H. 1919 S WHEELING AVE, STE 200 74104 #737-09-1985 L1992 IM *020 †20

ECKENRODE, John Lyman. 6585 S YALE AVE, STE 701 74136 #025-07-1980 L2007 HO PLM *020 †20

ECONOMIDIS, Nicholas C. ■ 74101 #041-01-1952 L1953 IM *071 †20

EDWARDS, David Lloyd, Jr. 1705 E 19TH STE 503 74104 #041-01-1963 L1967 OPH *071 †35

EDWARDS, Jeanne Mary. 1717 S UTICA AVE, STE 200 74104 #011-03-1977 L1982 N *020

EISEN, Barry Reed. 1725 E 19TH ST STE 600, TULSA GASTROENTEROLOGY, IN 74104 #039-01-1980 L1981 GE *020 †20

ELFRINK, Loui G, Jr. 1111 S SAINT LOUIS AVE, OU PHYSICIANS FAMILY MEDIC 74120 #023-12-1980 L1996 FM AM *020 †18

EL-HALABI, Issam M. 4502 E 41ST ST 74135 #575-01-1988 L1993 PG PD *020 †55

ELLIOTT, Randolph Chas. 5018 E 68TH ST, STE 200 74106 #048-12-1973 L1977 OBG *020 †30

ELLIS, Dalton Jane. 7600 S LEWIS AVE 74136 #654-01-2006 L2006 FP *012

ELLIS, Nancy L C Davis. 7802 S 99TH PL 74133 #027-01-1981 L2003 R *020 †80

ELLIS, Robert Geo. 6161 S YALE AVE 74136 #056-05-1965 L1973 RO *071 †80

EL-RAHEB, Morad Labib. 1145 S UTICA AVE, PRIMARY CARE GROUP 74104 #915-02-1984 L1992 IM *020 †20

ELSAYED, Mohamed Hany. 744 W 9TH ST, OSU MED CTR 74127 #915-04-1982 L2000 PD NPM *020 †18,55

EL-SHARIF, Fayza S. 2808 S SHERIDAN RD 74129 #915-04-1966 FM *100

EMEL, Thomas Jeffrey. 6475 S YALE AVE STE 301 74136 #039-01-1979 L1980 FSM OSM *020 †18

EMERSON, Amy Nisbett. 4502 E 41ST ST, DEPT PEDS 74135 #027-01-2000 L2004 PD *100 †55

EMERSON, Christopher D. 6839 S CANTON AVE, ANESTHESIOLOGISTS INC 74136 #039-01-1994 L1995 AN *020 †05

ENDRES, Robert Kendall. 4502 E 41ST ST, PED DEPT 74135 #039-01-1948 L1948 PD *071 †55

ENGLES, Marsha Howerton. 8803 S 101ST EAST AVE, SPECIALISTS PC 74133 #039-01-1986 L1987 OBG *020 †30

ENSLEY, Ralph Douglas. 10505 E 91ST ST, STE 150 74133 #048-12-1986 L1993 CD *020 †20

ESPIRITU, Anna Marie Sant. 7600 S LEWIS AVE 74136 #748-02-2004 L2006 FP *012

EXON, Walter Jay. 1245 S UTICA AVE 74104 #039-01-1973 L1976 PD *020 †55

EZENWA, Emeka Kyrian. PO BOX 35220 74153 #690-04-1982 L1998 OBG *020 †30

FAHEY, Patrick Jos, Jr. 7012 S UTICA AVE, PHYSICAL REHAB MEDICINE, P 74136 #035-09-1992 L1998 PM PME *020

FARISH, Joseph Key. ■ 74136 #004-01-1954 L1960 AN *071 †05

FARISH, Kent Galloway. 3218 S 79TH EAST AVE 74145 #048-12-1980 L1983 FM *020 †18

FARMER, Charles Alton, Jr. 7601 E APACHE ST, AEROCARE MEDICAL TRANSPORT 74115 #004-01-1971 L1974 EM *020 †16

FARRAR, Amy Louise. 7600 S LEWIS AVE 74136 #017-20-1993 L1994 FM *020 †18

FEEN, Alan Edward. 2121 S YORKTOWN AVE STE 7 74114 #041-02-1968 L1977 RO *020 †80 ‡

FEGHALI, Jean Elias. 8414 E 101ST ST 74133 #605-01-1991 L1992 PD *020 †55

FEHER, Steven Anthony. 6160 S YALE AVE 74136 #039-01-2002 L2003 GS *020 †85

FEILD, Eugene Gray. 6600 S YALE AVE STE 1315 74136 #048-12-1964 L1968 ORS *020 †40

FELL, David Alan. 6901 S OLYMPIA AVE 74132 #048-04-1970 L1975 NS *020 †25

FENGLER, Scott Arthur. 6565 S YALE AVE STE 902, KELLY PROFESSIONAL BLDG. 74136 #056-06-1985 L1998 CRS *020 †85,10

FERMO, Joe C, Jr. 2325 S HARVARD AVE 74114 #748-07-1956 L1976 P *072

FERMO, Merli Gorospe. 5970 E 31ST ST STE 0, FERMO CLINIC 74135 #748-07-1956 L1976 P GP *020

FIDEL, Marcus James. 7122 S SHERIDAN RD, # 2 74133 #034-01-2004 L2007 FPP *012

FIELDING, Allan Spencer. 2000 S WHEELING AVE, STE 1110 74104 #039-01-1977 L1984 NS *020 †25

FIELDING, Roy. 6161 S YALE AVE 74136 #035-09-1953 L1966 IM CD *071

FIELDS, Daniel David. 4502 E 41ST ST 74135 #005-12-1991 L1992 FM *020 †18

FINCHER, Stephen Glen. 6465 S YALE AVE STE 704, WARREN CLINIC INTERNAL MED 74136 #004-01-1990 L1991 IM *020 †20

FINER, Janis Rae. 1919 S WHEELING AVE, STE 404 74104 #039-01-1986 L1987 IM *020 †20

FIORAVANTI, Bernard Louis. 1120 S UTICA AVE 74104 #039-01-1977 L1978 DR VIR *020 †80 ‡

FIRST, Jerry Dale. 1705 E 19TH ST, STE 800 74104 #039-01-1972 L1973 IM CD *020

FISHER, John Dumas. 3010 S HARVARD AVE, STE 220 74114 #004-01-1975 L1976 DR *020 †80

FISHER, Kevin T. 6465 S YALE AVE, STE 900 74136 #039-79-1993, ▲ L1994 GS TRS *020

FITTER, John Frederick. 1923 S UTICA AVE 74104 #039-01-1998 L2003 DR *020 †80

FITTER, William Frederick. 1923 S UTICA AVE 74104 #539-05-1973 L1987 CLP PCH *020 †50

FITTS, Vlad. 6585 S YALE AVE STE 405 74136 #781-01-1959 L1976 NEP IM *071

FITZGERALD, Ellen Beth. 1145 S UTICA AVE 74104 #036-01-1979 L1983 OBG *074 †30

FITZ SIMONS, Louis E, Jr. ■ 74135 #045-01-1953 L1963 U *071 †95

FLECKENSTEIN, James L. 6901 S OLYMPIA AVE, DEPT. OF RADIOLOGY 74132 #054-04-1984 L2003 DR RNR *040 †80

FLESNER, Kelly R. 1265 S UTICA AVE, STE 300 74104 #048-14-1995 L2003 END *020 †20

FLORES, Leandrita Randi. 7600 S LEWIS AVE, IN HIS IMAGE FAM PRACT RES 74136 #034-01-2003 L2004 FM *020 †18

FLYNN, James Patrick. 10109 E 79TH ST 74133 #028-34-1961 L1992 RO *020 †80

FLYNN, Laurie Wolford. 1725 E 19TH ST, STE 800 74104 #027-01-2000 L2006 SO *020 †85 ‡

FOGLI, Michael John. 9228 S MINGO RD STE 200, OKLAHOMA HEART INSTITUTE 74133 #005-02-1998 L2005 CD *020 †20

FOLLY, Komi Semenou. ■ 74105 #893-01-2002 L2007 IM *012

FORD, William Richard. 4870 S LEWIS AVE 74105 #039-01-1973 L1974 P ADP *020 †75

FORE, Frank Neal. 6804 S CANTON AVE, STE 110 74136 #048-02-1974 L1975 TS *020 †85,90

FORREST, John B. 10901 E 48TH ST 74146 #039-01-1976 L1983 U *020 †95

FORTNER, Stacy Melinda. 4502 E 41ST ST 74135 #039-01-1999 L2000 PD *020

FOSSEY, Mark Douglas. 4502 E 41ST ST, UNIV OF OKLAHOMA 74135 #039-01-1977 L1978 P IM *040 †20,75

FOSTER, Michael Chas. 2325 S HARVARD AVE, STE 108 74114 #039-01-1981 L1982 FM FPG *020 †18

FOWLER, Johnny Mckay, Jr. 6161 S YALE AVE 74136 #012-22-1999 L2002 IM *020 †20

FOX, Mark Douglas. 4502 E 41ST ST 74135 #047-05-1997 L2002 MPD *050 †20,55

FRAME, John Raymond. 6475 S YALE AVE, STE 410 74136 #028-02-1979 L1980 GS VS *020 †85

FRAME, Lynn Edward. 1725 E 19TH ST, STE 501B 74104 #039-01-1975 L1976 OBG LM *020 †30

FRAMJEE, Sami Rumi. 2000 S WHEELING AVE, STE 1110 74104 #704-09-1973 L1981 ORS *020 †40

FRANDEN, Christine E. 6565 S YALE AVE STE 312 74136 #011-02-2000 L2001 IM *020 †20 ‡

FRAYSER, James Scott. ■ 74136 #039-05-1990 L1995 OS *020 †20

FRAZIER, Jerome. 4502 E 41ST ST, FAMILY PRACTICE 74135 #051-75-2007, ▲ OBG *012

FREEBERG, Sheldon Ygnacio. ■ 74104 #048-02-2006 L2006 IM *012

FREIDENBERGER, John Busch. 603 E PINE ST 74106 #039-01-1969 L1970 FM EM *071

FRIEND, Jonathan David. 1923 S UTICA AVE, PHYSICIANS 74104 #039-01-1979 L1980 AN *020 †05

FROST, Elizabeth Lyn. 9906 S YALE AVE, SOUTH TULSA ANESTHESIOLOGY 74137 #019-02-1989 L1993 AN *020 †05

FROST, Mark Irwin. 3902 E 51ST ST 74135 #018-03-1979 L1983 OBG *020 †30

FU, Jay. 6465 S YALE AVE, STE 507 74136 #243-43-1982 L2001 NEP *020 †20

FUCCI, Mei-Chien. 10151 E 11TH ST 74128 #038-41-1980 L1994 BBK PTH *030 †50

FULLER, Alen Munson. 1725 E 19TH STE 100 74104 #039-01-1961 L1961 OTO A *072 †45 ‡

FUMIA, Fred Danl. 6565 S YALE AVE, STE 601 74136 #035-09-1975 L2000 MFM OBG *020 †30

GAFFNEY, Frank John. 1265 S UTICA AVE STE 300, OKLAHOMA HEART INSTITUTE 74104 #035-09-1992 L2004 CD *020 †20

GAJJAR, Aakash Hasu. 4502 E 41ST ST, DEPARTMENT OF SURGERY 74135 #048-13-2004 L2005 GS *012

GALLES, Mark Anthony. 6585 S YALE AVE STE 1150 74136 #039-01-1994 L1999 **IM** *020 †20
GALLOWAY, N Linda. RR 8 BOX 410 74106 #039-01-1951 **PHP OS** *020
GANN, Ron M. 1111 S SAINT LOUIS AVE, OU FAMILY MEDICINE 74120 #039-79-2005, ▲ L2006 **FP** *012
GARBER, Eugene Bradley, Jr. 1784 S UTICA AVE 74104 #021-06-1976 L1985 **PS OTO** *020 †45,65 ‡
GARFINKEL, Fred. 1265 S UTICA AVE, STE 102 74104 #035-47-1973 L1978 **PUD IM** *020 †20
GARNER, Pamela R. 1111 S SAINT LOUIS AVE, OU HEALTH SCIENCES CENTER 74120 #039-79-2005, ▲ L2006 **FP** *012
GARNICA, Adolfo Dolores. 635 W 11TH ST, OSU PHYSICIANS - HOUSTON P 74127 #005-02-1969 L1984 **PD** *020 †55,19
GARRETT, Charles Walter. 6606 S YALE AVE 74136 #039-01-1984 L1989 **OPH OS** *020 †35 ‡
GARRETT, Robert Cole. 2000 S WHEELING AVE # 1100 74104 #039-01-1982 L1984 **TS** *020 †85,90
GARY, Walter Hubert. ■ 74135 #047-06-1956 L1961 **R** *071 †80
GASKA, Mary Ann. ■ 74137 #048-04-1998 L2008 **NEP** *100 †20
GASPAR, Harvey Lee. 9322 E 41ST ST 74145 #039-01-1961 L1961 **IM CD** *071 †20
GASTON, Gary Lynn. 1923 S UTICA AVE 74104 #039-01-1979 L1980 **PD** *020
GATCHELL, Frank Gaffney. ■ 74106 #039-01-1948 L1948 **GS** *071 †85
GAWEY, Stephen John. 1819 E 19TH ST, STE 302 74104 #039-01-1979 L1980 **IM** *020 †20
GEARHART, John Kelley. 6528 E 101ST ST, STE I 74133 #039-01-1973 L1974 **FM** *020 †18
GEBETSBERGER, Michael S. 6565 S YALE AVE STE 312 74136 #039-01-1994 L1998 **IM** *020 †20
GEFFEN, William Aaron. 4502 E 41ST ST, UNIV OF OK COL OF MED 74135 #048-12-1971 L1975 **PD** *020 †55
GEHRING, Paul James. 2000 S WHEELING AVE # 800, 2000 S WHEELING SUITE 800 74104 #038-41-1989 L1994 **OBG** *020 †30
GEIDL, David Joseph. 7600 S LEWIS AVE, FAMILY MEDICAL CARE 74136 #004-01-2006 L2007 **FP** *012
GELVEN, Paul Lemmel. 1923 S UTICA AVE 74104 #028-03-1992 L1996 **PTH** *020 †50
GENGLER, Jeffrey William. 9402 S 73RD EAST PL 74133 #036-05-1999 L2004 **AN** *100 †05
GEORGE, Sandy. ■ 74132 #422-01-2006 L2006 **IM** *012
GEORGY, Ibrahim Adly. 9322 E 41ST ST 74145 #915-04-1976 L1997 **IM** *020 †20
GEURIN, James Roy. 1923 S UTICA AVE 74104 #047-06-1984 L1993 **RO** *020 †80
GHANNOUM, Haysam. 4502 E 41ST ST 74135 #305-01-1999 L2002 **IM** *100 †20 ‡
GIBBENS, Jennifer Wall. 1805 E 15TH ST, JENNIFER GIBBONS MD 74104 #039-01-1983 L1984 **OBG** *020 †30
GIBBS, Rachel Lucile. 3902 E 51ST ST 74135 #039-01-1987 L1990 **OBG** *020 †30
GIBSON, Charles Roy. ■ 74132 #039-01-1955 L1955 **OM GS** *071 †85
GIBSON, Gwendolyn Louise. 4502 E 41ST ST 74135 #039-01-1986 L1987 **PD** *040 †55
GICHINGA, Monicah Wanjiku. 1611 S UTICA AVE, PMB 414 74104 #577-01-1997 L2002 **IM** *020 †20
GIDDENS, Jimmy Donald. 1809 E 13TH ST, STE 400 74104 #039-01-1968 L1968 **GS** *020 †85
GIKUNDA, Priscilla Kinya. 2808 S SHERIDAN RD 74129 #577-01-2004 L2007 **IM** *012
GILBERT, Scott Everett. ■ 74114 #039-01-1980 L1985 **FPS PS** *075
GILBERT-GERSON, Cynthia E. 4500 S GARNETT RD, TULSA X-RAY LAB, INC 74146 #005-14-1990 L2005 **DR** *020 †80
GILBERTSON, Gary Frans. ■ 74104 #026-04-1964 L1974 **CRS GS** *071 †85,90
GILE, Terry M. 2448 E 81ST ST, STE 363 74137 #039-79-1982, ▲ L1983 **AN PME** *020
GILLER, Sandra Paola. 6160 S YALE AVE, OU MEDICAL CENTER 74136 #039-01-2002 L2004 **GS** *020
GILLEY, Laura Beth. 4502 E 41ST ST 74135 #039-01-2005 L2006 **P** *012
GILLOCK, Thomas Douglas. 6839 S CANTON AVE, ANESTHESIOLOGISTS INC 74136 #039-01-1982 L1983 **AN** *020 †05 ‡
GILLOCK, William Robt. 7170 S BRADEN AVE, STE 175 74136 #039-01-1979 L1980 **OM OAR** *020 †18,20
GINUGU, Prasanna Lakshmi. 4502 E 41ST ST, DEPARTMENT OF PSYCHIATRY 74135 #496-31-1994 L2003 **P** *020
GIRARD, Charles Merritt. 4111 S DARLINGTON AVE, RADIOLOGY CONSULTANTS OF 74135 #048-13-1972 L1991 **R NM** *020 †80,28
GIST, Joel Keith. 1919 S WHEELING AVE # 304 74104 #039-01-1964 L1964 **PD** *020 †55
GLADD, Debbie A. 744 W 9TH ST, TULSA REG MED CTR 74127 #039-79-2002, ▲ L2003 **RHU** *012
GLAZE, Kathleen Ann. 1145 S UTICA AVE STE 514 74104 #039-01-1981 L1982 **GYN** *020 †30
GLEASON, Ondria Chris. 4502 E 41ST ST, UNIVERSITY OF OKLAHOMA SCH 74135 #030-05-1994 L1998 **P** *040 †75
GOEN, Rayburne W. 1919 S WHEELING AVE 74104 #007-02-1939 L1945 **CD IM** *071 †20
GOEN, Rayburne W, Jr. ■ 74136 #039-01-1969 L1969 **TS** *071 †85,90
GOLBABA, Bobby Babak. ■ 74137 #039-01-2008 *012
GOLD, Robert Max. 6465 S YALE AVE, NEPHROLOGY SPECIALISTS OF 74136 #016-11-1979 L1984 **NEP IM** *020 †20
GOLDBERG, Marc Andrew. 2000 S WHEELING AVE, STE 501 74104 #036-07-1988 L1996 **OPH** *020 †35
GOLDENSTERN, Linda. 1919 S WHEELING AVE, STE 204 74104 #048-04-1976 L1980 **IM** *020 †20
GOLDMAN, Harold Earl. 2241 E SKELLY DR 74105 #024-07-1954 L1958 **N** *020 †55 ‡
GOMEZ, Michael R. 6161 S YALE AVE 74136 #048-13-1986 L2003 **NPM PD** *020 †55
GONZALEZ, Jorge Antonio. 1245 S UTICA AVE 74104 #847-11-1984 L1995 **N OS** *020
GONZALEZ, Troy Dana. 744 W 9TH ST 74127 #005-18-1997 L2003 **DR** *020 †80
GOODLOE, Jeffrey M. 4502 E 41ST ST STE 2E24, OU CLGE OF MSF DEPT EMERG 74135 #048-13-1995 L2007 **EM** *020 †16
GOPAL, Chitra K. 6161 S YALE AVE, SAINT FRANCIS HOSPITAL 74136 #496-34-1992 L2007 **IM** *100 †20
GORDON, Andrew Robt, II. 1919 S WHEELING AVE 74104 #039-01-1991 L1992 **IM PD** *020
GORDON, Richard Allen. 1245 S UTICA AVE 74104 #039-01-1977 L1978 **PD** *020 †55
GORDON, Sherri Long. 2000 S WHEELING AVE, STE 300 74104 #039-01-1992 L1993 **PD** *072 †55
GOREE, Chas Stroder, Jr. 4815 S SHERIDAN RD STE 108 74145 #039-01-1965 L1965 **FM** *020
GOSNELL, Charles Ray. ■ 74145 #039-01-1967 L1968 **DR NR** *020 †80
GOTTEHRER, Andrew. 1265 S UTICA AVE STE 102 74104 #005-14-1985 L1991 **PUD CCM** *020 †20
GRAHAM, H Vondale, Jr. 1919 S WHEELING AVE, STE 200 74104 #004-01-1969 L1973 **IM** *020 †20
GRAHAM, Hugh C, Jr. 1919 S WHEELING AVE, STE 304 74104 #016-02-1959 L1961 **PD PDA** *020 †55
GRANT, Sophia Racquel. 4502 E 41ST ST, DEPARTMENT OF PEDIATRICS 74135 #047-07-1993 L2006 **PD** *020 †55
GRASS CULP, Marilyn K. 9245 S MINGO RD, UTICA PARK CLINIC 74133 #048-12-1993 L1994 **FM** *020 †18
GRAY, Gena Carol. 1725 E 19TH ST, STE 400 74104 #039-01-1989 L1994 **OBG** *020 †30
GRAY, J Robert. 1923 S UTICA AVE, STE 400 74104 #039-01-1978 L1979 **FM** *020 †18
GRAY, William Knight. 1120 S UTICA AVE 74104 #039-01-1982 L1983 **EM** *020 †16
GRAYSON, Nancy E. 4755 E 91ST ST 74137 #039-01-1985 L1991 **P PPN** *020 †75 ‡
GREEFF, Pierre Jean. 10109 E 79TH ST 74133 #836-02-1966 L1998 **GS** *020 †85
GREEN, Gregory Albert. 6600 S YALE AVE 74136 #039-01-1958 L1958 **GYN** *071 †30
GREEN, James Douglas. 2511 E 21ST ST 74114 #039-01-1957 L1957 **IM** *071
GREEN, Kendall B. 3800 N MINGO RD, AMERICAN AIRLINES, INC. 74116 #035-19-1983 L1994 **OM IM** *030 †20,70
GREEN, Susan Diane. 1145 S UTICA AVE, STE 367 74104 #048-14-1995 L2003 **PTH** *020 †50
GREENAWALT, James Wm. 6839 S CANTON AVE, ANESTHESIOLOGISTS INC 74136 #039-01-1983 L1984 **AN PME** *020 †05 ‡
GREGG, Lawrence J. 2121 E 21ST ST, TULSA DERMATOLOGY CLINIC 74114 #039-01-1970 L1971 **D** *020 †15
GREGG, Patricia Ann. 1923 S UTICA AVE 74104 #011-02-1987 L2007 **PTH PCP** *020 †50 ‡
GREGORY, Julia Kay. 6475 S YALE AVE, ORTHOPEDIC C 74136 #019-02-2002 L2003 **FSM** *020 †55
GREWAL, Shaun Gobindsing. ■ 74104 #039-01-2008 *012
GRIBBIN, Karen Holt. 9322 E 41ST ST 74145 #038-43-1986 L1987 **IM** *020 †20
GRIFFIN, Chelsey Diane. 4502 E 41ST ST, FAMILY PRACTICE 74135 #039-79-2007, ▲ **FP** *012
GRIFFIN, James Lynn. 4415 S HARVARD AVE, STE 100 74135 #017-20-1977 L1982 **ORS** *020 †40
GRIFFIN, Michael Warren. 6465 S YALE AVE, STE 900 74136 #039-79-1998, ▲ L1999 **GS** *020 †85
GRIFFITH, Kristy M. 2325 S HARVARD AVE, STE 400 74114 #039-01-1999 L2001 **P** *020 †75
GRIFFITHS, David Wesley. 2325 S HARVARD AVE, STE 108 74114 #039-01-1985 L1986 **FM** *020 †18
GRIGG, Mary Leann. ■ 74114 #039-01-2007 L2007 **IM** *012
GROSS, Worth Miller. ■ 74105 #016-06-1943 L1947 **ORS** *071 †40
GROSSERODE, Mark Henry. 6565 S YALE AVE, STE 812 74136 #030-05-1986 L1992 **IM** *020 †20
GROVES, Stephen Wilder. 9102 S TOLEDO AVE, STE C 74137 #007-02-1991 L1995 **PO** *020 †35
GRUBB, Robert Dale. 1980 UTICA SQ STE 250 74114 #016-06-1944 L1950 **IM** *071
GRUBB, William Robt. 1705 E 19TH ST, STE 400 74104 #039-01-1974 L1975 **IM** *020 †20
GUEVARA, Robert Stanley. 1111 S SAINT LOUIS AVE 74120 #048-02-2004 L2005 **FPP** *012
GUNDA, Arun. 4502 E 41ST ST, OKLAHOMA COLLEGE 74135 #496-23-2003 L2004 **FP** *012
GURKOWSKI, Larry John. ■ 74112 #039-01-1984 L1985 **NEP** *020 †20
GUSTAFSON, Gerald Edward. 6465 S YALE AVE, SURGICAL ASSOCIATES INC 74136 #028-03-1961 L1967 **GS** *071 †85
GUSTAVSON, Edward E. 1145 S UTICA AVE, STE 262 74104 #024-01-1970 L1997 **NPM** *020 †55
HA, Quyen Thanh. 1705 E 19TH ST 74104 #305-01-2004 L2006 **IM** *020
HAAS, Robert Chas. 1923 E 21ST ST 74114 #041-12-1983 L1991 **CD IM** *020 †20
HACKL, Frank J. 2448 E 81ST ST, STE 363 74137 #048-13-2002 L2007 **AN** *100
HAGGARD, David Kline. ■ 74105 #030-05-1962 L1966 **OBG** *071 †30
HAGGE, Maryhelen. 8803 S 101ST EAST AVE, STE 260 74133 #018-03-1982 L1993 **AN** *020 †05
HAGLUND, Roger Verner. 1435 S UTICA AVE, TULSA UROLOGIC CLINIC, INC 74104 #026-04-1954 L1959 **U** *071 †95
HAJDUK, Michael Brian. ■ 74133 #654-01-1998 L2002 **IM** *020 †20
HALE, Arthur E. 1725 E 19TH ST # 6, TULSA GASTROENTEROLOGY, IN 74104 #039-01-1973 L1974 **GE IM** *071 †20
HALE, Jack Edward. 6565 S YALE AVE, STE 410 74136 #021-01-1954 L1959 **PTH** *071 †50
HALL, Brian K. 6465 S YALE AVE STE 515 74136 #039-01-1981 L1982 **OBG** *020 †30
HALL, David William. 8803 S 101ST EAST AVE, STE 110 74133 #047-05-1994 L2000 **OTO** *020 †45
HALL, Heather Lyle. 6655 S YALE AVE, LAUREATE PSYCHIATRIC CLINI 74136 #039-01-1998 L1999 **P** *020 †75
HALL, Theodore Ray. ■ 74110 #010-03-1977 L1983 **U** *020
HALL, William Edward. 6465 S YALE AVE STE 515 74136 #039-01-1955 L1955 **OBG** *020 †30
HALLQUIST, Stone Matthew. 6565 S YALE AVE STE 912 74136 #016-06-1963 L1970 **U** *020 †95
HALTERMAN, Mark Wells. 1120 S UTICA AVE 74104 #039-01-1988 L1996 **AN** *020 †05
HAMIDUZZAMAN, Nida. ■ 74133 #654-01-2006 L2007 **IM** *012
HAMILL, Sarah Kathleen. 4502 E 41ST ST, FAMILY PRACTICE 74135 #039-79-2007, ▲ **FP** *012
HAMILTON, Donald R. 4502 E 41ST ST 74135 #039-01-1981 L1982 **PD ADL** *020 †55
HAMILTON, Frank Garrison. 7600 S LEWIS AVE 74136 #040-02-1979 L1982 **FM** *020 †18
HAMILTON, Herbert Edward. 4111 S DARLINGTON AVE 74135 #021-06-1985 L1994 **VIR FM** *020 †80,18
HAN, Patrick Pilgyun. 1919 S WHEELING AVE, STE 504 74104 #019-02-1997 L2006 **NS** *020
HANDEL, Carolyn J Hair. 8086 S YALE AVE, PMB 14 74136 #010-01-1963 L2003 **DR** *020 †80
HANDEL, Stanley Fredric. 744 W 9TH ST 74127 #048-02-1965 L2003 **DR RNR** *071 †80
HANDEL-RAZDAN, Cheryl C. 6465 S YALE AVE, STE 815 74136 #048-15-1993 L1994 **OBG** *020 †30
HANEY, Walter Patrick. 3010 S HARVARD AVE, STE 220 74114 #017-20-1967 L1974 **DR** *020 †80
HANSARD, James Gordon. 6839 S CANTON AVE, ANESTHESIOLOGISTS INC 74136 #048-02-1986 L1991 **AN** *020 †05
HARDY, Homer D, Jr. 8115 S MEMORIAL DR, OMNI MEDICAL GROUP, INC. 74133 #039-01-1949 L1949 **GP GS** *072 †18
HARKEY, Michael Rowe. 2738 E 51ST ST, STE 290 74105 #039-01-1969 L1970 **ATP PCP** *020 †50
HARMAN, Mark Loring. 1145 S UTICA AVE, STE 460 74104 #030-05-1982 L1995 **OBG** *020 †30
HARMON, Charles Kemper. 6465 S YALE AVE, STE 900 74136 #028-02-1966 L1976 **GS** *071 †85
HARMON, Kelly Renee. 6565 S YALE AVE, STE 201 74136 #039-01-1995 L1996 **PD** *020 †55
HARNEY, Ned Trevor. 1120 S UTICA AVE 74104 #047-06-1956 L1961 **IM** *071 †20
HARNISH, Stephen Norman. 6262 S SHERIDAN RD, SHADOW MOUNTAIN BEHAVIORAL 74133 #034-01-1976 L1991 **P** *020 †75
HARPER, David Lee. 10901 E 48TH ST 74146 #004-01-1971 L1974 **U** *020 †95
HARP-WETZ, Carrie Ann. 2808 S SHERIDAN RD, UNIV OF OK COLL MED-TULSA 74129 #039-79-2006, ▲ L2007 **PD** *012
HARRIS, David Jay. 4111 S DARLINGTON AVE, RADIOLOGY CONSULTANTS OF 74135 #039-01-1992 L1993 **DR** *020 †80
HARRIS, David Wayne. 6160 S YALE AVE 2ND FL 74136 #039-01-1983 L1984 **IM END** *020 †20
HARRIS, Robert Chas. 1120 S UTICA AVE 74104 #004-01-1977 L1986 **IM CCS** *020 †20

■ = Address Information Privacy Protected

HARRIS, Tiari Avakian. 1923 S UTICA AVE, EMPLOYEE HEALTH SERVICE 74104 #039-05-1985 L1986 **OM** *020 †70
HARRIS, William Keith, Jr. 8803 S 101ST EAST AVE, STE 205 74133 #039-01-1994 L1995 **OBG** *020 †30
HARRISON, Gene H. ■ 74136 #039-01-1950 L1950 **FM** *071 †18
HARRISON, Henry Allen. ■ 74114 #039-01-1998 L1998 **EM** *100
HARRISON, William Earl. 1919 S WHEELING AVE STE 40 74104 #048-04-1958 L1966 **HS ORS** *071 †40
HART, Lisa E. 744 W 9TH ST 74127 #039-79-2002, ▲ L2004 *020
HARTSELL, Brent D. 1923 S UTICA AVE 74104 #048-12-1987 L1992 **PTH IM** *020 †50
HASEGAWA, Alan Akira. 6655 S YALE AVE, LAUREATE PSYCHIATRIC CLINI 74136 #005-06-1981 L1990 **P IM** *020 †75
HASKELL, Henry Devereux. 1923 S UTICA AVE 74104 #001-02-2002 L2006 **DMP** *100 †50
HASSMANN, Gary C. ■ 74137 #039-01-1969 L1991 **ORS** *020 †40
HASTINGS, John Danl. 1725 E 19TH ST, STE 202A 74104 #028-34-1965 L1978 **N AM** *020 †75,70
HASWELL, Glenn Lee. 1705 E 19TH ST, STE 600 74104 #010-01-1967 L1981 **MFM** *020 †30
HATHAWAY, Paul Walter. 6160 S YALE AVE, FL 3 74136 #039-01-1964 L1964 **N IM** *071 †20
HAUGER, Kim R. 4111 S DARLINGTON AVE, RADIOLOGY CONSULTANTS OF 74135 #039-01-1981 L1986 **R NR** *020 †80 ‡
HAUGER, Robert Burnett. 6600 S YALE AVE STE 600 74136 #039-01-1991 L1994 **IM** *020 †20
HAUGH, Michael Joe. ■ 74135 #028-34-1963 L1969 **N** *071
HAWASLI, Omar. ■ 74137 #875-01-2001 L2006 **IM** *100 †20
HAWKINS, Henry Meek, Jr. 6161 S YALE AVE 74136 #004-01-1964 L1971 **CD** *071 †20
HAWKINS, William Henry. 1919 S WHEELING AVE, STE 302 74104 #004-01-1993 L1994 **OTO** *020 †45
HAYES, Amy Nicole. 7600 S LEWIS AVE, FAMILY MEDICAL 74136 #010-01-2004 L2006 **FM** *100 †18
HAYES, Jeanne O'Keefe. 2032 E 38TH ST 74105 #039-01-1984 L1985 **PD** *020 †55
HEATON, Diane Marie. 1120 S UTICA AVE, DEPT RADIATION ONCOLOGY 74104 #016-11-1988 L1994 **RO** *020 †80
HECK, Darrell Daniel, Jr. 1611 S UTICA AVE, # 217 74104 #039-01-1997 L2001 **AN** *020 †05
HEFFRON, Kathleen Ann. 1120 S UTICA AVE, STE G100 74104 #039-01-1979 L1983 **OBG** *020 †30
HEIBERGER, Brandon Joe. 6161 S YALE AVE 74136 #035-01-1996 L2000 **EM** *020 †16
HEINBERG, Charles Eugene. 5020 E 68TH ST 74136 #021-01-1966 L1973 **OTO** *020 †45
HELLER, Virginia Ruth. 3311 E 46TH ST 74135 #039-01-1993 L1994 **CHP** *020
HELMY, Amgad Farouk. 6161 S YALE AVE, LEVEL B 74136 #915-03-1996 L2006 **IM** *020 †20
HEMPHILL, Robert Lee. 1115 W 17TH ST 74107 #039-01-1966 L1966 **FOP ATP** *071 †50
HENDREN, Ryan Lane. ■ 74105 #004-01-2001 L2007 **PCP** *100 †50
HENDRICKS, James Warren. 2000 S WHEELING AVE, STE 300 74104 #047-05-1976 L1978 **PD** *020 †55
HENDRICKS, Randall Lane. 6160 S YALE AVE 74136 #019-02-1980 L1987 **ORS** *020 †40
HENDRIX, John Robert. 6161 S YALE AVE, ST. FRANCIS/WARREN CLINIC 74136 #039-01-2003 L2006 **IM** *020 †20
HENDRIX, Paul Grover. 2000 S WHEELING AVE, STE 1000 74104 #046-01-1979 L1980 **IM** *020 †20
HENLEY, Charles E. 1111 S SAINT LOUIS AVE 74120 #039-79-1977, ▲ L1997 **FM** *020 †18
HENRY, Sarah E. 2738 E 51ST ST STE 290, TULSA MEDICAL LAB LLC 74105 #028-46-2002 L2007 **HMP** *100
HENSELY, Dawn. 4502 E 41ST ST, FAMILY PRACTICE 74135 #039-79-2006, ▲ *012
HEPNER, Timothy Wade. 1725 E 19TH ST, STE 800 74104 #039-01-1989 L1990 **GS** *020 †85
HERBEL, Randall Wade. 3218 S 79TH EAST AVE, STE 200 74145 #019-02-1997 L2002 **FM** *020 †18
HERBST, Aunna Cannon. 4502 E 41ST ST, FAMILY PRACTICE 74135 #039-79-2007, ▲ **FP** *012
HESS, Philip James. 6465 S YALE AVE STE 704, WARREN CLINIC INTERNAL MED 74136 #039-01-1983 L1984 **IM** *020 †20
HICKS, Benjamin Loy. ■ 74137 #039-01-2007 L2007 **MPD** *012
HICKS, William Kenneth. 6966 S UTICA AVE 74136 #025-01-1954 L1967 **DR** *020 †80
HIDY, W Dean. ■ 74136 #004-01-1953 L1954 **GS OS** *071 †85
HIGBEE, Paul Thos. 1919 S WHEELING AVE, STE 108 74104 #039-05-1984 L1985 **FM** *020 †18
HIGGINS, Christopher Jame. ■ 74137 #035-01-2006 **IM** *012
HIGGINS, Donald John. 6600 S YALE AVE STE 800 74136 #016-11-1989 L1997 **IM** *020 †20
HIGGINS, James Ray. 7912 E 31ST CT, STE 320 74145 #035-45-1977 L1985 **CD IM** *020 †20
HILL, Arthur Victor L. 1124 S SAINT LOUIS AVE 74120 #143-02-1958 L1977 **NEP** *071
HILL, Charles Hayward. 1705 E 19TH ST STE 304 74104 #039-01-1987 L1988 **P** *020 †75
HILL, Erick John. 1919 S WHEELING AVE, STE 200 74104 #409-10-1976 L1985 **IM** *020
HILL, Erin Noelle. 2840 E 51ST ST, STE 200 74105 #039-79-2001, ▲ L2002 *020
HILL, Patricia Ann. 2447 E 25TH PL 74114 #039-01-1992 L1994 **OBG GS** *020
HINDS, Manuel John A. 1725 E 19TH ST, SURGERY INC 74104 #035-01-1957 L1967 **GS GP** *071 †85
HITZEMAN, David F. 635 W 11TH ST, COLLEGE OF OSTEOPATHIC MED 74127 #028-78-1974, ▲ L1976 **IM** *040
HOFF, Stuart Dexter. 1705 E 19TH ST STE 300 74104 #048-12-1984 L1991 **CRS GS** *020 †85,10
HOFFMAN, Todd Gregory. 1717A S UTICA AVE 74104 #039-01-1999 L2002 **EM** *020 †16
HOGE, Arthur F, Jr. ■ 74135 #021-01-1949 L1972 **GP ON** *072
HOLDERNESS, Alan Wm. 1809 E 13TH ST, THE ORTHOPAEDIC CENTER 74104 #016-11-1960 L1981 **ORS** *020 †40
HOLLAND, William Thos. 1923 S UTICA AVE 74104 #056-06-1948 L1955 **P** *071
HOLLAWAY, Rodney Roy. 1919 S WHEELING AVE, STE 404 74104 #007-02-1976 L1983 **FM** *020 †18
HOLMES, Cynthia Lindsey. 2738 E 51ST ST, STE 290 74105 #039-01-1996 L2003 **PCP** *020 †50
HOLT, Gregory Reece. 1809 E 13TH ST, THE ORTHOPAEDIC CENTER 74104 #039-01-1986 L1987 **ORS OSM** *020 †40
HOLT, Orville U. ■ 74136 #039-01-1952 L1952 **GP** *072
HOLT, Stephanie Cay. 1923 S UTICA AVE 74104 #016-02-1980 L2006 **ATP CLP** *020 †50
HONAKER, Jack Dennis. ■ 74135 #039-01-1953 L1953 **FM PHP** *071 †18
HONG, Ju-Lun. 6161 S YALE AVE 74136 #243-43-1983 L2002 **PCC** *020 †20
HOOD, John Raymond. 6565 S YALE AVE, STE 1200 74136 #039-01-1982 L1983 **GE IM** *020 †20
HOOD, Ronald Gene. 4415 S HARVARD AVE, STE 100 74135 #039-01-1987 L1988 **ORS** *020 †40
HOOK, Kevin Michael. 6839 S CANTON AVE, ASSOCIATED ANESTHESIOLOGIS 74136 #039-01-1999 L2000 **AN** *100 †05 ‡
HOOS, Tracy. 4502 E 41ST ST, FAMILY PRACTICE 74135 #039-79-2007, ▲ **PD** *012
HOOSER, Clifton Wallace. 4111 S DARLINGTON AVE, STE 700 74135 #048-04-1971 L1977 **DR NM** *071 †80,28
HOOVER, Ruth Ann. 6600 S YALE AVE STE 650 74136 #018-03-1978 L1985 **OBG** *020 †30
HORNE, Edwin Geo, Jr. ■ 74136 #039-01-1963 L1963 **FM** *071 †18
HOSKISON, Thomas Karl. 4502 E 41ST ST, SCHUSTERMAN CENTER CLINIC 74135 #039-05-1990 L1991 **IM** *020 †20
HOUSTON, Robert Alan. 4815 S HARVARD AVE STE 403 74135 #021-01-1965 L1970 **GP** *071 †05 ‡
HOWARD, Charles Anthony. 1725 E 19TH ST, SPECIALIST 74104 #039-01-1983 L1984 **GS CCS** *040 †85
HOWARD, Jeff W. 9001 S 101ST EAST AVE, MINGO VALLEY MEDICAL GROUP 74133 #048-02-1993 L1994 **FM** *020 †18
HOWARD, Paul Anthony. 6465 S YALE AVE, STE 614 74136 #039-01-1970 L1971 **PS HS** *020 †65
HOYLE, Nicole Andrea. ■ 74105 #039-01-2006 L2006 **OBG** *012
HOYT, Bradley Dean. 1245 S UTICA AVE 74104 #048-04-1992 L1996 **IM** *020 †20
HUANG, Stephen Robert. 1111 S SAINT LOUIS AVE 74120 #016-42-2002 L2004 **FSM** *020 †18
HUBBARD, Lori Ann. 1919 S WHEELING AVE, STE 500 74104 #039-01-2000 L2004 **OBG** *020 ‡
HUBNER, John Eldon. 2000 S WHEELING AVE, STE 1100 74104 #039-01-1993 L1994 **IM** *020 †20
HUBNER, Michael Lamkee. 1245 S UTICA AVE 74104 #030-05-1995 L1998 **IM** *020 †20
HUBNER, Michelle Phillips. 2431 E 61ST ST STE 310 74136 #039-01-1994 L1999 **CHP** *020 †75
HUDKINS, Bruce Eric. 6802 S OLYMPIA AVE, STE 200 74132 #039-01-1992 L1997 **OTO** *020 †45
HUDSON, Joseph Clayton. ■ 74105 #039-01-2008 *012
HUDSON, Lloyd A. 7316 E 91ST ST 74133 #020-02-1994 L1998 *020
HUDSON, Robert Etchison. 6585 S YALE AVE, CARDIAC SURGERY OF TULSA 74136 #039-01-1970 L1971 **TS** *071 †85,90
HUETTNER, Timothy Louis. 5555 E 71ST ST STE 7100 74136 #023-07-1976 L1981 **RHU IM** *020 †20
HUEY, Rodney Leigh. 1400 S BOSTON AVE 74119 #048-02-1976 L1977 **IM** *030 †20
HUFF, Steven Gary. 4500 S GARNETT RD 74146 #039-01-1985 L2003 **AN** *020 †05
HUFFMAN, Angela Desiree. 1120 S UTICA AVE, TULSA HILLCREST ANESTHESIO 74104 #032-01-1998 L2002 **AN** *020
HUGHES, J Patrick. 6565 S YALE AVE STE 704 74136 #039-01-1966 L1967 **PD** *020 †55
HULVER, Ryan Newton. 744 W 9TH ST, TULSA REGIONAL MEDICAL CE 74127 #039-79-2003, ▲ L2004 **AN** *020
HUM, Martina C. 6161 S YALE AVE 74136 #048-13-1990 L1997 **PHO PD** *020 †55
HUMPHREY, George Bennett. 4502 E 41ST ST, PEDIATRICS UNIV OK COLLEGE 74135 #016-02-1960 L1971 **PD HEM** *071 †55
HUNEKE, John Willard. 2021 S LEWIS AVE, STE 450 74104 #017-20-1958 L1966 **OPH PS** *071 †35
HUNTER, Christopher C. 1120 S UTICA AVE 74104 #048-13-1991 L1997 **FM** *020 †18 ‡
HUNTER, Gerard Jay. 1717 S UTICA AVE STE 101 74104 #035-03-1974 L1979 **OPH OS** *020 †35
HURD, Katherine Grace. 7600 S LEWIS AVE, FAMILY MEDICAL CARE 74136 #054-04-2005 L2006 **FP** *012
HUREWITZ, David Solomon. 1727 S UTICA AVE 74104 #041-13-1967 L1975 **A IM** *020 †20,03
HUSAIN, Shashi Anand. 1145 S UTICA AVE STE 520 74104 #495-36-1969 L1981 **N IM** *020
HUSSAIN, Iftikhar. 6565 S YALE AVE, STE 209 74136 #704-01-1990 L2006 **IM AI** *040 †03,20
HUTCHISON, Sandra Lowe. ■ 74137 #820-02-2006 L2006 **FP** *012
HUTTO, William Thomas, Jr. 10632 S MEMORIAL DR, # 5 74133 #039-01-1998 L2002 **EM** *020 †16
HUTTON, James Philip. 1923 S UTICA AVE 74104 #048-14-1979 L1984 **ID IM** *020 †20 ‡
HWANG, Stephen Sen-Yu. 2000 S WHEELING AVE, STE 700 74104 #244-05-1987 L1997 **GE** *020 †20
HYDER, Jamal Nasar. 1725 E 19TH ST STE 501, OF TULSA INC 74104 #704-02-1987 L1992 **IM** *020
ILLIG, William Patrick. 2738 E 51ST ST, STE 290 74105 #010-02-1963 L1971 **PTH** *020 †50
IMHOFF, Lynne Henson. 1120 S UTICA AVE 74104 #039-01-1980 L1981 **AN PME** *020 †05
INBODY, Donald Reid. 6161 S YALE AVE 74136 #039-01-1956 L1956 **P** *071
INHOFE, Nancy Susan. 2815 S SHERIDAN RD, COLLEGE OF MEDICINE-TULSA 74129 #028-03-1985 L1989 **PD** *040 †55
IRVIN, Richard Lynn. 10505 E 91ST ST 74133 #048-13-1984 L1993 **CD** *020 †20
IRWIN, Richard Craig. 4520 S HARVARD AVE STE 200, & CTR FOR FAMILY PSYCHOLOG 74135 #039-01-1979 L1980 **DBP** *020 †55 ‡
ISOLA, Mopelola Idowu. 6161 S YALE AVE 74136 #690-02-1990 L2007 **IM** *020 †20
IVANOFF, John Geo. 8803 S 101ST EAST AVE, STE 100 74133 #041-07-1984 L1994 **CD IM** *020 †20
IVINS, Douglas John. 1111 S SAINT LOUIS AVE, OU FAMILY MED 74120 #033-06-1995 L2002 **FM** *040 †18
JABBOUR, Antoine Ibrahim. 4415 S HARVARD AVE, STE 100 74135 #039-01-1990 L1991 **OSM** *020 †40
JABOUR, Robert. ■ 74152 #047-06-1954 L1956 **GS** *071
JACKSON, Ronald Earl. 6465 S YALE AVE STE 900 74136 #048-78-1978, ▲ L1979 **GS** *020
JACKSON, William Lynn. 6151 S YALE AVE, PEDIATRIC CARDIOLOGY OF 74136 #039-01-1974 L1975 **CD PD** *020 †55
JACOB, Martin Lee. ■ 74105 #016-02-1980 L2006 **OBG** *020 †30
JACOBS, Lawrence A. 5555 E 71ST ST STE 7100, STE 7100 74136 #039-01-1969 L1974 **RHU IM** *020 †20
JACOBS, Luster Irving. 1623 S UTICA AVE 74104 #039-01-1979 L1980 **EM FM** *020 †18
JAIN, Sanjeev. 10109 E 79TH ST, CANCER TREATMENT CENTERS O 74133 #495-43-1997 L2008 **HO** *020 †20
JAMES, Mark Stephen. 9912 E 21ST ST 74129 #039-01-1988 L1989 **FM** *020 †18
JANZEN, Mark Andrew. 3010 S HARVARD AVE STE 220 74114 #062-01-1985 L1993 **DR** *020 †80
JAROLIM, Dala Joy. 4502 E 41ST ST 74135 #039-01-1975 L1976 **IM ON** *040 †20
JEGATHESAN, Subramania. 1705 E 19TH ST, STE 701 74104 #495-16-1962 L1974 **PDS** *020 †85
JELLEY, David Herbert. 4502 E 41ST ST 74135 #039-01-1986 L1987 **PDE** *020 †55
JELLEY, Martina Jan. 4444 E 41ST ST 74135 #039-01-1986 L1987 **IM** *040 †20
JENKINS, Christopher D. 7600 S LEWIS AVE 74136 #039-01-1994 L1995 **FM** *020 †18
JENKINS, David Wilkinson. 1923 S UTICA AVE 74104 #038-06-1963 L1970 **GE IM** *071 †20
JENKINS, Edward W. 7410 LOCH NESS CIR 74132 #050-02-1951 L1960 **TS CD** *071 †85,90
JENNINGS, John David. 9001 S 101ST EAST AVE, STE 350 74133 #306-01-1985 L1987 **FM** *020 †18
JENNINGS, John Houston. 4111 S DARLINGTON AVE, RADIOLOGY CONSULTANTS OF 74135 #039-01-1993 L1997 **DR** *020 †80

■ = Address Information Privacy Protected

JENNINGS, Wm Clifford. 1725 E 19TH ST, SPECIALIST 74104 #004-01-1976 L1977 **GS** *020 †85
JESIOLOWSKI, Keith Alan. 8414 E 101ST ST 74133 #030-06-1978 L1983 **FM** *020 †18
JESUDASS, Richard R. ■ 74133 #495-27-1982 L1997 **GE** *020 †20
JIANG, Alice Hsiaowen. ■ 74119 #039-01-2005 L2005 **FM** *100
JIN, Marvin Y. 8596 E 101ST ST, STE D 74133 #583-06-1971 L1976 **CHP P** *020 †75
JOHNSEN, Debra Lynn Smith. 1245 S UTICA AVE 74104 #048-02-1988 L1989 **PD** *074 †55
JOHNSEN, Gregory Dennis. 1265 S UTICA AVE, STE 300 74104 #039-01-1988 L1989 **IC CD** *020 †20
JOHNSON, Chandrahasan A. 2408 E 81ST ST, STE 100 74137 #495-27-1954 L1985 **DR** *071 †80
JOHNSON, Christopher Vaug. 4502 E 41ST ST, COLL MEDICINE-TU 74135 #019-02-2005 L2006 **FPP** *012
JOHNSON, Craig Stephen. 6655 S YALE AVE 74136 #039-01-1986 L1987 **CRS** *020 †85,10
JOHNSON, James Albert, Jr. 8803 S 101ST EAST AVE 74133 #004-01-1975 L1976 **GS** *020 †85
JOHNSON, Jeffrey Allen. 1623 S UTICA AVE 74104 #039-01-2002 L2006 **EM** *100
JOHNSON, Jennifer Marie. ■ 74104 #004-01-2005 L2007 **PD** *012
JOHNSON, Lawrence Revel. 1923 S UTICA AVE, REGIONAL MEDICAL LABORATOR 74104 #032-01-1995 L2004 **HMP** *020 †50
JOHNSON, Ralph Sellers. 2815 S SHERIDAN RD, ADULT MEDICINE CLINIC 74129 #048-13-2004 L2006 **IM** *020
JOHNSON, Satyabama. ■ 74137 #495-27-1952 L1985 **NM IM** *071 †28
JONES, Birgit K S. 6655 S YALE AVE 74136 #858-02-1966 L2000 **CHP P** *071 †75
JONES, Collette. 1611 S UTICA AVE # 217 74104 #039-01-1995 L1999 **AN** *020 †05
JONES, Craig S. ■ 74105 #019-02-1944 L1950 **IM CD** *071 †20
JONES, Forrest Henry. ■ 74114 #019-02-1954 L1975 **FM OS** *071 †18
JONES, Janet Kay. 10011 S YALE AVE STE 200 74137 #039-01-1996 L1998 **PD** *020 †55
JONES, Kristy Lee. 6161 S YALE AVE LE, WARREN CLINIC, INC 74136 #039-01-2003 L2005 **IM** *020 †20
JONES, Nina Camille. 2408 E 81ST ST 74137 #039-01-1978 L1979 **DR** *020
JONES, Pete. 529 E 36TH ST N 74106 #306-01-1984 L1994 **FM** *020
JOSEPH, Sheba Mary. 7600 S LEWIS AVE 74136 #495-31-2003 L2007 **FP** *012
JOSEPHSON, John Francis. 4415 S HARVARD AVE, STE 100 74135 #561-01-1975 L1980 **ORS** *020 †40 ‡
JUBELIRER, David P. 6202 S LEWIS AVE, STE A 74136 #005-06-1972 L1978 **PD PDI** *020 †55
KACERE, Richard David. 1923 E 21ST ST, NEBRASKA HEART INSTITUTE 74114 #026-08-1992 L2007 **CD** *020 †20
KACHE, Ashok. 1145 S UTICA AVE STE 403 74104 #495-57-1973 L1982 **PM** *020 †60
KALAPURA, Thomachan. 1923 E 21ST ST 74114 #495-44-1993 L2001 **CD** *020 †20
KALBFLEISCH, John M. 10505 E 91ST ST, STE 150 74133 #039-01-1957 L1957 **CD** *071 †20
KALKAT, Prabhdeep. 2808 S SHERIDAN RD 74129 #496-08-2001 L2005 **MPD** *100
KALKAT, Tejwant. 6161 S YALE AVE 74136 #495-29-1992 L1999 **IM** *020 †20
KAMP, George H. 6161 S YALE AVE, 5TH FL PICU 74136 #004-01-1960 L1966 **R** *071 †80
KANESHIGE, Alan Mitsuo. 9228 S MINGO RD STE 200, OKLAHOMA HEART, INC. 74133 #030-06-1985 L1995 **CD** *020 †20
KARATHANOS, Angela. 1120 S UTICA AVE, NEWBORN SPECIALISTS OF 74104 #418-01-1969 L1980 **NPM PD** *020 †55
KARATHANOS, Michael. 2642 E 21ST ST STE 130 74114 #418-01-1970 L1980 **N** *020
KARIBASSAPPA SHIVASHANKAR, . ■ 74133 #495-98-2003 L2007 **IM** *012
KARLAK, Julia A. 1725 E 19TH ST STE 602 74104 #048-14-1982 L1983 **IM** *020 †20
KATHURIA, Chitralekha. 8115 S MEMORIAL DR 74133 #495-45-1991 L2001 **FM** *020 †18
KATSIS, Steven Blaine. 6465 S YALE AVE, STE 900 74136 #030-05-1993 L1994 **CCS** *020 †85
KATZ, Stewart Jay. 1923 E 21ST ST 74114 #039-01-1979 L1985 **CD** *071 †20
KAUL, Rajat. 1124 S SAINT LOUIS AVE, STE 61 74120 #495-36-1983 L1998 **NEP IM** *020 †20
KAUTH, John Edward. 6161 S YALE AVE 74136 #026-04-1954 L1959 **DR NM** *071 †80,28
KAYSER, Michael A. 6465 S YALE AVE STE 1015, WARREN CLINIC - GENETICS 74136 #039-79-2000, ▲ L2001 **MG** *020 †55,19
KEEFE, Elisa Jo. ■ 74136 #039-01-2007 L2007 **PD** *012
KELLER, Alan Marvin. 6475 S YALE AVE, STE 201 74136 #039-01-1973 L1978 **ON HEM** *020 †20
KELLER, Scott Allen. 7600 S LEWIS AVE 74136 #039-05-1988 L1989 **FM** *020 †18
KELLEY, Mark Alan. 1705 E 19TH ST STE 512, HOLLIMAN MED BLDG 74104 #039-01-1967 L1968 **P** *020 †75 ‡
KELLEY, Michelle Renee. 1923 S UTICA AVE 74104 #039-01-1996 L1997 **FM** *020 †18
KELLY, Douglas A. 10109 E 79TH ST 74133 #067-01-1991 L1996 **RO** *020 †80
KELLY, Garry Wayne. 1541 N SHERIDAN RD 74115 #039-01-1970 L1971 **OM GP** *020 †70 ‡
KEMPE, Paul Wm. 1265 S UTICA AVE, STE 105 74104 #048-12-1985 L1999 **TS VS** *020 †85,90
KENKEL, Thos Christopher. 1124 S SAINT LOUIS AVE, NEPH SPEC OF OKLA 74120 #038-41-1981 L1986 **NEP IM** *020 †20
KENNEDY, Craig Allen. 4500 S GARNETT RD 74146 #040-02-1978 L1984 **EM FM** *020 †16,18 ‡
KENNEDY, George Richard. ■ 74137 #056-05-1947 L1955 **GS** *071 †85
KENNEDY, Grace R. 6585 S YALE AVE, STE 1200 74136 #039-79-1988, ▲ L1989 **PCC** *020 †20
KENNEDY, John. 7912 E 31ST CT, PRUNETWORK OF TULSA-PPO 74145 #005-16-1962 L1975 **AN** *020
KERMANSHAHI, Kaveh. 7600 S LEWIS AVE 74136 #858-03-1988 L1991 **FM** *020 †18
KERN, Thomas Joseph. 4502 E 41ST ST, ADULT MEDICINE CLINIC 74135 #039-01-2005 L2006 **IM** *012
KETCHUM, Hall. ■ 74132 #016-06-1946 L1952 **OBG** *071 †30
KETTERL, Petra Jasmin. 10109 E 79TH ST 74133 #047-20-1990 L2004 **HO** *020
KEVENEY, John Jos, Jr. 1124 S SAINT LOUIS AVE, STE 61 74120 #041-02-1969 L1980 **NEP IM** *020 †20
KEYLADA, Hany Heshmat. ■ 74136 #915-10-1989 L1999 **FM** *100 †18
KHAN, Sameena. 4415 S HARVARD AVE, STE 202 74135 #035-47-1994 L2002 **OPH** *020 †35
KHATTAB, Jihad. 6585 S YALE AVE, STE 701 74136 #875-01-1989 L1999 **ON HO** *020 †20
KHOUW, Andrew S. 6160 S YALE AVE 74136 #048-12-1985 L1991 **END IM** *020 †20 ‡
KILBURY, Merlin Joe. 4308 S PEORIA AVE # 702 74105 #004-01-1972 L1973 **EM** *030 †85
KILPADIKAR, Anil Amarnath. 4111 S DARLINGTON AVE, RADIOLOGY CONSULTANTS OF 74135 #495-28-1983 L2006 **DR** *020 †80
KIM, Insung. 2815 S SHERIDAN RD 74129 #039-01-1982 L1983 **IM IMG** *040 †20
KIMBERLING, Matthew T. 6151 S YALE AVE, PEDIATRIC CARDIOLOGY OF 74136 #039-01-1994 L2000 **PDC** *020 †55
KINDRED, Michael Gerard. 4502 E 41ST ST, DEPARTMENT OF SURGERY 74135 #007-02-2003 L2004 **GS** *012
KING, David Michael. 6160 S YALE AVE, WARREN CLINIC SPRINGER BLD 74136 #028-02-1969 L1974 **GE** *020 †20
KING, Don Robt, II. 10109 E 79TH ST 74133 #010-01-1972 L1983 **IM OS** *020 †20
KING, John L, Jr. 6160 S YALE AVE, SPRINGER CLINIC, INC 74136 #048-12-1992 L2002 **GS** *020 †85
KING, Joy Dent. ■ 74137 #010-01-1972 L1983 **GYN** *072 †30
KING, Lisa Rayburn. 9001 S 101ST EAST AVE #280, SOUTHCREEK INTERNAL MED 74133 #039-01-1990 L1994 **IM** *020 †20
KIRK, Kenneth John. 8596 E 101ST ST STE B 74133 #039-01-1984 L1985 **IM** *040 †20
KIRK, Mary Carolyn. 1120 S UTICA AVE, STE G100 74104 #039-01-1987 L1991 **OBG** *020 †30
KIRK, Robert Gene. 1145 S UTICA AVE, STE 1109 74104 #016-02-1973 L1981 **PS** *020 †65
KIRKPATRICK, Gregory B. 6161 S YALE AVE 74136 #039-01-1984 L1986 **PHO PD** *020 †55
KISHNER, Leonard Lee. ■ 74136 #056-06-1946 L1950 **PD DBP** *072 †55
KLENDA, Elizabeth Eileen. ■ 74105 #039-01-2008 *012
KLIEWER, Allis Liu. 6151 S YALE AVE, PEDIATRIC CARDIOLOGY OF 74136 #039-01-1991 L1992 **PDC** *020 †55
KLIEWER, Douglas Bruce. 6465 S YALE AVE, STE 1002 74136 #039-01-1991 L1997 **GE** *020 †20 ‡
KLINE, Kristina Michelle. 1120 S UTICA AVE 74104 #039-01-1994 L1995 **FM** *020 †18
KLOS, Kevin John. 8110 S YALE AVE 74137 #039-01-2000 L2005 **N** *020 †75
KNIFE CHIEF, Chas Dennis. 8803 S 101ST EAST AVE, SPECIALISTS PC 74133 #005-18-1982 L1983 **OBG** *020 †30
KNIGHT, Joseph. 1502 S BOULDER AVE 74119 #035-47-1979 L2006 **ID IM** *020 †20
KNIPPERS, John Carroll. 7512 E 91ST ST, SOUTH ULSA PEDIATRICS 74133 #039-01-1981 L1982 **PD** *020 †55
KODURI, Uma. ■ 74133 #495-21-1986 L1994 **IM** *020 †20
KOEHLER, James R. 7322 E 91ST ST, TULSA SURICAL ARTS 74133 #001-02-1999 L2003 **CS** *020
KOHRS, Rainer. 6839 S CANTON AVE, ANESTHESIOLOGISTS INC 74136 #409-12-1993 L2000 **AN** *020 †05
KOK, William John. 2122 S 67TH E AVE, STE D 74129 #039-05-1983 L1984 **AM GP** *020
KOLMAN, Brett Herbster. 2448 E 81ST ST, STE 1650 74137 #039-01-1997 L1998 **DR** *020 †80
KONDOS, Frank David. 8136 S MEMORIAL DR 74133 #039-01-1983 L1984 **FM OM** *020 †18
KOONTZ, Douglas R. 6767 S YALE AVE A, NEUROSURGERY SPECIALISTS 74136 #039-01-1981 L1982 **NS** *020 †25
KOSBAB, Frederic Paul G. ■ 74170 #407-01-1945 L1982 **P** *071 †75
KOWALSKI, Michael Bryan. 2808 S SHERIDAN RD 74129 #305-01-2004 L2007 **IM** *012
KOZLOWSKI, Anne Elisabeth. 1923 S UTICA AVE 74104 #039-79-2000, ▲ L2001 **R** *020
KRAFT, David Price. 6585 S YALE AVE, STE 630 74136 #028-03-1976 L1979 **FM FPG** *020 †18
KRAFT, James Edward. ■ 74114 #021-01-1948 L1949 **OPH** *071 †35
KRAMER, John C. 7125 S BRADEN AVE, STE A 74136 #024-01-1950 L1956 **PD PDP** *020 †55
KRAMER, Robert Lewis. ■ 74105 #039-01-1956 L1956 **OPH** *071 †35
KRANZ, Robert Lang. 6839 S CANTON AVE, ANESTHESIOLOGISTS INC 74136 #014-01-1975 L1981 **AN** *020 †05
KRASNOW, Robert. ■ 74114 #869-04-1954 L1957 **IM PUD** *071
KRAUTTER, Paul Marsh. 2325 S HARVARD AVE, STE 108 74114 #048-02-1980 L1986 **FM GS** *020 †18
KRIEGER, Ronald Carl. 4111 S DARLINGTON AVE, RADIOLOGY CONSULTANTS OF 74135 #039-01-1980 L1981 **DR** *020 †80 ‡
KRIETMEYER, George R. ■ 74105 #028-02-1951 L1954 **PD** *071
KRISA, Peggy Julia. 1919 S WHEELING AVE, STUITE 404 74104 #039-01-1987 L2000 **IM** *020 †20
KRISHNA, Raja. 6161 S YALE AVE 74136 #039-01-1998 L2003 **IM** *020 †20
KRONFELD, Lydia Ballinger. 6655 S YALE AVE, LAUREATE PSYCHIATRIC CLINI 74136 #041-01-1955 L1980 **P PYA** *071
KRUTKA, Donna Jean. 1919 S WHEELING AVE # 304, TULSA PEDIATRIC AND ADOLES 74104 #028-03-1973 L1978 **PD PSM** *020 †55
KUFDAKIS, James. 1245 S UTICA AVE 74104 #042-03-1984 L2006 **IM** *020 †20
KUGLER, Kenyon Kline. 1919 S WHEELING AVE, STE 600 74104 #019-02-1968 L1975 **NS** *071 †25
KULLER, Melisa Gail. 1120 S UTICA AVE 74104 #048-13-2002 L2007 **RO** *020
KUMAR, Kartik Sampath. ■ 74137 #048-12-2007 **IM** *012
KUMAR, Kishore. 2808 S SHERIDAN RD, DEPT MED 74129 #704-02-2002 L2007 **MPD** *012
KUMAR, Naveen Nandigama. 10159 E 11TH ST, STE 100 74128 #495-99-1990 L1996 **P** *020 ‡
KUMAR, Shivanna Vijaya. ■ 74137 #495-99-1978 L1984 **P** *020
KUYKENDALL, Tracy Dee. 1245 S UTICA AVE, DERMATOLOGY ASSOCIATES OF 74104 #004-01-2003 L2004 **D** *020 †15
LA BARRE, Gary Carl. ■ 74133 #019-02-1962 L1976 **OBG** *071 †30
LAD, Chandan Dattatraya. 3218 S 79TH EAST AVE 74145 #039-01-2000 L2001 **FM** *020 †18 ‡
LAD, Jyoti Dattatraya. 2815 S SHERIDAN RD, OU DEPARTMENT OF PEDIATRIC 74129 #495-17-1971 L1981 **PD** *020 †55
LADE, Arvid. 6600 S YALE AVE 74136 #039-05-1988 L1989 **IM** *020 †20
LA FROMBOISE, Dawn Marie. 7010 S YALE AVE STE 215, ASSOCIATED CENTERS FOR THE 74136 #037-01-2003 L2004 **P** *020
LAHR, Stevan E. 4502 E 41ST ST, DEPARTMENT OF PSYCHIATRY 74135 #039-79-2004, ▲ L2005 **FPP** *012
LAKIN, Tracey Lynn. 1120 S UTICA AVE, STE G100 74104 #021-06-1998 L2002 **OBG** *020 †30
LA MAR, Walter Larry. 1923 S UTICA AVE 74104 #039-01-1973 L1974 **PTH** *062 †50
LAMBERT, Ruben. 2808 S SHERIDAN RD 74129 #275-02-1984 **FM** *100
LAMBRECHT, Bradley Dean. 6839 S CANTON AVE, ANESTHESIOLOGISTS INC 74136 #048-12-1994 L1999 **AN** *020 †05
LAMOTTE, Jeremy Paul. 1717A S UTICA AVE 74104 #016-43-2003 L2004 **FM** *020 †18
LANDGARTEN, Steven. 1245 S UTICA AVE 74104 #035-15-1966 L1972 **IM NM** *020 †28,20
LANDON, Pamela Cecile. 6475 S YALE AVE, STE 201 74136 #021-05-1994 L1999 **HO** *020 †20
LANE, Connie Jo. 4111 S DARLINGTON AVE, STE 425 74135 #039-01-1983 L1984 **IM P** *020 †20
LANGERAK, Alan David. 1810 E 15TH ST, CANCER CARE ASSOCIATES 74104 #003-01-1990 L1994 **HO** *020 †20
LANTZ, Gordon Dennis. 1919 S WHEELING AVE, STE 404 74104 #048-15-1975 L1980 **IM END** *020 †20
LANTZ, Peter Edwin. 6585 S YALE AVE, STE 1150 74136 #039-01-1983 L1984 **IM** *020 †20
LAO, Esther Sun. 7600 S LEWIS AVE 74136 #010-02-2003 L2004 **FM** *100 †18
LARSON, Lora J. 1705 E 19TH ST, SPECIALISTS PC 74104 #039-01-1981 L1982 **OBG** *020 †30 ‡
LARSON, Nancy Christene. 2808 S SHERIDAN RD 74129 #039-79-2005, ▲ L2006 **MPD** *012
LAUGHLIN, Brent Walker. 3534 E 51ST ST 74135 #004-01-1980 L1981 **FM** *020 †18
LAUGHLIN, Richard Lloyd. 4111 S DARLINGTON AVE, STE 700 74135 #039-01-1975 L1980 **DR NR** *020 †80 ‡
LAUINGER, Phyllis J White. ■ 74105 #035-01-1972 L1973 **GP** *075
LAWLER, Sidney Seay. 1919 S WHEELING AVE, STE 700 74104 #039-01-2002 L2003 **IM** *020 †20

■ = Address Information Privacy Protected

LAWLESS, Michael Albert. 4111 S DARLINGTON AVE, STE 700 74135 #038-41-1995 L2004 DR *020 †80

LAWSON, Reginald. ■ 74136 #422-01-2005 L2006 IM *020

LAWSON, Robert B. 1120 S UTICA AVE, NEWBORN SPECIALISTS OF 74104 #039-79-1983, ▲ L1984 GP *020

LAZARO-ZANO, Mercedes. 9001 S 101ST EAST AVE, STE 280 74133 #748-10-1981 L1994 IM *020 †20

LE, Kim Oanhthi. 6934 S LEWIS AVE 74136 #047-06-2003 L2007 DR *012

LE, Tho Dinh. 6151 S YALE AVE STE 400 74136 #051-01-1988 L2007 CD IM *020 †20

LE, Uyen Phuong. 4502 E 41ST ST 74135 #039-01-1999 L2000 PD *020 †55

LEACH, James Randal. 10901 E 48TH ST 74146 #016-11-1962 L1968 U *071 †95

LEDBETTER, Bryan K. 1111 S SAINT LOUIS AVE, OU HEALTH SCIENCES CENTER 74120 #039-79-2005, ▲ L2006 FP *012

LEDBETTER, Marcialee. 4502 E 41ST ST 74135 #039-01-1989 L1997 CHP P *020 †75

LEE, David. 8801 S 101ST EAST AVE, SOUTHCREST ANESTHESIA GROU 74133 #049-01-1987 L2000 AN *020 †20

LEE, Felicia R. 2448 E ADMIRAL BLVD, XAVIER MEDICAL CLINIC 74110 #048-02-1987 L2007 IM *020 †20

LEE, Gary R. 1120 S UTICA AVE 74104 #048-13-1987 L1988 FM *020 †18

LEE, James Choon-Yung. 4502 E 41ST ST 74135 #005-12-2004 L2005 IM *012

LEE, Laura L. 4111 S DARLINGTON AVE 74135 #039-01-1979 L1980 DR *020 †80

LEE, Melissa Anne. ■ 74133 #016-01-2005 L2006 IM *012

LEHMAN, Mark David. 2121 E 21ST ST, TULSA DERMATOLOGY CLINIC 74114 #048-15-1992 L1996 D *020 †15

LEIMBACH, Wayne N, Jr. 1265 S UTICA AVE, STE 300 74104 #016-06-1979 L1986 CD IM *020 †20

LEINEN, Jason Matthew. 1111 S SAINT LOUIS AVE 74120 #039-01-2006 L2007 FP *012

LENHART, Michael E. 1120 S UTICA AVE, NEWBORN SPECIALISTS OF 74104 #028-79-1987, ▲ L1988 NPM *020

LEON, Phillip Joseph. 4502 E 41ST ST, THE UNIVERSITY OF OKLAHOMA 74135 #048-02-2002 L2003 P *100 †75

LEONARD, Steven Bernard. 4111 S DARLINGTON AVE, RADIOLOGY CONSULTANTS OF 74135 #039-01-1987 L1992 DR *020 †80

LEPAK, Christopher Jason. 1717A S UTICA AVE 74104 #039-01-1999 L2003 EM *020 †16

LEPERE, Kristopher M. 6160 S YALE AVE 74136 #039-01-1999, ▲ L2000 MPD *020 †20,55 ‡

LEROY, Adam David. ■ 74135 #011-02-2003 L2006 FM *100

LESIKAR, George J. 6839 S CANTON AVE, ANESTHESIOLOGISTS INC 74136 #048-02-1968 L1978 AN *071 †05

LESTER, Patrick David. 2408 E 81ST ST, STE 100 74137 #039-01-1965 L1965 DR PDR *071 †80 ‡

LESTER, Stephen T. 6585 S YALE AVE STE 1110 74136 #039-01-1987 L1988 AN PME *020 †05 ‡

LETCHER, Frank Scott. 111 E 1ST ST 74103 #028-02-1967 L1976 NS *071 †25

LEVESTON, Steven Allan. 1919 S WHEELING AVE, STE 404 74104 #035-03-1973 L2007 END IM *020 †20

LEVINE, Jonathan Eliot. 6160 S YALE AVE, WARREN CLINIC 74136 #019-02-1998 L2002 HOS *020 †20

LEVIT, Simon Albert. 1725 E 19TH ST, STE 703 74104 #016-42-1963 L1969 CD IM *020 †20

LEWIS, Alan Garth. 6475 S YALE AVE STE 301, EASTERN OK ORTHOPEDIC CENT 74136 #019-02-1978 L1983 ORS EM *020 †40

LEWIS, Kevin L. 3501 E 31ST ST 74135 #048-13-1995 L1996 PCC SME *020 †20

LEWIS, William. 6565 S YALE AVE, INTER ID INC 74136 #048-02-1990 L1996 ID *020 †20

LEYSER, Larry James. 6151 S YALE AVE STE 303 74136 #021-05-1980 L2006 IM CD *020 †20

LI, Mary Huisiu. 6151 S YALE AVE STE 305, PEDIATRIC SURGERY INC. 74136 #016-11-1989 L1998 PDS CCS *020 †85

LIND, Timothy Alan. 1923 S UTICA AVE 74104 #003-01-1971 L1978 R RNR *020 †80 ‡

LINDSAY, Jeff Don. 6839 S CANTON AVE 74136 #024-01-1985 L1990 AN *020 †05

LINDSAY, Patricia Mae. ■ 74136 #016-11-1971 L1981 IM NEP *072

LINDSEY, Jason. 7306 S LEWIS AVE # 100 74136 #025-76-2004, ▲ L2005 FM *020 †18

LINS, Marilyn Elaine. ■ 74112 #019-02-1968 L1969 NS N *071

LIPE, Bill Herman. 4111 S DARLINGTON AVE, RADIOLOGY CONSULTANTS OF 74135 #039-01-1969 L1970 R PDR *020 †80

LISDELL, Leslie. 10505 E 91ST ST SU 74133 #048-15-1993 L2005 FM OBS *020 †18

LITWILLER, Scott Eric. 10901 E 48TH ST, UROLOGICSPECIALISTS OF OKL 74146 #017-20-1989 L1999 U *020 †95

LIU, Christine Y. 7600 S LEWIS AVE, FAMILY MEDICAL CARE 74136 #021-01-2005 L2007 FP *012

LIVINGSTON, Harry Earl. 6585 S YALE AVE, STE 200 74136 #012-05-1957 L1964 ORS *071 †40

LOCKHART, James B, Jr. 6465 S YALE AVE STE 900, WARREN PROF BLDG 74136 #027-01-1964 L1971 GS *020 †85

LODES, Patricia Elaine. 1919 S WHEELING AVE, GYNECOLOGY & OBSTETRICS 74104 #039-01-1987 L1988 OBG *020 †30

LOEHR, Anthony Edward. 8803 S 101ST EAST AVE, STE 110 74133 #039-01-1971 L1977 OTO *020 †45

LOFGREN, Darla Jean. 1145 S UTICA AVE, STE 460 74104 #039-01-1996 L1997 OBG *020

LOHREY, John Howard. 1810 E 15TH ST, CANCER CARE ASSOCIATES 74104 #039-01-1994 L1995 HO PD *020 †20,55

LONG, Cynthia A. 4500 S GARNETT RD, STE 840 74146 #004-01-1988 L1991 VIR *020 †80

LONG, Eric. 1923 S UTICA AVE, PHYSICIANS 74104 #039-79-2000, ▲ *100 †05

LONG, Jerome Myron. 9322 E 41ST ST, PRIMARY CARE 74145 #039-01-1981 L1987 IM *020 †20

LOPER, Tracy Shawn. 1714 S QUINCY AVE 74120 #654-01-2000 L2003 FM *020 †18,75

LOPEZ-MEJIA, Gerardo. ■ 74119 #039-01-2006 L2006 FP *012

LORTON, Jay Darin. 6475 S YALE AVE STE 301, EASTERN OK ORTHOPEDIC CENT 74136 #039-01-1995 L1996 ORS OSM *020 †40

LOSACCO, Dominic. 6565 S YALE AVE STE 706 74136 #025-07-1967 L1974 P *020 †75 ‡

LOUGHRIDGE, Billy Paul. 1705 E 19TH ST 74104 #039-01-1961 L1961 TS *071 †85,90 ‡

LOVE, James Tyre, Jr. 1727 S UTICA AVE, THE ALLERGY CLINIC OF TULS 74104 #008-02-1991 L1996 AI *020 †55,03

LOVE, Wallace Bond. 9322 E 41ST ST, TULSA VA OUTPATIENT CLINIC 74145 #039-01-1970 L1971 IM GE *020 †20

LOVELACE, Kelli Ann. 2121 E 21ST ST 74114 #039-01-2003 L2004 D *020 †15 ‡

LOVELESS, Donald E. 3902 E 51ST ST 74135 #039-01-1982 L1986 OBG *020 †30

LOVELESS, Donald Everett. ■ 1923 S UTICA AVE #004-01-1954 L1967 FM *071

LOVELESS, Jana Richards. 6465 S YALE AVE STE 704 74136 #039-01-2001 L2002 IM *020

LOWE, Michael Shawn. 1809 E 13TH ST, STE 400 74104 #039-01-1994 L1996 GS *020 †85

LOWEN, Deborah E. 2829 S SHERIDAN RD, CHILDRENS JUST CTR 74129 #036-05-1993 L2001 PD OS *020 †55

LOYD, Jefferson Carl. 1623 S UTICA AVE 74104 #028-78-1977, ▲ L1978 EM *020 †16

LOZANO, Jose Eduardo. ■ 74135 #048-15-1998 L2003 IM *020 †20

LOZANO ZALDIVAR, Alejandro. ■ 74133 #649-30-2005 L2007 OBG *012

LUC, Richard August. ■ 74136 #039-01-1981 L1982 P *020 †75

LUCENTA, Bryan Allen. 6151 S YALE AVE STE 303 74136 #048-02-1984 L1985 CD IM *020 †20

LUDLOW, Stacey Leigh. 3401 E 21ST ST 74114 #048-13-1992 L1997 GP PD *012

LUESSENHOP, Christian P. 6475 S YALE AVE STE 202 74136 #010-02-1985 L1995 ORS OAR *020 †40

LUISKUTTY, Thomas C. 6600 S YALE AVE, STE 900 74136 #039-01-1994 L1995 IM *020 †20

LUNDT, Cynthia Rae. 6151 S YALE AVE, PEDIATRIC CARDIOLOGY OF 74136 #039-01-2000 L2006 PDC *100 †55

LUNN, Rhonda Badeen. 6465 S YALE AVE STE 815 74136 #039-01-1980 L1981 OBG *020 †30 ‡

LUXENBERG, Nina Lynn. 1923 S UTICA AVE 74104 #033-06-1996 L2002 R *020 †80

LYNCH, Joseph Patrick. 6585 S YALE AVE STE 701, WILLIAM MEDICAL BUILDING 74136 #010-02-1986 L1999 ON *020 †20

LYNCH, Robert Edwin. 9228 S MINGO RD 74133 #039-01-1967 L1969 CD IM *020 †20

LYONS, George David. 4111 S DARLINGTON AVE, 4111 S DARLINGTON, SUITE 7 74135 #035-09-1992 L1999 DR *020 †80

MACEDO, Aisha Ann. ■ 74137 #035-47-2005 L2007 OPH *012

MACEDO, Elizabeth E. 5315 E 101ST PL 74137 #495-31-1975 L1992 DR *020 †80

MACKEY, Robert Warren. 6465 S YALE AVE STE 412 74136 #021-01-1963 L1966 PD FM *071 †55

MADAJ, Debra Kaye. 1245 S UTICA AVE 74104 #039-01-1987 L1993 IM *020 †20

MADAJ, Thomas Edward. 1245 S UTICA AVE 74104 #039-01-1985 L1986 IM *020 †20

MAGUIRE, Bernard J, Jr. 2815 S SHERIDAN RD 74129 #019-02-1960 L1965 PD *071 †55 ‡

MAHAFFEY, Robert Mark. 2325 S HARVARD AVE STE 108 74114 #048-12-1977 L1983 FM OM *020 †18

MAHALDAR, Anshinee. 7304 S 99TH EAST AVE, APT 717 74133 #496-17-2002 L2006 IM *012

MAHMOOD, Tahir. ■ 74137 #704-21-1990 L1997 IM *020 †20

MAJID, Pirzada Abdul. 10505 E 91ST ST, STE 150 74133 #495-15-1959 L1993 CD IM *020

MALIK, Shamim A. 1120 S UTICA AVE, NEWBORN SPECIALISTS OF 74104 #704-06-1974 L1982 NPM PD *020 †20

MALLOY, Michael Andrew. 1430 TERRACE DR, ARTHRITIS 74104 #039-01-1997 L1999 RHU *020 †20

MALONE, David Gerald. 1919 S WHEELING AVE 74104 #019-02-1986 L1995 NS GS *020 †25

MAMALIS, Nicholas D. 6465 S YALE AVE, STE 1002 74136 #012-05-1977 L1982 GE IM *020 †20 ‡

MAMMANA, Robert B. 6151 S YALE AVE, STE 302 74136 #010-02-1970 L1997 TS GS *020 †85,90

MANGE, Mona S. 3218 S 79TH EAST AVE, WARREN CLINIC 74145 #605-01-1966 L1981 PD *071 †55 ‡

MANN, Christopher Darin. 1111 S SAINT LOUIS AVE 74120 #039-01-2003 L2004 FM *020 †18

MANSUR, Laurence Ray. 6475 S YALE AVE STE 202, WARREN CLINIC 74136 #039-01-1968 L1969 OSM ORS *020 †18

MAPLES, Wesley Keith. 6901 S OLYMPIA AVE 74132 #039-01-1992 L1993 IM *020 †20

MAQSOOD, Asim. ■ 74135 #704-01-2000 L2006 FM *020

MARBERRY, Thomas Alan. 4415 S HARVARD AVE, STE 100 74135 #039-01-1975 L1976 ORS OSM *020 †40

MARINO, Gregory. 1923 S UTICA AVE, PHYSICIANS 74104 #039-01-1981 L1982 AN *020

MARKMAN, Bruce Scott. 6465 S YALE AVE, STE 202 74136 #550-02-1996 L2003 ORS *020 †40

MARPLE, Richard Neil. 5018 E 68TH ST STE 110 74135 #039-01-1973 L1974 IM ISM *020 †20

MARSHALL, Richard Allen. 6151 S YALE AVE STE 100, ST FRANCIS HOSPITAL 74136 #039-01-1955 L1955 IM HEM *071 †20

MARTENS, Jason Donald. 4500 S GARNETT RD, STE 919 74146 #039-01-2001 L2002 DR *020 †80

MARTENS, Mark G. 1145 S UTICA AVE, STE 460 74104 #010-01-1982 L2002 OBG ID *040 †30

MARTIN, Alan Lee. 1919 S WHEELING AVE, STE 606 74104 #039-01-1989 L1990 RHU PPR *020 †55,20

MARTIN, David Chas. 1725 E 19TH ST STE 602 74104 #039-01-1982 L1983 IM *020 †20

MARTIN, Dean Erwin. 2121 S COLUMBIA AVE, STE 301 74114 #039-01-1981 L1982 CHP P *020 †15

MARTIN, Edward Thos. 9228 S MINGO RD STE 200 74133 #038-43-1991 L1998 CD IM *020 †20

MARTIN, Fred Richard. 1725 E 19TH ST 74104 #039-01-1957 L1957 PS *071 †65

MARTIN, Jimmy Chas. 1445 E 51ST ST STE 110 74135 #039-01-1974 L1975 FM *020 †18

MARTIN, Michael J. 6565 S YALE AVE STE 1200, 1200 KELLEY PROF BLDG 74136 #048-13-1989 L1990 GE *020 †20

MARTIN, Samuel Gene. ■ 74133 #039-01-2007 L2007 P *012

MARTUCCI, Martin Leo. 2000 S WHEELING AVE, STE 600 74104 #048-12-1997 L2002 APM *020 †05

MASON, Clinton Kenneth. 6839 S CANTON AVE, ANESTHESIOLOGISTS INC 74136 #039-01-1990 L1991 AN *020 †05

MASOOD, Tariq. 1245 S UTICA AVE 74104 #704-02-1990 L1995 IM *020 †20 ‡

MATHERS, Mark Lee. 1844 E 15TH ST 74104 #039-79-1983, ▲ L1984 PS *020

MATHUR, Ashish. 4502 E 41ST ST, DEPT OF FAMILY PRAC 74135 #048-30-2001 L2006 FM *020

MATTHEWS, Kirsten Dale. 4502 E 41ST ST, THE UNIVERSITY OF OKLAHOMA 74135 #039-01-2001 L2002 PYG *100 †75

MAUERMAN, George Schmid. 6475 S YALE AVE STE 301, EASTERN OKLA ORTHOPEDIC CE 74135 #035-01-1963 L1970 ORS *020 †40

MAURITSON, Donald Forsyth. 4021 S HARVARD AVE 74135 #056-06-1948 L1954 R NM *071 †80,28

MAW, Gilbert Maylon. 1120 S UTICA AVE, 4W-4502 74104 #036-07-1970 L1982 PTH *071 †50

MAXWELL, Michael Kent. 1919 S WHEELING AVE # 404 74104 #039-01-1984 L1985 IM *020 †20

MAYER, Renae Lyne. 1810 E 15TH ST 74104 #039-01-1997 L2002 IM *020 †20

MAYFIELD, Christy D. 8803 S 101ST EAST AVE, STE 230 74133 #039-01-1997 L1998 FM *020 †18 ‡

MAYFIELD, James Donald. 1705 E 19TH ST 74104 #048-04-1961 L1970 PUD IM *071 †20

MAYOZA, James Clarke. 6122 E 61ST ST 74136 #027-01-1961 L1965 ORS OSS *020 †40

MAYS, Steven Scott. 8803 S 101ST EAST AVE, STE 165 74133 #048-14-1983 L1984 FM *020 †18

MC ANULTY, Brent Cannon. 2808 S SHERIDAN RD, DEPT IM 74129 #004-01-2003 L2007 MPD *012

MC CLANAHAN, Edwin Kent. 1923 S UTICA AVE, ST JOHNS MEDICAL CENTER 74104 #039-01-1973 L1974 EM *020 †16

MC CLURE, Bradley Allen. 6655 S YALE AVE 74136 #039-01-2001 L2004 P *020 †75

MC COLLUM, Jeffrey Scott. 1111 S SAINT LOUIS AVE, OU PHYSICIANS FAMILY MEDICI 74120 #028-34-1984 L2004 FM *020 †18

MC CORMACK, Steven Todd. 6757 S YALE AVE, A I ADVANCE IMAGING 74136 #039-01-1989 L1991 **RNR** *020 †80

MC COY, Cynthia Joan. 3105 E SKELLY DR, STE 305 74105 #039-01-1993 L1994 **FM** *020 †18 ‡

MCCREARY, Edwin Lynn. 1810 E 15TH ST, CANCER CARE ASSOCIATES 74104 #422-01-1998 L2001 **HO** *020 †20

MC CUNE, John Michael. 1809 E 13TH ST, STE 400 74104 #019-02-1980 L1981 **GS** *020 †85

MC DONALD, Joseph Leo. 4415 S HARVARD AVE, AMBULATORY ANESTHESIA INC 74135 #030-05-1958 L1966 **AN OS** *071 †05

MC ELWAIN, David Leroy. 4111 S DARLINGTON AVE, STE 425 74135 #039-01-1983 L1984 **P N** *020 †75

MC ENTEE, Charles Wm. 6151 S YALE AVE, STE 304 74136 #039-01-1976 L1977 **CD IM** *020 †20

MC GEE, James Michael. 1809 E 13TH ST, STE 400 74104 #039-01-1978 L1984 **GS SO** *040 †85

MC GETTIGAN, Marie C. 1120 S UTICA AVE, NEWBORN SPECIALISTS OF 74104 #041-02-1986 L2007 **NPM PD** *020 †55

MCGUIRE, Angela M. 1111 S SAINT LOUIS AVE 74120 #039-79-2005, ▲ L2006 **FP** *012

MCHAM, Scott Allen. 1810 E 15TH ST 74104 #039-79-1997, ▲ L2000 **HO** *020 †20

MC HENRY, Teressa Joan. 1705 E 19TH ST, SPECIALISTS PC 74104 #019-02-1988 L1993 **OBG** *020 †30

MC KEOWN, Kevin Jay. 6839 S CANTON AVE, ASSOCIATED ANESTHESIOLOGIS 74136 #039-01-1997 L1998 **AN** *020 †05

MC NEER, James Frederick. 6465 S YALE AVE, STE 808 74136 #036-07-1972 L1978 **CD IM** *020 †20

MC NULTY, Gerard Jos. 6600 S YALE AVE, STE 900 74136 #039-01-1989 L1990 **IM** *020 †20

MC SHANE, William Robt. ■ 74119 #010-01-1947 L1952 **OBG** *071

MEDAGODA, Rumali Samani. 2815 S SHERIDAN RD, UNIVERSITY OF OKLAHOMA 74129 #220-01-2001 L2006 **PD** *020 †55

MEDAPALLI, Raj Kiran. 4502 E 41ST ST, ADULT MEDICINE CLINIC 74135 #496-31-2001 L2007 **IM** *012

MEDAWAR, Michel Simon. 2738 E 51ST ST, STE 290 74105 #021-05-1961 L1969 **PTH** *020 †50

MEDINA-HIDALGO, Jose R. 1923 E 21ST ST 74114 #319-01-1961 L1971 **CD** *020

MEDLIN, Mark Alan. 744 W 9TH ST 74127 #039-01-1988 L1989 **P** *020 †75

MEDLOCK, Thomas Richard. 2000 S WHEELING AVE # 510 74104 #039-01-1965 L1965 **NEP IM** *020 †20

MEEHAN, James Cyril, Jr. 4444 S HARVARD AVE, MILLS EYE ASSOCIATES, INC 74135 #039-01-1998 L1999 **OPH** *020

MEESE, Mark Russell. 6465 S YALE AVE, STE 900 74136 #039-01-1985 L1986 **GS OS** *020 †85

MEHNERT-KAY, Susan Ann. 1111 S SAINT LOUIS AVE, OU PHYSICIANS FAMILY MEDIC 74120 #039-01-1990 L1991 **FM** *020 †18

MEIXEL, Steven Alan. 1111 S SAINT LOUIS AVE, OU PHYSICIANS FAMILY MEDIC 74120 #047-05-1975 L2000 **FM** *020 †18

MELICHAR, Lucinda Anne F. 1515 N HARVARD AVE, STE C 74115 #019-02-1968 L1970 **GP** *075

MELICHAR, Robert Melo. 1923 S UTICA AVE 74104 #019-02-1970 L1977 **GS** *020 †85

MELTON, Edward G. 4502 E 41ST ST, PSYCHIATRY CLINIC 74135 #039-01-2004 L2006 **P** *012

MERCER, Melville Metcalfe. 6839 S CANTON AVE, ANESTHESIOLOGISTS INC 74136 #039-01-1986 L1987 **AN** *020 †05 ‡

MERIFIELD, David Oswald. 9912 E 21ST ST 74129 #025-07-1957 L1964 **OTO** *072 †45

MERRIMAN, John Edward. 2325 S HARVARD AVE STE 308 74114 #065-05-1947 L1976 **PME CD** *020

MEYERS, Scott William. 1440 TERRACE DR 74104 #039-01-1994 L1995 **D** *020 †15

MEYROWITZ, David Michael. 2325 S HARVARD AVE, STE 603 74114 #062-01-1975 L1994 **IM** *020 †20

MIHELICH, Thomas Danl. 1245 S UTICA AVE 74104 #039-01-1981 L1982 **IM** *020 †20

MILLAR, James Stuart. 1111 S SAINT LOUIS AVE 74120 #039-01-1978 L1979 **FM MDM** *020 †18

MILLER, Archibald Sanford. 6585 S YALE AVE STE 315, WILLIAM MEDICAL BUILDING 74136 #048-02-1980 L1985 **PS FPS** *020 †65

MILLER, Bernadette Maria. ■ 74105 #039-01-2005 L2007 **IM** *012

MILLER, Dan Eugene. 2929 S GARNETT RD, TULSA EMER MED CTR 74129 #039-01-1969 L1971 **EM OM** *071

MILLER, Floyd Freeman. ■ 74135 #039-01-1956 L1956 **AI IM** *071 †20,03 ‡

MILLER, George Lance. 1705 E 19TH ST, STE 201 74104 #039-01-1964 L1964 **ON HEM** *020 †20

MILLER, George Steven. 1145 S UTICA AVE, STE 202 74104 #048-02-1975 L1984 **CHN PD** *020 †55,75

MILLER, Gerald Chas. 1923 S UTICA AVE 74104 #030-05-1964 L1964 **GS** *071 †85

MILLER, Jack Milton. 1145 S UTICA AVE STE 60, DEPARTMENT OF OB/GYN 74104 #016-11-1968 L2002 **OBG AM** *020 †30

MILLER, Jack Steven. 10901 E 48TH ST 74146 #039-01-1977 L1978 **U** *020 †95

MILLER, Loren Valmore. 2840 E 51ST ST STE 210 74105 #036-07-1947 L1954 **PD** *020 †55

MILLER, Oren Francis, III. 10901 E 48TH ST 74146 #028-34-1991 L2004 **UP PHP** *020 †95

MILLER, Robert E. 1802 E 19TH ST, ST JOHN KRAVIS BUILDING 74104 #046-01-2006 L2008 **GS** *012

MILLS, Miriam V. 3401 E 21ST ST 74114 #048-04-1974 L1979 **PD OMM** *020 †55

MILSTEN, Marc Steven. 10901 E 48TH ST 74146 #039-01-1989 L1994 **U** *020 †95 ‡

MILTON, Mark Allen. 1923 E 21ST ST, HEART CENTER OF TULSA 74114 #048-02-1997 L2004 **ICE** *020 †20

MIN, Wonhong David. 6767 S YALE AVE, STE A 74136 #039-01-1994 L1996 **NS** *020 †25

MINIELLY, John Andrew. 1923 S UTICA AVE 74104 #065-06-1962 L1980 **PTH NEP** *071 †50

MINOR, David Blake. 1516 S YORKTOWN PL 74104 #048-12-1980 L1984 **D** *020 †15

MINOR, Dwane Blake. ■ 74135 #039-01-1954 L1954 **D** *071 †15

MIRANDA, Ricardo. 1923 S UTICA AVE, NCIU 7E 74104 #649-33-1979 L1988 **NPM PD** *020 †55

MITCHELL, David Ray. 10109 E 79TH ST 74133 #039-01-1983 L1995 **P** *020 †75

MITCHELL, Franklin Louis. 1725 E 19TH ST, SURGERY, INC 74104 #023-07-1955 L1955 **GS TS** *030 †85,90

MITCHELL, Gregory Lynn. 1515 N HARVARD AVE 74115 #039-01-1986 L1987 **EM FM** *020 †18

MITCHELL, Jeffrey Raymond. 6655 S YALE AVE 74136 #023-01-1971 L1998 **CHP** *030 †75

MITCHELL, Karen Michele. 1809 E 13TH ST STE 400 74104 #010-02-1996 L2007 **CRS** *020 †85,10

MITCHELL, Ord Jehu. 5533 E 107TH PL 74137 #004-01-1970 L1974 **N** *071

MITCHELL, Robert Edward. 1725 E 19TH ST, SPECIALIST 74104 #039-01-2002 L2005 **GS** *020

MITTAL, Yogesh. 1809 E 13TH ST, THE ORTHOPAEDIC CENTER 74104 #048-12-1998 L2004 **ORS** *020 †40

MIZELL, James Cagle. 6964 S 69TH EAST AVE 74133 #047-06-1972 L1973 **IM** *020 †20

MOCNIK, Jack Johnny, Jr. 4720 S HARVARD AVE, STE 102 74135 #019-02-1975 L1983 **R** *062 †80

MOFFITT, Melba Jean. ■ 74112 #019-02-1985 L1986 **FM** *075 †18

MOLNAR, Gabriella E. ■ 74105 #473-01-1950 L1959 **PM** *071 †60

MONCADA, Franz. 6465 S YALE AVE STE 408 74136 #176-01-1970 L1976 **PD NPM** *020 †55

MONROE, Calvin Peitrei. 1334 N LANSING AVE, MORTON COMP HLTH 74106 #016-11-2001 L2005 **OBG** *020

MOORAD, Nicholas Eid. 9322 E 41ST ST, VA OUTPATIENT CLINIC 74145 #039-01-1968 L1972 **IM** *020

MOORE, Charles Strand. 1717A S UTICA AVE 74104 #012-05-2003 L2004 **FM** *100 †18

MOORE, Douglas Roger. 1623 S UTICA AVE 74104 #004-01-1972 L1973 **EM** *020 †16

MOORE, Joseph Michael. ■ 74137 #039-01-2003 L2004 **MPD** *100 †20,55

MOORE-FARRELL, Laura G. 4500 S GARNETT RD, STE 300 74146 #048-14-1989 L1994 **DR** *020 †80

MORGAN, Anne Kristen. 6565 S YALE AVE, STE 704 74136 #039-01-1988 L1992 **PD** *020 †55

MORGAN, Debra Lynn. 8803 S 101ST EAST AVE, STE 260 74133 #039-01-1979 L1980 **AN** *020 †05

MORGAN, Harley Bascom. 8803 S 101ST EAST AVE, STE 115 74133 #005-12-1977 L1990 **CHN** *020 †55,75

MORGAN, Rocky Max. 1725 E 19TH ST, STE 800 74104 #039-01-1988 L1990 **GS** *020 †85

MORREL, Dana Ramsey. 9425 S MINGO RD 74133 #039-01-1991 L1992 **IM** *020 †20

MORRIS, Dennis Wayne. 6839 S CANTON AVE, ANESTHESIOLOGISTS INC 74136 #039-01-1982 L1983 **AN** *020 †05 ‡

MORRIS, Edward Jos. 10505 E 91ST ST, STE 150 74133 #038-06-1987 L1993 **CD IM** *020 †20

MORRIS, Lonnie Fay. 720 W 7TH ST 74127 #028-03-1978 L1979 **P CHP** *020

MORROW, Gay. ■ 74114 #010-01-1947 L1948 **P AN** *020 †05

MORSE, Robert Michael. 1111 S SAINT LOUIS AVE 74120 #016-11-1969 L2000 **FM PHP** *040 †18 ‡

MORTON, Robert Cameron. 1120 S UTICA AVE, 4W-4502 74104 #041-13-1960 L1968 **AN** *071 †05

MOSEMAN, Scott Edward. 8662 E 101ST PL 74133 #048-16-1999 L2004 **P** *020 †75

MOULT, Robert Gene. 3010 S HARVARD AVE, STE 220 74114 #048-78-1986, ▲ L2000 **DR** *020

MOVVA, Venkatesh. 6565 S YALE AVE STE 212, THE PAIN AND SPORTS CENTER 74136 #495-50-1989 L1998 **IM** *020 †20

MOWRY, John Dean. 1919 S WHEELING AVE, STE 302 74104 #030-05-1977 L1982 **OTO** *020 †45

MUCKALA, Kenneth Arthur. 2325 S HARVARD AVE STE 108, HARVARD FAMILY PHYS PC 74114 #026-04-1967 L1987 **FM FPG** *020 †18

MULHOLLAND, J Andrew. 1145 S UTICA AVE STE 262 74104 #039-01-1964 L1964 **OBG** *071 †30

MURPHY, Arthur Jos, III. 6565 S YALE AVE STE 902, MURPHY MEDICINE PC 74136 #016-06-1973 L1978 **ORS** *020 †40

MURPHY, Linda Brittenham. 6565 S YALE AVE, STE 902 74136 #039-01-1977 L1978 **PD** *020 †55

MURPHY, Nancy Ann. 2808 S SHERIDAN RD, UNIV OF OK COLL OF MED-TUL 74129 #039-79-2006, ▲ L2007 **P** *012

MURPHY, Patrick Lee. 10125 S SHERIDAN RD, VILLAGE SOUTH STE G 74133 #039-01-1981 L2003 **FM** *020 †18

MURR, Indira Marie. 1717A S UTICA AVE, MAGNUM HEALTHCARE, INC. 74104 #048-04-2002 L2005 **EM** *020 †16

MURRAY, Debra Louise. 6565 S YALE AVE, INTER ID INC 74136 #026-04-1997 L2004 **ID** *020 †20

MURRAY, James Andrew. 6465 S YALE AVE STE 101 74136 #028-34-1962 L1970 **A** *020 †55,03

MURRELL, Steven Samuel. 2808 S SHERIDAN RD, DEPT FM 74129 #661-02-2007 L2007 **FP** *012

MUTHALALY, Bobby Koshy. 1923 E 21ST ST STE 101 74114 #495-37-1985 L1998 **NEP IM** *020 †20

MUTZIG, Elizabeth Montez. 1717 S UTICA AVE, BLDG B 74104 #039-01-1988 L1989 **IM** *020 †20

MYERS, Adam Lees. 8803 S 101ST EAST AVE, STE 230 74133 #021-06-1996 L1997 **FM** *020 †18

MYERS, Jennifer L. 5033 E 84TH ST 74137 #039-01-1981 L1982 **FM** *071 †18

MYERS, Rodney Lee. 1245 S UTICA AVE 74104 #039-01-1983 L1984 **N** *020 †75

NAHAR, Jane. 2815 S SHERIDAN RD, ADULT MEDICINE CLINIC 74129 #496-49-2002 L2006 **IM** *020 †20

NAHAR, Julie. ■ 74136 #496-49-2005 L2006 **IM** *012

NAHRA, Marsha Ann. 6600 S YALE AVE, STE 650 74136 #055-01-1997 L1999 **OBG** *020 †30

NAIMEH, Laudy George. 9311 S MINGO RD 74133 #605-01-1989 L2000 **AI** *020 †03,55

NAIR, Baishali. 1145 S UTICA AVE, STE 1105 74104 #913-07-1996 L2004 **IM** *020 †20

NASEER, Shazli. 1111 S SAINT LOUIS AVE, OU FAMILY MEDICINE 74120 #704-02-1996 L2005 **FM** *100 †18

NAYLOR, Mark Franklin. 1705 E 19TH ST, STE 502 74104 #048-15-1981 L1992 **D IM** *050 †20,15

NEAL, James Hal, Jr. ■ 74133 #039-01-1943 L1946 **GS** *071 †85

NEAL, Royden Wayne. 1923 E 21ST ST, HEART CENTER OF TULSA INC 74114 #028-02-1958 L1967 **CD IM** *071 †20

NEAL, Victor Ray. 6839 S CANTON AVE 74136 #039-01-1957 L1957 **AN** *071 †05

NEBERGALL, Robert Wm. 802 S JACKSON AVE, TULSA ORTHOPEDIC SURGEONS 74127 #018-75-1981, ▲ L1982 **ORS** *020

NEEL, James David. ■ 74135 #039-01-2008 *012

NEEL, James Harrison. ■ 74105 #039-01-2007 L2007 **GS** *012

NELSON, Robert Andrew. ■ 74136 #019-02-1948 L1955 **IM** *071

NELSON, Robert Howard. 8803 S 101ST EAST AVE, STE 110 74133 #039-01-1973 L1979 **OTO A** *020 †45

NEMEC, James Jos. 1265 S UTICA AVE, STE 300 74104 #030-06-1984 L1994 **CD IM** *020 †20

NESBIT, William Hugh. 1111 S SAINT LOUIS AVE, DEPT OF FAM PRACTICE 74120 #036-01-2006 L2008 **NS** *012

NETTLES, John Barnwell. 1145 S UTICA AVE STE 600, UNIV OF OK TULSA 74104 #045-01-1944 L1969 **OBG** *020 †30

NEVINNY-STICKEL, Hans B. 10109 E 79TH ST 74133 #154-02-1951 L1990 **ON IM** *071

NEWELL, Sara Lee. 6160 S YALE AVE, SPRINGER CLINIC, INC 74136 #018-03-1975 L1982 **RHU IM** *020 †20

NEWNAM, Michael B. 2325 S HARVARD AVE, STE 208 74114 #039-01-1994 L2001 **FM** *020 †18

NGO, Loc Kim. 2929 S GARNETT RD 74129 #039-01-1997 L2000 **EM** *020 †16

NGUYEN, Hai Long. 1611 S UTICA AVE, # 414 74104 #039-01-2003 L2005 **IM** *020 †20

NGUYEN, Hoang Dung Nhu. 1111 S SAINT LOUIS AVE 74120 #942-01-1991 L2007 **FP** *012

NGUYEN, Mykhanh Connie. 9320 S MINGO RD 74133 #005-14-1990 L2007 **RO** *020 †80

NIBLETT, Randy Lee. 4111 S DARLINGTON AVE #700, TULSA RADIOLOGY ASSOC 74135 #048-02-2000 L2005 **DR** *020 †80

NICHOLSON, Joseph M. 8801 S 101ST EAST AVE 74133 #039-79-1990, ▲ L1993 **FM** *030 †18
NICKEL, Timothy Joseph. 1727 S UTICA AVE 74104 #019-02-1998 L2004 **IM AI** *020 †20,03
NIERENBERG, David Marc. 1725 E 19TH ST, STE 501 74104 #039-01-1985 L1986 **IM** *020 †20
NIGAM, Rupesh. 2808 S SHERIDAN RD 74129 #495-73-1997 **IM** *100
NIGHTENGALE, Markham Lee. 6465 S YALE AVE, STE 1002 74136 #039-01-1988 L1993 **GE** *020 †20 ‡
NILSON, Arthur C. 10011 S YALE AVE, STE 100 74137 #039-79-1990, ▲ L1995 **OBG** *020 †30
NOLAND, Stacy L. 1919 S WHEELING AVE, STE 500 74104 #039-79-2003, ▲ L2004 **OBG** *020
NONWEILER, Edward Oscar. 6465 S YALE AVE, OKLAHOMA, INC, SUITE 704 74136 #048-04-1957 L1962 **U** *071 †95
NORRIS, Brent Lane. 6565 S YALE AVE STE 910, TRAUMA SPECIALISTS, PC 74136 #012-01-1989 L2006 **OTR ORS** *020 †40
NORTH, Phoenix Senna. 7600 S LEWIS AVE 74136 #040-02-2004 L2005 **FM** *020 †18
NOSSAMAN, Brent C. 4415 S HARVARD AVE, STE 100 74135 #039-79-1991, ▲ L1992 **ORS** *020
NUNLEY, Caleb Andrew. ■ 74133 #039-01-2007 L2007 **FP** *012
NUNN, Thomas V. 4564 S HARVARD AVE, STE B 74135 #039-79-1981, ▲ L1982 **OTO SME** *020
OCHOA, Daniela Alessandra. 1802 E 19TH ST 74104 #048-16-2005 L2007 **GS** *012
OCHOA LOPEZ, Jesus Maria. 7600 S LEWIS AVE, FAMILY MEDICAL CARE 74136 #847-17-1994 L2006 **FM** *100 †18
OCONNELL, Margaret Payton. ■ 74105 #039-01-2008 *012
O'DELL, Jennifer Faye. 1145 S UTICA AVE, STE 367 74104 #039-01-1994 L1995 **PTH** *020
OGLESBEE, Lana Hart. 6465 S YALE AVE, STE 615 74136 #039-01-1988 L1989 **OBG** *020 †30
OGLESBY, Aletha Cress. 9245 S MINGO RD, UTICA PARK CLINIC 74133 #039-01-1978 L1979 **FM GPM** *020 †18
O'HARE, Brady James. 4502 E 41ST ST, DEPT OF SURGERY 74135 #030-05-2003 L2004 **GS** *012
O'HERN, Dustin Lee. ■ 74129 #039-01-2008 *012
OKADA, Robert Dean. 6151 S YALE AVE STE 304, WARREN CLINICS 74136 #041-01-1973 L1985 **CD** *020 †20
OKWUASABA, Peter Azuka. 8803 S 101ST EAST AVE, STE 350 74133 #690-06-1986 L2006 **ID** *020 †20
OLIVE, Suzanne Renee. 1725 E 19TH ST STE 200 74104 #021-01-1980 L1989 **PUD AI** *020 †20,03
OLSEN, Mark Roger. 6475 S YALE AVE, STE 201 74136 #056-05-1992 L1998 **ON** *020 †20
OLSON, Christopher Parks. 1923 S UTICA AVE 74104 #039-01-1977 L1978 **EM** *020 †16
OLSON, Darwin Dee. 2325 S HARVARD AVE, STE 108 74114 #308-07-1981 L1983 **FM EM** *020 †18
O'MEILIA, William J. ■ 74136 #028-34-1946 L1950 **IM CD** *071 †20
OWENS, Dion La Point. 6262 S SHERIDAN RD, SHADOW MOUNTAIN BEHAVIORAL 74133 #033-06-2000 L2006 **CHP** *020 †75
OWENS, Lisa. 1120 S UTICA AVE, NEWBORN SPECIALISTS OF 74104 #039-79-1989, ▲ L1990 **NPM PD** *020 †55
PADMANABHAN, Sailatha. 1145 S UTICA AVE, STE 1105 74104 #496-39-2000 L2004 **IM** *020 †20
PAGEL, Warren W. 1611 S UTICA AVE, PMB 217 74104 #010-02-1975 L1978 **AN** *020
PALEPU, Pavan Narayana. ■ 74137 #104-01-2006 L2007 **FPP** *012
PALESANO, Richard Lewis. 1919 S WHEELING AVE, STE 302 74104 #039-01-1988 L1989 **OTO** *020 †45
PALMER, James Owen. 1923 S UTICA AVE 74104 #047-05-1981 L1989 **ATP** *020 †50
PALMERI, Joseph Matthew. ■ 74134 #039-01-2008 *012
PALOMINO, Victor R. 1809 E 13TH ST, THE ORTHOPAEDIC CENTER 74104 #025-76-1998, ▲ L2004 **OSM** *020
PANICKER, Ritwick. 9320 S MINGO RD, SOUTH TULSA CANCER CTR 74133 #495-27-1982 L1999 **ON HEM** *020 †20
PARHAM, Daran Lane. 1919 S WHEELING AVE, STE 500 74104 #039-01-1994 L1995 **OBG** *020
PASCUCCI, Daniel Ian. ■ 74105 #039-01-2007 L2007 **IM** *012
PASRICHA, Alok Pratap. 1245 S UTICA AVE 74104 #495-30-1995 L2005 **N** *020
PASRICHA, Alpana Java. 802 S JACKSON AVE, TULSA INC 74127 #496-07-1994 L2003 **NEP** *100 †20
PATEL, Jayen Harshad. 2000 S WHEELING AVE, BELLEVUE HOSPTIAL CENTER 74104 #024-05-2002 L2007 **AN** *100 †05
PATEL, Nicole Marie. 7322 E 91ST ST, TULSA SURGICAL ARTS 74133 #016-01-2002 L2007 **GS** *100 †85
PAUDEL, Nishant. 4502 E 41ST ST, FAMILY PRACTICE 74135 #672-05-2002 L2007 **FP** *012
PAUL, Eric Michael. 4502 E 41ST ST, OUHSC DEPT OF SURGERY 74135 #004-01-2004 L2006 **GS** *012
PAUL, Robert Elwood. 6717 S YALE AVE STE 107 74136 #039-01-1988 L1989 **FM** *020
PAUL, Roger Ray. ■ 74137 #039-01-1957 L1957 **IM** *071 ‡
PAULSEN, Robert Allan. 1919 S WHEELING AVE #LL100, OMNI FAMILY PHYSICIANS 74104 #039-05-1988 L1989 **FM** *020 †18
PAULSEN, Stephen Murray. 6585 S YALE AVE, STE 1020 74136 #039-01-1994 L1995 **PS** *020 †85,65
PELEG, Ika I. 4444 E 41ST ST, UNIV OF IOWA HOSP & CLINIC 74135 #409-23-1982 L2007 **GE** *020 †20
PELZL, Jon T. 4502 E 41ST ST 74135 #048-12-2005 L2006 **GS** *012
PENDELL, Geo Mumford, III. 9001 S 101ST EAST AVE 74133 #039-01-1991 L1992 **FM** *020 †18
PENTECOST, Diane Lynn. 1923 S UTICA AVE, PHYSICIANS 74104 #039-01-1986 L1987 **AN** *020 †05
PERONA, John Lee, Jr. ■ 74137 #039-01-2007 L2007 **IM** *012
PERRYMAN, Philip Ward. 4502 E 41ST ST, DEPARTMENT OF INTERNAL MED 74135 #039-01-1972 L1973 **IM** *020 †20
PERRYMAN, Robert G. 1923 S UTICA AVE 74104 #039-01-1946 L1947 **GS** *071 †85
PESCHKE, Lars Alexander. 7600 S LEWIS AVE 74136 #409-36-1999 L2002 **FM** *020 †18
PETCULESCU, Pia R. ■ 74119 #781-01-1952 L1977 **P** *071
PETERS, Myra A. ■ 74114 #001-02-1949 L1950 **ORS** *071 †40
PETERS, Walter James, Jr. 8131 S MEMORIAL DR, STE 106 74133 #039-01-1996 L1997 **OPH** *020 †35
PETERSON, Carl Ronald. 1801 E 71ST ST 74136 #049-01-1960 L1982 **P OS** *071 †75
PETTIGROVE, Bruce B, II. 6606 S YALE AVE STE 220 74136 #039-01-1980 L1981 **OPH** *020 †35
PETTY, Norman Charles. ■ 74136 #028-03-2000 L2007 **FM** *020 †18
PFEIFER, Donald Richard. ■ 74105 #039-01-1959 L1959 **PD** *072 †55
PHAM, Angie Khuevi. ■ 74137 #039-01-2004 L2005 **PTH** *012
PHELPS, Willis Franklin. 6600 S YALE AVE, STE 1000 74136 #039-01-1963 L1963 **FM MDM** *071 †18 ‡
PHILLIPS, John Wm, Jr. 1725 E 19TH ST, STE 800 74104 #004-01-1967 L1974 **GS** *020 †85
PHILLIPS, Kenneth Edward. 2929 S GARNETT RD 74129 #039-79-2000, ▲ L2001 **FM** *020
PHILLIPS, Preston John. 6465 S YALE AVE STE 304 74136 #024-01-1990 L2005 **ORS** *020 †40
PHOENIX, James Timothy. 1919 S WHEELING AVE, STE 200 74104 #039-01-2004 L2006 **IM** *020 †20
PIERATT, Michelle Mabel. 1120 S UTICA AVE 74104 #305-01-1996 L1998 **AN** *020 †05
PIERRE, Harold Luco. 1145 S UTICA AVE, STE 110 74104 #045-01-1999 L2003 **AN** *020 †05
PINSON, Robert Thomas. 6161 S YALE AVE 74136 #039-79-1987, ▲ L1988 **EM PEM** *020 †16
PIPER, Kenneth Walter. 6475 S YALE AVE, STE 410 74136 #056-05-1969 L1976 **IM** *020 †20
PISARIK, Paul. 1111 S SAINT LOUIS AVE, UNIVERSITY OF OKLAHOMA 74120 #016-11-1981 L2006 **FM** *020 †18
PITTMAN, Gregory Ross. 1809 E 13TH ST, STE 400 74104 #039-01-1985 L1986 **GS OS** *020 †85
PITTS, Ryan A. 1111 S SAINT LOUIS AVE, OU PHYSICIANS FAMILY MEDIC 74120 #016-76-2001, ▲ L2002 **FM** *020 †18
PLACE, Christopher Lee. 7600 S LEWIS AVE, FAMILY MEDICAL CARE OF TUL 74136 #021-06-1995 L1996 **FM** *020 †18
PLASTER, Rodney Lynn. 6475 S YALE AVE STE 301, EASTERN OK ORTHO CTR 74136 #039-01-1980 L1986 **ORS EM** *020 †40
PLOST, Gerald Neal. 1725 E 19TH ST STE 200 74104 #039-01-1979 L1984 **PUD CCM** *020 †20 ‡
PLUNKET, Daniel C. 2815 S SHERIDAN RD, OU PHYSICIANS PEDIATRIC CL 74129 #012-05-1952 L1975 **PD PHO** *071 †55 ‡
POHL, David Leon. 8801 S 101ST EAST AVE, SOUTHCREST ANESTHESIA GROU 74133 #007-02-2000 L2004 **AN** *100 †05
POLIN, Gerald Mark. 6655 S YALE AVE 74136 #041-02-1961 L1988 **P** *071 †75
POLLAK, Charity Ann. 1245 S UTICA AVE STE 130 74104 #039-01-2001 L2002 **PD** *020 †55
POTTS, David Wm. 1923 S UTICA AVE 74104 #039-01-1975 L1976 **IM PTH** *020 †50,20
POWEL, Virginia A. 6161 S YALE AVE, PICU 74136 #023-01-1992 L1999 **CCP** *020 †55
POWELL, Charles Clayton. 7600 S LEWIS AVE 74136 #039-05-1985 L2004 **FM** *020 †18
POWELL, Curtis Ryan. 10901 E 48TH ST, UROLOGIC SPECIALISTS OF OK 74146 #023-12-1991 L2003 **U** *020 †95 ‡
POWELL, Terry Douglas. 6161 S YALE AVE 74136 #019-02-1968 L1969 **RO** *020 †80 ‡
POWERS, Matthew Geo. 1923 S UTICA AVE 74104 #048-04-1973 L1980 **R OS** *020 †80
PRABHALA, Anuradha. 6160 S YALE AVE 74136 #495-01-1989 L2003 **IM** *020 †20
PRITCHARD, Charles R. 10901 E 48TH ST 74146 #004-01-2002 L2007 **U** *020
PROPES, Katherine L. 6655 S YALE AVE, LAUREATE PSYCHIATRIC CLINI 74136 #030-06-2001 L2005 **P** *020 †75
PROTHRO, George Wm. ■ 74145 #028-02-1945 L1968 **PHP FM** *072
PROUGH, Stanley Gene. 115 E 15TH ST 74119 #039-01-1976 L1977 **REN GYN** *020 †30
PUCKETT, Jerry Hanson. 6160 S YALE AVE, 3RD FL 74136 #004-01-1975 L1979 **OTO HNS** *020 †45
PUCKETT, Ladonna Carole. 6160 S YALE AVE 3RD FL, SPRINGER CLINIC, INC 74136 #039-01-1999 L2000 **PD** *020 †55
PUE, Wayne Harold. 8414 E 101ST ST 74133 #039-01-1973 L1974 **IM** *020 †20
PULS, Christopher M. 4502 E 41ST ST 74135 #028-34-1996 L2005 **CHP** *020 †75
PURSER, Jane Theotokatos. 9311 S MINGO RD 74133 #007-02-1987 L1993 **AI IM** *020 †20,03
PYLE, Vanlinh P. 1145 S UTICA AVE STE 1105, ADULT MEDICINE CLINIC 74104 #048-15-2004 L2005 **IM** *020 †20
QUADEER, Naveed Abdul. ■ 74136 #039-01-2008 *012
QUAY, Jennifer Beth. ■ 74133 #039-01-2005 L2007 **IM** *012
RABE, Frank Edward. 4500 S GARNETT RD STE 919, TULSA X-RAY LAB, INC 74146 #038-40-1977 L1997 **DR** *020 †80
RAE, Alton W. 3218 S 79TH EAST AVE 74145 #048-02-1995 L1997 **FM** *020 †18
RAGHURAMAN, Vasudevan U. 1919 S WHEELING AVE, BERNSEN BLDG 74104 #495-31-1981 L2006 **GE IM** *020 †20
RAHHAL, Scott Edward. 6475 S YALE AVE STE 301, EASTERN OKLAHOMA ORTHOPEDI 74136 #039-01-1989 L1990 **OSM** *020 †40
RAINE, Randall C. 6600 S YALE AVE, STE 800 74136 #039-79-1996, ▲ L1997 **IM** *020 †20
RAINES, Richard Dean. 1923 E 21ST ST 74114 #028-03-1966 L1974 **CD IM** *020 †20
RALEY, David Brian. 7779 E 106TH ST 74133 #039-01-1995 L1998 **PD** *020 †55
RAMEY, Jeri Lynn. 6839 S CANTON AVE, ANESTHESIOLOGISTS INC 74136 #039-01-1997 L1998 **AN** *020 †05 ‡
RAMEY, Palmer Ryburn, Jr. 6585 S YALE AVE, STE 1020 74136 #039-01-1971 L1972 **PS GS** *020 †85,65
RAMOS, Oscar De Leon. ■ 74128 #748-01-1956 L1977 *020
RANDLE, Jack Edward. ■ 74137 #019-02-1954 L1976 **OM GP** *071
RANNE, Richard Douglas. 10515 S 71ST EAST AVE 74133 #003-01-1977 L1989 **PCS PDS** *020 †90,85
RAO, Janhavi S. 9425 S MINGO RD 74133 #048-04-1997 L2001 **MPD** *020 †20,55
RAO, Madhusudan Gujar. 1145 S UTICA AVE STE 367, TULSA DIAGNOSTIC INC 74104 #495-98-1986 L2002 **PTH PHP** *020 †50
RAO, Peter Alan. 5544 S LEWIS AVE, STE 600 74105 #041-01-1989 L2004 **P** *020 †75
RAO, Rohini Seshappa. 4502 E 41ST ST, DEPARTMENT OF SURGERY 74135 #048-04-1999 L2002 **GS** *020
RAPACKI, Thomas Francis. 1919 S WHEELING AVE, STE 504 74104 #023-12-1989 L2006 **NS** *020 †25
RAPTOU, Alexander D. 6585 S YALE AVE, STE 500 EASTERN OKLAHOMA O 74136 #038-40-1960 L1972 **PM** *071 †60
RATLIFF, Gregory Earl. 2107 E 15TH ST 74104 #039-01-1984 L1985 **PS** *020 †65
RAY, Arlis G. 5640 S MEMORIAL DR 74145 #039-01-1976 L1977 **GP EM** *020
RAZDAN, Tito Aurobindo. 6160 S YALE AVE 74136 #048-15-1993 L1994 **IM** *020 †20
REAGAN, William Paul. ■ 74133 #023-07-1955 L1998 **FM IMG** *071 †70,18
REANTASO, Antonio Apostol. 4502 E 41ST ST 74135 #748-01-1992 L2000 **P** *020 †75
REBURN, Michael Anthony. 4500 S GARNETT RD STE 9 74146 #030-06-1990 L1995 **DR** *020 †80
REDDEN, Larry Leigh. 6151 S YALE AVE STE 400, CARDIOLOGY OF TULSA, INC 74136 #021-01-1977 L1980 **EM HOS** *020 †16
REDDY, Srikanth K. 8803 S 101ST EAST AVE # 2 74133 #495-16-1986 L1998 **PM** *020 †60
REED, Lawrence Alexander. 3606 N CINCINNATI AVE 74106 #010-03-1960 L1961 **IM GS** *071
REESE, Joe Lyndle. 6585 S YALE AVE STE 1150 74136 #039-01-1983 L1984 **IM EM** *020 †20
REID, William Richard. 1705 E 19TH ST STE 510 74104 #039-01-1955 L1956 **P** *020
REINKING, Richard A. 3910 E 51ST ST 74135 #039-01-1979 L1980 **FM** *020 †18
REINOSO, Luis Alberto. ■ 74135 #737-01-1957 L1966 **GP P** *071
REINOSO PEREZ, Blas Enriq. 4502 E 41ST ST, FAMILY PRACTICE 74135 #308-04-2001 **IM** *012
REINSTEIN, Ned Mark. 7171 S YALE AVE STE 101 74136 #035-08-1966 L1973 **OPH** *020 †35
REVELIS, Andreas Frank. 2000 S WHEELING AVE # 600 74104 #039-01-1996 L2000 **APM** *020
REYNOLDS, Freddie Albert. ■ 74145 #039-01-1962 L1962 **PHP** *071 †70
RHODES, Rollie Emer. 5020 E 68TH ST 74136 #020-02-1957 L1965 **OTO A** *020 †45

RIBAK, Brian. 1923 S UTICA AVE, PHYSICIANS 74104 #035-03-1970 L1977 **AN** *020 ‡

RIBAUDO, Lauralee Howe. 2000 S WHEELING AVE, STE 800 74104 #039-01-1999 L2003 **OBG** *020 †30

RICHTER, Ralph Walter. 1705 E 19TH ST STE 406, ST JOHN JOLLIMAN BLDG 74104 #035-01-1956 L1975 **N P** *020 †75

RICKNER, Thomas Wm. 6160 S YALE AVE 74136 #017-20-1973 L2003 **U** *020 †95

RICKS, Carole N. 3218 S 79TH EAST AVE 74145 #004-01-1971 L1993 **DR** *020 †20

RIPPY, Steven Todd. 4502 E 41ST ST, DEPARTMENT OF PEDIATRICS 74135 #422-01-2004 L2006 **PD** *020

RIVERO, Dennis Palmer. 6475 S YALE AVE STE 202, WARREN CLINIC ORTHOPEDIC 74136 #935-07-1981 L2006 **ORS** *020 †40

ROBARDS, Victor L, Jr. 10901 E 48TH ST 74146 #039-01-1961 L1961 **U** *071 †95

ROBERTSON, Lowell James. 6161 S YALE AVE 74136 #039-01-1989 L1990 **IM** *075

ROBINOWITZ, Bernard N. 6565 S YALE AVE STE 508 74136 #021-01-1970 L1974 **D** *020 †15

ROBINSON, Richard D. ■ 74134 #048-16-1988 L1989 **FM** *020 †18

ROBINSON, Richard Keith. ■ 74133 #019-01-1989 L1991 **IM RHU** *020 †20

ROCKLIN, Marc Stephen. 4735 E 91ST ST STE 200, TULSA COLON & RECTAL SURGE 74137 #023-01-1983 L1990 **CRS GS** *020 †85,10

RODERICK, Jana Nicole. ■ 74107 #016-76-2007, ▲ *012

RODGERS, James Allen. 6565 S YALE AVE, STE 709 74136 #039-01-1976 L1977 **NS OSS** *020 †25

RODGERS, Richard Warner. 1623 S UTICA AVE 74104 #039-01-1974 L1975 **EM** *020 †16

ROEMER, Howard. 1623 S UTICA AVE 74104 #035-08-1974 L1979 **EM** *020 †16,18 ‡

ROGERS, Sara Lynne. 1120 S UTICA AVE, 4W-4502 74104 #045-04-1994 L2001 **AN** *020 †05

ROJAS SANTAMARIA, Isabel. ■ 74133 #264-10-1994 L2007 **PD** *012

ROLLER, Don R. 4720 S HARVARD AVE STE 102, FAMILY CARE OF TULSA 74135 #039-01-1975 L1976 **FM** *020 †18

ROMAN, Divina Lucas. 1919 S WHEELING AVE, STE 200 74104 #748-10-1989 L1993 **IM PD** *020

ROMAN, Emmanuel Jesus. 10159 E 11TH ST STE 100, VA BEHAVIORAL MEDICINE CLI 74128 #748-10-1989 L1993 **P** *020

ROMAN, Lucilo Reyes. ■ 74133 #748-02-1955 L1971 **FM** *071 †18

ROMASANTA, Tara Marie. ■ 74104 #039-01-2008 *012

RONK, David Augustine. 5780 S PEORIA AVE 74105 #039-01-1971 L1972 **GYN OBS** *020 †30

RONK, James Frederick. 6465 S YALE AVE, STE 215 74136 #030-06-1989 L1993 **OPH OS** *020 †35 ‡

ROOKS, James Vernon. 1802 E 19TH ST, STE 301 74104 #039-01-1995 L1996 **IM** *020 †20

ROSE, Susan Anita. 1725 E 19TH ST 74104 #039-01-1983 L1984 **GS** *020 †85

ROSELL, Louis V. ■ 74132 #028-79-1945, ▲ L1945 **GP** *071

ROSS, James M. 8803 S 101ST EAST AVE, STE 230 & 245 74133 #048-15-1999 L2000 **FM** *020 †18

ROSS, William Bruce. 6151 S YALE AVE, STE 304 74136 #039-01-1975 L1982 **CD IM** *020 †20

ROTHENBACH, Thomas Alexan. 6151 S YALE AVE STE 305, PEDIATRIC SURGERY INC 74136 #042-12-1997 L2006 **PDS** *020 †85

ROUBEIN, Leor David. 6160 S YALE AVE 74136 #021-06-1980 L2004 **GE** *020 †20

ROWLAND, Mark D. 6565 S YALE AVE STE 812, INTER ID INC 74136 #039-01-1979 L1980 **ID IM** *020 †20

ROYCE, Michael Gordon. 6839 S CANTON AVE 74136 #039-01-2000 L2004 **AN** *020 †05

ROYE, John Andrew. 6151 S YALE AVE, STE 304 74136 #039-01-1971 L1972 **IM** *020

ROZSA, Tamerlane. 2738 E 51ST ST 74105 #039-01-1983 L1990 **PTH** *020

RUBIS, Brent Albert. 8803 S 101ST EAST AVE #270 74133 #028-34-1994 L2000 **PS HS** *020 †65

RUFFING, John Edwin. 3218 S 79TH EAST AVE 74145 #049-01-1977 L1978 **EM IM** *020 †16

RUIZ, Carmen. 2715 E 19TH ST, 1725 EAST 19TH STREET 74104 #024-01-1996 L2003 **CRS** *020 †85,10

RYAN, Karen Smallwood. 7820 E 15TH PL, RYAN OCCUPATIONAL MED. SRV 74112 #018-03-1985 L1993 **OM** *020 †70

RYKER, David E. 6565 S YALE AVE, STE 802 74136 #004-01-1967 L1970 **OBG FM** *020 ‡

RYLANDER, Edward Erk. 7600 S LEWIS AVE 74136 #039-05-1985 L1986 **FM PLM** *020 †18

SACRA, John Carl. 1417 N LANSING AVE, EMERGENCY MEDICAL SERVICES 74106 #039-01-1970 L1971 **EM IM** *040 †20,16

SADDORIS, Mary Louise. ■ 74132 #039-01-1965 L1965 **EM** *071

SAFA, Cynthia Shaklee. 3401 E 21ST ST 74104 #039-01-1985 L1986 **PD** *071 †55

SAFDAR, Zia-Ui-Haq M. ■ 74134 #704-21-1991 L1998 **AN** *020

SAINT, Richard Baker. 10901 E 48TH ST, 10901 E 48 ST S 74146 #017-20-1984 L1990 **U GS** *020 †95

SAIZOW, Ronald Barry. 4502 E 41ST ST, THE UNIVERSITY OF OKLAHOMA 74135 #039-01-1980 L1981 **IM** *040 †20

SAKIRGIL, Enis. 7600 S LEWIS AVE 74136 #902-07-1996 L2006 **FP** *012

SALAMY, Joseph. 4770 S HARVARD AVE, STE 200 74135 #039-01-1944 L1945 **FM OS** *071

SALIBA, Khalil Michel. 6655 S YALE AVE 74136 #605-01-1987 L2000 **P** *020 †75

SANDERS, Raymond Jos. 1120 S UTICA AVE, ARNOT OGDEN MEDICAL CENTER 74104 #033-06-1985 L2007 **NPM** *020 †55

SANDERS, Sherri Lynn. 4502 E 41ST ST 74135 #011-04-1997 L2000 **IM** *040 †20

SANDLER, David Abraham. 1265 S UTICA AVE, STE 300 74104 #010-02-1996 L2003 **CD** *020 †20

SANFORD, Wm Craig, IV. 1717A S UTICA AVE, ST JOHN URGENT CARE CLINIC 74104 #020-02-1976 L1981 **EM FM** *020 †16,18

SANGHVI, Purvi Jai. 4502 E 41ST ST 74135 #495-76-1996 L2006 **IM** *020

SAWHENY, Eva. ■ 74133 #473-04-2004 L2007 **IM** *012

SAWHENY, Nitin. ■ 74133 #473-04-2006 L2007 **IM** *012

SAWYER, William Perry, II. 8803 S 101ST EAST AVE, STE 110 74133 #039-01-1982 L1983 **OTO HNS** *020 †45

SAXON, Bruce Chas. 1923 S UTICA AVE, PHYSICIANS 74104 #039-01-1984 L1985 **AN** *020 †05

SAY, Mehmet Burhan. 4502 E 41ST ST 74135 #902-10-1946 L1978 **MG PD** *030 †55,19

SCARBROUGH, Catherine Pat. 7600 S LEWIS AVE 74136 #047-06-2005 L2007 **FP** *012

SCHECHTER, Ruben. 6161 S YALE AVE 74136 #132-01-1977 L1988 **NPM PD** *050 †55

SCHECK, David Nathan. 1120 S UTICA AVE, NEWBORN SPECIALISTS OF 74104 #011-03-1987 L1994 **ID IM** *020 †20

SCHELBAR, E Joe. 6585 S YALE AVE STE 1200 74104 #019-02-1975 L1980 **GP PYG** *020 †20

SCHIECHE, Christoph. ■ 74134 #408-30-1997 L2006 **IM** *012

SCHILLER, Thomas David. 6565 S YALE AVE, STE 1200 74136 #028-03-1978 L1983 **GE** *020 †20

SCHNETZER, George W, III. 6151 S YALE AVE, CANCER CARE ASSOCS 74136 #041-01-1964 L1972 **ON HEM** *071 †20

SCHNITKER, Jonathan C. 4111 S DARLINGTON AVE, STE 700 74135 #048-12-1987 L1995 **DR** *020 †80

SCHOEFFLER, Lee Earl. 7171 S YALE AVE 74136 #039-01-1970 L1971 **OPH N** *020 †35

SCHRAM, David Douglas. 1923 E 21ST ST, STE 101 74114 #039-01-1990 L1995 **NEP** *020 †20

SCHRUM, David I. ■ 74136 #036-05-1944 L1979 **PD** *071 †55

SCHUCHMAN, Abe. ■ 74145 #017-20-1947 L1947 **M** *075

SCHUMACHER, Shawn David. 1923 S UTICA AVE, PHYSICIANS 74104 #039-01-2000 L2001 **AN** *020 †05

SCHWARTZ, David Lewis. 2000 S WHEELING AVE, STE 401 74104 #041-12-1969 L1973 **OPH** *020 †35

SCHWARTZ, Stanley Newton. 6600 S YALE AVE STE 1200, 1 CLINIC TOWER 74136 #035-19-1971 L1977 **ID IM** *020 †20

SCOTT, Jane Scalet. 4520 S HARVARD AVE, STE 200 74135 #039-01-1988 L1994 **PD** *020 †55

SCOTT, John Edward. ■ 74137 #021-05-1944 L1953 **IM** *071

SCOTT, Martin Edward. 6160 S YALE AVE 1S, SPRINGER CLINIC, INC 74136 #041-02-1979 L1983 **IM** *020

SCOTT, Michael Greg. 550 S PEORIA AVE, RESOURCE CENTER 74120 #055-01-1992 L1993 **FM** *020 †18

SCOTT, Reginald Gene. 6839 S CANTON AVE, ANESTHESIOLOGISTS INC 74136 #039-01-1983 L1986 **AN** *020 †05 ‡

SCOTT, Richard Dean. 6600 S YALE AVE STE 850 74136 #039-01-1962 L1962 **FM** *020

SCOTT, Robert Lewis. 6161 S YALE AVE, ADMIN NORTH 74136 #023-07-1960 L1967 **END IM** *071 †20

SCOTT, Steve Cameron. 1923 E 21ST ST 74114 #039-01-1988 L1994 **CD IM** *020 †20

SEARCY, Robert Adrian. 4720 S HARVARD AVE, STE 100 74135 #039-01-1965 L1965 **IM CD** *071 †20

SEEFELDT, Gerald Mark. 9001 S 101ST EAST AVE, STE 270 74133 #039-01-1981 L1986 **FM** *020 †18

SEELY, Jennifer Lynn. ■ 74114 #039-01-1996 L2001 **GP P** *062

SEIDEL, Donald Richard. PO BOX 52588 74152 #019-02-1989 L1993 **D** *020 †15 ‡

SEIFERT, Richard Weber. 1145 S UTICA AVE STE 909 74104 #048-02-1976 L1977 **GE** *020

SEKHAR, Rajagopal V. 2815 S SHERIDAN RD, INTERNAL MEDICAL CLINIC 74129 #495-52-1993 L2001 **IM** *100 †20

SERRANO, Elka. 4502 E 41ST ST, UNIVERSITY OF OKLAHOMA 74135 #039-01-2005 L2006 **P** *012

SETH, Raman. 1503 SOUTHWEST BLVD, APT 15C 74107 #495-09-2001 L2006 **FP** *012

SETTER, Kenneth R. 2000 S WHEELING AVE # 300 74104 #019-02-1976 L1981 **FP** *020 †55

SEVIER, Billy Ray. 1705 E 19TH ST 74104 #004-01-1967 L1972 **IM END** *071 †20

SEXAUER, John Michael. 6151 S YALE AVE, CANCER CARE ASSOC 74136 #028-34-1965 L1973 **ON HO** *071 †20

SEXTER, Scott Howard. 3910 E 51ST ST, WARREN CLINIC 74135 #039-01-1987 L1988 **FM** *020 †18

SHAFFER, Rodney Glyn. 4111 S DARLINGTON AVE, STE 700 74135 #305-01-2000 L2006 **RNR** *020 †80

SHAH, Pat R. 8414 E 101ST ST 74133 #496-38-1973 L1981 **PD** *020 †55

SHANE, John Marder. 74114 #039-01-1967 L1969 **REN GYN** *071 †30

SHARMA, Bharat Bhushan. 4502 E 41ST ST 74135 #495-05-1974 L1981 **PDI PD** *020 †55

SHARMA, Chandini. 4502 E 41ST ST, COMANCHE CTY MED CLINIC 74135 #496-07-1991 L2006 **IMG** *020 †20

SHAUKAT, Muhammad Imran. 1334 N LANSING AVE 74106 #704-01-1995 L2004 **IM** *020

SHAW, Ronald Blane. 1705 E 19TH ST, STE 302 74104 #054-04-1978 L1979 **IM CD** *020 †20

SHEEHAN, William Ward. ■ 74120 #056-06-1964 L1981 **PTH HMP** *071 †50

SHEFFNER, Steven Elliott. 4111 S DARLINGTON AVE, RADIOLOGY CONSULTANTS OF 74135 #028-02-1979 L1991 **VIR DR** *020 †80

SHELLABARGER, Paul A. 1809 E 13TH ST STE 400 74104 #004-01-1972 L1973 **GS** *020 †85

SHENDRIK, Igor. 1923 S UTICA AVE 74104 #913-04-1986 L2004 **PTH** *020 †50

SHEPARD, Robert M, Jr. ■ 74132 #021-01-1941 L1942 **GS TS** *071 †85

SHEPHEARD, Russell Thos. 3242 E ADMIRAL PL, CARE FAMILY MEDICAL 74110 #039-01-1991 L1993 **EM** *020

SHERBURN, Eric Wallis. 6802 S OLYMPIA AVE, STE 300 74132 #039-01-1993 L2000 **NS** *020 †85

SHINKARENKO, Alexandr Dan. 7600 S LEWIS AVE, C/O JOHN MCVAY 74136 #913-29-2000 L2007 **FP** *012

SHINKARENKO, Irina Anatol. 7600 S LEWIS AVE, C/O JOHN MCVAY 74136 #913-29-1999 L2007 **FP** *012

SHIRKEY, Albert Lauck. ■ 74136 #048-04-1958 L1964 **TS CD** *071 †85,90

SHOLL, David Spencer. 2325 S HARVARD AVE, STE 108 74114 #039-01-1975 L1977 **FM** *020 †18

SHOUN, Shelley Dawn. 1145 S UTICA AVE STE 60 74104 #104-01-2004 L2006 **OBG** *012

SHRESTHA, Sagun. 10109 E 79TH ST, CANCER TREATMENT CTR 74133 #495-45-1990 L2005 **HO** *020 †20

SHRESTHA, Shravan K. 1802 E 19TH ST STE 400, ATTN WENDY DAVIS 74104 #160-02-1987 L1996 **IM** *020 †20

SHUNATONA, Baptiste B, III. 4720 S HARVARD AVE, STE 100 74135 #024-01-1985 L1986 **FM** *020 †18

SIBLEY, Leslie. 6585 S YALE AVE, STE 701 74104 #026-04-1994 L2000 **HO** *020 †20

SIDDIQUI, Ali. 1923 S UTICA AVE, NCIU 7E 74104 #495-56-1973 L1984 **NPM PD** *020 †55

SIDEMAN, Matthew Jay. 1725 E 19TH ST, SPECIALIST 74104 #048-13-1996 L2002 **VS GS** *020 †85

SIEGLER, David Jonathan. 6465 S YALE AVE, STE 320 74136 #048-12-1991 L1996 **CHN PD** *020 †75 ‡

SIEMENS, Christopher Ross. 6161 S YALE AVE 74136 #039-01-2000 L2004 **OTO PDO** *020 †45

SIEMENS, Roger Albert. 6465 S YALE AVE, STE 900 74136 #035-45-1969 L1976 **GS** *020 †85

SIEX, Neal W. 1923 S UTICA AVE, PHYSICIANS 74104 #039-79-1991, ▲ L1997 **AN** *020 †05

SIMCOE, Charles Wm. PO BOX 3348 74101 #039-01-1959 L1959 **OPH** *071 †35

SIMMONDS, Aba Marie. ■ 74133 #020-02-1987 L1992 **AN** *020 †15

SIMMONS, Larry Keith. 8110 S YALE AVE 74137 #039-79-1989, ▲ L1994 **N** *020

SIMON, Norman Morris. 1725 E 19TH ST STE 600 74104 #016-42-1969 L1977 **GE IM** *071 †20

SIMON, Parker Lee. 4502 E 41ST ST, OU DEPARTMENT OF PEDIATRIC 74135 #039-79-2003, ▲ L2004 **NPM** *012 †55

SIMONS, Nathan Trevor. 1111 S SAINT LOUIS AVE, OU PHYSICIANS FAMILY MEDIC 74120 #039-01-2005 L2007 **FP** *012

SINGH, Raymattie. 1717A S UTICA AVE, ST JOHN URGENT CARE CLINIC 74104 #913-09-1994 L2005 **FM** *100 †18

SINGLETARY, Thomas A. 4526 E 102ND ST, GUARDIAN ANESTHESIA SERVIC 74137 #048-02-1985 L1989 **AN** *020 †05 ‡

SISLER, Jerry. 1919 S WHEELING AVE, ORTHOPEDIC SURGERY CTR 74104 #028-02-1958 L1963 **ORS** *071 †40

SISLER, Kathleen Marie. 6585 S YALE AVE STE 200, CENTRAL STATE ORTHO SPEC 74136 #039-01-1991 L1992 **PM** *020 †60
SKIB, Robert Alan. 4026 S YORKTOWN PL 74105 #035-03-1978 L1996 **DR** *020 †80
SKONICKI, Jonathan Josef. 4502 E 41ST ST, COLLEGE OF MEDICINE 74135 #039-01-2005 L2006 **P** *012
SLAGLE, Richard Corbin. 10505 E 91ST ST, COR DIAGNOSTICS, LLC 74133 #039-01-1969 L1969 **CD** *020 †20
SLATER, James Chas. 4802 S 109TH EAST AVE 74146 #039-01-1986 L1987 **ORS OAR** *020 †40
SLOTHOUR, Edward Frank. 7600 S LEWIS AVE, FAMILY MEDICAL CARE OF TUL 74136 #041-13-1959 L1979 **FM** *020 †18 ‡
SLUSSER, Kimberly Ann. 9425 S MINGO RD 74133 #041-14-2001 L2004 **PD** *020 †55
SMALLWOOD, Sharon C. 1120 S UTICA AVE 74104 #039-01-1997 L1998 **FM** *020 †18
SMARINSKY, Richard Wm. 1923 S UTICA AVE, PHYSICIANS 74104 #039-01-1981 L1982 **AN** *020 †05
SMITH, Andrew William. ■ 74114 #039-01-2004 L2004 **AN** *012
SMITH, Hale Michael. 603 E PINE ST, MORTON CLINIC 74106 #010-02-1982 L1987 **IM** *020
SMITH, Henry Percy. 7419 E 67TH PL 74133 #039-01-1961 L1962 **FM** *071 †18
SMITH, John Herbert. ■ 74136 #039-01-1956 L1956 **HS ORS** *071 †40
SMITH, Kirk Michael. 9001 S 101ST EAST AVE, STE 300 74133 #018-03-1999 L2003 **FM** *040 †18
SMITH, Lanette Fay. 1120 S UTICA AVE, # G200 74104 #039-01-1994 L1995 **GS** *020 †85
SMITH, Michael Burwell. 10901 E 48TH ST 74146 #039-01-1967 L1967 **U** *020 †95
SMITH, Michael Scott. 3534 E 51ST ST 74135 #039-01-1998 L2001 **EM** *020 †16
SMITH, Nicole Autumn. 4502 E 41ST ST, UNIVERSITY OF OKLAHOMA COL 74135 #104-01-2004 L2006 **PD** *020 †55
SMITH, Rebecca Lynn. 1265 S UTICA AVE, STE 367 74104 #038-43-1994 L2002 **CD** *020
SMITH, Rex Neal. 5021 S FULTON AVE 74135 #038-06-1992 L1995 **CLP PTH** *020 †50
SMITH, Robert Louis, Jr. 9228 S MINGO RD STE 200, OKLAHOMA HEART INSTITUTE 74133 #039-01-2000 L2007 **IC** *020 †20
SMITH, Sarah Melissa. ■ 74135 #039-01-2008 *012
SMITH, Sean Lindsey. 1145 S UTICA AVE, STE 367 74104 #039-01-1994 L1999 **PTH** *020 †50
SMITH, Steven Alan. 9940 E 81ST ST 74133 #017-20-1979 L1985 **D IM** *020 †20,15
SMITH, Tracy Todd. 1919 S WHEELING AVE, STE 700 74104 #039-01-1994 L1995 **IM** *020 †20 ‡
SMITH, Vernon Thos. 6585 S YALE AVE, STE 1200 74136 #048-12-1981 L1982 **PUD IM** *020 †20
SNEDDEN, Jack Robin, III. 8803 S 101ST EAST AVE, STE 230 & 245 74133 #026-04-1997 L1999 **FM CCM** *020 †18
SNIDER, Gerald Albert. 4415 S HARVARD AVE, STE 204 74135 #039-01-1970 L1971 **FM EM** *075 †18
SNYDER, Diane Michel. 550 S PEORIA AVE, RESOURCE CENTER 74120 #039-01-1995 L1996 **MPD** *020 †55
SOKKAR, Hazem Hussein. 4833 S SHERIDAN RD, STE 408 74145 #915-04-1984 L1998 **P CHP** *020
SOLANO, Ambrose Anthony. 5906 E 31ST ST 74135 #007-02-1977 L1978 **IM EM** *020 †20
SOMMERS, Jack Milton. 218 W 6TH ST 74119 #039-01-1981 L1982 **FM MDM** *030 †18 ‡
SOOD, Alka Gupta. 10011 S YALE AVE, STE 200 74137 #048-14-1984 L1987 **PD ADL** *020 †55
SOOD, Sanjiv. 10011 S YALE AVE, STE 200 74137 #495-03-1980 L1989 **PD** *020 †55
SORIA, Manuel Elmido. 1801 E 7TH ST 74136 #748-01-1955 L1985 **P N** *071 †75
SORRELS, Christopher W. 6161 S YALE AVE 74136 #004-01-1999 L2003 **MPD** *020 †20,55
SOUS, Ziad. 1606 S ATLANTA AVE 74104 #875-02-1990 L1993 **IM** *020 †20
SPAIN, Michael Gene. 10505 E 91ST ST, STE 200 74133 #039-01-1982 L1983 **CD IM** *030 †20
SPANN, James C. 1265 S UTICA AVE, STE 105 74104 #004-01-1991 L1998 **TS GS** *020 †85,90
SPILLARS, Rodger Brannon. 8803 S 101ST EAST AVE # 29 74133 #039-01-1996 L1998 **IM** *020 †20
SPLANE, Bruce Lee. 3902 E 51ST ST, WARREN CLINIC 74135 #039-01-1982 L1983 **OBG** *020 †30
SRIDHARA, Srividya. ■ 74137 #495-62-2003 L2006 **IM** *012
STABLER, Larry Gene. ■ 74128 #039-01-1966 L1974 **FM** *020
STAFFORD, Andrea Elizabet. 1145 S UTICA AVE, HILLCREST MEDICAL GROUP 74104 #654-01-2004 L2007 **IM** *100 †20
STAFFORD, Paul Ryan. 2424 E 21ST ST STE 320, ORTHOPEDIC TRAUMA SERVICES 74114 #017-20-1997 L2006 **ORS** *020 †40
STAFIRA, Jeffrey Scott. 4111 S DARLINGTON AVE, RADIOLOGY CONSULTANTS OF 74135 #039-01-2002 L2003 **DR** *020 †80
STAMILE, Richard Martin. 4802 S 109TH EAST AVE, TULSA BONE & JOINT ASSOCIA 74146 #035-06-1968 L1975 **ORS** *020 †40
STANGEBY, Patrick John. ■ 74105 #039-01-2004 L2004 **P** *012
STANLEY, Keith Ladon. 6475 S YALE AVE, STE 301 74136 #039-01-1984 L1985 **FSM FM** *020 †18 ‡
STANTON, Paul Degraff. 6465 S YALE AVE, STE 1002 74136 #048-12-1986 L1987 **GE** *020 †20 ‡
STARK, Jodie Adams. 6839 S CANTON AVE 74136 #039-01-1958 L1958 **AN** *071
STARKEY, Cindi Rae. 1923 S UTICA AVE 74104 #021-05-2000 L2006 **PTH** *020 †50
STEARNS, Frederic Wm. 8803 S 101ST EAST AVE 74133 #048-04-1968 L1978 **D AM** *020 †15 ‡
STEARNS, Gillian Lind. ■ 74105 #039-01-2008 *012
STEICHEN, Kevin Eugene. 4720 S HARVARD AVE, STE 100 74135 #039-01-1983 L1984 **FM** *020 †18
STERLING, Robert Shannon. 10011 S YALE AVE STE 100, TULSA WOMEN'S HEALTH CARE 74137 #039-01-2001 L2005 **OBG** *020
STEVENS, Kristin Marie. 6465 S YALE AVE, STE 414 74136 #028-34-2001 L2002 **PD** *030 †55
STEVENS, Matthew Bret. 8803 S 101ST EAST AVE, STE 230 74133 #039-05-1988 L1991 **FM** *020 †18
STEVENSON, Carl Ronald. 6161 S YALE AVE 74136 #039-01-1966 L1966 **AN** *071 †05
STEWART, Charles Eaton. 6161 S YALE AVE, DEPARTMENT OF RADIATION ON 74136 #048-12-2001 L2006 **RO** *020
STEWART, Charles Edward. 4502 E 41ST ST, STE 2B-09 74135 #041-12-1973 L2007 **EM** *030 †16
STEWART, Charles Vincent. 6161 S YALE AVE 74136 #039-01-1986 L1987 **AN** *020 †05
STEWART, Jeffrey David. 4720 S HARVARD AVE 74135 #039-01-1992 L1993 **MFM OBG** *020 †30
STICKNEY, Randall Harwood. 4500 S GARNETT RD STE 9 74146 #048-02-1977 L1987 **DR** *020 †80
STIVERS, Bruce Rutherford. ■ 74133 #047-06-1964 L1972 **ORS OSM** *071 †40
STOCKTON, Darin Kent. 2325 S HARVARD AVE, STE 108 74114 #039-01-1994 L1995 **IM** *020 †20
STOESSER, Bruce Carlton. 10901 E 48TH ST 74146 #035-06-1968 L1975 **U** *020 †95 ‡
STOLTZFUS, Inez. 7600 S LEWIS AVE, FAMILY MEDICAL CARE 74136 #041-15-2005 L2006 **FP** *012
STONEHOCKER, Terri Kay. 2325 S HARVARD AVE STE 40, FAMILY & CHILDREN'S SERVIC 74114 #039-01-1999 L2000 **P** *020
STORTS, Deanna Sue. 550 S PEORIA AVE, RESOURCE CENTER 74120 #039-01-1982 L1983 **CHP P** *020 †75
STOTLER, Wesley M. 4415 S HARVARD AVE, STE 100 74135 #039-79-1996, ▲ L1997 **ORS** *020
STOUT, Donald Roy. 1120 S UTICA AVE 74104 #048-04-1964 L1970 **GYN** *071 †30 ‡
STOUT, Spencer Roy. ■ 74105 #039-01-1993 **PTH** *100
STRANGE, Jimmy Ray. 1923 S UTICA AVE 74104 #039-01-1959 L1959 **PTH** *071 †50
STRANSKY, Alan Jerome. 1120 S UTICA AVE 74104 #040-02-1971 L2003 **PTH** *062 †50
STREET, Daron Gene. 6475 S YALE AVE, STE 201 74136 #039-01-1990 L1991 **GO** *020 †30
STREIGHT, Robert Alan. 4500 S GARNETT RD 74146 #039-01-1982 L1983 **DR** *020 †80
STRICKLAND, Stuart K. 1120 S UTICA AVE 74104 #048-12-1988 L1993 **R** *020 †80
STRINGER, William E. 6600 S YALE AVE, STE 850 74136 #039-01-1993 L1995 **FM** *020 †18
STRNAD, Charles Martin. 6475 S YALE AVE, STE 201 74136 #016-42-1981 L1982 **ON HEM** *020 †20
STUDEBAKER, Ira John, Jr. 6809 E 83RD ST 74133 #039-01-1996 L1997 **PD OS** *075 †55
STUDEBAKER, Susan Nelson. 4502 E 41ST ST, UNIVERSITY OF OKLAHOMA 74135 #039-01-1996 L1997 **PD** *020 †55
STURDEVANT, William F. 744 W 9TH ST 74127 #028-78-1964, ▲ L1968 **AN** *071
SUKU, Suraj. 2808 S SHERIDAN RD 74129 #422-01-2005 L2007 **IM** *012
SULLIVAN, Garrett Gray. 1111 S SAINT LOUIS AVE 74120 #019-02-2004 L2007 **FP** *012
SUMMERS, Heather Belford. 6565 S YALE AVE SU 74136 #039-01-1999 L2001 **OBG** *020 †30
SURBECK, William Lawrence. 1919 S WHEELING AVE, STE 606 74104 #039-01-1988 L1989 **RHU IM** *020 †20
SWAFFORD, Melvin Ray. 1756 S UTICA AVE 74104 #004-01-1953 L1960 **AN** *071 †05
SWANSON, Robert G. 6161 S YALE AVE, DEPT OF RADIATION ONCOLOGY 74136 #028-02-1991 L1999 **RO** *020 †80
SWARTZ, John Frederick. 1923 E 21ST ST STE 200 74114 #041-09-1956 L1993 **FM IMG** *020
SWENNING, Todd Allen. 6475 S YALE AVE, STE 301 74136 #046-01-1997 L2005 **ORS** *020 †40
SWOPE, Melanie Kay. ■ 74104 #016-06-2008 *012
SWYDEN, Steven Neal. 6161 S YALE AVE, (ATTN: EMPLOYEE HEALTH) 74136 #039-01-1986 L1987 **OM FM** *020 †70
SYED, Nayyar Tauheed. 4019 E 51ST PL 74135 #704-02-1993 L1999 **ON** *012 †20
TAGHAVI ZARGAR, Soheil. ■ 74136 #517-12-2002 L2006 **FP** *012
TAHMOORESZADEH, Hooman. 1111 S SAINT LOUIS AVE 74120 #517-12-2001 L2006 **FP** *012
TAN, Poly. 1620 E 12TH ST 74120 #039-01-1969 L1999 **P** *020 †75
TANDON, Satwant. ■ 74136 #495-69-1974 L1994 **P** *020 †75
TARAKJI, Muhammad Anas. 1120 S UTICA AVE 74104 #875-02-2001 L2006 **IM** *020 †20
TATE, Emmett Lee. 4111 S DARLINGTON AVE, STE 700 74135 #020-02-1974 L1981 **DR PDR** *020 †80 ‡
TATE, Melita Louise. 6160 S YALE AVE 74136 #039-01-1999 L2000 **MPD** *020 †20,55
TATUM, Harvey Arthur. 1145 S UTICA AVE STE 701 74104 #039-01-1980 L1981 **GE IM** *020 †20
TAUBMAN, Kevin Edward. 1725 E 19TH ST, SPECIALIST 74104 #654-01-1999 L2007 **VS** *100 †85
TAYLOR, Edward Leon. 2000 S WHEELING AVE, STE 1000 74104 #048-12-1980 L1981 **IM** *020 †20
TAYLOR, James Richard. 1923 S UTICA AVE 74104 #016-02-1982 L1986 **ATP** *020 †50
TAYLOR, Oneita Floydette. 10109 E 79TH ST, DEPT OF RADIATION ONCOLOGY 74133 #019-02-1981 L1986 **RO** *020 †80 ‡
TAYLOR, Robert Anthony. ■ 74136 #039-01-1964 L1964 **GYN** *071 †30
TAYLOR, Walter J. 4111 S DARLINGTON AVE, RADIOLOGY CONSULTANTS OF 74135 #048-14-1990 L1996 **VIR** *020 †80
TENNEY, Richard Frank. 1919 S WHEELING AVE, NEUROSURGERY INC 74104 #039-01-1959 L1959 **NS** *071 †25
TERRELL, Dana L. 5428 E 109TH ST, CITYWIDE ANESTHESIA OF TUL 74137 #039-79-1989, ▲ L1990 **AN** *020
TERRY, Kimberly Kay. 1245 S UTICA AVE 74104 #039-01-1991 L1992 **PD** *020 †55
TETER, C Mark. 3343 S YALE AVE 74135 #039-01-1981 L1982 **FM** *020 †18
TETER, Christopher B. 6600 S YALE AVE STE 975 74136 #039-01-1977 L1978 **IM** *020
THAIYANANTHAN, G. ■ 74112 #005-02-2001 L2007 **NS** *100
THAMBUSWAMY, Michael. ■ 74136 #039-01-2008 *012
THIPPESWAMY, Tejaswi Bhar. ■ 74105 #495-99-2001 L2007 **FP** *012
THNG, Mark Li-Ken. 1611 S UTICA AVE, PMB 414 74104 #046-01-1993 L1994 **IM** *020
THOMAS, Darren Alan. 1705 E 19TH ST, STE 302 74104 #039-01-2001 L2002 **MPD** *020 †20,55
THOMAS, David Beynon. 6161 S YALE AVE 74136 #003-01-1972 L1977 **GS** *071 †85 ‡
THOMAS, Michael Leon. 802 S JACKSON AVE STE 505, OSU CENTER FOR HEALTH SCIE 74127 #004-01-1996 L2004 **GS** *020
THOMAS, Richard Doyle. 4802 S 109TH EAST AVE, TULSA BONE & JOINT ASSOCIA 74146 #039-01-1997 L1998 **ORS** *020 †40
THOMAS, Sanjay Mathew. 7600 S LEWIS AVE, IN HIS IMAGE FAM PRACT RES 74136 #035-03-2003 L2004 **FM** *020 †18
THOMAS, Sherri Lee. 10505 E 91ST ST SU 74133 #039-05-1986 L1987 **FM** *020 †18
THOMPSON, C Thos. 6161 S YALE AVE 74136 #024-01-1948 L1955 **GS** *071 †85
THOMPSON, John Raymond. 6565 S YALE AVE STE 807 74136 #039-01-1979 L1980 **OBG** *020
THOMPSON, Mark Leslie. ■ 74112 #305-01-2006 L2007 **IM** *012
THOMPSON, Mary. 1623 S UTICA AVE 74104 #036-08-1982 L1985 **EM** *020 †16
TIETZE, Pamela Hodges. 9001 E 101ST ST, STE 300 74133 #039-01-1984 L1993 **FM OBS** *040 †18
TINES, Stephen Chas. 10026 S MINGO RD STE A, PMB 332 74133 #030-05-1979 L1987 **DR** *020 †80
TIPTON, John Wylie. 1111 S SAINT LOUIS AVE, OU PHYSICIANS FAMILY MEDIC 74120 #039-01-1972 L1973 **FM** *020 †18
TISDALE, Alfred Dent, Jr. ■ 74132 #021-01-1958 L1988 **PTH** *071 †50
TODD, Clell Vaughn. ■ 74112 #039-01-1980 L1981 **PD** *062 †55
TOMECEK, Frank Jos, Jr. 6802 S OLYMPIA AVE, STE 300 74132 #017-20-1987 L1993 **NS SCI** *020 †25
TOUCHET, Bryan Keith. 4502 E 41ST ST 74135 #039-01-1993 L1994 **P** *020 †75
TOUGHANIPOUR, Abbas. 8803 S 101ST EAST AVE, STE 365 74133 #012-05-1993 L2000 **TS** *020 †85,90
TOWNSEND, Raymond Earl. 1923 S UTICA AVE 74104 #054-04-1969 L1981 **OPH** *020 †35
TOWSLEY, Daniel Kent. 110 W 7TH ST, STE 2520 74119 #048-12-1978 L1981 **GS** *071 †85
TRAINO, Philip J, Jr. 4111 S DARLINGTON AVE, RADIOLOGY CONSULTANTS OF 74135 #022-75-1993, ▲ L2001 **DR** *020 †80
TRAMONTE, Vallory John, II. 7600 S LEWIS AVE 74136 #031-01-2004 L2006 **FP** *012
TRAN, Yen My. 6565 S YALE AVE STE 610 74136 #039-01-1994 L1998 **OBG** *020 †30

■ = Address Information Privacy Protected

TRAUB, David Alan. 7614 E 91ST ST, STE 180 74133 #048-02-1993 L1994 IM *020

TREDWAY, Donald Ray. 115 E 15TH ST 74119 #016-11-1966 L1978 REN OBG *020 †30

TREHAN, Sanjeev. 10505 E 91ST ST, STE 150 74133 #495-27-1989 L2001 CD *020 †20

TRIPATHY, Sudip. 6600 S YALE AVE STE 800 74136 #039-01-1993 L1994 IM *020 †20

TROMBKA, Lawrence Henry. 3333 E 77TH ST 74136 #649-31-1982 L1987 P *020 ‡

TROXLER, Mark A. 1919 S WHEELING AVE, STE 200 74104 #039-79-1995, ▲ 1996 IM ISM *020 †20

TRUJILLO, Jose Eduardo. 4500 S GARNETT RD STE 840 74146 #048-12-1976 L1980 DR *071 †80

TRUONG, Nhan P. 4111 S DARLINGTON AVE, RADIOLOGY CONSULTANTS OF 74135 #048-12-1988 L1993 DR *020 †80

TRUONG, Thomas Nicholas. 4502 E 41ST ST, FAMILY PRACTICE 74135 #028-78-2003, ▲ L2005 *100

TUMLISON, Joel Adam. 7600 S LEWIS AVE 74136 #004-01-2005 L2006 FP *012

TURNER, Sarah Schafer. 1923 S UTICA AVE 74104 #010-02-2003 L2007 AN *020

UDUPA, Anand Deviprakash. 6465 S YALE AVE, STE 507 74136 #495-94-1978 L1999 IM NEP *020

UNTERSEHER, Chris Allen. ■ 74119 #030-05-2005 L2007 FPP *012

UTZ, Megan Elizabeth. ■ 74105 #039-01-2008 *012

UY, Nathan Wilson. 1923 S UTICA AVE 74104 #019-02-1998 L2004 RO *080

VAID, Anil Kishan. 1111 S SAINT LOUIS AVE 74120 #495-03-1989 L2005 FM *020 †18

VAIDYA, Ashwini K. 8803 S 101ST EAST AVE, STE 335 74133 #039-01-1999 L2003 D *020 †15

VAIDYA, Atul Makarand. 8803 S 101ST EAST AVE, STE 110 74133 #039-01-1998 L2003 OTO *020 †45

VAN NEWKIRK, Laura E. 2738 E 51ST ST, STE 290 74105 #041-07-1995 L2000 PTH *020 †50

VAN SCHOYCK, Patrick. 9001 S 101ST EAST AVE, MINGO VALLEY MEDICAL GROUP 74133 #039-01-1984 L1985 FM *020 †18 ‡

VAUGHN, Jerrod Lee. ■ 74114 #039-01-2007 L2007 GS *012

VENUGOPAL, Annie. 1705 E 19TH ST STE 501 74104 #495-27-1974 L1981 PM *020 †60

VETETO, Kenneth Wm. 6585 S YALE AVE, STE 1150 74136 #039-01-1987 L1988 IM *020 †20

VILLAMIL MORA, Miguel Ang. ■ 74133 #264-04-1995 L2006 IM *100

VITANZA, Alfred Thos. 1923 S UTICA AVE, DEPARTMENT OF NEONATOLOGY 74104 #561-01-1981 L1986 NPM *020 †55

VOLAK, Patrick Robt. 6465 S YALE AVE, 715 WARREN MEDICAL BUILDIN 74136 #039-01-1985 L1986 GE *020 †20 ‡

VON HARTITZSCH, Barry. 6465 S YALE AVE, NEPHROLOGY SPECIALISTS OF 74136 #671-01-1964 L1974 NEP IM *020

VOSBURGH, John Beecher. 4802 S 109TH EAST AVE 74146 #019-02-1964 L1968 ORS *020 †40

VOSS, Harold Matthew, Jr. 1120 S UTICA AVE 74104 #021-05-1983 L1986 AN *020 †05 ‡

WACKOWSKI, Michael Jos. 4041 S BIRMINGHAM AVE 74105 #028-03-1992 L1993 IM *020 †20

WACKOWSKI, Rebecca M. 1919 S WHEELING AVE, STE 404 74104 #048-13-1992 L1993 IM *020 †20

WADE, Jerome Byron. 1145 S UTICA AVE, STE 365 74104 #032-01-1977 L1984 N IM *020 †20

WAGNER, Patrice D. 2808 S SHERIDAN RD 74129 #039-79-2006, ▲ L2007 OBG *012

WALKER, Christina Celeste. 6475 S YALE AVE SU 74136 #016-02-2004 L2007 FSM *012 †18

WALKER, James Chas. ■ 74136 #004-01-1956 L1964 N *071

WALKER, James Dea Roe. 1923 S UTICA AVE, PHYSICIANS 74104 #039-01-1987 L1995 AN *020 †05

WALKER, Leslie Kirsten. 6585 S YALE AVE STE 701, OKLAHOMA ONCOLOGY, INC 74136 #039-01-2000 L2006 ON *020 †20

WALLACE, Erik Allen. 4444 E 41ST ST 74135 #028-02-2000 L2003 IM *020 †20 ‡

WALLACE, Suzanne Green. 2829 S SHERIDAN RD 74129 #043-01-2000 L2003 PD *020 †55 ‡

WALLER, Mark Wm. 1923 S UTICA AVE, PHYSICIANS 74104 #039-01-1991 L1992 AN *020 †05

WALTERS, Rustin Chanc. ■ 74105 #028-34-2001 L2002 GS *020

WAN, Sang Sandra. 2000 S WHEELING AVE 74104 #039-01-1988 L1992 PD *020 †55

WANAHITA, Anna. 1725 E 19TH ST STE 50 74104 #506-23-1999 L2007 N *020

WANG, Xi-Ling. 9322 E 41ST ST, VA OUTPATIENT CLINIC 74145 #243-44-1986 L1998 FM *071 †18

WARLICK, Ethan Aaron. 6161 S YALE AVE, CARE CENTER 74136 #019-02-1996 L1999 PD *020 †55

WARNOCK, Julia Katherine. 4502 E 41ST ST, UNIVERSITY OF OKLAHOMA 74135 #047-06-1984 L1993 P PYG *050 †75

WARREN, James Walter. 8181 S LEWIS AVE 74137 #047-07-1973 L1982 IM *075

WASIQUE, Maria. 1611 S UTICA AVE STE 414 74104 #704-16-1999 L2003 IM *020

WATERS, Victor Owen. 1120 S UTICA AVE, 4W-4502 74104 #039-01-1969 L1970 AN EM *020 †05,16

WATERS, Victor Virgil. ■ 74136 #041-13-1984 L1986 IM CCM *020 †20

WATSON, John Skelly. 1120 S UTICA AVE 74104 #030-05-1967 L1968 GS *071 †85

WATSON, William Gray, II. 1923 S UTICA AVE, PHYSICIANS 74104 #039-01-1992 L1993 AN *020 †05

WATT, Richard Hugh, Jr. 1245 S UTICA AVE, STE 240 74104 #048-04-1961 L1971 IM ON *030 †20

WATTS, Walter Edwin, IV. ■ 74133 #039-01-2008 *012

WEBB, James Robert, Jr. 2408 E 81ST ST, STE 900 74137 #039-01-1999 L2000 MSR PME *062 †80 ‡

WEBB, Randall Madison. 8110 S YALE AVE 74137 #039-01-1986 L1987 N *020 †75

WEBER, Carolyn Arleen. ■ 74136 #039-01-1985 *074

WEHRS, Roger E. ■ 74136 #030-05-1952 L1958 NO OTO *071 †45

WEIDNER, Vicky. 1623 S UTICA AVE 74104 #039-01-1984 L1985 EM *020 †16

WEINSTEIN, Jay Justin. 2424 E 21ST ST 74114 #048-12-1972 L1973 OBG *072 †30

WEISS, Mark Justin. 1717 S UTICA AVE, STE 107 74104 #041-13-1968 L1969 OPH OS *020 †35

WEISZ, Michael Alan. 4502 E 41ST ST 74135 #039-01-1988 L1989 IM *040 †20

WEKSLER, Luiz. 1120 S UTICA AVE, PHYSICIANS, INC. 74104 #187-03-1970 L2001 AN PME *020 †05 ‡

WELDEN, Shirley Jean. 2140 S HARVARD AVE, STE 105 74114 #039-05-1984 L1985 IM PM *020 †05

WELLES, Edward Hunter, IV. ■ 74133 #047-06-1998 *100

WELLS, Michelle S. 2808 S SHERIDAN RD 74129 #039-79-2005, ▲ L2007 FP *012

WENGER, Bruce Elliott. 1923 S UTICA AVE 74104 #019-02-1961 L1967 AN *071 †05

WENGER, Jill Goff. 1705 E 19TH ST, STE 302 74104 #039-01-1993 L1997 IM *020 †20

WENGER, Matthew Anthony. 4500 S GARNETT RD STE 9 74104 #039-01-1986 L1987 AN PME *020 †05 ‡

WENGER, Peter Bruce. 4720 S HARVARD AVE, STE 100 74135 #039-01-1993 L1997 FM *020 †18

WENGER, Theodore R. ■ 74136 #039-01-1949 L1949 AN *071

WERLLA, Vanessa. 2626 E 21ST ST, STE 6 74114 #039-01-1980 L1981 P *020 †75

WESTBROOK, Amy Rene. ■ 74114 #039-01-2000 *100

WHEELER-HARRINGTON, Keely. 2808 S SHERIDAN RD 74129 #039-79-2006, ▲ 2007 P *012

WHITE, David William. 5020 E 68TH ST 74136 #047-05-1984 L1990 NO OTO *020 †45

WHITE, James Edwin. ■ 74105 #039-01-1954 L1954 ORS OS *071 †40

WHITE, Julie Montague. 9423 E 95TH CT, TULSA OUTPATIENT SURGERY C 74133 #041-07-1991 L1993 EM *020 †16

WHITE, Robert Stanley. 2704 S VICTOR AVE 74114 #021-05-1959 L1965 PTH *020 †50

WHITE, Thomas Wallace. 3010 S HARVARD AVE, STE 220 74114 #039-01-1981 L1982 DR *020 †80

WHITENECK, James M. 1265 S UTICA AVE, STE 105 74104 #039-01-1979 L1987 TS *020 †85,90

WHITLOCK, Boyd Otho. 1919 S WHEELING AVE 74104 #039-01-1962 L1962 IM *071

WHITLOCK, Bryan Richard. 3319 E 46TH ST 74135 #039-01-1992 L1993 PS *020

WHITTAKER, Runako Deshawn. 1334 N LANSING AVE 74106 #005-02-1998 L2003 PD *020 ‡

WIEMAR, Kenneth Edwin. 1919 S WHEELING AVE, GYNECOLOGY & OBSTETRICS 74104 #048-02-1976 L1980 OBG *020 †30

WIESEMEYER, Dan L. 1923 S UTICA AVE, PHYSICIANS 74104 #028-46-1979 L1987 AN *020 †05

WILEY, Cara Denise. ■ 74839 #039-01-2005 L2006 GS *012

WILEY, Thomas Elmer, III. 4111 S DARLINGTON AVE, RADIOLOGY CONSULTANTS OF 74135 #048-12-1991 L2005 VIR DR *020 †80

WILKE, Gisele Catherine. 6839 S CANTON AVE 74136 #035-45-1996 L2003 AN *020 †05

WILKIN, Michael N. 10901 E 48TH ST 74146 #048-15-1999 L2005 U *020 †95

WILLARD, Susan Chaiser. 9001 S 101ST EAST AVE, STE 200 74133 #039-79-1983, ▲ L1984 GP *020

WILLIAMS, Gregory Patrick. 2738 E 51ST ST, STE 290 74105 #039-01-1974 L1975 PTH FM *020 †50

WILLIAMS, Janice Lee. 4720 S HARVARD AVE, STE 102 74135 #039-01-1996 L1997 FM *020 †18

WILLIAMS, Nancy. 1923 S UTICA AVE, OMNI MEDICAL GROUP, INC 74104 #039-01-2001 L2002 IM *020

WILLIAMS, Regina Lee. 2001 S GARNETT RD, STE F 74128 #026-04-1972 L1989 *020

WILLIAMS, Richard B. PO BOX 700863 74170 #019-02-1953 L1983 R OS *071 †80

WILLIAMS, Robert Bretch. ■ 74105 #021-01-1955 L1960 OBG *071 †30

WILLIAMS, Ryan Raymond. 2829 S SHERIDAN RD 74129 #049-01-2001 L2007 OS *100 †55

WILLIAMSON, Jay M. 10011 S YALE AVE, STE 100 74137 #039-79-1990, ▲ L1991 OBG *020

WILLISON, Frederick Wayne. 1923 S UTICA AVE, RADIATION ONCOLOGY 74104 #051-04-1989 L1997 RO *020 †80

WILLISTON, Laurel Katrina. 7600 S LEWIS AVE 74136 #048-16-2000 L2001 FM *020 †18 ‡

WILSON, Robert Keith. 6160 S YALE AVE 74136 #048-04-1972 L1998 PUD IM *030 †20

WILSON, Robert Wesley. 1120 S UTICA AVE 74104 #039-01-1977 L1978 EM *020 †16

WILSON, Victoria Nichole. 1923 S UTICA AVE 74104 #039-01-1998 L1999 EM *020 †16

WISEMAN, Steven Ray. 1435 S UTICA AVE 74104 #039-01-1991 L1992 IM *020 †20

WISENBAUGH, Thos Willard. 6151 S YALE AVE STE 400, CARDIOLOGY OF TULSA 74136 #038-40-1977 L1998 IM CD *050 †20

WITT, Richard Earl. ■ 74137 #039-01-1941 L1943 OM GS *071 †85

WOLF, Curtis Vandyne, II. 1145 S UTICA AVE, STE 362 74104 #039-01-1992 L1996 OPH *020 †35

WOLF, Jennifer Rae. 1245 S UTICA AVE 74104 #001-02-1996 L1997 PD *020 †55

WOLFE, James J. 1623 S UTICA AVE 74104 #004-01-1972 L1973 EM *020 †16

WOLFF, Eugene G. ■ 74105 #039-01-1934 AN A *071 †05

WOO, Van Hoy. 1120 S UTICA AVE, DEPT OF RADIATION THERPY 74104 #028-34-1991 L1994 RO *020 †80 ‡

WOOD, Chad Nathaniel. 1111 S SAINT LOUIS AVE, FAMILY PRACTICE RESIDENCY 74120 #049-01-2003 L2004 FM *020 †18

WOOD, Virgil W. 6600 S YALE AVE, STE 800 74136 #021-01-1952 L1956 IM *071

WOODRUFF, Conchita L. 1145 S UTICA AVE, STE 500 74104 #045-01-1998 L2002 OBG *020 †30

WOOLARD, Kent Alan. 6839 S CANTON AVE, ANESTHESIOLOGISTS INC 74136 #039-01-1981 L1982 AN *020 †20,05

WOOSLEY, Julie Anne. 6901 S OLYMPIA AVE, TSSH DEPT OF ANESTHESIOLOG 74132 #039-01-1997 L2001 AN *020 †05

WOOSLEY, Ronald Edward. 1919 S WHEELING AVE, STE 504 74104 #020-12-1968 L1982 NS *020 †25

WORLEY, Brian David. 6585 S YALE AVE, STE 1200 74136 #039-01-1990 L1999 PCC IM *020 †20

WORLEY, Kay Lisabeth. 6585 S YALE AVE, WILLIAMS BLDG., SUITE 620 74136 #039-01-1990 L1999 N *071 †75

WORTMANN, Dorothy H W. 2815 S SHERIDAN RD, DEPT OF PEDIATRICS 74129 #019-02-1971 L2000 RHU PD *075 †55

WRIGHT, Andrew David. 10901 E 48TH ST 74146 #019-02-1999 L2006 U *020 †95

WYLIE, Lori Jessica. 6161 S YALE AVE 74136 #048-04-1998 L2003 EM *020 †16

XING, Jian. 6465 S YALE AVE STE 704, WARREN CLINIC INTERNAL MED 74136 #243-95-1984 L1994 IM *020 †20

YARBOROUGH, William H. 4502 E 41ST ST 74135 #039-01-1977 L1978 IM ADM *040 †20

YATES, William Robt. 4502 E 41ST ST, SCHUSTERMAN CTR 74135 #039-05-1977 L1997 P FM *020 †75,18

YEARY, Edwin Curtis. 1725 E 19TH ST, STE 800 74104 #048-04-1974 L1980 GS VS *020 †85

YELVERTON, Jodi Leigh. 9322 E 41ST ST 74145 #021-06-1990 L1996 PM *020 †60

YOON, Myeong Sook. 8801 S 101ST EAST AVE 74133 #028-02-1994 L2000 DR *020 †80

YOUMAN, Kari Elizabeth. 2808 S SHERIDAN RD, PSYCHIATRY DEPARTMENT 74129 #039-01-2006 L2007 P *012

YOUMANS, Roger Lee. 1725 E 19TH ST STE LL103 74104 #019-02-1958 L1980 GS *071 †85

YOUNG, David Spencer. 6839 S CANTON AVE, ANESTHESIOLOGISTS INC 74136 #039-01-1980 L1991 AN *020 †05 ‡

YOUNG, Linda. 1245 S UTICA AVE 74104 #035-06-1967 L1975 IM DIA *020

YOUNG, Richard J J. 1120 S UTICA AVE 74104 #035-06-1967 L1975 GE IM *071

YOUNG, Timothy Ray. 1923 S UTICA AVE STE 200 74104 #039-01-1980 L1983 IM *030 †20

YOUNT, Brian James. 4502 E 41ST ST, OU COLLEGE OF MED 74135 #019-02-1999 L2004 MPD *020 †55,20

ZAIDI, Syed Muhammad Hamm. 2808 S SHERIDAN RD, DEPT FM 74129 #704-20-2003 FP *012

ZANDI, Farshid Adam-Amir. 1815 E 15TH ST 74104 #305-01-1999 L2001 IM *020 †20

ZANETAKIS, Ellen Irene. 1430 TERRACE DR, ARTHRITIS 74104 #038-44-1982 L1987 RHU IM *020 †20

ZANOVICH, Terry Lee. 2000 S WHEELING AVE # 800 74104 #039-01-1974 L1975 OBG *020 †30

ZARINTASH, Kioumars. 1145 S UTICA AVE 74104 #010-03-1968 L1974 AN *071 †05

ZEKAUSKAS, Raymond Andrew. 1725 E 19TH ST, STE 800 74104 #033-05-1971 L1978 **GS** *020 †85
ZETIK, Donald Frank, Jr. 2000 S WHEELING AVE 74104 #048-04-1996 L1999 **PD** *020 †55 ‡
ZOLLER, Robert Parker. 1923 E 21ST ST 74114 #018-03-1964 L1971 **CD IM** *020 †20
ZOMER, Yohanan Shmuel. 9228 S MINGO RD, STE 100 74133 #550-02-1974 L1976 **PD** *020 †55
ZORSKY, Paul Edward. 6585 S YALE AVE, STE 701 74136 #008-02-1978 L1981 **ON HEM** *020 †20
ZWIESLER, Daniel James. 1145 S UTICA AVE STE 60 74104 #004-01-2004 L2005 **OBG** *012

TUTTLE – GRADY

SPARKS, Rhonda Agnes. 4805 E HIGHWAY 37, URGENT MEDCARE CLINIC 73089 #039-01-1994 L1995 **FM** *020 †18

VINITA – CRAIG

ALLENSWORTH, Edward Wayne. 803 N FOREMAN ST 74301 #039-01-1961 L1961 **FM** *030 †18 ‡
AMRUD, Diaram. EASTERN ST HOSP-FAM PRAC 74301 #308-03-1978 L1979 **GP** *020
BLEVINS, Walter E. ■ 74301 #039-01-1951 L1951 **P** *071
COOPER, Martin Thomas. 715 N FOREMAN ST 74301 #065-01-1982 L1994 **FM** *020
DEZA, Ernesto Cabangal. PO BOX 69, EASTERN STATE HOSP 74301 #748-01-1951 L1978 **P** *020
GUTIERREZ, Nicasio G. PO BOX 69, 442-104 E 250 RD 74301 #748-01-1955 L1978 **P GP** *071
HORTON, Terry Ray. 715 N FOREMAN ST 74301 #039-01-1986 L1989 **FM** *020 †18 ‡
KOHL, Russell Wade. 36488 S HIGHWAY 82, GRAND LAKE MEDICAL PARK 74301 #039-01-2002 L2003 **FM** *100
KRIVENKOV, Andre Michael. PO BOX 69 74301 #913-37-1939 **GP** *020
LANIER, Paul Robinson. EASTERN STATE HOSPITAL RD 74301 #004-01-1959 L1967 **P CHP** *020
MATT, Leslie Nicholas. PO BOX 69 74301 #473-01-1938 *020
NEER, Charles Sumner, II. 74301 #041-01-1942 L1946 **ORS** *075 †40
NUNEZ, Joaquin A. ■ 74301 #264-04-1952 L1978 **P GS** *071
PINKERTON, Clarence B. ■ 74301 #039-01-1953 L1953 **P** *071
TYRRELL, Mickey Ray. 803 N FOREMAN ST 74301 #422-01-2002 L2005 **FM** *020 †18
VADHAWKAR, Vishnu Narayan. EASTERN STATE HOSPITAL RD 74301 #496-38-1943 L1973 **P GP** *020
VILLAREAL, Robert Francis. 715 N FOREMAN ST 74301 #039-01-2000 L2003 **FM** *020 †18 ‡

WAGONER – WAGONER

DENNY, Petie Ann. 1317 S DEWEY AVE, CMG FAMILY CLINIC 74467 #039-01-1999 L2000 **FM** *020 †18
FIELDER, Charles Thos. 1200 W CHEROKEE ST, WAGONER COMMUNITY HOSP 74467 #039-01-1981 L1982 **DR** *020
HALL, William Alan. 1200 W CHEROKEE ST 74467 #039-01-1977 L1978 **EM** *020
HANNA, Bryan Casey. 1200 W CHEROKEE ST 74467 #048-02-2000 L2001 **FM** *020 †18
HUDGENS, John Clark, Jr. ■ 74467 #021-01-1955 L1973 **GYN** *071 †30

WAKITA – GRANT

GRAVES, Donald L. PO BOX 27, 552 W OSAGE 73771 #035-09-1945 L1969 **FM GP** *071 †18

WALTERS – COTTON

GOSS, Larry Gene. 102 N BROADWAY ST 73572 #039-01-1973 L1974 **GP FM** *020
LASHLEY, Floyd J, Jr. 402 N BROADWAY ST 73572 #039-01-1960 L1960 **FM** *020 †18

WARR ACRES – OKLAHOMA

BIEHLER, Larry Loyd. 7301 N COMANCHE AVE 73132 #039-01-1962 L1962 **PD** *071
FISHER, Cary Ardis. 7301 N COMANCHE AVE 73132 #039-01-1989 L1990 **FM** *020 †18
JACKSON, Kenneth Charles. 7301 N COMANCHE AVE 73132 #012-01-1975 L1976 **PD AI** *020 †55
MADOUX, Demille Winston. 5911 WATERWOOD CIR 73132 #039-01-1985 L1986 **EM FM** *020 †18
MUSALLAM, L Sam. 7304 N COMANCHE AVE, HEFNER WEST MEDICAL CLIN, 73132 #039-01-1977 L1978 **FM** *020 ‡
SCHAUFELE, Julie Anne. 7301 N COMANCHE AVE 73132 #039-01-2000 L2001 **FM** *020 †18
STONE, Jennifer June. ■ 73122 #039-01-2008 *012

WATONGA – BLAINE

BOHLMAN, Curtis Owen. 500 N CLARENCE NASH BLVD 73772 #039-01-1965 L1965 **FM** *071 †18
CAGUNGUN, Julio M, Jr. RR 1 BOX 34A 73772 #748-07-1965 L1982 **GP GS** *020
CARPENTER, Byron Lee. 203 N WEIGLE AVE 73772 #039-01-1993 L1999 **FM** *020 †18
CARTER, Richard Scott. 500 N CLARENCE NASH BLVD 73772 #039-01-2002 L2003 **FM** *020 †18
PETRY, George Rodney. RR 2 BOX 336, DIAMONDBACK CORRECTIONAL F 73772 #305-01-2002 L2004 **FM** *020 †18
SCHENK, Curtis Andrew. 407 N CLARENCE NASH BLVD, BOX 669 73772 #039-01-1974 L1975 **FM** *020 †18
SPENCER, Robert Gordon. 500 N CLARENCE NASH BLVD 73772 #039-01-2002 L2004 **FM** *020 †18
TALLEY, Michael Roger. 500 N CLARENCE NASH BLVD 73772 #039-01-1979 L1982 **FM** *020 †18

WAURIKA – JEFFERSON

STOUT, Harold. U S HWYS 70 & 81 73573 #039-01-1960 L1960 **FM** *071 †18

WAYNOKA – WOODS

HULL, Susan Marie. ■ 73860 #019-02-2008 *012

WEATHERFORD – CUSTER

AARON, Michael Edward. 213 N ILLINOIS ST 73096 #039-01-1983 L1984 **FM** *020 †18
ARGANBRIGHT, Terry Kim. 215 N KANSAS ST 73096 #039-01-1980 L1983 **FM** *020 †18
BADGETT, Blake Allen. 211 N ILLINOIS ST 73096 #039-01-1999 L2002 **FM** *020 †18
DIXON, Thomas A. 1204 E MAIN ST 73096 #039-01-1976 L1977 **FM** *020 †18
HUSER, John Marshall. PO BOX 627 73096 #039-01-1958 L1959 **FM** *071 †18
HUSER, John Marshall, III. 517 E FRANKLIN AVE 73096 #039-01-1987 L1990 **FM** *020 †18
LAWRENCE, Gary Monroe. 215 N KANSAS ST 73096 #039-01-1980 L1983 **FM** *020 †18
MCLEMORE, Dustin James. ■ 73096 #039-01-2008 *012

WELLING – CHEROKEE

DAHLMANN, Kathleen Anna. 27753 S WELLING RD, TENKILLER BEHAVIORAL SERVI 74471 #004-01-1979 L1992 **PD** *020 †55

WESTVILLE – ADAIR

SUTTON, Diane Gray. ■ 74965 #041-07-1980 L1984 **IM** *020

WEWOKA – SEMINOLE

CROWSON, Glenn A. 1401 W 1ST ST 74884 #654-01-1981 L1982 **FM OM** *020 †18 ‡

WILBURTON – LATIMER

TRENT, David Lee. 209 NW 3RD ST 74578 #039-01-1964 L1976 **GS** *071
VALBUENA, Ricardo M. 1107 W MAIN ST 74578 #748-07-1965 L1979 **GP GS** *020

WOODWARD – WOODWARD

BERDECIA, Joseph. 1611 MAIN ST STE 203 73801 #012-01-1990 L2007 **FM** *020 †18
BROWN, Richard Dennis. 1502 OKLAHOMA AVE 73801 #039-01-1982 L1983 **FM** *020 †18
CAO, Hiep Andrew. 1824 KANSAS AVE 73801 #019-02-1996 L1999 **FM** *020
CHEN, Fong-Hsiung. 908 19TH ST 73801 #244-04-1970 L1977 **GS GE** *071 †85
CHIOU, Helen Shwu-Fen. 1818 KANSAS AVE 73801 #244-04-1972 L1977 **IM** *020
CHLEBORAD, Janice Louise. 1017 17TH ST 73801 #030-05-1984 L1988 **PD** *020 †55
GADBERRY, Walter Leslie. 1222 10TH ST STE 11 73801 #048-16-1991 L1996 **GS** *020
GARNER, James Ray. 1000 15TH ST 73801 #039-01-2000 L2002 **FM** *020
HUENERGARDT, Brenda Kay. 1650 MAIN ST STE B 73801 #039-01-1997 L2002 **GS** *020 †85
JIA, Gregory Y. 908 19TH ST, STE 1 73801 #243-47-1987 L1995 **U** *020 †95
KEITH, Howard Barton. 1650 MAIN ST 73801 #039-01-1957 L1963 **GS TS** *071 †85,90
LESTER, Michael Leon. 1818 KANSAS AVE, AGAPE HEALTH CARE PLLC 73801 #011-03-1978 L2006 **IM EM** *020
MC GARRY, Thomas Francis. 908 19TH ST, OKLAHOMA CARDIOVASCULAR 73801 #041-02-1985 L1991 **CD IM** *020 †20
MORRIS, William Theodore. 1650 MAIN ST, WOODWARD HEALTHLINK 73801 #039-01-1960 L1960 **ORS** *071 †40
PARROTT, Kenneth De Wayne. 900 17TH ST 73801 #039-01-1977 L1979 **FM** *020 †18
PULS, Alan Richard. 1650 MAIN ST 73801 #048-02-1980 L1981 **CD IC** *020 †20
RAY, Jason Scott. 1111 HILLCREST DR 73801 #039-01-1997 L1998 **FM** *020 †18
RAY, Kathryn Anne. 1111 HILLCREST DR, DRS. RAY PLLC 73801 #039-01-1997 L1998 **FM** *020 †18
SCHMIDT, Dwayne Allen. 908 19TH ST, OKLAHOMA CARDIOVASCULAR 73801 #039-01-1983 L1984 **CD IM** *020 †20
SCOTT, Larry B. 1650 MAIN ST, STE C 73801 #039-79-1998, ▲ L2004 **OTO** *020
SUTTON, John David. 1810 KANSAS AVE 73801 #039-01-1983 L1984 **IM** *020 †20
THOMPSON, Webb Maddux, III. 900 17TH ST 73801 #039-01-1987 L1988 **DR VIR** *020
WAGNER, Alan Marvin. 1024 MAIN ST 73801 #038-40-1974 L2005 **OBG** *020 †30

WRIGHT CITY – MCCURTAIN

WEST, Michael Curtis, Jr. PO BOX 680, GOOD HONEST MEDICIINE 74766 #037-01-1996 L1997 **GP** *020

WYNNEWOOD – GARVIN

ROBBERSON, James Kent. 116 E ROBERT S KERR BLVD 73098 #039-01-1977 L1978 **FM** *020 †18
SIMS, Cheryl Ford. 1303 PROSPECT CIR 73098 #039-01-1985 L1986 **FM** *020

YUKON – CANADIAN

ANDERSON, Michael Blake. 520 S MUSTANG RD 73099 #039-01-1979 L1980 **OM** *020 †18
ARAMBULA, Martha B. 1445 HEALTH CENTER PKWY 73099 #048-02-1993 L1994 **PD** *020 †55
BOURNE, Catrina Felice. 1205 HEALTH CENTER PKWY 73099 #039-01-2000 L2003 **FM** *020 †18 ‡
BOWEN, Dina M. 1445 HEALTH CENTER PKWY 73099 #039-01-1994 L1995 **PD** *020 †55

■ = Address Information Privacy Protected

BUDRICH, Evette Denise. 520 S MUSTANG RD 73099 #039-01-1994 L1995 **MPD** *020

BULLOCK, William Riley. ■ 73099 #036-01-1958 L1967 **CD IM** *071

BUNDY, John Mc Call. 520 S MUSTANG RD 73099 #039-01-1981 L1982 **FM EM** *020 †18

CASTRO NATAL, Norma Iris. ■ 73099 #308-03-1980 L2004 *100

CIGLAR, Steven. ■ 73099 #011-04-2003 L2005 **DR** *012

CORDUM, Myron Alfred. ■ 73099 #039-01-1962 L1962 **GP GS** *071

COURTNAY, William G. 1201 HEALTH CENTER PKWY 73099 #039-79-1994, ▲ L1995 **EM** *020

CULVER, David Lawrence. 1201 HEALTH CENTER PKWY, CANADIAN VALLEY REGIONAL H 73099 #039-01-1990 L1991 **AN** *020

DEES, Brett Randall. ■ 73099 #039-01-2007 L2007 **N** *012

DRABEK, Steven Alan. 436 S MUSTANG RD, YUKON FAMILY CLINIC 73099 #039-01-1984 L1985 **FM PLM** *020 †18

FETZER, Larry Dean. ■ 73099 #048-04-1964 L1965 **IM** *071

FIEGENER, Meredith Lynn. ■ 73099 #039-01-1983 L1984 **AN** *040 †05

FLORES, Catherine Barrett. 415 E MAIN ST, STE B 73099 #048-02-1989 L1994 **PD** *020 †55

FLORES, Javier A. 415 E MAIN ST, BLDG B 73099 #048-02-1994 L1995 **PD** *020

FRIESE, Athena Jane. 1205 HEALTH CENTER PKWY, STE 100 73099 #039-01-1982 L1983 **FM** *020 †18

FURGESON, Michael Douglas. 508 W VANDAMENT AVE, STE 100 73099 #039-01-1984 L1985 **FM OBG** *020 †18

GREER, Marek Tavis. ■ 73099 #039-01-1997 L2003 **GS** *020

HAGOOD, Brady Scott. 1205 HEALTH CTR PKWY 73099 #039-01-2000 L2002 **GS** *020 †85

HAMLETT, Sean Ray. 1205 HEALTH CENTER PKWY, STE 250 73099 #039-79-1999, ▲ L2000 *020

HANES, Alecia A. 508 W VANDAMENT AVE, STE 210 73099 #039-01-1982 L1983 **PD** *020 †55

HINE, Jerry Randal. ■ 73099 #039-01-2008 *012

JOHNSON, Michael Brandon. ■ 73099 #039-01-2008 *012

JOLLIFF, Kevin Lee. ■ 73099 #039-01-2004 L2006 **GS** *012

KHAN, Aleem Muhammad. ■ 73099 #704-02-1987 *100

KUMAR, Kirtida Gurjar. 520 S MUSTANG RD 73099 #495-27-1979 L1990 **GE IM** *020 †20

LACKEY, James David. 1205 HEALTH CENTER PKWY, MEDICAL OFF BLDG STE 240 73099 #039-01-1974 L1975 **OBG** *020 †30 ‡

LINDLEY, H Wain. 303 ANNAWOOD DR 73099 #039-01-1979 L1981 **P CHP** *020 †75

LINGENFELTER, Paul B. ■ 73099 #039-01-1933 L1934 **GS PUD** *071

LIVINGSTON, Tanya Leigh. 1205 HEALTH CENTER PKWY, STE 100 73099 #039-01-1999 L2000 **FM** *020 †18

LOCKWOOD, Robert James. 1205 HEALTH CENTER PKWY, STE 100 73099 #039-01-1999 L2000 **FM** *020 †18

MEKIS, John. 508 W VANDAMENT AVE, STE 100 73099 #473-02-1959 L1972 **GP** *071

MILLIGAN, Trey. 520 S MUSTANG RD, C/O MERCY AFTER HOURS 73099 #039-01-1998 L1999 **GP** *020 †18

MIRANDA, Mary Ann Venita. ■ 73099 #495-31-1999 L2006 **IM** *020 †20

MOLLOY, Allen Rogers. 125 W MEADE DR 73099 #039-01-2001 L2002 **VIR** *020 †80

NGUYEN, Jimmy Quang. 10417 LEICESTER DR 73099 #039-01-2005 L2006 **DR** *012

PAPPY, Raji Mathew. ■ 73099 #422-01-2005 L2007 **IM** *012

PINAROC, Nestor Fernandez. 520 S MUSTANG RD 73099 #039-01-1994 L1995 **FM** *020 †18 ‡

QURESHI, Farhan Mujtaba. 1205 HEALTH CENTER PKWY, STE 210 73099 #704-24-1987 L1998 **IM** *020 †20

REED, Emily Kathleen. 1205 HEALTH CENTER PKWY, STE 100 73099 #004-01-1995 L1996 **MPD** *020 †20,55

RICKNER, Kyle Wade. 1205 HEALTH CENTER PKWY 73099 #038-06-1998 L1999 **FM** *020 †18

SAMARA, Ilona E. ■ 73099 #039-01-2004 L2007 **FP** *012

SCHWARZ, Kristallena S. 1201 HEALTH CENTER PKWY 73099 #039-01-1996 L1998 **FM** *020 †18

SHEPHERD, James Daniel. ■ 73099 #039-01-2007 L2007 **GS** *012

SIEMS, Ami Leigh. 808 S MUSTANG RD, CANADIAN VALLEY FAMILY CAR 73099 #039-01-1988 L1989 **FM** *020 †18

SIPES, Billy Hugh. 520 S MUSTANG RD 73099 #039-01-1974 L1975 **GP** *020

SOO, Chenglun. 1205 HEALTH CENTER PKWY 73099 #020-12-1993 L1999 **ORS OSS** *020 †40

STOCKERT, Kassi Deanne. ■ 73099 #039-01-2008 *012

STUDEBAKER, Marion Kent. 520 S MUSTANG RD 73099 #039-01-1973 L1974 **FM** *020 ‡

TAYLOR, Stephanie Lynn. 1205 HEALTH CENTER PKWY, STE 100 73099 #039-01-2001 L2002 **GS** *020 †85

VERNIER, Stephen Lavern. 520 S MUSTANG RD 73099 #039-01-1993 L1994 **FM** *020 †18

WELDEN, William Lee. 436 S MUSTANG RD 73099 #039-01-1993 L1994 **FM** *020 †18 ‡

WOODCOCK, Luther Monroe. ■ 73099 #039-01-1980 L1981 **ID** *030

ALBANY – LINN

ADAMO, Harry Tony. 1046 6TH AVE SW 97321 #016-43-1975 L1978 **EM FM** *020 †18

ANDERSON, Kenneth Clair. 2615 WILLETTA ST SW, STE C2 97321 #018-03-1962 L1970 **ORS** *071 †40

BAIN, Matt Rodney. 2605 WILLETTA ST SW, STE D1 97321 #040-02-1998 L2001 **FM** *020 †18

BARTELL, Donald Robert. 1030 29TH AVE SW, MID-VALLEY PROFF PARK 97321 #005-15-1962 L1963 **GP OS** *071

BARTLETT, Mark Gordon. 734 ELM ST SW 97321 #035-45-1995 L2001 **PD** *020 †55

BASSINGER, Larry Lee. 2615 WILLETTA ST SW, STE C2 97321 #040-02-1962 L1963 **GP** *020

BENTSON, Lynn Anne. 1086 7TH AVE SW 97321 #040-02-1987 L1988 **IM** *020 †20

BOHMAN, Bruce Robt. 1046 6TH AVE SW 97321 #040-02-1977 L1978 **EM** *020 †16

BOYD, Lisa Ann. 734 ELM ST SW 97321 #003-01-1999 L2005 **PD** *020 †55

BROOKS, Allen Geo. 1046 6TH AVE SW 97321 #040-02-1978 L1982 **N** *020 †75

CAMP, John R. ■ 97322 #016-11-1947 L1948 **GP** *071

CARLSON, A Eugene. 705 ELM ST SW STE 300 97321 #019-02-1954 L1958 **OPH** *071 †35

CHAPIN, Pamela Jo Seewald. 1700 GEARY ST SE 97322 #007-02-1992 L1993 **FM** *020 †18

CLARK, Thomas Fuess. 1086 7TH AVE SW, STE 101 97321 #048-04-1973 L1976 **IM** *020 †20

CONKLIN, Thomas Roscoe. 1046 6TH AVE SW 97321 #040-02-1963 L1965 **FM** *071 †18

CROW, Kenneth Arthur. ■ 97321 #056-05-1964 L1973 **PTH FOP** *071 †50

CROY, Jeffrey Francis. 1046 6TH AVE SW, ALBANY ANESTHESIA PC 97321 #035-45-1991 L1996 **AN** *020 †05

DEEMS, Theodore R. ■ 97321 #016-06-1951 L1951 **FM** *071

DENGLER, Wolfgang Amadeus. 1046 6TH AVE SW, ALBANY GEN HOSP-EMERGENCY 97321 #005-02-1973 L1984 **EM GPM** *020 †16

EBY, Lawrence S. ■ 97322 #025-01-1961 L1966 **EM** *071 †85

ECKROTH, Michelle Diane. 734 ELM ST SW 97321 #005-12-1988 L1996 **PD** *020 †55

ELLISON, Elizabeth Leigh. ■ 97321 #021-01-1993 L1999 **P** *100

ELLISON, Monty Ross. 909 ELM ST SW 97321 #021-01-1962 L1970 **HS ORS** *071 †40

ENDICOTT, William R. ■ 97322 #040-02-1945 L1946 **GP** *071

EWANCHYNA, Kevin Daniel J. 1046 6TH AVE SW 97321 #068-01-1992 L1997 **FM** *030 †18

FLETCHER, Steven Richard. ■ 97321 #011-03-1980 L1981 **PTH** *020 †50

FROTHINGHAM, Edward Paul. 734 ELM ST SW 97321 #005-02-1995 L1999 **PD** *020 †55

GAEKWAD, Satyajeet Y. 705 ELM ST SW, STE 300 97321 #028-46-1992 L2006 **GS** *020 †85

GENSTLER, Darrell Eugene. 2700 14TH AVE SE 97322 #005-12-1977 L1984 **OPH** *020 †35

GILSDORF, Richard Chas. ■ 97321 #040-02-1963 L1967 **AN** *071

GOBY, Gary Albert. 1700 GEARY ST SE 97322 #028-34-1968 L1973 **FM** *020 †18

GRADIN, Dan. 2715 WILLETTA ST SW, STE B 97321 #040-02-1990 L2001 **OPH** *020 †35

GRAY, Mary J. COURT HOUSE ANNEX, LINN COUNTY HEALTH CLINIC 97321 #028-02-1949 L1991 **OBG** *071 †30

GREAVES, Paul Michael. 1046 6TH AVE SW, ALBANY ANESTHESIA PC 97321 #040-02-1994 L1995 **AN** *020 †05

HAFFNER, David Lee. 1046 6TH AVE SW 97321 #005-12-1971 L1973 **EM** *020

HAFFNER, Wesley Harry. ■ 97322 #005-12-1941 **GP R** *071

HALL, C Robt. 920 8TH AVE SW 97321 #025-07-1963 L1971 **U** *020 †95

HARADA, Mary Kay. 705 ELM ST SW STE 300 97321 #041-13-1985 L1990 **GS** *020 †85

HICKEY, John Edward. 1705 WAVERLY DR SE 97322 #054-04-1980 L1987 **FM** *020 †18

HOLMES, Henry Howard. 1700 GEARY ST SE, GEARY STREET CLINIC 97322 #005-02-1973 L1980 **OM FM** *020 †18

HOPKIN, Joel Kenneth. 1040 24TH AVE SW 97321 #048-15-1998 L2001 **GS** *020

HOVEY, Margaret Anne. 705 ELM ST SW, STE 200 97321 #056-06-1994 L1998 **OBG** *020 †30

HUME-RODMAN, Constance. 1086 7TH AVE SW, STE 101 97321 #008-02-1985 L1998 **IM** *020 †20

HURD, E Lew. ■ 97321 #040-02-1939 L1940 **GP** *071

IRVINE, David Jos. 2605 WILLETTA ST SW, STE D1 97321 #040-02-1982 L1985 **FM** *020 †18

JURANI, Othella Ann. 1705 WAVERLY DR SE 97322 #031-01-1999 L2006 **FM** *020 †18

KANDA, Parveen. 1700 GEARY ST SE 97322 #031-01-2002 L2006 **FM** *100 †18

KARAMI, Nilgoon. ■ 97321 #517-08-1997 L2004 **IM** *020

KAST, John Michael. 950 29TH AVE SW 97321 #016-42-1988 L2001 **NS** *020 †25

KAYE, Samuel Martin. 1086 7TH AVE SW, STE 101 97321 #031-01-1980 L1981 **IM** *020 †20

KENAGY, Benjamin Eugene. 2715 WILLETTA ST SW 97321 #016-06-1955 L1959 **FM GP** *071

KENYON, Richard Jos. 620 ELM ST SW, ALBANY ANESTHESIA PC 97321 #035-09-1957 L1971 **AN** *071 †05

KLEVE, Roger Albert. 620 ELM ST SW, ALBANY ANESTHESIA PC 97321 #016-43-1967 L1973 **AN** *072 †05

KNOWLES, Kara Melissa. 734 ELM ST SW 97321 #048-04-2004 L2007 **PD** *020 †55

LANDERS, Roger Q, III. 1046 6TH AVE SW 97321 #018-03-1982 L1993 **PTH** *020 †50

LARSEN, Jonathan Lorenzo. 705 ELM ST SW, STE 200 97321 #016-06-1993 L2000 **OBG** *020 †30

LAZAROFF, Elizabeth Cohn. 213 WATER AVE NW STE 40, LINN COUNTY MENTAL HEALTH 97321 #019-02-1988 L1994 **P** *020 †75

LEAR, William J, Jr. 1086 7TH AVE SW, STE 101 97321 #030-05-1978 L1982 **IM** *020 †20

LEES, John. 2715 WILLETTA ST SW 97321 #033-05-1965 L1969 **OPH** *020 †35

LINCOLN, Elizabeth Anne. 1700 GEARY ST SE 97322 #025-12-1997 L2002 **FM** *020 †18

MADSEN, Bruce William. 2715 WILLETTA ST SW, STE B 97321 #016-42-1999 L2003 **OPH** *020 †35

MARTIN, Rolland A. PO BOX 460 97321 #040-02-1949 L1950 **OM** *071

MAY, Takiko Monica. 1086 7TH AVE SW 97321 #001-06-2000 L2004 **IM** *020 †20

MC CARLEY, Tim D. 1052 29TH AVE SW 97321 #039-01-1994 L2001 **P** *020

MILLER, Gregg M. 1046 6TH AVE SW 97321 #040-02-1989 L1994 **GS** *020 †85

MILLER, Rose Caroline. 1700 GEARY ST SE, GEARY ST FAMILY PRACTICE 97322 #056-05-1989 L1994 **FM** *020 †18

MOORE, Harry Daniels. 1705 WAVERLY DR SE, SPECIALTY MEDI 97322 #004-01-1964 L1967 **GP** *020

MOORE, Robert Gary. 631 ELM ST SW STE 201 97321 #040-02-1972 L1980 **U** *020 †95

MORGAN, Lynn Spaulding. 1100 7TH AVE SW 97321 #032-01-1979 L1984 **FM** *020 †18

MULKEY, Daniel David. 1086 7TH AVE SW, STE 101 97321 #048-04-1973 L1976 **IM** *020 †20

NAIBERT, James Richard. 1705 WAVERLY DR SE 97322 #018-03-1981 L1995 **FM** *020 †18

NEAL, Stanley King. 2605 WILLETTA ST SW, STE D1 97321 #040-02-1972 L1975 **FM** *020

NEWCOMB, Susan Annette. 1100 7TH AVE SW, CALAPOOIA FAM MED GRP 97321 #041-07-1981 L1983 **IM** *020 †20

NEWMAN, Stephen Roy. 400 NW HICKORY AVE, # 200 97321 #056-06-1989 L1998 **ORS** *020 †40

OHLING, Dirk Anthony. 2605 WILLETTA ST SW, STE D1 97321 #040-02-1995 L1998 **FM** *020 †18

OLSEN, Armin Boone. ■ 97322 #017-20-1963 L1973 **OTO AM** *071 †45

ORIGER, William J. 1046 6TH AVE SW, ALBANY GENERAL HOSPITAL 97321 #030-05-1973 L1975 **FM MDM** *030 †18

OTIS, Patricia Sue. 1705 WAVERLY DR SE, ALBANY FAM & SPEC MEDICINE 97322 #030-05-2004 L2007 **FM** *020 †18

OUELLETTE, Laura Merie. ■ 97322 #040-02-1986 L1988 **FM** *020 †18

OWEN-THAYER, Rebekah K. 1100 7TH AVE SW 97321 #005-18-1992 L1995 **IM** *020 †20

PAKUNPANYA, Rachael Marie. 1705 WAVERLY DR SE 97322 #021-06-2003 L2006 **FM** *020 †18

PARK, Jung Yearl. ■ 97322 #583-09-1964 L1971 **GS** *071 †85

PATTON, Jaimy Theron. 1046 6TH AVE SW, ALBANY ANESTHESIA PC 97321 #056-06-1989 L1993 **AN** *020 †05

PAUL, Adam Bradley. 734 ELM ST SW 97321 #030-05-2001 L2007 **PD** *020 †55

PERRYMAN, Dana Dyan. 734 ELM ST SW 97321 #011-03-1992 L1995 **PD** *020 †55

PETERSEN, Glenn Alan. 1100 7TH AVE SW STE A 97321 #040-02-1980 L1983 **FM** *020 †18

POTTER, Michael Lewis. 1700 GEARY ST SE, FIRST CARE PHYSICIANS 97322 #040-02-1989 L2001 **FM FSM** *020 †18

PROTAIN, Adam Christian. ■ 97322 #007-02-2008 *012

RAFALSKI, Thomas A. 1086 7TH AVE SW, STE 101 97321 #017-20-1985 L1988 **IM** *020 †20

RAPP, Robert S. 1705 WAVERLY DR SE 97322 #041-09-1964 L1970 **AI PD** *071 †55,03

RAY, Marie Annette. 705 ELM ST SW, STE 300 97321 #016-42-1990 L1997 **GS** *020 †85

ROBINSON, Jeffrey E. 1705 WAVERLY DR SE 97322 #040-02-1993 L1996 **FM** *020 †18

RYCKMAN, Albert Edward. 631 ELM ST SW, STE 202 97321 #054-04-1976 L1987 **GE GP** *020 †20

SALISBURY, Dana. 734 ELM ST SW 97321 #016-11-1996 L1999 **PD** *020 †55

SANSOME, Kenneth Neil. ■ 97321 #026-04-1972 L2006 **FM** *020 †18

SCHINDELL, Scott Arthur. 1700 GEARY ST SE 97322 #054-04-1997 L2000 **FM** *020 †18

SERRILL, W Scott. 1050 7TH AVE S 97321 #028-03-1971 L1977 **D** *020 †18

SHERMAN, Michael Gerard. 1700 GEARY ST SE, SAMARITAN HEALTH PHYSICIAN 97322 #030-06-1999 L2003 **MPD** *020 †20,55

SILVER, Allan J. ■ 97322 #005-16-1962 L1975 **GP** *071

SMITH, Kenneth David. 1705 WAVERLY DR SE, ALBANY FAMILY MEDICINE 97322 #061-01-1992 L1998 **FM** *020 †18

SMOLEN, Gale A. 445 3RD AVE SW, LINN COUNTY MENTAL HLTH CL 97321 #005-12-1976 L1979 **P** *020

SOLENSKY, Roland. 1705 WAVERLY DR SE 97322 #035-47-1995 L2002 **AI A** *020 †03,55

SOUTH, Charles Danl, III. 705 ELM ST SW, STE 200 97321 #005-02-1963 L1971 **OBG** *020 †30

STANLEY, Rick Dean. 400 NW HICKORY AVE, # 200 97321 #012-05-1971 L1978 **ORS** *020 †40

STEGEMAN-OLSEN, Jenny Lee. 1705 WAVERLY DR SE 97322 #040-02-1997 L2000 **FM** *020 †18

STOBART, Olga Vilyamovna. 1046 6TH AVE SW 97321 #913-81-1996 L2007 **IM** *020 †20

SWAN, Christopher Paul. 1705 WAVERLY DR SE, ALBANY FAMILY & SPECIALTY 97322 #040-02-1977 L1978 **FM** *020 †18

TEPLICK, Stanley Bruce. 2310 14TH AVE SE, CENTER FOR SIGHT ALBANY 97322 #041-09-1977 L1991 **OPH** *020 †35

THAYER, Douglas Buchanan. 1100 7TH AVE SW 97321 #005-18-1992 L1995 **FM** *020 †18

THROOP, George Reeves, III. ■ 97321 #028-02-1970 L1974 **N** *062 †75

VANASCHE, Thomas Edward. 1046 6TH AVE SW 97321 #040-02-1977 L1979 **FM** *020 †18

VANDIVER, Robert Fred. 445 3RD AVE SW 97321 #046-01-1983 L1984 **P** *020

WARD, John Reznor, Jr. 1700 GEARY ST SE 97322 #040-02-2000 L2003 **FM** *020 †18

WEINSTEIN, Louis Walter. 1086 7TH AVE SW, STE 101 97321 #048-04-1973 L1976 **IM NEP** *020 †20

WHEELER, Patrica Leigh. 1700 GEARY ST SE 97322 #040-02-1990 L1993 **FM** *020 †18

WONG, Paul Y. 1040 7TH AVE SW, FIRSTCARE PHYSICIANS 97321 #748-10-1973 L1981 **OBG AM** *071 †30

WREN, Rodney Louis. 631 ELM ST SW, STE 204 97321 #040-02-1981 L1985 **OBG** *020

ZOLLINGER, Matthew Dean. 1700 GEARY ST SE 97322 #030-06-1999 L2003 **MPD** *020 †20,55

ALOHA – WASHINGTON

BLACKMAN, Jon Arthur. 1881 NW 185TH AVE, STE 300 97006 #028-02-1974 L1977 **FM** *020 †18

COLBRY, Kyran Gerald. 20870 SW ROSA DR 97007 #040-02-2001 L2004 **EM** *020 †16

DAVIDSON, Howard Andrew. 1881 NW 185TH AVE STE 207 97006 #041-12-1996 L1998 **PD** *020 †55

DELPLANCHE, Curtis Gregor. ■ 97007 #130-01-2002 L2007 **N** *100

DENMAN, Timothy Mark. 18345 SW ALEXANDER ST, STE A 97006 #056-06-1972 L1974 **OPH** *020 †35

GOSWAMI, Pompy Zillie. 1881 NW 185TH AVE, STE 300 97006 #495-18-1994 L2005 **FM** *020 †18

GUPTA, Sunita. 1881 NW 185TH AVE, STE 300 97006 #496-20-1995 L2000 **FM** *020

HEEG, James Christopher. 17175 SW TV HWY 97006 #068-01-1990 L1995 *100

JARMAN MILLER, Daniel M. 17175 SW TV HWY 97006 #040-02-1988 L1989 **IM GP** *020

KASARANENI, Yamuna. 1881 NW 185TH AVE STE 100, TANASBOURNE URGENT CARE 97006 #495-11-1987 L2002 **FM** *020 †18

KINGMAN, John. 1881 NW 185TH AVE STE 101, TANASBOURNE IMMEDIATE CARE 97006 #040-02-1979 L1991 **EM D** *020 †15,18

SANDHU, Neelwant Singh. ■ 97006 #040-02-2005 **PM** *012

WILLIAMS, Patrick Scott. 1881 NW 185TH AVE STE 102 97006 #040-02-1992 L1999 **FM** *020 †18

ANTELOPE – WASCO

RIEDLINGER-WIGGENHORN, F. 43 MEVLANA BHAGWAN ST 97001 #869-04-1975 L1985 *100

ASHLAND – JACKSON

ACKROYD, Alan Wile. ■ 97520 #049-01-1974 L1999 **EM IM** *020 †20,16

ALI, Zakir Musfique. 1801 HWY 99 N 97520 #495-18-1990 L2004 **N** *020 †75

ALLRED, Lyle Eugene. 855 WINDEMAR DR 97520 #005-06-1976 L1989 **EM FM** *020 †16

ANDERSON, Keith Frederick. ■ 97520 #005-11-1959 L1960 **AN** *071 †05

ATOR, Pamela Ruth. 280 MAPLE ST 97520 #040-02-1993 L1994 **IM** *020 †20

BARTON, John W. 280 MAPLE ST, DEPARTMENT OF RADIOLOGY 97520 #016-43-1967 L1975 **DR** *075 †80

BECICH, Joan N. ■ 97520 #005-19-1978 L1988 AN *020 †05
BLOOM, Michael Abram. ■ 97520 #041-02-1962 L1963 IM CD *071 †20
BRADSHAW, Donna M. 251B MAPLE ST 97520 #035-45-1991 L2001 PHO *020 †55
BROOKLER, Morton Irving. ■ 97520 #062-01-1958 L1991 RHU IM *071 †20
BROWN, Willard Leroy. 1875 HIGHWAY 99 N, INSIGHT RESOURCES INC 97520 #038-41-1957 L1979 GYN *071 †30
CALHOUN, Roselyn J. ■ 97520 #010-03-1980 L1982 P *020
CALLANAN, David Anthony. 132 N MAIN ST STE 103 97520 #143-03-1977 L1993 CHP *020 †75
CAMPBELL, Alan Bonham. 280 MAPLE ST 97520 #034-01-1989 L1994 FM *020 †18
CARY, Stephen Clarke. 743 N MAIN ST 97520 #008-01-1961 L1991 VS GS *071 †85
CAVAZOS, Martha Marie. 280 MAPLE ST 97520 #048-14-1997 L2004 END *100 †20 ‡
CENSOR, John Jacob. ■ 97520 #759-01-1946 GP *071
CHAMBERS, David Warner. 628 N MAIN ST 97520 #005-06-1986 L1998 OTO AM *020 †45
CHANG, Rhet. ■ 97520 #035-46-1977 L1991 IM *020
CHATROUX, Sylvia Seroussi. 400 W HERSEY ST 97520 #035-48-1987 L1991 FM *020 †18
CHENOWETH, Richard Glenn. 2305 ASHLAND ST STE C, PMB 407 97520 #016-11-1963 L1972 OPH *071 †35
CHOW, Craig Chong. 743 N MAIN ST 97520 #038-06-1985 L1990 GE IM *020 †20
CHRISTLIEB, Dee Edward. 935 SISKIYOU BLVD 97520 #040-02-1980 L1981 FM *020 †18
CLARK, Peter Lawrence. 280 MAPLE ST 97520 #024-05-1965 L1973 U *020 †95
CLARKE, John Carleton. ■ 97520 #005-02-1954 L1955 GS *071 †85
COREY, Ellen C. ■ 97520 #038-41-1989 L2000 EM *020 †16
COTT, Joshua Michael. ■ 97520 #051-01-2002 L2006 EM *020 †16
CRADDICK, Joyce Wilson. ■ 97520 #041-01-1957 L1995 PDC *074 †55
CRAIG, Joseph Deafner. ■ 97520 #038-40-1947 L1951 IMG PHP *071 †55
CRAWFORD, Robert David. ■ 97520 #005-02-1972 L1973 AN *020 †05
DELGADO, John Palsted. 148 E HERSEY ST 97520 #005-14-1987 L1990 FM *020 †18
DIEHL, Douglas Kent. 255 MAPLE ST, ASHLAND ANESTHESIA ASSOCIA 97520 #035-20-1982 L2002 AN *020 †05
DOEDE, Katherine Gonzalez. ■ 97520 #016-02-1967 L1968 FM IMG *020 †18
DOUMA, Allen Jacob. ■ 97520 #051-04-1975 L1977 GP *030
DUNN, James Edwin, II. 1801 HWY 99 N 97520 #023-01-1960 L1974 NS TRS *020 †25
ENNS, Gordon Lee. 280 MAPLE ST, ASHLAND EMERGENCY ASSOCIAT 97520 #041-01-1976 L1977 GP EM *020
EPSTEIN, William Stuart. 648 N MAIN ST 97520 #048-02-1979 L1983 OPH *020 †35
EWALD, Thomas Mc Connell. 595 N MAIN ST, STE 1 97520 #036-07-1972 L1975 FM PMM *020
FAIRCLOTH, James Ramsay. ■ 97520 #025-01-1954 L1955 P PYA *071 †75
FALKNER, Douglas Jay. ■ 97520 #038-06-1988 L2001 EM *020 †16
FALLON, Michael David. ■ 97520 #028-34-1977 L1978 PTH *050 †50
FENNELL, Robert H, Jr. ■ 97520 #051-04-1943 L1943 PTH *071 †50
FREEMAN, James Alvin. ■ 97520 #028-03-1969 L1969 CD IM *071 †20
FRIED, Yvonne Suzanne. 540 CATALINA DR 97520 #005-19-1979 L1992 OBG *020 †30
GAGNON, Elliott Bruce. ■ 97520 #040-02-2001 L2007 PS *020
GODARD, Denise Marie-F. ■ 97520 #067-02-1963 L1968 R *071 †80
GOODING, Matthew Kirk. 125 MAPLE ST 97520 #051-04-1967 L1972 FM *020 †18
GOODMAN, Mark Clifford. 333 N MAIN ST 97520 #035-08-1998 L2005 EM *020
GORDON, Deborah L. 1607 SISKIYOU BLVD 97520 #005-02-1979 L1986 FM EM *020 †18
GREENBERG, Mark Randy. 638 N MAIN ST 97520 #005-06-1981 L1993 AN PMM *020 †20,05
HALD, Christian Peter. 280 MAPLE ST 97520 #026-04-1952 L1952 FM *071 †18
HARRIS, Karen Diane. 246 CATALINA DR, LITHIA WMS CARE STE #5 97520 #018-03-1982 L1992 OBG *020 †30
HEBERT, Clifton Barclay. 2220 ABBOTT AVE 97520 #048-12-1985 L2002 AN *020 †05
HITES, Clifford Anthony. 6429 SHALE CITY RD 97520 #005-02-1971 L1974 IM EM *020 †20
HOFFMAN, Paul Geo. 1801 HWY 99 N, STE 2 97520 #005-15-1981 L1992 GS *020 †85
HONSINGER, Patrick Kelly. 241 MAPLE ST 97520 #034-01-1995 L1998 FM *072 †18
INBAR, Daria E. 1257 SISKIYOU BLVD 97520 #550-01-1997 L2003 P *020 †75
JARVIS, Thomas B. ■ 97520 #049-01-1952 L1987 PTH *071 †50
JOHNSON, Allen Duane. 628 N MAIN ST 97520 #005-11-1973 L1978 IM *020 †20
JOHNSON, Bruce Everett. 241 MAPLE ST 97520 #030-05-1967 L1972 PLM FM *071 †18
JOHNSTON, Tim Frederick. ■ 97520 #007-02-2004 L2007 FM *020 †18
JONES, David Scott. 595 N MAIN ST, STE 2 97520 #005-19-1974 L1975 FM *020 †18
KANE, Fred James. ■ 97520 #041-12-1954 L1955 P *030
KAUFMAN, Annick-Marie Vot. 1801 HIGHWAY 99 N 97520 #305-01-2002 L2007 GS *020
KEEVIL, Jean A Henderson. 935 SISKIYOU BLVD 97520 #005-02-1972 L1974 FM *071
KING, Charles Herschel. ■ 97520 #023-01-1956 L1963 AN PUD *071 †05
KIRKPATRICK, David Cowan. ■ 97520 #012-01-1970 L1978 OS *020 †75
KNOBLICH, Guenther Olaf. 269 MAPLE ST, ASHLAND ORTHOPEDIC ASSOC 97520 #005-11-1995 L2007 ORS *020 †40
KOLO-CARON, Lucinda Marie. 1025 SISKIYOU BLVD 97520 #032-01-1999 L2002 FM *020 †18
KOUTNIK, Debra Lynn. 251B MAPLE ST, ASHLAND PEDIATRICS 97520 #005-02-1988 L1994 PD PHP *020 †55
KUZMITZ, Andrew Anthony. 595 N MAIN ST, STE 1 97520 #005-14-1976 L1980 FM *020 †18
LEE, Jonathan Hilder. 628 N MAIN ST 97520 #026-08-2001 L2005 OTO *020 †45
LEHRBURGER, Gerry David. 1639 JACKSON RD, JACKSON HOUSE 97520 #007-02-1978 L1979 EM *020 †16
LOVICH, Stephen Frank. 521 N MAIN ST, STE 2 97520 #023-12-1984 L2003 PS *020 †65,85
LUCAS, William E. ■ 97520 #035-01-1950 L1988 ON GYN *020 †30
MATHER, Craig Stanley. 595 N MAIN ST, STE 1 97520 #005-14-1976 L1980 FM EM *020 †18
MAURER, John Gaffney. 280 MAPLE ST 97520 #047-06-1967 L1975 ORS *020 †40
MC COIN, Cameron. 1257 SISKIYOU BLVD 97520 #048-13-1991 L2004 FM *020 †18
MC DONALD, Lorraine Kay. 1250 SISKIYOU BLVD, STUDENT HEALTH & WELL CTR 97520 #016-02-1996 L2002 FM *020 †18
MICHAEL, Philip F. ■ 97520 #035-19-1979 L1983 PUD CCM *020 †20
MONTGOMERY, Mary Ann. ■ 97520 #016-06-1973 L1976 P *020 †75
MORNINGSTAR, Howard W. 370 E HERSEY ST 97520 #008-01-1989 L1996 FM NTR *020 †18
MORRIS, Richard Lee. 280 MAPLE ST 97520 #040-02-1978 L1984 FM *020 †18
MORRISON, Douglas Petrie. 280 MAPLE ST 97520 #005-02-1975 L1982 ORS *020 †40
MURPHY, George B, Jr. ■ 97520 #024-01-1951 L1981 CD GS *075 †85
NITZBERG, Jerome Stanford. ■ 97520 #041-02-1961 L1978 FM *071 †18
OLSON, Cynthia Lee. 246 CATALINA DR STE 5 97520 #010-02-1988 L1998 GYN *020 †30
O'SULLIVAN, Glen S. 280 MAPLE ST 97520 #917-21-1984 L1999 ORS *020 †40
PEARSON, Julie Seidl. 246 CATALINA DR, STE 5 97520 #016-11-1996 L2000 GYN *020 †30
PHILLIPS, Philip Harry. 280 MAPLE ST, ASHLAND COMMUNITY HOSPITAL 97520 #041-12-1972 L1994 EM IM *020 †20,16
POKORNY, Gert Eugen. ■ 97520 #407-05-1961 L1969 OBG *071 †30
POWELL, Gerald Francis. ■ 97520 #056-06-1957 L1963 PD *071 †55
POWELL, Geraldine L K. ■ 97520 #023-07-1964 L1964 GE PD *040 †55
RAYMAN, Mark Brooks. ■ 97520 #038-43-1979 L1994 P *020
REECK, Jay Berkley. 628 N MAIN ST 97520 #036-07-1998 L2003 OTO *020 †45
REYNOLDS, John Ross. 280 MAPLE ST 97520 #041-02-1947 L1948 IM *071
RODDEN, William Stephen. 246 CATALINA DR, RETINA & VITREOUS CENTER 97520 #051-04-1985 L1990 OPH *020 †35
ROLLINS, Jani Rene. 1025 SISKIYOU BLVD 97520 #005-02-1994 L1999 FM *020 †18
ROSE, Robin Lorie. 2305 ASHLAND ST, STE C121 97520 #003-01-1991 L1994 FM *020 †18
ROSS, Franklin H, Jr. 565 A ST, UNIT 100 97520 #019-02-1970 L1976 OBG *020 †30
ROTH, James Alan. ■ 97520 #026-04-1969 L1977 OTO *020 †45
RYAN, Donald Kevin. 292 GRESHAM ST 97520 #010-02-1964 L1982 DR *071 †80
SAGER, John Lawrence. 595 N MAIN ST 97520 #016-06-1991 L1992 FM *020 †18
SAKRADSE, Alfred. 333 RAVENWOOD PL 97520 #035-20-1974 L1976 EM IM *020 †20,16
SAMMONS, William M. ■ 97520 #021-01-1950 L1951 GP FM *072 †18
SCHILLING, Wendy L. 628 N MAIN ST 97520 #005-18-1993 L1994 IM *020 †20
SHEIBANI, Shahrzad. 400 W HERSEY ST 97520 #038-40-1996 L2002 IM *020 †20
SMITH, Leo Michael. ■ 97520 #005-06-1968 L1969 EM *075 †16
SNOOK, David Wallace. 280 MAPLE ST, BOX 248 97520 #025-01-1970 L1979 EM IM *020 †20
SORIANO, Miriam. 420 WILLIAMSON WAY 97520 #005-11-1986 L1989 FM *020 †18
STEELE, Elizabet Helen. 628 N MAIN ST 97520 #003-01-1987 L1988 OTO *020 †45
STEINSIEK, James Wm. 280 MAPLE ST, ASHLAND COMMUNITY HOSPITAL 97520 #004-01-1985 L2001 AN FM *020 †05,18
STEWART, Bert Montgomery. 1801 HIGHWAY 99 N, STE B 97520 #005-12-1989 L2001 GS TRS *020 †85
STEWART, Tamara Renee. 1801 HIGHWAY 99 N, STE B 97520 #005-12-1994 L2001 EM *020 †16
STONE, Leslie Peterson. ■ 97520 #054-04-1984 L2000 FM *020 †18
STONE, Peter Michael. 595 N MAIN ST, STE 2 97520 #054-04-1987 L2000 FM EM *020 †18
STRUM, Stephen Bruce. ■ 97520 #016-02-1968 L1984 ON IM *020 †20
SUNDEEN, Reinhold A. ■ 97520 #025-01-1942 L1946 P *071
SUNDIN, Ted Tryggve. 149 CLEAR CREEK DR, UNIT 102 97520 #858-02-1985 L1989 P *020 †75
SWANSON, Gary Lee. ■ 97520 #026-04-1972 L1983 AN *020 †05
THURSTON, Philip Albert. ■ 97520 #035-03-1966 L1973 IM *020 †20
TOWNSEND, Hal Scott. 280 MAPLE ST 97520 #024-01-1984 L1990 ORS *020 †40
TRAYNOR, John Lewis. 595 N MAIN ST 97520 #028-34-1966 L1971 OTO *020 †45
TRAYNOR, Sean Jos. 628 N MAIN ST 97520 #040-02-1992 L1993 OTO *020 †45
WALKER, Elspeth Mair. ■ 97520 #352-06-1948 L1967 PHP *071
WAY, Anthony Eugene. ■ 97520 #005-02-1968 L1969 MDM U *071 †95
WEBB, Alan Jack. 280 MAPLE ST 97520 #010-01-1983 L1988 ORS *020 †40
WILLIAMS, Diane C. 251 MAPLE ST 97520 #040-02-1971 L1977 PD PHO *072 †55
YOUNG, Scott Clifford. 521 N MAIN ST 97520 #067-01-1978 L1993 PS HS *020

ASTORIA – CLATSOP

ARMINGTON, William G. 2111 EXCHANGE ST 97103 #056-06-1982 L2007 DR RNR *020 †80
ASHLEY, Scott Edward. 2120 EXCHANGE ST, STE 209 97103 #027-01-2000 L2003 FM *020 †18
BANHOLZER, John Arthur. 2111 EXCHANGE ST 97103 #038-41-1963 L1973 OPH *071 †35
CHARLES, Ellen. 2111 EXCHANGE ST 97103 #495-27-1957 L1977 OBG *071 †30
COWAN, Amy Nicole. ■ 97103 #014-01-2006 L2006 ORS *012
DUNCAN, Thomas Scott. 595 18TH ST 97103 #040-02-1971 L1974 FM *020 †18
GLANTZ, Daniel Scott. 2055 EXCHANGE ST, STE 230 97103 #048-04-1993 L1997 OPH *020 †35 ‡
GLANTZ, Edie Yungyee. 2055 EXCHANGE ST, STE 230 97103 #048-04-1992 L1997 N *020 †75
HAYNER, Paul John Louis. 1230 MARINE DR, STE 201 97103 #010-02-1999 L2003 IM *020 †20
HOLLAND, Robert Leslie. 550 22ND ST 97103 #048-16-1984 L2002 OBG *020 †30
HONL, Thomas Carl. ■ 97103 #040-02-1964 GP U *075
KEIZER, Russell James. 2120 EXCHANGE ST, STE 203 97103 #040-02-1965 L1972 ORS *020 †40
KETTELKAMP, Richard Geo. 515 15TH ST 97103 #018-03-1956 L1961 OBG GP *071
LINEHAN, Charles Kenneth. ■ 97103 #005-06-1954 L1956 GP *020 †18
LITTLE, Roy J. 2111 EXCHANGE ST 97103 #010-01-1982 L1990 FM *020 †18
LIU, Kwang-San. 2111 EXCHANGE ST 97103 #038-06-1987 L2008 OBG *020 †30
MADHAVARAPU, Ramchandra R. 2120 EXCHANGE ST, STE 202 97103 #495-57-1980 L2004 PD *020 †55
MERRILL, Katherine. 2055 EXCHANGE ST, STE 190 97103 #056-06-1994 L1997 FM *020 †18
MERTEN, Carolyn Anita. 2111 EXCHANGE ST, COLUMBIA MEMORIAL HOSP 97103 #016-43-1978 L1984 EM *020 †20
MILLER, Roger Wm. 2095 EXCHANGE ST 97103 #054-04-1967 L2003 OTO *020 †45
MITTAN, Daniella Mariana. 2120 EXCHANGE ST STE 200 97103 #550-02-1995 L2002 END *020 †20
NAIRN, Angela Stock. 2055 EXCHANGE ST, STE 190 97103 #040-02-1996 L2000 FM *020 †18
NATZKE, Richard H. 2111 EXCHANGE ST 97103 #005-02-1949 L1991 IM PLM *020 †20
NEIKES, Robert Donald. ■ 97103 #030-06-1943 GP *071
PARK, Sangkun. 2120 EXCHANGE ST STE 200 97103 #583-01-1977 L1993 IM *020
PETERSON, Robert Dallas. 2055 EXCHANGE ST STE 210 97103 #041-02-1976 L2006 ON HEM *020 †20
PLAGATA, Edith Marie V. ■ 97103 #748-02-1944 L1968 EM GYN *071
SABAHI, Houman. 2055 EXCHANGE ST, STE 170 97103 #040-02-1983 L1996 R EM *020 †80
SASAKI, Truman Makoto. 2055 EXCHANGE ST, STE 290 97103 #040-02-1969 L1975 GS *020 †85
SMITH, Brenda Pearl. 2111 EXCHANGE ST, COLUMBIA MEMORIAL HOSPITAL 97103 #036-08-1997 L2000 EM *020 †16
STEINMANN, Leroy W. ■ 97103 #025-01-1949 L1953 GP ORS *071
STRYKER, Mark Spencer. 515 15TH ST, ANGEL MEDICAL 97103 #028-02-1963 L1967 IM *020
STULL, Paul Denning. ■ 97103 #010-02-1967 L1972 U *020 †95
SUK, Samuel Soong. 2120 EXCHANGE ST, STE 103 97103 #028-46-1996 L1999 FM *020 †18
VOELLER, Paul Frederick. 2200 EXCHANGE ST 97103 #037-01-1980 L1983 IM *020
ZAGATA, Joseph Lawrence. 2111 EXCHANGE ST 97103 #040-02-1974 L1976 EM *020 †16

AUMSVILLE – MARION

BRADSHAW, Douglas E. ■ 97325 #018-03-1945 L1955 PD *071

HOTAN, Tanie. PO BOX 139, AUMSVILLE MEDICAL CLINIC 97325 #040-02-1998 L2001 **FM** *020 †18

AURORA – MARION

ANGELL, Richard Henry. ■ 97002 #026-04-1968 L1975 **CHP** *071 †75
BROWN, Paul M. ■ 97002 #024-01-1949 L1954 **GS TS** *071 †85
BRYAN, James Henry. 22285 YELLOW GATE LN NE, STE 102 97002 #040-02-1990 L1993 **EM** *020 †16
HOUSE, William Fouts. PO BOX 510 97002 #005-06-1953 L1953 **NO** *071 †45
VANDERBEEK, Gretchen Eliz. PO BOX 273, 21215 SAYRE DR NE 97002 #040-02-2008 *012

BAKER CITY – BAKER

ALANKO, Randy Arlen. 3325 POCAHONTAS RD 97814 #054-04-1981 L1986 **FM** *020 †18
DAVIS, James Edward. 3705 MIDWAY DR 97814 #040-02-1976 L1980 **OPH AM** *020 †35
DE LASHMUTT, Steven A. 3325 POCAHONTAS RD 97814 #040-02-1977 L1980 **IMG IM** *020 †20
DE VOS, Gary Steven. 3325 POCAHONTAS RD 97814 #040-02-1976 L1979 **EM FM** *020 †18
HERIZA, Nancy Clare. 2040 8TH ST 97814 #005-02-1981 L1985 **FM** *020 †18
HOFMANN, Charles Edward. 3820 17TH ST 97814 #040-02-1978 L1981 **IM** *020 †20
KOSTOL, Carl R. ■ 97814 #067-01-1951 **GP** *071
LAMB, Eric Ryan. 3950 17TH ST STE A, E OR MED ASSOC LLC 97814 #040-02-1999 L2002 **FM** *020 †18
LEVINGER, Laurence Wilson. 2805 10TH ST 97814 #008-01-1971 L1978 **GS** *020 †85
MC KIM, Menzie, Jr. 3175 POCAHONTAS RD 97814 #041-02-1947 L1951 **GP GS** *071
MC KIM, Robert Menzie. 3175 POCAHONTAS RD 97814 #041-02-1964 L1965 **FM** *020 †18
NOWAK, Diane Patricia. 3950 17TH ST STE A, E OR MED ASSOC LLC 97814 #007-02-1997 L2000 **FM** *020 †18
PETTERSON, Jon E. 3175 POCAHONTAS RD 97814 #019-02-1975 L1978 **FM** *020 †18
SCHOTT, Jonathan David. 3950 17TH ST STE A, E OR MED ASSOC LLC 97814 #040-02-1996 L1998 **FM** *020 †18
SMITHSON, Jesse Daniel. 3950 17TH ST STE A, E OR MED ASSOC LLC 97814 #005-06-1997 L2000 **FM** *020 †18
STIFF, Carl Edward. 3325 POCAHONTAS RD 97814 #040-02-1956 L1960 **GYN** *020
TYLKA, Barbara Lynn. 3325 POCAHONTAS RD, ST ELIZABETHS HOSP 97814 #032-01-1986 L1998 **GS** *020 †85

BANDON – COOS

ABBOTT, John Edward. 110 10TH ST SE, BANDON MEDICAL GROUP 97411 #040-02-1964 L1968 **GP** *071
AITCHISON, Gregory Allen. 1295 OREGON AVE SE 97411 #003-01-1979 L1982 **P** *020
BATES, Janet Marie. 110 10TH ST SE, NORTH BEND MEDICAL CENTER 97411 #060-01-1990 L1995 *020
BATES, Kenneth Robert J. 900 11TH ST SE, MAIL: 89569 SUNNY LOOP LAN 97411 #060-02-1980 L1996 **FM** *020
BRAZER, John Wm. 900 11TH ST SE 97411 #030-05-1969 L1970 **FM** *020 †18
BROWN, Robert Ray. ■ 97411 #005-15-1962 L1975 **GP** *071 †18
DOHNER, V Alton. ■ 97411 #007-02-1965 L1966 **P IM** *071
GRECU, Eugen Ovidiu. ■ 97411 #781-03-1964 L1975 **END IM** *071 †20
INOUYE, Allan Ames. 900 11TH ST SE 97411 #054-04-1974 L1991 **GS TS** *020 †90,85
MC CLAVE, Gail Koch. 780 2ND ST SE 97411 #021-05-1994 L2001 **FM IM** *020 †20,18
MOEHRING, Carl John. 110 10TH ST SE 97411 #026-04-1971 L1972 **IM** *020
PASTERNAK, Mark Andreas. 900 11TH ST SE, SOUTHERN COOS HOSP HLTH CT 97411 #308-07-1983 L1990 **FM OS** *020 †18
RIDDICK, Robert Steven. ■ 97411 #043-01-1984 L1985 **TS** *020 †85,90
SPRINGER, James L. 110 10TH ST SE 97411 #654-01-1987 L1991 **FM** *020 †18
STAGGENBORG, Richard K. 1010 1ST ST SE 97411 #040-02-1988 L1996 **P** *020 †75 ‡
STORMO, Megan Marie. 475 ELMIRA AVE SE, STE 201 97411 #035-45-2002 L2007 **FM** *020 †18
SUAREZ DOMINGUEZ, Carlos. 110 10TH ST SE 97411 #737-06-2000 L2006 **FM** *020 †18
TOTH, Elizabeth Ann. ■ 97411 #021-05-1964 L1964 **IM EM** *020 †20,16,18
TREVINO, Maria Teresa. 1010 1ST ST SE STE 100 97411 #056-06-1981 L1983 **FM** *020 †18 ‡
WELLS, Wilfred Douglas. ■ 97411 #005-12-1964 L1965 **DR** *071 †80

BEATTY – KLAMATH

CORNELSEN, Rodney Ray. PO BOX 248, 32150 GODOWA SPRINGS RD 97621 #005-12-1965 L1966 **ORS** *071 †40

BEAVER – TILLAMOOK

TURNEY, Albert Warren. ■ 97108 #028-34-1966 L1966 **AS FM** *071

BEAVERTON – WASHINGTON

ABBOTT, Bruce David. ■ 97007 #056-06-1994 L1998 **AN** *075
AGUILAR, Edita Soriano. 2935 SW CEDAR HILLS BLVD 97005 #748-02-1991 L2004 **PD** *020 †55
AIJAZI, Shadab Nasreen. ■ 97007 #704-08-1979 L1991 **PTH** *020 †50
ALTENHOFEN, Christopher J. 8950 SW NIMBUS AVE 97008 #040-02-1989 L1990 **DR** *020 †80
APODACA, Raquel Marie. 1881 NW 185TH AVE STE 207, TANASBOURNE PEDS 97006 #041-13-1995 L1997 **PD** *020 †55
ASSAD, Osama Fouad. 1315 NW 185TH AVE 97006 #915-07-1982 *100
AZHAR, Ezra. 3415 SW 187TH AVE 97006 #495-15-1971 L1984 **FM** *020
BACKSTROM, Robert Lawrence. 4855 SW WESTERN AVE 97005 #040-02-1970 L1974 **GP OS** *071
BALLARD, Luke Justin. ■ 97006 #035-45-2003 L2004 **DR** *012
BARKER, David H. ■ 97006 #023-01-1945 L1948 **R** *071 †80
BARR, Ian Lewis. 15455 NW GREENBRIER PKWY, # PKW-130 97006 #143-01-1966 L1975 **IM** *020 †20
BATES, John Robert. 14780 SW OSPREY DR 97007 #040-02-2002 L2002 **P** *100
BATES, Mark Gardner. 15950 SW MILLIKAN WAY 97006 #020-12-1992 L2003 **NEP** *020 †20

BENZ, Alfred Brooke. 1960 NW 167TH PL 97006 #040-02-1980 L1985 **ORS** *020 †40
BILLS, Richard Wm. 4855 SW WESTERN AVE, BEAVERTON MEDICAL OFFICE 97005 #005-02-1976 L1984 **IM ID** *020 †20
BINDAL, Vandana Niraj. 14314 SW ALLEN BLVD 97005 #495-30-1997 L2001 **IM** *020 †20
BLAIR, Harold Raymond. 4855 SW WESTERN AVE 97005 #539-01-1958 L1965 **PD** *020 †55
BLEAZARD, Scott Lee. ■ 97005 #005-06-2003 L2003 **DR** *012
BLEDSOE, Laura Elizabeth. 15950 SW MILLIKAN WAY 97006 #040-02-1992 L1993 **PD** *020 †55
BLOCK, Kelly Dawn. 4855 SW WESTERN AVE, KAISER PERMANENTE - BEAVER 97005 #040-02-1996 L1997 **IM** *020 †20
BOYD, James Thomas. ■ 97006 #007-02-2008 *012
BOYD, Lisa D. 14195 SW MILLIKAN WAY 97005 #048-02-1993 L2007 **P CHP** *020 †75
BRECKENRIDGE, S N. 14325 SW BONNIE BRAE ST 97005 #220-01-1961 L1978 **PTH** *020 †50
BROWN, Thomas R, II. 1500 NW BETHANY BLVD, STE 100 97006 #025-12-1984 L1987 **DR** *020 †80
BURTON, Brent Thos. 1865 NW 169TH PL, STE 201 97006 #049-01-1978 L1979 **UM EM** *020 †70,16
BUTLER, Priscilla. 4855 SW WESTERN AVE 97005 #007-02-1977 L1979 **FM** *020 †18
CAHN, Paul Jeffrey. 14385 SW ALLEN BLVD, STE 101 97005 #016-42-1989 L1994 **IM END** *020
CALDERON, Leona Raymundo. ■ 97007 #748-08-1960 L1975 **P** *071
CAVE, Colin Robt. 4855 SW WESTERN AVE 97005 #005-02-1989 L1994 **OTO HNS** *020 †45
CHANDRAN, Prasanna Rama. 15950 SW MILLIKAN WAY 97006 #038-40-1997 L2006 **FM** *020 †18
CHERN, Laurie. 1881 NW 185TH AVE, STE 300 97006 #051-04-1995 L1998 **FM** *020 †18
CHING, Gerald Dock Sung. 1960 NW 167TH PL, STE 100 97006 #035-01-1974 L1976 **PD** *020 †55
CIRINO, Nicole Harrington. 16110 SW REGATTA LN, WILDWOOD PSYCHIATRIC RESOU 97006 #016-43-1999 L2005 **P** *020 †75
CLARK, Edgar Erastus. 1500 NW BETHANY BLVD, STE 100 97006 #005-02-1968 L1975 **R NM** *020 †80,28
CLARK, Roy Malcolm. 8905 SW NIMBUS AVE, STE 300 97008 #352-07-1957 L1962 **AN** *020 †05
CLARKE, Mary Jolianne. 4855 SW WESTERN AVE, C/O KAISER PERANENTE 97005 #040-02-1983 L1988 **FM** *020 †18
COBURN, William P. 4855 SW WESTERN AVE 97005 #054-04-1953 L1963 **OBG OS** *071 †30
COLLINS, Jan Michael. 4855 SW WESTERN AVE, KAISER CLINIC 97005 #019-02-1965 L1967 **IM OS** *020 †20
CONANT-NORVILLE, David O. 15050 SW KOLL PKWY STE A2 97006 #040-02-1982 L1983 **CHP P** *020 †75
CONDON, Robert J. ■ 97007 #030-05-1944 L1944 **IM OM** *071
CONTORER, Paul. 4855 SW WESTERN AVE 97005 #016-06-1960 L1966 **D** *020 †15
COSTANTINI, Raymond Alexa. ■ 97007 #003-01-2004 L2004 **IM** *100
COX, Janie Mae. 4855 SW WESTERN AVE, KAISER PERM BEAVERTON MEDI 97005 #028-02-1983 L1994 **PD** *020 †55
DACONES, Imelda. 4855 SW WESTERN AVE, DEPT OF INTERNAL MEDICINE 97005 #016-02-1996 L1999 **IM** *020 †20
DANTAS, Leonora Manzano. 4855 SW WESTERN AVE 97005 #748-10-1963 L1969 **IM** *071 †20
DANTAS, Stella Marie. 4855 SW WESTERN AVE 97005 #040-02-1991 L2001 **OBG** *020 †30
DARDIS, Page Yvonne. 4855 SW WESTERN AVE, BEAVERTON MEDICAL OFFICE 97005 #040-02-1995 L1998 **IM** *020 †20
DEFRANK, Mary Patricia. 1881 NW 185TH AVE 97006 #040-02-1990 L1991 **OPH** *020 †35
DENMAN, Susan Tobey. 18345 SW ALEXANDER ST 97006 #021-01-1980 L1981 **DMP** *020 †15
DICK, Daniel Woods. ■ 97005 #045-04-2005 L2006 **P** *012
DONOHUE, Jennifer Jo. 4855 SW WESTERN AVE 97005 #024-01-1988 L1995 **FM** *020 †18
DOUGLASS, Jaypaul Weston. ■ 97008 #040-02-2008 *012
D'SOUZA-KAMATH, Reewen C. 15950 SW MILLIKAN WAY 97006 #495-52-1989 L2006 **IM** *020 †20
DUNLAP, Scott Griffith. 4855 SW WESTERN AVE 97005 #038-06-1976 L1979 **IM** *020 †20
DURAN, Christina Cruz. 15950 SW MILLIKAN WAY, PORTLAND CLINIC - BEAVERTO 97006 #038-43-1998 L2001 **FM** *020 †18
EATON, Alice Audrey. 17895 NW EVERGREEN PKWY, WESTSIDE PEDIATRIC CLINIC 97006 #040-02-1989 L1990 **PD** *020 †55
EGAN, John M. 8152 SW HALL BLVD # 134 97008 #539-04-1951 L1967 **AN OS** *071 †05
EGLI, Julie Ann. 12250 SW 2ND ST 97005 #047-05-1992 L1998 **P** *020
ELZINGA, Lawrence Wayne. 1920 NW AMBERGLEN PKWY, STE 150 97006 #005-02-1981 L1982 **IM NEP** *020 †20
EVANS, Cody Jon. ■ 97006 #040-02-2006 L2006 **P** *012
FELDSTEIN, Adrianne C. 4855 SW WESTERN AVE, KAISER PERMANENTE OH DEPT 97005 #010-01-1981 L1982 **OM PHP** *030 †70
FILIPEK, Maureen Suzanne. 8950 SW NIMBUS AVE 97008 #040-02-2000 L2000 **DR** *020 †80
FINLEY, Paul Ernest. 1881 NW 185TH AVE 97006 #012-05-1992 L1997 **OPH** *020 †35
FISH, Warren Lester. ■ 97006 #005-12-1961 L1974 **OBG** *071 †30
FISHER, Erin Ruth. ■ 97007 #050-02-2007 L2007 **PD** *012
GALE, John Goddard, Jr. 4855 SW WESTERN AVE, STE MH 97005 #011-03-1978 L1984 **CHP P** *020 †75
GANNETT, David Endicott. 15700 SW GREYSTONE CT, PACIFIC ONCOLOGY CANCER CT 97006 #054-04-1992 L1998 **RO** *020 †80
GARD, Timothy Lee. 1881 NW 185TH AVE 97006 #040-02-1988 L1989 **OPH** *020 †35
GASS, Susan Danielle. 4855 SW WESTERN AVE 97005 #016-42-1988 L1992 **D** *020 †15
GEORGE, Robert Andrew. 15050 SW KOLL PKWY STE A2 97006 #021-05-1970 L1977 **P CHP** *020 †18,75
GILLIES, Michael David. ■ 97006 #040-02-1977 L1978 **EM IM** *020
GILLIGAN, John F. 4510 SW HALL BLVD 97005 #308-11-1984 L1996 **FM** *020 †18
GONZALEZ, David Gerard. 15950 SW MILLIKAN WAY, THE PORTLAND CLINIC 97006 #040-02-1990 L1993 **FM** *020 †18
GRACIA, Michael F. ■ 97007 #275-01-1955 L1970 **P PHP** *012
GROTTING, Michael Alan. 4855 SW WESTERN AVE 97005 #034-01-1986 L1988 **IM** *020 †20
GUEORDJEVA, Petya Nikolov. 2935 SW CEDAR HILLS BLVD, VIRGINIA GARCIA MEMORIAL H 97005 #198-02-1993 L2004 **IM** *020 †20
GUNDUPALLI, Anitha. 15950 SW MILLIKAN WAY 97006 #495-70-1996 L1999 **IM** *020 †20
HABERMAN, Joseph Jeffrey. 8950 SW NIMBUS AVE 97008 #040-02-1988 L1989 **R** *020 †80
HALL, Ellen Annette. 4855 SW WESTERN AVE, KAISER BEAVERTON PEDIATRIC 97005 #040-02-1985 L1988 **PD** *020 †55
HAM, Jay Bruce. ■ 97005 #005-12-2006 L2006 **IM** *012
HAMILL, Douglas Jos. 4855 SW WESTERN AVE, KAISER-BEAVERTON 97005 #054-04-1981 L1984 **PD** *040 †55
HANKENSON, Lori Gail. 17895 NW EVERGREEN PKWY, WESTSIDE PEDIATRIC CLINIC 97006 #040-02-1984 L1989 **PD** *020 †19,55

HARRIS, William David. ■ 97005 #041-09-1955 L1956 **IM PUD** *071

HASHIMA, Jason Naoki. ■ 97008 #040-02-2003 L2003 **OBG** *100

HAUG, Walter A. ■ 97007 #040-02-1944 L1946 **PTH CLP** *071 †50

HEICHELHEIM, Karen Ruth. 1960 NW 167TH PL, STE 100 97006 #048-12-1983 L1993 **PD** *020 †55

HELMS, Deborah Blair. 4855 SW WESTERN AVE, 4855 SW WESTERN AVE 97005 #045-01-1980 L1988 **PD** *020 †55

HELZERMAN, Ralph Franklin. 1881 NW 185TH AVE 97006 #025-01-1967 L1971 **OPH GP** *020 †35

HERRING, Don Puckett. 4855 SW WESTERN AVE 97005 #047-05-1974 L1977 **FM** *020 †18

HILDEBRAND, Jeanne Kay. ■ 97007 #019-02-1990 L1993 **IMG** *020 †20

HILL, Christian Nissen. 2935 SW CEDAR HILLS BLVD, VIRGINIA GARCIA MEMORIAL H 97005 #024-07-1991 L1992 **PHP** *020 †18

HIRATZKA, Jayme Ryan. ■ 97005 #038-41-2006 L2006 **ORS** *012

HOANG, Lan To. ■ 97006 #040-02-2007 L2007 **IM** *012

HOHL, Richard David. ■ 97005 #017-20-1958 L1976 **IM** *020 †20

HOUGHTON, Richard Collins. 8905 SW NIMBUS AVE, STE 300 97008 #041-09-1947 L1949 **AN** *020 †05

HOWARD, Ann Johnson. 16110 SW REGATTA LN 97006 #005-14-1985 L1991 **P CHP** *020 †75

HUGHES, Jason Jones. ■ 97006 #003-75-2007, ▲ L2007 **IM** *012

HWANG, Jay Kyung. ■ 97006 #054-04-1989 L1991 **AN** *020 †05

IMBRIE, Gregory Adair. ■ 97007 #024-05-2007 **IM** *012

IVERSEN, Deani Kay. 4855 SW WESTERN AVE, KAISER PERMANENTE - OB/GYN 97005 #026-04-1996 L2000 **OBG** *020 †30

IWANIEC, James U. ■ 97006 #048-14-1993 L1994 **IM** *020 †20

JARDINI, Mark Stephen. 4855 SW WESTERN AVE, BEAVERTON KAISER OFFICES 97005 #005-06-1983 L1989 **FM** *020 †18

JAUCH, Nancy Ann. 4855 SW WESTERN AVE 97005 #040-02-1985 L1989 **OBG** *020 †30

JOHNSON, Leslie Ann. 4510 SW HALL BLVD, PACIFIC MEDICAL GROUP - BE 97005 #054-04-1994 L2004 **FM** *020 †18

JONES, Tori Aline. 4855 SW WESTERN AVE, KAISER PERMANENTE 97005 #056-06-1995 L2006 **FM** *020 †18

JUNG, Terresa Shaoying. 15950 SW MILLIKAN WAY 97006 #025-12-1995 L1999 **OBG** *020 †30

KARR, Merilee Deborah. 4855 SW WESTERN AVE, KAISER PERMANENTE/BEAVERTO 97005 #054-04-1988 L1989 **FM** *062 †18

KELLY, Jennifer Suzanne. ■ 97007 #040-02-2005 L2006 **OBG** *012

KEYS, Alice De Saavedra. 9570 SW BEAVERTN HLSDL HWY 97005 #021-01-1983 L1985 **P** *071

KILBER, Eric Hunter. 4855 SW WESTERN AVE 97005 #046-01-1999 L2003 **D** *020 †15

KILGORE, James Marvin, Jr. ■ 97008 #048-02-1952 L1968 **P N** *071 †75

KISOR, Kimberly L. 4885 SW WESTERN AVE, KAISER PERMANENTE 97005 #040-02-1998 L1999 **IM** *020 †20

KOCARNIK, Daniel Robt. 8950 SW NIMBUS AVE 97008 #040-02-1986 L1987 **DR** *020 †80

KOMANAPALLI, Christopher. ■ 97007 #005-14-2001 L2001 **GS** *012

KOPPULA, Sandhya Vani. 17200 NW CORRIDOR CT, STE 112 97006 #495-58-1982 L1994 **D** *020 †15

KOTAMARTI, Ramu Rao. 4855 SW WESTERN AVE 97005 #037-01-1998 L2000 **IM** *020 †20

KOVACH, Joshua Robert. ■ 97005 #026-04-2004 L2004 **PD** *012 †55

KRAAKEVIK, Jeff Allen. 15425 SW BEAVERTON CREEK CT, CREEK CT 97006 #018-03-2000 L2004 **N** *020 †75

KRANENBURG, Andy Jon. ■ 97008 #039-01-2003 L2003 **ORS** *012

KRUER, Michael Christophe. ■ 97007 #003-01-2005 L2007 **PD** *100

LANDFIELD, Alexander Davi. ■ 97006 #020-12-2006 L2006 **N** *012

LAU, Kendrick Munkit. ■ 97008 #041-09-1993 L1994 **FM** *020 †18

LEE, Anthony H. 4670 SW WASHINGTON AVE 97005 #583-09-1964 L1988 **FM** *020 †18

LEHMAN, Theodore Henry. 4690 SW WASHINGTON AVE, BEAVERTON MEDICAL CLINIC 97005 #030-05-1953 L1955 **U** *071 †95

LEONARD, Douglas Terry. ■ 97007 #050-02-2004 L2004 **NPM** *012 †55

LIBKE, Albert Walter, Jr. 9000 SW GEMINI DR, STE 15 97008 #054-04-1971 L1972 **GS** *071

LIMCHIU, Luis V, Jr. 20565 SW TUALATIN VALY HWY, STE 336 97006 #748-11-1982 **NEP** *020

LOBB, Ray S. ■ 97007 #020-02-1950 L1952 **GP IM** *072

LUMACO, Darell Roy. 1881 NW 185TH AVE 97006 #054-04-1972 L1978 **OPH FM** *020 †18,35

LUTFI, Eman M R T. 17895 NW EVERGREEN PKWY, WESTSIDE PEDIATRIC CLINIC 97006 #584-01-1990 L1999 **PD** *020 †55

LYONS, Mary Lorraine. 4855 SW WESTERN AVE 97005 #016-42-1978 L1985 **D** *020 †15

LYTLE, Creighton L. ■ 97008 #041-02-1948 L1950 **FM** *020

MAC KAY, James Hart. 3601 SW MURRAY BLVD 97005 #048-12-1972 L1973 **IM** *020 †20

MAKO, Jeffrey Philip. ■ 97007 #025-01-2008 *012

MALECHA, Monika Agatha. 15950 SW MILLIKAN WAY 97006 #047-06-1995 L2006 **OPH** *020 †35

MALINOW, Manuel Rene. 505 NW 185TH AVE 97006 #132-01-1944 L1966 **CD** *071

MANDEL, Scott Harlow. 4855 SW WESTERN AVE 97005 #040-02-1977 L1979 **PDE** *075 †55

MANILDI, Barbara Ann. 4855 SW WESTERN AVE 97005 #005-02-1961 L1968 **OBG** *071 †30

MANOHARI, Shekherm Vijaya. ■ 97007 #495-59-1988 *100

MARTIN, Paul David. 14525 SW MILLIKN WAY 44569, GASWORK.COM 97005 #048-04-1983 L1983 **AN OS** *020 †05

MAYBERRY, Jennifer Purdy. 8950 SW NIMBUS AVE 97008 #004-01-1994 L1998 **DR** *020 †80

MC CALL, John Oppie, Jr. ■ 97008 #035-19-1942 **GYN** *071 †30

MC CORMACK, Miranda C. 5040 SW GRIFFITH DR, STE 201 97005 #041-15-1999 L2005 **FM** *020 †18

MCKIEL, Vanessa. 2935 SW CEDAR HILLS BLVD, VA GARCIA MEM HLTH CTR 97005 #061-01-1998 L1999 **FM** *020 †18

MC MAHON, Patrick John. 4855 SW WESTERN AVE 97005 #040-02-1981 L1986 **OTO** *030 †45

MEHTA, Bina. 4855 SW WESTERN AVE 97005 #043-01-1997 L2001 **PD** *020 †55

MEIER, Douglas Lloyd. 15950 SW MILLIKAN WAY 97006 #018-03-1994 L1999 **OPH** *020 †35

MICHELS, Kevin Scott. ■ 97007 #040-02-2004 L2004 **OPH** *012

MILLER, Gerald Wendall. 1960 NW 167TH PL STE 103 97006 #068-01-1977 L1990 **OS** *020

MILLER, Keith Edward. 14795 SW MURRAY SCHOLLS DR, STE 121 97007 #025-07-1982 L1994 **FM** *020 †18

MIRTORABI, Mehdi M. 2155 NW 173RD AVE, STE 102 97006 #409-21-1995 L2000 **IM** *020 †20

MOONEY, William Marcel. 15700 SW GREYSTONE CT 97006 #019-02-1973 L1977 **IM ON** *020 †20

MOORE, Heather M. 1960 NW 167TH PL, STE 100 97006 #048-13-1992 L1995 **PD** *020 †55

MOSHER, M Luther. 3800 SW CEDAR HILLS BLVD, STE 160 97005 #016-11-1938 L1938 **P** *071

MOSHOFSKY, Dean Arthur. 1960 NW 167TH PL, STE 100 97006 #040-02-1983 L1984 **PD** *020 †55

MUMFORD, Dwight C. 11020 SW BEAVRTN HLSDL HWY 97005 #040-02-1972 L1973 **OPH** *020 †35

MURPHY, Joseph Doran. 4855 SW WESTERN AVE 97005 #028-34-1996 L2005 **OBG** *020 †30

NEIL, Edwin Jack. ■ 97005 #049-01-1982 L1983 **AN** *075

NEWMAN, Stewart Swagler. 15050 SW KOLL PKWY, STE A2 97006 #038-40-2001 L2006 **PFP** *020 †75

NGUYEN, Huong Thien. ■ 97007 #005-11-2006 L2006 **IM** *012

NIEHUS, Douglas Richard. 1881 NW 185TH AVE STE 300, PROVIDENCE MEDICAL GROUP T 97006 #040-02-1993 L1996 **FM** *020 †18

NILSEN, Luanne B. 4855 SW WESTERN AVE 97005 #040-02-1986 L1987 **PD** *020 †55

NOLTE, Minerva D T. ■ 97007 #020-02-1968 L1971 **OS A** *075 †55

NOMURA, Fred Masaru, Jr. 4855 SW WESTERN AVE 97005 #054-04-1962 L1968 **PD** *020 †55

NORTON, Henry Holmes. ■ 97008 #040-02-1933 **GP** *071

NOTESTINE, Ronald Lee. ■ 97008 #040-02-1977 L1979 **AN** *020

OH, Albert S. 15950 SW MILLIKAN WAY 97006 #035-47-1994 L2005 **IM** *020 †20

OLENICK, Jeffrey Scott. 14795 SW MURRAY SCHOLLS DR, STE 121 97007 #056-05-1978 L1983 **FM** *020 †18

OVERBECK, Becky R. 4855 SW WESTERN AVE 97005 #056-06-1995 L1999 **OBG** *020 †30

OVERBECK, Kevin Scott. 4855 SW WESTERN AVE 97005 #048-02-1996 L2000 **OBG** *020 †30

PALM, Kathleen Marie. 15950 SW MILLIKAN WAY 97006 #038-45-1986 L1995 **PD** *020 †55

PARK, Jae Ok. 14455 SW ALLEN BLVD # 101 97005 #583-06-1969 L1983 **IM** *020

PATEL, Sonel P. 4510 SW HALL BLVD, PACIFIC MED GRP 97005 #068-01-2000 L2006 **FM** *020

PATTAMANUCH, Nicole Sawan. ■ 97006 #035-08-2008 *012

PELLICCIOTTI, Mary Gail. 4855 SW WESTERN AVE 97005 #026-04-1978 L1985 **FM** *020 †18

PERCELL, Breanna Loreen. ■ 97007 #040-02-2007 L2007 **FP** *012

PERLIS, Marvin S. ■ 97008 #025-01-1950 L1951 **IM** *071 †20

PERRY, Kyle Andrew. ■ 97006 #041-13-2002 L2007 **GS** *100 †85

PETERS, Bruce Alfred. ■ 97007 #040-02-1961 L1963 **ADM** *071

PETERSON, Lee H. 1881 NW 185TH AVE 97006 #021-01-1965 L1971 **OPH** *071 †35

PHAM, Pierre Quang. 4855 SW WESTERN AVE, KAISER PERMANENTE 97005 #005-18-1987 L1991 **OBG** *020 †30

PICKER, Louis Jeffrey. ■ 97007 #005-02-1982 L2000 **IG CLP** *020 †50

PINIEWSKI, Brigitte M. 8605 SW CREEKSIDE PL 97008 #061-01-1987 L2003 **GP** *050

PITTA, Sreedevi. 1881 NW 185TH AVE, STE 300 97006 #495-62-1997 L2004 **FM** *020 †18

PURCELL, Deborah Kay. 17895 NW EVERGREEN PKWY, WESTSIDE PEDIATRIC CLINIC 97006 #040-02-1979 L1980 **PD** *020 †55

PUZISS, Abe. 3800 SW CEDAR HILLS BLVD, STE 250 97005 #040-02-1939 L1940 **GP** *071

PUZISS, Paul Martin. 3800 SW CEDAR HILLS BLVD, STE 250 97005 #054-04-1971 L1979 **ORS** *020 †40

RAHKOLA MCCORMICK, Sarah. ■ 97006 #040-02-2005 L2005 **IM** *012

RATH, Robert Stuart. 14125 SW FARMINGTON RD 97005 #040-02-1978 L1981 **FM** *020 †18

REAM, Amy Colmer. 8905 SW NIMBUS AVE, STE 300 97008 #031-01-1986 L1987 **AN** *020 †05

REED, Sandra M. 4855 SW WESTERN AVE, DEPT OF OB GYN 97005 #005-02-1990 L1994 **OBG** *020 †30

REGALIA, Cheryl C. ■ 97007 #005-18-1991 L2008 **FM** *020 †18

REID, Vicki Lynne. 4855 SW WESTERN AVE, KAISER PERMANENTE - BEAVER 97005 #040-02-1994 L1997 **FM** *020 †18

REYNOLDS, Walter C. ■ 97006 #040-02-1949 L1953 **FM** *071 †18

ROGERS, Richard Allan. ■ 97008 #016-06-1944 L1948 **P** *071 †75

ROHRBACK, Janelle Marie. 15950 SW MILLIKAN WAY 97006 #028-34-2001 L2005 **D DS** *020 †15

ROSENBAUM, Howard Scott. 16110 SW REGATTA LN 97006 #040-02-1976 L1989 **P** *020 †75

ROSENBERG, Jack Allen. 1881 NW 185TH AVE # 20 97006 #012-05-1966 L1973 **PD PDC** *020 †55

ROSS, Donald Euan. ■ 97005 #143-06-1966 **TS** *100

RUBY, Michelle Butzer. 4855 SW WESTERN AVE, KAISER BEAVERTON CLNC 97005 #028-02-1986 L1987 **PD** *020 †55

RUSSELL, Bruce Allen. 9963 SW NIMBUS AVE 97008 #047-05-1990 L1994 **D** *020 †15

RYDELL, Gale Anne. 1960 NW 167TH PL, STE 100 97006 #031-01-1987 L1991 **PD** *020 †55

SALDIVAR, Robert John. 4855 SW WESTERN AVE DEPT F 97005 #005-18-1987 L1988 **FM** *020 †18

SANDOR, Steven Matthew. 4855 SW WESTERN AVE 97005 #803-03-1964 L1971 **OBG** *020 †30

SARDA, Rajkumar L. 4855 SW WESTERN AVE 97005 #495-01-1966 L1973 **OBG** *020 †30

SASAKI, Edwin Hideo. ■ 97007 #054-04-1955 L1970 **AN** *071

SAWYER, Attilia Marie. 4855 SW WESTERN AVE, DEPT. OF OTOLARYNGOLOGY 97005 #050-02-1992 L1993 **OTO** *020 †45

SCHUSTER, Erika Dale. 4855 SW WESTERN AVE # OB 97005 #028-02-1983 L1989 **OBG** *020 †30

SCHWEIGER, Annette M. 1881 NW 185TH AVE, STE 300 97006 #409-23-1991 L1995 **FM** *020 †18

SEAPY, Robert Wesley. 8950 SW NIMBUS AVE 97008 #005-14-1967 L1973 **DR** *020 †80

SEKHRI-BREADEN, Radhika. 4855 SW WESTERN AVE, KAISER PERMANTENTE BEAVERT 97005 #005-02-1996 L2000 **IM** *020 †20

SEPPALA, Marvin David. 8285 SW NIMBUS AVE, STE 148 97008 #026-08-1984 L1988 **P ADP** *030

SERRANO, Luz Marcela. 15950 SW MILLIKAN WAY 97006 #649-27-1997 L2006 **FM** *020 †18

SHELBY, J Teresa. 12250 SW 2ND ST 97005 #020-02-1978 L1979 **CHP P** *075 †75 ‡

SIEMIENCZUK, Joseph. 3601 SW MURRAY BLVD STE 45 97005 #040-02-1978 L1981 **IM** *020 †20

SILBERGER, Jenny Ruth. 4855 SW WESTERN AVE, BEAVERTON MEDICAL OFFICE 97005 #040-02-1999 L2000 **IM** *020 †20

SILVERMAN, Burton L. 4510 SW HALL BLVD 97005 #048-04-1966 L1995 **FM** *020 †18

SIMIC, Aleksandra. 15700 SW GREYSTONE CT, PACIFIC ONCOLOGY 97006 #957-02-1992 L2002 **HO** *020 †20

SMITH, Gary Alan. 1881 NW 185TH AVE, STE 101 97006 #005-12-1976 L1979 **FM** *020 †16,18

SMITH, K Ronald. 4690 SW WASHINGTON AVE 97005 #040-02-1956 L1961 **IM** *071 †20

SMITH, Leo Arthur. ■ 97007 #040-02-2006 L2006 **FP** *012

SMITH, N Dean. 4690 SW WASHINGTON AVE 97005 #040-02-1949 L1950 **IM** *071 †20

SMITH, Susan Patricia. ■ 97075 #005-18-1979 L1986 **P IM** *020 †20,75

SOSNOVEC, Milan. 12250 SW 2ND ST 97005 #016-11-1973 L1977 **P** *020

SPARR, Landy Ferris. 15390 NW WOODED WAY 97006 #056-05-1976 L1979 **P** *020 †75

SPIELMAN, Sheldon. 4855 SW WESTERN AVE 97005 #035-19-1956 L1966 **OBG** *020 †30

SPINDEL, Eliot Robt. 505 NW 185TH AVE 97006 #024-01-1982 **IM** *020

SPOERKE, Nicholas Jon. ■ 97007 #035-09-2005 L2005 **GS** *012

STEINBERG, Ellen. ■ 97005 #043-01-1991 L2007 **PD PDE** *020 †55

STEVENS, Douglas Clifford. PO BOX 500 97075 #005-11-1979 *075
STONE, Janine Ann. 4855 SW WESTERN AVE, KAISER PERMANENTE-BEAVERTO 97005 #028-03-1995 L2006 **FM** *020 †18
TADROS, Nicholas Nasry. ■ 97008 #040-02-2008 *012
TAKLA, Gamil Nassif. 4250 SW CEDAR HILLS BLVD 97005 #330-01-1949 L1964 **GS** *071 †85
THEEL, Marylynn. 12250 SW 2ND ST 97005 #040-02-1990 L1991 **CHP** *020 †75
THOMAS, Stephen John, Jr. 17600 SW ALEXANDER ST 97006 #040-02-1971 L1972 **ORS** *040
THURMOND, Amy Suzanne. 8950 SW NIMBUS AVE 97008 #005-14-1982 L1983 **DR** *020 †80
TOCHEN, Mark Lawrence. 4855 SW WESTERN AVE 97005 #047-06-1969 L1974 **PD GP** *020 †55
TRAN, Fawn. 14795 SW MURRAY SCHOLLS DR, STE 121 97007 #040-02-1997 L2000 **FM** *020 †18
TROCHMANN, Rebekah Ann. 15950 SW MILLIKAN WAY, THE PORTLAND CLINIC 97006 #040-02-1986 L1987 **IM** *020 †20 ‡
TRUJILLO, Miguel Ramon. 97006 #034-01-2007 L2007 **OBG** *012
TRUSZKOWSKI, Anthony Jos. 4855 SW WESTERN AVE 97005 #056-06-1958 L1970 **IM** *071
TUBBS, Warren Scott. 8950 SW NIMBUS AVE 97008 #050-02-1991 L1995 **DR** *020 †80
ULMER, Mary Ellen. 15950 SW MILLIKAN WAY, PEDS PORTLAND CLINIC 97006 #016-06-1992 L1998 **PD** *020 †55
URBACH, Stacey Lisa. ■ 97006 #065-01-1995 L1999 **PD** *100 †55
USHMAN, David Paul. 4855 SW WESTERN AVE 97005 #003-01-1975 L1991 **EM OM** *020 †16,70
VANDENBARK, Margaret S. 4855 SW WESTERN AVE, KAISER PERMANENTE 97005 #054-04-1977 L1978 **FM** *040 †18
VILHAUER, Sandra Lynne A. 1881 NW 185TH AVE STE 201 97006 #040-02-1969 L1970 **PD** *020 †55
VU, Dam. ■ 97006 #941-01-1959 L1980 **PHP GP** *071
VU, Trung Thanh. ■ 97007 #040-02-2006 L2006 *020
WARE, Marsha Diane. 1881 NW 185TH AVE, STE 101 97006 #011-03-1987 L1988 **IM** *020 †20
WARNOCK, Gerald Lloyd. 8950 SW NIMBUS AVE 97008 #040-02-1958 L1961 **R OS** *020 †80
WASMANN, Samuel Ivan. ■ 97005 #040-02-2005 L2006 **IM** *012
WILBRANDT, Hans Robt. ■ 97007 #869-04-1957 L1960 **OPH OS** *071 †35
WINTER, Virginia Kathleen. 97006 #038-45-1983 L1984 **OBG** *020 †30
WISE, Richard Wm. 4855 SW WESTERN AVE 97005 #026-04-1979 L1980 **IM** *020 †20
WITTKOPP, George F. 5040 SW GRIFFITH DR # 102 97005 #056-05-1970 L1977 **P** *071
WRIGHT, Craig Lyle. 3601 SW MURRAY BLVD, STE 45 97005 #054-04-1988 L2004 **FM** *030 †18
WYLLIE, Julius. 3601 SW MURRAY BLVD, STE 45 97005 #048-14-2003 L2005 **FM** *020
WYMAN, Scott Christopher. ■ 97006 #040-02-2008 *012
ZELTZER, Paul Jos. 6107 SW MURRAY BLVD, APT 141 97008 #869-05-1966 L1973 **P PA** *020
ZURITA, Marcelo Jose. ■ 97008 #847-02-1979 *071

BEND – DESCHUTES

ABSALON, Jeffrey Vincent. 2115 NE WYATT CT, STE 101 97701 #040-02-1991 L1992 **IM** *020 †20
ACKERMAN, Diana Ruth. 2400 NE NEFF RD, STE A 97701 #005-15-2002 L2006 **OBG** *020
ADAMS, Thomas W. ■ 97701 #016-06-1949 L1961 **GS TS** *071 †85
AHMED, Mary Ann. 2400 NE NEFF RD, STE A 97701 #016-02-1990 L2001 **OBG** *020 †30
ALLEN, John Robt. 1501 NE MEDICAL CTR DR, CENTER DRIVE 97701 #048-13-1990 L1995 **IM** *020 †20
ALLISON, Dawn S. 1510 SW NANCY WAY, STE 1 97702 #038-40-1993 L2000 **D** *020 †15
ALLRED, Raphael Montana. 2855 NW CROSSING DR, STE 102 97701 #049-01-1998 L2002 **FM** *020 †18
ALTIG, Donald William. ■ 97702 #005-14-1962 L1963 **AN OS** *020 †05
ALUL, Ida H. 2275 NE DOCTORS DR STE 6 97701 #028-46-1988 L2001 **OPH** *020 †35
ANDREWS, Robert E, Jr. 1303 NE CUSHING DR, STE 100 97701 #001-02-1995 L1999 **PM** *020 †60
ANGELES, Adam Peter. 2450 NE MARY ROSE PL, STE 200 97701 #005-02-1992 L2005 **PS** *100
ANTOLAK, Kathleen C. 1501 NE MEDICAL CTR DR, CENTER DRIVE 97701 #026-04-1981 L2001 **FM** *020 †18
ARCHER, Stephen Barry. 2084 NE PROFESSIONAL CT, ADVANCED SURGICAL CARE 97701 #047-06-1991 L2001 **GS** *020
ASKEW, Aaron Eugene. 1303 NE CUSHING DR, STE 100 97701 #040-02-1996 L2002 **ORS** *020 †40
AYERS, Charles Herbert. 2300 NE NEFF RD 97701 #016-11-1955 L1956 **FM IMG** *020 †18
AZIN, Gregg Darius. 1501 NE MEDICAL CENTER DR 97701 #040-02-1996 L2002 **GS** *020 †85
BACHMAN, James J. 535 NE GREENWOOD AVE 97701 #038-41-1978 L1979 **FM** *020 †16,18
BACKUS, Mark Andrew. 2115 NE WYATT CT, STE 101 97701 #036-07-1993 L2000 **IM** *020 †20
BALENTINE, Larry Thos. 2200 NE NEFF RD, STE 302 97701 #019-02-1977 L1991 **RHU IM** *020 †20
BALLIN, Daniel S. ■ 97701 #028-02-1983 L2006 **EM** *020 †20,16
BARNHOUSE, Dean Brooks. ■ 97701 #040-02-1966 L1969 **OM EM** *071 †16
BARRETT, Joseph Alton. 2500 NE NEFF RD 97701 #040-02-1991 L2003 **P** *020 †75
BEARD, Timothy Lee. 1501 NE MEDICAL CENTER DR 97701 #056-05-1994 L1999 **GS** *020 †85
BECK, Charles Lynn. ■ 97701 #026-04-1971 L1980 **DR** *072 †80
BEIER, Marlis Anne. 2400 NE NEFF RD, STE A 97701 #025-01-1978 L1983 **OBG** *071 †30
BELL, John Carl. 2500 NE NEFF RD 97701 #028-02-1970 L1974 **IM** *100
BELL, Michael Lance. ■ 97701 #040-02-2002 L2007 **CN** *020 †75
BELZA, Mark Gregory. 2200 NE NEFF RD, STE 200 97701 #031-01-1983 L1991 **NS** *020 †25
BENNETT, Craig Allison. ■ 97702 #048-04-1959 L1959 **FM** *071
BENSMILLER, Diane E. ■ 97702 #040-02-1977 L1978 **IM** *020 †20
BERREEN, John Patrick, Jr. 2275 NE DOCTORS DR, STE 2 97701 #050-02-1990 L2000 **OPH** *020 †35
BERROTH, Margaret E. ■ 97702 #407-10-1954 **PTH** *071 †50
BERRY, Douglas Foreman. 2400 NE NEFF RD, STE B 97701 #041-13-1974 L1981 **PS** *071 †85
BERRY, Lewis Wilson. ■ 97701 #041-13-1942 L1946 **GP OM** *100
BERUBE, Stacy Clifton. 1820 MONTEREY PNES 97701 #040-02-1973 L1978 **PD** *020 †55
BIGLER, Edward Wm. 18 NW OREGON AVE, HIGHLAKES CLNC 97701 #007-02-1959 L2002 **EM FM** *020
BIRSCHBACH, Jane Marie. 2500 NE NEFF RD 97701 #051-07-1993 L1997 **GYN** *020 †30
BLECHMAN, Jennifer Abby. 18 NW OREGON AVE, HIGHLAKES HEALTH CARE 97701 #034-03-1997 L2002 **FM** *020 †18
BLIZZARD, John David. PO BOX 5577, SURGEONS, PC 97708 #027-01-1989 L1997 **TS VS** *020 †85,90

BOCHNER, Richard H. 1501 NE MEDICAL CENTER DR 97701 #048-04-1985 L2004 **GE IM** *020 †20
BOEHM, Frederick P, III. 2200 NE PROFESSIONAL CT, CENTRAL OREGON PEDIATRICS 97701 #054-04-1971 L1978 **PD** *020 †55
BOGGESS, Jeffrey Paul. 1501 NE MEDICAL CENTER DR 97701 #011-02-1975 L1980 **FM** *020 †18
BOILEAU, Michel Adeodat. 2090 NE WYATT CT 97701 #040-02-1973 L1974 **U** *020 †95
BOONE, Robert Floyd. 1501 NE MEDICAL CENTER DR 97701 #005-18-1974 L1983 **ON IM** *020 †20
BOYLE, Edward M. 1501 NE MEDICAL CENTER DR 97701 #026-04-1992 L2001 **TS** *020 †85,90
BRAICH, Theodore Anthony. 1501 NE MEDICAL CENTER DR 97701 #040-02-1979 L2003 **ON HEM** *020 †20
BREWER, Jack Alan. 2090 NE WYATT CT, STE 101 97701 #056-05-1985 L1986 **U** *020 †95
BROWN, Avery Michael. 2421 NE DOCTORS DR 97701 #005-11-1973 L1974 **N** *071 †75
BROWN, Daniel Fleming. 2200 NE PROFESSIONAL CT 97701 #040-02-1967 L1968 **OBG** *020 †20
BROWN, Mary Patricia B. 1820 MONTEREY PNES 97701 #040-02-1967 L1968 **PD** *020 †55
BROWN, Patrick Brian. 1460 NE MEDICAL CENTER DR, CENTRAL OREGON RADIOLOGY 97701 #040-02-1983 L1989 **DR GP** *020 †80
BRUNDAGE, Bruce Howard. 1501 NE MEDICAL CENTR DR D, BEND MEMORIAL CLINIC 97701 #033-05-1965 L1998 **CD IM** *040 †20
BRYAN, Bradley Bent. ■ 97702 #067-01-2001 L2007 **PTH** *100 †50
BUCHHOLZ, Gary David. 2421 NE DOCTORS DR 97701 #003-01-1977 L1985 **N** *020 †75
BUCKLEY, Theresa Marie. 2042 NE WILLIAMSON CT, STANFORD MED. CTR., DEPT O 97701 #016-06-1997 L2008 **N** *020 †75
BUEHLER, Knute Carl. 2200 NE NEFF RD, STE 200 97701 #023-07-1991 L1992 **ORS** *020 †40
BUEHLER, Patricia Owen. 1100 WATT WAY 97701 #023-07-1990 L1992 **OPH** *020 †35
BULL, Tammy Ann. 63870 W QUAIL HAVEN DR, EAST CASCADE WOMEN'S GROUP 97701 #020-12-1986 L1999 **OBG** *020 †30
BURKET, Bradley John. 2100 NE WYATT CT, STE 101 97701 #040-02-1993 L1994 **FM** *020 †18
BURTON, William Young, Jr. 2500 NE NEFF RD 97701 #040-02-1965 L1970 **OBG** *020 †30
BUSBY, Dean Joseph. 1460 NE MEDICAL CTR DR, CENTER DRIVE 97701 #054-04-1995 L2001 **RNR** *020 †80
BUZZAS, George Rodney. 2500 NE NEFF RD 97701 #030-06-1993 L1998 **GS** *020 †85
CADE, Richard Martin. 2088 NE KIM LN, STE A 97701 #005-14-1974 L1993 **FM** *020 †18
CAGNEY, Patricia Lynne. ■ 97702 #005-06-1987 L1990 **PD** *071 †55
CALHOUN, William Ivan. ■ 97701 #040-02-1966 L1970 **OPH GP** *071 †35
CAMPAGNA, Emily Joan. ■ 97701 #035-46-2008 *012
CAMPBELL, Keith Eugene. ■ 97701 #005-06-1989 L1990 **OS GP** *020
CAMPBELL, Wm Lawrence. 2100 NE WYATT CT, STE 202 97701 #048-12-1973 L2006 **P** *020 †75
CANTOR, Arthur Saml. 1501 NE MEDICAL CENTER DR 97701 #041-01-1977 L1978 **GE HEP** *020 †20
CARLILL, Dianne M. ■ 97701 #005-12-1979 L1983 **OBG** *020 †30
CARLSEN, Thomas James. 2600 NE NEFF RD 97701 #026-04-1975 L1981 **ORS OS** *020 †40
CARNAHAN, Clarence Edgar. ■ 97701 #005-12-1954 L1955 **P** *071 †75
CARNES, Joyce Ann. 2500 NE NEFF RD, ST CHARLES MEDICAL CNTR 97701 #034-01-1972 L1975 **EM** *020 †20
CARROLL, John Paul. 2500 NE NEFF RD 97701 #035-03-1961 L1970 **ORS** *071 †40
CARROLL, Linda Rose. 18 NW OREGON AVE, HIGH LAKES HEALTH CARE 97701 #038-06-1990 L2001 **PM** *020 †60
CARROLL, Mary Fiona. 1501 NE MEDICAL CENTER DR, CENTER DRIVE 97701 #539-03-1993 L2005 **IM** *020 †20
CARTER, Forrest Rea. ■ 97702 #003-01-1973 L1974 **OBG** *071
CARTER, Leslie Ann. 2115 NE WYATT CT, STE 101 97701 #040-02-2000 L2004 **D** *020 †15
CARUSO, Kimberly Jean. 2200 NE PROFESSIONAL CT 97701 #026-04-1993 L2006 **PD** *020 †55
CARVER, Ronald Ellis. ■ 97702 #048-04-1967 L1970 **OBG** *071 †30 ‡
CHAFFEY, Ben Taft. ■ 97707 #040-02-1960 L1991 **GS IM** *020 †95
CHAFFEY, Paula Jean Good. ■ 97702 #067-01-1964 L1975 **OS** *020
CHANG, Linyee. 2500 NE NEFF RD, CTRL OR CANCER TX CTR 97701 #040-02-1990 L1991 **RO** *020 †20
CHRISTENSEN, Jeness M. 18 NW OREGON AVE, HIGH LAKES HEALTH CARE 97701 #748-29-1990 L2005 **IM** *020 †20
CHUNN, Charles John. 1820 MONTEREY PNES 97701 #054-04-1971 L1975 **PD ID** *020 †55
CLARK, Christopher. 2400 NE NEFF RD, STE A 97701 #028-34-1978 L1998 **OBG** *020 †30
CLAUTICE-ENGLE, Traci L. 1460 NE MEDICAL CENTER DR, CENTRAL OREGON RADIOLOGY 97701 #007-02-1988 L1998 **DR** *020 †80
COCHRAN, Quinten W. ■ 97701 #040-02-1943 L1947 **P PD** *072 †55
COE, Michael Romaine. 2600 NE NEFF RD STE 1, NEUROMUSCULOKSELETAL CENTE 97701 #016-42-1985 L1993 **ORS HS** *020 †40
COMBS, Darrel Thos. 1501 NE MEDICAL CENTER DR 97701 #040-02-1968 L1976 **CD IM** *020 †20
COMERFORD, Thomas James. 2500 NE NEFF RD 97701 #005-15-1973 L1982 **RO** *020 †80,20
CONNER, Patrick Lorin. 1501 NE MEDICAL CENTER DR, BEND MEMORIAL CLINIC 97701 #054-04-1961 L1965 **GP** *071
CONRAD, A K, Jr. 2042 NE WILLIAMSON 97701 #016-02-1978 L1985 **PUD IM** *020 †20
CORNELIUS, Pierce Austin. ■ 97702 #018-03-1957 L1962 **AN** *071 †05
CORSO, John Louis. 1302 NE 3RD ST, IMMEDIATE CARE CENTERS 97701 #016-42-1985 L1995 **IM** *020 †20
COULTER, Mary Ellen. ■ 97701 #035-03-1975 L1983 **FM IM** *020 †18
COURTNEY, Thomas Lukens. 2200 NE PROFESSIONAL CT, CENTRAL OREGON PEDIATRICS 97701 #051-01-1993 L2004 **PD IM** *020 †55
COUTIN, David Bryan. 2446 NE DOCTORS DR, ALLERGY ASTHMA ASSOCS 97701 #010-02-1982 L1994 **AI** *020 †20
COVEY, Marlene Anne. ■ 97702 #038-45-1985 L2006 **OBG** *020 †30
CREELMAN, Thomas James. 2500 NE NEFF RD 97701 #054-04-1974 L1976 **FM** *020 †18
CROSBY, Jack Henry. 1501 NE MEDICAL CENTER DR, BEND MEMORIAL CLINIC 97701 #016-11-1960 L1969 **IM** *071 †20
CUDDIHY, Richard Geo. 1501 NE MEDICAL CENTER DR 97701 #035-06-1991 L2005 **PD** *020 †20
DAVIES, James Clifford. ■ 97701 #020-02-1955 L1963 **GP** *071
DAVIS, Mary Jane. 2500 NE NEFF RD 97701 #054-04-1987 L1991 **OBG** *020 †30
DAWSON, John Andrew. 18 NW OREGON AVE 97701 #060-02-1993 L1999 **FM** *020 †18
DECKER, Susan Jane. 2500 NE NEFF RD, ST CHARLES MEDICAL CENTER 97701 #018-03-1991 L1994 **EM** *020 †16
DEDRICK, David Lars. 2042 NE WILLIAMSON CT 97701 #051-04-1994 L1996 **PCC SME** *020 †20

■ = Address Information Privacy Protected

DEEKS, Charles K. ■ 97702 #005-02-1949 L1978 U *071

DELGADO, William. ■ 97702 #030-06-1995 L1998 D *020 †15

DELP, James Rodney. 321 NE FRANKLIN AVE, JAMES R DELP MD PC 97701 #041-02-1959 L1965 OPH *071 †35

DEPPER, Joel Michael. 1250 NE 3RD ST, STE B100 97701 #028-02-1974 L1994 RHU AI *020 †20,03

DESMOND, Brian Patrick. 1501 NE MEDICAL CENTER DR 97701 #049-01-1999 L2004 OPH *020 †20

DI GIULIO, Christopher P. 63595 HUNNELL RD, STE 120 97701 #041-13-1998 L2006 FM *020 †20

DIMMIG, Jason Wade. 2275 NE DOCTORS DR, STE 6 97701 #050-02-2001 L2005 OPH *020 †35

DONLEY, Charles Edward. ■ 97701 #030-06-1942 L1942 R *071

DONLEY, Michael James. 1460 NE MEDICAL CENTER DR, CENTRAL OREGON RADIOLOGY 97701 #040-02-1973 L1974 DR *020 †80 ‡

DONNELLY, David Alan. 2115 NE WYATT CT STE 201, BEND VA CBOC 97701 #040-02-1979 L1981 IM *020 †20

DREWS, Kenneth Lester. ■ 97701 #422-01-2003 L2003 FM *100

DRUTMAN, Jeffrey. 1460 NE MEDICAL CENTER DR, CENTRAL OREGON RADIOLOGY 97701 #005-02-1987 L1993 DR *020 †80

EAST, Samuel Reed. 1501 NE MEDICAL CENTER DR 97701 #040-02-1967 L1973 OPH *071 †35

EASTWOOD, Ivan Roy. 1501 NE MEDICAL CENTER DR, BEND MEMORIAL CLINIC 97701 #023-07-1965 L1972 GE IM *071 †20

EBERLE, Craig. 2381 NE CONNERS AVE 97701 #035-08-1974 L1983 OBG *071 †30

ECKMAN, Paul Bates. ■ 97702 #001-02-1960 L1975 N *020 †75

ELLIS, William John. ■ 97701 #016-06-1957 L1962 U *071 †95

ERAKER, Stephen Andrew. 2115 NE WYATT CT, BEND VA CLINIC 97701 #040-02-1971 L1972 IM PHP *020 †20

ERTLE, Alan Richard. 2500 NE NEFF RD 97701 #040-02-1980 L1985 PUD IM *030 †20

ETTINGER, Richard Howard. 1501 NE MEDICAL CENTER DR 97701 #016-06-1948 L1954 IM *071 †20

FAWCETT, Richard Wayne. 1501 NE MEDICAL CTR DR, CENTER DRIVE 97701 #023-07-1993 L2001 ID *020 †20

FELTON, Lloyd James. ■ 97702 #035-45-1970 L1973 OBG *020 †30

FIET, Norman Arthur. ■ 97707 #018-03-1965 L1971 DR *071 †80

FITZSIMMONS, Thomas David. 1501 NE MEDICAL CENTER DR, U/T HSC AT SAN ANTONIO 97701 #025-01-1986 L2002 OPH PHP *020 †35

FITZSIMONS, Josephine M. 2500 NE NEFF RD, ST CHARLES REHAB 97701 #016-06-1985 L1992 PM *020 †20

FLANNERY, Joseph Wayne. 2229 SE PILATUS LN 97702 #038-41-1997 L2003 IM *020 †20

FLATT, John Roger. ■ 97702 #016-06-1953 L1954 FM *072

FOHRMAN, Daniel Evan. 1501 NE MEDICAL CENTER DR 97701 #016-42-1974 L1980 RHU IM *020 †20

FORD, Perry W. ■ 97702 #007-02-1951 L1954 GP *071

FORD, Theodore Rowe. 2041 NE WILLIAMSON CT, STE B 97701 #016-06-1988 L1995 AN *020 †05

FOSTER, Thomas Newton, Jr. ■ 97701 #005-11-1966 L1973 DR NM *071 †80,28

FREDSTROM, David Allan. 1247 NE MEDICAL CENTER DR, STE 3 97701 #030-05-1969 L1973 FM *020 †18

FREI, Gary John. 1501 NE MEDICAL CENTER DR 97701 #016-02-1978 L1983 GS VS *020 †85

FRIESS, Carter Christian. 2450 NE MARY ROSE PL, STE 120 97701 #056-06-1972 L1974 OTO PS *020 †45

GALLAGHER, Gary Lyle. 2041 NE WILLIAMSON CT, STE C 97701 #040-02-1991 L1999 PS *020 †65

GALLIVAN, Ryan Paul. 2450 NE MARY ROSE PL, STE 120 97701 #041-02-1996 L2002 OTO *020 †45

GALLIVAN, William Ryan. ■ 97701 #028-34-1956 L1956 OBG *071 †30

GARRETT, Stuart Gardner. 1501 NE MEDICAL CENTER DR 97701 #020-12-1975 L1976 FM *020 †18

GARZA, Erin Mc Guire. 2200 NE PROFESSIONAL CT, CENTRAL OREGON PEDIATRIC A 97701 #025-12-1994 L2003 PD *020 †55

GINGOLD, Brett Ian. 1303 NE CUSHING DR 97701 #050-02-1997 L2003 ORS *020 †40

GOLDSMITH, Neal A. 1501 NE MEDICAL CENTER DR, BEND MEMORIAL CLINIC 97701 #017-20-1950 L1958 GS *071 †85

GOLDSTEIN, Rick Niel. 1501 NE MEDICAL CTR DR, CENTER DRIVE 97701 #040-02-1986 L1990 IM IMG *020 †20

GREENLEAF, Delmar Lewis. 804 NE 3RD ST 97701 #005-14-1979 L1991 FM *071 †18

GRIFFIN, Craigan Todd. 2275 NE DOCTORS DR, STE 9 97701 #005-12-1999 L2004 CN *100 ‡

GUTMANN, Caroline Berth. 2200 NE PROFESSIONAL CT 97701 #050-02-1995 L2000 PD *020 †55

HA, Chae Mihngreg. 1303 NE CUSHING DR, STE 100 97701 #054-04-1998 L2004 ORS *020 †40

HADDEN, Anthony G, Jr. 2275 NE DOCTORS DR, STE 2 97701 #005-12-1999 L2006 NS *100 ‡

HAKALA, Robert Michael. 1501 NE MEDICAL CENTER DR 97701 #040-02-1967 L1970 FM *071 †18

HALL, Brooke Tate. 18 NW OREGON AVE, HIGH LAKES HEALTH CARE 97701 #025-07-2000 L2006 IM *020 †20

HALL, James Augustus, III. 2200 NE NEFF RD, CENTER FOR ORTHOPEDIC & NE 97701 #035-15-1991 L2005 ORS *020 †40

HAMBLIN, Derek Blaine. 1501 NE MEDICAL CENTER DR 97701 #040-02-1995 L2002 FM *020 †18

HAMLIN, Jefferson Andrew. ■ 97701 #005-12-1965 L1968 R *062 †80

HAMMETT, John B. PO BOX 6018, 1501 NE MEDICAL CENTER DRI 97708 #036-01-1965 L1991 GE IM *020 †20

HANINGTON, Kenneth R. 1303 NE CUSHING DR, STE 100 97701 #010-02-1981 L2007 HS ORS *020 †40

HANSON, Ronald Dean. 1460 NE MEDICAL CENTER DR, CENTRAL OREGON RADIOLOGY 97701 #003-01-1980 L1985 DR *020 †80

HARLESS, Keith Weston. 2500 NE NEFF RD, CASCADE HEALTHCARE COMMUNI 97701 #040-02-1972 L1973 PUD CCM *020 †20

HARP, Gregory Merrill. 1302 NE 3RD ST, ST CHARLES IMMEDIATE CARE 97701 #019-02-1978 L1991 EM *020 †16

HARRIS, Michael Norwood. 1501 NE MEDICAL CENTER DR 97701 #012-01-1977 L1980 IM *020 †20

HATLESTAD, Christopher L. 365 NE GREENWOOD AVE, STE 3 97701 #016-45-1990 L2002 FM *020 †18

HAVARD, Robert Hale. 86 SW CENTURY DR, STE 250 97702 #005-19-1985 L1996 FM *020 †18

HAYES, J Edward. ■ 97702 #019-02-1961 L1963 PS HS *071 †65

HEDGES, Brenda Kay. 2200 NE PROFESSIONAL CT, ASSOCIATES 97701 #005-18-1993 L1996 PD *020 †55

HEGEWALD, Matthew James. 1501 NE MEDICAL CENTER DR, BEND MEMORIAL CLINIC 97701 #016-02-1988 L1995 PUD CCM *020 †20

HENDERSON, Sidney E, III. 1501 NE MEDICAL CENTER DR 97701 #005-18-1977 L1979 GE IM *020 †20

HENDRICKS, Zeke Leroy. 60625 TETON CT 97702 #005-15-1967 L1984 DR *020 †80 ‡

HERZ, William Steven. 2500 NE NEFF RD 97701 #040-02-1978 L1979 P *020 †75 ‡

HIGGINS, Andrew Patrick. 1501 NE MEDICAL CENTER DR 97701 #007-02-1993 L1999 GS *020 †85

HILL, Timothy Alan. 2200 NE NEFF RD, STE 200 97701 #025-01-1990 L1995 PM *020 †60

HILLES, Alan Craig. 1501 NE MEDICAL CENTER DR 97701 #040-02-1970 L1976 FM *020 †18

HINZ, Anthony Christopher. 2200 NE NEFF RD, STE 100 97701 #054-04-1993 L1999 ORS *020 †40

HOESLY, James Michael. 1501 NE MEDICAL CENTER DR 97701 #040-02-1982 L1983 D IM *020 †20,15

HOFFMAN, Gary Lee. 516 SW 13TH ST, STE 202 97702 #025-01-1967 L1975 GS *020 †85

HOFFMEISTER, Alan Chas. 2500 NE NEFF RD 97701 #005-14-1974 L1976 NPM PD *020 †55 ‡

HOGAN, Robert Emmett. 1460 NE MEDICAL CENTER DR, CENTRAL OREGON RADIOLOGY A 97701 #025-12-2000 L2006 DR *100 †80

HOLLOWAY, Sandra K. 1501 NE MEDICAL CTR DR, CENTER DRIVE 97701 #019-02-1984 L2006 GE IM *020 †20

HOLMBOE, Jeffrey Arthur. 2200 NE NEFF RD, STE 200 97701 #023-01-1984 L1990 ORS *020 †40

HORNSBY, Michelle Ann. 1375 NW KINGSTON AVE, KIDS CENTER 97701 #017-20-1992 L1995 FM *020 †18

HOWELL, Jane Ann. 2400 NE NEFF RD, STE A 97701 #046-01-1988 L2001 OBG *020 †30

HUGHES, Joseph Alton. 2500 NE NEFF RD, CENTRAL OREGON PATHOLOGY 97701 #049-01-1998 L2006 PTH *020 †50

IRELAND, Stephen Paul. 2421 NE DOCTORS DR 97701 #040-02-1977 L1992 N *020 †20,75

IWANIEC, Lynn Marie. ■ 97701 #025-01-1994 L2007 IM *020 †20

JACOBS, Joseph Randall. 1501 NE MEDICAL CENTER DR 97701 #019-02-1972 L1996 FM *020 †18

JADERBORG, Jana Marie. 2084 NE PROFESSIONAL CT 97701 #019-02-1995 L2002 GS *020 †85

JAMES, Kimberly Lu. 2450 NE MARY ROSE PL, STE 220 97701 #023-12-1995 L2006 OBG *020 †30

JETT, Kris Joyce. 1102 NE 4TH ST 97701 #040-02-1981 L1986 GYN OBG *071 †30

JETT, Thomas Edward. 1460 NE MEDICAL CENTER DR, CENTRAL OREGON RADIOLOGY 97701 #040-02-1981 L1986 DR *020 †80

JOHNSON, Brenda Camille. 2160 NE WILLIAMSON CT 97701 #040-02-1993 L2001 IM *020 †20

JOHNSON, Donald Richard. ■ 97701 #005-11-1961 L1965 OPH *071 †35

JOHNSON, James Edward. 1460 NE MEDICAL CENTER DR, CENTRAL OREGON RADIOLOGY 97701 #054-04-1982 L1988 DR *020 †80

JOHNSON, Joseph Michael. 2650 NE COURTNEY DR, SOUTHWEST MEDICAL ASSOCIAT 97701 #041-14-1977 L2007 GS VS *030 †85

JOHNSON, Paul Jennings. 2088 NE KIM LN STE A, JOHNSON & CADE FP LLC 97701 #026-04-1980 L1983 FM *020 †18

JOHNSON-BAILIE, Valerie. 2200 NE PROFESSIONAL CT, CENTRAL OREGON PEDIATRIC A 97701 #030-05-1980 L1989 PD NPM *020 †55

JONES, Andrew Douglas. 1501 NE MEDICAL CENTER DR 97701 #026-04-1998 L1999 GS *020 †85

JUDD, James Lewis. 2500 NE NEFF RD 97701 #040-02-1978 L1979 PTH *020 †50

KEBLER, Richard Scott. 1501 NE MEDICAL CENTER DR 97701 #017-20-1979 L1987 NEP IM *020 †20

KELLEY, Harley Duncan. ■ 97701 #040-02-1959 L1962 GS VS *072 †85

KENDRICK, Michael M. ■ 97701 #007-02-1971 L1979 NS *071 †25

KERKOCH, Frank Robt. 1460 NE MEDICAL CENTER DR 97701 #016-11-1956 L1960 R DR *071 †80

KERRIGAN, Terence Jos. ■ 97701 #056-06-1954 L1955 AN *071

KJOBECH, Steven Dean. 1460 NE MEDICAL CENTER DR, CENTRAL OREGON RADIOLOGY 97701 #054-04-1995 L2001 VIR *020 †80

KNAPP, Stephen Lee. 726 NW WALL ST 97701 #005-19-1977 L1979 GP *020

KOCH, Albert Frederick. 1501 NE MEDICAL CENTER DR 97701 #016-02-1999 L2005 CD *020 †20

KOCUREK, Kathryn Marie. 2160 NE WILLIAMSON CT, FALL CREEK INTERNAL MEDICI 97701 #005-02-1989 L2003 IM *020 †20

KOEHLER, Thomas Frederick. 1460 NE MEDICAL CENTER DR, CENTRAL OREGON RADIOLOGY 97701 #005-18-1997 L2003 *020 †80

KOLLER, Richard Lynn. 2275 NE DOCTORS DR, STE 9 97701 #038-06-1976 L1997 N P *020 †75

KORNFELD, Stephen Brian. 1501 NE MEDICAL CENTER DR 97701 #005-06-1982 L1983 HO *020 †20

KOTEEN, Glenn Michael. 19055 MT MCLOUGHLIN LN 97701 #023-01-1979 L2004 GE IM *020 †20

KOWALSKI, Darren Michael. 1501 NE MEDICAL CENTER DR, BEND MEMORIAL CLINIC 97701 #040-02-1996 L2001 GS *020 †85

KRAL, Kevin Michael. 2065 NE WILLIAMSON CT, STE A 97701 #051-01-1977 L1990 AI PD *020 †55,03

KRANTZ, Heather B. 2330 NE DIVISION ST, STE 7 97701 #019-02-1989 L1993 OBG *020 †30

KRIEVES, David Allan. 1460 NE MEDICAL CENTER DR, CENTRAL OREGON RADIOLOGY 97701 #040-02-1977 L1979 DR NM *020 †80 ‡

KUHAR, Maryjeanne. 2577 NE COURTNEY DR 97701 #041-12-1983 L1988 OBG *020 †30

LAKOVICS, Magnus. 2100 NE WYATT CT STE 202 97701 #035-15-1971 L1992 P *030 †75

LAPINE, Armond Maurice, Jr. 2705 NE CONNERS AVE STE B, POB 6416 97701 #035-06-1997 L2004 CD *100 †20

LARGENT, Barbara Jean. 1375 NW KINGSTON AVE, KIDS CENTER 97701 #017-20-1993 L1996 FM *020 †18

LA SALA, Matthew Robt. 1501 NE MEDICAL CENTER DR 97701 #051-04-1992 L1993 IM *020 †20

LAUGHLIN, James Carlyle. 2500 NE NEFF RD, 2ND FL 97701 #033-05-2000 L2007 ICE *020 †20

LAWS, William Craig. 2450 NE MARY ROSE PL, STE 120 97701 #048-04-1968 L1974 OTO *020 †45

LEAR, Jerry Gene. 1501 NE MEDICAL CENTR DR D, BEND MEMORIAL CLINIC 97701 #040-02-1965 L1973 GS TS *071 †85

LEE, Carol Frost. 1558 SW NANCY WAY, STE 101 97702 #040-02-1976 L1979 IM *020

LEE, Gilbert Brownell. 1558 SW NANCY WAY STE 101 97702 #040-02-1976 L1979 **IM** *020
LEE, William Richard. ■ 97701 #040-02-1964 L1967 **OTO FPS** *071
LEFFEL, Linda Joann. 1310 NE CUSHING DR, STE D 97701 #040-02-1985 L1993
  PS GS *020 †85,65
LEMEE, Madeline T. 18 NW OREGON AVE 97701 #028-46-1987 L1995 **IM** *020 †20
LEVY, Mark. 2200 NE NEFF RD STE 200, NEUROMUSCULOSKELETAL CTR/C 97701
  #012-05-1992 L2006 **NS** *020 †25
LEWIS, Lisa Jo. 2075 NE WYATT CT, HOSPICE CENTER HOUSE 97701 #005-06-1990 L2001
  IM PHP *020 †20
LINDSEY, Kenneth Hart. 2500 NE NEFF RD 97701 #040-02-1995 L1996 **FM EM** *020 †18
LITCHFIELD, Ralph Verlin. 1501 NE MEDICAL CENTER DR 97701 #040-02-1964 L1965
  FM *071 †18
LYNCH-MILLER, Alison Kay. 25 NW LOUISIANA AVE, STE 100 97701 #005-02-1989 L1991
  OBG *020 †30
MAC CLOSKEY, Craig. 2600 NE NEFF RD STE 1 97701 #040-02-1968 L1970 **ORS** *062 †40
MAC DONELL, Richard Allen. 339 SW CENTURY DR STE 103 97702 #010-02-1995 L2000
  IM *020 †20
MAC KENZIE, David Allan. 1900 NE 3RD ST STE 106 97701 #067-01-1964 L1978
  PD ORS *030 †60
MADDOX, John Mark. 2084 NE PROFESSIONAL CT 97701 #047-20-1997 L2003 **CRS** *020 †85
MAGNUS, Peter David. ■ 97701 #035-15-1967 L1979 **PD FM** *020 †55
MAHONEY, James Widmann. 2500 NE NEFF RD, ST CHARLES MEDICAL CTR 97701
  #041-02-1972 L1973 **AN** *071 †05
MALONEY, Nancy Hinterberg. 1501 NE MEDICAL CENTER DR 97701 #056-05-1982 L1986
  PM *020 †60
MARA, Michael Lee. 1303 NE CUSHING DR, STE 100 97701 #025-01-1990 L1995 **ORS** *020 †40
MARCINEK, Helenka M. 2500 NE NEFF RD, BEND FIRE/SCMC ER DEPT 97701
  #065-09-1974 L1977 **EM** *020,16
MARTIN, Laurie Ann. 1460 NE MEDICAL CENTER DR, CENTRAL OREGON RADIOLOGY 97701
  #028-34-1995 L2000 **DR NM** *020 †80,28
MASON, Lyman Gates. ■ 97701 #010-01-1955 L1957 **ORS** *071 †40
MASSINE, Russell Edmund. ■ 97702 #040-02-1998 L2004 **NEP** *020 †20
MASTRANGELO, Michael John. 2450 NE MARY ROSE PL, STE 210 97701 #017-20-1992 L1998
  GS *020 †85
MATHEWS, Robert Clifton. 1501 NE MEDICAL CENTER DR, BEND MEMORIAL CLINIC 97701
  #040-02-1983 L1984 **OPH** *020 †35
MCCABE, Frances Margaret. 2500 NE NEFF RD, EMERGENCY MEDICINE 97701
  #005-11-1991 L2002 **EM** *020 †16
MC CARTHY, Patrick J. 2084 NE PROFESSIONAL CT 97701 #031-01-1980 L1983
  DIA END *020 †10
MC CLURE, Katie Brenna. 2500 NE NEFF RD, SW WASHINGTON MEDICAL CENT 97701
  #024-07-2000 L2000 **EM** *100
MC COWAN, Donald H. ■ 97701 #041-01-1946 L1956 **PTH R** *020 †50
MC DONALD, Lynn B. 2500 NE NEFF RD 97701 #039-01-1976 L1980 **OS** *020 †16
MC GEARY, George Danl. ■ 97701 #026-04-1945 L1948 **PTH NM** *071 †50
MC GRANAHAN, Thos Timmons. 18160 COTTONWOOD RD, # 793 97707 #038-41-1957 L1969
  AN *071 †05
MC GUIRE, James Patrick. 2500 NE NEFF RD, ST CHARLES - SOUND INPATIE 97701
  #056-06-1982 L2006 **IM** *020 †20
MC LELLAN, Bruce Arleigh. 2500 NE NEFF RD, HEART CENTER 2ND FL 97701
  #005-19-1982 L1988 **CD IM** *020 †20
MEADOR, Mary. 115 NW GREELEY AVE 97701 #035-20-1989 L1990 **EM** *020 †18
MILLER, Bruce Hyatt. PO BOX 5337, 37 WINNERS CIR 97708 #035-08-1963 L1970
  D DMP *050 †15
MILLER, Craig Revere. 2500 NE NEFF RD 97701 #005-12-1977 L1981 **EM** *020 †16
MILLER, Meredith Rae. 2090 NE WYATT CT, STE 101 97701 #048-12-2002 L2007 **U** *020
MILLS, Gary Michael. ■ 97701 #038-41-1969 L1985 **AN** *020 †05
MONCHAMP, Travis Louis. 2084 NE PROFESSIONAL CT, ADVANCED SPECIALTY CARE 97701
  #035-09-2000 L2006 **END** *020 †20,28
MONTEVERDI, Anthony Josep. 2100 NE WYATT CT STE 202 97701 #063-01-2000 L2005
  P *020 †75
MONTOYA, Angelina Marie. 1011 SW EMKAY DR, STE 101 97702 #030-06-1992 L2005
  CHP *020 †75
MOORE, Joel August, Jr. 2200 NE NEFF RD, STE 200 97701 #021-01-1999 L2005 **ORS** *100 †40
MOORE, Kathleen R. 1303 NE CUSHING DR, STE 100 97701 #040-02-1989 L1996 **OSS** *020 †40
MORRISON, Elliot Irwin. 724 NW FEDERAL ST 97701 #035-08-1957 L1993 **CHP P** *072 †75
MORRISSEY, John F. ■ 97702 #024-01-1949 L1950 **GE** *071 †20
MOSBRUCKER, Cynthia M. ■ 97701 #016-06-1990 L2006 **OBG OS** *020 †30
MUDGETT, John Scott. 55075 HUNTINGTON RD 97707 #305-01-1985 L1999 **P PFP** *020
MULLER, Thomas J. 2095 NW TRENTON AVE 97701 #030-06-1962 L1969 **DR NM** *071 †80,28
MURPHY, John Anthony. 2381 NE CONNERS AVE, 2381 NE CONNERS AVENUE 97701
  #046-01-1993 L2000 **OBG** *020 †30
NEEB, Andrew David. 2090 NE WYATT CT 97701 #056-06-2001 L2006 **U** *020 †95
NELSON, James Orville. 2200 NE NEFF RD, STE 200 97701 #005-18-1990 L1994 **PM** *020 †60
NEUMANN, Holm Wolfram. ■ 97701 #021-01-1966 L1973 **ORS LM** *072 †40
NEWBY, Norwyn Robt. 2600 NE NEFF RD STE 1, NEUROMUSCULOSKELETAL CENTE 97701
  #040-02-1970 L1980 **NS** *071 †25
NIBLER, Patricia Ann. 2160 NE WILLIAMSON CT, FALL CREEK INTERNAL MEDICI 97701
  #040-02-1996 L1999 **IM** *020 †20
NIXON, Brigitte Kate. 2500 NE NEFF RD, CENTRAL OREGON PATHOLOGY 97701
  #054-04-2000 L2000 **PTH** *020 †50
NOBLE, Gavin Leslie. ■ 97701 #035-15-1999 L2006 **CD** *100 †20
NONWEILER, Blake Alan. 2200 NE NEFF RD, STE 200 97701 #048-12-1989 L1996
  ORS OSM *020 †40
NORBURG, Mary Anne. 2577 NE COURTNEY DR, DESCHUTES COUNTY HEALTH DE 97701
  #005-12-1981 L1991 **OBG** *020 †30
NOVAK, Linda Christine. 2275 NE DOCTORS DR, STE 6 97701 #016-43-1984 L1985
  OPH *020 †35
O'CONNOR, Scott Troy. 1501 NE MEDICAL CENTER DR 97701 #041-15-1999 L2005
  OPH *020 †35
OERTLEY, Robert E. ■ 97709 #018-03-1951 L1952 **ID GPM** *071
O'HOLLAREN, Brian Timothy. 2090 NE WYATT CT, STE 101 97701 #040-02-1983 L1989
  U *020 †95
OPPENHEIMER, Karen Lee. 1501 NE MEDICAL CENTER DR 97701 #035-47-1996 L2005
  IM *020 †20
OWENS, Harry Robt, Jr. 2500 NE NEFF RD 97701 #028-34-1966 L1966 **MDM OS** *040 †18

PALACIO, Peter Edward. 2450 NE MARY ROSE PL, STE 220 97701 #025-12-1993 L2001
  OBG *020 †30
PALMER, Edward O'Hare. 2500 NE NEFF RD 97701 #003-01-1977 L1995 **EM** *020 †16
PAULSON, Larry Edward. 2200 NE NEFF RD, STE 200 97701 #031-01-1991 L2007 **PM** *020 †60
PEEPLES, Neal James. 2500 NE NEFF RD 97701 #056-05-1992 L2001 **EM** *020 †16
PETERS, Gerald Eugene, Jr. 1501 NE MEDICAL CENTER DR 97701 #038-41-1988 L2005
  D *020 †15
PIERSON, Christine Marie. 409 NE GREENWOOD AVE, STE 101 97701 #054-04-2000 L2005
  IM *020
PINNICK, Robert Volney. 1501 NE MEDICAL CENTER DR 97701 #019-02-1977 L1982
  NEP IM *020 †20
PINSON, Era Louise. ■ 97701 #004-01-1974 L1975 **OBG** *020 †20
PLATT, Ernest Nelson. 21155 TUMALO RD 97701 #005-12-1970 L1971 **FM** *075 †18
PONTE, Laurie Diane. 1080 MOUNT BACHELOR DR 97702 #025-12-1987 L1990 **FM** *020 †18
POOL, Stephen Edward. 2500 NE NEFF RD, CENTRAL OREGON PATHOLOGY 97701
  #067-01-1995 L2001 **DMP** *020 †50
POWELL, James Hargrave. ■ 97702 #047-05-1969 L1973 **AN** *020 †05
QUINN, Robert Thomas. 2450 NE MARY ROSE PL, STE 200 97701 #040-02-1996 L2002
  PS *020 †65
RAGAIN, Kermit Victor. ■ 97702 #040-02-1965 L1973 **DR EM** *020
RAPACZ, Brian Russell. 2500 NE NEFF RD, ST CHARLES MEDICAL CNTR 97701
  #040-02-1994 L1995 **EM** *020 †16
REDWINE, David Byron. 2190 NE PROFESSIONAL CT 97701 #048-04-1973 L1975
  GYN *020 †30
REED, William Job. 2500 NE NEFF RD, EMERG DEPT 97701 #056-06-1992 L2002 **EM** *020 †16
REICHERT, Susan Karen. 125 NW GREELEY AVE 97701 #038-41-1981 L1989 **PD OMM** *020 †55
RITCHIE, James Lewis. 2516 NW O BRIEN CT, CARDIOVASCULAR CONSULTS 97701
  #038-06-1967 L2002 **CD IM** *020 †20
RITZENTHALER, James C. 2300 NE NEFF RD, VOLUNTEERS IN MEDICINE CLI 97701
  #007-02-1981 L1982 **IM** *020 †20
ROGERS, Michael Sean. 1501 NE MEDICAL CTR DR, CENTER DRIVE 97701 #036-05-1994 L2005
  IM *020 †20
ROGERS, Stephen Roberts. 61535 S HIGHWAY 97, STE 9 97702 #005-06-1962 L1969
  GYN *020 †30
ROGG, Emilie Margarethe. 1501 NE MEDICAL CTR DR, CENTER DRIVE 97701
  #008-02-1996 L2004 **FM** *020 †18
ROSEN, Ronald Danl. 116 NE 5TH ST 97701 #649-01-1985 L1991 **IM AN** *020 †20
ROSENBERG, David Bruce. 2500 NE NEFF RD 97701 #051-04-1993 L2005 **EM** *020 †16
ROSENFIELD, Michael F. 1247 NE MEDICAL CENTER DR, STE 3 97701 #038-06-1974 L1998
  FM *020 †18
ROSENTHAL, Anthony James. 19237 DUTCHMAN CT 97702 #016-06-1966 L2004
  P PYA *030 †75
ROTONDI, Richard John. 60245 WOODSIDE RD 97702 #005-02-1968 L1975 **FM DR** *071 †80
RUSSELL, Hans G. 1501 NE MEDICAL CENTER DR 97701 #422-01-1998 L2001 **FM** *020 †18
RYAN, Michael G. 1303 NE CUSHING DR, STE 100 97701 #048-02-1986 L1996
  ORS GS *020 †40
SALTON, Gillian Greta. 2500 NE NEFF RD, ST. CHARLES MEDICAL CENTER 97701
  #032-01-2001 L2005 **EM** *100 †16
SAMPSON, Mark Edison. 2500 NE NEFF RD, EMERGENCY ROOM 97701 #040-02-1980 L1994
  IM EM *020 †20,16
SANDOVAL, David. 1501 NE MEDICAL CENTER DR 97701 #737-01-1985 L2001
  IM RHU *020 †20
SAN MIGUEL, Richard Hays. ■ 97707 #035-08-1965 L1968 **DR R** *020 †55,80
SCALLON, Quinn Marie. 409 NE GREENWOOD AVE # 101, THE COMMUNITY CLINIC-
  BEND 97701 #016-02-1998 L2005 **FM** *020 †18
SCHABEN, Laura Joelle. 2275 NE DOCTORS DR, NORTHSTAR NEUROLOGY 97701
  #030-05-2000 L2004 **N** *020 †75
SCHLOESSER, David T. 2421 NE DOCTORS DR, NEUROLGY OF BEND LLC 97701
  #019-02-1991 L2000 **N** *020 †75
SCHNEIDER, Eric Joseph. 1501 NE MEDICAL CENTER DR, BEND MEMORIAL CLINIC 97701
  #035-06-1993 L1996 **FM** *020 †18
SCHNEIDER, Roger Alan. 2500 NE NEFF RD, CENTRAL OREGON PATHOLOGY 97701
  #048-04-1967 L1976 **PTH** *071 †50
SCHOCK, Todd A. 1893 NE NEFF RD 97701 #048-12-1996 L1999 **GS** *020
SCOTT, Kim Shana. ■ 97701 #056-05-1985 L1996 **EM** *075 †16
SEWELL, Robert Dalton. 1375 NW KINGSTON AVE, KIDS CENTER 97701 #005-12-1975 L1982
  PD *020 †55
SHANNON, Robert Lee, Jr. 1303 NE CUSHING DR, STE 100 97701 #040-02-1998 L2003
  ORS GS *020 †40
SHAPIRO, William Herbert. 20890 89TH ST 97701 #016-42-1954 L2000 **P** *020
SHARPE, Dean Roy. 2500 NE NEFF RD 97701 #016-06-1975 L1983 **MDM** *030 †85
SHEPARDSON, Stanley Oral. 2275 NE DOCTORS DR, STE 6 97701 #040-02-1969 L1970
  OPH GP *020 †35
SHULTZ, Paula Kay. ■ 97701 #034-01-1983 L2007 **PDR** *020 †80
SHULTZ, Stephen Mitchell. 1460 NE MEDICAL CTR DR, CENTER DRIVE 97701
  #005-02-1985 L2006 **DR IM** *020 †80
SICOTTE, Mary Patricia. 2500 NE NEFF RD, ST CHARLES MEICAL CENTER 97701
  #040-02-1997 L2006 **IM** *020 †20
SIKES, Robert Anthony. 2500 NE NEFF RD 97701 #005-15-1969 **AN** *071
SIMNING, Patrick L. 1501 NE MEDICAL CENTER DR 97701 #023-12-1986 L1989 **FM** *020 †18
SINGER, Brett David. ■ 97702 #005-14-1989 L1993 **EM** *020 †16
SINGER, Craig Martin. ■ 97701 #040-02-1985 L2007 **EM** *020 †16
SINGLETARY, Dejuan. 2100 NE WYATT CT, STE 202 97701 #005-06-1995 L2005 **CHP P** *020 †75
SMART, Martin Lindsey. 409 NE GREENWOOD AVE # 101, THE COMMUNITY CLINIC OF
  BE 97701 #049-01-1996 L2007 **FM** *020 †18
SMITH, Carla Sue. 2500 NE NEFF RD, STE 200 97701 #048-04-1997 L2003 **ORS OTR** *020 †40
SMITH, Mary Gwendolen. ■ 97701 #917-25-1956 L1963 **GP GPM** *071
SMITH, Randall Carl. 2500 NE NEFF RD, ST.CHARLES MEDICAL CENTER 97701
  #005-18-1986 L1994 **AN** *020 †05
SMITH, Scott Thomas. 2500 NE NEFF RD, SOUND INPATIENT PHYSICIANS 97701
  #041-15-1999 L2005 *020 †20
STANGLAND, Kenneth James. 2500 NE NEFF RD, ANESTHESIA DEPARTMENT 97701
  #040-02-1981 L1985 **AN** *020 †05
STEINER, Linda Ann. ■ 97701 #018-03-1999 L2007 **PD** *020 †55
STEVENS, Scott Xavier. 2275 NE DOCTORS DR STE 6, PILOT BUTTE MED CTR 97701
  #039-05-1986 L1997 **OPH** *020 †35

STEWART, Brian Kirk. 2500 NE NEFF RD, CENTRAL OREGON PATHOLOGY 97701 #035-20-1989 L1999 **PTH MM** *020 †50
STEWART, David Cecil. 2200 NE NEFF RD, STE 200 97701 #054-04-1985 L1990 **PM** *020 †60
STRAGAND, James John. 2084 NE PROFESSIONAL CT, ADVANCED SURGICAL CARE 97701 #048-12-1985 L2000 **GE IM** *020 †20
SVENDSEN, Dale Scott. 1820 MONTEREY PNES 97701 #040-02-1985 L1990 **PD** *020 †55
TAJCHMAN, Urszula W. 2500 NE NEFF RD, THE HEART CENTER, ST CHARL 97701 #023-07-1993 L2001 **PDC** *020 †55
TAKLA, Nora Vanessa. 2090 NE WYATT CT, STE 101 97701 #012-05-1994 L1999 **U** *020 †95
TAPELBAND, Gerda Ellen. 2160 NE WILLIAMSON CT, FALL CREEK INTERNAL MEDICI 97701 #005-07-1992 L1997 **IM** *020 †20
TARBET, Edward Mitchell. 2500 NE NEFF RD 97701 #031-01-1984 L1985 **FM GS** *020 †18
TELLER, John D. 1501 NE MEDICAL CTR DR, CENTER DRIVE 97701 #040-02-1982 L1990 **FM** *020 †18
TENG, Daniel Yuwen. 115 SW ALLEN RD, DEACONESS MEDICAL CENTER 97702 #043-06-1994 L2006 **FM** *020 †18
THAYER, David T. 2300 NE NEFF RD, VOLUNTEERS IN MEDICINE 97701 #043-01-1976 L1982 **HS ORS** *020 †40
THOMAS, Robert Lawrence. 2200 NE NEFF RD, STE 200 97701 #038-41-1984 L1995 **ORS** *020 †40
THOW, George Bruce. ■ 97702 #065-01-1954 L1958 **CRS** *071 †85,10
TIEN, Raymond. 2200 NE NEFF RD, STE 200 97701 #016-11-1996 L1997 **NS** *020
TORNAY, Pamela Lall. 2500 NE NEFF RD 97701 #025-07-1988 L1998 **EM** *020 †16
TORNAY, Todd Cameron. 2500 NE NEFF RD, ST. CHARLES MEDICAL CENTER 97701 #006-12-1988 L1998 **EM** *020 †16
TRIPP, Michael Raattama. ■ 97701 #026-04-1972 L1979 **GE IM** *071 †20
TUFT, Stewart, Jr. 1501 NE MEDICAL CENTR DR D, BEND MEMORIAL CLINIC 97701 #040-02-1967 L1968 **FM** *020 †18
UGALDE, Viviane. 2200 NE NEFF RD STE 200 97701 #031-01-1988 L2007 **PM SCI** *020 †60
URI, Lisa Jill. 18 NW OREGON AVE, HIGH LAKES HEALTHCARE 97701 #041-09-1997 L2006 **FM** *020 †18
VADER, Virginia Lee. 2500 NE NEFF RD, CENTRAL OREGON PATHOLOGY 97701 #034-01-1997 L2002 **PTH** *020 †50
VAN CAMP, Paul Michael. 115 SW ALLEN RD, AESTHETICS MD 97702 #005-18-1979 L1995 **FM EM** *020 †16,18
VAUGHAN, Darin Davis. 1501 NE MEDICAL CENTER DR 97701 #007-02-2001 L2006 **PD** *020 †55
VERHEYDEN, James Richard. 2200 NE NEFF RD, STE 200 97701 #056-05-1997 L2003 **HS** *020 †40
VERHEYDEN, Jean S. 2450 NE MARY ROSE PL, STE 120 97701 #010-01-1995 L2004 **OTO** *020 †45
VILLANO, Michael Eusebio. 2400 NE NEFF RD STE B 97701 #036-05-1995 L2001 **OTO GS** *020 †45
VLESSIS, Angelo Anthony. 2500 NE NEFF RD 97701 #040-02-1989 L1990 **TS** *020 †85,90
WAGNER, Marc Anthony. 2200 NE NEFF RD, STE 200 97701 #005-12-2000 L2004 **PM** *100 †60
WALHOF, Debra Sue. ■ 97701 #033-05-1989 L2007 **PD** *020 †55
WALTHER, Cara Elizabeth. 1303 NE CUSHING DR, STE 100 97701 #032-01-1993 L1999 **OSM** *020 †40
WARD, Brad Allen. 2200 NE NEFF RD, CENTER FOR ORTHOPEDIC 97701 #027-01-1990 L2002 **NS** *020 †25
WARLICK, Thomas Anthony. 1501 NE MEDICAL CENTER DR 97701 #040-02-1971 L1977 **FM** *020 †18
WATFORD, John Wesley. ■ 97702 #001-06-2003 L2004 **IM** *100 †20
WEED, Linton Gilmore, II. ■ 97702 #056-05-1954 L1956 **PS** *071 †65
WEEKS, Michael Lorn. 2400 NE NEFF RD STE A 97701 #003-01-1985 L1989 **OBG** *020 †30
WENDEL, Thomas Herbert. 1501 NE MEDICAL CENTER DR 97701 #040-02-1984 L1985 **UCM FM** *020 †18
WETTSTEIN, Michael Eugene. 2500 NE NEFF RD, ATTN: GAIL MORRISON 97701 #005-12-1997 L2001 **AN** *020 †05
WHITSELL, Paul Franklin. 2500 NE NEFF RD 97701 #019-02-1965 L1973 **U** *071 †95
WIGLE, Rodney Phillip. 1693 SW CHANDLER AVE # 250 97702 #040-02-1977 L1982 **ORS** *020 †40
WIGNALL, William Bruce. 1247 NE MEDICAL CENTER DR, STE 3 97701 #030-05-1970 L2005 **FM** *040 †18
WILLIAMS, Marc Vincent. 2577 NE COURTNEY DR, DESCHUTES COUNTY MENTAL HE 97701 #005-06-1989 L2001 **P** *020 †75
WOLLMUTH, Jason Roland. ■ 97701 #040-02-1998 L2006 **IC** *100 †20
WOLLMUTH, Kimberly Anne. 2200 NE PROFESSIONAL CT, CENTRAL OREGON PEDIATRIC 97701 #040-02-1999 L2006 **PD** *020 †55
WOODS, Richard Henry. 2500 NE NEFF RD 97701 #054-04-1957 L1965 **IM ON** *020 †20
WORTHINGTON, Jack C. 2500 NE NEFF RD, ST CHARLES MEDICAL CENTER 97701 #005-02-1981 L1986 **EM** *020 †18,16
WRAY, Anita Downing. 1501 NE MEDICAL CENTER DR 97701 #035-01-1993 L1994 **IM** *020 †20
YARBROUGH, Wm Michael. ■ 97701 #021-01-1976 L1976 **OBG** *071 †30
YOCOM, Laurel B. 2500 NE NEFF RD, CENTRAL OREGON PATHOLOGY 97701 #017-20-1979 L1987 **PTH** *062 †50
YOUNG, Eddy Andrew. 1501 NE MEDICAL CENTER DR, BEND MEMORIAL CLINIC 97701 #016-06-1986 L1993 **CD IM** *020 †20
YOUNGER, Cheryl Lynn. 2500 NE NEFF RD, CENTRAL OREGON PATHOLOGY 97701 #040-02-1994 L2002 **PTH** *020 †50
YUNDT, Kent Douglas. 2275 NE DOCTORS DR, STE 2 97701 #047-05-1991 L1999 **NS** *020 †25
ZAMAN, Tonbira Syeda. 1501 NE MEDICAL CENTER DR, ST VINCENT CATHOLIC MEDICA 97701 #035-08-2000 L2006 **PCC** *020 †20
ZIRKER, Douglas Karl. 2747 NE CONNERS AVE 97701 #049-01-1975 L1979 **D** *020 †15

BLACHLY — LANE

MENTZER, Richard Lynn. 20270 BLACHLY GRANGE RD, LAKE CREEK MED CLINIC 97412 #005-02-1972 L1973 **GP** *020

BLACK BUTTE — DESCHUTES

GARCIA, Randal Lee. ■ 97759 #005-12-1979 L1983 **FM EM** *075 †18
WINCHESTER, Lynn W. ■ 97759 #049-01-1954 L1955 **AN** *071 †05

BLUE RIVER — LANE

MALO, Douglas Stanley. ■ 97413 #040-02-1979 L1980 **ORS** *020 †40

BORING — CLACKAMAS

BENNETT, Gaylord Wayne. ■ 97009 #041-02-1957 L1958 **PD CHN** *071 †55
HANSON, Mark C L. ■ 97009 #026-04-1945 **IM** *071 †20

BROOKINGS — CURRY

BISGROVE, Michael Edward. PO BOX 190 97415 #045-01-1985 L1986 **FM** *020 †18
CALVIN, Donald Dean. ■ 97415 #005-15-1962 L1975 **AN PME** *071
GRAHAM, William Haines. ■ 97415 #005-12-1956 L1957 **GP** *020
GROVES, Katrina. 585 5TH ST 97415 #041-07-1989 L1995 **FM** *020 †18
HARMAN, Charles Ellsworth. ■ 97415 #028-34-1960 L1963 **N P** *071 †75
HAUSER, Robert Wayne. ■ 97415 #005-12-1954 L1955 **AN OS** *075
KRICK, Warren Jerome. 585 5TH ST 97415 #035-01-1963 L2003 **P** *020 †75
LEIGHTON, Alexander C. 555 5TH ST, STE 2 97415 #040-02-1998 L2001 **IM** *020 †20
LEIGHTON, Juliane Listl. 555 5TH ST STE 2, SUTTER COAST HLTH CTR 97415 #048-14-1998 L2001 **IM** *020 †20
MILSTONE, Stanley J. ■ 97415 #041-09-1949 L1950 **P** *071 †75
PATEL, Jitendra Chunibhai. 97825 SHOPPING CENTER AVE, OR 97415-0326 97415 #496-11-1980 L1987 **IM** *020 †20
PETZOLD, Robert Warren. 585 5TH ST, BROOKINGS MEDICAL CENTER 97415 #019-02-1976 L2003 **OM FM** *020 †70,18
RANSMEIER, Robert E, Jr. 19921 WHALESHEAD RD 97415 #007-02-1957 L1964 **P** *071 †75
RERING, Clifford H. PO BOX 6429 97415 #660-03-1935 L1952 **RO R** *071
RUTH, Cynthia Moore. 109 SCHOONER BAY RD 97415 #005-14-1980 L1999 **P** *020 †75
SAVILLE, Wendy. ■ 97415 #016-11-1978 L1979 **P** *020 †75
SILVER, Mark Edward. 446 OAK ST, BROOKINGS HARBOR MED CTR 97415 #005-14-1985 L1988 **FM A** *020 †18
VAUGHN, Anna C. ■ 97415 #352-07-1951 L1961 **GP IMG** *072
VOIGT, Alfred Edward. ■ 97415 #016-43-1952 L1954 **P** *071

BROWNSVILLE — LINN

BARRON, Diana V Bailey. PO BOX 218 97327 #005-06-1980 L1983 **FM** *020 †18
HOLT, Donald Edwin. ■ 97327 #010-01-1959 L1960 **IM** *020

BURNS — HARNEY

FITZPATRICK, Tom Mark. 559 W WASHINGTON ST 97720 #030-05-1987 L1990 **FM** *020 †18
JOHNSTON, Kevin Allen. 559 W WASHINGTON ST 97720 #040-02-1999 L2002 **FM** *020 †18
MORRISON, Robert Oliphant. 557 W WASHINGTON ST 97720 #040-02-1956 L1958 **GP GS** *072
NICHOLSON, Gerald James. 557 W WASHINGTON ST 97720 #060-01-1948 L1959 **GS CD** *071 †18
OLSON, Stephen Eric. 557 W WASHINGTON ST, HARNEY DISTRICT HOSPITAL 97720 #035-01-1982 L1991 **GS** *020 †85
RICHARDS, Thomas Allen. 557 W WASHINGTON ST 97720 #007-02-1978 L1987 **FM** *020 †18
SPENCE, William Scott. 559 W WASHINGTON ST 97720 #040-02-1999 L2002 **FM** *020 †18
WHITE, Frank G. 557 W WASHINGTON ST 97720 #030-05-1951 L1954 **FM** *071 †18

CAMP SHERMAN — JEFFERSON

STRAUMFJORD, Marianne S. 26266 SW METOLIUS MEDWS DR 97730 #040-02-1969 L1970 **P FM** *071 †75

CANBY — CLACKAMAS

ALBRIGHT, Bernard Ralph. ■ 97013 #040-02-1954 L1955 **GP** *071
BRIDGEMAN, Deona Lynn. 345 N GRANT ST 97013 #040-02-1997 L2000 **FM** *020 †18 ‡
EWBANK, Shawn Albert. 452 NW 1ST AVE 97013 #040-02-1996 L1999 **FM** *020 †18
HUGHSON, Daniel Lee. 1185 S ELM ST 97013 #040-02-1981 L1982 **IM** *020 †20
MITCHELL, David Bruce. 158 SW 2ND AVE 97013 #060-01-1974 L1988 **FM** *020
PARSONS, David Paul. 1185 S ELM ST 97013 #040-02-1992 L1998 **GS** *020 †10,85
PIZZUTI, Anselmo. 1185 S ELM ST 97013 #040-02-1966 L1970 **PD** *020 †55
WARREN, Amanda Sue. 117 NE 3RD AVE 97013 #026-04-1998 L2001 **FM** *020 †18
WARREN, Trent Brian. 117 NE 3RD AVE 97013 #049-01-1997 L2000 **FM** *020 †18

CANNON BEACH — CLATSOP

LEONELLI, Leo Philip. ■ 97110 #030-06-1954 L1955 **EM AM** *071 †70
SCHWARTZ, Robert H. ■ 97110 #035-45-1962 L1963 **AI PD** *071 †55,03

CANYONVILLE — DOUGLAS

COOKSLEY, Fred Beynon. 495 SW IST STREET 97417 #005-15-1962 L1975 **OS GP** *071
LEIBOLD, Werner. 251 NORTH MAIN ST 97417 #649-14-1965 L1979 **FM EM** *075 †18
TIWARI, Anandita. ■ 97417 #495-47-1996 L2005 **IM** *020 †20

CARLTON — YAMHILL

RICHARDSON, Carol A. ■ 97111 #038-43-1991 L1994 **OBG** *020 †30

CAVE JUNCTION — JOSEPHINE

MILLER, Kristin K. 319 CAVES HWY 97523 #056-05-1996 L1999 **FM** *020 †18

MULLARKEY, Donna Eileen. 25647 REDWOOD HWY, SISKIYOU COMMUNITY HEALTH 97531 #026-08-1996 L1999 FP *020 †18

NORDAL, James Danl. 319 CAVES HWY 97523 #040-02-1990 L1993 FM *020 †18

VERSTEEG, Charles Neil. 441 S JUNCTION AVE 97523 #040-02-1943 L1947 GP GS *071

CENTRAL POINT – JACKSON

ARTHUR, Thomas D. ■ 97502 #067-01-1973 L1983 FM *020

BROWN, Kenneth Aaron. ■ 97502 #040-02-1977 L1995 EM FM *020 †16

GILMOUR, David Richard. 524 MANZANITA ST, CENTRAL POINT MEDICAL GROU 97502 #041-14-1974 L1981 FM *020 †18

HALL, James Whitney, III. ■ 97502 #024-01-1958 L1973 IM ID *071 †20

HULL, Brandan A. 524 MANZANITA ST, PROVIDENCE MEDICAL GROUP 97502 #049-01-2001 L2002 FM *020 †18

OLSEN, Neil Marvin. 524 MANZANITA ST 97502 #028-02-1996 L2003 FM FSM *020 †18

PONS, R Kenneth. 132 MANZANITA ST 97502 #036-01-1966 L1976 PS GP *020 †85,65

ROBERTS, Daniel Devee. 524 MANZANITA ST 97502 #040-02-1967 L1971 FM *071 †18

RUDISILE, Michael Edward. 524 MANZANITA ST, PHYSICIAN 97502 #056-06-2000 L2007 FM *020 †18

SPRUNG, Roma Jane. 524 MANZANITA ST 97502 #396-18-1984 L1994 IM *074 †20

TAHER, Ahmed Abdel. 524 MANZANITA ST, CENTRAL POINT PROVIDERS 97502 #056-06-1992 L1996 FM *020 †18

CHARLESTON – COOS

BILLS, Frederick Gurdon. ■ 97420 #005-11-1945 L1945 EM *075

CHESHIRE – LANE

BAIN, Robert W. ■ 97419 #024-05-1952 L1953 PTH P *071 †50

CHRISTMAS VALLEY – LAKE

O'DELL, Lawrence Wayne. ■ 97641 #040-02-1957 L1961 OPH *071 †35

CLACKAMAS – CLACKAMAS

ABUFADIL, Samer Halim. 10180 SE SUNNYSIDE RD 97015 #039-01-1998 L2007 IM *020 †20

ACKERMAN, Douglas A. 10180 SE SUNNYSIDE RD, DEPT OF UROLOGY 97015 #047-05-1988 L1989 U *020 †95

ALBERTS, Michelle Joy. 12360 SE SUNNYSIDE RD 97015 #040-02-1994 L1999 FM *020 †18

ALGENIO, Rachel Gamo. 10100 SE SUNNYSIDE RD, MT TALBERT MEDICAL OFFICE 97015 #038-06-1998 L2002 OBG *020 †30

ANDERSON, Bruce Carl. 10180 SE SUNNYSIDE RD 97015 #005-14-1976 L1979 IM ORS *020

ANDERSON-COWELL, Laurel R. 9290 SE SUNNYBROOK BLVD, STE 220 97015 #035-15-1988 L1998 AI *020 †20,03

ANDRICH, Angela Marie. 9800 SE SUNNYSIDE RD, MT SCOTT MEDICAL OFFICE 97015 #031-01-1991 L1992 P *020 †75

ARMSTRONG, Barbara Jean. 10220 SE SUNNYSIDE RD #REG 97015 #026-04-1982 L1988 PTH *071 †50

ATCHESON, Regina B Ross. 10180 SE SUNNYSIDE RD 97015 #040-02-1972 L1974 EM *020 †16

AZAR, Leesa Marie. 10180 SE SUNNYSIDE RD 97015 #040-02-1993 L1994 IM *020 †20

AZIMI-ZONOOZ, Aryan. 10180 SE SUNNYSIDE RD, KAISER PERMANENTE-SUNNYSID 97015 #028-34-1993 L1994 NPM *020 †55

BACHHUBER, Stephen Ryan. 10180 SE SUNNYSIDE RD, KAISER SUNNYSIDE MED CTR 97015 #056-06-1975 L1980 AN *020 †05

BACHMAN, Keith Howard. 10180 SE SUNNYSIDE RD, SUNNYSIDE MEDICAL OFFICE 97015 #005-18-1992 L1993 IM *020 †20

BAKER, Elaine Rose. 9800 SE SUNNYSIDE RD 97015 #040-02-1980 L1986 GE *020 †20

BALAKRISHNAN, Kirthika. 10180 SE SUNNYSIDE RD, KAISER SUNNYSIDE MEDICAL C 97015 #495-94-1998 L2002 IM *020 †20

BANDARI, Vijayalakshmi. 10180 SE SUNNYSIDE RD, KAISER SUNNYSIDE 97015 #495-57-1997 L2001 IM *020 †20

BARRETT, Michael John. 10180 SE SUNNYSIDE RD 97015 #040-02-1979 L1989 PD *020 †55,03

BASCO, Matthew Gregory. 9800 SE SUNNYSIDE RD, KAISER PERMANENTE, MT SCOT 97015 #035-45-2000 L2000 D *020 †15

BEAM, Richard Roy. 10180 SE SUNNYSIDE RD 97015 #040-02-1984 L1987 IM *020 †20

BEHARY, Patra Ann. 10180 SE SUNNYSIDE RD, HOSPITALIST DEPT 97015 #016-11-1994 L1997 IM *020 †20

BELL, Julian William. 10180 SE SUNNYSIDE RD, KAISER - SUNNYSIDE MEDICAL 97015 #035-09-2000 L2006 PCC *100 †20

BENEDETTI, Jeremy Angelo. 10100 SE SUNNYSIDE RD, KAISER PERMANENTE 97015 #038-43-1996 L2004 PS *020 †85,65

BIEBERACH, Maribel D. 9800 SE SUNNYSIDE RD, PHYSIATRY DEPT 97015 #715-01-1977 L2000 PM *020 †60

BISIO, James Michael. 10180 SE SUNNYSIDE RD, SUNNYSIDE MEDICAL CENTER 97015 #040-02-1977 L1979 GS PD *020 †85

BLACKETOR, Paula Dawn. 10180 SE SUNNYSIDE RD 97015 #048-15-1984 L1990 OBG *020 †30

BOARDMAN, David Laurence. 9900 SE SUNNYSIDE RD, KAISER SUNNYSIDE MEDICAL C 97015 #005-19-1992 L1999 ORS *020 †40

BOHME, Winhard Uwe. 12360 SE SUNNYSIDE RD, NORTHWEST PRIMARY CARE 97015 #067-01-1969 L1976 FM *020 †18

BOOK, Katrin Ina. 10180 SE SUNNYSIDE RD 97015 #409-33-2000 L2007 AN *020

BOOKSTEIN, Kenneth Harry. 10180 SE SUNNYSIDE RD, KAISER PERMANENTE 97015 #021-01-1997 L2003 DR *020 †80

BOWMAN, Carla Jean. 10180 SE SUNNYSIDE RD, KAISER SUNNYSIDE MEDICAL O 97015 #035-08-1998 L2001 FM *020 †18

BRITVAN, Leora Jan. 10180 SE SUNNYSIDE RD, KAISER - SUNNYSIDE 97015 #005-06-1988 L2006 IM *020 †20

BROCK, Mitch Edmond. 9900 SE SUNNYSIDE RD 97015 #048-04-1986 L1995 OTO HNS *020 †45 ‡

BROOKS, Martha Louise. 9800 SE SUNNYSIDE RD 97015 #025-01-1982 L1985 PD *020 †55

BROWN, Ben Maurice. 10180 SE SUNNYSIDE RD, KAISER SUNNYSIDE MED CTR 97015 #005-11-1969 L1983 DR P *020 †75,80

BROWN, Mary Kathryn. 9290 SE SUNNYBROOK BLVD, STE 200 97015 #051-01-1993 L2005 PD *020 †55

BUFFORD, Heather Lynn. 10100 SE SUNNYSIDE RD, KAISER PERMANENTE MT. TALB 97015 #028-02-2001 L2005 OBG *020 †30

BURNS, Beryl Margaret. 9800 SE SUNNYSIDE RD, KAISER, MT SCOTT 97015 #836-02-1976 L1981 PD *020 †20

BURT, Richard Arthur. 9900 SE SUNNYSIDE RD 97015 #012-05-1995 L1996 U *020 †95

BURTON, Lisa. 10180 SE SUNNYSIDE RD, KAISER SUNNYSIDE MEDICAL C 97015 #049-01-1988 L1996 FM FSM *020 †18

BYTNAR, Daniel William. 10180 SE SUNNYSIDE RD, KAISER SUNNYSIDE MEDICAL C 97015 #028-03-2003 L2007 *100

CALABIA, Belinda Serrano. 9290 SE SUNNYBROOK BLVD, SUNNYSIDE MED GRP 97015 #038-43-1989 L1990 IM *020 †20

CALAWA, Christopher Alan. 9800 SE SUNNYSIDE RD, KAISER MT SCOTT MED OFFICE 97015 #024-16-1981 L1993 IM OM *020 †20

CAMPBELL, Patricia T. 9800 SE SUNNYSIDE RD, KAISER MT SCOTT MEDICIAL O 97015 #040-02-1998 L1999 PD *020 †20

CARNEVALE, Tony John. 10180 SE SUNNYSIDE RD 97015 #016-43-1992 L1993 EM *020 †16

CARNEY, Maureen Louise. 9900 SE SUNNYSIDE RD 97015 #040-02-2001 L2001 PM *100 †60

CHAN, Tsoi Tsuen. 10200 SE SUNNYSIDE RD, KAISER FOUNDATION HOSP LAB 97015 #462-01-1966 L1973 PTH *020 †50

CHANDHOKE, Paramjit Singh. 10100 SE SUNNYSIDE RD, NW PERMANENTE-MT. TALBERT 97015 #038-06-1984 L2006 U *020 †95

CHANG, Aileen Derhuei. 9900 SE SUNNYSIDE RD 97015 #035-06-1991 L2002 GE *020 †20

CHANG, Chang-Shee. 10100 SE SUNNYSIDE RD 97015 #385-02-1963 L1973 GS *071 †85

CHANG, Naun. 10180 SE SUNNYSIDE RD, DEPT OF ANESTHESIA-KSMC 97015 #041-02-1995 L1999 AN *020 †05

CHEBAC, Carmen Gheorghe. 9800 SE SUNNYSIDE RD, MT SCOTT MEDICAL OFFICE 97015 #781-02-1987 L1998 IM *020 †20

CHO, Josephine. 10180 SE SUNNYSIDE RD, KAISER PERMANENTE 97015 #035-06-1993 L2000 DR *020 †80

CHOO, Christine E. 10180 SE SUNNYSIDE RD 97015 #035-46-1996 L1997 IM *020 †20

CHUNG, Jane Yujin. 10180 SE SUNNYSIDE RD 97015 #005-12-1999 L2004 IM *020 †20

CIRILLO, Fred. 10180 SE SUNNYSIDE RD, KAISER SUNNYSIDE MEDICAL C 97015 #005-02-2002 L2006 *100 †16

CLARK, Gregory Lynn. 10180 SE SUNNYSIDE RD 97015 #023-01-1983 L1993 N *020 †75

CLARKE, David Dean. 9900 SE SUNNYSIDE RD 97015 #008-02-1979 L1984 GE IM *020 †20

COLBACH, Josephine K T. 10200 SE SUNNYSIDE RD, SUNNYSIDE MEDICAL CNTR 97015 #016-06-1964 L1970 EM *020 †16

COLLIER, Jeanine Shannon. 10151 SE SUNNYSIDE RD 97015 #016-11-1987 L1998 P OS *020

CONSTIEN, Maria Ravelli. 9800 SE SUNNYSIDE RD 97015 #036-08-1983 L1990 PD *020 †55

CORNELL, Floyd Michael. 10001 SE SUNNYSIDE RD, STE 100 97015 #039-01-1975 L2005 OPH OS *020 †35

CORONADO, Stephanie. 10180 SE SUNNYSIDE RD 97015 #005-18-1983 L1984 OBG GYN *020 †30

CORRIGAN, Robert Francis. 10100 SE SUNNYSIDE RD, OCCUPATIONAL MED CLINIC 97015 #040-02-1957 L1958 ORS *071 †40

CURTIS, Audrey Ellen. 10100 SE SUNNYSIDE RD, MT TALBERT MED OFFICE 97015 #005-02-1995 L2002 OBG *020 †30

DEMAS, Larry Ross. 9900 SE SUNNYSIDE RD 97015 #039-01-1971 L1989 OTO *020 †45

DENNIS, James Warren. 9900 SE SUNNYSIDE RD 97015 #016-06-1972 L1989 GS *020 †85

DION, Garry Roger. 10180 SE SUNNYSIDE RD 97015 #040-02-1975 L1976 OS *020 †80

DONOHOE, Martin Thos. 10180 SE SUNNYSIDE RD, KAISER SUNNYSIDE MEDICAL C 97015 #005-14-1990 L1997 IM *020 †20

DOWNEY, Valerie Anne. 10180 SE SUNNYSIDE RD, SUNNYSIDE MEDICAL CENTER 97015 #038-40-1994 L1996 IM HOS *020 †20

DWORKIN, Lawrence Alan. 10200 SE SUNNYSIDE RD, KAISER SUNNYSIDE HOSP 97015 #038-41-1975 L1977 PTH NM *020 †50

DWYER, Marianne. 9800 SE SUNNYSIDE RD 97015 #038-41-1978 L1980 PD *020 †55

DYKSTRA, Richard Henry. 9800 SE SUNNYSIDE RD, MOUNT SCOTT OFFICE 97015 #018-03-1977 L1981 IM *020 †20

EBBING, Jonathan James. 10180 SE SUNNYSIDE RD 97015 #016-01-2002 L2006 P *020 †75

EBNER, Stephen Jos. 10180 SE SUNNYSIDE RD 97015 #040-02-1977 L1982 ORS *020 †40

EICKHOFF, Leo Edward, III. 9900 SE SUNNYSIDE RD 97015 #028-34-1988 L1989 GE *020 †20

ELS, Lisa Powell. 10100 SE SUNNYSIDE RD, KAISER-SUNNYSIDE MEDICAL C 97015 #054-04-1996 L1997 IM *020 †20

EURMAN, Peggy Toba. 9800 SE SUNNYSIDE RD 97015 #005-18-1982 L1983 IM *020 †20

EXALL, John Stuart. 10180 SE SUNNYSIDE RD 97015 #040-02-1976 L1979 EM *020 †20,16

FELCHER, Andrew Harry. 10180 SE SUNNYSIDE RD, KAISER-SUNNYSIDE MEDICAL C 97015 #035-45-1994 L1997 IM HOS *020 †20

FELDMAN, George Walter. 10180 SE SUNNYSIDE RD 97015 #025-01-1972 L1973 IM *020 †20

FERRELL, Michael Douglas. 9800 SE SUNNYSIDE RD 97015 #035-46-1977 L1996 IM *020 †20

FORREST, Laurie Beth. 10180 SE SUNNYSIDE RD 97015 #035-45-1980 L1984 DR *020 †80

FORSYTH, Matthew John. 10100 SE SUNNYSIDE RD 97015 #025-01-1982 L1983 U *020 †95

FOWLER, Julia Elizabeth. 10100 SE SUNNYSIDE RD 97015 #021-01-2002 L2006 OBG *020

FREDERICK, Elizabeth Ann. 9800 SE SUNNYSIDE RD, DEPT OF INTERNAL MEDICINE 97015 #016-01-1986 L1989 IM *020 †20

GALAVIZ, Manuel Raymond. 10200 SE SUNNYSIDE RD, DEPT OF FAMILY PRACTICE 97015 #005-19-1980 L1983 FM *020 †18

GARBER, Seth Lee. ■ 97086 #024-01-1976 L1979 IM *030 †20

GARCIA, Gregory Gilbert. 9290 SE SUNNYBROOK BLVD, STE 120 97015 #016-11-1990 IM *100

GARCIA, Gregory P. 9290 SE SUNNYBROOK BLVD, BLV STE120 97015 #748-01-1992 L2002 IMG *020 †20

GARNAND, Jennifer G. 10180 SE SUNNYSIDE RD 97015 #003-01-2000 L2000 IM *020 †20

GASOW, Shelly Lynn. 9290 SE SUNNYBROOK BLVD, STE 120 97015 #026-04-1997 L2007 FM *020 †18

GASS, Brooke Ryan. 10180 SE SUNNYSIDE RD, KAISER SUNNYSIDE MEDICAL C 97015 #005-18-1990 L1992 PD *020 †55

GEORGE, Walter F. 9290 SE SUNNYBROOK BLVD, STE 210 97015 #035-20-1971 L1991 IM OM *020 †20

GILBERT, Mark Allen. 10180 SE SUNNYSIDE RD, KAISER SUNNYSIDE MED CTR 97015 #056-06-1990 L1991 AN *020 †05

GILL, Frederick Francis. 10180 SE SUNNYSIDE RD 97015 #056-06-1983 L1984 AI PD *020 †55,03

GISWOLD, Mary Elizabeth. 10100 SE SUNNYSIDE RD, MT. TALBERT MEDICAL OFFICE 97015 #056-05-1998 L1999 GS *020 †85

GLAUBER, Harry Steven. 10180 SE SUNNYSIDE RD, KAISER PERMANENTE 97015 #836-01-1978 L1987 END *020 †20

GOLDSMITH, Seth Leopold. 10100 SE SUNNYSIDE RD 97015 #038-06-1998 L2004 ORS *100 †40

GOLDSTEIN, Melvyn Edward. 10180 SE SUNNYSIDE RD 97015 #041-12-1967 L1981 AN *020 †05

GONZALES, Susanna Marie. 10180 SE SUNNYSIDE RD 97015 #010-01-1997 L2006 IM *020 †20

GOODKIN, Peter Elliot. 9775 SE SUNNYSIDE RD # 500, SUNNYSIDE HEALTH CTR 97015 #005-14-1974 L1975 DS D *020 †15 ‡

GOODLOE, Trudy Lee. 10180 SE SUNNYSIDE RD, KAISER SUNNYSIDE MEDICAL C 97015 #005-18-1977 L1983 DR *020 †80

GRAY, Rafael. 10163 SE SUNNYSIDE RD, STE 490 97015 #021-01-1991 L2005 P *020 †75

GRAY, Siobhan Heidi. 10180 SE SUNNYSIDE RD, KAISER SUNNYSIDE MEDICAL C 97015 #017-20-1996 L1999 IM *020 †20

GRIFFIN, Keith Henry. 10163 SE SUNNYSIDE RD 97015 #040-02-1972 L1973 P *020 †75

GRISHKEVICH, Maksim V. 10001 SE SUNNYSIDE RD, STE 120 97015 #913-06-1995 L2001 IM *020 †20

GROMAN, Steven Ronald. 10100 SE SUNNYSIDE RD, DEPT OF ORTHOPEDICS 97015 #023-07-1977 L1988 ORS *020 †40

GROSS, Bennett Raymond. 9800 SE SUNNYSIDE RD 97015 #038-06-1995 L2004 IM *020 †20

GUNSON, Karen Lou. 13309 SE 84TH AVE, STE 100 97015 #040-02-1981 L1982 FOP *040 †50

HAJARIZADEH, Homayon. 10100 SE SUNNYSIDE RD 97015 #040-02-1987 L1988 VS *020 †85

HALL, Winthrop Huntington. 10180 SE SUNNYSIDE RD, NORTHWEST PERMANENTE 97015 #054-04-1997 L2002 DR *020 †80

HALPERT, Luis Emilio. 10180 SE SUNNYSIDE RD 97015 #649-01-1953 L1962 U *071 †95

HARNER, Marvin Harold. 9800 SE SUNNYSIDE RD 97015 #018-03-1968 L1973 PD NEP *020 †55

HEDMANN, Shaun Anthony. 10180 SE SUNNYSIDE RD 97015 #023-07-1981 L1986 CD IM *020

HENDRICKS, Curtis John. 10180 SE SUNNYSIDE RD 97015 #026-04-1952 L1955 OBG *071 †30

HERSON, Michael Kevin. 10180 SE SUNNYSIDE RD 97015 #016-42-1981 L1991 END DIA *020 †20

HICKETHIER, Cheryl Beth. 14831 SE 82ND DR 97015 #005-12-1985 L1987 FM GPM *020 †70

HICKS, Frances F. 9800 SE SUNNYSIDE RD, NW PERM 97015 #027-01-1970 L1979 PD *020 †55

HIESTAND, Jenna Alane. 10180 SE SUNNYSIDE RD, SUNNYSIDE MEDICAL CENTER 97015 #028-02-1999 L2008 P *020 †75

HIGGINS, Sharon Marie. 9800 SE SUNNYSIDE RD 97015 #030-05-1975 L1979 OTO *020 †45

HOEVET, Michael Ray. 10180 SE SUNNYSIDE RD, KAISER SUNNYSIDE HOSPITAL 97015 #048-04-1970 L1973 EM *020 †16

HOFFMANN, Dieter F, Jr. 9800 SE SUNNYSIDE RD 97015 #016-11-1983 L1984 OTO NO *020 †45

HONG, Gene Geo. 15630 SE 90TH AVE 97015 #005-11-1989 L1990 OS *020 †20

HORACEK, Jeffrey Jay. 9290 SE SUNNYBROOK BLVD, STE 120 97015 #039-01-1992 L1993 IM *020 †20

HORAN, Clayton Thos. 10180 SE SUNNYSIDE RD, SURGICAL SERVICES, ANESTHE 97015 #005-19-1981 L1993 AN *020 ‡

HOTAKI, Leila Marrie. 9800 SE SUNNYSIDE RD 97015 #040-02-1992 L1995 PD *020 †55

HOUSE, Robert Wesley. 10100 SE SUNNYSIDE RD 97015 #040-02-1978 L1979 OBG *020 †30

HUANG, Susan Ann. 10180 SE SUNNYSIDE RD 97015 #005-14-1988 L1994 DR *020 †80

HURT, Mark Robt. 10180 SE SUNNYSIDE RD, KAISER SUNNYSIDE MEDICAL C 97015 #016-11-1982 L1997 DR *020 †80

HWEE, Yinkan. ■ 97015 #040-02-2005 L2005 GS *012

ISRAEL, Jeffrey Morris. 9800 SE SUNNYSIDE RD 97015 #040-02-1976 L1977 OTO *020 †45

JACOBS, Paul Orrin. 9900 SE SUNNYSIDE RD 97015 #005-14-1967 L1972 PM *020 †20,60

JACOBSON, Karin Thea. 9800 SE SUNNYSIDE RD 97015 #005-14-2003 L2003 FM *020 †18

JANSSEN, Tonya Joan. 10180 SE SUNNYSIDE RD, KAISER SUNNYSIDE MEDICAL C 97015 #040-02-1996 L1999 FM *020 †18

JENKINS, Loren Edward. 9900 SE SUNNYSIDE RD 97015 #048-04-1985 L1990 OSS ORS *020 †40

JOHNSON, Jeannine Sheree. 10180 SE SUNNYSIDE RD 97015 #054-04-1999 L2000 PD *020 †55

JOHNSON, Jeffrey Eaton. 9900 SE SUNNYSIDE RD, SUNNYBROOK MEDICAL OFFICE 97015 #035-20-1993 L1994 U *020 †95

JONES, Marla Kay. 10180 SE SUNNYSIDE RD, KAISER SUNNYSIDE MED CTR 97015 #040-02-1985 L1986 DR *020 †80

JOYNER, Lisa Camille. 9800 SE SUNNYSIDE RD, KAISER MOUNT SCOTT MED CTR 97015 #047-06-1995 L1998 IM *020 †20

KANE, Joseph Alan. 9900 SE SUNNYSIDE RD 97015 #024-01-1974 L1980 IM *020 †20

KANG, Kenneth Myungdei. 9900 SE SUNNYSIDE RD 97015 #014-01-1991 L1992 D *020 †15

KAROLLE, Beth Lynne. 10180 SE SUNNYSIDE RD 97015 #025-01-1993 L2000 CD *020 †20

KENNEDY, Scott Richard. ■ 97086 #040-02-2006 L2006 AN *012

KHAN, Yiichiang. 10100 SE SUNNYSIDE RD, KAISER MT TALBERT MEDICAL C 97015 #385-02-1963 L1972 ORS *020 †40

KHANDEKAR, Aasma Alim. 10180 SE SUNNYSIDE RD, KSMC/UCC 97015 #047-06-2000 L2004 DBP *012 †55

KOCH, Susan E. 10180 SE SUNNYSIDE RD 97015 #041-14-1980 L1998 D PD *020 †55,15

KOSTA, Louis Daniel. 9900 SE SUNNYSIDE RD 97015 #007-02-1974 L1984 GS *020 †85

KOWALEWSKA, Maria Halina. 10180 SE SUNNYSIDE RD, KAISER SUNNYSIDE MEDICAL C 97015 #759-03-1984 L2002 DR *020 †80

KUNKE, Carol Kohlbacher. ■ 97015 #039-01-1982 L1996 AN *020

LADIZINSKY, Daniel Alan. 10100 SE SUNNYSIDE RD, MT TALBERT OFFICE 97015 #025-01-1984 L1999 PS *020 †85,65

LAKE, Robin Michael. 10180 SE SUNNYSIDE RD, CARDIOLOGY 97015 #048-04-1975 L1990 CD IM *020 †20

LAMBERT, Sarah Elizabeth. 10100 SE SUNNYSIDE RD 97015 #005-15-2002 L2006 OBG *020

LAMKA, Melanie Ann. 13229 SE 127TH AVE 97015 #048-04-2000 L2002 EM *020

LANDAUER, Kathryn C. 10180 SE SUNNYSIDE RD, KAISER PERMANENTE 97015 #051-01-1995 L1997 IM *020 †20

LANE, Ernest Aaron. 10180 SE SUNNYSIDE RD 97015 #016-11-1955 L1956 GP *071

LARSEN, Kenneth David. 10180 SE SUNNYSIDE RD, SUNNYSIDE HOSPITAL 97015 #011-02-1983 L1989 AN *020 †05

LAVERY, Daniel Philip. 10180 SE SUNNYSIDE RD, KAISER PERMANENTE DEPT-CAR 97015 #033-05-1981 L1999 CD *020 †20

LAWRENCE, Amy Renick. 10180 SE SUNNYSIDE RD, DEPT EM 97015 #005-02-1996 L1999 EM LM *020 †16

LAWRENCE, Geoffrey Talbot. 9900 SE SUNNYSIDE RD, KAISER SUNNYBROOK CLINIC 97015 #003-01-1973 L1978 OTO HNS *020 †45

LAYNE, Cheryl A. 10180 SE SUNNYSIDE RD, KAISER SUNNYSIDE MEDICAL C 97015 #024-07-1999 L2003 IM *020 †20

LEE, Chong W. 10180 SE SUNNYSIDE RD 97015 #035-19-1977 L1985 PUD AI *020 †20,03

LEE, Thomas Eugene. 10180 SE SUNNYSIDE RD, KAISER-SUNNYSIDE MEDICAL C 97015 #005-15-1993 L2006 EM *020 †16 ‡

LEFRANC, Yves Arturo. 13435 SE 97TH AVE 97015 #649-13-1986 L2001 FM *020 †18

LEIDER, Karen E. 10180 SE SUNNYSIDE RD 97015 #036-07-1975 L1981 EM *020 †16

LEIGHTON, Dawn Christine. 10180 SE SUNNYSIDE RD, KAISER PERMANENTE 97015 #040-02-1998 L2002 EM *020 †16

LENG, Mith. 10180 SE SUNNYSIDE RD 97015 #040-02-1994 L2007 FM *071 †18

LEONARD, Nicholas Markham. 10180 SE SUNNYSIDE RD, KAISER SUNNYSIDE MEDICAL C 97015 #010-02-1994 L1997 EM *020 †16

LEONG, Calvin Yuen. 10180 SE SUNNYSIDE RD 97015 #011-02-1978 L1981 IM *020 †20

LEVINE, Steven Mark. 9800 SE SUNNYSIDE RD 97015 #010-02-1975 L1997 IM *020 †20

LEWISON, Karen Pomian. 10180 SE SUNNYSIDE RD, DEPT OF RADIOLOGY 97015 #035-09-1992 L2002 NM *020 †80,28

LEWMAN, Larry Victor. 13309 SE 84TH AVE, STE 100 97015 #019-02-1967 L1971 FOP *050 †50

LI, Alvin Yichieh. 10180 SE SUNNYSIDE RD, KAISER PERMANENTE 97015 #054-04-1982 L1983 AN FM *020 †18,05

LIE, Kenneth George. 10180 SE SUNNYSIDE RD, DEPT OF ANESTHESIOLOGY 97015 #038-06-1998 L2003 AN *020 †05

LIEBERMAN, Stephen F. 10180 SE SUNNYSIDE RD 97015 #005-06-1977 L1978 U PYA *020 †95

LIEBO, Jeffrey Stephen. 9800 SE SUNNYSIDE RD, KAISER SUNNYSIDE MEDICAL C 97015 #026-04-1970 L1990 PD *020 †55

LIFTON, Ilyse Danielle. 10180 SE SUNNYSIDE RD 97015 #041-14-2001 L2005 PD *020 †55

LINMAN, John Edwin. 10100 SE SUNNYSIDE RD 97015 #048-13-1976 L1980 OBG *020 †30

LINMAN, Sally Ruth. 10180 SE SUNNYSIDE RD 97015 #048-13-1976 L1980 OBG *020 †30

LIPPY, Frank Taggart. 10180 SE SUNNYSIDE RD, KAISER SUNNYSIDE MEDICAL C 97015 #038-06-1999 L2001 EM *020 †16

LIU, Zheru. 10220 SE SUNNYSIDE RD, REGIONAL LABORATORY 97015 #243-47-1987 L2000 PTH *020 †50

LLOYD, Clee Everett. 9800 SE SUNNYSIDE RD 97015 #040-02-1978 L1979 OTO AM *020 †45

LOCH, James Robt. 10100 SE SUNNYSIDE RD 97015 #025-07-1976 L1985 ORS *030 †40

LOHMAN, Ronald Lee. 9900 SE SUNNYSIDE RD, KAISER - SUNNYBROOK 97015 #016-42-1979 L1984 ORS GS *020 †40

LORENCE, Thomas Allen. 10180 SE SUNNYSIDE RD 97015 #040-02-1976 L1977 IM *020 †20

LUDEMANN, Robert. 10100 SE SUNNYSIDE RD, KAISER-SUNNYSIDE - MT TALB 97015 #035-08-1995 L1996 GS *020 †85

LUNDSGAARDE, Thorsten. 10180 SE SUNNYSIDE RD 97015 #019-02-1997 L2006 FM *020 †18

LUTFIYYA, Waleed Lutfi. 10100 SE SUNNYSIDE RD, ORLANDO REGIONAL HEALTHCAR 97015 #030-05-2001 L2007 CRS *020

MAC GREGOR, Rebecca Spann. 10180 SE SUNNYSIDE RD, KAISER SUNNYSIDE MEDICAL C 97015 #048-15-1985 L2001 DR *020 †80

MACLIN, Martha Lynn. 10180 SE SUNNYSIDE RD 97015 #054-04-1987 L1994 DR *072 †80

MAC MILLAN, Ian Currie. 10180 SE SUNNYSIDE RD 97015 #065-05-1956 L1961 RHU IM *071 †20

MAND, Christopher Chas. 10108 SE SUNNYSIDE RD D, SUNNYSIDE MEDICAL CENTER 97015 #038-40-1988 L1991 IM *020 †20

MARKEY, Brian James. 10180 SE SUNNYSIDE RD, KAISER SUNNYSIDE MEDICAL C 97015 #005-18-1982 L1993 R VIR *020 †80

MARTIN, Claudia H. 10180 SE SUNNYSIDE RD, SUNNYSIDE MED CTR, DEPT OF 97015 #067-01-1988 L2002 NS *020

MASTANDUNO, Michael. 9290 SE SUNNYBROOK BLVD, STE 210 97015 #035-19-1978 L1985 ON HEM *075

MCGEE, Kerry Robinson. 9800 SE SUNNYSIDE RD, MT. SCOTT PEDIATRIC CLINIC 97015 #051-01-2003 L2003 PD *020 †55

MC GUIRE, John Thomas. 10180 SE SUNNYSIDE RD 97015 #016-11-2002 L2002 IM *100 †20

MEDNICK, Wendy L. 9800 SE SUNNYSIDE RD, C/O NW PERMANENTE 97015 #005-14-1987 L1995 IM *020 †20

MEEKER, Huey J. 9775 SE SUNNYSIDE RD # 800, SUNNYSIDE INTERNAL MEDICIN 97015 #005-18-1992 L1993 IM *020 †20

MERCURIO, Roderick Scott. 10180 SE SUNNYSIDE RD, KAISER SUNNYSIDE MEDICAL C 97015 #005-12-1997 L2002 DR *020 †80

MESSINGER, Jon Michael. 12042 SE SUNNYSIDE RD, # 603 97015 #005-12-1986 L1993 P *020

MEYERS, Wendy Susan. 10180 SE SUNNYSIDE RD, KAISER SUNNYSIDE MEDICAL C 97015 #034-01-1995 L1998 IM *020 †20

MICK, Alfred Mark. 12360 SE SUNNYSIDE RD, NORTHWEST PRIMARY CARE GRP 97015 #030-06-1967 L1970 GP *020 †18

MIKKELSEN, Susan Lee. 10180 SE SUNNYSIDE RD, KAISER SUNNYSIDE - PULMONO 97015 #018-03-1999 L2003 PCC *020 †20

MINKUNAS, Darian Vincent. 10163 SE SUNNYSIDE RD, STE 490 97015 #038-45-1995 L1997 P *020 †75

MISRA, Sounak Nick. 9290 SE SUNNYBROOK BLVD, STE 120 97015 #028-46-2001 L2004 IMG *020 †20

MOIEL, David Lee. 10100 SE SUNNYSIDE RD 97015 #021-01-1969 L1979 GS *020 †85

MOLITOR, John Thos. 10180 SE SUNNYSIDE RD, KAISER SUNNYSIDE MED CTR 97015 #040-02-1969 L1976 EM IM *071 †20,16

MORROW, Terry Allen. 10180 SE SUNNYSIDE RD, INPATIENT SERVICE 97015 #036-01-1985 L1986 IM *020 †20

MULARSKI, Karen Smith. 10180 SE SUNNYSIDE RD, KAISER PERM SUNNYSIDE 97015 #005-18-1998 L1999 IM HOS *020 †20

MULCAHY, Peggy Ann. 10180 SE SUNNYSIDE RD, ANESTHESIA DEPT 97015 #016-06-1986 L2000 AN *020 †05

MURAMATSU, Marc Seichi. 9900 SE SUNNYSIDE RD, DEPARTMENT OF DERMATOLOGY 97015 #028-34-1981 L1992 D *020 †15

NAG, Tushar Kanti. 10180 SE SUNNYSIDE RD 97015 #495-38-1954 L1968 NS *020

NAYAK, Navin Narayan. 9290 SE SUNNYBROOK BLVD, STE 120 97015 #041-12-2000 L2000 IM *020 †20

NELSON, Christopher Paul. 10100 SE SUNNYSIDE RD 97015 #041-01-1977 L1983 GS *020 †85

NELSON, Clifford Conrad. 13309 SE 84TH AVE STE 100, OREGON MED EXAM OFC 97015 #040-02-1989 L1990 FOP ATP *062 †50

NELSON, John Herbert. 10180 SE SUNNYSIDE RD 97015 #003-01-1977 L1978 IM *020 †20

NELSON, John Mauer. 10180 SE SUNNYSIDE RD, SUNNYSIDE KAISER MED CENTE 97015 #035-19-1975 L1988 **EM IM** *020 †20,16

NEVILLE, Malina Oana. 10180 SE SUNNYSIDE RD, KAISER SUNNYSIDE MEDICAL C 97015 #040-02-2001 L2001 **IM** *020

OBADIAH, Joseph Michael. 9900 SE SUNNYSIDE RD, DEPT DERM 97015 #036-07-1999 L2006 **D** *020 †15 ‡

OBUCHOWSKI, Christopher A. 10180 SE SUNNYSIDE RD, KAISER SUNNYSIDE MEDICAL C 97015 #041-14-1994 L1998 **DR** *020 †80

OH, Michael Chihong. ■ 97086 #040-02-2007 **GS** *012

OLSON, Neal Reinhart. 10220 SE SUNNYSIDE RD 97015 #028-02-1976 L1981 **ATP CLP** *020 †50

OLSON, Richard Milton, Jr. 10180 SE SUNNYSIDE RD 97015 #040-02-1981 L1982 **IM** *020 †20

OLTMANS, J Boyd-Wickizer. 9800 SE SUNNYSIDE RD, MOUNT SCOTT MEDICAL OFFICE 97015 #040-02-2002 L2002 **PD** *020 †55

ONO, Hirohisa. 9800 SE SUNNYSIDE RD, DEPT OF NEUROSURGERY 97015 #572-08-1959 L1982 **NS** *020 †25

ORCHARD, Reynold Graham. 9775 SE SUNNYSIDE RD SU, WILLAMETTE FALLS IMMEDIATE 97015 #165-08-1982 L2000 **FM EM** *020 †18

OTA, Jeremy Kayne. 10180 SE SUNNYSIDE RD 97015 #040-02-1972 L1982 **EM IM** *020 †20,18,16

PAPE, Gary Wayne. 9290 SE SUNNYBROOK BLVD, STE 120 97015 #040-02-1986 L1987 **IM** *020 †20

PARK, Robert T. 10100 SE SUNNYSIDE RD, MOUNT TALBERT MEDICAL OFFI 97015 #024-07-1994 L2006 **OBG** *020 †30

PEACOCK, Willis Edward. 10100 SE SUNNYSIDE RD, KAISER PERMANENTE OCCUP HE 97015 #040-02-1959 L1963 **FM OM** *071 †18

PIERSON, Jeffrey Scott. 10100 SE SUNNYSIDE RD, KAISER PERMANENTE 97015 #040-02-1988 L1989 **GPM** *020 †20,70

POLANSKY, Carolyn M. 9800 SE SUNNYSIDE RD 97015 #041-07-1973 L1974 **EM** *020

PRASAD, Atanu. 10180 SE SUNNYSIDE RD 97015 #035-19-1993 L2000 **VIR** *020 †80

RAE, Christopher Jason. 10180 SE SUNNYSIDE RD, KAISER PERMANENTE - SUNNYS 97015 #040-02-1996 L2003 **FM** *020 †18

RAETHER, Paul Michael. 9800 SE SUNNYSIDE RD 97015 #026-04-1979 L1982 **PM** *020 †60

RAHIMTOOLA, Sahra V. 10180 SE SUNNYSIDE RD, KAISER SUNNYSIDE MED CTR 97015 #040-02-2001 L2003 **IM** *020

RAMASUBRAMANIAN, Ramiah. 10180 SE SUNNYSIDE RD, MEDICAL CENTER 97015 #495-04-1979 L2003 **AN CCA** *020 †05

RANA, Vandana Hiren T. 9775 SE SUNNYSIDE RD, STE 200 97015 #495-56-1980 L1988 **PHP** *020

RAO, Maya Kuthethur. 10180 SE SUNNYSIDE RD, KAISER-SUNNYSIDE MEDICAL C 97015 #035-46-2002 L2002 **NEP** *012 †20

RASTOGI, Rahul. 10180 SE SUNNYSIDE RD, KAISER PERMANENTE 97015 #038-44-1996 L2005 **EM OBG** *020 †16

REGA, Peter Richard. 9800 SE SUNNYSIDE RD 97015 #035-19-1974 L1977 **IM** *020 †18,20

RICCELLI, Louis Patrick. ■ 97015 #054-04-1999 L2000 **RNR** *100 †80

RICHARDSON, Robert Hugo. 10200 SE SUNNYSIDE RD 97015 #026-04-1964 L1977 **PUD IM** *020 †20

RIDEOUT, Kenneth Marvin. ■ 97015 #040-02-1956 L1957 **GP** *071

ROBINSON, Jeanne B. 10180 SE SUNNYSIDE RD 97015 #048-04-2004 L2007 **IM** *100 †20

ROBINSON, Mindi Lynn. 9290 SE SUNNYBROOK BLVD, STE 120 97015 #040-02-2002 L2005 **FM** *020 †18

ROSENFELD, Alan Richard. 10180 SE SUNNYSIDE RD, KAISER SUNNYSIDE MEDICAL C 97015 #035-08-1971 L1984 **CD IM** *020 †20

ROTTER, Tricia Scholes. 10180 SE SUNNYSIDE RD, KAISER PERMANENTE - SUNNYS 97015 #047-05-2002 L2006 **EM** *100 †16

SADDISON, Diana K. 10180 SE SUNNYSIDE RD, KAISER SUNNYSIDE MEDICAL C 97015 #048-02-1981 L1995 **IM** *020 †85,20

SADRO, Claudia Theresa. 10180 SE SUNNYSIDE RD, DEPT OF RADIOLOGY 97015 #061-01-1993 L2002 **DR** *020 †80

SAGAWA, Jason Hiroshi. 10180 SE SUNNYSIDE RD, KAISER SUNNYSIDE MEDICAL C 97015 #014-01-1975 L1979 **IM** *020 †20

SAGE, Joan D. 9800 SE SUNNYSIDE RD 97015 #033-06-1984 L1985 **PD OS** *020 †55

SANDVIG, Roy James. 10180 SE SUNNYSIDE RD 97015 #028-34-1954 **GS** *072 †85

SAQUETON, Angelito De C. 9800 SE SUNNYSIDE RD, KAISER PERMANENTE 97015 #748-01-1962 L1974 **D** *071 †15

SCHAFIR, Karoline. 10180 SE SUNNYSIDE RD, PEDIATRIC URGENT CARE CLIN 97015 #048-04-1990 L1995 **PD** *020 †55

SCHEMM, George Walker. 10180 SE SUNNYSIDE RD 97015 #025-01-1955 L1964 **NS** *071 †25

SCHIEDLER, Michael Gerard. 9800 SE SUNNYSIDE RD 97015 #040-02-1980 L1986 **VS GS** *020 †85

SCHMIDT, David Martin. 10180 SE SUNNYSIDE RD, KAISER SUNNYSIDE MEDICAL C 97015 #036-07-1987 L1998 **NS** *020 †20

SCHMIDT, Linda Erika. 10001 SE SUNNYSIDE RD, STE 140 97015 #024-16-2000 L2003 **CHP** *100 †75

SCHWARZ, James Arthur. 10180 SE SUNNYSIDE RD, DEPT OF SURGERY 97015 #005-02-1980 L1989 **GS ON** *020 †85

SCHWEITZER, Timothy Paul. 9900 SE SUNNYSIDE RD, SUNNYBROOK MEDICAL OFFICE 97015 #039-01-1999 L2006 **ORS HS** *020 †40

SHAH, Sapna Shirish. 9290 SE SUNNYBROOK BLVD, OREGON PEDIATRICS-NE PORTL 97015 #041-15-2003 L2007 **PD** *020 †55

SHAW, John Chas. 10100 SE SUNNYSIDE RD 97015 #040-02-1974 L1975 **OBG** *020

SHEEDY, Gina Man-Mui. 9775 SE SUNNYSIDE RD, STE 100 97015 #041-13-1988 L1990 **GPM** *020 †70 ‡

SHEN, Mary. 10180 SE SUNNYSIDE RD, KAISER SUNNYSIDE MEDICAL C 97015 #040-02-1986 L1987 **IM** *020 †20

SHERGILL, Ravinder. 13518 SE 97TH AVE 97015 #495-29-1992 L2004 **PCC** *020 †20

SILVERBLATT, Adam Edward. 10180 SE SUNNYSIDE RD 97015 #041-02-2000 L2000 **GE** *020

SKAVARIL, James Vincent. 9290 SE SUNNYBROOK BLVD, STE 120 97015 #040-02-1995 L1997 **IM** *020 †20

SMITH, Dana Sainsbury. 10180 SE SUNNYSIDE RD, KAISER PERMANENTE 97015 #047-05-2000 L2001 **OTO** *100 †45

SNYDER, Stephan Mark. 10180 SE SUNNYSIDE RD 97015 #005-06-1979 L1984 **IM** *020 †20

SPINDEL, Steven Jay. 10180 SE SUNNYSIDE RD, KAISER SUNNYSIDE MEDICAL C 97015 #010-01-1989 L1990 **ID** *020 †20

STANDRIDGE, Walter L. 10180 SE SUNNYSIDE RD, BROOKSIDE CENTER 97015 #004-01-1990 L2008 **P** *020 †75

STARK, Edward Harlan. 10100 SE SUNNYSIDE RD, MT TALBERT CLINIC 97015 #040-02-1964 L1971 **ORS** *071 †40

STEINKELER, Cara Nicole. 10180 SE SUNNYSIDE RD 97015 #040-02-1996 L1999 **IM** *020 †20

STEPHENS, Sheree Diane. 9800 SE SUNNYSIDE RD 97015 #010-01-1991 L2002 **IM** *020 †20

STEWART, Kathy Lynn. 10100 SE SUNNYSIDE RD 97015 #040-02-1984 L1991 **OBG** *020 †30

STOEBER, Troy Christopher. 9290 SE SUNNYBROOK BLVD, STE 200 97015 #030-06-1998 L2002 **PD** *020 †55

STOLZBERG, Stephen M. 10163 SE SUNNYSIDE RD #490 97015 #035-46-1967 L1974 **P N** *020 †75

STRAUSS, Richard. 10180 SE SUNNYSIDE RD, KAISER SUNNYSIDE MEDICAL C 97015 #005-06-1977 L1978 **CD** *020 †20

STUTZMAN, Donald Paul. 10180 SE SUNNYSIDE RD, KAISER - SUNNYSIDE MEDICAL 97015 #041-01-1980 L1984 **CD** *020 †20

SWANSON, Jeffrey Todd. 10180 SE SUNNYSIDE RD 97015 #003-01-1994 L1996 **IM** *020 †20

TAHIR, Mian Mohammad. 10180 SE SUNNYSIDE RD 97015 #704-02-1955 L1970 **NS** *020

TAMANAHA, Reid. 10180 SE SUNNYSIDE RD, KAISER PERMANENTE 97015 #014-01-1996 L2002 **EM** *020 †16

TAMASHIRO, Daniel S. 9800 SE SUNNYSIDE RD, KAISER MT. SCOTT CLINIC 97015 #014-01-1990 L2001 **IM** *020 †20

TOAL, Thomas Roderick, Jr. 9900 SE SUNNYSIDE RD 97015 #003-01-1986 L1996 **ORS** *020 †40

TOTONCHY, Matti Abbo. 10180 SE SUNNYSIDE RD 97015 #528-01-1961 L1972 **U** *020 †95

TWOMBLY, Daniel Cavanagh. 10180 SE SUNNYSIDE RD 97015 #048-04-1982 L1988 **FM** *020 †18

UNITAN, Carol Lisensky. 10180 SE SUNNYSIDE RD, KAISER SUNNYSIDE MEDICAL 97015 #040-02-1988 L1989 **AN** *020 †05

VANDELINDT, David James. 9800 SE SUNNYSIDE RD, KSMC MTS-MH 97015 #047-05-1994 L1996 **PYG** *020 †75

VARAN, Richard Anthony. 9800 SE SUNNYSIDE RD, KAISER PERMANENTE - MT. S 97015 #040-02-2002 L2002 **FM** *020 †18

VESCO, Kimberly Kristine. 10100 SE SUNNYSIDE RD, DEPT OF OB/GYN 97015 #005-18-1997 L2001 **OBG** *020 †30

VESSELY, Laurie Hurtado. 10180 SE SUNNYSIDE RD, ENDOCRINOLOGY 97015 #040-02-1993 L1994 **END** *020 †20

WALLACE, Carol Ann. 10180 SE SUNNYSIDE RD 97015 #032-01-1977 L1985 **R PDR** *020 †80

WARD, Barbara Ola. ■ 97015 #038-40-1980 L1987 **IM** *020 †20

WARDWELL, Noel Rabb, Jr. ■ 97086 #038-41-1999 L2005 **PCC** *100 †20

WEIL, David Saml. 10180 SE SUNNYSIDE RD 97015 #028-02-1974 L1977 **OBG** *020 †30

WEINSTEIN, Mitchell Alan. 10180 SE SUNNYSIDE RD, KAISER SUNNYSIDE MED CTR 97015 #041-02-1969 L1991 **NS** *020 †25

WERNER, Jeffrey Allen. 10180 SE SUNNYSIDE RD 97015 #005-06-1972 L2005 **CD IM** *020 †20

WHITEHEAD, Guy, III. 10180 SE SUNNYSIDE RD, CLINIC C 97015 #026-08-1980 L1988 **FM** *020 †18

WIDMAN, Travis James. 9900 SE SUNNYSIDE RD, SUNNYBROOK MEDICAL OFFICE 97015 #054-04-2003 L2004 **D** *020 †15

WILKS, Rebecah Maureen. 10180 SE SUNNYSIDE RD, KAISER SUNNYSIDE MEDICAL C 97015 #005-18-1998 L2004 **EM** *020 †16

WOJESKI, William V. 10100 SE SUNNYSIDE RD 97015 #036-07-1974 L1981 **GS LM** *020 †85

WOLK, Adam Gregory. 10180 SE SUNNYSIDE RD, KAISER SUNNYSIDE MEDICAL C 97015 #005-19-2003 L2007 **IM** *100 †20

WONG, Richard. 10180 SE SUNNYSIDE RD 97015 #005-14-1973 L1979 **OBG** *020 †30

WOO, John Tak. 9800 SE SUNNYSIDE RD, MT SCOTT CLINIC 97015 #008-01-1979 L1980 **IM** *020 †20

WOOD, James Edward. 10180 SE SUNNYSIDE RD, KAISER SUNNYSIDE MEDICAL 97015 #026-08-1998 L2003 **IM** *020 †16

WOZNIAK, Mark Anthony. 9800 SE SUNNYSIDE RD 97015 #048-02-1991 L1992 **IM** *020 †20

WRIGHT, Robert Edwin. 10100 SE SUNNYSIDE RD, TALBERT M 97015 #917-19-1969 L1978 **HS TRS** *020 †40

WU, Jianyi. 10180 SE SUNNYSIDE RD, KAISER - DEPT OF CARDIOLOG 97015 #243-21-1982 L2004 **ICE** *020 †20

WYLLER, Alf Edward. 10100 SE SUNNYSIDE RD 97015 #056-05-1975 L1979 **OBG** *020

YAMASE, Melvin Hitoshi. 9290 SE SUNNYBROOK BLVD 97015 #014-01-1986 L1987 **IM** *020 †20

YANG, Caroline Y. 9800 SE SUNNYSIDE RD 97015 #028-46-1995 L2000 **OTO** *020 †45

YOUNG, Christopher Ray. 13309 SE 84TH AVE, ATE 100 97015 #048-14-1998 L1999 **FOP** *020 †50

ZARELLI, Greg R. 10180 SE SUNNYSIDE RD, KAISER SUNNYSIDE MEDICAL C 97015 #048-04-1996 L2000 **N** *020 †75

ZELAYA, Antonio Diaz. 9800 SE SUNNYSIDE RD 97015 #341-01-1969 L1996 **NS** *020 †25

ZENTHOEFER, Peter. 10100 SE SUNNYSIDE RD, KAISER PERM. NW 97015 #040-02-1980 L1986 **OBG** *020 †30

CLATSKANIE – COLUMBIA

GRAYSON, Charles Elbert. ■ 97016 #005-11-1942 L1942 **R DR** *071 †80

KEIZER, John Phil. ■ 97016 #040-02-1937 L1937 **OPH** *071 †35

COLTON – CLACKAMAS

EATON, John H. ■ 97017 #024-01-1950 L1951 **R** *072 †80

COOS BAY – COOS

ADAMS, Curtis Dale. 4225 CAPE ARAGO HWY 97420 #040-02-1962 L1976 **ORS** *071 †40

ALBERTSON, Carl U. 1900 WOODLAND DR 97420 #049-01-1950 L1951 **FM** *071

AMEND, Eric Kenneth. 1750 THOMPSON RD 97420 #038-43-2001 L2006 **OBG** *020

ARBAN, William Jos. 1750 THOMPSON RD 97420 #045-01-1986 L2007 **FM FSM** *020 †18

BACH, Terrance Stephen. 1750 THOMPSON RD 97420 #037-01-1981 L1984 **FM** *020 †20

BARBOUR, Scott Allen. 2699 N 17TH ST 97420 #028-34-1996 L2008 **ORS** *020 †40

BERT, Jeffrey Kent. 2699 N 17TH ST, SOUTH COAST ORTHOPAEDIC 97420 #007-02-1967 L1975 **ORS** *020 †40

BHANDARI, Amit. 1900 WOODLAND DR, NORTH BEND MEDICAL CTR 97420 #496-09-1998 L2005 **IM** *020 †20

BHATOYA, Jagdev R. 1900 WOODLAND DR 97420 #495-03-1985 L2007 **IM** *020 †20

BICKEL, Jeffrey Carl. 2650 N 17TH ST 97420 #016-11-1990 L1995 **DR** *020 †80

BRILL, Peter Wm. 1775 THOMPSON RD 97420 #030-05-1973 L2003 **EM OS** *040 †16

BROWN, Kathleen Mitchell. 1750 THOMPSON RD, BAY CLINIC, LLP 97420 #051-07-1988 L1998 **D IM** *020 †20,15

BUFTON, L. 1925 THOMPSON RD 97420 #040-02-1984 L1990 **N** *020 †75

CARTER, Dallas Arthur. 1900 WOODLAND DR 97420 #040-02-1987 L1993 **FM PLM** *020 †18

CHEUNG, Lance Kwangyung. ■ 97420 #030-06-2003 L2007 **PM** *100

CLARK, Richard Douglas. 1775 THOMPSON RD, BAY AREA HOSPITAL 97420 #035-01-1986 L2003 **DR** *020 †80

CLARKE, Terrell Lynn. 1750 THOMPSON RD 97420 #040-02-1969 L1974 **PD** *020 †55

COELHO, Paul Christopher. 1957 THOMPSON RD 97420 #016-02-1995 L2005 **PM** *020 †60

COLLINS, Harold Theodore. 1900 WOODLAND DR 97420 #038-40-1968 L1975 **U** *020 †95 ‡

COTTEL, Charles Edward. ■ 97420 #040-02-1944 **IM** *071 †20

COTTMAN, Gordon Wayne. 1750 THOMPSON RD 97420 #054-04-1986 L1996 **IM** *075 †20

CRANE, Douglas Gordon. 1900 WOODLAND DR, NORTH BEND MED CTR 97420 #047-20-1998 L2000 **IM** *020 †20

CURCIN, Aleksandar. 2699 N 17TH ST, SOUTH COAST ORTHOPAEDIC 97420 #005-14-1987 L2005 **OSS** *071 †40

DAVIS, Jon Steven. 2699 N 17TH ST, SOUTH COAST ORTHOPAEDIC 97420 #054-04-1978 L1993 **ORS** *071 †40

DELEON, Jenni C. 1900 WOODLAND DR 97420 #050-02-1997 L2004 **PD** *020 †55

ELLERBY, Richard Allen. 1900 WOODLAND DR 97420 #040-02-1966 L1973 **ON IM** *020 †20

FLANAGAN, John Dean. 682 S COOS RIVER RD 97420 #040-02-1944 L1947 **GP GS** *071

FREUDENBERG, Kenneth Robt. 2699 N 17TH ST 97420 #005-12-1971 L1977 **ORS** *071 †40

GABERT, Barbara Joan. 1775 THOMPSON RD 97420 #048-12-1970 L1974 **EM FM** *020

GERBER, Robert Wm. 1900 WOODLAND DR, NORTH BEND MEDICAL CENTER 97420 #270-02-1987 L1992 **FM** *020 †18

GISS, Steven Randall. 1900 WOODLAND DR 97420 #038-41-1995 L2000 **GS** *020 †85

GIVENS, Jeffery Stuart. 1900 WOODLAND DR 97420 #060-02-1994 L1996 **FM** *020

GOODMAN, Jay Maury. ■ 97420 #016-02-1970 L1976 **IM** *071 †20

GROOM, Debra Ann. 1775 THOMPSON RD, BAY AREA HOSPITAL 97420 #005-06-1983 L2004 **PTH** *020 †50

GROTH, Stephan John. 1750 THOMPSON RD 97420 #019-02-1993 L2000 **OBG** *020 †30

GRUCHACZ, Catherine Ann. 833 ANDERSON AVE, STE 1 97420 #033-05-1983 L1991 **GYN** *020 †30

GUMBS, Brian Lawrence. 1750 THOMPSON RD 97420 #035-46-1997 L2006 **PD** *020 †55

HAMILTON, Laurie Linn. 1900 WOODLAND DR, NORTH BEND MEDICAL CENTER 97420 #039-79-2000, ▲ L2004 **OBG** *020 †30 ‡

HANEY, Susan Theresa. 1775 THOMPSON RD, BAY AREA HOSPITAL 97420 #018-03-1998 L2001 **EM** *020 †16

HENKE, Joseph Martin. 1750 THOMPSON RD 97420 #025-07-1967 L1973 **IM** *020 †20

HOBSON, Shaun Michael. 2699 N 17TH ST, SOUTH COAST ORTHOPAEDIC 97420 #048-12-1991 L2001 **ORS** *020 †40

HOEWING, William Homer. 1775 THOMPSON RD DEPT GP 97420 #030-05-1964 L1964 **EM** *071

HOOGEVEEN, Johannes T. 1900 WOODLAND DR 97420 #660-03-1959 L1978 **FM CLP** *071 †18

HOSACK, William David. 1775 THOMPSON RD 97420 #040-02-1970 L1971 **PTH** *020 †50

HUNTER, Robert Walter. 1900 WOODLAND DR 97420 #014-01-1995 L2006 **IM** *020 †20 ‡

HURBIS, Charles Gerard. 2695 N 17TH ST 97420 #025-01-1985 L1990 **OTO FPS** *020 †45

JACKSON, Nicole Jenee. ■ 97420 #032-01-2000 **IM** *100

JANY, Richard Stephen. 1900 WOODLAND DR, NORTH BEND MEDICAL CENTER 97420 #028-34-1982 L1990 **ORS OAR** *020 †40

JENSON, Carl Rydell. 1775 THOMPSON RD 97420 #040-02-1984 L1992 **RO** *020 †80

KEAN, William Paul. 1900 WOODLAND DR 97420 #048-12-1947 L1947 **PD A** *074

KEIZER, Philip John. 1900 WOODLAND DR 97420 #040-02-1962 L1967 **GS** *071 †85

KING, William D. 1900 WOODLAND DR 97420 #023-01-1976 L1984 **IM** *020 †20

KOBRIN, Lowell Edmund. 1900 WOODLAND DR 97420 #041-02-1971 L1978 **OBG OS** *020 †30

KOWALL, James Paul. 750 THOMPSON RD, BAYCLINIC 97420 #011-02-1984 L2000 **IM** *020 †20

KUSUDA, Leo. 1900 WOODLAND DR, NORTH BEND MEDICAL CTR 97420 #028-02-1981 L2007 **U** *020 †95

LA GESSE, Philip Carey. 1775 THOMPSON RD 97420 #054-04-1989 L1990 **PDP PD** *020 †55

LANZA, Miguel Victor. 1750 THOMPSON RD, BAY CLINIC 97420 #005-02-1980 L2003 **PDA** *020 †55

LARSON, Frank Andrus. 1900 WOODLAND DR, NORTH BEND MEDICAL CTR 97420 #028-34-1987 L1992 **GS** *020 †85

LEVY, Robert Kent. ■ 97420 #051-01-1972 L1982 **IM OS** *062 †20

LINDSAY, Charles M. 1900 WOODLAND DR 97420 #049-01-1950 L1952 **FM** *071 †18

LOTMAN, Anton Erikovich. 1925 THOMPSON RD 97420 #913-01-1981 L2005 **N** *020 †75

MAEYENS, Edgar, Jr. 375 PARK AVE STE 5 97420 #047-06-1969 L1973 **D DMP** *020 †15

MALCOLM, William Richard. 1775 THOMPSON RD 97420 #041-13-1965 L1973 **OS** *020 †30

MARTIN, James Johnston. 2085 THOMPSON RD 97420 #040-02-1961 L1973 **P** *020 †20

MASLONA, Andrew Rowe. ■ 97420 #035-47-1998 L2008 **IM** *020 †20

MC ANDREW, Thomas Francis. 1900 WOODLAND DR 97420 #005-19-1985 L1988 **FM** *020 †18

MC INTYRE, Henderson M. 1775 THOMPSON RD, PATHOLOGY DEPT 97420 #049-01-1977 L1981 **PTH** *020 †50

MC KELVEY, Carla D. 1900 WOODLAND DR, NORTH BEND MEDICAL CENTER 97420 #048-13-1993 L1996 **PD** *020 †55

MORGAN, Joseph T. 1750 THOMPSON RD 97420 #007-02-1960 L1966 **A** *020 †55

MORIARTY, William James. 1900 WOODLAND DR 97420 #041-01-1988 L1996 **IM** *020 †20

MUDAY, Theresa Aileen. 750 CENTRAL AVE, STE 202 97420 #025-12-1996 L2000 **FM** *020 †18 ‡

MUENCHRATH, John Kelley. 1900 WOODLAND DR 97420 #040-02-1992 L1997 **U** *020 †95

MUKAIDA, Frank Yutaka. 1900 WOODLAND DR 97420 #025-12-1996 L2000 **OBG** *020

MULLER, Christopher M. 1900 WOODLAND DR 97420 #031-01-1985 L1990 **IM NEP** *020 †20

MURRAY, Wayne Lee. 1750 THOMPSON RD 97420 #040-02-1959 L1962 **IM** *071

NANDA, Rohit. 1775 THOMPSON RD 97420 #028-34-1997 L2001 **EM** *020 †16

OELKE, David Edward. 1900 WOODLAND DR 97420 #016-11-1966 L1974 **IM** *020 †20

O'LEARY, Jay Francis. 1750 THOMPSON RD 97420 #054-04-1958 L1964 **PD** *071 †55

ORSEL, Douglas Paul. 1775 THOMPSON RD, BAY AREA HOSPITAL-EMERG. D 97420 #005-19-1983 L1999 **EM IM** *020 †16

PARK, Jonathon. 1900 WOODLAND DR 97420 #042-03-1994 L2002 **FM** *020 †18 ‡

PARVIN, Dara. 1957 THOMPSON RD 97420 #054-04-1993 L1999 **ORS** *020 †40

PITTENGER, Basil. 1900 WOODLAND DR 97420 #054-04-2001 L2004 **IM** *020

PORTEOUS, Danielle Renea. 1750 THOMPSON RD 97420 #030-06-1999 L2003 **PD** *020 †55

PYLMAN, Michael Lester. 2699 N 17TH ST, SOUTH COAST ORTHOPAEDIC 97420 #010-01-1989 L1992 **AN PME** *020 †05

QUINN, Michael Stephen. ■ 97420 #040-02-1969 L1971 **DR** *071 †80

RABIN, Donna Lee. 1900 WOODLAND DR 97420 #016-01-1977 L1981 **PD OS** *020 †55

RAVURI, Rajesh. 1900 WOODLAND DR 97420 #495-11-1997 L2002 **IM** *020 †20

REAGAN, Charles Peter. 1865 THOMPSON RD, P O BOX 1436 97420 #046-01-1993 L1994 **P** *100

REMY, Delbert Lee. PO BOX 3190, 600 MILUK DR 97420 #040-02-1964 L1968 **FM** *071

RICHARDSON, Warren Steven. 1900 WOODLAND DR 97420 #016-01-1977 L1981 **IM CCM** *020 †20

RIZEA, Alina Iuliana. 1750 THOMPSON RD 97420 #781-01-1997 L2005 **IMG** *020

SCHANDELMEIER, Gregory. 1750 THOMPSON RD, BAY CLINIC 97420 #036-08-2000 L2004 **IM** *020

SCHMIDT, Merle Chas. 1900 WOODLAND DR, NORTH BEND MEDICAL CENTER 97420 #016-11-1957 L1964 **OBG** *071 †30

SHARMAN, Kenton Douglas. 1900 WOODLAND DR 97420 #035-03-1980 L1984 **FM OBS** *020 †18

SHIMOTAKAHARA, Steven G. 1900 WOODLAND DR 97420 #067-01-1978 L1993 **OTO HNS** *020 †45

SHININGER, Jack Benj. 1775 THOMPSON RD 97420 #040-02-1965 L1972 **R** *020 †80

SHIREMAN, Frances. 1900 WOODLAND DR 97420 #028-46-1978 L2003 **IM** *020 †20

SHULSINGER, Oded Z. 1900 WOODLAND DR 97420 #016-42-1971 L1977 **IM** *020 †20

SMITH, Anthony J. 61343 PIERSON RD 97420 #035-01-1952 L1958 **ORS** *072 †40

SOMERA, Geraldine Ann Jav. 1900 WOODLAND DR 97420 #040-01-1999 L2006 **IM** *100 †20

STEINBERG, Susann Joyce. ■ 97420 #035-03-1966 L2003 **FM OM** *020 †18

TERSIGNI, Steven Alan. 1900 WOODLAND DR 97420 #049-01-1990 L1995 **GS VS** *020 †85

THOREN, Theodore Fred. 1750 THOMPSON RD 97420 #007-02-1911 L1977 **PD** *020 †55

UNO, John Makoto. 620 COMMERCIAL AVE 97420 #005-02-1968 L1973 **U** *020 †95

VANDERHEIDEN, John Peter. 1750 THOMPSON RD 97420 #030-06-1965 L1973 **GS** *071

VELDSTRA, Brad Dean. ■ 97420 #056-06-1993 L1996 **EM** *020 †16

VON DIPPE, Patrick B. 1775 THOMPSON RD, BAY AREA HOSPITAL 97420 #005-06-1989 L2006 **EM** *020 †16

WALKER, James Vincent, Jr. 465 ELROD AVE, QUALICENTER COOS BAY 97420 #038-06-1970 L1977 **NEP IM** *020 †20

WEBSTER, William Wallace. 1900 WOODLAND DR 97420 #019-02-2002 L2007 **OTO** *020

WEIMER, Dennis Dorr, Jr. 2085 THOMPSON RD 97420 #035-06-1995 L2005 **P** *020

WHITNEY, Alan Lawrence. 2699 N 17TH ST, SOUTH COAST ORTHOPAEDIC 97420 #023-01-1973 L1978 **ORS** *020 †40

WILLIS, Roger Cecil. PO BOX 3190 97420 #003-01-1993 L2006 **FM** *020 †18

WISE, Larry Keith. ■ 97420 #016-11-1992 L2005 **P** *020

WOODS, James Patrick. 1775 THOMPSON RD, DEPT OF EMERGENCY MEDICINE 97420 #005-19-1989 L1993 **EM** *020 †16

YOST, Jon Craig. 1750 THOMPSON RD, BAY CLINIC 97420 #040-02-2000 L2003 **PD** *020 †55

COQUILLE – COOS

BASSETT, Gerald Robt. 240 N COLLIER ST 97423 #005-11-1959 L1961 **PHP FOP** *071 †70

CASSIM, Muthalib Mohammed. 940 E 5TH ST 97423 #917-10-1968 L1978 **GS TS** *020 †85

COUNTS, Jon Calvin. 790 E 5TH ST 97423 #040-02-1970 L1981 **FM** *020 †18

CROSON, William Blevins. 790 E 5TH ST 97423 #016-11-2002 L2007 **FM** *020 †18

FAROOQ, Shiraz. 940 E 5TH ST, COQUILLE VALLEY HOSPITAL 97423 #704-26-1996 L2004 **GS CCS** *020 †85

GURNEY, Edmund Reed. 790 E 5TH ST 97423 #040-02-1947 **FM OBG** *020 †18

HENKEN, Dale Preston. ■ 97423 #040-02-1969 L1975 **PD PDC** *071 †55

KELLER, Nancy. 790 E 5TH ST 97423 #040-02-1989 L1992 **FM** *020 †18

OTTEMILLER, Dennis Evan. 855 W CENTRAL ST 97423 #001-02-1987 L1992 **OPH** *020 †35

YOUNG, Richard Loren. ■ 97423 #012-05-1976 L1980 **OBG** *020

CORNELIUS – WASHINGTON

BYERLY, Laura Ruth. 85 N 12TH AVE 97113 #040-02-1990 L1991 **FM** *020 †18

HINDEL, Ingeborg Laura. 85 N 12TH AVE, VIRGINIA GARCIA CLINIC 97113 #008-02-1993 L1997 **FM** *020 †18

HOLLES, Gregory. 85 N 12TH AVE, VIRGINIA GARCIA CLINIC 97113 #048-02-1990 L1999 **FM** *020 †18

JACOBS, Lyn Carol. PO BOX 568 97113 #035-45-1995 L1998 **FM** *020 †18

MACIAS, Victor Orosco. ■ 97113 #649-38-1991 **FM EM** *040

MECKLEM, Gregory Todd. ■ 97113 #040-02-1977 L1981 **ORS** *020 †20

MORRISON, James Roy. ■ 97113 #028-02-1965 L1970 **P** *040 †75

NAKAO, Calvin Yoshiki. ■ 97113 #040-02-1967 L1968 **GO GYN** *071 †30

TROTT, Barbara Ellen. 85 N 12TH AVE 97113 #005-15-1991 L1997 **IM** *020 †20

TURNER, M Ann. 85 N 12TH AVE, VIRGINIA GARCIA MEMORIAL 97113 #005-06-1972 L1994 **FM IM** *020 †20

WOOD, John Franklin. ■ 97113 #005-17-1962 **FM** *071

ZEAITER, Farouk Mohammad. ■ 97113 #781-01-1986 *100

CORVALLIS – BENTON

ALLENDER, M Patrick. 3680 NW SAMARITAN DR, THE CORVALLIS CLINIC PC 97330 #055-01-1984 L1995 **PD** *020 †55

AMADOR, Carolina D. 530 NW 27TH ST, BENTON COMMUNITY HEALTH CE 97330 #012-01-1998 L2002 **PD** *020 †55

ANDERSON, Content E. 3517 NW SAMARITAN DR, STE 201 97330 #040-02-1997 L1998 **FM** *020 †18

ANKER, Anthony Leo. 3600 NW SAMARITAN DR 97330 #040-02-1989 L1992 **EM ETX** *020 †16

ATHA, Timothy Carlton. 3600 NW SAMARITAN DR 97330 #048-02-1978 L2007 **CD** *020 †20

ATHAY, Steven Grant. 3680 NW SAMARITAN DR 97330 #040-02-1976 L1977 **IM** *020 †20

AUSTIN-SEYMOUR, Mary M. 501 NW ELKS DR, RADIATION ONCOLOGY ASSOC. 97330 #016-02-1978 L2006 **RO** *020 †20

BAKER, Richard Kiger. ■ 97330 #040-02-1954 L1956 **GS** *071

BARRETT, Daniel Patrick. 3680 NW SAMARITAN DR 97330 #040-02-1993 L1996 **FM** *020 †18

BARTLEY, Beverly Denise. 3615 NW SAMARITAN DR, STE 10 97330 #030-06-1991 L1995 **IM** *020 †20

BASHEY, Jaffer Husain. 3640 NW SAMARITAN DR, CORVALLIS OR STE 210 97330 #051-07-1992 L1993 **U** *020 †95
BENTON, Nick Chas. 444 NW ELKS DR, P O BOX 3005 97330 #040-02-1986 L1992 **OTO EM** *020 †45
BERRY, John Robt. 3680 NW SAMARITAN DR 97330 #005-11-1957 L1960 **PD** *071 †55
BIBLER, Darrel D, Jr. 3680 NW SAMARITAN DR 97330 #024-01-1961 L1968 **GS TS** *071 †85
BLACK, Mary Ellen Eels. 4002 NW WITHAM HILL DR 97330 #021-05-1969 L2004 **P EM** *020 †75
BOLKER, Norman. ■ 97330 #030-05-1942 L1942 **R** *071 †80
BOMBECK, Christopher A. 3680 NW SAMARITAN DR, THE CORVALLIS CLINIC 97330 #016-11-1994 L2001 **GS** *020 †85
BOND, Richard Alden. 975 NW SPRUCE AVE 97330 #025-01-1968 L1975 **FM GS** *075
BOOTS, Donald Sydney. OREGON STATE U STU HLTH SE 97330 #040-02-1955 L1957 **GP** *071
BOYD, Jeff Lee. 2314 NW KINGS BLVD, STE A 97330 #003-01-1999 L2005 **DR** *020 †80
BOYLE, Jodell Jane. 3640 NW SAMARITAN DR, STE 270 97330 #036-07-1987 L1991 **OBG** *020 †30
BOZIEVICH, Clara A. 1600 SW WESTERN BLVD STE 3 97333 #023-01-1990 L1998 **P** *020 †75
BRANT, Michael David. 3680 NW SAMARITAN DR, CORVALLIS CLINIC, UROLOGY 97330 #028-03-1990 L2005 **U** *020 †95
BRAUTI, Erling F. 3615 NW SAMARITAN DR 97330 #040-02-1953 L1954 **R** *071 †80
BUCHANAN, John Lawrence. 3680 NW SAMARITAN DR 97330 #024-01-1960 L1976 **END IM** *020 †20
BURTON, Robert Mc Mahon. 3615 NW SAMARITAN DR # 100 97330 #020-02-1984 L1985 **IM DIA** *020 †20
BYRAM, Bruce Patrick. 3680 NW SAMARITAN DR 97330 #026-04-1981 L1985 **FM** *020 †18
BYRD, Sally Ruth. 444 NW ELKS DR 97330 #005-11-1982 L2002 **OPH IM** *020 †20,35
CADDY, Lance Joshua. 3600 NW SAMARITAN DR 97330 #030-05-1972 L1980 **AN** *020 †05 ‡
CARD, Amy Marie. 3680 NW SAMARITAN DR 97330 #028-03-1997 L2001 **OBG** *020 †30
CARR, Margaret Anne. 3517 NW SAMARITAN DR, STE 201 97330 #005-19-1998 L2007 **FM** *020 †18
CHAIMOV, Alan Lucien. ■ 97330 #040-02-1954 L1955 **OPH** *071 †35
CHIKKALINGAIAH, Nicola. ■ 97330 #043-01-1994 L1997 **FM** *020 †18
CHIKKALINGAIAH, Ravi. ■ 97330 #032-01-1993 L1994 **AN** *020 †05
CHO, Susan Sunghee. 3680 NW SAMARITAN DR, ASHBURY BUILDING 97330 #035-08-1992 L2000 **PCC** *020 †20
CHOW, Hsichao. 3680 NW SAMARITAN DR 97330 #005-19-1981 L2007 **GS GE** *020 †20
CHOWNING, Oscar Clayton. 3680 NW SAMARITAN DR 97330 #019-02-1956 L1962 **OTO** *071 †45
CLARK, Charlene Carroll. 201 PLAGEMAN BLDG 97331 #025-07-1978 L1980 **IM** *020 †20
CLEARY, Bryce Lawrence. 3680 NW SAMARITAN DR 97330 #040-02-1993 L1996 **FM** *020 †18
CONN, Fletcher F. ■ 97333 #030-05-1950 L1952 **FM** *071
COOK, Wallace Holly. ■ 97333 #038-41-1945 L1945 **GS LM** *071 †85
COPELAND, Ronald Harold. 3680 NW SAMARITAN DR 97330 #007-02-1963 L1969 **OBG** *071 †30
CRONK, Richard Vincent. 2755 SW FAIRMONT DR 97333 #024-01-1965 L1974 **ORS OSM** *030 †40
CSANKY, Judith Erika. 3517 NW SAMARITAN DR, STE 101 97330 #473-04-1983 L1999 **GE** *020 †20
CURTIS, Brian Marshall. 3680 NW SAMARITAN DR 97330 #047-05-1997 L2001 **IM** *020 †20
CURTIS, Michelle Jennifer. 3680 NW SAMARITAN DR, THE CORVALLIS CLINIC 97330 #047-05-1997 L2001 **OBG** *020 †30
DALE, Paul Danl. 3600 NW SAMARITAN DR 97330 #040-02-1980 L1991 **EM** *020 †18,16
DE SOYZA, Shanilka N. 201 PLAGEMAN BLDG, OREGON STATE UNIVERSITY ST 97331 #038-41-1993 L1995 **FM** *020 †18
DESPOT-JOVANOVIC, Maja. ■ 97330 #957-02-1973 L1999 **AN** *071
DICKSON, Ilana Fredrica. 3517 NW SAMARITAN DR, STE C 97330 #010-03-1995 L2003 **PD** *020 †55
DOHERTY, Melissa Jane. 3600 NW SAMARITAN DR 97330 #040-02-2000 L2003 **EM** *020 †16
DOWNEY, D Bryce. 2075 NW GRANT AVE 97330 #011-04-1977 L1989 **P CHP** *020 †75
DUNCAN, Brian Richard. 3600 NW SAMARITAN DR 97330 #035-09-1996 L2002 **EM** *020 †16
ELDER, Henry Irwin. 2045 NW GRANT AVE 97330 #040-02-1978 L1981 **P FM** *020 †18
EMBRY, Alan L. 3600 NW SAMARITAN DR 97330 #034-01-1979 L2000 **FM** *020 †18
ENBOM, John Arthur. 3640 NW SAMARITAN DR 97330 #021-01-1966 L1968 **OBG** *020 †30
ERICKSON, Eldon Le Roy. ■ 97333 #040-02-1960 L1961 **IM DIA** *071 †20
ERKKILA, John Charles. ■ 97330 #026-04-1971 L1979 **ORS** *020 †40
FADDIS, David Michael. 3615 NW SAMARITAN DR, STE 201 97330 #005-06-1979 L2005 **GS ON** *020 †85
FEDERIUK, Carol Sue. 3600 NW SAMARITAN DR 97330 #005-15-1986 L1990 **ESM EM** *020 †16
FERGUSON, William Russell. 444 NW ELKS DR 97330 #036-01-1973 L1975 **FM OM** *020
FICKENSCHER, Larry Geo. 201 PLAGEMAN BLDG, OREGON STATE UNIV 97331 #016-11-1968 L1978 **PD PHO** *020 †55
FISHER, Donald Dean. ■ 97330 #030-05-1957 L1959 **OS GP** *071
FISHER, Trevor Alan. 3600 NW SAMARITAN DR 97330 #054-04-1992 L1995 **EM** *020 †16
FOLTS, Lynd Louis. ■ 97333 #040-02-1943 **AI PD** *071 †55,03
FOULKE, Ted E. ■ 97330 #038-06-1951 L1955 **IM** *071
FOX, Linda K. 3640 NW SAMARITAN DR, STE 270 97330 #005-02-1989 L1995 **OBG** *020 †30
FREY, Bruce Edward. 3600 NW SAMARITAN DR 97330 #040-02-1988 L1989 **RO IM** *020 †80
FROST, Janice L Serven. 410 NW WALNUT BLVD, STE A 97330 #054-04-1983 L1990 **CD IM** *020 †20
FU, Xinyu. 3680 NW SAMARITAN DR, DEPT. OF HEMATOLOGY/ONCOLO 97330 #243-72-1988 L2004 **IM** *020 †20
FURST, John N. ■ 97333 #026-04-1939 **U** *071 †95
FUSETTI, Lydia Ann. 1835 NW KINGS BLVD, DIXON CREEK PROFESSIONAL C 97330 #041-14-1977 L1980 **PD OS** *020 †55
GALLANT, James David. 1128 NE 2ND ST STE 101 97330 #023-01-1978 L1981 **IM OM** *072
GAMELIN, Lara Jae. 2400 NW KINGS BLVD 97330 #068-01-1993 L1996 **FM** *020 †18
GARRETT, Troy Alan. 3517 NW SAMARITAN DR, STE 201 97330 #005-19-1988 L1992 **FM** *020 †18
GOLDNER, Alan Paul. 3600 NW SAMARITAN DR 97330 #026-04-1984 L2002 **EM** *020 †16
GOLDNER, Mari. 3680 NW SAMARITAN DR 97330 #024-01-1989 L2003 **CCM** *020 †20
GOODWIN, Steven Kent. 3640 NW SAMARITAN DR, STE 160 97330 #017-20-1985 L1993 **NS** *020 †25
GOTCHALL, John Ivan. 3680 NW SAMARITAN DR, THE CORVALLIS CLINIC 97330 #040-02-1985 L1993 **PUD CCM** *020 †20
GRAHAM, Connie Brenda. 3517 NW SAMARITAN DR, SAMRITAN FAM MED STE 201 97330 #068-01-1993 L1996 **FM** *020
GRAHAM, Craig Donald. 3517 NW SAMARITAN DR, STE 201 97330 #068-01-1992 L1996 **FM** *020 †18
GRAHAM, James Fisher. 3680 NW SAMARITAN DR 97330 #038-40-1955 L1955 **GP** *071
GRIFFITH, Thomas Kane. 3640 NW SAMARITAN DR 97330 #018-03-1955 L1987 **OBG** *020 †30
GUEMPEL, Ulrike Maria. 3680 NW SAMARITAN DR, THE CORVALLIS CLINIC 97330 #020-02-1995 L2001 **IM** *020 †20
GULICK, James Wharton. 3600 NW SAMARITAN DR 97330 #051-04-1974 L1977 **AN** *020 †05 ‡
HABERMAN, Abigail Lee. 330 NW ELKS DR, STE C 97330 #040-02-1988 L1989 **D** *020 †15
HALL, Clifford Allan. 3680 NW SAMARITAN DR, CORVALLIS CLINIC 97330 #035-01-1968 L1973 **PUD CD** *020 †20
HAMILTON, Jennifer O. 3509 NW SAMARITAN DR, INPATIENT PSYCHIATRY 97330 #050-02-2000 L2005 **P** *020 †75
HANDS, Lester Maxwell. 1128 NE 2ND ST STE 101, CORVALLIS INTERNAL MEDICIN 97330 #005-12-1980 L1987 **FM** *020 †18
HAO, Wei. 3680 NW SAMARITAN DR, MEDICINE/ASBURY BUILDING 97330 #243-47-1986 L2006 **END** *020 †20
HARDING, George Thos. 3640 NW SAMARITAN DR, G THOMAS HARDING JR MD PC 97330 #054-04-1958 L1966 **GS OS** *071 †85
HART, David Arthur. 1300 NW HARRISON BLVD # B1 97330 #025-12-1989 L1995 **P** *020 †75
HART, Jeannine C. 3600 NW SAMARITAN DR 97330 #012-01-1987 L1995 **AN** *020 †05 ‡
HART, Thomas J, Jr. ■ 97330 #026-04-1962 L1971 **OBG** *071 †30
HATHAWAY, Shawn Rey. 3517 NW SAMARITAN DR, STE C 97330 #019-02-1999 L2002 **PD** *020
HAUSKEN, Donna Lyn. 3600 NW SAMARITAN DR 97330 #040-02-1993 L1994 **AN** *020 †05 ‡
HAVARD, Richard Clayton. 2298 NW KINGS BLVD 97330 #005-06-1984 L2002 **PS HS** *020 †85,65
HECK, David Jos. 2438 NW PROFESSIONAL DR 97330 #026-04-1979 L1991 **P** *020 †75
HICKERSON, Jess W. 400 NW WALNUT BLVD, STE 300 97330 #040-02-1981 L1984 **OBG** *020 †30
HINCKLE, Peter Anthony. ■ 97330 #028-34-1971 L1993 **GS CD** *020 †85
HINDS, Kathleen Mae. 710 NW 11TH ST 97330 #025-12-1984 L1999 **AN** *020 †05
HISTAND, Phillip Claude. 201 PLAGEMAN BLDG, OSU STUDENT HEALTH SERVICE 97331 #016-06-1976 L1989 **IM** *020 †20
HOCHFELD, Paul Robt. 3600 NW SAMARITAN DR, GOOD SAMARITAN REG MED CTR 97330 #005-18-1978 L1979 **EM GP** *020 †16
HUANG, David Taochun. 444 NW ELKS DR 97330 #010-01-1992 L1996 **OPH** *020 †35
HUDSON, Peter C. 3680 NW SAMARITAN DR 97330 #019-02-1977 L1982 **GS** *020 †85
HUERTA-ENOCHIAN, Glenn S. 400 NW WALNUT BLVD, STE 300 97330 #005-19-1983 L1984 **OBG** *020 †30
HUFSMITH, Sandra Jean. 2294 NW KINGS BLVD STE 102 97330 #048-13-1978 L1982 **OPH** *020 †35
HULL, John Arthur. ■ 97330 #016-06-1956 L1957 **AN** *071 †05
HULT, John E. ■ 97330 #028-02-1949 L1954 **PD A** *071 †55
HUNTINGTON, Michael Carl. ■ 97330 #040-02-1967 L1971 **RO** *071 †80 ‡
HUYNH, Kien. 3600 NW SAMARITAN DR 97330 #034-01-1998 L2002 **IM HOS** *020 †20
IGERSHEIMER, Walter W. ■ 97339 #024-07-1944 L1949 **P** *071 †75
ITO, Bruce Yoshitaka. 2298 NW KINGS BLVD, CORVALLIS RADIOLOGY PC 97330 #040-02-1974 L1977 **DR** *020 †80
JOHNSON, Brett Anders. 3600 NW SAMARITAN DR 97330 #040-02-2001 L2004 **EM** *020 †16
JORDAN, Elizabeth Bowles. ■ 97333 #023-07-1992 **PD** *100
KANTOR, Joseph Ralph. 3640 NW SAMARITAN DR 97330 #030-05-1958 L1964 **GS** *071 †85
KAUL, Bette V Purtzer. ■ 97330 #040-02-1957 L1972 **A** *071
KELLER, Cecilia A. 444 NW ELKS DR, P O BOX 3005 97330 #034-01-1980 L1984 **N** *020 †75
KENNEDY, James Jeremy. ■ 97330 #010-01-1974 L1980 **D** *020 †15
KENYON, Peter Dale. 501 NW ELKS DR 97330 #041-01-1975 L1984 **IM ON** *020 †20
KERR, Donald Thos. 3860 NW SAMARITAN BLVD 97330 #040-02-1963 L1964 **GP** *071
KILLEFER, Peter, Jr. 3600 NW SAMARITAN DR, GOOD SAMARITAN REG MED CTR 97330 #005-06-1985 L2000 **EM IM** *020 †20,16
KLIEWER, David D. ■ 97333 #024-01-1951 L1957 **ON HEM** *071 †20
KNAPP, Wallace H, Jr. 3680 NW SAMARITAN DR 97330 #017-20-1968 L1971 **D DMP** *020 †15 ‡
KNIGHT, Charles Buarque. ■ 97333 #035-01-2001 L2007 **RNR** *020 †80
KOLARSKY, Kenneth John. 2835 NW SKYLINE DR 97330 #026-04-1997 L2002 **OS** *020 †16
KORN, Howard Norris. 3615 NW SAMARITAN DR, STE 200 97330 #005-14-1972 L1979 **PS GS** *071 †85,65
KOSKI, James Robt. 3680 NW SAMARITAN DR 97330 #040-02-1984 L1988 **IM** *020 †20
KRAFT, Robert Allen. ■ 97330 #054-04-1953 L1954 **ORS** *075 †40
KRAUSS, John Chas. 3680 NW SAMARITAN DR 97330 #025-07-1963 L1969 **OBG** *071 †30
KREUSSER, Edward Halse. ■ 97330 #005-11-1968 L1969 **ORS** *071 †40
KRUEGER, Diane Marie. 3600 NW SAMARITAN DR 97330 #040-02-1994 L1998 **AN** *020 †05 ‡
KRUMREY, Jacqueline Jill. 3640 NW SAMARITAN DR, STE 160 97330 #018-03-1992 L2006 **OTR** *020 †40
LADD, John Raymond. 3680 NW SAMARITAN DR 97330 #025-01-1962 L1969 **RHU IM** *020 †20
LAFRANCE, Richard Arthur. 3680 NW SAMARITAN DR 97330 #035-45-1972 L1977 **N IM** *020 †75
LANG, John Le Roy. ■ 97330 #030-05-1954 L1959 **CLP PTH** *071 †50
LANNAN, Robin Lynne. 3680 NW SAMARITAN DR 97330 #040-02-1986 L1989 **IM** *020 †20
LATTERI, Joseph Anthony. ■ 97339 #028-34-1948 L1948 **P** *020
LAWRENCE, Janel Marie. 3680 NW SAMARITAN DR 97330 #046-01-1995 L1998 **IM** *020 †20
LEE, Amey Yin-Chi. 3680 NW SAMARITAN DR, CORVALLIS CLNC 97330 #005-06-1991 L1995 **OBG** *020 †30
LEE, Chee Yan. 3680 NW SAMARITAN DR 97330 #038-43-1998 L2007 **IM** *020 †20
LEMAN, Craig B. 3680 NW SAMARITAN DR, THE CORVALLIS CLINIC 97330 #024-01-1952 L1957 **GP GS** *030 †85
LEWIS, Todd Jay. 2211 NW PROFESSIONAL DR, STE 100 97330 #024-05-1978 L1984 **ORS** *020 †40
LI, Hong. 3600 NW SAMARITAN DR 97330 #243-46-1982 L2001 **AN** *020 †05 ‡
LI, Hua. 3680 NW SAMARITAN DR 97330 #243-46-1985 L2005 **HO** *020 †20
LIBERATORE, Marcia A. 917 NW GRANT AVE 97330 #007-02-1981 L2003 **EM** *020 †16
LINDBERG, Matthew Lee. 3600 NW SAMARITAN DR, STE E350 97330 #054-04-2000 L2001 **CD** *020 †20
LINDNER, Paula Rae. 530 NW 27TH ST, BENTON COUNTY HEALTH DEPT 97330 #028-03-1997 L2002 **FM** *020 †18
LLOYD, William Koenig. 2298 NW KINGS BLVD, CORVALLIS RADIOLOGY PC 97330 #019-02-1967 L1971 **DR** *020 †80
MAJER, Martin. 3680 NW SAMARITAN DR, HUNTSMAN CANCER INSTITUTE 97330 #286-07-1987 L2007 **IM** *020 †20
MALKIN, Leon Harvey. 3640 NW SAMARITAN DR 97330 #024-05-1971 L1989 **ORS** *071 †40
MARCIN, Michael Sean. ■ 97330 #028-34-1999 L2006 **CHP** *100

MARRIOTT, William Robt Vi. ■ 97330 #005-06-1947 L1947 **D IM** *071
MAURER, Michael Andrews. 3600 NW SAMARITAN DR 97330 #016-42-1998 L2003 **EM** *020 †16
MAY, Michael Andrew. 3509 NW SAMARITAN DR 97330 #030-05-1980 L1991 **P** *030 †75
MC ATEE, Scott James. 3680 NW SAMARITAN DR, ASBURY BLDG 97330 #028-02-1991 L2004 **ORS** *020
MC CANN, Andrea Joy. 3640 NW SAMARITAN DR # 270 97330 #048-14-1997 L2001 **OBG** *020 †30
MC GRATH, David Michael. ■ 97330 #654-01-1987 L1992 **AN** *020
MC KITRICK, Delmar Blake. ■ 97330 #030-05-1953 L1956 **FM** *071
MC NABB, Craig David. 3640 NW SAMARITAN DR, STE 160 97330 #040-02-1989 L1993 **PM** *020 †60
MC NEILL, Christopher J. 444 NW ELKS DR, CORVALLIS CLINIC 97330 #035-01-1968 L2004 **GE IM** *030 †20
MERRILL, Milo Keefe. ■ 97333 #030-06-1948 L1949 **R** *071
METZLER, Eunju Rhee. 3680 NW SAMARITAN DR 97330 #047-06-1992 L1995 **PD** *020 †55
MEYER, Birgit. ■ 97330 #409-39-1996 L2005 **CHP** *100
MILLER, Jill Ann. 3680 NW SAMARITAN DR 97330 #018-03-1981 L1995 **PD** *020 †55
MILLER, Scott Flinn. 1128 NE 2ND ST, STE 101 97330 #030-06-1974 L1977 **FM IM** *020
MOHAMMED, Mohammed S. 3640 NW SAMARITAN DR, STE 250 97330 #915-03-1976 L1991 **IM NEP** *020
MOLITCH, Howard Ian. 2314 NW KINGS BLVD STE A, P O BOX 1418 97330 #005-14-1988 L1996 **DR** *020 †80
MONTGOMERY, Abbe Elizabet. 3600 NW SAMARITAN DR 97330 #041-15-2002 L2007 **EM** *020
MONZON, Gary Robt. 3600 NW SAMARITAN DR 97330 #041-02-1987 L2000 **AN** *020 †05 ‡
MORCOS, Carol Knudsen. 3680 NW SAMARITAN DR 97330 #028-03-1993 L1997 **OBG** *020 †30
MORGAN, Kelly Ann. 3600 NW SAMARITAN DR 97330 #007-02-2001 L2007 **AN** *020
MOULVI, Farzana S. 3517 NW SAMARITAN DR, STE C 97330 #704-16-1988 L2002 **PD** *020 †55
MULL, Jeffrey Chas. OSU STUDENT HLTH CTR 97330 #041-12-1980 L1983 **GP** *020
MYERS, David Neil M. ■ 97330 #836-01-1957 L1978 **AN** *071 †05
NAGAMOTO, Toshio. 3615 NW SAMARITAN DR, STE 201 97330 #030-06-1990 L1995 **GS VS** *020 †85
NAHM, Ohnn. 3615 NW SAMARITAN DR, STE 203 97330 #041-07-1995 L2004 **NEP** *020 †20
NEBEKER, Robbie Ned. 530 NW 27TH ST, BENTON CTY HEALTH DEPT 97330 #056-06-1995 L1998 **P** *020 †75
NELSON, Jared William. 2400 NW KINGS BLVD, CORVALLIS FAMILY MEDICINE 97330 #040-02-1989 L1991 **FM** *020 †18
NEVILLE, Stephen Vernia. 3680 NW SAMARITAN DR 97330 #023-07-1972 L1979 **HEM ON** *020 †20
NEWMAN, James Clair. ■ 97333 #040-02-1958 L1963 **P** *071 †75
NOBLE, Cynthia Ann. 3640 NW SAMARITAN DR, STE 270 97330 #040-02-1992 L1993 **OBG** *020 †30
NOREK, George Louis. 3680 NW SAMARITAN DR, CORVALLIS CLINIC 97330 #016-43-1968 L1975 **ON IM** *020 †20
NORVICH, Robert Cyrus. 3509 NW SAMARITAN DR 97330 #024-07-1973 L1978 **P** *020
NUDELMAN, Stanley Jay. 3615 NW SAMARITAN DR # 201, STE 201 97330 #028-02-1963 L1991 **IM** *020 †20
NUSRALA, James Michael. 3680 NW SAMARITAN DR 97330 #028-02-1968 L1971 **PD** *020 †55
O'HARE, Patricia Marie. 2358 NW KINGS BLVD, STE 100 97330 #040-02-1993 L1994 **D** *020 †15
OLCOTT, Stephen W. 3517 NW SAMARITAN DR # 201 97330 #035-06-1975 L1996 **FM** *020 †18
O'MEARA, Leslie Anne. 3600 NW SAMARITAN DR, GOOD SAMARITAN REG MED CTR 97330 #024-16-1993 L2001 **NEP** *020 †20
OVREGAARD, Arthur Leonard. ■ 97330 #040-02-1948 L1949 **DR** *071 †80
OXENHANDLER, Harry Steven. 2438 NW PROFESSIONAL DR 97330 #028-03-1967 L1976 **GP OS** *020
OYARZUN, Juan Rodrigo. 3600 NW SAMARITAN DR #E300 97330 #231-05-1985 L2000 **TS** *020 †85,90
PARKER, Charles S. 3680 NW SAMARITAN DR 97330 #028-02-1982 L1983 **IM** *020
PEERY, Winifred Ebbert. ■ 97330 #040-02-1946 **OBG GP** *071
PHELPS, James Robertson. 3517 NW SAMARITAN DR, STE C 97330 #038-06-1986 L1994 **P** *020 †75
PHILLIPS, Jason L. 3615 NW SAMARITAN DR, STE 100 97330 #048-04-2000 L2003 **IM** *020 †20
PHILLIPS, Wayne Howard. GOOD SAMARITAN HOSP 97330 #030-05-1964 L1969 **PTH GP** *071 †50
PIEPMEIER, Edward Harman, Jr. 2400 NW KINGS BLVD, CORVALLIS FAMILY MEDICINE 97330 #048-02-2003 L2006 **FM** *020 †18
PIERCEY, Sydney Camille. 444 NW ELKS DR 97330 #040-02-1996 L2000 **N** *020 †75
POOLE, Robert Richard. 3680 NW SAMARITAN DR, THE CORVALLIS CLINIC 97330 #040-02-1972 L1973 **U** *020 †95
PROPST, Michael T. ■ 97330 #040-02-1966 L2001 **FOP PTH** *020 †50
RAMPTON, Mark Edmond. 2400 NW KINGS BLVD, CORVALLIS FAMILY MEDICINE 97330 #040-02-1977 L1983 **FM EM** *020 †18
RAY, Emily Elizabeth. ■ 97330 #005-11-2006 **IM** *012
READ, Robert Allen. 3615 NW SAMARITAN DR, STE 201 97330 #007-02-1986 L1998 **GS** *020 †85
REEVES, William Barry. 3600 NW SAMARITAN DR, GOOD SAMARITAN REG MED CTR 97330 #039-01-1977 L1978 **IM** *020 †16
REGAN, Michael John. ■ 97333 #056-06-1959 L1965 **AN** *071 †05
REPLOEG, Mark David. 3680 NW SAMARITAN DR, THE CORVALLIS CLINIC 97330 #028-02-2000 L2005 **N** *100 †75
RILEY, James Anthony. ■ 97330 #040-02-1943 **IM CD** *071 †20
RINALDI, Phillip Anthony. 3600 NW SAMARITAN DR 97330 #048-13-1989 L1999 **AN** *072 †05 ‡
ROBERSON, Frank Clifford. ■ 97333 #048-04-1973 L1979 **NS** *020 †25
ROBERTS, Paul Alfred. ■ 97333 #016-11-1957 **OS** *050
RUNG, Laura Simon. 444 NW ELKS DR 97330 #041-13-1978 L1983 **PM** *020 †60
RUSHING, James Louis. 2310 NW KINGS BLVD 97330 #048-12-1969 L1997 **IM PUD** *020 †18,20
SCHMITT, Edward Jos. 3680 NW SAMARITAN DR 97330 #048-04-1979 L1984 **PD** *074 †55
SCHOCH, Winnifred A. 1600 SW WESTERN BLVD, STE 330 97333 #067-01-1978 L2000 **CHP P** *020 †75
SCHWARTZ, Gregory David. 3517 NW SAMARITAN DR, STE 101 97330 #550-02-2000 L2006 **GE** *020 †20
SHOTTON, Francis Thos, Jr. ■ 97330 #051-01-1969 L1969 **OPH OS** *071 †35
SHUMWAY, Wendy Elizabeth. 1600 SW WESTERN BLVD, STE 330 97333 #041-01-1987 L2000 **P** *020 †75
SIMPSON, Rhonda Naomi. 3615 NW SAMARITAN DR, STE 100 97330 #005-02-1982 L1992 **IM** *020 †20

SMITH, Barry Charles. 3600 NW SAMARITAN DR, INPATIENT CARE SERVICE 97330 #040-02-1994 L2005 **IM** *020 †20
SMITH, Cindy Jean. 4455 NE HIGHWAY 20, CHILDREN'S FARM HOUSE 97330 #038-45-1990 L2003 **CHP P** *020 †75
SOBOTKA, Jon Duane. 2045 NW GRANT AVE 97330 #054-04-1984 L1988 **P** *020 †75
SOLBERG, Bryon Allen. 3600 NW SAMARITAN DR # AN 97330 #005-18-1987 L1991 **AN** *020 †05
SOLGAARD, Lesle Ann. PO BOX 1052 97339 #016-43-1990 L1992 **OBG** *075 †30 ‡
SOSKIC, Vukman. ■ 97330 #957-01-1990 L2007 **IM** *020 †20
SPANN, Stefan Oliver. ■ 97330 #024-07-1991 L1996 **EM** *020 †16
STARR, Kenneth G. 5680 SW AIRPORT PL, REACH AIR MEDICAL SERVICE 97333 #048-15-1997 L2000 **EM** *020 †16
STEELE, Robert Edwin, Jr. 3680 NW SAMARITAN DR 97330 #024-01-1963 L1971 **ORS** *071 †40
STEVENS, Ryan Richard. 1867 NW KINGS BLVD 97330 #040-02-1995 L2000 **OTO** *020 †45
STORNIOLO, Cosimo Nicola. 3615 NW SAMARITAN DR 97330 #035-01-1990 L2000 **IM** *020 †20
SUDAKIN, Daniel Lee. 310 NW 5TH ST, STE 107 97330 #025-07-1994 L1996 **OM PTX** *020 †70
SWIFF, Rebecca Maria. 1600 SW WESTERN BLVD, STE 330 97333 #048-12-1989 L1995 **CHP** *020
TAKUSH, Donald Raymond. 3680 NW SAMARITAN DR, THE CORVALLIS CLINIC 97330 #054-04-1976 L1984 **FM PHP** *020 †18
TARR, Danson M. ■ 97330 #005-11-1936 L1936 **OBG** *071 †30
TAYLOR, Mark A. 3600 NW SAMARITAN DR STE E 97330 #566-01-1987 L2003 **TS** *020 †90,85
TERHUNE, Chas Alfred, Jr. 3680 NW SAMARITAN DR 97330 #016-06-1963 L1969 **IM ID** *020 †20
THOMAS, Frank Dayton. 3680 NW SAMARITAN DR 97330 #028-03-1965 L1969 **IM NEP** *071 †20
THOMSON, Bruce Edward. 2400 NW KINGS BLVD, CORVALLIS FAMILY MEDICINE 97330 #040-02-1990 L1991 **FM** *020 †18 ‡
TSAI, Chen I. 970 NW CIRCLE BLVD 97330 #242-28-1949 L1964 **NS** *020
TURNER, Pamela Elizabeth. 3680 NW SAMARITAN DR 97330 #008-02-1982 L1985 **IM** *020 †20
VALEVICH, Christina Marie. ■ 97333 #036-08-2004 L2007 **PD** *020
VAN OLST, James Harold. 3640 NW SAMARITAN DR 97330 #018-03-1956 L1963 **ORS** *071 †40
VASDEV, Surinder Mohan. 3517 NW SAMARITAN DR, STE 101 97330 #917-26-1984 L1992 **IM** *020 †20
VERHOOGEN, Robert Herman. 833 NW BUCHANAN AVE STE 9 97330 #869-04-1968 L1969 **PD** *020 †55
VICTOR, William Harold. ■ 97330 #035-19-1945 L1962 **GP** *071
WAGNER, Sheldon Leon. 3600 NW SAMARITAN DR 97330 #056-05-1957 L1963 **OM IM** *040
WALDRON, Elizabeth Hunt. ■ 97330 #016-01-1980 L1992 **IM** *075 †20
WALLACE, Mary Ann. 3509 NW SAMARITAN DR 97330 #040-02-1997 L1999 **IM** *030 †20
WANG, Rong. 3680 NW SAMARITAN DR 97330 #243-47-1988 L2004 **IM** *020
WATKINS, Judith Anne. 3509 NW SAMARITAN DR, SAMARITAN MENTAL HEALTH 97330 #028-03-2000 L2000 **P** *100 †75
WATKINS, Kerry Elaine. 3600 NW SAMARITAN DR 97330 #048-02-2001 L2005 **IM** *020 †20
WATROUS, Willis G. ■ 97330 #005-02-1945 L1945 **AN** *071 †05
WEISENSEE, Fredrick W. 3615 NW SAMARITAN DR, STE 100 97330 #040-02-1986 L1987 **IM** *020 †20
WEISMAN, Karen. 2310 NW KINGS BLVD 97330 #016-06-1992 L1995 **IM** *020
WIGGINS, Lloyd Harvey. ■ 97330 #028-34-1981 L1982 **IM** *020 †20
WILLCOX, Todd Michael. 3517 NW SAMARITAN DR, STE 100 97330 #040-02-1996 L2007 **PS** *020 †85,65
WILLIAMS, Walter Scott. 530 NW 27TH ST 97330 #012-01-1998 L2002 **FM** *020 †18
WILSON, Ethan Benj, II. 3600 NW SAMARITAN DR, GOOD SAMARITAN REG MED CTR 97330 #005-02-1977 L1979 **EM** *020 †16
WINTERS, Peter H V. ■ 97330 #660-01-1954 L1960 **P EM** *071 †75
WIRTH, Robert Barton. 3680 NW SAMARITAN DR 97330 #011-02-1980 L2000 **GP** *020 †20
WOBIG, Ronald Dean. 1122 NE 2ND ST 97330 #040-02-1993 L1996 **ORS OSM** *020 †40
WOLF, Edward Charles. 3680 NW SAMARITAN DR, THE CORVALLIS CLINIC 97330 #016-43-1994 L1997 **IM** *020 †20
WOLFE, Douglas Randall. 330 NW ELKS DR, STE A 97330 #005-11-1974 L1980 **OPH** *020 †35
WONG, Michael Lyn. 3680 NW SAMARITAN DR, THE CORVALLIS CLINIC, PC 97330 #051-01-1972 L1976 **PD ID** *020 †55
WOOD, Robert Jackson. 1807 NW KINGS BLVD, MIDVALLEY ORAL AND FACIAL 97330 #021-05-2002 L2005 **GS** *020
WOODWARD, Barton Clarke. 3600 NW SAMARITAN DR 97330 #047-20-1989 L1990 **AN** *020 †05 ‡
WRIGHT, David Wendell. OREGON ST UNIV HLTH SERV 97331 #005-19-1972 L1974 **GP** *020

COTTAGE GROVE – LANE

AMAGASU, Misha Wataru. 1515 VILLAGE DR 97424 #041-12-1999 L2002 **EM** *020 †16
APPLETON, Michael Charles. ■ 97424 #005-15-1962 L2007 **HPM IM** *020
BARKER, Gerald Allan. 1515 VILLAGE DR 97424 #016-11-1975 L1998 **FM** *020 †18
BRAZIE, Joseph V. ■ 97424 #040-02-1954 L1955 **NPM PD** *071 †55
BURKE, James Richard. 1340 BIRCH AVE, WOMEN'S HEALTH CLINIC 97424 #040-02-1985 L1994 **OBG** *075 †30
CRAVER, William Dillon. ■ 97424 #048-12-1970 L1986 **AN** *071 †05,18
CRONIN, Kimberly Ann. 1515 VILLAGE DR 97424 #051-07-1992 L1997 **FM** *020 †18
DISHER, William Allen. ■ 97424 #040-02-1969 L1970 **GP** *071 †18
GEROW, Thomas Albert. 1515 VILLAGE DR 97424 #025-07-1971 L1972 **P** *020
HARRISON, James Frederick. 1515 VILLAGE DR, COTTAGE GROVE COMM HOSP 97424 #056-06-1981 L1992 **FM** *020 †18
JACKSON, Kathleen Anne. 1515 VILLAGE DR 97424 #020-12-1985 L1991 **IM** *020 †20
MAIER, Kenneth Robt. 1445 GATEWAY BLVD 97424 #040-02-1965 L1969 **FM EM** *020 †18
MC MAHAN, Hugh Ballard. 1312 CHESTNUT AVE, COTTAGE GROVE MEDICAL IMAG 97424 #051-04-1971 L1972 **DR** *071 †80
MOLDOVAN, Georgene. 1515 VILLAGE DR 97424 #041-12-1976 L2007 **GS** *020 †16
MOSER, Michael Lee. 1515 VILLAGE DR 97424 #016-42-1978 L1994 **IM** *020 †18
NORRIS, Paul Gregory. 1515 VILLAGE DR 97424 #040-02-1973 L1974 **EM** *020 †16
SARVER, Patrick John. 1445 GATEWAY BLVD 97424 #048-12-1980 L1988 **FM** *020 †18
SCHAFER, Norman John. 1340 BIRCH AVE 97424 #030-05-1968 L1971 **FM OS** *071 †18
SEO, Un Sok. 1515 VILLAGE DR 97424 #005-12-2002 L2005 **EM** *020 †16
SHAVER, Mark Johnathan. 1515 VILLAGE DR 97424 #025-01-2004 L2004 **FM** *020 †18

■ = Address Information Privacy Protected

STOWELL, Christian R. 1515 VILLAGE DR 97424 #040-02-1995 L1998 **FM** *020 †18
TORGUSON, Lyle Robin. 1515 VILLAGE DR, S. LANE MEDICAL GROUP 97424 #026-04-1988 L2005 **FM P** *020 †18
WIECKOWSKA, Zuzanna Maria. 1515 VILLAGE DR 97424 #016-45-2001 L2006 **IMG** *020 †18,20

CRESWELL – LANE

HANSEN, Richard Arthur. 600 DALE KUNI RD, STE 210 97426 #005-12-1969 L2000 **GP GPM** *020
HOAGLAND, Daniel A. PO BOX 159, 98 W OREGON AVE 97426 #005-14-1979 L1999 **FM EM** *020 †18

CULVER – JEFFERSON

MACK, Maureen A Connolly. PO BOX 190 97734 #040-02-1973 L1974 **PD** *074 †55

DALLAS – POLK

BENTON, Deane W. ■ 97338 #026-04-1943 L1975 **P OS** *071
EDWARDSON, Christopher W. 641 SE MILLER AVE 97338 #068-01-1982 L1983 **FM** *020
ELGERSMA, Vincent Vance. 641 SE MILLER AVE, DALLAS FAMILY MEDICINE 97338 #060-01-1993 L1995 **FM** *020 †18
ESBENSHADE, John Fowler. 201 SE WASHINGTON ST, STE B 97338 #165-07-1982 L1984 **PD** *020 †55 ‡
HODA, Mohammed Q. 550 SE CLAY ST 97338 #704-03-1961 L1973 **ORS** *020 †40
HOLM, Richard Neal. ■ 97338 #040-02-1980 L1983 **AN** *020 †05
LATULIPPE, Steven Arthur. 531 SE CLAY ST 97338 #005-12-1997 L2000 **FM OBS** *020 †18
ORDONEZ, Carlos Benj. 591 SE CLAY ST 97338 #649-14-1975 L1986 **U** *020
POHL, Daryl David. 550 SE CLAY ST 97338 #040-02-1975 L1982 **DR** *020 †80
REMINGTON, Gina P. 201 SE WASHINGTON ST, STE C 97338 #030-06-2001 L2004 **FM** *020 †18
REXIN, Douglas Allan. 850 MAIN ST, POLK COUNTY JAIL 97338 #005-12-1988 L1997 **GP HMP** *020
SCHNEIDER, James A. ■ 97338 #026-04-1953 L1953 **R** *071 †80
SMITH, Alison Lynn. 555 SE WASHINGTON ST 97338 #005-02-1983 L2007 **GS** *020 †85
SOTO, Alfredo Jose. 182 SW ACADEMY ST STE 30 97338 #051-04-1995 L1999 **CHP P** *020 †75
STRINGHAM, Charles Howard. 550 SE CLAY ST 97338 #020-12-1972 L1975 **EM OM** *020 †18
TILLEY, Robert John. 550 SE CLAY ST, EMERGENCY DEPARTMENT 97338 #035-01-1984 L1986 **EM** *020
WILLEY, Robert Franklin. 201 SE WASHINGTON ST 97338 #016-11-1972 L1978 **FM** *020
WILSON, Gayle Ray. 550 SE CLAY ST 97338 #005-12-1973 L1975 **FM** *020 †18

DAMASCUS – CLACKAMAS

BAKER, William Gallatin, Jr. ■ 97089 #012-05-1961 L1961 **GE IM** *071 †20
BRUMMEL-SMITH, Karen L. 23115 SE YELLOWHAMMER ST 97089 #005-06-1983 L1995 **FM** *020 †18
HICKERSON, Thomas Hassel. 14530 SE ROYER RD 97089 #005-12-1973 L1978 **FM** *020 †18
LEE, Carma J. 14530 SE ROYER RD 97089 #034-01-1996 L1999 **FM** *020 †18
RIPPEY, William Edward. ■ 97089 #005-12-1954 L1955 **GS** *071
RUSCH, Roy Martin. 19695 SE WOODED HILLS DR 97089 #005-12-1965 L1972 **ORS** *071 †40
STEELE, Ryan. ■ 97089 #005-77-2007, ▲ L2007 **IM** *012
WHANG, Kee Sun. ■ 97089 #583-10-1963 L1977 **FM** *020

DAYS CREEK – DOUGLAS

MILLER, Arthur C. 16305 TILLER TRAIL HWY 97429 #005-12-1942 L1964 **GS TS** *071 †85,90

DAYTON – YAMHILL

SPROED, Robert Pete. ■ 97114 #005-12-1961 **GP** *071 †18

DEPOE BAY – LINCOLN

HARCOURT, Keith Frederic. ■ 97341 #040-02-1961 L1962 **GS** *071 †85
RUTTI, William Steven. ■ 97341 #038-41-1966 L1966 **D** *020 †15
STEIN, Donald Underwood. ■ 97341 #041-01-1963 L1967 **P** *071 †75

DEXTER – LANE

GORDON, Janine. ■ 97431 #836-01-1971 L1990 **P CHP** *020 †75
THOMPSON, William Sydney. ■ 97431 #016-11-1943 L1945 **EM** *071

DORENA – LANE

CASH, Gerolis S. ■ 97434 #039-01-1940 L1941 **GP** *071
LUNDQUIST, Jon Eric. ■ 97434 #017-20-1968 L1989 **ORS** *071 †40

DRAIN – DOUGLAS

HOLLAND, Joanne Marie. ■ 97435 #056-05-2001 L2001 **GP FM** *020

DUNDEE – YAMHILL

ATKINS, Tamara Zinaanne. ■ 97115 #054-04-2003 L2005 **FM** *100 †18
LEITCH, Gordon, Jr. ■ 97115 #023-07-1959 L1963 **OPH** *071 †35

EAGLE POINT – JACKSON

BROUSSARD, Nicholas D. ■ 97524 #021-05-1962 L1981 **GS** *071 †85
HANSEN, James E. ■ 97524 #051-04-1977 L2008 **IM** *020 †20
JOHNSON, Philip Kingston. ■ 97524 #005-12-1958 L1960 **GP OBG** *075
KELLY, Michael John. ■ 97524 #016-06-1962 L1963 **IM P** *071
MARK, Marsha Ellen F. ■ 97524 #014-01-1975 L1976 **GP** *071
WEISS, Murray John. 1776 ROGUE RIVER DR 97524 #005-06-1947 L1973 **CD DIA** *071 †20
YOUNG, Beverly Kay. PO BOX 815 97524 #012-01-1991 L1994 **PYG** *020 †75

ELKTON – DOUGLAS

FOUQUETTE, John Kenneth. ■ 97436 #005-19-1978 L1979 **GS** *020 †85

ELMIRA – LANE

CALLAHAN, Leta Teresa. ■ 97437 #027-01-1984 L1995 **FM** *020 †18
CARY, Pamela Joy. ■ 97437 #143-05-1968 L1974 **FM** *071 †18
CARY, Peter James. ■ 97437 #143-05-1970 L1974 **FM** *071 †18

ENTERPRISE – WALLOWA

EUHUS, Lowell Edward. 406 NE 1ST ST, P O BOX 430 97828 #040-02-1968 L1972 **FM** *020 †18
GRANDI, Renee Elisabeth. 406 NE 1ST ST 97828 #054-04-1999 L2002 **FM** *020 †18
POWERS, Elizabeth Carol. 406 NE 1ST ST, WINDING WATERS CLINIC 97828 #005-11-2003 L2003 **FM** *020 †18
SIEBE, Scott K. 406 NE 1ST ST 97828 #056-06-1978 L1979 **IM** *020 †20
WOODS, Lawrence L. ■ 97828 #005-02-1981 L1988 **EM** *020 †18

ESTACADA – CLACKAMAS

LLOYD, Chester S, Jr. ■ 97023 #005-12-1943 L1944 **FM GS** *071
RIES, Sanford Todd. ■ 97023 #048-12-1979 L1979 **R** *020 †80

EUGENE – LANE

ABEL, David James. 890 RIVER RD 97404 #018-03-1966 L1969 **FM** *071 †18
ABRAHAM, Richard M. 2650 SUZANNE WAY, STE 200 97408 #065-06-1978 L1979 **OM EM** *020 †70
ACKERMAN, Eric Alan. 2650 SUZANNE WAY, STE 200 97408 #049-01-1989 L1997 **GPM** *020
ADAMS, Lisa Marie. 1200 HILYARD ST, GROUP-HILYARD STREET 97401 #048-12-2000 L2005 **IM** *020 †20
ALEXANDER, Rajeev Lochan. 1200 HILYARD ST, STE S140 97401 #049-01-1995 L1997 **IM** *020 †20
ALFERO, Veronica. 132 E BROADWAY STE 621 97401 #035-20-1983 L1989 **P** *020 †75
ALLCOTT, John Volney, III. 655 E 11TH AVE, STE 8 97401 #036-01-1971 L1978 **IM** *020 †20
AMEEN, Khuram. 1200 HILYARD ST, STE S565 97401 #496-21-1991 L2001 **PCC** *020 †20
ANDERSON, Bradley Scott. 1255 HILYARD ST, EUGENE EMERGENCY PHYSICIAN 97401 #040-02-2003 L2006 **EM** *020 †16
ANDERSON, Gordon Phillips. 2830 CRESCENT AVE, CRESCENT FAMILY MEDICINE & 97408 #010-01-1979 L1984 **FM** *020 †18
ANDERSON, Richard Allan. 1800 HILYARD ALY 97401 #026-04-1956 L1963 **IM RHU** *071 †20
ANDRESEN, Bryan Lee. 242 COUNTRY CLUB RD, OF EUGENE-SPRINGFIELD, P.C 97401 #040-02-1986 L1990 **PM** *020 †60
ANDRESEN, Pamela Eileen. 2484 RIVER RD 97404 #040-02-1987 L1990 **FM** *020 †18
ARIAGNO, Richard Paul. ■ 97405 #016-11-1947 L1949 **PS** *072 †45
ARPAIA, Joseph Paul. 90 E 27TH AVE STE B 97405 #005-15-1990 L1996 **P** *020 †75
AUSTIN, Douglas John. 590 COUNTRY CLUB PKWY, STE A 97401 #035-46-1991 L1997 **OBG** *020 †30
BAGDADE, John David. 1200 HILYARD ST STE S200, PEACE HEALTH MEDICAL GROUP 97401 #035-20-1962 L1971 **END DIA** *050 †20
BAIRD, Diane Louise. 2550 WILLAKENZIE RD 97401 #014-01-1990 L1994 **D** *020 †15
BAKER, Clifton Earl. ■ 97401 #030-05-1955 L1961 **ORS** *071 †40
BAKER, Herbert Clow. ■ 97401 #040-02-1964 **IM GE** *071
BALDERSTON, Keith Douglas. 1200 HILYARD ST, STE S570 97401 #040-02-1992 L1993 **OBG** *020 †30
BALDWIN, Stanley Sherman. 1255 HILYARD ST, INSTITUTE 97401 #024-01-1965 L1973 **CD TS** *020 †85,90
BALLMAN, Robert John, Jr. 1162 WILLAMETTE ST, GROUP-DOWNTOWN EUGENE 97401 #038-41-1970 L1991 **IM EM** *020 †20
BALM, Michael Ross. 1200 HILYARD ST, STE S420 97401 #026-04-1991 L2002 **N CN** *020 †75
BALSOM, William Robt, III. 1650 CHAMBERS ST, WESTMORELAND FAMILY MED 97402 #054-04-1990 L1996 **FM** *020 †18
BARBOUR, Jacqueline Anne. 598 E 13TH AVE 97401 #025-12-1976 L1980 **GYN** *071 †30
BARKMAN, Michael Andrew. PO BOX 10905, SACRED HEART HOSP 97440 #017-20-1985 L1988 **EM** *020 †16
BARLOW, Loren Call. 1162 WILLAMETTE ST, GROUP-DOWNTOWN EUGENE 97401 #016-06-1951 L1955 **IM** *020 †20
BARNES, Deborah Ward. 1255 HILYARD ST 97401 #010-02-1986 L1992 **AN** *020 †05
BARNES, Robert Carlton. 1200 HILYARD ST, STE S200 97401 #048-12-1979 L2006 **IM ID** *020 †20
BARNHART, Richard Alan. 1200 HILYARD ST, STE S140 97401 #040-02-1980 L1985 **IM FM** *020 †20
BARSTOW, Tamara Kay. 4010 AERIAL WAY, GROUP-BARGER MEDICAL 97402 #019-02-1986 L1994 **PD** *020 †55
BASCOM, John Upton. ■ 97405 #016-06-1953 L1960 **GS** *071 †85
BASCOM, Thomas Hays. 1255 HILYARD ST 97401 #054-04-1984 L1991 **GS VS** *020 †85
BASKERVILLE, Mark John. 1255 HILYARD ST 97401 #023-07-1995 L2002 **AN EM** *020 †16,05
BASLAW, Beth Blumenstein. 1162 WILLAMETTE ST 97401 #025-07-1999 L2002 **FM** *020 †18
BAUMANN, Katherine Ann. 2830 CRESCENT AVE 97408 #005-02-1988 L1991 **PD** *020 †55

BAUMEISTER, Max, Jr. ■ 97408 #051-01-1945 L1946 **AN** *020 †05
BAUMGARNER, Gene Thos. ■ 97408 #041-02-1967 L1968 **U FM** *071 †95
BAXTER, Jeffrey Gerald. 4010 AERIAL WAY, GROUP-BARGER MEDICAL 97402 #025-12-1996 L2004 **FPG** *020 †18
BAYNES, Frank L. UNIV OF OREG SHC 97403 #038-41-1950 L1950 **OS GP** *020
BEAL, Sandy Lee. 1255 HILYARD ST 97401 #049-01-1980 L1989 **GS CCS** *020 †85
BEARDSWORTH, David. 1255 HILYARD ST, SACRED HEART MED CTR ANES 97401 #024-05-1975 L1994 **AN EM** *020 †20,05,16
BECHEN, William Shive. ■ 97405 #040-02-1963 L1963 **OBG** *071
BECKSTRAND, Katherine L. 1800 COBURG RD, GROUP-COBURG ROAD 97401 #005-14-1988 L1991 **FM** *020 †18
BELLER, Byrke O. 151 W 7TH AVE, PACIFIC WOMEN'S CENTER 97401 #041-02-1998 L2002 **OBG** *020 †30
BELLER, Klarissa Nelson. 3299 HILYARD ST 97405 #041-02-1999 L2002 **IM** *020 †20
BENDA, Paul Christian. 4010 AERIAL WAY 97402 #040-02-1996 L1997 **PD** *020 †55
BENNETT, Charles Stephen. 1255 HILYARD ST 97401 #040-02-1956 L1957 **AN** *071 †05
BENOIT, Fred Louis. 1162 WILLAMETTE ST 97401 #054-04-1957 L1968 **IM END** *071 †28
BENSON, Lyle M. 2101 BAILEY HILL RD 97405 #026-04-1946 L1953 **FM** *071 †18
BENT, Rebecca Clare. 1200 HILYARD ST STE S190 97401 #028-34-1983 L1995 **NPM PD** *020 †55
BERG, Brian Geo. 1255 HILYARD ST, PO BIX 50222 97401 #005-15-1980 L1997 **EM OM** *020 †16
BERGIN, Patrick John. 677 E 12TH AVE, STE N400 97401 #032-01-1980 L1988 **CD** *020
BERNARD, Walter David. 1255 HILYARD ST 97401 #028-46-1986 L1999 **AN** *020 †05
BERNSTEIN, Janet. ■ 97403 #035-15-1967 L1968 **P** *071
BETTERTON, Gillian M. 1162 WILLAMETTE ST 97401 #050-02-1992 L1996 **OBG** *020 †30
BEYERLEIN, Richard Alan. 151 W 7TH AVE STE 110 97401 #040-02-1985 L1989 **OBG** *020 †30
BIANCHINI, Luis Guillermo. 890 RIVER RD 97404 #019-02-1958 L1961 **FM GS** *071 †18
BICKERSTAFF, Linda K. ■ 97405 #028-03-1973 L1988 **GS VS** *071 †85
BIGLEY, Lorne Eugene. 890 RIVER RD, RIVER ROAD MEDICAL GROUP, 97404 #038-41-1987 L2001 **FM** *020 †18
BIRDSEYE, Michelle Lynn. 1200 HILYARD ST, STE S140 97401 #012-22-1989 L1995 **FM** *020 †18
BIRSKOVICH, Stephen F, Jr. 1755 COBURG RD # 4 97401 #016-43-1962 L1968 **IM RHU** *071 †20
BISHOP, John Walter. 2460 WILLAMETTE ST, PACIFIC EYE CENTERS 97405 #025-01-1946 **OPH** *071 †35
BISSONNETTE, Peter Martin. 1255 HILYARD ST 97401 #056-05-2001 L2005 **AN** *020 †05
BOCK, Kimberly Ann. 4010 AERIAL WAY, GROUP-BARGER MEDICAL 97402 #056-06-1999 L2003 **OBG** *020 †30
BODILY, Mark Norman. 1255 HILYARD ST, SACRED HEART MED CTR ANES 97401 #049-01-1985 L1989 **AN** *020 †05
BOESPFLUG, Michael P. 217 DIVISION AVE 97404 #054-04-1989 L1992 **FM** *020 †18
BOLZ, Christopher Wm. 4010 AERIAL WAY, GROUP-BARGER MEDICAL 97402 #030-06-1980 L1989 **FM** *020 †18
BOND, Daniel B. ■ 97401 #041-77-1942, ▲ L1946 **GP GS** *071
BONNER, Jocelyn Wolffe. 132 E BROADWAY, STE 430 97401 #036-07-1984 L1995 **P** *020 †75
BONZER, John Duane. 1255 HILYARD ST 97401 #041-13-1942 L1949 **IM** *071 †20
BOREN, Simona Sophia. 132 E BROADWAY, STE 830 97401 #286-13-1988 L2002 **RHU** *020 †20
BOST, Dawn Elizabeth. 1574 COBURG RD 97401 #003-01-1987 L1990 **IM** *020 †20
BOURESSA, Paul Glenn. 4010 AERIAL WAY, GROUP-BARGER MEDICAL 97402 #056-05-1993 L1996 **PD** *020 †55
BOVEE, Douglas Lee. 890 RIVER RD 97404 #011-02-1978 L1992 **IM ADM** *020 †20
BOYD, Stanley A. 890 RIVER RD 97404 #040-02-1949 **FM P** *071 †18
BRACKEBUSCH, Joyce Marie. 655 E 11TH AVE STE 9 97401 #040-02-1990 L1997 **OTO** *020 †45
BRADSHAW, Pilar Antonia. 1162 WILLAMETTE ST, GROUP-DOWNTOWN EUGENE 97401 #040-02-1995 L1997 **PD** *020 †55
BRANDT, Gary Edgar. 2830 CRESCENT AVE, CRECENT FAMILY MEDICINE & 97408 #010-03-1985 L1988 **FM** *020 †18
BRASTED, Robert C, Jr. 1162 WILLAMETTE ST 4TH FL, PEACEHEALTH BEHAV HEALTH 97401 #056-06-1984 L1988 **CHP P** *020 †75
BRE MILLER, Clifford E. 3525 HILYARD ST 97405 #025-01-1960 L1963 **FM** *071 †18
BREWSTER, Kurt Averytt. 401 E 10TH AVE, STE 240 97401 #048-15-1996 L1997 **IM** *020 †20
BRINTON, Donald Mackay. ■ 97401 #040-02-1947 **AN** *071 †05
BRINTON, Timmy Frank. ■ 97401 #040-02-1946 L1947 **AN** *071 †05
BROOKS, Theresa Gail. 1162 WILLAMETTE ST, PEACE HEALTH MEDICAL GROUP 97401 #040-02-1982 L1983 **PD** *020 †55
BROWN, Charles Corrigan. 44 CLUB RD STE 110 97401 #041-02-1958 L1964 **P** *072
BROWN, Phyllis Jean. 1255 HILYARD ST 97401 #040-02-1970 L1974 **IM** *071 †20
BROWN, Stanley Allen, Jr. UNIV OF OREG STU HLTH CTR 97403 #040-02-1952 **GP** *020
BRUNADER, Richard Edward. 4010 AERIAL WAY, PHMG- SENIOR HEALTH AND WE 97402 #010-02-1983 L2008 **FM IMG** *040 †18
BUCHANAN, Frank Randall. 995 WILLAGILLESPIE RD, STE 300B 97401 #021-01-1972 L1977 **OTO** *020 †45
BUCHANAN, Glenn Stewart. 520 COUNTRY CLUB PKWY 97401 #049-01-1998 L1999 **HO** *020 †20
BUCHANAN, Patricia A P. 890 RIVER RD 97404 #021-01-1973 L1976 **FM** *020 ‡
BUCK, Virginia M Boswell. 2201 WILLAMETTE ST, STE C 97405 #035-45-1971 L1979 **AI PD** *020 †55,03
BUDKE, Mary Anne. ■ 97408 #040-02-1980 L1981 **EM** *020 †16
BUEHRING, Lisa Marie. 1488 OAK ST 97401 #050-02-1991 L2004 **IM** *020 †20
BUIE, James Campbell. 1800 COBURG RD, GROUP-COBURG ROAD 97401 #012-01-1973 L1975 **IM AMI** *020 †20
BULLOCK, Michael Stephen. 520 COUNTRY CLUB PKWY 97401 #036-05-1974 L1981 **RO** *020 †80
BUNTMAN, Karen R. 74 E 18TH AVE, STE 1 97401 #016-11-1976 L1979 **GP** *020 †20
BUSTOS, Daniel Eduardo. 1162 WILLAMETTE ST 97401 #048-13-2003 L2007 **OPH** *020
BUTT, Steven Nolte. 920 COUNTRY CLUB RD, STE 200 97401 #030-05-1976 L1989 **IM** *020 †20
BUTTERS, Kenneth Philip. 55 COBURG RD 97401 #020-02-1971 L1980 **ORS** *020 †40
BYFIELD, Clyde Earl. 2484 RIVER RD 97404 #005-19-1979 L1991 **FM** *075 †18
BYLUND, Richard Kenneth. ■ 97401 #040-02-1956 L1957 **FM** *071 †18
BYRNE, Donna Marie. 1580 VALLEY RIVER DR, STE 210 97401 #010-02-1986 L1992 **FM** *020 †18
CAESAR, Richard Irwin. ■ 97405 #005-19-1980 L1981 **EM** *075 †16
CALDER, Carol David. 1200 HILYARD ST STE S-200, PEACE HEALTH MEDICAL GROUP 97401 #048-12-1964 L1969 **DIA IM** *020 †20
CAMPBELL, Patrick Milton. 1200 HILYARD ST, STE S140 97401 #005-15-1988 L2006 **IM END** *020 †20
CARDEN, Priya Joseph. 1200 HILYARD ST, STE S-140 97401 #016-06-2002 L2007 **IM** *100 †20
CAROLAN, Robert Mills. 1200 HILYARD ST, STE S565 97401 #024-01-1967 L1979 **IM PUD** *020 †20
CARRICABURU, Robert A. 1255 HILYARD ST 97401 #030-06-1999 L2003 **AN** *020 †05
CARTER, William Franklin. ■ 97405 #012-05-1957 L1957 **OBG** *071 †30
CASSELL, Sidney L I. 132 E BROADWAY STE 830 97401 #028-02-1971 L1978 **RHU** *020 †20
CASTALDO, Domenico N. 1255 HILYARD ST 97401 #048-02-1998 L2002 **AN** *020 †05
CATON, John Robt, Jr. 520 COUNTRY CLUB PKWY 97401 #056-06-1990 L2006 **HO** *020 †20
CHAMBERLAIN, Craig Edwin. 677 E 12TH AVE, EUGENE GASTROENTEROLOGY 97401 #040-02-1978 L1991 **GE IM** *020 †20
CHAMPER, Robert Johns. 1550 OAK ST, STE 7 97401 #035-46-1987 L1999 **OPH** *020 †35
CHAPLIN, Jill Jeanette. 1162 WILLAMETTE ST, GROUP-DOWNTOWN EUGENE 97401 #024-16-1987 L2006 **FM** *020 †18
CHAPMAN, Robert Stanton. ■ 97401 #040-02-1968 L1969 **GP OS** *030
CHARBONNEAU, Johnna Marie. 217 DIVISION AVE 97404 #045-01-1999 L2002 **FM** *020 †18
CHENG, Yan-Yan Valdez. 450 COUNTRY CLUB RD STE 30 97401 #051-07-1993 L2002 **P** *020
CHERNE, Scott Anthony. 1125 DARLENE LN, STE 100 97401 #005-12-1985 L1989 **OPH** *020 †35
CHICOLA, Cathryn Lynn. 1255 HILYARD ST 97401 #021-01-1984 L1999 **DR** *020 †80
CHO, Albert Ray. 1255 HILYARD ST, SACRED HEART MED. CTR. - A 97401 #003-75-2002, ▲ L2007 **AN** *020
CHOI, Hyungki. 1200 HILYARD ST STE S520 97401 #016-02-1992 L2006 **N** *020 †75
CHOU, Alice Hsing-Fen. 2233 WILLAMETTE ST 97405 #028-46-1992 L1997 **AI** *020 †20,03
CHRISTENSEN, Tannika. 890 RIVER RD, RIVER ROAD MEDICAL GROUP 97404 #049-01-2001 L2007 **FM** *100 †18
CHRISTIE, Leonard Geo, Jr. 1255 HILYARD ST 97401 #041-13-1965 L1982 **CD IM** *020 †20
CHRISTOFERSON, Kent W. 1255 HILYARD ST 97401 #026-04-1951 L1955 **OPH** *071 †35
CHRISTON, James Alexander. 1200 HILYARD ST, STE S565 97401 #016-06-1988 L2006 **PCC SME** *020 †20
CHRONES, George August. ■ 97405 #040-02-1985 L1988 **FM** *020 †18
CHUNG, George Kau Tai. ■ 97408 #016-02-1966 L1995 **TS** *075 †85,90
CHURCH, Linda Louise. 1650 CHAMBERS ST 97402 #016-06-1974 L1977 **FM** *071 †18
CIESIELSKI, Paula Ford. UNIV OREGON STUD HLTH CTR 97403 #040-02-1978 L1981 **IM** *020 †20
CIRKOVIC, George H. PO BOX 50160 97405 #065-09-1973 L1980 **N CHN** *020 †75
CIRULLO, Ronald Eugene. 920 COUNTRY CLUB RD, STE 200A 97401 #005-15-1987 L1993 **IM** *020 †20
CLEARY, Karen Anne R. ■ 97440 #028-02-1975 L1980 **PTH** *050 †50
COCKRELL, John L. ■ 97405 #028-02-1943 L1943 **GYN** *071 †30
CODA, Barbara Ann. 1515 OAK ST 97401 #008-01-1984 L2000 **AN** *020 †05
COHN, Alan J. 41 W 19TH AVE 97401 #028-03-1971 L1972 **P FM** *020
COLASURDO, Mike A. 1200 HILYARD ST, STE S190 97401 #040-02-1984 L1985 **NPM PD** *020 †55
COLASURDO, Susan Grover. 132 E BROADWAY, STE 621 97401 #040-02-1984 L1985 **CHP P** *020 †75
COLEMAN, Sarah Lynn. 1255 HILYARD ST 97401 #035-45-1999 L2002 **EM** *020 †16
COLLIS, Dennis Kenneth. 55 COBURG RD 97401 #028-02-1963 L1970 **ORS** *020 †40
COLWELL, Frances J. 1155 DARLENE LN, # 145 97401 #041-07-1951 L1973 **ADL PD** *071
CONTY, Orlando. 4135 QUEST DR 97402 #056-05-1997 L2005 **FM** *020 †18
CONWAY, William Dennis. 995 WILLAGILLESPIE RD, STE 300A 97401 #025-01-1958 L1963 **OTO HNS** *072 †45
COOPER, Brant Lawrence. 4010 AERIAL WAY, GROUP-BARGER MEDICAL 97402 #003-01-1996 L2000 **OBG** *020 †30
COPPERMAN, Terry. 3525 HILYARD ST 97405 #014-01-1975 L1976 **FM** *020
CORDES, Kathleen Kay. 401 E 10TH AVE, STE 250 97401 #026-08-1984 L1989 **FM** *020 †18
COX, William Edward. 1162 WILLAMETTE ST, GROUP-DOWNTOWN EUGENE 97401 #020-02-1971 L1978 **OPH** *020 †35
CRENWELGE, Katherine E. 2830 CRESCENT AVE 97408 #048-14-2004 L2007 **PD** *020 †55
CRIST, Robert Vincent. 2727 LEO HARRIS PKWY, ATHLETIC DEPARTMENT 97401 #017-20-1961 L1965 **FM FSM** *020 †18
CROCKER-WENSEL, Karen. 1180 PATTERSON ST, STE 3-A 97401 #018-03-1989 L1999 **P** *020 †75
CROOKS, Desmond Anthony. 2401 RIVER RD 97404 #040-02-1990 L1994 **EM** *020 †16
CURTIN, Paul G. 2484 RIVER RD 97404 #025-01-1987 L1993 **FM** *020 †18
CUTLER, Ralph Garr. 244 COUNTRY CLUB RD 97401 #049-01-1960 L1968 **PS HS** *071 †65
CYTRYNBAUM, Leo. 1200 HILYARD ST, STE S140 97401 #035-09-1993 L1996 **IM** *020 †20
DANIEL, Lee Buell. 244 COUNTRY CLUB RD 97401 #047-05-1984 L1999 **PS GS** *020 †85,65 ‡
DANIELSON, Christa. 3299 HILYARD ST, GROUP-SOUTH EUGENE 97405 #021-01-1986 L1996 **FM** *020 †18
DART, Paul Elliot. ■ 97405 #026-08-1984 L1985 **OMM** *020
DATZMAN, Marylin Ann. 1200 HILYARD ST 97401 #017-20-1978 L1999 **PUD IM** *020 †20
DAUGHERTY, Robert Guy. 2484 RIVER RD 97404 #026-04-1976 L1985 **FM** *020 †18
DAVIS, Robert Howard. 1550 OAK ST STE 3 97401 #005-02-1964 L1971 **OPH** *071 †35
DAY, Michael Louis. ■ 97401 #040-02-1997 L2006 **EM** *020 †16
DAYTON, Jerome Howard. 1255 HILYARD ST 97401 #026-04-1958 L1963 **PD** *071 †55
DEAN, Philip Wray. 2650 SUZANNE WAY, STE 200 97408 #056-06-1973 L1978 **EM OM** *071 †16
DEAN, William Mark. 3225 WILLAMETTE ST 97405 #021-01-1967 L2005 **P** *020 †75
DEATON, Charles Edwin, Jr. 1200 HILYARD ST STE S410 97401 #038-40-1971 L1979 **DR** *020 †80
DEDERER, Alexander. 1255 HILYARD ST 97401 #005-12-1945 L1955 **GS FM** *072
DE FRANK, Louis Paul. ■ 97405 #016-43-1961 L1962 **EM** *071
DE FREEST, Melissa Sue. 1255 HILYARD ST 97401 #040-02-2003 L2006 **EM** *020 †16
DEGGE, James Rolland. ■ 97404 #041-13-1943 **ORS** *071 †40
DEGNER, George Green. ■ 97408 #040-02-1971 L1972 **GP** *020 †18
DEGUIRE, John James. 1125 DARLENE LN, STE 100 97401 #016-11-1988 L2004 **OPH** *020 †35
DE HAAS, David Robt, Jr. 1255 HILYARD ST 97401 #041-09-1980 L1995 **GS** *020 †85
DEKKER-JANSEN, Anita Joan. 2401 RIVER RD STE 101 97404 #660-02-1979 L1985 **OM** *020 †70
DENEKAS, Brian David. 132 E BROADWAY STE 601 97401 #048-14-1984 L1985 **N** *020
DERLACKI, Donald Bratton. ■ 97402 #054-04-1984 L1985 **GP** *020
DEUTCH, David Sherman. 1162 WILLAMETTE ST, GROUP-DOWNTOWN EUGENE 97401 #005-19-1985 L1989 **OPH** *020 †35
DIAZ, Dennis Dale. 1200 HILYARD ST, STE S-200 97401 #011-03-1983 L2002 **FPS HNS** *020 †45

■ = Address Information Privacy Protected

DICKINSON, John Thos. 1255 HILYARD ST 97401 #025-07-1969 L1973 **GS CD** *020 †85
DIEHL, Antoni Mills. 1650 CHAMBERS ST 97402 #026-04-1948 L1953 **PDC PD** *071 †55
DIEHL, Michael Anthony. 1580 VALLEY RIVER DR, STE 210 97401 #039-01-1979 L1984 **PD ADL** *020 †55
DIERMAYER, Marion. 135 E 6TH AVE, HEALTH & HUMAN SERVICES 97401 #005-14-1988 L1997 **IM** *020 †20
DIETEL, Daniel Merrill. 1255 HILYARD ST 97401 #017-20-1987 L1991 **EM** *020 †16
DITOMASSO, John Paul. 755 E 11TH AVE, STE 200 97401 #040-02-1989 L1995 **PCP** *020 †50
DITTO, De Wayne Edwin. 940 COUNTRY CLUB RD, MCKENZIE SURGERY CENTER 97401 #040-02-1967 L1970 **AN GP** *020 †05
DOERKSEN, Juanita Pearl D. 1162 WILLAMETTE ST 97401 #062-01-1991 L1998 **FM** *020 †18
DONIELSON, David Wayne. 1255 HILYARD ST 97401 #040-02-1984 L1988 **AN** *020 †05
DOTTERS, Deborah J. 1200 HILYARD ST, STE S510 97401 #005-14-1979 L1989 **GO GYN** *020 †30
DOUGLAS, Ben Harold, II. 3321 W 11TH AVE 97402 #027-01-1985 L1995 **FM** *020 †18
DREYER, Cynthia Ann. 743 COUNTRY CLUB RD 97401 #018-03-1979 L1983 **D** *020 †15
DUKE, David John. 1255 HILYARD ST, INSTITUTE 97401 #016-06-1982 L1991 **TS VS** *020 †85,90
DUKEMINIER, William Mark. 3299 HILYARD ST, GROUP-SOUTH EUGENE 97405 #005-14-1976 L1980 **IM** *020 †20
DUNN, Joseph Scott. 360 S GARDEN WAY, STE 101 97401 #005-15-1988 L1997 **PME AN** *020 †05 ‡
DUNN, Michael Robt. 1255 HILYARD ST 97401 #005-02-1964 L1970 **OS PD** *020 †55
DUNPHY, John Englebert. 1162 WILLAMETTE ST, GROUP-DOWNTOWN EUGENE 97401 #005-02-1976 L1980 **PD** *020 †55
DU PRIEST, Robt White, Jr. 655 E 11TH AVE, STE 2A 97401 #040-02-1969 L1975 **VS GS** *020 †85
DZUBAY, Leita M. 1162 WILLAMETTE ST, GROUP-DOWNTOWN EUGENE 97401 #040-02-1998 L1999 **PD** *020 †55
EDWARDS, Melissa Dawn. 590 COUNTRY CLUB PKWY # B 97401 #040-02-1993 L1994 **OBG** *020 †30
EKSTROM, Judith Lynn. 940 COUNTRY CLUB RD 97401 #040-02-1983 L1989 **AN** *020 †05
EMERY, Scott. 1200 HILYARD ST, STE S-420 97401 #054-04-1975 L2006 **N** *020 †75
EMORY, Sylvia Ann. 1650 CHAMBERS ST 97402 #040-02-1988 L1989 **FM** *020 †18
ENGLAND, Donald Linklater. 755 E 11TH AVE, RADIANT RESEARCH-EUGENE 97401 #040-02-1947 L1949 **IMG IM** *050 †20
ENGLANDER, Raymond Neal. 1200 HILYARD ST, STE S-420 97401 #017-20-1972 L1978 **N GP** *030 †75
ERICKSON, Carl David. ■ 97402 #005-11-1968 L1969 **GP** *075
ETGES, Thomas Jeffrey. ■ 97403 #038-41-1989 L1993 **FM** *074 †18
EUSTIS, Michael Thos. 1255 HILYARD ST 97401 #016-01-1984 L1991 **PD** *020 †55
EVENSEN, Karen Elizabeth. 1162 WILLAMETTE ST, PHMG DEPT ORTHO 97401 #025-01-1998 L2007 **ORS** *020
EWING, Thomas Neil. 1162 WILLAMETTE ST, GROUP-DOWNTOWN EUGENE 97401 #028-02-1983 L1989 **FM** *020 †18
FARKHONDEPAY, Keyhan. 1550 OAK ST, STE 7 97401 #030-06-1988 L1992 **OPH** *020 †35
FARMER, Jane Kim. 1200 HILYARD ST, GROUP-HILYARD STREET 97401 #005-06-1986 L1991 **IM** *020 †20
FELDMAN, Daniel Philip. 1255 HILYARD ST 97401 #012-01-2000 L2004 **AN** *020 †05
FELTER, Frederick Chas. 940 COUNTRY CLUB RD, MCKENZIE SURGERY CENTER 97401 #040-02-1967 L1970 **AN** *020 †05
FERGUS, Emily Best. 1255 HILYARD ST 97401 #041-12-1950 L1965 **NEP IM** *071 †20
FERGUSSON, Kent Dayman. 1650 CHAMBERS ST 97402 #016-06-1964 L1968 **FM** *071 †18
FERRY, Kristian Martin. 360 S GARDEN WAY, STE 290 97401 #056-06-1994 L2001 **GS** *020 †85
FILARSKI, Stanley A, Jr. ■ 97404 #035-15-1967 L1975 **ORS** *071 †40
FILLINGAME, Ralph Alan. 1162 WILLAMETTE ST, GROUP-DOWNTOWN EUGENE 97401 #028-02-1979 L1984 **FM** *020 †18
FINDLAY, Ronald A. ■ 97405 #040-02-1952 L1958 **GP** *071
FINE, I Howard. 1550 OAK ST STE 5 97401 #024-05-1966 L1970 **OPH** *020 †35
FINKELSTEIN, Richard G. 1255 HILYARD ST 97401 #023-01-1982 L1989 **AN** *020 †05
FISH, Mathews Benarr. 1255 HILYARD ST, INSTITUTE 97401 #005-02-1959 L1973 **NM PTH** *071 †50,28
FISHER, Erik Ward. 2411 MARTIN L KING, JR BLV 97401 #008-01-1981 L1992 **P** *020 †75
FITZPATRICK, Daniel C. 1200 HILYARD ST, STE S600 97401 #018-03-1997 L2002 **ORS** *020 †40
FLANAGAN, Latham, Jr. 655 E 11TH AVE STE 8 97401 #036-07-1961 L1965 **GS OS** *071 †85
FLEISCHLI, Gerald Jos. 1232 UNIVERSITY OF OREGON, UNIVERSITY HEALTH CENTER 97403 #005-11-1967 L1991 **FM PHP** *020 †18
FLYNN, Sharon Hope. 1200 HILYARD ST, STE S-140 97401 #010-01-2000 L2003 **IM** *020 †20
FONTUS, Snell. 1053 HIGH ST 97401 #010-03-1989 L1997 **GS** *020 †85
FOSTER, George Lovell. 1200 HILYARD ST, STE S-450 97401 #054-04-1967 L1976 **PDS GS** *020 †85
FOX, Don. ■ 97401 #040-02-1948 L1950 **IM** *071 †20
FRANK, Philip Randall. 1200 HILYARD ST 97401 #028-78-1981, ▲ L2001 **CHP P** *020 †75
FRANZ, Jennifer. 1580 VALLEY RIVER DR, STE 210 97401 #035-48-2001 L2005 **OBG** *020 †30
FREEDMAN, Basil Eric. ■ 97405 #836-02-1967 L1976 **P CHP** *020
FRIEDRICH, Eugene V, Jr. 3855 SPRING BLVD 97405 #019-02-1974 L1985 **P** *020 †75
FRISON, Linda Diane. 1162 WILLAMETTE ST 97401 #040-02-1974 L1979 **OBG** *020 †30
FRYE, Ivan Lyle. ■ 97404 #048-02-1966 L1982 **GP** *071 †18
FRYEFIELD, David C. 520 COUNTRY CLUB PKWY 97401 #038-41-1980 L1984 **RO** *020 †80
FUERTH, Deborah Ruth. 3299 HILYARD ST, GROUP-SOUTH EUGENE 97405 #005-06-1984 L1987 **PD** *020 †55
FUERTH, John Hans. ■ 97405 #154-07-1954 L1956 **PD HEM** *072 †55
FULTS, Miriam. ■ 97405 #040-02-1989 L1995 **PD** *020 †55
GALLO, Catherine Jane. 74B CENTENNIAL LOOP 97401 #021-01-1981 L1987 **NS** *020 †25
GAMET, Douglas John. 1162 WILLAMETTE ST, GROUP-DOWNTOWN EUGENE 97401 #017-20-1973 L1975 **PD** *020 †55
GANTER, Peter Werner. 920 COUNTRY CLUB RD, STE 200A 97401 #409-05-1983 L1990 **IM EM** *020 †20
GARANT, Marc. 920 COUNTRY CLUB RD, STE 100A 97401 #067-02-1992 L2002 **R RNR** *020 †80
GARDBERG, Mikael Klas A. ■ 97405 #869-01-1969 L1983 *020
GARFINKEL, Michael Evan. 1650 CHAMBERS ST, WESTMORELAND MEDICAL CLINI 97402 #036-01-1984 L1992 **FM** *020 †18
GARNER, Lois Lee. 3321 W 11TH AVE 97402 #041-01-1978 L2003 **IM** *030 †20
GARRETT, Audrey P. 1200 HILYARD ST, STE S510 97401 #035-01-1993 L2002 **OBG GO** *020 †30
GEISLER, Anita Apte. 2830 CRESENT AVE 97408 #038-44-1991 L1994 **PD** *020 †55
GEMMELL, Julie Gubrud. 520 COUNTRY CLUB PKWY 97401 #005-02-1989 L1990 **RO** *020 †80
GERONDALE, Norbert Paul. 100 RIVER AVE, VA MEDICAL CLC 97404 #025-07-1985 L1988 **IM** *020 †20
GILL, Geoffrey Joseph. 1200 HILYARD ST, STE S140 97401 #030-06-2003 L2007 **OBG** *020
GILLILAND, Kathryn Grace. 920 COUNTRY CLUB RD, STE 200A 97401 #028-34-1990 L1993 **IM** *020 †20
GILSON, Ronald Arthur. 1162 WILLAMETTE ST, GERONTOLOGY INSTITUTE 97401 #018-03-1970 L1973 **FM FPG** *020 †18 ‡
GLADSTONE, Igor M, Jr. 1200 HILYARD ST, STE S190 97401 #054-04-1981 L1992 **NPM PD** *020 †55
GLASSER, Gary Loren. 100 RIVER AVE 97404 #005-15-1975 L1985 **IMG IM** *020 †20
GLIZA, Waleed Amar. 1200 HILYARD ST, PEACEHEALTH MEDICAL GROUP 97401 #613-02-1999 L2007 **IM** *100
GLOVER, Warren Maywood. 1255 HILYARD ST, INSTITUTE 97401 #054-04-1977 L1990 **CD TS** *020 †85,90
GOINS, Steven Carter. 1200 HILYARD ST, STE S420 97401 #045-01-1979 L1988 **N CHN** *020 †55,75
GOLDEN, Patrick Francis. 1426 OAK ST 97401 #056-06-1964 L1969 **NS** *071 †25
GOLDENBERG, Jeffrey Mark. 2460 WILLAMETTE ST 97405 #061-01-1988 L1990 **FM** *020 †18
GOLODNER, Ellen Hope. 1162 WILLAMETTE ST 97401 #021-01-1984 L2006 **IM GS** *020 †20
GONENNE, Jonathan. 677 E 12TH AVE, EUGENE GASTROENTEROLOGY 97401 #067-01-1998 L2005 **GE** *100 †20
GORDON, Glenn Geoffrey. ■ 97403 #040-02-1979 L1989 **EM FM** *020 †18,16
GORDON, Glenn M. ■ 97403 #048-02-1947 L1955 **GS TS** *071 †85,90
GORDON, Rebecca Grace. 1639 E 19TH AVE 97403 #040-02-1990 L1997 **CHP ADP** *072
GORDON, Steven G. 1255 HILYARD ST, P O BOX 1479 97401 #024-01-1993 L1996 **IM** *020 †20
GORRIN, Neal Richard. 1200 HILYARD ST, STE S570 97401 #030-06-1984 L2006 **GS** *020 †85
GORY, Dennis Jos. 677 E 12TH AVE STE N400 97401 #040-02-1975 L1980 **CD IC** *020 †20
GRAHAM, Robert Douglas. 1860 COBURG RD, MONARCH MEDICAL WEIGHT LOS 97401 #048-13-1994 L1999 **EM** *020 †16
GREENFIELD, I Lawrence. ■ 97405 #005-14-1981 **MM CLP** *050
GREENFIELD, Lawrence S. ■ 97405 #016-42-1972 L1973 **IM IMG** *075 †20
GRIFFIN, Galen R. 2484 RIVER RD 97404 #048-15-1996 L2000 **FM** *020 †18
GRIMM, James Timothy. 572 W 11TH AVE 97401 #056-06-1984 L1994 **CHP** *071
GRIPP, Mark Lawrence. ■ 97401 #035-47-2005 **IM** *012
GUNDERMAN, Suzanne. ■ 97405 #017-20-1980 L1980 **AN** *071
GUTHEIM, William Geo. 1200 HILYARD ST, STE S470 97401 #051-04-1991 L2003 **NEP IM** *020 †20
HABER, M Joshua. 360 S GARDEN WAY, STE 101 97401 #038-06-1991 L1994 **FM** *020 †18
HACKER, Gail Jean. 4000 E 30TH AVE, LANE COMMUNITY COLLEGE 97405 #016-06-1983 L1998 **FM** *020 †18
HACKER, Robert John. 1255 HILYARD ST 97401 #030-05-1977 L1989 **NS** *020 †25
HAGENGRUBER, Daniel Roy. 1255 HILYARD ST 97401 #056-05-1991 L1995 **AN** *020 †05
HAHN, Michael John. 755 E 11TH AVE, STE 200 97401 #028-03-1972 L1979 **D PTH** *020 †50
HAINES, John Herbert. 1550 OAK ST STE 3 97401 #045-01-1987 L1991 **OPH** *020 †35
HALL, Roger Clement. 920 COUNTRY CLUB RD, STE 100A 97401 #019-02-1966 L1973 **DR NR** *020 †80
HALLIDAY, Andrea Lois. 1410 OAK ST 97401 #024-01-1986 L2005 **NS** *020 †25
HALPERT, Scott David. 1650 CHAMBERS ST 97402 #016-42-1972 L1976 **PD FM** *020 †55
HALVORSON, Gary David. ■ 97403 #028-02-1982 L1988 **EM** *020 †16
HAMMOCK, Lauren Anita. ■ 97403 #011-02-1999 L2007 **DMP** *020 †50
HAMMOND, Christopher C. 1162 WILLAMETTE ST, UNM HEALTH SCIENCE CENTER 97401 #056-05-2001 L2007 **PD CCP** *020 †55
HANSEN, Douglas Alan. 722 E 11TH AVE 97401 #054-04-1993 L1999 **PTH DMP** *020 †50
HANSON, George Edward. ■ 97401 #016-11-1958 **GYN** *071 †30
HARGROVE, John Curtis. 2137 OLIVE ST 97405 #028-34-1974 L1980 **AN** *071 †05
HARLOR, Allen Douglas, Jr. 1800 COBURG RD, GROUP-COBURG ROAD 97401 #038-40-1961 L1966 **PD OS** *072 †55
HARRIS, Stephanie Ann. 1200 HILYARD ST, STE S450 97401 #040-02-1979 L1984 **N** *074 †75
HARTMAN, Carolyn Mickus. 1180 PATTERSON ST, STE 3-A 97401 #016-45-1985 L1997 **P** *020 †75
HARTMAN, Laura Jan. 940 COUNTRY CLUB RD 97401 #041-09-1987 L2002 **AN** *020 †20,05
HASBACH, Thomas James. 1162 WILLAMETTE ST, GROUP-DOWNTOWN EUGENE 97401 #041-12-1977 L2004 **ORS** *020 †40
HATFIELD, Peter Lawrence. 590 COUNTRY CLUB PKWY 97401 #048-12-1969 L1970 **OBG GP** *020 †30
HAUGEN, Julie Ann. 151 W 7TH AVE STE 110, PACIFIC WOMENS CTR 97401 #018-03-1991 L1997 **OBG** *020 †30
HAUGEN, Matthew Milo. 590 COUNTRY CLUB PKWY, STE B 97401 #040-02-1991 L1995 **OBG** *020 †30
HAUGEN, Richard Dean. 590 COUNTRY CLUB PKWY, STE B 97401 #018-03-1959 L1966 **OBG** *071 †30
HAUGHOM, John Lee. 677 E 12TH AVE STE N500 97401 #005-02-1975 L1980 **IM** *020 †20
HAYES, Anne Marie. 492 E 13TH AVE 97401 #030-06-1956 L1960 **P** *071 †75
HAYES, Tod Vernard. 1255 HILYARD ST 97401 #040-02-1999 L2002 **EM** *020 †16
HAYFLICK, Susan Judith. 901 E 18TH AVE 97403 #041-14-1985 L1993 **MG CG** *050 †19,55
HEAMAN, Allen Paul. 3299 HILYARD ST 97405 #001-02-1997 L2001 **FM** *020 †18
HEEREMA, Mark Stephen. 1200 HILYARD ST, STE S140 97401 #048-04-1974 L1977 **ID IM** *020 †20
HELMS, Paul Maben. 2411 MARTN LTHR KNG JR 97401 #048-02-1978 L1986 **P OS** *020 †75
HEMPHILL, William Jos. ■ 97405 #039-01-1947 L1948 **D** *072 †15
HENDERSON, Hugh Richard. 44 CLUB RD, STE 110 97401 #028-34-1969 L1971 **P CHP** *020
HENDRICKSON, Sarah M S. 572 W 11TH AVE 97401 #041-01-1972 L1974 **FM** *074 †18
HENERY, Julie Carpenter. 1200 HILYARD ST, STE S140 97401 #040-02-1997 L1998 **IM** *020 †20
HERBERT, Lauren Jean. 1162 WILLAMETTE ST, GROUP-DOWNTOWN EUGENE 97401 #040-02-1987 L1996 **PD** *020 †55
HERZ, Michael Glenn. 755 E 11TH AVE, STE 200 97401 #040-02-1975 L1978 **GYN PTH** *020 †50
HESKETT, Elizabeth Anne. 1162 WILLAMETTE ST, GROUP-DOWNTOWN EUGENE 97401 #030-06-1993 L1996 **PD** *020 †55
HIATT, Christopher Lang. 1580 VALLEY RIVER DR, STE 210 97401 #038-40-1965 L1970 **OTO** *020 †45
HIBBARD, Mark E. 1255 HILYARD ST 97401 #035-03-2001 L2005 **AN** *020 †05
HICKS, Richard Eldon. 1200 HILYARD ST STE S-51 97401 #024-01-1963 L1976 **TS** *071 †85,90
HILL, Donald Howard. 3203 WILLAMETTE ST 97405 #018-03-1953 L1957 **FM** *071 †18
HILL, Heather Renee. 1255 HILYARD ST, SACRED HEARTS MED CENTER 97401 #028-03-1998 L2008 **P** *020 †75
HILLS, David Kendall. 1755 COBURG RD 97401 #007-02-1957 L1958 **GP OS** *072 †18

HIRONS, Larry Washburn. 1162 WILLAMETTE ST, GROUP-DOWNTOWN EUGENE 97401 #040-02-1966 L1969 **GP** *020 †18

HOBBS, Donald Nichols. 677 E 12TH AVE STE N510 97401 #028-02-1965 L1973 **GS** *020 †85

HOCKEY, Arthur Alfred. 485 SPYGLASS DR 97401 #017-20-1959 L1967 **NS** *071 †25

HOEFLICH, Bert Jos. ■ 97403 #048-04-1946 L1952 **PD** *071 †55

HOELLRICH, Rudolf Glenn. 55 COBURG RD, SLOCUM CENTER 97401 #040-02-1997 L2003 **OSM** *020 †40

HOFFMAN, Richard Scott. 1550 OAK ST, STE 5 97401 #021-01-1987 L1994 **OPH** *020 †35

HOLCOMB, William Irving. 65 W 30TH AVE, # 607 97405 #038-06-1943 **IM** *071

HOLMES, Robert Ogden. ■ 97401 #005-02-1943 L1943 **PTH CLP** *071 †50,28

HOLO, Mary Lyn. 2830 CRESCENT AVE 97408 #054-04-1989 L1992 **PD ADL** *020 †55

HOLTZAPPLE, John B Iii. 4010 AERIAL WAY, GROUP-BARGER MEDICAL 97402 #036-01-1995 L1998 **FM PD** *020 †18

HOOVER, Reynolds K. 495 OAKWAY RD 97401 #040-02-1949 L1950 **IM** *071 †20

HORTON, Christy Ann. 1200 HILYARD ST, STE S200 97401 #039-01-1978 L2004 **PUD IM** *020 †20

HOSKINS, Blaine Lynn. 1255 HILYARD ST 97401 #054-04-1962 **GYN GP** *071 †30

HOSKINS, Wesley Wayne. 3217 W 11TH AVE, VOLUNTEERS IN MEDICINE CLI 97402 #040-02-1947 L1949 **FM** *071 †18

HOUCK, Jeffrey Allen. 755 E 11TH AVE, STE 200 97401 #038-40-1984 L1990 **PTH** *020 †50

HOUSE, Theresa Lynn. 217 DIVISION AVE 97404 #038-40-1993 L1996 **FM** *020 †18

HOVERSTEN, Glen. 1162 WILLAMETTE ST, GROUP-DOWNTOWN EUGENE 97401 #016-11-1973 L1987 **CRS GS** *020 †10,85

HUDSON, Norman Paul. 2479 OAKMONT WAY 97401 #016-11-1975 L2000 **RHU IM** *020 †20

HUEBERT, Kory Douglas. 1200 HILYARD ST, STE S-140 97401 #019-02-1993 L2007 **IM** *020 †20

HUNTS, John Howard. 2550 WILLAKENZIE RD 97401 #003-01-1990 L1995 **OPH PSH** *020 †35

HYLTON, James Bernard. 655 E 11TH AVE, STE 8 97401 #025-12-1989 L1990 **IM** *020 †20

ING, Eliesa Ann. ■ 97405 #050-02-2006 L2007 **IM** *020

INOUYE, Takashi. ■ 97405 #017-20-1951 L1951 **GP GS** *071

IRBE, Dainis. 4725 VILLAGE PLAZA LOOP, STE 101 97401 #913-16-1985 L2001 **N** *020 †75

IRVING, Barbara Kay. 1255 HILYARD ST 97401 #056-05-1985 L2002 **AN** *020 †05

ISUANI, Bernardo Hugo. 1255 HILYARD ST 97401 #048-02-1996 L2004 **R VIR** *020 †80

JACKSON, James Kenneth. U OR STU HLTH CTR FAM PRAC 97403 #026-04-1973 L1979 **FM ADL** *020 †18

JACKSON, Stephanie Laurel. 1200 HILYARD ST, STE S-140 97401 #028-02-1993 L2002 **IM DIA** *020 †20

JACOBS, Wesley Ray. ■ 97408 #040-02-1960 L1961 **MDM CD** *030 †20

JACOBSON, Kirk Douglas. 1488 OAK ST 97401 #040-02-1974 L1975 **IM ID** *020 †20

JACOBSON, Kraig Warren. 1488 OAK ST 97401 #040-02-1974 L1975 **A IM** *020 †20,03 ‡

JACOBSON, Leonard Dale. 65 W 30TH AVE # 624 97405 #040-02-1941 **GS** *071 †85

JACOBSON, Robert Bruce. 598 E 13TH AVE 97401 #026-04-1970 L1971 **GYN OS** *020 †30

JAKIOUS, Laura Lee. 1162 WILLAMETTE ST, GROUP-DOWNTOWN EUGENE 97401 #056-05-1981 L1985 **FM** *020 †18

JARRETT, John Reginald. 655 E 11TH AVE, STE 2 97401 #016-06-1965 L1972 **PS** *071

JARVIS, Barry Saml. 1162 WILLAMETTE ST, GROUP-DOWNTOWN EUGENE 97401 #061-01-1981 L1984 **GP** *020

JEFFERSON, Tom Alan. 770 E 11TH AVE 97401 #051-01-1973 L1974 **FM** *030 †18

JENSEN, Joan Mary. 1200 HILYARD ST, GROUP-HILYARD STREET 97401 #056-05-1984 L1988 **N** *020 †75

JEWELL, Mark Laurence. 630 E 13TH AVE 97401 #019-02-1973 L1979 **PS** *020 †65 ‡

JEWETT, Brian Arthur. 1200 HILYARD ST, STE S600 97401 #047-05-1995 L2001 **ORS** *020 †40

JEWETT, Paula Jane. 598 E 13TH AVE, WOMENS'S CARE 97401 #047-05-1995 L2001 **OBG** *020 †30

JOCUMS, Stephanie B. 1200 HILYARD ST, STE S140 97401 #047-05-1995 L1999 **IM** *020 †20

JOEHNK, Finn Jeffrey. 1162 WILLAMETTE ST, GROUP-DOWNTOWN EUGENE 97401 #028-34-1988 L1991 **PD** *020 †55

JOHANSEN, George Wallace. 1200 HILYARD ST, STE S-200 97401 #016-11-1956 L1964 **OTO** *020 †45

JOHN, Robert Herman. 570 LAWRENCE ST 97401 #026-04-1956 L1965 **OPH** *071 †35

JOHNSON, Philip John. 1255 HILYARD ST 97401 #048-12-1968 L1971 **EM** *071

JOHNSON, Scott Howard. 2460 WILLAMETTE ST, SOUTH TOWNE FAMILY MEDICIN 97405 #036-05-1993 L1994 **FM** *020 †18

JOHNSTON, Hugh Baker. 1650 CHAMBERS ST 97402 #005-11-1958 L1963 **IM HEM** *071 †20

JOHNSTON, Richard Robt. 1255 HILYARD ST, ANESTHESIA DEPT 97401 #018-03-1967 L1972 **AN** *071 †05

JONES, Brian Geo. 2484 RIVER RD 97404 #005-14-1986 L1989 **FM** *020 †18

JONES, Brian Paul. 1255 HILYARD ST 97401 #040-02-1994 L2002 **AN** *020 †05

JONES, Donald Crawford. 55 COBURG RD 97401 #021-05-1973 L1979 **ORS** *020 †40

JONES, Martin Luther, Jr. 1180 PATTERSON ST, STE 4 97401 #021-01-1970 L1974 **IM** *020 †20

JONES, Paul Wesley. ■ 97408 #036-07-1963 L1964 **N** *071 †75

JONES, Robert Frost. 1488 OAK ST 97401 #007-02-1970 L1977 **AI PD** *071 †55,03

JORDAN, John Scott. 1255 HILYARD ST 97401 #005-14-1988 L1993 **AN PME** *020 †05

JUNIOR, Emma Lee Arell. 3299 HILYARD ST, GROUP-SOUTH EUGENE 97405 #005-11-1979 L1998 **IM** *020 †20

KAMARU, Setiawan. 1255 HILYARD ST 97401 #025-76-1999, ▲ L2004 **AN** *020 †05

KAPLAN, Paul Franklin. 1232 UNIVERSITY OF OREGON, UNIVERSITY HEALTH CENTER 97403 #005-14-1974 L1975 **GYN REN** *071 †30

KARASEK, Michael Eugene. 689 E 19TH AVE 97401 #039-01-1972 L1977 **N PME** *020 †75

KARREN, Kent Anderson. 1550 OAK ST, STE 3 97401 #056-06-1986 L2000 **OPH** *020 †35

KATZ, Vern Louis. 1200 HILYARD ST, STE S570 97401 #005-14-1979 L1989 **OBG** *040 †30

KAY, Peter Shin. 677 E 12TH AVE, EUGENE GASTROENTEROLOGY 97401 #016-02-1991 L1997 **GE IM** *020 †20

KEENE, Foster Fred. 1255 HILYARD ST 97401 #005-11-1959 L1961 **CD** *071

KEEVER, Joe Clark. ■ 97405 #040-02-1946 L1975 **CRS GS** *071 †85

KEHL, Sarah K. 1488 OAK ST 97401 #016-42-1999 L2007 **PD AI** *020 †55,03

KEHN, Brent Douglas. 755 E 11TH AVE, STE 200 97401 #030-05-1967 L1978 **PTH NM** *020 †50,28

KEIPER, Glenn Lee, Jr. 1410 OAK ST 97401 #038-41-1991 L1997 **NS** *020 †25

KERNS, Thomas Albert. 648 E 16TH AVE 97401 #030-06-1943 L1946 **ADM** *072

KERRIGAN, Daniel P. 755 E 11TH AVE, STE 200 97401 #040-02-1983 L2000 **PTH** *020 †50

KHAN, Mohammad Habib. 1200 HILYARD ST, STE S200 97401 #305-01-1998 L2002 **IM** *020 †20

KIBBEY, Allen Paul. ■ 97401 #040-02-1966 L1969 **AN** *020 †05

KILEY, James Hunter. 1200 HILYARD ST, STE S200 97401 #012-01-2000 L2007 **N** *020 †75

KILTIE, Harriet. ■ 97403 #803-05-1957 **IM** *071

KIM, Julie Eum-Jung. ■ 97401 #005-12-2002 L2007 **EM** *020 †16

KIM, Martha Blanche. 1162 WILLAMETTE ST 97401 #032-01-1995 L2002 **OBG** *020 †20,30

KIM, R I. 2830 CRESCENT AVE, CRESCENT FAMILY MEDICINE & 97408 #021-05-1991 L1999 **PD** *020 †55

KIMBALL, Reid R. 4055 ROYAL AVE, SPC 99 97402 #049-01-1951 L1957 **P** *020 †75

KINCADE, Richard Gede, Jr. 1162 WILLAMETTE ST, GROUP-DOWNTOWN EUGENE 97401 #005-19-1982 L1985 **FM** *020 †18

KITCHEL, Scott Harold. 74B CENTENNIAL LOOP 97401 #040-02-1981 L1986 **ORS** *020 †40

KJAER, George Christian D. ■ 97405 #054-04-1959 L1965 **P** *071 †75

KNACKSTEDT, James Joy. 995 WILLAGILLESPIE RD, STE 300C 97401 #030-05-1981 L1986 **OTO** *020 †45

KNECHT, Gregory Lee. 677 E 12TH AVE, EUGENE GASTROENTEROLOGY 97401 #019-02-1973 L1977 **GE IM** *020 †20

KNOWLTON, David Alexander. 1755 COBURG RD, MCKENZIE FAMILY PRACTICE 97401 #033-06-1990 L1997 **FM** *020 †18

KOCH, Charles Bernard. ■ 97401 #016-11-1954 L1968 **GP** *071 †18

KOESTER, Michael Charles. 55 COBURG RD, ORTHOPEDIC HEALTHCARE NW 97401 #031-01-1996 L1998 **PD** *020 †55

KOESTER, Steven Elmer. 2460 WILLAMETTE ST 97405 #038-43-1980 L1986 **FM** *020 †18

KOH, Paul Seungjoon. 1255 HILYARD ST, ORGEON HEART & VASCLR INST 97401 #016-06-1994 L1997 **TS** *020 †85,90

KOKKINO, Andrew James. 1255 HILYARD ST 97401 #016-06-1992 L2000 **NS** *020 †25

KOLLMORGEN, Christine F. 1200 HILYARD ST, STE 450 # S 97401 #024-05-1991 L1998 **GS** *020 †85

KORDESCH, Catherine B. 3299 HILYARD ST, GROUP-SOUTH EUGENE 97405 #038-41-1980 L1984 **PD** *020 †55

KOSEK, Peter Single. 360 S GARDEN WAY, STE 101 97401 #005-14-1988 L1994 **AN PME** *020 †05

KOVACEVIC, Luci Mario. 2650 SUZANNE WAY STE 200, CASCADE HEALTH SOLUTIONS 97408 #030-06-2000 L2007 **OM** *030 †70

KOVACH, Peter Anthony. 520 COUNTRY CLUB PKWY, WILLAMETTE VALLEY CANCER C 97401 #040-02-1978 L1983 **ON** *020 †20 ‡

KRATKA, Reed Frank. 1200 HILYARD ST STE S470 97401 #005-06-1981 L1982 **IM NEP** *020 †20

KRATKA, Tina Debbas. 677 E 12TH AVE, EUGENE GASTROENTEROLOGY 97401 #035-45-1982 L1983 **GE IM** *020 †20

KRAUSE, Mark Scott. 1255 HILYARD ST 97401 #005-12-1991 L1994 **AN** *020 †18,05

KRAYNYAK, Michael John, Jr. 4010 AERIAL WAY, GROUP-BARGER MEDICAL 97402 #036-05-2001 L2004 **FM** *020 †18

KROHN, Don Ray. ■ 97408 #025-01-1956 L1957 **OBG** *071 †30

KWON, Iksung. 1125 DARLENE LN 97401 #042-02-1998 L2005 **OPH** *020 †35

LAMBERG, Jennifer Lane. 1162 WILLAMETTE ST, GROUP-DOWNTOWN EUGENE 97401 #032-01-1999 L2005 **IMG** *020 †20

LAMBROS, Steven Andrew. 1162 WILLAMETTE ST, GROUP-DOWNTOWN EUGENE 97401 #003-01-1980 L1989 **FM** *020

LAMOREAUX, Lisa Laray. 1162 WILLAMETTE ST, GROUP-DOWNTOWN EUGENE 97401 #040-02-1989 L2004 **ORS OSM** *020 †40

LANHAM, John Marc. ■ 97401 #010-01-1962 L1963 **OM FM** *071 †18

LANTZ, Brett Alan. 55 COBURG RD 97401 #039-01-1985 L1990 **ORS** *020 †40

LARI, Richard Lawrence. 1200 HILYARD ST, GROUP-HILYARD STREET 97401 #016-06-1982 L1998 **IM** *020 †20

LARKIN, Jeffrey Kevin. 4010 AERIAL WAY, GROUP-BARGER MEDICAL 97402 #026-04-1981 L2001 **FM** *020 †18

LARSEN, Robb Nels. 1200 HILYARD ST, STE S520 97401 #021-01-1997 L2006 **ORS** *020 †40

LARSON, Robert Le Roy. 1200 HILYARD ST, STE S600 97401 #010-01-1953 L1959 **ORS** *071 †40

LAURIE, Michael Aaron. 4010 AERIAL WAY, GROUP-BARGER MEDICAL 97402 #005-06-1987 L1996 **IM** *020 †20

LAZOWSKI, Eugene S. ■ 97405 #759-03-1940 **PD PM** *071

LEDUC, Louise Elizabeth. 1162 WILLAMETTE ST, PEACEHEALTH MEDICAL GROUP 97401 #041-14-2000 L2008 **FM OBS** *020 †18

LEE, Adriana. ■ 97404 #539-04-2002 L2002 **PDC** *100 †55

LEE, Gary Laurence. 520 COUNTRY CLUB PKWY, WILLIAMSON VLY CANCER CTR 97401 #040-02-1978 L1984 **ON HEM** *020 †20

LEE, Jae Hyun. 520 COUNTRY CLUB PKWY 97401 #010-01-1995 L2001 **HO** *020 †20

LEE, Richard Herbert. 1200 HILYARD ST, STE S140 97401 #007-02-1993 L1997 **OBG** *020 †30

LEFFORD, Jotham Jay. 1162 WILLAMETTE ST, GROUP-DOWNTOWN EUGENE 97401 #035-46-1995 L2006 **FM** *020 †18

LEMON, Herbert C. UNIV OF OREGON 97403 #030-05-1960 L1964 **GP** *074

LETOVSKY, John Milton, Jr. 1162 WILLAMETTE ST, GROUP-DOWNTOWN EUGENE 97401 #007-02-1993 L1996 **IM MDM** *020 †20

LEWIS, Randall Stewart. 1162 WILLAMETTE ST 97401 #018-03-1970 L1976 **GYN** *020 †30

LEYVA-YAPUR, Oscar. ■ 97405 #308-03-1985 L1999 **P** *020

LIN, Victor Kochi. 242 COUNTRY CLUB RD, OF EUGENE-SPRINGFIELD, P.C 97401 #005-02-1993 L1997 **PM** *020 †60

LINDQUIST, Richard John. 363 HIGH ST, MONARCH MEDICAL WEIGHT LOS 97401 #054-04-1984 L1989 **FM** *020 †18

LIPKIN, John Osmond. 1200 HILYARD ST, STE S-460 97401 #038-41-1966 L1972 **P** *030 †75

LIST, Patrick Brendan. 55 COBURG RD 97401 #038-43-2000 L2007 **ISM** *020 †20

LITCHMAN, Mark Arthur. 1650 CHAMBERS ST 97402 #040-02-1975 L1978 **FM** *020 †18

LITTELL, Frank H. 1200 HILYARD ST, STE S200 97401 #040-02-1984 L1985 **IM** *020 †20

LIU, Curtis Roy. ■ 97401 #041-02-1978 L1988 **ATP HMP** *020 †50

LIVERMORE, Douglas Scott. 2830 CRESCENT AVE, CRESCENT FAMILY MED & PEDI 97408 #056-05-1973 L1976 **PD** *020 †55

LOCKFELD, Alexandre Josef. 1200 HILYARD ST STE S420 97401 #010-01-1985 L1990 **N** *020 †75

LOESCHER, Richard Alvin. ■ 97405 #024-01-1965 L1972 **GE IM** *071 †20

LONG, George M. ■ 97401 #040-02-1953 L1962 **GS VS** *072

LOOMIS, Robert Chas. ■ 97401 #040-02-1960 L1961 **U** *071 †95

LUX, William David. 1800 COBURG RD, GROUP-COBURG ROAD 97401 #030-05-1973 L1981 **PD GP** *020 †55

LYNCH, Nancy Maureen. 1200 HILYARD ST STE S600, NORTHWEST PC 97401 #028-02-1990 L1996 **ORS** *020 †40

LYON, Mark Batchelder, III. 3299 HILYARD ST, GROUP-SOUTH EUGENE 97405 #016-42-1988 L1993 **FM** *020 †18

MACHA, Thomas Jos. 55 COBURG RD, SLOCUM CENTER 97401 #010-01-1983 L1988 **ORS** *020 †40

7744

■ = Address Information Privacy Protected

MACKEY, Amanda Belle. 1200 HILYARD ST, STE S460 97401 #020-02-2003 L2007 **P** *020
MACMASTER, William R, Jr. 1232 UNIVERSITY OF OREGON, UNIVERSITY HEALTH CENTER 97403 #016-06-1996 L2004 **FM** *020 †18
MAC RITCHIE, Martha Jean. 242 COUNTRY CLUB RD, OF EUGENE-SPRINGFIELD, P.C 97401 #025-01-1980 L1984 **PM** *030 †60
MAGENIS, Ruth E Heath. 901 E 18TH AVE 97403 #017-20-1952 L1974 **OS PD** *050 †55,19
MAHADEVAN, Karthik. 1200 HILYARD ST, STE S565 97401 #495-59-1995 L2006 **PCC** *020 †20
MAIER, William Paul. 633 E 11TH AVE 97401 #003-01-1980 L1991 **RHU IM** *020 †20
MALINER, Jerome S. 115 W 8TH AVE, STE 220 97401 #035-08-1953 L1960 **D A** *071 †15
MANDIGO, Katherine Velma. ■ 97405 #061-01-1988 *100
MANN, Thomas Weimar. 1255 HILYARD ST 97401 #040-02-1962 L1963 **GP ID** *020
MANWILL, James Lee. 920 COUNTRY CLUB RD, STE 100A 97401 #040-02-1990 L1992 **DR** *020 †80
MARCUS, Richard Wm. 1255 HILYARD ST, STE 600 97401 #048-02-1979 L2006 **N** *020 †75
MARKS, Kevin. 1162 WILLAMETTE ST, GROUP-DOWNTOWN EUGENE 97401 #036-01-1998 L2001 **PD** *020 †55
MARKS, Steven Don. 32729 SKYHAWK WAY 97405 #038-06-1973 L1994 **MDM FM** *030 †18
MARZANO, Louis Anthony. 923 COUNTRY CLUB RD, STE 100 97401 #056-06-1968 L1975 **OBG** *020 †30
MASTERSON, Kathleen M. ■ 97401 #012-05-1984 L1990 **PTH** *071 †50
MATTERI, Richard Eugene. 1255 HILYARD ST 97403 #040-02-1969 L1975 **ORS** *020 †40
MAXWELL, Winston Earl. 1162 WILLAMETTE ST, GROUP-DOWNTOWN EUGENE 97401 #040-02-1962 L1964 **IM** *020 †20
MC CAFFREY, John Francis. ■ 97401 #016-43-1978 L1982 **R** *020 †80
MCCARTHY, Amy Patricia. 1200 HILYARD ST, STE S140 97401 #040-02-1992 L1996 **OBG** *020 †30
MC CARTHY, Denis Marble. 755 E 11TH AVE, STE 200 97401 #040-02-1999 L2002 **PTH PCP** *020
MC CARTHY, John Denis. ■ 97405 #035-45-1955 L1956 **OM IM** *071
MC CARTHY, Jose Elsa C. ■ 97403 #396-06-1963 L1981 **P** *071
MC CLAIN, Ken Ronald. 1232 UNIVERSITY OF OREGON, UNIV HLTH CTR 97403 #005-02-1994 L1997 **IM** *020
MC CLUSKEY, William R. ■ 97405 #026-04-1947 L1947 **GP** *071 †55
MC CONNELL, Ross S. ■ 97401 #041-01-1952 L1953 **OM** *071 †70
MC DUFFIE, Richard W, Jr. 1200 HILYARD ST 97401 #040-02-1967 L1974 **U** *020 †95
MC FARLANE, Joe Robert, III. 755 E 11TH AVE, STE 200 97401 #048-14-2002 L2007 **DMP** *020 †50
MC GIRR, Stephen John. 1255 HILYARD ST 97401 #048-04-1982 L1990 **NS** *020 †25
MC GLADE, Charles Thos. 1255 HILYARD ST 97401 #035-20-1983 L1988 **VIR R** *020 †80
MC GLOTHLIN, Regina Dwyer. 1200 HILYARD ST, STE S460 97401 #010-02-1978 L1982 **P** *020 †75
MC HAN, James Albert. ■ 97405 #005-12-1958 L1959 **GP** *020
MCKENZIE, Barry A. 2852 WILLAMETTE ST, # 506 97405 #040-02-1983 L1984 **HO HEM** *020 †20
MC NIECE, Dawn Marie. ■ 97405 #005-02-1981 L1996 **CHP** *020 †75
MC WHORTER, William Paul. 1162 WILLAMETTE ST 97401 #048-12-1969 L1976 **IM GPM** *020 †20,70
MEHL, Roger Lee. ■ 97405 #023-01-1961 L1971 **TS GS** *071 †85,90
MEHLHAFF, Dawn Leslie. 4010 AERIAL WAY 97402 #040-02-1991 L1998 **IM** *020 †20
MELDRUM, David Garth. 743 COUNTRY CLUB RD 97401 #031-01-1999 L2005 **PS** *020 †65
MELTON, John Gregg. 1255 HILYARD ST 97401 #034-01-1985 L1989 **AN** *020 †05
MERRICK, John Patrick. 1162 WILLAMETTE ST, GROUP-DOWNTOWN EUGENE 97401 #040-02-1973 L1977 **FM** *020 †18
MEYER, Floyd Paul, Jr. ■ 97401 #021-01-1971 L1972 **OS** *020
MEYERS, David Scott. 755 E 11TH AVE, STE 200 97401 #025-01-1972 L1977 **PTH** *020 †50
MILLER, Christopher Geo. 74B CENTENNIAL LOOP 97401 #038-41-1987 L1993 **NS** *020 †25
MILLER, David Scott. 995 WILLAGILLESPIE RD # 200 97401 #040-02-1977 L1979 **PD** *020
MILLER, Gordon Covalt. 1255 HILYARD ST 97401 #038-41-1955 L1955 **DR** *071 †80
MILLER, Jacqueline B. PO BOX 369 97440 #005-06-1949 L1952 **PTH** *071 †50
MILLER, Sandra Elizabeth. 4135 QUEST DR, OREGON MEDICAL GROUP-WEST 97402 #025-12-2002 L2005 **PD** *020 †55
MILLER, William Alan. EUGENE EMER PHYSICIANS PC 97405 #024-07-1980 L1985 **EM** *020 †16
MILLER, William Richey. ■ 97405 #039-01-1942 L1948 **IM** *071 †20
MILSTEIN, Michael Jason. 920 COUNTRY CLUB RD, STE 100A 97401 #017-20-1988 L2006 **R** *020 †80
MINOR, John David. 2233 WILLAMETTE ST 97405 #047-06-1966 L1974 **AI** *072 †55,03
MINZ, Rene Barbara. ■ 97405 #056-06-1984 L1988 **FM** *020 †18
MIRHEJ, Michael Andrew. 1162 WILLAMETTE ST, GROUP-DOWNTOWN EUGENE 97401 #048-12-1992 L2003 **GE** *020 †20
MITCHELL, Timothy Alan. 1200 HILYARD ST, STE S460 97401 #016-11-1983 L2003 **P PYA** *020 †75
MITCHELL, William Barbee. 1255 HILYARD ST 97401 #054-04-1964 L2000 **IM** *020 †70
MOHLER, Craig Gifford. 55 COBURG RD 97401 #028-03-1986 L1992 **ORS** *020 †40
MONES, Stewart Levow. 217 DIVISION AVE 97404 #035-46-1995 L1998 **FM** *020 †18
MOORE, Beth Marie. 2484 RIVER RD 97404 #012-05-1987 L2001 **FM** *020 †18
MORAN, Sandra Lee. PO BOX 369, PATHOLOGY CONSULTANTS PC 97440 #040-02-1985 L1990 **D DMP** *050 †50
MORGAN, Donna Marie. 360 S GARDEN WAY, STE 101 97401 #016-06-1992 L2002 **APM** *020 †05
MORGAN, Glenn Wilkinson. 1255 HILYARD ST 97401 #040-02-1973 L1979 **EM FM** *020 †18
MORICH, Dieter Hermann. ■ 97408 #005-06-1972 L1976 **IM ON** *020 †20
MORRAY, Darian Wm. 920 COUNTRY CLUB RD, STE 100A 97401 #005-02-1980 L1983 **DR FM** *020 †18,80
MORRIS, James Robt. 2401 RIVER RD STE 101 97404 #005-19-1979 L1980 **FM PMM** *020 †18
MORRIS, Lynn Alper. 4135 QUEST DR 97402 #018-03-1978 L2001 **FM** *020 †18
MORRIS, Robert Roy. ■ 97405 #016-02-1942 L1980 **P** *071 †75
MORSE, Nancy Marie. 890 RIVER RD, RIVER ROAD MEDICAL CENTER 97404 #056-05-1997 L2003 **FM** *020 †18
MOSHOFSKY, William Gerald. 3299 HILYARD ST, PEACEHEALTH MEDICAL GROUP 97405 #040-02-1980 L1982 **FM** *020 †18
MOSSBERG, Jane Elizabeth. 655 E 11TH AVE, STE 4 97401 #035-01-1978 L1987 **IM** *020 †20
MOVASSAGHI, Kiumars. 1550 OAK ST STE 4 97401 #024-01-1995 L2002 **PS** *020 †65
MOYER, Donald Glenn. ■ 97405 #026-04-1955 L1968 **D** *071 †15
MUNDALL, John Newton. 1200 HILYARD ST STE S420, EUGENE SP 97401 #005-15-1969 L1975 **N** *071 †75

MURDOCK, James Lawrence. 85969 S WILLAMETTE ST 97405 #028-02-1963 L1969 **GS VS** *071 †85
MURPHEY, Laine Jerry. 1200 HILYARD ST, STE S140 97401 #040-02-1995 L2005 **IM PA** *020 †20
MURPHY, Christopher H. 1200 HILYARD ST, STE S-200 97401 #048-13-2000 L2001 **CCM** *012
MUSA, Byron Ulysses. 1162 WILLAMETTE ST 97401 #040-02-1956 L1957 **END IM** *071 †20
MYERS, Lew Barclay. ■ 97405 #040-02-1960 L1964 **N** *071
NAGATA, Robb Kaoru. 1255 HILYARD ST 97401 #014-01-1997 L2004 **AN** *020 †05
NAGEL, Larry James. ■ 97401 #040-02-1974 L1978 **ORS** *020 †40
NEARY, Jane Marie. 1755 COBURG RD, MCKENZIE FAMILY PRACTICE 97401 #019-02-1988 L1991 **FM** *020 †20
NEGUS, Lynn Dorraine. ■ 97405 #041-09-1965 L1966 **CHP PD** *071 †55
NEUBAUER, Steven William. ■ 97408 #016-06-1993 L2000 **EM** *020 †18
NGUYEN, Hoang Chau T. 1255 HILYARD ST, INSTITUTE 97401 #039-01-1992 L2006 **TS** *020 †85,90
NGUYEN, Luat Trong. 1255 HILYARD ST 97401 #041-14-1993 L1998 **CCA** *020 †05
NICHOLS, David Eugene. 1255 HILYARD ST, ANESTHESIA DEPARTMENT 97401 #028-03-1970 L1975 **AN** *020 †05
NICKLIN, Adrienne. 1255 HILYARD ST 97401 #035-45-2000 L2006 **FM OBS** *020 †18
NISSEL, Martin. ■ 97405 #035-09-1944 L1951 **RO R** *071 †80
NOH, Seong Jeong. 1200 HILYARD ST, GROUP-HILYARD STREET 97401 #025-01-2001 L2005 **MPD** *020 †20,55
NOONAN, J Chris. 74B CENTENNIAL LOOP STE 30 97401 #026-04-1983 L2005 **ORS OSS** *020 †40
NOPARSTAK, Irwin H. ■ 97405 #016-11-1964 L1971 **P** *071
NORLAND, James Thomas. ■ 97401 #016-02-1995 L1999 **IM** *020 †20
NOSCE, Rachel Jean. 217 DIVISION AVE 97404 #041-12-2002 L2005 **FM** *020 †18
NOTENBOOM, Hans Tobias. 111 W 52ND AVE 97401 #040-02-1997 L1998 **EM** *020 †16
OBERST, Byron Jos. 1200 HILYARD ST STE S410, ANESTHESIA DEPARTMENT 97401 #030-05-1974 L1978 **AN** *071 †05
O'BRIEN, Donald Jos. 5329 DONALD ST 97405 #016-06-1963 L1971 **U EM** *071 †95
O'FALLON, Kerry Kenneth. 3321 W 11TH AVE 97402 #019-02-1966 L1969 **FM** *071 †16
OFNER, Steven. 992 COUNTRY CLUB RD, STE 101 97401 #040-02-1984 L1989 **OPH** *020 †35 ‡
OGDEN, Thomas Edwin. ■ 97405 #005-02-1954 L1955 **OS** *050
OLSON, Donald Philip. 920 COUNTRY CLUB RD, STE 200A 97401 #005-19-1974 L1975 **IM** *020 †20
ONSTAD, Thomas Alfred. 923 COUNTRY CLUB RD, STE 100 97401 #026-04-1962 L1969 **U** *071 †95
PACKER, Mark. 1550 OAK ST STE 5 97401 #005-19-1991 L2000 **OPH** *020 †35
PALMAN, Cynthia Lynn. 1232 UNIVERSITY OF OREGON, UNIVERSITY HEALTH CENTER 97403 #041-01-1990 L2002 **P** *020 †75
PALMEN, Bradley Dean. 1255 HILYARD ST 97401 #049-01-1983 L1986 **AN** *020 †05
PALMER, Susan Kay. ■ 97404 #056-05-1973 L2002 **AN AM** *020 †05 ‡
PANUM, Pamela Anne. 1162 WILLAMETTE ST 97401 #026-04-1979 L1983 **OBG** *020 †30
PARDINI, Aaron William. 1200 HILYARD ST, STE S200 97401 #654-01-2000 L2006 **END** *020 †20
PARK, Jay Young. 1162 WILLAMETTE ST, GROUP-DOWNTOWN EUGENE 97401 #005-11-1992 L1997 **D** *020 †15
PARK, Woo Jin Paul. ■ 97408 #005-12-1993 L1995 **IM** *020
PARKER, Leslie Claire. 1255 HILYARD ST 97401 #051-01-1987 L2002 **AN** *020 †05
PARSHALL, William Andrew. 1255 HILYARD ST 97401 #024-01-1955 L1965 **GS** *071 †85
PATRICELLI, Peter Martin. 1755 COBURG RD, STE 3 97401 #024-01-1971 L1973 **IM FM** *020 †18
PAVLOSEK, Libor. 1200 HILYARD ST, GROUP-HILYARD STREET 97401 #286-04-1993 L2001 **AN** *020 †05
PEDERSON, Charles Leonard. 2650 SUZANNE WAY, STE 200 97408 #035-09-1997 L2004 **OM** *020
PELINKA, Leslie Rae. 1162 WILLAMETTE ST, 505 RARNASSUS AVE BOX 0110 97401 #049-01-2000 L2007 **PD** *020 †55
PELZ, Robert Kellogg. 1162 WILLAMETTE ST 97401 #023-01-1992 L2002 **ID CCM** *020 †20
PEREZ, Arneyo. 2484 RIVER RD 97404 #264-08-1994 L1999 **FM** *020 †18
PERLMAN, Barry Jay. 1255 HILYARD ST 97401 #035-03-1988 L1995 **AN IM** *020 †20,05
PETERSEN, Mario C. 901 E 18TH AVE 97402 #132-01-1981 L2005 **PD** *040 †05
PETERSON, Thomas David. 1178 CHARNELTON ST, EUGENE SPORTS & ORTHOPAEDI 97401 #056-05-1973 L1974 **PRS OMM** *020
PFRENDER, Ann Rogers. ■ 97401 #025-01-1966 L1967 **OS N** *062 †75
PFRENDER, Richard Eugene. ■ 97401 #025-01-1962 L1963 **P PFP** *062 †75
PHELPS, Randall Alan. 901 E 18TH AVE, CDRC/OHSU 97403 #054-04-2001 L2007 **PD** *100 †55
PHIFER, Robert Louis. ■ 97405 #024-01-1944 L1957 **ORS** *071 †40
PHILLIPS, Daniel Lee. 677 E 12TH AVE, EUGENE GASTROENTEROLOGY 97401 #040-02-1980 L1984 **GE** *020 †20
PHILLIPS, Gregory Matthew. 55 COBURG RD, UNIV OF WASHINGTON 97401 #305-01-2002 L2007 **PM** *100 †60
POLANSKY, John Derr. 2460 WILLAMETTE ST 97405 #041-13-1968 L1975 **OPH** *020 †35
POLCHERT, Susan Elizabeth. 3143 RIVERPLACE DR 97401 #030-05-1982 L1990 **P ADM** *020 †75
POLLACK, Bonita Corinne. ■ 97405 #033-06-1988 L1989 **FM** *020 †18
POMRANKY, Lisa Marie. 55 COBURG RD 97401 #025-07-2003 L2007 **FSM** *100 †18
PRINCEN, William R. ■ 97401 #040-02-1975 L1977 **EM GP** *020 †16
PUGSLEY, Mary Phyllis. 920 COUNTRY CLUB RD, STE 200A 97401 #028-02-1977 L1988 **IM ID** *020 †20
PURVIS, Mattox L, Jr. 1200 HILYARD ST STE S470 97401 #012-05-1966 L1973 **IM NEP** *020 †20
PYFER, Charles Merryman. 890 RIVER RD, RIVER ROAD MEDICAL GROUP 97404 #018-03-1959 L1960 **GP DR** *071
QUALTERE-BURCHER, Paul. 1162 WILLAMETTE ST 97401 #003-01-1991 L2002 **OBG** *020 †30
QUAM, Clyde Milton. 1200 HILYARD ST STE S410 97401 #040-02-1964 L1965 **AN** *071 †05
QUILLIN, Elizabeth P. 909 LAWRENCE ST 97401 #048-02-1992 L1995 **FM** *020 †18
RADMORE, Barbara J. 4055 ROYAL AVE SPC 99 97402 #040-02-1950 L1951 **P DR** *071 †75
RAGGE, Bonnie Lynn. ■ 97401 #011-03-1971 L1972 **GP** *020
RAISKIN, Alex Oleg. 1255 HILYARD ST, SACRED HEART MED CENTER 97401 #913-35-1997 L2007 **AN** *020
RAMSEY, Mary Jo Premuda. 1162 WILLAMETTE ST, INTERNAL MEDICINE 97401 #012-02-1990 L1991 **IM** *020
RANSOM, Charlotte Anne. ■ 97404 #019-02-2004 L2007 **EM** *020
RATTANASAMPHAN, Worawan. 4010 AERIAL WAY, GROUP-BARGER MEDICAL 97402 #891-04-1996 L2005 **IM** *020 †20 ‡
RAWLINS, Sherrie Ann. ■ 97405 #050-02-2002 L2007 **N** *100

REAVES, Michael Ernest. 2411 MARTIN L KING JR 97401 #040-02-1977 L1981 **P** *020 †75

REDDY, Neema. 217 DIVISION AVE 97404 #495-99-1998 L2005 **FM** *020 †18

REGALI, James Jos. 923 COUNTRY CLUB RD, STE 100 97401 #056-06-1968 L1975 **OBG** *072 †30

REILLY, Erin Patricia. 1162 WILLAMETTE ST, GROUP-DOWNTOWN EUGENE 97401 #007-02-1990 L1993 **FM** *020 †18

REILLY, Martha May. 1200 HILYARD ST, S-140 97401 #041-01-1987 L1997 **OBG** *020 †30

REMLINGER, Donald Elmer. 1162 WILLAMETTE ST 97401 #040-02-1958 L1960 **CD IM** *020

REUL, Charles Geo. ■ 97408 #035-01-1964 L1970 **N** *072 †75

RICE, Dwayne Lee. 1650 CHAMBERS ST 97402 #040-02-1974 L1977 **FM** *020 †18

RICHENSTEIN, Victor B. 44 CLUB RD, STE 110 97401 #016-42-1987 L1995 **P CHP** *020 †75

RICHTERICH, Gregory Chas. 992 COUNTRY CLUB RD, STE 201 97401 #040-02-1980 L1981 **D** *020 †15

RIGGS, Johnnie Wayne. 1162 WILLAMETTE ST, GROUP-DOWNTOWN EUGENE 97401 #005-19-1979 L2004 **FM EM** *020 †18

RINEHART, Robin Rene. 1200 HILYARD ST, STE S140 97401 #038-45-1999 L2000 **NEP** *020 †20

ROBERTS, John Paul. 4010 AERIAL WAY 97402 #048-13-1991 L2000 **IMG** *020 †20

ROBERTS, Ronda Marjorie. 1639 E 19TH AVE 97403 #005-18-1990 L1993 **PD P** *020 †55

ROBINHOLD, Daniel Guy. ■ 97401 #023-07-1965 L1972 **CD IM** *071 †20

ROBINSON, Brian Lindsay. 1255 HILYARD ST 97401 #040-02-1980 L1986 **AN IM** *020 †20,05

ROCKEY, Harold Clement. 1255 HILYARD ST 97401 #016-06-1953 L1954 **ORS** *071 †40

ROE, Thomas Leroy Willis. 1162 WILLAMETTE ST, GROUP-DOWNTOWN EUGENE 97401 #040-02-1961 L1967 **PD** *062 †55

ROGERS, Beverly R. 401 E 10TH AVE STE 470 97401 #056-05-1967 L1974 **P** *020

ROHR, Candice Melanie. 2233 WILLAMETTE ST 97405 #021-01-1974 L1978 **AI PD** *020 †55,03

ROMM, Richard Ethan. 677 E 12TH AVE STE N400 97401 #035-19-1970 L1975 **CD** *020 †20

ROY, Steven Peter. 132 E BROADWAY, STE 830 97401 #836-02-1967 L1978 **GP** *020

RUFF, Stanley James. 360 S GARDEN WAY STE 290, OREGON MEDICAL GROUP 97401 #007-02-1975 L1976 **GS** *020 †85

RUGHANI, Indulal Kalidas. 1200 HILYARD ST, STE S-565 97401 #025-07-1969 L1978 **PCC IM** *020 †20

RUSCHEINSKY, Delta Dawn. ■ 97405 #041-02-2000 L2003 **FM** *020 †18

RUSHTON, Andrew Scott. 1255 HILYARD ST 97401 #039-01-2000 L2001 **AN** *020 †05

RUSIN, Grant Michael. ■ 97405 #010-01-1977 L2000 **AN** *020 †05

RUTTAN, Gregory C. 1200 HILYARD ST, STE S200 97401 #011-02-2002 L2003 **IM** *020 †20

RYAN, Thomas Francis. 1590 E 13TH AVE, UNIV OF OREGON HEALTH CENT 97403 #051-01-1970 L2003 **GP FM** *020

SAKAL, Christopher David. 1200 HILYARD ST, STE S140 97401 #550-02-2004 L2007 **IM** *020 †20

SALERNO, James Donald. 1200 HILYARD ST STE S410 97401 #005-02-1969 L1975 **AN** *071 †05

SALISBURY, Patrick John. 1255 HILYARD ST, SACRED HEART MED CTR ANEST 97401 #038-41-2003 L2007 **AN** *020

SAMPLEY, Howard R. 1200 HILYARD ST 97401 #048-04-1987 L2002 **P** *020 †75

SANDERSON, Laura Rockey. 2830 CRESCENT AVE 97408 #016-45-1997 L2000 **PD** *020 †55

SATTENSPIEL, John Edward. 1800 MILLRACE DR 97403 #003-01-1979 L1980 **FM** *020 †18

SAXMAN, Karl Albert. 920 COUNTRY CLUB RD, STE 200A 97401 #005-18-1993 L1996 **IM** *020 †20

SCARBOROUGH, Allison L. 4010 AERIAL WAY, GROUP-BARGER MEDICAL 97402 #010-01-1984 L2000 **IM** *020 †20

SCHAEFER, Susan Ansley. ■ 97404 #010-02-2001 L2007 **AI** *020 †55,03

SCHAFFER, Rodney Warner. 400 E 2ND AVE STE 105 97401 #041-01-1987 L1990 **FM OS** *020 †18

SCHAUER, Robert Mark. 1200 HILYARD ST, STE 450 # S 97401 #026-04-1976 L1985 **GS OS** *020 †85

SCHEPERGERDES, Stephan M. 2484 RIVER RD 97404 #010-02-1986 L1992 **FM** *020 †18

SCHLICHTING, Joyce Louise. 1255 HILYARD ST, SACRED HEART MEDICAL CENTE 97401 #010-02-1991 L2000 **AN** *020 †18

SCHMIDT, Erica Lynne. 2401 RIVER RD, SANTA CLARA MEDICAL CLINIC 97404 #025-07-1991 L1994 **FM** *020 †18

SCHNAPPER, Tina Schwarz. 590 COUNTRY CLUB PKWY, STE B 97401 #028-34-1996 L2000 **OBG** *020 †30

SCHROEDER, Donald Joseph. 3203 WILLAMETTE ST 97405 #030-06-1964 L1971 **ORS** *062 †40

SCHUELKE, Dennis Max. 1162 WILLAMETTE ST, PEACE HEALTH MEDICAL GROUP 97401 #018-03-1972 L1978 **OBG** *071 †20

SCHWARZ, Edward Ross. 920 COUNTRY CLUB RD, STE 200A 97401 #016-43-1998 L2001 **IM** *020 †20

SCHWARZ, Ross Jonathan. 920 COUNTRY CLUB RD, STE 200A 97401 #035-09-1978 L1981 **FM** *020 †18

SCHWERZLER, Ronald Jos. 616 E 16TH AVE 97401 #040-02-1968 L1971 **ADM** *020

SCURLOCK, Donna K. U OF O STUDENT HLTH SERV 97403 #035-48-1976 L1979 **FM FSM** *020 †18

SEDDON, Thomas Kennard. ■ 97405 #028-03-1971 L1973 **IM** *020 †16

SEIDEL, Kristi Lynn. 3525 HILYARD ST, SOUTH HILYARD CLINIC 97405 #019-02-1996 L2001 **FM** *020 †18

SEIDL-FRIEDMAN, Jessica. 1200 HILYARD ST, STE S-140 97401 #041-13-1994 L1998 **OBG** *020 †30

SEIDMAN, Craig Scott. 1255 HILYARD ST 97401 #041-01-1994 L2002 **VS** *020 †85

SELF, James Leland. 1162 WILLAMETTE ST, GROUP-DOWNTOWN EUGENE 97401 #036-05-1968 L1977 **EM GP** *030 †16

SHAPIRO, Matthew Scott. 55 COBURG RD, ORTHOPEDIC HEALTH CARE NW 97401 #035-01-1983 L2000 **ORS OSM** *020 †40

SHARRER, John Harris. 1755 COBURG RD, MCKENZIE FAMILY PRACTICE 97401 #583-01-1981 L1984 **FM** *020 †18

SHEININ, Matthew Gilbert. ■ 97405 #035-46-1970 L2005 **IM ADM** *071 †20

SIEBS, John Armin. 1255 HILYARD ST 97401 #039-01-1947 L1948 **AN** *071 †05

SIMMONS, Geoffrey Stuart. 1162 WILLAMETTE ST, GROUP-DOWNTOWN EUGENE 97401 #016-11-1969 L1974 **IM GP** *020 †20

SIMS, Annette Chang. ■ 97401 #011-04-2002 L2007 **OPH** *100 †35

SINGER, Kenneth Martin. 55 COBURG RD 97401 #035-01-1965 L1972 **ORS N** *020 †40

SINKEY, Donald B. ■ 97405 #018-03-1952 L1955 **EM GP** *072

SJOLUND, Geo Clarence, Jr. ■ 97408 #023-01-1965 L1965 **PHP** *071 †70

SKAGGS, Gregory Chas. 1162 WILLAMETTE ST, GROUP-DOWNTOWN EUGENE 97401 #051-01-1992 L1996 **FM FSM** *020 †18

SKELL-CERF, Victoria Anne. 1232 UNIVERSITY OF OREGON, STUDENT HEALTH CENTER 97403 #036-07-1979 L1996 **FM** *020 †18

SMITH, Richard C, Jr. ■ 97401 #005-11-1969 L1989 **EM** *020

SMITH, Ronald Dwain. 1255 HILYARD ST 97401 #040-02-1987 L1991 **AN** *020 †05

SMYTHE, Caroline C. 1892 WILLAMETTE ST 97401 #045-01-1989 L2000 **P** *020 †75

SOPER, Margaret Swenson. ■ 97405 #024-01-2006 L2007 *012

SPANGLER, William Edmund. 1550 OAK ST STE 3 97401 #041-09-1962 L1970 **OPH** *071 †35

SPENCER, Eric Ashby. 1860 COBURG RD, MEDICAL WEIGHT LOSS CENTER 97401 #040-02-1998 L2003 **EM** *020 †16

SPENCER, John Henry. ■ 97401 #018-03-1947 L1953 **OM GS** *071 †85

SPRINGATE, Kenneth Albert. ■ 97405 #018-03-1960 L1968 **OTO A** *072 †45

STAFL, Jan Honza. 151 W 7TH AVE, STE 110 97401 #016-06-1981 L1994 **GYN OS** *020 †30 ‡

STANTON, Charles Joseph. 1200 HILYARD ST, STE 450 # S 97401 #005-19-1982 L1987 **GS VS** *020 †85

STEED, Michael W. 1200 HILYARD ST STE S330, OREGON IMAGING CENTER 97401 #060-01-1986 L1993 **DR FM** *020 †80

STEMMER, August Ludwig. ■ 97405 #024-01-1955 L1956 **HNS FPS** *020 †45

STENSHOEL, Tamara Ann. 151 W 7TH AVE STE 110, PACIFIC WOMENS CTR 97401 #040-02-1988 L1992 **OBG** *020 †30

STEPHENSON, Max Jesse. 1255 HILYARD ST 97401 #040-02-1955 L1958 **PD PDC** *071 †55

STERN, Anna E. 1800 MILLRACE DR 97403 #005-18-2003 L2007 **GPM** *100 †70

STEWART, Gary Malcolm. ■ 97405 #040-02-1965 L1969 **OPH GP** *071 †35

ST GEORGE, Brian Paul. 1255 HILYARD ST 97401 #040-02-2000 L2004 **AN** *020 †05

STITES, Thomas Pennington. 360 S GARDEN WAY, STE 290 97401 #040-02-2002 L2007 **GS** *020 †85

STOCK, Ronald Dwight. 1162 WILLAMETTE ST, GROUP-DOWNTOWN EUGENE 97401 #030-05-1984 L1989 **FM** *020 †18

STOUT, Jonathan. 995 WILLAGILLESPIE RD, STE 200A 97401 #016-01-1980 L1988 **FM** *020 †18

STOWELL, Erik Douglas. 242 COUNTRY CLUB RD, OF EUGENE-SPRINGFIELD, P.C 97401 #040-02-1987 L2000 **PM** *020 †60

STRAUB, Timothy Allen. 1200 HILYARD ST STE 600AT, HEALTHCARE NORTHWES 97401 #038-06-1980 L1985 **ORS** *020 †40 ‡

STRIMLING, Bruce Sanford. 4135 QUEST DR 97402 #016-11-1966 L1971 **PD** *020 †55

STRUTIN, David Michael. 920 COUNTRY CLUB RD, STE 200A 97401 #016-11-1979 L1984 **IM OM** *020 †20

SULAIMAN, Olugbenga Omota. 1200 HILYARD ST STE S600, OHN 97401 #690-02-1992 L2007 *100

SUNADA, Fay Yukiko. 1800 COBURG RD, GROUP-COBURG ROAD 97401 #023-12-1988 L1999 **PD** *020 †55

SUNKOMAT, Julia Nathalie. ■ 97405 #409-42-1997 L2007 **IM** *050 †20

SWANGARD, Robert James. 1255 HILYARD ST 97401 #409-05-1971 L1979 **VS GS** *020 †85

TAGGART, Phillip Ray. 920 COUNTRY CLUB RD, STE 200A 97401 #040-02-1976 L1978 **IM** *020 †20

TAUBE, Michelle Jolton. 2830 CRESCENT AVE, CRESCENT FAM MED 97408 #005-19-1987 L2000 **FM** *020 †18

TAVAKOLIAN, Jason Darius. 1200 HILYARD ST, STE S600 97401 #032-01-1999 L2005 **ORS** *020 †40

TEAL, Donald Fraser. 901 E 18TH AVE 97403 #048-12-1965 L1975 **PS HS** *020 †85,65

TEARSE, Robert Geo. 4725 VILLAGE PLAZA LOOP, STE 101 97401 #005-19-1977 L1982 **SME N** *020 †75

TEH, Swee Hoe. ■ 97404 #539-04-1996 L2005 **GS** *100 †85

TELLER, George W. ■ 97402 #007-02-1950 L1950 **GP GYN** *071

TERHES, John Michael. 360 S GARDEN WAY, STE 290 97401 #040-02-1998 L1999 **GS** *020 †85

THOMPSON, Paul Allen. 1255 HILYARD ST, ANESTHESIA DEPARTMENT 97401 #028-02-1992 L2001 **AN** *020 †05

THOMSON, Matthew John. 1255 HILYARD ST 97401 #049-01-2000 L2006 **VIR** *020 †80

THRALL, Thomas Michael. 2650 SUZANNE WAY, STE 200 97408 #017-20-1979 L1994 **OS IM** *020 †20

TREZONA, Thomas P. 1200 HILYARD ST STE S550 97401 #040-02-1985 L1995 **SO GS** *020 †85

TRITCH, Todd Patrick. 1255 HILYARD ST, ANESTHESIA DEPT SACRED HEA 97401 #040-02-1992 L1997 **AN** *020 †05

TRUNK, Gary. ■ 97404 #005-15-1967 L1968 **IM PUD** *071 ‡

TSAI, David S W. 1200 HILYARD ST STE S410, RADIOLOGY ASSOCIATES PC 97401 #028-46-1989 L2005 **DR** *020 †80

TUFARIELLO, Jennifer M. 590 COUNTRY CLUB PKWY, STE B 97401 #035-06-1994 L1998 **OBG** *020 †30

TURNER, Frank Nelson. ■ 97401 #041-01-1967 L1974 **PUD IM** *071 †20

TURVEY, Douglas Eugene. 100 RIVER AVE 97404 #016-11-1976 L1977 **FM FPG** *020 †16

UMBACH, Thomas Walter. 1200 HILYARD ST, STE S570 97401 #051-04-1996 L2006 **GS** *020 †85

UNGER, James Edwin. 3299 HILYARD ST, GROUP-SOUTH EUGENE 97405 #048-12-1980 L1996 **PD** *020 †55

VAN ERT, Timothy John. 1232 UNIVERSITY OF OREGON, UNIV HLTH SERV 97403 #005-19-1982 L1989 **FM** *020 †18

VAN PETT, Kasia. 74B CENTENNIAL LOOP 97401 #005-11-1991 L1997 **NS** *020

VELARDE, Robert Louis. 995 WILLAGILLESPIE RD, STE 100 97401 #005-02-1972 L1975 **PD** *020 †55

VERGAMINI, Jerome Carl. 2411 MARTIN L KING, JR. BLVD. 97401 #056-05-1965 L1974 **P CHP** *020 †75 ‡

VICKERS, I. Samuel. 755 E 11TH AVE, STE 200 97401 #005-02-1967 L1986 **PTH FOP** *020 †50

VIRAMONTES, Jose. 360 S GARDEN WAY, STE 290 97401 #056-06-1999 L2007 **VS** *020 †85

VITUMS, Vitolds Chas. 1200 HILYARD ST, STE S565 97401 #010-01-1968 L1971 **PUD** *020

VIVEK, Prashant Pammal. ■ 97405 #038-44-2000 L2007 **OTO** *020 †45

VON HIPPEL, Josephine B R. 74 E 18TH AVE 97401 #024-01-1956 L1968 **P** *020

WADIE, George Michel. 1200 HILYARD ST, STE S-450 97401 #915-02-1994 L2007 **GS** *100 †85

WALKER, H Douglas. 4415 HILYARD ST 97405 #030-06-1960 L1961 **GE IM** *071 †20

WALKER, Lisa Moran. 132 E BROADWAY STE 825 97401 #028-34-1995 L2003 **P** *020 †75

WALKER, Tommy R. 48 #048-04-1953 L1953 **AN** *071 †05

WALSH, Teresa G. 132 E BROADWAY 97401 #048-15-1979 L1989 **P** *020 †75

WALTER, Matthew Burtnett. 1200 HILYARD ST, STE S565 97401 #054-04-1992 L1998 **PCC IM** *020 †20

WALTON, Christopher Noel. 55 COBURG RD, MCKENZIE ORTHOPEDIC GROUPP 97401 #041-13-1985 L1991 **ORS** *020 †40

WASNER, Cody Keith. 1200 EXECUTIVE PKWY, STE 300 97401 #040-02-1974 L1981 **RHU IM** *020 †20

WATSON, Milton Russell. ■ 97405 #054-04-1960 L1992 **GS VS** *071 †85

WEBB, Michael David. 3225 WILLAMETTE ST STE 2 97405 #048-13-1981 L1988 **P** *020 †75

WEINER, Karen. 1680 CHAMBERS ST 97402 #005-06-1994 L1996 **PD** *020 †55

WEINSTEIN, Michael D. 1162 WILLAMETTE ST, GROUP-DOWNTOWN EUGENE 97401 #035-48-1976 L1977 **GP** *020
WEISETH, Warren M. 1800 LAKEWOOD CT, BOX 114 97402 #016-01-1940 L1946 **PD** *071
WELCH, Timothy B. 911 COUNTRY CLUB RD, STE 100 97401 #005-12-1995 L1996 **GS** *020
WELLER, Kathrin Annette. 242 COUNTRY CLUB RD, OF EUGENE-SPRINGFIELD, P.C 97401 #024-05-1989 L1993 **PM** *020 †60
WENDLAND, Merideth M. 520 COUNTRY CLUB PKWY 97401 #054-04-2001 L2006 **RO** *020 †80
WENSEL, Jeffrey Paris. 920 COUNTRY CLUB RD, STE 100A 97401 #018-03-1990 L1991 **RNR** *020 †80
WETTSTEIN, Lamont Aaron. 755 E 11TH AVE, STE 200 97401 #005-12-2000 L2004 **PTH** *020 †50
WHEATLEY, Lisa Maureen. 920 COUNTRY CLUB RD, STE 200A 97401 #016-43-1986 L1999 **AI IM** *020 †20,03
WHITE, David L. 1255 HILYARD ST 97401 #035-46-1963 L1972 **FM PHP** *020 †70
WHITE, David Mckinley. 1200 HILYARD ST, GROUP-HILYARD STREET 97401 #007-02-1991 L2002 **GS** *020 †85
WHITEHEAD, Danny Lamar. ■ 97405 #027-01-1982 L1982 **IM** *020 †20
WHITELEY, H Edmond. 1180 PATTERSON ST, STE 3-A 97401 #056-06-1974 L1999 **P** *020 †75
WHITMORE, James M. 1255 HILYARD ST 97401 #035-45-1981 L1982 **AN IM** *020 †20,05
WIBLE, Pamela L. 217 DIVISION AVE 97404 #048-02-1993 L1996 **FM** *020 †18
WICKMAN, Douglas William. 1200 HILYARD ST, STE S200 97401 #033-06-1995 L2002 **IM** *020 †20
WILEY, Kathleen M. 1232 UNIV OF OREGON 97403 #005-02-1972 L1979 **IM** *020 †20
WILKEN, Kathleen E. 1200 HILYARD ST, GROUP-HILYARD STREET 97401 #040-02-1978 L1989 **N** *020 †75
WILKEN, Robert Wayne. 1200 HILYARD ST, RADIOLOGY ASSOCIATES PC 97401 #026-04-1957 L1957 **DR** *071 †80
WILL, Geo Frederick, Jr. 1162 WILLAMETTE ST 97401 #035-20-1964 L1967 **OBG** *071 †30
WILLIAMS, David James. 1755 COBURG RD 97401 #018-03-1959 L1962 **GP** *020
WILLIAMS, Scott C. 1255 HILYARD ST, EUGENE EMERGENCY PHYSICANS 97401 #040-02-2001 L2004 **EM** *020 †16
WILSON, Edward Francis. ■ 97405 #008-01-1963 L1971 **PTH OS** *071 †50
WILSON, John D. 1200 HILYARD ST, STE S560 97401 #017-20-1971 L1977 **ID IM** *020 †20
WILSON, Leslie. 677 E 12TH AVE, STE N110 97401 #067-01-1952 L1957 **GS GP** *071 †80
WILSON, Paul Frederick. 1255 HILYARD ST 97401 #040-02-1947 L1954 **P CHP** *071
WILSON, Paul Lloyd. 1255 HILYARD ST 97401 #040-02-1972 L1979 **DR** *020
WILSON, Thomas Jos. 4510 S SHASTA LOOP 97405 #040-02-1969 L1974 **DR** *072 †80
WILSON, Timothy Lee. 1878 HAPPY LN 97401 #005-11-1987 L1996 **FM OM** *020 †18
WILTSE, William Earle. ■ 97404 #030-05-1955 L1956 **OS GP** *071 †18
WITKIN, David Bruce. 1800 COBURG RD 97401 #007-02-1977 L1983 **IM** *020 †20
WONG, John Che. 1255 HILYARD ST, SACRED HEART MED CTR 97401 #005-19-1991 L1997 **EM** *020 †20,16
WONG, Lorna Joy. 1800 COBURG RD, GROUP-COBURG ROAD 97401 #056-05-1990 L1993 **PD** *020 †55
WOODWARD, Kenneth Allan. 1255 HILYARD ST, ANESTHESIA DEPT 97401 #041-12-1999 L2007 **AN** *020 †05
WOODWORTH, Charles Baxter. ■ 97440 #035-15-1972 L1977 **GP** *020
WU, William Chinhai. 677 E 12TH AVE, EUGENE GASTROENTEROLOGY 97401 #054-04-1988 L1991 **GE IM** *020 †20
WUEST, Thomas Kurt. 55 COBURG RD, ORTHOPEDIC & FRACTURE CLIN 97401 #018-03-1987 L1992 **ORS OTR** *020 †40
WYZINSKI, Peter Wm. 360 S GARDEN WAY, STE 101 97401 #067-01-1977 L1985 **OPH** *050 †35
YANG, Donald K. 677 E 12TH AVE, EUGENE GASTROENTEROLOGY 97401 #041-01-1998 L2004 **GE** *020 †20
YARBROUGH, Donald E. 1200 HILYARD ST, STE S570 97401 #001-02-2000 L2006 **GS** *100 †85
YATES, Ati Urban. 1200 HILYARD ST STE S- 97401 #025-12-1993 L2008 **OS P** *020 †20
YEH, Hsiang-Sen Robert. 4010 AERIAL WAY 97402 #244-08-1987 L2005 **FPG** *020
YODER, Steven Michael. 1162 WILLAMETTE ST, GROUP-DOWNTOWN EUGENE 97401 #017-20-1977 L2005 **FM** *020 †18
YORK, Heather Lynne. 590 COUNTRY CLUB PKWY, STE B 97401 #025-12-1996 L2000 **OBG** *020 †30
YORK, John Robt. 590 COUNTRY CLUB PKWY, STE B 97401 #025-07-1970 L1973 **GYN** *020 †30
YOUNG, Gary Paul. 1255 HILYARD ST 97401 #040-02-1979 L1980 **EM** *020 †20,16
YUAN, Isaac. 1255 HILYARD ST 97401 #040-02-1980 L1983 **AN** *020 †05
ZEMAN, William Frederick. 1255 HILYARD ST, INSTITUTE 97401 #030-05-1972 L1979 **CD IM** *050 †20
ZIEMSKI, Glenn E. 1162 WILLAMETTE ST, GROUP-DOWNTOWN EUGENE 97401 #048-14-1991 L2004 **EM** *020 †16

FAIRVIEW – MULTNOMAH

STONEY, Gordon Adair. ■ 97024 #038-41-1955 L1964 **R** *071 †80 ‡

FLORENCE – LANE

ASHLEY, Phoebe Anne. 1845 HIGHWAY 126, STE H 97439 #056-06-1994 L2003 **CD** *020 †20
BOGE, Veldon C, Jr. PO BOX 17000 97439 #024-05-1949 L1968 **GP** *071
BOWER, Fred A. 400 9TH ST 97439 #038-40-1953 L1956 **FM** *071 †18
BRAUER, Albert James. ■ 97439 #030-05-1955 L1955 **GP FM** *071
CHAMBERS, Joseph Williams. 1845 HIGHWAY 126, STE H 97439 #008-01-1984 L1999 **CD IM** *020 †20
CHAPPELL, Jay Hamilton. 1845 HIGHWAY 126, STE H 97439 #005-19-1982 L1991 **CD IM** *020 †20
COOK, Stephen Lloyd. 1845 HIGHWAY 126, STE H 97439 #008-01-1983 L2002 **CD IM** *020 †20
DANIGELIS, Matthew James. 400 9TH ST 97439 #050-02-1997 L2003 **EM** *020 †16
DAY, William Timothy. 330 9TH ST, SURGICAL CLINIC 97439 #021-06-1981 L1991 **GS EM** *020 †85,16
DODSON, Anthony Lynn. 380 9TH ST, PRIMARY CARE BUILDING 97439 #040-02-1989 L1990 **FM** *020 †18
DUNLAP, Lawrence Bruce. 400 9TH ST 97439 #005-15-1968 L1972 **EM GP** *020 †18,16
EKSTROM, Jon Edward. 400 9TH ST 97439 #040-02-1983 L1989 **DR** *020 †80
FITZGIBBONS, James F. 1845 HIGHWAY 126, STE H 97439 #065-01-1972 L1973 **HEM ON** *020 †20
GORMAN, John Donnell. 400 9TH ST 97439 #040-02-1984 L1985 **DR GP** *020 †80
GRIMME, John David. 400 9TH ST 97439 #038-41-1999 L2005 **RNR** *020 †80
GUNDRY, John Winterson. 1845 HIGHWAY 126, STE H 97439 #040-02-1992 L2001 **CD** *020 †20
GUPTA, Akshay Satyarthi. 400 9TH ST 97439 #021-05-1997 L2005 **RNR** *020 †80
HAWN, Jerold A. 1845 HIGHWAY 126, STE H 97439 #010-02-1967 L1971 **CD IM** *020 †20
HOCKING, Dana Marie. 380 9TH ST 97439 #025-12-1999 L2006 **OBG** *020 †30
HODULIK, Michael J. 380 9TH ST, PRIMARY CARE BUILDING 97439 #056-05-1988 L1991 **FM** *020 †18
HOFF, Douglas Gerald. 1845 HIGHWAY 126, STE H 97439 #028-03-1995 L2004 **U** *020 †95
HORSLEY, Thomas Arthur. ■ 97439 #005-12-1945 L1947 **U** *071
HOWISON, Peter Wm. 380 9TH ST, PRIMARY CARE BUILDING 97439 #038-40-1975 L1994 **FM** *020 †18
ISHAM, Mary Louise. PO BOX 2978 97439 #005-18-1985 L1991 **ORS** *071 †40
JABR, Fadi Ibrahim. 380 9TH ST, HEALTH ASSOCIATES OF PEACE 97439 #605-01-1997 L2003 **IM** *020 ‡
JACQUES, Robert Leonard. 340 9TH ST, PO BOX 6000 97439 #005-12-1973 L1995 **IM** *020 †20
KIPPEN, James Duncan. 400 9TH ST 97439 #062-01-1997 L2004 *020 †80
LAU, Samuel. 1845 HIGHWAY 126, STE H 97439 #030-06-1988 L2000 **CD IM** *020 †20
LITIN, Robert B. 1845 HWY 126, STE H 97439 #026-04-1953 L1959 **U** *072 †95
MC CLELLAND, James H. 1845 HIGHWAY 126, STE H 97439 #008-02-1983 L1986 **CD IM** *020 †20
MC KIMMY, Roger Milford. 1845 HIGHWAY 126, STE H 97439 #040-02-1988 L1994 **U** *020 †95
MEHLHAFF, Bryan Allyn. 1845 HIGHWAY 126, STE H 97439 #040-02-1990 L1997 **U** *020 †95
MENEN, Michael Jo. 1845 HIGHWAY 126, STE H 97439 #056-06-1997 L2003 **CD** *020 †20
MICHELS, Lee Gordon. 400 9TH ST 97439 #054-04-1970 L1977 **R RNR** *020 †80
MURRAY, Todd Ingalls. ■ 97439 #035-01-1994 L2007 **EM** *020 †16
NAQVI, Khurram. 380 9TH ST 97439 #308-13-1999 L2005 **IM** *100
PADGETT, Richard Cameron. 1845 HIGHWAY 126, STE H 97439 #036-01-1988 L1998 **CD IM** *020 †20
PARK, David. 400 9TH ST 97439 #016-11-1996 L2004 **GS** *020 †85
PEARSON, Paul Eric. 380 9TH ST, PRIMARY CARE BUILDING 97439 #005-06-1989 L1993 **FM** *020 †18
PHUNTSHOG, Kalsang W. 400 9TH ST 97439 #495-14-1987 L1994 **IM** *020 †20
POSA, Idalee Pia Caballer. 380 9TH ST, PRIMARY CARE BUILDING 97439 #748-11-1996 L2004 **FM** *100 †18
RANTON, Jennifer A. 390 9TH ST 97439 #041-13-1996 L2007 **FM** *020 †18 ‡
REDDY, Ramakota Kandula. 1845 HIGHWAY 126, STE H 97439 #041-01-1990 L2001 **ICE CD** *020 †20
REESE, Randy Lee. 380 9TH ST 97439 #038-43-1977 L1992 **FM IMG** *020 †18
SAENGER, David Robert. 1845 HIGHWAY 126, STE H 97439 #005-11-1997 L2004 **CD** *020 †20
SCHWARTZ, Michael Norman. ■ 97439 #035-20-1964 L1965 **P ADP** *020 †75
SHEARER, Ronald Noble. 380 9TH ST, PRIMARY CARE BUILDING 97439 #040-02-1980 L1995 **IM** *020 †20
SMITH, Albert Andrew. 400 9TH ST, PEACE HARBOR HOSPITAL 97439 #010-01-1979 L1993 **EM** *020 †16
SMITH, David Ralph. 400 9TH ST, PEACE HARBOR HOSPITAL 97439 #048-14-2002 L2005 **EM** *020
STRUKEL, Robert James. 2006 HIGHWAY 101, PMB 330 97439 #026-04-1973 L1978 **ORS** *030 †40 ‡
TROJAN, Matthew Reed. 1845 HIGHWAY 126, STE H 97439 #012-05-1999 L2007 **CD** *100 †20
TURLEY, Kevin. ■ 97439 #056-06-1972 L1975 **PCS TS** *071 †85,90
ULMAN, Richard Walden. 85595 HIGHWAY 101 97439 #018-03-1953 L1955 **FM GS** *071 †18
URICH, Raoul Walwyn. ■ 97439 #038-40-1944 L1944 **PTH FOP** *072 †50
VALENTINE, Matthew W. 400 9TH ST 97439 #040-02-1999 L2003 **EM** *020 †16
VERGARA, Melanie Kathryn. 380 9TH ST 97439 #748-30-2000 L2004 **IM** *020
WOOLSEY, Jeff Brian. 1845 HIGHWAY 126, STE H 97439 #018-03-2001 L2006 **GS** *020 †95
WOZNIAK, Andrea Stuart. 1845 HIGHWAY 126, STE H 97439 #012-01-1999 L2005 **U** *020 †95
YOUNG, Stephanie T. 400 9TH ST 97439 #036-07-1990 L2006 **DR** *020 †80

FOREST GROVE – WASHINGTON

ADAMS, Parks Madden, Jr. ■ 97116 #005-06-1972 L1973 **FM** *071 †18
ARMERDING, Paul T. 1809 MAPLE ST 97116 #016-06-1979 L1991 **FM EM** *020 †18
ARMSTRONG, Scott Chester. 1809 MAPLE ST 97116 #040-02-1984 L1999 **P PYG** *020 †75
BOOTH, Marilyn Jean. 3305 19TH AVE 97116 #040-02-1979 L1982 **FM** *020 †18
BOURS, William Alsop, IV. 3303 19TH AVE 97116 #024-01-1970 L1972 **FM** *020 †18
DEMOTT, Megan Christine. 1809 MAPLE ST 97116 #023-07-2002 L2008 **PTX** *012 †16
DOUGLAS, James Edward. 1809 MAPLE ST 97116 #041-14-1994 L2001 **P** *020 †75
EICHNER, Robert James, Jr. 1809 MAPLE ST 97116 #038-41-1978 L1980 **EM IM** *020 †20,16
FALLER, Christopher Augus. 1809 MAPLE ST 97116 #040-02-2004 L2007 **EM** *020
FREDRICKSON, Richard H. 1809 MAPLE ST 97116 #026-04-1979 L1981 **P** *020
GRAY, Timothy J, II. 1909 MOUNTAIN VIEW LN, STE 200 97116 #041-77-2001, ▲ L2002 **FM** *020
HAMILTON, Raeann Denise. 1809 MAPLE ST 97116 #041-02-1999 L2002 **EM** *020 †16
HONIS, Gretel Elizabeth. 1809 MAPLE ST 97116 #050-02-2003 L2006 **EM** *020
IRVINE, David Nerseth. 1809 MAPLE ST 97116 #005-19-1977 L1988 **EM** *020 †16
KEMPER, Nicole Jackson. ■ 97116 #040-02-2005 L2005 **IM** *012
KORCHINSKI, Jean Ann. 3307 19TH AVE 97116 #005-06-1978 L1979 **IM IMG** *020 †20
LONG, Katherine Rose. 1911 MOUNTAIN VIEW LN, STE 200 97116 #012-01-2001 L2003 **PD** *020 †55
LYNCH, Conley Joseph. 1825 MAPLE ST, MAPLE ST CLINIC PC 97116 #054-04-1995 L1998 **FM** *020 †18 ‡
MEYER, Sabine Clara. 1809 MAPLE ST 97116 #409-25-1981 L2006 **P** *020 †75
MILLER, Andrew James. 1809 MAPLE ST 97116 #035-08-2003 L2006 **EM** *020
MITCHELL, John Carhart. 1809 MAPLE ST 97116 #005-12-1999 L2002 **EM** *020 †16
NASH, Maureen Cecilia. 1809 MAPLE ST 97116 #019-02-1997 L2005 **PYG IM** *020 †20,75
NOYES, Edwin Arland. ■ 97116 #005-12-1959 L1960 **FM** *071 †18
PEDEMONTE, Mark Stephen. ■ 97116 #030-06-1978 L1979 **AN** *020 †05
RATNAYAKE, Mahinda Takesh. 1809 MAPLE ST 97116 #017-20-2004 L2007 **EM** *020
RAYMOND, Robert Craig. 1809 MAPLE ST 97116 #016-11-1992 L2002 **EM** *020 †16
ROBB, Marvin John. 1809 MAPLE ST 97116 #040-02-1939 **GP** *071
SEWARD, Robert Lynn. ■ 97116 #056-05-1966 L2004 **IM** *020 †20
ZEITZER, Mark Eric. 1809 MAPLE ST 97116 #003-01-2002 L2008 **EM** *020 †16

FOX – GRANT

GERSTNER, Phillip Leon. 55958 COOK ALLEN LN 97856 #049-01-1965 L1970 **GS** *020 †85

GASTON – WASHINGTON

BRAUN, Joyce Elaine Braak. PO BOX 277 97119 #025-07-1964 L1968 **P** *075
CAMPBELL, Joe Herald. 27751 NW OLSON RD 97119 #005-11-1967 L1971 **EM** *020
SANDERS, David Gregg. ■ 97119 #005-14-1991 L1994 **FM** *020

GEARHART – CLATSOP

REDEKOP, Jacob Benj. PO BOX 2061 97138 #016-06-1960 L1961 **ORS GS** *071 †40
VANDER WAAL, Steven Craig. 3619 HIGHWAY 101 N, GROUP 97138 #018-03-1976 L1984
  IM *020 †20

GLADSTONE – CLACKAMAS

CHUNG, Robert T. ■ 97027 #583-03-1963 L1976 **P GP** *071
GARD, David Henry. ■ 97027 #649-14-1977 L1980 **FM** *020 †18
HOESLY, Frederick Charles. ■ 97027 #040-02-1962 **PHP** *071
MATHIESEN, Merrill Duane. ■ 97027 #005-12-1948 L1948 **FM OS** *071
TAI, Slater. 880 82ND DR, WESTERN PSYCHOLOGICAL/COUS 97027 #026-04-1996 L2000
  P *020 †75

GLENEDEN BEACH – LINCOLN

COOKSON, Peter James. ■ 97388 #010-02-1969 L1973 **PTH FM** *075 †50
DAVIS, Harvey D. ■ 97388 #035-06-1951 L1958 **IM** *071
HEINEMANN, Mitchell W. 273 SALISHAN DR 97388 #040-02-1944 L1947 **PTH** *071 †50

GOLD BEACH – CURRY

BAILES, John Douglas. 210 WALKER ST 97444 #028-79-1963, ▲ L1964 **GP** *071
BOLIN, Robert Bruce. 94180 2ND ST 97444 #007-02-1966 L1985 **IM HEM** *071 †20
CHERRY, Cherry. 94180 2ND ST 97444 #035-05-1985 L2003 **HO** *020 †20
COOK, Bret Alan. 94180 2ND ST 97444 #016-42-1994 L2000 **HO** *020 †20
DRUZDZEL, Maciej Janusz. 94220 4TH ST 97444 #759-03-1978 L1993 **FM** *020 †18
EYRE, John Thos. 94220 4TH ST, RADIOLOGY CGH HOSPITAL 97444 #054-04-1970 L1977
  DR *072 †80
FERNANDO, Nihal Nicetus. ■ 97444 #220-01-1966 L1975 **END IM** *071 †20
NICKELS, Russell Arthur. 94220 4TH ST 97444 #038-06-1967 L1976 **FM OBG** *020 †18
WILLIAMS, Reginald G, Jr. 94220 4TH ST 97444 #041-13-1971 L1972 **FM EM** *020 †18

GRAND RONDE – POLK

GERRITZ, Glenn A. 9615 GRAND RONDE RD, GRAND RONDE HLTH & WELLNES 97347
  #040-02-1970 L1975 **FM IM** *020 †20
LAM, Daniel Francis. 9615 GRAND RONDE RD, HEALTH/WELLNESS CENTER 97347
  #051-01-1992 L1993 **CHP P** *020 †75
PRATT, Teresa Diane. 9615 GRAND RONDE RD, GRAND RONDE HEALTH CTR 97347
  #010-01-1987 L2003 **FM** *020 †18

GRANTS PASS – JOSEPHINE

ABDUN-NUR, David John. 741 NE 6TH ST 97526 #005-06-1981 L1994 **FM OM** *020 †18
ABU GHALYOUN, Bader Moh'D. ■ 97526 #575-01-2003 L2007 **IM** *020
AHMED, Hala Mohamed Aly. 125 NE MANZANITA AVE, SISKIYOU COMMUNITY HEALTH 97526
  #915-02-1996 L2006 **FM** *100 †18
AHMED, Mohamed Gad Hassan. 500 RAMSEY AVE, THREE RIVERS COMMUNITY HOS 97527
  #915-04-1997 L2006 **IM** *100 †20
AL-KHOUDARI, Amer. ■ 97527 #875-01-2000 L2007 **IM** *020 †20
ANANTHAKRISHNAN, Shubha. 1619 NW HAWTHORNE AVE, STE 201 97526
  #495-59-1997 L2006 **NEP** *020 †20
APPLEBY, David Mitchell. 1619 NW HAWTHORNE AVE, STE 210 97526 #016-01-1980 L1986
  HS ORS *020 †40
ARMSTRONG, William F. ■ 97526 #024-01-1938 L1946 **IM** *071
BALLANTYNE, Robin Scott. 500 RAMSEY AVE 97527 #005-02-1968 L1972 **DR** *071 †80
BARONE, Rosemarie. 500 RAMSEY AVE 97527 #043-01-1988 L1991 **IM** *020 †20
BASIT, Abdul. 124 NW MIDLAND AVE, STE 110 97526 #704-04-1997 L2003 **IM** *020 †20 ‡
BATTEY, Richard Roy. 700 RAMSEY AVE, STE 101 97527 #021-06-1989 L1993 **OBG** *020 †30
BEACHY, Linford Dale. ■ 97527 #017-20-1971 L2006 **FM** *020 †18
BENTS, Robert Thurston. 520 RAMSEY AVE STE 102 97527 #040-02-1990 L1991 **ORS** *020 †40
BRANDES, Thomas Richard. 495 RAMSEY AVE 97527 #005-02-1969 L1973 **IM** *020 †20
BROWN, Caroline Jean. 495 RAMSEY AVE 97527 #005-02-1983 L1990 **FM** *020 †18
BRYNER, Marcus Alan. 500 RAMSEY AVE, 3 RIVERS COMM. HOSP.-RADIOL 97527
  #005-12-2000 L2006 **VIR** *020 †80
BURWELL, Douglas Trane. 520 RAMSEY AVE, STE 101 97527 #005-14-1972 L1996
  CD IM *020 †20
CANDELARIA, David D. 1505 NW WASHINGTON BLVD 97526 #007-02-1989 L1992 **FM** *020 †18
CATE, Joyce Y G. ■ 97526 #040-02-1967 L1974 **PTH** *062
CHU, Grace Tena. ■ 97526 #016-01-1980 L1986 **IM** *020 †20
CHUA, Joseleeto Uy. 1601 NE 6TH ST 97526 #748-01-1994 L2004 **N** *020
COHEN, Felicia. 700 RAMSEY AVE STE 101, WOMENS HEALTH CENTER 97526
  #011-02-1997 L2001 **OBG** *020 †30
COHEN, Richard Schley. 1600 NW 6TH ST 97526 #016-11-1973 L1977 **HNS OTO** *071 †45
COLLINS, Elbert Campbell. 495 RAMSEY AVE, GRANTS PASS CLINIC 97527
  #016-01-1981 L1986 **OBG** *020 †30

COOPER, James Carter, II. ■ 97526 #017-20-1971 L2005 **CHP P** *020 †75
COULAM, Curtis Richard. 500 RAMSEY AVE 97527 #049-01-1967 L1982 **R** *020 †80
COUNTISS, John Spencer. 495 RAMSEY AVE 97527 #028-02-1987 L1993 **IM** *020 †20
DEATHERAGE, Mark F. 1600 NW 6TH ST, GRANTS PASS SURGICAL 97526 #040-02-1974 L1979
  GS *020 †85
DICKERMAN, Elias. 749 NW KINNEY ST, P O BOX 231 97526 #048-13-1979 L1980
  N MDM *062 †75 ‡
DOOLITTLE, Charles H. 1505 NW WASHINGTON BLVD 97526 #043-01-1975 L1998
  ON IM *020 †20
DOWD, James Daniel. 625 RAMSEY AVE, STE A 97527 #005-18-1988 L1994
  ORS OSM *020 †40 ‡
DUGAN, James Michael, II. ■ 97527 #649-14-1984 L1987 **PD CCM** *020 †55
EOFF, Janet Marie. 1505 NW WASHINGTON BLVD, THREE RIVERS COMMUNITY HOS 97526
  #040-02-1987 L1988 **IM** *020 †20
ERMSHAR, Jon Edwinlloyd. 1716 WILLIAMS HWY 97527 #005-12-1988 L1991
  FM OBS *020 †18
FAWCETT, Cory Scott. 1600 NW 6TH ST, GRANTS PASS SURGICAL 97526 #040-02-1988 L1993
  GS VS *020 †85
FEAR, Daniel Roy. 1600 NW 6TH ST, STE S 97526 #040-02-1990 L1995 **OTO** *020 †45
FERGUSON-WILCOX, P A. 714 NW A ST 97526 #005-12-1996 L2001 **CHP** *020
FOREMAN, Mark A. 625 RAMSEY AVE STE A, GREATNER ORTHO PC 97527
  #048-13-1993 L1998 **ORS** *020 †40
FOUTZ, Steven Riggs. 124 NW MIDLAND AVE # B 97526 #040-02-1988 L1991 **FM** *020 †18
FRISBIE, Richard Duane. ■ 97526 #030-05-1956 L1963 **PD** *071 †55
GAMBRILL, Raymond, III. 700 RAMSEY AVE, STE 101 97527 #023-01-1968 L1972
  GYN *020 †30
GENTRY, Robert Mark. 1585 NW WASHINGTON BLVD 97526 #005-19-1975 L1978 **FM** *020 †18
GETTY, George Lucian. 214 NE OUTLOOK AVE 97526 #051-01-1976 L1983 **U** *020 †95
GLEFFE, Dan Phillip. 1587 NW WASHINGTON BLVD 97526 #025-01-1984 L1987 **FM** *020 †18
GOVE, Jon Duane. 500 RAMSEY AVE 97527 #038-40-1967 L1975 **DR** *020 †80
GRELL, Frieda Louise. 1475 NE 7TH ST 97526 #041-07-1962 L1977 **AN** *074 †05
GROENHOUT, Edward Guy. 495 RAMSEY AVE 97527 #034-01-1992 L2003 **IM** *020 †20
HADDAD, Haitham Boulos. 495 RAMSEY AVE 97527 #005-12-1993 L1994 **IM** *020 †20
HALFMANN, Lee Roger. ■ 97527 #007-02-1964 L1992 **FM** *074 †18
HAMAD, Ezedeen. 500 RAMSEY AVE 97527 #875-01-2001 L2007 **IM** *100
HAMANN, Barry Colfax. 741 NE 6TH ST 97526 #005-12-1990 L1993 **FM** *020 †18
HAMILTON, Lorene L. 1215 NE 7TH ST STE D 97526 #003-75-2001, ▲ L2005 **FM** *020
HANCOCK, Brian. 841 NE 7TH ST 97526 #308-11-1985 L1991 **FM** *020 †18
HANSEN, Gary R. 500 RAMSEY AVE, DEPT OF RADIOLOGY TRCH 97527 #028-02-1975 L1998
  DR PDR *020 †80
HARDING, Dean H. ■ 97526 #019-02-1943 L1943 **FM** *071 †18
HECOX, Douglas Baldwin. 201 SW L ST 97526 #041-15-1999 L2005 **NEP** *020 †20
HILL, Bernard Wm. 500 RAMSEY AVE 97527 #040-02-1973 L1976 **FM EM** *020 †18
HOELLRICH, Robert Geo. 520 RAMSEY AVE, STE 204 97527 #038-41-1969 L1977 **GS** *020 †85
HOFFMAN, Gregory Robert. 495 RAMSEY AVE 97527 #049-01-1998 L2001 **FM** *020 †18
HOLT, Anthony Wesson. ■ 97526 #026-04-1969 L1974 **FM** *071 †18
HONG, Fang Yen. 715 NW DIMMICK ST 97526 #385-02-1967 L1972 **PTH** *020 †50
HOWARD, Douglas James. 1505 NW WASHINGTON BLVD 97526 #061-01-1977 L1978
  EM *020 †16
HUANG, Chuck I-Chi. 1619 NW HAWTHORNE AVE # 20 97526 #422-01-2000 L2007
  END *020 †20
HUGHES, Kathleen Ann. 711 RAMSEY AVE 97527 #056-05-1984 L2006 **CHP P** *020 †75
ISERT, Justin August. ■ 97526 #056-06-1960 L1965 **IM** *071
JACKSON, Lyle Thos. ■ 97526 #016-11-1974 L1977 **FM** *071 †18
JASTI, Anil Kumar. 500 RAMSEY AVE, C/O APOGEE HOSPITALISTS 97527 #496-35-1998 L2005
  IM *020 †20
JOHNSON, Robert R. 524 NE 7TH ST 97526 #039-01-1944 L1951 **GP** *020
JORIZZO, Paul Albert. 881 NE 7TH ST 97526 #035-45-1982 L1983 **OPH** *020 †35
KATTENHORN, Lowell Dean. 700 NW DIMMICK ST 97526 #005-12-1941 L1971 **FM GS** *071
KENDALL, Warren W. ■ 97527 #039-01-1968 L1975 **ORS** *071 †40
KERR, Erin Louise. ■ 97526 #005-18-1988 L1995 **PD** *020 †55
KHO, Yung Kan. 1601 NE 6TH ST 97526 #409-19-1971 L1981 **N OS** *020 †55,75
KOHLER, George Danl. ■ 97526 #005-14-1961 L1962 **FM** *075
KOHN, William Lee. 495 RAMSEY AVE 97527 #005-14-1974 L1977 **PD** *020 †55
KRUSE, Theodore Clair. 495 RAMSEY AVE 97527 #005-02-1973 L1977 **EM IM** *020 †20
LATTIN, Anna Marie. ■ 97527 #048-16-2004 L2004 **FM** *100
LEAVITT, Rodney Derrick. 1226 NE 7TH ST, CASCADE EYE CARE CENTER 97526
  #005-12-2002 L2006 **OPH** *020
LEAVITT, Russell Jeffery. 1226 NE 7TH ST 97526 #005-15-1968 L1974 **OPH GP** *020 †35
LOELIGER, Eric Jay. ■ 97527 #035-09-2002 L2007 **EM** *020 †16
LOWE, James Richard. 1600 NW 6TH ST, GRANTS PASS SURGICAL 97526 #031-01-1999 L2004
  GS *020 †85
LUTHER, Andrew Donald. 495 RAMSEY AVE, GRANT PASS CLINIC 97527 #040-02-1995 L1998
  FM *020 †18
MADHAVAN, Ranganathan Gur. 500 RAMSEY AVE 97527 #495-37-2000 L2007 **IM** *020 †20
MAFFETT, Mark James. 1226 NE 7TH ST 97526 #047-05-1990 L1994 **OPH** *020 †35 ‡
MARCHINI, Carlos E. 874 NE 7TH ST 97527 #737-06-1983 L1990 **PUD CCM** *020 †20 ‡
MC CARTHY, Janice Louise. 500 RAMSEY AVE 97527 #040-02-1990 L1991 **DR** *020
MEDLEY, Tamara Clark. 700 RAMSEY AVE, STE 101 97527 #041-07-1998 L2002 **OBG** *020 †30
MERLO, Heather Calleen. ■ 97526 #305-01-2006 **100**
MERRITT, Douglas R. 1226 NE 7TH ST 97526 #048-14-1986 L1990 **OPH** *020 †35
MILLER, Rebecca. 1505 NW WASHINGTON BLVD, OCCUPATIONAL HEALTH 97526
  #028-34-1997 L2001 **FM** *020 †18
MOLINE, Daniel Lee. 124 NW MIDLAND AVE 97526 #054-04-1969 L1974 **FM** *020 †18
MONTGOMERY, Robt Ames, III. 1601 NW HAWTHORNE AVE 97526 #048-14-1990 L1994
  AN *020 †05
MOOS, Mitchell Andrew. 715 NW DIMMICK ST 97526 #016-11-1964 L1969 **U** *020 †95
MORRIS, Thomas Jack. 495 RAMSEY AVE 97527 #021-01-1972 L1975 **IM** *020 †20
MURRAY, Philip Bruce. 495 RAMSEY AVE 97527 #011-02-1976 L1990 **IM IMG** *020 †20
OEHLING, David Clague. 1600 NW 6TH ST, GRANTS PASS SURGICAL 97526
  #040-02-1966 L1971 **GS VS** *020 †85
OPEL, Markus. 495 RAMSEY AVE 97527 #409-12-1989 L1994 **IM** *020 †20
OTTIS, Larry Melvin. ■ 97526 #040-02-1963 L1964 **OPH** *071 †35
PALADUGU, Bhanu Prasad. 500 RAMSEY AVE 97527 #495-50-1995 L2006 **IM** *100 †20
PERRY, Bruce Edgar. 1619 NW HAWTHORNE AVE, STE 102 97526 #025-12-1983 L1989
  ORS OSM *020

■ = Address Information Privacy Protected

PERRY, Eric Matthew. 495 RAMSEY AVE, GRANTS PASS CLINIC 97527 #030-06-1994 L1999 IM *020 †20

PERSONIUS, Bradley Earl. 500 RAMSEY AVE 97527 #005-12-1984 L1998 **CD IM** *020 †20

PILCHER, Jason Clayton. 741 NE 6TH ST, MOUNTAIN VIEW FAMILY PRACI 97526 #048-16-2002 L2005 **FM** *020 †18

POWELL, Tamara Marie. 741 NE 6TH ST 97526 #051-04-1995 L1998 **FM** *020 †18

POWELL, Theodore Herbert. 495 RAMSEY AVE, GRANTS PASS CLINIC 97527 #005-12-1974 L1979 **GS** *020 †20

PRINS, Ben. ■ 97527 #005-06-1966 L1972 **IM GE** *020 †20

PROCKNOW, David Neal. 500 RAMSEY AVE 97527 #005-12-1984 L1990 **EM FM** *020 †18

PURTZER, Frank J. 1100 NE 7TH ST 97526 #040-02-1952 L1953 **GP** *071

RASMUSSEN, Richard Dean. 1309 NE 6TH ST 97526 #005-18-1989 L1993 **D** *020

REED, Craig. 131 NE B ST 97526 #040-02-1994 L2001 **P CHP** *020

RENAUD, Maurice Paul. ■ 97527 #050-02-1966 L1973 **ORS** *071 †40

REYNOLDS, Bruce Navin. 1600 NW 6TH ST, 9 97526 #024-07-1985 L1995 **OTO FPS** *020 †45

RIST, Peter P. ■ 97527 #409-19-1983 L2001 **IM** *020 †20

ROBERTS, Timothy Edward. 495 RAMSEY AVE 97527 #041-09-1998 L2001 **FM** *020 †18

RONDEAU, Mark Allen. 124 NW MIDLAND AVE, STE J 97526 #050-02-1997 L2000 **FM** *020 †18

ROSE, Philip Montgomery. 715 NW DIMMICK ST, HOSPITAL & HEALTH CENTER 97526 #040-02-1986 L1990 **DR** *020 †80

SAGER, William Jos. 500 RAMSEY AVE, APOGEE HOSP OFC 97527 #016-06-1959 L1972 **IM** *020 †20

SCHULTE, Brett Jon. 1600 NW 6TH ST, GRANTS PASS SURGICAL 97526 #054-04-1988 L1997 **GS** *020 †85

SELINGER, Daniel Steven. 495 RAMSEY AVE 97527 #016-11-1970 L1980 **IM ID** *020 †20

SELINGER, Rosemary C. 495 RAMSEY AVE 97527 #034-01-1977 L1980 **IM P** *020

SEXTON, Harold. 1215 SW G ST 97526 #040-02-1967 L1968 **P FM** *030

SINCLAIR, Ronald Stuart. 495 RAMSEY AVE 97527 #028-03-1983 L1987 **IM** *020 †20

STEINBRENNER, Roger Ward. 181 NW BUNNELL AVE 97526 #010-01-1965 L1972 **IM** *020 †20

STEINMAN, Beverly. 1505 NW WASHINGTON BLVD 97526 #005-12-1979 L1983 **FM** *020 †18

STEINMAN, William Douglas. 125 NE MANZANITA AVE 97526 #005-12-1979 L1983 **FM** *020 †18

STOWELL, Bruce Robt. 495 RAMSEY AVE 97527 #028-34-1979 L1982 **IM** *020 †20

STRONG, Brandi. 495 RAMSEY AVE, GRANTS PASS CLINIC 97527 #063-01-2001 L2004 **FM** *020 †18

SYMENS, June Lorraine. 201 SW L ST 97526 #046-01-1983 L1988 **NEP IM** *020 †20

TANK, Gerhard W. 125 NE MANZANITA AVE 97526 #056-05-1953 L1957 **OBG** *071 †30

TRANDINH, Chutuoc C. 124 NW MIDLAND AVE 97526 #024-07-1996 L2003 **IM** *020 †20

TRUMP, David Schick. 97527 #012-08-1959 L1959 **PDS OS** *071 †85,90

TUREK, Thomas Martin. 124 NW MIDLAND AVE 97526 #026-04-1970 L1972 **FM** *071 †18

TURNER, Dorothy May. ■ 97526 #005-12-1956 L1957 **GP GYN** *074

TYNER, Sandra J. 118 NE MANZANITA AVE 97526 #041-12-1976 L1980 **FM** *075 †18

VANHORNE, James Robt. 702 RAMSEY AVE, STE 112 97527 #041-09-1990 L1996 **ORS OAR** *020 †40

VAN HORNE, Robert G. ■ 97527 #035-01-1952 L1955 **IM CD** *071 †20

VILLONA, Barbra Ursa. 500 RAMSEY AVE 97527 #041-12-1995 L2001 **EM** *020 †16 ‡

WIGGERS, Marcel. 495 RAMSEY AVE 97527 #005-12-1996 L2004 **IM** *020 †20 ‡

WILLIAMS, Jeffrey Grey. 162 NE BEACON DR STE 103, VALLEY IMMEDIATE CARE 97526 #036-08-1983 L1990 **EM** *020 †16

WILLIAMS, Richard Andrew. 741 NE 6TH ST 97526 #005-18-1993 L1996 **FM PD** *020 †18

WILLIAMSON, Neil Robt. 243 NE C ST 97526 #040-02-1967 L1981 **P** *020

WOOD, Jonathan Allan. 500 RAMSEY AVE, POX 1750, GRANTS PASS, 975 97527 #005-12-1994 L2000 **VIR** *020 †80

YOUNG, David Franklin. 1309 NE 6TH ST 97526 #040-02-1977 L1981 **D GP** *020 †15

GRESHAM – MULTNOMAH

ACKER, Donald Watson. ■ 97080 #040-02-1954 L1971 **D GP** *071 †15

ALLEN, Robert Morris. 24800 SE STARK ST, LEGACY MOUNT HOOD MEDICAL 97030 #040-02-2004 L2007 **IM** *100 †20

ANDERSON, John Charles. 831 NW COUNCIL DR, STE 130 97030 #005-12-2000 L2006 **OSM** *020 ‡

BACHHUBER, Thomas Edward. ■ 97080 #056-05-1956 L1957 **ORS** *071 †40

BAILEY, Robert Burns. 440 NW DIVISION ST # 100 97030 #040-02-1985 L1986 **IM** *020 †20

BARNHART, Mary Kathleen. 831 NW COUNCIL DR, STE 212 97030 #005-12-1979 L1987 **GS VS** *020 †85

BERGER, Daniel Robert. 24800 SE STARK ST, LEGACY MT. HOOD MEDICAL CE 97030 #024-16-1999 L2002 **EM** *020 †16

BLATCHFORD, Douglas Mills. 24850 SE STARK ST STE 200 97030 #040-02-1968 L1969 **OBG** *020 †30

BRENNER, Joel Benton. 24800 SE STARK ST, MT HOOD MEDICAL CENTER 97030 #024-07-1975 L1976 **EM** *020 †16

BROSE, Daniel J. 25500 SE STARK ST STE 101 97030 #038-41-1952 L1953 **GS** *020 †85

BROWN, Adam Lee. ■ 97030 #040-02-1995 L2005 **PD** *020

BROWN, Marshall F. 100 W POWELL BLVD 97030 #026-04-1953 L1953 **FM** *071

BUCKMAN, Christy Richter. 24076 SE STARK ST, STE 230 97030 #025-01-1996 L2006 **OTO** *020 †45

BURRESS, Donald Allen. 711 NE HOOD AVE 97030 #035-01-1962 L1969 **OPH** *020 †35

CALCAGNO, Frank Anthony. 24850 SE STARK ST, STE 150 97030 #040-02-1996 L1999 **PD** *020 †55

CALCAGNO, John Anthony. 24850 SE STARK ST, STE 150 97030 #040-02-1985 L1986 **PD** *020 †55

CARPENTER, Kevin Richard. 440 NW DIVISION ST 97030 #040-02-1990 L1997 **FM** *020 †18

CARTER, Kelly Annette. 24850 SE STARK ST, STE 200 97030 #054-04-1991 L1995 **OBG** *020 †30

CAVALLI, Richard Ernest. 2850 SE POWELL VALLEY RD 97080 #040-02-1961 L1962 **PD** *071 †55

CHAUMETON, Amy Katherine. 24800 SE STARK ST 97030 #040-02-1998 L1999 **IM** *020 †20

CHEN, Michael Chihtung. 2850 SE POWELL VALLEY RD, STE 100 97080 #016-02-1992 L1998 **IM** *020 †20

CHIOU, Normy Yushang. 600 NE 8TH ST 97030 #040-02-2003 L2007 **FM** *020 †18

CHOONG, Stephen K M. 501 NE HOOD AVE STE 205 97030 #539-04-1970 L1977 **GS VS** *020 †85

COWELL, Vernon Lee, Jr. 25500 SE STARK ST STE 101, COLUMBIA SURG SPECIALISTS 97030 #010-02-1989 L1997 **GS CCS** *020 †85

CRAFT, Richard Wayne. 24900 SE STARK ST, STE 202 97030 #040-02-1986 L1989 **IM** *020 †20

CUSTIS, John Marc. 24900 SE STARK ST STE 109 97030 #040-02-1971 L1974 **IM** *020 †20

DALES, Bret Hardin. 24988 SE STARK ST, STE 100A 97030 #031-01-1991 L1998 **ORS OAR** *020 †40

DAVIDSON, Marc Romayne. 24076 SE STARK ST, STE 110 97030 #011-04-1991 L1992 **OSM ORS** *020 †20

DAVIS, Phyllis Gloria. 400 NE 7TH ST, MT HOOD COMMUNITY MENTAL 97030 #040-02-1947 L1949 **P** *071

DE LANE, Larry Rex. ■ 97030 #048-02-1971 L1971 **FM** *071 †18

DELORIT, Gary John. 24076 SE STARK ST, STE 230 97030 #056-06-1968 L1972 **OTO HS** *071 †45

DESAI, Samir Bharat. 24988 SE STARK ST, PACIFIC ONCOLOGY 97030 #038-44-1998 L2005 **IM** *020 †20

DESHMUKH, Sunita Madhukar. 440 NW DIVISION ST, PMG/GRESHAM 97030 #495-28-1992 L2001 **IMG** *020 †20

DOWSETT, Gordon Alexander. 24076 SE STARK ST, STE 230 97030 #040-02-1968 L1969 **OTO HNS** *071 †45

DUNN, Stuart Craig. 24988 SE STARK ST, ST#200 97030 #048-04-1995 L1998 **PD** *020 †55

EDGERTON, Glen Russell. 24800 SE STARK ST, MT HOOD MED CNTR 97030 #005-12-1958 L1959 **IM GP** *072

EGSIEKER, Mary Alison. 24988 SE STARK ST, STE 200 97030 #040-02-1999 L2003 **PD** *020 †55

EIDENBERG, Peter Jos. III. 400 NE ROBERTS AVE 97030 #041-02-1964 L1967 **GP** *071 †18

EISENSTEIN, Ben Ephriam. 24800 SE STARK ST 97030 #005-15-1962 L1975 **R NM** *020 †80,28

EKI, Norman Toshiaki. 2150 NE DIVISION ST # 103, PEDIATRIC ASSOC GRESHAM 97030 #040-02-1979 L1982 **PD** *020

EL-KHAL, Jamaal David. ■ 97080 #305-01-2004 L2007 **FM** *100

EMMERICH, Gregory David. 2150 NE DIVISION ST, STE 103 97030 #040-02-1986 L1989 **PD** *020 †55

FENNELL, Kenneth Owen. 4603 SE 16TH CT 97080 #040-02-1987 L1989 **PD** *020 †55

FISHER, George Alan. ■ 97030 #040-02-1942 L1943 **GP** *071

FORTES, Williefred M. 831 NW COUNCIL DR, STE 201 97030 #024-01-1988 L1996 **PS** *020 †65

FREEARK, George L. ■ 97080 #016-11-1951 L1952 **FM** *071 †18

FROMMLET, Michael. 24800 SE STARK ST, EMERGENCY DEPARTMENT 97030 #035-03-1990 L1994 **EM** *020

FUTTERMAN, Jay Brandon. 500 NW 20TH ST 97030 #016-01-2003 L2003 **OPH** *020

GHAHERI, Bobak Amir. 24076 SE STARK ST, STE 230 97030 #038-40-2002 L2002 **OTO** *020

GIEDWOYN, Jerzy Olgierd. 24900 SE STARK ST, STE 103 97030 #759-03-1963 L1970 **CD IM** *020 †20

GLEASON, Lee Arthur. ■ 97030 #040-02-1961 L1962 **FM OS** *020 †18

GULLO, Allison Scott. 24076 SE STARK ST 97030 #036-08-1994 L2006 **AN** *020

GULLO, Gregory. 831 NW COUNCIL DR STE 300 97030 #038-06-1980 L2005 **APM AN** *020 †05

GYERKO, Peter Robt. 24988 SE STARK ST STE 20 97030 #017-20-1986 L1987 **PD** *020 †55

HARRELL, Andrea Lynne. 24850 SE STARK ST STE 200 97030 #040-02-2003 L2007 **OBG** *020

HARRIS, John Thos. ■ 97080 #028-02-1971 L1976 **ORS** *071 †40

HART, Mark Vincent. 24988 SE STARK ST, STE 320 97030 #040-02-1988 L1991 **IM** *020 †20

HENNINGER, Amy Katherine. 600 NE 8TH ST 3RD FL, MULTNOMAH CNTY HLTH DEPT - 97030 #034-01-1996 L1997 **FM** *020 †18

HENRIQUES, Robert Wallace. 600 NE 8TH ST STE 300, MULTNOMAH COUNTY OREGON 97030 #033-05-1986 L2005 **FM** *020 †18

HOBSON, Jon Michael. 440 NW DIVISION ST 97030 #040-02-1993 L1994 **IM** *020 †20

HOSKO, Mark Eric. 2850 SE POWELL VALLEY RD 97080 #056-06-1985 L1986 **UCM** *030

HUYSSOON, Kathryn Lyn. 24988 SE STARK ST, STE 300 97030 #039-01-1993 L1994 **IM** *020 †20

JACKSON, Steven Colin. 600 NE 8TH ST STE 300, EAST COUNTY HEALTH CLINIC 97030 #031-01-1980 L1984 **EM** *020 †20,16

JOHN, Michelle Lynette. 24988 SE STARK ST, LEGACY CLINIC MOUNT HOOD 97030 #056-06-2000 L2000 **IM** *020

KALEZ, Robert Lee. 24900 SE STARK ST STE 208 97030 #030-06-1957 L1961 **U** *020 †95

KARSTEN, Nancy B. 24800 SE STARK ST # EM, LEGACY MT HOOD MEDICAL CEN 97030 #025-01-1977 L1978 **GP** *020 †16

KINSTETTER, Denise Dawn. 1217 NE BURNSIDE RD, STE 301 97030 #056-06-1988 L1991 **PD PHO** *020 †55

KLATT, Keith D. 2850 SE POWELL BLVD, STE 100 97080 #048-13-1987 L1988 **UCM GP** *020

KNUDSEN, Anne Meredith. 24988 SE STARK ST, STE 200 97030 #047-05-2000 L2004 **OBG** *020

KURUP, Anupama G. 24988 SE STARK ST, PACIFIC ONCOLOGY 97030 #035-45-1999 L2005 **HO** *020 †20

LADOGANA, Anthony S. 24800 SE STARK ST, LIMS 97030 #048-12-1993 L2003 **IM** *020 †20

LAUB, Jordan M. 24800 SE STARK ST, C/O EMERGENCY DEPT 97030 #033-05-1983 L1988 **EM OM** *020 †16

LEAF, Kelly Ray. 24800 SE STARK ST, EMERGENCY DEPARTMENT 97030 #005-12-1997 L2001 **FM** *020 †18

LEE, Matthew Elliot. 440 NW DIVISION ST 97030 #040-02-1995 L1999 **GPM** *100 †18

LEHTI, Patrick Michael. 24900 SE STARK ST STE 208 97030 #005-18-1978 L1979 **GS VS** *020 †85

LIANG, Yale Yeayiaw. 831 NW COUNCIL DR 97030 #023-01-1996 L2007 **FM** *020 †18

LIN, Wei-Hsung. 24900 SE STARK ST, GRESHAM INTERNAL MEDICINE 97030 #243-21-1983 L1996 **IM** *020 †20

LOCKWOOD, Darrell Robt. 24900 SE STARK ST STE 109 97030 #040-02-1968 L1973 **IM END** *020 †20

LOGAN, Norman Dean. ■ 97080 #040-02-1955 L1957 **ORS** *071 †40

MAC GREGOR, Malcolm D. 24800 SE STARK ST 97030 #040-02-1953 L1954 **GP** *075

MAHMOOD, Fayyaz. 24988 SE STARK ST STE 300, MTH CLINIC P C 97030 #704-01-1979 L1990 **IM** *020 †20

MAHR, Peter Nicholas. 600 NE 8TH ST STE 300, EAST COUNTY HEALTH CENTER 97030 #032-01-1998 L1999 **FM** *020 †18

MALLETT, Richard J. ■ 97030 #040-02-1949 **GP OS** *075

MANESS, Steven D. 400 NE ROBERTS AVE, ROBERTS ST CLINIC PC 97030 #048-14-1988 L1991 **IM** *020 †20

MANSOURI, Roya. 24076 SE STARK ST, STE 230 97030 #021-01-1999 L2004 **OTO** *020 †45

MC CLUSKEY, Edward A. 831 NW COUNCIL DR, STE 300 97030 #005-12-1989 L1993 **PMM AN** *020 †05

MC GOWAN, Patrick Jos. 24900 SE STARK ST STE 202 97030 #030-06-1991 L1994 **IM** *020 †20

MC KAY, Lorne Douglas. 24900 SE STARK ST STE 104 97030 #062-01-1972 L1985 **OPH** *020

MEADOWS, Mary Elizabeth. 440 NW DIVISION ST, PROVIDENCE MEDICAL GROUP 97030 #016-06-1998 L2001 **FM** *020 †18

MESTAD, Renee Elizabeth. 2150 NE DIVISION ST # 202 97030 #019-02-1998 L2002 **OBG** *020 †30

MILLER, Barbara Ann. 24800 SE STARK ST 97030 #040-02-1982 L1983 **AN** *020 †05 ‡
MILLER, Mark Nathan. 2850 SE POWELL BLVD # RO, GRESHAM URGENT CARE CENTER 97080 #021-05-1982 L1983 **IM** *020 †20
MILLIGAN, Glen Alvin. 24076 SE STARK ST, STE 230 97030 #048-04-1966 L1971 **OTO** *071 †45
MONNIER, Janet Rose. 831 NW COUNCIL DR STE 101 97030 #035-08-1989 L2004 **FM** *020 †18
MUELLER, Martin Chas. ■ 97080 #030-06-1948 L1950 **ORS** *071 †40
MURRAY, Michael Len. 24800 SE STARK ST, EMERGENCY DEPT 97030 #025-01-1980 L1981 **EM** *020 †16
NEAL, Dean Elton. 500 NW 20TH ST 97030 #040-02-1959 L1963 **OPH** *020 †35
NGUYEN, Nhat Quang. 831 NW COUNCIL DR, STE 300 97030 #019-02-2000 L2006 **APM** *020
ORDONEZ, Julio Alberto. 24900 SE STARK ST STE 209 97030 #132-02-1971 L1978 **NS** *020 †25
OSBORNE, Howard Ilo. ■ 97030 #005-12-1958 L1959 **GP** *071
PAJARILLO, Carmela Crisos. 440 NW DIVISION ST 97030 #748-08-2000 L2006 **FM** *020 †18
PALMROSE, Thomas William. ■ 97030 #040-02-1996 L2004 **PTH** *012 †20
PANWALA, Kathryn Victoria. 24950 SE STARK ST 97030 #054-04-1998 L2000 **RO** *020 †80
PAQUETTE, Julie Ann. 440 NW DIVISION ST, PMG GRESHAM 97030 #026-04-2000 L2001 **FM** *020 †18
PHIPPS, Richard Boyd. 1217 NE BURNSIDE RD # 704 97030 #040-02-1972 L1979 **D** *020 †15
PIEPGRASS, Sterling Robin. 2850 SE POWELL VALLEY RD, STE 100 97080 #010-01-1975 L1980 **IM AM** *020
PILLAI, Murali K. 24800 SE STARK ST 97030 #495-66-1990 L2004 **AN** *020 †05 ‡
PIZARRO, Renato Vitalis. ■ 97030 #748-01-1960 L1981 **FM PHP** *071
PODETT, Paul V. 24900 SE STARK ST, STE 205 97030 #305-01-1988 L1993 **FM EM** *020 †18
PUNJA, M Manohar. 24900 SE STARK ST, STE 103 97030 #495-33-1965 L1973 **CD IM** *020
RANA, Hiren Thakorbhai. 4101 NE DIVISION ST 97030 #495-37-1979 L1985 **P** *020 †75 ‡
RICHARD, Christen Kay. 1380 E POWELL BLVD 97030 #037-01-2000 L2001 **OPH** *020 †35
ROBERTS, Paul Wofford. 24900 SE STARK ST, WOMEN'S CLINIC PC 97030 #040-02-1968 L1971 **P** *020
ROCKOVE, Shammai. 24076 SE STARK ST, STE 310 97030 #016-01-1989 L1995 **U** *020 †95 ‡
ROMAINE, Richard Allen. ■ 97030 #040-02-1960 L1967 **D** *071 †15
SARGENT, Austin Underwood. 2850 SE POWELL BLVD, STE 206 97080 #067-01-1957 L1998 **AI IM** *020
SAYSON, Robert Chey. ■ 97030 #748-02-1974 L1980 **IM** *020 †20
SCHIAFFINO, Ellen. 440 NW DIVISION ST 97030 #917-04-1982 L1990 **IMG IM** *020 †20
SCHUEMANN, Sonia Johanna. 2850 SE POWELL VALLEY RD, STE 100 97080 #031-01-1991 L1998 **FM OS** *020 †18
SELIGMAN, Mark. 24988 SE STARK ST, PACIFIC ONCOLOGY 97030 #018-03-1971 L1979 **ON** *020 †20
SHAH, Amit Rajni. 600 NE 8TH ST 97030 #041-09-1997 L2000 **FM** *020 †18
SHAWLER, William Richard. 24800 SE STARK ST, MT HOOD MED CTR 97030 #005-12-1973 L1976 **EM OBS** *020 †16
SPRUNGER, Lewis Wm. 1550 NW EASTMAN PKWY, STE 100 97030 #038-02-1970 L1983 **CHP P** *030 †55,75
STOVER, Wilbur H. ■ 97030 #028-02-1952 L1952 **FM** *040 †18
TALLEY, Ernest Alfred. 501 NE HOOD AVE STE 340 97030 #040-02-1969 L1972 **GP** *020 †18
TOLAND, Kent Chas. 24076 SE STARK ST, STE 310 97030 #040-02-1988 L1993 **U** *020 †95
TRIGGS, Richard Arthur. ■ 97030 #010-01-1964 L1965 **AN** *071 †55,05
UTTERBACK, Thomas Duncan. 24800 SE STARK ST 97030 #040-02-1965 L1970 **ORS** *020 †40
VAJDOS, Margaret Adelle. 501 NE HOOD AVE STE 215 97030 #048-14-1985 L1996 **END IM** *020 †20
WILLEFORD, Vincent A. 24800 SE STARK ST 97030 #040-02-1980 L1985 **AN** *020 †05 ‡
WILLEY, Metta Elizabeth. 24988 SE STARK ST, STE 200 97030 #051-07-2004 L2004 **PD** *020 †55
WOBIG, Roger John. 24076 SE STARK ST, STE 230 97030 #040-02-1994 L1999 **OTO** *020 †45
WONG, Charles Men. 2850 SE POWELL VALLEY RD, STE 100 97080 #040-02-1980 L1986 **IM** *020 †20
WU, June K. 2150 NE DIVISION ST, STE 103 97030 #048-14-1988 L1991 **PD** *020 †55
YANKE, B Edward. 2150 NE DIVISION ST 97030 #005-76-1986, ▲ L1991 **OBG** *062
ZOOK, John Edwin. 25500 SE STARK ST STE 101, SURGICAL CLINIC 97030 #040-02-1954 L1966 **GS** *072 †85

HALFWAY — BAKER

HAMMAR, Michael Duncan. 36086 MCFADDEN LN 97834 #026-04-1965 L1980 **GS** *020 †85
MOORE, Lois Ann. ■ 97834 #051-01-1969 L2004 **R** *020 †80

HAPPY VALLEY — CLACKAMAS

BODIE, Mary Margaret. 12322 SE 126TH AVE 97086 #016-43-1981 L1990 **IM** *020 †20
BUYS, Robert John. 12100 SE STEVENS CT, STE 106 97086 #035-20-1979 L1983 **OPH** *020 †35
CHALMERS, Brent Earl. 12050 SE STEVENS RD, STE 400 97086 #040-02-1982 L1983 **OPH** *020 †35
CHANG, Winston. ■ 97086 #035-09-2006 L2007 **AN** *012
CLELAND-ZAMUDIO, Suzanne. 9200 SE 91ST AVE, STE 200 97086 #040-02-1993 L1998 **OTO HNS** *020 †45
DEREMER, Shawn M. 12444 SE SPENCER CT 97086 #422-01-1996 L2000 **AN** *020 †05
DOMREIS, John Stephen. 9200 SE 91ST AVE STE 320 97086 #035-09-1997 L1998 **GS** *020 †85
FAHEEH, Ali Reza. ■ 97086 #011-02-1998 L2005 **OD** *020
FRANZ, Thomas Jos. ■ 97086 #040-02-1965 L1971 **D** *050
GROSSNICKLE, Douglas Reed. ■ 97086 #040-02-1979 L1982 **IM IMG** *020 †20 ‡
GUERIN, Susan Beth. ■ 97086 #040-02-1983 L1984 **PTH DMP** *020
IUGA, Laura Maria. 9200 SE 91ST AVE, STE 200 97086 #007-02-2002 L2007 **OTO** *020
KELLOGG, Jordi Xirinachs. 9200 SE 91ST AVE STE 340 97086 #005-06-1994 L2001 **NS** *020
LEE, Shaotsu Thos. ■ 97086 #385-02-1953 L1962 **AN CCM** *071 †05
LEWIS, Angela Michelle. ■ 97086 #041-13-2000 L2007 **SO** *100 †85
LI, Kai. ■ 97086 #243-33-1992 L2006 **IM** *020 †20
LUM, Andrew Mark. 14110 SE ALDRIDGE RD 97086 #014-01-1986 L2007 **IM** *020 †20
MANALO, Rowena Lor. ■ 97086 #005-12-1996 L2003 **FM** *020 †18
MARSH, Peter Bradley. 12100 SE STEVENS CT # 106 97086 #040-02-1993 L1998 **OPH** *020 †35
MOSER, Jeffrey Steven. ■ 97086 #035-09-1998 L2005 **DR** *020 †80
NELSON, Jennifer Lynn. ■ 97086 #051-04-1998 L1998 **GS** *100
RAJ, Pritham Mohan. ■ 97086 #023-01-1997 L2006 **IM P** *020 †20,75

ROWLING, Jason C. ■ 97086 #018-75-2002, ▲ L2007 **AN PMM** *020 †05
SCHMIDT, J Robert. ■ 97086 #038-41-1940 L1954 **PHP** *071
STOLL, Michael E. 11750 SE 82ND AVE, CLACKAMAS PORTLAND 97086 #011-02-1984 L1985 **DR EM** *020 †80
TIBBLES, Larry Lyman. 8601 SE 141ST CT 97086 #040-02-1969 L1974 **OS** *100 †13
TULL, James Anthony. 12100 SE STEVENS CT # 106 97086 #039-01-1980 L1993 **OPH** *020 †35
VARELA, Adrian Eduardo. 9200 SE 91ST AVE STE 200, MT SCOTT EAR, NOSE, AND TH 97086 #011-03-1999 L2005 **OTO** *020 †45
WALKER, Tracy. 9200 SE 91ST AVE 97086 #040-02-1990 L1992 **IM** *020 †20
WENTZIEN, James Bond. 12100 SE STEVENS CT, STE 106 97086 #018-03-1990 L1991 **OPH** *020 †35
WILLIAMS, Juliann Kiraly. 12100 SE STEVENS CT, STE 106 97086 #016-02-1991 L1997 **OPH** *020 †35
WOODS, Matthew Travis. ■ 97086 #003-01-2005 L2007 **D** *012

HEPPNER — MORROW

GRANT, Donald J. 564 PIONEER DR, PIONEER MEMORIAL HOSPITAL 97836 #060-01-1965 L1968 **AN** *020

HERMISTON — UMATILLA

AL-AKHAL, Malek Hussein. 610 NW 11TH ST 97838 #605-01-2000 L2005 **FM** *020 †18
BERECZ, Robert James. 610 NW 11TH ST STE 33 97838 #005-12-1966 L1974 **GS** *020 †85
CAMPAGNA, Paul Anthony. 600 NW 11TH ST, GOOD SHEPHERD MED GRP 97838 #040-02-1980 L1981 **PD** *020 †55
CARLSON, Bruce Donald. 236 E NEWPORT AVE 97838 #056-06-1969 L1971 **FM PHP** *020 †18
CARPENTER, Richard Allen. 600 NW 11TH ST, STE E27 97838 #005-12-1973 L1974 **ORS** *020
DENTON, Robert John. 645 W ORCHARD AVE STE 3 97838 #040-02-1969 L1971 **P** *020
EARL, Derek T. 600 NW 11TH ST, STE E15 97838 #028-78-2000, ▲ L2001 **FM** *020 †18 ‡
ELDER, Terry. 600 NW 11TH ST, STE 100 97838 #040-02-1984 L1993 **AS TRS** *020
FARNEY, Thomas Leo. 600 NW 11TH ST STE E37 97838 #016-45-1979 L1987 **GS VS** *020 †85
FISHER, Deo Flaiz. 600 NW 11TH ST, FAMILY HEALTH ASSOCIATES 97838 #005-12-1973 L1979 **FM GPM** *020 †18
FLAIZ, Richard Allan. 610 NW 11TH ST, STE E21 97838 #005-12-1978 L1981 **OTO FPS** *020 †45
FLAIZ, T Douglas. 600 NW 11TH ST, FAMILY HEALTH ASSOCIATES 97838 #005-12-1972 L1973 **FM** *020 †18
FULPER, James Chas. 610 NW 11TH ST 97838 #017-20-1964 L1982 **EM OM** *020
GARCIA, Rafael Roberto. 600 NW 11TH ST, STE E-37-DEPT OF PD 97838 #005-02-1975 L2007 **PD** *020 †55
GIFFORD, Joseph Robt, Jr. 1050 W ELM AVE STE 110 97838 #005-12-1973 L1974 **GP FM** *020 ‡
GREGORY, Winn Harrison. 600 NW 11TH ST STE E10 97838 #036-01-1975 L2000 **GS** *020 †85
HUTCHINS, Phillip Maurice. 78068 ORDNANCE RD, CO MEDICAL CLINIC 97838 #005-12-1983 L2002 **OBG** *020 †70
JOHN, Marvin Martin. 610 NW 11TH ST 97838 #040-02-1954 L1955 **FM PME** *071
JOHNSON, Milton J. 975 W ORCHARD AVE 97838 #005-12-1949 L1950 **GP** *020
JOHNSON, Richard Fletcher. 600 NW 11TH ST, STE E37 97838 #027-01-1959 L1984 **OBG** *071 †30
JONES, Vicky Ayano. 2127 NW DUSK DR 97838 #035-19-2008 *012
MEHARRY, Le Roy Irwin. 610 NW 11TH ST 97838 #649-14-1971 L1978 **GP** *071
OGLESBAY, Michael L. 1050 W ELM AVE, STE 110 97838 #028-78-1995, ▲ L2002 **FM** *020 †18
OLTMAN, Guy Eugene. 600 NW 11TH ST, FAMILY HEALTH ASSOCIATES 97838 #005-12-1978 L1985 **FM** *020 †18
ORDINARIO, Maria Margarit. 610 NW 11TH ST 97838 #748-01-1998 L2004 **IM** *020
ORTIZ, George Abelard. 115 W HERMISTON AVE 97838 #005-12-1970 L1975 **IM GP** *020
PATEL, Rupa. ■ 97838 #033-05-1998 L2005 **OBG** *020 †30
RICKETTS, Edward A, Jr. 600 NW 11TH ST STE 109 97838 #041-02-1969 L1994 **IM CLP** *020
RUDD-MC COY, Nancy A. 600 NW 11TH ST STE E19 97838 #038-40-1980 L1999 **OBG** *020 †30
SOUDAH, Kathryn Lynn. 822 S HIGHWAY 395, # 314 97838 #665-01-2002 L2007 **FM** *020 †18
SWENA, Stewart Donald. 600 NW 11TH ST, STE E12 97838 #005-12-1982 L1992 **FM** *020 †18
TINIO, Frederick Gutierre. 600 NW 11TH ST, STE E37 97838 #748-01-1998 L2004 **IM** *020
TRAVERS, Leroy Albert C. 610 NW 11TH ST, HOSPITAL 97838 #065-01-1970 L1994 **R** *020 †80
TRUPP, Gary Victor. 600 NW 11TH ST, STE E37 97838 #005-12-1981 L2000 **OBG** *020 †30
TUDOR, Robert Chas. 1050 W ELM AVE, COLUMBIA PROFESSIONAL PLZ 97838 #005-02-1963 L1970 **OPH** *071 †35
VEALE, Robert Lorne. 1050 W ELM AVE, STE 210 97838 #068-01-1970 L1976 **FM** *020
WARNER, Michael Alan. 1070 W ELM AVE, E. OREGON REG. SURGERY CTR 97838 #036-07-1990 L1991 **OPH FPS** *020 †35
ZIEGLER, Jacquelyn Louise. 595 NW 11TH ST 97838 #005-11-2002 L2005 **FM** *020 †18

HILLSBORO — WASHINGTON

ABBOTT, David Frederick. 730 SE 7TH AVE, STE D 97123 #917-30-1968 L1974 **FM IM** *020
ABTIN, Keyvan. 333 SE 7TH AVE, STE 4050 97123 #026-04-1994 L2000 **NS** *020 †25
ACHAR, Guruajachar P L. 335 SE 8TH AVE 97123 #495-33-1966 L1978 **P** *075
ADOLPHS, Shawna Eileen. ■ 97124 #026-04-2006 L2006 **IM** *012
AEBI, Lisa Marie. 19400 NW EVERGREEN PKWY, SUNSET MEDICAL OFFICE 97124 #041-07-1995 L1998 **FM** *020 †18
AKHTAR, Salman. ■ 97123 #704-01-1984 L1996 **AN** *020 †05
ALEDO, Erenio Keoni. 21255 NW JACOBSON RD, STE 500 97124 #049-01-2002 L2003 **FM** *020
ALLEN, Nechol Leigh. 364 SE 8TH AVE, STE 200 97123 #034-01-2000 L2006 **GS** *100 †85
ALVAREZ, Lynn. 3000 NW STUCKI PL STE 220 97124 #003-75-2000, ▲ L2000 **P** *020 †75
ANDREWS, David Anker. 620 SE OAK ST STE A 97123 #040-02-1971 L1974 **OBG** *020 †30
APAU, Richard Kaukapono. 730 SE OAK ST, STE G 97123 #014-01-1991 L1997 **IM** *020
ARRINGTON, Sadie Ruth. 333 SE 7TH AVE, STE 5050 97123 #034-01-1978 L1980 **FM** *020 †18
AUGEE, Hollis Lyle. 335 SE 8TH AVE 97123 #040-02-1963 L1965 **AN AM** *020
AUSTIN, John Charles. 21255 NW JACOBSON RD, STE 500 97124 #025-01-2000 L2006 **OSM** *020
AWE, William Chester. 730 SE OAK ST, STE J 97123 #048-04-1958 L1964 **PHP** *020 †85,70
BAKER, Daniel Lloyd. 19400 NW EVERGREEN PKWY 97124 #010-02-1973 L1985 **PD HEM** *020 †55

■ = Address Information Privacy Protected

BALEN, Robert Francis. 512 E MAIN ST 97123 #028-34-1963 L1969 **OPH PS** *071 †35
BALLARD, James R. ■ 97124 #049-01-2007 L2007 **GS** *012
BARICH, Frank Charles. 730 SE OAK ST, STE G 97123 #018-03-2000 L2001 **IM** *020 †20
BARTLEY, Cynthia. 335 SE 8TH AVE RM 3318, SOUND INPATIENT PHYS 97123 #035-20-1988 L1995 **IM** *020 †20
BENNETT, Sylvana Elspeth. 364 SE 8TH AVE STE 205, AND GYNECOL 97123 #054-04-2003 L2007 **OBG** *020
BERGERON, Lester Leo. 364 SE 8TH AVE, STE 300A 97123 #040-02-1960 L1961 **OTO HNS** *072 †45
BERGQUIST, Bradley James. 527 SE BASELINE ST, STE F 97123 #054-04-1976 L1983 **NS** *020 †25
BIRD, Megan. 364 SE 8TH AVE, STE 205 97123 #040-02-2002 L2006 **OBG** *020
BISHOP, Jennifer Ellen. 335 SE 8TH AVE, TUALITY HEALTH CARE 97123 #033-06-2001 L2005 **IM** *100
BLAIR, Neil Frederick. 19400 NW EVERGREEN PKWY, SUNSET MEDICAL OFFICE 97124 #016-02-1990 L1993 **IM** *020 †20
BROWN, Greg Wm. 445 E MAIN ST STE 100 97123 #040-02-1989 L1996 **PD** *020 †55
BROWN, Katherine Ann. 1575 NE ARRINGTON RD 97124 #040-02-1989 L1996 **OBG FM** *020 †18,30
BYERLY, Robert Gene. 545 SE OAK ST STE F 97123 #040-02-1976 L1981 **PUD IM** *020 †20
CARO, James Edward. 900 SE OAK ST, STE 201 97123 #005-06-1983 L1993 **OTO HNS** *020 †45
CARR, Kirsten Marie Winn. 21255 NW JACOBSON RD # 500 97124 #040-02-2003 L2006 **FM** *020 †18
CHANG, Von Van. 5880 NE CORNELL RD, STE B 97124 #054-04-1999 L2002 **FM** *020 †18
CHAPIN, William C. 266 W MAIN ST, HLTH CNTR 97123 #041-07-1998 L1999 **END** *012 †20
CHEE, Peter Man Yuen. 21255 NW JACOBSON RD, STE 500 97124 #061-01-1996 L2002 **FM** *020 †18
CHEN, Wan-Jui. 364 SE 8TH AVE, STE 101 97123 #244-04-1985 L2000 **CN N** *020 †75
CHITWOOD, Bryan C. 19400 NW EVERGREEN PKWY, KAISER PERMANENTE 97124 #040-02-1994 L1997 **FM** *020 †20
CHOWDHURY, Masuma. 364 SE 8TH AVE, STE 301 97123 #160-07-1994 L2004 **IMG** *020 †20
CHOWDHURY, Mustaquim F. 730 SE OAK ST, STE G 97123 #160-02-1988 L2000 **IM** *020 †20
CLARKE, Edward Francis. 324 SE 9TH AVE STE D 97123 #040-02-1972 L1977 **IM** *020 †20
CLARKE, Nicholas Edward. 335 SE 8TH AVE, STE 201 97123 #040-02-1997 L2003 **END** *020 †20
COLETTI, John Milton, Jr. 335 SE 8TH AVE 97123 #035-20-1964 L1973 **ORS** *020 †40
COOK, Bernard Geoffrey. 335 SE 8TH AVE 97123 #068-01-1966 L1975 **AN** *071 †05
CORBIN, Christine Marie. 4660 NE BELKNAP CT STE 109, NORTHWEST GYN ASSOC LLC 97123 #038-44-1990 L2001 **GYN** *020 †30
CRUZ, Linda Irene. 730 SE OAK ST, TUALITY PHYSICIANS 97123 #060-02-1993 L1996 **FM D** *020 †20
CURRIE, Stuart John. 7545 SE TUALATN VLY HWY HI 97123 #016-01-1996 L2002 **FM** *020 †18
CUSTINO, Derrick Eugene. 19400 NW EVERGREEN PKWY 97124 #016-42-1996 L1999 **FM** *020 †18
DAHLQUIST, Nanette Dudley. 445 E MAIN ST, ST 100 97123 #040-02-1985 L1986 **PD** *020 †55
DAI, Charlotte Yue. 299 SE 9TH AVE, TUALITY/OHSU CANCER CENTER 97123 #041-01-2002 L2007 **RO** *100
DE MORGAN, Nicholas P. 19400 NW EVERGREEN PKWY 97124 #917-26-1962 L1979 **FM** *020 †20
DENESUK, Allison May. 730 SE OAK ST, TUALITY PHYSICIANS 97123 #060-01-1989 L1995 *100
DHADLI, Rupinder K. 6125 NE CORNELL RD, STE 320 97124 #038-06-1998 L2001 **OMF** *020
DISNEY, Jeffrey Dwane. 335 SE 8TH AVE, EMERGENCY DEPT 97123 #023-12-1990 L2002 **EM** *020 †16
DUMITRESCU, Alina Ioana. 22115 NW IMBRIE DR # 279 97124 #005-14-1996 L2001 **EM** *020 †16
EBERLE, Thomas Marion. 19400 NW EVERGREEN PKWY 97124 #040-02-1980 L1985 **IM** *020 †20
EILERS, Anton Farny. 349 SE 7TH AVE 97123 #035-20-1965 L1971 **ORS** *020 †40
ELLISON, John Harold. 2373 NW 185TH AVE # 459 97124 #040-02-1959 L1963 **IM GE** *075 †20
ENGLE, Patricia Marie. 364 SE 8TH AVE STE 301 97123 #017-20-2003 L2003 **IM** *020 †20
FIELDS, Robert Dwain. 730 SE OAK ST, TUALITY PHYSICIANS 97123 #048-04-1967 L1972 **FM** *020
FLEMMER, Kristen E. 333 SE 7TH AVE STE 5550 97123 #056-05-1992 L1993 **FM** *020 †18
FLORES, Marcella M. 7545 SE TV HWY 97123 #005-02-1973 L1976 **EM** *020 †16
FRANKHOUSE, Joseph H. 333 SE 7TH AVE, STE 5500 97123 #012-05-1990 L1997 **CRS** *020 †85
FREEDMAN, Samuel Polen. 335 SE 8TH AVE 97123 #041-02-1974 L1975 **EM** *020 †16
FREEMAN, Ian Lionel. 335 SE 8TH AVE, TUALITY COMMUNITY HOSPITAL 97123 #649-33-1982 L1999 **IM** *020 †20
FRIEDMAN, Daniel Keith. 364 SE 8TH AVE 97123 #041-03-1997 L1999 **N** *020 †75
FUNG, Hui-Ning Juju. 5625 NE ELAM YOUNG PKWY, STE 200 97124 #047-06-1996 L1999 **FM** *020 †18
GABEL, Steven Phillip. 900 SE OAK ST, STE 201 97123 #016-43-1995 L2001 **OTO FPS** *020 †45
GARBOWICZ, Leon. ■ 97123 #056-06-1962 L1969 **CHP P** *020
GARDNER, Amy Louise. 1200 NE 48TH AVE, STE 700 97124 #040-02-1991 L1991 **IM** *020 †20
GENT, Gregory Lee. 620 SE OAK ST, STE E 97123 #040-02-1974 L1978 **OBG** *020 †30
GIBBS, Gerald Everett. 405 SE 8TH AVE 97123 #005-02-1974 L1979 **ON IM** *020 †20
GILBERTS, Thomas Duane. 364 SE 8TH AVE, STE 301 97123 #040-02-2000 L2003 **IM** *020 †20
GILLINGHAM, Todd Sawyer. 5555 NE ELAM YOUNG PKWY, PMG/ORENCO 97124 #039-01-1995 L2000 **FM** *020 †18
GORDON, Steven Lewis. 19400 NW EVERGREEN PKWY 97124 #005-14-1981 L1982 **IM** *020 †20
GREENBERG, Mathew Scott. ■ 97124 #047-06-2000 L2008 **PTH** *100 †50 ‡
GULLO, Geoffrey Michael. 335 SE 8TH AVE, MEDICAL IMAGING GROUP OF 97123 #035-06-1994 L2003 **DR** *020 †80
GUPTA, Seema Radheshyam. ■ 97124 #496-38-1993 L2005 **IM** *100
GUTIERREZ, Monique. 445 E MAIN ST, STE 100 97123 #040-02-2001 L2004 **PD** *020 †55
HALL, Suzanne Mae. 5555 NE ELAM YOUNG PKWY 97124 #040-02-1979 L1980 **CD IM** *020 †20
HAPKE, Ronald Jack. 232 SE 7TH AVE 97123 #016-02-1992 L1995 **EM** *020 †16
HEBERLE, Wendi L. ■ 97124 #040-02-1997 L1998 **AN** *020 †05
HELAK, Agnieszka Krystyna. 335 SE 8TH AVE, DEPARTMENT OF ANESTHESIOLO 97123 #759-10-1991 L2003 **AN** *100 †05
HENDRICKSON, Jennifer Rai. 364 SE 8TH AVE, STE 205 97123 #035-08-1997 L2004 **OBG** *020 †30
HENNEBOLD, Karla Lea. 19400 NW EVERGREEN PKWY, SUNSET MEDICAL OFFICE 97124 #049-01-2000 L2000 **PD** *020 †55

HERMENS, Kenneth Anthony. 862 SE OAK ST, STE 3B 97123 #040-02-1979 L1980 **ORS** *020 †40
HERNANDEZ, Alexander M. ■ 97123 #847-04-1961 L1970 **P** *071
HEYDON, Kim M. 5555 NE ELAM YOUNG PKWY, PMG ORENCO 97124 #026-04-1993 L2002 **FM** *020 †18
HICKEN, Michael Powel. 5880 NE CORNELL RD STE B 97124 #060-01-1996 L2002 **FM** *020 †18
HILDEBRANT, Nathan James. 335 SE 8TH AVE #012-12-1999 L1999 **AN** *020 †05
HILLS, Barbara J. 364 SE 8TH AVE STE 101 97123 #037-01-1987 L1991 **N** *020 †20
HINCKLEY, James Herbert. 335 SE 8TH AVE 97123 #035-03-1998 L2001 **IM** *020 †20
HINKLEY, Andrea N. 19400 NW EVERGREEN PKWY 97124 #011-02-1999 L2002 **PD** *020 †55
HOEKSEMA, Catharina Ann. 333 SE 7TH AVE STE 4350 97123 #054-04-1995 L2000 **GS** *020 †85
HORNICK, Laurence Michael. 335 SE 8TH AVE, MEDICAL IMAGING GROUP OF 97123 #005-06-1970 L1975 **R RO** *020 †80
HUTCHINSON, Russell E. ■ 97124 #040-02-1943 L1946 **GP** *030
JAYARAMAN, Saramati. ■ 97124 #041-15-2003 L2008 **OBG** *100
JOHNSON, Lois Ann. 335 SE 8TH AVE, TUALITY COMMUNITY HOSPITAL 97123 #032-01-1982 L1990 **DR NM** *020 †20
KAPKA, Tanya Juliette. 226 SE 8TH AVE, VIRGINIA GARCIA MEM HLTH 97123 #040-02-2001 L2006 **FM** *020 †18
KELLY, Brian Wilbur. 545 SE OAK ST STE F 97123 #040-02-1976 L1977 **IM PUD** *020 †20
KENDALL, Carmen Gail. 5555 NE ELAM YOUNG PKWY 97124 #039-01-2000 L2004 **FM** *020 †18
KIM, Jinho. 335 SE 8TH AVE, MEDICAL IMAGING GROUP OF 97123 #040-02-1992 L1997 **DR** *020 †80
KORDASH, Terry George. 19400 NW EVERGREEN PKWY, SURGERY OFFICE 97124 #016-43-1995 L1999 **IM** *020 †20
KRACKE, Arthur Dale. 335 SE 8TH AVE 97123 #067-01-1958 L1961 **DR** *072 †55,80
KRAVITZ, Jay David. 155 N 1ST AVE MS 5, HUMAN SVS 97123 #021-01-1972 L1973 **PHP** *020 †16,70
KRISHNAMURTHY, G T. 335 SE 8TH AVE, TUALITY COMMUNITY HOSPITAL 97123 #495-09-1964 L1977 **NM IM** *020 †28
KRISHNAMURTHY, Shakuntla. 335 SE 8TH AVE, TUALITY COMMUNITY HOSPITAL 97123 #495-37-1968 L1977 **NM PTH** *020 †50,28
KU, Natalie. 335 SE 8TH AVE, MEDICAL IMAGING GROUP OF 97123 #025-01-1993 L2001 **VIR** *020 †80
KUKLINSKI, Piotr Pawel. 372 SE 6TH AVE 97123 #759-07-1978 L1994 **IM** *020 †20
KUMAR, Samudyatha A. 19400 NW EVERGREEN PKWY, SUNSET MEDICAL OFFICES 97124 #495-99-1998 L2002 **IMG** *020 †20
KUSTRITZ, Karen Louise. 333 SE 7TH AVE STE 5550 97123 #026-04-1995 L1998 **FM OBS** *020 †18
KWON, Susan B. 5880 NE CORNELL RD, STE B 97124 #048-13-1993 L1998 **FM** *020 †18
LA GASSE, David John. 349 SE 7TH AVE 97123 #035-20-1964 L1977 **ORS** *071 †40
LAKE, Jeremy Matthew. 232 SE 7TH AVE 97123 #054-04-1999 L2002 **GE** *020 †20
LAMPTON, Sarah Lisbeth. 425 SE BASELINE ST, CASCADE ORTHOPEDICS 97123 #051-01-1997 L2002 **ORS** *020
LARSEN, Raymond Vaughn. 1200 NE 48TH AVE, STE 700 97124 #030-06-1981 L1982 **FM** *020 †18
LARSON, Curtis John. 232 SE 7TH AVE 97123 #005-06-1985 L1994 **GE** *020 †20
LAWSON, Frances K. 335 SE 8TH AVE 97123 #016-42-1992 L2000 **EM** *020 †16
LEE, David Sukmin. 545 SE OAK ST STE C 97123 #016-06-1996 L2005 **IC** *020 †20
LEWIN, Kenneth Ward. 335 SE 8TH AVE, TUALITY COMMUNITY HOSPITAL 97123 #040-02-1954 L1978 **R** *071 †80
LEWIS, Albert Mc Rae. ■ 97124 #016-43-1955 L1960 **GP GS** *071 †85
LEWIS, Marc Erin. 333 SE 7TH AVE, STE 5050 97123 #049-01-1997 L2000 **FM** *020 †18
LOEHDEN, Otto Louis. ■ 97124 #040-02-1958 L1961 **GS VS** *071 †85
MAHARG, Patrick Ebert. 19400 NW EVERGREEN PKWY 97124 #005-06-1968 L1990 **FM** *020 †18
MANDI, Anandhi. 445 E MAIN ST, STE 100 97123 #495-37-1993 L2000 **PD** *020 †55
MARTENS, Robert Glen. ■ 97124 #062-01-1964 L1977 **GP** *020 †18
MARTIN, Christine Louise. 445 E MAIN ST, STE 100 97123 #050-02-2003 L2007 **PD** *020 †55
MC CARTHY, Joseph Patrick. 561 SE OAK ST 97123 #306-01-1988 L1995 **FM** *020 †18
MC PHEE, Cynthia Ann. 19400 NW EVERGREEN PKWY, KAISER SUNSET CLINIC 97124 #040-02-1998 L2001 **PD** *020 †55
MEJIA, Manuel S. ■ 97124 #748-02-1956 L1977 **P** *020 †75
MILLESON, Thomas Hugh. 335 SE 8TH AVE, MEDICAL IMAGING GROUP OF 97123 #040-02-1977 L1979 **DR** *020 †80
MINSON, Susan L. 335 SE 8TH AVE 97123 #040-02-1981 L1982 **AN** *020 †05
MITCHELL, Michael Darren. 545 SE OAK ST, STE C 97123 #021-01-1999 L2007 **CD** *020 †20
MOON, Stephen Patrick. 335 SE 8TH AVE 97123 #040-02-1991 L1992 **EM GP** *020
MORRIS, Christopher Roder. 21255 NW JACOBSON RD, STE 500 97124 #654-01-2003 L2007 **MPD** *020
MURLEY, Joseph Michael. 215 SW ADAMS AVE, M/S: 33 97123 #024-07-1971 L1994 **EM GP** *030 †18
MURPHY, Brenda. 364 SE 8TH AVE, STE 301 97123 #018-03-2000 L2005 **IM** *020
MURPHY, Jeremiah C. 333 SE 7TH AVE, STE 4500 97123 #018-03-2000 L2005 **U** *020 †95
NARDONE, David A. ■ 97124 #010-02-1968 L1975 **IM** *020 †20
NASH, Robert Rowland. 6020 NE ALDER ST 97124 #016-02-2003 L2003 **PD** *020 †55
NASON, Dana Richard. 445 E MAIN ST, STE 100 97123 #040-02-1981 L1982 **PD** *020 †55
NELSON, Carol Jean. 19400 NW EVERGREEN PKWY, SUNSET MEDICAL OFFICE 97124 #056-05-1980 L1984 **CHP P** *020 †75
NELSON, James Dean. ■ 97124 #040-03-1962 L1969 **ORS** *020 †40
NGUYEN, Bich-Hang Khac. ■ 97123 #028-46-1995 L2008 **AN** *020 †05
OH, Charles Changyop. 730 SE OAK ST, STE I 97123 #056-06-1994 L1997 **CD** *020 †20
OH, Kelly Kyung. 5555 NE ELAM YOUNG PKWY, DEPT OF COMM/FAMILY MEDICI 97124 #038-06-1993 L2006 **FM** *020 †18
OLDS, Julie Ann. 364 SE 8TH AVE, STE 205 97123 #041-14-2003 L2007 **OBG** *020
OLNEY, John Edward. ■ 97123 #030-05-1969 L1976 **EM GP** *020
O'NEILL, Michael James. 356 SE 9TH AVE 97123 #030-06-1984 L1987 **FM** *020 †18
ORFANAKIS, Nick George. 335 SE 8TH AVE 97123 #049-01-1970 L1976 **PTH** *030 †50
ORR, Samuel Robt. ■ 97124 #040-02-1947 L1951 **GP** *071
OSTROWSKI, Krzysztof J. 335 SE 8TH AVE, TUALITY COMMUNITY HOSP 97123 #759-12-1990 L1997 **AN** *020 †08
PATEL, Kishoree J. 19400 NW EVERGREEN PKWY 97124 #495-48-1973 L1990 **IM PUD** *020 †20
PATTEE, Burton Chas. 333 SE 7TH AVE, STE 5050 97123 #023-01-1968 L1971 **FM** *020 †18
PETER, Anna Preeti. 19400 NW EVERGREEN PKWY 97124 #495-31-1998 L2002 **IM** *020

PETERSON, Donald Anders. 349 SE 7TH AVE 97123 #040-02-1974 L1975 **ORS** *020 †40
PFEFER, Chad Thomas. 545 SE OAK ST STE A 97123 #056-06-1997 L1998 **IM** *020 †20
PICO, Mark Henry. 21255 NW JACOBSON RD STE 5 97124 #026-04-2003 L2007 **MPD** *020
PICOLOGLOU, Elizabeth A. 335 SE 8TH AVE 97123 #017-20-2002 L2002 **IM** *020 †20
PINKERT, Ted Charles. 335 SE 8TH AVE 97123 #026-04-1974 L1975 **PTH NM** *020 †50
PITMAN, William G. ■ 97124 #041-13-1961 L1966 **AN** *020 †05
PLATT, William D. 405 SE 8TH AVE 97123 #056-06-1973 L1978 **N** *020 †75
POWELL, Bruce F. ■ 97123 #041-07-1988 L1997 **N** *020 †75
PRAKASH, Kesavan. 364 SE 8TH AVE, STE 301 97123 #495-42-2000 L2005 **IM** *020 †20
PRICE, Linda Christensen. 364 SE 8TH AVE, STE 200 97123 #005-12-1992 L1996 **OBG** *020 †30
PROMISLOFF, Steven David. 545 SE OAK ST 97123 #041-09-1969 L1991 **CD** *020 †20
RAJAGOPAL, Shobana. 19400 NW EVERGREEN PKWY 97124 #495-22-1997 L2004 **FM** *020
RASK, Bart. 349 SE 7TH AVE 97123 #040-02-1989 L1993 **OSM** *020 †40
RASK, Patrick Henry. 335 SE 8TH AVE 97123 #031-01-1994 L1998 **EM** *020 †16
RATCLIFFE, James David. 335 SE 8TH AVE, MEDICAL IMAGING GROUP OF 97123 #034-01-1972 L1973 **DR** *020 †80
REICHLE, John Roger. 1200 NE 48TH AVE, STE 700 97124 #040-02-1992 L1993 **GPM** *012
REYES, Vincent Pedro. 333 SE 7TH AVE, STE 5200 97123 #005-06-1982 L1990 **CD IC** *020 †20
RHOADS, Kenneth Llewellyn. 333 SE 7TH AVE, STE 5200 97123 #007-02-1974 L1979 **CD IM** *050 †20
RISSER, Amanda Leigh. 226 SE 8TH AVE 97123 #005-11-2002 L2002 **FM** *100 †18
ROBINSON, David Lee. 620 SE OAK ST STE A 97123 #040-02-1966 L1974 **OBG** *071
ROSALES, Edmundo. 324 SE 9TH AVE STE F 97123 #005-14-1978 L1990 **IM** *020 †20
ROSALES, Isabel Casillas. 21210 NW MAUZEY RD, W. PSYCHOLOGICAL/COUNSELIN 97124 #005-14-1982 L1990 **P CHP** *020 †75
ROSENBLATT, Chas Ronald. 232 SE 7TH AVE 97123 #028-34-1968 L1976 **GE** *020 †20
ROTBERG, Nicola Sarah. 364 SE 8TH AVE, STE 205 97123 #050-02-1995 L2001 **OBG** *020 †30
RUF, James Eli. 21255 NW JACOBSON RD, STE 500 97124 #030-06-1997 L2005 **ORS** *020 †40
RUSSELL, Wayne Henry J. 3295 NE 4TH AVE, 2 97124 #062-01-1963 L1996 *020
SADOWSKI, Todd Joseph. 333 SE 7TH AVE STE 4500, WESTSIDE UROLOGY ASSOC LLP 97123 #038-40-1998 L2003 **U** *020 †95
SALOUM, Richard Dennis. ■ 97124 #040-02-1959 L1961 **FM IM** *075
SAUNDERS, Shad Stephen. ■ 97124 #036-05-2005 L2005 **OPH** *012
SCHAER, John Arlen. 232 SE 7TH AVE 97123 #040-02-1986 L1989 **GE** *020 †20
SCHMIDT, Robert Edwards. 333 SE 7TH AVE, STE 4500 97123 #040-02-1993 L1998 **U** *020 †95
SCOTT, Jennifer Alison. 3000 NW STUCKI PL, STE 220 97124 #003-01-2000 L2000 **P** *020 †75
SENASHOVA, Olga Sergeevna. ■ 97123 #040-02-2006 L2006 **IM** *012
SHIPLEY, Calvert John. 19400 NW EVERGREEN PKWY, KAISER SUNSET MEDICAL CLIN 97124 #060-01-1977 L1979 **FM OS** *020 †20
SMITH, Roger Garrett. 335 SE 8TH AVE 97123 #024-07-1964 L1967 **IM** *020
SNIDER, Robert Wm. ■ 97123 #035-15-1985 L2004 **FM A** *071 †18
SONG, Chin Kyong. 364 SE 8TH AVE, STE 301 97123 #048-18-1999 L2003 **IM** *020 †20
STEWARD, Sean. ■ 97123 #005-15-1991 L1995 **FM** *020 †18
STOIANTSCHEWSKY, R R. ■ 97124 #407-30-1952 L1962 **IM** *020
STONE, Mark Randolph. 405 SE 8TH AVE 97123 #005-15-1996 L2003 **HO** *020 †20
STONER, Ryan Edward. 2038 NW ALOCLEK DR, STE 205 97124 #007-02-2002 L2002 **FM** *100
STRAUHAL, Monika. 2778 NW PALAZZA WAY 97124 #409-10-1988 L2007 **PD** *020 †55
SUITS, Gregory Wm. 900 SE OAK ST, STE 201 97123 #036-01-1990 L1991 **OTO** *020 †45
SWEETMAN, Per. 19400 NW EVERGREEN PKWY 97124 #040-02-1975 L1977 **P** *020 †75
SY, Jeffrey Dela Cruz. 19400 NW EVERGREEN PKWY 97124 #748-02-1990 L2005 **IM IMG** *020 †20
SZEKELY, Otto Andreas. 335 SE 8TH AVE 97123 #473-01-1951 L1985 **AN** *071
TAHER, Mohammed Abu. 364 SE 8TH AVE STE 3 97123 #160-02-1987 L2000 **IM** *020 †20
TEED, Ronald Lewis, Jr. 425 SE BASELINE ST 97123 #040-02-1990 L1993 **ORS** *020 †40
TODD, Kathryn Ann. 335 SE 8TH AVE 97123 #040-02-1989 L1990 **PD** *020 †55
TOREN, Michael Stuart. 545 SE OAK ST STE C 97123 #008-01-1969 L1973 **CD** *020 †20
TSAI, Clifford Kwokleung. 335 SE 8TH AVE, TUALITY COMMUNITY HOSPITAL 97123 #054-04-1989 L1990 **AN EM** *020 †05
URSTADT, Donna S. 335 SE 8TH AVE 97123 #012-01-1984 L1996 **PTH** *020 †50
VINIKOOR, Nancy Heather. 1770 SW NEUGEBAUER RD 97123 #041-09-1986 L1987 **IM** *020 †20
WALTERS, Kevin Craig. 1200 NE 48TH AVE, STE 700 97124 #023-12-1993 L2005 **OM** *020 †70
WATSON, Randy D. 545 SE OAK ST STE D 97123 #040-02-1982 L1983 **GE IM** *020 †20
WEINGARTEN, David Scott. 364 SE 8TH AVE STE 30 97123 #033-05-1989 L1995 **IM** *020 †20
WEYL, Allan David. ■ 97123 #051-04-1972 L1973 **P** *075
WILLIAMS, Fred Crump. 333 SE 7TH AVE, STE 4250 97123 #048-04-1983 L2004 **NS** *020 †25
WILTRAKIS, Mark Geo. ■ 97123 #016-11-1973 L1977 **CD IM** *071 †20
WITTLAKE, William A. ■ 97124 #005-12-1976 L1980 **EM** *020 †16
YOUNG, David Yew Wing. 333 SE 7TH AVE 97123 #021-01-1966 L1974 **U** *020 †95
YUAN, Edmund. 335 SE 8TH AVE, DEPT OF ANESTHESIOLOGY 97123 #038-06-1989 L1990 **AN** *020 †05 ‡

HINES – HARNEY

HAYNIE, Holland Hoyt. ■ 97738 #041-12-2004 L2006 **PD** *100

HOOD RIVER – HOOD RIVER

ACOSTA, Orlando Ravenet. 849 PACIFIC AVE 97031 #051-04-1992 L1995 **FM** *020 †18
BAILEY, George Marion. 810 13TH ST, ALL WOMENS HEALTH 97031 #040-02-1979 L1981 **OBG** *020 †30
BECKER, Stephen Gerard. 1108 JUNE ST 97031 #028-03-1978 L1979 **FM** *020 †18
BRAUER, James Martin. 1021 JUNE ST 97031 #040-02-1984 L1987 **FM** *020 †18
CARTER, Grover C. 1790 MAY ST 97031 #005-11-1945 L1951 **GS ON** *071 †85
CARTER, Ralph Albert. 1304 MONTELLO AVE, HOOD RIVER MED GRP PC 97031 #040-02-1974 L1975 **GP** *020
CHADWICK, Philip David. 2149 CASCADE AVE, STE 106A-300 97031 #005-06-1987 L1995 **EM** *020 †16
CHAMBERS, Charles E. 810 13TH ST, ALL WOMENS HEALTH 97031 #048-14-1989 L2001 **OBG** *020 †30
CHAMBERS, Elizabeth G. 814 13TH ST, PROVIDENCE GORGE COUNSELIN 97031 #048-14-1989 L2000 **P** *020
COGSWELL, James Howard. 811 13TH ST 97031 #030-05-1967 L1973 **R** *020 †80

CZARNECKI, Maria Lisa. 1304 MONTELLO AVE 97031 #041-13-1996 L2002 **FM** *020 †18
DE SITTER, Linda Law. 2690 MAY ST 97031 #005-06-1984 L1987 **FM** *020 †18
DIETZ, Thomas Edward. 811 13TH ST, ER 97031 #048-04-1986 L1987 **EM** *020 †18
DILLON, Kristen Gail. 1108 JUNE ST, COLUMBIA GORG FAM MED 97031 #005-02-1996 L2000 **FM** *020 †18
DURKAN, John Alexander. 902 12TH ST 97031 #024-05-1979 L1986 **ORS** *020 †40
EPSTEIN, Beth. ■ 97031 #023-07-1988 L1997 **FM** *020 †18
FALZ, Stefanie. 1304 MONTELLO AVE 97031 #060-01-2002 L2003 **FM** *020 †18
FAUTH, Miriam Duncan. 849 PACIFIC AVE, LA CLINICA DE CARINO 97031 #034-01-2002 L2002 **FM** *020 †18
FERBER, Daniel Edwin. 811 13TH ST 97031 #040-02-1993 L1994 **CHP P** *020 †75
FINSTAD, Terrance Allen. ■ 97031 #051-04-1992 L1998 **DR** *020 †80
FOSTER, Martin Chad. 811 13TH ST 97031 #047-07-2000 L2005 **DR** *020 †80
GARCIA, John Michael. 1151 MAY ST 97031 #007-02-1973 L1999 **GS** *020 †85
GAY, Anthony Scott. 1108 JUNE ST 97031 #040-02-1987 L1991 **FM** *020 †18
GREENWALD, Howard Lee. 810 13TH ST 97031 #040-02-1985 L1991 **OBG** *020 †30
HAMADA, Paul Masaru. 1784 MAY ST 97031 #035-01-1965 L1969 **IM GP** *020 ‡
HARRIS, Michael Robt. 1304 MONTELLO AVE 97031 #033-05-1988 L1991 **FM** *020 †18
HAUTY, Michael Geo. 1151 MAY ST 97031 #048-12-1983 L1984 **GS TRS** *020 †85
HAYES, Robert Preston B. 1410 MAY ST, COLUMBIA RIVER EYE CENTER 97031 #040-02-1968 L2000 **OPH** *071 †35
HAYNIE, Charles Calvin. 814 13TH ST 97031 #028-03-1969 L1977 **GS** *071 †85
HEITMAN, Laura Anne. 1021 JUNE ST 97031 #007-02-1989 L1997 **FM** *020 †18
HENDERSON, J Allan. ■ 97031 #040-02-1953 L1954 **FM** *071 †18
HENSON, Robin Blunt. 917 11TH ST 97031 #041-12-1984 L2002 **OBG** *030 †30
HERING, H Douglas. 902 12TH ST 97031 #040-02-1962 L1992 **ORS** *020 †40
HUNT, Travis Lee. 1304 MONTELLO AVE 97031 #025-07-1996 L1999 **FM** *020 †18
JOURNEAU, Janice Wallace. 810 13TH ST 97031 #023-07-1991 L1992 **GS** *020 †85
KHAN, Zarin Parvez. ■ 97031 #917-02-1964 L2001 *100
LARIOS, Ramon. ■ 97031 #056-06-2004 L2005 **AN** *012
MACCABEE, David Lev. 1151 MAY ST 97031 #005-19-1996 L1999 **GS** *020 †85
MACCABEE, Mendy Shay. 1151 MAY ST, PROVIDENCE HOOD RIVER MEMO 97031 #054-04-1998 L1999 **OTO** *020 †45
MACK, Annie Seapan. ■ 97031 #048-13-2001 L2006 **MPD** *100 †20,55
MARSH, Alexander Elliott. ■ 97031 #017-20-2002 L2006 **EM** *020
MOORE, Kathleen Baker. 2149 CASCADE AVE, PMB 239 97031 #020-12-1979 L2003 **EM** *020 †16
OLSON, June Ann. ■ 97031 #007-02-1985 L1990 **PTH** *020 †50
PENDLETON, Michael L. 1108 JUNE ST 97031 #041-01-1980 L1986 **FM** *020 †18
PENNINGTON, James Wm. 1021 JUNE ST 97031 #048-02-1980 L1992 **FM** *020 †18
PETERSEN, Ryan Christian. 1151 MAY ST 97031 #040-02-2000 L2001 **IM** *020 †20
POBANZ, Sam. 13TH & MAY STS 97031 #017-20-1944 L1944 **GP IM** *071
REGALBUTO, Gary J. 1410 MAY ST 97031 #005-19-1976 L1980 **IM** *020 †20 ‡
RIGERT, Trey Allen. 1010 10TH ST, COLUMBIA PAIN MANAGEMENT 97031 #040-02-1989 L2001 **PM PME** *020 †60
ROBINSON, Laurel Anne. 810 13TH ST 97031 #039-01-1985 L2001 **GYN** *020 †30
ROBINSON, William Jos. ■ 97031 #039-01-1985 L2001 **PD** *055
ROSE, Donald Alfred. ■ 97031 #007-02-1963 L1964 **GP** *020
SAGER, Daniel Swink. 811 13TH ST, 1151 MAY STREET 97031 #038-06-1986 L1990 **IM** *020 †20
SALTZMAN, Michael Jacob. 1151 MAY ST, UROLOGY CLINIC 97031 #051-07-1991 L1998 **U** *020 †95
SCHAEFER, Kerry Abbot. ■ 97031 #056-05-2007 L2007 **FP** *012
SIREN, Greg P. ■ 97031 #539-06-1987 L1996 **FM** *020 †18
SJOBLOM, Janet Rae. 1304 MONTELLO AVE 97031 #054-04-1995 L1999 **FM** *020 †18
SLOAN, Luke Bradley. 917 11TH ST 97031 #028-03-1991 L2000 **D** *020
SMITH, Shelley Rae. 1790 MAY ST 97031 #026-04-1994 L1997 **OBG** *020
SOVA, Ivan Mark. 13TH & MAY ST, PROVDNCE HOOD RVR MEM HOSP 97031 #060-01-1988 L1995 **EM** *020 †20
THOMPSON, Warren Butler. 1304 MONTELLO AVE 97031 #040-02-1945 L1948 **FM** *071 †20
TURBES, Sandra Jeanne. 849 PACIFIC AVE 97031 #026-04-2001 L2005 **FM** *020 †18
VIRK, Reetinder S. 811 13TH ST 97031 #048-12-1986 L1990 **EM FM** *040 †18
VOGT, Stephen Paul. 1151 MAY ST 97031 #050-02-1996 L1997 **IM** *020 †20
WADE, James Belknap. 3413 BROOKSIDE DR, PHYSICIAN AND SURGEON 97031 #054-04-1957 L1962 **FM** *071
WELLS, Stanley Everett. PO BOX 537 97031 #018-03-1931 **GP GS** *071
WILHELM, Thomas James. ■ 97031 #054-04-1987 L1988 **IM** *020
WYMORE, Robert Adolphus. 1304 MONTELLO AVE 97031 #026-04-1959 L1962 **GP** *071

INDEPENDENCE – POLK

YOUNG, Paul Darrah. 9515 BUENA VISTA RD 97351 #040-02-1965 L1968 **GP** *020

ISLAND CITY – UNION

TRUDEL, Terry Allen. ■ 97850 #067-01-1969 L1977 **P** *020

JACKSONVILLE – JACKSON

BUCHALTER, Ira Harold. ■ 97530 #035-46-1970 L1971 **OTO** *020 †45
COBB, Jill. ■ 97530 #019-02-1981 L1999 **FOP** *020 †50
DIAZ, Jessica Helen. 725 N 5TH ST STE 101 97530 #038-06-1999 L2005 **FM** *020 †18
EASTERDAY, Jerry L. ■ 97530 #028-03-1977 L1979 **P** *062
HARRELL, Carl Edward. ■ 97530 #048-13-1975 L1983 **DR** *020 †80
HAZELTINE, John S. ■ 97530 #035-06-1964 L1967 **OTO** *071 †45
MOOSMAN, Carver L. ■ 97530 #035-09-1951 L1953 **GP GS** *071 †18
MORIKONE, Hiromu. ■ 97530 #005-12-1953 L1954 **OS GP** *071
PUSCAS, James Clarence. ■ 97530 #040-02-1961 L1962 **GP** *020
RENNIE, Ian Drummond. ■ 97530 #352-03-1961 L1968 **OS NEP** *062
SHOWERMAN, Earl Roy. 7498 UPPER APPLEGATE RD 97530 #025-01-1970 L1974 **EM PHP** *020 †16
STERNENBERG, Darice K. ■ 97530 #028-02-1993 L1999 **IM** *020 †20
THOMAS, George Edward. ■ 97530 #051-04-1970 L2004 **PTH** *075 †50

■ = Address Information Privacy Protected

TINSLEY, Thomas James. ■ 97530 #016-06-1947 L1958 **PTH** *071 †50
VUCICEVIC, Mijo. PO BOX 268, 884 HILL ST 97530 #957-01-1955 L1970 **FM OM** *071 †18
WARREN, Ward Beecher. ■ 97530 #017-20-1939 L1946 **IM CD** *071 †20
WATSON, Andrew Mark. 7208 HIGHWAY 238 97530 #040-02-1994 L1997 **FM** *020 †18

JEFFERSON – MARION

HORBEEK, Johannes H. PO BOX 170 97352 #660-01-1956 L1977 **OPH** *071 †35
VARNER, Foy Earl, Jr. PO BOX 190, PMB 22008 97352 #048-13-1977 L1977 **FM** *020

JOHN DAY – GRANT

GROUT, Andrea Lee. 180 FORD RD 97845 #040-02-2000 L2005 **FM** *020 †18 ‡
HOLLAND, Robert E, Jr. 135 FORD RD 97845 #056-06-1985 L1988 **FM** *020 †18
JACKSON, John Guider. 180 FORD RD 97845 #021-01-1987 L1988 **FM** *020 †18
JANSSEN, Andrew Gerard. 180 FORD RD 97845 #040-02-2002 L2005 **FM** *020 †18
MERRILL, Marion Theodore. ■ 97845 #035-01-1948 L1958 **GP** *071 †18
THOMAS, Keith Jay. 170 FORD RD, BLUE MOUNTAIN HOSPITAL 97845 #016-45-1987 L2005 **GS** *020 †85

JOSEPH – WALLOWA

BAYNES, Lewis Banfield. ■ 97846 #040-02-1978 L1982 **GP** *020 †18
BOYD, Ralph Devee. 100 N EAST ST 97846 #041-14-1973 L1989 **FM OBS** *020 †18
CAINE, Kirsten Tallent. PO BOX 1038, 100 N EAST ST 97846 #035-03-2002 L2002 **FM** *020 †18
SHEAHAN, Emily Ann. 100 N EAST ST, WALLOWA MOUNTAIN MED 97846 #007-02-2002 L2002 **FM** *020 †18
STONEBROOK, Philip Ray. ■ 97846 #040-02-1970 L1973 **GP FM** *071
THOMPSON, John Burdell. PO BOX 563 97846 #012-05-1963 L1963 **NS N** *071 †25

JUNCTION CITY – LANE

BAILEY, Douglas Dwight. 355 W 3RD AVE 97448 #005-06-1982 L1985 **FM** *020 †18
FLETCHALL, Gale Frederick. 430 W 7TH AVE 97448 #025-01-1955 L1956 **FM** *020
FLETCHALL, Marlon Gale. 430 W 7TH AVE, GROUP-JUNCTION CITY 97448 #040-02-1968 L1974 **FM** *020 †85
GAMBEE, John Edwin. 93244 HIGHWAY 99 S 97448 #040-02-1966 L1975 **GPM** *020 †95
MONTOYA, Justin Matthew. 355 W 3RD AVE 97448 #040-02-1999 L2002 **FM** *020 †18
WILLEY, Arthur John. 355 W 3RD AVE 97448 #054-04-1987 L1990 **FM** *020 †18

KEIZER – MARION

APPLEGATE, Roger Howard. ■ 97303 #040-02-1980 L2006 **FM** *020 †18
BHASIN, Sunil. 4925 RIVER RD N STE 231 97303 #005-18-1987 L2000 **PD ORS** *020
CARP, Stephen Andrew. 5900 INLAND SHORES WAY N 97303 #028-79-1999, ▲ L2002 *020
CHANDLER, Robin. 5900 INLAND SHORES WAY N 97303 #040-02-1994 L1996 **IM** *020 †20
FOULKE, Fred Geo. 5900 INLAND SHORES WAY N, SALEM CLINIC AT INLAND SHO 97303 #038-06-1983 L1997 **FM** *020 †18
GROSSO, Gene. ■ 97303 #028-34-1954 L1958 **OBG** *071 †30
HALE, Carolyn Irene. 5900 INLAND SHORES WAY N, STE 202 97303 #040-02-1975 L1977 **D** *020 †15
JAMIESON, Jay Alexander. 5100 RIVER RD N 97303 #016-06-1980 L1983 **FM** *020 †18
KURIAN, Julie P. 5100 RIVER RD N 97303 #048-14-1991 L1994 **FM** *020 †18
LOGANBILL, Heidi Anne. 174 SHORE POINTE PL N #202 97303 #032-01-1991 L1996 **N** *020 †75
MANSFIELD, Peggy Sue. ■ 97303 #040-02-1980 L1981 **NEP IM** *074 †20
NEAHRING, Richard K. 5750 INLAND SHORES WAY N 97303 #016-06-1989 L1998 **OPH** *020 †35 ‡
ROWELL, David Paul. 5750 INLAND SHORES WAY N 97303 #028-02-1979 L1980 **OPH** *020 †35
STICE, Scott Erik. 5750 INLAND SHORES WAY N 97303 #045-01-1994 L2000 **OPH** *020 †35
WANG, Jeffrey Tsehsin. 5900 INLAND SHORES WAY N 97303 #056-06-1992 L1993 **IM** *020 †20

KING CITY – WASHINGTON

TRAN, Dat Duc. 11820 SW KING JAMES PL #30 97224 #305-01-2001 L2005 **FM** *020 †18

KLAMATH FALLS – KLAMATH

ANTONIUS, John Ivan Blair. 2865 DAGGETT AVE 97601 #062-01-1955 L1971 **PTH** *050 †50 ‡
BAKKE, Kathleen Marie. 1905 MAIN ST, KLAMATH MEDICAL CLINIC 97601 #040-02-1995 L1998 **FM** *020 †18
BALME, Benjamin F. 2200 BRYANT WILLIAMS DR 97601 #008-01-1966 L1967 **ORS** *020 †40
BAUMAN, Beverly Helene. 2865 DAGGETT AVE 97601 #005-02-1987 L1997 **EM PEM** *020 †55,16
BAY, Nathan Brian. ■ 97603 #028-34-2007 L2007 **FP** *012
BEAMAN, Robert Paul. 1903 AUSTIN ST STE B 97603 #038-43-1989 L1992 **FM** *020 †18
BEERY, Heidi Margaret. ■ 97601 #040-02-2007 L2007 **FP** *012
BEGGS, James Neil. 2300 CLAIRMONT DR 97601 #026-04-1974 L1986 **FM MDM** *030 †18
BELL, John D. 2865 DAGGETT AVE 97601 #049-01-1957 L1966 **OBG** *071 †30
BENSON, Daniel Orville. 2615 ALMOND ST 97601 #005-12-1973 L1975 **OPH** *020 †35
BERVEN, Blake Dennis. 2616 CLOVER ST 97601 #016-02-1968 L1972 **IM** *020 †20
BEUS, Kirt Scott. 2581 UHRMANN RD 97601 #028-34-2000 L2005 **OTO** *020 †45
BIDLEMAN, Steven Kent. 2680 UHRMANN RD STE A 97601 #040-02-1970 L1973 **FM** *020 †18
BOHNEN, Robert Frank. 2610 UHRMANN RD 97601 #035-01-1965 L1991 **ON HEM** *071 †20
BOICE, John Allison. 3698 S 6TH ST 97603 #018-03-1969 L1991 **OM RHU** *030 †20
BRADBURY, Mark F. 2200 BRYANT WILLIAMS DR 97601 #028-34-1986 L1997 **GS VIR** *020 †85
BREAZEALE, Bretton Howard. 2865 DAGGETT AVE, MERLE WEST MEDICAL CENTER 97601 #005-12-2000 L2006 **VIR** *100 †80
BREITENSTEIN, Ralph A. 2865 DAGGETT AVE 97601 #040-02-1969 L1989 **IM GE** *020 †20

BRITSCH, Jerri Linn. 1905 MAIN ST, KLAMATH MEDICAL CLINIC 97601 #005-19-1987 L1990 **FM** *020 †18
BRUNSWICK, Jay Eric. 3737 SHASTA WAY, STE A 97603 #040-02-1992 L1995 **EM** *020 †16
BRUNSWICK, John Philip. ■ 97603 #067-01-1960 L1968 **PD** *071 †55
BURKE, Mary Catherine. 2580 DAGGETT AVE 97601 #024-07-1996 L2000 **OBG** *020 †30
BURY, Charles Danl. 2300 CLAIRMONT DR 97601 #041-13-1966 L1970 **FM GS** *020 †18
CALVERT, James Francis, Jr. 2801 DAGGETT AVE, CASCADE EAST FAM PRACTICE 97601 #010-01-1976 L1992 **FM** *040 †18
CALVERT, James Lee. 2801 DAGGETT AVE 97601 #005-11-1972 L1989 **IM OS** *020
CASEY, Michael Joe. 2200 BRYANT WILLIAMS DR, STE 1 97601 #048-02-1973 L1979 **ORS HS** *020 †40
CHASE, Brandon David. ■ 97601 #035-15-2007 L2007 **FP** *012
CHERRY, Nicola Jean. 2301 MOUNTAIN VIEW BLVD, STE A 97601 #040-02-1997 L1999 **PD CCP** *020 †55
CHIURA, Allen Nhamo. 2200 BRYANT WILLIAMS DR, STE 7 97601 #041-07-1992 L2005 **U** *020 †95
CHRISTENSEN, Chas Leonard. 2684 CAMPUS DR 97601 #016-43-1980 L1981 **IM** *020
CHUDOBA, Jeffrey Wm. 2575 CAMPUS DR, # 303 97601 #011-02-1990 L1999 **DR** *020 †80
COFAS, Charles Keith. 2682 CAMPUS DR 97601 #048-02-2002 L2005 **IM** *020
COSTA-CORPACIU, Ruxandra. 2200 BRYANT WILLIAMS DR, STE 7 97601 #781-01-1991 L2004 **N** *020 †75
CRITES, Savannah Noel. ■ 97601 #036-01-2006 L2006 **FP** *012
DASSOFF, David Scott. 1905 MAIN ST 97601 #005-19-1987 L1990 **FM** *020 †18
DOW, Sean B. 2850 DAGGETT AVE 97601 #019-02-1986 L1993 **PUD CCM** *020 †20
ECCLES, Ralph P. 2865 DAGGETT AVE 97601 #005-76-1982, ▲ L2003 **FM DIA** *040 †18 ‡
EDWARDS, Robert N, Jr. 4509 S 6TH ST, STE 311 97603 #018-03-1978 L1986 **PTH NM** *062 †50
EPPEL, Konrad Joseph. ■ 97601 #021-05-2001 L2006 **EM** *020
ERLANDSON, Gordon Owen. ■ 97603 #016-06-1945 L1951 **PD** *071
FARIS, John Walton. ■ 97603 #035-45-1974 L1990 **P** *075
FAY, Mark Terence. 2640 BIEHN ST, STE 300 97601 #028-02-1983 L1989 **OPH** *020 †35
FELLOWS, Carol. ■ 97601 #034-01-1972 L1989 **RO IM** *071 †80
FORD, Charles Frederick. ■ 97601 #017-20-1947 L1948 **AM OBG** *071 †30
FRIDINGER, William Chas. 1692 COVE POINT RD, KINGSLEY FIELD 97601 #023-01-1972 L1973 **EM** *071
GAILIS, Glenn Geo. 1905 MAIN ST 97601 #018-03-1970 L1973 **FM** *020 †18
GANONG, Carrie Atwell. 2310 MOUNTAIN VIEW BLVD 97601 #001-06-1990 L2007 **PDE** *020 †55
GLIDDEN, Alden Bruce. 2680 UHRMANN RD STE B 97601 #025-07-1969 L1970 **FM** *020 †18
GONSOWSKI, Charles T. ■ 97601 #005-02-1994 L1998 **AN** *020 †05
GOODMAN, Mark Stephen. 2900 DAGGETT AVE 97601 #040-02-1992 L1997 **DR** *020 †80
GRAHAM, Robert Wm. 1000 PINE ST 97601 #005-12-1957 L1961 **OPH** *020 †35
GRAHAM, Teresa Roleen. 1000 PINE ST 97601 #005-12-1992 L1995 **OPH** *020 †35
HAAS, Marcy Ann. ■ 97601 #041-02-2002 L2007 **FM** *020 †18
HALE, Robin Rand. 1000 PINE ST 97601 #054-04-1977 L1980 **FM** *020 †18
HARTMANN, Gerald Robt. 2865 DAGGETT AVE 97601 #016-43-1971 L1977 **N EM** *020 †75
HEIDINGER, Wendell C. 2300 CLAIRMONT DR 97601 #005-12-1990 L1994 **FM** *020 †18
HERR, Vincent Dean. ■ 97601 #040-02-1990 L1991 **AN** *020 †05
HILSINGER, K Leigh. 2580 DAGGETT AVE 97601 #038-43-1987 L1996 **OBG** *020 †30
HOBBS, John M, Jr. 2865 DAGGETT AVE 97601 #021-01-1972 L1986 **OBG** *020 †30
HOLLANDER-RODRIGUEZ, J C. 2801 DAGGETT AVE 97601 #040-02-2000 L2000 **FM** *020 †18
HUNT, Calvin Lawson. 97603 #040-02-1943 L1947 **A IM** *071
JACKMAN, Robert Paul. 2801 DAGGETT AVE, CASCADES EAST FAMILY PRACT 97601 #010-01-1994 L2000 **FM** *020 †18
JAMISON, Robert Ellis. 2865 DAGGETT AVE, C/O MERLE WEST MEDICAL CEN 97601 #005-14-1976 L1983 **PTH NM** *020 †50
JENSEN, Eric Richard. 2865 DAGGETT AVE 97601 #049-01-1999 L2002 **EM** *020 †16
JODKO, Stefan Joxef. 2865 DAGGETT AVE, MERLE WEST MEDICAL CENTER 97601 #759-06-1982 L1993 **AN** *020 †05
JOHNSON, Cory Todd. 3000 BRYANT WILLIAMS DR, STE 100 97601 #028-34-1998 L2002 **OBG** *020
KAHN, Heather Alaine. 2801 DAGGETT AVE 97601 #016-42-1999 L2001 **FM** *020
KHAN, Gauhar Raza. 2200 BRYANT WILLIAMS DR, KLAMATH HEART CLINIC 97601 #704-25-1996 L2005 **IC CD** *020 †20
KHAN, Mahi Mobeen. 2074 S 6TH ST 97601 #917-14-1996 L2007 **IM** *100
KIRSCHENMANN, Todd Jerome. 2865 DAGGETT AVE 97601 #046-01-2001 L2005 **AN** *020 †05
KLEEMAN, John Jos. 1905 MAIN ST 97601 #010-02-1979 L1984 **FM** *020 †18
KLUMP, Thomas Edward. 2865 DAGGETT AVE 97601 #041-02-1963 L1971 **NS** *071 †25
KNUDSEN, Karl Robert. 2200 BRYANT WILLIAMS DR, STE 1 97601 #028-34-1998 L2007 **ORS** *020 †40
KOCHEVAR, Mark Stanley. 1905 MAIN ST 97601 #007-01-1955 L1956 **FM AM** *020 †18
KRAMER, Bradley Alan. 2640 UHRMANN RD, CANCER TREATMENT CENTER 97601 #056-06-1992 L2006 **RO** *020 †80
KUBAC, George, Jr. 2200 BRYANT WILLIAMS DR, STE 3 97601 #060-01-1984 L1997 **IM** *020 †20
LA BUWI, Charles Michael. 2310 MOUNTAIN VIEW BLVD, KLAMATH PEDIATRIC CLNC 97601 #056-05-1975 L1978 **PD** *020 †55
LAMANUZZI, Sarah Ann. 2074 S 6TH ST, KLAMATH OPEN DOOR FAMILY P 97601 #005-18-2003 L2006 **FM** *020 †18
LANG, Kathie Jean. 3737 SHASTA WAY, STE A 97603 #051-04-1975 L2000 **FM** *020 †18
LEE, Kil Nam. ■ 97601 #583-03-1953 L1972 **IM** *020
LEPARD, Kevin Olin. ■ 97601 #026-08-1997 L2000 **EM** *020 †16
LE VERNOIS, Earle Mose. 2865 DAGGETT AVE 97601 #025-01-1960 L1965 **GS TS** *071 †85
LOUDERBOUGH, Henry C. 2865 DAGGETT AVE, SKY LAKES MEDICAL CENTER 97601 #034-01-1972 L1989 **AN** *020 †05
MACHADO, Randal Alan. 1905 MAIN ST 97601 #005-14-1983 L1986 **FM** *020 †18
MAGEE, Kenneth Kellogg. ■ 97601 #040-02-1963 L1967 **IM** *020
MARAIRE, Jacqueline N. 2301 CLAIRMONT DR 97601 #035-01-1992 L2005 **NS** *020
MARX, Frank Geoffrey. 2614 CLOVER ST 97601 #005-14-1971 L1977 **IM PD** *020 †20,55
MAYLAND, Gabriel Rama. 2074 S 6TH ST, KLAMATH OPEN DOOR FAMILY P 97601 #016-42-2003 L2006 **FM** *020 †18
MCCLURE, Cori Anne. ■ 97601 #047-05-2004 L2005 **EM** *100
MC CLURE, Edward Thos. 2200 BRYANT WILLIAMS DR, STE 2 97601 #005-14-1973 L1978 **GS** *020 †85
MC DOWELL, Dale Sterling. 2200 BRYANT WILLIAMS DR, STE 3 97601 #054-04-1970 L1979 **CD IM** *020 †20

■ = Address Information Privacy Protected

MC KELLAR, Jon Gregory. 2300 CLAIRMONT DR 97601 #014-01-1976 L1979 **FM** *020 †18
MEADOWS, Allison Demarris. ■ 97601 #017-20-2007 L2007 **FP** *012
MEDINA, Laurel Faye. 2801 DAGGETT AVE 97601 #654-01-2005 L2005 **FP** *012
MEINIG, Martin Lyn. 3000 BRYANT WILLIAMS DR, STE 119 97601 #041-09-1998 L2007 **OBG** *020 †30
MELNICK, Sharon Kay. 905 MAIN STE 412 97601 #054-04-1982 L1993 **P LM** *074 †75
MERHOFF, George Craig. ■ 97601 #005-02-1969 L1975 **GS VS** *071 †85
METZ, Arielle Anna. 3000 BRYANT WILLIAMS DR, STE 110 97601 #010-01-2001 L2007 **OBG** *020 †30
MILLER, Esteban Enrique. 2074 S 6TH ST 97601 #025-01-1999 L2002 **FM** *020 †18
MIRANDE, Raul Ari. 2200 BRYANT WILLIAMS DR, S. OREGON CTR - OBESITY SU 97601 #005-02-1990 L1995 **GS** *020 †85
MITCHELL, Benjamin Jacob. 2581 UHRMANN RD, WEST PHYSICIANS SVCS 97601 #038-41-2000 L2006 **EM** *020 †16
MONTES, Miguel Angel. 2865 DAGGETT AVE, KLAMATH FALLS 97601 #048-14-1992 L2001 **PTH** *062 †50
MOORE, Laura Lynn. 3737 SHASTA WAY, STE A 97603 #040-02-1987 L1988 **IM** *020
NAGABATTULA, Neelima. 2801 DAGGETT AVE 97601 #496-24-1996 L2005 **FP** *012
NARKEWICZ-JODKO, Joanna B. 2200 BRYANT WILLIAMS DR 97601 #759-06-1982 L1993 **CD** *020 †20
NEHREN, Norma Jean. 12190 OLD FORT RD 97601 #047-07-1993 L2002 **FM** *020 †18
NOVAK, James Francis. 1905 MAIN ST, KLAMATH MEDICAL CLINIC 97601 #040-02-1970 L1971 **FM** *020 †18
ORLANDO, Marc David. 3000 BRYANT WILLIAMS DR, STE 220 97601 #040-02-1996 L2001 **GS** *020 †85
OTOSKI, Richard Edward. 2303 CLAIRMONT DR 97601 #034-01-1971 L1978 **D GP** *020 †15 ‡
OTTEMAN, Richard Henry. 2130 OLD FORT RD 97601 #030-05-1958 L1960 **AN OS** *071
PANOSSIAN, David Harold. 2688 CAMPUS DR 97601 #025-12-1989 L1995 **PUD** *020 †20
PAUL, Leslie Vivian. 3810 S 6TH ST 97603 #016-42-1996 L1997 **FM** *020 †18
PAYNE, Robert David. ■ 97601 #040-02-1945 L1946 **GS GP** *071
PENOYAR, Jonathan Broder. 2801 DAGGETT AVE 97601 #038-06-2006 L2006 **FP** *012
PEREZ GIL, Harold. 2801 DAGGETT AVE 97601 #264-05-2002 L2005 **FP** *012
PHELPS, Stephen Benjamin. ■ 97601 #028-34-2003 L2006 **EM** *020 †16
POWELL, Suzanne Helen. ■ 97601 #054-04-2007 L2007 **FP** *012
PUNGAN, Ramona. 2631 CROSBY AVE, KLAMATH INTERNAL MEDICINE 97603 #781-01-1995 L2003 **END** *100 †20
PURVIS, Janey Mae. 2801 DAGGETT AVE, PROGRAM, MERLE WEST MEDICA 97601 #065-10-1986 L1995 **FM PME** *020 †18
RAIFE, Michael James. 2640 BIEHN ST 97601 #021-01-1973 L2001 **U AM** *020 †95
REEDER, David Dalmer. 2865 DAGGETT AVE 97601 #040-02-1963 L1966 **GS** *020 †85
REISCHER, Kristin Ganscho. 2801 DAGGETT AVE, CASCADES E FP 97601 #035-45-2004 L2004 **FM** *020 †18
REY, Alejandro. 2074 S 6TH ST, KLAMATH HEALTH PARTNERSHIP 97601 #935-02-1994 L2002 **FM** *020 †18
ROGERS, Scott Michael. ■ 97601 #038-40-2007 L2007 **FP** *012
ROSS, Robert George. 2801 DAGGETT AVE 97601 #065-01-1984 L1995 **FM FSM** *040 †18
RUDD, Francis Van Bukey. 2865 DAGGETT AVE 97601 #005-11-1964 L1972 **U** *071 †95
SALISBURY, Jeffrey Aaron. ■ 97603 #031-01-2004 L2007 **EM** *020
SAYERS, Ross V. ■ 97603 #165-04-1953 L1958 **OPH PHP** *071
SCOTT, Aaron Parry. 2800 DAGGETT AVE, CASCADES EAST FAMILY PRACT 97601 #036-05-1995 L1997 **FM** *020 †18
SCULLY, Michael Vincent. 3810 S 6TH ST 97603 #050-02-1996 L1997 **FM** *020 †18
SEARS, Robert Carlton. 2801 DAGGETT AVE 97601 #020-12-2001 L2006 **OS** *100 †55,75
SHIPMAN, Grover Gene. 2801 DAGGETT AVE, OHSU KLAMATH FALLS 97601 #004-01-2003 L2003 **FM** *100 †18
SHIRTS, Steven R. 2865 DAGGETT AVE 97601 #054-04-1975 L2000 **OBG** *020 †30
SIDEY, Atarah Evemartin. ■ 97601 #005-12-2005 L2006 **FP** *012
SINDMACK, Gregory. 2686 CAMPUS DR 97601 #016-02-1976 L1992 **GYN** *020 †30
SMITH, Philip M. 2615 ALMOND ST 97601 #048-15-2000 L2005 **OPH IM** *020
SOHO, Sandra. PO BOX 235 97601 #040-02-1967 L1968 **GYN GP** *075
STUROS, Curtis Jon. 2210 N ELDORADO AVE, KLAMATH YOUTH DEVELOPMENT 97601 #025-01-1992 L1993 **CHP** *075
SUTKUS, Amy Lynne. ■ 97601 #040-02-2006 L2007 **FP** *012
SWETLAND, Eric Brian. 2865 DAGGETT AVE, OPERATING ROOM 97601 #016-42-1993 L1997 **AN** *020 †05
SWETLAND, John Frederick. ■ 97601 #005-18-1991 L1995 **AN** *020 †05
SWETLAND, Lawrence Albert. ■ 97601 #056-05-1960 L1962 **AN** *020
TACKEY, Edward Opom. 2625 CROSBY AVE 97603 #412-02-1990 L2003 **IM RHU** *020 †20
TAMPLEN, William Kyle. 2485 DAGGETT AVE 97601 #005-19-1974 L1983 **DR** *020 †80
THEIN, Michael David. 3939 S 6TH ST # 119 97603 #005-06-1991 L1992 **P** *020 †75
THOMAS, Michelle Anne. 2074 S 6TH ST, KLAMATH HEALTH PARTNERSHIP 97601 #056-05-1999 L2002 **FM** *020 †18
TICE, Raymond S. ■ 97603 #019-02-1938 **GS** *071
TODD, Douglas Haymore. 3000 BRYANT WILLIAMS DR, STE 200 97601 #010-01-1987 L1988 **OTO FPS** *020 †45
TRAINA, Pamela Ann. 3150 S 6TH ST, BASIN IMMEDIATE CARE 97603 #024-07-1980 L1983 **EM** *020 †16
TUTTLE, Kenneth Lee. ■ 97601 #005-11-1964 L1968 **GS VS** *020 †85
WARD, Elisabeth Baldwin. ■ 97601 #041-07-1932 L1934 **GP** *071
WARREN, Wendy Ann. 2865 DAGGETT AVE 97601 #010-01-1989 L1992 **FM** *020 †18
WARWICK, Tracy Michelle. 2310 MOUNTAIN VIEW BLVD, KLAMATH PED CLC 97601 #040-02-1999 L2002 **PD** *020 †55
WAYLAND, Joan Trowbridge. ■ 97601 #008-01-1966 L1976 **CHP** *071 †75
WAYLAND, Jon Sewell. ■ 97601 #008-01-1966 L1976 **U** *071 †95
WENNER, Karl Conrad. 2200 BRYANT WILLIAMS DR, STE 1 97601 #011-03-1984 L1989 **ORS** *020 †40
WHIPPLE, Galen Charter. ■ 97601 #026-04-2005 L2007 **FP** *012
WIENCEK, Jeffrey Gerard. 2575 CAMPUS DR, SPECIALIST, MERLE WEST MED 97601 #016-02-1995 L2006 **IM** *020 †16
WILSON, John Aaron. 2310 MOUNTAIN VIEW BLVD 97601 #019-02-1978 L1981 **PD** *020 †55
WILSON, Margaret Leslie. ■ 97601 #034-01-2008 *012
WIRSING, Nellie May. 2801 DAGGETT AVE 97601 #056-05-2003 L2003 **FM** *100 †18
WOODY, Helene Priscilla. ■ 97601 #005-17-1962 L1975 *100
YOUNG-TRIPP, Sawar Chalut. 2801 DAGGETT AVE, OHSU KLAMATH FALLS 97601 #054-04-2006 L2006 **FP** *012

ZOOLKOSKI, Christopher D. 2801 DAGGETT AVE, CASCADE EAST FAMILY PRACTI 97601 #040-02-2000 L2001 **FM** *020 †18
ZWARTVERWER, Frederick L. 2301 MOUNTAIN VIEW BLVD, STE A 97601 #056-05-1975 L1978 **PD** *020 †55

LA GRANDE – UNION

ALLEN, David Williams. 1100 J AVE 97850 #036-07-1968 L1973 **IM** *071 †20
ALLEN, Matthew Weslee. 900 SUNSET DR 97850 #040-02-1999 L2003 **DR** *020 †80
ALLEN, Wesley Irvin. 710 SUNSET DR 97850 #049-01-1960 L1964 **FM PHP** *071 †18
BUMP, Stephen Robt. 506 4TH ST 97850 #028-34-1988 L1989 **IM** *020 †20
CHASTEEN, Kenneth Ray. 1806 COVE AVE, UNION CO FIRE AND DMS STAT 97850 #020-02-1974 L2002 **EM FM** *020 †18,16
CONKLIN, Bryan Richard. 710 SUNSET DR 97850 #654-01-1998 L2001 **FM** *020 †18
DENSMORE, Gregg Stanley. 700 SUNSET DR STE F 97850 #056-06-1983 L1993 **ORS** *020 †40
DUCHOW, Allison Joyce. 900 SUNSET DR 97850 #054-04-1993 L1994 **GS** *020 †85
FULLER, Dee Lowell. ■ 97850 #040-02-1958 L1987 **OBG** *071 †30
GERACI, Thomas Kent. ■ 97850 #038-41-1974 L1977 **PD** *020 †55
GLEESON, Timothy Chas. 307 C AVE 97850 #040-02-1973 L1979 **AN** *020 †05
GRAHAM-DAVIS, Stanley K. 506 4TH ST 97850 #048-04-1981 L1987 **IM** *020 †20
GRAYSON, Kevin David. 612 SUNSET DR, LA GRANDE PEDIATRIC CLKC 97850 #041-07-1997 L2001 **PD** *020 †55
HADDOCK, Richard Austin. 900 SUNSET DR 97850 #040-02-1970 L1973 **FM** *020 †18
HALSTEAD, William Elbert. 1501 6TH ST STE C 97850 #045-01-1995 L2001 **CHP P** *020
HARRISON, Gayle Ann. 612 SUNSET DR, GRANDE RONDE HOSP. CHILDRE 97850 #040-02-1994 L1996 **PD** *020
HETRICK, Michael Alan. 612 SUNSET DR 97850 #038-40-1979 L1982 **PD** *020 †55
HIBBERT, Milo La Von. 610 SUNSET DR 97850 #040-02-1977 L1979 **OBG** *040 †30
HOLECEK, Richard J. 710 SUNSET DR STE F 97850 #016-11-1969 L1973 **GS** *020 †85
JENSEN, Susan Stevens. 710 SUNSET DR 97850 #054-04-1996 L1999 **FM** *020 †18
JONES, K Kemps. 506 4TH ST 97850 #040-02-1957 L1964 **IM** *072 †20
KOPP, James Robt. 710 SUNSET DR 97850 #040-02-1974 L1975 **ORS** *020 †40
MATTHEWS, James Michael. 900 SUNSET DR 97850 #040-02-1974 L1975 **AN** *020 †05
MC CARTHY, R Patrick. 700 SUNSET DR STE A 97850 #019-02-1982 L1983 **U** *020
MC QUEEN, Michael Hugh. 700 SUNSET DR, STE G 97850 #040-02-1995 L1996 **FM** *020 †18
MEYERS, Susan Elizabeth. 900 SUNSET DR 97850 #040-02-1977 L1978 **AN EM** *020 †05
MINOGUE, Richard Patrick. ■ 97850 #035-08-1971 L1979 **IM EM** *020 †20
MONTEE, Kim Ray. 710 SUNSET DR STE C, KIM R. MONTEE, M.D., P.C. 97850 #040-02-1997 L1998 **FM** *020 †18
MOSIMAN, William Edward. 1100 K AVE 97850 #016-45-1983 L1984 **CHP P** *020 †75
MUTCH, Kelly Ray. 62462 IGO LN 97850 #054-04-1983 L1989 **IM EM** *020 †20
NEELEY, Betsy Ann. 506 4TH ST 97850 #038-45-1988 L1989 **IM** *020 †20
OLER, Ralph Clyde. 709 AQUARIUS WAY, ST BENEDICTS FAMILY MED. C 97850 #040-02-1972 L1973 **OBG FM** *020 †18,30
PETRUSEK, Joseph Louis. 710 SUNSET DR 97850 #056-06-1970 L1975 **OTO A** *020 †45 ‡
PETTIT, William A. 1404 GEKELER LN 97850 #048-14-1987 L1992 **OPH IMG** *020
RICE, Joel Douglas. 1101 I AVE 97850 #036-01-1986 L1993 **P** *020 †75
RICE, Susan K. 506 4TH ST 97850 #036-01-1987 L1993 **ID** *020 †20
ROBINSON, Dale Craig. 610 SUNSET DR, GRANDE RONDE HOSP. WOMEN'S 97850 #016-02-1990 L2006 **OBG** *020 †30
SCHAEFER, John Edward. 710 SUNSET DR, STE C 97850 #056-06-1992 L1995 **FM** *020 †18
SCHOENFELDER, Ellen K. 710 SUNSET DR 97850 #026-04-1983 L1988 **FM** *020 †18
SCHOENFELDER, Timothy K. 2519 COVE AVE 97850 #026-04-1983 L1987 **AN PME** *020 †05
SCHROEDER, Ted Reece. 900 SUNSET DR, EASTERN OREGON RADIOLOGY 97850 #040-02-1970 L1972 **DR R** *071 †80
SILTANEN, Randy Anton. 900 SUNSET DR, GRAND RONDE HOSPITAL 97850 #040-02-1986 L1997 **DR** *020 †80
SMITH, Lehlia Pia. 710 SUNSET DR, LA GRANDE FAMILY PRACTICE 97850 #065-09-1989 L1995 *020
THOMSON, Brook Allen. 610 SUNSET DR 97850 #023-12-1993 L2004 **OBG** *020 †30
WARREN, Donald Orland. 700 SUNSET DR, STE F 97850 #019-02-1974 L1980 **ORS HS** *020 †40
WEBER, James B. 1101 I AVE 97850 #041-12-1978 L1994 **PD** *020 †55
WINDE, James W. 700 SUNSET DR, STE C 97850 #048-15-1993 L1997 **FM** *020 †18

LAKE OSWEGO – CLACKAMAS

AFLATOONI, Nosratollah. PO BOX 1811 97035 #517-01-1969 *074
ANDERSON, Thomas Arden. ■ 97035 #040-02-1978 L1981 **IM** *020 †20
BADER, Max Christian. ■ 97035 #054-04-1961 L1980 **ADL GPM** *071 †70
BAER, Daniel Matthew. 3240 UPPER DR 97035 #035-09-1957 L1964 **CLP PTH** *030 †50
BAKER, James Wm. 3975 MERCANTILE DR, STE 158 97035 #056-05-1970 L1974 **PDA PD** *020 †55,03
BARON, Daryl Wm. 16463 BOONES FERRY RD, STE 300 97035 #016-11-1985 L1986 **IM** *020 †20
BAYER, Richard Edward. 16463 BOONES FERRY RD, OLSON INTERNAL MEDICINE 97035 #028-46-1978 L1979 **IM** *075 †20
BELLOWS, Michael Scott. 1928 PALISADES TERRACE DR 97034 #025-01-1960 L1997 **GP** *020 †18
BENOWICZ, Robert Emery. ■ 97035 #040-02-2006 L2006 **PD** *100
BHAVAN, Falguny Patel. ■ 97035 #040-02-2005 L2005 **IM** *012
BLANCHARD, John A. ■ 97034 #040-02-1950 L1952 **IM CD** *071 †20
BLUHM, James Scott. 4103 MERCANTILE DR 97035 #040-02-1988 L1990 **PD** *020 †55
BOUMA, Donald Jay. 16463 BOONES FERRY RD 97035 #025-01-1972 L1975 **IM END** *020 †20
BRUNS, Brenda Marie. ■ 97035 #054-04-1977 L1996 **EM IM** *030 †20,16
BURGESS, Elisa Anneli. 16865 BOONES FERRY RD, HP GROVE BUILDING, STE 101 97035 #040-02-1993 L1994 **PS** *020 †85,65
BURKE, Lucien Francis. ■ 97035 #012-12-1966 L1974 **R** *071 †80
BYRD, Walton Edward. 17685 65TH AVE, STE 300 97035 #028-02-1959 L1964 **ADM** *020
CAMP, Frederick Albert. ■ 97035 #048-04-1963 L1970 **OTO** *071 †45
CARR, Elizabeth Ann. 4103 MERCANTILE DR 97035 #051-01-1988 L1993 **PD** *020 †55
CARSWELL, Harold A. ■ 97035 #012-01-1952 L1952 **CRS** *071 †10
CARVER, Thomas Gwynn. 6405 ROSEWOOD ST, STE B 97035 #039-01-1980 L2001 **OM FM** *020 †70,18

CECH, James Mark. 3975 MERCANTILE DR, STE 216 97035 #035-45-1982 L1983 **OPH** *020 †35
CHAN, Susan Esther. ■ 97035 #040-02-1999 L2000 **GE** *020 †20
CHANG, Kyoung Sook. 2942 SW ORCHARD HILL PL 97035 #583-01-1960 L1983 **AN** *040 †05
CHENG, Keith. 17542 MARDEE AVE 97035 #005-12-1982 L1990 **CHP** *020 †75
CHENOWETH, John Barrows. 201 B AVE, STE 285 97034 #017-20-1998 L1999 **CHP** *020
CHILDERS, Ann Marie. ■ 97034 #040-02-1992 L1995 **CHP P** *020
COHEN, Richard Alan. 9 MONROE PKWY, STE 280 97035 #016-42-1981 L1986 **P** *020 †75
CONRAD, Edward E, Jr. 550 3RD ST 97034 #040-02-1980 L1981 **IM** *020 †20
COPELAND, Mc Cague B. ■ 97034 #007-02-1952 L1957 **IM** *072 †20
COPPOCK, Homer Cary. ■ 97034 #016-02-1941 L1947 **FM** *071
DAHL, Laura Lee. 4103 MERCANTILE DR 97035 #056-06-1990 L1991 **PD** *020 †55
DARLING, Marion Jean N. 16699 BOONES FERRY RD, STE 210 97035 #060-02-1981 L1997 **FM** *020 †18
DAUT, Dennis Paul. ■ 97035 #016-11-1963 L1990 **PTH HEM** *071 †50
DE MARIA, F John. ■ 97034 #627-01-1952 **OBG** *020 †30
DENMAN, Joseph Dewitt. 3975 MERCANTILE DR, STE 216 97035 #021-01-1980 L1981 **OPH AM** *020 †35
DENNISON, Gretchen E. ■ 97034 #005-02-1990 *074
DENSLOW, Brenda Lynn. ■ 97034 #035-45-1983 L1988 **EM** *020 †16
DURHAM, Maureen J. ■ 97035 #008-02-1982 L1984 **IM** *075
DYGERT, Timothy Nilo. ■ 97035 #017-20-2004 L2005 **IM** *012
ELY, Gayle Kathryn. 340 OSWEGO POINTE DR # 2 97034 #046-01-1994 L1998 **P** *020
ENLOE, Stephen Robt. 16463 BOONES FERRY RD 97035 #040-02-1969 L1975 **IM** *020 †20
ERICKSON, Kenneth Reed. 5 CENTERPOINTE DR, STE 400 97035 #005-12-1981 L1982 **N P** *020 †75
ESCHBACH, Mary Patricia. ■ 97034 #054-04-1981 L1991 **EM** *020 †20
EUSTERMAN, Jos Huntimer. 851 A AVE, WOEMS 97034 #026-04-1957 L1963 **OM LM** *062 †70
FARRIS, Linda Marie. 3975 MERCANTILE DR, MERCANTILE MEDICAL GROUP 97035 #040-02-1978 L1980 **IM** *072 †20
FIGUERAS, Dominic Anthony. 3 MONROE PKWY, STE P 97035 #005-14-1990 L1991 **AN** *020 †05
FISCHER-WRIGHT, Ruth A. 4015 MERCANTILE DR, STE 200 97035 #054-04-1987 L2004 **FM** *020 †18
FISHERMAN, William Harold. ■ 97035 #048-02-1967 L2005 **DR** *020 †80
FOX, James Edwin. ■ 97034 #025-01-1965 L1966 **PTH** *062 †50
FULLER, Stephen. 16001 QUARRY RD 97035 #539-04-1968 L1989 **ORS HS** *072 †40
FURMAN, Robert Howard. 17704 JEAN WAY, STE 101 97035 #035-45-1994 L1999 **OTO** *020 †45
GEARHART, Lauren Marlene. 16463 BOONES FERRY RD 97035 #040-02-1988 L1989 **IM** *020 †20
GEIGER, Barbara W. ■ 97035 #038-45-1983 L1985 **IM FM** *020 †20
GEIGER, Robert Randolph. ■ 97035 #005-02-1978 L1987 **EM** *020 †16
GLASS, Simon David. 4500 KRUSE WAY STE 100 97035 #023-01-1964 L1983 **P** *020 †75
GOODMAN, Richard Harvey. ■ 97034 #041-01-1976 L1987 **IM** *050 †20
GOODMAN, Shawn. 4035 MERCANTILE DR, STE 201 97035 #041-07-1981 L1983 **OPH** *020 †35
GORRELL, Guy W. ■ 97035 #040-02-1953 L1954 **OS GS** *071 †85
GRAHAM, Christopher Lee. ■ 97035 #040-02-2006 **EM** *012
GRAHAM, Donald Raymond. ■ 97035 #037-01-1976 L1977 **EM** *020 †16
GREENE, Randy Hale. 5 JUAREZ ST 97035 #005-12-1971 L1977 **R EM** *062 †80
GRIMWOOD, David C. ■ 97035 #035-45-1952 L1953 **GP GS** *071
GROSS, George Frederick. ■ 97035 #005-11-1967 L1970 **GS** *071 †85
GROSSMAN, Perry. ■ 97035 #041-13-1961 L2002 **PD** *020 †55
HARP, Kristina E. 17704 JEAN WAY, STE 105 97035 #005-06-1993 L1994 **IM** *020 †20
HARRIS, Henry Freeman. 4309 OAKRIDGE RD 97035 #004-01-1973 L1974 **IM** *020 †20
HASHIGUCHI, Steven A. 16463 BOONES FERRY RD, THE OLSON MEMORIAL CLINIC 97035 #051-01-1986 L1987 **IM** *020 †20
HAYES, Jeffrey Benton. 17685 65TH AVE, STE 300 97035 #038-43-1975 L1981 **FM ADM** *020 †18
HAYNES, Tana Marie. ■ 97034 #040-02-1995 L2003 **CD** *020
HENSALA, John David. ■ 97034 #023-01-1960 L1968 **P** *020 †75
HEWITT, Margaret Almeda. 4035 MERCANTILE DR STE 210 97035 #017-20-1978 L1981 **D** *020 †15
HOFFMAN, Jeffrey Ernest. 16463 BOONES FERRY RD 97035 #005-12-1977 L1980 **PD** *020 †55
HOLM, Victor Martin. ■ 97035 #018-03-1956 L1977 **P** *071 †75
HONG, Molly. 47 DA VINCI ST 97035 #043-01-2001 L2001 **FM** *020 †18
HOOPER, Jody Elizabeth. ■ 97034 #010-01-1998 L2007 **PTH** *100
HUBERTY, Erika Schettler. 17704 JEAN WAY, STE 101 97035 #048-12-2000 L2006 **OTO** *100 †45
HUTCHENS, Tyra Thornton. ■ 97034 #040-02-1945 **CLP NM** *071 †50,28
INGALA, Anthony. ■ 97034 #005-02-1942 L1942 **GS OS** *071 †85
JENIKE, Clarence A. ■ 97034 #026-04-1960 L1960 **PHP** *030 †70
JONES, Wilbert Robert. ■ 97035 #038-41-1998 L2006 **IM** *020 †20
JOSIFEK, Lorraine Frances. 3 MONROE PKWY STE P-450, COLUMBIA MEDINFORMATICS 97035 #020-12-1972 L1989 **N PD** *074 †55,75
KAALAAS, Allen Louis. ■ 97034 #016-11-1961 L1965 **OBG OS** *071
KASSAY, Kara Michele. 17704 JEAN WAY, STE 105 97035 #056-06-1996 L1999 **FM** *020 †18
KECK, Kevin Wm. 17323 BERGIS FARM DR 97034 #005-19-1975 L1999 **IM PD** *030 †20,55
KEMPLER, Geraldine Dina. 16463 BOONES FERRY RD, STE 400 97035 #040-02-1996 L1998 **PD** *020 †55 ‡
KEPPEL, William H. 5 CENTERPOINTE DR STE 400 97035 #040-02-1979 L1986 **P** *020
KHAN, Muhammad. ■ 97035 #308-11-1997 L2006 **IM** *012 †18
KIDD, David. ■ 97034 #025-07-1984 L1993 **IM** *020 †20
KIESSLING, Peter Jonathan. 4235 W BAY RD 97035 #051-01-1964 L1976 **PTH CLP** *020 †50
KILPATRICK, Paula Diane. 4035 MERCANTILE DR, STE 101 97035 #040-02-1983 L1984 **IM** *020
KITTAMS, Brian Kenneth. 16463 BOONES FERRY RD 97035 #054-04-1978 L1989 **PD** *020 †55
KJELSTRUP, Sissel M. 17704 JEAN WAY STE 102 97035 #023-07-1989 L1990 **D** *020 †15
KLECAN, Eugene Edward, Jr. 16869 65TH AVE STE 244 97035 #034-01-1970 L1986 **P PFP** *062 †75
KNOWLES, Jeffrey J. 4500 KRUSE WAY, STE 100 97035 #065-06-1978 L2000 **P ADM** *020 †75
KRALL, Noah L. ■ 97035 #035-08-1946 L1957 **IM** *071 †20
KRIPPAEHNE, Suzanne L. ■ 97035 #040-02-1996 L1998 **GS** *020
KYSAR, John E. ■ 97035 #030-05-1951 L1951 **P** *071 †75
LABHARD, Michael Edison. ■ 97035 #056-06-1976 L1979 **PD** *050 †19,55
LATHAM, George Hughie. 333 S STATE ST # 299 97034 #021-01-1965 L1971 **OS PD** *020 †55
LEES, Martin Henry. ■ 97035 #352-07-1955 L1964 **PDC NPM** *071 †55
LEWIS, Ashley Moore. ■ 97034 #040-02-2005 **IM** *012
LEWIS, Darren Blaine. 4015 MERCANTILE DR, STE 200 97035 #011-02-1989 L2007 **FM** *020 †18
LEWIS, Sue Ann. 17704 JEAN WAY STE 105 97035 #040-02-1994 L1995 **IM FM** *020 †20
LINKER, Wendy Jane. 17685 65TH AVE, STE 300 97035 #005-19-1987 L1997 **P** *020 †75
LINTON, Anne Elizabeth. ■ 97034 #038-06-1989 L1999 **P** *020 †75
LUTT, Joseph Randall. ■ 97035 #030-05-2004 L2004 **RHU** *012 †20
MAIER, Joel Patrick. 17720 JEAN WAY, STE 100 97035 #040-02-1996 L2006 **PS** *100 †85,65
MANDELBLATT, Steven Jay. 414 7TH ST 97034 #041-09-1981 L1982 **IM ADM** *020 †20
MARBLE, Michael Raymond. 16869 65TH AVE # 507 97035 #016-06-1967 L1976 **ORS** *020 †40
MARCEL, Leonard Jos. 18475 CRESTLINE DR 97034 #030-06-1968 L1974 **P** *020 †75
MARKEE, R Kent. ■ 97034 #040-02-1946 L1962 **GS** *071 †85
MARSHALL, William Robt. 1811 S SHORE BLVD, BOX 992 97034 #001-02-1958 L1969 **PS** *071 †85,65
MARTIN, Darcy A. 220 FOOTHILLS RD, P O BOX 999 97034 #016-06-1986 L1987 **CHP** *020 †75
MATAR, Adel Fahmy. ■ 97034 #330-02-1951 L1971 **TS** *071 †85,90
MAYOCK, Ellen Kyte. 16463 BOONES FERRY RD 97035 #040-02-1993 L1994 **IM** *020 †20
MC CRARY, Monica L. 17704 JEAN WAY STE 102, LAKE OSWEGO DERMATOLOGY 97035 #048-02-1994 L1999 **D** *020 †15
MC GOVERN, Peter John. ■ 97034 #539-03-1958 L1976 **AN** *071
MICHAELS, Claire E. 15110 BOONES FERRY RD, STE 230 97035 #016-43-1989 L1998 **OS** *074
MILLAN, Monica Alonso. ■ 97035 #231-01-1968 L1979 **REN PTH** *050 †50
MILLER, Philip Gene. 16463 BOONES FERRY RD, OLSON PEDIATRIC CLINIC 97035 #018-03-1977 L1981 **PD** *020 †55
MONTGOMERY, John C. ■ 97034 #025-01-1943 L1944 **PD** *071 †55
MOOKINI, Ruth Konane. ■ 97034 #014-01-1979 L1981 **IM NM** *020
MOORE, Barbara Kay. ■ 97034 #040-02-1989 L1990 **EM** *020 †16
MOSES, Irving I. ■ 97034 #005-16-1962 L1975 **PTH OS** *020
MULCAHY, Maureen Molly. 17704 JEAN WAY, STE 101 97035 #003-01-1993 L1994 **OTO A** *020 †45
MYKLEBUST, Monica. 4015 MERCANTILE DR, STE 200 97035 #026-04-1993 L2008 **FM** *020 †18
NEGREANU, Diana Claudia. ■ 97035 #781-03-1991 L2004 **END** *020
NELSON, Hans-Gerhardt E. 16455 BOONES FERRY RD 97035 #007-02-1949 L1987 **PD ADL** *020 †55
NEPVEU, Laura. 16463 BOONES FERRY RD, STE 300 97035 #050-02-1992 L1993 **IM** *020 †20
OBYE, John Roger. ■ 97035 #040-02-1966 L1967 **GP** *075
OIKAWA, Robert Yoichi. 3 MONROE PKWY, STE P PMB 450 97035 #023-07-1979 L1989 **CD** *071 †20
OSTER, Robert Arthur. ■ 97034 #048-02-1960 L1960 **OBG** *071 †30
PALING, Michael R. 12 EL GRECO ST 97035 #917-09-1971 L1994 **DR** *020 †80
PALMER, Donald. 16463 BOONES FERRY RD #400 97035 #016-11-1968 L1972 **PD** *020
PANG, Alvan Wei-Kuang. 16463 BOONES FERRY RD 97035 #054-04-1972 L1974 **PD** *020 †55
PEARSON, James Michael. 2 CAMELOT CT, DEPT. OF DIAGNOSTIC RADIOL 97034 #045-01-1984 L1997 **DR** *020 †80
PEASLEE, Mary Lillo. ■ 97034 #005-02-1987 L1993 **PHP** *020
PETERSON, Larry Len. 16877 65TH AVE 97035 #040-02-1980 L1981 **D** *020 †15 ‡
PETROFF, Mark Adler. 17720 JEAN WAY, STE 100 97035 #040-02-1982 L1989 **FPS OTO** *020 †45
PITT, Andrew Edward. 17704 JEAN WAY, STE 102 97035 #040-02-1986 L1989 **D** *020 †15
PORTMAN, Oscar Wm. ■ 97035 #024-01-1954 L1955 **OS** *071
POTTER, Bryce Earl. 15962 BOONES FERRY RD 97035 #054-04-1975 L1979 **HNS PS** *020 †45
PYLE, Donald. ■ 97035 #035-20-1947 L1948 **CD IM** *071
RABIE, Ezra. ■ 97034 #067-01-1974 L1986 **GP** *020 †16,70
RASHID, Kristina R. 4015 MERCANTILE DR, STE 200 97035 #054-04-1999 L2004 **FM** *020 †18
REHM, Christina Gertrud. ■ 97035 #409-19-1976 L1998 **TRS CCM** *020 †85
REIMER, Gerald Ray. ■ 97035 #039-01-1963 L1964 **N** *062
ROBINSON, Lee David. 4035 MERCANTILE DR STE 206 97035 #040-02-1983 L1987 **FPS OTO** *020 †45
ROE, Lynne Diane. ■ 97034 #005-15-1971 L1999 **D DMP** *020 †15
ROSENBLOOM, Jay Stanton. 4103 MERCANTILE DR 97035 #040-02-1996 L1998 **PD** *020 †55
ROWLAND, Willard Danl. ■ 97034 #028-02-1940 L1947 **PS** *071 †65
RUBIN, Stephen Lester. 4035 MERCANTILE DR 97035 #035-09-1970 L1975 **GS** *071
RUFF, Ronnie Harry. 4040 DOUGLAS WAY, STE 110 97035 #005-18-1982 L1991 **AN** *020 †05
SACCO, Russell N. ■ 97034 #056-05-1960 L1963 **LM U** *071 †95
SACHDEV, Naina. 123 C AVE 97034 #016-42-1984 L1989 **IM GPM** *020
SAMOIL, Daniela. 15962 BOONES FERRY RD 97035 #781-01-1984 L1997 **CD IM** *020 †20
SAWWAF, Abeer Walid. ■ 97035 #605-01-1998 L2002 **PS** *012 †85
SCHILLER, Donald Jos. ■ 97034 #040-02-1974 L1977 **EM** *020 †20,16
SCHNEPPER, Judith M. ■ 97035 #005-12-1973 L1977 **DR** *020 †80
SCHOENBERG, Erik Darrell. 201 B AVE, STE 225 97034 #024-05-1993 L2000 **FPS OTO** *020 †45
SCHUNK, Jack Phillip. 4103 MERCANTILE DR 97035 #040-02-1983 L1984 **PD** *020 †55
SESSIONS, Frances Pope. 310 1ST ST, STE 302 97034 #028-02-1958 L1962 **P** *020
SHEA, Kelly Suzanne. ■ 97034 #033-06-2004 L2007 **HO** *012 †20
SHIBUE, Charles Tatsuo. ■ 97035 #041-09-1965 L1975 **PTH** *020 †50
SHIPKEY, Fredrick H, Jr. ■ 97035 #010-01-1952 L1955 **ATP** *020 †50
SHIPPS, Fred Coulter, Jr. ■ 97035 #038-06-1945 **OS** *071 †80
SHOCHAT, Einav. ■ 97034 #056-05-2005 L2006 **DR** *012
SICARD, Gregorio Arquel. ■ 97034 #033-05-1998 L2003 **IM** *020 †20
SMITH, Ingrid Christina. ■ 97034 #035-19-1999 L2001 *100
SOTTA, Robert Paul. 17704 JEAN WAY, STE 105 97035 #010-02-1979 L1991 **ORS** *020 †40
STARK, Allen Lytton. 340 OSWEGO POINTE DR STE 2 97034 #048-04-1974 L1988 **P PYA** *020 †75
STARK, Carol L R. 340 OSWEGO POINTE DR # 205 97034 #048-04-1974 L1988 **P CHP** *020 †75
STEVENS, Jeffrey S. 929 COUNTRY COMMONS LN 97034 #005-11-1968 L1975 **NM DR** *020 †80,28
SWANSON, John Walter. 16001 QUARRY RD 97035 #018-03-1970 L1978 **ORS LM** *062 †40 ‡
TABOR, Gareth Aubrey. 27 S STATE ST, STE 240 97034 #048-13-1986 L1987 **OPH** *020 †35
TAYLOR, Ryan Lee. 16819 GREENBRIER RD 97034 #040-02-1992 L1995 **DR NM** *020 †80,28
THOMPSON, John Wallace. 16001 QUARRY RD 97035 #040-02-1959 L1960 **ORS** *072 †40
TOMPKIN, Jane Elizabeth. 3312 DUNCAN DR 97035 #007-02-1992 L1993 **EM** *020 †16
TONGUE, Andrea Cibis. 4035 MERCANTILE DR, STE 201 97035 #028-02-1966 L1971 **OPH** *020 †35
TOROSLU, Cigdem. ■ 97034 #028-03-2003 L2007 **PD** *020 †55

■ = Address Information Privacy Protected

TRINH, Thomas Toan. 4035 MERCANTILE DR, STE 103 97035 #021-01-1995 L1998 **FM** *020 †18
TYREE, Wesley Andrew. ■ 97035 #028-34-2002 L2004 **IM** *100 †20
VERVLOET, Albert F C. 4255 OAKRIDGE RD 97035 #660-03-1961 L1966 **IM PUD** *030
VESSELY, Jon Carper. 97034 #038-41-1963 L1971 **ORS** *020 †40
VIJJESWARAPU, John D. ■ 97035 #495-11-1954 *100
WALTERS, Marc Haskell. ■ 97035 #054-04-1983 L1984 **GE IM** *020 †20
WARE, Carrie M. ■ 97035 #040-02-1982 L1983 **IM** *020 †20
WARREN, Jamie Breanne. ■ 97035 #030-05-2006 L2006 **PD** *012
WATKINS, James Edward. ■ 97035 #016-11-1985 L2006 **AN EM** *020 †05
WATSON, John Brown. ■ 97034 #065-09-1985 L1990 *100
WATTS, Thomas W, Jr. ■ 97034 #040-02-1951 L1952 **AI PUD** *071 †03
WEIL, Stephen Alan. 4035 MERCANTILE DR, STE 101 97035 #035-03-1968 L1971 **IM OSS** *020 †20
WESTCOTT, Gary Ray. ■ 97035 #028-34-1992 L1995 **PD** *075
WHITE, David Karl. 5335 SW MEADOWS RD STE 380 97035 #035-46-1993 L1995 **CHP P** *075
WHITE, Stephen James. 17704 JEAN WAY, STE 101 97035 #012-05-1999 L2004 **OTO** *020 †45
WILKINSON, Justin Thomas. ■ 97035 #005-02-2007 L2007 **TY** *012
WOLF, Susan Irene. 17332 BROOKHURST DR 97034 #008-02-1984 L1990 **DR** *020 †80
YAZHARI, Ramine Hooshang. ■ 97035 #016-06-1999 L2002 **EM** *020 †16
YU, Julie S. 4035 MERCANTILE DR, STE 201 97035 #028-46-1994 L2003 **PO OPH** *020 †35
YUTAN, Elizabeth Uy. ■ 97035 #035-09-2001 L2006 **RNR** *100 †80

LAKEVIEW – LAKE

BOMENGEN, Robert Wm. 624 S J ST 97630 #040-02-1969 L1972 **FM GS** *020 †18
CLARKE, Spencer Alan. 624 S J ST 97630 #040-02-1996 L1999 **FM** *020 †18
GALLAGHER, Timothy Adrian. 624 S J ST 97630 #038-41-1995 L1998 **FM** *020 †18
HUSSEY, Stephen Arthur. 624 S J ST 97630 #041-13-1994 L2000 **FM** *020 †18
ROBERTSON, Lewis Campbell. 629 CENTER ST 97630 #040-02-1948 **GP CD** *071
STRIEBY, William Jerry. 18385 HWY 395 97630 #040-02-1946 L1947 **GP** *020

LANGLOIS – CURRY

CHINOWSKY, Heather M. ■ 97450 #352-01-1961 L1963 **P** *072

LEBANON – LINN

ALLEY, Richard Loren. 425 N SANTIAM HWY, MID-VALLEY MEDICAL GROUP 97355 #040-02-1972 L1973 **GP GS** *071 †85
APTER, Roy Jay. 525 N SANTIAM HWY 97355 #010-01-1972 L1979 **PTH** *020 †50
BABBEL, Robert Welker. 525 N SANTIAM HWY 97355 #049-01-1980 L1993 **DR RNR** *020 †80
BAILEY, John Victor. 55 TWIN OAKS AVE, STE A1 97355 #005-12-1996 L2000 **OBG** *020 †30
BARISH, William Gregory. 325 PARK ST, LEBANON CLINIC 97355 #051-01-1981 L1990 **FM** *020
BAUER, James Dean. 55 TWIN OAKS AVE, STE A1 97355 #038-41-1987 L1991 **OBG** *020 †30
BELL, Richard Kristopher. 525 N SANTIAM HWY, SAMARITAN LEBANON COMMUNIT 97355 #031-01-2002 L2006 **FM** *100 †18
BELOZER, Mary Lou Lucille. 425 N SANTIAM HWY, MIDVALLEY MEDICAL GROUP 97355 #040-02-1994 L1997 **FM** *020 †18
BURKETT, Patrick Robt. ■ 97355 #007-02-1960 L1979 **OTO GP** *071 †45
BUSLETTA, Angela Virginia. 55 TWIN OAKS AVE, STE A1 97355 #060-01-1993 L1998 *020
CHERVENAK, Carol Louise. 325 PARK ST 97355 #003-01-1984 L1990 **FM** *020 †18
CLAUTICE, Leslie Ann. 525 N SANTIAM HWY 97355 #040-02-1982 L1987 **DR** *020 †80
COLLIER, Christopher W. 425 N SANTIAM HWY, MID-VALLEY MEDICAL PLAZA 97355 #048-12-2002 L2008 **OBG** *100 †18
DEFREES, Gail Cmatthias. 525 N SANTIAM HWY, LEBANON HOSPITAL 97355 #040-02-1982 L1984 **EM** *020
DONNELLY, Mark William. 1050 W OAK ST, LEBANON FIRE DISTRICT 97355 #040-02-1999 L2001 **EM** *020 †16
EHLERS, David Mershon. 525 N SANTIAM HWY 97355 #051-04-1984 L1985 **DR IM** *020 †20,80
ESHLEMAN, Leon Clarence. 525 N SANTIAM HWY 97355 #040-02-1977 L1980 **EM FM** *020 †18,16
EVANS, Richard Call. 191 N MAIN ST 97355 #041-02-1984 L1987 **FM** *020 †18
FINK, Brigitte Dette. 425 N SANTIAM HWY 97355 #036-05-1999 L2003 **OBG** *020 †30
FLESHMAN, Keith. 525 N SANTIAM HWY 97355 #040-02-1957 L1961 **ORS** *020
FORRESTER, Alden Page. 525 N SANTIAM HWY 97355 #005-12-1999 L2002 **FM** *020 †18
FORTUNE, Michael Arthur. 525 N SANTIAM HWY 97355 #028-02-1982 L1984 **PTH** *020 †50
GALLUP, Donald Noel, Jr. 425 N SANTIAM HWY, SAMARITAN HLTH PHYS MED PL 97355 #060-01-1994 L1998 *020 †18
HAEBERLIN, James Richard. 55 TWIN OAKS AVE, STE C1 97355 #020-12-1975 L1979 **GS VS** *020 †85
HAMLIN, Jefferson Andrew. 525 N SANTIAM HWY 97355 #005-12-1991 L1996 **DR** *020 †80
HEIN, Janine Natalie. 20 E AIRPORT RD 97355 #011-04-1997 L2000 **FM** *020 †18
HEIN, John Edward. 425 N SANTIAM HWY 97355 #011-04-1997 L2000 **FM** *020 †18
HILL, Terrance Allen. 55 TWIN OAKS AVE, STE D2 97355 #024-01-1973 L1982 **GE IM** *020 †18,20
HINDMARSH, Richard Arthur. 425 N SANTIAM HWY, MID VALLEY MEDICAL PLAZA 97355 #068-01-1980 L2005 **FM** *020 †18
HOGAN, Stephen Faust. 525 N SANTIAM HWY 97355 #012-01-1981 L1986 **PTH** *020 †50
INMAN, Robert Davies. ■ 97355 #065-10-1974 **RHU IM** *050 †20
JOHNSON, Howard Le Roy. 55 TWIN OAKS AVE, STE C1 97355 #040-02-1967 L1968 **GS GP** *071 †85
KAUFFMAN, Darrel Leroy. ■ 97355 #054-04-1981 L1986 **ORS** *020
LEAR, William J, Sr. ■ 97355 #030-05-1951 L1951 **IM** *072 †20
LEE, Shi Hyo. 55 TWIN OAKS AVE STE A2 97355 #583-09-1962 L1975 **PD** *071 †55
LITTLE, Francis Leo. 425 N SANTIAM HWY, MID VALLEY MEDICAL GROUP 97355 #025-07-1968 L1973 **IM** *020 †20
MAC EWAN, Karen Lee. 525 N SANTIAM HWY 97355 #005-19-1983 L1998 **DR PD** *020 †80
MASKELL, Laura Kathleen. 525 N SANTIAM HWY, SAMARITAN LEBANON COMMUNIT 97355 #040-02-1986 L1987 **EM OM** *020
MATSUBA, Kevin Kenji. 525 N SANTIAM HWY 97355 #061-01-1990 L2003 **DR** *020 †80
MATTHEWS, Bruce E. 425 N SANTIAM HWY 97355 #040-02-1983 L1986 **FM** *020 †18

MC COY, Randy J. 425 N SANTIAM HWY, MID-VALLEY MEDICAL PLAZA 97355 #040-02-1993 L1996 **IM** *020 †20
MC QUARRIE, Shauna Leigh. 425 N SANTIAM HWY 97355 #062-01-1994 L1998 **FM** *020
MOLITOR, John Jos, Jr. 525 N SANTIAM HWY 97355 #005-12-1992 L1998 **DR** *020 †80
NELSON, Perry Vincent. 525 N SANTIAM HWY 97355 #005-06-2002 L2002 **IM** *020 †20
NELSON, Thadeus Leroy. 325 PARK ST 97355 #018-03-1974 L1977 **FM** *020 †18
ORWICK, Kenneth Leroy. 325 PARK ST 97355 #040-02-1974 L1979 **FM FPG** *020 †18
PAULSON, Reed Eric. 525 N SANTIAM HWY, LEBANON COMMUNITY HOSPITAL 97355 #030-06-1984 L1995 **FM** *020 †18
PHELPS, Anna-Maria. 525 N SANTIAM HWY 97355 #048-13-1988 L1994 **PTH** *020 †50
PLISKIN, Leslie Arthur. 525 N SANTIAM HWY, EMERGENCY ROOM 97355 #016-06-1976 L1979 **EM FM** *020 †16,18
ROBERTSON, Wm Carl, Jr. 55 TWIN OAKS AVE, STE D5 97355 #017-20-1967 L1974 **ORS** *020 †40
RUSSELL, Roger K. ■ 97355 #649-14-1970 *075
SALISBURY, Sedrick Alan. 425 N SANTIAM HWY, MID VALLEY MEDICAL GROUP 97355 #040-02-1985 L1988 **IM HOS** *020 †20
SAUNDERS, Gregory Elton. 55 TWIN OAKS AVE, STE C1 97355 #005-12-1985 L2004 **GS** *020 †18
SHORTRIDGE, Terry Wayne. 55 TWIN OAKS AVE # C 97355 #040-02-1979 L1989 **GS** *020 †85
WESSELS, Dennis Harm. 425 N SANTIAM HWY 97355 #018-03-1963 L1977 **FM** *071 †18
WESTERMEYER, Raymond E. 55 TWIN OAKS AVE STE A1, EAST LINN HEALTH CENTER 97355 #005-12-1975 L1978 **IM** *020 †20
WIMMER, Robert Dale. ■ 97355 #003-01-1973 L1976 **IM** *071 †20
WOPAT, Richard Carl. 325 INDUSTRIAL WAY 97355 #056-05-1975 L1976 **FM OBS** *020 †18

LINCOLN CITY – LINCOLN

BOHLMAN, John Edward. 2870 NE WEST DEVILS LAK RD, C/O LINCOLN CITY MEDICAL C 97367 #005-12-1979 L1983 **IM EM** *030 †20,16
BREAM, Randall Vincent. 3100 NE 28TH ST, SAMARITAN SURGICAL CLINIC 97367 #016-42-1980 L2000 **CD** *020
BROWN, Craig Ackerman. 3043 NE 28TH ST 97367 #005-18-1994 L1997 **FM** *020 †18
CHEEK, Michael Golden. 2870 NE W DEVILS LK RD 97367 #005-12-1979 L1983 **OBG OS** *020 †30 ‡
DREILING, Roger Jos. 3100 NE 28TH ST, SAMARITAN SURGICAL CLINIC 97367 #019-02-1978 L1998 **CD** *020 †20
EGAN, Michael Comerford. 3100 NE 28TH ST, STE B 97367 #010-01-1968 L2004 **GS CCS** *020 †85
FRASER, Marilyn J. 2870 NE W DEVILS LK RD 97367 #061-01-1982 L1990 **FM** *020
GREEN, Raymond Phillip. ■ 97367 #065-01-1957 L1961 **IM CD** *020
HALFERTY, Michael Joseph. 3043 NE 28TH ST, EMERGENCY MEDICAL 97367 #030-05-1995 L2002 **EM** *020 †16
HANDLEY, Brian Craig. 3043 NE 28TH ST, EMGY DEPT 97367 #016-42-1976 L1990 **EM** *020
HOQUE, Nazmul. 3043 NE 28TH ST 97367 #243-47-1991 L2000 **GE IM** *100 †20
KAYE, Robert John, Jr. 3043 NE 28TH ST 97367 #005-12-1961 L1962 **EM** *020
KITZMAN, Mark Michael. 2930 NE WEST DEVILS LAK RD, STE 3 97367 #030-05-1975 L1991 **IM** *075
KORT, Daniel Duane. 2930 NE WEST DEVILS LAK RD, STE 3 97367 #005-12-1987 L1992 **OBG** *020
KUMAR, Vinjamuri Vinod. 3043 NE 28TH ST 97367 #495-21-1982 L1993 **IM CD** *020 †20
MARKER, Thomas L. 3100 NE 28TH ST, SAMARITAN SURGICAL CLINIC 97367 #025-12-1979 L1988 **CD IM** *020 †20
MINER, William Jos. ■ 97367 #005-14-1968 L1974 **PD PHP** *020 †55
NIEHAUS, Karen Marie. 2870 NE WEST DEVILS LAK RD 97367 #005-12-1983 L2003 **IM** *020 †20
OGDEN, Lesley Jill. 3043 NE 28TH ST 97367 #045-01-2003 L2003 **EM** *020 †16
ORDELHEIDE, Karl Douglas. 2870 NE W DEVILS LK RD 97367 #005-12-1976 L1980 **IM** *020 †18
ORTON, Darrell Dean. 3043 NE 28TH ST, SAMARITAN NORTH LINCOLN HO 97367 #010-01-1998 L1999 ‡
PETERSON, Preston Horsley. 165 NW LANCER ST 97367 #023-01-1943 L1951 **GYN** *071 †30
PITMAN, Archie Oran, Jr. ■ 97367 #040-02-1957 L1958 **OS GP** *020
QUINN, Stephen Frederick. 3043 NE 28TH ST 97367 #036-01-1980 L1988 **DR** *050 †80
THOMPSON, Albert Prather. 3043 NE 28TH ST 97367 #005-12-1979 L1982 **FM EM** *020 †16,18
WASSMUTH, Dale Robert. ■ 97367 #018-03-1962 L1963 **P IM** *071 †20

LYONS – LINN

KING, William Frank. ■ 97358 #028-34-1964 L1966 **AN PUD** *071

MADRAS – JEFFERSON

BEAMER, Leland P, Jr. 76 NE 12TH ST 97741 #018-03-1968 L1974 **FM GS** *020 †18
BINGHAM, Christiane A. PO BOX 10, JESUS GROVE 97741 #409-19-1975 L1985 *100
EL-ATTAR, Suzanne M. 76 NE 12TH ST, MADRAS MEDICAL GROUP, P.C 97741 #041-12-1993 L1997 **FM** *020 †18
EVANS, David Vreeland. 76 NE 12TH ST, MADRAS MEDICAL GROUP, PC 97741 #041-12-1993 L1997 **FM** *020 †18
FUENTES, Molly Marie. ■ 97741 #025-01-2008 *012
KEMPER, Carlos Kirk. 470 NE A ST 97741 #019-02-1963 L1968 **FM EM** *071 †18
LIEUALLEN, Douglas Willia. 76 NE 12TH ST 97741 #040-02-1972 L1974 **FM** *020 †18
LILLY, Albert Jackson, III. 470 NE A ST, EMERGENCY DEPT. 97741 #051-07-1997 L2000 **EM** *020 †16
MANNING, Thomas Martin. 470 NE A ST 97741 #040-02-1980 L1983 **FM** *020 †18
MATTHEWS, Tracy Lee. ■ 97741 #040-02-1987 L1994 **FOP** *100
MEREDITH, Geo Alexander. PO BOX 10 97741 #917-21-1968 *100
PLANT, Gary Michael. 76 NE 12TH ST 97741 #047-20-2002 L2004 **FM** *020 †18
ROSS, John K. 910 SW HIGHWAY 97 STE 104 97741 #035-19-1977 L2001 **IM** *020 †20
RUDD, Stephen Miles. ■ 97741 #036-08-1991 L1994 **FM** *020 †18
SANDILANDS, John Robt. ■ 97741 #040-02-1969 L1974 **GS FM** *020 †85
SAVAGE, Leonard Dewitt. 470 NE A ST, MOUNTAIN VIEW HOSPITAL 97741 #054-04-1982 L1996 **EM** *020 †18
SHAPIRO, Edward A. 480 NE A ST 97741 #030-06-1975 L2006 **OBG** *020 †30

■ = Address Information Privacy Protected

SIDELL, Jonathan Edward. 480 NE A ST, MADRAS WOMEN'S CLINIC 97741 #025-07-1989 L1990 **OBG** *020 †30
THOMAS, Evan Watson. ■ 97741 #040-02-1943 **GP** *071
TUREK, Nicholas Thomas. 480 NE A ST 97741 #040-02-2001 L2004 **FM** *020 †18

MANZANITA – TILLAMOOK

HOLLOWAY, James Wix. ■ 97130 #040-02-1944 L1945 **U** *071
LOEHNING, Robert Wm. ■ 97130 #038-06-1954 L1954 **AN** *071 †05
SAXON, Richard Geo. ■ 97130 #016-11-1946 L1949 **OTR** *071 †40

MAPLETON – LANE

UNDERWOOD, Rex John. ■ 97453 #040-02-1955 L1961 **AN** *020 †05

MC KENZIE BRIDGE – LANE

BAUGH, John Ray. PO BOX 2022, 54721 MCKENZIE RIVER DR 97413 #048-12-1958 L1996 **OBG GYN** *020 †30 ‡

MCMINNVILLE – YAMHILL

ANASZ-KOPECKA, Beata. 375 SE NORTON LN, STE A 97128 #759-12-1988 L2004 **IM** *020 †20
ANDERSON, Marcella M. 254 NE NORTON LN, PHYSICIANS MEDICAL CENTER 97128 #054-04-1982 L1986 **PD** *020 †55
ARNOLD, Joseph Byrd. 627 N EVANS ST, YAMHILL CTY ADULT PROGRAMS 97128 #001-02-1969 L1976 **P** *020 †75,18
ARROYO, Francisco L. 392 NE NORTON LN 97128 #005-02-1977 L1999 **EM FM** *020 †18,16
BANKS, Gordon Earl. 2700 SE THREE MILE LN, UNIT 303 97128 #016-02-1977 L1998 **N** *020 †75 ‡
BARKER, George Thos. 320 SE BAKER ST 97128 #040-02-1973 L1983 **OBG** *020 †30
BHATIA, Vishal. 2700 SE STRATUS AVE, UNIT 403 97128 #913-65-1998 L2006 **IM** *020 †20
BLAKE, Christopher Alan. 355 SE BAKER ST 97128 #040-02-1976 L1977 **ORS** *020 †40
BLEDSOE, Stephen Wayne. 2700 SE STRATUS AVE, WILLAMETTE VALLEY MEDICAL 97128 #054-04-1986 L2006 **AN** *020 †05
BLIVEN, Matthew James. 254 NE NORTON LN, PHYSICIANS MEDICAL CENTER 97128 #040-02-1993 L1996 **FM** *020 †18
BOUTIN, Nancy Stidham. 2700 SE STRATUS AVE, STE A 97128 #040-02-1983 L1984 **RO** *020 †80
BRONSON, Betsy Jean. 325 NE EVANS ST 97128 #056-06-1987 L1996 **DR** *020 †80
BROTT, Leslie Michelle. 254 NE NORTON LN, PHYSICIANS MEDICAL CENTER 97128 #048-13-2000 L2000 **FM** *020 †18 ‡
CADDELL, Cara Marie. 254 NE NORTON LN 97128 #028-34-2003 L2006 **PD** *020 †55
CASE, Kay E. 2700 SE THREE MILE LN, UNIT 405 97128 #054-04-1991 L1995 **OBG** *020 †30
CHANYAPUTHIPONG, Sunisa. 115 NE MAY LN, VIRGINIA GARCIA MEMORIAL H 97128 #539-04-2001 L2005 **FM** *020 †20
CHRISTENSEN, Stephen E. 2700 SE STRATUS AVE, WILLAMETTE VALLEY MEDICAL 97128 #031-01-1994 L1999 **IM** *020 †20
COLLIER, Emerson Jos. 2700 SE THREE MILE LN 97128 #040-02-1944 L1947 **U** *071 †95
CYPROVA, Neda. 2700 SE STRATUS AVE 97128 #286-13-1996 L2006 **IM** *020 †20
DE MASTER, Robert John. 2700 SE THREE MILE LN 97128 #056-05-1973 L1996 **AN** *020 †05
ECKER, Richard Ivan. 706 NE EVANS ST 97128 #025-12-1974 L1979 **D** *020 †15
EDELMAN, Steven Herbert. 325 N EVANS ST 97128 #005-11-1969 L1975 **DR NM** *020 †80
ERIKSEN, Jacqueline M. 254 NE NORTON LN, PHYSICIANS MEDICAL CENTER 97128 #040-02-1997 L2000 **FM** *020 †18
FORD, John Richard. 375 SE NORTON LN, STE A 97128 #040-02-1998 L2001 **IM** *020 †20
GASSER, Leslie Ann. ■ 97128 #034-01-1982 L1983 **FM** *074
GEHRSITZ, Leta B. ■ 97128 #040-02-1953 L1956 **OPH** *071
GIBSON, Scott. 851 N BAKER ST 3 97128 #005-12-1984 L1985 **IM** *020 †20
GIGENA, Manuel. 375 SE NORTON LN 97128 #132-02-1989 L2002 **GS** *100
GRANATIR, Robert Francis. 2700 SE THREE MILE LN 97128 #054-04-1966 L1975 **ON HEM** *020 †20
GRINICH, Nicholas Peter. 235 SE NORTON LN STE A 97128 #040-02-1985 L1986 **OPH OS** *020 †35
HADDELAND, Paul Jaret. 2700 SE THREE MILE LN 97128 #040-02-1988 L1991 **FM** *020 †18
HAGLAND, Lester A. ■ 97128 #040-02-1953 L1955 **GS OS** *071 †85
HANSON, Leonard B. 440 E 8TH ST BOX 635 97128 #040-02-1949 L1952 **FM GS** *071
HEDGES, Allan John. 235 SE NORTON LN, STE B 97128 #033-05-1991 L2005 **OBG** *020 †30
HEIMULLER, Brent William. 254 NE NORTON LN, PHYSICIANS MEDICAL CENTER 97128 #040-02-1993 L1994 **PD** *020 †55
HEISER, John Michael. 175 E 1ST ST, MCMINNVILLE FIRE DEPARTMENT 97128 #040-02-1987 L1988 **EM** *020 †16
HOCH, Holly Anne. 627 NE EVANS ST, YAMHILL CNTY ADULT PROG 97128 #040-02-1997 L1999 **P** *020 †75
HOOVER, Harold Roger. 254 NE NORTON LN, PHYSICIANS MEDICAL CENTER 97128 #005-06-1975 L1977 **GS** *020 †85
HURTY, Alan Wayne, II. 2700 SE STRATUS AVE, UNIT 303 97128 #040-02-1993 L1994 **CD** *020 †20
HUSTON, Crittenden. 420 NE 5TH ST 97128 #040-02-1953 L1954 **FM** *072 †18
HYDER, Ashley. 2163 NW 2ND ST 97128 #041-13-2003 L2004 **FM** *020 †18
INKELES, Stephen Bruce. 254 NE NORTON LN, PHYSICIANS MEDICAL CENTER 97128 #016-43-1979 L1982 **IM NTR** *071 †20
INMAN, Leslie William. 420 NE 5TH ST 97128 #040-02-1962 L1964 **DR GP** *020 †80
JACOBSON, John Lee. 2700 SE STRATUS AVE 97128 #040-02-1975 L1977 **EM** *020 †16
KANG, Matthew Young. 2700 SE STRATUS AVE, STE A 97128 #012-02-1995 L2002 **RO** *020 †80
KATZ, Susan F. 254 NE NORTON LN 97128 #040-02-1981 L1983 **PD CHP** *071 †55
KENDRICK, Richard R. ■ 97128 #049-01-1957 L1958 **AN** *071
KENYON, Clifford Francis. 2700 SE STRATUS AVE, UNIT 302 97128 #040-02-1972 L1973 **FM** *020 †18
KHOURY, George Mousa. 2700 SE STRATUS AVE, WILLAMETTE VALLEY MEDICAL 97128 #875-01-1993 L2006 **IM** *020 †20

KIMANI, Richard Kibe. 375 SE NORTON LN, STE A 97128 #577-01-1992 L2004 **IM** *100
KISER, George Craig. 851 N BAKER ST 97128 #048-13-1981 L1982 **U** *020 †95
KNOTT, Everett Leslie. ■ 97128 #039-01-1972 L1975 **AN** *020
KREMER, Dag. 375 SE NORTON LN STE A 97128 #917-04-1968 L1995 **NEP IM** *020
LARKIN, Gail Gier. ■ 97128 #041-01-1982 L1991 **FM** *020 †18
LAUTENBACH, John C. 349 SE BAKER ST 97128 #407-21-1966 L1974 **IM** *072
LAVELLE, Michael Thomas. 254 NE NORTON LN 97128 #016-43-1999 L1999 **U** *020 †95
LOWE, Bruce Alan. 254 NE NORTON LN 97128 #019-02-1976 L1988 **U** *020 †95
MARTIN, Klaus. 310 SE BAKER ST 97128 #060-01-1974 L1976 **FM** *020
MARTIN, Randall Lee. 2700 SE THREE MILE LN 97128 #017-20-1980 L1986 **AN GPM** *020 †05
MC COY, Michael Paul. 325 N EVANS ST 97128 #019-02-1978 L1980 **DR** *020 †80
MILLER, Margaret Jean. 254 NE NORTON LN, PHYSICIANS MEDICAL CENTER 97128 #040-02-1979 L1982 **PD** *020 †55
MORRISON, Susan Anne. 1900 NE HIGHWAY 99W, STE A 97128 #021-01-1993 L1994 **GPM FM** *020 †18
NEELD, John Barton. 2700 SE STRATUS AVE, UNIT 301 97128 #049-01-1989 L1997 **OBG** *020 †30
NELSON, John Douglas. 821 NE HIGHWAY 99W 97128 #005-12-1984 L1987 **FM** *020 †18
NGUYEN, Kimya Anch L. 375 SE NORTON LN, STE A 97128 #025-76-1995, ▲ L2003 **GE** *020
NIELSEN, Catherine Harris. 235 SE NORTON LN 97128 #021-06-1991 L1995 **OBG** *020 †20
NOLAN, Raymond P. 254 NE NORTON LN 97128 #038-41-1974 L1977 **IM** *020 †20
NYQUIST, Theodore T. 2163 NW 2ND ST 97128 #005-12-1990 L1993 **FM** *020 †18
O'BRIEN, Catherine Anne. 2700 SE STRATUS AVE, SUTIE A 97128 #005-19-2000 L2003 **HO** *020 †20
O'LEARY, John J, Jr. ■ 97128 #025-01-1946 L1948 **IM** *072
PASSO, Michael Scott. 235 SE NORTON LN 97128 #017-20-1979 L1982 **OPH** *020 †35
PATHIAL, Kishore G. 2700 SE STRATUS AVE, UNIT 303 97128 #495-31-1983 L1993 **PCC SME** *020 †20
PETERSON, Mary Elizabeth. 2700 SE STRATUS AVE, UNIT 403 97128 #034-01-1988 L2006 **P** *020 †75
PETERSON, Rod Harvey. 2700 SE STRATUS AVE, UNIT 403 97128 #007-02-1979 L2006 **P** *020 †85,75
PFENDLER, David Fink. 1322 SW BAKER ST 97128 #026-04-1967 L1975 **OTO** *020 †45
PIERCE, William Crawford. 2700 SE STRATUS AVE, STE A 97128 #005-14-1987 L1994 **ON HEM** *020 †20
PITRE, Thomas Melford. 254 NE NORTON LN 97128 #035-08-1970 L1971 **U** *020 †95
PITTENGER, Robert G. ■ 97128 #040-02-1950 L1951 **IM HEM** *071 †20
POST, Jay Howard. 325 N EVANS ST 97128 #016-11-1978 L1987 **VIR** *020 †80
RADZIK, Jan. 349 SE BAKER ST 97128 #759-01-1981 L1991 **FM** *020 †20
RESCHLY, Gary Keith. 420 NE 5TH ST 97128 #018-03-1968 L1969 **FM** *071 †18
REYNOLDS, Marion C. 115 NE MAY LN, C/O VGMHC 97128 #040-02-1992 L1995 **FM** *020 †18
RODRIGUEZ CARLON, Ricardo. 2700 SE STRATUS AVE 97128 #048-04-1983 L1993 **EM FM** *020 †20
ROSE, Mark Craig. 535 E 5TH ST, CORRECTIONAL FACILITY 97128 #040-02-1983 L1985 **EM A** *020 †20
RUDEN, Nathan Michael. ■ 97128 #051-01-2006 *012
RUMBAUGH, Lori Cayford. 2700 SE STRATUS AVE # 303 97128 #028-34-1993 L1994 **IM** *020 †20
SANDBERG, John Robt. 2700 SE STRATUS AVE 97128 #016-11-1974 L1978 **EM** *020 †16
SCHIEBER, Scott Eric. 2163 NW 2ND ST 97128 #038-43-1994 L1997 **FM** *020 †18
SCHLOSSSTEIN, Edythe M. 375 SE NORTON LN, STE E 97128 #054-04-1992 L1996 **IM** *020 †20
SCHMIDT, Kenneth Gregory. 254 NE NORTON LN, PHYSICIANS MEDICAL CENTER 97128 #040-02-1983 L1984 **IM** *020 †20
SCOLTOCK, John Wilson. 435 N EVANS ST 97128 #018-03-1970 L1973 **FM** *020 †18 ‡
SHAVER, Kyle John. ■ 97128 #041-01-2004 L2007 **EM** *020
SHEPARD, Virginia D. 2700 SE THREE MILE LN 97128 #040-02-1982 L1983 **FM** *075 †18
SIEPMANN, David Benjamin. 325 N EVANS ST, MCMINNVILLE IMAGING ASSOC 97128 #040-02-2000 L2005 **DR** *020 †80
SIMON, Steven Donald. 207 NE 19TH ST 97128 #056-06-1982 L1998 **FM FPG** *020 †18
SIMS, Eleanor Calucag. 1900 N HIGHWAY 99W STE A, HEALTH CENTER 97128 #748-02-1979 L2003 **FM** *020 †18 ‡
SPARKS, Warren Bradford. 2700 SE THREE MILE LN 97128 #048-12-1971 L1988 **EM FM** *020 †18,16
SPEAR, Eugene Michael. 2700 SE STRATUS AVE, UNIT 406 97128 #040-02-1985 L1992 **CD IM** *020 †20
SPIELVOGEL, Allan. ■ 97128 #035-46-1968 L1969 **EM** *071 †16
STEELE, Thomas Mc Keown. 2700 SE STRATUS AVE, WILLIAMETTE VALLEY MED CEN 97128 #036-07-1996 L1998 **EM IM** *020 †20
STEPHENS, Michael David. 2700 SE STRATUS AVE 97128 #038-40-1975 L1979 **IM** *020 †20
STONEBRIDGE, James Harold. 235 SE NORTON LN 97128 #054-04-1968 L1973 **OPH EM** *071 †35
STOUT, Kevin Bryan. 2700 SE STRATUS AVE, WILLAMETTE VALLEY MEDICAL 97128 #019-02-1984 L2006 **AN** *020 †05
STRANBURG, Clifford Oscar. 254 NE NORTON LN 97128 #035-15-1965 L1967 **U** *020
SWENSSON, Erik Earl. 375 SE NORTON LN STE A 97128 #028-02-1979 L1997 **GS VS** *020 †85
TEAL, Stephen Wiley. 717 SW GILSON ST 97128 #040-02-1968 L1973 **ORS OSM** *071 †40
THOMSON, Charlotte Ann S. ■ 97128 #061-01-1962 **AN** *071
THORNTON, Craig Edward. 254 NE NORTON LN, PHYSICIANS MEDICAL CENTER 97128 #040-02-1985 L1986 **IM** *020 †20
TOPPING, John Wm. 2700 SE STRATUS AVE, UNIT 401 97128 #054-04-1990 L1996 **OTO FPS** *020 †45
ULLRICH, James Robt. 353 SE BAKER ST 97128 #005-15-1973 L1997 **IM** *020 †20
VAN PATTEN, Peter Kurt. 375 SE NORTON LN, STE C 97128 #054-04-1980 L2002 **ORS TRS** *020 †40
VAN UCHELEN, Paul Arthur. 851 N BAKER ST 97128 #660-01-1957 L1966 **IM** *020
VAN ZYL, Kenneth C. ■ 97128 #018-03-1943 **OS GP** *071
VINING, Jacky Roy. 14825 SW HIDDEN HILLS RD 97128 #040-02-1980 L1981 **IM** *020 †20,16
WEINSTEIN, Julia Ann. ■ 97128 #034-01-1995 L1998 **P** *020
WILLIAMSON, Theodore Jos. 2700 SE STRATUS AVE, STE A 97128 #011-02-1975 L1978 **RO** *020 †80
WINKLER, Albert, Jr. 353 SE BAKER ST 97128 #040-02-1964 **FM OBG** *071 †18
WINKLER, Craig Allen. 2700 SE STRATUS AVE 97128 #040-02-1986 L1987 **IM** *072 †20
ZAKAIB, George Salem. 2700 SE STRATUS AVE, MCMINNVILLE ORTHOPEDIC -HA 97128 #055-01-1972 L2002 **ORS HS** *020 †40

MEDFORD – JACKSON

AARONSON, John Philip. 2435 HERITAGE WAY 97504 #005-17-1962 **GP AN** *020

ADEN-WANSBURY, Cory. ■ 97501 #005-06-1971 L2002 **OTO HNS** *071 †45

ADESMAN, Peter Wm. 2860 CREEKSIDE CIR, GASTROENTEROLOGY 97504 #016-11-1979 L1980 **GE** *020 †20

AHMANN, Gerald Black. 2828 E BARNETT RD 97504 #036-07-1974 L1982 **ON IM** *020 †20

ALFORD, Amanda Bole. 2620 E BARNETT RD STE H, ANESTHESIA ASSOCIATES OF M 97504 #035-46-1999 L2006 **AN** *020 †05

ALFTINE, Anne Elise. 555 BLACK OAK DR, STE 100 97504 #018-03-1995 L1998 **IM** *020 †20

ALFTINE, Christopher D. 555 BLACK OAK DR STE 100, MEDFORD MED CLNC 97504 #018-03-1995 L1998 **IM** *020 †20

AMES, Bruce Anthony, Jr. 1111 CRATER LAKE AVE, APOGEE MEDICAL GROUP 97504 #422-01-1998 L2001 **FM** *020 †20

AMPEL, Kenneth Robt. 1698 E MCANDREWS RD, STE 400 97504 #040-02-1973 L1976 **IM OM** *020 †20

APOSTOL, John Gus. 815 E MAIN ST 97504 #040-02-1965 L1968 **OPH** *020 †35

ARNDT, Byron Chas. 2825 E BARNETT RD, VISTA PATHOLOGY, P.C. 97504 #056-06-1975 L1990 **PTH DMP** *020 †50

ASUDANI, Kusum Bhawandas. 1111 CRATER LAKE AVE 97504 #496-54-2002 L2006 **IM** *020 †20

AUGUST, Lynne. 650 ROYAL AVE # 12 97504 #028-02-1973 L1978 **PD** *075

BAILEY, George Winthrop. 1698 E MCANDREWS RD, STE 400 97504 #016-43-1978 L1981 **IM** *020 †50,20

BAILEY, Lisa Gaye. 1005 E MAIN ST 97504 #025-07-1990 L1997 **P ADP** *020 †75

BANDLER, Mack Kenneth. 692 MURPHY RD 97504 #003-01-1981 L1986 **DR** *020 †80

BARNETT, William Albert. 2620 E BARNETT RD STE H, ANESTHESIA ASSOC OF MEDFOR 97504 #048-04-1974 L1977 **AN** *020 †20

BARRETT, Frederick Jerald. 2620 E BARNETT RD STE H, MEDFORD, PC 97504 #017-20-1967 L1979 **AN** *020 †20

BARROWS, Edward Bruce. 1698 E MCANDREWS RD, STE 280 97504 #005-19-1983 L1993 **U** *020 †95

BARRUS, Loren Rodney. 2925 SISKIYOU BLVD 97504 #049-01-1984 L1989 **OPH** *020 †35

BARSS, Theodore Parker. ■ 97504 #010-01-1947 L1949 **AN** *071 †05

BAUER, Tino Frank. 2640 E BARNETT RD, STE E-333 97504 #408-30-1998 L2006 **IM** *100 †20

BECKSTEAD, Jay Hadley. 1111 CRATER LAKE AVE, STE 3 97504 #049-01-1974 L1990 **PTH HMP** *050 †50

BELAFSKY, Caryn Beth. 229 W STEWART AVE 97501 #021-01-1994 L1998 **MPD PD** *020 †55

BENTON, James Michael. 781 BLACK OAK DR STE 102 97504 #038-41-1973 L1976 **OM EM** *020 †16

BERGSTROM, Ralph Wm., Jr. ■ 97504 #026-04-1964 L1973 **FM** *071 †18

BERNARD, Roger Peterick. 748 STATE ST 97504 #024-01-1964 L1972 **GS VS** *071 †85

BERRYMAN, James Thos., Jr. 1698 E MCANDREWS RD, STE 400 97504 #016-06-1967 L1972 **IM** *020 †20

BIERAUGEL, Jean Therese. 555 BLACK OAK DR STE 100, MCPC FAMILY PRACTICE 97504 #026-04-1976 L1996 **FM** *020 †20

BILLONI, Philip Joseph. 2825 E BARNETT RD 97504 #041-13-1997 L2003 **IM** *020 †20

BINETTE, Alan Andrew. 691 MURPHY RD STE 232 97504 #016-02-1981 L1985 **OBG** *020 †30

BLANCHE, Robert N. 2900 DOCTORS PARK DR 97504 #036-05-1993 L1997 **IM** *020 †20

BLOOM, Heidi Taylor. 2780 E BARNETT RD 97504 #041-01-1995 L2002 **HS** *020 †40

BOBEK, Eileen M. 2825 E BARNETT RD, ROGUE VALLEY MEDICAL CENTE 97504 #035-06-1996 L2002 **EM** *020 †16

BOBEK, Miroslav Patrick. 2900 STATE ST 97504 #035-06-1995 L2002 **NS** *020 †25

BOLTON, Thomas Cornish. 840 ROYAL AVE STE 1 97504 #016-06-1947 L1947 **ORS** *071 †40

BRADSHAW, Mark Allen. 1005 E MAIN ST, BLDG B 97504 #027-01-1991 L2003 **P** *020 †75

BRANDENBURG, Danl Richard. 1698 E MCANDREWS RD, STE 400 97504 #040-02-1980 L1982 **IM** *020 †20

BRAWNER, John Clifton. 520 MEDICAL CENTER DR, STE 300 97504 #051-04-1975 L1984 **GS VS** *020 †85

BRENDER, Erin Bernadette. 2825 E BARNETT RD 97504 #034-01-2002 L2006 **IM** *100 †20

BROWER, Jon Russel. 520 MEDICAL CENTER DR, STE 200 97504 #003-01-1998 L2006 **CD** *020 †20

BRUMMER, Stephen David. 2960 DOCTORS PARK DR 97504 #051-04-1976 L1983 **IM IMG** *020 †20

BUCCINO, Kenneth Robert. 2825 E BARNETT RD, ROGUE VALLEY MEDICAL CENTE 97504 #005-11-1994 L1998 **EM** *020 †16

BUCK, Robert Hoem. ■ 97504 #021-01-1947 L1947 **PTH CLP** *062 †50

BUI, Thong Tien. 1698 E MCANDREWS RD, STE 280 97504 #035-06-1991 L1996 **U** *020 †95

BUJOSA, Pedro Carlos. 1698 E MCANDREWS RD, STE 300 97504 #005-19-1989 L2003 **FM** *020 †18

BURKE, Denise Ann. 749 GOLF VIEW DR UNIT A 97504 #030-06-1988 L1992 **D** *020 †15 ‡

BURKET, Brent Alexander. 3617 S PACIFIC HWY, LCDV 97501 #040-02-1993 L2002 **FM** *020 †18

BURKET, John Mc Vey. 749 GOLF VIEW DR, UNIT A 97504 #018-03-1960 L1966 **D DMP** *071 †15

BURT, Steven Ray. 2620 E BARNETT RD STE H 97504 #049-01-1997 L2001 **AN** *020 †05

BYERS, Cornelia Mei. 2780 E BARNETT RD # 32 97504 #017-20-1976 L1977 **PM IM** *020 †20,60

BYERS, Malcolm S. 2151 HOBERT ST 97504 #030-05-1947 L1947 **FM P** *020 †18

CALHOUN, Jos Bryant, Jr. ■ 97504 #018-03-1965 L1966 **OPH** *071 †35

CAMPAGNA, Mario J. 2900 STATE ST 97504 #040-02-1952 L1957 **OS NS** *071 †25

CANNON, Steve Gregory. 2620 E BARNETT RD STE H 97504 #005-02-1997 L2002 **AN** *020 †05

CARBONELL, Miguel Gonzalo. 3190 STATE ST, STE 102 97504 #024-07-1988 L1996 **OBG** *020 †30

CARLINI, Walter Gino. 2900 STATE ST 97504 #005-11-1988 L1993 **N CN** *020 †75

CARMECI, Charles. 2954 SISKIYOU BLVD 97504 #051-04-1993 L2002 **TS** *020 †85,90

CASTILLO, Juan Manuel. 520 MEDICAL CENTER DR, STE 300 97504 #035-19-1994 L2003 **VS** *020 †85

CASTILLO, Sherry Jo. 2859 STATE ST, STE 102 97504 #048-12-1995 L2003 **FM** *020 †18

CATALANO, David John. 2019 AERO WAY, STE 103 PMB 388 97504 #005-12-1982 L1990 **RO** *071 †80

CENDEJAS, Fernando. 2900 DOCTORS PARK DR, STE 200 97504 #005-11-1989 L1995 **IM** *020 †20

CHAMBERLAIN, Steven E. 2780 E BARNETT RD, STE 200 97504 #040-02-1978 L1984 **ORS** *020 †40

CHAMBERLAND, David L. 1365 POPLAR DR 97504 #040-02-2001 L2006 **RHU** *020

CHAMBERLAND, Shireen Nico. 555 BLACK OAK DR, STE 100 97504 #040-02-2001 L2006 **FM** *020 †18

CHARLES, Marcelin. 555 BLACK OAK DR, STE 100 97504 #035-19-1979 L2006 **FM** *020 †18 ‡

CIURLIK, Magdalena. ■ 97504 #759-09-1997 L2001 **AN** *100

COFER, Herman D. ■ 97501 #019-02-1949 L1978 **GP** *071

COLLIER, James Curtis. 132 W MAIN ST, STE 103 97501 #011-04-1990 L1996 **CHP** *020

CONWAY, Gregory Earle. 750 MURPHY RD 97504 #030-06-1997 L2000 **PD** *020 †55

CONWELL, John Wm., Jr. 1457 E MCANDREWS RD 97504 #038-06-1952 L1962 **N** *072

COOK, James Carl, Jr. 940 ROYAL AVE, UNIT 450 97504 #021-01-1976 L2007 **CD IM** *020 †20

COOK, Stephen Jay. 842 E MAIN ST, MEDFORD RADIOLOGICAL GROUP 97504 #039-01-1970 L1976 **DR OS** *071 †80

CORDEIRO, Maria E. 940 ROYAL AVE, UNIT 350 97504 #067-01-2001 L2005 **OBG** *020 †30

CORSON, John Stadler. ■ 97504 #040-02-1964 L1967 **ORS** *020 †40

COSMANN, Brian. 842 E MAIN ST, MEDFORD RADIOLOGICAL GROUP 97504 #918-01-1966 L2002 **DR** *020 †80

CRAFT, William Bradley. 940 ROYAL AVE UNIT 420, PMB/SISKIYOU SURGICAL 97504 #049-01-1994 L2001 **GS** *020 †85

CRUICKSHANK, James C. 1698 E MCANDREWS RD # 220, CANCER EAR, NOSE & THROATC 97504 #035-03-1975 L1993 **OTO** *020 †45

CULLEN, Edward Clark. 555 BLACK OAK DR STE 100 97504 #005-18-1982 L1990 **IM EM** *020 †20

CUTLER, Mary Frances. 1307 W MAIN ST 97501 #005-02-1988 L1997 **FM** *020 †18

DARLINGTON, Kristina Eliz. 842 E MAIN ST 97504 #005-76-2001, ▲ L2007 *020

DAUTERMAN, Kent W. 520 MEDICAL CENTER DR 97504 #023-07-1994 L2002 **IC CD** *020 †20

DAVIS, Michael A. 1610 E MCANDREWS RD, PMG/MEDFORD PEDIATRICS 97504 #056-05-1965 L1966 **PD** *020 †55

DAVIS, Michael Adam. 1610 E MCANDREWS RD, BLDG M 97504 #028-02-1993 L2002 **PD** *020 †55

DE BON, Francis Louis. ■ 97504 #005-02-1944 L1945 **AN** *071 †05

DEMPSEY, Jackson Tyler. 1005 E MAIN ST 97504 #034-01-1982 L1989 **P** *020

DE WING, Michelle Deborah. 1698 E MCANDREWS RD, STE 100 97504 #005-06-1995 L2001 **TS** *012 †85

DE YARMAN, Kent Houston. 493 MURPHY RD 97504 #018-03-1974 L1979 **AI PD** *020 †55,03

DIBB, Charles R. 2828 E BARNETT RD 97504 #016-42-1985 L1992 **HO IM** *020 †20

DICKERSON, Gordon Wayne. 2798 E BARNETT RD 97504 #019-02-1959 L1964 **AN** *071 †05

DIENEL, Nicholas Hans. ■ 97504 #041-01-1972 L1977 **CD** *020 †20

DIXON, Sandra Denniston. 2825 E BARNETT RD, ROGUE VALLEY MEDICAL CENTE 97504 #035-45-1965 L1986 **P CHP** *020

DODGE, James Theo, Jr. 940 ROYAL AVE UNIT 450, PMG CARDIOLOGY 97504 #054-04-1991 L2006 **IC CD** *020 †20

DRIVER, Timothy Robt. 2900 DOCTORS PARK DR, STE 100 97504 #040-02-1975 L1977 **U** *020 †95

DRYLAND, David Ian. 1365 POPLAR DR 97504 #035-15-1994 L2001 **RHU** *020 †20

DUNN, William Laurent. ■ 97504 #016-42-1978 L1993 **FM** *071 †18

DU VIVIER, Derick Rene. 2620 E BARNETT RD STE H, ANESTHESIA ASSOCIATES 97504 #012-05-1998 L2002 **AN** *020 †05

DYSART, Bonnar Wood. ■ 97504 #005-11-1956 L1963 **IM** *020 †20

EATON, Mark Adalbert. 520 MEDICAL CENTER DR, STE 300 97504 #041-01-1994 L2001 **VS** *020 †85

ECKERT, Robert Walter. 19 MYRTLE ST, COMMUNITY HEALTH CENTER 97504 #005-19-1994 L2002 **FM** *020 †18

ECKERT, Robin Carol. 1111 CRATER LAKE AVE, STE 3 97504 #005-19-1994 L2001 **PCP** *020

EDDY, Richard Lowell. 221 W STEWART AVE, STE 101 97501 #041-02-1961 L1998 **END** *020 †20

EDSON, Steven Bryan. 842 E MAIN ST, MEDFORD RADIOLOGICAL GROUP 97504 #041-02-1978 L2001 **DR PDR** *020 †80

EMORI, H Walter. 1104 E JACKSON ST 97504 #005-12-1966 L1975 **RHU IM** *020

FARAONI, James David, Jr. 2620 E BARNETT RD STE H 97504 #040-02-2001 L2001 **AN** *020 †05

FAUGHNAN, Kerri Ann. 1307 W MAIN ST 97501 #007-02-2001 L2005 **FM** *020 †18

FAUGHT, William Earl. 520 MEDICAL CENTER DR, STE 300 97504 #016-45-1987 L1994 **VS GS** *020 †85

FENG, Guoping. ■ 97504 #243-52-1986 L2005 **IM** *020 †20

FENNELL, Dan Frederic. 555 BLACK OAK DR, STE 300 97504 #007-02-1980 L1990 **PUD IM** *020 †20

FENNELL, Michael Scott. 842 E MAIN ST, MEDFORD RADIOLOGICAL GROUP 97504 #030-06-1993 L1999 **DR** *020 †80

FLETCHER, Gary Allan. 2620 E BARNETT RD STE H, MEDFORD, PC 97504 #054-04-1968 L1973 **AN** *020 †05

FLETCHER, Janet V. ■ 97504 #054-04-1968 L1973 **GP FM** *020

FOLSOM, David Lowell. 2954 SISKIYOU BLVD, CARDIOVASCULAR & THORACIC 97504 #049-01-1987 L1994 **TS** *020 †85,90

FORD, Christina Mc Grath. 2640 E BARNETT RD, STE E-333 97504 #020-02-2000 L2004 **IM** *020

FORSYTH, John Willard. 555 BLACK OAK DR, STE 200 97504 #028-02-1965 L1971 **CD IM** *071 †20

FOSTER, Paul D. 555 BLACK OAK DR 97504 #018-03-1958 L1959 **GS** *071 †85

FRIED, Frederick E. 2933 DOCTORS PARK DR, PSYCHIATRIC ASSOC 97504 #869-05-1966 L1976 **P** *071 †75

FRIERSON, James Alan. 691 MURPHY RD, STE 114 97504 #048-12-1976 L1982 **PD ADL** *020 †55

FULLER, Beverly Frances. 3170 STATE ST, MEDFORD WOMEN'S CLINIC 97504 #047-05-1988 L1992 **OBG** *020 †30

GALLEN, John Thomas. 555 BLACK OAK DR, STE 100 97504 #041-02-1999 L2004 **END** *020 †20

GALT, David Leland. 2780 E BARNETT RD, STE 200 97504 #005-06-1982 L1988 **OSM OAR** *020 †40

GARDNER, Hugh Willis. ■ 97504 #025-07-1962 L1967 **P LM** *030

GARRARD, Christopher Jay. 1111 CRATER LAKE AVE, PROVIDENCE HOSPITAL 97504 #049-01-1970 L1974 **EM** *020 †16

GARRETT, Ryan Joseph. 1111 CRATER LAKE AVE, MEDICAL CENTER 97504 #038-45-2000 L2006 **EM** *020 †16

GELL, Jonathan. 2825 E BARNETT RD 97504 #043-01-1975 L1980 **OS RHU** *030 †20

GENSKOW, Gordon Lee. 2798 E BARNETT RD 97504 #040-02-1981 L1982 **AN** *020

GERBER, Robert C. 460 MURPHY RD 97504 #005-06-1964 L1970 **RHU IM** *071 †20

GERDES, Clint Matthew. 842 E MAIN ST 97504 #030-06-2000 L2006 **DR** *020 †80

GIBBS, Frederic A, Jr. 940 ROYAL AVE UNIT 100B, PROVIDENCE HOSP RAD ONCOLO 97504 #005-11-1969 L1998 **RO** *071 †80

■ = Address Information Privacy Protected

GILLETTE, Patrick James. 2825 E BARNETT RD 97504 #649-36-1984 L1991 **IM** *020 †20

GILMORE, Gerald Thomas. 842 E MAIN ST 97504 #018-03-1968 L1975 **DR** *020 †80

GLATTE, Hayden Avery, Jr. 555 BLACK OAK DR, MEDFORD MEDICAL CLINIC 97504 #016-06-1961 L1967 **END IM** *020 †20

GONZALEZ, Gregory J. 1600 DELTA WATERS RD, STE 107 97504 #040-02-1984 L2002 **PD EM** *020 †55

GRAMLEY, Molly Mc Cormick. 19 MYRTLE ST, COMMUNITY HEALTH CENTER 97504 #035-01-1996 L2006 **IM** *020 †20

GRANT, David Michael. 2620 E BARNETT RD STE H, MEDFORD, PC 97504 #048-13-1974 L1975 **AN** *020 †05

GRANT, Peter Alan. 473 MURPHY RD 97504 #048-15-1982 L1985 **PM CN** *020 †60

GREENLEAF, Stephen M. ■ 97504 #038-06-1987 L1989 **P** *020

GRIMM, Philip John. 842 E MAIN ST, MEDFORD RADIOLOGICAL GROUP 97504 #030-06-1976 L1977 **DR** *020 †80

GROSS, Brian Walter. 520 MEDICAL CENTER DR, STE 200 97504 #035-45-1976 L1982 **CD IM** *020 †20

HAGLOCH, Nancy Lee. 4732 OAK TREE CIR, PROVIDENCE MEDICAL GROUP 97504 #005-18-1993 L1997 **OBG** *020 †30

HALEY, Tracy. 1698 E MCANDREWS RD, STE 100 97504 #005-19-1998 L2003 **GS** *020 †85

HALL, Brian Edwards. 2825 E BARNETT RD 97504 #049-01-2001 L2005 **AN** *020 †05

HALL, Roger Verge. 2954 SISKIYOU BLVD 97504 #049-01-1982 L1982 **TS** *020 †85,90

HAMMOND, Thomas John. 2620 E BARNETT RD STE H, ANESTHESIA ASSOC. OF MEDFO 97504 #054-04-1990 L1998 **AN** *020 †05

HARKER, Lee Clesson. 2825 E BARNETT RD, ROGUE VALLEY MED CNT 97504 #005-18-1980 L1994 **NPM PD** *020 †55

HARLOW, Elliott Lee. ■ 97504 #007-02-1944 L1955 **D** *071 †15

HARRIE, Robert R. 1698 E MCANDREWS RD, STE 100 97504 #037-01-1983 L2001 **GS** *020 †85

HARRIS, Linda Ruth. 1307 W MAIN ST 97501 #018-03-1978 L1985 **OBG** *020 †30

HARRIS, Victoria Vanorden. 2825 E BARNETT RD, ROGUE VALLELY MEDICAL CENT 97504 #049-01-1996 L2000 **EM** *020 †16

HAUGEN, Kenneth Duane. 940 ROYAL AVE, DEPARTMENT OF 97504 #005-12-1994 L1999 **RO** *020 †80

HAULK, Anthony Alan. 2860 CREEKSIDE CIR, GASTROENTEROLOGY 97504 #043-01-1979 L1998 **GE IM** *020 †20

HAVEMAN, Craig Norman. 2825 E BARNETT RD, DEPT RAD/ONCO 97504 #028-34-1982 L1991 **RO IM** *020 †20,80

HEBERT, Richard Joseph. ■ 97501 #056-06-1964 L1972 **GE** *071 †20

HEHN, Sean Thomas. 2828 E BARNETT RD 97504 #056-06-1998 L2004 **HO** *020 †20

HELMAN, Edward Allan. 1017 ROYAL AVE 97504 #056-06-1971 L1975 **FM OM** *020 †70

HENDERSON, Ronald Lee. 2780 E BARNETT RD, STE 200 97504 #060-01-1983 L1990 **ORS** *020 †40

HERRMANN, Susan Mcnew. 2620 E BARNETT RD STE H, MEDFORD, PC 97504 #054-04-1991 L1995 **AN PME** *020 †20

HERSCH, Steven Lawrence. 2640 E BARNETT RD, STE E-333 97504 #005-06-1986 L2002 **IM** *020 †20

HEUSCHER, Ruth Bertha. ■ 97504 #869-05-1948 L1976 **OPH GP** *071

HEYERMAN, Richard Danl. 1698 E MCANDREWS RD, STE 300 97504 #016-06-1979 L1983 **FM** *020 †18

HIGBEE, Kathleen Anne. 2900 DOCTORS PARK DR, FAMILY PRACTICE GROUP II 97504 #025-12-1978 L1990 **EM FM** *020 †18

HILDRETH, Douglas Howard. 555 BLACK OAK DR, HERBERT H SIX MD 97504 #025-01-1965 L1972 **GS CD** *071 †85

HOFSTETTER, Seth Morris. 842 E MAIN ST, MEDFORD RADIOLOGICAL GROUP 97504 #033-06-1989 L1994 **DR VIR** *020 †80

HOLBERT, Thomas Robt. 2825 E BARNETT RD 97504 #047-06-1972 L1987 **GYN** *020 †30

HOPKINS, Jon Lacey. 1111 CRATER LAKE AVE 97504 #010-01-1993 L2006 **IM** *020

HOUGH, David Matthew. 750 MURPHY RD, SOUTHERN OREGON PEDIATRICS 97504 #005-02-1992 L1998 **PD** *020 †55

HOUGH, Mary Cavill. 750 MURPHY RD, SOUTHERN OREGON PEDIATRICS 97504 #005-02-1992 L1998 **PD** *020 †55

HUBBERT, Theodore Earl. 842 E MAIN ST, MEDFORD RADIOLOGICAL GROUP 97504 #021-05-1993 L1999 **VIR** *020 †80

HUDSPETH, E Ray. ■ 97504 #048-02-1951 L1951 **GYN** *071 †30

HUSTON, James Edward. ■ 97504 #038-41-1956 L1956 **OBG** *072 †30

HUSUM, Kurt William. ■ 97504 #038-40-2004 **DR** *012

HUSUM, William Chas. 2900 DOCTORS PARK DR 97504 #038-43-1972 L1975 **IM** *020 †20

HUTCHINGS, Roger Herrick. 2825 E BARNETT RD 97504 #030-05-1960 L1987 **NEP FM** *072 †20

HUTCHINSON, Peter Brian. 1698 E MCANDREWS RD, STE 400 97504 #067-01-1963 L1969 **IM ID** *020 †20

HUTCHISON, Rebecca Warren. 2640 E BARNETT RD, STE E-333 97504 #027-01-1989 L2002 **IM** *020 †20

HUTH, Mark Michael. 520 MEDICAL CENTER DR 97504 #021-05-1985 L1994 **CD IM** *020 †20

HWANG, Harvey. 2620 E BARNETT RD STE H, MEDFORD, PC 97504 #005-02-1982 L1987 **AN** *020 †55,05

IANORA, Alfred A, Jr. ■ 97501 #561-01-1964 L1968 **FM** *075

IGELMAN, Jon David. 2959 SISKIYOU BLVD STE B, DERMATOLOGY & LASER ASSOCI 97504 #048-04-1986 L1999 **D** *020 †15

IMPERIA, Paul Steven. 2727 E BARNETT RD, MEDICAL EYE CENTER 97504 #035-03-1983 L1991 **OPH IM** *020 †20,35

INGMAN, Margaret Jean. 2825 E BARNETT RD 97504 #040-04-1962 L1987 **NPM** *071 †55

INGRAM, Gary Lohrenz. 2620 E BARNETT RD STE H, MEDFORD, PC 97504 #040-02-1971 L1977 **AN** *020

JACKSON, John Wm. 1698 E MCANDREWS RD, STE 400 97504 #019-02-1978 L1982 **IM** *020 †20

JACKSON, Roberta Lynn. 692 MURPHY RD, MEDFORD RADIOLOGICAL GROUP 97504 #005-12-1982 L1988 **DR** *020 †80

JACOBSON, Heidi Leverenz. 2860 CREEKSIDE CIR, GASTROENTEROLOGY 97504 #036-01-1985 L1990 **IM** *020 †20

JACOBSON, Kris N. 2860 CREEKSIDE CIR, GASTROENTEROLOGY 97504 #040-02-1983 L1990 **GE IM** *020 †20

JAFFAR, Ahsan. 2825 E BARNETT RD, SOUTHERN OREGON HOSPITALIS 97504 #704-19-2001 L2007 **IM** *020 †20

JAMES, Richard Ernest. 2780 E BARNETT RD, STE 200 97504 #054-04-1966 L1976 **ORS** *020 †40

JENSEN, Robert M. 1353 E MCANDREWS RD 97504 #010-01-1984 L1991 **PS GS** *020 †85,65

JETT, Patricia Lu. 2825 E BARNETT RD, ROGUE VALLEY MEDICAL CTR 97504 #040-02-1990 L1991 **NPM PD** *020 †55

JOHNSON, Diana Michele. 1111 CRATER LAKE AVE 97504 #028-03-1987 L1992 **EM** *020 †16

JOHNSON, Donald Harvey. 691 MURPHY RD, STE 122 97504 #049-01-1993 L1997 **PD** *020 †55

JOHNSON, William Warren. ■ 97504 #016-06-1953 L1954 **GP** *071

JOHNSTON, George David. 460 MURPHY RD, PAIN CARE OF OREGON 97504 #005-14-1970 L1971 **ORS OSS** *020 †40

JONES, Alan Mc Clung. 1111 CRATER LAKE AVE, EMERGENCY DEPARTMENT 97504 #005-11-1976 L1995 **FM** *020 †18

JONES, Ronald Dale. 691 MURPHY RD, STE 209 97504 #048-04-1988 L1994 **PD** *020 †55

KAHN, Daniel Aaron. 2620 E BARNETT RD STE H, MEDFORD, PC 97504 #021-01-1988 L1994 **AN** *020 †05

KAHN, Karen Tresser. 19 MYRTLE ST, COMMUNITY HEALTH CLINIC 97504 #021-01-1989 L1994 **GP** *030

KARCHMER, Richard Kent. 2828 E BARNETT RD 97504 #028-02-1969 L1976 **ON HEM** *020 †20

KAUFMAN, Robert Gould. 2691 HERITAGE WAY 97504 #040-02-1962 L1963 **OBG OS** *071 †30

KEARNS, John Cameron. 2620 E BARNETT RD STE H, MEDFORD, PC 97504 #019-02-1968 L1974 **AN** *020 †05

KELLER, Lisa Kay. 940 ROYAL AVE, UNIT350 97504 #005-19-1977 L2007 **OBG** *020 †30

KELLY, Alan John. 221 W STEWART AVE, STE 101 97501 #031-01-1994 L1998 **IM** *020 †20

KERWIN, Edward Michael. 3860 CRATER LAKE AVE 97504 #007-02-1988 L1993 **AI IM** *020 †20,03

KEY, James S. ■ 97504 #048-02-1952 L1952 **D** *071 †15

KIM, Milton Wallace. ■ 97501 #014-01-1977 L1978 **GS** *075 †85

KING, Julie Ann. 3170 STATE ST, MEDFORD WOMEN'S CLINIC 97504 #005-12-1998 L1999 **OBG** *020 †30

KING, Kristine Michelle. ■ 97504 #035-01-2001 L2005 **MG** *020 †19

KIRKPATRICK, Douglas B. 2900 STATE ST, MEDFORD NEUROLOGICAL CLINI 97504 #036-07-1969 L1991 **NS** *071 †25

KOCH, Thomas Chas. 1600 DELTA WATERS RD, STE 107 97504 #005-19-1975 L1990 **EM FM** *020 †16

KOHLER, Susan Elizabeth. 2828 E BARNETT RD 97504 #041-01-1986 L1996 **HEM ON** *020 †20

KOLSBUN, John Arthur. 2640 E BARNETT RD, STE E-333 97504 #054-04-1993 L1994 **IM** *020 †20

KOTLER, Todd Stuart. 520 MEDICAL CENTER DR 97504 #005-11-1982 L1989 **CD IM** *020 †20

KRONMAN, Karen Rae. 940 ROYAL AVE, UNIT 350 97504 #026-08-1979 L2003 **OBG** *020 †30

KUHL, Jason Michael. 97504 #040-02-2004 L2004 **IM** *020 †18

KUHL, Karin Boutacoff. ■ 97504 #040-02-2004 L2004 **IM** *100 †20

KUO, Wie-Peng. 1698 E MCANDREWS RD, STE 100 97504 #041-13-2002 L2007 **GS** *020

LAOHABURANAKIT, Petey. 555 BLACK OAK DR STE 300 97504 #891-01-1996 L2004 **PCC** *020 †20

LAURY, Daniel Henri. 786 STATE ST 97504 #035-46-1988 L1992 **OBG REN** *020 †30

LEMANNE, Dawn. 748 STATE ST 97504 #005-02-1988 L1996 **ON** *020 †20

LEVIN, Lawrence Brent. 1365 POPLAR DR 97504 #014-01-1981 L2002 **RHU** *020 †20 ‡

LEWIS, Jack Byron. 1698 E MCANDREWS RD, PROVIDENCE PLAZA, SUITE 28 97504 #040-02-1994 L1996 **U** *020 †95

LICHTENSTEIN, Roy. 1698 E MCANDREWS RD, STE 300 97504 #035-09-1971 L1977 **FM** *020 †18

LIGHTHEART, Kenneth M. 520 MEDICAL CENTER DR 97504 #040-02-1994 L2000 **CD** *020 †20

LINDEN, Dennis Henry John. 2900 DOCTORS PARK DR 97504 #060-01-1983 L1996 **IM** *020 †20

LINZMEYER, Kristin Marie. 520 MEDICAL CENTER DR 97504 #040-02-2000 L2001 **CD** *020 †20

LJUNGKVIST, Valerie Ann. 750 MURPHY RD, SOUTHERN OREGON PEDIATRICS 97504 #050-02-2002 L2005 **PD** *020 †55

LOOS, James Christian. 2900 DOCTORS PARK DR, STE 100 97504 #035-09-1999 L1999 **U** *020

LOUDERMILK, Allison. 1111 CRATER LAKE AVE, STE 3 97504 #048-02-1996 L2001 **PTH** *020 †50

LOUIE, Jeffrey Allen. 2900 STATE ST 97504 #005-15-1980 L1987 **NS** *020 †25

LOWENGART, Ruth A. 2627 SISKIYOU BLVD STE 100 97504 #005-06-1981 L1994 **ISM OMM** *020 †20,70

LUPINETTI, Flavian Mark. 940 ROYAL AVE, UNIT 450 97504 #023-07-1978 L2005 **TS** *020 †85,90

MAC KINNON, Susan K. ■ 97504 #010-02-1975 L1986 **IM RHU** *020 †20 ‡

MARGULIES, Thomas Daniel. 229 W STEWART AVE 97501 #028-02-1978 L1996 **IM** *020 †20

MARTIN, Christina Louise. 2940 DOCTORS PARK DR 97504 #016-06-1979 L1990 **PD MG** *020 †19,55

MARTIN, David Jansonius. 520 MEDICAL CENTER DR 97504 #032-01-1989 L1996 **CD ICE** *020 †20

MARTIN, Eric Lou. 2900 DOCTORS PARK DR, STE 100 97504 #040-02-1988 L1993 **U** *020 †95

MARTINEZ, Patricia Elena. ■ 97504 #048-16-1992 L1994 **PD** *020 †55

MARTINEZ, Patrick F. 1307 W MAIN ST 97501 #048-16-1992 L2006 **FM** *020 †18

MATTHEWS, Minor Edwin. 520 MEDICAL CENTER DR, STE 100 97504 #036-07-1967 L1972 **CD** *071 †20

MATTHEWS, William Ellis. ■ 97504 #005-11-1960 L1966 **ORS** *062 †40

MATZ, Paul David. 555 BLACK OAK DR STE 100, MCPC FAMILY PRACTICE 97504 #005-19-1978 L1981 **FM** *020 †18

MAUKONEN, Larry Jon. 897 ROYAL AVE STE B 97504 #038-41-1971 L1975 **N OS** *020

MAYER, Paul Thos. 3617 S PACIFIC HWY, LA CLINICA DEL VALLE FAM. 97501 #005-19-1991 L2000 **FM** *020 †18

MAYER, Roland Melvin. ■ 97504 #016-06-1947 L1947 **GS** *071 †85

MCANALLY, James L. 842 E MAIN ST 97504 #001-02-2002 L2008 **DR** *100 †80

MC ARDLE, Mona J. 1600 DELTA WATERS RD, STE 107 97504 #049-01-1993 L1994 **IM** *020 †20

MCCASKILL, Michael F. 2825 E BARNETT RD 97504 #056-05-1975 L1977 **EM FM** *020 †16

MC CULLOUGH, Leslie Lee. 815 N CENTRAL AVE STE C, VALLEY IMMEDIATE CARE, LLC 97501 #054-04-1975 L1978 **FM ADM** *020 †18

MCDONELL, Meleisa. 1648 E MCANDREWS RD, BLDG D 97504 #665-01-2000 L2001 **PM** *100 †60

MC GILL, Theodore Jon. 2620 E BARNETT RD STE H, ANESTHESIA ASSOC OF MEDFOR 97504 #048-02-1991 L1995 **AN** *020 †05

MC INTOSH, Donn Keith. ■ 97504 #040-02-1956 L1961 **ORS** *071 †40

MC INTYRE, Robert Dennis. 1089 MEDFORD CTR # 417 97504 #040-02-1969 L1972 **AN** *071 †05

MC LAUGHLIN, John R. ■ 97504 #016-11-1946 L1953 **OBG** *071 †30

MC NEAL, Travis Alan. 1698 E MCANDREWS RD, STE 400 97504 #016-42-1999 L2002 **IM** *020 †20

MEHTA, Manish. ■ 97504 #496-21-2000 L2006 **IM** *020 †20
MELNYK, Vera Olga. ■ 97504 #035-45-1982 L1983 **RHU IM** *020 †20
MELSON, John Anderson. 897 ROYAL AVE, STE B 97504 #017-20-1967 L1968 **N** *020 †75
MENDELSON, Jeri Kersten. 2959 SISKIYOU BLVD, STE B 97504 #004-01-1998 L2002 **D** *020 †15
MENDOZA, Noriecel Dimayug. 3144 STATE ST 97504 #748-01-1998 L2006 **END** *020
MENGIS, Christopher L, Jr. ■ 97504 #021-01-1951 L1959 **IM** *071 †20
METWALLY, Yaser Abdel A. 2780 E BARNETT RD 97504 #915-04-1986 L2001 **GS** *020
METZ, Gordon Luther. 2825 E BARNETT RD, DUBS CANCER CTR/RVMC 97504 #041-02-1995 L2001 **RO** *020 †80
MEYERDING, Elliott Eugene. 2931 DOCTORS PARK DR 97504 #040-02-1977 L1984 **GS** *020 †85
MEYERDING, Eugene V. 1111 CRATER LAKE AVE 97504 #026-04-1947 L1955 **GS** *071 †85
MICHELS, Kendall Richard. 760 GOLF VIEW DR, UNIT 200 97504 #040-02-1998 L1999 **NEP** *020 †20
MILLER, Maria Dawn. 1600 DELTA WATERS RD, STE 107 97504 #062-01-1989 L1994 **FM** *020
MILLER, Robin Hardy. 916 TOWN CENTER DR, TRIVNE INTERGRATIVE MEDICI 97504 #016-11-1979 L1980 **IM** *050 †20
MILLER, William Jos. ■ 97504 #028-02-1943 L1944 **IMG PD** *071 †55
MILLIGAN, Lee David. 2825 E BARNETT RD, ROGUE VALLEY MEDICAL CENTE 97504 #010-01-1997 L2000 **EM** *020 †16
MILLS, Michael Evan. 750 MURPHY RD, SOUTHERN OREGON PEDIATRICS 97504 #025-01-1995 L2000 **MPD PD** *020 †20,55
MINSER, Allen Chas. 2825 E BARNETT RD 97504 #035-15-1959 L1968 **EM PM** *071 †16
MOLINA-KIRSCH, Hernan. ROGUE VALLEY MEM HOSP, DEPT PATH 97501 #429-01-1977 L1980 **PTH** *040 †50
MOORE, Frank Arthur, Jr. ■ 97504 #005-02-1960 L1966 **OBG** *071 †30
MORAN, Mark Geo. 520 MEDICAL CENTER DR 97504 #005-14-1975 L1981 **IC CD** *020 †20
MORGAN, Christopher Riley. 2859 STATE ST, STE 102 97504 #040-02-1989 L1994 **IM PD** *020 †55,20
MORGAN, Lorie Jane. 2859 STATE ST, STE 102 97504 #040-02-1989 L1994 **GYN** *020 †30
MORRISON, Brian James. ■ 97504 #016-11-1987 L1998 **CD PDC** *020 †20
MULLEN, Eric Thomas. 940 ROYAL AVE, UNIT 110 97504 #036-05-1999 L2004 **RO** *020 †80
MURDOCH, Louis Lee. 2635 SISKIYOU BLVD 97504 #030-05-1960 L1965 **PD** *071 †55
NAOOM, Isam B.. 1111 CRATER LAKE AVE 97504 #528-03-1980 L2006 **IM** *020 †20
NARUS, Michael Steven. 2900 STATE ST 97504 #028-79-1971, ▲ L1977 **CHN N** *020 †75
NAUGLE, Floyd Philip. 781 BLACK OAK DR, STE 102 97504 #041-13-1960 L1966 **OM GS** *020
NAVERSEN, Douglas Norman. 2959 SISKIYOU BLVD, STE A 97504 #038-40-1973 L1982 **D DMP** *020 †15 ‡
NELSON, Stephen L. 2859 STATE ST, STE 102 97504 #021-01-1990 L1994 **FM** *020 †18
NEMZEK, William Raphael. 842 E MAIN ST, MEDFORD RADIOLOGICAL GROUP 97504 #035-03-1969 L2000 **DR** *071 †80
NEWLAND, Gary L. 1111 CRATER LAKE AVE, STE 3 97504 #038-40-1970 L1973 **PTH** *072 †50
NIXON, Randal Ray. 2825 E BARNETT RD 97504 #039-01-1989 L1990 **NP IM** *020 †50
NOYCE, Nancy Anne. 711 MEDFORD CTR 97504 #005-02-1985 L1988 **IM** *020 †20
NOYES, Peter Ford. 20 S BARNEBURG RD 97504 #035-45-1971 L1974 **TS GS** *071 †85
ODDO, Curtis Todd. 816 W 10TH ST 97501 #016-11-1990 L2000 **PD** *020 †55
OLIVA, Matthew Steven. 2727 E BARNETT RD 97504 #054-04-1999 L2006 **OPH** *020 †35
OLSHAUSEN, Kai Philipp. 3156 STATE ST 97504 #408-30-2002 L2006 **IM** *020 †20
OLSON, Henry Warren. 827 SPRING ST 97504 #040-02-1968 L1976 **U** *071 †95
OLSON, James Norman. 1111 CRATER LAKE AVE, STE 3 97504 #054-04-1972 L1976 **PTH FOP** *020 †50
O'NEAL, Nancy C. 520 MEDICAL CENTER DR, STE 300 97504 #048-12-1991 L2007 **GS** *020 †85
ORDAL, John Chas. 555 BLACK OAK DR, STE 300 97504 #005-11-1975 L1981 **PUD** *020 †20
OROZCO, Rachael. 1698 E MCANDREWS RD, STE 300 97504 #024-07-1999 L2004 **FM** *020 †18
OURSLER, Judith Redd. 691 MURPHY RD, STE 202 97504 #023-07-1989 L1994 **D** *020 †15
OVERLAND, Eric Stephen. 555 BLACK OAK DR, STE 300 97504 #026-04-1970 L1980 **PUD** *020 †20
PADDOCK, Robert L. ■ 97504 #005-12-1953 L1954 **GP** *071
PADEN, Philip Y. 221 W STEWART AVE STE 110 97501 #035-46-1982 L1983 **OPH DIA** *020 †35
PALAMARA, Alan Geo. 940 ROYAL AVE, UNIT 350 97504 #033-05-1973 L1977 **OBG** *020 †30
PALM, William Harold. 3617 S PACIFIC HWY, LA CLINIC DEL VALLE 97501 #047-07-1995 L2001 **FM** *020 †18
PARKS, Kevin Wilson. 3860 CRATER LAKE AVE, STE A 97504 #005-18-2001 L2006 **AI** *020 †20,03 ‡
PATTERSON, Bruce Lowell. 520 MEDICAL CENTER DR, STE 200 97504 #041-01-1990 L1996 **CD** *020 †20
PATTERSON, James Fulton. ■ 97504 #024-01-1944 L1948 **IM GE** *071 †20
PEARD, Garrett Hamilton. 555 BLACK OAK DR, MEDFORD MEDICAL CLINIC 97504 #041-12-1996 L2002 **IM** *020 †20
PENA, Eric Antonio. 520 MEDICAL CENTER DR 97504 #011-04-1990 L2003 **CD** *020 †20
PENNER, Thomas Peter. 1600 DELTA WATERS RD, STE 107 97504 #005-12-1988 L2003 **FM** *020 †18
PETERSON, Ashley. 229 W STEWART AVE, FAMILY PRACTICE GROUP PC 97501 #035-01-1992 L1998 **FM** *020 †18
PETERSON, Earl Duane. 2780 E BARNETT RD, STE 200 97504 #048-12-1963 L1973 **ORS** *020 †40
PETERSON, Mark Delano. 2780 E BARNETT RD 97504 #040-02-1988 L1994 **ORS** *020 †40
PHILLIPS, Kimberly A. 555 BLACK OAK DR 97504 #005-76-2000, ▲ L2003 **FM** *020 †18
POISSON, Brett Arthur. 2828 E BARNETT RD 97504 #836-01-1992 L2002 **HO** *020 †20
PORZECANSKI, Ilana. 2825 E BARNETT RD, ROGUE VALLEY MEDICAL CENTE 97504 #539-04-2002 L2007 **CCM** *100 †20
POST, James Theodore. 920 ROYAL AVE 97504 #005-02-1957 L1963 **OTO** *071 †45
POTTER, Michael Wm. 935 TOWN CENTER DR STE A 97504 #040-02-1975 L1996 **NS** *020 †25
POWELL, Diane Hennacy. ■ 97504 #023-07-1983 L2004 **P** *020 †75
PRULHIERE, Jon Darin. 1200 MIRA MAR AVE, ROGUE VALLEY MANOR CLINIC 97504 #040-02-1998 L2002 **FM** *020 †18
PURTZER, Thomas John. 1322 E MCANDREWS RD, STE 101 97504 #040-02-1979 L1981 **PME NS** *020 †25
RABINOVITCH, Ruth Ann. 2941 DOCTORS PARK DR 97504 #054-04-1978 L1984 **ID IM** *020 †20
RAMSEY, Anthony Eugene. 3190 STATE ST, STE 101 97504 #016-06-1972 L1979 **OBG IM** *020 †30
RANIELE, Dean Peter. 760 GOLF VIEW DR, UNIT 200 97504 #038-41-1984 L1990 **IM** *020 †20
REEDY, Michael Thane. 1111 CRATER LAKE AVE, STE 3 97504 #017-20-1983 L1990 **PTH CLP** *020 †50
REKK, Ariadna Irma. ■ 97504 #007-02-1955 L1958 **PTH** *071 †50
RETZLAFF, John Albert. 2727 E BARNETT RD 97504 #024-01-1957 L1963 **OPH** *071 †35
RHEE, Kenneth James. 2825 E BARNETT RD, ROGUE VLY MED CTR DEPT EM 97504 #005-14-1975 L1998 **EM GPM** *020 †70,16
RING, Eric Wallace. 229 W STEWART AVE 97501 #048-15-1997 L1998 **FM** *020 †18
RINKOFF, Jeffrey Stephen. 841 ALDER CREEK DR 97504 #048-04-1979 L1996 **OPH OS** *020 †35
RIZVI, Mujahid Ali. 2828 E BARNETT RD 97504 #704-25-1997 L2006 **HO** *020 †20
ROSS, Carissa Marie. 3170 STATE ST 97504 #039-01-2002 L2006 **OBG** *020
ROSS, Donald Andrew. 2900 STATE ST 97504 #017-20-1983 L2000 **NS** *020 †25
ROSTYKUS, Paul Steven. 787 W 8TH ST, JACKSON COUNTY SHERIFFS OF 97501 #054-04-1981 L1988 **FM EM** *020 †18
ROTE, Joan M. 3190 STATE ST, STE 101 97504 #038-40-1979 L1989 **OBG** *020 †30
ROWE, Melvin John, III. 1314 CENTER DR UNIT B, PMB 509 97501 #025-01-1966 L1999 **N CN** *071 †75
ROZKALNS, Baiba. ■ 97504 #065-01-1966 L1967 **ON HEM** *071
RULON, Michael Preston. 691 MURPHY RD STE 210 97504 #016-06-1980 L1984 **OBG** *020 †30
RUTHERFORD, Morrison. ■ 97504 #035-20-1943 L1947 **OBG** *071 †30
SACKS, Yale. 2825 E BARNETT RD 97504 #035-08-1964 L1965 **ON HEM** *020 †20
SAFLEY, Gary Hueston. 750 MURPHY RD 97504 #005-15-1967 L1973 **PD** *020 †55
SANCHEZ, Oscar Adolfo. 2900 STATE ST 97504 #847-11-1991 L2004 **NS** *020 †75
SANDEFUR, Jere L. 2825 E BARNETT RD, ROGUE VALLEY MEDICAL CENTE 97504 #005-12-1980 L1990 **RO** *020 †80
SANFORD, Kenneth Gary. 2640 E BARNETT RD, E-333 97504 #040-02-2000 L2007 **FM** *100 †18
SASSER, S Michael. 1762 E MCANDREWS RD STE D 97504 #040-02-1974 L1975 **P PFP** *020 †75
SAUER, Karen L. 1307 W MAIN ST 97501 #048-13-1993 L1996 **FM** *020 †18
SAVAGE, Alison Diana. 748 STATE ST 97504 #016-43-1991 L1997 **HEM** *020 †20
SAVIERS, Daniel Alan. 2780 E BARNETT RD STE 320 97504 #038-44-1986 L1990 **PM** *020 †60
SAVINO, Joseph Mark. 460 MURPHY RD 97504 #005-12-2000 L2005 **AN** *100 †05
SCHAEFER, Richard Alan. 520 MEDICAL CENTER DR 97504 #035-45-1969 L1972 **CD** *071 †20
SCHLEINITZ, Paul Fritz. 2860 CREEKSIDE CIR, GASTROENTEROLOGY 97504 #010-02-1974 L1975 **GE IM** *020 †20
SCHNUGG, Stephen Jos. 520 MEDICAL CENTER DR, STE 200 97504 #005-14-1975 L1990 **CD IM** *020 †20
SCHOENHALS, Joseph Alvin. 555 BLACK OAK DR, STE 300 97504 #049-01-1973 L2003 **PUD CCM** *020 †20
SCHROEDER, Paul Wm. 1910 E BARNETT RD, STE 102 97504 #040-02-1979 L1983 **GYN** *020 †30
SCHULTZ, Paul Norman. 2925 SISKIYOU BLVD 97504 #034-01-1985 L1993 **OPH** *020 †35
SCHWARTZ, John Andrew. 940 ROYAL AVE UNIT 420 97504 #038-41-1978 L1989 **VS GS** *020 †85
SHAMES, James Gordon. 1005 E MAIN ST, BLDG A 97504 #041-09-1971 L1972 **FM** *020 †18
SHEKHAR, Stephen Shashank. 812 NADIA WAY 97504 #495-29-1966 L1976 **GP** *020 †30
SIBLEY, Barbara Jean. 750 MURPHY RD, SOUTHERN OREGON PEDIATRICS 97504 #005-11-1991 L1994 **PD** *020 †55
SILLS, Shawn Michael. 460 MURPHY RD 97504 #005-12-1999 L2004 **APM** *020 †05
SIMONS, Jarid Allan. ■ 97504 #051-04-1974 L1975 **PA GP** *050
SINNOTT, Robert Casserly. 842 E MAIN ST, MEDFORD RADIOLOGY 97504 #047-06-1972 L1984 **DR R** *020 †80 ‡
SIX, Herbert H. 2931 DOCTORS PARK DR 97504 #028-03-1965 L1973 **GS TS** *020 †90,85
SMITH, Davis Seaton. 691 MURPHY RD, STE 216 97504 #040-02-1965 L1970 **PD** *020 †55
SOHL, Bryan Douglas. 2825 E BARNETT RD, MATERNAL FETAL MEDICINE CL 97504 #005-18-1984 L1988 **NPM OBG** *020 †30
SOUTHWORTH, William Chas. 1390 BIDDLE RD STE 101, CENTER FOR OCCUPATIONAL ME 97504 #005-02-1969 L1979 **IM EM** *020 †20,16
SPITELLIE, Pete Hunter. 2727 E BARNETT RD 97504 #054-04-1995 L2007 **OPH** *100 †05
STANFORD, Ray Edmund. ■ 97504 #005-14-1966 L1970 **ATP** *071 †50
STEFFEN, Christel Ann. 1111 CRATER LAKE AVE 97504 #016-76-2002, ▲ L2005 **EM** *020 †16
STEINSIEK, Jill Tilley. 555 BLACK OAK DR, STE 100 97504 #004-01-1987 L2003 **FM** *020 †18
STEPHENSON, Robert Wayne. 1111 CRATER LAKE AVE, STE 3 97504 #049-01-1983 L1988 **PTH** *020 †50
STERNENBERG, Paul L, III. 2780 E BARNETT RD 97504 #028-02-1993 L1999 **HS** *020 †40
STEWART, William Robt. 842 E MAIN ST 97504 #018-03-1957 L1965 **R** *071 †80
STIEGLITZ, Lary P. 691 MURPHY RD, STE 224 97504 #025-12-1983 L1989 **FM** *020 †18
STRAM, Harold M. ■ 97504 #005-15-1962 L1975 **OPH** *071
STREET, David Lee. 520 MEDICAL CENTER DR, STE 300 97504 #005-19-1981 L1988 **GS VS** *020 †85
STRICKLAND, Heather. 2940 DOCTORS PARK DR 97504 #005-02-1989 L1992 **PD** *020 †55
STRINGER, Brian Douglas. 2825 E BARNETT RD 97504 #671-01-1951 L2002 **GS CD** *071
STRINGER, Kenneth Dale, Jr. 760 GOLF VIEW DR, UNIT 200 97504 #005-06-1997 L1999 **NEP** *020 †20
STUART, Bryan James. 1600 DELTA WATERS RD, STE 107 97504 #021-01-1975 L1979 **EM FM** *020 †18,16
STUART, Ronald Rae. 2825 E BARNETT RD 97504 #054-04-1958 L1965 **GP PD** *020 †55
STUMPFF, Lawrence Chas. 2940 DOCTORS PARK DR 97504 #019-02-1974 L1978 **PD** *020 †55
SUE, Adrian Gregory. 1698 E MCANDREWS RD, STE 300 97504 #005-12-1992 L1995 **FM** *020 †18
SUE, Loralee D. 1698 E MCANDREWS RD, STE 300 97504 #005-12-1992 L1995 **FM** *020 †18
SULLIVAN, Kevin John. 2900 STATE ST 97504 #040-02-1967 L1973 **N** *020 †75
SWANSON, Richard Lee. 920 ROYAL AVE 97504 #026-04-1959 L1960 **OTO** *071 †45
TANGEMAN, F Thos. 555 BLACK OAK DR, STE 230 97504 #035-45-1966 L1973 **OBG** *020 †30
TARA, Mona Mynnel. 2640 E BARNETT RD, STE E-33 97504 #030-06-1986 L1987 **PUD CCM** *020 †20
TAYLOR, Bruce Fraser. 2825 E BARNETT RD 97504 #005-14-1971 L1976 **PD** *020 †55
TAYLOR, Sandra Jean. 2828 E BARNETT RD 97504 #048-15-1998 L2005 **HO** *020 †20
TEEGARDEN, David Whitmore. 1307 W MAIN ST 97501 #005-11-1971 L2003 **FM** *020 †18
TENNYSON, Eugene H, Jr. ■ 97504 #054-04-1960 L1968 **NS N** *071 †25
TEPLITZ, Raymond L. ■ 97504 #005-15-1962 L1975 **PTH OS** *071
THEEN, James Wm. 2825 E BARNETT RD 97504 #016-11-1975 L1989 **END IM** *020 †20
THOENE, Jennifer. 1307 W MAIN ST 97501 #040-02-1995 L2002 **FM** *020 †18
THOMPSON, Jeffrey Dodd. 2951 DOCTORS PARK DR, PSYCHIATRIC ASSOC 97504 #040-02-1967 L1968 **P** *020
THOMPSON, Matthew Dennis. 2620 E BARNETT RD STE H 97504 #005-06-1992 L1999 **AN** *020 †05
THORSON, Stuart Harley. 555 BLACK OAK DR, STE 300 97504 #054-04-1979 L1984 **PUD IM** *020 †20

■ = Address Information Privacy Protected

TICE, Martin Raymond. 1111 CRATER LAKE AVE, PROVIDENCE HOSPITAL 97504 #040-02-1977 L1978 **EM** *020 †16

TOBIAS, Joel Allan. 2941 DOCTORS PARK DR 97504 #041-01-1963 L1978 **TS CD** *071 †85,90

TOMLINSON, Daniel Alan. 3170 STATE ST 97504 #019-02-1981 L1988 **OBG** *020 †30

TRASK, David M. 492 MURPHY RD 97504 #040-02-1983 L1984 **D** *020 †15 ‡

TRAUL, David Karl. 520 MEDICAL CENTER DR, STE 300 97504 #056-06-1991 L1999 **VS** *020 †85

TREGER, Thomas Roy. 1111 CRATER LAKE AVE, STE 3 97504 #054-04-1978 L1984 **PTH MM** *062 †50

TRENARY, Sarah Mc Kinley. ■ 97504 #039-01-1995 L1998 **PD** *020 *55

TREW, Helen. 2921 DOCTORS PARK DR 97504 #060-02-1963 L1974 **FM** *020

TRIBELHORN, Donna Elena. 2640 E BARNETT RD, STE E-333 97504 #010-01-1984 L1993 **IM** *020 †20

TRIBELHORN, Dwight R. 2959 SISKIYOU BLVD, STE B 97504 #010-01-1984 L1993 **D DS** *020 †15 ‡

TROWBRIDGE, Barry Michael. 1111 CRATER LAKE AVE, EMERGENCY DEPT 97504 #040-02-1973 L1975 **EM GP** *020 †20,16

TROYCHAK, Michael Joseph. 842 E MAIN ST, MEDORD RADIOLOGICAL GROUP 97504 #040-02-1982 L1983 **NM DR** *020 †80,28

TRUJILLO, Robert Jos. 2620 E BARNETT RD STE H, MEDFORD, PC 97504 #005-02-1984 L1988 **AN** *020 †05

TRYON, Brian Christopher. 842 E MAIN ST 97504 #041-15-2000 L2007 **DR** *020 †80

TURCKE, Donald Andrew. 842 E MAIN ST 97504 #041-13-1962 L1970 **R NM** *072 †80,28

UPTON, Thomas Edward. 2825 E BARNETT RD 97504 #016-06-1954 L1960 **AN** *071 †05

URBANSKI, Richard Stanley. 212 MARIPOSA TER 97504 #025-07-1985 L1988 **EM** *020 †16

VALENTINE, William Newton. ■ 97504 #021-01-1942 L1948 **HEM IM** *071 †20

VAN VALKENBURG, Jon Kane. 555 BLACK OAK DR, STE 100 97504 #021-01-1992 L1999 **FM** *020 †18

VAN ZEE, Bruce Elbert. 2868 CREEKSIDE CIR 97504 #040-02-1970 L1977 **NEP IM** *020 †20

VERI, John-Paul Daniel. 2780 E BARNETT RD, STE 200 97504 #067-01-1996 L2002 *020

VERSTEEG, Chas Neil, Jr. 2780 E BARNETT RD, STE 200 97504 #040-02-1970 L1981 **ORS OSM** *020 †40

WADGAONKAR, Pushkar S. 2825 E BARNETT RD, DIV OF NEONATOLOGY 97504 #496-38-1989 L2004 **NPM** *020 †55

WALKER, David Howard. 2900 STATE ST, MEDFORD NEUROLOGICAL /SPIN 97504 #036-07-1998 L2005 **NS** *020

WALKER, John Allan. 2860 CREEKSIDE CIR, GASTROENTEROLOGY 97504 #048-12-1973 L1977 **GE** *020 †20

WALSTROM, Charles John. ■ 97504 #067-01-1954 L1960 **GYN OS** *071 †30

WALTERS, Harry Lyle. 4340 INDEPENDENCE SCHOL RD 97501 #040-02-1967 L1968 **FM R** *020 †18 ‡

WANG, Yujen. 2859 STATE ST, STE 103 97504 #024-07-1996 L2002 **OPH** *020 †35

WATSON, Frank Herrington. 2825 E BARNETT RD 97504 #041-01-1962 L1970 **PTH** *071 †50

WATSON, John Robt. ■ 97504 #026-04-1947 L1959 **GYN** *071 †30

WAYMAN, Daniel Macdowell. 555 BLACK OAK DR, STE 210 97504 #031-01-1986 L1991 **OTO HNS** *020 †45

WAYMAN, Kathryn Emiko. 2620 E BARNETT RD, STE H 97504 #031-01-1988 L1992 **IM** *020 †05

WEHAGE, Marie Annette. 19 MYRTLE ST, SOUTHERN OREGON HOSPITALIS 97504 #040-02-1994 L1996 **IM** *020 †20

WEINMAN, Darrell Theodore. 2780 E BARNETT RD, STE 200 97504 #026-04-1960 L1968 **ORS OS** *020 †40

WEISEL, John T. ■ 97504 #040-02-1952 L1953 **OPH** *071 †35

WELCH, John Lewis. 1698 E MCANDREWS RD 97504 #016-06-1944 L1946 **IM** *071 †20

WELLS, Steven Leonard. 1307 W MAIN ST 97501 #005-19-1988 L1996 **FM** *020 †18

WILEMAN, Louis W. ■ 97504 #005-06-1949 L1949 **R** *071 †80

WILKINSON, George Ray. 2954 SISKIYOU BLVD 97504 #018-03-1972 L1987 **TS GS** *020 †85,90

WILLIAMS, Keith Barton. 555 BLACK OAK DR STE 100 97504 #049-01-1983 L1990 **IM** *020 †20

WINTER, Todd Alin. 555 BLACK OAK DR, STE 100 97504 #040-04-1993 L1996 **IM** *020 †20

WINTERS, Gregory Francis. 2860 CREEKSIDE CIR, GASTROENTEROLOGY 97504 #016-43-1996 L2002 **GE** *020

WITT, Lanita Carol. 777 MURPHY RD, OB/GYN GROUP PC 97504 #023-07-1975 L1986 **GYN** *020 †30

WOODS, Dirk Winston. 2825 E BARNETT RD, EMERGENCY DEPARTMENT 97504 #010-01-1988 L2002 **EM** *020 †16

WORLAND, Ronald Glenn. 2959 SISKIYOU BLVD STE A 97504 #035-45-1970 L1977 **PS HS** *020 †85,65

WORTHYLAKE, Ralph D. ■ 97504 #040-02-1949 L1952 **PM P** *071

YEAKEY, Patrick Carl. 1698 E MCANDREWS RD, STE 300 97504 #047-05-1996 L2001 **FM** *020 †18

YOO, Jong Hyeon. 1111 CRATER LAKE AVE, APOGEE MEDICAL 97504 #583-13-1991 L2006 **IM** *020 †20

YOUNG, Heather Joy. 750 MURPHY RD, SOUTHERN OREGON PEDIATRICS 97504 #005-14-1994 L2004 **PD** *020 †55

YOUNG, Martin Kenneth. 2940 DOCTORS PARK DR 97504 #007-02-1993 L2000 **PD** *020 †55

ZAMANIAN, Maryam. 555 BLACK OAK DR, STE 300 97504 #858-02-1995 L2006 **PCC** *020

MERLIN – JOSEPHINE

GURDIN, Jonathan Michael. PO BOX 1402 97532 #021-01-1973 L1974 **ORS DR** *020

LOTSPEICH, Daniel Forrest. ■ 97532 #038-06-2003 L2003 **NEP** *012 †20

MILL CITY – LINN

BARNES, Lawrence Ray, Jr. 825 NW SANTIAM BLVD 97360 #017-20-1973 L1974 **FM EM** *020 †18

MILTON FREEWATER – UMATILLA

FRY, Scott Timothy. 10 NE 5TH AVE 97862 #005-12-2002 L2005 **FM** *020 †18

HURWITZ, Gary Lee. PO BOX 356, 84329 EASTSIDE RD 97862 #028-34-1990 L1999 **EM** *020 †16

SEELY, Howard Clinton. ■ 97862 #005-12-1953 L1953 **EM PM** *071

MILWAUKIE – CLACKAMAS

ANDERSON, J Chris. 10330 SE 32ND AVE, STE 205 97222 #001-02-1998 L2002 **FM** *020 †18

ARKLESS, Tyler Manfred. 4825 SE ALLEN RD 97267 #040-02-1991 L1992 **FM** *100

BENNETT, Frank M. 13505 SE RIVER RD # 238 97222 #026-04-1950 L1952 **FM GS** *071

BERGSTROM, Christina Ng. 10150 SE 32ND AVE 97222 #021-01-2006 L2006 **FP** *012

BLACKTHORNE, Steven James. 10150 SE 32ND AVE 97222 #040-02-1985 L1986 **IM** *020 †20

BRADLEY, Matthew Walter. ■ 97222 #017-20-2004 L2004 **ORS** *012

BUDDEN, Moir Mahendra K. 10202 SE 32ND AVE, STE 502 97222 #495-27-1963 L1977 **GS VS** *020 †85

BURGHER, Kristin Janeice. ■ 97222 #010-02-2007 L2007 **FP** *012

BURNESS, Jessica O. 10330 SE 32ND AVE STE 2 97222 #043-01-2001 L2001 **FM** *020 †18

CALLAGHAN, Elizabeth E. 3033 SE MONROE ST, NORTHWEST PRIMARY CARE GRO 97222 #038-41-1997 L1998 **FM** *020 †18

CHAN, Michael Mingyin. 10150 SE 32ND AVE 97222 #054-04-1992 L1998 **DR** *020 †80

COHEN, Deborah Janet. 10150 SE 32ND AVE, PMH RADIOLOGY DEPT 97222 #040-02-1988 L1989 **DR** *020 †80

CORTI, George Nicholas. 2403 SE MONROE ST STE A 97222 #028-34-1945 L1947 **GP ORS** *020

COURTNEY, Donel R. ■ 97267 #028-34-1989 L1990 **GS** *020 †85

DONKLE, James Byron. 10150 SE 32ND AVE 97222 #056-05-1960 L1961 **GP** *071

DUMLER, Cynthia Esther. 3033 SE MONROE ST 97222 #030-05-1993 L2002 **FM** *020 †18

EL YOUSSEF, Raphael. ■ 97222 #894-01-1999 L2005 **GS** *012

FORTLAGE, Donald Wm. 10202 SE 32ND AVE STE 201 97222 #005-06-1963 L1968 **PD OS** *020 †55

FRANCHUK, Jennifer Ann. ■ 97222 #056-06-2006 L2006 **FM** *100

GERHARDT, John Jos. ■ 97267 #154-01-1948 L1968 **PM** *071 †60 ‡

GILLANDERS, William Ross. 10330 SE 32ND AVE, STE 205 97222 #005-02-1972 L2000 **FM FPG** *030 †18

GREEN, Michael Sean. 10202 SE 32ND AVE, STE 703 97222 #025-12-1992 L1993 **N IMG** *020 †75

HARDIMAN, John Bradley. 10202 SE 32ND AVE, STE 101 97222 #040-02-1965 L1968 **ORS** *071 †40

HATHAWAY, Elwood Norton. ■ 97222 #024-05-1941 L1949 **ORS** *071 †40

HERBER, Jennifer Dawn. ■ 97222 #040-02-2005 L2005 **FP** *012

HOFFMAN, Brent Lee. 17070 SE MCLOUGHLIN BLVD, FAMILY CARE MEDICAL CLINIC 97267 #028-78-2001, ▲ L2004 **FM** *100

HOLEMAN, Thomas Alfred. 10202 SE 32ND AVE, STE 501 97222 #048-02-1964 L1969 **D** *071

HOMER, Speros D, III. 10150 SE 32ND AVE, PROVIDENCE MILWAUKEE HOSPI 97222 #012-01-1994 L1996 **EM** *020 †16

JACQMOTTE, Nathalie J. 3033 SE MONROE ST 97222 #040-02-1999 L2002 **FM** *020 †18

JOHNSON, Harold Desmond. 10202 S E 32D ST 97222 #067-01-1960 L1977 **OBG** *020 †30

KAUFFMAN, Susan M. 6902 SE LAKE RD 97267 #040-02-1981 L1983 **NEP IM** *020 †20

KAY, Joel Richard. ■ 97222 #025-07-1971 L1976 **GP** *020 †18

KEITH, Douglas Scott. 6902 SE LAKE RD, STE 100 97267 #026-08-1987 L1996 **NEP** *100 †20

KEMENY, Scott Jorge. 10150 SE 32ND AVE 97222 #016-11-2000 L2001 **IM** *020 †20

KNOX, David Glen. 10150 SE 32ND AVE, PROV MILWAUKIE HOSP 97222 #054-04-1977 L1980 **EM** *020 †16

KOEKKOEK, Douglas Alan. 10150 SE 32ND AVE, PROVIDENCE HOSPITALIST SO. 97222 #040-02-1988 L1989 **IM** *020 †20

KOZA, Robert John. ■ 97267 #030-05-1953 L1953 **GP** *071

LANDCHILD, Melinda. 10150 SE 32ND AVE, MILWAUKIE HOSPITAL 97222 #054-04-2002 L2002 **FM** *100 †18

LARSON, Ronald Keith. 10150 SE 32ND AVE 97222 #040-02-1980 L1988 **DR NM** *020 †18,80,28

LIN, Nancy. 10330 SE 32ND AVE, STE 305 97222 #035-46-1997 L2004 **OBG** *020 †30

LINDSEY, Judith Ann. 2305 SE WASHINGTON ST #105 97222 #032-01-1990 L1991 **IM** *020 †20

MADSEN, Lynn Elise. 10150 SE 32ND AVE, MILWAUKIE HOSPITAL 97222 #050-02-2003 L2003 **FM** *020 †18

MAGSARILI, Karl. 6975 SE LAKE RD 97267 #026-04-1995 L1998 **FM** *020 †18

MARAS, James Edward. 10150 SE 32ND AVE 97222 #040-02-1974 L1975 **EM** *020 †16

MASLEN, David Robert. 10024 SE 32ND AVE 97222 #409-21-1991 L1996 **IM** *020 †20

MAYER, Dennis Owen. 3033 SE MONROE ST 97222 #040-02-1971 L1977 **IM** *020 †20

MC CARTHY, William Henry. 3033 SE MONROE ST 97222 #030-06-1959 L1967 **IM R** *071 †20

MC DONALD, Patrick G. ■ 97267 #040-02-1989 L1993 **AN** *020

MCGEBROFF, Helen. 10150 SE 32ND AVE 97222 #905-02-2003 L2004 **FM** *100

MIYAKE, Scott Keola. 6902 SE LAKE RD, STE 100 97267 #014-01-2000 L2000 **NEP IM** *020 †20 ‡

MOONEY, Kathleen Marie. 17070 SE MCLOUGHLIN BLVD 97267 #028-02-1997 L2006 **PD** *020 †55

MORENO, Claudine Yvonne. 10330 SE 32ND AVE, STE 205 97222 #005-19-1997 L1998 **IMG FPG** *020 †18

MOURNIAN, Geraldine Berni. 10150 SE 32ND AVE 97222 #032-01-2004 L2004 **FM** *020 †18

NIELSEN, Jo Anne. 10150 SE 32ND AVE 97222 #048-04-1980 L1983 **PD** *020 †55

NISHIKAWA, Mural Jones. 10024 SE 32ND AVE 97222 #041-15-1999 L1999 **IM** *020 †20

NOBLE, Susan Carla. 4230 SE KING RD, # 206 97222 #422-01-1985 L1988 **AN IM** *020 †05

OEHLER, Richard Harvey. ■ 97267 #056-05-1961 L1962 **GP** *072

OSTERLUND, Tracey Kathlee. ■ 97222 #040-02-2007 L2007 **FP** *012

PARK, So Yun. 10150 SE 32ND AVE, PROVIDENCE MILWAUKIE 97222 #035-03-2006 L2006 **FP** *012

PAUL, Lisa Balk. 3033 SE MONROE ST 97222 #040-02-1991 L1992 **IM** *020 †20

PETERSON, Christina E. 19001 SE MCLOUGHLIN BLVD 97222 #005-06-1982 L1983 **N** *020

POSTLES, William Terrance. 10150 SE 32ND AVE 97222 #040-02-1954 L1957 **OM** *071

RAGSDALE, John Wm. 10330 SE 32ND AVE, STE 340 97222 #028-34-1985 L1986 **GS** *020 †85

REDMOND, Steven J. 10150 SE 32ND AVE, PROVIDENCE HOSPITALIST S.E 97222 #054-04-1990 L1991 **IM** *020 †20

RYAN, Mitchell R. ■ 97222 #040-02-1990 L1999 **PCP** *020 †50

SANDOZ, Ivan Luis. 10202 SE 32ND AVE, STE 702 97222 #038-40-1957 L1961 **U** *071 †95

SCHAUB, John Stephen. ■ 97222 #040-02-1964 L1965 **PMM IM** *071

SCHMICKRATH, Sarah Jean. ■ 97222 #040-02-2008 *012

SCOTT, Donald H. 10150 SE 32ND AVE 97222 #040-02-1962 L1966 **OBG** *072 †30

SHARIFICHAPMAN, Nazanin. ■ 97267 #040-02-2005 L2005 **IM** *012

SLADE, Barbara Ann. 6135 SE KING RD 97222 #036-01-1979 L1980 **PTH** *062 †50

SOLTERS, John Stanley. 6902 SE LAKE RD 97267 #041-12-1972 L1987 **IM NEP** *020 †20

STARK, James Edgar. 10150 SE 32ND AVE, PROVIDENCE MIWAUKIE HOSPIT 97222 #001-06-1988 L2003 **PDR** *020 †80

SUGALSKI, Matthew Thomas. 10202 SE 32ND AVE, STE 101 97222 #035-01-1998 L2005
OSM *020
SUGARMAN, Sharon E. ■ 97222 #010-03-1999 L2006 **GPM** *020 †70
SUNDSETH, Jason Dean. 10150 SE 32ND AVE 97222 #041-02-2000 L2000 **EM** *020 †16
SWARNER, Warner Blake. 6400 SE LAKE RD, STE 325 97222 #005-12-1974 L1979 **P** *020 †75
TAN, Dennis Chan. 10330 SE 32ND AVE, STE 305 97222 #016-42-2003 L2007 **OBG** *020
THOMAS, Christopher Owen. 6902 SE LAKE RD, LAKE ROAD NEPHROLOGY CENTE 97267
#019-02-1995 L1997 **NEP** *020
THORP, Micah L. 6902 SE LAKE RD, LAKE ROAD NEPHTOLOGY CLINI 97267 #018-75-1995,
▲ L1996 **NEP** *020 †20 ‡
TODD, Jerry Houghton. 10150 SE 32ND AVE 97222 #040-02-1944 **GP** *071
UNDERWOOD, Fred Lee. 10150 SE 32ND AVE 97222 #040-02-1973 L1975 **EM GP** *020 †16
VEILLET, Raymond. 10150 SE 32ND AVE 97222 #067-03-1961 L1967 **GS** *071 †85
VERDIECK, Alexandra. 3033 SE MONROE ST, NORTHWEST PRIMARY CARE 97222
#035-47-1996 L1997 **FM** *020 †18
ZHANG, Yufei. 10024 SE 32ND AVE 97222 #047-06-1998 L2000 **IM** *020 †20

MITCHELL — WHEELER

BELKNAP, Russell Lee. ■ 97750 #040-02-1960 L1961 **GYN GP** *020

MOLALLA — CLACKAMAS

STEINMETZ, Eric Vincent. ■ 97038 #040-02-2001 *100
WILLEFORD, Allison B. PO BOX 189, 110 CENTER ST 97038 #048-04-1951 L1953
FM GYN *071 †18

MONMOUTH — POLK

AFFLEY, Harry J, Jr. ■ 97361 #005-06-1951 L1976 **GP GS** *071 †85
BOESPFLUG, Randy Roy. 345 MONMOUTH AVE N, STUDENT HEALTH/COUNSEL SER 97361
#007-02-1980 L1987 **FM** *020 †18
BRUST, Richard Duane. ■ 97361 #040-02-1959 L1962 **GP** *071 †18
CARDEN, Geoffrey Hayden. 180 ATWATER ST N, TOTAL HEALTH COMMUNITY CLI 97361
#047-20-2000 L2003 *020 †18
SCHIFERL, Michael Joseph. 180 ATWATER ST N 97361 #056-05-2001 L2006 **FM** *020 †18

MONROE — BENTON

JEPSEN, Daniel Certen. 25904 GREEN PEAK RD, 13TH STREET AND AGATE 97456
#005-02-1970 L1974 **FM** *020

MOSIER — WASCO

BLACKWELL, Rose Ann. ■ 97040 #048-12-1983 L1984 **OBG** *020 †30

MOUNT ANGEL — MARION

DOMST, James Edward. 690 N MAIN ST 97362 #016-11-1999 L2005 **FM** *020 †18
KOSCHMANN, Faith Luanne. 690 N MAIN ST 97362 #038-43-1998 L2005 **FM** *020 †18
MC DONALD, Robert Wilson. 690 N MAIN ST 97362 #005-14-1978 L1981 **FM FPG** *020 †18
PETERS, Virgil Eugene. ■ 97362 #019-02-1962 L1967 **GP GS** *071
RAMOS, Mayda. 690 N MAIN ST, MT ANGEL FAMILY MEDICINE 97362 #042-03-1981 L1993
IM GE *020 †20
WOOD, Barbara Ann. ■ 97362 #035-09-1946 L1972 **PHP** *071

MOUNT HOOD PARKDALE — HOOD RIVER

HARVEY-SMITH, Warwick. ■ 97041 #143-03-1964 L1997 **DR PUD** *030 †20,80

MYRTLE CREEK — DOUGLAS

PHILLIPS, Mark C. 860 N MYRTLE RD 97457 #005-06-1986 L1994 **FM** *020
ROOS, John Christian. ■ 97457 #005-12-1944 L1944 **PTH FOP** *071 †50

MYRTLE POINT — COOS

BEBER, Ernest Frederick. MYRTLE POINT MED CTR 97458 #026-04-1940 **GP** *020
GURNEY, Edmund Reed. 324 4TH ST 97458 #040-02-1974 L1977 **GP** *020
ROBERTSON, Maria Noella P. ■ 97458 #748-02-1990 L1998 **IMG IM** *020 †20
ROESEL, Charles Michael. 324 4TH ST, 324 4TH ST 97458 #654-01-1994 L1997 **FM** *020 †18
SINNOTT, James Joseph. 324 5TH ST 97458 #018-03-1981 L1984 **FM** *020 †18

NEHALEM — TILLAMOOK

CROSS, Leland Loyal. ■ 97131 #016-06-1952 L1967 **PM** *071 †60
GIBSON, Steven Mitchell. ■ 97131 #003-01-1985 L1989 **IM** *020 †20
SCHLUTER, Harold G. ■ 97131 #025-01-1944 L1945 **GYN** *071 †30
STEWART, Robert H. ■ 97131 #005-16-1962 L1975 **GP** *020

NEOTSU — LINCOLN

JOHNSON, Marcus Paul. PO BOX 925 97364 #005-02-1967 L1974 **R** *071 †80
SHIPLEY, Glen Stuart. PO BOX 870, 1838 NW 52ND DR 97364 #040-02-1959 L1974
GP P *020 †75

NESKOWIN — TILLAMOOK

HARUDA, Fred D. PO BOX 1024 97149 #016-02-1976 L1981 **N** *020 †55,75 ‡

NETARTS — TILLAMOOK

MARTIN, Brian Kamanuokala. ■ 97143 #014-01-1987 **P** *074

NEWBERG — YAMHILL

ACKER, Robert Leroy. ■ 97132 #040-02-1964 L1969 **VS** *071 †85
ADAMSON, Daryl Albert. 501 VILLA RD 97132 #040-02-1978 L1980 **DR** *020 †80
BAILEY, William M. 308 VILLA RD, STE 114 97132 #040-02-1983 L1986 **FM** *020 †18
BERG, Helge Richard. ■ 97132 #040-02-1977 L1980 **EM** *020 †16
BERGQUAM, Nina Lew. 1003 PROVIDENCE DR, STE 210 97132 #035-09-1997 L1999
IM *020
BUCKLER, Robert E. 414 N MERIDIAN ST # 6153 97132 #010-02-1976 L1983 **P PHP** *040 †75
BUCKLER, Robert Paul. 414 N MERIDIAN ST # 6153 97132 #017-20-1947 L1948 **GP** *075
BUI, Kim Lanthi. 1003 PROVIDENCE DR, STE 210 97132 #041-02-1995 L2001 **GS** *020 †85
CARABALLO, Cynthia D. 1003 PROVIDENCE DR, STE 210 97132 #038-40-1995 L2001
FM *020 †18
CAUTHORN, Ross Alfred. 501 VILLA RD 97132 #040-02-1980 L1981 **DR IM** *020 †80
CHA, Stephanie W Chan. 1003 PROVIDENCE DR, STE 110 97132 #018-03-1997 L1999
IM *020 †20
CHINN, Crispin Anthony. 501 VILLA RD 97132 #054-04-1997 L1998 **DR** *020 †80,28
CONNELL, Robert Merritt. ■ 97132 #018-03-1955 L1964 **PTH** *071 †50
COVARRUBIAS, Diego Jose. 501 VILLA RD 97132 #005-15-1997 L2004 **RNR** *020 †80
COVEY, Douglas Paul. 501 VILLA RD 97132 #048-04-1973 L1976 **GS VS** *071 †85
CRONE, Richard Allan. 1003 PROVIDENCE DR, STE 325 97132 #054-04-1973 L2005
CD IM *020 ‡
CROY, Thomas Jos. 310 VILLA RD STE 108 97132 #040-02-1991 L1992 **ORS** *071 †40
CULVER, Ronald Eugene. 308 VILLA RD STE 116, NEWBERG PEDIATRIC CLINIC 97132
#056-05-1971 L2001 **PD** *020
CUMMINGS, John Lawrence. 506 VILLA RD 97132 #005-14-1969 L1970 **FM** *020 ‡
DIRE, Tony John. 501 VILLA RD 97132 #010-02-1991 L1992 **DR** *020 †80
DOUGLASS, Jeffrey Matthew. 1003 PROVIDENCE DR, STE 110 97132 #040-02-1999 L2000
GE *020 †20
FIELDHOUSE, M Hester. ■ 97132 #040-02-1965 L1967 **FPG GP** *071
FISHER, Richard Matthew. 1003 PROVIDENCE DR, STE 210 97132 #035-47-1991 L2000
GS *020 †85
FORBES, Alvis Ray. ■ 97132 #054-04-1978 L1980 **ORS** *020 †40
FOX, Christina Areti. 501 VILLA RD 97132 #035-01-1995 L2005 **DR** *020 †80
GALASSO, Robert Thos. 501 VILLA RD, PROVIDENCE NEWBERG HOSP 97132
#033-05-1984 L1985 **EM** *020
HAZARD, James Vernon. 501 VILLA RD 97132 #005-19-1995 L1997 **DR** *020 †80
HOLMAN, David Chas. 501 VILLA RD 97132 #040-02-1968 L1972 **DR** *020 †80
ISAACSON, Julie. 410 VILLA RD 97132 #005-06-1977 L1978 **ORS** *020 †40
JAHNKE, Jonathan David. 307 E HANCOCK ST 97132 #018-03-1983 L1985 **OPH EM** *020 †35
JEWELL, Steven Edward. 501 VILLA RD 97132 #005-18-1978 L1979 **EM** *020 †16
JOHNSON, David Paul. 1003 PROVIDENCE DR, STE 340 97132 #023-01-1983 L1987
OBG *020 †30
JOHNSON, Leah Jane. 501 VILLA RD 97132 #040-02-1992 L1993 **DR** *020 †80,28
KERN, Stanley Dale. ■ 97132 #019-02-1960 L1962 **FM** *071 †18
KIMBRELL, Michael Rusten. 1001 PROVIDENCE DR 97132 #055-01-1975 L1977 *020
KRIER, David Brice. 501 VILLA RD 97132 #019-02-1979 L1982 **FM EP** *020 †18
KUTTNER, Charles Herman. 1901 ESTHER ST, HAZELDEN SPRINGBROOK 97132
#048-02-1973 L1976 **P** *020 †75
LEA, James Allen. 1901 ESTHER ST, HAZELBEN SPRINGBROOK 97132 #040-02-1972 L1973
ADM ADP *020
LOUBE, Daniel Ira. ■ 97132 #010-01-1987 L2005 **PUD SME** *020 †20
MANKA, Maya J. 308 VILLA RD, STE 116 97132 #286-06-1967 L1977 **PD** *020 †55
MATTHEWS, James Nicholas. 2880 HAYES ST, NEWBERG URGENT CARE & MEDI 97132
#040-02-1988 L1990 **GP** *020
MAVEETY, Patrick Roswell. 701 E 3RD ST 97132 #040-02-1978 L1983 **GE IM** *020 †20
MC CLURE, Donald K, Jr. ■ 97132 #054-04-1966 L1975 **PTH BBK** *071 †50
MCCULLEY, Harry G, Jr. 501 VILLA RD 97132 #045-01-1976 L1977 **GS** *020 †85
MC NALLY, Steve Paul. 1003 PROVIDENCE DR, STE 110 97132 #028-34-1987 L1991
IM PD *020 †20
MC QUEEN, Robert Jerome. 2880 HAYES ST 97132 #040-02-1983 L1986 **FM** *020 †18
MENDENHALL, Andrew. 1003 PROVIDENCE DR, STE 210 97132 #040-02-2000 L2000
FM *020 †18
MITCHELL, Frederick Lee. 2505 PORTLAND RD, STE 100 97132 #040-02-1996 L1998
IM *020 †20
MONTO, George Luther. ■ 97132 #016-02-1961 L1961 **GE IM** *071 †18
MORIMOTO, Alan Kenji. 501 VILLA RD 97132 #034-01-1999 L2006 **R NRN** *020 †80
NAHM, Kevin II. 308 VILLA RD, STE 116 97132 #583-03-1971 L1980 **OBG** *020 †30
PAQUETTE, Janet Denson. 22955 NE NORTH VALLEY RD, STE 23 97132 #016-42-1985 L1986
EM *020 †16
PARK, Sun Jung. 1515 PORTLAND RD, PMG/NEWBERG INTERNAL MEDIC 97132
#016-01-1995 L2003 **CCM** *020 †20
PEARSON, Harris Leroy. 506 VILLA RD # A 97132 #026-04-1961 L1962 **GP** *020
PETERS, Judith Lee. 501 VILLA RD 97132 #016-45-1985 L1990 **DR** *020 †80
PINNEO, James S. ■ 97132 #041-13-1950 L1953 **GP FM** *071 †18
PORTER, Birch Ann. 1003 PROVIDENCE DR, PROVIDENCE INTERNAL 97132
#014-01-1989 L1995 **IM** *020 †20
PORTER, Gregory Gordon. 1003 PROVIDENCE DR, STE 210 97132 #054-04-1981 L2004
OTO *020 †45
PUSKAS, John Michael. 310 VILLA RD, STE 107 97132 #028-03-1972 L1977 **OTO** *075
ROBERTS, Wayne E. ■ 97132 #028-02-1951 **FM** *071
RODGERS, Tamara J. 1003 PROVIDENCE DR, STE 210 97132 #005-12-1992 L1996 **FM** *020 †18
ROLL, John Douglas. 501 VILLA RD 97132 #017-20-1981 L2002 **DR RNR** *020 †80
ROSALES, Camilo. 1003 PROVIDENCE DR, STE 210 97132 #005-14-1982 L2006 **GS** *020 †85

SELLARS, Kevin Randall. 1003 PROVIDENCE DR, STE 110 97132 #305-01-1997 L2001 IM *020 †20

SETHI, Stephen David. 1003 PROVIDENCE DR, STE 210 97132 #016-43-2002 L2002 IM *020 †20

SHUKLA, Lee Wolpin. 501 VILLA RD 97132 #035-03-1981 L1988 R PD *020 †80

SILVERS, Leonard L. 501 VILLA RD 97132 #040-02-1953 L1955 IM *071

SILVESTRE, David Gerard. 1003 PROVIDENCE DR, STE 210 97132 #005-02-1991 L1996 FM *020 †18

SOKOL, Evangeline. 501 VILLA RD 97132 #040-02-1981 L1983 EM *071 †16

SPENSLEY, Patrick Anthony. 221 VILLA RD 97132 #028-34-1989 L1996 FM *020 †18

STADTLANDER, Sean M. 1003 PROVIDENCE DR, STE 110 97132 #048-13-1988 L1995 IM *020 †20

STROTHER, John Michael. 310 VILLA RD, PACIFIC ONCOLOGY 97132 #041-14-2000 L2000 HO *020 †20

SWINDLE, Jeremy Scott. ■ 97132 #021-01-2003 L2006 FM *020 †18

TAKAHASI, Gary Wayne. 310 VILLA RD, PACIFIC ONCOLOGY 97132 #014-01-1984 L1985 HEM *020 †20

TOWNSEND, Stephen Forrest. 1003 PROVIDENCE DR, STE 110 97132 #048-04-1975 L1976 IM *071 †20

VAN EATON, John Gregory. 1001 PROVIDENCE DR 97132 #016-11-1987 L1989 IM *020 †20

VU, An Cong. 450 VILLA RD 97132 #941-01-1972 L1986 GP GPM *020

WEGHORST, George R. 1003 PROVIDENCE DR, STE 210 97132 #048-13-1972 L1975 GYN *020 †30

WEISS, Kathleen M. ■ 97132 #005-06-1978 L1981 IM *075 †20

WHITTAKER, Kenneth Andrew. 506 VILLA RD 97132 #035-01-1993 L1994 PD *020 †55

WILLIAMS, Vern Randal. 1901 ESTHER ST, HAZELDEN SPRING BROOK 97132 #014-01-1984 L1985 IM *020 †20

WILSON, Jennifer Marie. 1003 PROVIDENCE DR, STE 210 97132 #040-02-2001 L2001 IM *020 †20

ZEBELMAN, Wayne David. 1001 PROVIDENCE DR 97132 #054-04-2003 L2006 FM *020

ZINCK, Steven E. 501 VILLA RD 97132 #005-19-1995 L2001 DR *020 †80

NEWPORT — LINCOLN

ADLER, Michael Paul. 775 SW 9TH ST, STE H 97365 #017-20-1976 L1977 OBG *020 †30

ARBEENE, Richard Chas. ■ 97365 #035-45-1973 L1978 ORS GS *020 †40

BEAR, Gregory Reed. 351 SW 7TH ST 97365 #016-06-1990 L1991 DR *020 †80

BEEMER, Richard Keith. PO BOX 2067 97365 #054-04-1965 L1967 GS *074

BICE, David Mandus. 1010 SW BAY 97365 #065-05-1974 L1976 GP IMG *020

BLOS'E, Patricia Wall. 1600 N COAST HWY, SEA TOWNE CTYARD 97365 #047-05-1968 L2001 P ADP *075

BRITTAIN, Edward Humeston. 930 SW ABBEY ST 97365 #048-04-1965 L1971 *071 †30

BURNS, Stephen Macbain. 775 SW 9TH ST STE A 97365 #011-04-1976 L1979 PD *020 †55

BUTLER, Gerald Ray. 1010 SW COAST HWY, STE 101 97365 #039-01-1968 L1976 ORS *020 †40

CARSON, H Joshua. 930 SW ABBEY ST 97365 #005-06-1985 L1986 EM *020 †16

CELY, William Frederick. 775 SW 9TH ST STE 4, HOSPITAL 97365 #049-01-1977 L1981 OBG *020 †30

DE BLOIS, Thomas Edward. PO BOX 2031 97365 #023-12-1990 L2002 CHP *020 †75

FLESHER, Ryan Scott. 930 SW ABBEY ST 97365 #055-02-1999 L2007 EM *020 †16

FOBI, Aloysius Nchinda. 930 SW ABBEY ST 97365 #040-02-1999 L2002 EM *020 †16

FOX, Richard Leroy. 930 SW ABBEY ST 97365 #018-03-1966 L1993 FM *020 †18

FRASER, William R. 930 SW ABBEY ST 97365 #061-01-1981 L1990 *020

GRUZD, Douglas Chester. 930 SW ABBEY ST 97365 #030-05-1979 L2003 EM FM *020 †16,18

HAEG, James Peirce. ■ 97365 #054-01-1984 L2002 IM *020 †18

HARRIS, Bryan Duane. 775 SW 9TH ST STE B, PACIFIC COMMUNITIES HOSP.A 97365 #019-02-1994 L1997 IM *020 †20

JOHANSSON, Kris Kerstin. 930 SW ABBEY ST 97365 #038-41-1976 L1993 GS PD *020 †16

KACZMAREK, Jack Jay. 36 SW NYE ST 97365 #036-01-1983 L1984 P *020 †75

KONOWALCHUK, David Paul. 775 SW 9TH ST STE B 97365 #065-09-1975 L1991 PS *020 †65

KONOWALCHUK, Thomas Wm. ■ 97365 #065-09-1979 L1987 U *020 †95

LEDGER, Gabriel Baird. 930 SW ABBEY ST 97365 #024-01-2001 L2005 EM *020 †16 ‡

LEE, Wayland Sherrod. 904 SW BAY ST 97365 #005-11-1965 L1976 OTO A *071 †45 ‡

LEHRER, John Baptist. 775 SW 9TH ST, STE G 97365 #026-04-1994 L1997 FM *020 †18

LEVANN, Helen Patricia. 36 SW NYE ST, FQHC 97365 #919-07-1976 L1980 IM EM *020 †20

LONG, David Craig. 775 SW 9TH ST STE B 97365 #040-02-1977 L1980 IM FM *020 †20

MC UNE, Russell Hal. 930 SW ABBEY ST 97365 #054-04-1996 L1999 EM *020 †16

MICHNOWSKA, Maria Zofia. 1010 SW COAST HWY, STE 201 97365 #759-03-1987 L2007 IM *020 †18

MIDDELMAN, Francine. PO BOX 1730 97365 #660-01-1954 L1965 P *071

NORTH, Richard Lee. 930 SW ABBEY ST 97365 #025-01-1974 L2001 FM *020 †18

PERSONETT, Gregg Linden. 929 SW BAY ST, SAMARITAN PACIFIC SURGICAL 97365 #040-02-1976 L1977 GS VS *020 †85

PETERSON, Michael J. 862 SE 5TH ST 97365 #005-02-1969 L1975 DR *020 †80

QUINN, Julia M. 930 SW ABBEY ST 97365 #048-15-1990 L2006 EM *020 †16

RIGGS, Russell Westlyn. 930 SW ABBEY ST 97365 #048-04-1993 L2001 EM *020 †16

ROBBINS, Jerry Joel. 1010 SW COAST HWY STE 201 97365 #038-06-1971 L1977 EM *020 †20

ROHRBACK, Scott Matthew. 930 SW ABBEY ST 97365 #028-34-2001 L2005 EM *100 †16

SCHEINBERG, Samuel. 930 SW ABBEY ST 97365 #047-06-1965 L1973 ORS *072 †40

SCHRINER, Carol Lynn. 1103 SW MARK ST 97365 #048-03-1983 L1984 PD *020 †55

SCHWARTZ, Frank Edwin. 775 SW 9TH ST, FRANK E SCHWARTZ MD PC 97365 #041-12-1943 L1977 OPH *071 †35

STEVENS, Kenneth M. ■ 97365 #040-02-1963 L1964 OTO FPS *071 †45

THUESON, Gary Lee. 930 SW ABBEY ST 97365 #048-02-1981 L1987 FM *020 †18

VILBIG, Glory Joan. ■ 97365 #048-02-1960 L1975 IM *072 †20

WATANABE, Bruce Michio. 1010 SW COAST HWY STE 101, ASSOCS 97365 #005-14-1990 L1995 ORS *020 †40

WATKINS, John F. 1010 SW COAST HWY, STE 201 97365 #035-45-1997 L2000 IM *020

WINDLE, Gordon A. ■ 97365 #028-34-1951 L1952 GP *071

NORTH BEND — COOS

BERNDT, Jack Edward. 1860 VIRGINIA AVE, STE 9 97459 #046-01-1985 L2004 AN *020 †05

BERNSTEIN, William James. 1890 WAITE ST STE 3 97459 #005-02-1976 L1980 N *071 †75

BRILL, I Wm. ■ 97459 #017-20-1939 L1946 P *071 †75

CHURCH, John Odell, IV. PO BOX 368 97459 #028-34-1987 L1993 P *020

FREEMAN, Donald Eugene. ■ 97459 #030-05-1965 L1977 AN PME *071 †05

GILBERT, Jane. 3585 BROADWAY ST, BAY EYE CLINIC 97459 #003-01-1999 L1999 OPH *020 †05

HOLBERT, James A. 2330 BROADWAY ST 97459 #018-03-1953 L1956 ORS *071 †40

KINSLEY, Stephen Jay. 2000 CONNECTICUT AVE, USCG GROUP NORTH BEND 97459 #038-41-1987 L1988 EM *020 †16

KINTNER, Jon Chas. 3585 BROADWAY ST, BAY EYE CLINIC 97459 #038-06-1985 L1989 OPH *020 †18

LYNASS, William Jay. ■ 97459 #046-01-1984 DR *100

MA, Colin. 3585 BROADWAY ST 97459 #917-09-1982 L1987 OPH OS *020 †35

MAY, Mark Barry. 1860 VIRGINIA AVE, STE 9 97459 #065-01-1968 L1977 AN *020 †05

MESQUITA, John Anthony. ■ 97459 #005-15-1996 L1998 *020 †05

POAGE, Donald Ellis. 1890 WAITE ST 97459 #054-04-1955 L1963 GS *071

RUSU, Daniel Mihai. 1860 VIRGINIA AVE, STE 9 97459 #781-01-1997 L2005 AN *020 †05

TUCKER, Rochelle Roberta. 1975 MCPHERSON ST 97459 #026-08-1998 L2002 P *020 †75

TYSON, Hugh Kingsbury. 2000 CONNECTICUT AVE 97459 #038-06-1968 L2003 GP GP *020 †55

WORKHOVEN, Merrill N. 1860 VIRGINIA AVE, STE 9 97459 #030-05-1968 L1974 AN *020 †05

NORTH PLAINS — WASHINGTON

ADAMS, George Beverly. ■ 97133 #067-01-1956 L1960 OS GP *071

BUMP, Forrest E. 10245 NW GLENCOE RD, TUALITY N. PLAINS MEDICAL 97133 #020-02-1946 L1947 GP *071

GARDNER, Marion Lee, Jr. 10245 NW GLENCOE RD 97133 #040-02-1990 L1992 FM *020 †18

KEMP, Judith Marie. 10245 NW GLENCOE RD 97133 #048-02-2001 L2006 FM *100 †18

LEAVITT, Mark Keith. ■ 97133 #011-02-1979 L1980 IM IMG *062 †20

MEARS, Michelle Linda. 10395 NW GLENCOE RD, STE 200 97133 #026-04-1986 L1994 FM *020 †18

OAKLAND — DOUGLAS

LIAN, Yi Yvonne. 1393 OLD TOWN LOOP RD 97462 #035-47-1994 L1998 IM *020 †20

ONTARIO — MALHEUR

BABIJ, Roman John. 1050 SW 3RD AVE STE 2600 97914 #016-11-1981 L1986 GS *020 †85

BARLOW, Brad Lynn. 351 SW 9TH ST 97914 #049-01-1996 L1999 EM *020 †16

BOYLE, Joseph Danl. 351 SW 9TH ST, HOLY ROSARY MEDICAL CENTER 97914 #030-06-1991 L1994 EM *020 †16

BRAINARD, Scott Cree. 351 SW 9TH ST 97914 #051-04-1946 L1947 EM *071 †85,90

BRAUER, David Wm. 335 SW 13TH ST 97914 #030-06-1986 L1989 FM *020 †16

BROOKE, Cynthia Lee. 1050 SW 3RD AVE, STE 200 97914 #054-04-1986 L2005 OBG *020 †30

BURDIC, Joseph Thorn. ■ 97914 #040-02-1952 L1952 P GP *071

CEGNAR, Janet Marie. 964 W IDAHO AVE, SNAKE RIVER RADIOLOGY 97914 #054-04-1987 L1993 DR *020 †80

CHRISTIE, David Beaumont. 1050 SW 3RD AVE, STE 2200 97914 #007-02-1986 L1999 OPH *020 †35

DANIELS, Dorin Slater. 351 SW 9TH ST 97914 #016-02-1956 L1957 FM *071 †18

DE LA PAZ, Nora Francisco. 932 W IDAHO AVE STE 101 97914 #748-08-1967 L1977 PD *020 †55

DUNBRASKY, Sandra Jean. 1219 SW 4TH AVE, UNIT 1 97914 #040-02-1991 L1992 PD *020 †55

FIELD, James Chas. 1050 SW 3RD AVE 97914 #034-01-1942 L2006 CD *020 †20

GAMBINO, John. 964 W IDAHO AVE, SNAKE RIVER RADIOLOGY 97914 #033-06-1988 L1996 DR IM *020 †80

GERING, Paul Chris, Jr. 915 SW 3RD AVE 97914 #040-02-1993 L1994 FM PLM *020 †18

HERIZA, Thomas James. 702 SUNSET DR 97914 #030-06-1993 L1997 P *020 †75

HINCHMAN, David Andrew. 1050 SW 3RD AVE 97914 #007-02-1992 L2001 CD *020 †20

MANN, James Raymond. 915 SW 3RD AVE 97914 #049-01-1952 L1964 GP *071

MC KEE, M Christine. 1219 SW 4TH AVE UNIT 1, ST. ALPHONSUS MEDICAL GROU 97914 #033-05-1989 L2007 PD *020 †55

NAGATA, David Esteban. 1050 SW 3RD AVE, STE 3200 97914 #132-07-1998 L2003 IM *020 †20 ‡

OYER, Frederick Ray. 964 W IDAHO AVE 97914 #016-06-1969 L1983 DR AM *020 †80

PEDEN, Joseph Carroll, III. 351 SW 9TH ST 97914 #028-02-1971 L1976 GP *020

PETERSON, Andrew C. 351 SW 9TH ST 97914 #030-06-1969 L1975 IM PUD *020 †20

PETERSON, Eugene Eugene. 894 SW 4TH AVE 97914 #039-01-1987 L1996 ORS *020 †40

PHILLIPS, Jeffrey F. 351 SW 9TH ST 97914 #040-02-1977 L1979 EM *020 †16

PHILLIPS, John Henry. 1037 SW 5TH AVE 97914 #003-01-1974 L1978 IM *020

PITTS, Jeffrey Church. 251 SW 19TH ST, ONTARIO SURGERY CENTER 97914 #035-06-1978 L1983 OPH AM *020

PLUMMER, Patrick Martin. 1050 SW 3RD AVE STE 2500 97914 #019-02-1984 L1989 OTO HNS *020 †45

REICH, Steven Chas. 1050 SW 3RD AVE, STE 3200 97914 #056-01-1987 L1992 OTO *020 †45

RYSENA, Eric C. 351 SW 9TH ST, HOLY ROSARY MEDICAL CTR 97914 #048-13-1989 L1994 PTH *020 †50

RYSENGA, Julie Ream. 351 SW 9TH ST 97914 #048-13-1988 L1994 OPH PO *020 †35

SANDERS, Wilfred N. ■ 97914 #028-05-1943 L1944 GP *071

SCHANTZEN, Gayle Whitmer. 7 SW 3RD AVE 97914 #037-01-1993 L2002 FM *020 †18

SCOTT, Lester Wm. 351 SW 9TH ST 97914 #040-02-1947 L1948 GS GP *071 †85

SCOTT, Matthew Anderson. 351 SW 9TH ST, HOLY ROSARY MEDICAL CENTER 97914 #016-11-2001 L2004 EM *020 †16

SMITH, Morris Henry, Jr. 351 SW 9TH ST, C/O HOLY ROSARY HOSPITAL E 97914 #051-04-1964 L1984 IM OS *020 †16

SNYDER, Paul J. 335 SW 13TH ST, PHYS PRIMARY CARE CTR 97914 #025-12-1978 L1983 IM *020

SOLIPURAM, Arun Kumar Red. 269 SW 19TH ST, OREGON MEDICAL ASSOCIATES 97914 #495-21-2000 L2005 IMG *020 †20

SPARLING, Susan K.. 7 SW 3RD AVE 97914 #305-01-2000 L2006 FM *100 †18

SPOKAS, Frank J, Jr. 1050 SW 3RD AVE, STE 2600 97914 #016-11-1982 L1991 **GS** *020 †85
STARK, Fred Richard. 351 SW 9TH ST 97914 #016-11-1963 L1975 **IM AI** *020 †20,03
STOUNE, John Lawrence. 1050 SW 3RD AVE, STE 3200 97914 #028-34-1971 L1992
　IM *020 †20
TANAKA, Augustus M. 351 SW 9TH ST 97914 #035-08-1951 L1958 **GS** *071 †85
TESNOHLIDEK, Barbara Rahe. 351 SW 9TH ST, HOLY ROSARY MEDICAL CENTER 97914
　#054-04-1989 L1994 **AN** *020 †05
TESNOHLIDEK, Dwaine A. 1050 SW 3RD AVE, STE 2600 97914 #054-04-1989 L1994
　GS *020 †85
THOMPSON, William C. 351 SW 9TH ST 97914 #026-08-1989 L1999 **PTH PCH** *020 †50
TIPTON, Willis Matt. 351 SW 9TH ST, HOLY ROSARY HOSPITAL 97914 #028-34-1963 L1967
　R OS *071 †80
TYLER, Donald E. ■ 97914 #040-02-1950 L1951 **U** *020 †95
WOOD, David Gary. 984 W IDAHO AVE 97914 #019-02-1973 L2002 **DR** *020 †80
WU, Clifford L. 1219 SW 4TH AVE, UNIT 1 97914 #067-01-1995 L2007 **PD** *020 †20,55
YEAGER, Robert Thos. 964 W IDAHO AVE, SNAKE RIVER RADIOLOGYPC 97914
　#054-04-1988 L1998 **DR** *020 †80
ZIA, Arqam. 1050 SW 3RD AVE, STE 3200 97914 #704-02-1996 L2003 **IM** *020 †20
ZIEMANN-GIMMEL, Patrick. 1050 SW 9TH AVE STE 3200, HOLY ROSARY MED CTR 97914
　#409-33-1997 L2004 **AN** *100 †05

OREGON CITY – CLACKAMAS

ANTOLIK, John Jos. 728 MOLALLA AVE STE C 97045 #031-01-1984 L1985 **GS** *020 †85
AUGUSTINE, Ray J. 406 7TH ST 97045 #016-11-1973 L1991 **IM** *071
BANGS, Cameron Clarence. 728 MOLALLA AVE 97045 #050-02-1964 L1967 **IM CD** *071
BARTH, William Chas. 728 MOLALLA AVE 97045 #040-02-1989 L1992 **FM** *020 †18
BARTON, George Nicholas. 16807 S CLACKAMAS RIVER DR 97045 #023-01-1984 L1988
　EM *020 †16
BEILSTEIN, Michelle Cobur. 1508 DIVISION ST, STE 15 97045 #005-06-1997 L2004 **GE** *020 †20
BESPALY, Michael. 1510 DIVISION ST STE 1 97045 #305-01-1992 L1997 **APM** *020 †18,05
BOCK, Charles Joseph, Jr. 1306 DIVISION ST 97045 #016-06-1993 L1998 **OPH PO** *020 †35
BRAINARD, William S. ■ 97045 #005-15-1962 L1975 **GP DIA** *071
BROWN, Ann Elizabeth. 1500 DIVISION ST 97045 #040-02-1977 L1979 **EM IM** *071 †20,16
BURKE, William Romney. 1510 DIVISION ST STE 10 97045 #040-02-1970 L1978 **U** *020 †95
BURNHAM, Austin Clark. 1404 DIVISION ST STE 5 97045 #028-34-1982 L1983 **GS VS** *020
BUUCK, David Alan. 1505 DIVISION ST 97045 #056-05-1988 L1994 **OSM** *020 †40
CARLTON, Sharrel Marie. 1508 DIVISION ST, STE 205 97045 #005-06-1993 L2000 **OBG** *020 †30
CHITTY, Jack Lamont. 1001 MOLALLA AVE, STE 100 97045 #016-11-1959 L1965
　IM CD *071 †20
CLARKE, Ronald. 14279 GLEN OAK RD 97045 #858-03-1985 L1990 **PD** *020 †55
CLELAND, Donald Lockhead. 605 HIGH ST 97045 #040-02-1958 L1960 **GS** *020 †85
CONNOR, Rodney Wm. 1001 MOLALLA AVE, STE 100 97045 #018-03-1974 L1977
　IM ID *020 †20
COOPER, Arthur Denton. 1500 DIVISION ST 97045 #040-02-1978 L1979 **OBG** *020 †30
CORDOVA, Lee Jos. 1001 MOLALLA AVE, STE 100 97045 #054-04-1968 L1974 **IM** *020 †20
DALY, Michael James. ■ 97045 #005-14-1968 L1981 **NM IM** *020 †20,28
DAVIES, William Mellott. 1510 DIVISION ST, STE 110 97045 #032-01-1982 L2003 **IM** *020 †20
DAVIS, James E. 1500 DIVISION ST 97045 #040-02-1953 L1954 **GP** *020 †18
DE LA BRUERE, Beverly. 1500 DIVISION ST 97045 #019-02-1983 L1987 **FM** *020 †18
DIVINE, Ronald Wayne. 1500 DIVISION ST, RIVER RADIOLOGISTS 97045 #046-01-1995 L1999
　NM *020 †80,28
DODSON, Darlene Joyce. 1508 DIVISION ST STE 205 97045 #054-04-1992 L1993 **OBG** *020 †30
EDWARDS, George Marvin. 1001 MOLALLA AVE, STE 100 97045 #040-02-1974 L1975
　IM PUD *020
EILERSEN, Christopher R. 1420 JOHN ADAMS ST, OREGON CITY FAMILY 97045
　#040-02-1996 L1999 **FM** *020 †18 ‡
FARLEY, James Alan. 610 JEFFERSON ST 97045 #028-02-1969 L1973 **P** *020
FEENEY, Robert. ■ 97045 #041-01-1944 L1949 **P CHP** *071
FONKEN, Royce Leon. 1306 DIVISION ST 97045 #003-01-1984 L1985 **OPH** *020 †35
GARG, Sandeep. 1510 DIVISION ST, STE 110 97045 #495-43-1989 L1997 **CD** *020 †20
GOLDENBERG, Richard. 1510 DIVISION ST, STE 200 97045 #024-05-1984 L1994 **IM** *020 †20
GOODWIN DE MCCLENDON, Jenn. 1500 DIVISION ST, WILLAMETTE FALLS HOSPITAL 97045
　#040-02-2003 L2003 **FM** *100
GREALISH, Scott C. 1306 DIVISION ST, OREGON EYE CARE 97045 #016-11-1992 L1993
　OPH *020 †35
GREEN, John Albert, III. 516 HIGH ST 97045 #049-01-1974 L1980 **AI FM** *020
GREENSTREET, Michael M. ■ 97045 #040-02-1976 L1977 **EM** *020 †16
GRUCELLA, Christina Marie. 1510 DIVISION ST, STE 280 97045 #040-02-1988 L1989
　PD *020 †55
HALL, Wendy L. 1508 DIVISION ST STE 205, WOMENS HLTH CTR OR OREGON 97045
　#043-01-1999 L2000 **OBG** *020 †30
HARRY, Raymond Chas. 1500 DIVISION ST 97045 #040-02-1985 L1988 **PTH** *020 †50
HAWKINS, June. 14279 S GLEN OAK RD, STE 204 97045 #352-07-1962 L1981
　AI IM *020 †20,03
HAYS, Marcia Lee. 998 LIBRARY CT, CLACKAMAS COUNTY MEN HLT C 97045
　#005-19-1973 L1975 **P CLP** *020 †75
HEWITT, J Ivan. ■ 97045 #040-02-1960 L1961 **ADM** *071
HICKMAN, Charles Murrel. 1420 JOHN ADAMS ST 97045 #018-03-1963 L1967 **FM** *071
HOLMES, Keith Davis. 605 HIGH ST, CLELAND CLINIC 97045 #040-02-1960 L1969 **GS** *071 †85
INMAN, Robert E. 1500 DIVISION ST 97045 #018-75-1965, ▲ L1970 **AN** *071 ‡
INTILE, Joseph Anthony. 516 HIGH ST 97045 #035-09-1957 L1968 **IM** *071
JAMES, Frank Russell. 110 CENTER ST 97045 #034-01-1977 L1978 **IM GP** *020 †20
JAMISON, Kevin J. 1510 DIVISION ST, STE 180 97045 #040-02-1991 L1992 **N** *020 †75
JEFFREYS, Timothy Jay. 1510 DIVISION ST, STE 280 97045 #040-02-1987 L1988 **PD** *020 †55
JOE, Murray Douglas. 1508 DIVISION ST STE 115 97045 #030-05-1974 L1975 **OTO A** *020 †45
JUAREZ, Ralph Augustine. 1510 DIVISION ST, STE 200 97045 #005-02-1988 L1989
　PUD CCM *020 †20
KAESCHE, W Curtis. 1505 DIVISION ST 97045 #049-01-1968 L1969 **ORS** *020 †40
KAMINSKI, Stephen Michael. 1500 DIVISION ST, WILLAMETTE FALLS HOSP 97045
　#025-12-1990 L1992 **AN** *020 †05
KASKAN, Lisa Joy. 998 LIBRARY CT 97045 #040-02-1986 L1987 **CHP P** *020 †75
KIM, Samuel Hyunseong. 1500 DIVISION ST 97045 #008-01-2001 L2001 **EM** *020 †16
KLEIN, David Leo. ■ 97045 #017-20-1978 L1982 **DR** *020

KUNKE, Terry Alan. 1306 DIVISION ST, EYEHEALTH NORTHWEST 97045 #039-05-1986 L1995
　OPH *020 †35
LAMOREAUX, Le Roy Francis. ■ 97045 #040-02-1956 L1959 **AN** *020 †05
LARSON, Raelene Hanks. 1500 DIVISION ST 97045 #018-03-1982 L1988 **OBG** *071 †30
LEEDY, Daniel Allan. 1508 DIVISION ST, STE 115 97045 #040-02-1990 L1991 **OTO** *020 †45
LINDBERG, Bethany Joy. 1510 DIVISION ST STE 28 97045 #040-02-2004 L2004 **PD** *020 †55
LINDQUIST, David James. 1500 DIVISION ST 97045 #026-04-1972 L1973 **EM** *020 †16
MATSUNAGA, Don Wm. 998 LIBRARY CT, CLACKAMAS COUNTY MENTAL HE 97045
　#016-11-1984 L1985 **P** *020
MC KINNEY, John Kevin. 1306 DIVISION ST, EYEHEALTH NORTHWEST 97045
　#048-04-1987 L1998 **OPH PHP** *020 †35
MC LEAN, Edward Norris. 1306 DIVISION ST, OREGON EYE CARE 97045 #023-07-1947 L1950
　OPH *071 †35
MILLER, Maria Nelida. 702 JOHN ADAMS ST 97045 #748-01-1962 L1976 **FM** *020 †18
NIELSEN, Michael Paul. 1508 DIVISION ST, STE 205 97045 #049-01-1978 L1982 **OBG** *020 †30
NORRIS, Thaddeus Michael. 1420 JOHN ADAMS ST, OREGON CITY FAMILY 97045
　#040-02-1969 L1978 **FM** *020 †18
OERTHER, Frederick John. ■ 97045 #025-07-1963 L1964 **NEP** *071
OKINO, Gary Satoshi. 1500 DIVISION ST 97045 #040-02-1967 L1968 **AN** *071 †05
PASS, David A. 1500 DIVISION ST 97045 #011-04-1982 L1988 **AN** *071 †05
PHILIPS, Ronald Wayne. 13884 CONWAY DR 97045 #005-12-1955 L1956 **R** *020 †80
PIDGEON, Wayne M. 1500 DIVISION ST 97045 #040-02-1951 L1952 **P** *071
PYRCH, William J. 1500 DIVISION ST 97045 #040-02-1951 L1952 **GP GS** *071
RASOR, William Thos. 1508 DIVISION ST, STE 25 97045 #040-02-1971 L1976 **FM** *020 †18
RESK, James Matthew. 14279 S GLEN OAK RD 97045 #025-07-1990 L1993 **PD** *020 †55
RYDLUND, Kelly William. 1508 DIVISION ST STE 115, KELLY W. RYDLUND, MD 97045
　#030-05-1994 L2005 **OTO** *020 †45
SALISBURY, Nancy Jane. 1500 DIVISION ST 97045 #005-18-1982 L1983 **OBG** *020 †30
SCHILKE, John Frederick. 184 HARDING BLVD 97045 #008-01-1965 L1969 **PD FM** *020 †55
SCHMIDT, Frederick Geo. 1508 DIVISION ST, STE 205 97045 #025-01-1961 L1968
　OBG *020 †30
SCHNELL, Susan Kae. ■ 97045 #030-06-1985 L1986 **FOP PTH** *020
SERRES, Edward Jos. 1510 DIVISION ST, STE 210 97045 #030-06-1966 L1974 **GS** *020 †85
SEWELL, Jon Chas. 729 MOLALLA AVE, MOLALLA PLAZA 97045 #004-01-1963 L1969
　R *071 †80
SHILLING, Joel Mac Gregor. 1500 DIVISION ST 97045 #025-01-1964 L1971 **PTH PCP** *020 †50
SMUCKER, Ray Eldon. 1500 DIVISION ST 97045 #040-02-1981 L1984 **FM** *020 †18
STEPHENSON, Robert Eugene. 1500 DIVISION ST, DIAGNOSTIC IMAGING 97045
　#019-02-1978 L1992 **DR** *020 †80
STEVENS, Rudolph B. 702 JOHN ADAMS ST 97045 #016-11-1949 L1950 **GYN GP** *071 †85
STROMBERG, Paul Kenneth. 1306 DIVISION ST 97045 #034-01-1987 L1988 **OPH IM** *020 †35
SUSANKA, Elisabeth A. 1508 DIVISION ST, STE 205 97045 #040-02-1993 L1994 **OBG** *020 †30
TAYLOR, Cornelia Mann. 1500 DIVISION ST 97045 #040-02-1990 L1993 **HOS** *020 †20 ‡
WEEKS, Gaylord Clinton. 1500 DIVISION ST 97045 #040-02-1959 L1960 **FM** *071 †18
WENNHOLD, Kim. 998 LIBRARY CT, CCMH OREGON CITY HILLTOP C 97045
　#049-01-1996 L1998 **P** *020 †75
WINJUM, Jon Martin. 1420 JOHN ADAMS ST, OREGON CITY FAMILY 97045 #018-03-1993 L1996
　FM *020 †18 ‡
WOLLMUTH, Robert Lonnie. 1508 DIVISION ST, STE 15 97045 #040-02-1970 L1977
　GE *020 †20
YARRIS, Jonathan Peter. 1500 DIVISION ST, WILLAMETTE FALLS HOSPITAL 97045
　#040-02-2005 L2005 **EM** *012
YASENCHAK, Christopher A. 1510 DIVISION ST, STE 130 97045 #041-14-1999 L2006
　HO *020 †20
YOO, Ji Hyun. 1500 DIVISION ST 97045 #583-04-2003 L2007 **IM** *020 †20

OTIS – LINCOLN

FRANKEL, Henry. 6695 NE SAL-LA-SEA DR 97368 #035-19-1935 L1937 **OPH** *071 †35
MASS, Robert E. ■ 97368 #040-02-1951 L1956 **HEM ON** *071 †20
PETTERSON, Carl A. ■ 97368 #019-02-1942 L1954 **IM** *071

PACIFIC CITY – TILLAMOOK

THOMPSON, Jeremy Heward. ■ 97135 #539-03-1960 L1978 **PA IM** *071

PENDLETON – UMATILLA

ADAMS, Bart Ardell. 1050 SOUTHGATE, E OREGON EYE CARE SURG CTR 97801
　#005-18-1985 L1994 **OPH** *020 †35
ADAMS, Bradley Scott. 1416 SW COURT AVE 97801 #019-02-1996 L2001 **ORS** *020 †40
ADAMS, Lawrence James. 1601 SE COURT AVE 97801 #016-11-1978 L1991 **PTH** *020 †50
ALDAPE, Mark Andrew. 1601 SE COURT AVE 97801 #054-04-1993 L1994 **PTH** *020 †50
ALPERIN, Michael David. PO BOX 160, HEALTH CENTE 97801 #024-01-1984 L1997
　FM *020 †50,18
ANDREWS, Kevin Robt. 1100 SOUTHGATE, PENDLETON INTERNAL 97801 #030-06-1989 L2005
　IM *020 †20
BAXTER, J Albert. 125 SE COURT AVE STE 8 97801 #038-06-1955 L1956 **P ADP** *020
BITTNER, Jules Frederick. ■ 97801 #040-02-1947 **IM P** *071 †20
BLAIR, Roger Paul. 1100 SOUTHGATE STE 7, BLUE MTN DIAGNOSTIC IMG 97801
　#030-06-1988 L1996 **DR** *020
BOSS, Robert John. 911 SW COURT AVE 97801 #649-14-1972 L1976 **IM** *020
BOWER, Andrew Lee. 1600 SE COURT PL, STE 100 97801 #038-41-1996 L2005 **GS VS** *020 †85
BRANDT, Alan Dale. 125 SE COURT AVE, STE 4 97801 #054-04-1960 L1967 **IM OS** *071
CAMBIER, Jacob Warren. 1100 SOUTHGATE STE 7 97801 #005-02-1972 L1978 **DR** *020 †80
CARNEIRO, Jose. 1601 SE COURT AVE, APOGEE MEDICAL GROUP 97801 #770-02-1975 L2007
　IM *020 †20
CARRINGTON, John Mitchell. 602 SE BYERS AVE 97801 #021-06-1974 L1994 **D** *020 †15
COLLIS, Langley Reyburn. 1601 SE COURT AVE 97801 #005-11-1965 L1967 **GS** *071 †85
DALE, Allan Walter. 1601 SE COURT AVE 97801 #026-04-1978 L2008 **EM P** *020 †18,16
DATTA, Deepshikha. 1601 SE COURT AVE 97801 #495-79-1989 L2002 **PTH** *020 †50
DAVIDSON, Peter James. 2600 WESTGATE, EASTERN OREGON PSYCHIATRIC 97801
　#054-04-1985 L1991 **P** *020 †75

■ = Address Information Privacy Protected

DENTON, Clayton Lee. 714 SW DORION AVE 97801 #039-01-1982 L1992 **IM ADL** *075
DIEHL, Joseph Henry, Jr. 125 SE COURT AVE, STE 1 97801 #040-02-1970 L1971 **GP** *071
EARLY, Kendall Stewart. ■ 97801 #030-05-1967 L1976 **U** *020 †95
ERICKSON, Frank Albert. 109 NE ELLIS AVE 97801 #016-42-1981 L1992 **DR OS** *020 †80
FELDER, Jerald Barnard. PO BOX 1513 97801 #048-04-1959 L1995 **AM OTO** *030 †45,70
GIERL, Paul Richard. 434 SE 3RD ST 97801 #056-05-1983 L1997 **PTH** *020 †50
GORDON, Laura Sidney. 1100 SOUTHGATE, STE 6 97801 #016-06-1982 L1992 **U** *020 †95
GRAHAM, Gloria Ann. 105 HOSPITAL DR, BOX A 97801 #561-01-1975 **P GP** *020
GUENTHER, Donald C. 1600 SE COURT PL, STE L01 97801 #005-15-1969 L1974 **PD** *020 †55
HELOU, Khalil Y. 1601 SE COURT AVE 97801 #605-01-1973 L1982 **PTH** *020 †50
HITZMAN, Jonathan C. 1600 SE COURT PL, STE 201 97801 #016-01-1988 L1997 **FM** *020 †18
HOLMES, Cynthia Bos. 1601 SE COURT AVE 97801 #005-06-1991 L2002 **DR** *020 †80
JOHNSON, Richard Haviland. 135 SE 1ST ST 97801 #040-02-1962 L1972 **P** *071 †75
KHALEEQ, Erum Syed. 2600 WESTGATE, E OREGON PSYCHIATRIC CENTE 97801 #306-01-1986 L2002 **P** *020 †75
KOVACHEVICH, Larry Lee. ■ 97801 #028-34-1973 L1974 **FM ADM** *020 †18
LUNDQUIST, Christopher J. 1100 SOUTHGATE #005-12-1976 L1980 **FM** *020 †18
MAERCKS, Lisa Rani. 1601 SE COURT AVE 97801 #011-03-1999 L2002 **EM** *020 †16
MARIER, Cheryl L Quimby. 1304 SE COURT PL 97801 #007-02-1980 L1984 **OBG** *020 †30
MARIER, Daniel Leo. 1100 SOUTHGATE, PENDLETON INTERNAL 97801 #035-19-1975 L1984 **IM** *020 †20
MARKHAM, Juliet Kristina. 1304 SE COURT PL 97801 #025-12-1995 L2006 **OBG** *020
MC BEE, John Malcolm. 1600 SE COURT PL, STE 102 97801 #010-02-1986 L1994 **GS GE** *020 †85
MILLER, Friedrich V B. ■ 97801 #035-06-1965 L1970 **P PD** *071 †55
NEAL, Steven Lloyd. 702 SW DORION AVE 97801 #048-13-1982 L1987 **OTO** *020 †45
NELSON, George Everette. 1100 SOUTHGATE, STE 2 97801 #054-04-1965 L1975 **IM** *071 †20
PAGE, John Marshall. 1601 SE COURT AVE 97801 #040-02-1982 L1985 **EM AM** *020 †18
PARK, Hyung Dong. 1601 SE COURT AVE 97801 #583-10-1982 L2006 **IM** *100 †20
PETERSON, Dale Jay. 1601 SE COURT AVE 97801 #025-12-1985 L1988 **FM** *020 †18
PICKEN, Andrew James. ■ 97801 #038-06-1993 L2002 **IM** *020 †20
RAMIREZ, Nicholas Dumpit. ■ 97801 #748-01-1957 L1972 **FM GS** *071
RANCIER, Marco Antonio. ■ 97801 #308-01-1958 L1976 **P** *071
RICHARDS, David Alan. 1601 SE COURT AVE 97801 #019-02-1994 L1997 **FM** *020 †18
RICKMAN, Sara Schweigert. 1600 SE COURT PL, STE L01 97801 #028-34-1992 L1998 **PD** *020 †55
RUCKER, Casey James. 1601 SE COURT AVE 97801 #040-02-1987 L1988 **EM IM** *020 †20
SAWYER, James Brion. 1601 SE COURT AVE 97801 #019-02-1961 L1968 **PTH** *072 †50
SEKIYA, Utako. 2600 WESTGATE, EASTERN OREGON PSYCHIATRIC 97801 #572-04-1984 L2000 **P** *020 †75
SIMONS, Stanley John, Jr. 1100 SOUTHGATE, PENDLETON EYE CLINIC PC 97801 #026-04-1961 L1962 **OPH** *071 †35
SITZ, William Norman. 1100 SOUTHGATE, PENDLETON INTERNAL 97801 #028-02-1974 L1975 **IM EM** *020 †20
STEFANCIK, Rudy Wallis. 1606 SE COURT AVE 97801 #048-02-1982 L2001 **PTH FOP** *020 †50
TILL, Bruce L. ■ 97801 #035-45-1949 L1950 **OPH** *071 †35
TILL, Virginia Edwards. ■ 97801 #035-45-1949 L1950 **AN** *071 †05
TOWNSLEY, Malcolm C. 1601 SE COURT AVE, C/O ST. ANTHONY HOSPITAL 97801 #010-02-1993 L1997 **IM** *020 †20
VAN HOUTEN, Grant Chris. 2500 WESTGATE 97801 #040-02-1973 L1974 **FM** *020 †18
WEEKS, Charles Thos. 1416 SE COURT AVE 97801 #016-11-1966 L1978 **ORS OSM** *020 †40 ‡
WENDLER, Sheldon O. 1601 SE COURT AVE 97801 #040-02-1982 L1988 **FM** *020 †20
WIGLEY, Terry Lee. 1100 SOUTHGATE STE 4 97801 #005-12-1990 L1996 **OTO** *020 †45
WINN, Patricia J. 411 SE 14TH ST 97801 #040-02-1982 L1986 **OBG** *020 †30
WYLAND, Rhonda Lynn. 1600 SE COURT PL STE L1 97801 #040-02-1986 L1988 **PD** *020 †55
ZEIGLER, Gary Michael. 1601 SE COURT AVE 97801 #049-01-1999 L2002 **EM** *020 †16

PHILOMATH — BENTON

ACKERMAN, Jayne Anne. ■ 97370 #050-02-1976 L1991 **GP GPM** *020
BRALY, Berton E. ■ 97370 #039-01-1951 L1951 **AN** *071
CLARK, Ellis Richard. ■ 97370 #024-01-1982 L1988 **AN** *020 †05
CUTSFORTH, David H, Jr. 1219 APPLEGATE ST 97370 #040-02-1973 L1977 **FM** *020 †18
FOLEY, Shawn Jay. ■ 97370 #046-01-1994 L1998 **FM** *020 †18
GROSZ, Carl Robt. ■ 97370 #007-02-1957 L1958 **GS** *071 †85
GRUBE, David Raymond. 1219 APPLEGATE ST 97370 #040-02-1973 L1977 **FM GP** *020 †18
WOOD, William Travers. ■ 97370 #038-06-1938 L1940 **GP PD** *072

PHOENIX — JACKSON

HIEBER, Frank Reynolds. ■ 97535 #016-43-1954 L1999 **IM** *071 †20
WEBB, Eric Seth. 205 FERN VALLEY RD STE A 97535 #045-01-1986 L1991 **FM EM** *020 †18

PILOT ROCK — UMATILLA

JOHNSTON, Charles Edgar. 68619 SHAW RD 97868 #051-04-1962 L1970 **P GP** *020 ‡
KOCH, Richard Arthur. PO BOX CC 97868 #040-02-1954 L1955 **GP PHP** *071

PORT ORFORD — CURRY

FLAXEL, John Thad. 525 MADRONA ST 97465 #040-02-1963 L1964 **OPH** *020 †35 ‡
GRAHAM, Debra Ann. 525 MADRONA ST 97465 #035-19-1992 L1997 **OPH** *020 †35
JARVIS, William Robt. 42338 PARKWOOD DR 97465 #048-14-1974 L1974 **ID GPM** *050 †55
KIMBALL, Robert Mark. ■ 97465 #021-01-1940 L1941 **ORS** *071 †40
PITCHFORD, Thomas E. 525 MADRONA ST, CURRY FAMILY MEDICAL 97465 #010-01-1982 L1987 **GPM** *062
SAYANI, Ian. ■ 97465 #803-05-1948 L1971 **ORS** *071

PORTLAND — CLACKAMAS

ANDERSON, Howard John. ■ 97267 #005-14-1966 L1970 **D** *071 †15

ARMENTROUT, Herbert L. ■ 97222 #040-02-1942 **IM** *071
BAIRD, Carol Miller. 10150 SE 32ND AVE 97222 #040-02-1996 L1998 **IM** *020 †20
BASHAM, Chandra Marie. ■ 97267 #023-07-2005 L2007 **EM** *100
BECKER, Sara Kristine. 3033 SE MONROE ST 97222 #025-01-1977 L1978 **FM** *020 †18
BERGERON, Gary Alfred. ■ 97222 #040-02-1969 L1973 **CD IM** *071 †20 ‡
BISCHEL, John David. 2100 SE LAKE RD 97222 #040-02-1962 L1964 **CHP P** *020 †18
BLANCHARD, Donald Lynn. ■ 97086 #040-02-1973 L1974 **OPH** *071 †35
BLATT, Jonathan Matthew. 10150 SE 32ND AVE 97222 #016-42-1983 L1990 **PME** *020 †05 ‡
BOGGS, C Carter. ■ 97222 #040-02-1965 L1969 **EM IM** *071
BROWN, Benjamina Nina. 3033 SE MONROE ST 97222 #014-01-2004 L2004 **FM** *020 †18
BUHL, Walter Richard. 3033 SE MONROE ST 97222 #035-01-1971 L1972 **FM NM** *020 †18
CALHOUN, Craig William. 10150 SE 32ND AVE 97222 #028-34-1999 L2003 **AN** *020 †05 ‡
CARVALHO, Victoria F. 8305 SE MONTEREY AVE # 220 97086 #495-41-1969 L1979 **PM** *020 †60
CHEN, Jeffrey Che-Hsiung. ■ 97086 #385-03-1964 L1971 **END IM** *020 †20
DAVIS, Frederick Sterling. ■ 97267 #051-01-1955 L1955 **OPH** *020 †35
EMERICK, Charles Walton. ■ 97222 #030-06-1956 L1963 **OTO** *071 †45
FELDMAN, Donald. 3300 SE DWYER DR, STE 300 97222 #035-19-1954 L1956 **ATP CLP** *071 †50
HUGHES-FOX, Laura Violet. ■ 97086 #041-77-2005, ▲ L2005 **FP** *012
IRISH, R Ann. 13505 SE RIVER RD # 181 97222 #038-06-1957 L1957 **OPH PD** *071 †35
KASARANENI, Suresh. 10202 SE 32ND AVE, STE 101 97222 #495-50-1982 L2000 **ORS** *020
KAWAHARA, Cara Leonechiyo. ■ 97267 #021-01-2005 L2005 **FP** *012
KLEIN, Elizabeth Wanzer. 10330 SE 32ND AVE, STE 205 97222 #005-06-1986 L1991 **FM** *020 †18
KLEIN, Linda. ■ 97222 #041-07-1994 L1996 **FP** *012
LOWELL, Lawrence M. ■ 97222 #040-02-1936 L1937 **TS** *071
MONTEVERDI, Theresa Lynn. ■ 97222 #040-02-1994 **OS** *062
OLSON, Deanna Kay. 3250 SE LLEWELLYN ST 97222 #005-12-1986 L1991 **GS** *020 †85
QUICK, Jack Malcolm. ■ 97267 #005-02-1961 L1962 **PD** *071 †55
RUESCH, Paul David. 10202 SE 32ND AVE, STE 101 97222 #025-07-1990 L2003 **ORS OSM** *020 †40
SCHERMAN, Quinten. ■ 97267 #040-02-1945 L1948 **GYN** *071 †30
SCHNEIDER, Arnold J. 13505 SE RIVER RD 97222 #005-02-1943 L1944 **GP GS** *071
SHEARER, David Merle. ■ 97222 #041-01-1962 L1963 **NM OS** *071 †28,20
SPECHT, Elmer E. ■ 97268 #035-01-1950 L1953 **ORS** *071 †55,60,40
TALBOT, Cynthia Elizabeth. 10330 SE 32ND AVE, STE 205 97222 #005-02-1983 L1997 **FM** *020 †18
TASK, Stephen Alexander. 7000 SE THIESSEN RD 97267 #005-15-1965 L1968 **FM AM** *020 †18
TAYLOR, Eugene E. 13505 SE RIVER RD # 136 97222 #028-02-1945 L1961 **P CHP** *020 †70,75

PORTLAND — MULTNOMAH

AABY, Aazy Arthur. 1955 NW NORTHRUP ST, OREGON MEDICAL EYE CLINIC 97209 #038-06-1979 L1985 **OPH PO** *020 †35 ‡
ABBASSIAN, Soraya Ann. 10373 NE HANCOCK ST, STE 117 97220 #003-01-1998 L1999 **IM** *020 †20
ABBEY, Kenneth Robert. 3181 SW SAM JACKSON PRK RD, UHS 2 97239 #005-18-2001 L2005 **AN** *020 †05
ABDU, Emun Na. ■ 97239 #025-01-2004 L2004 **NS** *012
ABENDROTH, Francena Diane. 3181 SW SAM JCKSN PRK RD R, NEUROLOGY DEPARTMENT-OHSU 97239 #040-02-2001 L2001 **CN** *100
ACAR, Feridun. 3181 SW SAM JCKSN PRK RD R, DEPTOF NEUROLOGICAL SURGER 97239 #902-05-1998 L2006 *100
ACHORD, Thaddeus Claar. 1962 NW KEARNEY ST # L101 97209 #005-12-1968 L1977 **P** *071
ACHTERMAN, Christopher A. 501 N GRAHAM ST, STE 200 97227 #028-02-1972 L1980 **ORS OP** *020 †40
ACOSTA, Stephen C. 4805 NE GLISAN ST 97213 #005-14-1976 L1996 **EM GP** *020 †16
ADAMS, Gregory Thomas. ■ 97239 #040-02-2006 L2006 **GS** *012
ADAMS, John Philip. 3181 SW SAM JACKSON PRK RD 97239 #352-05-1992 L2002 *071
ADAMS, Karen E. 3181 SW SAM JCKSN PRK RD R 97239 #048-14-1988 L1989 **OBG** *020 †30
ADAMS, Michael Laurin. 3600 N INTERSTATE AVE, OCCUPATIONAL MEDICINE DEPT 97227 #045-01-1974 L1993 **OM FM** *020 †18,70
ADELMAN, Stephen Edward. 1846 SE LADD AVE 97214 #035-19-1962 L1969 **IM NM** *020 †20
ADKINS, Samantha Rae. 177 NE 102ND AVE 97220 #056-06-2003 L2007 **OBG** *020
ADLER, Adam Harris. ■ 97239 #040-02-2007 L2007 **FP** *012
ADLER, David E. 1040 NW 22ND AVE, STE 630 97210 #035-08-1988 L1999 **NS** *020 †25
ADLER, Michael. 2250 NW FLANDERS ST, STE 20 97210 #005-18-1993 L1994 **D** *020 †15 ‡
ADLHOCH, George Peter. 500 NE MULTNOMAH ST, STE 100 97232 #016-43-1954 L1961 **ORS** *020 †40
AEBI, Ernest Phelps. 500 NE MULTNOMAH ST STE 10 97232 #040-02-1964 L1967 **OPH** *071 †35
AFROSE, Sadeka. 2801 N GANTENBEIN AVE, & HEAL 97227 #160-06-1998 L2005 **IM** *100
AGATE, Nishita Ninad. 2801 N GANTENBEIN AVE 97227 #496-15-2001 L2004 **IM** *100
AGENO, Shaun Lowell. ■ 97209 #035-19-2004 L2007 **CD** *012 †20
AGHAMOHAMMADI, Sara. ■ 97239 #040-02-2008 *012
AGHAYAN, Aric Samad. ■ 97239 #028-46-2003 L2007 **GS** *012
AGNEW, Anna Maria. ■ 97239 #040-02-2006 L2006 **PD** *012
AHMAD, Asma Sultana. 177 NE 102ND AVE 97220 #016-06-1995 L2003 **OBG** *020 †30
AHMANN, Andrew Jos. 3181 SW SAM JACKSON PRK RD, OHSU DIABETES CTR 97239 #007-02-1980 L1990 **END IM** *020 †20
AHN, Alicia Meredith. ■ 97239 #040-02-2004 L2004 **IM** *020 †20
AHRENS, Merrill Marshall. 19500 SE STARK ST, ROCKWOOD MEDICAL CENTER 97233 #016-06-1989 L1992 **IM** *020 †20
AIONA, Michael David. 3101 SW JACKSON PARK RD 97201 #005-15-1977 L1986 **OS ORS** *020 †40
AKTAS, Seref. 3101 SW SAM JACKSON PRK RD 97239 #902-05-1990 **OP** *100
ALBAUGH, Jeffrey S. 1111 NE 99TH AVE 97220 #054-04-1974 L1975 **GE IM** *020 †20
AL-BEDAIWI, Waleed Ahmed. 2241 LLOYD CTR 97232 #797-01-1994 L2001 **FM** *020
ALBERT, Thomas W. 3181 SW SAM JACKSON PARK RD 97239 #024-01-1977 L1979 **FPS** *020
ALBERTS, Bennett Irvin. 10373 NE HANCOCK ST 97220 #030-05-1960 L1965 **OBG OBS** *020 †30
ALBERTS, Lisa Marie. 300 N GRAHAM ST, STE 200 97227 #041-07-1995 L1997 **IM** *020 †20

ALBRICH, John Michael. 1015 NW 22ND AVE, GOOD SAMARITAN HOSPITAL 97210 #016-02-1975 L1977 **EM** *020 †20,16

ALBRIGHT, Jeffreys David. 135 NE 102ND AVE, FRACTURE CLINIC 97220 #032-01-1992 L1998 **OSM** *020 †40

ALDEN, Richard John. 2386 NW HOYT ST 97210 #040-02-1988 L1989 **CHP** *020 †75

ALDRED, Jason Lamar. ■ 97213 #047-06-2003 L2003 **N** *100

ALEXANDER, Deborah Ann. 4805 NE GLISAN ST, STE BG05 97210 #041-02-2000 L2000 **IM** *020 †20

ALEXANDER, Jonathan S. 500 NE MULTNOMAH ST, STE 100 97232 #033-06-1999 L2003 **D** *020 †15 ‡

ALEXANDER, Priscilla W. 233 NE 102ND AVE 97220 #048-02-1988 L1992 **DR** *020 †80

ALEXANDRIDIS, Alexis Regi. ■ 97239 #035-09-2006 L2006 **GS** *012

ALFERES, John, Jr. 3550 N INTERSTATE AVE 97227 #040-02-1982 L1983 **IM** *020 †20

ALI, Cyrus. ■ 97219 #034-01-2003 L2003 **GS** *012

ALI, Shazia. 3181 SW SAM JACKSON PRK RD, RD DE 97239 #005-18-2006 L2006 **IM** *012

ALIABADI-WAHLE, S. 5050 NE HOYT ST, STE 347 97213 #040-01-1995 L2001 **GS** *020 †85

ALIABARGHOUI, Farnoush. ■ 97239 #016-42-2000 L2000 **ON** *100

ALIYEVA, Gulnara Davud. 3181 SW SAM JACKSON PRK RD, OR HLTH SCI UNIV HOSP 97239 #913-19-1994 L2005 **FP** *012

ALLADA, Gopal. 2241 LLOYD CTR 97232 #025-01-1994 L1998 **PCC** *020 †20

ALLEN, Amelia E Massman. ■ 97201 #028-02-1966 L1974 **GP** *071

ALLEN, Elizabeth Shaw. 3710 SW US VETRNS HSPTL RD, P3-MED 97239 #011-04-1991 L1992 **IM** *020 †20

ALLEN, Erin Jane. ■ 97201 #028-46-2002 L2006 **D** *100

ALLEN, Kirby Lawrence. ■ 97201 #028-02-1966 L1972 **RO** *071 †80

ALLEN, Richard. 3181 SW SAM JACKSON PRK RD 97239 #035-09-1965 L1967 **OBG** *040 †30

ALLENMAYCOCK, Chloe Andre. 5050 NE HOYT ST STE 540, MED CTR 97213 #040-02-2006 L2006 **AN** *012

ALLPORT, Robert B. ■ 97212 #038-06-1953 L1991 **OS** *071 †55

ALMAN, Kristina Rae. 3710 SW US VETRNS HSPTL RD 97239 #016-01-1984 L1990 **END IM** *020 †20

AL MAZROU, Khalid A. S.. ■ 97239 #797-01-1995 L2002 *100

ALTFAS, Jules Richard. 2525 NW LOVEJOY ST, STE 403 97210 #010-01-1970 L1976 **P GP** *020 †75

ALUMKAL, Joshi J. 3181 SW SAM JACKSON PRK RD, PARK ROAD 97239 #048-04-1998 L2006 **ON** *100 †20

AL-UZRI, Amira. 707 SW GAINES ST, M/C CDRCP 97239 #528-01-1978 L2001 **PD** *020 †55

ALVARES CORREA, Luiz Otav. 3181 SW SAM JCKSN PRK RD R 97239 #187-67-1994 L2005 *100

AMATO, Daniel Frank. 5050 NE HOYT ST, STE 454 97213 #040-02-1971 L1974 **IM** *020 †20 ‡

AMATO, Paula. 3303 SW BOND AVE, STE CH10F 97239 #065-01-1989 L2007 **REN** *020 †30

AMES, Alan Williams. 2222 NW LOVEJOY ST STE 512, HEART CENTERS OF AMERICA 97210 #008-01-1960 L1968 **CD IM** *071 †20

AMON, Robert Bickford. ■ 97201 #025-01-1965 L1973 **D GPM** *071 †70,15

AMUNDSON, Joel Aaron. 4445 NE FREMONT ST, THE CHILDREN'S CLINIC 97213 #035-46-2003 L2006 **PD** *020 †20

ANDERSEN, Brent David. 120 NW 14TH AVE, STE 300 97209 #040-02-1990 L1991 **AN** *020 †05 ‡

ANDERSEN, Eldon Dean. 3600 N INTERSTATE AVE 97227 #005-02-1967 L1972 **HEM ON** *020 †20

ANDERSEN, Peter Edward. 2241 LLOYD CTR 97232 #028-02-1988 L1989 **OTO** *020 †45

ANDERSEN, Steven Scott. 5050 NE HOYT ST, STE 353 97213 #025-07-1986 L1990 **PM** *020 †60

ANDERSON, Bradley M. 3550 N INTERSTATE AVE, EAST INTERSTATE MEDICAL OF 97227 #041-09-1987 L1995 **ADM FM** *020 †18

ANDERSON, Clifford Joe. 233 NW 16TH AVE 97209 #030-05-1970 L1975 **AI RHU** *020 †20,03

ANDERSON, Eric Carl. ■ 97239 #035-08-2006 L2006 **IM** *012

ANDERSON, James Curtis. 3181 SW SAM JACKSON PRK RD, CR135 97239 #030-05-1990 L2001 **RNR** *020 †80

ANDERSON, Jodee Marie. 501 N GRAHAM ST STE 265, NORTHWEST NEWBORN SPECIALI 97227 #047-07-1998 L2006 **NPM** *100 †55

ANDERSON, John Arthur. 3414 N MONTANA 97227 #047-07-1967 L1971 **IM ORS** *071 †20

ANDERSON, Joseph Danl. 120 NW 14TH AVE, STE 300 97209 #040-02-1982 L1984 **AN** *020 †05 ‡

ANDERSON, Julie Catherine. 3181 SW SAM JCKSN PRK RD R, MAILBOX: UHN 80 97239 #021-05-2004 L2004 **P** *012

ANDERSON, Lance Emanuel. 921 SW WASHINGTON ST, STE 460 97205 #025-12-1996 L1998 **P** *020

ANDERSON, Ross Watson. 5050 NE HOYT ST STE 255, LAURELHURST WOMEN'S CLINIC 97213 #067-01-1971 L1976 **OBG** *020 †30

ANDERSON, Sharon. 3181 SW SAM JCKSN PRK RD R, L463 97239 #021-05-1979 L1980 **IM NEP** *020 †20

ANDERSON, Stephanie S. 1015 NW 22ND AVE 97210 #005-02-1997 L2000 **IM** *020 †20

ANDERSON, Thomas Jeffrey. ■ 97201 #025-12-2006 L2006 **PD** *012

ANDERSON, Warren Le Roy. 1322 SW UPLAND DR 97221 #005-11-1970 L1975 **N** *020 †75

ANDREWS, Kahlil Jihad. ■ 97219 #005-02-1995 L2007 **PS** *012 †85

ANDRUS, Sarah Elizabeth. 3181 SW SAM JCKSN PRK RD R, M/C: CDW-EM 97239 #010-02-2003 L2006 **EM** *100 †16

ANGELOS, Patrick Constant. ■ 97239 #045-01-2006 L2006 **OTO** *012

ANKER, Roberto Juan Julio. 202 NW 20TH AVE 97209 #231-01-1983 L1999 **PTH** *020 †50

ANTEZANA, David Fernando. 5050 NE HOYT ST, STE 418 97213 #026-04-1994 L2002 **NS** *020 †25

ANTON, Amy Pape. ■ 97221 #040-02-2008 *012

ANTONISKIS, Andris. 5050 NE HOYT ST, STE 235 97213 #030-05-1975 L1976 **ADM IM** *020 †20

ANTONISKIS, Diana. 3550 N INTERSTATE AVE 97227 #030-05-1982 L1991 **ID IM** *020 †20

ANTONOVIC, John. 501 N GRAHAM ST STE 415 97227 #957-01-1961 L1969 **CD IM** *020 †20

ANUKAM, Uzoeshi Iheanacho. ■ 97217 #010-03-2006 **IM** *012

ARCHIE, Patrick Hinton. ■ 97213 #047-06-2005 L2005 **P** *012

ARDANS, Jeanette Alison. 3181 SW SAM JCKSN PRK RD R, UHN 80 97239 #010-01-2005 L2005 **P** *012

ARINIELLO, Edward A. 3500 N INTERSTATE AVE 97227 #033-05-1963 L1971 **GS** *020 †85

ARMIJO MEDINA, Hector Ale. 3181 SW SAM JCKSN PRK RD R, OHSU 97239 #451-01-2000 L2006 *100

ARMOUR, Rebecca Lew. 3303 SW BOND AVE, FL 11 97239 #025-12-2002 L2003 **OPH** *100

ARMSBY, Laurie Bertanyi. 3181 SW SAM JCKSN PRK RD R, PARK RD. 97239 #005-11-1994 L2006 **PDC** *012

ARMSTRONG-MURPHY, Maria A. 1040 NW 22ND AVE, STE 320 97210 #422-01-1997 L2006 **IM** *020 †20,60

ARNOLD, Deborah Lynn. ■ 97239 #054-04-1998 L2000 **DR** *020 †80

ARORA, Bhaskar Leelakrish. ■ 97239 #495-26-2002 L2007 **IM** *020 †20

ARTHUR, Christine Carol. 3550 N INTERSTATE AVE, DEPARTMENT OF PSYCHIATRY 97227 #917-09-1971 L1977 **P LM** *020 †75

ARTIS, Kathryn Amelia. ■ 97239 #035-47-2007 L2007 **IM** *012

ARUN, Shikha. 545 NE 47TH AVE, STE 106 97213 #495-05-1989 L1997 **IM** *020 †20

ASAPH, James Wellington. 507 NE 47TH AVE 97213 #040-01-1962 L1974 **TS** *071 †85,90 ‡

ASBY, Dennis Dudley. 4212 NE BROADWAY 97213 #018-03-1967 L1973 **IM** *020 †20

ASCOLI, Richard V. ■ 97239 #051-04-1974 L1975 **EM** *020

ASHCRAFT, Lisa Ann. 10000 SE MAIN ST, STE 205 97216 #040-02-1996 L1999 **IM** *020 †20

ATKINSON, Roland Moore. 3181 SW SAM JCKSN PRK RD R, PSYCH OP02 97239 #005-11-1961 L1978 **P** *030 †75

AUDI, Ramiz. ■ 97232 #030-06-2005 L2006 **IM** *012

AUGSBURGER, Jay Alan. 3181 SW SAM JCKSN PRK RD R, RESIDENCY TRAINING 97239 #038-41-2007 L2007 **P** *012

AUST, Bonnie Jean. 500 NE MULTNOMAH ST STE 10, PHYSICIANS AND SURGEONS 97232 #048-13-1979 L1998 **PD** *020 †55

AUSTIN, Donald Franklin. ■ 97239 #040-02-1965 L1969 **GPM PHP** *030 †70

AUSTIN, Juliana Lapanich. 707 SW GAINES ST, M/C: CDRC-P 97239 #025-01-2001 L2006 **PDE** *012

AUSTIN-GETSFRID, Wade Mil. 2800 N VANCOUVER AVE # 230, 2800 N VANCOUVER ST 230 97227 #143-11-2005 L2006 **IM** *012

AVERY, Anne Katharine. 97215 #054-04-1996 L1998 **HMP** *020

AVERY, Caryn Elizabeth. ■ 97214 #040-02-2008 *012

AVERY, Daniel Ivan. ■ 97239 #040-02-2008 *012

AVIDAN, Alexander Olivier. ■ 97239 #869-01-1988 L2001 *100

AVISON, Kathrine Elaine. 5050 NE HOYT ST, STE 469 97213 #040-02-1975 L1976 **IM** *020 †20

AXEL, Neil J. 2801 N GANTENBEIN AVE 97227 #048-16-1982 L1986 **AN** *020 †05 ‡

AXMAN, Michael Mark. 500 NE MULTNOMAH ST, DEPT OF OB-GYN 97232 #067-01-1967 L1971 **OBG** *020 †30

AXMAN, Stephanie. ■ 97211 #040-02-2006 L2006 **P** *012

AXTELL, Andrea Dawn. ■ 97212 #040-02-2007 L2007 **IM** *012

AZAR, Joseph Khalil, II. ■ 97239 #040-02-2003 L2008 **DR** *012

AZARBAL, Amir Farzin. ■ 97239 #035-01-2005 L2005 **GS** *012

AZEVEDO, Christina Janell. ■ 97203 #040-02-2007 L2007 **IM** *012

AZIZ, Michael Fekri. 3181 SW SAM JCKSN PRK RD R 97239 #038-40-2001 L2005 **AN** *020 †05

AZORR, Michael Albert. 2209 LLOYD CTR 97232 #040-02-1967 L1971 **IM** *071 †20

BABAIE, Ashkan. 1111 NE 99TH AVE 97220 #005-18-1998 L2007 **CD** *020 †20

BABSON, S Gorham. 3181 SW SAM JACKSON PRK RD 97239 #040-02-1936 **NPM PD** *071 †55

BACHMAN, Daniel M. ■ 97219 #040-02-1952 L1956 **IM RHU** *071 †20

BACK, Stephen Arthur. 3181 SW SAM JCKSN PRK RD R, HRC 5 97239 #005-15-1990 L1999 **N** *020 †75

BADER, Stephen Blake. 5050 NE HOYT ST, LEVEL B 97213 #054-04-1984 L1991 **RO IM** *020 †20,80

BADRA, Mohammad Ibrahim. ■ 97239 #605-01-1997 L2004 **OP** *020

BAERTLEIN, Richard Dean. 3600 N INTERSTATE AVE, DEPT OF OCCUPATIONAL HEALT 97227 #040-02-1987 L1992 **OM IM** *020 †20,70

BAGBY, Grover Carlton. 2241 LLOYD CTR 97232 #048-04-1968 L1971 **HEM ON** *050 †20

BAGBY, Susan Key Pound. 3314 SW US VETRNS HSPTL RD, PP262 97239 #048-04-1970 L1975 **NEP IM** *050 †20

BAGEAC, Alexandru C. ■ 97201 #024-01-1997 L2005 **R NM** *020 †80,28 ‡

BAGO, Attila Gyorgy. 2241 LLOYD CTR 97232 #473-01-1994 L2001 *020

BAHAR, Alistair. ■ 97205 #051-01-1998 L1999 **END** *020 †20

BAHR, Alison Kim. ■ 97214 #040-02-2005 L2005 **IM** *012

BAHRE, Frederick Gerard. ■ 97219 #028-34-1980 L1996 **IM** *020 †20

BAILEY, Steven Theodore. 3375 SW TERWILLIGER BLVD, CASEY EYE PHYSICIANS & SUR 97239 #018-03-2002 L2006 **OPH** *100

BAINS, Amarprit Singh. ■ 97239 #040-05-2007 L2007 **IM** *012

BAIRD, Michael David. 2825 NE BRAZEE 97212 #040-02-1957 L1958 **IM** *071

BAIRD, Rebecca May. 500 NE MULTNOMAH, STE 100 97232 #040-02-2002 L2002 **PD** *020 †20

BAJOREK, Mark Michael. 4411 SW VERMONT ST 97219 #038-40-1986 L1991 **FM** *020 †18

BAKER, Barbara Jean. 3355 SE POWELL BLVD 97202 #024-05-1970 L1993 **P CHP** *020 †55,75 ‡

BAKER, Charles Frederick. ■ 97209 #031-01-2001 L2008 **NPM** *020 †55

BAKER, Dawn Jimenez. ■ 97206 #003-01-2005 L2005 **IM** *012

BAKER, Diane R Haas. 1706 NW GLISAN ST, STE 2 97209 #038-40-1971 L1974 **D** *020 †15

BAKER, Mary Lee. 4212 NE BROADWAY ST 97213 #040-02-1980 L1983 **PD** *020 †55

BAKER, Peter Russell. ■ 97206 #003-01-2005 L2005 **PD** *012

BAKER, Phillip Donald. 1750 SW HARBOR WAY, STE 100 97201 #049-01-1993 L1994 **DR** *020 †80

BAKKE, Patrick Gary. 3181 SW SAM JACKSON PRK RD, UH 2 97239 #040-02-2001 L2002 **AN** *100 †05

BALAJI, Seshadri. 707 SW GAINES ST, CDRC-P 97239 #495-16-1983 L2000 **PDC** *020 †55

BALASINGAM, Vijayabalan. 3181 SW SAM JCKSN PRK RD R, M/C L472 97239 #067-01-1996 L2002 **NS** *020

BALASUBRAMANIAN, K. ■ 97239 #495-16-1957 L1973 **P** *071

BALASUBRAMANIAN, V. ■ 97202 #495-04-1964 L2004 **P** *020 †75

BALD, Douglas. 4805 NE GLISAN 97213 #005-14-1974 L1975 **ORS** *020 †40

BALDENHOFER, Craig A. ■ 97209 #021-06-2004 L2008 **GS** *012

BALDWIN, James Lester. 5050 NE HOYT ST STE 138 97213 #040-02-1968 L1969 **ORS** *071 †40

BALDWIN, Maureen Katherin. ■ 97221 #040-02-2007 L2007 **OBG** *012

BALENTINE, Jennifer Lanay. 2222 NW LOVEJOY ST, STE 504 97210 #007-02-1998 L1999 **OPH** *020 †35

BALKOVICH, Michael Eric. 5050 NE HOYT ST STE 515 97213 #040-02-1975 L1984 **HS PS** *020 †85,65

BALL, Melvyn John. 2241 LLOYD CTR 97232 #065-01-1963 L1989 *020

BALLINGER, James Ray. 3710 SW US VETRNS HSPTL RD, PORTLAND VA MED CTR 97239 #011-02-1976 L1977 **DR RP** *020 †80

BALOG, Carl Csaba. 527 SE 39TH AVE, OREGON PAIN ASSOCIATES 97214 #473-01-1988 L1995 **AN IM** *020 †20,05

BANE, James Edward. 1120 SW 3RD AVE 4TH FL, CORRECTIONS HEALTH 97204 #050-02-1983 L1999 **IM** *020 †20

BANITT, Peter F. 1040 NW 22ND AVE, STE 660 97210 #018-03-1989 L1999 **CD IM** *020 †20

BANKER, Katherine Ann. 3181 SW SAM JCKSN PRK RD R, OREGON HLTH & SCI UNIV 97239 #030-06-2006 L2006 **PD** *012

BANKES, Carl Raymond. 5201 SW WESTGATE DR, STE 111 97221 #005-12-1960 L1969
AN *020

BANKOWSKI, Brandon Jon. 2222 NW LOVEJOY ST, STE 304 97210 #010-02-1998 L2005
OBG *020 †30

BANKS, Mark Franklin. 2801 N GANTENBEIN AVE 97227 #422-01-1998 L2007 CCP *020 †55

BANNER, Richard Lionel. 507 NE 47TH AVE 97213 #035-01-1963 L1978 CD IM *071 †20

BAR, Anna Alexandra. 3303 SW BOND AVE, MC CH5D 97239 #035-19-2001 L2002 D *020 †15

BARAKAT, Suzette Lee. ■ 97239 #040-02-2008 *012

BARBOSA, Ronald Robert, Jr. 501 N GRAHAM ST STE 580 97227 #028-34-1999 L2006
TRS CCS *85

BARCLAY, Glen Newkirk. 300 N GRAHAM ST, STE 420 97227 #005-14-1975 L1981
PD GE *020 †55

BARDANA, Emil John, Jr. 3181 SW SAM JACKSON PRK RD, OP34 97239 #067-01-1961 L1967
AI RHU *020 †20,03

BARDARO, Sergio Jose. 1040 NW 22ND AVE STE 500 97210 #132-11-1998 L2006 *100

BARHAM, Robert Edward. ■ 97215 #049-01-1969 L1973 U *071 †95

BARKER, Alan Freund. 2241 LLOYD CTR 97232 #028-03-1970 L1976 PUD IM *040 †20 ‡

BARLOW, Darryk Wayne. 10101 SE MAIN ST, STE 2004 97216 #054-04-1990 L2003
OTO *020 †45

BARMACHE, Michael. 3181 SW SAM JACKSON PRK RD, OR HLTH SCI UNIV 97239
#035-08-1975 L1977 EM IM *040 †20,16

BARMADA, Adam. 501 N GRAHAM ST, STE 200 97227 #016-11-1996 L2002 ORS *020 †40

BARNATAN, Marcos Fabian. 501 N GRAHAM ST, STE 415 97227 #847-04-1986 L2002
VS TRS *020 †85

BARNES, Lynne J. ■ 97221 #048-13-1985 L2001 PTH PCP *012

BARNETT, Christine Mckeow. 3181 SW SAM JACKSON PRK RD, RD IN 97239
#026-04-2006 L2006 IM *012

BARNWELL, Stanley Lamons. 2241 LLOYD CTR 97232 #047-05-1983 L1991 NS *020 †25

BAROCHIA, Amisha Vipul. 5050 NE HOYT ST, STE 540 97213 #496-26-2000 L2002 PCC *012

BARONE, Christopher M. 1200 NW 23RD AVE, GOOD SAMARITAN 97210 #035-03-1999 L2001
IM *012

BARRETT, Brandon Jon. ■ 97219 #040-02-2006 L2006 IM *012

BARRETT, Krista Kae. 2801 N GANTENBEIN AVE 97227 #054-04-1997 L2000 PD *020 †55

BARRETT, Robin Wachunas. 2222 NW LOVEJOY, STE 619 97210 #038-40-1997 L2001
OBG *020 †30

BARRIATUA, Robert Duane. 10123 SE MARKET ST, C/O PORTLAND ADVENTIST HOS 97216
#054-04-1984 L1985 EM *020 †16

BARRY, John Maynard. 3303 SW BOND AVE, MAIL CODE CH10U 97239 #026-04-1965 L1969
U TTS *020 †95 ‡

BARSKY, Relly Fay. 12615 NE HALSEY ST 97230 #836-02-1956 L1981 FM *071

BARSOTTI, Michael Maurice. 3653 SE 34TH AVE, SOUTHEAST HEALTH CTR 97202
#054-04-1974 L2004 IM END *020 †20

BARSOTTI, Richard John. 10535 NE GLISAN ST, METROPOLITAN PEDIATRICS, L 97220
#040-02-1976 L1982 PD *020 †20

BARTON, George Simpson. 500 NE MULTNOMAH ST 97232 #040-02-1956 L1962 N *020

BARTON, Lane Wick, III. 3600 N INTERSTATE AVE 97227 #040-02-1985 L1989 PM *020 †60

BARTON, Robert Earl. 2241 LLOYD CTR 97232 #048-12-1983 L1991 PD DR *040 †80

BARTRUFF, James M. 3303 SW BOND AVE, M/S: CH9G 97239 #035-45-1992 L1993 IM *020 †20

BASCO, Hilary Reiter. 4212 NE BROADWAY ST, BROADWAY MEDICAL CLINIC LL 97213
#035-45-2000 L2000 PD *020 †55

BASCOM, Paul Benj. 2241 LLOYD CTR 97232 #040-02-1986 L1991 IM *020 †20

BASEL, Donald Gerhard. 3181 SW SAM JCKSN PRK RD L, OHSU 97239 #836-01-1994 L2007
MG *012

BASKIN, Lester Michael. 2222 NW LOVEJOY ST STE 406 97210 #040-02-1995 L1996
IM *020 †20

BASKIN, Michael Shale. 2228 NW PETTYGROVE ST, STE 150 97210 #054-04-1961 L1963
ORS *020 †40

BASNETT, Seema. ■ 97239 #495-26-2001 L2007 P *100

BASS, Jennifer Lynn. 3550 N INTERSTATE AVE 97227 #035-19-1994 L2005 PD *020 †55

BASS, Sarah. ■ 97206 #051-01-2004 L2014 IM *012

BATTALIA, Brian W. 6312 SW CAPITOL HWY, # 502 97239 #040-02-1983 L1984 IM *020

BATTALIA, Jack Edward. ■ 97212 #040-02-1946 L1947 OS GS *071 †85

BAUER, Jason Richard. 2701 NW VAUGHN ST STE 425, MAIL: PO BX 10768 97210
#040-02-2000 L2006 DR *100 †80

BAUER, John Eric. 4212 NE BROADWAY ST 97213 #040-02-1980 L1983 IM *020 †20

BAUER, Maxine Elaine. 5050 NE HOYT ST STE 421, PROVIDENCE PROFESSIONAL PL 97213
#012-05-1995 L1997 OBG *020 †30

BAUGH, Stephen Frederick. 1130 NW 22ND AVE, STE 220 97210 #028-34-1995 L1998
IM *020 †20

BAUMANN, Christina Isabel. ■ 97239 #025-01-2007 L2007 IM *012

BAUMEISTER, Frank J, Jr. 1130 NW 22ND AVE, NORTHWEST 97210 #011-02-1961 L1970
GE *030 †20

BAUSENBACH, Karin Helene. 19500 SE STARK ST 97233 #056-06-1993 L1997 PD *020 †55

BAXTER, Brett Rand. 4805 NE GLISAN ST, STE BG05 97213 #035-03-1999 L2002 IM *020 †40

BAXTER, Maureen O'Brien. ■ 97214 #007-02-2001 L2002 PDR *012 †80

BAY, Nathan Anderson. 120 NW 14TH AVE, STE 300 97209 #016-42-2002 L2006 AN *020 †05 ‡

BAYNE, Aaron Patrick. ■ 97239 #047-05-2002 L2002 GS *100

BAYNE, Lydia L. ■ 97201 #005-02-1984 L2000 N *071 †75

BAYS, Judith A. 2801 N GANTENBEIN AVE 97227 #005-18-1972 L1984 PD OS *071 †55

BAZELL, Marti. 2631 N MISSISSIPPI AVE, LIFEWORKS NW 97227 #016-01-1981 L1990
CHP FM *020 †18,75

BEAHRS, John Oakley. VET ADMIN M C, DEPT PSYCH 97207 #005-11-1969 L1980 P *030 †75

BEALE, Linda Sue. 5050 NE HOYT ST STE 353, OREGON REHAB MEDICINE 97213
#025-01-1993 L2002 PM *020 †60

BEALS, Rodney Kenneth. 3181 SW SAM JACKSON PRK RD, OHSU/OP13B DEPT OF
ORTHO 97239 #040-02-1956 L1958 ORS *040 †40

BEAMAN, Douglas Neal. 501 N GRAHAM ST, STE 250 97227 #025-01-1989 L1995
ORS *020 †40

BEAMER, Virginia L. ■ 97202 #038-41-1960 L1960 CD IM *030

BEAN, James. 3181 SW SAM JACKSON PRK RD, RD IN 97239 #040-02-2006 L2006 IM *012

BEARD, James Christopher. 1130 NW 22ND AVE 97210 #036-01-1976 L1991 END DIA *020 †20

BEARD, Tracey Elizabeth. ■ 97239 #040-02-2008 *012

BEASLEY, Geoffrey Enochs. 3181 SW SAM JCKSN PRK RD R, M/S: CB669 97239
#011-03-1977 L1979 GP *020

BEASLEY, Mary Beth. 4805 NE GLISAN ST, DEPT OF PATHOLOGY 97213 #021-01-1993 L2003
PTH *020 †50

BEAVER, Thomas Allen. 19500 SE STARK ST, ROCKWOOD MEDICAL OFFICE 97233
#016-43-1982 L1990 IM *020 †20

BECHER, Judith Carolyn. 5329 NE MARTIN LUTHER KING 97211 #007-02-1995 L1997
IM *020 †20

BECHTOLD, Marcia Anne. 7705 SE DIVISION ST, KAISER PERMANENTE-DIVISION 97206
#041-01-1984 L1989 IM *020 †20

BECK, Jonathan Jay. ■ 97239 #005-14-1986 L1987 OS GPM *075

BECKER, Brian Denney. ■ 97239 #040-02-2008 *012

BECKETT, Brooke Renee. ■ 97212 #018-03-2005 L2006 DR *012

BEDERKA, Bryce. 501 N GRAHAM ST, STE 200 97227 #016-11-2001 L2007 OSM *020

BEDNAREK, Paula Helen. 3181 SW SAM JCKSN PRK RD R 97239 #016-06-2000 L2004
OBG *020 †30

BEECHER, Heather. 1321 NE 99TH AVE, STE 200 97220 #035-08-1981 L1986 FM *020 †18

BEER, Tomasz Michal. 3303 SW BOND AVE CH14R 97239 #023-07-1991 L1992 ON *020 †20

BEERS, Douglas Kent. 2800 N VANCOUVER AVE # 230 97227 #005-02-1977 L1984 IM *040 †20

BEHEL, Sarah Hover. 2311 NW NORTHRUP ST, STE 201 97210 #038-41-1983 L1994 P *020 †75

BEHLE, Kristin Marie. 5329 NE MARTIN LUTHER KING, NORTHEAST HEALTH CENTER 97211
#005-02-1995 L1997 FM *020 †18

BELKNAP, Charles Sabin. 1130 NW 22ND AVE STE 400 97210 #040-02-1962 L1963 IM DIA *020

BELL, David Bishop. 1130 NW 22ND AVE STE 3, HEALTHFIRST MEDICAL GROUP 97210
#007-02-1969 L1974 PD *020 †55

BELL, Lynne Adams. 1040 NW 22ND AVE, NSC 600 97210 #005-18-1991 L1992 N *020 †75

BELL, Richard Bryan. 1849 NW KEARNEY ST STE 30 97209 #036-01-1997 L2001 *020

BELL, Robert Frank. ■ 97205 #039-01-1961 L1980 D DMP *071 †15

BELLANT, Jodeanne Kay. 501 N GRAHAM ST, STE 265 97227 #040-02-1981 L1982 PD *020

BELLANT, Richard Paul. 97220 #040-02-1981 *020

BENDA, Gerda Ida Marie D. 2241 LLOYD CTR 97232 #407-19-1962 L1969 NPM PD *071 †55

BENGTSON, George Wesley. 4212 NE BROADWAY ST, BROADWAY MEDICAL CLINIC 97213
#040-02-1988 L1991 PD *020 †55

BENNER, Kent G. 1111 NE 99TH AVE 97220 #005-14-1977 L1981 HEP GE *040 †20

BENNETT, H Stanley. 219 W BURNSIDE ST 97209 #024-01-1945 L1990 IM *072 †20

BENNETT, Robert Martin. 3181 SW SAM JACKSON PRK RD, PARK RD 97239
#917-26-1964 L1976 RHU IM *040 †20

BENNETT, William Gerald. 2801 N GANTENBEIN AVE 97227 #030-05-1970 L1973
PDR NM *020 †18,28,80

BENNETTS, Roland Wm. 1130 NW 22ND AVE, NORTHWEST 97210 #005-11-1973 L1975
GE IM *020 †20

BENSCHING, Katherine S. 2800 N VANCOUVER AVE, STE 230 97227 #016-11-1989 L1990
IM *020 †20

BENTZ, Charles Jos. 2400 SW VERMONT ST 97219 #056-06-1988 L1989 IM *020 †20

BERGER, Stephen Paul. ■ 97221 #005-11-1985 L1987 P *020

BERGMAN, Anders Stellan F. 3181 SW SAM JCKSN PRK RD R, OHSU 97239
#858-02-1974 L2004 *020

BERGSTROM, Richard Walter. 1130 NW 22ND AVE 97210 #054-04-1983 L1990
END IM *020 †20

BERGSTROM, Robert William. 2020 SE 182ND AVE 97233 #035-06-1986 L2002 IM *020 †20

BERGTHOLD, James Harold. ■ 97210 #056-06-1992 L1993 IM *050 †20

BERKEY, Richard Eric. 2801 N GANTENBEIN AVE, EMANUEL HOSPITAL & HEALTH 97227
#051-01-1990 L1994 EM *020 †16

BERLIN, Michelle. 3181 SW SAM JACKSON PRK RD, UHN-50 OHSU 97239 #038-41-1986 L2002
PHP OBG *050 †70,30

BERLINER, Harold Martin. PO BOX 319 97207 #012-01-1958 L1958 IM OS *071

BERNARD, Leah Suzanne. 3181 SW SAM JCKSN PRK RD R, M/C: L-458 97239
#007-02-2002 L2006 OBG *100 †20

BERNARDO, Augusto Dayrit. 500 NE MULTNOMAH ST STE 10 97232 #748-02-1956
GS *071 †85

BERNEY, Bertram W. 181 NE 102ND AVE 97220 #010-01-1982 L1990 IM *020 †20,70

BERNSTEIN, Eric Daniel. 4805 NE GLISAN ST, STE 6N40 97213 #036-01-1999 L2000
HO *020 †20

BERRY, Michael Barnard. 120 NW 14TH AVE, STE 300 97209 #007-02-1995 L2004
AN *020 †05 ‡

BERRY, Tracey Ione. 120 NW 14TH AVE, STE 300 97209 #054-04-1990 L1995 AN *020 †05 ‡

BERRYBIBEE, Erin Nicole. ■ 97239 #040-02-2008 *012

BERSELLI, Robert A. 501 N GRAHAM ST, STE 350 97227 #010-02-1964 L1971
ORS GS *020 †40

BERTHELSDORF, Siegfried R. ■ 97205 #040-02-1939 L1942 PYA P *071 †75

BERTOLA, James Mark. ■ 97214 #040-02-2001 L2001 AN *100

BETLINSKI, Jonathan P. 3181 SW SAM JCKSN PRK RD R, OHSU DEPARTMENT OF
PSYCHIA 97239 #005-12-2002 L2006 P *100

BEYER, Kiran Elizabeth. ■ 97214 #010-01-2003 L2003 EM *020 †16

BEZDIKIAN, Vatche Krikor. ■ 97209 #024-05-2003 L2008 AN *100

BHARGAVA, Sushama A. 3500 N INTERSTATE AVE, NUCLEAR MEDICINE DEPT 97227
#495-56-1984 L1999 IM NM *020 †20

BHAT, Sumeeth Mangalore. ■ 97266 #056-06-2005 L2006 FP *012

BHAYANI, Rajendra Damodar. 3181 SW SAM JCKSN PRK RD R 97239 #495-22-1996 L2003
OTO *100 †45

BIAGIOLI, Frances Emily. 4411 SW VERMONT ST 97219 #038-43-1995 L1997 FM *020 †18

BIETZ, Duane Stanley. 2241 LLOYD CTR 97232 #005-12-1965 L1975 CD TS *071 †85,90

BIGELOW, Dan Reid. ■ 97219 #062-01-1948 ORS *072

BIGELOW, John Chas. 2226 NW PETTYGROVE ST, NORTHW SURGICAL ASSOCS INC 97210
#054-04-1959 L1963 TS *071 †85,90

BIGLER, Robert D, II. 3600 N INTERSTATE AVE 97227 #043-01-1977 L1997 HO IM *020 †20

BIGLEY, Robert H. 3181 SW SAM JACKSON PRK RD 97239 #040-02-1953 L1958
HEM *050 †20,19

BILBAO, Joseph. 500 NE MULTNOMAH ST STE 10 97232 #035-01-1955 IM *020 †20

BILLERBECK, Elizabeth Ann. 120 NW 14TH AVE, STE 300 97209 #030-06-1984 L1985
AN *020 †05 ‡

BILLINGS, James Emery. 2225 LLOYD CTR 97232 #056-05-1956 L1957 IM *071

BILLINGSLEY, Kevin G. 3181 SW SAM JCKSN PRK RD R, M/S L223 97239 #023-07-1989 L1990
GS *020 †85

BILOTTI, Anthony Keith. 1509 SW SUNSET BLVD, STE 2E 97239 #040-02-1990 L1993
EM *020 †16

BILSTROM, Evan Jon. ■ 97212 #040-02-2005 L2005 IM *012

BINDER, Marc Karl. ■ 97209 #010-01-1972 L1977 GE IM *071 †20

BINGHAM, Leon Price. PO BOX 16233 97292 #005-12-1961 L1969 PTH *071 †50

BIRCH, Alexander A, Jr. 3181 SW SAM JCKSN PRK RD R 97239 #025-01-1963 L1981
AN *071 †05

BIRD, Charles Benj. 3181 SW SAM JCKSN PRK #R, OHSU DEPT/ORTHO & REHAB OP 97239 #041-01-1964 L1968 **ORS OAR** *020 †40

BIRECREE, Elizabeth Ann. 1020 SW TAYLOR ST, STE 750 97205 #047-05-1986 L1988 **P** *020 †75

BIRK, Bruce Jordon. 2525 NW LOVEJOY ST STE 200 97210 #048-12-1996 L1999 **PD** *020 †55

BIRKEMEIER, Susan Gail. 1015 NW 22ND AVE 97210 #040-02-1973 L1975 **OBG** *020 †30

BIRNDORF, Norman Irwin. 500 NE MULTNOMAH ST, STE 100 97232 #016-11-1964 L1971 **HEM ON** *020 †20

BISCHOF, John Kelly. PO BOX 8459, 2130 SW FIFTH AVE 97207 #028-03-1990 L1991 **P** *020

BISHOP, B Daniel. 3181 SW SAM JACKSON PRK RD, OR HLTH SCI UNIV SCH MED 97239 #040-02-2005 **EM** *012

BISSELL, Daniel Myers. 1509 SW SUNSET BLVD, STE 2E 97239 #007-02-2002 L2005 **EM** *020 †16

BISSINGER, Randall Craig. 120 NW 14TH AVE, STE 300 97209 #037-01-1988 L1992 **AN** *020 †05 ‡

BISSONNETTE, John Maurice. 2241 LLOYD CTR 97232 #067-01-1964 L1973 **MFM** *050 †30

BISSONNETTE, Lynne Louise. 2250 NW FLANDERS ST, STE 306 97210 #005-15-1973 L1977 **P** *020

BIX, Desiree. 1130 NW 22ND AVE STE 320 97210 #409-38-1989 L1995 **PD** *020

BLACK, Franklin Owen. 4805 NE GLISAN ST 97213 #028-03-1963 L1982 **OTO** *020 †45

BLACK, Joseph Loren. 3181 SW SAM JCKSN PRK RD R 97239 #040-02-1980 L1982 **IM** *020 †20

BLACK, Peter Kenneth. 4805 NE GLISAN ST, STE BG05 97213 #040-02-2000 L2003 **IM** *020 †20

BLAIR, Letrice. ■ 97239 #040-02-2008 *012

BLAKE, Jennifer Lynn. ■ 97201 #030-06-2007 L2007 **PD** *012

BLANCHARD, Shawn Henry. 3181 SW SAM JACKSON PRK RD, PARK ROAD 97239 #040-02-1992 L1995 **FM** *020 †18

BLANCHETTE, Mary Alice. 3181 SW SAM JACKSON PRK RD, UH 2 97239 #054-04-1985 L1986 **AN** *020 †05

BLAND, Lisa Barnett. 97202 #040-02-2003 L2003 **U** *012

BLAND, Zachary Martin. ■ 97202 #040-02-2003 L2003 **DR** *100

BLANK, Eugene. ORE HLTH SCI U SCH MED, DEPT RAD 97201 #023-07-1954 L1972 **R PD** *020 †55,80

BLANKE, Charles David. 3181 SW SAM JACKSON PRK RD 97239 #016-06-1988 L1998 **ON** *020 †20

BLASCO, Peter Anthony. 707 SW GAINES ST, CHILD DEVELOPEMENT & REHAB 97239 #035-20-1972 L1999 **PD** *020 †55

BLATT, Alice Day Pasel. ■ 97230 #016-11-1957 L1977 **OS** *075

BLATT, David Howard. 120 NW 14TH AVE, STE 300 97209 #005-15-1982 L1990 **AN** *030 †05

BLATT, Philip Edward. 4212 NE BROADWAY ST 97213 #048-04-1957 L1957 **IM** *071

BLAUVELT, Andrew. 3303 SW BOND AVE, DEPT - DERMATOLOGY 97239 #025-12-1988 L2004 **D** *050 †15

BLECHSCHMIDT, Paul T. 2311 NW NORTHRUP ST 97210 #041-09-1955 L1956 **IM CD** *071

BLEKIC, Amela. 3181 SW SAM JACKSON PRK RD 97239 #957-08-1990 L2005 **P** *012

BLENNING, Carol Elizabeth. 3930 SE DIVISION ST 97202 #005-18-1988 L1996 **FM** *020 †18

BLESSING, David Rae. 10803 SE CHERRY BLOSSOM DR 97216 #016-06-1971 L1974 **FM** *020 †18

BLEY, Dennis E. 4212 NE BROADWAY ST, HILLSBORO INTERNAL MEDICIN 97213 #018-75-1997, ▲ L2004 **IM** *020 †20

BLEY, Desiree Shawn. 5050 NE HOYT ST STE 421 97213 #028-34-1994 L2004 **OBG** *020 †30

BLISS, David Wm. 501 N GRAHAM ST, PEDIATRIC SURGERY 97227 #005-18-1990 L2001 **GS** *020 †85

BLIZIOTES, Matthew M. 2241 LLOYD CTR 97232 #011-03-1976 L1990 **END IM** *020 †20

BLOCK, Jerald Joseph. 2330 NW FLANDERS ST, STE 202 97210 #035-46-1994 L1999 **P** *020 †70

BLOMBERG, Adam Alexander. 5050 NE HOYT ST, PROVIDENCE PORTLAND INT ME 97213 #054-04-2005 L2008 **IM** *012

BLOMQUIST, Robert Henry. 5055 N GREELEY AVE 97217 #056-05-1960 L1969 **IM** *071 †20

BLOOM, Harvey Martin. ■ 97212 #035-09-1962 L1963 **FM** *020 †18

BLOOM, Joseph David. 3181 SW SAM JCKSN PRK RD R, L102 97239 #035-46-1962 L1977 **P PFP** *071 †75

BOBEK, Lesley Nicole. 1200 NW 23RD AVE, GOOD SAMARITAN 97210 #040-02-2006 L2006 **IM** *012

BOBENRIETH, Susanne K. 541 NE 20TH AVE, STE 210 97232 #023-01-1998 L2001 **FM** *020 †18

BOEHLAND, Andrea Nichole. ■ 97209 #040-02-2007 L2007 **EM** *012

BOEHNLEIN, James Kevin. 3181 SW SAM JCKSN PRK RD R, UHN 80 97239 #038-06-1980 L1981 **P** *020 †75

BOETTCHER, Erica Cristine. ■ 97219 #040-02-2006 L2007 **IM** *012

BOGARDUS, Carol. ■ 97239 #040-02-1977 L1978 **IM** *071 †20

BOGART, Amelia Lynnanakel. ■ 97202 #045-04-2008 *012

BOHLEY, Michael Francis. 10201 SE MAIN ST, STE 20 97216 #038-43-1988 L1989 **PS GS** *020 †85,65

BOLES, Matthew Stephen Am. 120 NW 14TH AVE, STE 300 97209 #422-01-2003 L2007 **AN** *020

BOLTON, Bruce Kirk. 120 NW 14TH AVE, STE 300 97209 #040-02-1988 L1989 **AN** *020 †05 ‡

BOLTON, Robert L. 120 NW 14TH AVE, STE 300 97209 #040-02-1985 L1986 **AN IM** *020 †20,05 ‡

BOMBERGER, Shana Alexandr. ■ 97205 #040-02-2006 L2006 **IM** *012

BONAFEDE, Rosario Peter. 5050 NE HOYT ST, PROVIDENCE ARTHRITIS 97213 #836-02-1974 L1989 **RHU** *020 †20

BONAZZOLA, Michael Flynn. 3181 SW SAM JACKSON PRK RD, MAIL CODE OP04 97239 #040-02-1978 L1979 **IM** *020 †20

BONNER, Svetlana. 2250 NW FLANDERS ST STE 1 97210 #035-47-1985 L1989 **P** *020 †05

BOOKER, Michael Scott. 2647 NE 33RD AVE 97212 #016-11-1988 L1989 **FM** *020 †18

BORDEN, James Prentice. 1015 NW 22ND AVE 97210 #028-46-1990 L1991 **IM** *020 †20

BORKAN, Eugene Lester. 4805 NE GLISAN ST, MENTAL HEALTH SERVICES 97213 #035-45-1971 L1972 **P** *020 †20

BORREGO, Clarisa. 3710 SW US VETRNS HSPTL RD, MEDICAL CENTER/PORTLAND DI 97239 #049-01-1992 L1993 **IM** *020 †20

BORZY, Michael Steven. 707 SW GAINES ST 97239 #023-07-1972 L1981 **PD IG** *050 †55,03

BOSHKOV, Lynn K. 3181 SW SAM JACKSON PRK RD 97239 #067-01-1981 L1999 **IM HEM** *020 †20

BOSKER, Gideon. 1015 NW 22ND AVE, GOOD SAMARITAN HOSPITAL 97210 #028-02-1976 L1978 **IM** *071 †20,16

BOSKIND, Jeffrey F. 10000 SE MAIN ST, STE 408 97216 #005-12-1991 L1998 **TS GS** *020 †90,85

BOST, Meghan Mary Emma. ■ 97211 #025-12-2005 L2005 **AN** *012

BOSTON, Bruce Alan. 707 SW GAINES ST 97239 #040-02-1988 L1989 **PDE** *020 †55

BOTWINICK, Ora Naomi. 9000 N LOMBARD ST 97203 #035-47-1983 L1992 **FM** *020 †18

BOUDREAU, Eilis Ann. 3181 SW SAM JACKSON PRK RD, MAIL CODE L226 97239 #035-15-1996 L1998 **N** *020 †75

BOURDETTE, Dennis Neil. 3181 SW SAM JACKSON PRK RD, MAIL CODE L226 97239 #005-19-1978 L1980 **N** *050 †75

BOVERMAN, Harold Irwin. 2250 NW FLANDERS ST STE 30 97210 #016-02-1956 L1969 **PYA CHP** *071 †75

BOVERMAN, Joshua Findley. 1027 E BURNSIDE ST 97214 #040-02-1993 L1994 **P** *020 †75

BOWEN, Judith Lynn. 3181 SW SAM JCKSN PRK RD R, MAIL CODE: L475 97239 #032-01-1981 L1997 **IM** *040 †20

BOWER, Elizabeth Ann. 3181 SW SAM JACKSON PRK RD, PARK RD 97239 #008-01-1991 L1993 **IM** *050 †20

BOWER, Michael Clifford. 1321 NE 99TH AVE, STE 100 97220 #028-34-1973 L1974 **IM** *020 †20

BOWERFIND, William M. 1111 NE 99TH AVE 97220 #038-06-1996 L2003 **PCC** *020 †20

BOWMAN, Jennifer Lynn. 1121 NE 2ND AVE 97232 #020-02-1999 L2004 **P** *020 †75

BOX, Thomas Wm. 120 NW 14TH AVE STE 300, OREGON ANESTHESIOLOGY GROU 97209 #040-02-1985 L1991 **AN** *020 ‡

BOYER, Julie Ina. 3181 SW SAM JACKSON PRK RD 97239 #005-19-2000 L2002 **GS** *100

BOYER, Mary Palumbo. ■ 97214 #028-34-1992 L1993 **PD** *020 †55

BOYER, Nathaniel Marion. ■ 97214 #041-12-1999 L2003 **OBG** *100 †30

BOYLES, Sarah Benson. ■ 97214 #041-12-1999 L2003 **OBG** *100 †30

BOYLES, Sarah Benson Hami. 3181 SW SAM JCKSN PRK RD R, M/S L466 97239 #041-14-1998 *100

BRACIS, Raymond Benj. 1015 NW 22ND AVE # 200 97210 #041-13-1971 L1975 **ID IM** *020 †20

BRADEEN, Resa Lynn. 10535 NE GLISAN ST, STE 300 97220 #020-02-1990 L1991 **PD** *020 †55

BRADY, Raymond Edward. 233 NW 16TH AVE 97209 #039-01-1970 L1977 **AI PD** *020 †55,03

BRADY, William John. 1750 SW SKYLINE BLVD, STE 120 97221 #040-02-1958 L1962 **FOP PTH** *062 †50

BRANER, Dana Armenvon. 707 SW GAINES ST, OREGAN HEALTH SCIENCE UNI 97239 #035-46-1986 L1992 **PD** *020 †55

BRANHAM, Virginia Gail. 97201 #040-02-2003 L2007 **OBG** *100

BRANT-ZAWADZKI, Bolek. 5050 NE HOYT ST STE 511 97213 #035-45-1965 L1967 **GS VS** *020 †85

BRAUN, Esmond. 222 SW COLUMBIA ST, STE 1400 97201 #025-07-1955 L1965 **GS U** *071 †85,95

BRAUNS, Lars. 3181 SW SAM JCKSN PRK RD R, OHSU DEPT/ANESTHESIOLOGY 97239 #409-40-1999 L2001 *100

BRAY, Harry Edward. 1111 NE 99TH AVE, THE OREGON CLINIC PC 97220 #836-01-1984 L1991 **GE** *020 †20

BRAZIEL, Rita Merle. 2241 LLOYD CTR 97232 #034-01-1977 L1984 **PTH** *020 †50

BRECKENRIDGE, Marie A. ■ 97202 #220-01-1961 L1978 **P** *020 ‡

BREDA, Michael Alexander. 1130 NW 22ND AVE, STE 420 97210 #023-07-1985 L1994 **GS OS** *020 †85

BREEN, Neff Russell. 3550 N INTERSTATE AVE, KAISE PERMANETE INTERSTATE 97227 #054-04-1992 L2004 **P** *020 †75

BREEN, Roy Eugene, III. 1040 NW 22ND AVE, STE 580 97210 #005-15-1978 L1980 **CRS GS** *020 †10,85

BREEN, Ruvin Victor. 2701 NW VAUGHN ST STE 150, KAISER PERMANENTE 97210 #062-01-1981 L1990 **GPM** *020 †70

BREEZE, Matthew James. 4104 SE 82ND AVE, STE 250 97266 #040-02-2002 L2003 **FM** *020 †18

BREITINGER, Anne Marie. 1130 NW 22ND AVE STE 410 97210 #030-05-1999 L2001 **GE** *020 †20

BREM, Jerome Barnett. 800 SW 13TH AVE 97205 #024-07-1970 L1977 **RHU IM** *020 †20

BREMNER, Rebecca Anne. 2250 NW FLANDERS ST, STE 20 97210 #005-19-2001 L2002 **D** *020 †15

BRENES, Phillip Michael. 707 SW GAINES ST 97239 #005-02-1966 L1970 **PD** *020 †55

BRENNEKE, Stephen Louis. 3510 NE 122ND AVE STE 103 97230 #040-02-1971 L1978 **ORS** *020 †40

BRETT, Darrell Cameron. 10101 SE MAIN ST STE 1006 97216 #065-06-1977 L1983 **NS** *020 †25

BREWER, Malcolm Irvin, Jr. ■ 97230 #028-34-1964 L1968 **OPH** *071 †35

BRINDLE, Ted Ian. ■ 97201 #025-07-2003 **NS** *012

BRINKS, Mitchell Vaughn. 3600 N INTERSTATE AVE, KAISER - INTERSTATE - OPHT 97227 #040-02-1992 L1993 **OPH** *020 †35

BRISCHETTO, Brenda Joy. 2241 LLOYD CTR 97232 #028-02-1996 L2000 **FM** *020 †18

BROBERG, Craig Stanford. 3181 SW SAM JACKSON PRK RD, UHN 62 DIVISION OF CARDIOL 97239 #005-02-1996 L2000 **CD** *100 †20

BROCK, Timothy David. ■ 97239 #040-02-2008 *012

BROD, Lissa Simone. ■ 97209 #035-47-2005 L2006 **N** *012

BRODEUR, Michael Toner H. 8332 SE 13TH AVE 97202 #067-01-1956 L1965 **CD IM** *020 †20

BRODHACKER, James Earl. 500 NE MULTNOMAH ST # 100 97232 #028-34-1965 L1970 **IM ID** *030 †20

BRODSKY, Matthew Aaron. 3181 SW SAM JCKSN PRK RD R, M/S OP32 97239 #035-47-1996 L2002 **N** *020 †75

BRODY, Benjamin Lee. 19500 SE STARK ST, PAC. MED. GRP, OREGON CITY 97233 #056-06-1999 L2002 **IM** *020 †20

BROMLEY, Peter Joseph. 3181 SW SAM JCKSN PRK #R, OHSU DOTTER INSTITUTE L605 97239 #060-01-1993 L1999 **DR** *020 †80

BROOCK, Gerald Jay. ■ 97209 #025-01-1963 L2007 **ORS HS** *071 †40

BROOCK, Heather Ann. 3181 SW SAM JCKSN PRK RD R 97239 #025-01-1995 L1998 **IM** *020 †20

BROOKFIELD, Mari Lackey. ■ 97215 #016-11-1988 L1990 **GS** *020

BROOKS, Rachel Ellen. ■ 97214 #025-01-1979 L1993 **PM** *020 †60

BROOKSBY, Gerald Armond. 800 SW 13TH AVE 97205 #026-04-1973 L1974 **OPH** *071 †35

BROWDER, James Albert. 3181 SW SAM JACKSON PRK RD 97239 #048-02-1955 L1972 **PM PD** *020 †55

BROWN, Dawson Scott. ■ 97219 #040-02-2007 L2007 *012

BROWN, George Allen. 3181 SW SAM JCKSN PRK RD R, M/C OP31 97239 #040-02-1969 L2003 **ORS** *020 †40

BROWN, Heather Noelle. 10000 SE MAIN ST, STE 205 97216 #038-45-1998 L2001 **IM** *020 †20

BROWN, Ian Alexander. ■ 97213 #067-01-1944 L1964 **N** *072 †75

BROWN, Jay Patrick. 545 NE 47TH AVE, PROVIDENCE MEDICAL GROUP 97213 #040-02-1987 L1991 **IM** *020 †20

BROWN, Jeffery Tyler. ■ 97239 #034-01-2007 L2007 **GS** *012

BROWN, Jeffrey Josiah. 501 N GRAHAM ST 97227 #010-01-1982 L1986 **N OTO** *020 †75

■ = Address Information Privacy Protected

BROWN, Juliet Patricia. 97239 #005-14-2001 L2004 **DR** *020 †80
BROWN, Kimberly. ■ 97208 #016-11-1998 L1998 **GS** *100 †85
BROWN, Richard Maurice. ■ 97221 #054-04-1973 L1975 **NM FM** *020 †28,18
BROWN, Robert Scott. 120 NW 14TH AVE, STE 300 97209 #056-06-1989 L1997
   AN PMM *020 †05 ‡
BROWN, Timothy Mather. 12612 SE STARK ST 97233 #050-02-1976 L1981 **D EM** *020 †50,15
BROWN, William John. 501 N GRAHAM ST STE 265, NW NEWBORN SPECIALISTS 97227
   #040-02-1976 L1981 **NPM** *071 †55
BROWNING, Joan Marie. 3600 N INTERSTATE AVE 97227 #040-02-1981 L1987
   OM GPM *020 †70
BRUCE, Kevin Robert. ■ 97239 #040-02-2006 L2006 **IM** *012
BRUNER, Amy Ruth. 2222 NW LOVEJOY ST, STE 619 97210 #051-04-1993 L1997 **OBG** *020 †30
BRUNETT, Patrick Howard. 3181 SW SAM JACKSON PRK RD, PARK CDWEM 97239
   #041-12-1990 L1994 **EM** *020 †16
BRUSS, Reginald David. 6833 SW 65TH AVE, OREGON ANESTHESIOLOGY GROU 97219
   #028-02-1975 L1977 **AN** *020 †05 ‡
BRYAN, Ross Emery. ■ 97211 #026-08-2005 L2005 **EM** *012
BRYANT, Richard Edward. 3181 SW SAM JACKSON PRK RD, L-457 97239 #028-02-1958 L1973
   ID IM *020 †20
BUBALO, Frances Shen. ■ 97221 #017-20-1991 L1992 **IM** *020
BUBOLTZ, Melissa Beth. 3181 SW SAM JCKSN PRK RD R, UHN 80 97239 #026-08-2003 L2003
   P *100
BUCHAN, George Colin. ■ 97239 #067-01-1958 L1960 **NP PTH** *040 †50
BUCHAN, Melissa L Lehman. 3181 SW SAM JACKSON PRK RD 97239 #041-01-1961 L1963
   FM *071 †18
BUCHHOLZ, Mark Thomas. 2801 N GANTENBEIN AVE, LEGACY EMANUEL HOSPITAL-PI 97227
   #054-04-1996 L2005 **CCP** *020 †55
BUCKLEY, David Ignatius. 3181 SW SAM JCKSN PRK RD R, FP 97239 #034-01-1993 L1999
   FM *020 †18
BUCKLEY, Philip Douglas. 4805 NE GLISAN ST 97213 #039-05-1990 L1991 **IM** *020 †20
BUCKMASTER, John Gilbert. 3181 SW SAM JACKSON PRK RD, OHSU L466 97239
   #040-02-1980 L1981 **OBG MFM** *020 †19,30
BUCKON, Matthew Edward. 120 NW 14TH AVE, STE 300 97209 #051-01-1987 L1991
   AN *020 †05 ‡
BUDDEN, Sarojini Sylvia. 2801 N GANTENBEIN AVE, DEPT OF PEDIATRIC PROGRAM 97227
   #495-27-1962 L1977 **PD OS** *020 †55
BUEHL, Robert Victor. 10300 NE HANCOCK ST, WOODLAND PARK HOSPITAL 97220
   #035-03-1977 L1981 **IM** *020 †20,16
BUEHLER, Jeffrey Charles. 1130 NW 22ND AVE STE 410, NORTHWEST
   GASTROENTEROLOGY 97210 #035-20-1998 L1999 **GE** *020 †20
BUEHLER, Mark James. 5050 NE HOYT ST STE 660 97213 #040-02-1981 L1982
   ORS HS *020 †40
BUERK, Pilar Hewitt. 2525 NW LOVEJOY ST STE 200 97210 #025-07-1992 L1993 **PD** *020 †55
BUERK, Todd Garrett. 4805 NE GLISAN ST, PORTLAND PROVIDENCE MED CE 97213
   #040-02-1992 L1993 **EM** *020 †16
BUIST, A Sonia. 3181 SW SAM JACKSON PRK RD, OHSU, MAIL CODE UHN 67 97239
   #803-02-1964 L1970 **PUD** *050
BUIST, Neil Robertson M. 3181 SW SAM JACKSON PRK RD 97239 #803-02-1956 L1970
   PD MG *020 †19
BULGER, Arthur R. 11510 SE STARK ST 97216 #054-04-1973 L1976 **EM** *020
BULGER, Roberta A. 11510 SE STARK ST 97216 #054-04-1970 L1976 **FM** *020
BULLOCK, Pamela L. 5050 NE HOYT ST, STE 540 97213 #005-12-1981 L1997 **IM** *020 †20
BUMSTED, Tracy Nicole. 707 SW GAINES ST, STE CDRCP 97239 #049-01-2000 L2000
   PD *020 †55
BUNCKE, Geoffrey Harry. 3181 SW SAM JACKSON PRK RD, #L352-1 DIV OF PLSTC
   SURG 97239 #036-07-1984 L2002 **HS PS** *020 †65
BUNNAGE, Steven Michael. 120 NW 14TH AVE, STE 300 97209 #040-02-1981 L1982
   AN IM *020 †20,05 ‡
BURBANK-SCHMITT, Emma R. ■ 97219 #024-16-2007 L2007 **N** *012
BURCH, Grant Hartley. 707 SW GAINES ST, MAIL CODE CDRC-P 97239 #026-04-1988 L1996
   PDC *020 †55
BURCHELL, Mary Fowler. 2801 N GANTENBEIN AVE 97227 #008-02-1984 L2000 **PD** *020 †55
BURCHIEL, Kim James. 3181 SW SAM JCKSN PRK RD R, L472 97239 #005-18-1976 L1989
   NS PMM *020 †25
BURFORD, Patricia Anne. 5050 NE HOYT ST STE 157 97213 #919-05-1987 L1993
   END OS *020 †20
BURGERMEISTER, Geo Emil. 507 NE 47TH AVE 97213 #056-05-1962 L1965 **DR** *071 †80
BURGOYNE, Claude Francis. 1225 NE 2ND AVE, 3RD FL 97232 #026-04-1987 L2006
   OPH *020 †35
BURKE, Andrew Garrett. 3181 SW SAM JACKSON PRK RD, OR HLTH SCI UNIV HOSP 97239
   #003-01-2006 L2007 **DR** *012
BURKE, Elaine M. 3181 SW SAM JACKSON PRK RD 97239 #035-46-1988 L1989
   DR NM *020 †28,80
BURKE, Ralph Leonard. 10300 NE HANCOCK ST 97220 #040-02-1973 L1976 **IM PD** *020 †20
BURKE, Robert Tustin. 500 NE MULTNOMAH ST, STE 100 97232 #040-02-1977 L1980
   FM OS *020 †18
BURLESON, David Oliver. 120 NW 14TH AVE, STE 300 97209 #004-01-1984 L1987 **AN** *020 ‡
BURLONE, Suzanne. ■ 97219 #036-01-2007 L2007 **OBG** *012
BURNS, Beech Stephen. ■ 97239 #040-02-2008 *012
BURNS-DIESING, Elizabeth. ■ 97202 #034-01-2000 L2001 **IM** *020
BURRELL, John Michael. 120 NW 14TH AVE, STE 300 97209 #003-01-1983 L1988
   AN IM *020 †20,05 ‡
BURREN, Christine Pamela. 3181 SW SAM JACKSON PRK RD, PEDS NRC5 OHSU 97239
   #143-02-1987 **PDE** *100
BURROUGHS, Duane Alan. 501 N GRAHAM ST, STE 100 97227 #039-01-1972 L1975
   IM *020 †20
BURRY, Kenneth Arnold. 3303 SW BOND AVE, STE CH10F 97239 #005-15-1968 L1971
   REN OBG *020 †30 ‡
BURRY, Mary Tweedy. 2241 LLOYD CTR 97232 #005-15-1969 L1971 **NR R** *020 †80
BURT, Alex Robt. 25 NW 23RD PL STE 6, PMB 129 97210 #054-04-1987 L1988 **P** *071 †75
BURTON, Deidre Lavonne. 1130 NW 22ND AVE STE 320 97210 #040-02-1991 L1992
   PD *020 †55
BURUSNUKUL, Prinyarat. ■ 97201 #891-02-1994 L2008 **CHN** *012
BUSCARINI, Maurizio. ■ 97239 #561-17-1991 L2006 **U** *100
BUTELA, Heather Leigh. 3181 SW SAM JCKSN PRK RD R, OHSU 97239 #041-12-2007 L2007
   FP *012

BUTLER, Carolyn Amelia. PO BOX 19243 97280 #748-10-1982 L1984 **N PD** *020 †55
BUTLER, John Lowe. ■ 97232 #023-07-1946 L1946 **P** *071
BUTRUILLE, Frank Richard. ■ 97239 #040-02-2007 L2007 **AN** *012
BUTTERFIELD, William Chas. 500 NE MULTNOMAH ST STE 10 97232 #008-01-1959 L1984
   GS TS *071 †85
BUTTON, Gavin John. 5050 NE HOYT ST, STE 318 97213 #024-07-1999 L2005 **ORS** *020 †40
BUTTON, Morris. 5051 SE HAWTHORNE BLVD 97215 #016-11-1967 L1973 **HS** *072 †40
BUXBAUM, Asher. 97219 #550-01-1962 L1975 **CD IM** *020 †18
BUXMAN, James Henry. 5050 NE HOYT ST, STE 240 97213 #005-02-1970 L1972 **FM** *020 †18
BUYS, Susan Linville. 3500 N INTERSTATE AVE 97227 #019-02-1979 L1983 **AN** *020 †05
BYRD, Dan Madison, IV. 3181 SW SAM JACKSON PRK RD, # L586 97239 #048-12-2003 L2003
   HO *012 †20
BYRD, Greg Dee. ■ 97239 #028-02-2005 L2005 **ORS** *012
BYRNE, William John. 707 SW GAINES ST, DIRECTOR GASTROENTEROLOGY/ 97239
   #038-40-1972 L2006 **GE PD** *020 †55
CAFFARATTI, Barbara Rose. 500 NE MULTNOMAH ST STE 10 97232 #040-02-1976 L1977
   IM *020 †20
CAFFERKY, Edwin A. ■ 97216 #005-12-1953 L1953 **CD IM** *071
CAFFERKY, Ronald Edwin. 5055 N GREELEY AVE 97217 #005-12-1976 L1989 **P** *020 †75
CAHILL, Mark Patrick. ■ 97211 #054-04-2006 L2006 **IM** *012
CAIN, Joanna M. 3181 SW SAM JCKSN PRK RD R 97239 #030-06-1977 L2001
   OBG GO *030 †30
CALDWELL, Avalo V. 5919 SE BELMONT ST, MT TABOR FAMILY MEDICAL 97215
   #039-01-1950 L1969 **FM** *020 †18
CALDWELL, Lawrence Edward. 120 NW 14TH AVE, STE 300 97209 #005-02-1987 L1993
   GS *020 †05 ‡
CALKINS, Mark Dennis. 10123 SE MARKET ST 97216 #005-12-1991 L2000 **CCA** *020 †05 ‡
CALLAHAN, Kerry Ben. 541 NE 20TH AVE STE 210 97232 #040-02-1989 L1990 **FM** *020 †18
CALLEN, Kenneth Eugene. 3710 SW US VA HOSP RD 97201 #028-03-1965 L1981 **P** *020 †75
CALLEY, Nicholas. 10123 SE MARKET ST, DIAGNOSTIC RADIOLOGIST PC 97216
   #040-02-1981 L1982 **DR EM** *020 †80
CAMACHO, Samuel Albert. 10201 SE MAIN ST 97216 #005-12-1982 L1998 **CD** *020 †20
CAMACHO, Sandra. ■ 97219 #042-01-1989 L2007 **NM IM** *062
CAMERON, Michelle Hannah. ■ 97219 #005-02-2003 L2005 **N** *012
CAMP, Gregory V. 2014 SE 59TH AVE 97215 #010-01-1974 L1987 **IM HEM** *020 †20
CAMPBELL, Jeff Allen. ■ 97212 #018-03-2007 L2007 **IM** *012
CAMPBELL, John Jeffrey. 2801 N GANTENBEIN AVE, EMANUEL HOSPITAL 97227
   #038-43-1981 L1982 **IM OS** *020 †20
CAMPBELL, John Richard. 745 SW GAINES ST, CDW-7 97239 #019-02-1958 L1968
   PDS *071 †85
CAMPBELL, Joyce A Atlee. 2230 NW PETTYGROVE ST, STE 220 97210 #016-11-1968
   CLP *071 †50
CAMPBELL, Pamela Anne. 3181 SW SAM JCKSN PRK RD R, OP-26 97239 #010-02-2000 L2002
   APM *100 †05
CAMPBELL, Robert Allen. 3181 SW SAM JCKSN PRK #R 97239 #005-02-1958 L1961
   PN *050 †55
CAMPBELL, Robert Perry. 3610 NE 82ND AVE, STE 100 97220 #040-02-1976 L1977
   OM GPM *030 †70
CAMPBELL, Stephen M. 5050 NE HOYT ST, PROVIDENCE ARTHRITIS 97213
   #005-18-1976 L1977 **RHU IM** *040 †20
CANAVOSIO, Federico Maria. 3101 SW SAM JACKSON PRK RD, PARK RD 97239
   #132-02-2001 L2006 **IM** *012
CAPPS, Robert Truman. ■ 97206 #056-05-1954 L1955 **AN** *071 †05
CAPPUCCINI, Fabio. 3181 SW SAM JCKSN PRK RD R 97239 #561-01-1985 L2002
   OBG *020 †30
CARDWELL, Beth Alison. 3181 SW SAM JCKSN PRK RD R 97239 #041-01-1984 L1995
   CHP *020 †55
CAREY, Marc Brandon. 4104 SE 82ND AVE STE 250, PROVIDENCE FAMILY MEDICINE 97266
   #040-02-2003 L2003 **FM** *020 †18
CARLISLE, James Robt. 5050 NE HOYT ST STE 240 97213 #005-18-1985 L1990 **FM** *020 †18
CARLSON, Hans Lowell. 3181 SW SAM JACKSON PRK RD, PK. RD. 97239 #040-02-1992 L1997
   PM *020 †60
CARLSON, Jonathan Dennis. ■ 97239 #005-12-2001 L2001 **NS** *012
CARLSON, Nels Loyal. 3181 SW SAM JACKSON PRK RD, PARK RD 97239 #040-02-1992 L1999
   PM *020 †60
CAROLAN, Amy Denise. 4805 NE GLISAN ST, RM BG05 97213 #035-09-1999 L1999
   IM *020 †20
CARON, Dania A. ■ 97201 #061-01-1984 L1986 **IM** *020 †20
CARON, Gordon Anton. 8250 N LOMBARD 97203 #917-30-1957 L1967 **FM D** *020
CARPENTER, Dalton Remell. 3710 SW US VETRNS HSPTL RD, PORTLAND VA MEDICAL
   CENTER 97239 #001-02-1973 L1974 **ORS HS** *020 †40
CARPENTER, James David. ■ 97239 #048-04-1955 L1955 **P** *071
CARPENTER, Tammily Rose. 120 NW 14TH AVE STE 300, OREGON ANESTHESIOLOGY
   GROU 97209 #016-02-2003 L2004 **AN** *020
CARPENTIERI, Ugo. 3181 SW SAM JCKSN PRK RD R 97239 #561-10-1953 L1994
   HEM ON *071 †55
CARR, Chad Lawrence. ■ 97210 #021-01-2004 L2004 **IM** *100 †20
CARR, Richard Dale. 3181 SW SAM JACKSON PRK RD, ANESTH UHS-2 97239
   #014-01-1984 L1990 **AN PD** *020 †05,55
CARR, Thomas Patrick. 3710 SW US VETRNS HSPTL RD 97239 #023-01-1988 L1999
   IM *020 †20
CARRICO, Emily Ann. 1509 SW SUNSET BLVD STE 2 97239 #020-12-1997 L1998 **EM** *020 †16
CARROLL, Brendan Cargill. 10000 SE MAIN ST, STE 110 97216 #010-02-1994 L1998
   OBG *020 †30
CARROLL, Gregory Shawn. 1221 SW 10TH AVE, SUITE1407 97205 #021-01-1995 L2005
   EM *020 †16
CARROLL, Michael Edward. 5050 NE HOYT ST, STE 454 97213 #030-05-1989 L1990
   IM *020 †20
CARRUTH, Michael Edward. ■ 97216 #011-03-1991 L1994 **IM** *100 †20
CARTER, Charles Conrad. 3181 SW SAM JACKSON PRK RD, MAIL CODE L226 97239
   #040-02-1948 L1950 **N** *071 †75
CARTER, Gina Marie. ■ 97202 #003-01-2006 L2006 **PD** *012
CARTWRIGHT, Ian. 120 NW 14TH AVE, STE 300 97209 #917-28-1976 L1980 **AN** *020 †05 ‡
CARTY, Peter Christopher. 10000 SE MAIN ST, STE 205 97216 #024-07-1998 L2000 **IM** *020 †20
CASE, Laurel G. ■ 97230 #019-02-1949 L1954 **GP** *071
CASEY, Daniel Edward. ■ 97239 #051-01-1972 L1976 **P** *020 †75

CASEY, Janice Eileen. 120 NW 14TH AVE, STE 300 97209 #028-03-1978 L1979 **AN** *020 ‡

CASMIER, Angela Slaymaker. ■ 97239 #054-04-2005 L2005 **P** *012

CASPAR, George Heyden. 10819 SE STARK ST STE 200 97216 #040-02-1961 L1963 **OPH** *071 †35

CASPERSEN, Leroy Skibsted. 2222 NW LOVEJOY ST, STE 619 97210 #040-02-1956 L1960 **OBG** *020 †30

CASSIDY, Robert Hugh. 120 NW 14TH AVE, STE 300 97209 #040-02-1982 L1985 **AN** *020 †05 ‡

CASSON, Henry. 3181 SW SAM JACKSON PRK RD 97239 #352-06-1959 L1976 **AN PA** *040 †05

CASTLE, Jessica Rose. 3181 SW SAM JCKSN PRK RD R 97239 #040-02-2004 L2004 **END** *012 †20

CAVANAUGH, Megan M. 511 SW 10TH AVE STE 714, COLON RECTAL SURGICAL 97205 #550-02-1997 L2004 **CRS** *020 †85,10

CAWTHON, Mary Lawrence. 6327 SW CAPITOL HWY STE C, PMB 140 97239 #040-02-1982 L1983 **PHP GP** *030

CEBALLOS, Carlos. 10300 NE HANCOCK ST 97220 #264-04-1967 L1981 **AN** *020

CEDERGREEN, Jamie Cristin. 3181 SW SAM JACKSON PRK RD, RD L5 97239 #048-04-2006 L2006 **IM** *012

CEDFELDT, Andrea Siddons. ■ 97212 #032-01-2000 L2000 **IM** *020 †20

CENTERWALL, Willard R. 3181 SW SAM JACKSON PRK RD 97239 #008-01-1952 L1987 **OS PD** *071 †55,70,19

CEREGHINO, James Jos. 3181 SW SAM JACKSON PRK RD, OREGON HLTH & SCI UNIV 97239 #040-02-1964 L1965 **N** *050

CETAS, Justin Schultz. ■ 97217 #003-01-2002 L2002 **NS** *012

CHA, Christine Myungsook. 4805 NE GLISAN ST 97213 #025-01-1993 L2003 **RO** *020 †80

CHAFFIN, Albert Ellsworth. ■ 97212 #038-43-2006 L2006 **PD** *012

CHAKRAPANI, Sanjay Durgam. ■ 97201 #040-02-2002 L2007 **RNR** *012 †80

CHAMIE, Rima. ■ 97214 #040-02-2002 L2002 **FM** *100 †18

CHAN, Anita Yuen-Fai. 177 NE 102ND AVE 97220 #462-01-1982 L1998 **OBG** *020 †30

CHAN, Farn Huei. 97219 #064-01-2004 L2005 **IM** *012

CHAN, Joe Munjung. 3181 SW SAM JACKSON PRK RD, DEPT RAD 97239 #040-02-2005 L2007 **DR** *012

CHAN, Wiley Vernon. 500 NE MULTNOMAH ST 97232 #025-01-1980 L1984 **IM** *020 †20

CHAN, Yuen Ming. 5329 NE M L K BLVD, NORTHEAST HEALTH CENTER 97211 #040-02-1984 L1990 **PD** *020 †55

CHANDLER, Stephen Grover. 3600 N INTERSTATE AVE 97227 #067-01-1966 L1971 **IM** *020 †20

CHANDRABOSE, Rekha K. ■ 97239 #036-01-2004 L2004 **GS** *100

CHANG, Aimee Sison. 2222 NW LOVEJOY ST, STE 304 97210 #005-18-1998 L2007 **OBG REN** *030

CHANG, Bill Hoon. 3181 SW SAM JCKSN PRK RD R, DOENBECHER CHILDREN'S HOSP 97239 #040-02-2000 L2000 **PHO** *100 †55

CHANG, Eric Chienyeh. 3181 SW SAM JCKSN PRK RD R, M/C: NRC-3 97239 #035-45-2002 L2006 **ID** *012 †20,55

CHANG, Eugene Yonchia. ■ 97239 #048-04-2001 L2001 **GS** *012

CHANG, Kuo-Chian. 3550 N INTERSTATE AVE, KAISER PERMANENTE 97227 #244-02-1969 L1977 **AI PD** *020 †55,03

CHANG, Peggy S. 3181 SW SAM JCKSN PRK RD R, SCIENCE UNIV 97239 #065-06-2003 L2006 **PHO** *012

CHANG, Te-Yu Ruth. 7705 SE DIVISION ST, KAISER PERMANENTE 97206 #025-01-2002 L2002 **FM** *100 †18

CHANG, Yeachyng Kathy. 3742 NE 22ND AVE 97212 #019-02-1999 L2005 **OM** *020 †70

CHAN KAI, Brian Tsiwah. 3375 SW TERWILLIGER BLVD 97239 #056-06-2003 L2007 *100

CHAPMAN, Carolyn Nobuko. 1321 NE 99TH AVE, STE 100 97220 #005-15-1990 L2007 **FM** *020 †18

CHAUHAN, Ranjana. 2335 NW RALEIGH ST, UNIT 405 97210 #038-44-1999 L2005 **OPH** *020 †35

CHAWLA, Renu. 2400 SW VERMONT ST, FANNO CREEK CLINIC LLC 97219 #495-47-1994 L1999 **IM** *020 †20

CHEEK, David Burton Chas. 120 NW 14TH AVE, STE 300 97209 #005-12-1981 L1985 **AN PME** *020 †05 ‡

CHELSKY, Ronald. 10201 SE MAIN ST, STE 10 97216 #048-14-1985 L1986 **CD IM** *020 †20

CHEN, Chang-Yu. 2801 N GANTENBEIN AVE 97227 #665-01-2005 L2006 **IM** *012

CHEN, Christine S. 19500 SE STARK ST, KAISER PERMENENTE-ROCKWOOD 97233 #048-13-2001 L2001 **PD** *020 †55

CHEN, Grace. 97219 #025-01-2003 L2004 **PMM** *012

CHEN, Jefferson Wm. 501 N GRAHAM ST STE 580, LEGACY EMANUEL HOSP 97227 #023-07-1987 L1999 **NS** *020 †25

CHEN, Jenjen. ■ 97239 #040-02-2008 *012

CHEN, John Taofan. 3500 N INTERSTATE AVE 97227 #036-01-1986 L1992 **IM** *020 †20

CHEN, Joyce Chiyi. 3181 SW SAM JACKSON PRK RD, OREGON HEALTH & SCIENCE UN 97239 #036-07-1999 L2000 **PS** *012

CHEN, Michael Shihjay. 819 SE MORRISON ST STE 275 97214 #028-03-2000 L2003 **FM** *020 †18

CHEN, Qing. 3181 SW SAM JACKSON PRK RD, OHSU 97239 #243-76-1982 L2000 **PTH** *020 †50

CHEN, Yi-Ching. 1200 NW 23RD AVE, GOOD SAMARITAN 97210 #010-01-2006 L2006 **IM** *012

CHENG, David. ■ 97209 #012-01-2006 L2007 **DR** *012

CHERNESKY, Michele Anne. 500 NE MULTNOMAH ST, NORTHWEST PERMANENTE PC 97232 #010-01-1989 L1997 **DR** *020 †80

CHESNUT, Randall Matthew. 2241 LLOYD CTR 97232 #054-04-1984 L1996 **NS GS** *020 †25

CHESNUTT, Asha N. 1111 NE 99TH AVE, OREGON CLNC 97220 #051-01-1988 L1996 **NS** *020 †20

CHESNUTT, James Clive. 3303 SW BOND AVE, OHSU ORTHOPAEDICS- SPORTS 97239 #040-02-1999 L1995 **FM FSM** *020 †18

CHESNUTT, Mark Sherman. 2241 LLOYD CTR 97232 #040-02-1986 L1996 **IM** *020 †20

CHESTLER, Robert Jay. 10502 NE WASCO ST 97220 #040-02-1985 L1989 **OPH** *020 †35

CHIA, Dennis Jay. 707 SW GAINES ST, CDRC-P 97239 #024-05-1998 L2001 **PDE** *100 †55

CHIA, Samuel Kah. 3101 SW SAM JCKSN PRK RD R 97239 #143-03-1999 L2007 *012

CHIASSON, Marcelle C. 4055 SW GARDEN HOME RD, STE 1 97219 #065-09-1962 L1972 **OS PM** *020 †05

CHIEN, Grace Lynn. P-8-ANES, PORTLAND VA MC ANESTH SVC 97201 #023-07-1985 L1989 **AN** *020 †05

CHILDERS, David Courtland. ■ 97219 #016-42-2007 L2007 **IM** *012

CHIM, Ha Jimmy. 3181 SW SAM JACKSON PRK RD, OR HLTH SCI UNIV 97239 #023-01-2007 L2007 **GS** *012

CHIN, Homer Lu-Shih. 500 NE MULTNOMAH ST, STE 100 97232 #032-01-1980 L1993 **IM OS** *030 †20

CHING, Alexander C. 3181 SW SAM JACKSON PRK RD, MAILCODE OP31 97239 #035-01-2001 L2006 **ORS** *020

CHING, Chester Sung. 10201 SE MAIN ST, STE 27 97216 #048-04-1990 L1997 **NEP IM** *020 †20

CHING, Katherine Huanglin. ■ 97239 #040-02-2007 **GS** *012

CHINN, Edwin K. 500 NE MULTNOMAH ST STE 10 97232 #025-01-1978 L1983 **PTH** *020 †50

CHIPMAN, Clark Douglas. ■ 97221 #019-02-1972 L1980 **EM OM** *016

CHIU, Andrew Alex. 120 NW 14TH AVE STE 300, OREGON ANESTHESIOLOGY GROU 97209 #040-02-1988 L1995 **APM** *020 †05 ‡

CHIU, Catherine Sueling. 10535 NE GLISAN ST, METROPOLITAIN PEDIATRIC, L 97220 #017-20-1995 L1998 **PD** *020 †55

CHIU, Vincent Shin Wai. 500 NE MULTNOMAH ST STE 10 97232 #028-34-1956 L1959 **GE IM** *020 †20

CHO, Benjamin L. 3181 SW SAM JCKSN PRK RD R, L586 97239 #016-01-2001 L2004 **HO** *012

CHO, Sherwin Yong. ■ 97214 #016-01-2003 L2007 **N** *100

CHO, Sungeyun David. ■ 97239 #003-01-2003 L2003 **GS** *012

CHOE, Marietta Hajung. 4104 SE 82ND AVE, STE 250 97266 #005-19-1993 L1996 **FM** *020 †18

CHOO, Esther Kim. 3181 SW SAM JCKSN PRK RD R, MAIL CODE CR114 97239 #008-01-2001 L2007 **EM** *100 †16

CHOONG, Meeiyng. 2400 SW VERMONT ST, FANNO CREEK CLINIC LLC 97219 #005-06-1991 L1992 **IM** *020 †20

CHOU, Roger. 3181 SW SAM JCKSN PRK RD R, M/S L475 97239 #016-06-1995 L1997 **IM** *020 †20

CHOU, Sun Wen. 2241 LLOYD CTR 97232 #005-14-1977 L1985 **IM ID** *040 †20

CHOW, John Laphong. 120 NW 14TH AVE, STE 300 97209 #056-06-1994 L1999 **AN CCA** *020 †05 ‡

CHOW, Lawrence Changlun. 3181 SW SAM JACKSON PRK RD, PARK ROAD 97239 #025-01-1995 L2005 **DR** *020 †80

CHRISTANTE, Dara Heisler. ■ 97201 #048-02-2004 L2004 **GS** *012

CHRISTENSEN, Clarence A. 2241 LLOYD CTR 97232 #025-01-1956 L1957 **FM** *071 †35

CHRISTENSEN, Laurie E. 3375 SW TERWILLIGER BLVD, CASEY EYE INSTITUTE 97239 #040-02-1982 L1990 **OS** *020 †35

CHRISTENSEN, Marilyn. 1225 NE 2ND AVE 97232 #040-02-1961 L1963 **AN EM** *071

CHRISTOPHERSON, Rose. PORTLAND VA MEDICAL CENTER, AN SERVICE PS-ANES 97207 #041-14-1982 L1997 **AN** *020 †05

CHUGH, Sumeet Singh. 3181 SW SAM JACKSON PRK RD, PARK ROAD 97239 #495-29-1988 L1999 **ICE** *020 †20

CHUI, Stephen Yun-Chi. 3181 SW SAM JCKSN PRK RD R, MNP 3225, MAIL CODE #L586 97239 #036-07-1996 L2006 **HO** *020 †20

CHUN, Colleen S Y. 3181 SW SAM JACKSON PRK RD R, MAIL CODE: CDRCP 97239 #014-01-1984 L1990 **PD** *020 †55

CHUNG, Kathryn Anne. 3181 SW SAM JACKSON PRK RD, MAIL CODE L226 97239 #060-01-1994 L1995 **N** *020 †20

CHUNG, Kelly Denise. 3303 SW BOND AVE, FL 11 97239 #005-12-1989 L1994 **OPH** *020 †35

CHURCH, Phyllis G B. 2232 NW PETTYGROVE ST 97210 #040-02-1967 L1971 **DIA IM** *020

CIESLAK, Paul Raymond. 800 NE OREGON ST STE 772, OREGON DEPT OF HUMAN SVCS 97232 #038-40-1986 L1995 **PHP ID** *030 †20

CINOCCO, Dawnrenee. 2800 N VANCOUVER AVE, LEGACY CLINIC EMANUEL 97227 #007-02-2005 L2005 **IM** *012

CIOFFI, George A. 1040 NW 22ND AVE STE 200, GOOD SAMARITAN HOSPITAL 97210 #045-04-1987 L1991 **OPH** *020 †35

CIRINO, Anthony C. 3600 N INTERSTATE AVE, CENTRAL INTERSTATE MEDICAL 97227 #016-43-2000 L2005 **OPH** *100 †35

CISZEWSKI, Aleksandra Ann. ■ 97209 #035-15-2005 L2005 **IM** *012

CLAPPISON, Valerie. ■ 97221 #040-02-1977 L1978 **P** *075 †75

CLARK, Amanda Lou. 3181 SW SAM JACKSON PRK RD R 97239 #020-02-1981 L1982 **OBG OS** *020 †30

CLARK, Brinton Carey. 5050 NE HOYT ST, STE 540 97213 #005-02-2001 L2005 **IM** *020

CLARK, Liisa Oakes. ■ 97239 #040-02-2008 *012

CLARK, Louise Helen. 2701 NW VAUGHN ST, STE 140 97210 #025-01-1983 L1995 **FM** *020 †18

CLARK, Melissa Christman. ■ 97210 #010-02-2007 L2007 **EM** *012

CLARK, Wayne Marston. 3181 SW SAM JACKSON PRK RD, MAIL CODE L226 97239 #040-02-1985 L1990 **N** *050 †75

CLAYTON, Michael John. 4805 NE GLISAN ST, STE BG05 97213 #005-14-1998 L2003 **IM** *020 †20

CLEARY, Timothy Shannahan. 5050 NE HOYT ST STE 454 97213 #748-01-1981 L1984 **IM** *020 †20

CLEGG, Stacey. ■ 97239 #043-01-2005 L2005 **IM** *012

CLELAND, John Eastmure. 3610 NE 82ND AVE 97220 #040-02-1957 L1958 **OBG** *071 †30

CLEMENTS, Christopher Mic. 1200 NW 23RD AVE, GOOD SAMARITAN 97210 #016-42-2007 L2007 **IM** *012

CLEVELAND, Minot. 1015 NW 22ND AVE 97210 #017-20-1979 L1980 **IM** *020 †20

CLEVEN, Jeffrey C. 800 SW 13TH AVE 97205 #025-01-1974 L1977 **IM** *020 †20

CLOCK, Charlotte Ann. 3181 SW SAM JCKSN PRK RD R, M/S: L458 97239 #019-02-2000 L2000 **OBG** *100 †30

CLOUTIER, Robert Louis. 2241 LLOYD CTR 97232 #050-02-1995 L2001 **PEM** *020 †16

COAKLEY, Brian Arrinza. ■ 97239 #040-02-2007 **GS** *012

COBANOGLU, Mustafa Adnan. 3181 SW SAM JACKSON PRK RD, PARK ROAD 97239 #902-03-1974 L1982 **TS** *020 †85,90

COCHRAN, Roy E. 4800 SW MACADAM AVE # 400 97239 #030-05-1951 L1957 **MDM GS** *071

COCHRAN, Terence H. PO BOX 5050 97208 #040-02-1941 **PTH** *071 †50

COCKBURN, Robert Milroy. 4805 NE GLISAN ST 97213 #040-02-1955 **FM** *071 †18

COCKRELL, Janice Louise. 2801 N GANTENBEIN AVE, DEVELMT & REHAB 97227 #016-06-1972 L1992 **PM PD** *020 †55,60

COFFIN, Galen H. 500 NE MULTNOMAH ST STE 10 97232 #005-12-1949 L1967 **AN GP** *071

COHEN, David Earl. 3314 SW US VETRN HOSP RD, HOSP. RD 97239 #024-01-1987 L1990 **GE** *020 †20

COHEN, David Mason. 2241 LLOYD CTR 97232 #041-02-1986 L1996 **NEP IM** *050 †20

COHEN, James Isaac. 3710 SW US VETRNS HSPTL RD, DEPT OTO 97239 #062-01-1978 L1988 **OTO HNS** *020 †45

COHEN, Jason Aaron. 3181 SW SAM JCKSN PRK RD R, OREGON HEALTH & SCIENCE UN 97239 #016-02-2003 L2003 **IM** *020 †20

COHEN, Marguerite P. 1130 NW 22ND AVE STE 520 97210 #005-06-1981 L1983 **OBG** *020 †30

COHEN, Milton Tepper. 5858 SW CHELTENHAM DR, MINOR INJURY CLINIC 97239 #028-02-1974 L1975 **EM** *020,16

COHEN, Norman Allen. 3181 SW SAM JCKSN PRK RD R, UHS-2 97239 #023-07-1985 L2002 **AN** *020 †05 ‡

COHEN, Richard Chas. 3550 N INTERSTATE AVE 97227 #016-42-1971 L1974 **PD** *020 †55

COHEN, William. 1015 NW 22ND AVE 97210 #040-02-1935 L1935 **IM PUD** *071 †20

■ = Address Information Privacy Protected

COHEN, Zori Beth. 3550 N INTERSTATE AVE, KAISER PERMANENTE 97227 #035-15-1978 L1995 **ADL PHP** *020 †55

COIT, William Eccles. 2701 NW VAUGHN ST, PORTLAND 97210 97210 #040-02-1981 L1982 **DR** *020 †80

COLBACH, Edward M. 4805 NE GLISAN ST 97213 #016-06-1964 L1970 **P** *072 †75

COLE, Frederic Jack, Jr. 501 N GRAHAM ST, STE 580 97227 #036-05-1983 L2006 **GS TRS** *020 †85

COLEMAN, Clifford Adams. 3930 SE DIVISION ST 97202 #005-11-2000 L2000 **FM GPM** *020 †18,70

COLEMAN, Fred Hughes, III. 300 N GRAHAM ST, STE 100 97227 #016-06-1974 L1978 **MFM OBG** *020 †30

COLEMAN, Roger Alan. ■ 97221 #040-02-2004 L2005 **AN** *012

COLER, Fred Kent. 921 SW WASHINGTON ST, STE 812 97205 #032-01-1993 L1996 **P** *020 †75

COLIP, Charles Leroy. 10000 SE MAIN ST STE 203, GASTROENTEROLOGY ASSOCIATE 97216 #017-20-1973 L1978 **GE IM** *020 †20

COLLINS, Judith Furman. 3181 SW SAM JACKSON PRK RD 97239 #045-01-1977 L1981 **GE IM** *020 †20

COLLINS, Kristan Cranmer. 4212 NE BROADWAY ST, BROADWAY MEDICAL CLINIC 97213 #048-04-1987 L1991 **PD** *020 †55

COLLINS, Lydia Helen. 3181 SW SAM JACKSON PRK RD, OB-GYN DEPT UHN50 97239 #016-43-1985 L1989 **OBG** *020 †30

COLLINS, Michael Sean. 1130 NW 22ND AVE, STE 120 97210 #045-01-1977 L1981 **GYN** *020 †30

COLMAN, Laurence. 2386 NW HOYT ST 97210 #035-01-2001 L2001 **CHP** *020 †75

COLORITO, Anthony Ivar. 1515 NW 18TH AVE, STE 300 97209 #035-01-1994 L2000 **OSM** *020 †40

COLVARD, Maryann. 1849 NW KEARNY ST, SUMMIT RESEARCH NETWORK 97209 #054-04-1991 L1997 **IM** *020 †20

COLVILLE, Christopher M. ■ 97201 #025-01-2003 L2004 **AN** *020

COLWELL, Fred Gustav. ■ 97205 #038-41-1955 L1962 **PD** *020 †55

COMBS, John Wm. ■ 97296 #054-04-1964 L1981 **PTH** *071

COMEAU, Maurice Jos. 3600 N INTERSTATE AVE 97227 #040-02-1964 L1967 **OTO HNS** *071 †45

COMSTOCK, Wendy J. 2311 NW NORTHRUP ST STE 20 97210 #056-05-1986 L1988 **P** *020 †75

CONANT, Keith David. 1130 SW MORRISON ST, STE 250 97205 #040-02-1997 L1999 **P** *020

CONE, Molly May. ■ 97239 #040-02-2006 L2006 **GS** *012

CONLIN, Michael. 3303 SW BOND AVE, MAIL CODE C H 10 U 97239 #048-13-1989 L1990 **U** *020 †95

CONNELLY, Lloyd George. ■ 97219 #005-19-2005 L2005 **EM** *012

CONNELLY, Timothy John. 120 NW 14TH AVE, STE 300 97209 #016-06-1987 L2001 **AN PA** *050 †05 ‡

CONNOR, William E. 2241 LLOYD CTR 97232 #018-03-1950 L1975 **OS NTR** *050 †20

CONOUR, James Anthony. 2130 SW 5TH AVE, STE 210 97201 #016-45-1999 L2005 **P** *100 †75

CONSTANTE, Marylou. 4805 NE GLISAN ST 97213 #054-04-1985 L1991 **FM** *020 †18

CONSTIEN, Daniel John. 5919 SE BELMONT ST 97215 #028-03-1981 L1990 **FM** *020 †18

CONTI, Paul Matthew. 1445 SW WESTWOOD DR 97239 #005-11-2001 L2007 **P** *020 †75

COODLEY, Gregg. 2400 SW VERMONT ST, FANNO CREEK CLINIC LLC 97219 #005-18-1985 L1990 **IM** *040 †20

COODLEY, Marcia K. 2400 SW VERMONT ST, FANNO CREEK CLINIC 97219 #033-05-1986 L1990 **IM** *020 †20

COOK, Charles Milton. 120 NW 14TH AVE STE 300, OREGON ANESTHESIOLOGY GROU 97209 #005-12-1983 L1986 **AN EM** *020 †05 ‡

COOK, David Michael. 3181 SW SAM JCKSN PRK RD R, M/S L607 97239 #028-34-1963 L1970 **END IM** *020 †20

COOK, David N. ■ 97206 #005-11-1953 L1953 **P** *071

COOK, Justin Otis. 1015 NW 22ND AVE, LEGACY GOOD SAMARITAN HOSP 97210 #040-02-2001 L2005 **IM** *020 †16

COOK, R Edward. 10123 SE MARKET ST DEPT P 97216 #005-12-1973 L1974 **PTH PCP** *020 †50

COOK, Ted A. 3181 SW SAM JACKSON PRK RD, PARK RD 97239 #048-04-1964 L1982 **FPS HNS** *020 †45

COOKE, Harriet. ■ 97239 #011-02-1984 L1985 **GP** *020

COOLEY, Ann Marie. ■ 97211 #040-02-2008 *012

COONEY, Thomas Gregory. 3710 SW US VETRNS HSPTL RD 97239 #010-02-1975 L1982 **IM** *040 †20

COOPER, Clifford. 800 SW 13TH AVE 97205 #056-06-1976 L1979 **IM** *020 †20

COOPER, Jimmy Lee. 3181 SW SAM JCKSN PRK RD R, CDW-EM 97239 #023-12-1996 L2005 **EM** *020 †16

COOPER, Larry Paige. 3550 N INTERSTATE AVE 97227 #005-19-1972 L1974 **P** *020 †75

COPELAND, Kimberly Hope. 2801 N GANTENBEIN AVE, LEGACY EMANUEL HOSPITAL 97227 #040-02-1991 L1998 **PD PEM** *020 †55

COPPERMAN, Jack. 120 NW 14TH AVE, STE 300 97209 #011-03-1965 L1968 **AN** *020 †05 ‡

CORBIN, Laura Lynn. ■ 97209 #005-19-2005 L2005 **PD** *012

CORE, Michael Anthony. ■ 97212 #040-02-2008 *012

COREY, Gwyn. 12451 NE ROSE PKWY 97230 #040-02-1999 L1999 **P** *020

CORLESS, Christopher Lee. 2241 LLOYD CTR 97232 #028-02-1988 L1994 **PTH** *020 †50

CORMAN, David Lawrence. 3181 SW SAM JCKSN PRK RD R, OHSU 97239 #016-42-2005 L2005 **IM** *012

CORN, Gerald Robt. PO BOX 4327 97208 #005-02-1973 L2006 **FM MDM** *030 †18

CORNUTT, David Patrick. 4805 NE GLISAN ST, PROVIDENCE MEDICAL CENTER 97213 #040-02-1985 L1986 **EM** *020 †20

CORRIERE, Marlene Michele. 10300 NE HANCOCK ST, WOODLAND PARK HOSPITAL 97220 #041-13-1989 L1997 **IM** *020 †55,20

CORTESE, David Anthony. ■ 97239 #040-02-2006 L2006 **OSM** *020

CORWIN, Raymond Sykes. 5440 SW WESTGATE DR, PORTLAND GYNECOLOGY CLINIC 97221 #036-05-1963 L1966 **OBG END** *071 †30

COSTA, Daniel Jungkeit. 3181 SW SAM JCKSN PRK RD R, UHN-80 97239 #031-01-2003 L2003 **P** *020

COSTANTINO, Mary Marcelle. ■ 97239 #005-14-2001 L2002 **DR** *020 †80

COTTERELL, Coral Wm. ■ 97230 #030-06-1954 **OBG** *071 †30

COUGHLIN, James Michael. 4212 NE BROADWAY ST 97213 #054-04-2000 L2000 **PD** *020 †55 ‡

COUROGEN, William Peter. 3325 N INTERSTATE AVE 97227 #041-02-1962 L1973 **ORS** *020 †40

COX, Andrew Gordon. 2311 NW NORTHRUP ST, STE 202 97210 #040-02-1993 L2001 **VIR** *020 †80

COZZENS, Jessica Dawn. ■ 97266 #040-02-2007 L2007 **FP** *012

CRANK, Christine Louise. ■ 97239 #040-02-2008 *012

CRANMER, Malia Annmongini. ■ 97201 #003-01-2006 L2006 **PD** *012

CRAVEN, Robert Edward. 5819 SE JOHNSON CREEK BLVD 97206 #030-06-1957 L1962 **R** *071 †80

CRAWFORD, Anthony Edward. ■ 97202 #040-02-2008 *012

CRAWFORD, Brooke Michelle. ■ 97239 #040-02-2007 L2007 **GS** *012

CRAWFORD, Dennis Charles. 3181 SW SAM JCKSN PRK RD R, OHSU 97239 #024-05-1995 L2002 **ORS** *020 †40

CRAWFORD, Edgar Daniel. 10803 SE CHERRY BLOSSOM DR 97216 #040-02-1975 L1978 **FM** *020 †18

CRAWFORD, Julie Takeuchi. ■ 97239 #003-01-2003 L2003 **OBG** *020

CRAWFORD, Thos Irving, II. 5050 NE HOYT ST STE 445 97213 #048-12-1980 L1984 **OPH** *020 †35

CRAWSHAW, Ralph Shelton. ■ 97210 #035-19-1947 L1960 **P PHP** *071 †75

CREITZ, Bonnie Jean. 2400 SW VERMONT ST, FANNO CREEK CLINIC LLC 97219 #040-02-1977 L1979 **IM OS** *020 †20 ‡

CRISERA, Richard Vincent. ■ 97219 #040-02-1960 L1961 **PTH NM** *071 †50,28

CRISLIP, Mark Alden. 1015 NW 22ND AVE RM 2, DEPT OF MEDICINE 97210 #040-02-1983 L1990 **ID** *020 †20

CRISLIP, Rodney Linwood. 507 NE 47TH AVE 97213 #038-06-1957 L1959 **CD PUD** *071 †20

CRISPELL, Kathy Ann. 3181 SW SAM JACKSON PRK RD 97239 #021-01-1990 L1991 **IM** *020 †35

CRIST, Audrey Ann. 19500 SE STARK ST, KAISER - ROCKWOOD 97233 #017-20-2003 L2004 **FM** *020 †18

CRISTOFANI, Daniel L. 5415 SW WESTGATE DR 97221 #010-02-1975 L1979 **OBG GP** *020 †30

CRITTENDEN, Marka Rae. ■ 97219 #026-08-2004 L2004 **RO** *012

CROCENZI, Todd Shane. 4805 NE GLISAN ST, STE 6N40 97213 #041-02-1994 L2005 **HO** *012

CROMBIE, Terry Shawn. 3001 N GANTENBEIN AVE, CHILD/ADOLESCENT TREATMENT 97227 #005-12-1994 L2002 **CHP** *020 †75

CROOK, Larry Dennis. 4337 SE SALMON ST 97215 #040-02-1971 L1974 **IM CCM** *020 †20

CROOK, Stephen Russell. 10000 SE MAIN ST, STE 408 97216 #005-12-1995 L2000 **GS VS** *020 †85

CROSS, Robert Laurance, Jr. 3181 SW SAM JACKSON PRK RD, UHS-2 97239 #001-02-1993 L1993 **AN** *020 †05

CROUSE, Robert Charles. 800 SW 13TH AVE 97205 #040-02-2003 L2006 **IM** *020 †20

CROVER, Jeana Marie. 10803 SE CHERRY BLOSSOM DR 97216 #040-02-2002 L2005 **FM** *020 †18

CROWLEY, William Joseph. 120 NW 14TH AVE, STE 300 97209 #003-01-1993 L1994 **AN** *020 †05 ‡

CRUMPACKER, Robert Wm. 10000 SE MAIN ST STE 307 97216 #019-02-1968 L1974 **N** *020 †75

CRUZ, Francisco, III. ■ 97209 #048-12-2001 L2003 **HMP** *012 †50

CRYSTAL, Chad Scott. 1015 NW 22ND AVE, DEPART EMERGENCY MEDICINE 97210 #016-06-2000 L2007 **EM** *020 †16

CULBERT, Emily Christina. ■ 97215 #054-04-2001 L2003 **OBG** *100

CULL, Anthony Salvatore. 3181 SW SAM JCKSN PRK RD R, UHN-80 97239 #016-11-2002 L2002 **P** *100 †75

CULL, Thomas Francis. 120 NW 14TH AVE, STE 300 97209 #010-02-2001 L2007 **AN** *100

CUMMINGS, Paul James. 2801 N GANTENBEIN AVE, RM 4100 97227 #028-02-1993 L2004 **IM** *020 †20

CUMMINGS, Rhett James. 1111 NE 99TH AVE 97220 #039-01-1997 L2004 **PCC** *100 †20

CUPLER, Edward James. 3181 SW SAM JCKSN PRK RD R, CR 120 97239 #038-40-1988 L2005 **N** *050 †75

CURIOSO, Evelyn A P. 5050 NE HOYT ST, STE 315 97213 #748-10-1993 L2001 **N OPH** *020 †75

CURL, Franklin Dale. 4805 NE GLISAN ST 97213 #047-05-1962 L1972 **PTH NM** *020 †50,28

CUROSH, Nancy Ann. 5050 NE HOYT ST, STE 234 97213 #003-01-1986 L1991 **END IM** *020 †20

CURRAN, Susan Margaret. 1800 SW 6TH AVE, PORTLAND STATE UNIV ST HLT 97201 #028-46-1986 L1987 **IM** *020 †20

CURTI, Brendan David. 4805 NE GLISAN ST, STE 6N40 97213 #010-02-1985 L2002 **ON IM** *050 †20

CUSHMAN, Francis Ray. ■ 97209 #038-06-1960 L1960 **PTH** *030 †50

CUTHILL, Sara Lynn. 3550 N INTERSTATE AVE, INTERSTATE MED OFF EAST 97227 #035-19-1996 L2003 **PD** *020 †55

CUYLER, James Paul. 1849 NW KEARNEY ST STE 200 97209 #060-01-1976 L1992 **PDO** *020 †45

CYNKUTIS-SIMON, Magdalena. ■ 97239 #040-02-1995 L2004 **FM** *100

DAACK, Aloys Julius. ■ 97202 #005-17-1962 L1975 **GP** *071

D'AGOSTINO, Anthony N. 3181 SW SAM JACKSON PRK RD 97239 #035-06-1958 L1974 **ATP NP** *020 †20

DAHLKE, Katherine Marie. 1025 NE 33RD AVE 97232 #025-07-1983 L1993 **IM** *020 †20

DAHLMAN, James Edwin. 2222 NW LOVEJOY ST, STE 619 97210 #025-01-1961 L1962 **GYN** *071 †30

DAILEY, Roger Allan. 3303 SW BOND AVE, FL 11 97239 #026-08-1982 L1983 **OPH** *020 †35

DALE, D Duane. 2386 NW HOYT ST 97210 #054-04-1975 L1978 **P PYA** *020 †75

DALKE, Kathellen Casey. 3550 N INTERSTATE AVE 97227 #051-07-1988 L1989 **OBG** *020 †30

DALROS, Launa Marie. ■ 97211 #040-02-2005 L2005 **IM** *020

D'AMATO, Charles Roland. 3101 SW SAM JCKSN PRK RD R 97239 #041-09-1979 L2003 **ORS** *020 †40

DANA, Bruce Wilson. 10101 SE MAIN ST, STE 1012 97216 #024-01-1975 L1976 **ON HEM** *050 †20

DANCE, David Gerald. 3375 SW TERWILLIGER BLVD, CASEY EYE INSTITUTE 97201 #048-04-2005 L2005 **OPH** *012

DANCZYK, Rachel Collette. ■ 97211 #017-20-2007 L2007 **GS** *012

DANESHMAND, Siamak. 3303 SW BOND AVE, DIV OF UROLOGY CH 10U 97239 #005-19-1996 L2004 **U** *020 †95

DANIEL, Morad Milad. 3710 SW US VETRNS HSPTL RD, P3NEUR 97239 #056-06-2002 L2003 **N** *100 †75

DANIELS, Alan Hunter. ■ 97239 #040-02-2008 *012

DAOUD, Katja Fawzieh. 5050 NE HOYT ST, PROVIDENCE ARTHRITIS 97213 #038-41-1997 L2000 **RHU** *020 †20

DARBY, Charles Lowell. 4212 NE BROADWAY ST 97213 #048-04-1981 L1982 **IM** *020 †20

DARK, Allison Carrell. ■ 97202 #040-02-2005 L2007 **P** *012

DARWICH, Hani. 2644 NW THURMAN ST 97210 #035-09-1998 L2006 **EM** *020 †16

DAS, Asish Kumar. 3181 SW SAM JACKSON PRK RD, UH 2 97239 #496-18-1980 L2001 **AN** *020 †05

DA SILVEIRA, Eduardo B V. PO BOX 1034 97207 #187-03-1995 L2006 **GE** *020 †20

DATENA, Stephen Jay. 3181 SW SAM JACKSON PRK RD 97239 #017-20-1984 L1993 **GS CCS** *050 †85

DAVENPORT, Thomas W. 120 NW 14TH AVE, STE 300 97209 #409-21-1991 L2001 **AN** *020

DAVEY, Michael Patrick. 3710 SW US VETRNS HSPTL RD 97239 #035-20-1982 L1988 **RHU** *050 †20

DAVID, Roger Chas. 1955 NW NORTHRUP ST, EYEHEALTH NORTHWEST 97209 #041-01-1969 L1975 **OPH** *020 †35

DAVIDOFF, Leslie. 181 NE 102ND AVE, EAST PORTLAND MED ASSOC 97220 #040-02-1997 L2000 **GPM OM** *020 †70 ‡

DAVIDSON, Hugh R. ■ 97236 #056-05-1951 L1968 **P GP** *071

DAVIES, Crispin Henry Cou. 3181 SW SAM JCKSN PRK RD R, OHSU-CARDIOLOGY UHN-62 97239 #917-25-1986 L2000 *020 †20

DAVIES, Laura Hall. 300 N GRAHAM ST, STE 200 97227 #024-16-1998 L2002 **RHU** *020 †20

DAVIS, Craig Stephen. 3550 N INTERSTATE AVE 97227 #047-06-1988 L1997 **IM** *020 †20

DAVIS, Ellen Jean. ■ 97202 #040-02-2007 L2007 **IM** *012

DAVIS, J Steven. 10000 SE MAIN ST, STE 105 97216 #005-12-1973 L1977 **PD** *020 †55

DAVIS, Lowell Evan. 2241 LLOYD CTR 97232 #020-12-1980 L1986 **OBG** *020 †30

DAVIS, Michael Wade. 2222 NW LOVEJOY ST STE 619 97210 #005-19-1998 L2000 **OBG** *020 †30

DAVIS, Molly Katherine. 3181 SW SAM JCKSN PRK RD R, UHN 80 97239 #054-04-2001 L2002 **N** *012 †75

DAVIS, Nina Sarah. 3181 SW SAM JCKSN PRK RD R, KPV-7C 97239 #035-45-1980 L2001 **U** *020 †95

DAVIS, Robert Michael. 3600 N INTERSTATE AVE 97227 #004-01-1984 L1990 **OM** *020 †70

DAVOLT, William Wray. 5055 N GREELEY AVE 97217 #025-01-1969 L1973 **OBG** *020 †30

DAWLEY, Douglas Lee. 1111 NE 99TH AVE 97220 #005-11-1980 L1986 **CD IM** *020 †20

DAWSON, Elizabeth Sims. ■ 97209 #035-20-2004 L2005 **D** *012

DAWSON, Lynne Elaine. 10123 SE MARKET ST, DEPT RAD ONCOLOGY 97216 #054-04-1978 L1986 **RO** *020 †80

DAY, Floyd Douglas. 2252 LLOYD CTR 97232 #040-02-1959 L1960 **FM** *020 †18

DAYA, Mohamud R. 3181 SW SAM JCKSN PRK RD R, MAIL CODE CDW-EM ORG HLTH 97239 #061-01-1984 L1985 **EM** *020 †16

DEALE, Shirley. 5050 NE HOYT ST, STE 422 97213 #060-01-1950 L1974 **P** *071

DEAN, Kevin L. ■ 97221 #005-02-2003 L2004 **EM** *020 †16

DEARDORFF, David Alva. 4805 NE GLISAN ST, STE BG05 97213 #055-01-1989 L2001 **MPD PD** *020 †55,20

DE CASTRO, Enrique C M. 2222 NW LOVEJOY ST STE 619 97210 #649-01-1957 L1961 **OBG** *020 †30

DEENEY, John Michael. 2386 NW HOYT ST 97210 #040-02-1960 L1967 **CHP P** *062

DEERING, Darcy Elizabeth. 2801 N GANTENBEIN AVE 97227 #040-02-1997 L1998 **IM** *020 †20

DEFFEBACH, Mark Elbert. 2241 LLOYD CTR 97232 #040-02-1981 L2001 **PUD IM** *020 †20

DE FONTES, Deane Chas. 12710 SE DIVISION ST, MID-COUNTY HEALTH CTR 97236 #005-14-1990 L2003 **FM** *020 †18

DEGREGORIO, Barry Thos. 501 N GRAHAM ST, NORTHWEST 97227 #036-01-1990 L1991 **GE** *020 †20

DEININGER, Michael Werner. 2241 LLOYD CTR 97232 #409-20-1994 L2002 *020

DEIORIO, Nicole Marie. 3181 SW SAM JACKSON PRK RD, PARK RD 97239 #010-01-1996 L2000 **EM** *012 †16

DEISSEROTH, Kate Benedict. ■ 97239 #016-06-2003 L2003 **ORS** *012

DEITZ, Estill Nickell. 10123 SE MARKET ST 97216 #035-08-1946 L1944 **IM** *075

DE JESUS-RENTAS, Gilberto. 3181 SW SAM JACKSON PRK RD, MAIL CODE UHN-80 97239 #308-13-2000 L2007 **PFP CHP** *012

DELASHAW, Johnny B, Jr. 3303 SW BOND AVE, M/C: CH8N 97239 #054-04-1983 L1992 **NS** *020

DE LA TORRE, Barbara. ■ 97202 #048-02-2005 L2005 **P** *012

DELBAUM, Andrew Robt. 3500 N INTERSTATE AVE 97227 #028-02-1976 L1979 **CD** *075 †20

DELGADO, Gregory T. ■ 97239 #040-02-2002 L2003 **GS** *100

DELLINGER, Karen Kaiser. 3181 SW SAM JACKSON PRK RD, PARK RD 97239 #016-06-1993 L1994 **N** *020 †75

DELLINGER, Michael Dean. 3181 SW SAM JACKSON PRK RD, OHSU DEPT OF INTERNAL MED 97239 #067-01-1992 L1993 **IM** *020 †20

DE LOOZE, Theodore Howard. 2801 N GANTENBEIN AVE 97227 #040-02-1976 L1981 **AN** *105 ‡

DELOUGHERY, Thomas Grier. 3181 SW SAM JCKSN PRK RD R 97239 #017-20-1985 L1986 **HEM IM** *020 †20

DE MARS, Ronald Victor. 10201 SE MAIN ST STE 20 97216 #040-02-1971 L1982 **PS** *020 †85,65

DEMETRION, George Byron. 2400 SW VERMONT ST, FANNO CREEK CLINIC LLC 97219 #010-01-1994 L1996 **IM** *020 †20

DE MOTS, Henry, Jr. 3181 SW SAM JACKSON PRK RD, DEPT CARD UHN-62 97239 #016-06-1966 L1974 **CD** *030 †20

DEMUNTER, Jodi Kim. 1321 NE 99TH AVE, STE 200 97238 #023-01-2000 L2000 **FM** *020 †18

DEMUTH, Robert John. ■ 97239 #035-45-1959 L1979 **PS HS** *071 †85,65

DENARD, Patrick Joel. ■ 97217 #032-01-2005 L2005 **ORS** *012

DENKER, John Thos. 5919 SE BELMONT ST, MT TABOR FAMILY MEDICAL 97215 #040-02-1980 L1981 **GP FPG** *020

DENMAN, Mary Anna. 3181 SW SAM JACKSON PRK RD, DEPT OB/GYN DIV OF UROGYNE 97239 #031-01-2001 L2005 **OBG** *100

DENNEY, D Duane. 3181 SW SAM JCKSN PRK RD R 97239 #040-02-1957 L1958 **P IM** *040 †75

DENNINGHOFF, Erik Peter. 97210 #012-05-2005 L2005 **EM** *012

DENTE, Jenny Maria. ■ 97209 #034-01-2005 L2005 **PD** *012

DEODHAR, Atulya Achyut. 3181 SW SAM JCKSN PRK RD R, OREGON HLTH & SCI UNIV 97239 #495-28-1987 L1998 **RHU** *012

DERBY, Craig Stuart. 120 NW 14TH AVE, STE 300 97209 #005-18-1992 L2006 **AN** *020 †05

DERSTINE, Christina Trost. ■ 97206 #017-20-2006 L2006 **PD** *012

DERVAN, Celia Katherine. 3181 SW SAM JCKSN PRK RD R 97239 #016-11-2002 L2002 **CD** *012 †20

DERVAN, Sarah Ann. 2222 NW LOVEJOY ST STE 505, CASCADE PHYSICIANS 97210 #035-09-2000 L2000 **IM** *020 †20

DESAI, Rohit. 12518 NE AIRPORT WAY, STE 110 97230 #495-23-1979 L1992 **IM** *020 †20

DESAI, Sima Suresh. 3181 SW SAM JCKSN PRK RD R, M/S L 97239 #034-01-1994 L1996 **IM** *020 †20

DE SILVERMAN, Carmen G. ■ 97205 #737-01-1965 L1978 **GP** *020

DE SIMONE, June Marie. 4212 NE BROADWAY ST 97213 #056-05-1993 L1994 **PD** *020 †55

DETLEFSEN, Stephanie P. 3550 N INTERSTATE AVE 97227 #010-02-1996 L1999 **IM** *020 †20

DEUTSCH, Evan Mark. 500 NE MULTNOMAH ST, STE 100 97232 #038-40-2001 L2008 **EM** *020 †16

DEVARAJAN, Sumathi. 3930 SE DIVISION ST 97202 #495-09-1993 L2001 **FM FPG** *020 †18

DEVENEY, Clifford Wayne. 3181 SW SAM JCKSN PRK RD R 97239 #005-02-1969 L1987 **GS** *050 †85

DEVENEY, Karen Elsa Suhr. 3181 SW SAM JACKSON PRK RD, PARK RD 97239 #005-02-1972 L1987 **GS** *020 †85

DEVERE, Theresa Schroeder. 3303 SW BOND AVE, DEPT - DERMATOLOGY 97239 #048-04-1997 L2001 **D** *020 †15

DE VOE, Jennifer E. 4411 SW VERMONT ST, GABRIEL PARK FHC 97219 #024-01-1999 L2001 **FM** *020 †18

DEVOE, Meg Anne. ■ 97239 #040-02-2008 *012

DEW, Leighanne. 10101 SE MAIN ST, STE 2004 97216 #012-01-1992 L1998 **OTO** *020 †45

DE WETTE, Nicolaas Willem. 265 N BROADWAY ST, NORTHWEST CANCER SPECIALIS 97227 #660-04-1988 L2001 **RO** *020 †80

DEYO, Richard Alden. 3181 SW SAM JACKSON PRK RD, FAMILY MED MAIL CODE FM 97239 #041-14-1975 L2007 **IM** *050 †20

DEYOUNG, Keith Richard. ■ 97219 #016-02-2006 L2006 **FP** *012

DE YOUNG, Patricia Ann. ■ 97239 #025-01-1956 L1972 **PTH** *074 †50

DHOOT, Dilsher Singh. 2800 N VANCOUVER AVE, LEGACY CLINIC EMANUEL 97227 #040-02-2006 L2006 **OPH** *012

DHULST, Marie-Louise. 800 SW 13TH AVE 97205 #041-09-1995 L1996 **IM** *020 †20

DHUNGEL, Birat. 3181 SW SAM JCKSN PRK RD R 97239 #160-11-2002 L2006 **GS** *012

DIBBERN, Donald A, Jr. 511 SW 10TH AVE STE 1307, ALLERGY CLNC LLC 97205 #041-01-1996 L2001 **A IM** *020 †20,03

DICARLO, Timothy Jos. 3710 SW US VETRNS HSPTL RD 97239 #040-02-1992 L1996 **IM** *020

DIEPENHORST, Lisa Lynn. 5050 NE HOYT ST, STE 359 97213 #025-12-2002 L2006 **OBG** *020

DIERAUF, Susan Stephens. 3550 N INTERSTATE AVE, E. INTERSTATE MEDICAL OFFI 97227 #005-18-1992 L1998 **PD** *020 †55

DIERKS, Eric Jackson. 1849 NW KEARNEY ST STE 300, ERIC J DIERKS MD DMD 97209 #020-02-1979 L1990 **HNS FPS** *020 †45

DIETZE, Margaret R. ■ 97221 #041-12-1952 L1953 **PD** *071 †55

DI GREGORIO, Frank A. 5050 NE HOYT ST STE 523, OREGON PEDS PC NE-PTLD 97213 #040-02-1989 L1992 **PD** *020 †55

DILLON, Deborah Carolyn. 501 N GRAHAM ST STE 445 97227 #836-03-1986 L2003 **OBG** *020 †30

DINGES, Emily Marie. ■ 97239 #040-02-2007 L2007 **GS** *012

DINNEEN, James Clark. 135 NE 102ND AVE 97220 #040-02-1962 L1963 **ORS** *075

DI PAOLA, John David. 4709 N LAGOON AVE 97217 #033-06-1982 L1983 **ORS** *020 †40

DIPIERO, Albert Raniero. 3181 SW SAM JACKSON PRK RD, OHSU GENERAL MEDICINE, L47 97239 #005-02-1991 L1996 **IM** *020 †20

DIRKX, Tonja Lisa. 3314 SW US VETRN HOSP RD, HOSP ROAD 97239 #005-19-1998 L1999 **NEP** *020 †20

DISHMAN, Jess Morrell. 500 NE MULTNOMAH ST STE 10 97232 #016-06-1962 L1971 **OBG** *020 †20

DITMORE, Harry Boaz. ■ 97239 #024-01-1953 L1964 **GP GS** *020 †85,90

DITTRICH, Kenneth Chas. ■ 97219 #060-01-1980 **EM** *020 †16

DIWAN, Tayyab Shabbir. ■ 97209 #038-06-2001 L2005 **GS** *100

DIXON, Harold Romain, Jr. ■ 97216 #005-12-1945 L1945 **AN** *071 †05

DIXON, Tara Denise. 4323 NE HAZELFERN PL 97213 #012-22-2000 L2003 **GS** *100 †85

DIXON, Walker B, III. ■ 97219 #048-15-1997 L2001 **P** *020 †75

DOBSCHA, Steven Keith. 3710 SW US VETRNS HSPTL RD, RD P3 97239 #008-01-1988 L1998 **P** *020 †75

DOBSON, Donald P. 1015 NW 22ND AVE 97210 #024-05-1950 L1953 **AN** *071 †05

DODGE, David Lowell. 4805 NE GLISAN ST 97213 #028-02-1966 L1980 **PTH NM** *071 †50,28

DODSON, Lisa Grill. 3303 SW BOND AVE 97239 #035-48-1988 L1989 **FM** *020 †20

DODSON, Thomas Wm. 1015 NW 22ND AVE 97210 #035-09-1982 L1992 **P PFP** *020 †75 ‡

DOGAN, Aclan. 2241 LLOYD CTR 97232 #902-03-1986 L2001 **NS** *100

DOGGETT, Joseph Stone. 5050 NE HOYT ST STE 540 97213 #001-06-2004 L2004 **ID** *012 †20

DOGRA, Meenakshi. 4805 NE GLISAN ST 97213 #496-17-1991 L2001 **APM** *020 †05

DOGRA, Vivek. 3181 SW SAM JCKSN PRK RD R, M/S-UHN67 97239 #496-17-1987 L2001 **CCM** *100 †20

DOLAN, Philip Jarvis. 800 SW 13TH AVE 97205 #021-05-1973 L2005 **GE** *020 †20

DOLIN, Leigh Chas. 545 NE 47TH AVE 97213 #035-08-1971 L1977 **IM** *071 †20

DONAGHU, Laura Isbell. ■ 97212 #040-02-1999 L2000 **FM** *020 †18

DONOVAN, Deirdre Eileen. 3181 SW SAM JCKSN PRK RD R 97239 #010-02-2001 L2002 **FM** *100 †18

DORATOTAJ, Shirin. 2801 N GANTENBEIN AVE 97227 #041-02-2003 L2006 **PHO** *012 †55

DORDEVICH, Dejan Milorad. 545 NE 47TH AVE STE 301 97213 #054-04-1971 L1977 **ID** *050 †20,03

DORNFEST, Franklyn David. 4411 SW VERMONT ST 97219 #836-02-1965 L2003 **FM** *030

DORR, David Andrew. 3181 SW SAM JCKSN PRK RD R 97239 #028-02-1999 L2000 **IM** *020 †20

DORSEN, Michael. 501 N GRAHAM ST STE 500, LEGACY NEUROSURGERY CLINIC 97227 #143-02-1969 L1999 **NS** *020 †25

DORSEY, Carla Gallati. 2386 NW HOYT ST 97210 #051-01-1986 L1990 **P** *020 †75

D'OSTROPH, Andrea Olsen. 200 SW MARKET ST STE L120 97201 #040-02-1997 L1998 **OPH** *020 †35

DOUGAN, Ronald Craig. 500 NE MULTNOMAH ST 97232 #056-05-1957 L1974 **OM EM** *071

DOUGHERTY, Nancy Kathleen. 10101 SE MAIN ST STE 1004 97216 #919-05-1988 L1992 **FM** *020 †18

DOUGHTON, Robert P. 2342 SE 57TH AVE 97215 #040-02-1959 L1963 **OS OBG** *075 †30

DOUGLAS, Bruce Clayton. 10803 SE CHERRY BLOSSOM DR 97216 #005-12-1981 L1984 **FM** *020 †18

DOUGLAS, Daniel Ray. 2241 LLOYD CTR 97232 #005-02-1989 L1993 **EM** *020 †16

DOUGLASS, George M, Jr. 2230 NW PETTYGROVE ST, STE 140 97210 #040-02-1996 L1999 **EM** *020 †16

DOUGLASS, Kristen. 2812 SW BERTHA BLVD 97239 #040-02-1996 L1999 **PD** *020 †55

DOUVILLE, Emery C. 1111 NE 99TH AVE 97220 #005-14-1982 L1991 **TS** *020 †85,90

DOUZDJIAN, Viken. 1040 NW 22ND AVE, TRANSPLANT SURGERY NSC 480 97210 #065-09-1985 L2001 **GS** *020 †85

DOVE, Phillip Michael. 5050 NE HOYT ST STE 540, PROVIDENCE 97213 #041-14-2007 L2007 **IM** *012

DOVER, Eric Alan. 11705 NE GLISAN ST 97220 #005-14-1985 L1991 **FM** *020 †18

DOW, Joshua Empedocles. ■ 97217 #054-04-2004 L2004 **CHP** *012

DOW, Russell Alfred. 2222 NW LOVEJOY ST STE 522 97210 #024-07-1974 L1976 **GYN** *020 †30

DOWIDAR, Bassim Martin. 2801 N GANTENBEIN AVE, LEGACY EMANUEL HOSPITAL 97227 #054-04-2003 L2005 **EM** *020 †16

DOWLING, Anna Rinehart. ■ 97239 #005-14-2005 L2005 **OBG** *012

■ = Address Information Privacy Protected

DOWNES, Hall. 3181 SW SAM JACKSON PRK RD, DPT PHRM 97239 #024-01-1959 L1963 OS AN *030 †05

DOWNS, Brian William. 3181 SW SAM JCKSN PRK RD R, M/S PV-01 97239 #036-01-2000 L2005 OTO *100 †45 ‡

DOWSETT, Peter John. ■ 97212 #040-02-1965 L1970 OBG *071 †30

DOYLE, Edward James. ■ 97209 #016-06-1964 L1974 R GP *071 †80

DOYLE, Sally Elizabeth. 1919 NW LOVEJOY ST 97209 #048-04-1985 L2005 OBG *020 †30

DRAKE, Brian Eugene. 10000 SE MAIN ST, STE 309 97216 #048-15-1997 L2001 OBG *020 †30

DRAKE, Richard Franklin. 1015 NW 22ND AVE 97210 #040-02-1959 L1961 NEP IM *071 †20

DRAKOS, Nicholas Anthony. ■ 97210 #038-41-1979 L1989 P *020

DRASIN, Dena. ■ 97202 #020-02-1980 L2002 CHP P *020 †75

DRASIN, George F. 800 SW 13TH AVE 97205 #056-05-1967 L2002 R DR *020 †80

DREISIN, Robert Barry. ■ 97239 #016-02-1971 L1983 PUD NS *071 †20

DREYER, Richard Frederick. 2525 NW LOVEJOY ST, STE 300 97210 #023-07-1977 L1986 OPH OS *020 †35

DREYER, Thomas Morgan. 2241 LLOYD CTR 97232 #016-11-1972 L1983 PS HNS *020 †45,65 ‡

DRINKA, Geo Frederick S. 2250 NW FLANDERS ST, STE 306 97210 #023-07-1975 L1984 CHP *020 †75

DROUKAS, Paul Craig. 707 SW GAINES ST, CDRC-P 97239 #040-02-1977 L1980 PDC PD *020 †55

DRUKER, Brian Jay. 3181 SW SAM JCKSN PRK RD R, L 592, BASIC SCIENCE 5383 97239 #005-18-1981 L1993 ON IM *020 †20

DRUMMOND, Jane Olmsted. 7705 SE DIVISION ST, KAISER PERMANENTE 97206 #005-19-1995 L1997 IM *020 †20

DUBOSE, Robert Adams. 2222 NW LOVEJOY ST, STE 315 97210 #036-01-1999 L2007 TS *020 †85

DUCKLER, Lawrence. 500 NE MULTNOMAH ST STE 10 97232 #056-05-1950 L1954 GS AS *020 †85

DUELL, Paul Barton. 3181 SW SAM JACKSON PRK RD, L465 97239 #040-02-1983 L1984 IM END *050 †20

DUFF, William. 4805 NE GLISAN ST 97213 #803-03-1965 L1975 ORS *020 †40

DUFFY, Regan Melissa. ■ 97206 #040-02-2007 L2007 IM *012

DUGONI, James Edward. 4805 NE GLISAN ST, PROVIDENCE MEDICAL CENTER 97213 #011-03-1981 L1982 IM *020 †20,16

DULL, Peter Matthew. 3181 SW SAM JCKSN PRK RD R, OREGON HEALTH SCIENCE UNIV 97239 #056-05-1997 L1998 ID *020 †20

DULUDE, Richard Donophen. 120 NW 14TH AVE, STE 300 97209 #025-07-1985 L1994 AN IM *020 †20,05 ‡

DUMSER, Bruce Theodore. 3181 SW SAM JACKSON PRK RD, RD AN 97239 #018-03-2005 L2005 AN *012

DUNCAN, David Gale. ■ 97211 #030-06-1936 L1937 GP *071

DUNCAN, William Cary, III. 5400 SW MENEFEE DR, STE 300 97239 #035-01-1962 L1971 VS GS *020 †85

DUNHAM, Tom Robt. 10373 NE HANCOCK ST, STE 115 97220 #024-01-1967 L1974 IM END *020 †20

DUNITZ, Neal Allan. 4805 NE GLISAN ST 97213 #025-01-1981 L1994 IM *020 †20

DUNKLEY, Brian Lynn. 500 NE MULTNOMAH ST # 100, M/S: KPB-5 97232 #040-02-1984 L1989 DR *020 †80

DUNKS, Kelli Joan. ■ 97216 #005-12-1997 L2005 EM *100

DUNLAP, Jennifer Beth. ■ 97239 #048-12-2003 L2005 PTH *012

DUNN, Mark Derral. ■ 97239 #048-12-2007 L2007 FP *012

DUNN, Patrick Marshall. 1130 NW 22ND AVE STE 220, LEGACY CLINIC NW 97210 #040-02-1979 L1980 IM *020 †20

DUNN, Stephen Richard. 3181 SW SAM JACKSON PRK RD, STE L588 97239 #018-03-1968 L2005 U *020 †95

DUNST, Christy Martinez. 1040 NW 22ND AVE, STE 560 97210 #007-02-1998 L2006 GS *020 †85

DUPLAIN, Ellen P. 10000 SE MAIN ST, STE 205 97216 #060-02-2000 L2000 IM *020 †20

DUPRE, Marcel Wilfred. 10123 SE MARKET ST, ADVENTIST MEDICAL CENTER 97216 #034-01-1991 L2003 EM *020 †16

DURFEE, David Allan. ■ 97202 #040-02-1968 L1969 OPH *020 †35

DURHAM, James Booth. 4805 NE GLISAN ST, PROVIDENCE MEDICAL CENTER 97213 #028-03-1974 L2002 DMP *020 †50

DURHAM, Stephanie Phinney. ■ 97215 #040-02-2003 L2004 FM *100

DUTTA, Sajal. 5050 NE HOYT ST, STE 516 97213 #005-06-1996 L2002 U *020 †95

DUTY, Brian Donald. ■ 97239 #040-02-2004 L2004 U *012

DU VALL, Clyde Henry, Jr. ■ 97221 #040-02-1946 OPH *071 †35

DWORKIN, Ronald Jeffrey. 5050 NE HOYT ST, INFECTION CONSULTANTS LLP 97213 #035-47-1984 L1990 ID IM *040 †20

DYER, Edward Alexander. 3181 SW SAM JACKSON PRK RD, RD IN 97239 #005-18-2005 L2005 IM *012

DYSON, Robert Duane. 177 NE 102ND AVE 97220 #040-02-1977 L1978 OBG *020 †30

DZIURZYNSKI, Kristine. 3303 SW BOND AVE, M/S: CH8N 97239 #001-06-2000 L2007 NS *100

EARHART, Amy Susan. 97212 #040-02-1991 L1995 FM PD *020 †18,55

EASTMAN, James Warren. 1631 NE BROADWAY 104 97232 #026-04-1966 L1970 P *020

EBERT, Stephen Arnold. 2701 NW VAUGHN ST, STE 140 97210 #040-02-1969 L1973 IM *020 †20

ECKSTROM, Elizabeth Nancy. 3181 SW SAM JCKSN PRK RD B 97239 #056-05-1990 L1991 IMG *100 †100

EDELMAN, Alison Beth. 3181 SW SAM JCKSN PRK RD R 97239 #040-02-1997 L1999 OBG *020 †30

EDELMAN, Jeffrey David. 2241 LLOYD CTR 97232 #035-01-1989 L2000 PUD IM *020 †20

EDEN, Kathryn Elizabeth. 1015 NW 22ND AVE 97210 #040-02-2003 L2003 IM *020 †20

EDGAR, Eric Matthew. ■ 97219 #039-01-2005 L2005 N *012

EDGAR, Katherine Jean. ■ 97232 #040-02-1931 L1936 OS *071 †55

EDHOLM, Karli Michelle. 97213 #040-02-2007 L2007 IM *012

EDMUNDS, Lorna Elizabeth. 3303 SW BOND AVE, FL 11 97239 #836-02-1989 L2003 *100

EDWARDS, Donald Gene. 545 NE 47TH AVE, PROVIDENCE MEDICAL OFFICE 97227 #040-02-1959 L1960 IM *071

EDWARDS, James Mark. 2241 LLOYD CTR 97232 #047-05-1981 L1982 VS GS *020 †85

EDWARDS, Jennifer Holt. ■ 97214 #051-01-2006 L2006 EM *012

EDWARDS, Raymond Scott. 2801 N GANTENBEIN AVE, LEGACY EMANUEL HOSPITAL 97227 #016-42-1994 L1999 DR *020 †20

EDWARDS, S Renee. 3181 SW SAM JCKSN PRK RD R, MAIL CODE L466 97239 #016-43-1989 L1999 GYN OS *020 †30

EGAN, Robert Arthur. 3181 SW SAM JCKSN PRK #R, L-226 97239 #056-06-1993 L1994 N *020 †75

EGENER, Barry Evan. 1130 NW 22ND AVE, STE 220 97210 #035-20-1979 L1981 IM *020 †20

EGSIEKER, Erik Lloyd. 10201 SE MAIN ST, STE 23 97216 #012-01-1998 L2003 EM *020 †16

EHRLICH, Elizabeth Susan. ■ 97214 #035-09-2002 L2004 IM *020 †20

EHRLICH, Ian K. 2801 N GANTENBEIN AVE 97227 #550-02-1986 L1992 AN *020 †05 ‡

EHST, Benjamin David. 3303 SW BOND AVE, OHSU DEPT OF DERM CH16D 97239 #026-04-2003 L2007 D *020 †15

EID, Tarek. 2801 N GANTENBEIN AVE, LEGACY EMMANUEL HOSP & MED 97227 #875-01-2002 L2004 IM *012 †20

EIDEMILLER, Larry Raymond. 1130 NW 22ND AVE STE 500 97210 #040-02-1966 L1968 GS VS *020 †85

EIFF, M Patrice. 3303 SW BOND AVE 97239 #056-06-1983 L1990 FM *020 †18

EILERS, Gregory Matthew. ■ 97239 #040-02-2004 L2004 OBG *012

EISEN, Glenn Miles. 3181 SW SAM JCKSN PRK RD R, M/S L-461 97239 #035-46-1987 L2003 GE *020 †20

EISENBERG, Douglas Brian. 500 NE MULTNOMAH ST, STE 100 97232 #011-02-1981 L1992 DR *020 †80

EISENBERG, Jay David. ■ 97239 #048-04-1978 L1979 PD PDP *020 †55

ELDER, Charles Robt. 7705 SE DIVISION ST 97206 #024-05-1987 L1991 IM *020 †20

ELDER, Leslie Dale. ■ 97239 #031-01-1987 L1992 FM *072 †18

EL-EBIARY, Fouad Hussein. 9111 NE SUNDERLAND AVE, OREGON DEPT OF CORRECTION 97211 #915-03-1964 L1981 GP GS *020

ELFERING, Sarah Liv. ■ 97209 #026-04-2006 L2006 IM *012

ELIA, Joseph Rocco. ■ 97210 #036-01-2007 L2007 PD *012

ELL, Kristen Rene. 5050 NE HOYT ST STE 523 97213 #040-02-1998 L2001 PD *020 †55

ELLEGALA, Dilantha B. 3181 SW SAM JCKSN PRK RD R, M/S: L472 97239 #054-04-1996 L2005 NS *020

ELLENBY, Miles Steven. 707 SW GAINES ST, CDRCP 97239 #016-02-1991 L2000 CCP PD *020 †55

ELLER, Jorge Luis. 3181 SW SAM JCKSN PRK RD R, M/S L472 97239 #187-14-1994 L2004 NS *020

ELLIOT, Diane Louise. 3181 SW SAM JACKSON PRK RD 97239 #028-02-1976 L1979 IM ISM *050 †20

ELLIS, Michelle Claire. ■ 97219 #034-01-2006 L2006 GS *012

ELLISON, Catherine Marie. 5050 NE HOYT ST, STE 315 97213 #040-02-1982 L1983 N *020 †75

ELLISON, David Hoadley. 2241 LLOYD CTR 97232 #016-01-1978 L1979 NEP IM *020 †20

ELMORE-BIEG, Susan. 1631 SW COLUMBIA ST 97201 #007-02-1988 L1996 P *020

ELSAS, Siegward Markus. 3181 SW SAM JCKSN PRK RD R, CR-120 97239 #409-44-1990 L2002 N *100 †75

EMARA, Khaled Mohamed. ■ 97239 #915-04-1990 L2005 OTR *100

EMENS, Jonathan Scott. 3181 SW SAM JCKSN PRK RD R, OREGON HEALTH & SCIENCE UN 97239 #024-16-1998 L1999 P *020 †75

EMERSON, Michael Vaughn. 3375 SW TERWILLIGER BLVD, CASEYE INST 97239 #008-01-2001 L2005 OPH *100 †35

EMERY, Rachel Elizabeth. ■ 97219 #040-02-2008 *012

EMMERICH, Joseph Leo. 4212 NE BROADWAY ST, BROADWAY MED CLINIC 97213 #016-11-1959 L1965 PD PDA *071 †55

EMMONS, Sandra L. 3181 SW SAM JCKSN PRK RD R 97239 #054-04-1985 L1986 OBG *020 †30

ENDERS, Walter Rudolf. ■ 97204 #040-02-1947 L1987 OPH *071 †35

ENDO, Carol Yoshie. 2800 N VANCOUVER AVE, STE 165 97227 #016-02-1991 L2007 PD *020 †55

ENESTVEDT, Charles K. ■ 97239 #016-06-2003 L2003 GS *012

ENGLAND, Jennifer Jones. ■ 97218 #016-01-1991 L1992 FM *020 †18

ENGLANDER, Wayne Douglas. 12710 SE DIVISION ST, MULTNOMAH COUNTY HEALTH DE 97236 #040-02-1993 L1994 IM *020 †20

ENGLE, Daniel James. 4110 SE HAWTHORNE BLVD 97214 #048-13-1999 L2003 CHP *100

ENGSTAD, Kai Erik. ■ 97209 #422-01-2001 L2006 TS *012 †85

ENGSTROM, Todd Wm. 727 SW BURNSIDE, OLD TOWN CINIC 97209 #016-06-1986 L1990 IM *020 †20

ENOMOTO, Tonya Miko. ■ 97239 #043-01-2001 L2001 AN *012

ENSMINGER, Shauna Lynne. 4920 N INTERSTATE AVE 97217 #060-01-1991 L1996 FM *020 †18 ‡

ENSROTH, Kenneth Alan. 3001 N GANTENBEIN AVE 97227 #025-12-1988 L2001 CHP P *020 †75

EPLEY, John Macnaughton. 545 NE 47TH AVE, STE 212 97213 #040-02-1957 L1965 NO *020 †45

EPNER, Elliot Mark. 3181 SW SAM JCKSN PRK RD R, M/S 97239 #035-01-1983 L2003 ON IM *020 †20

EPSON, Martin Fitzgerald. 3181 SW SAM JCKSN PRK RD R, RESIDENCY TRAINING 97239 #035-01-2007 L2007 P *012

EPSTEIN, Matthew David. ■ 97239 #040-02-2007 TY *012

EPSTEIN, Robert Warren. 800 SW 13TH AVE 97205 #041-01-1971 L1974 IM *020 †20

ERBGUTH, Peter H P. 3101 SW SAM JACKSON PRK RD 97239 #407-20-1964 L1971 AN *020 †05

ERDE, Karen M. 9936 SE WASHINGTON ST, PROVIDENCE PALLIATIVE CARE 97216 #035-48-1976 L1977 FM *020 †18

ERHARDT-EISEN, Eliza E. ■ 97210 #033-05-1988 L1989 PD *020 †55

ERICH, Louis Richard. ■ 97216 #005-12-1955 L1956 OBG *071 †30

ERICKSON, Benjamin James. ■ 97210 #035-09-2006 L2006 IM *012

ERICKSON, Douglas Bernard. 120 NW 14TH AVE, STE 300 97209 #005-12-1975 L1978 AN *020 †05

ERICSON, Gary Duane. 1235 NE 47TH AVE, STE 245 INTERHOSPITAL PHYS 97213 #056-06-1992 L1997 MDM *030 †20

EROGLU, Yasemen. 707 SW GAINES ST, MAILCODE CDRCP 97239 #902-05-1982 L2003 PG *020

ERSSON, Ole L. 1120 SW 3RD AVE 4TH FL, MCDC 97204 #040-02-1995 L1997 FM *020 †18

ERTEN-LYONS, Deniz. 3710 SW US VETRNS HSPTL RD, P3NEUR 97239 #902-05-1998 L2001 N *020

ERTZBERGER, Briar Leigh. ■ 97239 #035-46-2002 L2002 EM *100 †16

ESELIUS, Erik Philip. 4805 NE GLISAN ST DEPT RAD 97213 #056-06-1962 L1977 R *020 †80

ESHELMAN, Melissa. 4805 NE GLISAN ST # 3E 97213 #048-12-1988 L1994 P CHP *020 †75

ESHRAGHI, Niknam. 501 N GRAHAM ST STE 555 97227 #040-02-1993 L1994 GS OS *020 †85

ESSELINK, Barbara Joy. ■ 97220 #056-05-2006 L2006 IM *012

ESSINK, Beal Greg. 2230 NW PETTYGROVE ST, STE 120 97210 #030-05-1996 L1999 P *020 †75

EVANS, Bradley Harold. 1111 NE 99TH AVE, THE OREGON CLINIC, P.C. 97220 #005-02-1984 L1991 **CD IM** *020 †20

EVANS, Harry C. ■ 97219 #056-05-1952 **AN** *071 †05

EVANS, John Ebenezer, III. 120 NW 14TH AVE STE 300 97209 #040-02-1980 L1983 **AN IM** *020 †20,05 ‡

EVANS, William Byrd. 501 N GRAHAM ST STE 465, NORTHWEST GASTROENTEROLOGY 97227 #051-04-1961 L1966 **GE IM** *071

EVANS-SMITH, Mari Kay. 2525 NW LOVEJOY ST, STE 200 97210 #005-12-1989 L1992 **PD** *020 †55

EVENS, Timothy Earl. 19500 SE STARK ST 97233 #005-12-1973 L1975 **EM GS** *020

EVERED, John Ohara. ■ 97202 #021-01-1996 L1999 **NPM** *012 †55

EVERS, Kathryn S Hussey. 3715 N INTERSTATE AVE, OVERLOOK BLDG 97227 #023-01-1969 L1973 **P** *030

EVERSON, Teresa Ann. 3181 SW SAM JACKSON PRK RD, RD DE 97239 #038-43-2005 L2005 **FP** *012

EVERTS, Edwin Curtiss. 2241 LLOYD CTR 97232 #040-02-1962 L1965 **HNS OTO** *040 †45

EWING, Dawn Dillman. 3181 SW SAM JACKSON PRK RD, MAIL CODE UHS2 97239 #018-03-1998 L2003 **AN** *020 †05

FABER, Holly Ilena. 19500 SE STARK ST 97233 #035-47-2002 L2006 **MPD** *020 †20,55

FABRICANT, Loic James. ■ 97239 #040-02-2008 L2008 *012

FAGNAN, Lyle James. 3181 SW SAM JACKSON PRK RD, OHSU MAILCODE L222 97239 #040-02-1971 L1977 **FM** *050 †18

FAHRBACH, Thomas Richard. 10000 SE MAIN ST, STE 205 97216 #005-12-1988 L1994 **FM** *020 †18

FAIGEL, Douglas Arrick. 3181 SW SAM JACKSON PRK RD 97239 #041-01-1990 L1996 **GE IM** *020 †20

FAIRBANKS, Stacy Lynn. 2800 N VANCOUVER AVE STE 2, LEGACY CLINIC EHHC 97227 #040-02-2007 L2007 **IM** *012

FAIRLEY, Nora Lou. 10373 NE HANCOCK ST # 115 97220 #040-02-1970 L1974 **P** *020 †75 ‡

FAKLER, Cathy Rae. 501 N GRAHAM ST 97227 #056-06-1992 L2001 **NPM** *020 †55

FALARDEAU, Julie. 3303 SW BOND AVE, FL 11 97239 #067-02-1996 L2004 *020 †35

FALK, Neil A. 2415 SE 43RD AVE STE 100 97206 #025-01-1992 L1993 **P** *020 †75

FAN, Guang. 3181 SW SAM JACKSON PRK RD 97239 #243-47-1986 L2001 **HMP** *020 †50

FAN, Jessie. 120 NW 14TH AVE, STE 300 97209 #033-06-1999 L2007 **AN** *020 †05

FARKAS, Peter. ■ 97210 #036-01-2003 L2003 **IM** *100 †20

FARMER, Bruce Arthur. 3557 SE HAWTHORNE BLVD 97214 #040-02-1983 L1984 **GS** *020

FAROGHI, Arman. 2801 N GANTENBEIN AVE, LEGACY EMANUEL HOSPITAL HE 97227 #005-11-1994 L1996 **EM** *020 †16

FARR, John George. ■ 97239 #040-02-2008 *012

FARR, William F. 3303 SW BOND AVE, FL 11 97239 #040-02-1960 L1963 **OPH** *020 †35 ‡

FARRELL, Lori Joan. 300 N GRAHAM ST STE 200 97227 #040-02-1999 L1999 **IM** *020 †20

FARRIS, Clyde Alan. 10101 SE MAIN, STE 1012 97216 #005-11-1973 L1978 **ORS** *020 †40

FARRIS, Kendra H. ■ 97239 #016-06-1982 L1986 **PD** *020 †55

FARRIS, R David. 2801 N GANTENBEIN AVE 97227 #005-18-1981 L1986 **AN OS** *020 †05 ‡

FAUSEL, Craig Stephen. 1111 NE 99TH AVE 97220 #035-15-1976 L1984 **GE IM** *020 †20

FAUSEL, Rebecca Ann. ■ 97221 #010-01-2008 *012

FAWCETT, Kate Ayers. ■ 97210 #035-03-2007 L2007 **OBG** *012

FAZELI, Flora. 2801 N GANTENBEIN AVE, LEGACY EMANUEL HOSPITAL 97227 #165-01-1990 L2003 **IM** *020

FEARL, James Douglas. 5415 SW WESTGATE DR 97221 #040-02-1965 L1970 **OBG** *020 †30

FEDOR, Preston Joseph. ■ 97206 #040-02-2008 *012

FELDMAN, Kenneth Don. 501 N GRAHAM ST STE 580 97227 #005-02-1971 L1985 **GS PTH** *020 †50,85

FELLMAN, Kelley Susanne. 3181 SW SAM JCKSN PRK RD R, MAIL CODE: DC7P 97239 #048-14-2001 L2001 **P** *020 †75

FELT, Jessica Lynn. ■ 97213 #035-45-2007 L2007 **TY** *012

FENNERTY, Michael Brian. 3181 SW SAM JACKSON PRK RD, PARK RD 97239 #030-06-1980 L1994 **GE IM** *020 †20

FENTON, Lynn Ann. 3181 SW SAM JACKSON PRK RD, UH 2 97239 #040-02-1992 L1997 **AN** *040 †05

FERGUSON, Edward C. ■ 97239 #056-06-1951 L1952 **GS OS** *020

FERGUSON, Felicia A. 3181 SW SAM JCKSN PRK RD R, CDW-3 97239 #054-04-1995 L2001 **CN** *100 †18,75

FERGUSON, James Wm. 18750 SE STARK ST 97233 #031-01-1981 L1982 **IM GP** *020

FERGUSON, Roger Kent. ■ 97249 #049-01-1966 L1967 **IM PA** *071 †20

FERRE, Barbara K. 1130 NW 22ND AVE STE 320 97210 #016-11-1980 L1981 **PD** *020 †55

FERRELL, Cynthia Lynn. 707 SW GAINES ST, STE CDRCP 97239 #031-01-1992 L1993 **PD** *040 †55

FERROGGIARO, Anthony A. ■ 97212 #041-14-1993 L1999 **EM** *020 †16

FEUQUAY, Derek Matthew. ■ 97213 #003-01-2006 L2006 **IM** *012

FEUQUAY, Kathryn. ■ 97239 #003-01-2006 L2006 **FP** *012

FIELDS, Scott Allen. 3303 SW BOND AVE 97239 #054-04-1986 L1987 **FM** *040 †18 ‡

FILES, Matthew Dalton. ■ 97206 #027-01-2007 L2007 **PD** *012

FILLMORE, David John. 545 NE 47TH AVE, STE 215 97213 #008-01-1984 L2001 **DR VIR** *020 †80

FINCH, Gregory Dale. 3101 SW SAM JCKSN PRK R, SHRINERS HOSPITAL 97239 #671-02-1992 L2001 *100

FINES, Mary Lenore. 3710 SW US VETRNS HSPTL RD 97239 #040-01-1976 L1990 **IM** *020 †20

FINK, Sharon Marie. 1321 NE 99TH AVE, STE 100 97220 #026-04-1995 L1997 **FPG** *020 †20

FINKLE, Eugene Donald. ■ 97212 #005-02-1944 L1945 **GYN GP** *071 †30

FINLEY, Jennifer Horowitz. 2801 N GANTENBEIN AVE 97227 #012-05-1992 L1997 **AN** *020 †05 ‡

FINNEGAN, Colleen Amanda. 1130 NW 22ND AVE, STE 220 97210 #024-07-1999 L2000 **IM** *020 †20

FIREMAN, Marian. 3710 SW VETERANS HOSPTL RD, PORTLAND VA MEDICAL CENTER 97239 #050-02-1982 L1984 **P ADP** *020 †75

FIRTH, Thomas Alan. 5050 NE HOYT ST STE 235 97213 #422-01-1982 L1987 **IM** *020 †20

FISHER, Alan Murray. 10000 SE MAIN ST, STE 309 97216 #038-40-1970 L1991 **OBG** *020 †30

FISHER, Nancy Ann. 120 NW 14TH AVE, STE 300 97209 #051-01-1978 L1984 **AN CCM** *020 †05 ‡

FISHER, Pamela Ann. 707 SW GAINES ST, OHSU CDRCP 97239 #040-02-1986 L1987 **PD D** *020 †55

FISHER, Peter B. 5314 NE IRVING ST 97213 #035-48-1976 L1977 **NEP IM** *020

FISHER, Thomas E. 3181 SW SAM JACKSON PRK RD 97239 #028-78-2007, ▲ L2007 **OBG** *012

FITCH, Handly F. 510 NE 49TH AVE # 620 97213 #040-02-1951 **ORS** *071 †40

FITCHEN, John Hardy. ■ 97202 #035-45-1971 L1976 **HEM ON** *050 †20

FITZGERALD, Patrick Lee. 2701 NW VAUGHN ST, STE 140 97210 #051-04-1980 L1981 **IMG IM** *020 †20

FIX, Arthur Howard. 18750 SE STARK ST 97233 #038-41-1956 L1959 **GP** *071

FLAMING, Michael Boyd. 5050 NE HOYT ST, STE 655 97213 #040-02-1982 L1989 **OTO HNS** *020 †45

FLATH, Thomas Oakley. 5050 NE HOYT ST, STE 359 97213 #018-03-1973 L1974 **OBG** *020 †30

FLAXEL, Christina Joy. 3303 SW BOND AVE, FL 11 97239 #040-02-1989 L1989 **OPH** *020 †35

FLEGEL, Kathryn Jane. 3181 SW SAM JACKSON PRK RD, OHSU DEPT OF PSYCHIATRY 97239 #031-01-1981 L1983 **CHP P** *020 †75

FLEISCH, Juergen Marcus. 3181 SW SAM JCKSN PRK RD R, OHSU 97239 #409-19-1996 L2005 *100

FLEISCHMAN, Angela G. ■ 97239 #005-11-2005 L2005 **HO** *012

FLEMING, William H. 3181 SW SAM JACKSON PRK RD, UHN73C 97239 #062-01-1987 L1997 **ON** *020 †20

FLEMMING, Jeffrey Edward. 5050 NE HOYT ST, STE 660 97213 #040-02-1983 L1984 **ORS OSS** *020 †40

FLESERIU, Maria. 3181 SW SAM JCKSN PRK RD R, BTE 472 97239 #781-04-1993 L2006 **END IM** *100 †20

FLICK, Bonnie J. 3001 N GANTENBEIN AVE, LEGACY EMANUEL-CHILD/ADOLE 97227 #048-13-1988 L2006 **CHP PD** *020 †75

FLORA, Kenneth Donald. 1111 NE 99TH AVE 97220 #040-02-1988 L1989 **GE** *020 †20

FLOREK, Robt Constantine. 1040 NW 22ND AVE STE 660 97210 #026-04-1977 L1991 **ICE CD** *020 †20

FLYNN, Jessica Mary. 3181 SW SAM JCKSN PRK RD R, MAIL CODE FM 97239 #025-01-2003 L2003 **FM** *100 †18

FLYNN, Thomas Francis. 5050 NE HOYT ST STE 422 97213 #031-01-1989 L1990 **P** *020 †75

FLYTHE, Jennifer Elizabet. ■ 97213 #036-01-2006 L2006 **IM** *012

FO, Crystal Gay Seu Lin. ■ 97239 #014-01-2007 L2007 **N** *012

FOEGE, Robert Christian. 2801 N GANTENBEIN AVE, LEGACY 97227 #054-04-2005 L2005 **AN** *012

FOG, Joseph Richard. ■ 97209 #038-06-1980 L1982 **AN** *020

FOGEL, Gerald Irving. 2250 NW FLANDERS ST STE 30 97210 #025-01-1962 L1996 **PYA P** *020 †75

FOLEY, Marni. 800 SW 13TH AVE 97205 #056-06-1996 L1999 **IM** *020 †20

FOLEY, Matthew Ian. 501 N GRAHAM ST STE 415, LEGACY COLUMBIA VASCULAR 97227 #056-06-1995 L1998 **VS** *020 †85

FORD, Michaeline Marie. 97227 #050-02-2005 L2005 **PD** *012

FORD, Peter S. ■ 97220 #040-02-1951 L1952 **FM** *071 †18

FORD, Randall S. 120 NW 14TH AVE, STE 300 97209 #040-02-1988 L1989 **AN** *020 †05 ‡

FORREST, Steven Bruce. 500 NE MULTNOMAH ST STE 10 97232 #035-45-1980 L1984 **AN** *020 †05

FORTSCH, Byron Lynne. 500 NE MULTNOMAH ST STE 10 97232 #040-02-1957 L1960 **OTO** *071 †45

FOSS, Craig William. 10000 SE MAIN ST, STE 205 97216 #054-04-1987 L1995 **IM ID** *020 †20

FOSS, Erik William. 10123 SE MARKET ST 97216 #001-02-2000 L2006 **DR** *100 †80

FOSTER, Thomas Vernon, Jr. ■ 97210 #012-01-1973 L1976 **P MDM** *030 †75

FOSTER, Walter Theodore. 1130 NW 22ND AVE STE 120 97210 #047-06-1968 L1973 **OBG** *071

FOWLER, Laura Marie. ■ 97239 #040-02-2008 *012

FRANCIS, Peter James. 3303 SW BOND AVE, FL 11 97239 #917-14-1992 L2007 *100

FRANK, Andrew Dorson. 3550 N INTERSTATE AVE, KAISER PERMANENTE 97227 #035-46-1983 L1989 **IM** *020

FRANK, Brian Elliot. ■ 97239 #040-02-2008 *012

FRANK, Edmund Halbert. 2241 LLOYD CTR 97232 #038-41-1978 L1984 **NS** *020

FRANKEL, Herman Morris. 9045 SW BARBUR BLVD 97219 #035-01-1962 L1968 **GPM PD** *020 †55

FRANKS, Lawrence Jos. 10000 SE MAIN ST STE 305 97216 #016-06-1969 L1975 **NS** *071 †25

FRANZ, Michael Andrew. ■ 97215 #017-20-1999 L2000 **CHP** *020 †75

FRANZINI, Daisy Aparecida. 1015 NW 22ND AVE, GSH DEPT OF PATHOLOGY T100 97210 #187-55-1975 L1991 **PTH PCP** *020 †50

FRAUNFELDER, Frederick W. 3303 SW BOND AVE, FL 11 97239 #040-02-1994 L1996 **OPH** *020 †35

FRAUNFELDER, Fredrick T. 3303 SW BOND AVE, FL 11 97239 #040-02-1960 L1962 **OPH** *030 †35

FREED, Gregory Allen. 1220 SW 3RD AVE STE 1173 97204 #030-05-1978 L2006 **EM OM** *020 †18

FREED, Marcia. 2250 NW FLANDERS ST STE 30 97210 #036-07-1973 L1977 **P CHP** *020 †75

FREEMAN, Dwight Warren. 2800 N VANCOUVER AVE, STE 130 97227 #016-11-1955 L1977 **ORS** *071 †40

FREEMAN, Judith Anne. 3181 SW SAM JACKSON PRK RD, UH 2 97239 #917-01-1970 L1998 **AN** *020 †05

FREID, Jakob Forrest. ■ 97219 #030-06-2006 L2006 **EM** *012

FREIERMUTH, Leo J. 4805 NE GLISAN ST 97213 #040-02-1954 L1960 **IM GE** *071

FREITAG, Corona Maria. ■ 97219 #031-01-2001 L2001 **IM** *020

FRENCH, Loren Keith. ■ 97202 #040-02-2006 L2006 **EM** *012

FREW, Patricia Marie. ■ 97211 #040-02-2008 *012

FRIDGE, Jacqueline Louise. 300 N GRAHAM ST, STE 420 97227 #917-13-1987 L2007 **PG** *020 †55

FRIEDMAN, Eric Ian. 5050 NE HOYT ST STE 317 97213 #041-12-1983 L1984 **GS SO** *020 †85

FRIEDMAN, Raymond F. 3181 SW SAM JACKSON PRK RD, KVP-7M 97239 #040-02-1957 L1959 **DR PDR** *020 †20

FRIEDMAN, Scott Andrew. 3181 SW SAM JACKSON PRK RD, UHN 80 97239 #038-40-2004 L2004 **P** *012

FRIEDMAN, Steven Alan. 500 NE MULTNOMAH ST # 100, NORTHWEST PERMANENTE 97232 #041-01-1985 L1996 **OBG** *020 †30

FRIEND, Sean Michael. 5635 NE ALAMEDA ST, THE ROSE CITY CLINIC 97213 #041-12-1994 L1996 **IM** *020 †20

FRIESS, Darin Morgan. 3181 SW SAM JCKSN PRK RD R, M/C: RE-OP31 97239 #021-01-1999 L2006 **ORS** *020

FRISCH, David Chas. 511 SW 10TH AVE, STE 1006 97205 #026-04-1942 L1952 **D** *072 †15

FRISTOE, Frank H. ■ 97219 #028-03-1966 L1971 **PTH** *020 †50

FROME, Britton Anne. 501 N GRAHAM ST, STE 250 97227 #041-15-1999 L2000 **HS** *020 †40

FROMME, Erik Karl. 2241 LLOYD CTR 97232 #039-01-1994 L1996 **IM PLM** *050 †20

FROST, Deborah Love. 4805 NE GLISAN ST, SUITE BG 05 97213 #054-04-2003 L2003 **IM** *020 †20

FROST, Megan Marie. ■ 97239 #019-02-2006 L2006 **GS** *012

FRUEHLING, Carolyn Ann. 611 SW CAMPUS DR, M/C: SD176 97239 #018-03-1976 L1976 **PD** *020 †55

■ = Address Information Privacy Protected

FUCHS, Eugene Frederick. 3303 SW BOND AVE, FL 10 97239 #050-02-1970 L1972 **U** *040 †95

FULSHER, Remy W. 10101 SE MAIN ST, STE 2011 97216 #038-40-1950 L1954 **OBG** *071 †30

FUNG, Alice W. ■ 97219 #048-13-2001 L2007 **DR** *100 †80

FUNK, Nathan Daryl. ■ 97239 #018-03-2007 L2007 **IM** *012

FURNARY, Anthony Paul. 2241 LLOYD CTR 97232 #041-02-1984 L1992 **TS CD** *020 †85,90

FUROY, Daniel Justin. ■ 97209 #014-01-2007 L2007 **TY** *012

FURR, Maxwell Charles. ■ 97201 #041-02-2006 L2006 **OTO** *012

FUSS, Martin Hanns Ferdin. 3181 SW SAM JACKSON PRK RD, L3 97239 #409-10-1994 L2006 *100

GABOR, Ferenc. 500 NE MULTNOMAH ST STE 10 97232 #473-03-1954 L1961 **U** *071 †95

GAIL, Anna Snajdr. ■ 97205 #008-01-1969 L1970 **DR** *071 †80

GAIL, Thomas A. ■ 97217 #040-02-1962 L1963 **FM D** *071 †18

GAINES, Jeffrey Thomas. 10000 SE MAIN ST, STE 214 97203 #025-01-2001 L2006 **EM** *020 †16

GAJEWSKI, James Leonard. 3181 SW SAM JCKSN PRK RD R, U MAILCODE L586 97239 #041-13-1983 L1985 **HEM ON** *020 †20

GALEN, Edward Alan. 1130 NW 22ND AVE, NORTHWEST 97210 #040-02-1975 L1976 **GE IM** *020 †20

GALEY, William Ted. PO BOX 1034, VET ADMIN MED CTR 97207 #040-02-1976 L1977 **OS PTH** *030 †50

GALIC, Vijaya. 3181 SW SAM JACKSON PRK RD, PARK RD 97239 #054-04-2004 L2006 **OBG** *012

GALLISON, Claudia Jean. 120 NW 14TH AVE, STE 300 97209 #038-45-1984 L1986 **AN** *020 †05 ‡

GANCHER, Stephen Theo. 3550 N INTERSTATE AVE, EAST INTERSTATE - NEUROLOG 97227 #036-05-1980 L1982 **N** *040 †75

GANDLER, Howard I. 2311 NW NORTHRUP ST, STE 207 97210 #048-12-1982 L1992 **RHU IM** *020 †20

GANZINI, Linda Kay. 3710 SW US VETRNS HSPTL RD, MC:R&D66 97239 #040-02-1983 L1984 **PYG P** *020 †75

GARDINER, Sara Kathryn. 1318 NW 20TH AVE, STE A 97209 #005-02-1997 L2005 **P** *020 †75

GARDNER, David Puryear. 2525 NW LOVEJOY ST 97210 #047-06-1975 L1978 **N** *071 †75

GARG, Anuj. 1200 NW 23RD AVE, LEGACY CLINIC GOOD SAMARIT 97210 #495-44-2000 L2003 **IM** *020 †20

GARLID, Keith David. ■ 97210 #023-07-1961 **OS** *050

GARLINGER, Mary Patricia. 0236 SW RIDGE DR, C/O DONALD MCCONNELL 97219 #035-45-1967 L1972 **OS PD** *020 †55

GARNER, Bennett Weil. 1020 SW TAYLOR ST STE 685 97205 #016-43-1977 L1999 **CHP P** *020 †75

GARNJOBST, William Martin. 510 NE 49TH AVE 97213 #040-02-1945 **CRS GS** *071 †85,10

GARRETT, Lara Young. 4531 SE BELMONT ST, STE 250 97215 #040-02-2000 L2001 **IM** *020 †20

GARRISON, Henry Byron. ■ 97212 #024-01-1968 L1974 **CD** *071 †20

GARTNER, Katharine Mary. 120 NW 14TH AVE, #300 OREGON ANESTH GRP PC 97209 #010-01-1968 L1970 **AN PUD** *020 †05

GARVEY, Deborah Loomis. 5319 SW WESTGATE DR, STE 241 97221 #014-01-1988 L1989 **AN** *020 †05

GARVEY, Scott Anthony. 1111 NE 99TH AVE 97220 #040-02-1985 L1992 **CD IM** *020 †20

GARVIN, Roger Doyle. 4411 SW VERMONT ST 97219 #040-02-1985 L2007 **FM** *040 †18

GARZOTTO, Mark Greg. 3181 SW SAM JACKSON PRK RD, STE L588 97239 #021-05-1990 L2000 **U** *020 †95

GASKELL, Karen Elizabeth. 10101 SE MAIN ST, STE 3001 97216 #005-12-1974 L1997 **OPH** *020

GASTON, Patrick James. 3181 SW SAM JACKSON PRK RD, RD IN 97239 #021-01-2005 L2005 **IM** *012

GATTER, Ken Marcus. 2241 LLOYD CTR 97232 #030-05-1995 L1998 **PTH** *020 †50

GATTEY, Devin M. 3303 SW BOND AVE, FL 11 97239 #005-19-1995 L1999 **OPH** *020 †35

GAUDINO, James A, Jr. 800 NE OREGON ST STE 370, FAM HEALTH IMMUN PROG 97232 #005-19-1985 L2004 **PHP GPM** *050 †70

GAUGER, John Wm. 1437 SW COLUMBIA ST, STE 200 97201 #018-03-1939 L1940 **AN GP** *071

GAUMOND, Ethan William. 120 NW 14TH AVE, STE 300 97209 #010-02-2000 L2001 **AN** *020 †05 ‡

GAVAGAN, Justine Arden. 5050 NE HOYT ST STE 511 97213 #056-05-1999 L1999 **GS** *020 †85

GAVLICK, Milton J, Jr. 1750 NW NAITO PKWY, STE 100B 97209 #043-01-1982 L1984 **IM** *020 †20,70

GAY, Richard Gene, Jr. 1040 NW 22ND AVE, STE 660 97210 #019-02-1978 L1979 **CD IM** *020 †20

GE, Shugang. 10000 SE MAIN ST, STE 207 97216 #243-32-1986 L2005 **IM** *020 †20

GEARHART, Mark Ross. 3267 SE HAWTHORNE BLVD 97214 #040-02-1979 L1982 **EM GP** *020 †16

GEDENK, Monique. 4920 N INTERSTATE AVE 97217 #035-48-1993 L1996 **FM** *020 †18

GEE, Arvin. 3181 SW SAM JCKSN PRK RD R, M/S: MC-L223A 97239 #016-11-2003 L2003 **CCS** *012

GEELAN, Kim Marie. 120 NW 14TH AVE, STE 300 97209 #040-02-1990 L1991 **AN** *020 †05 ‡

GEHEB, Michael Albert. 3181 SW SAM JACKSON PRK RD, OR HLTH SCI U # CR9-6 97239 #025-07-1973 L2000 **CCM IM** *030 †20

GEHRING, Brian Jos. 3500 N INTERSTATE AVE, KAISER PERMANETE INTERSTAT 97227 #040-02-1983 L1984 **DR** *020 †80

GEISSAL, Erik Dorn. ■ 97212 #024-07-2006 L2006 **IM** *012

GEIST, Howard James. ■ 97221 #024-01-1955 L1965 **ORS** *071 †40

GEISTWHITE, Robert Lynn. 2330 NW FLANDERS ST, STE 105 97210 #017-20-1996 L2000 **P** *020 †75

GELB, Michael Ethan. 1318 NW 20TH AVE, STE A 97209 #035-47-1998 L2006 **P** *020 †75

GELLER, Pamela Edith. 2525 NW LOVEJOY ST, CASCADE PHYSICIANS PC 97210 #026-04-1975 L1982 **PD** *020 †20

GELLMAN, Richard Evan. 501 N GRAHAM ST STE 250, SUMMIT ORTHOPAEDICS 97201 #008-01-1991 L2001 **ORS** *020 †40

GELOW, Jill Michelle. ■ 97209 #040-02-2004 L2007 **CD** *012 †20

GEORGE, Margaret Ann. 1015 NW 22ND AVE, LEGACY GOOD SAMARITAN HOSP 97210 #048-02-2002 L2003 **IMG** *100 †20

GERBIC, Elizabeth Paige. ■ 97202 #040-02-2005 L2006 **AN** *012

GERHARD, Glenn Thos. 3181 SW SAM JCKSN PRK RD R, DEPARTMENT OF MEDICINE, L4 97239 #016-11-1982 L1988 **NTR GP** *020 †20

GERTZ, Ryan James. ■ 97219 #005-06-2008 L2007 **IM** *012

GESCHKE, Wilfred Arthur. 10101 SE MAIN ST, STE 1012 97216 #005-12-1966 L1975 **HEM ON** *020 †20

GESTELAND, Katherine Mary. 3181 SW SAM JCKSN PRK RD R 97239 #049-01-2001 L2005 **OBG** *040

GEVURTZ, John Milton. 1015 NW 22ND AVE 97210 #040-02-1962 L1967 **PD HEM** *071

GHANDOUR, Jihad Ibrahim. ■ 97221 #605-01-1995 L1996 **IM** *020 †20

GHASSEMI, Sahar. ■ 97205 #006-01-2001 L2008 **GE** *020

GHAZNAVI, Shuja. 2244 LLOYD CTR 97232 #704-01-1961 L1972 **CD IM** *071

GHITEA, Oliver. 2801 N GANTENBEIN AVE 97227 #005-12-1995 L1999 **AN** *020 †05 ‡

GIANELLI, Thomas Jos. ■ 97201 #040-02-1948 L1949 **GS GP** *071 †85

GIANNOTTI, Andrew G. 120 NW 14TH AVE STE 300, OREGON ANESTHESIOLOGY GROU 97209 #048-14-1998 L2002 **AN** *020 †05 ‡

GIBBENS, Janet Lee. 5050 NE HOYT ST, STE 421 97213 #040-02-1983 L1987 **OBG** *020 †30

GIBBS, Daniel Marion. 1040 NW 22ND AVE, STE 420 97210 #012-05-1980 L1986 **N** *020 †75

GIBSON, Jennifer Margaret. 1200 NW 23RD AVE 97210 #035-03-2000 L2000 **IM** *100 †20

GIBSON, Jeremy Leighton. ■ 97239 #040-02-2008 *012

GIBSON, Sylvia. 4805 NE GLISAN ST BH16, PROVIDENCE PORTLAND MED CT 97213 #056-06-1997 L1999 **IM** *020 †20

GICKING, Richard Crooks. 2801 N GANTENBEIN AVE, DEPT OF MEDICINE 97227 #010-01-1992 L1993 **HOS AMI** *020 †20

GIDEONSE, Nicholas L. 3930 SE DIVISION ST 97202 #038-06-1991 L1992 **FM OBS** *020 †18

GIEDWOYN-MIZGAJSKA, A A. 1880 SW 6TH AVE, PSU STUDENT CTR - HLTH & C 97201 #759-04-1998 L2004 **FM** *020 †18

GIESY, Jerry Donald. 501 N GRAHAM ST, UROLOGY CLINIC PC 97227 #040-02-1959 L1960 **U** *020 †95

GILBAUGH, James H, Jr. 3181 SW SAM JACKSON PRK RD, MAIL CODE L 588 97239 #040-02-1963 L1966 **U** *071 †95

GILBERT, David Norman. 5050 NE HOYT ST, INFECTION CONSULTANTS LLP 97213 #040-02-1964 L1967 **ID IM** *040 †20

GILBERT, James Leo. 47 SW BANCROFT ST 97239 #012-01-2003 L2003 **IM** *100 †20

GILBERT, Jon Saxon. ■ 97239 #032-01-2000 L2005 **AN** *012

GILBERT, Judy Langdon. 2801 N GANTENBEIN AVE 97227 #040-02-1979 L1981 **FM OBS** *020 †18

GILBERTSON, Jessica L. 3181 SW SAM JCKSN PRK RD R, M/S DC7P 97239 #036-01-1994 L2002 **CHP** *020 †20

GILDEN, Daniel Jos. 2801 N GANTENBEIN AVE, STE 4100 97227 #028-03-1985 L1989 **IM** *020 †20

GILES, Donald Everett. 10000 SE MAIN ST, STE 408 97216 #005-12-1974 L1980 **GS VS** *020 †85

GILHOOLY, Joseph Thos. 707 SW GAINES ST, MC - CDRCP 97239 #014-01-1980 L1981 **PD NPM** *020 †55

GILKEY, Gawain Mitchell. ■ 97213 #017-20-2000 L2000 **PCC** *020 †20

GILLCRIST, Amy Katherine. 545 NE 47TH AVE, STE 106 97213 #040-02-1996 L1999 **IM** *020 †20

GILMARTIN, Lori Ann. 4212 NE BROADWAY ST, PHYSICIANS AND SURGEONS 97213 #010-02-1991 L1992 **PD** *020 †55

GINGRICH, Richard Allen. 10000 SE MAIN ST, STE 309 97216 #005-12-1956 L1957 **GS** *071 †85

GINOCCHIO, Christopher J. 501 N GRAHAM ST, STE 515 97227 #005-18-1992 L1993 **N** *020 †75

GIPSON, Teresa Frances. 3181 SW SAM JACKSON PRK RD 97239 #010-02-1994 L1996 **FM** *020 †18

GIRARD, Donald Edward. 3181 SW SAM JCKSN PRK RD R, OREGON HEALTH & SCIENCE UN 97239 #048-04-1969 L1975 **IM** *040 †20

GIRAUD, George David. 2241 LLOYD CTR 97232 #060-02-1982 L1985 **CD** *020 †20

GIRAUDIER, Maurice E J. 3500 N INTERSTATE AVE, INTERSTATE AMBULATORY SURG 97227 #068-01-1967 L1979 **DR OS** *020 †80

GLASS, Andrew Geo. 3600 N INTERSTATE AVE 97227 #041-01-1965 L1970 **OS PD** *020 †55

GLASS, Laurel Ellen. 0324 SW ABERNATHY ST 97239 #005-02-1974 L1976 **OS P** *030

GLASSER, Debra L. 5909 SE DIVISION ST 97206 #024-16-1980 L1981 **IM** *072 †20

GLENN, Char. 2222 NW LOVEJOY ST, STE 422 97210 #040-02-1995 L1996 **IM** *020 †20

GLOEKLER, Eberhard. 3414 N. KAISER CTR DR 97227 #407-19-1956 L1964 **IM N** *071

GMELCH, Benjamin Scott. 2801 N GANTENBEIN AVE 97227 #040-02-2004 L2004 **AN** *012

GOBBO, Robert William. 4104 SE 82ND AVE, STE 250 97266 #005-14-1984 L1989 **FM** *020 †18

GODARD, Sally Lynn. 3181 SW SAM JCKSN PRK #P 97239 #040-02-1981 L1983 **CHP** *020 †75

GODBEY, Joel Stephen. 3550 N INTERSTATE AVE, IMMUNE DEFICIENCY CLINIC 97227 #858-03-1985 L1988 **IM** *020 †20

GOEBEL, Melissa Marie. 831 N WATTS ST 97217 #033-05-2003 L2006 **IM** *100 †20

GOEKE, James Eldon. 120 NW 14TH AVE, STE 300 97209 #026-04-1985 L1998 **AN IM** *020 †20,05 ‡

GOETSCH, Martha Frances. 3181 SW SAM JACKSON PRK RD, RD UHN 97239 #036-01-1974 L1976 **OBG** *020 †18

GOH, Kai-Oon. 1040 NW 22ND AVE, DEVERS EYE INSTITUTE 97210 #143-06-1993 L2001 *100

GOKHALE, Dalika D. 3550 N INTERSTATE AVE, DEPT OF OB/GYN 97227 #005-14-1987 L1997 **OBG** *020 †30

GOLD, Jeffrey Allen. 3181 SW SAM JCKSN PRK RD R, M/C UHN-67 97239 #035-19-1995 L2005 **PCC IM** *050 †20

GOLD, Robert David. 5050 NE HOYT ST STE 422 97213 #024-05-1976 L1997 **P** *020 †16,75

GOLDBERG, Charles Barry. 8332 SE 13TH AVE 97202 #016-11-1973 L1978 **FM AI** *072 ‡

GOLDBERG, Kenneth Chas. 407 NE 12TH AVE, STE 200 97232 #025-07-1988 L1989 **PHP** *020

GOLDBERG, Leonard Marvin. 501 N GRAHAM ST, STE 400 97227 #040-02-1955 L1957 **CD IM** *020 †20

GOLDBERG, Linn. 2241 LLOYD CTR 97232 #010-01-1975 L1977 **IM** *050 †20

GOLDBERG, Marshall Colman. 18750 SE STARK ST 97233 #023-01-1966 L1973 **IM GPM** *020 †70

GOLDBERGER, David B. 12770 SE STARK ST 97233 #038-44-1998 L1999 **IM** *020 †20

GOLDEN, Eve Ruth. 2800 N VANCOUVER AVE, STE 165 97227 #041-01-1996 L2007 **PHO** *020 †55

GOLDENBERG, Daniela Celia. 1130 NW 22ND AVE, STE 220 97210 #781-02-1995 L2001 **IM** *020 †20

GOLDFARB, Jaime. ■ 97215 #132-01-1955 L2008 **PD** *020 †55

GOLDMAN, David Wallace. ■ 97201 #040-02-1982 L1988 **FM** *075 †18

GOLDMAN, Jennifer Ann. ■ 97239 #040-02-2008 *012

GOLDMAN, Marvin C. 10000 SE MAIN ST 97216 #040-02-1950 L1958 **GE IM** *071 †20

GOLDMAN, Michael Jay. 1130 NW 22ND AVE 97210 #035-09-1972 L1977 **RO** *071 †80

GOLDMAN, Robert Kenneth. 3181 SW SAM JCKSN PRK RD R, MAIL CODE P3SURG 97239 #016-06-1990 L1991 **GS** *020 †85

GOLDOR, Cynthia Jane. 19500 SE STARK ST, KAISER PERMANENTE MEDICAL 97233 #005-15-1990 L2005 **OBG** *020 †30

GOLDRING, Maureen Burke. 2222 NW LOVEJOY ST STE 606 97210 #008-02-1976 L1997 **CD** *020 †20

GOLDSTEIN, Brahm N. 3181 SW SAM JCKSN PRK RD R, OREGON HEALTH SCIENCES 97239 #035-15-1981 L1994 **PD** *020 †55

GOLSHANI, Kiarash. ■ 97239 #040-02-2002 L2002 **NS** *012
GONZALEZ, Julio Andres. 3303 SW BOND AVE, COM PAIN CENTER-CH4P 97239 #231-02-1990 L2003 **APM** *020
GONZALEZ-VITALE, Juan C. 2801 N GANTENBEIN AVE 97227 #726-01-1971 L1989 **PTH PCP** *020 †50
GOODNIGHT, Scott H, Jr. 3181 SW SAM JACKSON PRK RD, DPT HEM 97239 #040-02-1964 L1968 **HEM IM** *040 †20
GOODREAU, Renee Nicole. 3181 SW SAM JCKSN PRK RD R, SCIENCE UNIV 97239 #025-01-2006 L2006 **OBG** *012
GOODSTEIN, George. 4540 NE GLISAN ST 97213 #054-04-1982 L1983 **IMG IM** *020 †20
GOODWIN, Katie Maureen. ■ 97209 #010-02-2006 L2006 **IM** *012
GOODWIN, Peter A. 3181 SW SAM JCKSN PRK RD R 97239 #836-02-1951 L1978 **FM** *040 †18
GOOGINS, John A. ■ 97221 #023-01-1950 L1965 **PHP** *071
GOPAL, Yasodha Rangulu. 2525 NW LOVEJOY ST, STE 200 97210 #010-01-1994 L2001 **PD** *020 †55
GORANSON, Eric Alastair. 3181 SW SAM JACKSON PRK RD, RD PATHO 97239 #040-02-2006 L2006 **PTH** *012
GORANSON, Eric Edwin. 1020 SW TAYLOR ST STE 640 97205 #010-01-1970 L1977 **P** *020 †18,75
GORDON, Geoffrey H. 3500 N INTERSTATE AVE 97227 #005-15-1976 L1984 **IM P** *040 †20
GORE, Randall Deaver. 5050 NE HOYT ST, STE 203 97213 #016-42-1971 L1972 **IM** *020 †20 ‡
GORMAN, Paul Northrop. 3181 SW SAM JCKSN PRK RD R, OREGON HEALTH & SCIENCE UN 97239 #016-01-1980 L1984 **IM IMG** *050 †20
GORNBEIN, Gordon Jeffrey. 120 NW 14TH AVE, STE 300 97209 #028-34-1980 L1982 **AN** *020 †05 ‡
GORONDY, Susan Collins. 1040 NW 22ND AVE, STE 330 97210 #041-02-1980 L2004 **OBG** *020 †30
GORRILL, Marsha Jan. 3303 SW BOND AVE, STE CH10F 97239 #011-02-1981 L1992 **OBG** *020 †30
GOSHORN, David Ross. ■ 97209 #045-04-2008 *012
GOSLIN, Kimberly Louise. 5050 NE HOYT ST, STE 315 97213 #051-01-1991 L1998 **N** *020 †75
GOSPODNETICH, Thomas Geo. 500 NE MULTNOMAH ST STE 10 97232 #040-02-1973 L1974 **EM** *020 †16
GOSS, Bennett Steven. 5050 NE HOYT ST, STE 540 97213 #550-02-2003 L2003 **EM** *012 †20
GOSSELIN, Marc V. 2241 LLOYD CTR 97232 #067-01-1991 L2001 **DR** *020 †80
GOURLEY, Brett Lee. ■ 97239 #040-02-2008 *012
GOURZIS, James Theophile. 1420 NW LOVEJOY ST APT 705 97209 #062-01-1963 L1964 **PA** *071
GRACE, Michael Patrick. ■ 97211 #018-03-2003 L2006 **FM** *100 †18
GRADY, Scott P. 1130 NW 22ND AVE 97210 #067-01-1996 L2002 **END** *020 †20
GRAFE, Marjorie Ruth. ■ 97221 #005-11-1985 L1999 **ATP NP** *050 †50
GRAFF, Julie Nicole. ■ 97202 #010-01-2003 L2003 **HO** *012 †20
GRAGNOLA, Thomas Glen. 2400 SW VERMONT ST, FANNO CREEK CLINIC LLC 97219 #010-02-1994 L1997 **IM** *040 †20
GRAHAM, Alan Scott. 707 SW GAINES ST, OHSU 97239 #005-18-1997 L2004 **CCP** *020 †55
GRAHAM, Brent Allen. 120 NW 14TH AVE, STE 300 97209 #035-09-1989 L1999 **AN** *020 †05 ‡
GRAHAM, Tanith Marlyn. 120 NW 14TH AVE, STE 300 97209 #027-01-1981 L1982 **AN** *020 †20,05 ‡
GRAHAM-SCHUFF, Kathryn E. 2241 LLOYD CTR 97232 #034-01-1991 L1992 **END** *020 †20
GRAMZA, Ann Wild. 3181 SW SAM JCKSN PRK RD R, L586 97239 #038-40-2000 L2004 **HO** *100 †20
GRANT, Elizabeth Ann. ■ 97239 #040-02-2008 *012
GRANT, Katrina Michelle. ■ 97206 #026-08-2006 L2006 **FP** *012
GRANT, Nancy Marie. 5050 NE HOYT ST, STE 421 97213 #056-06-1993 L1997 **OBG** *020 †30
GRASSI, Maurizio. 3181 SW SAM JACKSON PRK RD 97239 #561-17-1983 **PUD CD** *100
GRASSO-KNIGHT, Guido Sole. 3181 SW SAM JCKSN PRK RD R, OHSU 97239 #035-47-2007 L2007 **FP** *012
GRAUER, Susan Elaine. 2241 LLOYD CTR 97232 #038-41-1986 L1990 **CD IM** *020 †20
GRAVES, Rachel Sinex. 97214 #005-02-2005 L2005 **FP** *012
GRAY, Cynthia Ellis. 1318 NW 20TH AVE STE A 97209 #038-06-1991 L2005 **P PYA** *020 †75
GRAY, David Michael. ■ 97210 #035-06-2003 L2007 **HMP** *012 †50
GREEDER, Glenn Alan. 19500 SE STARK ST 97233 #016-11-1984 L1985 **IM** *020 †20
GREEN, Andrew Todd. ■ 97210 #654-01-2003 L2008 **GS** *012
GREEN, Edward Francis. 4037 NE TILLAMOOK ST 97212 #056-05-1979 L1983 **P** *020 †75
GREEN, Gerald Stanley. 1015 NW 22ND AVE DEPT R 97210 #005-02-1963 L1969 **R** *020 †80
GREEN, Rory Eric. 3550 N INTERSTATE AVE 97227 #041-12-1985 L1986 **P** *020 †75
GREEN, Sharon Sarah. ■ 97214 #040-02-2007 L2007 **PD** *012
GREENBERG, Craig Phillip. 10101 SE MAIN ST STE 3012 97216 #016-43-1980 L1988 **END IM** *020 †20
GREENBERG, Daniel Lee. ■ 97221 #016-42-1987 L2006 **HEM IM** *020 †20
GREENBERG, Gary Michael. 10201 SE MAIN ST STE 10, NORTHWEST CARDIOVASCULAR I 97216 #056-05-1985 L1986 **CD IM** *020 †20
GREENBERG, Lawrence M. ■ 97202 #026-04-1959 L1959 **CHP P** *050 †75
GREENE, June. 19500 SE STARK ST 97233 #040-02-1995 L2003 **IM** *020 †20
GREGG, Jessica Lampkin. 3181 SW SAM JCKSN PRK RD R, M/C: L475 97239 #034-01-1998 L1999 **IM** *020 †20
GREGORY, Cecilia Dolores. 1200 SW 20TH AVE 97205 #010-01-1966 L1968 **P ADM** *072 †75,70
GREGORY, Kenton Wayne. 1121 NE 2ND AVE 97232 #005-06-1980 L1991 **IC CD** *020 †20
GREGORY, William Thomas. 3181 SW SAM JCKSN PRK RD R 97239 #005-06-1994 L1997 **GYN** *050 †30
GREVE, John Jay. 2228 NW PETTYGROVE ST, STE 150 97210 #018-03-1962 L1967 **PUD IM** *071 †20
GREWE, Kathy. 300 N GRAHAM ST, STE 320 97227 #040-02-1983 L1990 **CD IM** *020 †20
GREWE, Ray Victor. 501 N GRAHAM ST, STE 545 97227 #040-02-1947 L1948 **NS** *071 †25
GREWE, Scott Roberts. 1 N CENTER COURT ST, ORTHOPEDICS NORTHWEST 97227 #040-02-1983 L1990 **ORS OSM** *012
GREWENOW, Ronald Doermann. 3710 SW US VETRNS HSPTL RD 97239 #040-02-1973 L1974 **IM** *020 †20
GRIERSON, Alfred James. ■ 97213 #040-02-1946 **FM** *071
GRIES, Heike. 3181 SW SAM JCKSN PRK RD R, OHSU - UHS2 97239 #409-33-1996 L2007 **PAN** *020
GRIEVE, Gary Allen. 200 SW MARKET ST STE L120 97201 #060-01-1975 L1991 **OPH** *020 †35
GRIFFEE, Matthew James. 3181 SW SAM JCKSN PRK RD R, M/S UHS-2 97239 #054-04-2001 L2004 **AN** *100
GRIFFIN, Christopher Boos. 6327 SW CAPITOL HWY, STE C # 106 97239 #040-02-1988 L1993 **DR** *020 †80

GRIFFIN, John Wm. 10101 SE MAIN ST STE 2001 97216 #005-12-1968 L1973 **RHU IM** *020 †20
GRIGSBY, John Wallace. 1015 NW 22ND AVE 97210 #048-02-1973 L1982 **EM** *030 †16
GRILLO, S Phillip. ■ 97219 #017-20-1940 L1941 **GS GP** *071
GRIMM, Nancy R. ■ 97239 #023-07-1956 L1965 **P CHP** *071 †75
GRIMM, Robert John. 2455 NW MARSHALL ST STE 14 97210 #025-01-1961 L1968 **N** *020 †75
GRIPEKOVEN, Price. 2565 NW LOVEJOY ST, OREGON ORTHOPEDIC CLINIC 97210 #035-20-1966 L1973 **ORS** *072 †40
GRISWOLD, Herbert E, Jr. 3181 SW SAM JACKSON PRK RD 97239 #040-02-1943 L1948 **CD IM** *050 †20
GRITZKA, Thomas Lehman. ■ 97202 #024-01-1963 L1972 **ORS OS** *062 †40
GROMLICH, Tiffany Drinaso. ■ 97239 #040-02-2007 L2007 **IM** *012
GROMPE, Markus. 3181 SW SAM JCKSN PRK RD R 97239 #409-41-1983 L1992 **OS PD** *020 †19,55
GROSE, Jared Dale. ■ 97239 #040-02-2008 *012
GROSS, Neil Dwayne. 3181 SW SAM JCKSN PRK RD R, M/C: PV01 97239 #040-02-1998 L1999 **OTO** *020 †45
GROSS, Robert John. 2386 NW HOYT ST 97210 #012-05-1966 L1978 **P OBG** *020 †30,75
GROSSENBACHER, Edward A. 2525 NW LOVEJOY ST, STE 400 97210 #040-02-1964 L1971 **ORS** *020 †40
GROSSMAN, Charles Milton. 610 SW ALDER ST, STE 500 97205 #035-19-1941 L1947 **IM** *020 †20
GROSZ, Anna Helen. ■ 97212 #041-01-2002 L2002 **OTO** *020
GROTH, Harry Edwin. 5050 NE HOYT ST, STE 660 97213 #056-05-1955 L1958 **ORS** *071 †40
GROVER, John Allen. 3500 N INTERSTATE AVE 97227 #026-04-1960 L1968 **CD IM** *071 †20
GROVER, Myron Roberts. OR HLTH SCI UNV DPT PSCYCH 97201 #035-20-1954 L1959 **IM OS** *071
GRUND, Steven Lee. 3181 SW SAM JCKSN PRK RD R, SCIENCE UNIV 97239 #031-01-2000 L2003 **PCC** *100 †20
GRUNER, Sam Evans. 2311 NW NORTHRUP ST, STE 202 97210 #041-01-1986 L1992 **DR** *020 †80
GUAPPONE, Kenneth Paul. 1631 NE BROADWAY ST, PMB 140 97232 #038-40-1981 L1982 **IM** *020 †20
GUBLER, Kelly Dean. 501 N GRAHAM ST STE 580 97227 #018-75-1981, ▲ L2001 **GS CCS** *020 †70,85
GUDMAN, Jonathan Todd. 120 NW 14TH AVE, STE 300 97209 #040-02-1981 L1985 **AN PME** *020 †05 ‡
GUERIN, Larry L. 545 NE 47TH AVE, STE 306 97213 #040-02-1983 L1984 **D** *020 †15
GUEVARA, John Chas. 120 NW 14TH AVE, STE 300 97209 #005-14-1987 L1995 **AN** *020 †05 ‡
GUGGENHEIM, Rainer Victor. ■ 97201 #035-09-1958 L1959 **OBG PHP** *071 †30
GUIDO, Annette Diane. 7705 SE DIVISION ST 97206 #008-01-1981 L1985 **IM** *020 †20
GUISE, Jeannemari Renee. 3181 SW SAM JCKSN PRK RD R 97239 #054-04-1992 L1998 **OBG EP** *050 †30
GUITTEAU, John Newton. 3108 NE 181ST AVE 97230 #040-02-1984 L1985 **EM** *020 †16
GUITTEAU, Michelle Suzann. 5050 NE HOYT ST STE 540 97213 #003-01-1994 L1996 **IM** *020 †20
GULTEKIN, Sakir H. ■ 97239 #902-05-1986 L2004 **NP N** *050 †50
GUNASEKARAN, Nilana S. 3550 N INTERSTATE AVE, KAISER - EAST INTERSTATE M 97227 #010-02-1998 L2004 **FM** *020 †18
GUPTA, Maneesh. 3181 SW SAM JACKSON PRK RD, OR HLTH SCI UNIV HOSP 97239 #496-43-2000 L2005 **IM** *012
GUPTA, Sanjeev. 3101 SW SAM JACKSON PRK RD, SHRINERS HOSPITAL 97239 #143-03-2000 L2006 **IM** *100
GUSTAFSON, Raymond Thos. ■ 97230 #056-05-1955 L1957 **GP** *071 †18
GUSTAVSSON, John Enar. 2311 NW NORTHRUP ST, RADIOLOGY CONSULTANTS INC 97210 #035-45-1993 L2003 **DR** *020 †80
GUYER, William D. 3710 SW US VETRNS HSPTL RD 97239 #040-02-1953 L1954 **ORS** *020 †40
GWINNELL, Esther Maria. 319 SW WASHINGTON ST #1015 97204 #054-04-1979 L1981 **P PFP** *020 †75
HAAS, Helmut. 3710 SW US VETRNS HSPTL RD 97239 #026-04-1958 L1975 **PUD IM** *071 †20
HABRICH, Diana Lynn. 3600 N INTERSTATE AVE 97227 #030-05-1986 L1987 **OPH** *020 †35
HACKENBRUCK, Mary Hanley. 1732 SE ASH ST 97214 #040-04-1968 L1975 **P OS** *071
HACKETT, Amy Schultz. 3181 SW SAM JACKSON PRK RD 97239 #040-02-2000 L2000 **NEP** *020 †20
HACKMANN, Hilary Rachael. ■ 97219 #016-42-2007 L2007 **PD** *012
HAFERBECKER, Dustin Richa. ■ 97239 #040-02-2007 L2007 **PD** *012
HAGAN, Dawn Carla. ■ 97239 #048-13-2002 L2002 **AN** *012
HAGEN, Arlene Debora. 2386 NW HOYT ST, HOYT STREET PSYCHIATRISTS 97210 #026-08-1989 L1995 **CHP** *020 †75
HAGEN, Chad Cameron. 3181 SW SAM JACKSON PRK RD, MAIL CODE: CR-139 97239 #054-04-2002 L2002 **P** *100 †75
HAGEN, Kerry Brent. 1955 NW NORTHRUP ST, EYE HEALTH NORTHWEST 97209 #005-12-1984 L1993 **OPH** *020 †35
HAGG, Daniel Stuart. 3181 SW SAM JACKSON PRK RD R, M/S UHN-67 97239 #048-12-2000 L2000 **PCC** *100 †20
HAHN, Charles Raymond. 2228 LLOYD CTR 97232 #039-01-1964 L1972 **D PS** *020 †15 ‡
HAHN, Kenneth Alan. ■ 97212 #041-14-2004 L2007 **EM** *100
HALE, David Richard. 500 NE MULTNOMAH ST STE 10 97232 #040-02-1967 L1970 **EM** *020
HALL, David Zachary. 10201 SE MAIN ST, STE 29 97216 #005-12-1998 L2006 **GPM** *020 †70
HALL, Michael Lee. 2801 N GANTENBEIN AVE, & HEAL 97207 #054-04-2007 L2007 **TY** *012
HALL, Stephen B. 3181 SW SAM JCKSN PRK RD R, RM 323/UHN67 97239 #040-02-1982 L1991 **PUD IM** *020 †20
HALLIN, Roger W. 2222 NW LOVEJOY ST STE 315, NORTHW SURGICAL ASSOC INC 97210 #067-01-1952 L1953 **VS TS** *071 †85
HALLSTROM, Jon Fjacob. ■ 97239 #040-02-2008 *012
HALMOS, Peter Steven. 10101 SE MAIN ST STE 205 97216 #030-06-1999 L1999 **IM** *020 †20
HALPERIN, Ruben Olivier. 5050 NE HOYT ST, STE 540 97213 #012-05-1993 L2005 **IM** *020 †20
HALPIN, Valerie Jo. 1040 NW 22ND AVE STE 500, OREGON WEIGHT LOSS SURGERY 97210 #028-02-1997 L2008 **GS OS** *020 †20
HALVERSON, Harold W. ■ 97215 #005-12-1949 L1949 **EM** *071
HALVORSON, Stephanie Ann. 3181 SW SAM JCKSN PRK RD R, M/S 97239 #026-04-2001 L2001 **IM** *100 †20
HAM, John Marshall. 3181 SW SAM JACKSON PRK RD, MAILCODE L590 97239 #005-12-1980 L2001 **GS TTS** *020 †85
HAM, L Bruce. 10101 SE MAIN ST STE 3012 97216 #005-12-1974 L1976 **CCS** *100 †85
HAMEL, Edward Eugene. 10535 NE GLISAN ST STE 30, METROPOLITIAN PEDIATRICS, 97220 #054-04-1985 L1986 **PD** *020 †55
HAMILTON, Bronwyn E. 3181 SW SAM JACKSON PRK RD, MAIL CODE CR13 97239 #005-12-1996 L2003 **RNR** *020 †80

■ = Address Information Privacy Protected

HAMILTON, George Quentin. 10123 SE MARKET ST 97216 #005-15-1971 L1973 **CD** *020
HAMILTON, Norman Gregory. 2250 NW FLANDERS ST, STE 306 97210 #040-02-1977 L1983 **P** *020 †75
HAMILTON, Richard N. 5050 NE HOYT ST, STE 359 97213 #041-02-1996 L1999 **OBG** *020 †30
HAMLIN, Virgil L, Jr. 5050 NE HOYT ST STE 235 97213 #007-02-1963 L1967 **IM** *020
HAMMERSTAD, John Philip. 3181 SW SAM JACKSON PRK RD, MAIL CODE OP32 97239 #016-02-1964 L1972 **N** *040 †75
HAN, Esther. ■ 97219 #012-05-2006 L2006 **GS** *012
HANCEY, James Orlo. 3181 SW SAM JACKSON PRK RD, PARK RD 97239 #040-02-1986 L1987 **P** *020 †75
HAND, Karen Wendy. 3181 SW SAM JACKSON PRK RD, UH 2 97239 #917-07-1994 L2005 *020
HANDELMAN, Irvin Lewis. 2525 NW LOVEJOY ST, STE 100 97210 #026-04-1969 L1976 **OPH** *020 †35
HANDY, John Rutherfoord. 1111 NE 99TH AVE 97220 #036-07-1983 L1997 **TS GS** *020 †85,90
HANEL, Christopher V. 1880 SW 6TH AVE, PSU STUDENT HEALTH CENTER 97201 #040-02-1997 L1998 **FM** *020 †75
HANEY, Elizabeth. 3181 SW SAM JCKSN PRK RD R, L-475 97239 #010-02-1997 L1999 **IM** *020 †20
HANEY, Robert Frank. 2330 NW FLANDERS ST 97210 #040-02-1958 **OPH** *071 †35
HANFT, Rachelle Titiana. ■ 97232 #051-04-2007 L2007 **FP** *012
HANIFIN, Jon M. 3303 SW BOND AVE, MAIL CODE CH16D 97239 #056-05-1965 L1972 **D AI** *020 †15
HANLEY, Patrick L. 10000 SE MAIN ST STE 402 97216 #025-07-1981 L1987 **ORS OSM** *020 †40
HANNA, Cheryl Elizabeth. 3181 SW SAM JACKSON PRK RD, OREGON HLTH SCIENCES UNIV 97239 #005-18-1976 L1978 **PDE** *020 †55
HANNA, Ward P. 120 NW 14TH AVE, STE 300 97209 #040-02-1982 L1983 **AN** *020 †05 ‡
HANS, Gurpreet K. 2801 N GANTENBEIN AVE 97227 #065-01-2005 L2005 **IM** *012
HANSCHKA, Mark Richard. 1020 NE 2ND AVE, STE 200 97232 #024-01-1961 L1962 **OBG** *071 †30
HANSEN, Eric Borg. 120 NW 14TH AVE, STE 300 97209 #025-01-1994 L1998 **AN** *020 †05 ‡
HANSEN, Jill Rachel. 2801 N GANTENBEIN AVE 97227 #005-14-1997 L2000 **IM** *020 †20
HANSEN, Juliana Ehrman. 3181 SW SAM JCKSN PRK RD R, OHSU DIVISION OF PLASTIC S 97239 #054-04-1988 L1996 **PS** *020 †85,65
HANSEN, Keith Sherman. 265 N BROADWAY 97227 #036-05-1971 L1978 **HEM ON** *020 †20
HANSEN, Paul Danl. 1040 NW 22ND AVE, STE 560 97210 #054-04-1988 L1996 **GS SO** *020 †85
HANSEN, Susan Marie. 2400 SW VERMONT ST, FANNO CREEK CLINIC LLC 97219 #040-02-1986 L1995 **IM** *020 †20
HANSEN, Thomas Allan. 501 N GRAHAM ST STE 455 97227 #025-01-1966 L1974 **OS IM** *074 †20
HANSEN, Thomas Edward. 1121 NE 2ND AVE 97232 #040-02-1979 L1983 **P PYG** *020 †75
HANSEN, Vincent Edward. 250 NE 181ST AVE, STE A 97230 #005-12-1976 L1977 *020
HANSON, Angela Jean. 3181 SW SAM JACKSON PRK RD, RD IN 97239 #007-02-2006 L2006 **IM** *012
HANSON, Eric Leif. 301 NE KNOTT ST 97212 #024-07-1994 L2006 **D** *020 †15
HARA, George S. 1015 NW 22ND AVE 97210 #040-02-1953 L1956 **GYN** *020 †30
HARBIN, Jonathan R. ■ 97227 #025-12-2006 L2006 **P** *012
HARBISON, Tom William. 3550 N INTERSTATE AVE, KAISER PERMANENTE - E1N 97227 #051-04-1997 L1999 **IM** *020 †20
HARBURG, Thomas David. 7705 SE DIVISION ST 97206 #025-01-1979 L1980 **IM** *020 †20
HARDIMAN, Karin Marie. ■ 97239 #001-02-2004 L2004 **GS** *012
HARDIN, Chelsea Seare. 3181 SW SAM JACKSON PRK RD 97239 #049-01-2000 L2000 **GS** *020
HARDING, Cary Owen. 707 SW GAINES ST, OREGON HEALTH SCIENCE UNIV 97239 #054-04-1987 L1999 **PD** *020 †55,19
HARDMAN, Joseph Augustus. ■ 97213 #005-18-2003 L2007 **IM** *100 †20
HARDY, Deborah Anne. 2241 LLOYD CTR 97232 #005-11-1989 L1999 **PD** *020 †55
HARGUNANI, Christopher A. 2222 NW LOVEJOY ST, STE 622 97210 #010-02-2001 L2001 **OTO** *100 †45
HARGUNANI, Dana Elizabeth. 3181 SW SAM JCKSN PRK RD R, MAILCODE CDRCP 97239 #010-02-2001 L2001 **PD** *100 †55
HARPER, Richard Jos. 3710 SW US VETRN HOSP RD, BOX 1031 97239 #040-02-1989 L1990 **EM** *020 †16
HARRINGTON, Mark S. 1509 SW SUNSET BLVD, STE 2E 97239 #040-02-1996 L1997 **IM** *020 †20
HARRIS, Homer H. 900 NE 81ST AVE, UNIT 381 97213 #040-02-1945 L1948 **PTH FOP** *071 †50
HARRIS, Merrill Gwyn. 4805 NE GLISAN ST STE BG05 97213 #005-20-2000 L2000 **IM** *020 †20
HARRIS, Monica Williams. 545 NE 47TH AVE, STE 106 97213 #024-07-1984 L1993 **IM OM** *020
HARRIS, Norman Ernest. 10123 SE MARKET ST 97216 #048-04-1974 L1978 **DR** *020 †80
HARRIS, Richard Lawrence. 2220 SW 1ST AVE 97201 #036-01-1958 L1965 **IM** *071
HARRIS, William Kiley. 3600 N INTERSTATE AVE 97227 #041-01-1962 L1970 **OPH** *020 †35
HARRISON, Charles William. 5319 SW WESTGATE DR, STE 241 97221 #836-02-1956 L1978 *071
HARRISON, Marvin W. 501 N GRAHAM ST, PEDIATRIC SURGERY 97227 #035-06-1970 L1976 **PDS** *020 †85
HARRISON, Matthew James. ■ 97239 #038-41-2006 L2006 **ORS** *012
HARRISON, Rebecca Ann. 3181 SW SAM JCKSN PRK RD R, BTE 119 97239 #026-04-1994 L1996 **IM** *020 †20
HARRSKOG, Lars Ola. 3181 SW SAM JACKSON PRK RD, UH 2 97239 #858-02-1983 L1998 *020
HARSANY, Robert Milton. 10000 SE MAIN ST STE 3 97216 #005-12-1973 L1977 **GYN** *020 †30
HART, Melanie Nicole. PO BOX 1034, MED CTR 97207 #005-19-1996 L1998 **IM** *020 †20
HART, Robert Alan. 2241 LLOYD CTR 97232 #005-18-1992 L1998 **ORS** *020 †40
HARTER, Jeffrey Douglas. 4805 NE GLISAN ST, PROVIDENCE PORTLAND MEDICA 97213 #048-02-1993 L1994 **SP** *020 †50
HARTFORD, Emily Marie. ■ 97239 #040-02-2008 *012
HARTMAN, Ralph A. 120 NW 14TH AVE, STE 300 97209 #023-12-1987 L1998 **AN** *020 †05 ‡
HARTMAN, Shelley Renee. 10535 NE GLISAN ST, STE 300 97220 #040-02-1993 L1995 **PD** *020 †55
HARTMEYER, Michael Layman. 120 NW 14TH AVE, STE 300 97209 #039-01-2002 L2003 **AN** *100 †05
HARTOCH, Richard Stephen. 2241 LLOYD CTR 97232 #028-02-1984 L1989 **IM** *020 †20,16
HARTWELL, Laurel Ann. ■ 97202 #035-47-2007 L2007 **IM** *012
HARUKUNI, Izumi. 3181 SW SAM JACKSON PRK RD R, UHS2 97239 #572-23-1988 L2005 **AN** *020 †05
HARVEY, James Chas. 120 NW 14TH AVE, STE 300 97209 #040-02-1977 L1978 **AN** *020 †05 ‡
HARVEY, Mark Alan. 3930 SE DIVISION ST 97202 #048-13-2001 L2001 **FM** *020
HARVEY, Thomas Pascal. 2647 NE 33RD AVE 97212 #048-04-1977 L1978 **FM** *020 †18

HASENAUER, James Joseph. ■ 97201 #422-01-1998 L2007 **DR** *100 †80
HASTINGS, William L. 120 NW 14TH AVE, STE 300 97209 #032-01-1992 L1993 **AN** *020 †05
HASUIKE, Toshi. 97219 #040-02-1959 L1961 **P** *075
HASWELL, Howard P. ■ 97216 #035-45-1942 L1949 **AN** *071 †05
HATCHER, Peter Wolverton. 9000 N LOMBARD ST, NORTH PORTLAND HEALTH CLIN 97203 #024-01-1995 L1996 **FM** *020 †18
HATEGAN, Liana Felicia. 3181 SW SAM JACKSON PRK RD, OR HLTH SCI UNIV HOSP 97239 #781-03-1984 L2007 **PFP** *012
HATFIELD-KELLER, E. 2241 LLOYD CTR 97232 #040-02-1993 L1994 **EM** *020 †16
HATTENHAUER, Mark Thos. 3181 SW SAM JACKSON PRK RD R, M/S UHN62 97239 #040-02-1966 L1970 **IC IM** *020 †20
HAUBRICH, Mark Paul. 120 NW 14TH AVE, STE 300 97209 #056-06-1982 L1986 **PAN PD** *020 †05,55 ‡
HAUGEN, Obert Desmond. 2801 N GANTENBEIN AVE, LEGACY EMANUEL HOSPITAL 97227 #060-01-1962 L1971 **DR** *071 †80
HAUN, Thomas Milton. ■ 97221 #030-06-1957 L1958 **GE IM** *071
HAUSER, Analene Joanne. ■ 97239 #008-01-2002 L2002 **OBG** *020
HAUSER, Peter Paul. ■ 97210 #051-01-1981 L2003 **P** *050 †75
HAWLEY, Virginia L Frank. 2801 N GANTENBEIN AVE 97227 #035-06-1972 L1973 **AN** *020 †05 ‡
HAY, Gordon Cave. 3101 SW SAM JCKSN PRK RD R, SHRINERS HOSP FOR CHILDREN 97239 #143-06-1991 L2006 *100
HAYDEN, James Bernard. 3181 SW SAM JACKSON PRK RD, DEPT OF ORTHOPEDICS OP-31 97239 #040-02-1996 L1997 **OMO ORS** *020 †40
HAYES, Daniel Peter. 4444 SW CORBETT 97239 #049-01-1971 L1973 **P IM** *075
HAYES, Margaret Mary. 3181 SW SAM JACKSON PRK RD, PARK RD 97239 #040-02-1994 L1996 **FM** *020 †18
HAYES, Roby Francis. 10000 SE MAIN ST, STE 408 97216 #039-05-1984 L1991 **GS CCS** *020 †85
HAYES-LATTIN, Brandon M. 3181 SW SAM JACKSON PRK RD R, MAILCODE L586 97239 #054-04-1997 L1998 **HO** *020 †20
HAYWARD, Arthur D Alanson. 2701 NW VAUGHN ST, STE 140 97210 #035-01-1972 L1977 **IM** *020 †20
HEARN, James Duff. ■ 97239 #040-02-1963 L1965 **AN** *071
HECKLER, Adrienne Michell. 3181 SW SAM JACKSON PRK RD, OR HLTH SCI UNIV HOSP 97239 #041-02-2007 L2007 **GS** *012
HEDBERG, Katrina. ■ 97212 #040-02-1985 L1991 **PHP** *062 †70
HEDGES, Jerris Robt. 3181 SW SAM JACKSON PRK RD, L-102 SCHOOL OF MEDICINE 97239 #054-04-1976 L1989 **EM** *030 †16
HEDRICK, Leigh Austin. 3181 SW SAM JCKSN PRK RD R 97239 #040-02-2005 L2005 **P** *012
HEFFERNAN, Robert Edward. 4212 NE BROADWAY ST 97213 #024-07-1975 L1978 **PD** *020 †55
HEFFNER, John Edward. 5050 NE HOYT ST STE 540, MEDICAL EDUCATION 97213 #005-14-1974 L2006 **PUD IM** *020 †20
HEGGE, Frederick N. 2801 N GANTENBEIN AVE, EMANUEL HOSPITAL 97227 #056-05-1968 L1977 **OS NM** *020 †20,28
HEGNELL, Lars Goran. 3181 SW SAM JACKSON PRK RD, UH 2 97239 #858-05-1986 L2002 *020
HEIFERMAN, Miriam Frances. 500 NE MULTNOMAH ST, STE 100 97232 #035-46-1977 L1999 **PD PDC** *020 †55
HEIN, Scott James. ■ 97239 #005-12-2002 L2006 **AN** *100
HEINONEN, Mark Brian. 500 NE MULTNOMAH ST, STE 100 97232 #010-01-1991 L2007 **AN** *020 †05
HEINRICH, Michael Chas. 2241 LLOYD CTR 97232 #023-07-1984 L1985 **HEM ON** *020 †20
HEINTZ, Ronald Terrence. 1121 NE 2ND AVE, OREGON STATE HOSPITAL 97232 #040-02-1982 L1983 **P** *020 †75
HEINTZMAN, John David. 3181 SW SAM JCKSN PRK RD R, OHSU 97239 #041-13-2002 L2002 **FM** *020 †18
HEITSCH, Richard Carlton. 163 NE 102ND AVE, BLDG V 97220 #056-06-1970 L1979 **GS** *020 †20
HELFAND, Mark. 3710 SW US VETRNS HSPTL RD, PO BOX 1034 P3 MED 97239 #016-11-1984 L1992 **IM** *020 †20
HELFET-HILLIKER, Daniel. ■ 97206 #024-16-2003 L2003 **P** *012
HELLER, Kimerlynn Michell. 177 NE 102ND AVE 97220 #025-76-2003, ▲ L2007 **OBG** *020
HELMS, Melissa Ann. ■ 97201 #007-02-2006 L2006 **IM** *012
HELWIG, Jonathan Austin. 10123 SE MARKET ST, DIAGNOSTIC RADIOLOGISTS, P 97216 #048-02-1999 L2000 **RNR** *100 †80
HENDERSON, Jean C. 120 NW 14TH AVE, STE 300 97209 #030-06-1978 L1979 **AN** *020 †05 ‡
HENDERSON, Robin Gregory. 1130 SW MORRISON ST, STE 600 97205 #049-01-1969 L1976 **P** *020 †75
HENDIN, A Perry. 501 N GRAHAM ST, STE 100 97227 #550-03-1989 L1992 **IM** *020 †20
HENDRICKSON, Irene C. 5050 NE HOYT ST, STE 540 97213 #030-06-2000 L2001 **IM** *100
HENDRICKSON, Robert G. 3181 SW SAM JCKSN PRK RD R, CSB - 550 97239 #035-08-1997 L2002 **EM ETX** *020 †16
HENKEL, Gary Frederick. 2230 NW PETTYGROVE ST, STE 220 97210 #005-15-1995 L1998 **EM** *020 †16
HENNER, William David. 3181 SW SAM JACKSON PRK RD 97239 #041-01-1977 L1988 **ON IM** *050 †20
HENRY, Helen Lawrence. 2330 NW FLANDERS ST, STE 207 97210 #005-02-1987 L1988 **IM** *020 †20
HENRY, Michael. 506 NE 49TH AVE 97213 #539-02-1950 L1959 **AN** *071 †05
HENRY, Thomas Paul. 3510 NE 122ND AVE STE 207 97230 #040-02-1975 L1978 **FM** *020 †18
HENSHAW, Eric Thomas. 120 NW 14TH AVE, STE 300 97209 #040-02-1991 L1996 **AN** *020 †05
HENSTROM, Michael James. 6312 SW CAPITOL HWY # 502, NORTHWEST ACUTE CARE SPECI 97239 #038-40-2004 L2004 **EM** *020
HERBST, Jeffrey Robert. 5331 SW MACADAM AVE, STE 210 97239 #040-02-1975 L1977 **EM** *020
HERCHER, Michelle Ann. ■ 97205 #040-02-2008 *012
HERDER, Kimberly Jean. 5050 NE HOYT ST, STE 454 97213 #060-01-1994 L1997 **IM** *020 †20
HERIZA, Elizabeth Louise. ■ 97213 #040-02-1978 L1979 **PD** *020 †55
HERMENS, Jeanne Marie. 120 NW 14TH AVE, STE 300 97209 #040-02-1980 L1983 **AN** *020 †05
HERNANDEZ, Jo Carolyn. 4805 NE GLISAN ST, PROVIDENCE MEDICAL CENTER 97213 #048-02-1979 L1987 **PTH** *020 †50
HERR, Daniel Bret. 120 NW 14TH AVE, STE 300 97209 #040-02-1984 L1987 **AN IM** *020 †05
HERRICK, Timothy Leland. 4110 SE HAWTHORNE BLVD, PMB 251 97214 #016-06-1983 L1988 **FM** *040 †18
HERRINGTON, Robert Ramsey. ■ 97239 #001-02-2003 L2003 **EM** *100 †16

HERSH, William Richard. 3181 SW SAM JACKSON PRK RD, BICC 97239 #016-11-1984 L1990 **IM** *050 †20

HERZBERG, Alex Maurice. 3181 SW SAM JACKSON PRK RD, DEPT OF ORTHOP REHAB 97239 #054-04-1992 L1998 **ORS** *020 †40

HERZIG, Daniel Owen. 3181 SW SAM JCKSN PRK RD R, MAIL CODE L-223A 97239 #047-05-1999 L2005 **CRS GS** *020 †85,10

HERZKA, Andrea Susan. 3181 SW SAM JCKSN PRK RD R 97239 #005-02-1999 L2005 **OSM** *100

HESKETT, Tammy Alyce. 2801 N GANTENBEIN AVE, EMANUEL HOSP DEPT PD 97227 #040-02-1985 L1988 **PD** *020 †55

HESLA, John S. 2222 NW LOVEJOY ST, STE 304 97210 #040-02-1982 L1999 **REN OBG** *020 †30

HESLA, Richard Bryan. 2801 N GANTENBEIN AVE, EMANUEL HOSPITAL 97227 #040-02-1984 L1990 **DR** *020 †80

HESSMAN, Crystal Joy. ■ 97214 #019-02-2007 L2007 **GS** *012

HESTER, Eric James. ■ 97221 #007-02-2001 L2004 **D** *020 †15

HETHERINGTON, Arthur F. ■ 97207 #041-12-1970 L1989 **OBG** *071 †30

HETTINGER, Barbara Diane. ■ 97201 #051-01-2004 L2004 **IM** *100

HETTWER, Werner Herbert. 3181 SW SAM JCKSN PRK RD R, OHSU 97239 #409-16-1996 L2003 *100

HETZLER, P Wendy. 120 NW 14TH AVE, STE 300 97209 #016-43-1976 L1979 **AN OBG** *020 †30,05

HEUSER, Rose Gabrielle. ■ 97210 #040-02-2007 L2007 **IM** *012

HEWSON, Jennifer Marie. ■ 97239 #021-01-2007 L2007 **OBG** *012

HICKAM, David Howard. 3710 SW US VETRNS HSPTL RD, VETERANS HOSPITAL 97239 #005-02-1977 L1982 **IM** *030 †20

HICKOK, Durlin Edward. ■ 97211 #025-01-1973 L1975 **MFM PHP** *020 †30

HICKS, James Stowers. 3181 SW SAM JACKSON PRK RD, UH 2 97239 #027-01-1970 L1979 **AN** *040 †05

HIGGINS, Ivanhoe B, Jr. 5050 NE HOYT ST, STE 640 97213 #023-01-1971 L1977 **ORS** *020 †40

HIGGINSON, Grant Kenneth. 800 NE OREGON ST, STE 930 97232 #040-02-1976 L1988 **GPM PHP** *030 †70

HIKES, David Christopher. 5050 NE HOYT ST STE 668, PORTLAND JOINT RECON CLNC 97213 #025-07-1977 L1978 **ORS** *020 †40

HILBELINK, Todd Ronald. 5314 NE IRVING ST 97213 #038-40-1996 L2001 **NEP** *020 †20

HILL, Curtis Lyle. 510 NE 49TH AVE # 510 97213 #024-01-1963 L1967 **NS** *071

HILL, Jonathan Grant. 2222 NW LOVEJOY ST, STE 315 97210 #005-06-1975 L1983 **TS** *020 †85,90

HILL, Joshua Robert. ■ 97221 #040-02-2004 L2004 **DR** *012

HILLIER, Teresa Anne. 3800 N INTERSTATE AVE, CENTER FOR HEALTH RESEARCH 97227 #040-02-1990 L1991 **END IM** *050 †20

HILLS, William Louis. 3181 SW SAM JCKSN PRK RD R, M/S- L226 97239 #031-01-2003 L2003 **N** *100

HINDAHL, David Scott. 19500 SE STARK ST, NORTHWEST PERMANENTE-ROCKW 97233 #016-11-1983 L1984 **FM** *020 †18

HINK, Carrie Elizabeth. ■ 97228 #056-06-2004 L2004 **GS** *012

HINSHAW, Bruce M. 120 NW 14TH AVE, STE 300 97209 #396-38-1988 L1993 **AN** *020 †05 ‡

HIPSHMAN, Lawrence. 3181 SW SAM JACKSON PRK RD, OHSU DEPT OF PSYCH 97239 #025-07-1977 L1998 **OS P** *020 †75

HIRSCH, Anne Marie. 4212 NE BROADWAY ST 97213 #019-02-1989 L1990 **IM** *020 †20

HIRSCH, Dale Douglas. 1111 NE 99TH AVE, THE OREGON CLINIC, P.C. 97220 #019-02-1989 L1990 **CD IM** *020 †20

HIRSCH, Rebecca Leah. 500 NE MULTNOMAH ST, STE 100 97232 #016-42-2000 L2007 **P** *020

HIRSCHFIELD, Beth Lynne. 4610 SE BELMONT ST STE 60 97215 #051-04-1976 L1979 **PHP PD** *020

HIRUKI, Tadaaki. 3003 SW 11TH AVE 97239 #060-01-1986 L1999 **ATP** *020 †50

HO, Julia. ■ 97227 #028-46-1997 L2004 **D** *020 †15

HOCKING-KELTNER, Leila. ■ 97221 #038-06-1987 L1988 **IM** *020

HODGES, Marian Osborne. 5050 NE HOYT ST, STE 540 97213 #035-01-1985 L1986 **IMG IM** *040 †20

HODGSON, Richard Arthur. 2222 NW LOVEJOY ST, STE 607 97210 #040-02-1956 L1961 **OTO** *020 †45

HODGSON, Richard Sterling. 1849 NW KEARNEY ST, STE 300 97209 #040-02-1983 L1984 **OTO NO** *020 †45

HODSON, Robert Walter. 1111 NE 99TH AVE 97220 #040-02-1981 L1987 **CD IM** *020 †20

HOEFLICH, Molly Lynn. 5050 NE HOYT ST STE 25 97213 #040-02-1981 L1986 **PM** *020 †60

HOELTER, Jenny. ■ 97230 #040-02-2004 L2007 **PD** *020 †55

HOESLY, Megan Elizabeth. 3181 SW SAM JCKSN PRK RD R 97239 #040-02-2003 L2007 **PD** *100 †55

HOFF, Steven Frederick. 5050 NE HOYT ST, STE 660 97213 #030-06-1973 L1978 **ORS** *020 †40

HOFFMAN, Martin Ambrose. ■ 97212 #026-04-1972 **IM** *020

HOFFMAN, William Franklin. 3710 SW US VETRNS HSPTL RD, MNTL HLTH DIV P35C, VAMC 97239 #056-05-1981 L1982 **P** *020 †75

HOGARTH, Penelope. 3181 SW SAM JACKSON PRK RD, MAIL CODE L226 97239 #007-02-1994 L2000 **IM** *020 †75

HOLDEN, Donald H. 1015 NW 22ND AVE 97210 #008-01-1944 L1953 **OTO A** *071

HOLDEN, Jeremy Paul. 1111 NE 99TH AVE 97220 #040-02-2001 L2007 **GE** *020

HOLDEN, William Edward. 2241 LLOYD CTR 97232 #038-41-1968 L1973 **PUD IM** *050 †20

HOLLAND, Daniel Ray. 10819 SE STARK ST, STE 200 97216 #048-12-1993 L1998 **OPH** *020 †35

HOLLAND, John Michael. 3181 SW SAM JCKSN PRK L337, RADIATION ONCOLOGY DEPT 97239 #028-02-1989 L1994 **RO** *020 †80

HOLLIDAY, Jennifer Lynne. ■ 97221 #040-02-2008 L2008 *012

HOLLOPETER, Sarah Marie. 3181 SW SAM JCKSN PRK RD R, OHSU 97239 #054-04-2003 L2003 **FM** *020 †18

HOLLOWAY, Kelli L. 4800 SW MACADAM AVE, STE 325 97239 #028-46-1988 L2001 **P** *020

HOLMES, Aaron Karl. ■ 97213 #040-02-2007 L2007 **FP** *012

HOLMES, David Marsh. 1650 NW FRONT AVE STE 180, LEGACY OCCUP HLTH CLN AVA 97209 #040-02-1956 L1957 **AM AN** *071 †05

HOLMES, John Eric. ■ 97221 #005-14-1957 L1958 **N OS** *040 †75

HOLMES, Stephen Clark. 120 NW 14TH AVE, #300 OREGON ANESTH GRP PC 97209 #040-02-1990 L1994 **AN** *020 †05 ‡

HOLTZMAN, Sally Jane. 501 N GRAHAM ST, STE 445 97227 #024-01-1991 L1997 **OBG** *020 †30

HOMAN, James Allen. ■ 97215 #019-02-2002 L2007 **RNR** *012 †80

HONG, Chih-Ho Hilary. 3181 SW SAM JCKSN PRK RD R 97239 #065-01-1997 L2002 *100 †15

HONG, Dennis. 1040 NW 22ND AVE STE 500, OREGON WEIGHT LOSS SURGERY 97210 #065-01-1996 L2002 **GS** *020

HONG, Robert Bumsuk. 6254 SW BURLINGAME AVE A 97239 #035-06-1987 L2000 **IM** *020

HOOVER, Annette Larie. ■ 97214 #005-12-2005 L2005 **IM** *012

HOPE, Andrew Patrick. ■ 97221 #035-01-2002 L2007 **AI** *020 †20,03

HOPKINS, Katharine Lee. 3181 SW SAM JCKSN PRK RD R, OHSU M/C- DC7R 97239 #005-02-1989 L2001 **PDR DR** *020 †80

HOPKINS, Robert Samuel. 3303 SW BOND AVE, MAIL CODE CH16D 97239 #051-01-2006 L2006 **D** *012

HOPPE, Hanno. 3181 SW SAM JCKSN PRK RD R 97239 #409-20-2001 L2006 *100

HORACEK, Ashley Elizabeth. 1012 SW KING AVE # 350 97205 #039-01-1993 L1994 **P** *100 †75

HORENSTEIN, Marcus M. ■ 97220 #040-02-1941 L1943 **IM** *072 †20

HORENSTEIN, Velma J. 10300 NE HANCOCK ST 97220 #040-02-1953 L1954 **IMG IM** *072

HORN, Albert Curtis, III. 4805 NE GLISAN ST 97213 #048-12-1974 L1976 **EM** *071 †16

HORN, Jean-Louis Edouard. 3181 SW SAM JACKSON PRK RD, UH 2 97239 #165-07-1986 L1999 **AN** *020

HORNER, Peder Elbert. 3181 SW SAM JCKSN PRK RD R, MAIL CODE L605 97239 #019-02-2002 L2003 **DR** *100 †80

HOROWITZ, Brandon Zane. 2241 LLOYD CTR 97232 #035-03-1979 L1997 **EM** *040 †20,16

HOROWITZ, Irving J. ■ 97202 #025-01-1952 L1953 **RO** *071 †80

HORRALL, Mary Beth. 800 SW 13TH AVE 97205 #039-01-1986 L1989 **PD** *020 †55

HORTON, William Arnold. 3101 SW SAM JACKSON PRK RD, SHRINERS HOSP CHILDREN 97239 #019-02-1971 L1994 **OS IM** *050 †20,19

HOSSEINION, Shahram. 3942 SE HAWTHORNE BLVD 97214 #040-02-2003 L2003 **FM** *020 †18

HOSTETLER LIPPY, Saskia. 833 SW 11TH AVE STE 250 97205 #038-06-2001 L2001 **P** *100

HOTELLING, Hillary Brooke. 5119 NE 57TH AVE 97218 #012-01-1993 L1994 **IM** *020 †20

HOU, Emmeline Fei. ■ 97210 #005-18-2001 L2001 **CD** *020

HOU, Vivian Ying. 3181 SW SAM JACKSON PRK RD, UH 2 97239 #023-07-1991 L1996 **AN** *020 †05

HOUFF, Anne Maija. ■ 97213 #016-42-2006 L2006 **IM** *012

HOUGHTON, Donald Cary. 2241 LLOYD CTR 97232 #040-02-1972 L1973 **PTH NEP** *030 †50

HOULE, Richard Paul. 426 SW STARK ST 5TH FL 97204 #048-04-1981 L1982 **GP** *020

HOUSMAN, Tamara Salam. 507 NE 47TH AVE, STE 204 97213 #020-02-1997 L2006 **D DS** *020 †15

HOVAGUIMIAN, Hagop. 2241 LLOYD CTR 97232 #875-02-1977 L1984 **TS GS** *020 †85,90

HOWARD, Janet Marie. 19500 SE STARK ST 97233 #305-01-1987 L1997 **PD** *020 †55

HOWARD, Perry H, Jr. 4805 NE GLISAN ST 97213 #021-01-1983 L1990 **PTH** *072 †50

HOWATT, Janis Lynn. 4212 NE BROADWAY ST, BROADWAY MEDICAL CLINIC, L 97213 #041-07-1993 L1994 **IM** *020 †20

HOWELL, Gary Alan. 545 NE 47TH AVE, STE 215 97213 #027-01-1991 L2000 **DR** *020 †80

HOWELL, Laurene Lona. ■ 97202 #005-02-1982 L1983 **OTO** *075 †45

HOWELL, Walter Lyall, III. 120 NW 14TH AVE, STE 300 97209 #021-01-1981 L1983 **AN** *020 †05 ‡

HOWIESON, John. 2241 LLOYD CTR 97232 #019-02-1955 L1959 **R N** *071 †80,75

HRBEK, Marjorie Jean. 4212 NE BROADWAY ST, BROADWAY MEDICAL CLINIC 97213 #030-05-1997 L2000 **IM** *020 †20

HSU, Irene Shiaoyun. 3375 SW TERWILLIGER BLVD, OHSU/CASEY EYE INST 97239 #041-02-2002 L2007 **OPH PO** *020

HSU, Richard Lihren. 1321 NE 99TH AVE, STE 100 97220 #016-11-1995 L1998 **IM** *020 †20

HU, Charles Yan. 2801 N GANTENBEIN AVE 97227 #056-06-1999 L2003 **MPD OS** *020 †20

HU, Meituck. 2801 N GANTENBEIN AVE, LEGACY 97227 #014-01-2004 L2004 **IM** *020

HUANG, Betty Frances. 1111 NE 99TH AVE 97220 #025-01-1997 L2003 **GE** *020 †20

HUANG, Enoch Teen. 10201 SE MAIN ST, STE 9 97216 #021-01-1996 L2005 **EM** *020 †16

HUANG, Hahn. 0836 SW CURRY ST, UNIT 600 97239 #035-09-2001 L2001 **PTH** *100

HUANG, James Zhiyan. 2241 LLOYD CTR 97232 #243-76-1984 L2001 **HMP** *020 †50

HUANG, Theodore Tingche. 5050 NE HOYT ST STE 540, PROVIDENCE PORTLAND MED CT 97213 #035-03-1999 L2002 **IM** *100

HUANG, Xiaoyan. 1111 NE 99TH AVE, THE OREGON CLINIC, PC 97220 #005-11-1995 L1996 **CD** *020 †20

HUBER, Stanley J. 5050 NE HOYT ST, OREGON RETINAL ASSOCIATES 97213 #040-02-1965 L1967 **OPH AM** *071 †35

HUFFMAN, Jennifer Clare. 501 N GRAHAM ST STE 330, DEPARTMENT OF PEDIATRIC NE 97227 #034-01-2002 L2007 **CHN** *020

HUGHES, Grant Buehler. 2525 NW LOVEJOY ST STE 405 97210 #041-13-1944 L1955 **P** *072

HUGLI, Olivier William. ■ 97221 #869-05-1988 **IM** *100 †20

HUH, Seung Young. 3181 SW SAM JCKSN PRK RD R, OHSU 97239 #572-30-1997 L2004 **EM** *100

HULL, Paul Quilliam. 2222 NW LOVEJOY ST, STE 408 97210 #054-04-1963 L1968 **CD IM** *020

HULTON, Leslie Gail. 1130 NW 22ND AVE, STE 520 97210 #005-15-1980 L1982 **OBG** *020 †30

HULTSCH-SMITH, Sara E. 4805 NE GLISAN ST, # 6N40 97213 #041-02-1984 L1997 **IM** *020 †20

HUMMEL, Errett E, Jr. 1 CENTER CT, STE 110 97227 #040-02-1966 L1971 **NS** *020 †25

HUMPHREY, Linda Louise. 3710 SW US VETRNS HSPTL RD, PORTLAND VA MEDICAL CENTER 97239 #040-02-1983 L1984 **GPM IM** *050 †20,70

HUNG, Arthur. 3181 SW SAM JACKSON PRK RD, PARK RD 97239 #038-40-1997 L2002 **RO** *020 †80

HUNG, May-Ho. 120 NW 14TH AVE STE 300 97209 #572-20-1967 L1972 **AN** *020 †05 ‡

HUNG, Sian Ming. 545 NE 47TH AVE, STE 321 97213 #385-02-1963 L1972 **OS CLP** *075

HUNGERFORD, Linda M. 1321 NE 99TH AVE, STE 100 97220 #040-02-1992 L1993 **IM** *020 †20

HUNSAKER, Shona Rae. 3181 SW SAM JCKSN PRK RD R, M/S L-475 97239 #054-04-2002 L2002 **IM** *100 †20

HUNTER, Alan Jos. 2241 LLOYD CTR 97232 #004-01-1991 L1992 **IM** *020 †20

HUNTER, John Greenleaf. 2241 LLOYD CTR 97232 #041-01-1981 L2001 **GE GS** *020 †85

HUNTER, Maya Koike. 501 N GRAHAM ST STE 375, PEDIATRIC ENDOCRINOLOGY 97227 #004-01-1989 L1992 **PDE** *020 †55

HUNTER, Valerie. 545 NE 47TH AVE STE 215 97213 #048-02-1983 L1996 **DR** *020 †80

HUNTLEY, Sonia. 19500 SE STARK ST, KAISER PERMANENTE ROCKWOOD 97233 #005-18-1990 L1991 **IM** *020 †20

HUNTWORK, Bruce Leslie. ■ 97212 #010-01-1955 L1973 **GS GP** *040

HURLIMAN, Amanda Kathleen. ■ 97202 #040-02-2006 L2006 **OBG** *012

HURTADO, Arnold V. 3800 N INTERSTATE AVE 97227 #024-07-1952 L1956 **IM** *050 †20

HURWITZ, Joshua Joseph. ■ 97239 #040-02-2008 *012

HURWORTH, Mark Alexander. 3101 SW SAM JCKSN PRK RD R 97239 #836-02-1995 L2004 *100

HUSSAIN, Sanaa. ■ 97209 #875-01-1986 L2008 **SP** *020

HUSTON, Robert Karl. 501 N GRAHAM ST STE 265 97227 #040-02-1972 L1978 **NPM** *020 †55

HUTCHENS, Michael Paul. 3181 SW SAM JACKSON PRK RD, UH 2 97239 #023-01-1999 L2000 **CCA** *100 †05

■ = Address Information Privacy Protected

HUTCHINSON, James Emlen. ■ 97201 #041-01-1962 L1966 **P PTH** *072 †50,75

HWANG, Alice. 5050 NE HOYT ST, STE 256 97213 #028-46-1998 L2005 **HO IM** *020 †20

HWANG, Esther C. 3710 SW US VETRNS HSPTL RD, P3RHEUM 97239 #005-18-2000 L2000 **RHU** *100 †20

HWANG, Henry Chen. 120 NW 14TH AVE STE 300, OREGON ANESTHESIOLOGY GROU 97209 #025-01-2003 L2007 **AN** *100

HWANG, Thomas Sangchul. 3303 SW BOND AVE, FL 11 97239 #005-18-1999 L2003 **OPH** *020 †35

HYDE, Jason Karl. ■ 97212 #010-01-1998 L2006 **HMP** *020 †50

HYDE, Karl Grant. 120 NW 14TH AVE, STE 300 97209 #021-01-1999 L2005 **AN** *020 †05 ‡

HYMAN, Milton D. ■ 97232 #035-08-1937 L1946 **RO** *071 †80

HYMAN, Selma B Shapiro. ■ 97232 #035-19-1938 L1945 **RO** *071 †80

HYUN, Chris Byung. 800 SW 13TH AVE 97205 #016-06-1994 L2006 **GE** *020 †20 ‡

IBSEN, Laura Marie. 707 SW GAINES ST, OHSU DEPT PEDS CDRCP 97239 #005-18-1989 L1998 **CCP** *020 †55

ILES-SHIH, Lulu. 3181 SW SAM JACKSON PRK RD, RD IN 97239 #003-01-2006 L2006 **IM** *012

ILLINGWORTH, David Roger. 2241 LLOYD CTR 97232 #011-02-1976 L1977 **IM** *050 †20

IMATANI, James, Jr. 5050 NE HOYT ST, STE 610 97213 #007-02-1980 L1981 **GS** *020 †85

INGBAR, Jonathan. ■ 97209 #038-06-1985 L1990 **P IM** *020 †75,20 ‡

INGRAM, Shirley Blaine. 3181 SW SAM JACKSON PRK RD 97239 #048-04-1979 L1981 **RHU IM** *062 †20

IQBAL, Bland. 3181 SW SAM JACKSON PRK RD, RD MC 97239 #704-02-1990 L2007 **IM** *100 †20

IRISH, C Edwin. 1130 NW 22ND AVE 97210 #050-02-1974 L1975 **GS TS** *020 †85

IRONSIDE, Keith L, Jr. 10300 NE HANCOCK ST 97220 #026-04-1967 L1975 **PUD SME** *071

IRONSIDE, Robert Bruce. 1040 NW 22ND AVE STE 620 97210 #016-43-1971 L1973 **IM** *020 †20

IRVINE, Douglas Harvey. 120 NW 14TH AVE, STE 300 97209 #025-01-1987 L1996 **AN** *020 †05 ‡

IRVINE, Gregory Wm. 1 N CENTER COURT ST, ORTHOPEDICS NORTHWEST 97227 #025-01-1978 L1985 **ORS EM** *012

IRVINE, Harry S, Jr. ■ 97230 #040-02-1946 L1947 **OBG GP** *071

IRVINE, Jill Christina. 3101 SW SAM JCKSN PRK RD R, SHRINERS HOSPITALS FOR CH 97239 #025-01-1982 L1985 **AN** *020 †20

IRWIN, Robert Peter. 833 SW 11TH AVE, STE 915 97205 #040-02-1985 L1986 **PA IM** *020 †20

ISAACS, Gwen F. 12615 NE HALSEY ST 97230 #062-01-1975 L1978 **FM** *020

ISAACSON, Terah Christina. ■ 97219 #019-02-2006 L2006 **GS** *012

ISENBARGER, Daniel Wayne. ■ 97231 #010-02-1991 L2007 **IC** *012

ISENHATH, Scott Normile. 3303 SW BOND AVE, CH16-D 97239 #054-04-2004 L2005 **D** *012

ISHAG, Mona Tarig I. 13705 NE AIRPORT WAY 97230 #848-01-1993 L2002 **PTH** *020 †50

ISLEY, Michelle Marie. 3181 SW SAM JCKSN PRK RD R, M/C: UHN 50 97239 #026-04-2002 L2006 **OBG** *020

ISMACH, Richard Brian. ■ 97239 #005-02-1991 L2004 **EM** *020 †20,16

ISOM, John Burnace. ■ 97221 #047-05-1954 L1964 **N PD** *040 †55

ISRAEL, Robert Scott. 10123 SE MARKET ST 97216 #041-01-1984 L1993 **DR** *020 †16,80

ISRAEL, Zvi Harvey. 3181 SW SAM JACKSON PRK RD, OHSU DEPT NEURO SURGERY 97239 #917-07-1986 L1999 *100

ISRAELIT, Arnold H. 5314 NE IRVING ST 97213 #035-06-1964 L1975 **NEP IM** *020 †20

ISRAELIT, Sallie Ellen. 5314 NE IRVING ST 97213 #047-05-1998 L2005 **NEP** *020 †20

IVASHKOV, Julia. 3181 SW SAM JCKSN PRK RD R, OHSU 97239 #913-60-1989 L2003 *100

IVERSON, Duane Roger. 2222 NW LOVEJOY ST, STE 505 97210 #016-06-1971 L1975 **IM** *020 †20

IZENBERG, Seth David. 501 N GRAHAM ST STE 580, PACIFIC SURGICAL PC 97227 #043-01-1980 L1998 **GS TRS** *020 †85

JACKSON, Constance Janene. 4800 SW MACADAM AVE, STE 350 97239 #040-02-1992 L1993 **P** *020 †20

JACKSON, Seth Huntington. 511 SW 10TH AVE, STE 905 97205 #051-01-1968 L1977 **GYN** *020 †30

JACKSON, Shannon E. 5050 NE HOYT ST, STE 540 97213 #005-12-2003 L2003 **IM** *100 †20

JACOB, Stanley Wallace. 3181 SW SAM JACKSON PRK RD, MAIL CODE L225 97239 #038-40-1948 L1962 **GS** *071 †85

JACOBOWITZAMES, Deborah K. ■ 97239 #036-07-2005 L2005 **FP** *012

JACOBS, Kenneth Allan. 2801 N GANTENBEIN AVE 97227 #041-12-1997 L2001 **OBG** *020 †30

JACOBS, Marc Allan. 1111 NE 99TH AVE 97220 #005-18-1992 L1999 **PCC** *020 †20

JACOBS, Melissa Ann. ■ 97209 #035-20-2000 L2007 **DR** *100 †80

JACOBSEN, Gary Anton. 6327 SW CAPITL HWY #C #211 97239 #040-02-1967 L1973 **ADM OS** *062

JACOBSON, Eric Steven. 1015 NW 22ND AVE 97210 #024-01-1965 L1973 **PTH** *020 †50

JACOBSON, Gail Harriet. 6312 SW CAPITOL HWY, STE 502 97239 #040-02-1987 L1988 **IM** *020 †20

JACOBSON, Sig-Linda. 2241 LLOYD CTR 97232 #005-06-1978 L1988 **MFM** *020 †30

JACOBSON, Timothy Dennis. 500 NE MULTNOMAH ST, STE 100 97232 #026-08-1998 L1999 **HOS** *020 †20

JACOBY, David Bernard. 3181 SW SAM JCKSN PRK RD R, M/C UHN-67 97239 #035-09-1980 L2003 **IM** *020 †20

JAFFE, Arthur C. 707 SW GAINES ST, STE CDRCP 97239 #010-02-1970 L1990 **PD** *030 †55

JAHNKE, Kristoph. 3181 SW SAM JCKSN PRK RD R, OHSU 97239 #408-09-2001 L2005 *100

JAIN, Meera. 5050 NE HOYT ST STE 540, SUITE 540 97213 #011-03-1994 L1997 **IM** *020 †20

JALLAD, Rima Huda. 3710 SW US VETRNS HSPTL RD, PORTLAND VA MED CTR 97239 #875-01-1984 L1995 **IMG IM** *020 †20

JAMES, Robert Lewis. ■ 97215 #005-12-1956 L1957 **AN** *020

JAMES, Tricia Torgensen. ■ 97230 #007-02-2008 *012

JAMISON, Richard Lindsay. 1040 NW 22ND AVE, STE 560 97210 #026-08-1993 L1998 **GS** *020 †85

JAMOND, Michael Thos. 3710 SW US VETRNS HSPTL RD, P-3 ANES PORTLADN VAMC 97239 #010-01-1985 L1987 **AN** *020 †05

JAN, Jay Cp. 1040 NW 22ND AVE, STE 500 97210 #041-02-1996 L2003 **GS** *020 †85

JANNUZZI, Joseph David. 500 NE MULTNOMAH ST STE 10 97232 #025-07-1962 L1987 **ORS** *071 †40

JANOFF, Kenneth A. 5050 NE HOYT ST STE 411 97213 #041-13-1978 L1979 **VS GS** *020 †85

JANOSY, Norah Ruth. ■ 97206 #035-01-2004 L2004 **AN** *020

JANSELEWITZ, Steven James. ■ 97210 #038-40-1998 L2004 **PM** *020 †60

JANZEN, Timothy Paul. 10803 SE CHERRY BLOSSOM DR, FAMILY PHYSICIANS 97216 #040-02-1987 L1990 **FM** *020 †20

JARNBERG, Per-Olof. 3181 SW SAM JACKSON PRK RD, UH 2 97239 #858-02-1969 L1994 **AN** *020

JEFFERY, David Andrew. 3415 SE POWELL BLVD 97202 #016-43-1998 L2001 **P** *020 †75

JENE, Joanne. 2801 N GANTENBEIN AVE 97227 #040-02-1960 L1961 **AN** *020 †05 ‡

JENKINS, Linda Hudak. ■ 97214 #008-01-1988 L1989 **P** *020 †75

JENKINS, Randall David. 501 N GRAHAM ST STE 340 97227 #038-45-1980 L1981 **PN PD** *020 †55

JENKINS, Richard Ross. 7705 SE DIVISION ST, DIVISION MED CTR 97206 #008-01-1988 L2006 **IM** *020 †20

JENNINGS, Lori Ann. ■ 97212 #016-11-2006 L2006 **PD** *012

JENNINGS-PETERSON, Dawn. ■ 97239 #038-06-2005 L2006 **FP** *012

JENSEN, Jeffrey Thos. 3181 SW SAM JACKSON PRK RD, DEPT OF OB-GYN L-466 97239 #012-05-1984 L1985 **OBG** *020 †30

JESPERSON, Tricia Noelle. ■ 97202 #028-78-2007, ▲ L2007 **IM** *012

JETMALANI, Ajitkumar N. 3181 SW SAM JACKSON PRK RD 97239 #040-02-1983 L1988 **CHP P** *020 †75

JETMALANI, Shobha N. 2250 NW FLANDERS ST, STE 20 97210 #040-02-1987 L1988 **D** *020 †15

JEW, Ben Christopher. 1121 NE 2ND AVE, OREGON STATE HOSPITAL 97232 #056-05-1997 L2006 **P** *020 †20

JHOOTY, Ameet. 2801 N GANTENBEIN AVE, LEGACY INPATIENT MEDICAL S 97227 #495-45-1996 L2003 **IM** *020 †20

JHOOTY, Rajvir Singh. 3181 SW SAM JACKSON PRK RD 97239 #305-01-2002 L2003 **IM** *020

JHOOTY, Ramnik S. 300 N GRAHAM ST, STE 320 97227 #035-15-1994 L2002 **CD IM** *020 †20

JIMENEZ, Anna Maria. 8935 SE POWELL BLVD 97266 #005-15-1998 L1999 **GPM** *020 †18

JIMENEZ, Walkiria R. ■ 97205 #035-47-2007 L2007 **IM** *012

JIN, Justin Sungho. 3181 SW SAM JACKSON PRK RD R 97239 #021-01-2004 L2004 **ID** *012 †20

JOBE, Blair Anderson. 3181 SW SAM JACKSON PRK RD, L223A 97239 #030-06-1993 L1994 **GS** *020 †85

JOHANSEN, Laurens Foster. 4805 NE GLISAN ST 97213 #005-12-1987 L1989 **FM** *020 †18

JOHANSEN, Luther Wendell. 18750 SE STARK ST 97233 #005-12-1962 L1974 **GP** *020 †18

JOHANSON, Ryan Eric. 120 NW 14TH AVE, STE 300 97209 #040-02-2003 L2007 **AN** *020

JOHNSON, Amy Adelle. 4805 NE GLISAN ST, STE BG05 97213 #056-05-1996 L2001 **IM** *020 †20

JOHNSON, David Spires. 1015 NW 22ND AVE 97210 #028-02-1948 L1970 **PTH CLP** *020 †50

JOHNSON, F Leonard. 2241 LLOYD CTR 97232 #043-03-1969 L1996 **PHO** *071 †55

JOHNSON, Gordy Elliot. 300 N GRAHAM ST, STE 200 97227 #054-04-1994 L1996 **IM** *020 †20

JOHNSON, Gregory Lloyd. 15845 SE BYBEE DR 97236 #035-08-1994 L2004 **DR** *020 †80

JOHNSON, Guy Edward. ■ 97202 #035-09-2007 L2007 **IM** *012

JOHNSON, John Bradley. 120 NW 14TH AVE, STE 300 97209 #040-02-1985 L1986 **AN** *020 †05 ‡

JOHNSON, Joshua Laurence. 5050 NE HOYT ST, STE 315 97213 #021-01-1999 L1999 **N** *020 †75

JOHNSON, Katherine L. 8935 SE POWELL BLVD, ROSEWOOD FAMILY HEALTH CEN 97266 #043-01-2002 L2005 **FM** *020 †18

JOHNSON, Kyle Patrick. 3181 SW SAM JCKSN PRK RD R, OREGON HEALTH SCIENCES UNI 97239 #039-01-1992 L1993 **CHP** *020 †75

JOHNSON, Lisa Kristina. 5050 NE HOYT ST STE 359 97213 #040-02-1999 L1999 **OBG** *020 †30

JOHNSON, Lloyd E. 500 NE MULTNOMAH ST STE 10 97232 #056-05-1953 L1954 **PD ADL** *020 †55

JOHNSON, Martin Clifton. 5201 SW WESTGATE DR, STE 111 97221 #005-11-1959 L1968 **NS N** *071 †25 ‡

JOHNSON, Mary Elizabeth. ■ 97266 #008-01-1983 L1984 **IM** *020 †20

JOHNSON, Melissa Divan. 3181 SW SAM JACKSON PRK RD, SCIENCE UNIV/C 97239 #036-01-2006 L2006 **EM** *012

JOHNSON, Michael Bruce. 3101 SW SAM JCKSN PRK RD R, SHRINERS HOSP FOR CHILDREN 97239 #143-08-1991 L2001 **OP** *100

JOHNSON, Michael Singer. 500 NE MULTNOMAH ST STE 10 97232 #025-07-1973 L1974 **FM** *020 †18

JOHNSON, Nancy Kelly. 800 SW 13TH AVE 97205 #040-02-1990 L1991 **PD** *020 †55

JOHNSON, Natasha Rae. ■ 97239 #056-05-2003 L2003 **IM** *020 †20

JOHNSON, Nathalie Mcdowel. 1130 NW 22ND AVE STE 500 97210 #051-04-1986 L1992 **GS** *020 †85

JOHNSON, Pamela Marie. ■ 97202 #001-02-2004 L2004 **EM** *012

JOHNSON, Stephen Morris. 2801 N GANTENBEIN AVE 97227 #054-04-1983 L2002 **PD PDI** *020 †20

JOHNSON, Steven Wm. 3710 SW US VETRNS HSPTL RD, PORTLAND VA MED CTR 97239 #007-02-1985 L1988 **N** *020

JOHNSON, Susan Harrington. 5436 SE 28TH AVE 97202 #016-11-1987 L1991 **OBG** *020 †30

JOHNSON, Thomas Harry. 3620 N INTERSTATE AVE 97227 #051-04-1979 L1983 **RO** *020 †80

JOHNSON, Trevor Raymond. 3181 SW SAM JACKSON PRK RD, OSHU STE R 97239 #917-10-1988 L2000 *100

JOHNSTON, Bradford Dixon. ■ 97210 #041-12-2004 L2007 **EM** *100

JOHNSTONE, Bruce Beal. 1121 NE 2ND AVE 97232 #040-02-1961 L1962 **P** *020

JONES, Benjamin Beacham. 4805 NE GLISAN ST 97213 #041-13-1953 L1954 **OBG** *071 †18

JONES, Brian Alan. ■ 97210 #017-20-2005 L2005 **GS** *012

JONES, Eric Iversen. 1040 NW 22ND AVE, STE 168 97210 #035-48-1998 L2002 **OPH** *020 †35

JONES, Gary Richard. 3181 SW SAM JCKSN PRK RD R, PED 97239 #040-02-1980 L1995 **PHO PD** *020 †55

JONES, Huw Lloyd. 3181 SW SAM JACKSON PRK RD, OHSU STE R 97239 #917-01-1991 L2000 *100

JONES, James M, Jr. 2311 NW NORTHRUP ST, STE 202 97210 #048-04-1969 L1976 **R** *020 †80

JONES, Kenrick Anthony. 3550 N INTERSTATE AVE, INTERNAL MEDICINE DEPT 97227 #054-04-1993 L1996 **IM** *020 †20

JONES, Mark Anthony. 3181 SW SAM JCKSN PRK RD R, MAIL CODE OP11 97239 #049-01-1999 L2001 **VS** *012

JONES, Mary Elizabeth. 1015 NW 22ND AVE, GOOD SAMARITAN HOSPITAL AC 97210 #041-07-1978 L1983 **EM** *020 †16

JONES, Nikolas Alexander. 6312 SW CAPITOL HWY, STE 502 97239 #038-41-2003 L2003 **EM** *020 †16

JONES, Richard Theodore. 3181 SW SAM JACKSON PRK RD 97239 #040-02-1956 L1958 **OS** *030

JONES, Robert Steven. 19500 SE STARK ST 97233 #040-02-1985 L1994 **IM** *020 †20

JONES, Scott Berian. 1515 NW 18TH AVE, STE 300 97209 #041-01-1982 L1983 **ORS** *020 †40

JONES, Sean Eric. 3550 N INTERSTATE AVE 97227 #008-01-1986 L1987 **IM** *020 †20

JONES, Stephen Richardson. 2282 NW NORTHRUP ST # 27 97210 #018-03-1966 L1975 **IM ID** *030 †20

JORDAN, Michael Colin. 2241 LLOYD CTR 97232 #030-06-1967 L1998 **IM ID** *030 †20

JORDAN, Rosa Garcia. 1130 NW 22ND AVE, STE 220 97210 #005-19-1995 L2006 **IM** *020 †20

JOSLIN, Timothy Alan. 3303 SW BOND AVE, OHSU FAMILY MEDICINE 97239 #010-01-2004 L2004 **FM** *100 †18
JOVANOVIC, Vesna Ann. 2020 SE 182ND AVE, ADVENTIST HEALTH MEDICAL G 97233 #005-19-1998 L2001 **FM** *020 †18
JOVIN, Thomas Michael. ■ 97239 #023-07-1964 **OS** *100
JUI, Jonathan. 1 SE 2ND AVE, AMR NORTHWEST 97214 #025-07-1976 L1977 **EM ID** *030 †20,16
JUMP, Sarah Mynette. ■ 97211 #026-08-2005 L2005 **EM** *012
JUNN, Edward H C. 9724 NW SKYVIEW DR 97231 #065-06-1988 L2000 **EM** *020 †16
JUTLA, Rajninder Kaur. ■ 97201 #905-02-2001 L2007 **PMM** *012
JUVINALL, Fawn Melanie. 2800 N VANCOUVER AVE, STE 230 97227 #038-43-2002 L2002 **END** *012 †20
KABRUN, Eli. 6441 SW CANYON CT, STE 100 97221 #836-02-1956 L1981 *071
KADNER, William. 3500 N INTERSTATE AVE 97227 #035-19-1965 L1972 **R DR** *020 †80
KAGEN, David Ira. 3181 SW SAM JACKSON PRK RD 97239 #023-01-2000 L2000 **IM** *020 †20
KAHANER, Nancy R. 5415 SE MILWAUKIE AVE, STE 1 97202 #035-75-1982, ▲ L1987 **GYN** *020
KAI, Mari. 5050 NE HOYT ST, STE 540 97213 #035-01-1993 L1994 **IM** *020 †20
KAIMAKTCHIEV, Vassil Bori. 3181 SW SAM JACKSON PRK RD, PATHOLOGY DEPT L113 97239 #198-01-1999 L2001 **NP** *012 †50
KALBFLEISCH, Norman Dana. 2241 LLOYD CTR 97232 #054-04-1987 L1988 **EM** *020 †16
KALISIAK, Angela A. 2311 NW NORTHRUP ST STE 1, NORTHWEST CANCER SPECIALIS 97210 #008-02-1983 L1992 **IM** *071 †20
KALLGREN, Mark Andrew. 800 SW 13TH AVE 97205 #003-01-1989 L1993 **PME AN** *040 †05 ‡
KALLGREN, Mary Jo G. 10201 SE MAIN ST, STE 23 97216 #003-01-1995 L1997 **IM** *100
KAM, Benjamin Cheechu, Jr. 3181 SW SAM JACKSON PRK RD, OP31 97239 #021-01-1995 L1999 **ORS** *020 †40
KAMMER, Huldrick. 5050 NE HOYT ST STE 540 97213 #016-06-1941 L1949 **END IM** *071 †20
KANE, Michael Edward. 120 NW 14TH AVE, STE 300 97209 #026-04-1990 L2000 **AN** *020 †05 ‡
KANE, Peter Jos. 5050 NE HOYT ST STE 256 97213 #016-43-1965 L1972 **HEM ON** *020 †20
KANESHIRO, Bliss E. 3181 SW SAM JACKSON PRK RD 97239 #014-01-2001 L2005 **OBG** *100
KANGAS-GATES, Kay. 1321 NE 99TH AVE, STE 100 97220 #040-02-1995 L2001 **IM** *020 †20
KANSAGARA, Devan Lalit. 3710 SW US VETRN HOSP RD, P3HSRD PORTLAND VA MED CTR 97239 #008-02-2001 L2005 **IM** *050
KAO, Amy. 707 SW GAINES ST, CDRC-P 97239 #016-06-1997 L2003 **CHN** *020 †55,75
KAO, Robert. 3550 N INTERSTATE AVE 97227 #005-14-1969 L1971 **GP** *020 †28
KAPLAN, Andrew W. 2801 N GANTENBEIN AVE, LEGACY EMANUEL HOSPITAL 97227 #035-19-1978 L1983 **DR PD** *020 †80
KAPLAN, Stephanie Heindel. 120 NW 14TH AVE, STE 300 97209 #036-01-1992 L1999 **AN** *020 †05 ‡
KAPLAN BERNDSEN, Kimberly. ■ 97239 #042-03-1999 L2005 **AN** *020
KAPPES, Joji. 3550 N INTERSTATE AVE 97227 #005-06-1973 L1978 **RHU IM** *050 †03,20
KARAMLOU, Kasra. 1130 NW 22ND AVE, PACIFIC ONCOLOGY 97210 #010-01-1996 L2000 **HO** *020 †20
KARANOUH, Dia D. ■ 97221 #917-24-1991 L1996 **END** *020 †20
KARL, Diane M Richters. 10000 SE MAIN ST, STE 403 97216 #035-20-1970 L1994 **DIA END** *020 †20
KARR, Daniel John. 3303 SW BOND AVE, FL 11 97239 #011-02-1978 L2006 **OPH PD** *020 †35
KARULF, Matthew Ryan. 3181 SW SAM JCKSN PRK RD R, UHN 67 97239 #007-02-2001 L2005 **PCC** *012 †20
KASKOWITZ, Alexa Pfeffer. ■ 97211 #040-02-2008 *012
KASSAR, Paul. 4805 NE GLISAN ST, STE BG05 97213 #038-40-2001 L2001 **IM** *020
KASTEN, Thomas Lloyd. 2801 N GANTENBEIN AVE 97227 #005-02-2000 L2003 **FM** *020 †18
KATON, Ronald Melvin. 3181 SW SAM JCKSN PRK RD R 97239 #016-42-1966 L1970 **GE** *020 †20
KAUFMAN, John Andrew. 2241 LLOYD CTR 97232 #024-05-1982 L2000 **DR OBG** *020 †80
KAUFMAN, Louis W. ■ 97201 #025-01-1946 L1948 **GS** *071 †85
KAUFMANN, Christoph Robt. 501 N GRAHAM ST, STE 580 97227 #023-12-1982 L2002 **GS TRS** *020 †85
KAUL, Matthew Peter. ■ 97202 #040-02-1987 L1987 **PM** *020 †60
KAUL, Sanjiv. 3181 SW SAM JACKSON PRK RD, PARK ROAD 97239 #495-45-1975 L2006 **CD IM** *050 †20
KAYE, Jeffrey Alan. 3181 SW SAM JACKSON PRK RD, MAIL CODE L226 97239 #035-09-1980 L1988 **N PYG** *050 †75
KAYNARD, Joyce Christine. 1130 NW 22ND AVE, STE 220 97210 #016-06-1986 L1987 **IM** *020 †20
KAZEMY, Abdul Hai. 3710 SW US VETRNS HSPTL RD, PORTLAND VA MED CTR/ PRIMA 97239 #118-01-1975 L2004 **IM** *020 †20
KAZMIERSKI, Eugeniusz A. 545 NE 47TH AVE, STE 106 97213 #759-03-1963 L1970 **IM GE** *020 †20
KEAN, Jaime Ellen. 5050 NE HOYT ST STE 359 97213 #038-06-1994 L1998 **OBG** *020 †30
KEARL, Richard Bryant. 2525 NW LOVEJOY ST, STE 307 97210 #056-05-1977 L1980 **OBG** *020
KEARSLEY, Jennifer Bitere. ■ 97212 #008-02-2005 L2006 **IM** *012
KEELER, Donald Kerry. 2801 N GANTENBEIN AVE 97227 #005-18-1981 L1987 **AN** *020 †20,05 ‡
KEEPERS, George Alan. 3181 SW SAM JCKSN PRK RD R 97239 #048-04-1977 L1978 **P** *020 †75
KEGEL, Gary. 3181 SW SAM JCKSN PRK RD R, SCIENCES UNIV 97239 #041-02-2005 L2005 **ORS** *012
KEHOE, Brenda Lynn. 501 N GRAHAM ST, STE 445 97227 #040-02-1985 L1986 **OBG** *020 †30
KEHR, Elizabeth Lee. 3181 SW SAM JCKSN PRK RD R, OP-30 97239 #035-45-2002 L2002 **IM** *100 †20
KELEMEN, Katalin. ■ 97201 #473-03-1991 L2007 **HMP** *100 †50
KELL, Anne Corinne D. ■ 97202 #054-04-2000 *100
KELLER, Frederick Saul. 3181 SW SAM JCKSN PRK RD R, MAIL CODE L605 97239 #041-01-1968 L1974 **DR VIR** *030 †80
KELLOGG, Henry Jos. 5050 NE HOYT ST 97213 #030-05-1952 L1955 **OPH OS** *071
KELLOGG, Matthew Maxwell. 120 NW 14TH AVE, STE 300 97209 #031-01-2001 L2005 **AN** *020 †05 ‡
KELLY, Frank Joseph. 10201 SE MAIN ST # 27, STE 27 97216 #539-06-1988 L1996 **IM** *020 †20
KELLY, Imelda Calubaquib. 12615 NE HALSEY ST, ADVENTIST MED CTR - HAZELW 97230 #748-20-1988 L2002 **FM** *020 †18
KELLY, Stephen Patrick. 120 NW 14TH AVE, #300 OREGON ANESTH GRP PC 97209 #040-02-1978 L1979 **AN** *020 †05 ‡
KELTNER, Llew. ■ 97221 #038-06-1984 **OS OM** *071
KEMALYAN, Nathan Arthur. 501 N GRAHAM ST, STE 555 97227 #005-14-1987 L1988 **GS TRS** *020 †85
KEMMER, Kathleen Anne. 3181 SW SAM JACKSON PRK RD, MAIL CODE L586 97239 #026-04-1996 L2000 **HO** *020 †20
KEMP, Jonathan Robert. 5050 NE HOYT ST, STE 245 97213 #035-06-1993 L1998 **OPH IM** *020 †35
KEMPLE, Kip Louis. 2311 NW NORTHRUP ST, STE 207 97210 #040-02-1972 L1977 **RHU IM** *020 †20
KENDALL, Adam Rock. ■ 97201 #005-06-2003 L2007 **PLM** *100 †18
KENDALL, Brian August. ■ 97213 #054-04-2005 L2005 **IM** *012
KENDALL, John Walker. 3181 SW SAM JACKSON PRK RD, L-607 97239 #054-04-1956 L1961 **IM END** *071
KENDRICK, Angela. 3181 SW SAM JACKSON PRK RD, PARK RD 97239 #036-01-1982 L1983 **AN IM** *040 †20,05
KENISTON, Richard Chace. 333 SW 5TH AVE STE 300, BETTER BUSINESS BUREAU 97204 #040-02-1975 L1983 **CLP NTR** *050 †50
KENNEDY, John Halisey. 1040 NW 22ND AVE 97210 #038-40-1957 L1972 **PM** *071 †60
KENNEDY, Rebecca H. 3550 N INTERSTATE AVE 97227 #025-01-1999 L2000 **FM** *020 †18
KENNY, Sharon Louise. ■ 97219 #040-02-1999 L1999 **IM** *020 †20
KENT, Jay Frederick. 3600 N INTERSTATE AVE, NORTHWEST PERMANENTE R.C. 97227 #019-02-1963 L1971 **OTO** *020 †45
KEPPEL, Cynthia Reyes. ■ 97221 #748-02-1969 L1976 **P** *020 †75
KEPPEL, John Ford. 1111 NE 99TH AVE STE 200 97220 #035-45-1973 L1976 **PUD** *020 †20
KERMAN, Freda. 3550 N INTERSTATE AVE, HEALTH CENTER EAST MED OFF 97227 #041-07-1981 L1987 **ID IM** *020 †20
KERN, James M. 5050 NE HOYT ST, STE 454 97213 #035-06-1976 L1981 **IM** *020 †20
KESSLER, Stephen. 3181 SW SAM JACKSON PRK RD 97239 #028-34-1965 L1974 **PTH** *020 †50
KETTLER, Mark David. 10123 SE MARKET ST 97216 #025-01-1976 L1987 **DR** *020 †20,80
KHAJANCHEE, Yashodhan Sha. 501 N GRAHAM ST, STE 120 97227 #495-20-1992 L1999 *020
KHALILI, Barzin. 511 SW 10TH AVE, STE 1301 97205 #019-02-2000 L2000 **AI** *020 †20,03 ‡
KHAN, Sajid A. ■ 97205 #035-15-2003 L2007 **GS** *012
KHAW, Kevin Peaung. 10201 SE MAIN ST, STE 25 97216 #035-03-1999 L2007 **RHU** *020 †20
KHINE, Albert Henry. 800 SW 13TH AVE 97205 #010-02-2001 L2007 **IM** *100
KHURMA, Vandana. ■ 97209 #038-41-2001 L2007 **RHU** *020
KIEST, Calvin Herrick. 1015 NW 22ND AVE 97210 #040-02-1955 L1956 **ORS PM** *071 †40
KILLEN, Ronald Hugh. 5319 SW WESTGATE DR, STE 241 97221 #021-01-1979 L1988 **AN** *020 †05
KILLINGBECK, Anne Carissa. ■ 97219 #056-06-2007 L2007 **IM** *012
KIM, Charles Young Joong. 3181 SW SAM JCKSN PRK RD R, L223 97239 #016-11-2000 L2000 **GS** *100 †85
KIM, David Sungjin. ■ 97219 #016-11-2003 L2007 **FM** *020 †18
KIM, Edward. ■ 97210 #017-20-2002 L2006 **N** *100
KIM, Eric Hoon. 120 NW 14TH AVE # 300, STE 300 97209 #040-02-1992 L1994 **AN** *020 †05 ‡
KIM, Harold Hyonsoo. 911 NW 18TH AVE 97209 #035-46-1997 L2004 **OTO** *020 †75,45
KIM, James Yongjae. 10101 SE MAIN ST STE 1001, SPECIALISTS NORTHW 97216 #005-12-1993 L2003 **APM** *100 †18,60
KIM, Janice Jihyun. ■ 97214 #054-04-2006 L2007 **AN** *012
KIM, Jennifer Woojin. ■ 97219 #036-07-2005 L2005 **IM** *012
KIM, Jenny Eun. 3181 SW SAM JCKSN PRK RD R, OHSU 97239 #016-11-2006 L2007 **FP** *012
KIM, Jim Chinhwan. 3600 N INTERSTATE AVE, FL 2 97227 #005-12-1997 L1999 **RHU** *020 †20
KIM, Joseph Jyongwon. 2801 N GANTENBEIN AVE, LEGACY 97227 #031-01-2005 L2005 **IM** *012
KIM, Julie Ann. 501 N GRAHAM ST, NORTHWEST 97227 #056-05-1992 L1993 **GE** *020 †20
KIM, Lauren Hyun Hee. 3181 SW SAM JCKSN PRK RD R, M/C OP 09 ARTH & RHUEM 97239 #035-48-1997 L2004 **RHU** *020 †20
KIM, Shane Kyong. 10819 SE STARK ST STE 200 97216 #035-19-2001 L2007 **OPH** *100 †35
KIM, Sik Kiyoshi. 2801 N GANTENBEIN AVE, EMANUEL HOSPITAL, L+D UNIT 97227 #030-06-1987 L2000 **OBG** *020 †30
KIM, Song Jin. 9000 N LOMBARD ST, NORTH PORTLAND HEALTH CENT 97203 #035-19-1995 L2002 **IM** *020 †20
KIM, Won Kyu. 10300 NE HANCOCK ST, PHYSICIAN'S HOSPITAL 97220 #583-09-1966 L1974 **OBG** *020 †30
KIMBERLEY, Stephen L. 2050 NW LOVEJOY ST 97209 #040-02-1979 L1981 **IMG GPM** *020 †20
KINEALY, Meghan Bridget. 2738 SW RUTLAND TER 97205 #028-46-1997 L2002 **PD** *020 †55
KING, Douglas Hoff. 501 N GRAHAM ST, STE 220 97227 #054-04-1979 L1985 **PDC** *020 †55
KING, Leslie Patrice. 3636 NE 9TH AVE 97212 #051-01-1996 L1997 **EM** *020
KING, Valerie Jean. 3181 SW SAM JACKSON PRK RD, ROAD, MAILCODE 97239 #036-01-1991 L2004 **FM OBG** *050 †70,18
KINGERY, Frederick A J. 2250 NW FLANDERS ST 97210 #035-19-1953 L1959 **D** *071 †15
KINGMA, Mary Christine. 10201 SE MAIN ST STE 2, CTR/BUILDING 3 97216 #040-02-2001 L2007 **NEP** *100
KINGSBURY, Daniel Jos. 2801 N GANTENBEIN AVE, LEGACY EMANUEL HOSP 97227 #047-06-1988 L2000 **PPR** *020 †55
KINGSTON, Harry Geo G. 3181 SW SAM JACKSON PRK RD 97239 #836-01-1967 L1982 **AN OS** *020
KINNE, Jane Evelyn. 3710 SW US VETRNS HSPTL RD 97239 #034-01-1995 L1997 **IM** *020 †20
KINSFATER, Craig. 3181 SW SAM JACKSON PRK RD, OR HLTH SCI UNIV SCH OF ME 97239 #040-02-2005 L2006 **GS** *100
KINSMAN, Kirsten Jeanne. 1111 NE 99TH AVE 97220 #025-07-1990 L1993 **GE** *020 †20
KINZIE, John David. 3181 SW SAM JCKSN PRK RD R 97239 #054-04-1963 L1977 **P** *020 †75
KINZIE, John Mark. 3181 SW SAM JCKSN PRK RD R, M/S UHN 80 97239 #040-02-1999 L2004 **P** *020 †75
KIRALY, Laszlo Nicholas. ■ 97211 #016-06-2002 L2002 **CCS** *100
KIRBY, Aileen Lanette. 707 SW GAINES ST, M/C CDRCP 97239 #005-12-1992 L2001 **CCP PD** *020 †55
KIRK, Edward Paul. 2241 LLOYD CTR 97232 #917-29-1961 L1976 **OBG** *071 †30
KIRSCH, Jeffrey Robt. 3181 SW SAM JACKSON PRK RD, UH 2 97239 #025-01-1983 L2002 **AN** *040 †05
KIRZ, Louise Ida. 2801 N GANTENBEIN AVE 97227 #054-04-1984 L1997 **AN** *020 †05 ‡
KISS, Sandor Raymond. 120 NW 14TH AVE # 300, STE 300 97209 #038-06-1991 L1996 **AN** *020 †05 ‡
KITZIS, Alejandro Lionel. ■ 97201 #033-05-1998 L1999 **EM** *020 †55,16
KIYASU, Phillip Kunisada. 1111 NE 99TH AVE 97220 #021-01-1987 L1994 **IM** *020 †20
KIZZIAR, Ronald William. 5251 NE GLISAN ST BLDG A 97213 #005-12-1997 L1998 **RNR** *020 †80
KLAM, Cheri Nicole. ■ 97211 #005-12-2003 L2006 **FM** *020
KLASS, Alvin Manly. 1890 NE 162ND AVE 97230 #040-02-1963 L1964 **OPH** *071
KLAUS, Lorissa Esther. 19500 SE STARK ST, KAISER - ROCKWOOD MEDICAL 97233 #035-15-1997 L2003 **FM** *020 †18

7780

■ = Address Information Privacy Protected

KLEIN, Andrea Eva. 120 NW 14TH AVE, STE 300 97209 #781-03-1999 L2005 **AN** *020 †05 ‡
KLEIN, Arnold Jay. 3500 N INTERSTATE AVE, INTERSTATE MED OFF S RADIO 97227 #005-06-1986 L1991 **DR VIR** *020 †80
KLEIN, Eran Patrick. ■ 97239 #010-02-2004 L2004 **N** *012
KLEIN, Eve Leah. ■ 97211 #024-16-2006 L2006 **N** *012
KLEIN, Michael Louis. 3303 SW BOND AVE, FL 11 97239 #016-06-1967 L1976 **OPH** *020 †35
KLEIN, Robert Frederick. 3710 SW US VETRNS HSPTL RD 97239 #005-02-1980 L1989 **END IM** *050 †20
KLEIN, Roger Lawrence. ■ 97219 #016-43-1958 L1970 **AN** *040 †05
KLEIN, William M. 3101 SW SAM JACKSON PRK RD, PARK ROAD 97239 #040-02-1989 L1997 **AN** *020 †05
KLEINMAN, Mark Allen. 500 NE MULTNOMAH ST, STE 100 97232 #016-42-1981 L1982 **FM** *020 †18
KLIKS, Bernard Ross. 1040 NW 22ND AVE, STE 660 97210 #026-04-1967 L1976 **CD IM** *020 †20
KLIZAS, Sarah Ann. ■ 97239 #051-01-2002 L2005 **ID** *100 †20
KLOPFENSTEIN, Bethany J. 3181 SW SAM JCKSN PRK RD R, M/S L607 97239 #040-02-1999 L1999 **END** *100 †20
KLOPFER, Keith C. ■ 97239 #033-05-1998 L2000 **FM** *030
KLOSTER, Frank Ellis. 3181 SW SAM JACKSON PRK RD 97239 #018-03-1958 L1964 **CD IM** *071
KNIGGE, Kandice Leigh. 3181 SW SAM JACKSON PRK RD 97239 #049-01-1992 L1996 **GE** *020 †20
KNIGHT-RICHARDSON, N. 3181 SW SAM JCKSN PRK RD R 97239 #048-14-1984 L1992 **P** *020 †75
KNOLL, Julie Ann. ■ 97217 #040-02-2005 L2005 **IM** *012
KNOPF, Gregory Michael. 4805 NE GLISAN ST 97213 #040-02-1976 L1977 **FM** *020 †18
KNOX, Mary Lucretia. 3550 N INTERSTATE AVE, EAST INTERNATIONAL MED OFF 97227 #005-02-1989 L1990 **OBG** *020 †20
KNOX, William Raymond. 500 NE MULTNOMAH ST STE 10 97232 #007-02-1948 L1948 **OBG** *071 †30
KNUDSEN, Wendy Parker. 3500 N INTERSTATE AVE, KAISER INTERSTAT SURGI CEN 97227 #005-11-1976 L1977 **AN OBS** *020 †05
KOCH, Thomas Kenneth. 707 SW GAINES ST, CDRC-P 97239 #005-18-1977 L1998 **CHN N** *020 †55,75
KOEHLER, David Lawrence. 500 NE MULTNOMAH STE 10 97232 #016-06-1957 L1966 **IM** *071 †20
KOELLER, David Martin. 707 SW GAINES ST 97239 #016-11-1982 L2000 **PD** *020 †55,19
KOERNER, Ines Pia. 3181 SW SAM JCKSN PRK RD R 97239 #409-05-1997 L2006 *100
KOESEL, Richard Joseph. 4805 NE GLISAN ST, PROVIDENCE PORTLAND MEDICA 97213 #035-46-1997 L2001 **RNR** *100 †80
KOFFEL, Bettylou. 25 NW 23RD PL, STE 6 PMB 432 97210 #041-07-1978 L1997 **AN** *020 †05
KOH, Jeffrey Lee. 3181 SW SAM JACKSON PRK RD, UH 2 97239 #025-07-1985 L2000 **AN** *020 †05,55
KOH, Wui-Leong. 7705 SE DIVISION ST, KAISER PERMANENTE 97206 #005-12-1994 L2003 **FM** *020 †18
KOHATSU, Wendy Gaye. 3303 SW BOND AVE, M/C FM 97239 #005-14-1994 L2003 **FM** *020 †18
KOHLER, Peter Ogden. 3181 SW SAM JACKSON PRK RD 97239 #036-07-1963 L1989 **IM END** *071 †54
KOHN, Melvin Adam. 800 NE OREGON ST STE 730, OREGON DEPT OF HUMAN SERV 97232 #024-01-1990 L1999 **PD** *030 †55,70
KOHNEN, Paul Wm. PRVDNCE MED CTR, DPT PTH 97213 #023-07-1965 L1978 **PTH OS** *020 †50
KOLBECK, Kenneth John. 3181 SW SAM JCKSN PRK RD R, M/S - L605 97239 #016-11-2000 L2006 **VIR** *100 †80
KOLER, Robert Donald. 3181 SW SAM JACKSON PRK RD 97239 #040-02-1947 **OS IM** *071 †20,19
KOLESNIKOVA, Violetta Ale. 3181 SW SAM JACKSON PRK RD 97239 #913-18-1988 L2005 **PTH** *012
KOMISAROF, Jeffrey Aaron. 3181 SW SAM JCKSN PRK RD R, OREGON HEALTH & SCIENCE UN 97239 #041-01-1999 L2003 **CCM** *100 †20
KONEZ, Orhan. 545 NE 47TH AVE STE 215, RADIOLOGY SPECIALISTS OF N 97213 #902-01-1990 L2007 **PDR** *020 †80
KONKOL, Richard Jos. 3550 N INTERSTATE AVE, PEDIATRIC NEUROLOGY 97227 #010-02-1979 L1992 **PD N** *020 †75
KORCHEVA, Veselina Boriso. 3181 SW SAM JACKSON PRK RD 97239 #198-01-1999 L2006 **PTH** *012
KORERSHI, Safina. ■ 97202 #035-06-2005 L2005 **FP** *012
KORI, Isaac. 3181 SW SAM JACKSON PRK RD, STE R 97239 #550-01-1990 L2002 *100
KORTHUIS, P Todd. 2241 LLOYD CTR 97232 #016-42-1991 L2002 **IM** *020 †20
KOSITCH, Alexander M. 3550 N INTERSTATE AVE 97239 #051-01-1983 L1984 **IM** *020 †20
KOSKI, Gregory Joel. 3325 N INTERSTATE AVE 97227 #026-04-1979 L1985 **ORS** *012
KOSLIN, D Bradley. 3181 SW SAM JACKSON PRK RD, PARK ROAD 97239 #038-43-1981 L1993 **DR** *040 †80
KOSTINER, Dana Ruth. 3325 N INTERSTATE AVE 97239 #010-01-1994 L2002 **MG IM** *020 †20,19
KOSYDAR, Charles Alexande. ■ 97239 #040-02-2007 L2007 **TY** *012
KOUSKOV, Oleg Sergeevich. ■ 97239 #913-32-1997 L2006 **PCC** *012 †20
KOVACSOVICS, Tibor J. 3181 SW SAM JACKSON PRK RD, UHN-73C 97239 #869-04-1981 L2003 **HO** *020
KOZAK, Blaine Eugene. 2801 N GANTENBEIN AVE, EMANUEL HOSPITAL 97227 #054-04-1979 L1980 **DR VIR** *020 †80
KOZAK, Richard John. ■ 97214 #035-06-1994 L1996 **EM** *020 †16
KOZIN, Eliana Lois. 3181 SW SAM JACKSON PRK RD 97239 #539-06-2007 L2007 **IM** *012
KRAJBICH, Joseph Ivan. 3101 SW SAM JCKSN PRK RD R 97239 #065-01-1975 L1993 **OP ORS** *020
KRASNOW, Sharon Marie. ■ 97221 #049-01-1988 L1991 **N** *020
KRATZER, John Robert. 2386 NW HOYT ST 97210 #017-20-2003 L2003 **P** *100
KRAUSE, Valerie Ann. 2241 N WATTS ST 97217 #016-06-1997 L1998 **FM** *020 †18
KREMKAU, Edna Louise B. 507 NE 47TH AVE, THE OREGON CLINIC, P.C. 97213 #040-02-1965 L1994 **CD** *072 †20
KRENKEL, Aaron Paul. ■ 97202 #056-06-2005 L2005 **P** *012
KRET, Marcus Robert. ■ 97209 #016-42-2008 *012
KRIEGER, Walter Reed. 1620 SW TAYLOR ST STE 300 97205 #040-02-1978 L1979 **AN** *071 †05 ‡
KRIPPAEHNE, Marion Larsen. 3181 SW SAM JACKSON PRK RD 97239 #040-02-1948 L1950 **IM IMG** *071

KRISHNAMOORTHY, Brintha. ■ 97214 #016-06-2005 L2005 **IM** *012
KRISHNAN, Brinda Shree. ■ 97232 #051-04-2000 L2000 **P** *020 †75
KRISHNASAMY, Prasannavenka. 2800 N VANCOUVER AVE, LEGACY CLINIC EMANUEL 97227 #495-94-2003 L2007 **IM** *012
KRISHNASWAMI, Sanjay. 501 N GRAHAM ST, STE 300 97227 #041-13-1996 L2005 **PDS** *020 †85
KRISTIN, Staci Lyn. 1509 SW SUNSET BLVD, STE 2E 97239 #040-02-2002 L2002 **EM** *020 †16
KRIZ, Petra. 120 NW 14TH AVE, STE 300 97209 #286-09-1996 L2006 **AN** *020 †05
KROL, Alfons Lucian. 3303 SW BOND AVE, DEPT - DERMATOLOGY 97239 #060-01-1975 L2002 *020 †15
KRON, Jack. 3181 SW SAM JACKSON PRK RD, DIV OF CARDIOLOGY UHN62 97239 #012-05-1978 L1979 **ICE IM** *020 †20
KROOK, Peter Michael, Jr. 3500 N INTERSTATE AVE, MEDICAL OFFICE 97227 #028-02-1975 L1979 **DR** *020 †80
KRUGER, Kristine Ann. 3930 SE DIVISION ST, RICHMOND HEALTH CENTER 97202 #040-02-1998 L2001 **FM** *020 †18
KRUM, Robert Joel. 13705 NE AIRPORT WAY STE C, AIRPORT WAY LAB 97230 #040-02-1991 L1992 **PTH** *020 †50
KRUSCHWITZ, Dohn Royal. 2220 SW 1ST AVE 97201 #018-03-1966 L1995 **GP** *020
KRUSE, Karen Marie. 1015 NW 22ND AVE 97210 #034-01-1990 L1991 **IM** *020 †20
KUANG, Anna Aitsi. 3181 SW SAM JCKSN PRK RD R, M/C: L352A 97239 #035-20-1994 L2005 **PS** *100 †65
KUBOTA, Susan Yuri. 2801 N GANTENBEIN AVE 97227 #035-06-1991 L1992 **AN** *020 †05 ‡
KUCERA, Paul Robt. 5050 NE HOYT ST, STE 454 97213 #016-11-1979 L1986 **GYN GO** *020 †30
KUEHL, Kerry Stephen. 3181 SW SAM JACKSON PRK RD, O.H.S.U MAILCODE CR110 97239 #005-12-1994 L1996 **IM** *020 †20
KUEHNEL, Edward Geo. 10201 SE MAIN ST 27 97216 #035-08-1970 L1975 **NEP IM** *020 †20
KUETHER, Todd Allen. 5050 NE HOYT ST, STE 418 97213 #019-02-1993 L1994 **NS** *020 †25
KUJOVICH, Jody Lynn. 265 N BROADWAY ST 97227 #024-01-1989 L1995 **HO** *020 †20
KULASAVAGE, Alice P R. ■ 97216 #016-11-1943 **GYN** *071 †30
KULIK, James Paul. 3225 N INTERSTATE AVE, PAIN MANAGEMENT CLINIC 97227 #021-05-1997 L2001 **PM** *020 †60
KULLBERG, Patricia Ann. 426 SW STARK ST, 8TH FL 97204 #040-02-1979 L1984 **FM PHP** *030 †18
KULLNAT, Jonathan Aaron. 2801 N GANTENBEIN AVE, LEGACY 97227 #040-02-2005 L2005 **DR** *012
KUNIHOLM, Erin Fairbank. ■ 97211 #036-07-2002 L2005 **EM** *020 †16
KUNIO, Nicholas Robert. ■ 97239 #016-11-2007 L2007 **GS** *012
KUO, Lena Fungwen. 2801 N GANTENBEIN AVE, MEDICAL STAFF OFFICE 97227 #035-20-2002 L2007 **PD** *020 †55
KURMASKIE, Jennifer. 2800 N VANCOUVER AVE, STE 165 97227 #011-04-1993 L2001 **PD** *020 †55
KURRE, Peter. 3181 SW SAM JACKSON PRK RD, CDRCP 97239 #409-39-1991 L2004 **PHO** *020 †55
KURZ, Frank Jos. 2222 NW LOVEJOY ST, STE 505 97210 #048-04-1977 L1979 **IM** *020 †20
KURZ, Paul Allen. 3375 SW TERWILLIGER BLVD 97239 #038-40-1998 L2006 **OPH** *012 †35
KWONG, Karen Lynn. 2241 LLOYD CTR 97232 #038-06-1990 L2002 **GS** *020 †85
KYRIAKOPOULOS, Damianos D. 3600 N INTERSTATE AVE 97227 #418-02-1967 L1975 **OTO** *020 †45
KYSER, James Phililp. 501 N GRAHAM ST, STE 220 97227 #038-40-1999 L2005 **PDC** *100 †55
LA, Mike Quocchau. ■ 97239 #040-02-2008 *012
LABBY, Daniel H. 3181 SW SAM JCKSN PRK RD R 97239 #040-02-1939 L1945 **P IM** *040 †20
LABBY, David. 3303 SW BOND AVE, FL 9 97239 #017-20-1990 L1991 **IM** *020 †20
LACHMAN, Alan Barry. 3181 SW SAM JACKSON PRK RD 97239 #023-01-1962 L1965 **D** *071 †15
LACKOWSKI, Douglas M. 3600 N INTERSTATE AVE, CENTRAL INTERSTATE MED OFF 97227 #045-04-1992 L1993 **HEM** *020 †20
LA FRANCHI, Stephen Henry. 707 SW GAINES ST, DEPT OF PEDIATRICS 97239 #005-14-1969 L1971 **END PD** *020 †20
LAHIJI, Patrice Mc Gowan. ■ 97202 #033-05-1994 L1999 **RO** *020 †80
LAHTI, Elizabeth Pepper. 2491 SW SHERWOOD DR 97201 #016-11-2002 L2002 **IM** *100 †20
LAI, Albert. ■ 97239 #040-02-2008 *012
LAIDLEY, Tracy Lynn. 501 N GRAHAM ST STE 100 97227 #035-19-1992 L1993 **IM** *020 †20
LAIRD, Robert James. 5050 NE HOYT ST, STE 445 97213 #040-02-1968 L1975 **OPH** *071 †35
LAKDAWALLA, Hussain M. ■ 97212 #495-37-1995 L2006 **AN** *020 †05
LAKIN, Paul Conrad. 2241 LLOYD CTR 97232 #007-02-1964 L1971 **DR OS** *020 †80
LALLI, Richard Arthur. ■ 97201 #040-02-1956 L1960 **OPH** *071 †35
LALOR, Molly Margaret. ■ 97239 #040-02-2007 L2007 **IM** *012
LALWANI, Kirk. 3181 SW SAM JACKSON PRK RD, UH 2 97239 #495-52-1988 L1999 **AN PD** *020
LAMB, Rick Dwayne. 3710 SW US VETRNS HSPTL RD, VA MEDCIAL CENTER - PORTLA 97239 #005-18-1984 L1984 **EM** *020 †16
LAMKIN, Thomas David. ■ 97212 #016-06-1988 L2003 **PHO** *020 †55
LANDON, Rachel Elizabeth. 3600 N INTERSTATE AVE, INTERSTATE MEDICAL OFFICE 97227 #016-02-1994 L1999 **OPH** *020 †35
LANDRETH, Eugene Williams. ■ 97239 #040-02-1948 L1952 **CLP PTH** *071 †50
LANDRY, Gregory James. 3181 SW SAM JACKSON PRK RD, MAIL CODE OP11 97239 #056-05-1991 L1992 **VS** *020 †85
LANFORD, Windsong Hollis. 3181 SW SAM JACKSON PRK RD, OR HLTH SCI UNIV HOSP 97239 #021-01-2000 L2007 **PYG** *012 ‡
LANG, Barbara Ann. 1321 NE 99TH AVE, STE 200 97220 #040-02-1999 L2000 **FM** *020 †18
LANG, Michael Peter. ■ 97239 #035-01-2004 L2005 **IM** *012
LANGDON, Theresa Anne. 181 NE 102ND AVE 97220 #016-01-1986 L1987 **FM** *020 †18
LAPIDUS, Alexander D. 1125 SE 47TH AVE 97215 #005-19-2000 L2000 **EM** *100
LARNER, Albert Ernest. 2228 LLOYD CTR 97232 #065-01-1959 L1963 **D A** *020
LARSEN, David Stephen. 3181 SW SAM JCKSN PRK RD R, OHSU 97239 #028-34-2002 L2006 **AN** *100 †05
LARSEN, Greg Christian. 2241 LLOYD CTR 97232 #054-04-1978 L1985 **CD IM** *020 †20
LARSEN, Jerry Kemp. 1027 E BURNSIDE ST, ABUSERS 97214 #040-02-1968 L1971 **P** *020
LARSEN, Kenna. ■ 97209 #034-01-2003 L2003 **ORS** *012
LARSEN, Walter G. 2250 NW FLANDERS ST, STE 20 97210 #005-06-1960 L1961 **D** *020 †15
LARSON, Dawn Marie. ■ 97214 #017-20-2004 L2007 **AN** *012
LASH, Emilyflore Edwards. ■ 97239 #040-02-2008 *012
LASHLEY, David Brian. 2230 NW PETTYGROVE ST, STE 210 97210 #040-02-1993 L1994 **UP** *020 †95
LASZEWSKI, Jayne Anne. 1940 NE BROADWAY 97232 #056-05-1997 L1999 **P** *020

LATHAM MARKIN, Catherine. 3181 SW SAM JCKSN PRK RD U, M/S UHN67 97239 #040-02-1992 L1993 **PCC** *020 †20

LATTIN, Jason Arlen. 3181 SW SAM JACKSON PRK RD 97239 #054-04-2003 L2003 **GS** *012

LAUER, Andreas Katsuya. 3303 SW BOND AVE, FL 11 97239 #039-01-1994 L1999 **OPH** *020 †35

LAUNEY, Donna Suzanne. 233 NE 102ND AVE 97220 #021-05-1989 L1993 **R** *020 †80

LAW, Ivan Pe. 2707 NE 33RD AVE 97212 #209-01-1964 L1977 **ON IM** *020 †20

LAWRENCE, David Mc Kinnon. 3500 N INTERSTATE AVE 97227 #020-12-1966 L1977 **PHP GP** *030 †70

LAWRENCE, Robert. 3550 N INTERSTATE AVE 97227 #056-06-1976 L1980 **AI PD** *020 †55,03

LAWRENCE, Stuart Alan. 2801 N GANTENBEIN AVE 97227 #007-02-1972 L1975 **PD** *020

LAYNE, Matthew Wagner. 2801 N GANTENBEIN AVE 97227 #024-07-1999 L2003 **AN** *020 †05 ‡

LAZAR, Burton Wayne. 800 SW 13TH AVE, THE PORTLAND CLINIC 97205 #016-45-1985 L1988 **IM PTH** *020 †20

LE, Daitrang Elizabeth. 3181 SW SAM JCKSN PRK RD R, M/C: UHN62 97239 #008-01-1993 L2005 **CD** *020 †20

LE, Khoi Ha. 545 NE 47TH AVE 97213 #014-01-2004 L2004 **IM** *020 †20

LE, Thienluong. ■ 97239 #040-02-2008 *012

LE, Vien Voquang. 3181 SW SAM JCKSN PRK RD R, SCIENCE UNIV 97239 #018-03-2002 L2007 **CCM** *012 †20

LEACH, Benjamin H. ■ 97219 #048-12-2005 L2005 **IM** *012

LEAVERTON, Gary Howard. 511 SW 10TH AVE STE 714 97205 #040-02-1955 L1956 **CRS GS** *072 †85,10

LE BLANC, Erin Scalley. 3181 SW SAM JCKSN PRK RD R, M/S- L607 97239 #008-01-1995 L1998 **END** *100 †20

LEBRON, Francisco Arturo. ■ 97239 #042-01-2000 L2004 **AN** *100 †05

LECLAIR, Catherine Marie. 3181 SW SAM JCKSN PRK RD R 97239 #050-02-1995 L1997 **OBG** *020 †30

LE CLAIR, Susan Lewis. 120 NW 14TH AVE, STE 300 97209 #023-12-1990 L2001 **AN** *020 †05 ‡

LEE, Alisa Beth. ■ 97239 #026-04-2006 L2007 **PD** *012

LEE, Brent Younghoon. ■ 97201 #005-12-2006 L2006 **IM** *012

LEE, Carol Ellen. 2801 N GANTENBEIN AVE 97227 #025-01-1978 L1982 **AN** *020 †05 ‡

LEE, Dae Young. ■ 97232 #012-01-2004 L2005 **GS** *012

LEE, David Michael. 3303 SW BOND AVE, STE CH10F 97239 #008-01-1993 L2000 **OBG** *020 †30 ‡

LEE, David Techang. 10123 SE MARKET ST, PORTLAND ADVENTIST MEDICAL 97216 #038-43-1993 L1994 **IM** *020 †20

LEE, Donnie. 1220 SW 3RD AVE, STE 476 97204 #041-01-1984 L1995 **FM** *020 †18

LEE, G Prentiss. 1015 NW 22ND AVE, STE 307 97210 #040-02-1943 **GS** *071 †85

LEE, Harold. 10101 SE MAIN ST STE 2016 97216 #040-01-1982 L1985 **PM** *020

LEE, Harry Arbaugh. ■ 97201 #007-02-1961 L1963 **OBG** *071 †30

LEE, Hyung-Suk Tommy. 2801 N GANTENBEIN AVE 97227 #065-05-2000 L2005 *100

LEE, Jennifer Jin. 3181 SW SAM JACKSON PRK RD, DEPT RAD 97239 #005-02-2005 L2007 **DR** *012

LEE, John S. 2363 NW FLANDERS ST 97210 #035-01-1994 L1999 **PS** *020 †65

LEE, Ken Kyung-Hoon. 3303 SW BOND AVE CH5D, DEPT - DERMATOLOGY 97239 #035-20-1990 L1995 **D** *020 †20,15

LEE, Melinda Ann. 13007 NE GLISAN ST 97230 #005-02-1979 L1981 **IMG IM** *050 †20

LEE, Michael. 800 SW 13TH AVE, THE PORTLAND CLINIC 97205 #016-06-1982 L1987 **GS** *020 †30

LEE, Michael Sukmin. 2525 NW LOVEJOY ST, STE 100 97210 #008-01-1993 L2004 **OPH** *020 †35

LEE, Misa Melissa. 1015 NW 22ND AVE, LEGACY GOOD SAMARITAN HOSP 97210 #056-06-1994 L1999 **RO** *020 †80

LEE, Patrick Yuk-Hoi. 511 SW 10TH AVE, COLON RECTAL SURGICAL 97205 #016-06-1988 L1990 **CRS SO** *020 †85,10

LEE, Randall A. 1015 NW 22ND AVE, CASCADE PATHOLOGY SERVICES 97210 #049-01-1976 L1987 **PTH** *020 †50

LEE, Raymond. 3181 SW SAM JACKSON PRK RD, SCIENCE UNIV/C 97239 #010-02-2005 L2005 **EM** *012

LEE, Tack-Shin. 3101 SW SAM JACKSON PRK RD 97239 #143-11-1995 L2005 *100

LEE, Wai Leong. 5050 NE HOYT ST, STE 155 97213 #028-02-1995 L2001 **RHU** *020 †20,03

LEE, Wai Ming. 3500 N INTERSTATE AVE, DEPARTMENT OF ANESTHESIOLO 97227 #040-02-1992 L1993 **AN PME** *020 †05

LEEBORG, Nicky Jo. ■ 97206 #035-15-2003 L2003 **PTH** *100 †50

LEFLER, William Stephen. ■ 97215 #012-01-2007 L2007 **IM** *012

LEFOR, Michael John. 1111 NE 99TH AVE 97220 #040-02-1996 L2002 **PCC** *020 †20

LEGER, Andre Robert. 3181 SW SAM JCKSN PRK #R, OHSU DEPT/GEN SURG 97239 #034-01-1996 L1997 **GS** *020 †85

LEGG, Edith Alfredda. ■ 97212 #048-02-1997 L1998 **U** *020 †95

LEGGETT, James E, Jr. 5050 NE HOYT ST, INFECTION CONSULTANTS LLP 97213 #020-12-1980 L1999 **ID IM** *040 †20

LE GRAS, Marc D. 501 N GRAHAM ST, STE 220 97227 #067-01-1987 L1996 **PDC** *020 †55

LEI, Stan Sizheng. 800 SW 13TH AVE 97205 #243-47-1983 L1998 **AN** *020 †05 ‡

LEIBOVITZ, Joshua Robert. 1509 SW SUNSET BLVD STE 2E, SPECIALISTS 97239 #005-15-1996 L1998 **EM** *020 †16

LEIGH, Janet Marilyn. 19500 SE STARK ST, ROCKWOOD MEDICAL OFFICE 97233 #005-15-1986 L1987 **OBG** *020 †20

LEIMERT, Joseph Thompson. 3550 N INTERSTATE AVE 97227 #035-01-1973 L1980 **ON IM** *020 †20

LEIVA, Maria C. 2705 E BURNSIDE ST STE 114 97214 #264-04-1983 L2004 **OBG** *020 †30

LEMAN, Richard Farwell. 800 NE OREGON ST, STE 730 97232 #040-02-1989 L1991 **FM** *020 †18

LEMLEY, Craig Augustus. 2525 NW LOVEJOY ST, STE 100 97210 #054-04-2001 L2007 **OPH** *020 †35

LEMMER, John Henry, Jr. 2222 NW LOVEJOY ST, STE 315 97210 #040-02-1979 L1991 **TS** *020 †85,90

LENG, Poh Hock. 2801 N GANTENBEIN AVE, LEGACY HEALTH SYSTEM 97227 #825-01-1991 L2004 **IM** *020 †20

LENNARZ, William. 1509 SW SUNSET BLVD, STE 2E 97239 #051-01-1985 L2004 **PD** *020 †55

LEON, Dolores Anne. 120 NW 14TH AVE, STE 300 97209 #040-02-1975 L1977 **AN** *071 †05 ‡

LEON, Fernando. ■ 97205 #649-01-1955 L1962 **TS** *071 †85,90

LEON, Jeffrey Edward. 2801 N GANTENBEIN AVE 97227 #045-14-1985 L1989 **AN** *020 †05 ‡

LEONARD, Heather. 5050 NE HOYT ST STE 540, MEDICAL CE 97213 #018-03-2002 L2002 **IM** *020 †20

LEONARD, Hubert Arnold. 1040 NW 22ND AVE, STE 420 97210 #040-02-1973 L1974 **N IM** *020 †75

LEONHARDT, Danny Earsel. 2800 N VANCOUVER AVE # 201, LEGACY EMANUEL CHILDREN'S 97227 #016-02-1995 L2007 **PD** *020 †55

LESSELROTH, Blake Justin. ■ 97217 #021-01-2000 L2000 **IM** *100 †20

LESTER, Linda Baker. 3181 SW SAM JACKSON PRK RD 97239 #054-04-1988 L1989 **END** *020 †20

LETKO, Erik. 3375 SW TERWILLIGER BLVD, CASEY EYE INSTITUTE 97239 #286-13-1994 L2005 **OPH** *012

LE TOURNEAU, Jennifer L. 3181 SW SAM JCKSN PRK RD R, M/S: UHN 67 97239 #005-76-2000, ▲ L2000 **CCM** *012 †20

LEUNG, Paul Ka-Hing. 3181 SW SAM JCKSN PRK RD R 97239 #051-04-1981 L1982 **P** *020 †75

LEVANDA, Carole. 1130 NW 23RD AVE # 520 97210 #011-02-1983 L1984 **OBG** *020 †30

LEVERETTE, Roger Barr. 800 SW 13TH AVE 97205 #031-01-1987 L1988 **IM** *020 †20

LEVIN, Dina Jane. 177 NE 102ND AVE, BLDG V 97220 #035-46-1993 L1997 **OBG** *020 †30

LEVIN, Tedd. 5919 SE BELMONT ST, MT TABOR FAMILY MEDICAL 97215 #016-06-1982 L1986 **FM GPM** *020 †70,18

LEVITTE, Marc Geo. 2400 SW VERMONT ST, FANNO CREEK CLINIC LLC 97219 #048-04-1976 L1990 **IM** *020 †20 ‡

LEVITTE, Susan Schutzman. VET ADMIN MED CTR P3MHDC 97207 #048-04-1981 L1990 **P** *020 †75

LEWINSOHN, David Michael. 2241 LLOYD CTR 97232 #005-11-1989 L1998 **CCM** *020 †20

LEWIS, Barbara Kathleen. 550 SW JACKSON ST, 9205 SW BARNES ROAD 97201 #020-02-2001 L2006 **MPD** *100 †20,55

LEWIS, David Warren. 2241 LLOYD CTR 97232 #005-19-1993 L1994 **DR** *020 †28,80

LEWIS, Linda M. 5050 NE HOYT ST STE 454, PROVIDENCE MEDICAL GROUP 97213 #017-20-1991 L1992 **IM** *071 †20

LEWIS, Marcia Ann. ■ 97215 #054-04-1981 L1984 **EM IM** *020 †20,16

LEWIS, Michael Scott. 1130 NW 22ND AVE STE 220, LEGACY CLINIC NORTHWEST 97210 #012-01-1980 L1983 **PUD CCM** *020 †20

LEWIS, Paul Francis. 6315 SE 15TH AVE 97202 #005-11-1987 L1996 **PD** *050 †55

LEWIS, Ralph Carl. 5050 NE HOYT ST STE 255, LAURELHURST WOMEN'S CLINIC 97213 #005-18-1981 L1983 **OBG** *020 †20

LEWIS, Sandra Jean. 2222 NW LOVEJOY ST, STE 606 97210 #005-11-1977 L1985 **CD IM** *020 †20

LEWIS, Timothy Wade. 4805 NE GLISAN ST, EMERGENCY DEPARTMENT 97213 #054-04-1991 L1992 **EM** *020 †16

LEWY, Alfred James. 3181 SW SAM JACKSON PRK RD, # L469 97239 #016-02-1973 L1980 **P OS** *050 †75

LEZAK, Myron Burton. 2400 SW VERMONT ST, FANNO CREEK CLINIC LLC 97219 #016-02-1969 L2001 **GE** *020 †20

LI, Melissa Kay. ■ 97210 #040-02-1995 L2004 **FOP** *020 †50

LI, Miao. 2801 N GANTENBEIN AVE 97227 #035-15-2002 L2002 **IM** *020 †20

LI, Xiaokui. ■ 97201 #243-79-1988 **IM** *012

LIAO, Eric Bin. ■ 97201 #041-12-2004 L2005 **IM** *100

LIAO, Jimmy Mingyuh. 1321 NE 99TH AVE, STE 100 97220 #025-01-2001 L2002 **FM** *020 †18

LIAO, Teresa Hsueh. ■ 97201 #023-01-1986 L2000 **AN** *020 †05

LIBBY, Louis Samuels. 1111 NE 99TH AVE 97220 #010-01-1977 L1985 **PUD CCM** *020 †20

LIBERMAN, Llewelyn Eric. ■ 97221 #024-01-1945 L1959 **IM END** *072 †20

LICKTEIG, Karen Hummer. 1130 NW 22ND AVE STE 320 97210 #048-12-1991 L1998 **PD** *020 †55

LIEBERMAN, David Alan. 3181 SW SAM JACKSON PRK RD 97239 #025-01-1976 L1977 **GE** *040 †20

LIEBERMAN, Michael Ian. 3181 SW SAM JCKSN PRK RD R, OR HEALTH SCI UNIV 97239 #005-18-1991 L1992 **IM** *020 †20

LIEBREICH, Brian Scott. 4805 NE GLISAN ST, 3 E MENTAL HEALTH ADMIN 97213 #040-02-1985 L1989 **P** *020 †75

LIEDEL, John Wm. 7707 SW CAPITOL HWY 97219 #038-40-1974 L1975 **PD** *020 †55

LIEL, Meghan Shaw. ■ 97213 #036-07-2006 L2006 **IM** *012

LIEM, Timothy King. 3181 SW SAM JACKSON PRK RD, # OP-11 97239 #005-06-1990 L2001 **VS GS** *020 †85

LIGHTHALL, Jessica Grace. ■ 97239 #040-02-2008 *012

LILES, Elizabeth G. 3550 N INTERSTATE AVE 97227 #063-01-2003 L2004 **IM** *100 †20

LILLIS, Joseph Vincent. ■ 97214 #010-02-2005 L2005 **D** *012

LIM, Christopher N H. 5050 NE HOYT ST, STE 610 97213 #060-01-1974 L1979 **GS ON** *020 †20

LIM, Lei Yuan. 3181 SW SAM JACKSON PRK RD, OR HLTH SCI UNIV HOSP 97239 #064-01-2004 L2007 **GE** *012 †20

LIM, Lyndell Lee Ping. 3375 SW TERWILLIGER BLVD, CASEY EYE INSTITUTE 97239 #143-02-1996 L2005 *100

LIMBAUGH, Kevin James. ■ 97221 #023-01-2003 L2003 **DR** *012

LIN, David W. 3600 N INTERSTATE AVE, INTERSTATE MED OFFICE 97227 #048-04-1991 L1992 **OTO** *020 †45

LIN, Hsinchen Jean. ■ 97219 #012-01-2004 L2004 **GS** *012

LIN, Jennifer Shihwei. ■ 97215 #035-19-2000 L2005 **IM** *020 †20

LIN, Lianne Liangjung. ■ 97239 #040-02-2008 *012

LIN, Wendy. 3550 N INTERSTATE AVE, KAISER PERMANENTE 97227 #016-02-1989 L2004 **PD** *020 †55

LINCK, Leesa Marie. 1591 SE MAPLE AVE 97214 #005-02-1992 L1995 **MG** *020 †19,55

LINCOLN, Douglas Ronald, III. ■ 97206 #021-01-2007 L2007 **PD** *012

LIND, Renae Louise. 1040 NW 22ND AVE, STE 330 97210 #026-08-1987 L1988 **OBG** *020 †30

LINDAU, Mark Schloff. 2801 N GANTENBEIN AVE 97227 #026-04-1970 L1976 **PD** *020 †55

LINDBERG, John Francis. 1420 NW LOVEJOY ST, LOFT 409 97209 #054-04-1975 L1979 **IM** *020 †20,16

LINDELL, Thomas David. 0227 SW PALATINE HILL RD R 97219 #005-11-1967 L1970 **GS VS** *020 †85

LINDNER, Jonathan. ■ 97221 #048-12-1990 L2005 **CD** *020 †20

LINDQUIST, Richard Harmon. ■ 97202 #020-02-1947 L1959 **GS** *071

LINDSAY, James Niles. 2801 N GANTENBEIN AVE, EMANUEL CHILDREN'S HOSPITA 97227 #005-18-1980 L1996 **CCP PEM** *020 †55,16

LINDSAY, Kurt Daniel. ■ 97239 #040-02-2004 L2004 **N** *012

LINGAS, John. 2250 NW FLANDERS ST # 306 97210 #060-01-1959 L1970 **CHP P** *071 †75

LINK, Holger Werner. 707 SW GAINES ST, MAIL CODE: CDRCP 97239 #409-07-1994 L2001 **PDP PD** *020 †55

LINN, Merritt Lewis. ■ 97210 #040-02-1961 L1964 **OPH** *071 †35

LIPMAN, Derek Spencer. 2525 NW LOVEJOY ST STE 208 97210 #836-02-1966 L1977 **OTO** *020 †20

LIPPERT, Dennis Michael. 10000 SE MAIN ST STE 205, ADMISSION AND MANAGEMENT 97216 #051-07-2004 L2004 **IM** *020 †20

LIPPINCOTT, Tyler Bertram. 233 NE 102ND AVE, 8950 SW NIMBUS AVE 97220 #024-07-1986 L1990 **DR** *020 †80

LIPTON, Sarah Jan. ■ 97206 #008-02-2005 L2005 **IM** *012

LISAC, Gerald Thos. 5050 NE HOYT ST, ORTHOPEDICS SPECIALISTS PC 97213 #040-02-1963 L1964 **ORS** *071 †40

LISSMAN, Thomas Larry. 4506 SE BELMONT ST, STE 204 97215 #040-02-1998 L1999 **P** *020 †75

LITT, Robert Joseph. 3181 SW SAM JCKSN PRK RD R, UHN-62 97239 #016-02-1999 L2002 **CD** *020 †20

LITTLE, James Russell, Jr. 202 NW 13TH AVE 97209 #007-02-1998 L1999 **FM** *020 †18

LITVACK, Zachary Naren. ■ 97209 #043-01-2003 L2003 **NS** *012

LITWER, Lawrence Ronald. 4117 NE COUCH ST 97232 #165-08-1980 L1990 **EM FM** *020 †18,16

LIU, Cynthia Hsiyenn. 10123 SE MARKET ST 97216 #012-01-1999 L2003 **AN** *020 †05 ‡

LIU, Kenneth Chanying. ■ 97239 #005-06-2001 L2001 **NS** *012

LIU, Ming Hui. 3181 SW SAM JCKSN PRK RD R, OHSU 97239 #243-76-1984 L2004 *100

LIU, Robyn Ann. 3181 SW SAM JCKSN PRK RD R, MAIL CODE FM 97239 #019-02-2003 L2003 **FM** *100 †18,70

LIVINGSTON, Catherine Jea. 3181 SW SAM JACKSON PRK RD, RD - 97239 #024-01-2005 L2005 **FP** *012

LLOYD, Jonathan Reynolds. ■ 97219 #020-12-2008 *012

LLOYD, Michael John. 3375 SW TERWILLIGER BLVD 97239 #048-12-2004 L2005 **OPH** *012

LLOYD, Spencer Blunt. 5050 NE HOYT ST STE 540, MEDICAL CE 97213 #049-01-2005 L2005 **IM** *012

LO, Jamie Oiting. ■ 97239 #040-02-2008 *012

LOBITZ, Caroline Rockwell. ■ 97239 #016-06-1942 L1943 **OS** *071

LOCHNER, Jennifer E. 3303 SW BOND AVE 97239 #056-05-1999 L2000 **FM** *020 †18

LOCK, Jesse Maxwell. 3181 SW SAM JACKSON PRK RD, DCH105 97239 #035-03-2002 L2002 **PD** *020 †55

LOCKEY, Christopher James. 2833 NE FLANDERS ST 97232 #038-41-2003 L2003 **PFP** *012

LOEB, Felix Faust. ■ 97201 #024-01-1955 L1980 **PYA P** *020 †75

LOEB, Loretta L Roseman. ■ 97201 #041-12-1957 L1980 **PYA CHP** *020 †75

LOEB, Nancy Anne. 3550 N INTERSTATE AVE 97227 #018-03-1979 L1987 **IM EM** *020 †20,16

LOEB, Sandra G. 2801 N GANTENBEIN AVE 97227 #041-13-1989 L1996 **AN** *020 †55,05 ‡

LOEBNER, Mindy Sue. 5050 NE HOYT ST, STE 240 97213 #038-06-1989 L1991 **FM** *020 †18

LOEFFLER, Ann Marie. 2801 N GANTENBEIN AVE 97227 #026-04-1987 L2003 **PDI** *020 †55

LOERA, Nikolas Francis. ■ 97239 #040-02-2008 *012

LOFBERG, Katrine Margreth. 3181 SW SAM JACKSON PRK RD, OR HLTH SCI UNIV HOSP 97239 #054-04-2007 L2007 **GS** *012

LOFTIN, Kara Jeanne. ■ 97206 #048-13-2007 L2007 **PD** *012

LOGAN, Jacqueline Susan. PO BOX 19055 97280 #040-02-1995 L1998 **IM** *020 †20

LOGAN, Judith Rose. 3181 SW SAM JACKSON PRK RD, OHSU/MAIL CODE BICC 97239 #005-06-1976 L1987 **EM** *020 †16,18

LOMBARDI, Lorinna H. ■ 97202 #005-11-2005 L2006 **OPH** *012

LOMBOS, Natividad C. 10300 NE HANCOCK ST 97220 #748-08-1965 L1982 **GP** *030

LONG, Wm Broughton, III. 501 N GRAHAM ST STE 580, PACIFIC SURGICAL PC 97227 #023-01-1968 L1983 **TRS CD** *030 †85,90

LONGAKER, Christopher Jay. 511 SW 10TH AVE STE 714 97205 #038-41-1968 L1976 **CRS** *071 †10

LOOMIS, Anna Catherine. 1321 NE 99TH AVE, STE 200 97220 #051-01-1998 L1999 **FM** *020 †18

LOOMIS, John Stebbins, III. 18750 SE STARK ST 97233 #016-06-1978 L1996 **PD EM** *020 †18,55

LOPEZ, Charles Dayrit. 3181 SW SAM JCKSN PRK RD R, M/C L586B 97239 #005-02-1991 L2001 **IM** *020 †20

LOPEZ-BERMEJO, Abel. 3181 SW SAM JACKSON PRK RD, PED NRC 5/OHSU 97239 #847-07-1991 **PDE** *100

LORBER, Eileen Mary. ■ 97219 #040-02-1996 *100

LORENSEN, Gilda Jane. 3500 N INTERSTATE AVE 97227 #036-07-1981 L1983 **OBG** *020 †30

LORENZ, Linda R. 3550 N INTERSTATE AVE 97227 #040-02-1986 L1987 **PD** *020 †55

LORENZO, Cedric S. ■ 97201 #014-01-2000 L2007 **GS** *020

LORIAUX, Donald Lynn. 3181 SW SAM JCKSN PRK RD R 97239 #048-04-1967 L1990 **END HOS** *040 †20

LORIAUX, Marc Maurice. ■ 97239 #040-02-1997 L2001 **HMP** *020 †50

LORTS, Gregory Byron. 4805 NE GLISAN ST 97213 #040-02-1974 L1975 **EM** *020 †16

LOU, Jau-Shin. 3181 SW SAM JACKSON PRK RD, PARK RD 97239 #244-02-1979 L1999 **N** *050 †75

LOVELESS, Mark Olin. ■ 97212 #016-06-1975 L1980 **ID** *062 †20

LOVERDE, Vernon Douglas. ■ 97202 #028-02-1968 L1971 **IM PUD** *020 †20

LOVITZ, Robert Scott. 10123 SE MARKET ST 97216 #035-46-1988 L1992 **AN** *020 †05 ‡

LOVRIEN, Everett Winslow. 3181 SW SAM JACKSON PRK RD 97239 #026-04-1959 L1968 **PD MG** *020 †55,19

LOW, Lewis Lee. 1015 NW 22ND AVE, LEGACY GOOD SAMARITAN HOSP 97210 #028-34-1988 L2003 **CCM IM** *020 †20

LOW, Malcolm John. 3181 SW SAM JCKSN PRK RD R, OHSU-VOLLUM INSTITUTE L474 97239 #035-03-1979 L1990 **END** *071 †20

LOWAS, Stefanie Rose. 3181 SW SAM JACKSON PRK RD R, PEDIATRIC HEMATOLOGY ONCOL 97239 #041-14-2002 L2005 **PHO** *012 †15

LOWE, Robert Augustus. 3181 SW SAM JACKSON PRK RD R, M/C CR114 97239 #005-19-1977 L2001 **PHP** *050 †20,16

LOWENKOPF, Theodore John. 3181 SW SAM JACKSON PRK RD 97239 #041-02-1993 L2000 **N** *020

LOWENSOHN, Richard Irwin. 3181 SW SAM JACKSON PRK RD R 97239 #005-06-1970 L1986 **MFM OBS** *040 †30

LOWTHER, Dale Loys Walker. ■ 97212 #040-02-1961 L1962 **IM GE** *071

LU, Kim Champion. 3181 SW SAM JCKSN PRK RD R, M/S L223A 97239 #024-01-1997 L2005 **CRS GS** *020 †85,10

LU, Mary Weichin. 3181 SW SAM JCKSN PRK RD R, UHN 80 97239 #005-11-2002 L2002 **P** *100 †75

LU, Xiaodong. 120 NW 14TH AVE, STE 300 97209 #243-39-1984 L2002 **AN** *020 †05 ‡

LUCIDI-PHILLIPI, Carrie A. ■ 97221 #005-19-1999 L2002 **PD** *020 †55

LUDWICK, Annameika Eve. 3181 SW SAM JACKSON PRK RD, SCIENCE UNIV/C 97239 #040-02-2006 L2006 **EM** *012

LUEM, Carl Dominick. ■ 97239 #040-02-2008 *012

LUFT, Kimberly F. 3550 N INTERSTATE AVE, KAISER PERMANENTE EAST 97227 #005-19-1998 L1999 **PD** *020 †55

LUFT, Ulrich Cameron. 3181 SW SAM JCKSN PRK RD R, M/S UHN 62 97239 #040-02-2001 L2003 **IC** *012 †20

LUM, Donald Foon. 1111 NE 99TH AVE 97220 #005-19-1988 L1989 **GE** *020 †20

LUND, Cynthia Lee. 2707 NE 33RD AVE 97212 #056-06-1997 L2000 **FM** *020 †18

LUNDBLAD, James R. 2241 LLOYD CTR 97232 #035-01-1990 L1991 **END** *050 †20

LUNDEBERG, Duane Allen. 2222 NW LOVEJOY ST STE 622 97210 #040-02-1977 L1978 **OTO** *020 †45

LUOH, Shiuhwen. 3710 SW US VETRNS HSPTL RD, PORTLAND VA MED CTR 97239 #244-02-1986 L2003 **ON HEM** *020 †20

LUPU, Vitalie Dionis. 10000 SE MAIN ST, STE 307 97216 #913-50-1994 L2006 **N CN** *075

LUSK, Robert C. 5050 NE HOYT ST, INFECTION CONSULTANTS LLP 97213 #048-02-1988 L1991 **ID** *020 †20

LUTHER, Douglas Robt. 5050 NE HOYT ST STE 422 97213 #040-02-1989 L1990 **P** *020

LUTSEP, Helmi Liia. 3181 SW SAM JACKSON PRK RD, MAIL CODE L226 97239 #026-08-1988 L1996 **N** *020 †75

LUTY, Jeffrey Alexander. ■ 97231 #040-02-1993 L1994 **IM** *020

LUZIER, Jonah Hamblin. 3181 SW SAM JACKSON PRK RD, MAIL STOP L340 97239 #019-02-2000 L2002 **DR** *012 †80

LYCETTE, Jennifer Lynn. 3600 N INTERSTATE AVE 97227 #054-04-2000 L2003 **HO** *100 †20

LYNAM, Clifford David. 710 SW 2ND AVE 97204 #020-11-1979 L1981 **P** *020

LYON, Douglas Raymond. 426 SW STARK ST, 8TH FL 97204 #035-45-1992 L1993 **FM** *020 †18

LYTOLLIS, William. 7002 SW 5TH AVE 97219 #040-02-2000 L2000 **NEP** *020 †20

MA, Kimberly Kari. ■ 97239 #047-05-2007 L2007 **OBG** *012

MAC ARTHUR, Carol J. 3181 SW SAM JACKSON PRK RD 97239 #005-14-1984 L2002 **PDO OTO** *020 †45

MACDONALD, Ian Donald. 2230 NW PETTYGROVE ST, STE 220 97210 #040-02-1944 L1945 **D** *071

MACDONALD, Ian Donald. 1015 NW 22ND AVE, GOOD SAMARITAN HOSP 97210 #040-02-1983 L1984 **IM** *020 †20

MAC DONALD, Steven Eric. 2801 N GANTENBEIN AVE 97227 #040-02-1983 L1984 **AN IM** *020 †05 ‡

MAC DOUGALL, Malcolm P. ■ 97239 #048-12-1949 L1953 **AN** *071

MACHT, Madison. ■ 97211 #040-02-2004 L2004 **IM** *012 †20

MACK, Donald Merrill. 11510 SE STARK ST 97216 #005-12-1956 L1974 **GP** *075

MACK, Gordon K. 3181 SW SAM JACKSON PRK RD, OR HLTH SCI UNIV 97239 #068-01-1994 L2000 **PDC** *100 †55

MACK, James Loren. 800 SW 13TH AVE 97205 #028-34-1961 L1965 **IM PUD** *071

MACKERT, Christine Louise. ■ 97212 #028-02-1962 L1964 **AN** *071 †05

MACKETT, Milton C T. 10000 SE MAIN ST, STE 408 97216 #005-12-1968 L1994 **GS VS** *020 †85

MAC LEAN, Scot Robert. 3434 SW KELLY AVE 97239 #041-07-1997 L2005 **P** *020 †75

MAC LOWRY, James Don. 3181 SW SAM JACKSON PRK RD 97239 #035-01-1960 L1994 **CLP** *030 †50

MAC MURDY, Karen Stevens. ■ 97210 #010-01-1993 L2001 **ICE CD** *020 †20

MAC NICHOL, Jennifer Lynn. 1015 NW 22ND AVE 97210 #040-02-1984 L1985 **IM** *020 †20

MAC VEIGH, Michael S. 426 SW STARK ST 4TH FL 97204 #024-16-1988 L1989 **IM OS** *020 †20

MADANI, Hajra. 2801 N GANTENBEIN AVE 97227 #704-02-1996 L2004 **IM** *020

MADEY, Steven Michael. 501 N GRAHAM ST, STE 250 97227 #035-01-1989 L1997 **ORS** *020 †40

MADILL, Janet Sue. 1015 NW 22ND AVE APT T200 97210 #040-02-1977 L1978 **IM** *020 †20

MADISON, Dana Lawrence. 3181 SW SAM JACKSON PRK RD, HRC-3 97239 #008-02-1998 L1999 **END** *100 †20

MADISON, Lisa D. 707 SW GAINES ST, DEPT OF PEDIATRICS CDRCP 97239 #008-02-1999 L2000 **PDE** *100 †55

MADNICK, Ellen Gale. 3303 SW BOND AVE, M/S: CH9G 97239 #035-19-1983 L1986 **OS IM** *020 †20

MADRIAGO, Erin Janelle. 3181 SW SAM JACKSON PRK RD, RD DE 97239 #005-19-2004 L2004 **PDC** *012 †55

MADRIGAL, Elis. ■ 97239 #040-02-2008 *012

MAGARET, Nathan David. ■ 97214 #040-02-2003 L2003 **EM** *100 †16

MAGARIAN, Gregory James. 3181 SW SAM JCKSN PRK RD R, OHSU-OP30 97239 #011-03-1997 L1980 **IM** *040 †20

MAGID, Safa Taha. ■ 97239 #040-02-2007 **IM** *012

MAGNELL, Corey Elizabeth. ■ 97239 #035-01-1999 L2006 **GS** *100 †85

MAGNUSSON, Arnar Roy. 3181 SW SAM JCKSN PRK RD R 97239 #054-04-1982 L1985 **EM IM** *030 †20,16

MAHAN, Robert Scott. ■ 97209 #047-05-1987 L1996 **DR** *020 †80

MAIER, Marissa Marie. ■ 97217 #040-02-2007 L2007 **IM** *012

MAJEED, Fareeha. 2801 N GANTENBEIN AVE, LEGACY EMMANUEL HOSP & MED 97227 #704-06-1988 L2004 **IM** *012

MAK, Arkady. ■ 97232 #005-02-1994 L1996 *100

MAK, Larry Wei. ■ 97239 #047-06-2006 L2006 **P** *012

MAKKER, Vishal James. 5050 NE HOYT ST, STE 204 97213 #048-13-1995 L2002 **NS** *020

MAKLER, Michael Thos. ■ 97239 #016-06-1966 L1976 **CLP NM** *030 †50,28

MALACHOWSKI, Jon Chas. 800 SW 13TH AVE 97205 #759-01-1982 L1985 **FM** *020 †18

MALEMPATI, Suman. 3181 SW SAM JCKSN PRK RD R 97239 #028-02-1996 L2002 **PHO** *100 †55

MALJIAN, Meroujan Ardziv. 3181 SW SAM JCKSN PRK RD R, UHN-80 97239 #654-01-1999 L2006 **PFP** *020 †75

MALKOSKI, Stephen Paul. 5111 SE BOISE ST 97206 #034-01-2000 L2001 **PCC** *012 †20

MALOMO, Alfred Adebayo. 3710 SW US VETRNS HSPTL RD, MEDICAL C 97239 #690-01-1990 L2002 **IMG** *100 †20

MALOTT, Richelle Louise. 3181 SW SAM JCKSN PRK RD R, OHSU-DEPT OF PATHOLOGY-L47 97239 #005-12-1986 L1996 **PTH** *020 †50

MANDIBERG, Joseph J. 5050 NE HOYT ST STE 640 97213 #025-07-1974 L1978 **ORS** *020 †40

MANKIN, Leonard Alan. 3181 SW SAM JACKSON PRK RD, STE L475 97239 #032-01-1992 L2005 **IM** *020 †20

MANLEY, Robert Elliot. 10201 SE MAIN ST, STE 25 97216 #005-12-1968 L1975 **ORS** *020 †40

MANN, Jason. 3600 N INTERSTATE AVE, HEMATOLOGY - ONCOLOGY 97227 #010-01-1975 L2000 **ON IM** *020 †20

MANNING, James Foster. 1040 NW 22ND AVE, STE 620 97210 #054-04-1986 L1987 **IM** *020 †20

MANSBERGER, Steven L. 1040 NW 22ND AVE, STE 200 97210 #017-20-1995 L2000 **OPH** *020 †35

MANSON, Thomas Spalding. 120 NW 14TH AVE, STE 300 97209 #021-05-1979 L1981 **AN** *020 †05 ‡

MANSOOR, Atiya. 2241 LLOYD CTR 97232 #704-06-1983 L1999 **PTH** *020 †50

MANSOOR, David John. ■ 97239 #040-02-2004 L2004 **P** *012

MARCUM, Ronald Gale. 3181 SW SAM JCKSN PRK RD R 97239 #040-02-1969 L1972 **OBG** *030 †30

MARCUS, Elaine Rae. 6445 N GREELEY AVE, MULLIKEN MEDICAL CENTER 97217 #035-19-1984 L2001 **FM** *020 †18

MARFORI, Jennifer Elvira. 3181 SW SAM JCKSN PRK RD R, L457 97239 #051-04-2000 L2000 **ID** *020 †20

MARGOLES, Mark Nelson. 12710 SE DIVISION ST 97236 #005-15-1987 L1998 **FM** *020 †18

MARICLE, Robert Alan. 3181 SW SAM JCKSN PRK RD R, MAIL CODE UHN8OT 97239 #040-02-1975 L1976 **P** *020 †20,75

MARIN, Oscar San Martin. 1015 NW 22ND AVE 97210 #231-01-1952 L1971 **N** *040

MARKEE, Joe Eldridge, Jr. 265 N BROADWAY ST, METRO CLINIC 97227 #036-07-1965 L1965 **OBG** *071 †30

MARKEE, R Janan. 5050 NE HOYT ST STE 540, MEDICAL CE 97213 #054-04-2003 L2003 **IM** *100 †20

MARKIW, Juliana. PO BOX 6584 97228 #407-16-1947 **P OS** *071

MARKS, Daniel Lee. 707 SW GAINES ST, OHSU MAILCODE CDRCP 97239 #054-04-1995 L1998 **PDE** *050 †55

MARKS, Karen Celia. 120 NW 14TH AVE, STE 300 97209 #005-15-1984 L1985 **AN OBG** *020 †05 ‡

MARKS, Karen Sue. 11540 NE INVERNESS DR, HEALTH 97220 #028-03-1982 L1990 **FM GPM** *020 †70

MARQUARDT, Victor C, Jr. 3181 SW SAM JACKSON PRK RD 97239 #030-05-1957 L1969 **PTH** *020 †50

MARQUART, Clark Thos. ■ 97232 #017-20-1973 L1973 **GP** *020

MARQUEZ, Carol Madellaine. 3181 SW SAM JCKSN PRK RD R, M/S L337 97239 #005-02-1987 L1993 **RO** *020 †80

MARQUIS, Malcolm Mylrae. 3303 SW BOND AVE, FL 11 97239 #040-02-1961 L1962 **OPH** *020 †35

MARR, Curtis. 1130 NW 22ND AVE, STE 220 97210 #040-02-1988 L1989 **IM** *020 †20

MARR, Kieren A. 3181 SW SAM JCKSN PRK RD R, MC NRC-03 97239 #041-09-1993 L2007 **ID** *020 †20

MARR, Lance Terry. 5050 NE HOYT ST, STE 514 97213 #040-02-2001 L2001 **GS** *100

MARSAL, Scott William. 5050 NE HOYT ST STE 540 97213 #038-40-1993 L1994 **IM** *020 †20

MARSH, Brian James. 120 NW 14TH AVE, STE 300 97209 #040-02-1984 L1985 **AN** *020 †05 ‡

MARSH, Sarah Louise. ■ 97211 #040-02-2004 L2004 **IM** *100 †20

MARSHALL, Philip Dana. 1220 SW MORRISON ST, STE 900 97205 #017-20-1994 L1996 **GPM** *020

MARSHALL, William F. 300 N GRAHAM ST, STE 420 97227 #047-05-1981 L1989 **PG PD** *020 †55

MARTENS, Thomas Jos. ■ 97230 #056-05-1957 L1970 **ORS** *071 †40

MARTIN, Albert Chas. 500 NE MULTNOMAH ST STE 10 97232 #016-11-1944 L1949 **OM GP** *071

MARTIN, Matthew Jeffrey. 501 N GRAHAM STE 580, PACIFIC SURGICAL P.C. 97227 #024-05-1998 L2006 **CCS** *020 †85

MARTIN, Robert Thos. 3500 N INTERSTATE AVE 97227 #040-02-1979 L1980 **EM** *020 †18,16

MARTINDALE, Robert Geo. 3181 SW SAM JACKSON PRK RD, # L223A 97239 #010-01-1984 L2005 **NTR GS** *020 †85

MARTINEZ, Juan-Carlos. 3303 SW BOND AVE CH16D 97239 #026-08-2003 L2007 **D** *012 †15

MARTINEZ-DE CASTRO, R. 2222 NW LOVEJOY ST, STE 619 97210 #035-09-1987 L1991 **OBG** *020 †30 ‡

MARTINSON, Charles Lewis. 1130 NW 22ND AVE, NORTHWEST RENAL CLINIC INC 97210 #040-02-1963 L1964 **NEP IM** *071

MARTON, Keith Ian. 1919 NW LOVEJOY ST, LEGACY HEALTH SYSTEM 97209 #005-11-1970 L1999 **IM** *030 †20

MARTY, Nanette Cheryl. 3303 SW BOND AVE, 9TH FLOOR, CH9G 97239 #054-04-1993 L1998 **IM** *020 †20

MASHRU, Sandeep Hashmukh. 3600 N INTERSTATE AVE, DEPT OF ONCOLOGY 97227 #496-30-1991 L2004 **HO IM** *020 †20

MASKELL, George Murray. 3930 SE DIVISION ST, OHSU RICHMOND CLINIC 97202 #040-02-1964 L1965 **FM** *020 †18

MASON, Michael Stanley. 1040 NW 22ND AVE STE 440 97210 #040-02-1955 L1956 **NS** *020 †25

MASS, Michele Kimberly. 3181 SW SAM JACKSON PRK RD, MAIL CODE L226 97239 #040-02-1983 L1986 **NP PTH** *020 †75

MASSENGALE, Oliver N. ■ 97221 #023-07-1955 L1963 **PD** *071 †55

MASTALERZ, Katarzyna Agni. ■ 97210 #041-12-2007 L2007 **IM** *012

MASTRANDREA, Mark Wm. 120 NW 14TH AVE, STE 300 97209 #040-02-1984 L1985 **AN** *020 †05 ‡

MATHERS, William Dean. 3303 SW BOND AVE, FL 11 97239 #005-11-1973 L1999 **OPH AN** *020 †05,35

MATHEW, Julia Marie. ■ 97210 #024-05-2005 L2005 **IM** *012

MATHEW, V Molly. 500 NE MULTNOMAH ST STE 10 97232 #495-31-1957 L1976 **AN** *071

MATSEN, Laura Jane. ■ 97239 #040-02-2005 L2005

MATSON, Paul Arthur. 3710 SW US VETRNS HSPTL RD, PORTLAND VAMC 97239 #046-01-1987 L1988 **IM** *020 †20

MATSUMURA, Andrea Loran. 3550 N INTERSTATE AVE, INTRENAL MEDICINE 97227 #048-13-1999 L2001 **IM** *020 †20

MATTERI, Robert Keith. 2222 NW LOVEJOY ST, STE 304 97210 #012-05-1978 L1983 **REN GYN** *020 †20,30

MATTEUCCI, Neil Arthur. PO BOX 1034, 3710 SW US VETERANS HOSP 97207 #054-04-1988 L1990 **P** *020

MATTHEWS, Annette Marie. 3181 SW SAM JCKSN PRK RD R, M/S 97239 #040-02-2001 L2001 **P** *100

MATTHIEU, Sharlene Debra. 10000 SE MAIN ST STE 105 97216 #040-02-2002 L2005 **PD** *020 †55

MATTISON, Steven James. 120 NW 14TH AVE, STE 300 97209 #005-12-1984 L1990 **AN** *020 †05 ‡

MAUNDER, Richard John. 1235 NE 47TH AVE, STE 148 97213 #010-01-1977 L1995 **OS PUD** *030 †20

MAURO, Michael John. 3181 SW SAM JACKSON PRK RD, MAIL CODE UHN 73C 97239 #032-01-1994 L2004 **HEM IM** *020 †20

MAVITY, Laura Kelly. 2701 NW VAUGHN ST, STE 140 97210 #025-12-1999 L1999 **IM** *020 †20

MAY, Michael J. 3600 N INTERSTATE AVE, KAISER- CENTRAL INTERSTATE 97227 #038-40-1994 L2004 **OPH** *020 †35

MAYBERRY, John Clark. 3181 SW SAM JACKSON PRK RD, OREGON HEALTH SCIENCES UNI 97239 #040-02-1986 L1987 **GS TRS** *020 †85

MAYO, Jennifer Burch. ■ 97217 #040-02-2006 L2006 **OBG** *012

MAYS, Maureen Ellen. 3181 SW SAM JCKSN PRK RD R, MC UHN-62 97239 #031-01-1998 L2005 **CD VM** *020 †18

MAYS, Thelma Jean. 1620 SW TAYLOR ST, STE 300 97205 #005-12-1985 L1991 **AN** *020 †05

MAZIARZ, Richard Thos. 2241 LLOYD CTR 97232 #024-01-1979 L1992 **IM HEM** *050 †20

MAZUR, Dennis John. 3710 SW US VETRN HOSP RD, VA MEDICAL CENTER (P3-MED) 97239 #005-11-1979 L1987 **IM** *020 †20

MCALARNEY, E Kelly Whitso. ■ 97232 #045-04-2001 L2006 **NM** *012

MC ALLISTER, Leslie. 1040 NW 22ND AVE STE 207 97210 #014-01-1987 L1997 **N** *020 †75

MC ANDREW, Stephanie Ann. ■ 97221 #018-03-2002 L2002 **FM** *100 †18

MC ANINCH, Malcolm Lewis. 300 N GRAHAM ST STE 200 97227 #041-02-1981 L1982 **IM** *020 †20

MC ANULTY, David Allen. 6327 SE MILWAUKIE AVE 97202 #005-19-1987 L1991 **FM** *020 †18

MC BARRON, Frank Dana. 5251 NE GLISAN ST, HEART RESEARCH 97213 #030-06-1959 L1964 **IM** *050 †20

MCCALL, Bryant Ralph. ■ 97213 #054-04-2004 L2004 **IM** *100

MC CALLUM, Michele Dawn. 7705 SE DIVISION ST 97206 #056-06-1994 L1997 **IM** *075 †20

MCCARN, Kate Elizabeth. ■ 97239 #051-01-2005 L2005 **OTO** *012

MC CARRON, David Alan. 120 NW 9TH AVE, STE 216 97209 #041-01-1971 L1977 **NEP IM** *050 †20

MC CARTHY, Geoffrey Wm. 677 NW MELINDA AVE, CLACKAMAS COMM. HEALTH CLI 97210 #035-03-1974 L2006 **AM FM** *030 †18

MC CARTHY, Mary K. 2311 NW NORTHRUP ST STE 20 97210 #040-02-1982 L1983 **P CHP** *020 †75

MCCARTNEY, Lyndsey. 3181 SW SAM JACKSON PRK RD 97239 #917-04-2000 L2007 **FP** *012

MC CAUSLAND, Aaron David. ■ 97212 #054-04-1997 **IM** *100

MCCLAIN, Erik James. 2801 N GANTENBEIN AVE 97227 #661-02-2007 L2007 **IM** *012

MCCLUNG, Michael Roy. 5050 NE HOYT STE 651 97213 #048-12-1969 L1976 **OS** *020 †20

MCCLURE, Ashley Elisabeth. ■ 97239 #040-02-2008 *012

MC COMB, Gordon Lee. 5847 NE 122ND AVE, STE 201 97230 #056-05-1958 L1959 **FM** *071 †18

MC CONNELL, Donald Bruce. 3181 SW SAM JACKSON PRK RD 97239 #040-02-1968 L1974 **GS CCS** *020 †85

MC COY, Gregory Buel. 1015 NW 22ND AVE 97210 #047-05-1981 L1982 **U** *020 †95

MC COY, Robin Beth. 707 SW GAINES ST, CHILD DEVELOPMENT & REHABI 97239 #035-45-1997 L2007 **PD** *020 †55

MC CREARY, John Chalmer. 2801 N GANTENBEIN AVE 97227 #012-01-1999 L2003 **AN** *020 †05 ‡

MC CULLAR, Frank Wayne. 4805 NE GLISAN ST 97213 #040-02-1972 L1977 **EM PD** *020 †55,16

MCCULLOUGH, Elizabeth Hop. ■ 97217 #011-02-2007 L2007 **IM** *012

MCCUNE, Christina Ann. ■ 97206 #048-04-2004 L2005 **DR** *012

MCDANELD, Logan Matthew. ■ 97219 #007-02-2006 L2006 **N** *012

MC DANIEL, Philip Lee. 10803 SE CHERRY BLOSSOM DR, SOUTH TABOR FAMILY PHYSICI 97216 #016-11-1974 L2003 **IM** *020 †20

MC DONALD, John Arthur. 3600 N INTERSTATE AVE, KAISER PERMANENTE 97227 #016-02-1971 L1974 **OM EM** *020 †16

MC DONALD, Michael Gene. 10101 SE MAIN ST STE 2004 97216 #005-12-1975 L1981 **OTO SME** *020 †45

MCDONALD, Tasha Lee. 3181 SW SAM JCKSN PRK RD R, M/S: L337 97239 #040-02-2004 L2004 **RO** *012

MCELVANY, Matthew Dean. ■ 97219 #005-19-2007 L2007 *012

MC EVOY, Cindy T. 707 SW GAINES ST, OREGON HEALTH SCIENCE UNIV 97239 #016-43-1985 L1999 **NPM PD** *020 †20

MC EVOY, Kevin Michael. 1130 NW 22ND AVE, UROLOGY CLINIC PC 97210 #016-43-1985 L1999 **GS U** *020 †95

MCFADDEN-GERBER, Leslie N. ■ 97201 #036-01-2007 IM *012

MC FARLAND, Bentson Hayes. 2241 LLOYD CTR 97232 #054-04-1979 L1981 **P PHP** *050 †75

MC FARLANE, Donald R. ■ 97202 #026-04-1953 L1974 **R OS** *071 †80

MC FARLANE, Robert Alan. 2801 N GANTENBEIN AVE, DEPT OF SURGERY 97227 #040-02-1960 L1962 **TS GS** *072 †85,90

MC GANN, Judeth Kathleen. 501 N GRAHAM ST, STE 355 97227 #035-03-1993 L2006 **PHO** *055

MC GEHEE, Matthew James. 3303 SW BOND AVE, FL CH4P 97239 #016-11-2003 L2007 **PMM** *012

MC GRAW, Terrence Thos. 3181 SW SAM JACKSON PRK RD, UH 2 97239 #016-43-1979 L1993 **AN** *020 †55,05

MC GUIRE, James Smith. 500 NE MULTNOMAH ST, STE 100 97232 #005-18-1987 L2000 **NPM** *020 †55

MC INTYRE, Christin Jane. 2250 NW FLANDERS ST # 306 97210 #019-02-1999 L1999 **P** *020 †75

MC IRVIN, David Michael. 2801 N GANTENBEIN AVE 97227 #422-01-1982 L1991 **PDC PD** *020 †55

MC IVOR, Andrew Craig. 800 SW 13TH AVE, THE PORTLAND CLINIC 97205 #036-05-1988 L1993 **GS VS** *020 †85

MCKEE, Rohini. 1040 NW 22ND AVE STE 560 97210 #495-52-1998 L2006 **GS** *100 †85,10

MC KELVEY, Robert Smith. 2241 LLOYD CTR 97232 #032-01-1974 L1998 **CHP P** *030 †75

MC KENNA, Ian Gregory. 6312 SW CAPITOL HWY 502, SPECIALIST 97239 #051-04-1992 L1996 **EM** *020 †16

MCKENZIE, Mary Suzanne. ■ 97239 #040-02-2007 L2007 **IM** *012

MCKEOGH, Donogh Fahey. 2241 LLOYD CTR 97232 #539-04-1993 L1999 **CD** *020 †20

MC KEOWN, Jana K. 1040 NW 22ND AVE, STE 320 97210 #028-78-2002, ▲ L2006 **PM** *020

MC KOWNE, Frank James. 3500 N INTERSTATE AVE 97227 #035-15-1971 L1978 **DR** *020 †80

MC LACHLAN, Murray James. 6312 SW CAPITOL HWY 502 97239 #016-06-2002 L2006 **EM** *100 †16

MC LARTY, Charles Arthur. 10123 SE MARKET ST 97216 #047-06-1987 L1988 **IM** *075

MC MENOMEY, Sean Oleary. 3181 SW SAM JACKSON PRK RD, STE L472 97239 #028-34-1987 L1988 **OTO** *020 †45

MC MULLAN, J Bart, Jr. 100 SW MARKET ST MSE12A, OF ORGON 97201 #027-01-1967 L1972 **IM** *030 †20

MC NAMARA, Michael Peter. 2850 NW NICOLAI ST, KAISER PERMANENTE 97210 #005-02-1987 L1994 **PD** *020 †55

MC NEILL, Donald Lee. 2933 SW FAIRVIEW BLVD 97205 #040-02-1962 L1965 **EM GS** *030 †16

MC NEILL, George. 2214 LLOYD CTR, GEORGE MCNEILL MD PC 97232 #065-06-1964 L1973 **ORS** *071 †40

MCNELLEY, Erin Elizabeth. ■ 97239 #035-01-2006 L2006 **IM** *012

MCNICHOL, Margaret Irene. 6327 SE MILWAUKIE AVE 97202 #041-02-1996 L1998 **FM** *020 †18

MC QUESTON, John Andrew. 501 N GRAHAM ST, MOB SUITE 320 97227 #023-12-1984 L2005 **PD** *020 †55

MC RAE, Yan Robert. ■ 97219 #012-01-2002 L2003 **AN** *100 †05

MEAD, Jay Harvey. 5125 SW MACADAM AVE, STE 200 97239 #005-02-1976 L1984 **PTH BBK** *062 †50

MECKLEM, Nicholas Keith. 120 NW 14TH AVE, STE 300 97209 #040-02-1973 L1974 **AN** *020 †05 ‡

MECKLER, Garth David. ■ 97214 #024-01-1997 L2006 **PD** *020 †55

MECKLING, Kent Forrest. 2801 N GANTENBEIN AVE 97227 #005-12-1997 L2003 **AN** *020 †05 ‡ ‡

MEDAK, Ruth Ellen Evelyn. 1130 NW 22ND AVE, STE 520 97201 #016-11-1973 L1974 **IM** *040 †20

MEDRANO, Evelyn Villena. 800 SW 13TH AVE 97205 #748-01-1970 L1977 **IM EM** *020

MEECHAN, Robert J. ■ 97266 #040-02-1953 L1954 **PD** *071 †55

MEES, Leonard Roger. ■ 97206 #035-45-1972 L1973 **GP** *075

MEGHASHYAM, Janhavi. 4805 NE GLISAN ST 97213 #495-33-1993 L2000 **IM** *020 †20

MEHREN, Laura Sue. 13705 NE AIRPORT WAY, KAISER PERM AIRPORT WAY RE 97230 #040-02-1983 L1984 **PTH HMP** *020 †50

MEIER, Linda M. 3600 N INTERSTATE AVE, KAISER PERMANENTE 97227 #005-11-1985 L1986 **OPH** *020 †35

MEIER, Werner Richard. 3434 SE POWELL BLVD 97202 #065-10-1972 L1973 **AN** *020 †05

MEIGHAN, Stuart Spence. 1015 NW 22ND AVE 97210 #803-05-1945 L1962 **OS** *062

MEIHOFF, Erich Jonathan. 1130 NW 22ND AVE, STE 220 97210 #021-01-2001 L2001 **IM** *020

MEIHOFF, Walter Edwin. 510 NE 49TH AVE # 611 97213 #040-02-1959 L1961 **GE** *020 †20

MELARAGNO, Anthony Joseph. ■ 97212 #038-40-1973 L2001 **HEM** *071 †20

MELCHER, William Lee. 3550 N INTERSTATE AVE 97227 #041-07-1986 L1995 **IM RHU** *020 †20

MELMAN, Mark Alan. 2801 N GANTENBEIN AVE 97227 #028-03-1983 L1984 **AN** *020 †05 ‡

MELNICK, Alan L. 3181 SW SAM JACKSON PRK RD, MAIL CODE: FM 97239 #024-07-1977 L1978 **PHP FM** *020 †70,18

MELNYK, Clifford Stephen. 2241 LLOYD CTR 97232 #061-01-1959 L1967 **GE IM** *071

MENASHE, David Scott. 5050 NE HOYT ST, STE 514 97213 #040-02-1983 L1989 **ON U** *020 †95

MENASHE, Jeffrey Irving. 10101 SE MAIN ST, STE 1012 97216 #040-02-1981 L1989 **ON HEM** *020 †20

MENASHE, Victor D. 3181 SW SAM JACKSON PRK RD, CDRD-P 97239 #040-02-1953 L1954 **PDC OS** *020 †55

MENDELSON, Robert Allen. 2525 NW LOVEJOY ST STE 200 97210 #040-02-1959 L1963 **PD** *040 †55

MENGELBERG, Brigitte. 500 NE MULTNOMAH ST STE 10 97232 #407-07-1957 L1973 **OBG** *071 †30

MENGIS, Matilda Martha. 5432 N ALBINA AVE 97217 #016-06-1992 L2002 **P** *020 †75

MERA, Csaba Leslie. 601 SW 2ND AVE, ODS COMPANIES 97204 #005-12-1972 L2000 **PD PHO** *030 †55

MERCER, Rachel. ■ 97239 #005-02-2006 L2007 **AN** *012

MERKEL, Matthias Johannes. 3181 SW SAM JACKSON PRK RD, UH 2 97239 #409-16-1997 L2005 *100

MERKENS, Mark John. 2241 LLOYD CTR 97232 #035-15-1972 L1989 **PD** *020 †55

MERRICK, Todd Richard. 5050 NE HOYT ST, STE 540 97213 #038-45-2004 L2004 **IM** *020 †20

MERRILL, Patrick Andrew. 300 N GRAHAM ST STE 1, 300 N GRAHAM #100 97227 #048-04-1980 L1986 **NPM OBG** *020 †30

MERTENS, Mark Jos. 800 SW 13TH AVE 97205 #040-02-1981 L1985 **AN** *020 †05 ‡

MERTENS, Ronald Edward. 3550 N INTERSTATE AVE 97227 #005-02-1973 L1981 **N IM** *020 †20,75

MESSAMORE, Erik L. 3710 SW VETERANS HOSPTL RD, MENTAL HEALTH DIV P35C 97239 #016-11-1997 L1998 **P** *020

METCALFE, James. 3181 SW SAM JACKSON PRK RD 97239 #024-01-1946 L1949 **CD IM** *071 †20

METRICK, Michele Edith. 501 N GRAHAM ST, STE 330 97227 #016-42-1981 L2001 **N PD** *020 †55,75

METZ, Paul. 2455 NW MARSHALL ST, STE 2A 97210 #040-02-1939 L1940 **GS GP** *071

METZ, Samuel. 120 NW 14TH AVE # 300, STE 300 97209 #040-01-1980 L1999 **AN** *020 †05 ‡

METZGER, Mark Steven. 10101 SE MAIN ST, STE 3008 97216 #025-01-1995 L2002 **ORS** *020 †40

MEUNIER, Kathleen Ann. 500 NE MULTNOMAH ST, STE 100 97232 #047-05-1981 L1989 **DR** *020 †80

MEURER, Joseph Peter, Jr. 200 SW MARKET ST, STE L120 97201 #040-02-1974 L1978 **OPH** *020 †35

MEYER, Eric David. 4805 NE GLISAN ST DEPT EM 97213 #003-01-1988 L1989 **EM** *020 †16

MEYER, Erika Kempler. 1130 NW 22ND AVE, STE 300 97210 #024-01-2000 L2000 **PD** *020 †55

MEYER, James V. ■ 97202 #048-02-1953 L1953 **PS** *071 †65

MEYER, Mary Margaret. 2330 NW FLANDERS ST SU 97210 #054-04-1979 L1989 **NEP IM** *020 †20

MEYER, Rodica Negrea. 3550 N INTERSTATE AVE 97227 #781-01-1988 L2001 **P** *020 †75

MEYER, Sam Lee. 1120 NW 20TH AVE, STE 108 97209 #040-02-1961 L1962 **OPH PTH** *071 †35

MEYERHOFF, Jeffrey David. 2386 NW HOYT ST 97210 #016-01-1989 L1991 **P** *020 †20

MEYERS, Christina Michel. ■ 97211 #040-02-2005 L2005 **FP** *012

MEYERS, Gabrielle. 3181 SW SAM JCKSN PRK RD R, M/C: UHN 73C 97239 #016-02-1998 L1999 **HO** *100 †20

MICHAELS, Andrew Jacob. 2801 N GANTENBEIN AVE, STE 130 97227 #041-12-1988 L1998 **GS TRS** *020 †85

MICHAELSON, Ellen M. 4650 SW MACADAM AVE, STE 100 97239 #024-16-1982 L1993 **HEM IM** *020 †20

MICHAUD, Andre-Paul. ■ 97239 #018-03-2006 L2006 **AN** *020

MIDGEN, Craig Aaron. 3181 SW SAM JACKSON PRK RD, RD PA 97239 #048-12-2006 L2006 **PTH** *012

MIELKE, Beverly Ann. ■ 97239 #040-02-2008 *012

MIHELIC, David Theodore. 1750 NW NAITO PKWY, STE 100 97209 #040-02-1982 L1983 **IM** *020 †20

MIKSOVSKY, Petr. 19500 SE STARK ST, KAISER - ROCKWOOD MEDICAL 97233 #286-04-1986 L2002 **OBG** *020 †20

MILANO, Christina Elizabe. ■ 97212 #005-02-2005 L2005 **FP** *012

MILCZUK, Henry Alexander. 3181 SW SAM JACKSON PRK RD, UNIVERSITY PV-01, 97239 #005-19-1985 L1994 **OTO PDO** *020 †45

MILES, Marie Ann. ■ 97221 #005-14-2004 L2004 **PD** *020 †55

MILLAN, Juan Carlos. 1225 NE 2ND AVE 97232 #031-21-1968 L1968 **PTH** *030 †50

MILLER, Ben John. 120 NW 14TH AVE, STE 300 97209 #016-42-1990 L2005 **AN** *020 †05

MILLER, Debbie Lee. 2565 NW LOVEJOY ST, STE 100 97210 #054-04-1983 L1989 **D** *020 †20,15

MILLER, Diane L. 3181 SW SAM JCKSN PRK RD R, OHSU DEPT OF ANESTHESIOLOG 97239 #040-02-1992 L1993 **AN CD** *020 †05

MILLER, Elmer Bowman. 2801 N GANTENBEIN AVE 97227 #028-02-1943 L1943 **PM EM** *071 †85

MILLER, F Wm. 10373 NE HANCOCK ST, STE 115 97220 #021-01-1968 L1972 **IM OM** *020 †20

MILLER, Helen Carney. 3181 SW SAM JCKSN PRK RD R, M/C - CDW-EM 97239 #038-41-1987 L1993 **PD PE** *020 †20

MILLER, Jay David. 1 CENTER CT STE 110, MEDICINE 97227 #025-01-1964 L1966 **NS** *030 †25

MILLER, Jeffrey A. 6647 SE THORBURN ST 97215 #040-02-1980 L1981 **EM** *020

MILLER, Jessica Ward. ■ 97212 #028-02-2002 L2007 **PAN** *012 †20

MILLER, Jill Elaine. 3181 SW SAM JCKSN PRK RD R 97239 #040-02-1995 L1998 **IM** *020 †20

MILLER, Lani Joyce. 2705 E BURNSIDE ST STE 114 97214 #005-02-1979 L1982 **OBG** *020 †30

MILLER, Laura Ann. 11510 SE STARK ST 97216 #040-02-1981 L1982 **FM** *020 †20

MILLER, Michael Jos. 3181 SW SAM JACKSON PRK RD, PARK RD. 97239 #040-02-1960 L1975 **PD OS** *020

MILLER, Robert Leslie. 500 NE MULTNOMAH ST STE 10 97232 #040-02-1970 L1971 **OS FM** *075

MILLER, Robert Skeith. ■ 97219 #040-02-1955 L1958 **DR** *071 †80

MILLER, Thomas Lynn. 4805 NE GLISAN ST 97213 #030-06-1956 L1958 **FM** *071

MILLIUS, Rebecca Adele. 5919 SE BELMONT ST, MT TABOR FAMILY MEDICAL 97215 #040-02-2001 L2004 **FM** *020 †18

MILLS, Andrew John. 3181 SW SAM JACKSON PRK RD, RD IN 97239 #040-02-2003 L2006 **IM** *012

MINETTE, Mary Sara. 2241 LLOYD CTR 97232 #018-03-1993 L1996 **PDC** *020 †55

MINJAREZ, Renee C. ■ 97239 #048-12-2002 L2002 **GS** *012

MIRACLE, Max Vernon. 11510 SE STARK ST 97216 #005-12-1957 L1958 **FM** *071

MIRKA, Alar. 1130 NW 22ND AVE, STE 220 97210 #040-02-1982 L1983 **IM OS** *020 †20

MIRKIN, Dana Brian. 3181 SW SAM JACKSON PRK RD, # CB550 97239 #016-11-1977 L1995 **OM** *030 †70

MISAKI, Chieko. 10000 SE MAIN ST, STE 205 97216 #040-02-1998 L1999 **IM** *020 †20

MISHLER, Richard Matthew. 10000 SE MAIN ST, STE 205 97216 #017-20-1997 L1999 **IM** *020 †20

MISKO, John Charles. 501 N GRAHAM ST STE 500 97227 #040-02-1958 L1960 **NS** *071 †25

MISRA, Sahana. ■ 97209 #016-01-1993 L1997 **PYG** *020 †75

MITAL, Meena. ■ 97217 #025-12-2004 L2004 **IM** *100 †20

MITCHELL, Alison Margaret. 8935 SE POWELL BLVD, ROSEWOOD FAMILY HLTH CTR 97266 #026-04-2000 L2004 **FM** *020 †20

MITCHELL, Brandon Warren. 3181 SW SAM JCKSN PRK RD R 97239 #305-01-2006 L2006 **FP** *012

MITCHELL, Brian Alexander. ■ 97215 #038-40-2006 L2007 **AN** *012

MITCHELL, Erica. ■ 97210 #007-02-1996 L2003 **GS** *100 †85

MITTAL-HENKLE, Anuja. ■ 97221 #005-14-1997 L2004 **NEP** *100 †20

MIURA, Lisa Noelle. 2800 N VANCOUVER AVE 97227 #041-01-1997 L1998 **IMG** *020 †20

MIZUSHIMA, Aoi Nathalia. 4920 N INTERSTATE AVE 97217 #056-05-2001 L2001 **FM** *020 †18

MOHAN, Vishnu. 1015 NW 22ND AVE R200 97210 #495-45-1992 L2003 **IM** *020 †20 ‡

MOHTADI, Kourosh. 120 NW 14TH AVE # 300, STE 300 97209 #040-02-1992 L1993 **AN** *020 †05 ‡

MOISA, Radu Cosmin. 3181 SW SAM JACKSON PRK RD 97239 #781-04-1999 L2005 **FP** *012

MOLINA, Lisa Karlasusan. 3500 N INTERSTATE AVE 97227 #056-06-1984 L1996 **OBG** *020 †30

MONES, Andrew Irving. 300 N GRAHAM ST, STE 200 97227 #035-47-1994 L1996 **IM** *020 †20

MONETA, Gregory Louis. 3181 SW SAM JCKSN PRK RD R, OP-11 97239 #024-01-1980 L1988 **VS TRS** *020 †85

MONETA, Michael Dean. 120 NW 14TH AVE, STE 300 97209 #010-01-1985 L1992 **AN** *020 †05

MONROE, Marcus Matthew. ■ 97221 #028-03-2005 L2005 **OTO** *012

MONSON, Dinelli Marina. ■ 97221 #056-05-2006 L2007 **OPH** *012

MONSON, William Jos. 120 NW 14TH AVE, STE 300 97209 #040-02-1982 L1987 **AN IM** *020 †05 ‡

MONTANARO, Anthony. 511 SW 10TH AVE, ALLERGY CLINIC LLC 97205 #054-04-1978 L1981 **RHU A** *020 †20,03

MONTANO, Noelle Elizabeth. ■ 97214 #021-01-2001 L2006 **RNR** *020 †80

MONTGOMERY, Rosalyn Marie. 2241 LLOYD CTR 97232 #034-01-1986 L1991 **OP** *020 †40

MONTGOMERY, Stuart Mead. 5050 NE HOYT ST, STE 318 97213 #016-06-1994 L2000 **ORS** *020 †40

MOORE, Charles Patrick. ■ 97212 #054-04-1970 L1975 **PM RHU** *071 †20,60

MOORE, James Alan. 800 SW 13TH AVE 97205 #040-02-1994 L1998 **AN** *020 †05 ‡

MOORE, Laurie Jo. 3181 SW SAM JCKSN PRK RD R 97239 #040-02-1974 L1975 **P** *020 †75

MOORE, Mark Owen. 97213 #054-04-2005 L2005 *100

MOORE, Michael Andrew. 10123 SE MARKET ST 97216 #038-40-1975 L1977 **PTH** *020 †50

MOORE, Rachael Lynne. 3303 SW BOND AVE, CH16D 97239 #005-18-2005 L2006 **D** *012

MOORE, Robert Hugh. ■ 97208 #051-01-1963 L1975 **PD PHP** *030 †55

MOORE, Robert Jameson. 2801 N GANTENBEIN AVE 97227 #040-02-1955 L1956 **U** *072 †95

MOORHEAD, John Couper. 3181 SW SAM JACKSON PRK RD, CDW-EM 97239 #065-05-1975 L1978 **EM** *040 †16

MORELAND, Alisha Rolonda. ■ 97232 #010-01-2007 *012

MOREY, Peter Samuel. 1220 SW MORRISON ST STE 13 97205 #054-04-2001 L2001 **P** *100

MORGAN, Clarence Lorenzo. 500 NE MULTNOMAH ST STE 10 97232 #024-01-1958 L1967 **PD CD** *071 †55

MORGAN, James Stuart. 4805 NE GLISAN ST, STE BH16 97213 #051-04-1978 L1980 **IM** *020 †20

MORGAN, Terry Knud. 3181 SW SAM JACKSON PRK RD, RD MC 97239 #049-01-2000 L2005 **PCP** *100

MORGANROTH, Melvin Lee. 1111 NE 99TH AVE 97220 #025-01-1978 L1990 **PUD IM** *020 †20

MORIARTY, Allison Marie. ■ 97239 #040-02-2006 L2006 **GS** *012

MOROYE, Marc Minoru. 10201 SE MAIN ST STE 12, INTERNAL MEDICINE ASSOCIAT 97216 #014-01-1992 L1995 **IM** *020 †20

MOROZOVA, Lyudmila V. ■ 97266 #040-02-2008 *012

MORRIS, Isaac Cherrington. ■ 97239 #040-02-2008 *012

MORRIS, Katherine Teresa. 1040 NW 22ND AVE, STE 540 97210 #040-02-1996 L1999 **SO GS** *020 †85

MORRIS, Lisa Michelle. ■ 97214 #019-02-2007 L2007 **OTO** *012

MORRIS, Melanie Sanders. ■ 97239 #047-06-2003 L2003 **GS** *012

MORRIS, William James. 500 NE MULTNOMAH ST STE 10 97232 #025-01-1981 L1982 **PD** *071 †55

MORRISON, John Carl. 3303 SW BOND AVE, FL 11 97239 #040-02-1977 L1978 **OPH EM** *020 †20

MORRISON, Lynne Lorraine. 3303 SW BOND AVE, DERMATOLOGY DEPT. 97239 #040-02-1982 L1983 **D** *020 †15

MORROW, Charles E. 5050 NE HOYT ST STE 511 97213 #056-06-1978 L1988 **VS GS** *020 †85

MORROW, Daniel Kent. ■ 97218 #005-12-2007 L2007 **PD** *012

MORTON, John Mark. 800 SW 13TH AVE 97205 #030-05-1976 L1990 **IM** *020 †20
MORTON, William Edwards. 3181 SW SAM JACKSON PRK RD 97239 #054-04-1955 L1967 **GPM OM** *030 †70
MOSES, Robb Edwin. 3181 SW SAM JACKSON PRK RD, MEDICAL GENETICS L103 97239 #023-07-1966 L1991 **MG** *050 †19
MOSESON, Bertha Alicia. 500 NE MULTNOMAH ST STE 10 97232 #005-11-1975 L1977 **GPM** *020 †30,70
MOSHTAEL, Naghmeh. 3111 SW SAM JCKSN PRK RD R, DC 10 S 97239 #040-02-2002 L2002 **PD** *020
MOSSEFIN, Catherine Jane. 3181 SW SAM JCKSN PRK RD R, UHN-80 97239 #040-02-2002 L2002 **ADP** *020
MOVIUS, Rosalie Louise. 1020 SW TAYLOR ST, STE 448 97205 #040-02-1992 L1993 **IM** *020
MOWRY, Jeanne Ann. 3550 N INTERSTATE AVE, EAST INTERSTATE MEDICAL OF 97227 #005-18-1988 L1994 **PD PN** *020 †55
MOY, Esther. ■ 97239 #040-02-2008 *012
MOYLAN, Mark Christopher. ■ 97206 #028-03-2002 L2002 **EM** *020 †16
MOYNIHAN, Kelley Colleen. ■ 97221 #005-19-2005 *100
MRAK, Nayade I. 120 NW 14TH AVE, OREGON ANESTHESIOLOGY GROU 97209 #048-14-2001 L2005 **AN** *020 ‡
MUDERSPACH, Ib Bernhardt. 10000 SE MAIN ST, STE 207 97216 #005-12-1971 L1974 **IM** *020
MUEGGE, Paula Ann. ■ 97217 #030-05-2004 L2004 **IM** *012 †20
MUELLER, Reid Vance. 2241 LLOYD CTR 97232 #007-02-1987 L1997 **PS GS** *020 †85,65
MUENCH, John Philip. 4181 SW SAM JCKSN PRK #R, MAIL CODE: SM 97239 #025-07-1989 L1995 **FM** *020 †18
MULARSKI, Richard Anthony. 3800 N INTERSTATE AVE 97227 #003-01-1996 L1997 **PCC PLM** *050 †20
MULLEN, John Thos. 2388 NW LOVEJOY ST 97210 #005-18-1988 L1997 **EM** *020 †16
MULLEN, Robert D. 5635 NE ALAMEDA ST 97213 #010-01-1982 L1983 **IM** *020 †20
MULLER, Martin C. 120 NW 14TH AVE STE 300 97209 #869-01-1977 L1990 **AN CCA** *020 †05
MULLER, Melinda Jean. 1200 NW 23RD AVE 97210 #040-02-1996 L1997 **IM** *020 †20
MULLER, Roger Allan. 4380 SW MACADAM AVE, STE 570 97239 #040-02-1990 L1993 **EM** *020 †16
MULLINS, Richard James. 3181 SW SAM JACKSON PRK RD, # L223A 97239 #024-07-1974 L1977 **TRS GS** *020 †85
MUNOZ, Sonia Uyen. ■ 97219 #040-02-1999 L1999 **P** *100
MURAMOTO, Osamu. 3550 N INTERSTATE AVE, DEPT. OF NEUROLOGY 97227 #572-03-1974 L1991 **N IM** *020 †75
MURPHY, David Alexander. 1015 NW 22ND AVE 97210 #048-02-1972 L1974 **GPM NTR** *030 †70
MURPHY, Deborah Jane. 541 NE 20TH AVE, STE 210 97232 #054-04-1996 L1997 **FM** *020 †18
MURPHY, Edward Simon. 2241 LLOYD CTR 97232 #016-02-1971 L1977 **CD IM** *020 †20
MURPHY, Gregory Lee. 3710 SW US VETRNS HSPTL RD, EAST CBOC 97239 #027-07-1993 L2001 **FM** *020 †18
MURPHY, Laura. 19500 SE STARK ST 97233 #005-06-1998 L2004 **PD** *020 †55
MURPHY, Melissa Denise. 3710 SW US VETRNS HSPTL RD, P O BIX 1035 97239 #016-42-1996 L1998 **IM** *020 †20
MURRAY, Jennifer Helen. 1130 NW 22ND AVE, STE 520 97210 #041-02-1995 L1998 **OBG** *020 †75
MURRAY, Scott Michael. 10735 SE STARK ST STE 203 97216 #038-41-1983 L1987 **P ADP** *020 †75
MURROW, Mark David. 2801 N GANTENBEIN AVE, & HEAL 97227 #003-01-2007 L2007 **TY** *012
MYALL, Robert Wm. 611 SW CAMPUS DR, DEPT OF ORAL & MAXFACL SUR 97239 #061-01-1975 L2001 **OS** *040
MYERS, Edmund. 2408 SE 16TH AVE 97214 #040-02-1990 L1991 **P** *020 †75
MYERS, Gloria J. 2400 SW VERMONT ST, FANNO CREEK CLINIC LLC 97219 #035-47-1985 L1986 **IM** *020 †20
MYERS, Gordon C. ■ 97203 #040-02-1950 L1951 **GP** *072
MYERS, Kathleen Mary. 6312 SW CAPITOL HWY, STE 502 97239 #014-01-1979 L1995 **P CHP** *020 †75
MYERS, Kristin K. 1321 NE 99TH AVE, STE 200 97220 #040-02-1997 L2000 **FM** *020 †18
MYERS, Lee Donald. PO BOX 1036, VAMC OUTPATIENT CLNC 97207 #005-12-1980 L1985 **GP** *020
MYINT, Maung Win. 3550 N INTERSTATE AVE, INTERSTATE MEDICAL OFFICE 97227 #209-01-1986 L1998 **IM** *020 †20
NADIG, Shrinath Kalaseshw. 3181 SW SAM JCKSN PRK RD R, OHSU 97239 #495-23-1983 L2006 *100
NADOL, Gregory Scott. 800 SW 13TH AVE 97205 #017-20-1993 L1998 **AN** *020 †05 ‡
NAEMURA, Joe Shigeru. 12235 NE ROSE PKWY 97230 #040-02-1957 **AN** *071 †05
NAGY, Melba Louisa. ■ 97209 #033-05-2001 L2005 **DR** *020 †80
NAIK, Arpana Madhukant. 3181 SW SAM JCKSN PRK RD R, M/S L223A 97239 #035-19-1996 L2004 **GS** *020 †85
NAIMARK, Willow Nicole. ■ 97221 #035-09-2006 L2006 **P** *012
NAITO, Ronald Warren. 800 SW 13TH AVE 97205 #040-02-1978 L1982 **IM** *020 †20
NAJJAR, Hazim Yosef. ■ 97239 #797-01-1997 L2002 **PTH** *100 †19
NAKADATE, K James. ■ 97216 #040-02-1939 **AN** *071
NAKAI, Hitomi. 2801 N GANTENBEIN AVE 97227 #305-01-2005 L2005 **IM** *012
NAKAMURA, Alvin Kenji. 10000 SE MAIN ST, STE 309 97216 #005-12-1988 L1992 **OBG** *020 †30
NAKATA, Thomas Yukio. 3710 SW US VETRNS HSPTL RD 97239 #005-14-1972 L1973 **CHP P** *075
NAKAYAMA, Clyde H. 120 NW 14TH AVE, STE 300 97209 #014-01-1976 L1977 **AN CCA** *020 ‡
NAMAN, Leslie Rodney. 5055 N INTERSTATE AVE 97217 #010-01-1967 L1974 **IM** *020 †20
NANCE, Dale Russell. 10123 SE MARKET ST 97216 #048-04-1976 L2006 **DR** *020 †80
NANCE, Robert Walter, Jr. 3181 SW SAM JACKSON PRK RD, OHSU M/S OP-23 97239 #011-02-1978 L1991 **DR NM** *020 †80
NARAPASETTY, Kalpana. 2801 N GANTENBEIN AVE 97227 #495-50-2002 L2005 **IM** *012
NASH, George Austin. 5415 SW WESTGATE DR 97221 #040-02-1948 **PD** *071
NASSIRI, Naiem. ■ 97239 #040-02-2008 *012
NATSIOS, Peter Andrew. 3181 SW SAM JACKSON PRK RD 97239 #012-01-1984 L1985 **P** *020 †75
NAUGLER, Scott Edward. 3303 SW BOND AVE, MAIL CODE: CH6D 97239 #004-01-1996 L2000 **GE** *100 †20
NAUTIYAL, Jaishanker. 3620 N INTERSTATE AVE 97227 #016-02-1988 L2000 **RO** *020 †80
NAYAK, Alice Catherine. ■ 97202 #041-12-2000 L2000 **IM** *020 †20
NAYLOR, Jack. ■ 97220 #040-02-1957 **GS** *071 †85
NAZEMI, David Christopher. ■ 97219 #048-15-2000 L2006 **IM** *020 †20

NAZEMI, Kellie Jean. 3181 SW SAM JACKSON PRK RD, M/C: 97239 #048-15-2000 L2006 **PHO** *100 †55
NEAL, Cheryl Ruth. ■ 97231 #040-02-1974 L1975 **IM** *071 †20
NEAL, Edward Griffin. ■ 97213 #034-01-1988 L1989 **IM** *020 †20
NEDROW, Anne Ruth. 3181 SW SAM JACKSON PRK RD, SCIENCE UNIV 97239 #040-02-1983 L1984 **IM** *020 †20
NEEDLE, Jennifer Susan. ■ 97209 #010-03-2000 L2007 **CCP** *100 †55,20
NEFF, Kent Edward. ■ 97221 #041-01-1965 L1970 **P** *030
NEILSON, Duncan Reese, Jr. 300 N GRAHAM ST, STE 100 97227 #023-07-1969 L1974 **OBG** *030
NEILSON, Leslie. ■ 97210 #040-02-1995 L2001 **P** *020 †75
NELSON, Bella Asako. 5050 NE HOYT ST STE 540 97213 #040-02-2007 L2007 **IM** *012
NELSON, Heidi Dawn. 3181 SW SAM JACKSON PRK RD 97239 #026-04-1985 L1986 **IM PHP** *020 †20
NELSON, Joanne Claire. 501 N GRAHAM ST, STE 555 97227 #016-06-1973 L1974 **GS** *020 †85
NELSON, Joshua Dayalan. 2701 NW VAUGHN ST, STE 350 97210 #005-19-2001 L2006 **P** *100
NELSON, Joshua Herbert. 1125 NW 21ST AVE STE B 97209 #056-06-2003 L2003 **NEP** *012 †20
NELSON, Lisa Ann. 4445 SW BARBUR BLVD, STE 104 97239 #049-01-1991 L1992 **IM** *020 †20
NEMECEK, Eneida R. 3181 SW SAM JACKSON PRK RD, OREGON HLTH & SCIENCE UNIV 97239 #042-01-1996 L2005 **PHO** *050 †55
NERNESS, Curtis Reed. 10000 SE MAIN ST, STE 205 97216 #005-12-1989 L1993 **IM** *020 †20
NESBIT, Gary Merlin. 2241 LLOYD CTR 97232 #026-04-1986 L1994 **NR** *020 †80
NEUMAN, Michael Jay. 4805 NE GLISAN ST, DEPARTMENT OF RADIOLOGY 97213 #056-05-1986 L2001 **DR** *020 †80
NEUMAYER, Stephanie K. ■ 97213 #030-06-2007 L2007 **PD** *012
NEUVONEN, Pekka Tapani. 3181 SW SAM JACKSON PRK RD 97239 #374-02-1976 L2002 *100
NEUWELT, Edward Allen. 3181 SW SAM JACKSON PRK RD, MAIL CODE L603 97239 #007-02-1972 L1981 **NS** *020 †25
NEVIS, Harold Chaim. 3550 N INTERSTATE AVE, KAISER EIN MEDICAL OFFICE 97227 #016-02-1966 L1970 **IM** *020
NEWGARD, Craig Douglas. 3181 SW SAM JACKSON PRK RD R, MAIL CODE CR-114 97239 #016-43-1997 L2002 **EM EP** *020 †16
NEWHALL, Elizabeth P. 501 N GRAHAM ST, STE 445 97227 #005-19-1979 L1984 **OBG** *020 †30
NEWHALL, James Fellows. 511 SW 10TH AVE, STE 905 97205 #005-19-1980 L1984 **FM** *020 †18
NEWTON, Patricia Anne. 1200 NW 23RD AVE 97210 #051-04-1976 L1977 **IM IMG** *020 †20
NEWTON, William Lee. 1000 SW VISTA AVE, NO. 903 97205 #038-40-1971 L1992 **P** *020 †75
NG, John Danl. 3375 SW TERWILLIGER BLVD, CASEY EYE INST 97239 #010-01-1988 L2000 **OPH AM** *020 †35
NGUYEN, Hanh Ngoc. 6523 SE KNIGHT ST 97206 #040-02-2003 L2003 **CHP** *012
NGUYEN, Hoang Quangduc. 5050 NE HOYT ST STE 540, MEDICAL CE 97213 #054-04-2002 L2002 **IM** *020 †20
NGUYEN, Hung Trung. 3710 SW US VETRNS HSPTL RD 97239 #942-01-1979 L2007 **IM** *020 †20
NGUYEN, Luan Van. 4805 NE GLISAN ST 97213 #941-01-1961 L1979 **GP** *071
NGUYEN, Nganlien T. 10201 SE MAIN ST, STE 12 97216 #040-02-1984 L1985 **IM** *020 †20
NGUYEN, Tuan A. 2050 NW LOVEJOY ST 97209 #048-15-1989 L1997 **PS** *072 †85,65
NGUYEN-HUYNH, Anh T. 3181 SW SAM JACKSON PRK RD, PHYSICIANS PAV PV01 97239 #024-01-1999 L2006 **OTO** *050 †45
NICHOLS, Craig Randal. 4805 NE GLISAN ST, STE 6N40 97213 #040-02-1978 L1998 **ON HEM** *050 †20
NICHOLS, Dane Jeffrey. 3181 SW SAM JACKSON PRK RD, MAIL CODE UHN-67 97239 #040-02-1981 L1998 **CCM** *020 †20
NICHOLS, Gregory Bunton. 1111 NE 99TH AVE 97220 #030-06-1943 **DR** *071 †80
NICHOLS, Mark David. 3181 SW SAM JCKSN PRK RD R 97239 #005-19-1979 L1981 **OBG** *020 †30
NICHOLS, Michael J. 3710 SW US VETRNS HSPTL RD, MED. SERV/VAMC 97239 #043-01-1976 L1990 **PTH** *020 †55,50
NICHOLSON, Eugene Pendlet. ■ 97213 #012-01-2005 L2005 **PD** *012
NICHOLSON, Henry Stacy. 2241 LLOYD CTR 97232 #012-01-1985 L1997 **PHO PD** *020 †55
NICHOLSON, Svati Valia. ■ 97213 #012-01-2005 L2005 **PD** *012
NICKEL, Robert Elwood. 2241 LLOYD CTR 97232 #005-02-1971 L1980 **PD** *020 †55
NICOLAIDIS, Christina M. 2241 LLOYD CTR 97232 #005-01-1993 L1994 **END** *020 †20
NICOLOFF, Alexander D. 2222 NW LOVEJOY ST STE 419 97210 #026-04-1993 L1994 **VS GS** *020 †85
NIECE, William K. 10300 NE HANCOCK ST 97220 #040-02-1951 L1954 **GP OS** *071
NIELSEN, Erik Wm. 10201 SE MAIN ST, STE 20 97216 #005-12-1978 L1981 **AN** *020 †05
NIELSEN, Nathan Dean. 3181 SW SAM JCKSN PRK RD R, SCIENCE UNIV 97239 #036-07-2004 L2004 **CCM** *012 †20
NIEMANN, Petra Susanne. 3181 SW SAM JCKSN PRK RD R, M/C: L608 97239 #409-16-1999 L2001 **CCM** *100
NIGHTINGALE, Janice H T. ■ 97201 #035-09-1945 L1977 **PD PHP** *071 †55
NILAVER, Gajanan. 3181 SW SAM JACKSON PRK RD 97239 #495-04-1970 L1985 **N** *050
NILES, Nelson Robinson. 3181 SW SAM JCKSN PRK #R 97239 #035-02-1947 **ATP** *071 †50
NILES, Sally Lindsay. 1040 NW 22ND AVE, STE 320 97210 #040-02-1986 L1987 **PM IM** *020 †60
NIOSI, Willemina. 700 NE MULTNOMAH ST, STE 560 97232 #660-01-1963 L1980 **CHP PD** *071 †55,75
NITTA, Kenneth Masahiro. 10123 SE MARKET ST, DEPT RAD ONCOLOGY 97216 #028-34-1983 L1986 **RO** *020 †80
NJONJO, Margaret Nduta. ■ 97239 #026-04-2005 L2005 **IM** *012
NOALL, David Lawrence. 501 N GRAHAM ST 97227 #040-02-1972 L1973 **ORS** *020 †40
NOBLE, Stephen Leonard. ■ 97239 #017-20-2006 L2006 **GS** *012
NOEL, Gordon Lee. 3710 SW US VETRNS HSPTL RD 97239 #035-01-1967 L1993 **IM END** *030 †20
NOFFSINGER, Julie Marie. 2801 N GANTENBEIN AVE, MEDICAL STAFF OFFICE 97227 #016-45-2000 L2007 **PD** *020 †55
NOLAN, James Thos. 5050 NE HOYT ST STE 515, PROVIDENCE PROF PLAZA 97213 #040-02-1978 L1986 **HS PS** *020 †65
NOLAND, Carter. 10101 SE MAIN ST, STE 3001 97216 #005-12-1964 L1972 **OPH** *020 †35
NOLES, Lorna Michele. ■ 97215 #040-02-2001 L2001 **AN** *100 †05
NOLT, Dawn Lynn. 3181 SW SAM JACKSON PRK RD, PARK ROAD 97239 #010-01-1996 L2006 **PDI** *020 †55
NORLING, Mark Allen. 120 NW 14TH AVE STE 300 97209 #040-02-1987 L1991 **AN PME** *020 †05 ‡
NORMAN, Douglas James. 3181 SW SAM JACKSON PRK RD, PARK RD 97239 #054-04-1972 L1979 **NEP IG** *020 †20

■ = Address Information Privacy Protected

NORRIS, Eric Stephen. 300 N GRAHAM ST, STE 200 97227 #041-09-1998 L2002 **FM** *020 †18
NORRIS, James Douglas. 500 NE MULTNOMAH ST, STE 100 97232 #007-02-1969 L1972
  IM *020 †20
NORRIS, Patricia Lynn. 2222 NW LOVEJOY ST, STE 412 97210 #040-02-1994 L1998 **D** *020 †15
NORTH, Jeffrey Paul. 3303 SW BOND AVE, MAIL CODE 16D 97239 #005-02-2006 L2006 **D** *012
NORTH, Neshe Ella. 300 N GRAHAM ST, STE 320 97227 #004-01-1989 L1990 **CD** *020 †20
NORTON, Robert Louis. 2241 LLOYD CTR 97232 #032-01-1977 L1980 **EM IM** *020,16
NORTON, Walter Edgar. 10123 SE MARKET ST 97216 #040-02-1963 L1964 **FM** *020 †18
NORWOOD, Kevin Glen. 501 N GRAHAM ST, STE 355 97227 #045-04-1996 L2003
  PHO *055
NOVAK, Freddie Patrick D. 1220 SW MORRISON ST # 1100 97205 #040-02-1984 L1988
  AN *075
NOVY, Miles Jos. 3181 SW SAM JCKSN PRK #R 97239 #024-01-1963 L1970 **OBG PD** *050 †30
NUDELMAN, Phillip Leo. 833 SW 11TH AVE STE 717 97205 #040-02-1943 L1948 **IM** *075
NUNLEY, William Ronnie. 97206 #020-02-2004 L2004 **P** *012
NUTT, John Gordon, Jr. 3181 SW SAM JACKSON PRK RD, DEPT NEUROLOGY OP-32 97239
  #048-04-1970 L1979 **N PA** *050 †75
NYE, Jerry Earl. 2222 NW LOVEJOY ST, STE 401 97210 #005-02-1965 L1971 **HS GS** *020 †85,65
NYENDAK, Melissa Rose. 3181 SW SAM JACKSON PRK RD 97239 #550-02-2002 L2002
  ID *100 †20
OAKES, Elizabeth Anne. 2801 N GANTENBEIN AVE 97227 #005-11-1989 L1991 **AN** *020 †05 ‡
OBESTER, James Alan, Jr. 3181 SW SAM JCKSN PRK RD R, SCIENCE UNIV 97239
  #040-02-2001 L2002 **AN** *100 †05
O'BRIEN-WILLIAMS, Jennifer. 120 NW 14TH AVE, OREGON ANESTHESIOLOGY GRP 97209
  #008-01-1992 L2001 **AN** *020 †05 ‡
OCHOA, Jose L. 1040 NW 22ND AVE, STE 600 97210 #231-03-1961 L1986 **N** *050
OCKNER, James Lee. 2701 NW VAUGHN ST, STE 425 97210 #030-05-1992 L1997
  DR RNR *020 †80
O'CONNELL, William R. 3500 N INTERSTATE AVE 97227 #020-02-1968 L1977 **GS** *020 †85
O'CONNOR, Terrence Richar. ■ 97219 #005-02-2004 L2005 **EM** *012
O'DWYER, Michael Eamon. 3181 SW SAM JCKSN PRK RD R, M/C CR145 97239
  #539-05-1990 L2000 **HO** *100
OFFENSTEIN, Heather B. 3181 SW SAM JCKSN PRK RD R 97239 #016-42-2003 L2003
  PCC *012 †20
OGISU, Tatsuro. 1920 NW JOHNSON ST, STE 116 97209 #036-05-1994 L1998 **PM** *020
O'GLASSER, Avital Yehudit. ■ 97239 #041-02-2007 L2007 **IM** *012
OGLE, David Jeffrey. 10748 NE HALSEY ST 97220 #305-01-1989 L1997 **FM NTR** *020 †18
O'HANLEY, Kelly Lou K. ■ 97213 #045-01-1977 L1979 **OBG** *020
O'HANLEY, Peter Donald. ■ 97213 #045-01-1979 L1980 **IM** *020 †20
O'HARA, Michael Francis. 2241 LLOYD CTR 97232 #035-45-1975 L2002 **PTH GS** *050 †50
O'HEARN, Daniel James. 2241 LLOYD CTR 97232 #035-15-1991 L2002 **PCC** *020 †20
O'HEARN, James Y. 500 NE MULTNOMAH ST, STE 100 97232 #016-11-1978 L1981 **IM** *020 †20
O'HEARN, Mary Elizabeth. 3181 SW SAM JCKSN PRK RD R, M/C L-475 97239
  #005-11-1986 L1997 **IM** *020 †20
O'HERRON, Patrick Joseph. ■ 97239 #003-01-2004 L2005 **GS** *012
OHMAN, Kimberly Ann. 3181 SW SAM JACKSON PRK RD, SCIENCE UNIV/C 97239
  #048-12-2006 L2006 **EM** *012
O'HOLLAREN, Mark Thos. 511 SW 10TH AVE, ALLERGY CLINIC LLC 97205 #040-02-1980 L1983
  IM A *020 †20,03
O'HOLLAREN, Patrick Sean. 2801 N GANTENBEIN AVE 97227 #040-02-1987 L1994
  UP *020 †95
OHOTTO, Anthony Arthur. ■ 97214 #026-04-1994 L2004 **FPG** *020 †18
OKEN, Barry S. 3181 SW SAM JACKSON PRK RD, CR120 97239 #036-05-1978 L1986
  N *050 †75
OKEN, Stuart Lee. 5055 N GREELEY AVE 97217 #020-12-1966 L1978 **P** *020 †75
OKEREKE, Linda Ijeoma. 3600 N INTERSTATE AVE, CENTRAL INTERSTATE OFFICE 97227
  #028-46-2001 L2007 **PM** *020 †60
OKIES, Joseph Edward. 115 SW WRIGHT AVE 97205 #048-04-1967 L1973 **TS** *020 †85,90
OLBRICH, Gary David. 727 SW BURNSIDE 97209 #005-11-1973 L1990 **ADM** *030 †20
O'LEARY, Thomas Jos. 500 NE MULTNOMAH ST STE 10 97232 #028-34-1958 L1962 **GP** *071
OLLER, Dale Tobin. 5319 SW WESTGATE DR STE 10 97221 #040-02-1991 L1992 **P** *020 †75
OLMSCHEID, Richard Hubert. ■ 97212 #040-02-1969 L1973 **N** *100 †75
OLSEN, George Duane. OR HLTH SCI U PHAR L 221 97201 #024-01-1966 L1970 **OS** *040
OLSON, Amanda E. ■ 97239 #003-03-2006 L2006 **OBG** *012
OLSON, Barry Dean. 120 NW 14TH AVE, STE 300 97209 #040-02-1973 L1974 **AN** *020 †05 ‡
OLSON, Janice Faye. 2801 N GANTENBEIN AVE 97227 #049-01-1985 L1999 **PHO PD** *020 †55
OLSON, Jeffrey Stephen. 3181 SW SAM JCKSN PRK RD R, M/S PV310 97239
  #003-01-2001 L2001 **GE** *012
OLSON, Lisa Ann May. ■ 97211 #040-02-2008 *012
OMIZO, Molly Nothman. 5050 NE HOYT ST STE 626, SUITE 626 97213 #040-02-1990 L1991
  IM *050 †20
OMIZO, Russ Tatsuto. 2801 N GANTENBEIN AVE, RADIATION ONCOLOGY 97227
  #040-02-1993 L1994 **RO** *020 †80
OMURA, Susan Emily. 2801 N GANTENBEIN AVE, EMERCGENCY DEPARTMENT 97227
  #001-02-1991 L2002 **PD** *020 †55
O'NEAL, Natasha Ingvoldst. 3181 SW SAM JACKSON PRK RD, OR HLTH SCI UNIV SCH
  MED 97239 #040-02-2005 L2007 **FP** *012
ONEAL, Seth Edward. 2801 N GANTENBEIN AVE, LEGACY 97227 #040-02-2006 L2006 **TY** *012
O'NEILL, Elizabeth Ruth. 1321 NE 99TH AVE, STE 200 97220 #056-05-2000 L2000 **FM** *020 †18
O'NEILL, Oisin R. 5050 NE HOYT ST, STE 418 97213 #539-06-1985 L1992 **NS** *020 †25
OPDYKE, Kerry Elizabeth. ■ 97219 #007-02-2006 L2006 **P** *012
OPPENHEIMER, Jeffrey H. ■ 97219 #010-02-1984 L2006 **NS** *020 †25
OPPENHEIMER, Margaret Ann. ■ 97220 #028-03-2007 L2007 **IM** *012
OPTON, James Curtis. 120 NW 14TH AVE, STE 300 97209 #040-02-2003 L2004 **AN** *020
O'REILLY, Margaret Mary. 2241 LLOYD CTR 97232 #021-01-1995 L1997 **OBG** *020 †30
OREN, Tamara Lynn. 7705 SE DIVISION ST, KAISER DIVISION CLINIC 97206 #040-02-2002 L2005
  FM *020 †18
ORFALY, Robert M. 3181 SW SAM JCKSN PRK RD R 97239 #067-01-1991 L1999 **OAR** *020 †40
ORFANAKIS, Dolores T. 2801 N GANTENBEIN AVE, EMANUEL HOSP & HEALTH CTR 97227
  #049-01-1970 L1976 **PD** *020 †30
ORLANDO, Marc Vincent. ■ 97239 #038-45-2006 L2006 **GS** *012
ORLOFF, Susan Louise. 3181 SW SAM JACKSON PRK RD 97239 #005-02-1984 L1995
  GS *020 †85
O'ROURKE, Robert Ward. 3181 SW SAM JACKSON PRK RD, DEPT GEN SURG L223A 97239
  #005-14-1993 L2001 **GS** *020 †85
ORSINI, Caroline Mariejos. ■ 97232 #032-01-2006 L2006 **FP** *012

ORTIZ, Justin Philip. 3181 SW SAM JCKSN PRK RD R, DEPT OF ANESTHESIOLOGY 97239
  #024-01-2002 L2004 **AN** *012
ORWOLL, Eric Smith. 2241 LLOYD CTR 97232 #023-01-1974 L1975 **END** *050 †20
ORWOLL, Rebecca Lynn. 5050 NE HOYT ST STE 256, PC 97213 #040-02-1979 L1980
  HO IM *020 †20
OSBORN, Richard Alan. ■ 97212 #005-14-1977 L1983 **DR** *020 †80
OSBORN, Timothy M. 611 SW CAMPUS DR, SD-522 97239 #040-02-2008 *012
OSBORNE, Michael Vernon. 5440 SW WESTGATE DR, DRIVE #220 97221 #054-04-1990 L1991
  PD AI *020 †55,03
OSBORNE, Molly Lee. 3181 SW SAM JACKSON PRK RD, PK ROAD 97239 #007-02-1979 L1981
  CCM PUD *050 †20
O'SHEA, John Jos. 5050 NE HOYT ST STE 138 97213 #010-02-1992 L2002 **OSM ORS** *020 †40
OSMUNDSEN, Blake Carter. 5050 NE HOYT ST STE 255, LAURELHURST WOMEN'S
  CLINIC 97213 #021-01-1987 L1991 **OBG** *020 †30
OSTERGARD, Arthur Eric. 123 NE 3RD AVE STE 24, UNITED STATES POSTAL SERVI 97232
  #038-40-1973 L1973 **OM MDM** *071
OSTERMEYER, Claudia D. 19500 SE STARK ST 97233 #836-01-1984 L1991 **IM** *020 †20
O'SULLIVAN, Mark D. 3101 SW SAM JACKSON PRK RD 97239 #143-02-1981 **OP** *020
OTIS, Carol Louise. ■ 97239 #005-06-1975 L1979 **IM OS** *074 †20
O'TOOLE, Julie Kathleen. 2800 N VANCOUVER AVE # 118, KARTINI CLINIC, PC 97227
  #409-39-1980 L1991 **PD ADL** *020 †55
OTT, Charlotte C. ■ 97211 #048-04-2002 L2007 **MPD** *020 †20,55
OTT, Gary Yee. 1111 NE 99TH AVE 97220 #041-02-1983 L1991 **TS** *050 †85,90
OTTINGER, Ayland Midgley. 2222 NW LOVEJOY ST STE 315 97210 #023-01-1958 L1962
  IM *071
OXMAN, Gary Lyle. 426 SW STARK ST 8TH FL 97204 #026-04-1978 L1979 **PHP** *030 †70
OYAMA, Karen Anne. 13705 NE AIRPORT WAY 97230 #040-02-1990 L1991 **PTH** *062 †50
PACKARD, Daniel Newell. 4805 NE GLISAN ST 97213 #018-75-2004, ▲ L2005 **IM** *012
PAGE, Amy Elizabeth. ■ 97239 #041-07-1994 L1997 **IM** *012
PAGE, Michael Allen. 2801 N GANTENBEIN AVE, LEGACY 97227 #025-01-2006 L2006 **OPH** *012
PAGE, Tanya Lorraine. 3110 SE SALMON ST 97214 #035-47-2002 L2002 **FM** *020 †18
PAGE, Urlin Scott. 2222 NW LOVEJOY ST STE 315, NORTHWEST SURGICAL ASSOC I 97210
  #040-02-1959 L1961 **TS** *071 †85,90
PAGEL, Keith Jos. 3710 SW US VETRNS HSPTL RD, MEDICAL CENTE 97239
  #040-02-1987 L1997 **PM** *020 †60
PAISLEY, John Wm. 2801 N GANTENBEIN AVE, DEPT PEDIATRICS 97227 #024-01-1973 L1989
  PD ID *020 †55
PAIVA, Eduardo Dos Santos. 3181 SW SAM JACKSON PRK RD, STE L329A 97239 #187-08-1992
  RHU *100
PAK, Jonathan T. ■ 97209 #041-13-2007 L2007 **IM** *012
PAK, Suzanne Yongchu. 800 SW 13TH AVE 97205 #041-01-1995 L2001 **AN** *020 †05 ‡
PALMER, Earl A. 3303 SW BOND AVE, FL 11 97239 #036-07-1966 L1974 **OPH PD** *020 †55,35
PALMER, Rebecca Lynn. 3181 SW SAM JCKSN PRK RD R, OHSU - CDW-EM 97239
  #036-05-2005 L2005 **EM** *012
PALMER, Roberta Rose. ■ 97202 #005-12-1970 L1974 **AN** *020 †05
PALMROSE, Frank Edgar. 120 NW 14TH AVE, STE 300 97209 #040-02-1985 L1986
  AN *020 †05 ‡
PALTROW, Kenneth Guy. 1015 NW 22ND AVE 97210 #035-09-1958 L1966 **P** *020 †75 ‡
PAN, Xianghua. 2801 N GANTENBEIN AVE 97227 #243-47-1988 L2002 **AN** *020 †05 ‡
PANCOAST, Patricia N. 120 NW 14TH AVE, STE 300 97209 #005-12-1988 L1996
  AN IM *020 †20,05 ‡
PANCOAST, Patrick M. 120 NW 14TH AVE, STE 300 97209 #005-12-1991 L1999 **AN** *020 †05 ‡
PANDURANGAN, Suresh. 3181 SW SAM JACKSON PRK RD, OR HLTH SCI UNIV HOSP 97239
  #495-04-1994 L2005 **PAN** *100
PANIKER, Parwathi V. 3600 N INTERSTATE AVE, NW PERMANENTE CENTRAL INTE 97227
  #003-01-1995 L2005 **D** *020 †15
PANOSCHA, Rita. 3181 SW SAM JACKSON PRK RD 97239 #036-01-1986 L2002 **PD** *020 †55
PANTELY, George Alexander. 3181 SW SAM JACKSON PRK RD, PARK ROAD 97239
  #056-05-1971 L1973 **CD IM** *062 †20
PANYUTICH, Alexander V. 3600 N INTERSTATE AVE, NORTHWEST PERMANENTE PC 97227
  #913-32-1982 L2004 **HO IM** *020 †20
PAPAK, Joel Nathaniel. ■ 97217 #040-02-2007 L2007 **IM** *012
PAPPAS, James Thos. 5050 NE HOYT ST STE 428 97213 #005-11-1966 L1967 **U FM** *020 †95
PARAFINA, Hedi O. ■ 97209 #048-12-1987 L1989 **P** *075 †75
PARENT, Joseph Adrien, Jr. 1750 SW HARBOR WAY STE 245 97201 #035-03-1965 L1972
  GE IM *020 †20
PARK, Jin S. 10000 SE MAIN ST, STE 205 97216 #048-13-1998 L1999 **IM** *020 †20
PARK, Paul S. ■ 97209 #035-09-1996 L1997 **IM** *020
PARKER, Frank. 3303 SW BOND AVE, DEPT - DERMATOLOGY 97239 #054-04-1958 L1977
  D IM *020 †20,15
PARKER, Richard Allen. 3314 SW US VETRN HOSP RD, HOSPITAL RD. 97239
  #017-20-1971 L1975 **NEP IM** *020 †20
PARKER, Stephen Jennison. 2241 LLOYD CTR 97232 #050-02-1995 L1999 **EM** *020 †16
PARRISH, Earl Harrison. 2241 LLOYD CTR 97232 #028-02-1964 L1972 **PS CS** *020 †85,65
PARSHLEY, Marianne Cook. 1321 NE 99TH AVE, STE 100 97220 #032-01-1984 L1985
  IM *020 †20
PARSHLEY, Philip Ford, Jr. 1500 SW 1ST AVE STE 620 97201 #024-01-1956 L1964
  GS OS *030 †85
PARSONS, Bowen Stewart. ■ 97205 #021-01-1985 L1992 **IM** *020
PARSONS, William Ronald. 2222 NW LOVEJOY ST STE 518 97210 #048-04-1960 L1968
  NS *071 †25
PARTRIDGE, John W. ■ 97221 #016-02-1945 L1957 **IM DIA** *071 †20
PARTSAFAS, Aaron Wayne. ■ 97239 #040-02-2004 L2004 **GS** *012
PASADHIKA, Sirichai. 3375 SW TERWILLIGER BLVD, OHSU CASEY EYE INSTITUTE 97239
  #891-01-1998 L2007 *100
PASQUINE, Ginevra Lois. ■ 97211 #024-07-2004 L2005 **IM** *012
PATCHIN, Daniel Marvin. 10000 SE MAIN ST, STE 309 97216 #005-12-1966 L1973
  OBG *071 †30
PATEL, Chirag R. 1200 NW 23RD AVE 97210 #048-78-2002, ▲ L2002 **IM** *020 †20
PATEL, Zara Marzban. 3181 SW SAM JACKSON PRK RD, APT L102 97239 #040-02-2005 L2007
  OTO *012
PATRICK, Shawn Timothy. 2222 NW LOVEJOY ST STE 606 97210 #056-06-1994 L2001
  CD *020 †20
PATRIZIO, Glen Richard. 1235 NE 47TH AVE, STE 148 97213 #040-02-1999 L2002
  MPD IM *100 †18
PATTERSON, Emma Jean. 1040 NW 22ND AVE STE 50, OREGON WEIGHT LOSS
  SURGERY 97210 #065-01-1993 L2000 **GS** *020 †85

PATTINSON, Kara Laure. 1306 NW HOYT ST, STE 205 97209 #040-02-2001 L2001 **CHP** *020

PATTON, Gregory Alan. 265 N BROADWAY ST, NW CANCER SPECS 97227 #048-04-1977 L2001 **RO MDM** *020 †80 ‡

PATTON, Leslie J. 3181 SW SAM JACKSON PRK RD, # L587 97239 #040-02-1991 L1992 **IM** *020 †20

PATTON, Phillip Edward. 3303 SW BOND AVE, STE CH10F 97239 #021-01-1980 L1986 **OBG** *020 †30

PATZEL, Jerome C. 120 NW 14TH AVE, STE 300 97209 #019-02-1978 L1980 **AN** *020 †05 ‡

PAUDYAL, Sunita. 5050 NE HOYT ST STE 540, PROVICENCE 97213 #672-03-2005 L2007 **IM** *012

PAULL, David Parmenter. 510 NE 49TH AVE 97213 #038-06-1945 L1955 **U** *071 †95

PAULSON, Lorien Mary. ■ 97217 #005-18-2007 L2007 **OTO** *012

PAWLIK, Theodore David. 501 N GRAHAM ST STE 265, NORTHWEST NEWBORN SPECIAL] 97227 #041-13-1998 L2007 **PD** *020 †55

PAXTON, Don Alan. ■ 97211 #047-20-2004 L2005 **AN** *012

PAXTON, Harold Denver. 3181 SW SAM JACKSON PRK RD 97239 #023-07-1948 L1956 **NS** *071 †25

PAYNE, Jane Gregory. ■ 97206 #049-01-2002 L2002 **P** *100

PAYNE, Roy Alpha. ■ 97266 #040-02-1955 L1956 **IM** *071

PAYSSE, Jeanette Claire. 5217 SE 28TH AVE, COLUMBIA HILLS FAMILY MEDI 97202 #021-01-1999 L2006 **IM** *020

PEARSE, Harper Davis. ■ 97221 #049-01-1963 L1971 **RO ON** *071 †95,80

PEARSON, John Albert. 3800 N INTERSTATE AVE 97227 #005-06-1972 L1977 **PD N** *020 †55

PECK, James Jos. 1136 NW 22ND AVE 97210 #040-02-1972 L1981 **GS VS** *020 †85

PEDERSEN, Andrew Dale. 5050 NE HOYT ST, STE 655 97213 #040-02-1991 L1995 **OTO** *020 †45

PEDERSEN, Donal Harry. 507 NE 47TH AVE, STE 103 97213 #040-02-1969 L1972 **CD** *071 †20

PEEL, Anne Rutherford. 3181 SW SAM JACKSON PRK RD 97239 #040-02-2007 L2007 **IM** *012

PEEL, Lynda Rose. 2222 NW LOVEJOY ST, STE 505 97210 #032-01-1998 L1999 **IM** *012

PEIMER, Corinne Baldwin. 3181 SW SAM JCKSN PRK RD R, OHSU 97239 #025-12-2007 L2007 **FP** *012

PEIZNER, David Stephen. 300 N GRAHAM ST, STE 320 97227 #028-34-1987 L2003 **CD** *020 †20

PEJOVIC, Tanja Branko. 3181 SW SAM JCKSN PRK RD R 97239 #957-02-1984 L2003 **OBG GO** *020 †30

PENA, Porfirio. 5050 NE HOYT ST, STE 203 97213 #040-02-1986 L1987 **IM** *020 †20

PENG, Louis Ingting. 5050 NE HOYT ST, STE 454 97213 #024-07-1995 L1997 **IM** *020 †20

PENNY, Heather Michelle. ■ 97202 #040-02-2007 L2007 **FP** *012

PENSA, Mellisa Ann. ■ 97239 #008-02-2008 *012

PERCHINSKY, Michael John. 2801 N GANTENBEIN AVE 97227 #060-01-1989 L1991 **GS** *100 †85

PEREIRA, Leonardo Mr. 3181 SW SAM JCKSN PRK RD R 97239 #041-01-1997 L2004 **OBG** *020 †30

PEREIRA, Natasha Lynn. 1040 NW 22ND AVE, STE 500 97210 #067-01-1998 L2004 *100

PERLMAN, David Weil. ■ 97221 #040-02-1974 L1975 **UCM** *020

PERNICE, Nicholas James. ■ 97201 #035-19-1967 L1968 **DR** *020 †80

PERRIN, Eugene Rene. 2363 NW FLANDERS ST 97210 #035-20-1959 1971 **PS** *020 †85,65

PERRY, David Long, Jr. 1130 NW 22ND AVE, STE 220 97210 #005-11-1968 L1972 **IM** *020 †20

PERRY, Judith Adams. 3550 N INTERSTATE AVE, KAISER - INTERSTATE MEDICA 97227 #005-12-1972 L1998 **P** *020 †75 ‡

PERSON, Thomas David. 3181 SW SAM JCKSN PRK RD R, M/S L-223 97239 #024-05-2001 L2001 **GS** *012

PERSSE, Timothy Francis. 2282 NW NORTHRUP ST, STE 21 97210 #012-01-1983 L2001 **IM** *020 †20

PETERING, Ryan Carl. ■ 97239 #047-20-2006 L2006 **FP** *012

PETERS, Brandon Richard. ■ 97219 #040-02-2008 *012

PETERS, Jon F. 2647 NE 33RD AVE, FAMILY MEDICAL GROUP NORTH 97212 #048-12-1988 L1992 **FM** *020 †18

PETERSEN, Arnold L, II. 10101 SE MAIN ST STE 2011 97216 #005-12-1966 L1971 **OBG** *020 †30

PETERSEN, Bryan Dale. 2241 LLOYD CTR 97232 #040-02-1986 L1987 **DR** *040 †80

PETERSEN, Ronald Raymond. 1111 NE 99TH AVE 97220 #040-02-1982 L1983 **CD ICE** *020 †20

PETERSON, Amie Louise. 3181 SW SAM JCKSN PRK RD R, M/C: OP32 97239 #012-01-2001 L2007 **N** *100 †75

PETERSON, Dawn Misora. ■ 97211 #028-78-2006, ▲ L2006 **IM** *012

PETERSON, Preston L. 1130 NW 22ND AVE STE 220 97210 #048-15-2001 L2001 **IM IMG** *020

PETERSON, Robert Wm. 3600 N INTERSTATE AVE 97227 #035-09-1986 L1993 **PD** *020 †55

PETROSKE, James Lawrence. 2250 NW FLANDERS ST, STE 103 97210 #040-02-1959 L1965 **P** *075 †75

PETRUNIN, Chuck Gregory. 2241 LLOYD CTR 97232 #031-01-1996 L1999 **HO** *020 †20

PETTIT, Jody Lea. 5050 NE HOYT ST STE 5 97213 #051-04-1994 L1997 **IM** *020 †20

PETTY, Wm Mc Candless, Jr. 5804 SW GILLCREST CT 97221 #028-34-1966 L1974 **GO GYN** *071 †30

PEZZONI, Kimber Lee. 3181 SW SAM JACKSON PRK RD, UHN 80 97239 #040-02-2004 L2004 **CHP** *012

PHAL, Pramit Minesh. 3181 SW SAM JCKSN PRK RD R, OHSU 97239 #143-02-1996 L2004 *100

PHAM, Minh Quang. 120 NW 14TH AVE STE 3 97209 #048-12-2002 L2007 **AN** *100 †05

PHAM, Thanhlong Duc. ■ 97230 #040-02-2005 L2005 **FP** *012

PHELPS, Carolyn Michelle. ■ 97239 #040-02-2007 L2007 **P** *012

PHILBECK, Kerry Noelle. 3181 SW SAM JACKSON PRK RD 97239 #011-04-2001 L2001 **IM** *100

PHILLIPS, Charles Robt. 3181 SW SAM JCKSN PRK RD R, M/S UHN 67 97239 #010-01-1990 L1991 **PCC** *020 †20

PHILLIPS, Jeanne Vesey. 1111 NE 99TH AVE 97220 #024-01-1997 L2004 **CD** *020 †20

PHILLIPS, Michael Gregory. 1111 NE 99TH AVE 97220 #040-02-1986 L1992 **GE IM** *020 †20

PHILLIPS, Nancy Anne. ■ 97221 #021-05-1985 L1992 **P** *020 †75

PHILLIPS, Richard Harvey. 4805 NE GLISAN ST 97213 #040-02-1960 L1964 **P** *020

PICKETT, Mary Ellis. 2241 LLOYD CTR 97232 #005-02-1994 L2000 **IM** *020 †20

PIEDRA, Mark Peter. ■ 97201 #026-08-2006 L2006 **NS** *012

PIENIAZEK, John. 8935 SE POWELL BLVD, WORKER CLIN 97266 #759-01-1999 L2004 **FM** *020 †18

PIERCE, David Albert. 800 SW 13TH AVE 97205 #016-06-1978 L2000 **FM** *020 †18

PILLERS, De-Ann Margaret. 2241 LLOYD CTR 97232 #040-02-1984 L1987 **NPM PD** *040 †55

PILLETTE, Stacey Jean. 6312 SW CAPITOL HWY, PMB 192 97239 #040-02-2000 **P** *100

PINTER, Jergensen David. 707 SW GAINES ST, PEDIATRIC NEUROLOGY, CDRC- 97239 #005-14-1990 L2007 **CHN PD** *020 †55,75

PIPER, Kalman John. 3101 SW SAM JCKSN PRK RD R, SHRINERS HOSP 97239 #143-05-1998 L2006 *100

PITSCH, Trevor John. ■ 97219 #056-05-2005 L2006 **AN** *012

PLATTER, Daniel Laurence. 503 NE LAURELHURST PL 97232 #030-06-1999 L2002 **EM** *020 †16

PLUMB, Donald Frederick. 5050 NE HOYT ST, STE 245 97213 #005-15-1968 L1971 **OPH** *020 †35

PODMORE, Patricia. 3181 SW SAM JACKSON PRK RD 97239 #919-05-1977 **D** *100

POINDEXTER, Charles W. 5319 SW WESTGATE DR, CHARLES W POINDEXTER MD PC 97221 #040-02-1966 L1970 **AN GP** *071

POLACKWICH, Alan Scott. ■ 97209 #011-03-2008 *012

POLENSEK, Natasha Andrea. 3303 SW BOND AVE, 9TH FL 97239 #040-02-1990 L1991 **PD** *020 †55

POLLACK, David Alan. 3181 SW SAM JACKSON PRK RD, DEPT PSYCH OP-02 97239 #039-01-1973 L1976 **P** *020 †75

POLLAK, Kelly Ann. ■ 97209 #040-02-2008 *012

POLO, Oscar Raphael. 5050 NE HOYT ST, STE 421 97213 #039-01-1987 L1993 **OBG FM** *020 †18,30

POMMIER, Rodney Francis. 3181 SW SAM JCKSN PRK RD D, L-619 97239 #040-02-1983 L1984 **GS** *020 †85

POMPILIO, Jenny Elizabeth. 3550 N INTERSTATE AVE, EAST INTERSTATE MEDICAL OF 97227 #020-02-1996 L2000 **IM** *020 †20

POORMAN, Jay Clifford. 501 N GRAHAM ST, NORTHWEST 97227 #028-02-1988 L1989 **GE** *020 †20

POOTHULLIL, Antony Mathew. 3600 N INTERSTATE AVE, NORTHWEST PERMANENTE 97227 #048-04-1999 L2005 **OPH** *020 †35

POPE, Donna Lynn. 5319 SW WESTGATE DR, STE 241 97221 #048-14-1990 L1991 **AN** *020 †05

POPLI, Lokesh. 2801 N GANTENBEIN AVE 97227 #496-09-2003 L2006 **IM** *012

PORTER, David Wm. 2525 NW LOVEJOY ST, STE 200 97210 #040-02-1973 L1975 **PD** *020 †55

PORTER, George Alvin. 2241 LLOYD CTR 97232 #040-02-1957 L1958 **IM NEP** *040

PORTER, Mark Darragh. 3101 SW SAM JACKSON PARK R, 3101 SW SAM JACKSON PARK R 97239 #539-03-1990 L2006 **ORS** *100

POSNER, Jonathan Eric. 3181 SW SAM JCKSN PRK RD R, MAIL CODE: DC7P 97239 #035-08-2001 L2007 **CHP** *012

POST, Robert Henshaw. 1015 NW 22ND AVE 97210 #035-20-1960 L1968 **ORS** *071 †40

POTLA, Madhu Mala. 1321 NE 99TH AVE, STE 100 97220 #495-21-1996 L2001 **IM** *020 †20

POTTER, Robert Lyman. ■ 97230 #019-02-1964 L1965 **IM IMG** *071 †20

POTTS, Ronald Glenn. 500 NE MULTNOMAH ST, STE 100 97232 #038-41-1969 L1973 **EM** *030 †16

POWE, Larry Kenneth. ■ 97211 #047-07-1972 L1973 **PD N** *030 †55,75

POWELL, Christian Harring. ■ 97213 #539-04-2005 L2005 **IM** *012

POWELL, Constance Anne. 2455 NW MARSHALL ST STE 12 97210 #040-02-1982 L1983 **P NM** *020 †75

POWELL, James Norval. 5331 SW MACADAM AVE, BENEFIT RESOURCES INC 97239 #005-15-1966 L1973 **PD** *020 †55

POWERS, James Harrison. 2386 NW HOYT ST 97210 #047-05-1996 L2004 **CHP** *020 †75

POWERS, Jason John. 3500 N INTERSTATE AVE, PHYSICIAN/SURGEONS 97227 #010-01-1995 L1998 **GE** *020 †20

POWERS, Kara. 0615 SW PALATINE HILL RD, COUNSELING CENTER 97219 #047-05-1996 L2004 **P** *020 †75

POWERS, Michael Ray. 3181 SW SAM JCKSN PRK RD R, OHSU 97239 #040-02-1985 L1986 **PD** *050 †55

POYDENCE, Kristen M. ■ 97239 #038-45-2007 L2007 **GS** *012

POYOUROW, Erik. ■ 97239 #040-02-2008 *012

PRATER, Richard Neal. 4805 NE GLISAN ST 97213 #040-02-1957 L1962 **FM** *071

PRAVEEN, Anur Venkatachal. 3181 SW SAM JCKSN PRK RD R, SCIENCE UNIV 97239 #496-22-2002 L2007 **PHO** *012

PREDD, Florian Martin. ■ 97209 #017-20-1963 L1963 **GS** *072 †85

PREMYSLER, Raisa C. 12710 SE DIVISION ST, MID-COUNTY HEALTH CLINIC 97236 #913-18-1979 L1988 **PHP GP** *020

PRENDERGAST, Wm John, III. 1955 NW NORTHRUP ST, EYEHEALTHNW 97209 #040-02-1967 L1969 **OPH** *020 †35

PRESCOTT, S James, Jr. 5050 NE HOYT ST, STE 359 97213 #045-01-1978 L1982 **OBG** *020 †30

PRESENT, Sarah Dalen. ■ 97218 #021-01-2007 L2007 **FP** *012

PRESS, Richard Dale. 2241 LLOYD CTR 97232 #038-06-1988 L1993 **PTH** *020 †50

PRESSMAN, Peter Scott. ■ 97239 #040-02-2008 *012

PRICE, Eric W. 2647 NE 33RD AVE 97212 #048-12-1997 L2000 **FM PD** *020 †18

PRICE, Ernest H. 4805 NE GLISAN ST 97213 #030-05-1952 L1953 **FM** *071 †18

PRICE, Geraldine Gill. 5050 NE HOYT ST, STE 204 97213 #047-06-1949 L1949 **P** *071 †20

PRICE, Kursteen S. 233 NW 16TH AVE, ALLERGY ASTHMA & DERMATOLO 97209 #067-01-1996 L2002 **AI** *020 †20,03

PRIEST, Ryan Alexander. 3181 SW SAM JACKSON PRK RD, DEPT RAD 97239 #040-02-2006 L2007 **DR** *012

PRIHODA, James Sheldon. 3325 N INTERSTATE AVE, WEST INTERSTATE MEDICAL OF 97227 #016-11-1985 L1986 **END DIA** *020 †20

PRIKIS, Marios. ■ 97201 #473-01-2000 L2007 **NEP** *012 †20

PRIMACK, Steven Lloyd. 2241 LLOYD CTR 97232 #016-02-1987 L1994 **DR** *020 †80

PRITCHARD, Monique E. 2241 LLOYD CTR 97232 #050-02-1997 L2000 **PD** *020 †55

PRO, Stephan Lee. ■ 97239 #019-02-2004 L2004 **ORS** *012

PROWS, Ralph Merrill. 200 SW MARKET ST 97201 #021-01-1977 L1994 **IM** *020

PRUETT, David Rollins. 3710 SW US VETRNS HSPTL RD 97239 #016-42-1995 L1997 **EM** *020 †20

PRUETT, Jill Elizabeth. 1015 NW 22ND AVE, R 200 97210 #035-20-1993 L1994 **IM** *020 †20

PULITO, Geraldine. 120 NW 14TH AVE, STE 300 97209 #010-02-1973 L1976 **AN** *020 †05 ‡

PULLIAM, Joseph Patrick. 1130 NW 22ND AVE, STE 640 97210 #040-02-1979 L1981 **NEP CCM** *071 †20

PURANDARE, Amar Yeshwant. ■ 97239 #305-01-2000 L2005 **DR** *020 †80

PURNELL, Jonathan Quentin. 3181 SW SAM JACKSON PRK RD, MS L607 97239 #040-02-1986 L2000 **END** *020 †20

PUSCH, Allen Lewis. ■ 97239 #023-07-1960 L1967 **ATP CLP** *071 †50

PUTZ, Eric Jon. 2222 NW LOVEJOY ST, STE 606 97210 #054-04-1994 L2002 **ICE** *020 †20

QAISI, Waleed Ghazi. 2801 N GANTENBEIN AVE, ATTN: XRAY DEPT 97227 #020-12-1994 L2001 **DR** *020 †20

QUAN, Glenda Gia. ■ 97211 #005-19-2003 L2003 **GS** *012

QUARTERMAN, Renee Laverne. 800 SW 13TH AVE 97205 #036-07-1996 L2001 **GS** *020 †85

QUARUM, Merrit Laird. 700 NE MULTNOMAH ST, STE 1200 97232 #040-02-1986 L1987 **OS IM** *020

QUINN, Joseph Francis. 3181 SW SAM JACKSON PRK RD, MAIL CODE CR 131 97239 #005-06-1990 L1991 **N** *050 †75

■ = Address Information Privacy Protected

QUINT, Peter Andrew. 2801 N GANTENBEIN AVE, DEPT PEDIATRICS 97227 #007-02-1978 L1988 PD *020 †55

QUTISHAT, Ala Said. ■ 97210 #575-01-1989 L1994 PTH *020

RADCLIFFE, Carla C. 6736 NE KILLINGSWORTH ST, STE 100 97218 #038-06-1992 L2000 FM *020 †18

RADECKI, Patrick Louis. 2222 NW LOVEJOY ST STE 607 97210 #038-40-1973 L1983 N PM *020 †60

RADER, Anne Elizabeth. 2241 LLOYD CTR 97232 #030-05-1992 L1998 PTH *020 †50

RADHAKRISHNAN, Latha S. 3181 SW SAM JCKSN PRK RD R, MAILCODE L607 97239 #495-19-1996 L2002 END *100 †20

RADOSTITZ, Julie Carol. 0615 SW PALATINE HILL RD, LEWIS/CLARK COLL. STUDENT 97219 #040-02-1993 L1994 IM *020

RADOULOVA, Kristina Nikol. 3181 SW SAM JACKSON PRK RD, RD DE 97239 #198-01-1996 L2006 CHP *012

RADOVICH, Nicholas Daniel. ■ 97239 #007-02-2002 L2002 PTH *020 †50

RAGGIO, Julie. 10201 SE MAIN ST STE 27 97216 #048-12-1998 L2006 NEP IM *020 †20

RAGURAM, Parthasarathy. 5314 NE IRVING ST, & NEPHRO 97213 #495-04-1989 L2001 NEP *020

RAHIMTOOLA, Aly. 1111 NE 99TH AVE 97220 #016-43-1996 L1999 CD *020 †20 ‡

RAHME, Jason Ghassan. 4805 NE GLISAN ST STE BG05 97213 #041-12-1992 L1998 IM *020 †20

RAHN, Gregory John. 120 NW 14TH AVE, STE 300 97209 #005-06-1975 L1989 AN *020 †05

RAINES, J Richard. ■ 97212 #039-01-1935 DR *071 †80

RAINKA, Brian Alexander. ■ 97219 #025-12-2004 L2004 IM *100 †20

RAITT, Merritt Hanson. 2241 LLOYD CTR 97232 #005-18-1986 L1994 CD IM *020 †20

RAJ, Katelyn A. 3620 N INTERSTATE AVE 97227 #036-07-2001 L2006 RO *020

RALLS, Rayann Marie. 120 NW 14TH AVE STE 300, GROUP PC 97209 #054-04-2002 L2007 AN *020

RALSTON, Gregory Lee. 4805 NE GLISAN ST, EMERGENCY DEPARTMENT 97213 #005-02-1977 L1978 GS *020 †16

RAMAN, Arun. 3181 SW SAM JCKSN PRK RD R, OHSU 97239 #894-01-1999 L2007 GS *012

RAMOZ, Reuben Rudy. ■ 97206 #040-02-1998 L2007 IM GP *020

RAMSEY, John Patrick. ■ 97214 #021-01-2005 L2005 IM *012

RAMSEY, Monica Rau. ■ 97214 #021-01-2005 L2005 IM *012

RAMSEYER, Joshua Andrew. 1040 NW 22ND AVE STE 420, THE NEUROLOGICAL CLINIC 97210 #026-04-2001 L2001 N *100

RAMSTHEL, Donald Dale. 4610 SE BELMONT ST, STE 60 97215 #040-02-1960 L1961 IM *071

RAMZY, Ameen Ishak. 501 N GRAHAM ST STE 580 97227 #030-05-1975 L2000 GS TRS *020 †85

RANDALL, Geneva Jeanne. ■ 97232 #019-02-2004 L2005 DR *012

RANDHAVA, Karan S. 3181 SW SAM JCKSN PRK RD R, DCH7P 97239 #016-11-2002 L2003 CHP *012

RANKIN, Alan Batson. 4805 NE GLISAN ST, STE BG05 97213 #047-06-1999 L2000 IM *020 †20

RANSOM-SCHWAEBER, Mary M. 3303 SW BOND AVE, M/C: CH8C 97239 #036-05-2000 L2006 N CN *075

RAPPAPORT, Daniel Mark. 3550 N INTERSTATE AVE 97227 #005-06-1975 L1978 PD *020 †55

RARICK, Mark Urban. 3600 N INTERSTATE AVE 97227 #005-06-1980 L1991 HEM IM *020 †20

RASANEN, Juha Pekka. 3181 SW SAM JCKSN PRK RD R 97239 #374-03-1984 L2006 *100

RASH, Sean Michael. 3181 SW SAM JCKSN PRK #R 97239 #030-06-1991 L1992 PD *020 †55

RASHAD, Abdel Latif. 3181 SW SAM JACKSON PRK RD 97239 #915-02-1959 MM CLP *030

RASHEED, Derek Alan. ■ 97202 #036-07-2004 L2004 IM *100 †20

RATANASOPA, Sarah Queen. ■ 97239 #005-11-2005 L2005 PD *012

RATIGAN, Owen Michael. ■ 97201 #007-02-2007 L2007 IM *012

RATKOVEC, Ranae Marie. 1111 NE 99TH AVE 97220 #030-05-1984 L1991 CD IM *020 †20

RAUM, William Jos. 1040 NW 22ND AVE STE 500 97210 #038-43-1992 L2008 IM END *050

RAVICHANDRAN, Pasala S. 3181 SW SAM JCKSN PRK RD R, M/C L353 97239 #495-04-1979 L1999 GS TS *020

RAWLINSON, Janet Louise. 545 NE 47TH AVE, STE 106 97213 #010-01-1988 L1989 IM *020 †20

RAY, Judith Ann. PO BOX 4207 97208 #012-05-1975 L1983 PTH *020 †50

RAYHILL, Stephen Corrigan. 3181 SW SAM JACKSON PRK RD, MAIL CODE L590 97239 #035-01-1987 L2004 GS TTS *020 †85

READ, Jamie N. 833 SW 11TH AVE STE 628 97205 #054-04-1985 L1995 P *020 †75

READ, Ralph Lewis. 2900 SE STEELE ST 97202 #026-04-1969 L1999 DR *020 †80

READ, Vern. ■ 97212 #040-02-1977 L1981 P *074

REAGAN, Bonnie. 541 NE 20TH AVE, STE 210 97232 #040-02-1984 L1985 FM *020 †18

REAGAN, Joshua David. 541 NE 20TH AVE, STE 210 97232 #005-02-2000 L2000 FM *020 †18

REAGAN, Peter Lindley. 541 NE 20TH AVE STE 210, PORTLAND FAMILY PRACTICE 97232 #040-02-1977 L1978 FM *020 †20

REARDON, Thomas Robt. 10123 SE MAIN ST 97216 #007-02-1959 L1962 GP *071

REAUME, Ralph B. 507 NE 47TH AVE 97213 #028-02-1953 L1955 CD IM *071 †20

REAY, Caroline. 545 NE 47TH AVE, STE 106 97213 #010-01-1990 L1991 IM *020 †20

REBAGLIATI, Gerard Steve. 3181 SW SAM JCKSN PRK RD R, MAIL CODE CDW-EM 97239 #040-02-1985 L1989 EM *020 †20

REBAGLIATI, Mary Benowitz. 500 NE MULTNOMAH ST, STE 100 97232 #040-02-1985 L1988 PD *020 †55

RECHT, Michael. ■ 97221 #056-05-1992 L2007 PHO *072 †55

REDDY, Pulla Raghu. 3181 SW SAM JCKSN PRK RD R, M/C: BTE 119 97239 #495-21-1987 L2005 IM *100 †20

REDWINE, Robin L. 1121 NE 2ND AVE 97232 #040-02-1982 L1988 FM LM *020 †18

REED, Matt Harold. 800 SW 13TH AVE, THE PORTLAND CLINIC LLP 97205 #005-02-1982 L1993 GS *020 †85

REEDER, Joan Leslie. 426 SW STARK ST 8TH FL, MULTNOMAH COUNTY HEALTH DE 97204 #038-43-1990 L2000 IM *020 †20

REESE, Rebecca Louise. 1312 E BURNSIDE ST 97214 #024-07-1993 L1994 IM *020 †20

REGAN, David Harold. 5050 NE HOYT ST, STE 256 97213 #005-06-1969 L1973 ON HO *020 †20

REGAN, James Kevin. 1111 NE 99TH AVE 97220 #040-02-1991 L1998 GE *020 †20

REGMI, Anuj. 1015 NW 22ND AVE, LEGACY CLINIC GOOD SAMARIT 97210 #913-84-2000 L2005 IM *012

REICH, Jerome Mark. 3550 N INTERSTATE AVE 97227 #035-15-1962 L1969 PUD IM *020 †20

REID, Eric Scott. 3181 SW SAM JACKSON PRK RD, OR HLTH SCI UNIV SCH MED 97239 #040-02-2005 L2005 GS *100

REID, John Barlow, III. 1515 NW 18TH AVE, STE 300 97209 #040-02-1998 L2000 ORS *020 †40

REIDY, Peter Childs. ■ 97210 #035-09-2007 L2007 IM *012

REINHART, Steven Earl. 1111 NE 99TH AVE, STE-201 97220 #040-02-1978 L1979 CD *020 †20

REISS, Betty Eve Stein. 19500 SE STARK ST 97233 #035-15-1968 L1973 PD *020 †55

REISS, Jacob Anderson. 3325 N INTERSTATE AVE, WEST INTERSTATE MEDICAL OF 97227 #035-15-1968 L1973 CG CCG *020 †55,19

REKITO, Nikki Burlingame. ■ 97239 #012-01-2005 L2005 AN *012

RELLER, Mark Douglas. 707 SW GAINES ST, CDRCP 97239 #038-41-1977 L1984 PDC PD *020 †55

RENNER, Regina-Maria. 3181 SW SAM JACKSON PRK RD 97239 #409-38-2001 L2005 OBG *012

RENOUARD, Douglas Edward. 4212 NE BROADWAY ST, BROADWAY MEDICAL CLINIC, L 97213 #040-02-1994 L1998 IM *020 †20

REPLOGLE, Marilyn Louise. 2801 N GANTENBEIN AVE, LEGACY EMANUEL HOSPITAL 97227 #040-02-1999 L2002 IM *020 †20

RESNICK, Barbara E. 2250 NW FLANDERS ST, STE 205 97210 #035-45-1990 L1995 D *020 †20

RESNICK, Michael Philip. 4805 NE GLISAN ST 97213 #038-41-1971 L1975 P ADP *020 †75

RETONDO, Margaret Joan. 426 SW STARK ST, HIV CLINIC 4TH FL 97204 #024-01-1988 L1992 IM *020 †20

REULER, James Bruce. VET ADMIN HOSP NO 11C 97207 #016-02-1973 L1975 IM *020 †20

REYNOLDS, Christopher M. 5050 NE HOYT ST, OREGON HEMATOLOGY 97213 #035-20-1991 L2005 HO IM *020 †20

REYNOLDS, Dale C. 4805 NE GLISAN ST 97213 #030-05-1952 L1953 GP *071 †18

REZNICK, Leah Greenhill. 3303 SW BOND AVE, FL 11 97239 #035-45-2002 L2002 OPH *100

REZNIK, Oleg. 3930 SE DIVISION ST 97202 #035-08-2000 L2003 FM *020 †18 ‡

RHEE, Connie Meeyoung. ■ 97239 #016-06-2005 L2005 IM *012

RHETT, Carolyn N. 3181 SW SAM JCKSN PRK RD R 97239 #039-01-1999 L1999 EM *020 †16

RICE, Jeffrey Daryl. 2250 NW FLANDERS ST STE 30 97210 #041-13-1987 L1988 P *020 †75

RICE, Mary Jo. 707 SW GAINES ST, CDRC-P 97239 #026-04-1978 L1983 PDC *020 †55

RICE, Robert Douglas. ■ 97239 #023-12-2006 GS *012

RICH, David Wm. ■ 97210 #040-02-1964 L1966 N *071

RICH, Gerald Barton. 1849 NW KEARNEY ST STE 202 97209 #040-02-1975 L1981 SME N *020

RICH, Larry Francis. 3303 SW BOND AVE, FL 11 97239 #040-02-1970 L1971 OPH *020 †35

RICH, Phoebe. 2565 NW LOVEJOY ST, STE 200 97210 #040-02-1984 L1985 D *020 †15

RICHARD, Samuel Wm. 10123 SE MARKET ST 97216 #040-02-1979 L1986 FM *020 †18

RICHARDS, Amanda Beatrice. ■ 97239 #046-01-2005 L2006 OPH *012

RICHARDS, Jay Stephen. 120 NW 14TH AVE, #300 OREGON ANESTH GRP PC 97209 #040-02-1988 L1989 AN *020 †05 ‡

RICHARDS, Jeffrey James. 3110 NE 33RD AVE, STE 1 97212 #056-06-1991 L2004 P *020

RICHARDSON, Mark Andrew. 2241 LLOYD CTR 97232 #045-01-1975 L2001 OTO PDO *020 †45

RICHERT-BOE, Kathryn E. 3600 N INTERSTATE AVE 97227 #019-02-1974 L1977 ON HEM *020 †20

RICHINS, Scott Whitear. ■ 97239 #040-02-2008 *012

RICHMOND, Judith Anita. 3330 SW CARAWAY CT 97219 #038-06-1982 L2002 GS AM *020

RICKER, Mari Anoushka. 3930 SE DIVISION ST 97202 #040-01-2002 L2002 FM *100 †18

RICKETT, Hamish Wm. 120 NW 14TH AVE, STE 300 97209 #040-02-1992 L1993 AN *020 †05 ‡

RIDDLE, Matthew Casey, Jr. 2241 LLOYD CTR 97232 #024-01-1964 L1967 DIA IM *050 †20

RIDDLE, Stephanie Kane. 3500 N INTERSTATE AVE, INTERSTATE SOUTH 97227 #040-02-1995 L1999 IM *020 †05

RIHA, Gordon Miles. 3181 SW SAM JACKSON PRK RD, OR HLTH SCI UNIV HOSP 97239 #048-04-2007 L2007 GS *012

RILEY, Keith Bernard. 3550 N INTERSTATE AVE, EIN-3 97227 #005-06-1983 L1988 ID IM *020 †20

RILEY, Matthew Ryan. 300 N GRAHAM ST, STE 420 97227 #040-02-1999 L1999 PG *100 †55

RILEY, Steven Joseph. 3181 SW SAM JCKSN PRK RD R, UHN 62 97239 #018-03-2000 L2003 CD *020 †20

RIMBERG, Clytie Sharon R. 4212 NE BROADWAY ST 97213 #041-13-1986 L1987 D *020 †15

RINKEVICH, Diana Beatriz. ■ 97221 #132-01-1980 L2006 IM *100 †20

RIPPEY, Wesley Edward. 10000 SE MAIN ST, STE 408 97216 #005-12-1976 L1980 GS VS *020 †85

RISCHITELLI, Donald Gary. 3181 SW SAM JCKSN PRK RD R, OR HLTH SCIENCES UNIV VHN 97239 #048-04-1987 L1988 OM *020 †70

RISHEL, Lisa L. ■ 97239 #040-02-2007 L2007 PD *012

RITCHIE, Phyllis S B. ■ 97201 #040-12-1992 L2002 ID *020 †20

RITMANIS, Andris. ■ 97202 #040-02-1956 L1957 GP *071

RITTER, Michelle Lee. 19500 SE STARK ST 97233 #054-04-1997 L2002 FM *020 †18

RIVAS, Henry Rainier. 11510 SE STARK ST 97216 #649-14-1978 L1986 FM *020 †18

ROAST, Andrea Bobbie. 5050 NE HOYT ST, STE 540 97213 #025-12-1999 L2000 IM *020 †20

ROBB, Douglas Allan. 3550 N INTERSTATE AVE 97227 #040-02-1973 L1977 P *020 †75

ROBB, James Vernon. 2801 N GANTENBEIN AVE 97227 #040-02-1968 L1975 AN *020 †05 ‡

ROBERTS, Colin Matthew. 707 SW GAINES ST, CDRC-P ROOM 1255 97239 #041-02-1995 L2001 CHN *020 †75

ROBERTS, Janet L. 2330 NW FLANDERS ST, STE 201 97210 #005-02-1968 L1975 D OS *020 †15

ROBERTS, Lauren Whipple. 541 NE 20TH AVE STE 210 97232 #032-01-1981 L1982 FM *020 †18

ROBERTS, Peter H R. 5050 NE HOYT ST STE 359 97213 #040-02-1962 L1964 OBG *071 †30

ROBERTSON, Deborah Graham. 6312 SW CAPITOL HWY, HWY STE#502 97239 #040-02-1999 L1999 EM *020

ROBERTSON, Jos Edmond, Jr. 3303 SW BOND AVE, FL 11 97239 #017-20-1978 L1982 OPH *030 †35

ROBERTSON, Lawrence D, Jr. 1220 SW 3RD AVE STE 476 97204 #027-01-1978 L1982 GPM PHP *030 †55

ROBERTSON, Patricia Anne. 3181 SW SAM JCKSN PRK RD R 97239 #021-01-2000 L2004 OBG *020

ROBERTSON, Walter Peter. ■ 97239 #021-01-2001 L2004 CD *020 †20

ROBIE, Andrew Christopher. 3930 SE DIVISION ST 97202 #038-41-2005 L2005 FP *012

ROBINS, Berklee. 3181 SW SAM JACKSON PRK RD, UHS-2 97239 #035-47-1989 L1996 PAN AN *020 †05

ROBINSON, Dan Lee. 3181 SW SAM JACKSON PRK RD, UH 2 97239 #030-05-1982 L1995 PAN AN *040 †05

ROBINSON, Debra Lynn. 4805 NE GLISAN ST, DEPT OF EMERGENCY MEDICINE 97213 #041-01-1989 L1993 EM *020 †16

ROBINSON, Gregory Earl. 10201 SE MAIN ST, STE 12 97216 #005-12-1989 L1990 IM *020 †20

ROBINSON, Jamie Lorrine. ■ 97209 #041-02-2003 L2003 OTO *012

ROBINSON, Lane David. 120 NW 14TH AVE, STE 300 97209 #054-04-1993 L1994 AN *020 †05 ‡

ROBINSON, Margaret Lynn. 4805 NE GLISAN ST 97213 #028-02-1977 L1982 DR *020 †80

ROBINSON, Stephen Tim. 3181 SW SAM JACKSON PRK RD, DEPT ANESTHE-UHS-2 97239 #054-04-1982 L1986 AN *020 †05

ROBINSON, Terri Elizabeth. ■ 97236 #005-14-2002 L2004 **DR** *020
ROBINSON, Valerie R Pond. 120 NW 14TH AVE, STE 300 97209 #040-02-1983 L1987
   AN *040 †05 ‡
ROBLEY, Michael Warren. 120 NW 14TH AVE, STE 300 97209 #422-01-1983 L1989
   AN *020 †05 ‡
ROCKEFELLER, Melissa Swee. 500 NE MULTNOMAH ST, NORTHWEST PERMANENTE 97232
   #054-04-2004 L2007 **EM** *020
RODDY, John Michael. 4212 NE BROADWAY ST 97213 #030-06-1957 L1962 **DR RO** *020 †80
RODDY, Timothy James. 300 N GRAHAM ST, STE 200 97227 #056-05-1984 L1985
   IM IMG *020 †20
RODGERS, Michael Sean. 3181 SW SAM JCKSN PRK RD R 97239 #671-02-1991 L2003 *100
RODGERS, William Harry. 2241 LLOYD CTR 97232 #035-45-1983 L1999 **PCP ATP** *020 †50
RODRIGUEZ, Glenn Sumner. 1235 NE 47TH AVE STE 299 97213 #038-06-1981 L1989
   FM IMG *030 †18
RODRIGUEZ, Hector M. 1820 SW VERMONT ST, STE A 97219 #011-75-1990, ▲ L1991
   IM *020 †20
RODRIGUEZ, Luis Felipe. 13007 NE GLISAN ST 97230 #737-06-1991 L2006 **IMG** *020 †20
RODRIGUEZ, Maria Isabel. ■ 97239 #040-02-2004 L2004 **OBG** *012
RODRIGUEZ, Sarah Allie. 3181 SW SAM JACKSON PRK RD, PARK ROAD 97239
   #020-12-1996 L1998 **GE** *100 †20
RODUNER, Gregory Kenneth. 10373 NE HANCOCK ST, STE 216 97220 #040-02-1967 L1971
   PS *020 †65
ROESSLER, Peter Michael. 120 NW 14TH AVE, STE 300 97209 #005-15-1992 L1996
   AN *020 †05 ‡
ROFFE, Shirley. 1015 NW 22ND AVE, NORTHUP #32 97210 #021-05-1983 L1985 **P** *020 †75
ROGERS, Brian T. 707 SW GAINES ST, CHILD DEVELOPMENT AND REHA 97239
   #016-43-1979 L2002 **PD** *020 †55
ROGERS, Mary Therese. ■ 97219 #030-06-2007 L2007 **PD** *012
ROGERS, Sarah Ruth. ■ 97206 #040-02-2008 *012
ROGERS, Wayne Russell. 2222 NW LOVEJOY ST, STE 606 97210 #047-06-1947 L1956
   CD IM *071 †20
ROGOSIN, Shane Orion. 3181 SW SAM JACKSON PRK RD, OR HLTH SCI UNIV SCH MED 97239
   #040-02-2004 L2004 **IM** *100 †20
ROHLF, Sherri Nicole. 120 NW 14TH AVE, STE 300 97209 #019-02-1998 L2005 **AN** *020 †05 ‡
ROHLFING, Ronald Durant. 10123 SE MAIN 97216 #007-02-1957 L1961 **GP** *020
ROMANAGGI, Don V. 1920 NW JOHNSON ST 97209 #016-43-1960 L1962 **A IM** *071 †03
ROMANOWSKI, Andrew. 1955 NW NORTHRUP ST, OREGON MEDICAL EYE CLINIC 97209
   #036-01-1983 L1984 **OPH** *020 †35
RONEY, Ryan Patrickmul. 120 NW 14TH AVE, STE 300 97209 #056-05-2001 L2006
   AN *020 †05 ‡
ROONEY, Kellie Anne. ■ 97210 #010-02-2007 L2007 **IM** *012
ROOT, Daniel B. 2228 NW PETTYGROVE ST # 1, OREGON SLEEP ASSOCIATES 97210
   #048-04-1991 L1992 **PCC** *020 †20
ROOT, Leslie L. 501 N GRAHAM ST STE 100 97227 #040-02-1994 L1996 **IM** *020 †20
ROSCH, Josef. 3181 SW SAM JCKSN PRK #R 97239 #286-02-1950 L1976 **VIR** *071
ROSE, Christine Marie. ■ 97239 #028-34-2005 L2005 **PD** *012
ROSE, Jennifer Ann. ■ 97211 #028-34-2003 L2003 **IM** *020 †20
ROSE, Lauren Hollingswort. ■ 97212 #040-02-2005 L2005 **PD** *012
ROSE, Paul David. 2801 N GANTENBEIN AVE 97227 #040-02-1985 L1989 **AN** *020 †05 ‡
ROSEN, Donald Edward. 3181 SW SAM JACKSON PRK RD, PARK ROAD 97239
   #019-02-1984 L1999 **P** *020 †75
ROSENBAUM, Edward E. ■ 97221 #030-05-1938 L1938 **RHU** *071 †20
ROSENBAUM, James Todd. 3303 SW BOND AVE, FL 11 97239 #008-01-1975 L1985
   RHU OPH *050 †20
ROSENBAUM, Richard Barry. 5050 NE HOYT ST, STE 315 97213 #024-01-1971 L1977
   N IM *020 †20,75
ROSENBAUM, Robert Alan. 5050 NE HOYT ST, STE 315 97213 #023-07-1968 L1973
   N *020 †75 ‡
ROSENBAUM, Thomas Jay. 2222 NW LOVEJOY ST STE 516 97210 #040-02-1973 L1978
   NS *020 †25
ROSENBAUM, William M. 1015 NW 22ND AVE 97210 #030-05-1940 L1949 **GP** *072 †85
ROSENBERG, Daniel Matthew. 1321 NE 99TH AVE, STE 200 97220 #035-45-2000 L2000
   FM *020 †18
ROSENBERG, Julie Ellen. 2250 NW FLANDERS ST, STE 101 97219 #010-01-2001 L2001 **P** *100
ROSENBERG, Kenneth D. ■ 97212 #024-07-1973 L1977 **AI PHP** *020 †70
ROSENBERG, Mark R. 5050 NE HOYT ST, PROVIDENCE MEDICAL CENTER 97213
   #041-12-1978 L1980 **IM** *074 †20
ROSENBLUM, Keren. ■ 97213 #028-02-2004 L2004 **OBG** *012
ROSENBLUM, Stuart Michael. 2800 N VANCOUVER AVE, STE 130 97227 #040-02-1980 L1983
   AN *020 †05 ‡
ROSENCRANTZ, David R. 2222 NW LOVEJOY ST, STE 416 97210 #040-02-1966 L1968
   U *075 †95
ROSENFELD, Ron Gershon. 3181 SW SAM JCKSN PRK #R, OREGON HEALTH SCIENCES
   UNI 97201 #005-11-1973 L1994 **PDE** *050 †55
ROSENFELD, Sally Ann. 2701 NW VAUGHN ST STE 140, KAISER PERMANENTE 97210
   #040-02-1984 L1989 **IM** *020 †20
ROSENFELD, Seth Shephard. 7705 SE DIVISION ST 97206 #005-19-1979 L1981 **IM** *020 †20 ‡
ROSENFIELD, Richard Brian. 120 NW 14TH AVE, STE 200 97209 #038-41-1996 L2000
   OBG *020 †30
ROSENHEIM, Sidney H. 4805 NE GLISAN ST 97213 #016-06-1963 L1972 **PTH NM** *020 †50,28
ROSENKRANZ, Michael Paul. 120 NW 14TH AVE, STE 300 97209 #028-34-1979 L2007
   AN *020 †05
ROSENQUIST, Roger Dale. 10000 SE MAIN STE 406 97216 #005-12-1972 L1980 **U** *020
ROSENTHAL, Eli Aviv. 1040 NW 22ND AVE STE 660 97210 #040-04-16-1991 L1992 **CD** *020 †20
ROSOFF, Jack Philip. 325 NW 21ST AVE, STE 203 97209 #050-02-1986 L1987 **EM** *020
ROSS, Alicia Marie. 3181 SW SAM JCKSN PRK RD R 97239 #040-02-1999 L1999 **CD** *100 †20
ROSS, John Edward. 120 NW 14TH AVE 97209 #040-02-1983 L1986 **AN** *020 †05 ‡
ROSSMILLER, Sarah Rebecca. ■ 97239 #005-06-2006 L2006 **OTO** *012
ROSSON, Constance Lynn. 3181 SW SAM JACKSON PRK RD, PARK RD 97239
   #040-02-1982 L1987 **IM** *020 †20
ROTH, Isadora. ■ 97219 #005-06-2001 L2001 **IM** *020
ROTHBERGER, Sophia M. ■ 97239 #036-01-2004 L2004 **OBG** *012
ROTHGERY, Marc Chagall. ■ 97219 #035-03-2008 *012
ROTHMAN, Ilan Jose Daniel. ■ 97219 #231-01-2001 L2007 **PAN** *012
ROTTER, Steven Mark. 1820 SW VERMONT ST, STE I 97219 #056-06-1986 L1987 **IM GPM** *020
ROTWEIN, Peter Scott. 3181 SW SAM JACKSON PRK RD, STE R 97239 #035-46-1975 L1997
   END DIA *050 †20

ROWAN-KELLY, Michael Char. ■ 97221 #143-01-1977 L2006 **FP** *012
ROWELL, Susan Evelyn. 3181 SW SAM JCKSN PRK RD R, MAILCODE: L611 97239
   #005-19-2000 L2006 **CCS** *100 †85
ROWLAND, Margaret Stevens. 315 SW 5TH AVE, STE 900 97204 #038-41-1977 L1992
   FM *030 †18
ROY, Dennis Robt. 3101 SW SAM JACKSON PRK RD, SHRINERS HOSP FOR CHILDREN 97239
   #012-01-1975 L2003 **OP** *020 †40
ROZANSKY, David Joel. 3181 SW SAM JCKSN PRK RD R, M/C CDRC-D 97239
   #005-18-1994 L2001 **PN** *020 †55
ROZEBOOM, Sarah Ann. 500 NE MULTNOMAH ST # 100, NW PERMANENTE PC-LOCUM
   TEN 97232 #025-01-2002 L2005 **PD** *020 †55
RUBIN, Glenn Julian. 3500 N INTERSTATE AVE 97227 #039-01-1978 L1982 **AN** *020 †05
RUBIN, Gregory Samuel. 19500 SE STARK ST, KAISER PERMANENTE NORTHWES 97233
   #035-46-2004 L2004 **IM** *020 †20
RUBINSTEIN, Richard Allan. 5050 NE HOYT ST, STE 138 97213 #040-02-1986 L1987
   ORS OSM *020 †40
RUDEN, Edward Leslie. 7705 SE DIVISION ST, KAISER FNDN-PED 97206 #033-05-1976 L1998
   PD *020 †55
RUDNER, Glenn Allen. 25 NW 23RD PL STE 6 PMB 20 97210 #025-07-1993 L2003
   PTH FOP *020 †50
RUE, George H, Jr. ■ 97215 #005-12-1949 L1949 **AN** *075 †05
RUEDA, Jose Fernando. ■ 97214 #264-04-1991 L2004 **IM NEP** *020 †20
RULLMAN, David Russell. 2220 SW 1ST AVE 97201 #038-41-1957 L1962 **IM ON** *071 †20
RUMINSON, Glenn Edrum. 10000 SE MAIN ST STE 2 97216 #005-12-1970 L1975 **P** *020 †75
RUNCKEL, Douglas Newell. 13705 NE AIRPORT WAY, STE C 97230 #040-02-1971 L1974
   PTH EM *020 †50
RUPERT, Jennifer Leigh. 3550 N INTERSTATE AVE 97227 #054-04-2001 L2001 **OBG** *020 †30
RUSA, Renata. 3181 SW SAM JACKSON PRK RD, PARK RD 97239 #033-05-1991 L1998
   AN *020 †05,75
RUSH, John Boyd. 1015 NW 22ND AVE 97210 #048-04-1962 L1970 **CD IM** *071 †20
RUSHOLD, Warren Elliott. 10123 SE MAIN ST 97216 #005-12-1973 L1989 **IM GP** *020 †20
RUSSAK, Fern Gilda. 3550 N INTERSTATE AVE, KAISER INTERSTATE MEDICAL 97227
   #005-06-1987 L2003 **PD** *020 †55
RUSSELL, Brent Austin. 3181 SW SAM JACKSON PRK #R, OREGON HEALTH SCIENCE UNIV 97239
   #001-02-1997 L1998 **EM** *020 †16
RUSSELL, Paul Stephen. 2250 NW FLANDERS ST 97210 #048-02-1957 L1965 **D DMP** *071 †15
RUSSMAN, Barry Sheldon. 3101 SW SAM JACKSON PRK RD, PARK ROAD 97239
   #024-07-1963 L1997 **N PD** *020 †55,75
RUST, Cuchulain Luke. ■ 97219 #032-01-2007 L2007 *012
RUSTIN, Arnold. ■ 97210 #018-03-1950 L1954 **U** *071 †95
RUTH, Amy. 10373 NE HANCOCK ST, STE 200 97220 #005-15-1988 L1999 **CHP P** *020 †75
RUUD, David Henry. 3414 N KAISER CTR DR 97227 #046-01-1980 L1981 **PDR N** *020 †75
RYAN, Christopher Walter. 3181 SW SAM JACKSON PRK RD, CR 145 97239
   #035-15-1994 L2003 **HO IM** *020 †20
RYAN, Kelly Anne. 3181 SW SAM JACKSON PRK RD, OR HLTH SCI UNIV HOSP 97239
   #010-02-2007 L2007 **GS** *012
RYAN, Thomas Edward. ■ 97210 #056-05-1952 L1953 **ORS** *071 †40
SABBAJ, Alfredo. 3181 SW SAM JACKSON PRK RD, MAIL CODE UHN-52 97239
   #024-07-1997 L2001 **EM** *020
SABIN, Charlene Oda. 1811 NE 8TH AVE 97212 #040-02-1977 L1978 **CHP PD** *020 †55
SACEDA, Sonia Fantonial. 3710 SW US VETRNS HSPTL RD 97239 #748-09-1961 L1973
   AN *040
SACK, Robert Leroy. 3181 SW SAM JACKSON PRK RD, PARK RD 97239 #040-02-1968 L1978
   P SME *040 †75
SACK, William Hyink. 2241 LLOYD CTR 97232 #040-02-1960 L1963 **CHP P** *020 †55,75
SACKS, Lawrence H. 10735 SE STARK ST, STE 100 97216 #035-47-1988 L1989 **P** *020 †75
SADDORIS, Thomas J, II. 169 NE 102ND AVE 97220 #041-13-1968 L1976 **AI IM** *020 †20,03
SAFRA, Jessica Alice. ■ 97210 #035-09-2007 L2007 **IM** *012
SAHA, Somnath. 3710 SW US VETRNS HSPTL RD, PORTLAND VAMC 97239
   #005-02-1991 L2000 **IM** *050 †20
SAHN, David Jonathan. 2241 LLOYD CTR 97232 #040-01-1969 L1992 **PDC PDA** *020 †55
SAHNI, Nishant. ■ 97239 #495-41-2001 L2007 **ID** *012 †20
SAHNI, Ritu. 3181 SW SAM JACKSON PRK RD, M/C CDW-EM 97239 #021-01-1993 L2002
   EM *040 †16
SAIER, Fulton Leroy. 800 SW 13TH AVE, PORTLAND CLINIC 97205 #028-34-1970 L1974
   OBG *071 †30
SAILLER, Deborah Anne. 500 NE MULTNOMAH ST, STE 100 97232 #026-08-1987 L1990
   FM *020 †18
SAINT CLAIR, Nicole R. ■ 97239 #054-04-2004 L2004 **OBG** *012
SALINDONG-DARIO, Nemecia. 300 NE MULTNOMAH ST 97232 #748-01-1968 L1981 **P** *020
SALINSKY, Martin Craig. 3181 SW SAM JCKSN PRK RD R, CDW-3 97239 #035-48-1980 L1988
   N IM *020 †75
SALINSKY, Michael Scott. 19500 SE STARK ST 97233 #016-06-1994 L1997 **PD** *020 †55
SALK, Darrell John. ■ 97219 #023-07-1974 L1975 **OS PD** *050 †55,19
SALLAY, Brian Scott. 2241 LLOYD CTR 97232 #028-34-1993 L1994 **IM** *020 †20
SALLY, Mitchell Brett. 3181 SW SAM JCKSN PRK RD R 97239 #036-01-2004 L2004 **GS** *012
SALVADOR, Marina Espos. ■ 97230 #748-07-1968 *100
SAMBASIVAN, Chitra Neela. ■ 97239 #041-13-2004 L2005 **GS** *012
SAMMIS, Annabelle Loretta. 2801 N GANTENBEIN AVE 97227 #054-04-2003 L2003 **IM** *100 †20
SAMOUILIDIS, Leo T. 7306 SE 30TH AVE 97202 #033-05-1994 L1999 **PD** *020 †55
SAMPLES, John Randall. 3375 SW TERWILLIGER BLVD, CEI 97239 #005-18-1977 L1983
   OPH N *020 †35
SAMPSON, James Horton. 1200 NW 23RD AVE, LEGACY CLIN GOOD SAMARITAN 97210
   #012-01-1976 L1979 **GP** *020
SAMPSON, Jone Elizabeth. 3181 SW SAM JCKSN PRK ND, DEPT OF GENETICS, L-103 97239
   #010-01-1986 L1995 **OBS** *020 †19,30
SAMUELS, Mary Helen. 2241 LLOYD CTR 97232 #024-01-1983 L1993 **END IM** *020 †20
SANBORN, Rachel Elizabeth. 3181 SW SAM JACKSON PRK RD, OREGON HEALTH AND
   SCIENCE 97239 #040-02-1999 L2004 **HO** *100 †20
SANCHEZ, Jaime. ■ 97239 #005-11-2004 L2005 **AN** *012
SANDBERG, C Joan. 3500 N INTERSTATE AVE 97227 #039-01-1987 L1993 **DR** *020 †80
SANDBERG, Scott Alan. 3500 N INTERSTATE AVE 97227 #005-14-1987 L1993 **DR** *020 †80
SANDERS, Michelle Lorene. ■ 97214 #035-45-2004 L2004 **IM** *100 †20
SANDQUIST, Chloe Anne. 3181 SW SAM JCKSN PRK #R, OHSU 97239 #028-02-2000 L2000
   GS *020 †85
SANDQUIST, Michael A. 5050 NE HOYT ST, STE 418 97213 #034-01-1997 L1999 **NS** *020

■ = Address Information Privacy Protected

SANDS, Mark W. 2801 N GANTENBEIN AVE, LEGACY CLINIC 97227 #048-13-2005 L2005 IM *012

SANGHVI, Parag R. ■ 97239 #012-01-2003 L2004 RO *012

SANTA, John S. 3181 SW SAM JACKSON PRK RD, OHSU-FAMILY MEDICINE 97239 #024-07-1976 L1977 IM *030 †20

SANTAELLA, Ricardo Miguel. 97239 #048-04-2004 L2004 OPH *012

SANTOS, Bryant Obbe. 120 NW 14TH AVE, STE 300 97209 #051-04-1993 L1997 AN *020 †05 ‡

SARFF, Maryclare Suzanne. ■ 97211 #016-45-2003 L2003 GS *012

SARGENT, David James. 10101 SE MAIN ST, STE 2015 97216 #040-02-1977 L1981 OBG *020

SARKAR, Subhajit. 3181 SW SAM JCKSN PRK RD, OHSU 97239 #917-03-1995 L1995 IM *012

SASAKI, Aaron Takuji. 2801 N GANTENBEIN AVE 97227 #040-02-2002 L2002 PS *020

SASAKI, Anna Theresa W. 2241 LLOYD CTR 97232 #042-01-1974 L1985 IM *020 †20

SASEK, Dean Andrew. ■ 97209 #040-02-2002 L2008 EM *020 †16

SASHIDA, Yasunori. 3181 SW SAM JCKSN PRK RD R 97239 #572-35-1987 L2001 *100

SASLOW, George. 2241 LLOYD CTR 97232 #024-01-1940 L1957 P *071 †75

SATTERBERG, Brett Lee. ■ 97221 #040-02-1999 L2007 P *100

SATTERFIELD, Deborah Anne. 1321 NE 99TH AVE STE 200, PROVIDENCE FAMILY MEDICINE 97220 #005-15-1979 L1993 FM *020 †18

SATTERFIELD, James H. ■ 97212 #028-02-1955 L1960 CHP P *071 †75

SATTLER, Scott Clayton. 3181 SW SAM JCKSN PRK RD R, SCIENCE UNIVER 97239 #010-01-1997 L2006 PS *012 †85

SATYANARAYAN, Kadavil R. 3600 N INTERSTATE AVE 97227 #495-37-1968 L1976 PM *020 †60

SAUER, David Austin. 2241 LLOYD CTR 97232 #040-02-1996 L2001 PTH *020 †50

SAULINO, Evan Theodore. 97232 #028-02-2000 L2000 FM *020 †20

SAULSON, Roger Moss. 10819 SE STARK ST STE 200 97216 #048-13-1985 L1992 OPH OS *020 †35

SAULTZ, John Wm. 3303 SW BOND AVE 97239 #038-40-1979 L1986 FM *040 †18

SAUNDERS, James Alan. 10819 SE STARK ST STE 200 97216 #040-02-1960 L1964 OPH *071 †35

SAUTTER, Nathan Benjamin. ■ 97201 #025-01-2001 L2007 OTO *100

SAUVAIN, Melanie M C. 3181 SW SAM JCKSN PRK RD R, MAIL CODE UHN-89 97239 #054-04-1984 L1985 IM OM *020 †12

SAVA, Daniela Bianca. ■ 97239 #781-01-1997 L2002 CHP *020 †75

SAVOY, Alan Drew. 1111 NE 99TH AVE 97220 #031-01-1999 L2005 GE *100 †20

SAX, David Eric. 3660 N INTERSTATE AVE 97227 #056-06-1995 L2000 IM *020

SAX, Tracy Williams. 5050 NE HOYT ST, STE 315 97213 #040-02-1995 L2000 CN *020 †75

SAYLAM, Fevzi Argun. 3181 SW SAM JACKSON PRK RD, DPT SRG 97239 #902-10-1970 TS PUD *100

SAYLER, Clinton Bruce. 1015 NW 22ND AVE, RADIOLOGY CONSULTANTS INC 97210 #005-11-1958 L1965 R *071 †80

SCANLAN, Richard Michael. 2241 LLOYD CTR 97232 #005-14-1980 L1983 PTH GS *020 †50

SCHAAL, Michael Stephen. ■ 97239 #038-40-2001 L2005 PDC *012 †55

SCHAER, Christi Anne. 12710 SE DIVISION ST, MID-COUNTY HEALTH CENTER 97236 #005-14-1984 L1989 IM *020 †20

SCHAFER, Donald W E. 10123 SE MARKET ST 97216 #040-02-1963 L1970 PTH *071 †50

SCHAFER, Sean David. ■ 97232 #005-06-1987 L2006 EP *020 †18

SCHAUMBERG, Thomas Hyland. 1111 NE 99TH AVE 97220 #007-02-1986 L1987 PUD IM *020 †20

SCHENCK, Joseph Paul, Jr. ■ 97239 #003-01-2002 L2005 ORS *100

SCHILLING, Phillip James. 5251 NE GLISAN ST, BLDG A 97213 #030-06-1969 L1974 R *071 †80

SCHILPEROORT, Steven John. 500 NE MULTNOMAH ST STE 10 97232 #040-02-1974 L1978 ORS *020 †40

SCHIMSCHOCK, James R. 97210 #026-04-1961 L1967 CHN N *071 †75

SCHINDLER, Joshua Sandvig. ■ 97205 #002-1998 L2005 OTO *020 †45

SCHIPPER, Paul Henry. 3181 SW SAM JCKSN PRK RD R, M/S L353 97239 #018-03-1996 L2004 TS *020 †85,90

SCHJELDERUP, Christine D. 3325 N INTERSTATE AVE 97227 #056-06-1986 L1987 IM *020 †20

SCHLESSMAN, Katherine Mar. 3303 SW BOND AVE 97239 #038-06-2005 L2005 FP *012

SCHLIPPERT, William Chas. 10000 SE MAIN ST, STE 203 97216 #041-13-1971 L1978 GE IM *020 †20

SCHLUETER, Jamie. 3181 SW SAM JACKSON PRK RD, UHN53 OHSU 97239 #048-15-1998 L1999 EM *020 †16

SCHMAHMANN, Sandra. 2241 LLOYD CTR 97232 #836-01-1984 L2001 DR *020 †80

SCHMERTZLER, Leslie E. 19500 SE STARK ST 97233 #005-02-1976 L1979 IM *020 †20

SCHMIDT, David Eugene. 3550 N INTERSTATE AVE, DEPT PEDIATRICS 97227 #040-02-1980 L1985 PD *020 †55

SCHMIDT, James Frederick. 5050 NE HOYT ST, STE 410 97213 #040-02-1969 L1970 NS *020 †25

SCHMIDT, Terri Ann. 4216 NE 30TH AVE 97211 #040-02-1985 L1986 EM *020 †16

SCHMIDT, Waldemar A, IV. 2241 LLOYD CTR 97232 #040-02-1969 L1970 PCP PTH *020 †50

SCHMITKE, Amy Marie. 5050 NE HOYT ST, STE 359 97213 #012-05-1996 L2000 OBG *020 †30

SCHMITT, Amy Elizabeth. 2801 N GANTENBEIN AVE 97227 #040-02-2001 L2001 IM *020 †20

SCHMITZ, Kelli Ruth. ■ 97212 #040-02-2004 L2006 DR *100 †80

SCHNADIG, Ian Denison. ■ 97214 #016-01-2002 L2002 HO *012 †20

SCHNEIDER, Harry Joseph. 1239 SW WOODS ST 97239 #917-07-1988 GS *100

SCHNEIDER, Heidi Marie. ■ 97239 #040-02-2007 FP *012

SCHOEPFLIN, Gerald S. 10000 SE MAIN ST STE 208 97216 #005-12-1970 L1977 RHU IM *020 †20 ‡

SCHONE, Hildegard A E. 2020 SE 182ND AVE 97233 #005-12-1970 L1973 PD *020 †55

SCHRATTENHOLZER, Thomas F. 2801 N GANTENBEIN AVE 97227 #005-12-1999 L2004 APM *020 †05 ‡

SCHRAY, Mark Fredrick. 1130 NW 22ND AVE 97210 #040-02-1979 L1990 RO *020 †80

SCHREIBER, Martin Allen. 3181 SW SAM JACKSON PRK RD, MAIL CODE L223A 97239 #038-06-1988 L2002 GS *020 †85

SCHREINER, Mitchal Aric. ■ 97208 #016-06-2002 L2006 GE *012 †20

SCHROEDER, Alfred James. 5050 NE HOYT ST STE 655 97213 #025-01-1957 L1958 OTO *071 †45

SCHROEDER, David Arthur. 1040 NW 22ND AVE, STE 660 97210 #033-06-1997 L1998 CD *020 †20

SCHROEDER, Garrett Paulra. 3181 SW SAM JACKSON PRK RD, OR HLTH SCI UNIV HOSP 97239 #030-06-2006 L2007 DR *012

SCHULMAN, Peter Mark. ■ 97209 #050-02-2000 L2007 CCA *100 †05

SCHULTZ, Megan Farrell. 2801 N GANTENBEIN AVE, EMANUEL HOSPITAL 97227 #056-05-2001 L2001 PD *020 †55

SCHUMAN, Earl Stanley. 1130 NW 22ND AVE STE 300 97210 #005-15-1969 L1974 GS *020 †85

SCHUTZ, Ronald Walter. 2222 NW LOVEJOY ST, STE 512 97210 #016-11-1975 L1978 CD IM *020 †20

SCHWAB, Pascale. 3181 SW SAM JCKSN PRK RD R, M/S: OP-09 97239 #048-14-1994 L2006 IM *020 †20

SCHWARTZ, Dafna Lorge. ■ 97213 #005-18-2004 L2004 OBG *012

SCHWARTZ, Jonathan Meier. 3181 SW SAM JACKSON PRK RD, STE 310 97239 #550-02-1991 L2001 GE *020 †20

SCHWARTZ, Lawrence David. 1220 SW MORRISON ST STE 11, PORTLAND VAMC V3MHC 97205 #005-14-1981 L1982 P *020 †20

SCHWARTZ, Martin Lerner. 3550 N INTERSTATE AVE, KAISER-PERMANENTE INTERSTA 97227 #036-07-1973 L1977 OBG *020 †30

SCHWARTZ, Rhonda Lynn. 2311 NW NORTHRUP ST, STE 201 97210 #035-46-1989 L1993 P *020 †75

SCHWARTZ, Thomas Murrow. 4104 SE 82ND AVE, STE 250 97266 #056-05-1994 L1998 FM *020 †16

SCHWARZ, Timothy William. 2230 NW PETTYGROVE ST, STE 220 97210 #038-06-1995 L1997 EM *020 †16

SCHWEIGERT, Daniel S. ■ 97209 #048-13-1990 L2007 FM *020 †18

SCHWEINFURTH, Joseph D. 5300 SW LANDING SQ # NO-10 97239 #016-06-1950 L1955 GS *071

SCHWIEBINGER, Gerald Wm. 10000 SE MAIN ST STE 406 97216 #056-05-1948 L1950 U *072 †95

SCHWINOF, Kristine Mina. ■ 97219 #040-02-2007 L2007 IM *012

SCIONTI, Joseph Anthony. ■ 97202 #003-01-2007 L2007 IM *012

SCORVO, Sean Kristofer. 1509 SW SUNSET BLVD, STE 2E 97239 #040-02-1998 L2000 EM *020 †16

SCOTT, Ann Grace. 500 NE MULTNOMAH ST 97232 #056-06-1995 L1997 OBG *020 †30

SCOTT, David Lewis. 3181 SW SAM JACKSON PRK RD R, M/C L590 97239 #016-06-1997 L2005 TTS *020 †85

SCOTT, David Russell. ■ 97201 #007-02-2006 L2006 IM *012

SCOTT, James Porter. ■ 97212 #024-01-1972 L1976 FM *030 †18

SCOTT, Kelly Faith. 1130 NW 22ND AVE, STE 220 97210 #040-02-1985 L1986 IM *020 †20

SCOTT, Peter Norman. 2801 N GANTENBEIN AVE 97227 #003-01-1983 L1986 AN GP *020 †05 ‡

SCRIBNER, Gregory Clark. 11510 SE STARK ST 97216 #005-12-1986 L1991 IM *020 †20

SCURRY, Melanie Tae. 12710 SE DIVISION ST, MIDCOUNTY HLTH CTR 97236 #007-02-1992 L1993 IM *020 †20

SEARS, Gosha Malgorzata. 3181 SW SAM JACKSON PRK RD, RD FA 97239 #020-12-2006 L2006 FP *012

SEETHARAMAN, Subramaniam. 3181 SW SAM JCKSN PRK RD R 97239 #495-16-1984 L2002 FP *012

SEGAL, Gerald Marc. 1015 NW 22ND AVE 97210 #016-06-1979 L1986 ON HEM *020 †20

SEGALL, Jocelyn Ann. 3181 SW SAM JCKSN PRK RD R, MAIL CODE OP11 97239 #048-02-2000 L2005 VS *100 †85

SEGEL, Sally Yael. 3181 SW SAM JCKSN PRK RD R 97239 #005-11-1994 L2004 OBG *020 †30

SEGURA, Jennifer R. ■ 97239 #048-13-2003 L2003 IM *020 †20

SEHGAL, Raj T. ■ 97209 #048-12-2005 L2005 IM *012

SEITZ, Gregory William. ■ 97213 #040-02-2007 L2007 IM *012

SEKHON, Harmanjatinder Si. 3181 SW SAM JACKSON PRK RD, DEPT OF PATH BOX L113 97239 #496-16-1981 L2000 PCP *100 †50

SELDEN, Karen B. 25 NW 23RD PL, STE 6 97210 #024-01-1993 L2000 PS *020 †65

SELDEN, Nathan R. 3303 SW BOND AVE, OHSU NEUROSURGERY, CH8N 97239 #024-01-1993 L2000 NS *020 †25

SELLS, Clifford Wayne. 707 SW GAINES ST, CDRCP 97239 #056-06-1988 L1996 ADL PD *020 †55

SELVA, Karin A. 707 SW GAINES ST, DEPT OF PEDIATRICS CDRCP 97239 #035-06-1996 L2000 PDE *020 †55 ‡

SEMLER, Herbert J. 2330 NW EVERETT ST, EXECUTIVE CARDIOLOGY 97210 #040-02-1953 L1955 CD PDC *020 †20

SEMLITZ, Linda Jan. 2386 NW HOYT ST 97210 #043-01-1978 L1988 CHP P *030 †75

SEMONSEN, Kevin Geo. 2311 NW NORTHRUP ST, STE 202 97210 #005-06-1989 L1990 DR VIR *020 †80

SENDERS, Wilbur L. 4805 NE GLISAN ST 97213 #040-02-1950 L1953 IM *071 †20

SENFT, Robert Arthur. 3715 N INTERSTATE AVE, NORTHWEST PERMANENTE P.C. 97227 #041-02-1960 L1969 IM *071 †20

SEQUEIRA, Sandy M. 10000 SE MAIN ST, STE 105 97216 #422-01-1997 L2000 PD *020 †55

SERA, Valerie Anne. 3181 SW SAM JCKSN PRK RD R, UHS 5D-11 97239 #051-04-1995 L2003 AN *020 †05

SERES, Joel Leonard. 5440 SW WESTGATE DR, THE HIGHLAND BLDG STE 300 97221 #041-02-1958 L1967 NS PMM *071 †25

SERES, Steven Paul. 501 N GRAHAM ST, STE 100 97227 #041-02-2000 L2000 IM *020 ‡

SEROPIAN, Michael A. 3181 SW SAM JACKSON PRK RD, UH 2 97239 #065-09-1990 L1998 AN *020 †05

SERRURIER, Laurence R. 1015 NW 22ND AVE 97210 #005-11-1955 L1961 IM *072 †20

SHACKLETON, Dustin Deloyc. ■ 97205 #005-19-2005 L2005 PTH *012

SHAFFCHIN, Cynthia Jane. 4411 SW VERMONT ST 97219 #025-12-2003 L2003 FM *100 †18

SHAH, Kirit S. 171 NE 102ND AVE 97220 #495-23-1971 L1981 U *020 †95

SHAH, Mona Kamal. 1509 SW SUNSET BLVD, STE 2E 97239 #040-02-1994 L1997 EM *020 †16

SHAKER, Kamal Gem. 10201 SE MAIN ST STE 11 97216 #915-04-1977 L1994 PUD CCM *020 †20

SHAMIE, Neda. 1040 NW 22ND AVE, STE 200 97210 #005-02-1998 L2005 OPH *020 †35

SHANGRAW, Robert Edward. 3181 SW SAM JACKSON PRK RD, UH 2 97239 #035-03-1985 L1990 AN GS *020 †05

SHANLEY, Chloe Matilda. ■ 97202 #048-02-2007 L2007 IM *012

SHAPIRO, David Scott. ■ 97239 #008-02-2002 L2007 CCS *012

SHAPIRO, Philip. ■ 97201 #016-11-1969 L1985 P *030 †75

SHARDY, Deborah Lynn. 501 N GRAHAM ST, STE 355 97227 #038-41-1999 L2006 PHO *100 †55

SHARMA, Srilakshmi Missul. 3182 SW SAM JACKSON PARK R, OHSU CASEY EYE INSTITUTE 97239 #917-02-1998 L2006 *100

SHAUGHNESSY, Robin Day. 707 SW GAINES ST, M/S CDRC-P 97239 #040-02-1990 L1993 PD *020 †55

SHAW, Jonathan Glazer. ■ 97210 #024-01-2006 L2006 FP *012

SHAW, Michelle Roseann. ■ 97214 #040-02-2006 L2006 EM *012

SHAW, Tatyana Evgenievna. 3303 SW BOND AVE, MC CM16D 97239 #040-02-2005 L2005 D *012

SHEHDEV, Ann Smith. ■ 97201 #040-02-1996 L2002 PTH *020 †50

■ = Address Information Privacy Protected

SHELEY, Robert Curtis. 1015 NW 22ND AVE, GOOD SAMARITAN HOSPITAL 97210 #040-02-1988 L1989 **IM** *020 †80

SHELLEY, Matthew Michael. 2230 NW PETTYGROVE ST, STE 220 97210 #040-02-1988 L1989 **PD** *020 †55

SHELY, William Walter, III. 2222 NW LOVEJOY ST STE 315, THE OREGON CLINIC, P.C. 97210 #016-01-1985 L1986 **TS** *020 †85,90

SHENSON, David Levitt. 3600 N INTERSTATE AVE, NORTHWEST PERMANENTE 97227 #020-12-1996 L1997 **IM** *020 †20

SHEPARD, Andrew Joshua. 1509 SW SUNSET BLVD, STE 2E 97239 #040-02-2001 L2004 **EM** *020 †16

SHEPPARD, Brett C. 3181 SW SAM JCKSN PRK RD R, L223A 97239 #016-42-1984 L1985 **GS SO** *020 †85

SHER, Paul Phillip. 3264 SW FAIRMOUNT BLVD 97239 #028-02-1965 L1965 **CLP IM** *030 †50

SHERICK, Stephen Vincent. ■ 97239 #007-02-2006 L2006 **EM** *012

SHERSHOW, Lee Wolfe. 2250 NW FLANDERS ST, STE 300 97210 #005-06-1967 L1998 **P PYA** *020 †75

SHI, Yongbing. 3181 SW SAM JCKSN PRK RD R 97239 #243-95-1983 L1999 **OTO** *020

SHICK, Paul Ellsworth, Jr. 3710 SW US VETRNS HSPTL RD 97239 #021-01-1946 **GE** *030 †55

SHIELDS, Ambrose B. 97239 #019-02-1940 L1941 **GS CRS** *071 †85

SHIH, Mark M. 2241 LLOYD CTR 97232 #026-04-1994 L1999 **OS** *020 †60,55

SHIIBA, Kayleen Noriko. 4845 NE GLISAN ST, EMERGENCY DEPT 97213 #040-02-1989 L1990 **EM** *020 †16

SHILEY, Samuel Gardner. 2222 NW LOVEJOY ST, STE 622 97210 #005-15-1999 L1999 **OTO** *020 †45

SHIM, Uhngchoon Brenda. ■ 97232 #054-04-2002 L2002 **IM** *100 †20

SHIN, Chu Ri. 3181 SW SAM JCKSN PRK RD R, SCIENCE UNIV 97239 #038-40-1999 L2006 **PHO** *012

SHIN, Kyung Hee. 1234 SE 122ND AVE 97233 #583-03-1964 L1977 **AN** *030

SHIRES, Robbie J Martin. ■ 97219 #040-12-1947 L1950 **PD OS** *074

SHNEIDMAN, Robert James. 3500 N INTERSTATE AVE 97227 #048-14-1982 L1983 **GE IM** *020 †20

SHOJAEI, Mehrdad. ■ 97296 #517-03-1990 L2007 **IM** *100

SHUFORD, Terry Scott. 3181 SW SAM JACKSON PRK RD, DPT RAD 97239 #040-02-1979 L1982 **DR** *020

SHULTS, William Thos. 1040 NW 22ND AVE STE 200 97210 #048-04-1968 L1971 **OS OPH** *071 †35

SHY, Hogan Howie. ■ 97239 #005-19-2003 L2003 **IM** *020 †20

SIAW, Caleb. 10101 SE MAIN ST, CALEB SIAW M D PC 97216 #649-14-1970 L1978 **OBG** *020

SIBELL, David Matthew. 3181 SW SAM JACKSON PRK RD, UH 2 97239 #050-02-1992 L1997 **AN** *020 †05

SIDDAPPA, Vinay K. 4805 NE GLISAN ST, STE BG05 97213 #012-05-1996 L2003 **IM** *020 †20

SIDOFF, Bonnie Ellen L. 4805 NE GLISAN ST, PROVIDENCE HOSP. EMERG. DE 97213 #021-01-1978 L1979 **EM** *020 †16

SIEGAL, Lori. 2701 NW VAUGHN ST, MONTGOMERY PARK OFFICE 97210 #005-02-1988 L1998 **IM** *020 †20

SIEGEL, Dawn Heather. ■ 97221 #056-05-1998 L2007 **D** *100 †15

SIEGEL, Joshua Ben. 120 NW 14TH AVE, STE 300 97209 #550-02-1987 L1999 **IM** *020 †20,05 ‡

SIEGEL, Michael Anthony. 3500 N INTERSTATE AVE 97227 #048-04-1985 L1990 **DR** *020 †80

SIKER, David Alan. 1800 NE 2ND AVE, PORTLAND NEUROVASCULAR 97212 #011-03-1992 L2000 **DR** *020 †80

SIKORA, Brooke Christine. 3303 SW BOND AVE, MC CH16D 97239 #012-05-2006 L2007 **D** *012

SILBERBACH, Gary Michael. 3181 SW SAM JCKSN PRK RD R, MAIL CODE CDRC-P 97239 #038-40-1979 L1988 **PDC** *020 †55

SILBERT, Lisa Carolyn. 3181 SW SAM JACKSON PRK RD, MAIL CODE L226 97239 #017-20-1996 L2000 **CN** *020 †75

SILEN, Mark Lawrence. 501 N GRAHAM ST, PEDIATRIC SURGERY 97227 #024-01-1980 L1999 **GS PDS** *020 †85

SILVA, Rafael. 2311 NW NORTHRUP ST, STE 202 97210 #048-02-1998 L2004 **DR** *020

SILVER, David Jay. 5050 NE HOYT ST STE 238 97213 #024-01-1967 L1975 **NS** *020 †20

SILVER, David Mark. 6327 SE MILWAUKIE AVE 97202 #051-01-1983 L1987 **FM** *020 †18

SIMASKO, Joel Loren. 19500 SE STARK ST, KAISER PERMANENTE ROCKWOOD 97233 #054-04-1980 L2000 **IM** *020 †20

SIMON, Joseph Harris. ■ 97202 #041-09-1963 L1964 **FM** *071 †18

SIMON, Laurel Lee. 4212 NE BROADWAY ST 97213 #040-02-1990 L1992 **IM** *020 †20

SIMON, Roger Pawcoast. 1225 NE 2ND AVE, LEGACY RESEARCH 97235 #035-20-1971 L2000 **N IM** *050 †20,75

SIMON, Shannon Kaye. 3303 SW BOND AVE, SCIENCE UNIV 97239 #054-04-2006 L2007 **D** *012

SIMONE, Eric Anthony. 501 N GRAHAM ST, STE 373 97227 #005-02-1990 L2007 **PDE** *020 †55

SIMPSON, Cedric B. ■ 97209 #048-13-1990 L1991 **IM** *020 †20

SIMPSON, Eric Lawrence. 3303 SW BOND AVE, DEPT - DERMATOLOGY 97239 #048-12-1998 L1999 **D** *020 †15

SIMPSON, Jennifer Dale. 3550 N INTERSTATE AVE, EAST INTERSTATE KAISER 97227 #017-20-1987 L1992 **IM** *020 †20

SINCLAIR, Jack Edwin. ■ 97206 #040-02-1957 L1958 **NS** *075

SINGER, Ellen Louise. 3500 N INTERSTATE AVE, EMERGENCY CENTER 97227 #035-45-1990 L1995 **IM PD** *020 †55,20

SINGH, Bhawar. 3500 N INTERSTATE AVE, AMBULATORY SURGERY CENTER 97227 #671-01-1960 L1966 **AN** *020 †05

SINGH, Sukhwant Nikkikaur. ■ 97209 #021-01-2005 L2006 **IM** *012

SINGSON, Peter Paul. PO BOX 4381 97208 #016-06-1994 L2006 **OBG** *020 †30

SISK, Clark Edmund. 3600 N INTERSTATE AVE 97227 #028-02-1978 L1980 **D** *020 †15

SISLER, Frank O. 2455 NW MARSHALL ST 97210 #017-20-1946 L1948 **P NTR** *071

SKACH, William R. 3181 SW SAM JACKSON PRK RD, PARK ROAD 97239 #024-01-1983 L1987 **HEM ON** *050 †20

SKAU, David Arlyn. 10000 SE MAIN ST, STE 105 97216 #005-12-1979 L1989 **PD** *020 †55

SKILES, Paul Vincent. 2230 NW PETTYGROVE ST, STE 220 97210 #010-01-1994 L1996 **EM** *020 †16

SKINNER, Martin David. 545 NE 47TH AVE, PROV MED GRP 47TH 97213 #035-45-1966 L1991 **IM IMG** *020 †20

SKINNER, Susan T Hunt. 3181 SW SAM JACKSON PRK RD, OHSU PEDIATRICS 97239 #040-02-1989 L1992 **PD** *030 †55

SKLENICKA, Scott R. ■ 97219 #040-02-2008 *012

SKOKAN, Michael David. 1111 NE 99TH AVE 97220 #040-02-1992 L2001 **PCC** *020

SKOOG, Steven John. 3303 SW BOND AVE, MAIL CODE CH10 U 97239 #040-02-1976 L1992 **UP EM** *020 †95

SKRLIN, Sara Marie. ■ 97239 #026-04-2006 L2007 **AN** *012

SLACK, Jennifer Michelle. 501 N GRAHAM ST STE 100, CASCADE PHYSICIANS, PC 97227 #003-01-2004 L2004 **IM** *020 †20

SLATER, Matthew Simon. 3181 SW SAM JCKSN PRK RD R, L353 97239 #051-07-1993 L1994 **CCS TTS** *020 †85,90

SLAUGHTER, Sarah Ellen. 5050 NE HOYT ST, INFECTION CONSULTANTS LLP 97213 #017-20-1990 L1991 **ID** *020 †20

SLAVIN, Richard Eugene. 2801 N GANTENBEIN AVE 97227 #165-02-1959 L1988 **PTH** *020 †50

SLEESMAN, Jay Bryant. ■ 97209 #028-03-2003 L2003 **AN** *020

SLEPACK, Jerry M. 500 NE MULTNOMAH ST, STE 100 97232 #041-01-1968 L1974 **IM** *020 †20

SLICKERS, Jennifer Ellen. 707 SW GAINES ST, CDRC-P 97239 #051-01-2000 L2000 **PN** *100 †55

SLIFMAN, Nancy Rae. ■ 97221 #024-07-1974 L1978 **D IG** *020 †55,15

SLIGER, Holly Marie. 1015 NW 22ND AVE, GOOD SAMARITAN 97210 #539-04-2005 L2005 **IM** *012

SLOUGH, Cristian Martin. 3181 SW SAM JCKSN PRK RD R, OHSU 97239 #917-12-2000 L2005 **OTO** *012

SMART, Mary Alison. ■ 97212 #012-01-1999 L2005 **AN** *020 †05

SMILEY, Peter W. 501 N GRAHAM ST, STE 555 97227 #061-01-1968 L1975 **CRS** *020 †10,85

SMILKSTEIN, Martin Jay. 3181 SW SAM JACKSON PRK RD, EMERGENCY MEDICINE 97239 #005-19-1979 L1991 **EM** *040 †16

SMITH, Christine. 7929 SW 37TH AVE STE B 97219 #021-05-1983 L2006 **P PYA** *020 †75

SMITH, Cristina Ann. ■ 97206 #040-02-2004 L2004 **PTH** *012

SMITH, Daryl I. 120 NW 14TH AVE, STE 300 97209 #043-01-1984 L2005 **AN PHP** *020 †05 ‡

SMITH, David Lloyd. 3710 SW US VETRNS HSPTL RD 97239 #038-41-1975 L1976 **RHU IM** *050 †20

SMITH, David Morrison. ■ 97205 #017-20-1987 L1988 **P** *020 †75

SMITH, Dennis Bernard. 2241 LLOYD CTR 97232 #035-03-1965 L1986 **N** *071 †75

SMITH, Frederic Warren. 3710 SW US VETRNS HSPTL RD 97239 #035-20-1956 L1987 **GE IM** *071 †20

SMITH, Gary Mac. 2250 NW FLANDERS ST # 301 97210 #030-05-1970 L1978 **P** *020

SMITH, James Dettmer. 3181 SW SAM JACKSON PRK RD, OHSU DEPT-OTOLARYNGOLOGY 97239 #018-03-1965 L1968 **OTO PDO** *040 †45

SMITH, Jason Patrick. 97239 #028-03-2005 L2005 **GS** *100

SMITH, Jeanene Ann. 2241 LLOYD CTR 97232 #040-02-1984 L1988 **FM** *020 †18

SMITH, John Washburn, II. 5050 NE HOYT ST STE 256 97213 #041-02-1981 L1996 **ON** *020 †20

SMITH, Justine Ruth. 3303 SW BOND AVE, FL 11 97239 #143-01-1989 L2000 *020

SMITH, Kevin Ray. 10373 NE HANCOCK ST, ST 115 97220 #030-05-1993 L1994 **PYG** *020 †75

SMITH, Leyla Akan. 500 NE MULTNOMAH ST, STE 100 97232 #902-04-1982 L1998 **PD OS** *020 †55

SMITH, Mary Anne De Witt. ■ 97221 #035-20-1959 L1966 **P** *071

SMITH, Robert Jos, Jr. 265 N BROADWAY ST 97227 #041-01-1961 L1967 **IM** *030 †20

SMITH, Robert Wm. ■ 97221 #040-02-1969 L1972 **AN FM** *020 †05

SMITH, Scott Warren. 541 NE 20TH AVE, STE 210 97232 #054-04-1983 L1985 **FM** *020 †18

SMITH, Stephen Mark. 3181 SW SAM JCKSN PRK RD R, OHSU DEPT/MEDICINE NRC3 97239 #917-04-1990 L2000 **PCC** *020

SMITH, Sue Ann. 707 SW GAINES ST, CDRCP 97239 #005-14-1988 L1989 **NPM** *020 †55

SMITH, Timothy Lee. 3181 SW SAM JACKSON PRK RD, M/C PV-01 97239 #038-41-1991 L2005 **OTO** *020 †45

SMITH, Virginia Jane. 3550 N INTERSTATE AVE, KAISER PERMANENTE OB/GYN 97227 #005-06-1979 L1981 **OBG** *020 †30

SMITH, Ward Tolbert. 1849 NW KEARNEY ST, STE 201 97209 #041-01-1965 L1970 **P GP** *050

SMITH, Wendy Jane. 3550 N INTERSTATE AVE, KAISER PERMANENTE ,NORTHWE 97227 #035-01-1991 L1998 **OBG** *020 †30

SMITH, William Brewster. 1040 NW 22ND AVE, THE NEUROLOGICAL CLINIC 97210 #033-05-1972 L1975 **NTR** *071 †75

SMITH, William Louis. 123 NE 3RD AVE STE 315 97232 #024-05-1957 L1962 **NS** *072 †25

SMITH-CUPANI, Kimberly A. 1321 NE 99TH AVE, STE 200 97220 #010-01-1986 L1992 **FM** *020 †18

SMITHPETER, Margaret Vane. ■ 97220 #034-01-2007 L2007 **IM** *012

SMITS, Ariel Kathleen. 4411 SW VERMONT 97219 #028-02-1999 L2000 **GPM** *020 †18,70

SMOOD, Jackson Danl. 4805 NE GLISAN ST, EMERGENCY DEPT 97213 #054-04-1991 L1992 **EM** *020 †16 ‡

SMUCKER, Lonnie Lee. 5050 NE HOYT ST, STE 240 97213 #040-02-1991 L1992 **FM** *020 †18

SNEDECOR, Philip A. ■ 97210 #040-02-1953 L1955 **GS** *071 †85

SNODGRASS, Roy Glenn. ■ 97201 #019-02-1955 L1963 **N** *071 †75

SNYDER, David Brian. 501 N GRAHAM ST STE 375, PROGRAM 97227 #017-20-1987 L1988 **PDE** *020 †55

SNYDER, Kristen Marie. 3710 SW US VETRNS HSPTL RD, PORTLAND VA MEDICAL CENTER 97239 #040-02-1998 L2000 **P** *020

SO, Norman Kai-Yan. 1040 NW 22ND AVE, STE 420 97210 #917-03-1980 L1993 **N CN** *020 †75

SODERSTROM, Evan Andrew. 1015 NW 22ND AVE, R 200 97210 #040-02-2001 L2001 **IM** *020

SOHAEY, Roya. 3181 SW SAM JACKSON PRK RD, OHSU DIAGNOSTIC RADIOL L34 97239 #016-06-1987 L2000 **R** *020 †80

SOIFER, Betsy Ellen. 3710 SW US VETRNS HSPTL RD, PORTLAND VETERANS AFFAIRS 97239 #041-07-1983 L1987 **AN CCM** *020 †05

SOKOLOFF, Mitchell H. 3303 SW BOND AVE, CH 10 U 97239 #005-11-1991 L2004 **U ON** *020 †95

SOLD, Denise Nicole. ■ 97239 #040-02-2008 *012

SOLER, Zachary Michael. 3181 SW SAM JACKSON PRK RD, RD DE 97239 #036-05-2004 L2004 **OTO** *012

SOLHJEM, Matthew Curtis. 5050 NE HOYT ST, LEVEL B 97213 #026-04-2000 L2005 **RO** *020 †80

SOLOMON, Andrew Jay. ■ 97239 #035-47-2005 L2005 **N** *012

SOLOMON, Joel Stuart. 3181 SW SAM JACKSON PRK RD, PARK ROAD 97239 #028-02-1993 L2005 **HS** *020 †65

SOLONDZ, David Keller. ■ 97214 #024-07-2005 L2005 **FP** *012

SOLOTAROFF, Rachel. ■ 97214 #032-01-2001 L2003 **IM** *100

SOMOGYI, Lehel. 1111 NE 99TH AVE 97220 #957-01-1989 L2004 **GE IM** *020 †20

SONDERLEITER, Joseph Paul. 5410 SW MACADAM AVE, STE 200 97034 #034-01-1975 L2003 **CHP P** *020 †75

SONG, Howard Kim. 3181 SW SAM JCKSN PRK RD R, M/S L353 97239 #005-11-1994 L2004 **TS** *020 †85,90

SONG, Meong-Gum. 3181 SW SAM JACKSON PRK RD 97239 #583-02-1976 **TS** *020

SONNELAND, Jane Ellen. 1321 NE 99TH AVE, STE 100 97220 #047-06-1973 L1974 **FM** *020 †18

SOO, Brendan Cheng. 3101 SW SAM JCKSN PRK RD R 97239 #143-02-1996 L2007 *100

SOO, Edward W. 5050 NE HOYT ST STE 256 97213 #048-15-1988 L1998 **ON HEM** *020 †20

■ = Address Information Privacy Protected

SOOT, Scott Johannes. 5050 NE HOYT ST, STE 610 97213 #040-02-1994 L1997 **GS** *020 †85
SORENSEN, Everett A. ■ 97221 #040-02-1946 L1949 **GP** *071
SORENSEN, Mary Lynn. 9220 SW BARBUR BLVD, STE 119-196 97219 #040-02-2005 L2005 **GS** *012
SOSA, Sonia Elena. ■ 97211 #016-11-2007 L2007 **FP** *012
SOUCY, Adrienne Elise. ■ 97209 #026-04-2006 L2006 **IM** *012
SOULE, Duncan Edward. 1312 E BURNSIDE ST #025-01-1983 L1993 **PM** *020 †60
SOULE, George Melton. 511 SW 10TH AVE STE 604 97205 #036-05-1978 L1979 **P** *020
SOULE, Jordana Liane. 3181 SW SAM JACKSON PRK RD 97239 #040-02-2000 L2000 **GS** *100
SOWELL, Richard C. ■ 97292 #040-02-1954 L1955 **PUD IM** *074
SPACKMAN, Kent Alan. 3181 SW SAM JACKSON PRK RD, OHSU-BICC 97239 #060-01-1979 L1989 **BBK CLP** *050 †50
SPARKMAN, Miriam Grace. ■ 97239 #040-02-2008 L2008 *012
SPECHT, H David, Jr. ■ 97206 #005-12-1967 L1974 **PTH NM** *071 †50,28
SPECTOR, Gary C. PO BOX 17394 97217 #028-34-1975 L1980 **OBG** *100
SPEIRS, Robert T, III. 3500 N INTERSTATE AVE, INTERSTATE MEDICAL OFFICE 97227 #035-01-1984 L1990 **DR** *020 †80
SPENCER, David Conlee. 745 SW GAINES ST, M/C CDW-3 97239 #026-04-1993 L1999 **CN** *020 †75
SPENCER, Dennis Wayne. 200 SW MARKET ST, AETNA HEALTH PLANS-OREGON 97201 #012-01-1978 L1989 **IM** *020 †20
SPENCER, Scott Simner. 3181 SW SAM JCKSN PRK RD R 97239 #040-02-2005 L2005 **PD** *012
SPERLIN, Andrew G. 4531 SE BELMONT ST, STE 250 97215 #054-04-1978 L1998 **IM** *020 †20
SPEROFF, Leon. 3181 SW SAM JACKSON PRK RD 97239 #038-06-1961 L1977 **END OBG** *020 †30
SPIGHT, Donn Hatiim. 3181 SW SAM JACKSON PRK RD, MAILCODE L223A 97239 #016-06-1999 L2006 **GS** *100 †85
SPIRO, David Mark. 3181 SW SAM JACKSON PRK RD, MAIL CODE CDW-EM 97239 #005-02-1991 L1994 **PEM PD** *020 †55
SPISAK, William. 7910 NE FAILING ST 97213 #025-07-1979 L1982 **IM** *020
SPITALE, Patricia. 707 SW GAINES ST, OHSU - CDRC-P 97239 #035-06-1991 L2003 **PD** *020 †55
SPIVAK, Laura Ann. 3181 SW SAM JCKSN PRK RD R, M/C CB550 97239 #041-13-2001 L2005 **ETX** *020 †16 ‡
SPRAGUE, Carol Lee. 3710 SW US VETRNS HSPTL RD, P3GP1 97239 #016-43-1993 L1994 **IM** *020 †20
SPRAGUE, Lisa Ann. 3181 SW SAM JACKSON PRK RD, PARK RD 97239 #054-04-1988 L1996 **OBG** *020 †20,30
SPRINGER, Leonard. ■ 97239 #036-07-1964 L1964 **D** *071 †15
SPURGEON, Stephen E. 3181 SW SAM JCKSN PRK RD R, M/S BTE-119 - H. CROWELL 97239 #041-02-2002 L2002 **HO** *012 †20
STACEY, Brett Russell. 3303 SW BOND AVE, 4TH FL 97239 #025-01-1986 L1996 **AN PMM** *020 †05
STAJDUHAR, Karl. 3181 SW SAM JACKSON PRK RD, DIV OF CARDIO UHN 62 97239 #041-12-1983 L2005 **ICE CD** *020 †20
STALLINGS, Ronald Victor. 4426 NE 38TH AVE 97211 #308-07-1982 L2004 **AN EM** *050
STANDAGE, Blayne Allan. 1130 NW 22ND AVE STE 300, OREGON SURG CONSTLS 97210 #005-11-1980 L1981 **GS** *020 †85
STANDISH, Myles Patrick. 120 NW 14TH AVE, STE 300 97209 #036-05-1989 L1990 **AN** *020 †05 ‡
STANEK, Ann Marie. ■ 97219 #054-04-2003 L2003 **OBG** *020
STANGELAND, Ray Gregory. 1750 SW HARBOR WAY 97201 #038-06-1974 L1975 **EM** *020 †16
STANKE, Roger Willard. 5055 N GREELEY AVE, PED URGENCY CARE CLINIC 97217 #016-11-1971 L1974 **PD** *071 †55
STANTON, Robert Edward. 3477 NE PEERLESS PL 97232 #005-02-1957 L1965 **PD** *071 †55
STAPLETON, Joseph Paul. 120 NW 14TH AVE, #300 OREGON ANESTH GRP PC 97209 #040-02-1982 L1983 **AN** *020 †05 ‡
STARK, Donald Byron. 2705 E BURNSIDE ST 97214 #035-20-1958 L1959 **GS VS** *071
STARK, Karen L. 2222 NW LOVEJOY ST STE 504, ASSOCIATES LLC 97210 #028-02-1996 L2004 **OPH** *020 †35
STARK, William Kenneth. ■ 97212 #040-02-1955 L1956 **GP OS** *071
STARR, Albert. 5319 SW WESTGATE DR, STE 255 97221 #035-01-1949 L1957 **TS CD** *020 †85,90
STARR, Ian Richard. ■ 97239 #040-02-2008 *012
STATKUS, Nicholas Jerome. ■ 97219 #040-02-2004 L2004 **DR** *012
STEARNS, Angela Murray. 5050 NE HOYT ST, STE 469 97213 #056-06-1993 L1994 **IM** *020 †20
STECKER, Eric Carl. 3181 SW SAM JCKSN PRK RD R, UHN 62 97239 #056-05-1998 L1999 **CD** *020 †20
STEELE, Eric Alan. 3375 SW TERWILLIGER BLVD, CASEY EYE INST 97239 #048-04-2001 L2002 **OPH** *020 †35
STEELMAN, Robert Joe. 707 SW GAINES ST, OHSU PEDIATRIC CRITICAL CA 97239 #055-01-1993 L2001 **PD CCP** *020 †55
STEINBERG, Mary A Edwards. 707 SW GAINES ST 97239 #026-04-1980 L1986 **PD** *020 †55
STEINBERG, Zachary Louis. ■ 97209 #010-01-2007 L2007 **IM** *012
STEINER, Elizabeth. 3181 SW SAM JACKSON PRK RD, PARK RD 97239 #024-16-1991 L1992 **FM** *020 †18
STEINER, Robert David. 707 SW GAINES ST, MAILCODE CDRC-P 97239 #056-05-1987 L1996 **CBG PD** *050 †55,19
STEINFELDT, Matthew Paul. ■ 97239 #040-02-2007 **PD** *012
STEINKELER, Jeffrey Alan. 120 NW 14TH AVE, STE 300 97209 #017-20-1983 L1987 **AN** *020 †05 ‡
STEINMETZ, Laurel Kay. ■ 97219 #018-03-2006 L2006 **PD** *012
STELLWAY, David L. 120 NW 14TH AVE, STE 300 97209 #016-42-1981 L1982 **AN** *020 †05 ‡
STELZER, Keith Jeffrey. 1400 NW IRVING ST 97209 #005-14-1989 L2000 **RO** *040 †80
STEMPEL, James Ernest. 5050 NE HOYT ST, STE 359 97213 #040-02-1978 L1980 **OBG** *020 †30
STENGER, Robert John. ■ 97206 #023-07-2006 L2006 **FP** *012
STENZEL, Matthew Jerome. 120 NW 14TH AVE, STE 300 97209 #539-06-1989 L1996 **AN PAN** *020 †05
STENZEL, Molly Sue. 3500 N INTERSTATE AVE 97227 #040-02-1994 L2004 **ID** *020 †20
STENZEL, Peter. 2241 LLOYD CTR 97232 #040-02-1966 L1978 **PTH** *062 †50
STEPHAN, Jon Scott. 10123 SE MARKET ST 97216 #005-12-1992 L1996 **AN** *020 †05 ‡
STEPHENS, Craig Lee. 1321 NE 99TH AVE STE 20, GATEWAY FAMILY MEDICINE 97220 #005-06-1980 L1993 **FM** *020 †18
STEPHENS, Elizabeth Anne. 5050 NE HOYT ST, STE 540 97213 #047-05-1994 L1996 **END** *020 †20

STEPHENS, John W. 1015 NW 22ND AVE 97210 #060-01-1944 **DIA** *071
STEPHENS, Kevin Michael. ■ 97206 #036-01-2005 L2005 **PD** *012
STEPHENSON, David Andrew. ■ 97201 #040-02-2005 L2008 **IM** *012
STEVENS, Eugene Archer. 6445 N GREELEY AVE, PACIFIC MEDICAL GROUP 97217 #030-05-1969 L1973 **FM EM** *020 †18
STEVENS, Janice Robinson. OREGON HEALTH SCIENCE UNIV, DEPT OF PSYCHIATRY 97201 #024-05-1949 L1955 **P N** *050 †75
STEVENS, Jill Marie. 3181 SW SAM JACKSON PRK RD, RD PE 97239 #040-02-2006 L2006 **PD** *012
STEVENSON, Craig Clark. 2530 NE 38TH AVE 97212 #020-12-1977 L1978 **PD OS** *062 †55
STEVENSON, Linda Kay. 120 NW 14TH AVE, STE 300 97209 #028-02-1987 L1992 **AN** *020 †05 ‡
STEVENSON, Ronald Carlo. ■ 97239 #005-18-1991 L2000 **OBG FSM** *020 †30
STEVENSON, Windy. 707 SW GAINES ST, STE CDRCP 97239 #019-02-1999 L1999 **PD** *020 †55
STEVLAND, Nelson Peter. 500 NE MULTNOMAH ST, STE 100 97232 #018-03-1973 L1979 **N P** *020 †75
STEWART, Lowan Han. 3714 SE ALDER ST 97214 #034-01-2001 L2001 **EM** *020 †16
STEWART, Tanya Lugliani. 5835 NE 122ND AVE STE 135 97230 #024-07-1999 L1999 **PLM IM** *030 †20
STIBOLT, Thomas Bodley. 500 NE MULTNOMAH ST, STE 100 97232 #016-01-1975 L1985 **PUD** *020 †20
STILES, Charlotte Esther. ■ 97218 #054-04-2006 L2006 **GS** *012
STILWELL, Jane Elizabeth. 14046 SE ELLIS ST 97236 #040-02-1976 L1977 **IMG IM** *020
STILWELL, Kamela Suzanne. 10000 SE MAIN ST, STE 105 97216 #047-05-1994 L1997 **PD** *020 †55
STOEHR, Thomas Michael. 2241 LLOYD CTR 97232 #056-05-1996 L1998 **DR** *020
STOELK, Eugene Merle. 1750 SW HARBOR WAY, STE 200 97201 #018-03-1980 L1986 **REN** *020 †30
STOKES, Karen Renee. 120 NW 14TH AVE, STE 300 97209 #054-04-1991 L2001 **AN** *020 †05 ‡
STONE, Berton Hamilton. 19500 SE STARK ST, KAISER PERMANENTE ROCKWOOD 97233 #040-02-1994 L1997 **IM** *020 †20
STONE, Elizabeth Jean. 5051 SE HAWTHORN BLVD #101 97215 #016-06-1967 L1973 **PS** *072 †65
STONE, Sean Michael. ■ 97212 #036-05-1999 L2008 **EM** *020 †16
STONER, Jo Anne Marie. 3181 SW SAM JCKSN PRK RD R, M/C: UHS-2 97239 #020-02-1989 L2005 **AN** *020 †05
STORK, Linda Claudette. 3181 SW SAM JACKSON PRK RD, PARK RD 97239 #035-01-1979 L2002 **PHO PD** *040 †55
STORK, Philip Jacques. 3141 SW SAM JCKSN PRK #L47 97239 #035-01-1984 L1989 **IM PTH** *100
STORRS, Frances Judy. 3303 SW BOND AVE, DEPT- DERMATOLOGY 97239 #035-20-1964 L1965 **D** *020 †15
STOSUR, Harriet Russell. 500 NE MULTNOMAH ST, STE 100 97232 #035-45-1995 L1997 **OBG** *020 †30
STOUMBOS, Vasiliki Diane. 2222 NW LOVEJOY ST STE 411 97210 #023-07-1983 L1984 **OPH IM** *020 †20,35
STOUT, Ann Ulmer. 3303 SW BOND AVE, FL 11 97239 #048-04-1984 L2000 **OPH PO** *020 †35
STOUT, John Timothy. 3303 SW BOND AVE, FL 11 97239 #048-04-1989 L2000 **OPH PO** *020 †35
STOYANOVA, Veneta Dimitro. 3181 SW SAM JCKSN PRK RD R, M/S - DCH, DC7P 97239 #198-01-1996 L2005 **P** *100
STRASFELD, Lynne Meryl. 3181 SW SAM JCKSN PRK RD R, OHSU-INFECTIOUS DISEASES 97239 #008-01-1996 L2006 **ID** *020 †20
STRATFORD, Travis William. ■ 97239 #040-02-2000 L2001 **DR** *100 †80
STRATTON, Geraldine Lee. 6312 SW CAPITOL HWY # 502 97239 #024-01-1997 L2006 **IM EM** *020 †16
STRAUBE, Kurt R. ■ 97221 #154-07-1952 L1960 **R IM** *071 †80
STRAUSBAUGH, Larry James. 2241 LLOYD CTR 97232 #048-04-1971 L1985 **ID IM** *020 †20
STRAUSS, Wayne Lawrence. 1111 NE 99TH AVE 97220 #054-04-1999 L2004 **IM** *020 †20
STRBA, Jaroslav Peter. 120 NW 14TH AVE, STE 300 97209 #286-11-1991 L1997 **AN** *020 †05 ‡
STREAM, Glen Ritchie. 12518 NE AIRPORT WAY, STE 110 97230 #040-02-1979 L1982 **FM** *020 †18
STREAR, Christopher M. ■ 97202 #041-01-1994 L2002 **EM** *020 †16
STRELICH, Katie Rebecca. 10201 SE MAIN ST, STE 10 97216 #049-01-1996 L1997 **CD** *020 †20
STROUP, Christina Louise. 3181 SW SAM JCKSN PRK RD R, 3181 SW SAM JACKSON PARK R 97239 #550-04-2006 L2006 **FP** *012
STUART, Roger Conrad. 120 NW 14TH AVE, STE 300 97209 #040-02-1978 L1979 **AN** *020 †05 ‡
STUBBS, Ervin Gene. 707 SW GAINES ST, OREGON HEALTH SCIENCE UNIV 97239 #018-03-1964 L1971 **CHP P** *071 †75
STUBENRAUCH, Peter Charle. ■ 97213 #016-01-2004 L2004 **IM** *020 †20
STULL, John Davis. 3181 SW SAM JCKSN PRK RD R, CB-669 97239 #028-02-1978 L1998 **GPM** *020 †55,70
STUPFEL, J Frank. 4805 NE GLISAN ST 97213 #028-34-1946 L1947 **FM** *071
STURGES, Stanley Gordon. 921 SW WASHINGTON ST STE 5, CERES BEHAVIORAL HLTH 97205 #005-12-1955 L1983 **P** *071 †75
SU, Eustacia. 2241 LLOYD CTR 97232 #038-41-1978 L1984 **EM PD** *040 †55,16
SUHLER, Eric Barton. 3303 SW BOND AVE, FL 11 97239 #048-12-1995 L2002 **OPH** *020 †35
SUKUMAR, Mithran S. 3181 SW SAM JCKSN PRK RD R, L353 97239 #495-27-1990 L1999 **TS** *020 †85,90
SUKUMAR, Shirin Ruth. 1200 NW 23RD AVE, LEGACY CLINIC GOOD SAMARIT 97210 #495-27-1995 L2000 **IMG** *020 †20 ‡
SULLIVAN, Fred R, Jr. 3710 SW US VETRNS HSPTL RD, M/S P3MED 97239 #004-01-1970 L2003 **HEM IM** *020 †20
SULLIVAN, Joseph Wm. 5050 NE HOYT ST, STE 240 97213 #005-02-1985 L1990 **FM PD** *020 †18
SULLIVAN, Michael Edward. ■ 97221 #040-02-1989 *050
SULLIVAN, Peter Damian. 3181 SW SAM JACKSON PRK RD, PARK RD 97239 #005-19-1994 L1996 **IM** *020 †20
SULLIVAN, Scot Alan. 833 SW 11TH AVE, STE 833 97205 #039-01-1995 L1999 **OPH** *020 †35
SUMMERS, Gordon Wm. 510 NE 49TH AVE 97213 #040-02-1965 L1967 **HNS OTO** *071 †45
SUN, Hai. 3181 SW SAM JACKSON PRK RD, OR HLTH SCI UNIV HOSP 97239 #032-01-2007 L2007 **GS** *012
SUNDERLAND, Cecille O. 3181 SW SAM JACKSON PRK RD 97239 #035-15-1962 L1967 **PDC PD** *020 †55
SUNENSHINE, Rebecca H. 3181 SW SAM JACKSON PRK RD, PARK ROAD 97239 #017-20-1998 L1999 **ID** *100 †20

SUNG, Esther Mary. ■ 97232 #048-12-2004 L2005 **AN** *012
SUNG, Jennifer. 3181 SW SAM JACKSON PRK RD, RD L5 97239 #048-04-2005 L2006 **GS** *012
SUPER, Elizabeth Rachel. ■ 97202 #054-04-2005 L2005 **PD** *012
SURIANO, Kimberly Ann. 501 N GRAHAM ST, STE 445 97227 #005-15-1995 L2002 **OBG** *020 †20
SURMAN, Dusan Josip. 847 SW 58TH AVE 97221 #869-02-1959 L1965 **OBG EM** *020 †30 ‡
SUSSMAN, Michael David. 3101 SW SAM JACKSON PRK RD 97239 #023-01-1967 L1992 **OP** *071 †35
SUTTON, James Craig. 500 NE MULTNOMAH ST STE 10 97232 #018-03-1958 L1964 **OPH** *071 †35
SUWANJINDAR, Papassorn. 3710 SW US VET RD 97201 #891-02-1969 L1977 **PTH** *020 †50
SUZUKI, Aijiro Pascal. ■ 97209 #019-02-2000 L2001 **DR** *100 †80
SUZUKI, Carol Michie. 1130 NW 22ND AVE, STE 520 97210 #005-19-1996 L2000 **OBG** *020 †30
SWANSON, Neil Axel. 3303 SW BOND AVE, DEPT - DERMATOLOGY 97239 #035-45-1976 L1989 **D PS** *020 †15
SWANSON, Veronica C. 3181 SW SAM JACKSON PRK RD, UH 2 97239 #016-06-1992 L2000 **AN PAN** *020 †05
SWANSTROM, Lee Leray. 1040 NW 22ND AVE, STE 560 97210 #030-06-1983 L1984 **GS VS** *020 †85
SWARZTRAUBER, Karleen. 3181 SW SAM JACKSON PRK RD, MAIL CODE L226 97239 #021-01-1991 L2000 **N** *020 †75
SWEENEY, April Louise. ■ 97206 #033-05-2007 L2007 **P** *012
SWEENEY, Dennis Patrick. 1111 NE 99TH AVE 97220 #026-04-1975 L2001 **GE IM** *020 †20
SWEERUS, Kelly Ann. ■ 97239 #040-02-2008 *012
SWEIGERT, Karen M. 1040 NW 22ND AVE STE 330, CASCADE WOMEN'S HEALTH PC 97210 #035-48-1985 L1989 **OBG** *020 †30
SWENSON, Keith Howard. 5050 NE HOYT ST STE 454 97213 #028-02-1970 L1974 **D IM** *020 †15,20
SWETNAM, Leah Alice. ■ 97202 #021-01-2002 L2002 **NEP** *012 †20
SWIDE, Christopher Edward. 3181 SW SAM JACKSON PRK RD, UH 2 97239 #050-02-1987 L1988 **AN** *020 †05
SWITLYK, Paul Anthony. 1515 NW 18TH AVE, STE 300 97209 #033-05-1979 L1983 **ORS** *020 †40
SYTSMA, Virginia Johnston. 2701 NW VAUGHN ST STE 140, CONTINUING CARE SERVICES 97210 #028-34-1985 L1992 **IM** *020 †20
TAGGART-WIESBERG, Tracy. ■ 97211 #040-02-2001 L2001 **GS** *020
TAI, Cynthia. 3314 SW US VETRNS HSPTL RD, OHSU DEPT. NEPHROLOGY PP26 97239 #026-04-1996 L2000 **NEP** *020 †20
TAJ, Nazhat. 19500 SE STARK ST 97233 #028-03-2000 L2005 **MPD** *020 †20,55
TAKANO, Lina M A. 800 SW 13TH AVE 97205 #014-01-1996 L1997 **IM OS** *020 †20
TAKIGUCHI, Rodd Hisao. 3181 SW SAM JACKSON PRK RD, PARK ROAD 97239 #040-02-2001 L2005 **D** *012
TAKLA, Victor Nabil. 120 NW 14TH AVE, STE 300 97209 #040-02-1985 L1989 **AN** *020 †05 ‡
TALBOT, John Michael. 233 NE 102ND AVE 97220 #040-02-1962 L1981 **DR OTO** *040 †45,80
TALBOT, Thomas Edward. 1015 NW 22ND AVE 97210 #040-02-1945 **OPH** *071 †35
TAM, Lori Mon. ■ 97239 #040-02-2007 L2007 **IM** *012
TAMARAPPOO, Balaji K. ■ 97239 #041-15-2002 L2002 **CD** *012 †20
TAM SU, Anita. 545 NE 47TH AVE, STE 310 97213 #462-01-1967 L1995 **PD** *030 †55
TANGUM, Michael Ross. 1015 NW 22ND AVE, GSH R-200 97210 #048-02-1996 L1998 **IM** *020 †20
TANNE, Emanuel. 1015 NW 22ND AVE 97210 #035-08-1962 L1973 **OPH** *071 †35
TANNER, Gerald E. 3181 SW SAM JACKSON PRK RD, UH 2 97239 #016-43-1968 L1974 **AN** *040 †05
TANNER, Joan K. ■ 97231 #040-02-1966 L1967 **GP** *071
TARNASKY, John Walter. 501 N GRAHAM ST STE 525 97227 #040-02-1961 L1965 **OBG** *071 †30
TARRANT, Kevin Joseph. 120 NW 14TH AVE, STE 300 97209 #016-43-1990 L2002 **AN** *020 †05 ‡
TARRO, Jimmie Nick. 5331 SW MACADAM AVE, STE 307 97239 #049-01-1966 L1970 **IM** *071
TASSON, Dana Paul. 921 SW WASHINGTON ST STE 8 97205 #025-01-1993 L1994 **P** *071 †75
TAUBENBERGER, Peter. ■ 97293 #409-16-1953 L1983 **IM GP** *062
TAUBMAN, Robert Edward. 2153 SW MAIN ST 97205 #030-05-1960 L1961 **P** *020
TAVAN, Emmanuel Trungtoan. ■ 97239 #040-02-2007 L2007 **IM** *012
TAVELLI, Bert Gregory. 1130 NW 22ND AVE, STE 330 97210 #007-02-1982 L1986 **D** *020 †15
TAWFIK, Joyce Mary. ■ 97221 #041-12-2008 *012
TAYLOR, Benjamin Nathan. 1750 NW NAITO PKWY, HEALTH NORTHWEST, SUITE 10 97209 #040-02-1984 L1991 **FM** *020 †18
TAYLOR, Claudia Paula. ■ 97213 #005-02-2002 L2004 **D** *020 †15
TAYLOR, Derek Carr. 1130 NW 22ND AVE, NORTHWEST 97210 #049-01-1998 L2001 **GE** *020 †20
TAYLOR, Howard Scott. 10000 SE MAIN ST STE 307 97216 #012-01-1988 L1994 **N** *020 †75
TAYLOR, Lee Alan. 3101 SW SAM JCKSN PRK RD R, SHRINERS HOSPITAL FOR CHIL 97239 #048-12-1982 L1986 **AN** *030 †05
TAYLOR, Lloyd M. 3181 SW SAM JCKSN PRK RD R, DIVISION OF VASULAR SURGER 97239 #036-07-1946 L1950 **GS TS** *071 †85,90
TAYLOR, Lloyd M. 2241 LLOYD CTR 97232 #036-07-1973 L1977 **VS GS** *020 †85
TAYLOR, Mary Margaret. ■ 97221 #040-02-1996 L2000 **P** *100
TAYLOR, Matthew Hiram. 3181 SW SAM JCKSN PRK RD R, M/C: L-586 97239 #040-02-2005 L2007 **HO** *012
TAYLOR, Robert Brown. 3181 SW SAM JCKSN PRK #R, MAIL CODE: SM 97239 #041-13-1961 L1984 **FM OS** *040 †18
TAYLOR, William Frederick. ■ 97201 #050-02-1983 L2002 **FM** *020 †18
TAYLOR, William Holmes. 3181 SW SAM JACKSON PRK RD, OHSU DIV. PLASTIC & RECONS 97239 #005-12-1947 L1976 **GS HS** *040
TCHERVENIVANOV, Nikolay G. 120 NW 14TH AVE, STE 300 97209 #198-02-1985 L2003 **PAN** *020 †05 ‡
TEENY, Parry Saml. 3434 NE 170TH PL 97230 #040-02-1978 L1979 *100
TEGTMEYER, Kenneth Bren. 707 SW GAINES ST, MC CDRCP, DEPT OF PEDIATRI 97239 #026-04-1992 L2001 **CCP** *020 †55
TELERANT, Robin Michelle. ■ 97210 #005-19-2007 L2007 **IM** *012
TERRALL, Vance L. 910 NE 47TH AVE 97213 #040-02-1945 **GP** *020
TERRY, Annie B. 707 SW GAINES ST, DEPT OF PEDS/CDRCP 97239 #035-06-1971 L1977 **GE PD** *020
TERRY, David Gerard. 2241 LLOYD CTR 97232 #028-34-1990 L1996 **DR** *020 †80
TERRY, Mark Andrew. 1040 NW 22ND AVE N200, DEVER'S EYE INSTITUTE 97210 #028-34-1979 L1991 **OPH** *035 †35

TESTER, Patrick Wm. 10535 NE GLISAN ST 97220 #050-02-1991 L1992 **IM** *020 †20
TEWARI, Devansu Sujata. 3181 SW SAM JACKSON PRK RD 97239 #005-15-1997 L2006 **OBG** *020 †30
TEWFIK, Michael H. 300 N GRAHAM ST, STE 200 97227 #040-02-1997 L1999 **IM** *020 †20
THAYER, James Robt. 426 SW STARK ST, 5TH FL 97204 #017-20-1982 L1983 **IM** *075
THEARD, Angele. 2801 N GANTENBEIN AVE 97227 #016-11-1989 L2001 **AN** *020 †05 ‡
THIESING, John Tyler. ■ 97219 #040-02-2002 L2002 **DR** *100 †80
THOITS, Joseph Ryan. ■ 97214 #051-01-2007 L2007 **P** *012
THOMAS, Charles Richard. 3181 SW SAM JCKSN PRK RD R, DEPT OF RADIATION MEDICINE 97239 #016-11-1985 L2006 **RO ON** *020,80
THOMAS, Gregory Alan. 3181 SW SAM JACKSON PRK RD, OHSU CDRC-P 97239 #040-02-1981 L1991 **PD PHO** *020 †55
THOMAS, James Phillip. 909 NW 18TH AVE 97209 #041-14-1985 L1992 **OTO** *020 †45
THOMAS, Larry Richard. 2222 NW LOVEJOY ST STE 622 97210 #038-40-1972 L1973 **OTO** *020 †45
THOMAS, Mildred Mae. ■ 97217 #040-02-1954 **OBG** *071 †30
THOMASSON, Catherine Lynn. 724 SW HARRISON ST, SERVICE 97201 #025-07-1983 L1984 **IM** *075 †20
THOMPSON, Alivia Karin. ■ 97227 #035-45-2002 L2002 **GS** *012
THOMPSON, Betty Blomquist. 3181 SW SAM JACKSON PRK RD 97239 #040-02-1959 L1962 **AN** *071 †05
THOMPSON, Christopher J. 800 SW 13TH AVE 97205 #040-02-1983 L1984 **IM** *020 †20
THOMPSON, Curtis Troy. ■ 97201 #040-04-1990 L2002 **DMP** *020 †50
THOMPSON, David Prescott. 3181 SW SAM JCKSN PRK RD R, BAIRD HALL 18 97239 #019-02-1969 L1972 **IM OM** *020 †20,70
THOMPSON, Eric Michael. ■ 97214 #030-05-2006 L2006 **NS** *012
THOMPSON, John Jones. 13705 NE AIRPORT WAY, STE C 97230 #008-01-1974 L1982 **PTH** *062 †50
THOMPSON, Mark Alan. 4805 NE GLISAN ST 97213 #038-41-1992 L1996 **FM** *020 †18
THOMPSON, Michelle Renee. ■ 97239 #040-02-2006 L2006 **IM** *012
THOMPSON, Rebecca Newton. ■ 97239 #005-11-2003 L2006 **P** *100 †70
THOMPSON, Sarah Kathryn. 3181 SW SAM JACKSON PRK RD 97239 #060-02-1999 L2004 *100
THOMSON, Gregory John. 501 N GRAHAM ST, STE 260 97227 #025-07-1990 L2001 **ORS** *020 †40
THONG, Bob. ■ 97290 #054-04-2006 L2006 **IM** *012
THORBORG, Per Arnold J. 3181 SW SAM JACKSON PRK RD, DEPT OF ANESTHESIOLOGY 97239 #858-06-1978 L1999 **CCA AN** *020
THORPE, John D. ■ 97201 #028-02-1952 L1956 **PTH NM** *072 †50
THUKKANI, Nundhini. ■ 97239 #040-02-2004 L2004 **GE** *012 †20
THUNDER, Timothy Carl. 4805 NE GLISAN ST, STE BG05 97213 #031-01-1997 L2000 **IM** *020 †20
THYGESEN, Megan Emily. 13007 NE GLISAN ST, PROVIDENCE ELDER PL 97230 #040-02-1999 L2000 **IMG** *020 †20 ‡
TIERNEY, Rhonda Cynthia. 4805 NE GLISAN ST 97213 #048-12-2002 L2002 **IM** *020 †20
TILFORD, David Lee. 3181 SW SAM JCKSN PRK RD R 97239 #019-02-1970 L1979 **PHO PD** *071 †55
TING, Frances T. 10000 SE MAIN ST, STE 408 97216 #019-02-1996 L2002 **GS** *020 †85
TING, Helen Charing. 3181 SW SAM JCKSN PRK RD R, OHSU DEPT/ SURGERY L223 97239 #061-01-2000 L2001 *100
TIPPETTS, Rebekha K. 2801 N GANTENBEIN AVE 97227 #049-01-1998 L2001 **EM** *020 †16
TIRUMALI, Nagendra R. 3600 N INTERSTATE AVE 97227 #495-33-1974 L1983 **ON HEM** *020 †20
TITUS, Bradley Geo. 10123 SE MARKET ST 97216 #025-01-1984 L1990 **IC CD** *020 †20 ‡
TOBIN, Nora Ann. 10123 SE MARKET ST 97216 #038-43-1981 L1982 **IM IMG** *020 †20
TOENNIESSEN, Linda Marie. 511 SW 10TH AVE STE 604 97205 #005-12-1978 L1979 **P** *020 †75
TOFFLER, William L. 3181 SW SAM JCKSN PRK RD R, OHSU-FM 97239 #051-04-1976 L1979 **FM FSM** *040 †18
TOLAN, Tod Frederick. 1620 SW TAYLOR ST STE 300, OREGON ANESTHESIOLOGY GROU 97205 #040-02-1975 L1977 **AN** *020 †05 ‡
TOLLE, Susan Willis. 3181 SW SAM JACKSON PRK RD, PK RD 97239 #040-02-1977 L1981 **IM** *040 †20
TOLOSA, Jorge Enrique. 3181 SW SAM JACKSON PRK RD, L-458 97239 #264-04-1982 L2004 **OBG** *020 ‡
TOMITA, Tatsuo. 611 SW CAMPUS DR, DEPT OF INTEGRATIVE BIOS 97239 #572-35-1965 L2005 **PTH** *050 †50
TORRES, Samuel Ernesto. 10123 SE MARKET ST 97216 #005-12-1976 L1980 **AN** *020 †05 ‡
TORRES, Vicente A. ■ 97239 #034-01-2004 L2004 **EM** *100
TORRES-VINCENZI, Alfonso. 2220 NW PETTYGROVE ST 97210 #019-02-1956 L1963 **IM OS** *020
TOWNES, John Manchester. 3181 SW SAM JACKSON PRK RD, L457 OHSU 97239 #023-07-1990 L1995 **ID** *020 †20
TOY, Richard Michael. ■ 97209 #035-45-1998 L1999 **EM** *020 †16
TRAER, Elie Abraham. ■ 97209 #048-12-2006 L2006 **IM** *012
TRAJANO, Nicole Suzanne. 3181 SW SAM JACKSON PRK RD 97239 #016-43-1999 L2000 **FM** *020 †18
TRAN, Vuong Van. 8106 NE WASCO ST 97213 #941-01-1977 L1995 **IM** *020 †20
TRAUTMAN, Paul. 5055 N GREELEY AVE 97217 #021-01-1944 L1955 **GS PDS** *071 †85
TRAUTMAN, Stephanie Alice. ■ 97209 #048-12-2004 L2005 **D** *012
TRAUTMANN, Phillip R. 2521 NW WESTOVER RD 97210 #056-05-1961 L1963 **CHP** *071
TRAYNER, Jennifer Kristi. ■ 97239 #040-02-2008 *012
TRAYNOR, Michael Paul. ■ 97209 #040-02-2000 L2005 **OBG** *100 †30
TREIBLE, Timothy James. 135 NE 102ND AVE 97220 #056-06-1982 L1987 **ORS EM** *020 †40
TRENOUTH, Roland Stewart. ■ 97219 #007-02-1968 L1969 **CD** *071 †20
TROUT, Alechia Marie. ■ 97219 #025-76-1999, ▲ L2007 **PAN** *012
TROXELL, Megan Leigh. 3181 SW SAM JACKSON PRK RD, L471 97239 #005-11-2000 L2004 **PTH** *020 †50
TRUAX, Richard Allan. 10123 SE MARKET ST 97216 #018-03-1961 L1970 **P** *071
TRUBOWITZ, Phoebe Rowand. 3600 N INTERSTATE AVE, KAISER/NW HEMATOLOGY/ONGOL 97227 #024-05-1993 L2000 **HO** *020 †20
TRUEWORTHY, Bryan Robert. 4805 NE GLISAN ST, EMERGENCY DEPARTMENT 97213 #019-02-2001 L2006 **EM** *020
TRUEWORTHY, Robert Chas. ■ 97201 #028-02-1966 L2007 **PHO PD** *071 †55
TRUNKEY, Donald Dean. 3181 SW SAM JACKSON PRK RD, O H S U 97239 #054-04-1963 L1986 **TRS GS** *020 †85
TRUONG, Ngoccam Thi. 6236 NE HALSEY ST 97213 #941-01-1975 L1984 **GP** *020
TRUTT, Simon Michael. ■ 97212 #035-08-1970 L1975 **P** *071 †75

■ = Address Information Privacy Protected

TSAI, James C. 545 NE 47TH AVE, STE 215 97213 #038-40-1996 L2002 **DR** *020 †80
TSAI, Jenny Jien-I. 3181 SW SAM JCKSN PRK RD R, M/C DC7P 97239 #539-06-1998 L2001 **P** *020 †75
TSAI, Nancy Formosa. 10000 SE MAIN ST, STE 200 97216 #016-11-1997 L2007 **IM** *020 †20
TSEN, Andrew Cho. 2222 NW LOVEJOY ST, STE 315 97210 #019-02-1988 L1996 **TS** *020 †85,90
TSENG, Ann G. 4411 SW VERMONT ST, OHSU - GABRIEL PARK CLINIC 97219 #023-01-2003 L2006 **FM** *020 †18
TSENG, Paul Chienchung. 1130 NW 22ND AVE, STE 630 97210 #023-01-1982 L1990 **GO GYN** *020 †30
TSO, Michael Y. 10803 SE CHERRY BLOSSOM DR 97216 #043-01-1994 L1996 **FM** *020 †18
TSUJIMURA, James K. 2222 NW LOVEJOY ST, JAMES K TSUJIMURA MD PC 97210 #040-02-1960 L1962 **OPH** *071 †35
TUCHSCHMIDT, James Arnold. PO BOX 1034, PORTLAND VA MEDICAL CENTER 97207 #028-03-1980 L1981 **CCM PUD** *020 †20
TUFTS, Emily. 3181 SW SAM JACKSON PRK RD 97239 #041-13-1950 L1951 **PD** *040 †55
TUHY, John Edmund. ■ 97201 #040-02-1938 L1949 **PUD** *071
TURNBULL, Isaiah Richard. ■ 97203 #028-02-2008 *012
TURNER, David Avery. 2250 NW FLANDERS ST STE 30 97210 #016-02-1966 L1974 **P PYA** *020 †75
TURNER, Erick Howard. 3710 SW US VETRN HOSP RD, P3MHDC 97239 #040-02-1989 L1990 **P** *020 †75
TURNER, Nicole Renee. ■ 97216 #040-02-2008 *012
TURNER, William Geo, Jr. 2228 NW PETTYGROVE ST, STE 150 97210 #028-02-1969 L1979 **IM PUD** *075 †20
TUSHLA, Sean Patrick. 4805 NE GLISAN ST, STE BG05 97213 #030-06-1996 L2002 **IM** *020 †20
TWEEDT, Kenneth Geo. 1015 NW 22ND AVE, GOOD SAMARITAN HOSPITAL 97210 #016-06-1980 L1981 **GP IM** *020 †20
TYLER, Jeffrey Richard. 10529 NE HALSEY ST 97220 #016-11-1978 L1984 **IMG** *020 †20,55
TYNE, Kari Louise. ■ 97202 #056-05-2002 L2005 **FM** *100 †18
UECKER, Nathaniel Emmett. 2801 N GANTENBEIN AVE, LEGACY 97227 #305-01-2002 L2006 **GS** *012
UEECK, Brett Allen. 611 SW CAMPUS DR, OHSU-DEPT OMS 97239 #040-02-2003 L2004 **GS** *020
UFFERMAN, Aaron Matthew. ■ 97239 #016-43-2007 L2007 **IM** *012
UJIKI, Michael Bryant. ■ 97205 #016-06-2000 L2007 **GS** *100 †85
ULLOTH, Karen Sue. 2222 NW LOVEJOY ST STE 322 97210 #005-12-1982 L1990 **GS** *020 †85
ULMER, Todd Wm. 10101 SE MAIN ST 97216 #005-11-1990 L1997 **ORS** *020 †20,40
UMAPATHY, Krishnamurthy. ■ 97239 #496-32-1996 L2005 **CCM** *020
UMBREIT, Eric Charles. ■ 97239 #040-02-2007 L2007 **GS** *012
UNGERLEIDER, Ross Michael. 3181 SW SAM JCKSN PRK RD R, M/C DC8S 97239 #016-01-1977 L2001 **PCS TS** *020 †85,90
UNITAN, Robert Steven. 3500 N INTERSTATE AVE, KAISER PERMENTENTE 97227 #041-13-1987 L1988 **PUD CCM** *020 †20
UPHOFF, Eugene John. 4805 NE GLISAN ST 97213 #007-02-1968 L1973 **FM** *020 †18
URANKAR, Rakhee Nandakuma. 3181 SW JACKSON PARK RD, OHSU 97201 #495-01-1993 L2000 **GS** *100
URBA, Walter John. 4805 NE GLISAN ST, STE 6N40 97213 #011-02-1981 L1993 **ON** *050 †20
URBACH, Daniel J. 2525 NW LOVEJOY ST, STE 402 97210 #012-05-1989 L1990 **IM** *020 †20
U'REN, Harold Merle. 1015 NW 22ND AVE 97210 #040-02-1935 L1937 **OPH** *071 †35
U'REN, Richard Cameron. 1735 NW IRVING ST 97209 #067-01-1964 L1965 **P IM** *062 †75
URI, Andrew Jos. 10201 SE MAIN ST, STE 11 97216 #041-01-1982 L1992 **PUD IM** *020 †20
URQUHART, Jennifer Lynn. 3181 SW SAM JCKSN PRK RD R, OHSU 97239 #025-07-2003 L2003 **GE** *012 †20
URSIN, Ekhard Karl. 500 NE MULTNOMAH ST STE 10 97232 #154-02-1951 L1961 **IM** *071 †20
USHER, Vernon Howard. 10123 SE MARKET ST 97216 #005-12-1968 L1975 **AN** *020
UY, Olivia Tan. 10123 SE MARKET ST 97216 #748-01-1968 L1976 **PTH DMP** *062 †50
VAGNEROVA, Kamila. 3181 SW SAM JACKSON PARK RD, UH 2 97239 #286-07-1997 L2004 *020
VAJTAI, Petra Lucia. ■ 97219 #035-09-2001 L2002 **PDR** *100 †80
VALE, Elaine Sue. 800 SW 13TH AVE 97205 #016-01-1982 L1987 **FM** *020 †18
VALEN, Jonathan Joseph. 5441 SW MACADAM AVE, STE 102 97239 #021-01-1998 L2000 **P** *020
VALERIO, Donald Anthony. 2400 SW VERMONT ST, FANNO CREEK CLINIC LLC 97219 #035-19-1996 L2002 **IM** *020 †20
VALLABHANATH, Prashanth. 1955 NW NORTHRUP ST, EYEHEALTH NORTHWEST 97209 #025-01-1994 L2000 **OPH** *020 †35
VALLEROY, Marie Lucetta. 1040 NW 22ND AVE, STE 320 97210 #048-13-1979 L1982 **PM** *020 †60 ‡
VALLS, Luis. 4212 NE BROADWAY ST 97213 #011-02-1990 L1991 **IM** *020 †20
VALLS, Luis Antonio. ■ 97239 #275-01-1953 L1966 **IM** *071
VAN, Philbert Yuan. ■ 97239 #041-15-2005 L2005 **GS** *012
VAN BUSKIRK, Edmund M. 1015 NW 22ND AVE 97210 #024-05-1968 L1979 **OPH** *071 †35
VAN DEN BERG, Anton Alber. 3181 SW SAM JCKSN PRK RD R, OHSU 97239 #836-02-1971 L2004 *100
VANDERHOEVEN, Jeroen Pete. ■ 97214 #041-15-2006 L2006 **OBG** *012
VANDERMOLEN, William J. 120 NW 14TH AVE, STE 300 97209 #040-02-1985 L1986 **AN** *020 †05
VANDER WERFF, Laura Marie. 3181 SW SAM JCKSN PRK RD R, SCIENCE UNIV 97239 #030-05-2003 L2003 **CCM** *012 †20
VANDEUSEN, Shawn Kelly. 1122 NE 192ND AVE 97230 #040-02-1999 L2003 **EM** *020 †16
VANDE ZANDSCHULP, Corey J. 501 N GRAHAM ST, STE 250 97227 #010-02-2000 L2000 **ORS** *020
VANEK, Chaim. 3181 SW SAM JCKSN PRK RD R, M/S L607 97239 #040-02-1999 L2003 **END** *100 †20
VANGELISTI, Garrett R. 1040 NW 22ND AVE, STE 610 97210 #001-02-1999 L1999 **PS** *012 †85
VANHO, Anthony. 265 N BROADWAY ST 97227 #049-01-1996 L2002 **HO** *020 †20
VAN HOUTEN, Laura Elizabe. ■ 97239 #040-02-2005 L2005 **OBG** *012
VAN KLEEK, Cecil Albert. ■ 97219 #040-02-1959 **OS** *075
VANN, Robert Eldred. 500 NE MULTNOMAH STE 10 97232 #016-06-1961 L1968 **DR** *071
VANSANT, Janine Tracy. ■ 97239 #040-02-2008 *012
VAN SCOY, H Virginia. ■ 97219 #007-02-1956 L1960 **P IM** *071
VARDANEGA, Lorelie Anne. 2801 N GANTENBEIN AVE, LEGACY EMANUEL HOSPITAL/EM 97227 #040-02-1995 L1999 **EM** *020 †16
VARGHESE, Simmy. ■ 97202 #043-01-2006 L2006 **IM** *012
VAUGHN, Janice Marie. 120 NW 14TH AVE, STE 300 97209 #054-04-1978 L1981 **AN** *020 †05 ‡
VEA, Henry Walter. 1015 NW 22ND AVE, LEGACY GOOD SAM HOSP RADIO 97210 #054-04-1980 L1985 **DR NM** *020 †20,28,80
VEGAS, Carl David. ■ 97219 #011-02-2005 L2005 **DR** *012

VELAMOOR, Gautam Rangaraj. ■ 97239 #054-04-2000 L2005 **TS** *020 †85
VEMULAKONDA, Gurunadh A. 3181 SW SAM JCKSN PRK RD R, OHSU - CASEY EYE INSTITUTE 97239 #028-02-2002 L2006 **OPH** *020
VENIGALLA, Sridevi. 3181 SW SAM JACKSON PRK RD 97239 #496-24-2001 L2002 **NPM** *012
VENTRES, William Brainerd. 12710 SE DIVISION ST, MID-COUNTY HEALTH CENTER 97236 #026-04-1984 L1996 **FM** *020 †18
VERSCHUEREN, David Shane. ■ 97209 #040-02-2007 **GS** *012
VERZOSA, Frances Ventura. 10535 NE GLISAN ST STE 100, 10535 NE GLISAN STREET 97220 #748-01-1972 L1982 **GP PTH** *020
VESTERGAARD, Anne Friis. 4212 NE BROADWAY ST 97213 #040-02-1995 L1997 **PD** *020 †55
VETTO, Anne Amelia. 97201 #040-02-1984 L1987 **RHU IM** *020 †20
VETTO, John Tyson. 3181 SW SAM JACKSON PRK RD, PARK RD 97239 #040-02-1982 L1991 **GS** *020 †85
VIGELAND, Theodore John. 3181 SW SAM JACKSON PRK RD, PARK RD 97239 #040-02-1968 L1969 **ORS** *020 †40
VIGIL, Kimberly L. 7705 SE DIVISION ST 97206 #048-13-1995 L1999 **PD** *020 †55
VIGRAN, Richard Ira. 545 NE 47TH AVE, STE 215 97213 #005-15-1981 L1987 **DR** *020 †80
VILLEGAS, Lydia Antonieta. 5050 NE HOYT ST STE 240, CASCADE FAM MED 97213 #031-01-1992 L1993 **FM** *020 †18
VINES, Jennifer Lee. 3181 SW SAM JACKSON PRK RD, OHSU DEPT OF FAMILY MEDICI 97239 #043-01-2002 L2002 **FM** *100 †18,70
VINING, Ella Rutledge. 19500 SE STARK ST, KAISER PERMANENTE ROCKWOOD 97233 #041-01-2001 L2001 **IM** *100
VINIS, Lawrence Howard. 120 NW 14TH AVE, STE 300 97209 #021-01-1973 L1991 **AN GP** *020 †05
VINOCUR, Marcela Judith. 1821 SE ANKENY ST, PORTLAND HLTH & WELLNESS 97214 #017-20-1989 L1990 **P** *020
VISSERS, Robert John. 2801 N GANTENBEIN AVE, EMANUEL HOSP DEPT EMGY MED 97227 #065-06-1990 L2004 **EM** *020 †16
VITELLS, Aharon. 2701 NW OVERTON ST 97210 #550-01-1980 L1996 **EM** *020 †16
VOELKER, Courtney C. ■ 97239 #043-01-2007 L2007 **OTO** *012
VOLCHOK, Sabine. ■ 97202 #040-02-2008 *012
VOLKOV, David Morris. ■ 97201 #005-12-2005 L2006 **AN** *012
VOOKLES, Jennifer Frances. 3181 SW SAM JACKSON PRK RD, UH 2 97239 #054-04-1995 L1999 **APM** *020 †05
VORE, John Victor. 8250 N LOMBARD ST 97203 #017-20-1959 **FM** *071 †18
VORPAHL, Jessica Lynn. 3181 SW SAM JCKSN PRK RD R, MAIL CODE CB669 97239 #056-05-2004 L2004 **FM** *020 †18
VOTH, Irvin Geo. 97212 #035-45-1944 **IM** *071 †20
VOVES, Arley L. 120 NW 14TH AVE, STE 300 97209 #040-02-2002 L2003 **AN** *100 †05 ‡
VRIESMAN, Paul. ■ 97230 #660-03-1963 L1978 **FM** *071
WACHSMUTH, Benjamin Danie. ■ 97206 #028-03-2004 L2004 **FM** *020 †18
WADDELL, Bronwyn Meredith. ■ 97214 #040-02-2005 L2006 **PD** *012
WADDICK, Michael Anthony. 4104 SE 82ND AVE, STE 250 97266 #056-05-1998 L2006 **FM** *020 †18
WADE, Fredrick David. 4805 NE GLISAN ST 97213 #040-02-1963 L1964 **ORS** *071 †40
WADE, Mel Dean. 800 SW 13TH AVE 97205 #040-02-1982 L1986 **AN** *020 †05 ‡
WAGAR, David Antony. 3181 SW SAM JCKSN PRK RD R 97239 #040-02-1998 L2007 **OBG** *020 †30
WAGNER, Barbara Elaine. 10123 SE MARKET ST 97216 #041-13-1972 L1973 **EM** *020 †16
WAGNER, David G. ■ 97217 #017-20-1951 L1951 **AN** *071
WAGNER, David Gerben. 3181 SW SAM JACKSON PRK RD #R, MAIL CODE: SM 97239 #040-02-1967 L1968 **FM** *020 †18 ‡
WAGNER, Mark Bastian. 5050 NE HOYT ST, STE 318 97213 #041-13-2001 L2001 **ORS** *100
WAGNER, Mary Kathryn. 1130 NW 22ND AVE, STE 320 97210 #048-02-1984 L1986 **PD** *020 †55
WAGNER, Matthew Dale. ■ 97214 #040-02-2002 L2002 **GS** *100
WAGNER, Tamara Lee. 3181 SW SAM JACKSON PRK RD 97239 #021-01-2003 L2003 **PD** *100 †55
WAHBA, Ihab Michel. 3314 SW US VETRN HOSP RD, DIV OF NEPHROLOGY PP262 97239 #915-02-1991 L1997 **NEP** *020 †20
WAHLE, Mark John. 4805 NE GLISAN ST, PPMC ATTN EMERGENCY DEPT 97213 #005-19-1993 L2001 **EM** *020 †16
WAHTO, Lorinda C. 3181 SW SAM JACKSON PRK RD, MAIL STOP UHS 2 97239 #005-12-1994 L2005 **AN** *020 †05 ‡
WALDMAN, James Roger. 10819 SE STARK ST, STE 200 97216 #005-02-1970 L1976 **OPH** *020 †35
WALDRAM, Joseph Patrick. 3710 SW US VETRNS HSPTL RD, PORTLAND VA MEDICAL CTR EM 97239 #040-02-1981 L1990 **EM** *020 †16
WALKER, Dean Stanton. 2801 N GANTENBEIN AVE 97227 #005-18-1991 L1996 **AN** *020 †05 ‡
WALKER, Roger D. 3181 SW SAM JACKSON PRK RD R, OHSU GAINES HALL, 156 97239 #039-01-1972 L1997 **P** *020 †75
WALL, Danielle Dell. ■ 97206 #005-19-2003 L2003 **PCC** *012 †20
WALL, Michael. 2241 LLOYD CTR 97232 #036-01-1973 L1978 **NP** *040 †55
WALL, Wendy Susan. 3181 SW SAM JACKSON PRK RD, DEPT NEUROLOGY L226 97239 #065-05-1985 L1991 **P** *020 †75
WALLACE, James Michael, Jr. ■ 97239 #040-02-2008 *012
WALLEN, Linda Diane. 707 SW GAINES ST, OREGON HLTH SCIENCES UNIV 97239 #035-47-1979 L1994 **NPM PD** *012 †55
WALTA, Douglas Craig. 1111 NE 99TH AVE 97220 #026-04-1968 L1976 **GE IM** *020 †20
WALTERS, Lee. 545 NE 47TH AVE, STE 106 97213 #041-01-1977 L2004 **OS IM** *050 †20
WALWORTH, Jill Terece. 4805 NE GLISAN ST, RM BH16 97213 #026-04-1997 L1999 **IM** *020 †20
WANDEL, Hans-Guenter. 2241 LLOYD CTR 97232 #407-33-1956 L1962 **DR** *020 †80
WANG, Amy. ■ 97239 #016-11-2002 L2005 **GE** *012 †20
WANG, Anne Hsiaoyuen. 1111 NE 99TH AVE 97220 #040-02-1987 L1997 **GE IM** *020 †20
WANG, James Yu. 120 NW 14TH AVE, STE 300 97209 #243-46-1985 L2000 **AN** *020 †05 ‡
WANG, Jian-Sheng. 2801 N GANTENBEIN AVE 97227 #243-64-1982 L1998 **AN** *020 †05 ‡
WANG, May Sing. 1056 SW GAINES ST 97239 #011-02-2001 L2001 **FM** *020 †18
WANG, Paul Yung-Kai. 2241 LLOYD CTR 97232 #065-01-1984 L2001 **DR** *020 †80
WANG, Pei-Li. 3181 SW SAM JCKSN PRK #R, OHSU 97239 #016-11-1999 L1999 **NEP** *100 †20
WANG, Samuel James. 3181 SW SAM JCKSN PRK RD R, M/C: L337 97239 #005-11-1996 L2006 **RO** *012 †20
WANG, Tom D. 2241 LLOYD CTR 97232 #016-06-1981 L1986 **FPS** *020 †45
WANG, Warren York. 500 NE MULTNOMAH ST, STE 100 97232 #067-01-1994 L2000 **AN** *020 †05
WANLASS, Wendy Ann. VETERANS HOSP RD, 3710 SOUTHWEST US 97207 #051-01-1977 L1981 **IMG IM** *040 †20

WANTOCH, Peter John. 10300 NE HANCOCK ST 97220 #067-01-1969 L1978 **DR** *020

WARD, Abner Michael. ■ 97209 #036-01-2002 L2007 **ORS** *012

WARD, Thomas Towey. 3181 SW SAM JACKSON PRK RD 97239 #054-04-1971 L1987 **IM** *020 †20

WARD, William Arthur. 7705 SE DIVISION ST, DIVISION CLINIC 97206 #040-02-1977 L1981 **IM** *020 †20

WARD, William Joseph. 3181 SW SAM JACKSON PRK RD, OREGON HLTH & SCI UNIV 97239 #016-02-2005 L2005 **IM** *012

WARD, William Kenneth. 1130 NW 22ND AVE STE 400 97210 #007-02-1978 L1986 **DIA IM** *020 †20

WARDA, Robert Francis. 10000 SE MAIN ST, STE 302 97216 #005-12-1998 L2001 **FM** *020 †18

WARDEN, Craig Robt. 3181 SW SAM JACKSON PRK RD, CDWM 97239 #007-02-1988 L1989 **PD EM** *020 †55,16

WARE, Mary Ann. 426 SW STARK ST, 3RD FL 97204 #049-01-1977 L1982 **IM** *020 †20

WARNE, Clinton Lee. 120 NW 14TH AVE STE 300, OREGON ANESTHESIOLOGY GROU 97209 #035-19-1986 L2001 **IM** *020 †20,05

WARNOCK, Robert H, Jr. ■ 97232 #036-01-1980 L2006 **GYN** *020 †30

WARREN, Johanna Beth. 4411 SW VERMONT ST 97219 #016-06-2003 L2003 **FM** *100 †18

WARRINGTON, Thomas Patric. ■ 97239 #026-08-2006 L2006 **FP** *012

WASHTOK, Christopher P. 120 NW 14TH AVE, STE 300 97209 #030-06-2002 L2003 **AN** *100 †05 ‡

WASTON, Wendy Irene. 500 NE MULTNOMAH ST STE 10 97232 #040-02-1980 L1981 **IM** *020 †20

WATASE, Taketo. 3181 SW SAM JACKSON PRK RD 97239 #572-58-2003 L2007 **EM** *012

WATERMAN, Kimberley Robt. 2023 NW KEARNEY ST 97209 #061-01-1979 *100

WATKINS, Angela Nicole. 5050 NE HOYT ST STE 540, MEDICAL CE 97213 #040-02-2006 L2006 **OPH** *012

WATKINS, Robert Camp. 3550 N INTERSTATE AVE 97227 #040-02-1978 L1979 **P EM** *075 †75

WATNICK, Suzanne Gwen. 2241 LLOYD CTR 97232 #024-16-1995 L2002 **NEP** *020 †20

WATT, David Geo. 500 NE MULTNOMAH ST, 15TH FL 97232 #014-01-1982 L1992 **AN** *020 †05

WATT, Jonathan Vincent. 10123 SE MARKET ST 97216 #005-12-1973 L1974 **OBG** *020

WATTERS, Jennifer Marie. 3181 SW SAM JCKSN PRK #R, OHSU 97239 #048-12-2000 L2000 **GS** *100 †85

WATZKE, Robert C. 3303 SW BOND AVE, FL 11 97239 #056-05-1952 L1984 **OPH** *071 †35

WAWRUKIEWICZ, Anthony S. 500 NE MULTNOMAH ST, STE 100 97232 #020-02-1979 L1980 **DR** *020 †80

WAX, Mark Kenneth. 2241 LLOYD CTR 97232 #065-01-1980 L1998 **OTO** *020 †45

WAYSON, Kim Alan. 5050 NE HOYT ST, STE 418 97213 #040-02-1978 L1982 **NS** *020 †25

WEAVER, Alice Elaine. 19500 SE STARK ST 97233 #040-02-1990 L1991 **OBG** *020 †30

WEAVER, Scott Alan. 3500 N INTERSTATE AVE, RADIO DEPT INTERSTATE MED 97227 #041-14-1984 L1992 **DR** *020 †80

WEBER, Emily Kathleen. ■ 97239 #041-12-2008 *012

WEBER, Larry Alan. 120 NW 14TH AVE, STE 300 97209 #040-02-1976 L1977 **AN** *020 †05 ‡

WEBSTER, Devon Jean. 3303 SW BOND AVE CH14R, OHSU -HEMATOLOGY/ONCOLOGY 97239 #005-11-1999 L2000 **HEM** *100 †20

WEBSTER, Kim Barclay. 2525 NW LOVEJOY ST, STE 408 97210 #031-01-1982 L1987 **FM** *020 †18

WECHTER, Mary Ellen. ■ 97219 #026-08-2000 L2007 **GYN OBG** *020 †30 ‡

WEE, Tienahn. 233 NE 102ND AVE, EPIC IMAGING 97230 #035-01-1996 L2006 **DR** *020 †80

WEEKS, Ann E Anthony. 2250 NW FLANDERS ST # 301 97210 #012-05-1975 L1976 **PYA** *020 †18

WEEKS, Douglas Alan. 2241 LLOYD CTR 97232 #005-12-1974 L1981 **PTH** *020 †50

WEHBY, Monica. 5050 NE HOYT, STE 418 97213 #048-04-1988 L1997 **NS** *020 †25

WEI, Kevin Stephen. 3181 SW SAM JACKSON PRK RD, OR HLTH & SCI UNIV 97239 #065-01-1989 L2005 **CD** *020 †20

WEI, Wei. 3181 SW SAM JCKSN PRK RD R, OHSU 97239 #243-52-1992 L2005 **GS** *012

WEICK, Walter Joe. ■ 97202 #040-02-1967 L1990 **MFM OBG** *071 †30

WEILL, Beau Christopher. 3181 SW SAM JCKSN PRK RD R, MAIL CODE CDRCP 97239 #035-03-2003 L2003 **PD** *100 †55

WEINSOFT, Anne Michelle. ■ 97214 #040-02-2007 L2007 **IM** *012

WEINSTEIN, Jason Samuel. ■ 97215 #007-02-2003 L2003 **NS** *012

WEINSTEIN, Marvin Jerome. ■ 97209 #040-02-1955 L1957 **IM LM** *071 †20

WEINSTEIN, Mayer Howard. 1220 SW MORRISON ST STE 52 97205 #024-07-1967 L1974 **P** *020 †75

WEINSTEIN, Ralph Elliott. 265 N BROADWAY ST, NORTHWEST CANCER SPECIALIS 97227 #035-15-1982 L1990 **ON HEM** *020 †20

WEINTRAUB, Ira Michael. 1515 NW 18TH AVE, STE 300 97209 #017-20-1976 L1981 **ORS** *020 †40

WEIS, Patrick Denis. 3181 SW SAM JCKSN PRK RD R, SCIENCE UNIV 97239 #033-02-2012 L2006 **PCC** *020 ‡

WEISBERG, Stuart Gordon. 1971 NW OVERTON ST, STUART WEISBERG MD LLC 97209 #056-06-2000 L2000 **P ADP** *020

WEISS, Joseph Benj. 2241 LLOYD CTR 97232 #035-19-1988 L2002 **IM** *020 †20

WEISSERT, Wesley R. ■ 97232 #040-02-1945 L1947 **P** *071

WEISSKIRK, Margaret A. ■ 97239 #040-02-2008 *012

WEISSMAN, Jane Lisa. 3181 SW SAM JCKSN PRK RD R, OHSU M/C CR-135 97239 #035-01-1983 L1999 **DR** *020 †80

WEKSLER, Nicole Barron. ■ 97211 #040-02-2005 L2006 **IM** *012

WELBORN, Jody M. 1111 NE 99TH AVE, THE OREGON CLINIC, P.C. 97220 #040-02-1984 L1992 **CD IM** *020 †20

WELCH, Thomas Patrick. 2408 SE 16TH AVE 97214 #054-04-1991 L1992 **P PFP** *020 †75 ‡

WELDON, Heather Emily. 5050 NE HOYT, STE 255 97213 #017-20-1996 L1999 **OBG** *020 †30

WELEBER, Richard Gordon. 3303 SW BOND AVE, FL 11 97239 #040-02-1967 L1972 **OPH** *020 †35,19

WELKE, Karl Frederick. 3181 SW SAM JCKSN PRK RD R, M/S L353 97239 #016-11-1994 L2004 **TS** *020 †85,90

WELLER, Kirk Land. 501 N GRAHAM ST STE 515 97227 #054-04-1990 L1991 **N** *020 †75

WELLS, Clay Norris. 3439 NE SANDY BLVD # 330 97232 #021-05-1946 L1946 **OBG PHP** *072

WELLS, Elmer Robert. 10101 SE MAIN ST STE 3008 97216 #005-12-1962 L1973 **ORS HS** *040 †40

WELLS, Robert Lee. 5050 NE HOYT ST, STE 240 97213 #040-02-1979 L1982 **FM** *020 †18

WELLS, Ronald Scott. ■ 97239 #047-05-2000 L2005 **PDC** *012 †55 ‡

WENGER, David Joel. ■ 97221 #040-40-1978 L1981 **IM** *020,16

WERNER, John Scott. ■ 97212 #038-41-1978 L1978 **PD** *020 †55

WERNICK, Richard. 5050 NE HOYT ST, PROVIDENCE ARTHRITIS 97213 #010-02-1973 L1981 **RHU IM** *062 †20

WERTHEIM, Michael Sean. ■ 97212 #836-02-1998 L2003 *020

WESENBERG, Karen Joan. 1111 NE 99TH AVE 97220 #040-02-1996 L1999 **PCC** *020 †20

WEST, Patrick Leight. 3181 SW SAM JCKSN PRK RD R, OREGON POISON CENTER 97239 #051-01-2004 L2004 **EM** *020

WEST, Ulla Christina. 3600 N INTERSTATE AVE 97227 #005-06-1971 L1980 **OPH** *071 †35

WESTBROOK, Gary Lee. 3181 SW SAM JACKSON PRK RD, MAIL CODE L474 97239 #038-06-1976 L1987 **N IM** *050 †20

WESTERBERG, Harry. ■ 97217 #040-02-1943 L1947 **GS TS** *071

WESTERMEYER, Richard J. 800 SW 13TH AVE 97205 #005-12-1983 L1987 **AN** *020 †05 ‡

WHEELER, David Timothy. 3303 SW BOND AVE, FL 11 97239 #005-18-1988 L1997 **OPH** *020 †20

WHEELER, Justin Daniel. ■ 97217 #043-01-2005 L2005 **FP** *012

WHEELER, Nicole Marie. ■ 97239 #038-40-2003 L2003 **GS** *100

WHELER, Glynne Henry T. 3181 SW SAM JCKSN PRK RD R, UHN 80 97239 #143-02-1966 L1990 **P** *020 †55,75

WHITE, Charles Thayer. ■ 97219 #036-01-2007 L2007 **FP** *012

WHITE, Clifton Robt, Jr. 3303 SW BOND AVE, DEPT- DERMATOLOGY CH5-D 97239 #005-14-1971 L1975 **D DMP** *020 †15

WHITE, Jocelyn Cameron. 1025 NW 22ND AVE R200 97210 #035-19-1987 L1988 **PLM** *020 †20

WHITE, Keith Allen. 2241 LLOYD CTR 97232 #040-02-1976 L1977 **FM EM** *020 †18

WHITE, Kevin Patrick. ■ 97202 #041-02-2002 L2003 **DMP** *012 †15

WHITE, Sandra Linne. ■ 97239 #005-12-2004 L2004 **PTH** *012

WHITEFORD, Mark H. 1040 NW 22ND AVE, STE 560 97210 #023-01-1991 L1999 **CRS** *020 †85,10

WHITHAM, Ruth Hilary. 3181 SW SAM JACKSON PRK RD, OHSU USH42 97239 #016-02-1978 L1979 **N** *030 †20,75

WHITING, James. PORTLAND VA MED CTR, DEPT RAD 114P 97207 #067-01-1964 L1969 **DR** *020 †80

WHITLOCK, Evelyn Patricia. 3800 N INTERSTATE AVE 97227 #017-20-1979 L1981 **GPM PHP** *050 †70

WHITLOCK, Matthew Charles. ■ 97206 #036-01-2005 L2005 **IM** *012

WHITNEY, Diane F. 1220 SW MORRISON ST, STE 525 97205 #060-02-1976 L1977 **P** *020

WICHIENKUER, Promporn Pau. ■ 97239 #040-02-2007 L2007 **IM** *012

WIEBE, Alton Enoch. 6445 N GREELEY AVE 97217 #040-02-1957 L1958 **FM** *071 †18

WIENS, Donald Avery. 1015 NW 22ND AVE, EMERGENCY DEPT 97210 #040-02-1983 L1984 **EM** *020 †16

WIESNER, Don Robt. ■ 97220 #010-01-1975 L1976 **P** *071 †75

WILBORN, Sandra Lee. 1130 NW 22ND AVE, NORTHWEST 97210 #031-01-1981 L1989 **GE IM** *020 †20

WILCOX, Carl Roger. 12774 SE STARK ST 97233 #649-14-1974 L1978 **FM** *071

WILCOX, Ruth Ellen. 10000 SE MAIN ST, STE 302 97216 #649-14-1974 L1979 **FM** *020

WILDER, Mary Helen. 5511 SE HAWTHORNE BLVD, WESTERN SEMINARY 97215 #040-02-1963 L1967 **OBG FM** *071

WILDES, Julia Woodruff. 2241 LLOYD CTR 97232 #024-05-1975 L1992 **PTH** *020 †50

WILDIN, Robert Sean. 3181 SW SAM JACKSON PRK RD, OHSU L-103 97239 #005-02-1985 L1997 **PD MG** *020 †55,19

WILKINS, Marguerite Davis. 3710 SW US VETRNS HSPTL RD, P3-MED 97239 #054-04-2002 L2007 **IM** *020 †20

WILL, Erin Marianne. ■ 97201 #045-04-2007 L2007 **P** *012

WILLET, Michael Bradley. 5228 NE HOYT ST BLDG B 97213 #003-01-1988 L1992 **P PYG** *020 †75

WILLIAMS, Alexis Ann. ■ 97212 #010-01-2005 L2008 **FP** *012

WILLIAMS, Christopher P S. 2241 LLOYD CTR 97232 #040-02-1958 L1968 **OS PD** *071 †55

WILLIAMS, Danielle Christ. 3601 SW RIVER PKWY, STE 812 97239 #050-02-2008 *012

WILLIAMS, Jennifer Fogle. 120 NW 14TH AVE, STE 300 97209 #012-05-2001 L2003 **OBG** *020 †30

WILLIAMS, Jonathan Snow. ■ 97239 #040-02-2008 *012

WILLIAMS, Kalaiselvi. ■ 97202 #043-01-2000 L2002 **GPM** *100 †70

WILLIAMS, Lara Jeannette. 501 N GRAHAM ST, STE 445 97227 #048-16-2000 L2004 **OBG** *020 †30

WILLIAMS, M Lanier A. ■ 97211 #035-01-1963 L1967 **PD OS** *071 †55

WILLIAMS, Paul C. 3181 SW SAM JACKSON PRK RD, # L 97239 #004-01-1969 L1991 **NS** *020 †25

WILLIAMS, Sandra Shizue. 545 NE 47TH AVE, STE 106 97213 #014-01-1984 L1986 **IM** *020 †20

WILLIAMS, William Paul. ■ 97219 #028-78-1940, ▲ L1941 **LM FM** *071

WILLIS, Brian Richard. 3500 N INTERSTATE AVE, KAISER PERMANENTE GI DEPT 97227 #016-11-1985 L1986 **GE IM** *020 †20

WILPER, Andrew Peter. 3181 SW SAM JACKSON PRK RD, PARK ROAD 97239 #054-04-2003 L2003 **IM** *100 †20

WILSON, Brittany Anne. ■ 97239 #040-02-2004 L2004 **D** *012

WILSON, Courtney Laurel. ■ 97239 #040-02-2008 *012

WILSON, David Franklin. 911 NW 18TH AVE 97209 #018-03-1963 L1970 **NO OTO** *020 †45

WILSON, David Jean. 3303 SW BOND AVE, FL 11 97239 #048-04-1981 L1982 **OPH** *030 †35

WILSON, Elisa Anne. ■ 97239 #005-12-2004 L2006 **FP** *012

WILSON, Frank Rupp. ■ 97209 #005-02-1967 L1968 **N** *020 †75

WILSON, Michael Eugene. ■ 97239 #040-02-2008 *012

WILSON, Reed Calhoun. 2525 NW LOVEJOY ST, STE 400 97210 #021-01-1969 L1975 **N** *020 †20,75

WILSON, Robert Darryl. 120 NW 14TH AVE STE 300, OREGON ANESTHESIOLOGY GROU 97209 #005-12-1974 L1977 **AN** *020 †05 ‡

WILSON, William H. 3181 SW SAM JCKSN PRK RD R, MAIL CODE UHN-79 97239 #041-01-1981 L1989 **P** *040 †75 ‡

WILSON, William Slate. 3181 SW SAM JACKSON PRK RD, PARK ROAD 97239 #040-02-1964 L1972 **GS VS** *020 †85

WINCHESTER, David Kevin. 10000 SE MAIN ST STE 404 97216 #040-02-1983 L1984 **U** *020 †95

WINCHESTER, Karen. 200 SW MARKET ST 97201 #041-01-1989 L1998 **OPH** *020 †35

WINKLER, Carey Lynn. 4016 NE 9TH AVE 97212 #040-02-1984 L1986 **MFM OBG** *020 †30

WINTER, Elizabeth Lyn. 2801 N GANTENBEIN AVE 97227 #048-04-1996 L1999 **IM** *020 †20

WINTER, William Edward. 265 N BROADWAY ST, NORTHWEST CANCER SPECIALIS 97227 #051-01-1996 L1999 **OBG** *020 †30

WINTERBERG, Pamela Dietz. ■ 97239 #023-01-2006 L2006 **PD** *012

WINTERBOTTOM, Lisa M. 3710 SW US VETRNS HSPTL RD, P-3 MED 97239 #043-01-1992 L1993 **IM** *020 †20

WINTERS, Nancy Claire. 2241 LLOYD CTR 97232 #035-46-1983 L1987 **CHP P** *020 †75

WINTHROP, Kevin Loring. 3181 SW SAM JACKSON PRK RD, ROAD, CEI 97239 #040-02-1998 L2004 **IM** *100 †20

WIRTH, Norman Valentine. ■ 97239 #030-06-1959 L1962 **OPH** *071 †35
WISE, Cathryn Lee. 703 NE HANCOCK ST, DSI 97212 #005-18-1983 L1984 **NEP IM** *020 †20
WISE, Todd Vance. 10000 SE MAIN ST, STE 207 97216 #047-05-1996 L1999 **IM** *020 †20
WITT, Albert Carl. ■ 97219 #040-02-1958 L1972 **EM GP** *071
WITTEMYER, Melaura. 3181 SW SAM JCKSN PRK RD R 97239 #040-02-1996 L2002 **IM** *020 †20
WITTERT, Gary A. 3181 SW SAM JCKSN PRK #R 97239 #836-01-1983 **END** *100
WITTWER, Erica Danelle. ■ 97230 #049-01-2007 L2007 **TY** *012
WOBIG, John Lee. 3181 SW SAM JACKSON PRK RD 97239 #040-02-1964 L1967 **OPH** *071 †35
WOFFORD, Tara Lauren. ■ 97239 #040-02-2008 L2007 **
WOLF, Ariane Ingrid. 3660 SE 20TH AVE 97202 #035-45-1994 L1997 **FM** *020 †18
WOLF, Solomon. 3181 SW SAM JCKSN PRK RD R 97239 #913-15-1987 L1995 **P** *020 †75
WOLFE, Bruce Mc Laren. 3181 SW SAM JACKSON PRK RD, BTE223 97239 #028-34-1967 L2006 **GS NTR** *020 †85
WOLFE, Gordon F. 8250 N LOMBARD ST 97203 #016-11-1945 L1949 **GP A** *071 †18
WOLFE, Jeffry Kirby. 120 NW 14TH AVE, STE 300 97209 #040-02-1980 L1981 **AN** *020 †05 ‡
WOLFE, Kirk Dana. 1818 SE DIVISION ST 97202 #028-34-1986 L1993 **CHP P** *020 †75
WOLFE, Marika Deena. ■ 97211 #040-02-2008 *012
WOLFE, Valerie Anne. 5050 NE HOYT ST STE 240 97213 #054-04-1993 L1994 **FM** *020 †18
WOLFENSON, Elena H. 5254 N EMERSON DR 97217 #649-01-1968 L1992 **P CHP** *075 †75
WOLFER, Viktoriya Drofyak. ■ 97239 #040-02-2008 *012
WOLFF, Lawrence Jos. 2241 LLOYD CTR 97232 #028-03-1964 L1968 **PHO PD** *020 †55
WOLFSON, Deborah Ruth. 545 NE 47TH AVE, STE 325 97213 #905-02-2001 L2001 **IM** *020
WONG, Brian. 3181 SW SAM JCKSN PRK RD R, M/C NRC-3 97239 #035-08-1974 L2006 **ID IM** *020 †20
WONG, Brian Kinyun. ■ 97239 #014-01-2002 L2002 **GS** *012
WONG, Dexter Munming. ■ 97239 #024-05-2005 L2007 **IM** *012
WONG, Franklin S. 700 NE MULTNOMAH ST, STE 460 97232 #014-01-1977 L1980 **PM** *030 †60
WONG, Jamie Ryan. ■ 97239 #040-02-2003 L2004 **DR** *012
WONG, Joseph Ping Cheung. 120 NW 14TH AVE STE 300, OREGON ANESTHESIOLOGY GROU 97209 #462-02-1988 L1998 **AN** *020 †05 ‡
WONG, Sharon Elizabeth. 10000 SE MAIN ST, STE 110 97216 #005-12-1989 L1993 **OBG** *020 †30
WONG, Victor Waidor. ■ 97239 #024-05-2005 L2005 **GS** *012
WONG, Wayne. 3500 N INTERSTATE AVE, KAISER INTERSTATE MEDICAL 97227 #040-02-1987 L1990 **IM** *020 †20
WONNACOTT, Amanda Marie. 5050 NE HOYT ST STE 540, PROVIDENCE PORTLAND 97213 #040-02-2006 L2006 **
WOO, Brian M. 3181 SW SAM JACKSON PRK RD, OR HLTH SCI UNIV SCH OF ME 97239 #040-02-2006 L2006 *012
WOO, See Sim. 2701 NW VAUGHN ST STE 140, KAISER PERMANENTE 97210 #056-05-1985 L1986 **IM** *020 †20
WOO, Winston Howard. 120 NW 14TH AVE, STE 300 97209 #040-02-1996 L2000 **AN** *020 ‡
WOOD, Charles Macdonald. 19500 SE STARK ST, ROCKWOOD CLINIC 97233 #035-01-1981 L1982 **IM** *020 †20
WOOD, Terry Dale. 3375 SW TERWILLIGER BLVD, CASEY EYE INSTITUTE 97239 #036-05-1998 L1999 **OPH** *020 †35
WOOD, Turner Anderson, III. 5050 NE HOYT ST, OREGON HEMATOLOGY 97213 #004-01-1961 L1999 **ON HEM** *020 †20
WOOD, William Jos. 5050 NE HOYT ST, STE 317 97213 #012-05-1980 L1987 **OS** *020 †85
WOODS, Kathryn Anne. 707 SW GAINES ST DEPT PEDI, OHSU 97239 #917-20-1988 L2004 *100
WOODS, Todd D. 10373 NE HANCOCK ST, STE 137 97220 #016-06-1986 L1990 **CN N** *020 †75
WOODWARD, Anthony Harvey. ■ 97219 #917-09-1964 L1997 **ORS** *030 †40
WOODWARD, Daniel J. 3181 SW SAM JACKSON PRK RD, DEPT OF ANESTH BTE-2 97239 #048-13-1998 L2003 **PAN** *020 †05
WOODWORTH, James V. ■ 97230 #040-02-1946 L1950 **IM** *071 †20
WOOLLEY, Charles Todd. 10101 SE MAIN ST, STE 3008 97216 #036-07-1994 L2002 **ORS** *020 †40
WORKMAN, Kimberly Leigh. 501 N GRAHAM ST, STE 250 97227 #005-02-2000 L2005 **ORS** *020
WOROBEY, Alexander Lee. 5319 SW WESTGATE DR, STE 241 97221 #040-02-1972 L1974 **AN** *020 ‡
WORTHINGTON, Richard Lee. 500 NE MULTNOMAH ST STE 10 97232 #040-02-1968 L1974 **GPM PTH** *020 †18
WOSKOW, Lorraine Belinda. 2222 NW LOVEJOY ST STE 505 97210 #005-18-1994 L1996 **IM** *020 †20
WRIGHT, David James. 5819 SE JOHNSON CREEK BLVD 97206 #048-12-1960 L1971 **DR** *020 †80
WRIGHT, Gregory Lyle. 120 NW 14TH AVE, STE 300 97209 #016-11-1973 L1977 **AN** *020 †05 ‡
WRIGHT, Maureen A. 500 NE MULTNOMAH ST # 100, 16TH FL 97232 #040-02-1987 L1988 **IM** *020 †20
WRIGHT, Sharon Leanne. ■ 97202 #035-09-2007 L2007 **GS** *012
WU, David Edward. 2222 NW LOVEJOY ST STE 606 97210 #040-02-1993 L1994 **CD** *020 †20
WU, Hsiao-Chi David. 4920 N INTERSTATE AVE 97217 #003-01-1997 L2006 **FM** *020 †18
WU, Jennifer Ngokeling. ■ 97239 #040-02-2007 L2007 **GS** *012
WU, Joanne. 6327 SE MILWAUKIE AVE 97202 #036-07-2004 L2004 **FM** *100 †18
WU, Vivian Faye. ■ 97219 #010-03-2004 L2004 **OTO** *012
WUTTE, Paula Jane. 120 NW 14TH AVE, STE 300 97209 #038-06-1986 L1996 **AN** *020 †05
WYATT, Solange Marie. 3181 SW SAM JCKSN PRK RD R 97239 #056-05-1997 L2004 **OBG** *020 †30
WYLIE, Linda Sueanna. ■ 97219 #005-12-1995 L1996 **AN** *020 †05
WYMAN, Michael B. 5050 NE HOYT ST, STE 318 97213 #040-02-1983 L1984 **ORS** *020 †40
WYNNE, Thomas Donald. 3620 N INTERSTATE AVE 97227 #035-45-1990 L1995 **RO** *020 †80
WYRICK, Jared James. ■ 97221 #056-06-2005 L2005 **IM** *012
XU, Hongshi. 3181 SW SAM JCKSN PRK RD R, OHSU 97239 #243-58-1987 L2006 **IM** *012
YACKEL, Thomas Roger. 3181 SW SAM JACKSON PRK RD, MAIL CODE L-475 97239 #010-01-1996 L2000 **IM** *030 †20
YADAV, Vijayshree. 3181 SW SAM JACKSON PRK RD, UHS42 97239 #495-12-1994 L1997 **N** *020 †75
YAKIMOVSKY, Yoram. 2801 N GANTENBEIN AVE 97227 #011-02-1978 L1981 **AN GP** *020 †05 ‡
YAMASAKI, Stacy Akashi. 545 NE 47TH AVE STE 215, RAIOLOGY SPECIALIST NW 97213 #035-48-1987 L1988 **DR IM** *020 †80
YAMASHITA, Daisuke. 3181 SW SAM JACKSON PRK RD 97239 #572-41-2000 L2006 **FP** *012
YANASE, Lisa Rietz. 5050 NE HOYT ST, STE 315 97213 #036-01-1994 L2005 **N PM** *020 †75
YANDLE, Molly Moran. 541 NE 20TH AVE, STE 210 97232 #040-02-1996 L1997 **IM** *020 †18
YAO, Lisa Karin. 1111 NE 99TH AVE, THE OREGON CLINIC 97220 #025-07-1998 L2006 **CD** *020 †20,55

YARRIS, Lalena Michelle. 3181 SW SAM JCKSN PRK RD R, MAILCODE CDW-EM 97239 #040-02-2002 L2002 **EM** *100 †16
YASUDA, Naoki. 3181 SW SAM JACKSON PRK RD 97239 #572-35-1970 L1985 **END** *050
YASUI, Homer. ■ 97216 #041-09-1949 **GS** *071 †85
YEAGER, Richard Allan. 2241 LLOYD CTR 97232 #019-02-1971 L1975 **VS GS** *020 †85
YEE, Joyce Anne. ■ 97201 #034-01-2005 L2006 **AN** *012
YEGGY, Julie Elizabeth. 2800 N VANCOUVER AVE # 230 97227 #005-02-1991 L1994 **IM** *040 †20
YEO, Alan Soonsong. 2415 SE 43RD AVE, PLAZA 97206 #040-02-2000 L2000 **P** *020 †75
YERTON, Jeremiah Ezekiel. ■ 97219 #019-02-2007 L2007 **EM** *012
YI, Eun Jung. ■ 97206 #040-02-2007 L2007 **IM** *012
YOKEN, Jonathan. 1955 NW NORTHRUP ST 97209 #028-34-1997 L2001 **OPH** *020 †35
YONKE, Nicole Joy. ■ 97239 #040-02-2007 L2007 **FP** *012
YOO, Jung Uck. 3181 SW SAM JCKSN PRK RD R, M/S OP31 97239 #016-02-1984 L2004 **ORS** *020 †20
YORK, Douglas Graham. ■ 97219 #036-01-2007 L2007 **GS** *012
YORK, Duncan James. 10000 SE MAIN ST, STE 205 97216 #021-06-2003 L2003 **IM** *020 †20
YOSHINAGA, Monica Ann. 2701 NW VAUGHN ST STE 16 97210 #036-07-1976 L1980 **IM** *020 †20
YOUNG, Donald Andrew, III. 5050 NE HOYT ST, STE 514 97213 #025-07-1963 L1964 **U** *020 †95
YOUNG, Jeffrey Scott. 5847 NE 122ND AVE, STE 201 97230 #040-02-1990 L2000 **FM** *020 †18
YOUNG, Jonathan Byron. 120 NW 14TH AVE, #300 OREGON ANESTH GRP PC 97209 #040-02-1984 L1987 **AN** *020 †05 ‡
YOUNG, Kimberly Kristine. ■ 97210 #005-11-2006 L2006 **FP** *012
YOUNG, Lauretta Lee. 3550 N INTERSTATE AVE, INTERSTATE MED EAST KAISER 97227 #040-02-1980 L1981 **P** *020 †75
YOUNG, Neal Hong. ■ 97227 #016-42-2007 L2007 **TY** *012
YOUNG, Robert Chenzong. 3600 N INTERSTATE AVE, EDGAR F KAISER HEALTH CENT 97227 #244-06-1968 L1978 **PM GP** *020 †60
YOUNG, Scott Allen. 3600 N INTERSTATE AVE 97227 #008-01-1975 L1981 **ORS** *020 †40
YOUNGER, Eldon Wilfrid. 3181 SW SAM JCKSN PRK RD R 97239 #040-02-1962 **PD** *071 †55
YU, Aaron Tsau-Yuen. ■ 97209 #024-05-1997 L2005 **DR** *012 †18
YU, Jessica Anne. ■ 97239 #040-02-2008 L2008 *012
YU, Kelvin Chiu. 5050 NE HOYT ST STE 610, PROVIDENCE PROFESSIONAL PL 97213 #005-02-1990 L1997 **GS** *020 †85
YU, Lijuan. 7705 SE DIVISION ST, DIVISION MED 97206 #243-63-1983 L2005 **PD** *020 †55
YURLOV, Vladislav Vladimi. 3181 SW SAM JCKSN PRK RD R, L223 97239 #913-85-1996 L2007 **GS** *012
YUTAN, Paul Uy. 5050 NE HOYT ST, STE 454 97213 #422-01-1997 L2002 **IM** *020 †20
ZACHAREK, Preeti Malani. ■ 97239 #025-07-1995 L2003 **IMG** *020 †20
ZALD, Philip Benjamin. ■ 97239 #025-01-2005 L2005 **OTO** *012
ZALLEN, Garret Seth. 501 N GRAHAM ST, PEDIATRIC SURGERY 97227 #007-02-1994 L2004 **PDS** *020 †85
ZAMAN, Atif. 3181 SW SAM JACKSON PRK RD 97239 #024-07-1991 L1994 **GE** *020 †20
ZANONE, Beata Maria. 2801 N GANTENBEIN AVE 97227 #759-04-1989 L1999 **AN** *020 †05 ‡
ZARLING, Craig Frederic. 2386 NW HOYT ST 97210 #056-05-1985 L1990 **P IM** *020 †75
ZARLING, Suzanne Sawicki. 3500 N INTERSTATE AVE 97227 #056-05-1985 L1990 **AN** *020 †05
ZAUGRA, Christopher John. 4805 NE GLISAN ST, STE BG05 97213 #025-07-1996 L1999 **IM** *020 †20
ZAVANELLI-MORGAN, Barbara. 1015 NW 22ND AVE 97210 #041-02-1979 L1980 **END** *072 †20
ZBINDEN, Arthur Francis. 2228 NW PETTYGROVE ST, OREGON SLEEP ASSOCIATES 97210 #040-02-1967 L1969 **PUD IM** *020 †20
ZEGZULA, Henry Danl, Jr. 1015 NW 22ND AVE 97210 #028-34-1991 L1992 **PS** *020 †65
ZEIGLER, Timothy David. 6312 SW CAPITOL HWY # 502 97239 #041-01-1995 L1998 **EM** *020 †16
ZELKO, John Robt. 501 N GRAHAM ST, STE 580 97227 #014-01-1978 L1983 **GS** *020 †85
ZELLER, Katharine Margret. 1130 NW 22ND AVE, STE 220 97210 #040-02-1985 L1986 **IM** *020 †20
ZELLER, Werner Emanuel. ■ 97220 #040-02-1937 L1938 **GP** *071 †85
ZENEL, Jos Alexander, Jr. 707 SW GAINES ST, STE CDRCP 97239 #010-02-1980 L1996 **PD** *020 †55
ZERBE, Kathryn Jane. 4800 SW MACADAM AVE # 340 97239 #041-13-1978 L2001 **P PYA** *020 †75 ‡
ZERZAN, Charles J, Jr. 500 NE MULTNOMAH ST STE 10 97232 #056-06-1951 L1968 **GE IM** *071 †20
ZHAI, Juan. 2801 N GANTENBEIN AVE 97227 #243-47-1988 L2001 **AN** *020 †05 ‡
ZHONG, Weimin William. 120 NW 14TH AVE, STE 300 97209 #243-47-1987 L2000 **AN** *020 †05 ‡
ZHOU, Minhao. ■ 97239 #012-01-2003 L2003 **GS** *012
ZHUANG, Liyan. 3181 SW SAM JCKSN PRK RD R 97239 #243-92-1995 L2007 **GS** *012
ZIA, Joy Kai-Yang. 3181 SW SAM JCKSN PRK RD R, SCIENCE UNIV 97239 #014-01-2006 L2006 **OBG** *012
ZIEVERINK, William D. 1809 NW JOHNSON ST, FRANCINE SIEGAL MD PC 97209 #023-07-1968 L1974 **P** *072 †75
ZIGMAN, Aviva Jacoby. 2230 NW PETTYGROVE ST, STE 220 97210 #005-02-1993 L2001 **EM OBG** *020 †16
ZIMMERMAN, Angela Tay. 3181 SW SAM JACKSON PRK RD, UH 2 97239 #038-41-1993 L1999 **AN** *020
ZIMMERMAN, James Lawrence. ■ 97239 #040-02-2007 *012
ZIMMERMAN, Richard Clyde. 501 N GRAHAM ST, STE 200 97227 #040-02-1957 L1958 **ORS** *071 †40
ZINK, Karen Anne. ■ 97221 #028-02-2004 L2004 **GS** *012
ZOLNA MCLANE, Janae Donah. ■ 97239 #040-02-2007 L2007 **FP** *012
ZONANA, Jonathan. 707 SW GAINES ST, CHILD DEVELOPMENT 97239 #041-01-1972 L1979 **MG PD** *020 †55,19
ZORNOW, Mark Herbert. 3181 SW SAM JACKSON PRK RD, UHS 2 97239 #011-03-1980 L1999 **AN** *020 †05
ZUBERI, Nauphyll Sabih. ■ 97219 #704-01-1991 L2007 **P** *020 †75
ZUSMAN, Ehud Israel. 800 SW 13TH AVE 97205 #041-13-1994 L2001 **U** *020 †95
ZWEHL-BURKE, Sarah Louise. 6312 SW CAPITOL HWY, STE 502 97239 #005-02-2003 L2006 **EM** *020 †16

PORTLAND – WASHINGTON

ABEL, David Eric. 9701 SW BARNES RD, STE 299 97225 #035-15-1992 L2003 **MFM** *020 †30

ABRAHAMS, Matthew S. ■ 97229 #028-02-2001 L2007 **AN** *100 †05

ACHAR, Sudha. 1815 SW MARLOW AVE STE 102 97225 #495-33-1966 L1978 **P** *020

ADAMS, Ryan Dwight. ■ 97229 #030-05-2006 L2006 **IM** *012

AEPFELBACHER, Franz C. 9427 SW BARNES RD STE 498, COLUMBIA CARDIOLOGY ASSOCI 97225 #409-16-1991 L2002 **CD** *020 †20

AHMAD, Aftab. 9155 SW BARNES RD, STE 240 97225 #495-12-1963 L1974 **CD** *020

AHMAD, Aftab. 9155 SW BARNES RD STE 240 97225 #704-02-1961 L1973 **IM** *020

AHMAD, Masud. 9427 SW BARNES RD, STE 498 97225 #704-04-1966 L1974 **CD IM** *020 †20

AHMAD, Rehan Saeed. 9155 SW BARNES RD, COLON & RECTAL SURGICAL 97225 #919-05-1992 L2003 **CRS** *020 †85,10

ALBERTY, Roger Ellis. 9155 SW BARNES RD, STE 211 97225 #019-02-1968 L1973 **GS VS** *030 †85

ALBRICH, Jerald Edward. 9205 SW BARNES RD 97225 #040-02-1965 L1968 **RO U** *020 †95,80

ALEXANDER, Hugh E. 9555 SW BARNES RD, CHILDRENS CLINIC PC 97225 #048-02-1988 L1992 **PD** *020 †55

ALEXANDER, Philip T. 9701 SW BARNES RD, STE 140 97225 #005-14-1982 L1983 **VS GS** *020 †85

ALHARETHI, Rami. 8440 SW OLESON RD 97223 #875-02-1995 L2005 **CD** *100 †20

ALSOUFI, Bahaaldin K. ■ 97225 #875-01-1995 L2002 **TS** *020 †85,90

ALTER, Dale Newton. 6455 SW 90TH AVE 97223 #028-34-1986 L1997 **IM** *020

ANDERSEN, Jay Christopher. 9555 SW BARNES RD, STE 150 97225 #019-02-1996 L2004 **HO** *020 †20

ANDERSON, John Wesley. 9450 SW BARNES RD, STE 230 97225 #007-02-1968 L1977 **P** *071 †75

ANDERSON, Thomas Patrick. 9370 SW GREENBURG RD, WASHINGTON BLDG STE 602 97223 #041-01-1968 L1974 **IM** *020 †20,70

ANDONE, Andreea Luiza. 9701 SW BARNES RD, STE 110 97225 #781-05-1998 L2001 **NEP** *020

ANDREWS, Christopher Ray. 9340 SW BARNES RD, STE 529 97225 #012-01-1992 L1993 **EM** *020 †16

ANDREWS, Julie Ward. 9205 SW BARNES RD 97225 #012-01-1992 L1993 **EM** *020 †16

ANSARI, Yasmin. ■ 97229 #496-27-1997 L2001 **IMG** *020 †20

ANTONOVIC, Sandra Ana. 12442 SW SCHOLLS FERRY RD, STE 205 97223 #005-06-1990 L2002 **PD** *020 †55

ATKIN, Edward. 9205 SW BARNES RD 97225 #026-04-1977 L1981 **D IM** *020 †15

AU, Phillip Kwok-Hay. 9205 SW BARNES RD, WEST PAVILION SECOND FLOOR 97225 #005-14-1979 L1987 **CD IM** *020 †20

AXLEY, Michael Shawn. 9205 SW BARNES RD, PROVIDENCE ST VINCENTS MED 97225 #035-20-1999 L2003 **AN** *012 †20

BACH, Mary Ho-Mong. 9205 SW BARNES RD STE 20 97225 #054-04-2007 L2007 **IM** *012

BAER, William Bruce. ■ 97229 #020-02-1965 L1970 **OPH** *071 †35

BAINS, Naseem Kaur. ■ 97229 #021-05-1996 L2006 **IM** *020 †20

BAIR, Donald Glen. 9701 SW BARNES RD STE 200 97225 #040-02-1976 L1982 **OBG** *020 †30

BAKER, Adam Parks. ■ 97223 #028-03-2008 *012

BAKER, George Griffith. 9205 SW BARNES RD, WP-200, CARDIOLOGY 97225 #007-02-1965 L1974 **CD IM** *071 †20

BAKKE, John Noel. 9205 SW BARNES RD, # WP200 97225 #041-01-1974 L1981 **IM ID** *020 †20

BALDWIN, Christopher R. 9205 SW BARNES RD 97225 #040-02-2003 L2004 **IM** *020 †20

BALISH, Martin Joseph. 9155 SW BARNES RD, STE 336 97225 #056-05-1993 L1994 **OPH** *020 †35

BARBER, Erika Marie. ■ 97229 #030-05-2007 L2007 **IM** *012

BARKHUIZEN, Andre. 6640 SW REDWOOD LN STE 301 97224 #836-01-1984 L1997 **RHU** *020 †20

BARLOW, Robert Pentz. 12400 NW CORNELL RD, SUNSET FAMILY PRACTICE 97229 #034-01-1982 L1990 **FM** *020 †18

BARNETT, Arthur J. ■ 97224 #010-02-1950 L1972 **IMG FM** *071 †18

BARRY, Harold Bruce. 12400 NW CORNELL RD, SUNSET FAMILY PRACTICE GRO 97229 #654-01-1997 L2001 **FM** *020 †18

BATIUK, Thomas David. 9701 SW BARNES RD, STE 110 97225 #060-01-1985 L1990 **IM** *020 †20

BEAGLE, Gregory Lee. 9400 SW BARNES RD, STE 250 97225 #016-45-1989 L1994 **DR** *020 †80

BEAUMONT, Ralph Harrison. 9205 SW BARNES RD 97225 #036-07-1976 L1997 **P** *020 †75

BECKERMAN, James Gregg. 9427 SW BARNES RD, STE 498 97225 #024-01-1999 L2006 **CD** *020 †20

BEDELL, Jane Eckmann. 11920 SW GREENBURG RD, BODY IMAGING RADIOLOGY 97223 #040-02-1981 L1982 **DR** *020 †80

BEESON, Steven Carter. 9155 SW BARNES RD STE 340 97225 #040-02-1986 L1987 **IM** *020 †20

BELL, Diana Elizabeth. 9427 SW BARNES RD, STE 599 97225 #040-02-1985 L1989 **OBG** *020 †30

BELLVILLE, Chas Geo, Jr. 9205 SW BARNES RD 97225 #012-05-1974 L1979 **P** *020 †75

BENDRE, Suhas Chandrakant. 9155 SW BARNES RD STE 240 97225 #495-01-1988 L2001 *100

BENNETT, William Michael. 9701 SW BARNES RD, STE 110 97225 #016-06-1963 L1970 **IM NEP** *020 †20 ‡

BENTLEY, Robert Wells. 13240 SW PACIFIC HWY, STE 200 97223 #040-02-1983 L1984 **OPH** *020 †35

BERGSTROM, John Ove. 9155 SW BARNES RD, STE 634 97225 #040-02-1964 L1965 **GYN** *020 †30

BERKELEY, Edward Winston. ■ 97225 #902-10-1965 L1977 **NS** *071

BERLAND, John Edward. 417 SW 117TH AVE STE 100, PROVIDENCE SUNSET MEDICAL 97225 #040-02-1968 L1972 **IM** *020 †20 ‡

BERNARDS, Walter Camiel. ■ 97229 #040-02-1960 L1964 **AN** *071 †05

BIEMER, James Jos, Jr. 9135 SW BARNES RD, STE 863 97225 #010-02-1986 L1990 **IM** *020 †20

BITTS, Laura Kay. 6640 SW REDWOOD LN 97224 #016-43-1992 L2003 **FM** *020 †18

BIZOVI, Kenneth Elie. 9340 SW BARNES RD STE 2, OHSU CSB 550 97225 #035-15-1990 L1998 **EM** *020 †16

BLACK, Whitney Erin. ■ 97225 #028-46-2002 L2008 **DR** *100

BLAHNIK, Michael Robt. 9340 SW BARNES RD STE 20 97225 #040-02-1976 L1977 **EM** *020 †16

BLAIR, Gregory Paul. 9155 SW BARNES RD, OREGON PULMONARY ASSOC PC 97225 #049-01-1977 L1982 **CCM PUD** *020 †20

BLANK, Bruce Henry. 9205 SW BARNES RD 97225 #040-02-1972 L1975 **U** *071 †95 ‡

BLAYLOCK, Paul Douglas. ■ 97229 #047-06-1972 L1973 **EM LM** *020 †16

BLODGETT, Beth. 9370 SW GREENBURG RD, GRANT BLDG SUITE O 97223 #056-06-1978 L1987 **PD** *030 †55

BLUMBERG, Jack Burton. 9370 SW GREENBURG RD, WASHINGTON BLDG, STE 602 97223 #005-11-1956 L1958 **GS TS** *020 †85

BLUMEN, Herbert. ■ 97229 #047-06-1959 L1960 **DR** *071 †80

BOICOURT, Orville Willis. 9205 SW BARNES RD 97225 #019-02-1959 L1965 **CD IM** *071 †20

BOLTON, Robert Earl. 8555 SW APPLE WAY STE 130, OREGON ANESTHESIOLOGY GRP 97225 #005-12-1943 L1943 **GP** *071 †18

BONTA, Michelle Da Costa. 417 SW 117TH AVE, STE 210 97225 #024-01-2000 L2001 **D** *020 †15

BOOKIN, Stephen Oscar. 9205 SW BARNES RD 97225 #018-03-1969 L1973 **DIA END** *020 †20

BOOTH, James L, Jr. 9205 SW BARNES RD 97225 #047-06-1972 L1974 **PTH** *062 †50

BOSS, Diana Kathryn. 9205 SW BARNES RD STE 20, VINCENT MEDICIAL 97225 #012-01-2004 L2004 **IM** *100 †20

BOYER, Stephen Jos. 9340 SW BARNES RD, OREGON EMERGENCY PHYSICIAN 97225 #007-02-1977 L1979 **EM** *071 †16

BRENTLINGER, Eric Robt. 9205 SW BARNES RD 97225 #007-02-1989 L1990 **EM** *020 †16

BRIDENBAUGH, R Harlan. 9205 SW BARNES RD 97225 #040-02-1966 L1969 **P** *071 †75

BRODSKY, Trina A. 9555 SW BARNES RD, WOMENS HEALTH ASSOC., LLC 97225 #014-01-1984 L2000 **OBG** *020 †30

BROWN, Daniel Baken. 9155 SW BARNES RD, STE 336 97225 #056-05-1992 L2000 **OPH** *020 †35

BROWN, David James. 9205 SW BARNES RD 97225 #040-02-1956 **PTH NM** *071 †50,28

BROWN, Phyllis Ann. 9427 SW BARNES RD, STE 395 97225 #005-18-1981 L1982 **OBG** *020 †30

BROWNING, Scott Morgan. 9155 SW BARNES RD, COLON & RECTAL SURGICAL 97225 #023-01-1991 L2000 **CRS** *020 †85,10

BRYAN, Bradley Thomas. 9205 SW BARNES RD, PROVIDENCE HOSPITALIST WES 97225 #020-12-1993 L1995 **IM** *020 †20

BRZANA, Jessica Allison. ■ 97223 #035-09-2006 L2006 **IM** *012

BUBALO, John M. 9155 SW BARNES RD STE 401 97225 #016-43-1947 **GYN** *020

BURDZIK, Eberhard G. ■ 97229 #407-16-1954 L1978 **P CHP** *071

BURNINGHAM, Alan Richard. 9250 SW HALL BLVD 97223 #040-02-2000 L2006 **OTO FPS** *020 †45

BURRIS, Terry Eugene. 6950 SW HAMPTON ST STE 150, NORTHWEST CORNEAL SVCS 97223 #019-02-1977 L1986 **OPH** *020 †35 ‡

BUSBY, Richard Colin. 9155 SW BARNES RD, STE 930 97225 #007-02-1981 L1986 **PS** *020 †85,65

BUTCHER, Jean Elizabeth. ■ 97225 #028-02-1981 L1986 **IMG** *020 †20

BUTLER, Jay B V. 11782C SW BARNES RD, # 300 97225 #021-01-1965 L1969 **OS** *071 †40

BUTLER, Jay B V. 11782 SW BARNES RD STE 300 97225 #021-01-1988 L1994 **OSM** *020 †40

CAI, Xiaohong. ■ 97229 #243-76-1983 L2002 **PTH** *020 †50

CALVERLEY, Thomas Craig. 9340 SW BARNES RD, STE-202 97225 #040-02-1987 L1988 **EM** *020 †16

CAMPBELL, Timothy Jos. 9427 SW BARNES RD, STE 598 97225 #040-02-1964 L1965 **PDS** *020 †85

CANEPA, Clifford Steven. 9155 SW BARNES RD STE 532 97225 #035-03-1983 L1984 **PS GS** *020 †65

CAREY, Thomas Christopher. ■ 97229 #040-02-1969 L1974 **U GS** *071 †95

CARLSON, Misty Lynn. ■ 97229 #041-12-2003 L2003 **PDC** *012 †55

CARTER, Christopher R. 9701 SW BARNES RD, WEST HILLS 97225 #040-02-1978 L1983 **GE** *020 †20

CARTER, Dale M. 12400 NW CORNELL RD, SUNSET FAMILY PRACTICE 97229 #035-03-1984 L2004 **PMM N** *020 †75

CAULFIELD, Todd Alan. 9427 SW BARNES RD, STE 498 97225 #010-01-1994 L2001 **CD** *020 †20

CAUTHORN, Richard Wm. 8835 SW CANYON LN, STE 236 97225 #040-02-1957 L1959 **AN** *071 †05

CHALASANI, Sunita. ■ 97229 #422-01-1996 L1999 **IM** *020

CHAN, Patrick John. 9155 SW BARNES RD, STE 430 97225 #016-43-1966 L1972 **OPH** *020 †35

CHANDRAN, Rubin. 9701 SW BARNES RD, STE 110 97225 #028-02-1998 L2003 **NEP** *020 †20

CHANG, David Jin-Woo. ■ 97229 #008-01-1998 L2007 **RNR** *020 †80

CHANG, Renee Mc Lean. 417 SW 117TH AVE, STE 210 97225 #040-02-2003 L2003 **D** *020 †15

CHANG, Yee Tiffany. 10250 SW GREENBURG RD, LINCOLN BLD 4 97223 #016-06-1999 L2002 **IM** *020 †18

CHAN-LAZARRA, Cynthia Ann. 9205 SW BARNES RD 97225 #042-02-2000 L2006 **MPD** *100

CHARLES, Antony Joseph. 9205 SW BARNES RD STE 2, DEPT OF INTERNAL MEDICINE 97225 #495-59-1993 L2003 **HO** *012 †18,20

CHAWLA, Sushma. 9205 SW BARNES RD 97225 #495-47-1964 L1975 **PTH** *020 †50

CHEN, Jeff. ■ 97225 #031-01-2005 L2006 **AN** *012

CHILD, Gilbert Carl. 9155 SW BARNES RD, STE 336 97225 #039-01-1974 L1978 **OPH** *020 †35 ‡

CHOKSI, Vaishali R. ■ 97229 #495-96-1991 L2007 **R** *020 †80

CLAYBURGH, Daniel Robert. ■ 97291 #016-02-2008 *012

COBER, Sheldon Ray. 9155 SW BARNES RD, STE 930 97225 #041-13-1990 L2000 **PS HS** *020 †85,65

COHAN, Stanley Lawrence. 9427 SW BARNES RD, STE 595 97225 #035-08-1968 L1999 **N** *020 †75

COHEN, Lawrence Jack. ■ 97225 #023-01-1934 L1947 **ORS** *072

COLLINS, Scott Andrew. 10215 SW HALL BLVD 97223 #048-04-1987 L1991 **D** *020 †15

CONNOLLY, Coleen Ann. 417 SW 117TH AVE, STE 100 97225 #040-02-1994 L1997 **IM** *020 †20

COOK, Margaret Mary. ■ 97229 #038-44-2006 L2006 **IM** *012

COVE, Matthew Edward. 9205 SW BARNES RD STE 20, ST VINCENT MEDICAL CENTER 97225 #917-13-1999 L2004 **IM** *100 †20

COVER, Cameron John. 9155 SW BARNES RD, STE 304 97225 #040-02-1998 L2005 **ID** *020 †20

COX, Brian Matthew. 12400 NW CORNELL RD, SUNSET FAMILY PRACTICE 97229 #033-05-1978 L1979 **IM** *040 †20

CRAIG, David Harrin. 9205 SW BARNES RD 97225 #026-04-1975 L1979 **EM** *020 †16

CRAWFORD, Robert Richard. 9205 SW BARNES RD STE 200, PROVIDENCE ST VINCENT KAIS 97225 #005-06-1989 L1997 **CD** *020 †20

CRISTOFANI, Cynthia B. 9205 SW BARNES RD, 5TH FLOOR SOUTH 97225 #010-02-1975 L1980 **CCP PD** *020 †55

CROSS, James Austin. 9555 SW BARNES RD STE 100 97225 #018-03-1967 L1970 **OBG** *071 †30

CROWLEY, Kirsten E. 9427 SW BARNES RD STE 395 97225 #005-14-2001 L2001 **PD** *020 †55

DAO, Linh Duy. 9205 SW BARNES RD 97225 #048-16-1999 L2000 **IM** *020 †20

DA PRATO, Robert Arthur. ■ 97229 #005-14-1972 L2001 **A** *030

DARM, Marcia Gail. 9427 SW BARNES RD, STE 599 97225 #040-02-1978 L1979 **OBG** *020 †30

DAVITT, James S. 11782 SW BARNES RD, STE 300 97225 #048-14-1994 L2001 **ORS** *020 †40

DE BOLT, William Leonard. ■ 97229 #040-02-1958 L1979 **N** *071 †75

DE GUZMAN, Gregorio B, Jr. ■ 97223 #748-08-1968 L1983 **AN** *020

DELACRUZ, Emmanuel A, Jr. ■ 97225 #048-14-2001 L2007 **HSP** *012

DE LAMELENA, Violeta T. 9155 SW BARNES RD 97225 #040-02-1996 L1997 **GS** *020 †85

DENES, Alexander Eugene, Jr. 11782 SW BARNES RD STE 300 97225 #028-46-2001 L2007 **ORS OSM** *100

DENNIS, Daniel Leslie. 9205 SW BARNES RD 97225 #040-02-1958 L1959 **GS** *071 †85

DEODHAR, Hem Atulya. 9701 SW BARNES RD, STE 110 97225 #495-28-1982 L1998 **IM** *020 †20

DE VORE, Joanne Grace. 9555 SW BARNES RD, CHILDRENS CLINIC PC 97225 #051-01-1994 L1997 **PD** *020 †55

DHOOT, Jaspreet Kaur. ■ 97229 #040-02-2008 *012

DICKSON, Alfred Holden. ■ 97229 #005-06-1959 L2004 **GS CD** *030 †85

DINE, David Elliott. 9427 SW BARNES RD, STE 595 97225 #021-01-1964 L1975 **N IM** *020 †20,75

DION, Danielle Marie. 9701 SW BARNES RD, STE 200 97225 #047-05-2003 L2007 **OBG** *020

DIRK, Kenneth Charles. 9205 SW BARNES RD, EM DEPT 97225 #030-06-1996 L1997 **EM** *020 †16

DOMOND, Yolanda Clara. 9205 SW BARNES RD, 1ST FL 97225 #010-03-2003 L2007 **MPD** *020 †20,55

DONOHUE, Elizabeth Kip. 9155 SW BARNES RD, STE 430 97225 #035-15-1990 L1998 **OPH** *072 †35

DOOLEY, Timothy Allen. 9555 SW BARNES RD 97225 #026-04-1973 L1975 **OBG** *020 †30

DOSHI, Heena S. 12400 NW CORNELL RD, SUNSET FAMILY PRACTICE 97229 #495-32-1985 L1993 **FM OBS** *020 †18

DOUEK, Karen A. 9701 SW BARNES RD, STE 110 97225 #065-01-1987 L1990 **NEP** *020 †20

DOUGAN, Kim Elizabeth. ■ 97229 #040-02-2008 *012

DOUGLASS, Lucy Marie. 12442 SW SCHOLLS FERRY RD, STE 100 97223 #054-04-2003 L2006 **FM** *020 †18

DRAKE, Matthew Georgenson. ■ 97225 #003-01-2007 L2007 **IM** *012

DREW, Mary J. ■ 97223 #007-02-1983 L2007 **PTH** *020 †50

DRLICA, Karen Janette. ■ 97225 #040-02-1974 L1976 **CHP P** *020

DROTTAR, Beverly. ■ 97229 #025-07-1980 L2001 **FM** *020 †18

DUFFENS, Kurt Robt. 9205 SW BARNES RD, EMERGENCY DEPARTMENT 97225 #019-02-1980 L1978 **EM IM** *020 †20,16

DUNHAM, Marcia Jeanne. 9205 SW BARNES RD 97225 #040-02-1985 L1986 **IM** *020 †20

DUNLAP, Gerald Acheson. ■ 97225 #040-02-2007 L2007 **IM** *012

DUWELIUS, Paul Jude. 11782 SW BARNES RD, STE 300 97225 #030-06-1982 L1988 **ORS** *020 †40

EARDLEY, Dianne C. 417 SW 117TH AVE, STE 200 & 210 97225 #836-01-1984 L1994 **IM** *020 †20

EDWARDS, Edward Gary. 9370 SW GREENBURG RD 97223 #047-06-1962 L1967 **NPM PD** *071 †55

EDWARDS, Pamela Jean. 3833 NW MORTENSEN TER 97229 #028-34-1989 L1990 **P** *020 †75

EFTEKHARI, Mohmad. ■ 97223 #517-07-1975 L1978 **PTH NM** *020 †20

EGANS, Michael Frank. 9205 SW BARNES RD 97225 #040-02-1970 L1976 **OTO** *020 †45

EGRESSY, Katarine Von Lan. ■ 97229 #550-04-2004 L2007 **IM** *012

EKLUND, G W. 11920 SW GREENBURG RD, BODY IMAGING RADIOLOGY 97223 #048-02-1960 L1971 **DR** *020 †80

ELLERBROOK, Randy Lee. 9155 SW BARNES RD STE 238, WESTSIDE INTERNAL MEDICINE 97225 #040-02-1970 L1973 **IM** *020 †20

EMPEY, Marcel Alva. ■ 97225 #040-02-1954 L1955 **FM** *071

ENGLANDER, Honora Lesley. 9205 SW BARNES RD, HOSPITALIST GROUP 97225 #024-16-2003 L2003 **IM** *020 †20

ENGLEHART, Michael Shawn. ■ 97223 #056-06-2002 L2002 **GS** *012

ENGLISH, Woodruff J, II. 9205 SW BARNES RD, 1ST FL 97225 #035-01-1972 L1978 **IM ID** *020 †20

ENGLUND, Karen Jean. 9205 SW BARNES RD, SOCIAL SERVICES DEPT 97225 #054-04-1998 L1999 **IM** *020 †20

ENGRAV, Mary Beth. 9205 SW BARNES RD, ST VINCENT HOSPITAL 97225 #030-06-1990 L1991 **EM** *020 †16

ERB, Danielle Laure. 1815 SW MARLOW AVE, STE 110 97225 #040-02-1986 L1990 **PM** *020 †60

ERICKSEN, Michael Kent. 9135 SW BARNES RD, STE 763 97225 #049-01-1995 L1998 **PD** *020 †20

ERICKSEN, Wayne Gordon. 15875 SW 72ND AVE 97224 #040-02-1946 **DR** *071 †80

ESMER, Ertan Raif. 9250 SW HALL BLVD 97223 #055-01-1996 L2005 **OTO** *020 †45

ESPARZA, Brian Paul. 9205 SW BARNES RD, VINCENT HOSPITAL 97225 #054-04-2003 L2007 **P** *020

EYLER, Steven Wm. 10152 SW WINDWOOD WAY 97225 #024-01-1977 L1993 **AN** *020 †05

FAGAN, Charles Augustine. 9205 SW BARNES RD 97225 #040-02-1955 L1956 **ORS** *071 †40

FANCHER, Bradley Stanford. 417 SW 117TH AVE, STE 100 97225 #040-02-1979 L1981 **IM** *020 †18,20

FEI, Haihua. 6600 SW HAMPTON ST 97223 #243-16-1983 L2001 **PTH** *020 †50

FEIGHNER, Jennifer Anne. 9205 SW BARNES RD, 1ST FL 97225 #021-01-2003 L2003 **IM** *020 †20

FELDMAN, Peter Michael. 9427 SW BARNES RD 97225 #165-04-1971 L1977 **GS VS** *020 †85

FELDMAN, Virginia M. 9205 SW BARNES RD 97225 #025-01-1972 L1975 **PD** *020 †55

FELIX, Jacob Kilian. ■ 97229 #056-05-1971 L1972 **NPM PD** *071 †55

FERGUSON, Casey Elizabeth. ■ 97225 #048-02-2000 L2007 **IM** *020

FERRIER, Cynthia Jane. 9427 SW BARNES RD 97225 #005-02-1981 L1983 **IM** *030 †20

FIFE, William Charle. 9400 SW BARNES RD, STE 250 97225 #041-13-1996 L2002 **DR** *020 †80

FIKS, Vladimir. 10305 SW PARK WAY STE 300, ADVANCED PAIN MGMT CTR 97225 #913-17-1987 L1995 **APM AN** *020 †05

FLETCHER, Wm Sigourney. ■ 97225 #024-01-1955 L1960 **ON GS** *071 †85

FLICK, Gregory Robt. 9205 SW BARNES RD, OREGON PULMONARY ASSOC PC 97225 #041-01-1977 L1989 **PUD IM** *020 †20

FLOTEN, Harkness Storm. 9155 SW BARNES RD, STE 240 97225 #040-02-1971 L1978 **GS TS** *020 †85,90

FLOWERS, Karen Louise. 9250 SW HALL BLVD 97225 #025-07-1996 L2006 **FM** *020 †18

FOJTASEK, Robert G. 9205 SW BARNES RD, C/O HOSPITALIST OFFICE 97225 #048-15-1999 L2000 **IM** *020 †20

FOSTER, Mary. 9205 SW BARNES RD 97225 #048-12-1987 L1988 **PD** *020 †55

FOX, Shirley Ann. 9555 SW BARNES RD STE 100 97225 #026-04-1992 L1996 **OBG** *020 †30

FRABACK, Ronald Chas. 9155 SW BARNES RD, STE 314 97225 #040-02-1969 L1971 **RHU IM** *020 †20,18

FRANK, Matthew Carstens. ■ 97229 #007-02-2001 L2007 **HMP** *100 †20

FREEMAN, Norman Robt. 9427 SW BARNES RD STE 100, DEPT OF NEUROLOGY 97225 #021-01-1978 L2002 **N** *020 †75

FREER, Steven David. 9205 SW BARNES RD, STE 20 97225 #035-45-1988 L2003 **IM** *020 †20

FRIC, Frank. 9155 SW BARNES RD STE 33 97225 #154-01-1957 L1963 **IM** *020

FRIEDMAN, Lynn Kari. 9900 SW WILSHIRE ST, STE 210 97225 #056-05-1981 L1984 **P** *020 †75

FROMHERZ, Scott Douglas. 7450 SW BEVELAND RD, STE 120 97223 #010-02-1999 L2005 **N SME** *020 ‡

FROOM, Donald Woodrow. 9155 SW BARNES RD STE 534 97225 #040-02-1966 L1967 **NEP IM** *020 †20

FUCHS, Kyle Ivy Cohen. 9427 SW BARNES RD 97225 #005-02-1976 L1981 **PUD** *050 †20

FUCHS, Peter Cornelius. 9205 SW BARNES RD 97225 #023-01-1963 L1964 **CLP PTH** *071 †50

FULMER, Alison. 9205 SW BARNES RD 97225 #005-15-1988 L1989 **CD IM** *020 †20

FULSANG, Elise Jan. 9205 SW BARNES RD, SUTIE 2800 97225 #040-02-2000 L2001 **IM** *020 †20

GABBARD, Wesley Alan. 6663 SW BEAVERTN HLSDL HWY 97225 #047-06-1998 L2004 **NEP** *020

GADBAW, Matthew James. 9205 SW BARNES RD, 5TH FL SOUTH 97225 #054-04-2000 L2004 **MPD** *020

GAO, Guangqiang. 9205 SW BARNES RD # LL33 97225 #243-58-1986 L2001 **GS** *012

GARLITZ, Betsy. ■ 97225 #040-02-1989 L1990 **GPM** *100

GASCH, Bernard Andreas. 9701 SW BARNES RD, STE 130 97225 #056-06-1997 L2003 **D** *020 †20,15

GATELY, Hugh Louis, Jr. 9155 SW BARNES RD, STE 240 97225 #056-05-1978 L1979 **TS** *075 †85,90

GATES, Gary Franklin. 9205 SW BARNES RD, PROVIDENCE ST VINCENT MED 97225 #005-11-1964 L1976 **NM R** *071 †80,28

GEARY, Gregory Lance. 9701 SW BARNES RD, STE 140 97225 #048-02-1978 L1983 **VS GS** *020 †20

GEDDES, Gary Ross. 12400 NW CORNELL RD, SUNSET FAMILY PRACTICE 97229 #062-01-1974 L1977 **GP EM** *020 ‡

GEORGE, Samuel Everett. 9229 #028-02-1980 L1982 **CD IM** *020 †20

GERRITY, Martha Susan. ■ 97223 #016-06-1980 L1982 **IM** *020 †20

GERRY, Jeffrey Ira. 9155 SW BARNES RD STE 440 97225 #040-02-1986 L1990 **PM** *020 †60

GHANEM, Tamer Abdelhalim. ■ 97223 #049-01-2002 L2007 **OTO** *100

GIBSON, Richard Frank. 11308 SW 68TH PKWY 97223 #038-06-1981 L1996 **EM FM** *050 †16,18

GIBSON, Robt Clayton, III. 9205 SW BARNES RD 97225 #036-01-1966 L1974 **CD IM** *020 †20

GIESBRECHT, Raymond E. ■ 97224 #040-02-1965 L1966 **P GP** *071

GIGER, Paul Thomas. 9205 SW BARNES RD, PSVMC BEHAVIORAL HEALTH AD 97225 #003-01-1997 L1998 **P** *020 †20,75

GIL, Richard Xavier. ■ 97225 #016-02-2008 *012

GILBERT, Wayne Francis. 9427 SW BARNES RD 97225 #028-34-1987 L1988 **GS** *020 †85

GILL, Samuel Fenton. 11782C SW BARNES RD, # 300 97225 #040-02-1955 L1959 **HS ORS** *071 †40

GILLESPIE, Robert James. 9555 SW BARNES RD, CHILDRENS CLINIC PC 97225 #040-02-1997 L2001 **PD** *020 †55

GLASSBERG, Kathryn Jo. ■ 97225 #040-02-2006 L2006 **IM** *012

GLUCK, Lori. 15285 NW CENTRAL DR, PMG/BETHANY 97229 #024-07-1997 L1998 **FM** *020 †18

GLUCKMAN, Robert Allen. 9205 SW BARNES RD # 2800 97225 #016-02-1982 L1991 **IM** *040 †20

GLUCKMAN, Ty Justin. 9427 SW BARNES RD, STE 498 97225 #016-06-1997 L2006 **CD** *100 †20

GOEL, Anita A. 9155 SW BARNES RD, STE 314 97225 #917-18-1989 L2001 **RHU** *020 †20

GOLDSTEIN, Michael Jacob. ■ 97225 #005-06-2008 *012

GOODALL, Patrick Thompson. 9155 SW BARNES RD, STE 304 97225 #005-11-1971 L1974 **IM ID** *020 †20

GOODRICH, Louann. 9340 SW BARNES RD 97225 #040-02-1985 L1986 **IM** *020 †20

GOSEWEHR, Jim Alan. 9555 SW BARNES RD, STE 150 97225 #056-05-1983 L1995 **OBG** *020 †30

GRAHAM, Barbara Ann. 12672 NW BARNES RD, STE 100 97229 #040-02-1987 L1988 **IM** *020 †20

GRAHAM, Michael Haw. ■ 97229 #018-03-1964 L1965 **ORS OS** *071 †40

GRASLEY, Andrew Barnes. ■ 97229 #040-02-1994 L1996 **GS** *020

GRASS, Henry. 9155 SW BARNES RD, STE 418 97225 #038-41-1971 L1974 **P** *020

GRAZER, Richard Edward. 11175 SW LYNNVALE DR, PORTLAND VA MEDICAL CENTER 97225 #024-16-1980 L1982 **EM IM** *020 †20,16

GREEN, Janette Eddy. 9155 SW BARNES RD STE 340 97225 #048-15-1992 L1993 **IM** *020 †20

GREEN, Marvin F. ■ 97225 #018-03-1951 L1957 **OPH** *071 †35

GREENBERG, Laura Hope. 9205 SW BARNES RD 97225 #005-18-1983 L1987 **GYN REN** *020 †30

GREWE, Kent Michael. 9205 SW BARNES RD 97225 #040-02-1983 L1984 **NS** *020 †25

GRIFFIN, Kirby. 9370 SW GREENBURG RD # 101 97223 #010-01-1966 L1967 **OM IM** *020 †70

GRUENBERG, Daniel Richard. 9555 SW BARNES RD, STE 150 97225 #028-34-1988 L1995 **HO** *020 †20

GRUNKEMEIER, David Morris. 9701 SW BARNES RD, STE 300 97225 #005-18-2000 L2000 **GE** *100 †20

GRUNKEMEIER, Miriam Natal. 2065 NW MILLER RD, BOX 518 97229 #005-14-2000 L2000 **PTH** *012

GUFFEE, Guy Keel. ■ 97223 #048-02-1962 L1969 **GS GP** *071 †85

GUINN, Debra Nadler. 9701 SW BARNES RD, STE 299 97225 #005-07-1989 L2004 **OBG** *020 †30

GUZIEC, Janice Arlene. 9205 SW BARNES RD 97225 #016-01-1980 L1984 **IM** *020 †20

GWILLIAM, Suzanne Jane. 6640 SW REDWOOD LN, STE 100 97224 #065-10-1982 L1993 **FM** *020 †18

HABER, Seymour. 9400 SW BARNES RD, RADIOLOGY GROUP PC 97225 #035-08-1954 L1965 **R DR** *071 †80

HAGMAN, Heidi Marie. 9155 SW BARNES RD, STE 238 97225 #040-02-1992 L1993 **IM** *020 †20

HAJDU, Laszlo. 9155 SW BARNES RD STE 240 97225 #473-01-1979 L1996 *100

HAL, Jeffrey Terrance. 9250 SW HALL BLVD 97223 #012-21-1999 L2005 **DR** *020 †80 ‡

HALPERIN, Blair David. 9427 SW BARNES RD STE 490 97225 #025-07-1984 L1985 **CD IM** *020 †20

HAMBY, John Edward. 12250 SW GARDEN PL, NWOMC 97223 #040-02-1985 L1987 **FM EM** *020

HAMDAN, Naji Mohamed. 9205 SW BARNES RD 97225 #010-03-1995 L1997 **IC** *020 †20

HAN, Iris Jakon. 9555 SW BARNES RD, CHILDRENS CLINIC PC 97225 #046-01-1996 L2001 **PD** *020 †55

HANLEY, John Franklin. ■ 97223 #038-40-1954 L1955 **AN** *071

HANSEN, Eric Keith. 9205 SW BARNES RD 97225 #040-02-2002 L2007 **RO** *100

HANSEN, Matthew Lee. ■ 97225 #038-06-2007 L2007 **EM** *012

HARRIS, James Edward. 9370 SW GREENBURG RD, STE 101 97223 #040-02-1991 L1992 **OM IM** *040 †20,70

HASAN, Shagufta. 15280 NW CENTRAL DR, S. TWIN BLDG, STE 204 97229 #704-06-1980 L1998 **GS** *020 †18 ‡

HASSELL, Miles. 9155 SW BARNES RD, STE 302 97225 #143-06-1988 L1992 **IM** *020 †20

HAUNG, James. ■ 97229 #385-04-1966 L1976 **AN** *020

HAWKEY, Mitchell Alan. 9701 SW BARNES RD, STE 110 97225 #040-02-1997 L1999 **NEP** *020 †20

HAYES, Robert Paul. 9155 SW BARNES RD, STE 422 97225 #040-02-1980 L1983 **IM** *020 †20

HAYHURST, John Orville. 11785 SW CORBY DR, STE 300 97225 #040-02-1970 L1971 **ORS** *071 †40

HAYMOND, Janice Eileen. 9427 SW BARNES RD STE 39 97225 #005-06-1985 L1986 **OBG** *020 †30

HAYS, Zanice Elizabeth. 9427 SW BARNES RD STE 590 97225 #012-05-1998 L2001 **IM** *020 †20

HEDGES, Jason Charles. ■ 97223 #031-01-2004 L2004 **U** *012

HEDTKE, James L. 9340 SW BARNES RD, STE 202 97225 #040-02-1986 L1987 **EM** *020 †16

HEFELE, Mary C. 9427 SW BARNES RD, ORTHOPEDICS/MJP 97225 #036-01-1988 L1994 **OMO** *020 †40

HEIDEN, James Steve. ■ 97229 #025-01-1966 L2004 **NS** *071 †25

HEINONEN, Larry Allan. 9701 SW BARNES RD, WEST HILLS 97225 #040-02-1974 L1975 **GE IM** *020 †20

HELIKSON, Mary Alice. 9427 SW BARNES RD, MOTHER JOSEPH PLZ STE 598 97225 #005-11-1972 L2001 **PDS CCS** *020 †85

HELLER, Lloyd Emerson, Jr. 9400 SW BARNES RD, STE 250 97225 #041-09-1993 L1999 **DR** *020 †80

HENDRICKS, Edward L. ■ 97229 #040-02-1949 L1984 **PD** *071 †55

HERTLER, Craig Kevin. 9555 SW BARNES RD 97225 #056-05-1985 L1986 **OTO** *020 †45

HILL, David Walker. 9205 SW BARNES RD, VINCENT MEDICAL 97225 #041-02-1984 L1985 **IM** *020 †20

HILL, Timothy Bradley. 9205 SW BARNES RD, STE MT2800 97225 #005-12-2005 L2005 **IM** *012

HINEDI, Kareem Aref. 9205 SW BARNES RD, HOSPITALIST OFFICE 97225 #539-06-2000 L2003 **IM HOS** *020 †20

HIRSH, Thomas Frederick. 9250 SW HALL BLVD 97223 #026-04-1985 L1990 **DR** *020 †80

HITCHCOCK, Emily Ellen. 9205 SW BARNES RD, STE MT-2800 97225 #041-01-1998 L2002 **IM** *020 †20

HOBSON, Susan A. 9155 SW BARNES RD, STE 634 97225 #040-02-1999 L2000 **OBG** *020 †30

HOCHENEDEL, Todd Ashley. 9155 SW BARNES RD, STE 205 97225 #021-05-1995 L1996 **IM** *020 †20

HOFFMAN, Walter Gary. 9555 SW BARNES RD, STE 100 97225 #028-34-1987 L1988 **OBG** *020 †30

HOHF, Steven M. 9155 SW BARNES RD, STE 205 97225 #024-01-1973 L1990 **IM** *020 †20

HOLT, Lois M Nelson. ■ 97229 #019-02-1944 L1947 **OS** *071

HOLZGANG, Curtis Ray. 9205 SW BARNES RD # 20 97225 #040-02-1963 L1964 **IM** *020 †20

HOPPOCK, John S. 9205 SW BARNES RD 97225 #035-01-1976 L1977 **EM OS** *020 †16

HORENBLAS, Lindsey Waine. 9205 SW BARNES RD 97225 #065-01-1974 L1979 **EM** *030 †16

HOWE, Richard Harold. 12442 SW SCHOLLS FERRY RD, SCHOLLS IMMEDIATE CARE, ST 97223 #008-01-1974 L1976 **IM** *020 †20

HOWELL, Beth Ann. 7327 SW BARNES RD # 821 97225 #003-01-1979 L1980 **P N** *062 †75

HOWTON, Joseph Conrad. 9340 SW BARNES RD, STE 202 97225 #041-01-1984 L2005 **EM** *020 †16

HUDSON, Timothy Howard. 9205 SW BARNES RD 97225 #054-04-1996 L2004 **IC** *020 †20

HUGHES, Wendy Michele. 9427 SW BARNES RD 97225 #040-02-1979 L1980 **ORS HS** *020 †40

HULL, Daniel Jos. 9340 SW BARNES RD STE 20 97225 #025-01-1981 L1992 **EM PD** *020 †55,16

HUYNH, Maiphuong Thi. 9205 SW BARNES RD, ST VINCENT HOSP 97225 #054-04-1989 L1990 **IM** *020 †20

HYDER, Dan Morris. ■ 97225 #039-01-1978 L1986 **PTH CLP** *020 †50

IGUIDBASHIAN, John Paul. 9155 SW BARNES RD STE 240 97225 #025-07-1986 L1995 **TS** *020 †85,90

ILIAIFAR, Sakineh Sadat. ■ 97229 #040-02-1994 L2003 **PCC** *020 †20

IMBRIE, J Donald. ■ 97229 #040-02-1959 L1960 **OTO** *071 †45

INAHARA, Toshio. ■ 97225 #040-02-1950 L1951 **VS VIR** *071 †85

ING, Frederic Yau Wong. 9205 SW BARNES RD 97225 #017-20-1963 L1968 **AN** *071 †05

IP, Benjamin Hinmeng. 12442 SW SCHOLLS FERRY RD, STE 100 97223 #048-04-1993 L2007 **FM** *020 †18 ‡

JACOBSON, Ben Erik. 9400 SW BARNES RD, STE 307 97225 #040-02-1995 L2006 **DR RNR** *020 †80

JACOBY-LOW, Gail Ann. 9427 SW BARNES RD, STE 395 97225 #550-02-1988 L1995 **PD** *020 †55

JAN, Elroy Yi. 9205 SW BARNES RD, HOSPITALIST - 5TH FLOOR SO 97225 #047-06-2002 L2006 **MPD** *020 †20,55

JANISSE, Thomas Leo. 9205 SW BARNES RD 97225 #025-07-1975 L1988 **EM PD** *020 †16,05

JANOFF, Daniel Mark. 9135 SW BARNES RD, STE 663 97225 #005-15-1999 L2000 **U** *020

JARVIS, Noel Marie. 8835 SW CANYON LN STE 236 97225 #026-04-1999 L2000 **P** *020 †75

JAYARAM, Ashok. 9155 SW BARNES RD, STE 934 97225 #495-73-1973 L1996 **AN** *020 †05

JAYARAM, Navnit Kaur. 9155 SW BARNES RD, STE 934 97225 #496-07-1976 L1996 **AN** *020 †05

JEAN-BAPTISTE, Firmine. 9427 SW BARNES RD, STE 395 97225 #035-08-1994 L2001 **OBG** *020 †30

JENDRZEJEWSKI, John W. 9701 SW BARNES RD, WEST HILLS 97225 #040-02-1974 L1976 **GE IM** *020 †20

JENKINS, Michael Hawley. 14120 NW SPRINGVILLE RD 97229 #040-02-1962 L1975 **EM PTH** *020 †50,18

JENSEN, James Waldemar, II. 9155 SW BARNES RD STE 5, OREGON EMERGENCY PHYSICIAN 97225 #017-20-1941 L2001 **OS** *020 †55,16

JEWETT, Stiles Turner, Jr. 12400 NW CORNELL RD # 200, THE WALDORF CTR FOR PLAS 97229 #016-06-1968 L1979 **PS GS** *020 †85,65

JIRIES, Katie Lynne. ■ 97223 #040-02-2008 *012

JOERKE, Frank. 9205 SW BARNES RD, ST VINCENT MEDICAL CENTER 97225 #409-19-1991 L2005 **IM** *012

JOHNSON, Ben Webb. 9701 SW BARNES RD, STE 200 97225 #037-01-2000 L2004 **OBG** *020

JOHNSON, Jeffrey Philip. 9427 SW BARNES RD STE 595 97225 #035-01-1990 L2000 **NS** *020 †25

JOHNSON, Merlin Harvey. ■ 97229 #016-43-1941 L1949 **OPH** *071 †35

JOHNSON, William Ellis. 9155 SW BARNES RD 97225 #005-06-1989 L1996 **GS** *020 †85

JONES, Darren Randolph. 9427 SW BARNES RD, STE 490 97225 #054-04-1996 L2004 **ICE** *020 †20

JONES, Lee Anna. 9205 SW BARNES RD 97225 #054-04-1986 L1995 **RHU** *020 †20

JULIEN, Robert Michael. 9205 SW BARNES RD 97225 #005-15-1977 L1978 **AN** *071

KAHN, Marcia Anne. 14600 NW CORNELL RD 97229 #021-05-1977 L1989 **P** *020 †75

KANSAL, Raman. 11920 SW GREENBURG RD, BODY IMAGING RADIOLOGY 97223 #048-04-1999 L2005 **VIR** *100 †80

KAPLAN, Paul David. 9135 SW BARNES RD STE 963 97225 #024-07-1975 L1980 **OTO** *020 †45

KARLSSON, Anna Ulfsdotter. 9555 SW BARNES RD, STE 100 97225 #018-03-1996 L2000 **OBG** *020 †30

KATZ, Jeffrey Lee. 7421 SW BRIDGEPORT RD, STE 220 97224 #051-04-2000 L2003 **FM** *020 †18

KAVITT, Henry H. ■ 97225 #026-04-1938 L1938 **DR** *071 †80

KAYNARD, Alan Howard. 9701 SW BARNES RD, WEST HILLS 97225 #040-02-1997 L2000 **GE** *020 †20

KAYSER, Edwin Allen, Jr. 11782 SW BARNES RD, STE 300 97225 #035-20-1965 L1967 **ORS** *020 †40

KEANE, J Michael. 9155 SW BARNES RD, STE 422 97225 #021-01-1965 L1973 **U** *071 †95

KEARNS, Brian John. 9205 SW BARNES RD, PROVIDENCE HOSPITALISTS WE 97225 #040-02-2002 L2001 **IM HOS** *020 ‡

KEATING, Angela Blanche. 9427 SW BARNES RD, STE 395 97225 #026-04-1993 L2003 **OBG** *020 †30

KEDAR, Arvind. 9205 SW BARNES RD 97225 #495-23-1962 L1978 **OBG U** *020 †30

KEDAR, Lopa Aravind. 14740 NW CORNELL RD, STE 160 97229 #495-23-1964 L1978 **OBG** *020 †30

KEIZUR, Lowell Walter. ■ 97225 #040-02-1946 **U** *071 †95

KENNEDY, Kathleen Anne. 9205 SW BARNES RD, DEPARTMENT OF PERINATOLOGY 97225 #005-02-1984 L1985 **OBG MFM** *020 †20

KENNEDY, Michael Patrick. 7300 SW CHILDS RD, OREGON HEALTH SCIENCE UNIV 97224 #025-07-1995 L2002 **ORS** *020 †40

KENNEFICK, Thomas Michael. 9701 SW BARNES RD, STE 110 97225 #016-01-1989 L1990 **IM** *020 †20

KEY, Douglas Jeffrey. 9555 SW BARNES RD STE 390 97225 #005-02-1968 L1974 **D** *020 †15

KHAKI, Ali Adnan. 9155 SW BARNES RD STE 8 97225 #528-01-1979 L2000 **GS** *020 †85

KHARY, Victorya Vladi. 417 SW 117TH AVE, STE 200 & 210 97225 #040-02-1998 L1999 **IM** *020 †20

KIELICH, Andrea M. 9205 SW BARNES RD 97225 #010-02-1976 L1978 **IM IMG** *020 †20

KILO, Mary Nathanson. 9205 SW BARNES RD, DEPT OF PATHOLOGY 97225 #045-01-1989 L2000 **PTH HMP** *020 †50

KIM, Edsel U. 9155 SW BARNES RD 97225 #035-19-1996 L2003 **OTO FPS** *020

KIM, Evelyn. 9340 SW BARNES RD, STE 202 97225 #011-04-1996 L1998 **EM NS** *020 †16

KIMURA, Hidenao. 417 SW 117TH AVE, STE 200 & 210 97225 #010-02-1992 L1996 **IM** *020 †20

KINDUELL, Kevin Kyle. 9205 SW BARNES RD, HOSPITALIST DIVISION 97225 #017-20-2004 L2004 **IM** *100 †20

KING, James Thos, Jr. 9155 SW BARNES RD 97225 #012-01-1966 L1977 **VS** *071 †85

KITZHABER, John Albert. ■ 97225 #040-02-1973 L1974 **EM** *020

KLEIKAMP, Theodore Jos. 417 SW 117TH AVE, STE 100 97225 #054-04-1982 L1983 **IM** *020 †20

KLEIN, Deena R. 9205 SW BARNES RD 97225 #035-46-1968 L1974 **P** *020 †75

KLEIN, Marla Marie. 9495 SW LOCUST ST 97223 #005-19-1993 L1997 **D** *020 †15 ‡

KLOTZ, Michael Moore. 9427 SW BARNES RD, STE 395 97225 #054-04-1986 L2002 **OBG** *020 †30

KLUBERT, David Matthew. 9205 SW BARNES RD 97225 #038-43-1977 L1978 **FM** *020 †18

KNAPP, Hilary Katherine. 9555 SW BARNES RD, STE 255 97225 #030-05-2003 L2003 **PD** *020 †55

KOELLER, Paula Hirsh. 9427 SW BARNES RD, STE 590 97225 #026-04-1985 L2001 **ADL** *020 †55

KORMAN, Laura Anne. 9555 SW BARNES RD 97225 #024-07-1991 L1992 **OBG** *020 †30

KOSKI, Stephanie Ann. 9155 SW BARNES RD, STE 238 97225 #026-04-2000 L2000 **IM** *020 †20

KOSTINER, Anthony Ivan. 97223 #041-01-1968 L1973 **DR** *020 †80

KOVAL, George. 9701 SW BARNES RD, WEST HILLS 97225 #041-12-1978 L1983 **GE IM** *020 †20

KRISCIUNAS, Victor. 12400 NW CORNELL RD, SUNSET FAMILY PRACTICE 97229 #062-01-1974 L1977 **FM GPM** *020 ‡

KRULEWITCH, Harry Scott. 4838 SW SCHOLLS FERRY RD, NORTHWEST GERIATRICS 97225 #016-11-1975 L1976 **FPG** *020 †18

KRUPA, Lawrence Theodore. 1675 SW MARLOW AVE STE 204, & DEVELOPMENTAL 97225 #040-02-1969 L1976 **PD** *071 †55

KUMAR, Sandeep. ■ 97223 #018-03-2005 L2005 **GS** *012

KUMAR, Suniti. ■ 97225 #024-16-1997 L2004 **FM** *020 †18

KURIAN, Jason Brian. ■ 97225 #056-06-2001 L2007 **OSM** *020

KWIECIEN, Marni Sue. 9701 SW BARNES RD, STE 200 97225 #031-01-1998 L1999 **OBG** *020 †30

LACAYANGA, Imelda P. 9427 SW BARNES RD, STE 395 97225 #748-01-1981 L1995 **PD** *020 †55

LACOUR, Kevin Charles. ■ 97229 #021-05-1999 L2006 **DR** *100 †80

LAHR, Tiffany Robin. ■ 97223 #041-15-2005 L2006 **PD** *012

LAHTI, Jeffrey Paul. 9205 SW BARNES RD, PROVIDENCE ST. VICENT MED 97225 #016-06-1999 L2002 **EM** *020 †16

LAIDLER, James Robt. ■ 97225 #005-06-1985 L1997 **AN PME** *020 †05

LAIRSON, Edward Joseph. 11782 SW BARNES RD STE 300 97225 #040-02-1996 L2003 **PM PME** *020 †60

LANGER, Lucy Ruwitch. 9555 SW BARNES RD, STE 150 97225 #005-11-2000 L2007 **HO** *020 †20

LANIER, Keith Singleton. 9155 SW BARNES RD STE 533 97225 #007-02-1971 L1984 **HEM** *020 †20

LARSON, L Wm. ■ 97225 #026-04-1952 L1957 **IM** *071

LAU, Leslie. ■ 97225 #539-04-1953 L1968 **AN** *071

LAYMAN, Charles Donald. 9155 SW BARNES RD STE 220 97225 #040-02-1975 L1977 **HS PS** *020 †65,85 ‡

LAYNE, Gregory David. ■ 97229 #040-02-1975 L1977 **PD** *071 †55

LAZARUS, Howard M. 9155 SW BARNES RD, STE 840 97225 #067-01-1991 L2002 **PCC** *020 †20

LE, Priscilla Diem. 9205 SW BARNES RD 97225 #040-02-1997 L1999 **IM** *020 †20

LEAF, David Nathanael. 9135 SW BARNES RD, STE 663 97225 #016-11-1967 L1971 **U** *020 †95

LE BLANC, Benjamin Harrel. 417 SW 117TH AVE, 2ND FL 97225 #008-01-1995 L1998 IM *020 †20

LEDBETTER, Randi Rae. 9155 SW BARNES RD, STE 219 97225 #040-02-1978 L1991 OBG FM *020 †18,30

LEE, Georgia Mason. ■ 97225 #040-02-1947 L1948 PYA CHP *071

LEE, Somnit. ■ 97224 #054-04-2007 L2007 IM *012

LEE, Thomas. 9701 SW BARNES RD, STE 299 97225 #041-01-1995 L2002 OBG *020 †30

LEE, Ting David, Jr. ■ 97229 #024-01-1957 L1964 CD IM *072 †20

LEONARD, Claudia Suzanne. 9205 SW BARNES RD, # 2800 97225 #024-01-1990 L1995 IM *020 †20

LESTER, Steven Edward. 9427 SW BARNES RD 97225 #054-04-1986 L1987 GS *020 †85

LEWIS, Stacy Kay. 9155 SW BARNES RD, STE 533 97225 #028-02-1988 L1998 ON HEM *020 †20

LEWIS, Wesley Alfred. 9155 SW BARNES RD 97225 #040-02-1981 L1983 OTO *020 †45

LIM, Kit Yeng. ■ 97229 #048-16-2005 L2005 PD *100

LINDGREN, John Arthur. 9155 SW BARNES RD STE 401 97225 #040-02-1968 L1972 OTO HNS *020 †45

LINDGREN, Thomas Wm. ■ 97225 #040-02-1975 L1976 OPH *071 †35 ‡

LINDQUIST, Mary Maher. 9427 SW BARNES RD, STE 595 97225 #016-11-1984 L1985 IM *020 †20

LIPKE, Michael Charles. 9427 SW BARNES RD, MOTHER JOSEPH PLAZA 97225 #035-06-1999 L2006 U *100 †95

LIU, Minghui. ■ 97225 #243-76-1984 L2000 TS *100

LOBITZ, John Rockwell. 9701 SW BARNES RD, WEST HILLS 97225 #040-02-1974 L1978 GE IM *020 †20

LONG, David Douglas, Jr. 9427 SW BARNES RD, MOTHER JOSEPH PLAZA 97225 #035-03-1966 L1971 HS ORS *030 †40

LORBER, Bradford Benton. 12250 SW GARDEN PL 97223 #040-02-1994 L2000 PM *020 †60

LORENCE, Elke Patricia. 9205 SW BARNES RD, 1ST FL 97225 #671-01-2000 L2005 IM *100 †20

LORISH, Frederick Chas. ■ 97229 #041-01-1941 L1942 IM CD *071

LORISH, Thomas Robt. 9205 SW BARNES RD # REHAB 97225 #051-05-1985 L1989 PM *020 †60

LOUIE, Jeannie. 9205 SW BARNES RD 97225 #040-02-1990 L2000 RO *020 †80

LOWENSTEIN, Keith G. 9450 SW BARNES RD STE 270 97225 #035-03-1989 L1992 CHP P *020 †75

LOWENSTEIN, Shelley. 4888 NW BETHANY BLVD 97229 #035-03-1989 L1992 FM *020 †18

LOWY, Richard Otto. ■ 97229 #033-05-1965 L1973 RO *071 †80

LUBARSKY, Suzanne Lynne. 9205 SW BARNES RD STE 3, PROVIDENCE ST VINCENT MED 97225 #051-07-1988 L1996 OBG *020 †30

LUBISCHER, James Thos. 9205 SW BARNES RD #010-02-1978 L1979 PD PN *020 †55

LUM, Catherine Kay. 9155 SW BARNES RD STE 9 97225 #005-14-1993 L2007 PDE *020 †55

LUNDBERG, Laury Edward. ■ 97229 #040-02-1960 L1962 OM FPG *020

LUU, Vien Thao. 417 SW 117TH AVE STE 200 97225 #409-24-1985 L1997 IM *020 †20

LYON, Peter Baker. 9155 SW BARNES RD, STE 205 97225 #023-07-1977 L1981 IM *020 †20

MA, Alison Yi. ■ 97229 #040-02-2006 L2006 IM *012

MA, Oscar John. ■ 97225 #010-01-1990 L2006 EM *030 †16

MACKLES, Lawrence F. 10490 SW EASTRIDGE ST 97225 #035-15-1971 L1984 P *020

MAGILKE, Dave Dean. 9427 SW BARNES RD STE 394 97225 #040-02-1990 L1996 OTO FPS *020 †45

MAJOR, Kevin Michael. 9155 SW BARNES RD STE 830 97225 #038-43-1998 L2006 VS *020 †85

MAKAR, Rosemary R. 9205 SW BARNES RD DEPT PAT, VINCENTS MEDICAL 97225 #584-01-1986 L2002 PTH HMP *020 †50

MALECHA, Mark J. ■ 97225 #759-03-1981 L1991 ATP *020 †50

MALEKZADEH, Arash. 9205 SW BARNES RD, ST. VINCENT HOSPITAL 97225 #517-01-1994 L2003 AN *020 †05

MANNING, Marilyn Poulsen. ■ 97229 #054-04-1986 L1987 OBG *020 †30

MAREADY, Douglas Milan. ■ 97225 #021-01-2006 L2006 IM *012

MARIK, Devapriya. 9155 SW BARNES RD STE 240 97225 #495-14-1986 L1994 *020

MARIK, Laszlo. ■ 97223 #473-02-1996 L2004 *100

MARTIN, Carolyn Johanna. ■ 97225 #025-07-1996 L2006 EM *020

MARTINEZ-POYER, Juan Luis. 9701 SW BARNES RD, STE 299 97225 #935-01-1984 L2003 OBG *020 †30

MASARIE, Fred E, Jr. ■ 97225 #040-02-1982 L1984 OS *050

MASARIE, Kathleen S. ■ 97225 #040-02-1982 L1991 PD *020 †55

MASENHIMER, Harry W, Jr. ■ 97224 #023-07-1953 L1960 IM *020

MASSAR, John Cliffton. ■ 97223 #040-02-1948 L1951 D *020 †15

MASSART, Mylynda Beryl. ■ 97223 #040-02-2006 L2006 FP *012

MATHESON, Robert Taylor. 9495 SW LOCUST ST, STE G 97223 #049-01-1973 L1975 D EM *050 †15

MAYER, Brian Jacob. 9205 SW BARNES RD, 5TH FLOOR SOUTH 97225 #017-20-2002 L2006 IM *020 †20

MC ALLISTER, William R. 9155 SW BARNES RD, STE 419 97225 #016-06-1962 L1964 GS *020 †85

MC ANULTY, John H, Jr. 9205 SW BARNES RD 97225 #024-07-1969 L1974 CD GP *020 †20

MC BRIDE, William Fenton. 4475 SW SCHOLLS FERRY RD, STE 150 97225 #060-01-1978 L1995 GP *020

MC CARTOR, Harold Robt. ■ 97225 #005-14-1961 L1972 P GE *075 †20

MC CLOSKEY, Margaret Mary. 9135 SW BARNES RD, STE 763 97225 #007-02-1987 L1990 PD *020 †55

MC CLUSKEY, Lisa Louise. 9555 SW BARNES RD, STE 150 97225 #040-02-1992 L1999 OBG *020 †30

MC DEVITT, Robert John. ■ 97229 #028-34-1955 L1956 P *071 †75

MC DOWELL, Susan F H. 9205 SW BARNES RD 97225 #038-06-1971 L1976 FM EM *020 †18

MCGEHEE-KELLY, Margo Anne. 7752 SW CHASE LN 97223 #024-01-1990 L2003 IM *020 †20

MCGREW, Gabrielle Marieba. ■ 97223 #005-19-2005 L2005 IM *012

MCILRAITH, Marlo Lenox. 15220 NW LAIDLAW RD, DOERNBECHER PEDIATRICS WES 97229 #005-18-1996 L2000 PD *020 †55

MC KANNA, Candace Kay. 9155 SW BARNES RD STE 418 97225 #056-05-1974 L1978 P *030

MCKEOWN, Michael John. ■ 97224 #024-01-1961 L1967 OBG OS *071 †30

MC KILLOP, Robert Graf. ■ 97229 #016-06-1956 L1962 ORS *071 †40

MEALY, Katherine E. ■ 97229 #047-07-1981 L1981 GPM FM *020

MEGA, Michael Steven. 9427 SW BARNES RD, COGNITIVE ASSESSMENT CLINI 97225 #010-01-1988 L1993 N *020 †75

MEHR, Seth Travis. 9205 SW BARNES RD, DEPT OF EMERGENCY 97225 #012-05-2000 L2000 EM *020 †20

MEINKE, Ann Elizabeth. ■ 97225 #040-02-2007 L2007 IM *012

MELLICK, Laura Jeanne. 2020 SW ABERCROMBIE PL, 2020 SW ABERCROMBIE PL 97225 #035-46-1988 L1992 EM *020 †16

MELVIN, Kenneth E W. 9205 SW BARNES RD STE 20 97225 #671-01-1958 L1972 END *071 †20

MELVIN, Marcus W. 9200 SW BARNES RD 97225 #671-01-1963 L1973 PS HS *020 †85,65

MENDELSON, Martin. ■ 97225 #035-48-1976 L1978 FM *062 †18

MERSHON, Christopher E. 9427 SW BARNES RD, KAISER - MOTHER JOSEPH PLA 97225 #040-02-1984 L1985 U *020 †95

MEUNIER, Paul Anthony. 11920 SW GREENBURG RD, BODY IMAGING RADIOLOGY 97223 #050-02-1981 L1989 DR *020 †80

MEYER-STROM, Paul M. 1225 NW MURRAY RD, STE 210 97229 #040-02-1983 L1988 CHP P *020 †75

MILES, Catherine. 9205 SW BARNES RD 97225 #040-02-1987 L1988 PTH *072 †50

MILLER, Janice Paulette. 9155 SW BARNES RD, STE 205 97225 #038-40-1994 L1996 IM *020 †20

MILLER, Jeffrey Glenn. 15220 NW LAIDLAW, STE 100 97229 #005-14-1991 L1999 PD *020 †55

MILLER, Matthew Walter. ■ 97225 #026-04-2007 L2007 OTO *012

MILLER, Thomas Scott. 9155 SW BARNES RD, STE 205 97225 #040-02-1971 L1976 IM GP *020 †20

MINAKATA, Kenji. 9155 SW BARNES RD, STE 240 97225 #572-01-1994 L2001 *020

MITIN, Timur. 9205 SW BARNES RD STE 20 97225 #024-07-2007 L2007 IM *012

MIZGAJSKI, Adam. 9205 SW BARNES RD, HOSPITALIST GROUP 97225 #759-04-1997 L2003 IM *020

MOHAMEDY, Imran Arif. 9205 SW BARNES RD # 20, ST VINCENT HOSP MED CTR 97225 #539-06-2000 L2002 IM *020

MOLLER, Hans Stern, III. 11782 SW BARNES RD, STE 300 97225 #038-43-1977 L1984 ORS *020 †40

MOON, David Kyungchun. 9205 SW BARNES RD, 1ST FL 97225 #003-01-1995 L2001 IM *020 †20

MOORE, Linda Yvonne. 9555 SW BARNES RD 97225 #005-18-1987 L1988 OBG *020 †30

MOORE, Michael Trevor. 9155 SW BARNES RD STE 205 97225 #048-13-1992 L1995 IM *020 †20

MORELAND, Kathryn. 9155 SW BARNES RD, STE 238 97225 #004-01-1979 L1992 IM *020 †20

MORENO, Raymond. 9340 SW BARNES RD, STE 202 97225 #043-01-1997 L2001 EM *020 †16

MORRIS, Amy Lee. 9427 SW BARNES RD, MOTHER JOSEPH PLAZA 97225 #034-01-1995 L2002 GS *020 †85

MORRIS, Marianne Cecile. 9427 SW BARNES RD, STE 395 97225 #040-02-1986 L2002 OBG *020 †30

MORRISON, Laura Yun. 9555 SW BARNES RD, STE 100 97225 #025-01-1999 L2004 OBG *020

MORROW, Mark Jay. 9427 SW BARNES RD, STE 595 97225 #024-05-1982 L2005 N OPH *020 †75

MOURDJINIS, Athanasios. ■ 97223 #418-01-1960 CD IM *020

MUKUL, Liberato Vadillo. ■ 97225 #005-06-1997 L2008 OBG *020 †30

MURRAY, Eric Leon. 9427 SW BARNES RD, STE 590 97225 #054-04-1998 L1999 IM *020 †20

MURTHY, Madhavi. 417 SW 117TH AVE, STE 100 97225 #495-09-1994 L1998 IM *020 †20

NASSON, Scott Lyngklip. ■ 97229 #010-01-1996 L2007 OSM *020 †40

NATHAN, Ranjana S. 12442 SW SCHOLLS FERRY RD, STE 106 97223 #495-33-1988 L1993 IM *020 †20

NATTER, Carl Edward. ■ 97229 #056-05-1960 L1961 OBG *071 †30

NATTER, Jean Anne Russell. ■ 97229 #056-05-1960 L1961 OS *071

NEIFING, James Lester. 9155 SW BARNES RD, STE 317 97225 #016-11-1986 L1987 END IM *020 †20

NELSON, Andrew Creighton. ■ 97229 #054-04-2007 L2007 EM *012

NEVREKAR, Dipti Venkatesh. ■ 97223 #040-02-2008 *012

NEWMAN, Barry M. 9427 SW BARNES RD, STE 598 97225 #035-48-1976 L2007 PDS GS *020 †85

NEWMAN, Elise. 9205 SW BARNES RD, ST. VINCENT'S HOSPITAL 97225 #049-01-1999 L2000 IM *020 †20

NICHOLS, William David. 9555 SW BARNES RD, CHILDRENS CLINIC PC 97225 #007-02-1977 L1982 PD PUD *020 †55

NORRIS, Susan L. ■ 97229 #060-01-1980 L1988 FM *050 †18

NOTTINGHAM, Ralph Edward. 9427 SW BARNES RD, MOTHER JOSEPH PLAZA 97225 #054-04-1973 L1978 PUD CCM *020 †20

NUNEZ, Dale Lee. ■ 97229 #048-13-1973 L1982 AN *020 †05

NYLUND, Karin Sandra. 9205 SW BARNES RD 97225 #047-06-1999 L2000 CHP P *100 †75

OGRYZLO, Karen. 9555 SW BARNES RD 97225 #065-05-1993 L2004 OBG *020 †30

OH, George Richard. 9427 SW BARNES RD 97225 #005-11-1980 L1985 GS *020 †85

OKUBO, Tadashi. 9205 SW BARNES RD, DEPT SURG 97225 #572-52-1974 TS *100

O'LEARY, Maura Ann. 8105 SW VALLEY VIEW DR 97225 #040-02-2002 L2007 FM *100 †18

OLLER, Sarah Rachel. ■ 97223 #035-47-2003 L2003 PD *020 †55

OLSON, Christine. 9427 SW BARNES RD, DEPT OF SURG 97225 #026-04-1996 L1998 GS *020 †85

OLSON, Donald Roy. 2505 NW PINNACLE DR, STE 209 97229 #040-02-1963 L1965 MDM IM *071 †20

OLSON, Terrence Jos. 417 SW 117TH AVE, STE 200 & 210 97225 #040-02-1988 L1992 IM *020 †20

OLSSON, Adam Richard. ■ 97229 #041-15-2006 L2007 *020

O'NEILL, Susan B. ■ 97229 #539-06-1986 L1992 AN *020

ONO, Alfred Kazuo. 9555 SW BARNES RD 97225 #026-04-1971 L1973 OBG *020 †30

ORMAN, Melissa R. 9340 SW BARNES RD, STE 202 97225 #005-11-1995 L1999 EM *020 †16

ORMAN, Robert Barton. 9340 SW BARNES RD, STE 202 97225 #012-05-1995 L2000 EM *020 †16

OSBORN, Roger Cook. 9205 SW BARNES RD, STE WP200 97225 #048-12-1978 L1989 CD CCM *020 †20

OSERAN, Daniel Spencer. 9427 SW BARNES RD, STE 490 97225 #005-18-1979 L1992 ICE *020 †20

OSMAN, Shukri Aden. 9701 SW BARNES RD, STE 110 97225 #040-02-1996 L1999 NEP *020 †20

OTTO, Lesley Nicoloff. 9155 SW BARNES RD, STE 634 97225 #026-04-1993 L1994 OBG *020 †20

OWENS, Michael Martin. 9701 SW BARNES RD, WEST HILLS 97225 #019-02-1997 L2003 GE *050 †20

OYAMA, Albert A. 9205 SW BARNES RD 97225 #040-02-1953 PTH CLP *071 †50

PALLA, Suvarna Reddy. 6640 SW REDWOOD LN 97224 #495-65-1992 L1999 M *020 †75

PANDIPATI, Santosh. 9701 SW BARNES RD, STE 299 97225 #025-01-2000 L2007 OBG *020 †30

PANOW, Naima Stephen. 9370 SW GREENBURG RD 97223 #528-01-1959 L1978 OBG *071

PANWALA, Sanjiv Manharlal. 9205 SW BARNES RD, ST VINCENTS HOSP HOSP OFC 97225 #054-04-1993 L2000 **IM** *020 †20

PARK, Eun Kyung. ■ 97225 #047-06-2005 **P** *012

PATEL, Ashit Gajendra. ■ 97223 #305-01-2000 L2007 **ICE** *012 †20 ‡

PATEL, Jayant. 9205 SW BARNES RD 97225 #495-48-1973 L1989 **GS IG** *020 †85

PAUSIG, Ronald Gerald. 9205 SW BARNES RD 97225 #038-41-1978 L1980 **IM** *020 †20

PAYNE, Susan Dannette. 9427 SW BARNES RD, STE 395 97225 #005-15-1991 L2000 **OBG** *020 †30

PAZ, Francisco Miguel. 9205 SW BARNES RD STE 20, VINCENT HOSPITAL 97225 #026-04-2005 L2005 **IM** *012

PEASLEE, David Blanchard. 9205 SW BARNES RD #005-19-1989 L1993 **EM** *020 †16

PEEL, David H. 9340 SW BARNES RD, STE 202 97225 #050-02-1991 L1993 **EM** *020 †16

PELMAS, Carol Jean. 9427 SW BARNES RD 97225 #032-01-1985 L1993 **OSM GS** *020 †40

PENA, Angeles. 15220 NW LAIDLAW RD, OHSU DOERNBECHER PEDIATRIC 97229 #005-02-1992 L2001 **PD** *020 †55

PERDUE, Nicole Lynn. 9205 SW BARNES RD 97225 #025-12-2002 L2006 **MPD** *020 †20,55

PEREDNIA, Douglas Alan. ■ 97225 #028-02-1984 L1991 **D** *020 †20

PERKINS, Dahra Diane. ■ 97225 #005-06-2005 L2005 **FP** *012

PERKINS, Norris H. ■ 97223 #040-02-1953 **IM OS** *071

PERRONE, Theresa Lynn. ■ 97225 #035-08-1978 L2002 **PTH** *050 †50

PETER, David R. 6640 SW REDWOOD LN, THE PORTLAND CLINIC SOUTH 97224 #035-45-1988 L1994 **FM** *020 †18

PETRILLO, Raymond Jos. 9701 SW BARNES RD, STE 110 97225 #041-02-1984 L1990 **NEP IM** *020 †20

PETTERSEN, Teri Lynne. 9555 SW BARNES RD, CHILDRENS CLINIC PC 97225 #001-02-1985 L1986 **PD** *020 †55

PHELAN, John Patrick. PO BOX 25184 97298 #539-02-1959 L1964 **DR** *071 †55,80

PHILLIPS, Paul Mathew. ■ 97229 #038-41-2003 L2007 **OPH** *012

PHINNEY, Edward S. 9155 SW BARNES RD STE 217 97225 #034-01-1981 L1982 **GS** *020 †85

PINEDA, Jorge Alberto, Jr. ■ 97229 #028-03-2003 L2004 **AN** *100

PLUEDEMAN, Carin Kay. 9735 SW SHADY LN, STE 200 97223 #040-02-1993 L1994 **FM** *020 †18

POHOWALLA, Parvez J. 9427 SW BARNES RD, STE 390 97225 #495-20-1970 L1984 **CHN PHP** *020

POKORNY, David Jos. 9155 SW BARNES RD STE 839 97225 #030-06-1978 L1980 **D** OS *020 †15

POLIAKOFF, Claude S. ■ 97229 #035-01-1964 L1967 **GS** *071 †85

POPPE, John Karl. ■ 97225 #035-45-1937 L1946 **TS** *071 †85,90

POTTS, Richard Lindley. ■ 97229 #649-01-1960 **GP OS** *071

PRINS, Renee Carolyn. ■ 97223 #005-12-2006 L2006 **IM** *012

PULS, Henry Thomas. ■ 97225 #019-02-2007 L2007 **PD** *012

PURNELL, Susanne. 9555 SW BARNES RD, CHILDRENS CLINIC PC 97225 #050-02-1990 L2001 **PD** *020 †55

PUTERBAUGH, James Stephen. 9155 SW BARNES RD, STE 422 97225 #005-14-1973 L1974 **IM** *020 †20

PUTNAM, James Stanley. 9400 SW BARNES RD, STE 250 97225 #040-02-1982 L1983 **DR** *020 †20

QUILES, Nitza I. 9555 SW BARNES RD, STE 270 97225 #042-01-1988 L1999 **PD** *020 †55

QUILICI, Nate Dominic. 9205 SW BARNES RD, DEPT OF RADIOLOGY 97225 #040-02-1966 L1971 **RNR R** *020 †80

RADDISH, Michele. 9205 SW BARNES RD, JERRY FRENCH CHILD ST VIN 97225 #016-43-1982 L2001 **PD** *020 †55

RAGADE, Jagdish Rammohan. 9205 SW BARNES RD 97225 #495-17-1996 L2007 **P** *020 †75

RAGADE, Namrata Jhamb. ■ 97229 #495-17-1996 L2007 **ID IM** *020 †20

RAGLIONE, U W. 9205 SW BARNES RD 97225 #040-02-1952 L1953 **GS** *071 †85

RAITIERE, Martin Norman. 9900 SW WILSHIRE ST STE 22 97225 #048-13-1983 L1989 **P** *020 †75

RANADE, Nalini M. ■ 97229 #495-28-1959 L1978 **PD** *071 †55

RATH, Brett Michael. 6640 SW REDWOOD LN, CARMAN MED PLAZA 97224 #040-02-1980 L1994 **FM** *020 †18

REDDI, Rohini. ■ 97229 #051-04-2007 **IM** *012

REDDOCH, Jana Marie. 9155 SW BARNES RD, PORTLAND GYN/ONC #416 97225 #010-01-1989 L1990 **GO GYN** *020 †30

REDDY, Jayaprakash Davlap. ■ 97224 #495-37-2002 L2006 **IM** *020 †20

REED, Stacy Nicole. 9205 SW BARNES RD # 20, PROVIDENCE ST VINCENTS 97225 #040-02-2006 L2006 **IM** *012

REGER, Vincent Alan. 9155 SW BARNES RD STE 406 97225 #040-02-1981 L1990 **GS** *020 †85

REINDL, Elizabeth Ann. 9427 SW BARNES RD, STE 395 97225 #028-34-1996 L2000 **OBG** *020

REITZ, Thomas Max. 9205 SW BARNES RD, ST. VINCENT HOSP EMERGENCY 97225 #019-02-1998 L2000 **EM** *020 †16

RENDLEMAN, Neal James. 10305 SW PARK WAY, STE 300 97225 #010-01-1981 L1982 **IM** *020 †20

RENWICK, Stephen Einar. 9427 SW BARNES RD #005-06-1989 L1998 **ORS** *020 †40

REULE, G Ronald. ■ 97225 #040-02-1956 L1957 **U** *071 †95

REUTHER, Cecille Herrera. 9450 SW BARNES RD, STE 200 97225 #748-10-1991 L2004 **P** *020 †75

REYNOLDS, Lisa Anne. 9555 SW BARNES RD, CHILDRENS CLINIC PC 97225 #005-14-1991 L1994 **PD** *020 †55

RIBBINK, Philippa J. 9205 SW BARNES RD 97225 #035-20-1991 L1997 **OBG** *020 †30

RICHARDS, Oren Rogers, Jr. 9205 SW BARNES RD 97225 #040-02-1947 L1949 **IM** *071

RICHMAN, Edward Merle. 9555 SW BARNES RD, CHILDRENS CLINIC PC 97225 #028-02-1971 L1976 **PD** *020 †55

RIDDICK, Carl Anthony. 9155 SW BARNES RD, STE 840 97225 #023-07-1984 L1997 **PCC** *020 †20

RILEY, Beth Ann. 9427 SW BARNES RD, STE 395 97225 #005-11-1992 L1996 **OBG** *020 †30

RIORDAN, John Philip. 9155 SW BARNES RD STE 240 97225 #671-01-1980 *100

ROBINSON, Paul James. 15404 SW 116TH AVE, OREGON MEDICAL EYE CLINIC 97224 #008-01-1955 L1960 **OPH** *072 †35

RODGERS, Michael Kenneth. 9205 SW BARNES RD 97225 #005-12-1993 L1996 **FM** *020 †18

ROGAN, Alice. 3019 NW MONTARA LOOP 97229 #048-13-1995 L2004 **CHP** *020 †75

ROHRER, Daniel C. 9155 SW BARNES RD, STE 210 97225 #035-09-1987 L1988 **NS** *020 †20

ROL, Alida Neeltje. 9205 SW BARNES RD 97225 #005-07-1980 L1982 **OBG** *020 †30

ROSE, Charissa. 9205 SW BARNES RD 5E 97225 #040-02-1994 L2001 **P** *040 †75

ROSEN, Marvin. 6663 SW BEAVERTN HLSDL HWY, PMB 291 97225 #035-01-1967 L1972 **P** CHP *020 †55,75

ROTHENBERGER, Gary Byron. ■ 97223 #040-02-1965 L1966 **GS VS** *071 †85

ROUNDY, Neil Edmund. ■ 97223 #003-01-2007 L2007 **GS** *012

ROZELLE, Christopher Lawr. ■ 97225 #028-34-2005 L2005 **PTH** *012

RUSHANAEDY, Agustinus. 9427 SW BARNES RD 97225 #165-04-1975 L1985 **U** *020 †95

RUSHING, Rodney Scott. 9555 SW BARNES RD, STE 150 97225 #047-06-1996 L2003 **GO OBG** *020 †30

RYAN, William Michael. 9155 SW BARNES RD, STE 733 97225 #021-01-1978 L1990 **IM IMG** *020 †20

RYDZIK, Beata Ludmila. 9427 SW BARNES RD, STE 495 97225 #025-01-2000 L2004 **D** *020 †15

SACHDEV, Naveen. 9155 SW BARNES RD, STE 41 97225 #495-58-1980 L1984 **CD IM** *020 †20

SACKER, Allan Ray. 9205 SW BARNES RD 97225 #056-06-1988 L1989 **PTH** *020 †50

SACKS, Martine Richardson. 9205 SW BARNES RD, CENTER FOR CHILDERN 97225 #035-47-1988 L1989 **PD** *020 †55

SALTER, Kelli D. ■ 97229 #007-02-2003 L2003 **GS** *012

SAMAGH, Gunjeet Kaur. 15285 NW CENTRAL DR, STE 100 97229 #065-09-1999 L2005 **FM** *020 †18

SANCHEZ, Carlos David. 9340 SW BARNES RD, STE 202 97225 #036-07-2002 L2002 **EM** *020 †16

SANDERSON, Margaret Olwen. ■ 97229 #061-01-1974 L1992 **FM** *074 †18

SANDMEIER, Robert H. 9250 SW HALL BLVD 97223 #034-01-1991 L1997 **ORS OSM** *020 †40

SANDS, Vicki Marie. 9155 SW BARNES RD STE 529 97225 #040-02-1991 L1994 **EM** *020 †16

SANG, Nora Michelle. 9555 SW BARNES RD 97225 #040-02-1994 L1996 **OBG** *020 †30

SASADEUSZ, Kevin Joseph. 9400 SW BARNES RD, STE 307 97225 #038-41-1996 L2001 **DR** *020 †80

SCHAFIR, Alexander David. 9205 SW BARNES RD, STE MT2800 97225 #005-14-1988 L1993 **IM** *020 †20

SCHMIDT, Joshua Don. ■ 97225 #040-02-2004 L2005 **GS** *100

SCHNEIDER, Edward Michael. ■ 97225 #040-02-1961 L1962 **PTH GS** *071 †50

SCHNEIDER, Erin E. ■ 97225 #040-02-2008 *012

SCHOOLFIELD, Matt Wayne. ■ 97223 #046-01-2002 L2007 **TS** *012 †85

SCHULTZ, Sarah Virginia. ■ 97225 #017-20-2006 L2006 **IM** *012

SCHUTT, Gregory Paul. 9340 SW BARNES RD STE 20 97225 #056-06-2000 L2000 **EM** *100 †16

SCHWAB, Tara Ann. ■ 97225 #016-43-2004 L2004 **PD** *020 †55

SCHWARZ, Gerald Robt. 9155 SW BARNES RD, UROLOGY CONSULTANTS P.C 97225 #028-02-1963 L1974 **U** *071 †95

SCHWENNINGER, Mary F. 9555 SW BARNES RD, STE 270 97225 #023-01-1975 L1978 **PD** *071 †55

SCOTT, Bj. 417 SW 117TH AVE, 2ND FL 97225 #045-01-1994 L1997 **IM** *020 †20

SCOTT, David Ross. 9205 SW BARNES RD 97225 #067-01-1972 L1977 **PTH MM** *062 †50

SCRIVEN, Alistair Jeremy. 9205 SW BARNES RD, NW PERMANENTE PC 97225 #028-02-1990 L2003 **PUD** *020 †20

SEELEY, Miles Kenneth. 9555 SW BARNES RD, STE 100 97225 #040-02-1974 L1975 **OBG** *020 †30

SEHDEV, Paul Singh. 9155 SW BARNES RD, STE 931 97225 #019-02-1993 L1994 **ID** *020 †20

SEUNG, Steven Kysung. 9205 SW BARNES RD 97225 #016-02-1994 L1998 **RO** *020 †80

SEYMOUR, John Patrick. 9205 SW BARNES RD 97225 #040-02-1989 L1990 **GPM** *020 †20,70

SHAFFER, Brian Scott. 9135 SW BARNES RD, STE 663 97225 #024-01-1986 L1994 **U** *020 †95

SHAH, Maulin Piyush. 9205 SW BARNES RD 97225 #048-04-2000 L2006 **IM** *020

SHAKIR, Maha Sabah. ■ 97229 #528-03-1993 L2002 **GS** *020 †85

SHANAHAN, Michael Bruce. 9205 SW BARNES RD, WEST PAVILLION 2002 97225 #056-05-1976 L1981 **IM** *020 †20

SHARFF, Jeffrey Alan. 9205 SW BARNES RD, ST VINCENT HOSPITAL 97225 #040-02-1977 L1978 **EM** *020 †20,16

SHARFF, Katie Anne. ■ 97291 #016-02-2008 *012

SHAWKY, Hesham Abdel F. 9155 SW BARNES RD, STE 240 97225 #915-02-1980 L1995 *100

SHERBIN, Vandy Lee. 850 SW 67TH PL 97225 #038-06-1990 L2000 **PCC** **IM** *020 †20

SHERMAN, Linda Ann. ■ 97225 #041-02-1979 L1981 **PHM IM** *071 †50,20

SHERTZ, Michael David. 9340 SW BARNES RD, STE 202 97225 #035-09-1996 L1999 **EM** *020 †16

SHIELDS, Paul Dixon. ■ 97225 #040-02-1967 L1968 **AN** *071

SHIN, Sejung. 13305 NW CORNELL RD, STE C 97229 #016-11-1990 L2000 **EM** *020 †16

SHIRZAD, Khalid. ■ 97223 #030-06-2004 L2004 **ORS** *012

SHUMAKER, Douglas Allen. 9701 SW BARNES RD, WEST HILLS RD #040-02-1994 L1995 **GE** *020 †20

SHUMATE, Lillian. ■ 97225 #748-08-1967 L1973 **OBG** *020 †30

SHUTE, David Evan. 9427 SW BARNES RD, STE 590 97225 #016-11-1984 L1985 **IM** *020 †20

SIGURDSSON, Hannes Jon S. 9205 SW BARNES RD, BEHAVIROAL HEALTH DIVISION 97225 #484-01-1987 L2002 **P** *020 †75

SIMKOFF, William Louis. 9427 SW BARNES RD, STE 498 97225 #038-41-1975 L1981 **CD** *020 †20

SIMMONS, Robert D. 9205 SW BARNES RD 97225 #028-34-1963 L1972 **PS** *071 †85,65

SIMPSON, Theresa Sue. 9555 SW BARNES RD, STE 100 97225 #054-04-1988 L1989 **OBG** *020 †30

SINGH, Taranpreet. 9155 SW BARNES RD, STE 240 97225 #495-29-1983 L2000 *100

SIQUEIRA, Carmelindo. 9155 SW BARNES RD STE 310 97225 #187-03-1970 L1982 **CD IM** *020 †20

SKINNER, Robert Edward. 9427 SW BARNES RD 97225 #040-02-1985 L1987 **U** *020 †95

SKLAR, Ronald Stuart. 9205 SW BARNES RD STE 380, KAISER PERINAIAL OFFICE 97225 #038-41-1982 L1983 **NPM PD** *020 †55

SKOGRAND, Richard Paul. 9205 SW BARNES RD 97225 #040-02-1984 L1985 **EM** *020 †16

SLEVEN, Rodger Alan. 9701 SW BARNES RD STE 300 97225 #005-02-1976 L1977 **GE IM** *020 †20

SLOAN, Angela Renee. 9155 SW BARNES RD, STE 302 97225 #007-02-1996 L1998 **IM** *020 †20

SMILEY, Clayton Michael. 9701 SW BARNES RD, STE 110 97225 #016-02-1998 L2007 **NEP** *020 †20

SMITH, James Kenneth, Jr. 9155 SW BARNES RD, STE 314 97225 #012-01-1985 L1998 **RHU IM** *020 †20

SMITH, Robert Keith. 9427 SW BARNES RD, MOTHER JOSEPH PLAZA 97225 #040-02-1975 L1977 **ORS EM** *020 †40

SNYDER, Kelvin Kenneth. 9555 SW BARNES RD, STE 255 97225 #019-02-1980 L1986 **AN PD** *020 †55

SOGN, Richard Randolph. 9900 SW WILSHIRE ST STE 26 97225 #005-15-1980 L1989 **P CHP** *020 †75 ‡

SOHLBERG, Rolf Charles. 11782 SW BARNES RD, STE 300 97225 #054-04-1988 L1994 **HS** *020 †40

SOHN, Richard Hoon. 9427 SW BARNES RD, STE 498 97225 #023-07-1995 L2004 **IC** *020 †20

SOLOMON, Nitikul S. ■ 97229 #891-02-1991 L2005 **PG** *020 †55

SONG, Xiang-Hong. ■ 97229 #243-43-1990 L2001 **IM** *020 †20
SOOT, Ilmar. 11782 SW BARNES RD, STE 300 97225 #040-02-1966 L1968 **ORS** *020 †40
SPENCE, Donna Kay. 1675 SW MARLOW AVE 97225 #048-02-1996 L1999 **PD** *020 †55
SPRINGER, John Henry. 9370 SW GREENBURG RD STE O 97223 #016-43-1957 L1960
   PD *071 †55
STANFORD, Edward Jos. 9900 SW WILSHIRE ST, STE 260 97225 #036-05-1989 L1990
   CHP *020 †75
STANGER, Mary Ellen. 9155 SW BARNES RD, STE 306 97225 #041-07-1957 L1972
   CHN *071 †55
STANLEY, Lauren Keith. 9205 SW BARNES RD 97225 #040-02-1962 L1965 **AN** *071 †05
STEED, Leslie Marie. 9701 SW BARNES RD, STE 110 97225 #054-04-1987 L1988
   IM NEP *020 †20
STEELE, Arthur F S, Jr. ■ 97229 #040-02-1969 L1972 **OPH** *020 †35
STEINBERG, Richard Wm. 9205 SW BARNES RD 97225 #026-04-1979 L1981 **U** *020 †95
STEVENS, Kristin R. 417 SW 117TH AVE, STE 200 & 210 97225 #048-04-1998 L2003
   D *020 †15 ‡
STEWART, Timothy W. 9555 SW BARNES RD, STE 100 97225 #040-02-1984 L1985
   OBG *020 †30
STOCK, Christine L. 9205 SW BARNES RD, ST VINCENT'S HOSPITAL 97225
   #011-04-2004 L2004 **IM** *100 †20
STONE, Jason Richard. 9450 SW BARNES RD, STE 200 97225 #005-14-2001 L2006 **P** *020 †75
STONE, Lee Jayson. 9701 SW BARNES RD, WEST HILLS 97225 #028-34-1989 L2001
   GE IM *020 †20
STRAIN, Donna Dorothy. 9205 SW BARNES RD, STE 200 97225 #063-01-1976 L1978
   IM *020 †20
STRAUSS, Mitchell John. 9427 SW BARNES RD, STE 395 97225 #028-34-1991 L1999
   OBG *020 †30
STULL, Carol Grammer. 9555 SW BARNES RD, STE 100 97225 #028-02-1978 L1998
   OBG *020 †20
SUH, Hyun Sook. 9155 SW BARNES RD, STE 317 97225 #005-19-1987 L1993 **IM END** *020 †20
SULTANY, Gary Lee. 9155 SW BARNES RD, STE 314 97225 #026-04-1976 L1982
   RHU IM *020 †20
SUN, Christopher. 9205 SW BARNES RD STE 20, VINCENT MEDICAL 97225
   #919-02-2003 L2005 *100
SUTHERLAND, Donald Wood. 9427 SW BARNES RD, STE 498 97225 #024-01-1957 L1963
   CD IM *071 †20
SWANK, Roy Laver. ■ 97225 #016-06-1935 L1954 **ON** *071 †75
SWANSON, Jeffrey Scott. 9427 SW BARNES RD, STE 596 97225 #396-04-1977 L1979
   TS CD *020 †85,90
SYNA, Deborah R. 9155 SW BARNES RD, STE 531 97225 #048-02-1988 L1992 **N CN** *020 †75
TAITANO, Anthony Marion. 9555 SW BARNES RD, STE 100 97225 #014-01-1977 L1979
   OBG *020 †30
TAKAHASHI, Tetsuro. ■ 97224 #572-03-1960 L1975 **P CHP** *020 †75
TANABE, Calvin Tsugio. 9155 SW BARNES RD STE 440 97225 #040-02-1964 L1965
   NS *040 †25
TANK, Julia Elizabeth. 9701 SW BARNES RD, STE 110 97225 #040-02-1987 L1988
   NEP *020 †20
TARAZI, Nabil Yousef. 9155 SW BARNES RD, STE 240 97225 #605-01-1982 L1997
   TS GS *020 †85,90
TATSUMI, Robert Louis. 9695 SW MELNORE ST 97225 #040-02-2002 L2003 **ORS** *100
TAYLOR, Gregory Chas. 9205 SW BARNES RD, PROVIDENCE ST. VINCENT MC 97225
   #014-01-1988 L2001 **AN** *020 †05
TEN EYCK, James Richard. 9205 SW BARNES RD 97225 #040-02-1963 L1974
   PS GS *071 †85,65
TENNANT, Robert Edward. 11785 SW CORBY DR, STE 300 97225 #010-02-1984 L1990
   ORS U *020 †40
THIGPEN, Kathy Ann. 9205 SW BARNES RD, PROVIDENCE ST VINCENT MEDI 97225
   #016-42-1993 L1994 **CD** *020 †20
THOMAS, Paul Norman. 11790 SW BARNES RD, STE 140 97225 #032-01-1985 L1988
   PD *020 †20
THOMASON, Mary A L. 12442 SW SCHOLLS FERRY RD, STE 100 97223 #040-02-1999 L2007
   IM *020 †20
THOMPSON, Catherine W. 9555 SW BARNES RD, CHILDRENS CLINIC PC 97225
   #041-01-1982 L1983 **PD** *020 †55
THOMPSON, James Edward. 9340 SW BARNES RD, STE 202 97225 #040-02-1997 L1999
   EM *020 †16
THOMPSON, Mollie E. 9155 SW BARNES RD, STE 314 97225 #034-01-1997 L1998
   RHU *020 †20
THOMPSON, Rodney Lee, Jr. 9155 SW BARNES RD, STE 529 97225 #026-04-1997 L2000
   EM *020 †20
THOMPSON, Steven Keith. ■ 97225 #422-01-1984 L1988 **PTH** *020 †50
THONGOUTHAITHIP, Viyada. 9155 SW BARNES RD, STE 310 97225 #244-02-1972 L1981
   CD IM *020 †20
THUM, Lisa Ann. 9427 SW BARNES RD, STE 395 97225 #048-04-1994 L1998 **OBG** *020 †30
TIEU, Brandon Hoavinh. ■ 97223 #039-01-2002 L2002 **GS** *012
TOMKORIA, Smita. 9555 SW BARNES RD, CHILDRENS CLINIC PC 97225 #039-01-1997 L2004
   PD *020 †55
TOMLINSON, Mark William. 9701 SW BARNES RD, STE 299 97225 #025-07-1985 L2000
   MFM OBG *020 †30
TOPINKA, John August, Jr. 9155 SW BARNES RD STE 430, THE EYE CLINIC PC 97225
   #038-41-1964 L1974 **OPH IM** *020 †10
TRAJANO, Cesar Antonio. 9735 SW SHADY LN, STE 104 97223 #026-04-1990 L1991 **GP** *020
TRAN, Diane Hoa. ■ 97225 #039-01-2000 L2004 **IM** *100 †05
TRAN, Man Minh. 9205 SW BARNES RD STE 20, VINCENT HOSPITAL 97225
   #016-06-2003 L2004 **IM** *100 †20
TRAUSCH, Ann Manion. 9205 SW BARNES RD 97225 #040-02-1993 L1997 **FM** *020 †18
TRENHOLME, Stuart Edward. 9155 SW BARNES RD, STE 431 97225 #054-04-1972 L1977
   IM CD *020
TRUMBO, Roy Wade. ■ 97223 #020-12-2004 L2004 **IM** *020 †20
TSAI, Richard Zelos. 417 SW 117TH AVE, STE 200 & 210 97225 #028-02-1998 L2001
   IM *020 †20
TSENG, Daniel. 9155 SW BARNES RD 97225 #016-11-1999 L1999 **GS** *020 †85
TURCO, Ronald. 9011 SW BEAVERTN HLSDL HWY, STE 2B 97225 #041-02-1966 L1973
   PYA *020 †75
TURKER, Ronald Jeff. 9427 SW BARNES RD, KAISER -ORTHOPEDICS 97225
   #035-15-1987 L1998 **OP** *020 †40

TURNER, Craig Douglas. 9155 SW BARNES RD, STE 422 97225 #005-18-1994 L2000
   U *020 †95
TURNER, Fredrick Wm. ■ 97225 #040-02-1957 **P** *071
TURNER, Lance Drayton. 6655 SW HAMPTON ST, STE 110 97223 #040-02-1991 L1992
   CHP *020 †20
TURNER, Lisa S. 417 SW 117TH AVE, 2ND FL 97225 #016-02-1993 L2000 **D** *020 †15
UDDIN, Minhaz Mohammed. 9205 SW BARNES RD, PROVIDENCE HEART INSTITUTE 97225
   #160-04-1977 L2003 *020
UNDERHILL, Kelly Jane. 9205 SW BARNES RD, DEPT OF RADIATION ONCOLOGY 97225
   #065-05-1992 L2006 **RO** *020 †80
UNGER, Phillip Stephen. 3415 SW VISTA DR 97225 #017-20-1968 L1973 **IM** *020 †20
URMAN, Marvin J. ■ 97223 #040-02-1951 **FM** *071
URRY, Mary Stewart. 7170 SW GARDEN HOME RD 97223 #352-08-1960 L1969 **GP PD** *071 †55
UTKE, Maria Gabriele. ■ 97225 #037-01-1988 L1990 **GP** *020
VALLEJO, Ronald. 9250 SW HALL BLVD, THE PORTLAND CLINIC 97223 #748-20-1988 L2004
   IM *020 †20
VANDERHEYDEN, Nicole Mari. ■ 97229 #016-11-2000 L2000 **CCS** *020 †85
VAN DER VEER-HARRIS, E. 6650 SW REDWOOD LN, STE 150 97224 #040-02-1998 L2000
   IM *020 †20
VANKO, Mark Marshall. 9340 SW BARNES RD, STE 202 97225 #016-43-1987 L1988
   EM *020 †16
VAN SICKLE, David Gordon. ■ 97225 #010-01-1966 L1970 **IM GE** *071
VAWTER, Michael Harry. 9427 SW BARNES RD, STE 498 97225 #030-06-1968 L1989
   CD IM *020 †20
VELTMAN, Larry Louis. 9555 SW BARNES RD, STE 100 97225 #040-02-1968 L1975
   OBG *020 †30
VENNES, George J, Jr. ■ 97229 #040-02-1958 L1963 **PTH NM** *071 †50
VETTO, R Mark. 9155 SW BARNES RD, PETROFF FACIAL SURGERY 97225 #041-02-1949 L1963
   GS VS *071 †85,90
VLACHOU, Maria. ■ 97225 #418-02-1995 L2007 *100
VON BORSTEL, Robert C, II. 9450 SW BARNES RD STE 23 97225 #040-02-1995 L1999
   P *020 †75
VOSS, Charles Bradley. 9205 SW BARNES RD 97225 #055-01-1983 L1993 **IM** *020 †20
VU, Kim-Chi. 9555 SW BARNES RD STE 27 97225 #040-02-1995 L1999 **PS** *020 †65
WADIA, Yasmin. 9155 SW BARNES RD, STE 240 97225 #496-07-1983 L1997 *020
WAGNER, Fredrick Chas. 9205 SW BARNES RD, DEPT OF RADIATION ONCOLOGY 97225
   #005-14-1971 L1976 **RO** *020 †80
WAGNER, Patricia L. 9155 SW BARNES RD, STE 205 97225 #040-02-1984 L1985 **IM** *020
WAGNER, Robert Bastian. 9205 SW BARNES RD 97225 #041-13-1972 L1973 **FM** *020 †18
WAINWRIGHT, Stacey Ann. ■ 97229 #032-01-1996 L2000 **END** *020 †20
WALCZYK, Michael Hanley. 9701 SW BARNES RD, STE 110 97225 #041-09-1981 L1982
   NEP *020 †20
WALDMANN, George Edwin. 9600 SW OAK ST STE 340 97223 #040-02-1965 L1970
   FM *030 †18 ‡
WALDORF, Kathleen Anne. 12400 NW CORNELL RD, STE 200 97229 #010-02-1986 L1991
   PS *020 †65
WALKEY, Marilyn Mills. ■ 97223 #035-03-1979 L1993 **DR** *020 †80
WALLER, Frederick T. 9155 SW BARNES RD, STE 211 97225 #040-02-1972 L1974 **NS** *020 †25
WALSH, Craig Robert. 9427 SW BARNES RD, STE 498 97225 #040-02-1994 L2002
   CD IM *020 †20
WALTEMATH, Charles Louis. ■ 97225 #028-03-1960 L1968 **AN** *040 †05
WAN, Feng. 9155 SW BARNES RD STE 240 97225 #243-76-1983 L1995 *020
WANG, Su. ■ 97229 #243-70-1983 L2003 **PCP** *020 †50
WARHUS, Damon Anthony. 9555 SW BARNES RD, STE 100 97225 #005-18-1997 L2001
   OBG *020 †30
WASHUT, Tammy Lynn. ■ 97223 #040-02-2006 L2006 **GS** *012
WATRING, Watson Glenn. ■ 97225 #055-01-1963 L1963 **GO GYN** *071 †30
WATSON, James Mac Donald. 7255 SW HUNT CLUB LN, 97280 97223 #016-02-1949 L1968
   N *020 †75
WATSON, Peter Town. 9701 SW BARNES RD STE 299 97225 #041-01-1973 L1979
   MFM *020 †30
WAYSON, Barbara. 9205 SW BARNES RD 97225 #040-02-1986 L1987 **EM** *020 †16
WEBBER, John David. 11501 SW PACIFIC HWY, STE 100 97223 #040-02-1965 L1966
   GS *072 †85
WEEKS, Jeffrey Power. 12442 SW SCHOLLS FERRY RD 97223 #012-05-1975 L1976
   FM *020 †18
WEINSTEIN, Amy Samara. 9205 SW BARNES RD 97225 #040-02-1996 L2004 **DR** *020 †80
WEIRICH, Samuel Draper. 9205 SW BARNES RD 97225 #010-01-1986 L1994 **ORS** *020 †40
WEISMAN, Russell, Jr. ■ 97229 #038-06-1946 L2006 **BBK HEM** *071 †20
WENTROSS, Sally Janine. 9701 SW BARNES RD, STE 200 97225 #025-12-1990 L1991
   OBG *020 †30
WEPRIN, Jeffrey Joseph. 9701 SW BARNES RD, STE 300 97225 #038-41-2000 L2006
   GE *020 †20
WESTON, Mark Cecil. 9155 SW BARNES RD, STE 210 97225 #030-05-1990 L2000
   ORS *020 †40
WETTACH, George Randolphe. ■ 97224 #051-07-2006 L2006 **PTH** *012
WHEATLEY, Michael John. 9205 SW BARNES RD 97225 #025-01-1985 L1992 **PS** *020 †85,65
WHITE, Charles Stephen. 9205 SW BARNES RD 97225 #040-02-1976 L1979 **EM** *020 †16
WICKLUND, Roger Allen. 9427 SW BARNES RD 97225 #056-05-1974 L1975 **U** *020 †95
WIEST, John Walter. 9155 SW BARNES RD STE 321 97225 #005-14-1979 L1985 **VS GS** *020 †85
WILKINS, John Howard. 9155 SW BARNES RD, STE 430 97225 #040-02-1983 L1984
   OPH IM *020 †20,35
WILKINS, Paul California. ■ 97225 #048-04-1948 L1960 **OPH** *071 †35
WILKINSON, David B. 9427 SW BARNES RD, STE 595 97225 #067-01-1999 L1999 **CN** *020 †75
WILLIAMSON, Merle Dean. 9205 SW BARNES RD 97225 #040-02-1982 L1985 **AN** *020 †05
WILLIAMSON, Weldon Kent. 9155 SW BARNES RD, STE 321 97225 #036-05-1993 L1994
   VS *020 †85
WILLIS, Dale Michael. 9155 SW BARNES RD, STE 931 97225 #040-02-1981 L2000
   PDE *020 †55
WILLIS, David Wm. 1675 SW MARLOW AVE, STE 204 97225 #041-02-1976 L1977
   PD CHP *020 †55
WILLS, David Max. 13200 SW PACIFIC HWY 97223 #040-02-1977 L1980 **FM** *020 †18
WILSON, Addison Ray. 15285 NW CENTRAL DR 97229 #040-02-1989 L1992 **FM** *020 †18
WILSON, Geoffrey Marks. 9427 SW BARNES RD, STE 498 97225 #035-01-1988 L1995
   CD *020 †20
WILSON, James Edward. 9205 SW BARNES RD 97225 #040-02-1981 L1985 **AN** *020

WILSON, John Walsh. 9205 SW BARNES RD 97225 #040-02-1966 L1973 **CD IM** *071 †20

WILSON, Michael Allen. 9427 SW BARNES RD 97225 #025-01-1981 L1987 **CD IM** *020 †20

WILSON, Robert Joseph. 15755 SW SEQUOIA PKWY, ORTHOPEDICS NORTHWEST 97224 #003-01-1977 L1982 **ORS** *020 †40

WISDOM, David Scott. 11782C SW BARNES RD, # 300 97225 #021-05-1965 L1970 **ORS** *071 †40

WITHERSPOON, Scott Robert. ■ 97229 #028-34-2003 L2007 **OPH** *100

WITTKOPP, Beverly L. 9555 SW BARNES RD, CHILDRENS CLINIC PC 97225 #056-05-1971 L1977 **PD RHU** *020 †55

WOLF, Ronald Frank. 9155 SW BARNES RD, STE 940 97225 #040-02-1987 L1995 **GS SO** *020 †85

WOOD, James Anderson. 9155 SW BARNES RD, STARR WOOD CHAPMAN AHMAD 97225 #040-02-1957 L1958 **TS** *020 †85,90

WRIGHT, Karen Lee. 1815 SW MARLOW AVE STE 206 97225 #031-01-1993 L1995 **GP GPM** *020

WRIGLEY, Keith Allen, Jr. 9205 SW BARNES RD 97225 #035-01-1970 L1977 **GE IM** *071 †20

WU, Yingxing. ■ 97225 #243-47-1996 *100

YANG, Rui. ■ 97229 #244-09-1990 L2007 *100

YEH, Susan. ■ 97225 #005-06-1995 L1998 **IM** *020 †20

YERBY, Mark Smythe. 9427 SW BARNES RD STE 595 97225 #050-02-1976 L1977 **N PHP** *075

YOUKER, Gerald Duane. 9205 SW BARNES RD 97225 #005-12-1971 L1975 **END DIA** *020 †20

YOUNG, Brian Phillip. ■ 97229 #028-34-1998 L2006 **CCM** *100 †20

YOUNG, Jeffery Thos. 9155 SW BARNES RD, ST. VINCENT HOSP & MEDICAL 97225 #040-02-1981 L1982 **P** *020 †75

ZECHNICH, Andrew Douglass. 9340 SW BARNES RD STE 20 97225 #038-41-1989 L1990 **EM** *020 †16

ZHOU, Ting Ting. ■ 97229 #040-02-2008 *012

ZIGMAN, Andrew F. 9427 SW BARNES RD, MOTHER JOSEPH PLAZA 97225 #067-01-1993 L2001 **PDS** *020 †85

ZIMMERMAN, Paul Michael. 9205 SW BARNES RD 97225 #025-01-1978 L1979 **EM** *020 †16

ZIVIN, Lawrence Sheldon. PO BOX 91578 97291 #024-01-1962 L1969 **N** *071 †75

ZOUBEK, Jaroslava. 9135 SW BARNES RD 97225 #025-01-1985 L1992 **U** *020 †95

ZWEBER, Sarah Rhoades. 9155 SW BARNES RD, STE 205 97225 #005-19-1992 L1993 **IM** *020 †20

POWELL BUTTE – CROOK

HAYES, Donald Keith. ■ 97753 #014-01-1999 **FM** *062

PRINEVILLE – CROOK

ANDERSON, David Dale. ■ 97754 #040-02-1971 L1979 **GS** *020 †85

ATTEBERRY, Yo Herman. 1201 NE ELM ST 97754 #040-02-1998 L2001 **EM** *020 †16

BUSBY, Tina Marie. 375 NW BEAVER ST STE 101, OCHOCO COMMUNITY CLINIC 97754 #054-04-1995 L2002 **FM** *020 †18

CLEVELAND, David Jonathan. 1103 NE ELM ST 97754 #047-20-2001 L2005 **FM** *020 †18

CRASKA, Linda Carol. 1103 NE ELM ST 97754 #028-03-1995 L2002 **FM** *020 †18

DILLOW, Leslie Margaret T. ■ 97754 #040-02-1972 L1974 **OBG** *071

DIXON, Lester Jonathan. 1201 NE ELM ST 97754 #040-02-1987 L2002 **EM** *020 †16

FALCK, Jack C. 1201 NE ELM ST 97754 #048-15-2003 L2006 **EM** *020 †16

GREEN, Margaret Alma. ■ 97754 #040-02-1984 L1985 **OM** *030 †70

HAMON, Beta Jo. 991 NE 3RD ST 97754 #045-01-1989 L2002 **FM** *020 †18

HODGES, Holly J. 1103 NE ELM ST, PIONEER HLTH CARE ASSOC 97754 #040-02-1993 L1996 **FM OBS** *020 †18

IWANYK, Eugene Jos. 411 NW 3RD ST, RESTORE VISION CENTERS 97754 #023-12-1986 L2005 **OPH** *020

KAIB, John Jos. 1201 NE ELM ST 97754 #038-41-1984 L1987 **EM** *020 †16

KING, Maggie Jean. 1103 NE ELM ST 97754 #040-02-2003 L2006 **FM** *020 †18

KNOWER, Michael Edward. 1251 NE ELM ST, STE 1A 97754 #040-02-1985 L1988 **FM PLM** *020 †18

MAGARET, David Ernest. 1201 NE ELM ST 97754 #030-05-1969 L2004 **IM GE** *020 †20

MATHESON, Thomas Edward. 1201 NE ELM ST 97754 #048-04-1962 L1969 **FM** *020 †18

MESKE, Curtis Andrew. 1201 NE ELM ST 97754 #026-04-1994 L2003 **FM** *020 †18 ‡

NICHOLS, Russel James. 1201 NE ELM ST 97754 #040-02-1998 L1999 **FM** *020 †18

PARDINI, Ricci Stefan. 1201 NE ELM ST 97754 #036-05-1998 L2001 **EM** *020 †16

RICHARDS, Christopher F. 1201 NE ELM ST 97754 #005-18-1993 L2001 **EM** *040 †16

RODE, Matthew. 1201 NE ELM ST 97754 #040-02-2002 L2003 **FM** *020 †18

SPROAT, Ronald Wm. 1251 NE ELM ST 97754 #040-02-1972 L1981 **GS VS** *020 †85

THOMAS, Denison Mauran. 260 W 4TH ST 97754 #040-02-1992 **FM OS** *071

WEEKS, James Arthur. 1103 NE ELM ST 97754 #034-01-1986 L2002 **FM** *020 †18

WILLIAMS, Bruce Neal. 1103 NE ELM ST 97754 #040-02-1980 L1984 **FM** *020 †18

WOODHALL, Barrett Jereme. 1201 NE ELM ST 97754 #038-43-2005 L2008 **EM** *012

RAINIER – COLUMBIA

LAHTI, Richard Edward. ■ 97048 #040-02-1955 L1956 **FM** *071

REDMOND – DESCHUTES

ADAMSKI, Andrew Wade. 1273 NW CANAL BLVD, ST CHARLES MED CTR 97756 #040-02-1996 L1999 **FM** *020 †18

AMBROSON, Roger Dean. 737 SW CASCADE AVE 97756 #026-04-1963 L1964 **FM** *071 †18

ANDERSON, Charles K. 244 NW KINGWOOD AVE 97756 #037-01-1982 L1986 **AN** *020 †05

BACKUP, Phillip Henry. ■ 97756 #050-02-1946 L1948 **AN** *071 †05

BARSTOW, William H, IV. 213 NW LARCH AVE STE A 97756 #005-19-1989 L1999 **OBG** *020 †30

BASS, Jerry Jerome. 5795 NW HOMESTEAD WAY 97756 #040-02-1963 L1965 **AN** *071 †05

BOE, Stephen Lawrence. 244 NW KINGWOOD AVE 97756 #040-02-1982 L1987 **AN FM** *020 †18,05

BOLT, Richard Henry. ■ 97756 #016-11-1970 L2005 **ORS** *071 †40

BORGEN, Jennings O. ■ 97756 #054-04-1950 L1953 **GYN OS** *071 †30

CARNEY, Timothy H. 244 NW KINGWOOD AVE 97756 #040-02-1996 L1998 **AN** *020 †05

CHOO, Darryl Itsuo. 1604 S HIGHWAY 97 # 340 97756 #014-01-1993 L2004 **CCS** *020

CLARIDGE, William Cullers. 211 NW LARCH AVE 97756 #040-02-1976 L1979 **FM** *020 †18

CRAVEIRO, Robert Jos. 244 NW KINGWOOD AVE 97756 #005-14-1977 L1988 **AN** *020 †16,05

CROSS, Steven Wilson. 215 NW KINGWOOD AVE # 140, CENT OR FAM MED PC 97756 #040-02-1976 L1978 **FM** *020 †18

DETWILER, James Kennedy. 211 NW LARCH AVE 97756 #045-01-1971 L1975 **FM** *020 †18

ERNST, Thomas Neil. 211 NW LARCH AVE 97756 #005-19-1977 L2002 **PD** *040 †55

FIXOTT, Dawnamarie T. 1001 NW CANAL BLVD 97756 #040-02-2002 L2002 **FM** *020 †18

FLAHERTY, Kevin Leo. 244 NW KINGWOOD AVE 97756 #040-02-1983 L1988 **AN** *020 †05

FOGARTY, David Paul. 2300 SW GLACIER PL, BLDG A 97756 #005-18-1994 L2000 **ORS** *020 †40

FREELING, Michael Radford. 244 NW KINGWOOD AVE 97756 #054-04-2001 L2005 **AN** *020 †05 ‡

FRY, Robert J. ■ 97756 #041-13-1952 L1953 **ORS** *071 †40

GANGAN, Celso A. 1245 NW 4TH ST, STE 201 97756 #748-02-1987 L2001 **IM** *020 †20

GILSDORF, John William. ■ 97756 #041-01-1962 L1966 **ORS** *071 †40

GOODMAN, Lori P. 244 NW KINGWOOD AVE 97756 #025-01-1986 L1994 **AN IM** *020 †05

GORMAN, Susan P. 1001 NW CANAL BLVD, THE WOMENS CENTER 97756 #016-43-1993 L2001 **OBG** *020 †30

HANLON, John Timothy. 333 NW LARCH AVE 97756 #040-02-1974 L1975 **CD** *020 †20

HANSON, Richard Anthony. 244 NW KINGWOOD AVE 97756 #054-04-2002 L2003 **AN** *100 †05

HARTLEY, Jack Warnock. 1245 NW 4TH ST, STE 101 97756 #005-06-1980 L1981 **GS** *030 †85

HAWMAN, Artyce Lee. ■ 97756 #040-02-1963 L1964 **AN** *071 †05

HENRICH, Le Roy M, Jr. ■ 97756 #010-01-1960 L1968 **OS** *030 †95

HOPKINS, Benj Theodore. 244 NW KINGWOOD AVE 97756 #041-02-1981 L1989 **AN** *020 †05

IRBY, Pamela Jo. 211 NW LARCH AVE 97756 #005-11-1993 L1997 **FM** *020 †18

JACOBSON, Scott Robt. 1315 NW 4TH ST, APT A 97756 #005-14-1988 L1995 **OSM** *020 †40

JOHNSON, Steven Folke. 1523 NW CANAL BLVD, STE 100 97756 #016-06-1973 L1979 **U** *020 †95

JONES, Lucian Rustin. 244 NW KINGWOOD AVE 97756 #007-02-2001 L2005 **AN** *020 †05

KARMY, James Roy. 333 NW LARCH AVE 97756 #005-12-1973 L1979 **ORS** *020 †40

KENNY, Rose Jeannine. 246 W ANTLER AVE, FAMILY CARE CENTER 97756 #024-07-1995 L2001 **FM** *020 †18

KONING, Marinus H. 1253 N CANAL C 97756 #660-06-1969 L1978 **GS** *020 †85

KUEHN, Richard Allyn. ■ 97756 #018-03-1958 L1962 **FM AM** *071 †18

KUHL, Robert Dean. ■ 97756 #056-05-1967 L1968 **AN** *071 †05

LAND, John Charles. 244 NW KINGWOOD AVE # 110 97756 #040-02-1996 L2001 **GS** *071 †85

LANGSJOEN, Ralph Julian. ■ 97756 #026-04-1958 L1963 **FM NEP** *020 †18

LANSING, Raymond Chas. 244 NW KINGWOOD AVE 97756 #030-06-1991 L2005 **AN PMM** *020 †05

LETOURNEAU, L Scott. 244 NW KINGWOOD AVE 97756 #050-02-1990 L1998 **AN** *020 †05

LONGERBEAM, Jerrold Kay. ■ 97756 #040-02-1948 L1953 **GS VS** *071 †85

MACY, John Albert. 215 NW KINGWOOD AVE # 150 97756 #040-02-1977 L1999 **FM** *020 †18

MARTIN, William Guy. 1541 NW CANAL BLVD, REDMOND SPECIALTY CLINIC 97756 #054-04-1993 L1996 **HO** *020 †20

MC CAULEY, Jimmy Dale. ■ 97756 #028-03-1986 L1996 **FM** *020 †18

MC COOK, Joe Thomas, Jr. 211 NW LARCH AVE 97756 #051-07-2003 L2006 **FM** *020 †18

MC ELROY, Guy Bruce. 645 NW 4TH ST 97756 #040-02-1995 L1998 **FM** *020 †18

MILLER, Patrick C. 244 NW KINGWOOD AVE 97756 #050-02-2002 L2007 **AN** *100 †05

MORTON, Mark Johnston. ■ 97756 #038-40-1970 L1978 **CD** *040 †20

MURPHY, Daniel J. 211 NW LARCH AVE 97756 #010-02-1981 L1995 **FM** *020 †18

MURPHY, Thomas Robert. 333 NW LARCH AVE 97756 #035-09-1993 L1999 **PCC** *020 †20

NARY, Jeffrey Clark. 244 NW KINGWOOD AVE 97756 #005-12-1991 L2006 **AN** *020 †05

NORRIS, Sheryl Lynn. 211 NW LARCH AVE 97756 #040-02-1990 L1992 **FM** *020 †18 ‡

OSBORN, Mark M. ■ 97756 #019-02-1973 L1991 **IM EM** *071 †20 ‡

PALMER, Harold Derek. 213 NW LARCH AVE 97756 #054-04-1992 L1995 **IM** *020 †20

PARTON, Edward Richard. 244 NW KINGWOOD AVE 97756 #005-15-1992 L1999 **AN** *020 †05

PEAT, George B. ■ 97756 #041-12-1968 L1969 **GS GP** *074 †85

PECK, Lanford Lampart. 213 NW LARCH AVE, STE B 97756 #008-01-1994 L1999 **OBG** *020 †30

PHILP, Margaret Jane. 211 NW LARCH AVE 97756 #005-19-1977 L2002 **PD** *020 †55

PRICE, Michael Ernest. 211 NW LARCH AVE 97756 #040-02-1981 L1984 **FM** *030 †18

RAUDY, Todd Matthew. 244 NW KINGWOOD AVE 97756 #040-02-1995 L2001 **AN** *020 †05

REAGAN, Zed Majerus. 244 NW KINGWOOD AVE 97756 #010-02-2001 L2005 **AN** *020 †05

ROSCELLI, John Donald. ■ 97756 #054-04-1972 L1980 **PN PD** *040 †55

SARMIENTO, David Keith. 244 NW KINGWOOD AVE 97756 #005-12-2000 L2004 **AN** *100

SCHAEFER, Patricia Kathy. 1253 NW CANAL BLVD 97756 #041-02-1977 L1991 **EM FM** *020 †18,16

SMITH, Eric Brian. 244 NW KINGWOOD AVE 97756 #054-04-2003 L2007 **AN** *020

SMITH, Todd Richard. 244 NW KINGWOOD AVE 97756 #056-06-1994 L2002 **AN** *020 †05

SPRANGEL, Kellie M. 236 NW KINGWOOD AVE, STE B 97756 #040-02-1996 L1997 **IM** *020 †20

STACK, Roger Dwyer. 211 NW LARCH AVE 97756 #040-02-1948 L1949 **FM** *020 †05

ST CLAIR, Bradley Alan. 244 NW KINGWOOD AVE 97756 #005-12-1990 L2001 **AN** *020 †05

STERNFELD, Mark David. 236 NW KINGWOOD AVE, STE B 97756 #040-02-1990 L1991 **IM** *071 †20

STUDT, Sara Ann. 244 NW KINGWOOD AVE 97756 #005-12-1987 L2000 **AN PD** *020 †05

THORNE, Richard Malcolm. ■ 97756 #016-43-1964 L1974 **OS GYN** *030 †30

TRAUSTASON, Oli Isfeld. 813 SW HIGHLAND AVE, THE EYE SURGERY INSTITUTE 97756 #005-12-1974 L1976 **OPH GP** *020 †35

TRETHEWAY, David Martin. 236 NW KINGWOOD AVE, STE B 97756 #040-02-1985 L1986 **IM** *020 †20

TSAI, Lulu S. 1001 NW CANAL BLVD 97756 #041-09-1994 L2006 **P** *020 †75

VALENTI, Mark Anthony. 211 NW LARCH AVE 97756 #054-04-1979 L1983 **FM EM** *020 †18

VANMETER, Blake Harrison. 244 NW KINGWOOD AVE 97756 #051-01-1995 L1998 **AN** *020 †05

WICKRAMASINGHE, Ashton Se. 1245 NW 4TH ST, STE 201 97756 #243-72-1989 L2007 **IM** *020 †20

WILKIN, Michael Gage. 244 NW KINGWOOD AVE 97756 #019-02-1968 L1969 **AN GP** *020 †05

WILKINSON, John Darrin. 244 NW KINGWOOD AVE 97756 #025-01-1986 L1998 **AN** *020 †05

WILSON, Robert Dillon. ■ 97756 #040-02-1956 L1957 **IM A** *071 †20

WIMBERLY, Julianne Stack. 244 NW KINGWOOD AVE 97756 #040-02-1993 L2004 **AN** *020 †05

WOOD, Anthony Joseph. 244 NW KINGWOOD AVE 97756 #040-02-1994 L1996 **AN** *020 †05

REEDSPORT – DOUGLAS

FABER, Clinton. 1313 HIGHWAY 101 S 97467 #049-01-1970 L1971 **GP** *020

FONG, Julita Angela Chin. ■ 97467 #005-11-1958 L1959 **PTH** *071 †50
HARRIS, Dale Edward. 620 RANCH RD 97467 #033-06-1980 L1986 **FM** *020 †18
IVANITSKY, Michael M. 600 RANCH RD, SPECIALTY CLINIC 97467 #026-08-1993 L2000 **ORS** *020 †40
LANDAUER, Janet Leah. 385 RANCH RD 97467 #040-02-1998 L2001 **IM** *020 †20
LAW, Robert Duncan. 620 RANCH RD, DUNES FAMILY HEALTH CARE 97467 #040-02-1988 L1989 **FM** *020 †18
MC LEAN, Rickard Wm. 600 RANCH RD 97467 #040-02-1948 L1951 **FM** *071 †18
PATIN, Janet Emilie. 620 RANCH RD 97467 #038-40-1994 L1996 **FM** *020 †20
PETROFES, Michelle. 620 RANCH RD 97467 #024-01-1980 L1986 **FM** *020 †18
PRADHAN, Eva. ■ 97467 #672-02-2000 L2008 **IM** *020 †20
THAPA, Yiyakchu Jung. ■ 97467 #672-02-2000 L2008 **IM** *020 †20
VAIL, Ronald Evan. 620 RANCH RD, DUNES FAMILY HEALTH CARE 97467 #051-04-1998 L1999 **FM** *020 †18
WELKER, Kenneth Jay. 385 RANCH RD 97467 #054-04-1982 L2000 **GS TS** *020 †85
ZLATEV, Tinko Ivanov. 600 RANCH RD 97467 #012-01-1992 L2003 **DR** *020 †80

RHODODENDRON – CLACKAMAS

WEAVER, Orville Eugene. 21152 E MOUNTAIN CREEK CIR 97049 #025-01-1956 L1996 **FM** *020 †18

RIDDLE – DOUGLAS

BASKETT, Leslie D. ■ 97469 #005-15-1962 L1975 **GP** *071

ROCKAWAY – TILLAMOOK

KRAUS, James Calvin. ■ 97136 #040-02-1962 L1967 **P** *072
WILLIAMS, Ceilous L. ■ 97136 #051-01-1954 L1958 **IM OM** *071

ROGUE RIVER – JACKSON

JENSEN, Robert David. ■ 97537 #005-02-1967 L1980 **PTH MDM** *072 †50
MILLER, John Seldon. ■ 97537 #005-02-1943 **EM** *071 †30
VERZEANO, Marcel. 265 MURPHY GULCH RD 97537 #561-16-1936 **N** *071

ROSEBURG – DOUGLAS

ABACAN, Cynthia Caparros. 2395 NW STEWART PKWY, THE WELLNESS CLINIC 97470 #748-01-1997 L2005 **END IM** *020 †20 ‡
AGARWAL, Diwaker. 1813 W HARVARD AVE, ROSEBURG RADIOLOGIST 97470 #495-05-1994 L2004 **DR** *020 †80
ALVARADO, Hernan Carlos. 272 MEDICAL LOOP, STE E 97470 #231-05-1973 L2006 **U** *020 †95
AMEREDES, Faye Ellen. 2460 NW STEWART PKWY, STE 230 97470 #038-75-1987, ▲ L2000 **GYN** *020 †30
ANDERSON, Harold F. 1813 W HARVARD AVE STE 202, DOUGLAS CLINIC 97470 #010-01-1964 L1971 **IM** *020
ASHRAF, Naeem. 511 W UMPQUA ST 97470 #704-09-1983 *074
AXFORD, Paul C. 1813 W HARVARD AVE, STE 436 97470 #065-05-1983 L2006 **OBG** *020 †30
BAKER, Rola P. 2282 NW TROOST ST, STE 102 97470 #016-43-1976 L1990 **FM** *020 †18
BENNETT, Robert John. 1813 W HARVARD AVE, ROSEBURG RADIOLOGIST 97470 #005-19-1975 L1982 **DR EM** *020 †80
BERGREEN, Peter Wm. 341 MEDICAL LOOP, STE 100 97470 #040-02-1965 L1976 **U** *020 †95
BILDER, Paul Andre. 1813 W HARVARD AVE STE 214 97470 #035-03-1970 L1976 **PUD IM** *020
BITTER, Douglas Allen. 272 MEDICAL LOOP, STE 160 97470 #005-15-1981 L1989 **PS** *020 †65,85
BLACK, Frederick James. 2282 NW TROOST ST, STE 103 97470 #049-01-1971 L1977 **FM** *071 †18
BLACK, Joseph Michael. 615 DAIRY LOOP RD 97470 #005-02-1995 L1997 **FM** *020 †18
BLEJERU, Monica Maria. ■ 97470 #781-02-1995 L2007 **IM** *020 †20
BLEJERU, Radu-Mihai Mihai. ■ 97470 #781-02-1995 L2008 **IM** *020
BLUM, Steven Allen. 913 NW GARDEN VALLEY BLVD 97470 #005-19-1994 L1998 **IM** *020 †20
BOGART, Larry Frank. 179 NW TRUST ST 97470 #067-01-1965 L1997 **P** *020 †75
BOGGS, Jerry David. 2460 NW STEWART PKWY, STE 200 97470 #040-02-1991 L1998 **N** *020 †75
BOLDUC, Diane. 340 MEDICAL LOOP 97470 #067-03-1999 L2002 **FM** *020 †18
BOTHWELL, Roger Stuart K. 913 GARDEN VALLEY BLVD, ROSEBURG VA MEDICAL CENTER 97470 #040-02-1968 L1969 **GS VS** *020 †85
BOU MERHI, Gabriel Farid. 2395 NW STEWART PKWY, THE WELLNESS CLINIC 97470 #605-01-1999 L2003 **IM** *020 †20
BOURDAGES, Howard Robt. 913 NW GARDEN VALLEY BLVD, VA MEDICAL CTR ROSEBURG 97470 #035-45-1988 L2003 **GS VS** *020 †85
BOWER, Richard John. ■ 97470 #038-40-2004 L2007 **EM** *020
BRADLEY, Arlene Dianne. ■ 97470 #028-34-1988 L1989 **IM** *020 †20
BRADLEY, Mark Edward. VAMC ROSEBURG DIV, DEPT AMBULATORY CARE 97470 #028-34-1987 L1989 **END** *020 †20
BRANDENBURGER, Lisa Ann. 2564 NW EDENBOWER BLVD, STE 126 97470 #038-41-1993 L2006 **GE** *020 †20
BRITTAIN, Shelley G. ■ 97470 #036-08-1989 L2007 **IM** *020 †20
BRUNS, Bart Joseph. 2801 NW MERCY DR 97470 #030-06-1992 L1999 **AN PME** *020 †05
BURPEE, Jon Chas. 1435 QUAIL LN 97470 #040-02-1968 L1975 **OPH** *071 †35
BYMASTER, Angela Jo. ■ 97470 #018-03-2006 L2007 **FP** *012
CALDWELL, Ann Dumont. 2801 NW MERCY DR 97470 #017-20-1997 L2006 **AN** *020 †05
CASEBOLT, Gerald L. ■ 97470 #005-12-1949 L1949 **CRS GS** *071 †85
CERVI SKINNER, Kjell R. ■ 97470 #132-01-1965 L1987 **GS GP** *020
CITRONE, Michael Jos. 1887 W HARVARD AVE, P O BOX 1547 97470 #023-12-1991 L2004 **DR** *020 †80
CLINGER, David Hadley. 913 GARDEN VALLEY BLVD, VETERANS AFFAIRS MEDICAL C 97470 #017-20-1977 L1979 **FM** *020 †18

CONGDON, Robert Neilson. 2570 NW EDENBOWER BLVD, STE 100 97470 #040-02-1983 L1986 **FM** *040 †18
DANDY, Gary Blaine. 2570 NW EDENBOWER BLVD, STE 100 97470 #010-01-1981 L1989 **FM** *020
DANNENHOFFER, Robert Loui. 2460 NW STEWART PKWY, STE 104 97470 #035-03-1980 L1989 **PD PN** *020 †55
DAS, Ashoke Kumar. VA MED CTR DPT SUR 97470 #495-02-1961 L1974 **GS VS** *071 †85
DAUTERMAN, John Frederick. 2700 NW STEWART PKWY 97470 #036-07-1996 L2001 **PTH** *020 †50
DAVEN, Joel Robt. 1813 W HARVARD AVE, STE 206 97470 #024-05-1975 L1990 **N CHN** *020 †75
DONAHOO, Stanley E. ■ 97470 #054-04-1963 L1971 **ORS** *072 †40
DRIVER, Matthew Scott. 2570 NW EDENBOWER BLVD, STE 100 97470 #040-02-1980 L1982 **FM** *020
EDWARDS, James S, Jr. ■ 97470 #005-06-1969 L1976 **GS ORS** *071 †85
ENGSTROM, Gerald Wilhelm. 1813 W HARVARD AVE STE 427 97470 #016-06-1982 L1987 **GYN** *020 †20
FELDMAN, Howard Joel. 2700 NW STEWART PKWY, STE 200 97470 #035-46-1975 L2006 **CD IM** *020 †20
FLETCHER, Marion D. ■ 97470 #005-15-1962 L1975 **FM** *071
FRANTZ, Robert Herman. 913 NW GARDEN VALLEY BLVD 97470 #023-07-1946 **IM** *071
GADE, Jay Norman. 2579 EDENBOWER BLVD 97470 #040-02-1993 L1997 **D** *020 †15
GARCIA, Aixa Z. 913 NW GARDEN VALLEY BLVD, COW CREEK HEALTH-WELLNESS 97470 #308-03-1985 L2006 **FM** *020 †18
GARG, Neelam. ■ 97470 #496-07-1996 L2008 **PD** *012
GHEBREDNGHIL, Luul. 913 NW GARDEN VALLEY BLVD 97470 #056-06-1986 L1991 **IM** *020 †20
GILBERT, Robert Martin. ■ 97470 #040-02-1954 L1955 **OPH** *071
GILCHRIST, Doherty Irene. 1361 DOERNER RD 97470 #031-01-1994 L1997 **IM** *020 †20
GLADDING, Timothy F, Jr. 2700 NW STEWART PKWY, DEPT OF PATHOLOGY 97470 #017-20-1992 L1997 **PTH** *020 †50
GLASER, David. 2801 NW MERCY DR, STE 241 97470 #649-01-1970 L2003 **GE IM** *020 †20
GLASSMAN, Anthony Lee. 1813 W HARVARD AVE, STE 241 97470 #040-02-1990 L1996 **PM** *020 †60
GOMBART, Augustin Karl. 532 W UMPQUA ST 97470 #023-01-1966 L1974 **GP** *020
GOODWIN, Allen. 2564 EDENBOWER BLVD 97470 #040-02-1990 L1993 **PM** *020 †60
GOSLINE, Sylvia K. 545 W UMPQUA ST 97470 #040-02-1978 L1980 **RO** *020 †80
GOSMAN, Razvan I. 2460 NW STEWART PKWY, STE 103 97470 #781-03-1993 L2003 **PUD SME** *020 †20
GRADY, Connie Lorraine. 2395 NW STEWART PKWY 97470 #040-02-1995 L1998 **IM** *020 †20
GRAY, Andrea Varner. 2569 NW EDENBOWER BLVD 97470 #040-02-1995 L1999 **OPH** *020 †35
GRAY, Jason Fredrick. 2801 NW MERCY DR 97470 #040-02-1996 L2000 **AN IM** *020 †05 ‡
GREGG, Patrick Joseph. 341 MEDICAL LOOP, STE 120 97470 #041-07-1998 L2003 **OPH** *020 †35
GROSHONG, Aric Alan. 1813 W HARVARD AVE, NORTH RIVER PEDIATRICS 97470 #040-02-1992 L1993 **PD** *020 †55
GROSHONG, Jacquelyn O. 2460 NW STEWART PKWY, STE 104 97470 #040-02-1992 L1993 **PD** *020 †55
GUISLER, Paul David. 1813 W HARVARD AVE, ROSEBURG RADIOLOGIST 97470 #005-12-1994 L2000 **DR** *020 †80
HAINES, Gregory Allen. 2801 NW MERCY DR 97470 #039-01-1990 L1991 **AN** *020
HALL, Larry Jene. 1813 W HARVARD AVE, STE 140 97470 #040-02-1963 L1964 **PD** *071 †55
HANSEN, Bret Richard. 2801 NW MERCY DR, STE 330 97470 #039-01-1993 L2002 **GS** *020 †85
HARDING, R Michael. 209 CEDAR TREE DR 97470 #040-02-1982 L1983 **EM IM** *020 †16
HARPOLE, Thomas Jos. 2560 NW MEDICAL PARK DR 97470 #040-02-1975 L1980 **GE IM** *020 †20
HASHEM, Bassam. 2460 NW STEWART PKWY, STE 103 97470 #875-02-1994 L2004 **PCC** *020 †20
HAWES, Virginia M. 2570 NW EDENBOWER BLVD, STE 100 97470 #048-02-1984 L2002 **IM** *020 †20
HAYES, Brian Eugene. 1813 W HARVARD AVE, STE 100 97470 #048-13-1976 L1988 **ORS OSM** *020 †40
HIGGINS, Laura Ann. ■ 97470 #028-34-2003 L2007 **EM** *020
HISEY, Bradner Lyle. ■ 97470 #028-02-1963 L1969 **OS** *030
HOLLANDER, Maureen Fencl. 1813 W HARVARD AVE STE 201, DOUGLAS MED CLINIC 97470 #016-11-1981 L1988 **PD** *020 †55
HOLLANDER, William Thos. 2700 NW STEWART PKWY # 100 97470 #016-42-1981 L1988 **OBG** *020 †30
HOLT, Robert Gary. PO BOX 1547, 1887 W HARVARD AVE 97470 #021-01-1972 L2006 **DR** *020 †80
HORSTKAMP, John Anthony. 171 MEDICAL LOOP, STE 150 97470 #005-14-1985 L2003 **FM** *020 †18
HUTCHESON, Bellenden Rand. ■ 97470 #016-06-1947 L1951 **P CHP** *071 †75
JANNELLI, Chris Anthony. 139 CLYDE WILLIAM LN 97470 #040-02-1987 L1988 **IM** *020 †20
JAWORSKI, Gerry Andrew. 2282 NW TROOST ST, STE 101 97470 #062-01-1989 L1992 **FM** *020 †18
JONES, Henry Earl. 2579 EDENBOWER BLVD 97470 #021-01-1965 L1995 **D** *071 †15
JORDAN, Elena Ruth. 2801 NW MERCY DR STE 200 97470 #005-14-1977 L1981 **AN** *020
JORDAN, Ernest Wm. ■ 97470 #005-12-1947 L1947 **GP** *071
KALAI KUMAR, Neil R. 2510 EDENBOWER BLVD, STE 176 97470 #495-04-1986 L2001 **IM** *020 †20
KEYS, Clyde Arthur. 340 MEDICAL LOOP 97470 #020-02-1988 L1993 **FM** *020 †18
KREMSER, Cynthia Brownson. 2700 NW STEWART PKWY # 200 97470 #016-02-1979 L1987 **CD IM** *071 †20
KREMSER, Paul Converse. 2700 NW STEWART PKWY, # 200 97470 #016-02-1979 L1987 **GS** *020 †20
KRNACIK, Michael John. 2801 NW MERCY DR, STE 300 97470 #048-04-1997 L2002 **ORS** *020 †40
KRONNER, Richard F. 1443 UPPER CLEVLND RPDS RD 97470 #005-12-1964 L1972 **GS** *071 †85
LAWSON, Kenneth Lee. 1394 FISHER RD 97470 #005-12-1978 L1992 **GS** *020 †85
LEE, Joel Harvey. 1813 W HARVARD AVE, STE 423 97470 #005-06-1967 L1974 **IM P** *020
LESLIE, James Russell. 1813 W HARVARD AVE, STE 201 97470 #308-03-1964 L1978 **IM** *020 †20
LIENERT, Richard Eugene. 545 W UMPQUA ST 97470 #040-02-1969 L1970 **RO** *020 †80
LINDEN, Kenneth L. 1813 W HARVARD AVE, ROSEBURG RADIOLOGIST 97470 #056-06-1978 L1990 **DR** *020 †80

LORENZO, Rodolfo Bunanig. 913 NW GARDEN VALLEY BLVD 97470 #748-02-1965 L1979 GE IM *020

LUNDH, Henrik Anker B. 1682 NW HUGHWOOD CT 3 97470 #054-04-1957 L1961 IM NEP *020

LUNDY, Theresa M. 913 GARDEN VALLEY, VA HOSP 97470 #026-04-1982 L1983 IM *020 †20

MARJANOVIC, Danijela. PO BOX 1272 97470 #957-03-1962 L1981 FM OM *071

MATSON, Mary Ross. ■ 97470 #041-13-1951 L1953 CLP *071 †60

MATTHEWS, William T. ■ 97470 #040-02-1953 GP *071

MAYO-LORENZO, Mila A. ■ 97470 #748-01-1963 PD *074

MC CANN, Deidre Ann. 2801 NW MERCY DR 97470 #003-01-1995 L2002 AN *020 †05

MC CART, Charles Wm. 1290 NE CEDAR ST, DOUGLAS COUNTY FIRE DISTRI 97470 #040-02-1992 L1995 EM OM *020 †16

MENDELSON, Scott. 2700 NW STEWART PKWY, MERCY MEDICAL CENTER 97470 #016-11-1996 L2000 P *020 †75

MICHALEK, Louis F. ■ 97470 #054-04-1950 L1954 GP A *071

MIDDLEKAUFF, George Wiles. 2750 W HARVARD AVE, P O BOX 1426 97470 #016-06-1971 L1982 P *020 †75 ‡

MOOERS, Robert R. ■ 97470 #040-02-1952 L1953 FM *072 †18

MOORE, Barbara Ellen. 4311 MELQUA RD 97470 #005-02-1966 L2005 FPG *020

MORLANG, Adolph. ■ 97470 #035-15-1966 L1973 R *020 †80

NEDITA, Luana-Ionela N. 272 MEDICAL LOOP STE B 97470 #781-01-1994 L2004 PCC *020 †20

NGUYEN, Duke Duc Hoang. 2460 NW STEWART PKWY, STE 102 97470 #917-24-1996 L2004 GE *020 †20

OLESKOWICZ, Jeanette H. 913 NW GARDEN VALLEY BLVD 97470 #033-06-1990 L1992 P *020 †75

OLIPHANT, Charles R. ■ 97470 #028-34-1943 L1944 FM GS *071 †18

ONDRACEK, Ted Charles. 2700 NW STEWART PKWY, MERCY MED CTR 97470 #018-03-1996 L2004 SP *020 †50

O'NEIL, Michael Chas. 272 MEDICAL LOOP, STE C 97470 #048-04-1975 L1981 ON IM *020

OTTENHEIMER, Edward J, III. 544 W UMPQUA ST STE 203 97470 #031-01-1982 L1997 ON HEM *020 †20

OWENS, David Edwin. 1813 W HARVARD AVE, STE 207 97470 #005-15-1968 L1975 OTO FPS *020 †45

PATTERSON, Chas Stephen. 1122 NE GARDEN VALLEY BLVD, STE 107 97470 #019-02-1967 L1971 N GP *020 ‡

PICKREL, Susan G. 621 W MADRONE ST 97470 #045-01-1988 L2000 CHP *020 †75

POWELL, John Lynn. 2570 NW EDENBOWER BLVD, STE 100 97470 #040-02-1993 L1996 FM *020 †18

POWELL, Timothy James. 2570 NW EDENBOWER BLVD, STE 100 97470 #040-02-1977 L1980 FM *020 †18

RACHITA, Corina Gabriela. 2395 NW STEWART PKWY, THE WELLNESS CLINIC 97470 #781-01-1997 L2003 IM *020 †20

RACHITA, Mircea S. 1813 W HARVARD AVE, STE 241 97470 #781-01-1997 L2003 IMG *020 †20

RAJENDRAN, Ranganathan. 2220 NW STEWART PKWY 97470 #495-04-1985 L2004 IM NEP *020 †20

RAMSEY, Bruce Allen. 2700 NW STEWART PKWY 97470 #056-05-1997 L1998 IM *020 †20

REICHERTER, Paul Douglas. 1813 W HARVARD AVE, STE 310 97470 #019-02-1998 L2002 D *020 †15

RENNICK, Ronald Leslie M. 2700 STEWART PKWY DR 97470 #060-01-1970 L1977 FM *020 †18

RICHARDS, Julee Kay. 341 MEDICAL LOOP STE 110 97470 #026-04-1987 L1991 D *020 †15

RICHARDSON, George E. ■ 97470 #005-12-1944 L1944 GP *071

ROADY, William Ross. 2750 W HARVARD AVE 97470 #040-02-1968 L1973 AN *020

ROBINSON, Brad Eric. 2570 NW EDENBOWER BLVD, STE 101 97470 #024-05-1978 L1990 ID IM *020 †20

ROSE, Gordon Frederik. 544 W UMPQUA ST, STE 104 97470 #065-01-1984 L1989 GP *020

SALBADOR, Gus William. 727 SE CASS AVE, STE 325 97470 #040-02-1994 L1997 P *020

SANTIBANEZ, Jorge. 1813 W HARVARD AVE, STE 241 97470 #649-04-1998 L2003 IM *020 †20

SATHIANATHAN, Jairus. 2700 NW STEWART PKWY, MERCY MEDICAL CENTER 97470 #422-01-2001 L2005 IM *020

SCHALAU, Daphne Behrens. 1813 W HARVARD AVE STE 542 97470 #051-01-1992 L1996 OBG *020 †30

SCHEUFELE, Mia L. 2460 NW STEWART PKWY, STE 200 97470 #048-12-2000 L2004 N *020 †75

SCHNEIDER, Richard F. ■ 97470 #028-02-1947 L1947 P OS *071

SCHREINER, Carl Sturgis. 2801 NW MERCY DR 97470 #039-01-1993 L1999 OTO *020 †45

SCOTT, James Dennis. 2700 STEWART PKWY DR 97470 #028-34-1966 L1971 OTO *072 †45

SEALS, Christine M. 2504 NW MEDICAL PARK DR 97470 #005-12-1995 L2000 FM *020 †18

SEELY, Bradley Harvey. 341 MEDICAL LOOP STE 12 97470 #035-03-1987 L1991 OPH *020 †35

SEPULVADO, Polly Maria. 573 NE STEPHENS 97470 #021-05-1974 L1990 IM *020 †20

SEWELL, Linda L. 1813 W HARVARD AVE, STE 542 97470 #056-06-2002 L2006 OBG *020

SKOGLUND, Roy Wm, Jr. 2700 STEWART PKWY DR 97470 #047-06-1963 L1972 U *020 †95

SMITH, David Marc. 2700 NW STEWART PKWY, MERCY MEDICAL CENTER 97470 #005-14-1986 L1989 EM *020

SODER, Eric Albert. 2570 NW EDENBOWR BLVD #101 97470 #019-02-1973 L1979 GS *020 †85

SOYKE, Jennifer Mae. 2700 NW STEWART PKWY, EMERG DEPT MMC 97470 #040-02-1988 L1995 FM EM *020 †18

SPENCE, Christopher R. 2801 NW MERCY DR, STE 330 97470 #041-02-1996 L2005 GS *020 †85

SPROED, John Dennis. 868 NW GARDEN VALLEY BLVD 97470 #005-12-1963 L1964 CD IM *020

STANHISER, Daniel Edward. 544 W UMPQUA ST STE 102 97470 #005-12-2001 L2004 FM *020 †18

STANTON, Stephen Kent. 2750 W HARVARD AVE 97470 #019-02-1974 L1980 AN *020 †05

STEVENS, Richard K. PO BOX 927 97470 #038-41-1960 L1960 R *071 †80

STODDARD, Donald Wayne. 1813 W HARVARD AVE STE 214 97470 #040-02-1993 L1996 IM *020 †20

STREITZ, William Leonard. 1813 W HARVARD AVE STE 20 97470 #026-04-1968 L1975 ORS *020 †40

TALIK, Jill Carmen. 1813 W HARVARD AVE, NORTH RIVER PEDIATRICS 97470 #003-01-1996 L1999 PD *020 †55

THOMPSON, Thomas Hunter. 2508 NW MEDICAL PK DR 97470 #019-02-1978 L1984 ORS *020 †40

THRALL, Sharon Ann Reiser. 2460 NW STEWART PKWY 97470 #003-01-1974 L1977 FM PHP *030 †18

TOTOIAN, Doru Aurelian. 544 W UMPQUA ST STE 201 97470 #781-05-1998 L2003 IM *020 †20

TOWNSEND, William Bradley. 1813 W HARVARD AVE STE 423 97470 #038-43-1997 L2001 IM *020 †20

TUCKER, Todd St John. 1813 W HARVARD AVE, STE 211 97470 #021-06-1996 L1999 *020

TURNER, Richard Nichols. 913 NW GARDEN VALLEY BLVD, VETERANS AFFAIRS MEDICAL C 97470 #005-15-1984 L1995 P *020 †75

UNRUH, John Wm. ■ 97470 #030-05-1945 OPH *071 †35

VAJDA, Robert Allen. ■ 97470 #038-06-1965 L1972 IM GE *071

VAN ANROOY, Michael David. 2801 NW MERCY DR, STE 300 97470 #016-01-1988 L1998 ORS *020 †40

VAN DIS, Frederic Jan. 2700 NW STEWART PKWY, STE 200 97470 #025-01-1976 L1980 CD *020 †20

VARGAS-BOZO, Jose. 340 MEDICAL LOOP 97470 #176-01-1968 L1981 OBG *020

VENES, D J. 913 NW GARDEN VALLEY BLVD, VA ROSEBURG HEALTHCARE SYS 97470 #035-19-1987 L1989 IM *020

VENIGALLA, Srividya. ■ 97470 #496-24-1999 L2003 IM *020 †20

VILK, Victor Joseph. PO BOX 1547 97470 #023-01-1962 R NM *071 †80

VU, Vanessa Thien. 2801 NW MERCY DR, STE 200 97470 #035-48-1987 L1991 AN PA *020 †05

WAHLS, Steven Alan. 2570 NW EDENBOWER BLVD, STE 100 97470 #016-01-1981 L1984 FM *020 †18

WALCH, John James. ■ 97470 #030-06-1963 L1965 P *020

WALKER, Leslie Vernor. ■ 97470 #021-05-1982 L1983 CD IM *020 †20

WANG, Yan. ■ 97470 #243-33-1983 L2001 PP *100 †50

WARREN, Jerry Gene. 1813 W HARVARD AVE, ROSEBURG RADIOLOGIST 97470 #007-02-1965 L1972 R NM *071 †80 ‡

WESTON, Jon-Marc. 2435 NW KLINE ST 97470 #041-09-1977 L1991 OPH *020 †35

WHEELER, Gary Edward. 1813 W HARVARD AVE, STE 423 97470 #051-04-1971 L1984 RHU IM *020 †20

WILLIAMS, Joseph Henry. 1729 W HARVARD AVE STE 4 97470 #005-12-1943 L1944 GP GPM *071

WILLIAMS, Susan Lai. 2801 NW MERCY DR, STE 300 97470 #048-13-2001 L2007 ORS *100

WILSON, Stewart M, Jr. 341 MEDICAL LOOP, STE 120 97470 #019-02-1968 L1974 OPH *020

WONDERLY, Donald Eric. 2460 NW STEWART PKWY, OR, 97495 97470 #005-12-1995 L1999 OBG *020

YATES, Bryan Douglas. 621 W MADRONE ST 97470 #054-04-1990 L1999 P *020 †75

YOUNG, Elizabeth B. ■ 97470 #010-01-1963 L1972 GPM PD *071 †55

YOUNG, Stanley Burkle. 1813 W HARVARD AVE, STANLEY B YOUNG MD PC 97470 #010-01-1962 L1972 ORS GS *071 †40

YUN, James M. 2801 NW MERCY DR, STE 330 97470 #041-09-1996 L2006 OTO *020 †45

ZASTROW, Arlan G. 320 MEDICAL LOOP 97470 #048-15-1974 L1979 FM *020 †18

ZIDD, Peter Leon. 913 NW GARDEN VALLEY BLVD, VETERANS AFFAIRS MED CTR 97470 #048-12-1972 L1981 IM *020 †18,20

ZIPP, Paul Arthur. ■ 97470 #005-02-1971 L1978 DR *020 †80

SAINT HELENS – COLUMBIA

APONTE, Jennifer Ellen. 270 COLUMBIA BLVD, COLUMBIA RIVER FIRE & RESC 97051 #024-01-1995 L2000 EM *020 †16

AZHAR, Naiyar. 500 N COLUMBIA RIVER HWY, STE 6 97051 #704-02-1981 L1990 PD *020 †55

BREMMER, Matthew Scott. ■ 97051 #023-01-2008 *012

BROOKHART, John Howard. 515 N COLUMBIA RIVR HWY #A 97051 #040-02-1972 L1977 IM *020

KAEMPF, Michael Jerome. 500 N COLUMBIA RIVER HWY, UROLOGY CLINIC PC 97051 #040-02-1972 L1976 U *020 †95

KELLY, Janet Ruth. 525 N COLUMBIA RIVER HWY 97051 #016-11-1973 L1985 FM *020 †18

LEHMAN, Marykay. 500 N COLUMBIA RIVER HWY, STE 6 97051 #025-12-2001 L2005 PCC *012 †20

LOOSLI, Charles Gary. 525 N HIGHWAY 97051 #049-01-1958 L1961 GS GP *071 †85

LOSLI, Steven Mason. 500 N COLUMBIA RIVER HWY 97051 #040-02-1991 L1992 IM *020 †20

MARK, Susan Lord. 500 N COLUMBIA RIVER HWY, STE 6 97051 #010-01-1987 L1992 IM *020 †20

MINTER, Mikeanne. 500 N COLUMBIA RIVER HWY, LEGACY ST HELENS CLINIC 97051 #048-13-2000 L2000 IM *020 †20

MUEHLECK, Geo Ernest, Jr. ■ 97051 #021-01-1944 L1950 FM *071 †18

PERRETTA, Louis Julius. 105 S 12TH ST, COLUMBIA RIVER FIRE & RESC 97051 #035-45-1983 L1987 EM *020 †16

RITCHIE, Christopher S. 500 N COLUMBIA RIVER HWY, STE 7 97051 #005-06-1993 L1996 FM *020 †18

SHEPHERD, Richard Lee. ■ 97051 #028-03-1962 L1972 CD *071 †20

TESAR, Paul Louis. 525 N HIGHWAY 97051 #024-01-1969 L1976 ORS GS *020 †40

TETZ, Rhonda Louise. 500 N HIGHWAY, STE 6 97051 #005-12-1996 L1998 IM *020 †20

VIDESLEMUS LOPEZ, Eduardo. 500 N COLUMBIA RIVER HWY, LEGACY CLINIC - ST HELENS 97051 #270-02-1995 L2007 IM *020 †20

WILLIAMS, Daniel Ray. 500 N COLUMBIA RIVER HWY, LEGACY CLINIC ST HELENS 97051 #014-01-2002 L2005 IM *100 †20

SALEM – MARION

AARON, Martha H. 4742 LIBERTY RD S # 140 97302 #040-02-1994 L2001 CHP *020 †75

ADAMS, Ralph Edwin. 2925 RYAN DR SE 97301 #040-02-1956 L1957 DR MDM *071 †80

AGA, Vimal Mohun. 2600 CENTER ST NE, OREGON STATE HOSP 97301 #496-10-1992 L2003 PYG P *020 †75

AGUILAR, Janet L Espejo. ■ 97302 #005-14-1985 L1986 PD PDI *020 †55

ALLAN, Joseph Harmer. 3099 RIVER RD S, STE 150 97302 #031-01-1981 L1983 OTO NO *020 †45

ALTMAN, Kathryn Lee. 2020 CAPITOL ST NE 97301 #047-20-1997 L2003 FM *020 †18

ALTSCHUL, Martin Steven. 2400 LANCASTER DR NE 97305 #023-07-1976 L1984 PD *020 †55

ANDERSON, Craig Douglas. 4999 SKYLINE RD S, STE 150 97306 #056-05-1988 L1997 AN *020 †05 ‡

ANDERSON, Philip Warren. 2925 RYAN DR SE 97301 #054-04-1966 L1975 R *071 †80 ‡

ANDERSON, Robert F. 1489 STATE ST 97301 #040-02-1943 ORS *071

ATKINSON, Dee Daryl. 857 MEDICAL CENTER DR NE 97301 #040-02-1962 L1963 FM GP *020 †18

AUERBACH, James Allen. 3482 LIBERTY RD S 97302 #050-02-1974 L1980 GP *020

AUSTIN, Edwin Neal. 960 LIBERTY ST SE STE 170 97302 #005-14-1985 L1996 PS *020 †85,65 ‡

AYERS, John Martin, Jr. 5125 SKYLINE RD S 97306 #054-04-1970 L1987 ORS *020 †40

AZADPOUR, Maziar. 875 OAK ST SE, STE 5040 97301 #517-01-1994 L2006 IC *020 †20

BABE, Rodney Scott. 528 COTTAGE ST NE STE 320 97301 #032-01-1994 L1999 P *020 †75

BACULI, Raymond Mecija. 1155 MISSION ST SE, STE 108 97302 #054-04-2000 L2005 FM *020 †18 ‡

■ = Address Information Privacy Protected

BAILEY, Thomas Allen. 875 OAK ST SE STE 5030 97301 #018-03-1962 L1969 **U** *020 †95
BAILLY, Daniel James. 885 MISSION ST SE 97302 #005-14-1976 L1981 **CD** *020 †20
BAIN, Robert Verne. ■ 97302 #040-02-1957 L1960 **GP** *020
BALLARD, John Mc Neil. 1600 STATE ST 97301 #048-04-1989 L1994 **ORS** *020 †40
BALMER, David Maurice. 245 COMMERCIAL ST SE # 220, MID-VALLEY IPA 97301 #539-06-1970 L1979 **GPM OS** *030 †70
BALMER, Paul Timothy. 755 MEDICAL CENTER DR NE 97301 #040-02-1979 L1983 **FM** *020 †18
BARBER, Martin Steven. 665 WINTER ST SE 97301 #040-02-1971 L1980 **GS TS** *030 †85
BASKIN, Hugh Alan. 2478 13TH ST SE 97302 #007-02-1974 L1977 **PD** *020 †55
BASSETT, Martin Lawrence. 700 BELLEVUE ST SE, STE 240 97301 #040-02-1975 L1983 **IM END** *020 †20
BAUMANN, Howard Wayne. 2020 CAPITOL ST NE 97301 #038-41-1969 L1976 **GE IM** *020 †20
BEAL, Melissa Lou. 665 WINTER ST SE, SALEM HOSPITAL 97301 #040-02-1983 L1984 **PTH GS** *020 †50
BEARD, Duane Gary. 665 WINTER ST SE 97301 #040-02-1963 L1965 **OBG** *020 †30
BEARDSLEY, G Donald. 665 WINTER ST SE 97301 #040-02-1947 L1949 **NTR** *071 †95
BECKER, Jerry Ray. 1600 STATE ST, WILLAMETTE ORTHOPEDIC GROU 97301 #047-06-1961 L1968 **ORS** *020 †40
BECKLEY, Brandon Everett. 665 WINTER ST SE, MAIL: PO BX 14001 97301 #040-02-2003 L2006 **EM** *020
BECKMAN, Robert Clarence. ■ 97306 #030-05-1955 L1957 **IM** *071 †20
BELAND, Mary Katherine. 5125 SKYLINE RD S, SKYLINE MEDICAL OFFICE 97306 #005-14-1978 L1995 **IM** *020 †20
BENNINGTON DAVIS, M E. 1127 OAK ST SE 97301 #040-02-1989 L1990 **P** *020 †75
BERANEK, Steven Ray. 1600 STATE ST 97301 #039-05-1986 L2003 **ORS TRS** *020 †40
BERNARDO, Peter Augusto. 700 BELLEVUE ST SE, STE 230 97301 #040-02-1987 L1992 **GS CCS** *020 †85
BERZINS, Uldis Janis. 655 MEDICAL CENTER DR NE 97301 #005-11-1977 L1985 **OPH** *020 †35
BINGHAM, Richard Douglas. 2478 13TH ST SE 97302 #050-02-1985 L1996 **OS CHP** *050 †75
BLAKE, Erik David. 1002 BELLEVUE ST SE 97301 #012-05-1995 L1999 **PM** *020 †60
BLEVINS, Joseph Wendell. ■ 97301 #023-01-1947 L1954 **OM PHP** *071
BONG, Cliffton Tinghong. 960 LIBERTY ST SE, STE 140 97302 #056-06-1996 L2003 **ID IM** *020 †20
BOWEN, Michael James. 2020 CAPITOL ST NE 97301 #034-01-1977 L1992 **OBG** *020 †30
BOYD, Harold Stuart. 1600 STATE ST, WILLAMETTE ORTHO GRP 97301 #005-15-1968 L1976 **ORS** *020 †40
BRISTOL, Thomas Lindsey. 665 WINTER ST SE 97301 #040-02-1972 L1975 **FM** *071 †18
BROOKS, Ulista Jean. 2600 CENTER NE, OREGON STATE HOSPITAL 97310 #040-02-1975 L1977 **IM** *020 †20
BROWN, Jeffery Chas. 5050 SKYLINE VILLAG LOOP S 97306 #019-02-1988 L2006 **IM** *020 †20
BROWN, Willard Robt. 2250 STRONG RD SE 97310 #019-02-1956 L1978 **FM PHP** *072 †70,18
BRUMBAUGH, Raymond Brian. 2561 CENTER ST NE 97301 #007-02-1998 L2002 **PM** *020 †60
BRUTON, Orin Hugh. 875 OAK ST SE STE 5080 97301 #028-34-1966 L1974 **CD** *020
BRYLSKI, James Ronald. ■ 97306 #035-06-1960 L1986 **CHP P** *062 †75
BUCHANAN, Jack. 1002 BELLEVUE ST SE 97301 #016-11-1979 L1982 **GP** *020
BUCK, Michael D. 875 OAK ST SE, STE 3010 97301 #025-12-1974 L1978 **GE IM** *020 †20
BUCKLEY, Christopher Paul. 665 WINTER ST SE 97301 #005-14-1997 L2003 **FM** *020 †18
BURGIN, Heather Joy. 2020 CAPITOL ST NE 97301 #028-02-1996 L1997 **IM** *020 †20
BURR, John Bartlett. ■ 97302 #061-01-1957 L1969 **ORS OS** *072 †40
BURROWS, Stephen Leon. 2925 RYAN DR SE 97301 #028-02-1995 L2000 **DR OS** *020 †80
BURTON, Timothy Angus. ■ 97302 #025-01-1969 L1971 **P ADL** *075
BUZA, Robert Chas. 875 OAK ST SE, STE 5085 97301 #025-07-1966 L1973 **NS** *020 †25
BYRKIT, James Edmund. 2020 CAPITOL ST NE 97301 #005-12-1983 L1987 **IM MDM** *030 †20
CAIN, Roselee Gilbert. 875 OAK ST SE, STE 3070 97301 #056-06-1992 L1993 **P** *020 †75
CAREY, Thomas Joseph, Jr. ■ 97302 #016-43-1962 L1964 **IM** *071
CARLSON, Deborah Lee. 1578 COMMERCIAL ST SE 97302 #048-04-1996 L2001 **CHP P** *020 †75
CARLSON, Kenneth Michael. 891 23RD ST NE 97301 #048-04-1996 L2001 **PD** *020 †55
CARNEY, Douglas Michael. 960 LIBERTY ST SE, STE 150 97302 #003-01-1973 L1976 **IM** *020 †20
CARNEY, Jean Mary. 2400 LANCASTER DR NE 97305 #054-04-1970 L1985 **PD A** *020 †03,55
CARTER, Bruce. 875 OAK ST SE, STE 4060 97301 #038-40-1973 L1983 **PS GS** *020 †85,65 ‡
CASTERLINE, Vernon Dale. 665 WINTER ST SE 97301 #040-02-1948 L1950 **GP** *071
CHAMBERLIN, Cecil Rhodes. 1234 COMMERCIAL ST SE 97302 #039-01-1955 L1955 **CHP** *071 †75
CHAMBERLIN, Thomas Jay. 1234 COMMERCIAL ST SE 97302 #040-02-1990 L1991 **END** *020 †20
CHAN, Mark Tekseng. 2400 LANCASTER DR NE, DEPT OF ALLERGY 97305 #016-43-1992 L2006 **AI** *020 †55,03
CHANDRAGIRI, S. 665 WINTER ST SE, SALEM HOSPITAL 97301 #496-39-1986 L2000 **P** *020 †75
CHAU, Y Michael. 2020 CAPITOL ST NE 97301 #028-02-1996 L2008 **OBG** *020 †30
CHEN, Cher-Yao. 2600 CENTER ST NE 97310 #270-01-1998 L2005 **P** *020
CHESTER, John Buist, Jr. 3628 DOGWOOD DR S 97302 #048-12-1957 L1969 **OS ORS** *020 †40
CHONG, Laura Jean. 2020 CAPITOL ST NE 97301 #056-06-1990 L1999 **OBG** *020 †30
CHOPRA, Carol. 5125 SKYLINE RD S, SKYLINE MEDICL OFFICE 97306 #025-07-1990 L1994 **OBG** *020 †30
CHRISTIANSEN, Gregory A. 1020 LIBERTY ST SE 97302 #049-01-2000 L2006 **OPH** *100 †35
CHU, John Jen-Chu. 665 WINTER ST SE 97301 #242-09-1946 L1976 **GP PUD** *020
CLARKE, Christine G S. 875 OAK ST SE STE 4010 97301 #023-12-1995 L2006 **GS** *020 †85
CLARKE, George Andrew. 875 OAK ST SE, STE 4010 97301 #023-12-1995 L2006 **GS** *020 †85
CLEARY, Andrew John. ■ 97317 #030-06-2008 L2008 *012
CLOYD, Linda Barrueco. 2600 CENTER ST NE 97310 #748-01-1966 **P** *071
CLOYD, William Harrison. ■ 97302 #048-02-1945 L1956 **P** *020
COHEN, Charlotte Hurwitz. 2600 CENTER ST NE 97310 #016-11-1945 L1973 **CHP P** *071
COLLADA, Mauricio, Jr. 1344 LIBERTY ST SE 97302 #011-04-1977 L1983 **NS** *020 †25
COLLINS, Calvin John. 939 OAK ST SE, STE 202 97301 #024-01-1958 L1972 **GS VS** *071 †85
COLLINS, Richard Duncan. 2925 RYAN DR SE 97301 #040-02-1985 L1986 **DR** *020 †80
CONTINO, Joseph Philip. 2020 CAPITOL ST NE 97301 #016-43-1988 L1994 **GS** *020 †85
COOK, Frederick Geo. 5050 SKYLINE VILLAG LOOP S 97306 #041-12-1977 L1981 **FM** *020 †18
COOPER, Robert Ramon. ■ 97302 #018-03-1954 L1960 **OTO** *071 †45
COPLON, Barry Keith. 2400 LANCASTER DR NE, KAISER LANCASTER MED OFC 97305 #051-04-1985 L1994 **IM** *020 †20
COST, Gregory Alan. 875 OAK ST SE, STE 5030 97301 #041-12-1991 L1997 **U** *020 †95
COURTNEY, Erin Frances. 5125 SKYLINE RD S 97306 #030-06-1994 L1997 **PD** *020 †55
COX, Deborah. 1155 MISSION ST SE, STE 108 97302 #049-01-1989 L1996 **PD** *020 †55
CRAIG, Eric Wm Scott. 1296 COMMERCIAL ST SE 97302 #040-02-1964 L1966 **IM NEP** *071
CRAMER, Loy Ermal. ■ 97317 #040-02-1956 L1961 **ORS PM** *071 †40
CRUISE, Dale Alan. ■ 97302 #030-05-1961 L1970 **OBG** *071 †30
CUNNINGHAM, Linda Elaine. 5050 SKYLINE VILLAG LOOP S, THE DOCTORS CLINIC 97306 #016-11-1982 L1983 **IM** *020 †20
CURNELL HEGGEN, Kimberly. 891 23RD ST NE 97301 #040-02-1992 L1993 **PD** *020 †55 ‡
CURRIE, John Morgan. 2441 GREAR ST NE, DERMATOLOGY CLINIC 97301 #039-01-1963 L1970 **D AM** *020 †15
DACKER, Evelin Rebeca. 1155 MISSION ST SE STE 205 97302 #038-06-1993 L1996 **FM** *020 †18
DALY, Edward Francis, Jr. 821 SAGINAW ST S 97302 #048-12-1974 L1975 **P** *020 †75
DANIELS, John Paul. 2020 CAPITOL ST NE, SALEM CLNC 97301 #005-14-1993 L1996 **FM** *020 †18
DANIELS, John Paul. 2020 CAPITOL ST NE 97301 #056-05-1965 L1966 **GP PHP** *075
DANNER, Robert Eugene. 865 MEDICAL CENTER DR NE 97301 #030-05-1957 L1958 **GP** *071
DASSENKO, Ivan. 665 WINTER ST SE 97301 #018-03-1956 L1962 **AN** *071
DAVIDSON, Benton John. 1344 LIBERTY ST SE, STE 2 97302 #010-01-1988 L1999 **N** *020 †75
DAVIES, Robert Roy. 5050 SKYLINE VILLAG LOOP S, THE DOCTORS CLINIC 97306 #016-76-1982, ▲ L1983 **IM** *020 †20
DAVIS, Stanley Keith. 2730 BOLTON TER S 97302 #040-02-1945 L1952 **PTH CLP** *071 †50
DAYTON, Beth. 875 OAK ST SE, STE 4010 97301 #054-04-1985 L1992 **GS** *020 †85
DELGADO, Yara Lia. 3896 BEVERLY AVE NE, BLDG J 97305 #042-01-1999 L2007 **FM** *020 †18
DENTON, Samuel J. 2441 GREAR ST NE, DERMATOLOGY CLINIC 97301 #040-02-1982 L1983 **D** *020 †15
DEVORSS, James Ernest. 665 WINTER ST SE 97301 #010-01-1966 L1973 **CD IM** *020
DIAZ, Heather Nicole. 3896 BEVERLY AVE NE, VIRGINIA GARCIA MEMORIAL H 97305 #040-02-1999 L2006 **FM** *020 †18
DICKER, Lance Matthew. 875 OAK ST SE, STE 5070 97301 #035-08-2002 L2007 **NEP** *020 †20
DIETER, Kay Lynn. 5125 SKYLINE RD S, DEPT OF MENTAL HEALTH 97306 #037-01-1989 L1990 **P** *020
DI IACONI, Daniel Ernest. ■ 97302 #056-06-1942 L1953 **GS** *071
DINSMORE, Suzanne. 2395 CENTER ST NE 97301 #040-02-1979 L1983 **PD** *075 †55
DONOVAN, John Stephen. 3099 RIVER RD S, STE 150 97302 #028-02-1987 L1992 **OTO** *020 †45
DONOVAN, Roxanne Sue. 1002 BELLEVUE ST SE 97301 #054-04-1987 L1991 **PM** *020 †60
DRAVIS, Donald. 2600 CENTER ST NE, OREGON STATE HOSPITAL 97310 #033-05-1992 L1999 **PFP** *020 †75
DUDLEY, Winston C. ■ 97302 #023-01-1951 L1960 **IM** *072 †20
DURAN, Michael Paul. 2600 CENTER ST NE 97301 #034-01-1989 L1995 **CHP P** *020 †75
DURNING, Jonathan C. 875 OAK ST SE, STE 4010 97301 #054-04-1991 L1996 **GS** *020 †85
EASON, David Mac. 2600 CENTER ST NE, OREGON STATE HOSPITAL 97301 #036-01-1982 L1983 **P** *020 †75 ‡
EAST, Marcus Allan. 655 MEDICAL CENTER DR NE 97301 #041-14-2002 L2006 **OPH** *020
EBEL, Ronald Geo. 1020 LIBERTY ST SE 97302 #038-41-1959 L1966 **OPH** *071 †35
EDELBLUTE, Timothy Scott. 665 WINTER ST SE 97301 #040-02-1994 L1997 **EM** *020 †16
EDMONDS, David Lee. 5050 SKYLINE VILLAG LOOP S 97306 #040-02-1984 L1987 **FM** *020 †18
EIKREM, Richard Svante. 5050 SKYLINE VILLAG LOOP S 97306 #040-02-1975 L1976 **FM** *020 †18
EISENHUT, Deborah Ann. 2020 CAPITOL ST NE 97301 #040-02-1981 L1986 **GS** *020 †85
ELKINS, David Allen. 875 OAK ST SE, STE 5030 97301 #005-12-1997 L2003 **U** *020 †95
ELKINS, Gina Maria. ■ 97302 #025-12-1988 L1989 **GPM** *071 †18
ELMGREN, David Todd. 875 OAK ST SE, STE 5030 97301 #040-02-1969 L1970 **U** *020 †95
EM, Makkalearn. 875 OAK ST SE, STE 3010 97301 #041-01-1996 L2005 **GE** *100 †20
EMBICK, Richard Paul. ■ 97302 #056-05-1943 L1976 **ORS** *072 †40
ERICKSON, Raymond Leroy. 2450 12TH ST SE 97302 #040-02-1944 L1946 **OPH** *071 †35
ESCHELMAN, Lawrence Thos. 3099 RIVER RD S, STE 150 97302 #005-11-1964 L1967 **OTO** *071 †45
ETZEL, Fara K. 891 23RD ST NE, CHILDHOOD HEALTH ASSOCIATE 97301 #048-14-1999 L1999 **PD** *020 †55
EVANS, Joseph Mark. 5125 SKYLINE RD S, SKYLINE MEDICAL OFFICE 97306 #017-20-1983 L1996 **GS CCS** *020 †85
EYRE, James M, Jr. 250 CHURCH ST SE, STE 102 97301 #040-02-1996 L1998 *020
FAIRFAX, Carolyn Sue. 5050 SKYLINE VILLAG LOOP S 97306 #040-02-1988 L1989 **FM** *020 †18
FARMER, Samuel Graham. 2450 12TH ST SE 97302 #054-04-1979 L1986 **OPH** *020 †35
FARMER-CUNNINGHAM, Becky. ■ 97306 #054-04-1979 L1986 **AN** *020
FARNELL, Gerald Francis. 2020 CAPITOL ST NE 97301 #026-08-1994 L1997 **FM** *020 †18
FARTHING, David Grant. 2925 RYAN DR SE 97301 #005-19-1983 L2003 **R** *020 †80
FAULK, Charles Edward, Jr. ■ 97302 #040-02-1975 L1977 **P** *020
FEDOR, Elana. 1234 COMMERCIAL ST SE, LINCOLN INTENAL MEDICINE A 97302 #035-19-1992 L2007 **IM** *020 †20
FEDOR, Matthew. 885 MISSION ST SE, 575 S 70TH ST 97302 #028-02-1992 L2007 **ICE CD** *020 †20
FERRELL, Bert L. 100 HIGH ST SE, STE 200 97301 #047-06-1953 L1956 **GP** *072 ‡
FIALLOS-MONTERO, Denis. 2600 CENTER ST NE, OREGON STATE HOSP 97310 #451-01-1967 L1995 **P OS** *020 †75
FICKLE, Marvin Dwane. 2600 CENTER ST NE, OREGON STATE HOSPITAL 97301 #005-06-1977 L1992 **P** *020 †75
FISCHL, Mark Richard. 2020 CAPITOL ST NE 97301 #054-04-1994 L2001 **IM** *020 †20
FITZGERALD, John Edward. 2020 CAPITOL ST NE 97301 #539-03-1975 L1994 **FM** *020 †18
FLEMING, Timothy Wrea. ■ 97302 #005-02-1986 L1991 **U** *020 †95
FLETEMIER, Heidi Louise. 755 MEDICAL CENTER DR NE, DRIVE NE 97301 #016-43-2002 L2005 **FM** *020 †18
FOGLESONG, Mark Evan. 1600 STATE ST 97301 #040-02-1991 L1996 **ORS** *020 †40
FORSYTHE, David Andrew. 5125 SKYLINE RD S 97306 #045-04-1994 L2003 **ORS** *020 †40
FORTNER, Lucille Lanier. 665 WINTER ST SE 97301 #040-02-1940 L1945 **IMG IM** *071
FRANK, Frederick Herman. 2020 CAPITOL ST NE, SALEM CLINIC 97301 #005-11-1998 L2002 **OBG** *020 †30
FRENCH, John Allan. 1002 BELLEVUE ST SE 97301 #048-04-1984 L1987 **PM** *020 †60
FRITZ, Michael Louis. ■ 97302 #040-02-1967 L1969 **AN** *020 †05
FRITZ, Steven Edward. 2600 CENTER ST NE, OREGON STATE HOSPITAL 97301 #035-45-1986 L1987 **P** *020 †75
FROMWILLER, Travis Eugene. 2925 RYAN DR SE 97301 #056-06-2001 L2007 **DR** *020 †80
FU, Irene Hsiaolan. 2020 CAPITOL ST NE 97301 #005-18-2000 L2003 **FM** *020 †18
FURLONG, Thad Eugene. 2600 CENTER ST NE 97310 #040-02-1955 L1958 **P** *020

■ = Address Information Privacy Protected

GABR, Mark T. 180 RAMSGATE SQ S, STE 150 97302 #915-03-1976 L1987 **N OS** *020 †75 ‡
GAISER, Donald Frederick. 939 OAK ST SE 97301 #054-04-1959 L1966 **GS VS** *071 †85
GALLAGHER, William Jos. 665 WINTER ST SE 97301 #019-02-1968 L1976 **ORS** *020 †40
GARRISON, Cort Reid. 1234 COMMERCIAL ST SE 97302 #005-06-1986 L1987 **END IM** *062 †20
GATES, Lawrence Keith, Jr. 875 OAK ST SE STE 3010 97301 #036-07-1986 L2002 **GE IM** *020 †20
GEANEY, Casey John. ■ 97301 #056-06-1997 L2006 **AI** *020 †03,55
GEORGE, Michael John. 665 WINTER ST SE 97301 #018-03-1997 L2003 **DR** *020 †80
GHALILI, Kamran. 885 MISSION ST SE, SALEM CARDIOLOGY ASSOCIATE 97302 #035-46-1982 L2006 **CD IM** *020 †20
GILBERT, Jon Michael. 891 23RD ST NE 97301 #040-02-1969 L1975 **PD** *020 †55
GILLESPIE, William G, III. 2020 CAPITOL ST NE 97301 #040-02-1993 L1996 **IM** *020 †20
GIROD, John Cooper. 960 LIBERTY ST SE, STE 140 97302 #040-02-1976 L1981 **ID IM** *020 †20
GLASER, Joseph Paul. 5125 SKYLINE RD S, KAISER PERMANENTE 97306 #041-02-1968 L2003 **GE IM** *020 †20
GLOTZBACH, Robin Kay. 2400 LANCASTER DR NE 97305 #019-02-1985 L1999 **OS OPH** *020 †35
GOESER, Christopher D. 1165 UNION ST NE, STE 100 97301 #016-11-1994 L1999 **DR MSR** *020 †80
GOETZ, Robert Lee. 2478 13TH ST SE 97302 #030-06-1967 L1971 **PD** *071 †55
GOLDBERG, Bruce Warren. 500 SUMMER ST NE E-15, DEPARTMENT OF HUMAN SERVIC 97301 #035-47-1982 L1992 **FM** *030 †18
GOODENBERGER, Michael E. 665 WINTER ST SE 97301 #018-03-1986 L1990 **D** *020 †15
GORDIN, Raylene L. 700 BELLEVUE ST SE 97301 #056-06-1991 L1996 **ORS** *020 †40
GORDON, Matthew Seth. 875 OAK ST SE STE 1080, RADIATION ONCOLOGY DEPT 97301 #016-42-1987 L1998 **RO** *020 †80
GOTTSCHALK, Wolfram F. 700 BELLEVUE ST SE, WOLFRAM F GOTTSCHALK MD PC 97301 #407-16-1959 L1973 **PS GS** *072 †65
GOW, Jack Alexander. 1309 LIBERTY ST SE 97302 #060-01-1967 L1977 **OPH** *071
GOWING, David. ■ 97308 #008-01-1959 L1963 **P GP** *071 †05,75
GRAU, Keith Edward. 2400 LANCASTER DR NE 97305 #041-09-1976 L2006 **IM IMG** *020 †20
GRAVEN, Kendall Endre. 2020 CAPITOL ST NE 97301 #028-03-1987 L1989 **FM** *020 †18
GREEN, Sidney Irvine. 2925 RYAN DR SE 97301 #040-02-1976 L1982 **DR** *020 †80
GREENWOOD, Ernest P. 665 WINTER ST SE 97301 #040-02-1944 **FM** *071
GRIFFIN, Warren L, III. 2478 13TH ST SE 97302 #001-02-1992 L1996 **PD** *020 †55
GRIFFITHS, Dondeena Rae. 2925 RYAN DR SE 97301 #011-04-1981 L1990 **DR NR** *020 †80
GRUBER, Matthew. 490 MILLER ST SE 97302 #026-04-1951 L1951 **GP** *071
GU, Ruili. 665 WINTER ST SE 97301 #243-16-1986 L1993 **IM** *020 †20
HALL, Roy Ernest. 2020 CAPITOL ST NE 97301 #040-02-1966 L1971 **FM** *020 †18
HAN, Kwang-Hoon. 1234 COMMERCIAL ST SE, PHYS BUILDING GRP 97302 #583-02-1994 L2003 **RHU** *020 †20
HANNIG, John Richard. ■ 97306 #026-04-1981 L2005 **OBG** *020 †30
HANSEN, Ole. 2605 STATE ST, OREGON STATE PENITENTIARY 97310 #068-01-1970 L1979 **FM** *020
HANSLITS, Michael L. 2925 RYAN DR SE, SALEM RADIOLOGY CONSULTANT 97301 #025-01-1980 L1986 **DR VIR** *020 †80
HARE, Michael James. 665 WINTER ST SE 97301 #025-07-1975 L1976 **EM** *020
HARMON, Elizebeth Rose. 875 OAK ST SE STE 4090 97301 #040-02-1984 L1988 **OBG** *020 †30
HARMON, Harold Ralph. 1234 COMMERCIAL ST SE 97302 #047-06-1984 L1997 **IM PD** *020 †20
HARPER, Cynthia Marie. 5050 SKYLINE VILLAG LOOP S 97306 #025-01-1980 L1986 **FM** *020 †18
HARRINGTON, Leon Oliver. 1645 LIBERTY ST SE 97302 #025-01-1974 L1977 **CHP P** *062 †75
HARRIS, John Thos. 2600 CENTER ST NE, OREGON STATE HOSPITAL 97301 #036-01-1992 L2004 **ADP P** *020
HARRIS, W Andrew. 1309 LIBERTY ST SE 97302 #051-01-1969 L1974 **OPH** *071 †35
HARRISON, David Chaim. 2925 RYAN DR SE 97301 #051-01-1988 L1993 **R** *020 †80
HARVEY, Harmon Thos. 801 MISSION ST SE 97302 #040-02-1973 L1979 **IM** *020 †20
HASBROOK, John B. 665 WINTER ST SE 97301 #018-03-1966 L1967 **AN** *020 †05
HAY, Alan Reid. 875 OAK ST SE, STE 5030 97301 #023-07-1983 L1989 **U** *020 †95
HEINECK, Susan Marie. 3700 HAGERS GROVE RD SE 97317 #056-05-1992 L2002 **IM** *020 †20
HEITZ, Carl Jos, Jr. 5125 SKYLINE RD S, SKYLINE MED OFF RAD 97306 #024-05-1970 L1990 **DR OS** *020 †80
HELMAN, Manya Blumberg. 700 BELLEVUE ST SE, STE 285 97301 #038-06-1988 L1990 **FM** *020 †18
HENNIG, Arnella Catherine. 875 OAK ST SE, STE 1080 97301 #007-02-1984 L1991 **RO FM** *020 †80
HEROS, Robert David. 2480 LIBERTY ST NE STE 180 97301 #047-06-1999 L2007 **PM** *020 †60
HIEBERT, Eugene Lloyd. 4999 SKYLINE RD S, SALEM, 97303 97306 #030-05-1980 L1982 **AN** *020 †05
HIKES, Charles Edward, III. 2450 12TH ST SE 97302 #025-07-1971 L1974 **OPH** *071 †35
HIPPEN, Robert L, Jr. 5125 SKYLINE RD S, SKYLINE MEDICAL OFFICE 97306 #047-06-1984 L1989 **DR** *020 †80
HITTLE, Gretchen Lynn. 1002 BELLEVUE ST SE 97301 #040-02-1992 L1993 **IM** *020 †20
HOANG, Hoa Thanh. 5050 SKYLINE VILLAG LOOP S, THE DOCTORS' CLINIC 97306 #040-02-1994 L1997 **IM** *020 †20
HOFELDT, Ronald Lloyd. 665 WINTER ST SE 97301 #040-02-1972 L1976 **P** *020 ‡
HOGAN, Daniel Frederick. 5050 SKYLINE VILLAG LOOP S 97306 #028-34-1958 L1968 **FM** *020 †18
HOLCOMB, Frederick Duane. 2020 CAPITOL ST NE 97301 #054-04-1956 L1961 **OBG** *072 †30
HOLLEY, W Lawrence. 1490 STANDISH CT SE 97302 #016-43-1966 L1972 **PD END** *071 †55
HOLLOWAY, William David. PO BOX 14001, 665 WINTER ST 97309 #039-01-1982 L2006 **FM MDM** *030 †18
HOLM, Carl Ludwig. ■ 97308 #040-02-1943 L1956 **ORS** *071 †40
HOLME, Stanley Lawrence. PO BOX 8100 97303 #025-01-1960 L1963 **FM** *071 †18
HOOK, James David. 1002 BELLEVUE ST SE 97301 #048-02-1993 L1997 **PM OM** *020 †60
HOPKIN, Cristina Isela. 2266 MISSION ST SE 97302 #048-15-1998 L2001 **FM** *062 †18
HORWITZ, Alexander Earle. 702 CHURCH ST NE 97301 #047-20-1984 L1995 **PFP N** *020 †75
HOWARD, Antje Heckmann. 755 MEDICAL CENTER DR NE, MEDICAL CENTER 97301 #041-02-1992 L1998 **FM** *020 †18
HUBBARD, Jerry Leroy. 875 OAK ST SE STE 5060 97301 #048-02-1978 L1979 **NS** *020 †25
HUEWE, Philip Jos. ■ 97302 #018-03-1958 L1959 **OTO PS** *020 †45
HUGHES, William Arvan. 1234 COMMERCIAL ST SE 97302 #005-15-1977 L1980 **IM** *020 †20
HUNT, Richard Allen. 5340 14TH PL S 97306 #030-06-1996 L1997 **IM** *020 †20
HUUN, Paul Emanuel. 2020 CAPITOL ST NE 97301 #021-01-1987 L1993 **IM** *020 †20
HYNDMAN, Nina Joanne. 2478 13TH ST SE 97302 #040-02-1998 L2003 **PD** *020 †55
ICOVINO, Joanne Marie. 2250 STRONG RD SE 97310 #035-48-1981 L1984 **PD** *020 †55
ILG, Antoinette. 891 23RD ST NE 97301 #040-02-1994 L1996 **PD** *020 †55
INGLE, Robert Maurice. 2400 LANCASTER DR NE 97305 #028-02-1977 L1989 **GP OM** *020 †70
INNES, Arthur James. ■ 97306 #803-01-1965 L1972 **GS TS** *071 †85
IRWIN, Mary Rosamund. 2600 CENTER ST NE, OREGON STATE HOSPITAL CLIN 97301 #061-01-1973 L1974 **FM** *074 †18
ISMAIL, Saleh Ali. 801 MISSION ST SE, SALEM PULMONARY ASSOCIATES 97302 #605-01-2000 L2007 **PCC** *100
JACKSON, Robert Clinton. 665 WINTER ST SE 97301 #040-02-1947 L1955 **GYN OBG** *071 †30
JAECKS, Ronald Dale. 5125 SKYLINE RD S 97306 #005-12-1981 L1997 **GS** *020 †85
JAMES, Matthew. 665 WINTER ST SE 97301 #040-02-1976 L1982 **EM** *071
JAPPAY, Elisabeth Lee. 665 WINTER ST SE # 5303 97301 #005-06-1986 L2006 **IM** *020 †20
JENSEN, Joseph Edgar, Jr. ■ 97317 #067-01-1955 L1960 **ORS** *071 †40
JENSEN, Linda Louise. 3150 LANCASTER DR NE, DISABILITY DETERMINATION S 97305 #054-04-1981 L1988 **PM PMM** *020 †60
JETMALANI, Naraindas B. 665 WINTER ST SE 97301 #917-30-1946 **P PYA** *075
JOHANSON, Constance May. 665 WINTER ST SE 97301 #040-02-1980 L1983 **FM OM** *020
JOHNSON, Bradley Loyal. 1165 UNION ST NE, STE 100 97301 #068-01-1975 L1997 **DR FM** *020 †80
JOHNSON, Bruce Clark. 3099 RIVER RD S # 150 97302 #040-02-1986 L1987 **OTO FPS** *020 †45
JOHNSON, Charles Raymond. 665 WINTER ST SE, SALEM HOSPITAL EMERGENCY D 97301 #040-02-1976 L1980 **EM FM** *020 †18,16
JOHNSON, Karen Diane. 665 WINTER ST SE 97301 #068-01-1978 L1984 **FM** *020
JOHNSON, Linda Bernice. 665 WINTER ST SE, SALEM HOSPITAL-EMERGENCY D 97301 #040-02-1983 L1984 **EM OM** *020 †16
JOHNSON, Martin C, II. 801 MISSION ST SE 97302 #005-18-1987 L1996 **CCM** *020 †20
JOHNSON, Sharon Bradway. 3150 LANCASTER DR NE, DHS/SPD/DDS 97305 #040-02-1985 L1986 **IM** *020 †20
JONES, Gary Jos. 2925 RYAN DR SE 97301 #024-01-1979 L1985 **R** *020 †80
JOQUE, Laura Ann. 875 OAK ST SE, STE 4030 97301 #025-12-2000 L2007 **IM** *100 †20
JURA, Randell Peter. 4666 COMMERCIAL ST SE 97302 #005-12-1977 L1980 **FM** *020 †18
JUURMA, Anneliis. 5125 SKYLINE RD S 97306 #040-02-1997 L2000 **IM** *020 †20
KAHAN, Thomas Aaron. 700 BELLEVUE ST SE STE 245 97301 #007-02-1972 L1978 **GYN** *020 †30
KAMINENI, Raghunandan. 885 MISSION ST SE 97302 #495-57-1995 L2005 **CD** *100 †20
KAVKA, Alicia Beth. 285 LIBERTY ST NE, STE 390 97301 #016-01-1979 L1980 **PTH** *020 †50
KEHRLI, Martin Alan. 3700 HAGERS GROVE RD SE 97317 #040-02-1982 L1984 **AN** *020
KEILLOR, George Westley. 2600 CENTER ST NE 97310 #040-02-1963 L1964 **P** *020
KELBER, Michael Wilford. 2365 GREAR ST NE 97301 #028-34-1974 L1977 **FM** *020 †18
KELLY, Pete Benville. 2925 RYAN DR SE 97301 #054-04-1966 L1972 **DR** *071 †80
KELLY, Robert Bryan. 665 WINTER ST SE, SALEM HOSPITAL EMERGENCY D 97301 #040-02-1994 L1997 **EM** *020 †16
KELLY, Robert Rhodee. 665 WINTER ST SE 97301 #012-05-1971 L1977 **EM IM** *020 †20,16
KENNEDY, Brian Dennis. 5125 SKYLINE RD S 97306 #051-04-1974 L1990 **FM OS** *020 †18
KENNEY, Kay Alain Haglund. 5125 SKYLINE RD S, KAISER PERMANENTE 97306 #040-02-1971 L1972 **AN** *071
KENOYER, Joseph Karl. 665 WINTER ST SE 97301 #040-02-1991 L1994 **EM** *020 †16
KIM, Jiyoun Elizabeth. 2020 CAPITOL ST NE 97301 #048-02-1999 L2006 **GS** *020 †85
KIM, Kiku Emilei. 5125 SKYLINE RD S, KAISER - SKYLINE MEDICAL O 97306 #014-01-1995 L2006 **CHP** *020 †75
KIRK, Christopher Jon. 245 COMMERCIAL ST SE, STE 200 97301 #031-01-1983 L1984 **IM IMG** *030 †20
KIRKPATRICK, Ryan David. 665 WINTER ST SE 97301 #040-02-2001 L2005 **EM** *020 †16
KITCHIN, Tina Ciesiel. 500 SUMMER ST NE #E10, DHS SNRS & PEOPLE DISBLTS 97310 #040-02-1978 L1989 **PD** *020 †55
KLEMENT, John Chas. 1234 COMMERCIAL ST SE, PHYSICIANS BLDG GROUP 97302 #016-06-1983 L1985 **IM** *071 †20
KOLETAR, Vincent John. 2478 13TH ST SE 97302 #031-01-1993 L1994 **PD** *020 †55
KONICK, Larry. ■ 97302 #040-02-1983 L1992 **PTH** *020 †50
KRAUSE, Albert Henry, Jr. 875 OAK ST SE 97301 #028-02-1965 L1973 **TS** *071 †85,90
KRUSE, Thomas Vernon. ■ 97302 #038-06-1974 L1978 **D** *020 †15
LACE, James Kenneth. 891 23RD ST NE 97301 #038-41-1974 L1977 **PD** *020 †55
LACKIDES, Gregory Andrew. 2020 CAPITOL ST NE, SALEM CLINIC, P.C. 97301 #005-11-1994 L1998 **IM** *020 †20
LAHR, Martin Bruce. 3150 LANCASTER DR NE, DHS/SPD/DDS 97305 #040-02-1979 L1981 **PD OS** *030 †55
LAI, Wallace. 885 MISSION ST SE 97302 #020-12-1991 L1992 **CD** *020 †20
LAING, Susan Craig. 5125 SKYLINE RD S 97306 #040-02-1982 **FM** *020 †18
LANDERS, Karen Ann. 3180 CENTER ST NE, MARION COUNTY HEALTH DEPT 97301 #018-03-1983 L1991 **PD** *020 †55,70
LARAMORE, Rosemary. ■ 97302 #048-04-1967 L2000 **P** *020
LARO, Eric Adrian. 5050 SKYLINE VILLAG LOOP S, LOOP S 97306 #024-07-1998 L2003 **GS** *020 †85
LASERSOHN, William Bock. ■ 97306 #038-06-1960 L1986 **OBG** *071 †30
LEE, Eva Yihua Wang. 1296 COMMERCIAL ST SE, STE 102 97302 #243-16-1987 L2003 **NEP IM** *020 †20
LEE, Myron Louie. 5050 SKYLINE VILLAG LOOP S 97306 #040-02-1976 L1983 **FM** *020 †18
LEE, Paul Chonghoon. 5125 SKYLINE RD S, SKYLINE OFFI 97306 #043-01-1986 L1998 **ORS** *020 †40
LENOX, Jeff David. 875 OAK ST SE, STE 3070 97301 #040-02-1990 L1991 **P** *020 †75
LEONARD, Dann Kevin. 700 BELLEVUE ST SE, NORTHBANK PLAZA SUITE 280 97301 #040-02-1984 L1992 **PS HS** *020 †85,65
LEONARDO, Victor Jos. 1165 UNION ST NE, DIAGNOSTIC IMAGING 97301 #030-06-1991 L1992 **DR** *020 †80 ‡
LEWIS, Robert Lynn. 665 WINTER ST SE 97301 #028-03-1962 L1963 **EM GP** *020 †16
LICHTER, David John. 5125 SKYLINE RD S, KAISER PERMANENTE SKYLINE 97306 #008-01-1983 L1984 **FM** *020 †18
LIEURANCE, Richard C. 2400 LANCASTER DR NE 97305 #021-01-1984 L1999 **OPH** *020 †35
LIND, Andrea Kay. 966 12TH ST SE, PACIFIC FAMILY MEDICAL CEN 97302 #040-02-1997 L2005 **FM** *020 †18
LITTLE, Alison Smith. 255 CAPITOL ST NE, OHPR 5TH FLR PUB SERV BLVD 97310 #056-06-1984 L1990 **FM** *030 †18
LIU, Michael Liangsun. 1390 LIBERTY ST SE 97302 #033-05-1986 L1998 **NS OSS** *020 †25
LIUM, James Howard. 285 LIBERTY ST NE, STE 390 97301 #040-02-1946 L1949 **ATP** *020 †50
LOEWEN-THOMAS, Ian Glen. 2020 CAPITOL ST NE 97301 #068-01-1992 L1997 **FM** *020

■ = Address Information Privacy Protected

LONG, James Wm. 1020 LIBERTY ST SE, OREGON EYE CTR 97302 #056-05-1971 L1977 **OPH** *020 †35

LONIGAN, Robert Michael. 801 MISSION ST SE 97302 #021-01-1968 L1978 **PUD IM** *040 †20

LOWRY, James Phillip. 885 MISSION ST SE 97302 #005-12-1982 L1994 **CD** *020 †20

LUGENBILL, Cheryl Ann. 939 OAK ST SE STE 162 97301 #030-06-1984 L1993 **OBG FM** *020 †30

LUNDEBERG, Kenneth Arthur. 665 WINTER ST SE 97301 #041-13-1953 L1967 **R** *071 †80

LUNDMARK, Gregory James. ■ 97308 #056-06-1965 L1966 **OTO PS** *072 †45

MACKAMAN, Bert James. 665 WINTER ST SE 97301 #048-02-1974 L1978 **D** *071 †15

MAGILNER, Mark. 285 LIBERTY ST NE, STE 390 97301 #041-02-1996 L2000 **PTH PCP** *020 †50

MAHONEY, Timothy Michael. 665 WINTER ST SE 97301 #028-34-1968 L1976 **IM** *050 †20

MANOCHA, Ritu. 875 OAK ST SE STE 4090, SALEM WOMEN'S CLINIC INC 97301 #422-01-2001 L2006 **FM** *020 †18

MANSON, Alan Lee. 5125 SKYLINE RD S 97306 #031-01-1980 L1989 **U** *020 †95

MARLOWE, Michael Adam. 5125 SKYLINE RD S, DEPT PEDS 97306 #035-15-1997 L2000 **PD** *020 †55

MARVEL, Steven Lee. 801 MISSION ST SE 97302 #040-02-1979 L1990 **PUD IM** *020 †20

MARVIN, Judy Lynn. 665 WINTER ST SE, SALEM HOSPITAL 97301 #054-04-1998 L2005 **OBG** *020 †30

MASSON, Donald Winston. 5050 SKYLINE VILLAG LOOP S 97306 #054-04-1967 L1976 **GS** *071 †85

MATTHEWS-BRYLSKI, Beverly. 2600 CENTER ST N.E., OREGON STATE HOSPITAL 97310 #021-01-1972 L1986 **P** *020

MATTHEY, Carl Henry, Jr. 6345 JOSEPH ST SE 97317 #649-01-1964 L1969 **GP** *020

MAY, Charles Milton. 801 MISSION ST SE 97302 #028-03-1966 L1974 **RHU IM** *020 †20

MC DONALD, Clark Elliott. 285 LIBERTY ST NE, STE 390 97301 #047-06-1988 L1992 **PTH** *020 †50

MCDONALD, James Robert. 875 OAK ST SE, STE 4000 97301 #054-04-1968 L1978 **A IM** *020 †20,03

MC GEE, Charles Duane. 700 BELLEVUE ST SE, STE 220 97301 #035-45-1967 L1973 **GYN** *020 †30

MC KEOWN, Laurie Grace. ■ 97302 #025-01-1986 L1988 **GS** *020

MCNAUGHTON, Lauren. 2685 4TH ST NE 97301 #048-04-1983 L1987 **PD** *020 †55

MC NAUGHTON, Robert H. 1073 OAK ST SE, SALEM MEDICAL OFFICES 97301 #067-01-1949 L1978 **OBG** *071

MEAD, Richard Jos. 681 COTTAGE ST NE 97301 #063-01-1973 L1979 **P ADM** *020 †75

MEJIA, Carmelo S. 5125 SKYLINE RD S 97306 #748-20-1988 L1997 **IM** *020 †20

MESSER, John Blake. 665 WINTER ST SE, SALEM HOSPITAL MEMORIAL UN 97301 #035-45-1968 L1977 **EM** *020 †20

METZGER, Laura Erickson. 2020 CAPITOL ST NE, SALEM CLINIC, PC 97301 #005-06-1986 L1992 **AI IM** *020 †20,03

MEYER, John Edward. 2600 CENTER ST NE, OREGON STATE HOSPITAL 97301 #040-02-1977 L1979 **P** *020

MHOON, John Mark. 875 OAK ST SE, STE 5030 97301 #004-01-1995 L2000 **U** *020 †95

MICHAELS, Rodney Douglas. 1585 LIBERTY ST SE, FIREHOUSE DIABETES & ENDOC 97302 #308-11-1985 L1990 **END IM** *020 †20

MIKESKA, Brett Wayne. 1430 COMMERCIAL ST SE 97302 #654-01-1999 L2005 **NEP** *020 †20

MIKESKA, Claudia R. 4676 COMMERCIAL ST SE #308 97302 #654-01-2000 L2007 **IM** *020

MILLER, Debbie Lee. 1234 COMMERCIAL ST SE 97302 #016-11-1987 L2001 **IM** *020 †20

MILLER, George Earl. 891 23RD ST NE 97301 #038-06-1971 L1976 **PD FM** *020 †55

MILLER, Gordon Arthur. 2001 COMMERCIAL ST SE 97302 #005-12-1975 L1979 **OPH** *020 †35

MILLER, James Frederick. 1127 OAK ST SE 97301 #016-11-1991 L2001 **P ADP** *020 †75

MILLER, Michael Ransley. 1127 OAK ST SE, SALEM HOSPITAL 97301 #040-02-1975 L1979 **PYG P** *020 †75

MILLER, Owen Geo. ■ 97302 #040-02-1943 **D** *071 †15

MOE, Gordon Harlan. 2020 CAPITOL ST NE 97301 #040-02-1979 L1984 **GS** *071 †85

MOLINA, Reginaldo Romero. 1445 STATE ST 97301 #005-02-1978 L1996 **AN** *020 †05

MORENO, William Arthur. 432 LANCASTER DR NE 97301 #005-12-1957 L1958 **FM** *071 †18

MORGAN-JAHANSHIR, Lavena. 700 BELLEVUE ST SE, STE 210 97301 #016-45-1994 L1998 **OBG** *020 †30

MORRIS, Christy Ann. ■ 97317 #005-18-2006 L2006 **IM** *012

MORRISON, Thomas Lloyd. ■ 97302 #010-01-1955 L1961 **FM** *071 †18

MOSS, Jerry Franklin. 5125 SKYLINE RD S 97306 #040-02-1978 L1982 **FM** *020 †18

MOZELL, Everett James. 2020 CAPITOL ST NE 97301 #035-15-1983 L1984 **GS VS** *020 †85

MUELLER, Robert Louis. ■ 97302 #040-02-1948 L1949 **R NM** *071 †80

MUNKENBECK, Frances C. 875 OAK ST SE, STE 5080 97301 #016-02-1980 L1996 **CD ICE** *020 †20

MURPHY, Michael Andrew. 875 OAK ST SE, STE 5090 97301 #041-02-1980 L1989 **MDM LM** *030 †30

MURRAY, Amy Miok. 4666 COMMERCIAL ST SE, SOUTH SALEM SPINE AND REHA 97302 #050-02-1993 L1994 **P** *020

MYERS, Robert Wayne. 1165 UNION ST NE STE 10 97301 #021-01-1993 L1998 **DR** *020 †80

NAIR, Rajan Vijayachand. 2020 CAPITOL ST NE 97301 #003-01-1992 L1999 **GS** *030 †85

NEAHRING, Jennifer Chi. 875 OAK ST SE, STE 5070 97301 #016-06-1989 L1998 **NEP IM** *020 †20

NEUBURG, Janet. 2400 LANCASTER DR NE 97305 #003-01-1975 L1980 **FM** *050 †70,18

NGUYEN, Chuong Huan. 2400 LANCASTER DR NE 97305 #005-02-1993 L1997 **IM** *020 †20

NISBET, William. 960 LIBERTY ST SE STE 100 97302 #035-03-1971 L1977 **PS GS** *020 †65

NISHIOKA, Gary Jim. 3099 RIVER RD S, STE 150 97302 #048-13-1990 L1997 **OTO FPS** *020 †45

NOBIS, Chris Eric. 2400 LANCASTER DR NE 97305 #017-20-1981 L1989 **IM** *020 †20

NONWEILER, Rebecca T. 1445 STATE ST 97301 #005-15-1990 L1996 **AN D** *020 †05 ‡

NORTON, Claire Elaine. 665 WINTER ST SE, SUITE5305 97301 #001-02-2000 L2005 **IM** *020 †20

NOVOA, Jose Otoniel. 2925 RYAN DR SE 97301 #010-03-1992 L1998 **NM** *020 †80,28

NUNES, Anne A. 2020 CAPITOL ST NE 97301 #028-78-1997, ▲ L2000 **FM** *020 †18

NURRE, Mark Jeremy. 3750 HAZELGREEN RD NE 97305 #018-03-1977 L1980 *020

OH, Eliza. 960 LIBERTY ST SE, STE 140 97302 #305-01-1998 L2003 **IM** *020 †20

OLSEN, Beverly Joan. 665 WINTER ST SE 97301 #056-06-1954 L1959 **PD PHP** *071

OLSHER, Neil Burton. 5125 SKYLINE RD S, KAISER PERMANENTE- SKYLINE 97306 #005-15-1974 L1998 **OBG** *020 †30

OLSON, David Lawrence. 2020 CAPITOL ST NE, SALEM CLINIC, PC 97301 #054-04-1988 L1995 **IM** *071 †20

OLSON, Donald Ray. 2480 LIBERTY ST NE, STE 120 97301 #056-05-1961 L1986 **NS PMM** *020 †25

OLSON, Mark Warren. 2400 LANCASTER DR NE 97305 #040-02-1972 L1975 **FM** *020 †18

ORLOWSKI, Edward Peter. 875 OAK ST SE, STE 4030 97301 #017-20-1976 L1982 **ON HEM** *020 †20

ORTEGA, Salvador Marcial. 755 MEDICAL CENTER DR NE, MEDICINE CEN 97301 #005-02-1991 L1994 **FM** *020 †18

ORWICK, Donald Lee. 2020 CAPITOL ST NE 97301 #040-02-1979 L1982 **FM** *020 †18

PAPPAS, Anthony Geo. 1155 MISSION ST SE, STE 105 97302 #018-03-1968 L1969 **DR GP** *020 †80

PAROSA, James Francis. 801 MISSION ST SE 97302 #040-02-1974 L1978 **PUD IM** *020 †20

PASS, Michael Melton. 2925 RYAN DR SE 97301 #040-02-1999 L2004 **DR** *020 †80

PATI, Prasanna Kumar. 665 WINTER ST SE 97301 #495-13-1949 L1975 **P OS** *072 †75

PEDERSEN, Niels F. 4676 COMMERCIAL ST SE, STE 168 97302 #048-15-1999 L2006 **FM** *020 †18

PEKALSKA, Krystyna A. 2400 LANCASTER DR NE 97305 #759-09-1973 L1997 **IM** *020 †20

PERKINS, Marsh Olin. ■ 97302 #026-04-1942 L1942 **AN** *071

PERRIN, Paul Julian. 1881 BROADWAY ST NE, APT 7 97301 #143-07-1974 L1984 **AN EM** *020

PETERSON, Gordon Kermit. 8229 GORDAN ST SE 97301 #016-06-1957 L1963 **IM** *071

PETERSON, Mark S. 1535 LIBERTY ST SE 97302 #040-02-1984 L1989 **GS** *020 †85

PETERSON, Patricia. 2020 CAPITOL ST NE 97301 #054-04-1990 L1994 **OBG** *020 †30 ‡

PITTMAN, Rick De Witt. 1535 LIBERTY ST SE 97302 #040-02-1981 L1988 **VS GS** *020 †85

POLLARD, Harry Saml. 665 WINTER ST SE 97301 #048-02-1958 L1965 **AN AM** *071 †05

POLLARD, Marcus Lee. 1600 STATE ST, WILLAMETTE ORTHOPEDIC GROU 97301 #021-05-1979 L1986 **ORS** *020 †40

PONEC, Robert James. 875 OAK ST SE, STE 3010 97301 #005-06-1987 L1997 **GE** *020 †20

PORTER, Philip B. 665 WINTER ST SE 97301 #025-01-1949 L1953 **FM** *071

POTTER, Gregory Deloss. 5125 SKYLINE RD S 97306 #005-06-1974 L1975 **GE** *050 †20

POULSON, Don E. 875 OAK ST SE, STE 3060 97301 #040-02-1953 L1971 **ORS** *071 †40

POZAR, John Mark. 998 CAPITOL ST NE, P O BOX 12444 97301 #021-01-1966 L1972 **GP ADM** *071 †50

PRIOLLAUD, Logan Petrus. ■ 97302 #040-02-2003 L2003 **AN** *020

PRITCHARD, Amy Leigh. ■ 97302 #040-02-2004 L2005 **EM** *020

PROFFITT, James Lawrence. ■ 97301 #019-02-1996 L2006 **IM** *020 †20

PROFFITT, Pamela Ruth. ■ 97306 #041-13-1999 L1999 **HMP** *100

PROKHOROVA, Maria V. 2600 CENTER ST NE, OREGON STATE HOSP 97310 #913-06-1989 L1999 **P** *030 †75

PUERINI, Michael Thos. 3405 DEER PARK DR SE, OREGON STATE CORRECTION IN 97310 #030-06-1984 L1987 **FM** *020 †18

PUGMIRE, Jonathan Edward. PO BOX 2687 97308 #034-01-1998 L2002 **OBG** *020 †30

PURNELL, William Ebbert. 855 MEDICAL CENTER DR NE 97301 #024-05-1948 L1955 **R** *071 †80

PURNELL, Wm Ebbert, Jr. 1155 MISSION ST SE, STE 105 97302 #040-02-1980 L1986 **DR** *020 †80

PUSCAS, Mark S. 665 WINTER ST SE, SALEM HOSPITAL 97301 #048-13-1989 L1990 **EM** *020 †20

QUIJANO, Lerma Ocapan. 608 LANCASTER DR SE 97317 #748-09-1969 L1977 **GP** *020

QUIJANO, Oscar Manubag. 608 LANCASTER DR SE 97317 #748-09-1968 L1976 **FM** *020

RAHE, Richard Henry. ■ 97302 #054-04-1961 L1962 **P** *050 †75

RAPPAPORT, Michael Steven. 2600 CENTER ST NE, OREGON STATE HOSPITAL 97301 #038-41-1987 L1997 **P PYG** *071 †75

RASMUSSEN, Michelle Anne. 966 12TH ST SE, STE 130 97302 #040-02-1997 L2000 **FM** *020 †18

RASMUSSEN, Peter Alan. 875 OAK ST SE, STE 4030 97301 #016-11-1971 L1980 **ON** *020 †20

REICHLIN, Kay M. 2600 CENTER ST NE 97310 #007-02-1975 L1987 **P CHP** *040 †75

REICHLIN, Scott Mitchell. 2600 CENTER ST NE 97301 #007-02-1978 L1987 **P** *020 †75

REILLY, Philip John. 2600 CENTER ST NE 97310 #056-06-1953 **N** *040

RENNE, Jeanine Yvonne. ■ 97302 #048-04-1996 L2000 **LM** *062

REYES-MOLYNEUX, Nancy J. 875 OAK ST SE, STE 1080 97301 #016-43-1992 L1999 **RO** *020 †80

REYNOLDS, Dennis Elroy. ■ 97306 #026-04-1966 L1981 **CHP P** *020 †75

REY-ROSA, Alvaro E. 2400 LANCASTER DR NE 97305 #429-02-1990 L2001 **PDP** *020 †55

REY-ROSA, R Kirsten. 2400 LANCASTER DR NE, NORTHWEST PERMANENTE 97305 #035-03-1995 L2001 **FM** *020 †18

RICOY, Rebecca Luisa. 821 SAGINAW ST S 97302 #016-02-1988 L1992 **P** *020 †75

RILEY, Richard Leon. ■ 97302 #005-06-1961 L1962 **CHP PD** *020 †55

RIOS, Gloria Adriana. 5125 SKYLINE RD S, DEPT OF SURGERY 97306 #021-01-1994 L2000 **GS** *020

RIVERS, Leslie Dwight. 700 BELLEVUE ST SE, STE 300 97301 #030-05-1960 L1970 **AN** *071

ROBERTS, Donald Allen. ■ 97302 #035-20-1966 L1971 **IM** *020 †20

ROBERTS, John Mark. 875 OAK ST SE, STE 5040 97301 #056-05-1977 L1988 **ORS** *020 †40

ROBINSON, Brett Wm. 693 36TH AVE NE, SALEM FAMILY MEDICINE 97301 #005-12-1989 L1992 **FM** *020 †18

ROBINSON, Michael Edwin. 2600 CENTER ST NE, OREGON STATE HOSPITAL 97301 #048-02-1980 L1989 **P** *020 †75

ROEMELING, Bradley Joe. 2400 LANCASTER DR NE 97305 #026-04-1984 L1991 **FM** *071 †18

ROGOSIN, Steven Roy. 5050 SKYLINE VILLAG LOOP S 97306 #016-11-1970 L1976 **IM** *020 †20

ROHWER, Michael Demuth. 3993 FAIRVIW INDSTRL DR SE 97302 #026-04-1978 L1979 **IM** *020 †20

ROLLINGS, John Wm. 875 OAK ST SE STE 5060 97301 #028-02-1977 L1980 **FM** *020 †18

RONAI, Melanie Anne. 2478 13TH ST SE, SALEM PEDIATRIC CLC 97302 #040-02-1991 L1997 **PD** *020 †55

RONAI, Peter Michael. 2925 RYAN DR SE 97301 #143-03-1962 L1979 **R NM** *071 †28,80

ROSENFELD, Justin Elias. ■ 97302 #550-02-2004 L2007 **EM** *020

ROTH, Daniel Lewis. 2400 LANCASTER DR NE, DEPT OF INTERNAL MEDICINE 97305 #016-42-1989 L1992 **IM** *020

RUIZ-MARTINEZ, Luvy. 2600 CEMTER STREET N.E. 97310 #682-01-1978 L1988 **P** *020

RUSSELL, Franklin Howard. 2600 CENTER ST NE 97310 #027-01-1963 L1967 **GP P** *071

RUTHVEN, Daryl Spencer. 2575 CENTER ST NE, COUNSELING & TREATMENT SVC 97301 #007-02-1987 L1988 **P** *020 †75

SAAVEDRA, Benjamin. 2020 CAPITOL ST NE, SALEM CLINIC, P.C. 97301 #054-04-1986 L1989 **FM** *020 †18

SADLER, Jared R. 2925 RYAN DR SE 97301 #048-12-2002 L2007 **RNR** *012 †80

SAINT-JUST, Donald D. 2600 CENTER ST NE 97301 #031-01-1993 L1999 **CHP P** *020

SALOMON, Herbert. 665 WINTER ST SE 97301 #016-42-1971 L1978 **GE IM** *020 †20

SANDERS, Dorin M. 891 23RD ST NE 97301 #035-09-1997 L2000 **PD** *020 †55

SANDOR, Carol Thomas. 285 LIBERTY ST NE, STE 390 97301 #005-18-1984 L1990 **ATP CLP** *020 †50

SAUNDERS, Barney Sutton. 2600 CENTER ST NE 97310 #010-01-1963 L1969 **IM GP** *020 †20

SAYRE, Lewis Warren. 665 WINTER ST SE, SALEM MEMORIAL HOSPITAL 97301 #040-02-1976 L1977 **EM FM** *020 †18,16

■ = Address Information Privacy Protected

SAZIE, Elizabeth Suzanne. 4005 AUMSVILLE HWY SE, HEALTH SERVICES DIVISION 97317 #067-02-1975 L1980 **IM PHP** *020 †20
SCANLAN, Kathleen Ann. 2925 RYAN DR SE 97301 #040-02-1979 L2000 **DR GS** *020 †80
SCHMIDGALL, James Robt. 2925 RYAN DR SE 97301 #040-02-1974 L1977 **DR EM** *020 †80
SCHMIDT, David Frank. 1660 OAK ST SE, PORTLAND VA MEDICAL CENTER 97301 #010-01-1984 L1996 **IM AM** *020 †20
SCHNEIDER, Raymond A. 665 WINTER ST SE 97301 #035-45-1952 L1953 **AN** *071 †05
SCHONBLOM, Jon Walker. ■ 97302 #065-01-1964 L1978 **OBG** *071 †30
SCHRADER, Jerry Lee. ■ 97302 #019-02-1961 L1965 **P** *071 †75
SCHULTE, John W. 560 WINTER ST SE 97301 #028-02-1952 L1962 **PD** *071
SCHULTHEISS, Edward H. 875 OAK ST SE STE 3010 97301 #016-11-1982 L1983 **GE IM** *020 †20
SCHUMACHER, Gordon F. ■ 97301 #056-06-1954 L1959 **GYN** *071 †30
SCHUNK, George James. ■ 97306 #016-11-1946 L1952 **PDA GP** *072 †03,55
SCRUGGS, Thomas Murphy. ■ 97306 #023-07-1957 L1986 **U** *071 †85,95
SEETO, Keifong. 1344 LIBERTY ST SE 97302 #243-81-1986 L1996 **N** *020 †75
SEGAL, Richard John. 875 OAK ST SE STE 5050 97301 #033-06-1986 L1991 **IM** *020 †20
SELLER, Vicki Lynn. 633 JASON ST NE 97301 #017-20-1980 L1985 **GYN** *020 †30
SERVAIS, Edmund Gary. 2450 12TH ST SE 97302 #065-10-1978 L1982 **OPH** *020 †35
SESSIONS, David L. 665 WINTER ST SE 97301 #028-02-1958 L1962 **PD P** *071 †55
SEWELL, Dan Ardrey. ■ 97302 #028-02-1966 L1971 **PD PDC** *020 †55
SEWELL, Dan Gulliver. 1600 STATE ST 97301 #028-02-1993 L2002 **ORS** *020 †40
SHADWICK, Constance F. 2400 LANCASTER DR NE 97305 #041-13-1975 L1998 **D** *020 †18,15
SHAW, Enoch David. 700 BELLEVUE ST SE, STE 225 97301 #495-08-1963 L1973 **ORS** *020 †40
SHELTON, Steven Robt. 1880 LANCASTER DR NE, URGENCY CARE CLINIC 97305 #040-02-1980 L1983 **GP** *030
SHIN, Hyong. 2020 CAPITOL ST NE 97301 #054-04-1992 L1993 **IM** *020 †20
SHULTZ, Theodore Graham. 801 MISSION ST SE 97302 #017-20-1973 L1979 **PUD IM** *020 †20
SILVA, Louisa Mary. 3709 RIVERDALE RD S 97302 #005-14-1979 L1981 **GPM** *020
SILVER, John. 801 MISSION ST SE 97302 #024-05-1990 L2001 **PCC IM** *020 †20
SIMS, Jonathan Tippet. 855 MEDICAL CENTER DR NE, H LEE MOFFITT CANCER CTR & 97301 #011-04-2001 L2007 **DR** *020 †80
SKACH, Lorraine Elizabeth. 2600 CENTER ST NE, OREGON STATE HOSP 97301 #040-02-1984 L1987 **P PFP** *020 †75
SKARADA, Douglas John. 3099 RIVER RD S, STE 150 97302 #036-07-1996 L2001 **OTO** *020 †45
SLAMA, James Oliver. 665 WINTER ST SE 97301 #005-02-1958 L1963 **GS TS** *071 †85
SLOAN, Robert Louis. 665 WINTER ST SE, C/O ED- SALEM HOSPITAL 97301 #024-05-1988 L2001 **EM** *020 †16
SLOOP, Richard Donald. 700 BELLEVUE ST SE, RICHARD D SLOOP MD PC 97301 #040-02-1956 L1957 **GS TS** *072 †85
SMILLIE, Kent. 1489 STATE ST 97301 #035-03-1997 L2007 **OSM** *020 †40
SMOLIN, Michael Frederick. 2925 RYAN DR SE 97301 #041-13-1978 L1987 **DR** *020 †80
SNIDER, Malcolm Pratt. 875 MEDICAL CENTER DR NE 97301 #056-05-1978 L1983 **ORS** *020 †40
SOLOMON, Adam. 5050 SKYLINE VILLAG LOOP S 97306 #023-01-1993 L1996 **IM** *020 †20
SORNSON, Elmer Theodore. 655 MEDICAL CENTER DR NE 97301 #018-03-1961 L1966 **OPH** *020 †35
SPRAY, Charles Cranston. 500 SUMMER ST NE 1ST FL 97310 #016-06-1958 L1964 **IM** *062
SRINIVASAN, Shashi Kumar. 2441 GREAR ST NE, DERMATOLOGY CLINIC 97301 #495-59-1992 L2006 **D** *020 †20,15
STABLES, Derek Peter. 2925 RYAN DR SE 97301 #917-03-1960 L1981 **DR IM** *071
STACK, Sean Patrick. 2925 RYAN DR SE, SALEM RADIOLOGY CONSULTANT 97301 #040-02-1994 L1997 **DR** *020 †80
STAGEMAN, James H, III. 5050 SKYLINE VILLAG LOOP S, THE DOCTORS CLINIC 97306 #030-05-1994 L1997 **FM** *020 †18 ‡
STALFIRE, Joseph. 5125 SKYLINE RD S, SKYLINE MEDICAL OFFICE 97306 #048-13-1996 L2000 **OBG** *020 †30
STANFORD, Thad Chas. ■ 97302 #025-01-1958 L1965 **ORS LM** *062 †40
STANLEY, William Maltas. 3777 COMMERCIAL ST SE 97302 #040-02-1967 L1970 **EM OS** *020
STEELE, Robert Lowell. 755 MEDICAL CENTER DR NE 97301 #007-02-1984 L1993 **IM END** *020 †20
STEKETEE, Kirsten Gay. 665 WINTER ST SE 97301 #040-02-1991 L1994 **EM** *020 †16
STEVENS, John Andres. 1600 STATE ST 97301 #016-02-1967 L1975 **ORS HS** *020 †40 ‡
STEVENS, Thomas Ray. 655 MEDICAL CENTER DR NE 97301 #056-05-1965 L1974 **OPH** *020 †35
STEWART, Stephen Ray. 830 SAGINAW ST S 97302 #040-02-1974 L1976 **AI RHU** *020 †20,03
STILES, William Keith. 885 MISSION ST SE, SALEM CARDIO ASSOC PC 97302 #040-02-1978 L1983 **CD** *020 †20
STOESSL, Jeffrey Scott. 2020 CAPITOL ST NE 97301 #051-01-1992 L1995 **FM** *020 †18
STOR, Richard Arthur. 5125 SKYLINE RD S, KAISER - SKYLINE CLINIC 97306 #007-02-1972 L1979 **IM NEP** *020 †20
STRAND, Floyd Loren. 665 WINTER ST SE 97301 #036-01-1975 L1976 **EM** *020 †18,16
STRAUMFJORD, Agnar Allen. 2600 CENTER ST NE 97310 #040-02-1955 L1956 **P** *071 †75
STRINGHAM, Renee. 665 WINTER ST SE 97301 #020-12-1972 L1975 **FM FPG** *020 †18
STRUM, Gregory Maurice. 2380 HEATH ST S, P O BOX 4030 97302 #016-11-1979 L1983 **ORS OSM** *020 †40
SULLINALES, Lisa Carol. 2400 LANCASTER DR NE 97305 #034-01-1997 L2003 **PD** *020 †55
SWIFT, Gregory Lee. 2400 LANCASTER DR NE 97305 #016-06-1971 L1974 **FM** *020 †18
TACKETT-NELSON, Steven C. 821 SAGINAW ST S 97302 #028-03-1974 L1988 **P** *020 †75
TATARSKI, Petko Pentchev. 1234 COMMERCIAL ST SE 97302 #198-02-1987 L2004 **IM** *020 †20 ‡
TATE, David Michael. 2020 CAPITOL ST NE 97301 #054-04-1984 L1987 **IM** *020 †20
TAYLOR, Denise Adele. 3896 BEVERLY AVE NE, BLDG J 97305 #054-04-1994 L2006 **FM** *020 †18
TAYLOR, Duane Franklin. 665 WINTER ST SE 97301 #040-02-1961 L1965 **CD IM** *020
TAYLOR, Robert Ellis. ■ 97302 #047-06-1962 L1965 **FM** *030
TEMPLE, Brian Walter. 891 23RD ST NE, CHILDHOOD HEALTH ASSOC. OF 97301 #539-04-2004 L2007 **PD** *012
THALER, Joseph J. 5050 SKYLINE VILLAG LOOP S 97306 #038-06-1974 L1978 **IM** *020 †20
THOMAS, Gregory Martin. 665 WINTER ST SE 97301 #040-02-1980 L1983 **FM** *020 †18
THOMAS, James Melvin. 700 BELLEVUE ST SE STE 2 97301 #040-02-1969 L1973 **GYN** *071
THOMPSON, Clark Russell. 3099 RIVER RD S, STE 150 97302 #018-03-1982 L1987 **OTO** *020 †45
THOMPSON, Margaret June. 665 WINTER ST SE 97301 #039-01-1968 L1973 **RO** *071 †80
THOMPSON, Ralph Eugene. ■ 97302 #040-02-1955 L1956 **P GP** *071
THORSETT, David Andrew. 1600 STATE ST 97301 #028-02-1991 L1996 **ORS** *020 †40
THURSTON, Timothy Allen. 5125 SKYLINE RD S 97306 #016-02-1989 L1998 **AN** *020 †05
TIBOLT, Robert E. 655 MEDICAL CENTER DR NE 97301 #048-13-1988 L1989 **OPH** *020 †35
TIFFANY, Natasha Marie. 875 OAK ST SE, STE 4030 97301 #040-02-1998 L2001 **HO** *020 †20
TILEY, Frederick Wm. 665 WINTER ST SE 97301 #035-01-1963 L1970 **ORS** *020 †40
TOBIN, Richard W, Jr. 1600 STATE ST, WILLAMETTE ORTHOPEDIC GROU 97301 #041-02-1984 L1993 **ORS** *020 †40
TOLAND, Charles Wesley. 665 WINTER ST SE 97301 #018-03-1961 L1969 **GP** *071 †30
TRAN, Hung Dinh. 875 OAK ST SE STE 3070 97301 #040-02-1989 L1990 **P** *020 †75
TRANDAFIR, Simona I. 665 WINTER ST SE, SALEM HOSPITAL 97301 #781-01-1982 L2002 **IM** *020 †20
TRELEAVEN, Joseph H. ■ 97302 #060-01-1950 L1956 **P** *072 †75
TRUDEAU, Joseph Douglas. 1165 UNION ST NE 97301 #056-06-1995 L2001 **DR** *020 †80
TRUONG, Dung Xuan. 2561 CENTER ST NE 97301 #040-02-2001 L2005 **PM** *020 †60
TSANG, Howard Wai. 2168 LANCASTER DR NE 97305 #040-02-1986 L1997 **OM IM** *020 †70
TURCOT, Jeffrey Louis. 875 OAK ST SE, STE 5085 97301 #011-04-1986 L1992 **FM** *020 †18
TURK, Kyong Tae. 885 MISSION ST SE, SALEM CARDIOLOGY ASSOCIATE 97302 #041-01-1979 L2006 **ICE CD** *020 †20
VANDERBURGH, Mark Peter. 3494 LIBERTY RD S 97302 #038-45-1987 L2001 **FM** *020 †18
VANDERVEER, Penny Lee. 285 LIBERTY ST NE, STE 390 97301 #010-01-1988 L2000 **PTH** *020 †50
VAN RONZELEN, Michael Geo. 875 OAK ST SE, STE 4010 97301 #028-03-1972 L1979 **GS TS** *020 †85
VAN VOLKINBURG, Earl Jon. 875 OAK ST SE STE 5050 97301 #040-02-1970 L1974 **IM** *020 †20
VEENHUIZEN, Janice C. 1127 OAK ST SE 97301 #060-02-1987 L2003 **P** *020 †75
VERBURG, David Lee. 2400 LANCASTER DR NE 97305 #005-15-1976 L1989 **P** *020 †75
VETTER, William Laughlin. 5125 SKYLINE RD S 97306 #005-14-1978 L2007 **ORS HS** *020 †40
VOIGT, Allan E. ■ 97302 #040-02-1951 L1953 **OS** *071
VOLKMANN, Robert Michael. 665 WINTER ST SE 97301 #026-04-1979 L1984 **OBS** *020 †18
WAGNER, Charles John. 875 OAK ST SE STE 4000 97301 #030-05-1975 L1984 **AI PDA** *020 †55,03
WALKER, Kirk. 875 OAK ST SE, STE 5080 97301 #040-02-1989 L1991 **EM OS** *020 †20
WALKER, Shawn Michael. 2020 CAPITOL ST NE 97303 #048-12-1975 L1978 **IM** *075
WANG, Edwin Yen. 1165 UNION ST NE, STE 100 97301 #025-01-1997 L2007 **DR R** *020 †80
WARD, Jeffrey Steven. 875 OAK ST SE, STE 5030 97301 #040-02-1966 L1973 **U** *020 †95
WARNER, Russell Beebe. 1309 LIBERTY ST SE, EYE CARE PHYSICIAN 97302 #028-34-1999 L2003 **OPH** *020 †35 ‡
WASENMILLER, James Edwin. 885 MISSION ST SE 97302 #005-12-1973 L1980 **CD IM** *020 †20
WEARN, Frederick G. 665 WINTER ST SE 97301 #038-06-1978 L1982 **R** *020 †80
WEDEL, E Paul. 141 LANCASTER DR NE 97301 #040-02-1950 L1951 **GP N** *071
WEEBER, Charles E. ■ 97302 #018-03-1951 L1952 **GP** *071
WEEBER, Jerome Creighton. ■ 97302 #018-03-1958 L1965 **ON** *071 †95
WEEKS, Patricia June. 2020 CAPITOL ST NE 97301 #061-01-1983 L1994 **FM** *020 †18
WEILER, Karin Diane. 2478 13TH ST SE 97302 #005-02-1994 L1997 **PD** *020 †55
WEST, David Marold. 1305 CANNON ST SE 97302 #048-04-1976 L1980 **OBG** *020 †30
WEST, Hans Christian. 2020 CAPITOL ST NE 97301 #012-05-1975 L1981 **GE IM** *020 †20
WEST, Niels Jespersen. ■ 97302 #297-01-1941 L1957 **ORS** *071 †40
WESTFALL, Andrew. 2450 12TH ST SE 97302 #040-02-1999 L2000 **OPH** *020 †35
WESTFALL, Mary Ann. 3150 LANCASTER DR NE 97305 #025-01-1980 L1981 **PM** *020 †60
WHITMAN, Walter Howard. 1430 COMMERCIAL ST SE 97302 #023-01-1971 L1978 **NEP IM** *020 †20
WILD, Anne Marie. 755 MEDICAL CENTER DR NE, WILLAMETTE FAMILY MEDICAL 97301 #040-02-1983 L1984 **FM** *020 †18
WILSON, Benjamin R. 700 BELLEVUE ST SE STE 290 97301 #005-06-1979 L1980 **GS** *020 †85
WILSON, Charles Edward. 1220 HANSEN AVE S, SALEM EMERG PHYSICANS P.C 97302 #016-11-1970 L1975 **EM** *020 †16
WILSON, Kenneth Mitchell. 1600 STATE ST, WILLAMETTE ORTHOPEDIC GROU 97301 #048-02-1981 L1989 **HS** *020 †40
WILSON, Richard A. 885 MISSION ST SE 97302 #028-34-1975 L1983 **CD NM** *020 †20
WILSON, Thomas Allen. 2478 13TH ST SE, SALEM PEDIATRIC CLNC 97302 #003-01-1978 L1981 **PD** *020 †55
WINKLER, Thomas Robin. 875 OAK ST SE, STE 4030 97301 #007-02-1978 L1983 **TS** *020 †85,90
WINNER, Dennis Donald. 665 WINTER ST SE 97301 #025-07-1980 L1981 **EM GS** *020 †16
WINTHROP, Loring Herbert. 2020 CAPITOL ST NE 97301 #005-02-1971 L1973 **FM** *020 †18
WIRSIG, Jennifer Ellen. 2478 13TH ST SE, SALEM PEDIATRIC CLINIC 97302 #040-02-2000 L2003 **PD** *020 †55
WOLF, Mark Timothy. 665 WINTER ST SE 97301 #054-04-1999 L1999 **PYG** *020 †75
WOLF, Robert Michael. 1127 OAK ST SE, SALEM PSYCHIATRIC CENTER 97301 #030-06-1995 L1997 **P** *020 †75
WOOD, John Waterbury. 665 WINTER ST SE 97301 #040-02-1963 L1968 **OPH** *071 †35
WOODS, Richard Allen. 5125 SKYLINE RD S, SALEM MEDICAL OFFICE 97306 #017-20-1983 L1984 **IM** *020 †20
WRIGHT, Sarah D. 2478 13TH ST SE 97302 #041-14-1980 L1985 **PD ADL** *020 †55
WU, Debbie Chia. ■ 97302 #028-02-1995 L2003 **PCP** *020 †50
XU, Yu. ■ 97302 #048-04-2003 L2006 **PD** *020 †55
YAMANAKA, Masatoshi. 2400 LANCASTER DR NE 97305 #572-41-1976 L1988 **ORS** *020 †40
YORK, Julie Elizabeth. 875 OAK ST SE, STE 5085 97301 #048-04-1994 L2006 **NS** *020 †25
YUE, Ourania. 857 MEDICAL CENTER DR NE 97301 #418-01-1973 L1990 **IM** *020
YUREVICH, Nina. 2600 NE CENTER STREET, OREGON STATE HOSPITAL 97310 #913-52-1956 L1982 **P PHP** *020
ZIRSCHKY, Robert Guy. 1600 STATE ST, WILLAMET ORTHOPEDIC GROUPQ 97301 #040-02-1984 L1985 **ORS** *020 †40
ZUK, Timothy Tolander. 3494 LIBERTY RD S 97302 #060-01-1991 L2002 **FM** *020 †18
ZURFLIEH, Patricia Jaye. 2600 CENTER ST NE, OREGON STATE HOSPITAL 97301 #036-01-1991 L1994 **P** *020 †75

SALEM – POLK

AUSTIN, Wallace O. ■ 97304 #005-11-1953 L1953 **PD PDC** *071 †55
BRAY, James Donald. ■ 97304 #019-02-1961 L1965 **P** *072 †75

■ = Address Information Privacy Protected

BROSKIE, Nancy Elaine. 525 GLEN CREEK RD NW STE 2 97304 #036-01-1991 L1992
 P *020 †75
BYERLY, Olin M. ■ 97304 #016-11-1951 L1952 **FM OS** *071 †18
COOK, Joseph Wright. ■ 97304 #041-01-1943 L1943 **GP** *020
DOWNS, Edward Hume. ■ 97304 #005-06-1948 L1955 **GS** *071 †85
ELTZROTH, Kimberly Sue. 1320 TITAN DR NW, SALEM WOMEN'S CLINIC 97304
 #024-07-1997 L2006 **OBG** *020 †30
FAIRFAX, Walter A, Jr. ■ 97304 #054-04-1952 L1961 **OPH** *071 †35
HAEVERNICK, Kenneth B. ■ 97304 #040-02-1959 L1960 **GP** *072
HANZEL, Lumier Erving. 4700 SALEM DALLAS HWY NW, # 88 97304 #030-05-1958 L1963
 AN *071 †05
HEDER, James Earl. 1275 WALLACE RD NW 97304 #041-13-1973 L1979 **FM** *020 †18
HOWELL, Harold Blane. ■ 97304 #048-04-1966 L1972 **EM GP** *020 †16,05
HURSEY, Phyllis Deshun. 1233 EDGEWATER ST NW 97304 #010-03-1989 L2005 **FM** *020 †18
JOBE, David L. ■ 97304 #030-06-1975 L1977 **P** *020
KEARNS, Albert Ralph. ■ 97304 #040-02-1966 L1991 **IMG** *071
KOLTA, Laslo Emory. 1255 WALLACE RD NW, PRIMARY CARE WEST 97304 #023-01-1974 L1983
 IM *020 †20 ‡
LARGE, Lance Brandon. 150 KINGWOOD AVE NW #026-04-2000 L2000 **FM** *020 †18 ‡
LOBERG, Lance Gregory. 150 KINGWOOD AVE NW 97304 #054-04-1979 L1982 **FM** *020 †18
NOCEK, Cynthia S. 150 KINGWOOD AVE NW, C/O WEST SALEM CLINIC 97304
 #035-03-1983 L1991 **IM** *020 †20
ORAN, Gwendolyn Alta. 150 KINGWOOD AVE NW, NORTHWEST HUMAN SERVICES 97304
 #051-01-1999 L2004 **FM** *020 †18
PRICE, Harvey Bruce. 150 KINGWOOD AVE NW 97304 #016-06-1959 L1964 **FM EM** *020 †16,18
SIMMONS, Thomas Britt. 150 KINGWOOD AVE NW, WEST SALEM CLINIC 97304
 #060-01-1981 L1996 *020
STRAUMFJORD, Jon V, Jr. ■ 97304 #040-02-1953 L1958 **CLP PTH** *071 †50
SUCKOW, George Robt, Jr. 1245 EDGEWATER ST NW 97304 #040-02-1960 L1961
 P LM *020 †75
SULT, Elizabeth Hogan. 1808 WESTHAVEN AVE NW 97304 #024-01-1951 L1959 **PD** *071
SULT, Francis L. ■ 97304 #024-01-1951 L1958 **PD** *071 †55
SUND, Sheila Lynn. 1015 3RD ST NW, WILLAMETTE VALLEY HOSPICE9 97304
 #005-15-1984 L1989 **PLM N** *030 †75
THOMAS, Heidi S. 1275 WALLACE RD NW 97304 #040-02-1980 L1983 **IM** *020 †20
TIHANYI, Katie E. 1255 WALLACE RD NW 97304 #068-01-1977 L1983 **GP GYN** *020 ‡
TRAN, Drissana T. 1015 3RD ST NW 97304 #040-02-1992 L1993 **IM** *050
VAN ZANTEN, Pamela Mae. ■ 97304 #040-02-1998 **FM** *100
WHITE, John Deason. 865 KINGWOOD DR NW 97304 #021-05-1960 L1968 **NS** *072 †25
YAMAGUCHI, Eugene Yukio. 1275 WALLACE RD NW, WEST SALEM FAMILY PRACTICE 97304
 #005-19-1983 L1986 **FM** *020 †18
YOUNG, Terence Howe. 1205 WALLACE RD NW 97304 #014-01-1975 L1979 **FM** *020

SANDY — CLACKAMAS

BLOME, Randall Eric. 17055 RUBEN LN 97055 #038-43-1986 L1992 **FM** *020 †18
CHA, Michael J. 17055 RUBEN LN 97055 #005-12-1994 L2001 **FM** *020 †18
COURSER, Darel Eugene. ■ 97055 #649-14-1968 L1969 **ORS GS** *071
FULTON, Robert Dalzell. ■ 97055 #038-06-1942 L1942 **PD GP** *071 †55
KANDT, Robert. ■ 97055 #005-12-1962 L1965 **AN** *071
LEAKOS, Richard James. 36860 INDUSTRIAL WAY 97055 #068-01-1995 L1998 *020
LEAVITT, Elton D. ■ 97055 #040-02-1950 L1953 *071
LIAN-LEAF, Eunice Ripoh. 17055 RUBEN LN 97055 #005-12-1998 L2001 **FM** *020 †18
MILLER, Jos Leggett, Jr. ■ 97055 #016-02-1936 **IM** *071 †20
MOELLENHOFF, Robert Wm. ■ 97055 #028-03-1959 L1989 **IM CD** *071
NICHOLSON, Stephen Frank. 36860 INDUSTRIAL WAY 97055 #040-02-1980 L1983 **FM** *020 †18
PARSON, Victor G. ■ 97055 #018-03-1951 L1974 **AN** *071
SWIRIDOFF, Eric Eugene. 36860 INDUSTRIAL WAY 97055 #005-12-1986 L1994 **FM EM** *020 †18
WYLES, Jean Marie. ■ 97055 #040-02-1987 L1992 **PM** *020 †60

SCAPPOOSE — COLUMBIA

RUGGE, John Bruin. 51377 SW OLD PORTLAND RD, STE C 97056 #008-01-1999 L2000
 GPM *020 †18,70
WU, Karyee. 51377 SW OLD PORTLAND RD, STE C 97056 #024-07-1999 L2002 **FM** *020 †18

SEAL ROCK — LINCOLN

CRAWFORD, Raymond B. ■ 97376 #005-12-1949 L1949 **CD** *071 †20

SEASIDE — CLATSOP

ARNAEZ, Gerardo Enrique. 727 S WAHANNA RD, PROVIDENCE NORTH COAST CLI 97138
 #016-02-1998 L2002 **IM** *020 †20
BLANCHE, Jeffrey Alan. 725 S WAHANNA RD 97138 #005-12-1975 L1981 **DR** *020
COCKCROFT, Ben David. 727 S WAHANNA RD, NORTHCOAST MEDICAL CENTER 97138
 #005-15-1986 L1989 **FM EM** *020 †18
DOWLATDAD, Ali. 727 S WAHANNA RD 97138 #917-23-1964 L1984 **GS** *020
DUEKER, George Edgar. 727 S WAHANNA RD, PROVIDENCE NORTH COAST CLI 97138
 #028-02-1961 L1994 **U** *071 †95
GRECO, Dominique. 727 S WAHANNA RD 97138 #054-04-1996 L2000 **FM** *020 †18
HUDDLESTON, Lisa Ann. 727 S WAHANNA RD, PROVIDENCE NORTH COAST CLI 97138
 #040-02-1991 L1994 **FM EM** *020 †18
LINDGREN, Jonathan Scott. 725 S WAHANNA RD, PROVIDENCE SEASIDE HOSP ER 97138
 #040-02-1998 L1999 **FM EM** *020 †18
LYONS, Jennifer Lee. 727 S WAHANNA RD 97138 #017-20-1992 L1993 **OPH PO** *020 †35
MC BRIDE, Jonathan Eg. 727 S WAHANNA RD 97138 #035-09-2003 L2006 **FM** *020
MEYER-ARENDT, Erica Amely. 580 AVENUE U 97138 #409-21-1949 L1977 **GP** *071
MITCHELL, Winston A. 725 S WAHANNA RD 97138 #040-02-1959 L1963 **R** *020 †80
OPIE, Timothy Martin. 725 S WAHANNA RD, PROVIDENCE SEASIDEHOSPITAL 97138
 #054-04-1998 L2003 **IM** *020 †20

PATIL, Ravindra Ramdas. 727 S WAHANNA RD 97138 #496-38-1984 L1998 **IM** *020 †20
RAND, William Chas. 725 S WAHANNA RD 97138 #005-14-1975 L1990 **ORS OS** *020
SHAFFER, Walter Everett. 727 S WAHANNA RD 97138 #005-02-1976 L1976 **FM** *020
SISK, James Victor. 725 S WAHANNA RD, PROV SEASIDE HOSP EMERG 97138
 #016-11-1982 L1983 **FM** *020 †18
SMART, Christopher Roy. 725 S WAHANNA RD, PROVIDENCE SEASIDE HOSPITA 97138
 #060-01-2000 L2006 **FM** *020 †18 ‡
SOLLER, Richard V. ■ 97138 #306-01-1983 L1989 **IM** *020
STARR, Charles Roger. 725 S WAHANNA RD 97138 #056-05-1956 L1968 **PS** *071 †65
STEFANELLI, Joann G. 580 AVENUE U, SEASIDE URGENT CARE 97138 #033-05-1985 L1996
 OBG *020 †30
STEFANELLI, Mark Anthony. 580 AVENUE U, SEASIDE URGENT CARE 97138
 #033-05-1986 L1996 **IM EM** *020 †20
STELSON, Hugh Carrier. 727 S WAHANNA RD 97138 #005-06-1978 L1982 **FM** *020 †18
WALCZAK, Karin. 580 AVENUE U 97138 #297-01-1974 L1987 **FM** *020 †18
WAYNE, Robert. 727 S WAHANNA RD 97138 #030-06-1969 L1978 **GS** *020 †85
WERNER, Sandra Vianna. 727 S WAHANNA RD 97138 #187-25-1978 L2000 **FM** *020 †18
ZOBELL, Richard L. 727 S WAHANNA RD 97138 #049-01-1990 L2006 **U** *020 †95

SELMA — JOSEPHINE

MECHLING, Katherine Ann. 18173 REDWOOD HWY BOX 847, CLEAR CREEK FAM
 PRACT 97538 #010-01-1992 L1995 **FM** *020 †18

SHADY COVE — JACKSON

SHARKEY, Frances Faison. ■ 97539 #035-19-1959 L1992 **PD** *072 †55

SHERIDAN — YAMHILL

COLLINS, David M. 222 SE JEFFERSON ST, SHERIDAN MEDICAL CENTER 97378
 #068-01-1978 L1984 **FM** *020
DHALIWAL, Jaspal Singh. ■ 97378 #495-03-1981 L2005 *100
HAGGLUND, Hal Gene. ■ 97378 #040-02-1977 **GP** *071
MOLLOY, James Patrick, III. 950 SE SHERIDAN RD, WESTERN YAMHILL MEDICAL C 97378
 #048-14-1983 L1986 **FM** *020 †18
NAGY, Frank Michael. ■ 97378 #041-09-1962 L1968 **OPH** *020 †35

SHERWOOD — WASHINGTON

ASHLEY, Bradford Clifford. 16770 SW EDY RD, STE 315 97140 #040-02-1994 L1996
 AM P *020 †70
ATKINSON, Tamara Marie. ■ 97140 #040-02-2008 *012
BECK, Edmund Choongki. 16770 SW EDY RD, STE 102 97140 #055-01-1997 L2000
 FM *020 †18 ‡
CORDOVA, Gilbert Michael. ■ 97140 #019-02-1964 L1969 **DR** *020 †80
ELLINGSON, Todd William. ■ 97140 #040-02-2003 L2007 **GS GS** *012
GILMORE, Phyllis Claire. 16770 SW EDY RD, STE 102 97140 #021-05-1977 L2001 **FM** *020 †18
HEAVEY, Laurence Ross. ■ 97140 #005-18-1980 L1986 **DR** *020 †80
JOHNSON, Michael Wayne. 21887 SW SHERWOOD BLVD, STE C 97140 #016-43-1976 L1977
 IM *020 †20
JOHNSON, Steven Warner. 16770 SW EDY RD, STE 102 97140 #054-04-1976 L2000
 FM *020 †18
KANNING, Nathan Christian. ■ 97140 #019-02-2002 L2002 **GS** *012
MARTIN, Bridget Charleen. 16770 SW EDY RD, PMG/SHERWOOD 97140 #048-02-2002 L2003
 FM *020 †18
MC DOWELL, Lyle B. ■ 97140 #007-02-1962 L1965 **EM N** *020
MEHTA, Jessica N. 16770 SW EDY RD, PROVIDENCE MEDICAL GROUP 97140
 #028-46-1996 L2006 **D** *020 †15
MILLER-DAVIS, Jennifer W. 22198 SW FISK TER, PMG/NEWBERG 97140 #019-02-2002 L2006
 OBG *012 †20
NOONAN, William Donald. ■ 97140 #040-02-1991 L1994 **OPH** *020
RAJANI, Bhavesh. 16770 SW EDY RD 97140 #917-08-1989 L2002 **FM MDM** *020 †18
ROLLIN, Sarah Jane. 16770 SW EDY RD 97140 #051-07-2000 L2006 **PD** *020 †55
STEVENS, Kenneth Richards. ■ 97140 #049-01-1966 L1968 **RO** *071 †80
SWEENEY, Joseph Danl. 16770 SW EDY RD 97140 #028-34-1987 L1990 **PD** *020 †55
TODD, David Steven. ■ 97140 #040-02-1963 L1967 **ORS** *071 †40
WALKER, Sara Careen. ■ 97140 #011-04-2001 L2006 **P** *020 †75
WHITE, Anna G. 16078 SW TUALATIN SHRWD RD 97140 #012-05-1999 L2004 **FM** *020 †18
WILSON, Jacob Hayes. ■ 97140 #040-02-1964 L1969 **N** *071
YU, Maggie Kate. 20015 SW PACIFIC HWY, STE 221 97140 #005-14-1997 L2002 **FM** *020 †18

SILVERTON — MARION

BAYLIES, Howard N, Jr. ■ 97381 #005-02-1977 L2003 **IM** *020 †20
BERNER, Neal Eugene. ■ 97381 #019-02-1972 L2006 **FM** *020 †18
BLOCK, Richard Allan. 342 FAIRVIEW ST, SILVERTON HOSPITAL 97381 #016-11-1974 L2004
 ORS *020 †40
BLOUNT, Elizabeth Jane. 335 FAIRVIEW ST 97381 #005-15-1984 L2001 **FM** *020 †18
BROWN, Eric Trent. 342 FAIRVIEW ST, SILVERTON HOSPITAL 97381 #005-12-1994 L1997
 EM *020 †16
CHISHOLM, Robert William. 342 FAIRVIEW ST, SILVERTON HOSPITAL 97381
 #048-13-2001 L2001 **EM** *020 †16
CLIMER, Curtis Mark. 408 WELCH ST 97381 #040-02-1982 L1983 **IM** *020 †20
DALISKY, Denis Jon. 406 WELCH ST 97381 #016-11-1975 L1987 **OBG** *020 †30
DAVIES, Olwyn Kenneth. 410 WELCH ST 97381 #040-02-1955 L1956 **GP** *020
DOJAQUEZ, Katherine C. 3745 EDISON RD NE, MAIL: POX 1425 97381 #024-01-1995 L2004
 OBG *020 †30
GABE, Michael Dana. 402 WELCH ST 97381 #056-06-1979 L1989 **FM** *020 †18
GILLIAM, John A, II. ■ 97381 #048-12-1995 L1998 **FM OBS** *020 †18

■ = Address Information Privacy Protected

GRADY, Michael Edward. 442 MCCLAINE ST, MCCLAINE STREET CLNC 97381 #040-02-1976 L1983 **FM** *020 †18

GREIG, Shandra Denise. 335 FAIRVIEW ST 97381 #040-02-1993 L1996 **FM** *020 †18

GRUBER, Meegan. 342 FAIRVIEW ST, SILVERTON HOSPITAL 97381 #016-11-2000 L2005 **PS** *100 †65

HARRIS, Daniel Kimball. 342 FAIRVIEW ST, LANCASTER FAMILY HEALTH CE 97381 #040-02-1993 L1996 **FM OBS** *020 †18

HEIDINGER, Harvey Eugene. ■ 97381 #005-12-1960 L1963 **PHP PD** *030

HOUTS, Katie E. 335 FAIRVIEW ST 97381 #040-02-1996 L1999 **FM** *020 †18

JENSEN, Brett Terry. 342 FAIRVIEW ST, SILVERTON HOSPITAL 97381 #005-11-2004 L2004 **EM** *020

LARSON, Andrea Karin. 335 FAIRVIEW ST 97381 #016-01-1984 L1992 **FM** *020 †18

LARSON, Robert Lee, Jr. 335 FAIRVIEW ST 97381 #005-12-1985 L1992 **FM** *020 †18

LEMMERS, Michael John. 342 FAIRVIEW ST 97381 #005-11-1985 L1986 **U** *020 †95

LORD, Frank King. 342 FAIRVIEW ST 97381 #040-02-1971 L1974 **EM** *020 †18

MC NEILLY, Gordon C. ■ 97381 #016-11-1944 L1945 **GP** *071

NADEL, Vivienne. PO BOX 596 97381 #917-04-1971 L1978 **IM** *074

NEALON, James Patrick. 450 WELCH ST 97381 #030-05-1996 L2001 **GS** *020 †85

NINO, Henry E. 454 WELCH ST, SILVERTON SPECIALISTS 97381 #005-14-1970 L2006 **N CN** *020 †75

NORTH, Eric Morgan. ■ 97381 #040-02-2004 L2007 **FM** *020 †18

O'HALLORAN, Elizabeth K. ■ 97381 #036-07-2003 L2005 **FM** *100 †18

ORR, Rodney Earl. 335 FAIRVIEW ST 97381 #040-02-1976 L1979 **FM** *020 †18

PETERS, Sarah Mae. 605 WELCH ST 97381 #030-05-1988 L1991 **FM** *020 †18

PETERS, Timothy Roy. 605 WELCH ST, NORTHWEST FAMILY MEDICINE 97381 #019-02-1988 L1991 **FM** *020 †18

RENARD, Brooke Denise. 406 WELCH ST 97381 #030-05-1996 L2000 **OBG** *020 †30

ROSBOROUGH, Robert James. 335 FAIRVIEW ST, RODNEY E ORR MD 97381 #040-02-1993 L1996 **FM** *020 †18

ROWLEY, Mark Calvin. 400 WELCH ST 97381 #016-02-1981 L1993 **OBG** *020 †30

ROWLEY, Michele Betrice. ■ 97381 #016-02-1986 L1994 **P** *020

SANFORD, Clinton Chas. 333 FAIRVIEW ST 97381 #054-04-1973 L1976 **FM** *020 †18

SHREYER, Eugene S. ■ 97381 #005-12-1949 L1949 **AN** *071

SPADY, Herbert Arthur. ■ 97381 #028-02-1955 L1956 **ORS** *071 †40

SPARKS, Danny Chas. 123 BREYONNA WAY 97381 #040-02-1973 L1976 **PD EM** *020 †55,16

WALKER, James Grant. 347 FAIRVIEW ST, SILVERTON FAMIILY CLINIC 97381 #040-02-1978 L2005 **FM** *020 †18 ‡

WATERS, Harris J. 450 WELCH ST 97381 #005-14-1981 L1988 **GS VS** *020 †85

WICKS, Michael David. 347 FAIRVIEW ST 97381 #040-02-1971 L1974 **FM** *020 †18

WILEY, Cameron James. 342 FAIRVIEW ST 97381 #040-02-1957 L1964 **R** *071 †80

SISTERS – DESCHUTES

ASAY, Lyal Duane. ■ 97759 #008-01-1950 L1953 **PD** *071 †55

BASSFORD, Paul Stanley. PO BOX 3500 97759 #048-04-1955 L1956 **P** *071

BENSON, William Lee. ■ 97759 #018-03-1966 L1982 **OBG PTH** *071 †30

BUCK, Mylon Lee. 69200 BARCLAY DR 97759 #028-02-1958 L1959 **FM OS** *071 †18

FAN, May Shan. 231 E CASCADE 97759 #005-02-1987 L1990 **FM** *020 †18

GRISHAM, Philip Leo. ■ 97759 #039-01-1962 L1964 **N GP** *071 †18

HARNER, Donald S. ■ 97759 #005-17-1962 L1975 **AN** *071 †05

RIES, John Peter. ■ 97759 #026-04-1970 L1976 **PD** *020 †55

SPRANG, Harry Edward. ■ 97759 #038-40-1945 **P** *020

STEPHENSON, Wayland A. ■ 97759 #019-02-1942 L1952 **N** *071 †75

SOUTH BEACH – LINCOLN

BROOKSBY, Wilford A. ■ 97366 #016-06-1943 L1944 **P N** *071 †75

SPRINGFIELD – LANE

AHLEN, John Vernon. 2280 MARCOLA RD, SPRINGFIELD FAMILY 97477 #018-03-1974 L1976 **FM** *020 †18

AHLEN, Patricia Park. 2280 MARCOLA RD, SPRINGFIELD FAMILY 97477 #018-03-1974 L1976 **FM** *020 †18 ‡

AMATO, Jacqueline Marie. 175 W B ST, STE D 97477 #016-02-1994 L2001 **CHP** *020 †75

AMES, Stephan Anthony. 147 S 52ND PL 97478 #040-02-1987 L1989 **FM D** *020 †18

ARORA, Rashi. 1460 G ST, APOGEE MEDICAL GROUP 97477 #495-41-2000 L2006 **IM** *020 †20

BABCOCK, Cristin Jane. 3100 MARTN LTHR KNG JR 97477 #036-01-1983 L1987 **OBG** *020 †30

BAUMANN, John Albert. ■ 97477 #036-07-1962 L1962 **FM** *020

BECKWITH, Jeffrey Drew. 2280 MARCOLA RD, SPRINGFIELD FAMILY 97477 #016-06-1971 L1976 **FM** *020 †18

BENDER, Robert Alan. 1460 G ST 97477 #017-20-1968 L1973 **IM** *020 †20

BERGIN, Marie Bliscemi. 960 16TH ST, STE 303 97477 #032-01-1982 L1988 **IM** *020 †20

BERKMAN, Marvin Ivan. 1462 I ST 97477 #038-40-1966 L1973 **AN** *071 †05

BETTMAN, Thomas Coulter. 1462 I ST 97477 #024-01-1969 L1974 **AN** *020 †05

BLYTON, Barry Duane. 1457 G ST, OREGON UROLOGY INSTITUTE R 97477 #017-20-1990 L2007 **RO** *020 †80

BOWERS, Ann Pauline. 1460 G ST, EMERGING DEPT 97477 #054-04-1992 L1995 **EM** *020 †16

BRENDLER, Sarah Jane. 960 16TH ST, STE 208 97477 #005-18-1982 L1983 **GE IM** *020 †20

BRONICEL, Benjamin J. 1460 G ST 97477 #049-01-1996 L2001 **EM** *020 †16

BUCK, Richard Otis. 1705 CENTENNIAL BLVD, STE 2 97477 #035-45-1971 L1979 **AI PUD** *071 †55,03

BUTDORF, Steven Joseph. 147 S 52ND PL 97478 #011-03-1981 L1984 **FM** *020 †18

CARSON, Mark Robert. 2400 HARTMAN LN, UROLOGY HEALTHCARE 97477 #018-03-1996 L2002 **U** *020 †95

CARTER, John Linus. 40820 MCKENZIE HWY 97478 #018-03-1962 L1967 **P CHP** *062

CARTER, Terrence Edgar. 1435 G ST 97477 #054-04-1966 L1974 **ORS** *071 †40

CHANCE, Stacy Ryan. 1007 HARLOW RD, STE 210 97477 #047-05-2002 L2006 **MPD** *020 †55,20

CHARLES, Robert John. 1460 G ST, CASCADE MEDICAL ASSOCIATES 97477 #054-04-1997 L2006 **EM** *020 †16

CHAVIN, Paul Anthony. 1403 F ST 97477 #016-43-1971 L1977 **OBG** *020 †30

CLAEYS, Donald Walter. 1462 I ST 97477 #016-43-1970 L1976 **AN MDM** *071 †05

DAVENPORT, Charles K. ■ 97478 #005-02-1946 L1947 **OM IM** *071

DAVIDSON, Lee Warren. 1460 G ST 97477 #049-01-1996 L1999 **EM** *020 †16

DAVIS, Fredric Willis. ■ 97478 #048-04-1964 L1972 **ORS** *071 †40

DIAZ, Paul Richard. 1462 I ST 97477 #040-02-2001 L2001 **AN** *020 †05

DI MARCO, David Sean. 2400 HARTMAN LN, UROLOGY HEALTHCARE 97477 #028-34-1998 L2005 **U** *020 †20

DISSANAYAKE, Magha S. 223 Q ST, Q STREET INTERNISTS LLC 97477 #913-92-1986 L1998 **IM** *020 †20

DOS REIS, Leslie. 960 N 16TH ST STE 103, MCKENZIE MEDICAL IMAGING 97477 #024-01-1969 L1973 **DR** *020 †80

EDSALL, Jean Ann. 1007 HARLOW RD, STE 210 97477 #005-19-1988 L2005 **FM** *020 †18

ELLISON, Dennis Lynn. 1611 J ST 97477 #040-02-1969 L1970 **U** *071 †95

ERDE, Alison Joan. 147 S 52ND PL 97478 #011-02-1987 L2001 **P** *020 †18

ERPELDING, Richard F. 1717 CENTENNIAL BLVD STE 7 97477 #026-04-1967 L1974 **ORS** *071 †40

ESRIG, David. 2400 HARTMAN LN, UROLOGY HEALTHCARE 97477 #016-43-1986 L1998 **U GS** *020 †95

EVERETT, Rolanda R. 2000 19TH ST 97477 #005-12-1992 L1998 **PD** *020 †55

FEDOROV, Alec. 1435 G ST 97477 #005-14-1993 L2000 **ORS** *020 †40

FITZGERALD, Kathleen M. 960 N 16TH ST, STE 207 97477 #005-19-1980 L1991 **N** *020 †75

FLETCHER, Mark Justin. 1435 G ST, OREGON MEDICAL GROUP 97477 #010-01-1999 L2006 **ORS** *100

GAGE, Miriam Enid. 1640 G ST, RIVERSTONE CLNC 97477 #005-18-1993 L2004 **FM** *020 †18

GEE-GOTT, Lana. 2280 MARCOLA RD 97477 #051-07-1998 L2006 **FM** *020 †18

GEISLER, Eric Langer. 147 S 52ND PL 97478 #038-44-1991 L1994 **FM** *020 †18

GHANDOUR, Hassan Ali. 960 16TH ST, STE 303 97477 #605-01-1987 L1996 **IM ID** *020 †20

GREEN, Frederick Norman. 3100 MARTN LTHR KNG JR, PO BX 70368 97477 #007-02-1980 L1985 **GYN** *020 †30

GRENIER, Catherine Ann. 1460 G ST 97477 #021-05-1979 L2001 **PD** *020 †55

GUILD, Robert Evan. 3831 MAIN ST, STE 101 97478 #005-02-1974 L1977 **FM** *020 †18

GUNDERMAN, Robert Edward. 860 BELTLINE RD 97477 #038-41-1979 L1988 **DR NM** *020 †80

HARRINGTON, Sarah E. 1403 F ST 97477 #054-04-2000 L2000 **OBG** *020 †20

HEJINIAN, Anna Carolyn. 2280 MARCOLA RD, SPRINGFIELD FAMILY 97477 #005-02-1995 L2004 **FM** *020 †18

HEMSLEY, Gregory Barton. 1460 G ST 97477 #038-41-1989 L1993 **PD** *020 †55

HERRING, Mark Owen. 960 N 16TH ST STE 207 97477 #032-01-1980 L1986 **N** *020

HIRTZ, Susan Kathleen. 1717 CENTENNIAL BLVD, S KATHLEEN HIRTZ 97477 #005-02-1982 L1985 **GPM FSM** *072

HOKARI, Naoko. 1442 S A ST 97477 #035-47-1999 L2004 **PD** *020 †55

HUANG, Richard Hao. 1007 HARLOW RD, UNIV OF CALIFORNIA IRVINE 97477 #005-15-2001 L2007 **IM** *020

HUFFMAN, Todd Alan. 1442 S A ST 97477 #038-40-1992 L1996 **PD** *020 †55

HURTADO, Martin. 2280 MARCOLA RD, SPRINGFIELD FAMILY 97477 #005-15-1993 L2004 **FM** *020 †18

JACKSON, Larry Arthur. 1460 G ST 97477 #005-12-1972 L1973 **FM PHP** *020 †18

JAMES, Stanley Lawrence. 1435 G ST 97477 #018-03-1962 L1967 **ORS OSM** *072 †40

JEFFREY, Douglas Paul. 2280 MARCOLA RD, SPRINGFIELD FAMILY 97477 #040-02-1978 L1979 **FM** *020 †18

JOHNSON, J Allen. 2000 N 19TH ST, VALLEY CHILDRENS CLINIC 97477 #005-06-1966 L1969 **PD** *071 †55

JOLL, Larry Ervin. 1621 CENTENNIAL BLVD, FAIRFIELD MEDICAL CLINIC 97477 #040-02-1968 L1969 **FM** *071 †18

JONASSON, David Craig. 1110 N 18TH ST 97477 #040-02-1972 L1973 **FM** *075 †18

KAO, Jaylynn Lee. 2000 19TH ST 97477 #056-06-1989 L2007 **PD** *020 †55

KAPLAN, Michelle Lynn. 147 S 52ND PL 97478 #005-06-2001 L2006 **FM** *020 †18

KATUL, Munir Jibrail. 2400 HARTMAN LN, STE 200 97477 #605-01-1962 L1969 **U** *071 †95

KEIZER, Philip John, Jr. 860 BELTLINE RD 97477 #028-34-1994 L1998 **DR** *020 †80

KELLEY, William Mark. 960 N 16TH ST, STE 208 97477 #005-11-1999 L2006 **IM** *020 †20

KINTZ, Jesse Jos. 1705 CENTENNIAL BLVD STE 2, SUITE 5 97477 #048-12-1971 L1978 **PUD** *020 †20

KITTERMAN, James F. 1460 G ST 97477 #040-02-1976 L1977 **D** *020 †15 ‡

KLOS, Martin Mark. 3831 MAIN ST STE 105 97478 #040-02-1983 L1992 **AN** *020 †05

KNAPP, Todd Lowell. 1007 HARLOW RD, STE 210 97477 #049-01-1995 L2001 **D** *020 †15

KOLLMORGEN, Thomas Arthur. 2400 HARTMAN LN, UROLOGY HEALTHCARE 97477 #018-03-1992 L1998 **U** *020 †95

KONRADI, Melanie. 1403 F ST 97477 #054-04-2002 L2006 **OBG** *020

LE CLAIR, Gary James. 3100 MARTN LTHR KNG JR 97477 #040-02-1971 L1975 **GYN** *020 †30

LEVY, Jonathan. 1717 CENTENNIAL BLVD STE 6 97477 #035-06-1971 L1974 **FM** *071

LONGSTRETH, Paul Lambert. 960 N 16TH-103 97477 #048-04-1972 L1980 **R** *020 †80

LUNDSGAARD, Douglas K. 1435 G ST 97477 #018-03-1969 L1980 **ORS** *020 †40

MACKEY, John Austin. 1460 G ST, MCKENZIE-WILLIAMETRE MEDIC 97477 #003-01-1975 L1979 **EM** *020 †16 ‡

MARIE, Sally. 2280 MARCOLA RD, SPRINGFIELD FAMILY 97477 #038-41-1982 L1985 **FM** *020 †18

MARKOWITZ, Nathan Roy. 960 N 16TH ST, STE 208 97477 #026-04-1985 L1986 **GE IM** *020 †20

MASTERSON, Michael Daniel. 2400 HARTMAN LN STE 300, OREGON SURGICENTER 97477 #012-05-1984 L1990 **AN** *020 †05

MC CAFFERTY, Dennis E. 1460 G ST 97477 #040-02-1954 L1958 **IM** *071 †20

MC CORKLE, Elizabeth Jean. 1403 F ST 97477 #012-01-1992 L1999 **OBG** *020 †30

MC HOLICK, William J. 1435 G ST 97477 #040-02-1951 L1952 **ORS** *071 †40

MEYERS, Mark Stanley. 2280 MARCOLA RD, SPRINGFIELD FAMILY 97477 #040-02-1996 L1999 **FM** *020 †18

MICHAELIS, Barbara Ann. 860 BELTLINE RD 97477 #035-15-1991 L1999 **DR** *020 †80

MILLER, Shadi Imani. 1007 HARLOW RD, STE 210 97477 #005-18-1999 L2004 **MPD** *020 †20,55

MOFFITT, Robert Arthur. ■ 97477 #040-02-1955 L1956 **FM** *071

MOHA-JERIN, Amir Hooshang. 1605 G ST 97477 #517-01-1959 L1973 **D** *071 †15

MONJI, Zena Ione. 1403 F ST 97477 #005-19-1991 L1995 **OBG** *020 †30

MONTICELLI, Michael A. 2260 MARCOLA RD 97477 #051-04-1992 L1998 **HO** *020 †20

MORISHITA, Megumi M. 1403 F ST 97477 #056-06-2000 L2005 **OBG** *020

MORLEY, Alexander K, III. 1460 G ST, MCKENZIE-WILLAMETTE HOSPIT 97477 #007-02-1979 L1993 **EM FM** *020 †16,18

MYERS, Larry Richard. 1640 G ST, COMMUNITY HEALTH CTR OF LN 97477 #003-01-1975 L1998 **FM** *020 †18

NADEL, William Michael. ■ 97477 #016-02-1971 L1987 **GS** *071 †85
NEWBOULD, Samantha Jane. 1007 HARLOW RD, STE 210 97477 #039-01-2000 L2003 **FM** *020 †18
NYONATOR, Edem Kobla. 1460 G ST 97477 #412-01-1998 L2005 **IM** *020 †20
OJHA, Chandra Shekhar. 1460 G ST 97477 #495-49-1984 L2006 **IM** *020 †20
OLSON, Eric Geo. 1605 G ST 97477 #040-02-1973 L1979 **D** *020 †15
OPPENHEIMER, Linda Gay. 960 16TH ST, STE 303 97477 #016-11-1984 L1987 **IM** *020 †20
PARK, Harry Hyungjin. 1007 HARLOW RD, STE 120 97477 #005-12-1997 L2003 **GE** *020 †20
PAULSON, Daniel Keith. 2280 MARCOLA RD, SPRINGFIELD FAMILY 97477 #056-05-1998 L2001 **FM** *020 †18 ‡
PHELPS, David Charles. 1007 HARLOW RD, STE 210 97477 #040-02-2001 L2005 **FM FSM** *020 †18
RANDLE, Richard Edward. 86734 MAHOGANY LN 97478 #005-19-1979 L1983 **N** *020
REYES, Marilou Laude. 2000 19TH ST 97477 #030-06-2001 L2005 **PD** *020
RICHEY, Troy Kent. 1605 G ST 97477 #028-34-1989 L1997 **D** *020 †15
SCHNAPPER, Marc Brian. 1460 G ST 97477 #028-34-1996 L2000 **EM** *020 †16
SHEERIN, Daniel Vinson. 1435 G ST 97477 #010-01-1998 L2004 **ORS OTR** *020 †40
SINGH, Jaswinder Kaur. 960 16TH ST, STE 303 97477 #495-08-1983 L2000 **IM** *020 †20
SMOLUCH, Leslie Paul. 1110 N 18TH ST, STE 3 97477 #016-43-1971 L1977 **OPH** *020 †35
SOHLBERG, Olof Erick. 2400 HARTMAN LN, UROLOGY HEALTHCARE 97477 #054-04-1986 L1992 **U GS** *020 †95
STENGER, John Richard. ■ 97478 #050-02-1956 L1974 **OBG** *071 †30
STREK, William B. 175 W B ST, STE D 97477 #024-16-1985 L1999 **P PYG** *020 †75
STRGAR, Franc. 175 W B ST STE B 97477 #026-04-1990 L1997 **P CHP** *020 †75
TANNENBAUM, Chas Shepard. ■ 97478 #024-01-1957 L1992 **OPH** *071 †35
TELEW, Nicholas W. 175 W B ST STE B 97477 #038-44-1986 L1991 **P** *020 †75
THIEDE, Stephan Gerhard. 860 BELTLINE RD 97477 #036-01-1998 L2005 **RNR R** *020 †80
THOMPSON, Gail Wesley. 960 N 16TH ST STE 311 97477 #026-04-1959 L1987 **GS** *071
TOM, William David. 1007 HARLOW RD, STE 310 97477 #016-42-1999 L2004 **OTO** *020 †45
TOMLINSON, Craig Philip. ■ 97478 #056-06-1988 *100
TRAN, Khoi My. 1007 HARLOW RD, STE 120 97477 #005-15-1994 L2000 **GE** *020 †20
URBEN, Susan Louise. 1007 HARLOW RD, STE 210 97477 #005-02-1992 L1998 **OTO** *020 †45
WALKER, Brady Raymond. 2400 HARTMAN LN, UROLOGY HEALTHCARE 97477 #040-02-1996 L2001 **U** *020 †95
WHITSEL, Carol Elaine. 960 16TH ST, STE 303 97477 #005-06-1987 L1991 **IM** *020 †20
WILHITE, Steven Lewis. 960 N 16TH ST, STE 203 97477 #040-02-1967 L1974 **GS VS** *020 †85
WOOD, Thomas Rodman. 341 MAIN ST 97477 #038-06-1960 L1983 **OPH** *020 †35
YORK, Catherine Anne. 3100 MARTN LTHR KNG JR 97477 #036-05-2000 L2004 **OBG** *020
YOUNG, Clayton W. 2000 19TH ST 97477 #005-12-1992 L1996 **PD** *020 †55

STANFIELD — UMATILLA

JONES, Gerald Austin. ■ 97875 #005-12-1954 L1955 **FM** *071

STAYTON — MARION

AULD, Brian Murray. 1401 N 10TH AVE 97383 #040-02-1980 L1991 **EM FM** *020 †16
BORELLA, Lori Ann. ■ 97383 #030-06-2000 L2004 **AN** *020 †05
BOUGHN, Richard Cutler. 1377 N 10TH AVE 97383 #007-02-1973 L1976 **FM** *020 †18
DEGNER, George Matthew. 1373 N 10TH AVE, SANTIAM MEMORIAL HOSPITAL 97383 #040-02-1998 L2000 **IM** *020 †20
FITZPATRICK, Jeanne L. 1401 N 10TH AVE, STE 200 97383 #054-04-1978 L2002 **FM** *020
FOSTER, David Wm. 1401 N 10TH AVE, STE 200 97383 #040-02-1978 L1980 **FM** *020 †18 ‡
FRASER, Gregory Mark. 1373 N 10TH AVE 97383 #060-01-1985 L1998 **FM** *020 †18
GILBERTS, John Howard. 1401 N 10TH AVE 97383 #019-01-1963 L1964 **FM** *020 †18
GOOCH, Ritchie Belton. 1377 N 10TH AVE 97383 #054-04-1973 L1979 **FM** *020
HADDEN, Scott Thomas. 1401 N 10TH AVE 97383 #040-02-1998 L2001 **FM** *020 †18
INGHAM, Claire Elizabeth. 1401 N 10TH AVE 97383 #005-06-1989 L2006 **FM** *020 †18
JORGENSEN, Damian Eric. 1401 N 10TH AVE # 2 97383 #040-02-2002 L2007 **FM** *020 †18
KLASS, Wm Arnold Stuart. 1375 N 10TH AVE 97383 #068-01-1957 L1975 **GP** *071
MC GREEVY, Robert Gerard. 1371 N 10TH AVE 97383 #005-02-1991 L1992 **GS** *020 †85
NEUMANN, Paul Jay. 1401 N 10TH AVE, STE 100 97383 #040-02-2000 L2002 **FM** *020 †18
SEPPALA, Fay Ellen. 1371 N 10TH AVE 97383 #025-07-1977 L2006 **GS** *020 †85
SIMS, Thomas Jack. 1377 N 10TH AVE 97383 #030-06-1970 L1973 **OS** *020 †18
STRATTON, Nicolas John. 1369 N 10TH AVE 97383 #005-15-1995 L2004 **ORS** *020 †40
VAN VEEN, Thos Augustine. 1401 N 10TH AVE STE 100 97383 #040-02-1963 L1964 **FM** *020 †18
VERMONT, Beth. 1371 N 10TH AVE 97383 #035-09-1983 L2004 **OBG** *020
VON BORSTEL, Eric Reid. 1401 N 10TH AVE 97383 #040-02-1994 L1998 **AN** *020 †05
WISER, Amy Londergan. 1401 N 10TH AVE 97383 #041-15-2003 L2007 **FM** *020 †18
WISER, Eric Milton. 1401 N 10TH AVE 97383 #041-13-2003 L2007 **FM** *020 †18
YEAGER, Dean Alan. 1375 N 10TH AVE STE A 97383 #056-05-1989 L1992 **FM OBS** *020 †18

SUBLIMITY — MARION

CLAPPISON, Gordon B. ■ 97385 #018-03-1951 L1968 **AN** *071 †05

SUNRIVER — DESCHUTES

ABRAMS, Harvey Allen. #7 TAN OAKLANE 97707 #016-42-1964 L1972 **AN OS** *071
ANTLE, Robert C. 21 ALBRELLO CIR 97707 #025-07-1950 L1951 **OPH** *071 †35
BENDING, Glenville C. 18160 COTTONWOOD RD, # 154 97707 #065-06-1952 L1971 **OPH AM** *071 †35
CAMPBELL, Donald Duane. ■ 97707 #030-05-1960 L1960 **AN** *071 †05
CARLSON, Donald Warren. 2000 EDGEWOOD DRIVE #111 97707 #005-11-1964 L1987 **DR** *071 †80
EADE, Gilbert G. 18160 COTTONWOOD RD, # 771 97707 #054-04-1951 L1952 **PS** *071 †65
HAJNY, Robert Geo. 18160 COTTONWOOD RD # 746 97707 #018-03-1970 L1972 **AN** *020 †05
HALL, I Scott. 18160 COTTONWOOD RD, PMB 459 97707 #005-14-1973 L2001 **IM** *071 †20 ‡
HILL, Malcolm Campbell. ■ 97707 #352-07-1953 L1959 **DR** *071 †80
LONG, Avard Chipman. PO BOX 3163 97707 #067-01-1944 L1946 **IM GP** *071

MALEY, Joseph Clift. 18160 COTTONWOOD RD # 710 97707 #040-02-1968 L1972 **AN** *071 †05
MC GRANAHAN, Thomas C. 18160 COTTONWOOD RD # 793 97707 #054-04-1951 L1952 **AM FM** *071 †18
MILLER, Richard Russell. ■ 97707 #040-02-1965 L1996 **CD IM** *071 †20
PORTER, Giles Stevens. 57233 QUAIL LANE 97707 #008-01-1943 L1946 **EM** *071
PRIBNOW, Jock Thos. ■ 97707 #040-02-1972 L1975 **OM** *071 †70,18
SPAULDING, Leland Clair. 18160 COTTONWOOD RD # 422 97707 #005-12-1956 L1967 **GS** *071 †85
STONE, Albert James, Jr. 18160 COTTONWOOD RD, # 499 97707 #040-02-1980 L1989 **EM** *020 †16

SUTHERLIN — DOUGLAS

BURNS, William Thos, III. PO BOX 246 97479 #005-11-1944 L1946 **PD** *075 †55
GUEST, Mary Teju. ■ 97479 #005-12-1993 L1994 **FM** *020 †18
KADAS, Warren A. 1007 W CENTRAL AVE 97479 #026-04-1949 L1949 **FM OPH** *071 †18

SWEET HOME — LINN

BLAKE, Alan Noel. 679 MAIN ST 97386 #054-04-1985 L1988 **FM** *020 †18
DOWLING, Harold Bader. ■ 97386 #054-04-1954 L1956 **GP** *071
HARTMANN, Ronald Allan. 2242 MAIN ST 97386 #176-03-1958 L1973 **FM GS** *074 †18
HINDMARSH, May Ann. 679 MAIN ST, SWEET HOME FAMILY MEDICINE 97386 #068-01-1992 L1994 **FM** *020 †18
HINDMARSH, Timothy Edward. 679 MAIN ST, SWEET HOME FAMILY MEDICINE 97386 #068-01-1992 L1994 **FM** *020 †18
THORNTON, Thomas Leon. ■ 97386 #040-02-1961 L1963 **GYN OBS** *071 †30

TALENT — JACKSON

BASIN, Karen Sue. 1310B TALENT AVE 97540 #005-18-1986 L1991 **RHU IM** *020 †20
BIRNEY, Rodney Stuart. ■ 97540 #010-01-1985 L1989 **PYA** *020 †75
CANFIELD, Craig Jennings. ■ 97540 #040-02-1957 L1958 **PA IM** *030 †20
GREENE, Rudy Robt. 268 S PACIFIC HWY 97540 #065-01-1978 L1998 **RHU ISM** *020 †20
JOSHUA, Susan Caroline. ■ 97540 #020-02-1986 L2003 **P** *020
LOFGREN, Lars Borge. ■ 97540 #858-03-1946 L1965 **PYA** *071
MOORE, Donald Scott. ■ 97540 #028-02-1958 L1958 **IM GE** *020 †20
O'TOOLE, Richard Dennis. ■ 97540 #035-20-1963 L1971 **ID IM** *020 †20
SAIKEVYCH, Irene Ann. ■ 97540 #016-06-1976 L1977 **CCG PTH** *071 †50,19
SWARTZ, William Harold. ■ 97540 #025-01-1962 L1963 **OBG** *071 †30

TERREBONNE — JEFFERSON

ALLUMBAUGH, Thomas Lee. ■ 97760 #005-19-2000 L2003 **FM** *020 †18
LOCKER, Rachel E. ■ 97760 #001-06-1993 L1996 **FM** *020 †18

THE DALLES — WASCO

BELLANCA, Helen Katherine. 425 E 7TH ST, LA CLINICA DEL CARINO 97058 #016-06-1996 L1997 **FM** *020 †18
BLAIR, Gretchen Elizabeth. 1810 E 19TH ST, STE 210 97058 #054-04-1990 L1999 **IM** *020 †20
BRUCE-BEAMAN, Michele K. 1620 E 12TH ST 97058 #025-01-1990 L1996 **CCP** *020 †55
BURNHAM, Erin M. 1400 W 8TH ST, MID-COLUMBIA FIRE & RESCUE 97058 #040-02-1995 L1997 **EM** *020 †16
BURNS, Angus Keith. 1700 E 19TH ST S1, MID COLUMBIA MEDICAL CENTE 97058 #032-01-1985 L1990 **AN** *020 †05
CAPEK, Michael. 1700 E 19TH ST, MID COLUMBIA MED CTR 97058 #016-06-1981 L1986 **DR** *020 †80
CAPEK, Vlastimil. ■ 97058 #286-02-1950 L1969 **R** *072 †80
CARDOSI, Paul Jos. 1700 E 19TH ST 97058 #032-01-1992 L1993 **IM** *020 †20
CASTANARES, Tina Doris. 425 E 7TH ST, LA CLINICA DEL CARINO 97058 #005-06-1980 L1984 **FM PHP** *030
COLFELT, Brenda Marie. 425 E 7TH ST, LA CLINICA DEL CARINO 97058 #054-04-1990 L1994 **FM** *020 †18
DAVIS, Richard James. 1400 W 8TH ST, MID-COLUMBIA FIRE/RESCUE 97058 #038-40-1978 L1980 **EM** *020 †16
DEY, Nirad Kumar. 1700 E 19TH ST 97058 #495-19-1957 L1970 **GS** *071 †85
DION, Denise M. 400 E SCENIC DR STE 2343 97058 #035-45-1990 L1991 **PYG** *020
EDWARDS, James Matthew. ■ 97058 #016-11-2005 L2005 **IM** *012
ELLIOTT, John D. 1700 E 19TH ST 97058 #048-15-1999 L2002 **EM** *020 †16
FAHERTY, James Chas. 1810 E 19TH ST, STE 209 97058 #056-06-1992 L1993 **OBG** *020 †30
FIELD, Frederick George. 1700 E 19TH ST, MID COLUMBIA MEDICAL CENTE 97058 #021-01-1998 L2005 **AN** *020 †20
FORD, Charles Roy. 1815 E 19TH ST STE 1 97058 #038-40-1970 L1977 **OTO** *020 †45
FORD, David Christian. 1700 E 19TH ST, MID-COLUMBIA MEDICAL CENTE 97058 #038-40-2001 L2005 **AN** *020 †05
GINGRICH, Gary Allen. 1805 E 19TH ST 97058 #005-12-1977 L1985 **U** *020 †95
GRANT, Lisa Christine. 1810 E 19TH ST STE 225 97058 #021-01-2000 L2000 **N** *020 †75
HAMILTON, William C. 1810 E 19TH ST STE 225, APT 225 97058 #047-06-1976 L1985 **GS** *020 †85
HANKINS, Corinda Marie. 1620 E 12TH ST 97058 #017-20-1999 L2003 **PD** *020 †55
HODGE, Thomas Harold. 1700 E 19TH ST 97058 #040-02-1973 L1978 **IM SME** *020 †20
IRVINE, Brendon Robert. 425 E 7TH ST, THE DALLES CLINIC 97058 #061-01-1993 L1995 **OS** *020 †18
KELLY, Daniel Jos. 405 E 7TH ST, COLUMBIA RIVER EYE CLINIC 97058 #040-02-1978 L1980 **OPH** *020
KICE, Edward Everett, III. 1700 E 19TH ST, MID COLUMBIA MEDICAL CENTE 97058 #028-03-1969 L1973 **AN NS** *020 †05
KREHBIEL, Rodney A. 425 E 7TH ST, LA CLINICA DEL CARINO 97058 #048-13-1993 L1996 **FM** *020 †18

LARSON, Jennifer Lynne. 1700 E 19TH ST, EMERGENCY DEPARTMENT 97058 #040-02-2002 L2002 **EM** *100 †16
MACK, David Arthur. 1810 E 19TH ST STE 209 97058 #028-79-1972, ▲ L1973 **OBG** *020 †30
MAC MILLAN, James E, Jr. 408 E 4TH ST 97058 #038-40-1979 L1981 **P** *020
MATHISEN, Jeffrey Robert. 1810 E 19TH ST, STE 225 97058 #017-20-1996 L2001 **GS** *020 †85
MCALLISTER, Marc Ward. ■ 97058 #023-07-2004 L2006 **U** *012
MC DANIEL, David Schwab. 405 E 7TH ST 97058 #040-02-1959 L1960 **OPH OS** *071 †35
MC DONELL, Miriam Dorothy. ■ 97058 #005-15-1991 L1993 **OBG** *020 †30
MC LENNON, Stephen Alfred. 1620 E 12TH ST 97058 #016-43-1986 L1991 **FM** *020 †18
MELBY, Gregory Brian. 1620 E 12TH ST 97058 #056-05-1995 L2003 **FM** *020 †18
MERRISS, Martin Danl. 425 E 7TH ST 97058 #040-02-1943 **OBG GP** *071
MILLER, Charles Prescott. 1730 E 12TH ST 97058 #010-01-1991 L1999 **FM** *020 †18
MILLS, Victor David. ■ 97058 #039-01-1938 **GYN** *071
MOON, Paul O. 1810 E 19TH ST, STE 225 97058 #041-02-1987 L1993 **GS** *020 †85
MORRIS, Daniel S. 1825 E 19TH ST 97058 #040-02-1972 L1973 **IM PUD** *020 †20
MOSER, Emily Ann. 1810 E 19TH ST, STE 225 97058 #032-01-1985 L1990 **N** *020 †75
NICHOL, Thomas Andrew. 1825 E 19TH ST STE 3 97058 #007-02-1986 L1989 **IM** *020 †20
OPHEIM, Georgia Nel. 1620 E 12TH ST 97058 #054-04-1983 L1984 **PD** *020 †55
PERUZZO, Peter A. 1620 E 12TH ST 97058 #040-02-1971 L1974 **FM** *020 †18
POTTER, Bryan O'Neil. 1810 E 19TH ST, STE 225 97058 #038-41-1995 L2004 **GS** *020 †85
PROCTOR, Kerry Scully. ■ 97058 #050-02-2001 L2007 **PTH** *100 †50
PROCTOR, Matthew David. 1815 E 19TH ST, STE 1 97058 #050-02-2001 L2007 **OTO** *100 †45
QUIST, Paul David. 1700 E 19TH ST 97058 #040-02-1985 L1986 **DR** *020
RAMEY, Brendan B. 425 E 7TH ST 97058 #054-04-1998 L2005 **FM** *020 †18
RICHARDSON, Judy. 1810 E 19TH ST, STE 211 97058 #032-01-2001 L2003 **FM** *100 †18
SCHUBERT, Frederick, Jr. 1700 E 19TH ST 97058 #040-02-1983 L1984 **PTH** *072 †50
SERRA, Constance May. 425 E 7TH ST, LA CLINICA DEL CARINO 97058 #038-40-1995 L1997 **FM** *020 †18
SESSIONS, Hal Rucks, III. 1810 E 19TH ST STE 225 97058 #047-06-1974 L1981 **GS** *071 †85
SHOLAR, J Brent. 1700 E 19TH ST, EMER DEPT MIDCOLUMBIA MED 97058 #012-05-1988 L1993 **EM** *040 †16
STANLEY, Gregory Mark. 1715 E 12TH ST 97058 #040-02-1997 L2003 **ORS OSM** *020 †40
STARRETT, Richard Paul. 425 E 7TH ST, LA CLINICA DEL CARINO 97058 #040-02-1987 L1997 **FM** *020 †18
STAVER, Robert Allen. 1715 E 12TH ST 97058 #007-02-1967 L1974 **ORS** *020 †40
SWARTZ, Philip Kinsell. 1620 E 12TH ST 97058 #041-13-1958 L1977 **GS** *071 †85
TAKANO, Takeo. ■ 97058 #572-13-1941 L1958 **IMG P** *071
TAYLOR, Samuel Gale. 1800 E 19TH ST, CELILO CANCER CTR 97058 #068-01-1969 L2003 **ON** *020 †20
UNHANAND, Nartnucha. 1700 E 19TH ST, MID-COLUMBIA MED CTR 97058 #048-02-1978 L1982 **DR** *062 †80
VAN EATON, Arthur Hunt. 1700 E 19TH ST 97058 #040-02-1969 L1971 **PTH GP** *020 †50
VOGEL, Deborah A. 1700 E 19TH ST 97058 #024-05-1990 L1991 **EM** *020 †16
WILCOX, Dean Morrison. ■ 97058 #040-02-1955 L1956 **GP** *071 †18
WILKINSON, Albert E. THE DALLES CLINIC 97058 #040-02-1949 L1951 **GP** *020
YUHAS, Frances May. 818 W 6TH ST STE 4 97058 #040-02-1991 L1992 **IM UCM** *020 †20

TIGARD – WASHINGTON

AL-MULLA, Zaid S. 9735 SW SHADY LN STE 300, HORIZON PEDIATRICS PC 97223 #584-01-1990 L1999 **PD** *040 †55
ANDERSON, Robert Lynn. ■ 97224 #040-02-1957 L1958 **AN OS** *020 †05
ATKINS, Charles Burwell. ■ 97224 #040-02-1932 L1933 **R** *071
BAKOS, Ladislav Ivan. 13240 SW PACIFIC HWY, STE 200 97223 #286-04-1967 L1975 **OTO FPS** *020 †45
BERNEY, Joyce Margaret. 13200 SW PACIFIC HWY 97223 #054-04-1983 L1988 **FM** *020 †18
BILSTROM, David Edwin. 9370 SW GREENBURG RD, STE 311 97223 #018-03-1970 L1977 **PD AI** *020 †55,03
BLETTEL, Milton Louis. 9900 SW HALL BLVD, STE 200 97223 #048-13-1986 L1987 **IM** *020 †20
BOBOIA, Dorina S. 12442 SW SCHOLLS FERRY RD, STE 100 97223 #781-01-1967 L1985 **IM** *075
BOHLING, Joel Ivan. 9735 SW SHADY LN, STE 100 97223 #030-05-1976 L1979 **FM** *020 †18
BOLTON, Philip Manning. 11895 SW GREENBURG RD 97223 #035-03-1995 L1996 **P** *020 †75
BOWMAN, Ronald Ray. 9445 SW LOCUST ST 97223 #040-02-1985 L1986 **ORS** *020 †40
BRODSKY, Anatoly G. 13200 SW PACIFIC HWY 97223 #040-02-1999 L2001 **FM** *020 †18
BUEFFEL, Bernard H, III. 9370 SW GREENBURG RD, STE 205 97223 #034-01-1970 L1976 **PD** *020 †55
BULOSAN, Emedio B. PO BOX 230084 97281 #748-01-1967 L1978 **GP** *020
CHIAPUZIO, Robert. ■ 97224 #040-02-1956 L1957 **GP** *020
CLACK, Susan Marie. 13200 SW PACIFIC HWY 97223 #040-02-1984 L1985 **FM** *020 †18
COOLEY, William Chas. 9407 SW MAPLEWOOD DR # 148 97223 #038-06-1979 L1980 **AN** *020 †05
CORBETT, Brett Charles. 12442 SW SCHOLLS FERRY RD, PROVIDENCE SCHOLLS CLINIC 97223 #005-19-1999 L1999 **FM** *020 †18
DARM, Jerry Roy. 9735 SW SHADY LN STE 203 97223 #040-02-1976 L1977 **EM CLP** *020 †16
DEGRAAUW, Jennifer Ann. ■ 97223 #021-05-2004 L2004 **IM** *012 †20
DE KLOTZ, Richard Leonard. 12442 SW SCHOLLS FERRY RD, STE 205 97223 #030-06-1966 L1969 **PD** *020 †55
DENKER, Arthur Gilman. ■ 97224 #040-02-1952 L1953 **OM GS** *071
DRURY-BROWN, Marcie Kay. ■ 97223 #005-12-2002 L2002 **PDE** *012
EDELSON, Richard Henry. 7300 SW CHILDS RD, STE B 97224 #040-02-1987 L1994 **OSM ORS** *020 †40
GERHARD, Amy Lynn. ■ 97224 #016-11-2004 L2006 **FM** *100 †18
GIVI, Babak. ■ 97224 #517-01-2000 L2002 **GS** *012
GLAUBKE, John A. 13200 SW PACIFIC HWY 97223 #017-20-1949 L1953 **GP** *071
GRAHAM, Daniel Lee. 13200 SW PACIFIC HWY 97223 #040-02-1977 L1980 **FM** *020 †18
GREENLEAF, Jonathan E. 7300 SW CHILDS RD 97224 #024-05-1985 L1990 **ORS OSM** *020 †40
GRUBER, Frank. ■ 97224 #869-05-1958 R *020 †80
GUNN, Carol Elizabeth. 9370 SW GREENBURG RD, STE 101 97223 #005-19-2001 L2002 **IM** *100 †20,70
HAKKINEN, Frederick S. 15350 SW PACIFIC HWY, LEGACY CLINIC KING CITY 97224 #040-02-1968 L1969 **IM IMG** *020
HARTFORD, James Thos. 9370 SW GREENBURG RD, STE 201 97223 #040-02-1961 L1962 **PD** *020 †55
HENDERSON, Winnie Wanyin. ■ 97224 #040-02-2004 L2004 **GS** *012
HOLT PAMOVSKIS, Aina J. ■ 97224 #594-01-1957 L1971 **P** *071
HORTSCH, Michael Paul. 13200 SW PACIFIC HWY 97223 #040-02-1985 L1988 **FM** *020 †18
ISGRO, Melodie Kayoko. 12442 SW SCHOLLS FERRY RD, STE 100 97223 #011-03-1995 L2000 **EM** *020 †16
JHOOTY, Sukhraj Kaur. 15298 SW ROYALTY PKWY, LEGACY CLINIC TIGARD 97224 #495-29-1995 L2003 **IM** *020 †20
KAO, David Ming Fung. 15895 SW 72ND AVE STE 250 97224 #065-09-1992 L2001 **D** *020 †20,15
KARAMLOU, Tara Bhat. ■ 97224 #048-04-1999 L1999 **GS** *012
KIM, Aileen Hyunoak. 12442 SW SCHOLLS FERRY RD 97223 #040-02-1989 L1990 **IM** *020 †20
LAM, Summer Ray. ■ 97223 #014-01-2005 L2005 **IM** *012
LANGSDORF, Lawrence Lyman. 12442 SW SCHOLLS FERRY RD, STE 100 97223 #005-06-1978 L1993 **DIA END** *020 †20
LARSEN, Robert G. ■ 97224 #042-03-2007 **EM** *012
LEE, Joyce L. 7175 SW BEVELAND RD, STE 205 97223 #047-20-2002 L2002 *020
MAC HAFFIE, Reginald A. ■ 97224 #007-02-1948 L1948 **FM A** *071
MANSFIELD, Charles Owen. ■ 97224 #040-02-1943 L1944 **FM OS** *071
MARTIN, Kenneth Lyle. 15298 SW ROYALTY PKWY 97224 #054-04-1972 L1977 **IM** *020 †20
MCCALL, Susan Vandervalk. 6950 SW HAMPTON ST, STE 130 97223 #040-02-1986 L1995 **GPM ADM** *030 †70
MC CLESKEY, Michael Thos. 13200 SW PACIFIC HWY 97223 #040-02-1972 L1978 **FM** *020 †18
MC MILLAN, Mischelle. 9900 SW HALL BLVD, STE 200 97223 #049-01-1994 L1996 **IM** *020 †20
MOHAMMED, Imran. ■ 97224 #495-16-2001 L2007 **PCC** *012 †20
MON PERE, Philip Matthew. 9735 SW SHADY LN, METROPOLITAN CLINIC PC 97223 #005-19-1989 L1991 **RHU IM** *075
MOOS, Steven Gabriel. 9600 SW OAK ST, STE 350 97223 #040-02-1995 L1996 **GS** *020
MURPHY, Kevin James. 7300 SW CHILDS RD 97224 #005-06-1998 L2004 **ORS OSM** *020 †40
NAGAPPAN, Poombavai O. 12442 SW SCHOLLS FERRY RD 97223 #495-59-1995 L2000 **IM** *020 †20
NEWBERRY, Stephen Glenn. 13200 SW PACIFIC HWY 97223 #040-02-1985 L1990 **FM** *020 †18
NORTH, Raymond Robt. 7300 SW CHILDS RD, STE B 97224 #040-02-1967 L1973 **ORS OSM** *020 †40
REMBER, Katrenka Rae. 13200 SW PACIFIC HWY, PACIFIC MEDICAL GROUP 97223 #040-02-1987 L1988 **FM** *020 †18
ROSS, Marla. 10215 SW HALL BLVD 97223 #005-18-1982 L1993 **D IM** *020 †20,15
SCHWARTZ, Benjamin Jos. 9735 SW SHADY LN, STE 100 97223 #038-41-1975 L1977 **EM** *020
SEGAL, Lesley Kay. 12442 SW SCHOLLS FERRY RD, STE 100 97223 #026-04-1988 L1989 **IM** *020 †20
SHAKIBA, Peyman. ■ 97223 #305-01-2000 L2007 **FM** *100 †18
SHENOY, Raghuveer B. 12442 SW SCHOLLS FERRY RD, STE 100 97223 #495-37-1991 L1997 **IM** *020 †20
SMAKA, Todd Jeffery. ■ 97223 #017-20-2003 L2006 **AN** *012
SMITH, Walter Aldine, Jr. 9250 SW HALL BLVD 97223 #012-01-1969 L1973 **ORS** *020 †40
SOLEM, Dana Lyman. 6950 SW HAMPTON ST, STE 310 97223 #048-02-1974 L1979 **P OS** *020
SPANGLER, Ronald Lee. 7455 SW BEVELAND RD 97223 #054-04-1986 L1990 **P** *020 †75
SPITTEL, D Michael. PO BOX 23786 97281 #060-01-1968 L1982 **GP CD** *020 †85
TAHIR, Jahanara. 12442 SW SCHOLLS FRY RD #2, STE 201 97223 #704-02-1956 L1980 **OBG** *020
ULAM, Sandra Lynn. 9735 SW SHADY LN, STE 100 97223 #040-02-1994 L1997 **IM** *020 †20
VESSELY, Michael Brent. 9250 SW HALL BLVD 97223 #040-02-1986 L1994 **OAR ORS** *020 †40
WALL, Eric Martin. 13221 SW 68TH PKWY, STE 200 97223 #165-07-1977 L1985 **FM PHP** *050 †18
WEBER, Stephen Michael. ■ 97224 #024-05-2003 L2003 **OTO** *012
WILSON, David Leroy. 9370 SW GREENBURG RD, STE T 97223 #040-02-2005 L2005 **AN** *012
YOUNG, Robert Christopher. 13200 SW PACIFIC HWY 97223 #054-04-1983 L1984 **FM** *020 †18
ZALMA, Alysa Dawn. 7455 SW BEVELAND RD 97223 #024-07-1997 L2001 **P** *020 †75

TILLAMOOK – TILLAMOOK

ADAMS, Marcia Jennifer. 801 PACIFIC AVE, TILLAMOOK COUNTY HEALTH DE 97141 #035-08-1990 L1993 **FM** *020 †18
ALFONSO, Jose Raul. ■ 97141 #275-01-1956 L1959 **GP AN** *020
BENNETT, Michael Johnson. 1000 3RD ST 97141 #011-02-1977 L1980 **AN** *020 †05
BETLINSKI, Paul Edward. 1000 3RD ST 97141 #005-12-1973 L1979 **FM** *020 †18
BOWMAN, Mark R. 1000 3RD ST, TILLAMOOK COUNTY GENERAL H 97141 #038-44-1991 L1994 **EM** *020 †16
BRADBURN, David Arthur. 980 3RD ST, STE 200 97141 #024-16-1995 L1998 **FM** *020 †18
BRUS, Nancy Aamodt. ■ 97141 #005-12-1985 L1988 **FM** *020 †18
CALLANDER, Wendy Joy. 1000 3RD ST 97141 #040-02-1992 L1993 **IM** *020
CUTLER, David Lloyd. 906 MAIN AVE, TILLAMOOK FAMILY COUNSELIN 97141 #038-40-1967 L1977 **P** *040 †75
DENNIS, Paul J. 1000 3RD ST 97141 #010-02-1976 L2003 **AN** *020 †05
FAX, J Nicholas, Jr. 1000 3RD ST 97141 #040-02-1966 L1969 **ORS** *071 †40
FELLMAN, Robert G. 1000 3RD ST, OREGON EYE SPECIALISTS PC 97141 #030-05-1966 L1969 **OPH** *071 †35
GAVER, Paul Edgar. ■ 97141 #005-12-1945 L1984 **AN** *072 †05
GERKEN, Brittany J.. 980 3RD ST, STE 500 97141 #654-01-2002 L2006 **OBG** *020
HILL, Calvin Ray. 980 3RD ST, STE 200 97141 #005-12-1975 L1979 **IM** *020 †20
HUNT, Clyde Ernest. 1107 3RD ST 97141 #040-02-1970 L1976 **ORS** *071 †40
KALIHER, Howard. 1000 3RD ST 97141 #026-04-1944 L1944 **GP PHP** *071
LARWEH, Maxwell Larm. 1011 3RD ST 97141 #412-01-1999 L2005 **IM** *020 †20
MC COLGIN, Gene Coates. 1000 3RD ST, TILLAMOOK COUNTY HOSPITAL 97141 #040-02-1987 L1997 **FM EM** *020 †18
MEIER, Benius Karl, Jr. 980 3RD ST, STE 200 97141 #005-12-1994 L1997 **FM** *020 †18
MOHR, Lyle Rowland. 980 3RD ST, STE 100 97141 #005-12-1971 L1976 **GS** *020 †85
MUNLY, James Christopher. 1000 3RD ST 97141 #040-02-1980 L1983 **FM EM** *020 †16,18
NEITLING, Stanley Jos, Jr. 1107 3RD ST 97141 #040-02-1980 L1982 **ORS** *020 †40
PARSONS, Rex Richard. 1011 3RD ST 97141 #040-02-1980 L1981 **IM** *020
PITTS, Todd Alan. 980 3RD ST STE 200 97141 #031-01-1992 L2007 **GS** *020 †85
RICHARDSON-TOLLERTON, J. 2325 BILYEU AVE W, P O BOX 69 97141 #005-19-1992 L1995 **FM** *020 †18
RINEHART, Harry Herbert. 1000 3RD ST 97141 #040-02-1972 L1978 **FM** *020 †18
ROBERTS, Craig Stanley. 1000 3RD ST 97141 #028-02-1983 L1988 **EM** *020 †18

■ = Address Information Privacy Protected

ROESENER, Fremont F. 1000 3RD ST 97141 #005-12-1973 L1974 **OBG** *020 †30
SAYLER, Glen Walter. 980 3RD ST 97141 #005-12-1974 L1978 **FM** *020 †18
THOMAS, Griffith Lloyd. TILLAMOOK GEN HOSPITAL 97141 #005-12-1964 L1968 **DR NM** *030 †80
TURNEY, Matthew Warren. 1000 3RD ST, 1105 5TH ST 97141 #056-06-1995 L2000 **EM** *020 †16
VEVERKA, Michael John. 1000 3RD ST, TILLAMOOK CNTY GEN HOSP 97141 #026-04-1975 L1977 **DR** *020 †80

TOLEDO – LINCOLN

COWAN, Tavis Lee. ■ 97391 #040-02-1997 L2004 **FM** *020 †18
KAUFFMAN, Dennis Lee. 1744 NW HIGHWAY 20, SAMARITAN TOLEDO CLINIC 97391 #026-04-1979 L1980 **GP** *071

TROUTDALE – MULTNOMAH

BIER, Emily Cupp. 1700 SW 257TH AVE, MEDICAL CENTER 97060 #040-02-1992 L1993 **FM** *020 †18
BLANFORD, Anthony Lee. ■ 97060 #035-06-1989 L2007 **P** *020 †75
HAUPTMANN, Mary Christine. 24601 SE STARK ST 97060 #028-46-1980 L1982 **OPH** *020 †35
HOGGARD, John Thos, III. 1700 SW 257TH AVE, GRESHAM TROUTDALE FAMILY M 97060 #040-02-1972 L1973 **FM GP** *071 †18 ‡
SCOTT, Brenda Diane. 113 W HISTORC CLMB RVR HWY 97060 #040-02-1995 L1998 **FM** *020 †18

TUALATIN – WASHINGTON

ALLISON, Gina Renee. 19250 SW 65TH AVE STE 300 97062 #054-04-2001 L2001 **OBG** *020 †30
AMES, Stephen Keith. 19260 SW 65TH AVE, STE 275 97062 #021-05-1982 L2004 **PD** *020 †55
APPLEBAUM, Brian Alec. 19250 SW 90TH AVE 97062 #005-19-2000 L2006 **GE** *020 †20
ARMSBY, David Henry. 19260 SW 65TH AVE, CHILDRENS CLINIC PC 97062 #005-11-1994 L2005 **PD** *020 †55
ARORA, Monika. ■ 97062 #040-02-2008 *012
ASH, Paul Richard. 19260 SW 65TH AVE, STE 220 97062 #005-14-1971 L1976 **N P** *020 †75 ‡
ASPER, Paul Ansgar. 5557 SW NATCHEZ ST, PAUL ASPER MD 97062 #054-04-1955 L1958 **GP** *020
AZAR, Robby Jos. 19250 SW 65TH AVE, STE 220 97062 #040-02-1992 L1993 **GS** *020 †85
BALLARD, James Covey. 19250 SW 65TH AVE, OREGON ORTHOPEDIC & 97062 #048-04-1997 L2003 **ORS OAR** *020 †40
BARLOW, Catherine Crider. 19185 SW 90TH AVE, TUALATIN 97062 #034-01-1982 L1990 **CHP P** *020 †75
BARTON, Sandra Jean. 19185 SW 90TH AVE, KAISER PERMANENTE 97062 #040-02-1988 L1997 **IM PD** *020 †55,20
BEATTY, Peter T. 6464 SW BORLAND RD STE A4 97062 #036-07-1988 L1996 **DR** *020 †80
BERGER, Jon M. 19875 SW 65TH AVE 97062 #062-01-1975 L1978 **FM** *020
BLACK, Bradford Todd. 19250 SW 65TH AVE, OREGON ORTHOPEDIC & 97062 #024-07-1994 L2002 **ORS** *020 †40 ‡
BLAKE, Susan. 19185 SW 90TH AVE 97062 #056-06-1993 L1994 **FM** *020 †18
BLUHM, Jeffrey Martin. 19250 SW 65TH AVE, OREGON PULMONARY ASSOC PC 97062 #054-04-1991 L1998 **PCC SME** *020 †20
BOCCHI, Jay Alan. 6464 SW BORLAND RD, STE A4 97062 #040-02-1980 L1981 **DR** *020 †80
BOSTON, Tammi Kaye. 19875 SW 65TH AVE 97062 #040-02-1987 L1996 **IM** *020 †20
BRADDOCK, John Rodgers. 19300 SW 65TH AVE 97062 #040-02-1974 L1975 **EM OM** *020 †16
BRODY, Eric Ernest. 19185 SW 90TH AVE, KAISER PERMANENTE 97062 #016-06-1971 L1979 **PD** *020 †20
BROMS, Anton Kersten. 19250 SW 65TH AVE, STE 300 97062 #048-04-1973 L1977 **OBG** *020 †20
BURGOINE, Gary Andrew. 19250 SW 65TH AVE, STE 300 97062 #040-02-2000 L2000 **OBG** *020
BURNER, Todd William. 19875 SW 65TH AVE 97062 #056-06-2001 L2004 **RHU** *012
CANNON, Sara Jane Laun. 19260 SW 65TH AVE, CHILDRENS CLINIC PC 97062 #056-05-1995 L1997 **PD** *020 †55
CARLTON, Steven Mc Guire. 19300 SW 65TH AVE 97062 #031-01-1982 L1993 **AN** *020 †05 ‡
CHANG, Chong Chong. 19875 SW 65TH AVE 97062 #005-18-1982 L1983 **OBG** *020 †30
CHANG, Chun-Yang. 19250 SW 90TH AVE 97062 #048-04-1996 L2002 **GE** *020 †20
CHANG, Edward Hsiaokua. 19260 SW 65TH AVE, STE 435 97062 #023-01-1989 L2000 **HO IM** *020 †20
CHESTER, Catherine Ann. 19185 SW 90TH AVE, TUALATIN MEDICAL OFFICE 97062 #056-06-1994 L2001 **IM** *020 †20
CHRISTENSEN, William Robt. 19260 SW 65TH AVE, STE 340 97062 #048-02-1968 L1968 **IM CD** *020
CONGER, Allard John, III. 19250 SW 65TH AVE, STE 300 97062 #040-02-1975 L1979 **OBG** *020 †30
CONNALL, Timothy Patrick. 19801 SW 72ND AVE, STE 160 97062 #035-19-1990 L2002 **PS** *020 †85,65
COOK, David W. 19250 SW 65TH AVE, STE 240 97062 #040-02-1984 L1985 **GS VS** *020 †85
COOK, Robert Dale. 19875 SW 65TH AVE, STE 201 97062 #028-03-1963 L1969 **ORS OS** *020 †40
CORSO, Magdalenne Marie. 19300 SW 65TH AVE 97062 #016-43-2001 L2004 **PD** *020 †55
CRAFT, Robert Michael. 19260 SW 65TH AVE, CHILDRENS CLINIC PC 97062 #040-02-1991 L1992 **PD** *072 †55
CRAMER, Andrew Benj. 19250 SW 65TH AVE, STE 220 97062 #040-02-1986 L1987 **GS VS** *020 †85
CRAVEN, James P. 19250 SW 65TH AVE, STE 220 97062 #040-02-1989 L1994 **GS** *020 †85
CRIM, Catherine Elizabeth. 19250 SW 65TH AVE STE 300, WOMENS HEALTHCARE ASSOCIAT 97062 #005-19-1986 L1991 **OBG** *020 †30
CRUMPACKER, Nancy S. 19250 SW 65TH AVE STE 320 97062 #019-02-1975 L1978 **ON** *020 †20
DAVIES, William D. 19260 SW 65TH AVE, STE 420 97062 #016-11-1952 L1953 **OS** *071 †85
DAVIS, Debra Kaye. 19185 SW 90TH AVE, KAISER TUALATIN FAMILY PRA 97062 #040-02-1995 L1998 **FM** *020 †18
DAVIS, Terry Lane. 19185 SW 90TH AVE, TUALATIN MEDICAL OFFICE 97062 #048-02-1972 L1989 **FM** *020 †18
DELANEY, Jaymee E. 19260 SW 65TH AVE, STE 270 97062 #040-02-1994 L1997 **IM** *020

DEVERE, Todd R. 19260 SW 65TH AVE, STE 280 97062 #048-04-1996 L2001 **N** *020 †75
DODGE, Rodney Wayne. 6464 SW BORLAND RD, STE B5 97062 #030-05-1986 L1990 **EM** *020 †16
DONNELLY, Wm Augustus. 6464 SW BORLAND RD STE A2 97062 #035-20-1973 L1982 **TS** *020 †85,90
EMEIS, William Emil. ■ 97062 #030-06-1964 L1965 **OBG** *071 †30 ‡
ENGLISH, John Canisius. 6464 SW BORLAND RD STE A4 97062 #040-02-1959 L1961 **R** *020 †80
EVETTS, Brent K. 19875 SW 65TH AVE STE 260 97062 #054-04-1991 L1997 **CRS** *020 †10,85
EY, Frederick S. 19260 SW 65TH AVE, PACIFIC ONCOLOGY 97062 #040-02-1984 L1985 **HEM ON** *020 †20
FERRIN, William Myron, III. 19250 SW 90TH AVE 97062 #047-05-1986 L1992 **GE IM** *020 †20
FIELDER, Kathleen Louise. 19260 SW 65TH AVE, STE 435 97062 #041-07-1978 L1979 **ON HEM** *020 †20
FOLEY, Mary Elizabeth. ■ 97062 #017-20-1983 L1984 **EM** *071 †16
FORSYTHE, John Thos. 19205 SW 65TH AVE, STE 110 97062 #025-01-1977 L1982 **IM** *020 †20
FRAHM, Kenneth Harold. 19300 SW 65TH AVE, LEGACY MERIDIAN PARK HOSP 97062 #056-06-1973 L1976 **AN** *020 †05 ‡
FRANCO, Reynaldo Danilo T. 19300 SW 65TH AVE, UNIT 1A 97062 #654-01-2003 L2003 **IM** *020 †20
FULLMAN, Jeffrey Drew. 19250 SW 65TH AVE, STE 110 97062 #040-02-1980 L1983 **IM** *020 †20
GARDNER, Michael Paul. 19250 SW 65TH AVE, STE 235 97062 #040-02-1995 L2000 **U** *020 †95
GILSTER, Jason C. 19250 SW 65TH AVE, STE 240 97062 #021-01-1996 L1999 **GS** *020 †85
GIROLAMI, Stephen Gordon. 19250 SW 65TH AVE, WOMENS HEALTHCARE ASSOCIAT 97062 #028-34-1983 L1991 **OBG** *020 †30
GLEASON, Daniel Lee. 19260 SW 65TH AVE, CHILDRENS CLINIC PC 97062 #028-02-1977 L1979 **PD** *020 †55
GOMEZ, Miguel Angel. 19260 SW 65TH AVE, STE 420 97062 #025-01-1986 L2001 **CD** *020 †20
GORIN, Aaron Daniel. 6464 SW BORLAND RD 97062 #010-01-1997 L2002 **PS CS** *020 †65
HADEED, Bassam George. 19260 SW 65TH AVE, STE 275 97062 #566-01-1981 L1995 **PD** *020 †20
HALE, Lloyd Dean. 6464 SW BORLAND RD STE B1 97062 #040-02-1968 L1969 **PS** *071 †65
HATCH, Thomas Robt. 19250 SW 65TH AVE, STE 250 97062 #040-02-1978 L1979 **U** *020 †95
HIROSHIGE, Stephen Nobuo. 19300 SW 65TH AVE 97062 #038-43-1989 L1990 **AN** *020 †05 ‡
HODA, Katherine Mary. ■ 97062 #040-02-2003 L2003 **GE** *012 †20
HOLMES, Bruce Neal. 19875 SW 65TH AVE STE 100 97062 #048-14-1982 L1995 **FM** *020 †18
HOPPERT, Jonathan Herman. 19250 SW 65TH AVE, STE 100 97062 #056-05-1972 L1977 **ORS** *020 †40
HUBERTY, David Patrick. 19250 SW 65TH AVE, OREGON ORTHOPEDIC & 97062 #030-06-2000 L2006 **ORS** *100
HUE, Heather Jane. 19300 SW 65TH AVE 97062 #034-01-1999 L2000 **IM** *020 †20 ‡
HUEBERT, Jimmy Dee. 6464 SW BORLAND RD, STE D2 97062 #030-05-1995 L2001 **IM ISM** *020 †20
JOHNSON, Kevin R. 19250 SW 65TH AVE, STE 220 97062 #040-02-1989 L1990 **GS** *020 †85
KAEDER, Collin Scott. 19300 SW 65TH AVE 97062 #020-12-1973 L1976 **AN** *020 †05 ‡
KAFROUNI, John Pierre. 19875 SW 65TH AVE, REHABILITATION MEDICINE 97062 #005-12-1998 L2002 **PM** *020 †60
KARIMI, Misagh. 19260 SW 65TH AVE, PACIFIC ONCOLOGY 97062 #010-01-1996 L2005 **HO** *020 †20
KARLIN, Manuel David. 19875 SW 65TH AVE 97062 #005-19-1980 L1982 **IM** *020 †20
KATES, Robin Sean. 6464 SW BORLAND RD, STE A4 97062 #005-15-1989 L1997 **DR** *020 †80
KEENEN, Timothy Lynn. 19260 SW 65TH AVE STE 270 97062 #028-34-1979 L1988 **OSS OTR** *020 †40
KILGORE, James Alfred. 19250 SW 65TH AVE, STE 365 97062 #049-01-1980 L1983 **PS HS** *020 †65
KILTY, John Edmund. 19260 SW 65TH AVE, CHILDRENS CLINIC PC 97062 #008-01-1995 L1997 **PD** *020 †55
KIM, Jin-Hee. 19250 SW 65TH AVE, UROLOGY CLINIC PC 97062 #005-14-1995 L2002 **U** *020 †95
KLAS, Paul Anthony. 19875 SW 65TH AVE 97062 #040-02-1994 L1998 **D** *020 †15
KLOBUCNIK, Robert Leonard. 19300 SW 65TH AVE 97062 #038-43-1994 L2000 **EM** *020 †16
KOON, David Chichiu. 19875 SW 65TH AVE, REHABILITATION MEDICINE 97062 #041-09-1997 L2001 **PM** *020 †60
LACE, Christopher James. ■ 97062 #040-02-2003 L2004 **AN** *020
LANDERS, Maeran Chung. 19255 SW 65TH AVE, STE 260 97062 #041-01-2000 L2001 **D** *020 †15
LARSON, William David. 19300 SW 65TH AVE 97062 #040-02-1976 L1977 **OPH** *020 †35
LAUER, Brian Avery. 19260 SW 65TH AVE, CHILDRENS CLINIC PC 97062 #021-01-1969 L1989 **PD** *020 †55
LAWLOR, Jennifer Kathleen. 19875 SW 65TH AVE, REHABILITATION MEDICINE 97062 #005-02-1993 L1997 **PM IM** *020 †60
LESLIE, Robin Rae. 19185 SW 90TH AVE, KAISER TUALATIN MEDICAL OF 97062 #023-01-1987 L1990 **PD** *020 †55
LEW, Ronald Jay. 19250 SW 90TH AVE 97062 #035-19-1995 L2002 **GE** *020 †20
LINDQUIST, Grant Richard. 19250 SW 65TH AVE, STE 215 97062 #040-02-1981 L1982 **OPH** *020 †20,35
LIU, Louis Hsitien. 19185 SW 90TH AVE 97062 #012-05-1990 L2001 **FM** *020 †18
LONG, Eric Wm. 6485 SW BORLAND RD STE G 97062 #054-04-1969 L1977 **FM** *020 †60
LOPEZ, Carl Emil. 6464 SW BORLAND RD 97062 #005-14-1978 L1984 **R OS** *020 †80
LUCK, Cameron Dean. 19260 SW 65TH AVE, CHILDRENS CLINIC PC 97062 #040-02-1984 L1985 **PD** *020 †55
LUTTMER, Collette Marie. 19300 SW 65TH AVE, 1820 SW VERMONT 97062 #041-09-1995 L1998 **IM** *020 †20
MAHON, Brian Robt. 6464 SW BORLAND RD, STE 14-4 97062 #035-15-1991 L1996 **RNR** *020 †80
MALLETT, Barbara S. 6464 SW BORLAND RD, STE C1 97062 #019-02-1986 L1991 **APM OS** *020 †05
MALOS, Michael John. 6464 SW BORLAND RD, STE A2 97062 #040-02-1978 L1979 **NS** *020 †25
MASON, Steven Jon. 19250 SW 90TH AVE 97062 #040-02-1975 L1976 **GE** *020 †20
MAUER, Jason Dale. 6464 SW BORLAND RD, STUITE C-1 97062 #005-18-1990 L2003 **APM** *100 †05
MC BEE, Patrick Gilbert. 19875 SW 65TH AVE, STE 260 97062 #010-02-1987 L1996 **GS** *020 †85
MC CRAW, Louis Henry. 19300 SW 65TH AVE 97062 #027-01-1963 L1973 **PS** *020 †85,65
MC KINSTRY, Mark Leo. 19875 SW 65TH AVE, LEAGACY CLINICS TUALATIN 97062 #040-02-1988 L1989 **IM** *020 †20

MC WEENEY, Thomas Philip. 19250 SW 65TH AVE, OREGON ORTHOPEDIC & 97062 #010-02-1985 L1990 **ORS** *020 †40

MC WILLIAMS, Jeffrey E. 19260 SW 65TH AVE, STE 435 97062 #040-02-1989 L1990 **ON HEM** *020 †20

MIGCHELBRINK, Suzanne L. 19205 SW 65TH AVE, STE 110 97062 #056-06-1998 L1999 **IM** *020 †20

MONSON, Robert B. ■ 97062 #040-02-1944 L1946 **GP** *075

MORGAN, Shawn Michael. 19250 SW 65TH AVE, STE 220 97062 #054-04-1996 L2001 **GS** *020 †85

MORITA, Lloyd Tetsuo. 6464 SW BORLAND RD 97062 #054-04-1968 L1974 **IM** *020 †20

MYERS, Emily Kay. 19875 SW 65TH AVE, LEGACY TUALATIN CLINIC 97062 #005-02-1997 L2001 **FM** *020 †18

NELSON, David Wesley, Jr. 6464 SW BORLAND RD, STE A4 97062 #045-01-1978 L1985 **DR** *020 †80

NOGEIRE, Christopher J. 6464 SW BORLAND RD STE C5 97062 #035-09-1973 L1980 **ON HEM** *020 †20

NORTH, F Chester. 19185 SW 90TH AVE 97062 #004-01-1981 L1982 **IM** *020 †05,20

O'BRIEN, Mary L. 19185 SW 90TH AVE, KAISER - TUALATIN CLINIC 97062 #041-09-1969 L1975 **PD** *020 †55

OLMSTEAD, Drea Cable. 19250 SW 65TH AVE, STE 300 97062 #054-04-1990 L1991 **OBG** *020 †30

OLSON, Kevin Donald. 19260 SW 65TH AVE, STE 435 97062 #040-02-1988 L1991 **ON** *020 †20

OYAMA, Kevin Keith. 19300 SW 65TH AVE, LEGACY MERIDAN PARK HOSP 97062 #040-02-1989 L1990 **PTH GP** *020 †50

PARSONS, Michael Robert. 19260 SW 65TH AVE, STE 420 97062 #035-01-1998 L2005 **CD** *020 †20

PATAROQUE, Benito G. 6485 SW BORLAND RD 97062 #748-01-1989 L2001 **IM** *020 †20

PETERSON, Chad Allan. ■ 97062 #040-02-2003 L2003 **U** *012

PETERSON, David Atley. 19300 SW 65TH AVE #026-04-1965 L1966 **PTH** *071 †50

PEW, Lisa Meyer. 19250 SW 65TH AVE, STE 300 97062 #028-34-1992 L1993 **OBG** *020 †30

PFISTER, Michael Eli. 6464 SW BORLAND RD STE A4, TUALATIN IMAGING PC 97062 #038-06-1992 L1997 **DR VIR** *020 †80 ‡

PHIPPS, Thomas Arthur. 19260 SW 65TH AVE, STE 220 97062 #040-02-1982 L1986 **N** *020 †75

PULITO, Joseph F. 6485 SW BORLAND RD, STE E 97062 #010-02-1973 L1977 **GS OS** *020 †85

RASMUSSEN, Kerry Jean. 19185 SW 90TH AVE, TUALATIN MEDICAL OFFICE 97062 #040-02-2000 L2000 **FM** *020 †18

REEVE, Gwen Johanna. 19875 SW 65TH AVE STE 100, LEGACY CLINIC 97062 #051-07-1997 L1998 **IM** *020 †20

REX, John Marvin, Jr. ■ 97062 #040-02-1980 L1983 **IM PHP** *020 †20

REYNOLDS, Walter Joseph. 6485 SW BORLAND RD, STE F 97062 #041-02-1967 L1977 **U** *071 †95

RISS, Gretchen Barber. ■ 97062 #040-02-1978 L1981 **FM** *020 †18

ROSENBLOOM, Frank Sy. 6464 SW BORLAND RD, STE B2 97062 #495-98-1990 L1996 **IM** *020 †20

ROVANG, James Thos. 19300 SW 65TH AVE, MERIDIAN PARK HOSP 97062 #040-02-1983 L1984 **EM** *020 †16

RUDIN, Marilyn Lucile. 19250 SW 65TH AVE, OREGON PULMONARY ASSOC PC 97062 #040-02-1973 L1974 **SME PUD** *020 †20

RUDOFF, Joanne C. 6475 SW BORLAND RD, OB/GYN STE L 97062 #041-14-1979 L1989 **GYN** *020 †30

RUDOFF, John Mark. 6475 SW BORLAND RD STE L 97062 #041-13-1983 L1989 **CD IM** *020 †20

RUYBALID, Kristina Marie. ■ 97062 #028-02-2002 L2006 **AN** *020

SAKS, Seldon K. 19300 SW BOONES FERRY RD, STE 5 97062 #016-11-1982 L1988 **IM** *020 †20

SAMMOND, Elizabeth. 19875 SW 65TH AVE, STE 100 97062 #005-19-1998 L2002 **IM** *020 †20

SAMSON, Liza Delacruz. 19875 SW 65TH AVE, STE 100 97062 #005-19-1996 L2000 **FM** *020 †18

SANDERS, Shari Ann. 19165 SW 90TH AVE, KAISER THALATIN MED OFFICE 97062 #005-02-2001 L2001 **IM IMG** *020

SCHADER, James Brian. 19875 SW 65TH AVE, STE 201 97062 #010-02-1977 L1982 **ORS** *020 †40

SCHAFF, Paul E. 19300 SW 65TH AVE 97062 #040-02-1951 L1953 **AN** *020

SCHIELE, Mark Stephen. 19250 SW 90TH AVE 97062 #005-19-1989 L1992 **GE IM** *020 †20

SCHRINSKY, Daniel Craig. 19250 SW 65TH AVE, STE 300 97062 #056-06-1972 L1973 **OBG** *020 †30

SEDGEWICK, Terrence A. 19250 SW 65TH AVE, OREGON ORTHOPEDIC & 97062 #025-07-1987 L1993 **ORS OSM** *020 †40

SHAH, Anil. 19300 SW 65TH AVE, LEGACY MERIDIAN PARK HOSPI 97062 #160-10-1987 L2004 **IM** *020 †20

SHAH, Rupa Kirit. 19260 SW 65TH AVE, STE 275 97062 #495-89-1974 L1984 **PD** *020 †55

SIDOFF, Michael Luby. 19300 SW 65TH AVE 97062 #056-05-1973 L1978 **EM** *020 †16

SKEETERS, C Edward. 19250 SW 65TH AVE, STE 235 97062 #017-20-1967 L1971 **U** *020 †95

SLUSS, Michael Paul. 19260 SW 65TH AVE, STE 280 97062 #026-04-1976 L2005 **N** *020 †75

SMART, Kari Lyn. 19185 SW 90TH AVE 97062 #040-02-1996 L1998 **PD** *020 †55

SMITH, Christine Wessels. 19260 SW 65TH AVE, CHILDRENS CLINIC PC 97062 #011-04-1992 L1999 **PD** *020 †55

SNOW, Susan Dale. 6485 SW BORLAND RD, STE D 97062 #034-01-1983 L1989 **P** *020

SOLDEVILLA, Francisco X. 19250 SW 65TH AVE, STE 260 97062 #016-11-1984 L1985 **NS** *020 †25

SOOT, Laurel C. 19250 SW 65TH AVE, STE 240 97062 #054-04-1994 L1997 **GS** *020 †85

SPADY, George Pettit, II. 6464 SW BORLAND RD, STE D1 97062 #040-02-1985 L1988 **IM** *020 †20

STEWART, Marguerite Ruth. 19250 SW 65TH AVE STE 300, WOMEN'S HEALTH CARE ASSOC. 97062 #025-07-1985 L2000 **OBG** *020 †30

SWARTZ, Kim Raymond. 19260 SW 65TH AVE, STE 240 97062 #008-01-1980 L1982 **GS VS** *020 †85

TEN HULZEN, David Ross. 6464 SW BORLAND RD STE D3 97062 #030-05-1982 L1984 **OMF** *020

TERRY, Toni Lee. 19875 SW 65TH AVE STE 10 97062 #034-01-2001 L2001 **IM** *020

THIESSEN, Curtis Richard. ■ 97062 #062-01-1983 L1985 **ESM OM** *020 †70

TONGUE, John Richard. 6485 SW BORLAND RD 97062 #028-34-1972 L1973 **ORS HS** *020 †40

TOOVY, David Aron. 19300 SW 65TH AVE, MERIDAN PARK HOSP ER 97062 #016-11-1991 L1993 **EM** *020 †16

TRAINES, Mark Leslie. ■ 97062 #048-04-1981 L1990 **IMG IM** *020 †20

TRELSTAD, Donald Axton. 19260 SW 65TH AVE, STE 420 97062 #035-01-1973 L1974 **CD** *020 †20

TRICKEY, Andrew Robert. 19300 SW 65TH AVE, MERIDIAN PARK HOSPITAL ER 97062 #012-05-1997 L1998 **EM** *020 †16

TRIPP, Larry Clifford. ■ 97062 #007-02-1959 L1961 **FM OS** *071 †18

UNRAU, Audrey Christina. 19260 SW 65TH AVE, CHILDRENS CLINIC PC 97062 #034-01-1994 L1997 **PD** *020 †55

VAN ALLEN, Michael Ross. 19255 SW 65TH AVE, STE 210 97062 #040-02-1986 L1987 **HS** *020 †40

VESSELY, Michelle Bleynat. 6485 SW BORLAND RD STE B 97062 #036-01-1988 L1994 **OTO** *020 †45

VICK, Harold Gregory. 19250 SW 65TH AVE, STE 300 97062 #040-02-1970 L1973 **OBG** *020 †30

WALDRAM, David Wm. 3025 SW BORLAND RD 97062 #040-02-1966 L1973 **ORS GP** *020 †40

WALLACE, Jason Rene. 6464 SW BORLAND RD STE A4, TUALATIN IMAGING, PC 97062 #048-02-2001 L2007 **AR** *020 †80

WALLIS, Kristin Robinson. 19260 SW 65TH AVE, CHILDRENS CLINIC PC 97062 #040-02-1989 L1994 **PD** *020 †55

WARD, Gary Allen. 19875 SW 65TH AVE, REHABILITATION MEDICINE 97062 #026-04-1972 L1974 **PM OS** *020 †60

WEINGARTEN, Franklin S. 19250 SW 65TH AVE, STE 265 97062 #016-02-1976 L1979 **FM EM** *020 †18

WEISS, James Edward. 19365 SW 65TH AVE, STE 200 97062 #040-02-1966 L1973 **D** *020 †15

WELLS, Hilary Ann. 19185 SW 90TH AVE, TUALATIN MEDICAL OFFICE 97062 #041-12-1998 L2002 **PD** *020 †55

WESTLY, Laurel Margaret. 19185 SW 90TH AVE, NW KAISER PERMANENTE 97062 #040-02-2002 L2003 **FM** *020 †18

WHITE, Michael Chas. 19300 SW 65TH AVE, LEGACY MERIDIAN PARK 97062 #040-02-1976 L1979 **EM** *020 †16

WILCOX, Linda Conkling. ■ 97062 #016-43-1982 L1983 **PD** *071 †55

WILLIS, Norman Robt. 6489 SW BORLAND RD 97062 #005-14-1971 L1975 **RO** *020 †80

WOLFE, Gordon Lee. 19205 SW 65TH AVE, STE 110 97062 #040-02-1975 L1976 **IM** *020 †20

WOLTJER, Randall Lee. ■ 97062 #047-05-1994 L2006 **PTH** *020 †50

WOOD, Gregg Donald. 19300 SW 65TH AVE 97062 #040-02-1943 L1946 **GP GS** *071

WU, Philip. 19185 SW 90TH AVE 97062 #038-41-1976 L1983 **PD** *020 †55

YEAGER, Julie Fiene. 19260 SW 65TH AVE, CHILDRENS CLINIC PC 97062 #005-06-1991 L1997 **PD** *020 †55

YEE, Kevin Wung Hong. 19260 SW 65TH AVE, PACIFIC ONCOLOGY 97062 #005-14-1996 L1999 **HO** *020 †20

ZHU, Xianghong. 19185 SW 90TH AVE, TUALATIN MEDICAL OFFICE 97062 #243-18-1982 L2002 **FM** *020 †18

TURNER – MARION

COULTER, James Arthur. ■ 97392 #054-04-1954 L1976 **NS** *071 †25

WIGHT, Bennett Allen, Jr. ■ 97392 #048-02-1962 L1970 **P N** *071

UMATILLA – UMATILLA

DANNER, William Bruce. ■ 97882 #047-06-1956 L1973 **GP** *071

ZIELINSKI, Steven Robt. 1890 7TH ST 97882 #016-06-1982 L1985 **IM LM** *020 †20

UMPQUA – DOUGLAS

JOHNS, Clara Ritchie. ■ 97486 #016-02-1941 L1957 **IM PHP** *071 †70

VALE – MALHEUR

JAGELSKI, Aaron Thos. 789 WASHINGTON ST W 97918 #040-02-1992 L2004 **FM OBS** *020 †18

KOPP, Clarence John. 1500 HIGHWAY 20 26 97918 #040-02-1947 L1948 **FM OS** *071

VENETA – LANE

FLOYD, David Alan. 25045 DUNHAM AVE 97487 #024-01-1972 L1974 **GP** *020

VIDA – LANE

STENSTROM, William Harold. ■ 97488 #023-01-1947 L1955 **OBG ADM** *020 †30

WALDPORT – LINCOLN

BOWMAN, Donald Brand. ■ 97394 #040-02-1957 L1962 **CD IM** *071

LEAKE, James R. ■ 97394 #035-45-1949 L1955 **IM IMG** *071

MAERCKS, Ralph Owen. ■ 97394 #036-05-1957 L1957 **P** *071

MOYAR, John Borland. ■ 97394 #041-01-1943 L1944 **NS** *071 †25

THOMPSON, James Melvin. 150 HWY 101 97394 #040-02-1976 **GP** *020

WRAZEN, Jennifer Lynn. 150 SW ARROW 97394 #035-06-1996 L1999 **PD** *020 †55

WARRENTON – CLATSOP

SHEN, Henry John. 2185 SE 12TH PL, USCG GROUP ASTORIA MEDICAL 97146 #032-01-1982 L1985 **FM AM** *020 †18

WELCHES – CLACKAMAS

MEDINA, Juan Jose. ■ 97067 #649-14-1954 L1964 **AN** *071

VAN DYKE, Alan Ronald. ■ 97067 #040-02-1968 L1974 **R** *071 †80

WEST LINN – CLACKAMAS

ADAMS, William R. ■ 97068 #008-01-1952 L1954 **PTH MG** *062 †50

BARBEE, Daniel Garth. ■ 97068 #036-07-1995 L2003 **EM** *020 †16
BIRENBAUM, Georges. ■ 97068 #020-12-1967 L1968 **OPH FPS** *071 †35
BROWN, Mark Vincent. ■ 97068 #038-40-1975 L1976 **FM** *071 †18
BRUECHERT, Robert Wayne. ■ 97068 #040-02-1957 L1959 **OPH** *071 †35
CAMPBELL, David Douglas. 18654 WILLAMETTE DR 97068 #007-02-1979 L1984
    FM OM *020 †70,16,18
CAMPBELL, Wiley Leigh. ■ 97068 #040-02-1955 L1956 **OPH OS** *071 †35
CARR, William Alexander. ■ 97068 #036-07-1966 L1976 **ORS** *071 †40
CHANG, Lisa Minhuey. ■ 97068 #016-02-2001 L2007 **IM** *020
CHAPMAN, Richard Dennis. 23730 SW STAFFORD HIL DR D 97068 #035-20-1961 L1970
    TS *020 †85,90
COALE, Franklin S. 18380 WILLAMETTE DR, STE 201 97068 #040-02-1981 L1987
    OTO HNS *020 †45
COLEMAN, Randall Chaney. 21810 WILLAMETTE DR 97068 #040-02-1978 L1979 **OBG** *020 †30
COMBS, Gregory Lloyd. 1830 BLANKENSHIP RD, STE 100 97068 #047-05-1986 L1987
    PS *020 †65
COOLEY, Laura Lynn. 1750 BLANKENSHIP RD, STE 275 97068 #054-04-1997 L2000
    PD *020 †55
CRAWFORD, Steven Russell. 22490 SW MOUNTAIN RD 97068 #054-04-1975 L1977 **GP** *020
DAVIS, Richard Franklin. 28976 SW PETES MOUNTAIN RD, 28976 SW PETES MOUNTAIN
    RO 97068 #005-02-1974 L1989 **AN** *020 †05 ‡
DE VRIES, John Cornelius. ■ 97068 #025-01-1962 L1967 **AN** *071
ENDO, Joyce Sachie. 18380 WILLAMETTE DR, STE 202 97068 #005-14-1988 L1991
    FM OBG *020 †18
FARLEY, David Brian. 18380 WILLAMETTE DR, STE 202 97068 #024-01-1986 L1989
    FM *020 †18
FOGGIA, Riccardo Rudolfo. 26075 SW MOUNTAIN RD 97068 #040-02-1959 L1963 *020
FRANZKE, Ronald Oscar. 1980 WILLAMETTE FALLS DR, STE 230 PMB 263 97068
    #005-12-1965 L1974 **OTO** *020 †45
FRENZEL, William Lee. ■ 97068 #040-02-1974 *075
GODBEY, Grant Tyrone. ■ 97068 #040-02-1981 L1988 **CHP** *020 †75
GRIESER, Gerhard Matthew. ■ 97068 #065-06-1966 L1976 **NS** *071 †25
HARRIS, Mary Martha. ■ 97068 #005-19-1981 L1989 **PD** *020 †55
HILL, Robert Eugene. ■ 97068 #001-02-1967 L1975 **DR** *020
KANG, John J. ■ 97068 #035-48-1991 L2000 **EM** *020 †16
KARL, Andrea Ingrid. 29355 SW PETES MOUNTN RD R 97068 #040-02-2001 L2005 **PM** *100
LAIRD, Sheri Lee. 22400 S SALAMO RD STE 101C 97068 #017-20-1995 L1999
    PD IM *020 †20,55
LANDRUM, Connie Lou. ■ 97068 #005-02-1971 L1978 **EM** *020 †16
LUCAS, Linda Margaret. ■ 97068 #040-02-1980 L1981 **IM** *020 †20
LUCAS, Scott Tindall. ■ 97068 #040-02-1980 L1988 **DR** *020
MC DONOUGH, Colin M. 18676 WILLAMETTE DR # 100, INTERNAL MEDICINE 97068
    #048-12-1988 L1991 **IM** *020 †20
MICKEL, Stephen Dale. 6301 PALOMINO WAY 97068 #040-02-1979 L1981 **EM GP** *020 †16
MILLER, Michael Scott. 3475 RIVERKNOLL WAY 97068 #025-01-1973 L1974 **EM** *020 †16
MISHRA, Naveen Ram. 1800 BLANKENSHIP RD STE 20 97068 #005-76-2002, ▲ L2002 **P** *020
MOLENDYK, John Mark. 3049 S ROXBURY DR 97068 #005-11-1966 L1972 **RO** *020 †80
NEMEC, Jaroslav F. ■ 97068 #286-02-1958 L1978 **AN** *020
NICHOLS, Michael Norman. ■ 97068 #040-02-1967 L1970 **AN** *071
NORCOM, Derek Franklin. ■ 97068 #039-01-1994 L1998 **FM** *072 †18
PARVARESH, Guy A. ■ 97068 #517-01-1956 L1964 **P** *071 †75
POPOWICH, Yale Sands. 1830 BLANKENSHIP RD, STE 100 97068 #041-07-1998 L2004
    PS *020 †85
ROA, Veronica. ■ 97068 #308-02-1988 L2001 **HO** *020 †20
ROWER, Jeremy Andrew. ■ 97068 #038-41-1997 L2006 **IM** *020 †20
SALTZBERG, George Henry. ■ 97068 #016-11-1965 L1990 **OM FM** *020 †18
SAN MIGUEL, Virginia V. 21810 WILLAMETTE DR 97068 #048-02-1991 L2005 **OBG** *020 †30
SCOTT, Ryan Gary. 18380 WILLAMETTE DR, STE 202 97068 #040-02-1996 L1999
    FM OBS *020 †18
SORENSEN, Theresa M. 18380 WILLAMETTE DR STE 20, HEALTH CENTER 97068
    #026-04-2000 L2001 **FM** *100 †18
SPEER, Christian Albert. ■ 97068 #409-21-1995 L2007 **GE** *100 †20
TELASHA, David Paul. 22650 SW MOUNTAIN RD 97068 #010-02-1979 L1984 **OBG** *071 †30
TENISON, Michael David. ■ 97068 #040-02-2002 L2006 **EM** *020 †16
TINDALL, Elizabeth Ann. ■ 97068 #017-20-1977 L1978 **RHU IM** *020 †20
TRUAX, Jan Marie. ■ 97068 #040-02-1986 **IM** *074
UNO, Hideo. ■ 97068 #572-32-1955 **PTH OS** *050
WEEKS, Melanie Sue. ■ 97068 #030-05-1979 L1982 **AN** *020
WILSON, Paula Rea. ■ 97068 #001-02-1981 L1983 **P** *020
WUSTRACK, Karl Otto. 1830 BLANKENSHIP RD, STE 100 97068 #008-01-1970 L1973
    PS GS *020 †85,65
YANNEY, James Ferris M. 1800 BLANKENSHIP RD, STE 195 97068 #030-06-1986 L1987
    OMF GS *020
ZACK, Steven Edward. ■ 97068 #025-07-1975 L1976 **AN** *020 †05 ‡
ZIMMERMAN, Michael A. ■ 97068 #020-02-1978 L2007 **FM** *075 †18

WHEELER — TILLAMOOK

SKIRVING, John H. ■ 97147 #030-06-1943 **FM GS** *071

WHITE CITY — JACKSON

CLARK, Thomas Leonard. 8495 CRATER LAKE HWY 97503 #040-02-1976 L1988 **EM GP** *020
DEMIAN, Pamela Grace. 8495 CRATER LAKE HWY 97503 #649-33-1981 L1994 **FM** *020 †18
FUSON, Thomas J. ■ 97503 #038-06-1943 **GP GS** *071 †85
HARRIS, Garry Christopher. 8495 CRATER LAKE HWY, VA SOUTHERN OREGON REHAB 97503
    #038-41-1966 L1998 **OTO** *020 †45
JUAN, Gerardo. 8495 CRATER LAKE HWY 97503 #748-02-1966 L1972 **P PYG** *020 †75
KIRKMAN, Ada Darleen. 8495 CRATER LAKE HWY 97503 #045-01-1978 L1979 **P** *020 †75
MEBANE, Andrew Hill. 8495 CRATER LAKE HWY 97503 #001-06-1977 L1978 **P MDM** *030 †75
MORRISON, Mary Jane. 8495 CRATER LAKE HWY, VA-DOM PM & R 97503 #036-05-1972 L1972
    PM GP *030 †60
MORTIMER-LAMB, Chas Derek. 8495 CRATER LAKE HWY 97503 #061-01-1965 L1974
    OM GP *020 †18

NAYMIK, Robert John. 8495 CRATER LAKE HWY 97503 #038-43-1973 L1974 **IM** *020 †20
NEILL, Mary Langford. 8495 CRATER LAKE HWY 97503 #056-06-1985 L1986 **IM** *020 †20
NELSON, Randall Ray. 8495 CRATER LAKE HWY 97503 #040-02-1983 L1987 **IM** *020 †20
OURSLER, David Paul. 8495 CRATER LAKE HWY, VETERAN'S ADMINISTRATION 97503
    #023-07-1988 L1994 **NEP** *020 †20
REN, Junlong. 8495 CRATER LAKE HWY, SOUTHERN OREGON VA REHABIL 97503
    #243-47-1970 L2003 **PM PME** *020
SHAW, Steven Henderson. 8495 CRATER LAKE HWY 97503 #047-07-1993 L1994 **IM** *020 †20
THOMPSON, Neal Thornton. 8495 CRATER LAKE HWY 97503 #036-01-1983 L1999
    IM CCM *020 †20
TURNER, Robert M. VA DOMICILIARY 97503 #054-04-1950 L1951 **GP PD** *071
WHITE, Steven Maxwell. 8495 CRATER LAKE HWY, SO OREGON REHAB CTR 97503
    #055-01-1972 L1994 **GP** *020

WILDERVILLE — JOSEPHINE

POTTER, Charles D. 525 INGALLS LN 97543 #025-01-1968 L1973 **ORS** *020 †40

WILSONVILLE — CLACKAMAS

BERNARD, Richard M. ■ 97070 #016-02-1950 L1951 **FM** *072 †18
CHAUDHURI, Jhuma. ■ 97070 #035-19-2003 L2006 **IM** *100 †20
CLARK, Grant Cowan. PO BOX 9000, 24499 SW GRAHAM FERRY RD 97070
    #005-02-1965 L1979 **FM** *020 †18
FIROOZI, Kamran. ■ 97070 #517-01-1993 L2005 **PCC** *020 †20
GARCIA, Ester Abarguez. 30045 SW PARKWAY AVE 97070 #748-01-1965 L1976 **IM** *020
GEARHART, Lenly Marlin. ■ 97070 #018-03-1964 L1968 **P** *071 †75
GUISS, Russell Loran. ■ 97070 #040-02-1943 L1944 **P GS** *071 †85
HARTWIG, James Henry. 24499 SW GRAHAMS FRY RD, FERRY RD 97070 #054-04-1957 L1997
    GP *020
HU, Funan. ■ 97070 #242-16-1942 L1955 **OS DMP** *071 †15
HUSBAND, Lynn Sherman. ■ 97070 #040-02-1960 L1961 **AN** *020 †05
MASON, Herbert Eugene. ■ 97070 #040-02-1939 **GP** *071
MEEK, Edward C, Jr. ■ 97070 #023-07-1944 L1945 **PTH** *071 †50
MELVIN, Kenneth Paul. ■ 97070 #671-01-1998 L2001 **FM** *020 †20
MINARD, Eugene W. ■ 97070 #005-11-1949 L1975 **P PHP** *071 †70,75
MURRAY, William Norbert. ■ 97070 #016-11-1948 **DR** *071
OSTLUND, Roland D. ■ 97070 #019-02-1950 L1969 **RO** *071 †80
RITZMANN, Dorothy Reese. ■ 97070 #028-02-1944 L1944 **DR** *071 †80
RITZMANN, Leonard W. ■ 97070 #028-02-1945 L1954 **CD IM** *071 †20
SCHENK, John Frederick. ■ 97070 #040-02-1972 L1974 **AN** *020 †05
SEBASTIAN, George Edward. ■ 97070 #040-11-1955 L1956 **P** *071 †75
SIMON, Jack Howard. PO BOX 3980, JACK SIMON 97070 #056-05-1979 L2007 **R** *020 †80
SINCLAIR, Colin Edward. ■ 97070 #062-01-1957 L1963 **A HEM** *071 †20
SMYTH, Kenneth D. ■ 97070 #040-02-1953 L1957 **PM** *072 †60
STENSTROM, David Andrew. ■ 97070 #040-02-2008 *012
STEVENS, Catherine. ■ 97070 #024-05-1979 L2007 **NPM PD** *020 †55
STORINO, Henry E. ■ 97070 #030-06-1953 L1954 **N** *072
TAFT, James Walter. ■ 97070 #035-06-1943 L1966 **GP** *071
WALKER, Scott L. ■ 97070 #036-05-1950 L1970 **DR** *071
WILSON, Norman James. ■ 97070 #023-01-1935 L1937 **PUD** *020 †85,90
ZEPS, David John. 24130 SW GAGE RD 97070 #056-06-1971 L1975 **IMG IM** *020 †20,18

WINCHESTER — DOUGLAS

FLETCHER, C Weldon. ■ 97495 #005-15-1962 L1975 **GP** *020
MC CLURE, Jack B. 273 THORA CIRCLE DR 97495 #016-02-1950 L1955 **GS TS** *071 †85,90
TAN, Alfonso O. ■ 97495 #748-01-1954 L1982 **IM** *071 †20
YEAGER, Thomas D. ■ 97495 #041-01-1978 L1981 **PD PHP** *071 †55

WINCHESTER BAY — DOUGLAS

FRENCH, William Richmond. ■ 97467 #040-02-1954 **GS** *071 †85
HERYFORD, Daniel Albert. ■ 97467 #040-02-1954 L1961 **R** *071 †80

WOODBURN — MARION

ALTIZER, Mercedes Fairfax. 1390 MERIDIAN DR, WOODBURN FAMILY CLINIC 97071
    #054-04-1953 L1968 **GP OBS** *072
BANKS, Heather Susann. 1175 MOUNT HOOD AVE 97071 #056-06-1998 L2002 **FM** *020 †18
BOHLMAN, Donald Keith. ■ 97071 #005-12-1961 L1963 **GP** *071
BOYD, Stacy Lynne. 974 N CASCADE DR, WOODBURN INTERNAL MEDICINE 97071
    #040-02-1997 L2000 **IM** *020 †20
BRAMAN, Marcus Allan. 1475 MOUNT HOOD AVE 97071 #005-12-1995 L1999 **GPM** *020 †70
BROYHILL, Julie Christine. 1390 MERIDIAN DR, SILVERTON HOSP. WOODBURN F 97071
    #040-02-1999 L2000 **FM** *020
CHUN, Denise Meilin. 1175 MOUNT HOOD AVE 97071 #005-14-1998 L2003 **FM** *020 †18
DZIADOS, Joseph Edward. 1475 MOUNT HOOD AVE, SILVERTON HOSPITAL IMMEDIA 97071
    #030-06-1977 L2005 **FM PHP** *020 †70,18
ENTENA, Monchito C. 1350 MERIDIAN DR, NORTHWOOD OFFICE PARK 97071
    #748-02-1970 L1980 **FM** *020 †20
EPSTEIN, Roger Jay. 693 GLATT CIR 97071 #041-14-1974 L2002 **GE** *020 †20
GOLDEN, Maurice Franklin. 974 N CASCADE DR 97071 #040-02-1986 L1990 **IM** *020 †20
GOURLEY, Edward Wayne. ■ 97071 #040-02-1948 L1954 **IM** *071
GRIFFIN, Page Bynum. 1175 MOUNT HOOD AVE 97071 #021-01-1996 L1999 **FM** *020 †18
HARTOG, Robert Cecil L. 1002 N BOONES FERRY RD, LEGACY CLINIC WOODBURN 97071
    #060-02-1979 L1995 **FM** *020 †18
HAYES, John Russell. 1175 MOUNT HOOD AVE 97071 #030-06-2002 L2005 **FM** *020 †18
HUANG, Joseph Hudson. 1175 MOUNT HOOD AVE 97071 #016-06-1999 L2003 **FM** *020 †18
LINDEROTH, Diana Marie. 1390 MERIDIAN DR, WOODBURN PEDIATRIC CLINIC 97071
    #040-02-2002 L2005 **PD** *020 †55

MASHKURI, Javad Scott. 1175 MOUNT HOOD AVE 97071 #035-08-1995 L1999 **EM** *012 †18

MC COLL, Mary Ellen. 1390 MERIDIAN DR, WOODBURN FAMILY CLINIC 97071 #065-01-1968 L1999 **FM** *020

MC DONALD, Patrick Chas. 685 EVERGREEN RD 97071 #654-01-1980 L1984 **FM** *020 †18

POWER, Juliette Marie. 1390 MERIDIAN DR 97071 #041-07-1998 L2001 **FM** *020 †18

READ, Tracy Lynn. 1390 MERIDIAN DR, WOODBURN FAMILY PRACTICE 97071 #060-01-1994 L1996 **FM** *020 †18

SAVAGE, Jeanne Selby. ■ 97071 #040-02-1999 L2003 **FM** *020 †18

SCHULTZ, Charles Merle. ■ 97071 #040-02-1958 L1961 **GP D** *075

SCHUMACHER, John Paul. 1475 MOUNT HOOD AVE, SILVERTON HOSP IMMEDIATE C 97071 #045-01-1979 L1997 **FM** *020 †18

STANFORD, Gary E. ■ 97071 #016-11-1977 L1983 **GP EM** *020 †16

STEINBERG, Richard Henry. 1390 MERIDIAN DR 97071 #035-46-1970 L1973 **PD P** *020 †55

SURBAUGH, Mark Frederick. 1390 MERIDIAN DR 97071 #040-02-2002 L2002 **FM** *020 †18

WALLACE, Jennifer Lyn. 1002 N BOONES FERRY RD 97071 #025-01-2000 L2003 **FM** *020 †18

WHITSON, Joseph P. 1475 MOUNT HOOD AVE, SILVERTON HOSPITAL IMMEDIA 97071 #048-78-1992, ▲ L2002 **FM** *020 †18

ZAWADA, Eleanor. 976 N CASCADE DR, WOODBURN MEDICAL CLINIC 97071 #010-02-1996 L1999 **IM** *020 †20

YACHATS – LINCOLN

KING, Philip S, III. 897 OCEAN VIEW DRIVE 97498 #030-05-1952 L1953 **PM** *071 †60

WIKLER, Joan Grier. 5600 NE GOODWIN AVE 97498 #041-01-1980 L1990 **FM** *075

YONCALLA – DOUGLAS

ANDERSON, A Keith. ■ 97499 #005-12-1953 L1954 **GP OS** *071

ABINGTON – MONTGOMERY

ACHANTA, Latha Madhavi. 1200 YORK RD 19001 #495-11-2004 L2007 **IM** *012

ADDONIZIO, V Paul. 1200 OLD YORK RD, PORTER INST FOR VALVULAR 19001 #035-20-1974 L1977 **TS** *020 †80,90

ALDERSON, Skip Michael. ■ 19001 #041-15-2005 L2005 **DR** *012

ALI, Aliya. 1200 OLD YORK RD, ABINGTON MEMORIAL HOSPITAL 19001 #422-01-1999 L2001 **IM ISM** *020 †20

ANDREWS, Willard Guy, III. 1200 OLD YORK RD, STE 1W 19001 #041-02-1980 L1985 **ON IM** *020 †20

ANGOTTI, Donna M. 1584 OLD YORK RD 19001 #041-09-1987 L1990 **GS** *020 †85

ANIGATI, Juan Carlos. 1200 OLD YORK RD 19001 #132-01-1958 L1964 **AN** *020 †05

ANOIA, Elizabeth Joanne. 1200 OLD YORK RD, STE 210 19001 #010-02-1999 L2006 **U** *020 †95

AQUILINA, Patrick Michael. 1235 OLD YORK RD, STE 222 19001 #041-13-1998 L2000 **ICE** *020 †18,20

ARMSTRONG, Thomas A. 1550 OLD YORK RD 19001 #041-13-1978 L1981 **OPH** *020 †35

ATKINS, Robert F. 1200 OLD YORK RD, DEPT OF ANESTHESIOLOGY 19001 #024-16-1980 L1988 **AN CCM** *020 †20,05

AYDIN, Ali Nejat. 1186 HIGHLAND AVE 19001 #902-03-1952 L1964 **CHP P** *071

AYUB, Bilal. 1200 OLD YORK RD, ABINGTON MEMORIAL HOSPITAL 19001 #704-21-2003 L2006 **IM** *012

BAIR, John E. 1200 OLD YORK RD, ABINGTON MEMORIAL HOSP 19001 #041-12-1992 L1995 **EM** *020 †16

BALARATNA, Asoka. 1235 OLD YORK RD STE 222 19001 #038-06-1995 L1999 **CD** *020 †20

BALDASSANO, Robert N. 1309 HIGHLAND AVE 19001 #035-08-1984 L1987 **PD GE** *020 †55

BALL, Andrew Gordon. 1200 OLD YORK RD, ABINGTON MEM HOSP-EMERG MD 19001 #033-06-1988 L1990 **EM** *030 †20,16

BANIFATEMI, Reza. 1200 OLD YORK RD 19001 #473-03-1997 L2001 **IM** *020

BARMAT, Larry Ian. 1245 HIGHLAND AVE, STE 404 19001 #041-13-1991 L1993 **OBG** *020 †30

BELLARY, Siddharth Somash. 1200 YORK RD, ABINGTON MEM HOSP 19001 #495-99-2005 L2008 *100

BERGER, Bruce C. 1235 OLD YORK RD, MED PLZ STE 222 19001 #041-02-1974 L1975 **CD** *020 †20

BIKO, David Matthew. ■ 19001 #010-02-2004 L2005 **DR** *012

BLAZES, Christopher Km. 1200 OLD YORK RD, ABINGTON MEMORIAL HOSPITAL 19001 #035-45-1997 L2001 **EM** *020 †16

BOMMADEVARA, Deepthi Kris. 1200 YORK RD, ABINGTON MEM HSP 19001 #496-74-2006 L2008 *012

BONANNI, Fernando Benito. 1235 OLD YORK RD, STE G28 19001 #041-09-1990 L1992 **GS OS** *020 †85

BORGE, Richard Peter, Jr. 1235 OLD YORK RD, STE 222 19001 #041-02-1991 L1994 **CD** *020 †20

BOSSE, Christopher Gerard. 1235 OLD YORK RD, ABINGTON PULMONARY & 19001 #033-06-1987 L1990 **PUD** *020 †20

BRAUN, Todd Ian. 1235 OLD YORK RD, ASSOCIATES IN INFECTIOUS 19001 #041-09-1981 L1982 **ID IM** *020 †20

BRENNAN, Alicia Ann. 1200 OLD YORK RD, 4TH FLOOR, 1 HIGHLAND 19001 #023-07-1994 L1996 **PD** *020 †55 ‡

BRENNAN, Laura Kaye. 1200 OLD YORK RD 19001 #041-12-2001 L2001 **PD** *050 †55

BUSSLER, Brandon Lee. 1200 OLD YORK RD, ABINGTON MEMORIAL HOSPITAL 19001 #041-02-2002 L2002 **FM** *100 †18

CAMILO-LITTLE, Martha M. 1245 HIGHLAND AVE, STE 305 19001 #308-07-1983 L1992 **PYG P** *020 †75

CARROLL, Pamela Tennille. 1200 OLD YORK RD, DEPT OF MED EDU 19001 #422-01-2006 L2006 **OBG** *012

CARSON, Sam Leon. 1200 OLD YORK RD 19001 #041-13-1986 L1987 **P PYG** *020 †75

CASSIN, Maureen. 1235 OLD YORK RD, ASSOCIATES IN INFECTIOUS 19001 #041-15-2001 L2001 **ID** *020

CHANG, Eddie. 1200 OLD YORK RD, DEPT OF NEONATOLOGY 19001 #041-02-2000 L2003 **NPM** *020 †55

CHARLES, Robert Seth. 1235 OLD YORK RD, STE 210 19001 #041-13-1980 L1981 **U** *020 †95

CHERNEY, Paul J. 1200 OLD YORK RD 19001 #041-01-1949 L1950 **PTH BBK** *072 †50 ‡

CHEYNEY, James B, II. 1200 OLD YORK RD 19001 #041-02-1951 L1952 **GP** *071

CHIGUCHI, Miki. 1200 YORK RD 19001 #572-74-1997 L2005 **OBG** *012

COHEN, Adam Matthew. 1235 OLD YORK RD, STE 222 19001 #035-47-1997 L2000 **CD** *020 †20

COHEN, Avraham Naphtali. 1550 OLD YORK RD 19001 #035-46-1990 L1998 **OPH** *020 †35

COHEN, Marc Curtis. 1235 OLD YORK RD, STE 222 19001 #035-46-1979 L1981 **CD** *020 †20

COLE, Karin Lorraine. 1200 OLD YORK RD 19001 #024-07-2004 L2004 **GS** *012

COLT, Cathy Ann. 1550 OLD YORK RD 19001 #024-01-1984 L1985 **OPH** *020 †35

COMBER, John Thos. 1200 OLD YORK RD, ABINGTN MEM HSP EMERG DEPT 19001 #041-02-1991 L1993 **EM** *020 †16

COMPERATORE, David M. 1200 OLD YORK RD, EMERGENCY TRAUMA CENTER 19001 #041-02-1998 L2001 **EM** *020 †16

COOPER, Barry Robt. 1128 OLD YORK RD 19001 #041-01-1973 L1974 **FM FPG** *020 †18 ‡

COOPER, Murray Stephen. 1245 HIGHLAND AVE 19001 #041-13-1971 L1972 **OBG** *071 †30

COZEN, Bennett H. 1400 OLD YORK RD 19001 #041-13-1984 L1985 **IM** *020

CRAMER, Arnold Jeffrey. 1865 OLD YORK RD 19001 #041-02-1981 L1982 **IM** *020 †20

CRAPARO, Frank Joseph. 1235 OLD YORK RD, STE 119 19001 #308-07-1982 L1987 **MFM OBG** *020 †30

CUSTER, Diane E. 1200 OLD YORK RD 19001 #041-14-1988 L1990 **P** *020 †75

CUTLER, Jack. 1200 OLD YORK RD 19001 #041-13-1951 L1952 **OBG** *071 †30

CUTLER, Larry Alan. 1235 OLD YORK RD, STE 210 19001 #041-13-1978 L1979 **U** *020 †95

DAGO-OC, Joseph Rey Cheng. 1200 YORK RD, ABINGTON MEMORIAL HOSPITAL 19001 #748-02-2005 L2007 **IM** *012

DAY, Harvey James. 1200 OLD YORK RD, ROSENFELD CANCER CENTER 19001 #041-09-1953 L1954 **HEM ON** *071 †20

DEE, Robert Raymond. 1235 OLD YORK RD, ASSOCIATES IN INFECTIOUS 19001 #041-13-1981 L1982 **ID** *030 †20

DEGAPUDI, Bhargavi. 1200 OLD YORK RD, DEPT OF MED EDU 19001 #495-65-2002 L2005 **IM** *012

DHAND, Monica. ■ 19001 #041-13-2007 *012

DHANKECHA, Hemant Vallabh. 1200 YORK RD, ABINGTON MEMORIAL HOSPITAL 19001 #495-22-1997 L2007 **GS** *012

DIDUSZYN, Jorge Maria. 1245 HIGHLAND AVE, STE 302 19001 #132-01-1996 L2002 **IMG** *020 †20

DINAKAR, Satishchandra. 1200 YORK RD, DEPT OF INTERNAL MED 19001 #495-04-2001 L2003 **IM** *100 †20

DIZON, Ruben Ong. ■ 19001 #748-08-1991 L1995 **IM** *100

DOMERACKI, Frank Robt. 1200 OLD YORK RD 19001 #041-13-1987 L1988 **DR IM** *020 †20,80

DORMONT, Paul John. 1245 HIGHLAND AVE 19001 #041-01-1967 L1968 **P OS** *020

DUBOW, Scott Ryan. ■ 19001 #041-01-2001 L2003 **AN** *012 †55

EDELSON, Mitchell Ira. 1200 OLD YORK RD, RCC 1-W 19001 #041-02-1991 L1997 **GO** *020 †30

EDIAE, Jude Osaretin. 1200 OLD YORK RD, ABINGTON MEMORIAL HOSPITAL 19001 #690-06-1999 L2006 **IM** *012

EDO-OHONBA, Osaze. 1200 OLD YORK RD, ABINGTON MEM HOSP 19001 #690-06-1998 L2005 **IM** *012

EINHORN, Kenneth Howard. 1245 HIGHLAND AVE, OTOLARYNGOLOGY ASSOCIATES 19001 #010-02-1983 L1989 **OTO** *020 †45

EISENSTAEDT, Richard Saml. 1200 OLD YORK RD, STE 2B 19001 #016-11-1973 L1978 **HEM IM** *040 †20

EKIZIAN, Stephanie H. 1200 OLD YORK RD 19001 #033-05-1994 L1997 **IM** *020 †20

ELLISON, Richard T, Jr. 1200 OLD YORK RD 19001 #051-01-1952 L1952 **PD** *072 †55

ESKIN, David Joel. 1235 OLD YORK RD STE 222 19001 #041-01-1967 L1968 **CD** *071 †20

FARIS, Mary Rachel. 1200 OLD YORK RD, STE 1W 19001 #041-02-1979 L1995 **ON HEM** *020 †20

FASSLER, Steven Adam. 1235 OLD YORK RD, STE G20 19001 #041-13-1995 L2001 **CRS** *020 †85,10

FETCHO, Carole Louise. 1245 HIGHLAND AVE, STE 104 19001 #041-13-1964 L1965 **EM OM** *020 †16

FIERSTEIN, Jeffrey S. 1200 OLD YORK RD 19001 #041-01-1977 L1979 **CD IM** *020 †20

FIREMAN, Andrew Scott. 1235 OLD YORK RD, STE 222 19001 #041-02-1988 L1990 **CD** *020 †20

FISHER, Steven Frederick. 1200 OLD YORK RD, ABINGTON MEMORIAL HOSPITAL 19001 #025-01-1998 L2004 **EM** *020 †16

FLICKINGER, Haviland. 1200 OLD YORK RD 19001 #041-02-1956 L1957 **AN PME** *071 †05

FRANK, Robert L. 1200 OLD YORK RD 19001 #041-02-1953 L1959 **OPH** *071 †35

FRANKEL, Arthur Mark. 1200 OLD YORK RD 19001 #041-13-1978 L1979 **GS** *020 †85

FRIEDENHEIM, Richard E. 1235 OLD YORK RD, ABINGTON PULMONARY & 19001 #041-01-1988 L1990 **PUD CCM** *020 †20

GABLE, Sundee Lynn. 1400 OLD YORK RD, STE A 19001 #016-06-1997 L1999 **IM** *020 †20

GALLAGHER, Sidhbh. 1200 YORK RD, ABINGTON MEMORIAL HOSPITAL 19001 #539-04-2006 L2007 **GS** *012

GARZA, Mary B. 1200 OLD YORK RD, CHOP CONNECTION-1 HIGHLAND 19001 #041-01-1999 L2001 **PD** *020 †55

GEORGE, Eric. 1550 OLD YORK RD 19001 #041-09-1991 L1997 **OPH** *020 †35

GEWIRTZMAN, Steven Mark. 1200 OLD YORK RD 19001 #035-19-1984 L1987 **PD** *020 †55

GLASER, Barry Louis. 1200 OLD YORK RD 19001 #041-09-1964 L1965 **GS** *020 †85 ‡

GLASS, Kristen Marie. ■ 19001 #041-12-2003 L2003 **NPM** *012 †55,20

GLIJANSKY, Alex. 1579 OLD YORK RD 19001 #935-01-1917 **P** *020 †75 ‡

GLOWACKI, Stanley James. 1200 OLD YORK RD 19001 #041-07-1988 L1994 **AN** *020 †05

GOEL, Jaya. 1200 OLD YORK RD, DEPT OF MEDICINE 19001 #495-41-1996 L2005 **IM** *100 †20

GOLDHAHN, Richard T, Jr. 1200 OLD YORK RD, ABINGTON MEM HOSP 19001 #041-13-1964 L1965 **PTH DMP** *020 †50

GOLDSTEIN, Richard Allan. 1235 OLD YORK RD, SUITE 222 LEVY MEDICAL PLA 19001 #041-14-1975 L1994 **CD NM** *020 †20

GONZALEZ, Eric Humberto. 1200 OLD YORK RD 19001 #041-02-1983 L1984 **EM** *020 †16

GOODMAN, David Alan. 1200 OLD YORK RD DEPT ANES 19001 #041-02-1983 L1984 **AN** *020 †05

GOODMAN, Katy Elizabeth. ■ 19001 #041-02-2005 L2005 **FP** *012

GOODMAN, Matthew Aron. 1200 OLD YORK RD 19001 #041-13-1995 L1997 **IM** *020 †20

GORE, Ashwini Prabhakar. 1200 YORK RD, DEPT OF INTERNAL MED 19001 #496-42-2002 L2003 **IM** *100 †20

GOTTLIEB, Charles David. 1235 OLD YORK RD, STE 222 19001 #041-01-1981 L1983 **CD IM** *040 †20

GREEN, George Raymond. 1235 OLD YORK RD, STE 110 19001 #041-01-1962 L1964 **AI IM** *020 †03,20

GREENBERG, Richard Evan. 1235 OLD YORK RD, STE 210 19001 #035-20-1976 L1982 **U** *020 †95

GREENBERG, Vivian N. 1245 HIGHLAND AVE, STE 505 19001 #025-07-1980 L1981 **GYN** *020 †30

GRIFFITH, Annette Y. 1200 YORK RD, ABINGTON MEMORIAL HOSPITAL 19001 #035-08-1976 L1984 **DR** *020 †20,80,28 ‡

GROSSMAN, Linda Beth. 1235 OLD YORK RD, STE 222 19001 #041-13-1994 L1997 **CD** *020 †20

GROSSMAN, Sheila Servetz. 1200 OLD YORK RD 19001 #041-02-1986 L1987 **FM** *020 †18

GRUENER, Daniel M. 1128 OLD YORK RD 19001 #654-01-1984 L1990 **PME P** *020 †75

GUJJA, Deepa. 1200 OLD YORK RD, ABINGTON MEMORIAL HOSPITAL 19001 #496-66-2004 L2006 **IM** *012

HANBY, Forwood Evans. 1200 OLD YORK RD, 4 HIGHLAND BLDG - AMH 19001 #041-01-1959 L1960 **R RO** *071 †80

HANJANI, Parviz. 1200 OLD YORK RD, 1 WIDENER 19001 #517-01-1965 L1978 **GO** *020 †30

HARKINS, F Thomas. 1200 OLD YORK RD 19001 #041-09-1990 L1998 **EM** *020 †16

HARPER, Steven Gary. 1235 OLD YORK RD, STE G20 19001 #041-13-1983 L1984 **CRS** *020 †85,10

HARRIS, Lee James. 1245 HIGHLAND AVE, STE 401 19001 #035-46-1984 L1989 **N CN** *020 †75

HARVEY, Edith Elizabeth. 1200 OLD YORK RD 19001 #041-01-1938 L1941 **OPH** *071

HASSEY, Joseph Anthony. 1235 OLD YORK RD, ASSOCIATES IN INFECTIOUS 19001 #041-13-1991 L1994 **IM ID** *020 †20

HERBERT, Scott Howard. 1200 OLD YORK RD, ABINGTON MEMORIAL 19001 #035-19-1987 L1988 **RO IM** *020 †80

HERRERA DE JUANA, Santiago. 1200 YORK RD 19001 #649-13-2003 L2005 **GS** *012

HETZEL, Christine M. 1235 OLD YORK RD, STE 222 19001 #041-13-1995 L1997 **IM** *020 †20

HIRSHBERG, Steven Jay. 1235 OLD YORK RD, STE 210 19001 #024-05-1991 L1993 **U** *020 †95

HOFMANN, Mary Mc Loone. 1245 HIGHLAND AVE 19001 #041-13-1988 L1990 **IMG** *020 †20

HOLLINGER, Mary Katherine. ■ 19001 #041-02-2003 L2003 **AN** *100

HOPE, Paul Ronald. 1200 OLD YORK RD, ABINGTON MEMORIAL HOSP 19001 #041-14-1989 L1993 **EM** *020 †16

HOPKINSON, John H, III. 1245 HIGHLAND AVE, STE 106 19001 #041-13-1960 L1961 **OBG** *020 †30

HORMAN, Marc Joel. 1200 OLD YORK RD 19001 #041-09-1966 L1967 **PUD IM** *020

HORNER, Daniel Warren, Jr. 1235 OLD YORK RD, STE 110 19001 #041-02-1963 L1964 **CD IM** *020 †20

HORVATH, David Addis. 1245 HIGHLAND AVE, STE G05 19001 #041-02-1990 L1993 PS *020 †85,65

HORVICK, David. 1200 OLD YORK RD, ABINGTON MEMORIAL 19001 #041-02-1982 L1984 RO *020 †80

HUCK, George Francis. 1200 OLD YORK RD 19001 #041-13-1954 L1955 PTH *072 †50

IDAHOSA, Osamudiamen. 1200 OLD YORK RD 19001 #690-06-1999 L2004 IM *100 †20

IZES, Joseph Keith. 1245 HIGHLAND AVE STE G- 19001 #041-02-1986 L1987 U *020 †95

JACOBSTEIN, Jerome Geo. 1200 OLD YORK RD 19001 #041-01-1967 L1982 NM *020 †28

JAGADEESH, Simha Vivek. 1200 OLD YORK RD, DEPT OF INTERNAL MEDICINE 19001 #495-37-2001 L2004 IM *100 †20

JAGEN, Cynthia Eve. 1200 OLD YORK RD 19001 #035-19-2002 L2005 IM *020 †20

JALIL, Lilian Lucinda. 1235 OLD YORK RD, STE 113 19001 #035-19-1996 L1998 IM *020 †20

JAMIAS, Augusto Angel Gar. 1200 OLD YORK RD 19001 #748-10-2000 L2003 GS *012

JAN, Muhammad Fuad. 1200 OLD YORK RD 19001 #495-51-2000 L2002 IM *020 †20

JOHNSEN, Hege. 1200 YORK RD, DEPT OF GEN SURG 19001 #473-02-2003 L2006 GS *012

JOHNSON, Heather Marie. 1200 OLD YORK RD DEPT FAM 19001 #041-02-1997 FM *100

JOSLOFF, Robert Kevin. 1200 OLD YORK RD 19001 #041-02-1989 L1991 GS *020 †85

JUBELIRER, Robert Alan. 1200 OLD YORK RD 19001 #041-13-1980 L1981 GS VS *020 †85 ‡

KARUR, Vinit Gopal. 1200 OLD YORK RD, ABINGTON MEMORIAL 19001 #495-23-2000 L2006 IM *030

KELLY, John Jos. 1235 OLD YORK RD, ASSOCIATES IN INFECTIOUS 19001 #024-07-1977 L1983 ID IM *030

KELSO, Don Robt. 1245 HIGHLAND AVE STE 103 19001 #041-13-1958 L1959 CRS GS *020 †85

KENNEDY, Tara Lynn. ■ 19001 #041-02-2004 L2004 GS *012

KENWORTHY, Harry Jos. 1235 OLD YORK RD, STE 222 19001 #041-09-1961 L1962 IM *020 †20

KIDWELL, Kendel Grant. 1200 OLD YORK RD, DEPT EMERGENCY MEDICINE 19001 #038-40-1980 L1986 EM *020 †16

KIM, Hans Young. 1200 OLD YORK RD, DEPT OF RADIOLOGY 19001 #035-03-1999 L1999 DR *100 †80 ‡

KIMBALL, Randall Mark. ■ 19001 #035-03-2007 L2007 GS *012

KISH, Karen Jean. 1200 OLD YORK RD 19001 #041-15-2003 L2003 GS *012

KISHAN, Channarayapatna V. 1200 OLD YORK RD 19001 #495-09-1995 L1999 CD IC *020 †20

KLEBACK, John Michael, III. 1200 OLD YORK RD 19001 #041-15-1999 L2001 PD *020 †55 ‡

KLOTZ, Roy Gilbert. 1200 YORK RD DPT PATH 19001 #041-13-1957 L1958 PTH *020 †50

KLUGHERZ, Bruce Douglas. 1235 OLD YORK RD, STE 222 19001 #036-07-1992 L1994 CD *020 †20

KOLFF, Jeffrey Willem. 1245 HIGHLAND AVE STE 600 19001 #038-06-1999 L2001 GS *020 †85

KOLLROS, Peter Richard. 1917 GUERNSEY AVE, ABINGTON PEDIATRIC NEURO 19001 #016-02-1982 L1988 CHN *020 †55,75

KONERU, Kalyana Chakravar. 1200 OLD YORK RD, ABINGTON MEMORIAL 19001 #496-24-2001 L2006 IM *012

KOSTACOS, Emanuel James. 1235 OLD YORK RD STE 222, ABINGTON MEDICAL SPECIALIS 19001 #035-01-1998 L2001 CD *020 †20

KRAVITZ, Bernard Jos. 1200 OLD YORK RD 19001 #041-01-1961 L1962 IM *020 †20

KUKORA, John Steven. 1245 HIGHLAND AVE STE 305 19001 #025-01-1973 L1984 GS *030 †85

LAMBERG, Randy Evan. 1200 OLD YORK RD 19001 #041-09-1983 L1985 AN *020 †05

LATTA, Richard Andrew. 1235 OLD YORK RD, STE 119 19001 #041-07-1986 L1988 OBG MFM *020 †30

LAVY, Alexandra. ■ 19001 #550-01-1975 L1984 *100

LEE, Melissa Quynh. 1235 OLD YORK RD STE G10 19001 #041-13-2002 L2002 IM *020 †20

LEVETTE, Andrew R, Jr. 1200 OLD YORK RD, ABINGTON MEM HOSP DPT ANES 19001 #010-03-1983 L1985 AN CCM *020 †05

LOBANOV, Pavel Vladimirov. 1200 YORK RD, ABINGTON MEM HOSP 19001 #913-32-1998 L2004 AN *012

LUCENTE, Vincent R. 1200 OLD YORK RD 19001 #035-48-1985 L1993 GYN OS *020 †30 ‡

LYNCH, Joseph Michael. 1200 OLD YORK RD 19001 #041-13-1972 L1986 ID IM *050 †20

MACKEY, Amy M. 1200 OLD YORK RD, ABINGTON PRIMARY WOMEN'S H 19001 #041-13-1996 L1999 OBG *020 †30

MALLAVARAPU, Vamshi Krish. 1200 YORK RD, DEPT OF INTERNAL MED 19001 #496-01-2001 L2003 IM *100 †20

MALONEY, Donald W. ■ 19001 #041-01-1952 L1953 IM PUD *071 †20 ‡

MANCHIKALAPUDI, Rama Bind. 1200 OLD YORK RD 19001 #495-50-2003 L2006 IM *012

MANDA, Yugandhar Reddy. 1200 YORK RD, ABINGTON MEMORIAL HOSPITAL 19001 #495-21-2001 L2007 IM *012

MANN, Denise Lynn. 1200 OLD YORK RD, DEPT OF ANESTHESIA 19001 #041-01-1986 L1987 AN *020 †05

MARGARIDA, Leopoldo E. ■ 19001 #035-20-1950 L1954 DR *071 †80

MATEO, Michael Glenn. 1200 OLD YORK RD, 1ST FLOOR RORER BLDG 19001 #033-06-1987 L1988 AN IM *020 †05 ‡

MATHERS, Keith Jeffrey. 1200 OLD YORK RD STE 2B, ABINGTON MEMORIAL HOSPITAL 19001 #041-02-2006 L2006 OPH *012

MC DONALD, Thos Alexander. 1200 OLD YORK RD 19001 #041-13-1977 L1978 OBG *020 †30

MC GARVEY, Marguerite L. 1200 OLD YORK RD 19001 #041-02-2002 L2002 RHU *020 †20

MC LAUGHLIN, Jason Ryan. 1200 OLD YORK RD, TRAUMA CENTER 19001 #041-15-1999 L2006 EM *020 †16

MC MULLEN, Paul David. 1200 OLD YORK RD, EMER MEDICINE 19001 #035-48-1990 L1992 EM *020 †16,20

MEDWAY, Marc Jay. 1200 OLD YORK RD 19001 #041-02-1977 L1978 PM *020 †60

MERCADER, Luis. 1200 OLD YORK RD, ANESTHESIA DEPARTMENT 19001 #042-01-1988 L1991 AN *071 †05

MERCURIO, Eduardo. 1200 OLD YORK RD 19001 #010-01-2003 L2003 OBG *020

MILLER, Alan Edward. 1200 OLD YORK RD STE 2B, ABINGTON MEMORIAL HOSPITAL 19001 #005-19-2004 L2004 PM *012

MILLER, Audrey Frances. 1245 HIGHLAND AVE, STE 505 19001 #025-01-1991 L2007 OBG *020 †30

MINO, Robert D. 1245 HIGHLAND AVE STE G03 19001 #010-02-1981 L1987 U OS *020 †95

MINTER, Catherine L. 1200 OLD YORK RD 19001 #028-78-2007, ▲ L2007 OBG *012

MISHEL, Henry Stuart. 1235 OLD YORK RD, ABINGTON PULMONARY & 19001 #041-09-1974 L1975 PCC IM *020 †20

MISHRA, Richa. 1200 YORK RD 19001 #495-41-2004 L2006 IM *012

MITCHELL, Christina Marie. ■ 19001 #041-02-2005 L2005 IM *012

MOGHBELPOUR, May Chinmaye. 1200 YORK RD, ABINGTON MEMORIAL HOSPITAL 19001 #672-02-2003 L2007 IM *012

MOLINARI, Wm John, Jr. 1200 OLD YORK RD 19001 #041-02-1968 L1969 AN *020 †05

MOORE, James Thos. 1208 HIGHLAND AVE 19001 #041-07-1980 L1981 GS TRS *020 †85

MORAGIANNI, Vasiliki A. ■ 19001 #041-15-2005 L2005 OBG *012

MUDY, Karol. 1200 YORK RD, ABINGTON MEMORIAL HOSPITAL 19001 #759-10-2004 L2007 GS *012

MUSHO, Michael A. 1235 OLD YORK RD STE G10 19001 #041-09-1987 L1988 IM *020 †20

MUTTREJA, Manoj Rana. 1235 OLD YORK RD, STE 222 19001 #041-01-1995 L1997 CD *020 †20

NEFT, Evan Edward. ■ 19001 #035-47-2008 L2008 *012

NEIMOLLER, Ulrich Marcus. 1235 OLD YORK RD, SUITE 222, LEVY MEDICAL PL 19001 #409-32-1987 L1996 IM *020 †20

NEJMAN, Joseph Henry. 1235 OLD YORK RD STE G20 19001 #041-13-1979 L1980 CRS GS *020 †10,85

NELSON, Michael Jay. 1200 OLD YORK RD, DEPT EM 19001 #041-02-1995 L2005 EM *020 †16

NEWMAN, Seth Louis. 1200 OLD YORK RD 19001 #041-13-1997 L2000 GS *020 †85

NIEMAN, Roger Elsworth. 1235 OLD YORK RD, ASSOCIATES IN INFECTIOUS 19001 #023-07-1973 L1977 ID IM *020 †20

NUSSBAUM, Michael Lynn. 1208 HIGHLAND AVE 19001 #017-20-1982 L1987 GS AS *020 †85

O'CONNELL, Brendan G. 1200 OLD YORK RD, ABINGTON MEMORIAL HOSPITAL 19001 #041-13-2003 L2003 GS *012

O'GRADY, Timothy John. 1200 OLD YORK RD 19001 #033-06-1986 L1987 AN PME *020 †05

OLKEN, Mark David. 1200 OLD YORK RD, 4 HIGHLAND BLDG - AMH 19001 #024-07-1958 L1962 DR *071 †80

OLOFSSON, Beatrix Astrid. ■ 19001 #041-15-2007 L2007 IM *012

ONIFER, Theodore Michael. 1200 OLD YORK RD 19001 #041-13-1948 L1950 IMG IM *071

OPATT, Diane Mary. 1245 HIGHLAND AVE STE 604 19001 #041-13-2000 L2005 GS *020 †85 ‡

ORMAN, Jack Morton. 1200 YORK RD 19001 #041-01-1937 L1938 GP *071

OSINUSI, Olukemi Abimbola. 1200 OLD YORK RD 19001 #690-01-2001 L2005 IM *012

OSTRUM-PAUL, Phyllis. ■ 19001 #041-09-1950 L1951 IM *071

PAK, Ho. 1584 OLD YORK RD 19001 #041-13-1993 L1995 GS *020 †85

PANDIT, Srijana Pradhan. 1200 YORK RD, ABINGTON MEM HSP 19001 #672-02-2002 L2008 *100

PANDIT, Trailokya Nath. 1200 YORK RD, ABINGTON MEMORIAL HOSPITAL 19001 #672-02-2003 L2007 IM *012

PANSE, Sagar Jayant. 1200 YORK RD, DEPT OF INTERNAL MED 19001 #496-42-2002 L2003 NEP *012 †20

PARSONS, Richard E. 1200 OLD YORK RD, ABINGTON MEMORIAL HOSPITAL 19001 #041-13-1987 L1992 VS *020 †85

PASUPULETI, Sundeep. 1200 OLD YORK RD, DEPT OF MEDICINE 19001 #495-62-2000 L2003 IM *100 †20

PATEL, Rajni Bhakhabhai. 1200 OLD YORK RD 19001 #495-22-1981 L1990 PD *020 †55 ‡

PAUL, Gerson S. ■ 19001 #041-09-1949 L1950 OBG *071 †30

PEFF, Ann Bowling. 1245 HIGHLAND AVE 19001 #051-01-1978 L1987 IM *040 †20

PELEG, David. 1200 OLD YORK RD, STE 109 19001 #550-01-1990 L2006 OBG *012

PENDLETON, James Lowrie. 1245 HIGHLAND AVE STE 208 19001 #041-01-1957 L1958 P *071 †75

PENNER, Gary Edward. 1200 OLD YORK RD, ABINGTON MEMORIAL HOSPITAL 19001 #041-02-1995 L1997 EM *020 †16

PERNYESZI, Gabor, Jr. ■ 19001 #008-02-2006 L2006 FP *012

PERRY, Bethany Lynn. 1200 OLD YORK RD, MOB 206 19001 #041-13-1997 L2000 OBG *020 †30

PETROV, Mihail Todorov. 1200 OLD YORK RD 19001 #198-01-1986 L2002 AN *100

PETRUCCI, William Gary. 1235 OLD YORK RD, STE 222 19001 #041-09-1982 L1983 CD IM *020 †20

PEZZI, Christopher M. 1245 HIGHLAND AVE, STE 604 19001 #041-02-1982 L1983 SO GS *020 †85

PEZZI, Pio Julius. 1208 HIGHLAND AVE 19001 #561-17-1953 L1959 GS ORS *071 †85

PIELEANU, Adrian. 1200 YORK RD, ABINGTON MEMORIAL HOSPITAL 19001 #781-01-2004 L2007 IM *012

PIELEANU, Irina. 1200 YORK RD, ABINGTON MEMORIAL HOSPITAL 19001 #781-01-2004 L2007 IM *012

PILLA, Thomas Edward. 1200 OLD YORK RD 19001 #041-02-1944 L1945 IM OS *072

POKORNY, John Henry. 1245 HIGHLAND AVE, STE G05 19001 #286-13-1971 L1992 PS *071 †65

POKORNY, Kelli Brown. 1200 OLD YORK RD, CHIEF OF STAFF OFFICE 19001 #041-13-2000 L2001 DR *020 †80

POLAVARAPU, Harsha Vineet. 1200 YORK RD, ABINGTON MEMORIAL HOSPITAL 19001 #495-58-2003 L2007 GS *012

POLIN, Joel Ian. 1200 OLD YORK RD, # 109 19001 #041-13-1961 L1962 OBG MFM *030 †30 ‡

POSATKO, Barbara Anne. 1200 OLD YORK RD, ABINGTON HOSP DEPT ANES 19001 #041-13-1980 L1981 AN *020 †05

PRAMICK, Michelle Renee. ■ 19001 #041-02-2007 L2007 IM *012

RAMACHANDRAN, Swetha. 1200 OLD YORK RD, ABINGTON MEMORIAL HOSPITAL 19001 #496-21-2003 L2006 IM *012

RAMZAN, Zeeshan. 1200 YORK RD, DEPT OF INTERNAL MED 19001 #704-01-2000 L2003 IM *100 †20

REDMOND, John, III. 1200 OLD YORK RD, STE 1W 19001 #012-05-1974 L1990 ON HEM *020 †20

REED, Conrad C. 1235 OLD YORK RD, ABINGTON PULMONARY & 19001 #409-21-1989 L1998 PCC *020 †20

REESE, Walter David. 1200 OLD YORK RD 19001 #041-13-1946 L1947 GYN *071 †20

REGAN, Lora S. 1245 HIGHLAND AVE, STE 106 19001 #005-14-1985 L1993 OM IM *020 †20,70

REICHARD, Rita A. 1200 OLD YORK RD, ABINGTON MEM HOSP 19001 #041-13-1991 L1994 IMG *020 †20

REILLY, Eugene Francis. 1200 OLD YORK RD, DEPT OF SURGERY, AMH 19001 #041-02-2002 L2002 GS *100 ‡

RENDON, Roberto. 1245 HIGHLAND AVE 19001 #429-01-1955 L1968 N PN *071 †55

RESTREPO JARAMILLO, Ricard. 1200 OLD YORK RD 19001 #264-13-2000 IM *012

REZVANI, Masoud. 1200 YORK RD, ABINGTON MEM HOSP 19001 #517-12-2002 L2004 GS *012

RICHTER, Melvyn Paul. 1200 OLD YORK RD 19001 #041-09-1971 L1975 RO *020 †80

ROEDIGER, Paul Margerum. 1200 YORK RD, DIXON BLDG 19001 #041-02-1958 L1959 IM *071 †20

ROSENBERG, Manuel. 1200 OLD YORK RD, DEPT OF MEDICINE 19001 #041-13-1977 L1978 ID IM *020 †20

ROSENFELD, Philip Allan. 1245 HIGHLAND AVE, OTOLARYNGOLOGY ASSOCIATES 19001 #041-02-1967 L1968 OTO *020 †45

ROSENN, Marc Frederick. 1235 OLD YORK RD STE 119 19001 #035-47-1984 L1986 OBG MFM *020 †30

■ = Address Information Privacy Protected

ROSENTHAL, Ronald Stanley. 1235 OLD YORK RD, STE 210 19001 #041-13-1964 L1965 **U** *071 †95

RUTH, Miriam Christina. ■ 19001 #003-01-2007 L2007 **OBG** *012

SAI, Karthikeyan. 1200 YORK RD 19001 #495-70-2001 L2005 **IM** *012

SAMAHA, A Michael, Jr. 1235 OLD YORK RD, STE 210 19001 #024-05-1984 L1986 **GS U** *020 †95

SANDSTROM, Frank Theo, Jr. 1245 HIGHLAND AVE 19001 #041-13-1970 L1971 **OBG** *020 †30

SANKINENI, Abhinav. 1200 YORK RD, ABINGTON MEM HSP 19001 #496-74-2006 L2008 *012

SASSO, Philip John. 1200 OLD YORK RD, DEPARTMENT OF ANESTHESIOLO 19001 #041-02-1988 L1990 **AN** *020 †20,05

SCHINFELD, Jay Scott. 1245 HIGHLAND AVE STE 601 19001 #041-02-1974 L1986 **CCP REN** *020 †30

SCHMUTZLER, Robert Carl, III. 1200 OLD YORK RD 19001 #041-13-1965 L1966 **GS** *020 †85 ‡

SCHNEIDER, Doron. 1200 OLD YORK RD, DEPT OF MEDICINE 19001 #033-05-1994 L1997 **IM** *020 †20

SCHRAGER, Ralph M. 1200 OLD YORK RD, ABINGTON MEMORIAL HOSP 19001 #041-01-1983 L1985 **PD NPM** *020 †55

SCHRECK, Roger Irvin. ■ 19001 #038-06-1984 L1985 **PTH IM** *020 †20,50

SCHWARTZ, Joel. 1245 HIGHLAND AVE STE 202 19001 #041-09-1965 L1966 **P CHP** *030 †75

SCHWARTZ, Laurence Milton. 1245 HIGHLAND AVE, STE 403A 19001 #041-01-1961 L1962 **P** *020 †75

SHAH, Pranav Punyadhan. 1200 YORK RD, DEPT OF INTERNAL MED 19001 #495-23-2002 L2004 **IM** *100 †20

SHAHIN, Mark Shahram. 1200 OLD YORK RD, ROSENFIELD CANER CTR 19001 #016-06-1993 L2001 **OBG GO** *020 †30

SHAIKH, Asif Mohammed. 1208 HIGHLAND AVE 19001 #496-38-1994 L2001 **HO** *100 †20

SHETH, Nirav Gopalbhai. 1200 YORK RD, ABINGTON MEM HOSP 19001 #495-23-2002 L2005 **IM** *012

SHIBUTANI, Yasushi F. 1235 OLD YORK RD, STE 210 19001 #035-01-1987 L1989 **U** *020 †95

SHIH, Yu-Chen. 1200 OLD YORK RD STE 2B, ABINGTON MEMORIAL HOSPITAL 19001 #244-04-2004 **IM** *012

SHILDKROUT, Kenneth. 1200 OLD YORK RD 19001 #035-03-1985 L1989 **EM ESM** *020 †16

SHRESTHA, Ruby. ■ 19001 #041-02-2005 L2005 **OBG** *012

SHRIVASTAVA, Aseem. 1200 YORK RD, ABINGTON MEM HOSP 19001 #672-03-2002 L2005 **IM** *012

SILVER, Deborah Lee. 1200 OLD YORK RD # 4H, ABINGTON MEMORIAL HOSP 19001 #035-19-1989 L1993 **PD** *020 †55

SILVERMAN, Stanley Philip. 1235 OLD YORK RD, ABINGTON PULMONARY & 19001 #041-09-1982 L1984 **PUD IM** *020 †20

SINGH, Vijay. 1200 YORK RD, DEPT OF INTERNAL MED 19001 #495-37-2001 L2004 **RHU** *012 †20

SLAVIN, James Wm. 1200 OLD YORK RD 19001 #038-06-1966 L1971 **PS** *020 †65

SMITH, David Gary. 1200 OLD YORK RD 19001 #041-13-1977 L1982 **IM** *020 †20

SMITH, Stephen John. 1235 OLD YORK RD, STE 119 19001 #033-05-1988 L1990 **MFM** *020 †30 ‡

SMYSER, Linda Mansfield. 1200 OLD YORK RD, 1ST FLOOR HIGHLAND BLDG 19001 #028-34-1985 L1987 **PD** *020 †55

SOMKUTI, Stephen Geo. 1245 HIGHLAND AVE, REPRODUCTIVE MEDICINE 19001 #036-01-1989 L1995 **OBG** *020 †30

SOOD, Geetika Nisha. 1235 OLD YORK RD, ASSOCIATES IN INFECTIOUS 19001 #041-13-1996 L2000 **ID** *020 †20

SPIRITOS, Michael David. 1200 OLD YORK RD, ROSENFELD CANCER CENTER 19001 #035-20-1983 L1987 **HEM ON** *020 †20

STEPHENS, Paul, Jr. 1309 HIGHLAND AVE 19001 #036-07-1983 L1987 **PDC PD** *020 †55

STERNSCHUSS, Gina. ■ 19001 #913-48-1997 L2005 **OBG** *012

STROBOS, Eben Heathcliff. 1200 YORK RD 19001 #550-02-2005 L2005 **GS** *012

SULLIVAN, Theodore Robert. 1245 HIGHLAND AVE 600, ABINGTON HOSPITAL OFFICE B 19001 #041-13-1988 L1990 **VS** *020 †85

SURYADEVARA, Sree Kiran. ■ 19001 #894-01-2001 L2005 **GS** *012

SWE, Nandar Min. 1200 YORK RD, DEPT OF INTERNAL MED 19001 #209-01-2001 L2004 **IM** *100

TANEL, Ronn Eli. 1200 OLD YORK RD 19001 #011-02-1988 L1998 **PDC NPM** *020 †55

TANGRI, Sabrena Kumari. 1200 OLD YORK RD STE 2B, ABINGTON MEMORIAL HOSPITAL 19001 #661-03-2005 L2006 **IM** *012

TEICH, Stephen Michael. 1235 OLD YORK RD 19001 #035-08-1978 L1983 **CD IM** *020 †20

TEY, Steven. 1200 OLD YORK RD, DEPARTMENT OF RADIOLOGY 19001 #035-19-1991 L1997 **VIR** *020 †80

TIJANI, Lukman Aderoju. 1200 OLD YORK RD 19001 #690-02-1988 L2001 **HO** *012 †20 ‡

TOLL, Norma Spear. 1200 OLD YORK RD 19001 #041-13-1982 L1985 **CHP P** *020

TOPPUR RAMANAKUMAR, Ajay. 1200 YORK RD, DEPT OF INTERNAL MED 19001 #496-21-2003 L2005 *012

TUMPATI, Prabhakara Rao. 1200 YORK RD, DEPT OF INTERNAL MED 19001 #495-21-1997 L2004 **IM** *100 †20

TURK, Adam Theodore. 1200 OLD YORK RD 19001 #051-04-1981 L1982 **FM** *020 †18

UDAYASANKAR, Jayalakshmi. 1200 OLD YORK RD, ABINGTON MEMORIAL HOSPITAL 19001 #495-59-1995 L2001 **END** *012 †20

URFFER, Paul Allen. 1200 OLD YORK RD, DEPT RAD 19001 #041-01-1961 L1962 **R OS** *071 †80

VACHRANUKUNKIET, T. 1200 OLD YORK RD 19001 #891-01-1970 L1973 **PM** *020 †60

VALENTI, Salvatore M. 1200 YORK RD 19001 #041-13-1967 L1968 **PTH** *020 †50

VALENTINE, John Howard. 1200 OLD YORK RD 19001 #041-01-1967 L1968 **P** *020 †75

VANGA, Amaresh Reddy. 1200 OLD YORK RD, DEPT OF INTERNAL MED 19001 #495-65-2000 L2002 **IM** *100 †20

VAN SCOTT, Eugene Jos. ■ 19001 #016-02-1948 L1968 **D OS** *071 †15

VAVA, Mihaela V. 1200 OLD YORK RD, DEPT OF RADIOLOGY 19001 #781-06-1993 L2001 **DR** *020 †80

VEERAPUTHIRAN, Muthu Kuma. 1200 OLD YORK RD, ABINGTON MEM HOSP 19001 #495-16-2003 L2005 **IM** *012

VOGEL, Eric William. 1200 OLD YORK RD, C/O DREXEL UNIVERSITY COM 19001 #041-07-1994 L1996 **IM** *040 †20

WAGMAN, Albert D. 1245 HIGHLAND AVE, STE 401 19001 #041-01-1953 L1954 **N SME** *020 †75

WALDFOGEL, Shimon S. 1245 HIGHLAND AVE STE 308, ABINGTON MEMORIAL HOSP 19001 #550-04-1984 L1986 **P PYG** *075 †75

WATSON, Robert A, III. 1235 OLD YORK RD, STE 222 19001 #020-02-1982 L1985 **CD IM** *020 †20

WAY, Deborah Jane. 1200 OLD YORK RD, ABINGTON MEMORIAL HOSPITAL 19001 #041-13-2001 L2001 **IMG** *020 †20

WEINTRAUB, William Henry. 1245 HIGHLAND AVE, STE 604 19001 #024-01-1964 L1979 **PDS** *020 †85

WEISS, Richard David. 1200 OLD YORK RD 19001 #041-13-1965 L1966 **R NM** *020 †80

WEISS, Steven Joshua. 1245 HIGHLAND AVE STE 105 19001 #041-07-1980 L1981 **TS** *020 †90,85

WERNER, Dean Richard. 1200 OLD YORK RD, ANESTHESIA ASSOCIATES OF A 19001 #041-13-2000 L2001 **AN** *020 †05

WILMOTH, Jason Gordon. 1245 HIGHLAND AVE, OTOLARYNGOLOGY ASSOCIATES 19001 #041-02-1996 L2001 **OTO** *020 †45

WU, Cheryl Tsailuen. 1200 OLD YORK RD, ABINGTON MEMORIAL HOSPITAL 19001 #033-05-2003 L2003 **PD** *020 †55

YARLAGADDA, Madhavi. 1200 OLD YORK RD, ABINGTON MEM HOSP 19001 #495-21-2003 L2005 **IM** *012

YAZMAJIAN, Dina Rosa. 1235 OLD YORK RD, STE 222 19001 #035-19-1989 L1991 **CD** *020 †20

ZAKRZEWSKI, Kevin Michael. 1235 OLD YORK RD, STE 113 19001 #041-02-1988 L1990 **IM** *020 †20

ZEBLEY, David Mark. 1235 OLD YORK RD, STE G20 19001 #041-13-1989 L1992 **CRS** *020 †85,10

ZHANG, Zhongyu. 1245 HIGHLAND AVE, STE 207 19001 #243-45-1983 L1996 **PM** *020 †60

ZINMAN, Raezelle. 1309 HIGHLAND AVE 19001 #067-01-1973 L1998 **PDP** *020

ACME – WESTMORELAND

MC LEOD, Roderick R. ■ 15610 #060-01-1951 L1957 **P** *072 †75

AKRON – LANCASTER

JACKSON, T Scott. 101 S 7TH ST 17501 #039-05-1982 L1983 **FM** *020 †18

SHAFER, Virginia Ella E. 101 S 7TH ST, CONESTOGA FAMILY PRACTICE 17501 #041-13-1980 L1981 **EM** *020 †16,18

TRINH, Khiet Ngoc. 101 S 7TH ST 17501 #051-04-1997 L2000 **FM** *020 †18

WASKOWICZ, Bruce Craig. 101 S 7TH ST 17501 #051-04-1988 L1990 **FM** *020 †18

ALBION – ERIE

KROEMER, Peter Otto. 155 E STATE ST, ALBION FAMILY PRACTICE 16401 #035-06-1981 L1982 **FM** *020 †18

ALBRIGHTSVILLE – CARBON

LESITSKY, Neil. ROUTE 903, PENN-KIDDER MEDICAL CENTER 18210 #041-09-1986 L1987 **FM** *020 †18

ALBURTIS – BERKS

DEWAR, Kate Marie. ■ 18011 #041-77-2007, ▲ L2007 *012

LUIZZA, Anthony George. ■ 18011 #041-15-2006 L2006 **EM** *012

MILIA, David Joseph. ■ 18011 #056-06-2004 L2005 **GS** *012

NEWTON, Yolanda Marie. ■ 18011 #036-08-2004 L2004 **OBG** *012

SACCO, James M. ■ 18011 #041-77-2006, ▲ L2006 **FM** *100

ALDAN – DELAWARE

ACKROYD, David Alan. 772 E PROVIDENCE RD, STE 96 19018 #041-09-1989 L1992 **PD** *020 †55

BANADDA, Bezareli. 770 E PROVIDENCE RD # 112 19018 #905-01-1982 L1995 **IM** *020 †20

DOBRACKI, Alyson E. ■ 19018 #041-77-2007, ▲ L2007 **IM** *012

HUYETTE, John Newell. 38 SPRINGFIELD RD 19018 #041-14-1979 L1981 **FM** *020 †18

KIM, Roy Jung Woo. ■ 19018 #036-01-1997 L2002 **PD** *020 †20,55

MITRA, Chandan. ■ 19018 #160-02-1997 L2005 **IM** *012

RODRIGUEZ, Angel M. ■ 19018 #042-02-2007 L2007 **GS** *012

ALEXANDRIA – HUNTINGDON

REEDER, Charles Frederick. ■ 16611 #035-20-1947 L1948 **FM OS** *071 †18

STEWART, Harold Wm. PO BOX 376, MAIN ST 16611 #041-02-1945 L1946 **EM** *020

ALIQUIPPA – BEAVER

AGARWAL, Amrit. 200 PLEASANT DR 15001 #496-38-1962 L1972 **RHU IM** *071 †20

ALOI, Frank Philip. 2139 BRODHEAD RD 15001 #041-09-1995 L1999 **AI** *100 †20,03

ANDERSON, Victor Saml. ■ 15001 #016-11-1965 L1969 **HS** *071 †65

BEIS, Athena Cleo. 1 HOSPITAL DR 15001 #305-01-1998 L2001 **IM** *020 †20

BONNER, Brian Keith. 524 FRANKLIN AVE 15001 #041-12-2001 L2001 **FM** *020 †18

BORZUTSKY, Carlos. 2020 MAIN ST 15001 #231-01-1968 L1973 **DR** *020

COLBURN, Nancy Therese. 2500 HOSPITAL DR 15001 #038-43-1985 L1987 **AN** *020 †05

D'ANTONIO, Amy Patricia. ■ 15001 #010-02-1992 L2006 **PM PRS** *020 †60

DESAI, Jitendra Maganlal. 1 HOSPITAL DR, ALLEGHENY UROLOGY ASSOCIA 15001 #495-01-1963 L1973 **U** *020 †95

EDELMANN, Werner Jos. ■ 15001 #035-01-1958 L2000 **U** *071 †95

EGLESTON, Leon Alan. 2500 HOSPITAL DR 15001 #041-12-1972 L1974 **GS GP** *020 †85

ELYADERANI, Morteza K. 2500 HOSPITAL DR, RADIOLOGY DEPARTMENT 15001 #517-01-1967 L1987 **R** *020 †80,28

FIKE, Leanne Marie. ■ 15001 #041-13-2007 L2007 **TY** *012

GANDHE, Ashwini. 2360 HOSPITAL DR 15001 #495-20-1999 L2002 **IM** *020 †20

HUGHES, Elizabeth D O S. 2139 BRODHEAD RD STE 1 15001 #917-22-1967 L1978 **PM IM** *020

KAUL, Ramesh. 2500 HOSPITAL DR 15001 #495-36-1979 L1998 **PUD IM** *020 †20

KAVIC, Alexander John. ■ 15001 #041-09-1967 L1971 **EM** *020 †16

■ = Address Information Privacy Protected

KOSANOVICH, Mitchell A. 1315 MAIN ST 15001 #041-07-1998 L2000 **EM** *020 †16

MEDICH, George F. 2500 HOSPITAL DR 15001 #041-12-1977 L1980 **ORS OSM** *071

MOKA, Ganapathirao. 2450 MILL ST 15001 #495-11-1965 L1979 **GP GS** *020 †16

MORTIMER, Gregory Paul. ■ 15001 #041-14-1985 L1986 **FM** *030 †18

MORTIMER, Marcia Thompson. ■ 15001 #041-12-1985 L1986 **FM** *020 †18

NEGRINI, Bryan Paul. 2360 HOSPITAL DR 15001 #025-01-1993 L1995 **IM** *020 †20

NOTARO, John. 2349 MILL ST 15001 #561-17-1962 L1965 **FM IM** *072 †18

PALLAN, Laura Anne. 2500 HOSPITAL DR 15001 #041-12-1989 L1991 **OPH** *020 †35 ‡

PATEL, Manojkumar R. 2448 MILL ST 15001 #495-23-1967 L1975 **OPH EM** *020 †35

POPE, Roxanne. ■ 15001 #010-03-1995 L1999 **PD** *100

PRIOLA, James Nicholas. 99 BUSS RD 15001 #018-75-1990, ▲ L1991 **FM** *020 †18

SHAW, William I. 2020 MAIN ST 15001 #041-12-1962 L1963 **R** *020 †80

SHETTY, Kandavar Narayan. 2349 MILL ST 15001 #495-37-1962 L1972 **CD IM** *020 †20

SHETTY, Sarvotham N. 2369 MILL ST 15001 #495-37-1992 L1997 **IM** *020 †20

SIA, Jose Ku. 2285 BRODHEAD RD 15001 #748-01-1969 L1973 **FM CD** *020

SIMONS, Bernie Michael. 99 BUSS RD 15001 #055-02-1990 L1993 **FM** *020 †18

SINGH, Amarjeet Rana. 1 HOSPITAL DR 15001 #495-29-1972 L1976 **CD** *020 †20

TAPYRIK, Nicholas. 2500 HOSPITAL DR 15001 #041-01-1975 L1980 **PUD IM** *020 †20

TATUM, James Klaber. 2299 BRODHEAD RD 15001 #030-06-1977 L1986 **FM** *020 †18

THOMAS, Harold D, Jr. ■ 15001 #041-12-1954 L1955 **FM OBG** *020

TWERSKI, Abraham Joshua. RR 2, DEPT PSYCH 15001 #056-06-1959 L1961 **P** *071 †75

VELLANI, Zuleikha. 99 AUTUMN ST 15001 #704-25-1996 L2000 **FM** *020 †18 ‡

ZERNICH, Stephen, Jr. ■ 15001 #041-12-1946 L1947 **GS** *071

ZERNICH, Wallace. HOSPITAL DR 15001 #041-12-1951 L1953 **FM** *071 †18

ALLENTOWN – LEHIGH

ABBOUD, Michael John. 1200 S CEDAR CREST BLVD 18103 #422-01-2005 L2005 **GS** *012

ABDULHAY, Gazi. 1611 POND RD STE 101, STE 101 18104 #902-10-1972 L1988 **GYN GO** *020 †30

ABDULLAH, Ibrahim. ■ 18109 #041-15-2007 L2007 **EM** *012

ABRAMS, Albert Danl. 1401 N CEDAR CREST BLVD, STE 201 18104 #041-13-1975 L1976 **RHU IM** *020 †20

ACKAH, Elena Alexandrovna. 421 W CHEW ST, DEPT OF FAMILY PRACTICE 18102 #913-09-2003 L2006 **FP** *012

ADAMS, Milton Stephen. 1610 E EMMAUS AVE 18103 #010-03-1963 L1964 **CHP P** *020 †75 ‡

ADOLPHINE, Roline L. ■ 18109 #035-15-2002 L2007 **CCS** *012

AGARWALA, Sumon Kumar. 1259 S CEDAR CREST BLVD, STE 323 18103 #033-05-1999 L2004 **END** *020 †20

AHMED, Basil Sebri. 1240 S CEDAR CREST BLVD, STE 305 18103 #528-01-1979 L1998 **HO** *020 †20

AHMED, Khawaja Nadeem. 1200 S CEDAR CREST BLVD 18103 #305-01-2005 L2005 **IM** *012

AHMED, Shameer. 1200 S CEDAR CREST BLVD 18103 #495-50-2001 L2007 **IM** *012

AKHTER, Waseem. 1736 W HAMILTON ST 18104 #704-02-1993 L1998 **NPM PD** *020 †55

ALBAKER, Osamah Jaber. ■ 18109 #584-01-1996 L2001 **N** *020

ALCHAER, Maha. 421 W CHEW ST, SACRED HEART HOSP 18102 #875-02-1996 L2004 **FM** *100 †18

ALI, Aras Omar. 400 N 17TH ST, FAIRGROUNDS SURGICAL CTR 18104 #528-01-1993 L2001 **AN** *05

ALLMON, Donna M. 1736 W HAMILTON ST 18104 #041-15-2000 L2003 **EM** *020

ALTMAN, Howard Bruce. 1259 S CEDAR CREST BLVD, STE 100 18103 #041-07-1989 L1992 **DMP PTH** *062 †50 ‡

ALTOBELLI, John Anthony. 1230 S CEDAR CREST BLVD 18103 #051-04-1967 L1968 **PS** *020 †65

ALTOMARE, Frank Jos. 421 W CHEW ST, SACRED HEART HOSPITAL 18102 #041-09-1959 L1960 **NR R** *071 †80,28

AMRO, Rafic A. 402 N 2ND ST 18102 #875-01-1969 L1979 **GS GP** *030

ANBARI, Kevin Kinan. 250 CETRONIA RD, STE 303 18104 #041-01-2000 L2001 **ORS OAR** *100

ANDERKO, Frank Thos. 1603 LEHIGH PKWY N 18103 #041-09-1944 L1945 **GP** *072

ARANGIO, George Anthony. 5925 TILGHMAN ST, STE 200 18104 #035-20-1969 L1971 **ORS OFA** *020 †40 ‡

ARDIRE, Anthony Jos. ■ 18104 #041-13-1978 L1979 **PD** *075 †55

ARORA, Smita. 450 W CHEW ST, STE 101 18102 #495-43-1986 L2001 **FM** *020 †18

ASO, Linda Balagon. 1600 HANOVER AVE, ALLENTOWN STATE HOSP 18109 #748-09-1966 L1973 **OBG** *020

ATTEWELL, Rosemarie. 421 W CHEW ST 18102 #041-13-1983 L1985 **FM EM** *020 †18

AUCH-RICCI, Ella M. ■ 18104 #041-07-1939 L1940 **GP** *071 †18

AUTERI, Anthony G. 451 W CHEW ST, STE 401 18104 #041-01-1984 L1987 **GE IM** *020 †20 ‡

BABCOCK, Karen Ruth. 1227 W LIBERTY ST, STE 303 18102 #033-06-1993 L2007 **PD** *020 †55 ‡

BADELLINO, Michael Marc. 1240 S CEDAR CREST BLVD, STE 308 18103 #041-13-1983 L1985 **PM** *020 †85

BAIRD, Rowan Chantel Ales. 1200 S CEDAR CREST BLVD 18103 #422-01-2005 L2006 **FP** *012

BANNON, Kevin Robt. 1255 S CEDAR CREST BLVD, STE 3600 18103 #035-08-1980 L2000 **DR RNR** *020 †80

BARBOUR, Peter J. 1250 S CEDAR CREST BLVD, STE 405 18103 #041-13-1974 L1978 **N** *020 †75

BARCHUGOVA, Olga. 4TH AND CHEW STS, SACRED HEART HOSPITAL 18102 #913-76-1999 L2007 **FP** *012

BARILLA, Donald Edward. 401 N 17TH ST, STE 215 18104 #041-09-1970 L1971 **END DIA** *020 †20

BARONE, Anthony. ■ 18103 #035-09-1964 L1971 **AN** *071 †05

BARRACO, Robert Don. 1240 S CEDAR CREST BLVD, STE 308 18104 #033-06-1989 L2003 **GS CCS** *020 †85

BARRETT, Stephen Joel. 1200 S CEDAR CREST BLVD 18103 #035-01-1957 L1958 **OS P** *071

BARRON, Lloyd Eugene, II. 1240 S CEDAR CREST BLVD, STE 103 18104 #041-09-1970 L1971 **HO ON** *020 †20

BATTISTA, Richard David. 250 CETRONIA RD, STE 100 18104 #041-02-1993 L1995 **HS ORS** *040 †40

BAUSCH, Andrew N. 1616 W ALLEN ST 18102 #041-01-1982 L1984 **OPH** *020 †35

BAUTISTA, Florante C. ■ 18103 #748-07-1965 L1975 **U** *020

BAYLOR, Richard D. 2901 HAMILTON BLVD, UNIT 100 18103 #041-02-1985 L1986 **FM** *020 †18

BEGANY, Diane Patricia. 2801 W HIGHLAND ST 18104 #041-13-1988 L1991 **CCP** *020 †55

BELLUCCI, Kirsten Shelby. ■ 18104 #035-46-1999 L2002 **DMP** *020

BELMAN, Alexander S. 1255 S CEDAR CREST BLVD, STE 3600 18103 #869-02-1961 L2004 **R** *020 †80

BELMONT, Donald Jeffrey. 1202 S CEDAR CREST BLVD, STE 500 18103 #041-01-1977 L1983 **CD IM** *020 †20

BEMAN, Scott William. 1240 S CEDAR CREST BLVD, STE 208 18103 #051-07-1995 L1999 **GS** *020 †85

BEMPORAD, Joshua A. 1255 S CEDAR CREST BLVD, STE 3600 18103 #035-09-1995 L2002 **RNR** *020 †80

BENN, Keisha. 1200 S CEDAR CREST BLVD, DIV OF OB/GYN 18103 #035-08-2005 **OBG** *012

BENZEL, Stanley. 1255 S CEDAR CREST BLVD, STE 3600 18103 #041-02-1969 L1976 **R** *020 †80

BERGAMASCHI, Roberto Cami. 1240 S CEDAR CREST BLVD, STE 308 18103 #561-03-1982 L2003 **GS CRS** *020

BERGER, Alan. 1210 S CEDAR CREST BLVD #1 18103 #041-13-1976 L1977 **VS TRS** *020 †85

BERGER, Paul Matthew. 1240 S CEDAR CREST BLVD 18103 #023-01-1994 L1996 **U** *020 †95

BERKOWITZ, Neal Jerrold. 141 W EMMAUS AVE 18103 #041-01-1979 L1980 **FM** *020 †18

BERNHARD, Kenneth Alan. 1901 W HAMILTON ST 18104 #041-01-1982 L1983 **CD IM** *020 †20

BEST, Richard Arthur. ■ 18102 #917-21-1968 *100

BHATTI, Yasmin I. ■ 18104 #704-15-1996 L2005 **PM** *100 †60

BHULLAR, Shaminder Singh. 1200 S CEDAR CREST BLVD, TRANSITIONAL YEAR 18103 #038-45-2007 L2007 **TY** *012

BILLEN, Denise Margaret. 421 W CHEW ST, SACRED HEART HOSP 18102 #308-07-1982 L1988 **EM PD** *020

BINGHAM, Jonathan B, II. 1230 S CEDAR CREST BLVD, STE 302 18103 #035-01-1999 L2004 **U** *020 †95 ‡

BISHOP, Ellen Bryant. ■ 18104 #025-01-1978 L1981 **PD** *020 †55

BLINDER, Jeffrey Stuart. 1255 S CEDAR CREST BLVD, STE 3600 18103 #051-04-1976 L1981 **VIR** *071 †80

BLOOMFIELD, Cheryl A.. 1210 S CEDAR CREST BLVD, STE 3600 18103 #422-01-2003 L2003 **IM** *100 †20

BOLLINGER, Barbara Kay. ■ 18103 #020-02-1989 L1993 **FOP** *020 †50

BONOS, Chas Theodore, III. ■ 18104 #041-09-1970 L1971 **EM OM** *020

BOO, Ki Taick. 1322 W HAMILTON ST 18102 #583-10-1966 L1975 **IM GP** *020 ‡

BOORSE, Richard Chas. 1240 S CEDAR CREST BLVD, STE 208 18103 #041-13-1985 L1987 **GS** *020 †85

BORACK, Carol Anne. 401 N 17TH ST 18104 #036-01-1998 L2004 **FM** *020 †18

BOULAY, Richard Mark. 400 N 17TH ST, STE 201 18104 #041-12-1990 L1992 **OBG** *020 †30

BRADY, John Gregory. 1259 S CEDR CRST BLVD #100, ADVANCED DERMATOLOGY 18103 #041-77-1980, ▲ L1981 **D** *020 †20

BRANDECKER, Thomas. 798 HAUSMAN RD 18104 #010-02-1986 L1989 **IM IMG** *020 †20

BRENNER, Scott Murray. 401 N 17TH ST, ABC PEDIATRICS 18104 #033-05-1991 L1995 **PD** *020 †55

BRESNAN, Kristin Annachim. 1730 W CHEW ST, FAMILY MEDICINE 18104 #041-13-2005 L2005 **FPP** *012

BRETZ, Karen Ann. 400 N 17TH ST, FAIRGROUNDS SURGICAL CTR 18104 #041-13-1978 L1979 **AN IM** *020 †20,05

BREWER, Cheryl Ann. 1611 POND RD, STE 101 18104 #017-20-1985 L2007 **OBG** *020 †30

BRISLIN, Kenneth James. 250 CETRONIA RD, STE 100 18104 #041-13-1998 L2001 **ORS** *020 †40

BROOKS, Charles Michael. 3131 COLLEGE HEIGHTS BLVD, STE 1200 18104 #041-02-1968 L1969 **GE IM** *020 †20 ‡

BROSS, Ronald Jos. 451 W CHEW ST STE 401 18102 #041-02-1992 L1994 **GE** *020 †20 ‡

BROTHERS, Muriel Annette. 1628 W CHEW ST, 1ST FL 18102 #665-01-2007 L2007 **FP** *012

BROWN, Christopher Lee. 1255 S CEDAR CREST BLVD, STE 3600 18103 #041-02-1972 L1973 **DR** *020 †80

BROWN, Donald Craig. 451 W CHEW ST, STE 409 18102 #033-06-1994 L2001 **GS** *020 †05

BROWN, Kimberly Clouser. 1605 N CEDAR CREST BLVD, STE 610 18104 #041-01-1990 L1992 **PD** *020 †55

BUCHANAN, Harry W, IV. 400 N 17TH ST STE 200 18104 #051-01-1979 L1983 **OPH** *020 ‡

BUCKLEY, Ronald John. 1208 HANOVER AVE 18109 #041-13-1977 L1978 **FM** *020 †18

BUNIN, Lisa Sharon. 1611 POND RD STE 403 18104 #023-07-1984 L1988 **OPH FPS** *020 †35

BUONANNO, Anthony P, Jr. 1255 S CEDAR CREST BLVD, STE 2200 18103 #035-08-1993 L1997 **MPD** *020 †55,20

BURKE, James Addison. 1250 S CEDAR CREST BLVD, STE 300 18103 #035-20-1984 L1990 **CD CCM** *020 †20

BURKHOLDER, Thomas Oliver. 400 N 17TH ST, STE 101-106 18104 #041-13-1974 L1975 **OPH** *020 †35

BURLEW, Brian Prentice. 1540 E RACE ST, REAR 18109 #041-13-1985 L1986 **PUD IM** *020 †20

BURTAINE, Jeffrey Edward. 2100 MACK BLVD, MACK TRUCKS INC 18103 #033-05-1969 L1970 **FM** *020 †18,70

BUXBAUM, Jodie Lynn. 1245 S CEDR CRST SU301, ALLENTOWN ANESTHESIA ASSOC 18103 #041-13-1988 L1991 **AN IM** *020 †05

CACCESE, David Michael. 401 N 17TH ST 18104 #041-01-1970 L1971 **IM** *020 †20

CAMASTO, Angela Marie. 1200 S CEDAR CREST BLVD 18103 #035-06-1997 L2000 **PD** *020 †55

CAMICI, Stefano. 1210 S CEDAR CREST BLVD, STE 1100 18103 #561-16-1976 L2000 **NS** *020 †25

CAMPBELL, Faunda Nicola. ■ 18104 #041-15-2004 L2004 **OBG** *012

CAMPBELL, Stephen Scott. ■ 18104 #010-02-2000 L2007 **NS** *100

CAMPION, John F. 1251 S CEDAR CREST BLVD, STE 202A 18103 #035-19-1978 L1990 **CHP P** *020 †75

CAMPOS, Luis Ismael. 101 S 17TH ST, LPRSCPC CAMPOS 18104 #649-14-1976 L1981 **GS** *020 ‡

CANDAL, Jorge Alfredo. 421 W CHEW 18102 #132-01-1976 L2003 **FM** *100

CANDAL, Mario Alberto. 451 W CHEW ST, STE 310 18102 #132-01-1965 L1974 **OBG** *020 †30

CANDIO, Joseph Anthony. 1230 S CEDAR CREST BLVD, STE 201 18104 #041-13-1976 L1977 **IM NTR** *020 †20

CAPREZ, John C. 24 S 18TH ST 18104 #041-77-1999, ▲ L1999 **AN** *020 †05

CARNEY, David Paul. 798 HAUSMAN RD 18104 #041-09-1974 L1975 **IM** *020 †20

CARPENTER, E Joel, IV. ■ 18103 #041-01-1962 L1963 **GP** *020 ‡

CARROLL, Leslie Frances. 6083 HAMILTON BLVD 18106 #561-01-1978 L1990 **PD** *020 †55

CARTER, Debra Lynne. 401 N 17TH ST 18104 #023-07-1994 L1997 **PD** *020 †55

CARVER, Bala Bansal. 1200 S CEDAR CREST BLVD 18103 #495-08-1967 L1972 **PTH BBK** *020 ‡

CASSEL, John Joel. 1255 S CEDAR CREST BLVD, STE 1200 18103 #041-02-1973 L1978 **CD IM** *020 †20

CASTALDO, John Edward. 1250 S CEDAR CREST BLVD, STE 405 18103 #032-01-1979 L1982 N *020 †75 ‡

CASTELEIN, Delilah Anchet. 421 W CHEW ST 18102 #748-29-2002 L2007 FP *012

CELANI, Victor James. 1275 S CEDAR CREST BLVD, STE 301 18103 #041-02-1973 L1978 OS GS *020 †85

CERCIELLO, Mark James. 451 W CHEW ST 18102 #041-09-1964 L1965 ORS OS *020 †40

CESANEK, Paul Bernard. ■ 18103 #041-13-2004 L2004 GS *012

CHAI, Mark Douglas. 1200 S CEDAR CREST BLVD 18103 #041-09-1988 L1990 PM IM *020 †20,60

CHAKRABARTI, Pradip Kumar. 1210 S CEDAR CREST BLVD, STE 3300 18103 #495-39-1980 L2000 GS *020

CHANG, Chris C N. 1259 S CEDR CRST BLVD #210 18103 #244-02-1969 L1974 PDS GS *020 †85

CHANG, In-Ho. 1251 S CEDAR CREST BLVD, STE 212C 18103 #583-02-1963 L1973 AN *071

CHAUDHARY, Pushpi P. 3110 HAMILTON BLVD 18103 #495-17-1982 L1995 P *020 †75

CHEN, Juh-Huey. 1600 HANOVER AVE 18109 #385-04-1967 L1973 PD *071 †55

CHENG, Harvey Steven. 401 N 17TH ST STE 109 18104 #041-13-1977 L1978 OPH *020 †35

CHERNOFSKY, Michael A. 1230 S CEDAR CREST BLVD, STE 204 18103 #035-46-1982 L1988 PS HS *020 †65

CHIADIS, James Michael. 421 W CHEW ST 18102 #041-09-1980 L1983 PTH *020 †50 ‡

CHIKAMI, Gary Kenji. 644 BENNER RD, APT 102 18104 #005-18-1979 L1981 ID IM *050 †20

CHILD, Proctor L. ■ 18103 #035-08-1949 L1967 PTH *071 †50

CHIN, Katherine Ching. 1200 S CEDAR CREST BLVD, DEPT MED 18103 #041-15-2006 L2006 IM *012

CHONG, Pearlie Pao Ee. 1200 S CEDAR CREST BLVD, DEPT OF INTERNAL MED 18103 #065-06-2006 L2006 IM *012

CHOVANES, George Ivan. 325 N 5TH ST # 3 18102 #041-01-1981 L1983 NS *020 †25

CHOWDARY, Raj P. 1230 S CEDAR CREST BLVD, STE 204 18103 #495-11-1970 L1985 PS *020 †85,65

CHUHRAN, Craig Michael. ■ 18104 #041-13-2004 L2004 IM *020 †20

CHUNG, Heiwon. 1240 S CEDAR CREST BLVD, STE 205 18103 #187-04-1989 L1997 GS *020 †85

CHUNG, Johnny Sheayuan. 250 CETRONIA RD, STE 301 18104 #033-05-1998 L2001 PS *020 †65

CHYUNG, Dennis Kwak. 1245 S CEDAR CRST BLVD #301, FAIRGROUNDS SURGICAL CTR 18103 #041-13-1993 L1997 AN OS *020 †05

CIFELLI, John Riggio. 325 N 5TH ST, THIRD FLOOR 18102 #033-05-1993 L2000 GS *020

CILIBERTI, Michael David. 250 CETRONIA RD STE 103, CTR/ALLERGY & ASTHMA CARE 18104 #035-09-1988 L1991 AI *020 †20,03

CLAIR, David Lee. 1230 S CEDAR CREST BLVD, STE 302 18103 #041-02-1984 L1991 U GS *020 †95 ‡

CLAUSER, Gary Wilbur. 1210 S CEDAR CREST BLVD 18103 #041-13-1998 L2000 IM *020

COHEN, Laurie Ann. 1517 POND RD 18104 #035-75-1986, ▲ L1988 PD *020 †55

COLEMAN, Sarah Grace. ■ 18103 #041-15-2005 L2005 IM *012

COLLER, Daniel Harold. 450 W CHEW ST, STE 101 18102 #041-13-1974 L1975 FM *020 †18

COLLINS, J John. 1245 S CEDAR CREST BLVD, ALLENTOWN ANESTHESIA ASSOC 18103 #010-02-1982 L1984 AN *020 †05

COMBS, William G, Jr. 451 W CHEW ST, STE 104 18102 #041-12-1984 L1985 IC CD *020 †20

CONNERS, Christopher J. 1255 S CEDAR CREST BLVD, STE 3600 18103 #041-07-1985 L1990 DR *020 †80

CONNOLLY, Rae Lynne. 450 W CHEW ST, STE 101 18102 #422-01-2003 L2003 FM *100 †18

CONSUELOS, Michael Joseph. 401 N 17TH ST, DEPT OF PEDS 18104 #041-01-1994 L1996 PD *020 †55

CORCORAN, Matthew Harold. 1259 S CEDAR CREST BLVD, STE 323 18103 #010-02-1995 L2004 END *020 †20

CORLEONE, Dalia Adnan. 1628 W CHEW ST 18102 #528-01-1997 L2007 FP *012

CORNELL, James Frederic. 451 W CHEW ST 18102 #035-15-1976 L1979 GE IM *020 †20

CORPUS, Kathalina Andres. 1200 S CEDAR CREST BLVD 18103 #748-01-2000 L2004 FM *100 †14

COSTELLO, Kelly Lee. 401 N 17TH ST STE 311 18104 #041-01-1994 L1996 PD *020 †55

COX, David Alan. 1250 S CEDAR CREST BLVD, STE 300 18103 #016-02-1982 L2006 IM *020 †20

COX, John Fordyce. 1255 S CEDAR CREST BLVD, STE 3600 18103 #041-02-1984 L1985 DR *020 †80

CRIPE, Chad C. 1245 S CEDAR CREST BLVD, STE 301 18103 #041-15-2004 L2004 AN *012

CRISWELL, Samuel Winn. ■ 18106 #041-13-1968 L1969 FM *071 †18

CUSICK, Richard J. 535 E EMMAUS AVE 18103 #035-46-1972 L1974 PM *020 †18 ‡

CZAJKOWSKI, Thomas John. 421 W CHEW ST 18102 #041-02-1986 L1987 FM *020 †18

DADAY, Joseph M, III. 4825 W TILGHMAN ST 18104 #041-13-1979 L1980 FM *020 †18

DALEY, James Joseph. 501 SAINT JOHN ST, GOOD SHEPHERD PHYSICIAN GR 18103 #033-06-1995 L2003 PM OS *020 †80

D'AMBROSIO, Anthony Willi. 1628 W CHEW ST 18102 #305-01-2006 L2007 FP *012

DANDEGIAN, Albert Nishan. 1255 S CEDAR CREST BLVD, STE 3600 18103 #041-09-1991 L1996 DR *020 †80

DANGLEBEN, Dale Alvin. 1255 S CEDAR CREST BLVD, STE 1100 18103 #041-14-2000 L2001 CCS *020 †85

DANIELS, Anita Carolyn. 6083 HAMILTON BLVD 18106 #033-06-1993 L1995 PD *020

DEDANIA, Kishorkumar. 1600 HANOVER AVE 18109 #495-48-1980 L1983 P PYG *020 †75

DEDIO, Robert. 1575 POND RD STE 203 18104 #035-19-1985 L1986 OTO *020 †45 ‡

DEEB, Ramon John. 1251 S CEDAR CREST BLVD, ALLENTOWN ANESTHESIA ASSOC 18103 #041-01-1961 L1962 AN *071 †05

DE FALCIS, Delphy F. 24 S 18TH ST 18104 #041-77-1993, ▲ L1994 AN *020 †05

DEHOFF, John Howard. 1255 S CEDAR CREST BLVD, STE 3600 18103 #051-07-1991 L1995 IM *020 †20

DE LA VEGA, Guillermo Ant. 401 N 17TH ST STE 300 18104 #737-01-1996 L2002 OBG *020 ‡

DEL VECCHIO, Philip Jos. ■ 18104 #010-02-1959 L1991 IM GPM *071 †20

DESHPANDE, Vilas. 401 N 17TH ST, STE 307 18104 #495-01-1973 L1981 PD *020 †55

DEUTSCHER, Sigismond. ■ 18104 #187-03-1954 L1974 FM *071 †70

DHOTRE, Dheeraj. ■ 18103 #495-09-2001 L2007 IM *012

DICKEY, Lorraine Roberts. ■ 18104 #030-05-1987 L2004 NPM PD *020 †55

DICKSON, Thomas Bruce, Jr. 250 CETRONIA RD 18104 #041-13-1966 L1967 ORS *020 †40

DIMICK, Anthony Lewis. 401 N 17TH ST 18104 #007-02-1989 L1997 PD *020 †55

DONMOYER, Theodore Lewis. ■ 18104 #041-13-1958 L1959 CD IM *071 †20

DOSTAL, Julie Ann. 1730 W CHEW ST 18104 #026-04-1981 L1982 FM EM *020 †18

DRAUCH, Eugene Wm. ■ 18102 #041-13-1957 L1958 EM *071

DROBIL, Jeffrey L. 1245 S CEDAR CREST BLVD, STE 301 18103 #041-77-1994, ▲ L1995 AN *020 ‡

DUBOV, Wayne Eric. 250 CETRONIA RD, STE 100 18104 #035-08-1988 L1992 PM SCI *020 †60

DUNN, Jerome. ■ 18104 #041-13-1968 L1969 AI PD *071 †55,03

DUNNE, Laura Marie. 798 HAUSMAN RD 18104 #028-34-1999 L2003 FM FSM *020 †18

DUPONT, Paul G. 451 W CHEW ST 18102 #035-48-1990 L1995 RNR *020 †80 ‡

DURKIN, Raymond Andrew. 1202 S CEDAR CREST BLVD, STE 500 18103 #041-09-1989 L1991 CD *020 †20

EARNEST, Tamar D. ■ 18104 #041-13-1968 L1969 GS TRS *071 †85

EBERWEIN, Sigrid B. 1210 S CEDAR CREST BLVD, SURG SPEC OF LEHIGH VLY-BU 18103 #409-33-1990 L2002 PS *020

ECHEVARRIA, Linda Angela. ■ 18102 #003-75-2007, ▲ L2007 *012

ECONOMOU, Nicholas Dimitr. ■ 18104 #041-13-2006 L2006 IM *100

EDFORD, Kim B. 1200 S CEDAR CREST BLVD, DEPT MED 18103 #041-77-2007, ▲ L2007 IM *012

EL-BECK, Munier Abraham. 1200 S CEDAR CREST BLVD 18103 #305-01-2004 L2005 IM *012

ELLSWEIG, Bruce Alan. 1251 S CEDAR CREST BLVD, STE 102A 18103 #041-02-1974 L1975 FM *020 †18

ESLER, James Wallace, Jr. 451 W CHEW ST 18102 #041-01-1960 L1961 AN *071 †05

ETCHASON, Jeffrey Allen. ■ 18104 #017-20-1988 L2006 IM *020 †20

EUTSLER, Eric Paul. ■ 18104 #041-15-2008 *012

FABIAN, Mary P. 1101 W EMAUS AVE, EMAUS AVE FAMILY PRACT 18103 #041-14-1990 L1993 FM *020 †18

FAIDLEY, Jeffrey Ray. 119 N 15TH ST 18102 #041-14-1998 L2001 IM *020 †20

FALATYN, Stephen Paul. 250 CETRONIA RD, STE 250 18104 #035-20-1990 L1995 ORS *020 †40

FALCONE, Domenico. 1245 S CEDAR CREST BLVD, STE 301 18103 #041-02-1974 L1975 AN *020 †05

FARBOWITZ, Steven. 1601 W LIBERTY ST 18102 #305-01-1982 L1985 FM EM *020 †18

FARRELL, John David. 798 HAUSMAN RD, STE 200 18104 #035-15-1975 L1978 FM *020 †18

FASSL, Joseph John. 1200 S CEDAR CREST BLVD 18103 #041-13-1970 L1971 EM *020 †16

FEENEY, Robert Anthony. 3710 BROADWAY 18104 #041-13-1961 L1962 FM *071 †14

FERGUSON, Kale Patrick. 1200 S CEDAR CREST BLVD, LEHIGH VALLEY HOSP 18103 #422-01-2002 L110 *012

FERNSLER, Sarah Jane. 501 N 17TH ST, STE 212 18104 #041-14-1976 L1979 PD *020 †55

FETZER, Arthur Eugene. 1230 S CEDR CRST BLVD #302 18103 #035-20-1967 L1973 U *020 †95

FINCH, Frank Gerard. 1605 N CEDR CRST BLVD #602 18104 #041-14-1984 L1985 IM *020 †20

FINNEGAN, Walter James. 4949 LIBERTY LN, STE 10 18106 #041-02-1969 L1972 ORS GP *020 †40

FINNERTY, Sarah. 1243 S CEDAR CREST BLVD, LEHIGH VALLEY HOSPITAL HEA 18103 #016-11-1996 L2002 EM *020 †16

FITZGIBBONS, John P, Jr. 1200 S CEDAR CREST BLVD 18103 #035-15-1964 L1988 NEP IM *030 †20

FITZSIMONS, Thomas Robt. 1255 S CEDAR CREST BLVD, STE 3600 18103 #041-14-1973 L1980 PDR *020 †80

FOGELMAN, Sandra. 798 HAUSMAN RD 18104 #187-18-1986 L1992 IM FM *020 †20

FOLIO, Beth A S. 322 S 17TH ST 18104 #023-07-1985 L1986 OBG *071 †30

FOOSKAS, Stephen Perry. 1200 S CEDAR CREST BLVD 18103 #041-07-1984 L1985 EM IM *020 †20

FOSTER, Hilary Fitzgerald. ■ 18103 #055-75-2007, ▲ L2007 *012

FRAILEY, Wm Wasson, Jr. ■ 18103 #041-13-1968 L1969 GS *020 †85

FRANKENFIELD, Bruce A. 2200 W HAMILTON ST STE 203 18104 #041-01-1957 L1958 IM *071

FREED, Kelly Marie. 1255 S CEDAR CREST BLVD, STE 3600 18103 #041-02-1991 L1993 DR *020 †20

FREUDENBERGER, Ronald S. 1250 S CEDAR CREST BLVD, STE 300 18103 #035-15-1989 L2007 CD IM *020 †20

FRIEDBERG, Milton. 1240 S CEDAR CREST BLVD 18103 #041-13-1951 L1953 ON HNS *072 †85

FRIEDMAN, Eliot Lawrence. 1240 S CEDAR CREST BLVD, STE 408 18103 #016-02-1981 L2002 ON IM *020 †20

FRIEL, Timothy James. 1200 S CEDAR CREST BLVD 18103 #024-01-1994 L1999 ID *020 †20

FRIESS, Henry Michael. 421 W CHEW ST, DEPT OF 18102 #033-05-1990 L1996 RNR *020 †80

FRY, Robinson G. 1575 POND RD, STE 201 18104 #041-77-1956, ▲ L1957 GS CRS *071

FUGAZZOTTO, Pasquale Jos. 401 N 17TH ST 18104 #035-03-1958 L1964 PD *020 †55

FULLAN, Debra M. 400 N 17TH ST, FAIRGROUNDS SURGICAL CTR 18104 #033-75-1988, ▲ L1992 AN *020 †05

FUNKE, Saralee. 1200 S CEDAR CREST BLVD, 2ND FL 18103 #041-13-1987 L1987 FOP *020 †20

GALASSI, Joseph Wm, Jr. 400 N 17TH ST, FAIRGROUNDS SURGICAL CTR 18104 #041-09-1991 L1993 AN PME *020 †05

GALGON, John Paul. 1210 S CEDAR CREST BLVD, STE 2300 18103 #041-02-1960 L1961 PUD IM *020 †20

GALLAGHER, Hugh Stephen. 1202 S CEDAR CREST BLVD 18103 #041-01-1961 L1962 CD IM *020 †20

GARCIA, Jose Ramon. 451 W CHEW ST STE 306 18102 #041-02-1978 L1980 IM IMG *020 †20

GARECA, Marcelo G. 1251 S CEDAR CREST BLVD 18103 #132-02-1992 L1998 ID *020 †20

GASTINGER, Joseph Wm. 1251 S CEDAR CREST BLVD 18103 #041-13-1974 L1975 IM *100 †24

GAYLOR, Donald H. 1200 S CEDAR CREST BLVD 18103 #035-45-1949 L1972 TS GS *020 †85,90

GAYLOR, Theodore Henry. 1251 S CEDAR CREST BLVD, STE 110 18103 #165-06-1975 L1979 OTO *020 †45

GERCHMAN, Leroy Benj. 3710 BROADWAY, WEST END MEDICAL GROUP 18104 #025-12-1972 L1973 FM *020 †18

GERHARDT, Susan Gail. 1210 S CEDAR CREST BLVD, STE 2300 18103 #041-09-1998 L2000 PCC *020 †20

GERNERD, Ross M. 951 N 4TH ST 18102 #041-13-1949 L1950 EM *020

GERTNER, Eric Justin. 1605 N CEDAR CREST BLVD, STE 610 18104 #033-06-1992 L1994 IM *020 †20

GERTNER, Ian M. 17TH & CHEW ST, DEPT NEO 18104 #047-07-1977 L1983 NPM *020 †55

GEVIRTZ, Jeffrey Louis. 1251 S CEDAR CREST BLVD 18103 #033-06-1986 L1991 U *020 †95

GIANGIULIO, Dennis Jos. 1240 S CEDAR CREST BLVD, STE 305 18103 #041-09-1980 L1982 ON IM *020 †20

GIBBS, Jeffrey Taylor. ■ 18103 #041-15-2007 GS *012

GINSBERG, Gene Howard. 798 HAUSMAN RD 18104 #041-02-1972 L1973 IM IMG *020 †20

GITTLEMAN, Mark Alan. 400 N 17TH ST STE 202 18104 #041-01-1969 L1970 GS SO *020 †85

GLANVILLE, Carlos Javier. 1200 S CEDAR CREST BLVD, DEPT OF GENERAL SURGERY 18103 #042-02-2006 L2006 GS *012

GLAZERMAN, Larry R. 250 CETRONIA RD, STE 350 18104 #041-02-1976 L1977 OBG *020 †30 ‡

GLUECK, David Geo. 1200 S CEDAR CREST BLVD 18103 #041-09-1980 L1981 **FM OM** *020 †18

GOLDFARB, Daniel David. 121 N CEDAR CREST BLVD 18104 #035-08-1973 **P** *020 †75

GOLDFARB, Harold Jonas. 501 N 17TH ST STE C, LIBERTY SQ MED CTR 18104 #024-07-1961 L1968 **OPH** *020 †35

GOLDMAN, Gary Lon. 5000 W TILGHMAN ST, STE 240 18104 #038-04-1977 L1980 **AN** *020 †05 ‡

GOLDMAN, Peter Harry. 1251 S CEDAR CREST BLVD, RM 207D 18103 #035-09-1968 L1969 **FM** *020 †18

GOLDNER, David Brian. 1250 S CEDAR CREST BLVD, STE 300 18103 #041-07-1980 L1981 **CD** *020 †20

GOLDSMITH, Charles P. ■ 18103 #041-13-1940 L1941 **OPH** *071 †35

GOODREAU, James Jos P. 1259 S CEDAR CREST BLVD, STE 301 18103 #021-05-1972 L1981 **VS GS** *020 †85

GOONEWARDENE, Shanth A. 2024 LEHIGH ST, PATHOLOGY DEPARTMENT 18103 #041-02-1995 L1998 **PTH PCP** *020 †50

GOPAL, Tirunilayi A. 250 CETRONIA RD, STE 305 18104 #495-01-1971 L1976 **OBG** *020 †30

GOR, Devang Mahesh. 1255 S CEDAR CREST BLVD, STE 3600 18103 #496-38-1995 L2003 **RNR** *020 †80

GORDON, Charles Alan. 798 HAUSMAN RD 18104 #041-02-1972 L1973 **IM** *020 †20 ‡

GORDON, Michael Jules. 1575 POND RD, STE 203 18104 #033-05-1966 L1973 **OTO** *020 †45

GORDON, Richard Efrem. 2200 W HAMILTON ST, STE 200 18104 #011-02-1975 L1978 **GS** *020

GOY, Richard Frank. 1243 S CEDAR CREST BLVD, HEALTHWORKS 18103 #035-08-1987 L1998 **OM** *020

GRAHAM-BROCK, Shayla D. ■ 18104 #043-01-2006 L2006 **FP** *012

GREYBUSH, Joseph Nicholas. 401 N 17TH ST, STE 301 18104 #041-13-1966 L1967 **OBG** *020 †30

GRISKA, Linda Ann Birkner. 1255 S CEDAR CREST BLVD, STE 3600 18103 #041-07-1972 L1973 **DR OS** *020 †20

GROSS, Paul Kenneth. 401 N 17TH ST STE 304 18104 #041-01-1972 L1973 **P** *020 †75

GRUNDMANN, Ina Johanna. ■ 18104 #023-01-2002 L2005 **FP** *012

GUARINO, Edward Francis. 451 W CHEW ST STE 309 18102 #561-17-1981 L1988 **PS HS** *020 †65

GUBERNICK, Julie Ann. 1255 S CEDAR CREST BLVD, STE 3600 18103 #041-01-1990 L1993 **DR IM** *020 †20 ‡

GUILES-LACEY, Stacey Lynn. 401 N 17TH ST, STE 203 18104 #041-14-1997 L2005 **MPD** *020 †20,55

GULOTTA, Paul. 1202 S CEDAR CREST BLVD, JAINDL PAVILION STE 500 18103 #041-14-1983 L1984 **CD IM** *020 †20

GUNDEL-BREHM, Caroline J. 1240 S CEDAR CREST BLVD, STE 410 18103 #041-13-2003 **IM** *100 †20

GUPTA, Arvind Kumar. 421 W CHEW ST, SACRED HEART HOSPITAL 18102 #305-01-1996 L1998 **IM** *020 †20

GUZMAN, Lourdes Lacap. 1600 HANOVER AVE 18109 #748-01-1955 L1973 **IM P** *071

GUZZO, Joseph Carl. 1230 S CEDAR CREST BLVD, STE 301 18103 #028-34-1971 L1973 **NEP IM** *020 †20 ‡

HABIG, Joseph A, II. 798 HAUSMAN RD 18104 #041-02-1983 L1984 **FM** *020 †18

HALIBEY, Zirka Maria. 1611 POND RD, STE 101 18104 #021-01-1982 L1983 **OBG** *020 †30

HALLOCK, Geoffrey Gaddis. 1230 S CEDR CRST #BLV-306 18103 #041-02-1975 L1982 **PS HS** *020 †85,65

HAMADANI, Houshang G. 2895 HAMILTON BLVD, STE 103 18104 #517-01-1963 L1978 **P CHP** *020 †75

HAMATI, Husam Fayez Y. 2634 W LIBERTY ST 18104 #286-03-1983 L1992 **PTH** *020 †50

HAMILTON, Jerome Matthew. 421 W CHEW ST, FAMILY PRACTICE CTR 18102 #422-01-2003 L2005 *100

HANNA, Wafa S. 951 N 4TH ST 18102 #875-02-1983 L1992 **FM** *020 †18 ‡

HANSROTE, Louis Wilbur. 401 N 17TH ST STE 309, CHILDRENS HEART CTR 18104 #561-17-1985 L1991 **PDC PD** *020 †55

HARDIN, William Downer. 1259 S CEDAR CREST BLVD, STE 210 18103 #021-01-1979 L2008 **PDS GS** *020 †85

HARMAN, Robert Golden. 1200 S CEDAR CREST BLVD 18103 #041-13-1957 L1958 **GP** *020

HARPER, Gregory Randall. 1240 S CEDAR CREST BLVD, STE 408 18103 #035-03-1976 L1996 **ON** *020 †20

HARR, Douglas Paul. 2895 HAMILTON BLVD, STE 101 18104 #041-13-1973 L1974 **IM NM** *020 †20,28

HARRIS, Katherine Ann. 1240 S CEDAR CREST BLVD, STE 103 18103 #041-14-1994 L2002 **HO IM** *020 †20

HARRIS, Kenneth Hirson. 1255 S CEDAR CREST BLVD, STE 3600 18103 #041-13-1974 L1975 **DR NM** *020 †80 ‡

HARRIS, Stanley R. ■ 18104 #917-06-1955 L1968 **RO NR** *071 †80

HARVEY, Kenneth Lee. 421 W CHEW ST 18102 #041-13-1957 L1958 **GP** *071

HASTINGS, Leo Jos. ■ 18104 #041-02-1955 L1956 **GP** *072

HAWK, Gregor Mc Clearn. 250 CETRONIA RD, STE 100 18104 #061-01-1990 L1998 *020 †40

HAWKINS, Christopher A. 250 CETRONIA RD, STE 100 18104 #023-01-1995 L2001 **OSM** *020 †40

HAYFORD, Kweku Amoanu. 1240 S CEDAR CREST BLVD, STE 410 18103 #032-01-2001 L2004 **IM** *020

HAZLETT, Shawn M. 401 N 17TH ST, STE 212 18104 #041-77-2000, ▲ L2001 **NEP** *020 †20

HELWIG, Kyle Andrew. 421 W CHEW ST 18102 #033-05-1991 L1995 **GE** *020 †20 ‡

HENRIQUEZ, Jack Anthony. ■ 18104 #041-13-1974 L1975 **EM** *020 †16

HENRIQUEZ VENTURA, L C. 6083 HAMILTON BLVD 18106 #308-01-1966 L1985 **PD** *020

HERMANY, Debra K. 421 W CHEW ST 18102 #041-77-1985, ▲ L1986 **EM FM** *020

HERTZ, Jonathan. 1210 S CEDAR CREST BLVD, STE 2300 18103 #041-01-1978 L1983 **PUD** *020 †20

HILL, Kina Teria Danyelle. 1200 S CEDAR CREST BLVD 18103 #422-01-2005 L2005 **IM** *012

HO, Oi Lan. 1600 HANOVER AVE 18109 #572-10-1965 L1984 **P** *071 †75

HOANG, Nghia Trong. 1255 S CEDAR CREST BLVD, STE 2200 18103 #041-77-2003, ▲ L2003 **IM** *100

HOFER, Michael. 450 W CHEW ST, SACRED HEART HOSPITAL 18102 #286-13-2001 L2003 **FM** *100 †18

HOFFMAN, Andre H. 451 W CHEW ST, STE 409 18102 #055-01-2000 L2002 **AN** *020

HOFFMAN, Arthur David. 3710 BROADWAY STE 101 18104 #041-13-1975 **CD IM** *020 †20

HOFFMAN, Errin James. 1255 S CEDAR CREST BLVD, STE 3600 18103 #041-02-1995 L1997 **DR** *020 †80

HOFFMANN, Ursula Maria. 421 W CHEW ST 18102 #041-01-1978 L1979 **FM** *020 †18

HOFFMAN-TERRY, Margaret L. 825 N CEDAR CREST BLVD 18104 #041-13-1989 L1991 **ID IM** *040 †20

HOLLAND, Clarence A, Jr. 451 W CHEW ST STE 407 18102 #041-13-1972 L1977 **GS OS** *020 †85

HOMAN, Joan Elizabeth. 1250 S CEDAR CREST BLVD, STE 300 18103 #010-01-2000 L2005 **CD** *020

HONG, John. 1240 S CEDAR CREST BLVD, STE 308 18103 #038-41-1992 L2007 **CCS** *020 †85

HORSTMANN, Rosemary A. 1251 S CEDAR CREST BLVD 18103 #041-02-1972 L1974 **P** *020 †75

HORTNER, Michael Steven. 421 W CHEW ST 18102 #041-12-1980 L1986 **FM** *020 †18

HOUIDES, Athanasios C. ■ 18104 #041-09-1967 L1968 **GS** *020 †85

HOUSHMAND, Elizabeth B. ■ 18103 #042-02-2001 L2002 **IM** *050 †20

HOWARD, Jerry Lee. 1200 S CEDAR CREST BLVD 18103 #422-01-2004 L2005 **GS** *012

HOWARD, Pamela Anne. 1240 S CEDAR CREST BLVD, STE 308 18103 #010-01-1993 L2004 **GS** *020 †85

HUBER, Stephen Joseph. 1255 S CEDAR CREST BLVD, STE 3600 18103 #041-14-1996 L2000 **VIR** *020 †80

HUDSON, Howard E. 1245 S CEDAR CREST BLVD, ALLENTOWN ANESTH ASC #301 18103 #041-01-1967 L1968 **AN GP** *020 †05

HUMMEL, James Patrick. PO BOX 3880, 1202 S CEDAR CREST BLVD 18106 #041-13-1996 L2007 **ICE** *020 †20

HUSAIN, Arif. 1600 HANOVER AVE 18109 #495-21-1978 L1992 **P** *020 †75

HYMAN, David Sheldon. ■ 18104 #051-04-1975 L1976 **OPH PME** *071 †35

IKEDA, Jane Yuriko. ■ 18104 #023-12-1987 L1990 **PD** *020 †55

INNIS, Patricia Ann S. ■ 18104 #067-01-1965 L1966 **FM** *071 †18

IOBST, William Francis. 1210 S CEDAR CREST BLVD, STE 3600 18103 #041-02-1982 L1983 **RHU IM** *020 †20

ISAYEV, Yevgeniy. 1250 S CEDAR CREST BLVD, STE 405 18103 #913-05-1992 L2002 **N** *020 †75

ISRAEL, Howard A. 1605 N CEDAR CREST BLVD, STE 605 18104 #011-04-1985 L1990 **AI IM** *020,03

ISRAEL, Karyn Joan. 451 W CHEW ST, STE 405 18102 #033-06-1984 L1999 **ON HEM** *020 †20

IYENGAR, Nandini Bhargav. 850 S 5TH ST, COASTAL FAMILY HEALTH CENT 18103 #495-99-1987 L1997 **PD** *020 †55

JACOBETZ, Dianne Renee. 1227 W LIBERTY ST, STE 303 18102 #041-14-1996 L1998 **PD** *020 †55

JACOBS, Larry Eugene. 1250 S CEDAR CREST BLVD, STE 300 18103 #041-07-1982 L1983 **CD** *040 †20

JAEGER, Christine Ann. ■ 18103 #036-05-1988 L1995 **IM** *020 †20

JAEGER, Robert Mason. 1240 S CEDAR CREST BLVD, STE 210 18103 #035-06-1947 L1955 **AM** *071 †25

JAFFE, John Saml. 1605 N CEDAR CREST BLVD, STE 411 18104 #035-19-1970 L1977 **U MDM** *095

JAIN, Sweety. 1730 W CHEW ST, LEHIGH VALLEY FAMILY HEALT 18104 #495-02-1985 L1994 **FM** *040 †18

JAJOO, Anurita. 1255 S CEDAR CREST BLVD, STE 3600 18103 #495-30-1997 L2004 **DR** *020 †80

JAN, Tayyaba Saeed. 7615 TILGHMAN ST 18106 #704-09-1978 L1982 **PD** *020 †55

JANCO, Jennifer Ann. 1227 W LIBERTY ST, STE 303 18102 #041-09-1997 L1999 **PD** *020 †55

JAUNZEMIS, Irma Lisete. ■ 18105 #594-01-1940 L1963 **GP** *071

JAZAERI, Omid. ■ 18103 #422-01-2003 L2003 **GS** *012

JIMENEZ, Soraya E. 1210 S CEDAR CREST BLVD 18103 #308-02-1992 L2004 **N** *020 †75

JIN, Hong. 401 N 17TH ST 18104 #243-21-1982 L2000 **PDC** *020 †55

JONES, David Geo. 1616 W ALLEN ST, BAUSCH & JONES EYE ASSOC 18102 #041-02-1965 L1966 **OPH** *020 †35

JONES, Edward Russell. ■ 18104 #007-02-1973 L1988 **OM IM** *062 †20,70

JONES, Kenneth Lee. ■ 18103 #010-02-2001 L2003 **EM** *020 †16

JOYCE, Kevin Francis. 421 W CHEW ST 18102 #010-02-1987 L1990 **IM** *020 †20

JULES, Marie Esther. 2548 W TILGHMAN ST 18104 #654-01-1991 L2004 **FM** *020 †18

JUNG, Jay Soo. 400 N 17TH ST, FAIRGROUNDS SURGICAL CTR 18104 #583-02-1962 L1970 **AN PD** *071 †55,05

JUNG, Serena Ann. 24 S 18TH ST 18104 #041-13-1993 L1997 **AN** *020 †05

JUNKER, Barnett J. ■ 18102 #035-19-1951 L1971 **AN** *071 †05

KABRA, Ashish Navneet. 1200 S CEDAR CREST BLVD, LEHIGH VALLEY HOSP 18103 #917-08-2006 L2006 **IM** *012

KAINZ, Gregory Francis. 1200 S CEDAR CREST BLVD, LEHIGH VALLEY HOSP 18103 #041-77-2006, ▲ L2006 **OBG** *012

KALE, Sanjay Dattatreya. 1600 HANOVER AVE, ALLENTOWN STATE HOSPITAL 18109 #495-57-1974 L1984 **AN** *020

KALOLA, Chirag Jay. 850 S 5TH ST 18103 #021-01-2003 L2007 **PM** *100

KANCHANA, Sulada. 1250 S CEDAR CREST BLVD, STE 405 18103 #025-07-1998 L2004 **N** *020 †75

KANE, Vivien Gene. 1255 S CEDAR CREST BLVD, STE 3600 18103 #035-48-1980 L1982 **DR** *020 †80

KAPOOR, Arun A. 24 S 18TH ST 18104 #035-48-1991 L1996 **AN PME** *020 †05

KARESS, Gina. 1210 S CEDAR CREST BLVD, STE 3600 18103 #041-14-1988 L1990 **IM** *020 †20

KAROUNOS, Garry Chas. 2200 W HAMILTON ST 18104 #033-06-1987 L1989 **OBG** *020 †30

KASPRENSKI, Matthew A. 1200 S CEDAR CREST BLVD 18103 #041-09-1957 L1958 **FM OS** *071 †18

KASPRENSKI, Matthew Louis. 1483 SHELBURNE CT 18104 #041-09-1983 L1984 **IM** *020 †20

KASUNDRA, Parshottam N. 1600 HANOVER AVE 18109 #495-23-1976 L1984 **IM EM** *020 †20

KATZ, Aaron David. 3710 BROADWAY 18104 #033-06-1994 L1998 **FM** *020 †18

KATZ, Barbara. 401 N 17TH ST 18104 #024-05-1979 L1980 **P** *075 †75 ‡

KATZ, Barbara Levin. 401 N 17TH ST 18104 #041-02-1976 L1999 **PD ADL** *020 †55 ‡

KAUFMAN, Barre Douglas. 1405 N CEDAR CREST BLVD 18104 #041-01-1955 L1956 **RHU IM** *071 †20

KAUFMAN, Daniel. 1405 N CEDAR CREST BLVD, STE 115 18104 #041-01-1983 L1988 **D** *020 †15

KAUFMAN, Jay Harris. 1210 S CEDAR CREST BLVD, STE 2300 18103 #041-01-1976 L1979 **PUD SME** *020 †20

KAVCHOK, Joseph, Jr. 2015 W HAMILTON ST, STE 103 18104 #042-01-1979 L1981 **OPH** *020 †35

KAZAHAYA, Masayuki. 1251 S CEDAR CREST BLVD, STE 307 18103 #041-09-1990 L1992 **OPH** *020 †35

KAZIMIR, Michal. 1200 S CEDAR CREST BLVD, DEPT OF INTERNAL MED 18103 #305-01-2003 L2004 **IM** *100

KEAN, Dennis Wm. 401 N 17TH ST, STE 204 18104 #041-13-1968 L1969 **PD** *071 †55

KEBLISH, Peter A, Jr. 250 CETRONIA RD, STE 100 18104 #041-09-1962 L1963 **ORS** *020 †40

KEGLOVITZ, Lisa. 1245 S CEDR CRST BLVD #301, ALLENTOWN ANESTHESIA ASSOC 18103 #024-05-1992 L2000 **AN** *020 †05

KEIL, Loretta Witczak. 450 W CHEW ST, SACRED HEART HOSP 18102 #041-07-1980 L1981 **IM** *040 †20

KELLER, Amy F. 400 N 17TH ST, FAIRGROUNDS SURGICAL CTR 18104 #021-01-1994 L1999 **AN** *020 †05

KELLEY, Chas Francis, Jr. ■ 18103 #041-12-1975 L1976 **PD** *020 †55

KENDER, Mark A. 1210 S CEDAR CREST BLVD, STE 3600 18103 #041-09-1983 L1985 **EM IM** *020 †20

KENVIN, John Edward. 1240 N 36TH ST, ALLENTOWN 18104 #041-13-1954 L1955 **PD** *071 †55

KENVIN, Monica Magnant. ■ 18104 #041-13-1963 L1965 **PD** *071

KEVITCH, Robert Blaine. 250 CETRONIA RD 18104 #041-13-1983 L1984 **PS** *020 †65

KHALIFA, Suha Falah. 450 W CHEW ST, SACRED HEART HOSPITAL 18102 #575-02-1999 L2003 **FM** *100 †18

KHAN, Elizabeth Acton. 4825 W TILGHMAN ST, STE 200 18104 #041-07-1991 L1993 **FM** *020 †18

KHAN, Nina. 798 HAUSMAN RD, STE 240 18104 #704-06-1996 L2006 **IM** *020 †20

KHAN, Yasin Nisar. 4825 W TILGHMAN ST 18104 #041-09-1985 L1985 **PME AN** *020 †05

KHANANI, Najma. ■ 18103 #422-01-1997 L2003 **OS** *100 †75

KHINDRI, Chetan Dev. 1040 S CEDAR CREST BLVD 18103 #495-03-1956 L1968 **TS VS** *071 †85,90

KHUBCHANDANI, Indru T. 1275 S CEDAR CREST BLVD 18103 #495-01-1956 L1968 **CRS** *020 †10

KIBELSTIS, John Alexander. 1251 S CEDAR CREST BLVD 18103 #041-01-1964 L1965 **PUD PCC** *071 †20

KIESEL, Robert. 400 N 17TH ST STE 20, SUITE 200 18104 #035-03-1960 L1963 **OPH** *020 †35

KIM, David Daewhan. 4825 W TILGHMAN ST 18104 #023-01-1990 L2001 **APM** *100 †60

KIM, Jin Il. 1245 S CEDAR CREST BLVD, STE 301 18103 #583-03-1964 L1972 **AN** *020

KIM, Larry Inlip. 1245 S CEDAR CREST BLVD, STE 301 18103 #041-02-2002 L2002 **AN** *100 †05

KIMMEL, Deborah Netsky. 501 SAINT JOHN ST, GOOD SHEPERD REHAB HOSP 18103 #041-07-1984 L1990 **PM** *020 †60

KINTZEL, James Edward. 1230 S CEDAR CREST BLVD, EASTERN PENN NEPHRO ASSOCI 18103 #041-01-1964 L1967 **NEP** *020 †20

KISTLER, Kermit K. 17TH & LIBERTY ST, LIBERTY SQUARE MED CTR 18104 #041-09-1943 L1948 **OPH** *072

KLAASSEN, Johanna H. 1251 S CEDAR CREST BLVD 18103 #660-04-1961 L1975 **CHP P** *020 ‡

KLEAVELAND, Jos Patrick. 1250 S CEDAR CREST BLVD, STE 300 18103 #035-01-1976 L1980 **CD IM** *050 †20

KNAPPER, Elizabeth Jean. 2895 HAMILTON BLVD 18104 #041-07-1967 **D** *071

KNECHT, Charles Lewis. 3131 COLLEGE HEIGHTS BLVD, STE 1200 18104 #041-02-1957 L1958 **R** *071 †80

KNIBBE, Pieter. ■ 18104 #660-01-1961 L1966 **CD IM** *071 †20

KNOUSE, Mark Christian. 1210 S CEDAR CREST BLVD 18103 #010-02-1982 L1983 **ID** *020 †20

KO, Dong H. 4825 W TILGHMAN ST, STE 200 18104 #025-07-1994 L2001 **PM PME** *020 †60

KOCH, Thomas Jacob. 1575 POND RD, STE 203 18104 #041-14-1982 L1987 **OTO** *020 †45

KONDUR, Prabhakara Rao. 1245 S CEDAR CREST BLVD, STE 301 18103 #495-50-1971 L1974 **AN** *020 †05

KOSTELNIK, Francis V. 421 W CHEW ST 18102 #041-02-1958 L1959 **CLP** *071 †50,28

KOVACS, Robert Joseph. 1230 S CEDAR CREST BLVD, STE 201 18103 #041-14-1979 L1980 **IM IMG** *020

KOVAR, Charles Edward. ■ 18103 #041-12-1956 L1957 **OBG** *071 †30

KRATZER, Glenn Stanley. 798 HAUSMAN RD 18104 #041-13-1974 L1975 **IM** *020 †20

KRAVITZ-SCHUBACH, Sharon. 4166 FAWN TRAIL RD, MEDICAL IMAGING OF LV PC 18104 #035-09-1990 L1996 **DR** *020 †80

KREITHEN, Harold. 401 N 17TH ST STE 211 18104 #041-09-1961 L1962 **A IM** *020 †03,20

KRICUN, Robert. 1255 S CEDAR CREST BLVD, STE 3600 18103 #041-13-1972 L1973 **DR** *020 †80

KRIEG, Susan Louise. ■ 18104 #041-12-1999 L2004 **EM** *020 †16

KRISCH, Ronald Avery. 1200 S CEDAR CREST BLVD 18103 #041-09-1978 L1979 **CHP P** *020 †75 ‡

KRISUKAS, Vera J Palmer. ■ 18104 #041-13-1944 L1945 **FM IMG** *072 †18

KRUKLITIS, Robert Jay. 1210 S CEDAR CREST BLVD, STE 2300 18103 #010-02-1997 L2001 **PCC** *020 †20

KUNDUR BHATIA, Aruna. 375 W LINDEN ST LOWR LEVEL, STEP- BY-STEP, INC 18102 #495-99-1989 L1998 **P** *020

KURTZ, Kenneth Stephen. 1255 S CEDAR CREST BLVD, STE 3600 18103 #041-02-1998 L2003 **DR** *020 †80

KUSHNICK, Howard Jay. 400 N 17TH ST, STE 101-106 18104 #021-01-1991 L1999 **OPH** *020 †35

KUSNIERCZYK, Michelle K. 1730 W CHEW ST 18104 #041-77-2004, ▲ L2004 **FM** *020

KUTTY, Shooja. 1227 W LIBERTY ST, STE 303 18102 #495-09-1996 L2005 **PD** *100

LABI, Maria C. 501 SAINT JOHN ST, GOOD SHEPHERD REHAB HOSPIT 18103 #035-06-1985 L1986 **P** *020 †60

LABIB, Maged Afifi. 421 W CHEW ST, DEPT OF FAMILY PRACTICE 18102 #915-10-1999 L2006 **FP** *012

LAM, Carl Augustus. ■ 18103 #041-09-1963 L1965 **OBG** *071 †30

LAND, Samuel D. 1200 S CEDAR CREST BLVD, 2ND FL 18103 #051-04-1988 L1996 **FOP** *020 †50

LANG, Gregory Michael. 440 S 15TH ST 18102 #041-12-1973 L1974 **OBG REN** *075 †30

LANG, John Bradley. 400 N 17TH ST, FAIRGROUNDS SURGICAL CTR 18104 #041-77-1977, ▲ L1978 **AN** *020 †05

LAPOS, Linda L. 1255 S CEDAR CREST BLVD, STE 3900 18103 #041-13-1985 L1986 **CRS** *020 †85,10

LAPP, John Richard. 1600 HANOVER AVE 18109 #041-09-1954 L1955 **GP** *071

LARUSSA, Liborio. PO BOX 689, CEDAR CREST & 1-78 18105 #011-03-2002 L2002 **PD HOS** *020 †55

LATONA, Sandra Jean. 421 W CHEW ST 18102 #041-09-1992 L1999 **IM** *020 †20

LAUFER, Fred. 4501 CRACKERSPORT RD 18104 #035-03-1979 L1983 **FM DS** *020 †18

LAYDEN, Paul William, Jr. 1255 S CEDAR CREST BLVD, STE 2200 18103 #041-02-2003 L2003 **IM** *012

LEAHEY, Alan Brett. 400 N 17TH ST STE 102 18104 #010-02-1987 L1988 **OPH** *020 †35

LE DEAUX, Pamela Faye. 1251 S CEDAR CREST BLVD, STE 104B 18103 #033-06-1989 L1999 **FM** *020 †18

LEE, Dong Pill. ■ 18103 #583-04-1964 L1972 **GP GS** *071

LEHMAN, Douglas R. ■ 18103 #023-07-1994 L2007 **GS** *012 †18

LEMBERG, Paul Stewart. 1575 POND RD STE 203 18104 #043-01-1990 L1995 **OTO** *020 †45

LERNER, Samuel. 1245 S CEDAR CREST BLVD, STE 301 18103 #660-01-1961 L1972 **AN** *020 †05

LETCHER, Abby S. ■ 18102 #041-01-1995 L1998 **FM** *020 †18

LEVICK, Donald Lee. 401 N 17TH ST 18104 #041-07-1982 L1983 **PD** *020 †55

LEVICK, Mary Stahl. 401 N 17TH ST 18104 #041-07-1982 L1983 **PD** *020 †55

LEVIN, Kenneth. 2717 W WASHINGTON ST 18104 #041-02-1977 L1978 **DR NM** *020 †28,80

LEVIN, Vadim A. 1250 S CEDAR CREST BLVD, STE 300 18103 #913-01-1989 L1997 **ICE CD** *020 †20

LEVINE, Arthur Leon. 401 N 17TH ST, STE 212 18104 #035-46-1975 L1982 **NEP CCM** *020 †20 ‡

LEVINE, Charles Ray. 450 W CHEW ST, FIRST FLOOR 18102 #041-12-1972 L1973 **ORS** *020 †40

LEVITT, Lawrence Paul. 1210 S CEDAR CREST BLVD 18103 #035-20-1965 L1972 **N** *071 †75

LI, Peter Mark. 1250 S CEDAR CREST BLVD, STE 400 18103 #024-01-1993 L2001 **NS** *020 †25

LI, Qiang. 1255 S CEDAR CREST BLVD, STE 3600 18103 #243-38-1989 L2004 **RNR DR** *020 †80

LI, Yuebing. 1250 S CEDAR CREST BLVD, STE 405 18103 #243-32-1986 L2003 **N CN** *020

LIAW, Danny. 1240 S CEDAR CREST BLVD, VALLEY HOSPITAL,MCC410 18103 #035-01-2002 L2004 **IM** *100 †20

LIEBERMAN, Richard M. 1259 S CEDAR CREST BLVD #2 18103 #041-13-1980 L1984 **U** *020 †95 ‡

LIN, Zwu-Shin. 1200 S CEDAR CREST BLVD, LEHIGH VALLEY HOSP CTR 18103 #385-01-1964 L1972 **DR** *020 †80

LINDENMUTH, Jennifer Mari. ■ 18102 #041-14-2008 L2008 *012

LINDERMAN, Anna. 1517 POND RD 18104 #913-69-1979 L1996 **PD** *020 †55

LISTHAUS, Alan David. 400 N 17TH ST, STE 101-106 18104 #035-46-1985 L1992 **OPH OS** *020 †35

LIU, Henry Tsunyen. 1251 S CEDAR CREST BLVD, STE 102A 18103 #035-20-1996 L1998 **FM** *020 †18

LOCKER, Karen Elizabeth. 5000 W TILGHMAN ST, STE 240 18104 #033-06-1987 L1995 **AN PMM** *020 †05

LOFFREDO, Linda Susan. 2901 HAMILTON BLVD, UNIT 100 18104 #041-12-1989 L1992 **FM** *020 †20

LONDON, Richard L. 401 N 17TH ST, STE 207 18104 #041-01-1975 L1976 **GE IM** *020 †20

LONG, Elmer Chas, Jr. 401 N 17TH ST 18104 #023-01-1966 L1967 **PD** *020 †55

LOZANO, Daniel Dennis. 1240 S CEDAR CREST BLVD, STE 210 18103 #005-02-1994 L2004 **GS** *020 †85

LUSSER, Martha Ann. 1251 S CEDAR CREST BLVD, STE 301A 18103 #028-03-1970 L1976 **N CHN** *020 †55,75

LUTZ, Ronald A, Sr. 1200 S CEDAR CREST BLVD 18103 #041-09-1972 L1973 **EM IM** *020 †20,16

LYCETTE, Christopher A. 1210 S CEDAR CREST BLVD, STE 1100 18103 #035-01-1997 L2004 **NS** *020

LYNCH, Christopher Gerard. 451 W CHEW ST STE 103 18102 #539-04-1975 L1982 **PM R** *020 †20

MAC KENZIE, Richard Scott. 1240 S CEDAR CREST BLVD, STE 214 18104 #036-08-1982 L1983 **EM** *020 †16

MACKIN, Glenn A. 1250 S CEDAR CREST BLVD, STE 405 18103 #041-02-1983 L1991 **N IM** *020 †20,75

MADBAK, Firas George. ■ 18104 #020-12-2005 L2007 **GS** *100

MAFFEO, Alphonse Anthony. 1245 S CEDAR CREST BLVD #301, ALLENTOWN ANESTH ASSOC INC 18103 #035-15-1972 L1977 **AN** *020 †05 ‡

MAGGIONCALDA, John B. 1240 S CEDAR CREST BLVD, STE 310 18103 #041-02-1999 L2005 **U** *020 †95

MAJEED, Warqaa. 450 W CHEW ST, STE 204 18102 #528-01-1993 L2001 **N** *020

MAKWANA, Vipul Devshibhai. 1255 S CEDAR CREST BLVD, STE 2200 18103 #495-23-1999 L2001 **IM** *020 †20

MALACOFF, Robt Frederick. 1250 S CEDAR CREST BLVD, STE 300 18103 #008-01-1975 L1989 **CD ICE** *020 †60

MALHOTRA, Kamna. ■ 18103 #496-07-1999 L2004 **P** *020 †75

MALHOTRA, Rakesh. 1259 S CEDAR CREST BLVD, STE 310 18103 #495-45-1994 L2002 **IM** *020 †20

MALIK, Shehzad Masood. 1202 S CEDAR CREST BLVD, STE 500, P.O. BOX 3880 18103 #422-01-2001 L2001 **CD** *100

MALLICK, Rajani Kumari. 421 W CHEW ST 18102 #160-04-1996 L2002 **FM** *020 †18

MANHOFF, Dion Timur. 421 W CHEW ST 18102 #041-13-1989 L1992 **PTH PCP** *020 †50 ‡

MANTELL, Harriet Baylies. ■ 18103 #016-06-1950 L1952 **PD** *071 †55

MANZOUL, Saad Mahmoudada. ■ 18102 #038-06-2007 L2007 **TY** *012

MAO, Nancy Ann. ■ 18104 #033-06-1986 L1991 **IM FM** *020 †20

MARAN, Patricia Lynn. ■ 18103 #035-48-2004 L2004 **OBG** *012

MARCUS, Norman H. 1202 S CEDAR CREST BLVD, JAINDL PAVILION STE 500 18103 #035-19-1977 L1981 **ICE CD** *020 †20

MARGER, Bruce R, Jr. ■ 18104 #041-01-1944 L1945 **CD IM** *071 †20

MARGRAF, John Wm. 798 HAUSMAN RD STE 270, SUITE 270 18104 #051-01-1974 L1975 **N IM** *020 †20

MARKOWITZ, Moshe Kenneth. 401 N 17TH ST 18104 #035-48-2001 L2004 **PD** *020 †55

MARKSON, William. 1486 HAMPTON RD 18104 #025-01-1984 L1989 **CD** *020 †20

MARQUEZ, Mirelle Ann Mend. 4TH AND CHEW STS, SACRED HEART HOSPITAL 18102 #748-01-2004 L2007 **FP** *012

MARRACCINI, Rory Lavell. 1251 S CEDAR CREST BLVD, STE 202A 18103 #041-12-1999 L2002 **P** *020 †75

MARSH, Jeffrey Allen. 1210 S CEDAR CREST BLVD, STE 2300 18103 #038-44-1988 L2004 **IM PCC** *020 †20

MARTIN, James. 1148 S CEDAR CREST BLVD 18103 #422-01-1983 L1997 **FM** *040 †18

MARTIN, Patricia. 1255 S CEDAR CREST BLVD, STE 3600 18103 #041-01-1985 L2000 **DR** *020 †80

MARTIN, Richard T. 450 W CHEW ST, STE 101 18102 #062-01-1978 L2000 **FPG** *040 †18

MARTINEZ, Rafael Ernesto. 1245 S CEDAR CREST BLVD, STE 301 18103 #042-01-2003 L2004 **AN** *020

MARTINEZ, Tania Consuelo. 711 W CHEW ST 18102 #042-02-2003 L2003 **P** *020

MARTINO, Martin Anthony. 400 N 17TH ST, STE 201 18104 #041-09-1998 L2005 **OBG** *020 †30

MARTUCCI, John C. 1255 S CEDAR CREST BLVD, STE 3600 18103 #041-02-2002 L2007 **DR** *100 †80

MARTZ, Mark Noel. 421 W CHEW ST 18102 #023-07-1970 L1980 **TS GS** *071 †85,90

MARVI, David D. ■ 18104 #517-01-1954 L1964 **P CHP** *020

MATCHETT, Stephen C. 1247 S CEDAR CREST BLVD, STE 106B 18103 #035-45-1987 L1995 **IM** *020 †20

MATHIEU, Jeffrey Scott. 1730 W CHEW ST 18104 #008-02-1996 L1998 **FM** *020 †18

MATHIEU, Susan Snyder. 1730 W CHEW ST 18104 #041-07-1996 L1998 **FM** *020 †18

MATZ, Karen Marie. 1245 S CEDAR CREST BLVD, STE 201 18103 #041-09-1988 L1990 **OBG** *020 †30

MAYER, Eva. 1227 W LIBERTY ST, STE 303 18102 #033-06-1997 L2003 **PD** *020 †55

MC CAMBRIDGE, Matthew M. 1210 S CEDAR CREST BLVD, STE 2300 18103 #010-02-1992 L1995 **PCC** *020 †20

MC CONNELL, Jeffrey Ross. 250 CETRONIA RD, STE 100 18104 #041-02-1985 L1986 **ORS OSS** *020 †40

MC CULLOUGH, James L, Jr. 1275 S CEDAR CREST BLVD, STE 301 18103 #041-01-1980 L1988 **VS** *020 †85

MC DAID, Patrick Joseph. 250 CETRONIA RD, STE 303 18104 #041-13-1995 L1997 **ORS** *020 †40

MC DONALD, Judith Ann. 798 HAUSMAN RD 18104 #041-09-1975 L1976 **IM** *020 †20

MC DONALD, Kenneth M. ■ 18103 #065-09-1963 L1974 **VS GS** *071 †85

MC GEHEAN, Heather M. 2200 W HAMILTON ST, STE 111 18104 #047-05-2001 L2005 **PD** *020

MCGILL, Kimberly Michelle. ■ 18103 #038-06-2007 L2007 **OBG** *012

MC GINLEY, George Wm. 401 N 17TH ST STE 103 18104 #010-02-1967 L1969 **OPH** *020 †35

MC GINLEY, Thomas Chas. 450 W CHEW ST, STE 101 18102 #041-14-1992 L1995 **FM** *040 †18

MC GOFF, Mari Ann. 421 W CHEW ST 18102 #041-14-1990 L1992 **IM** *020 †20

MC GORRY, Dennis Michael. 401 N 17TH ST 18104 #041-02-1999 L2001 **FM** *020 †18

MC HUGH, James Gerard. 825 N CEDAR CREST BLVD 18104 #308-07-1981 L1985 **EM IM** *020 †20

MC LAUGHLIN, Kimberly Pat. ■ 18103 #041-15-2004 L2004 **OBG** *012

MC LOUGHLIN, Thomas M, Jr. 1200 S CEDAR CREST BLVD, P O BOX 689 18103 #036-07-1988 L1995 **AN** *020 †05

MEADE, Thomas Danl. 1243 S CEDAR CREST BLVD, STE 2500 18103 #041-02-1983 L1984 **ORS OSM** *020 †40

MECCA, John J. 3710 BROADWAY, WEST END MEDICAL GROUP 18104 #041-09-1966 L1968 **GP** *020

MEEHAN, David Jos. 401 N 17TH ST 18104 #028-03-1986 L1996 **PD** *020 †55

MEHTA, Nalini Bharat. 325 N 5TH ST 18102 #495-96-1972 L1977 **RO** *020 †80

MEHTA, Shashikant Jivram. ■ 18104 #495-96-1972 L1992 **IM** *020 †20

MELAMUT, Gerald L. 1150 N 28TH ST 18104 #041-77-1965, ▲ L1966 **FM** *071

MELMAN, Jay Elliott. ■ 18104 #051-07-1984 L1985 **OS** *020

MERKLE, Larry N. 401 N 17TH ST, STE 215 18104 #407-10-1966 L1968 **END IM** *020 †20 ‡

METREVELI, Ramaz Evgeni. 1200 S CEDAR CREST BLVD, LEHIGH VLY HOSP 18103 #913-23-1988 L2000 **CRS** *012 †85

MICHAEL, Eva R. 2527 E TEXAS BLVD 18103 #915-02-1976 L1995 **FM** *020 †18

MIKA, Brian Philip. 1251 S CEDAR CREST BLVD, STE 202A 18103 #016-11-2003 L2007 **P** *020

MILLER, Elizabeth Anne. ■ 18106 #035-19-2003 L2004 **ID** *012

MILLER, Gerald Molnar. 451 W CHEW ST 18102 #041-09-1971 **IM** *020 †20

MILLER, Joseph Abraham. 825 N CEDAR CREST BLVD 18104 #041-02-1955 L1956 **OBG** *071 †20

MILLER, Kerry Dane. 3131 COLLEGE HEIGHTS BLVD 18104 #041-13-1976 L1977 **RHU IM** *020 †20

MILLER, William Lloyd. 1730 W CHEW ST, LEHIGH VLY FMLY HLTH CTR 18104 #036-01-1977 L1979 **FM** *030 †18

MILLET, Brent Louis. 250 CETRONIA RD, STE 100 18104 #021-06-1989 L1994 **PM** *020 †60

MISHKIN, Mark Howard. 798 HAUSMAN RD, STE 240 18104 #035-09-1976 L1980 **IM** *020 †20 ‡

MISHRIKI, Yehia Y. 1210 S CEDAR CREST BLVD, STE 3600 18103 #016-43-1979 L1986 **IM** *040 †20

MISSELBECK, Timothy Scott. 1200 S CEDAR CREST BLVD 18103 #305-01-2002 L2003 **GS** *012

MOATZ, James D. 1200 S CEDAR CREST BLVD 18103 #041-13-1943 L1944 **GP** *071

MOHAMED-ALI, Abul-Kassim. 1200 S CEDAR CREST BLVD 18103 #913-15-1971 L1979 **IM** *020 †20 ‡

MOHAMMED, Muneeruddin Qua. PO BOX 689, LEHIGH VALLEY HOSPITAL 18105 #422-01-2006 L2007 **IM** *012

MONKOWSKI, Daniel Henry. 1210 S CEDAR CREST BLVD 18103 #041-02-2000 L2001 **ID** *020 †20

MOORE, Morgan Francis. ■ 18106 #035-08-1955 L1960 **P** *072

MORALES, Fermin Esteban. 1200 S CEDAR CREST BLVD 18103 #275-01-1985 L2003 **GS** *012

MORFFI, Oscar Andres. 401 N 17TH ST STE 307, LEHIGH VALLEY PEDIATRIC AS 18104 #308-05-1982 L1986 **PD** *020 †55

MORRISON, Alan N. 451 W CHEW ST, STE 405 18102 #035-08-1951 L1972 **HO IM** *071 †20

MORRISSEY, Wm Michael. 250 CETRONIA RD, STE 301 18104 #024-05-1992 L1996 **PS** *020 †65

MORSE, Richard Jason. 401 N 17TH ST STE 307 18104 #041-14-1986 L1989 **PD** *020 †55

MOSCA, Paul Jos. 1240 S CEDAR CREST BLVD, STE 205 18103 #051-01-1995 L2004 **GS** *020 †85

MOTLEY, Robert Jos. 1730 W CHEW ST, LEHIGH VALLEY FAMILY HEAL 18104 #041-02-1985 L1986 **FM FPG** *020 †18

MOTSAY, Stephen J. 1200 S CEDAR CREST BLVD 18103 #041-14-1988 L1990 **FM** *020 †18

MOUSSA, Sami H. 951 N 4TH ST 18102 #875-01-1987 L1997 **IM** *020 †20

MUJTABA, Bilal. ■ 18104 #704-29-2003 L2005 **IM** *012

MUJTABA, Najda Ansari. 421 W CHEW ST, SACRED HEART HOSP 18102 #704-02-2000 L2005 **FP** *012

MUKETE, Bertrand Njume. PO BOX 689, LEHIGH VALLEY HOSPITAL 18105 #422-01-2007 L2007 **IM** *012

MULLIN, Edward M, Jr. 1240 S CEDAR CREST BLVD, STE 310 18103 #035-01-1968 L1976 **U** *020 †95 ‡

MURPHY, Brian Patrick. 1240 S CEDAR CREST BLVD 18103 #010-01-1980 L1989 **U** *020 †95

MURPHY, Miles, II. 2200 W HAMILTON ST, STE 111 18104 #041-12-1997 L2000 **OBG** *020 †30

MYLNARSKY, Michael. 1245 S CEDAR CREST BLVD, STE 301 18104 #035-47-2003 L2007 **AN** *020

NADER, Joseph N. 401 N 17TH ST STE 308 18104 #264-04-1958 L1968 **CD IM** *020 ‡

NAEEM, Sobia. 4TH AND CHEW STS, SACRED HEART HOSPITAL 18102 #704-01-2005 L2007 **FP** *012

NAIR, Suresh G. 1240 S CEDAR CREST BLVD, STE 103 18103 #041-02-1984 L1985 **ON HEM** *020 †20

NAKTIN, Jaan Peter. 1240 S CEDAR CREST BLVD 18103 #041-02-1994 L1996 **ID** *020 †20

NEPOMUCENO, Sherwin Papa. 421 W CHEW ST, SACRED HEART HOSP 18102 #748-01-2001 L2004 **FM** *020 †18

NEUMANN, Peter Henry. 401 N 17TH ST, STE 105 18104 #041-09-1958 L1959 **FM PS** *072

NEWCOMB, James Allan. 1255 S CEDAR CREST BLVD, STE 3600 18103 #041-12-1986 L1992 **DR** *020 †80

NEWMAN, Christopher David. 1255 S CEDAR CREST BLVD, STE 2200 18103 #010-02-1998 L2006 **IM** *020 †20

NEWMAN, Heather Louisa. 1255 S CEDAR CREST BLVD, STE 3600 18103 #010-02-2000 L2006 **DR RNR** *100 †80

NGO, Hieu Van. 1736 W HAMILTON ST 18104 #941-01-1965 L1981 **DR** *062

NICHOLSON, Bruce David. 1240 S CEDAR CREST BLVD, STE 307 18103 #051-07-1983 L1992 **PMM PLM** *020 †05

NICKLIN, Sarah. 2166 S 12TH ST STE 402, OACIS SERVICES 18103 #032-01-1989 L1997 **FM EM** *020 †18

NIGGLEY, Cindy Monette. 1730 W CHEW ST 18104 #019-02-1990 L2002 **FM** *020 †18

NIMELY, Contah Stella. 421 W CHEW ST, SACRED HEART HOSP 18102 #610-01-1989 L2004 **FM** *100 †18

NOGUEIRA, Emanuel Florim. ■ 18104 #041-15-2006 L2006 **GS** *012

NOOR, Shahid. 421 W CHEW ST 18102 #704-24-2000 L2007 **FP** *012

NORELLI, Charles Clyde. 250 CETRONIA RD, STE 100 18104 #041-02-1983 L1984 **PM** *020 †60 ‡

NORMINGTON, Ernest Y, Jr. 1611 POND RD 18104 #041-09-1968 L1969 **OBG** *020 †30

NORRIS, Edward Robert. 1251 S CEDAR CREST BLVD 18103 #036-07-1996 L2003 **P** *020 †75

NOSAL, Jules. ■ 18103 #041-13-1961 L1962 **FM** *071

NUSCHKE, John D, Jr. 798 HAUSMAN RD 18104 #041-09-1983 L1984 **IM IMG** *020 †20

NWAIZUZU, Peter Chinedu. 450 W CHEW ST, SACRED HEART HOSPITAL 18102 #690-12-1998 L2003 **FM** *100

OBEID, Edmond. 951 N 4TH ST 18102 #875-03-1992 L2003 **FM** *020 †18

OBERLENDER, Steven Alan. 1259 S CEDR CRST BLVD #100, ADVANCED DEMATOLOGY ASSOC 18103 #041-02-1995 L2000 **D DS** *020 †15

OKUNSKI, Walter John. 1230 S CEDAR CREST BLVD, STE 204 18103 #035-15-1962 L1968 **PS** *020 †65

OLIVER, John Geo. ■ 18109 #041-02-1944 L1944 **FM** *071 †18

ORDWAY, Eugene Elliot, Jr. 1255 S CEDAR CREST BLVD, STE 1200 18103 #041-09-1977 L1979 **CD IM** *020 †20

ORIEL, Robert Jos. 1202 S CEDAR CREST BLVD, STE 500 18103 #041-09-1974 L1975 **CD IM** *020 †20

OROURKE, Daniel Kevin. 325 N 5TH ST, THIRD FLOOR 18102 #041-07-1988 L1992 **NS** *020 †25

ORR, Paul Lee. 2844 PENNSYLVANIA ST 18104 #041-07-1974 L1975 **P** *071 †75

OSBORNE, Mark Allen. 1255 S CEDAR CREST BLVD, STE 3600 18103 #016-02-1981 L1987 **OS DR** *020 †80

OSTERWALD, Bonnie E B. 1251 S CEDAR CREST BLVD, STE 109 18103 #035-47-1988 L1996 **OBG** *020 †30

OSTFELD, David Alan. 501 SAINT JOHN ST 18103 #035-15-1971 L1982 **DR GP** *020 †80

PADMANABHAN, Savitri. 1240 S CEDAR CREST BLVD, STE 103 18103 #496-07-1994 L2005 **HO** *020 †20

PADOLICK, Joseph Michael. 953 BELFORD RD, 18103 #041-13-1996 L1998 **HO IM** *100 †20

PAISTE, Juhan. 1245 S CEDAR CREST BLVD, STE 301 18104 #913-94-1988 L1996 **AN** *020 †05

PALUMBO, Robert Craig. 250 CETRONIA RD, STE 300 18104 #033-06-1986 L2002 **ORS OSM** *020 †40

PANDEY, Prasant. 1202 S CEDAR CREST BLVD, THE HEART CARE GRP 5TH FL 18103 #041-14-1997 L1999 **CD** *020 †20

PANTANO, James Albert. 1736 W HAMILTON ST 18104 #041-12-1970 L1975 **CD IM** *020 †20

PAONESSA, Nina. 1275 S CEDAR CREST BLVD 18103 #041-78-1998, ▲ L2003 **CRS** *020

PAPOLA, John Stephen. ■ 18104 #041-13-1982 L1983 **OTO** *071 †45

PARANICAS, Jamie Dimitria. 1202 S CEDAR CREST BLVD, STE 500 18103 #041-09-1984 L1985 **CD IM** *020 †20

PARAYIL, Mathew Johnson. 421 W CHEW ST, DEPT OF FAMILY PRACTICE 18102 #473-02-2004 L2006 **FP** *012

PARK, Sung Ho. 711 W CHEW ST 18102 #583-10-1968 L1972 **P** *020

PASCAL, Joseph. 1251 S CEDAR CREST BLVD #3 18103 #649-14-1972 **U GS** *020 †95

PASIMIO, Maria Raquel M. 401 N 17TH ST, STE 309 18104 #748-02-1994 L2005 **PDC** *020 †55

PASQUALE, Michael David. 1240 S CEDAR CREST BLVD, STE 308 18103 #010-02-1986 L1993 **CCS GS** *020 †85

PATEL, Bindi Shantilal. 702 N 38TH ST 18104 #038-44-1996 L1998 **FM** *020 †18

PATEL, Nainesh C. 1250 S CEDAR CREST BLVD, STE 300 18104 #305-01-1995 L2000 **IC** *020 †20

PATEL, Niketu M. 1575 POND RD STE 203 18104 #051-07-1995 L1998 **OTO HNS** *020 †45

PATEL, Vishal. 1200 S CEDAR CREST BLVD, LEHIGH VALLEY HOSP 18103 #422-01-2003 L2004 **IM** *100 †20

PATRO, Phalgunee. 1227 W LIBERTY ST, STE 303 18102 #495-13-1997 L2005 **PD** *020 †55

PATTISON, Elizabeth Percy. ■ 18103 #041-07-1960 L1961 **GP** *071

PAUL, George J. ■ 18104 #016-42-1954 L1983 **NTR GS** *071 †85

PEARCE, Richard Chas. 798 HAUSMAN RD, STE 240 18104 #041-13-1960 L1961 **FM** *020 †18 ‡

PEIFER, Maryann King. 1251 S CEDAR CREST BLVD, STE 104B 18103 #041-13-1987 L1989 **FM** *020 †18

PERIN, Lawrence Anthony. 2100 MACK BLVD 18103 #041-01-1972 L1974 **PHP OM** *020 †18

PETERS, Charles David. 401 N 17TH ST, STE 201 18104 #041-01-1958 L1959 **IM** *020 †20 ‡

PETERSON, Emily Ann. ■ 18103 #041-15-2003 L2003 **PS** *012

PETTINE, John Paul. 1259 S CEDAR CREST BLVD, STE 220 18103 #014-01-1996 L1998 **IM** *020 †20 ‡

PHELAN, William Jos. 2200 W HAMILTON ST STE 214 18104 #041-01-1973 L1980 **PD** *020 †55

PHILLIPS, Theodore Geo. 1240 S CEDAR CREST BLVD, STE 403 18103 #024-01-1983 L1990 **CD TS** *020 †85,90

PHIPPS, Virginia C. ■ 18104 #033-75-2000, ▲ L2003 **IM** *020 †20

PICKLE, Jacob H, IV. 3131 COLLEGE HEIGHTS BLVD 18104 #041-09-1984 L1985 **GE IM** *020 †20 ‡

PINKNEY, Kerrie Ann. 1200 S CEDAR CREST BLVD, 6TH FLR BOX 689 JAINDL 18103 #055-07-1994 L2003 **CCP** *020 †55

PINNAMANENI, Sreenivasa R. 1600 HANOVER AVE, ALLENTOWN STATE HOSPITAL 18109 #495-50-1969 L1992 **P** *020

PIOTROWSKI, Theresa Amy. 1251 S CEDAR CREST BLVD 18103 #010-02-1989 L2006 **FM** *020 †18

PLETCHER, Jonathan Robert. 400 N 17TH ST, STE 202 18104 #041-12-1994 L1996 **ADL** *020 †55

PLOWRIGHT, Leon Nicholas. ■ 18104 #041-14-2007 L2007 **OBG** *012

POLLICE, Paul Ferninano. 250 CETRONIA RD, STE 100 18104 #041-01-1994 L2000 **OAR** *020 †40

POPESCU, Dan. 1240 S CEDAR CREST BLVD, STE 305 18103 #781-01-1995 L2001 **IM** *020 †20

POST, Alison Beth. 2901 HAMILTON BLVD, UNIT 300 18103 #041-09-1996 L1999 **IM** *020 †20

POST, Robert. 1240 S CEDAR CREST BLVD, STE 103 18103 #035-06-1963 L1972 **ON HEM** *020 †20

POWERS, Victor John. 451 W CHEW ST STE 306 18102 #041-14-1981 L1982 **IM** *020 †20

PRAGER, David. 1240 S CEDAR CREST BLVD #016-42-1958 L1964 **ON HEM** *071 †20

PRELETZ, Rudolph John, Jr. ■ 18103 #041-02-1963 L1965 **GS** *071

PRESS, Danielle Maren. 1200 S CEDAR CREST BLVD, LEHIGH VLY HOSP 18103 #041-15-2007 L2007 **GS** *012

PRICE, Gregory Winston. 1255 S CEDAR CREST BLVD, STE 3600 18103 #023-01-1986 L2001 **DR** *020 †80

PRIMELO, Ralph Albert. 1605 N CEDAR CREST BLVD, STE 610 18104 #024-07-1986 L1993 **P** *020 †75

PROOTHI, Subhash Chander. 451 W CHEW ST, STE 405 18102 #495-69-1971 L1979 **ON HEM** *020 †20 ‡

PROVOST, George Louis. 1208 HANOVER AVE 18109 #041-13-1977 L1978 **FM** *020 †18

PRYBLICK, Judith Richmond. 3131 COLLEGE HEIGHTS BLVD, STE 1100 18104 #041-77-1989, ▲ L1990 **FM** *020

PUSCHAK, Russell Basil. ■ 18103 #041-09-1956 L1957 **PD** *071 †55

QUEVEDO, Jonathan Paul. 501 SAINT JOHN ST 18103 #035-01-1980 L1983 **PM** *020 †60

QURASHI, Sultana K. 421 W CHEW ST 18102 #704-09-1968 L1977 **IM** *020

QURESHI, Shabana Nadeem. 421 W CHEW ST #704-21-2000 L2005 **FP** *012

RADIO, Gregory John. 1611 POND RD 18104 #041-14-1973 L1974 **OBG PHP** *020 †30

RAHJOI MONFARED, Ziba. 124 E SUSQUEHANNA ST 18103 #308-11-1992 L2001 **FM** *100 †18 ‡

RAHMAN, Atira. 450 W CHEW ST 18102 #704-16-1990 L2004 **PD** *020 †55

RAI, Anil Kumar. 3110 HAMILTON BLVD, VETERANS ADMINISTRATION CL 18103 #496-09-1988 L1998 **P** *020 †20

RAI, Nisha. 1600 HANOVER AVE, ALLENTOWN STATE HOSPITAL 18109 #495-47-1971 L1981 **IM** *030

RAJASEKHARAN, Amirtha B. 3110 HAMILTON BLVD 18103 #495-04-1973 L1995 **IM** *020 †20

RAKHMANINE, Michael I. 1255 S CEDAR CREST BLVD, STE 3900 18103 #913-01-1989 L1999 **CRS** *020 †85,10

RAMANUJAM, Sandeep Ravi. 1628 W CHEW ST 18102 #422-01-2006 L2007 **FP** *012

RAMASAMY, Dhanalakshmi. 1255 S CEDAR CREST BLVD, STE 3800 18103 #495-94-1995 L2001 **CHP** *020 †75

RAPPAPORT, Daniel Michael. 1736 W HAMILTON ST 18104 #869-05-1984 L1986 **IM IMG** *020 †20

RATH, Manasija. 421 W CHEW ST, SACRED HEART HOSP 18102 #495-20-2000 L2004 **FPG** *012

RAVI, Sasikala. 1600 HANOVER AVE, ALLENTOWN STATE HOSPITAL 18109 #495-62-1980 L2000 **CHP** *020

RAY, Daniel Eric. 1210 S CEDAR CREST BLVD, STE 2300 18103 #038-40-1988 L1998 **CCM** *020 †20

RAY, Madhab. PO BOX 689, LEHIGH VALLEY HOSPITAL 18105 #495-02-1991 L2007 **IM** *012

REDENBAUGH, James Edwards. 1250 S CEDAR CREST BLVD, STE 405 18103 #041-12-1970 L1977 **N AM** *020 †75

REIHMAN, Kristin Clague. ■ 18103 #005-11-2004 L2004 **FP** *012

REILLY, James Frank. 1240 S CEDAR CREST BLVD, SURGICAL SPECIALISTS OF TH 18103 #041-02-1989 L1992 **CCS** *020 †85

REINHART, John Wm. ■ 18103 #041-13-1960 L1961 **GP** *020

RENGABHASHYAM, Padmanabha. 451 W CHEW ST STE 409, SHMA ANESTHESIA 18102 #495-42-1989 L2005 **AN** *020 †05

RESPET, Patrick Butler. 250 CETRONIA RD, STE 100 18104 #041-09-1968 L1969 **ORS TRS** *020 †40

RHODES, Luther V, III. 1210 S CEDAR CREST BLVD 18103 #016-43-1970 L1971 **ID IM** *020 †20

RIBAUDO, Vanessa Ann. ■ 18103 #035-09-2000 L2007 **PCC** *100 †20

RICE, Scott Alan. 401 N 17TH ST STE 311 18104 #041-13-1991 L1993 **PD** *020 †55

RIEDEL, C William. 1941 W HAMILTON ST, STE 100 HAMILTON OBGYN PC 18104 #041-77-1995, ▲ L1996 **OBG** *020

RIENZO, Robert James. 1255 S CEDAR CREST BLVD, STE 3600 18103 #035-09-1975 L1980 **NM DR** *020 †80,28 ‡

RITTENHOUSE, Eric Ray. 440 S 15TH ST 18102 #041-02-1991 L1993 **OBG** *020 †30

RIVERA, Diana Marina. 1200 S CEDAR CREST BLVD, DEPT MED 18103 #042-02-2007 L2007 **IM** *012

ROBB, Marie Eileen. 1255 S CEDAR CREST BLVD, STE 3600 18103 #041-02-1979 L1984 **DR** *020 †20

RODENBERGER, Bruce M. 1251 S CEDAR CREST BLVD, STE 108A 18103 #041-01-1961 L1962 **GYN** *071 †30

RODRIGUEZ, Ernesto. 1605 N CEDAR CREST BLVD, STE 610 18104 #042-03-1992 L1996 **OBG** *020

RODRIGUEZ, Victor R. 6083 HAMILTON BLVD 18106 #042-03-1980 L1985 **PD** *020 †55

ROIZIN, John Dennis. 1409 UNION BLVD, REAR ENTRANCE 18109 #067-04-1992 L1996 **OBG** *020 †30

ROJAS, Julio Renan. 501 N 17TH ST, STE 207 18104 #737-03-1969 L1974 **OPH** *020 †35

ROONEY, Kris Ann. PO BOX 689, 6TH FLOOR JAINDL 18105 #041-14-2004 L2004 **PD HOS** *012 †55

ROSE, Bruce Irwin. 1275 S CEDAR CREST BLVD, STE 3 18103 #011-02-1982 L1988 **REN GYN** *020 †30

ROSENBERG, Howard David. 1255 S CEDAR CREST BLVD, STE 3600 18103 #035-09-1976 L1982 **R** *020 †80

ROSENFELD, Edward Jay. 1255 S CEDAR CREST BLVD, STE 2220 18103 #041-02-1987 L1988 **IM** *020 †20

ROSS, James Matthew. 1210 S CEDAR CREST BLVD, STE 3600 18103 #033-06-1984 L1987 **RHU IM** *020 †20

ROSSI, Michael A. 1250 S CEDAR CREST BLVD, STE 300 18104 #043-01-1984 L1989 **CD IM** *030 †20

ROSSINI, Gerald John M. 1736 W HAMILTON ST 18104 #041-13-1998 L2004 **ORS OSM** *020 †40

ROVITO, Peter Francis. 842 N 19TH ST 18104 #041-13-1983 L1985 **GS** *040 †85

ROY, Priyanka P. 421 W CHEW ST 18102 #495-99-1991 L2004 **IM** *020 †20

RUELAS SALGADO, Miguel Sa. 421 W CHEW ST, DEPT OF FAMILY PRACTICE 18102 #649-46-2001 L2006 **FP** *012

RUHT, Barry Alan. 1605 N CEDAR CREST BLVD, STE 608 18104 #041-13-1975 L1976 **ORS** *020 †40

RUSH, Wendy Jean. 2901 HAMILTON BLVD 18103 #051-07-1984 L1985 **FM** *020 †18

RUSSO, Michael Richard. 1736 W HAMILTON ST 18104 #041-77-1978, ▲ L1979 **GPM** *071

RUST, Orion Albert. PO BOX 7017, LEHIGH VALLEY HOSP 18105 #045-04-1984 L1996 **OBG MFM** *020 †30

RYAN-MITLYNG, Theresa A. 1605 N CEDAR CREST BLVD, STE 610 18104 #026-04-1971 L1998 **PD** *030 †55

SAAVEDRA, Geraldo A. 823 W WALNUT ST 18102 #737-09-1988 L1999 **END IM** *020 †20

SADR, Farrokh S. 451 W CHEW ST STE 409 18102 #517-01-1966 L1975 **TS** *020 †85,90

SAEED, Imran. 1200 S CEDAR CREST BLVD, LEHIGH VLY HOSP 18103 #305-01-2001 L2007 **CRS** *012 †85

SALANDY, Shellyann M. 450 W CHEW ST, 2ND FL 18102 #010-03-1998 L2000 **PD** *020 †55

SALAS-LOPEZ, Debbie. 1200 S CEDAR CREST BLVD, JDMCC SUITE 410 18103 #033-05-1996 L2007 **IM** *020 †20

SALDUKAS, Diane Marie. 1200 S CEDAR CREST BLVD 18103 #041-13-1986 L1987 **EM** *020 †20

SALERNO, Francis Anthony. 1200 S CEDAR CREST BLVD 18103 #041-13-1974 L1975 **IM IMG** *020 †20

SALTZ, Stephanie Marie. 2200 W HAMILTON ST, STE 111 18104 #051-01-2002 L2002 **OBG** *100

SANDBERG, James A. 1202 S CEDAR CREST BLVD, STE 500 JAINDL PAVILION 18103 #024-16-1978 L1984 **CD IM** *020 †20

SANDHU, Rovinder Singh. ■ 18106 #041-02-1995 L1999 **CCS** *020 †85

SANTANIELLO, Marnie Sue. 4033 EVERGREEN RD, AVENTURA COMPREHENSIVE CAN 18104 #041-14-2002 L2002 **GS** *100 †85

SANTIAGO RIVERA, Jose E. 1200 S CEDAR CREST BLVD 18103 #308-13-2005 L2006 **IM** *012

SAPICO, Leizl Firme. 4TH AND CHEW STS, SACRED HEART HOSPITAL 18102 #748-31-2005 L2007 **FP** *012

SARACHEK, Norman Saul. ■ 18103 #041-01-1964 L1965 **CD IM** *071 †20

SARUBIN, Daniel Ronald. 421 W CHEW ST 18102 #041-13-1969 L1970 **DR R** *071 †80

SARVER, Gwendolyn R. 1611 POND RD STE 400 18104 #041-14-2003 **PD** *020 †20

SAUNDERS, Celeste Marie. 1243 S CEDAR CREST BLVD, HEALTHWORKS 18103 #041-13-1983 L1986 **EM OM** *020 †16 ‡

SAWARES, Hani Iskander. 3110 HAMILTON BLVD, ALLENTOWN VETERANS CLINIC 18103 #915-03-1972 L1997 **IM** *020 †20

SAWYNA, Vitaly. 2224 W LIBERTY ST 18104 #041-07-1981 L1982 **GS** *020 †85

SAXENA, Anil. 1600 HANOVER AVE 18109 #496-09-1976 L1984 **CHP P** *020 †75

SCAFFIDI, John Jos, Jr. 2200 W HAMILTON ST, STE 103 18104 #033-06-1988 L1997 **OBG** *020 †30

SCAGLIOTTI, Chas John L. 1255 S CEDAR CREST BLVD, STE 1100 18103 #561-11-1970 L1972 **GS** *020 †80

SCHAEFGEN, Madalyn. 1251 S CEDAR CREST BLVD, STE 104B 18103 #041-02-1982 L1983 **FM** *074 †18

SCHAIRER, Henry Louis, Jr. 1230 S CEDAR CREST BLVD, STE 301 18103 #033-05-1996 L1998 **NEP** *020 †20

SCHELLENBERG, Andrea. 1245 S CEDAR CREST BLVD, INC/STE 301 18103 #041-14-1995 L1997 **AN** *020 †05

SCHELLENBERG, Joseph B. 1210 S CEDAR CREST BLVD, STE 2300 18103 #041-01-1993 L1995 **PCC** *020 †20

SCHENCK, Paul Henry. 5239 HAMILTON BLVD 18106 #033-05-1970 L1975 **OPH** *020 †35

SCHILKE, Clifford Harold. 1501 N CEDAR CREST BLVD, STE 101 18104 #041-09-1978 L1979 **P IM** *020 †75

SCHOCHET, Elie. ■ 18104 #025-12-2003 L2003 **GS** *012

SCHOLL, Harvey Wm, Jr. 1791 AIRPORT RD 18109 #041-02-1967 L1968 **R** *020 †80 ‡

SCHUKA, Edward Anthony. 450 W CHEW ST, SACRED HEART HOSPITAL 18102 #654-01-2000 L2002 **FM** *020 †18

SCHUMAECKER, Matthew M. 1250 S CEDAR CREST BLVD, STE 300 18103 #067-01-2000 L2004 **CD** *020 †20

SCHWANN, Nanette Margaret. 1245 S CEDAR CREST BLVD, STE 301 18103 #024-05-1989 L1995 **AN** *020 †05

SCHWARTZ, Janet H. 1255 S CEDAR CREST BLVD, THE GUIDANCE PROG STE 3800 18103 #035-46-1978 L1982 **P** *020 †75 ‡

SCHWARTZ, Michael David. 401 N 17TH ST 18104 #041-01-1986 L1989 **PD** *020 †55

SCHWIEP, Francis. 1210 S CEDAR CREST BLVD, STE 2300 18103 #024-05-1978 L1988 **IM PUD** *020 †20

SCHWINGE, Elaine Alice. 2895 HAMILTON BLVD STE 103 18104 #041-07-1945 L1946 **P** *071 †75

SCORZA, William Edwin. 1200 S CEDAR CREST BLVD, DEPT OBG 18103 #035-08-1981 L2008 **MFM OBG** *020 †30

SCOTT, Carolyn Simpson. 1611 POND RD, STE 101 18104 #041-13-1990 L1993 **OBG** *020 †30

SCOTT, Steven Alfred. 401 N 17TH ST 18104 #041-02-1982 L1983 **IMG IM** *020 †20

SECKINGER, Raymond P. 451 W CHEW ST, STE 403 18102 #041-02-1953 L1954 **P** *071 †75

SEMBROT, Joseph Thos. 3110 HAMILTON BLVD 18103 #041-13-1961 L1962 **IM DIA** *071 †20 ‡

SENFT, Karen E. 850 S 5TH ST, GOOD SHEPHERD REHAB HOSPIT 18103 #041-14-1979 L1981 **OS** *020 †55

SEXTON, Scott Edwin. 250 CETRONIA RD STE 303, OAA ORTHOPAEDIC SPECIALIST 18104 #033-05-2000 L2007 **ORS** *020

SHAFF, Darryn Ivor. 1255 S CEDAR CREST BLVD, STE 3600 18103 #041-09-1994 L1996 **VIR** *020 †80

SHAH, Kamalesh T. 1210 S CEDAR CREST BLVD, STE 3700 18103 #495-23-1982 L1989 **GS TRS** *020 †85

SHAH, Kumar. 1200 S CEDAR CREST BLVD 18103 #661-02-2006 **IM** *012

SHAH, Surendra Shantilal. 1736 W HAMILTON ST 18104 #496-38-1974 L1979 **ON HEM** *020 †20

SHAHEEN, James C. 1245 S CEDAR CREST BLVD, STE 301 18103 #041-14-1994 L1997 **AN** *020 †05

SHAHIN, Islam. 1251 S CEDAR CREST BLVD, STE 3600 18103 #033-06-2000 L2005 **VIR IM** *100 †80 ‡

SHALABY, Waleed S. 400 N 17TH ST, STE 201 18104 #045-01-1996 L1999 **GO GYN** *020 †30

SHAMPAIN, Mark Philip. 3131 COLLEGE HEIGHTS BLVD 18104 #024-05-1972 L1981 **AI PDA** *020 †55,03

SHANE, John Jos. 1200 S CEDAR CREST BLVD 18103 #041-09-1961 L1962 **CLP** *020 †50

SHANER, Catharine Louise. 401 N 17TH ST, STE 307 18104 #041-09-1984 L1987 **PD** *071 †55

SHARIFF, Nasir. PO BOX 689, LEHIGH VALLEY HOSPITAL 18105 #496-39-1998 L2007 **IM** *012

SHARMA, Rita. ■ 18103 #422-01-2003 L2004 **FM** *100 †18

SHEKA, Karthik. 1255 S CEDAR CREST BLVD, STE 1200 18103 #422-01-1997 L2005 **CD** *020 †20

SHERWIN, Gerald Prettyman. 1240 S CEDAR CREST BLVD, STE 114 18103 #041-13-1966 L1967 **GS** *020 †85 ‡

SHIEH, Kan-Chien. 421 W CHEW ST 18102 #244-02-1973 L1976 **R** *020 †80

SHIELDS, Mary Susan. 1245 S CEDAR CREST BLVD 18103 #041-13-1977 L1978 **PD AI** *020 †55

SHIRK, Colby Michael. 2042 E HIGHLAND ST 18109 #041-14-2003 L2003 **EM** *020 †16

SHOEMAKER, Elliot Ivan. 1255 S CEDAR CREST BLVD, STE 3600 18103 #041-13-1983 L1984 **RNR IM** *020 †80

SHOEMAKER, Patricia L. 401 N 17TH ST 18104 #041-13-1980 L1981 **PD** *020 †55

SHOENBERGER, Douglas Chas. 421 W CHEW ST 18102 #041-09-1987 L1989 **FM** *020 †18

SHOLEHVAR, Javad. 1575 POND RD, STE 203 18104 #517-01-1961 L1970 **OTO** *071 †45

SHOLEVAR, Farhad. 451 W CHEW ST STE 403 18102 #517-01-1979 L1985 **P** *020 †75

SHORE, Stephen Richard. 798 HAUSMAN RD, STE 240 18104 #041-01-1972 L1974 **IM** *020 †20

SHORT, Glenn Montgomery. 401 N 17TH ST STE C207 18104 #041-09-1979 L1980 **GE** *020 †20

SIDDIQUE, Sultan Mahmud. 1250 S CEDAR CREST BLVD, STE 300 18103 #035-19-1997 L1999 **ICE** *020 †20

SILBERT, Ophira. PO BOX 689, CEDAR CREST & 1-78 18105 #035-45-2001 L2007 **NPM** *100 †55

SILVERBERG, Bruce J. 1250 S CEDAR CREST BLVD, STE 300 18103 #041-13-1973 L1974 **CD IM** *020 †20 ‡

SILVERBERG, Daniel Myron. 1255 S CEDAR CREST BLVD, STE 1400 18103 #041-12-1975 L1976 **U** *020 †95 ‡

SILVERMAN, Howard Ayres. ■ 18104 #051-04-1955 L1958 **FPG** *071 †18

SILVERMAN, Morton I. ■ 18104 #041-01-1938 L1939 **CD IM** *071

SINCLAIR, Michael Carson. 451 W CHEW ST, STE 409 18102 #005-02-1966 L1979 **CCS** *020 †85,90

SINGER, Gregory Mitchell. 227 S ROUTE 100 18106 #308-03-1986 L1994 **FM** *020 †18

SINGER, Raymond Lederer. 1240 S CEDAR CREST BLVD, STE 403 18103 #041-01-1984 L1985 **TS GS** *020 †85,90

SINGLETON, Gregory Noel. 451 W CHEW ST, STE 409 18102 #035-08-1991 L2004 **AN** *020 †05

SINNOTT, Robert J. 1255 S CEDAR CREST BLVD, STE 3900 18103 #041-77-1985, ▲ L1986 **CRS GS** *020 †85,10

SIRARD, Richard Barry, Jr. 1200 S CEDAR CREST BLVD, LEHIGH VALLEY HOSP 18103 #654-01-2006 L2006 **IM** *012

SKIBBA, Joshua Bennett. 1200 S CEDAR CREST BLVD 18103 #654-01-2002 L2002 **CD** *012 †20

SKORINKO, Kenneth Paul. 2200 W HAMILTON ST, STE 214 18104 #041-09-1980 L1983 **IC CD** *020 †20

SKWEIR, Leon Arthur. ■ 18103 #041-09-1963 L1964 **P** *020 †75

SLAVEN, Barry Howard. 1240 S CEDAR CREST BLVD, STE 308 18103 #041-13-1975 L1976 **GS** *020 †85

SLEDZ, Donald M. 451 W CHEW ST STE 205 18102 #010-02-1967 L1971 **U GP** *020 †95

SLOMPAK, Carol Ann. 401 N 17TH ST 18104 #041-02-1982 L1983 **IM IMG** *020 †20

SLYPER, Arnold Harvey. 400 N 17TH ST, STE 202 18104 #917-30-1972 L2006 **PD PDE** *020 †55

SMITH, Geo Sylvester, Jr. 421 W CHEW ST 18102 #041-13-1959 L1962 **OBG** *071 †30

SMITH, Jere Philip. 401 N 17TH ST, STE 307 18104 #041-13-1965 L1970 **PD** *020 †55

SMITH, Nicole Robin. ■ 18106 #041-01-2000 L2000 **IM** *100

SMITH, Stacey James. 1210 S CEDAR CREST BLVD, STE 3600 18103 #041-14-2001 L2001 **IM** *020

SNYDER, Jeffrey Curtis. 1255 S CEDAR CREST BLVD, STE 1200 18103 #041-02-1985 L1986 **CD IM** *020 †20

SNYDER, Rosalie Rutter. 4825 W TILGHMAN ST 18104 #041-07-1985 L1986 **FM** *020 †18

SNYDER, Stanley. 1200 S CEDAR CREST BLVD 18103 #041-13-1953 L1954 **OBG** *071 †30

SOHAGIA, Amitkumar Bhikha. 1255 S CEDAR CREST BLVD, STE 2200 18103 #495-22-2000 L2007 **IM** *020 †20

SOKOLOWSKI, D'Nese Mary. 1575 POND RD STE 104 18104 #041-02-1996 L1998 **OBG** *020 †30

SONG, Steven S. 451 W CHEW ST, STE 409 18102 #583-01-1961 L1971 **AN PME** *020 †05

SORATHIA, Lubna Tayyab. 421 W CHEW ST 18102 #704-02-1996 L2003 **FM** *100

SOSIS, Arthur Cyril. 1259 S CEDAR CRST BLVD 010 18103 #035-06-1967 L1970 **D** *020 †15 ‡

SOTIROPOULOS, Sara V. ■ 18104 #028-46-1983 L2004 **ID PD** *020 †55

SPANGLER, Nancy Kay. 250 CETRONIA RD, STE 100 18104 #041-14-1986 L1986 **OBG** *020

SPARANDERO, Frank. 421 W CHEW ST, SACRED HEART HOSPITAL 18102 #035-08-1974 L1982 **OM IM** *030 †20,70

SPIKOL, Lorraine. 1250 S CEDAR CREST BLVD, STE 405 18103 #041-02-1986 L1991 **N IM** *020 †75

SPRINGER, Mark Sanford. 825 N CEDAR CREST BLVD 18103 #041-09-1986 L1987 **FM** *020 †18

STAFFARONI, Mark Albert. 400 N 17TH ST, STE 101-106 18104 #041-02-1981 L1983 **OPH** *020 †35

STAMATAKOS, Michael John. ■ 18104 #041-09-1953 L1954 **R** *071 †80

STASIK, John Joseph. 1275 S CEDAR CREST BLVD 18103 #041-09-1969 L1970 **CRS GS** *020 †10,85

STECKEL, Timothy Eric. 798 HAUSMAN RD, STE 220 18104 #051-07-1997 L1999 **IM** *020 †20

STEERMAN, Samuel Nathan. ■ 18104 #041-02-2006 L2006 **GS** *012

STEIN, Arthur Victor. ■ 18104 #041-01-1980 L1982 **PS** *075

STEIN, David M. 1941 W HAMILTON ST, STE 102 18104 #048-02-1950 **IM** *020

STEIN, Stanley Irwin. 622 N BROAD ST 18104 #050-02-1959 L1963 **PD** *020 †55 ‡

STELLO, Brian. 1617 W CHEW ST 18102 #041-02-1988 L1990 **FM** *020 †18

STELZER, Frederic Arthur. 451 W CHEW ST STE 401 18102 #028-34-1974 L1975 **GE** *020 †20

STEPHENS, Harry Wm, Jr. ■ 18103 #407-10-1946 **NS GS** *071 †25

STERN, Mark. 421 W CHEW ST 18102 #041-13-1968 L1970 **IM END** *030

STEVENS, Sarah Lynn. 401 N 17TH ST STE 210, ADOLESCENT MED PED SPEC CA 18104 #035-08-1987 L1998 **PD IM** *020 †20

STOLL, Malaika Sarit. ■ 18104 #005-11-2004 L2004 **FP** *012

STOLZ, Ralph E. 1605 N CEDAR CREST BLVD, STE 609 18104 #028-79-1957, ▲ L1958 **GP ADM** *020

STONER, John Gillespie. 1259 S CEDAR CREST BLVD, NO 100 18103 #041-77-2006, ▲ L2006 **D** *012

STRASSMAN, Rima Linden. 1200 S CEDAR CREST BLVD 18103 #041-07-1991 L1994 **PD** *020 †55

STRAUSS, Robert Dixon. 1251 S CEDAR CREST BLVD, STE 110 18103 #041-13-1963 L1964 **OTO A** *071 †45

STROBEL, Richard J. 1210 S CEDAR CREST BLVD, PULMONARY ASSOCIATES 18103 #048-02-1985 L1999 **PUD SME** *020 †20

SUBZPOSH, Ruhi. 421 W CHEW ST, SACRED HEART HOSPITAL 18102 #495-77-1977 L1985 **NPM** *020 †55

SUBZPOSH, Syed. 451 W CHEW ST, STE 302 18102 #495-77-1977 L1985 **CD IM** *020 †20

SUGGS, Nora Ann. 1200 S CEDAR CREST BLVD 18103 #048-04-1977 L1981 **GS CCS** *020 †85

SUMNER, Andrew David. 1250 S CEDAR CREST BLVD, STE 300 18103 #041-14-1990 L1992 **CD** *020 †20

SUNDAY-HARTMAN, Dorothy I. 400 N 17TH ST, FAIRGROUNDS SURGICAL CTR 18104 #041-01-1985 L1987 **AN** *020 †05

SUPRUN, Harry Zvi. 1200 S CEDAR CREST BLVD 18103 #869-05-1952 L1992 **ATP** *020

SUSSMAN, David B. 214 N 31ST ST 18104 #016-42-1968 L1969 **ORS OTR** *050 †40

SUSSMAN, Elliot Jay. 825 N CEDAR CREST BLVD 18104 #024-01-1977 L1979 **IM** *030 †20

SUSSMAN, Sylvia. ■ 18104 #035-06-1960 L1969 **AN** *071 †05

SWANK, Mark Donald. 1255 S CEDAR CREST BLVD, STE 3600 18103 #041-14-1981 L1982 **DR VIR** *020 †80

SWINFARD, Ronald W. PO BOX 689, CEDAR CREST & I-78 18105 #028-03-1978 L2003 **D** *020 †15

SZENICS, Jonathan Michael. 1259 S CEDAR CREST BLVD, STE 245 18103 #033-06-1981 L1989 **OM** *020 †70

SZWERC, Michael Francis. 1240 S CEDAR CREST BLVD, STE 403 18103 #028-02-1992 L1998 **TS** *020 †85,90

SZYDLOWSKI, Gary Walter. 1240 S CEDAR CREST BLVD, STE 403 18103 #041-09-1986 L1987 **TS** *020 †85,90

TAEB, Parisima. 1200 S CEDAR CREST BLVD, LEHIGH VALLEY HOSPITAL 18103 #422-01-2006 L2006 **IM** *012

TAHIR, Mahmood Ahmad. 451 W CHEW ST STE 304 18102 #704-02-1973 L1979 **GS VS** *020

TALENTI, Donald Paul. 421 W CHEW ST 18102 #041-13-1995 L1999 **MPD PD** *020 †20,55

TALSANIA, Jay S. 250 CETRONIA RD, STE 100 18104 #041-13-1991 L1993 **ORS** *020 †40

TAN, Hoan Seng. 421 W CHEW ST, SACRED HEART HOSPITAL 18102 #506-01-1962 L1971 **DR** *071 †80

TASNEEM, Safia. 421 W CHEW ST 18102 #496-27-2003 L2005 **FP** *012

TAUS, John Kurt. 451 W CHEW ST, STE 401 18102 #041-77-1980, ▲ L1981 **GE** *020 †20

TEICHER, Erik Joshua. 1200 S CEDAR CREST BLVD 18103 #422-01-2004 L2005 **GS** *012

TENZER, Ryan Lawrence. 1200 S CEDAR CREST BLVD 18103 #041-09-1997 L1999 **EM** *020 †16

TERMINI, Joseph Thos. 421 W CHEW ST 18102 #035-09-1960 L1961 **GP** *071

TERREROS, Pavel Enrique. 451 W CHEW ST, STE 301 18102 #451-01-1989 L2002 **FM** *020 †18

TETLOW, Georgia Katherine. 850 S 5TH ST, GOOD SHEPHERD REHABILITATI 18103 #036-01-2004 L2004 **PM** *012

THANGARAJ, Madankumar. 850 S 5TH ST 18103 #495-42-1988 L2006 **APM** *020 †60

THOMAS, Alex Thadathil. 1600 HANOVER AVE, ALLENTOWN STATE HOSPITAL 18109 #495-31-1982 L1987 **P** *020 †75

THOMAS, Manju Mary. 450 W CHEW ST 18102 #495-52-1996 L2005 **PD** *020 †55

THOMAS, Steven John. 1200 S CEDAR CREST BLVD 18103 #036-08-1999 L1999 **PS** *100

THOMPSON, Gregory Errol. 325 N 5TH ST, THIRD FLOOR 18102 #021-01-1992 L2005 **NS** *020 †25

THOMPSON, Robert John. 1259 S CEDAR CREST BLVD, STE 100 18103 #041-13-1981 L1983 **D IM** *020 †20,15

TOFF, Kenneth J. 1517 POND RD 18104 #041-77-1979, ▲ L1980 **PD** *020 †55

TOONDER, F Geoffrey. 1259 S CEDAR CREST BLVD 18103 #035-06-1966 L1976 **TS** *020 †85,90

TORRES, Flor D. 501 N 17TH ST, STE 206 18104 #737-01-1989 L2001 **FM** *020 †18

TORRES, Julio E. 1611 POND RD STE 101, LEHIGH VLY WMNS CANCER CTR 18104 #264-04-1968 L1976 **HO HEM** *020

TOTLANI, Meena Rajender. 450 W CHEW ST, SACRED HEART HOSPITAL 18102 #495-01-1986 L2002 **FM** *100 †18

TOTLANI, Rajender Suresh. 401 N 17TH ST STE 307, LEHIGH VALLEY PEDIATRIC AS 18104 #495-85-1989 L1996 **PD** *020 †55

TRACHTMAN, Mark Steven. 400 N 17TH ST, STE 101-106 18104 #041-13-1987 L1992 **OPH PO** *020 †35

TRAN, Dung P. 711 W CHEW ST 18102 #409-32-1979 L1988 **P** *020 †75

TRAN, Hanhdung. 4TH AND CHEW STS, SACRED HEART HOSPITAL 18102 #305-01-2007 L2007 **FP** *012

TRAPASSO, Jos Gerard. 1240 S CEDAR CREST BLVD, STE 310 18103 #035-08-1987 L1994 **U** *020 †95

TRETTER, Margaret Sadako. 1255 S CEDAR CREST BLVD, STE 2200 18103 #041-77-1982, ▲ L1983 **IM IMG** *020 †20 ‡

TREVASKIS, Allan Edward. 1230 S CEDAR CREST BLVD, STE 204 18103 #023-01-1945 L1948 **PS** *071 †65

TREVISAN, Susan Garrett. 1255 S CEDAR CREST BLVD, STE 3600 18103 #041-07-1991 L1991 **DR** *020 †80

TROMBLE, Alice Marie. ■ 18106 #005-06-2005 L2005 **GS** *012

TUFFIASH, William Alan. 1251 S CEDAR CREST BLVD, STE 107 18103 #041-13-1970 L1977 **AI IM** *020 †20,03

UFBERG, Michael Harris. 3131 COLLEGE HEIGHTS BLVD 18104 #041-13-1966 **GE** *020 †20 ‡

UNJIA, Shaileshkumar M. 6536 FOREST KNOLL CT 18104 #495-23-1992 L1998 **IM** *020 †20

URANKAR, Nancy Anne. 798 HAUSMAN RD STE 240 18104 #038-06-1977 L1979 **IM IMG** *020 †20

UXER, Jennifer B. ■ 18103 #048-78-2006, ▲ L2006 **OBG** *012

UZOCHUKWU, Chizoba Dolly. 1200 S CEDAR CREST BLVD 18103 #035-75-2005, ▲ L2005 **OBG** *012

VALANCIUS, Daniel Thomas. 1255 S CEDAR CREST BLVD, STE 2200 18103 #041-02-2001 L2004 **IM** *020

VASU, Seema Balwantsingh. PO BOX 689, LEHIGH VALLEY HOSP 18105 #011-75-2005, ▲ L2005 **FP** *012

VEERABHADRAIAH, Jyothi. 3110 HAMILTON BLVD, OUTPAT CLINIC 18103 #496-35-1996 L2001 **IM** *020 †20

VELAS, Carlos M. 1600 HANOVER AVE 18109 #748-08-1966 L1984 **P** *020

VELASQUEZ, Jorge Alberto. ■ 18109 #264-16-1986 **IM** *100

VELAZQUEZ, Gilbert. ■ 18102 #041-15-2002 *100

VEMURI, Vijaya Sireesha. 421 W CHEW ST, DEPT OF FAMILY PRACTICE 18102 #672-04-2004 L2006 **FP** *012

VENIGALLA, Naveen. 1200 S CEDAR CREST BLVD, LEHIGH VLY HOSP 18103 #495-37-1999 L2006 **IM** *100

VERMA, Deepti. 1210 S CEDAR CREST BLVD, STE 2700 18103 #496-04-1996 L2002 **IM** *100 †20

VICHNIN, Michael Chad. 1255 S CEDAR CREST BLVD, STE 3600 18103 #041-02-1996 L2002 **DR** *020 †80

VIECHNICKI, Michael Bruce. 1611 POND RD STE 102 18104 #041-13-1966 L1967 **OBG** *020 †30

VILLAMARIN, Carlos Felipe. 124 E SUSQUEHANNA ST 18103 #737-05-1993 L2004 **FM** *020 †18

VILLENEUVE, Deborah Lee. 1611 POND RD, STE 101 18104 #041-12-1992 L1994 **OBG** *020 †30

VILLENEUVE, John Burton. 1611 POND RD STE 101, LEHIGH VLY WOMENS CANCER 18104 #005-06-1991 L1998 **GO GYN** *020 †30

VINCENT, Joseph Emerson. 1210 S CEDAR CREST BLVD, STE 3200 18103 #041-01-1964 L1971 **PUD** *030 †20

VIOLAGO, Katherine Rose F. 421 W CHEW ST 18102 #748-01-2003 L2006 **FP** *012

WACHTEL, Julie. ■ 18104 #005-76-2007, ▲ L2007 **EM** *012

WAHHAB, Samina. 842 N 19TH ST 18104 #041-09-1995 L1998 **PS** *020 †65

WALL, James Robt. 2895 HAMILTON BLVD 18104 #041-02-1972 L1974 **D** *020 †15
WAN, Cindy. 1245 S CEDAR CREST BLVD, SUITE301 18103 #041-15-2002 L2002 **AN** *100
WAPNER, John Michael. 2015 W HAMILTON ST 18104 #041-02-1954 L1955 **OPH OS** *071 †35
WARD, Thomas Alfred. 1251 S CEDAR CREST BLVD, STE 302C 18103 #041-02-1961 L1962 **ORS** *071 †40
WASKO, Robert. 1200 S CEDAR CREST BLVD 18103 #041-13-1958 L1959 **U OS** *071 †95
WASSERMAN, Ronald Elliot. ■ 18103 #041-12-1969 L1974 **N** *071 †75 ‡
WAXMAN, Andrea. 1575 POND RD, STE 101 18104 #035-19-1978 L1979 **OBG** *020 †30
WEBER, Cynthia Beier. 1227 W LIBERTY ST, STE 303 18102 #041-02-1989 L2003 **PEM PD** *020 †55
WEIGAND, Justin. ■ 18106 #041-15-2008 *012
WEINSTOCK, Michael Saul. PO BOX 689, EMERG MED JDMCC-214 18105 #016-42-1967 L1997 **EM PD** *030 †55,16
WEIS, James Carl. 250 CETRONIA RD, STE 100 18104 #041-13-1983 L1984 **ORS** *020 †18,40
WEISBROD, Lawrence M. ■ 18104 #035-19-1942 L1951 **ORS** *071 †40
WEISS, Patrice Marie. 17TH AND CHEW STS, DEPT OBG 18105 #041-09-1992 L1995 **OBG** *071 †30
WELKIE, John Francis. 1259 S CEDAR CREST BLVD, STE 301 18103 #041-02-1985 L1990 **VS G5** *020 †85
WENDLING, Mark Allen. 1251 S CEDAR CREST BLVD, STE 104B 18103 #041-14-1994 L1996 **FM** *020 †18
WERHUN, Anthony Thos. 825 N CEDAR CREST BLVD 18104 #041-02-1983 L1984 **EM IM** *020 †20
WHALEN, Thomas Vincent, Jr. 1240 S CEDAR CREST BLVD, DEPT OF SURGERY SUITE 210 18103 #024-05-1976 L1990 **PDS CCS** *040 †85 ‡
WHEELER, John Sargent. 401 N 17TH ST STE 109 18104 #061-01-1957 L1961 **PD** *071 †55
WHITSON, David Wayne. 2150 W WASHINGTON ST 18104 #041-14-1972 L1973 **FM GP** *020 †18
WIDGE, Toeruna Sunil. 400 N 17TH ST, FAIRGROUNDS SURGICAL CTR 18104 #495-01-1969 L1974 **AN** *020 †05
WILCOX, Benjamin James. 401 N 17TH ST, STE 212 18104 #041-13-2001 L2001 **NEP** *020 †20
WILEY, Susan Deaner. 1255 S CEDAR CREST BLVD 18103 #041-01-1978 L1980 **P** *020 †75
WILKES, Dawn'C. 421 W CHEW ST 18102 #306-01-1986 L1991 **FM** *020 †18
WILLIAMS, David Oplinger. ■ 18103 #041-09-1948 L1949 **GP** *071 †80
WILLS, Henry Donald. 450 W CHEW ST, # 204 18102 #041-13-1975 L1976 **N** *020 †75 ‡
WILSON, Eric Paul. 1275 S CEDAR CREST BLVD, STE 301 18103 #422-01-1989 L1993 **VS** *020 †85
WILSON, Richard Chase. 2200 W HAMILTON ST 18104 #041-02-1965 L1968 **IM CD** *071 †20
WOJCIK, Randolph. 1230 S CEDAR CREST BLVD, STE 204 18103 #422-01-1997 L2001 **PS** *020 †85,65
WOLF, John F. 1255 S CEDAR CREST BLVD 18103 #041-13-1982 **FM** *020 †18 ‡
WOLSON, Alan H. 1255 S CEDAR CREST BLVD, STE 3600 18103 #041-02-1967 L1968 **DR** *020 †80
WONG, Emily Lo. 1210 S CEDAR CREST BLVD, STE 2700 18103 #035-06-2000 L2008 **ID** *100 †20
WU, Edward Houston. 1210 S CEDAR CREST BLVD, STE 3600 18103 #035-19-2001 L2004 **IM** *040
WU, James Kuoching. 1240 S CEDAR CREST BLVD, STE 403 18103 #016-02-1993 L2001 **TS** *071 †90,85
YAMPOLSKY, Igor. 1600 HANOVER AVE, ALLENTOWN STATE HOSPITAL 18109 #913-09-1977 L2005 **P** *020 †75
YANG, Wen-Shiong. 400 N 17TH ST, FAIRGROUNDS SURGICAL CTR 18104 #244-04-1970 L1976 **AN PUD** *075 †05 ‡
YEAGER, Daniel Quenton. 501 SAINT JOHN ST 18103 #041-12-1987 L1991 **PM** *020 †60
YELLIN, Stanley E. 450 W CHEW ST, STE 101 18102 #024-05-1974 L1985 **FM** *040 †18
YEN, C L Tan Chun. 1736 W HAMILTON ST 18104 #748-01-1960 L1968 **GYN** *020 †30
YIP, Luke Chor-Kung. 1240 S CEDAR CREST BLVD, STE 308 18103 #242-07-1955 L1971 **TS** *071 †85,90
YOUNG, Eric Todd. 1210 S CEDAR CREST BLVD, STE 2700 18103 #024-05-1990 L2002 **ID IM** *020 †20
YOUNG, Wen. 1255 S CEDAR CREST BLVD, STE 3600 18103 #024-07-1996 L2004 **NR** *020 †80,28
YOUSEFI-ELMI, Aram. 1227 W LIBERTY ST, STE 303 18102 #517-08-1994 L2000 **PD** *020 †55
YOZVIAK, Joseph L. LEHIGH VALLEY HOSP, 17TH AND CHEW ST 18104 #041-77-2003, ▲ L2003 **IM** *020 †20
YULO, John Alster C. 1245 S CEDAR CREST BLVD, STE 301 18103 #748-10-1983 L1996 **PME PMM** *020 †60
ZAGER, Michael L. 2895 HAMILTON BLVD, STE 101 18104 #305-01-1991 L1993 **IM** *020 †20
ZELINKA, Marijo Ann. 1200 S CEDAR CREST BLVD 18103 #041-02-1984 L1989 **NPM PD** *020 †55
ZEMANEK, Kenneth James. 1251 S CEDAR CREST BLVD, STE 202A 18103 #033-06-1986 L1990 **P PYG** *020 †75 ‡
ZIEGENFUS, Warren L, III. ■ 18104 #041-13-1963 L1964 **FM FPG** *020
ZIENKIEWICZ, Joseph. 1251 S CEDAR CREST BLVD, STE 102A 18103 #041-77-2002, ▲ L2005 **FM** *020 †18
ZOHARY, Yasser Ali. ■ 18103 #915-03-1993 L2005 **FP** *012
ZOHN, Lawrence Keith. 1245 S CEDAR CREST BLVD, STE 301 18103 #035-08-1985 L1988 **AN** *020 †05

ALLISON PARK — ALLEGHENY

ABDULKADIR, Adegboyega Ab. ■ 15101 #690-03-1990 L2005 **NPM** *012 †55
ANDERSON, Richard Eric. ■ 15101 #041-12-1971 L1973 **IM** *020 †20 ‡
ANJAMPARATHIKAL, Yusuf S. 1908 WALLACE RD 15101 #496-21-1988 L1998 **IM** *020 †20
ARCHER, Stephanie Lynn. 4927 ROUTE 8 15101 #041-02-1992 L1998 **FM** *020 †18
ASTBURY, Jeffrey Chas. 4485 WILLIAM FLYNN HWY, BUTLER ANESTHESIA ASSOC PC 15101 #041-12-1992 L1996 **AN CCA** *020 †05
BANE, Brian Carl. ■ 15101 #018-03-2006 L2006 **AN** *012
BIGATEL, Todd Andrew. ■ 15101 #422-01-2001 L2004 **END** *020
BLAKLEY, John Bigler. #106 FOXCROFT, 1772 FERGUSON ROAD 15101 #041-13-1947 L1948 **ORS** *071 †40
CARDINAL, Jon Silvio. ■ 15101 #010-02-2003 L2003 **GS** *012
CASTRO, Augusto D. ■ 15101 #737-01-1953 L1967 **PTH CLP** *071 †50
CHALLINOR, Robert Bingay. 4218 CORTON CT 15101 #041-12-1948 L1949 **U** *071 †95

CHEN, Minzhi. ■ 15101 #243-40-1982 L2001 **AN** *020 †05
CHOPPING, Peter Terry. 3019 SWANSEA CRES W, ALLISON PARK 15101 #917-21-1946 L1976 **RO** *071 †80
COX, Lora Antionette. ■ 15101 #038-40-2006 L2006 **FP** *012
DECOSKEY, Darla Kathleen. ■ 15101 #041-13-1979 L1987 **CD** *075
DEKKER, Andrew. ■ 15101 #660-02-1958 L1963 **ATP PCP** *071 †50
DISHART, Paul Warren. ■ 15101 #056-01-1959 L1960 **FM IM** *040 †18
GEORGE, Jose P. RTE 8 COVENTRY SQ, STE 125A 15101 #649-33-1984 L1985 **IM** *020 †20 ‡
GLASSO, Louis Chas, Jr. ■ 15101 #561-01-1968 L1970 **ORS** *071
HACHE, John Joseph. ■ 15101 #041-12-2006 L2006 **AN** *012
HALTIGAN, Jill Eileen. ■ 15101 #023-01-2008 *012
HOLLERMAN, Charles Edward. ■ 15101 #035-20-1955 L1956 **PN PD** *071 †55
HUBER, Donald Jos. 511 FOXCROFT LN 15101 #041-12-1956 L1957 **FM** *071 †18
JANIK, Joseph Robt. ■ 15101 #041-12-1987 L1990 **AN** *020 †05 ‡
JARMOLOWSKI, Chester R. 2301 FERGUSON RD, DEPARTMENT OF RADIOLOGY 15101 #035-15-1973 L1974 **DR VIR** *020 †80
KEARNS, Kevin Joseph. ■ 15101 #041-14-1993 L1996 **IM** *020 †20
KRAM, John Edward. ■ 15101 #041-09-1943 L1944 **GP** *071
KULICH, Scott Michael. ■ 15101 #056-06-1996 L2001 **PTH** *020 †50
KUNKEL, Herbert Gerard. ■ 15101 #041-12-1954 L1955 **AN** *071 †05
KUNKEL, James Vachon. ■ 15101 #041-12-1982 L1983 **AN** *020 †05
KUSH, Margaret Barnard. 4284 WILLIAM FLYNN HWY 15101 #010-01-1972 L1973 **IM IMG** *020 †20
LAMPERSKI, Brendan Dale. 4068 MOUNT ROYAL BLVD, STE 101 15101 #041-12-1989 L1991 **IM** *020 †20
LAMPERSKI, Curtis Raymond. 4068 MT ROYAL BLVD 15101 #041-02-1979 L1980 **IM** *020 †20
LIM-CO, Rizalina Yu. ■ 15101 #748-01-1959 L1975 **PTH** *071 †50
LUDMER, Mario. ■ 15101 #132-01-1955 L1966 **NS** *071 †25
MANOV, Nagib. 4805 SHAMROGUE CT 15101 #957-08-1987 L2003 **FPG** *020 †20
MC GUIRE, Patricia M. 4284 WILLIAM FLYNN HWY 15101 #041-02-1979 L1981 **CHP P** *020 †75 ‡
MULLENS, Jerry Duane. ■ 15101 #422-01-2001 **P** *071
MUTHU, Kanagasabai. 2753 SHAMROCK DR, WESTERN PENNSYLVANIA HOSP 15101 #495-66-1978 L2002 **AN** *020 †05
NETTROUR, Walter S, IV. ■ 15101 #041-12-1991 **ORS** *020
PALMER, William David. ■ 15101 #041-12-1947 **GS** *071 †85
PARVA, Ghasem. 4790 WILLIAM FLYNN HWY 15101 #517-05-1965 L1972 **FM PTH** *071
PATEL, Anuj Kishor. ■ 15101 #041-12-2008 *012
RAU, Kimberly Anne. 4290 WILLIAM FLYNN HWY, ROUTE 8 15101 #010-02-1991 L1993 **D** *020 †20,15
RAZA, Kashif. ■ 15101 #704-04-1997 L2005 **ID** *100 †20
SCHENKER, Mara Lynne. ■ 15101 #016-02-2008 †012
SOBER, Diane Marie. 3402 ROUTE 8 15101 #041-07-1984 L1986 **OBG** *020 †30
SONEL, Elif. ■ 15101 #902-05-1991 L2000 **IM** *074 †20
TAYLOR, Lela Evelyn. ■ 15101 #055-02-2007 L2007 **FP** *012
THOMPSON, James Smillie. 125A COVENTRY SQ OFC 15101 #041-12-1959 L1960 **GP** *020
TLACHAC, Jonathan Gregory. ■ 15101 #049-01-2005 L2005 **AN** *012
WARD, R Wendell. ■ 15101 #041-01-1949 L1989 **IM PTH** *071
WILDER, David Wm. ■ 15101 #040-02-1966 L1971 **DR NM** *071 †80,28
WILLIAMS, Philip D, Jr. ■ 15101 #041-13-1956 L1957 **OPH** *071 †35
WU, Hsi-Yang. ■ 15101 #041-01-1993 L1999 **UP** *020 †95

ALTOONA — BLAIR

AGARWAL, Ramesh Kumar. 716 24TH ST 16602 #495-47-1964 L1973 **OTO A** *020 †45
AHMAD, Shabbir. 620 HOWARD AVE, 4TH FL 16601 #704-04-1981 L1992 **HO** *020 †20
AIGNER, William James. ■ 16602 #041-02-1962 L1963 **GP** *020
AKHTAR, Sulman. 2907 PLEASANT VALLEY BLVD, JAMES E. VAN ZANDT VA MEDI 16602 #704-02-1987 L1995 **IM** *020 †20
ALI, Asif. 2907 PLEASANT VALLEY BLVD, GERIATRICS DEPT #23 16602 #495-21-1986 L2005 **IMG** *020 †20
ALKHAFAJI, Ikbal. 2907 PLEASANT VALLEY BLVD, VA MEDICAL CENTER 16602 #875-01-1989 L1999 **PTH PP** *030 †50
ALKHAFAJI, Rajih. 810 VALLEY VIEW BLVD, BLAIR GASTROENTEROLOGY 16602 #528-01-1986 L1999 **GE** *020 †20
ANASTASI, John Salvatore. 620 HOWARD AVE, 7TH FL 16601 #036-05-1980 L1989 **TS GS** *020 †85,90
ANDREW, Oliver Terry. 2907 PLEASANT VALLEY BLVD 16602 #041-01-1965 L1967 **IM NEP** *020 †20
ANTON, Americo Bayona. 620 HOWARD AVE 16601 #737-03-1969 L1974 **PTH** *062 †50
ANTONOWICZ, Joseph L. 620 HOWARD AVE 16601 #035-45-1982 L1993 **P FM** *020 †18,75
APPLETON, Abraham T. 620 HOWARD AVE, OP 3 16601 #035-01-1981 L2004 **ORS GS** *020 †40
ARSHAD, Mohammad Naveed. 501 HOWARD AVE, ALTOONA HOSPITAL 16601 #704-21-1989 L2001 **FM** *020 †20
ASWATHAPPA, Sathya N. 615 6TH AVE 16602 #496-22-1992 L1996 **PD** *020 †55
AZAD, Aslam Mohamed. 1414 9TH AVE, STATION MEDICAL CENTER 16602 #422-01-2002 L2005 **PD** *020 †55
AZAR, Elie Michel. 2500 7TH AVE 16602 #605-01-1996 L2001 **DR** *020 †80
BARNES, Robert Frederick. 620 HOWARD AVE, ALTOONA HOSPITAL 16601 #041-09-1976 L1977 **IM** *071 †20
BARTKOWIAK, Anthony James. 1414 9TH AVE 16602 #035-06-1995 L1999 **IM** *020 †20 ‡
BARTKOWIAK, Liang R. 1701 12TH AVE 16601 #035-06-1995 L1999 **OBG** *020 †30
BATZEL, Linnane Rene. 620 HOWARD AVE, ALTOONA HOSPITAL EMERG. DE 16601 #041-02-1999 L2001 **EM** *020 †16
BAYSAL, Deniz. 620 HOWARD AVE 16601 #660-01-1998 L2004 **OTR** *020 †20
BECHTEL, Robert Todd. 501 HOWARD AVE, ALTOONA OPHTHALMOLOGY 16601 #051-04-1991 L1996 **OPH PO** *020 †35 ‡
BECKSTEAD, Donald Michael. 501 HOWARD AVE, STE F2 16601 #023-01-1984 L1985 **FM ADM** *040 †18
BEERS, Kenneth Leroy. 501 HOWARD AVE 16601 #020-12-1966 L1967 **FM** *071 †18
BELIS, Theodore Eugene. 2500 5TH ST 16601 #041-12-1977 L1982 **U** *071 †95
BERARDINELLI, John L. 501 HOWARD AVE, STE E1 16601 #041-02-1968 L1969 **PD** *071 †55
BERTOLINO, John Gerome. 2907 PLEASANT VALLEY BLVD, LATROBE AREA HOSPITAL FAMI 16602 #041-02-1983 L1984 **FM** *040 †18

BLESCIA, Jill S. 1414 9TH AVE 16602 #041-02-2003 L2003 **PD** *020 †55

BOCCAGNO, Patrick Michael. ■ 16602 #041-09-1958 L1959 **IM** *020

BOSSINGER, Steven Owen. 1701 12TH AVE, STE E 16601 #041-02-1991 L1996 **U** *020 †95

BOUCHARD, Matthew Peter. 620 HOWARD AVE, ALTOONA HOSPITAL 16601 #041-01-1997 L1999 **EM** *020 †16

BRADLEY, Vernon Francis. 501 HOWARD AVE, ALLEGHENY FAMILY PHYSICIAN 16601 #041-02-1958 L1959 **OBG** *020 †30

BRANDT, Craig S. 620 HOWARD AVE, FL 2 16601 #041-14-1980 L1981 **CD IM** *020 †20

BRZANA, Ronald Jos. 810 VALLEY VIEW BLVD, BLAIR GASTROENTEROLOGY ASS 16602 #041-13-1991 L1993 **GE IM** *020 †20

BUDD, Robert Michael. 501 HOWARD AVE, ALTOONA OPHTHALMOLOGY 16601 #041-12-1983 L1984 **OPH OS** *020 †35

BURK, Thomas Andrew. 1400 9TH AVE 16602 #047-06-1994 L1997 **IM** *020 †20

BURKE, James Paul. 501 HOWARD AVE STE F3, ALLEGHENY BRAIN & SPINE SU 16601 #001-02-1996 L2001 **NS** *020

CAMPBELL, Mark C. 615 HOWARD AVE STE 106 16601 #016-42-1992 L2002 **END IM** *020 †20

CAPRIOTTI, Richard Darrel. 1223 13TH AVE 16601 #041-09-1970 L1971 **OPH** *020 †35

CARDAKLI, Ufuk Fusun. 501 HOWARD AVE, ALTOONA OPHTHALMOLOGY 16601 #056-05-1988 L1993 **OPH** *020 †35

CHALFIN, Laura B. ■ 16602 #035-01-1983 L1984 **FM** *020 †18

CHOPRA, Ramesh Kumar. 1224 7TH AVE 16602 #209-01-1965 L1972 **PD** *020 ‡

CHUU, Wen-Min. 620 HOWARD AVE, 4TH FLOOR ONCOLOGY 16601 #244-02-1979 L2000 **HO** *020 †20

CLARK, Joseph Dale. 1414 9TH AVE, BLAIR MEDICAL ASSOC 16602 #041-14-1992 L1995 **N** *020 †75

COTTLE, Betty J Lowell. 2500 7TH AVE 16602 #035-19-1949 L1970 **AN OS** *071 †05

COVALESKI, Thomas Edward. 620 HOWARD AVE, LEXINGTON HOSPITALISTS, IN 16601 #041-14-1992 L1994 **IM** *020 †20

COWDEN, Michelle Lynn. 501 HOWARD AVE, STE F2 16601 #051-04-2005 L2005 **FP** *012

COWGER, David Lee. 620 HOWARD AVE, ALTOONA REGIONAL HLTH SYS 16601 #017-20-1979 L1982 **EM FM** *020 †18,16

CRAWFORD, Ralph Wm, Jr. 3014 PLEASANT VALLEY BLVD 16602 #041-02-1965 L1966 **FM OBG** *071 †30,18 ‡

CREVECOEUR, Carline Marie. 2613 8TH AVE, STE 1A 16602 #035-08-1989 L1993 **OBG** *020 †30

CRIDER, Donald Bryant. 501 HOWARD AVE 16601 #010-02-1953 L1961 **P N** *071 †75

DAVIES, Michael John. 501 HOWARD AVE 16601 #041-14-1999 L2000 **IM** *100 †20,03

D'CRUZ, Joseph Franklin. 615 6TH AVE 16602 #495-52-1970 L1973 **PD** *020 †55 ‡

DE FAY, Stanley. 620 HOWARD AVE, ALTOONA HOSP DEPT AN 16601 #035-08-1977 L1987 **AN PD** *020 †05

DE FRANCISCO, Lance Carl. 810 VALLEY VIEW BLVD, BLAIR GASTROENTEROLOGY 16602 #041-07-1979 L1980 **GE** *020 †20

DEHAAS, Sherri Lyn. 1414 9TH AVE, STATION MEDICAL CENTER 16602 #011-02-1999 L2001 **FM** *020 †18

DE KONING, Johannes L. ■ 16601 #660-03-1959 L1961 **FM** *071

DEL BAGGIO, Rebecca Lee. 1414 9TH AVE 16602 #041-12-1997 L2000 **PD** *020 †55

DIB, Suzanne Youssef. 501 HOWARD AVE STE F2, ALTOONA FAMILY PHYSICIANS 16601 #875-03-1994 L2007 **FP** *012

DIETRICK, Ronald Allen. 1701 12TH AVE STE A 16601 #041-12-1957 L1958 **GYN** *071 †30

DODSON, Brian Danl. 810 VALLEY VIEW BLVD, BLAIR GASTROENTEROLOGY 16602 #028-02-1987 L2000 **GE** *020 †20

DOLPHIN, Quentin Richard. 620 HOWARD AVE, ALTOONA HSPTL MENTAL HLTHC 16601 #041-02-1999 L2001 **P** *020 †75

DONOHUE, Christopher T. 620 HOWARD AVE, ARHS-ALTOONA CAMPUS ER 16601 #010-03-1992 L1998 **EM** *020 †16

DOWLUT, Mohammad A. 1400 LOGAN BLVD 16602 #869-05-1968 L1981 **IM EM** *020 †20

DRASS, Michael James. 1402 9TH AVE 16602 #041-14-1992 L1994 **AN PME** *020 †05

EBLING, Matthew Todd. 501 HOWARD AVE, STE F2 16601 #041-02-2003 L2003 **FM** *100 †18

EDGELL, Penne H. 1400 9TH AVE 16602 #041-14-1993 L1995 **FM** *020 †18

FAZI, Burt. 630 HOWARD AVE, CARDIOVASCULAR THORACIC SU 16601 #055-01-1982 L1983 **TS** *020 †85,90

FENELLO, Anthony Paul. 620 HOWARD AVE 16601 #041-12-1959 L1960 **IMG** *020

FISCHER, Edward Preston. 2613 8TH AVE 16602 #048-04-1965 L1992 **ON HNS** *071 †85

FLORES, Regino J. 1414 9TH AVE 16602 #042-02-1990 L1992 **FM** *020 †18

FOCHLER, Francis John. 501 HOWARD AVE 16601 #041-01-1962 L1963 **FPG** *071 †85

FORD, Alan Christopher. 1414 9TH AVE 16602 #023-01-1984 L1986 **CD IM** *020 †20

FOUSE, George W, Jr. 620 HOWARD AVE, ALTOONA HOSP EMER SVCS 16601 #041-07-1984 L1987 **EM DDL** *020 †16

GALBRAITH, David John. 1414 9TH AVE 16602 #041-12-1973 L1974 **PD** *020 †55

GAROFALO, James Harold. 1701 12TH AVE, INTOWNE SQUARE, SUITE G2 16601 #041-13-1999 L2006 **AN** *020 †05

GATES, Zane Herbert. 501 HOWARD AVE, STE B204 16601 #041-12-1995 L1998 **IM** *020 †20

GHARIB, Sayed Morteza. 1701 12TH AVE, STE G2 16601 #517-01-1987 L2003 **AN** *020

GHEBRE, Hailemicael. 2907 PLEASANT VALLEY BLVD, VA MEDICAL CTR 16602 #561-03-1984 L1991 **IM** *020

GIBBONS, William Port. ■ 16602 #041-01-1956 L1957 **PS** *071 †65

GILOT, Jean Baptiste M. ■ 16602 #440-01-1958 L1965 **AN IM** *071

GOLDSCHMIDT, Pauline. 501 HOWARD AVE, STE B110 16601 #396-06-1961 L1977 **CHP P** *071

GONZALEZ-CRUZ, Roberto. 3107 FAIRWAY DR 16602 #649-52-1997 L2006 **PS GS** *020 †65

GORE, Thomas Winfield. 601 HOWARD AVE, ALTOONA HOSP 16601 #020-02-1981 L1982 **EM FM** *020 †18

GRAB, Edmundo Manuel. 501 HOWARD AVE STE F1 16601 #132-01-1971 L1975 **GYN** *020 †30

GRIER, Jonathan. 2525 9TH AVE 16602 #035-19-1986 L1995 **GE** *020 †20

GUNGON, Carlos M. VA HOSPITAL 16603 #748-07-1964 L1973 **DR** *020

GUPTA, Anju. 312 CHESTNUT AVE 16601 #495-30-1992 L2002 **IM** *020 †20

GUPTA, Pawan Kumar. 2613 8TH AVE STE 4B 16602 #495-74-1989 L1998 **IM NEP** *020 †20

GURMAN, Andrew William. 3000 FAIRWAY DR 16602 #035-15-1980 L1986 **ORS HS** *020 †40 ‡

HAAS, Charles Michael. ■ 16602 #041-12-1972 L1973 **PTH** *030 †50

HADUCK, Leonard Anthony. 1414 9TH AVE 16602 #025-07-1968 L1971 **FM** *071 †18

HAERIAN ARDAKANI, Haleh. 1414 9TH AVE 16602 #517-04-2000 L2006 **END** *100 †20

HALL, James Philip. 620 HOWARD AVE 16601 #023-01-1982 L1983 **FM OM** *020 †18

HARTMAN, Craig W. 801 HOWARD AVE 16601 #041-14-1974 L1975 **PUD IM** *020 †20

HAWKINS, Richard F, Jr. RR 1 BOX 589A, RIGGLES GAP ROAD 16601 #051-04-1970 L1970 **DR** *020 †80

HEATON, Fred M. 501 HOWARD AVE, STE F2 16601 #041-77-2005, ▲ L2005 **FP** *012

HEMATILLAKE, Mabodawilage. 2907 PLEASANT VALLEY BLVD, ALTOONA VA MEDICAL CENTER 16602 #422-01-1992 L2006 **HEM** *020 †20

HIGGINS, David Earl. 501 HOWARD AVE, STE A107 16601 #034-01-1980 L1981 **OTO** *020

HOFFMAN, Salee Laopet. 620 HOWARD AVE 4TH FL, ALTOONA REGIOAL HEALTH SYS 16601 #572-12-1971 L1974 **ON HEM** *020

HOFFMAN, Tamara L. 620 HOWARD AVE 3RD FL, LEXINGTON HOSPITALISTS 16601 #041-78-2003, ▲ L2003 **FM** *020 †18

HOMMER, J Scott. ■ 16602 #041-01-1959 L1960 **FM** *071 †18

HOOVLER, Philip Wayne. 620 HOWARD AVE 16601 #041-13-1961 L1962 **MDM** *071 †18

HORMELL, Johnson Grant. 2612 PLEASANT VALLEY BLVD 16602 #654-01-1984 L1987 **FM GS** *020 †18

HOWELLS, Richard Charles. 501 HOWARD AVE 16601 #055-01-1996 L2000 **OTO** *020 †45

HOYNE, Patricia Mary. 1701 12TH AVE 16601 #010-02-1983 L1993 **OBG** *020 †30

HROMNAK, George. 620 HOWARD AVE, ALTOONA HOSP 16601 #016-11-1982 L1989 **P CHP** *020 †75

JAYARAJ, Arumugam B. 3109 FAIRWAY DR, KEYSTONE PAIN INSTITUTE 16602 #495-95-1975 L1998 **APM** *020 †05

JENKINS, Benjamin Chas. ■ 16602 #035-06-1954 L1955 **FM EM** *071 †18

JOHNSON, Paula Z. 1414 9TH AVE 16602 #041-12-1987 L1989 **IM CD** *020 †20

JOURDAIN, Luis Manuel. 620 HOWARD AVE, ALTOONA HOSP LAB SVCS 16601 #308-01-1962 L1970 **PTH ATP** *020 †50 ‡

JOYCE, Alice Plummer. 620 HOWARD AVE 16601 #041-07-1983 L1985 **D** *020 †15

JOYCE, John P. 620 HOWARD AVE 16601 #041-13-1983 L1984 **D IM** *020 †20,15

KACZOR, Stanley F. ■ 16602 #041-12-1949 L1950 **GP** *072

KALRA, Gurmeet Kaur. 501 HOWARD AVE STE F2, ALTOONA FAMILY PHYSICIANS 16601 #496-12-1996 L2007 **FP** *012

KANESHIKI, Neil Akira. 2525 9TH AVE STE 1B 16602 #033-06-1992 L1997 **GS VS** *020 †85

KANSAL, Kusum Rajgopal. 714 6TH AVE 16602 #495-49-1970 L1978 **OBG** *020 †30

KANSAL, Raj Gopal. 714 6TH AVE 16602 #495-03-1970 L1978 **U** *020 †95

KAPLAN, Stephen M. 810 VALLEY VIEW BLVD 16602 #041-01-1962 L1963 **GE IM** *071 †20

KARUNARATNE, E R. 620 HOWARD AVE, THE ALTOONA HOSPITAL 16601 #220-01-1969 L1973 **DR** *020 †80

KATARI, Raju S. 2907 PLEASANT VALLEY BLVD, VA MEDICAL CTR 16602 #649-33-1988 L1993 **IM** *020

KATTUPALLI, Geronami Paul. 501 HOWARD AVE STE F2, FAMILY PHYSICIANS-ALTO 16601 #495-50-2000 L2007 **FP** *012

KEATING, Mark Mc Keon. 620 HOWARD AVE, ALTOONA REGIONAL HEALTH SY 16601 #041-01-1990 L1993 **HEM** *020 †20

KHALOUF, Fred K. 2005 VALLEY VIEW BLVD 16602 #041-77-1981, ▲ L1982 **AN PME** *020 †05 ‡

KHOURY, Ziad. 1321 11TH AVE, CARDIOLOGY ASSO OF ALTOONA 16601 #875-01-1987 L1994 **IM CD** *020 †20

KIHM, Ronald H. 2500 7TH AVE 16602 #583-06-1964 L1982 **R NM** *020 †28,80

KOMARNENI, Sree Devi. 2907 PLEASANT VALLEY BLVD 16602 #495-50-1979 L1984 **P** *020

KUMAR, K Vijay. 2907 PLEASANT VALLEY BLVD, VA MEDICAL CENTER 16602 #495-21-1970 L1979 **N** *020

KWON, Jong Duk. 620 HOWARD AVE, RADIOLOGY DEPARTMENT 16601 #583-04-1963 L1972 **R** *020 †80

LAMPARD, Simon David. 1701 12TH AVE STE D 16601 #054-04-1989 L2000 **GS** *020 †85

LEE, David Richard. 1701 12TH AVE STE A 16601 #023-01-1984 L1987 **OBG** *020 †30

LI, Zhenhui. 1414 9TH AVE 16602 #243-78-1983 L2003 **N** *020 †75

LILLIE, Tracy Ann. 1414 9TH AVE 16602 #028-03-1996 L1998 **FM** *020 †18

LILLIS, Terence Owen. 501 HOWARD AVE STE F2, ALTOONA FAMILY PHYSICIANS 16601 #055-01-2004 L2004 **FM** *020 †18

LITTLEJOHN, John Dana. 2613 8TH AVE, STE B1 16602 #016-11-1977 L1998 **OBG** *020 †30

LOUTON, Fanny Xhajanka. 620 HOWARD AVE 16601 #045-01-1986 L1991 **FM GPM** *020 †18

LOUTON, Robert Brian. 3107 FAIRWAY DR 16602 #048-12-1982 L1989 **PS HS** *020 †65 ‡

LOYCHIK, Sandra Gray. 1701 12TH AVE, STE 3 16601 #035-06-1975 L1979 **N** *020

LUCAS, Timothy Alan. 620 HOWARD AVE 16601 #041-14-1994 L1997 **PCC PUD** *020 †20

LUKACS, Kornel. 312 UNION AVE 16602 #305-01-1983 L1986 **N** *020 †75

MACEK, Ralph Chas. 1414 9TH AVE 16602 #041-13-1966 L1967 **FM** *020 †18

MAGEE, Richard Saml. 501 HOWARD AVE, STE B109 16601 #041-13-1976 L1977 **GS TS** *020 †85

MAGLEY, Robert Scott. 620 HOWARD AVE 16601 #041-02-1982 L1983 **EM ESM** *020 †16

MAITRA, Subhashis. 2525 9TH AVE STE 1B, PURITAN PARK MEDICAL CENTE 16602 #033-06-1985 L1986 **VS GS** *020 †85

MANIGLIA, Anthony John. 1414 9TH AVE, BLAIR MEDICAL ASSOC 16602 #041-09-1978 L1979 **IM** *020 †20

MANNING, Thomas Alexander. 2950 FAIRWAY DR 16602 #025-01-1987 L2000 **DR** *020 †80

MANON, Marcos A. 501 HOWARD AVE, STE B110 16601 #308-11-1983 L1986 **NEP IM** *020 †20

MAZZIOTTI, Mario Chas. 2500 7TH AVE, BON SECOURS HOLY FAM 16602 #561-01-1973 L1976 **EM** *020

MC COY, Morgan M, II. 620 HOWARD AVE, ALTOUNA REG HLTH SYS 16601 #041-09-1968 L1969 **PTH** *062 †50

MC ELHANEY, Angela Dawn. 1414 9TH AVE 16602 #041-12-2000 L2001 **FM** *020 †18

MC KIBBIN, Ralph David. 810 VALLEY VIEW BLVD, BLAIR GASTROENTEROLOGY 16602 #041-09-1986 L1987 **GE HEP** *020 †20

MC KINNEY, Henry D. 1800 GRANT AVE 16602 #561-01-1969 L1971 **D A** *020 †15 ‡

MCLELLAN, Fiona Jane. 501 HOWARD AVE, BLDG C 16601 #917-29-1995 L1999 **FM** *040 †18

MEISNER, Marvin Henry. 620 HOWARD AVE 16601 #038-40-1963 L1970 **CD IM** *020 †20

METZGER, Amy Kathleen. 620 HOWARD AVE 16601 #038-41-1996 L2006 **P** *020 †75

MIRZA, Sara. 501 HOWARD AVE STE F2, FAMILY PHYSICIANS-ALTO 16601 #704-18-1991 L2006 **FM** *100

MORGAN, Vincent Francis. 205 TENNYSON AVE, STE C 16602 #308-07-1982 L1988 **PM** *020 †60

MOUSSA, Mohamad. 615 6TH AVE 16602 #875-01-1971 L1978 **PD** *020 †55 ‡

MURPHY, Matthew Joseph. 620 HOWARD AVE, ALTOONA HOSPITAL 16601 #041-14-1997 L1999 **EM** *020 †16

MUSHREF, Waleed. 201 LOGAN BLVD # 2 16602 #875-01-1989 L2002 **CHP** *020

NACKLEY, Daniel Anthony. 2907 PLEASANT VALLEY BLVD 16602 #051-01-1987 L1991 **OM** *020 †70

NAJI, Muhammad G. 1400 LOGAN BLVD, LAKEMONT MEDICAL CENTER 16602 #875-01-1974 L1994 **IM** *020 †20

NECHES, Norman Morris. 1414 9TH AVE 16602 #035-08-1968 L2005 **OBG OS** *020 †30

NETREBA, Jules Leonard. PO BOX 3068 16603 #869-02-1958 L1964 **IM** *071 ‡

NEWLIN, Matthew Evans. 1701 12TH AVE, STE D 16601 #041-02-1998 L2004 **GS** *020 †85

NICOLAS, Rudy. 2950 FAIRWAY DR 16602 #748-08-1968 L1976 **DR NM** *020

O'BRIEN, Thomas More. 615 HOWARD AVE, STE 105 16601 #041-02-1985 L1992 **OBG** *020 †30

■ = Address Information Privacy Protected

OLNEY, Franklin Blaze. 2950 FAIRWAY DR 16602 #041-13-1960 L1961 **DR GP** *071 †80
OPIDA, Ciceron Legaspi. 1915 VALLEY VIEW BLVD 16602 #748-01-1972 L1978 **N** *020 †75
OPIDA, Marina. 2500 7TH AVE 16602 #748-01-1971 L1980 **OBG** *020
OSAGIEDE, Emmanuel. 620 HOWARD AVE, ALTOONA REGIONAL HEALTH SY 16601 #690-01-1983 L2006 **RNR** *020 †80
OSGOOD, Carroll P, Jr. 501 HOWARD AVE, BLDGE E1 16601 #041-02-1965 L1973 **NS** *020 †25
OSORIO, Emmanuel P. 2918 6TH AVE 16602 #748-08-1964 L1971 **OBG** *020 †30
OSTAPOVICZ, Diana Marie. 620 HOWARD AVE, ONCOLOGY, ALTOONA HOSPITAL 16601 #041-09-1992 L1995 **RO** *100
PANDIT, Rashmikant S. 2613 8TH AVE, STE 4C 16602 #495-23-1982 L1990 **PUD IM** *020 †20
PATEL, Arun Rambhai. 2500 7TH AVE 16602 #495-37-1966 L1988 **DR** *020 †80
PAZCOGUIN, Silvino P. 2907 PLEASANT VALLEY BLVD 16602 #748-01-1965 L1978 **AS GS** *020
PERICHERLA, Venkata R R. 1710 6TH AVE 16602 #495-21-1990 L1998 **IM** *020 †20
POON, Mario John. 620 HOWARD AVE, FL 2 16601 #035-46-1977 L1990 **CD IM** *020 †20
POPOVICH, Jon Eric. 2907 PLEASANT VALLEY BLVD, ALTOONA VA MED CTR 16602 #041-01-1988 L1990 **IM** *020 †20 ‡
PRIMACK, Laurence Alan. 1701 12TH AVE, STE 3 16601 #035-03-1979 L1984 **N** *020 †75
RAHMAN, Mohammed J. 1414 8TH AVE 16602 #160-02-1972 L1995 **IM** *020 †20
RAHMAN, Mohammed Waliur. 620 HOWARD AVE, LEXINGTON HOSPITALISTS 16601 #160-06-1983 L1996 **IMG** *020 †20
RAJU, Padma Indukuri. 501 HOWARD AVE BLDG E 16601 #495-39-1963 L1984 **RO** *072
RAJU, Rudraraju. 620 HOWARD AVE 16601 #495-58-1972 L1979 **RO** *071 †80
RAMDAS, Jagadeesh. 1304 7TH ST 16601 #495-44-1988 L2002 **PHO PD** *020 †55
RAPOSAS, Angel Q. 501 HOWARD AVE, STE B110 16601 #748-07-1983 L1996 **IM** *020 †20
RASMUSSEN, David Michael. 610 HOWARD AVE, ALTOONA HOSP-DEPT ANESTH 16601 #051-04-1991 L1998 **AN** *020 †05
RESNIK, Paul Herbert. 1402 9TH AVE 16602 #016-42-1976 L2007 **AN** *020 †05
RICE, Patrick Douglas. 501 HOWARD AVE, BLDG F 16601 #005-12-1991 L1993 **FM** *020 †18
RICE, Philip Lynn. 620 HOWARD AVE, BLDG F 16601 #016-43-1971 L1997 **TS GS** *020 †85,90
RIFKAH, Elias Mounif. 100 CHESTNUT AVE 16601 #875-03-1988 L1998 **FM** *020 †18
ROBINSON, Jay Allen. 200 N 4TH AVE 16601 #041-02-1982 L1983 **FM OM** *020 †18
ROSCH, Jeffrey Marvin. 501 HOWARD AVE, A-201 16601 #041-02-1972 L1974 **A PUD** *020 †55,03
ROSENCRANTZ, Elliot. 622 HOWARD AVE, ALTOONA HOSP 16601 #308-07-1982 L1986 **P PYG** *020
RUHL, Terry Steven. 501 HOWARD AVE STE F2 16601 #035-06-1988 L1999 **FM** *040 †18
SALTZBURG, Michael C. 615 HOWARD AVE, EXECUTIVE HSE I STE 200 16601 #041-77-1977, ▲ L1978 **ORS PMM** *020
SANGIORGIO, Frank Edward. RR 6 BOX 341, WILLOW DRIVE 16601 #561-01-1966 L1978 **EM FM** *020 †18
SANKARAN, Manickam. 901 VALLEY VIEW BLVD # 10 16602 #495-04-1968 L1979 **IM EM** *020 †20
SCHATANOFF, David. 620 HOWARD AVE 16601 #041-09-1968 L1969 **RO FM** *071 †80
SCHLECHTER, Michael J. 1414 9TH AVE, STATION MEDICAL CENTER 16602 #041-09-1992 L1994 **IM** *020 †20
SCHMIDT, Stephen Lloyd. 620 HOWARD AVE 16601 #165-01-1977 L1981 **GS VS** *020 †85
SCHOCKER, Jack David. 620 HOWARD AVE 16601 #041-09-1977 L1978 **RO** *020 †80
SCHOKKER, Johannes. 1700 12TH AVE 16601 #025-01-1966 L2000 **GS** *020 †85
SCHROEDER, Sarah. 1701 12TH AVE, STE A 16601 #010-01-1991 L2000 **OBG** *020 †30
SCHULTZ, Paul Scott. 1701 12TH AVE, BLAIR COUNTY ANESTHESIA 16601 #041-07-1990 L1998 **AN** *020 †05
SEBASTIAN, Robin Day. ■ 16601 #049-01-2006 L2006 **FP** *012
SEYMOUR, Elizabeth Marya. 2529 BROAD AVE 16601 #041-02-1996 L2002 **FM** *020 †18 ‡
SHAHEEN, Robert Geo. 501 HOWARD AVE, STE B201 16601 #033-05-1961 L1964 **IM PUD** *020
SHARMA, Vivek Kumar. 2500 7TH AVE 16602 #495-14-1994 L2003 **RNR** *020 †80
SHENOUDA, Emeil Mofid. 620 HOWARD AVE 16601 #915-02-1993 L2003 **FM** *020 †18
SILVERMAN, Joseph Shepsel. 4304 LYNDALE RD 16602 #041-12-1959 L1960 **P** *020 †75 ‡
SINGH, Madhavi. 1414 9TH AVE 16602 #495-34-1995 L2003 **FM** *020 †18
SIRIPALA, Kumbalatara. 312 CHESTNUT AVE 16601 #220-01-1969 L1974 **IM NEP** *020 †20
SIRIPALA, Ranjini W. 310 CHESTNUT AVE 16601 #220-02-1970 L1978 **PD** *020
SKERL, Anton. 620 HOWARD AVE 16601 #041-14-1979 L1980 **FM** *020 †18
SMITH, Oronde Anthony. 620 HOWARD AVE 16601 #035-19-1998 L2007 **EM** *020 †16
SMOLARCZYK, Przemyslaw P. ■ 16601 #759-03-1982 L1991 **AN** *020 †05,20
SNEFF, Eugene M. 620 HOWARD AVE 16601 #041-09-1951 L1974 **ATP CLP** *071 †50
SPONSLER, Rodney Lee. ■ 16601 #041-02-1962 L1963 **PD** *071 †55
SPONSLER, Todd Allen. 501 HOWARD AVE, ALTOONA OPHTHALMOLOGY 16601 #041-14-1990 L1994 **OPH** *020 †35
STERN, Douglas D. 620 HOWARD AVE 16601 #041-77-1996, ▲ L1997 **EM** *020
STULL, Todd Edward. 810 VALLEY VIEW BLVD, BLAIR GASTROENTEROLOGY 16602 #041-09-1985 L1986 **GE IM** *020
SUBRAMANIA, Rajesh. 620 HOWARD AVE, LEXINGTON HOSPITALISTS INC 16601 #495-80-1992 L2002 **IM** *020 †20
SULEIMAN, Samer A. 2950 FAIRWAY DR 16602 #875-03-1990 L2006 **DR** *020 †80
SULLIVAN, Robert Danl. 2323 BROAD AVE 16601 #016-11-1979 L1984 **IM ID** *020 †20
SYMONS, John Taylor. 501 HOWARD AVE BLDG C 16601 #023-01-1979 L1980 **FM FPG** *040 †18
TEJWANI, Roop. 2500 7TH AVE, ANESTHESIA DEPT 16602 #495-30-1968 L1984 **AN IM** *020
THOMAS, Kochumol. ■ 16601 #495-63-1991 L2005 **FP** *012
THOMPSON, Holly Jean. 620 HOWARD AVE, DEPT OF EMERGENCY MEDICINE 16601 #041-14-1996 L1998 **EM** *020 †16
TILYOU, Mark Edward. 2500 7TH AVE 16602 #021-05-1978 L1980 **FM OBS** *020 †18
TRIFAN, Tudor Stefan M. 2907 PLEASANT VALLEY BLVD, ALTOONA VA MEDICAL CENTER 16602 #781-01-1983 L1991 **IM** *020 †20
VAN RIPER, Danl Frederick. 1701 12TH AVE, STE G2 16601 #041-09-1984 L1986 **AN** *020 †05 ‡
VERMA, Rakesh C. 600 PLEASANT VALLEY BLVD 16602 #495-03-1977 L1990 **AI PD** *020 †03,55
WADHWA, Dom. 2907 PLEASANT VALLEY BLVD 16602 #422-01-1982 L1985 **IM OBG** *020 †20
WAIBEL, John Thos Jos. 1701 12TH AVE 16601 #561-01-1973 L1978 **OBG** *020 ‡
WALTON, Barbara L. 620 HOWARD AVE, ALTOONA HOSPITAL LAB 16601 #051-04-1988 L1993 **PTH** *020 †50
WEBSTER, Paul F. ■ 16602 #041-12-1950 L1951 **R** *020
WERTZ, Jennifer Lynn. 501 HOWARD AVE, STE F2 16601 #041-14-1989 L1995 **CCM** *020 †20
WERTZ, Richard Andrew. 2500 7TH AVE 16602 #041-14-1988 L1992 **DR** *020 †80
WERTZ, Robert Elwood. 1701 12TH AVE 16601 #041-12-1960 L1961 **GS CD** *020 †85 ‡
WETZEL, Ann Marie. 501 HOWARD AVE STE E3 16601 #024-07-1981 L1985 **OBG** *020 †30
WHITMORE, Mason. 620 HOWARD AVE 16601 #035-20-1950 L1951 **R** *071 †80
WILFORD, Mark Russell. 1414 9TH AVE, STATION MEDICAL CENTER 16602 #025-07-1983 L1988 **END IM** *020 †20
WILLENBRING, Karen Marie. 620 HOWARD AVE 16601 #041-14-1998 L2000 **FM** *020 †18
WUSTROW, Heinz Juergen. ■ 16601 #407-20-1953 L1959 **PD** *071 †55
YOUNES, Nader. 615 6TH AVE 16602 #875-03-1990 L1997 **PD** *020 †55 ‡
YOUSHAW, Dennis Gordon. 1414 9TH AVE 16602 #041-09-1965 L1966 **GS TRS** *020 †85 ‡
YOUSSEF, Adnan M. 615 6TH AVE, PEDIATRIC HEALTHCARE ASSOC 16602 #875-03-1990 L2000 **PD** *020 †55 ‡
ZAMMAM, Hassan Yassin. 620 HOWARD AVE, RM 332 SCHOOL OF NURSING 16601 #875-01-1991 L1997 **IM EM** *020 †20
ZHANG, Ya. 2907 PLEASANT VALLEY BLVD, VA MEDICAL CTR ALTOONA 16602 #243-63-1982 L1999 **PTH** *020 †50
ZIMMERMAN, A Leonard. ■ 16601 #041-12-1958 L1968 **OTO** *071 †45
ZIMMERMAN, Raymond John. 2613 8TH AVE, ALTOONA REGIONAL HEALTH SY 16602 #045-04-1985 L1989 **FM** *020 †18
ZLUPKO, George M. 801 HOWARD AVE 16601 #041-02-1972 L1973 **PUD** *020 †20
ZLUPKO, Ryan Joseph. 1701 12TH AVE, STE A 16601 #041-02-2000 L2001 **OBG** *020 †30 ‡

ALUM BANK – BEDFORD

FOCKLER, Craig H. 121 ROLLING ACRES DR 15521 #016-76-1995, ▲ L1996 *020

AMBLER – MONTGOMERY

ADESANYA, Adenekan O. ■ 19002 #690-02-1987 *100
ADESANYA, Afoluso Aderonk. ■ 19002 #690-02-1987 **FM** *050
AIELLO, Kathleen Kuykenda. 602 S BETHLEHEM PIKE 19002 #041-02-2002 L2005 **PD** *020 †55
AMIN, Jagruti. 722 E BUTLER PIKE 19002 #495-17-1989 L1995 **CHP** *020 †75
AU, Susan Newbauer. 722 E BUTLER PIKE, THE HORSHAM CLINIC 19002 #041-13-1977 L1979 **P N** *020 †75
BAKER, Courtney Fredrick. ■ 19002 #041-09-1970 L1972 **P** *020 †75
BECKER, Jason Peter. 101 MATTISON AVE, # 2FL 19002 #041-02-2005 L2005 **EM** *012
BELL, Karen Ann. ■ 19002 #041-01-1994 L1997 **PTH** *020 †50
BISHOP, Robert Philip. ■ 19002 #010-03-1957 L1980 **IM OM** *020
BLOCK, Charles Alan. 808 NESBITT RD 19002 #041-13-1986 L1988 **PD** *020 †55
CARLSON, Bruce Edward. ■ 19002 #026-04-1968 L1969 **P PYA** *040 †75
CAVORSI, Kenneth Joseph. ■ 19002 #041-13-2007 L2007 **TY** *012
CHANG, Lily Sy. 105 JEM DR 19002 #748-01-1969 L2006 **AN** *020 †05
CLARKE, Joseph Francis. ■ 19002 #041-13-1962 L1963 **R OS** *071 †80
COCCHELLA, Miguel C. ■ 19002 #737-01-1984 L2003 **P** *020
COCHRAN, William C. ■ 19002 #041-13-1951 L1952 **GS** *071 †85
COMLY, Kathleen Mc Keag. 722 E BUTLER PIKE 19002 #041-02-1973 L1974 **CHP** *020 †75
CONGDON, James Boote. 722 E BUTLER PIKE, HORSHAM CLINIC 19002 #041-01-1977 L1979 **P** *020 †75
DECKER, Steven Edward. 500 WILLOW AVE 19002 #041-02-1974 L1975 **FM** *020 †18
DEGIROLAMO, Maria Pia. ■ 19002 #035-45-1986 L1987 **ID** *071 †20
DENMAN, Susan Jane. 321 NORRISTOWN RD, STE 100 19002 #035-15-1976 L1994 **IMG IM** *030 †20
DE WEER, Ann. 602 S BETHLEHEM PIKE 19002 #028-02-1991 L1993 **PD** *020 †55
DOAN, Hanhnhon. ■ 19002 #047-20-1995 L1999 **IM** *020
DU, Wei. 722 E BUTLER PIKE 19002 #243-72-1986 L2001 **P** *020 †75
DUCOMMUN-NAGY, Catherine. 126 S BETHLEHEM PIKE 19002 #869-04-1976 L1988 **P** *020
DYAKOVETSKY, Izabella. 722 E BUTLER PIKE, THE HORSHAM CLINIC 19002 #913-21-1983 L1998 **P** *020 †75
ELLIS, Michael David. 552 FULWELL CT 19002 #041-02-1970 L1971 **OBG** *020 †30
FARCHIONE, Elizabeth Ann. ■ 19002 #035-15-1980 L1990 **IM** *020 †20
FREEDMAN, Noah D. 722 E BUTLER PIKE 19002 #041-02-1990 L1992 **P** *020 †75
FREEDMAN, Steven James. ■ 19002 #024-07-1997 L2003 **IM** *020 †20
FREEMAN, Hillary N. ■ 19002 #041-13-2003 L2003 **IM** *100 †20
GENZ-REMSHARD, Bernadette. ■ 19002 #041-02-1979 L1979 **IM** *020
GOLD, Michelle Heather. ■ 19002 #041-12-2006 L2006 **DR** *012
HART, Francis Fisher. PO BOX 120 19002 #041-01-1936 L1939 **R OS** *100 †80
HSU, Elizabeth H. ■ 19002 #041-13-2001 L2001 **DR** *020 †80
HYATT, Glenn Alan. 1000 E WELSH RD 19002 #041-02-1978 L1980 **IM** *020 †20
KAPOOR, Ashika. 722 E BUTLER PIKE 19002 #033-06-2001 L2004 **CHP** *020 †75
KIM, Kyong Tai. ■ 19002 #583-02-1957 L1972 **GP P** *071
KOVAR, Robert Chas. 722 E BUTLER PIKE 19002 #041-13-1990 L1992 **CHP** *020 †75
KRAUSE, David Stuart. 1025 DENSTON DR 19002 #041-13-1977 L1979 **IM** *020 †20
KURTZ, John Stephen. ■ 19002 #041-13-1945 L1946 **OBG OS** *071
LIN, Paul Min. ■ 19002 #041-13-1954 L1954 **NS** *071 †25
MALISAN, Lucy Loredana. ■ 19002 #035-08-1988 L1991 **IM** *020 †20
MALONEY, Kathleen A. 1016 GLENDEVON CT 19002 #041-13-1979 **N** *020
MANDEL, Jeffrey Mark. ■ 19002 #041-09-1989 L1993 **OPH** *020 †35
MC ILHENNY, Paul Robt. 1747 CLINTON DR 19002 #041-13-1961 L1962 **CHP** *071
MIDDLETON, Patricia Jean. ■ 19002 #041-13-1964 L1965 **P** *020
MIEZIO, Stanley. ■ 19002 #056-05-1960 L1962 **P** *071 †75
MORRELL, James Francis. ■ 19002 #035-08-1946 **D** *071 †15
MUDE-NOCHUMSON, Hannah M. ■ 19002 #041-02-2005 L2005 **EM** *012
MUELLER, Patricia Powers. ■ 19002 #041-09-1978 L1980 **IM** *030 †20
MURRY, Martha Lillian. ■ 19002 #041-15-1999 L2001 **CHP** *020 †75
NELSON, Edward Blake. ■ 19002 #048-02-1974 L1989 **IM PA** *050 †20
NELSON, Franklin Stirling. ■ 19002 #024-01-1961 L1963 **GS** *071 †85
NOVITSKY, Mark Anthony, Jr. ■ 19002 #041-13-2006 **P** *012
NUGENT, Lynne Jennifer. ■ 19002 #041-02-1992 L1994 **P** *020 †75
NUTHI, Umadevi. 722 E BUTLER PIKE 19002 #495-21-1988 L1993 **CHP** *020 †75
OTTO, Dean Francis. 324 TENNIS AVE 19002 #041-02-1993 L1996 **EM** *020 †16
PATSON, Brian John. ■ 19002 #041-13-2006 L2006 **IM** *012
REED, David Templeton. 500 WILLOW AVE, LOWER LEVEL 19002 #041-01-1962 L1964 **FM** *071 †18
RESNICK, Brian. 1000 E WELSH RD, MAPLE GLEN MEDICAL ASSOCIA 19002 #041-77-1993, ▲ L1994 **IM** *020 †20
RHEE, Sang Ho. ■ 19002 #041-15-2007 L2007 **OBG** *012
ROEDER, Kathleen Marie. ■ 19002 #041-13-1968 L1969 **EM** *020 †16

ROMANZO, George M. 500 WILLOW AVE 19002 #041-02-1975 L1976 **FM** *020 †18
ROTH, Robert Lawrence. ■ 19002 #654-01-1981 L1993 **P IM** *020
ROTHKOPF, Lauren Hope. ■ 19002 #041-13-2007 L2007 **IM** *012
SANTANGELO, Marsha F. ■ 19002 #041-01-1985 L1986 **GS LM** *020
SARNOFF, Jeffrey Ray. 722 E BUTLER PIKE 19002 #561-07-1982 L1985 **P CHP** *020
SCARLETT, John Archibald. ■ 19002 #016-02-1977 L1978 **IM END** *050 †20
SCHOELLES, Karen Terrell. ■ 19002 #011-03-1978 L1980 **IM** *020
SEROTA, Fredric Tobin. 602 S BETHLEHEM PIKE 19002 #041-13-1971 L1972 **PD LM** *020 †55 ‡
SIAM, Nabil A. 722 E BUTLER PIKE, THE HORSHAM CLINIC 19002 #915-04-1981 L1994
  CHP P *075
SILVER, Laurence Mitchel. 1000 WELSH RD 19002 #041-13-1969 L1970 **IM** *071 †20
SILVERMAN, Arthur Ephraim. ■ 19002 #041-13-1959 L1960 **PM** *020 †60
SIMONSON, Andrew C. 722 E BUTLER PIKE 19002 #748-09-1988 L1994 **P CHP** *020
SINHA, Ranjan Kumar. 722 E BUTLER PIKE, THE HORSHAM CLINIC 19002 #495-15-1988 L2000
  PYG *020
SOLISH, Larry. 316 E ORMANDY PL 19002 #065-01-1969 L1975 **U** *020 †95
STEK, Michael, Jr. ■ 19002 #030-06-1969 L1970 **GPM IM** *030 †70
SWAMINATHAN, Mahesh. ■ 19002 #041-02-2003 L2005 **ID** *012 †20
THOMAS, Evan Jennings. 722 E BUTLER PIKE 19002 #041-13-1990 L1992 **P** *020
UDIS, David Scott. 518 MULLEN RD 19002 #041-07-1984 L1985 **DR IM** *020 †80
UKWU, Henrietta Ngazi. 1810 E BUTLER PIKE, 110 KENT DRIVE 19002 #690-07-1982 L1993
  ID IM *050 †20
URBANSKI, Timothy Edward. 500 WILLOW AVE 19002 #041-02-1971 L1972 **IM FM** *020 †20
WOLSKI, Kenneth Paul. ■ 19002 #016-06-1968 L1975 **RHU** *075
WOODWARD-LEE, Astrid E. 602 S BETHLEHEM PIKE, AMBLER PEDIATRICS 19002
  #048-04-1998 L2005 **PD** *020 †55
WYDAN, Anthony Geo. 1116 HORSHAM RD, STE 10 19002 #041-09-1991 L1993 **FM** *020 †18

AMBRIDGE — BEAVER

BACU, Geri Lynn. 1196 MERCHANT ST, SEWICKLEY VALLEY RHEUMATOL 15003
  #041-09-1990 L1993 **RHU** *020 †20
CASSOFF, Richard Geo. 1155 MERCHANT ST 15003 #041-12-1973 L1974 **IM** *020
CHEPONIS, George Baron. 1155 MERCHANT ST 15003 #035-45-1973 L1974 **IM** *020 †20
CRAIG, Donna Jean. 72 1ST ST, AMBRIDGE ARREA HEALTHCARE 15003 #041-12-1990 L1993
  FM *020 †18
FUCHS, Hans James. 1155 MERCHANT ST 15003 #038-06-1987 L1993 **IM** *020 †20
KARP, Michael Alan. 72 1ST ST 15003 #041-13-1988 L1991 **FM** *020 †18 ‡
LEVKOY, Barbara Runkle. 1155 MERCHANT ST 15003 #041-12-1983 L1986 **IM** *020 †20
OSTEN, Kathleen Marie. 72 1ST ST, AMBRIDGE AREA HEALTHCARE S 15003
  #041-02-1989 L1991 **FM** *020 †18 ‡
PERRY, Stephanie L. 1155 MERCHANT ST 15003 #041-14-1994 L1997 **IM** *020 †20
SCHOLLAERT, Richard A. 1155 MERCHANT ST 15003 #041-13-1973 L1974 **IM IMG** *020 †20

ANDALUSIA — BUCKS

PEDDINGHAUS, Marie Elisab. ■ 19020 #016-11-2004 L2004 **PTH** *012

ANNVILLE — LEBANON

CARMANY, Thomas Bear. 580 MOUNT PLEASANT RD 17003 #041-02-1962 L1963
  PTH *071 †50
CONNER, Garret Harding. ■ 17003 #010-01-1965 L1976 **ORS** *071 †40
ENGLE, David Michael. 475 N WEABER ST 17003 #041-15-2001 L2003 **FM** *020 †18
HEETER, David William. 475 N WEABER ST 17003 #041-77-1991, ▲ L1992 **FM** *020
HORWITZ, Alexandra A. 475 N WEABER ST, ANNEVILLE FAMILY MEDICINE 17003
  #041-13-2001 L2002 **MPD** *020
LEACH, Mark William. 10484 JONESTOWN RD 17003 #041-14-1996 L1998 **FM** *020 †18
LOOSE, George Thos. 475 N WEABER ST 17003 #041-77-1970, ▲ L1971 **FM** *020
LUDWIG, Karla Maria. ■ 17003 #050-02-1984 L1986 **HEM** *020
MATEER, Daniel T. 475 N WEABER ST 17003 #041-77-1993, ▲ L1995 **FM** *020 †18
NIELSEN, Robert Keith. 475 N WEABER ST 17003 #035-03-1975 L1976 **FM** *020 †18
POWELL, Dana Edward. 475 N WEABER ST 17003 #041-77-1990, ▲ L1991 **FM** *020
ROSS, Sudeep Jebaraj. ■ 17003 #496-35-2001 L2005 **FP** *012
SMITH, Brent Anthony. 475 N WEABER ST 17003 #041-77-1992, ▲ L1993 **GP** *020
SPAR, Brian Michael. 475 N WEABER ST 17003 #035-45-1976 L1979 **NEP IM** *040 †20
TAYLOR, Abraham Robert. ■ 17003 #041-02-2007 L2007 **FP** *012
TOWNSEND, Beth Veronica. ■ 17003 #041-14-2002 L2002 **P** *100
WELCH, John Benson. 10484 JONESTOWN RD 17003 #041-02-1999 L2001 **FM** *020 †18
WELCH, John Patrick. 10484 JONESTOWN RD 17003 #041-02-1981 L1982 **FM** *020 †18
WING, John Mccormick. ■ 17003 #051-07-1988 L2006 **AM GP** *020 †70

APOLLO — WESTMORELAND

MARTIN, Ruth Danette W. 311 N 2ND ST 15613 #041-12-1976 L1977 **FM** *020 †18
MCLAUGHLIN, Andrew Dale. ■ 15613 #023-12-2008 *012
MCLAUGHLIN, Sandra Sharan. ■ 15613 #023-12-2008 *012

ARCHBALD — LACKAWANNA

KELLY, Patrick J. ■ 18403 #028-34-1949 L1988 **ORS GS** *071 †40
SEPROSKY, Joseph Chas. 4 KELLY ST 18403 #041-09-1987 L1988 **FM** *020 †18
WRIGHT, Donald Conroy. ■ 18403 #011-03-1983 L1984 **IM** *075

ARDMORE — MONTGOMERY

ABROMS, Gene Mayer. ■ 19003 #024-01-1959 L1966 **P** *020 †75
ALLISON, William D. ■ 19003 #041-13-1950 L1951 **CD IM** *071
ANTER, Elad. ■ 19003 #550-01-2002 L2007 **CD** *012

BARTLETT, Alexandra S. 100 CHURCH RD, STE 300 19003 #041-13-1983 L1984 **PD** *020 †55
BASERGA, Susan J. ■ 19003 #008-01-1988 *100
BATTAGLIA, David R. 121 COULTER AVE STE 102 19003 #041-02-1988 L1990 **FM IMG** *020 †18
BLUM, Justin Tyler. ■ 19003 #023-01-2000 L2001 **DR** *100 †80
BRACE, Frederick Howes. 113 CRICKET AVE, P O BOX 271 19003 #041-01-1963 L1964
  CHP P *071
BROWN, Leslie Anne. 100 CHURCH RD, STE 100 #005-11-1987 L1989 **OPH** *020 †35
BUERK, Minerva Smith. ■ 19003 #041-07-1946 L1948 **D** *071 †15
CHERUKURI, Sudha. ■ 19003 #495-21-1992 L2005 **IM** *012
CHEVRES, Anita. 233 E LANCASTER AVE, STE 300 19003 #041-07-1986 L1988 **NM** *020 †28
COOPER, Joseph Helt. ■ 19003 #041-13-1954 L1955 **PTH CLP** *071 †50
CORAO, Diana Andreina. ■ 19003 #935-01-1997 L2000 **PTH** *100 †50
DIDARIO, A Geoffrey. 233 E LANCASTER AVE, STE 200 19003 #050-02-1997 L2002
  PD AI *100 †55,03
EHRLICH, Lori A. ■ 19003 #041-12-2007 L2007 **PD** *012
EPSTEIN, David Ezra. 121 COULTER AVE, STE 102 19003 #035-46-1979 L1980 **FM** *020 †18
ESCOVITZ, Gerald Howard. ■ 19003 #035-08-1962 L1969 **GE** *071 †20
FARREN, Rosemary C. ■ 19003 #063-01-1979 L1991 *100
FERRELL, Michael Stuart. ■ 19003 #036-05-2005 L2006 **DR** *012
FRIEDMAN, Josh Richard. ■ 19003 #041-01-1998 **PD** *100 †55
FRIEDMAN, Joshua. ■ 19003 #550-01-1988 L2000 **RHU** *020
GOBER, Michael David. ■ 19003 #023-01-2007 L2007 *012
GRAY, Frieda Gersh. ■ 19003 #035-09-1944 L1968 **OS IM** *071 †20
GREEN, Sean D. 9 E ATHENS AVE, STE 9B 19003 #041-09-1996 L1998 **FM** *020 †18
HAMILTON, Weston Thos. 105 SIBLEY AVE 19003 #041-13-1970 L1972 **P** *020 †75
HARRIS, John Eric. ■ 19003 #024-16-2005 L2006 **D** *012
HEIL, Charles G, Jr. ■ 19003 #041-02-1953 L1954 **OBG** *071 †30
HONEBRINK, Ann Louise. 130 VALLEY RD 19003 #041-07-1981 L1983 **OBG** *030 †30
HOROWITZ, Harvey Alan. 125 COULTER AVE 19003 #041-13-1968 L1969 **P** *020 †75
ISAAC, Lea M. ■ 19003 #028-78-2004, ▲ L2004 **OBG** *012
JONES, Daniel Cornell. 90 GREENFIELD AVE 19003 #047-07-1940 L1945 **FM PHP** *071
KELLY, Vernon Chas, Jr. 100 CHURCH RD STE 202 19003 #041-01-1970 L1972 **P CHP** *020 †75
KEMMERER-BROWN, Kelly M. 225 E ATHENS AVE, WU SCHOOL OF MEDICINE 19003
  #041-09-1996 L2007 **N** *020 †20,75
KING, Frank Harrison, Jr. 100 CHURCH RD, STE 300 19003 #041-13-1976 L1978 **PD** *020 †55
KRAVIS, Lillian B Panzer. 233 E LANCASTER AVE, MAIN LN ALLRGY & PULMONARY 19003
  #041-01-1943 L1944 **AI PD** *071 †55,03
KRAVITZ, Lawrence Bruce. ■ 19003 #660-01-1963 L1968 **P** *071
LABOR, James Xavier. 8 SHAWNEE RD 19003 #041-07-1996 L1999 **EM** *020 †16
LEVY, Susan Ellen. 128 CEDARBROOK RD 19003 #041-07-1978 L1979 **PD** *020 †55
LYNN, Jennifer Ruth. 100 CHURCH RD 19003 #041-15-1999 L2001 **OPH** *020 †35
MAC MURTRIE, Wm J A, Jr. 161 GOLFVIEW RD 19003 #041-01-1943 L1944 **GS CRS** *072 †85
MASTER, Stephen Reis. ■ 19003 #041-01-2002 L2002 *020 †50
MATTHIES, Frank Alexander. ■ 19003 #409-07-1993 L1998 **NM** *100 †28
MENAGED, Rachel Elise. ■ 19003 #035-46-2005 L2007 **PD** *012
MENDELSON, Lawrence Scott. 233 E LANCASTER AVE, STE 300 19003 #035-08-1990 L1992
  CD *020 †20
MOHMAND, Adam. ■ 19003 #759-09-1997 L2004 **CD** *012 †20
MOSCOTTI, Richard Wm. 119 COULTER AVE 19003 #041-09-1960 L1961 **P** *020 †75
NAKISBENDI, Kara Munira. 233 E LANCASTER AVE, STE 103 19003 #041-13-1994 L1998
  OBG *020 †30
OULIGIAN, John Chas. 121 COULTER AVE, STE 208 19003 #035-09-1978 L1993
  P PFP *020 †05,75
PARK, Jin. ■ 19003 #036-01-2002 L2007 **VIR** *012
PATEL, Seema Mahesh. 59 W LANCASTER AVE, SHANTI MED SPA & WELLNESS 19003
  #038-40-1994 L1999 **FM** *020 †18
POSENCHEG, Michael A. ■ 19003 #043-01-1999 L2002 **NPM** *100 †55
PRICE, Raymond Stephen. ■ 19003 #041-01-2004 L2004 **N** *012
REITANO, John. 121 COULTER AVE 19003 #035-15-1989 L1992 **P** *020 †75
RITTER, Baird S. ■ 19003 #041-01-1953 L1954 **CHP P** *062 †55,75
RODMAN, Theodore. ■ 19003 #041-01-1953 L1954 **PUD IM** *071 †20
RUBIN, Morton. ■ 19003 #041-77-1943, ▲ L1958 **FM** *071 †18
RUIZ, Camilo A. 170 LAKESIDE RD 19003 #011-75-2007, ▲ L2007 **OBG** *012
RUSK, John Michael. 133 COULTER AVE 19003 #041-01-1961 L1962 **CHP P** *020 †75
SANDLER, Susan Meredith. 121 COULTER AVE, STE 102 19003 #041-07-1989 L1991
  FM *040 †18
SANDO, Ralph Scott. 100 CHURCH RD, STE 100 19003 #041-13-1973 L1974 **OPH** *020 †35
SANDO, Ralph Scott, Jr. 100 CHURCH RD 19003 #041-13-1997 L2000 **OPH** *020 †35
SANDOVAL-BARRETT, Jessy. 121 COULTER AVE, STE 201 19003 #041-09-1993 L1995
  CHP P *020 †75
SARIS, Steven Demetrius. 100 CHURCH RD 19003 #041-09-1977 L1979 **IM PA** *020 †20
SELTZER, Elyse Gail. ■ 19003 #035-19-1990 L1992 **ID** *020 †20
SHAFIK, Marleine Ragaie. ■ 19003 #010-03-2006 L2006 **EM** *012
SINGLETARY, William Marle. 119 COULTER AVE STE 200 19003 #047-05-1973 L1985
  PYA CHP *020 †75
SMITH, Kaighn. 100 W LANCASTER AVE 19003 #041-01-1954 L1955 **OBG** *071 †30
SOUSER, Roslyn Coskery. 44 HAVERFORD RD 19003 #041-07-1966 L1967 **PS** *020 †85,65
SPENCER, H Newton. ■ 19003 #041-01-1950 L1955 **ORS OM** *072
SPENCER, Mary E J. ■ 19003 #041-01-1948 L1950 **ID PD** *100
STEERS, John Coster. 233 E LANCASTER AVE, STE 300 19003 #035-47-1990 L1992
  CD IM *020 †20
SWEINBERG, Sharon Kay. 233 E LANCASTER AVE, STE 200 19003 #041-14-1983 L1984
  AI PDA *020 †55,03 ‡
TANG, Shangguo. 120 E MONTGOMERY AVE, UNIT 303 19003 #243-23-1983 L2001 *100 †50
TOLIN, Laurie Beth Gordon. 100 CHURCH RD 19003 #024-07-1972 L1975 **D IM** *020 †15
TRONCELLTI, A Wayne. 1522 WYNNEWOOD RD 19003 #561-20-1971 L1974 **IM** *020
WEINSTEIN, Adam Jacob. ■ 19003 #041-13-2005 L2005 **N** *012
YEILDING, Newman Manly. ■ 19003 #041-02-1985 L1987 **HO** *050 †20
YOGO, Norihiro. ■ 19003 #017-20-2008 *012
YOKOGAWA, Naoto. ■ 19003 #572-30-1998 L2007 **RHU** *012 †20

ASHLAND — SCHUYLKILL

CHO, Chung Hyun. RT 61 17921 #583-01-1948 L1968 **AN OS** *020

DALLABRIDA, Marguerite R. 101 BROAD ST, ASHLAND REGIONAL MEDICL CT 17921 #041-07-1960 L1961 **GYN** *072
DAVIS, Jacob Lamar. ■ 17921 #041-13-1936 L1937 **GP OS** *075
GIRTON, Keith Eugene. 101 BROAD ST 17921 #038-40-1974 L1985 **ORS FM** *020 †18,40
GOLSORKHI, Mohammad. 93 BROAD ST STE 1C 17921 #517-06-1968 L1975 **GS VS** *020 †85
GREEN, Roy Carter, Jr. 1126 BEAVER DAM RD 17921 #041-09-1961 L1962 **AN** *020
MODY, Satish Kantilal. 101 BROAD ST 17921 #496-38-1969 L1973 **AN** *020
MONCAVAGE, Melissa Beth. ■ 17921 #041-02-2005 L2005 **OPH** *012
NAKKOUL, Anwar. 1023 W CENTER ST 17921 #875-01-1980 L1996 **IM** *020
NICHOLLS, Edith Evelyn. 1023 CENTRE ST 17921 #008-01-1926 L1940 **GP PD** *071
NICHOLLS, Joan Ethel. 101 BROAD ST 17921 #041-07-1955 L1956 **P** *071 †75
NICHOLLS, Richard Henry. 1023 CENTRE ST 17921 #041-13-1954 L1955 **GP** *071 †85
SCEARCE, Naomi Elaine. 101 BROAD ST 17921 #005-12-1995 L2003 **IM PD** *020 †20,55
SHAH, Vinay N. 101 BROAD ST 17921 #495-22-1971 L1986 **IM EM** *020
STEFOVIC, John Wm. 530 W CENTER ST 17921 #041-14-1984 L1985 **EM FM** *020
STRATTON, Robert G. 101 BROAD ST 17921 #041-13-1984 L1985 **FP** *020
VILLARREAL, Carlos X. 101 BROAD ST 17921 #649-30-1981 L1982 **GS VS** *020 †85

ASPINWALL — ALLEGHENY

BROWN, David Carl. ■ 15215 #041-01-1985 L1985 **IM** *075
BRUNO, Carmen Rosa. 135 FREEPORT RD 15215 #132-02-1971 L1975 **P CHP** *071 †75
BURKE, Timothy Ray. ■ 15215 #041-12-1996 L1998 **IM** *020 †20
CANNON, Glenn Martin, Jr. ■ 15215 #041-02-2000 L2002 **UP** *012
GIBSON, Margaret Elizabet. ■ 15215 #041-12-2005 L2005 **FP** *012
JACOBS, Micah Abram. 137 FREEPORT RD 15215 #038-43-2003 L2008 **ID IM** *012 †20
JANULEWICZ, John David. ■ 15215 #041-12-2005 L2005 *100
JOHNSON, Kim Graham. ■ 15215 #041-12-1999 L2000 **IM** *100
LASURE, Rex David. 50 FREEPORT RD, STE 500 15215 #055-01-1980 L2007 **EM FM** *020 †18,16
MC CARTHY, John J, Jr. 241 FREEPORT RD 15215 #041-12-1949 L1950 **GYN** *071 †30
PONTZER, Raymond Edward. 137 FREEPORT RD 15215 #041-07-1979 L1981 **ID IM** *020 †20
ROMANO, Joseph Michael. 137 FREEPORT RD 15215 #041-07-1975 L1976 **ID IM** *020 †20
SIEWERS, Christiane M F M. 135 FREEPORT RD 15215 #036-05-1962 L1973 **CHP P** *071 †75

ASTON — DELAWARE

DE LA CRUZ, Michael. ■ 19014 #035-15-2005 L2005 **PTH** *012
KESSLER, Woodrow Bertram. 4515 PENNELL RD 19014 #041-13-1962 **FM FPG** *020 †18
LEBITA, Mamerto M. 5904 CHICHESTER AVE 19014 #748-09-1975 L1983 **FM** *020 †18
MATADEEN-ALI, Chandra. ■ 19014 #566-01-1996 L2002 **IM** *100 †20
NOVIELLI, Karen Dare. 211 E PETERS LN 19014 #041-02-1987 L1989 **FM IMG** *040 †18
SCHWEIZER, Robert A. 3150 CONCORD RD 19014 #041-02-1979 L1981 **IM FM** *020
SURESHKUMAR, Ambika. 243 PENNELL RD A, ASTON MEDICAL ASSOC 19014 #690-02-1988 L1998 **IM** *020 †20
WARE, William Chas. 400 CHERRY TREE RD 19014 #041-09-1982 L1983 **IM** *020 ‡

ATGLEN — CHESTER

LOMBOY, Norma Trinidad. ■ 19310 #748-01-1958 L1970 **IM GP** *071
LOMBOY, Tito P, Jr. ■ 19310 #748-01-1958 L1969 **CLP PTH** *020 †50

ATHENS — BRADFORD

BECK, Jan. ■ 18810 #035-19-1960 L1965 **GS HNS** *071 †85
BECK, Paul Vincent. ■ 18810 #041-02-2006 L2007 **GS** *012
BLAKE, Monroe Onque. RD #2MOORE ROAD 18810 #010-03-1955 L1956 **FM** *071
FALKENBERG, Karl Jorg. ■ 18810 #407-20-1956 L1968 **OTO** *071 †45
GIORDANO, Debra Louise. ■ 18810 #041-07-1980 L1982 **PTH** *074
HAHN, Kurt R. 307 N MAIN ST 18810 #038-44-1982 L1986 **P PYG** *020 †75
HARVEY, Barbara J. 107 CENTER ST 18810 #008-01-1986 L1995 **IM** *020 †20
JACOBSON, Horace H H. ■ 18810 #064-01-1949 L1959 **RO** *075 †80
JONES, Edward Leslie, Jr. 412 S MAIN ST 18810 #024-05-1968 L1970 **FM EM** *020 †16,18
KELLY, John Anthony. PO BOX 189, 32 GREEN MOUNTAIN DR 18810 #539-04-1960 L1968 **PTH** *030 †50
LUFT, William Coleman. ■ 18810 #035-45-1956 L1967 **PTH** *071 †50
MIKAYA, Martin Losuba. 2031 ORANGE HILL RD 18810 #045-01-1980 L1983 **EM GS** *020 †16 ‡
NAGLE, Warren Chas. ■ 18810 #024-01-1953 L1958 **U** *071 †95
NASSER, Salah Nasrat. ■ 18810 #575-01-1987 L2000 **AN CD** *020 †05
PAUL, Stephen Edwin. RR 1 BOX 302 18810 #038-40-1969 L1992 **NS** *071 †25
WANAMAKER, John Lloyd. 735 S MAIN ST 18810 #041-01-1959 L1964 **CD IM** *071 †20

AUDUBON — MONTGOMERY

CRUFT, George Edward. ■ 19403 #016-11-1947 L1949 **GS** *071 †85

AVALON — ALLEGHENY

BRUNO, Jorge Cesar. 846 CALIFORNIA AVE, ALLEGENY EYE CTR 15202 #132-02-1970 L1975 **OPH** *020 †35
JANCARIK, John Peter. 824 CALIFORNIA AVE 15202 #041-12-1999 L2001 **NEP** *020 †20
OLSON, Mary. 910 CALIFORNIA AVE 15202 #041-12-1978 L1979 **OBG** *020 †30

AVELLA — WASHINGTON

BONI, Dino Richard, Jr. 1953 BRUSH RUN RD 15312 #047-07-1970 L1972 **GE IM** *071 †20 ‡

AVOCA — LUZERNE

DRUFFNER, Lewis C, Jr. 824 MCALPINE ST 18641 #041-02-1959 L1960 **GP** *071

KOZLOSKI, Maureen C. 180 MAIN ST 18641 #041-13-1987 L1989 **IM** *020 †20

AVONDALE — CHESTER

BINCK, Brian Walter. ■ 19311 #039-01-1997 L2005 **CCP** *020 †55
BLANKSON, Victor Nikoi. ■ 19311 #869-05-1972 L1978 **CCP** *030 †55
COFFEY-ZERN, Susan L. 113 SAINT ANDREWS DR 19311 #041-13-1992 L1997 **PD** *020 †55
DABBAGH, Omar. ■ 19311 #605-01-1982 L2006 **N PD** *020 †55,75
GELLER, Wayne Kevin. ■ 19311 #041-14-1982 L1983 **FM PHM** *050 †18
GIDUSKO, Kelly. ■ 19311 #041-13-2004 L2006 **AN** *012
HAUSLER, Fred C, Jr. ■ 19311 #041-09-1962 L1990 **AN** *071 †05
LI, Ryan Jeffrey. ■ 19311 #041-12-2008 *012
SOTO-DIAZ, Norberto E. ■ 19311 #264-18-1989 L1998 **ID** *050 †20
ZABEL, David Donald. 111 HARTEFELD DR 19311 #038-41-1990 L1998 **PS** *020 †65

BADEN — BEAVER

ALBERTS, Nancy Kay. 229 STATE ST 15005 #041-12-1979 L1980 **FM** *071 †18
HEIN, Jeffrey Paul. 1525 BEAVER RD 15005 #041-09-1992 L1994 **FM** *020 †18 ‡
KUNTZ, Andrew Thos. ■ 15005 #038-44-1990 L1993 **N** *020
SOLIMAN, Layla. ■ 15005 #038-43-2005 L2005 **P** *020

BAKERSTOWN — ALLEGHENY

DONALDSON, Joseph V. ■ 15007 #041-12-1944 L1945 **OM** *071 †70

BALA CYNWYD — MONTGOMERY

ABRAMSON, John. 333 E CITY AVE, STE 2 19004 #041-13-1971 L1972 **GE IM** *020 †20
ADENWALLA, Humaira Naseem. 1 BALA PLZ STE 402 19004 #704-02-2001 L2005 **IM** *012
AGNIHOTRI, Gauri. 1 BALA AVE, STE 118 19004 #495-50-1988 L1996 **P** *020 †75
AJMAL, Adnan. 1 BALA PLZ STE 402, MERCY CATH MED CTR INC 19004 #704-04-2000 L2004 **IM** *012
AKBAR, Ali. 1 BALA PLZ STE 402, MERCY CATH MED CTR INC 19004 #704-01-2002 L2005 **IM** *012
ANANDAPPA, Roshani T. ■ 19004 #016-11-2003 L2005 **PD** *100 †55
ARIFUDDOWLA, Abul Foyez M. 1 BALA PLZ STE 402, MERCY CATH MED CTR INC 19004 #160-02-1995 L2005 **IM** *012
ASNANI, Alpna Deepak. 1 BALA PLZ STE 402, MERCY CATH MED CTR INC 19004 #495-01-1988 L2000 **IM** *012
ASTROFF, Matthew Robt. 333 E CITY AVE, STE 2 19004 #012-05-1980 L1986 **GE IM** *020 †20
AUDAY, Jose Horacio. 1 BELMONT AVE, GSB BUILDING, SUITE 307 19004 #132-01-1953 L1962 **ORS** *071 †40
AYRES, Brandon Daniel. 40 MONUMENT RD, STE 104 19004 #033-06-2000 L2000 **OPH** *020 †35
BALAKRISHNAN, Priya. 1 BALA PLZ STE 402 19004 #496-23-2001 L2001 **IM** *020
BARNETT, Michael A. ■ 19004 #041-01-1996 L1999 **OTO** *020
BARNICA ELVIR, Victor Hug. 1 BALA PLZ STE 402, DEPT OF GENERAL SURGERY 19004 #649-43-2004 L2007 **GS** *012
BARRETT, Michael John. 1 BELMONT AVE, 620 GSB BLDG 19004 #041-14-1973 L1978 **CD IM** *020 †20 ‡
BECK, Sylvia Ruth. 40 MONUMENT RD FL 5 19004 #008-01-1982 L1983 **OPH** *020 †35
BENSER, Suzanne K. 555 E CITY AVE, STE 520 19004 #048-15-1988 L1990 **P PYA** *020 †75
BERKOWITZ, Darryl H. ■ 19004 #836-01-1993 L2001 **PAN** *100 †05
BLESHMAN, Michael Henry. 417 LINDY LN 19004 #041-09-1971 L1972 **DR** *030 †80
BONOVITZ, Jay Stuart. 191 PRESIDENTIAL BLVD, STE 111B 19004 #038-41-1969 L1973 **P** *072 †75
BORTIN, Leonard. 191 PRESIDENTIAL BLVD 19004 #041-09-1946 L1947 **IM** *071 †20
BRENNER, Ira. 10 PRESIDENTIAL BLVD STE 1 19004 #041-02-1976 L1979 **P PYA** *020 †75
BRODKEY, Amy Catherine. 191 PRESIDENTIAL BLVD, STE 113 19004 #041-01-1975 L1978 **P ADP** *020 †75
BRYAN, Frances Evans. 2 BALA PLZ STE IL40 19004 #023-07-1980 L1983 **IM** *075 †20
BRYANT, Winston M, Jr. 191 PRESIDENTIAL BLVD # W5 19004 #047-07-1960 L1961 **OPH** *071 †35
BURNS, Rosalie Annette. 191 PRESIDENTIAL BLVD 19004 #008-01-1956 L1964 **N** *030 †75
BYRNE, Jessica Price. ■ 19004 #010-02-1979 L1980 **P PYA** *020 †75
CARANDANG-PANIS, Norma H. ■ 19004 #748-01-1982 L1991 **PD PTH** *020 †55
CASKEY, Herbert Tarter. 401 E CITY AVE STE 820 19004 #041-02-1972 L1974 **IM** *020
CENGEL, Keith. ■ 19004 #016-11-2001 L2002 **RO** *100
CHAKABVA, Munyaradzi Stan. 1 BALA PLZ STE 402, MERCY CATH MED CTR INC 19004 #775-01-2002 L2005 **IM** *012
CHODOS, Wesley S. 1 BALA AVE, STE 120 19004 #018-75-1977, ▲ L1978 **REN** *071
CLOUGH, Howard Kenneth. 40 MONUMENT RD, FL 5 19004 #038-06-1948 L1957 **OPH** *071 †35
CO, Deborah Luz. 191 PRESIDENTIAL BLVD, STE 111B 19004 #041-01-1997 L1999 **P** *020 †75
COHEN, Michael Martin. GSB BUILDING STE 620, CITY & BELMONT AVE 19004 #041-02-1973 L1978 **N PMM** *020 †75
COHEN, Robyn Tracy. ■ 19004 #035-46-2000 L2007 **PDP** *020 †55
COPPERMAN, Gertrude F. 2 BALA PLZ STE 8 19004 #041-07-1949 L1950 **GP OSM** *071
CUMPEERAVUT, Pranom. PO BOX 398 19004 #891-01-1988 **AN** *100
DEMBE, Carol. ■ 19004 #032-01-1978 L1988 **EM** *020 †16
DEN, Robert Benjamin. ■ 19004 #024-01-2006 L2007 **RO** *012
DIAZ, Ruben Martinez. ■ 19004 #649-05-1954 L1965 **PTH GP** *020
DIDIZIAN, Noubar Hagop. 1 BALA PLZ STE 621, ORTHO & HAND SPEC PC 19004 #605-01-1967 L1973 **ORS HS** *020 †40
DI GIOVANNI, Ralph J, Jr. 501 BELMONT AVE 19004 #041-09-1998 L2000 **OPH** *020 †35
DOLSKY, Richard Laurence. 191 PRESIDENTIAL BLVD #105 19004 #024-07-1972 L1981 **PS OTO** *020 †45,65 ‡
EDWARDS, Arthur Mark. ■ 19004 #048-02-1979 L1987 **FM EM** *075 †18
ELLIS, Richard A. 142 MONTGOMERY AVE, RICHARD A ELLIS PC 19004 #041-02-1949 L1950 **OPH** *071 †35

■ = Address Information Privacy Protected

ENGINEER, Erach Hormasji. ■ 19004 #495-17-1954 L1967 **AN** *020
FARBER, Roger Evan. 1 BALA AVE, STE 130 19004 #041-01-1963 L1966 **N** *020 †75
FARKAS-SZALLASI, Tunde. ■ 19004 #473-04-1985 L2003 **PCP** *020 †50
FEINBERG, Michael P. 1 BALA AVE, STE 230 19004 #024-05-1973 L1986 **P PYA** *020 †75
FEJERDY, Francis Rudolf. ■ 19004 #473-01-1945 L1965 **GP GS** *071
FINDEN, Steven George. ■ 19004 #033-05-1999 L2001 **DR** *100 †80
FINK, Paul Jay. 191 PRESIDENTIAL BLVD, STE C132 19004 #041-13-1958 L1959 **P PYA** *020 †75
FISH, Jonathan D. ■ 19004 #035-15-2000 L2004 **PHO** *100 †55
FLEISCHER, Mark Harold. ■ 19004 #035-46-1974 L1976 **AN** *020 †05
FLOYD, Floyretta Joann. 111 PRESIDENTIAL BLVD, STE 220 19004 #033-06-1992 L1996 **FM** *020 †18
FOWLER, William P. 190 PRESIDENTIAL BLVD # 51 19004 #010-02-1981 L1982 **P** *020
FOX, Michael L. 100 PRESIDENTIAL BLVD, BRANDON CLINIC 19004 #654-01-1983 L1984 **GP PHL** *020 ‡
FRATTAROLI, Elio John. 1 BALA AVE STE 210 19004 #016-02-1978 L1979 **P PYA** *020 †75
FTAIHA, Zaki. 15 PRESIDENTIAL BLVD, STE 200 19004 #875-01-1973 L1987 **GS CD** *020 †85
GARBER, Jeffrey Geo. 555 E CITY LINE AVE, STE 100 19004 #020-02-1977 L1978 **FM EM** *020 †18
GENOVESE, Elizabeth. 2 BALA PLZ, STE 600 19004 #041-01-1983 L1986 **IM OM** *030 †20,70
GLADSHTEIN, Sonya. 2 BALA PLZ, LINE AVE 19004 #913-96-1970 L1984 **AN** *020
GOEBEL, Edward Jos. 11 BALA AVE 19004 #041-13-1989 L1991 **P PYG** *020 †75
GOGINENI, Rama Rao. 1 BALA AVE STE 118 19004 #495-57-1973 L1978 **P CHP** *020 †75
GOLDMAN, Marina. ■ 19004 #041-15-2000 L2001 **ADP** *012 †75
GOTSDINER, Denise Beth. ■ 19004 #041-13-1990 L1993 **PTH** *020 †50
GOULD, John Douglas. 555 E CITY AVE, STE 930 19004 #654-01-1988 L1992 **END IM** *020 †20
GOYAL, Vipin Kumar. 333 E CITY LINE AVE 19004 #041-07-1996 L2001 **OPH** *020 †35
GRAUB, Milton. 41 CONSHOHOCKEN STATE RD 19004 #041-09-1944 L1945 **PD** *072 †55
GRECO, Timothy Mark. 333 E CITY AVE, STE PL15 19004 #041-09-1989 L1991 **FPS** *020 †45
GREENBAUM, Marvin Henry. 501 BELMONT AVE 19004 #010-01-1979 L1982 **OPH** *020 †35
GREENBERG, Bram. ■ 19004 #041-09-1981 L1982 **PD** *040 †55 ‡
GREENBERG, Roger Alan. ■ 19004 #035-46-2000 L2007 **CLP** *020 †50
GREENE, Ronald Barry. 225 E CITY AVE, STE 105 19004 #041-13-1972 L1973 **ORS AM** *020 †40 ‡
GREENSPAN, Jack. ■ 19004 #041-09-1956 L1957 **P** *020 †75
GRUJIC, Dejan. ■ 19004 #422-01-2005 L2005 **GS** *100
HAAS, Eric Jason. ■ 19004 #550-04-2002 L2005 **PDI** *012 †55
HALPERN, Ethan Jos. 29 RADCLIFF RD 19004 #035-19-1985 L1991 **R** *020 †80
HARAN, Michal Zippora. ■ 19004 #550-01-1991 **PTH** *100 †20
HARMON, Eli Beller. 111 PRESIDENTIAL BLVD, STE 235 19004 #021-01-1954 L1959 **P ADP** *020
HOFFMAN, Jill Edwards. ■ 19004 #041-09-1989 L1991 **CHP** *071
HOOKER, Leah Rae. ■ 19004 #039-01-2003 L2006 **GE** *012
HOSALKAR, Hetal Harish. 1 BALA PLZ STE 402, MERCY CATH MED CTR INC 19004 #496-36-1995 L2005 **AN** *012
HSU, Jason. 40 MONUMENT RD, STE 104 19004 #041-01-2001 L2002 **OPH** *020 †35
HUDDLESTON, Christie Ann. 1 BALA AVE, STE 308 19004 #041-07-1978 L1979 **P** *020 †75
HUSSAIN, Mahnaz. 1 BALA PLZ STE 402, MERCY CATH MED CTR INC 19004 #704-21-2000 L2005 **IM** *012
IQBAL, Rashid. ■ 19004 #704-01-2000 L2003 **IM** *020 †20
JOHNSTON, Esther Mascaro. 555 E CITY AVE STE 500, LOWENTHAL & ABRAMS PC 19004 #041-09-1972 L1992 **FM** *062 †18
JOHNTZ, Susan Estill. 115 CYNWYD RD 19004 #041-07-1989 L1991 **P** *020 †75
KALANI, Ghassem. 191 PRESIDENTIAL BLVD, STE W1A 19004 #517-01-1971 L1985 **PM** *020 †60
KALLEN, Roland Gilbert. ■ 19004 #035-01-1960 L1974 **IM HEM** *050
KATCHMAN, Jerome J. 190 PRESIDENTIAL BLVD, UNIT 416 19004 #041-02-1960 L1961 **D GP** *071
KAUR, Primal Jyot. 1 BALA PLZ STE 402 19004 #495-03-2003 **IM** *012
KHAN, Meher Sami. 146 MONTGOMERY AVE STE 200 19004 #704-06-1979 L1981 **AI** *020 †55,03
KHOURY, Jacques A. 333 E CITY AVE, STE 2 19004 #605-02-1970 L1974 **GE IM** *020 †20
KINSTLICK, Emanuel. 9 UNION AVE 19004 #041-02-1966 L1967 **DR** *071 †80
KIRSHBAUM, Bernard A. ■ 19004 #041-02-1950 L1951 **D** *071 †15
KLEINERT, Bradley Andrew. ■ 19004 #041-77-2007, ▲ L2007 *012
KLUFT, Richard Philip. 111 PRESIDENTIAL BLVD, STE 238 19004 #024-01-1968 L1969 **P PYA** *020 †75 ‡
KOHLER, John Patrick. 301 E CITY LINE AVE # 250 19004 #016-02-1976 L1984 **PMM GS** *020 †85,90
KOREVAAR, Wilhelmina C. 1 BELMONT AVE, STE 315 19004 #008-01-1977 L1981 **PMM AN** *020 †05 ‡
KRENZEL, Archibald R. 191 PRESIDENTIAL BLVD 19004 #041-09-1949 L1950 **P PYA** *071 †75
KUH, Elizabeth Nancy. 3 CYNWYD RD 19004 #024-05-1985 L1986 **P** *020 †75
KUMAR, Ajay. 1 BALA PLZ STE 402, MERCY CATH MED CTR INC 19004 #495-69-2003 **IM** *012
LAUFER, Terri Marilyn. 12 PENARTH RD, 12 PENARTH ROAD 19004 #035-01-1987 L1998 **RHU** *020 †20
LEE, May Wing-Kim. ■ 19004 #041-07-1958 L1962 **PD** *020 †55
LEFKOE, Roy Thos. 301 E CITY AVE STE 235 19004 #041-12-1970 L1971 **ORS OSM** *020 †40
LEHRER, Jenifer K. 555 E CITY AVE STE 1170 19004 #041-01-1998 L2001 **GE** *020 †20 ‡
LEVY, Steven H. 555 E CITY AVE, STE 210 19004 #041-09-1975 L1976 **P** *020
LIACHOWITZ, Claire H. SUTTON TERRACE NO 501 19004 #035-01-1956 L1957 **PM** *071 †60
LIANG, Howard S. ■ 19004 #243-21-1940 L1962 **AN** *071 †05
LICHTENSTEIN, Stephen B. 40 MONUMENT RD STE 104 19004 #041-02-1974 L1975 **OPH OS** *020 †35 ‡
LIEBERMAN, Amara A. 1 BALA PLZ, STE 620 19004 #005-14-1990 L1995 **D** *020 †15
LIEZ, Joshua. ■ 19004 #041-01-2006 L2006 **IM** *012
LIT, Joan Ava. 555 E CITY AVE, ASSOCIATES 19004 #041-07-1987 L1988 **END IM** *020 †20
LIU, Aaron Liu. 42 CONSHOHOCKEN STATE RD, UNIT 6A 19004 #041-13-1997 L2000 **IMG** *020 †18
LIU, Chiashang Jason. ■ 19004 #041-01-2006 L2006 **DR** *012
LIU, Renyu. 1 BALA PLZ STE 402 19004 #243-49-1990 L2004 **AN** *012
LIU, Tzu-Shang Thomas. ■ 19004 #041-01-2003 L2003 **ORS** *012
LLUBERES, Jocelyn. 190 PRESIDENTIAL BLVD, UNIT 413 19004 #308-13-1999 L2001 **CHP** *100 †75
LONG, William Donald, III. ■ 19004 #041-02-2007 *012
LONGANECKER, Nicole Renee. ■ 19004 #047-05-2005 **IM** *012
LOW, Julie Ann. 146 MONTGOMERY AVE STE 301 19004 #035-01-1982 L1989 **P** *020 †75
LUSH, David Theodore. 333 E CITY AVE, STE IL27 19004 #028-34-1976 L1979 **IM IMG** *020 †20
LUSTIG, Herbert S. 15 PRESIDENTIAL BLVD STE 2 19004 #035-46-1968 L1971 **CHP P** *020 †75
M, Satya Narayana Reddy. 1 BALA PLZ STE 402 19004 #496-22-2005 **IM** *012
MAGEE, Joni Lahr. 191 PRESIDENTIAL BLVD, STE W1 19004 #041-07-1968 L1969 **OBG** *020 †30
MALEKI, Jahangir. 100 PRESIDENTIAL BLVD, THE PAGODA BLDG 3RD FL 19004 #409-37-1988 L1997 **N** *020 †75
MAMO, Jubran Geo. ■ 19004 #605-01-1946 L1955 **OPH** *020 †35
MARCHLINSKI, Francis E. ■ 19004 #041-01-1976 L1978 **CD** *020 †20
MARKOWITZ, Elizabeth A. 312 LLANDRILLO RD 19004 #028-02-1991 L2001 **FM** *020 †18
MARLOWE, Frank Irwin. 40 MONUMENT RD, STE 500 19004 #041-12-1963 L1971 **OTO HNS** *020 †45 ‡
MATCHETT, Myrtle O. ■ 19004 #919-03-1971 L1974 **CHP P** *020 †75
MATHISEN, Jane Marietta. 1 BALA AVE STE 118 19004 #008-01-1985 L1986 **P OBG** *020 †75
MC KENZIE, Clancy Douglas. 191 PRESIDENTIAL BLVD, STE 3W, P.O. BOX 345 19004 #025-01-1962 L1965 **P OS** *020 †75
MEISLER, Jeanne Shamai. 11 BALA AVE 19004 #041-07-1971 **P PD** *020 †75
MERCOGLIANO, Giancarlo. 333 E CITY AVE, STE 2 19004 #041-09-1983 L1984 **GE IM** *040 †20
MEYERS, Karl Robt. ■ 19004 #035-03-1963 L1971 **PTH** *020 †50
MEZROW, Craig K. 15 PRESIDENTIAL BLVD, STE 200 19004 #035-47-1996 L2001 **PS** *020 †65 ‡
MILLER, Herman. 50 BELMONT AVE # NO-510 19004 #041-13-1940 L1941 **GP CRS** *072
MILSTEIN, Harold Jacob. 301 E CITY AVE STE 119 19004 #033-05-1975 L1977 **D** *020 †15 ‡
MORY, Aaron Karl. 308 LEVERING MILL RD 19004 #041-02-2005 L2005 **AN** *012
MOSENKIS, Judith Blum. 167 UPLAND TER 19004 #035-46-1996 L2003 **PYG** *020
MOY, M Louis. ■ 19004 #016-43-1996 L1999 **U** *020 †95
MRUK, Claudia Celeste. 2 BALA PLZ STE IL27 19004 #041-07-1977 L1978 **IM** *020 †20
MUMTAZ, Khurram. 1 BALA PLZ STE 402, DEPT OF INTERNAL MED 19004 #704-20-2001 L2004 **IM** *012 †20
NAGELBERG, Steven Brooks. 555 E CITY AVE, STE 930 19004 #035-01-1978 L1985 **END IM** *020 †20
NARASIMHA RAO, Archana. 1 BALA PLZ STE 402, MERCY CATH MED CTR INC 19004 #496-24-2003 L2005 **N** *012
NASSER, Syed Kamal. 1 BALA PLZ STE 402 19004 #704-02-1996 L2005 **IM** *012
NEWMAN, Gary Alan. 333 E CITY AVE, STE 2 19004 #041-01-1979 L1980 **IM** *050 †20
OBERSTEIN, Paul Eliezer. ■ 19004 #038-40-2006 L2006 **IM** *012
OFER, Dafna. ■ 19004 #550-02-1997 L2004 **SME** *012 †55
ORELLANA, Charles Francis. 2 BALA PLZ, STE IL27 19004 #041-01-1992 L1994 **IM** *020 †20 ‡
PADMA, Hymavathi. 1 BALA PLZ STE 402 19004 #495-21-1996 L2004 **IM** *100
PALMACCIO, Anthony J. 100 PRESIDENTIAL BLVD, THIRD FLOOR 19004 #041-07-1973 L1975 **ORS** *020
PALYA, Aniruddha Venkates. 1 BALA PLZ STE 402 19004 #496-21-2002 L2005 **IM** *012
PARENS, Henri. 111 PRESIDENTIAL BLVD, STE 133 19004 #021-01-1959 L1964 **PYA CHP** *020
PARK, Carl Hyunsuk. 40 MONUMENT RD STE 104, OPHTHALMIC SUBSPECIALTY CN 19004 #026-08-1997 L2003 **OPH** *020 †35
PERILSTEIN, Paul Kramer. ■ 19004 #041-02-1942 **CD IM** *071
PERVEZ, Ayesha. 1 BALA PLZ STE 402, MERCY CATH MED CTR INC 19004 #160-02-2001 **IM** *012
PHILIPS, Andrew J. 2 BALA PLZ, INTERMEDIATE LEVEL STE 35 19004 #035-46-1977 L1978 **OPH** *020 †35
PIETRA, Giuseppe. ■ 19004 #561-03-1955 L1970 **PTH** *071 †50
PLANTE, Lauren Anne. ■ 19004 #035-46-1984 L1991 **OBG MFM** *020 †05,30
POLISHOOK, Robert D. 11 BALA AVE STE 27 19004 #041-01-1967 L1968 **P** *020 †75
POLLARD, Emily Frances. 555 E CITY LINE AVE, STE 1170 19004 #047-07-1984 L1996 **PS GS** *020 †85,65
PRO, Michael James. 40 MONUMENT RD 19004 #041-15-2001 L2006 **OPH** *020 †35
PRUSKY, Paul Murray. 1 BELMONT AVE STE 519 19004 #024-01-1955 L1969 **GP OS** *020
RANA, Amira. 1 BALA PLZ STE 402, DEPT OF INTERNAL MED 19004 #704-21-2000 L2003 **IM** *100
REAPE, Kathleen Zinger. 1 BELMONT AVE FL 11 19004 #041-01-1991 L1995 **OBG** *050 †30
REDDY, Jyothsna Budibetta. 1 BALA PLZ STE 402, MERCY CATH MED CTR INC 19004 #496-39-1988 L2004 **AN** *012
RICHARDS, Rafael Mayo. ■ 19004 #041-13-2000 L2005 **AN** *020
RODGERS, Carla. 2 BALA PLZ, STE 300 19004 #016-01-1980 L1988 **P LM** *062 †75
ROHTBART, Meyer. 191 PRESIDENTIAL BLVD, STE 110 19004 #025-01-1971 L1972 **P** *020 †75
RUCINSKA, Ewa J. ■ 19004 #759-07-1959 **OS N** *050
SABIR, Aaliya Parveen. ■ 19004 #060-01-2002 L2003 **PD** *100
SACKS, Harry Jack. 335 BALA AVE 19004 #035-46-1986 L1987 **PHM PD** *020 †55 ‡
SAMPSON, Matthew Gordon. ■ 19004 #051-01-2005 L2005 **PD** *012
SANFACON, Cheryl Lynn. 111 PRESIDENTIAL BLVD 19004 #024-07-1978 L1979 **P** *020 †75
SARIN, Lov K. 40 MONUMENT RD STE 104 19004 #495-12-1955 L1967 **OPH** *020 †35
SBARBARO, John Louis. BELMONT & CITY LINE AVE 19004 #041-09-1955 L1956 **ORS** *071 †40
SCHEER, Abraham. 45 E CITY AVE, # 431 19004 #308-07-1980 L2005 **CHN CHP** *020
SCHMIDT, Courtland Mercer. 40 MONUMENT RD, STE 104 19004 #041-01-1956 L1987 **GS** *071 †85
SCHMIDT, Richard Geo. 15 PRESIDENTIAL BLVD, STE 300 19004 #041-14-1980 L1982 **ORS** *020 †40
SCHWAB, Morton E. 41 CONSHOHOCKEN STATE RD A 19004 #041-13-1942 L1943 **P** *071 †75
SCHWARTZ, Edward Saul. 1 BALA PLZ 19004 #035-08-1967 L1981 **IM FM** *075 †18
SCHWELL, Ari Brett. ■ 19004 #035-46-1991 L1995 **EM** *020 †16
SELTZER, Jonathan. 225 E CITY AVE, STE 15 19004 #041-01-1988 L1994 **CD** *020 †20
SESTOPAL EPELMAN, Monica. ■ 19004 #132-02-1989 L2004 **DR** *020
SHAHABDEEN, Simi. 1 BALA PLZ STE 402, MERCY CATH MED CTR INC 19004 #495-31-2001 L2005 **IM** *012
SHAPIRO, Stuart Howard. 34 LLANBERRIS RD 19004 #035-06-1968 L1981 **PHP GP** *030 †80,28,70
SHERWIN, William Kevin. 1 BALA PLZ STE 620 19004 #041-01-1975 L1976 **D** *020 †15 ‡
SHRESTHA, Sachin Lal. 1 BALA PLZ STE 402 19004 #672-02-2003 L2006 **IM** *012
SILVERSTEIN, Leonard I. ■ 19004 #035-19-1979 L1985 **U IM** *050 †95 ‡
SMITH, Randall Norman. 100 PRESIDENTIAL BLVD 19004 #041-13-1973 L1974 **ORS PME** *020 †40
SMITH, William Thomas. ■ 19004 #035-48-2000 L2003 **NEP** *020 †20
SOLOMON, Mark P. 191 PRESIDENTIAL BLVD, STE LN24 19004 #035-19-1978 L1979 **PS GS** *020 †65,85
SOLOTOFF, Stephen Alan. 191 PRESIDENTIAL BLVD, STE 103 19004 #041-07-1981 L1982 **D** *020 †15

■ = Address Information Privacy Protected

SONDER, Hestor Molly. 2 BALA PLZ STE IL41 19004 #041-13-1976 L1978 **OBG** *020 †30
SOSKIS, David Aaron. ■ 19004 #008-01-1968 L1971 **P** *062 †75
SPECTOR, Jordan Andrew. ■ 19004 #035-46-2003 L2007 **EM** *100
SPIERER, Morris. 122 BIRCH AVE 19004 #035-46-1969 L1971 **IM PUD** *020 †20
SRIKANTHAN, Shruthi H. 24 E PRINCETON RD 19004 #496-21-1994 L2002 **AN** *020 †05
SROUJI, Maurice Nakhleh. ■ 19004 #605-01-1953 L1966 **PDS** *071 †85
STARSNIC, Mary Ann. 108 TALL TREES DR 19004 #041-02-1973 L1974 **AN** *020 †05
STEIN, Joel. BELMONT/CITY GSB BLDG 323 19004 #041-09-1962 L1963 **GYN** *071 †30
STEINBERG, J Arthur. ■ 19004 #041-01-1962 L1964 **FM** *040 †18
STEINBERG, Stanley B. 190 PRESIDENTIAL BLVD, UNIT 602 19004 #041-13-1952 L1953 **R** *020 †80
STEINMAN, David. 191 PRESIDENTIAL BLVD, STE 111B 19004 #041-07-1988 L1990 **P PYA** *020 †75
STEINMAN, Ruth Herman. 1 BALA AVE, STE 230 19004 #041-07-1987 L1989 **PYG** *020 †75
STERN, Joshua E. ■ 19004 #035-46-2003 L2006 **GE** *012
STOLLER, Jason Zachariah. ■ 19004 #041-01-1999 L2002 **NPM** *020 †15
STRATON, Joseph Benedict. 150 MONUMENT RD STE 300, WISSAHICKON HOSPICE 19004 #041-02-1997 L1999 **FM PLM** *030 †18
STREISFELD, Neil Todd. 555 E CITY AVE, STE 930 19004 #035-09-1979 L1982 **END IM** *020 †20
STUNZ, Ronald Wm. 1 BALA PLZ, HEALTH CARE BUSINESS RESOU 19004 #396-27-1978 L1981 **EM IM** *030 †20,16
SUBBARAMAN, Aparna. 1 BALA PLZ STE 402, MERCY CATH MED CTR INC 19004 #495-70-2001 L2005 **IM** *012
SUMMERS, Jane Marans. 146 MONTGOMERY AVE, STE 301 19004 #010-02-1985 L1986 **P** *020 †75
TAKAWIRA, Ngano Tongesai. 1 BALA PLZ STE 402, DEPT OF INTERNAL MED 19004 #775-01-2000 L2004 **IM** *020 †20
TESSLER, Cheryl Lynn. ■ 19004 #041-01-1998 †100
THORNTON, James Jos, III. 333 E CITY AVE, STE 2 19004 #041-13-1964 L1965 **GE IM** *020 †20
THOTA, Subhashini. 1 BALA PLZ STE 402 19004 #495-65-2000 L2003 **IM** *020 †20
TIKHONOVA, Elizaveta Vile. 1 BALA PLZ STE 402, DEPT OF INTERNAL MED 19004 #913-01-1997 L2002 **IM** *020 †20
TIPPERMAN, Richard. 40 MONUMENT RD, STE 104 19004 #035-45-1984 L1985 **OPH N** *020 †35
TOKHI, Ashish. 1 BALA PLZ STE 402, MERCY CATH MED CTR INC 19004 #495-12-2002 L2005 **IM** *012
TSE, Rose Lou. 191 PRESIDENTIAL BLVD # 20 19004 #041-07-1960 L1961 **IM RHU** *020 †20
TYAGI, Isha. 1 BALA PLZ STE 402 19004 #495-12-2001 L2005 **IM** *012
URICCHIO, Joseph F. 2 BALA PLZ 19004 #024-07-1949 L1954 **CD IM** *071 †20
VACCARO, Vincent Michael. 1 BALA AVE, STE 120 THE KEATING BLDG 19004 #041-02-1968 L1969 **OBG** *040 †30
WATANABE, Yoshio. ■ 19004 #572-20-1951 L1971 **CD IM** *020
WEERASINGHE, Chandra M P. 555 E CITY AVE STE 210 19004 #220-01-1970 L1987 **P CHP** *020 †75
WEINBERGER, Abraham. ■ 19004 #550-01-1970 **RHU** *100
WEINBERGER, Tal Esther. 29 BALA AVE STE 224, BALA CHILD & FAM ASSOC 19004 #041-01-2001 L2001 **P** *020 †75
WEISS, Kenneth Jay. 333 E CITY AVE STE 300 19004 #041-09-1973 L1979 **P PFP** *020 †75
WEISS, Robert. 191 PRESIDENTIAL BLVD 19004 #041-13-1967 L1968 **IM** *020 †20 ‡
WELL, David S. ■ 19004 #041-01-2007 L2007 **TY** *012
WERRIN, Marguerite W. ■ 19004 #041-07-1974 L1975 **ID IM** *071 †20 ‡
WILSON, Rachel Marie. ■ 19004 #041-13-2008 *012
WILSON, Richard Philip. 40 MONUMENT RD, STE 104 19004 #028-03-1973 L1975 **OPH** *030 †35
WIMMER, Robert Saml. 345 LLANDRILLO RD 19004 #041-13-1972 L1976 **PHO PD** *020 †55
WOLF, Lisa Carol. ■ 19004 #041-02-1984 L1985 **IM** *020
WOODS, Timothy Alan. 333 E CITY LINE AVE # IL40, 2 BALLA PLAZA 19004 #023-07-1979 L1983 **IM IMG** *020 †20 ‡
ZACHIAN, Toby Frank. 2 BALA PLZ, STE IL17 19004 #041-01-1992 L1995 **D** *020 †15
ZHAO, Iris Ginron. 1 BALA PLZ STE 213, C/O PAUL INGLESBY 19004 #243-47-1970 **OPH** *020
ZITIN, Marc Allen. 2 BALA PLZ STE IL30, 333 EAST CITY LINE AVENUE 19004 #041-09-1985 L1987 **GE IM** *020 †20
ZUL-E-HUMA, None. 1 BALA PLZ STE 402 19004 #495-51-2003 **IM** *012
ZWILLENBERG, Seth. 40 MONUMENT RD, STE 500 19004 #035-08-1981 L1982 **OTO FPS** *020 †45

BANGOR – NORTHAMPTON

CAPOBIANCO, Frank M. ■ 18013 #041-09-1945 L1946 **U GS** *071 †95
CAPOBIANCO, Frank Michael. ■ 18013 #041-09-1973 L1974 **OM EM** *020 †16,70
DE FRANCO, Mary Ellen. 316 WASHINGTON BLVD 18013 #308-11-1983 L1999 **PD** *020
ROMANO, Nicholas Michael. 104 S 2ND ST 18013 #041-09-1977 L1978 **FM** *020 †18
STANCOMBE, Wesley Ray. ■ 18013 #041-09-1954 L1955 **GP** *071

BARNESBORO – CAMBRIA

DANDREA, Raymond L. PO BOX 213, 1304 PARK AVE 15714 #041-02-1951 L1952 **GP GS** *071
SEMADAR, Joseph. ■ 15714 #550-01-1964 L1983 **PD** *071

BARTONSVILLE – MONROE

VESCE, Joseph P. ■ 18321 #016-42-1951 L1951 **FM OS** *071

BATH – NORTHAMPTON

AHMAD, Iftikhar. 6649 CHRISPHALT DR STE 101 18014 #704-16-1988 L1997 **IM** *020 †20
BLOSE, Linda Kay. 6649 CHRISPHALT DR 18014 #041-09-1983 L1984 **IM** *030 †20
BOND, William Franklin. ■ 18014 #041-02-1995 L1998 **EM** *020 †16
ERICKSON, Craig William. 586 MOORESTOWN DR, NORTHERN LEHIGH PRIMARY CA 18014 #041-14-1999 L2001 **FM** *020 †20
GUERRA, Reynaldo C. 108 E NORTHAMPTON ST 18014 #748-01-1974 L1984 **FM** *020

MILLER, Janet Elizabeth. 586 MOORESTOWN DR, NORTHERN LEHIGH PRIMARY CA 18014 #041-14-1999 L2002 **IM** *020 †20
ORSI, James M. 2225 YOST RD 18014 #033-05-1967 L1973 **AN** *071 †05
SORATHIA, Iqbal. 6649 CHRISPHALT DR STE 101 18014 #704-16-1984 L1990 **IM** *020 †20
STRATEFF, Liselotte H. ■ 18014 #407-04-1951 L1960 **AN** *071

BAUSMAN – LANCASTER

ECKERT, Patrick Quinn. ■ 17504 #041-13-2006 L2006 **FP** *012
STEHMAN, Charles Christop. ■ 17504 #041-15-2008 *012

BEAR CREEK TOWNSHIP – LUZERNE

PALENCAR, Andrea. ■ 18702 #041-07-1993 L1999 **FM** *020 †18
TICZON, Andres Rivera. 2989 BALD MOUNTAIN RD 18702 #748-07-1965 L1972 **CD IM** *020 †20 ‡

BEAR LAKE – WARREN

BULGER, Jennifer Louise. 227 ARDEN RD, BAILEY HILL RD 16402 #035-06-1998 L2000 **FM** *020 †18

BEAVER – BEAVER

ALBRIGHT, Deborah Dawn. 701 SHARON RD 15009 #041-12-1997 L2007 **AI** *020 †03,55
BAGLIO, Corrado M. ■ 15009 #561-04-1951 L1966 **PTH** *020 †50
BANSAL, Prabha. 1000 DUTCH RIDGE RD, U P M C/H V H S C C 15009 #496-07-1968 L1975 **RO** *020 †80 ‡
BASKA, John Kevin. 701 5TH ST, ONE BEAVER PLACE 15009 #010-01-1974 L1975 **IM** *020 †20
BEGG, Richard J. 500 SHARON RD 15009 #539-06-1986 L1987 **CD IM** *020 †20
BELICH, Stephen Chas. 93 BOUNDRY LN 15009 #041-13-1973 L1975 **GS CRS** *020 †85
BOAL, William Erwin S. 219 3RD ST 15009 #041-12-1940 L1941 **GP** *071
BRABSON, Howard W. 699 3RD ST 15009 #041-02-1951 L1952 **GP** *071
BRANDT, Robert I. 1000 DUTCH RIDGE RD 15009 #041-09-1960 L1965 **GS TS** *071 †85
BRENNAN, Richard Everall. 1000 DUTCH RIDGE RD, MEDICAL CENTER 15009 #041-02-1972 L1973 **DR** *020 †80
BRETT, George William, III. 701 5TH ST, ONE BEAVER PLACE 15009 #041-13-1977 L1978 **IM** *020 †20 ‡
BROCK, Justin. 131 DUNCAN CIR 15009 #048-12-2008 *012
BRODY, Michael Chas. 1000 DUTCH RIDGE RD 15009 #051-04-1984 L1986 **AN** *020 †05
BURGER, Joseph Geo. 1000 DUTCH RIDGE RD 15009 #041-12-1955 L1956 **OBG** *071 †30
BUSH, Francis. 1000 DUTCH RIDGE RD 15009 #041-12-1943 L1944 **GP** *071
CAHILL, Lisa Jenkins. ■ 15009 #023-01-1983 L1984 **EM PD** *020 †55,16
CAREY, Brian Coleman. 500 SHARON RD 15009 #041-15-2000 L2001 **IC** *020 †20
CARL, Beverly Ann. 500 MARKET ST, ASSOCIATION OF SPECIALTY 15009 #041-12-1979 L1981 **PS** *020 †20
CECCARELLI, Amerigo N. 250 COLLEGE AVE 15009 #041-12-1990 L1992 **PD** *020 †55
CHAMOVITZ, Bruce Norton. 1000 DUTCH RIDGE RD, MEDICAL CENTER OF BEAVER C 15009 #041-12-1977 L1982 **IM ID** *040 †20
CHEN, Carolyn Chihui. 1000 DUTCH RIDGE RD, BEAVER VALLEY PATHOLOGY 15009 #011-03-1991 L1996 **PTH HMP** *020 †50
CONE, Alexander Scott. 3345 TUSCARAWAS RD 15009 #041-12-1968 L1969 **GP** *020
CONTE, Anthony A. ■ 15009 #035-06-1950 L1951 **OS AN** *072
COOK, Amanda Marie. 1200 SHARON RD, STE 202 15009 #041-14-2001 L2005 **OPH** *020
COZZA, Michael R, Jr. 1360 SHARON RD 15009 #847-01-1973 L1978 **FM** *020 †60
CROZIER, David Jack. 690 STATE AVE 15009 #041-13-1954 L1955 **OBG** *071 †30
CROZIER, James Allen. 690 STATE AVE 15009 #041-09-1974 L1975 **OBG** *020 †30
CRUMRINE, Richard Seiple. 5230 TUSCARAWAS RD 15009 #041-02-1962 L1963 **OTO** *020 †45
CUDDY, Vincent Don. 1300 5TH ST 15009 #041-09-1957 L1958 **GS TS** *071 †85
CULYBA, Michael John. 1000 DUTCH RIDGE RD, HERITAGE VLY HLTH SYS 15009 #016-43-1972 L1979 **IM** *030 †20
DANIELS, George Francis. 1700 3RD ST 15009 #016-06-1982 L1993 **U** *020 †95
DEACON, Robert Edwin. 250 COLLEGE AVE, TRI-STATE PEDIATRIC 15009 #041-07-1996 L1999 **PD** *020 †55
DEL GRANDE, Richard E. 1000 DUTCH RIDGE RD, ANESTHESIA DEPARTMENT 15009 #055-01-1981 L1984 **AN IM** *020 †20,05
DUMPE, Pamela Mc Kee. 2325 GYPSY GLEN RD 15009 #041-09-1982 L1983 **IM** *020 †20
DUSENBERRY, Sarah Jo. ■ 15009 #041-07-1984 L1985 **EM** *020 †16
ELSON, James Jos. 605 SHARON RD 15009 #016-43-1980 L1981 **IM** *050 †20
ENGLE, Carolyn P. 1030 BEANER HOLLOW RD 15009 #055-01-1990 L1992 **ORS** *020 †40
ERUKHIMOV, Jeffrey A. 1425 3RD ST 15009 #913-16-1980 L1995 **PCC** *020 †65
ESKENDRI, Nasser. 1000 DUTCH RIDGE RD 15009 #517-01-1971 L1977 **OBG** *020 †30
EUBANKS, Marc Joseph. 1000 DUTCH RIDGE RD 15009 #041-13-1996 L1998 **EM** *020 †16
FARLAND, Monica Louise. 1211 3RD ST, ASSOC OF INTERNAL MED 15009 #041-09-1991 L1993 **IM** *020 †20
FERRI, William Albert, Jr. 1030 BEANER HOLLOW RD, UPMC CANCER CENTER BEAVER 15009 #024-05-1986 L1987 **ON HEM** *020 †20
FIGUCIA, David Alan. 701 5TH ST, AGH INTERNAL MEDICINE 15009 #023-01-1993 L1996 **IM** *020 †20
FLORES, Angel. 500 SHARON RD 15009 #308-02-1978 L1990 **CD** *020 †20
FLYNN-MCGARVIE, Nancy. 274 3RD ST 15009 #422-01-1993 L1997 **FM** *020 †18
GAGNE, Jane Read. 274 3RD ST STE 100, CENTER MEDICAL ASSOICATES, 15009 #024-16-1992 L1994 **FM** *020 †18
GOLTZ, Gerald Marvin. 1000 DUTCH RIDGE RD 15009 #041-12-1973 L1974 **END NEP** *020 †20
GRAY, Herbert Mann. 1000 DUTCH RIDGE RD 15009 #165-04-1965 L1971 **GP** *020 ‡
HAYES, Oliver Wesley, III. 1000 DUTCH RIDGE RD, HERITAGE VALLEY HEALTH SYS 15009 #025-76-1981, ▲ L2006 **EM** *040 †16
HEINLE, Edward William. ■ 15009 #024-16-2005 L2005 **PM** *012
HEINLE, Edward Wm, Jr. ■ 15009 #041-12-1958 L1959 **ON IM** *071 †20
HEINLE, Michael Scott. 1211 3RD ST, ASSOCIATES OF INTERNAL MED 15009 #041-12-1990 L1993 **IM** *020 †20

HELSING, Walter John. ■ 15009 #041-13-1945 L1946 **ORS OS** *071 †40
HERALD, Geoffrey Richard. 1300 5TH ST 15009 #023-01-1980 L1982 **GS VS** *020 †85
HERTFORD, Joann Fiorito. 628 MARKET ST 15009 #033-06-1986 L1987 **FM** *020 †18
HIRSCH, Bernard. 1030 BEANER HOLLOW RD 15009 #055-01-1970 L1977 **ORS** *020 †40
HOCKENBERRY, Sherry Lynn. 1000 DUTCH RIDGE RD, DEPT OF EMERGENCY MEDICINE 15009 #041-14-1993 L1995 **EM** *020 †16
HOOVER, Paul Michael. 647 3RD ST 15009 #016-43-1986 L1987 **PM** *020 †60
HOVENDEN, Anthony Lennox. 701 5TH ST, P O BOX 570 15009 #917-24-1958 L1980 **RO** *071 †80
IZQUIERDO, Wilson. 1000 DUTCH RIDGE RD, DEPT OF FAMILY PRACTICE 15009 #649-38-1999 L2006 **FM** *100
JACKSON, Timothy Louis. 500 SHARON RD 15009 #041-09-1989 L1991 **IM** *020 †20
JADOON, Muhammad Shamsher. 1000 DUTCH RIDGE RD 15009 #704-24-1995 L2003 **FM** *100 †18
JONES, Hilary Sarah. 250 COLLEGE AVE, TRISTATE PEDIATRIC ASSOC 15009 #055-01-1994 L1997 **PD** *020 †55
KAYE, Andrew Stuart. 1030 BEANER HOLLOW RD, ASSOCIATION OF SPECIALTY 15009 #041-12-1988 L1990 **ORS** *020 †40
KIM, Sun Yeong. 1000 DUTCH RIDGE RD 15009 #035-46-1995 L2000 **PTH** *020 †50
KNAPP, Robert Chas. 701 SHARON RD 15009 #041-09-1980 L1981 **END IM** *020 †20
KRAUS, Kathryn Elaine. 701 SHARON RD 15009 #041-12-1977 L1979 **AI IM** *020 †20,03
KRAYER, Nicholas H, Jr. 1000 DUTCH RIDGE RD 15009 #041-12-1951 L1952 **IM PUD** *071
KWIAT, Michael Anthony. 1360 SHARON RD 15009 #035-15-1987 L1991 **P PYG** *075
LA FORTE-MOORE, Anne. 1211 3RD ST 15009 #566-01-1980 L1993 **CHP P** *020
LANCASTER, Stewart Lloyd. 1030 BEANER HOLLOW RD, UPMC CANCER CTR 15009 #041-14-1982 L1987 **ON** *020 †20
LARACUENTE, Benjamin. 1201 3RD ST 15009 #308-01-1961 L1970 **PD** *020
LEHMAN, John David. 1030 BEANER HOLLOW RD, ASSOCIATION OF SPECIALTY 15009 #041-13-1991 L1993 **ORS** *020 †40
LEPIANE, Richard Michael. 500 SHARON RD, VALLEY INTERNAL MEDICINE 15009 #041-07-1982 L1993 **FM IMG** *020 †18
LIM, Jung Taick. ■ 15009 #583-08-1969 L1973 **PTH** *074 †50
LINS, Jeffrey Allen. 500 SHARON RD 15009 #036-05-1984 L1985 **CD IM** *020 †20 ‡
LOFFREDA-MANCINELLI, C. 1000 DUTCH RIDGE RD 15009 #561-17-1980 L1986 **AN** *020 †05
LUCERO, Prudencio C. 500 SHARON RD 15009 #748-10-1988 L1993 **CD IM** *020 †20
LUELLEN, John Russell. 1000 DUTCH RIDGE RD, THE MEDICAL CENTER, BEAVER 15009 #041-14-1996 L1998 **EM** *020 †16
LUKE, Seema. 500 SHARON RD, VALLEY INTERNAL MEDICINE 15009 #065-06-1993 L1998 **FM** *020 †18
MARCUS, Gary Jay. 1000 DUTCH RIDGE RD, BEAVER VALLEY PATHOLOGY 15009 #055-01-1970 L1974 **ATP CLP** *071 †50
MARION, Roy Haines. 1000 DUTCH RIDGE RD 15009 #041-12-1957 L1958 **GP OBG** *071 †18
MARKOWITZ, Hank Evan. 300 S WALNUT LN, STE 100 15009 #561-17-1978 L1983 **DR** *020 †80 ‡
MARSHALL, John Schoeller. 701 5TH ST, ONE BEAVER PLACE 15009 #041-01-1954 L1955 **IM GE** *071
MC CORMICK, Mark Wilson. 1000 DUTCH RIDGE RD 15009 #055-01-1975 L1976 **OBG** *020 †30
MC CREARY, Thomas Wm, III. ■ 15009 #041-01-1955 L1956 **NM IM** *071 †20,28
MCNEILL, Laura. 1000 DUTCH RIDGE RD 15009 #016-01-1991 L1994 **AN** *020 †05
MEUSER, Robert Martin. 1300 5TH ST, ASSOCIATION OF SPECIALTY 15009 #038-45-1988 L1990 **GS** *020 †85
MIANO, Lidia. ■ 15009 #561-10-1950 L1965 **GP** *071
MICHAEL, Thomas Peter. 1000 DUTCH RIDGE RD 15009 #041-01-1985 L1986 **EM** *020 †18
MICHEL, John Paul. 1200 SHARON RD, STE 200 15009 #041-09-1975 L1976 **FM IMG** *030 †18 ‡
MIN, Tae Cheol. 1000 DUTCH RIDGE RD, BEAVER VALLEY PATHOLOGY 15009 #583-03-1968 L1970 **IM PTH** *020
NAVARRO, Catherine Sembra. ■ 15009 #748-19-2000 L2005 **FP** *012
NAWROCKI, Mary F. ■ 15009 #028-34-1952 L1956 **PM** *071
NEELEY, Steven Wm. 1000 DUTCH RIDGE RD, ANESTHESIA DEPARTMENT 15009 #047-06-1983 L1984 **AN** *020 †05 ‡
NIGAM, Rajendra Kumar. 1607 3RD ST 15009 #495-41-1977 L1987 **P CHP** *020 †75
O CONNOR, William Francis. 1000 DUTCH RIDGE RD 15009 #041-12-1976 L1977 **AN** *020 †05
OTTING, James Joseph. ■ 15009 #038-43-2006 L2007 **PM** *012
OVADIA, Philip Craig. 1000 DUTCH RIDGE RD 15009 #041-02-1998 L2005 **TS VS** *020 †85
PALOMBO, Christopher J. 1000 DUTCH RIDGE RD, FL 0 15009 #041-14-1988 L1990 **OBG** *020 †30 ‡
PANGBURN, Thomas L M. 1000 DUTCH RIDGE RD 15009 #041-12-1993 L1995 **EM** *020 †16
PATRICK, David Brice. 1700 3RD ST 15009 #041-12-1970 L1977 **U** *020 †95
PETERSON, William Michael, II. ■ 15009 #041-14-2008 L2008 **P** *012
PHAN, An Kieu. 1000 DUTCH RIDGE RD 15009 #942-01-1992 L2003 **FM** *020
PIERSON, Edward Chas. 1000 DUTCH RIDGE RD 15009 #038-40-1991 L1994 **P** *020 †75
PUPI, Paul Anthony. 1300 5TH ST, ASSOCIATION OF SPECIALTY 15009 #041-02-1966 L1967 **GS TS** *020 †85
RAFALKO, David Mark. 1301 RIVERSIDE DR 15009 #041-13-1974 L1975 **OTO** *020 †45 ‡
RAJ, Victor Soundararaj. 1000 DUTCH RIDGE RD 15009 #041-13-2001 L2005 **AN** *100
RAY, Annmarie. 1211 3RD ST 15009 #055-01-1988 L1990 **IM END** *020 †20
REITZ, John Donald. ■ 15009 #041-12-1948 L1949 **PTH** *071 †50
REYES, Saturnino Mercader. 1360 SHARON RD 15009 #748-02-1959 L1968 **GS EM** *071
REZNICK, Barry Richard. 1200 SHARON RD STE 201, ALLEGHENY NEUROLOGICAL ASS 15009 #041-12-1980 L1986 **N IM** *020 †20,75
RICH, John Jeffrey. 500 SHARON RD 15009 #539-06-1987 L1990 **CD IM** *020 †20
ROONEY, Joseph Wm. 701 SHARON RD, STE 1 15009 #011-04-1979 L1980 **CD IM** *020 †20
ROSCOE, Brandon M. 1000 DUTCH RIDGE RD 15009 #654-01-2006 L2006 **FP** *012
ROSCOE, Nico D. 1000 DUTCH RIDGE RD 15009 #654-01-2006 L2006 **FP** *012
RUMBAUGH, William P. 1000 DUTCH RIDGE RD, FL 0 15009 #041-02-1986 L1987 **OBG** *020 †30
SCHOUCHOFF, Adrienne Lee. 500 SHARON RD 15009 #041-09-1993 L1995 **CD** *020 †20
SEGAL, Allan. 1000 DUTCH RIDGE RD 15009 #041-13-1974 L1975 **GS VS** *020 †85
SEIBEL, Philip Scott. 1000 DUTCH RIDGE RD, CANCER TREATMENT CTR 15009 #045-01-1989 L1994 **TS** *020 †40
SHUMWAY, Gail Janet. ■ 15009 #026-04-1984 L1986 **FM** *020 †18
SLEMENDA, William Dennis. 500 SHARON RD 15009 #041-12-1979 L1982 **CD** *020 †20 ‡
SMITH, James Willard. 1000 DUTCH RIDGE RD, THE MDCL CTR PHYSCL THRPY 15009 #041-12-1958 L1959 **PCH GS** *062 †50

STIEGEL, Robert Mark. 701 5TH ST 15009 #016-11-1976 L1979 **D** *020 †15
STRAGAND, Jarod Paul. ■ 15009 #041-77-2006, ▲ L2006 **FP** *012
TAHA, Mohammad Taher. 1000 DUTCH RIDGE RD 15009 #104-01-2006 **FP** *012
TARABAY, Grace Raouf. 1030 BEANER HOLLOW RD 15009 #605-01-1997 L2004 **HO** *020 †20
THEL, Henry Chas, Jr. 1000 DUTCH RIDGE RD 15009 #010-02-1963 L1966 **OPH** *071 †35
TROY, Deborah Dawson. 300 S WALNUT LN STE 100, BRIGHTON RADIOLOGY ASSOC 15009 #045-01-1986 L1999 **DR** *020 †80
VASILAKIS, Alexander. 1000 DUTCH RIDGE RD, TSMG CARDIAVASCULAR & THOR 15009 #055-01-1985 L1990 **TS GS** *020 †85,90
VOGEL-SCIBILIA, Suzanne. 219 3RD ST, BEAVER COUNTY PSYCHIATRIC 15009 #041-12-1985 L1990 **P** *020 †75
WEBER, Susan Louise. 1201 3RD ST, TRI-STATE PULMONARY MEDICI 15009 #041-02-1985 L1987 **PUD IM** *020 †20
YAKISH, Jack Edward. 1030 BEANER HOLLOW RD 15009 #041-09-1981 L1982 **FM** *020 †18
YAKISH, Samuel Dale. 1030 BEANER HOLLOW RD, ASSOCIATION OF SPECIALTY 15009 #041-12-1979 L1980 **ORS** *020 †40
YANGSON, Anda Karleen Bal. 1000 DUTCH RIDGE RD 15009 #748-01-2001 L2005 **FP** *012
YOUNGDAHL, Paula Sun. 1000 DUTCH RIDGE RD, FL 0 15009 #041-01-1985 L1986 **OBG** *020 †30

BEAVER FALLS – BEAVER

BALDWIN, Thomas Marcy. ■ 15010 #041-12-1937 L1938 **OPH OTO** *071 †45
CHEEK, Edwin Wm. 2674 DARLINGTON RD 15010 #041-12-1974 L1975 **OBG** *020 †30 ‡
COLAVINCENZO, John Wm. ■ 15010 #016-43-1947 L1948 **AN** *071 †05
DAMAZO, Elpidio D. 619 15TH ST 15010 #748-07-1957 L1968 **FM** *020
DAMAZO, Natividad S. 619 15TH ST 15010 #748-01-1958 L1968 **FM** *020
DELLA TOFFALO, Deanne Mar. BEAVER MED CTR, DEPT FAM MED 15010 #041-77-2005, ▲ L2005 **FP** *012
DHAGAT, Satish Chandra. 701 5TH ST, ASSOCIATION OF SPECIALTY 15010 #495-22-1967 L1978 **U** *020 †95
DUMPE, Kevin Clayton. 1302 7TH AVE 15010 #041-09-1982 L1983 **OBG** *020 †30
EHRENBERG, Eric Eugene. 2620 CONSTITUTION BLVD 15010 #041-77-1991, ▲ L1992 **FM** *020 †18
FEDIN, Amber Lynn. THE MED CTR OF BEAVER FALL, DEPT FAM MED 15010 #041-78-2005, ▲ L2005 **FP** *012
FELDMEIER, Curtis Jos. 1307 6TH AVE 15010 #041-13-1980 L1981 **IM** *020 †20
FLORES, Elaine Rodriguez. 918 3RD AVE, THE MEDICAL CENTER BEAVER 15010 #748-10-2006 L2007 **FP** *012
FORCELLA, Luigi Robert. 918 3RD AVE 15010 #305-01-1998 L2001 **FM** *020 †18
GAPUZ, Donald Flores. 918 3RD AVE, THE MEDICAL CENTER BEAVER 15010 #759-18-2005 L2007 **100
GRIECO, Robert Louis. 2620 CONSTITUTION BLVD, STE B 15010 #051-04-1984 L1985 **FM** *020 †18 ‡
GUFFEY, Michael Tyson. 2400 DARLINGTON RD 15010 #041-02-2001 L2001 **FM** *020 †18
HENDRY, Stanley G. ■ 15010 #041-12-1951 L1952 **IM** *071
HOLMES, Amie E. ■ 15010 #038-40-2007 L2007 **GS** *012
JAIN, Rashima. 918 3RD AVE, THE MEDICAL CENTER BEAVER 15010 #305-01-2006 L2007 **FP** *012
JANSMA, David R, Jr. 918 3RD AVE, FAMILY PRACTICE CENTER 15010 #025-07-1988 L1990 **FM** *020 †18
JEAN, Danielle Saint Ulme. 918 3RD AVE, THE MEDICAL CENTER BEAVER 15010 #654-01-2005 L2007 **FP** *012
LAUER, James Howard. 1302 7TH AVE 15010 #010-02-1984 L1992 **OBG** *020 †30
LEHMAN, John Walter. 1415 6TH AVE 15010 #041-13-1958 L1959 **ORS** *071 †40
MARTSOLF, Robert Henley. 1302 7TH AVE 15010 #041-02-1976 L1977 **FM** *020 †18
MC KENNA, James Patrick. 918 3RD AVE, FAMILY PRACTICE CENTER 15010 #023-01-1980 L1987 **FM** *040 †18
PALGUTA, Robert Francis. 1065 SHENANGO RD 15010 #051-04-1989 L1991 **FM** *020 †18
PASCUA, Alexander V. 2400 DARLINGTON RD 15010 #748-02-1970 L1975 **PMM** *020
PRENDERGAST, Maurice D. 1307 6TH AVE 15010 #051-01-1979 L1980 **IM** *020 †20
RAGOOWANSI, Tulsidas N. 1628 8TH AVE 15010 #495-33-1962 L1973 **CD IM** *020
REDMOND, Wendy J. 918 3RD AVE 15010 #166-01-2002 L2005 **FP** *012
RODRIGUEZ, Jason Allen. 2620 CONSTITUTION BLVD, TSMG-TRINITY FAMILY PRACTI 15010 #038-40-1999 L2001 **FM** *020 †18
SABO, Erin Maureen. 1215 7TH AVE STE 2, GATEWAY REHAB CTR 15010 #041-12-1990 L1992 **P** *012
SARVER, Margaret Ellen. ■ 15010 #041-01-1958 L1960 **IM OS** *071 †20
SESTITO, Carl Gregory. 1307 6TH AVE 15010 #035-15-1991 L1993 **IM** *020 †20
STEELE, Garen Daxton. ■ 15010 #041-13-2004 L2004 **ORS** *012
STRAGAND, Suzanne Marie. 918 3RD AVE, FAMILY PRACTICE CTR 15010 #041-77-2006, ▲ L2006 **FP** *012
SWAN, Patrick Francis. ■ 15010 #539-02-1958 L1965 **AN OS** *100 †05
THOMA, Kevin C. ■ 15010 #654-01-1992 **IM** *100
VOGEL, Julius A. ■ 15010 #041-12-1959 L1960 **PD** *071 †55
WONG, Mailinn Eleana. 918 3RD AVE, MED CTR BEAVER PA 15010 #654-01-2006 L2007 **012
ZVONAR, Kristin Marie. 1307 6TH AVE 15010 #041-07-1998 L2001 **IM** *020 †20

BEAVER SPRINGS – SNYDER

GILFERT, Larry Yost. RR 1 17812 #041-09-1960 L1961 **EM FM** *071 †18

BEDFORD – BEDFORD

CHO, Doo Whan. 1243 SHED RD 15522 #583-09-1963 L1973 **P** *020 †75
GALLAGHER, Michael Donald. ■ 15522 #041-02-1985 L1986 **FM** *020 †18
JOHNSON, Sharon Rose. ■ 15522 #654-01-1986 L1990 **AN** *020 †05
LIPSKI, Edward Michael. 1243 SHED RD, BEDFORD-SOMERSET MH/MR 15522 #041-09-1970 L1971 **P** *020
NEWMAN, William Randolph. ■ 15522 #035-08-1956 L1980 **R RO** *071 †80
PALIN, William Edwin. PO BOX 637 15522 #041-12-1944 L1945 **GS** *071 †85
RAJAN, V K Suresh. 1243 SHED RD 15522 #495-04-1975 L1981 **P** *020 †75

SAMUEL, Christopher J. ■ 15522 #305-01-1991 L1997 **AN** *020 †05
SLICK, Gregory Dixon. 140 S ANDERSON ST 15522 #041-02-1981 L1982 **IM** *020
UMPIERRE, Anthony H. 608 E PITT ST 15522 #654-01-1983 L1986 **P** *020 †75

BEDMINSTER – BUCKS

DUANE, Julia Mc Elhinney. ■ 18910 #018-03-1941 L1951 **PD** *071 †55

BEECH CREEK – CLINTON

GINGRICH, David Neil. ■ 16822 #041-02-1981 L1983 **EM** *020 †16

BELLE VERNON – FAYETTE

BHATNAGAR, Bhavana. ■ 15012 #041-77-2007, ▲ L2007 **IM** *012
BROOKS, James L, III. 1645 ROSTRAVER RD, ROSTRAVER MEDICAL BLDG #50 15012 #055-01-1969 L1970 **FM** *030
BROOKS, James Locke, Jr. ■ 15012 #041-12-1943 L1944 **GP OBG** *071
CHAUHAN, Ambaram Vashram. 1645 ROSTRAVER RD 15012 #495-23-1973 L1978 **IM OS** *020 †20
CRUDO, Chito Mombay. 25 FAYETTE AVE # 251 15012 #748-01-1971 L1975 **GS GP** *020 †85
CRUDO, Karl Vincent. 25 FAYETTE AVE 15012 #748-01-2000 L2003 **FM** *100 †18
JONES-GORDON, Sandra. 1645 ROSTRAVER RD 15012 #041-12-1985 L1986 **IM** *020 †20 ‡
KAUL, Neerja. 1645 ROSTRAVER RD 15012 #495-34-1981 L2000 **IM** *020 †20
KHAN, Uzma H. 1645 ROSTRAVER RD 15012 #704-25-1992 L2002 **ID** *020 †20
KRISHNASWAMI, Subramania. 1645 ROSTRAVER RD 15012 #495-04-1970 L1982 **CD** *020 †20
LONG, Richard Alan. 1645 ROSTRAVER RD, STE 202 15012 #847-10-1975 L1976 **IM** *020
PEPPER, L Douglas. 728 BROAD AVE 15012 #041-02-1975 L1976 **FM** *020 †18
PEPPER, Maria Elizabeth. 728 BROAD AVE 15012 #041-02-2002 L2004 **FM** *020 †18
PINTO, Thomas B. 1645 ROSTRAVER RD 15012 #495-52-1974 L1979 **CD IM** *020 †20
RAMBHIA, Jethalal L. 1645 ROSTRAVER RD 15012 #495-01-1979 L1990 **CD** *020 †20
SAINSBURY, Cynthia Riedel. 1645 ROSTRAVER RD 15012 #041-07-1983 L1986 **GP EM** *020 †16
SHAH, Rajesh C. 133 FINLEY RD, TRICOUNTY MEDICAL PRACTICE 15012 #495-89-1987 L1994 **IM** *020 †20
URBAN, Robert Raymond. 853 FINLEY RD 15012 #041-12-1956 L1957 **FM** *020
VRABLIK, Kevin Allen. 800 PLAZA DR, STE 210 15012 #041-14-1993 L1995 **FM** *020 †18

BELLEFONTE – CENTRE

ABOUL-HOSN, Hussein F. 527 WILLOWBANK ST 16823 #396-26-1981 L1985 **IM** *020 †20
BENSON, David Richard. 141 MEDICAL PARK LN, STE 2 16823 #041-13-1962 L1963 **GP** *020 ‡
BURKE, Kevin Wayne. 420 HOLMES ST, WILLOWBANK BUILDING 16823 #051-07-1982 L1983 **P** *020
BURKE, P Brian. 819 E BISHOP ST 16823 #041-14-1985 L1987 **FM** *020 †18
CHASE, William D. 141 MEDICAL PARK LN 16823 #010-01-1973 L1974 **PD** *020 †55
COLLISON, Craig Harold. 141 MEDICAL PARK LN 16823 #036-05-1997 L2000 **PD** *020 †55
EGGLER, Betsey Louise. ■ 16823 #041-14-1975 L1976 **IM IMG** *020
GOLDSTEIN, Morton Saml. 625 LITTLE MARSHCREEK RD, WHISPERING PNS PERSNL CARE 16823 #041-12-1963 L1964 **IM** *075
HESTER, Christopher E. 141 MEDICAL PARK LN, STE 2 16823 #041-14-1993 L1996 **IM** *020 †20
HOELSCHER, Kenneth King. 550 W COLLEGE AVE 16823 #056-06-1961 L1983 **PM GP** *030 †60
HOLDERMAN, Michael H. 703 N ALLEGHENY ST 16823 #308-07-1982 L1983 **FM** *020 †18
HUFFARD, Robert Scott. 141 MEDICAL PARK LN 16823 #041-02-1984 L1985 **PD** *020 †55
HUGGINS, Allyson Anne. 141 MEDICAL PARK LN 16823 #041-02-2003 L2003 **PD** *020 †55
KAUFMAN, Kristie Lynn. 141 MEDICAL PARK LN 16823 #041-14-1994 L2000 **PD** *020 †55
MC CORMICK, George Milton. 141 MEDICAL PARK LN 16823 #041-01-1970 L1972 **PD** *020 †55
OESTERLING, Brett Robert. 819 E BISHOP ST 16823 #051-01-1997 L2000 **FM** *020 †18
ROZICK, Mark Steven. 819 E BISHOP ST 16823 #041-02-1983 L1984 **FM** *020 †18
SCHWAB, Rachel Suzanne. 141 MEDICAL PARK LN 16823 #023-12-1994 L1996 **PD** *020 †55
SHANNON, Dennis Augustin. 141 MEDICAL PARK LN, STE 2 16823 #041-02-1997 L2000 **IM** *020 †20
TRUDEL, Tracey Lynne. 141 MEDICAL PARK LN 16823 #038-40-1995 L1998 **PD** *020 †55
VORE, Steven Brooks. 141 MEDICAL PARK LN 16823 #051-04-1972 L1977 **PD** *020 †55
WINGERT, Charles H. ■ 16823 #041-01-1958 L1959 **D A** *071 †15
WOLFE, Joshua Bryan. ■ 16823 #041-02-2001 L2004 **EM** *020 †16

BELLEVILLE – MIFFLIN

CRANOR, John Ross. ■ 17004 #023-07-1939 L1949 **GS** *071 †85
FOWLER, Eric K. 5 HEDGEAPPLE DR 17004 #041-02-1989 L1992 **FM** *020 †18
HELFRICK, Marlin Wm. 17004 #041-07-1934 L1935 **GP** *071
SIKORSKY, Phyllis M. E MAIN EXT 17004 #041-02-1975 L1978 **FM** *020 †18
ZGLESZEWSKI, Edward J. 5 HEDGEAPPLE DR 17004 #041-13-1996 L1999 **FM** *020 †18

BELLEVUE – ALLEGHENY

BLINN, David Louis. 557 LINCOLN AVE, STE 104 15202 #030-06-1985 L1986 **IM ADM** *020 †20
DHAWAN, Neelam. 575 LINCOLN AVE, STE 201 15202 #496-07-1978 L1980 **FM** *020
DHAWAN, Ram Lal. 575 LINCOLN AVE, STE 201 15202 #041-03-1973 L1976 **CD IM** *020 †20
EDBERG, Sanford Howard. S JACKSON AVE 15202 #035-09-1954 L1966 **CLP PTH** *020 †50
HUSSAINI, Syed R. 340 LINCOLN AVE 15202 #495-57-1967 L1978 **IM CD** *020 †20
KILPATRICK, Megan Marie. 446 LINCOLN AVE, BELLEVUE PEDIATRICS 15202 #041-12-2005 L2005 **PD** *012
NATH, Lisa M. 575 LINCOLN AVE, STE 204 15202 #041-12-1993 L1993 **OPH** *020 †35
REED, David Mark. 575 LINCOLN AVE STE 104 15202 #041-12-1976 L1977 **IM IMG** *020 †20

BELLWOOD – BLAIR

HESS, Megan L. 503 MAIN ST 16617 #018-03-1987 L1989 **FM** *020 †18

BENSALEM – BUCKS

AHMAD, Sarfaraz. 3070 BRISTOL PIKE, STE 100 19020 #704-02-1964 L1972 **GS GP** *020 †85 ‡
ALMOMANI, Mohammad Ahmed. 2685 KNIGHTS RD, MOHAMMED ALMOMANI MD 19020 #575-01-1986 L1997 **PD** *020 †55
ANKIN, Lana G. ■ 19020 #041-77-2006, ▲ L2006 *012
ARCILLA, Joel Santos. ■ 19020 #748-10-1978 L1984 **IM** *075
BANSAL, Krishan. ■ 19020 #495-43-1970 L1976 **P** *020 †75 ‡
BELLETIERI, Christopher M. 2171 GALLOWAY RD 19020 #041-77-1996, ▲ L1997 **FM** *020
BLUE, Vincent Patrick. 3300 NESHAMINY BLVD # 216 19020 #041-02-1959 L1960 **EM IM** *071 †20
BOBROW, Joseph Sheldon. 107 THUNDER CIR 19020 #035-19-1961 L1982 **OBG OS** *020 †30
BROOKSSIENKIEWIC, Sara El. ■ 19020 #035-06-2005 L2005 **DR** *012
CHAEFSKY, Robert Louis. 3237 BRISTOL RD STE 206 19020 #041-13-1966 L1967 **P GP** *020
CHAUDHRY, Aaila Ijaz. ■ 19020 #704-21-2002 L2003 **OPH** *012
CHAUDHRY, Faisal Aziz. ■ 19020 #041-15-2008 *012
CHERNOVA, Tatyana. ■ 19020 #913-05-1981 L2006 **SP** *020 †50
COWAN, Clayton Jos. 2051 FINCH DR 19020 #041-02-1991 L1995 **CCA** *020 †05
CREECH, David Michael. ■ 19020 #041-15-2007 L2007 **TY** *012
DAVE, Ashesh Shivprasad. 2742 KNIGHTS RD, CENTER FOR MEDICAL CARE IN 19020 #495-23-1984 L2000 **IM** *020 †20
DIANGI, Yumi Taylor. ■ 19020 #041-01-2006 L2006 **IM** *012
DINOZO, Nelia Laja. ■ 19020 #748-01-1963 **FM GP** *020
DU PREE, Beth Baughman. 3300 TILLMAN DR, STE 309 19020 #041-09-1987 L1988 **GS TRS** *020 †85
EL NEMR, Mohammed Attia. ■ 19020 #915-03-1995 L2008 **OBG** *100
FABIANI, Cesar A. 3369 PROGRESS DR 19020 #132-09-1966 L1973 **P ADP** *020 †75
FAROOQ, Sabahat. 3034 KNIGHTS RD, KNIGHTS MEDICAL ASSOCIATES 19020 #704-20-1988 L1998 **IM** *020 †20
FAROOQ, Umar. 3034 KNIGHTS RD, KNIGHTS MEDICAL ASSOCIATES 19020 #704-20-1985 L1997 **IM** *020 †20
FRANQUES, Pascale. ■ 19020 #396-01-1993 **P** *100
GARCIA CARABALLO, Nohazara. ■ 19020 #409-10-1999 L2007 **P** *012
GAYMAN, Tara Lynn. ■ 19020 #041-15-2008 *012
GOCKEN, Mehmet Sabri. ■ 19020 #902-10-1951 L1976 **OS AN** *071
GUPTA, Abha Rani. 1442 STREET RD, GOVIND MEDICAL CENTER 19020 #041-01-2001 L2001 **DBP** *020
GUPTA, Nand Kishore. 1442 STREET RD 19020 #495-05-1965 L1979 **AN** *020
GUYER, Seymour Martin. ■ 19020 #005-17-1962 L1968 **OS GP** *071
HASHIM, Atia Shireen. ■ 19020 #704-02-1984 L2001 **GE** *020 †20
HUHN, Wolfgang Anton. 3101 BRISTOL RD 19020 #041-02-1972 L1973 **D DS** *020 †15 ‡
IHTESHAM, Mohammad. 1217 ORIOLE DR 19020 #902-03-1989 L1997 **PYG** *020
JASTI, Babu Rao. ■ 19020 #495-37-1989 L1998 **CD** *020 †20
JOHNY, Salini. ■ 19020 #495-31-2001 L2003 **IM** *020 †20
JOSEPH, Karel. ■ 19020 #495-63-1998 L2006 **IM** *100 †20
KHAN, Mohammad Irfan. ■ 19020 #704-01-1999 L2007 **GS** *012
KRISHER, Stacy Leanne. 3300 TILLMAN DR, STE 309 19020 #041-12-1996 L2001 **GS** *020 †85
LA ROSA, Vincent. 3554 HULMEVILLE RD 19020 #561-01-1979 L1984 **IM** *020 †20
LATHARI, Aydin Abyar. ■ 19020 #041-13-2007 L2007 **IM** *012
LAZOFSON, Harvey. 2846 KNIGHTS RD, KNIGHTS ROAD MEDICAL BLDG 19020 #041-13-1962 L1963 **FM CLP** *071
LEHOTZKY, Helen. 3701 OLD TREVOSE RD 19020 #041-07-1960 L1961 **PD OS** *030
LIEBERMAN, Jonathan Ira. ■ 19020 #041-13-2004 L2004 **DR** *012
LOGANI, Sanjay. ■ 19020 #495-45-1993 L2000 **PCP** *100 †50
MADDEN, Robert Abner. 3554 HULMEVILLE RD STE 106 19020 #041-09-1964 L1965 **IM** *020 †20
MARLEY, Wayne Michael. 1950 STREET RD, STE 100 19020 #035-15-1979 L1984 **D FPS** *020 †15 ‡
MCDERMOTT, Raymond Sean. 820 DURHAM PL 19020 #539-04-1992 L2002 **HO** *020
MEKAPATI, Jyothi. ■ 19020 #496-32-1998 L2001 **GE** *012 †20
MILLMAN, Brad. 1336 BRISTOL PIKE, WOODHAVEN ONE STE 201 19020 #041-09-1990 L1993 **OTO FPS** *020 †45
NAGARAKANTI, Rangadham. ■ 19020 #496-37-1999 L2001 **IM** *020
OOMMEN, Manoj George. ■ 19020 #041-13-2004 L2008 **IM** *100
PATEL, Nimish Dhirubhai. ■ 19020 #010-01-2005 L2005 **IM** *012
PATEL, Nirav D. ■ 19020 #010-01-2005 **IM** *012
PEARLSTEIN, Louis. 3070 BRISTOL PIKE, STE 124 19020 #041-77-1978, ▲ L1979 **N** *020 †75
QURESHI, Masud. ■ 19020 #308-07-1982 **CHP** *100
RAJAPREYAR, Indranee Nama. ■ 19020 #495-36-2002 L2008 **IM** *020 †20
RAMOS-BONNER, Luz Sicat. ■ 19020 #748-10-1998 L2006 **IMG** *020 †20
ROTENBERG, Scott Eric. ■ 19020 #010-02-2008 *012
SANDHU, Bakhshish Singh. 2938 KNIGHTS RD 19020 #308-07-1982 L1986 **IM** *020 †20
SANTHANAKRISHNAN, Jyothi. ■ 19020 #495-59-1993 L2006 **IM** *100
SAPONARO, Stephen Andrew. 3260 TILLMAN DR, STE 120 19020 #041-02-1992 L1997 **DR** *020 †80 ‡
SHAH, Akbar Raza. ■ 19020 #704-08-1982 L2004 **NR NM** *020
SHAH, Jitendra. 3103 HULMEVILLE RD, STE 104 19020 #495-76-1970 L1980 **PD** *020
SHETH, Kashmira R. ■ 19020 #495-22-1972 L1996 **PD** *071 †55
SMALLOW, Stevan Alan. 2846 KNIGHTS RD 19020 #041-07-1989 L1991 **IM** *020
SMITH, Ralph Wm. ■ 19020 #010-03-1942 L1944 **OBG GP** *071
STOTZ, June Ellen. 3655 HULMEVILLE RD # 311 19020 #041-09-1974 L1976 **P** *020 †75
TALPADA, Motibhai D. ■ 19020 #495-23-1981 L1997 **ID** *020 †20
THINGALAYA, Nita Krishnap. 138 STATE RD 19020 #495-17-2000 *100
THURHEIMER, Elizabeth A. 2259 BOWMAN AVE 19020 #041-13-1995 L1997 **FM** *020 †18
UGWUOKE, Emmanuel Aniebon. ■ 19020 #690-06-2001 L2005 **CHP** *020
URBANSKI, Linda Marie. ■ 19020 #041-13-1992 L1995 **EM** *020 †16
VANNOZZI, Brian Micheal. ■ 19020 #041-01-2003 L2003 **ORS** *012
WETTLAUFER, Marilyn R. ■ 19020 #010-02-1975 L1976 **OBG** *071 †30
WOLANIN, Marie Apolonia. ■ 19020 #041-15-2006 L2007 **IM** *012

WYDRO, Gerald Charles. 1197 WILLIAM PENN DR, TEMPLE UNIVERSITY HOSPITAL 19020 #041-13-1994 L1996 **EM** *020 †16

ZAKUTO, Alan Sheldon. 3237 BRISTOL RD 19020 #041-09-1970 L1971 **PD** *020 †55

BENTLEYVILLE – WASHINGTON

CHO, Yong Dae. 100 WILSON RD 15314 #583-10-1966 L1972 **FM FPG** *020 †18

EKBOTE, Seema Kurichh. 119 WILSON RD 15314 #041-07-1995 L1997 **IM** *020 †20

LACAVA, Theresa Jean. 100 WILSON RD 15314 #671-01-1990 L1997 **FM** *020 †18

BENTON – COLUMBIA

TEODORO, Jose Vicierra. ■ 17814 #748-02-1953 L1970 **EM IM** *071

BERLIN – SOMERSET

KAWCHAK, James. ■ 15530 #036-07-1952 L1976 **IM** *071

KLOSE, Paul L. ■ 15530 #041-12-1952 L1953 **IMG FPG** *072

BERNVILLE – BERKS

BROCK, David Carl. 7173 BERNVILLE RD 19506 #041-02-1976 L1978 **FM** *020 †18

DICASIMIRRO, John Arthur. ■ 19506 #041-02-1988 L1990 **FM FSM** *020 †20

MANN-HARBONIC, Barbara L. 7173 BERNVILLE RD 19506 #041-09-1998 L2000 **FM** *020 †18

STEWART, Thomas Allen. 7173 BERNVILLE RD 19506 #041-14-1975 L1976 **FM** *020 †18

BERWICK – COLUMBIA

ALLEY, Ali Abbas. 301 W 3RD ST 18603 #041-09-1956 L1957 **FM** *071 †18

ASEVEDO, Maria. 32 SHADY LN 18603 #021-01-1992 L2003 **OBG** *020 †30

ASHTON, Michael Robert. 2200 W FRONT ST 18603 #041-12-1999 L2002 **FM** *020 †18

BORGER, Annette Rae. 751 E 16TH ST, STE 400 18603 #041-02-1995 L1999 **MPD PD** *020 †20,55

BUTOI, Dan Stefan. 500 FOWLER AVE STE 202 18603 #781-06-1969 L1980 **IM** *020 †20

CAMPBELL, David Robt. ■ 18603 #041-13-1973 L1974 **FM** *074 †18

CHITTALIA, Aliasgar Zakir. R699 E 16TH ST 18603 #496-30-1993 L2002 **IM** *020 †20

CRAKE, Roger Fred. 695 E 16TH ST, STE C 18603 #041-02-1978 L1979 **GS** *020 †85 ‡

CRETELLA, Thomas Serafino. 301 E FRONT ST 18603 #041-09-1945 L1946 **FM AN** *071

DENNIS, James Brown, Jr. ■ 18603 #041-01-1966 L1978 **R NM** *072 †80

FERRIGNO, Carmen J, Jr. 701 E 16TH ST 18603 #033-05-1968 L1975 **R** *020 †80

FRANCIS, Leon Robt. 701 E 16TH ST 18603 #654-01-1981 L1983 **FM** *020 †18 ‡

GEGWICH, Frank. 1303 N MARKET ST 18603 #035-45-1970 L1976 **IM** *020 †20

GEGWICH, Joseph Frank. 701 E 16TH ST 18603 #033-05-1968 L1969 **IM** *071 †20

GIUGLIANO, Frank Dino. 523 FOWLER AVE 18603 #035-08-1978 L1982 **FM EM** *020 †18,16

GLICKMAN, Andrew S. 1401 HOLLY DR 18603 #305-01-1982 L1985 **AN** *020 †20

GO, David Yang Gaw. 301 W 3RD ST 18603 #748-08-1987 L1999 **FM** *020 †18

GORMLEY, James Bernard. ■ 18603 #041-02-1941 L1942 **GS** *071 †85

JOHN, M J. 701 E 16TH ST 18603 #495-52-1978 L1987 **IM PD** *020

JUSTO, Mona. 540 E 11TH ST 18603 #748-08-1990 L1997 **AN** *020 †05

KANOUSE, Gary Douglas. 695 E 16TH ST STE D 18603 #041-09-1985 L1986 **IM IMG** *020 †20

KASPUTIS, David Anthony. 701 E 16TH ST 18603 #035-15-1973 L1977 **AN PUD** *020 †05

KERBACHER, Daniel J. 701 E 16TH ST 18603 #030-06-1979 L1980 **EM** *020 †16

KREUZBURG, Robert Chas. 701 E 16TH ST 18603 #041-13-1963 L1964 **PD** *071 †55

MANUEL, Laureano Mallare. 701 E 16TH ST 18603 #748-08-1960 L1973 **IM CD** *071

MEHTA, Niharika. 695 E 16TH ST STE E 18603 #495-48-1970 L1984 **OBG EM** *020 †30 ‡

MILLER, G Geoffrey. 126 W FRONT ST 18603 #041-02-1977 L1980 **OPH** *020 †35

MOLITORIS, John, Jr. ■ 18603 #041-14-2007 L2007 **FP** *012

MUNESHWAR, Victor. 701 E 16TH ST 18603 #035-09-1991 L1995 **P** *020

ODEYEMI, Olutunde Olakunl. 701 E 16TH ST 18603 #690-05-1998 L2006 **IM** *100 †20

OGRIN, Cristina Gheorghe. 751 E 16TH ST, STE 400 18603 #781-08-1995 L2005 **END** *100 †20

OWUSU, Samuel. 2200 W FRONT ST 18603 #033-06-1997 L2002 **OBG** *020

PANDIKA, Emilio Harris. 701 E 16TH ST 18603 #506-23-1998 L2005 **IM** *020 †20

PRIBULA, Pavel. 751 E 16TH ST, STE 400 18603 #286-06-1988 L1999 **IM** *020 †20

PYLES, Mark Cullen. 695 E 16TH ST 18603 #041-09-1981 L1983 **GS HS** *020 †85

REID, Lawrence Michael. 1401 HOLLY DR 18603 #005-18-1982 L2005 **AN** *020 †05

SMITH, Alva Donald. 751 E 16TH ST, STE 200 18603 #566-01-1985 L1995 **CD** *020 †20

TANRIBILIR, Abdul Kerim. 301 E FRONT ST 18603 #902-10-1960 L1970 **IM GE** *071

UD-DIN, Mallhi Moin. 540 E 11TH ST 18603 #704-01-1983 L1995 **AN** *020

VEINO, Joyce. 699 E 16TH ST 18603 #041-14-1993 L1996 **FM** *020 †18

WIEGAND, Paul Joseph. 701 E 16TH ST 18603 #308-11-1988 L1996 **AN** *020

WITHERUP, Marilyn R F. 701 E 16TH ST, BERWICK HOSP CTR 18603 #041-07-1970 L1971 **EM** *020 †16

ZARETSKY, Jay Ross. 695 E 16TH ST, STE F 18603 #035-47-1988 L2008 **ORS** *020

BERWYN – CHESTER

ALVAREZ, J D. ■ 19312 #028-02-1997 L2000 **PTH** *100 †50

BLACK, Ronald Scott. ■ 19312 #023-07-1984 L1996 **IM** *020

BLODGETT, Randolph C. 244 LENAPE DR 19312 #050-02-1959 L1966 **RHU IM** *071 †20

BRENAN, Kelly Maureen. ■ 19312 #041-02-2004 **PTH** *012

CALDERON, Patricia. ■ 19312 #737-06-1987 L1999 **IM** *020 †20

CHAN-HO, Audrey. ■ 19312 #023-07-1992 L2000 **RHU** *020 †20

CHODOSH, Sanford. ■ 19312 #023-07-1952 L1952 **IM PUD** *062

CHOGICH, John Chas. ■ 19312 #041-13-1953 L1954 **R** *071 †80

COUGHLIN, Christina Marie. ■ 19312 #041-01-1999 L2001 **PHO** *020

DICKINSON, Edward Thos. 23 BRIDGE AVE, BERWYN FIRE COMPANY 19312 #035-48-1989 L1997 **EM** *020 †16

EASTON, Rachael Mary. ■ 19312 #028-02-1999 L2001 **END** *100 †20

EDELSON, Jeffrey Danl. ■ 19312 #065-01-1979 L1999 **PUD** *020

EICHNER, Lambert Geo. ■ 19312 #041-02-1954 L1955 **IM** *071

GAUTHIER, Harold Jos. ■ 19312 #021-06-1973 L1984 **GP** *020 †16

GAUTHIER, Martha Rojas. ■ 19312 #021-06-1973 L1974 **GP** *020

GOLDBERG, Eric Jay. 1172 PEBBLE SPRING DR 19312 #041-13-1976 L1977 **GS VS** *071

GOODMAN, Vicki Lynn. ■ 19312 #035-46-1998 L1998 **HO** *020

HARRIMAN, Gregory Robt. ■ 19312 #005-18-1981 L1983 **IG ID** *050 †20

HO, Andrew Pojung. ■ 19312 #005-18-1991 L1993 **CHP P** *020 †75

HO, Tony Weishiu. ■ 19312 #023-07-1991 L2000 **N** *050 †75

HTAIK, Tun Tin. ■ 19312 #209-01-1982 L2001 **VIR** *020 †80

KEON, Thomas Peter. ■ 19312 #065-09-1965 L1978 **AN** *071 †05

KOPELMAN, William Joseph. 604 HICKORY LN 19312 #036-08-1996 L2001 **EM** *020 †16

LACHMAN, Robert J. ■ 19312 #041-13-1949 L1950 **AN OS** *071 †05

MCCORMICK, Michael Edward. ■ 19312 #041-02-2006 L2006 **OTO** *012

MC KEOWN, John Jos, Jr. ■ 19312 #041-02-1947 L1948 **GS TS** *071 †85,90

MEADOWCROFT, James Arthur. ■ 19312 #041-02-1968 L1969 **ORS OSM** *071 †40

PONCE, Philip Oswald. ■ 19312 #041-01-2006 **IM** *012

RUDOLPH, Richard L. 978 HEATHERSTONE DR 19312 #033-05-1976 L1979 **IM PHM** *030 †20

SEDEHI, Daniel Ray. ■ 19312 #041-01-2006 **IM** *012

SHANKAR, Padmini. ■ 19312 #495-96-1980 **PD** *020

TUCCI, Mary Anne C. ■ 19312 #051-07-1989 L1993 **EM** *020 †16

WATSON, Brenda Lynne. ■ 19312 #065-01-1981 L2000 **FM** *075

WEBER, George Lawrence. 750 OLD LANCASTER RD, BENJAMINE WEST APT #510 19312 #041-02-1946 L1947 **OM GP** *071

ZACHARIAH, John Suku. ■ 19312 #496-22-1992 L2000 **GE** *020 †20

ZOURAS, Nicholas Louis. ■ 19312 #010-01-1957 L1962 **GPM CHP** *075

BETHEL PARK – ALLEGHENY

ADHAR, Gur Charan. 2000 OXFORD DR, STE 113 15102 #495-36-1976 L1988 **ICE CD** *020 †20

BARRETT, John Patrick. 1300 OXFORD DR, STE 2B 15102 #035-06-1996 L2001 **OBG** *020 †30

BOBBY, John Leslie. 2000 OXFORD DR, STE 100 15102 #041-77-1982, ▲ L1983 **FM** *020 †18

BORON, Ronald Louis. ■ 15102 #041-12-1968 L1974 **GS** *071 †85

BUONOCORE, Camille Marie. 2000 OXFORD DR, STE 130 15102 #035-06-1987 L1989 **END IM** *020 †20

DE MARINO, David Philip. 1300 OXFORD DR STE LLC 15102 #041-14-1981 L1987 **OTO HNS** *020 †45 ‡

DESAI, Saryu Jitendra. 1300 OXFORD DR, UPMC SO SURG CTR 15102 #495-23-1966 L1973 **AN** *020 †05

DEYARMIN, Brian Jos. 1000 HIGBEE DR, STE 104 15102 #041-14-1992 L1994 **FM** *020 †18

DI TULLIO, Nicholas P. 5187 LIBRARY RD 15102 #041-12-1994 L1996 **IM** *020 †20

FRITZ, Kevin John. 1300 OXFORD DR, STE 1B 15102 #038-43-2004 L2004 **IM** *020 †20

GENTILE, Anthony Fernando. 1300 OXFORD DR, STE 2B 15102 #041-12-1969 L1970 **OBG** *020 †30

GIBBS, Shelana Marie. 1000 HIGBEE DR, STE 108 15102 #038-44-1997 L2001 **PM** *020 †60

GREATHOUSE, Mark Kevin. 2000 OXFORD DR, STE 680 15102 #055-01-1983 L1984 **CD** *020 †20

GRIBIK, Michael. 4651 LIBRARY RD, BMA SOUTH HILL INC 15102 #041-12-1971 L1972 **NEP IM** *020 †20

HARTMAN, Harry S. ■ 15102 #041-12-1943 L1944 **GP GS** *071

HUMPHREYS, Kristin E. 1300 OXFORD DR, STE 1B 15102 #041-14-1999 L2005 **IM** *020 †20

KEITH, Scott Kelly. ■ 15102 #040-02-2006 L2006 **IM** *012

KOSKY, Jason Robert. ■ 15102 #041-15-2007 L2007 **GS** *012

KRISHNASWAMI, V. 2000 OXFORD DR, STE 113 15102 #495-16-1958 L1978 **CD IM** *020 †20 ‡

LANDFAIR, Roy Jos. 2000 OXFORD DR, STE 113 15102 #041-12-1972 L1974 **CD IM** *050 †20

LEE, Sang Gun. ■ 15102 #583-03-1971 L1982 **PM** *071 †60

LUPINETTI, Michael. 1300 OXFORD DR, STE 2B 15102 #055-01-1976 L1977 **OBG** *020 †30

MAROPIS, Christopher G. 2000 OXFORD DR, STE 115 15102 #055-01-1991 L1993 **OM FSM** *020 †18

MATHENY, Jeffrey Michael. 1000 HIGBEE DR, STE 106 15102 #041-14-1993 L2003 **OSM ORS** *020 †40

MC CLAIN, Edward J, III. 1300 OXFORD DR, STE 1B 15102 #055-01-1986 L1988 **ORS** *020 †40

MC GONIGAL, Michael P. ■ 15102 #051-01-1980 L1983 **FM** *020 †18

MELEN, Kimberly Ann. 1300 OXFORD DR, STE 2B 15102 #041-12-1975 L1982 **OBG** *020 †30

MEROS, Edward John. 35 HIGHLAND RD APT 4405 15102 #010-02-1989 L1994 **OM** *020 †70

NEISH, Pamela Rae. 1300 OXFORD DR, STE 1D 15102 #041-12-1984 L1992 **RHU IM** *020 †20

NELSON, William. ■ 15102 #041-15-2008 *012

NICHOLAS, Stephanie Lee. 1300 OXFORD DR, STE 2B 15102 #041-12-1989 L1991 **OBG** *020 †30

O'MALLEY, Donald F. 1000 HIGBEE DR, STE 106 15102 #041-12-1990 L1992 **ORS** *020 †40

OSIAL, Thaddeus A, Jr. 1300 OXFORD DR, STE 1D 15102 #041-12-1976 L1977 **RHU IM** *020 †20

PAUL, Michael David. 1300 OXFORD DR STE 1C 15102 #775-01-1971 L1979 **ORS** *020

POLLOCK, Burton Harold. 1300 OXFORD DR, STE 1D 15102 #041-01-1962 L1963 **RHU IM** *020 †20

POON, Edward Daichee. 1000 HIGBEE DR, STE 106 15102 #041-01-1992 L1998 **ORS** *020 †40

POPOVICH, John Edward. 2000 OXFORD DR, STE 680 15102 #041-12-1979 L1980 **FM** *020 †18

PRADHAN, Sulochana Laxman. ■ 15102 #495-22-1972 L1981 **PTH** *020 †50

PURIGHALLA, Uma. 3400 S PARK RD 15102 #041-07-1994 L1994 **IM** *020 †20

RANKIN, Samuel Glenn. ■ 15102 #041-12-1955 L1956 **FM** *072

RITTENHOUSE, Frank H. ■ 15102 #041-01-1942 L1943 **GP** *071

SALSBUREY, Donna Jean. ■ 15102 #038-40-1975 L1976 **NPM PD** *020 †55

SCHAEFER, Thomas Leon. 5791 BAPTIST RD 15102 #041-12-1983 L1984 **FM IMG** *020 †18

SCHEIN, George, II. 2311 BETHEL CHURCH RD 15102 #041-12-1970 L1972 **OTO** *020 †45

SCHWARTZ, Joel D. 1300 OXFORD DR STE LLC 15102 #041-12-1973 L1974 **OTO** *020 †45

SCOLIERI, Paul. 1300 OXFORD DR, STE LLC 15102 #041-12-1997 L2001 **OTO** *020 †45

SMITH, Patrick Neil. 1300 OXFORD DR, STE 1B 15102 #041-12-1997 L2001 **ORS** *020 †40

STAPOR, David J. 1000 HIGBEE DR, STE 106 15102 #028-34-1983 L1988 **ORS** *020 †40

SWANSON, Lee Ann. 1300 OXFORD DR, STE 2B 15102 #041-13-1983 L1987 **OBG** *020 †30

THOMAS, Theodore Barry. 100 BROUGHTON RD 15102 #041-12-1947 L1948 **IM OS** *020

UNG, Tuan-Anh L. ■ 15102 #041-12-1985 L1987 **GS** *020

VARMA, Rajiv Ranjan. 1300 OXFORD DR STE 1E, CHILDRENS HOSP 15102 #495-15-1974 L1980 **CHN PD** *020 †55,75

WARSHAW, Joel David. 2000 OXFORD DR, STE 440 15102 #041-12-1992 L1994 **IM** *020 †20

WAWROSE, Stephen F. 1300 OXFORD DR, STE LLC 15102 #041-02-1986 L1996 **OTO** *020 †45

■ = Address Information Privacy Protected

WAYLONIS, Joseph Robt. ■ 15102 #041-01-1954 L1955 **OBG** *071
WIDOWS, Robert J. ■ 15102 #035-09-1955 L1956 **AN** *071 †05
WOODITCH, Angela Corinne. ■ 15102 #041-13-2005 L2005 **AN** *012
WRIGHT, Richard Edwin. ■ 15102 #041-12-1956 L1957 **GP** *071
YOUNG, Elizabeth Ann. 1300 OXFORD DR, STE 1D 15102 #051-01-1981 L1983 **RHU IM** *020 †20
ZIELINSKI, John Joseph. ■ 15102 #047-06-1998 **IM** *100

BETHLEHEM – LEHIGH

AKSU, Ahmet. 1406 EATON AVE 18018 #902-01-1953 L1960 **AN IM** *071 †05
ALBRECHT, Robert Ashton. ■ 18018 #041-12-2005 L2005 **EM** *012
ALI, Arjumand. ■ 18018 #041-15-2006 L2006 **GS** *012
ARNER, Raymond Harvey. ■ 18018 #041-09-1960 L1961 **AN** *071 †05
BAYRI, Mehmet Fuat. 35 E ELIZABETH AVE 18018 #902-03-1951 L1966 **AN** *071 †05
BAZEL, Saeed. 65 E ELIZABETH AVE, STE 303 18018 #517-01-1969 L1973 **GS AS** *020 ‡
BEHAR, David. 206 E BROAD ST 18018 #041-09-1975 1980 **P CHP** *020 †75 ‡
BERGER, Jay Bennett. 77 W BROAD ST UNIT 14-1 18018 #041-02-1968 L1969 **IM** *020 †20 ‡
BERMAN, Scott Irwin. ■ 18018 #051-04-1985 L1986 **P PYG** *071 †75
BIEHUSEN, Frederick Chas. ■ 18018 #024-01-1946 L1947 **PD** *071 †55
BIGDELI, Homayoon. 65 E ELIZABETH AVE, STE 704 18018 #517-01-1971 L1974 **END** *020 †20
BOWEN, Dale Thos. ■ 18018 #041-13-1960 L1961 **FM** *020 †18
BRAINARD, Andrew Han. ■ 18018 #034-01-2007 L2007 **EM** *012
BURKEY, Seth Micah. ■ 18018 #041-13-2006 L2006 **EM** *012
CAMPBELL, Harold S, Jr. 65 E ELIZABETH AVE, STE 303 18018 #005-12-1970 L1982 **FM IM** *020 †20,18,16
CASSELBERRY, Erma J. ■ 18018 #041-09-1952 L1953 **PD A** *071 †55
CLOUSER, William F. ■ 18018 #041-02-1952 L1953 **GP OS** *020
DANESHDOOST, Leyla. 65 E ELIZABETH AVE, STE 704 18018 #517-01-1981 L1985 **END IM** *020 †20
DIAZ-BURNEY, Carmen Elisa. 1107 EATON AVE, STE B 18018 #308-03-1988 L1998 **P** *020 †75
ECHENBERG, Robert Jay. 623 W UNION BLVD UNIT 5 18018 #041-02-1965 L1971 **GYN PMM** *020 †30
FISHER, Jos Wallace, Jr. 19 E ELIZABETH AVE 18018 #016-43-1953 L1955 **PTH** *072 †50
FROSCH, Florence Mary. ■ 18018 #041-13-1938 L1939 **CHP** *071
FULINSKA, Elzbieta. 1107 EATON AVE, ST LUKE'S PSYCHIATRIC ASSO 18018 #759-03-1991 L2001 **P** *020 †75
GREENSPAN, Bruce Martin. 940 N NEW ST 18018 #041-13-1980 L1982 **OTO** *020 †45
HAGGERTY, Sally H Mosser. 204 E MARKET ST 18018 #041-01-1973 **GS** *071
HEIMBACH, Geo Zimmerman. ■ 18018 #041-09-1957 L1958 **R NM** *071 †80
HELMOLD, Marie Elisabeth. 940 N NEW ST, LEHIGH VALLEY DERMATOLOGY 18018 #035-03-1991 L1995 **D** *020 †15 ‡
HOFFMAN, John Edward. 35 E ELIZABETH AVE 18018 #041-09-1957 L1958 **IM GE** *071
KANABAR, Reena Vinodchand. ■ 18018 #024-07-2008 L2008 *012
KANG, Wade Wei. ■ 18018 #243-16-1991 L2003 **GS** *012
LAUDADIO, Saverio N. 493 LAKE DRIVE 18025 #028-79-1967, ▲ L1973 **P** *020
LYCHAK, John C. 35 E ELIZABETH AVE 18018 #041-02-1950 L1951 **P** *020 †75
MARCINCIN, Robert Paul. 35 E ELIZABETH AVE STE 38 18018 #016-02-1977 L1979 **NS** *020 †25
MEYERHUBER, Stephen Micha. ■ 18018 #422-01-2000 L2004 **AN** *020
MORALES, Gladys Dinorah. ■ 18018 #308-01-1956 L1967 **IM CD** *071
OLEWILER, H Newton, Jr. 1 E ELIZABETH AVE 18018 #041-01-1963 L1964 **IM** *020
ORR, Ross M. 35 E ELIZABETH AVE 18018 #051-04-1953 L1959 **GS** *071
PATTIN, Robin Marie. 1107 EATON AVE, STE B 18018 #035-46-2000 L2007 **CHP** *100
ROGERS, John Fletcher. 35 E ELIZABETH AVE 18018 #008-02-1973 L1978 **P PYA** *020 †75
SARAYNO-SAGGE, Perla. 35 E ELIZABETH AVE, STE 24 18018 #748-10-1973 L1986 **AN** *020
SCHADT, Daniel Calvin. 35 E ELIZABETH AVE, STE 30 18018 #041-09-1953 L1954 **IM** *020 †20
SCHARLE, William Timothy. 35 E ELIZABETH AVE, STE 37 18018 #012-01-1980 L1982 **IM** *020 †20
SCHWENDEMAN, David Lee. 623 W UNION BLVD 18018 #041-09-1978 L1980 **P** *020 †75
SENFT, Stephen Curvin. 940 N NEW ST 18018 #041-14-1979 L1981 **D** *020 †20,15 ‡
SHANLEY, David Brian. 35 E ELIZABETH AVE, STE 21A 18018 #077-01-1993 L1996 **FM** *020 †18
SHARMA, Amar Jeet. 940 N NEW ST 18018 #495-69-1967 L1980 **AI PG** *020 †55,03
SION, Ricardo. 35 E ELIZABETH AVE, STE 24 18018 #748-01-1977 L1995 **AN** *020
SMOCK, Regina Cudemo. 618 4TH AVE, STE 204 18018 #041-02-1980 L1981 **P** *020
SNYDER, Marsha W. 1107 EATON AVE, STE B 18018 #041-01-1980 L1981 **P** *020 †75
STEIN, Richard Norman. 701 N NEW ST 18018 #050-02-1963 L1966 **PD PDA** *020 †55
SWETERLITSCH, Louis Henry. 65 E ELIZABETH AVE 18018 #041-02-1960 L1961 **OPH** *020 †35
SWETERLITSCH, Louis Henry. 65 E ELIZABETH AVE 18018 #041-02-1992 L1996 **OPH** *020 †35
TONEY, Melinda Q. 623 W UNION BLVD UNIT 5, CENTER OF FAMILY HEALTH 18018 #012-05-1982 L1987 **FM** *020 †18
TRAUPMAN, Arnold F. 1313 LANARK ST 18018 #041-02-1973 L1974 **OPH** *020 †35
VASILY, David B. 940 N NEW ST 18018 #035-06-1975 L1976 **D** *020 †15 ‡
VIQAR, Syed Hasan. 1107 EATON AVE, STE B 18018 #305-01-1984 L1988 **P FM** *020
WALLACE, Edwin Andrew. ■ 18018 #041-01-1954 L1955 **PHP GP** *030
WEISMAN, Dale Max. 401 W BROAD ST 18018 #165-01-1977 L1978 **FM EM** *020 †18 ‡
WENG, Sam Sheng-San. 940 N NEW ST 18018 #244-04-1970 L1974 **IM OS** *020
ZALADONIS, Sylvia P. 1809 COLUMBINE AVE 18018 #041-07-1959 L1960 **FM** *071 †18

BETHLEHEM – NORTHAMPTON

ABGOTT, Michael Alan. 1545 BROADWAY 18015 #561-01-1977 L1979 **FM** *020 †18
ABO, Marc Neal. 2597 SCHOENERSVILLE RD, STE 207 18017 #035-46-1975 L1980 **GS AS** *020 †85
ACHARYA-GUPTA, Sonia. 801 OSTRUM ST 18015 #913-97-2001 L2007 **FP** *012
AGARWALA, Sanjiv S. 801 OSTRUM ST, ST LUKE'S HOSP & HLTH NTWK 18015 #496-33-1984 L1991 **ON HEM** *020 †20
AGUIRRE ALVARADO, Ricardo. 801 OSTRUM ST 18015 #132-01-2000 L2004 **OBG** *012
AHERN, Maryellen Patricia. ■ 18015 #041-09-1985 L1986 **AN** *020 †05
AHMAD, Nadeem V. 2649 SCHOENERSVILLE RD, LEHIGH VALLEY CARD ASSN 18017 #043-01-1993 L1999 **CD** *020 †20
AHMED, Sultan. ■ 18017 #704-01-1973 L1978 **RO** *020 †80
AIROLDI, James Andrew. 801 OSTRUM ST, STE 3 18015 #041-07-1993 L1995 **OBG** *020 †30

ALCOSEBA, Camilo Enrique. 801 OSTRUM ST 18015 #748-11-1973 L1977 **RO** *020 †80
ALEXANDRIN, Eugene. 2545 SCHOENERSVILLE RD, PATHOLOGY DEPARTMENT 18017 #913-04-1977 L1993 **PTH** *020 †50
AMORES, Edward D. ■ 18015 #035-01-2004 L2008 **EM** *012
ANDREWS, Charles Franklin. 2545 SCHOENERSVILLE RD, FL 1 18017 #041-09-1981 L1982 **RO** *020 †80
APFELBAUM, Jay Henry. 801 OSTRUM ST 18015 #028-34-1967 L1973 **AN** *020 †05
ARASTU, Mohammad Ishaq. 5325 NORTHGATE DR STE 208 18017 #495-21-1974 L1977 **END IM** *050 †20
ATTILIO, Michael Joseph. ■ 18015 #041-15-2005 L2005 **FP** *012
AVELLINI, Jami. 801 OSTRUM ST, DEPT OF MEDICINE 18015 #305-01-2006 L2006 **OBG** *012
BALOH, Frank Gerard. 1685 VALLEY CTR, PARKWAY, 200 18017 #041-14-1990 L1995 **OPH** *020 †35
BALSHI, Stephen Francis. 2597 SCHOENERSVILLE RD 18017 #041-02-1945 L1946 **OTO** *072 †45
BANAS, Michael Paul. 2775 SCHOENERSVILLE RD 18017 #041-01-1988 L1994 **ORS** *020 †40
BANDI, Padmaja. ■ 18017 #496-40-1993 L2006 **IM** *012
BARR, Gavin Chaundy. 2649 SCHOENERSVILLE RD, STE 201 18017 #041-02-1960 L1961 **IM CD** *030
BARR, Gavin Chaundy, Jr. ■ 18015 #041-02-1993 L1997 **EM** *020 †16
BARTOS, Joseph E. 2223 LINDEN ST 18017 #041-02-1948 L1949 **FM** *071
BATTISTELLA, Jessica Loui. 801 OSTRUM ST, DEPT OF OB/GYN 18015 #051-07-2006 **OBG** *012
BEALER, John Danl. ■ 18017 #041-02-1948 L1949 **OM GPM** *071 †70
BECKER, Eric David. 2045 WESTGATE DR STE 402 18017 #041-13-1986 L1987 **P** *020 †75
BELL, Joseph Gerard. 801 OSTRUM ST, STE 3 18015 #041-02-1986 L1987 **MFM OBG** *020 †30
BERRY, Marcos A. ■ 18017 #231-03-1990 **GS** *100 †85
BHATT, Surya Prakash. 801 OSTRUM ST 18015 #495-09-2001 L2006 **IM** *012
BINNIG, Holly Loraine. 2101 EMRICK BLVD, STE 201 18020 #041-15-1999 L2002 **FM** *020 †18
BITAR, Hussam. 801 OSTRUM ST, ST. LUKE'S HOSPITAL 18015 #875-02-2000 L2004 **GS** *012
BLAUTH, Jeanette Marie. 2545 SCHOENERSVILLE RD, FL 1 18017 #041-14-1994 L1996 **RO** *020 †80
BLEZNAK, Aaron David. 2597 SCHOENERSVILLE RD, STE 201 18017 #041-02-1983 L1988 **SO** *020 †85
BOCCHINO, Joseph Vincent. ■ 18017 #561-01-1972 L1977 **PS HS** *020 †65
BOLLINI, Sashidhar. 801 OSTRUM ST 18015 #308-11-1999 L2001 **IM** *100 †20
BOREEN, Stuart Michael. 525 BRIGHTON ST STE 202 18015 #041-02-1986 L1987 **AN** *020 †05
BOSOY, Dimitry. 801 OSTRUM ST 18015 #422-01-2005 L2005 **EM** *012
BOU ZGHEIB, Nadim Louis. 801 OSTRUM ST, ST LUKE'S HOSPITAL 18015 #605-03-2006 L2007 **OBG** *012
BOYLAN, James Jeremy. 5325 NORTHGATE DR, STE 101 18017 #035-19-1970 L1978 **GE IM** *020 †20
BOZORGNIA, Hassan. 4315 EASTON AVE, UNIT 1 18020 #517-01-1969 L1987 **PD** *020 †55 ‡
BRAU, Alan Seth. 4315 EASTON AVE, UNIT 2 18020 #035-47-1986 L1988 **PUD IM** *020 †20
BROGLE, Patrick Joseph. 801 OSTRUM ST 18015 #035-08-1993 L1999 **ORS** *020 †40
BURGER, Theodore P. ■ 18017 #041-13-1961 L1962 **FM GP** *071 †18
BURGEY, Gail E. 801 OSTRUM ST 18015 #054-04-1989 L1991 **OBG** *020 †30
CACERES SERRANO, Hector A. ■ 18017 #429-02-2004 **OBG** *012
CANLAS, Jolly B. 3897 ADLER PL STE 160, BLDG C 18017 #748-02-1976 L1985 **FM OS** *020
CARDIGES, Nicholas M. 801 OSTRUM ST, ST LUKES CANCER CENTER 18015 #023-01-1990 L1995 **RO** *020 †80 ‡
CARLIN, Hugh Michael. 801 OSTRUM ST 18015 #041-02-1980 L1985 **AN** *020 †05
CARMONA, Aldo. 1685 VALLEY CENTER PKWY 18017 #041-01-1984 L1985 **AN** *020 †05
CARNEY, Rebecca Kay. 801 OSTRUM ST 18015 #001-06-2005 L2005 **EM** *012
CHALUNKAL, Mathai Mathew. 801 OSTRUM ST 18015 #495-17-1987 L2005 **IM** *012
CHANG, Chi-Kue T. 3348 EASTON AVE 18020 #305-01-1986 L1991 **IM IMG** *020 †20
CHAPMAN, Christopher Nead. ■ 18017 #035-15-1999 L2000 **PTH** *012
CHEIPESH, Larisa Petrovna. 2830 EASTON AVE, PRACTICE RESI 18017 #913-13-1982 L2002 **FP** *012
CHEN, Edward C H. 5325 NORTHGATE DR, STE 101 18017 #244-04-1980 L1987 **GE IM** *020 †20
CHIAPELLA, Carla Diane. 2545 SCHOENERSVILLE RD 18017 #030-06-1984 L1991 **U** *020 †95
COJANU, Carmen. ■ 18015 #781-01-1987 L2007 **FM** *100
COJANU, Daniel Nelu. 801 OSTRUM ST 18015 #781-01-1990 L2004 **FM** *020 †18
COLE, Jack Eli. ■ 18017 #041-01-1941 L1942 **FM ID** *071 †18
CONRON, Richard W, Jr. 5325 NORTHGATE DR STE 204 18017 #022-75-1994, ▲ L1995 **GS** *020 †85
COPELAND, Ardeth Lee. 801 OSTRUM ST 18015 #041-15-1999 L2003 **HO** *100 †20
CORNFIELD, Dennis Borek. 2545 SCHOENERSVILLE RD, PATHOLOGY DEPARTMENT 18017 #041-01-1968 L1969 **HMP PTH** *020,50 ‡
COWAN, James A. 801 OSTRUM ST, ST LUKES HOSPITAL 18015 #065-01-1977 L1991 **IM MDM** *030 †20
COWEN, Malcolm Lee. ■ 18020 #041-02-1958 L1959 **FOP** *071 †50
COYLE, Bonnie. 801 OSTRUM ST 18015 #041-02-1989 L1995 **GPM** *020 †70
CUNNINGHAM, Crystal Marie. ■ 18017 #037-01-2006 L2006 **GS** *012
CUSTODIO, Edgardo Caparaz. ■ 18017 #748-01-1957 L1973 **DR** *071
DANESHDOOST, Ghodrat O. 1250 GREENWOOD DR 18017 #517-01-1971 L1977 **NS** *020 †25
DAVIDYOCK, John Michael. 3080 10TH ST 18020 #041-15-2001 L2003 **IM** *020
DE JOSEPH, Robert Louis. 2649 SCHOENERSVILLE RD, STE 301 18017 #041-09-1968 L1974 **CD** *020 †20
DELLERS, Elizabeth Ann. 2545 SCHOENERSVILLE RD, LEHIGH VALLEY HOSP PATH DP 18017 #035-45-1985 L1986 **PTH** *020 †50
DE LONG, William Geo, Jr. 801 OSTRUM ST 18015 #041-13-1978 L1979 **ORS** *020 †40 ‡
DESAI, Darius Cawas. 801 OSTRUM ST 18015 #041-02-1992 L1995 **SO GS** *020 †85
DE SOUSA, Hansel. 2775 SCHOENERSVILLE RD 18017 #060-02-1976 L1985 **AN PME** *020 †05
DI CONCETTO, Jos Anthony. 5325 NORTHGATE DR, STE 104 18017 #041-09-1978 L1981 **AI IM** *020,03
DIETRICH, Gary Jay. 801 OSTRUM ST DEPT R 18015 #041-13-1985 L1987 **DR** *020 †80
DIPPOLITO, Anthony D. 201 DRIFT CT 18020 #030-06-1979 L1980 **CRS** *020 †10,85
DITMARS, Douglas Detrick. 801 OSTRUM ST 18015 #041-13-1972 L1973 **ORS** *020 †40
DODSON, Donald Lynn. 801 OSTRUM ST 18015 #041-14-1982 L1983 **AN** *020
DOLPHIN, Basil. 2649 SCHOENERSVILLE RD, STE 102 18017 #041-02-1984 L1997 **OM GPM** *020 †70
DOTO, Joseph Benj. 425 BRIGHTON ST, STE202 P O BOX 5520 18015 #041-02-1966 L1967 **AN** *020 †05

DUBBELMAN-BANAS, Theresa. 4727 KATHI DR 18017 #041-01-1987 L1988 **FM PD** *020 †18

DUNNING, E Ruth. ■ 18017 #041-01-1943 L1944 **GP** *071

DUNNING, Kyle Gilbert. ■ 18017 #041-15-2004 L2004 **GS** *012

DUQUE, Welda Trilles. 1696 KEVIN DR 18015 #748-08-1980 L1997 **P** *020

EBERHARDT, Mary Helen. 801 OSTRUM ST, DEPT OF EMERGENCY MEDICINE 18015 #041-13-1988 L1999 **EM OM** *020 †16

EHRENFEUCHTER, Kurk E. 2775 SCHOENERSVILLE RD 18017 #041-77-1983, ▲ L1984 **AN** *071

EHRIG, Michael John. 2649 SCHOENERSVILLE RD, STE 201 18017 #041-14-1994 L1996 **IM** *020 †20

EL CHAAR, Maher Mahmoud. 801 OSTRUM ST, ST LUKES HOSP 18015 #605-01-2001 L2003 **GS** *012

ELLIS, Ross Edward. 2101 EMRICK BLVD, HEALTHWORKS 18020 #035-01-1996 L2004 **PSM** *020 †20

ENDER, Peter Todd. 801 OSTRUM ST, DEPT OF MED 18015 #041-13-1992 L1995 **ID** *020 †20

ENEA, Ned Alan. 5325 NORTHGATE DR, STE 100 18017 #041-14-1990 L1994 **VIR** *020 †80

EPISCOPIO, Jennifer Susan. 801 OSTRUM ST, NETWORK 18015 #041-15-2005 L2005 **OBG** *012

ERMOLOVICH, Tanya. 2101 EMRICK BLVD 18020 #041-77-1995, ▲ L1996 **D** *020

EYVAZZADEH, Camille. 5325 NORTHGATE DR, STE 101 18017 #517-01-1974 L1981 **CRS** *020 †85,10

FAROOQI, Asif. 4379 EASTON AVE UNIT 1 18020 #704-16-1986 L1997 **FM** *020 †18 ‡

FIELD, Ellen Meryl. 1665 VALLEY CENTER PKWY, STE 100 18017 #041-09-1978 L1982 **RHU PPR** *020

FIELDS, Esther L. 801 OSTRUM ST, INTERNAL MEDICINE OFFICE 18015 #041-77-2002, ▲ L2002 **PCC** *012 †20

FOGARTY, Kevin T. 5325 NORTHGATE DR, STE 100 18017 #035-08-1986 L1991 **DR IM** *030 †80

FOLANDER, Hal L. 214 WEDGEWOOD RD 18017 #035-19-1982 L1987 **VIR DR** *020 †80 ‡

FOLLMER, Don Clark. 2830 EASTON AVE, ST LUKES FAM PRACTICE CTR 18017 #041-01-1955 L1956 **FM** *071 †18

FOREST, Patti Green. 2830 EASTON AVE, ST LUKES FAMILY PRACTICE C 18017 #047-06-1991 L1997 **FM** *020 †18

FRIEDENBERG, Steven S. 5325 NORTHGATE DR, STE 100 18017 #035-09-1975 L1976 **DR** *020 †80

FURLONG-JULIA, Ellen Mary. 3201 HIGHFIELD DR 18020 #422-01-1981 L1982 **PD** *020 †55

GALLAGHER, James Gerald. 3445 HIGH POINT BLVD, STE 300 18017 #035-48-1986 L1994 **CD NC** *020 †20 ‡

GALTMAN, Lawrence M. 2380 SCHOENERSVILLE RD 18017 #041-07-1981 L1982 **PD** *020 †55

GARCIA, Gerardo M. 2649 SCHOENERSVILLE RD 18017 #649-14-1988 L1997 **GS** *020 †85

GARZIA, Fernando Marcelo. 2545 SCHOENERSVILLE RD, 4TH FL 18017 #038-40-1986 L1996 **TS** *020 †85,90

GAVIN, Monica Carezani. 3101 EMRICK BLVD STE 201 18020 #025-07-1991 L1997 **PD** *020 †55

GAYDOS, Thomas Leo. 801 OSTRUM ST 18015 #041-13-1961 L1962 **GYN** *071 †30

GERONIMO, Lauro S. 4379 WILLIAM PENN HWY 18020 #748-01-1955 L1973 **FM** *071

GHATAK, Parimal Kumar. 801 OSTRUM ST 18015 #495-02-1961 L1975 **PUD IM** *020 †20

GHEORGHE, Camelia Magda. 801 OSTRUM ST, ST LUKE'S HOSPITAL 18015 #781-02-2000 L2006 **FP** *012

GHETU, Maria V.. 2830 EASTON AVE, PRACTICE RESI 18017 #781-03-1982 L2003 **FPG** *020 †18

GHOOCHANI, Abbas Saberi. ■ 18017 #517-01-1969 L1987 **GE IM** *050 †20

GIBSON, Brett William. 2775 SCHOENERSVILLE RD 18017 #041-01-2001 L2001 **ORS** *020

GILLEN, George Patrick. ■ 18017 #041-13-1968 L1969 **R DR** *071 †80

GOENKA, Anamika. ■ 18015 #496-36-2001 L2006 **IM** *020 †20

GOLDMAN, Eugene Emmanual. ■ 18020 #005-19-2005 L2005 **EM** *012

GOMEZ, John Paul. 2545 SCHOENERSVILLE RD, 5TH FL 18017 #041-13-1998 L2004 **CHP** *020 †75

GONZALEZ, Abel Arturo. 2299 BRODHEAD RD, STE N 18020 #308-01-1982 L1988 **P** *020 †75

GONZALEZ, Miguel Angel. 608 PIERCE ST 18015 #035-46-1976 L1983 **FM** *020 †18

GONZALEZ, Rene Miguel. 2775 SCHOENERSVILLE RD 18017 #041-01-1983 L1985 **AN** *020 †05 ‡

GOODRICH, David Chas. 801 OSTRUM ST 18015 #041-13-1979 L1981 **AN** *020 †05

GOPAL, Gnanaprakash. 2101 EMRICK BLVD, STE 100 18020 #496-01-1984 L1991 **FM** *020 †18

GOPAL, Jyoti G. 2649 SCHOENERSVILLE RD, STE 201 18017 #495-82-1988 L1996 **FM** *020 †18

GOTSCH, Patricia Beck. 2830 EASTON AVE, ST LUKES FAMILY PRACTICE C 18017 #023-07-1988 L2005 **FM** *040 †18

GRAYNER, Scott Matthew. 801 OSTRUM ST, DEPT OF MEDICINE 18015 #905-02-2004 L2005 **FP** *012

GROSSMAN, Michael David. 801 OSTRUM ST, TRAUMA/SURGICAL CRITICAL C 18015 #005-14-1984 L1995 **CCS** *020 †85

GROVE, Dale Addison, Jr. 1545 BROADWAY 18015 #041-02-1956 L1957 **FM** *071 †18

GUPTA, Pooja. 801 OSTRUM ST 18015 #496-07-2001 L2007 **OBG** *012

GUPTA, Puneet. 2545 SCHOENERSVILLE RD, AT LEHIGH VALLEY HOSPITAL 18017 #495-36-1986 L2001 **PD** *020 †55

HEITLINGER, Leo Abraham. 801 OSTRUM ST, ST LUKE'S HOSPITAL 18015 #035-09-1978 L1999 **PG NTR** *030 †55

HELLER, Michael Bruce. 801 OSTRUM ST, DEPT OF EMERGENCY MEDICINE 18015 #035-15-1974 L1984 **EM IM** *040 †20,16

HERNANDEZ, Danny William. 608 PIERCE ST 18015 #033-06-1999 L2001 **FM** *020 †18

HERNANDEZ, Jon David. 2300 HIGHLAND AVE 18020 #005-14-1998 L2004 **HS** *020 †40

HILL, Robert Geo, Jr. 801 OSTRUM ST 18015 #041-02-1980 L1981 **EM** *020 †16

HODGES, Robert. 801 OSTRUM ST, ANES SPECIALISTS OF BETHLE 18015 #035-01-1992 L2002 **AN** *020 †05

HOEY, Brian Anthony. 801 OSTRUM ST, ST. LUKE'S TRAUMA CENTER 18015 #051-07-1994 L2000 **CCS** *020 †85

HOFFMAN, David Edward. 5325 NORTHGATE DR, STE 207 18017 #041-09-1984 L1986 **IM** *020

HOLUMZER, Clinton C. 2649 SCHOENERSVILLE RD, STE 201 18017 #041-13-1998 L2000 **IM** *020 †20

HORNE, Howard K. 801 OSTRUM ST 18015 #016-06-2000 L2000 **OBG** *020 ‡

HOSAKOTE SUBRAHMANYAM, Amb. 801 OSTRUM ST 18015 #496-21-2001 L2005 **FP** *012

HOWE, J Dale. 2775 SCHOENERSVILLE RD, COORDINATED HEALTH SYSTEMS 18017 #008-01-1962 L1963 **ORS** *071 †40

HUANG, Shaw Yeh. ■ 18020 #385-01-1967 **GP** *100

HUNSICKER, Robert Chas. 3445 HIGH POINT BLVD, STE 100 18017 #041-09-1966 L1967 **OTO** *020 †45

HUNTER, Carol Ann. 801 OSTRUM ST 18015 #041-09-1978 L1980 **FM** *020 †18

HYLAND, James Carroll. 2545 SCHOENERSVILLE RD, PATHOLOGY DEPARTMENT 18017 #041-02-1993 L1997 **PTH** *020 †50

IRANI, Mahakhurshid. 201 DRIFT CT 18020 #495-17-1978 L1981 **CRS** *020 †85,10

IYER, Manny Subramanian. 2300 HIGHLAND AVE 18020 #495-16-1977 L1984 **PS HS** *020 †85,65

JACOB, Jeena Mary. 2830 EASTON AVE, PRACTICE RESI 18017 #495-31-1999 L2005 **FP** *012

JACOB, Sharon Leigh. 801 OSTRUM ST 18015 #550-02-2004 L2004 **EM** *100

JAEGER, Randy. 2775 SCHOENERSVILLE RD 18017 #036-05-1988 L1993 **OSM** *020 †40

JAHRE, Jeffrey Allen. 801 OSTRUM ST 18015 #016-42-1970 L1978 **ID IM** *020 †20

JAIK, Nikhil Pollo. 801 OSTRUM ST, ST LUKE'S HOSP 18015 #496-23-2003 L2005 **GS** *012

JAIN, Praveer. 2649 SCHOENERSVILLE RD, STE 301 18017 #495-36-1982 L1995 **CD ICE** *020 †20

JAIN, Sandeep. 801 OSTRUM ST 18015 #495-30-1997 L2007 **IM** *012

JAJODIA, Anila Shyam. 801 OSTRUM ST 18015 #495-06-2002 L2005 **FM** *100

JIMENEZ, Michael Angel. 801 OSTRUM ST, ST LUKE'S HOSP 18015 #005-14-2006 L2006 **GS** *012

JOHNSON, Douglas Emil. 2005 CITY LINE RD 18017 #017-20-1972 L1979 **NEP IM** *020 †20

JOSEPH, Christopher John. ■ 18017 #041-77-2007, ▲ *012

JULIA, Ronald Richard. 3201 HIGHFIELD DR 18020 #422-01-1981 L1982 **IM** *020 †20

JUSINSKI, Michael G.. 2830 EASTON AVE, ST. LUKE'S FAMILY PRACTICE 18017 #759-01-2002 L2003 **FM** *020 †18

KANDULA, Hymavathy R. ■ 18017 #495-57-1970 L1979 **GP IMG** *071

KANDULA, Ravindra Reddy. 2649 SCHOENERSVILLE RD, STE 203 18017 #495-21-1964 L1974 **GS SO** *020 †85

KANNANGARA, Don Walter W. 801 OSTRUM ST 18015 #220-02-1966 L1976 **ID IM** *020 †20 ‡

KANNANGARA, Yogeswary. 2775 SCHOENERSVILLE RD 18017 #220-01-1965 L1976 **AN** *020

KANOFF, Steven Jay. 2663 SCHOENERSVILLE RD, MUHLENBERG MED CTR DRS CAM 18017 #041-13-1985 L1989 **OPH** *020 †35 ‡

KARPER, Laurence P. 2545 SCHOENERSVILLE RD 18017 #033-06-1988 L1997 **P ADP** *020 †75

KASARDA, David C. 801 OSTRUM ST, DEPT OF EMERGENCY MEDICINE 18015 #041-13-1997 L2001 **EM** *020 †16

KAUFMANN, Michael Wm. 2545 SCHOENERSVILLE RD, LEHIGH VLY HOSP 5TH FL 18017 #132-01-1976 L1991 **P PYG** *030 †75

KAYE, Glenn M. 2851 BAGLYOS CIR, STE 201 18020 #035-45-1991 L2000 **OTO CS** *020 †45

KEITH, Helen R Hesselman. 801 OSTRUM ST 18015 #041-09-1972 L1973 **PD PUD** *020 †55

KHALAJ HEDAYATI, Hediyeh. 2830 EASTON AVE 18017 #517-12-1997 L2007 **FP** *012

KIENZLE, Cheryl. 3445 HIGH POINT BLVD, STE 204 18017 #041-01-1985 L1986 **PD** *020 †55

KIRILLOVA, Lyudmila. 801 OSTRUM ST, ST LUKE'S HOSPITAL 18015 #913-77-1998 L2006 **IM** *012

KITEI, Susan Comer. 36 UNIVERSITY DR, LEHIGH UNIVERSITY STUDENT 18015 #041-09-1982 L1982 **GP** *020 ‡

KLAYTON, Tracy Lea. 801 OSTRUM ST, ST LUKE'S HOSPITAL 18015 #010-02-2007 L2007 **TY** *012

KOLESKY, Richard Andrew. 2545 SCHOENERSVILLE RD, LVH MUHLENBERG ANES DEPT 18017 #049-01-1988 L1990 **AN IM** *020 †20,05

KORRAPATI, Vamsimadhav Ch. ■ 18017 #496-24-2000 L2005 **IM** *012

KOSARAJU, Nitish. 801 OSTRUM ST 18015 #495-50-2003 L2006 **IM** *012

KOWALYSHYN, Theodore J. 2101 EMRICK BLVD, STE 100 18020 #041-09-1966 L1967 **IM HEM** *020 †20 ‡

KRAFCZYK, Michael Allen. 2830 EASTON AVE, ST LUKES FAM PRACTICE CTR 18017 #041-13-1993 L1995 **FSM** *100 †18

KRAYBILL, Margaret Ann. 1545 BROADWAY 18015 #041-09-1971 L1972 **IM** *020 †20

KRAYNICK, Benj Michael. 801 OSTRUM ST 18015 #041-09-1953 L1954 **ORS** *071 †40

KUEHNER, William Paul, III. 4311 EASTON AVE 18020 #041-02-1992 L1995 **IM** *020 †20

KUMARESAN, Vasumathy K. 3833 LINDEN ST, MILLER HEIGHTS MEDICAL ASS 18020 #495-42-1988 L1999 **IM** *020 †20

KUNDU, Kaushik. 5325 NORTHGATE DR, STE 201 18017 #495-44-1989 L1996 **IM** *020 †20

LAHAV, Erika. 2045 WESTGATE DR, STE 305 18017 #473-01-1974 L1985 **IM** *020 ‡

LAM, Nguyet-Cam Vu. 2830 EASTON AVE 18017 #905-02-2003 L2003 **FM** *100 †18

LASZLO, Ingrid M L. ■ 18020 #407-05-1964 L1971 **PD** *071 †55

LE, Thong Phuoc. 801 OSTRUM ST, ST LUKES HOSPITAL 18015 #024-07-1990 L1998 **ID IM** *050 †20

LEE, Ha-Lin Christina. 95 HIGHLAND AVE STE 100 18017 #016-11-1983 L1994 **REN GYN** *020 †30

LEET, Thomas Eugene. 2101 EMRICK BLVD 18020 #026-04-1967 L1970 **DR PDR** *020 †20,80 ‡

LEFROCK, Brian Abraham. 2775 SCHOENERSVILLE RD, ALBANY MEMORIAL HOSPITAL 18017 #035-09-1989 L2007 **AN** *020 †05

LEH, David W, Jr. 801 OSTRUM ST 18015 #041-02-1989 L1992 **IM** *020 †20

LEHRICH, Deborah Anne. 2151 EMRICK BLVD 18020 #008-02-1994 L1994 **HO** *020 †20

LENTZ, Conrad Lee. ■ 18017 #041-02-1960 L1961 **D** *071

LERMAN, Joel Martin. 2545 SCHOENERSVILLE RD, MUHLENBERG BEHAVIORAL HEAL 18017 #041-13-1985 L1986 **P** *020 †75

LEVIN, Larry Lewis. 2649 SCHOENERSVILLE RD, STE 201 18017 #041-13-1989 L1991 **IM** *030 †20

LEVIN, Marc Wm. 2101 EMRICK BLVD 18020 #041-07-1976 L1989 **D** *020 †18,15 ‡

LEVINSTEIN, Gene V.. 2597 SCHOENERSVILLE RD, STE 101 18017 #305-01-2000 L2001 **PM** *020 †60

LEWIS, Courtney Lynne. ■ 18017 #041-77-2007, ▲ L2007 *012

LIGHT, Harry Grim. ■ 18015 #041-02-1955 L1956 **GS** *071 †85

LIN, Wei-Shen W. 2775 SCHOENERSVILLE RD 18017 #035-15-1994 L1997 **ORS** *020 †40

LIPETSKAIA, Lioudmila. 801 OSTRUM ST 18015 #913-36-2000 L2005 **OBG** *012

LODEIRO, Jorge G. 801 OSTRUM ST, STE 3 18015 #935-04-1977 L2003 **MFM OBG** *020 †30

LONG, John Stephen. 1545 BROADWAY, S MTN FAMILY PRACTICE 18015 #041-02-1985 L1986 **FM** *020 †18

LONGO, Santo. 801 OSTRUM ST 18015 #041-02-1963 L1964 **PTH ON** *020 †50

LOVETT, Brian Dewitt. 801 OSTRUM ST, ST LUKE'S HOSPITAL 18015 #041-14-2004 L2004 **EM** *020

LOZO, Robert Leslie. 801 OSTRUM ST 18015 #654-01-2005 L2006 **OBG** *012

LUKAS, Lou Ann. 2101 EMRICK BLVD, HEALTH SPRING 18020 #030-05-1998 L2000 **FM** *020 †18

LUKASZCZYK, Thomas Andrew. ■ 18017 #041-09-1954 L1955 **PTH** *071 †50

MAIZEL, Rahkil. 801 OSTRUM ST, ST LUKES HOSP 18015 #913-19-1988 L2004 **FM** *020 †18

MALIK, Anup. 2310 HIGHLAND AVE 18020 #496-09-1979 L1996 **AN** *020 †05

MALKA, Ari R. ■ 18015 #011-02-2003 L2003 **EM** *100

MANDELKER, Eiran Moses. 2775 SCHOENERSVILLE RD 18017 #041-01-1992 L2005 **DR** *020 †80

MANE, David. ■ 18015 #041-13-2007 L2007 **GS** *012

MANNISI, John Anthony. 2649 SCHOENERSVILLE RD, STE 301 18017 #023-07-1980 L1990 **CD IM** *020 †20

7840

■ = Address Information Privacy Protected

MARCINCIN, Paul Gerard. 2597 SCHOENERSVILLE RD, STE 303 18017 #016-02-1983 L1988 D *020 †15

MARGIE, Walter E, Jr. ■ 18017 #041-13-1951 L1952 IM *071 †20

MASTROLIA, Ricardo Salvat. 801 OSTRUM ST, DEPT OF OB/GYN 18015 #305-01-2002 L2002 OBG *012

MATEJICKA, Anthony V, II. 2649 SCHOENERSVILLE RD, STE 201 18017 #041-77-1994, ▲ L1995 IM PHP *020 †20

MAZZA, Steven B. 2300 HIGHLAND AVE 18020 #033-05-1999 L2003 PM *020 †60

MCCARTNEY, John N. 801 OSTRUM ST, ST LUKE'S HOSPITAL 18015 #033-75-2007, ▲ L2007 IM *012

MC GEE, James Michael. 801 OSTRUM ST, EMERGENCY MEDICINE RESIDEN 18015 #031-01-2001 L2001 EM *020 †16

MCINTYRE, Patrick Edgar. 2597 SCHOENERSVILLE RD, COLLEGE HEIGHTS OB/GYN 18017 #041-09-1995 L1998 OBG *020 †30

MC WILLIAMS, Wayne F. 2649 SCHOENERSVILLE RD, STE 201 18017 #041-13-1996 L1998 IM *020 †20

MEEHAN, Kathleen Mary. 1545 BROADWAY, SOUTH MOUNTAIN FAMILY PRAC 18015 #041-13-1985 L1987 FM FPG *020 †18

MELANSON, Scott Wm. 801 OSTRUM ST, DEPT OF EMERGENCY MEDICINE 18015 #041-02-1987 L1989 EM *020 †16

MELITO, Brian Van. 2545 SCHOENERSVILLE RD, EMP DEPT 18017 #041-13-1982 L1983 EM *020 †16

MERCADO, Modesto Garcia. 4520 KATHI DR 18017 #748-10-1965 L1968 AN *071 ‡

MERLA, Amartej. 801 OSTRUM ST 18015 #495-11-2002 L2006 IM *012

MEROLA, Joseph C L. 801 OSTRUM ST 18015 #041-12-1969 L1970 OBG *020 †30

MILLER, Warren Alton. 1545 BROADWAY 18015 #041-02-1947 L1948 FM *071

MOHER, Heather Ellen. 2830 EASTON AVE, ST. LUKE'S FAMILY PRACTICE 18017 #022-75-2006, ▲ L2006 FP *012

MONTELEONE, Philip M. 2545 SCHOENERSVILLE RD, PEDIATRIC SPECIALISTS OF L 18017 #041-13-1985 L2000 PHO PD *020 †55

MORRIS, Patricia Ann. 801 OSTRUM ST 18015 #041-09-1979 L1981 AN IM *020 †05

MORRISON, Robert E. 5325 NORTHGATE DR, STE 206 18017 #016-42-1988 L1993 OPH *020 †35

MORTAZAVI, Steven Allie. 4250 FRITCH DR, VALLEY PAIN SPEC PC 18020 #035-15-1994 L1997 APM *020 †05

MOSCATO, Anthony Francis. 3525 HECKTOWN RD 18020 #041-09-1972 L1973 IM ON *020

MUNSON, Frederick J. 801 OSTRUM ST 18015 #041-01-1952 L1953 R NM *071 †80

MURPHY, Robert X, Jr. 2597 SCHOENERSVILLE RD, STE 206 18017 #035-19-1982 L1989 PS HS *020 †65

NAGRA, Rajwinder Singh. 801 OSTRUM ST 18015 #495-29-2002 L2005 IM *012

NAIR, Sindhu. 801 OSTRUM ST, ST. LUKE'S INTERNAL MEDICI 18015 #048-04-2004 L2008 IM *100 †20

NAIR, Suneesh Gopalan. 801 OSTRUM ST, ST LUKES HOSP 18015 #495-31-2001 L2004 IM *020 †20

NANDA, Rakesh Amar. 2830 EASTON AVE 18017 #665-02-2004 L2005 FP *012

NANDA, Sudip. 801 OSTRUM ST 18015 #495-02-1997 L2004 IM *100 †20

NARAYAN, Shesha S. ■ 18015 #495-09-1984 L1998 AN *020 †05

NASHLEANAS, Michelle E. 2101 EMRICK BLVD, STE 100 18004 #035-46-2003 L2004 FM *020 †18

NEUMAN, Joel David. 3650 NAZARETH PIKE 18020 #011-02-1986 L1992 R VIR *020 †80

NGUYEN, Michael Cao. 801 OSTRUM ST 18015 #041-02-2000 L2001 EM *020 †16

NIEWIAROWSKI, Tomasz J. 5325 NORTHGATE DR, STE 101 18017 #759-03-1982 L1986 GE IM *020 †20

NIMA ZEGARRA, Harry Marti. 801 OSTRUM ST, ST LUKE'S HOSPITAL 18015 #737-06-2003 L2007 IM *012

OLIVER, Patrick Anthony. ■ 18015 #051-04-2007 L2007 EM *012

O'ROURKE, Elizabeth M. ■ 18015 #021-01-1992 L1996 OTO *020 †45

OTERO, Jorge Antonio. 2223 LINDEN ST 18017 #042-01-1978 L1981 PD *020 †55

OVERBAUGH, Robert Hugh. 316 TRUMAN LN, PAIN SPECIALISTS OF GREATE 18020 #041-14-1997 L2001 APM *100 †05

OZA, Rajen P. 2151 EMRICK BLVD 18020 #495-89-1982 L1995 HO PTH *020 †20

PAJEL-SIO, Mary Anne A. 2551 BAGLYOS CIR, STE A10 18020 #748-02-1984 L1998 FM *020 †18

PAMULA, John Vijaya Kumar. 801 OSTRUM ST 18015 #495-11-1988 L2005 IM *012

PARIKH, Reshma. 801 OSTRUM ST, DEPT OF OB/GYN 18015 #495-01-1998 L2003 OBG *100

PARIKH, Shailesh Bansilal. ■ 18017 #495-76-1969 L1984 AN *020

PARKER, Jacqueline Cherie. ■ 18015 #041-14-1984 L1991 EM OM *020 †16

PATEL, Anish Sharad. 4250 FRITCH DR, VALLEY PAIN SPECIALIST PC 18020 #496-23-2000 L2006 APM AN *020

PATEL, Bharatkumar R. ■ 18017 #495-89-1980 L1996 IM *020

PATEL, Nimisha Praful. 801 OSTRUM ST, DEPT RADIATION ONCOLOGY 18015 #033-06-1989 L1995 DR RO *020

PATEL, Nitin Nalin. 2830 EASTON AVE, PRACTICE RESI 18017 #496-20-2003 L2004 FM *020 †18

PATTERSON, John William. 801 OSTRUM ST, DEPT OF EMERGENCY MEDICINE 18015 #041-02-1978 L1979 EM IM *020 †20,16

PATWARDHAN, Manasi Sanjay. 801 OSTRUM ST, ST LUKE'S HOSPITAL 18015 #495-28-2001 L2004 OBG *012

PENDURTHI, Tribhuvan K. 2649 SCHOENERSVILLE RD, STE 203 18017 #495-21-1979 L1995 SO GS *020 †85

PERCH, Steven Jay. 2545 SCHOENERSVILLE RD, FL 1 18017 #041-01-1991 L1993 RO *020 †80

PEREZ ACOSTA, Claudia Mar. 801 OSTRUM ST 18015 #649-53-2002 L2005 FP *012

PETERS, Walter K. 801 OSTRUM ST 18015 #407-10-1954 L1965 GP *020

PETERSEN, Charles Gerard. 5325 NORTHGATE DR, STE 209 18017 #024-07-1996 L2001 PCC SME *020 †20

PETRASEK, E Brian. 4379 EASTON AVE, STE 101 18020 #033-06-1993 L1997 FM *020 †18

PETRUCCELLI, Nicholas D. ■ 18017 #041-13-1954 L1955 FM *071 †18

PEYECHU, Judith Tombobi. 801 OSTRUM ST, ST LUKE'S HOSPITAL 18015 #409-46-2003 L2007 FP *012

PICHAIMUTHU, Poonguzhali. 801 OSTRUM ST, ST. LUKE'S HOSPITAL 18015 #495-04-1996 L2003 IM *100 †20

PIMENTEL, Gonzalo E. 2545 SCHOENERSVILLE RD, 2ND FLOOR, KOLB CENTER 18017 #935-01-1990 L1996 IM FM *020 †20

POMPONIO, Joseph G. ■ 18017 #050-02-1953 L1954 GP *071

PORTER, Matthew Edson. 801 OSTRUM ST, ST LUKES HOSPITAL 18015 #003-01-2004 L2005 EM *012

PORTNER, Marc Eric. 801 OSTRUM ST, TRAUMA / CRITICAL CARE 18015 #041-14-2003 L2003 EM *020

POTTERJONES, Christine. 2101 EMRICK BLVD, STE 100 18020 #041-13-2000 L2003 FM *020

PRAGER, David Alan. 2851 BAGLYOS CIR, STE 201 18020 #035-47-1986 L1994 OTO *020 †45

PRONCHIK, David Jos. 801 OSTRUM ST, ST LUKE'S HOSPITAL 18015 #041-13-1989 L1991 EM *020 †16

PUNDIAK, Terry James. 2545 SCHOENERSVILLE RD 18017 #041-09-1974 L1975 IM IMG *020 †20

QUILO, Felicidad F. 2545 SCHOENERSVILLE RD 18017 #748-01-1964 L1975 IM *020

QUINTANA, Benjamin Jos. 2663 SCHOENERSVILLE RD 18017 #005-14-1989 L1992 END IM *020 †20 ‡

QUIROS, Roderick Michael. 801 OSTRUM ST, ST. LUKE'S HOSPITAL & HEAL 18015 #048-14-1998 L2005 GS *100 †85

RAMOS, Jose Leon. 2223 LINDEN ST 18017 #042-01-1978 L1981 PD END *020 †55

RAPHAEL, Paul Stephen. 4436 LENOX DR 18017 #561-01-1969 L1972 PM OS *020 †60

RATANAWONGSA, Boosara. 2545 SCHOENERSVILLE RD, 3RD FL 18017 #035-01-1993 L2007 CHN PD *020 †55,75

REGAN, James Rodman. 801 OSTRUM ST 18015 #041-02-1956 L1957 IM *071 †20

REILLY, William Terence. 5325 NORTHGATE DR, STE 101 18017 #035-03-1987 L1996 CRS *020 †85,10

REITER, Christina M. ■ 18020 #033-06-2003 L2007 AN *020

REITER, Mark Howard. ■ 18020 #033-06-2003 L2007 EM *020 †16

RESTO, Migdalia. 801 OSTRUM ST 18015 #041-09-1993 L1995 NPM *020 †55

REYES, Lea Machado. 801 OSTRUM ST, ST LUKE'S HOSPITAL 18015 #748-31-2005 L2007 IM *012

RIAZ, Mohammad. 801 OSTRUM ST, ST LUKES HOSP 18015 #704-15-1982 L1993 PD NPM *020 †55

RILEY, Lee B. 801 OSTRUM ST, ST LUKES HOSPITAL 18015 #048-14-1986 L1992 GS *030 †85

RILEY, Valerie J. 801 OSTRUM ST 18015 #048-14-1987 L1992 OBG *020 †30

RISCH, Victor Rene. 2545 SCHOENERSVILLE RD, FL 1 18017 #041-09-1980 L1981 RO ON *020 †20,80

RIVERA, Jose Luis. ■ 18017 #024-01-1984 L1988 AN *020 †05

ROBSON, Peter Andrew. 39 UNIVERSITY DR 18015 #041-09-1987 L1990 OBG *020 †30

RODRIGUEZ, Marisa Lopez. ■ 18017 #041-15-2002 L2002 EM *020

ROGERS, Jennifer Rebecca. ■ 18015 #041-14-2008 L2001

ROLAND, Frederick H. ■ 18017 #041-02-1953 L1954 FM A *071 †18

ROTHMAN, Michael Ian. ■ 18017 #041-09-1984 L1988 R RNR *020 †80

RUDOLPH, Jason Willer. 3101 EMRICK BLVD, STE 112 18020 #016-42-1993 L1999 ORS OFA *020 †40

RUTKAUSKAS, Jonathon T. 801 OSTRUM ST, DEPT OF ANESTHESIA 18015 #041-13-2003 L2007 AN *020

SALEM, Mohamed Ibrahim. 301 BROADWAY, STE A 18015 #915-04-1994 L2003 IC *020 †20

SALEN, Philip Nathan. 801 OSTRUM ST, ST LUKES HOSPITAL 18015 #028-02-1990 L1992 EM *020 †20,16

SANCHEZ, Marcos Dionisio. 801 OSTRUM ST 18015 #665-01-1999 L1999 IM *020 †20

SANDERS, Christopher Mich. ■ 18015 #041-13-2007 L2007 GS *012

SANDHU, Ranvir Singh. 801 OSTRUM ST, ST LUKE'S HOSPITAL 18015 #496-31-1999 L2007 FP *012

SAQIB, Mohammad Najumus. 2005 CITY LINE RD 18017 #704-01-1987 L1998 NEP *020 †20

SARAGOVI, Armand Aquiles. 2101 EMRICK BLVD 18020 #132-01-1964 L1969 OS DR *020 †80 ‡

SARNO, Albert Peter, Jr. 801 OSTRUM ST, STE 3 18015 #005-06-1981 L1992 OBG MFM *020 †30

SAUER, Scott Thomas. 2597 SCHOENERSVILLE RD, GEORGETOWN DEPARTMENT OF 18017 #010-02-1998 L2001 ORS *020 †40

SAUNDERS, Charles Dean. 801 OSTRUM ST, ST LUKES HOSP 18015 #041-01-1967 L1968 U *030 †95

SCARLATO, Michael. 2545 SCHOENERSVILLE RD, PATHOLOGY DEPARTMENT 18017 #041-09-1965 L1966 ATP CLP *020 †50

SCARPINO, Leo Jos. 2775 SCHOENERSVILLE RD 18017 #035-15-1974 L1983 ORS *020 †40 ‡

SCHADT, Mark Edward. 5325 NORTHGATE DR, STE 204 18017 #041-02-1985 L1986 GS *020 †85

SCHENKEL, Eric J. 3101 EMRICK BLVD, STE 211 18020 #035-46-1976 L1978 AI IM *020 †20,03 ‡

SCHLEICHER, John Raymond, Jr. 801 OSTRUM ST, DEPT OF MEDICINE 18015 #422-01-2006 L2006 EM *012

SCHRAN, Seth Andrew. 801 OSTRUM ST, ST LUKE'S HOSPITAL 18015 #041-14-2006 L2006 PM *012

SCHWARTZ, Daniel Perez. ■ 18020 #041-02-2008 *012

SCHWARTZ, Luz Perez. 2775 SCHOENERSVILLE RD 18017 #035-46-1989 L1992 APM *020 †05

SCHWARTZ, Nathan. 2310 HIGHLAND AVE, CHS AMBULATORY SURGERY CEN 18020 #231-01-1972 L1990 PME PD *020 †55,05

SCLAFANI, Mia Jane. ■ 18017 #041-77-2007, ▲ L2007 *012

SEBASTIAN, Renato Bandoy. 396 TIMOTHY DR 18017 #748-01-1980 L1986 FM *020 †55

SEFCIK, Susan. ■ 18015 #035-03-1984 L1992 IM *020 †20

SEHWANI, Sunaina Guli. 801 OSTRUM ST, ST LUKES HOSP 18015 #748-01-2001 L2005 OBG *012

SELIG, Michael Bruce. 2545 SCHOENERSVILLE RD 18017 #308-07-1980 L1984 CD IM *020

SEXTON, Joseph Danl. 801 OSTRUM ST, ST LUKES HOSPITAL 18015 #010-01-1992 L1995 EM *020 †16

SHADLE, Chester Allen. 5325 NORTHGATE DR, STE100 18017 #041-01-1975 L1976 DR *020 †80

SHAIKH, Samir Rafiq. 39 UNIVERSITY DR, BOX G328 18015 #041-15-2006 L2006 IM *012

SHEETS, James Albert. 1023 STONE STACK DR 18015 #036-05-1961 L1965 CRS *071 †10

SHIELDS, David A. 5325 NORTHGATE DR, STE 205 18017 #041-09-1998 L2000 IM *020 †20

SHIELDS, Ralph Lyle. 5325 NORTHGATE DR, STE 205 18017 #036-07-1964 L1965 IM CD *071

SHUSTIK, Ofer Josef. 2101 EMRICK BLVD 18020 #550-02-1989 L1996 FM *020 †18

SILODIA, Alok. 801 OSTRUM ST, ST LUKE'S HOSPITAL 18015 #495-49-2001 L2007 IM *012

SILVER, David Foster. 801 OSTRUM ST 18015 #041-02-1992 L1999 GO GYN *020 †30

SINGH, Vasu. 2830 EASTON AVE, PRACTICE RESI 18017 #496-31-1997 L2003 FM *100 †18

SINHA, Vinaya K. ■ 18017 #495-75-1972 L1981 GS *075

SISSON, Ralph Steven. 801 OSTRUM ST, DEPT OF ANESTHESIA 18015 #041-01-1985 L1987 AN *020 †05

SLEDZ, Ann Marie. 5325 NORTHGATE DR, STE 100 18017 #041-07-1978 L1980 DR *020 †80

SNYDER, Chas Fisher, Jr. ■ 18017 #041-01-1946 L1947 ORS *071 †40

SOLGA, Steven Francis. 5325 NORTHGATE DR, STE 101 18017 #036-07-1997 L2007 GE *020 †20

SOM, David Baninn. ■ 18017 #007-02-2003 L2007 EM *012

STACKHOUSE, Duane Edwin. 801 OSTRUM ST 18015 #041-13-1961 L1962 **GP** *071

STAUFFER, Stanley S. ■ 18015 #041-02-1953 L1954 **AN** *071 †05

STEINBERG, David Marc. 801 OSTRUM ST 18015 #041-02-1994 L2001 **PCP PTH** *020 †50

STEINBOOK, Melvin. 2597 SCHOENERSVILLE RD 18017 #035-09-1974 L1980 **U GS** *020 †95

STEINER-FRIEL, Rochelle. 2597 SCHOENERSVILLE RD, COLLEGE HEIGHTS OB/GYN 18017 #041-09-1998 L2000 **OBG** *020 †30

STEWART, Lesley S. 2545 SCHOENERSVILLE RD, 3RD FL 18017 #048-12-1998 L2005 **PHO** *020 †55

STOLL, Scott Ronald. 2300 HIGHLAND AVE 18020 #007-02-1998 L2002 **PM PRS** *020 †60

STRAVINO, Vincent Darius. 2545 SCHOENERSVILLE RD 18017 #041-09-1960 L1963 **PM** *071 †60

STREUBERT, George Edward. 5328 NORTHGATE DR 18017 #010-01-1964 L1965 **R** *062 †80

STROMSKI, Christopher J. 801 OSTRUM ST, EMERGENCY MEDICINE 18015 #050-02-1997 L2000 **EM** *020 †16

STRUNK, William Milton. ■ 18015 #041-13-1946 L1947 **R NM** *071 †80

SUAREZ, Bernard. ■ 18020 #305-01-1998 **IM EM** *062

SUBZPOSH, Faiz Ali. ■ 18015 #041-15-2007 L2007 **IM** *012

SUNDAY, James Michael. 2597 SCHOENERSVILLE RD, STE 101 18017 #041-09-1994 L1999 **ORS** *020 †40

TACHOVSKY, Thomas Joseph. 2545 SCHOENERSVILLE RD 18017 #041-01-1962 L1963 **GS** *030 †85

TAMASKAR, Aparna Uday. 801 OSTRUM ST, ST LUKE'S HOSPITAL 18015 #495-49-1983 L2005 **FP** *012

TEJADA, Luis A. 3445 HIGH POINT BLVD, STE 300 18017 #264-18-1986 L1998 **CD IC** *020 †20

THIRUMURTI, Venugopal. 301 BROADWAY, STE A 18015 #495-94-1989 L2000 **CD** *020 †18

THOMPSON, Chas Frederick. 801 OSTRUM ST 18015 #041-09-1964 L1965 **FM** *071 †18

THORKILDSEN, Bruce Geo. 2597 SCHOENERSVILLE RD, STE 308 18017 #308-03-1980 L1995 **EM IM** *020 †20

TOLAYMAT, Naser. 2545 SCHOENERSVILLE RD, 3RD FL 18017 #875-01-1983 L2005 **PG PD** *020 †55

TORPIE, Richard J. 801 OSTRUM ST 18015 #041-09-1966 L1967 **RO** *020 †80

TUAZON, Hazel Alvaran. 801 OSTRUM ST, DEPT OF MEDICINE 18015 #748-31-2004 L2006 **OBG** *012

TURNER, Keith Scott. 5325 NORTHGATE DR, STE 101 18017 #035-15-1972 L1977 **GE IM** *020 †20

TWADDLE, Hugo Nicholl. 2649 SCHOENERSVILLE RD, STE 201 18017 #396-08-1980 L1985 **IM** *020 †20

UNGER, Andrew. 801 OSTRUM ST 18015 #005-14-1980 L1986 **NPM PD** *020 †55

UPPALAPATI, Sesha Spandan. 801 OSTRUM ST 18015 #495-21-2002 L2004 **IM** *020 †20

URBANO, Anthony Michael. 2649 SCHOENERSVILLE RD, STE 301 18017 #008-01-1981 L1990 **CD CCM** *020 †20

VALE, Steven. 216 NAZARETH PIKE, ACUITY LASER EYE & VISION 18020 #041-07-1988 L1990 **OPH** *020 †20,35 ‡

VANDER, James Franklin. 2300 HIGHLAND AVE, STE 201 18020 #025-01-1984 L1988 **OPH** *020 †35

VARLOTTA, Laurie. 801 OSTRUM ST 18015 #035-08-1985 L1989 **PUD PD** *020 †55

VEERARAGHAVAN, Nandihini. 2830 EASTON AVE, PRACTICE RESI 18017 #496-07-1993 L2003 **FSM** *012

VEGUNTA, Rajakumari. 118 SAUCON VIEW DR 18015 #495-11-1966 L1978 **IM** *020 †55,20

VENKATESH, Kota Raghupath. 801 OSTRUM ST, ST LUKE'S HOSP 18015 #496-33-1996 L2003 **GS** *012

VILLALUZ, Lucila Quinto. ■ 18020 #748-20-1984 L1996 **CHP** *020 †75

VINOD, Chacko. ■ 18017 #495-80-2001 L2005 **IM** *012

VIPPERLA, Kishore. 801 OSTRUM ST, ST. LUKES HOSPITAL 18015 #495-21-2002 L2006 **IM** *012

VISHWAKARMA, Moti Lal. 801 OSTRUM ST, ST LUKE'S HOSPITAL 18015 #672-04-2004 L2007 **FP** *012

VLAD, Oana. 801 OSTRUM ST, ST LUKES HOSP 18015 #781-01-2001 L2004 **IM** *012

VOSTINAK, William J. 2649 SCHOENERSVILLE RD, HEALTHWORKS 18017 #011-04-1977 L1999 **ORS** *071 †40

VYAS, Amy M. ■ 18015 #041-15-2003 L2005 **PD** *100 †55

WAGENER, Christopher F. ■ 18015 #010-02-2001 L2007 **ORS** *020

WALTERS, Clova Elaine. 3005 BRODHEAD RD 18020 #654-01-1982 L1986 **P** *020

WANINGER, Kevin Nicholas. 2830 EASTON AVE, FAMILY MEDICINE CENTER 18017 #041-13-1987 L1988 **FSM EM** *020 †16,18 ‡

WARE, Melanie Renee. 801 OSTRUM ST, ST LUKES HOSP 18015 #041-77-2006, ▲ L2006 **OBG** *012

WARHOLIC, Holli Marie. 801 OSTRUM ST 18015 #041-77-2005, ▲ L2005 **OBG** *012

WERTZ, Robert Elwood, II. 2545 SCHOENERSVILLE RD 18017 #041-14-1991 L1995 **AN** *020 †05

WHITE, Jennifer Lynn. 801 OSTRUM ST 18015 #035-08-2003 L2003 **EM** *020 †16

WILDRICK, Kenneth Harold. 4315 EASTON AVE 18020 #041-09-1969 L1970 **PUD CCM** *020 †20

XU, Shu G. 2545 SCHOENERSVILLE RD, PEDIATRIC SPECIALTY CENTER 18017 #243-75-1983 L2001 **CHN** *020

YEN, David Melicio. 3445 HIGH POINT BLVD, STE 100 18017 #041-01-1995 L1997 **OTO** *020 †45

ZALADONIS, Joseph James, Jr. 1665 VALLEY CTR PKWY, STE 120 18017 #041-07-1988 L1991 **D IM** *020,15 ‡

ZANDERS, Steven John. 801 OSTRUM ST 18015 #022-75-1999, ▲ L2000 **CCM** *020 †20

ZARRELLI, Stephen G. 2851 BAGLYOS CIR, STE 100 18020 #041-13-1991 L1994 **AN PME** *020 †05 ‡

ZEHNDER, Amy B. 801 OSTRUM ST, DEPT OF OB/GYN 18015 #654-01-2005 L2005 **OBG** *012

ZHENG, Tim Ming. 2545 SCHOENERSVILLE RD, PATHOLOGY DEPARTMENT 18017 #243-39-1983 L2001 **PTH** *020 †50

BIGLERVILLE — ADAMS

OLSON, Nora. ■ 17307 #023-01-2002 L2002 **FM** *100 †18

WALTHER, Bruce Edgar. 149 W HANOVER ST 17307 #041-07-1990 L1992 **FM** *020 †18

BIRCHRUNVILLE — CHESTER

COOK, Donald Hunter. ■ 19421 #041-09-1965 L1966 **PTH BBK** *071 †50

BIRDSBORO — BERKS

CHRISTENSEN, David Warren. 100 S SPRUCE ST 19508 #041-13-1967 **FM FPG** *020 †18

DENGLER, Robert E, Jr. ■ 19508 #041-13-1953 L1954 **EM** *072

MURR, Phyllis A G. 500 GREEN HILLS RD 19508 #041-07-1975 L1976 **FM FPG** *020 †18

NAPOLITANO, Michael A, Jr. 321 FURNACE RD, STE 100 19508 #033-05-1982 L1989 **IM PD** *020 †20,55

ROEDER, John Henry. ■ 19508 #041-13-1946 L1947 **AN** *071

BLAIRSVILLE — INDIANA

BESSER, Lisa Lynne. 56 CLUB LN 15717 #055-02-1991 L1995 **PD** *020 †18

BURNS, Mary Jo. 56 CLUB LN 15717 #038-43-1985 L1986 **PD** *075 †55

DAVOLI, Robert Louis. 135 E MARKET ST STE 108 15717 #041-02-1984 L1985 **FM** *020 †18

FOX, Paul Clyde. 56 CLUB LN 15717 #016-01-1979 L1991 **FM PD** *020 †18

GESSNER, Thomas Patrick. 56 CLUB LN 15717 #041-12-1968 L1972 **PD** *020 †55

HEASLEY, Eric Christopher. 155 E MARKET ST 15717 #038-43-1996 L1998 **IM** *020 †20

KLAIN, Matthew Newton. 155 E MARKET ST 15717 #041-12-1987 L1989 **IM** *020 †20

LOMBARDOZZI-LANE, Susan. 56 CLUB LN 15717 #041-14-1988 L1993 **PN** *020 †55

MAROON, Thomas John, Jr. 56 CLUB LN 15717 #036-07-1985 L1986 **PD** *020 †55

SANTARLAS, John Thos. 56 CLUB LN 15717 #041-02-1975 L1976 **FM** *040 †18

SCHERER, Bernard C. 135 E MARKET ST STE 108, BLAIRSVILLE OFFICE 15717 #041-02-1980 L1981 **FM** *020 †18

SHUHART, Dwayne Thos. 56 CLUB LN 15717 #023-01-1990 L1992 **PD IM** *020 †20,55

WHORRAL, Greg Scott. 56 CLUB LN 15717 #041-13-1991 L1995 **OBG** *020 †30

ZIMMERMAN, Robert Paul. 56 CLUB LN 15717 #041-02-1993 L1995 **FM** *020 †18

BLAKELY — LACKAWANNA

GALARDI, Tracey Boros. 200 MAIN ST, PAVUK PROFESSIONAL BUILDIN 18447 #041-09-1992 L1995 **IM** *020

LEIMAN, Paul M. 110 TERRACE DR, STE102 18447 #024-05-1974 L1978 **DR** *071 †80

VENTURA, Samuel R. 119 MAIN ST, VENTURA CONSULTANTS MD PC 18447 #748-08-1967 L1975 **OBG** *020

BLAKESLEE — MONROE

DIAZ, Renato Trinidad. RR 940 BOX 219, POCONO MED CTR 18610 #748-10-1966 L1970 **FM EM** *020

FINO, Gregory. PO BOX 40 18610 #422-01-1982 L1983 **FM** *020 †18

BLANCHARD — CENTRE

LANGE, Robert Alan. ■ 16826 #016-01-1977 L1978 **OS GP** *030 †20

BLANDON — BERKS

OUANO, Joselito Abayan. 11 INGOT DR 19510 #748-11-1991 L1995 **FM** *020 †18

WEICKER, Michelina Eva. ■ 19510 #561-17-1988 *100

XU, Jin. 11 INGOT DR 19510 #243-16-1983 L2000 **FM** *020 †18

BLAWNOX — ALLEGHENY

GIALAMAS, Antonio. ■ 15238 #051-04-1954 L1961 **PTH FM** *020

KUMARI, Sarita. ■ 15238 #495-15-1989 L2002 **CCM** *020 †20

LAMP, Clyde B, Jr. ■ 15238 #041-12-1945 L1946 **OTO NO** *071 †45

MARTIN, Thos Patrick, Jr. ■ 15238 #024-01-1987 L1987 **EM** *020 †20,16

MNUSKIN, Anna. ■ 15238 #913-06-1984 L1999 **PTH** *020 †50

MNUSKIN, Dmitriy. 113 SHANNON DR 15238 #913-99-1984 L1996 **AN** *020 †05

PANCHAL, Pravin Dahyabhai. 200 HIGHLAND RD 15238 #495-22-1965 L1974 **PM** *020 †60

SZYMKIEWICZ, Steven John. 121 FREEPORT RD 15238 #041-09-1982 L1983 **GP** *020

VARINDANI, Mahesh K. 307 FREEPORT RD 15238 #495-17-1979 L1985 **GE IM** *020 †20

BLOOMFIELD — ALLEGHENY

TULLOCH-REID, Desiree Mar. 4800 FRIENDSHIP AVE, WESTERN PENNSYLVANIA HOSP 15224 #566-01-1999 L2002 **IM** *100 †20

BLOOMSBURG — COLUMBIA

ABBOTT, Robert Thomas. ■ 17815 #051-07-2006 L2007 **DR** *012

ABUBAKER, Firas. ■ 17815 #875-02-1999 L2006 **IM** *020 †20

ACLE, Alejandro E. 549 FAIR ST, THE BLOOMSBURG HOSP ED 17815 #308-07-1982 L1986 **EM IM** *020 ‡

AVENIA, Ronald J. 410 GLENN AVE STE 302 17815 #010-02-1975 L1976 **OPH** *020 †35

BAYLOR, Kathy Eileen. 410 GLENN AVE, STE 2 17815 #041-02-1991 L1993 **FM** *020 †18

BECKER, Bruce. 301 OAK LN, BRUCE BECKER, M.D. 17815 #036-05-1977 L1981 **FM EM** *020 ‡

BOHAN, James Daniel. ■ 17815 #011-04-2005 L2005 **EM** *012

BRENNAN, John Peter. 549 FAIR ST 17815 #041-02-1991 L1996 **PTH** *020 †50

BURMAN, Dmitriy K. 410 GLENN AVE STE 2 17815 #913-16-1993 L2000 **PD** *020 †55 ‡

BYBEL, Gretchen. 2407 REICHART RD 17815 #041-09-1988 L1990 **FM** *020 †18

CAMPBELL, Ernest Wayne. 2407 REICHART RD 17815 #041-13-1963 L1964 **GP** *020

CHOPRA, Anuj Kumar. 2701 COLUMBIA BLVD, STE C 17815 #041-14-1995 L2001 **U** *020 †95

CHOPRA, Raj Paul. 326 MARKET ST 17815 #495-01-1957 L1967 **U** *071 †95

CHRISTIAN, Dean Arthur. 2407 REICHART RD 17815 #041-02-1983 L1984 **FM** *020 †18

CORSON, Thomas Clark. 549 FAIR ST 17815 #041-02-1957 L1958 **GYN** *072 †30

COYLE, Alice Regina. 6850 LOWS RD 17815 #041-09-1985 L1989 **ORS** *020 †40

■ = Address Information Privacy Protected

DE PAOLI, Rosemary T. 602 HONEYSUCKLE LN 17815 #041-14-1982 L1983 **D IM** *075 †20,15

DULA, David John. 1265 CHESTNUT ST 17815 #041-09-1976 L1977 **EM** *020 †16

ERWIN, Patrick Jerome. 410 GLENN AVE STE 203 17815 #033-05-1988 L1992 **GS** *020 †85

FERRARACCIO, Wm David. 603 FOWLERSVILLE RD 17815 #047-05-1973 L1997 **ORS** *020 †40

GEARY, Daniel Carroll. ■ 17815 #051-07-2006 L2006 **EM** *012

GERGITS, Franklyn R. 6850 LOWS RD, # 320 17815 #041-77-1992, ▲ L1993 **OTO A** *020

GO, Alfonso Hong Lim. 549 FAIR ST, BLOOMSBURG HOSP 17815 #748-11-1974 L1981 **AN** *020 †05

HARASYM, E Lawrence. 549 FAIR ST 17815 #041-13-1966 **GS GE** *020 †85

HASKELL, Gordon Alexander. 549 FAIR ST 17815 #041-09-1985 L1986 **FM EM** *020 †18

HERMANN, Mary Elizabeth. 549 FAIR ST, BLOOMSBURG HOSPITAL 17815 #048-15-1981 L1984 **EM GP** *020 †20,55

HIKES, Ryan Matthew. 410 GLENN AVE, STE 303 17815 #041-13-2001 L2001 **FM** *020

HUSKEY, Richard Edward. 410 GLENN AVE, BLOOMSBURG HOSPITAL 17815 #308-07-1981 L1991 **IMG IM** *020

HUTSON, Jody W. 410 GLENN AVE, STE Z 17815 #041-77-1988, ▲ L1989 **FM** *020 †18 ‡

JACOBSON, John. ■ 17815 #035-15-1985 L2005 **OPH** *071 †35

KARWAT, Mukesh Parmanand. 549 FAIR ST, BLOOMSBURGH HOSP 17815 #495-01-1976 L1986 **DR** *020

KOWALSKI-MC GRAW, Michele. 410 GLENN AVE, STE 2 17815 #041-13-1991 L1999 **FM** *020 †18

LEVINE, Myron A. 410 GLENN AVE, STE 2 17815 #041-12-1966 L1967 **OBG REN** *071 †30

LIU, Haiyan. ■ 17815 #243-75-1983 L2001 **PCP** *100 †50

MACIEJCZYK, John Francis. 16 DUKE OF GLOUCESTER 17815 #041-13-1999 L2004 **EM** *100

MANSURI, Faizmohamed Moha. 549 FAIR ST 17815 #654-01-1998 L2002 **IM** *020 †20

MARANCENBAUM, Daniel Arie. ■ 17815 #649-14-2002 L2002 **OBG** *012

MARTIN, Edmund Francis. 549 FAIR ST 17815 #422-01-1998 L2005 **IM** *020 †20

MELDRUM, Robert Wm. 410 GLENN AVE, STE 304 17815 #036-05-1967 L1971 **FM** *020 †18 ‡

MELOY, Robert Alain. 410 GLENN AVE, STE 304 17815 #041-12-2000 L2001 **IM** *020

MESCHTER, Steven Chase. 549 FAIR ST 17815 #041-14-1981 L1986 **PTH** *020 †50

MONTGOMERY, Ben Edward. 410 GLENN AVE STE 2, THE BLOOMSBURG HOSPITAL 17815 #041-02-2000 L2002 **OBG** *020

MUCCIOLO, Lisa. 6850 LOWS RD 17815 #010-02-1996 L1999 **RHU** *020 †20

NARMI, Jeffrey John. 549 FAIR ST 17815 #654-01-1984 L1986 **IM** *020 †20

NIKPARVARFARD, Mahdi. ■ 17815 #517-01-1994 L2002 **IM** *100 †20

OCKENHOUSE-DONATO, Ingrid. 2407 REICHART RD 17815 #041-07-1983 L1985 **IM** *020 †20

O'NEIL, Catherine. 6850 LOWS RD 17815 #041-02-1996 L1998 **FM** *020 †18

PANIKKAR, Ananda Krishna. 549 FAIR ST 17815 #220-02-1974 L1979 **AN** *020

PIERCE, Richard Norwin. 549 FAIR ST 17815 #036-01-1973 L1986 **PTH** *020 †50 ‡

RAKAUSKAS, William. 549 FAIR ST 17815 #041-07-1985 L1986 **P** *020 †75

RINGAWA, Peter Edwin. ■ 17815 #041-02-1960 L1961 **GP** *062

ROSE, Harry Joseph. 425 E 1ST ST, STE 201 17815 #041-09-1997 L1999 **IM** *020 †20 ‡

SEIDENBERG, Jennifer K. 3151 COLUMBIA BLVD, STE 100 17815 #041-14-1996 L2006 **PD** *020 †55

SEIDENBERG, Peter Harris. 3151 COLUMBIA BLVD, KING MEDICAL CARE INC 17815 #041-14-1996 L2006 **FM** *020 †18

SENGUPTA, Tapash Kumar. 2407 REICHART RD 17815 #160-08-1982 L1997 **PD** *020 †55

SMITH, Harold Alvin, Jr. 127 NORTH ST 17815 #036-07-1970 L1976 **EM** *020 †16

SRIVASTAVA, Pratima. 425 E 1ST ST, STE 101 17815 #496-07-1985 L2000 **OBG** *020 †30

SURACI, Aldo John. 549 FAIR ST 17815 #041-13-1981 L1982 **U** *020 †95

UMERAH, Nnaemeka Maduka. 425 E 1ST ST, STE 101 17815 #036-01-1994 L1997 **OBG** *020 †30

WEADER, Joseph Alvin. 549 FAIR ST 17815 #041-13-1966 L1970 **PD** *020 †55

WIDGER, John Edward. 439 E 1ST ST 17815 #041-02-1980 L1981 **GS** *020 †85

WILLIAMS, Mark Stanley. 6850 LOWS RD 17815 #041-77-1992, ▲ L1993 **ORS OSS** *020

YOST, Charles S. PO BOX 458 17815 #041-09-1941 L1946 **GS GP** *072

ZUMBO, Ann Marie. 410 GLENN AVE, STE 301 17815 #308-11-1984 L1988 **IM** *020 †20

BLOSSBURG – TIOGA

STEPCZAK, Wawrzyniec. 6 RIVERSIDE PLZ 16912 #759-04-1988 L1996 **IM** *020 †20

BLUE BELL – MONTGOMERY

ADESIDA, Oluremi C. 154 INVERNESS DR 19422 #690-01-1980 L1991 **NPM** *012 †55

ALEXANDER, Joe, Jr. 10 SENTRY PKWY # BL3-1, MERCK RESEARCH LABORATORIE 19422 #023-07-1987 L1999 **IM** *020

BAGARAZZI, Mark Leonard. 5 SENTRY PKWY W 19422 #033-05-1990 L1992 **PD** *020 †55

BAILEY, Robert S, Jr. 790 PENLLYN BLUE BELL PIKE, STE 102 19422 #041-09-1980 L1981 **OPH** *020 †35

BALDECK, Andrea Mae. ■ 19422 #041-01-1979 L1981 **AN IM** *071 †20,05

BARAKAM, Sreekar. ■ 19422 #495-70-1982 **AN** *100

BARR, Eliav. 785 JOLLY RD UNC-141, MERCK & CO INC 19422 #041-02-1986 L1995 **CD IM** *020 †20

BAUR, Andrew M. ■ 19422 #041-13-1989 L1989 **EM FM** *020

BEERS, Mark Howard. 785 JOLLY RD UND-100 19422 #050-02-1982 L1992 **IM IMG** *020 †20

BEGRAUD, Came-Ann. ■ 19422 #041-77-2007, ▲ **EM IM** *012

BERGER, James Michael. ■ 19422 #035-20-1985 L1996 **IM LM** *074 †20

BISCHOF, Ralph Oscar. 980 JOLLY RD U12S 19422 #033-06-1990 L1993 **FM** *020 †18

BLACKSTONE, Sherri Elise. ■ 19422 #041-13-1997 L1999 **END** *100 †20

BLUMENTHAL, Andrew R. 658 SKIPPACK PIKE STE 13 19422 #041-09-1980 L1981 **FM** *020 †18

BOTELHO, Stella Yates. PO BOX 1108 19422 #041-07-1949 L1955 **OS** *071

BRENNER, Barry Steven. 1777 SENTRY PKWY W, DUBLIN HALL 4TH FL 19422 #041-02-1976 L1979 **FM** *062 †18

BUTTZ, Charles Leland. 1777 SENTRY PKWY W, DUBLIN HALL 4TH FL 19422 #041-09-1986 L1988 **FM** *030 †18

CAINE, Ruth Harris. 1425 UNION MEETING RD, MAILSTOP U21N 19422 #041-09-1987 L1988 **IM OM** *030 †20

CAMPBELL, Kevin Martin. ■ 19422 #041-02-1983 L1984 **AN** *020 †05 ‡

CAPRIOTTI, Joseph Anthony. ■ 19422 #041-02-2003 L2004 **OPH** *100

CASE, Randall B. ■ 19422 #033-05-1977 L1978 **EM AM** *030 †16

CHADAGA, Pandeswaram C S. ■ 19422 #495-50-1967 L1973 **R** *020 †80

CHAN, Paul Kintanar. ■ 19422 #748-01-1954 L1967 **CD IM** *020

CLEMENT, Gordon S. 113 EVERGREEN CT 19422 #041-09-1965 L1966 **GS** *020 †85

COATES, James Gregory. 980 JOLLY RD, AETNA MAILSTOP U12S 19422 #028-34-1979 L2002 **IM** *030 †20

CONNOLLY, Joanna L Miller. 1777 SENTRY PKWY W, 110 DUBIN HALL 19422 #041-02-1976 L1977 **OBG** *020 †30

CONROY, James Francis. ■ 19422 #041-77-1965, ▲ L1970 **ON HEM** *071

CRAMER, Sondra. ■ 19422 #041-09-1989 L1991 **GE** *020 †20

CUTLER, Charles Michael. 980 JOLLY RD, AETNA BUILDING 1 19422 #035-19-1973 L1975 **IM GPM** *030 †20

DATTA, Satya Pall. ■ 19422 #704-01-1948 L1977 **P** *071

DOUGHERTY, Joseph F. 980 JOLLY RD BOX 1109 19422 #041-13-1980 L1983 **FM** *062 †18

ENGEL, Walter Celdo. ■ 19422 #041-09-1944 L1945 **GP** *071

FINKE, James Steven. 1777 SENTRY PKWY W, DUBLIN HALL 4TH FL 19422 #041-09-1986 L1987 **PD** *020 †55

FORMAN, Stanley Orkin. 470 SENTRY PKWY E, STE 200 19422 #041-09-1979 L1980 **AI** *020 †20,03

FOX, Jonathan C. 518 TOWNSHIP LINE RD, MERCK & CO., INC 19422 #016-02-1987 L1993 **CD** *050 †20

FRANK, Karen Ann. ■ 19422 #023-07-1989 L1992 **IM** *020 †20

FRIED, Scott Martin. 1515 DEKALB PIKE STE 100 19422 #035-75-1981, ▲ L1982 **HS PME** *020

FRIEDMAN, Deborah Anne. ■ 19422 #041-07-1984 L1985 **IM** *074

FRIEDMAN, Tara. 1740 WALTON RD, STE 100 19422 #035-01-1997 L2000 **IM PLM** *030 †20

GERETY, Robert John. ■ 19422 #010-01-1970 L1975 **ID PD** *020

GIANNASIO, Chas Vincent. 900 LENMAR DR STE B 19422 #041-09-1974 L1975 **P PYA** *020 †75

GOLDSTEIN, Marvin. ■ 19422 #041-02-1950 L1951 **IM CD** *071 †20

GOOD, Kolin Diane. 1717 SWEDE RD, STE 213 19422 #045-01-1994 L1997 **P** *020 †75

GORDON, Jeffrey Phillip. ■ 19422 #041-01-2008 *012

GORDON, Leonard Frank. 1700 GOVERNORS WAY 19422 #041-01-1977 L1978 **DR** *020 †80

GOVEIA, Michelle B. 785 JOLLY RD, RESEARCH LABORATORIES 19422 #010-01-1996 L2003 **PD** *020 †55

HOFFMAN, James Patrick. ■ 19422 #010-02-1965 L1971 **PD** *071

HORVATH, Ronald Jos. 7 BROMLEY DR 19422 #041-02-1964 L1965 **ORS** *020 †40

HWANG, Amy Hyunkyung. ■ 19422 #041-15-2008 *012

IGE, Abayomi O. ■ 19422 #690-08-1986 L1996 **CHP** *020 †75

JACOB, Shushan Binu. ■ 19422 #495-59-1997 L2001 **GS** *020

KAHN, Hyman Richard. 8 TALLY HO LN, WHITPAIN FARM 19422 #041-02-1956 L1957 **IM CD** *071 †20

KIM, Jason Yun. ■ 19422 #041-13-1998 L2000 **PDI** *020 †55

KOO, Phillip Jahyung. ■ 19422 #041-15-2005 L2005 **DR** *012

KRAVIS, Gary Ithamar. ■ 19422 #041-01-1961 L1962 **FM OM** *071 †18

LAMBERT, Marialisa. 1777 SENTRY PKWY W, STE 110 19422 #035-08-1990 L1996 **OBG** *020 †30

LEIBOLD, Debra Marie. ■ 19422 #041-01-1985 L1986 **IM PHM** *062 †20

LEIBOWITZ, Arthur Neil. 450 SENTRY PKWY E STE 102 19422 #041-13-1972 L1973 **PD MDM** *030 †55 ‡

LINDSAY, Carlotta M. 1777 SENTRY PKWY W, STE 110 19422 #041-02-1996 L1998 **FM** *020 †18

LINGENFELTER, Natalie E. ■ 19422 #041-77-2007, ▲ L2007 **FP** *012

LOPEZ, Gloria E. ■ 19422 #649-12-1993 **PTH** *020 †50

MAMI, Ahmed Gibril. ■ 19422 #613-02-1991 L2001 **GS** *100 †85

MC DANIEL, Annette S. 1777 SENTRY PKWY W, STE 110 19422 #038-06-1983 L1987 **OBG** *020 †30

MC FADDEN, Dominic Joseph. 653 SKIPPACK PIKE, BLUE BELL FAMILY PRACTICE 19422 #041-07-1997 L2000 **FM** *020 †18

MEZZANOTTE, John James. ■ 19422 #041-09-1948 L1949 **IM** *071

MILLER, Frank L. ■ 19422 #041-09-1941 L1942 **GP** *071

MIN, Insung. ■ 19422 #041-02-2007 *012

MINN, Fredrick Louis. ■ 19422 #011-02-1973 L1976 **PA GP** *071 ‡

MIRABILE, Robert Jos. 1050 DEKALB PIKE 19422 #041-02-1981 L1982 **PS OS** *020 †85,65

MONTAG, Mark Charles. 2004 MEADOW DR, NORTHEAST RETINA PC 19422 #041-12-1995 L2003 **OPH** *020 †35

MURRAY, John Patrick. ■ 19422 #041-02-1957 L1958 **FM** *071 †18

NEUMANN, Paul Marshall. 1777 SENTRY PKWY W, STE 110 19422 #041-01-1984 L1986 **OBG** *020 †30

NGUYEN, Bachyen Thi. 10 SENTRY PKWY, MERCK RESEARCH LAB BL 3-4 19422 #026-04-1985 L1995 **IM ID** *020 †20

NO, Benjamin. ■ 19422 #033-05-2005 **EM** *012

PARK, Milton Winfred. ■ 19422 #583-10-1962 L1979 **AN GP** *071

PATEL, Pragna Piush. 120 BROCHANT CIR, PRAGNA P PATEL MD PC 19422 #495-22-1982 L1993 **P** *020

PEET, David Carlisle, Jr. 721 SKIPPACK PIKE, STE 3 19422 #041-13-1974 L1975 **FM** *020 †18

PIEN, Gary Chaili. ■ 19422 #043-01-2003 L2006 **AI** *012 †55

ROSENFELD, Howard. 1635 SKIPPACK PIKE 19422 #041-13-1960 L1961 **FM IM** *020 †18

RUBIN, Paulette. ■ 19422 #041-07-1967 L1969 **P PYA** *071

RUTBERG, Franklin Leon. ■ 19422 #041-01-1938 L1939 **OTO** *071 †45

RUTBERG, Michael. 4 POMMEL LN 19422 #041-01-1966 L1967 **GS** *020 †85

SABLE, Carole Anne. 10 SENTRY PKWY # BL34, MERCK & CO 19422 #041-02-1987 L1996 **ID** *050 †20

SABLOSKY, Lester. ■ 19422 #041-09-1950 L1951 **FM CD** *071 †18

SAHOTA, Kulpreet Kaur. ■ 19422 #033-05-2005 L2006 **PM** *012

SATTLER, Carlos A. 785 JOLLY RD, UN-C141 19422 #737-06-1992 L1993 **PDI** *020 †55

SAX, Frederic Lee. 10 SENTRY PKWY, APT BL 3-6 19422 #035-01-1981 L1992 **CD IM** *050 †20

SCHALLER, James Anthony. ■ 19422 #041-01-1958 L1959 **GYN** *071 †30

SCHWARCZ, Harriet B. 725 SKIPPACK PIKE, 2ND FL 19422 #041-02-1979 L1982 **FM** *020 †18

SIEGEL, William. ■ 19422 #041-09-1958 L1959 **HEM** *072 †20,28

SIMPSON, Joseph W. ■ 19422 #041-02-1953 L1954 **OM GP** *071

SINGER, Joseph David. 721 SKIPPACK PIKE, STE 3 19422 #041-13-1983 L1987 **OBG** *020 †30

SINGHAL, Monika Desai. 1412 HEMPSTEAD CT 19422 #041-13-1996 L1997 **P** *020 †75

STROTHER, Byron Keith. 602 COUNTRY CLUB DR 19422 #038-06-2000 L2005 **P** *020

TANNEBAUM, Philip Jerome. ■ 19422 #041-13-1958 L1959 **IM** *071 †20

TEPPLER, Hedy. 10 SENTRY PKWY, MERCK & CO INC 19422 #024-01-1984 L1992 **ID IG** *071 †20

THORP, Tilman Ramsey. 790 PENLLYN BLUE BELL PIKE, STE 102 19422 #041-01-1962 L1963 **OPH** *020 †35

TIERNAN, Julia C. 653 SKIPPACK PIKE, BLUE BELL FAMILY PRACTICE 19422 #041-02-1999 L2001 **FM** *020 †18 ‡

■ = Address Information Privacy Protected

TORRES, Carlos Javier. ■ 19422 #041-13-2001 L2001 **IM** *100 †20
TRACHTENBERG, Jacob. 6198 BUTLER PIKE, STE 145 19422 #041-02-1971 L1996 **P** *020 †75
VALLOW, Ingeborg Gerber. ■ 19422 #041-13-1959 L1960 **FM OS** *020 †18
VARADA, Babu Krishna P. 1630 CHADWYCK PL 19422 #495-50-1971 L1979 **PM** *020 †60 ‡
VICHNIN, Michelle Denise. ■ 19422 #041-02-1991 L1998 **OBG** *020 †30
WILLIAMS, Gregory. ■ 19422 #010-03-1974 L1977 **CHP** *020 †75
WINER, Robert Ira. 1717 SWEDE RD, STE 213 19422 #038-40-1978 L1979 **N P** *020 †75
YUEN, Eric Choming. ■ 19422 #016-02-1989 L2003 **N CN** *050 †75
ZAGER, Warren Howard. 518 TOWNSHIP LINE RD, PLASTIC ASSOC 19422 #011-02-1997 L2000 **OTO** *020
ZAVITSANOS, Thomas Peter. ■ 19422 #041-13-1986 L1988 **PME AN** *020 †05 ‡
ZEITZER, Randi Rush. 725 SKIPPACK PIKE, PAREC PLAZA 2ND FL 19422 #041-02-1994 L1997 **FM** *020 †18
ZIMMERMANN, Albert W, Jr. 790 PENLLYN BLUE BELL PIKE, STE 102 19422 #041-01-1962 L1963 **OPH OS** *020 †35

BLUE RIDGE SUMMIT – FRANKLIN

GALLO, Gary Leonard. 14961 BUCHANAN TRL E 17214 #047-20-1996 L1998 **FM** *020 †18
RETTIG, Stephen Jos. 14961 BUCHANAN TRL E 17214 #020-02-1973 L1976 **FM** *020 †18

BOALSBURG – CENTRE

FRIED, Suzanne Ragin. ■ 16827 #035-46-1964 L1985 **P** *020
OH, Susan Y. 290 MEADOW LARK LN 16827 #583-08-1961 L1983 **P** *071
VAKHARIA, Vijay Himatlal. 181 MEADOW LARK LN 16827 #495-01-1980 L1991 **AN** *020 †05

BOILING SPRINGS – CUMBERLAND

JUMPER, Chadler Matthew. 210 FORGE RD, STE 2 17007 #041-14-2000 L2002 **FM** *020 †18 ‡
KASE, Paul Frederick. ■ 17007 #041-13-1954 L1955 **FM GP** *071
KOVACS, Donald James. 1358 LUTZTOWN RD 17007 #038-41-1976 L1977 **FM** *020 †18
RICKS, John Edward. 1261 KUHN RD 17007 #016-06-1972 L1980 **EM IM** *020 †20,16
WOOD, Bradford John. 1358 LUTZTOWN RD, YELLOW BREECHES FAMILY PRA 17007 #050-02-1978 L1981 **FM** *020 †18

BOLIVAR – WESTMORELAND

HIRSCH, William Paul. 207 WHITETAIL DR 15923 #041-12-1961 L1962 **GP FPG** *030

BOOTHWYN – DELAWARE

DEMBERT, Mark Lawrence. ■ 19061 #041-02-1975 L1976 **P PHP** *020 †70,75
GUERRIERI, Courtney Beth. ■ 19061 #041-02-2007 L2007 **D** *012
JALALI, Manoucher. 2211 CHICHESTER AVE, STE 102 19061 #517-07-1967 L1975 **GS** *020 †85
SOKOLOVE, Victoria S. ■ 19061 #041-01-2000 L2000 **FM** *100 †18

BOSWELL – SOMERSET

THOMPSON, William O'Brien. 430 STONYCREEK ST 15531 #041-02-1987 L1988 **FM** *020 †18

BOYERTOWN – BERKS

BERLAND, Laila Krauss. ■ 19512 #041-09-1988 *071
DITIZIO, Robert P. 23 N WALNUT ST 19512 #654-01-1989 L1992 **IM** *020
FOLEY, Francis Lamar, Jr. 146 S READING AVE 19512 #041-14-1983 L1984 **FM** *020 †18
GOLD, Alan Cary. ■ 19512 #041-02-1975 L1989 **OBG** *020 †30
HUNT, Jettie Vivian. ■ 19512 #045-01-1975 L1994 **BBK PTH** *020 †50
LOTZ, Michael Jay. PO BOX 314 19512 #035-01-1972 L1998 **PTH** *030 †50
MICKLE, James Douglas, Jr. 203 5TH AND MONTGOMRY #203 19512 #041-14-1975 L1976 **FM** *020
PECHSTEIN, George Richard. ■ 19512 #041-02-1948 L1949 **R** *071 †80
PETRUSO, Kimberly A. 23 N WALNUT ST 19512 #041-77-1997, ▲ L1998 **FM** *020

BRACKENRIDGE – ALLEGHENY

BERGER, Malcolm Paul. 985 PENN STE A 15014 #041-12-1971 L1976 **N P** *020 †75
BIDULA, Leo Paul, Jr. 985 PENN ST, ARTHRITIS & RHEUMATIC 15014 #041-13-1979 L1980 **RHU IM** *020 †20
CO, Deborah Jane. 985 PENN ST, ARTHRITIS & RHEUMATIC 15014 #748-02-1984 L1990 **RHU IM** *020 †20
KILLIAN, Paul Jeffery. 985 PENN ST, ARTHRITIS & RHEUMATIC 15014 #041-12-1972 L1980 **RHU IM** *020 †20
LESLIE, M Russell, Jr. 1030 BROADVIEW BLVD 15014 #041-12-1962 L1964 **ORS HS** *072 †40
LOWTHER, Holly A. 985 PENN ST, ARTHRITIS & RHEUMATIC 15014 #041-13-2001 L2006 **RHU IM** *020 †20
MEARS, Dana Christopher. 1030 BROADVIEW BLVD 15014 #352-09-1969 L1973 **ORS** *020 †40
MILLER, Michael David. 1030 BROADVIEW BLVD 15014 #025-07-1975 L1981 **ORS** *020 †40
ULIZIO, Anthony Richard. 1030 BROADVIEW BLVD 15014 #041-01-1980 L1982 **OTO HNS** *020 †45
WATSON, Anthony Douglas. 1030 BROADVIEW BLVD 15014 #016-06-1991 L1997 **ORS OFA** *020 †40

BRADDOCK – ALLEGHENY

ABU-HAMAD, Ghassan. 450 HOLLAND AVE 15104 #605-01-1984 L2005 **GS** *020 †85
ARAYA, Cleto Uy, Jr. 400 HOLLAND AVE DEPT ANES 15104 #748-01-1957 L1967 **AN** *071

ARLUK, Judith. 400 HOLLAND AVE 15104 #065-01-1979 L1983 **D DS** *020 †15
ASHOK, Krishnamurthy. ■ 15104 #495-59-1980 L1998 **HS** *100
BERK, H Ronald. 400 HOLLAND AVE, STE 206 15104 #038-40-1977 L1979 **N CN** *020 †20,75
BRUNING, Carl O, III. 450 HOLLAND AVE, STE 203 15104 #041-12-1988 L1996 **U OS** *020 †95
CHANDRA, Seethalakshmi T. 450 HOLLAND AVE STE 107 15104 #495-99-1982 L1986 **END IM** *020 †20
CHETLIN, Stuart Howard. 450 HOLLAND AVE 15104 #041-12-1965 L1967 **GS** *020 †85
DUBNER, Howard Murray. 450 HOLLAND AVE 15104 #035-19-1987 L1993 **GE IM** *020 †20
FELDMAN, Stewart Lewis. 450 HOLLAND AVE, STE 203 15104 #050-02-1971 L1979 **U** *020 †95
GOLDEN, Scott Alan. 450 HOLLAND AVE, UPMC BRADDOCK HOSPITAL 15104 #038-06-1991 L1996 **P** *020 †75
HALENDA, Gregory. 450 HOLLAND AVE, STE 203 15104 #041-02-1984 L1985 **U OS** *020 †95
HEATH, F Richard. 400 HOLLAND AVE # A-316 15104 #035-06-1982 L1988 **EM IM** *030 †16
HUGHES, Patrick H. 450 HOLLAND AVE 15104 #041-12-1953 L1954 **GS** *072 †85
KOSIC, Neven. 450 HOLLAND AVE, STE 112 15104 #957-01-1991 L1997 **IM** *020 †20
KRIFCHER, Charles. 400 HOLLAND AVE, UPMC BRADDOCK 15104 #021-01-1961 L1971 **PTH** *020 †50
LABATE, Steffanie Jaye. 400 HOLLAND AVE, UPMC BRADDOCK-ANESTH DEPT 15104 #041-01-1984 L1985 **AN** *020 †05 ‡
LEBOVITZ, Charles Neal. 450 HOLLAND AVE, # 102 15104 #041-12-1966 L1967 **GS** *020 †85
MANNING, James Albert. 400 HOLLAND AVE, UPMC BRADDOCK MEDICAL CENT 15104 #041-12-1965 L1966 **R** *020 †80
MATSUDA, Maria Teruko. 404 BRADDOCK AVE, MON VALLEY FAMILY PHYS LTD 15104 #019-02-1991 L1993 **FM** *020 †18
MENDOZA, Antonia Aoigan. 450 HOLLAND AVE 15104 #748-01-1983 L1993 **NEP** *020 †20
MENOTIADES, John C. 400 HOLLAND AVE 15104 #418-01-1968 L1981 **IM FM** *020
PATTERNAC, Stephen Thomas. 400 HOLLAND AVE, C/O MEDICAL STAFF OFFICE 15104 #041-09-1977 L1978 **FM ADM** *020 †18
PEARD, Robert James. 400 HOLLAND AVE, DEPT RADIOLOGY 15104 #055-01-1981 L1983 **R AR** *020 †80
ROSENBLOOM, Meyer A. 450 HOLLAND AVE 15104 #041-12-1937 L1938 **GP** *071
ROSVANIS, Thomas Kostas. 450 HOLLAND AVE, STE 203 15104 #038-40-1986 L1987 **U GS** *020 †95
SHAH, Shirish Nagindas. 400 HOLLAND AVE, STE 206 15104 #495-23-1960 L1972 **GE IM** *020
SMOLAR, Benjamin Richard. 400 HOLLAND AVE, STE 206 15104 #041-12-1991 L1993 **N** *020 †75
STEINFELD, Michael L. 400 HOLLAND AVE 15104 #035-06-1975 L1980 **CD CCM** *020 †20
TUNG, Alfred Sik To. 400 HOLLAND AVE 15104 #143-02-1968 L1973 **PME AN** *020 †05
WEITZEL, William Kenneth. 400 HOLLAND AVE 15104 #041-12-1948 L1949 **AN GS** *071 †85,05
YADAGIRI, Uma. 404 BRADDOCK AVE, MONVALLEY FAMILY PHY 15104 #495-65-1994 L2000 **FM** *020 †18
YEE, Emily Louise. 450 HOLLAND AVE 15104 #041-02-1990 L1993 **PUD CCM** *020 †20

BRADFORD – MCKEAN

AKHTAR, Muhammad Javed S. 199 PLEASANT ST STE 34 16701 #704-01-1971 L1981 **OTO** *020 †45
AL HATTAB, Eyad Sufian. 116 INTERSTATE PKWY, STE 22 16701 #575-01-1999 L2007 **HO** *020
ALI, Syedshah Dastagir. 195 PLEASANT ST 16701 #016-42-1994 L2000 **IM** *020 †20 ‡
ALLY, Syed Azim I. 116 INTERSTATE PKWY, PATHOLOGY DEPT BRMC 16701 #160-02-1980 L2003 **PTH ATP** *050 †50 ‡
BAZZOUI, Widad. 110 CAMPUS DR 16701 #528-01-1953 L1973 **P N** *020
BHAYANI, Shabir A. 54 BOYLSTON ST, # 2NFL 16701 #033-05-1982 L1987 **ORS** *020 †40
BREZNIK, John Douglas. 116 INTERSTATE PKWY # 156, BRADFORD HOSPITAL 16701 #026-04-1982 L1987 **EM AM** *020
CAMAS, John Michael. ■ 16701 #041-02-1977 L1992 **GS VS** *020 †85
DEE, Cecilio Cu. 116 156 INTERSTATE PKWY 16701 #748-01-1963 L1973 **PTH** *062 †50
DEFORNO, Donald Jack, Jr. 700 SOUTH AVE 16701 #041-13-1985 L1987 **ORS** *020
DZIONARA, Marek Stefan. 116 INTERSTATE PKWY, BRADFORD REG MED CTR 16701 #759-07-1968 L1992 **EM IM** *020
FOKSTUEN, Terje Sigbjorn. 110 CAMPUS DR 16701 #869-07-1956 L1982 **P** *020
GODFREY, David Kimball. 51 BOYLSTON ST 16701 #048-13-1977 L1989 **U** *020 †95
GONZALEZ, Luis. 181 INTERSTATE PKWY 16701 #264-11-1983 L1994 **GS** *020 †85
GRAHAM, Nathaniel Lars. 51 BOYLSTON ST 16701 #041-01-1983 L1985 **GS CRS** *020 †85
HAMIDI, Jafar Aval. 199 PLEASANT ST 16701 #517-04-1955 L1966 **OBG** *071 †30
HERBERT, Anita Jane. 116 INTERSTATE PKWY, BRADFORD REGIONAL MED 16701 #035-06-1963 L1964 **IM OM** *020 †20
HERRMANN, Steven Clarke. 116 INTERSTATE PKWY, STE 21 16701 #028-34-1995 L2005 **CD** *020 †20
ILAGAN, Petronio M. 116 INTERSTATE PKWY STE 32, BRADFORD NEUROSCIENCE 16701 #748-01-1970 L2005 **N OS** *020 †75
IRWIN, Glenn Edgar, Jr. 1223 E MAIN ST 16701 #041-14-1980 L1983 **IM EM** *020 †16
JACOBS, Martin. 125 MAIN ST, RM 205 16701 #396-04-1953 L1979 **IM** *020
JAVED, Muhammet T. 665 E MAIN ST 16701 #305-01-1986 L1995 **NEP IM** *020 †20
JUNG, Tinliung. 199 PLEASANT ST, BRADFORD PA 16701 16701 #385-02-1966 L1973 **OBG** *020 †20
KAPLAN, David Bennett. 116 INTERSTATE PKWY, BRADFORD REG MED CTR 16701 #041-13-1995 L2001 **PAN AN** *020 †05
KAUR, Hardish. ■ 16701 #495-03-1968 L2008 **P** *100
KONWINSKI, Edward S. ■ 16701 #035-15-1952 L1962 **GS** *071 †85
LAROCHE, Roger Renan. 199 PLEASANT ST STE 12 16701 #026-04-1987 L1992 **P ADM** *020 †75
MAGOUN, George Lester. 116 INTERSTATE PKWY 16701 #048-13-1985 L1988 **EM FM** *020 †18
MARRERO, Luis B. 23 KENNEDY ST, STE 302 16701 #847-10-1979 L1986 **GE IM** *020 †20
MC ELLIGOTT, James B. ■ 16701 #539-06-1979 L1984 **DR** *075 †28
MC NEIL, John. ■ 16701 #566-01-1956 L1979 *071
MILLER, Rebecca Truax. 116 INTERSTATE PKWY, # 42 16701 #035-06-2002 L2005 **PD** *020 †55
NADELLA, Venkateswararao. 6 N CENTER ST 16701 #496-01-1973 L1978 **FM EM** *020 ‡
OWENS, Jill Slike. 181 INTERSTATE PKWY, STE 2 16701 #041-12-1997 L1999 **FM** *020 †18 ‡
PRADHAN, Anil Gajanan. 195 PLEASANT ST 16701 #495-96-1972 L1976 **PD** *055
RAHMAN, Firoz Pushkin. 116 INTERSTATE PKWY 16701 #160-03-1988 L1999 **ADP** *100 †75
RAJESWARAN, Hemina. 195 PLEASANT ST, UNIT 3 16701 #496-34-1993 L2004 **PD** *020 †55
ROTSTEIN, Matthew I. ■ 16701 #065-01-1945 **GS OS** *075
ROUMANI, Faiez Ali. 195 PLEASANT ST UNIT 4, P O BOX 522 16701 #875-01-1973 L1979 **IM NEP** *020 ‡

■ = Address Information Privacy Protected

SALEH, Kamran. 24 W WASHINGTON ST 16701 #704-02-1989 L1994 **IM** *020 †20

SINGH, Dilbagh. 6 N CENTER ST 16701 #495-03-1966 L1978 **EM GP** *020

SOSIC, Abaz. 54 BOYLSTON ST 16701 #957-05-1987 L2000 **OBG** *020 †30

SZCZUPAK, Waldemar P. ■ 16701 #759-03-1975 L1986 **GS** *020 †18

TAHARA, Robert Wayne. 116 INTERSTATE PKWY, STE 31 16701 #035-06-1993 L2002 **VS GS** *020 †85

TANDON, Jagjit Singh. 8 N CENTER ST 16701 #495-08-1973 L1979 **ON HEM** *020 †20

VACCARO, Peter. 24 W WASHINGTON ST 16701 #035-46-1979 L1993 **IM** *020 †55

WEISS, Robert J. 2 MAIN ST 16701 #035-06-1975 L1979 **OPH** *020 †35

WONG, Samuel T. 2 MAIN ST 16701 #024-01-1988 L2008 **OPH** *100

ZEMEL, Reuben. 25 CHESTNUT ST 16701 #065-01-1958 L1966 **GS OS** *020 †85

BRADFORDWOODS – ALLEGHENY

ALEXEIEF, Leo. ■ 15015 #957-02-1936 L1952 **GP** *071

FAWCETT, James Love. 705 ELM RD 15015 #041-01-1955 L1956 **U** *071 †95

KANTER, Steven Lyle. ■ 15015 #048-13-1981 L1990 *030

KELLY, Eugene Wm. ■ 15015 #041-12-1946 L1947 **R** *020

LEBEC, David Richard. 88 FOREST RD 15015 #041-15-2000 L2004 **AN** *020 †05

RUMBLE, Chas Taylor, Jr. ■ 15015 #012-05-1962 L1966 **P PYA** *020 †75 ‡

BREINIGSVILLE – LEHIGH

ABENES, Gil A. ■ 18031 #748-07-1956 L1967 **AN GP** *072

FERRAN, Claudia. ■ 18031 #935-01-1999 L2003 **FM** *100 †18

GREATHOUSE, Shawn Travis. ■ 18031 #017-20-2008 *012

MONDSCHEIN, Joseph Frank. ■ 18031 #028-34-1982 L1988 **PUD CCM** *020 †20

O'NEILL, Oscar. ■ 18031 #042-03-2001 L2004 **FM** *020 †18

BRIDGEPORT – MONTGOMERY

CRAVETZ, Howard. 19 W 5TH ST 19405 #041-02-1955 L1956 **GP OM** *071

GBEDDY, Richard Kofi. ■ 19405 #041-02-2008 *012

IQBAL, Asjad. ■ 19405 #704-02-1994 *100

BRIDGEVILLE – ALLEGHENY

ADAIR, Dale Keith. 1607 MAYVIEW RD 15017 #041-12-1985 L1987 **P PYG** *020 †75

ARFFA, Robert Craig. 1370 WASHINGTON PIKE, STE 108 15017 #008-02-1979 L1986 **OPH** *020 †35

BEAR, Jonathan. 1601 MAYVIEW RD, MAYVIEW STATE HOSP 15017 #051-01-1996 L1999 **P** *020 †75

BEEREL, Roy Marcel. 1370 WASHINGTON PIKE, STE 206 15017 #308-03-1985 L1993 **IM** *020 †20

CHERUP, Lori Lyn. 701 BOYCE RD 15017 #035-01-1982 L1984 **PS** *020 †65

CHIESA, Nicolette. 1168 WASHINGTON PIKE 15017 #041-02-1989 L1992 **IM** *020 †20

COURTNEY, Dennis Jos J. 533 WASHINGTON AVE 15017 #649-30-1982 L1985 **OS AN** *020

CROCHIER, Lawrence John. 9506 SUNDANCE DR 15017 #038-43-1986 L2000 **FM** *020 †18

FATUR, Leo Matthew. 424 SHADY AVE 15017 #045-01-1976 L1977 **IM** *020 †20

FERRIS, Jennifer Newell. 1370 WASHINGTON PIKE, STE 207 15017 #010-01-1986 L1993 **PD NPM** *020 †55

GIGA, Judith Sue. 1370 WASHINGTON PIKE, STE 107 15017 #038-40-1975 L1978 **PD** *020 †55

GOPALANI, Aziz. 1601 MAYVIEW RD, MAYVIEW STATE HOSPITAL 15017 #495-97-1972 L1982 **P** *020

GOPALANI, Usha. 1601 MAYVIEW RD, MAYVIEW STATE HOSPITAL 15017 #495-97-1970 L1982 **P** *020

HUTCHINSON, Mindy Beth. 1370 WASHINGTON PIKE, STE 303 15017 #016-06-1985 L1991 **P CHP** *020 †75

JARIWALA, Leticia Quinto. 1601 MAYVIEW RD 15017 #748-01-1964 L1978 **GP PTH** *020

KARNIK, Reena Arwind. ■ 15017 #495-06-2000 L2003 **IM** *020 †20

KETYER, Edward C. 1370 WASHINGTON PIKE, STE 107 15017 #016-06-1987 L1988 **PD** *020 †55

KOHL, Sarah Elizabeth. 1370 WASHINGTON PIKE, STE 107 15017 #041-02-1986 L1997 **PD** *020 †55

KUSHNER, Donald Allen. 533 WASHINGTON AVE, STE 205 15017 #041-12-1989 L1991 **IM** *020 †20

LEE, Bang Hoon. 1601 MAYVIEW RD 15017 #583-03-1964 L1972 **GP EM** *020

MASSOUD, Sanaa Sabry. 1601 MAYVIEW RD, MAYVIEW STATE HOSPITAL 15017 #915-02-1966 L1981 **GP PHP** *020

MILLER, Robert Harold. 430 WASHINGTON AVE 15017 #041-12-1942 L1943 **GP** *100

NAM, Lam Van. 1601 MAYVIEW RD, MAYVIEW STATE HOSP 15017 #941-01-1971 L1979 **GP PTH** *020 †50

NASR, Farida M. 1601 MAYVIEW RD 15017 #915-03-1966 L1978 **CHP P** *020 †75

NEEL, Wendy Suzanne. 1370 WASHINGTON PIKE, STE 107 15017 #055-01-1998 L2001 **PD** *020 †55

O'TOOLE, Raymond Craig. 1370 WASHINGTON PIKE, STE 107 15017 #041-12-1994 L1996 **PD** *020 †55 ‡

PARIKH, Kiran Jagmahandas. 713 WASHINGTON AVE 15017 #495-56-1970 L1981 **GS FM** *020 ‡

PHILLIPS, Dennis Patrick. ■ 15017 #041-77-2007, ▲ L2007 **FP** *012

PURIGHALLA, Sri P S Raman. 533 WASHINGTON AVE, STE 205 15017 #495-58-1991 L1998 **IM** *020 †20

QUAYE, David. ■ 15017 #561-01-1971 L1977 **GS** *020

RECHTER, Sharon Gail. 1370 WASHINGTON PIKE, STE 303 15017 #011-02-1991 L1995 **P** *020 †75

RODRIGO, T M Nelson. 1601 MAYVIEW RD, MAYVIEW STATE HOSPITAL 15017 #220-01-1969 L1973 **PTH** *020

ROTHFUS, Helen F Tefft. 1601 MAYVIEW RD 15017 #010-01-1943 L1948 **GP** *071

ROY, Bhola Nath. 609 WASHINGTON AVE 15017 #495-75-1990 L2002 **IM** *020

SAENZ, Pedro Emilio. 1601 MAYVIEW RD 15017 #275-01-1953 L1968 **GP P** *071

SAFIER, Joel. 1370 WASHINGTON PIKE, STE 107 15017 #041-12-1964 L1967 **PD PDA** *071 †55

SCOTT, Cynthia Hartz. 1600 MAYVIEW RD 15017 #041-12-1971 L1978 **P CHP** *020 †75

SERRANO, Emma R. 1601 MAYVIEW RD, MAYVIEW STATE HOSPITAL 15017 #847-10-1964 L1967 **OS IMG** *020

TARASZEWSKI, Robert. 1601 MAYVIEW RD, MAYVIEW STATE HOSPITAL 15017 #038-44-1985 L1988 **PUD IM** *030 †20 ‡

VARMA, Swarna. 1370 WASHINGTON PIKE, STE L8 15017 #495-27-1975 L1980 **END** *020 †20

WALCZAK, Katherine Wagner. 1370 WASHINGTON PIKE, STE 107 15017 #010-01-1990 L1993 **PD** *020 †55

WHITAKER, Shannon E. ■ 15017 #035-15-2007 L2007 **FP** *012

ZALEWSKI, Pamela Ann. 1601 MAYVIEW RD, PSYCHIATRIC SERVICES AT MA 15017 #041-12-2002 L2002 **P** *100 †75

BRISTOL – BUCKS

ADIRAJU, Ramesh Kumar. 501 BATH RD, RENU CA RESRCH INSTITUTE 19007 #495-37-1985 L1988 **CD IC** *020 †20

ADRID, Augusto S. 501 BATH RD 19007 #748-01-1956 L1964 **GS OM** *020 †85

ANENE, Charles Azubike. 501 BATH RD, # 215 19007 #030-06-1985 L1998 **TS GS** *020 †85,90

ANTELO, Ronny Eduardo. 501 BATH RD, STE 211 19007 #847-02-1979 L1998 **N** *020

BEDNAREK, Joseph M. 501 BATH RD STE 208 19007 #049-01-1971 L1972 **GS** *020 †85

BOUSHRA, Nader Naguib. 501 BATH RD, LOWER BUCKS HOSPITAL 19007 #915-02-1982 L2004 **AN** *020 †05

BRITTON, Richard John. 501 BATH RD, LOWER BUCKS HOSPITAL 19007 #033-06-1996 L2001 **EM FM** *020 †18

BUI, Lehien Thi. 501 BATH RD 19007 #041-02-1994 L2000 **IM** *020 †20

CHACKO, George Vilangolil. 501 BATH RD 19007 #690-07-1987 L1998 **AN** *020 †05 ‡

CLABBER, Kim Marie. 501 BATH RD, STE 2F 19007 #026-04-1995 L1997 **OSM** *020 †40

CROWE, Elizabeth Ann. 245 MILL ST 19007 #041-07-1982 L1984 **GYN** *071 †30

DEL VECCHIO, Fredesuinda. 501 BATH RD, LOWER BUCKS HOSP 19007 #748-01-1953 L1983 **GP** *071

DURRANI, Mehmood Alam. 501 BATH RD, LOWER BUCKS HOSPITAL 19007 #495-51-1988 L2006 **CCA** *020 †05

FRANKEL, Christopher John. 501 BATH RD 19007 #033-06-1996 L1999 **NEP IM** *020 †20

GESTOSO, Romulo Glaraga. 501 BATH RD 19007 #748-01-1961 L1973 **EM** *020 †16

GHAURI, Rashida. 100 GREEN LN, STE 3 19007 #305-01-2001 L2001 **IM** *020 †20

GOLDBERG, Steven Paul. 100 GREEN LN, STE 3 19007 #041-12-1987 L1989 **CD IM** *020 †20

GOLDSTEIN, Michael David. 501 BATH RD, HEALTHWORKS 19007 #035-01-1983 L1991 **OM IM** *020 †20,70

HAIMOWITZ, Daniel. 501 BATH RD 19007 #041-02-1983 L1984 **IM IMG** *020 †20

HANN, Suhung. 501 BATH RD 19007 #583-02-1961 L1971 **AI PD** *075 †03

HASIUK, Aaron Saml. 501 BATH RD, STE 202 19007 #041-13-1977 L1981 **OBG** *020 †30

JUHNG, Hagwon. 501 BATH RD, LOWER BUCKS HOSPITAL 19007 #583-06-1988 L1996 **RHU** *020 †20

KEENAN, Paul Chas, Jr. 216 MILL ST 19007 #010-02-1983 L1987 **OPH** *020 †35

KETELS, Erk Arfst. 501 BATH RD 19007 #407-10-1958 L1961 **OBS** *071 †30

KONCHANIN, Lynn Marie. 501 BATH RD 19007 #035-03-1981 L1983 **PD ADL** *020 †55

LEDVIN, Veronika. 501 BATH RD 19007 #913-94-1998 L2003 **IM** *020 †20

LEE, Chanchi. 501 BATH RD, BUCKS COUNTY UROLOGY PC 19007 #385-04-1966 L1973 **U** *020 †95

LE PAR, Edwin. BATH ROAD AT ORCHARD, LOWER BUCKS HOSP DEPT RAD 19007 #041-02-1957 L1958 **R NM** *071 †20,80

MANNARINO, Anthony Peter. 216 MILL ST 19007 #010-02-1982 L1986 **OPH** *020 †35 ‡

MC ILVAINE, Paul W. ■ 19007 #041-02-1952 L1953 **FM** *071

MERSKY, Martin Ralph. 501 BATH RD 19007 #041-02-1975 L1976 **IM** *020 †20 ‡

PASQUALONE, Martin A. 501 BATH RD 19007 #654-01-1986 L1989 **IM EM** *020 †20

PATEL, Bhavna Chunibhai. 501 BATH RD 19007 #495-76-1968 L1981 **GP** *020

PATEL, Jayantilal R. 501 BATH RD, STE 209A 19007 #495-17-1969 L1978 **GP** *020

PATEL, Jaykumar C. 501 BATH RD, STE 208 19007 #496-38-1972 L1984 **PS HS** *020 †65,85 ‡

PATEL, Rajani. 501 BATH RD STE 210 19007 #495-17-1969 L1979 **P** *020 †75

PATRONE, Patrick Michael. 501 BATH RD, LAB LOWER BUCKS HOSPITAL 19007 #051-01-1984 L1988 **PTH** *020 †55

PEGUERO, Federico A. 501 BATH RD 19007 #308-01-1966 L1974 **TS OS** *072 †85 ‡

PILTZ-SEYMOUR, Jody. 216 MILL ST, CENTURY EYE CARE LTD 19007 #035-46-1984 L1990 **OPH** *020 †35

PITKOW, Ronald B. 900B OLD ORCHARD LN 19007 #041-01-1960 L1961 **ORS** *071 †40 ‡

RAIFORD, John Wm. 501 BATH RD 19007 #041-02-1955 L1959 **OBG** *071 †30

RAMPURE, Jaideep Mahadeva. ■ 19007 #496-01-1986 L2001 **DR** *100

ROMANO, Vincent Edwin. 256 RADCLIFFE ST, BOX 2174 19007 #035-08-1938 L1946 **GP** *071

SCHNEIDER, Amy Christina. ■ 19007 #041-77-2007, ▲ L2007 *012

SIMONS, Carl Irwin. 501 BATH RD 19007 #041-02-1959 L1960 **ORS** *020 †40

SONG, Sang Won. 501 BATH RD 19007 #583-01-1960 L1968 **PTH** *020 †50

SOSNOVSKY, Anna. 501 BATH RD, LOWER BUCKS HOSPITAL 19007 #913-69-1981 L1997 **NPM PD** *020 †55 ‡

STRAUSS, Richard Edwin. 501 BATH RD 19007 #041-02-1947 L1948 **D** *072 †15

SUBRAHMANYAM, Chivukula. 501 BATH RD 19007 #495-65-1972 L1985 **IM** *020 †20

TRUJILLO, Hernando. 501 BATH RD, STE 210 19007 #264-01-1950 L1966 **GS TRS** *020 ‡

WATOREK, Kazimierz M. 501 BATH RD 19007 #759-01-1984 L2000 **NPM** *020 †55 ‡

ZUCKERMAN, Nathan Jay. 501 BATH RD 19007 #035-15-1970 L1971 **OBG** *020 †30

BROAD TOP – HUNTINGDON

KISTLER, Dominick A. ROUTE 913 BOX 127, BROAD TOP MEDICAL CENTER 16621 #041-02-1989 L1991 **FM** *020 †18

BROCKPORT – ELK

MORGAN, Earl David. 5439 ROUTE 153 15823 #654-01-1984 L1986 **EM OS** *020 †20

BROCKWAY – JEFFERSON

ALLENBAUGH, Renee Marie. 1200 WOOD ST 15824 #041-14-1998 L2001 **FM** *020 †18

■ = Address Information Privacy Protected

DEVLIN, Albert Edward. 1100 MAIN ST 15824 #041-12-1947 L1949 **OM** *071
DEVLIN, James Edward. 1100 MAIN ST 15824 #041-02-1985 L1986 **FM** *020 †18
MC ANDREW, Joseph Edward. ■ 15824 #041-13-1982 L1993 **EM GP** *020
SCOTT, Suzanne Marie. 1200 WOOD ST 15824 #051-01-1998 L2005 **FM** *020 †18
WELCH, Frederick Wm. 1200 WOOD ST, CLINICARE HLTH CTR 15824 #028-34-1976 L1980 **GS** *075

BRODHEADSVILLE — MONROE

GOTCHEL, Mark Phillip. 13 KEVIN LN 18322 #036-05-1982 L1983 **OPH** *020 †35 ‡
GUPTA, Amitabha. 13 KEVIN LN 18322 #041-09-1993 L1995 **OPH** *020 †35
HIEMENZ, Donald Wm. OF BRODHEADSVILLE, FAMILY PRACTICE ASSOCIATES 18322 #041-13-1971 L1972 **FM** *020 †18 ‡
KENNY, Christine Anne. 12 KEVIN LN, PLEASANT VALLEY FAMILY PRA 18322 #041-15-2003 L2003 **FM** *020
KOTHARI, Kirit Kumar. ■ 18322 #496-38-1976 L1996 **FM** *020
MARTUCCI, William James. FAM PRAC ASSOC OF BRODHEAD 18322 #041-13-1971 L1972 **FM** *020 †18
YOUNG, Douglas Allen. 13 KEVIN LN 18322 #010-02-1990 L1992 **OPH OS** *020 †35 ‡

BROOKHAVEN — DELAWARE

ANDERSON, Carol Elizabeth. 1 MEDICAL CENTER BLVD 19015 #024-05-1972 L1983 **PD MG** *020 †55,19
BENDLIN, Arnaldo. ■ 19015 #726-01-1962 L1970 **OS GS** *071
BRAR, Adarshdip. ■ 19015 #495-43-1995 L2000 **IM** *100 †20
CHUNG, John Youngsong. ■ 19015 #041-13-2001 L2004 **GS** *020
GRECO, Jonathan Peter. 8 W BROOKHAVEN RD 19015 #041-09-1984 L1986 **IM GP** *020 †20
HUANG, Marian Mei En. 1 MEDICAL CENTER BLVD 19015 #041-02-1982 L1987 **NPM** *020 †55
KESSLER, Rex Keith. 8 W BROOKHAVEN RD 19015 #041-13-1977 L1978 **IM END** *020 †20
MANN, Irving Arnold. 2711 EDGMONT AVE 19015 #041-09-1957 L1958 **OBG** *071 †30
MILBURN, Christopher Anth. ■ 19015 #041-02-2008 *012
O'DEA, Thomas Patrick. 1 MEDICAL CENTER BLVD 19015 #033-05-1967 L1968 **GS** *020 †85
ROSEN, Jeffrey Keith. 100 E BROOKHAVEN RD 19015 #041-07-1987 L1989 **FM** *020 †18
SIDDIQUI, Wajid Ali. ■ 19015 #704-15-2001 L2005 **IM** *012

BROOKVILLE — JEFFERSON

BAUMUNK, Creston Neal. 100 HOSPITAL RD 15825 #016-01-1977 L1979 **ORS GS** *020
BEZIER, Jeffrey Lee. 50 WATERFORD PIKE, EDGEWORTH SQUARE 15825 #035-01-1982 L1983 **OPH** *020 †35
BHATNAGAR, Y Mohan. 75 PICKERING ST 15825 #495-36-1970 L1974 **OBG REN** *020 †30
CHAMBERS, Deborah Jo. 100 HOSPITAL RD 15825 #038-40-1995 L1998 **FM** *020 †18
CHAPA, Sukumar. 240 ALLEGHENY BLVD, STE A 15825 #495-21-1967 L1981 **GS** *020 †85
CONNOR, Susan Ann. 253 MADISON AVE STE A 15825 #041-12-1976 L1977 **FM** *020 †18
CONWELL, Francis L, Jr. ■ 15825 #041-12-1948 L1977 **DR** *071
DELOIA, Samuel Paul. ■ 15825 #041-13-2007 L2007 **TY** *012
GARRETT, Jeffrey S. 100 HOSPITAL RD 15825 #035-19-1981 L1988 **CD IM** *020 †20
GILFORD, Lawrence M. ■ 15825 #041-12-1959 L1960 **GP PD** *020 †55 ‡
GREENBERG, Steven Mark. 50 WATERFORD PIKE 15825 #025-07-1969 L1973 **OPH** *071 †35
HARVEY, Paul Earle. 100 HOSPITAL RD 15825 #055-01-1969 L1970 **EM FM** *020
LOVE, Stephen Clifford. 240 W MAIN ST, P O BOX 328 15825 #654-01-1981 L1984 **GP CCM** *020
MC KINLEY, Arthur R. ■ 15825 #041-13-1945 L1946 **OBG GP** *071
MC KINLEY, William M. 420 MAIN ST 15825 #035-03-1949 L1953 **GS GP** *071 †85
NANDHAKUMAR, Ayyavoo. 100 HOSPITAL RD, BROOKVILLE HOSPITAL 15825 #495-94-1974 L1992 **AN** *075
PATEL, Jayeshkumar A. 100 HOSPITAL RD, DEPT OF CARDIOTHORACIC SUR 15825 #965-01-1988 L2007 **TS** *020
PATEL, Jivanlal Maganlal. 2834 MAPLEVALE RD 15825 #495-22-1974 L1981 **CD IM** *020 †20
PENDLETON, Tanis Shasta. 100 HOSPITAL RD, BROOKVILLE HOSPITAL 15825 #422-01-1994 L2006 **AN** *020
PENDLETON, Timothy P. 111 SUMMIT ST, SUMMIT HEALTH CENTER 15825 #654-01-1987 L2006 **IM PUD** *020 †20
PIPER, Greta Lynn. ■ 15825 #041-15-2003 L2003 **GS** *012
REDDY, Jaiveer T. 82 BARNETT ST 15825 #495-65-1967 L1974 **U** *020
SAN JOSE, Nelia M. 100 HOSPITAL RD 15825 #748-10-1989 L1999 **P** *020 †75

BROOMALL — DELAWARE

ALTMAN, Charles Anthony. ■ 19008 #041-01-1992 L1995 **P** *020 †75
ANDERSON, Halette Lasker. 1991 SPROUL RD, BROOMALL PEDIATRIC 19008 #041-02-1985 L1987 **PD** *020 †55
BALLARD, Ian Matheson. 1991 SPROUL RD, STE 300 19008 #041-13-1962 L1963 **IM FM** *072 †18 ‡
BARNETT-SMITH, Rhoneise Y. 1991 SPROUL RD, BRYN MAWR FAMILY PRACTICE 19008 #051-01-2002 L2002 **FM** *100 †18
BAZZINI, Anthi S. ■ 19008 #418-02-1975 **P** *020
BEVILACQUA, John Edward. ■ 19008 #041-01-1954 L1955 **N CN** *071 †75
BISHARA, Girgis Greis. ■ 19008 #330-02-1951 L1971 **GP** *020
BOKEN, Patricia A. 1991 SPROUL RD, STE 300 19008 #040-02-1992 L2000 **FM** *020 †18
CHANDY, Sunil Alexander. ■ 19008 #041-13-2006 L2006 **AN** *012
CHANG, Catherine Diana. ■ 19008 #024-16-1987 L1989 **PTH IM** *100
CHIU, Priscilla Peilan. 1991 SPROUL RD, STE 300 19008 #041-15-2002 L2002 **FM** *100 †18
COLTON, Anne Elizabeth. 2004 SPROUL RD, RUSH UNIVERSITY MEDICAL CE 19008 #041-13-2001 L2001 **OSM** *020
DEL CONTE, Beth Ann. ■ 19008 #041-12-1984 L1985 **PD** *062 †55
EDELSTEIN, Mark Randy. 1999 SPROUL RD, MARPLE MEDICAL ASSOCIATES 19008 #023-01-1990 L1996 **CD** *020 †20
EMANUEL, E Stephen. ■ 19008 #041-02-1961 L1962 **OBG** *071 †30
FIENMAN, Norman Lester. 1991 SPROUL RD, BROOMALL PEDIATRIC SUITE 19008 #035-15-1966 L1984 **PD** *020 †55 ‡

FLEISCHER, Leroy Barry. 1999 SPROUL RD, STE 21 19008 #041-09-1985 L1987 **IM** *020 †20
FRAS, Christian Ivan. 1991 SPROUL RD, STE 300A 19008 #035-01-1994 L2004 **ORS** *020 †40
FUCHS, Ronald S. 580 REED RD 19008 #043-01-1992 L1998 **IM** *020 †20
GENOVESE, Cynthia Marie. 1991 SPROUL RD, STE 300 19008 #561-01-2001 L2006 **FP** *012
GIACOBBE, Rosamary. 1991 SPROUL RD, BROOMALL PEDIATRIC 19008 #041-07-1996 L1999 **PD** *020 †55
GLADSTONE, Julian Louis. 1999 SPROUL RD STE 25 19008 #041-01-1969 L1970 **CD IM** *020 †20
GRECO, Joseph Anthony. 1991 SPROUL RD, STE 300 19008 #041-02-1991 L1993 **FM** *020 †18
GUMINA, Thomas Francis. 1999 SPROUL RD 19008 #041-02-1959 L1960 **IM** *020
HARGROVE, Claudia Liane. 1991 SPROUL RD, BRYN MAWR FAMILY PRACTICE 19008 #409-21-1988 L2003 **FM** *100 †18
HARLIN, Stephen. 2000 SPROUL RD STE 200, MARPLE COMMONS 19008 #041-09-1986 L1988 **PS PRD** *020 †65 ‡
KAIDBEY, Kays Hussein. 505 PARK WAY, STE B 19008 #605-01-1968 L1976 **D** *050 †15
KENNEALLY, Barry Edmund. 1991 SPROUL RD, STE 300 19008 #041-02-1992 L1994 **FSM** *012 †18
KLINZING, Gerard F. 1991 SPROUL RD, STE 300 19008 #041-02-1980 L1981 **FM** *040 †18 ‡
LA BRICCIOSA, Joseph. 1999 SPROUL RD, STE 21 19008 #022-75-1985, ▲ L1988 **FM** *071 †18
LAOTHAMATAS, Jiraporn. ■ 19008 #891-01-1981 L1989 **DR** *100 †80
LAVERAN-STIEBAR, Rudolf L. 1991 SPROUL RD STE 200, LAWRENCE PARK OB/GYN 19008 #041-01-1993 L1997 **OBG** *020 †30
LEE, Frank Szechi. 823 MEADOWBROOK LN 19008 #024-01-1991 L1998 **PTH** *020 †50
LEVENBERG, Richard Jay. 2004 SPROUL RD, PREMIER ORTHOPAEDIC & 19008 #041-13-1988 L1990 **OSS ORS** *020 †40
LICHTENBERG, Richard A. 1999 SPROUL RD, MARPLE MEDICAL ASSOCIATES 19008 #024-05-1975 L1976 **CD IM** *020 †20
LISBERGER, Mark David. 1999 SPROUL RD, MARPLE MEDICAL ASSOCIATES 19008 #023-01-1978 L1981 **CD IM** *020 †20 ‡
LOGAN, Martha Louise. 2000 SPROUL RD, STE 300 19008 #067-01-1981 L1987 **IM** *020 †20 ‡
MAUSSER, E Ellen Vaugh. ■ 19008 #038-06-1949 L1983 **AN** *071 †05
MILLER, Curt Dwight. 2004 SPROUL RD, PREMIER ORTHOPAEDIC & 19008 #041-13-1979 L1980 **ORS** *020 †40
NG, Manyan. 1991 SPROUL RD, BROOMALL PEDIATRIC 19008 #035-06-1997 L1999 **PD** *020 †55 ‡
O'MAHONY, Lisa. 1991 SPROUL RD, BROOMALL PEDIATRIC 19008 #041-07-1981 L1983 **PD** *075 †55
PARTEM, Leslie Marie. 1991 SPROUL RD, STE 175 19008 #913-89-1978 L2002 **FP** *012
PRATSOS, Antonis. 1999 SPROUL RD, MARPLE MEDICAL ASSOCIATES 19008 #917-08-1993 L2002 **CD** *020 †20
RESNICK, Myron Ellis. 1999 SPROUL RD, MARPLE MEDICAL ASSOCIATES 19008 #041-09-1956 L1957 **CD IM** *072 †20
ROSENFELD, Ronald Norman. 2000 SPROUL RD STE 320 19008 #041-07-1974 L1975 **ORS** *020 †40
ROSENZWEIG, Max. ■ 19008 #041-02-1936 L1938 **GP U** *071
RUDO, Sharon F. 1991 SPROUL RD STE 200, LAWRENCE PARK OB/GYN 19008 #041-02-2000 L2001 **OBG** *020
SALITSKY, Sherwood Norman. 2193 W CHESTER PIKE 19008 #041-09-1957 L1958 **PD** *020 †55
SARDANOPOLI, Lisa Ann. 1991 SPROUL RD STE 625, MAIN LINE HEALTH CENTER LA 19008 #041-09-1991 L2001 **IM** *020 †20
SMOGER, Barry R. 123 DIANE DR STE 206 19008 #041-02-1977 L1979 **DR NM** *020 †80,28
STUMACHER, Roger Elias. 1991 SPROUL RD, STE 750 19008 #041-01-2003 L2003 **IM** *100 †20
SUERO, Felipe Francisco. ■ 19008 #847-02-1983 L2003 **AN** *020 †05
TULIN, Joanne Rachel. 1991 SPROUL RD, STE 625 19008 #041-02-2004 L2006 **IM** *100 †20
WALKER, Margaret Elaine. 2000 SPROUL RD, STE 300 19008 #041-09-1977 L1978 **IM** *020 †20
WOLK, Daniel Lee. 2000 SPROUL RD, STE 300 19008 #024-07-1981 L1982 **FM FPG** *020 †18
WOODRING, Albert Jos. 1999 SPROUL RD 19008 #041-13-1963 L1970 **OTO** *020 †45
YANG, Lynn Weiling. 419 LAWRENCE RD, MRCP 19008 #041-02-1995 L1997 **PM** *020 †60

BROWNFIELD — FAYETTE

WHITE, Carol Jean. ■ 15416 #041-12-1977 L1978 **FM** *020 †18

BROWNSVILLE — FAYETTE

BOBAK, Leopold. 125 SIMPSON RD 15417 #759-01-1968 L1978 **CD IM** *020
D'AURIA, Thomas Mario. 129 SIMPSON RD, STE 304 15417 #041-09-1944 L1945 **PD** *072 †55
DI LEO, Dominic Wm. 127 SIMPSON RD, STE C 15417 #041-12-1974 L1975 **CD IM** *020 †20
GANTI, Murty S. 125 SIMPSON RD, BROWNSVILLE HOS 15417 #495-11-1970 L1991 **IM** *020,16
GENNAULA, Charles Patrick. 125 SIMPSON RD 15417 #041-12-1991 L1993 **N** *020 †75
ISARIYAWONGSE, Prakorb. 129 SIMPSON RD STE 108 15417 #891-01-1965 L1973 **GS AS** *020
KIM, Kun Hyung. 125 SIMPSON RD 15417 #583-03-1962 L1976 **ORS** *071
PARK, Thomas Elliott. 125 SIMPSON RD 15417 #041-01-1942 L1944 **GP** *075
RAMSAY, Michael. 125 SIMPSON RD 15417 #539-03-1978 L1985 **DR** *020 †80
SAHAI, Anand Vasante. 125 SIMPSON RD 15417 #067-02-1990 L1996 **IM** *020 †20
SAHAI, Ashok Kumar. 1239 SIMPSON MNR 15417 #495-12-1968 L1979 **GS GP** *020
SEPESKY, Victoria M. 125 SIMPSON RD 15417 #041-12-1994 L1998 **PM** *020 ‡
SINGH, Malkit. 631 NATIONAL PIKE E, STE D 15417 #495-29-1974 L1980 **IM** *020 †20
WADHWANI, Bhagwan J. 129 SIMPSON RD 15417 #495-01-1963 L1969 **CD IM** *020 †20
ZAGLAMA, Mona Sabry. 125 SIMPSON RD, BROWNSVILLE GENERAL HOSP 15417 #915-04-1975 L1984 **PTH BBK** *020
ZAGLAMA, Nabil Edward. 104 SIMPSON RD # A 15417 #915-04-1976 L1984 **HEM ON** *074 †20

BRYN ATHYN — MONTGOMERY

KING, Cedric Sirbridge. 3039 HUNGINGDON PIKE 19009 #041-09-1942 L1943 **GS** *071

BRYN MAWR — DELAWARE

ABBOUD, Joseph Melki. 830 OLD LANCASTER RD 19010 #010-01-1997 L1999 **PCC** *020 †20

ABBOUDI, Jack. 830 OLD LANCASTER RD 19010 #033-06-1994 L1996 **HS** *020 †40

ABDER, Roxanne C. 919 CONESTOGA RD 19010 #035-19-2003 L2003 **OBG** *020

ABRAHAM, George. 130 S BRYN MAWR AVE, PSYCHIATRIC UNIT 19010 #495-80-1989 L2001 **P** *020 †75

ACHUFF, Barbara-Jo. 130 S BRYN MAWR AVE, PEDIATRICS OFFICE 19010 #041-02-1996 L1998 **PD** *020 †55

ADAMS, David John. 27 S BRYN MAWR AVE 19010 #041-13-1964 L1965 **ORS** *020 †40

ALEXANDER, Fred. ■ 19010 #023-01-1941 L1953 **IM PA** *071

ANDERSON, Ellen E. ■ 19010 #041-07-1969 L1971 **GS** *071

ANDERSON, Mark. ■ 19010 #041-15-2008 *012

ANID, Antun G. 226 FISHERS RD 19010 #605-01-1968 L2005 **OBG** *020

ANUGU, Rajeev. ■ 19010 #495-65-1996 L2004 **DR** *012

ARONZON, Boris. 937 E HAVERFORD RD 19010 #913-69-1985 L2004 **AN** *020 †05

ARUN KUMAR, Avinashi Soma. ■ 19010 #495-94-1994 L2007 **IM** *012

ASHBY, Bonnie Lee. 830 OLD LANCASTER RD, STE 108 19010 #041-02-1968 L1969 **IM ID** *020 †20

ASSARSSON, Erik David. 130 S BRYN MAWR AVE, THE BRYN MAWR HOSPITAL 19010 #033-06-1989 L1992 **RO** *020 †80

ASUNTO, Ann Mantua. 130 S BRYN MAWR AVE 19010 #748-11-2000 L2006 **FP** *012

ATKINS, Robert Raymond. 130 S BRYN MAWR AVE 19010 #041-01-1979 L1980 **GE IM** *020 †20

ATTIE, Alisa Melanie. ■ 19010 #041-01-1997 L1999 **PD** *020

AZER, Michele L. ■ 19010 #035-45-1997 L1999 **EM** *020 †16

BALICK, Alan Keith. 130 S BRYN MAWR AVE, STE 312 D WING 19010 #422-01-1989 L1992 **IM** *020 †20

BAR AD, Voichita. ■ 19010 #781-04-1992 L2006 *100

BARBARISI, Marchello J. 130 S BRYN MAWR AVE, BRYN MAWR HOSPITAL 19010 #033-06-1992 L1994 **DR** *020

BARNES, James D. ■ 19010 #041-02-1950 L1951 **IM PM** *071

BARTHOLD, Julia Spencer. 830 OLD LANCASTER RD, STE 201 19010 #016-06-1981 L1999 **UP GS** *020 †95

BASHKIN, Marisa Elizabeth. ■ 19010 #041-02-2007 L2007 **IM** *012

BATES, Barbara. ■ 19010 #035-20-1953 L1980 **IM** *072 †20

BAYLESS, Steven. ■ 19010 #041-13-1965 L1966 **PTH** *062 †50

BEKEN, Emre. 910 ACADEMY LN 19010 #902-21-1985 L1997 **IM** *020 †20

BENNETT, Jean. ■ 19010 #024-01-1986 **OS PD** *100

BENSON, John Richard. 1062 E LANCASTER AVE, STE 7 19010 #016-06-1955 L1956 **P PYA** *071 †75

BENSTOCK, Michael Aaron. 130 S BRYN MAWR AVE, BRYN MAWR HOSPITAL 19010 #010-02-1993 L1996 **RNR** *012 †55,80

BERBERIAN, Vicky Papazian. BRYN MAWR COLLEGE CAMPUS 19010 #041-07-1982 L1983 **FM** *020 †18

BERG, Bruce Jeffrey. 234 S BRYN MAWR AVE, STE 202 19010 #012-05-1983 L1986 **P ADP** *020 †75 ‡

BERGMANN, Leigh Scott. 919 CONESTOGA RD, BLD 1 STE 300 19010 #041-01-1986 L1997 **U GS** *020 †95

BERNSTEIN, Guy Thos. 245 S BRYN MAWR AVE 19010 #035-01-1982 L1988 **U** *020 †95 ‡

BERRY, Theodore Jos. ■ 19010 #041-02-1943 L1944 **IM** *071 †20

BLEIER, Esther Skorr. 937 E HAVERFORD RD, STE 204 19010 #035-20-1973 L1974 **AN** *020 †05

BLOOM, Peter Brower. 950 E HAVERFORD RD STE 302 19010 #041-01-1962 L1963 **P IM** *020 †75 ‡

BOMZE, Jeffrey Peter. 1201 COUNTY LINE RD, STE 200 19010 #041-01-1975 L1980 **PD ADL** *020 †55 ‡

BONNIGTON, Mark. 130 S BRYN MAWR AVE, MAIN LINE EMERGENCY 19010 #048-04-1981 L1988 **EM** *020 †16

BOOVA, Robert S. 830 OLD LANCASTER RD, STE 203 19010 #041-02-1977 L1978 **TS** *020 †85,90

BORGESE, Stephen C. 130 S BRYN MAWR AVE, MAIN LINE EMERGENCY 19010 #041-13-1991 L1996 **EM** *020 †16

BOTTGER, David Avery. 940 E HAVERFORD RD, STE 100 19010 #041-13-1982 L1990 **OTO PS** *020 †65,85

BRADY, James. 1062 E LANCASTER AVE STE 4 19010 #041-13-1983 L1984 **P** *020

BRAUN, Kenneth. ■ 19010 #035-19-1972 L2004 **OPH** *071 †35

BRISKIN, Jonathan Alan. 733 OLD LANCASTER RD, BOX 400 19010 #041-13-1981 L1982 **FOP ATP** *020

BROWER, Richard O, Jr. BRYN MAWR COLLEGE CAMPUS 19010 #165-01-1979 L1980 **IM EM** *020 †20

BRUNT, Manly Y, Jr. 864 GLENBROOK AVE 19010 #036-05-1948 L1953 **P** *072 †75

BUDWAY, Matthew James. 958 COUNTY LINE RD, CONESTOGA MEDICAL BLDG. 19010 #005-02-1996 L2005 **NS** *020 †25

BURKE, Francis X, III. 723 S ROBERTS RD, VANGUARD OCCUPATIONAL MED 19010 #041-13-1982 L1982 **EM FM** *020 †16

BURNS, Margaret Ann. 919 CONESTOGA RD 19010 #041-09-1991 L1995 **OBG** *020 †30

BURT, Theresa A. 933 E HAVERFORD RD 19010 #041-02-1974 L1975 **GE IM** *020 †20

BYREDDY, Sunila Reddy. 130 S BRYN MAWR AVE, 312 D-WING 19010 #495-37-1998 L2001 **IM** *020

BYRON, Martamarie. 130 S BRYN MAWR AVE, HOSP MED SVCS 19010 #041-02-1999 L2000 **IM** *020 †20

CAHILL, Matthew Paul. 130 S BRYN MAWR AVE 19010 #041-01-1955 L1956 **R OS** *020 †80

CANCELMO, Richard Peter. 130 S BRYN MAWR AVE 19010 #041-01-1955 L1956 **R OS** *020 †80

CANNON, Edward Jos. ■ 19010 #041-13-1948 L1950 **OPH** *071 †35

CAPUCAO, Joel Balbuena. 130 S BRYN MAWR AVE, PSYCHIATRIC UNIT 19010 #748-10-1992 L1999 **P** *020 †75

CARELLA, Richard John. BRYN MAWR COLLEGE CAMPUS 19010 #024-07-1966 L1983 **RO** *020 †80

CARPENTER, John T, Jr. 864 COUNTY LINE RD 19010 #041-01-1952 L1953 **OBG** *071 †30

CARR, Robert F, Jr. 130 S BRYN MAWR AVE, MAIN LINE PATHOLOGY ASSOC 19010 #023-01-1982 L1984 **PTH** *020 †50

CARRUTHERS, Catherine D. 101 S BRYN MAWR AVE # 201, COMPREHENSIVE BREAST CENTE 19010 #001-02-2001 L2006 **GS** *100 †85

CARSON, John S. ■ 19010 #041-01-1950 L1951 **AN** *071 †05

CARTY, James Byron, Jr. 830 OLD LANCASTER RD, STE 100 19010 #041-02-1970 L1971 **OPH** *020 †35

CASEY, Thomas James. 937 E HAVERFORD RD, STE 103 19010 #041-13-1972 L1975 **PD** *020 †55

CETNAR, Jeremy Paul. ■ 19010 #016-43-2002 L2006 **HO** *012 †20

CHECCHIO, Leonard Mario. 130 S BRYN MAWR AVE, MAIN LINE EMERGENCY 19010 #010-02-1980 L1991 **EM IM** *020 †20,16

CHELIKANI, Muralikrishna. ■ 19010 #495-58-1992 L2004 **IM** *100 †20

CHERNOFF, Robert Wesley. ■ 19010 #024-07-1959 L1960 **IM** *071 †20

CIRILLO-HYLAND, Victoria. 830 OLD LANCASTER RD, MEDICAL BLDG NORTH SUITE 1 19010 #041-01-1989 L1992 **D** *020 †15

CLAIR, Theodore Wm. 864 COUNTY LINE RD 19010 #041-09-1963 L1964 **PD** *020 †55 ‡

CLOSKEY, Gregory Mark. 130 S BRYN MAWR AVE, THE CLOTHIER BUILDING 19010 #010-02-1978 L1979 **NEP IM** *020 †55

COADY, Mary Luz K. 455 S ROBERTS RD 19010 #041-07-1962 L1963 **PD** *071 †55

COHEN, Steven Clark. 933 E HAVERFORD RD 19010 #023-07-1980 L1983 **HEM ON** *020 †20

COLETTA, Anthony Vincent. 830 OLD LANCASTER RD, STE 306 19010 #041-02-1979 L1980 **GS** *020 †85

COLLAZZO, Jack Alan. 933 E HAVERFORD RD 19010 #041-07-1990 L1994 **GE** *020 †20

COLLETT-SOLBERG, Paulo F. 130 S BRYN MAWR AVE, BRYN MAWR HOSPITAL 19010 #187-03-1989 L1994 **PDE** *020 †55

COLUMBO, Michele. 875 COUNTY LINE RD, STE 107 19010 #561-31-1983 L2000 **AI IM** *020 †20,03

COPLAN, James. 919 CONESTOGA RD, BLDG ONE 19010 #035-09-1973 L1975 **PD NDP** *040 †55

CORNELIUS, Chalmers E, III. 919 CONESTOGA RD, BLDG 2 19010 #041-01-1964 L1965 **D** *020 †15

CRAPARO, Jocelyn Lopez. 919 CONESTOGA RD 19010 #308-07-1983 L1988 **OBG MFM** *020 †30

CURRAN, Sean Connor. 830 OLD LANCASTER RD, STE 305 19010 #041-01-1999 L2001 **CD** *020 †20

DALY, Christopher Xavier. 130 S BRYN MAWR AVE, MAIN LINE EMERGENCY 19010 #010-02-1980 L1982 **EM IM** *020 †20,16

D'ANGELO, Marc Scott. 651 BLACK ROCK RD 19010 #649-14-1980 L1983 **N** *020 †75 ‡

DANOFF, David Mark. 130 S BRYN MAWR AVE, BRYN MAWR HOSPITAL 19010 #041-02-1971 L1975 **R DR** *040 †80

DAVIS, Deborah Ann. 830 OLD LANCASTER RD, STE 201 19010 #041-09-1980 L1982 **PAN CCP** *020 †55,05

DAWID, Suzanne Rachel. ■ 19010 #028-02-2000 L2001 **PD** *100 †55

DAY, Francis Peter. 130 S BRYN MAWR AVE 19010 #041-02-1981 L1982 **CD IM** *020 †20

DEASEY, Karen Kulik. 875 COUNTY LINE RD, 207 BRYN MAWR BLDG S 19010 #041-07-1976 L1977 **D** *020 †15

DELEA, Ellen. 830 OLD LANCASTER RD, STE 108 19010 #041-01-2000 L2003 **FM** *020 †18

DEL ROSARIO, J Fernando. 830 OLD LANCASTER RD, AVE/STE 201 19010 #748-10-1986 L1992 **PG PD** *020 †55

DENNE, Jennifer Leigh. 830 OLD LANCASTER RD # 306, SURGICAL SPECIALISTS PC 19010 #041-15-2001 L2001 **GS** *020 †85

D'ENTREMONT, Tracy S. 933 E HAVERFORD RD 19010 #041-14-1997 L1999 **HO** *020 †20

DE PILLIS, Vincent Jos. 130 S BRYN MAWR AVE 19010 #041-13-1954 L1955 **PTH NM** *020 †50,28

DERBY, Christopher Dean. 830 OLD LANCASTER RD, STE 2 19010 #025-01-1995 L2004 **PCS** *020 †85,90

DEVON, Ronit Karpati. ■ 19010 #041-01-1998 L2001 **DR** *100 †80

DIAMOND, Herbert. ■ 19010 #041-01-1947 L1948 **P PYA** *030 †75

DIETRICH, Christine E. ■ 19010 #035-06-1981 L1982 **DR** *020

DILLON, Edward Vansant. 130 S BRYN MAWR AVE, BLDG 306 19010 #041-01-1952 L1953 **GS** *020 †85

DILLON, Richard Snowdon. ■ 19010 #041-01-1959 L1962 **END DIA** *071 †20

DI PENTIMA, Maria Cecilia. 830 OLD LANCASTER RD, MEDICAL BLDG NORTH, SUITE 19010 #132-04-1987 L2000 **PD ID** *020 †55 ‡

DONOHOE, Dennis Jos. 130 S BRYN MAWR AVE 19010 #041-14-1978 L1979 **FM** *050 †18

DOUYON, Liselle. 130 S BRYN MAWR AVE, BRYN MAWR HOSPITAL 19010 #027-01-1986 L1989 **END** *020 †20

DRAGONETTI, Gerald C. 933 E HAVERFORD RD 19010 #041-07-1991 L1993 **GE** *020 †20

DRIES, Daniel Lee. ■ 19010 #056-05-1991 L2004 **CD** *020 †20

DUNCAN, Alfred E, III. ■ 19010 #041-01-1960 L1961 **P** *071

DUNCAN, Michael Paul. ■ 19010 #010-02-2007 L2007 **FP** *012

EISNER, Richard A. 830 OLD LANCASTER RD STE 2 19010 #033-05-1977 L1978 **N** *020 †75

ELEGBE, Oloruntoba Abiona. ■ 19010 #690-02-1983 L2004 **IM** *100

ELICKER, John Edward. 130 S BRYN MAWR AVE 19010 #041-02-1960 L1961 **EM GP** *020 †16

ELLIS, David J. 919 CONESTOGA RD BLDG ONE, STE 300 19010 #041-02-1981 L1984 **U** *020 †95

ELLMAN, Tamar Ahuva. 130 S BRYN MAWR AVE 19010 #041-02-2001 L2004 **PD** *100

EMLET, Michael Ray. 101 S BRYN MAWR AVE, STE 120 19010 #041-01-1987 L1996 **FM** *020 †18

ENOCHS, William Scott. 130 S BRYN MAWR AVE, BRYN MAWR HOSP 19010 #016-11-1989 L1997 **RNR DR** *020 †80

EYMONTT, Michael John. 130 S BRYN MAWR AVE 19010 #038-40-1959 L1972 **NM END** *071 †28

FALCHEK, Stephen Jos. 830 W LANCASTER AVE, STE 201 19010 #041-13-1992 L1994 **CHN** *020 †75,55

FARBER, Daniel Marc. 130 S BRYN MAWR AVE, DEPT OF EMERGENCY MEDICINE 19010 #041-01-2000 L2004 **EM** *020 †16

FARMAKIDIS, Constantine. ■ 19010 #035-45-2006 L2007 **IM** *012

FELDMAN, Arnold. 14 ELLIOTT AVE, STE 8 19010 #041-02-1962 L1967 **P PYA** *020 †75

FENICHEL, Gladys Susan. BRYN MAWR COLLEGE CAMPUS 19010 #041-13-1978 L1980 **P NS** *020 †75

FEUERSTEIN, Giora Z. ■ 19010 #550-01-1973 L1980 **PA GP** *050

FEWELL, John W U. ■ 19010 #051-01-1954 L1958 **PUD IM** *071

FILIP, John Robt. 830 OLD LANCASTER RD, STE 202 19010 #759-09-1964 L1970 **IM CD** *020 †20

FINE, Laurence David. 933 E HAVERFORD RD 19010 #051-04-1998 L2006 **N** *020 †75

FINKBINER, Rodman B. 933 E HAVERFORD RD 19010 #041-02-1953 L1954 **GE IM** *071 †20

FINKELSTON, Thomas Jay. 130 S BRYN MAWR AVE, BRYN MAWR HOSPITAL 19010 #041-07-1992 L1994 **AN** *020 †05

FISCHER, Carl R, Jr. BRYN MAWR COLLEGE CAMPUS 19010 #041-09-1945 L1946 **IM GP** *071

FISCHER, Newell. ■ 19010 #041-01-1961 L1962 **P** *040 †75

FISCHER, Ruth Simons. ■ 19010 #041-07-1962 L1964 **PYA CHP** *020 †75

FISHER, Andrew Wheeler. BRYN MAWR COLLEGE CAMPUS 19010 #035-45-1981 L1982 **IM** *020 †20

■ = Address Information Privacy Protected

FISHER, John Pedrick. 830 OLD LANCASTER RD, STE 305 19010 #051-04-1983 L1992 CD IM *020 †20

FLANAGAN, Michael Dennis. 937 E HAVERFORD RD, STE 103 19010 #041-01-1983 L1984 IM *020 †20

FLICK, Jonathan Andrew. 601 WOODLEAVE RD 19010 #035-01-1979 L1982 PG NTR *020 †55

FLORIN, Todd Adam. ■ 19010 #035-45-2005 L2005 PD *012

FRAZIER, Thomas Gibson. 101 S BRYN MAWR AVE # 201 19010 #041-01-1968 L1969 SO *020 †85

FREEDMAN, Lisa Beth. 1209 MONTGOMERY AVE 19010 #051-07-1995 L1997 FM *020 †18

FRIDAY, Gary H. 130 S BRYN MAWR AVE, GERHARD BLDG 1ST FL 19010 #041-13-1979 L1984 N IM *050 †75

FURMAN, Harold B. BRYN MAWR COLLEGE CAMPUS 19010 #041-02-1953 L1954 PD *071

GAROFALO, John Anthony. ■ 19010 #561-17-1974 L1976 ON AI *020

GEIGER, Mary E. 130 S BRYN MAWR AVE, BLG S 19010 #035-03-1965 L1966 P CHP *020

GILBERT, Elizabeth Merril. ■ 19010 #041-13-2005 L2007 IM *012

GILFOIL, James Henry. 864 COUNTY LINE RD 19010 #047-05-1972 L1973 P *020 †75

GILL, Frances M. ■ 19010 #016-02-1965 L1969 PD PHO *071 †55

GILLESPIE, Matthew James. 130 S BRYN MAWR AVE 19010 #041-13-1998 L2000 PDC *012

GILROY, Anne Frances. 1062 E LANCASTER AVE, ROSEMONT PLAZA 19010 #041-07-1985 L1986 EM *020 †16

GLASSNER, Michael J. 130 S BRYN MAWR AVE, STE 1000 D WING 19010 #035-03-1984 L1986 REN GYN *020 †30

GLUCK, Daniel Shellon. ■ 19010 #024-07-1982 L1993 NS *020

GNECCO, Sean Patrick. ■ 19010 #041-15-2003 L2003 EM *100

GODINEZ, Marye Hilda D D. ■ 19010 #028-34-1971 L1977 OS AN *071

GOLDENBERG, Marc Richard. 101 S BRYN MAWR AVE # 260 19010 #041-02-1973 L1983 TS GS *020 †85,90

GOLDMAN, Elizabeth Sarah. 1062 E LANCASTER AVE, STE 6 19010 #038-06-1999 L2001 P *020 †75

GOLDSTEIN, A Deborah Z. ■ 19010 #041-07-1962 L1963 PD *020 †55

GOLDSTEIN, Joel Benj. 860 W LANCASTER AVE 19010 #041-02-1961 L1962 CHP PYA *020 †75 ‡

GOLDSTEIN, Lisa Ilene. 1062 E LANCASTER AVE, ROSEMONT PLAZA SUITE 11 19010 #041-13-1987 L1994 P CHP *020 †75

GOPPELT, John Walter. 1201 COUNTY LINE RD 19010 #041-01-1955 L1956 P *020 †75 ‡

GOUDIE, Brett William. 830 OLD LANCASTER RD, STE 201 19010 #041-12-2000 L2006 PDC *100 †55

GRANETT, Jeffrey Roger. ■ 19010 #023-07-1968 L1987 CD IM *071 †20

GROSS, Peter Geo. 958 COUNTY LINE RD, STE 106 19010 #038-40-1982 L1982 OPH *020 †35

GROWNEY, Patrick Martin. 933 E HAVERFORD RD 19010 #010-02-1959 L1960 ON HEM *071 †20

GRUENBERG, Alan M. 950 E HAVERFORD RD, STE 302 19010 #047-06-1976 L1985 P PYA *020 †75

GRUJIC, Edina. 130 S BRYN MAWR AVE, MAIN LINE PATHOLOGY ASSOC 19010 #957-08-1975 L1998 PCP *020 †20

GUERRY, Richard Kennon. ■ 19010 #051-01-1970 L1972 OPH OS *071 †35

GUIDA, Jack Darryl. 130 S BRYN MAWR AVE, BRYN MAWR HOSPITAL 19010 #035-46-1997 L1999 NPM *020 †55

GUILLE, James T. 830 OLD LANCASTER RD, STE 201 19010 #422-01-1996 L1999 ORS *020 †40

GURUNATHAN, Shopana. 130 S BRYN MAWR AVE 19010 #496-69-2004 FP *012

HADDAD, Danny B. 829 W LANCASTER AVE, 2ND FL 19010 #041-02-2007 L2007 IM *012

HAMID, Nevan Ahmed. ■ 19010 #915-02-1980 PD *100

HARIGOVIND, Shalini. 130 S BRYN MAWR AVE, STE 312 19010 #496-28-1992 L2004 IM *020 †20

HARRISON, Frank S, Jr. 830 OLD LANCASTER RD, STE 305 19010 #041-01-1961 L1965 CD IM *071 †20

HARRISON, Joseph, Jr. 888 GLENBROOK AVE 19010 #041-13-1944 L1945 GP OM *072

HART, George Jonathan, III. 830 OLD LANCASTER RD, STE 206 19010 #023-01-1994 L2000 CN *020 †75

HASKIN, Marvin Edward. ■ 19010 #041-13-1955 L1956 R CD *030 †80

HAUPT, Donald Norman. 14 ELLIOTT AVE STE 4 19010 #041-14-1972 L1975 P *020 †75

HAUSMAN, David Henry. ■ 19010 #041-02-1947 L1948 PTH *071 †50

HELLER, Lisa J. 950 E HAVERFORD RD 19010 #041-01-1986 L1987 PD *020 †55

HENNING, Kelly Jo. ■ 19010 #024-07-1985 L1987 ID IM *020

HERRING, Christina Smith. 1030 E LANCASTER AVE, THE RADNOR HOUSE STE L-6 19010 #041-07-1975 L1977 P PME *020 †75

HERRING, Craig Richard. 130 S BRYN MAWR AVE, MAIN LINE EMERGENCY 19010 #041-14-1991 L1995 EM *020 †16

HERRMANN, Deborah R. ■ 19010 #041-01-1989 L1991 OPH *040 †35

HESSEN, Margaret Trexler. ■ 19010 #041-02-1982 L1983 ID IM *071 †20

HILFERTY, Daniel Jos, Jr. 840 MONTGOMERY AVE 19010 #041-02-1943 L1944 IM *071 †20

HILLIS, Nancy Haas. 130 S BRYN MAWR AVE 19010 #035-01-2001 L2003 PD *020 †55

HINGORANI, Arpita Jaideep. ■ 19010 #495-17-1995 L2004 DR *012

HIONIS, Roxane. 937 E HAVERFORD RD, STE 103 19010 #038-06-1989 L1991 IM *020 †20

HOBSON, John J. 937 E HAVERFORD RD, STE 103 19010 #041-02-1981 L1982 IM *020

HOLLANDER, Alexis Clay. 130 S BRYN MAWR AVE, BRYN MAWR HOSPITAL 19010 #041-13-1994 L1998 DR *020 †80

HOPKINS, F Thos. 830 OLD LANCASTER RD, STE 105 BRYN MAWR MEDICAL 19010 #023-07-1953 L1957 CD IM *071 †20

HOWKINS, John Henry F. 860 W LANCASTER AVE 19010 #035-01-1946 L1952 P *020 †75 ‡

HTIKE, Naing Lin. ■ 19010 #209-01-2002 L2007 IM *012

HUFF, Dale Sanborn. ■ 19010 #018-03-1962 L1969 CLP PTH *050 †50

HUFF, Denise Dennis. 194 FISHERS RD 19010 #018-03-1962 L1968 PD *020 †55

HUTH, Edward Janavel. ■ 19010 #041-01-1947 L1949 IM *071 †20

IQBAL, Linda Susan. 130 S BRYN MAWR AVE, 312 D-WING 19010 #028-34-1990 L2001 IM *020 †20

ISCHIROPOULOS, Patricia N. 919 CONESTOGA RD 19010 #001-02-1992 L1995 OBG *020 †30

JACKSON, Woody Herman. 101 S BRYN MAWR AVE 19010 #005-19-1993 L1997 FM *020 †18

JAIN, Manish. 130 S BRYN MAWR AVE, 321 H-WING 19010 #496-33-2002 L2006 IM *020 †20

JANZER, Sean Francis. 830 OLD LANCASTER RD, STE 105 19010 #041-09-1986 L1987 IC IM *020 †20

JESSAR, Ralph Alfred. ■ 19010 #041-01-1946 L1947 RHU IM *071

JUNG, Sungmi. ■ 19010 #583-06-1995 L2006 NP *100 †50

KAHN, Mark L. ■ 19010 #043-01-1987 L1999 IM *020 †20

KASPER, Vincent Peter, Jr. 937 E HAVERFORD RD, STE 204 19010 #041-02-2003 L2003 AN *020

KATZ, Stuart Ira. 1201 COUNTY LINE RD 19010 #041-01-1985 L1988 D *020 †15

KAUFFMAN, Frederic H. ■ 19010 #041-01-1981 L1983 IM *020,16

KAYE, Kendra Beth. 933 E HAVERFORD RD, BRYN MAWR MEDICAL SPECIALI 19010 #041-07-1987 L1988 RHU IM *020 †20

KELLER, Wayne Wm. 830 OLD LANCASTER RD, STE 305 19010 #041-01-1965 L1966 CD IM *020 †20

KENNING, James Alan. 958 COUNTY LINE RD 19010 #041-02-1974 L1980 NS *020 †25 ‡

KERN, Frank. 1201 COUNTY LINE RD 19010 #036-07-1968 L1976 D *071 †15

KERR, Kay Cundiff. BRYN MAWR COLLEGE HLTH CTR 19010 #041-07-1977 L1978 FM *020 †18

KHAN, Nuzhat. 130 S BRYN MAWR AVE, D-WING, SUITE 312 19010 #704-21-1989 L1999 IM *020 †20

KIM, Soo H. ■ 19010 #023-07-1998 L2001 OTO *020

KIRKPATRICK, William H. 830 OLD LANCASTER RD 19010 #038-41-1982 L1983 HS ORS *020 †40

KLEIN, Joel David. 830 W LANCASTER AVE, STE 201 19010 #041-09-1968 L1980 PD PDI *020 †55

KLINE, Mathilde R Saphir. 130 S BRYN MAWR AVE, BRYN MAWR HOSPITAL 19010 #038-06-1958 L1969 PTH *071 †50

KLINOW, Linda Faye. 950 E HAVERFORD RD 19010 #016-42-1981 L1983 PD *020 †55 ‡

KOCH, Cheryl Ann. 933 E HAVERFORD RD 19010 #041-14-1989 L1995 END *020 †20

KOHL, E James. ■ 19010 #041-13-1966 L1967 ORS *071 †40

KOLBERG, Heidi L. 245 N ITHAN AVE 19010 #023-07-1982 L1985 DR *020 †80

KOSARAJU, Siva Sankara Ra. 131 S BRYN MAWR AVE, DWING HMS 19010 #495-58-1983 L2002 IM *020 †95

KOTALIK, Frederick. 130 S BRYN MAWR AVE, MAIN LINE EMERGENCY 19010 #041-02-1988 L1991 EM *020 †16

KRAMAN, Franci R. 937 E HAVERFORD RD, STE 103 19010 #041-01-1987 L1988 IM *020 †20

KRAMER, Howard Barnet. 830 OLD LANCASTER RD, STE 105 19010 #041-13-2000 L2001 CD *020 †20

KRON, Violet S Samorodin. ■ 19010 #023-01-1955 L1960 CHP P *020 †75

KURTZMAN, Gary Jay. ■ 19010 #028-02-1981 L1983 HEM IM *050 †20

KUZNITS, Sagi Moses. 958 COUNTY LINE RD, CHESTMONT NEUROSURGICAL 19010 #041-13-1994 L2000 NS *020 †25 ‡

LAHUE-MORDY, Rhonda L. ■ 19010 #028-78-1988, ▲ L1989 IMG *071

LAMP, J Curtis. 888 GLENBROOK AVE 19010 #041-02-1944 L1944 PS *020 †65

LANCHONEY, Thomas Francis. 245 S BRYN MAWR AVE, CENTER FOR UROLOGIC CARE O 19010 #041-01-1997 L2001 U *020 †95

LANDER, William W. 888 GLENBROOK AVE 19010 #041-01-1949 L1950 FM IM *071 ‡

LAWRENCE, Thomas Edward. 937 E HAVERFORD RD, STE 103 19010 #041-07-1987 L1988 IM IMG *020 †20

LEDLIE, John Fletcher. 933 E HAVERFORD RD 19010 #048-04-1974 L1975 PUD IM *020 †20

LEE, Hoi Ko. 130 S BRYN MAWR AVE, EMERGENCY DEPT BRYN MAWR H 19010 #018-03-2003 L2003 EM *020 †20

LEE, Nancy Anne. 330 MILLBANK RD 19010 #035-19-1995 L2000 RNR *020 †80

LEE, Rotan. ■ 19010 #010-03-1938 L1939 GP PHP *071

LEHNER, William Edward. 130 S BRYN MAWR AVE 19010 #041-09-1976 L1977 FM EM *020 †18

LEINBERRY, Charles F, Jr. 101 S BRYN MAWR AVE, STE 300 19010 #041-02-1984 L1985 HS *020 †40 ‡

LENDENER, Stacey B. ■ 19010 #035-15-2003 L2003 PM *020

LE ROY, N Blair. 933 E HAVERFORD RD 19010 #035-20-1958 L1964 PUD IM *071

LEUNG, Lit Hung. ■ 19010 #462-01-1969 IM *100

LEUNG, Yiu Tak. ■ 19010 #041-02-2008 *012

LEVIN, Michele Andrea. ■ 19010 #024-01-2008 *012

LEVINE, Eleanor Rose. 130 S BRYN MAWR AVE, MAIN LINE EMERGENCY 19010 #016-06-1993 L2001 EM *020 †16

LEVITT, Robert. 933 E HAVERFORD RD 19010 #041-13-1974 L1975 GE IM *020 †20 ‡

LEWIS, George C, Jr. 875 COUNTY LINE RD 19010 #041-01-1944 L1945 GO GYN *072 †30

LIU, Hans Hamilton. 933 E HAVERFORD RD 19010 #024-01-1978 L1985 IM *020 †20

LOHNER, Ronald Adolf. 919 CONESTOGA RD, STE 1-200 19010 #033-06-1986 L1991 GS *020 †85,65

LOI, Thomas. 859 OLD LANCASTER RD # A10 19010 #035-15-2003 L2004 DR *012

LONG, Madeleine Loretta. 945 E HAVERFORD RD 19010 #041-07-1980 L1981 IM *071 †20

LONGAKER, Edwin D. BRYN MAWR COLLEGE CAMPUS 19010 #041-01-1943 L1944 GE OS *071 †20

LOWENTHAL, Joel Richard. BRYN MAWR MEDICAL BLDG S, STE 206 19010 #041-01-1963 L1964 FM *020 †18

LUTHRA, Veena. 635 S ITHAN AVE 19010 #495-17-1983 L1998 CHP *020 †75

MA, Edward. 130 S BRYN MAWR AVE, BRYN MAWR HOSP/HOSP MED SV 19010 #033-05-2000 L2001 IM *020 †20

MABASA, Abra Grize. 130 S BRYN MAWR AVE, BRYN MAWR HOSPITAL 19010 #759-18-2000 L2005 FP *012

MAC KENZIE, William Geo. 830 OLD LANCASTER RD, STE 201 19010 #061-01-1980 L1995 ORS OSS *020 †40

MAGEE, John Thos. BRYN MAWR COLLEGE CAMPUS 19010 #041-02-1957 L1958 IM NEP *072 †20

MAHEDAVI, Asma. ■ 19010 #041-13-2006 L2006 OBG *012

MALLER, Jacalyn Schlenger. 950 E HAVERFORD RD, STE 107 19010 #024-01-1984 L1986 PEM PD *020 †55

MANLOVE, Francis R. ■ 19010 #041-13-1938 L1940 P *071 †20

MANNAN, Mohammed Ashiq. 130 S BRYN MAWR AVE, STE 312 19010 #051-07-2002 L2006 IM *100 †20

MARCHANT, Frances E. 830 OLD LANCASTER RD, STE 209 19010 #041-02-1988 L1990 OTO *020 †45 ‡

MARCHIONNI, Christine. ■ 19010 #041-02-2007 L2007 P *012

MARINARI, Lawrence A. 875 COUNTY LINE RD, STE 112 19010 #041-01-1977 L1984 IM *020 †20

MARONE, Louis Anthony. ■ 19010 #041-02-2006 L2006 DR *012

MARTELLA, Arthur Thos. 830 OLD LANCASTER RD 19010 #041-02-1989 L1996 TS *020 †85,90

MARTIN, John Harvey. 933 E HAVERFORD RD 19010 #041-13-1958 L1959 RHU IM *071 †20

MARTIN, Martina M. 130 S BRYN MAWR AVE 19010 #041-02-1968 L1969 RHU IM *020 †20

MAYER, Henry Sawyer. 933 E HAVERFORD RD, BRYN MAWR MEDICAL SPECIALI 19010 #025-01-1971 L1973 CD IM *020 †20

MC CARTER, Thomas Gerald. 130 S BRYN MAWR AVE 19010 #041-09-1992 L1994 MDM IM *030 †20 ‡

MC CLURE, Charles P. 130 S BRYN MAWR AVE, 312 D-WING 19010 #041-02-1997 L1999 FM *020 †18

MC GINNIS, David Earl. 919 CONESTOGA RD BLDG ON 19010 #048-13-1987 L1990 **U** *020 †95

MC GOVERN, Angela Marie. 130 S BRYN MAWR AVE 19010 #041-02-2001 L2001 **NPM** *020 †55

MC KEE, Frank Wray. ■ 19010 #035-45-1943 L1954 **PTH OS** *071 †50

MC KENNA, Ernest La Place. 830 OLD LANCASTER RD, STE 209 19010 #041-02-1955 L1956 **OTO** *071 †45

MC KNIGHT, Lawrence K. 130 S BRYN MAWR AVE, HOSP/SUITE 312 D-WING 19010 #031-01-1997 L2000 **IM** *020 †20

MC NEAL, Geo Edward, Jr. 1128 WYNDON AVE 19010 #041-01-1961 L1962 **CLP** *030 †50

MC PHERSON, Margaret Bell. 130 S BRYN MAWR AVE 19010 #041-07-1989 L1991 **FM** *020 †18

MEARS, Ashley Wallace. 130 S BRYN MAWR AVE 19010 #024-07-1999 L2001 **FM** *020

MECHANICK, Stephen M. 14 ELLIOTT AVE, STE 9 19010 #041-01-1982 L1987 **P** *020 †75

MEIDT, Charles Eugene. 130 S BRYN MAWR AVE, STE 321 19010 #033-06-1988 L1990 **IM** *020 †20

MELHEM, Lina Y. 933 E HAVERFORD RD 19010 #001-06-1989 L2002 **END** *020 †20

MERKLIN, Lewis, Jr. 270 BEECHWOOD DR 19010 #041-13-1963 L1964 **P** *020 †45

MILLER, Donald Seth. 933 E HAVERFORD RD 19010 #035-19-1981 L1986 **RHU IM** *020 †20

MIRZA, Natasha. ■ 19010 #704-02-1983 L1993 **OTO** *020 †45

MOGHADAM, Abdol-Nabi. ■ #517-01-1949 L1962 **CD PDC** *071 †55

MOORE, Mary Elizabeth. 933 E HAVERFORD RD 19010 #041-13-1967 L1968 **RHU IM** *071 †20

MORROW, Vicki Olivia. 1062 E LANCASTER AVE, ROSEMONT PLAZA STE 18-D 19010 #036-08-1999 L2001 **CHP P** *020 †75

MURPHY, J Thomas, Jr. 888 GLENBROOK AVE 19010 #041-01-1957 L1958 **PYA** *071 †80

MURPHY, John Brien. 888 GLENBROOK AVE 19010 #028-03-1973 L1981 **PS** *071 †85,65

MURPHY, Stephen Gerard. 830 OLD LANCASTER RD, STE 201 19010 #035-01-1981 L1994 **PDS CCS** *020 †85

MUTHAURA, Patricia Nkatha. 919 CONESTOGA RD STE 104 19010 #010-03-2000 L2001 **OBG** *020 †30

MYERS, William S. 130 S BRYN MAWR AVE 19010 #041-77-1964, ▲ L1965 **FM** *020 †18 ‡

MYRICK, Steven Ronald. 830 OLD LANCASTER RD, STE 306 19010 #041-02-1981 L1983 **GS** *020 †85

NEALIS, Henry Jos. 875 COUNTY LINE RD, STE 202 19010 #041-01-1961 L1962 **OPH** *020 †35

NEIDECKER, Winifred Ann. 464 S ROBERTS RD 19010 #047-20-1985 L1990 **IM OBG** *020

NELSON, Wenonah Huston. 864 COUNTY LINE RD 19010 #041-07-1982 L1984 **PD** *020 †55

NEWHALL, Daniel L. BRYN MAWR COLLEGE CAMPUS 19010 #041-13-1972 L1973 **FM PM** *071 †18

NGUYEN, John Michael. 937 E HAVERFORD RD, STE 204 19010 #028-34-2001 L2001 **AN** *020 †05

NICKOLAS-SWATSKI, Karla. 1201 COUNTY LINE RD, STE 200 19010 #041-14-1991 L1993 **PD** *020 †55 ‡

NIKITINA, Svetlana. 830 OLD LANCASTER RD, STE 105 19010 #913-47-1990 L2003 **IM** *020 †20

NOONE, R Barrett. 888 GLENBROOK AVE 19010 #041-01-1965 L1966 **PS DS** *020 †85,65

NORWOOD, William Imon. 830 OLD LANCASTER RD, BLDG N. SUITE 201 19010 #007-02-1967 L1983 **TS** *020 †85,90

NWE, Khin May. ■ 19010 #209-01-1964 L1974 **AN** *071 †05

NYE, Robert Saml. 130 S BRYN MAWR AVE 19010 #041-07-1991 L1999 **IM** *020 †20

O'BRIEN, Kathleen Brigid. 130 S BRYN MAWR AVE 19010 #041-14-1996 L1999 **PD** *020 †55

O'REILLY, Robert Carlos. 130 S BRYN MAWR AVE 19010 #041-02-1990 L1992 **OTO** *020 †45

ORTIZ-ARDUAN, Alberto. ■ #847-13-1987 **NEP** *012

OSBORN, Hayler Herron. 130 S BRYN MAWR AVE, BRYN MAWR HOSPITAL 19010 #041-13-1968 L1969 **DR** *020 †20

OYELEWU, Richard Olayinka. 130 S BRYN MAWR AVE, "H-WING STE 321 19010 #690-02-1987 L2000 **IM** *020 †20 ‡

PACKARD, William Imbrie. 1062 E LANCASTER AVE, STE 8 19010 #041-09-1978 L1979 **P** *020 †75

PAJAK, Darian Michael. ■ 19010 #143-11-2001 L2004 **DR** *012

PALANT, Marina B. 875 COUNTY LINE RD, STE 105 19010 #913-09-1963 L1983 **IM** *020

PAPOLA, Gino Gaetano. ■ 19010 #041-13-1944 L1945 **GP IM** *020

PAPPANO, Jos Eugene, Jr. 875 COUNTY LINE RD 19010 #041-01-1961 L1962 **A IM** *071 †20,03

PARRY, Carolyn Elizabeth. ■ 19010 #041-02-1965 L1966 **R** *071 †80

PAULSON, James Arthur. 130 S BRYN MAWR AVE, MAIN LINE PATHOLOGY ASSOC 19010 #021-05-1983 L1988 **PCP** *020 †50 ‡

PAVAO, Jennifer Hardin. ■ 19010 #012-05-1985 L1987 **IM** *020 †20

PENAGALURU, Sreedhar. 130 S BRYN MAWR AVE, HOSPITAL MEDICAL SERVICES/ 19010 #495-50-1991 L2001 **IM** *020

PENG, Lee Li. 130 S BRYN MAWR AVE, 130 S BRYN MAWR AVENUE 19010 #243-76-1983 L2003 **HO** *020 †20

PIATT, Clarke U, II. 830 OLD LANCASTER RD, BRYN MAWR MEDICAL BUILDING 19010 #041-13-1995 L1997 **PCC** *020 †20

POOR, Leslie Ann Hamilton. 830 OLD LANCASTER RD, STE 305 19010 #041-07-1982 L1983 **CD IM** *020 †20

PORITSKY, Susan. 234 S BRYN MAWR AVE, STE 202 19010 #041-09-1978 L1979 **P** *020 †75

PRESSEL, David Michael. 130 S BRYN MAWR AVE 19010 #028-02-1993 L1997 **PD** *020 †55

PRICE, Henry Locher, Jr. ■ 19010 #041-01-1946 L1947 **AN** *071 †05

PRICE, Margaret Ann B. 950 E HAVERFORD RD STE 302 19010 #036-07-1982 L1984 **CHP PD** *020 †55,75

PRICE, Trevor Robt P. 950 E HAVERFORD RD STE 302 19010 #035-01-1969 L1985 **P IM** *020 †20,75

PRINCE, David Saml. 933 E HAVERFORD RD, BRYN MAWR MED SPECIALIST A 19010 #023-01-1979 L1987 **PUD CCM** *020 †20

QURESHI, Atif Ejaz. 130 S BRYN MAWR AVE, 312 D-WING 19010 #704-01-1995 L2000 **IM** *020 †20

RACKOW, David Lee. 130 S BRYN MAWR AVE 19010 #041-09-1980 L1981 **P** *020 †75

RADTKE, Wolfgang Arno K. 830 OLD LANCASTER RD, STE 201 19010 #409-12-1980 L2003 **PDC CD** *020 †55

RAGAVAN, Vanaja Vijaya. 831 AMIES LN 19010 #035-19-1976 L1981 **END IM** *030 †20

RANGARATHNAM, Candadai S. ■ 19010 #495-16-1957 L1972 **PS RO** *020

RAPP, Deborah. ■ 19010 #035-08-1983 L1984 **GP** *020

RATTAN, Sushil. 130 S BRYN MAWR AVE, RM 312 19010 #495-45-1983 L2001 **IM** *020 †20

REBER, Rose Marie J. ■ 19010 #033-05-1966 L1971 **NPM PD** *071 †55

REICHARD, Kirk Walker. 130 S BRYN MAWR AVE 19010 #041-01-1988 L1995 **PDS** *020 †85

REID, Christopher Jackson. 830 OLD LANCASTER RD, STE 206 19010 #041-02-1989 L1994 **N** *020 †75

REILLY, Kathleen Joyce. 603 PORTLEDGE DR 19010 #041-01-1989 L1991 **GS** *020 †85

REISS, Suzanne E. 860 W LANCASTER AVE 19010 #041-02-1988 L1993 **CHP P** *020 †75

RENDER, Jill Shafer. ■ 19010 #041-15-2000 L2008 **PD** *020 †55 ‡

RETIG, Jeffrey Norman. 933 E HAVERFORD RD 19010 #035-46-1979 L1984 **GE IM** *020 †20

RICHARDS, Cynthia Hinton. ■ 19010 #041-09-1988 L1990 **NM** *020 †28

RING, Ilona Raditz. ■ 19010 #473-01-1950 L1962 **PTH** *071 †50

RIORDAN, Thomas J. 1030 E LANCASTER AVE, STE L10 19010 #041-07-1993 L2003 **P ADP** *020 †75

ROBINSON, Harold Jerome. 830 OLD LANCASTER RD 19010 #041-01-1957 L1958 **CD IM** *071 †20

RODMAN, Mitchell Sanford. 24 N BRYN MAWR AVE # 171 19010 #041-01-1985 L1988 **NM** *071 †80,28

ROHR, Albert Schumm. 875 COUNTY LINE RD, STE 107 19010 #048-02-1977 L1978 **AI IM** *020 †20,03

ROLFE, Steven S. 14 ELLIOTT AVE 19010 #024-07-1975 L1983 **CHP PYA** *020 †75

ROMAN, Nancy Vivian. 130 S BRYN MAWR AVE, DEPT OF RADIOLOGY 19010 #041-07-1991 L1996 **PDR R** *020 †80

ROSE, David. 830 OLD LANCASTER RD, STE 306 19010 #035-01-1977 **ON GS** *020 †85

ROSEN, Alyssa Rachel. ■ 19010 #024-01-2008 L2012

ROSENBLUM, Jay S. 865 W LANCASTER AVE, FOX CHASE MEDICAL CENTER 19010 #035-46-1974 L1979 **DR** *020 †80 ‡

ROSENFELD, Jonathan F. 101 S BRYN MAWR AVE, STE 300 19010 #041-02-1999 L2005 **HS ORS** *100 †40

ROTH, Beverly R G. 860 W LANCASTER AVE 19010 #041-07-1971 L1973 **P CHP** *020 †75

ROWAN, Amy Beth. 14 S BRYN MAWR AVE STE 201 19010 #041-07-1987 L1990 **P** *020 †75

ROWLAND, Charlotte Waters. 130 S BRYN MAWR AVE, DEPT PATH 19010 #041-13-1948 L1968 **PTH** *071 †50

RUBIN, Jonathan Scott. ■ 19010 #008-02-1987 L2007 **PD** *020 †55

RUBINSTEIN, David. 1201 COUNTY LINE RD 19010 #275-01-1951 L1963 **P** *020 †75

RUDOLPH, Samuel Fogg. 1030 E LANCASTER AVE 19010 #041-02-1958 L1959 **OBG** *071 †30

RYAN, Michael Jos, Jr. 830 OLD LANCASTER RD, STE 306 19010 #019-02-1967 L1978 **CD** *020 †20

SACHDEVA, Rajeev. ■ 19010 #495-36-1975 L1976 **PTH OS** *020 †50

SAEDI, Nazanin Araghi. ■ 19010 #010-01-2007 L2007 **IM** *012

SAILES, Frederick Cortney. ■ 19010 #012-21-2003 L2003 **GS** *012

SALIM, Bozorgmehr. ■ 19010 #517-01-1955 L1968 **PTH** *072 †50

SALOMON, Alexander R. 130 S BRYN MAWR AVE 19010 #041-13-1989 L1991 **PD** *020 †55 ‡

SALWEN, Julia Kay. 130 S BRYN MAWR AVE, BRYN MAWR HOSPITAL 19010 #041-02-1994 L2000 **PDR** *020 †80

SANDERS, Lisa. 130 S BRYN MAWR AVE 19010 #008-01-1997 L2000 **IM** *040 †20

SANSONE, Thomas Christian. 101 S BRYN MAWR AVE, STE 220 19010 #041-01-1965 L1969 **U** *071 †95

SCHEIN, Deborah E. 1030 E LANCASTER AVE 19010 #041-15-1998 L2000 **PD** *020 †55

SCHEIN, Philip Saml. ■ 19010 #035-15-1965 L1984 **ON PA** *050 †20

SCHIFFMAN, Mara Suzanne. ■ 19010 #035-19-1984 L1985 **PD** *020 †55

SCHNALL, Sandra Faye. 933 E HAVERFORD RD 19010 #041-02-1979 L1980 **IM HEM** *020 †20

SCHOTLAND, Helena M. 830 OLD LANCASTER RD, MOB NORTH, SUITE 101 19010 #035-46-1988 L1992 **PUD SME** *020 †20

SCHWARTZ, Eric. ■ 19010 #550-02-1989 L1993 **GE** *020 †20

SHANMUGAN, Skandan. ■ 19010 #041-13-2007 L2007 **GS** *012

SHAPIRO, Aaron Lee. 1030 E LANCASTER AVE, STE L11 19010 #041-01-1987 L1987 **OTO** *020 †45

SHARPS, Lewis S. 1201 COUNTY LINE RD 19010 #041-02-1975 L1976 **ORS** *020 †40

SHORE, Neal Adam. 14 ELLIOTT AVE STE 2 19010 #041-01-1977 L1978 **P ADP** *020 †75

SHUKLA, Pragati. 830 OLD LANCASTER RD, STE 206 19010 #041-07-1997 L2003 **N** *020 †75

SIADATAN, Amir. 130 S BRYN MAWR AVE, STE 312 19010 #517-11-1996 L2001 *100

SIMON, Kathryn Karo. 130 S BRYN MAWR AVE, BRYN MAWR HOSPITAL 19010 #005-11-1978 L1987 **D OS** *020 †20

SIMON, Thomas Jay. ■ 19010 #005-18-1979 L1980 **GE IM** *050 †20

SIMPSON, Emma L. 130 S BRYN MAWR AVE 19010 #041-01-1980 L1981 **DR** *020 †80

SINCLAIR, Thomas Joseph. 130 S BRYN MAWR AVE, STE 312 19010 #041-02-2002 L2002 **IM HOS** *020 †20

SIVALINGAM, Jocelyn F. 933 E HAVERFORD RD 19010 #041-02-1987 L1988 **ID** *020 †20

SLAP, Gail B. ■ 19010 #041-01-1977 L1979 **ADL IM** *020 †20

SLATTERY, Thomas Raymond. ■ 19010 #041-13-2002 L2007 **DR** *012

SMITH, Jennifer Ann. 130 S BRYN MAWR AVE, FOURTH FLOOR A 19010 #041-02-2002 L2002 **AN** *012

SOHMER, Barbara Helene. ■ 19010 #023-07-1979 L1992 **CHP P** *020 †75

SOMERVILLE, Sheryl Ann. ■ 19010 #041-13-1960 L1961 **CHP P** *020

SORENSEN, Maryanne. 130 S BRYN MAWR AVE, BRYNN MAYR HOSPITAL 19010 #041-02-1982 L1984 **AN PD** *020 †55,05

SOROUSH, Mehrdad. 919 CONESTOGA RD, BLDG 1 19010 #051-01-1994 L1996 **U** *020 †95

SOWELL, Margaret Olivia. ■ 19010 #045-01-1990 L1992 **APM** *020 †20

SPITZER, Peter Gordon. 933 E HAVERFORD RD 19010 #041-05-1981 L1989 **ID IM** *020 †20

SQUADRITO, James F, Jr. 919 CONESTOGA RD, BLDG 1 19010 #041-02-1980 L1981 **U GS** *020 †95

STAHLMAN, Roy Alvin. ■ 19010 #041-13-1975 L1978 **EM** *020 †16

STAVIS, Robert Lawrence. 404 VALLEY GLEN DR 19010 #035-46-1976 L1981 **NPM PD** *020 †55

STAVROPOULOS, Lata T. ■ 19010 #016-43-1996 L2000 **IM** *020 †20

STEARNS, Jennifer Shaw. 937 E HAVERFORD RD 19010 #041-12-1997 L2005 **IM** *020 †20

STEIN, Eric Joel. 130 S BRYN MAWR AVE, BRYN MAWE HOSPITAL 19010 #041-01-1979 L1980 **DR VIR** *020 †80

STEINMEYER, Harry H, Jr. BRYN MAWR HOSPITAL 19010 #041-02-1951 L1952 **DR** *071 †80

STERIOUS, William John. 130 S BRYN MAWR AVE, MAIN LINE EMERGENCY 19010 #041-02-1998 L2000 **EM** *020 †16

STERNBERG, Cora. ■ 19010 #041-01-1977 L1978 **ON IM** *050 †20

STEVENS, Lloyd Weakley. ■ 19010 #041-01-1937 L1939 **GS** *071 †85

STEWART, David Arthur. BRYN MAWR HOSP 19010 #038-40-1962 L1967 **AN** *071 †05

STRAYER, David Rodney. ■ 19010 #005-14-1972 L1980 **ON IM** *050 †20

SUNG, Daniel John. 130 S BRYN MAWR AVE H-321 19010 #038-44-2003 L2003 **IM** *020 †20 ‡

SUTLIFF, Frederick P. BRYN MAWR MEDICAL BLDG 19010 #041-13-1946 L1947 **OPH** *071 †35

SWIHART, Jean O. 14 ELLIOTT AVE STE 8 19010 #041-07-1978 L1981 **P PYA** *020

SYKES, Linda K Stallings. 830 OLD LANCASTER RD, STE 206 19010 #048-02-1973 L1975 **N** *020 †75

TANG, Godffery Richard. 130 S BRYN MAWR AVE, STE 312 19010 #041-02-1994 L1996 **IM** *020 †20

TANTUCO, Irvin Co. ■ 19010 #748-01-1998 L2005 **IM** *100 †20
THALER, Malcolm Stuart. BRYN MAWR COLLEGE CAMPUS 19010 #036-07-1976 L1984 **IM** *020 †20 ‡
THANGADA, Vinod Kumar. 130 S BRYN MAWR AVE, STE 312 19010 #495-57-1993 L2001 **IM** *020 †20
THEURKAUF, Edward A. 933 E HAVERFORD RD 19010 #035-01-1954 L1955 **PUD IM** *020 †20
THOMPSON, James Wm. 245 S BRYN MAWR AVE 19010 #051-01-1960 L1967 **U GS** *020 †95
THOMPSON, Noble L, Jr. 1201 COUNTY LINE RD 19010 #041-02-1968 L1969 **R** *040 †80
TOAFF, Michael E. 1201 COUNTY LINE RD 19010 #550-01-1968 L1978 **GYN** *020 †30
TRAN, Thoai Qui. 130 S BRYN MAWR AVE, 3RD FLOOR H WING 19010 #033-05-1999 L2001 **IM** *020 †20
TRELLA, Tamara Ann. ■ 19010 #035-09-2004 L2005 **DR** *012
TRUMPP, Cynthia. 130 S BRYN MAWR AVE 19010 #016-06-1976 L1992 **PD ID** *020 †55
TURNER, Martha. 929 GLENBROOK AVE 19010 #041-13-1973 L1974 **P OS** *020 †75 ‡
UNDERWOOD, Mara Zagars. 937 E HAVERFORD RD, STE 204 19010 #041-13-1981 L1981 **AN** *020 †05
VAIDYA, Shailendra S. 910 ROSCOMMON RD 19010 #495-17-1968 L1973 **IM NEP** *020 †20
VERNACE, Joseph Victor. 101 S BRYN MAWR AVE, STE 200 19010 #041-02-1982 L1983 **ORS OSM** *020 †40
VIOLA, Paul Richard. 132 MORLYN AVE 19010 #035-15-1971 **P CHP** *071 †75
VOHRA, Pankaj. ■ 19010 #495-36-1988 **PD** *075 †55
WALKER, Angela Terese. 925 COUNTY LINE RD, P O BOX 440 19010 #047-07-1979 L2001 **IM OM** *040
WALLER, Joan C. 412 WYLDHAVEN RD 19010 #041-07-1973 L1974 **ID IM** *020 †20
WALSH, Shannon Jarosh. ■ 19010 #024-07-2002 L2004 **OBG** *020
WALZER, David Mark. 14 ELLIOTT AVE, STE 9 19010 #041-09-1978 L1979 **P** *020 †75 ‡
WANG, Monica H. ■ 19010 #385-02-1963 L1970 **FM** *071 †55
WARD, Michael Joseph, Jr. ■ 19010 #041-02-2003 L2007 **OPH** *100
WARREN, Kenneth C. BRYN MAWR COLLEGE CAMPUS 19010 #047-06-1949 L1953 **U** *071 †95
WEBER, Ronald Jay. BRYN MAWR COLLEGE CAMPUS 19010 #041-09-1976 L1977 **FM** *020 †18
WEHBE, Marwan Anis. 101 S BRYN MAWR AVE # 300, PA HAND CENTER 19010 #605-01-1976 L1981 **HS ORS** *020 †40
WEINGRAD, Tina Rose. BRYN MAWR HOSP, NUCLEAR MEDICINE DEPT 19010 #041-07-1978 L1979 **DR NM** *062 †80,28
WEINSTEIN, Steven Harley. 864 COUNTY LINE RD 19010 #041-02-1979 L1980 **P** *020 †75
WEISS, Fred Harvey. 130 S BRYN MAWR AVE 19010 #035-09-1971 L1987 **PD PDC** *020 †55
WESTAWSKI, Daniel B. 919 CONESTOGA RD, BLDG 2 19010 #041-02-1992 L1994 **PS HS** *020 †85,65
WILKERSON, L Douglas. 830 OLD LANCASTER RD, STE 309 19010 #012-05-1969 L1973 **CHN N** *020 †55,75
WILSON, William Wartman. BRYN MAWR COLLEGE CAMPUS 19010 #041-01-1942 L1943 **P N** *072 †75
WOLLMAN, Eve Elizabeth. ■ 19010 #035-45-1995 N *100
WOOD, James E, III. ■ 19010 #024-01-1949 L1954 **CD** *071
WOODY, Daniel Jos. ■ 19010 #041-13-1976 L1977 **TS GS** *020 †85,90
WU, Pearl May. 130 S BRYN MAWR AVE 19010 #016-06-1992 L1996 **IM** *020 †20
YEGUDKINA, Irina. 130 S BRYN MAWR AVE, STE 312 19010 #913-43-1989 L2005 **IM** *020 †20 ‡
ZAVOD, William S. 130 S BRYN MAWR AVE 19010 #041-02-1966 L1967 **PD OS** *020 †55
ZEIDMAN, Joan Helene. 919 CONESTOGA RD 19010 #041-13-1987 L1989 **OBG** *020 †30
ZELTSER, Ilia. 919 CONESTOGA RD, BLDG 1 19010 #035-48-2000 L2001 **U** *100
ZHU, Yun. 130 S BRYN MAWR AVE, SYSTEM/MED STAFF AFFAIRS O 19010 #243-44-1984 L2003 **AN** *020 †05
ZIHNI, Sherif Mohamed. ■ 19010 #308-13-2001 L2007 **FP** *012

BUCKINGHAM – BUCKS

CHAO, Jimmy Yee-Lee. ■ 18912 #244-03-1968 *074
WALSH, Simona Manuela. PO BOX 665, 4870 YORK RD 18912 #781-03-1989 L2002 **PD** *020 †55

BUFFALO MILLS – BEDFORD

FINDER, Marc Joel. 1433 BARD HOLLOW RD 15534 #041-02-1978 L1979 **EM GP** *020 †16

BURGETTSTOWN – WASHINGTON

ALEXANDER, Dan Geo. ■ 15021 #055-01-1986 L1988 **IM** *075 †20
DEROSA, Julie Kang. 1227 SMITH TOWNSHIP STT RD, CORNERSTONE CARE 15021 #055-01-1991 L1993 **FM** *020 †18
EVANS-WHEELER, Coleen G. 1227 SMITH TOWNSHIP STT RD 15021 #051-04-1986 L1995 **FM** *020 †18
HARPER, Thomas Geo. 86 STEUBENVILLE PIKE 15021 #041-12-1955 L1956 **FM** *020 †18
MULLEN, Brendan Thomas. ■ 15021 #041-15-2007 L2007 **TY** *012
RAGO, Mary Kendall. 560 STEUBENVILLE PIKE 15021 #028-03-1983 L2005 **OTO** *020 †45
TAYLOR, Aparna Vempaty. 1227 SMITH TOWNSHIP STT RD 15021 #038-44-2000 L2001 **FM** *020 †18
THIMMIAH, Ramesh. 560 STEUBENVILLE PIKE 15021 #496-22-1989 L1996 **IM** *020 †20

BURNHAM – MIFFLIN

DINSMORE, Harry H, Jr. 215 N BEECH ST 17009 #055-02-1991 L1997 **ORS** *020 †40
PATEL, Prakash J. 299 1/2 S LOGAN BLVD, LEWISTOWN CARDIOLOGY ASSOC 17009 #495-22-1979 L1988 **CD CCM** *020 †20
SHETH, Ketankumar R. 299 1/2 S LOGAN BLVD 17009 #495-23-1983 L1993 **CD** *020 †20
SUTHAR, Arvind Laljibhai. 299 1/2 S LOGAN BLVD 17009 #495-76-1978 L1984 **CD IM** *020 †20 ‡

BUTLER – BUTLER

ACEVEDO, Frederic Abalo. 389 NEW CASTLE RD 16001 #748-02-1982 L1988 **PUD IM** *020 †20
ADALJA, Amesh Ashok. ■ 16002 #654-01-2002 L2002 **ID** *012 †20

ADALJA, Ashok Natverlal. 325 NEW CASTLE RD 16001 #495-96-1970 **IM FM** *020 †20 ‡
ADAMS, Richard Francis. 579 THREE DEGREE RD 16002 #041-09-1979 L1979 **EM** *020 †16
ALTHOFF, Rodger Wm. 165 BRUGH AVE, STE 201 16001 #010-01-1972 L2003 **GS AS** *020 †85
AMOR IZNAGA, Leonardo. V A HOSPITAL 16001 #275-01-1947 L1974 **PM** *020
ASHBAUGH, William Heber. 100 EVANS RD STE A 16001 #041-02-1959 L1961 **PD OS** *020 †55
BAKER, Marvin Palange. 127 ONEIDA VALLEY RD, MORGAN II STE 202 16001 #649-14-1974 L1982 **CD IM** *020 †20
BALOURIS, Dean Anthony. 102 TECHNOLOGY DR, STE 120 16001 #041-12-1988 L1991 **OPH** *020 †35
BELL, Alexander Leighton. 301 1ST ST, STE 200 16001 #041-12-1985 L1988 **HS** *020 †40
BELLA, Paraluman R. 257 HENRICKS RD 16001 #748-01-1961 L1979 **PM** *062 †60
BELLA, Romeo H. PO BOX 1785 16003 #748-01-1958 L1973 **AN** *071
BENADO, David Nissim. 911 E BRADY ST 16001 #041-09-1991 L2001 **EM** *020 †16
BENAKANAHALLI, Manjunath. 233 THORNWOOD DR 16001 #496-39-1995 L2000 **IM** *020 †20
BHOJAK, Tejal Jitendra. 901 E BRADY ST, STE 103 16001 #495-17-1997 L2001 *020 †75
BODE, Frederick Wm, Jr. 911 E BRADY ST 16001 #041-02-1947 L1948 **OTO OS** *072 †45
BRAY, John Page. 911 E BRADY ST, BUTLER MEMORIAL HOSPITAL 16001 #019-02-1981 L1984 **AN PD** *020 †20
CAMPANELLA, Stephen D. 480 E JEFFERSON ST, STE C4 16001 #041-02-1981 L1987 **U** *020 †95
CARLSON, Nicole Lynn. 911 E BRADY ST, BUTLER HEALTH SYSTEM 16001 #041-14-1999 L2006 **OBG** *020 †30
CARLSSON, Mark Andrew. 200 RENAISSANCE DR 16001 #041-09-1982 L1983 **FM** *020 †18
CASTRO, Oscar Lopez. 111 WOODY DR 16001 #748-08-1991 L2003 **END IM** *020 †20
CHANNAPATI, Thippeswamy T. 342 N MAIN ST 16001 #495-72-1971 L1975 **IM** *020 †18
CHATTA, Fozia A. 1651 N MAIN ST 16001 #704-05-1983 L1993 **IM** *020 †20
CHRISTIE, William Clark. 357 N MAIN ST 16001 #039-05-1985 L1986 **OPH** *020 †35
COPE, Donald I. ■ 16001 #041-12-1953 L1954 **R** *071 †80
DE L'ETOILE, Helene. ■ 16001 #067-02-1978 L1982 *074
DEMBY, Dennis Mitchell. 1022 N MAIN ST EXT, STE B 16001 #041-13-1978 L1980 **IM** *020 †20
DICUCCIO, William A. 480 E JEFFERSON ST 16001 #041-02-1974 L1975 **FM FPG** *030 †18 ‡
DICUCCIO, William Carroll. 480 E JEFFERSON ST 16001 #041-02-2001 L2003 **FM** *020 †18 ‡
DRENNEN, James Kirk. 911 E BRADY ST 16001 #041-13-1957 L1957 **GS** *071 †85 ‡
DUBNANSKY, John Earle. 325 NEW CASTLE RD, VA MED CTR 16001 #041-12-1964 L1965 **AN** *020 †05
DUDECK, Carl R. ■ 16002 #041-02-1953 L1954 **GS** *071 †85
ELAWAR, Munir Youssef. 724 E BRADY ST 16001 #605-01-1978 L1984 **N** *020 †75
EL-KHATIB, Hazem N. 911 E BRADY ST 16001 #605-01-1987 L1998 **TS VS** *020 †85,90
EVANS, Jonathan Lynn. 911 E BRADY ST 16001 #035-01-1972 L1973 **DR PUD** *020 †20,80
FIEHLER, Paul Cecil. 389 NEW CASTLE RD 16001 #041-12-1976 L1977 **PUD IM** *020 †20
FITZSIMMONS, Wm Richard. ■ 16001 #041-12-1939 L1940 **OBG** *071 †30
FLOOD, Katherine Margaret. 325 NEW CASTLE RD, BUTLER VAMC 16001 #041-12-1982 L1987 **PM** *020 †60
FOSTER, Frederick G, Jr. 911 E BRADY 3RD FL 16001 #007-02-1968 L1974 **ADM PYG** *020 †75
GARCIA, Alfredo J. 312 W JEFFERSON ST, ALFREDO J GARCIA MD LTD 16001 #737-01-1958 L1964 **IM CD** *020
GEMPERLEIN, John L, Jr. ■ 16002 #041-12-1952 L1953 **PTH** *020 †50
GEORGE, Sarah. 911 E BRADY ST 16001 #495-83-1989 L2003 **PTH PCP** *020 †50
GHORBANIAN, Sakeneh N. 100 EVANS RD 16001 #517-01-1967 L1977 **PD** *050 †55
GOSSELIN, Robert Rene. 911 E BRADY ST, BUTLIN MEMORIAL HOSPITAL 16001 #067-02-1977 L1982 **EM** *020 †16
GREGG, Thomas S. 911 E BRADY ST DEPT RAD 16001 #041-12-1953 L1957 **R** *071 †80
GRIBIK, Joseph J, Sr. 911 E BRADY ST 16001 #041-12-1978 L1979 **IM** *020
HAJDUK, Istvan. 389 NEW CASTLE RD 16001 #473-01-1982 L1999 **PCC** *020 †20
HAN, Samuel I. 480 E JEFFERSON ST, STE A 16001 #385-01-1966 L1972 **IM** *020 †20
HANDLER, Ira Scott. 901 E BRADY ST, STE 103 16001 #035-06-1985 L1986 **P** *020 †75
HANNA, Sophie Sadek. 911 E BRADY ST, BUTLER MEDICAL PROVIDERS 16001 #915-10-1992 L2001 **APM PM** *020 †60
HO, Hung-Chi. 102 TECHNOLOGY DR STE 110, BUTLER REG CANCER CTR 16001 #244-04-1979 L1984 **RO PD** *020 †80 ‡
HOOTMAN, Barry Dunn. 301 1ST ST, ORTHOPEDIC ASSOC STE 200 16001 #041-12-1975 L1976 **ORS** *020 †40 ‡
HU, Kang Hing. 901 E BRADY ST, STE 301 16001 #244-03-1970 L1981 **U** *020 †95
JACOB, Rose. 325 NEW CASTLE RD, BUTLER VA MEDICAL CENTER 16001 #495-02-1985 L1992 **IM** *020 †20
JINDAL, Ripu Daman. 325 NEW CASTLE RD, VA MEDICAL CENTER 16001 #495-43-1991 L2000 **P** *020
JOHN, Benjamin. 325 NEW CASTLE RD 16001 #495-08-1983 L1988 **IMG** *020 †20
JORDAN, Lillian Lupinacci. 325 NEW CASTLE RD, BUTLER VA MEDICAL CENTER 16001 #038-41-1982 L1983 **IM NEP** *020 †20
KEDZIERSKI, Maciej M. 911 E BRADY ST, BUTLER MEMORIAL HOSPITAL 16001 #038-40-2003 L2007 **EM** *030 †16
KHAN, Mohammed Abdul Rahm. 114 E DIAMOND ST 16001 #035-09-2000 L2000 *020
KINSELLA, Mario Thos. 389 NEW CASTLE RD 16001 #539-03-1978 L1992 *020
KLINE, Lewis Reuel. 389 NEW CASTLE RD 16001 #041-14-1979 L1980 **PUD SME** *020 †20
KRAWCZUK, Agnieszka. 911 E BRADY ST, BUTLER MEMORIAL HOSPITAL 16001 #759-11-1991 L2003 **ID** *020 †20
LAUREANO, Eber Nantes. ■ 16001 #748-01-1955 L1967 **IM** *071
LAUREANO, Reynaldo E. 518 N MAIN ST LOWR LEVEL, LERA PROFESSIONAL BUILDING 16001 #748-01-1956 L1967 **IM** *071
LEIGHTON, Kevin L. 1022 N MAIN ST EXT, STE B 16001 #064-01-1991 L1995 **FM** *020 †18
LENKO, Philip Michael. 901 E BRADY ST, STE 100 16001 #035-03-1984 L1985 **OBG** *020 †30
LLOYD, George Thos. 408 GLENWOOD WAY 16001 #041-12-1985 L1990 **GS OS** *075 †85
MAALOUF, Tony Maurice. 407 W JEFFERSON ST STE B 16001 #605-03-1989 L1994 **GS VS** *020 †85
MADONNA, Frank Anthony. 911 E BRADY ST, BUTLER MEM HOS RADIOLOGY 16001 #041-09-1986 L1988 **DR VIR** *020 †80
MAHMOOD, Arshad. 216 W JEFFERSON ST 16001 #495-67-1975 L1986 **CD IM** *020 †20
MARWAHA, Asha. ■ 16002 #495-15-1964 L1975 **OBG** *020
MC GILL, A Thomas. 911 E BRADY ST 16001 #024-16-1985 L1986 **ID IM** *020 †20
MC GORRIAN, Grace Maureen. 112 HILLVUE DR, ISCMHC 16001 #032-01-1982 L1984 **P PFP** *020 †75
MC KEE, Robert Earl. 911 E BRADY ST 16001 #041-12-1948 L1949 **GS** *030 †85
MC NULTY, Timothy Patrick. 325 NEW CASTLE RD, BUTLER VA MEDICAL CENTER 16001 #041-12-1986 L1988 **PM** *020 †60

MEHTA, Varsha Jayantilal. 325 NEW CASTLE RD, VA MEDICAL CENTER 16001 #495-96-1970 L1974 **IM PUD** *030 †20

METCALFE, Marc Francis. 911 E BRADY ST 16001 #038-06-1984 L1990 **AN** *020 †05

MICHALAK, William Anthony. 911 E BRADY ST 16001 #035-08-1984 L1989 **ATP CLP** *020 †50 ‡

MIRANDA, Cesar P. 911 E BRADY ST 16001 #748-08-1957 L1971 **IM CD** *071

MITRA, Devashis A. 518 N MAIN ST 16001 #495-83-1985 L2000 **IM** *020 †20

MOORE, Ernest E. ■ 16002 #038-41-1946 L1947 **FM** *071 †18

MUSMANNO, Mark Clark. 480 E JEFFERSON ST, STE C4 16001 #041-12-1981 L1990 **U** *020 †95

NALLATHAMBI, Helga N. PO BOX 909 16003 #495-08-1960 L1972 **NEP NPM** *071

NALLATHAMBI, Swamikkan A. 131 E CUNNINGHAM ST 16001 #495-08-1960 L1971 **IM GE** *020 †20

NESBITT, Scott Alan. 1022A N MAIN ST, AVADA BUILDING 16001 #041-09-1988 L1990 **FM** *020 †18

NIETO, Victor Edgardo. 901 E BRADY ST, STE 301 16001 #341-01-1971 L1976 **GS** *020 †20

O'HALLARON, Helen Chun. 602 EVANS CITY RD STE 20 16001 #051-01-1985 L1989 **PD** *040 †55

ONUFREY, Victor Geo. 160 HINDMAN RD 16001 #041-02-1981 L1982 **RO** *020 †80 ‡

PATTERSON, Robert Brian. 911 E BRADY ST, DEPT PATH 16001 #021-01-1980 L2002 **PTH** *020 †50

PINEDA, Rosalinda A. ■ 16001 #748-08-1965 L1978 **IM GS** *100

PIRZADA, Raheela. 389 NEW CASTLE RD 16001 #704-20-1990 L1997 **PCC** *020 †20

POMERANTZ, Marc B. 325 NEW CASTLE RD, V A MED CENTER 16001 #041-09-1977 L1978 **IM** *020 †20

PRASAD, Mahadevappa M. 1651 N MAIN ST EXT 16001 #495-33-1972 L1980 **CD IM** *020 †20

PULLEKINES, Joseph W. 301 1ST ST, STE 200 16001 #041-12-1987 L1988 **ORS** *020 †40

RAJ, Moses S. 102 TECHNOLOGY DR, STE 110 16001 #495-50-1985 L2000 **HO** *020 †20

RAO, Edwin Jonathan P. 389 NEW CASTLE RD 16001 #748-10-1982 L1988 **CCM GS** *020 †20

RAVELLA, David L, Jr. 325 NEW CASTLE RD, BUTLER VA MEDICAL CEBTER 16001 #024-01-1962 L1964 **R NM** *071 †75,80

REEFER, John Chester. 1022B N MAIN ST 16001 #041-12-1977 L1978 **IM** *020 †20

RIZK, Wafa. 911 E BRADY ST 16001 #915-04-1969 L1973 **EM AM** *020 †18,16

ROCCHI, John Robert. 480 E JEFFERSON ST 16001 #055-01-1993 L1996 **IM PD** *020 †55,20 ‡

SAMUEL, Dhinesh John. 131 E CUNNINGHAM ST 16001 #041-12-1999 L2002 **MPD** *020

SARGENT, Stephen Ernest. 480 E JEFFERSON ST 16001 #041-13-1984 L1986 **IM PD** *020 †20,55

SCHMIDT, Harry Justus. ■ 16001 #025-01-1948 L1955 **GS** *071 †85

SEKARAN, Kamalesh. 480 E JEFFERSON ST 16001 #495-04-1963 L1973 **PD** *074 †55

SEKARAN, S K. 117 S MCKEAN ST 16001 #495-16-1962 L1971 **U** *020 †85,95

SEKHON, Manharpreet S. 325 NEW CASTLE RD, VA MEDICAL CENTER 16001 #495-29-1975 L1985 **IM** *020 †20

SETHI, Surendra Kumar. 230 S WASHINGTON ST 16001 #495-20-1962 L1972 **CD IM** *020 †20 ‡

SHETTER, Thomas Gerard. 480 E JEFFERSON ST 16001 #041-12-1982 L1983 **IM IMG** *020 †20

SOFFIETTI, John Hubert. 901 E BRADY ST STE 103 16001 #035-15-1980 L1981 **P PYG** *020 †75 ‡

SPINA, Carmen Michael. 129 E CUNNINGHAM ST 16001 #010-02-1943 L1944 **GP OBG** *075

SPINGOLA, Charles Edward. 301 1ST ST, STE 200 16001 #035-05-1982 L1987 **ORS** *020 †40

SRODES, Charles Henninger. 102 TECHNOLOGY DR, STE 110 16001 #035-01-1967 L1969 **HEM ON** *020 †20

SUBBIAH, Thevaraya N D. 122 S WASHINGTON ST 16001 #495-04-1971 L1979 **CD IM** *020 †20

TIBURCIO, Albino F, Jr. 100 EVANS RD 16001 #748-01-1958 L1968 **PD PDA** *071 †55

TOLENTINO, Julian Canlas. 316 N MAIN ST 16001 #748-08-1967 L1972 **OBG** *020 †30

TOLENTINO, Lilia B. VA MEDICAL CENTER 16001 #748-08-1965 L1970 **R RO** *071

TOPARLI, Ahmet. 1022 N MAIN ST EXT, STE B 16001 #902-09-1991 L2003 **IM** *020 †20

TOTH, Eva. 111 WOODY DR 16001 #473-02-1981 L1993 **END IM** *020 †20

TREDENNICK, Chas Nicholas. 1230 EAST DR 16002 #041-13-1960 L1961 **OPH** *020 †35

TROTTA, Michael Richard. 480 E JEFFERSON ST 16001 #055-01-1993 L1997 **IM** *020 †55,20 ‡

WAHL, Michael James. 200 RENAISSANCE DR, STE 403 16001 #041-14-1993 L1995 **FM** *020 †18

WELKER, Keith Bernhardt. 901 E BRADY ST 16001 #041-14-1986 L1990 **OTO** *020 †45 ‡

WICK, John Leroy. ■ 16001 #041-13-1963 L1964 **OPH** *071 †35

YOST, Charles Thos. 901 E BRADY ST 16001 #041-12-1974 L1975 **OTO A** *020 †45 ‡

ZADECKY, Leonard Bruce. 325 NEW CASTLE RD 16001 #041-13-1969 L1970 **IMG AM** *020 †20

ZAGGER, George Martin. ■ 16001 #041-02-1996 L1998 **FM** *020 †18

ZIMMERMAN, Greg Alan. 911 E BRADY ST 16001 #041-12-1991 L1995 **PM** *020 †60

CABOT – BUTLER

BEAN, Carl Bennett. ■ 16023 #016-06-1944 L1944 **R** *071 †80

SCHWARTZ, Susan F. ■ 16023 #023-01-1975 L1988 **IM** *020 †20

CALIFORNIA – WASHINGTON

CHADWICK, Lisa T. 415 3RD ST 15419 #041-15-2000 L2001 **FM** *020 †18

GANDHI, Anant J. 371 SKYLINE DR 15419 #495-37-1975 L1981 **IM IMG** *020 †20

GOSAI, Kamlesh Babarpuri. 371 SKYLINE DR 15419 #495-76-1980 L1988 **IM OM** *020

KEDARNATH, Siva. 371 SKYLINE DR 15419 #495-04-1980 L1989 **CD IM** *020 †20

KOMALAHIRANYA, Usa E. 166 SKYLINE DR 15419 #891-02-1962 L1972 **AN** *020 ‡

MARTIN, John Byron. 1152 WOOD ST 15419 #041-12-1972 L1973 **IM IMG** *020 †20 ‡

NINO, Raymond Frank. 87 3RD ST 15419 #654-01-1983 L1984 **FM** *020 †

PARK, Min Hi. 217 WOOD ST 15419 #583-10-1965 L1973 **FM** *020

PATANI, Hemant A. 371 SKYLINE DR 15419 #495-48-1995 L2003 **IM** *020

REDDY, Thugu Sahadeva. 371 SKYLINE DR 15419 #495-70-1989 L1999 **IM** *020 †20

CAMBRIDGE SPRINGS – CRAWFORD

MARTIN, Ronald Christian. 118 RAILROAD ST, BOX 241 16403 #748-01-1977 L1987 **GP OBG** *020

WELLS, Kippen Clift. ■ 16403 #035-45-1946 L1952 **IM OS** *071 †20

CAMP HILL – CUMBERLAND

ACHARYA, Ravi Dilipkumar. 1845 CENTER ST 17011 #495-76-1999 L2006 **RHU** *020

ADLESTEIN, Joseph. ■ 17011 #010-02-1950 L1951 **P** *072 †75

AGGARWAL, Shiv S. 503 N 21ST ST, HOLY SPIRIT HOSPITAL 17011 #495-69-1971 L1985 **P** *020

AHMED, Ali. 890 POPLAR CHURCH RD # 309 17011 #704-02-1963 L1983 **P PYA** *020

ALDOUS, Thomas Winder. HOLY SPIRIT HOSPITAL 17011 #049-01-1972 L1973 **EM GP** *020 †16

ALFANO, Salvatore Norman. ■ 17011 #041-07-1980 L1981 **EM** *020 †16 ‡

AL-SBAITI, Rabia Naim. 425 N 21ST ST, STE 204 17011 #875-01-1993 L1999 **IM** *020 †20

ANDERSON, Elizabeth Joan. 104 ERFORD RD 17011 #041-01-1989 L1993 **D** *020 †15 ‡

ANDERSON, William M. ■ 17011 #041-09-1967 L1968 **PUD CCM** *071 †20

ANDREWS, Janiece C. 890 POPLAR CHURCH RD, STE 410 17011 #041-14-1974 L1996 **CHP P** *020 †75

ARNOLD, Gordon Carl. 890 POPLAR CHURCH RD, MEDICAL ARTS BLDG SUITE 50 17011 #041-09-1964 L1965 **GS CRS** *071 †85

ARO, Jennifer M. 25 N 32ND ST 17011 #023-12-1992 L2002 **FM** *020 †18

ARORA, Ramesh. 503 N 21ST ST 17011 #495-05-1967 L1975 **EM ADM** *020 †16

AUERBACH, David Neil. 503 N 21ST ST 17011 #023-01-1979 L1981 **DR GS** *020 †80

AZIZKHAN, Reza Geo. 503 N 21ST ST 17011 #495-01-1949 L1966 **GS** *071 †85

BAGIAN, Robert G. 503 N 21ST ST 17011 #041-02-1979 L1979 **OM EM** *020 †16

BANZHOFF, Gordon K. 890 POPLAR CHURCH RD, STE 505 17011 #041-13-1952 L1953 **OBG** *071

BARTON, Frances Jane. 1524 CEDAR CLIFF DR 17011 #041-07-1976 L1977 **OPH** *020 †35

BARTON, John Odonnell. 104 ERFORD RD 17011 #041-09-1981 L1982 **D** *020 †15 ‡

BATTIN, Jasna P. 207 HOUSE AVE, CONNER, RICH ASSOCIATES 17011 #957-03-1981 L1994 **IM** *020

BEANE, Howard Carlton. 100 CORPORATE CENTER DR, STE 100 17011 #024-05-1957 L1961 **U** *071 †95

BEKAL, Shridhara. ■ 17011 #496-01-1975 **PD** *100

BELIS, John Alexander. 423 N 21ST ST, STE 300 17011 #041-02-1971 L1986 **U** *020 †95

BENEDICT, John Howard. 503 N 21ST ST 17011 #041-14-1982 L1984 **AN** *020 †05

BERGEY, Elizabeth Anne. 503 N 21ST ST 17011 #041-13-1992 L1996 **DR** *020 †80

BHATT, Anjali Gaurang. 503 N 21ST ST, DEPT PATH 17011 #495-01-1965 L1973 **PTH** *020 †50 ‡

BHYUN, Dae Soo. 503 N 21ST ST 17011 #583-01-1960 L1968 **R** *020 †80 ‡

BLAS, Alfredo L. 205 GRANDVIEW AVE, STE 402 17011 #748-02-1997 L2006 **NEP** *020 †20

BLOSCHICHAK, Andrew. 1800 CENTER ST 17089 #041-09-1982 L1983 **FM** *030 †18

BOSHNAKOVA, Sevdalina V. 25 N 32ND ST, VA OUTPATIEN CLINIC 17011 #198-03-1989 L1998 **IM** *020

BRECHT, James Allen. 503 N 21ST ST 17011 #041-02-1961 L1962 **CHP P** *020 †75

BRENT, Geoffrey John. 1524 CEDAR CLIFF DR 17011 #041-13-1993 L1997 **OPH** *020 †35

BRICKNELL, Paul Philip. 503 N 21ST ST 17011 #917-28-1958 L1969 **AN** *071 †05

BRONITSKY, Barbara G. 503 N 21ST ST 17011 #041-14-1977 L1979 **DR OS** *020 †80

BUCHANAN, Sarah. ■ 17011 #028-46-1999 L2004 **OBG** *012

BUENAVENTURA, Milagros P. ■ 17011 #748-01-1967 L1977 **P** *020 †75

CALAITGES, John Geo. 800 POPLAR CHURCH RD 17011 #035-15-1992 L1994 **VS** *020 †85

CAMPONOVO, Ernest John. 503 N 21ST ST 17011 #003-01-1981 L1990 **DR NM** *020 †80,28

CHARAN, Meena. 890 POPLAR CHURCH RD, STE 200 17011 #496-03-1981 L2003 **FM** *020 †18

CHARAN, Mohan Singh. 899 POPLAR CHURCH RD, PA-G1 CONSULTANTS 17011 #496-03-1981 L1997 **GE** *020 †20

CLADEL, Charles E, Jr. 503 N 21ST ST 17011 #035-15-1966 L1973 **CHP P** *020 †75

COLEMAN, Ernest Hamer, Jr. 4900 MARKET ST 17011 #041-02-1957 L1958 **OPH** *071 †35

CONNER, Kenneth Bruce. 207 HOUSE AVE, STE 101 17011 #041-09-1968 L1969 **IM** *071 †20

COWLEY, Allen Wilson. ■ 17011 #041-01-1929 L1931 **IM CD** *071 †20

DAGEN, J Edward. 503 N 21ST ST 17011 #041-14-1974 L1976 **U** *020 †95

DAGGS, Faith Devine. 423 N 21ST ST, #202 CENTER FOR WOMENS HLT 17011 #010-02-1995 L2000 **OBG** *020 †30

DAILEY, John R. 503 N 21ST ST 17011 #041-09-1990 L1992 **OPH** *020 †35 ‡

DALY, James Francis. 25 W SHORE DR 17011 #010-02-1962 L1966 **PD** *020 †55

DANNUNZIO, Donald R. 503 N 21ST ST 17011 #043-01-1993 L1998 **D DS** *020 †15 ‡

DAVIES, Mary Cecelia. ■ 17011 #041-15-2001 L2001 **IM** *100 †20

DAVIS, Stephen Jeffrey. 1863 CENTER ST 17011 #048-12-1974 L1981 **PUD A** *020 †20

DAVIS, William S. 3620 LOGAN CT 17011 #041-02-1952 L1953 **GS** *071 †85

DE LA CRUZ, Silvestre. 503 N 21ST ST, HOLY SPIRIT HOSPITAL 17011 #748-10-1973 L1983 **P** *020

DELINE, Constance Rose. 3720 MARKET ST 17011 #065-06-1986 L1998 **FM** *020 †18

DE LONE, Carrie L. 503 N 21ST ST, HOLY SPIRIT HOSPITAL 17011 #041-13-1985 L1990 **IM** *020 †20

DE LONE, Charles A, Jr. 503 N 21ST ST, HOLY SPIRIT HOSPITAL 17011 #041-01-1945 L1946 **MDM** *071 †30

DE LONE, Joseph Bert. 890 POPLAR CHURCH RD, STE 210 17011 #041-13-1985 L1990 **GS** *020 †85

DEL ROSARIO, Vivencio G. HOLY SPIRIT HOSP CMHC 17011 #748-01-1953 L1963 **P** *071

DESAI, Ahutiben Jayantibh. 205 GRANDVIEW AVE STE 210, SPIRIT PHYSICIAN SERVICES 17011 #495-23-2000 L2006 **IM** *020 †20

DESCHENE, Lori Everling. 3720 MARKET ST 17011 #050-02-1995 L2007 **PD** *020 †55

DONEGAN, Paul Maurice. 872 POPLAR CHURCH RD, PRISON HEALTH SERVICES,INC 17011 #024-16-1995 L1997 **IM** *020 †20

DOUGLAS, Elaine Johnson. 503 N 21ST ST, HOLY SPIRIT HOSPITAL 17011 #045-04-1994 L1996 **P** *020 †75

DOUGLAS, Svetlana V. 101 ERFORD RD, STE 101 17011 #913-60-1995 L2001 **IM** *020 †20

DUKKIPATI, Ravi. 897 POPLAR CHURCH RD, NEURORADIOLOGY CTR PC 17011 #065-09-1994 L2000 **CN** *020 †75

EDMUNDOWICZ, Alphonse C. ■ 17011 #041-09-1955 L1956 **CD IM** *071 †20

EVANCHO, Charles David. 503 N 21ST ST, DEPT PATH 17011 #051-04-1985 L1986 **CLP ATP** *062 †50,18

FAN, Chris Ying. 101 ERFORD RD, STE 101 17011 #051-01-1993 L1995 **END IM** *020 †20

FARHI, Vida Z. 503 N 21ST ST, HOLY SPIRIT HOSPITAL 17011 #517-01-1982 L1997 **IM** *020 †20

FARIES, Geo Bonnell, Jr. 503 N 21ST ST 17011 #041-02-1967 L1968 **GS GP** *020 †85 ‡

FEDOK, Frederick Geo. 101 ERFORD RD, STE 101 17011 #041-14-1979 L1983 **FPS HNS** *020 †16,45

FIELD, Douglas. 101 ERFORD RD, STE 101 17011 #041-02-1989 L1991 **PG** *020 †55

FITZSIMONS, Margaret M. 101 ERFORD RD, STE 101 17011 #539-05-1987 L1996 **IM NEP** *020 †20

FOX, James Miles. ■ 17011 #041-02-1964 L1965 **OM EM** *050

FRANTZ, Kathryn Marian. 890 POPLAR CHURCH RD, STE 508 17011 #023-07-1991 L1992 **IM** *020 †20

FREEDMAN, Donald Bernard. 890 POPLAR CHURCH RD, STE 508 17011 #041-01-1948 L1949 **IM** *071

FROMME, Kenneth Louis. 125 RODNEY LN 17011 #041-09-1960 L1961 **PD P** *071
FURLONG, Christopher B. 899 POPLAR CHURCH RD, PA GASTROENTEROLOGY CONSUL 17011 #041-02-1989 L2001 **GE** *020 †20
GAITHER, Herbert. ■ 17011 #023-01-1962 L1968 **IM NEP** *071 †20
GBEMUDU-JATTO, Claudette. 207 HOUSE AVE, CONNOR, RICH ASSOCIATES 17011 #690-03-1991 L2000 **IM** *020 †20
GEADAH, Fouad Adib. 503 N 21ST ST 17011 #605-01-1954 L1969 **OTO PS** *071 †45
GERACI, Gaspere C. PO BOX 235 17001 #035-06-1980 L1981 **FM EM** *020 †16,18
GHOSH, Supriyo U. 888 POPLAR CHURCH RD 17011 #496-38-1994 L2004 **IMG** *040 †20
GILARSKY, Bruce Philip. 503 N 21ST ST 17011 #035-19-1984 L1990 **DR** *020 †80
GOEL, Neeti Bhatia. 503 N 21ST ST 17011 #010-01-1998 L2004 **DR** *020 †80
GOLDBERG, Howard David. 503 N 21ST ST 17011 #023-01-1992 L2003 **VIR** *020 †80
GOLDSTEIN, Laurence. ■ 17011 #041-02-1970 L1973 **HEM OM** *020 †20
GOODMAN, Jay David. 503 N 21ST ST 17011 #041-13-1995 L1998 **VIR** *020 †80
GOODMAN, Robert Alan. 503 N 21ST ST 17011 #041-14-1999 L2001 **AN** *020 †05
GOULDY, Christine A. 503 N 21ST ST 17011 #041-14-1995 L1997 **DR** *020 †80
GRADZKI, Robert. 205 GRANDVIEW AVE, STE 402 17011 #759-03-1992 L2002 **NEP** *020 †20
GREENAWALD, Henry Adam. 425 N 21ST ST 17011 #041-02-1959 L1960 **FM** *071 †18
GREENBERG, David Lawrence. 503 N 21ST ST 17011 #048-13-1990 L2000 **DR OTO** *020 †80
GREINER, Ann S. 503 N 21ST ST 17011 #041-14-1984 L1985 **AN IM** *020 †05
GUSTAVSON, Roger B. 890 POPLAR CHURCH RD STE 5 17011 #041-13-1969 L1970 **IM** *020 †20
HAMSHER, James Ronald. 3399 TRINDLE RD 17011 #041-13-1964 L1965 **ORS** *020 †40
HARNER, Jeffrey David. 503 N 21ST ST 17011 #041-02-1981 L1983 **DR NM** *020 †80
HARRIS, Brian Walter. 503 N 21ST ST 17011 #020-02-1981 L1983 **DR R** *020
HART, James Clarke. 423 N 21ST ST, ATTN: MR. STEVE VICKERS 17011 #041-14-1977 L1978 **TS** *020 †85,90
HARTMAN, Michael J. ■ 17011 #023-01-2005 L2007 **OMF** *012
HARVEY, Todd John. 1857 CENTER ST 17011 #041-13-1990 L2000 **OPH** *020 †35
HERCEG, Stephen Jos. ■ 17011 #041-02-1957 L1958 **PS** *071 †65
HOLDER, Gertrude Clarissa. ■ 17011 #041-14-1997 L1999 **FM** *100 †18
HOOVER, Jesse Earl. 503 N 21ST ST 17011 #041-14-1999 L2001 **AN** *020 †05
HOTTENSTEIN, Daniel Wm. 503 N 21ST ST 17011 #041-01-1967 L1968 **R** *071 †80
IAMS, William Bowman. 423 N 21ST ST 17011 #016-06-1966 L1969 **TS VS** *020 †85,90
ISAACSON, Jon Eric. 880 POPLAR CHURCH RD, MILTON S HERSHEY MED CENTE 17011 #033-05-1991 L2000 **OTO NO** *040 †45
JACKSON, F Wilson, III. 423 N 21ST ST, STE 100 17011 #016-06-1992 L1995 **GE** *020 †20
JACKSON, Frank Wilson. 423 N 21ST ST STE 100 17011 #023-07-1959 L1962 **GE IM** *071 †20
JEFFERIES, Geo Edwin, III. 890 POPLAR CHURCH RD, STE 503 17011 #041-02-1968 L1969 **OBG** *071 †30
JONES, Samuel Luther. ■ 17011 #041-13-1955 L1956 **GP OS** *071
JORGE, Eduardo. 423 N 21ST ST, AMERICAN REHAB CTR 17011 #010-02-1979 L1980 **TS** *020 †85,90
JOYNER, David Mc Arthur. 3399 TRINDLE RD 17011 #041-14-1976 L1977 **ORS** *020 †40
JUDSON, John P. 503 N 21ST ST 17011 #010-02-1965 L1987 **EM LM** *030 †85,90
KAHLENBORN, Chris. 503 N 21ST ST, HOLY SPIRIT HOSPITAL 17011 #041-14-1988 L1991 **IM** *020 †20
KANENSON, William Lee. MEDICAL ARTS BUILDING, SUSQUEHANNA INTERNL MEDCN 17011 #041-02-1955 L1956 **IM** *071 †20
KEGEL, Erica C. ■ 17011 #041-14-1997 L1997 *100
KEHM, Robert Farrell. 503 N 21ST ST 17011 #041-02-1976 L1978 **DR PDR** *020 †80
KENNEDY, Rae Lynn. 101 ERFORD RD, STE 101 17011 #051-01-1998 L2001 **OBG** *020
KIM, Erich. 503 N 21ST ST 17011 #023-01-1973 L1987 **R** *020 †80
KINGSLEY, Charles Philip. 503 N 21ST ST, DEPT PATH 17011 #035-45-1981 L1990 **AN** *020 †05
KOLEV, Tania Dimitrova. 25 N 32ND ST, DEPT OF VETS AFFAIRS 17011 #198-04-1986 L1999 **IM** *020 †20
KORMIS, Karen Katherine. 899 POPLAR CHURCH RD 17011 #041-09-1991 L1996 **GE IM** *020 †20
KOST, Lewis Victor, Jr. 100 CORPORATE CENTER DR, STE 100 17011 #041-01-1961 L1962 **U** *020 †95
KRISHNAN, Harinidevi. 3456 TRINDLE RD, HAMPDEN PHYSICIAN ASSOC 17011 #496-22-1990 L2006 **IM** *020 †20
KUNKEL, Barbara Karlheim. 503 N 21ST ST 17011 #041-13-1965 L1968 **R** *040 †80 ‡
KUNKEL, Paul Augustine. 890 POPLAR CHURCH RD, STE 210 17011 #041-07-1987 L1988 **GS** *020 †85
KUSZTOS, Robert D. 207 HOUSE AVE, CONNER RICH ASOCIATES 17011 #473-01-1977 L1998 **IM** *020 †20
LAMARQUE, Edward Eugene. 2920 MARKET ST 17011 #561-17-1977 L1980 **IM** *020
LERRO, Desiree. 503 N 21ST ST 17011 #041-77-1989, ▲ L1990 **DR** *071
LEVIN, Barry Leon. 503 N 21ST ST 17011 #024-07-1966 L1969 **DR** *020 †80
LEVIN, Roger James. 880 POPLAR CHURCH RD, ASSOCIATED OTOLARYNGOLOGIS 17011 #023-01-1988 L1994 **HNS OTO** *020 †45
LEWIN, Stanley B. 425 N 21ST ST, HERITAGE CARDIOLOGY 17011 #035-06-1971 L1978 **CD IM** *020 †20
LEWIS, Maurice Jay. 890 POPLAR CHURCH RD, STE 508 17011 #041-02-1961 L1962 **IM** *020 †20
LITTON, Jason Jack. 3399 TRINDLE RD 17011 #035-08-1962 L1969 **ORS** *020 †40
LONG, David Allen. 4400 CARLISLE PIKE, PINNACLE HEALTH FAMILY CAR 17011 #041-13-1978 L1979 **FM** *020 †18
LONG, James Downey. 423 N 21ST ST, STE 202 17011 #051-01-1976 L1996 **OBG** *020 †30
LOWRY, Donald Jay. 425 N 21ST ST 17011 #041-12-1954 L1955 **IM** *071 †20
LULEY, Richard Frank. 503 N 21ST ST 17011 #041-12-1982 L1983 **FM** *020 †18
MAAS, Anthony E. HOLY SPIRIT HOSPITAL, WEST SHORE PATH ASSOCS INC 17011 #660-04-1953 L1967 **PTH CLP** *071 †50
MACALUSO, David Anthony. 101 ERFORD RD, STE 101 17011 #041-14-1996 L1998 **END** *020 †20
MAGARGLE, Rodney Lynn. 3335 MARKET ST 17011 #041-14-1973 L1974 **IM** *020
MALCOM, Ronald Hugh. 405 SAINT JOHNS CHURCH RD 17011 #012-01-1987 L1991 **RO** *020 †80
MANIU, Adrian Calin. 503 N 21ST ST 17011 #781-03-1993 L1999 **AN** *020 †05
MANNING, Anne Marie. 423 N 21ST ST, STE 201 17011 #041-14-1985 L1989 **OBG** *020 †30
MANNING, Richard Gerard. 890 POPLAR CHURCH RD, MED ARTS BLDG STE 210 17011 #041-02-1983 L1990 **GS** *040 †85
MAUE, Frederick Robt. 503 N 21ST ST, HOLY SPIRIT HOSP BEH HLTH 17011 #041-13-1980 L1981 **P N** *030 †75
MC INROY, Brian Donnal. 503 N 21ST ST 17011 #041-13-1992 L1997 **VIR** *020 †80
MEGHAPARA, Bhavinkumar Ka. 503 N 21ST ST 17011 #495-23-2002 L2007 **IM** *020
MICHALEK, Maria. 897 POPLAR CHURCH RD 17011 #286-06-1972 L1984 **N** *020
MILLER, Robin Kate. 503 N 21ST ST 17011 #010-03-1988 L1996 **P** *020 †75
MIRA, John Francis. 115 S SAINT JOHNS DR 17011 #030-06-1970 L1976 **P N** *020 †75
MIZE, David Scott. 423 N 21ST ST, STE 100 17011 #041-09-1997 L2000 **GE** *020 †20
MOOLA, Jagadeesh Kumar K. 503 N 21ST ST 17011 #495-72-1976 L1982 **P** *020 †75
MOSER, Richard Pershing, Jr. 503 N 21ST ST 17011 #023-01-1976 L1989 **DR** *040 †80
MUMTAZ, Mubashir Ahmed. 423 N 21ST ST, STE 301 17011 #704-25-1994 L2002 **TS** *020 †85,90
MUSSER, Robert Jay. 503 N 21ST ST 17011 #041-01-1965 L1966 **FM EM** *020 †18
NADAR, Venkatesh K. 425 N 21ST ST, HERITAGE CARDIOLOGY ASSOC 17011 #495-04-1985 L1993 **CD** *020 †20
NAJEM, Elias Shuaib. 503 N 21ST ST 17011 #033-05-1989 L1999 **R** *020 †80
NEWTON, Frederick Clark. 100 CORPORATE CENTER DR 17011 #055-01-1968 L1969 **RO R** *020 †80 ‡
NORATO, Joseph F. ■ 17011 #035-09-1965 L1968 **GP AN** *072 †05 ‡
O'CONNELL, Brent James. 100 SENATE AVE STE 1N, PA BLUESHIELD 17011 #041-02-1967 **PD** *030 †55
OLBES PRUDENCIO, Maria E. 503 N 21ST ST, HOLY SPIRIT HOSPITAL NIC4 17011 #748-08-1978 L1986 **NPM PD** *020 †55
OLEWILER, Dean B. ■ 17011 #041-02-1951 L1952 **GP OS** *071
ORMAN, Steven Kerry. 104 ERFORD RD 17011 #041-14-1972 L1976 **D DMP** *020 †15 ‡
OWENS, Russell Scott. 503 N 21ST ST 17011 #041-14-1987 L1988 **U** *020 †95
PARASCANDOLA, Salvatore A. 890 POPLAR CHURCH RD, STE 210 17011 #055-01-1984 L1986 **GS** *020 †85
PARIKH, Neelima Mukul. 503 N 21ST ST, WEST SHORE ANESTHESIA ASSO 17011 #495-21-1979 L1984 **AN** *020 †05
PARK, Sung Jin. 423 N 21ST ST, STE 301 17011 #051-01-1993 L2001 **TS** *020 †85,90
PARNES, Herbert Milton. 104 ERFORD RD 17011 #041-01-1962 L1963 **D DMP** *020 †15 ‡
PASTOR, James Alejo. 503 N 21ST ST 17011 #748-07-1971 L1983 **AN** *020
PASZEK, Michael John. 503 N 21ST ST, NEONATOLOGY 17011 #010-01-1973 L1978 **PD** *050 †55
PATTERSON, Leland Francis. 503 N 21ST ST 17011 #038-40-1963 L1969 **N PMM** *062 †75
PATTERSON, Lewis Thos. MEDICAL ARTS BLDG, KUNKEL SURGICAL GROUP 17011 #041-01-1955 L1956 **GS TS** *072 †85,90
PAUL, Laurence Howard. 503 N 21ST ST 17011 #308-07-1982 L1983 **IM** *020
PERNA, Francis Xavier. 1521 CEDAR CLIFF DR 17011 #041-09-1960 L1961 **END IM** *020
PETERS, David J. 899 POPLAR CHURCH RD 17011 #041-77-1992, ▲ L1993 **GE IM** *020 †20
PETKASH, David Gabriel. 25 N 32ND ST, VA MED OUTPATIENT CTR 17011 #308-07-1983 L1986 **P PFP** *020 †75
PHILLIPS, Vernon R. ■ 17011 #041-02-1942 L1943 **FM IM** *071
PROCOPIO, Frank. 153 S 32ND ST, TAN & GARCIA PC 17011 #056-06-1946 L1952 **PD ADL** *071 †55
PROPHET, Steven Allen. 888 POPLAR CHURCH RD 17011 #041-14-1993 L1995 **IM** *020 †20
PUVVALA, Sukumar. 503 N 21ST ST 17011 #495-21-1989 L2003 **DR** *020 †80
RABIN, Harold Steven. 503 N 21ST ST 17011 #035-08-1973 L1978 **DR** *020 †80
RASTOGI, Nita. 503 N 21ST ST 17011 #495-30-1986 L1994 **IM** *020 †20
RATLIFF, Sandra Smith. 25 W SHORE DR 17011 #041-09-1987 L1989 **PD** *020 †55
RAZZINO, Richard Alfred. 800 POPLAR CHURCH RD, VASCULAR ASSOCIATES 17011 #305-01-1982 L1987 **VS** *020 †85
REDDY, Palukuri Bharath K. ■ 17011 #308-13-1998 L2007 **P** *100
RICH, James Francis. 207 HOUSE AVE, STE 101 17011 #561-01-1974 L1976 **IM** *020 †20
RJEPAJ, Aida. 25 N 32ND ST, CORUP HILL COMMUNITY 17011 #120-01-1991 L2007 **P** *020 †75
ROBINSON, James Alan. 503 N 21ST ST 17011 #035-15-1980 L1982 **DR** *020 †80
ROSSI, John Anthony. 890 POPLAR CHURCH RD 17011 #041-14-1981 L1982 **VS GS** *020 †85
ROUMM, Alan David. 650 POPLAR CHURCH RD 17011 #041-02-1977 L1979 **RHU IM** *020 †20
SANDERSON, Douglas Kent. 205 GRANDVIEW AVE 17011 #023-07-1963 L1968 **ORS** *071 †40
SANDUSKY, Matthew Francis. ■ 17011 #041-13-2007 L2007 **TY** *012
SANFORD, Robert Geo. 1845 CENTER ST 17011 #041-09-1970 L1971 **RHU IM** *020 †20
SANGILLO, Mario M. 25 W SHORE DR 17011 #016-43-1979 L1981 **PD** *020 †55
SAVASTIO, Joseph Anthony. 503 N 21ST ST 17011 #041-09-1959 L1960 **OM** *075
SAYSON, Lilia M. 25 N 32ND ST 17011 #748-01-1962 L1973 **IM** *020 †20
SCHARFF, Nicholas. 75 UTLEY DR, STE 101 17011 #035-01-1974 L1975 **IM IMG** *030 †20
SCHIRO, John Chas. 503 N 21ST ST 17011 #041-02-1969 L1970 **IM** *020
SCHMALENBERGER, Kevin P. 503 N 21ST ST 17011 #041-12-1999 L2001 **AN** *020 †05 ‡
SCHUCKER, Forrest A. 890 POPLAR CHURCH RD, STE 200 17011 #041-13-1975 L1976 **GS** *071 †85
SHAPIRO, Andrew M. 880 POPLAR CHURCH RD 17011 #041-13-1987 L1989 **OTO PDO** *020 †45
SHARMA, Amita. 355 N 21ST ST, STE 300 17011 #495-43-1989 L1995 **P OS** *020 †75
SHARMA, Ranjana S. 503 N 21ST ST 17011 #495-74-1976 L1984 **IM FM** *020 †20
SHINDLER, Robert Lester. 1524 CEDAR CLIFF DR 17011 #041-13-1967 L1968 **OPH** *071 †35
SHRIFT, Craig Anthony. 3720 MARKET ST 17011 #041-09-1982 L1989 **PD** *020 †55
SHRIFT, Katherine G. 4076 MARKET ST, FAMILY MED CTR OF CAMP HIL 17011 #041-09-1982 L1989 **FM** *020 †18
SICKEL, Edward Francis. ■ 17011 #041-01-1958 L1959 **OTO HNS** *071 †45
SINGER, Paul Scott. 503 N 21ST ST 17011 #041-09-1990 L1994 **DR** *020 †80
SINGH, Sonia. 153 S 32ND ST 17011 #495-73-1990 L1998 **PD** *020 †55
SMITH, Maura. ■ 17011 #041-13-1983 L1986 **GPM CCM** *020
SMITH, Paul Howard. 100 CORPORATE CENTER DR, STE 100 17011 #011-03-1980 L1987 **U** *020 †95
SROUJI, Samir. 3438 TRINDLE RD 17011 #605-01-1964 L1976 **PS** *072 ‡
STANKOVIC, Ljubisa. 797 POPLAR CHURCH RD 17011 #957-02-1965 L1977 **IM** *020
STEGMAN, Mark Francis. 423 N 21ST ST, STE 202 17011 #038-41-1981 L1995 **OBG REN** *020 †30
STEWART, Richard Philip. 503 N 21ST ST 17011 #035-20-1965 L1971 **DR** *020 †80
STINE, Howard Edwin. 25 N 32ND ST 17011 #041-01-1943 L1944 **PUD IM** *020
STRYKER, John Alvin. 100 CORPORATE CENTER DR 17011 #025-01-1963 L1973 **RO** *071 †80 ‡
SULLIVAN, Gregory Benen. 503 N 21ST ST, HSH BEHAVIORAL HEALTH 17011 #010-01-1985 L1987 **P** *020 †75
SWEITZER, Brett Alan. ■ 17011 #041-13-2003 L2004 **ORS** *012
TABB, David Randy. 503 N 21ST ST 17011 #023-01-1984 L1986 **DR** *020 †80
TEGELER, James Allen. 503 N 21ST ST 17011 #023-01-1979 L1980 **RO PTH** *020 †50,80
TEPLIS, Alan Colman. 503 N 21ST ST 17011 #012-05-1982 L1982 **EM** *020

THOMAS, Gary Alexander. 101 ERFORD RD, STE 101 17011 #041-14-2001 L2001 **CN** *020

THOMAS, Holly Jo. 101 ERFORD RD, STE 101 17011 #041-14-1993 L1995 **OBG** *020 †30

TORCHIA, Joseph Anthony. 503 N 21ST ST, HOLY SPIRIT HOSPITAL 17011 #422-01-1987 L1990 **IM** *020 †20

TRAVISANO, Frank Jos. 423 N 21ST ST 17011 #023-01-1963 L1967 **TS** *071 †85,90

TRISTAN, Theodore A. ■ 17011 #030-05-1950 L1951 **DR** *071 †80

VANDER ARK, Wesley Dean. 890 POPLAR CHURCH RD, STE 300 17011 #036-05-1992 L2001 **OTO** *020 †45

VENBRUX, Henry Jos. 503 N 21ST ST, DEPT PATH 17011 #049-01-1979 L1981 **PTH** *020 †50 ‡

VICTORINA, Wilfred Marco. 890 POPLAR CHURCH RD, STE 503 17011 #649-38-1993 L2007 **END** *020 †20

WAGGENSPACK, Gerard Alan. 405 SAINT JOHNS CHURCH RD 17011 #021-06-1979 L1988 **R N** *020 †80

WENGER, Allen Steven. 423 N 21ST ST STE 300 17011 #041-14-1980 L1986 **U** *020 †95

WENGERT, Paul Andrew, Jr. 890 POPLAR CHURCH RD, STE 200 17011 #041-13-1967 L1968 **GS** *071 †85

WEST, Joseph E. 503 N 21ST ST, WEST SHORE ANESTHESIA ASSO 17011 #041-07-1988 L1992 **AN AM** *020 †05

WHITE, David Allan. ■ 17011 #041-07-1998 L2000 **EM** *020 †16

WITT, Christopher John. 890 POPLAR CHURCH RD, STE 300 17011 #024-07-1996 L2004 **OTO** *020 †45

WOLANIN-SAIFI, Suzanne V. 4400 CARLISLE PIKE, ANNACLE HEALTH FAMILY CARE 17011 #759-10-1991 L2000 **FM** *020 †18

WOLDORF, Norman Melvyn. 890 POPLAR CHURCH RD, AP 17011 #041-02-1964 L1965 **OTO** *071 †45 ‡

WOLF, Robert Edward. 205 GRANDVIEW AVE, STE 401 17011 #041-14-1988 L1991 **PS PSH** *020 †65

WON, Kwan H. 503 N 21ST ST 17011 #583-02-1960 L1971 **OTO GS** *020 †45

YATES, James Arthur. 205 GRANDVIEW AVE, STE 401 17011 #041-01-1960 L1962 **PS** *020 †65 ‡

YOUNG, Thomas Allen. 890 POPLAR CHURCH RD, STE 508 17011 #041-09-1990 L1992 **IM** *020 †20

YUCHA, Thomas Joseph. 3399 TRINDLE RD 17011 #041-13-1970 L1971 **ORS** *071 †40

ZIMMERMAN, Kathleen M. 3720 MARKET ST, HERITAGE PEDIATRICS 17011 #041-14-1999 L2003 **PD** *020 †55

CANONSBURG – WASHINGTON

AIELLO, Ronald James. 457 IRONWOOD DR, THE WASHINGTON HOSPITAL 15317 #041-15-2000 L2001 **FM** *020 †18

BAQUERO-BUENO, Mario Raul. 100 MEDICAL BLVD 15317 #319-01-1961 L1973 **GS TS** *020

BISSELL, Brad Joseph. ■ 15317 #041-02-2007 L2007 **EM** *012

CARMONA-KELLER, Diane. 400 SOUTHPOINTE BLVD, STE 110 15317 #024-01-1996 L2000 **OBG** *020 †30

CHAN, Brandon Willie. ■ 15317 #023-07-1993 L2005 **DR** *020 †80

CHANGCO, Alvaro N. 100 MEDICAL BLVD 15317 #748-01-1963 L1975 **FM EM** *020 †18

DEATRICH, Dylan Paul. ■ 15317 #041-14-2004 L2004 **FM** *020 †18

DICKEY, James Burl. 100 MEDICAL BLVD 15317 #039-05-1987 L1995 **OPH** *020 †35

FRONCZEK, Wm Michael, Jr. 100 MEDICAL BLVD 15317 #041-12-1966 L1967 **OPH** *020 †35

GALLETTA, Anthony S. 160 W PIKE ST 15317 #041-01-1964 L1967 **FM OS** *020 †18

GAUR, Surabhi. 116 AERIAL DR 15317 #041-13-2008 *012

GOLDBERG, Howard Ross. 100 MEDICAL BLVD 15317 #041-12-1997 L2001 **OTO HNS** *020 †45

HAPPEL, John Lindsay. 3035 WASHINGTON RD 15317 #041-12-1948 L1949 **GS** *071 †85

JOHNSON, Charles Julius. ■ 15317 #056-05-1959 L1963 **PS GS** *072 †85,65

KATHPAL, Gurbachan Singh. 100 MEDICAL BLVD 15317 #495-20-1968 L1975 **N** *020 †75

KATHPAL, Madeera. ■ 15317 #041-77-2007, ▲ L2007 *012

KEEN, Stephen Michael. 67 E PIKE ST 15317 #055-01-1999 L2001 **FM** *020 †18

KIM, Song Keun. 100 MEDICAL BLVD 15317 #583-10-1966 L1976 **GP** *020

KUMAR, Ashok. 2215 HILL CHURCH HOUSTN RD, STE 3A 15317 #495-30-1968 L1976 **IM CD** *020

LEE, John Ki. 100 MEDICAL BLVD, CANONSBURG GENERAL HOSPITA 15317 #583-10-1964 L1975 **AN OBG** *020 ‡

MOLINDA, Laurie Shirman. 400 SOUTHPOINTE BLVD, # 1-235 15317 #051-04-1987 L1989 **IM** *020 †20

MOOLTEN, Frederick London. ■ 15317 #024-01-1963 L2002 **IM** *050

MUTSCHLER, Thomas Anthony. 100 MEDICAL BLVD 15317 #041-12-1985 L1986 **OAR** *020 †40

NAHATA, Amit Kumar. 131 HILLPOINTE DR 15317 #035-03-1999 L2004 **NEP** *020 †20

PATEL, Shashikant V. 100 MEDICAL BLVD 15317 #495-76-1978 L1997 **PMM AN** *020

PECORA, Michael John. 100 MEDICAL BLVD 15317 #016-42-1981 L1989 **CD** *020 †20

SHARPNACK, Bruce Clark. 100 MEDICAL BLVD 15317 #041-12-1981 L1984 **FM OBS** *020 †18 ‡

SHAW, Jane Marr. ■ 15317 #012-01-1986 *074

SMITH, Gary Chas. 2001 WATERDAM PLAZA DR, STE 105 15317 #041-12-1992 L1998 **PD** *020 †55

THOMEIER, William Chas. 100 MEDICAL BLVD, MED IMAGING CANONSBURG GH 15317 #041-14-1984 L1990 **DR** *020 †80

VALLEJO, Manuel Curamen. 2215 HL CHURCH HSTN RD 15317 #748-01-1957 L1966 **GS** *071

WELKER, David Mathew. 100 MEDICAL BLVD 15317 #055-01-1996 L1998 **ORS** *020 †40

WILDENHAIN, Sarah Lehar. ■ 15317 #041-12-1987 L1990 **R RNR** *071 †80

ZAFAR, Tasneem Syed. 100 MEDICAL BLVD, CANONBURGH GENERAL HOSP 15317 #495-19-1970 L1976 **PTH** *020 †50

CARBONDALE – LACKAWANNA

AMIN, Quaser Ruhul. 37 HONESDALE RD, WHITES CROSSING MEDICAL GR 18407 #160-05-1984 L2004 **IM** *100 †20

BARRETT, Ronald Timothy. 141 SALEM AVE 18407 #041-01-1997 L1999 **U** *020 †95 ‡

CHAI, Min Suk. ■ 18407 #583-02-1959 L1973 **OBG** *020 †30

CRAPARO, Thomas James. 10 DUNDAFF ST 18407 #041-09-1977 L1978 **GP** *020 ‡

CREWS, John Everett, III. 141 SALEM AVE, MAXIS SURGICAL SERVICES 18407 #025-01-1996 L2007 **GS** *085

DAVIS, Neal Malcolm. 254 BROOKLYN ST, STE 1 18407 #041-77-1988, ▲ L1989 **FM** *020 †18 ‡

DE ANTONIO, John E. ■ 18407 #010-02-1951 L1953 **GP** *020

DINHOFER, David Steven. 100 LINCOLN AVE, MARIAN COMMUNITY HOSPITAL 18407 #021-01-1980 L2006 **DR IM** *020 †80

GILBERT, Jerald Blair. 100 LINCOLN AVE 18407 #005-14-1989 L1992 **U** *020 †95 ‡

GREGORY, Peter G. 100 LINCOLN AVE, MARIAN COMMUNITY HOSPITAL 18407 #473-01-1983 L1993 **DR** *020 †80

HAHN, Kon S. 100 LINCOLN AVE 18407 #583-10-1965 L1975 **OPH** *020

HOLMES, John Jos Francis. 100 LINCOLN AVE 18407 #041-01-1952 L1953 **GP** *071

JASON, William J. 141 SALEM AVE 18407 #035-01-1990 L1998 **ORS OSM** *020 †40

KOHN, Ira Joel. 141 SALEM AVE 18407 #033-05-1991 L1993 **U** *020 †95 ‡

MALLIK, Satish K. 185 FALLBROOK ST, TRICOUNTY HUMAN SERVICES C 18407 #495-41-1989 L1997 **P** *020

MASANKAY, Manuel Gatoula. 141 SALEM AVE 18407 #748-01-1961 L1970 **GS GP** *020

MIZIN, Lakshmi D J. 187 FALLBROOK ST 18407 #495-11-1970 L1981 **CD IM** *020 †20

MOGERMAN, Jeffrey Albert. 141 SALEM AVE 18407 #035-06-1977 L1982 **ORS** *020 †40 ‡

MORGAN, Albert P. ■ 18407 #041-13-1952 L1953 **OM AM** *071

MORO, Frank Michael. 150 BROOKLYN ST 18407 #422-01-1982 L1984 **IM** *020 †20 ‡

OLSEN, Kevin Harry. 100 LINCOLN AVE 18407 #008-02-1982 L1988 **CD** *020 †20

PETTINATO, Salvatore R. 92 SALEM AVE 18407 #056-06-1947 L1948 **GP OS** *071

ROCHE, James Jos. 150 BROOKLYN ST 18407 #041-02-1986 L1991 **GS VS** *020 †85 ‡

SALKO, Gregory Jos. 37 HONESDALE RD 18407 #041-02-1971 L1972 **FM FPG** *020 †18 ‡

SEBASTIANELLI, Mario Jos. 100 LINCOLN AVE 18407 #041-02-1962 L1963 **NEP IM** *020 †20

SHINGALA, Arun Jamnadas. 141 SALEM AVE 18407 #495-23-1969 L1974 **CD IM** *020 †20

SHOVLIN, John Michael. 185 FALLBROOK ST, TRI-COUNTY HUMAN SERVICES 18407 #041-02-1970 L1971 **P** *020 †75

SPEICHER, David Gerard. ■ 18407 #041-15-2004 L2004 **CCP** *012

SUNDAY, Michael Louis. 150 BROOKLYN ST 18407 #041-01-1988 L1990 **GS** *020 †85 ‡

TAROLI, Andrea. 44 N SCOTT ST 18407 #041-07-1984 L1988 **PD OS** *071 †55

WENGER, Norman Edward. RR 2 18407 #019-02-1956 L1975 **OS A** *075

WILDNER, Ralf G. 185 FALLBROOK ST 18407 #165-07-1985 L1996 **CHP** *020 †75 ‡

CARDALE – FAYETTE

MONTAGNA, David Julius. REPUBLIC FAIRBANKS RD 15420 #041-12-1963 L1964 **GP** *020

CARLISLE – CUMBERLAND

ABRAM, Adam Combs. 220 WILSON ST STE 200, PLASTIC SURGERY 17013 #047-05-1988 L1995 **GS** *020 †45

ALBRIGHT, David Parker. 45 SPRING RD 17013 #041-14-1983 L1991 **IM** *020 †20

ALSTER, Howard L. 246 PARKER ST 17013 #748-08-1979 L1983 **AN** *020 †20,05

ARMSTRONG, Jack Leonard. 220 WILSON ST, STE 211 17013 #041-14-1990 L1992 **AI OM** *020 †20,03

BAHIA, Jinan Omran Musa. 2 JENNIFER CT 17015 #528-01-1977 L1982 **DR NR** *020 †80

BAILEY, Bruce Olin. 450 GIBNER RD STE 1, DUNHAM US ARMY HEALTH CLIN 17013 #038-40-1975 L1993 **FM** *020 †18

BAKER, David Carlton. 19 BROOKWOOD AVE, STE 104 17015 #041-01-1982 L1989 **ORS** *020 †40

BEACHY, Ivan Edgar. 8 BROOKWOOD AVE 17015 #038-06-1964 L1965 **OBG** *071 †30

BEACHY, Stanley Creed. 19 SPRINT DR STE 2 17015 #023-01-1973 L1974 **GYN** *020 †30

BEHNKE, Andrew John. 40 BROOKWOOD AVE 17015 #041-14-1987 L1990 **END** *020 †20

BELLISSIMO, Joseph Bruno. 2 JENNIFER CT 17015 #041-14-1982 L1983 **DR IM** *020 †20

BERK, Theodore F. 241 ALEXANDER SPRING RD 17015 #041-02-1979 L1980 **GE IM** *020 †20

BERO, Christopher John. 220 WILSON ST, MASLAND ASSOCIATES INC 17013 #041-14-1999 L2001 **IM** *020 †20

BLACKSMITH, Gary List, Jr. ■ 17013 #041-14-1972 L1973 **FM** *071 †18

BLOOM, Brian Paul. 2 JENNIFER CT 17015 #023-01-1993 L1997 **VIR DR** *020 †80

BORGES, Wayne H. ■ 17013 #038-06-1944 L1958 **ON HEM** *071 †55

BOSHNAKOV, Tzvetalin A. 220 WILSON ST, STE 109 17013 #198-03-1989 L2001 **IM** *020 †20

BOWER, Douglas John. 220 WILSON ST, MASLAND ASSOCIATES INC 17013 #024-05-1984 L1993 **IM** *020 †20

BRANSCUM, George Paul, Jr. 850 WALNUT BOTTOM RD 17013 #004-01-1971 L1975 **FM IMG** *030 †18

BRAZEL, Joseph Francis. 220 WILSON ST, STE 109 17013 #041-13-1966 L1967 **IM HEM** *071 †20

BROCKMOLE, Dean Mark. 2 JENNIFER CT 17015 #028-34-1978 L1987 **DR** *020 †80

BROPHY, Dow Edward. 1921 SPRING RD, SPRING ROAD FAMILY PRAC 17013 #396-02-1979 L1982 **FM** *020 †18

BROWN, Wendy Katherine. ■ 17015 #024-16-1991 L2005 **P** *020 †75

BRYANT, David Shaun. 3 SPRINT DR, STE A 17015 #041-13-1994 L1999 **GS** *020 †85

BRYANT, David Willard. ■ 17013 #041-13-1967 L1976 **GS** *072 †85

BYRNE, William Edmund. 5 BROOKWOOD AVE 17015 #041-14-1975 L1977 **OBG** *020 †30

CAMPBELL, Joseph John. 816 BELVEDERE ST 17013 #041-01-1979 L1981 **VS GS** *020 †85

CAREY, Philip Dean. 360 ALEXANDER SPRING RD 17015 #038-06-1976 L1977 **PUD IM** *020 †20

CEGELSKI, Frank Chas. ■ 17013 #035-45-1959 L1968 **OBG** *071 †30

CENTENERA, Virgilio A. ■ 17015 #033-06-1992 L2007 **U** *020 †95

CHANG, Duck-Kyu. 361 ALEXANDER SPRING RD, MEDICAL CENTER 17015 #583-01-1966 L1972 **PTH CLP** *020 †50

CHERRY, Steven Bernard. 419 VILLAGE DR, STE 4 17015 #041-02-1979 L1980 **OBG** *020 †30

CHESS, Daniel Jos. 31 SPRINT DR, SURGERY CENTER 17015 #041-13-1991 L1994 **AN** *020 †05

CHO, John Ming. ■ 17013 #023-12-1988 L1990 **TS GS** *020 †85,90

CLARK, Linda Jean. 450 GIBNER RD, DUNHAM HEALTH CLINIC 17013 #041-12-1982 L1983 **PD** *020 †55

COHEN, Brian Eliot. 5 BROOKWOOD AVE 17015 #023-01-1989 L1993 **OBG** *020 †30

COOKE, Nora. 804 BELVEDERE ST 17013 #035-20-1974 L1978 **PD** *075 †55

COYLE, Johnson Graham. 246 PARKER ST 17013 #041-02-1978 L1981 **EM** *020 †16

CRIM, Laura Ehrhardt. 246 PARKER ST 17013 #010-02-1996 L2000 **EM** *020 †16

DEAN, Shervin Christopher. 2 JENNIFER CT 17015 #048-14-1993 L2005 **DR** *020 †80

DELROSARIO, Robert. 5 BROOKWOOD AVE 17015 #041-09-1991 L1994 **OBG** *020 †30

DE MUTH, William E, Jr. 17015 #041-01-1946 L1947 **GS TS** *020 †85,90

DOORLY, Thomas Joseph. ■ 17013 #041-02-1962 L1968 **PD PDA** *071

DORKO, Carl J. 5 BROOKWOOD AVE 17015 #038-41-1962 L1963 **OBG** *071 †30

DOYLE, Patrick J. 1 LONGSDORF WAY # 8, CUMBERLAND CROSSING 17015 #024-07-1950 L1987 **GPM PD** *072 †75 †20

DOORLY, Thomas Joseph. ■ 17013 #041-02-1962 L1968 **PD PDA** *071

DUSSINGER, Andrew Michael. 366 ALEXANDER SPRING RD 17015 #041-15-2000 L2007 **U** *020 †95

EHLY, George Wileman. 246 PARKER ST 17013 #041-09-1947 L1948 **EM OS** *071

ESKIN, Rose Nancy. 5 BROOKWOOD AVE 17015 #041-13-1993 L1997 **OBG** *020 †30

EVANS, David Bruce. 850 WALNUT BOTTOM RD 17013 #010-01-1966 L1968 **GYN** *020 †30

FARMER, Kenneth Lloyd, Jr. ■ 17013 #001-02-1975 L1980 **AM FM** *030 †18

FERRARO, Richard Edward. 2 JENNIFER CT, STE B 17015 #041-14-1999 L2001 **OTO** *020 †45 ‡

FRIERSON, Patricia Louise. 246 PARKER ST 17013 #001-02-1979 L2005 **EM** *020 †18,16

FRONKO, Gerald E. 246 PARKER ST, CARLISLE REG MED CTR ED 17013 #041-13-1991 L1993 **IM MPD** *020 †55,20

GALINDO, Jose, Jr. 49 BROOKWOOD AVE, CUMBERLAND VLY ENDCRNOLGYP 17015 #308-07-1981 L1988 **END IM** *020 †20

GATRELL, Cloyd Barton. ■ 17013 #051-04-1976 L1999 **EM FM** *020 †18,16

GIESSWEIN, Peter. 5 BROOKWOOD AVE 17015 #409-05-1983 L1987 **PS** *074 †85,65

GOMEZ, Patricia Shukla. 850 WALNUT BOTTOM RD 17013 #160-01-1993 L2005 **IM** *020 †20

GOULD-EARLEY, Mary Jean. 2 JENNIFER CT 17015 #056-05-1989 L1995 **DR VIR** *020 †80

GREEN, Thomas Jeffrey. 1 DUNWOODY DR 17015 #041-02-1966 L1970 **ORS** *020 †40

GRONKIEWICZ, Bruce V. 9 BROOKWOOD AVE 17015 #028-34-1983 L1993 **U** *020 †95

GROSSMAN, Melvyn L. 33 STATE AVE 17013 #869-04-1960 L1994 **P CHP** *071 †75

GUENIN, Mark Alan. 2 JENNIFER CT 17015 #041-01-1986 L1991 **DR** *020 †80

GUISTWITE, Kenneth R. 246 PARKER ST 17013 #041-13-1972 L1973 **FM** *020 †20

HALL, Robert Franklin, II. 246 PARKER ST 17013 #041-02-1967 L1971 **R NR** *072 †80

HARDESTY, James Lee. 850 WALNUT BOTTOM RD, BELVEDERE MEDICAL CENTER 17013 #051-07-1983 L1984 **GS** *020 †85

HARPER, Donald Scott. 220 WILSON ST, STE 213 17013 #049-01-1995 L2003 **AI** *020 †20,03

HARTZELL, David Larry. 37 BROOKWOOD AVE 17015 #041-14-1967 L1968 **OPH** *020 †35

HARTZELL, David Leigh. 37 BROOKWOOD AVE 17015 #041-14-1994 L1998 **OPH** *020 †35

HELY, Daniel Patrick. 1 DUNWOODY DR 17015 #033-05-1975 L1982 **ORS** *020 †40

HILDEN, Michael Francis. 45 SPRING RD 17013 #665-01-1998 L2002 **IM** *020 †20

HILLS, James Ronald. 2 JENNIFER CT 17015 #041-02-1994 L1996 **DR R** *020 †80

HIMMELREICH, Lester Leon. 220 WILSON ST, MASLAND ASSOCIATES INC 17013 #041-09-1982 L1983 **IM** *020 †20

HOFFMAN, Holly Christine. 246 PARKER ST 17013 #011-04-1982 L1985 **PD** *020 †55

HOFFMAN, Jay Lynn. 804 BELVEDERE ST 17013 #041-13-1978 L1980 **PD** *020 †55

HOLLEN, Robert Arthur. 850 WALNUT BOTTOM RD 17013 #041-13-1958 L1959 **FM** *071 †18

HOTCHNER, Harvey J. 25 SPRINT DR 17015 #654-01-1981 L2005 **IM ON** *020 †20

HOUGH, Rodney Kent. 246 PARKER ST 17013 #051-01-1970 L1971 **FM** *020 †18

HUERTER, Joachim J. 2 JENNIFER CT 17015 #048-02-1985 L1986 **DR** *020 †80

ISMAIL, Mohammad Khawar. 220 WILSON ST STE 210 17013 #704-15-1990 L2003 **N PME** *020

JANSON, Russell Robert. 5 BROOKWOOD AVE 17015 #041-13-1981 L1982 **OBG** *020 †30

JOHNSTON, James R, III. 850 WALNUT BOTTOM RD, WALNUT BOTTOM RADIOLOGY 17013 #024-01-1947 L1948 **GS** *071 †85

JOHNSTON, Marion Northup. ■ 17013 #041-07-1947 L1948 **PD** *071

JOZEFIAK, Judith Ann. 2 JENNIFER CT 17015 #041-13-1989 L1994 **DR** *020 †80

JURGENSEN, John Craig. 850 WALNUT BOTTOM RD 17013 #035-09-1966 L1981 **N IM** *030 †20,75

KANN, David Gordon. 850 WALNUT BOTTOM RD, # GRN-304 17013 #041-09-1984 L1985 **CD IM** *020 †20

KASALES, Claudia Jane. 2 JENNIFER CT 17015 #041-14-1986 L1987 **DR** *020 †80

KAUFFMAN, William Scott. 1921 SPRING RD 17013 #051-04-1988 L1991 **FM** *020 †18

KOCHERT, Erik Ian. ■ 17013 #041-02-2006 L2006 **EM** *012

KOLEV, Serge N. 850 WALNUT BOTTOM RD, STE 103 17013 #198-02-1982 L1998 **IM D** *020 †20

KOSENSKE, Ted Danl. 5 TYLER CT, STE B 17015 #041-12-1988 L1990 **AN** *020 †05

KREBS, Stephen Jay. 804 BELVEDERE ST 17013 #041-12-1973 L1975 **PD** *020 †55

KRETZING, Harold Geo. ■ 17013 #041-13-1959 L1960 **FM** *071 †18

KUSH, Mary-Kathleen L. 25 STATE AVE, STE A 17013 #041-14-1974 L1976 **P** *020

LASEK, Colette R. 850 WALNUT BOTTOM RD, GRN #102 17013 #035-06-1984 L1985 **CD IM** *020 †20

LEONARD, Kevin James. 2 JENNIFER CT 17015 #041-14-1986 L1987 **DR** *020 †80

LEWIS, Gregory Lee. 241 ALEXANDER SPRING RD 17015 #041-02-1975 L1976 **GE IM** *020 †20

LOEFFLER, John G, Jr. ■ 17013 #035-09-1949 L1955 **PD** *071 †55

LOH, Charles K. 246 PARKER ST, BOX 310 17013 #583-01-1966 L1971 **R** *020 †80

LOH, John J K. ■ 17013 #583-01-1967 L1976 **RO** *071 †80

LONGTON, Wallace Augustus. 5A SPRINT DR, CARLISLE HOSPITAL CANCER C 17015 #025-12-1993 L1997 **RO** *020 †80

MAN, Elena. 804 BELVEDERE ST 17013 #024-01-1993 L1995 **PD** *020 †55

MANDELL, Michael Jay. 2 JENNIFER CT 17015 #649-33-1983 L1984 **DR** *020 †80

MANFREDI, Rocco Louis. 5A MEL RON CT 17015 #041-14-1983 L1984 **P** *020 †75 ‡

MARKIEWICZ, Annmarie. 220 WILSON ST, STE 106 17013 #041-09-1986 L1987 **IM** *020 †20

MARTIN, Douglas James. 1511 HEMLOCK AVE 17013 #035-19-2001 L2001 **IM** *020 †80

MARTIN, Gerald Bernard. 64 S WEST ST 17013 #041-02-1975 L1976 **IM** *050

MASLAND, David Sharp. BELVEDERE MEDICAL CENTER, MASLAND ASSOCIATES INC 17013 #041-02-1948 L1949 **IM** *071 †20

MC GHEE, James Crawford. 850 WALNUT BOTTOM RD 17013 #018-03-1977 L1989 **A OTO** *074 †45

MILLER, Katie Jo. 381 ALEXANDER SPRING RD, EMERGENCY DEPARTMENT 17015 #041-12-1999 L2004 **EM** *020 †16

MIRA, Allan Jos. 220 WILSON ST STE 206 17013 #030-06-1972 L1973 **ORS** *020 †40

MONTELLO, Joan Mary. 220 WILSON ST 17013 #041-13-1975 L1976 **A AI** *020 †55,03

NITECKI, Juliusz C. 361 ALEXANDER SPRING RD, CARLISLE REGIONAL MED CTR 17015 #759-07-1991 L2000 **IM** *020

OATMAN, Brenda K. ■ 17015 #048-13-1995 L1997 **EM** *020 †16

OLIVERIO, James Anthony. 1 DUNWOODY DR 17015 #035-09-1994 L2005 **ORS** *020 †40

ONG, George P. 850 WALNUT BOTTOM RD 17013 #244-01-1969 L1979 **D DMP** *020

OPLINGER, Michael John. 1 DUNWOODY DR, APPALACHIAN ORTHOPEDIC CEN 17015 #035-09-1994 L2002 **ORS** *020 †40

PHELAN, William Jos. 2 TYLER CT 17015 #041-14-1982 L1984 **FM** *020 †18

PORTER, Albert Roberts. 2 JENNIFER CT 17015 #041-14-1982 L1984 **DR** *020 †80

PUMROY, Keith Spence. 850 WALNUT BOTTOM RD, WALNUT BOTTOM RADIOLOGY 17013 #023-01-1984 L1985 **DR** *020 †80

RAMIREZ, Jason Alexander. 1921 SPRING RD, SPRING ROAD FAMILY PRACTIC 17013 #041-15-1999 L2002 **FM** *020 †18

RANKIN, Larry Stephens. 220 WILSON ST, MASLAND ASSOC INC MED ARTS 17013 #038-06-1967 L1974 **CD IM** *071 †20

RAUBENSTINE, Deborah Ann. 804 BELVEDERE ST 17013 #041-14-1988 L1990 **PD** *020 †55

REID, Bryan Richard. 1921 SPRING RD 17013 #041-09-1998 L2001 **FM** *020 †18

ROEDER, Donald Kistler. 850 WALNUT BOTTOM RD 17013 #041-02-1961 L1962 **TS VS** *020 †85,90

ROSARIO, Eliseo. 804 BELVEDERE ST 17013 #035-46-1979 L1987 **PD** *020

ROYAL, David Robt. 850 WALNUT BOTTOM RD 17013 #041-12-1972 L1973 **DR** *020 †80

SCHLANSKY, Ronald Martin. 220 WILSON ST, STE 104 17013 #035-20-1975 L1976 **RHU IM** *020 †20

SCHWEITZER, Dina Lea. 419 VILLAGE DR, STE 4 17015 #023-12-1993 L2004 **OBG** *020 †30

SHELLEY, William Lawrence. ■ 17013 #041-01-1947 L1948 **GS CRS** *071 †85

SIGUENZA, Robt Frederick. 49 BROOKWOOD AVE, RODNEY K HOUGH MD & ASSOC 17015 #341-01-1980 L1981 **FM** *071 †18

SOLA, Julio. 246 PARKER ST, CARLISLE HOSPITAL 17013 #042-03-1985 L1989 **AN GS** *020

SPASIC, Alexandar. 816 BELVEDERE ST 17013 #957-02-1989 L1998 **FM** *020 †18

SPENCER, Douglas Murray S. ■ 17013 #041-01-1957 L1962 **PD** *071 †55

STOKEN, Drew Jos. 5 TYLER CT, OPHTHALMOLOGY & SURGICAL I 17015 #041-09-1983 L1984 **OPH** *020 †35

SWEER, Leon Wm. 850 WALNUT BOTTOM RD, # 105 17013 #008-01-1980 L1981 **PUD** *020 †20

TAYLOR, Debra Dawn. 220 WILSON ST, MASLAND ASSOCIATES INC 17013 #023-01-1986 L1987 **IM** *020 †20

THOMPSON, David Irvine. ■ 17013 #041-01-1942 L1943 **PD** *071 †55

THOMPSON, Lawrence K, III. 850 WALNUT BOTTOM RD 17013 #036-07-1961 L1994 **PS** *071 †65

THOMPSON, Robert Lee. 220 WILSON ST, MEDICAL ARTS BLDG STE 207 17013 #041-09-1960 L1961 **OPH** *071 †35

VERRECCHIO, Jonathan Jame. 2 OLD COACH LN LOT 180 17013 #041-77-1999, ▲ L2000 **GE** *020 †20

VICKERY, Jon Livingston. 3 JENNIFER CT, # B 17015 #016-11-1980 L1984 **N** *020 †75

VONAH, William Richard. 220 WILSON ST, MASLAND ASSOCIATES INC 17013 #041-02-1998 L2000 **IM** *020 †20

WAGAR, David Bruce. 2 JENNIFER CT 17015 #065-01-1987 L2003 **DR** *020 †80

WALLIN, Thomas Ernest. 5 BROOKWOOD AVE 17015 #026-04-1977 L1981 **OBG** *020 †30

WANG, Helen Chiungju. 220 WILSON ST STE 213 17013 #041-15-2001 L2001 **AI** *020 †55,03

WARREN, James William. 2 JENNIFER CT 17015 #041-13-1980 L1982 **DR** *020 †80

WEHMAN, Henry Jos. 33 STATE AVE, THE STEVENS CENTER 17013 #041-14-1982 L1984 **P** *020 †75

WEST, William James. BELVEDERE MEDICAL CTR 17013 #041-02-1960 L1962 **OBG** *071 †30

WHITCOMB, Luther M. 246 PARKER ST 17013 #041-13-1938 L1939 **EM GP** *071

WINN, Lauren Michaud. 19 SPRINT DR, STE 2 17015 #041-01-1992 L2006 **OBG** *020 †30

WISE, Scott Wm. 2 JENNIFER CT 17015 #041-14-1991 L1995 **DR** *020 †80

WISS, Raymond John. 220 WILSON ST 17013 #041-02-1955 L1956 **OTO A** *072 †45

WONG, Mabel Louise. 220 WILSON ST, 207 MEDICAL ARTS BUILDING 17013 #036-01-1995 L1999 **OPH** *020 †35

YOUNG, Kimberlee P. 450 GIBNER RD, DUNHAM ARMY MEDICAL CLINIC 17013 #001-06-1991 L1997 **FM** *020 †18

CARLISLE BARRACKS – CUMBERLAND

SMITH, Ronald E, Jr. 450 GIBNER RD STE 1, DUNHAM U.S. ARMY HEALTH CL 17013 #048-04-1989 L1991 **FM** *020 †18

CARMICHAELS – GREENE

CHADWICK, Joseph Eric, II. 601 W GEORGE ST, CARMICHAELS CLINIC 15320 #041-15-1999 L2001 **FM** *020 †20

IMRICH, Bernard John. 110 S PINE ST 15320 #055-01-1975 L1981 **IM GP** *020 †20

PHILLIPPI, Grover Hughes. ■ 15320 #041-12-1962 L1966 **D GP** *075

CARNEGIE – ALLEGHENY

ALCALA, Marco Antonio, Jr. ■ 15106 #422-01-2005 **GS** *100

CARTER, Jennifer Patrice. ■ 15106 #041-77-2007, ▲ L2007 *012

CHARNY, E Joseph. 41 THOMS RUN RD, WOODVILLE STATE HOSP 15106 #041-01-1954 L1955 **P PYA** *075 †75

CONOVER, Keith. 55 SIGRID DR 15106 #010-01-1984 L1985 **EM IM** *020 †20,16

COWAN, Thomas Walker, III. 916 IDLEWOOD AVE 15106 #012-01-1969 L1976 **ORS** *020 †40

DICKINSON, Peter Arthur. 1100 WASHINGTON AVE 15106 #026-04-1976 L1977 **IM IMG** *020

EDNIE, Brent. 25 W MAIN ST, WORKWELL 15106 #041-09-1992 L1995 **IM** *020 †20

EISENMAN, Susan Ann. 25 W MAIN ST 15106 #041-12-1988 L1990 **OM** *020

FABER, Lance. ■ 15106 #055-75-2007, ▲ L2008 *012

GRANT, Kathleen Jane. 100 BROADWAY ST 15106 #041-02-1976 L1978 **TS CD** *020 †85,90

HIGGS, Jessica Dermody. ■ 15106 #016-45-2004 L2007 **FSM** *012 †18

JHAVERI, Shalin Yogesh. ■ 15106 #041-13-2004 2004 **DR** *012

KUTSENKOW, Michael. 225 E MAIN ST 15106 #041-13-1952 L1953 **FM FPG** *071

MITAL, Amita. 1100 WASHINGTON AVE, STE 115 15106 #041-02-1992 L1994 **IM** *020 †20

PRINCE, Lester Otto. 25 W MAIN ST, WORKWELL 15106 #011-02-1987 L1990 **PM** *020 †60

RADASKY, E D. ■ 15106 #041-12-1953 L1954 **P GPM** *071

TROMPETER, Joseph I. 813 WASHINGTON AVE 15106 #041-12-1973 L1978 **PD HO** *020 †55

WATERS, Harry William, Jr. 202 MEADOWGROVE CIR 15106 #041-12-1983 L1985 **AN** *020 †05

CARROLLTOWN – CAMBRIA

CARNEY, David James. 387 THEATRE RD 15722 #010-02-1987 L1989 **U** *020 †95 ‡

WEBER, George Francis. 387 THEATRE RD 15722 #041-13-1984 L1987 **FM** *020 †18

CATASAUQUA – LEHIGH

HEFFELFINGER, Sean M. 1400 MAIN ST, MEDICAL CENTER 18032 #041-13-1998 L2000 **FM** *020 †18

LAUGHLIN, Mary E Bowyer. 530 HOWERTOWN RD 18032 #065-01-1922 L1953 **OS** *020

PETRO, Denis James. ■ 18032 #041-14-1971 L1974 **N PA** *030 †75

CATAWISSA – COLUMBIA

FRANCIS, William Leon. ■ 17820 #041-09-1964 L1965 **GP OS** *100

■ = Address Information Privacy Protected

SHEEHE, Dennis Michael. 353 MAIN ST 17820 #041-02-1983 L1986 **FM NTR** *020 †18
ZIMMERMANN, Gordon A. ■ 17820 #068-01-1989 L1995 **AN** *020 †05

CECIL – WASHINGTON

FAITH, Donald James. 3415 MILLERS RUN RD 15321 #041-12-1997 L1999 **FM** *040 †18

CENTER SQUARE – MONTGOMERY

CARCHEDI, Joseph A. 1200 DEKALB PIKE 19422 #561-17-1988 L1991 **EM IM** *020

CENTER VALLEY – LEHIGH

ALKASOV, Isabella. 5848 OLD BETHLEHEM PIKE, STE 101 18034 #913-31-1986 L2001 **FM** *020 †18
AYOS, Danilo Perido. ■ 18034 #748-08-1969 L1980 **EM GP** *020
BANACH, Stanley Francis. ■ 18034 #041-09-1964 L1965 **NEP** *071
BIGGAR, Stephen Richard. ■ 18034 #005-11-2000 *100
DERATZOU, Benjamin. ■ 18034 #041-12-1988 L1991 **AN** *020 †05
ERZURUM, Serhat I. 5848 OLD BETHLEHEM PIKE, STE 101 18034 #048-13-1989 L1991 **OBG** *020 †30
HERMANY, Paul L. ■ 18034 #041-02-1952 L1953 **FM** *071 †18
JIBILIAN, Amy Armen. 3800 SIERRA CIR, STE 100 18034 #033-06-1988 L1992 **PD** *020 †55
KANE, Bryan George. 5302 PINEVIEW DR 18034 #041-01-1998 L2002 **EM** *020 †16
KANE, Kathleen E. ■ 18034 #041-01-1999 L2003 **EM** *020 †16
MAUTHE, Robert Wm. 4676 ROUTE 309 18034 #051-04-1985 L1986 **PM** *020 †60
MORAN, John Anthony. ■ 18034 #023-01-1939 L1970 **GS GP** *071
MOSCA, Katharine Sidur. ■ 18034 #051-01-1991 L1994 **PD** *020 †55
QUINONES, Joanne N. ■ 18034 #008-01-1998 L2000 **OBG** *020
SAYLOR, Samuel. ■ 18034 #041-15-2007 L2007 **EM** *012
STUART, Wayne Christopher. 2755 STATION AVE, PA PROGRAM DESALES UNIVERS 18034 #045-01-1982 L1993 **OS ORS** *040 †42 ‡
TABOR, Richard John. ■ 18034 #041-09-1993 L1997 **EM** *020 †16
YOUNG, Thomas E. 4025 W HOPEWELL RD 18034 #305-01-1987 L1990 **IM IMG** *020 †20

CENTRAL CITY – SOMERSET

GRIFFITH, Glenn Geo. ■ 15926 #041-12-1956 L1957 **GS** *071 †85
KITSKO, William Thos. ■ 15926 #010-02-1953 L1954 **P CHP** *072 †75
QUINN, John R. ■ 15926 #041-12-1953 L1954 **AN** *071 †05

CENTRE HALL – CENTRE

CHAUDHRY, Rashid Sultan. 132 THE MEADOWS DR, MEADOWS PSYCHIATRIC CTR/UC 16828 #704-04-1983 L2001 **P** *020
MEHTA, Tushar Jayantilal. 132 THE MEADOWS DR 16828 #495-01-1981 L1994 **CHP** *020
PATEL, Nalin Gordhanbhai. 132 THE MEADOWS DR 16828 #495-76-1979 L1986 **P** *020 †75
RICHMAN, Craig Garry. 132 THE MEADOWS DR, THE MEADOWS PSYCHIATRIC CE 16828 #041-02-1988 L1990 **P PYG** *020 †75

CHADDS FORD – DELAWARE

BLUMBERG, Gabriele. ■ 19317 #165-03-1985 L1990 **NEP** *020 †20
CHEN, Hsiong. ■ 19317 #023-01-2005 L2006 **N** *012
GOLD, Alexander Michael. ■ 19317 #024-01-1995 L2001 **CD** *020 †20
HURFORD, Matthew Thomas. ■ 19317 #017-20-1995 L1999 **PTH** *020 †50
KAPADIA, Dilip Laxmikant. 11 RAVEN DR 19317 #495-98-1971 L1978 **DR NR** *020 †28
KOUSSIS, Carmela P. ■ 19317 #041-09-1962 L1963 **P** *020 †75
KRALL, Ronald Lee. ■ 19317 #041-12-1973 L1999 **N PA** *040 †75
LEFF, Richard Louis. 230 S FAIRVILLE RD 19317 #008-01-1984 L2000 **RHU IM** *020 †20
LIGO, Robert Norman. ■ 19317 #041-12-1954 L1955 **OM** *030 †70
LUBIC, Lowell G. ■ 19317 #041-12-1950 L1951 **N** *071 †75
LUSCAVAGE, Lonnie. 608 CHADDS FORD DR, STE 100 19317 #041-02-1996 L1998 **OPH** *020 †35 ‡
MAYEKAR, Ruta Ulhas. ■ 19317 #496-38-1979 L1984 **P CHP** *020 †75
O'BRIEN, Nora O'Flynn. ■ 19317 #539-02-1942 L1960 **PUD** *071
OCHS, Judith J S. ■ 19317 #041-13-1973 L2005 **PHO PD** *050 †55
PENZA, Brian Louis. ■ 19317 #041-77-2007, ▲ L2007 *012
PILEGGI, Cecile Marie. 100 RIDGE RD STE 12 19317 #422-01-1987 L1990 **FM** *020 †18
PORTER, Robert S. 15 ATWATER RD, MERCK & CO., INC. 19317 #041-09-1980 L1983 **EM** *062 †16
REDER, Robert Frank. 100 ENDO BLVD, ENDO PHARMACEUTICALS 19317 #035-47-1973 L1974 **PHM PDC** *050 †55
REINHARDT, Chas Francis. ■ 19317 #017-20-1959 L1959 **OM** *071 †70
SICA, Paul Anthony, Jr. ■ 19317 #041-02-1967 L1968 **D** *071 †15
TAPIA R., Raquel. ■ 19317 #308-01-1994 L2007 **PN** *100
UTIDJIAN, Levon Haig. ■ 19317 #035-19-2008 L2008 *012
WADDELL, James Graham. ■ 19317 #067-01-1955 L1956 **ORS** *071 †40
WAVREK, Dorothy Joan. ■ 19317 #041-02-2004 L2004 **PD** *020
WEINTRAUB, William Seth. ■ 19317 #023-07-1975 L1979 **CD** *050 †20

CHALFONT – BUCKS

ADOFO, Grace Laast. 1100 HORIZON CIR, STE 103 18914 #035-46-1983 L1993 **OBG** *020 †30
BAGNICK, Joseph F. 202 N MAIN ST 18914 #041-09-1987 L1997 **FM** *020 †18
BASEMAN, Alan Scot. ■ 18914 #041-02-1985 L1986 **FM FPG** *062 †18
BORANS, Stacy Mara. 703 ABBEY CT, ADVANCED MEDICAL STRATEGIE 18914 #041-09-1994 L1996 **IM** *020 †20
COHEN, Meryl Sahn. 500 W BUTLER AVE 18914 #035-48-1989 L1992 **PDC** *020 †55

CRABTREE, Loren H, Jr. 1 HIGHLAND DR 18914 #041-01-1961 L1962 **P CHP** *020
DACIER, Christine Marie. 202 N MAIN ST 18914 #041-01-1996 L1999 **FM** *020 †18 ‡
DYNAN, James Edward. 4309 COUNTY LINE RD 18914 #041-01-1960 L1961 **GS OS** *071 †85
FISSEL, Brett Scott. 1600 HORIZON DR STE 117, GWYNEDD FAMILY MEDICINE 18914 #041-13-1995 L1997 **FM** *020 †18
GAMO, Teofila Sarabia. ■ 18914 #748-01-1952 L1970 **FM EM** *071
GERSHENSON, Stephen Robt. 1700 HORIZON DR, STE 200 18914 #005-11-1971 L1973 **PD** *020 †55
GETZOW, Martin Brian. 1700 HORIZON DR STE 203 18914 #041-02-1983 L1988 **FM** *020 †18
GUSA, William Earl, Jr. 1300 HORIZON DR, STE 101 18914 #024-07-1985 L1994 **PMM PLM** *020 †05
KYRIAKOS, Raja Nicholas. ■ 18914 #033-05-2001 L2007 **MSR** *100 †80
LIEBERMAN, Bruce Lawrence. 202 N MAIN ST, CHALFONT FAMILY PRACTICE 18914 #041-09-1986 L1987 **FM** *020 †18
LOMAX, Walter P. 200 HIGHPOINT DR, STE 215 18914 #041-09-1957 L1958 **IM** *020
MACDONALD, Sarah Whiting. 1700 HORIZON DR, KIDS FIRST HIGH PT 18914 #056-06-1993 L1995 **PD** *020 †55
MATHEWS, Neilson Murray. 700 HORIZON DR, GRAND VIEW MEDICAL PRACTIC 18914 #051-04-1991 L1997 **FM FSM** *020 †18
MAYER, Oscar Henry. 500 W BUTLER AVE 18914 #041-12-1995 L1999 **PDP** *020 †55
MC GARVEY, Joseph F, Sr. 1100 HORIZON CIR, STE 103 18914 #041-01-1962 L1963 **CD IM** *020 †20 ‡
O'SHEA-CROCKER, Kathleen. 1700 HORIZON DR, STE 200 18914 #041-02-1997 L2000 **PD** *020 †55
OWENS, Clara Brewster. ■ 18914 #035-20-1931 L1933 **IM OS** *020
PIATOK, David Jos. 700 HORIZON DR, STE 106 18914 #041-09-1989 L1991 **END** *020 †20 ‡
POMERANTZ, Roger James. 711 HARVEST HILL DR 18914 #023-07-1982 L1990 **IM** *020 †20
RATE, William Richard. 700 HORIZON DR, HIGHPOINT CANCER CENTER 18914 #041-09-1984 L1985 **RO** *020 †80
ROBERTSON, Michael N. ■ 18914 #001-02-1983 L1983 **ID IM** *020 †20
ROSENBLUM, Frances Lee. 1700 HORIZON DR, STE 200 18914 #041-07-1975 L1976 **PD** *020 †55
SANTOS, Richard M. 1700 HORIZON DR 18914 #748-10-1989 L1998 **PD** *020 †55
SAVIOR, Deric Clyde. 207 SOMERSET CIR 18914 #041-15-2002 L2002 **HO** *012 †20
SENN, Francis Edmund, Jr. ■ 18914 #041-02-1956 **NS** *075 †25
SHAEFFER, Joseph Martin. 202 N MAIN ST, CHALFONT FAMILY PRACTICE 18914 #010-02-1977 L1979 **FM FPG** *020 †18
SIESHOLTZ, Thomas S. 700 HORIZON DR 18914 #041-13-1978 L1979 **ON IM** *020 †20
SMITH, Paul Dennis. ■ 18914 #021-01-1994 L2005 **PD** *020 †55
SUCHESKI, Brian Matthew. 700 HORIZON DR, STE 204 18914 #041-14-1995 L1998 **OPH** *020 †35
WALKER, Rebecca S. 700 HORIZON DR, STE 204 18914 #028-02-1989 L1994 **OPH** *020 †35
YOON, David A. 243 W BUTLER AVE 18914 #041-13-1990 L1994 **FM** *020 †18
ZIPIN, Howard S. 700 HORIZON DR 18914 #041-13-1994 L1996 **ON HEM** *020 †20 ‡

CHAMBERSBURG – FRANKLIN

AKMAL, Mohammad. 144 S 8TH ST, CHAMBERSBURG ANESTHESIA AS 17201 #704-15-1977 L2000 **APM** *020 †05
ALI, Jamal Fadhil. 754 NORLAND AVE, STE 208 17201 #528-04-1982 L1998 **N** *020 †75
ALI, Mohammed Zulfequar. 419 LIMEKILN DR, KEYSTONE MEDICAL ASSOCIATE 17201 #495-65-1997 L2005 **ID** *100 †16
ANDERSON, Thomas Eugene. 112 N 7TH ST 17201 #016-11-1983 L1984 **EM** *020 †16
ANGSTADT, Jo Ann. 112 N 7TH ST 17201 #041-14-1980 L1990 **FM** *020 †18
ANGULO, Armand Jules. 144 S 8TH ST STE 106 17201 #041-09-1958 L1964 **AN** *071
APOLLO, William Paul, Jr. 757 NORLAND AVE, MOFFITT HEART & VASCULAR 17201 #041-14-1991 L1994 **CD** *020 †20
ASHBY, John D. ■ 17201 #041-13-1943 L1968 **ORS** *071 †40
BACHINSKY, William B. 757 NORLAND AVE, MOFFITT HEART & VASCULAR 17201 #024-07-1990 L1992 **CD** *020 †20
BAILY, Robert. 757 NORLAND AVE, MOFFITT HEART & VASCULAR 17201 #016-06-1982 L1983 **CD** *062 †20
BALARAMAN, Govinda Chetty. 144 S 8TH ST STE 106 17201 #495-16-1965 L1973 **AN** *071 †05
BALHARA, Yogindra Singh. 761 5TH AVE, STE B 17201 #495-69-1970 L1996 **IM** *020 †20
BARTON, James Calvin. 4073 FRECON RD, 4073 FRECON ROAD 17202 #041-02-1964 L1966 **FM** *020 †18
BATOULI, Amirreza. 757 NORLAND AVE 17201 #035-47-1999 L2006 **DR** *020 †80
BEIDLER, Jon Garry. 19 5TH AVE 17201 #041-01-1962 L1963 **D** *071 †15
BENENATI, Carolyn. 757 NORLAND AVE, STE 206 17201 #035-09-1995 L2004 **OBG** *020 †30
BENNER, John Nolt. 2075 SCOTLAND AVE, MENNO HAVEN INC 17201 #041-09-1975 L1976 **IM** *020 †20
BLUM, Julia Elizabeth. 260 N 7TH ST 17201 #028-02-1983 L1990 **RO** *020 †80
BOKELMAN, Todd Allen. 757 NORLAND AVE, MOFFITT HEART & VASCULAR 17201 #041-09-1990 L1996 **CD** *020 †20
BOYLER, Lawrence John. 112 N 7TH ST 17201 #060-02-1976 L1980 **EM** *020 †16
BRANNAC, Patrick Gerard. 482 E WASHINGTON ST 17201 #539-04-1977 L1980 **EM** *020 †16
BRICKER, Samuel Quentin. 144 S 8TH ST STE 111 17201 #041-13-1979 L1980 **FM EM** *020 †18
BRILL, David Ritchie. 112 N 7TH ST 17201 #028-03-1967 L1972 **NM DR** *020 †80,28
BROWN, Gregory Patrick. 601 NORLAND AVE 17201 #038-40-1981 L1992 **PUD CCM** *020 †20
BROWN, Yvette Michelle. 757 NORLAND AVE STE 206, KEYSTONE WOMEN'S CARE 17201 #041-07-1997 L1999 **OBG** *020 †30
BRUBAKER, H Wallace, Jr. 757 NORLAND AVE STE 101 17201 #051-04-1980 L1983 **FM** *020 †18
BRUNO, Anthony. 120 N 7TH ST, STE 101 17201 #041-14-1987 L1991 **ORS** *020 †40
BUNDY, Thomas Wm. ■ 17202 #036-01-1967 L1970 **OBG** *071 †30
BURNS, Frank Duffryn. ■ 17202 #041-13-1948 L1950 **OBG** *071 †30
CABELLO, Stephanie San An. 755 NORLAND AVE 17201 #748-01-2001 L2007 **IM** *020 †20
CARTER, Stephen Lee. 757 NORLAND AVE, STE 208 17201 #016-11-1972 L1974 **GS TRS** *020 †85
CARUSO, John Robt. 757 NORLAND AVE, STE 201 17201 #051-07-1990 L1997 **NS SCI** *020 †25
CASHDOLLAR, Michael Roy. 755 NORLAND AVE, STE 100 17201 #055-01-1973 L1974 **ON IM** *020 †20
CHADWICK, Antonia Marie. 435 PHOENIX DR, STE A 17201 #010-02-1980 L1995 **IMG** *020 †20

CHAN, Jennifer Puiling. 820 5TH AVE 17201 #035-15-1997 L1999 **FM** *020 †18

CHANG, David. 757 NORLAND AVE, MOFFITT HEART & VASCULAR 17201 #016-42-1991 L1996 **CD IC** *020 †20

CHANG, John Chunlu. 755 NORLAND AVE, STE 202 17201 #041-09-1998 L2004 **OTO** *020 †45

CHARLESWORTH, Ernest E. 375 FLORAL AVE STE 1 17201 #041-12-1981 L1982 **FM** *020 †18

CHING, Henry Tawah. 757 NORLAND AVE 17201 #051-01-1986 L1995 **DR** *020 †80

CHO, Jay Jungho. 120 N 7TH ST, STE 205 17201 #583-01-1968 L1973 **PM PME** *020 †60

CLASSEN, Carolyn Farley. 2700 LUTHER DR, LUTHERAN HOME CARE SERVICE 17202 #041-02-1989 L1991 **IM** *020 †20

COLLI, Michael John. 757 NORLAND AVE, STE 206 17201 #035-45-1998 L2001 **PD** *020 †55

CONSEVAGE, Michael W. 757 NORLAND AVE, MOFFITT HEART & VASCULAR 17201 #041-14-1988 L1990 **PDC** *020 †55

CORIALE, Michael Mark. 112 N 7TH ST 17201 #035-15-1996 L1998 **EM** *020 †16

CRAMER, Harry Ralph. ■ 17201 #041-02-1944 L1945 **R** *071 †80

CRISPEN, John Willard. 112 N 7TH ST, THE CHAMBERSBURG HOSP 17201 #041-01-1966 L1967 **PTH GS** *071 †85,50

CRUZ, Betsie. 755 NORLAND AVE, STE 201 17201 #042-01-1987 L1995 **CD** *020 †20

CUKIER, Andrew Robt. 757 NORLAND AVE, STE 203 17201 #035-01-1989 L1997 **OTO** *020 †45

D'AMELIO, Frank Louis. 757 NORLAND AVE 17201 #041-07-1976 L1995 **DR NM** *020 †80

DAVIS, William Lee. 19 5TH AVE 17201 #036-05-1970 L1974 **D** *020 †15

DE LORENZO, Donald P, Jr. 835 5TH AVE 17201 #041-02-1980 L1981 **IM** *020 †20 ‡

DHANYAMRAJU, Sumitra. 820 5TH AVE 17201 #495-11-1979 L2007 **FM** *020 †18

DHAR, Sanjay. 761 5TH AVE, STE B 17201 #496-17-1997 L2002 *020 †20

DOBISH, Mark Peter. 120 N 7TH ST, STE 201 17201 #010-02-1982 L1984 **GE IM** *040 †20 ‡

DONAHOE, Michael Terrance. 112 N 7TH ST 17201 #010-01-1965 L1971 **CD IM** *020 †20 ‡

DRAWBAUGH, Edward John. 757 NORLAND AVE, STE 203 17201 #036-07-1974 L1982 **OTO** *071 †45

DRUCKENBROD, James Fred. 820 5TH AVE, KEYSTONE HEALTH CENTER 17201 #028-34-1972 L1973 **P** *020 †18,75

EARLY, Calvin Bud. 764 LINCOLN WAY E 17201 #038-40-1960 L1983 **NS** *071 †25

EBBITT, David Michael. 112 N 7TH ST, CHAMBERSBURG HOSPITAL 17201 #010-01-1992 L2006 **EM** *020 †16

ENDERS, John Gilbert. 835 5TH AVE 17201 #041-09-1972 L1973 **GE IM** *020 †20

FACCHINA, Stephen Leo. 825 5TH AVE, STE 102 17201 #010-03-2000 L2006 **OPH** *020 †35

FANELLI, Claude. 757 NORLAND AVE, MOFFITT HEART & VASCULAR 17201 #025-01-1982 L1983 **CD IM** *020 †20

FANG, Peter Jong Wei. 757 NORLAND AVE 17201 #010-01-1977 L1983 **DR** *020 †80

FERGUSON, Joe Rice. 820 5TH AVE 17201 #021-01-1978 L2002 **FM** *020 †18

FLACK, Stephen Brett. 820 5TH AVE, KEY STONE HEALTH CENTER 17201 #041-13-1997 L1999 **FM** *020 †18

FLANAGAN, Margaret Mary. 112 N 7TH ST 17201 #041-02-1980 L1981 **PTH GP** *020 †50

FRY, Robert Lee. 112 N 7TH ST 17201 #041-13-1957 L1958 **OPH** *072 †35

GALANIS, George. 757 NORLAND AVE 17201 #033-06-1999 L2005 **DR** *100 †80

GAUDIOSE, Michael Chas. 757 NORLAND AVE STE 101 17201 #038-40-1977 L1980 **FM** *020 †18

GROSSBERG, Michael F. 1942 SCOTLAND AVE 17201 #025-01-1976 L1986 **PD EM** *020 †55 ‡

GUTHRIE, David Arthur. 757 NORLAND AVE 17201 #055-01-1978 L1985 **GS VS** *020 †85

GUTIERREZ-MUNUZURI, Felix. 757 NORLAND AVE, MOFFITT HEART & VASCULAR 17201 #649-01-1970 L1977 **CD IM** *020 †20

HADDON, Harry Harter, Jr. ■ 17201 #041-13-1948 L1949 **IM** *072 †20

HALL, Mary Jo. 757 NORLAND AVE, STE 206 17201 #041-15-1999 L2002 **PD** *020 †55

HALL, Michael Dean. 757 NORLAND AVE, STE 104 17201 #038-40-1967 L1977 **PS** *020 †65

HANNAGAN, Erin A. 757 NORLAND AVE, STE 206 17201 #035-15-2003 L2006 **PD** *100

HARI, Padma Bala. 755 NORLAND AVE STE 201 17201 #495-66-1994 L2000 **CD** *020

HARRIS, Albin Warner. 765A 5TH AVE 17201 #023-01-1975 L1987 **NEP IM** *020 †20

HASAN, Ansuddin Syed. 601 NORLAND AVE, STE 201 17201 #422-01-2004 L2004 **FM** *020 †18

HASLETT, Katrina Nikole. 757 NORLAND AVE, STE 206 17201 #001-02-1996 L2004 **OBG** *020

HENDERSON, Stephen Dwight. 755 NORLAND AVE, STE 207 17201 #035-09-1994 L2004 **IM** *020 †20

HENDRICKSON, Donald Chas. 176 S COLDBROOK AVE, FRANKLIN CO PEDS 17201 #041-12-1973 L1976 **PD** *062 †55

HESS, David Robt. ■ 17202 #041-09-1939 L1940 **GP** *020

HOLMES, Brian. 757 NORLAND AVE, STE 201 17201 #041-14-1987 L1994 **NS** *020 †25

HOOPER, E Marie. 757 NORLAND AVE, STE 207 17201 #041-01-1981 L1982 **OBG** *020 †30

HOOVER, Wayne Clement. 835 5TH AVE 17201 #041-14-1987 L1990 **IM GE** *020 †20

HURLEY, James E, II. 757 NORLAND AVE, S CENTRAL SURG ASSOC 17201 #055-01-1982 L1987 **GS TS** *020 †85 ‡

HUSSAIN, Shabbar. 1035 WAYNE AVE 17201 #704-15-1978 L1983 **ORS** *020 †40

JABLIN, Peter Mark. 601 NORLAND AVE 17201 #041-01-1980 L1983 **PUD** *020 †20

JAMEEL, Mushtaq. 176 S COLDBROOK AVE 17201 #704-16-1991 L2000 **CHP** *100

JAPZON, Francisco G. 1610 ORCHARD DR 17201 #748-01-1959 L1970 **GS OM** *071 †85

JONES, Steven Rolfe. 757 NORLAND AVE, MOFFITT HEART & VASCULAR 17201 #010-01-1990 L1998 **CD** *020 †20,05

KAUFMAN, Matthew C. 757 NORLAND AVE, STE 206 17201 #041-14-2000 L2002 **PD** *020 †55

KENT, Carolyn Elizabeth. 757 NORLAND AVE, STE 206 17201 #041-14-1976 L1978 **PD** *020 †55

KENT, William David. 112 N 7TH ST 17201 #041-14-1976 L1977 **FM** *020 †18

KHALID, Amatul Basit. 1988 SCOTLAND AVE 17201 #704-05-1985 L1998 **IM PLM** *020 †20

KHALIFA, Nagib Maurice. 767 5TH AVE # A 17201 #330-02-1960 L1971 **U** *071 †95

KHATRI, Shella Asif. 533 S MAIN ST, HEALTH CENTER 17201 #704-16-1986 L2002 **P** *020 †75

KHOKHAR, Muhammad F. 835 5TH AVE 17201 #704-15-1987 L2002 **GE HEP** *020 †20

KHURSHID, Imtiaz. 601 NORLAND AVE 17201 #704-21-1989 L2002 **PUD** *020 †20

KIM, Sungjoo Brian. 755 NORLAND AVE, STE 202 17201 #041-13-1997 L2004 **OTO** *020 †45

KING, Joseph Aaron, Jr. 427 LIMEKILN DR, FRANKLIN FAMILY SERVICES 17201 #047-06-1965 L2000 **P** *020 †05

KISKADDON, James C. 144 S 8TH ST STE 110 17201 #016-42-1974 **OPH** *020 †35

KISTLER, Warren Douglas. ■ 17202 #041-13-1961 L1962 **OPH** *071 †35

KLINK, Paul Lowell. 3000 PHILADELPHIA AVE 17201 #035-15-1986 L1989 **FM** *020 †18

KLINKO, Christopher James. 767 5TH AVE, CHAMBERSBURG 17201 #023-12-1991 L2002 **U** *020 †95

KRAMER, William Alfred. 144 S 8TH ST 17201 #041-13-1979 L1980 **FM** *020 †18

KUMAR, Vasantha. 764 LINCOLN WAY E 17201 #495-33-1962 L1973 **NS** *020 †25

LAD, Rajnikant Purshottam. 176 S COLDBROOK AVE, UNIT 2 17201 #917-10-1983 L1993 **P** *020 †75

LAMPTON, Edward Wm, Jr. 757 NORLAND AVE 17201 #023-01-1971 L1988 **DR GP** *020 †80

LEITE, Helena Pires De So. 757 NORLAND AVE, STE 206 17201 #187-67-1979 L2005 **PD** *020 †55

LEVIN, Eric Marc. 144 S 8TH ST, STE 101 17201 #396-24-1980 L1982 **P** *020 †75

LEWANDOWSKI, Ann E. 757 NORLAND AVE 17201 #041-14-1985 L1986 **DR** *020 †80

LINE, Dennis Edward. 757 NORLAND AVE, MOFFITT HEART & VASCULAR 17201 #041-01-1973 **CD** *020 †20

LISTIJANI, Ira. 757 NORLAND AVE, STE 206 17201 #506-15-1996 L2007 **PD** *020 †55

LIU, Xu-Jing. 112 N 7TH ST, CHAMBERSBURG HOSPITAL 17201 #243-47-1993 L2002 **IM** *020 †20

LOWMAN, Karla Denise. 757 NORLAND AVE, SUMMIT HEALTH CENTER SUITE 17201 #051-04-1999 L2002 **FM** *020 †18

LUDWICK, David John. 825 5TH AVE, STE 102 17201 #041-13-1985 L1986 **OPH IM** *020 †20,35

MADARAS, Laszlo. 112 N 7TH ST 17201 #024-07-1993 L1996 **FM** *020 †18

MAGBOJOS, Quirico R. 112 N 7TH ST 17201 #748-02-1960 L1968 **IM PUD** *072

MAINI, Brijeshwar Singh. 757 NORLAND AVE, MOFFITT HEART & VASCULAR 17201 #495-08-1991 L1998 **CD** *020 †20

MALINOWSKI, Ewa Maria. 112 N 7TH ST, CHAMBERSBURG HOSPITAL 17201 #759-10-1985 L1998 **AN PME** *020 †05

MANDAK, Jeffrey Scott. 757 NORLAND AVE, MOFFITT HEART & VASCULAR 17201 #041-01-1991 L1993 **CD IM** *020 †20

MARTIN, Robert Edward. 757 NORLAND AVE, MOFFITT HEART & VASCULAR 17201 #051-04-1995 L2003 **IC** *020 †20

MARTZLUF, Douglas R. 757 NORLAND AVE STE 101 17201 #016-11-1977 L1980 **FM** *020 †18

MARX, David Glenn. 112 N 7TH ST 17201 #039-05-1988 L1991 **EM** *020 †18,16

MATZELLE, Donald William. 845 DUNCAN AVE 17201 #041-02-1962 L1964 **GS TS** *071

MC CARTY, Christine M. 755 NORLAND AVE, STE 201 17201 #041-07-1984 L1986 **TS** *020 †85,90

MC GEHEE, Daniel Lyndon. ■ 17201 #038-41-1970 L1978 **FM** *071 †18

MOCK, Joseph Phillips. ■ 17201 #041-01-1963 L1964 **R NM** *071 †80,28

MOLLOY, Christine M. 757 NORLAND AVE STE 207 17201 #021-01-1997 L2000 **OBG** *020 †30 ‡

MOZDY, Frank Edward. 601 NORLAND AVE, STE 210 17201 #041-09-1982 L1985 **FM** *020 †18

MUKHERJEE, Satyajit. 176 S COLDBROOK AVE 17201 #495-39-1989 L2001 **P PYG** *020 †75

NANBJOR, Arnfinn B. 755 NORLAND AVE, STE 201 17201 #693-01-1986 L2004 *100

NGUYEN, Thach Ngoc. 757 NORLAND AVE, MOFFITT HEART & VASCULAR 17201 #041-13-1984 L1985 **CD IM** *020 †20

O'MALLEY, Neil Patrick. 757 NORLAND AVE, STE 201 17201 #038-43-1989 L1991 **NS** *020 †25

ORANGE, Paul Douglas. 5 CANTERBERRY DR 17201 #654-01-1981 L1982 **FM** *020 †18

ORFAN, Nicholas Andrew. 1942 SCOTLAND AVE, STE 5 17201 #016-06-1984 L1996 **AI** *020 †20,03

OWENS, James Raymond. 820 5TH AVE 17201 #041-13-2001 L2001 **FM** *020 †18

PALMER, Michael Howard. 757 NORLAND AVE, FRANKLIN COUNTY HEART CENT 17201 #018-03-1977 L1978 **CD IM** *020 †20

PARK, Hong Sik. 120 N 7TH ST, STE 205 17201 #583-02-1970 L1978 **PM** *020 †60

PARK, Jae Ok. 120 N 7TH ST, STE 205 17201 #583-09-1968 L1978 **IM GP** *020 †60

PATEL, Chetankumar B. 414 EPIC DR 17201 #011-03-2000 L2006 *020 †35

PATTERSON, Anthony Edward. 757 NORLAND AVE, STE 101 17201 #041-02-2002 L2002 **FM** *020 †18

PATTI, Michael Jos. 820 5TH AVE, KEYSTONE FAMILY PRACTICE 17201 #041-02-1985 L1992 **FM** *020 †18

PAWLUSH, David Geo. 757 NORLAND AVE, MOFFITT HEART & VASCULAR 17201 #041-14-1983 L1985 **CD IM** *020 †20

PENNOCK, John Leslie. 755 NORLAND AVE, STE 201 17201 #041-13-1972 L1973 **TS** *020 †85,90

PETERSON, Todd Victor. 757 NORLAND AVE STE 203, PHYSICIANS 17201 #041-02-1996 L1998 **FM** *020 †18

PICCINI, Paul Allen. 757 NORLAND AVE, MOFFITT HEART & VASCULAR 17201 #041-02-1975 L1976 **CD IM** *020 †20 ‡

POTLURI, Ajith Kumar. 820 5TH AVE, KEYSTONE HEALTH CTR 17201 #495-57-1996 L2001 **P** *100 †75

PRICE, Alfred R. ■ 17201 #041-01-1950 L1952 **GP** *071

PYATT, Robert Sheridan. 757 NORLAND AVE 17201 #035-15-1975 L1978 **DR** *020 †80

QUESENBERRY, Paul Jos. 757 NORLAND AVE STE 101, PHYSICIANS 17201 #051-04-1991 L1994 **FM** *020 †18

RADLEY, Michael Gerald. 757 NORLAND AVE, STE 201 17201 #035-45-1988 L1994 **NS** *020 †25

RAHAUSER, David M. ■ 17201 #041-12-1950 L1951 **FM** *071

RAMIREZ, Constancio A. ■ 17202 #748-01-1955 L1965 **PTH** *071 †50

RICE, Keith S. 757 NORLAND AVE, MOFFITT HEART & VASCULAR 17201 #041-14-1996 L2000 **CD** *020

RICHARDS, Robert N. 1035 WAYNE AVE 17201 #041-13-1945 L1946 **ORS** *071 †40

RICHARDS, Robt Nathaniel. 1035 WAYNE AVE 17201 #041-13-1978 L1979 **ORS** *020 †40

RICTOR, Kenneth Wayne. 112 N 7TH ST 17201 #023-01-1985 L1986 **FM** *020 †18

RIZVI, Ghousia. ■ 17202 #704-06-1982 L2001 **PTH** *020 †50

ROBERTSON, Roger John. 120 N 7TH ST, STE 101 17201 #023-01-1980 L1989 **ORS** *020 †40

ROBINSON, James Wm. 112 N 7TH ST 17201 #041-02-1982 L1992 **FM** *020 †18

ROBINSON, John Fraley. 755 NORLAND AVE STE 101 17201 #306-01-1993 L1999 **ON HEM** *020 †20

ROSADO, Sulang. 757 NORLAND AVE, STE 207 17201 #042-02-2001 L2001 **OBG** *020

ROSEL, Romeo Canaya. ■ 17202 #748-09-1959 L1973 **EM GS** *071

SABRI, Philip Joseph. 757 NORLAND AVE 17201 #051-07-1980 L1982 **R NM** *020 †80

SAFI, Arshad Mahmood. 755 NORLAND AVE, STE 201 17201 #704-01-1988 L2004 **CD** *020 †20

SANTOS, Rudy Yabut. 112 N 7TH ST 17201 #422-01-1997 L2002 **IM** *020 †20

SARSFIELD, Jeffrey P. 120 N 7TH ST, STE 205 17201 #010-02-1981 L1995 **PM GS** *020 †60

SEMPOWSKI, Timothy Joseph. 112 N 7TH ST 17201 #041-77-1991, ▲ L1992 **AN** *020 †05

SENECAL, Keith Evan. 112 N 7TH ST, CHAMBERSBERG HOSP ER 17201 #041-02-1979 L1984 **EM** *020 †18

SHAMSUDDIN, Shaju. 260 N 7TH ST 17201 #495-33-1987 L1997 **RO IM** *020 †80

SHEEP, Andrew Evans. ■ 17201 #041-13-2006 L2007 *012

SHEEP, Robert E. 120 N 7TH ST, STE 206 17201 #041-14-1978 L1984 **GS TS** *020 †85

SHIVERS, Michael Edward. 757 NORLAND AVE 17201 #035-03-1988 L1997 **VIR** *020 †80

SIMPSON, Zachary Weeder. 1425 PHILADELPHIA AVE, MENNO HAVEN PHYSICIAN SERV 17201 #041-07-1994 L1998 **IMG** *020 †20

SOMERS, Ernest Edward. ■ 17201 #018-03-1948 L1950 **ORS** *071 †40

STRITE, James Aaron, Jr. 120 N 7TH ST STE 101 17201 #041-01-1966 L1967 **ORS** *020 †40

SUKERKAR, Niteen Narayan. 757 NORLAND AVE 17201 #496-38-1974 L1981 **DR** *020 †80

SWARTZ, Mark Alan. 761 5TH AVE STE D 17201 #041-09-1986 L1987 **FM FPG** *020 †18

TANG, Aylmer Chuakay. 755 NORLAND AVE, STE 201 17201 #748-02-1993 L2001 **CD** *020 †20

THANE, Thane Toe. 757 NORLAND AVE 17201 #209-03-1968 L1982 **DR NR** *020 †80

■ = Address Information Privacy Protected

TIJANI, Tunde Tolani. 415 LIMEKILN DR, # A 17201 #690-01-1978 L1995 **NEP** *020 †20
TOM, Albert. 120 N 7TH ST, STE 101 17201 #035-15-2000 L2006 **OSM** *020
TOMAS, Cecila. ■ 17201 #748-02-1965 L1971 **IM** *100
TYSLAND, Arne C. 1035 WAYNE AVE STE 1 17201 #297-02-1984 L2004 *020
VAN KIRK, James Keck. 435 PHOENIX DR 17201 #041-12-1957 L1958 **FM GP** *071
VARKEY, Mary. 820 5TH AVE 17201 #495-31-1989 L2004 **FM** *020 †18
WALSH, Timothy Patrick. 757 NORLAND AVE, MOFFITT HEART & VASCULAR 17201 #041-02-1983 L1987 **CD IM** *020
WATHNE, Jarl Thos. 112 N 7TH ST 17201 #010-02-1985 L1994 **OTO HNS** *020 †45
WHITE, Daryl Eugene. 144 S 8TH ST, STE 111 17201 #041-13-1980 L1981 **FM** *020 †18
WILLWERTH, Gerald Eugene. 112 N 7TH ST 17201 #041-14-1985 L1988 **EM** *020 †16
WILSON, Therese Marie. 2000 SCOTLAND AVE, CTR FOR DERMATOLOGY 17201 #021-05-1991 L2002 **D** *020 †15
WINGERD, Robert A. ■ 17201 #041-01-1953 L1954 **FM** *071 †18
YOUSUFUDDIN, Ali. 112 N 7TH ST, CHAMBERSBURG HOSPITAL 17201 #496-27-1991 L2003 **AN PME** *020 †05
YUREK, Mark Frederick. 1035 WAYNE AVE 17201 #308-03-1981 L1982 **FM OS** *020 †18
ZACHARY, Christopher H. 757 NORLAND AVE, MOFFITT HEART & VASCULAR 17201 #036-05-1990 L1993 **PDC** *020
ZORNOSA, John Paul. 757 NORLAND AVE, MOFFITT HEART & VASCULAR 17201 #041-09-1981 L1985 **ICE** *020 †20
ZUROWESTE, Edward Lee. 1331 S 7TH ST 17201 #038-41-1977 L1980 **FM** *020 †18

CHARLEROI – WASHINGTON

BROCKMEYER, Thomas F. 625 LINCOLN AVE, STE 107 15022 #008-01-1983 L1984 **ORS** *020 †40
D'ABARNO, Jennifer Vries. 1200 MCKEAN AVE 15022 #041-12-1992 L1994 **OBG** *020 †30
DAVE, Nikhil. 1200 MCKEAN AVE STE 103, ALLERGY & ASTHMA CARE 15022 #495-76-1980 L1990 **AI PDA** *020 †03,55
DERIENZO, Umberto Anthony. 17 ARENTZEN BLVD STE 101, VISTA ONE PROFESSIONAL CTR 15022 #041-13-1992 L1994 **FM** *020 †18
DREYER, Evan Benj. 17 ARENTZEN BLVD, STE 201 15022 #024-01-1984 L1997 **OPH** *020 †35
GIPSON, Larry La Ray. 305 MCKEAN AVE 15022 #041-12-1976 L1978 **OPH** *020 †35
KANDABAROW, Alexander. 625 LINCOLN AVE, STE 107 15022 #033-06-1982 L1984 **OSS** *020 †40
LANGENHEIM, Geosette A. 309 5TH ST, GEOSETTE A LALNGENHEIM MD 15022 #041-07-1957 L1958 **OBG GP** *071
LENTZ, Kenneth Howard. 625 LINCOLN AVE, STE 206 15022 #035-46-1975 L1976 **CD IM** *020 †20
LUTES, Ronald A. 17 ARENTZEN BLVD STE 102 15022 #041-77-1988, ▲ L1989 **NEP IM** *020
MALEPATI, K Durga. 323 MCKEAN AVE 15022 #495-65-1975 L1985 **PD FM** *020 †55
MC CONNELL, Peter Jos. 1200 MCKEAN AVE, STE 101 15022 #051-04-1985 L1992 **OBG** *020 †18,30
MITSOS, William John. 1200 MCKEAN AVE 15022 #041-12-1990 L1994 **OBG** *020 †30,18
NAYAR, Sudna Mohan. 17 ARENTZEN BLVD STE 102 15022 #495-31-1979 L1989 **IM NEP** *020 †20
SALOPEK, Edward Jude. 501 MCKEAN AVE STE 2 15022 #041-12-1995 L2002 **FM** *020 †18
SHETH, Malay Champak. 1200 MCKEAN AVE 15022 #033-05-1989 L1991 **OBG** *020 †30
SIMONS, Kathryn May. 1200 MCKEAN AVE 15022 #028-02-2001 L2001 **OBG** *020 †30
SOBOL, Bernard Harvey. 420 FALLOWFIELD AVE, BRNRD H SOBOL M D PC 15022 #407-10-1968 L1970 **OPH** *071
STOCKER, Kevin Dean. 1200 MCKEAN AVE 15022 #051-01-1989 L1991 **OBG** *020 †30
TISSENBAUM, Allan H. 625 LINCOLN AVE, STE 107 15022 #065-01-1988 L1993 **020 †40
WINGROVE, Rhonda Lynn. 17 ARENTZEN BLVD, VISTA SUITE101 15022 #041-07-1993 L1995 **FM** *020 †18
WIZDA, Marianne. 1200 MCKEAN AVE 15022 #041-13-1991 L1993 **GYN** *020 †30
ZINSSER, Michael H. 1200 MCKEAN AVE 15022 #041-01-1973 L1977 **OBG** *020 †30 ‡

CHELTENHAM – MONTGOMERY

AKBARIANBROJENI, A. ■ 19012 #517-01-1966 L1975 **OBG** *100
DEGUZMAN, Carmelita T. ■ 19012 #748-01-1966 L1978 **EM** *020
ETZIONI, Amos. ■ 19012 #550-03-1975 L1981 *100
GADEA, Ramon Arturo. 423 RYERS AVE 19012 #042-02-1989 L1994 **ID IM** *020 †20
KNIAZER, Barry. ■ 19012 #041-02-1968 L1969 **OBG** *071 †30
LEVY, William J. ■ 19012 #041-13-1951 L1952 **DR** *071 †80
MIRABELLI, Richard P. ■ 19012 #561-10-1959 L1962 **PD** *071 †55
MORGAN, Jason C. ■ 19012 #041-13-2003 L2003 **EM** *100 †16
SCHNEEBERG, J Myron. 7943 ROLLING GREEN RD 19012 #041-02-1958 L1959 **U** *030 †95
SCOTT, Sabriya Carolyn. ■ 19012 #041-15-2006 L2006 **FP** *012
TOUFEEQ KHAN, Taqi Fakher. 7 ELM AVE 19012 #704-01-1977 L2004 **GS** *020
TRINH, Trong Tony. ■ 19012 #041-15-2007 L2007 **IM** *012
TULUC, Madalina. 138 BEECHER AVE 19012 #781-02-1992 L2002 **SP** *100 †50

CHESTER – DELAWARE

AGRAWAL, Shrinkhla. 1 MEDICAL CENTER BLVD 19013 #495-67-2004 L2006 **PD** *012
AGUAYO OROZCO, Alberto. 1 MEDICAL CENTER BLVD 19013 #649-07-1993 L2005 **OBG** *012
ALDERFER, Kenneth Groff. 1 MEDICAL CENTER BLVD 19013 #041-02-1957 L1958 **IM PUD** *071
ALTOMARI, Gia Nina. 1 MEDICAL CENTER BLVD 19013 #041-14-1988 L1997 **PD** *020 †55
ANDERSEN, Carol Brumbalow. 1 MEDICAL CENTER BLVD, CROZER CHESTER HOSP 19013 #035-06-1983 L1986 **NPM PD** *020 †55
ANJUM, Fatima. 1 MEDICAL CENTER BLVD, CROZER-CHESTER MED CTR 19013 #704-20-2002 L2005 **IM** *012
ANTONIADES, Kristina E. 1 MEDICAL CENTER BLVD 19013 #374-01-1962 L1971 **ATP** *071 †50
APARNA ARUN, None. 30 MEDICAL CENTER BLVD, POB 1 19013 #495-85-2003 **PD** *012
ARMITAGE, Harry V. CORZER CHESTER MEDICAL CTR 19013 #041-02-1943 L1944 **GS** *071 †85
ARORA, Sat Pal. 30 MEDICAL CENTER BLVD, STE 303 19013 #495-36-1972 L1980 **NEP IM** *020 ‡
ARRIGO, Stephen Anthony. 1 MEDICAL CENTER BLVD, CROZER REG CANCER CTR 19013 #035-19-1983 L1985 **RO** *020 †20,80

ASOKAN, Kannya Parameshwa. 1 MEDICAL CENTER BLVD, DEPT MED 19013 #496-32-2001 L2005 **IM** *012
AUERBACH, Robert Lawrence. 30 MEDICAL CENTER BLVD, STE 205 19013 #422-01-1982 L1993 **PD** *020 †55
AZAD, Raman. 1 MEDICAL CENTER BLVD, DEPT OF MEDICINE 3 EAST 19013 #495-69-2001 **IM** *012
BAKER, David. 1 MEDICAL CENTER BLVD 19013 #016-42-1952 **PD CHN** *040 †55
BALIS, Sol. 1 MEDICAL CENTER BLVD, STE 400 19013 #041-02-1948 L1949 **AN** *071 †05
BALL, Susan Karen. 1 MEDICAL CENTER BLVD, CROZER-CHESTER MEDICAL CEN 19013 #041-01-1981 L1982 **P** *020 †75
BANERJEE, Audreesh. 1 MEDICAL CENTER BLVD, CROZER CHESTER MEDICAL CEN 19013 #036-07-2001 L2004 **PCC** *012 †20
BANEZ-FOGLER, Susan Kaye. 30 MEDICAL CENTER BLVD, STE 305 19013 #305-01-2000 L2000 **AN** *020
BARISH, Stuart S. 1 MEDICAL CENTER BLVD, STE 220 19013 #041-09-1989 L1991 **GE** *020 †20 ‡
BARR, Richard G. 1 MEDICAL CENTER BLVD 19013 #041-02-1953 L1954 **PD** *071 †55
BECH, Fritz Richard. 1 MEDICAL CENTER BLVD, CROZER-CHESTER MED CENTER 19013 #041-07-1985 L1997 **GS VS** *020 †85
BECKER, Lance Jay. 1 MEDICAL CENTER BLVD, DEPT OF RADIOLOGY 19013 #035-47-1995 L2001 **VIR** *020 †80
BEHNAM, Melody Shahrzad. 1 MEDICAL CENTER BLVD 19013 #305-01-2001 L2001 **OBG** *020
BERKOWITZ, Leonard B. 1 MEDICAL CENTER BLVD, STE 422 19013 #035-08-1972 **PUD IM** *020 †20
BERKOWITZ, Robert Philip. 1 MEDICAL CENTER BLVD #332, AMBULATORY CARE PAVILION 19013 #041-13-1984 L1985 **OBG** *020 †30
BERNSTEIN, Emily Beth. 1 MEDICAL CENTER BLVD, CCMC, POB 1 19013 #041-01-2001 L2001 **P** *020 †75
BHAGAT, Urvashi. 2600 W 9TH ST, KEYSTONE HLTH SYS COMM HOS 19013 #495-36-1978 L1993 **P CHP** *020 †75
BOGDANOFF, Bruce Michael. 1 MEDICAL CENTER BLVD, CROZIER CHESTER MED CENTER 19013 #041-09-1966 L1967 **N** *071 †75
BOGOTA ANGEL, Sandra Patr. 1 MEDICAL CENTER BLVD, DEPT OBG 19013 #264-01-1995 L2006 **OBG** *012
BOLLMANN, Andreas. 30 MEDICAL CENTER BLVD, STE 103 19013 #409-15-1995 L1998 **PD** *020 †55
BRADLEY-DODDS, Kelly A. 30 MEDICAL CENTER BLVD SU 19013 #041-02-1998 L2007 **PD** *020 †55
BRANDFASS, William Taylor. CHESTER CROZER MEDICAL CTR, ORTHOPAEDIC ASSOCIATES LTD 19013 #041-02-1955 L1958 **ORS** *071 †40
BREWER, Una Espenkotter. 30 MEDICAL CENTER BLVD, STE 205 POB I 19013 #041-02-1991 L1993 **PD** *020 †55
BRISKIN, Kenneth Brian. 2112 PROVIDENCE AVE 19013 #025-01-1989 L1997 **OTO** *020 †45
BROWN, Michele Susan. 1 MEDICAL CENTER BLVD, CROTTER CHESTER MED CTR 19013 #041-13-2003 L2003 **DR** *012
BROWN, Shannon S. 1 MEDICAL CENTER BLVD, CROZER CHESTER MEDICAL CEN 19013 #025-01-1994 L1997 **EM** *020 †16
BUDEIR, Mohammed Hassan. 1 MEDICAL CENTER BLVD, VIAVAQUA PAVILLON STE 440 19013 #875-02-1974 L1984 **GS TRS** *020 †85
BULTHUIS, Deanna Beth. 1 MEDICAL CENTER BLVD, CROZER CHESTER MEDICAL CEN 19013 #041-07-1997 L2003 **EM** *020 †16
BUONOCORE, Richard V. 1 MEDICAL CENTER BLVD, # 428 19013 #024-05-1989 L2000 **NS** *020
BURKE, John Kilgallen. 1 MEDICAL CENTER BLVD 19013 #041-02-1990 L1993 **OBG** *020 †30
CABRERA, Jose Ismael. 1 MEDICAL CENTER BLVD, STE 428 CROZER CHESTER MED 19013 #847-04-1977 L1980 **NS** *020 †25
CACHECHO, Riad. 1 MEDICAL CENTER BLVD, STE 440 19013 #875-01-1976 L2004 **GS CCS** *020 †85
CALMON, Julieta. 1 MEDICAL CENTER BLVD, CROZIER CHESTER MED CENTER 19013 #187-46-1982 L1986 **ID IM** *020 †20
CAPUTO, Kevin Patrick. 1 MEDICAL CENTER BLVD, OLD MAN BUILDING 19013 #035-15-1985 L1986 **P** *020 †75 ‡
CARPIO, Constantino P. ■ 19013 #748-08-1963 L1970 **FM GS** *020
CASTONGUAY, Nicole. 30 MEDICAL CENTER BLVD, PEDIATRIC RES 19013 #041-02-2005 L2005 **PD** *012
CHANG, Fu-Zen. 206 E 9TH ST 19013 #385-02-1970 L1982 **FM** *020 †18
CHERAYIL, Joseph M. 1 MEDICAL CENTER BLVD, DEPT OF MEDICINE/3 EAST 19013 #495-52-1981 L1999 **IM** *020 †20
CHINIWALA, Niyati Umesh. 1 MEDICAL CENTER BLVD, DEPT OF MEDICAL EDU 19013 #496-38-2004 L2006 **IM** *012
CHINTA, Jyothi. 1 MEDICAL CENTER BLVD, PM&R, GROUND FLOOR 19013 #495-50-1975 L1980 **PM** *020 †60
CHRISTOS, Nicholas John. 30 MEDICAL CENTR BLVD #103 19013 #033-05-1963 L1964 **PD** *020 †55
CLARK, James E. 1 MEDICAL CENTER BLVD 19013 #041-02-1952 L1953 **IM NEP** *071 †20
CLEMENTS, William W. 1 MEDICAL CENTER BLVD 19013 #041-02-1958 L1959 **FM** *071 †18
COHEN, Matthew Frederick. 1 MEDICAL CENTER BLVD 19013 #041-02-2001 L2001 **IM** *020
COLAVITA, Annette Marie. 30 MEDICAL CENTER BLVD, STE 202 19013 #041-09-1993 L1997 **PCC** *020 †20
CONRAD, Stephen David. 1 MEDICAL CENTER BLVD, CROZER CHESTER MED CENTER 19013 #041-02-1975 L1976 **IM** *020 †20
CONTINO, John Anthony. 1 UNIVERSITY PL, CROZER CHESTER MED CTR 19013 #041-13-1973 **EM IM** *020 †16
COOK, William Lee. 1 MEDICAL CENTER BLVD 19013 #041-09-1959 L1960 **GP** *071
COOPERMAN, Elliot Mark. 30 MEDICAL CENTER BLVD, STE 407, POB I 19013 #041-02-1968 L1969 **P** *020 †75
COYLE, William Anthony. 1 MEDICAL CENTER BLVD 19013 #041-02-1956 L1957 **ORS** *071 †40
DADA, Daniel Olushola. 230 E 24TH ST 19013 #041-01-1977 L1983 **PD** *020
DAVIS, Homer Bardo. 1 MEDICAL CENTER BLVD 19013 #041-13-1975 L1976 **U OPH** *020 ‡
DAWOUD, Magy Monir. 1 MEDICAL CENTER BLVD, CROZER EMERGENCY DEPT 19013 #033-05-1997 L2000 **EM** *020 †16
DEMBOFSKY, Cynthia Gombar. 1 MEDICAL CENTER BLVD, DEPT OF NEONLGY 19013 #008-02-1992 L1994 **NPM** *020 †55
DI GIOVANNI, Robert Jos. 30 MEDICAL CENTER BLVD, STE 101 19013 #028-34-1966 L1967 **VS** *020 †85
DOMER, Gregory Stewart. 1 MEDICAL CENTER BLVD, CROZIER CHESTER MEDICAL CE 19013 #422-01-1994 L2005 **VS** *020 †85

DONAHOO, Harry C, Jr. ■ 19013 #041-13-1941 L1942 **OBG OS** *071

DONTHU, Soujanya. 1 MEDICAL CENTER BLVD 19013 #495-21-2002 L2006 **IM** *012

EISEN, Carole Lynne. 1 MEDICAL CENTER BLVD, CASE MANAGMNT/UTILZTN REVW 19013 #041-07-1974 L1975 **OS NEP** *062 †20

EL-ROEIY, Albert. 1 MEDICAL CENTER BLVD, ACP STE #531 19013 #550-01-1982 L1992 **REN** *020 †30

FARIAS, Maria F. 30 MEDICAL CENTER BLVD, "STE 205, POB I" 19013 #495-17-1976 L1978 **PD** *020 †55

FAROOQI, Abdulbari K. 30 MEDICAL CENTER BLVD, STE 407, POB I 19013 #797-02-1989 L1997 **P** *020 †75

FERRER, Nelson Benito. 1 MEDICAL CENTER BLVD, AMBULATORY CARE PAVILION/S 19013 #715-01-1997 L2001 **PCC** *012

FINNESON, Bernard Earl. 1 MEDICAL CENTER BLVD 19013 #041-09-1948 L1949 **OS NS** *072 †25

FISHER, Adam Robt. 1 MEDICAL CENTER BLVD, ATTN; DEPT OF RADIOLOGY 19013 #041-01-1991 L1996 **DR** *020 †80

FITZPATRICK, Ruth Ann P. 1 MEDICAL CENTER BLVD, SUITE 424 POB 2 19013 #041-07-1967 L1970 **END DIA** *020 †20

FLORES, Lisa Estelle. 2600 W 9TH ST, CHES PENN HLTH SVCS 19013 #048-02-1981 L1987 **PD** *020 †55

FREDERIQUE, Pierre. 1 MEDICAL CENTER BLVD, STE 422 19013 #035-15-1998 L2001 **PCC** *020 †20

FUMBERG, Cecilia G. 1 MEDICAL CENTER BLVD, STE 3 19013 #132-01-1991 L1995 **ID** *020 †20

GARY, Robert John. 1 MEDICAL CENTER BLVD, ASSOCIATES IN UROLOGY 19013 #308-07-1982 L1986 **U GS** *020 †95

GERSTADT, Kimberly Ann. 1 MEDICAL CENTER BLVD, STE 3 19013 #041-02-1993 L1995 **ID** *020 †20

GHANEIE, Arezoo. 1 MEDICAL CENTER BLVD 19013 #409-25-1998 L2001 **HO** *020 †20 ‡

GODBOLE, Shyamali Vilas. 30 MEDICAL CENTER BLVD, PROF BLDG I STE 205 19013 #495-41-1975 L1994 **PD** *020 †55

GODFREY, John Trevor. 1 MEDICAL CENTER BLVD, STE 224 19013 #028-78-2001, ▲ L2001 **CD** *020 ‡

GOESER, Eugene. 1 MEDICAL CENTER BLVD 19013 #407-16-1962 L1966 **GP IM** *020

GOPAL, Asha. 2621 W 9TH ST 19013 #495-45-1972 L1978 **OBG** *020 †30

GORDON, Andrew Ryan. 1 MEDICAL CENTER BLVD, DEPT OF RADIOLOGY 19013 #041-01-2001 L2001 **DR** *020 †80

GRAYUM, Bradley Patrick. 1 MEDICAL CENTER BLVD, SUITE 533 A.C.P. 19013 #041-09-1983 L1988 **N OS** *020 †75

GRUNEWALD, Karl Edward. 1 MEDICAL CENTER BLVD 19013 #025-12-1980 L1987 **TS** *020 †85,90

GUBITOSI, Terry Ann. 1 MEDICAL CENTER BLVD, CCMC-DEPT OF NEONATOLOGY 19013 #033-05-1984 L1991 **PD CCM** *020 †55 ‡

GUILDAY, Robert Ernest. 1 MEDICAL CENTER BLVD, SURGICAL CARE ASSOCIATES 19013 #041-02-1990 L1993 **GS** *020 †85

GUNDA, Pavani. 1 MEDICAL CENTER BLVD, HOSPITALISTS OF DELAWARE C 19013 #496-21-2002 L2007 **IM** *020 †20

GUPTA, Madhavi. 1 MEDICAL CENTER BLVD 19013 #047-06-1999 L2003 **N** *020

HADLEY, Carolyn Beth. 1 MEDICAL CENTER BLVD, CROZIER CHESTER MED CTR 19013 #041-01-1981 L1983 **MFM OBG** *020 †30

HAGOPIAN, Edward Raymond. 1 MEDICAL CENTER BLVD, CROZIER CHESTER MED CENTER 19013 #041-02-1956 L1957 **TS GS** *071 †85,90

HAITH, Linwood Ross. 1 MEDICAL CENTER BLVD, SURGICAL CARE ASSOCIATES 19013 #024-01-1976 L1978 **GS CCS** *020 †85

HANNUM, Christopher F. 920 YARNALL ST 19013 #035-20-1983 L1984 **IM** *020

HARDAS, Anuradha D. 1 MEDICAL CENTER BLVD 19013 #495-98-1978 L1992 **CHP P** *020 †75

HARRIS, Lovell. 614 W 8TH ST 19013 #041-01-1974 L1977 **IM** *020

HARRIS, Mark Kendall. 1 MEDICAL CENTER BLVD, CROZER MEDICAL CENTER 19013 #041-13-1996 L2001 *020 †16

HEWLETT, Guy Stewart. 1 MEDICAL CENTER BLVD, ACP SUITE 332 19013 #041-02-1985 L1987 **OBG** *040 †30

HIEHLE, John F, Jr. 1 MEDICAL CENTER BLVD, CCMC RADIOLOGY 19013 #024-01-1987 L1988 **DR RNR** *020 †80

HIGGINS, Stephen Thos. 1 MEDICAL CENTER BLVD, 3RD FL 19013 #041-09-1989 L1992 **NPM** *020 †55

HIRSH, Leonard F. 1 MEDICAL CENTER BLVD 19013 #041-01-1970 L1971 **NS** *020 †25

HIRSH, Samuel Jay. 30 MEDICAL CENTER BLVD, STE 102 19013 #041-13-1970 L1971 **U** *020 †95

HO, Immanuel. 30 MEDICAL CENTER BLVD, POB 1 19013 #035-45-1988 L2001 **GE HEP** *020 †20

HOCH, Susan. 1 MEDICAL CENTER BLVD, STE 306/POB 1 19013 #016-02-1974 L1990 **RHU IM** *050 †20

HORVITZ, Nancy Joy. 1 MEDICAL CENTER BLVD, A.C.P. SUITE 532 19013 #041-13-1998 L2000 **NEP** *020 †20

HOWLAND, Vera G. 30 MEDICAL CENTER BLVD, SUITE 300 PROF BLDG I 19013 #041-09-1979 L1980 **IM** *020 †20

HULMAN, Sonia Elise. 1 MEDICAL CENTER BLVD, CROZER CHESTER MED CTR 19013 #038-43-1981 L1992 **NPM PD** *020 †55

HUMMER, Chas De Witt, Jr. 1 MEDICAL CENTER BLVD, PROFESSIONAL BLDG 2 STE 32 19013 #041-09-1963 L1964 **ORS** *020 †40

HUSTED, James Wethington. 1 MEDICAL CENTER BLVD, DPT RAD 19013 #035-20-1972 L1973 **DR** *020 †80

ISLAM, Raquibul. 125 E 9TH ST 19013 #160-02-1983 L1996 **IM** *020 †20

IWALOYE, Femi David. 1 MEDICAL CENTER BLVD 19013 #690-08-2001 L2006 **OBG** *012

JACKSON, Paul W. 2112 PROVIDENCE AVE 19013 #005-12-1953 L1954 **PS OTO** *071 †45,65

JAHSHAN, Antoine Elias. 1 MEDICAL CENTER BLVD 19013 #605-01-1971 L1976 **GO GYN** *020 †30

KAMINSKI, Mitchell A. 1 MEDICAL CENTER BLVD, STE 443 19013 #025-01-1979 L2001 **FM** *020 †18

KANE, Daniel Julien. 1 E BEACON LIGHT LN 19013 #539-06-1988 L1995 **PM** *020 †60

KAPLAN, Mark Alan. 1 MEDICAL CENTER BLVD, CROZIER CHESTER MED CENTER 19013 #041-09-1989 L1994 **PCP** *020 †50

KAPLAN, Stuart L. 1 MEDICAL CENTER BLVD, HERSHEY MEDICAL CENTER HO7 19013 #010-01-1965 L1966 **CHP P** *020 †75

KAUFFMAN, Christopher Ira. 1 MEDICAL CENTER BLVD, CROZER CHESTER MED CTR 19013 #041-09-1998 L2004 **P NUP** *020 †75 ‡

KAZMOUZ, Suhaib. 1 MEDICAL CENTER BLVD, CROZER-CHESTER MEDICAL CEN 19013 #875-02-2005 L2006 **PD** *012

KENI, Jyotsna Hassan. 30 MEDICAL CENTER BLVD, PEDIATRIC RESID 19013 #422-01-2003 L2004 **PD** *100

KHAN, Asad Ullah. 1 MEDICAL CENTER BLVD, STE 422 19013 #704-21-1984 L1997 **PCC** *020 †20

KHAN, Muhammad. 1 MEDICAL CENTER BLVD, CROZER ACP - SUITE 331 19013 #704-02-1986 L1996 **ID** *020 †20

KHIN, Khin. 2600 W 9TH ST, CROZER COMMUNITY HOSP 19013 #209-01-1982 L1994 **CHP** *020

KILIDDAR, Hussein Ali. 1 MEDICAL CENTER BLVD, STE 422 19013 #528-01-1994 L2000 **PCC** *100 †20

KIM, Ki Woong. 1 MEDICAL CENTER BLVD 19013 #583-03-1962 L1971 **R** *062 †80

KLAVAN, Marshall. 1 MEDICAL CENTER BLVD 19013 #051-04-1957 L1964 **OBG** *071 †30

KOCHHAR, Amrita. 1 MEDICAL CENTER BLVD, CROZER-CHESTER MED CTR 19013 #894-01-2002 L2005 **IM** *012

KOENIG, Johann Alois. 1450 EDGMONT AVE, STE 100 19013 #407-04-1954 L1962 **PTH CLP** *071 †50

KOLSKI, Gerald Brian. 30 MEDICAL CENTER BLVD, STE 205, POB I 19013 #035-20-1976 L1980 **PDA AI** *020 †55,03

KONG, Peiann. 1 MEDICAL CENTER BLVD, STE 532ACP 19013 #041-13-1998 L2002 **MPD** *020 ‡

KOOHDARY, Ali. 2600 W 9TH ST 19013 #517-01-1960 L1973 **GS** *020

KRESGE, Carrie Lee. 1 MEDICAL CENTER BLVD, CROZER CHESTER MED CTR 19013 #041-02-1988 L1991 **DR** *020 †80

LACHMAN, Joseph. 1 MEDICAL CENTER BLVD, STE 103 19013 #041-01-1937 L1938 **PD** *071 †55

LADINSKY, Glenn Alan. 30 MEDICAL CENTER BLVD, STE 303 19013 #025-12-2000 L2003 **NEP IM** *020 †20 ‡

LAINOFF, David. 1450 EDGMONT AVE, STE 100 19013 #035-45-1991 L2005 **IM** *020 †20

LAMOND, John Patrick. 1 MEDICAL CENTER BLVD, RADIATION ONCOLOGY 19013 #041-09-1991 L1998 **RO** *020 †80

LANDER, Kenneth R. 30 MEDICAL CENTER BLVD, STE 202 19013 #308-11-1986 L1991 **PCC** *020

LAVER, Arthur Terry. 1 MEDICAL CENTER BLVD, "ACP, STE 334" 19013 #041-09-1969 L1975 **OBG** *020 †30

LIND, Marita E G. 30 MEDICAL CENTER BLVD, STE 205 19013 #041-13-1992 L1995 **PD** *020 †55

LINDENBAUM, Gary Arlin. 1 MEDICAL CENTER BLVD, STE 231 19013 #041-13-1982 L1984 **GS TRS** *020 †85

LONDON, Gladys Z. 19TH AND PROVIDENCE AVE 19013 #041-09-1949 L1950 **GP** *071

LOUCKS, James Howe. 2600 W 9TH ST 19013 #041-02-1956 L1963 **OS IM** *040

LYNN, Justin Forest. 1 MEDICAL CENTER BLVD 19013 #041-13-2004 L2004 **PD** *012 †55

MACEDA, Jose Sixto. 1 MEDICAL CENTER BLVD, CRCC, SUITE 240 19013 #035-06-1998 L2001 **OBG** *020 †30

MAGALONG, Leslie Anne. 1 MEDICAL CENTER BLVD, CROZIER CHESTER MED CENTER 19013 #041-02-1993 L1996 **IM** *020 †20

MAHAJAN, Deepak Shridhar. 1 MEDICAL CENTER BLVD, STE 407 19013 #495-01-1982 L2001 **P** *020 †75

MALAMUT, Richard Ivan. 1 MEDICAL CENTER BLVD, STE 533ACP 19013 #041-09-1985 L1986 **N IM** *020 †75

MALAVIYA, Lalkrushna Chim. 1 MEDICAL CENTER BLVD #302, CROZER-CHESTER MED CTR 19013 #496-25-2002 L2004 **IM** *012

MALLAPPA, Ashwini. 1 MEDICAL CENTER BLVD 19013 #496-35-2004 L2006 **PD** *012

MAMIDI, Veena Rani. 1 MEDICAL CENTER BLVD 19013 #495-21-2000 L2006 **OBG** *012

MANNELLA, William John. 1 MEDICAL CENTER BLVD, DEPT OF SURGERY 19013 #041-09-1973 L1975 **GS VS** *020 †85

MARCUS, Roy Gordon. 30 MEDICAL CENTER BLVD, STE 303 19013 #041-13-1986 L1997 **NEP** *020 †20 ‡

MATTEUCCI, Barbara Maria. 1 MEDICAL CENTER BLVD, STE 306, POB I 19013 #041-02-1978 L1979 **RHU IM** *020 †20

MBADIWE, Chukwyemeka. 1 MEDICAL CENTER BLVD, CROZER CHESTER MEDICAL CEN 19013 #690-01-1974 L1979 **GS ORS** *020 †85

MC KELVY, Constance C. 1 MEDICAL CENTER BLVD, STE 335ACP 19013 #056-05-1991 L1993 **IM IMG** *071

MC LAUGHLIN, Edward. 1 MEDICAL CENTER BLVD, DEPT OF EMER MED 19013 #041-09-1972 L1973 **EM** *020 †16

MELNICK, Sandy Dean. 1 MEDICAL CENTER BLVD 19013 #041-01-1977 L1978 **P** *020 †75 ‡

MORA, Raquel Angelique. 1 MEDICAL CENTER BLVD, CROZER CHESTER MEDICAL CEN 19013 #033-05-1997 L2001 **EM PE** *020 †16

MORRIS, Sheldon Lewis. 1 MEDICAL CENTER BLVD, SUITE 104 - P O BOX I 19013 #041-02-1962 L1965 **OPH** *020 †35

MOUGHAN, Beth. 30 MEDICAL CENTER BLVD, STE 205, POB I 19013 #041-12-1989 L1991 **PD** *020 †55

MUDRICK, Marylyn Ann. 521 E 9TH ST 19013 #041-09-1982 L1982 **FM GPM** *020

MUETTERTIES, Craig Lee. PROF BLDG 1, MED CTR BLVD, STE 400 19013 #041-02-1975 L1976 **AN PME** *020 †05 ‡

MULLA, Wadia Rose. 1 MEDICAL CENTER BLVD, DEPT OB 19013 #038-44-1987 L1991 **CG MFM** *020 †19,30

NACHLIS, Allan David. 1 MEDICAL CENTER BLVD 19013 #041-09-1980 L1984 **OBG** *075 †30

NELSON, Stephen Craig. 1 MEDICAL CENTER BLVD, CROVER-CHESTER MED CTR 19013 #041-09-1975 L1976 **ID IM** *020 †20

NGUYEN, Adrienne Justine. 1 MEDICAL CENTER BLVD, ACP, STE 231 19013 #028-46-1996 L2006 **GE** *020 †20

NISBET, Bruce Cameron. 1 MEDICAL CENTER BLVD 19013 #041-13-2004 L2007 **EM** *100

NOUMOFF, Joel S. 1 MEDICAL CENTER BLVD, STE 441 19013 #035-19-1973 L1984 **OBG ON** *020 †30

O'HARA, Christopher. 30 MEDICAL CENTER BLVD, STE 205 19013 #041-12-1992 L2001 **PD** *020 †55

OKECHUKWU, Chike Nathan. 30 MEDICAL CENTER BLVD, STE 303 19013 #690-04-1987 L2001 **NEP** *020 †20 ‡

OLA, Khadija Sughra. 1 MEDICAL CENTER BLVD 19013 #704-02-1994 L2007 **P** *020

ORRACA-TETTEH, Joseph A. 230 E 24TH ST 19013 #412-01-1976 **OBS** *020 †30

PAIGE, Cathy Mc Pherson. 30 MEDICAL CENTER BLVD, STE 305 19013 #032-01-1982 L1984 **AN** *020 †05

PATEL, Nayankumar Rameshb. 1 MEDICAL CENTER BLVD 19013 #495-22-2003 L2006 **IM** *012

PATEL, Ragin Chandubhai. 1 MEDICAL CENTER BLVD 19013 #495-76-1996 L2005 **OBG** *012

PATTON, Mary Lou. 1 MEDICAL CENTER BLVD, SURGICAL CARE ASSOCIATES 19013 #038-43-1979 L1984 **GS CCS** *020 †85

PIECHOTA, Darren Frank. 1 MEDICAL CENTER BLVD, CROZER-CHESTER MEDICAL CEN 19013 #041-07-1991 L1993 **P CHP** *020 †75

PIERCE, Carl Lynn, Jr. 500 W 9TH ST 19013 #041-09-1982 L1984 **IM** *020

PIPPIDIS, Michael Nicolas. 1 MEDICAL CENTER BLVD 19013 #418-02-1954 L1962 **CHP P** *071

POBLETE, Katrina Papa. 30 MEDICAL CENTER BLVD, PEDIATRIC RESID 19013 #748-01-2000 L2004 **PD** *100

POWELL, Julia Lynn. 1 MEDICAL CENTER BLVD 19013 #041-15-2001 L2001 **OBG** *020 †30

PRASAD, Kalpana Raj. 1 MEDICAL CENTER BLVD, SUITE 407 POB 1 19013 #495-05-1993 L2000 **P** *020 †75

QUESADA ROJAS, Adrian. 1 MEDICAL CENTER BLVD #302, CROZER-CHESTER MED CTR 19013 #270-01-2000 L2006 **OBG** *012

RASTOGI, Neeti. 1 MEDICAL CENTER BLVD, DEPT OF MED EDUC 19013 #496-04-2003 L2005 **IM** *012

RAUNIO, Anne Marie. 1 MEDICAL CENTER BLVD 19013 #023-07-1976 L1980 **OBG** *040 †30

RAVREBY, William David. 1 MEDICAL CENTER BLVD 19013 #035-19-1968 L1975 **ID IM** *071 †20

RECLA, Lakambini Domen. 206 E 9TH ST 19013 #748-15-1985 L1996 **PD** *020 †55

RIDOUT, Daniel Lyman, III. 1 MEDICAL CENTER BLVD, STE 220 19013 #038-41-1979 L1981 **GE IM** *020 †20 ‡

RINKER, Barry Dale. 1 MEDICAL CENTER BLVD, STE 532-ACP 19013 #041-02-1981 L1989 **IM IMG** *020 †20

RIVERA, Rommel Lubiano. 30 MEDICAL CENTER BLVD, STE 407, POB I 19013 #748-10-1978 L1996 **P** *020

ROSA, Karena Margarita. 1 MEDICAL CENTER BLVD, CROZER CHESTER MED CENTER 19013 #041-13-2003 L2006 **EM** *020 †16

ROSENBERG, Frank. 1 MEDICAL CENTER BLVD, STE 306 19013 #041-09-1946 L1947 **IM** *071 †20

ROTHENBERG, Howard Paul. 1 MEDICAL CENTER BLVD 19013 #041-01-1968 L1969 **NM DR** *020 †80,28

RUBIN, Eric Matthew. 1 MEDICAL CENTER BLVD, CROZER-CHESTER MEDICAL CEN 19013 #033-06-1998 L2003 **DR** *020 †80

RUSSELL, Edward Rose. 1 MEDICAL CENTER BLVD, STE 440 19013 #041-02-1972 L1973 **GS** *020 †85

SABANAYAGAM, Ponnampalam. 1 MEDICAL CENTER BLVD 19013 #220-01-1965 L1973 **GS VS** *020 †85

SABILI, Erlinda Asa. 30 MEDICAL CENTER BLVD, STE 407, POB I 19013 #748-01-1982 L1996 **MP** *020 †20,75

SACHAROK, Cynthia Anne. 1 MEDICAL CENTER BLVD 19013 #041-02-1988 L1990 **FM** *020 †18

SAH, Pravin Kumar. 1 MEDICAL CENTER BLVD, CROZER-CHESTER MEDICAL CEN 19013 #672-03-2004 L2006 **PD** *012

SCHLAKMAN, Jonathan Todd. 1 MEDICAL CENTER BLVD, CROZER-CHESTER MEDICAL CEN 19013 #024-01-1995 L1995 **DR** *020 †80

SCOTT, Donna Pride. 30 MEDICAL CENTER BLVD, STE 205, POB I 19013 #041-07-1990 L1992 **PD** *020 †55

SHARMA, Sheetal. 1 MEDICAL CENTER BLVD 19013 #496-36-1997 L2005 **OBG** *012

SIGIDIN, Marina Y. 2600 W 9TH ST 19013 #913-06-1982 L1997 **FM** *020 †18

SINGH, Ramandip. 1 MEDICAL CENTER BLVD, MEDICINE RESIDENCY OFFICE 19013 #495-43-1995 L1999 **IM** *020 †20

SKALINA, Stefan Michael. 1 MEDICAL CENTER BLVD 19013 #038-06-1979 L1982 **DR PDR** *020 †55,80

SLASKY, Benjamin Simon. 1 MEDICAL CENTER BLVD, CROZER-CHESTER MEDICAL CEN 19013 #836-01-1956 L1978 **R OS** *020 †80

SMITH, Cathy Schanberger. 1 AVENUE OF THE STATES 19013 #270-02-1984 L1985 **IM OM** *020 †20

SMITH, Christopher James. 1 MEDICAL CENTER BLVD, ACP SUITE 233 19013 #024-07-1992 L2000 **VS** *020 †85

SMITH, Gisele. 1 MEDICAL CENTER BLVD, CROZER CHESTER MEDICAL CEN 19013 #038-06-1992 L1997 **P** *020 †75

SMOLOCK, Christopher John. 1 MEDICAL CENTER BLVD, NATHAN SPEARE REGIONAL BUR 19013 #041-02-2002 L2002 **GS** *012

SOKOL, Joel Harris. 1 MEDICAL CENTER BLVD, DEPT OF EMERGENCY MEDICINE 19013 #041-02-1975 L1980 **EM** *020 †16

SOLOWAY, Andrew Stuart. 30 MEDICAL CENTER BLVD, STE 407, POB I 19013 #041-12-1998 L2000 **P** *020 †75

SPECTOR, Harvey Benj. 1 MEDICAL CENTER BLVD, DPT PTH 19013 #035-46-1965 L1971 **PTH** *020 †50

SPERLING, Kevin Robert. 30 MEDICAL CENTER BLVD, STE 303 19013 #041-12-2000 L2005 **NEP** *100 †20

STANLEY, Michael Ian. CROZER CHESTER MED CTR, PROF BLDG 2 STE 428 19013 #033-05-1988 L1994 **NS** *020 †25

STEPANYAN, Hasmik. 1 MEDICAL CENTER BLVD #302, CROZER-CHESTER MED CTR 19013 #913-38-1994 L2004 **OBG** *012

STOCK, Joseph Rudy. 1 MEDICAL CENTER BLVD, DEPT OF RADIOLOGY 19013 #030-05-1974 L1979 **R** *020 †80

SWAMY, Priya. 1 MEDICAL CENTER BLVD, HAN REHAB ASSOCS 19013 #654-01-2000 L2001 **PM PMM** *020 †60 ‡

SWEENEY, Joan Dever. 1 MEDICAL CENTER BLVD, STE 533ACP 19013 #010-02-1993 L1997 **N** *020 †75

TARKIN, Neil Lewis. 1 MEDICAL CENTER BLVD, CROZIER CHESTER MED CENTER 19013 #035-09-1978 L1984 **GE** *020 †20

TAXIN, Richard Nathan. 1 MEDICAL CENTER BLVD, CROZER CHESTER MED CTR 19013 #041-01-1968 L1974 **DR** *071 †80

TCHONG, Kuo-Liang. 1 MEDICAL CENTER BLVD, POB II 19013 #385-02-1966 L1973 **PUD IM** *020 †20

THALER, Bruce Jay. 1 MEDICAL CENTER BLVD, CROZER-CHESTER MEDICAL CEN 19013 #028-02-1978 L2000 **DR NM** *020 †80

THANGALI VARADARAJU, Bharg. 1 MEDICAL CENTER BLVD, CROZER-CHESTER MEDICAL CEN 19013 #495-98-2003 L2006 **IM** *012

TIRO, Salud Urtula. 125 E 9TH ST, CHESPENN HEATLH SERVICES 19013 #748-02-1971 L1984 **PD** *020

TONOGBANUA, Gabino C. 2600 W 9TH ST, COMMUNITY DIV 19013 #748-08-1965 L1983 **P** *020

TOTINO, Joseph Anthony. 1 MEDICAL CENTER BLVD 19013 #041-02-1957 L1958 **OPH** *020 †35

TRAN, Tran Ngoc. 1 MEDICAL CENTER BLVD 19013 #941-01-1975 L1988 **PD NPM** *020 †55

TUCH, Arthur Franklin. 30 MEDICAL CENTER BLVD, STE 201 19013 #035-19-1965 L1969 **GE** *020 †20

UMEZ, Chinwe Oyeronke. 1 MEDICAL CENTER BLVD 19013 #905-02-2005 L2005 **PD** *012

VALLOTI, Joseph M. 721 FULTON ST 19013 #041-02-1949 L1950 **GP OM** *020 ‡

VIVACQUA, Raymond John. 1 MEDICAL CENTER BLVD, VIVACQUA PAVILION, STE 341 19013 #041-02-1960 L1961 **OM HEM** *020 †20

VOLFSON, Ilya. 1 MEDICAL CENTER BLVD, ASSOCIATES IN UROLOGY 19013 #035-03-1999 L2006 **U** *020 †95

VON LINGEN, Andreas. ■ 19013 #409-15-1970 **IM** *100

WALKER, Stephen Raymond. 1 MEDICAL CENTER BLVD, ASSOCIATES IN UROLOGY 19013 #041-02-1983 L1984 **U** *020 †95 ‡

WALLACH, Lawrence. 1 MEDICAL CENTER BLVD, PROFESSIONAL OFFICE BUILDI 19013 #041-09-1969 L1975 **END** *020 †20

WARFIELD, Anna Sturgis. 1 MEDICAL CENTER BLVD, CCMC POB 11 SUITE 424 19013 #041-01-1978 L1981 **END IM** *020 †20

WEBER, Andrew Michael. 1 MEDICAL CENTER BLVD, MEDICINE 3E 19013 #041-13-2004 L2004 **IM** *100 †20

WEIL, Susan Margot. 1 MEDICAL CENTER BLVD 19013 #043-01-1981 L1982 **GYN** *020 †30

WENDELL, Gary David. 1 MEDICAL CENTER BLVD #422 19013 #050-02-1982 L1983 **PUD** *020 †20

WESTBY, George Randolph. 1 MEDICAL CENTER BLVD 19013 #035-03-1970 L1973 **NEP IM** *020 †20 ‡

WEYN, Adrian Saltzman. 1 MEDICAL CENTER BLVD, CROZIER CHESTER MED CENTER 19013 #023-01-1958 L1964 **CD IM** *072

WILLIAMS, Susan Lyman. 1450 EDGMONT AVE, STE 100 19013 #035-15-1979 L1982 **NEP IM** *030 †20

WILLIS, English Dupree. 30 MEDICAL CENTER BLVD, STE 205, POB I 19013 #041-01-1978 L1983 **PD ADL** *020 †55

WILSON, C Amy. 1 MEDICAL CENTER BLVD, CROZER CHESTER MED CTR 19013 #041-07-1983 L1985 **DR** *020 †80

WITHAM, Rebecca Sue. 1 MEDICAL CENTER BLVD, SUITE 426 POB 3 19013 #035-01-1984 L1986 **PS GS** *020 †65

WITHERELL, John C. 1 MEDICAL CENTER BLVD, STE 104 19013 #041-02-1994 L1996 **OPH** *020 †35

WOOLF, Paul Danl. 1 MEDICAL CENTER BLVD, CROZER-CHESTER MEDICAL CTR 19013 #035-19-1968 L1999 **END IM** *030 †20

WU, Kai Qi. 1 MEDICAL CENTER BLVD, BLVD, ACP-332 19013 #041-13-2004 L2004 **OBG** *012

YAGNIK, Rekha. 2600 W 9TH ST 19013 #495-01-1966 L1973 **PD** *020 †55 ‡

YANG, Irene Jeesun. 1 MEDICAL CENTER BLVD, RADIOLOGY DEPT 19013 #041-01-1996 L2001 **DR** *020 †80

YANTIS, Judith B G. 30 MEDICAL CENTER BLVD, STE 407, POB I 19013 #041-07-1975 L1976 **P** *020 †75

ZENONE, Eugene Anthony. 1 MEDICAL CENTER BLVD, BLDG 2 19013 #041-09-1972 L1974 **IM GE** *020 †20

ZWEBEN, Alan H. 1 MEDICAL CENTER BLVD, STE 532-ACP 19013 #035-48-1981 L1982 **IM** *020 †20

CHESTER SPRINGS – CHESTER

ARMSTRONG, Donald Jos. ■ 19425 #041-02-1977 L1984 **EM** *020 †16

ARNDT, Isabelle Owen. ■ 19425 #041-13-1978 L1979 **P** *020

BALDIA, Liveo B. ■ 19425 #748-01-1958 L1970 **GS EM** *071

BURGOON, Jane Smiley. ■ 19425 #041-13-1947 L1948 **D PD** *072 †55

CIVIL, Richard Henry. ■ 19425 #038-06-1981 L1987 **N IM** *100

DAMPIER, Carlton Dennis. ■ 19425 #016-02-1978 L1988 **PHO PD** *020 †55

FATEHNEJAD, Saeed. ■ 19425 #517-05-1981 L1986 **RHU IM** *020 †20

GARG, Sherry Sushil. ■ 19425 #038-41-2003 L2004 **FM** *020 †18

GEER, Ralph Taggart. ■ 19425 #051-01-1965 L1971 **PUD IM** *071 †20,05

GOODMAN, Mark Lloyd. ■ 19425 #020-02-1975 L1976 **ORS HS** *020 †40

HWANG, Scott Nyshin. ■ 19425 #041-13-2001 L2002 **NRN** *012 †75,80

JORDAN, Henry Alvah. RD #1 HORSESHOE TRAIL 19425 #041-01-1962 L1963 **P** *071 †75

KANATALA, Roopesh Kumar. ■ 19425 #496-46-1999 **HO** *012

KHALIFA, John N.. 222 BYERS RD, VILLAGE HEALTH & MEDICAL C 19425 #305-01-2000 L2003 **FM** *020 †18

KLEIN, Amy Beth. ■ 19425 #041-15-1999 L2001 **PD** *020 †55

KRARAS, Christine Mary. 1043 HIGHVIEW DR 19425 #041-07-1987 L1991 **AN** *020 †05

KRISHNARAO, Premavathy. ■ 19425 #495-04-1986 *100

LEISE, Eleanor Olga. ■ 19425 #041-07-1964 L1965 **OBG** *071 †30

LIEN, William James. 412 CUMBERLAND LN 19425 #041-13-1997 L1999 **FM** *020 †18

MESIA, Cesar Igor. ■ 19425 #737-06-1992 L2004 **PDC IC** *020 †55

ORR, Daniel Gilbert. 134 POTTSTOWN PIKE 19425 #041-02-1983 L1984 **FM** *020 †18

RAFI, Rezvandokht. ■ 19425 #517-05-1981 L2002 **IM** *020 †20

ROMEO, Jeffrey Steven. ■ 19425 #041-09-1987 L2001 **IM** *020 †20

ROSS, Wayne Kenneth. ■ 19425 #041-02-1983 L1990 **NP PTH** *020 †50

RUBINSTEIN, Neal Abbe. ■ 19425 #041-01-1974 *100

SALAZAR-GRUESO, Edgar F. ■ 19425 #016-01-1982 L1998 **N** *050 †75

SCHROGIE, John Jos, Jr. ■ 19425 #008-01-1960 L1977 **PA** *071

SZABO, Veronika Rozsa. ■ 19425 #473-01-1984 *100

TORRISI, Vittorio. ■ 19425 #561-07-1967 L1980 **OBG** *075

VANDE POL, Christine J. 454 FAIRMONT DR 19425 #041-01-1979 L1992 **END** *020 †20

CHESTER TOWNSHIP – DELAWARE

CHURA, Justin Christopher. 1 MEDICAL CENTER BLVD, STE 441 19013 #041-01-2000 L2002 **OBG** *100

GLACKEN, Michael Francis. 2001 PROVIDENCE AVE 19013 #041-13-1984 L1985 **P** *020 †75

HIMELSTEIN, Rima Herold. 1701 UPLAND ST, GROUND FLOOR 19013 #041-01-1986 L1991 **PD ADL** *020 †55

KATZ, Leon. 1 MEDICAL CENTER BLVD, & BARIATRIC SURGERY / POLL 19013 #035-19-1996 L2006 **GS** *020 †85

LIEBERMAN, Douglas B. 1 MEDICAL CENTER BLVD, STE 403 19013 #024-07-1994 L1996 **IM** *020 †20

CHESTERBROOK – DELAWARE

BENDER, Christine Ellen. ■ 19087 #035-19-1991 L1993 **PTH** *020 †50

BENJAMIN, Fred. 701 LEE RD, STE 104 19087 #836-02-1943 L1963 **OBG** *071

BUFFAN, Adrienne E. 945 CHESTERBROOK BLVD 19087 #010-02-1997 L2005 **OBG** *020

COSTABILE, Rocco Jason. ■ 19087 #041-13-2006 L2006 **FP** *012
DEKTOR, Jodi Beth. ■ 19087 #041-12-2001 L2004 **PD** *100 †55
DOMBROWSKI, Keith Edward. ■ 19087 #035-08-2005 L2005 **N** *012
FIELD, Samuel. ■ 19087 #869-02-1936 L1937 **GP** *071
GARDINER, David Foulke. ■ 19087 #041-02-1997 L2000 **ID** *100 †20
GLOWACKI, Peter. ■ 19087 #041-02-1954 L1955 **P** *020 †75
GROSS, Daniel J. ■ 19087 #041-09-1952 L1956 **ORS** *071 †40
HATTI, Vikram Mysore. 10 ELAN LN 19087 #047-07-2000 L2005 **DR** *020 †80
HERNANDEZ, Edgar. ■ 19087 #308-03-1981 L1989 **CHP** *100
KLIBANER, Michael I. 725 CHESTERBROOK BLVD 19087 #913-06-1967 L1981
    ATP PTH *050 †50
LEBISCHAK, J Doris. ■ 19087 #422-01-1984 L1985 **CHP P** *020 †75
LYNCH, Robert Edward. ■ 19087 #041-02-1950 L1954 **R** *071 †80
MUNABI, Abraham K. 945 CHESTERBROOK BLVD, REPRODUCTIVE SCIENCE INSTI 19087
    #905-01-1975 L1990 **OBG END** *020 †30
POURDEHNAD, Michael T. ■ 19087 #016-42-2005 L2007 **IM** *012
QUILL, Joseph Redmond. ■ 19087 #041-13-1954 L1955 **CRS GS** *071 †40
REILLY, Ann Elizabeth. 500 CHESTERBROOK BLVD 19087 #041-02-1978 L1979 **IM** *020 †20
ROSEN, Susan Isaacs. 725 CHESTERBROOK BLVD 19087 #035-20-1978 L1979
    OPH PHM *062 †35
TREMBLAY, Gerald Fabian. 725 CHESTERBROOK BLVD 19087 #011-03-1980 L1982
    LM *020 †55,75
WEBBER, Carol P. 500 CHESTERBROOK BLVD 19087 #041-07-1965 L1967 **GYN** *071 †30

CHESWICK – ALLEGHENY

BRITTON, Brigit Christine. ■ 15024 #041-12-2005 **EM** *012
CHISMER, Michael Eugene. 221 RUSSELLTON DORSEYVL RD 15024 #051-04-1992 L1994
    FM *020 †18
DONALDSON, Denise J. ■ 15024 #010-03-1981 L1984 **IM** *020 †20,16
GLINSKI, Diane Elizabeth. ■ 15024 #041-14-2007 L2007 **FP** *012
KUO, Ryan Jon. ■ 15024 #008-01-2008 *012
MAHALE, Radha Sunil. 221 RUSSELLTON DORSEYVL RD, SMA DEER LAKES, PC 15024
    #496-42-2001 L2001 **FM** *020 †18
MARTIN, Timothy Hopkins. 221 RUSSELLTON DORSEYVL RD #041-15-2000 L2001
    FM *020 †18
MATTHEWS, John Thos. 221 RUSSELLTON DORSEYVL RD, DEER LAKES MED ASSOC 15024
    #041-12-1974 L1975 **FM** *071 †18
MORPHY, John Chas. PO BOX 299A 15024 #041-12-1968 L1969 **GP** *071 †18
PACEK, John. 715 FREEPORT RD 15024 #041-12-1956 L1957 **EM OS** *071
VALLEY, Robert Nelson. ■ 15024 #305-01-1984 L1985 **IM** *020
VIJAYVARGIYA, Anjana. ■ 15024 #495-20-1993 L2007 **PCP** *100 †50
WILFONG, Donald John, Jr. 105 HILL AVE 15024 #041-09-1979 L1980 **IM** *020 †20

CHICORA – BUTLER

EVANKO, David Allen. 160 MEDICAL CENTER RD, STE A 16025 #847-11-1981 L1982
    FM FPG *020 †18
RITTER, Paul R. ■ 16025 #041-12-1950 L1951 **NM** *071 †28

CHINCHILLA – LACKAWANNA

PANCHOLY, Dipti S. PO BOX 602, SAMIR B PANCHOLY LLC 18410 #035-48-1992 L1995
    IM *020 †20

CHURCHVILLE – BUCKS

AARONSON, Herbert G. ■ 18966 #041-02-1957 L1958 **P OS** *071 †75
CHAUDHRY, Shefali. ■ 18966 #035-20-1998 L2004 **PD** *020 †55
HUSLIN, Stanley Chas. ■ 18966 #041-13-1960 L1961 **OBG** *071 †30
SAXENA, Arjun. ■ 18966 #041-02-2006 L2006 **ORS** *012
SUPER, Leonid Eremeevich. ■ 18966 #913-86-1952 L1984 **OTO** *020

CLAIRTON – ALLEGHENY

ABER, John Michael. 1200 BROOKS LN, STE 140 15025 #041-09-1967 L1968 **GP** *020 †18
BALK, Marshall Louis. 575 COAL VALLEY RD, STE 111 15025 #041-01-1993 L1995
    ORS HS *020 †40 ‡
BARBATI, Alfonso John. 1200 BROOKS LN, SOUTHWEST 15025 #041-77-1984, ▲ L1984
    GE IM *020
BARRETT, John Sean L. 575 COAL VALLEY RD, STE 209 15025 #041-13-1983 L1984
    FM *020 †18
BERNS, David Herschel. 1200 BROOKS LN, JMA BUILDING 15025 #038-06-1983 L2002
    R N *020 †20
BIALY, Tracy Lynn. 575 COAL VALLEY RD, ZITELLI AND BRODLAND PC 15025
    #008-02-2001 L2007 **PRD** *012
BODNAR, Sharon Denise. ■ 15025 #010-02-1980 L1986 **DR** *020 †80
BOLDEN, Mary Carol. 565 COAL VALLEY RD 15025 #023-01-1981 L1982 **AN** *020 †05 ‡
BORRERO, Guillermo. 575 COAL VALLEY RD, STE 303 15025 #264-07-1967 L1973
    P SME *020 †75
BREJT, Mark. 1200 BROOKS LN, STE G70 15025 #056-06-1985 L1990 **DR** *020 †80
CHANDRA, Ramesh Rama. 575 COAL VALLEY RD, STE 460 15025 #495-33-1981 L1986
    CD IM *020 †20
CLINE, Charles Walker. 1200 BROOKS LN, STE 150 15025 #041-09-1983 L1984 **GS** *020 †85
COLLINS, Richard F, Jr. 1200 BROOKS LN, STE 240 15025 #010-01-1968 L1970 **ORS** *020 †40
CRABLE, Daniel John. 1200 BROOKS LN, STE 250 15025 #023-01-1992 L1994 **FM** *020 †18
CUTULY, Eugene. 2129 CONSTITUTION CIRCLE 15025 #041-12-1947 L1948 **GP** *071
DA COSTA, Joao B E. 565 COAL VALLEY RD 15025 #187-11-1969 L1975 **AN** *020 †05
DASHOTTAR, Nupur. 1200 BROOKS LN, STE 250 15025 #010-01-1996 L1998 **FM** *020 †18
DE MEDIO, Gabriel A. ■ 15025 #041-12-1951 L1952 **GP NM** *071
DIAMOND, Mark. 1925 ROUTE 51 15025 #041-12-1975 L1976 **PD** *020 †55

EARLE, Martin Francis. 575 COAL VALLEY RD, STE 404 15025 #010-01-1976 L1982
    ON *020 †20
ENCKE, Ted K. 1200 BROOKS LN, STE 240 15025 #041-13-1964 L1968 **ORS AM** *071 †40
ENRIQUEZ, Teresita Enrile. 1200 BROOKS LN STE G70, JEFFERSON MEDICAL ARTS BLD 15025
    #748-02-1971 L1974 **DR** *020 †20
EREVELLES, Christine. ■ 15025 #041-13-1990 L1992 **EM** *020 †16
FIERRO, Ronald Francis. 575 COAL VALLEY RD, STE 404 15025 #041-13-1983 L1984
    ON HEM *020 †20
FILIP, Patrick. 565 COAL VALLEY RD 15025 #781-04-2000 L2007 **AN** *100
FINE, Arthur Philip. 575 COAL VALLEY RD STE 372, SO HILLS MEDICAL BLDG STE 15025
    #422-01-1981 L1983 **GS GE** *020 †85
FINGERET, Arnold E. 1200 BROOKS LN, STE 150 15025 #035-06-1970 L1976 **GS** *020 †85
FREEMAN, Stephanie E. ■ 15025 #001-02-2000 L2004 **CCM** *020 †20 ‡
GAGIANAS, Peter John. 575 COAL VALLEY RD, STE 209 15025 #041-12-1987 L1989
    FM *020 †18 ‡
GALASKA, Henry Jos. 565 COAL VALLEY RD 15025 #038-41-1989 L1991 **AN** *020 †05
GANNON, Mark Patrick. 1200 BROOKS LN, STE 150 JMA BLDG 15025 #041-12-1986 L1987
    GS *020 †85
GOPAL, Krishnan A. 575 COAL VALLEY RD STE 301, JEFFERSON HOSPITAL MED BLD 15025
    #495-33-1962 L1980 **CRS** *020 †10,85 ‡
GORUN - GORUNESCU, Calin. 565 COAL VALLEY RD 15025 #781-05-1996 L2006 **AN** *100 †05
GRANDIS, Donald Jay. 575 COAL VALLEY RD, STE 516 15025 #051-04-1985 L1986 **IM** *020 †20
GREGG, Robert Alan. 565 COAL VALLEY RD 15025 #041-09-1981 L1984 **AN** *020 †05
GURNANI, Aruna. 575 COAL VALLEY RD, STE 510 15025 #495-16-1960 L1981 **PD** *020 †55
HART, Timothy Paul. 1925 ROUTE 51 15025 #041-12-1992 L1998 **PD** *020 †55
JALIL, Amjad. 575 COAL VALLEY RD, STE 507 15025 #704-02-1995 L1998 **HO** *020 †20
JOSON, Philip Michael. 1200 BROOKS LN, SOUTHWEST 15025 #041-09-1986 L1991
    GE IM *020 †20 ‡
JURIGA, Barbara M. 1200 BROOKS LN, STE 160 15025 #041-77-1990, ▲ L1992 **CD** *020 †20
KASUBA, Vida Regina. 565 COAL VALLEY RD 15025 #038-44-1988 L1992 **AN** *020 †05
KEMP, Amy Lynn. 565 COAL VALLEY RD 15025 #041-14-1997 L1997 **AN** *020 †05
KOMER, Louis Mark. 1200 BROOKS LN, STE 250 15025 #041-13-1991 L1993 **FM** *020 †18
KRAUSE, Seymoure. 575 COAL VALLEY RD, STE 460 15025 #041-12-1943 L1944
    CD IM *071 †20 ‡
KUMAR, Shashi. 1200 BROOKS LN, SOUTHWEST 15025 #495-14-1980 L1987 **IM GE** *020 †20
KUMARI, Pushpa. 1200 BROOKS LN STE 120 15025 #704-16-1993 L2003 **N** *020 †75
KUWIK, Richard James. 565 COAL VALLEY RD 15025 #035-06-1977 L1988 **AN IM** *020 †05
LA BARBERA, Anthony P. 1925 ROUTE 51 15025 #041-12-1993 L1995 **PD** *020 †55
LAMAN, Andrew David. 575 COAL VALLEY RD, STE 404 15025 #041-12-1996 L1998
    HO *020 †20
LAWSON, Robin Ann. 565 COAL VALLEY RD 15025 #041-12-1991 L1995 **CCA** *020 †20,05
LEMBERG, Jeffrey. 575 COAL VALLEY RD, STE 361 15025 #654-01-1982 L1986
    PM OS *020 †60 ‡
LESH, Mark Lee. 1200 BROOKS LN, STE 240 15025 #041-14-1993 L1996 **OSM** *020 †40
LEVIN, Kenneth Philip. 1925 ROUTE 51 15025 #041-12-2000 L2002 **PD** *020 †55
LILIENTHAL, David S. 575 COAL VALLEY RD STE 374, JEFFERSON INT MED PC 15025
    #041-12-1986 L1987 **IM** *020 †20 ‡
LIPMAN, Rodney Craig. 575 COAL VALLEY RD, CARDIOLOGY OFFICE 15025
    #041-14-1975 L1980 **CD IM** *020 †20
LO, Shih-Chieh. 1200 BROOKS LN, STE 280 15025 #244-06-1970 L1985 **IM NEP** *020
LOBUR, David Michael, Jr. ■ 15025 #041-02-2008 L2008 *012
MALLINGER, Michael I. 575 COAL VALLEY RD STE 405 15025 #041-12-1974 L1975
    IM IMG *020 †20 ‡
MC CENSKY, Gail Marx. 565 COAL VALLEY RD 15025 #041-12-1987 L1989 **AN** *020 †05
MC GROGAN, Martin Jos. 565 COAL VALLEY RD 15025 #041-09-1986 L1988 **AN** *020 †05
MEHTA, Rajesh Maharlal. 575 COAL VALLEY RD, STE 312 15025 #495-22-1983 L1994
    PM *020 †20,60
MIKHAEL, Nabil Harby. 1200 BROOKS LN 15025 #915-04-1985 L1997 **NEP IM** *020 †20
MINELLA, Ricci Anthony. 575 COAL VALLEY RD, CARDIOLOGY OFFICE 15025
    #010-01-1984 L1985 **CD IM** *020 †20
MINTON, Michael David. 565 COAL VALLEY RD 15025 #041-12-1981 L1982 **AN** *020 †05
MITRO, Robert Nicholas. 1200 BROOKS LN STE G10 15025 #041-77-1980, ▲ L1981
    NEP IM *020 †20
ORZA, Daniela V. 565 COAL VALLEY RD 15025 #781-05-1993 L2002 **AN** *020
PANDEY, Ramesh. 803 MILLER AVE 15025 #495-55-1970 L1993 **IM** *020 †20
PAPA, Frank Chas. ■ 15025 #305-01-1980 L1985 **DR** *020 †20
PARK, Chong Soon. 575 COAL VALLEY RD, STE 504 15025 #041-09-1989 L1994 **TS** *020 †90,85
PARK, Kyung Soon. 575 COAL VALLEY RD, STE 504 15025 #041-09-1992 L1999 **TS** *020 †90,85
PARK, Sang Bock. 575 COAL VALLEY RD, STE 504 15025 #583-02-1959 L1971
    TS VS *020 †85,90
PHANSE, Mohan Singh. 1200 BROOKS LN, SOUTHWEST 15025 #495-20-1968 L1973
    GE *020 †20
PHITAYAKORN, Chet. 575 COAL VALLEY RD, STE 365 15025 #891-02-1968 L1970
    TS *020 †85,90 ‡
PIROLI, Robert Jos. 575 COAL VALLEY RD 15025 #041-14-1983 L1984 **RO** *020 †80
PITUCH, Daniel William. 575 COAL VALLEY RD, STE 316 SH MED BLDG 15025
    #041-12-1994 L1996 **OS** *020 ‡
PORTZ, Matthew Chas. 1200 BROOKS LN, STE 250 15025 #041-13-1987 L1989
    FM IMG *020 †18
ROSARIO, Anjali C. 565 COAL VALLEY RD 15025 #495-17-1990 L1998 **AN** *020 †05
RUBIN, Daniel Albert. 575 COAL VALLEY RD STE 574, SOUTH HILLS MED BLDG 15025
    #035-06-1986 L1990 **CD IM** *020 †20,50
SAN PEDRO, Romeo Sioson. ■ 15025 #748-07-1961 L1973 **OBG** *071
SANTIAGO, Carlos Rafael. 575 COAL VALLEY RD STE 303, GUILLERMO BORRERO MD &
    ASC 15025 #847-10-1959 L1975 **P CHP** *020 †75
SCHNEIDER, Richard Roy. 575 COAL VALLEY RD, STE 464 JEFFERSON MED. OFF 15025
    #025-01-1973 L1983 **CD IM** *071 †20
SHARMA, Neelum. 575 COAL VALLEY RD, STE 209 15025 #495-39-1997 L2003 **FM** *100 †18
SMITH, Jack Ernest. 575 COAL VALLEY RD, CARDIOLOGY OFFICE 15025 #041-09-1984 L1985
    CD IM *020
SPILL, Ira Louis. 565 COAL VALLEY RD 15025 #035-19-1975 L1987 **AN OBG** *020 †05
SUTKOWSKI, Przemyslaw J. 1200 BROOKS LN, STE G10 15025 #759-12-1991 L1997
    NEP *020 †20
TAUBERG, Stuart Gregg. 575 COAL VALLEY RD STE 460 15025 #041-12-1985 L1986
    CD IM *020 †20
URBAN, Richard Stephen. 575 COAL VALLEY RD, STE 209 15025 #035-06-1979 L1980
    FM *020 †18

URBANO, Thomas H. 565 COAL VALLEY RD 15025 #748-08-1966 L1973 **AN GS** *020
VARTAZARIAN, Tigran N. 565 COAL VALLEY RD 15025 #913-38-1986 L2006 **AN** *05
WALLIA, Rajni. 575 COAL VALLEY RD, STE 264 15025 #495-20-1976 L1979 **NEP IM** †20
WATKINS, Brenda Ellen. 1925 ROUTE 51 15025 #041-12-1983 L1984 **PD** *020 †55
WEIDNER, Gregg Gerard. 565 COAL VALLEY RD 15025 #041-13-1988 L1992 **AN PME** *020 †05 ‡
WEIDNER, Lisa Ann. 565 COAL VALLEY RD 15025 #041-13-1981 L1982 **PME** *020 †05
WEINBERGER, Monte Brian. 575 COAL VALLEY RD, STE 507 15025 #045-01-1987 L1993 **NS** *020 †25
WILEN, Howard Orent. 1200 BROOKS LN, SOUTHWEST 15025 #654-01-1981 L1984 **GE** *020 †20
ZEMANICK, Mark Chas. 565 COAL VALLEY RD 15025 #041-13-1987 L1994 **AN** *020 †05 ‡

CLARIDGE – WESTMORELAND

CHOI, Charles Jungchul. ■ 15623 #023-01-1986 L1992 **PTH** *020 †50

CLARION – CLARION

ABDULLAH, Mohammad F. ■ 16214 #875-02-1986 L1995 **PHO** *020 †55
BOOK, Edward Eugene. ■ 16214 #038-40-1983 L1985 **GP** *020
CUNNINGHAM, Catherine A. 24 DOCTORS LN, STE 101 16214 #028-78-1998, ▲ L1999 **IM** *020 †20
DESAI, Haresh Indubhai. 1008 S 5TH AVE STE 201, CRICKLE WOOD CTR 16214 #495-48-1977 L1995 **A PD** *020 †55
FIELDING, Eric John. 1 HOSPITAL DR, CLARION HOSPITAL 16214 #039-01-1981 L1982 **DR** *020 †80
FREENOCK, Thomas F, Jr. 24 DOCTORS LN, STE 304 16214 #041-09-1984 L1985 **PM PRS** *020 †60 ‡
GANABATHI, Kumaresan. 24 DOCTORS LN, STE 301 16214 #495-42-1979 L1994 **U** *020
GUDAKUNST, Jane Belt. 24 DOCTORS LN, STE 102 16214 #038-45-1986 L1995 **FM** *040 †18
HAGERTY, Michael Francis. 1008 S 5TH AVE, PENNSYLVANIA HEART GROUP 16214 #041-02-1982 L1983 **CD IM** *020 †20
KO, Anne C Martin. 949 S 5TH AVE 16214 #017-20-1986 L1992 **PD** *020 †55
MAHER, Yvonne B. 1008 S 5TH AVE, PENNSYLVANIA HEART GROUP 16214 #010-02-1976 L1980 **CD** *020 †20
MATSON, Bart L. 1008 S 5TH AVE, STE 203 16214 #041-77-1987, ▲ L1988 **OBG** *020 †30
MYERS, John H. 1008 S 5TH AVE, STE 203 16214 #041-77-1988, ▲ L1989 **OBG** *020
PARK, Joseph Soo. ■ 16214 #051-01-2004 L2007 **ORS** *012
PERARD, Anie Gency. 1008 S 5TH AVE, STE 203 16214 #041-14-2000 L2005 **OBG** *020
POLATTY, Thomas Varn. ■ 16214 #018-75-1954, ▲ L1960 *071
PRIBADI, Krishnahari S. 2 HOSPITAL DR, CLARION PSYCHIATRIC CTR 16214 #506-05-1971 L1992 **CHP P** *020 †75
RADECKI, Thomas Edward. 1008 S 5TH AVE, STE 202 16214 #038-40-1973 L1974 **P** *050 †75
STAHLMAN, Frederick Boyd. ■ 16214 #041-12-1946 L1947 **GP** *072
SUMROK, Rick John. 1 HOSPITAL DR 16214 #048-14-2001 L2001 **EM** *020
TYNSKI, Zofia. ■ 16214 #759-01-1995 L2006 **PCP** *100
WONG, Hon Yuen. 1350 E MAIN ST 16214 #244-02-1973 L1975 **FM** *020 †16,18
YOHE, Frank James. 2 HOSPITAL DR 16214 #041-02-1978 L1979 **P** *020 †18,75
ZLOTNICKI, David Michael. ■ 16214 #041-07-1989 L1992 **FM** *020 †18

CLARKS GREEN – LACKAWANNA

BOYARSKY, Stephanie Anne. 102 N ABINGTON RD, STE 107 18411 #041-07-1988 L1990 **FM** *020 †18
CRUCIANI, Dominick A. ■ 18411 #010-02-1958 L1959 **OPH** *071 †35
FARRELL, Marla Judith. ■ 18411 #041-07-1991 L1994 **PD** *020 †55
JEWETT, Stephen R. 251 E GROVE ST 18411 #035-15-1946 L1949 **FM** *071
MC ANDREW, John Joseph. 319 N ABINGTON RD, ABINGTON MEDICAL CLINIC 18411 #010-02-1962 L1963 **FM** *071 †18
SMITH, Stafford Michael. 102 N ABINGTON RD, STE 103 18411 #422-01-1985 L1987 **CD IM** *020 †20

CLARKS SUMMIT – LACKAWANNA

ADONIZIO, Tanja. ■ 18411 #041-02-1996 L1999 **EM** *020 †16
BARNES, Willis Curtis. 115 DEPOT ST 18411 #041-09-1957 L1958 **AN** *071 †05
BLACK, Wm Alexander, Jr. ■ 18411 #041-09-1965 L1968 **NS N** *071 †25
BOLAND, Stanley W. 503 S STATE ST 18411 #065-09-1961 L1962 **OPH** *020 †35
BONESSI, James Vincent. 311 DAVIS ST 18411 #041-12-1956 L1957 **IM DIA** *071
BUXBAUM, Henry. STATE HOSP 18411 #407-26-1938 L1950 **P** *030 †75
CHO, Hyung Tai. 1451 HILLSIDE DR, CLARKS SUMMIT STATE HOSPIT 18411 #583-10-1965 L1973 **P** *071
CHOWDHURY, Mahdi Razeeb. ■ 18411 #041-02-2008 *012
CUPPLE, Peter Paul. 1451 HILLSIDE DR 18411 #041-09-1954 L1955 **P** *020 †75
DE LEO, Nicholas V A. ■ 18411 #561-10-1936 L1946 **GP IM** *071
DRUFFNER, Charles Richard. 1851 NEWTON RANSOM BLVD 18411 #041-02-1960 L1961 **IM** *071 †20
FRATTALI, Mary J. 503 S STATE ST, NORTHEASTERN EYE INST 18411 #041-02-1990 L1992 **OPH** *020 †35
GALELLA, Yvonne. 407 N STATE ST 18411 #041-77-2003, ▲ L2003 *020
GERFIN, Ernest Raymond. 707 N STATE ST 18411 #010-01-1967 L1968 **PTH** *020 †50
GRUZENSKI, William Paul. 1451 HILLSIDE DR, CLARKS SUMMIT STATE HOSP 18411 #065-09-1970 L1981 **P CHN** *030 †75
HOLLA, Vathsala Shripathi. ■ 18411 #495-09-1969 L1981 **NPM PD** *071 †55
HWAN, Jung Jang. 709 N STATE ST 18411 #385-02-1966 L1972 **OBG** *020 †30
JOSHI, Satish Kantilal. 1451 HILLSIDE DR, C S S HOSPITAL 18411 #495-22-1970 L1979 **P** *020
LEE, Jeffrey Yoonsuk. 1157 LACKAWANNA TRL 18411 #041-76-2002, ▲ L2003 **PM** *100
LEE, Susan C. 1451 HILLSIDE DR, CLARKS SUMMIT STATE HOSP 18411 #583-08-1966 L1973 **GP AN** *020
MAJESKI, Joseph Thos. 103 W GROVE ST 18411 #041-14-1980 L1982 **D** *020 †15

POLLINO, Vincent. 129 KIMBERLY CIR, RD 4 BOX 225E 18411 #649-14-1977 L1980 **EM FM** *020 †18,16
PRAHALAD, Ponathpur K. 319 N STATE ST 18411 #495-52-1978 L1981 **AN** *020 †05
PRAHALAD, Sheela Sunder R. 319 N STATE ST 18411 #495-47-1981 L1987 **IM IMG** *020 †20
ROE, Eugene Jos. ■ 18411 #041-15-1955 L1956 **FM** *071 †18
SABBAR, David. 1011 LEWIS LN 18411 #517-06-1965 L1973 **DR NM** *020 †28
SAMUELSEN, Thomas Spencer. 407 N STATE ST 18411 #041-13-1984 L1991 **GYN** *020 †30
STAMPIEN, Ted Michael, Jr. 103 W GROVE ST 18411 #041-02-1990 L2001 **D** *020 †15
SU, Virginia. ■ 18411 #016-02-2002 L2006 **OBG** *012
SU, William. ■ 18411 #041-15-2002 L2006 **AN** *100 †05
SUSEELAN, Rajeswari. ■ 18411 #495-59-1973 L1983 **FM IM** *020
SYMES, Dilwyn Edward. 421 S STATE ST, SPS OUTPATIENT BEHAVIORAL 18411 #305-01-1983 L1984 **P** *020 †75
WANG, Yao Chun. 1451 HILLSIDE DR 18411 #244-03-1963 L1981 **P** *020
WHITE, Barry E. 202 HIGHLAND AVE, 3RD FL 18411 #539-06-1957 L2004 **N** *020 †75
WITTMANN, Eric Karl. 1451 HILLSIDE DR, CLARKS SUMMIT STATE HOSP 18411 #308-12-1985 L1988 **FM OM** *020 †18
WOODLEY, Christopher C. 407 N STATE ST 18411 #041-13-1978 L1979 **FM EM** *020 †18
YOSS, Barry Stuart. ■ 18411 #035-03-1972 L1973 **NPM PD** *074 †55

CLARKSBURG – INDIANA

HOWARD, Marjorie Ellen. ■ 15725 #005-12-1966 L1969 **PD** *071 †55
UMALI, Cresencio Y. 29 SALTSBURG RD 15725 #748-08-1987 L1998 **FM** *020 †18
WAHBA, Haney Naguib. 29 SALTSBURG RD, JACKSONVILLE FAMILY MEDICI 15725 #915-02-1972 L1988 **FM PTH** *020 †18

CLARKSVILLE – WASHINGTON

BERGSTEIN, Jack Marshall. ■ 15322 #026-04-1982 L2003 **GS TRS** *020 †85

CLAYSBURG – BEDFORD

BULGER, Donald W. RR 2 BOX 1068A 16625 #041-12-1980 L1981 **FM** *020 †18 ‡
DUNMORE, Elizabeth Witmer. 2073 SCHELLSBURG RD 16625 #051-01-1991 L1994 **IM** *020 †20
GATTUSO, Joseph W, Jr. RR 2 BOX 1068A 16625 #023-01-1982 L1987 **CD IM** *020 †20
KOTALA, Stanley Herbert. RR 2 BOX 1068A, CLAYSBURG MEDICAL ASSOCIAT 16625 #041-13-1989 L1991 **FM** *020 †18
LASKARIS, Alice Marie. RR 2, BOX 1068A 16625 #041-14-1986 L1987 **FM** *020 †18
SCHULTZ, Edward Donald. ■ 16625 #041-12-1963 L1964 **GP** *071
SHANOUDY, Hany Fawzi. RR 2 BOX 1068A 16625 #915-02-1983 L1996 **CD IM** *020 †20

CLAYSVILLE – WASHINGTON

LANDENWITSCH, Frederick J. 1263 ROUTE 40 W 15323 #038-41-1989 L1991 **FM** *020 †18
RIHMLAND, Janine K. 1263 STATE ROUTE 40 W 15323 #038-06-1995 L1997 **FM** *020 †18
SKRENTA, Richard John. ■ 15323 #016-06-1965 L1966 **PS** *020 †65
ZIEGLER, Jay Montie. MAIN ST EXT 15323 #041-14-1977 L1978 **FM** *020 †18

CLEARFIELD – CLEARFIELD

ALBANESE, Ellenjeane. 809 TURNPIKE AVE 16830 #654-01-1986 L1988 **IM** *020 †20
BEDGER, Richard C, Jr. 809 TURNPIKE AVE, CLEARFIELD HOSPITAL 16830 #041-12-1983 L1984 **AN** *020 †05
BELL, Lawrence David. 807 TURNPIKE AVE, STE 120 16830 #038-40-1978 L1984 **ORS HS** *020 †40
BLEYAERT, Achiel Lucien. 809 TURNPIKE AVE, CLEARFIELD HOSPITAL 16830 #165-02-1957 L1972 **AN PME** *071 †05
BORON, Robert J. ■ 16830 #041-02-1957 L1958 **DR NM** *071 †28
CALLEY, William Doyle. 211 N 2ND ST 16830 #035-45-1958 L1970 **PD PHO** *071
CARDAMONE, Ralph Anthony. 10 S 2ND ST 16830 #422-01-1983 L1984 **CD IM** *020 †20
CARNEVALE, Thomas Anthony. 807 TURNPIKE AVE, STE 260 16830 #041-02-1983 L1989 **OBG** *020 †30 ‡
COOK, Richard Tramontina. 809 TURNPIKE AVE 16830 #041-02-1984 L1986 **PEM EM** *020 †16
CRUZ-VETRANO, Wilhelmina. 809 TURNPIKE AVE 16830 #748-08-1982 L1997 **OS** *020 †50
DOTSEY, Michael Thos. 807 TURNPIKE AVE 16830 #041-02-1972 L1976 **GS GYN** *020 †85
DUPONT, Philip Jos. 809 TURNPIKE AVE 16830 #041-02-1972 L1980 **GS** *075 †85
FABRE, John Arthur. 809 TURNPIKE AVE 16830 #028-34-1973 L1983 **OPH PD** *020 †35
HO, Allan Waiming. 517 W PINE ST 16830 #035-09-1994 L2002 **OBG** *020 †30
JONES, Ernest Price, Jr. 809 TURNPIKE AVE 16830 #041-02-1990 L1995 **EM** *020
KAO, Yi How. 807 TURNPIKE AVE, BOX 592 16830 #041-02-1976 L1977 **OTO SME** *020 †45
LUGUE, Amado Bamba, Jr. 809 TURNPIKE AVE 16830 #748-08-1963 L1971 **ORS PM** *020 †20
LUGUE, Carmela Sala. 809 TURNPIKE AVE 16830 #748-10-1963 L1972 **PD** *020 †55
LUNA, Fredesvinda Suba. 531 HANNAH ST 16830 #041-07-1967 L1973 **PD** *020 †55
LUNA, Roberto Silva. 809 TURNPIKE AVE 16830 #748-01-1966 L1976 **OBG** *020
MAC CARTHY, Justin D. 807 TURNPIKE AVE, STE 230 16830 #539-03-1966 L2006 **OTO** *020 †45
MOSCH, Geo Christian, II. 502 PARK AVE, STE A 16830 #048-12-1980 L1981 **FM** *020 †18
OBLEY, David Lee. 809 TURNPIKE AVE, IMAGING DEPT CLEARFIELD HO 16830 #041-12-1980 L1981 **DR** *020 †80 ‡
OPPENHEIMER, Philip Jos. ■ 16830 #041-13-1976 L1978 **PD** *071
POLINTAN, Rodolfo Sunga. 807 TURNPIKE AVE 16830 #748-01-1970 L1979 **ORS** *020 †40
ROMEO, Bruno J. 820 TURNPIKE AVE 16830 #561-17-1985 L1991 **PUD CCM** *020
SCHICKLING, Leonard F. 820 TURNPIKE AVE 16830 #041-02-1969 L1970 **IM HEM** *071 †20
SHEFFO, Gregory Scott. 809 TURNPIKE AVE, BOX 992 16830 #041-12-1989 L1992 **PD** *020 †55
SMEAL, Darren Michael. 820 TURNPIKE AVE 16830 #041-14-1996 L1999 **IM** *020 †20
TAGALA, Praxidio. 615 THOMPSON ST 16830 #748-10-1976 L1979 **OBG** *020
TAGALA, Rebecca Seribo. 809 TURNPIKE AVE 16830 #748-10-1976 **OBG** *071
THOMPSON, Sherri L Sortor. 809 TURNPIKE AVE 16830 #010-02-1992 L1998 **PD** *020 †55

TRINIDAD, Tito Bascon. 101 N 4TH ST 16830 #748-01-1964 L1971 **IM** *075
VETRANO, Joseph Anthony. 820 TURNPIKE AVE, LTD 16830 #035-08-1987 L1996 **IM** *020 †20
WILLIAMS, Richard George. 809 TURNPIKE AVE, BOX 992 16830 #035-06-1980 L1982 **DR NM** *020 †80
YINGLING, Douglas Bruce. 1212 TURNPIKE AVE 16830 #041-02-1978 L1983 **GS** *020 †85

CLEONA — LEBANON

DEMAIO, Raymond. 233 W PENN AVE 17042 #041-09-1992 L1995 **OPH** *020 †35
MILLER, Claude Jos. ■ 17042 #041-02-1959 L1960 **D** *071
MORASCO, Edward Raymond. ■ 17042 #539-02-1964 L1967 **GP D** *020

CLIFTON HEIGHTS — DELAWARE

ARKLES, Jeffrey Samuel. ■ 19018 #041-02-2007 L2007 **IM** *012
CHERREY, Morris J. ■ 19018 #041-77-1944, ▲ L1956 **RHU IM** *071
GAGLIARDO, Michael James. 201 WESTBROOK DR 19018 #308-07-1982 L1986 **FM** *020 †18
HARPER, Kristine Denisse. ■ 19018 #025-12-1980 L1985 **END IM** *020 †20

CLINTON — BEAVER

BAYUK, John David. 1254 ROUTE 30 15026 #041-12-1976 L1977 **FM** *020 †18

CLYMER — INDIANA

BERKEBILE, Mary Horner. 349 FRANKLIN ST 15728 #041-09-1984 L1986 **FM** *020 †18
DROZDIAK, Russell A. 349 FRANKLIN ST 15728 #041-14-1981 L1982 **FM** *020 †18
FLAHERTY, Janice Marie. ■ 15728 #030-06-1970 L1971 **FM** *020 †18

COAL TOWNSHIP — NORTHUMBERLAND

CHAKRABARTI, Alakananda. 101 HAKES ST 17866 #495-02-1987 L1998 **IM** *020 †20
FESNIAK, Henry Francis. 4203 HOSPITAL RD 17866 #041-14-1984 L1985 **CD IM** *020 †20
FUNKHOUSER, Geo Richard. 4200 HOSPITAL RD 17866 #023-01-1954 L1956 **R** *020 †80
HEROMIN, Thomas Jos. 4203 HOSPITAL RD 17866 #010-01-1981 L1982 **DR** *020 †80
HETRICK, Theodore L, Jr. 4200 HOSPITAL RD 17866 #041-13-1975 L1976 **EM** *020 †18,16 ‡
KOVALOVICH, Kaleen K. 4203 HOSPITAL RD 17866 #041-14-1995 L1997 **CHP** *020 †75
LIN, Paul Stephan. 4200 HOSPITAL RD, SUN ORTHOPAEDIC GROUP 17866 #041-13-1982 L1983 **ORS** *020 †40
MAGILL, John Thompson, III. 4200 HOSPITAL RD 17866 #041-13-1979 L1980 **ORS** *071 †40
MARTIN, John Campbell. 4200 HOSPITAL RD 17866 #065-01-1954 L1966 **PTH** *071 †50
MARTIN, Thomas Louis. 4200 HOSPITAL RD 17866 #041-12-1996 L2001 **ORS** *020 †40
REISH, William Gale. 4200 HOSPITAL RD, SUN ORTHOPAEDIC GROUP 17866 #041-13-1968 L1969 **ORS** *020 †40
SEN, Sanjay Kumar. 4201 HOSPITAL RD 17866 #496-05-1988 L2000 **IM** *020 †20
TWIGGAR, Edward Vernon. ■ 17866 #041-01-1967 L1968 **GS** *075 †85
VARANO, Vincent James. 4203 HOSPITAL RD 17866 #041-02-1967 L1972 **GE IM** *020 †20
WAGNER, Jere L. 4200 HOSPITAL RD 17866 #041-02-1980 L1981 **FM** *020 †18

COALDALE — SCHUYLKILL

BOBROWSKI, Daniel. 360 W RUDDLE ST 18218 #041-09-1986 L1991 **GS VM** *020 †85
BODISH, Eric Jules. 360 W RUDDLE ST 18218 #041-14-1986 L1988 **IM** *020 †20
EL SHAWARBY, Amr O. 360 W RUDDLE ST 18218 #915-08-1983 L1997 **GS VS** *020
MEHOLCHICK, Jean Marie. 360 W RUDDLE ST, ST LUKES MINERS MEM HOSP 18218 #041-07-1973 L1975 **EM FM** *020
MILLER, Richard Eli. 360 W RUDDLE ST 18218 #041-01-1941 L1942 **GYN GP** *071 †30
RAVITZ, Gerald Alan. 360 W RUDDLE ST 18218 #055-01-1967 L1974 **U** *020 †95
SAHOO, Dilliswar. 48 W PHILLIPS ST, BOX 25 18218 #495-79-1972 L1982 **IM** *020
UMALI, Idona Caballes. 360 W RUDDLE ST, ST LUKES MINERS MEM HOSSP 18218 #748-01-1965 L1968 **AN** *071
ZACHER, Joseph Anthony. 360 W RUDDLE ST, DEPT OF RADIOLOGY 18218 #033-05-1986 L1992 **R** *020 †80 ‡

COALPORT — CLEARFIELD

ERVIN, Lawrence M, Jr. MAIN 16627 #035-20-1953 L1955 **GP** *071

COATESVILLE — CHESTER

AINSLIE, George Wm, Jr. 1400 BLACKHORSE HILL RD 19320 #024-01-1969 L1979 **P** *030 †75
AL-ANNOUF, Nabil. 201 REECEVILLE RD 19320 #875-01-1983 L1991 **PTH PCP** *020 †50
BAMEZAI, Vitasta. 217 REECEVILLE RD, STE C 19320 #913-92-1989 L2004 **IM** *020 †20
BARTELS, John Harold. 213 REECEVILLE RD, STE 13 19320 #051-01-1982 L1987 **ID IM** *020 †20
BELL, Robert Lloyd. 1400 BLACKHORSE HILL RD 19320 #041-12-1947 L1948 **NS N** *071 †25,28
BILYAK, Aileen. 201 REECEVILLE RD, STE A 19320 #041-15-1999 L2001 **OBG** *020 †30
BINDER, Martin G. 201 REECEVILLE RD 19320 #041-01-1953 L1954 **OBG** *071 †30
BINNING, Chhinder Pal S. 213 REECEVILLE RD, STE 34 19320 #495-03-1975 L1986 **N GP** *020
BOUCHER, Brian Robert. 525 HIGHLAND BLVD, STE 106 19320 #041-02-1997 L1999 **FM** *020 †18
BURGESS, Geoffrey Marsden. 525 HIGHLAND BLVD, STE 106 19320 #041-14-1975 L1978 **FM** *020 †18
BURNS, Sandra J. 495 HIGHLAND BLVD, STE 100 19320 #035-47-1995 L1998 **PD** *020 †55
BUSTONERA, Linda G. VET ADMIN HOSP, DEPT PSYCH 19320 #748-01-1966 L1973 **P** *020 †75
BUTLER, Charles H. 134 N 4TH AVE 19320 #047-07-1953 L1954 **GP** *071
CEPPA, Federico Ariel. 213 REECEVILLE RD, STE 23 19320 #010-03-1999 L2004 **GS** *100 †85

CHADA, Vijaya. 201 REECEVILLE RD 19320 #495-70-1996 L2003 **IM** *100 †20
CHELLAPPA, Sheila. 1400 BLACKHORSE HILL RD, PRIMARY CARE 111 19320 #495-27-1978 L1998 **IM** *030 †20
CHEN, Qiping. 201 REECEVILLE RD, BRANDYWINE HOSPITAL 19320 #243-25-1982 L2003 **AN** *020 †05
CIACCI, Vincent Wm. ■ 19320 #041-02-1942 L1943 **EM** *071
CRUSSIAH, Leah K. 1400 BLACKHORSE HILL RD 19320 #495-08-1966 L1981 **FM OBG** *071
DENLINGER, John Kenneth. 201 REECEVILLE RD, BRANDYWINE HOSP 19320 #041-01-1968 L1969 **AN** *020 †05
DUNFEE, Robin Ann. 125 DAVIS RD 19320 #041-02-1990 L1992 **FM** *020 †18
EBNER, Steven Adam. 201 REECEVILLE RD, DEPT OF RADIOLOGY 19320 #035-19-1988 L1990 **DR** *020 †80
FITZPATRICK, Kenneth John. 213 REECEVILLE RD, STE 21 19320 #035-08-1993 L1995 **U** *020 †95
FREESE, Andrew. 213 REECEVILLE RD, STE 33 19320 #024-01-1990 L1993 **NS** *020 †25
FU, Libang. 229 DANIELLE LN 19320 #243-99-1982 L2000 **AN** *020 †05
GINTY, Meghan Ann. 1029 E LINCOLN HWY 19320 #041-13-2001 L2003 **FM** *020 †18
GLOCKSON, Barbara. 1400 BLACKHORSE HILL RD, VETERANS AFFAIRS MEDICAL C 19320 #759-04-1968 L1996 **IM** *020 †20
GOETZ, John Michael. 1400 BLACKHORSE HILL RD 19320 #035-08-1983 L1991 **IM** *020 †20
GOLDBLUM, Kenneth David. 217 REECEVILLE RD, STE C 19320 #028-02-1985 L1986 **IM IMG** *020 †20
GOLDEN, Michael F. 1400 BLACKHORSE HILL RD 19320 #016-02-1958 L1963 **P IMG** *071
GOMER, Susheil K. 1400 BLACKHORSE HILL RD, VA MEDICAL CENTER 19320 #649-33-1980 L1986 **IM** *020
HANSPAL, Reena Kaur. 1400 BLACKHORSE HILL RD, VA MEDICAL CENTER 19320 #495-47-1974 L1983 **PM** *020 †60
HARE, Jeffrey Louis. 201 REECEVILLE RD 19320 #041-13-1989 L1991 **DR AR** *020 †80
HARRIS, James R. 1400 BLACKHORSE HILL RD, V A MEDICAL CENTER 19320 #023-01-1949 L1956 **PHP P** *030 †75
HOLSTEIN, James John. 201 REECEVILLE RD 19320 #041-02-1967 L1968 **DR** *020 †80 ‡
HUNG, Jeffrey Liu. 201 REECEVILLE RD 19320 #055-01-1994 L1996 **VIR** *020 †80
HYUN, Min Ja. 1400 BLACKHORSE HILL RD, MEDICAL CENTER 19320 #583-08-1969 L1973 **P** *071 †75
JAHROMI, Heidar K. 213 REECEVILLE RD STE 22 19320 #517-01-1965 L1975 **N CHN** *020 †75 ‡
JUDGE, James Wm. 213 REECEVILLE RD STE 28 19320 #010-02-1982 L1986 **OPH** *020 †35
KHOSHGAVAR, Peyman. 1400 BLACKHORSE HILL RD, VETERANS AFFAIRS MEDICAL C 19320 #305-01-1998 L2005 **P** *020
KHURSHID, Gauhar. 1400 BLACKHORSE HILL RD, VA MEDICAL CENTER 19320 #704-16-1990 L2004 **P** *020 †75 ‡
KLUFAS, Alexander J. 423 E CHESTNUT ST 19320 #561-17-1981 L1983 **IM** *020 †20
KYADA, Jatin Babubhai. 201 REECEVILLE RD, DEPT OF MED/BRANDWYINE HOS 19320 #495-48-1995 L2002 **IM** *020 †20
LEE, Daniel. 723 MERCHANT ST 19320 #010-03-1945 L1946 **GP CD** *071
LEE, Sang Ha. 1400 BLACKHORSE HILL RD 19320 #583-02-1951 L1995 **ON IM** *071
LIN, Sheng Kai. 213 REECEVILLE RD, STE 10 19320 #649-33-1981 L1985 **AN PME** *020 †05
LINGINENI, Kavitha. 1400 BLACKHORSE HILL RD, VA MEDICAL CENTER 19320 #496-24-1991 L2006 **IM** *020 †20
LYNESS, Samuel Stewart. 213 REECEVILLE RD, STE 34 19320 #041-12-1959 L1960 **NS** *020 †25
LYONS, Christine. 217 REECEVILLE RD, BRANDYWINE OB GYN 19320 #041-13-1983 L1986 **OBG** *020 †30
MAGEE, Joan Marie. 495 HIGHLAND BLVD, STE 100 19320 #041-07-1981 L1983 **PD** *020 †55
MARCUS, Donald J. 1400 BLACKHORSE HILL RD 19320 #041-01-1961 L1962 **N IM** *020 †75
MEDVETZ, Lisa Ann. 213 REECEVILLE RD, PROF OFC BLDG ST #23 19320 #041-02-1994 L1996 **GS** *020 †85
MEMON, Naim A. 1400 BLACKHORSE HILL RD, VAMC COATESVILLE 19320 #704-02-1987 L1996 **PYG P** *020 †75
MEYERS, Frederic Alan. 213 REECEVILLE RD STE 17 19320 #010-01-1983 L1984 **GE IM** *020 †20
MONASTERIO, Jose Ramiro. 201 REECEVILLE RD 19320 #132-05-1969 L1971 **GS VS** *071
MOXLEY, T Wayne. 217 REECEVILLE RD, STE A 19320 #051-04-1977 L1981 **OBG** *020 †30
NAM, Theodore S. 1400 BLACKHORSE HILL RD, CVAMC-BLDG 39B, ACOS-MH 19320 #023-12-1982 L1986 **P** *020 †75
NATHAN, David Arthur. 201 REECEVILLE RD 19320 #010-02-1987 L1988 **EM** *020 †16
NIKAS, Marianne Ruth. 525 HIGHLAND BLVD, STE 106 19320 #041-14-1997 L1999 **FM** *020 †18
O'BRIEN, Christine Morris. 1400 BLACKHORSE HILL RD, COATESVILLE VETERANS MEDIC 19320 #041-13-1993 L1996 **P** *100
PANNALA, Neetu Reddy. 201 REECEVILLE RD 19320 #496-30-1995 L2004 **IM** *020 †20
PATEL, Ajaykumar S. 1400 BLACKHORSE HILL RD, VA MEDICAL CENTER (11) 19320 #495-23-1997 L2001 **IMG** *020 †20
PATUKAS, Peter C. ■ 19320 #041-09-1962 L1963 **FM OM** *071 †18
PLOTZKER, Richard Ivan. 213 REECEVILLE RD STE 38 19320 #561-17-1971 L1973 **GE IM** *020 †20 ‡
PLOURDE, Nancy Karen. 201 REECEVILLE RD 19320 #050-02-1979 L1981 **DR** *020 †80
POLINER, Hime Saul. ■ 19320 #041-13-1936 L1937 **FM** *071 †18
PUREWAL, Amarpal K. 201 REECEVILLE RD 19320 #495-10-1985 L2007 **IM PD** *020 †55,20
QURESHI, Tanveer Jamal. 1400 BLACKHORSE HILL RD, COATESVILLE VA MEDICAL CEN 19320 #305-01-1998 L2001 **IM** *020 †20
RABAH, Raida. 213 REECEVILLE RD STE 22A 19320 #875-01-1985 L1994 **ID IM** *020 †20
RAO, Sailaja Satturu. 201 REECEVILLE RD, APOGEE PHYSICIANS 19320 #495-13-2000 L2004 **IM** *020 †20
RICKELS, Michael R. 201 REECEVILLE RD 19320 #041-01-1999 L2001 **END** *100 †20
RILL, Michael Philip. 201 REECEVILLE RD 19320 #041-14-1985 L1988 **FM** *020 †18
ROBY, Ross. ■ 19320 #041-01-1950 L1953 **P CHP** *071
SATRIALE, Richard Faust. 201 REECEVILLE RD 19320 #308-07-1982 L1986 **IM FM** *020 †20
SATRIALE, Robert O. 213 REECEVILLE RD 19320 #308-07-1982 L1986 **PUD CCM** *020 †20
SCHLESS, Arthur Paul. 213 REECEVILLE RD, STE 17 19320 #041-01-1964 L1967 **P** *071 †75
SHORI, Amit Kumar. 201 REECEVILLE RD, BRANDYWINE HOSPITAL 19320 #038-43-2000 L2003 **IM** *020 †20
SIROHI, Arun. 1400 BLACKHORSE HILL RD 19320 #496-09-1981 L1984 **IM** *020 †20
SNYDER, Robert Dourte. 201 REECEVILLE RD, BRANDYWINE HOSPITAL 19320 #041-13-1976 L1977 **EM OS** *062 †16
SPIVACK, Jordan Gary. 495 HIGHLAND BLVD, STE 100 19320 #041-07-1998 L2000 **PD** *020 †55
STEPHENSON, James Bryant. 203 E LINCOLN HWY, BOX 1454 19320 #035-03-1977 L1978 **GP OM** *020 †85

STOKES, Louis Campbell. 201 REECEVILLE RD 19320 #010-03-1936 L1938 **FM OBG** *071

STRAM, Ronald Louis. 201 REECEVILLE RD 19320 #035-47-1988 L2006 **EM** *020 †16

TOUSSAINT, Yardlie. 217 REECEVILLE RD, BRANDYWINE OB GYN 19320 #035-75-1999, ▲ L2001 **OBG** *020

UHLER, Gene Frederick. 525 HIGHLAND BLVD, STE 106 19320 #033-05-1987 L1990 **FM** *020 †18

URBANO, Michael John, Jr. 213 REECEVILLE RD, STE 32 19320 #033-05-1993 L1996 **IM** *020 †20

USMANI, Saadat Sultana. 1400 BLACKHORSE HILL RD, DEPARTMENT OF VETERANS AFF 19320 #704-06-1960 L1978 **P PYG** *020 †75

VON ZEMENSZKY, Elisabeth. 1400 BLACKHORSE HILL RD, HOSPITAL 19320 #409-10-1974 L1987 **P** *020

WALCZAK, Anne France. 213 REECEVILLE RD, STE 26 19320 #042-02-1986 L1988 **END** *020 †20

WEDEEN, Robert S. ■ 19320 #035-45-1951 L1956 **ORS** *071 †40

WELLS, Harold Edward. 1400 BLACKHORSE HILL RD, DEPT. OF VETERANS AFFAIRS 19320 #041-01-1978 L1981 **PUD IM** *020 †20

WELLS, Harriet Van Horne. 1400 BLACKHORSE HILL RD 19320 #024-05-1963 L1965 **P** *020 †75

WENGER, Robert K. 201 REECEVILLE RD 19320 #041-07-1983 L1984 **TS** *020 †85,90

YAO, Yulin. 1400 BLACKHORSE HILL RD 19320 #385-01-1957 L1968 **IM IMG** *071 †20

YEUNG, Horatio Himtai. 201 REECEVILLE RD, BRANDWINE HOSPITAL RADIOLO 19320 #028-02-1982 L1984 **IM** *020 †80

ZELLER, Erwin Rudolf. ■ 19320 #038-40-1956 L1960 **R NM** *020 †80,28

COCHRANVILLE – CHESTER

MILLS, Randell Lee. RR 2 19330 #024-01-1986 *100

COGAN STATION – LYCOMING

VAN ESS, Lester Jay. ■ 17728 #041-09-1947 L1948 **GS** *020

COLLEGEVILLE – MONTGOMERY

ABISSI, Christopher Jos. 1250 S COLLEGEVILLE RD, GLAXO SMITH KLINE 19426 #035-45-1977 L1978 **N IM** *020 †75

AYALA, Alejandro Raul. 500 ARCOLA RD 19426 #187-13-1992 L2002 **END** *020 †20

BELASCO, Robert. 555 2ND AVE, STE B100 19426 #041-13-1973 L1974 **CD CCM** *020 †20

BELBER, Arthur David. 555 2ND AVE, STE B100 19426 #041-13-1979 L1980 **CD CCM** *020 †20

BERGER, Bruce M. 409 2ND AVE STE 201, STRESSGEN BIOTECH INC 19426 #021-01-1977 L1989 **IM PA** *050 †20

BICHAY, Mournir Assaad. 12 VICTORIA CIR 19426 #915-02-1953 L1971 **P** *020

BLUM, Michael David. 500 ARCOLA RD 19426 #035-19-1983 L1995 **PDI PD** *050 †55

BLYSKAL, Daria Florence. ■ 19426 #041-15-2007 L2007 **FP** *012

BORISUTE, Hannah R. ■ 19426 #035-45-1995 L2002 **IM** *050 †20

BRIGANDI, Richard A. 1250 S COLLEGEVILLE RD, GLAXO SMITH KLINE 19426 #041-02-1997 L2000 **PD PA** *062 †55 ‡

BROGAN, Donald Robert. 1 IRON BRIDGE DR, STE 100 19426 #305-01-1986 L1997 **PD** *020

BULLER, Richard Edward. 1250 S COLLEGEVILLE RD, GLAXOSMITHKLINE 19426 #048-04-1977 L1978 **GO OBG** *020 †30

BURELLE, Sara K. 500 ARCOLA RD 19426 #001-02-1994 L1997 **IM** *062 †20

BURLINGTON, Donald Bruce. ■ 19426 #025-01-1975 L1977 **ID IM** *030 †20

CASEY, Paul Robt, Jr. 555 2ND AVE, STE B100 19426 #041-13-1975 L1977 **CD** *020 †20

CASTY, Frank. ■ 19426 #041-13-1986 L1986 **PUD CCM** *050 †20

CENTER, Kimberly Joy. 500 ARCOLA RD G-3201, WYETH PHARM 19426 #041-07-1997 L1999 **PDI** *050 †55 ‡

CHAIKIN, Philip. 500 ARCOLA RD # H35, RHONE POULENC RORER 19426 #033-05-1987 L1988 **PA PHM** *050

CLEAVER, Dorothy M G. ■ 19426 #041-13-1951 L1952 **P N** *071 †75

COHEN, Christopher John. 500 ARCOLA RD G4208, 34TH ST AND CIVIC CTR BLVD 19426 #008-01-1995 L1998 **PDI** *020 †55

COMER, Gail Marie. 500 ARCOLA RD, WYETH RESEARCH 19426 #035-46-1978 L1980 **GE IM** *040 †20

DASCHER, John James, Jr. ■ 19426 #041-13-1969 L1970 **DR NM** *071 †80

DEL CONTE, Anthony, III. 500 ARCOLA RD, WYETH PHARMACEUTICALS 19426 #041-12-1984 L1985 **GYN** *050 †30

DERIVAN, Albert Thos. 229 PAPERBIRCH DR 19426 #033-05-1966 L1985 **P CHP** *050 †75

DESAI, Ketan Girish. 1250 S COLLEGEVILLE RD # U 19426 #495-73-1985 L1993 **AI** *020 †20

DOGHRAMJI, Paul Peter. 555 2ND AVE, STE C-300 19426 #041-02-1982 L1983 **FM** *020 †18 ‡

DOMAN, David Michael. ■ 19426 #032-01-2006 L2007 **ORS** *012

DUKART, Gary. 500 ARCOLA RD, WYETH RESEARCH 19426 #041-02-1980 L1980 **PHM** *050

FARRELL, Paul Edward, Jr. ■ 19426 #051-04-1980 L1987 **PD GP** *020 †55

FELDMAN, Debra S. 500 ARCOLA RD 19426 #035-15-1984 L1985 **IM IMG** *020 †20

FEYSSA, Eyob Lemma. ■ 19426 #366-03-1995 L2007 **IM HEP** *020 †20

FINCH, Eric Michael. 1 IRON BRIDGE DR STE 100, TRAPPE PEDIATRIC CARE 19426 #033-05-2002 L2005 **PD** *020 †55

FITZPATRICK, Lorraine A. 1250 S COLLEGEVILLE RD, GLAXOSMITHKLINE 19426 #016-02-1980 L2006 **END IM** *050 †20

FLITMAN, Lauren Michelle. ■ 19426 #654-01-2000 L2001 **PD** *020 †20

FUHR, Wendy E. 599 ARCOLA RD 19426 #035-03-1996 L1999 **FM** *020 †18

GAZDICK, Mary Anne. 50 W 3RD AVE, STE 400 19426 #041-09-1981 L1983 **PD** *020 †55

GOLDMAN, Mitchell Joel. 500 ARCOLA RD, MAIL STOP H31 19426 #038-06-1989 L1992 **PCC** *020 †20

GRANEY, William Francis. ■ 19426 #041-01-1975 L1990 **AN EM** *050 †05

HAMMOND, Isaac Wm. 1250 S COLLEGEVILLE RD 19426 #011-03-1989 L2002 **IM** *050

HESS, Ivan Wilmer. ■ 19426 #041-09-1943 L1944 **GP** *071

HONIG, Susan Flamm. ■ 19426 #016-06-1983 L2005 **ON IM** *020 †20

ISAACMAN, Daniel Jay. 500 ARCOLA RD, G3203 19426 #041-01-1984 L1986 **PD PEM** *020 †55

JONES, Thomas Vincent. 500 ARCOLA RD, WYETH 19426 #035-45-1983 L1998 **IM IMG** *050 †20

KANE, Cecelia Patrice. 500 ARCOLA RD, STE E6234 19426 #048-15-1992 L2007 **P** *020 †75

KARLSTADT, Robyn Gail. 1250 S COLLEGEVILLE RD, UP 3415 19426 #024-05-1974 L1988 **GE IM** *050 †20

KEIM, Jon Alan. 1 IRON BRIDGE DR 19426 #654-01-1989 L1992 **FM** *020 †18

KORIMILLI, Annapurna Devi. ■ 19426 #495-11-1990 L2004 **GE** *012

KORNER, Paul. 500 ARCOLA RD # 23 19426 #016-43-1991 L2001 **OBG** *020 †30

KRZYSPIAK, Barbara P. 3770 RIDGE PIKE 19426 #759-03-1978 L1982 **PD** *020 †55 ‡

KURRASCH, Regina H. 500 ARCOLA RD, A5154 19426 #035-08-1979 L1998 **PHM RHU** *050 †20

LAWSON, Scott Raymond. ■ 19426 #041-02-1981 L1983 **EM** *075

LEI, Junyi. 100 KESTREL DR 19426 #243-38-1982 L2007 **ATP** *062

LEVIN, Jeremey. 1250 S COLLEGEVILLE RD 19426 #016-11-1987 L2002 **IM** *020 †20

LEWIS-LEBEN, Carlene A.. ■ 19426 #035-06-2007 **OBG** *012

LOH, Evan. 500 ARCOLA RD, WYETH RESEARCH 19426 #024-01-1985 L1994 **CD IM** *020 †20

MALDONADO, Samuel David. 500 ARCOLA RD, WYETH RESEARCH GRA 19426 #451-01-1983 L1991 **ID PD** *055

MARKS, Gilbert Lynn. 1250 S COLLEGEVILLE RD, UP4215 19426 #001-06-1983 L1984 **ID IM** *050 †20

MC CALLUM, Stewart Wm. 1250 S COLLEGEVILLE RD, UP 4420 19426 #065-01-1992 L1998 **U** *020 †95

MELOY, John H. ■ 19426 #041-13-1953 L1954 **GP GPM** *072

MENDIS, Chandira K. 599 ARCOLA RD, UPPER PROVIDENCE FAM MED 19426 #275-01-1994 L2000 **FM** *020 †18

MERCIER, Richard John. 555 2ND AVE, STE B100 19426 #041-09-1980 L1981 **CD IM** *020 †20

MILON, Charles F. 555 2ND AVE # C 19426 #041-13-1949 L1952 **AI** *071 †03

MINES, Daniel. 500 ARCOLA RD 19426 #041-01-1985 L1986 **IM EP** *050 †20,16

MOLTA, Charles Thos. 500 ARCOLA RD, # E6232 19426 #396-28-1983 L2008 **RHU IM** *020 †20

NEUBERT, David Patrick. 130 W MAIN ST, STE 144 PMB 316 19426 #035-45-2003 L2006 **EM** *020 †16

OFFUTT, Laura Anne. 500 ARCOLA RD 19426 #016-06-1994 L1996 **IM** *020 †20

ORCZYK, Gayle Penniman. 500 ARCOLA RD 19426 #033-06-1979 L1997 **END** *020 †20

OSEI, Suzette Y. 1250 S COLLEGEVILLE RD, MAIL CODE 4340 19426 #412-01-1988 L1999 **END** *020 †20

PICKAR, James Harrison. 500 ARCOLA RD, E5202 19426 #011-02-1978 L1982 **OBG** *050 †30

PORTNOY, Alison Dean. 1250 S COLLEGEVILLE RD 19426 #008-01-1999 L2001 **EM PA** *050 †16

POSENER, Joel Alexander. 500 ARCOLA RD A-3, WYETH RESEARCH 19426 #067-01-1987 L2004 **P** *050 †75

RAHMAN, Nasifa. ■ 19426 #160-02-1995 L2003 **P** *020

RAO, Gayathri Sudhakar. 599 ARCOLA RD, MAIN LINE HEALTH CENTER 19426 #496-07-1979 L1988 **PD** *020 †55

RAPHAEL, Stephen Alan. 409 2ND AVE STE 301 19426 #016-42-1970 L1974 **A** *040 †55,03

REDDY, Karunakar K. ■ 19426 #496-26-1991 *100

REIFE, Ross Alexander. 500 ARCOLA RD, WYETH PHARMACEUTICALS 19426 #035-01-1978 L1990 **N** *050 †75

ROWE, Jeffery James. ■ 19426 #665-01-1999 L2003 **PM** *020 †60 ‡

ROYCHOWDHURY, Debasish F. 1250 S COLLEGEVILLE RD, UP 4420 19426 #495-36-1984 L1989 **IM** *020 †20

SACCAR, Michael. 50 2ND AVE 19426 #041-77-1976, ▲ L1977 **FM** *071

SAVARESE, John Jos. ■ 19426 #033-05-1982 L1983 **OS** *050

SCAROLA, Joseph Alexander. ■ 19426 #023-07-1973 L1977 **RHU IM** *075 †20

SCHRANZ, Jennifer Ann. 500 ARCOLA RD, G3204 19426 #065-01-1989 L1998 **ID** *020 †20

SCHULMAN, Seth Lewis. 500 ARCOLA RD 19426 #033-05-1983 L1984 **PN PD** *050 †55

SCHURTZ, Rannette. 78 2ND AVE 19426 #041-15-2001 L2004 **IM** *020 †18

SEIFERT, Harry Abraham. 1250 S COLLEGEVILLE RD, BCSF MC-4340 19426 #041-13-1985 L1993 **PHM AN** *062 †05

SHACHAR, Or. 555 2ND AVE, STE C-850 19426 #024-05-1991 L1993 **N** *020 †75

SHAH, Shailen Ramesh. 555 2ND AVE STE C-750 19426 #495-33-1986 L1994 **AI PD** *020 †55,03

SHANKAR, Sadhna M. 1250 S COLLEGEVILLE RD, GLAXOSMITHKLINE, UP4420 19426 #495-36-1989 L1997 **PD** *020 †55

SIGAL, Adam Peter. ■ 19426 #041-09-1996 L2002 **EM** *020

STILES, Gary Lester. 500 ARCOLA RD, # D6206 19426 #047-05-1975 L2004 **CD** *020 †20

SWEETMAN, Robert Wm. 1250 S COLLEGEVILLE RD, UP4220 19426 #016-42-1988 L2005 **PHO PD** *020 †20

TALAMO, Robert Jos. 555 2ND AVE, STE D-201 19426 #041-02-1983 L1984 **FM** *020 †18

TINKELMAN, Brad Jay. 555 2ND AVE, STE C-850 19426 #041-07-1992 L1997 **N** *020 †75

TOURIAN, Karen Astrid. 500 ARCOLA RD, WYETH RESEARCH 19426 #036-07-1989 L1995 **P ADP** *050 †75

TSAI, Li Chen. 599 ARCOLA RD, UPPER PROV PEDIATRICS 19426 #187-03-1987 L1994 **PD** *020 †55

TURNER, Mary Ellen E. 500 ARCOLA RD 19426 #010-02-1977 L1983 **PD PN** *020 †55

VERVERELI, Kathleen O. 598 ARCOLA RD, 2ND FL 19426 #041-02-1989 L1991 **AI PD** *050 †55,03

VIGDERMAN, Robert Joshua. 599 ARCOLA RD 19426 #010-01-1991 L1994 **IM** *020 †20

VILLASIN, Jose. ■ 19426 #748-02-1968 L1975 **PTH** *020

WANG, Jingsong. 500 ARCOLA RD 19426 #243-49-1986 L2006 **IM** *020 †20

WEBER, Allan Arthur. 555 2ND AVE, STE C-850 19426 #041-12-1993 L2000 **N** *020 †75

WHITE, Scott Matthew. 500 ARCOLA RD 19426 #041-14-1990 L1992 **ID** *020 †20

WIGGINTON, John Marc. ■ 19426 #025-01-1989 L1992 **PHO PD** *020 †55

WILSON, Judith Pflueger. ■ 19426 #041-07-1974 L1975 **GP** *020

WISSEL, Paul Stephen. 1250 S COLLEGEVILLE RD 19426 #035-01-1979 L1989 **PA ON** *050 †20

WISWE, Birgit M. 555 2ND AVE, STE 300 19426 #048-13-1989 L1992 **FM** *020 †18

YEUNG, Paul Pojen. ■ 19426 #035-01-1992 L1999 **CHP** *020 †75

YOUSSEF, Nawal A. 3770 RIDGE PIKE 19426 #915-04-1974 L1987 **PD GP** *020 ‡

YU, Jenny S. 500 ARCOLA RD 19426 #035-01-1996 L1998 **IM** *050 †20 ‡

ZAPOTOK, Dawn Marie. 599 ARCOLA RD, UPPER PROVIDENCE PEDIATRIC 19426 #041-13-1994 L1996 **PD** *020 †55

COLLINGDALE – DELAWARE

CRANE, Janet Elizabeth. 222 CLIFTON AVE 19023 #041-07-1977 L1978 **IM P** *020 ‡

MALZ, Martin Adam. 614 CLIFTON AVE 19023 #759-01-1984 L1987 **IM IMG** *020

MC GILL, Herman I. ■ 19023 #041-13-1979 L1981 **IM IMG** *020 †20

RICHARDS, Paul S, Jr. 923 MACDADE BLVD 19023 #035-09-1952 L1953 **NTR GP** *071

COLMAR – MONTGOMERY

DETWEILER, Thomas Craig. 2405 N BROAD ST 18915 #422-01-1982 L1983 **IM GP** *020 †20 ‡
GOTLIEB, Jerry. 2515 N BROAD ST, STE 215 18915 #041-09-1963 L1964 **U** *020 †95 ‡
MOIDEL, Robert Arnold. 262A BETHLEHEM PIKE, STE 100 18915 #041-01-1976 L1981 **RHU IM** *020 †16
THOMAS, Audra. ■ 18915 #016-11-1996 L2005 **EM** *020 †16
WYSZKOWSKI, Rafal Jan. 262 BETHLEHEM PIKE, STE 103 18915 #759-03-1989 L1997 **AN** *020 †05

COLUMBIA – LANCASTER

ALEJOS, Melito P. 523 LOCUST ST 17512 #748-01-1969 L1973 **OBG** *020
CARRUTHERS, Ralph B. 306 N 7TH ST 17512 #041-09-1964 L1967 **FM** *020
DEGENHARD, Joseph Gerard. 306 N 7TH ST 17512 #036-01-1998 L2001 **FM** *020 †18
HERNANDEZ, Janario Flores. 237 N 7TH ST 17512 #748-01-1968 L1973 **IM** *020 †20
JENSEN, Alvin Christian. PO BOX 926 17512 #041-09-1946 L1950 **OBG OS** *100
LAJINIAN, Shoghag A. ■ 17512 #605-01-1990 L1997 **OBG** *020 †30
LEHMAN, Michael Scott. 17512 #041-14-1999 **P** *062
RUTT, Clarence Henry. 255 N 6TH ST 17512 #041-09-1957 L1958 **GS** *071 †85
SRITULANONDHA, Nowaratana. 631 POPLAR ST 17512 #748-08-1962 L1972 **AN** *071

CONEMAUGH – CAMBRIA

WISNIEWSKI, John Michael. 340 1ST ST 15909 #759-03-1986 L1990 **IM** *020 †20

CONESTOGA – LANCASTER

DOE, Robert Gorham. ■ 17516 #032-01-1978 L1979 **EM FM** *062 †18,16

CONFLUENCE – SOMERSET

RENTSCHLER, Lawrence L. 710 ODEN ST, FAMILY HEALTH CARE 15424 #023-12-1986 L1988 **GP** *020

CONNEAUT LAKE – CRAWFORD

BAZYLAK, Robert Andrew. 12387 CONNEAUT LAKE RD 16316 #041-12-1972 L1973 **FM EM** *020 †16,18 ‡
MARTIN, James W, Jr. ■ 16316 #041-01-1943 L1944 **GP** *071
MOYERS, Robert Nile. ■ 16316 #041-12-1962 L1963 **FM** *071 †18
PIROCH, Joseph G. 7 LAKESIDE SQ 16316 #041-12-1962 L1964 **IM CD** *020
SPENCER, Dean Wm. 12387 CONNEAUT LAKE RD 16316 #010-02-1984 L1991 **FM** *020 †18

CONNELLSVILLE – FAYETTE

AL-FAKIH, Mouhanad. 261 E CRAWFORD AVE 15425 #875-01-1993 L2000 **IM** *020 †20 ‡
AL-SAADI, Khaldon. 420 E CRAWFORD AVE 15425 #875-01-1977 L1985 **GS GE** *020 †85
AREZA, Pablo Reyes. 15425 #748-02-1956 L1968 **AN** *020
ARTUSO, Frank Burke. 201 N PITTSBURGH ST 15425 #041-12-1981 L1982 **PM** *020 †60
BERONILLA, Hilarion A, Jr. 232 N PITTSBURGH ST 15425 #748-01-1960 L1973 **GS GP** *071
BITTNER, Liana. ■ 15425 #041-09-1998 L2000 **FM** *020 †18
CELESTINE, Gerald Thos. 401 E MURPHY AVE, HIGHLANDS HOSP 15425 #041-02-1984 L1985 **EM** *020 †18
COLVIN, William Ferry. RR 1 15425 #041-12-1945 L1946 **GP** *071
CONN, Richard Alan. 2616 MEMORIAL BLVD, STE B 15425 #041-14-2003 L2003 **FM** *020 †18
ENANY, Albert Kelly. 208 S ARCH ST, RIVERFRONT PROFF CTR. 15425 #056-06-1980 L1981 **IM** *020 †20
FARMER, Robert Clarence. 201 N PITTSBURGH ST 15425 #010-03-1967 L1968 **DR NR** *020 †80
FLORENTIN, Heriberto. 2618 MEMORIAL BLVD STE A 15425 #132-01-1967 L1974 **OBG EM** *020
FREMD, Mark Stuart. 205 N CARNEGIE AVE, FAMILY HEALTH CARE CENTER 15425 #035-08-1981 L1982 **FM GP** *020
GREENE, Robert K. 204 MEMORIAL BLVD 15425 #038-43-1976 L1995 **OBG** *020 †30
JANA, Barid Baran. 261 E CRAWFORD AVE 15425 #495-15-1965 L1972 **GS GP** *071 †85
JANADRI, Bchara F. 2618 MEMORIAL BLVD STE C 15425 #875-02-1986 L1993 **PD** *020 †55
KOZAK, William Joseph. 401 E MURPHY AVE, HIGHLANDS HOSPITAL 15425 #041-13-2000 L2003 **FM** *020 †18
KRAFTY, Mary Beth. 401 E MURPHY AVE 15425 #041-09-1982 L1983 **FM** *020 †18
NETAJI, Vinutha J. 232 N PITTSBURGH ST 15425 #496-20-1989 L2002 **FM** *020 †18
NEWILL, Domer Slater, Jr. ■ 15425 #561-01-1956 L1961 **IM OS** *071
OPPY, James Miller. 201 N PITTSBURGH ST STE 3A 15425 #025-07-1981 L1982 **FM** *020 †18 ‡
PERCY, Linda Kay. ■ 15425 #041-12-1985 L1987 **IM** *020 †20
PEREZ, Godofredo B. 134 S PITTSBURGH ST 15425 #748-01-1959 L1971 **FM** *075
SETTY, Polepalli S. 2900 MEMORIAL BLVD 15425 #495-62-1962 L1975 **IM PUD** *020 †20
SHAHOUD, Geith H. 413 E GIBSON AVE, HIGHLAND 15425 #875-01-1992 L2003 **P** *020 ‡
TIBERIO, Richard Alan. 201 N PITTSBURGH ST 15425 #041-12-1980 L1981 **IM** *020 †20

CONSHOHOCKEN – MONTGOMERY

ANDERSON, Robert Andrew. 1000 RIVER RD, STE 100 19428 #041-13-1972 L1973 **P** *071 †75
BALDASSANO, Marisa F. 20 ASH ST, STE 310 19428 #041-14-1992 L2001 **PTH** *020 †20,50
BARNES, Brent Aaron. ■ 19428 #041-77-2006, ▲ L2006 **IM** *012
BASHA, Suzanne Lrajjoub. ■ 19428 #041-13-2004 L2005 **OBG** *012
CASTELLANO, Patrick V. 917 FAYETTE ST 19428 #041-02-1959 L1960 **FPG GP** *020
CHAUDHARY, Chhaya S. 408 W RIDGE PIKE 19428 #495-74-1981 L1986 **PD** *020 †55
CIANFERONI, Antonella. ■ 19428 #561-06-1996 L2005 **PD** *100 †55
CLARK, John Andrew. 401 W 10TH AVE 19428 #007-02-1979 L1991 **IM GPM** *020 †20,70

DI LEONARDO, Mario.

DI LEONARDO, Mario. 20 ASH ST, STE 310 19428 #041-09-1985 L1986 **D** *020 †15
DOBERSTEIN, Timothy Frede. ■ 19428 #041-13-2006 L2006 **IM** *012
DRAPER, Kenneth Harry. 2177 HARTS LN, 2177 HARTS LANE 19428 #035-45-1960 L1969 **P** *020 †75
DUMIN, Michael Jeffrey. ■ 19428 #041-01-2002 L2002 **EM** *020 †16
FRACHT, Harvey Uval. 101 W ELM ST, STE 340 19428 #035-19-1994 L1998 **OPH** *020 †35
FRANKLIN, Rodney Duran. 117 E 4TH AVE 19428 #036-05-1995 L1997 **FM** *020 †18
GOLSORKHI, Anthony Ali. ■ 19428 #041-13-2001 *100
GRIFFIN, Thomas Danl. 20 ASH ST, STE 310 19428 #041-02-1980 L1982 **DMP D** *020 †50,15
HEEBNER, Jeffrey A. 103 E 5TH AVE 19428 #041-77-1995, ▲ L1996 **FM FPG** *020
HOURI, Pamela K. 1000 RIVER RD, STE 100 19428 #030-06-1994 L1996 **EM** *020 †16
HUBER, Irving Paul. 3004 BUTLER PIKE 6 19428 #035-15-1976 L1977 **EM IM** *020 †20,16
HULL, Sarah Christine. ■ 19428 #041-01-2008 *012
JOHNSON, Waine C. 20 ASH ST, STE 310 19428 #048-02-1953 L1962 **D DMP** *071 †15
KANTOR, Gary Richard. 20 ASH ST, STE 310 19428 #041-14-1982 L1987 **D DMP** *020 †15
KAUFFMAN, Patricia Joan. ■ 19428 #041-13-1993 L1996 **FOP** *062
KERN, Joseph F. ■ 19428 #041-15-2007 L2007 *012
KHANNA, Indira. ■ 19428 #495-34-1962 L1982 **P** *020
KHANNA, Kamal Nath. ■ 19428 #495-05-1963 L1978 **IM** *020
KOLTON, Michelle Mary. ■ 19428 #035-04-2004 RO *012
KRAMER, E Michael. 20 ASH ST, STE 310 19428 #035-03-1982 L1983 **DMP** *020 †15
KWON, Alan Fay. 625 RIDGE PIKE BLDG B, WILLS EYE SURGERY CENTER 19428 #005-02-1980 L1995 **AN FM** *020
LABOWSKIE, Eugene Melvin. 827 FAYETTE ST 19428 #041-09-1945 L1946 **FM** *071 †18
LEE, Susanne N. 20 ASH ST, STE 310 19428 #409-21-1999 L2001 **DMP** *100 †50
LUCKING, Steven Eric. ■ 19428 #041-01-1980 L1990 **CCM PD** *020 †55
MANNING, Richard Andrew. ■ 19428 #041-12-1961 L1962 **CHP** *071 †75
MIN, George Guiho. ■ 19428 #005-06-2001 L2006 **PS** *012
MOKASHI, Suyog Anil. ■ 19428 #024-07-2006 **GS** *012
NAIR, Usha C. 408 W RIDGE PIKE, SUNSHINE PEDIATRICS 19428 #496-38-1988 L1997 **PD** *020 †55
NEZOWITZ, Gregg David. 1000 RIVER RD, STE 100 19428 #035-09-1995 L1997 **EM** *020 †16
OH, Jung Duk. ■ 19428 #028-02-2007 L2007 **IM** *012
OVERBECK, Michael David. 1100 FAYETTE ST 19428 #041-02-1979 L1980 **IM** *020 †20
PUPEK, Stanley, Jr. ■ 19428 #041-09-1940 L1942 **GP OS** *020
RAFF, Sandra Beth. ■ 19428 #035-09-1971 L2003 **END DIA** *062 †20
RENZI, Stephen. 904 FAYETTE ST, MAIN LINE HEALTHCARE CONSH 19428 #041-78-2000, ▲ L2001 **IM** *020
RESNIK, Kenneth Scott. 20 ASH ST, STE 310 19428 #041-09-1990 L1992 **DMP** *020 †15
RUBIN, Janis Wolf. 117 E 4TH AVE 19428 #041-07-1978 L1979 **FM** *020 †18
SCHIMERT, Arnd P. 1 W ELM ST 19428 #473-01-1939 L1962 **R NR** *071 †80
SHELANSKI, Morris Victor. 151 E 10TH AVE 19428 #067-01-1947 L1949 **GP OS** *071
SPECK-STANG, Ellen L. 1100 E HECTOR ST STE 393, PROGEN HEALTH INC 19428 #041-14-1989 L1991 **PD** *020 †55
SPIELVOGEL, Richard Lee. 20 ASH ST, STE 310 19428 #035-45-1972 L1989 **D DMP** *020 †15
STODDARD, Jeffrey Jackson. 555 E NORTH LN, COVANCE 19428 #056-05-1988 L1998 **PD** *050 †55
VACCA, Peter John. 418 W 11TH AVE 19428 #041-02-1994 L1998 **AN** *020 †05
VON GERSDORFF, Gero D. ■ 19428 #409-06-1993 **IM** *100 †20
WARSOFSKY, Ilana Simone. ■ 19428 #010-01-2005 L2006 **DR** *012
WILLIAMS, Nicole Carmita. ■ 19428 #041-15-2003 L2004 **PTH** *012
WILTON, Edward A. ■ 19428 #041-02-1953 L1954 **GP** *020
WOODBURY, Deborah. 117 E 4TH AVE 19428 #041-01-1993 L1995 **FM** *020 †18
YANG, Un-Taek. ■ 19428 #583-02-1964 L1971 **AN GP** *071 †05

CONYNGHAM – LUZERNE

WARD, Mary Jane. ■ 18219 #008-02-1973 L1975 **GP IM** *020

COOPERSBURG – LEHIGH

ANDERSON, David W. ■ 18036 #023-12-1983 L2001 **PTH** *020 †50
BUDINETZ, Robert E. 629 W STATE ST 18036 #041-15-2002 L2002 **FM** *020 †18
DALE, James Allan. ■ 18036 #035-48-1978 L1979 **IM** *075
DE QUEVEDO, Robt Francis. 7096 BLOSSOM LN 18036 #041-02-1992 L1995 **CCA** *100 †05 ‡
FENSTERMACHER, Robt P, Jr. ■ 18036 #041-01-1948 L1949 **EM** *020
HUBER, Patricia A. ■ 18036 #048-02-1985 L1986 **AN** *020 †05
KRAFCZYK, Jill Anne. ■ 18036 #041-13-1993 L2000 **FM** *020 †18
LI, Min. ■ 18036 #243-16-1987 L2005 **D** *020
SARNOSKI, Christopher L. ■ 18036 #041-77-1998, ▲ L2006 **IC** *020 †20
STOCKTON, Peter Michael. ■ 18036 #003-01-2007 L2007 **EM** *012
URIBE, Manuel Ruiz. ■ 18036 #033-05-1985 L1999 **AN IM** *020 †05
WANG, Hai Ying. ■ 18036 #243-46-1986 L2000 **AN** *020
WOODRUFF, William Wharton. ■ 18036 #051-07-1981 L1989 **N R** *020 †80

COPLAY – LEHIGH

DEBOER, Emily Mae. ■ 18037 #012-05-2006 **PD** *012

CORAOPOLIS – ALLEGHENY

ADOKI, Iyalla. ■ 15108 #690-01-1972 L1980 **GP** *020
ARDINGER, Eric John. 1308 5TH AVE 15108 #041-78-2003, ▲ L2007 *100
BASSILIOS, Fouad Aziz. 935 THORN RUN RD, STE 214 15108 #915-02-1964 L1972 **IM** *020 †20
BOTTA, Samuel Anthony. 1187 THORN RUN RD STE 130, ONE THORN RUN CENTER 15108 #561-01-1982 L1984 **PS** *020
BRADEN, Frank Robt, Jr. 15108 #041-01-1933 L1934 **FM** *020
BUCHKO, Sheila Nadine. ■ 15108 #041-12-1978 L1979 **IM** *020
COCHENOUR, Donald Jerome. ■ 15108 #041-01-1978 L1981 **PTH** *074
COHEN, Ira J K. 980 BEAVER GRADE RD 15108 #023-01-1978 L1982 **D GP** *020 †15
COSSROW, Joel Irwin. 110 GATEHOUSE DR 15108 #041-02-1972 L1973 **R DR** *071 †80

CROCENELLI, Theresa Marie. 960 BEAVER GRADE RD, LOWR LEVEL 15108 #041-14-1997 L2000 **PD** *020 †55

CROWLEY, Patricia Ann. ■ 15108 #041-07-1959 L1960 **OBG** *071

CULIG, Carl Albert. 1992 EWINGS MILL RD 15108 #024-01-1980 L1981 **IM** *020 †20

D'ANTONIO, James Anthony. 725 CHERRINGTON PKWY, STE 200 15108 #041-12-1968 L1969 **ORS OAR** *020 †40

DENVER, Stanley David. 1150 THORN RUN ROAD EXT 15108 #035-47-1972 L1977 **OBG** *020 †30

D'ERAMO, Linda. ■ 15108 #041-77-2006, ▲ L2006 **FP** *012

DERIGGI, Leonard Alexis. 890 BEAVER GRADE RD 15108 #041-12-1990 L1993 **DR** *020 †80

DINES, George Louis. ■ 15108 #041-12-1939 L1940 **GS OS** *071 †85

DI TANO, Oriente. 725 CHERRINGTON PKWY, STE 200 15108 #041-12-1993 L1998 **HS ORS** *020 †40

FLINT, Eric Willard. 890 BEAVER GRADE RD 15108 #041-12-1984 L1987 **R N** *020 †80

GATES, Michael Edward. 1101 5TH AVE 15108 #055-01-2001 L2004 **FM** *020 †18

HASER, Heywood Albert. 725 CHERRINGTON PKWY, CHERRINGTON CORPORATE CENT 15108 #041-12-1966 L1970 **ORS** *071 †40

JAMES, Edward E. 1308 5TH AVE 15108 #041-77-1958, ▲ L1959 **FM** *071

JARRETT, Patricia J. ■ 15108 #041-12-1986 L1987 **P** *020 †75

JIAN, Parviz. 1150 THORN RUN RD EXT, STE 101 15108 #517-01-1968 L1981 **OBG** *020 †30

JUNGHANS, Siegfried Paul. 464 SHARON RD, BLACKBURN ROAD 15108 #407-08-1953 L1968 **PTH CLP** *072

KANIECKI, Vida Sheen. 960 BEAVER GRADE RD, LOWR LEVEL 15108 #028-02-1988 L1992 **PD** *020 †55

KARIMKHANI, Kobra. 938 BEAVER GRADE RD 15108 #517-01-1965 L1972 **GYN PTH** *020 †30

KLEIN, Milton J. 1352 5TH AVE 15108 #018-75-1977, ▲ L1983 **PM PMM** *020 †60

KLUTZ, Joseph Peter. 993 BRODHEAD RD 15108 #041-12-1976 L1977 **FM** *020 †18

KOSSOL, Janet Marie. 890 BEAVER GRADE RD 15108 #041-12-1980 L1981 **DR** *020 †80

KROSS, Timothy Jos. 935 THORN RUN RD 15108 #041-09-1971 L1984 **IM** *020 †20

LEVY, Jon Alexander. 725 CHERRINGTON PKWY, STE 200 15108 #041-12-1987 L1989 **ORS** *020 †40

LUPA, Maria Concetta. ■ 15108 #055-01-2003 L2007 **PAN** *012

MARATTA, Jan Wm. 986 BROADHEAD RD 15108 #561-01-1970 L1972 **GS GP** *020 ‡

MARFATIA, Ruta Sudhir. 1047 LINCOLN HIGHLANDS DR 15108 #496-41-2000 L2006 **FM** *020 †18

MARINELLI, Riccardo R. 935 THORN RUN RD, STE 102 15108 #041-12-1993 L1998 **APM AN** *020 †05

MATUS, Jacqueline Beth. 960 BEAVER GRADE RD, LOWR LEVEL 15108 #041-13-2004 L2005 **PD** *100 †55

MC GUIRE, Francis Edward. ■ 15108 #028-34-1954 L1955 **GS** *071

MIHOK, Michael Raymond. ■ 15108 #041-12-1977 L1978 **EM** *020 †16

MULHOLLAND, Jeffrey B. 725 CHERRINGTON PKWY, STE 200 15108 #051-01-1990 L1996 **OSM ORS** *020 †40

PARK, Nancy H. 993 BRODHEAD RD 15108 #041-12-1983 L1984 **FM** *020 †18 ‡

PATRICK, Gregory Brandon. 993 BRODHEAD RD 15108 #041-12-1976 L1977 **PUD IM** *020 †20

PEGRAM, Langdon. 960 BEAVER GRADE RD, LOWR LEVEL 15108 #048-16-1984 L1997 **PD** *020 †55

PITCAVAGE, James Geddes. 960 BEAVER GRADE RD, LOWR LEVEL 15108 #041-12-1960 L1965 **PD A** *020 †55

PUCEVICH, Chas Lawrence. 935 THORN RUN RD 15108 #021-01-1977 L1982 **RHU IM** *020 †18

PUCEVICH, Maria Valiente. 935 THORN RUN RD 15108 #021-01-1977 L1982 **D DMP** *020 †15

ROSEMAN, Sharon Renee. 993 BRODHEAD RD 15108 #041-06-1982 L1983 **GE IM** *020 †20 ‡

RYOO, In O. 205 COMMERCE DR 15108 #583-10-1966 L1975 **PD** *020 †55 ‡

SANGODEYI, Oluyemisi. 935 THORN RUN RD STE W201 15108 #690-01-1972 L1975 **GS PDS** *020 †85

SCHNEIDERMAN, Marc J. 1101 5TH AVE 15108 #016-42-1982 L1985 **FM** *020 †18 ‡

SCHWARTZ, Robert Louis. ■ 15108 #035-09-2006 L2007 **PD** *012

SCHWARTZ, Robert Sidney. ■ 15108 #035-09-1968 L1969 **PD** *020 †30

SEIFERT, Carol Lee. 890 BEAVER GRADE RD 15108 #041-02-1985 L1986 **DR** *020 †80

SINGLEY, Thomas Lower. ■ 15108 #041-02-1957 L1958 **EM** *071

SMITH, Gary Lee. 725 CHERRINGTON PKWY, STE 200 15108 #041-13-1978 L1979 **ORS** *020 †40

SOONTORRNNIYOMKI, Virawudh. ■ 15108 #891-02-1986 L1996 **NP** *100 †50

SPERLING, Vera Rachel. 890 BEAVER GRADE RD 15108 #038-41-1985 L1989 **DR** *020 †80

STEPHEN, Kristen Ann. 980 BEAVER GRADE RD, STE 10A 15108 #041-14-1993 L1997 **D** *020 †15

TANNEHILL, Norman Bruce. ■ 15108 #041-12-1942 L1943 **R** *074 †80

THOMAS, Stephen John. 725 CHERRINGTON PKWY, STE 200 15108 #041-12-1993 L1995 **ORS** *020 †40

VASQUEZ PEREZ, Ramon A. ■ 15108 #308-01-1956 L1973 *020

YAYLA, Huseyin. ■ 15108 #902-03-1947 L1971 **R** *071 †80

CORNWALL — LEBANON

DAVIS, Donna Jeanne. ■ 17016 #030-05-1993 L1996 **P** *020 †75

KNOLLE, Leslie R. 115 SPRUCE ST 17016 #407-10-1959 L1967 **GS** *071 †85

RIFFERT, Paul Maurer. ■ 17016 #041-02-1935 L1936 **GS** *071

ROVINSKI, Helen T. ■ 17016 #010-01-1943 L1944 **PM FPG** *071 †60

STEVENS, John M, Jr. PO BOX 125 17016 #041-01-1946 L1947 **P PYA** *071 †75

CORNWELLS HEIGHTS — BUCKS

CHIEMCHANYA, Surtrong. ■ 19020 #891-02-1972 L1976 **PTH** *020 †50

SANTOS, Rodolfo Jacinto. 6200 MADISON CT 19020 #748-02-1959 L1971 **IM** *071 †20

CORRY — ERIE

BARZYK, Peter P. 300 YORK ST 16407 #010-02-1968 L1977 **NEP IM** *020 †20

CORNELL, Lynne Lori. 315 YORK ST 16407 #041-13-1982 L1983 **FM** *020 †18

CORTINA, Gary John. 300 YORK ST 16407 #041-02-1986 L1987 **ORS** *020 †40

HALLIGAN, Rekha D. 300 YORK ST 16407 #048-14-1993 L1998 **NEP IM** *020 †20

HOU, Ching Wu. 210 N CENTER ST 16407 #244-05-1969 L1976 **OBG** *020 †30

LLOYD, Gerald Ray. 315 YORK ST 16407 #041-13-1963 L1966 **FM** *020

LOVERANES, Mariano. 706 WORTH ST 16407 #748-01-1972 L1980 **GS GP** *020

LUND, Kurt Edward. 1086 MEAD AVE 16407 #011-04-1991 L1993 **FM** *020 †18

MALHOTRA, Shailesh. ■ 16407 #496-09-1994 L2002 **IM** *020 †20

PASTERNACK, Jennifer M. ■ 16407 #038-06-1994 L1996 **P** *020 †75

PROY, Bernard Carl. 315 YORK ST 16407 #041-02-1980 L1981 **FM** *020 †18

RAMA, Sreedhar. 108 W SMITH ST 16407 #495-57-1999 L2006 **IM** *020

VASILOPOULOS, Nicholas N. 315 YORK ST 16407 #041-12-1959 L1960 **FM EM** *020

COUDERSPORT — POTTER

AKBARI, Saeed. 1001 E 2ND ST 16915 #517-01-1966 L1973 **U** *020 †95

BACKES, Celso Luiz. 1001 E 2ND ST, COLE MEDICAL CENTER 16915 #187-23-1965 L1974 **OBG** *020 †30

BHAT, Syed Bilal Ahmed. 1001 E 2ND ST 16915 #495-51-1992 L2001 **IM** *020 †20

BOWMAN, Douglas F, Jr. 1001 E 2ND ST 16915 #023-01-1978 L1979 **GP MDM** *020 ‡

CARAMIA, Christan Michael. ■ 16915 #654-01-2000 L2006 **AN** *100 †05

CRUZ, Moises Beltran, Jr. 1001 E 2ND ST 16915 #748-01-1955 L1966 **GS** *071

DELO, Jeffrey Scott. 1001 E 2ND ST 16915 #055-01-1993 L1996 **HO IM** *020 †20

GIANNOTTI, Bradley F. 1001 E 2ND ST 16915 #041-01-1991 L1993 **ORS OSM** *020 †40 ‡

HARASCHAK, Michael John, IV. 1001 E 2ND ST, IRWIN MEDICAL ARTS CTR 16915 #041-13-1999 L2001 **GS** *020

HORTON, Richard Curtis. 1001 E 2ND ST, EMERGENCY DEPT 16915 #041-12-1973 L1974 **EM FM** *020 †16

HYLTON, Connie Sue. 1001 E 2ND ST, CHARLES COLE MEMORIAL HOSP 16915 #051-07-2003 L2003 **IM** *020

KELLEY, William Thos. ■ 16915 #041-07-1976 L1979 **IM** *020 †16

KHANNA, Amit. 1001 E 2ND ST 16915 #665-01-2002 L2006 **FM SME** *020 †18

KHAYYAM, Umar. ■ 16915 #041-15-2008 *012

LLINAS, Alfredo Jose. 1001 E 2ND ST, IRWIN MEDICAL ARTS CENTER 16915 #264-01-1971 L1980 **GS VS** *020 †85 ‡

LUBIN, Jeffrey H. 1001 E 2ND ST 16915 #041-02-1980 L1981 **EM** *020 †16

MELLER, Rafael Andres. ■ 16915 #187-61-1997 L2000 **IMG** *020 †10

MILLER, Howard Jay. 71 ELK ST 16915 #041-13-1980 L1981 **IM** *020 †20

MOSCH, George C. 207 CARTEE ST 16915 #041-09-1946 L1947 **FM** *071 †18

NEERUKONDA, Sampath Kumar. 1001 E 2ND ST 16915 #495-57-1980 L1994 **P GPM** *020

NESTOR, Kalliopi Kapsalis. 1001 E 2ND ST 16915 #305-01-2000 L2001 **PM** *020

NURBHAI, Murtaza Ebrahim. 1001 E 2ND ST 16915 #905-01-1969 L1977 **OTO** *020 †45 ‡

PRESTON, Virginia B. 1001 E 2ND ST 16915 #048-02-1994 L1999 **FM OBS** *020 †18

QUTOB, Tarek Subhi. 1001 E 2ND ST, CHARLES COLE MEMORIAL HOSP 16915 #575-01-1995 L2003 **GE** *020 †20

RIGAS, Mary Ann. 1001 E 2ND ST 16915 #041-01-1987 L1989 **PD** *020 †55

ROSENBERRY, Clark Michael. 2914 DIVIDING RIDGE RD 16915 #038-41-2008 *012

SACKMAN, Michael. 1001 E 2ND ST, CHARLES COLE MEMORIAL HOSP 16915 #528-02-1988 L2006 **PD** *020

SHELLEY, Mark Hungerford. 1001 E 2ND ST 16915 #041-02-1982 L1983 **FM** *020 †18

SHIFRIN, Seth Philip. 1001 E 2ND ST, U S ROUTE 6 EAST 16915 #016-02-2000 L2005 **FSM** *020,55

VILLA, Francisco B. U S RT 6E R R 1 P O BOX 16915 #748-07-1960 L1968 **GP PD** *075 †55,18

WAGNER, Robert Edgar. 1001 E 2ND ST 16915 #041-09-1972 L1973 **IM** *020 †20

WAHLERS, Brenda Marshall. ■ 16915 #041-14-2002 L2002 **IM** *100 †20

WEI, Lawrence Clifton. 1001 E 2ND ST, IRWIN MEDICAL ARTS BLDG 16915 #035-19-1975 L1985 **OPH** *020 †35

WONGPAKDEE, Sobsan. COLE MEDICAL CENTER, SOBSAN WONGPAKDEE MD PC 16915 #891-02-1962 L1972 **GS CRS** *071 †10

WUST-SMITH, Marlene J. 1001 E 2ND ST 16915 #035-20-1989 L2006 **PD** *020 †55

COWANSVILLE — ARMSTRONG

VOGAN, Clifford. 882 E BRADY RD, CLIFFORD VOGAN, MD, PC 16218 #041-12-1976 L1979 **IM** *020 †20

CRANBERRY — VENANGO

BROOKER, David Robert. 6945 US 322, UNIT508 16319 #033-06-1989 L1991 **NEP IM** *020 †20

CRANBERRY TOWNSHIP — BUTLER

ACHALABUN, Pithaya. 1 SAINT FRANCIS WAY, UPMC PASSAVANT CRANBERRY 16066 #891-02-1970 L1977 **GS** *020 †16

AGUSTIN, Amelia V. 20397 ROUTE 19 STE 220, TWO LANDMARK NORTH 16066 #748-08-1965 L1974 **PD** *020 †15

AMOS, David B. 20826 ROUTE 19, STE 2 16066 #048-04-1994 L1996 **D** *020 †15

BANDARANAYAKE, Nisantha M. 20399 ROUTE 19, ONE LANDMARK NORTH STE 203 16066 #220-01-1969 L1975 **AN** *020 †05 ‡

BEARD, Denise Michele. ■ 16066 #041-12-1988 L1992 **IM** *020

BERGMAN, Gary Robert. 20130 ROUTE 19, PITTSBURGH GYNOB INC 16066 #055-01-1987 L1989 **OBG** *020 †30

BITAR, Henry Joseph, III. 213 EXECUTIVE DR, STE 340 16066 #041-01-1994 L1999 **PD** *020 †55

BOWMAN, Michael W. 20130 ROUTE 19 STE 1100, UPMC PASSAVANT 16066 #038-41-1980 L1983 **HS OFA** *020 †40

BRECK, H Jane Mikuliak. 20421 ROUTE 19, STE 201 16066 #041-02-1967 L1968 **PD OS** *020 †55

BUGARIJA, Nenad. 3104 UNIONVILLE RD, STE 180 16066 #957-01-1998 L2001 **IM** *020 †20

BUMBAUGH, James Howard. 20130 ROUTE 19, STE 1000 16066 #041-77-1984, ▲ L1985 **IM** *020 †20

CAMPBELL, Jennifer H. 3 SAINT FRANCIS WAY, STE 102 16066 #041-12-1980 L1981 **FM** *020 †18

CELIN, Scott Edward. 501 SMITH DR 16066 #028-02-1985 L1986 **OTO HNS** *020 †45

CONAWAY, Bruce Edward. 20397 ROUTE 19, 2 LANDMARK NORTH 16066 #041-14-1979 L1980 **FM FSM** *020 †18

CYPHER, Ronald Lloyd. 2001 EHRMAN RD, STE A 16066 #041-09-1980 L1981 **OBG** *020 †30
DAPPERT, Barbara. 3 SAINT FRANCIS WAY, STE 206 16066 #016-01-1985 L1991 **N** *020 †75
DAVIS, Donald Dean. ■ 16066 #008-01-1954 L1955 **GS** *071 †85
DELEO, Caesar Augustus. ■ 16066 #041-02-1987 L1989 **IM** *020 †20
DESHMUKH, Uday Uttamrao. ■ 16066 #495-45-1988 L1997 **IM** *020 †20
DINTINI, Jennifer Hope. 20130 ROUTE 19, PITTSBURGH GYNOB INC 16066 #055-75-2001, ▲ L2001 **OBG** *020
EVERETT, William G. ■ 16066 #041-12-1951 L1952 **OS** *071 †35
GOLD, Gordon Robt. 3104 UNIONVILLE RD STE 180 16066 #041-02-1973 L1974 **IM GP** *020 †20
GOLIKERI, Sarita Ganesh. ■ 16066 #422-01-1999 L2002 **FPG** *100 †18
HALL, Audrey Sadar. 20130 ROUTE 19, STE 1000 16066 #041-12-1989 L1991 **IM** *020 †20
HAMILTON, Robert Wayman. 20421 ROUTE 19, SOUTHW BUTLER URGENT CARE 16066 #041-12-1955 L1956 **GP** *071
HEIL, Brian Vassar. 144 EMERYVILLE DR, STE 110 16066 #041-12-1996 L1999 **PS** *020 †65
HILDENBRAND, Lisa Ann. 2001 EHRMAN RD, STE A 16066 #041-14-1993 L1996 **OBG** *020 †30
HORWIN, Samuel. 100 NORMAN DR APT 227 16066 #010-01-1935 L1935 **R** *071 †80
HUWE, Joseph Edward, Jr. 8050 ROWAN RD, STE 403 16066 #041-12-1988 L1990 **PD** *020 †55
JACKSON, Rebecca Renee. ■ 16066 #041-15-2008 *012
JACOBS, George A J. 20725 ROUTE 19 16066 #041-12-1946 L1947 **FM** *071
JAGIELLO, Ben Peter. 20399 ROUTE 19, ONE LANDMARK NORTH, SUITE 16066 #422-01-1983 L1988 **PUD GS** *020 †20
KIM, Anna Heasuk. 20421 ROUTE 19 16066 #041-14-1995 L1997 **PD** *020 †55
KOVEL, Arthur Jay. 20421 ROUTE 19, STE 201 16066 #010-02-1978 L1988 **PD** *020 †55
KUNKEL, Frank Alfred. 1 LANDMARK BLDG, OBAS INC 16066 #041-12-1985 L1986 **AN PME** *020 †05 ‡
LABELLA, John James. 20421 ROUTE 19, STE 201 16066 #035-15-1991 L1993 **NPM PD** *020 †55
LUCOT, Suzanne D. 127 AVERYS WAY 16066 #016-11-1994 L1996 **CHP** *020 †75
LUPARIELLO, Angelo D. 5 SAINT FRANCIS WAY, FMC CRANBERRY 16066 #010-02-1970 L1974 **NEP IM** *020 †20
MAHSOOB, Abdul-Hameed. 8001 ROWAN RD, STE 206 16066 #528-01-1959 L1971 **PD PDC** *071 †55
MAJEWSKI, Mary Lee. 20421 ROUTE 19, STE 201 16066 #041-12-1987 L1989 **PD** *020 †55
MAYER-COSTA, Carlos M. 2001 EHRMAN RD 16066 #033-05-1994 L1996 **FM** *020 †18
MOGHANI LANKARANI, Ali. ■ 16066 #517-08-2002 L2008 **IM** *012
MUSTOVIC, Ellen Haidet. 3 SAINT FRANCIS WAY # 209 16066 #035-45-1986 L1987 **PM** *020 †60 ‡
NOVEMBER, Stephen R. 3 SAINT FRANCIS WAY, ST FRANCIS MEDICAL CTR NOR 16066 #035-48-1978 L1983 **OBG** *020 †30
PAZIN, John Gregory. 20826 ROUTE 19, CRANBERRY MEDICAL ARTS-BLD 16066 #036-07-1996 L1999 **IM** *020 †20
PERRYMAN, Charles Alexand. 20130 ROUTE 19, PITTSBURGH GYNOB INC 16066 #165-01-1977 L1979 **OBG** *020 †30 ‡
PETERS, Daniel Robt. 105 BRANDT DR, STE 201 16066 #039-05-1985 L2006 **OPH AM** *020 †35
PETTAPIECE, Milton C, Jr. 20397 ROUTE 19, STE 300 TWO LANDMAKR N 16066 #024-05-1965 L1969 **OPH PO** *071 †35
POTTER, Robert Hugo. ■ 16066 #041-12-1955 L1956 **GP** *071
RICE, Samuel M. PO BOX 2005 16066 #008-01-1949 L1950 **FM GP** *072
RICHMOND, Jeffrey Allen. ■ 16066 #055-01-2001 L2005 **PCP** *100 †50
RIZZO, Melissa Ann. ■ 16066 #041-14-2001 *100 †35
ROCK, Ira Michael. 3 SAINT FRANCIS WAY, STE 104 16066 #035-06-1988 L1990 **OBG** *020 †30
SCHOGEL, Karen Lee. 213 EXECUTIVE DR, STE 200 16066 #050-02-1991 L1993 **IM** *020 †20
SEKAS, Gail. 3 SAINT FRANCIS WAY, ASSOCIATES 16066 #038-06-1979 L1985 **GE IM** *071 †20
SHARP, David Lee. 101 SMITH DR, STE 4 16066 #041-12-1979 L1980 **IM** *020 †20
SHEPARD, Kathleen Ann. 20130 ROUTE 19, STE 1000 16066 #008-01-1975 L1976 **PD** *071 †55
SIMMONS, Randon Calvin. 20397 ROUTE 19 STE 238 16066 #041-12-1974 L1975 **CHP P** *020 †75
ST ANDRE, Mary Louise. 20130 ROUTE 19, STE 1000 16066 #024-16-1977 L1982 **IM** *020 †20
STEPANOW, Samuel Jos. 213 EXECUTIVE DR, STE 240 16066 #041-09-1985 L1986 **IM** *020 †20
SUBRAMANIAM, Vijay. ■ 16066 #496-01-2000 L2004 **PCC** *012
VAJJHALA, Ravindra Nath. 1 SAINT FRANCIS WAY 16066 #496-04-1976 L1982 **EM** *020 †16
WAPENSKI, Joseph Albert. 401 SMITH DR STE 4 16066 #038-40-1978 L1989 **N NM** *020 †75,28
WECHT, Ingrid Anne. 20130 ROUTE 19, PITTSBURGH GYNOB INC 16066 #010-02-1995 L1997 **OBG** *020 †30
WHITMAN, Lewis Vincent. 20130 ROUTE 19, STE 1000 16066 #561-01-1977 L1979 **IM** *020 †20
WILLIAMS, Kathryn Anne. 20421 ROUTE 19, STE 201 16066 #041-12-2001 L2001 **PD** *020 †55
WUSYLKO, Michael. 20826 ROUTE 19, CRANBERRY MED ARTS BLDG 16066 #041-12-1977 L1979 **IM** *020 †20
YOUNG, Victoria Kuangcee. 2001 EHRMAN RD, STE A 16066 #047-20-2002 L2006 **OBG** *020
ZHAO, Chengquan. ■ 16066 #243-32-1983 L2001 **PTH** *100 †50
ZUNKIEWICZ, Mark Richard. ■ 16066 #038-43-2004 L2004 **GS** *012

CRANESVILLE — ERIE

REA, Jennifer Marie. ■ 16410 #021-05-2006 L2006 **GS** *012

CREIGHTON — ALLEGHENY

WANG, Xiaohong Helen. 521 FREEPORT RD 15030 #243-16-1983 L1999 **IM** *020 †20

CRESCENT — ALLEGHENY

KERR, Harry James, Jr. ■ 15046 #041-12-1948 L1949 **IM** *071

CRESCO — MONROE

ANTOLIN, Eleanor B. RR 2 BOX 2440 18326 #748-01-1990 L1997 **P** *020 †75
CALANDRA, Gary Bruce. ■ 18326 #040-02-1971 L1981 **IM ID** *071 †20,03

CRESSON — CAMBRIA

HILL, Jean-Claude P. PO BOX A 16630 #056-06-1987 **P** *020
LENZ, Patrick Kenneth. 792 GALLITZIN RD 16630 #041-02-1996 L1998 **FM** *020 †18
RAYMOND, Paul Anthony. 225 KEYSTONE AVE 16630 #041-02-1971 L1972 **FM FPG** *020 †18 ‡
REPKO, Dawn Marie. 792 GALLITZIN RD, MAINLINE MEDICAL ASSOC INC 16630 #041-14-1998 L2000 **FM** *020 †18
STEM, Lawrence Robt. 792 GALLITZIN RD, STE 108 16630 #041-14-1979 L1980 **FM EM** *020 †18
UBINA, Gilfred C. 815 2ND ST 16630 #748-08-1992 L2001 **FM** *020 †18

CRESSONA — SCHUYLKILL

HAFIZ, Tariq. 35 S SILLYMAN ST 17929 #704-02-1987 L1993 **IM CD** *020 †20

CROYDON — BUCKS

LEWIS, Philip Gaylord. 3100 STATE RD 19021 #023-07-1976 L1984 **PHP** *030 †70
ROGER, Aime K. ■ 19021 #041-09-1997 L2000 **IM** *020

CRUM LYNNE — DELAWARE

BILLBROUGH, Marguerite. 1553 CHESTER PIKE 19022 #010-02-1986 L1986 **OPH** *020 †35
NATALE, Sherry Grace. 1124 CHESTER PIKE 19022 #036-05-1986 L1989 **CHP P** *020 †75
RANA, Ashish Vasudev. 1553 CHESTER PIKE, STE 1 19022 #035-48-1992 L1995 **IM** *020 †20
SCOLES, Karen Schumann. 1553 CHESTER PIKE, STE 1 19022 #033-06-1983 L1985 **IM** *020 †20

CURWENSVILLE — CLEARFIELD

ELKINS, Carol Gay. 465 STATE ST STE A, PRIMARY CARE ASSOCS 16833 #041-02-1985 L1986 **FM** *020 †18
HAYS, Amy Lynne. 617 STATE ST 16833 #047-05-1990 L1993 **FM** *020 †18 ‡

DALLAS — LUZERNE

BRADLEY, Jeffrey Shane. ■ 18612 #028-03-2002 L2007 **P** *020
CHANG, Chun Sik. ■ 18612 #583-04-1966 L1972 **P** *020 †75
COOK, Glendon Elven. 16 CHURCH ST 18612 #041-15-2003 L2003 **FM** *020 †18
DAINIUS, Alfonsas. ■ 18612 #407-16-1960 L1973 **PHP FM** *062
GARCIA, Francisco L, Jr. ■ 18612 #748-01-1963 L1975 **P** *020
GAZA, Dennis John. N PIONEER AV MEADOWS 1 602 18612 #649-39-1978 L1982 **EM IM** *020
GREULICK, Joan Elizabeth. 16 CHURCH ST 18612 #035-03-1976 L1981 **PD** *020 †55 ‡
GROSSMAN, William King. ■ 18612 #041-02-1968 L1970 **P** *071 †75
HORA, James Francis. ■ 18612 #016-43-1957 L1966 **OTO HNS** *071 †45
HUTZ, David Paul. 40 DALLAS SHOPPING CTR, GEISINGER MEDICAL GROUP DA 18612 #041-15-1999 L2001 **IM** *020
JACOBS, Irvin. 16 CHURCH ST 18612 #041-02-1953 L1954 **FM PD** *020 †18
KIMPEL, Rebecca Irene. ■ 18612 #041-09-1987 L1989 **EM** *020 †20
KOEHL, C Warren, Jr. ■ 18612 #041-02-1956 L1957 **PTH NM** *071 †50
KOWALSKI, Joseph John. RR 4, BOX 173A 18612 #041-09-1968 L1969 **P** *020 †75
LEHMAN, Clinton James. LAKE 18612 #041-13-1960 L1961 **IM** *071
MAAS, Kurt Dalen. 609 MAIN RD, BOX B 18612 #041-09-1982 L1983 **FM** *020 †18
ORLANDO, Joseph Dominic. MOUNTAIN VIEW DRIVE R.D. 5 18612 #041-13-1962 L1964 **R** *020 †80
PATEL, Krishnakant A. 1180 MEMORIAL HWY, TWIN STACKS 18612 #496-41-1994 L2000 **FM** *020 †18
PUFFENBERGER, Mark W. 1180 MEMORIAL HWY, TWIN STACKS 18612 #041-13-1986 L1987 **FM** *020 †18
REICH, Harry. ■ 18612 #539-06-1970 L1975 **GYN OS** *020 †30
SARADA, Kamal Kishore. ■ 18612 #495-70-1992 L2007 **DR** *100 †80
SMITH, Harry A, Jr. 50 TERRACE ST 18612 #041-02-1954 L1955 **ORS** *071
VODZAK, Jennifer. ■ 18612 #041-15-2006 L2006 **PD** *012
WEINMAN, Herbert Michael. ■ 18612 #035-15-1965 L1994 **FM** *020 †18

DALLASTOWN — YORK

ARCIERI, Rocco R, II. 1010 BLYMIRE RD, DALLASTOWN MEDICAL 17313 #041-14-1995 L1998 **FM** *020 †18
DAUGHERTY, Donald T. ■ 17313 #041-07-1983 L1984 **FM** *071 †18
DOBISH, Michael John. 1010 BLYMIRE RD, DALLASTOWN MEDICAL 17313 #010-02-1975 L1976 **FM IM** *020 †18
FAVINO, Charles James. ■ 17313 #041-02-1963 L1964 **PTH** *071 †50
HEILAND, Angela Harty. 755 S PLEASANT AVE 17313 #035-09-2001 L2001 **FM** *100 †18
KRESGE, Dale Leslie. 1010 BLYMIRE RD, DALLASTOWN MEDICAL 17313 #041-12-1972 L1975 **IM** *020 †20
LACKEY, Robert M. 755 S PLEASANT AVE, 755 S PLEASANT AVE 17313 #023-01-1995 L1997 **FM** *020 †18
MARSALA, Jessica Sarah. ■ 17313 #041-14-2006 **FP** *012
MC GANN, Thomas R. 755 S PLEASANT AVE 17313 #010-02-1981 L1982 **FM** *020 †18
MOSSER, Kevin Henry. 757 S PLEASANT AVE 17313 #041-01-1979 L1981 **FM** *030 †18
NEUBURGER, David Lawrence. 1010 BLYMIRE RD, DALLASTOWN MEDICAL 17313 #041-14-1979 L1981 **FM** *020 †18
NOLL, Mindy Ann. 1010 BLYMIRE RD, DALLASTOWN MEDICAL 17313 #041-14-1999 L2004 **FM** *020 †18
PATTERSON, Cynthia Mae. 755 S PLEASANT AVE 17313 #041-09-1978 L1979 **FM** *020 †18
PIPER, Donald Evans. SOUTH PLEASANT AVE 17313 #041-13-1955 L1956 **FM** *071 †18
ROWAND, Randall Wm. 1010 BLYMIRE RD, DALLASTOWN MEDICAL 17313 #041-02-1978 L1984 **FM** *020 †18

■ = Address Information Privacy Protected

SCHWARTZKOPF, Paul Bruce. 755 S PLEASANT AVE 17313 #041-02-1987 L1989 **FM** *020 †18

DALTON – LACKAWANNA

DOVYDAITIS, Romas. RR 1 BOX 244, DECKER ROAD 18414 #165-01-1974 L1979 **DR** *020 †80
FAVINI, M Peter J. ■ 18414 #010-02-1953 L1954 **FM** *071
KLINE, Ben. 111 S TURNPIKE RD 18414 #041-02-1955 L1956 **GP OS** *072 ‡
KOTCHICK, E Donald. 210 BRAEWOOD RD, RD 3 18414 #041-02-1963 L1964 **FM** *020 †18
LARKIN, Vincent D, Jr. 205 SUGARBUSH RD 18414 #035-08-1974 **GS VS** *062 †85
MORI, Gino. RR 3, LILY LAKE ROAD 18414 #041-02-1958 L1959 **GS** *071 †85
NALEVANKO, Albert M. RR 3, SUGARBUSH RD 18414 #010-02-1965 L1966 **OTO** *071 †45 ‡
PALMER, Meade T. 114 WINDEMERE CIR 18414 #041-13-1985 L1992 **CCS** *020 †85
STEC, Eugene Geo. ■ 18414 #041-02-1954 L1955 **FM** *071 †18
WALKOWSKI, Edward Jos, Jr. RR 1 BOX 434A 18414 #422-01-1982 L1983 **DR** *062 †80

DAMASCUS – WAYNE

LAYTON, Bradley Wm. PO BOX 237, 1713 COCHECTON TPKE 18415 #041-02-1981 L1984 **FM** *020 †18

DANIELSVILLE – NORTHAMPTON

RICE, Natalie Marie. 1365 BLUE MOUNTAIN DR 18038 #041-02-1993 L1995 **FM** *020 †18

DANVILLE – MONTOUR

ACHARYA, Yuba Raj. 100 N ACADEMY AVE 17822 #672-03-2001 L2005 **IM** *012
ADHIKESAVAN, Leena Geetha. ■ 17821 #025-07-2006 L2007 **DR** *012
AGBARA, Onyinyechi Beverl. ■ 17821 #025-07-2006 L2007 **DR** *012
AHMAD, Fareed. 100 N ACADEMY AVE, FOSS 6 17822 #704-02-1990 L2004 **PDC** *020 †55
AHMED, Shaik Mohd Laeeq. 100 N ACADEMY AVE, DEPT OF ANESTHESIOLOGY 17822 #495-65-1993 L2005 **APM** *020 †60
AHOYA, Leah Eboso. ■ 17821 #008-01-2003 L2007 **OBG** *020
AIJAZ, Naghma Jabeen. 100 N ACADEMY AVE, GEISINGER HEALTH SYSTEM/PE 17822 #704-06-1994 L2005 **PDE** *020 †55
AJANS, Amy N. ■ 17821 #028-03-2004 L2005 **OPH** *012
AKMAL, Yasir Mohammad. 100 NO, OFFICE OF MED EDUCATION 17822 #539-03-2003 L2004 **GS** *012
AKULA, Surekha Venkata. ■ 17822 #495-11-1999 L2006 **IM** *012
AL-AGHA, Mouna A.. 100 N ACADEMY AVE 17822 #875-01-1992 L2006 **IM** *012
AL-AMIN, Tony Troublefiel. 100 NO, OFFICE OF MED EDUCATION 17822 #033-06-2002 L2002 **PMM** *012
ALESSI, Christopher M. 100 N ACADEMY AVE, GEISINGER HLTH SYS-VAS SUR 17822 #024-01-1998 L2007 **VS** *020 †85
ALESSI, Thomas Richard. 100 N ACADEMY AVE 17822 #033-05-1980 L1983 **AN** *071 †05
ALEXANDER, Ian Joseph. ■ 17822 #034-01-2004 L2004 **OTO** *012
ALI, Sarah Ashfaq. 100 N ACADEMY AVE, GEISINGER MEDICAL CENTER 17822 #704-02-1988 L1998 **IM** *020 †20
ALOMARI, Mohammad Ghaleb. ■ 17821 #575-01-1992 L1999 **PTH** *020 †50
ANTOHE, Jana Laura. 100 N ACADEMY AVE 17822 #781-03-1999 L2006 **IM** *012
ARIBANDI, Lavanya. 100 N ACADEMY AVE, GEISINGER MED CTR 17822 #495-21-1997 L2004 **IM** *100 †20
ARIBANDI, Manohar. 100 N AVE, GEISINGER MEDICAL CENTER 17822 #495-21-1990 L2003 **DR** *020 †80
ASHARAF, Abdul Rasheed. 100 N ACADEMY AVE 17822 #495-80-1990 L2003 **IM** *020 †20
ASLAM, Farhan. 100 NO, OFFICE OF MED EDUCATION 17822 #704-04-2001 L2003 **IM** *100
ASSAL, Chafik. ■ 17821 #875-02-2001 L2006 **CD** *012 †20
AWAD, Latif Labib. 1 N ACADEMY AVE 17821 #330-04-1964 L1974 **REN GYN** *020 †30
AYERS, Michael Lindsay. 100 N ACADEMY AVE 17822 #010-02-1993 L2001 **PCC** *020
AZEREDO, William James. 100 N ACADEMY AVE, GEISINGER HEALTH SYSTEM 17822 #035-15-2002 L2007 **OTO** *020
BAKER, Nevin Charles. ■ 17821 #041-77-2007, ▲ L2007 **IM** *012
BALDASSANO, Vincent F, II. 100 N ACADEMY AVE, TEMPLE UNIV HOSPITAL 17822 #041-02-1990 L1993 **OPH** *020 †35
BALZ, Thomas Patrick. 100 N ACADEMY AVE, GEISNGER MEDIAL CENTER 17822 #041-07-1980 L1983 **IM** *020 †20
BARACALDO, Juan Carlos. 100 N ACADEMY AVE 17822 #264-21-1997 L2006 **IM** *012
BATES, James S. ■ 17821 #041-12-1953 L1954 **GYN** *071 †30
BAUCOM, David Alan. 100 N ACADEMY AVE 17822 #033-06-1991 L1995 **AN** *020 †05
BAUER, Jacob Howard. 100 N ACADEMY AVE, GEISSINGER MED CENTER 17822 #050-02-2004 L2005 **D** *012
BAXTER, John Arthur. 1 N ACADEMY AVE, GEISINGER MEDICAL CENTER 17821 #041-09-1970 **DR R** *020 †80 ‡
BECK, John David. ■ 17822 #054-04-2007 L2007 **ORS** *012
BEHM LOPEZ, Robert. 100 N ACADEMY AVE 17822 #270-02-2000 L2005 **IM** *012
BELLINO, Paul Joseph, III. 100 N ACADEMY AVE 17822 #041-07-1993 L1995 **PD** *020 †55
BENKOVIC, Gregory Wm. 1 N ACADEMY AVE 17821 #010-01-1970 L1973 **IM GP** *020 †20
BENOIT, Charles Hector. 100 N ACADEMY AVE 17822 #019-02-1974 L1981 **TS** *020 †85,90
BENOTTI, Peter Norbert. 100 N ACADEMY AVE 17822 #024-07-1970 L2005 **GS** *020 †85
BERBERICH, Joel John. 100 N ACADEMY AVE, DIVISION OF ANESTHESIOLOGY 17822 #011-02-1980 L1989 **AN** *020 †05 ‡
BERGER, Peter B. 100 N ACADEMY AVE MC30-03, GEISINGER HEALTH SYSTEM 17822 #035-19-1983 L2006 **CD IM** *020 †20
BERMUDEZ, Maria Camila. 100 N ACADEMY AVE 17822 #264-16-2002 L2005 **IM** *012
BERTSCH, David John. 100 N ACADEMY AVE, GEISINGER MEDICAL CENTER 17822 #041-02-1985 L1987 **GS** *020 †85
BHATIA, Shyamsunder G. DEPT OF DERMATOLOGY, GEISINGER MED CTR 17822 #496-38-1963 L1973 **D DMP** *071 †15
BIEBER, Eric Jos. 121 SKYWARD DR 17821 #016-43-1986 L2001 **REN GYN** *020 †30
BILI, Androniki. ■ 17822 #418-02-1990 L2006 **AI** *020 †20
BILLAS, Anthony, Jr. NORTH ACADEMY AVE, 31-01 GEISINGER MED CTR 17822 #041-02-1982 L1983 **FM** *020 †18

BIRKETT, D Peter. 217 KATYS CHURCH RD 17821 #946-01-1957 L1970 **IMG P** *020 †75
BIRKETT, Dylan P. 100 N ACADEMY AVE, ANESTHESIOLOGY MC-20-25 17822 #035-15-1998 L2002 **AN** *020 †05
BISHAY, Ayman Asaad. ■ 17821 #915-04-1990 L2006 **PUD** *100
BISORDI, Joseph E. 1 N ACADEMY AVE 17821 #010-02-1975 L1975 **NEP** *030 †20
BITETTO, Daniel Peter. ■ 17821 #048-02-2004 L2004 **IM** *020 †20
BLANKENSHIP, James C. GEISINGER MED CTR, DEPT OF CARDIOLOGY 21-60 17822 #035-20-1980 L1980 **IC CD** *020 †20 ‡
BLANSFIELD, Joseph Alfred, Jr. 100 N ACADEMY AVE, MC 21-70 17822 #041-02-1999 L2001 **GS** *020 †85
BOCK, Glenn Howard. 100 N ACADEMY AVE, MC 13-39 17822 #028-03-1975 L2004 **PN PD** *050 †55
BOCTOR, Fouad Nassif. 100 N ACADEMY AVE, GEISINGER HEALTH SYSTEM 01 17822 #915-02-1984 L2006 **PTH BBK** *020 †50
BOGNER, Edward Walter. 100 N ACADEMY AVE 17822 #041-02-1977 L1978 **FM** *020 †18
BOLOS, Peter Rifat. ■ 17822 #011-04-2004 L2005 **DR** *012
BOULIS, Tharwat Stewart F. ■ 17821 #915-02-1998 L2004 **OBG** *012
BOULTON, Harold Michael. 100 N ACADEMY AVE, STE 20-05 17822 #005-12-2003 L2003 **EM** *100 †16
BOURG, Stacey Jean. ■ 17821 #021-06-2007 L2007 **PD** *012
BRADY, James Oherron. 100 N ACADEMY AVE 17822 #035-09-1983 L1984 **HEM** *020 †20
BROFFERIO, Alessandra. ■ 17821 #561-01-1998 L2005 **CD** *012 †20
BROGNA, Michael Chas. 200 STATE HOSPITAL DR, DANVILLE STATE HOSPITAL 17821 #308-03-1983 L1985 **IM** *020 †20
BROKHIN, Matvey. 100 N ACADEMY AVE, GEISINGER MEDICAL CENTER - 17822 #035-08-2002 L2007 **END** *020 †20
BRONOV, Oleg Erlenovich. 100 N ACADEMY AVE, GEISINGER MEDICAL CTR 17822 #913-97-1992 L2002 **IM** *100 †80
BROSS, James Edward. 100 N ACADEMY AVE 17822 #041-13-1980 L1981 **ID IM** *020 †20
BROWN, Frederick Gerdts. 100 N ACADEMY AVE 17822 #041-12-1961 L1962 **NEP IM** *071 †20
BROWN, Robert E. 100 N ACADEMY AVE 17822 #051-04-1966 L1973 **PTH** *050 †50
BRUNO, Pat Jos. 100 N ACADEMY AVE, 1ST FL 17822 #041-14-1972 L1976 **PD** *020 †55
BUCALOIU, Ion Dan. 100 N ACADEMY AVE 17822 #781-01-1998 L2001 **IM** *100
BUDINETZ, Tara Hope. 100 N ACADEMY AVE 17822 #041-77-2007, ▲ L2005 **OBG** *012
BULGER, John B. 100 N ACADEMY AVE, GEISINGER MED CTR 17822 #041-77-1995, ▲ L1996 **IM** *020 ‡
BURKE, Greg Francis. 100 N ACADEMY AVE 17822 #041-02-1988 L1990 **IM** *020 †20
BURNS, J Robt. 100 N ACADEMY AVE, GEISINGER MEDICAL CTR 17822 #041-09-1963 L1964 **CCM PUD** *020 †20 ‡
BURNSIDE, Joyce Ann. 100 N ACADEMY AVE, GEISINGER MEDICAL CENTER 17822 #041-13-1986 L1987 **CD** *020 †20
BUSH, David Chas. DEPARTMENT OF ORTHOPEDICS, GEISINGER MEDICAL CENTER 17822 #024-01-1969 L1977 **HS ORS** *020 †40
BUTCHER, Richard James. 100 N ACADEMY AVE 17822 #041-01-1973 L1974 **CD NM** *020 †18,20
BUZAS, Christopher J. ■ 17821 #041-77-2006, ▲ L2006 **GS** *012
BUZZINI, Sergio Russo. ■ 17821 #187-67-1990 L2007 **ADL** *020 †55
CABALLERO, Sandra Patrici. OF OBSTETRICS-GYNECOLOGY, DEPT 17822 #005-12-2007 L2007 **OBG** *012
CADENA, Alberto Jose. 100 N ACADEMY AVE 17822 #264-16-2002 L2005 **IM** *012
CAHILL, Thomas J. 100 N ACADEMY AVE 17822 #035-19-1952 L1953 **IM** *071
CAI, Qiangjun. 100 N ACADEMY AVE 17822 #243-49-1994 L2005 **IM** *012
CAMERON, Brian Howard. 1 N ACADEMY AVE 17821 #065-05-1980 L1992 **PDS** *050
CAMPBELL, Lisa Butenhoff. 100 N ACADEMY AVE, DEPT OF DERMATOLOGY #14-06 17822 #056-05-2002 L2003 **PRD** *100
CAMPBELL, Michael Andrew. 100 N ACADEMY AVE, GEISINGER MEDICAL CENTER 17822 #035-15-2005 L2005 **ORS** *012
CAPRILES DIAZ, Daniela Jo. 100 N ACADEMY AVE 17822 #935-01-2003 L2005 **IM** *012
CARDELLA, John Francis. 100 N ACADEMY AVE, GEISINGER HEALTH SYSTEM 17822 #025-01-1978 L1989 **R** *020 †20
CARLETON, Marta Johnson. N ACADEMY AVE, DEPT OF RADIOLOGY 17822 #038-43-1980 L1987 **DR** *020 †80
CARLSON, John Philip. GEISINGER MEDICAL CENTER, DEPT OF NEUROLOGY 17822 #041-14-1975 L1976 **N IM** *020 †20,75
CARNERO SALAZAR, Guillermo. 100 N ACADEMY AVE, GEISINGER MEDICAL CENTER 17822 #737-06-2000 L2007 **IM** *012
CARPENTER, Michael Harris. 100 NO, OFFICE OF MED EDUCATION 17822 #049-01-2004 L2004 **PD** *020 †55
CASTILLO, Cesar Augusto. DEPTARTMENT OF MEDICINE, GEISINGER HEALTH SYSTEM 17822 #308-05-2001 L2007 **AN** *012
CERA, Peter John, Jr. N. ACADEMY AVENUE, GEISINGER MEDICAL CENTER 17822 #041-02-1961 L1962 **PTH** *071 †50
CHALLMAN, Thomas Donovan. 100 N ACADEMY AVE 17822 #010-02-1991 L2002 **PD** *020 †55
CHAPMAN, John Hascall. 100 N ACADEMY AVE 17822 #051-01-1970 L1995 **CD IM** *030 †20
CHARNOFF, Nina Esther. ■ 17821 #035-08-1981 L2006 **AN** *020 †05 ‡
CHEPURNAYA, Iryna A. ■ 17821 #913-05-1987 L2005 **P** *020 †75
CHERUVATTATH, Rekha. ■ 17821 #495-02-1996 L2006 **GE** *012
CHO, Stephanie Yoon. 115 WOODBINE LN, GEISINGER DERMATOLOGY 17822 #041-02-2007 L2008 **D** *012
CHOI, Lydia Wooyoung. ■ 17822 #033-05-2002 L2007 **GS** *012
CHRISTIE, Alfred Douglas. 100 N ACADEMY AVE 17822 #048-02-1989 L1992 **RO** *020 †80
CHUDOW, Clara Jean. 100 N ACADEMY AVE, GEISINGER MEDICAL CENTER 17822 #035-19-1980 L2007 **DR** *020 †80
CINDRIC, Matthew Craig. ■ 17821 #055-01-2004 L2004 **GS** *012
CLEMENT, John Anthony. ■ 17821 #041-02-1969 L1971 **RO** *072 †80 ‡
COLANCECCO, Joseph Paul. 100 N ACADEMY AVE, GEISINGER MEDICAL CENTER 17822 #041-09-1974 L1975 **IM** *020 †20
COLE, James Monroe. 1 N ACADEMY AVE, GEISINGER MEDICAL CENTER 17822 #035-45-1946 L1955 **OTO** *071 †45
COLEMAN, Linda Lorraine. 2 MILLWOOD DR, 2 MILLWOOD DRIVE 17821 #041-02-1969 L1971 **DR** *020 †80
COLLINS, Scotty Ray. 100 NO, OFFICE OF MED EDUCATION 17822 #055-02-2002 L2002 **DR** *100 †80
COMBS, Loreli Lee. GEISINGER MED CTR, DEPT OF PEDIATRICS 17822 #051-07-2007 L2007 **PD** *012
CONCA, Dominick Michael. GEISINGER MEDICAL CENTER, DEPARTMENT OF RADIOLOGY 17822 #035-09-1970 L1973 **DR NM** *020 †80

CONROY, Michael Patrick. 100 N ACADEMY AVE 17822 #041-15-2003 L2007 **DMP D** *012 †15
CONSTANTINOU, Constantinos. 100 N ACADEMY AVE 17822 #759-03-2000 L2005 **GS** *012
COOK, James Alan. GEISINGER MED CTR, DEPT OF NEONATOLOGY 17822
  #041-02-1984 L1989 **NPM PD** *020 †55
CORTEZA, Benjamin A. 200 STATE HOSPITAL DR 17821 #748-01-1963 L1973 **IM** *020
COTARLAN-NISTOR, Vladimir. ■ 17822 #781-08-1996 L2005 **CD** *012
COVER, Kenneth Lewis. 100 N ACADEMY AVE 17822 #041-14-1989 L1991 **IM** *020 †20
CRONIN, Hyland Elizabeth. ■ 17821 #055-01-2006 L2007 **D** *012
CRUCIANI, Mary Catherine. 100 N ACADEMY AVE, GEISINGER MEDICAL CENTER 17822
  #010-02-1988 L1991 **IM** *020
CUETO, Josephine-Liezl Pa. ■ 17821 #028-34-2006 L2006 *012
CURRID, Aideen Mary. GEISINGER MEDICAL CTR, DEPT OF ANESTHESIA 20-25 17822
  #539-04-1972 L1998 **AN** *020 †05
CURRY, Thomas Andrew. 100 N ACADEMY AVE 17822 #041-01-1974 L1975 **PD** *020 †55
CURTIS, James L. ■ 17821 #010-01-1949 L1965 **OPH** *071 †35
DALENCOURT, Gregory. 100 N ACADEMY AVE, GEISINGER MED CTR 17822
  #305-01-2002 L2002 **GS** *100
DAMSTRA, Darin Dean. ■ 17821 #018-03-2003 L2004 **DR** *012
DANCEA, Horatiu Calin. 100 N ACADEMY AVE 17822 #781-01-1998 L2006 **GS** *012
DANCEA, Sorina. ■ 17821 #781-01-1999 L2007 **IM** *020
DANELLA, John Francis. 100 N ACADEMY AVE, C/O GEISINGER MEDICAL CENT 17822
  #041-02-1986 L1987 **U** *020 †95
DAVE, Harish R. 200 STATE HOSPITAL DR, DANVILLE STATE HOSPITAL 17821
  #495-22-1969 L1976 **GP RO** *030 †80
DAVIS, Duane Edwin. ACADEMY AVE, FOSS CLINIC 17822 #041-09-1971 L1972
  RHU IM *030 †20
DAVIS, Julia Christina. GEISINGER MED CTR, DEPT OF PEDIATRICS 17822 #050-02-2007
  PD *012
DEITRICK, John E, Jr. 100 N ACADEMY AVE 17822 #035-20-1966 L1968 **GS OS** *071 †85
DEITRICK, John English. 625 MOWERY RD 17821 #023-07-1933 L1952 **IM** *071
DELANEY, Amy Michelle. ■ 17821 #048-14-2007 L2007 **IM** *012
DEL CASTILLO, Joseph Bern. 100 NO, OFFICE OF MED EDUCATION 17822 #654-01-2002 L2003
  MPD *100
DEL VECCHIO, Leonard, Jr. 100 N ACADEMY AVE, DEPT OF RADIOLOGY 17822
  #041-02-1973 L1974 **DR** *020 †80
DERIAN, Edie Lillian. 100 N ACADEMY AVE, MAIL CODE 29-20 DPT OB/GYN 17822
  #016-43-1987 L2001 **OBG** *020 †30
DEROSA, Jaimie. 100 N ACADEMY AVE, DEPT OF OTOLARYNGOLOGY, MC 17822
  #035-06-2000 L2006 **OTO** *100 †45
DESANTIS, Joseph Gerard. 100 N ACADEMY AVE, DEPT PLASTIC SURGERY 17821
  #008-01-1984 L1986 **PS HS** *020 †85,65
DIEHL, David Lawrence. 100 N ACADEMY AVE # 21-11 17822 #005-14-1983 L2006
  GE IM *020 †20
DITTEL, Walter. ■ 17822 #270-02-2000 L2005 **MPD** *012
DOHSE, Lindsey Ann. 100 N ACADEMY AVE, DEPT OF DERMATOLOGY 17822
  #038-44-2006 L2007 **D** *012
DONOVAN, Julia Theresa. 100 N ACADEMY AVE, 29-20 GYN/ONCOLOGY 17822
  #010-02-1974 L2004 **GO OBG** *020 †30
DORION, Robert Patrick. 100 N ACADEMY AVE 17822 #429-01-1981 L1983
  PTH HMP *020 †50 ‡
DRINIS, Sophia. 100 N ACADEMY AVE 17822 #016-01-1996 L2004 **U** *020 †95
DUCHESNE, Shadi. 13 KIRKBRIDE DR, FEMALES 17821 #042-02-1987 L1991 **P** *020
DULA, Brian David. ■ 17822 #041-14-2004 L2005 **AN** *012
DUNNE, Anne Patricia. 100 N ACADEMY AVE, GEISINGER MED CTR RAD DEPT 17822
  #010-02-1978 L1984 **DR** *020 †80
DVORAK, Andrea Marie. ■ 17821 #035-15-2006 L2006 **PD** *012
EAGER, Matthew Robert. 100 N ACADEMY AVE 17822 #041-13-2003 L2003 **ORS** *012
ECKEL, Timothy Brainerd. 1410 BLOOM RD 17821 #041-13-1976 L1977 **FM** *020 †18 ‡
EDWARDS, Philip Douglas. 100 N ACADEMY AVE, GEISINGER HEALTH SYSTEM 17822
  #917-03-1989 L2006 *020
EKBERG, Norman Lee. ■ 17821 #030-05-1962 L1967 **PUD IM** *071 †20
EL-AROUSY, Hazem Mahmoud. 100 N ACADEMY AVE 17822 #915-02-1998 L2006 **GS** *012
ELLISON, Neil Michael. 100 N ACADEMY AVE 17822 #035-15-1973 L1979 **PLM** *020 †20
ELMORE, James R. 100 N ACADEMY AVE 17822 #008-02-1984 L1992 **VS GS** *020 †85
ELSTON, Dirk M. 100 N ACADEMY AVE, DEPT OF DERM GEISINGER 17822 #041-02-1982 L1985
  D DMP *040 †15 ‡
EMGE, Frederick Konrad. 100 N ACADEMY AVE, GEISINGER HEALTH SYSTEM 17822
  #035-03-1982 L2000 **PDC PD** *020 †55
ENARI, Denise Marion. 100 N ACADEMY AVE, GHS REHABILITATION HOSPITA 17822
  #422-01-1983 L1987 **PM** *020 †60
ERIAN, Yousef Yehia Nagib. ■ 17822 #915-04-2000 L2001 **IM** *100
ESCOBAR, Juan Ricardo. 100 N ACADEMY AVE, GEISINGER MED CTR 17822
  #264-16-1998 L2004 **IM** *100 †20
ESQUIBEL, Augusto Jose. ■ 17821 #187-04-1950 L1969 **P** *071 †75
EVANS, James Folpmers. 1 N ACADEMY AVE, DEPT OF GEN SURG 17821 #035-01-1971 L1980
  OS GS *020 †85
EVANS, Ronald. 100 N ACADEMY AVE 17822 #041-77-2003, ▲ L2003 **IM** *100 †20
FACKTOR, Michael Alan. 100 N ACADEMY AVE 17822 #025-01-1967 L2008 **AI PD** *020 †55,03
FANELLI, Gregory Carl. 115 WOODBINE LANE, GEISINGER ORTHOPAEDICS WOO 17822
  #041-14-1984 L1985 **ORS** *020 †40
FELBERG, Robert Adam. ■ 17821 #041-02-1994 L2007 **N** *020
FERNANDEZ CUARTAS, Carlos. 100 N ACADEMY AVE 17822 #264-16-1997 L2006 **IMG** *100
FEROZE, Mustafa. ■ 17821 #704-01-1985 L2000 **IM** *020
FERRINGER, Tammie C. 100 N ACADEMY AVE, GEISINGER MEDICAL CTR 17822
  #041-07-1998 L2001 **D DMP** *020 †15
FIGUEREDO DIETES, Tatiana. 100 N ACADEMY AVE, DEPT OF INTERNAL MED 17822
  #264-21-2000 L2007 **IM** *020
FISK, David Emery. 100 N ACADEMY AVE, DPT THOR MED GEISINGER MED 17822
  #038-06-1970 L1983 **PUD IM** *020 †20
FITZPATRICK, Michael Hugh. 100 N ACADEMY AVE, GEISINGER MEDICAL CENTER 17822
  #041-02-1992 L1996 **EM** *020,16
FLEURY, Margot Casas. ■ 17822 #051-07-2007 L2007 **PD** *012
FOLK, Jeffrey Randall. 100 N ACADEMY AVE 17822 #041-13-1982 L1983 **CD IM** *020 †20 ‡
FOLTZER, Michael Albert. 100 N ACADEMY AVE, MC 13-48 17822 #038-41-1981 L2002
  ID IM *020 †20
FRANKLIN, David Perdue. 100 N ACADEMY AVE, DEPT VASCULAR SRGY 17821
  #036-05-1983 L1989 **VS GS** *020 †85

FREEMAN, Allison Lee. 100 N ACADEMY AVE 17822 #065-01-1987 L2006 **AI PD** *020 †55
FRIEDENBERG, Scott M. 100 N ACADEMY AVE, PENN STATE GEISINGER 17822
  #041-13-1994 L1999 **CN** *020 †75
FRODEL, John Linton, Jr. 100 N ACADEMY AVE, MC -13-33 17822 #054-04-1981 L2003
  OTO FPS *020 †45
FULMER, Brant Robert. 1OO N ACADEMY AVE 17822 #041-13-1994 L2001 **U** *020 †95
GABRIELSEN, Jon Damon. 100 N ACADEMY AVE 17822 #017-20-1998 L2007 **GS** *100 †85
GALLAGHER, James Gerard. GEISINGER CLINIC-CANCER CE, DIV MEDICAL ONCOLOGY 17822
  #050-02-1975 L1980 **ON ID** *071 †20
GALT, Spencer Wm. 100 N ACADEMY AVE 17822 #041-09-1986 L2003 **VS** *020 †85
GARCIA-MAYORCA, Carlos A. 100 N ACADEMY AVE, CENTER 17822 #270-02-1989 L1996
  CD *020 †20
GARNICA, Sheila Viviana. ■ 17822 #264-21-1998 L2006 **OBG** *012
GASTON, Erin Jean. ■ 17822 #041-12-2004 L2004 **EM** *100
GEE, Nathan Gordon. ■ 17821 #035-45-2006 L2007 **DR** *012
GERHARD, Glenn Stephen. 100 N ACADEMY AVE, WEIS CTR FOR RESEARCH 17822
  #041-14-1986 L1989 **BBK** *050 †50
GHOSH, Sumit Bijoy. 100 N ACADEMY AVE 17822 #041-07-1994 L1999 **OBG** *020 †30
GHOSH, Tarit Kanti. 100 N ACADEMY AVE 17822 #495-38-1959 L1970 **OBG GO** *030 †30
GIBSON, Keith. 100 N ACADEMY AVE 17822 #041-02-1986 L1987 **FM** *020 †18
GIBSON, Wm Stephen, Jr. 100 N ACADEMY AVE, GEISINGER MEDICAL CENTER 17822
  #036-01-1961 L1964 **PDO OTO** *071 †45
GINN, Tommy Neal. ■ 17822 #012-01-1992 L2003 **OBG** *020 †18
GIRARD, Scott. 100 N ACADEMY AVE 17822 #041-77-2004, ▲ L2004 **IM** *100 †20
GO, Bernard-Dennis M. 100 N ACADEMY AVE, GEISINGER MEDICAL CENTER 2 17822
  #041-14-1993 L1998 **DR** *020 †80
GOLDBERG, Alan. 109 WOODBINE LN 17822 #041-02-1975 L1976 **CCM PUD** *020 †20
GORDNER, Jesse W, Jr. 410 FERRY ST 17821 #023-01-1936 L1937 **GP** *071
GOTOFF, Jill Maitland. 100 N ACADEMY AVE, SECTION PEDIATRIC NEUROLOG 17822
  #016-01-1986 L1996 **N PD** *020 †55,75
GOTOFF, Robert Alan. 100 N ACADEMY AVE, GEISINGER HEALTH SYSTEM 17822
  #016-01-1986 L1996 **ID IM** *020 †20
GRANT, Howard Rieger. GEISINGER HEALTH SYSTEM, 100 N ADCAMEY AVE 17822
  #010-01-1983 L1984 **PD** *030 †55
GREENE, Joseph Scott. 100 N ACADEMY AVE 17822 #036-05-1986 L1987 **OTO** *020 †45
GUADAGNO, Brian Peter. 100 N ACADEMY AVE, GEISINGER HEALTH SYSTEM 17822
  #035-03-2006 L2006 **MPD** *012
GUERRA VALENCIA, Jose Arm. 100 N ACADEMY AVE, GEISINGER MEDICAL CENTER 17822
  #737-06-2001 L2005 **IM** *012
GUIBORD, Nathalie M. 100 N ACADEMY AVE, GEISINGER MEDICAL CENTER 17822
  #067-01-1994 L1999 **OPH** *020 †35
GUILFOOSE, Mark Alan. 100 N ACADEMY AVE, NORTH ACADEMY AVE 17822
  #050-02-1983 L1984 **FM** *020 †18
GUTKNECHT, David Ross. 100 N ACADEMY AVE 17822 #035-20-1971 L1972 **IM** *020 †20
HADDADIANPOUR, Sedigheh. 100 N ACADEMY AVE, DEPT OF GME 17822 #517-13-1986 L2005
  OBG *012
HAHN, Thomas Francis. 100 N ACADEMY AVE, 1ST FL 17822 #010-02-1982 L1984 **PD** *020 †55
HAIDER, Fyeza Shafique. 100 N ACADEMY AVE 17822 #704-22-1998 L2005 **IM** *100
HAMORY, Bruce Hill. 100 N ACADEMY AVE, GEISINGER HEALTH SYSTEM 17822
  #048-04-1971 L1987 **ID IM** *030 †20
HAN, John Jin. 100 N ACADEMY AVE, DEPT OF ANESTGHLGY 17822 #010-01-1993 L1998
  APM AN *020 †05 ‡
HARRINGTON, Thos Michael. 100 N ACADEMY AVE, GEISINGER MEDICAL CENTER 17822
  #041-13-1976 L1977 **RHU** *020 †20
HARRISON, Harold Henry. 100 N ACADEMY AVE, MAIL STOP 01-31 17822 #016-11-1977 L2007
  CLP MG *030 †50
HARRISON, Thomas A. N ACADEMY AVE, GEISINGER MED CTR 21-60 17822
  #024-16-1980 L1988 **CD CCM** *020 †20
HARTER, Gary D. 100 N ACADEMY AVE 17822 #055-01-1988 L1994 **ORS GP** *020 †40
HARTLE, James E, II. 100 N ACADEMY AVE 17822 #035-46-1985 L1987 **NEP** *020 †20
HASEGANU, Laura Elena. 100 N ACADEMY AVE, GEISINGER MEDICAL CENTER 17822
  #781-01-1995 L2007 **IM** *012
HAUGEN, Thorsen. 100 N ACADEMY AVE, GEISINGER MED CTR 17822 #005-12-2007 L2007
  OTO *012
HAUPT, Marilyn T. 100 N ACADEMY AVE, GEISINGER MEDICAL CENTER 17822
  #035-20-1976 L2004 **CCM IM** *030 †20
HEDGES, Amy Elizabeth. ■ 17821 #051-07-2002 L2007 **PD** *012
HERGAN, Robert Ronald, Jr. 100 N ACADEMY AVE, DICKEY CLINIC GEN INTERNAL 17822
  #041-01-1994 L1997 **IM** *020 †20
HERMAN, Lori Jill. ■ 17821 #041-77-2007, ▲ L2007 **PD** *012
HICKS, Maria Isabel. 115 WOODBINE LIN, GEISINGER DERMATOLOGY 17822
  #264-16-1996 L2006 **IM** *012
HILL, Erik Norman. ■ 17822 #048-14-2005 L2006 **DR** *012
HINTON, Selena Marcanthia. 100 N ACADEMY AVE, GEISINGER HEALTH SYSTEM 17822
  #039-01-2001 L2001 **DR** *100 †20
HO, David Wei-Kang. 328 B MILL ST 17822 #422-01-2004 L2004 **MPD** *012
HOENNINGER, David William. ■ 17821 #038-41-2004 L2005 **DR** *012
HOFFER, Richard Scott. 304 RAILROAD ST 17821 #041-09-1976 L1982 **P OS** *020 †75
HOFFMAN, Kerrie Leigh. 100 N ACADEMY AVE, GEISINGER MEDICAL CENTER 17822
  #422-01-2006 L2007 **MPD** *012
HOSEY, Jonathan Patrick. 100 N ACADEMY AVE, GEISINGER CLINIC 17822 #041-09-1983 L1991
  N *020 †75
HOUSTON, John Bernard. 3 HEATHER HILLS DR 17821 #041-13-1963 L1964 **AN** *020 †05
HUBBARD, Cleon Randolph. 100 N ACADEMY AVE, MC 21-60 17822 #665-01-2000 L2000
  IC *012
IGNATOVSKYY, Vitaliy Y. ■ 17822 #913-05-1987 L2005 **GS** *012
INGRAHAM, Herbert John. 100 N ACADEMY AVE 17822 #023-07-1986 L1991 **OPH** *020 †35 ‡
INVERSO, Nicholas Anthony. 100 N ACADEMY AVE 17822 #041-02-1990 L1992 **GE** *020 †20
IZGUR, Vitaly. ■ 17822 #041-13-2005 L2005 **DR** *012
JACOBSEN, Greg Robert. ■ 17821 #038-43-2005 L2006 **D** *012
JEFFREYS, William H. 100 N ACADEMY AVE, GEISINGER CLINIC 17822 #035-20-1951 L1957
  N *020 †75
JIANG, Liangyong. 100 N ACADEMY AVE 17822 #243-93-1991 L2006 **IM** *012
JOHAL, Amitpal Singh. ■ 17822 #056-06-2003 L2006 **GE** *012 †20
JOHNSON, Lauren Adrienne. 100 N ACADEMY AVE, MC 27-10 17822 #035-01-1988 L1990
  NPM *020 †55

JONES, Frederick L, Jr. ■ 17821 #041-01-1956 L1960 **PUD IM** *071 †20
KALYANASUNDARAM, Arun. 100 N ACADEMY AVE, GEISINGER HEALTH SYSTEM 17822 #495-04-2000 L2002 **CD** *012 †20 ‡
KAMAL, Nazmi Ragheb. ■ 17822 #575-01-1985 L2000 **PCP** *020 †50
KASCHNER, Imme Sonja. DEPT OF PEDIATRICS, GEISINGER MED CTR 17822 #408-17-2002 L2005 **AN** *012
KAUFFMAN, Karl Frederic. 100 N ACADEMY AVE 17822 #305-01-2002 L2005 **EM** *100
KENNEDY, John Wm. ■ 17821 #041-02-1992 L1998 **END** *020 †20
KENNEDY, Thomas Leon. 100 N ACADEMY AVE, GEISINGER MEDICAL CENTER 17822 #035-15-1973 L1980 **OTO HNS** *020 †45 ‡
KENNESON, Maryann. ■ 17821 #020-12-2003 L2005 **U** *012
KHALIL, Maged Fouad. ■ 17821 #915-02-1999 L2007 **HO** *020
KHAN, Hassan John. 100 NO, OFFICE OF MED EDUCATION 17822 #011-04-2003 L2004 **DR** *012
KHAN, Sharif Sadullah. 100 N ACADEMY AVE, GEISINGER CANCER INSTITUTE 17822 #704-26-1996 L2005 **HEM** *100 †20
KHAN, Wasim. ■ 17821 #704-02-1991 L2004 **PDC** *020 †55
KHANDELWAL, Vivek Jugalki. 100 N ACADEMY AVE, GEISINGER MED CTR 17822 #495-80-2000 L2002 **IM** *100 †20
KHEIRI, Samir A. 100 N ACADEMY AVE, GEISINGER MEDICAL CENTER 17822 #915-03-1984 L2004 **HO** *020 †20
KHIANI, Kamal Jaikrishin. 100 N ACADEMY AVE, GEISINGER MEDICAL CENTER 17822 #035-15-1984 L1989 **GE** *020 †20 ‡
KHIANI, Kamal Jaikrishin. 100 NO, OFFICE OF MED EDUCATION 17822 #020-02-2003 L2004 **DR** *012
KIMBER, William J. 100 N ACADEMY AVE 17822 #041-01-1960 L1968 **CD IM** *071 †20
KINSEY, Robert H. GEISINGER MEDICAL CENTER, PULMONARY DISEASES 17822 #051-04-1978 L1983 **PD** *020 †55
KLEMPEL, Patrick R. ■ 17821 #037-01-2006 L2006 **EM** *012
KLENA, Joel C. 113 BLOOM ST 17821 #035-15-2001 L2001 **HS** *100
KNIGHT, Jesse Charles. ■ 17821 #012-22-2007 L2007 **OTO** *012
KNOTT, Kyle Carmichael. 100 N ACADEMY AVE, GEISINGER HEALTH SYSTEM 17822 #004-01-2004 L2007 **EM** *020
KOMAR, Michael John. 100 N ACADEMY AVE, GEISINGER MEDICAL CENTER 17822 #035-15-1984 L1989 **GE** *020 †20 ‡
KOTRU, Anil. 100 N ACADEMY AVE, DEPARTMENT OF TRANSPLANTAT 17822 #495-90-1993 L2006 *100
KRASEMAN, Stephen James. ■ 17821 #016-43-2005 L2006 **OTO** *012
KRISHNAN, Kalyan S. 100 N ACADEMY AVE 17822 #495-37-1971 L1976 **PMM AN** *020 †05
KRONENWETTER, Christopher. 100 N ACADEMY AVE, DEPT OF ANES 17822 #041-13-1988 L1992 **AN** *020 †05,18
KUPAS, Douglas Frank. 100 N ACADEMY AVE, EMGY MED 17822 #041-02-1990 L1992 **EM** *020 †16
LA FOLLETTE, Bruce F. DEPT OF ORTHOPAEDICS 21-30, PENN STATE GEISINGER CLINI 17822 #007-02-1957 L1983 **ORS** *071 †40
LAMBERT, Richard Leland. 100 N ACADEMY AVE, GEISINGER MEDICAL CENTER 17822 #010-03-2000 L2005 **CCP** *100 †55 ‡
LAMPARTER, Carol M. 3 WESNER LN, SUSQEHANNA MEDICAL CNSLTNT 17821 #041-02-1975 L1976 **FM** *075 †18
LANDWEHR, Douglas Mann. 100 N ACADEMY AVE, GEISINGER MEDICAL CENTER 17822 #021-01-1971 L1984 **NEP IM** *030 †20
LANGDON, David Robt. NORTH ACADEMY ROAD, GEISINGER MEDICAL CENTER 17822 #017-20-1976 L1989 **PD END** *020 †55
LARGENT, Jill Annette. 100 N ACADEMY AVE 17822 #035-03-1974 L1990 **PN PD** *050 †55
LAUBACH, Chas Andrew, Jr. HGHS CTR N 20-30 WOODBINE, GEISINGER HLTH PLAN 17822 #041-13-1943 L1944 **CD IM** *030 †20
LAW, Amy. 217 PINE ST 17821 #024-07-1992 L2001 **HO** *020 †20
LECHTEV, Tanya Batinova. 100 N ACADEMY AVE 17822 #198-02-1990 L2006 **MPD** *012
LEE, Ho Yan. GEISINGER HEALTH SYSTEM, DEPTARTMENT OF MEDICINE 17822 #010-02-2007 L2007 **IM** *012
LEICHT, Michael Jos. 100 N ACADEMY AVE, GEISINGER MEDICAL CENTER 17822 #041-13-1974 L1975 **EM IM** *020 †20,16
LEMA MEDINA, Pablo. 100 N ACADEMY AVE, GEISINGER MEDICAL CENTER 17822 #264-13-1993 L2007 **IM** *012
LENTZ, Mark Russel. 100 N ACADEMY AVE, GEISENGER MED CTR 17822 #041-02-1985 L1986 **IM GPM** *020 †20
LEONARD, Di Anne Jo. 100 N ACADEMY AVE, GEISINGER MEDICAL CTR 17822 #018-03-1981 L1987 **TRS** *040 †85
LIANG, Kaihui. 100 N ACADEMY AVE, GEISINGER MED CTR 17822 #243-76-1984 L2007 **PCP** *012
LIN, Fan. 100 N ACADEMY AVE 17822 #243-33-1984 L2000 **PCP** *012
LINES, Barbara A. 100 N ACADEMY AVE, WEIS CENTER 17822 #033-06-1992 L1995 **SP** *020 †50
LITWIN, Bryce Peyton. 100 N ACADEMY AVE 17822 #048-16-2002 L2002 **EM** *020
LIU, Jiabin. 100 N ACADEMY AVE 17822 #243-44-1996 L2006 **IM** *100
LODER, William A. 305 MAPLE ST 17822 #030-05-1990 L1992 **CCA** *020 †05
LOFTON, Holly Felecia. 17821 #012-01-2004 L2007 **IM** *100 †20
LOKHANDWALA, Juzar Onali. 100 N ACADEMY AVE 17822 #495-23-2001 L2002 **CD** *012 †20
LOMBARD-MC RIPLEY, Sharon. 100 N ACADEMY AVE 17822 #032-01-1982 L1986 **AN** *020 †05
LONG, Tanner Andrew. GEISINGER MED CTR, DEPT OF SURGERY 17822 #041-77-2007, ▲ L2007 **GS** *012
LOUNTZIS, Nektarios Ilias. 100 N ACADEMY AVE, GEISINGER MED CTR 17822 #041-13-2004 L2004 **D** *012
MAFFEI, Frank Anthony. 100 N ACADEMY AVE, DIV OF PEDIATRIC CRITICAL 17822 #035-46-1992 L1994 **CCP** *020 †55
MAHADEEN, Ziad I. ■ 17821 #575-01-1985 L1996 **CN** *020 †75
MAHMUD, Faruq. DEPT OF RADIOLOGY, GEISINGER MEDICAL CENTER 17822 #704-01-1970 L1977 **PDR DR** *020 †80
MAINALI, Roshan. 100 NO, OFFICE OF MED EDUCATION 17822 #672-03-2001 L2003 **IM** *100 †20
MAINALI (KHANAL), Sapana. 100 N ACADEMY AVE 17822 #672-03-2001 L2003 **IM** *100 †20
MAKARY, Adel Zaki. OF HEMATOLOGY/ONCOLOGY, DEPARTMENT 17822 #915-02-1960 L1974 **HEM IM** *020 †20 ‡
MAKSIMAK, Janis Felice. DEPT OF PEDIATRICS, GEISINGER MEDICAL CENTER 17822 #041-14-1978 L1983 **PD** *020 †55
MAKSIMAK, Martin. GEISINGER MEDICAL CENTER, DEPARTMENT OF PEDIATRICS 17822 #041-14-1978 L1983 **PG PD** *020 †55
MALERICH, Patricia G. 100 N ACADEMY AVE, DEPARTMENT OF DERMATOLOGY 17822 #038-40-2003 L2004 **D** *020 †15

MALONE, William J. GEISINGER CLINIC, DEPT OF GENERAL PEDIATRICS 17822 #035-15-1972 L1980 **PD ID** *020 †55
MANCHANDA, Aarush. ■ 17822 #495-45-2004 L2007 **CD** *012 †20
MARINO, Christopher Angel. 100 N ACADEMY AVE 17822 #748-02-2004 L2006 **IM** *012
MARKMANN, Denise Marie. 100 N ACADEMY AVE 17822 #041-02-2003 **PD** *100 †55
MARKS, Steven Jay. 100 N ACADEMY AVE 17822 #041-09-1988 L1991 **OPH** *071 †35
MARKS, Victor James. 100 N ACADEMY AVE 17822 #041-14-1978 L1983 **D IM** *020 †20,15
MAROON, Michele Senga. 1 N ACADEMY AVE, DEPT DERM 17821 #055-01-1986 L1987 **D** *020 †15 ‡
MARTIN, James S. 100 N ACADEMY AVE 17822 #023-07-1946 L1949 **FM** *072
MARTIN, Joseph Scott. 100 N ACADEMY AVE 17822 #041-12-1960 L1961 **NS** *020 †25
MARTINEZ, Zeferino. 11 VALLEY GREEN DR 17821 #649-04-1973 L1982 **ORS** *020 †40
MARTINSON, Mark Wayne. ■ 17821 #041-13-1979 L1983 **AN** *040 †05
MATEER, Harry Owen, Jr. DEPARTMENT OF OB/GYN 29-20, GEISINGER MEDICAL CENTER 17822 #041-02-1981 L1983 **OBG** *020 †30
MATHEWS, Benjamin John. 100 N ACADEMY AVE 17822 #308-13-2004 L2005 **MPD** *012
MATRAGRANO, Andrew Paul. 100 N ACADEMY AVE, GEISINGER MEDICAL CENTER 17822 #035-48-1974 L1981 **PUD IM** *020 †20
MATTISON, Mark Christian. ■ 17821 #005-12-2007 L2007 **MPD** *012
MC CORMICK, John Vincent. 100 N ACADEMY AVE 17822 #024-07-1962 L1965 **GE IM** *020 †20 ‡
MC COY, Alice Marie. 100 N ACADEMY AVE, GEISINGER MEDICAL CENTER 17822 #018-03-1998 L2005 **HEM** *020 †20
MC GEEHAN, Ann Marie. 100 N ACADEMY AVE, GEISINGER MEDICAL CENTER 17822 #041-02-1992 L1994 **DR NM** *020 †80
MCILVRIED, Robb. 100 N ACADEMY AVE 17822 #041-02-1996 L1999 **IMG** *020 †20
MCKENNA, Mark Edward. ■ 17821 #054-04-2005 L2005 **ORS** *012
MC KINLEY, David F. 100 N ACADEMY AVE 17822 #033-05-1981 L1987 **PD** *020 †20
MC MURRY, Fred Gifford. 100 N ACADEMY AVE, NEUROSURGERY 14-05 17822 #041-13-1970 L1971 **NS** *020 †25
MEADE, Paul Gerard. 100 N ACADEMY AVE 17822 #024-05-1986 L2004 **CRS GS** *020 †85,10
MEHR, Jagdeep Kaur. 100 N ACADEMY AVE, GEISINGER MED CTR 17822 #496-43-1997 L2004 **MPD** *012
MELTON, Robert Thomas. ■ 17822 #040-02-2006 L2006 **EM** *012
MENAPACE, Francis J, Jr. DEPT OF CARDIOLOGY, GEISINGER MED CTR 17822 #041-13-1970 L1971 **CD IM** *020 †20
MENTYKA, Mary Jean D. 100 N ACADEMY AVE 17822 #041-09-1982 L1983 **PD** *075 †55
MERY FERNANDEZ, Esteban. 100 N ACADEMY AVE, GEISINGER MED CTR 17822 #264-16-2004 L2007 **IM** *012
MIAO, Chuan Long. 100 N ACADEMY AVE 17822 #243-92-1996 L2006 **IM** *012
MILLER, Barbara Ann. 100 N ACADEMY AVE 17822 #041-14-1976 L1986 **HEM** *055
MILLER, David Daniel. ■ 17821 #041-12-2006 L2006 **EM** *012
MILLER, Oliver F, III. NORTH ACADEMY AVE, GEISINGER MEDICAL CENTER 17822 #041-01-1963 L1965 **D** *020 †15
MINNICH, Marie Elaine. 10 MURPHY RD 17821 #041-14-1981 L1982 **AN** *020 †05
MINNICH, Stephen James. 1 N ACADEMY AVE 17821 #041-14-1980 L1982 **AN** *020 †05
MIRENDA, William Michael. 100 N ACADEMY AVE 12-20, GEISINGER MEDICAL CENTER 17822 #041-02-1975 L1977 **ORS TRS** *020 †40
MITTAL, Jyoti. ■ 17821 #495-83-1989 L2002 **IM** *100
MITTAL, Sanjay. 100 N ACADEMY AVE, DEPT OF NEUROSCIENCES 17822 #495-49-1985 L2004 **N** *100 †75
MODESTO, Thomas Anthony. GEISINGER MEDICAL CTR 17822 #041-12-1974 L1975 **CD IM** *020 †20
MOKABBERI, Rasoul. 100 N ACADEMY AVE, GEISINGER MED CTR 17822 #517-08-1994 L2007 **CD** *012 †20
MOLINA MONTOYA, Paola And. 100 N ACADEMY AVE 17822 #264-03-1999 L2005 **IM** *012
MONTECALVO, Anthony Louis. 200 STATE HOSPITAL DR, DANVILLE STATE HOSPITAL 17821 #561-23-1981 L1983 **P** *030 †75 ‡
MONTOYA REBELLON, Juan Ca. 100 N ACADEMY AVE, GEISINGER MEDICAL CENTER 17822 #264-05-1985 L2007 **IM** *012
MOORE, Margrette Macfie. ■ 17821 #051-04-2005 L2007 **GS** *012
MORAN, John J. ■ 17821 #041-02-1952 L1953 **PTH** *071 †50
MORGAN, Howard E. 100 N ACADEMY AVE 17822 #023-07-1949 **OS** *030
MORRISON, Samuel Slemmons. 100 N ACADEMY AVE 17822 #024-01-1947 L1948 **PD** *071 †55
MOSS, Brian Warren. ■ 17822 #035-09-2005 L2005 **EM** *012
MOURAD, William Asad. ■ 17821 #038-40-2000 L2004 **GE** *100 †20
MOWAD, Joseph James. 100 N ACADEMY AVE, GEISINGER CLINIC 17822 #030-06-1961 L1962 **U** *020 †95
MOYA, Alexander Paul. 100 N ACADEMY AVE, GEISINGER MEDICAL CTR 21-7 17822 #010-02-1995 L2002 **PS** *020 †65
MUKHTAR, Hamid Bin. 100 N ACADEMY AVE 17822 #704-04-1985 L2001 **IM** *100
MURPHY, Timothy Jos. 100 N ACADEMY AVE 17822 #041-01-1991 L1996 **DR** *020 †80
MYERS, Scott Matthew. 100 N ACADEMY AVE, GEISINGER MEDICAL CENTER 17822 #041-02-1992 L1994 **PD** *020 †55
MYERS, Tamara Tennille. ■ 17821 #008-02-2007 L2007 **GS** *012
NADKARNI, Anupa Prashant. ■ 17822 #496-15-1992 L2006 **IM** *012
NAGI, Hesham I. 100 N ACADEMY AVE, GEISINGER MEDICAL CENTER 17822 #915-04-1976 L2000 **P** *020
NASSEF, Louis Andrew, Jr. 100 N ACADEMY AVE 17822 #036-01-1976 L1985 **CD IM** *020 †20
NEPAL, Manish. 100 N ACADEMY AVE 17822 #672-02-2004 L2006 **IM** *012
NESS, Ryan Jeffery. ■ 17821 #041-12-2001 L2006 **APM** *020 †05
NETREBKO, Pavlo I.. 100 N ACADEMY AVE, MC 21-60 17822 #913-10-1999 L2002 **CD** *012 †20
NEWELL, Wendy Susan. ■ 17822 #041-12-1989 L1992 **GS VS** *020 †85
NEWMAN, Eric Douglas. 100 N ACADEMY AVE 17822 #041-14-1983 L1986 **RHU IM** *020 †20 ‡
NI, Yanni. 100 N ACADEMY AVE 17822 #243-47-2000 L2006 **IM** *012
NICKLES, Thomas P. 100 N ACADEMY AVE, GEISINGER MEDICAL CENTER 17822 #048-13-1986 L2004 **DR** *020 †75,80
NIETO FONSECA, Carlos And. 100 N ACADEMY AVE, GEISINGER MEDICAL CENTER 17822 #264-10-2003 L2007 **IM** *012
NIKAM, Shivprasad Dattatr. 100 N ACADEMY AVE, DEPARTMENT OF 17822 #495-28-1995 L2005 **VS** *020 †85
NOBLE, Christine Althea. 100 N ACADEMY AVE 17822 #035-01-2003 L2007 **AN** *020
NORFOLK, Evan Ross. 100 N ACADEMY AVE, DEPT OF NEPHROLOGY (21-11) 17822 #035-15-1998 L2003 **NEP** *020 †20
NOTZ, Michaelyn Frances. 100 N ACADEMY AVE, GEISINGER HEALTH SYSTEM 17822 #041-77-2007, ▲ L2007 **MPD** *012

NOVAK, Gregg. 100 N ACADEMY AVE 17822 #041-78-2003, ▲ L2003 **MPD** *100 †20,55

NOVINGER, Quentin Thos. 100 N ACADEMY AVE, GEISINGER HEALTH PLAN 17822 #041-02-1977 L1979 **PD** *020 †55

OBRADOVIC, Gordana. 100 N ACADEMY AVE, GEISINGER MEDICAL CENTER 17822 #957-02-1996 L2007 **IM** *020

OBRADOVIC, Vladan Nikola. 100 N ACADEMY AVE 17822 #957-02-1990 L2006 **GS** *012

O'KEEFE, Mary. 100 N ACADEMY AVE, MC 01-37 17822 #011-02-1986 L1987 **IM** *020 †20

OLENGINSKI, Thomas Paul. DEPARTMENT OF RHEUMATOLOGY 17822 #041-14-1984 L1985 **RHU IM** *020 †20

OLSON, Michelle Marie. 100 N ACADEMY AVE, DEPT OF SURGERY MC 21-70 17822 #041-15-1999 L2004 **CRS GS** *020 †85,10

OPPERMANN, Brian Patrick. 100 N ACADEMY AVE, GEISINGER MEDICAL CENTER 17822 #055-01-2005 L2005 **IM** *012

OREN, Jess W, IV. 100 N ACADEMY AVE 17822 #041-12-1984 L1986 **IM CD** *020 †20

O'ROURKE, John Norbert. GEISINGER MEDICAL CENTER 17822 #033-05-1964 L1965 **A IM** *020 †03

O'ROURKE, Terence Leonard. 1 N ACADEMY AVE, GEISINGER MEDICAL CENTER 17821 #041-02-1960 L1961 **R** *020 †80

ORTEGON-ZAMBRANO, Berenice. 100 N ACADEMY AVE, GEISINGER MEDICAL CENTER 17822 #264-04-2001 L2007 **IM** *012

OWENS, David Evan. 100 N ACADEMY AVE 17822 #010-01-1971 L1973 **FPG FM** *020 †18

PADIGALA, Kiran Kumar. 100 N ACADEMY AVE 17822 #495-62-2000 L2003 **IM** *100 †20

PANCHOLY, Samir B. 100 N ACADEMY AVE 17822 #495-22-1987 L1992 **CD** *020 †20

PAOLUCCI, Stephen Jos. 100 N ACADEMY AVE 17822 #041-14-1982 L1984 **P AM** *020 †75 ‡

PAOLUCCI, Susan Leigh. 100 N ACADEMY AVE, DIV OF PSYCHIATRY 17822 #041-14-1982 L1984 **P AM** *020 †75 ‡

PARENTI, John Michael. 100 N ACADEMY AVE 17821 #041-13-1974 L1975 **PD ORS** *020 †40

PARK, Alyssa Marie. ■ 17822 #041-13-2006 L2006 **GS** *012

PARLADE, Albert Joseph. ■ 17821 #011-02-2005 L2005 **DR** *012

PATEL, Bakulesh Devjibhai. GEISINGER MEDICAL CENTER 17822 #495-17-1969 L1975 **NPM PD** *020 †55

PAULUS, Ronald Alan. 100 N ACADEMY AVE MC30-55, GEINSINGER HLTH SYSTEM 17822 #041-01-1988 L1989 **IM** *030

PAYTON, Thomas Frank. 100 N ACADEMY AVE 20-05 17822 #011-04-2001 L2001 **EM** *020 †16

PECK, Rachel Elizabeth. ■ 17821 #041-02-2005 L2005 **IM** *100

PECKHAM, Steven James. 100 N ACADEMY AVE 17822 #026-04-1995 L2005 **DMP** *020

PEMMASANI, Chandra Sekhar. 1404 RIDGEVIEW 17821 #495-21-2001 L2002 **IM** *100 †20

PEREZ, Carlos Ramon. 100 N ACADEMY AVE, IMMUNOLOGY & PULMONARY DIS 17822 #038-41-1981 L1996 **PDP PD** *020 †55

PETRICK, Anthony Thos. 100 N ACADEMY AVE, DEPT OF SURGERY 17822 #010-02-1989 L1996 **GS** *020 †85

PETRICK, Mary Grace. 100 N ACADEMY AVE, DERMATOLOGY MC14-06 17822 #010-02-1997 L2001 **D** *020 †15

PHARR, William Frederick. ■ 17821 #041-02-1965 L1966 **TS** *020 †85,90

PIERCE, James Clarence. ■ 17821 #024-01-1955 L1979 **GS** *071 †85

PILLUS, Sarah Ann. ■ 17822 #041-77-2007, ▲ L2007 **OBG** *012

PILLY, Vikas Kumar. 100 N ACADEMY AVE, GEISINGER MED CTR 17822 #305-01-2002 L2002 **PM** *020

PLATTE, Raisa Oleksandra. GEISINGER MEDICAL CENTER, DEPT OF OBSTETRICS-GYNECOL 17822 #913-97-1989 L2005 **OBG** *012

POHL, Christoph. 100 N ACADEMY AVE, DEPT OF RADIOLOGY 17822 #051-04-1987 L1997 **VIR DR** *020 †80

POLER, S Mark. 100 N ACADEMY AVE, GEISINGER MEDICAL CENTER 17822 #005-02-1978 L1990 **AN** *020 †05

POPLAWSKY, Deborah Ann G. 100 N ACADEMY AVE, GEISINGER MED CTR 17822 #041-13-1980 L1981 **OBG** *020 †30

POURMOGHADAM, Kamal K. 100 N ACADEMY AVE, JANET WEIS CHILDREN'S HOSP 17822 #035-03-1988 L1999 **TS** *020 †85,90

PRADHAN, Ramesh Chandra S. 100 N ACADEMY AVE 17822 #495-01-1956 L1973 **DR** *020 †80

PRIDE, Howard Bruce. 1 N ACADEMY AVE, DEPT DERM 14-02 17821 #050-02-1986 L1987 **D PD** *020 †20,55,15

PROUDAN, Vladimir Ivanovi. ■ 17822 #913-70-1986 L2005 **IM** *012

PULLER, Justin Parker. 100 NO, OFFICE OF MED EDUCATION 17822 #041-15-2004 L2004 **EM** *100

PURI, Puja Kumari. GEISINGER MED CTR, DEPT OF DERMATOLOGY 17822 #051-07-2004 L2007 **DMP** *012 †50

PYTKO, Valentine F, Jr. 100 N ACADEMY AVE 17822 #041-13-1954 L1955 **CD PUD** *071 †20

QUINTANA, Javier F. 100 N ACADEMY AVE 17822 #011-04-2002 L2004 **DR** *012

QUIRING, Mark Aaron. 100 N ACADEMY AVE 17822 #039-01-2005 L2005 **EM** *012

QURESHI, Anwer. 100 N ACADEMY AVE, GEISINGER MEDICAL CENTER 17822 #704-02-1988 L1996 **CD** *020 †20

RAGAB, Abdelhamed Lotfi. 100 N ACADEMY AVE 17822 #915-02-1980 L1997 **AN** *020 †05

RAHMAN, Omar. ■ 17821 #704-22-1996 L2000 **CCM** *100 †20

RAJU, Nagamalar. 100 N ACADEMY AVE 17822 #495-94-1998 L2005 **IM** *012

RAJU, Srirangarajan. 100 N ACADEMY AVE, GEISINGER MEDICAL CENTER 17822 #495-94-2004 L2007 **IM** *012

RAMBY, Alexis Lynn. ■ 17822 #022-75-2006, ▲ L2006 **PD** *012

RAMENOFSKY, Max Lantin. 100 N ACADEMY AVE 17822 #047-06-1965 L1972 **PDS GS** *020 †85

RAMSEY, Michael Lee. DEPT OF DERMATOLOGY, GEISINGER MEDICAL CENTER 17822 #048-04-1983 L1993 **D** *020 †15

RASHID, Zahid. 100 N ACADEMY AVE, GEISINGER HEALTH SYSTEM 17822 #704-01-1987 L1996 **GE** *020 †20

RAVIN, Karen Ann. 100 N ACADEMY AVE, JANET WEIS CHILDREN'S HOSP 17822 #041-02-1998 L2000 **PDI** *020 †55

REAMS, Carl Lewis. NORTH ACADEMY AVE, GEISINGER MEDICAL CENTER 17822 #041-02-1966 L1967 **OTO NO** *020 †45

REED, Douglas Richard. 100 N ACADEMY AVE 17822 #041-13-1990 L1992 **P** *020 †75

RESTREPO, Alejandro. 100 N ACADEMY AVE 17822 #264-03-1998 L2003 **ID** *012 †20

RIEHL, John Thomas. ■ 17821 #041-13-2006 L2006 **ORS** *012

RISTIN, Norman Ira. 100 N ACADEMY AVE 17822 #035-06-1967 L1968 **DR NM** *020 †80,28

RIVERA, Martha Monica. 100 N ACADEMY AVE, DEPARTMENT. M.C.29-20 17822 #264-06-1992 L2002 **OBG** *020 †30

ROBBINS, Larry Mark. 100 N ACADEMY AVE, GEISINGER MEDICAL CENTER 17822 #035-09-1988 L1999 **PAN AN** *020 †55,05

ROBERTSON, Spencer John. 100 N ACADEMY AVE 17822 #028-34-2004 L2005 **DR** *012

ROBINSON, Kristine Swinto. 100 N ACADEMY AVE, GEISINGER MEDICAL CENTER 17822 #055-01-2004 L2005 **EM** *012

ROSE, John Frank. ■ 17821 #035-20-1954 L1964 **U** *071 †95

ROSEN, Joseph H. 100 N ACADEMY AVE 17822 #041-02-1961 L1962 **R NM** *071 †80,28

ROTHERMEL, Franklin John. 407 LOCUST LN, GEISINGER MEDICAL CENTER 17821 #041-02-1967 L1968 **R** *020 †80

ROWE, Sean Andrew. ■ 17821 #051-07-2007 L2007 **EM** *012

RUKSTALIS, Daniel Brian. 100 N ACADEMY AVE, DEPARTMENT OF UROLOGY 17822 #051-07-1984 L1995 **U** *020 †95

SABRI, Mahmoud Talaat. 100 N ACADEMY AVE, DIV. OF PEDIATRIC GASTROEN 17822 #915-03-1990 L2000 **PG** *020 †55

SALAMA, Farag Asaad. 100 N ACADEMY AVE 17822 #915-04-1982 L2002 **OBG** *100

SALGADO CAMPO, Juan Carlo. 100 N ACADEMY AVE, M.C. 01-39 17822 #264-05-1999 L2004 **IM** *100 †20

SALVADOR, Jewel De Leon. 100 N ACADEMY AVE 17822 #748-02-2004 L2006 **PD** *012

SANCHEZ CUEVA, Patricio A. 100 N ACADEMY AVE 17822 #319-07-2000 L2005 **IM** *012

SANTOS DONOSO, Shadia Sam. 100 N ACADEMY AVE 17822 #715-01-1998 L2005 **IM** *012

SARIN, Sanjay. 9 RESERVOIR ST 17821 #496-09-1992 L2002 **CD** *012 †20

SARRIA, Ivan. GEISINGER MEDICAL CENTER, DEPT OF OBSTETRICS-GYNECOL 17822 #264-06-1993 L2004 **OBG** *012

SAUTER, Anthony Louis. GEISINGER MEDICAL CENTER 17822 #024-07-1992 L1994 **EM** *020 †16

SAYRE, Rodger Clarke. 100 N ACADEMY AVE 17822 #041-02-1983 L1984 **FM** *020 †18

SCHROEDER, Lisa Lorrae. ■ 17821 #056-05-2007 L2007 **IM** *012

SCHUERCH, Conrad. 100 N ACADEMY AVE, DEPT OF LAB MEDICINE 17822 #035-08-1975 L1981 **PTH** *030 †50

SCHULTZ, Michael F. 100 N ACADEMY AVE 17822 #054-04-1986 L1988 **NEP IM** *020 †20

SCHWARTZ, Jan Arthur. 1 N ACADEMY AVE, DEPT ANES 17821 #035-06-1975 L1976 **AN CCM** *020 †05,55

SCHWARTZMAN, Michael Seth. 100 N ACADEMY AVE, GEISINGER MEDICAL CENTER 17822 #051-04-1978 L2001 **NEP IM** *020 †20

SCORPIO, Ronald James. 100 N ACADEMY AVE, MC 21-70 17822 #051-07-1982 L2005 **GS** *020 †85

SCOTT, Charles Ivan, Jr. 100 N ACADEMY AVE 17822 #004-01-1959 L1988 **CG PD** *072 †55,19

SERRANO DONADO, Ricardo A. 100 N ACADEMY AVE 17822 #264-12-2003 L2006 **IM** *012

SEWELL, Lindsay Dane. 100 N ACADEMY AVE, DEPT OF DERM MC 14-06 17822 #010-01-2003 L2004 **PRD** *012 †12

SHAH, Chandresh Kumar. 200 STATE HOSPITAL DR, DANVILLE STATE HOSPITAL 17821 #495-20-1975 L1984 **IM** *020

SHARMA, Devesh. ■ 17821 #496-09-1994 L2003 **GS** *012

SHARMA, Smita. ■ 17821 #495-49-1995 L2003 **DR** *020 †80

SHARP, David Edward. 100 N ACADEMY AVE, GEISINGER MEDICAL CENTER 17822 #036-01-1973 L1995 **BBK CLP** *020 †50

SHELDON, David Garrabrant. 100 N ACADEMY AVE 17822 #041-12-1992 L2000 **GS** *020

SHIRANI, Jamshid. 100 N ACADEMY AVE B2160, GEISINGER MEDICAL CENTER 17822 #517-05-1980 L2000 **CD** *020 †20

SICILIANO, Zhanna Viktoro. 100 N ACADEMY AVE, GEISINGER MEDICAL CENTER 17822 #913-80-1998 L2007 **IM** *012

SIEGELMANN, Nava. 100 N ACADEMY AVE, GEISINGER MEDICAL CENTER 17822 #550-01-1988 L1994 **ON** *020

SIMMONS, Jennifer. 100 N ACADEMY AVE 17822 #041-13-1998 L2004 **U** *020 †95

SIMON, Bruce Jay. 100 N ACADEMY AVE, TRAUMA PROGRAM 20-18 17822 #035-09-1979 L1991 **TS GS** *020 †90,85

SIMS, Deborah W. 15 ERIN DR 17821 #025-01-1981 L2003 **GS** *020 †85

SINHA, Sangeeta. ■ 17821 #495-54-1991 L2001 **OBG** *020 †30

SKELDING, Kimberly Ann. ■ 17821 #016-06-1996 L1998 **IC** *100 †20

SKIENDZIELEWSKI, John Jos. 100 N ACADEMY AVE, GEISINGER MEDICAL CENTER 17822 #041-13-1973 L1974 **EM** *020 †16

SMIT, Jeffrey Ryan. ■ 17822 #005-12-2004 L2005 **GS** *012

SMITH, Joseph L. 100 N ACADEMY AVE, GEISINGER MEDICAL CENTER 17822 #035-20-1972 L1973 **IM ID** *020 †20

SMITH, Robert Edward. 100 N ACADEMY AVE, GASTROENTEROLOGY/MC 21-11 17822 #041-13-1982 L1983 **GE IM** *020 †20

SNOVER, Amy Jill. 100 N ACADEMY AVE, GEISINGER MEDICAL CENTER 17822 #010-01-1994 L1996 **EM** *020 †16

SNOWDEN, Marion Lynette. 100 N ACADEMY AVE, PENNSTATE GEISINGER MED CT 17822 #054-04-1985 L1997 **PM** *030 †60

SNOWDEN, Robert Reginald. ■ 17821 #026-04-2004 L2006 **DR** *012

SOGES, Laurence John. 100 N ACADEMY AVE, DEPT RADIOLOGY 17822 #051-01-1979 L1987 **DR RNR** *020 †80

SOLOSKO, Alexandra. ■ 17821 #041-78-2006, ▲ L2006 **PD** *012

SPAHR, Robert Carl. 100 N ACADEMY AVE, GEISINGER MED CTR 17822 #041-02-1969 L1970 **NPM** *020 †55

SPERA, Devin James. 100 NO, OFFICE OF MED EDUCATION 17822 #041-13-2004 L2004 **EM** *012

SPICER, Scott Michael. ■ 17821 #035-15-2005 L2005 **PD** *012

STARKEY, Ralph Herbert. 100 N ACADEMY AVE, GEISINGER MEDICAL CENTER 17822 #041-13-1970 L1977 **END IM** *020 †20

STECKER, Mark Menniti. 100 N ACADEMY AVE, GEISINGER MEDICAL CENTER 17822 #024-01-1984 L1985 **N** *020 †75

STEELE, Glenn Danl, Jr. 100 N ACADEMY AVE, MC 22-01 17822 #035-19-1970 L2001 **SO IG** *062 †85

STEEN, C A Edward. 100 N ACADEMY AVE, GEISINGER CLINIC 17822 #065-05-1976 L1990 **AN** *020 †05

STEMM, Joseph J. 100 N ACADEMY AVE, GEISINGER MED CTR 17822 #041-14-1980 L1994 **AN** *020 †05

STEWART, Kurtis Alan. ■ 17821 #038-43-2007 L2007 **GS** *012

STORM, Douglas William. ■ 17821 #016-01-2000 L2003 **U** *012

STORM, Randle Henry. 100 N ACADEMY AVE, GEISINGER MEDICAL CENTER 17822 #041-02-1984 L1993 **CD IM** *020 †20

STRICKLAND, Mary Lou. 100 N ACADEMY AVE, GEISINGER MEDICAL CENTER 17822 #051-04-1981 L1983 **DR** *020 †80

STRODEL, William Edward. 100 N ACADEMY AVE, DEPT OF SURGERY 17822 #025-01-1973 L2002 **GS** *040 †85

STUTZMAN, Joshua. 100 N ACADEMY AVE 17822 #041-77-2004, ▲ L2004 **OBG** *012

SUCANDY, Iswanto. 100 N ACADEMY AVE 17822 #506-02-2003 L2007 *100

■ = Address Information Privacy Protected

SUCK, Abyssinia F. ■ 17821 #748-01-1959 L1969 **IM IMG** *020
SUMFEST, Joel Michael. 100 N ACADEMY AVE, UROLOGY 13-16 17822 #041-02-1982 L2004 **UP** *020 †95
SUNDERLIN, Elaine Marie. ■ 17821 #041-02-2008 *012
SUTTON, Paul Lee. 1 N ACADEMY AVE 17821 #035-15-1973 L1978 **AI PD** *020 †55,03
SWANSON, Paul Joseph, Jr. 100 N ACADEMY AVE, GEISINGER MED CTR 17822 #036-08-1993 L2006 **OBG** *020 †30
TAYLOR, Amanda Ann. 100 N ACADEMY AVE 17822 #035-15-1997 L2003 **P** *020 †75
TESLIC, Kornelija. 100 N ACADEMY AVE, RADIOLOGY 17822 #957-07-1990 L2004 **RNR** *020 †80
THOMAS, Chadwick John. 100 N ACDAMEY AVE, DEPT OF DERM-M.C. 14-06 17822 #047-20-2001 L2002 **PRD** *020 †15
TOBIN, Richard Scott. 100 N ACADEMY AVE 17822 #035-45-1973 L2005 **FM** *020 †18
TOLAN, Keith Alan. 200 STATE HOSPITAL DR, SCI-MUNCY 17821 #055-02-1993 L1996 **P CHP** *020
TOMASAK, Tammy Elizabeth. ■ 17821 #041-77-2007, ▲ L2007 *012
TOMASZEWSKI, Daniel John. 100 N ACADEMY AVE 17822 #056-06-2004 L2004 **ORS** *012
TOMS, Steven A. 100 N ACADEMY AVE, CLEVELAND CLINIC FOUNDATIO 17822 #043-01-1989 L2007 **NS** *020 †25
TORRETTI, Dennis. 1 N ACADEMY AVE 17821 #023-07-1973 L1978 **RHU IM** *020 †20
TYLER, William Boyd, III. 100 N ACADEMY AVE 17822 #041-13-1970 L1974 **PTH** *020 †50
UDAS, Prakrita Bhushan. 100 N ACADEMY AVE, GEISINGER MEDICAL CENTER 17822 #672-03-2002 L2007 **IM** *012
UDEKWU, Anthony Okechukwu. 100 N ACADEMY AVE, PROFESSIONAL STAFFING MC 2 17822 #690-04-1979 L1987 **GS** *020 †85
ULRICH, Jan Niklas. 100 N ACADEMY AVE, GEISINGER MED CTR 17822 #409-16-2004 L2005 **OPH** *012
UMOH, Nsikak Jarlath. 100 N ACADEMY AVE, DEPT OF MED EDU 17822 #690-03-2004 L2006 **GS** *012
UNZUETA, Alberto. 100 N ACADEMY AVE 17822 #649-31-1994 L2005 **IM** *012
VARGHESE, Mini. ■ 17821 #035-48-2005 L2005 **U** *012
VARMA, Chintalapati V. 100 N ACADEMY AVE, DEPARTMENT OF TRANSPLANTAT 17822 #495-73-1984 L2006 **GS** *020
VATNER, Dorothy Eileen. ■ 17822 #051-01-1975 L1998 **CD PDC** *050
VELAGAPALLI, Mini Spoorth. 100 N ACADEMY AVE, GEISINGER MED CTR 17822 #495-04-2002 L2004 **IM** *020
VERDE, Franco. ■ 17822 #035-08-2006 L2007 **DR** *012
VILLAREAL, Alexander Maca. 100 N ACADEMY AVE, DEPT OF INT MED 17822 #176-05-2000 L2007 **SME** *020 †20
VIVINO, M Louella Lopez. ■ 17821 #748-02-1986 L2005 **N** *020 †75
VOLLMER, Timothy Paul. 1 N ACADEMY AVE 17821 #041-12-1981 L1982 **EM** *020 †16
VRABEC, Donald Paul. GEISINGER MEDICAL CENTER 17822 #041-12-1959 L1960 **OTO** *071 †45
VRABEC, Tamara Roseann. 100 N ACADEMY AVE, DEPT OF OPT 17822 #041-07-1985 L1987 **OPH OS** *020 †35 ‡
WALKER, James Mcclellan. 100 N ACADEMY AVE # 30-06 17822 #041-01-1989 L1991 **IM** *030 †20
WALKER, Robert Norman. ■ 17821 #016-11-2004 L2004 **DR** *012
WALLACE, Catherine Mary. 1 N ACADEMY AVE, GEISINGER MED CTR 17821 #035-09-1979 L1984 **CCP** *020 †55
WARNOCK, Ashley Ann. 100 NO, OFFICE OF MED EDUCATION 17822 #049-01-2004 L2004 **MG** *012 †55
WATSON, William Earl. 100 N ACADEMY AVE 17822 #038-43-1982 L2003 **CHN** *020 †55 ‡
WEBER, Valerie Dawn. 100 N ACADEMY AVE 17822 #041-01-1991 L1994 **IM** *020 †20
WEISS, David Lawrence. 100 N ACADEMY AVE, RADIOLOGY 17822 #041-02-1975 L1976 **DR** *020 †80
WESTHAFER, Jennifer L. ■ 17821 #041-14-2007 L2007 **IM** *012
WHITAKER, Mark Edward. 100 N ACADEMY AVE, DEPT OF OTOLARYNGOLOGY 17822 #041-14-1996 L1998 **OTO** *020 †45
WHITE, Charles Francis. 100 N ACADEMY AVE, GEISINGER MEDICAL CTR 17822 #041-13-1976 L1978 **ON IM** *020 †20
WIDMAIER, James Carl, Jr. 100 N ACADEMY AVE 17822 #023-01-1996 L1998 **ORS** *020 †40
WIDOM, Kenneth Andrew. 100 N ACADEMY AVE 17822 #023-01-1998 L2004 **CCS TRS** *020 †20
WILKERSON, Myra Lyn. 100 N ACADEMY AVE 17822 #055-02-1994 L1996 **PTH** *020 †50
WILLIAMS, John Lecoq. RR 7 BOX 47 17821 #035-01-1945 L1952 **R** *071 †80
WILLIAMS, Joseph Post, Jr. 100 N ACADEMY AVE, GEISINGER MEDICAL CENTER 17822 #005-02-1961 L2004 **NS N** *020 †85,25
WILLS, Alyson Ann. ■ 17821 #038-45-2005 L2005 **PD** *012
WILSON, Darrell Lynn. 100 N ACADEMY AVE, GEISINGER MEDICAL CENTER 17822 #031-01-1999 L2001 **EM** *020 †16
WILT, Elaine M. ■ 17821 #035-06-1974 L1983 **PDS** *020 †85
WINESETT, Douglas Edmond. 100 N ACADEMY AVE 17822 #027-01-1987 L1999 **PD** *020 †55
WINSTEAD, Johnathan Myles. 100 N ACADEMY AVE 17822 #047-20-2003 L2003 **OTO** *012
WISE, Melissa Thompson. GEISINGER MED CTR, DEPT OF DERMATOLOGY 17822 #020-02-2005 L2007 **D** *012
WOLFGANG, Gary Lamont. 100 N ACADEMY AVE 17822 #041-02-1967 L1968 **ORS** *020 †40
WOOD, William Edward. 100 N ACADEMY AVE, MEDICAL CENTER 17822 #045-04-1984 L1985 **OTO** *020 †45
WOODS, Edward Lawson. 100 N ACADEMY AVE 17822 #028-03-1977 L1990 **TS CD** *020 †85,90
WOOMERT, Cathleen Ann. 100 N ACADEMY AVE, GEISINGER MEDICAL CENTER 17822 #041-14-1987 L1989 **R** *020 †80
WUBBEL, Catherine. 100 N ACADEMY AVE 17822 #020-02-1993 L2007 **PDP PD** *020 †55 ‡
YAIKO, Jeffrey Thomas. ■ 17822 #422-01-2003 L2003 **AN** *100
YATSENKO, Nataliya V.. 100 N ACADEMY AVE, GEISINGER MEDICAL CENTER 17822 #913-10-1999 L2006 **PD** *012
YOHAI, Norma Helen. 100 N ACADEMY AVE, GEISINGER HEALTH CTR F-2 17822 #035-15-1990 L2001 **P** *020 †75
YOUNG, Kathy Lee. CRITICAL CARE, 110 N ACADEMY AVENUE 17822 #041-14-1996 L2003 **PCC** *020 †20 ‡
YOUSEFI, Marjan. 100 N ACADEMY AVE, GEISSINGER MEDICAL CENTER 17822 #010-01-2003 L2005 **D** *012
YUASA, Korta. ■ 17821 #033-06-1998 L2007 **GE** *020 †20
YUMEN, Omar. 100 N ACADEMY AVE, DEPT OF RADIATION ONCOLOGY 17822 #065-10-1979 L1984 **HEM** *020 †20,80

ZARCONI, Diane Rose. 100 N ACADEMY AVE 17822 #028-34-1986 L1995 **OBG** *020 †30
ZHANG, Kai. 100 N ACADEMY AVE 17822 #243-33-1984 L2001 **PTH HMP** *020 †50
ZHANG, Ping L. 100 N ACADEMY AVE 17822 #243-48-1986 L1999 **PTH** *020 †50
ZIJERDI, David Arman. 100 N ACADEMY AVE, GEISINGER MEDICAL CENTER 17822 #051-01-2003 L2003 **ORS** *012
ZIMMER, Cynthia Swartley. 698 AVENUE D, C/O ZIMMER, WILLIAM 17821 #041-01-1945 L1946 **GP** *071
ZLOTOWSKI, Steven Jeffrey. 100 N ACADEMY AVE, GEISINGER MEDICAL CENTER 17822 #041-07-1997 L1999 **EM** *020 †16
ZOTALIS, George. ■ 17821 #418-02-1986 L1998 **IM** *012 †50

DARBY – DELAWARE

ABEL BOENERJOUS, Rebakah. 1500 LANSDOWNE AVE, DEPT OF GME 19023 #496-27-2004 L2006 **IM** *012
ADAMS, Susan Elizabeth. 1503 LANSDOWNE AVE 19023 #041-02-1989 L1991 **PD** *020 †55
AHMADINEJAD, Ali Seyed. 1501 LANSDOWNE AVE, STE207 19023 #517-04-1975 L1979 **GS VS** *020 †85
ALAUDDIN, Mohammad. 1500 LANSDOWNE AVE, DEPT OF GME 19023 #160-02-1992 L2006 **IM** *012
ALBORNOZ, Marco A. 1503 LANSDOWNE AVE, STE 3010 19023 #270-02-1983 L1985 **RHU IM** *020 †20 ‡
ALUKO, Babajide Olufemi. 1500 LANSDOWNE AVE, DEPT OF MEDICAL EDUCATION 19023 #690-08-1998 L2005 **IM** *012
AMARAL, Rafael A. 1501 LANSDOWNE AVE, STE 205 19023 #042-02-1987 L1989 **GE IM** *020 †20
AMBADY, Prakash. MS 40, MERCY CATHOLIC MEDICAL CEN 19023 #496-69-2003 L2007 **IM** *012
AMER, Adel M. 1503 LANSDOWNE AVE, DEPT PEDS 19023 #915-04-1979 L1994 **PD** *020
ANDRIES, Raymond Carl. 1500 LANSDOWNE AVE 19023 #041-02-1980 L1980 **AN** *020 †05
ARMAO, Joseph J, Jr. 1500 LANSDOWNE AVE 19023 #041-02-1953 L1954 **FM FPG** *071
BALRAJ, Praveen Chandar. 1500 LANSDOWNE AVE, DEPT OF SURGERY, MS 082 19023 #495-94-2003 L2007 **GS** *012
BECKER, Joseph M. 1500 LANSDOWNE AVE, MERCY FITZGERALD HOSP 19023 #041-09-1971 L1972 **DR LM** *020 †80 ‡
BEKRET, Jeffrey Joseph. 1503 LANSDOWNE AVE, STE 3005 19023 #041-02-1973 L1974 **P PYG** *020 †75
BHATTARAI, Alok. 1500 LANSDOWNE AVE, MERCY CATHOLIC MEDICAL CEN 19023 #672-03-2005 L2006 **IM** *012
BICHARA, Wahib M. 1501 LANSDOWNE AVE, STE 105 MERCY IMAGING 19023 #330-02-1950 L1969 **R** *071 †80
BOBROW, Michael Lorne. 1500 LANSDOWNE AVE, DEPT OF RADIOLOGY 19023 #041-15-2003 L2003 **DR** *012
BOLMARCICH, Virginia A D. 1500 LANSDOWNE AVE 19023 #041-07-1971 L1972 **R** *020 †80
BRENNAN, Martin Tarsicius. 1500 LANSDOWNE AVE, FITZGERALD MERCY HOSPITAL 19023 #041-02-1957 L1958 **OTO** *020 †45
BROOKS, Michael Lee. 1500 LANSDOWNE AVE, DEPT RAD 19023 #041-09-1981 L1983 **DR RNR** *020 †80
BURKE, James Francis. 1501 LANSDOWNE AVE, MARK FINNEGAN 19023 #041-02-1977 L1979 **CD IM** *072 †20
CARNEY, Sharon Kathleen. 1500 LANSDOWNE AVE, MERCY FITZGERALD HOSPITAL 19023 #038-41-1991 L1993 **EM** *020 †16
CASTILLO, Orlando Alfonso. 1501 LANSDOWNE AVE STE 303 19023 #737-06-1983 L1993 **GS** *020 †85
CHAKRABORTY, Rebanta Kuma. MS 40, MERCY CATHOLIC MEDICAL CEN 19023 #495-39-2003 L2007 **IM** *012
CHE, Khanh. 1500 LANSDOWNE AVE 19023 #941-01-1973 L1984 **FM** *020 †18 ‡
CINCO, Flocerfina V. 20 N 9TH ST, DARBY FAMILY MEDICINE 19023 #748-08-1972 L1981 **GP AN** *020
COHEN, Norman Nathan. ■ 19023 #041-01-1956 L1957 **GE IM** *020 †20
COHN, Neil Randolph. 1503 LANSDOWNE AVE, STE 3005 19023 #041-02-1988 L1990 **P** *020 †75
CYNN, Won Sik. 1503 LANSDOWNE AVE 19023 #583-01-1961 L1972 **R** *020 †80
DEL GUERCIO, Edmund T. 1501 LANSDOWNE AVE, STE 201 19023 #041-09-1965 L1966 **NEP IM** *020 †20
DI GIOVANNI, Alphonse Jos. 1501 LANSDOWNE AVE, STE 108 19023 #041-09-1960 L1961 **GS VS** *020 †85
DOMINGO, Orville. 1501 LANSDOWNE AVE, STE 207 19023 #495-52-1972 L1976 **GS** *020 †85
DORSEY, Taffy Anne. 1503 LANSDOWNE AVE FL 1 19023 #010-02-1988 L1992 **OBG** *020 †30
DRAGANESCU, John Michael. 1501 LANSDOWNE AVE, STE 205 19023 #041-01-1983 L1986 **GE IM** *030 †20
DRAVID, Vikram Shashank. 1500 LANSDOWNE AVE 19023 #495-01-1982 L1991 **DR** *020 †80
EBBA, Celsus I. 869 MAIN ST 19023 #748-20-1985 L1991 **IM** *020 †20
EISER, Arnold Robt. 1500 LANSDOWNE AVE MS 31 19023 #016-06-1974 L1975 **IM** *030 †20
FARHEEN, Amtul Sakina. MS 40, MERCY CATHOLIC MEDICAL CEN 19023 #496-72-2005 L2007 **IM** *012
GALERA, Hugo. MERCY CATH MED CTR-SURG 19023 #847-02-1991 L1994 **GS** *100
GALINDO, Lorenzo Manuel. 1500 LANSDOWNE AVE 19023 #847-01-1982 L1987 **OS PTH** *020 †50
GANDIKOTA, Neetha. MS 40, MERCY CATHOLIC MC 19023 #495-62-2003 L2008 *100
GENOVA, Jacqueline K. 1503 LANSDOWNE AVE, STE 3002 19023 #198-04-1988 L1999 **PD** *020 †55
GEORGELOS, Panagiotis. 1503 LANSDOWNE AVE STE 300, STE 3002 19023 #041-13-1998 L2003 **PD** *020 †55
GHIMIRE, Raj Kumar. MS 40, MERCY CATHOLIC MEDICAL CEN 19023 #672-02-2003 L2007 **IM** *012
GILBERT, Mark. 1503 LANSDOWNE AVE, STE 3010 19023 #035-06-1980 L1981 **ID IM** *020 †20
GIORGIO, Quentin Marc. 1500 LANSDOWNE AVE 19023 #422-01-1981 L1983 **IM PHM** *062
GONZALES, Melchor J. ■ 19023 #748-07-1964 *020
GURAGAIN, Manish. MS 40, MERCY CATHOLIC MEDICAL CEN 19023 #672-02-2002 L2007 **IM** *012
HO, David Ming. 1500 LANSDOWNE AVE, DEPARTMENT OF SURGERY 19023 #104-01-2003 L2003 **FP** *012
HOFMAN, Walter I. 1500 LANSDOWNE AVE 19023 #869-01-1965 L1972 **PTH FOP** *020 †50 ‡

HUBSHER, Jay Wm. 1501 LANSDOWNE AVE STE 201 19023 #041-09-1981 L1985 **NEP IM** *020 †20

IM, Mary J. 1500 LANSDOWNE AVE, HOUSE STAFF OFFICE 19023 #583-08-2000 L2005 **AN** *012

IQBAL, Anwar. MS 40, MERCY CATHOLIC MC 19023 #704-20-2001 L2008 *100

IZES, Betsy Ann. 1500 LANSDOWNE AVE, DEPT OF RADIOLOGY 19023 #041-02-1987 L1993 **DR OS** *020 †80

JAISWAL, Suresh. MS 40, MERCY CATHOLIC MEDICAL CEN 19023 #672-07-2003 L2007 **IM** *012

JAMKHANA, Zafar Akram. MS 40, MERCY CATHOLIC MEDICAL CEN 19023 #495-62-2004 L2007 **IM** *012

JAY, Michael Corey. ■ 19023 #010-02-1999 L2006 **RNR** *020 †80

KAFLE, Prakash Mohan. MS 40, MERCY CATHOLIC MEDICAL CEN 19023 #160-05-2002 L2007 **IM** *012

KAIN, Thomas Michael, III. 1501 S LANSOOWNE VAE, NO 102 19023 #041-02-1969 L1971 **ORS IM** *020 †40

KAPLAN, Carol Ellen. 1500 LANSDOWNE AVE 19023 #033-05-1988 L1994 **DR** *020 †80

KHAN, Muhammad Riaz. 1500 LANSDOWNE AVE, DEPT OF GME 19023 #704-02-2001 L2006 **IM** *012

KHOURY, Mohsen Andre. 1500 LANSDOWNE AVE, MERCY FITZGERALD HOSPITAL 19023 #915-03-1972 L1988 **DR** *020

KIM, John Joongjin. 1501 LANSDOWNE AVE STE 209 19023 #583-03-1970 L1977 **OTO HNS** *020

KORMAN, Michael Jay. 1501 LANSDOWNE AVE STE 103 19023 #041-02-1981 L1982 **PUD IM** *020 †20 ‡

KUMAR, Rajender. 1500 LANSDOWNE AVE, DEPT OF GME 19023 #495-69-2000 L2006 **IM** *012

KURETU, Mwazhuwa L. 1503 LANSDOWNE AVE 19023 #047-07-1977 L1982 **CD TS** *020 †85,90

LEHMAN, Curtis Edward. 1500 LANSDOWNE AVE, DEPARTMENT OF 19023 #041-09-1997 L2003 **EM** *020 †16

MACK, Joan Minette. 1503 LANSDOWNE AVE 19023 #422-01-1981 L1983 **NM DR** *020

MAKOPOULOS, John. 1500 LANSDOWNE AVE 19023 #041-02-2003 L2003 **EM** *020 ‡

MASCARO PANKOVA, Andres A. 1500 LANSDOWNE AVE, MERCY FITZGERALD HOSP 19023 #231-01-2005 L2006 **GS** *012

MAYEKAR, Ulhas Vasant. 1503 LANSDOWNE AVE, STE 3005 19023 #496-38-1979 L1984 **P** *020 †75

MAYER, David Pierce. 1503 LANSDOWNE AVE 19023 #041-02-1975 L1976 **DR** *020 †80 ‡

MC COLLUM, Michael F. 1500 LANSDOWNE AVE 19023 #041-13-1986 L1987 **GYN OS** *020 †30

MC GINNIS, Andrew W H. 1501 LANSDOWNE AVE, STE 104 19023 #041-13-1970 L1971 **CD IM** *020 †20

MC NAMEE, William B, Jr. 1503 LANSDOWNE AVE 19023 #041-02-1977 L1979 **IM** *020 †20

MEHTA, Rohtesh S. 1500 LANSDOWNE AVE, MERCY CATHOLIC MEDICAL CEN 19023 #495-29-2003 L2006 **IM** *012

MEHTA, Tushar Bhaurai. 1500 LANSDOWNE AVE 19023 #495-22-1964 **FM** *020 ‡

MESETE, A Francis. 1501 LANSDOWNE AVE, STE 104 19023 #041-13-1967 L1968 **CD IM** *020 †20

MEYER, Allen Eric. 1501 LANSDOWNE AVE, STE 201 19023 #041-02-1974 L1976 **NEP IM** *020 †20

MODI, Niyati Dilipkumar. 1500 LANSDOWNE AVE, MERCY CATHOLIC MEDICAL CEN 19023 #495-89-2003 L2006 **IM** *012

MUKERJEE, Prashant Kumar. 1503 LANSDOWNE AVE # 300, MCMC S4 19023 #495-34-1961 L1975 **PUD IM** *020 †20

MULLER, Otto Friedrich. 1500 LANSDOWNE AVE # 3001 19023 #407-15-1954 L1961 **CD IM** *071 †20

MURPHY, John Jos. 1501 LANSDOWNE AVE, STE 304 19023 #041-01-1945 L1946 **U** *072 †85,95

MUSUKU, Mary Usha. 1500 LANSDOWNE AVE, MERCY CATHOLIC MED CTR 19023 #495-11-1992 L2006 **IM** *012

MUZONDI, Charles. MS 40, MERCY CATHOLIC MEDICAL CEN 19023 #775-01-2000 L2007 **IM** *012

NEALE, Jeffrey Allan. 1500 LANSDOWNE AVE, DEPARTMENT OF SURGERY 19023 #665-02-2004 L2004 **GS** *012

NEPAL, Manoj. 1500 LANSDOWNE AVE, DEPT OF GME 19023 #704-15-1997 L2006 **IM** *012

NIEDZIOLKA, Anna. 1500 LANSDOWNE AVE, MERCY CATHOLIC MEDICAL CEN 19023 #759-06-1995 L2006 **AN** *012

NORONHA, Anandprakash I. 1500 LANSDOWNE AVE 19023 #495-52-1971 L1978 **OBG** *020 †30

ONASANYA, Olukayode Oluse. 1500 LANSDOWNE AVE, DEPT OF GME 19023 #690-14-1998 L2006 **IM** *100

PARAMASIVAM, Vijayakumar. MS 40, MERCY CATHOLIC MC 19023 #495-16-2000 L2008 *100

PARSIA, K Shahi. 1501 LANSDOWNE AVE STE 202 19023 #517-01-1963 L1971 **P PYA** *071 †75

PASDAR, Homayoon. 1500 LANSDOWNE AVE 19023 #517-01-1960 L1969 **TS VS** *030 †85,90

PAVURALA, Ravi Babu. MS 40, MERCY CATHOLIC MEDICAL CEN 19023 #495-11-2003 L2007 **IM** *012

PILLAI, Ajay Raman. 1503 LANSDOWNE AVE, STE 3007 19023 #495-01-1986 L2001 **PCC** *020 †20

PLESA, Carmen Adeluta. 1500 LANSDOWNE AVE, DEPT IM 19023 #781-01-2003 L2006 **IM** *012

PRICE, Joseph John, Jr. 1501 LANSDOWNE AVE, STE 201 19023 #010-02-1987 L1989 **NEP** *050 †20

QAZI, Naila. MS 40, MERCY CATHOLIC MEDICAL CEN 19023 #704-09-2002 L2007 **IM** *012

RAEZER, David Michael. 1501 LANSDOWNE AVE STE 301 19023 #041-01-1968 L1969 **U** *020 †95 ‡

RAHMAN, Fahd. 1500 LANSDOWNE AVE, MAIL STOP 104 19023 #704-09-1999 L2003 **IM** *020 †20

RAMACHANDRA, Prashanth R. 1501 LANSDOWNE AVE, STE 305 19023 #495-73-1990 L1999 **GS** *020 †85

RATHER, Assar Ahmed. 1500 LANSDOWNE AVE, MERCY FITZGERALD HOSPITAL 19023 #495-51-2000 L2005 **GS** *012

RICCIARDI, Susan L. 1500 LANSDOWNE AVE FL W, MERCY FITZGERALD HOSP 19023 #041-02-1985 L1987 **IM** *030 †20

RIMAL, Anshu. 1500 LANSDOWNE AVE, DEPT OF GME 19023 #672-06-2004 L2008 **IM** *012

RIZVI, Rehana. 1500 LANSDOWNE AVE, DEPT OF GME 19023 #704-20-1993 L2006 **IM** *100

RUBY, Edward Bernard. 1501 LANSDOWNE AVE, STE 203 19023 #041-02-1971 **END IM** *020 †20

SABATINO, John Cono. 1503 LANSDOWNE AVE 19023 #033-06-1995 L2000 **DR** *020 †80

SALVO SOTO, Federico. 1500 LANSDOWNE AVE, MERCY CATHOLIC MEDICAL CEN 19023 #270-02-2002 L2006 **IM** *012

SANDBERG, Lars Johan Marc. 1500 LANSDOWNE AVE, MERCY FITZGERALD HOSPITAL 19023 #858-01-2000 L2005 **GS** *012

SANGA, Ricardo Reis. MS 40, MERCY CATHOLIC MEDICAL CEN 19023 #187-04-1998 L2007 **IM** *012

SCHRENZEL, Steven. 1500 LANSDOWNE AVE 19023 #016-42-1978 L1980 **AN** *020 †05

SEIFERT, Richard Allen. 1501 LANSDOWNE AVE STE 303, MERCY CATHOLIC MEDICAL CEN 19023 #308-07-1981 L1986 **CD IM** *020 †20

SHAH, Rajal Dhruvish. 1500 LANSDOWNE AVE, DEPT OF GME 19023 #495-76-2002 L2005 **IM** *012

SHARAF, Imran. 1500 LANSDOWNE AVE 19023 #704-20-1996 L2001 **AN** *100

SHRESTHA, Rijesh Raj. 1500 LANSDOWNE AVE, MERCY CATHOLIC MEDICAL CEN 19023 #672-02-2003 L2006 **IM** *012

SILVERMAN, Lee David. 1503 LANSDOWNE AVE, STE 3005 19023 #041-02-1988 L1990 **P** *020 †75

SINGH, Saurav Bahadur. MS 40, MERCY CATHOLIC MEDICAL CEN 19023 #672-03-2004 L2007 **IM** *012

SMILEY, Joseph Wm. 1501 LANSDOWNE AVE, STE 201 19023 #041-02-1965 L1966 **NEP IMG** *020 †20

SMITH, Robert Terry. 1503 LANSDOWNE AVE 19023 #035-08-1984 L1986 **IM** *030

SOLBERG, Byrne Lincoln. 1503 LANSDOWNE AVE, OUTPATIENT CENTER 19023 #041-13-1980 L1981 **PM** *020 †60

SRIVASTAVA, Mohit. 1500 LANSDOWNE AVE, DEPARTMENT OF SURGERY 19023 #038-44-2004 L2004 **GS** *012

STUARD, Ian Donald. FILZGERALD MERCY HOSPITAL, DEPT OF PATHOLOGY 19023 #035-45-1961 L1981 **PTH CLP** *071 †50

TESSLER, A Robt. 869 MAIN ST 19023 #041-09-1969 L1984 **FM** *020 †18

THAPA, Rupak. MS 40, MERCY CATHOLIC MC 19023 #672-05-2005 L2008 *100

TRAN, Loc V. 1501 LANSDOWNE AVE STE 3 19023 #942-01-1973 L1993 **IM** *020

TRAN, Son Dai. 1500 LANSDOWNE AVE, DEPT OF GME 19023 #942-01-1992 L2006 **IM** *012

TUPCHONG, Leslie. 1500 LANSDOWNE AVE 19023 #836-02-1971 L1985 **RO IM** *020 †80 ‡

TURCHI, Joseph John. 1503 LANSDOWNE AVE, STE 3007 19023 #041-02-1958 L1959 **ON HEM** *020 †20

TZARNAS, Chris D. 1501 LANSDOWNE AVE STE 20 19023 #418-01-1975 L1979 **PS GS** *020 †65,85 ‡

UNNISA, Rafat. MS 40, MERCY CATHOLIC MEDICAL CEN 19023 #495-65-2000 L2007 **IM** *012

USMAN, Mohammed Haris Ume. 1500 LANSDOWNE AVE &, BAILEY RD 19023 #704-02-2001 L2003 **IM** *020 †20

VENGOECHEA, Fabian Albert. 1500 LANSDOWNE AVE 19023 #264-12-1998 L2002 **IM** *100 †20

VIJAYKUMAR, Shalini. MS 40, MERCY CATHOLIC MEDICAL CEN 19023 #496-21-2003 L2007 **IM** *012

WADKE, Rahul Chandrakant. 1500 LANSDOWNE AVE, DEPT OF MEDICAL EDUCATION 19023 #496-25-2000 L2005 *100

ZOJWALLA, Maleka. 1500 LANSDOWNE AVE, FITZGERALD MERCY HOSP PATH 19023 #495-01-1968 L1972 **PTH PCP** *020 †50 ‡

DARLINGTON – BEAVER

KALENAK, Alexander Eric. 207A 2ND ST 16115 #041-09-1994 L1996 **FM** *020 †18 ‡

DAUPHIN – DAUPHIN

CORSON, Geoffrey Alan. ■ 17018 #041-09-1954 L1956 **GS OS** *071 †85

DAVIDSVILLE – SOMERSET

FRANK, William Henry. 2000 CAMBRIDGE DR, # 904 15928 #023-01-1945 L1949 **OM GS** *071

DELAWARE WATER GAP – MONROE

FOSTER, Ian Scott. PO BOX 257 18327 #035-08-1983 L1984 **FM** *020 †18 ‡

DELMONT – WESTMORELAND

ASPINALL, Alan Roy. 390 ROUTE 22, STE 200 15626 #041-07-1984 L1985 **FM** *020 †18

BOHNER, Mary Frank. 390 ROUTE 22, STE 200 15626 #035-06-1980 L1981 **FM** *020 †18

BRODSKY, Robert Lawrence. 390 ROUTE 22, STE 200 15626 #035-08-1983 L1984 **FM FPG** *020 †18

GIBSON, Ken. 6530 ROUTE 22 STE 200 15626 #041-02-1986 L1987 **FM** *020 †18

HERRON, Eugene William. 195 SHEFFIELD DR 15626 #041-12-1962 L1963 **FM FPG** *020 †18

HUBAHIB, Hannah Elma. ■ 15626 #748-09-1996 L2005 **PM** *100

ROMITI, Steven Lee. 6530 ROUTE 22, STE 200 15626 #041-12-1990 L2004 **FM** *020 †18

SEPP, Jennifer Lynn. 390 ROUTE 22, STE 200 15626 #041-78-1999, ▲ L2000 **FM** *020

SHEVCHIK, Grant John. 390 ROUTE 22, STE 200 15626 #041-01-1978 L1979 **FM FPG** *020 †18 ‡

DELTA – YORK

DOOLEY, John Malford. 205 CHESTNUT ST 17314 #051-07-1987 L1990 **FM** *020

MC FARLAND, Robert Peter. RR 1, THE NARDENHOUSE 17314 #041-13-1960 L1962 **GP P** *020

DENVER – LANCASTER

GILBERT, Christopher. ■ 17517 #041-77-2004, ▲ L2004 **IM** *100 †20

IMPERIAL, Sandy L. ■ 17517 #748-08-1989 L1997 **PTH** *020 †50

LEIS, Jacqueline Renee. ■ 17517 #033-05-2008 L2008 **IM** *020

NASH, James Douglas. 560 N 5TH ST 17517 #649-33-1981 L1984 **IM** *020

TRACHTE, Thomas Patrick. 63 W CHURCH ST 17517 #041-13-1977 L1978 **FM** *020 †18 ‡

DERRY – WESTMORELAND

JOUBERT, Ina Lynn. ■ 15627 #010-03-1984 L1990 **GP** *074

VIN, Prakash Kanaiyalal. 118 W 4TH AVE 15627 #495-23-1973 L1977 **IMG IM** *020 †20

DEVON – CHESTER

BODAPATI, Srinivas. ■ 19333 #495-70-1991 **IM** *012
BOLSTER, Richard Hawks. ■ 19333 #041-09-1945 L1946 **FM A** *072
BOMBERGER, John Henry A. ■ 19333 #041-13-1956 L1957 **PD OS** *071 †55
BRIGIDI, Antonette Jude. ■ 19333 #023-01-2004 L2004 **IM** *020 †20
CARON, Cynthia Marie. ■ 19333 #067-01-1983 L1988 **IM P** *020 †20
CLAYPOOL, William Dow. ■ 19333 #008-02-1976 L1978 **IM** *040 †20
DAMIANO, Robert Edward. ■ 19333 #025-01-1960 L1969 **PA** *071
DHAMANKAR, Minal Milind. ■ 19333 #496-48-1996 L2006 **IM** *012
DISTEFANO, Vincent James. 235 W LANCASTER AVE, DEVON MANOR STE 100 19333 #041-09-1963 L1964 **ORS** *020 †40
EARLEY, Laurence Elliott. ■ 19333 #036-01-1956 L1977 **IM** *071 †20
EASAW, Jacob. ■ 19333 #495-61-1984 **IM** *100
EMPER, William David. 235 W LANCASTER AVE, STE 100 19333 #024-01-1981 L1982 **ORS OSM** *020 †40
EREMUS, Joseph Lee. 235 W LANCASTER AVE, STE 100 19333 #041-13-1972 L1973 **ORS OFA** *020 †40
EVANGELISTA, Simplicio E. ■ 19333 #748-10-1964 L1972 **DR** *071 †80 ‡
FORSYTH, Kyle Landis. 139 BERKELEY RD, DEVON FAMILY PRACTICE 19333 #041-02-1984 L1985 **FM** *020 †18
FREEDMAN, Kevin Blake. 235 W LANCASTER AVE, STE 100 19333 #041-01-1995 L1998 **ORS** *020 †40
FURMAN, Frank Harold. 139 BERKELEY RD 19333 #041-14-1980 L1981 **FM** *020 †18
GALASSO, Jennifer Hosp. ■ 19333 #051-07-2001 L2004 **PD** *020 †55
GLASNER, Saul. ■ 19333 #041-02-1959 L1960 **PYA P** *020 †75
GOOD, Robert Paul. 235 W LANCASTER AVE, STE 100 19333 #041-02-1973 L1974 **ORS OSM** *020 †40
HARP, James Robt. 123 OLD LANCASTER RD, DEVEREUX MAPLETON MANOR 19333 #036-07-1961 L1969 **CHP P** *071 †05,75
HEDRICK, Holly Lee. ■ 19333 #036-07-1991 L1998 **PDS** *020 †85
JAEGER, Eugene A. 223 W LANCASTER AVE 19333 #041-02-1953 L1954 **P GP** *071
KEEFER, George J Pfahler. ■ 19333 #041-01-1939 L1940 **R** *071 †80
LAWLOR, Robert J. 139 BERKELEY RD 19333 #041-02-1977 L1978 **FM** *020 †18
LIPKOWITZ, Ronald Lee. 223 W LANCASTER AVE 19333 #035-03-1978 L1979 **P** *020 †75
LOREI, Matthew Peter. 235 W LANCASTER AVE, STE 100 19333 #041-01-1990 L1998 **ORS** *020 †40
MC GEE, Elizabeth Lewis. ■ 19333 #041-07-1949 L1950 **P CHP** *072 †55
MELLI, Maria Gombeda. 139 BERKELEY RD 19333 #041-02-1989 L1991 **FM** *020 †18
MORRIS, Jonathan Andrew. ■ 19333 #028-02-1992 L1993 **GS** *020
NARZIKUL, Gregory Tura. 139 BERKLEY RD 19333 #041-02-1988 L1990 **FM** *020 †18
NOWOSIWSKY, Taras. ■ 19333 #024-01-1958 L1985 **OM PHP** *071 †70
OBERWAGER, Andrew Whiting. ■ 19333 #024-01-2001 *100
OVERTON, Deborah C Stine. ■ 19333 #041-13-1969 L1970 **PD** *074
POOLE, Robert Michael. ■ 19333 #005-18-1984 L2006 **N IM** *020 †20,75
PORTER, Roger John. ■ 19333 #036-07-1968 L1992 **PA N** *050 †75 ‡
PRIEM, Robert Wahl. 139 BERKLEY RD 19333 #041-02-1985 L1986 **FM** *020 †18
RATTAN, Neeru Shashi. ■ 19333 #041-02-2002 L2002 **AN** *100 †05
ROSATO, Donald J. 176 E CONESTOGA RD 19333 #041-13-1959 L1960 **FM OS** *071 †18
RUBINO, Daniel Theodore. 176 E CONESTOGA RD 19333 #305-01-1996 L2001 **PM PME** *020
VANDER VEER, Joseph B, Jr. ■ 19333 #035-45-1965 L1967 **GS EM** *071 †85
VOGEL, R Lee. ■ 19333 #033-06-1980 L1981 **PDC PD** *020 †55
WALSH, Kevin Michael. 235 W LANCASTER AVE, STE 100 19333 #041-02-1998 L2001 **FSM** *020 †18
WHITELEY, Wm Henry, III. ■ 19333 #041-02-1943 **NS** *071 †25
WILSON, Donald Filmore. 260 CHURCH RD 19333 #041-02-1979 L1982 **OBG** *030 †30
WORLEY, William Ellis. 2 ILE DHUYERE, ARBORDEAU 19333 #041-01-1960 L1963 **OS** *030

DICKSON CITY – LACKAWANNA

BLONDEK, Stanley W. 890 VIEWMONT DR 18519 #306-01-1984 L1986 **PD** *020 †55 ‡
CRONIN, Randall C, Jr. 235 MAIN ST STE 109, ALLIED SERVICES-WORK MED 18519 #041-09-1977 L1990 **FM OM** *020 †18 ‡
DAWGERT, Francis Dennis. 920 VIEWMONT DR 18519 #028-34-1972 L1975 **PD** *020 †55
GLEESON, Michael Francis. 243 MAIN ST STE 301 18519 #308-07-1983 L1986 **GS** *020 †85
HENZES, Jack. 334 MAIN ST 18519 #041-02-1987 L1990 **ORS** *020 †40
MARX, John Henrey. 920 VIEWMONT DR 18519 #041-14-2004 L2004 **PDC** *012 †55
MC COY, Jill Fasciana. 890 VIEWMONT DR 18519 #041-15-2002 L2002 **PD** *020 †55
MECCA, Donato Dominick. 235 MAIN ST STE 121 18519 #041-13-1959 L1960 **OPH** *020 ‡
METZGER, Paul Christopher. 334 MAIN ST 18519 #041-09-1975 L1976 **ORS** *020 †40
OLESKI, Cynthia Marie. 542 BOULEVARD AVE 18519 #030-06-1998 L2001 **IM** *020 †20
RAMOS, Giovanni Greto. 312 BOULEVARD AVE 18519 #030-06-1998 L2002 **IM** *020
SAUTER, Martha Ann. 890 VIEWMONT DR 18519 #024-07-1992 L1995 **PD** *020 †55 ‡
SIGMAN, Mark James. 920 VIEWMONT DR 18519 #041-07-1998 L2001 **PD** *020 †55
TIGUE, Kathleen Ann. 920 VIEWMONT DR 18519 #041-13-1994 L2000 **PD** *020 †55
WALSH, Kathleen Iezzi. 890 VIEWMONT DR 18519 #010-02-1992 L1995 **PD** *020 ‡
WELBY, Timothy Damian. 920 VIEWMONT DR 18519 #041-13-1991 L1994 **PD** *020 †55
ZUKOSKI, Thomas Eugene. 920 VIEWMONT DR 18519 #041-02-1972 L1973 **PD** *071 †55

DILLINER – GREENE

WILSON, Alison. ■ 15327 #048-04-1996 L2001 **GS** *020 †85

DILLSBURG – YORK

ABRAHAM, Vanitha E. 204 MUMPER LN 17019 #495-95-1976 L1981 **FM** *020 †18
HEISE, Glen Edward. 204 MUMPER LN 17019 #041-14-1982 L1983 **FM** *020 †18
JACKSON, George Lyman. ■ 17019 #041-01-1948 L1949 **NM IM** *071 †28,20
LONERGAN, Robert Philip. 20 LOCUST LN, LONERGAN ORTHOPAEDICS 17019 #041-13-1965 L1967 **ORS GP** *020 †40

PORR, George Henry, Jr. ■ 17019 #041-13-1953 L1954 **P** *071
SHUMWAY, Clare Nelson, Jr. ■ 17019 #035-06-1948 L1972 **ADL PD** *071 †55
SHUMWAY, Jane Baldwin. ■ 17019 #008-01-1950 L1972 **P PD** *072
SPURRIER, David Jonathan. ■ 17019 #041-13-1973 L1980 **EM** *020
UNIACKE, Beverley P. 2 BARLO CIR STE A, PINNACLEHEALTH FAMILY CARE 17019 #055-02-1991 L1994 **FM** *020 †18
WAGNER, Kristina Mae. 2 BARLOW CIR 17019 #041-07-1990 L1993 **MPD** *020 †20,55

DINGMANS FERRY – PIKE

KRESSEL, Anja. ■ 18328 #409-21-1988 L1996 **IM** *020 †20 ‡
PATHAK, Lisa. 1409 ROUTE 739, BON SECOURS HEALTH PARTNER 18328 #035-47-1998 L2003 **MPD** *020 †20,55

DONORA – WASHINGTON

CORDERO, Edgar C. 627 MCKEAN AVE 15033 #748-01-1963 L1973 **GS GP** *020
CORDERO, Marc E.. 627 MCKEAN AVE 15033 #422-01-2002 L2007 **GS** *020 †85
PETRO, Dimitri Michael. 718 MCKEAN AVE 15033 #041-12-1960 L1961 **GP** *020

DOUGLASSVILLE – BERKS

BASTIDAS, Erin L. ■ 19518 #041-77-2007, ▲ **FP** *012
DE GUZMAN, Rodolfo Lim. ■ 19518 #041-01-1954 L1970 **EM** *071
FOSTER-MERROW, Sonya Mari. ■ 19518 #021-01-2002 L2007 **FM** *012
GUTHRIE, W James. ■ 19518 #016-06-1954 L1958 **IM CD** *071 †20
HOEPFNER, Elisabeth Anne. 193 OLD SWEDE RD 19518 #041-13-2002 L2003 **FM** *020 †18
HUSSAINI, Saira Niloufer. 193 OLD SWEDE RD 19518 #496-27-1992 L2001 **FM** *100 †18
KIMMEL, William Bradford. ■ 19518 #041-09-1992 L1996 **PTH** *020 †50
RASTOGI, Sanjay. 193 OLD SWEDE RD, BERKS FAMILY CARE 19518 #065-10-1992 L1996 **FM** *020 †18
SCULLY, John P. ■ 19518 #041-01-1939 L1940 **D** *071 †15
STRUNK, Jessika Marie. ■ 19518 #041-15-2008 L2008 *012
TADDONIO, William Scott. 193 OLD SWEDE RD 19518 #041-02-1986 L1987 **FM** *020 †18

DOVER – YORK

ALTLAND, Debra Mason. 3992 CARLISLE RD 17315 #051-01-1984 L1987 **FM** *020 †18
AMBROSE, Rachelle Lynne. 4020 CARLISLE RD 17315 #041-12-1999 L2002 **PD** *020 †55
DAUGHERTY, Sherod Lynn. ■ 17315 #041-07-1964 L1965 **OS** *074
DONATI, Theresa Ann. 4020 CARLISLE RD 17315 #041-02-1990 L1993 **IM** *020 †20
EBAUGH, Duane Wallace. 3992 CARLISLE RD 17315 #041-09-1965 L1966 **NPM** *020 †55
GOLDHAHN, Lawrence Jamesr. ■ 17315 #041-13-2008 L2008 *012
IMBODEN, Elizabeth Marie. 4020 CARLISLE RD 17315 #041-14-1994 L1996 **PD** *020 †55
NALLAPATI, Rajesh Kumar. 4020 CARLISLE RD 17315 #496-24-1993 L1998 **IM** *020 †20
NGO, Ly Thien. ■ 17315 #041-02-2008 *012
PAUL, Ronald Larry. ■ 17315 #067-01-1963 L1973 **NS** *071 †25
SMITH, Karen Mason. 3992 CARLISLE RD 17315 #051-01-1984 L1987 **FM** *020 †18
SMITH, Larry. 3992 CARLISLE RD 17315 #046-01-1984 L1987 **FM** *020 †18
TAYLOR, Brian Jeffrey. ■ 17315 #010-02-1998 L2003 **FM** *020 †18
WALLACE, Joseph, Jr. 17315 #023-01-1942 L1943 **OTO** *071 †45

DOWNINGTOWN – CHESTER

ABBOTT, David Marine, Jr. ■ 19335 #041-13-1971 L2004 **P** *020
ADAMS, Geo Hancock Nutt. 520 E LANCASTER AVE 19335 #045-01-1961 L1967 **P** *071
BACKUP, Dudley Clifford. 202 E LANCASTER AVE, MINQUAS AMBULANCE 19335 #041-09-1980 L1983 **EM** *020 †16
BARR, Charles Jay. 101 MANOR AVE 19335 #041-09-1980 L1982 **FM** *020 †18
BENINATI, Daniel David. 77 MANOR AVE STE 201 19335 #132-01-1969 L1973 **GYN NTR** *020 †30 ‡
BRADFORD, John David. ■ 19335 #051-04-1955 L1960 **GS** *071 †85
BROWN, Robert Chas. ■ 19335 #041-13-1942 L1946 **R** *071 †80
CARROLL, Robert T. ■ 19335 #041-02-1952 L1953 **IM HEM** *071
CLAY, Bettie West. BLACK HAWK APTS G5 19335 #041-13-1947 L1948 **IM** *071
DEMOLA, Philip. ■ 19335 #041-77-2007, ▲ L2007 *012
DORFMAN, Michael. 520 E LANCASTER AVE, HUMAN SVCS INC 19335 #041-09-1991 L1993 **P** *020 †75 ‡
DOUGHERTY, John Dennis. ■ 19335 #041-13-2002 L2002 **IMG** *020 †20
DUNSMORE, Lillian Drozd. ■ 19335 #041-09-1949 L1950 **CD IM** *071
DUNSMORE, Richard A. ■ 19335 #041-09-1949 L1951 **CD IM** *071 †20
D'URSO, Francesco. 4333 W LINCOLN HWY, WEDGWOOD CENTER PEDIATRICS 19335 #649-35-1985 L1991 **PD** *020 †55
DVORKIN, Daniel. 797 E LANCASTER AVE, STE 15 19335 #041-12-1967 L1968 **D** *020 †15
ELANCHENNY, Indranee. 711 E LANCASTER AVE, BLACK HAWK CONVENIENCE CEN 19335 #220-02-1973 L1982 **IM IMG** *020 †20
FRIEDMAN, Robert Marc. 77 MANOR AVE, STE 200 19335 #035-20-1984 L1986 **OBG** *020 †30
GEORGE, Joe. ■ 19335 #041-77-2004, ▲ L2004 **PD** *012
GUPTA, Angela. ■ 19335 #041-13-2007 L2007 **IM** *012
JAIN, Bina. ■ 19335 #496-34-2002 L2007 **IM** *100 †20
JINDAL, Dilip Kumar. 102 MADISON WAY 19335 #495-30-2001 L2007 **IM** *020 †20
KELLY, Edward A. 99 MANOR AVE 19335 #041-02-1973 L1976 **FM** *020 †18
KIMMEL, Irene V. 151 WOODBINE RD 19335 #041-07-1965 L1966 **GP** *075
KRISHNA, Narendra. 797 E LANCASTER AVE, ARTHUR BELSON & KRISHNA 19335 #495-03-1953 L1966 **OPH** *071 †35
LIVINGSTON, Robert Alan. ■ 19335 #023-07-1985 L1996 **PD ID** *020 †55
LUCINE, Albert A, Jr. 506 E LANCASTER AVE 19335 #041-01-1951 L1952 **OBG** *072 †30
MAC FADYEN, James Jos. 151 WOODBINE RD 19335 #041-09-1971 L1972 **P CHP** *020 †75
MALIREDDY, Jyothirmayi. ■ 19335 #495-70-1988 L2008 **FP** *012
MODLIN, Hyman Jos. ■ 19335 #803-09-1942 L1978 **GP P** *071

NAGARAJ, Susheela. ■ 19335 #495-33-1974 L1985 **IM ON** *020 †20
NELSON, Thomas. ■ 19335 #051-01-1964 L1964 **IM PD** *020 †55
NEWBROUGH, Robert Seymour. 455 BOOT RD, CCIU 19335 #055-01-1989 L1991
  CHP P *062 †75
NEWMAN, Richard August. ■ 19335 #016-11-1956 L1962 **P PYA** *020 †75
NORRIS, Monica Leigh. 101 MANOR AVE 19335 #041-07-1998 L2000 **FM** *020 †18
PEGG, John R Poynton. 38 ANSLEY DR 19335 #917-19-1950 L1973 **AN** *030 †05
PEOPLES, James Francis, III. ■ 19335 #422-01-2007 L2007 **GS** *012
RUSSO, Pierantonio. ■ 19335 #561-01-1978 L1988 **TS CD** *020
SALAM, Mahi. 106 SCHUBERT DR 19335 #915-02-1969 L1983 **PD** *020
SLAVISH, Lydia Gay. 77 MANOR AVE, STE 200 19335 #041-14-1985 L1989 **OBG** *020 †30 ‡
TAUB, Elizabeth H. ■ 19335 #048-04-1993 L2007 **PTH** *071
VADHER, Alpa. 110 HOPEWELL RD 19335 #041-13-1996 L1998 **FM** *020 †18
VAGHARI, Benjamin Ali. ■ 19335 #035-47-2006 L2006 **IM** *012
VILBERT, Eric Michael. ■ 19335 #067-01-2006 L2007 **DR** *012
WALSH, Steven James. ■ 19335 #041-14-2006 L2006 **EM** *012
WILLIAMS, Thomas M. 1306 DECATUR CT, BRADFORD GLEN 19335 #913-01-1972 L1984
  PD *020 ‡
WU CHEN, Wen Ying. ■ 19335 #270-01-1997 L2003 **N** *012

DOYLESTOWN – BUCKS

ABEL, David Robt. 5175 COLD SPRING CREMRY RD, STE 3 18902 #041-13-1986 L1987
  CHP *020 †75
ACHARYA, Pinak Sumant. 1980 S EASTON RD, STE 230 18901 #016-02-1997 L2001
  PCC *020 †20 ‡
ADELIZZI, Paul Jeffry. 595 W STATE ST, DOYLESTOWN HOSPITAL 18901 #041-13-1985 L1986
  DR *020 †20
ALEXANDER, Karen E. 14 MEMORIAL DR, STE B 18901 #041-02-1994 L1997 **FM** *020 †18
AUTERI, Joseph S. 595 W STATE ST 18901 #041-02-1986 L2007 **TS GS** *020 †85,90
BADAYOS, Alicia Parreno. 500 N WEST ST 18901 #748-01-1967 L1977 **P** *020
BARBA, William Philip, III. 708 N SHADY RETREAT RD, SUITES 3 & 4 18901 #041-13-1981 L1982
  PD *020 †55
BENZIO, Karl Gene, Jr. 800 W STATE ST, LIGHTHOUSE PSYCHIATRY #302 18901
  #033-05-1989 L1993 **P CHP** *040 †75
BERMAN, Jeffrey Marc. 708 N SHADY RETREAT RD, STE 9 18901 #041-14-1993 L1997
  GE HEP *020 †20
BERNSTEIN, Deborah R. 595 W STATE ST, DOYLESTOWN HOSPITAL 18901
  #041-07-1988 L1992 **PM** *020 †60
BILHEIMER, David Woodrow. ■ 18902 #041-01-1967 L1968 **IM** *071
BLACKBURN, Laurence Henry. ■ 18901 #023-07-1955 L1978 **OM AM** *071 †70
BOLAND, David Gerard. 14 MEMORIAL DR STE B, CENTRAL BUCKS SPECIALISTS 18901
  #047-05-1992 L1999 **CD** *020 †20
BOLAND, Francis B, Jr. 800 W STATE ST 18901 #041-02-1962 L1963 **ORS** *020 †40
BOSSE, Myhanh. 708 N SHADY RETREAT RD, STE 9 18901 #033-06-1987 L1990 **GE** *020 †20
BOURNE, Scott Earle. ■ 18902 #041-14-2005 L2005 **PTH** *012
BOYLAN, Angela C. ■ 18901 #038-06-1990 L1993 **OBG** *020 †30
BOYLAN, Douglas Neil. 103 PROGRESS DR 18901 #041-02-1993 L1999 **OSM** *020 †40
BRACKIN, George Gaul. 595 W STATE ST DEPT RAD 18901 #041-09-1970 L1972
  R GPM *020 †80
BRILLIANT, Lawrence Craig. 595 W STATE ST, DOYLESTOWN HOSP 18901 #035-48-1990 L1995
  EM *020 †16
BRODERMAN, Susan J. 310 FARM LN 18901 #041-09-1984 L1985 **IM** *020 †20
BROWN, Madeline Morgan. 1456 FERRY RD, UNIT 600 18901 #041-15-2002 L2004
  IM OS *020 †20 ‡
BRYAN, John Stever. 595 W STATE ST 18901 #024-01-1958 L1966 **ORS PM** *071 †40
BUCKWALTER, Jeffrey Allen. 103 PROGRESS DR, STE 200 18901 #036-01-1979 L1984
  OTO A *020 †45
BUINEWICZ, Brian Robt. 3655 ROUTE 202, STE 225-230 18902 #041-02-1985 L1986
  PS *020 †85,65
BURMAN, Sneh Prabha. 500 N WEST ST 18901 #495-45-1975 L1990 **P** *020 †75
BURROWS, Charles Brundage. 800 W STATE ST, STE 202 18901 #041-13-1993 L1995
  OAR *020 †40
CANDIA, Andrea Jane. 595 W STATE ST, DOYLESTOWN HOSPITAL 18901 #041-09-1980 L1981
  DR *020 †80
CANNELLA, Joseph M. ■ 18902 #065-05-1961 L1963 **OM** *071 †70
CHANG, Alan Weichieh. 599 W STATE ST, STE 200 18901 #041-01-1998 L2000 **GE** *020 †20
CHANG, Paul I. ■ 18902 #008-01-1986 L1992 **CD** *062 †20
CHAPIN, Scott Deeter. 253 W STATE ST 18901 #041-13-1988 L1995 **PS** *020 †85,65
CHERIAN, Pradip. 708 N SHADY RETREAT RD, STE 9 18901 #495-08-1982 L2000 **GE** *020 †20
CHIN, Victor Michael. 702 HYDE PARK 18902 #035-47-2002 L2006 **OPH** *020 †35
CHIRGWIN, Keith David. 3810 LANCASTER DR 18902 #035-46-1981 L1998 **ID IM** *050 †20
CHOBY, John Joseph. 708 N SHADY RETREAT RD 18901 #041-01-1962 L1963 **OBG** *071 †30
CHOI, Mark. 595 W STATE ST, DOYLESTOWN HOSP EMGY DEPT 18901 #033-06-1987 L1989
  EM *020 †16
COCHRAN, Daniel C. 3842 W BRANDON WAY 18902 #041-77-1997, ▲ L1998 **FM** *020 †18
CODY, Kieran Danl. 800 W STATE ST STE 202 18901 #041-09-1989 L1996 **ORS OSM** *020 †40
COLETTA, Daniel Jos. 301 S MAIN ST 18901 #033-05-1970 L1971 **GYN** *020 †30
COSTANZO, Ronald Joseph. 595 W STATE ST, DOYLESTON HOSPITAL, DEPART 18901
  #035-15-1990 L1993 **DR** *020 †80 ‡
COVERDALE, Edward J, III. 301 S MAIN ST, THE ATRIUM 18901 #041-02-1967 L1968
  IM *020 †20
CURCI, Joseph James. 16 N FRANKLIN ST 18901 #041-13-1972 L1973 **GS** *020 †85
DARNELL, Richard I. 595 W STATE ST 18901 #041-09-1940 L1941 **GP OS** *071
DE LA TORRE, Cesar A. 708 N SHADY RETREAT RD, STE 9 18901 #035-19-1996 L1998
  GE *020 †20
DEMOPOULOS, James Thos. ■ 18901 #035-08-1956 L1983 **PM** *071 †60
DERRICK, Bruce Melvin. 599 W STATE ST, STE 301 18901 #041-13-1975 L1976 **GS VS** *020 †85
DE VENUTO, Jos John, Jr. 485 N MAIN ST 18901 #041-13-1966 L1967 **OPH GS** *020 †35
DREW, Elizabeth A. 800 W STATE ST STE 100 18901 #041-09-1998 L2000 **FM** *020 †18
EHRLICH, Leonard David. 599 W STATE ST, STE 200 18901 #010-01-1972 L1973
  GE IM *020 †20
ESBENSHADE, James Jay. 14 MEMORIAL DR, STE A 18901 #041-09-1997 L1999 **FM** *020 †18
FITZGERALD, Jean O. 708 N SHADY RETREAT RD, STE 7 18901 #041-07-1985 L1988
  OBG *020 †30

FITZGERALD, Kevin Brian. 303 W STATE ST 18901 #048-04-1993 L1999 **U** *020 †95
FITZPATRICK, Francis T. 72 E STATE ST 18901 #041-02-1963 L1964 **PD** *071 †55
FITZPATRICK, John Raymond. ■ 18901 #041-13-2004 L2004 **GS** *012
FLASHNER, Steven Chas. 303 W STATE ST 18901 #041-02-1982 L1992 **U** *020 †95
FORD, Francis Wm. 16 N FRANKLIN ST 18901 #041-13-1972 L1973 **GS VS** *020 †85
FORSTER, Terrence John. 14 MEMORIAL DR STE D 18901 #025-07-1970 L1985
  RHU AI *020 †20,03
GALIANI, David Louis. 10 S CLINTON ST, THE LANDMARK BLDG 18901 #051-04-1999 L2003
  OPH *020 †35
GALIETTA, Gerald Edward. 5768 VALLEY STREAM DR 18902 #041-09-1967 L1969
  P AN *020 †05,75
GALLANT, Jane Tuller. 1456 FERRY RD, UNIT 600 18901 #051-01-1989 L1994 **IM** *020 †20
GAMZA, Francis Chas. ■ 18902 #041-09-1971 L1972 **ON HEM** *050 †20
GEJER, Eric R. 599 W STATE ST, STE 200 18901 #041-77-1999, ▲ L2000 **CD** *020
GITTLEN, Stanford Dale. 1980 S EASTON RD, STE 230 18901 #041-02-1982 L1983
  PCC IM *020 †20
GIUFFRIDA, Michael A. 312 HYDE PARK 18902 #024-07-1989 L1992 **PS** *020 †65
GKONOS, Peter James. 101 PROGRESS DR, STE B1ST 18901 #041-02-1978 L2000
  END IM *050 †20
GOOSENBERG, Eric Brad. 708 N SHADY RETREAT RD, STE 9 18901 #041-13-1984 L1985
  GE IM *020 †20
GRABOWSKI, Robert J. 807 N EASTON RD, STE 100 18902 #041-77-1998, ▲ L2000 **FM** *020
GRIBB, John J. 14 MEMORIAL DR, STE A 18901 #041-13-1954 L1955 **OBG** *071 †30
GROSS, Michael Bruce. 252 W SWAMP RD, STE 4 18901 #041-13-1973 L1975 **OBG** *020 †30
GRZYWACZ, Francis William. 599 W STATE ST, STE 200 18901 #041-15-2000 L2001
  CD *100 †20
GWYNNE, John Thos. ■ 18902 #036-07-1970 L1972 **END DIA** *050
HALE, Robert Henry. 599 W STATE ST, STE 200 18901 #041-09-1971 L1972 **IM GE** *020 †20
HANDY, Robert Wm. 800 W STATE ST, STE 202 18901 #041-13-1972 L1973 **ORS** *020 †40
HARRINGTON, Pamela J. 708 N SHADY RETREAT RD, KIDS FIRST CTRL NCJ #3-4 18901
  #041-15-2001 L2003 **PD** *020 †20
HARRIS, Katherine Kirby. 10 S CLINTON ST, STE 202 18901 #041-07-1983 L1984 **CHP** *020 †75
HARRISON, Brett Morgan. 599 W STATE ST STE 301 18901 #035-45-1985 L1986
  GS VS *020 †85
HARTMAN, Daniel Gerard. 5175 COLD SPRING CREMRY RD, STE 3 18902 #041-07-1988 L1990
  CHP *020 †75
HEISE, Caroline Ruth. 14 MEMORIAL DR STE A, DOYLESTOWN GYNECOLOGY 18901
  #047-05-1991 L1999 **GYN** *020 †30
HERB, Kathleen Elizabeth. ■ 18902 #041-07-1995 L1998 *020
HERMAN, Richard Michael. 103 PROGRESS DR, STE 200 18901 #041-13-1989 L1991
  OTO *020 †45
HERMANN, Christopher Paul. 301 S MAIN ST STE 2N 18901 #010-01-1976 L1979 **IM** *020 †20
HOLTZMAN, Henry Bruce. 800 W STATE ST STE 204 18901 #041-09-1974 L1975
  PUD IM *071 †20
HUEBNER, Elizabeth Stack. 708 N SHADY RETREAT RD, STE 9 18901 #016-43-2004 L2007
  GE *020 †20 ‡
IE, Darmakusuma. 700 W STATE ST, STE 100 18901 #021-01-1988 L1993 **OPH** *020 †35
JACOBS, Erika Lyn. ■ 18901 #035-19-2002 L2006 **MSR** *012 †80
JELLINEK, Sharon Lynn. 3655 ROUTE 202, STE 100 18902 #010-02-1988 L1999 **PD** *020 †55 ‡
JENNINGS, Bonnie Kimbell. 6166 STOVERS MILL RD 18902 #012-01-1981 L2005 **P** *020
JERDAN, Dennis Albert. 599 W STATE ST, STE 301 18901 #041-13-1998 L2000 **RHU** *020 †20
KANE, Haresh Shaba. 400 S MAIN ST, GREENLEAF NURSING HOME 18901 #473-04-2003 L2006
  IM *020
KAPLAN, Michael Alan. ■ 18902 #035-08-1983 L1989 **END PA** *050 †20
KARDISH, Thomas Jos. ■ 18901 #041-13-1959 L1960 **FM** *071 †18
KELEPOURIS, Nikoletta N. 101 PROGRESS DR, STE B1ST 18901 #418-01-1982 L1985
  END IM *020 †20
KENNY, Rose Mary. 595 W STATE ST, DOYLESTOWN HOSP LAB 18901 #041-02-1970 L1973
  PTH *020 †50 ‡
KESACK, Craig Danl. 595 W STATE ST 18901 #041-14-1989 L1992 **DR** *020 †80
KHANNA, Chanchal. 595 W STATE ST 18901 #495-03-1961 L1973 **PTH CLP** *020 †50
KIEVE, Carola Anne. 500 N WEST ST 18901 #041-13-1984 L1985 **P** *020 †75
KIM, Eun Ha. 500 N WEST ST 18901 #048-12-1991 L1994 **P** *020 †75
KISTHARDT, Anne Christian. ■ 18901 #041-02-1994 L1997 **OBG** *071 †30
KMETZO, James John. 315 W STATE ST, CENTRAL BUCKS CARDIOLOGY 18901
  #041-13-1983 L1989 **CD IM** *020⋅†20
KNOPF, Edwin Ronald. 595 W STATE ST 18901 #041-09-1964 L1967 **OS P** *030 †75
KOPACH, Michele. 595 W STATE ST 18901 #041-02-1986 L1998 **PDR R** *020 †80
KRICK, Andrew Earl. 310 FARM LN 18901 #041-09-1974 L1975 **IM** *020 †20
KUBOVSAK, Edward Geo. 595 W STATE ST, DOYLESTOWN HOSP EMERG DEPT 18901
  #041-07-1979 L1980 **EM** *020 †16
KWOK, Moody. 101 PROGRESS DR 18901 #041-13-1994 L1996 **HS** *020 †40
LAI, Naline Lerue. 595 W STATE ST 18901 #041-12-1994 L1996 **PD** *020 †55
LAPHEN, Jeffrey Thomas. 252 W SWAMP RD, STE 41 18901 #654-01-2003 L2003 **FM** *020 †18
LAQUER, K Geo. ■ 18901 #041-13-1951 L1952 **P** *071 †75
LATTA, Priscilla W. 595 W STATE ST 18901 #041-02-2002 L2002 **FM UM** *020 †18
LAUDENSLAGER, Elmer C. ■ 18901 #041-09-1943 L1944 **GP** *071
LAVELLE, Kenneth Gordon. 455 EAST ST, CENTRAL BUCKS AMBULANCE 18901
  #041-02-2004 L2004 **EM** *100
LE, Tuan Anh. 708 N SHADY RETREAT RD SU 18901 #051-01-1984 L1986 **OBG** *020 †30
LEE, Frank C. 702 HYDE PARK 18902 #041-14-2001 L2005 **OPH** *020 †35
LEE, Guy A. 101 PROGRESS DR 18901 #041-13-1993 L1995 **ORS OSS** *020 †40
LEISTER, Howard Alonza. ■ 18901 #041-02-1959 L1960 **FM GPM** *071 †18
LEONARD, Edward Harry. 595 W STATE ST 18901 #041-09-1990 L1993 **AN** *020 †05
LEVIN, Donald B. 360 N BROAD ST, STE 200 18901 #041-09-1967 L1968 **P** *020 †75
LEVY, Scott S. 595 W STATE ST, DOYLESTOWN HOSPITAL #305-01-1985 L1987
  NEP IM *020 †20
LIN, Daniel Yunchung. 599 W STATE ST, STE 100 18901 #010-02-2000 L2001 **NEP** *020 †20
LIPES, Jan Keith. ■ 18902 #035-46-1976 L1981 **OS FM** *030 †18
LIPKOWITZ, Jeffrey L. 700 W STATE ST, STE 100 18901 #041-13-1978 L1979 **OPH** *020 †35
LONGSHORE, Kristine E. 410 FARM LN 18901 #035-15-1995 L1997 **OPH** *020 †35 ‡
LUBINSKI, Stuart Mitchell. 708 N SHADY RETREAT RD, STE 9 18901 #041-01-1993 L1999
  GE IM *020 †20
MACKELL, James V, Jr. 800 W STATE ST, STE 202 18901 #041-02-1969 L1972 **ORS** *020 †40
MACKELL, Thomas Edward. 800 W STATE ST, STE 202 18901 #041-02-1972 L1975
  ORS *020 †40

MAGUIRE, Robert Thos. ■ 18902 #041-13-1977 L1983 **PD** *020 †55
MANCINI, David James. 101 PROGRESS DR 18901 #041-02-1995 L1996 **PM** *020
MARCHANT, Eric Alan. 401 HYDE PARK 18902 #041-13-1985 L1987 **PS** *020 †65
MARTYNEC, Bohdan. 301 S MAIN ST, STE 2 18901 #422-01-1981 L1983 **IM** *020 †20
MASCOLO, Richard. 315 W STATE ST, CENTRAL BUCKS CARDIO 18901 #035-15-1994 L2002 **CD IM** *020 †20
MASS, Stephen Christopher. 103 PROGRESS DR STE 200, SURGERY ASSOCIATES 18901 #036-07-1994 L1999 **OTO** *020 †45
MATOSSIAN, Cynthia. 702 HYDE PARK 18902 #041-14-1981 L1985 **OPH** *020 †35
MC EWAN, Jack Raymond. 14 MEMORIAL DR, STE A 18901 #033-05-1985 L1991 **FM** *020 †18
MC GARVEY, Joseph Francis. 599 W STATE ST STE 200 18901 #010-02-1989 L1995 **CD IC** *020 †20
MC HUGH, Joseph James. 595 W STATE ST 18901 #041-13-1981 L1982 **EM** *020 †16,20
MENNA, Vincent Jos. 402 HYDE PARK 18902 #041-09-1965 L1974 **PD** *020 †55
METCALF, Randy K. 78 S MAIN ST, STE 200 18901 #048-14-1983 L1989 **TS** *020 †85,90
MINEHAN, Kathryn Ann. 708 N SHADY RETREAT RD, SUITES 3-4 18901 #041-02-1986 L1989 **PD** *071 †55
MOHLINE, John D. ■ 18902 #022-75-2005, ▲ L2005 **MEM** *012
MOOMJIAN, Ara Sarkis. 595 W STATE ST 18901 #035-19-1975 L1977 **NPM PD** *020 †55
MORGAN, Cyrus Joseph. 599 W STATE ST 18901 #041-13-1999 L2004 **GS** *020 †85
MORSBACH, Louis Franklin. 599 W STATE ST, STE 200 18901 #041-07-1987 L1988 **GE IM** *020 †20
MOYER, Paul Robt. 595 W STATE ST 18901 #041-01-1967 L1970 **IMG IM** *020
MURRAY, Richard Scott. 210 FARM LN 18901 #033-06-1979 L1988 **GS** *020 †85
MYERS, Philip Adam. 310 FARM LN 18901 #041-07-1983 L1984 **IM** *020 †20
NADEL, Douglas Mark. 599 W STATE ST, STE 201 18901 #041-02-1992 L1994 **OTO** *020 †45 ‡
NAVARRO, Cyrilda Orillos. 252 BAILIWICK DR STE 6 18901 #748-02-1977 L1983 **PD** *020 †55 ‡
NESI, Daniel A. 800 W STATE ST 18901 #041-13-1963 L1965 **OTO A** *020 †45
NEVES, Jose Santos. ■ 18901 #770-04-1978 **TS** *020
NICHOLAS, Michael Dunston. 708 N SHADY RETREAT RD, STE 3 & 4 18901 #051-01-1995 L1998 **PD** *020 †55
NIESENBAUM, Leonard. 31 CEDAR WOODS CIR 18901 #041-09-1956 L1957 **PUD** *030 †20
NUNEZ, Ricardo. 500 N WEST ST 18901 #737-06-1991 L1999 **P** *020
O CONNOR, Robert Leo, III. ■ 18902 #041-02-1986 L1987 **AN** *020 †05
OPASS, Edward Scott. 500 N WEST ST 18901 #041-09-1980 L1981 **P PYA** *020 †75
ORPHANIDES, Timothy. 599 W STATE ST, STE 200 18901 #035-19-1983 L1985 **GE** *020 †20 ‡
PALONI, Lauri E. 708 N SHADY RETREAT RD, STE 3 18901 #035-15-1990 L1993 **PD** *074 †55
PARLEE, Donald Ewart. 595 W STATE ST 18901 #041-13-1959 L1960 **R RO** *020 †80
PATT, Richard H. 595 W STATE ST 18901 #010-02-1985 L2003 **OS** *020 †80
PATTON, Carla Saccarelli. 1456 FERRY RD, UNIT 600 18901 #041-07-1982 L1983 **IM** *020 †20
PELLETIER, Mary Ellen. 595 W STATE ST STE 308 18901 #041-13-1997 L1999 **IM** *020 †20
PETERS, Stanley Frederick. 401 S MAIN ST 18901 #041-02-1962 L1963 **FM IMG** *020 †18 ‡
PIERSON, Steven Bruce. 210 FARM LN 18901 #028-02-1977 L1983 **GS VS** *020 †85
PINES, Deborah Ann. 1960 S EASTON RD 18901 #041-07-1978 L1979 **P CHP** *020 †75
PLOTKIN, Stanley Alan. ■ 18902 #035-08-1956 L1958 **ID PD** *050 †55
POLESUK, Brian Steven. 595 W STATE ST, DEPT OF RADIOLOGY 18901 #033-06-1993 L1999 **DR** *020 †80
PRICE, Scott Keith. 595 W STATE ST 18901 #023-01-1992 L1997 **VIR** *020 †80
PRIEST, Brian Patrick. 595 W STATE ST, DOYLESTOWN HOSPITAL 18901 #033-05-1984 L1985 **TS** *020 †85,90
PRITCHARD, Charles Henry. 599 W STATE ST, STE 310 18901 #010-01-1983 L1986 **RHU IM** *020 †20
RAPKIN, Robert Michael. 54 E OAKLAND AVE # 200 18901 #024-07-1965 L1986 **P PYG** *020 †75 ‡
RECUPERO, Elizabeth A. 595 W STATE ST, ATTN: MEDICAL STAFF 18901 #028-78-1996, ▲ L1999 **MPD** *020 †20,55
REINHARDT, Sean Craig. 315 W STATE ST, CENTRAL BUCKS CARDIOLOGY 18901 #033-05-2000 L2007 **CD** *100 †20
RICHARDS, John Clifford. 595 W STATE ST 18901 #041-13-1952 L1953 **P OP** *071
RIM, Jeung Kyu. ■ 18901 #583-04-1963 L1972 **IM END** *071 †20
ROGAN, Rose M. ■ 18902 #033-05-1978 L1979 **PD** *071
ROLAND, Frank Hancock, Jr. 303 W STATE ST 18901 #036-07-1994 L2005 **U** *020 †95
ROSAN, Stuart William. 252 W SWAMP RD, STE 50 18901 #041-77-1975, ▲ L1976 **GP FM** *071 †18
ROSE-VALLEJO, Kathryn E. 14 MEMORIAL DR STE B, PRACTICE 18901 #051-04-1996 L2002 **FM** *020 †18
RUEBEL, Catherine M. ■ 18902 #010-02-1968 L1971 **PD** *020 †55
RUENES, Albert, Jr. 303 W STATE ST 18901 #035-01-1988 L1994 **U** *020 †95 ‡
SAINI, Rajnish. 599 W STATE ST, STE 200 18901 #043-01-1999 L2003 **CD** *020 †20
SANGRIGOLI, Renee Ann. 599 W STATE ST, STE 200 18901 #041-13-1993 L1995 **CD** *020 †20
SANGRIGOLI, Robert M. 599 W STATE ST, STE 200 18901 #041-13-1993 L1995 **CD** *020 †20
SANTORO, Anthony Francis. 599 W STATE ST STE 305, DOYLESTOWN DERM 18901 #041-01-1996 L1998 **D DS** *020 †15
SARIS, Anne Louise. 708 N SHADY RETREAT RD, STE 9 18901 #041-09-1976 L1977 **GE IM** *020 †20
SCHEINFIELD, Stephen D. 595 W STATE ST 18901 #165-02-1972 L1973 **DR** *020 †80
SCHILLING, Maria Mercedes. 599 W STATE ST, STE 308 18901 #041-07-1997 L1999 **IM HOS** *020 †20 ‡
SCHNUR, Elliot Howard. 201 FARM LN 18901 #035-09-1988 L1990 **FM** *020 †18
SCHONFELD, Margery Beth. 708 N SHADY RETREAT RD 18901 #035-03-1981 L1991 **PD** *020 †55
SCHWARZ, Richard Arthur. 14 MEMORIAL DR STE D 18901 #035-46-1981 L1983 **AI** *020 †55,03
SEMANOFF, Theophila C. 595 W STATE ST 18901 #935-01-1972 L1976 **PM R** *020 †60 ‡
SENDZIK, Nestor Ivan. 708 N SHADY RETREAT RD, STE 7 18901 #041-09-1976 L1978 **OBG** *020 †30
SHAH, Kamlesh Manher. 599 W STATE ST, STE 200 18901 #033-06-1999 L2001 **GE** *100 †20
SHAH, Kekul Bharat. 700 W STATE ST, STE 100 18901 #033-06-1998 L2004 **IM** *020 †35
SHETZLEY, Carl M. ■ 18902 #041-01-1951 L1952 **FM** *071
SHLEWIET, Basem Kaleem. 833 E BUTLER AVE, FOUNDATIONS BEHAVIORAL HEA 18901 #875-01-1994 L2001 **CHP** *020
SILBERMAN, David Alan. 800 W STATE ST, STE 300 18901 #041-01-1977 L1979 **PS OTO** *020 †45,65 ‡
SILIDKER, Mark Stuart. 595 W STATE ST, DOYLESTOWN HOSP-RADIOLOGY 18901 #033-05-1983 L2001 **DR NM** *020 †80
SILLARS, Charles H. PO BOX 1574 18901 #041-13-1945 L1946 **R** *071 †80
SMITH, David Alan. 252 W SWAMP RD STE 41 18901 #041-02-1984 L1985 **FM** *020 †18
SMITH, David Lawrence. 599 W STATE ST STE 200 18901 #041-01-1984 L1985 **CD IM** *020 †20
SMITH, Roger M F. 595 W STATE ST 18901 #010-02-1963 L1967 **P** *020 †75
SMULLEN, Sean Michael. 103 PROGRESS DR, STE 200 18901 #056-05-1988 L1990 **FPS OTO** *020 †45
SOMMERS, Dan. 4590 DERBY LN 18902 #033-05-1978 L1982 **IM** *020 †20,16
SOUILLIARD, Donald Henry. 595 W STATE ST, DOYLESTOWN HOSPITAL 18901 #041-13-1954 L1955 **PTH** *071 †50
SPIEGEL, William Allen. 599 W STATE ST, STE 300 18901 #041-13-1979 L1983 **A** *020 †55,03
SPIERS, Elizabeth M. 1456 FERRY RD, STE 405 18901 #048-02-1986 L1992 **D DMP** *020 †15
SPILLANE, Kathleen Susan. 595 W STATE ST 18901 #051-07-1993 L2004 **PM** *020 †60 ‡
SPITALNY, Sarah Michelle. 708 N SHADY RETREAT RD, STES. 3&4 18901 #041-15-2004 L2004 **PD** *100 †55
STARRELS, Michael E. 252 W SWAMP RD, STE 30 18901 #041-02-1971 L1975 **OPH** *071 †35
STELLA, Joseph Henry. 800 W STATE ST, STE 302 18901 #041-02-1982 L1983 **P** *020 †75
STELTZ, Marie Ann. ■ 18902 #041-13-1989 L1991 **P** *020
STHALEKAR, Ninad Durganan. 800 W STATE ST, STE 202 18901 #422-01-2001 L2005 **PMM** *020 †60
STIEFEL, Marc Aaron. 599 W STATE ST STE 201 18901 #035-09-2001 L2006 **OTO** *020 †45
STRAUS, Walter Lee. ■ 18902 #035-06-1986 L2003 **IM GE** *020 †20
SUGDEN, William Alfred. 595 W STATE ST 18901 #041-02-1961 L1962 **GP** *071
SZEKELY, Les Attila. 1980 S EASTON RD, STE 230 18901 #038-43-1990 L1992 **PCC SME** *020 †20
TATEM, Henry Randolph, III. 595 W STATE ST, DOYLESTOWN HOSPITAL 18901 #041-09-1963 L1965 **R NM** *071 †80,28
TOMLINSON, John Wesley. 10 S CLINTON ST 18901 #041-02-1962 L1963 **OPH** *020 †35
TONKONOW, Barry Lee. 275 S MAIN ST, STE 4 18901 #041-13-1975 L1976 **ON HEM** *020 †20
TOPORCER, Mary Barbara. 800 W STATE ST STE 303, SURGERY 18901 #041-09-1984 L1985 **D IM** *020 †20,15 ‡
TRAVERS, Eleanor May. 1282 ALMSHOUSE RD, STE 100 18901 #041-07-1966 L1967 **CLP PTH** *030 †50
TREDICI, Luis Mario. ■ 18901 #132-02-1956 L1971 **P** *020
TREIMAN, Philip Russell. 252 W SWAMP RD, STE 41 18901 #041-02-1993 L1995 **FM** *020 †18
TROTTA, Robert John. 595 W STATE ST, DOYLESTOWN HOSP PATH 18901 #035-19-1984 L2003 **PTH** *020 †50
TWEEDY, Charles Enzer, III. ■ 18901 #041-01-1965 L1999 **PD** *071 †55 ‡
TWYMAN, Roy Ervin. ■ 18902 #020-12-1982 L1983 **N** *050 †75
VANDERBEEK, Richard R. 14 MEMORIAL DR STE B 18901 #041-02-1958 L1959 **IM ON** *020 †20
VARRELL, James Ronald. 1730 S EASTON RD, BCCF, CFG/CORRECTIONAL MEN 18901 #033-06-1989 L1991 **CHP P** *020 †75
VERNACE, Melchiore A. 599 W STATE ST, STE 100 18901 #035-06-1987 L1997 **NEP IM** *020 †20
VIKOREN, Farah Hooshmand. 595 W STATE ST 18901 #517-01-1960 L1970 **OBG** *071 †30
WAGNER, Steven Craig. 595 W STATE ST, DOYLESTOWN HOSPITAL 18901 #041-02-1999 L2001 **VIR** *020 †80
WALHEIM, Jon Peter. 310 FARM LN 18901 #041-02-1970 L1975 **IM HOS** *020 †20
WASSEL, Antoinette C. 252 W SWAMP RD, STE 41 18901 #041-12-1997 L1999 **FM** *020 †18
WASSERBLY, Pamela Joan. 4656 DICKINSON WAY 18902 #041-02-1977 L1978 **PHP EM** *030 †16
WEATHERBY, Ellsworth, III. 595 W STATE ST 18901 #016-06-1978 L1987 **DR NM** *020 †80
WELSCH, Frank Anthony. 1980 S EASTON RD, STE 230 18901 #041-01-1974 L1975 **PUD IM** *020 †20
WELSH, Mary F. 2813 E FOX CHASE CIR 18902 #041-07-1971 L1994 **GS OS** *020 †85 ‡
WENGER, Robert Eric. 833 E BUTLER AVE, FOUNDATION BEHAVIORAL HEAL 18901 #041-13-1971 L1975 **P DS** *020 †75 ‡
WHITAKER, Joseph Michael. 103 PROGRESS DR, STE 300 18901 #041-09-1976 L1981 **ORS** *020 †40
WIEMANN, George Frederick. 315 W STATE ST, CENTRAL BUCKS CARDIOLOGY 18901 #035-47-1981 L1983 **CD IM** *020 †20
WIGGINS, William Stover. 41 E ASHLAND ST 18901 #036-05-1973 L1974 **N** *020 †20,75
WILLARD, Robert Joseph. 610 FARM LN 18901 #041-02-1998 L2001 **D** *020 †15
WILSON, Dale Frances. 595 W STATE ST 18901 #035-09-1996 L2000 **AN** *020 †05
WINNEG, Karen Pevar. 14 MEMORIAL DR, STE A 18901 #041-07-1988 L1990 **FM** *020 †18
YEH, Vivian Wenhan. 708 N SHADY RETREAT RD, STE 7 18901 #035-20-1992 L1994 **OBG** *020 †30
YOUNG, David J. 595 W STATE ST 18901 #041-77-1985, ▲ L1986 **PM** *020 †60 ‡
YOUNG, Linda M. 114 N MAIN ST 2ND FL 18901 #004-01-1985 L1994 **P** *020 †75
ZAKRZEWSKI, Paul J. 301 S MAIN ST, MEDICINE/ATRIUM/STE 2 SOUT 18901 #041-77-1996, ▲ L1997 **IM** *020 †20
ZAZOW, Paul Leslie. 22 S CLINTON ST 18901 #041-02-1976 L1985 **P** *020 †75 ‡
ZENOUZI, Sirus. 800 W STATE ST, STE 302 18901 #407-10-1958 L1967 **AN** *071 †05
ZIEGENFUSS, Jay F, Jr. 16 N FRANKLIN ST, STE 201 18901 #041-02-1967 L1968 **ON IM** *020
ZOLLER, Mary A. 14 MEMORIAL DR, STE A 18901 #035-19-1977 L1978 **FM** *020 †18

DRESHER – MONTGOMERY

BRODY, Myer. ■ 19025 #024-05-1932 L1934 **IM P** *071
CHERNOW, Claudia Groves. ■ 19025 #041-02-1982 L1983 **CHP P** *020 †75
COHEN, Sidney Allan. 152 GREEN VALLEY CIR 19025 #041-01-1982 L1983 **CD IM** *050 †20
GREENFIELD, William Stern. 1451 BROAD ST 19025 #041-13-1969 L1970 **P** *020 ‡
GROSSMAN, Lawrence Bruce. 1460 CATLIN WAY 19025 #041-13-1991 L1993 **GE** *020 †20
KIM, Chong Duk. 1430 LIMEKILN PIKE 19025 #583-08-1975 L1984 **IM** *020
KRAMER, Mark Steven. ■ 19025 #041-13-1976 L1977 **P PA** *050 †75
LEAVITT, Randi Yvette. ■ 19025 #028-02-1978 L1993 **IM IG** *030 †20,03
LEWIN, Bernard. 1750 LIMEKILN PIKE 19025 #008-01-1981 L1986 **DR VIR** *020 †80
MATHUR, Ajita Pratap. ■ 19025 #496-01-1997 L2007 **P** *100
MC GILL, Dorothy J. ■ 19025 #041-12-1985 L1987 **ID PD** *020
SCHATZ, Nathan. ■ 19025 #041-09-1962 L1963 **GE IM** *020 ‡
SCHWARTZ, Heinz Georg. ■ 19025 #041-13-1961 L1962 **CLP** *071 †50
SELLA, Walter Allan. 200 DRYDEN RD E, STE 3100 19025 #649-14-1980 **FPG IMG** *075
SILVERMAN, Robert Eliot. ■ 19025 #028-02-1978 L1993 **END IM** *050 †20
TEHRANI, Massoud Bakhsh. ■ 19025 #517-01-1956 L1961 **U** *071 †95
TURNER, Margo Eleanor. ■ 19025 #041-09-1979 L1981 **IM** *020

■ = Address Information Privacy Protected

WEINSTEIN, Lindsay Pricel. ■ 19025 #041-13-2007 **IM** *012
WINEGRAD, Albert I. ■ 19025 #041-01-1952 L1953 **DIA IM** *071 †20
WOO, Chee Houe. ■ 19025 #041-02-1998 L2003 **APM** *020 *05
WORTHINGTON, John J. 715 TWINING RD, STE 201 19025 #010-02-1959 L1967 **P** *020 †75
YUSCHAK, James Victor. 829 REDGATE RD 19025 #041-13-1985 L1986 **GS TRS** *020 †85 ‡

DREXEL HILL – DELAWARE

ADVANI, Asha Kamal. 5030 STATE RD, STE 2-900 19026 #025-07-1987 L1990 **PD** *020 †55
ARORA, Manju. 501 N LANSDOWNE AVE, FL 4 19026 #495-67-1973 L1980 **DR** *020 †80
ATKINSON, Gerald Russell. 3001 GARRETT RD STE C 19026 #041-02-1954 L1955 **IM** *020
BAKER, Richard Paul. ■ 19026 #041-02-1956 L1957 **PTH** *071 †50
BARR, Maura Irene. ■ 19026 #041-77-2007, ▲ L2007 **IM** *012
BECKWITH, William Robt. 2100 KEYSTONE AVE, STE 200 19026 #041-13-1964 L1965 **CD IM** *071 †20
BEDROSSIAN, Edward H, Jr. 4501 STATE RD 19026 #041-13-1978 L1981 **OPH** *020 †35
BENDITT, Milton Barry. ■ 19026 #041-07-1984 L1988 **AN** *020 †20
BENEDETTO, Anthony V. 2221 GARRETT RD 19026 #041-77-1974, ▲ L1975 **D CS** *020 †15
BENEDETTO, Ernest Alfred. 501 N LANSDOWNE AVE 19026 #561-25-1983 L1990 **D DS** *020 ‡
BLEEDEN, Edward M. 2231 GARRETT RD 33/35 19026 #041-09-1971 L1973 **IM** *020 †20
BLOCK, Ronald Mark. 501 N LANSDOWNE AVE 19026 #654-01-1981 L1983 **IM** *020 †20 ‡
BOCCIO, Remigio V. 501 N LANSDOWNE AVE, DEPT ANES DEL CNTY MEM HOS 19026 #035-15-1980 L1988 **AN CCM** *020 †20,05
BOXER, Louis Marc. 501 N LANSDOWNE AVE 19026 #041-07-1991 L1993 **AN** *020 *05
BRADLEY, Jason Todd. ■ 19026 #041-15-2004 L2004 **CD** *012 †20
BRISCOE, Clarence C. ■ 19026 #041-01-1935 L1939 **OBG** *071 †30
BURKE, Mary Theresa. 2100 KEYSTONE AVE, MEDICAL OFC BLDG STE 502 19026 #041-09-1980 L1982 **ON HEM** *020 †20
CALLANS, Linda S. 2100 KEYSTONE AVE, 1ST FLOOR, MOB 19026 #023-07-1986 L1989 **GS SO** *020 †85
CHAKHBAZOV, Abdoulla Arif. 501 N LANSDOWNE AVE, DEPT OF ANESTHESIA/DCMH 19026 #913-19-1988 L2002 **AN** *020 †05 ‡
CHOJNACKI, Karen Ann. 650 HARPER AVE 19026 #035-06-1995 L1997 **GS** *020 †85
CICCONE, Ronald Paul. 501 N LANSDOWNE AVE 19026 #041-09-1978 L1981 **FM** *020 †18 ‡
COLLINS, Joy Lynn. ■ 19026 #023-01-1996 L1998 **PDS** *020 †85
COLOMBO, John Mario, Jr. 5030 STATE RD, DREXELINE PROF BUILDING 19026 #041-02-1979 L1981 **IM IMG** *020 †20 ‡
COOLEY, Derek Dion. ■ 19026 #001-02-2002 L2005 **IM** *100 †20
COONEY, Marina Jean. 401 PILGRIM LN, STE 100 19026 #041-13-1992 L1994 **P** *020 †75
DANG, Mark Hanh Van. 2100 KEYSTONE AVE, STE 506 19026 #041-13-1991 L1995 **FM** *020 †18
DE GUZMAN-CAM, Brigida. 501 N LANSDOWNE AVE, DE COUNTY MEM HOSP 19026 #748-01-1962 L1969 **OBG** *071
DI LEONARDO, Francesca. 501 N LANSDOWNE AVE, DELAWARE COUNTY MEM HOSP 19026 #041-13-1987 L1992 **EM** *020 †16
DOMSKY, Steven Michael. ■ 19026 #041-13-2004 L2004 **IM** *100 †20
DUMOFF, Kimberly Laurie. ■ 19026 #035-06-2000 L2001 **PTH** *020 †50 ‡
ESPOSITO, John C. 501 N LANSDOWNE AVE 19026 #010-02-1951 L1952 **IM A** *020 ‡
FLETCHER, Peter Richard. 501 N LANSDOWNE AVE, DELAWARE COUNTY MEM HOSP 19026 #917-09-1974 L1987 **AN CCA** *020 †05
FOLEY, Brenda Ann. 501 N LANSDOWNE AVE, DEPT EMERGENCY MEDICINE 19026 #041-07-1998 L2002 **EM** *020 †16
FORNASIERI, Valerie Weil. 916 EDMONDS AVE 19026 #041-01-1991 L1993 **IM** *020 †20
FRIEDMAN, Ben-Zion. 501 N LANSDOWNE AVE, FL 4 19026 #041-01-1962 L1963 **DR** *020 †80
FURIA, Frederick Arthur. 2100 KEYSTONE AVE, STE 200 19026 #041-01-1968 L1969 **CD IM** *020 †20
FURIA, Robert. 3030 GARRETT RD 19026 #041-12-1976 L1977 **IM IMG** *020 †20
GALATI, Victor Geo. 2100 KEYSTONE AVE, STE 406 19026 #035-19-1972 **PUD IM** *071 †20
GAMBURG, Christine Chiosi. 501 N LANSDOWNE AVE, DEPT ANES 19026 #041-02-1982 L1986 **AN** *020 †05
GEVJAN, Armen Haik. 501 N LANSDOWNE AVE 19026 #041-09-1941 L1946 **FM** *071
GHAYAD, Pierre Y. 3001 GARRETT RD 19026 #605-02-1979 L1981 **U** *020 †95
GIBBONS, Ryan Charles. ■ 19026 #041-13-2007 *012
GILMAN, Philip B. 2100 KEYSTONE AVE, STE 700 19026 #041-02-1981 L1984 **GE IM** *020 †20
GOEHL, Kevin Henry. 5030 STATE RD, STE 2-900 19026 #010-01-1982 L1985 **PD** *020 †55
GOLDSCHMIDT, Joseph C, Jr. 3030 GARRETT RD 19026 #041-02-1985 L1986 **IM IMG** *020 †20
GOLLOTTO, Katie T. ■ 19026 #041-77-2005, ▲ **PM** *012
GORDON, Joseph Saml. 4017 GARRETT RD 19026 #041-01-1957 L1958 **IM CD** *071
GOULD, Rebecca. 2100 KEYSTONE AVE, STE 206 19026 #047-05-1999 L2001 **OBG** *020 †30 ‡
GOYAL, Suman. 501 N LANSDOWNE AVE 19026 #496-07-1960 L1978 **FM PD** *020 †20
GRANT, Bernard David. 501 N LANSDOWNE AVE 19026 #352-11-1946 L1962 **ORS** *020 †40
GUIRGUIS, Morris Fouad. 501 N LANSDOWNE AVE 19026 #915-04-1959 L1972 **IM CD** *020 ‡
HADFIELD, William Adrian, Jr. ■ 19026 #041-01-1946 L1947 **IMG IM** *071 †20
HAFT, Harold. 501 N LANSDOWNE AVE, DELAWARE COUNTY MEMORIAL H 19026 #035-08-1954 L1961 **OS N** *030 †25
HAIKEN, Jeffrey Allen. 501 N LANSDOWNE AVE, DEPT OF ANESTHESIA 19026 #165-06-1978 L1981 **AN IM** *020 †20,05
HAMILTON, Geraldine A E. 501 N LANSDOWNE AVE, 4TH FL 19026 #041-07-1967 L1968 **DR** *020 †80
HELETZ, Ido. ■ 19026 #023-01-2004 L2007 **CD** *012 †20
HENRY, Stephen James. 501 N LANSDOWNE AVE 19026 #047-06-1972 L1981 **NEP IM** *020 †20
HEWITT, Agnes Marie. 3 BLOOMFIELD AVE 19026 #654-01-2000 L2001 **FM** *020 †18
HUMFELD, Amy Lynn. ■ 19026 #010-01-2005 L2005 **PD** *020
IACOVELLA, Jackeline. 2100 KEYSTONE AVE, STE 406 19026 #270-01-1989 L1996 **ID IM** *020 †20 ‡
IWANTSCHEFF, Alexander. ■ 19026 #409-42-1982 L1987 **PUD** *020 †20
JACOBSON, Barry Jay. 2100 KEYSTONE AVE STE 707 19026 #041-02-1980 L1981 **OBG** *020 †30
JAMES, Alaina Janelle. ■ 19026 #048-04-2003 L2005 **D** *012
JEFFREY, William Lockhart. ■ 19026 #041-02-1955 L1962 **GP FOP** *072 †50
JOHNSON, Rebecca Warner. 5030 STATE RD STE 2-900 19026 #041-13-1981 L1983 **PD** *020 †55 ‡
JUDKINS, Alexander R. ■ 19026 #035-45-1996 L1999 **FOP** *020 †50
KAPLAN, Richard Zane. 2100 KEYSTONE AVE, STE 404 19026 #024-01-1985 L1987 **PD** *020 †55 ‡

KAVJIAN, Edward M. 501 N LANSDOWNE AVE 19026 #041-09-1939 L1940 **U** *071 †95
KELLY, Edward Aloysius. STATE RD ADDINGHAM AVE 19026 #041-02-1947 L1948 **FM** *071
KELLY, James Jos. ■ 19026 #041-02-1939 L1940 **GP IM** *071
KIM, Yong Mook. 501 N LANSDOWNE AVE, FL 4 19026 #583-01-1968 L1974 **R** *050 †80
KO, Victor Dragon. ■ 19026 #033-06-2003 L2006 **IM** *100 †20
KOSA, Namir B. 5030 STATE RD, STE 2-500 19026 #528-01-1973 L1995 **IM** *020 †20
KURTZ, Robert Melvyn. 501 N LANSDOWNE AVE, DELAWARE COUNTY MEM HOSP 19026 #036-07-1967 L1987 **R** *071 †80
LABAO-LARGOZA, Maria V. 2100 KEYSTONE AVE, STE 703 19026 #748-01-1985 L1993 **NEP** *020 †20
LANCIANO, Rachelle Marie. 501 N LANSDOWNE AVE, DELAWARE COUNTY MEM HOSP 19026 #041-07-1984 L1985 **RO** *020 †80 ‡
LANDOW, Craig Alan. 3001 GARRETT RD STE B 19026 #010-02-1995 L1998 **U** *020 †95
LA ROSA, David Francis. ■ 19026 #035-08-2000 L2003 **AI** *100 †20,03
LARSON, Emily Jo. ■ 19026 #041-77-2007, ▲ *012
LONG, Milly Ho. 2251 GARRETT RD 19026 #836-01-1981 L1986 **IM** *020
LONGO, Mary E. ■ 19026 #041-13-1943 L1944 **GP OS** *071
LO SASSO, Alisa. 518 BLYTHE AVE, LANKENAU FAMILY PRACTICE 19026 #041-02-1998 L2001 **PD** *020 †55
LOUKA, Elizabeth Bahiya. 501 N LANSDOWNE AVE 19026 #041-02-1999 L2001 **OBG** *020 ‡
LUONGO, Joseph C. 5030 STATE RD 19026 #010-02-1943 L1944 **PD** *071
MAKOON-SINGH, Eric M. 501 N LANSDOWNE AVE, DELAWARE COUNTY MEM HOSP 19026 #847-02-1973 L1982 **PS** *020
MALIN, Seth Arnold. 2100 KEYSTONE AVE, STE 407 19026 #041-02-1970 L1979 **GS** *020 †85 ‡
MARKIEWICZ, Deborah Ann. 501 N LANSDOWNE AVE, DEPT OF RAD/ONCLGY 19026 #016-06-1986 L1987 **RO** *020 †80 ‡
MATTHEWS, Lawrence M, Jr. 501 N LANSDOWNE AVE 19026 #041-02-1980 L1981 **PTH** *020 †50
MATULEWSKI, Thomas John. 2100 KEYSTONE AVE, STE 304 19026 #041-02-1974 L1975 **GS VS** *020 †85
MAY, Noah Ryan. ■ 19026 #041-77-2006, ▲ L2006 **GS** *012
MC CLOSKEY, David S. 2100 KEYSTONE AVE, STE 204 19026 #041-07-1983 L1984 **GS** *020 †85
MCCONNELL, Sean Alan. ■ 19026 #041-02-2005 L2005 **OBG** *012
MC CORMICK, Kathryn Joan. ■ 19026 #041-01-1981 L1983 **GS** *020 †85
MC GOWAN, William Edward. 2100 KEYSTONE AVE STE 307 19026 #041-01-1980 L1981 **U GS** *020 †95
MEYER, Andrew Scott. ■ 19026 #041-15-2003 L2003 **NPM** *012 †55
MILEWSKI, Leonard Francis. 2100 KEYSTONE AVE, STE 304 19026 #041-09-1981 L1983 **GS VS** *020 †85
MORENO, Carlos. 4601 STATE RD 19026 #737-01-1958 L1968 **GP EM** *020
MORGAN, Harry Edward. 501 N LANSDOWNE AVE, FL 4 19026 #047-07-1965 L1975 **DR** *020 †80,28
MORGAN, Melissa Ann. ■ 19026 #041-77-2006, ▲ L2006 **IM** *012
O'CONNELL, James Richards. 2100 KEYSTONE AVE, STE 307 19026 #041-09-1965 **U SO** *095
O'DONNELL, John Jos. 501 N LANSDOWNE AVE, DELAWARE COUNTY MEM HOSP 19026 #041-09-1974 L1978 **EM IM** *020 †20,16
ORTMEYER, James Wm. 2100 KEYSTONE AVE STE 407 19026 #041-07-1986 L1997 **IM** *020 †20
OTERI, Domenic L. 2100 KEYSTONE AVE STE 506 19026 #561-08-1985 L1995 **FM** *020 †18
OYESANMI, Olugbenga A. ■ 19026 #690-05-1991 **P** *100
PARVA, Mohamad-Mehdi. ■ 19026 #665-01-2006 L2007 **OBG** *012
PASSERO, Frank Chas. 2100 KEYSTONE AVE, STE 306 19026 #041-01-1973 L1974 **RHU IM** *020 †20
PATTERSON, Chris. 501 N LANSDOWNE AVE 19026 #418-01-1958 L1967 **FM IM** *072 †18
PEARSON, Stephanie Joy. 2100 KEYSTONE AVE, MOB 707 19026 #041-15-2001 L2001 **OBG** *020 †30
POWERS, Donald Vincent. 501 N LANSDOWNE AVE 19026 #041-02-1955 L1956 **NEP** *071 †20
PRESTEL, Thomas Francis. 2100 KEYSTONE AVE STE 407 19026 #010-02-1975 L1980 **PUD IM** *020 †20
RABINOWITCH, Bonnie Leigh. 2100 KEYSTONE AVE STE 406, HAN INFECTIOUS DISEASES 19026 #041-02-1988 L1990 **ID** *020 †20
RIGBY, Charles Edward, Jr. ■ 19026 #041-09-1943 L1944 **OM** *071
ROLLNIK, Elizabeth Gail. 5030 STATE RD, STE 2-900 19026 #035-47-1985 L1990 **PD** *020 †55
ROMNEY, Ralph O. 5030 STATE RD, STE 2-900 19026 #024-05-1983 L1991 **PD** *020 †55
ROMO, Victor Manuel. 4315 CEDAR LN 19026 #041-13-1995 L1998 **AN** *020 *05
ROPER, William Jason. ■ 19026 #049-01-2006 L2006 **EM** *012
RYAN, Marilyn. 2100 KEYSTONE AVE STE 308 19026 #035-15-1979 L1981 **END IM** *020 †20
SAADE, Rosalma. 501 N LANSDOWNE AVE, DELAWARE COUNTY MEM HOSP 19026 #041-09-1994 L1998 **DR** *020 †80
SAJADIEH, Ahmad. 7211 DREXEL BROOK APTS 19026 #297-02-1990 L1996 **IM** *100
SAMMARTINO, John Paul. 3019 GARRETT RD 19026 #041-09-1980 L1982 **OPH** *020 †35
SAMUELS, Pauline M. 3712 GARRETT RD 19026 #422-01-1990 L1992 **IM** *020
SCHARF, Ann Theresa. 501 N LANSDOWNE AVE, FL 4 19026 #041-13-1986 L1987 **DR VIR** *020 †80 ‡
SCHRAN, Albert Geo. 685 FERNE BLVD 19026 #041-02-1947 L1948 **GP IM** *071
SEARS, Alan Jeffrey. 2100 KEYSTONE AVE, STE 507 19026 #041-02-1978 L1979 **GE** *020 †20
SEBASTIAN, Justin Charles. ■ 19026 #495-99-2000 L2001 **PCC** *100
SHAH, Ranjit Ratilal. 501 N LANSDOWNE AVE, FL 4 19026 #495-76-1971 L1979 **DR FM** *020 †80
SHEIKH, Awais Ahmed. ■ 19026 #495-01-1999 L2006 **IM** *012
SLATER, Robert. 2100 KEYSTONE AVE STE 401, MEDICAL & CONFERENCE CTR 19026 #041-01-1967 L1968 **N** *020 †75 ‡
SLAVIN, Michael J. 2100 KEYSTONE AVE, STE 506 19026 #308-10-1984 L1986 **FM** *020 †18
SMITH, Monica Elizabeth. 2100 KEYSTONE AVE STE 502 19026 #041-07-1984 L1985 **ON** *020 †20
SOPPAS, Despina. 5030 STATE RD, STE 2-900 19026 #041-12-1979 L1981 **PD** *020 †55
SREEDHAR, Nandhini. 73 DREXELBROOK DR 19026 #495-04-1993 L2002 **IM** *100 †20
STALAM, Malini. 501 N LANSDOWNE AVE 19026 #495-98-1983 L1998 **ID** *020 †20
STAMPLER, Kate Marion. ■ 19026 #041-77-2007, ▲ L2007 *012
STATHACOS, Evangelia M. 501 N LANSDOWNE AVE 19026 #561-14-1980 L1984 **PD** *020 †18
STONE, Robert K. 501 N LANSDOWNE AVE 19026 #041-01-1949 L1951 **P** *071 †75
SUGAR, Miklos. 2300 GARRETT RD 19026 #409-16-1950 L1968 **PD** *071
SUH, Moon Ja. 2929 GARRETT RD 19026 #583-09-1966 L1988 **IM** *020

■ = Address Information Privacy Protected

SUNDMAKER, Wilfried K H. ■ 19026 #407-10-1953 L1962 **OTO** *071 †45
SZABO, Patricia Ellen. 5030 STATE RD, STE 2-500 19026 #473-01-1981 L1984 **GP** *020
TARGAN, Nathan Alpern. ■ 19026 #035-08-1943 L1951 **OS** *075
THEBERGE, Francois. 47 REVERE RD # 5 19026 #847-11-1994 L1998 **FM** *071
THORNTON, Anthony Michael. 501 N LANSDOWNE AVE 19026 #041-13-1990 L1994
    AN *071 †05
TIONGSON, Eleanor S. 2100 KEYSTONE AVE, STE 301 19026 #748-01-1968 L1976
    OBG *020 †30
TRIGOS, Wira. ■ 19026 #407-16-1952 L1963 **CHP** *071
TUMAIAN, Aram. 501 N LANSDOWNE AVE 19026 #781-01-1961 L1980 **AN** *071
VALA, Marc A. 501 N LANSDOWNE AVE 19026 #036-01-1993 L1998 **SP** *020 †50
VANDERBEEK, Paul Brannan. 501 N LANSDOWNE AVE, DELAWARE COUNTY MEM
    HOSP 19026 #041-02-1993 L1996 **EM** *020 †16
WANG, Yongping. ■ 19026 #032-01-2003 L2003 **PTH** *100 †50
WEINSTEIN, Michael Scott. 2100 KEYSTONE AVE STE 309, PULMONARY ASSOSCIATES OF
    D 19026 #041-15-2000 L2002 **PCC** *020 †20
WELZ, Werner Kurt Robt. 5248 RESERVATION RD 19026 #407-21-1945 L1959 **P N** *072 †75
WESTPHAL, Robert Darwin. ■ 19026 #047-05-1930 L1930 **IM** *071 †20
YOUHN, Deborah Dale. 2100 KEYSTONE AVE, STE 507 19026 #016-42-1998 L2007 **D** *020 †15
ZINTL, William John. 3001 GARRETT RD 19026 #041-01-1939 L1941 **GS** *071 †85

DRUMS – LUZERNE

ALLEN, Julia Roberta. ■ 18222 #041-07-1959 L1980 **P** *071 †75
BENYO, Philip John. 144 S OLD TURNPIKE RD 18222 #041-14-1978 L1979 **IM** *020 †20
BERGUSON, Paul David. ■ 18222 #041-02-1975 L1976 **AN** *071 †05
GRECO, Victor F. ■ 18222 #041-02-1951 L1952 **GS TS** *072 †85
KRAYNACK, Barry Jos. ■ 18222 #041-12-1973 L1976 **AN PMM** *071 †05 ‡
LARSSON, Ernst-Olof L. ■ 18222 #041-09-1977 L1978 **IM** *020 †20
MODY, Sushil Sudhakar. 11 WOODMERE DR 18222 #012-05-2000 L2003 **PD** *020 †55
MUMIE, Lawrence Eugene. ■ 18222 #041-09-1982 L1983 **FM** *020 †18
SATTAR, Shariq. ■ 18222 #748-12-1998 L2007 **IM** *020 †20
WASHINSKY, Jodi. ■ 18222 #041-13-2007 L2007 **IM** *012

DU BOIS – CLEARFIELD

AHN, John Joon. 145 HOSPITAL AVE STE 113 15801 #043-01-1987 L2003 **CD** *020 †20
ALLEN, John Edgar. ■ 15801 #041-12-1961 L1961 **P** *030
AMBROSE, Jayaseelan. 145 HOSPITAL AVE STE 113, DU BOIS REG CARDIOLOGY 15801
    #495-27-1985 L1997 **CD IM** *020 †20 ‡
ANAND, Sanjeev. 190 W PARK AVE, STE 6 15801 #308-11-1984 L1988 **NEP IM** *020 †20
ANGHELOIU, George Oliviu. 100 HOSPITAL AVE, DUBOIS REGIONAL MEDICAL CE 15801
    #781-03-1993 L2001 **CD** *020 †20
AUSTIN, Gregory Eric. 145 HOSPITAL AVE STE 200 15801 #024-07-1979 L1993 **FM** *020 †18
BALDERACH, Ronald Re. 635 MAPLE AVE, DRMC EAST 15801 #048-02-1971 L1975
    GS *020 †85
BARLEY, Samuel Benj. 145 HOSPITAL AVE STE 105, BOX 601 15801 #025-01-1958 L1971
    ORS OSM *071
BEAN, George Jos. 100 HOSPITAL AVE 15801 #041-07-1991 L1994 **PTH** *020 †50
BECK, Bonny Lorraine. 90 BEAVER DR, STE 21D 15801 #041-13-1981 L1982 **OPH** *020 †35
BHAGWANDIEN, Narendra. 100 HOSPITAL AVE, DRMC 15801 #660-02-1992 L1997
    IM *020 †20 ‡
BLAKESLEE, Colson E. ■ 15801 #041-77-1944, ▲ L1959 **FM** *071
BOBRIN, Bradford David. 635 MAPLE AVE, 3RD FL 15801 #041-09-1995 L2004 **PYG** *020 †75
BRADLEY, Thomas Jos. 100 HOSPITAL AVE 15801 #041-14-1977 L1978 **FM** *020 †18
CAMERON, Russell Edward. 100 HOSPITAL AVE 15801 #041-12-1986 L1999 **EM** *020 †16
CHERRY, James Paul. 145 HOSPITAL AVE, STE 313 15801 #021-01-1993 L1996 **U** *020 †95
CHERRY, Louis J. ■ 15801 #041-12-1953 L1954 **GS** *071
DE THOMAS, Ronald S. 145 HOSPITAL AVE, STE 313 15801 #035-03-1979 L1986 **ORS** *020 †40
DHANANI, Nizar H. ■ 15801 #704-03-1968 L1973 **IM** *071 †20
EL KASSAS, Hazem Fathlla. 100 HOSPITAL AVE, P O BOX 447 15801 #915-02-1988 L1993
    ON *020 †20
FALL, Stephen Mart. 145 HOSPITAL AVE, STE 206 15801 #036-05-1977 L1995 **TS** *020 †85,90
FATULA, George Michael. 529 SUNFLOWER DR 15801 #041-12-1971 L1972 **PD** *020 †55
FUGATE, Howard, Jr. 145 HOSPITAL AVE 15801 #041-02-1952 L1953 **IM DIA** *020 †20
FUGATE, James K, Jr. ■ 15801 #041-09-1981 L1994 **PD** *020 †55
FUGATE, James Kethledge. 529 SUNFLOWER DR 15801 #041-09-1956 L1958 **P** *071 †75
GANTALAO, Edgar B. 90 BEAVER DR STE 117D, CHILD & ADOLESCENT SERVICE 15801
    #748-14-1980 L2002 **CHP** *020 †20
GERHART, Guy Harold. ■ 15801 #041-09-1968 L1974 **IM** *020 †20
GRILL, Winfred Eugene. ■ 15801 #038-40-1943 L1946 **GP** *071
GROUT, Richard Everett. 635 MAPLE AVE APT C 15801 #005-12-1972 L2000 **NPM PD** *020 †55
HALLSTROM, Laun Robt. 145 HOSPITAL AVE STE 300 15801 #041-02-1989 L1995 **PM** *020 †60
HASSAN, Mohamed Ibrahim. 100 HOSPITAL AVE, DUBOIS REGIONSAL MEDICAL C 15801
    #915-02-1987 L2007 **NPM** *020 †55
HAYAT, Shaukat. 145 HOSPITAL AVE, DRMC NEUROSURGERY 15801 #704-04-1968 L1976
    NS GS *020 †25
HETZLER, Norman A, Jr. 145 HOSPITAL AVE, STE 202 15801 #041-09-1982 L1986
    GS VS *020 †90,85
HILL, William R. ■ 15801 #041-02-1952 L1953 **OPH** *071 †35
HRECZNYJ, Bohdan Nicholai. 100 HOSPITAL AVE 15801 #025-07-1985 L1987 **P CHP** *020 †75
HURWITZ, Larry Edward. 145 HOSPITAL AVE, STE 113 15801 #041-12-1968 L1969
    CD IM *020 †20
KENNARD, John Frederick. ■ 15801 #041-02-1957 L1958 **PTH** *071 †50
KOSCO, George Michael. 100 HOSPITAL AVE 15801 #041-13-1972 L1974 **DR** *020 ‡
KRATZ, Johannes Ruediger. ■ 15801 #024-01-2006 L2006 **GS** *012
KRATZ, Rudiger. 145 HOSPITAL AVE, STE 211 15801 #016-01-1973 L2002 **N** *020 †75
KULKARNI, Shashikant A. 38 OVERLOOK DR 15801 #495-98-1972 L2006 **DR** *020 †80
KUSH, Michael Joel. 145 HOSPITAL AVE, STE 106 15801 #016-43-1971 L1987
    MFM AM *020 †30
LANG, Stanley. 90 BEAVER DR, PRIMARY CARE ASSOCIATES AT 15801 #019-02-1978 L1981
    FM *020 †18
LEE, Albert C. 100 HOSPITAL AVE, HAHNE REGIONAL CANCER CENT 15801
    #063-01-1982 L1992 **ON** *020 †80

LUNDGREN, Eric Carl. 605 S MAIN ST 15801 #041-02-1986 L1988 **GS** *020 †85
LUNDGREN, Paula Ann. 605 S MAIN ST 15801 #041-02-1994 L1999 **GS** *020 †85
LUNDGREN, Wilbert Gene. DEPOSIT NATNL BANK BLDG, STE 204 15801 #041-02-1956 L1957
    GS *071 †85
MALHOTRA, Rajeev. 100 HOSPITAL AVE, DRMC BEHAVIORAL HEALTH CEN 15801
    #495-29-1976 L1999 **P PYG** *020 †75
MALIK, Javaid Ashraf. 100 HOSPITAL AVE, DEPT. OF ANESTHESIA 15801 #704-20-1990 L2003
    GS *020 †05 ‡
MALIK, Rajat P. 621 S MAIN ST 15801 #495-45-1977 L1979 **GE IM** *020 †20 ‡
MARCHIOLI, Carmine Carl. 100 HOSPITAL AVE, HAHNE REGIONAL CANCER CENT 15801
    #025-07-1990 L1992 **HO IM** *020 †20
MC KINLEY, Erin Arthur. 100 HOSPITAL AVE 15801 #041-13-1975 L1976 **EM** *020 †18,16
MC VAY, Edward John. 100 HOSPITAL AVE, BOX 447 15801 #010-02-1988 L1990
    OM IM *020 †70,20
MEILLER, Joan Mason. ■ 15801 #035-08-1952 L1994 **P CHP** *071 †75
MILLER, Adam Christopher. 90 BEAVER DR STE 101A 15801 #041-12-2002 L2002 **IM** *020
MILLER, Michal Ann. 145 HOSPITAL AVE, STE 204 15801 #051-07-1997 L1999 **PHO** *020 †55
MOORE, Le Roy Calvin. 145 HOSPITAL AVE, STE 113 15801 #041-09-1981 L1982
    IM CD *020 †20
MYERS, Lynn Austin, III. 145 HOSPITAL AVE STE 300 15801 #056-06-1986 L2001 **PM** *020 †60
O'BRYON, James Earl. 898 BEAVER DR 15801 #130-01-2001 L2006 **FM** *020 †18
OTT, Gary Dean. 145 HOSPITAL AVE, STE 315 15801 #041-14-1996 L1999 **OBG** *020 †30
PAISLEY, Kevin John. ■ 15801 #041-12-1996 L1998 **DR** *020 †80
PARLAVECCHIO, Dennis Sean. DEPOSIT BANK BLDG, DU BOIS FAMILY PRACTICE 15801
    #422-01-1981 L1982 **FM** *071 †18
PATHAK, Rajani Kanta. ■ 15801 #495-15-1956 L1979 **CD IM** *071 †20
PERKINS, Richard Putnam. ■ 15801 #035-01-1965 L1977 **MFM OCC** *020 †30 ‡
PIASIO, Mark Alfred. 145 HOSPITAL AVE STE 311 15801 #010-02-1982 L1989
    ORS OAR *020 †40
POPE, Jonathan Gaertner. 100 HOSPITAL AVE, DUBOIS REGIONAL MEDICAL CE 15801
    #016-06-1998 L2004 **ID** *020 †20
REESE, Sterling Scott. 145 HOSPITAL AVE, STE 113 15801 #024-05-1978 L1995 **CD** *020 †20
ROEMER, Paul Brian. 211 BEAVER DR 15801 #550-03-1996 L1999 **IM** *020 †20
ROSCOE, Gregory James. 871 BEAVER DR 15801 #561-01-1976 L1979 **OTO** *020 ‡
SAPRA, Manish. 100 CALDWELL DR 15801 #496-38-1998 L2003 **P** *020 †75
SCERBO, James Alexander. 145 HOSPITAL AVE STE 205 15801 #035-01-1979 L1982
    IM *020 †20 ‡
SCHACHTER, Larry Gene. 145 HOSPITAL AVE, STE 112 15801 #017-20-1978 L1987
    GS GP *020 †85
SELDEN, Basil Harris. 346 TREASURE LK, 346 TREASURE LAKE 15801 #041-01-1977 L1979
    IM *020 †20
SETH, Arun K. 215 HILLCREST DR 15801 #913-12-1976 L1994 **AN** *020 †05
SETHURAMAN, Venkat. 145 HOSPITAL AVE STE 311, DUBOIS REGIONAL MEDICAL CE 15801
    #041-07-1998 L2001 **ORS OSS** *020 †40
SHAH, Ghazanfar Ali. 100 HOSPITAL AVE, DUBOIS RADIOLOGISTS 15801 #704-01-1967 L1978
    R *020 †80
SHAH, Manjula Shirish. 629 S MAIN ST 15801 #495-23-1962 L1977 **GYN GS** *071
SHAH, Shirish Natwarlal. 629 S MAIN ST 15801 #495-23-1962 L1975 **GS GP** *020 †85
SHARMA, Navneet Kumar. 100 HOSPITAL AVE, DRMC 15801 #496-38-1999 L2004
    AN *020 †20 ‡
SIAR, William John. ■ 15801 #041-12-1963 L1964 **NPM PD** *020 †55 ‡
SIMPSON, Timothy Clark. 222 FALLEN TIMBER DR, 222 FALLEN TIMBER DRIVE 15801
    #024-16-1999 L2001 **EM FM** *020 †20
SMITH, Thomas Walter. 529 SUNFLOWER DR 15801 #008-01-1975 L1978 **OPH** *020 †35
SUSLOW, Gregory Richard. 100 HOSPITAL AVE, DUBOIS REG MED CTR 15801
    #305-01-1988 L1993 **PTH PCP** *020 †50 ‡
SUVARNAKAR, Jawahar N. 145 HOSPITAL AVE STE 105 15801 #495-01-1971 L1979
    IM *020 †20
THOMAS, Santha Mary. ■ 15801 #495-80-1971 L1983 **PD** *074
THOMAS, Thomas K. 38 W SCRIBNER AVE 15801 #495-38-1961 L1976 **U** *071 †95
TURKIN, Scott Robt. 90 BEAVER DR STE 121D, BEHAVIORAL HEALTH CENTER 15801
    #649-43-1992 L1996 **P MDM** *020 †20
VALIGORSKY, Paul J, II. 100 HOSPITAL AVE, DUBOIS REGONAL MEDICAL CEN 15801
    #654-01-1987 L1994 **AN** *020 †05
WONG, Karl. 100 HOSPITAL AVE, DE BOIS REG MED CTR 15801 #165-04-1973 L1977 **AN** *020 ‡
YOO, Tai Young. 145 HOSPITAL AVE STE 315 15801 #583-09-1962 L1973 **OBG** *071
ZIMET, Lewis Bruce. ■ 15801 #748-08-1981 L1994 **IM** *020

DUBLIN – BUCKS

WAKIM, Wakim Victor. 915 MANOR DR, GRANDVIEW HOSPITAL 18917 #605-03-2002 L2007
    IM *020 †20

DUNBAR – FAYETTE

EDGE, Fred Clayton. 1829 UNIVERSITY DR 15431 #654-01-1983 L1984 **PM PMM** *020
PEREZ-AQUINO, Erlinda B. 230 DOGWOOD DR 15431 #748-08-1969 L1976 **FM** *020

DUNCANNON – PERRY

BOLDEN, Patrick Thos. 51 BUSINESS CAMPUS WAY, STE 200 17020 #023-01-1978 L1979
    FM *020 †18
JENKINS, Rosemary. ■ 17020 #041-12-1979 L1980 **PTH PCP** *071 †50

DUNCANSVILLE – BLAIR

BURWELL, David Landon. 3 764 PLZ 16635 #305-01-2001 L2001 **FM** *020 †18
JACOBUS, Judith Lynn. 189 GLIMCHER DR 16635 #041-09-1987 L1989 **FM** *020 †18
KHALID, Mushtaq H. ■ 16635 #704-20-1981 L1999 **PTH** *020
MADDEN, Francis Patrick. ■ 16635 #041-02-1967 L1968 **IM GE** *020 †20
MARLOWE, Scott David. 317 HUNTERS PASS DR, MERCY MEDICAL IMAGING ASSO 16635
    #041-07-1988 L1990 **DR** *020 †80

MURPHY, Frederick T. 1125 OLD ROUTE 220 N, OSTEOPOROSIS CENTER 16635 #041-77-1993, ▲ L2000 **RHU** *020 †20

RANATUNGA, Don Kemananda. ■ 16635 #220-01-1964 L1975 **EM** *072

SHAW, Marianne Lynn. 1125 OLD ROUTE 220 N, OSTEOPOROSIS CTR/P O BOX 9 16635 #041-13-1993 L2004 **RHU** *020 †20

SOMMER, Vicki Marlene. 1125 OLD ROUTE 220 N 16635 #035-03-1977 L1982 **PD** *020 †55

VAN HORN, Stewart Dane. 176 VISION DR 16635 #005-18-1995 L2000 **OPH** *020 †35

DUNMORE – LACKAWANNA

ANTOGNOLI, William John. 781 KEYSTONE INDUSTRL PARK 18512 #041-02-1961 L1962 **PTH** *071 †50

BAIKADI, Madhava. 1110 MEADE ST, CENTER 18512 #495-37-1975 L1982 **RO** *020 †80

BARON, Andrew J. 751 KEYSTONE INDUSTRL PARK 18512 #041-02-1978 L1979 **R** *071 †80

BARSIGIAN, Carl. 1100 MEADE ST, HEMA & ONC ASSOC NEPA 18512 #041-02-1997 L1999 **HO IM** *020 †20

BATZEL, Edward Lee. 1416 MONROE AVE, STE 303 18509 #035-47-1978 L1993 **VS GS** *020 †85

BLOMAIN, Eric Wm. 1222 MARION ST 18512 #041-02-1973 L1976 **PS GS** *020 †65 ‡

BORLANDOE, Beverly C. 781 KEYSTONE INDUSTRL PARK 18512 #041-02-1972 L1978 **IM DMP** *020 †50

BRERETON, Harmar Denny. 1110 MEADE ST 18512 #041-12-1970 L1982 **RO ON** *020 †80

BROSCIUS, Michael B. 781 KEYSTONE INDUSTRL PARK 18512 #041-02-1988 L1994 **BBK** *020 †50

CONNORS, Charles F. 110 POTTER ST 18512 #041-01-1969 L1970 **FM** *071 †16,18

CRONKEY, Joseph E. 1210 ONEILL HWY 18512 #010-02-1972 L1973 **ORS** *020 †40

CURTIN, Charles Thomson. 781 KEYSTONE INDUSTRL PARK 18512 #041-02-1966 L1967 **PTH PCP** *071 †50

DAS, Amit. 1416 MONROE AVE, STE 201 18509 #495-02-1976 L1992 **N IM** *020 †75

DENAPLES, Louis Dominick. 1000 DUNHAM DR 18512 #025-01-1993 L1996 **EM** *020 †16

DHADUK, Vithalbhai D. 121 S APPLE ST, STE 1C 18512 #495-48-1980 L1985 **N** *020

DI SILVIO, Thomas Vernon. 901 KEYSTONE INDUSTRL PARK 18512 #016-43-1963 L1965 **PTH** *071 †50

DODGE, Nicholas David. 1401 ELECTRIC ST 18509 #041-13-1992 L1994 **IM** *020 †20

FALCON, John Gary. 1000 DUNHAM DR, EMERGENCY SERVICES PC 18512 #010-02-1988 L1998 **EM** *020 †16

FRANTZ, Linda Sebastian. 1039 ONEILL HWY 18512 #041-02-1985 L1986 **IM** *020 †20

FRICCHIONE, Patrick Josep. 769 KEYSTONE INDUSTRL PARK 18512 #041-13-1983 L1984 **OM EM** *020 †16

GENTILE, Anthony Jos. ■ 18509 #047-06-1948 L1949 **IM** *071

GIOMBETTI, Joseph John. 919 E DRINKER ST 18512 #041-02-1967 L1968 **FM** *020 †18

GOLDEN, Robert Jos. ■ 18509 #041-09-1943 L1947 **OPH** *071

GORDON, Michael H. 1401 ELECTRIC ST 18509 #041-07-1992 L1995 **IM** *020 †20 ‡

GUZEK, John R. 1173 CLAY AVE 18510 #041-12-1978 L1979 **IM** *020 †20

HIMES, Thomas Richard. 781 KEYSTONE INDUSTRL PARK, STE P 18512 #041-07-1977 L1979 **PTH** *020 †50

HLAVAC, Philip Joseph. 414 E DRINKER ST 18512 #035-03-1993 L2003 **NS** *020 †25

JANZE, Victor. ■ 18512 #957-03-1979 L1984 **GP** *075

LABEEB, Atef Waheeb. 781 KEYSTONE INDUSTRL PARK 18512 #915-04-1989 L2001 **PCP** *100 †50

MAGILL, John Wm. ■ 18512 #010-02-1964 L1988 **IM NEP** *071 †20

MC KENNA, Scot Robt. 1140 QUINCY AVE 18510 #041-02-1992 L1994 **PS GS** *020 †85,65 ‡

MORRIS, Gloria Joan. 1100 MEADE ST 18512 #045-01-1998 L2001 **HO** *020 †20

MOXEN, John M. 1000 MEADE ST, STE 201A 18512 #010-02-1981 L1982 **DR** *020 †80

O'BOYLE, James Patrick. ■ 18512 #010-02-1932 L1933 **OBG** *071

PIOTROWSKI, Thaddeus A. 769 KEYSTONE INDUSTRL PARK 18512 #305-01-1985 L1986 **FM** *020 †18

RHIEW, Francis Changnam. 1233 MONROE AVE 18509 #583-02-1964 L1973 **DR NM** *071 †28

RIENZI, Joseph. 1000 MEADE ST, STE 201B 18512 #035-06-1985 L1989 **DR NR** *020 †80

ROSS, Alan Nicholas. 781 KEYSTONE INDUSTRL PARK 18512 #041-12-1973 L1974 **PTH** *071 †50

ROSS, Gary Wayne. 781 KEYSTONE INDUSTRL PARK, STE P 18512 #041-09-1980 L1982 **FOP PTH** *071 †50

SEHIC, Azra M. 1000 MEADE ST, STE 102 18512 #957-08-1982 L1998 **PD PN** *020 †55

SKOVIRA, Edward Martin. 901 KEYSTONE PARK 18512 #010-02-1957 L1959 **PTH** *071 †50

STEINMETZ, James Cyril. 781 KEYSTONE INDUSTRL PARK, STE P 18512 #035-03-1984 L1993 **PTH** *020 †50

SUNDHEIM, James Lang. 1000 MEADE ST, STE 201B 18512 #041-01-1970 L1971 **DR** *020 †80

SUTTON, Charles Stewart. 1000 MEADE ST, STE 201B 18512 #005-11-1982 L1992 **DR VIR** *020 †80

TSANG, Chi Keung. 1110 MEADE ST 18512 #025-07-1988 L2001 **RO NM** *020 †80

VALENTI, Samuel Anthony. 769 KEYSTONE INDUSTRL PARK 18512 #041-07-1990 L1992 **IM** *020 †20

WON, Ok Hee. 781 KEYSTONE INDUSTRL PARK, STE P 18512 #583-08-1970 L1977 **PTH PCP** *020 †50

YODER, Michael Alan. 781 KEYSTONE INDUSTRL PARK, STE P 18512 #041-13-1997 L2001 **PCP** *020 †50

ZALE, Nannette Ruth. 1000 MEADE ST, STE 102 18512 #041-02-1994 L1998 **OPH** *020 †35

DUPONT – LUZERNE

BISCOTTI, Mauer Thomas. 526 MAIN ST 18641 #308-03-1981 L1983 **IM** *020 †20 ‡

DUQUESNE – ALLEGHENY

CHUGHTAI, Mubashar. 424 GRANT AVE 15110 #704-01-1974 L1984 **IM DR** *020

PRATT, Veronica Mc Clay. 2 DUQUESNE PLZ, DUQUESNE FAMILY HEALTH CTR 15110 #041-12-1995 L1997 **FM** *020 †18

DURHAM – BUCKS

MC HUGH, Margaret Therese. ■ 18039 #308-03-1985 L1991 **IM** *020 †20

DURYEA – LUZERNE

FASCIANA, Guy Michael. 605 MAIN ST 18642 #308-03-1981 L1983 **IM** *020

EAGLES MERE – SULLIVAN

CONIFF, Robert Francis. ■ 17731 #041-02-1958 L1959 **DIA IM** *071 †20

FREELAND, George Richard. ■ 17731 #041-02-1971 L1972 **IM GE** *071 †20

SABOL, Louise C Justin. ■ 17731 #041-07-1959 L1960 **OPH** *071 †35

SPAETH, Philip G. PO BOX 68 17731 #051-01-1951 L1953 **OPH** *071 †35

EAGLEVILLE – MONTGOMERY

AGUILO-SEARA, Miguel R. 104 EGYPT RD 19403 #308-04-1982 L1991 **N** *020

ALTOMONTE, Joseph Francis. 342 W GERMANTOWN PIKE 19403 #561-17-1963 L1964 **GP** *020

ARCILLA, Rene A. ■ 19403 #748-01-1952 L1966 **PDC** *071

BAZZAN, Anthony J. 2505 BOULEVARD OF TH GNRLS 19403 #561-11-1984 L1988 **IMG** *020 †20

BELLET, Robert Ernest. 1000 MADISON AVE 19403 #041-02-1968 L1969 **ON HEM** *062 †20

BENNETT, John Toscan. ■ 19403 #041-13-1961 L1962 **OBG** *071 †30

BERGNES, Manuel Arthur. ■ 19403 #035-08-1941 L1949 **FOP** *071 †50

BHARDWAJ, Anil Kumar. ■ 19403 #495-29-1988 L2001 **IM** *020

CARRILLO, Margaret A. 60 EAGLEVILLE RD, FACILITY 19403 #024-01-1978 L1986 **IM** *020 †20,16

CHOWDHARY, Kamlesh K. ■ 19403 #495-49-1961 L1980 **OBG** *020

COLCHER, Robert E. 1033 W GERMANTOWN PIKE 19403 #041-02-1950 L1951 **ADM GS** *020 †85

CORRADO, Gail Carol. 1033 W GERMANTOWN PIKE 19403 #041-02-1980 L1981 **P OS** *020

DANA, Adrian. ■ 19403 #041-07-1979 L1986 **PDS** *020 †55

DANTULURI, Hema Malini. ■ 19403 #496-27-1997 L2005 **PD** *020 †20

DOLPHIN, John Michael. 400 EGYPT RD 19403 #041-09-1947 L1948 **PTH** *071 †50

DRINKER, Anne Sandwith. 2819 COLONY DR 19403 #035-01-1944 L1963 **AN PD** *074

ECHIKSON, Edward H. 100 EAGLEVILLE RD, EAGLEVILLE HOSPITAL 19403 #035-08-1953 L1957 **IM** *020 †20

FERNANDES, Trina Doreen. ■ 19403 #041-15-2005 L2005 **IM** *012

GAGNON, Suzanne. 1000 MADISON AVE, LUITPOLD PHARM INC 19403 #024-05-1985 L1994 **IM** *020 †20

GANGULY, Rukmini Phani. ■ 19403 #495-27-1957 L1980 **GP OBG** *020

GHEITH, Shereen Mohamed F. ■ 19403 #915-04-1989 L2001 **PTH** *100 †50

GROW, David Volpe. ■ 19403 #561-16-1958 L1959 **LM IM** *074

GUPTA, Chitra Lekha. 400 EGYPT RD 19403 #495-45-1970 L1974 **PTH** *062 †50

HAMMERS, Karen R. 50 BEECH DR, MONTGOMERY COUNTY EMERGENC 19403 #041-02-1988 L1990 **P** *020 †75

HARMAN, Herbert Jay. 50 BEECH DR, MCES 19403 #051-01-2001 L2001 **P** *100 †75

HOLDBROOK, Thomas. 50 BEECH DR, MONTGOMERY CNTY EMERG SVC 19403 #412-01-1978 L1996 **P** *020 †75

HOLM, William Wendell. ■ 19403 #028-34-1965 L1971 **PD** *071 †55

HOPKINS, John Estaugh. ■ 19403 #041-01-1946 L1947 **EM** *071 †85

JHA, Jiwesh Chandra. ■ 19403 #495-54-1980 L1995 **P** *020

JOSHI, Asmita Shrikant. ■ 19403 #495-01-1989 L1997 **PD** *020 †55 ‡

JULIEN, Antoine. 100 EAGLEVILLE RD 19403 #440-01-1957 L1968 **P IM** *020

KASIBHOTLA, Sumabala. 1033 W GERMANTOWN PIKE, 1033 WEST GERMAN TOWN PIKE 19403 #495-62-1994 L2001 **IM** *020 †20

LAZARO-MORAN, Miguela. 130 BRANDON RD 19403 #748-01-1956 L1970 **FM** *071

LEONARD, Ronald Arthur. 700 W GERMANTOWN PIKE, STE 101 19403 #041-07-1982 L1987 **GE EM** *020

LEVIN, David Welsh. ■ 19403 #041-02-1947 L1948 **IM IMG** *072

LEYDECKER, Karen M. ■ 19403 #041-07-1977 L1978 **OS IMG** *071

LOWERY, Teresa. 1042 NICOLE DR 19403 #041-15-1999 L2001 **FM** *020 †18

MAGEN, Barry Greg. ■ 19403 #041-13-1994 L1996 **AN** *020

MAHAJAN, Radha Krishna. 2521 W MAIN ST 19403 #495-20-1971 L1977 **EM GP** *020 †16

MANDEL, Richard Jay. 716 W GERMANTOWN PIKE 19403 #041-02-1976 L1981 **ORS HS** *020 †40

MARTELLA, Arthur. 2525 W MAIN 19403 #041-02-1963 L1965 **GP** *020

MARTIN, Kahlil Justin. ■ 19403 #048-04-2007 **GS** *012

MARTINEZ, Jaime Omar. ■ 19403 #041-01-2003 L2003 **AN** *020

MAYER, Bernard W. ■ 19403 #041-02-1951 L1952 **AN** *071 †05

MEYER, Matthew Christophe. ■ 19403 #041-13-2007 L2007 **IM** *012

MUDE, Malini Rvinash. 100 EAGLEVILLE RD 19403 #495-17-1970 L1986 **P** *020 †75

MULDERS, Huub J. 2505 BOULEVARD OF TH GNRLS 19403 #660-05-1983 L1988 **IM** *020 †20

NICKLAS, Donald Alden. ■ 19403 #041-02-1973 L1974 **PD** *020 †50

PALMON, Roberto Pono. ■ 19403 #748-02-1970 L1976 **CHP P** *020

PATEL, Natvarbhai R. 2792 EGYPT RD 19403 #495-22-1968 L1977 **GP** *020

PATEL, Nilesh V. 2792 EGYPT RD 19403 #919-05-1984 L1993 **FM** *020 †18

PENA-ARIET, Maria Elena. 104 EGYPT RD 19403 #308-04-1980 L1991 **P** *020 †75

PETERS-STRICKLAND, T S. 50 BEECH DR, MCES 19403 #011-03-1990 L1999 **P ADP** *020 †75

QASIM, Mohammad. 50 BEECH DR, SERVICE 19403 #704-08-1981 L1997 **P** *020 †75

RELUZ-BERNAOLA, Javier S. ■ 19403 #847-04-1961 L1970 **EM OS** *071

SAGET, Garry. 100 EAGLEVILLE RD, EAGLEVILLE HOSPITAL 19403 #041-09-1993 L1996 **IM** *020

SANDERS, Jimmie Jerome. ■ 19403 #025-01-1977 L1995 **GS EM** *030 †85

SANSONE, Joann. ■ 19403 #041-77-1985, ▲ L1986 **OBG** *020

SCHEUERMAN, Walter Geo. ■ 19403 #025-01-1942 L1948 **NS** *071 †25

SCHWARTZ, Gerson. ■ 19403 #041-77-1953, ▲ L1958 **OS** *071

SEZER, Vedat Mehmet. 1033 W GERMANTOWN PIKE 19403 #902-03-1955 L1972 **D PD** *071

SHAH, Girish J. 100 EAGLEVILLE RD 19403 #495-22-1982 L1996 **P PYG** *020

SHAH, Rajnikant Keshavlal. 2121 W MAIN ST 19403 #495-22-1968 L1975 **FM IM** *030 †18

SOLOMIDES, Chamalambos C. ■ 19403 #409-02-1988 L1997 **PCP** *020 †50

SOWERBY, George Wm. 100 EAGLEVILLE RD 19403 #041-09-1981 L1983 **P PYA** *020

STHALAM, Dwarakanath. ■ 19403 #495-21-1982 **AN** *100

SUN, Elizabeth Anne. 700 W GERMANTOWN PIKE, STE 101 19403 #041-13-1976 L1977 **GE IM** *020 †20

THOMAS, James Washington. 342 W GERMANTOWN PIKE, STE 310 19403 #041-01-1990 L2001 **DR** *020 †80

TSAI, Yu Jen. 1846 W MAIN ST 19403 #244-04-1970 L1976 **GP** *020

VASU, Neetu Balwantsing. ■ 19403 #041-15-2007 L2007 **IM** *012

WILLIAMS, Barbara J K. 100 EAGLEVILLE RD, EAGLEVILLE HOSPITAL 19403 #041-02-1974 L1976 **P GP** *020 †75 ‡

WILSON, Llewellyn, Jr. ■ 19403 #018-75-1957, ▲ L1958 **OM FM** *071 †70

WOO, Chong Wook. ■ 19403 #583-03-1979 L1984 *100

WOOD, Madeline. 548 N TROOPER RD, RD 19403 #041-02-1989 L1991 **FM** *020 †18

WRABEL, Susana. ■ 19403 #132-01-1971 L1995 **P** *020

EAST BERLIN – ADAMS

BROWN, Michael Eugene. 105 4TH ST 17316 #041-13-1980 L1981 **FM** *020 †18

GARCIA, Jose Acerimo. 470 BERMUDIAN CREEK RD 17316 #748-07-1957 L1968 **GP IM** *020

GREER, Robert Bruce, III. 166 LAKE MEADE DR 17316 #024-01-1960 L1964 **ADM OS** *071 †40

HENRY, Mark Richard. 105 4TH ST, E BERLIN FAMILY MEDICINE 17316 #041-14-1992 L1994 **FM** *020 †18

HOFFACKER, Wynne Ann. 105 4TH ST, E BERLIN FAM MED 17316 #023-01-1990 L1995 **FM** *020 †18

NELSON, Edward Arnold. 105 4TH ST, EAST BERLIN FMLY MED 17316 #035-45-1978 L1979 **FM** *020 †18

EAST GREENVILLE – MONTGOMERY

LEVY, Jenni. 8580 KINGS HWY 18041 #035-09-1986 L1992 **IM** *040 †20

SCHOLL, Harvey Wm. 5TH AND JEFFERSON STS 18041 #041-02-1937 L1938 **GP** *071

EAST MC KEESPORT – ALLEGHENY

CHOI, Sean Ho. 333 LINCOLN HWY 15035 #583-04-1971 L1976 **IM** *020

MASTERS, Ruth V Snyder. 1144 BROADWAY ST 15035 #041-12-1935 L1936 **FM FPG** *071 †18

EAST NORRITON – MONTGOMERY

BRUCE, Christopher James. 2705 DEKALB PIKE, STE 309 19401 #033-05-1989 L2007 **CRS GS** *020 †85,10

HEITMAN, David W. ■ 19401 #005-77-2002, ▲ L2002 **GS** *020

LAWSON, Lori A. 2701 DEKALB PIKE, MERCY SUBURBAN HOSP 19401 #041-02-1991 L1993 **EM** *030 †16

MERMELSTEIN, Andrew Lee. 170 W GERMANTOWN PIKE, STE C2 19401 #035-19-1994 L1997 **RHU** *020 †20

METTER, Susan Ellen. 123 W GERMANTOWN PIKE, STE 2 19401 #041-07-1979 L1983 **AN** *020 †20,05

NORDEN, Daniel Kanof. 170 W GERMANTOWN PIKE, STE C2 19401 #041-13-1986 L1987 **RHU IMG** *020 †20

SHAH, Sanjay Mahendra. 2400 VINCENT WAY 19401 #042-02-2001 L2001 **APM** *020 †05

TRIOLA, Brian Richard. ■ 19401 #038-40-2002 L2002 **CD** *012 †20

WILSON, Brian Glenn. 123 W GERMANTOWN PIKE, STE 2 19401 #041-12-1992 L1999 **AN** *020

EAST PETERSBURG – LANCASTER

HARRIGER, Miles D. ■ 17520 #041-02-1952 L1953 **FM** *072

LABOSH, Timothy John. 5970 LEMON ST, GRP AT EAST PETERSBURG 17520 #039-05-1987 L1988 **FM** *020 †18 ‡

XAKELLIS, George C, Jr. 5970 LEMON ST, EAST PETERSBURG FAMILY HEA 17520 #041-12-1981 L1983 **FM FPG** *040 †18

EAST PITTSBURGH – ALLEGHENY

DORENCAMP, Donald Girard. ■ 15112 #041-09-1954 L1956 **N OS** *100 †20

EAST STROUDSBURG – MONROE

AHDIEH, Houman. 214 WASHINGTON ST 18301 #041-09-1990 L1995 **OPH** *020 †35

ALKHUJA, Samer. 239 E BROWN ST, MEDICAL ASSOC OF MONROE CO 18301 #875-01-1989 L2001 **PUD** *020 †20

ANDERSON, John Edward. 206 E BROWN ST, MERCY MEDICAL CENTER 18301 #005-12-1977 L1990 **TS** *020 †85,90

AROMIN, Romulo A. 206 E BROWN ST, POCONO MEDICAL CENTER 18301 #748-01-1990 L1995 **ADP** *020 †75

AZAM, Muhammad. 206 E BROWN ST, POCONO MEDICAL CENTER 18301 #704-05-1991 L2000 **GPM** *020 †20

BAIR, Jeffrey F. 239 E BROWN ST 18301 #035-19-1978 L1983 **CD IM** *020 †20

BAIRD, Robert Marshall. 206 E BROWN ST 18301 #041-02-1957 L1958 **NS OS** *071 †25

BARNES, Frederick John. 600 PLAZA CT STE C 18301 #035-20-1986 L1992 **ORS GS** *020 †40

BERMAN, Eli. 239 E BROWN ST 18301 #869-04-1958 L1962 **CD IM** *020 †20

BHAGAT, Rajesh Gamanlal. 292 E BROWN ST 18301 #495-96-1974 L1984 **AI PD** *020 †55,03

BHATT, Drupad Dilipkumar. 206 E BROWN ST 18301 #495-48-1977 L1987 **OTO** *020 †45

BIGATEL, David Alfred. 505 INDEPENDENCE RD, STE C 18301 #041-02-1990 L1993 **VS** *020 †85

BIGATEL, Levelle Drose. 505 INDEPENDENCE RD, STE C 18301 #011-02-1997 L2002 **FM** *020 †18

BLANCHFIELD, Patrick Thom. 206 E BROWN ST 18301 #305-01-2000 L2007 **AN** *020

BOLDEN, Brian Eric. 206 E BROWN ST, FAMILY CARE CENTER 18301 #025-01-1994 L2003 **IM** *020 †20

BORDAS, Jose Rafael. 200 E BROWN ST, POCONO KIDS PEDS 18301 #308-02-1993 L2007 **PD** *020 †55 ‡

BULETTE, Michael Dow. 206 E BROWN ST 18301 #041-07-1998 L2001 **EM** *020 †16 ‡

BUSCH, Michael Frederick. 505 INDEPENDENCE RD, STE A 18301 #041-13-1976 L1981 **ORS** *020 †40

BUTLER, Horace G. ■ 18301 #041-01-1943 L1947 **R** *071 †80

CAHILL, Colleen Diana. 206 E BROWN ST, POCONO MEDICAL CENTER 18301 #035-15-1999 L2002 **IM** *020 †20

CASALE, Peter John. 100 PLAZA CT STE A, POCONO MED GRP NEP CNSLTS 18301 #305-01-1984 L1986 **IM NEP** *020 †20

CERRA, Carmine J. 206 E BROWN ST, POCONO HOSPITAL PATHOLOGY 18301 #561-01-1979 L1983 **PTH** *020 †50

CHAITIN, Robert Frederick. 175 E BROWN ST 18301 #025-07-1980 L2007 **OBG** *020 †30

CHARLES, Gervais. 206 E BROWN ST 18301 #035-03-1997 L2000 **IM** *020 †20

CHAUDHRY, Mohammad Azhar. 228 INDEPENDENCE RD 18301 #704-01-1963 L1975 **PUD IM** *020 †20

CHEN, Yen Shou. ■ 18301 #024-05-1984 L1990 **GE IM** *020 †20

CHHABRIA, Bhavna Mahesh. 3 PARKINSON RD 18301 #495-16-1986 L2001 **IM** *100

CHHABRIA, Mahesh. 3 PARKINSON RD 18301 #495-01-1984 L1992 **N IM** *020 †75

CHUA, Michael Cheng. 206 E BROWN ST 18301 #035-09-1991 L1995 **AN** *020 †05

CHUN, Yoon-Taek. 263 PROSPECT ST 18301 #583-01-1972 L1984 **PD** *020 †55

CIBISCHINO, Maurizio. 600 PLAZA CT STE C, MOUNTAIN VLY ORTHO PC 18301 #033-06-1989 L1996 **ORS OSM** *020 †40

COHEN, Beth Ann. 371 E BROWN ST 18301 #041-09-1990 L1992 **N CN** *020 †75

COOPER, Colleen Ann. 206 E BROWN ST 18301 #035-47-1981 L1983 **PD** *020 †55

COVINGTON, Darell Tyrone. 500 PLAZA CT, STE C 18301 #041-14-1981 L1982 **CRS** *020 †10

DALAL, Umesh Isharlal. 100 PLAZA CT STE A, POCONO MED GRP NEP CNSLTS 18301 #495-48-1981 L1992 **IM NEP** *020 †20

DAVIS, Howard Zeleg. ■ 18302 #041-01-1977 L2007 **EM** *020 †16

DE FRANCO, Basil A. 206 E BROWN ST, PMC MEDICAL STAFF OFFICE 18301 #305-01-1994 L2000 **EM** *020 †16

DEGLER, Douglas Alan. 239 E BROWN ST STE C 18301 #010-02-1995 L1997 **IM** *020 †20

DE QUEVEDO, Robert F G. 175 E BROWN ST 18301 #041-13-1967 L1968 **OBG** *020 †30

DI IORIO, Emil John. 505 INDEPENDENCE RD, STE A 18301 #165-08-1978 L1983 **ORS HS** *020 †40

DIXON, Arthur S. 739 MILFORD RD, POCONO PEDIATRIC ASSOC 18301 #035-15-1981 L1990 **PD** *020 †55

DORON, David A. 239 E BROWN ST 18301 #231-01-1988 L1997 **CD** *020 †20

DRACOS, Frank John. 100 PLAZA CT, STE C 447 OFFICE PLAZA 18301 #041-01-1956 L1957 **ORS OSM** *071 †40

DUGAN, Gary Mitchell. 206 E BROWN ST 18301 #041-14-1985 L1986 **IM** *020 †20

EICHLER, George Robt. 296 E BROWN ST 18301 #041-13-1957 L1958 **ORS** *071 †40

ESTONILO, Rodrigo M. 100 EAGLESMERE CIR, STE 200A 18301 #748-09-1972 L1992 **NS** *020

EUFEMIO, Michael Anthony. 300 PLAZA CT STE B, RTE 447 18301 #010-02-1991 L1993 **U** *020 †95

FAMIGLIO, Linda Marie. 175 E BROWN ST, STE 202 18301 #041-09-1983 L1991 **CHN PD** *020 †55,75

FRANCESCANGELI, V, Jr. 500 PLAZA CT 18301 #041-13-1980 L1981 **IM** *020 †20

FREIMER, Martin. 100 PLAZA CT STE D 18301 #038-43-1985 L1997 **P EM** *020 †75

FUENTES, Jose N. 239 E BROWN ST 18301 #264-12-1981 L1997 **IM** *062 †20 ‡

GEROLD, Thomas Francis. 206 E BROWN ST, POCONO MEDICAL CENTER 18301 #035-09-1984 L2005 **GS** *020 †85

GIBBS, Judith A. 739 MILFORD RD 18301 #067-01-1972 L1980 **NPM** *075 †55

GODBOUT, Brett Patrick. 505 INDEPENDENCE RD, STE A 18301 #035-15-1982 L1990 **ORS** *020 †40

GOLD, Steven Elliot. 239 E BROWN ST 18301 #036-01-1994 L1997 **IM** *020 †20

GORTYCH-BARNES, Virginia. 206 E BROWN ST, POCONO MEDICAL CENTER 18301 #035-09-1987 L1993 **EM** *020 †16

GOVINDASAMY, Rajesh. 100 PLAZA CT, STE A 18301 #495-04-1993 L2002 **NEP** *020 †20

GRANET, Paul Jason. 500 PLAZA CT, STE D 18301 #010-02-1997 L2006 **CCS** *020

GREENBERG, Michael J. 231 E BROWN ST 18301 #035-47-1984 L1988 **RO** *020 †80 ‡

GRUSZKA, Francis Anthony. ■ 18301 #041-02-1957 L1958 **PTH** *071 †50

GULICK, Thomas Howard. 175 E BROWN ST 18301 #041-13-1972 L1973 **U** *020 †95

GUPTA, Giriwar Lal. 144 E BROWN ST 18301 #495-41-1957 L1975 **N IM** *020 †20,75

HALPERIN, M. ■ 18301 #154-07-1937 L1952 **GP** *062 †05

HAMILTON, Cheryl. 175 E BROWN ST, URBAN HEALTH PLAN INC 18301 #035-06-1980 L2004 **OBG** *020 †30

HAMILTON, Donna Lynn. ■ 18302 #041-02-1992 L1995 **PD** *020 †55

HAMILTON, Garry Affef. ■ 18301 #035-08-2000 L2004 **PD** *020

HAWKS, Ralph David. 500 PLAZA CT 18301 #033-05-1995 L1998 **IM** *020 †20

HAYNICZ, Peter. 206 E BROWN ST DEPT RAD 18301 #041-02-1962 L1963 **R** *020 †80

HODGE, Hugh Perry, Jr. ■ 18301 #041-09-1958 L1962 **OBG** *020 †20

HOFFMAN, James Kirk. 505 INDEPENDENCE RD, STE A 18301 #041-09-1990 L1996 **ORS** *020 †40

HUNSICKER, Llewellyn W. ■ 18301 #041-01-1946 L1947 **AS TRS** *071 †85

INDZONKA, Mark Francis. 505 INDEPENDENCE RD STE B, HEART CARE OF THE POCONOS 18301 #035-08-1986 L1989 **CD IC** *020 †20

INYANG, Udeme Udofia. 206 E BROWN ST 18301 #690-01-1986 L2004 **AN** *020

IQBAL, Muhammad Javed. 206 E BROWN ST, POCONO MEDICAL CENTER 18301 #704-01-1991 L2003 **DR** *020

JARAMILLO, John Joe. 175 E BROWN ST, STE 202 18301 #048-12-1983 L2004 **PDE** *020 †55

JENNINGS, Eugene Leslie. 175 E BROWN ST, STE 111 18301 #035-20-1988 L1999 **P** *020 †75

JOHNSON, Lorie Nicole. 175 E BROWN ST, STE 108 18301 #041-15-1999 L2002 **OBG** *020 †30

JORDAN, William Peter. 175 E BROWN ST, STE 107 18301 #065-09-1967 L1968 **GS** *020 †85 ‡

KATARA, Rajkumar Lachharam. 3 PARKINSON RD, MONROE COUNTY 18301 #495-65-1990 L2000 **IM** *020 †75

KATARA, Suman R. ■ 18301 #496-38-1991 L2001 **IM** *020 †60

KATZ, Howard Victor. 500 PLAZA CT, STE C 18301 #025-01-1986 L2003 **ORS** *020 †40

KAUDERER, John Geo, Jr. ■ 18301 #035-01-1964 L1970 **GE IM** *071 †20

KEMPF, Charles Tyler. 206 E BROWN ST 18301 #035-08-1977 L1979 **R** *020 †80

KENNEDY, Richard Paul. 206 E BROWN ST, POKENO MEDICAL CTR 18301 #011-02-1965 L1975 **DR NM** *020 †80,28

KERRIGAN, James Jos. 3 PARKINSON RD 18301 #041-02-1984 L1986 **N** *020 †75

KESSELRING, Wm Thos, Jr. 500 PLAZA CT 18301 #041-02-1979 L1980 **IM IMG** *020 †20

KHAN, Saadullah. 239 E BROWN ST, MEDICAL ASSOCIATES OF MONR 18301 #704-09-1973 L2005 **GE IM** *020 †20

KOSCIELNIAK, Dariusz E. 100 EAGLESMERE CIR, EAST BROWN MEDICAL ASSOC 18301 #759-04-1987 L1997 **IM** *020 †20

LAWRENCE, Philip H. 175 E BROWN ST, POCONO MEDICAL BLDG 18301 #020-02-1978 L1986 **OBG** *020 †30
LAZO, Deogracias Singson. 206 E BROWN ST 18301 #748-02-1963 L1996 **EM** *071 †16
LI, Fuhai. ■ 18302 #243-23-1986 L2006 **N** *020 †75
LIEGNER, Robert Mark. 206 E BROWN ST 18301 #030-06-1982 L1986 **EM IM** *020 †20
LIM, Ho-Im. ■ 18302 #583-03-1962 L1974 **PM** *020
LIRAG, Enrique Mendiola. 526 INDEPENDENCE RD 18301 #748-01-1991 L1997 **P** *020 †75
LUCCO, Angelo John. 210 MOUNT NEBO RD 18301 #033-06-1980 L1999 **IMG IM** *020 †20
LUCHETTI, Wayne Thomas. 505 INDEPENDENCE RD, STE A 18301 #041-01-1993 L1995 **OSM** *020 †40
LUDIVICO, Charles L. 600 PLAZA CT, STE D 18301 #041-13-1970 L1971 **RHU** *020 †20
LUNA, Aurelio Coronel. ■ 18301 #748-08-1957 L1972 **OBG GP** *071
MAGHSOUDLOU, Behzad. 239 E BROWN ST 18301 #035-48-1995 L2005 **N P** *020 †75
MALIK, Hussain G. 296 E BROWN ST 18301 #704-01-1969 L1976 **OTO** *020 †45
MARKOSI, Charles, Jr. 206 E BROWN ST 18301 #041-02-1963 L1965 **FM ORS** *071
MARTZ, Patricia Ann. 175 E BROWN ST, STE 115 18301 #041-09-1992 L1996 **GS** *020 †85
MC DONALD, Brian Francis. 239 E BROWN ST 18301 #561-01-1979 L1995 **IM OS** *020 †20
MEHTA, Mukesh Jayantilal. 175 E BROWN ST, STE 110 18301 #495-17-1974 L1982 **GS VS** *020 †85
MENIO, Gregory John. 300 E BROWN ST 18301 #041-13-1985 L1986 **ORS HS** *020 †40
MIELNICKI, Stanley D. 5221 MILFORD RD 18302 #305-01-1982 L1987 **FM** *020 †18
MILLER, Mary Beth. 175 E BROWN ST 18301 #007-02-1997 L2001 **OBG** *020
MIRIC, Slobodan Jovan. 230 INDEPENDENCE RD 18301 #957-07-1994 L2006 **N** *020
MOHYUDDIN, Moiz. 419 KING ST 18301 #704-01-1962 L1973 **P** *020
MOLINA, Ramon Basil. 206 E BROWN ST 18301 #041-02-1959 L1960 **FM** *071 †18
MORELLO, Dino Cono. ■ 18302 #041-13-1996 L1999 **FM** *020 †18
MORROW, Robert Edward. 206 E BROWN ST 18301 #033-05-1983 L1984 **P** *020 †75
MOYER, James Edward. 300 PLAZA CT STE B, RTE 447 18301 #016-01-1980 L1981 **U** *020 †95
NARVAEZ, Richard Alan. 206 E BROWN ST 18301 #041-13-1982 L1983 **CD IM** *020 †20
NEKURI, Suresh Kumar. 206 E BROWN ST, POCONO MEDICAL CENTER 18301 #495-58-1994 L2000 **IM** *020 †20
NICHOLS, Rufus A. ■ 18302 #165-04-1958 L1960 **OBG** *071 †30
NOSTRO, Anthony Frank. 206 E BROWN ST 18301 #035-15-1988 L2006 **AN** *020 †05
OGBOLU, Chukwudi Emmanuel. 206 E BROWN ST, POCONO MEDICAL CENTER 18301 #012-21-1999 L2003 **IM** *020 †20
PACIOTTI, Samuel Michael. 53 WELLSLEIGH CT, SPRING LAKE ESTATES 18301 #041-01-1980 L1982 **AN** *020 †05
PAGLIA, John Anthony. 600 PLAZA CT, 447 OFFICE PLZ STE C 18301 #010-02-1988 L1993 **ORS** *020 †40
PAPA, Thomas Michael. 206 E BROWN ST, POCONO MED CTR 18301 #561-17-1983 L1992 **ID IM** *050 †20
PASCAL, Harold James. 5006 POOLE RD 18301 #649-33-1980 L1981 **P** *020
PATEL, Darshan B. ■ 18302 #035-06-2000 L2002 **FM** *020 †18
PAUL, Boris. 391 E BROWN ST 18301 #913-49-1972 L1982 **VS GS** *020 †85
PEREZ, Alex D. 3 PARKINSON RD, NEUROLOGY ASSOCIATES OF MO 18301 #042-02-1999 L2005 **APM** *020
PEVNY, Ernest. ■ 18301 #286-03-1959 L1983 **FM AN** *020 †05
PLISKIN, Mark. 239 E BROWN ST 18301 #041-02-1962 L1963 **R** *020 †80
PONNATHPUR, Vidyashankar. 239 E BROWN ST 18301 #495-72-1989 L1999 **CD** *020 †20
POWERS, Brian Allan. 600 PLAZA CT, STE C 18301 #033-05-1986 L1991 **ORS** *020 †40
PRIMIANO, George Alexande. 500 PLAZA CT STE D, 447 OFFICE PLAZA 18301 #041-09-1968 L1975 **ORS HS** *020 †40 ‡
REZNIK, David. ■ 18301 #422-01-2002 L2007 **P** *100
RICHLIN, David Mark. 206 E BROWN ST, POCONO MED CTR-ANESTH DEPT 18301 #033-05-1974 L1993 **AN PME** *020 †05
ROSS, Daniel Ira. 214 WASHINGTON ST 18301 #035-15-1981 L1986 **OPH** *020 †35
RUSSO, David Peter. 175 E BROWN ST STE 115 18301 #041-09-1986 L1991 **GS VS** *020 †85
RYAN, William Francis. 500 PLAZA CT, STE D 18301 #035-08-1979 L1985 **ON IM** *020 †20
RYLKO, Patricia Ann. 373 E BROWN ST 18301 #041-13-1986 L1987 **IM CD** *020 †20
SAM, Catherine Thyra. 175 E BROWN ST 18301 #035-19-2000 L2002 **OBG** *020
SAMET, Sherwood Lawrence. 175 E BROWN ST STE 114 18301 #041-01-1954 L1955 **GYN** *020 †30
SAMUELS, Allen Jeffrey. 600 PLAZA CT, STE D 18301 #041-07-1984 L1985 **RHU IM** *020 †20
SANTHA, Akos Kalman. 206 E BROWN ST 18301 #473-04-1992 L1999 **N CN** *020 †75,20
SARAS, Harry Peter. 300 PLAZA CT, STE A 18301 #041-09-1982 L1983 **OPH IM** *020 †20,35 ‡
SCHUMAN, Michael H. 144 E BROWN ST 18301 #035-19-1961 L1997 **N P** *075 †75
SEDANI, Khemraj H. 400 PLAZA CT, STE A 18301 #495-96-1982 L1986 **IM PCC** *020 †20
SEDANI, Mayuri Khemraj. 400 PLAZA CT STE A 18301 #495-96-1986 L1997 **MPD PD** *020 †20,55
SFORZA-HUFFMAN, Carolina. 206 E BROWN ST, LABORATORY POCONO MED CTR 18301 #924-01-1984 L1998 **PCP** *020 †50 ‡
SHANKAR, Lakshmi. 206 E BROWN ST, ATTN:PEGGY RAISING 18301 #496-20-1993 L2002 **IM** *020 †20
SIBBERING, Georgine H. 5221 MILFORD RD 18302 #308-11-1984 L1988 **FM** *020
SINGH, Harpreet K. 144 E BROWN ST 18301 #495-29-1994 L2003 **IM** *100 †20
SINGH, Karan Deep. 239 E BROWN ST, MEDICAL ASSOCIATES OF MONR 18301 #495-03-1992 L2001 **CD IC** *020 †20
SINGH, Rajwinder. 206 E BROWN ST, POCONO MEDICAL CENTER 18301 #495-29-1992 L2003 **DR** *020 †80
SINGH, Ranju. 600 PLAZA CT, STE D 18301 #495-03-1993 L2004 **RHU** *020 †20
SMITH, Chester Lional, Jr. 369 E BROWN ST 18301 #010-03-1975 L1978 **GYN** *020 †30
STERLING, Ingrid M. 200 E BROWN ST 18301 #035-08-1997 L2000 **PD** *020 †55
SYED, Ali A. 206 E BROWN ST, POCONO MEDICAL CENTER 18301 #308-13-1998 L2005 **IM** *020 †20
SZELE, Krisztina. 206 E BROWN ST 18301 #473-04-1996 L2001 **PD** *020 †55
TARPINIAN, Vaghenag Vahe. 505 INDEPENDENCE RD 18301 #913-38-1974 L1987 **FM** *020 †18 ‡
TATU, William Francis. 206 E BROWN ST 18301 #041-02-1976 L1977 **DR** *020 †80
TAYLOR, Jeffrey Scott. 175 E BROWN ST, STE 202 18301 #041-13-1988 L1990 **PHO** *020 †55
TESFAYE, Abohawariat G M. 206 E BROWN ST 18301 #286-13-1991 L2004 **AN** *030
THOMAS, Winston William. 206 E BROWN ST 18301 #275-03-1993 L2007 **CCA** *100
THOMPSON, Jeffrey Wm. 505 INDEPENDENCE RD, STE A 18301 #041-01-1972 L1973 **OM GP** *020
TINSLEY, John Patrick. 206 E BROWN ST 18301 #041-14-1973 L1976 **PTH** *020 †50
TLEMCANI, Kaoutar. 500 PLAZA CT STE A, POCONO HEMATOLOGY & ONCOLO 18301 #655-01-1999 L2007 **HO** *020

TRACHTENBERG, Wm Mark. 214 WASHINGTON ST 18301 #041-09-1971 L1972 **OPH** *020 †35
TUCKERMAN, Krystyna. 175 E BROWN ST, STE 202 18301 #917-06-1967 L2002 **PDE NPM** *020 †55
TURNBERG, Martha A. 419A KING ST 18301 #041-07-1982 L1987 **CHP P** *020
UFONDU, Solibe Chikaodili. 302 E BROWN ST 18301 #033-06-1992 L1997 **FM** *020 †18
UFONDU, Uchenna Rebecca. 302 E BROWN ST 18301 #690-07-1991 L1997 **PD** *020 †55
UGLIK, Sheldon F. ■ 18301 #759-09-1980 **PTH** *072
VAHANVATY, Ramlah M. 419 KING ST 18301 #704-06-1987 L1993 **PD** *020 †55
VAN DER SLUIS, Ralf W. 232 INDEPENDENCE RD 18301 #660-05-1989 L1998 **N** *020 †75
VEGARI, Matt M. 230 INDEPENDENCE RD, NORTHEASTERN REHAB 18301 #517-05-1979 L1983 **N IM** *020 †20
WEBER, Otto R. 206 E BROWN ST 18301 #041-09-1951 L1952 **OBG** *071 †30
WEISS, Carl Broock, Jr. 505 INDEPENDENCE RD, STE A 18301 #035-20-1982 L1988 **ORS** *020 †40
WESTHEIM, Alan I. 239 E BROWN ST 18301 #035-19-1981 L1984 **D IM** *020 †20,15
WILLIAMS, Allister. 600 PLAZA CT STE C 18301 #041-02-2008 L2008 **ORS** *020
WONG, Lim Wai. 239 E BROWN ST, MEDICAL ASSOC OF MONROE CO 18301 #035-47-1994 L1997 **IM** *020 †20
YASWINSKI, Peter Theodore. 369 E BROWN ST 18301 #041-07-1980 L1983 **OBG** *020 †30

EASTON – NORTHAMPTON

ABRAHAM, George. 250 S 21ST ST 18042 #875-01-1998 L2007 **IM** *012
ABRAHAM, Joseph Mekhail. 41 COMMUNITY DR 18045 #875-01-1993 L2004 **FM** *020 †18
AKSADE, Artun. 919D GEORGE ST 18042 #902-05-1998 L2001 **GS** *020 †85
AMIN, Atul Kanaiyalal. 3729 NAZARETH RD, STE 201 18045 #495-01-1973 L1979 **PS HS** *020 †85,65
AMIN, Devendra Kanaiyalal. 3735 NAZARETH RD 18045 #495-17-1975 L1992 **CD IM** *020 †20
AMOROSO, Anthony C. 3735 EASTON NAZARETH HWY, STE 301 18045 #033-05-1985 L1986 **IM** *020 †20
ANCHA, Prasad R. 315 S 21ST ST 18042 #495-50-1979 L1988 **N** *020 †75
ANGELICO, Richard J. 2005 FAIRVIEW AVE, CARDIOTHORACIC SURGEONS OF 18042 #035-06-1978 L1986 **TS** *020 †85,90
ANTARIO, Joseph Michael. 2025 FAIRVIEW AVE, TWIN RIVERS UROLOGY PC 18042 #035-08-1986 L1993 **U GS** *020 †95
ARACKAL KRISHNAKURUP, Jay. 250 S 21ST ST 18042 #495-63-2002 L2006 **IM** *012
ARORA, Ashoni Kumar. 100 N 18TH ST 18042 #917-13-1989 L2002 **ID** *020 †20
ATIYEH, Ahmad M S. 111 N 4TH ST 18042 #915-04-1971 L1995 **PD** *020 †55
AUERBACH, Mark Howard. 3735 EASTON NAZARETH HWY, STE 301 18045 #038-06-1978 L1981 **IM** *020 †20
AUSTIN, Mariette. 2762 NAZARETH RD 18045 #041-09-1986 L1987 **ON** *020 †20
AVALLONE, Nicholas Joseph. 3735 EASTON NAZARETH HWY, STE 101 18045 #033-06-2001 L2007 **OSM** *020
AZHAR, Saba Fatima. 250 S 21ST ST, EASTON HOSPITAL 18042 #704-02-2001 L2006 **IM** *012
BABARIA, Namrata Gaurang. 250 S 21ST ST, EASTON HOSPITAL 18042 #496-41-2002 L2005 **IM** *012
BACHURINA, Marina Vladimi. ATTN TAMMY THATCHER, EASTON HOSP 18042 #913-84-2002 L2008 *100
BAKER, Richard P, III. 2925 WILLIAM PENN HWY, STE 104 18045 #041-02-1983 L1984 **OBG** *020 †30
BARRETO, Maria Suzette V. 1723 NORTHAMPTON ST 18042 #496-15-1983 L1995 **IM** *020 †20
BASTIDAS, Jaime Adolfo. 3729 NAZARETH RD, STE 201 18045 #033-05-1994 L2003 **PS** *100
BATCHU, Rama Rao. 250 S 21ST ST, EASTON HOSPITAL 18042 #495-58-1991 L2006 **IM** *012
BECKER, Martin S. 619 MCCARTNEY ST 18042 #041-01-1951 L1952 **OBG** *071 †30
BENSIMHON, Salomon Nessim. ■ 18042 #050-02-1962 L1963 **N P** *071
BETHALA, Mary Grace. 250 S 21ST ST 18042 #308-12-1987 L2001 **IM** *100
BHAGAT, Pragina Rajesh. 250 S 21ST ST 18042 #495-17-1973 L1984 **AN** *020 †05
BHAVSAR, Ashish Ashok. ATTN TAMMY THATCHER, EASTON HOSPITAL 18042 #422-01-2007 L2007 **GS** *012
BISSET, James F, Jr. 3311 NAZARETH RD 18045 #041-02-1962 L1963 **GYN** *071 †30
BLOCH, Robert Saml. 3735 EASTON NAZARETH HWY, STE 203 18045 #035-09-1979 L1986 **GS** *020 †85
BOONSWANG, Narongsak G. 2005 FAIRVIEW AVE STE A, CARDIOTHORACIC SURGEONS OF 18042 #041-13-1997 L2003 **TS** *020 †85
BOONSWANG, Pricha. 2358 GRUVER AVE 18045 #748-09-1966 L1973 **GS CRS** *020 †10,85
BOULIS, Eman Ramses. 250 S 21ST ST, EASTON HOSPITAL 18042 #915-02-1997 L2004 **IM** *100 †20
BRANDT, Thomas Dean. 3735 EASTON NAZARETH HWY, STE 206 18045 #016-43-1976 L1997 **R** *020 †80
BURKE, Dana Richard. 250 S 21ST ST, EASTON HOSPITAL RADIOLOGY 18042 #041-14-1979 L1984 **VIR DR** *020 †80 ‡
CASAIA, Mark Anthony. 2925 WILLIAM PENN HWY, STE 201 18045 #041-14-1995 L1998 **FM** *020 †20
CHADHA, Uday Kumar. 250 S 21ST ST 18042 #495-30-1981 L1988 **PD** *020 †55
CHAO, Fang-Yu. ATTN TAMMY THATCHER, EASTON HOSP 18042 #244-02-2005 L2008 *100
CHAPMAN, Christopher, Sr. 2690 KINGSTON RD 18045 #035-15-1979 L1986 **NM DR** *020 †80,28
CHENG, Edgar T. 3735 EASTON NAZARETH HWY, STE 206 18045 #035-15-1998 L2003 **NR** *020 †80,28
CHU, Ahn Suhnmi. 3735 EASTON NAZARETH HWY, STE 206 18045 #024-05-1993 L1999 **DR** *020 †80 ‡
CHYSHKEVYCH, Iryna Ihoriv. ATTN TAMMY THATCHER, EASTON HOSPITAL 18042 #913-57-1999 L2007 **IM** *012
CLARY, Anne Adolf. 250 S 21ST ST 18042 #041-09-1981 L1982 **IM** *040 †20
COCHRAN, James F. 2151 FAIRVIEW AVE 18042 #041-13-1963 L1969 **OPH GP** *020 †35
COHEN, Brian Kenneth. 250 S 21ST ST, EMERGENCY DEPT 18042 #035-08-1993 L2001 **EM** *020 †16
COLE, Andrew James. 3735 EASTON NAZARETH HWY, STE 206 18045 #041-13-1998 L2000 **DR** *020 †80
COPELY, Dean James. 3735 EASTON NAZARETH HWY, STE 206 18045 #010-02-1983 L1994 **DR** *020 †80
COSTACURTA, Gary Aldo. 2001 FAIRVIEW AVE 18042 #041-09-1984 L1985 **CD IC** *020 †20
COSTANZA, Agatha H. ■ 18045 #041-13-1959 L1960 **PD** *071
DADA, Bolanle Abosede. 250 S 21ST ST 18042 #690-14-1990 L2003 **IM** *020 †20

DALSANIYA, Keyurkumar Pur. ■ 18042 #496-41-2004 L2007 **IM** *012
D'AMATO, Thomas. ■ 18042 #305-01-1992 **P** *012
DAVIS, Edward Thos, III. 3213 NAZARETH RD 18045 #041-09-1978 L2004 **FM** *020 †18
DEOL, Jasbir Singh. 2209 LEHIGH ST 18042 #495-29-1960 L1971 **GS** *020 †85
DESAI, Barin G. ■ 18045 #495-01-1958 L1966 **P** *072 †75
DESHMUKH, Vrushali Uddhav. 250 S 21ST ST, EASTON HOSPITAL 18042 #496-30-2001 L2005 **IM** *012
DHARIWAL, Manoj K. ■ 18042 #665-01-2006 L2007 **GS** *012
DINSMORE, Barbara J. 250 S 21ST ST, NORTHAMPTON IMAGING SPECIA 18042 #035-20-1984 L1985 **R IM** *020 †80 ‡
DI SALVO, Eugene Isidore. 2005 FAIRVIEW AVE 18042 #041-01-1957 L1958 **ORS** *071 †40
DONEKER, Thomas Geo. ■ 18045 #041-02-1956 L1957 **OS AN** *071 †05
DORMAN, Sanford Alan. 250 S 21ST ST 18042 #010-01-1976 L1982 **PTH MM** *020 †50
DRATCH, Adam Douglas. 30 COMMUNITY DR 18045 #041-02-1993 L1995 **NEP IM** *020 †20
DURBACK, Mark A. 21 CORPORATE DR # 6 18045 #041-07-1981 L1982 **RHU IM** *020 †20
DY, Victor C. 3735 NAZARETH RD, STE 102 18045 #748-10-1971 L1974 **GS SO** *020 ‡
EGAN, Gregory. 3735 NAZARETH RD, STE 206 18045 #035-08-1991 L1999 **DR** *020 †80 ‡
ELDER, Eldon Glenn. 2205 LEHIGH ST 18042 #041-12-1943 L1944 **GP A** *071
ELMI, Farhad. 2001 FAIRVIEW AVE 18042 #517-01-1995 L2001 **CD** *020 †20 ‡
FEDULLO, Lisa Marie. 3735 EASTON NAZARETH HWY, STE 206 18045 #041-13-1981 L1982 **DR** *020 †80 ‡
FELDMAN, Michael Stephen. 250 S 21ST ST 18042 #035-08-1985 L1989 **AN** *020 †05
FERNANDEZ-LOPEZ, Ulpiano. ■ 18042 #847-04-1957 L1969 **P** *020
FERRANTE, Christopher R. 3735 EASTON NAZARETH HWY, STE 101 18045 #033-06-1996 L2001 **OAR** *020 †40
FERRY, Amy Eileen. 4051 FREEMANSBURG AVE 18045 #035-06-1994 L1997 **OBG** *020 †30
FORERO-BRIGGS, Leonor. 2925 WILLIAM PENN HWY, STE 201 18045 #033-05-1988 L2002 **FM** *020 †18
FOURNIER, Robert Scott. 3735 EASTON NAZARETH HWY, STE 206 18045 #010-02-1994 L1998 **NM** *020 †80,28 ‡
FRIEDMAN, Robert Lawrence. 3735 EASTON NAZARETH HWY, STE 101 18045 #005-14-1988 L1995 **ORS** *020 †40
FULETRA, Govindji B. 1950 HAY TER 18042 #495-48-1981 L1992 **IM** *020 †20
FURMAN, David Paul. 3735 EASTON NAZARETH HWY, STE 206 18045 #041-13-1998 L2004 **DR** *020 †80
GANDHI, Jinesh M. 1700 SULLIVAN TRL, STE 12 18040 #496-38-1992 L1999 **IM** *020 †20 ‡
GAURILOFF-ROTHENBERG, Jane. 3735 NAZARETH RD, STE 206 18045 #374-05-1995 L2006 **DR** *020 †80
GEIL, Patricia Anne. 2925 WILLIAM PENN HWY, STE 201 18045 #035-06-1994 L1997 **PD** *020 †55
GENTILE, M Cristina. ■ 18045 #041-13-1981 L1983 **GP** *075
GETZ, William Bernard. ■ 18040 #041-13-1957 L1958 **OPH** *071
GHIA, Pradeep Sujanmal. 123 S 22ND ST 18042 #496-38-1976 L1978 **CD IM** *020 †20
GHORAB, Khaled Mostafa. 250 S 21ST ST, EASTON HOSPITAL 18042 #915-04-1991 L2003 **GS** *012
GLAUSER, Todd Adam. 250 S 21ST ST 18042 #026-08-1993 L2006 **PTH** *020 †50
GOLDSTEIN, Jeffrey Eric. 607 HIGH ST, BAILEY HEALTH CENTER 18042 #035-09-1984 L1990 **EM IM** *020 †16
GOPALDAS, Raja Rajan. 250 S 21ST ST, EASTON HOSP 18042 #495-04-2001 L2002 **TS** *012 †85
GORDON, David Alan. 2005 FAIRVIEW AVE, # A 18042 #051-04-1980 L1988 **TS** *020 †85,90 ‡
GORLA, Manjeera. 250 S 21ST ST, EASTON HOSPITAL 18042 #495-58-2001 L2007 **IM** *020 †20
GOZUM, Carmen Zita. 25TH ST 18042 #748-02-1956 L1963 **OS PD** *071 †55
GRASSI, Joseph John. 3735 EASTON NAZARETH HWY, STE 101 18045 #561-01-1973 L1983 **PM** *020 †60
GREGA, Meagan Llewelyn. 607 HIGH ST 18042 #041-01-1997 L2006 **FM** *020 †18 ‡
GRUEN, Melissa Beth. 2200 SULLIVAN TRL 18040 #422-01-1999 L2004 **FM** *100 †18
GUERRA, Corazon Anastacio. 2205 LEHIGH ST 18042 #748-01-1974 L1983 **P** *020
GUPTA, Alok Kumar. ■ 18045 #495-36-2004 L2005 **GS** *012
GUPTA, Divya. ■ 18045 #016-06-2005 **OPH** *012
GUPTA, Jaideep. 250 S 21ST ST, EASTON HOSPITAL 18042 #495-45-1986 L2002 **NPM** *020 †55
GUPTA, Pramila Parveen. 3735 EASTON NAZARETH HWY 18045 #495-01-1984 L1989 **IM** *020 †20
GURUNATHAN-MANI, Sivaraman. 250 S 21ST ST 18042 #495-04-2000 **GS** *012
HAKIM, Harvey Jos. 3735 NAZARETH RD, STE 301 18045 #035-47-1992 L1996 **IM** *020 †20
HALPERN, Andrew Evan. 3735 EASTON NAZARETH HWY, STE 206 18045 #035-08-1996 L1999 **DR** *020 †80
HARADA, William Aiji. 250 S 21ST ST 18042 #041-13-1959 L1960 **PTH** *071 †50
HARRINGTON, Silvie. 250 S 21ST ST 18042 #286-07-2004 L2006 **GS** *012
HARVEY, Gregory David. 3735 EASTON NAZARETH HWY, STE 206 18045 #041-13-1978 L1982 **DR** *020 †80 ‡
HASAN, Ambreen. ATTN TAMMY THATCHER, EASTON HOSPITAL 18042 #704-26-1999 L2007 **IM** *012
HELMSTADTER-BECK, C. 21 CORPORATE DR, EASTON HOSP STE 9 18045 #035-09-1977 L1982 **PM** *020 †60
HOBART, John Hampden. ■ 18045 #035-01-1954 L1962 **OS LM** *071 †95
HONG, Tao. 250 S 21ST ST 18042 #243-52-1985 L2001 **AN** *020 †05
IARIKOVA, Elena Vladimiro. 250 S 21ST ST, EASTON HOSPITAL 18042 #913-92-1988 L2004 **IM** *020 †20
JACOBY, Jeanne Louise. 3044 HODLE AVE 18045 #041-14-1999 L2001 **EM** *020 †16
JAMISON, Jerry David. 250 S 21ST ST, EASTON HOSPITAL 18042 #041-13-1973 L1974 **EM** *020 †16
JANI, Nika. 250 S 21ST ST, DEPT OF MED 18042 #913-19-1998 L2006 **IM** *012
JANJUA, Aasia Daud. 250 S 21ST ST 18042 #704-26-1999 L2006 **IM** *012
JHAVERI, Harish S. 250 S 21ST ST, RADIOLOGY DEPARTMENT 18042 #495-23-1966 L1981 **NRN R** *020 †80
JONES, Stuart Andrew. 280 S 21ST ST 18042 #024-01-1972 L1978 **NM DR** *020 †80,28
JOSEPH, George Michael. 3735 EASTON NAZARETH HWY, STE 301 18045 #016-43-1961 L1964 **IM** *071
KAKODKAR, Vasundhara S. 1922 HAY TER 18042 #495-49-1968 L1987 **PD NPM** *020 †55
KANTOR, Nathan I. 2024 LEHIGH ST 18042 #016-42-1951 L1965 **AN** *071
KAZA, Chatargy S. 3735 NAZARETH RD, STE 102 18045 #495-11-1991 L2002 **GE IM** *020 †20
KEMP, David Garrett. 250 S 21ST ST, EASTON HOSPITAL 18042 #028-02-1967 L1995 **IM** *040 †20
KHALIGHI, Koroush. 2001 FAIRVIEW AVE 18042 #308-11-1986 L1992 **ICE CD** *020 †20
KHALLAFI, Hicham. 250 S 21ST ST, EASTON HOSPITAL 18042 #655-01-2001 L2005 **IM** *012
KIM, Doo Tae. 250 S 21ST ST, ANESTHESIA ASSOCIATES OF E 18042 #583-01-1965 L1973 **AN** *020 †05
KIM, Ih Chin. 6 IVY CT 18045 #583-02-1950 L1963 **PD** *071 †55 ‡
KIM, John Howe. 301 S 22ND ST 18042 #041-02-1989 L1995 **OBG** *020 †20,30
KOH, Wei-Loong Glenn. 250 S 21ST ST, EASTON HOSP 18042 #825-01-2000 L2004 **GS** *012
KOHLI, Harjeet Pal Singh. 250 S 21ST ST, EASTON HOSPITAL 18042 #495-36-1981 L1992 **GS** *020 †85
KONIA, Charles. SPRING HILL FARM 18042 #010-01-1959 L1968 **P** *020 †75
KOREN, James Peter, Jr. 3735 EASTON NAZARETH HWY, STE 203 18045 #038-40-1996 L2002 **GS** *020 †85
KOSHAR, Mark Irwin. 3735 EASTON NAZARETH HWY, STE 301 18045 #033-05-1974 L1975 **IM** *020 †20
KOZICKY, Peter Walter. 2111 WASHINGTON BLVD 18042 #016-42-1973 L1978 **ORS** *020 †40
KOZINN, Wesley Parker. 2061 FAIRVIEW AVE 18042 #038-41-1973 L1978 **ID IM** *020 †20
KRAMER, Kenneth. 250 S 21ST ST, SPECIALISTS 18042 #035-19-1972 L1976 **DR** *020 †80
KRISHNAMURTHY, Mahesh. 250 S 21ST ST, EASTON HOSPITAL 18042 #495-52-1996 L2005 **IMG** *100 †20 ‡
KSIAZEK, Stephen Jude. 241 N 13TH ST, PREMIER HEART SPECIALISTS 18042 #041-01-1991 L1994 **CD** *020 †20
KUMAR, Rashmi. 250 S 21ST ST, EASTON HOSPITAL 18042 #495-45-1996 L2004 **IM** *020 †20
LAMB, Elizabeth K. 250 S 21ST ST 18042 #041-07-1995 L1997 **OBG** *020 †30
LARGE, Hiram Stuart. ■ 18045 #051-01-1979 L1980 **AN** *020 †05
LASTIMOSA, Chona Bacay. 250 S 21ST ST, EASTON HOSPITAL 18042 #748-08-2002 L2006 **IM** *012
LEE, H C. 1825 NORTHAMPTON ST 18042 #583-01-1969 L1975 **PD** *020 †55
LEE, Jeen Hyung. 250 S 21ST ST 18042 #035-03-1986 L1987 **ATP CLP** *062 †50
LEE, Sang Tai. 2100 LEHIGH ST 18042 #583-01-1961 L1971 **OTO** *020
LEVIN, Arthur Lawrence. 50 S 18TH ST 18042 #024-01-1965 L1968 **PD OS** *074 †70
LEWIS, Irwin Holden. 41 COMMUNITY DR 18045 #041-01-1975 L1976 **IM FM** *020 †20 ‡
LITTLE, Thomas. 241 N 13TH ST 18042 #012-01-1981 L1990 **CD** *020 †20
LOGUIDICE, Vito Anthony. 3735 EASTON NAZARETH HWY, STE 101 18045 #035-15-1981 L1988 **OSS** *020 †40
LOWMAN, Gerald Farley. 250 S 21ST ST 18042 #041-14-1977 L1978 **PUD CCM** *020 †20
LUTKUS, Edward Richard. 250 S 21ST ST, EASTON HOSPITAL 18042 #016-43-1980 L2005 **EM** *020 †16
LYON, David Thos. 250 S 21ST ST, MEDICAL AFFAIRS 18042 #035-15-1971 L1974 **IM GE** *030 †20 ‡
MADANAT, John Paul. ■ 18042 #305-01-2007 L2007 **GS** *012
MAKHDOMI, Abdur Rashid. 2100 LEHIGH ST 18042 #495-04-1963 L1972 **IM** *020 †20
MAKHOUL, Khaldoun. 1901 HAY TER, STE 5 18042 #875-02-1993 L2003 **FM** *020 †18
MAKWANA, Ravindrakumar Tr. 250 S 21ST ST, EASTON HOSP 18042 #496-41-1998 L2004 **IM** *020 †20
MANJA, George Semaan. 3735 NAZARETH RD, STE 301 18045 #875-01-1989 L1995 **IM** *020 †20
MANN, Christopher Robt. 41 COMMUNITY DR, # 2 18045 #033-06-1990 L1997 **OBG** *020 †30
MANNE, Murali Krishna. 2430 BUTLER ST, # 110 18042 #496-23-1992 L2000 **NPM** *020 †55
MARELLA, Koteswararao V. 3735 NAZARETH RD, STE 202 18045 #495-50-1995 L2007 **U** *020
MARIAM, Uzma. 41 COMMUNITY DR 18045 #704-06-1988 L2004 **FM** *100 †18
MARLAPUDI, Prem K. 250 S 21ST ST 18042 #495-21-1982 L1987 **NPM PD** *020 †55 ‡
MAYER, Eric. 3735 EASTON NAZARETH HWY, STE 206 18045 #033-06-1997 L2003 **U** *020 †95
MC BRIDE, James Geo. 2061 FAIRVIEW AVE 18042 #041-02-1971 L1972 **OPH** *020 †35 ‡
MC DERMOTT, Annmarie A. 48 CREST BLVD 18045 #033-05-1995 L1999 **OBG** *020 †30
MC INTYRE, Patrick B. ■ 18045 #064-01-1978 L1991 **CRS** *100 †85,10
MC MAHON, Joseph F, Jr. ■ 18040 #041-01-1962 L1965 **ORS OSM** *071 †40
MC NELLIS, Donald Robt. 3729 EASTON NAZARETH HWY 18045 #056-06-1975 L1978 **U** *071 †95
MEHTA, Bharat Kumar. 2632 NAZARETH RD 18045 #495-75-1978 L1983 **IM** *020 †20
MEHTA, Sanjay Marc. ■ 18045 #041-14-1991 L1993 **TS** *020 †85,90
MELTZER, Arthur Howard. 3735 NAZARETH RD, STE 302 18045 #035-46-1982 L1990 **CD** *020 †20
MEPHARISHVILI, Zurab Avta. 250 S 21ST ST, EASTON HOSPITAL 18042 #913-23-1994 L2004 **IM** *020 †20
MITTAL, Manoj Kumar. 2061 FAIRVIEW AVE 18042 #495-03-1982 L1994 **IMG** *020 †20
MIXA, Dorothy Margaret. 250 S 21ST ST 18042 #759-09-1997 L2002 **IM** *100 †20
MOHAN, Brij. 2690 KINGSTON RD 18045 #495-45-1972 L1982 **DR NM** *020 †80
MOSSACK, Karin Elizabeth. ■ 18042 #016-76-2007, ▲ L2007 **IM** *012
MOYER, Rodney Donald. 2461 NAZARETH RD, REDI-CARE MED CTR 18045 #041-02-1956 L1957 **GP EM** *020
MUKHERJEE, Shanker. 20 COMMUNITY DR 18045 #495-15-1980 L1989 **GE IM** *020 †20
MULPRAMOOK, Chintana. 250 S 21ST ST 18042 #891-01-1971 L1974 **EM** *020 †20,16
MUNDI, Gurpreet S. 250 S 21ST ST, EASTON HOSPITAL 18042 #035-15-2003 L2007 **AN** *020
NAIR, Shalina. ■ 18040 #038-44-1999 L2001 **FM** *020 †18
NAJMI, Moosa. 2001 FAIRVIEW AVE 18042 #517-01-1958 L1968 **CD IM** *071 †20
NAT, Hridayesh Singh. 250 S 21ST ST, EASTON HOSPITAL 18042 #913-09-2000 L2005 **IM** *012
NENNI, Roger Dean. 400 S GREENWOOD AVE # 200 18045 #041-13-1986 L1987 **OBS** *020 †30
O'DONNELL, Nancy Jean. 250 S 21ST ST 18042 #041-07-1983 L1985 **OBG** *020 †30
OXFELD, Gary Michael. 3735 EASTON NAZARETH HWY, STE 206 18045 #041-13-1999 L2001 **DR** *020 †80
PANEBIANCO, Antonio. 2025 FAIRVIEW AVE, STE A 18042 #561-04-1960 L1964 **TS** *020 †85,90
PAPPACHEN, Binu Thomas. 250 S 21ST ST 18042 #496-35-1999 L2005 **IM** *012
PATEL, Chandulal. 2001 FAIRVIEW AVE 18042 #495-22-1980 L1998 **CD IM** *020 †20
PATEL, Nilam Suryakant. ■ 18045 #041-13-2002 L2005 **PCC** *012 †20
PATEL, Prashant. 3735 NAZARETH RD STE 206, PROGRESSIVE PHYSICIAN ASSO 18045 #041-13-1999 L2001 **VIR** *020 †80
PEACOCK, Thomas Edward. 50 S 18TH ST 18042 #041-13-1977 L1982 **ON HEM** *020 †20
PEQUENO, Rebecca Marsh. 3231 FREEMANSBURG AVE, SUBURBAN EMS 18045 #041-13-2001 L2001 **EM** *020 †16
PURSELL, Robert Neil. 30 COMMUNITY DR 18045 #561-01-1974 L1976 **IM NEP** *020 †20
QUEEN, Emily K. ■ 18042 #028-78-2007, ▲ **OBG** *012
RANA, Hiralal Natvarlal. 250 S 21ST ST, EASTON HOSPITAL 18042 #495-23-1997 L2004 **IM** *020 †20
RASO, Dominick J. 124 N 14TH ST 18042 #561-01-1958 L1960 **IM OS** *020
RASTOGI, Vijay. 250 S 21ST ST, DEPARTMENT OF SURGERY 18042 #495-49-1981 L2001 **GS** *020 †85 ‡

REDDY, Bhoompally Venkata. 3735 NAZARETH RD, STE 102 18045 #495-65-1990 L2001 GS *020 †85

REDSTONE, Ellen A. 3735 NAZARETH RD, STE 206 18045 #033-05-1992 L1999 VIR *020 †80 ‡

REINA, Charles Ricca. ■ 18045 #035-09-1974 L1976 ORS LM *062 †40

REINHART, Robert David. 3735 EASTON NAZARETH HWY, STE 206 18045 #028-02-1992 L1992 R OS *020 †80

REISCHEL, Ulrich Andreas. 250 S 21ST ST 18042 #033-05-1982 L1984 EM *020 †20,16

RICCARDI, Jay Scott. 3735 NAZARETH RD STE 20, PROGRESSIVE PHYSICIAN ASSO 18045 #035-48-1988 L2006 DR *020 †80

RINGOLD, Michael Aaron. 3735 EASTON NAZARETH HWY, STE 206 18045 #041-13-1995 L1997 VIR DR *020 †80 ‡

ROHATGI, Anita. ■ 18045 #495-15-1980 L1984 IM IMG *020 †20

ROHATGI, Anuja. 117 N 4TH ST 18042 #495-15-1985 L1999 IM *020 †20 ‡

ROHATGI, Chand. 3735 NAZARETH RD STE 103 18045 #495-14-1984 L1995 GS *020 †85 ‡

ROHATGI, Rajeev. 2001 FAIRVIEW AVE 18042 #495-36-1976 L1979 CD CCM *020 †20

ROSEN, Scott Ira. 2031 HAY TER 18042 #035-47-1988 L1990 U *020 †20

ROSENTHAL, Jarrod Evan. 3735 EASTON NAZARETH HWY, STE 206 18045 #035-19-2000 L2006 U *020 †95

ROSSI, Carla Marie. 3735 NAZARETH RD STE 201 18045 #305-01-1988 L1993 ID *020 †20

ROSSI, Cynthia Ann. 1412 SULLIVAN TRL, FORKS MEDICAL CENTER 18040 #041-09-1996 L1999 FM *020 †18

RUSSO, Joseph Patrick. 3735 EASTON NAZARETH HWY, STE 206 18045 #016-43-1998 L2004 DR *020 †80

SACHDEV, Ranjan. 2111 WASHINGTON BLVD 18042 #495-36-1974 L1981 ORS OS *020 †40

SALCEDO, Wilfredo Garcia. 250 S 21ST ST 18042 #748-08-1966 L1972 PTH *020 †50

SANTOS, Lambert-Ian Pasco. ATTN TAMMY THATCHER, EASTON HOSPITAL 18042 #748-10-2005 L2007 IM *012

SAUER, Thomas S. 2111 WASHINGTON BLVD 18042 #010-02-1972 L1978 ORS *020 †40

SCHIAVONE, Joseph Adriano. 2001 FAIRVIEW AVE 18042 #422-01-1985 L1986 CD IC *020 †20

SCHOEPPNER, Eric. 1723 NORTHAMPTON ST 18042 #409-34-1974 L1977 IM IMG *020 †20

SCHUBACH, Gregg David. 250 S 21ST ST, EASTON HOSPITAL 18042 #035-09-1990 L1996 R NM *020 †80,28

SCHWARTZMAN, Daniel M. 2925 WILLIAM PENN HWY, STE 104 18045 #035-19-1981 L1982 OBG *020 †30

SERFAS, Lee Sherwood. ■ 18045 #041-02-1948 L1949 GS TS *071 †85,90

SHAFI, Saima. 250 S 21ST ST, EASTON HOSPITAL 18042 #704-20-1999 L2001 IM *020 †20

SHARMA, Om Prakash. 2100 LEHIGH ST 18042 #495-36-1976 L1978 IMG IM *020 †20

SHEVTSIV, Yuriy Yevgenovy. 250 S 21ST ST, EASTON HOSPITAL 18042 #913-89-1992 L2005 IM *012

SHUKLA, Shwetanshu Mahesh. 250 S 21ST ST, EASTON HOSPITAL 18042 #496-42-2004 L2006 IM *012

SHURMAN, Andrew Marc. 3735 NAZARETH RD, STE 206 18045 #041-13-2000 L2001 RNR *100 †80

SIDHU, Harshinder Singh. 250 S 21ST ST 18042 #495-29-2004 L2007 IM *012

SILVER, Barry Evan. 250 S 21ST ST, EASTON HOSP EMERG DEPT 18042 #023-01-1985 L1990 EM PD *020 †55,16

SILVER, Ross Ian. 3735 NAZARETH RD, STE 206 18045 #035-20-2000 L2001 DR *100 †80

SIMPSON-SEBASTIANO, L. 3735 EASTON NAZARETH HWY, STE 206 18045 #033-05-1992 L2000 DR *020 †80

SINGH, Harinder K. 50 S 18TH ST, NEPHROLOGY HTN ASSOC OF LE 18042 #495-03-1990 L2005 NEP *020 †20

SINGH, Neeraj. 250 S 21ST ST, EASTON HOSP 18042 #495-03-1996 L2004 GS *012

SLADE, Robert Nason. 250 S 21ST ST 18042 #041-13-1987 L1990 EM *020 †16

SLOAN, Susan Potts. 2925 WILLIAM PENN HWY, STE 201 18045 #026-04-1998 L2007 IM *020 †20

SNYDER, Richard Wm. 30 COMMUNITY DR 18045 #041-13-1977 L1979 PUD CCM *020 †20 ‡

STABILE, Jerome G. 250 S 21ST ST 18042 #010-02-1956 L1962 TS VS *071 †85,90

STAIR, Susannah Mary. 205 S 22ND ST, COMMUNITY CARE CENTER 18042 #041-15-2000 L2004 MPD *020

STIGERS, Julie Ann. 3735 NAZARETH RD, STE 206 18045 #041-13-2001 L2001 DR *020 †80

STRAUSS, Jay Earl. 3735 EASTON NAZARETH HWY, STE 206 18045 #035-19-1980 L1986 DR *020 †80

SULTAN, Junaid. ■ 18045 #704-02-1996 L2007 PTH *020

TABASSUM, Nabeela. ATTN TAMMY THATCHER, EASTON HOSPITAL 18042 #496-27-1998 L2007 IM *012

TAHERI, Hamed. 250 S 21ST ST, DEPT OF MEDICINE 18042 #305-01-2006 L2006 GS *012

TAMARKIN, Frank Jeremy. 3735 EASTON NAZARETH HWY, STE 206 18045 #041-15-2000 L2007 U *020

THACHIL, Rajeeve Thomas. 226 S KATHRYN ST, EASTON PULMONARY & CRITICA 18045 #495-52-1986 L1998 PCC *020 †20

TOSHNIWAL, Pradip Kumar. 315 S 21ST ST 18042 #495-36-1974 L1977 N IM *020 †20,75 ‡

TOSHNIWAL, Renu. 315 S 21ST ST 18042 #495-45-1974 L1976 ID IM *020 †20 ‡

TREND, Christopher David. 3735 EASTON NAZARETH HWY, STE 206 18045 #033-06-2000 L2001 DR *020 †80

TRETYAKOV, Jekaterina. 250 S 21ST ST 18042 #913-16-1999 L2005 IM *012

TRIBBLE, Jana Kay. ■ 18045 #051-01-1980 L1982 PD *020 †55

TRIGIANO, Lucien L. ■ 18042 #041-13-1952 L1953 PM *071 †60

TUMA, Roman Alfred. 3735 NAZARETH RD 18045 #409-39-1992 L2004 ID *020 †20

UPDEGROVE, John Harvey. ■ 18045 #041-01-1947 L1948 GS *071 †85

VACHHANI, Manu. 3729 EASTON NAZARETH HWY, STE 101 18045 #495-48-1984 L1991 IM *020 †20

VADIVELU, Arunpriya. 250 S 21ST ST, EASTON HOSPITAL 18042 #495-94-1998 L2005 IM *020 †20

VALDIVIESO, Julio. 36 CREST BLVD 18045 #737-09-1975 L1983 NPM PD *020 †55 ‡

VAN DER VEER, Lindsley D, Jr. 2025 FAIRVIEW AVE 18042 #041-09-1976 L1981 GE *020 †20

VELEY, Eugene A.. 250 S 21ST ST 18042 #305-01-2001 L2007 PCC *020 †20

VELLORE, Thriveni R. 4260 FIELDSTONE DR, SIGAL CENTER FOR FAMILY 18045 #495-37-1993 L2002 FM *020 †18

VEMURI, Suresh. 250 S 21ST ST 18042 #495-21-1999 L2006 IM *020 †20

VERMA, Maheshwer Bux. 21 CORPORATE DR STE 4 18045 #495-05-1972 L1982 PD P *020 †55

VINAY, Gopalakrishna Rupa. 250 S 21ST ST, EASTON HOSPITAL-MEDICAL ST 18042 #496-39-1999 L2005 IM *020 †20

WALDEN, Thomas Bruce. 3729 EASTON NAZARETH HWY, STE LL2 18045 #041-07-1975 L1978 U GS *020 †95

WALKER, Stanley Robt. 21 CORPORATE DR STE 1 18045 #847-01-1974 L1976 IM IMG *020 †20

WANG, Chee-Kung. 250 S 21ST ST, ANESTHESIA DEPARTMENT 18042 #385-03-1963 L1972 AN *071

WARREN, Jonathan. 77 N 2ND ST 18042 #041-02-1967 L1970 IM *020 †20

WERLEY, John David. ■ 18045 #041-02-1954 L1955 R NM *071 †80

WILLARD, Brian Mc Kinley. 3729 EASTON NAZARETH HWY 18045 #041-02-1989 L1989 GS *020 †35

WILLARD, Donald Earl. 1901 HAY TER 18042 #041-02-1958 L1975 OPH *072 †35

WILLIAMS, John Morgan. 2111 WASHINGTON BLVD 18042 #033-06-1981 L1990 ORS OTR *020 †40

YALAMANCHI, Geeta Rao. 250 S 21ST ST, APOGEE MEDICAL GROUP 18042 #495-49-1993 L2006 IM *020 †20

YEISLEY, Geary Lee. 2025 FAIRVIEW AVE 18042 #041-09-1978 L1980 TS *020 †85,90

YU, Ju Yun. 3735 EASTON NAZARETH HWY, STE 302A 18045 #917-30-1997 L2005 FM *020 †18

ZELAZNICKA, Jolanta. 1901 HAY TER STE 2 18042 #759-03-1984 L1994 RHU IM *020 †20

EBENSBURG — CAMBRIA

BERGER, Karl. 1100 W HIGH ST 15931 #407-16-1968 L1975 PD HEM *020 †55

FIORICA, Vincent Michael. 1100 W HIGH ST, LAUREL UROLOGY INC 15931 #039-01-1983 L1988 U *020 †95 ‡

GOLDEN, Stanley John. ■ 15931 #041-14-2001 L2001 DR *020 †80

HOLSINGER, David Franklin. 1100 W HIGH ST, EBENSBURG FAM PRAC 15931 #041-12-1987 L1989 FM *020 †18

KOH, Enrique S. 1100 W HIGH ST 15931 #748-10-1987 L1993 FM *020 †18

LIGHTBOURN, Susan E. 203 ROYALWOOD DR, INTERNAL MEDICINE 15931 #010-03-1981 L1985 PD IM *020 †55

MAGLEY, Robert Chester. 1100 W HIGH ST 15931 #041-02-1956 L1957 FM EM *020 †18

MC KINLEY, Richard Graham. 236 JAMESWAY RD 15931 #018-03-1972 L1977 OBG *020 †30

MULLEN, Amy Jo. ■ 15931 #041-14-2007 L2007 *012

PIDUTTI, Richard Warren. 1100 W HIGH ST, LAUREL UROLOGY INC 15931 #065-05-1979 L1984 U GS *020 †95

REESE, Jack Wheeling. ■ 15931 #024-01-1953 L1963 GS *072 †85

REYES, Alfredo Mariano. 15931 #748-07-1954 L1966 GP *071

SMITH, William Prideaux. RR 2 BOX 192AA 15931 #041-12-1954 L1955 GP *071

WARIKOO, Shiban Kishan. 1100 W HIGH ST, LAUREL UROLOGY INC 15931 #495-51-1966 L1973 U *020 †95

EDGEMONT — DELAWARE

ABRAMS, Karen Lynn. ■ 19028 #041-02-1993 L1995 FM *020 †18

EDGEWORTH — ALLEGHENY

PARULIS, Albert Clem, Jr. 204 ORCHARD PL 15143 #649-14-1972 L1976 EM *020 †16

EDINBORO — ERIE

GETSON, William Russell. 450 ERIE ST 16412 #038-45-1989 L1995 FM *020 †18

MC GUIRE, Thomas Eugene. 208 WATERFORD ST 16412 #041-02-1982 L1983 FM OM *020 †18

MILLER, Tom R. 201 WATERFORD ST 16412 #035-15-1957 L1959 FM IM *071 †18

MORRIS, John Leroy. 450 ERIE ST 16412 #041-09-1960 L1961 FM OS *071 †18

STREIFF, John Jos, Jr. 450 ERIE ST 16412 #041-12-1986 L1987 FM *020 †18

EDWARDSVILLE — LUZERNE

CASTELLANO, Thomas John. 494 NORTHAMPTON ST, STE 2 18704 #035-01-1976 L1981 GE IM *020 †20

FARRELL, Dorothy Ann. 468 NORTHAMPTON ST 18704 #041-12-1977 L1978 N *020 †75 ‡

MC GRATH, Edmund Wm. ■ 18704 #035-09-1955 L1956 GP OS *020 ‡

PARK, Byung-Gook. ■ 18704 #583-15-1978 L2002 FM *020 †18

YUSUP, Ira Paula. ■ 18704 #506-01-1999 L2007 PD *020

EIGHTY FOUR — WASHINGTON

BOEHME, Kevin Geo. 845 ROUTE 519 15330 #041-12-1989 L1991 FM *020 †18

RICHARDSON, Ross E. ■ 15330 #041-02-1951 L1952 EM ORS *071

ELDERTON — ARMSTRONG

CIPPEL, Joseph Andrew, Jr. 116 MAIN STREET 15736 #041-14-1993 L1995 FM *020 †18

ELDRED — MCKEAN

ZIBILICH, Gloria Jean. PO BOX 509, 139 MAIN ST 16731 #023-01-1981 L1992 FM *020 †18 ‡

ELIZABETH — ALLEGHENY

BROWN, Charles Robt. 105 N 2ND AVE 15037 #041-12-1954 L1955 GP *071 †18

CAMPAGNA, James Thos. 605 SCENERY DR 15037 #305-01-1982 L1983 FM *020 †18

CHIESA, Raul Oscar. ■ 15037 #924-01-1980 L1997 PTH *062

DORMAN, Franklin L. ■ 15037 #041-02-1953 L1954 FM *071 †18

GORALCZYK, Edward J, Jr. 300 SCENERY DR 15037 #041-12-1977 L1978 FM FPG *020 †18

HOLMAN, Ingrid A. 1001 WEIGLES HILL RD 15037 #409-32-1979 L1980 FM *020 †18

KAZMI, Bushra. 121 N 2ND AVE 15037 #704-06-1991 FM *020

NAIK, Monica Ramesh. ■ 15037 #496-38-1996 L2004 PD *100 †55

SADASHIV, Santhosh Kukkad. ■ 15037 #496-37-1998 L2003 IM *020 †20

SKINNER, Douglas Van Dyne. 300 SCENERY DR 15037 #048-02-1977 L1978 **FM** *020 †18
WALK, Ryan Mcmahon. ■ 15037 #041-02-2007 *012

ELIZABETHTOWN - LANCASTER

BAER, Gerald Robt. 418 CLOVERLEAF RD, GRP AT NORLANCO MEDICAL 17022 #041-14-1988 L1990 **FM** *020 †18
BEIDLER, Lorin K. 418 CLOVERLEAF RD 17022 #023-01-2002 L2002 **FM** *020 †18
BOGERT, Eugeniapaul Reyes. 37 BROOKFIELD DR 17022 #041-07-1995 L1997 **FM** *020 †18
BOWER, Douglas William. ■ 17022 #041-14-2006 L2006 **AN** *012
BRIGUGLIO, John. 424 CLOVERLEAF RD 17022 #041-12-1995 L1997 **VIR DR** *020 †80
BRUBAKER, Paul Eugene. 418 CLOVERLEAF RD, GRP AT NORLANCO MEDICAL 17022 #041-13-1973 L1974 **FM** *020 †18
BRUBAKER, Samuel M. 332 OBERHOLTZER RD 17022 #041-01-1964 L1969 **GS** *071 †85
CARLSON, Lisa Christine. 1 CONTINENTAL DR, UNIV PHYS GRP 17022 #005-12-1996 L1998 **PD** *020 †55
CARTER, William Alvin. 418 CLOVERLEAF RD 17022 #036-07-1963 L1986 **IM ID** *050
CONLEY, Scott Christopher. 418 CLOVERLEAF RD, GRP AT NORLANCO MEDICAL 17022 #041-14-1997 L1999 **FM** *020 †18
COOK, Glenda J. 418 CLOVERLEAF RD, GRP AT NORLANCO MEDICAL 17022 #051-04-1991 L1993 **IM** *020 †20
EICHELBERGER, Dwight Otis. 418 CLOVERLEAF RD, GRP AT NORLANCO MEDICAL 17022 #023-01-1992 L1994 **FM** *020 †18
ESCH, Eric Lynn. 418 CLOVERLEAF RD, GRP AT NORLANCO MEDICAL 17022 #041-13-2000 L2002 **FM** *020 †18
FEINSTEIN, Alex. 424 CLOVERLEAF RD 17022 #041-02-1983 L1984 **DR** *020 †80
FORMAN, Irwin Harvey. ■ 17022 #561-01-1967 L1971 **P** *071
GISH, Martin Saml. ■ 17022 #041-13-1983 L1984 **EM FM** *020 †18
GISH, Robin Denise. 418 CLOVERLEAF RD, GRP AT NORLANCO MEDICAL 17022 #041-14-1985 L1987 **FM** *020 †18
GODSHALL, Stanley Moyer. 418 CLOVERLEAF RD, GRP AT NORLANCO MEDICAL 17022 #041-01-1969 L1971 **FM FPG** *020 †18
GOOD, Milton Shenk. 300 CONTINENTAL DR 17022 #041-09-1958 L1959 **FM** *071 †18
GORDON, Patricia Louise. ■ 17022 #038-44-1987 L2004 **OS PD** *020 †19,55
GRIFONE, Thomas Joseph. ■ 17022 #033-05-2003 L2003 **PTH** *100 †50
HAMMAN, John Shue. ■ 17022 #041-12-1948 L1949 **OBG OS** *071
HARNLY, Neal Stuart. 418 CLOVERLEAF RD, GRP AT NORLANCO MEDICAL 17022 #041-13-1990 L1992 **FM** *020 †18
HEWLETT, John Orange. ■ 17022 #041-02-1955 L1956 **IMG FM** *071
IRIANA, Sarah Mary. 1 CONTINENTAL DR 17022 #050-02-1993 L1995 **PD** *020 †55 ‡
JANESKY, Cindy. 424 CLOVERLEAF RD 17022 #041-14-1981 L1982 **R** *020 †80
KEGEL, Jennifer Lyn. 424 CLOVERLEAF RD 17022 #041-14-1992 L1996 **DR** *020 †80
KIPP, James Earl. 418 CLOVERLEAF RD, GRP AT NORLANCO MEDICAL 17022 #041-13-1970 L1973 **FM** *020 †18
KRAMER, Jeffrey Paul. 424 CLOVERLEAF RD 17022 #041-02-1996 L1999 **DR** *020 †80
KREIDER, Henry Lloyd. 300 CONTINENTAL DR 17022 #041-09-1959 L1960 **FM IMG** *071 †18
LANDIS, Alice Jane. ■ 17022 #041-01-2001 *100
LAWRENCE, David P. 424 CLOVERLEAF RD 17022 #041-01-1980 L1998 **DR OS** *020 †80
LE CLERC, Susan Marie. ■ 17022 #008-02-1981 L1983 **FM EM** *071 †18
LEHMAN, Bethany Jean. ■ 17022 #005-06-2008 *012
LEICHT, Paul F. 220 ANCHOR RD 17022 #041-02-1951 L1952 **PTH** *020
LINN, Robert Hayes. ■ 17022 #041-09-1941 L1942 **PEM CD** *071
MARTIN, Enos Danl. 595 OLD HERSHEY RD 17022 #041-14-1973 L1974 **P** *020 †75
MAST, John Jacob. 418 CLOVERLEAF RD, GRP AT NORLANCO MEDICAL 17022 #017-20-1996 L1998 **FPG** *012 †18
MC COY, Andrea. 1 CONTINENTAL DR 17022 #041-14-1986 L1987 **PD** *020 †55
MELLINGER, E S. 418 CLOVERLEAF RD, GRP AT NORLANCO MEDICAL 17022 #051-01-1993 L1997 **FM** *020 †18
MICHELITCH, Scott William. ■ 17022 #035-48-2003 L2004 **DR** *012
MILLER, Thomas Lynn. 418 CLOVERLEAF RD 17022 #038-43-1976 L1977 **FM** *020 †18
MOTTER, Daniel F. ■ 17022 #041-77-2004, ▲ L2004 **IM** *012
MOTTER, William C. 21 TEAKWOOD CIR 17022 #041-14-1995 L1998 **AN** *020 †05
OLIVES, Manuel. ■ 17022 #847-04-1953 L1963 **IMG FM** *071 †18
OTTO, Nicholas Paul. ■ 17022 #041-14-2005 L2005 **DR** *012
PERRY, Maurice Clive. 424 CLOVERLEAF RD 17022 #917-25-1974 L1998 **DR** *020 †80
RITTENHOUSE, Jeffrey B. 418 CLOVERLEAF RD, GRP AT NORLANCO MEDICAL 17022 #051-04-1988 L1990 **FM** *020 †18
SHERBAN, Paul Robt. 424 CLOVERLEAF RD 17022 #035-03-1974 L1978 **DR** *020 †80
SHUMAN, Leigh Swartley. 424 CLOVERLEAF RD 17022 #023-07-1978 L1992 **VIR DR** *020 †80
SMIGOCKI, Gene C, Jr. 424 CLOVERLEAF RD 17022 #047-05-1983 L1986 **DR** *020 †80
STEPHENS, Melissa Falk. ■ 17022 #024-01-1990 L1993 **IM** *020 †20
TANNA, Nitin K. 424 CLOVERLEAF RD 17022 #041-01-1990 L1998 **DR** *020 †80
WINSTANLEY, Robert A. ■ 17022 #041-13-1943 L1944 **AM OPH** *071 †35
YODER, John J. 418 CLOVERLEAF RD, GRP AT NORLANCO MEDICAL 17022 #041-12-1988 L1990 **FM** *020 †18
YUNGINGER, Richard C, Jr. 418 CLOVERLEAF RD, GRP AT NORLANCO MEDICAL 17022 #010-03-1985 L1986 **FM** *020 †18

ELKINS PARK - MONTGOMERY

ACHARYA, Ranjit V. ■ 19027 #495-76-1970 L1976 **N** *020 †75
ADONI, Leon. 8302 OLD YORK RD, BRIAR HOUSE 19027 #902-01-1946 L1959 **D** *071
ANGLES, Carmen Amelia. 60 TOWNSHIP LINE RD, MOSS REHAB PHYS MED ASSOC 19027 #041-13-1977 L1979 **PM** *020 †60
ARCE, A Anthony. ■ 19027 #041-13-1946 L1976 **P** *030 †75
ASKIN, Stanley Robt. 60 TOWNSHIP LINE RD 19027 #041-09-1973 L1974 **HS ORS** *020 †40 ‡
AZARVA, Harvey Laurence. 921 W CHELTENHAM AVE 19027 #041-09-1977 L1979 **IM** *020 †20 ‡
BEG, Raihana Rizvi. 7900 OLD YORK RD, 7900 OLD YORK RD STE 109A 19027 #704-02-1956 L1973 **P CHP** *020 †75 ‡
BENEZRA, Isak. ■ 19027 #902-01-1949 L1965 **AN** *071 †05
BERNSTEIN, Eric Ferenc. 8360 OLD YORK RD 19027 #008-01-1986 L1991 **D** *020 †15
BIRNBAUM, Michael David. 8380 OLD YORK RD, STE 200 19027 #035-15-1966 L1967 **REN GYN** *020 †30
BONN, Jerrold Charles. 7900 OLD YORK RD APT 106B, ELKINS PARK HOUSE 19027 #041-02-1962 L1963 **P** *020 †75
BRECHER, Eugene. 8302 OLD YORK RD, STE 100 19027 #041-09-1945 L1946 **IM** *071 †20
BRYANT-STEPHENS, Tyra C. 7513 VERNON RD, 7513 VERNON ROAD 19027 #036-05-1984 L1987 **PD** *020 †55
CARR, Zyad James. ■ 19027 #539-02-2005 L2005 **AN** *100
CHANDRASEKHARA, Mallipatn. ■ 19027 #495-33-1960 L1978 **PD** *020 †55
CHECK, Jerome Harvey. 7447 OLD YORK RD, COOPER CENTER OF IVF 19027 #041-09-1971 L1972 **REN END** *020 †20
CHO, Sooja. 60 TOWNSHIP LINE RD 19027 #024-07-2000 L2001 **PM** *020 †60 ‡
CHOMSKY, David E. ■ 19027 #041-13-1959 L1960 **IM** *020 †20
CHON, Hikon. ■ 19027 #583-02-1960 L1972 **R DR** *071 †80
CHRISTOU, Aristotle. 60 TOWNSHIP LINE RD 19027 #418-01-1956 L1965 **PTH OBG** *071 †50
COACHI, Daniel. 1831 W CHELTENHAM AVE 19027 #654-01-1991 L1998 **IM** *020 †20
COHEN, Eugene. 8302 OLD YORK RD, A13 19027 #005-17-1962 L1968 **R** *072
COHEN, Randi Jill. ■ 19027 #035-48-2006 L2007 **RO** *012
CORBMAN, Gene Robert. 8302 OLD YORK RD, STE B14 19027 #165-06-1976 L1977 **P** *020 †75 ‡
CROSS, Brian Jared. ■ 19027 #041-01-2005 L2005 **IM** *012
CROSS, Kevin Jay. ■ 19027 #041-01-2002 L2008 **PS** *012
DE BERADINIS, Camillo T. ■ 19027 #041-01-1941 L1942 **IM** *071 †20
DE LEON, Remedios B. 60 TOWNSHIP LINE RD 19027 #748-01-1955 *100
DHAR, Sunil Kumar. 2005A N JOHN RUSSELL CIR 19027 #495-48-1998 L2001 **IM** *020 †20
DOBERCZAK, Bohdan W. 7900 OLD YORK RD RM105A 19027 #041-09-1975 L1978 **P** *020 †75
DOMINICI CABRAL, Paul Gio. ■ 19027 #308-13-2001 L2007 **EM** *012
DON, Sidney Harry. 1939 W CHELTENHAM AVE, TRI COUNTY PEDIATRICS 19027 #041-01-1995 L1997 **PD** *020 †55
DORFF, Jonathan David. ■ 19027 #028-02-2002 L2002 **DR** *100 †80
DORNSTEIN, Perry I. 8302 OLD YORK RD, BRIARHOUSE 19027 #035-08-1960 L1965 **IM PTH** *071 †20
DRUBETSKY, Norman. 60 TOWNSHIP LINE RD 19027 #913-50-1970 L1982 **IM GP** *020
DUDA, John Robt. 60 TOWNSHIP LINE RD 19027 #041-13-1974 L1975 **ORS** *020 †40
ELLISON, Julius. ■ 19027 #041-13-1960 L1961 **CD IM** *071
ELMALEH, Miriam Kaiser. 60 TOWNSHIP LINE RD 19027 #041-01-1957 L1958 **FM OS** *020 ‡
ESQUENAZI, Alberto M. 60 TOWNSHIP LINE RD, MOSS REHAB 19027 #649-01-1982 L1984 **PM** *030 †60 ‡
FOREMAN, Joseph. 60 TOWNSHIP LINE RD 19027 #041-13-1949 L1950 **GS** *071 †85
FORMAN, Jack David. 8302 OLD YORK RD, BRIAR HOUSE - B2 19027 #047-06-1969 L1970 **P** *040 †75
FOXHALL, James Scott. ■ 19027 #056-05-2004 L2007 **FM** *020 †18
FRAKES, Shirley Irene. 60 TOWNSHIP LINE RD 19027 #041-13-1982 L1983 **IM** *020 †20
FRIEDMAN, Milton Louis. 60 TOWNSHIP LINE RD 19027 #041-02-1960 L1962 **GP** *020
GARCIA, Laureano Pedro. 60 TOWNSHIP LINE RD 19027 #275-01-1954 L1973 **IM FM** *020 †18 ‡
GITTERMAN, Jack Eugene. ■ 19027 #062-01-1955 L1960 **PYA CHP** *020
GNIADY, John Paul. ■ 19027 #021-05-2007 L2007 **GS** *012
GOODWIN, Mary Catherine. ■ 19027 #012-22-2005 L2005 **GS** *012
GOREN, Stanley E. ■ 19027 #041-09-1951 L1952 **PD** *071 †55
GREEN, William. ■ 19027 #041-09-1949 L1951 **IM IMG** *071
GREENBERG, Lawrence. ■ 19027 #035-08-1957 L2007 **OTO** *020 †45
GREENBERG, Steven Jay. 60 TOWNSHIP LINE RD 19027 #041-02-1967 L1968 **GYN GP** *071 †30
GUTOWICZ, Marcia Annette. 50 TOWNSHIP LINE RD, STE 222 19027 #041-13-1977 L1978 **VS GS** *020 †85
GUTTMANN, Gad Gerd. 60 TOWNSHIP LINE RD, # GROUND 19027 #407-05-1960 L1965 **ORS OFA** *071 †40
HAMPEL, Avraham. 60 TOWNSHIP LINE RD 19027 #561-19-1972 L1977 **OTO HNS** *020 †45 ‡
HANN, Richard Merrill. ■ 19027 #039-01-1974 *030
HAWRYLUK, Orest. ■ 19027 #028-03-1961 L1990 **PHP OM** *071 †70
HAYWARD, Kathleen Ann. 60 TOWNSHIP LINE RD, AT ELKINS PARK/DEPT EMERG 19027 #041-01-1992 L1995 **EM** *020 †16
HERRING, Allen Bernard. ■ 19027 #041-13-1958 L1959 **OS IM** *071 †20
HESKEL, Milton M. 50 TOWNSHIP LINE RD, STE 300 19027 #041-01-1948 L1950 **END** *020 †20
HONG, Kab Sun. 1349 W CHELTENHAM AVE, STE 201 19027 #583-01-1978 L1983 **PM** *020 †60
HONG, Sun Wha. 1333 W CHELTENHAM AVE, STE 105 19027 #583-08-1965 **OBG** *020 †30 ‡
HSIEH, Mingkuan. 60 TOWNSHIP LINE RD, MOSS REHAB HOSPITAL 19027 #025-07-1991 L1995 **PM** *020 †60
JOHNSON, Jill Denae. ■ 19027 #041-13-2007 L2007 **IM** *012
JOSEPH, Giliane. ■ 19027 #041-13-2005 **IM** *012
KAO, Allen. ■ 19027 #016-11-2004 L2005 **PM** *012
KAPLAN, Bernard. 60 TOWNSHIP LINE RD 19027 #041-09-1953 L1954 **GP** *020
KASSUTTO, Susan Rachelle. ■ 19027 #550-02-1987 L1988 **PD** *020 †55
KERSHBAUM, Carol M. ■ 19027 #041-07-1983 L1984 **FM PME** *020 †18
KIM, Jung Sun. 60 TOWNSHIP LINE RD 19027 #583-01-1961 L1969 **PD PHO** *071 †55
KOHN, Jeffrey Kenneth. ■ 19027 #041-02-1974 L1975 **P** *020
KOLANSKY, Harold. 7900 OLD YORK RD, STE 109B 19027 #010-02-1948 L1950 **PYA CHP** *020 †75 ‡
KOROPECKYJ, Natalia B. ■ 19027 #407-16-1948 L1959 **AN** *071
KUMAR, Ajay. 60 TOWNSHIP LINE RD, PHYSICAL MED & REHAB 19027 #495-36-1991 L2001 **PM** *020 †60
KWIK, Christine I. ■ 19027 #759-01-1962 L1973 **EM** *071 †16 ‡
LABE, Alexander. 60 TOWNSHIP LINE RD, ZASLOW PORTNER COHEN 19027 #041-01-1956 L1957 **GS** *071 †85
LEATHERWOOD, Donald F, II. 60 TOWNSHIP LINE RD 19027 #041-01-1987 L1988 **ORS HS** *020 †40
LEVIN, Jack Mann. ■ 19027 #041-13-1980 L1981 **EM FM** *020 †18
LEVINE, Richard Barry. 304 DOGWOOD LN, 304 DOGWOOD LANE 19027 #035-46-1969 L1974 **R NM** *020 †80 ‡
LEWIS, James Scott. 8380 OLD YORK RD, STE 110A 19027 #041-02-1982 L1987 **OPH OS** *020 †35
LOHIER, Raymond. 1831 W CHELTENHAM AVE 19027 #440-01-1962 L1975 **GP GS** *020 ‡
LUBOWITZ, Richard M. ■ 19027 #041-13-1952 L1953 **OPH** *071 †35
MANIN, Bradley Evan. 8302 OLD YORK RD, STE 100 19027 #041-07-1989 L1994 **IM** *020 †20
MAYER, Nathaniel Hyman. 60 TOWNSHIP LINE RD 19027 #035-46-1968 L1970 **PM** *020 †60 ‡
MEYER, Harold. 7900 OLD YORK RD, ELKINS PARK HOUSE APT 513B 19027 #041-02-1946 L1947 **PD** *071 †55

■ = Address Information Privacy Protected

MINERVA, Felicisima Bunyi. 60 TOWNSHIP LINE RD 19027 #748-07-1956 L1971 **AN** *071
MINERVA, Justino G. 60 TOWNSHIP LINE RD 19027 #748-01-1957 L1970 **AN PUD** *071
MIRSKY, Pamela Anne. ■ 19027 #041-13-2007 L2007 **P** *012
NAKHJAVAN, Fred Khan. 50 TOWNSHIP LINE RD, STE 120 19027 #517-01-1956 L1966
    CD IM *020 †20
NAMJOSHI GONZALEZ, Meera. ■ 19027 #041-13-2006 L2006 **AN** *012
OCAMPO, Romeo Talavera. ■ 19027 #748-01-1959 L1979 **GP EM** *071
PANZER, Eric Marshall. ■ 19027 #041-13-2005 L2005 **EM** *012
PATTON, Paula. ■ 19027 #028-02-1992 L1995 **IMG** *020 †20
PAUL, Madhulatha Anil. ■ 19027 #495-21-1961 L1981 **P** *020 †75
PELENSKY, Jeanne M. 60 TOWNSHIP LINE RD, PM & R DEPT 19027 #041-02-1975 L1976
    PM IM *020 †20,60 ‡
PEOPLES, Julia Rose. ■ 19027 #041-13-2005 L2005 **DR** *012
RAYATNAZARI, Ahmad-Hassan. 7447 OLD YORK RD 19027 #517-01-1961 L1975
    OBG GS *071 †30
RECIK, Halit. ■ 19027 #902-10-1953 L1966 **AN** *071
RICHMOND, Allen Chas. 632 FOXCROFT RD 19027 #041-02-1970 L1973 **OPH** *020 †35
RIZEN, Brian Kenneth. ■ 19027 #041-13-1966 L1967 **PD** *020 †55
ROSENTHAL, David Elliot. 8302 OLD YORK RD, BRIARHOUSE 19027 #041-02-1962 L1963
    IM CD *071 †20 ‡
SALOMON, Michelle Renee. ■ 19027 #021-05-2006 L2006 **GS** *012
SAREN, Beth L. ■ 19027 #035-48-1978 L1983 **IM** *020
SAULINO, Michael Francis. 60 TOWNSHIP LINE RD, MOSSREHAB 19027 #041-14-1993 L1995
    PM *020 †60 ‡
SCHARF, Renee Doris. 333 TOWNSHIP LINE RD 19027 #305-01-1982 L1983 **PM** *020 †60
SCHWARTZ, Harry Wm. 60 TOWNSHIP LINE RD 19027 #041-01-1985 L1986 **PM SCI** *020 †60
SEIN, Nyo Nyo. ■ 19027 #209-01-1979 L1994 **PD** *020 †55
SEITCHIK, Murray Wolf. ■ 19027 #041-09-1955 L1956 **PS** *071 †65
SILVERSTEIN, Daniel Mark. 8302 OLD YORK RD, STE 100 19027 #028-03-1992 L1995
    IM *020 †20
SKLAROFF, Robert B. 50 TOWNSHIP LINE RD, STE 130 19027 #041-02-1974 L1979
    ON HEM *020 †20
SMITH, Alvin H. ■ 19027 #041-02-1952 L1953 **FM PM** *071 †35
SONG, Michaela Chun Ja. 60 TOWNSHIP LINE RD 19027 #583-03-1962 L1971 **AN** *071
SRIDHARA, Channarayapatna. 60 TOWNSHIP LINE RD, MOSS REHAB/EINSTEIN ELKINS 19027
    #495-09-1973 L1977 **PM PMM** *020 †60
STAHL, Kathryn Michelle. ■ 19027 #041-15-2006 L2006 **EM** *012
STEIKER, Daniel David. ■ 19027 #035-08-1954 L1961 **PD** *071 †55 ‡
STOLOFF, Irwin L. ■ 19027 #041-02-1951 L1952 **IM ON** *072 †20
SUPNICK, Amy Beth. ■ 19027 #041-09-1991 L1996 **END** *020 †20
TATLONGHARI, Portia Marie. ■ 19027 #268-04-1989 **PD** *075
TAYLOR, Tisa Alexis. ■ 19027 #041-14-2007 L2007 *012
TELEGADIS, John. 333 TOWNSHIP LINE RD 19027 #305-01-1984 L1985 **IM** *020 †20 ‡
THAM, Allen Y. ■ 19027 #041-15-2005 L2005 **ORS** *012
THOMAS, Anila E. ■ 19027 #041-15-2008 *012
TIMKO, Mercedes Ann. ■ 19027 #041-15-2007 L2007 **FP** *012
TURK, Michael Ira. 315 YORKTOWN PLZ 19027 #051-07-2001 L2005 **P** *100 †75
VACHRANUKUNKIET, Theera. 60 TOWNSHIP LINE RD, MOSS REHAB ELKINS PARK 19027
    #041-01-2000 L2001 **PM** *020 †60 ‡
WATANABE, Thomas Ken. 60 TOWNSHIP LINE RD 19027 #016-11-1992 L2006 **PM** *020 †60
WIKOFF, Edward Kowal. 60 TOWNSHIP LINE RD, MOSS REHABILITATION HOSP 19027
    #041-13-1985 L1987 **PM** *020 †60 ‡
WILK GRABER, Mauricio. ■ 19027 #649-01-1979 L1982 **GS** *020 †85
YAZDANFAR, Shahriar. 401 TOWNSHIP LINE RD, STE A 19027 #517-01-1965 L1973
    IC CD *020 †20
YOON, Chung H. ■ 19027 #583-03-1959 L1976 **GP FM** *071 ‡
YOUNG, Geraldine Anne P. ■ 19027 #035-08-1951 L1959 **PTH** *071
YOUNG, Muriel Loretta. ■ 19027 #041-07-1962 L1964 **PD** *071 †55
YUN, Daniel Du Whan. 50 TOWNSHIP LINE RD, MAB STE 335 19027 #583-01-1958 L1967
    IM CD *020 ‡
YUNIS, Fernando Elias. 60 TOWNSHIP LINE RD 19027 #132-04-1970 L1980 **OBG** *020
ZIV, Amitai. ■ 19027 #550-01-1991 L1997 *020

ELKLAND – TIOGA

BOWER, Ryan Thomas. 103 FORESTVIEW AVE 16920 #041-09-1998 L2005 **FM** *020 †18 ‡
LARSON, Eleanor. MAIN ST 16920 #041-07-1930 L1931 **GP** *075

ELLIOTTSBURG – PERRY

GASULL, H Robt, Jr. ■ 17024 #041-13-1957 L1958 **FM** *071 †18

ELLWOOD CITY – LAWRENCE

BOZORG, Kamal Mirza A. 724 PERSHING ST 16117 #517-01-1969 L1994 **OBG** *020
CIOCCA, Joseph James. 724 PERSHING ST 16117 #041-12-1995 L1997 **OBG** *020 †30
COLANGELO, Anthony Baron. 510 PARK AVE, ELLWOOD FAMILY MED 16117
    #041-02-1978 L1979 **FM EM** *020 †16,18
FROMAN, Stephen Michael. 304 EVANS DR 16117 #041-09-1974 L1975 **OTO A** *020 †45
GARDNER, Morris Zachary. 724 PERSHING ST, ELLOWWD CITY HOSPITAL 16117
    #041-01-1963 L1978 **DR NM** *071 †80
KELLER, Frank Morris. 1673 ROUTE 65 16117 #165-04-1970 L1972 **FM** *020 †18
KIM, Uh Gwon. 419 SPRING AVE 16117 #583-10-1966 L1973 **AN** *071 †18
NANJUNDASWAMY, H C. 302 PETAIN ST 16117 #495-09-1971 L1978 **IM NEP** *020 †20
ORSINI, Michael Anthony. 304 EVANS DR 16117 #041-14-1978 L1979 **OTO A** *020 †45 ‡
PALATKA, Andrew Arthur. ■ 16117 #041-13-1947 L1948 **GP OM** *071
PINTO, Rekha. 748 PERSHING ST 16117 #496-34-2001 L2004 **IM** *020 †20
RAJASENAN, Vasudevan. 300 LAWRENCE AVE 16117 #495-31-1963 L1972 **CD IM** *020
RAYMUNDO, Ricardo B, III. 748 PERSHING ST 16117 #748-10-1967 L1973 **GP GS** *020
RAYMUNDO, Rosalinda R. 748 PERSHING ST 16117 #748-10-1967 L1975 **IM** *020 †20
ROSENBLOOM, Richard C. 304 EVANS DR, STE 301 16117 #041-09-1980 L1981
    CD IM *020 †20

SIMON, David Jeffrey. 724 PERSHING ST, ELLWOOD CITY HOSP 16117 #041-12-1975 L1976
    EM *020 †16
SNYDER, David Chas. 729 PERSHING ST, RM 402 16117 #025-01-1973 L1990 **GS** *020 †85
VOLPE, Peter Eugene. 724 PERSHING ST 16117 #054-04-1981 L1991 **P PYG** *020 †75
WILLIAMS, Karl Edward. 724 PERSHING ST, ELLWOOD CITY HOSP DEPT LAB 16117
    #041-12-1974 L1975 **PTH FOP** *020 †50
ZALAMEA, Petronio F. 755 MASSACHUSETTS ST, PETRONIO F ZALAMEA MD 16117
    #748-08-1960 L1969 **PD GP** *020

ELTON – CAMBRIA

PATTERSON, Richard John. ■ 15934 #041-09-1961 L1962 **IM OS** *075

ELVERSON – CHESTER

BOYER, Randal Allen. ■ 19520 #041-01-1937 L1939 **DR NM** *071 †80
LEONARD, Eileen Marie. ■ 19520 #033-06-1982 L1983 **IM** *020 †20
PERRY, John Francis. PO BOX 210 19520 #041-02-1970 L1972 **ORS** *020 †40
WENTZEL, Harvey Earl, Jr. 2082 RIDGE RD 19520 #041-02-1960 L1961 **OM D** *020 †70

ELWYN – DELAWARE

FRONDUTI, Ronald Anthony. 111 ELWYN RD 19063 #041-02-1977 L1978 **IM** *071 †20
OVERBY, Kim Jean. 111 ELWYN RD, ELWYN INC (CHILD WELFARE D 19063 #041-01-1982 L1984
    PD *050 †55

ELYSBURG – NORTHUMBERLAND

BOBEK, Francis Brian. 2 S MARKET ST 17824 #041-13-1981 L1982 **FM** *020 †18
FISCHER, Rolf Heinrich. ■ 17824 #407-10-1953 L1962 **FM EM** *071
PUGLIESE, Patrick Dale. 1 E MILL ST, ELYSBURG FIRE DEPARTMENT 17824
    #010-02-1982 L1983 **EM** *020 †16
RODRIGUEZ, Edsel Antonio. 10 W CENTER ST 17824 #023-01-1948 L1952 **GP** *020
WILLIAMS, Llewellyn A. ■ 17824 #422-01-1993 L1996 **AN** *020 †05

EMMAUS – LEHIGH

BUB, Carol Lisa. 619 DALTON ST 18049 #035-47-1993 L1996 **FM** *020 †18
BUB, Sam. 619 DALTON ST 18049 #836-02-1963 L1978 **FM IMG** *020 †18
COLON-RUIZ, Carlos L, Jr. 431 CHESTNUT ST 18049 #042-02-1995 L1999 **IM** *020 †20
COOPER, Marjorie Rush. 555 HARRISON ST 18049 #041-13-1991 L1993 **P** *020 †75
DE PUY, Amy Marie. ■ 18049 #041-02-2005 L2005 **OBG** *012
DEX, Walter John. ■ 18049 #041-01-1956 L1957 **DR** *072 †80
DRY, Frederick A. 730 HARRISON ST 18049 #041-01-1941 L1942 **GP FM** *020
EASTLAND, Theodore Wm, Jr. ■ 18049 #041-09-1963 L1965 **GP A** *071
GHITULESCU, Gabriela A. ■ 18049 #067-01-1992 **CRS** *100 †85,10
HEID, John N. 1040 CHESTNUT ST 18049 #028-78-1975, ▲ L1976 **FM** *020
HOLBROOK, Todd Reichert. 619 DALTON ST 18049 #041-07-1994 L1997 **FM** *020 †18
JOHNSON, Alan Wright. 2660 MOUNTAIN VIEW CIR 18049 #041-13-1975 L1976 **FM** *071 †18
KIM, Kyu Sun. ■ 18049 #583-01-1954 L1982 **PM** *071
KLOIN, Jay Elliot. 431 CHESTNUT ST 18049 #396-31-1975 L1977 **IM** *020 †20 ‡
KRAUS, Robert Michael. ■ 18049 #041-07-1979 L1980 **EM** *020 †16
LEE, Meng-Chao. 619 DALTON ST 18049 #011-75-1999, ▲ L2001 **HOS** *020 †18
LEHRICH, Henry E. 2887 SHEFFIELD DR 18049 #041-13-1962 L1965 **FM** *071 †18
MITCHELL, John Francis. 555 HARRISON ST 18049 #030-06-1977 L1978 **P N** *020
MOHTASHEMI, Kevin. 100 EAGLE DR, # 713 18049 #010-01-2003 L2004 **P** *012
PEARCE, John Greig. 2827 SHEFFIELD DR 18049 #671-01-1970 L1998 **DR LM** *020 †80
PETZ, Colin J. ■ 18049 #041-13-1983 L1985 **IM** *020 †20
SHALDERS, Deborah Ann. 1031 CHESTNUT ST 18049 #035-06-1987 L1990 **FM** *020 †18
TAN, Lian K P O. ■ 18049 #506-01-1962 L1971 **AN** *020
TANIGAWA, Koichi. ■ 18049 #572-12-1982 **CCA** *100
TELEO, Nicolas. ■ 18049 #187-45-1996 L2004 **GS** *012

EMPORIUM – CAMERON

BLACKBURN, Joseph Morgan. ■ 15834 #041-02-1955 L1956 **GP** *071
DANIELISZ, Petra. 90 E 2ND ST, KEYSTONE RURAL HEALTH 15834 #660-01-1993 L1997
    IM *020 †20
HIPPS, John G. 1333 RAINBOWS END 15834 #041-01-1953 L1954 **OM PHP** *020 †70
KCOMT, William Antonio. 275 E 4TH ST 15834 #737-01-1994 L2004 **RHU** *020 †20
LEIGH, Mary Merkle. ■ 15834 #041-01-1969 L1970 **AN** *100

ENOLA – CUMBERLAND

BLUTSTEIN, Richard Neal. 125 N ENOLA DR STE 101 17025 #041-02-1975 L1979
    PD NPM *020 †55
BRITTON, Llda Lynne. 98 S ENOLA DR, HOSPICE OF CENTRAL PA 17025 #004-01-1982 L1984
    IM *071 †20
DAVIS, Richard Lee. 4470 VALLEY ST 17025 #055-01-1980 L1984 **FM** *020 †18
ESPINO-OSTMAN, Zenaida L. 394 SAMPLE BRIDGE RD, HOME OFFICE 17025
    #748-08-1961 L1970 **AN** *020 ‡
GADANI, Pravin Ramjibhai. 30 E SHADY LN 17025 #496-38-1974 L1977 **IM** *020
GAWLAS, Michael Raymond. 1830 GOOD HOPE RD 17025 #041-77-1982, ▲ L1983
    FM *020 †18
HARM, Kenneth Robbins, Jr. 1830 GOOD HOPE RD 17025 #041-09-1976 L1977
    FM IMG *020 †18
HARR, Denise Flickinger. 1830 GOOD HOPE RD 17025 #041-14-1994 L1996 **FM** *020 †18
JOSEF, Ernest Michael. ■ 17025 #051-04-1988 L1990 **FM** *020
KOSZYK, Anita Michalina. ■ 17025 #759-01-2001 L2002 **HO** *012 †20

MACK, Vicki L. 125 N ENOLA DR, STE 101 17025 #005-14-1984 L1998 **PD** *020 †55
MADAR, Mercedes G. ■ 17025 #060-02-1995 L1998 **EM** *020 †16
MUMMAW, Lisa Ann. 4470 VALLEY ST 17025 #041-02-1988 **FM** *020 †18
NALLUSWAMI, Kumar. ■ 17025 #041-15-1987 L2001 **IM** *020
NEEMA, Swarnalatha. ■ 17025 #496-35-2001 L2007 **FM** *020 †18
PAPOUTSIS, Maria Patselas. 1830 GOOD HOPE RD, GOOD HOPE FAMILY PHYSICIAN 17025 #041-15-2001 L2001 **FM** *020 †20
ROLLER, Rebecca Lauren. ■ 17025 #041-14-2007 L2007 **TY** *012
ROWEHL, Jane Beebe. 1830 GOOD HOPE RD 17025 #035-46-1985 L1986 **FM** *020 †18
SANGILLO, Cathleen Krol. 1830 GOOD HOPE RD, GOOD HOPE FAMILY PHYSICIAN 17025 #016-43-1981 L1982 **FM** *020 †18
SHAH, Jagdish R. 30 E SHADY LN 17025 #495-22-1988 L2005 **N CN** *020 †75
SRIVASTAVA, Anupam. ■ 17025 #496-09-1997 L2006 **END** *020 †20
TOCKS, Jonathan Becket. 4470 VALLEY ST, CUMBERIAND FAMILY PRACTICE 17025 #025-01-1973 L1975 **FM** *020 †18
VOGEL, David Paul. 2250 MILLENIUM WAY, STE 400 17025 #010-02-1987 L1994 **PUD IM** *020 †20

ENON VALLEY – LAWRENCE

DE JESUS, Roman Y, Jr. 153 COREY LN 16120 #748-10-1967 L1973 **AN PME** *020 †05

EPHRATA – LANCASTER

ADUSUMILLI, Sandhya Kiran. 208 W MAIN ST, ASSOCIATES 17522 #496-24-1996 L2002 **RHU** *020 †20
ALLEN, Lisa Sherbin. 208 W MAIN ST, ASSOCIATES 17522 #041-09-1982 L1983 **RHU IM** *020 †20
ALTMAN, Richard Slee, Jr. 4140 OREGON PIKE 17522 #010-01-1974 L1978 **GE IM** *020 †20
BERKOWITZ, Alan Robt. 169 MARTIN AVE 17522 #041-01-1980 L1982 **AN** *020 †20
BROSBE, Robert Jon. 169 MARTIN AVE 17522 #041-07-1979 L1980 **R IM** *020 †20,80
BYBEL, Ann Marie. 175 MARTIN AVE, STE 125 17522 #041-14-1987 L1990 **OBG** *020 †30 ‡
CAMERINO, Edward Gabriel. 44 LANCASTER AVE 17522 #583-01-1983 L1988 **FM** *020 †18
CARINI, John Francis. 175 MARTIN AVE, STE 125 17522 #038-45-1987 L1991 **OBG** *020 †30
CHANDRASEKARAN, Obulakshmi. ■ 17522 #495-04-1997 L2006 **ID** *012 †20
CHON, Il Chun. 169 MARTIN AVE 17522 #041-07-1998 L2001 **IM** *020 †20
COEN, Patricia Elaine. 568 S STATE ST 17522 #007-02-1981 L1985 **IM END** *071
COLTON, Carl Goro. 4140 OREGON PIKE 17522 #035-06-1986 L1995 **GE** *020 †20
CONNELL, Daniel Charles. 4140 OREGON PIKE 17522 #041-02-1991 L1999 **GE IM** *020 †20 ‡
CONRAD, Wayne Ramsay. 175 MARTIN AVE, STE 315 17522 #041-14-1976 L1981 **ORS** *020 †40
COOK, Colleen Lee. 4221 OREGON PIKE 17522 #023-01-1986 L1992 **CCP PD** *020 †55
COTE, Peter Christopher. 169 MARTIN AVE 17522 #036-07-1979 L1987 **PTH** *020 †50
DEVENYI, Attila Geo. 4140 OREGON PIKE 17522 #041-14-1984 L1991 **PG** *020 †55
DORF, Steven. 177 N READING RD 17522 #041-77-1984, ▲ L1985 **OTO** *020
DURISEK, Debbie Belovich. 169 MARTIN AVE 17522 #041-14-1984 L1987 **DR** *020 †80
ELIA, James Michael. 11 S STATE ST 17522 #035-15-1994 L1997 **FM** *020 †18
EVANS, Charles Milton. 175 MARTIN AVE, STE 315 17522 #026-04-1967 L1972 **ORS** *020 †40
FASULO, Gregg Joseph. 175 MARTIN AVE, STE 315 17522 #010-02-1985 L1985 **ORS** *020 †40 ‡
FOLEY, T Raymond. 4140 OREGON PIKE 17522 #035-09-1980 L1986 **GE IM** *020 †20 ‡
FREDERICK, John Randall. 804 GRANDVIEW DR, STE 2 17522 #028-34-1983 L1984 **GS** *020 †85
GALANIS, Sotir Eft. ■ 17522 #781-01-1949 L1971 **FM ORS** *072
GARDNER, Cheryl Lynne. 460 N READING RD, THE EPHRATA CANCER CENTER 17522 #041-77-1990, ▲ L1991 **HO IM** *020
GIBAS, Alexandra Lynn. 4140 OREGON PIKE 17522 #035-47-1982 L1993 **GE IM** *020 †20
GIORDANO, Anthony James. 169 MARTIN AVE, EPHRATE COMM HOSPITAL 17522 #041-09-1967 L1968 **DR** *020 †80 ‡
HAGER, Christopher Lee. 1635 W MAIN ST, GROUP AT LINCOLN FAMILY 17522 #038-45-2003 L2003 **FM** *020 †18
HARNISH, David Miller. 208 W MAIN ST 17522 #041-02-1959 L1960 **GS ORS** *071 †85
HERSHEY, Curtis L. 1635 W MAIN ST, GROUP AT LINCOLN FAMILY 17522 #041-13-2003 L2003 **FM** *020 †18
HESS, Robert Buckwalter. 169 MARTIN AVE 17522 #041-13-1946 L1947 **GP** *020
HONG, Robert Dawson. 175 MARTIN AVE, FL 3 17522 #041-02-1993 L1995 **U** *020 †95
HOVENDEN, Susan Rebecca. 175 MARTIN AVE, STE 125 17522 #051-07-1994 L1996 **OBG** *020 †30
IRWIN, Joseph Jude. 561 W TROUT RUN RD, TROUT RUN FAMILY PRACTICE 17522 #041-01-1997 L1999 **FM OBS** *020 †18
IVES, William Leroy, Jr. 21 N STATE ST 17522 #023-12-1985 L1986 **GS CRS** *020 †85
JOSEPH, John Thos, III. 3440B ROTHSVILLE RD 17522 #025-07-1983 L2003 **CCM PUD** *020 †20
KELLY, James Michael. 1635 W MAIN ST, GROUP AT LINCOLN FAMILY 17522 #036-08-2003 L2003 **FM** *020 †18
KUHLENGEL, Keith Ralph. 175 MARTIN AVE, STE 340A 17522 #028-02-1982 L1990 **NS** *020 †25 ‡
KUNTZ, David Gordon, Jr. 175 MARTIN AVE, STE 315 17522 #041-13-1992 L1994 **ORS** *020 †40
LALANI, Mehul. 4140 OREGON PIKE 17522 #041-15-1999 L2001 **GE** *100 †20
LANCELLOTTI, Guiseppe. 157 N READING RD 17522 #561-10-1982 L1986 **PD** *075 †55
LAND, Rachiel Nettie. 169 MARTIN AVE, EPHRATA HOSPITAL 17522 #014-01-1992 L1996 **PTH PCP** *020 †50
LEAMAN, Phyllis Landis. 169 MARTIN AVE 17522 #041-13-1980 L1981 **EM** *020 †16
LEGASPI, Leopoldo P, Jr. 159 N READING RD 17522 #748-01-1994 L2001 **PD** *020 †55
LIWAG, Celerina. 159 N READING RD, BACA PEDIATRICS 17522 #748-08-1990 L2002 **PD** *020 †55
LOMBOY, Clifford Trinidad. 4140 OREGON PIKE 17522 #041-13-1986 L1992 **GE IM** *020 †20
LYET, J Paul, III. 175 MARTIN AVE 17522 #041-01-1979 L1980 **ORS** *020 †40
MC DONOUGH, Kathleen M. 1 COMMUNITY LN 17522 #035-45-1981 L1987 **N** *071 †75
MERTZ, Persila Vikoren. 169 MARTIN AVE 17522 #041-12-1987 L1989 **OPH** *020 †35
MIDCAP, Matthew E. 175 MARTIN AVE STE 220 17522 #055-01-1985 L1991 **AN PMM** *020 †05 ‡
MONACCI, William Thos. 175 MARTIN AVE, STE 340A 17522 #023-12-1987 L1990 **NS** *020 †25
MUNTEANU, Virgil Peter. 169 MARTIN AVE 17522 #041-09-1955 L1956 **OBG GP** *072

NAWA, John. 169 MARTIN AVE, 1ST FL 17522 #041-09-1990 L1994 **DR** *020 †80
OH, Jang Kyun. 169 MARTIN AVE, EPHRATA COMMUNITY HOSPITAL 17522 #583-01-1966 L1971 **DR RO** *020 †80
OUILIKON, Neva Andrea. 808 PLEASANTVIEW DR 17522 #035-06-2001 L2004 **IM** *020 †20
PARK, So H. 460 N READING RD, EPHRATA CANCER CENTER 17522 #583-04-1990 L1997 **HO** *020 †20
PEART, Raymond Edward. 175 MARTIN AVE, STE 315 17522 #041-14-1983 L1984 **ORS HS** *020 †40
PIEPGRASS, William Chas. 804 GRANDVIEW DR, STE 2 17522 #041-14-1975 L1981 **GS FM** *062 †85
POKORNEY, Bruce Howard. 4140 OREGON PIKE 17522 #051-01-1976 L1977 **GE IM** *030 †20
PORTER, Ira Stanley. 175 MARTIN AVE 17522 #041-02-1976 L1990 **ORS** *020 †40
POWERS, Stephen Langdon. 169 MARTIN AVE 17522 #024-07-1970 L1982 **P** *020 †75
REESE, Richard Wayne. 208 W MAIN ST, ASSOCIATES 17522 #041-12-1972 L1973 **RHU IM** *020 †20
ROGERS, Albert Kandle. 808 PLEASANTVIEW DR 17522 #041-02-1961 L1962 **IM CD** *020 †20
ROMMEL, F Michael. 175 MARTIN AVE, STE 300 17522 #041-02-1981 L1982 **U** *020 †95
ROSENBERG, Dale Jay. 4140 OREGON PIKE 17522 #041-02-1985 L1986 **GE IM** *020 †20 ‡
SARKER, Mary Ann. 169 MARTIN AVE 17522 #160-02-1976 L2001 **FM** *020 †18
SHEPHERD, Rebecca M. 208 W MAIN ST, ASSOCIATES 17522 #047-05-1999 L2006 **RHU** *100 †20
SHUGAR, Gary Lee. 169 MARTIN AVE 17522 #041-02-1974 L1975 **PTH** *020 †50
SIEBER, Paul Robert. 175 MARTIN AVE, FL 3 17522 #017-20-1982 L1984 **U** *020 †95
SMITH, David Marshall. 4140 OREGON PIKE 17522 #036-08-1999 L2000 **GE** *020 †20
SVETEC, David Andrew. 175 MARTIN AVE 17522 #041-01-1992 L1995 **U** *020 †95
TUCKMAN, Alan Scott. 175 MARTIN AVE, STE 315 17522 #035-15-1990 L1992 **ORS OFA** *020 †40 ‡
WALKER, Jon Gilchrist. 175 MARTIN AVE 17522 #055-01-1968 L1975 **U** *071 †95
WEAVER, Aaron Richard. 169 MARTIN AVE 17522 #041-13-1964 L1965 **GS FM** *071 †85
WEBER, Howard Scott. 169 MARTIN AVE 17522 #308-07-1983 L1987 **PDC PD** *020 †55
WEBER, Jeffrey Karlton. ■ 17522 #041-14-1993 L1995 **FM** *020 †18
WENGER, Marlin Esbenshade. 208 W MAIN ST, ASSOCIATES 17522 #041-13-1964 L1965 **RHU IM** *020 †20
WILLWERTH, James Wm. PO BOX 1002 17522 #041-02-1957 L1958 **R** *071 †80
WIRTH, Carole Zajac. 169 MARTIN AVE, X-RAY 17522 #041-14-1985 L1986 **DR** *020 †80
WOLBACH, Albert Bogh. 923 W MAIN ST 17522 #041-02-1958 L1959 **FM** *071
WOODARD, Christopher A. 175 MARTIN AVE, STE 300 17522 #011-04-1998 L2001 **U** *020 †95
ZARTMAN, Gary Matthew. 175 MARTIN AVE, STE 315 17522 #007-02-1986 L1994 **ORS IM** *020 †40

EQUINUNK – WAYNE

VAN NATTA, Fred Chas. 59 COYOTE LN 18417 #005-02-1968 L1988 **DR PD** *020 †55,80

ERDENHEIM – MONTGOMERY

BAKER, Linda Joyce. 7 WHITEMARSH AVE 19038 #005-18-1980 L1982 **PD** *020 †55
BENNETT, Arlene Parsons. ■ 19038 #041-01-1964 L1965 **P** *020 †75
BLACK, Maurice Wm. 415 GLENWAY RD 19038 #041-09-1953 L1954 **IM** *071
DE PAULA, Geraldine H F. ■ 19038 #035-06-1968 L1969 **P OS** *020 †75
FOREST, Jean Louise. 709 BETHLEHEM PIKE REAR 19038 #041-07-1955 L1966 **ADM PTH** *071 †50
GINSBERG, Craig Alan. 600 BETHLEHEM PIKE 19038 #041-09-1984 L1985 **CHP P** *020 †75
HANSON, Eric Paul. ■ 19038 #041-12-2002 L2002 **PPR** *012 †55
LAVIZZO-MOUREY, R J. 711 PAPER MILL RD 19038 #024-01-1979 L1982 **IM** *030 †20
SHAPIRO, Beverly. 717 BETHLEHEM PIKE 19038 #041-09-1975 L1976 **GP OS** *020
WITTELS, Heidi Linsk. 1006 PRESTON RD 19038 #041-09-1989 L1992 **PM** *020 †60
YOST, Robert Morris. 717 BETHLEHEM PIKE # C2 19038 #041-13-1955 L1956 **FM PD** *071 †18

ERIE – ERIE

ABD-AL-GHAFFAR, Amr Ahmad. 2500 W 12TH ST 16505 #915-03-1978 L1993 **ON** *020 †20
ABOGUNDE, Segun Eneji. 238 W 22ND ST, DIGESTIVE DISEASES OF NW 16502 #690-08-1987 L2000 **GE** *020 †20
ADELMAN, Michael. 135 E 38TH ST, ERIE VETERANSADMINISTRATIO 16504 #041-12-1981 L1982 **IM** *020 †20
AGARWALA, Vijaya Kumar. 225 W 25TH ST STE 408, DEPT OF ANESTHESIA 16502 #917-08-1979 L1996 **AN** *020 †05
AGRIS, Jacob Martin. 1910 SASSAFRAS ST, STE 300 16502 #048-04-1994 L2006 **RNR** *020
ALBANESE, Cheryl Lee. 104 E 2ND ST 16507 #041-02-1979 L1979 **FM** *030 †18
ALBAUGH, Mary Anne. 1330 W 26TH ST, SAFE HARBOR BEHAV HLTH 16508 #041-09-1982 L1984 **CHP P** *020 †75
ALBERT, John David. 201 STATE ST 16540 #041-12-1975 L1977 **AN PAN** *020 †05
ALI, Amjad. 104 E 2ND ST 16507 #704-25-1991 L2004 **GS OS** *020 †85
ALMISKY, Nabil Sadek. ■ 16509 #875-01-1960 L1973 **FM GP** *020 †18
ALMQUIST, John Foster. 5241 BUFFALO RD 16510 #041-12-1976 L1977 **FM** *020 †18
ANDERSON, Richard Jos. 232 W 25TH ST, SAINT VINCENT EMERGENCY DE 16544 #041-09-1992 L1994 **EM** *020 †16
ANDRIJIW, Roman. ■ 16509 #154-01-1955 L1962 **IM GP** *071
ANON, Jack Bryant. 3580 PEACH ST, ENT SPECIALISTS OF 16508 #038-41-1981 L1986 **OTO** *020 †45
APARICIO, Luis Felipe. 300 STATE ST, STE 204 16507 #737-01-1983 L1992 **PD** *020 †55
ARMET, Kerry Kathleen. 1645 W 8TH ST 16505 #035-03-1998 L2007 **PD** *020 †55
ARREOLA, Rodolfo, Jr. 104 E 2ND ST, HAMOT BARIATRCI SURGERY CE 16507 #043-01-1989 L2001 **GS** *020 †85
AYDIN, Haluk Kaya. 5515 PEACH ST, CHILD & ADOLESCENT PSYCH 16509 #902-19-1994 L2000 **CHP** *020 †75
BABEL, Douglas Bruce. 300 STATE ST STE 201, ERIE RETINAL SURG INC 16507 #019-02-1992 L2007 **OPH IM** *020 †35
BABINS, David Michael. 300 STATE ST, STE 400 16507 #041-09-1989 L1991 **ORS** *020 †40
BAJOREK, Edward John. 230 W 26TH ST 16508 #028-34-1954 L1955 **GS OM** *071 †85
BALDWIN, Bruce Wm. 4509 W RIDGE RD 16506 #654-01-1984 L1985 **FM** *071 †18

BALDWIN, Robert C. 300 STATE ST STE 201 16507 #041-14-1993 L2000 **OPH** *020 †35
BALSAN, Michael J, III. 201 STATE ST, NEONATAL INTENSIVE CARE UN 16550 #056-06-1983 L1984 **NPM PD** *020 †55
BARBER, Joseph C, Jr. 3580 PEACH ST, STE 100 16508 #041-12-1979 L1987 **CHN PD** *020 †55
BARBERO, Daniel J. 201 STATE ST 4, HAMOT MEDICAL CENTER 16550 #035-06-1994 L1998 **MPD PD** *020 †20,55
BARONE, Steven Michael. ■ 16503 #016-42-2002 L2007 **CRS** *012
BARTEAUX, John W. 1330 W 26TH ST 16508 #064-01-1960 L1989 **P CHP** *020
BAUMAN, Jeanne. 1645 W 8TH ST 16505 #041-14-1980 L1984 **DR** *020 †80
BAUMGRATZ, William A. 232 W 25TH ST, EMERGENCY DEPARTMENT 16544 #041-13-2000 L2001 **EM** *020 †16
BAXTER, Donald L, Jr. 3416 STATE ST 16508 #041-09-1983 L1992 **D IM** *020 †15
BEAVER, Warren Jeffry. 3822 COLONIAL AVE 16506 #041-09-1984 L1985 **FM** *020 †18
BEDNARSKI, Jeffrey John. 104 E 2ND ST, FL 7 16507 #010-02-1972 L1975 **GS TRS** *020 †85
BEDWELL, Scott Harold. 2626 SIGSBEE ST 16508 #041-09-1981 L1982 **GS VS** *020 †85
BEEBY, James Leonard. ■ 16506 #023-01-1957 L1972 **GS** *071 †85
BELL, Hershey Sheldon. 1858 W GRANDVIEW BLVD 16509 #065-01-1982 L2000 **FM** *040 †18
BENJAMIN, David Robt. 3416 STATE ST 16508 #041-12-1974 L1978 **D** *020 †20,15
BERGQVIST, Gunnar E. 410 CRANBERRY ST STE 310 16507 #041-12-1994 L2002 **PS CS** *020 †85,65
BESNER, Lance Alan. 120 E 2ND ST STE 348 16507 #035-06-1986 L1989 **P** *020 †75
BETZ, William Richard. 2701 EVANSTON AVE, STE 100 16506 #033-05-1982 L1983 **IM IMG** *020 †20
BHARWANI, Ishwer Lal. 406 PEACH ST, AGING 16507 #704-08-1979 L1997 **IMG** *020 †20
BHATTI, Zahida. 1202 STATE ST 16501 #495-30-1992 L2006 **ID** *020
BIENIEK, Russell Bruce. 201 STATE ST, EMERG DEPT ADM 16550 #024-16-1982 L1983 **EM** *030 †16
BINGHAM, Rodney Steven. 2409 STATE ST, STE 1R 16503 #010-03-1984 L1985 **PM** *020 †60
BINNER, Robert Arthur, Jr. 232 W 25TH ST 16544 #035-03-1980 L1996 **AN PD** *020 †05,55
BLAKE, Jeffery Irving. 2216 SOUTH SHORE DR 16505 #041-13-1973 L1977 **CD IM** *020 †20
BLILEY, Kirk Stephen. 333 STATE ST, STE 204 16507 #041-12-1982 L1983 **IM** *020 †20
BLOOM, R Lee. 1315 PENINSULA DR 16505 #016-76-1965, ▲ L1978 **ON HEM** *071
BLOOMSTINE, Mark Theodore. 204 W 26TH ST 16508 #010-02-1982 L1991 **ORS OFA** *020 †40
BOGGIO, Jose Luis. ■ 16505 #737-01-1994 L1998 **IM** *020
BONGUTU, Mbembo. 104 E 2ND ST, ROLAND E MILLER FAMILY MED 16507 #010-01-1995 L1997 **FM** *020 †18
BORCZON, Dennis Philip. 3939 W RIDGE RD, STE B40 16506 #041-09-1982 L1983 **CHP** *030 †75
BOROWSKI, David T. 2315 MYRTLE ST, STE 190 16502 #035-03-1985 L1999 **CD** *020 †20
BOWERS, Steven Kenneth. 135 E 38TH ST 16504 #041-13-1988 L1990 **IM** *020 †20
BOYLE, Richard Cyener. 1608 WALNUT ST 16502 #035-06-1958 L1959 **FM** *071 †18
BRERETON, William F. 2500 W 12TH ST 16505 #035-20-1963 L1971 **HO IM** *071 †20
BRIDGE, Raymond James. 1910 SASSAFRAS ST, STE 200 16502 #010-01-1980 L1981 **FM** *020 †18
BROTHERSON, Gary Thos. 1801 W 8TH ST 16505 #036-01-1980 L1984 **OPH** *020 †35
BROWN, Arthur Craig. 3216 STATE ST 16508 #049-01-1973 L1983 **CRS GS** *020 †85,10
BROWN, Christina Cordell. 3211 LIBERTY ST 16508 #041-13-1996 L2000 **OBG** *020 †30
BROWN, Christine Marie. 1700 PEACH ST STE 200 16501 #041-09-1991 L1993 **FM** *020 †18
BROWN, Gordon Earl. ■ 16508 #035-01-1957 L1988 **GS GYN** *075 †85
BROWN, Lisa Ann. 2314 SASSAFRAS ST, STE 306 16502 #038-44-2001 L2001 **PMM** *012 †18
BRUNNER-MARTINEZ, Kirstin. 1020 E 10TH ST 16503 #041-77-1986, ▲ L1986 **CHP PD** *020 †55,75
BRUNO, Sharon Marie. 4500 PINE AVE 16504 #038-41-1992 L1994 **FM** *020 †18
BRYDON, Jan Kirkland. 310 FRENCH ST 16507 #041-13-1978 L1983 **D IM** *020 †20,15
BRZOZOWSKI, Jan Francis. 311 W 24TH ST STE 303 16502 #016-43-1985 L1987 **OBG** *020 †30
BUETIKOFER, Jeffrey Alan. 2315 MYRTLE ST, STE 190 16502 #041-09-1983 L1990 **CD IM** *020 †20
BUSECK, Mark Sherwood. 204 W 26TH ST, ORTHOPAEDIC SURGEONS INC 16508 #041-01-1983 L1989 **ORS OSM** *020 †40
BUSHELL, Gordon J. 1330 W 26TH ST 16508 #010-02-1973 L1977 **P** *020 †75
BUTLER, Michael Dana. 120 W 2ND ST 16507 #050-02-1990 L1997 **TS** *020 †85,90
BYUN, Stanley Y. 2500 W 12TH ST 16505 #583-02-1969 L1987 **RO** *020 †80 ‡
CACCHIONE, Joseph Gerald. 2315 MYRTLE ST, STE 190 16502 #041-09-1985 L1991 **CD IM** *020 †20
CAIN, Sean Robert. 104 E 2ND ST, 7TH FL 16507 #038-43-2001 L2006 **GS** *020
CANDIB, Dorothy. 2314 SASSAFRAS ST, FAMILY MEDICINE CENTER 16502 #067-01-1981 L1984 **IM IMG** *020 †20
CARLSON, Derek C. ■ 16509 #422-01-1994 L2000 **CHP** *020
CARNES, Paul Phillip. 232 W 25TH ST 16544 #023-12-1990 L2002 **AN** *020 †05
CARNEVAL, Daniel C. ■ 16505 #028-78-1955, ▲ L1956 **ORS OSM** *071
CARVELLI, Joseph Anthony. 2059 W 8TH ST, PRIMARY CARE WEST 16505 #561-26-1983 L1985 **FM** *020 †18
CERMAK, Mary Beth. 300 STATE ST STE 205 16507 #041-13-1984 L1989 **ORS HS** *020 †40
CHADHA, Priyanka. ■ 16506 #495-83-2004 L2007 **FP** *012
CHAPMAN, Penelope. 2910 STATE ST 16508 #917-02-1986 L1995 **P** *020
CHARRON, Albert Eugene, Jr. 2821 E 27TH ST 16510 #041-09-1997 L2005 **FM** *020 †18
CHARRON, Amy R. 201 STATE ST, HAMOT MEDICAL CENTER 16550 #041-09-1997 L2005 **DR** *020 †80
CHEKKA, B Rao. 1611 PEACH ST, STE 225 16501 #495-11-1972 L1979 **PD NPM** *020 †55
CHEUNG, Wai C. 201 STATE ST, DEPT OF MED EDUCATION 16550 #030-05-1979 L1980 **FM** *020
CHINSKY, Kenneth David. 3580 PEACH ST, CHEST DISEASES OF 16508 #028-03-1985 L1991 **PUD CCM** *020 †20
CHINTA, Bharath Kumar. 232 W 25TH ST 16544 #495-65-1996 L2005 **DR** *020 †80
CHINTA, Suneetha. 232 W 25TH ST, DEPT OF MEDICAL EDUCATION 16544 #495-65-1996 L2005 **FP** *012
CHORAZY, Zdzislaw Jozef. 311 W 24TH ST, ALLIED UROLOGY ASSOCIATES 16502 #759-01-1975 L1981 **U** *020 †95
CHRISTIANSEN, Deanne. ■ 16509 #422-01-1982 L1991 **CHP P** *071
CHU, Winston Htin. 5215 PEACH ST, NEW PLASTIC SURGERY 16509 #209-03-1968 L1972 **PS GS** *020 †85,65
CLARK, Edward Chas. 311 W 24TH ST, STE 402 16502 #041-09-1983 L1995 **NEP IM** *020 †20
CLEMENTE, Jeffrey Earl L.. 232 W 25TH ST 16544 #748-10-2002 L2006 **FP** *012
COGLEY, Jonathan Ryan. ■ 16509 #041-13-2007 L2007 **GS** *012
COGLEY, Richard L. 232 W 25TH ST, ST VINCENT FAMILY MED 16544 #041-12-1978 L1979 **FM IMG** *030 †18
COLE, Dennis Gene. 4873 WOLF RD 16505 #041-09-1963 L1964 **ORS** *071 †40
COLE, Richard Allan. ■ 16508 #023-07-1974 L1978 **END DIA** *075 †20
COONEY, Michael James. 2314 SASSAFRAS ST, STE 200 16502 #041-09-1991 L1993 **IM** *020 †20
COOVER, Leonard R. 201 STATE ST 16550 #055-01-1982 L1985 **R NM** *071 †80
CREAGER, Andrew Jared. 201 STATE ST 16550 #036-01-1995 L2005 **PTH** *020 †50
CROSBY, Nicholas Excell. ■ 16505 #036-05-2008 *012
CROSS, Raquel. 201 STATE ST 16550 #649-01-1972 L1978 **IM** *020
CSIR, Floyd Marcus. 311 W 24TH ST STE 101, ALLIED UROLOGY ASSOCIATES 16502 #041-01-1969 L1976 **U** *020 †95
DAIL, Eric Michael. 215 HOLLAND ST 16507 #035-06-1971 L1980 **OBG** *071 †30
DAILEY, Ellen Elizabeth. 311 W 24TH ST STE 303 16502 #041-09-1979 L1981 **OBG** *020 †30
DAILEY, James Patrick. 300 STATE ST STE 201 16507 #035-20-1982 L1990 **OPH** *020 †35
DALTON, Brian Edward. 120 E 2ND ST STE 401 16507 #035-15-1983 L1984 **NS** *020 †25
D'ANGELO, George J. ■ 16506 #035-45-1951 L1958 **OS TS** *071 †85,90
DANIELE, Joseph Quentin. 232 W 25TH ST 16544 #016-43-1971 L1972 **GS** *020 †85
DAVISON, Maria Willa. 201 STATE ST, HAMOT EMERGENCY DEPT 16550 #032-01-1993 L2000 **EM** *020 †16
DECKER, Richard Lawrence. 510 CRANBERRY ST, STE 200 16507 #041-09-1982 L1983 **FM** *020 †18
DE FRANCO, Joseph Mariano. 232 W 25TH ST 16544 #038-41-1967 L1973 **IM** *071
DEFRANCO, Richard Jos. 201 STATE ST 16550 #035-45-1989 L1993 **OBG** *020 †30
DEIMEL, Joseph Francis. 145 W 23RD ST, STE 101 16502 #035-15-1973 L1974 **FM** *020 †18
DEJOHN, Matthew Ronald. 2808 STATE ST 16508 #025-01-2003 L2007 **P** *012
DE JOYA, German D. 201 STATE ST, HAMOT MEDICAL CENTER 16550 #748-10-1988 L1995 **CCM IM** *020 †20
DELULLO, James Anthony. 300 STATE ST, STE 400 16507 #038-45-1998 L2000 **ORS OSM** *100 †40
DE MATTEIS, James Albert. 120 E 2ND ST, FL 3 16507 #011-02-1978 L1984 **N OS** *020 †20,75
DEMJANENKO, Paul. 120 E 2ND ST, FL 2CD 16507 #041-09-1984 L1985 **CD IM** *020 †20
DENNISTON, Baron Takayuki. 4201 DION CT 16506 #024-05-1985 L1991 **P CHP** *020 †75
DEPOWSKI, Peter Louis. 201 STATE ST 16550 #035-03-1996 L2002 **HMP** *020 †50
DESHPANDE, Asha Sharad. 232 W 25TH ST, SAINT VINCENT HEALTH CENTE 16544 #495-56-1965 L1978 **PTH** *020
DESHPANDE, Sharadchandra. ■ 16506 #495-21-1958 L1970 **FM FPG** *071
DEXTER, David Wm. 104 E 2ND ST 7TH FL 16507 #035-15-1991 L2000 **GS TRS** *020 †85
DICOLA, Edward L. ■ 16506 #028-78-1946, ▲ L1950 *071
DIETEMAN, David Francis. 3190 GLENWOOD PARK AVE 16508 #016-43-1969 L1972 **D** *020 †15
DI STEFANO, Berardino. ■ 16509 #561-17-1956 L1967 **IM** *071 †20
DOGUN, Enakeme Stella. 1202 STATE ST, COMMUNITY HEALTH NET 16501 #690-06-1983 L1993 **PD** *020 †55
DREYFUS, Richard. 311 W 24TH ST, STE 402 16502 #035-08-1969 L1977 **NEP IM** *071 †20
DRISCOLL, Robert Alonzo. 232 NIAGARA POINT DR 16507 #030-06-1969 L1975 **R** *020 †80
DUBEY, Saroj Kumar. 232 W 25TH ST, SAINT VINCENT EMERGENCY 16544 #495-13-1956 L1973 **GP EM** *071 †16
DUDENHOEFER, Christian P. 2059 W 8TH ST 16505 #041-09-1988 L1990 **FM** *020 †18
DUDENHOEFER, Frederick J. 2202 W 15TH ST, STE 108 16505 #041-02-1969 L1976 **A IM** *020 †20,03
DUDENHOEFER, Kathleen C. 2314 SASSAFRAS ST, STE 200 16502 #041-02-1969 L1976 **PD** *040 †55
DUGAN, Robert Byron. 3211 LIBERTY ST, STE 101 16508 #050-02-1942 L1948 **OPH** *071 †35
DULABON, David Alexander. 104 E 2ND ST, 4TH FL 16507 #041-12-1973 L1974 **U** *020 †95
DULABON, George Robt. 201 STATE ST, HAMOT SHOCK TRAUMA 16550 #041-12-1991 L2001 **TRS CCS** *020 †85
DUNCOMBE, Michael Paul. 232 W 25TH ST 16544 #041-12-1972 L1977 **N** *020 †75 ‡
DUNN, David Dennis. ■ 16505 #041-02-1939 L1941 **GS** *071 †85
DUNN, Geoffrey Parker. 201 STATE ST 16550 #041-02-1979 L1984 **GS** *020 †85
DUSCKAS, George John. ■ 16505 #041-12-1945 L1946 **OTO** *071
EARICK, Michael Edward. 2626 SIGSBEE ST 16508 #041-09-1961 L1962 **OPH** *071 †35
ECKBERG, John James. 201 STATE ST 16550 #041-12-1943 L1944 **IM CD** *071 †20
EGGLESTON, Lisa K. 300 STATE ST, STE 301 16507 #055-01-2000 L2003 **PD** *020 †55
EISENBERG, Richard B. ■ 16509 #041-01-1942 L1943 **PTH BBK** *071 †50
EMANUELE, Tullio. 104 E 2ND ST, MEDICOR ASSOC INC 16507 #561-23-1982 L1989 **CD CCM** *020 †20
ENGEL, Edward E. 3317 LIBERTY ST 16508 #067-01-1984 L1985 **RHU IM** *020 †20
ENGEL, Eileen Georgia. 232 W 25TH ST, ST VINCENT EMERGENCY DEPT 16544 #041-12-1979 L1980 **EM IM** *020 †20,55,16
ENGEL, Gregory Scott. 104 E 2ND ST 16507 #041-12-1986 L1987 **GS** *020 †85
EPISCOPO, Frank Ronald. ■ 16509 #041-12-1954 L1955 **EM GS** *071 †85
ESTES, Michael Kevin. 3535 PINE AVE 16504 #041-15-2004 L2004 **FM** *020 †18
ESTRADA, Jason K. 3535 PINE AVE, ERIE PHYSICIANS NETWORK 16504 #748-01-1991 L2001 **IM** *020 †20
EULIANO, John Jos, Jr. 300 STATE ST STE 400A 16507 #010-02-1969 L1970 **ORS** *020 †40
EVANKOVICH, Michael R. 300 STATE ST, STE 302 16507 #041-14-1994 L1996 **U** *020 †95
FADRIGO, Andrea. 300 STATE ST STE 301, YOUR PEDIATRIC CONNECTION 16507 #748-01-1977 L1994 **PD** *020 †55
FAGENHOLZ, Linda S L. 3939 W RIDGE RD STE C2 16506 #024-07-1972 L1979 **PD** *020 †55
FAGENHOLZ, S Allen. 3939 W RIDGE RD, STE C2 16506 #035-45-1970 L1978 **PD PUD** *020 †55
FAROOQ, Ahmad. 135 E 38TH ST, VETERANS AFFAIR MEDICAL CT 16504 #704-20-1988 L2004 **IMG** *020 †20
FAZALARE, Joseph James. 201 STATE ST 16550 #055-01-2004 L2004 **ORS** *012
FERRARO, Robert Jos. 120 E 2ND ST 16507 #041-14-1977 L1982 **CD IM** *020 †20
FERRARO, Robert Wm. 120 E 2ND ST 16507 #030-06-1963 L1964 **ORS LM** *030 †40
FESSLER, Thomas J. 204 W 26TH ST 16508 #010-02-1981 L1987 **ORS** *020 †40
FILIPPI, Ronald Stephen. ■ 16502 #041-09-1985 L1986 **IM EM** *020 †20
FINE, Robert Melvin. 2500 W 12TH ST 16505 #010-01-1970 L1987 **RO GS** *020 †80
FINN, Joanne. 3211 LIBERTY ST, STE 103 16508 #041-12-1980 L1982 **OBG** *020 †30
FITZGIBBON, Leo David. 232 W 25TH ST 16544 #035-09-1987 L1989 **TS GS** *020 †85,90
FLAMINI, John A. 3504 STATE ST 16508 #016-43-1979 L1981 **N** *020 †75
FLICK, Kathryn Laverne. 406 PEACH ST, SENIOR HEALTHCARE SERVICES 16507 #038-43-1982 L1985 **FM** *020 †18
FOFUNG, Dopgima. ■ 16504 #010-03-1977 L1982 **GS CRS** *020
FOREHAND, Brett Ramsey. 232 W 25TH ST, SAINT VINCENT HEALTH CENTE 16544 #038-40-2000 L2003 **EM** *100 †16
FORNELLI, Rick Allen. 3580 PEACH ST, ENT SPECIALISTS OF 16508 #041-14-1995 L2000 **OTO HNS** *020 †45

7886

■ = Address Information Privacy Protected

FORTNA, Sandra Jane. 104 E 2ND ST 16507 #041-09-1988 L1990 **ID IM** *020 †20

FOWLER, Melissa Halpern. 232 W 25TH ST, DEPT OF PATHOLOGY 16544 #035-45-1998 L2003 **PTH** *020 †50

FOX, Bradley Preston. 3413 CHERRY ST, LIBERTY FAMILY PRACTICE 16508 #035-15-1991 L1993 **FM OBG** *020 †18

FRANCIS, Gerard R. 1330 W 26TH ST, CENTER FOR PERSONAL & FAMI 16508 #220-04-1987 L2000 **P** *020

FRANCIS, Paul. ■ 16509 #917-03-1957 L1963 **P** *071 †75

FRANKOVITCH, Karl Frank. 1645 W 8TH ST 16505 #016-43-1963 L1964 **ORS OSS** *072 †40

FREEMAN, Carl Rutledge. ■ 16509 #010-02-2006 L2006 **ORS** *012

FREEMAN, David Mark. 1351 W 6TH ST 16505 #041-09-1986 L1997 **PDC** *020 †55

FRYCZYNSKI, Thaddeus Paul. 232 W 25TH ST 16544 #041-02-1954 L1955 **CD IM** *071

FRYER, Theresa J. 3317 LIBERTY ST 16508 #017-20-1979 L1984 **RHU** *020 †20

FUH, Yen-Jen. 135 E 38TH ST 16504 #385-02-1963 L1997 **PUD IM** *071 †20

FURR, Charles Morris. 120 E 2ND ST 16507 #041-02-1970 L1972 **IC CD** *020 †20

GABRESKI, Ralph Charles. 135 E 38TH ST, VA MEDICAL CENTER 16504 #041-09-1993 L1996 **IM** *020 †20

GALLAGHER, Philip Edward. 2202 W 15TH ST 16505 #041-12-1976 L1981 **AI PD** *020 †55,03

GARCIA, Gerald Dion. 4355 PEACH ST 16509 #041-14-1983 L1984 **PS** *020 †85,65

GARCIA, Lydia. ■ 16505 #649-01-1972 L1991 **IM END** *020 †20

GAROUFALIS, Evgenia. ■ 16507 #306-01-1999 L2001 **FM** *020

GAUNA-ESTRADA, Maribelle. 406 PEACH ST, ERIE CENTER ON HEALTH & AG 16507 #748-01-1991 L2002 **IM** *020 †20

GEBHARDT, Bruce Cushman. 232 W 25TH ST, ST. VINCENT FAMILY MEDICIN 16544 #038-41-1987 L1989 **FM** *020 †18

GEIGLE, Carl Frederick. 3216 STATE ST 16508 #041-13-1939 L1940 **CRS** *071 †10

GEORGE, Jacob. 232 W 25TH ST 16544 #495-31-1966 L1972 **TS GS** *071 †85,90

GERMAN, Antonio Isaias. 201 STATE ST 16550 #050-02-1960 L1973 **PTH** *071 †50

GERMAN, David John. 204 W 26TH ST, ORTHOPAEDIC SURGEONS INC 16508 #038-40-1994 L1999 **ORS** *020 †40

GHANEM, Maged Mahmoud. 3535 PINE AVE 16504 #915-03-1998 L2004 **IM** *100 †20

GILMAN, Steven Adam. 120 E 2ND ST, STE 401 16507 #041-09-1989 L1995 **NS** *020 †25

GLASER, Alan Lawrence. 232 W 25TH ST 16544 #041-12-1985 L1989 **AN** *020 †05

GLENNON, Edward Joseph. 3216 STATE ST, RECTAL 2 COLON SURGERY INC 16508 #010-02-1987 L1992 **GS CRS** *020 †85,10

GMUER, Paul Jos. 238 W 22ND ST 16502 #035-08-1979 L1984 **GE** *020 †20

GOBBIE, Katherine Mary. 4815 THOROUGHBRED LOOP 16506 #055-01-1995 L1997 **FM** *020 †18

GOKHALE, Abhay Sudhir. ■ 16505 #024-07-2004 L2005 **RO** *012

GOLD, Jack. ■ 16509 #035-06-1953 L1954 **PD** *071 †55

GOLDBAUM, Abe Frank. 232 W 25TH ST, SAINT VINCENT HEALTH CENTE 16544 #016-11-1991 L1995 **PM** *020 †60

GOLDBERG, Aron T. 311 W 24TH ST 16502 #012-05-1996 L2005 **TS** *020 †85

GRIFFITH, Christina M. 232 W 25TH ST 16544 #041-78-2006, ▲ L2006 **FP** *012

GRIFFITH, Scott Alan. 2640 W 38TH ST 16506 #041-07-1992 L1997 **OPH** *020 †35

GUELCHER, Robert T. 3580 PEACH ST, OF NORTHWESTERN PENNSYLVAN 16508 #035-06-1960 L1967 **OTO** *071 †45

GUNDUZ, Paula Angela. 4000 STERRETTANIA RD 16506 #649-40-1980 L1984 **OBG** *020 †30

GUSTIN, Thomas Arthur. 1330 W 26TH ST, # 2NFL 16508 #041-12-1959 L1960 **P** *020 †75

GUTHLEBEN, John Geo. 1611 PEACH ST 16501 #028-34-1968 L1975 **OBG** *071 †30

GUTIERREZ, Matthew James. 201 STATE ST 16550 #035-06-1997 L2004 **IM** *020 †20

GUZZARDO, Michael Nick. 2560 W 12TH ST 16505 #021-05-1982 L1983 **EM FM** *071 †18,16

HAIBACH, Raymond Anthony. 145 W 23RD ST, STE 101 16502 #041-02-1978 L1979 **FM** *020 †18

HALT, Raymond Allan. 232 W 25TH ST, ST VINCENT HC 16544 #041-12-1972 L1973 **R** *020 †80

HARDNER, Rebecca Marie. 232 W 25TH ST, DEPT OF PATHOLOGY 16544 #035-06-1992 L1998 **PTH** *074 †50

HARDY, Heidrun D. 201 STATE ST, HAMOT MEDICAL CENTER 16550 #409-23-1971 L1978 **AN** *071 †05

HARRINGTON, Cassie J. 5241 BUFFALO RD, HARBOCREEK FAMILY PHY 16510 #054-04-1998 L2000 **FM** *020 †18

HAUPT, Daniele. 2626 SIGSBEE ST 16508 #041-14-1995 L1999 **GS** *020 †85

HAVERLY, Robert Frederick. 311 W 24TH ST, STE 301 16502 #035-06-1992 L1998 **OPH** *020 †35

HAVKO, Frederick Chas. 232 W 25TH ST 16544 #041-12-1987 L1993 **EM** *020 †16

HAYES, Kelly Lynne. 120 E 2ND ST, FL 2CD 16507 #050-02-1995 L2004 **IM** *020 †20

HEIBEL, Edward James. ■ 16504 #028-34-1954 L1955 **GP PHP** *020

HELSLEY, Scott Edward. 201 STATE ST 16550 #035-06-1998 L2002 **AN** *020

HENDRICKS, Wm Craig, Jr. ■ 16505 #041-01-1959 L1960 **NS** *071

HENRY, Scott Perrin. 300 STATE ST, STE 103 16507 #035-09-1983 L1988 **GE IM** *020 †20 ‡

HERBST, Charles Gregory. 3317 LIBERTY ST 16508 #041-09-1981 L1982 **RHU IM** *020 †20

HERGENROEDER, Paul F. 2500 W 12TH ST 16505 #041-13-1984 L1985 **HO** *020 †16,20

HILL, John Louis. 232 W 25TH ST 16544 #011-02-1983 L1983 **DR** *020 †80

HINES, Joseph Harry. 240 W 11TH ST, STE 2 16501 #035-09-1975 L1978 **END IM** *020 †20

HOOBLER, Randall James. 201 STATE ST 16550 #041-02-1985 L1988 **AN** *020 †05

HOOD, John Michael. 300 STATE ST STE 205 16507 #041-09-1985 L1987 **ORS HS** *020 †40

HOWELL, James Tennyson. ■ 16509 #004-01-2005 L2005 **ORS** *012

HOWER, Robert. 300 STATE ST, STE 103 16507 #041-78-2001, ▲ L2004 **GE IM** *020

HUDSON, Howard Lane. 201 STATE ST 16550 #041-12-1957 L1958 **R** *071 †80

HUTZEL, David Charles. 2701 EVANSTON AVE, STE 100 16506 #038-06-1996 L2002 **IM** *020 †20

HYATT, Floyd Richard. 232 W 25TH ST 16544 #041-12-1969 L1975 **R** *020 †80

IGNOCHECK, Anthony R. 104 E 2ND ST 16507 #041-14-1985 L1986 **FM** *040 †18

INTRIERI, Peter Michael. 201 STATE ST, HAMOT MEDICAL CENTER 16550 #041-12-1987 L1990 **EM** *020 †16

IYER, Hema. 232 W 25TH ST, ST VINCENT'S HEALTH CENTER 16544 #495-66-1994 L2004 **P** *020 ‡

IZZO, Mark Robt. 2315 MYRTLE ST, STE 190 16502 #041-07-1989 L1991 **CD** *020 †20

JACKSON, Thomas Richard. 2374 VILLAGE COMMON DR, STE 100 16506 #041-13-2002 L2002 **PMM PM** *020 †60

JADEJA, Mahendrasinh A. ■ 16506 #495-48-1980 L2000 **IM** *020

JAGEMAN, James Robt. 3530 PEACH ST, GREAT LAKES FAMILY MEDICIN 16508 #041-09-1973 L1974 **FM** *020 †18

JAGEMAN, John Chas. 4108 ZUCK RD 16506 #041-13-1973 L1974 **IM** *020 †20

JANA, Dilip Kumar. 2931 PEACH ST, INTERNAL MED ASSOCS 16508 #495-39-1960 L1977 **CD IMG** *020 †20

JEFFRESS, Andrea Toulson. 311 W 24TH ST STE 303 16502 #008-01-1996 L2000 **OBG** *020 †30

JENKINS, Jay Lee. 2500 W 12TH ST 16505 #041-01-1961 L1962 **HO ON** *020 †20

JEYAPALAN, Amelia Miro. 2626 SIGSBEE ST 16508 #041-09-1998 L2004 **GS** *020 †85

JOHANSEN, Robert Wm. 300 STATE ST STE 209 16507 #035-08-1971 L1972 **P** *020 †75

JOHNS, Walter Scott, IV. 213 E 41ST ST 16504 #041-14-1978 L1985 **IM** *020 †20

JOHNSTON, Craig Tyrrell. 2059 W 8TH ST 16505 #041-77-1981, ▲ L1982 **FM** *020 †18

JOY, Charles A. 4 W 34TH ST 16508 #035-06-1946 L1952 **IM** *071 †20

JOY, Charles Richard. 4 W 34TH ST 16508 #041-12-1978 L1987 **CHP P** *020 †75

JUN, Young Ae Kwon. 135 E 38TH ST, VA MEDICAL CENTER 16504 #583-08-1963 L1973 **IM** *020 †20

JURGENS, Kenneth H. 232 W 25TH ST 16544 #035-08-1971 L1977 **PTH** *071 †50

KAMINSKY, James Francis. ■ 16504 #028-34-1955 L1957 **AN** *071

KANG, Ajaipal Singh. 201 STATE ST, HAMOT MEDICAL CENTER 16550 #047-07-1998 L2004 **PS** *020 †85,65

KANG, Manjot Kaur. 3330 PEACH ST, STE 107 16508 #495-08-1995 L2001 **FM** *020

KARAMANIAN, Agop-Venelin. HAMOT MED CTR 16512 #198-01-1962 L1977 **AN** *020 †05

KEISTER, Stephen R. 300 STATE ST, STE 204 16507 #023-01-1945 L1946 **IM RHU** *071

KENNEDY, Grace Lorraine. 2116 EAST AVE 16503 #041-07-1985 L1997 **FM** *020 †18

KHERA, Dinesh C. 238 W 22ND ST 16502 #495-45-1975 L1980 **GE** *020 †20

KHERA, Ritu Bhalla. ■ 16509 #495-29-1976 L1981 **ATP CLP** *020 †50

KHOJA, Isam Ahmed. 120 E 2ND ST, STE 401 16507 #797-01-1988 L2001 **NS** *020 †25

KHOURI, Amer Sameer. 2500 W 12TH ST 16505 #575-01-1990 L1995 **HO IM** *020 †20

KIM, Samuel A. 444 W 8TH ST 16502 #654-01-1993 L1997 **CCA AN** *020 †05

KINKOPH, Robert Jos, II. 201 STATE ST 16550 #038-45-1992 L2000 **AN** *020 †05

KISSOONDIAL, Prem B. 1202 STATE ST 16501 #495-13-1991 L1995 **FM OBG** *020 †18

KLAWON, David Lee. 201 STATE ST 16550 #035-45-1972 L1976 **PTH** *020 †50

KNOLL, Judith M. 201 STATE ST, HAMOT MEDICAL CENTER 16550 #055-75-1990, ▲ L2004 **EM** *012 †18

KOCAN, Richard Steven. 232 W 25TH ST, SAINT VINCENT HEALTH CENTE 16544 #041-09-1981 L1982 **DR** *020 †80

KOHN, Helen J. 1611 PEACH ST STE 300 16501 #041-12-1967 L1969 **P OS** *020 †75

KOLARIK, Gary F. ■ 16505 #041-77-1989, ▲ L1990 **PM** *020 †60

KONDYLIS, Philip D. 3216 STATE ST, RECTAL AND COLON SURGERY I 16508 #024-16-1992 L1997 **CRS GS** *020 †85,10

KREMER, Edwin Shields. 3211 LIBERTY ST STE 103 16508 #041-12-1955 L1956 **OBG** *071 †30

KUHN, Richard Herman. 2314 SASSAFRAS ST STE 200 16502 #041-12-1961 L1962 **FM** *071 †18

KUKLINSKI, Lawrence M. 204 W 26TH ST 16508 #041-02-1978 L1979 **ORS** *071 †40

KURIC, Kevin Martin. 1700 PEACH ST STE 200, HEALTHY FAM PRIMARY CARE 16501 #041-02-1986 L1987 **FM** *020 †18

KURIEN, Sam. 5241 BUFFALO RD, HARBORCREEK FAMILY PHYS 16510 #035-08-1997 L2000 **FM** *020 †18

KUZMA, Kevin Robert. 201 STATE ST 16550 #036-05-2004 L2004 **ORS** *012

LAMAS, Carlos. 1526 PEACH ST, PATHOLOGY DEPARTMENT 16501 #847-04-1968 L1974 **PTH CLP** *020 †50

LAMBERTON, William David. 2005 W 8TH ST, STE 208 16505 #041-09-1953 L1954 **FM OS** *020 †18

LAMP, Albert L, Jr. ■ 16508 #024-05-1948 L1953 **PD** *071 †55

LANE, James Wm. 232 W 25TH ST, SAINT VINCENT FAST TRACK 16544 #041-09-1987 L1989 **FM** *020 †18

LARSON, Christopher E. 201 STATE ST, HAMOT MEDICAL CENTER 16550 #041-12-1986 L1987 **AN** *020 †05 ‡

LASHER, Jay D. ■ 16505 #010-01-1951 L1952 **GS OS** *071

LASHER, Robert Lemuel. ■ 16505 #041-13-1947 L1948 **GS** *072 †85

LAUER, Carl Gregory. 145 W 23RD ST, STE 303 16502 #026-08-1982 L1993 **VS GS** *020 †85

LAUKAITIS, Margaret Mary. 5241 BUFFALO RD 16510 #041-07-1978 L1979 **FM** *020 †18

LAVIN, David Michael. 135 E 38TH ST, ADMINISTRATION MEDIAL 16504 #041-02-1978 L1981 **IM** *030 †20

LAYE, Peter Manho. 2500 W 12TH ST 16505 #012-01-1989 L2000 **RO** *020 †80

LEE, Aung Pwint. 232 W 25TH ST 16544 #209-01-1976 L1987 **AN** *020 †05

LEEMHUIS, Ronald Paul. 1611 PEACH ST STE 320 16501 #041-14-1978 L1979 **FM** *020 †18

LEONARD, Maria Irma S. 300 STATE ST, STE 301 16507 #748-10-1985 L2005 **PD** *020 †55

LEVIN, Howard Myles. 2626 SIGSBEE ST 16508 #041-09-1981 L1982 **OPH** *020 †35

LEVINE, Jeffrey Harris. 201 STATE ST, HAMOT HOSP 16550 #035-46-1987 L1999 **TRS GS** *020 †85

LEVINSON, Peter Gasche. 215 HOLLAND ST 16507 #041-12-1983 L1984 **OBG** *020 †30

LEVY, Steven. 135 E 38TH ST 16504 #035-09-1981 L1991 **IM** *040 †20

LIEBENTRITT, Frank Jos. ■ 16505 #016-11-1973 L1985 **EM FM** *020 †18

LIPMAN, Sidney Philip. 3580 PEACH ST STE 106, OF NORTHWESTERN PENNSYLVAN 16508 #041-12-1976 L1980 **OTO** *020 †45

LOESCH, Daniel Vincent. 120 E 2ND ST, STE 401 16507 #041-07-1991 L1997 **NS** *020 †25 ‡

LONG, Richard Wm. 201 STATE ST, HAMOT MEDICAL CENTER 16550 #067-01-1976 L1988 **TS** *020 †85,90

LONGSTREET, Peter Leigh. 4845 W LAKE RD, STE 113 16505 #048-13-1989 L1993 **P** *020 †75

LUBAHN, John David. 300 STATE ST, STE 205 16507 #038-06-1975 L1981 **HS ORS** *020 †40

LUND, Peter Scott. 104 E 2ND ST, 4TH FL 16507 #038-44-1982 L1987 **U** *020 †95

LUPO, Robert Anthony. 204 W 26TH ST, ORTHOPAEDIC SURGEONS INC 16508 #038-06-1994 L1999 **ORS** *020 †40

LYONS, Carol A. 104 E 2ND ST, FIFTH FLOOR 16507 #041-09-1981 L1982 **DR** *020 †80

LYONS, Gary Williams. 225 W 25TH ST 16502 #041-12-1960 L1971 **TS** *071 †85,90

LYONS, John Cornelius. 104 E 2ND ST, STE 303 16507 #041-01-1980 L1981 **ORS** *020 †40 ‡

MAC KRELL, James Patrick. 2315 MYRTLE ST, STE 190 16502 #041-12-1983 L1984 **CD** *020 †20 ‡

MACLACHLAN, Margaret Jean. ■ 16511 #041-12-1952 L1953 **IM RHU** *071 †20

MACRINO, Sheri Jo. ■ 16504 #041-14-2005 L2005 **DR** *012

MAINZER, Francis Kirkwood. ■ 16509 #010-01-1959 L1960 **NS** *071 †25

MAKAROWSKI, Wm Stephen. 1781 W 26TH ST 16508 #016-43-1974 L1975 **RHU APM** *020

MAKOSKE, Theodore A. 135 E 38TH ST 16504 #048-16-1996 L1999 **GS** *020

MALASPINA, Paul James. 104 E 2ND ST 16507 #041-13-1994 L1996 **GS TRS** *020 †85

MANASSE, Howard Steven. 311 W 24TH ST, STE 301 16502 #035-08-1976 L1981 **OPH** *020 †35

MARASCO, Richard Michael. 2409 STATE ST 16503 #041-02-1961 L1962 **OPH** *020 †35

MARBEY, Mark Leonard. 2315 MYRTLE ST, STE 160 16502 #011-02-1975 L2007 **TS** *020 †85,90

MARCOULLIS, George P. 2500 W 12TH ST, THE REGIONAL CANCER CENTER 16505 #418-01-1974 L2004 **ON HEM** *020 †20

MARSH, Robert James. 311 W 24TH ST 16502 #010-02-1957 L1958 **U** *020 †95
MARSHALL, Jack Herbert. ■ 16505 #041-13-1960 L1961 **FM** *071 †18
MASCIA, Brett Anthony. 232 W 25TH ST, DEPT OF PATHOLOGY 16544 #035-06-1999 L2004 **PTH** *020
MASCIA, Kimberly Nadine. 213 E 41ST ST 16504 #051-01-2001 L2004 **IM** *100
MASON, Gregg Claude. 204 W 26TH ST 16508 #041-12-1984 L1985 **ORS** *020 †40
MATHEW, Thomas K. 3738 W 12TH ST 16505 #495-80-1973 L1975 **FM PD** *020 †18
MC ALLISTER, Raymond W. 3530 PEACH ST 16508 #041-13-1996 L1998 **FM** *020 †18
MCCORMICK, Kelly Reid. ■ 16505 #007-02-2006 L2006 **ORS** *012
MC DONALD, Ann Margaret. 3610 W 12TH ST, SOLUTIONS 16505 #041-13-1980 L1982 **P** *020 †75
MC GOVERN, Jeffrey P. 3580 PEACH ST, CHEST DISEASES OF 16508 #041-09-1990 L1992 **PCC CCM** *020 †20
MC INTOSH, Laura Jean. 2501 W 12TH ST, STE 4 16505 #041-12-1999 L2001 **FSM** *020 †18
MC KRELL, Jonathan Dale. 2314 SASSAFRAS ST, STE 200 16502 #041-12-1985 L1994 **FM FSM** *040 †18
MC NAMARA, Mary E. ■ 16511 #041-12-1978 L1979 **N P** *020 †75
MC NEELA, Peter Michael. 201 STATE ST, DEPT OF MED EDUCATION 16550 #035-06-1997 L1997 **FM** *100
MC NEILL, Donald Babbitt. 201 STATE ST 16550 #041-09-1948 L1949 **OBG** *071 †30
MECCA, Andrew Leonard. 2315 MYRTLE ST, STE 190 16502 #016-42-1988 L1998 **ICE CD** *020 †20
MECCA, William Leonard. 2315 MYRTLE ST, STE 190 16502 #028-34-1985 L1995 **CD IC** *020 †20
MEHTA, Santosh Kumari V. ■ 16505 #495-05-1956 L1968 **PTH** *020 †50
MICHAELIDES, Doros Nikita. 1611 PEACH ST 16501 #418-01-1964 L1973 **AI PUD** *020 †03,18
MICHALAK, Dennis Michael. 120 E 2ND ST 16507 #035-08-1976 L1985 **TS VS** *020 †90,85
MIKELONIS, Robert John. 2314 SASSAFRAS ST STE 200 16502 #041-12-1979 L1980 **FM** *020 †18
MIKIELSKI, Kevin J. 4002 SCHAPER AVE, STE A 16508 #041-78-1999, ▲ L1999 **CD** *020 †20 ‡
MINGEY, Deborah Lee. 232 W 25TH ST 16544 #041-09-1983 L1985 **AN OTO** *020 †05
MINGEY, John Richard. 213 E 41ST ST 16504 #041-02-1985 L1986 **IM** *020 †20
MINK, Kenneth Rodger. 3800 W 12TH ST 16505 #041-09-1992 L1992 **D** *020 †15
MIR, David J. 100 STATE ST STE 500 16507 #869-05-1954 L1965 **ORS HS** *071 †40
MIRONE, Paul John. 1600 PENINSULA DR, STE 9 16505 #038-40-1991 L1997 **FM AM** *020 †18
MISCHLER, Forrest Clair. 104 E 2ND ST STE A 16507 #038-41-1967 L1968 **GS** *071 †85
MIX, William Avery. 104 E 2ND ST 16507 #035-06-1977 L1983 **FM EM** *020 †18
MOLINA, Rene Pedro. 300 STATE ST, STE 302 16507 #847-05-1976 L1983 **U** *020
MONTOYA, Jaime H. 404 HOLLAND ST 16507 #264-10-1973 **R CD** *050 †80
MOORE, Susan Jane. 4671 W LAKE RD, CHILDRENS HLTH CARE WEST 16505 #041-14-1987 L1989 **PD** *020 †55
MOUBARAK, Jean. 120 E 2ND ST, FL 2CD 16507 #605-02-1990 L1999 **CD IM** *020 †20
MOZDY, Lauren Marie. ■ 16505 #041-02-1986 L1995 **DS AN** *020 †05
MRAZ, James Edward. ■ 16509 #041-12-1962 L1963 **ORS** *071 †40
MRAZ, John Paul. ■ 16505 #025-01-1960 L1968 **D** *071 †15
MUCCIO, Daniel J. 1910 SASSAFRAS ST, STE 300 16502 #041-13-1985 L1986 **NS GS** *020 †25
MUKHTAR, Mohammad Jawad. 201 STATE ST 16550 #308-13-2001 L2003 **FM** *020 †18
MUNIYAPPA, Ramesh. 3535 PINE AVE, FIRST FLOOR 16504 #496-01-1993 L2006 **IM** *100 †20
MURPHY, Patrick John. 1600 PENINSULA DR, STE C 16505 #305-01-2000 L2001 **FM** *020 †18 ‡
MYERS, Daniel T. 232 W 25TH ST 16544 #041-02-1992 L1994 **EM** *020 †16
NADWORNY, Howard Alan. 2314 SASSAFRAS ST, STE 310 16502 #050-02-1978 L1984 **ID IM** *020 †20
NAGLE, Richard Wm. 201 STATE ST 16550 #041-13-1979 L1983 **DR** *020 †80
NAIR, Krishnan K. 1611 PEACH ST, STE 320 16501 #495-31-1967 L1975 **OTO** *071 †45
NANJUNDAPPA, Aravinda. 2315 MYRTLE ST, STE 190 16502 #496-33-1994 L2007 **IC** *020 †20
NECHLEBA, Jeffrey Anthony. 300 STATE ST, STE 400 16507 #035-06-1999 L2001 **ORS** *020 †40
NEDRESKY, Joseph Peter. 201 STATE ST 16550 #041-12-1979 L1984 **DR NM** *020 †80
NEER, Gary Lee. 3330 PEACH ST, STE 104 16508 #038-41-1986 L1994 **FM** *020 †18
NEGI, Prabhu Dayal Singh. ■ 16506 #495-05-1963 L1983 **GS** *071 †85
NEGRON, Angel Manuel. 104 E 2ND ST 16507 #935-02-1980 L1987 **N PD** *071 †55
NEWELL, Paul Michael. 104 E 2ND ST 16507 #041-02-1981 L1982 **ID IM** *020 †20
NEYLON, Michael Patrick. 3939 W RIDGE RD, STE B7 16506 #041-09-1986 L1987 **FM** *020 †18
NOVAK, Kevin Joseph. 201 STATE ST 16550 #026-04-1986 L1990 **AN** *020 †05
ODONNELL, Steven T. 232 W 25TH ST 16544 #041-78-2005, ▲ L2005 **FP** *012
OLJESKI, Stephen Andrew. 232 W 25TH ST 16544 #036-01-2000 L2006 **RNR** *020 †80
OMAR, Alaeeldin A. 232 W 25TH ST 16544 #915-04-1985 L2002 **PD NPM** *020 †55
ONNEN, Jeremy David. ■ 16506 #025-01-2007 L2007 **ORS** *012
OPPENHEIM, David Enoch. 232 W 25TH ST 16544 #035-08-1980 L1987 **DR** *050 †80 ‡
ORINICK, Michael, III. 135 E 38TH ST 16504 #041-12-1991 L1994 **PM** *020 †60
OVERARE, David Esohwode. 238 W 22ND ST, HILLSIDE FAMILY MEDICINE 16502 #690-06-1987 L2001 **FM** *020 †18 ‡
OVERFIELD, Edward M. 3580 PEACH ST, STE 103 16508 #010-02-1967 L1970 **PUD IM** *071 †20
PAHAPILL, Peter Ain. 120 E 2ND ST STE 401, TRI-STATE NEUROLOGICAL SUR 16507 #065-01-1992 L2001 **NS** *020 †25
PAHUJA, Deepak. 3535 PINE AVE STE 1, ST VINCENT HEALTH CENTER/ 16504 #495-45-2000 L2005 **MPD** *020 †55,20
PARK, Chong Shick. 143 E 2ND ST 16507 #583-02-1968 L1977 **PM** *020 †60
PARKS, Barry Owen. 232 W 25TH ST 16544 #041-14-1987 L1990 **DR GS** *020 †80
PATEL, Kantilal C. 444 W 8TH ST 16502 #495-22-1971 L1983 **AN PME** *020 †05
PATEL, Shailesh Dahyabhai. 5424 CIDER MILL RD 16509 #495-89-1983 L1993 **IM** *020 †55,20
PATEL, Vinod M. 238 W 22ND ST 16502 #496-38-1966 L1975 **GE IM** *020 †20
PAUL, David Brownlie. ■ 16514 #023-01-1962 L1964 **P OS** *071
PELKOWSKI, Timothy Daniel. 3822 COLONIAL AVE, STE A 16506 #038-06-1997 L1999 **FM FSM** *020 †18
PENA, Pedro Manuel. 1645 W 8TH ST 16505 #264-04-1967 L1974 **R** *020 †80
PENG, Zengling. 2240 E 38TH ST, STE 200 16510 #243-39-1982 L2003 **FM** *020 †18
PEPICELLO, James Anthony. 201 STATE ST 16550 #041-09-1974 L1975 **OS** *030 †85
PERKINS, Rob Kieran. 201 STATE ST, HOSPITALIST GROUP 16550 #041-15-1998 L2008 *020 †20
PETERSON, Ross C. 2315 MYRTLE ST, STE 190 16502 #041-12-1999 L2002 **CD IM** *020 †20
PETRELLA, Richard Wm. 120 E 2ND ST, FL 2CD 16507 #041-09-1983 L1984 **CD IM** *020 †20
PETT, Stephen Donohoe, Jr. 120 E 2ND ST 16507 #010-01-1971 L1982 **TS VS** *020 †85,90
PHELPS, William R. 104 E 2ND ST STE 201, SPECIALISTS 16507 #041-09-1975 L1976 **GS** *020 †85
PICARDO, Carla Marie. 225 W 25TH ST, ERIE WOMEN'S HEALTH PARTNE 16502 #036-05-1998 L2002 **GPM** *100 †30,70
PIERCE, Trenton Lyle. 201 STATE ST 16550 #005-12-1999 L2005 **AN** *020 †05
PINEIRO, Gerardo Jose. ■ 16506 #010-03-1992 L2003 **EM** *020 †16
PREGLER, Frank C. 5515 PEACH ST 16509 #041-77-1988, ▲ L1989 **FM FPG** *020
PRYLINSKI, Gregory V. 201 STATE ST 16550 #041-09-1982 L1984 **GS** *020 †85
PYKE, O'Neil Joseph. 201 STATE ST 16550 #038-40-1997 L2000 **IM** *020 †20
PYLES, John Ralph. 717 STATE ST 16501 #019-02-1979 L1981 **FM EM** *020 †18,16
RADDER, Debora J. 5241 BUFFALO RD 16510 #041-07-1978 L1979 **FM OS** *020 †18
RAHNER, Richard Arthur. ■ 16509 #035-06-1958 L1959 **ORS** *071 †40
RAI, Jithendra. 2620 SIGSBEE ST 16508 #495-72-1988 L2000 **APM** *020 †60
RAJ, Stephen Soundararaj. 201 STATE ST, DEPT OF ANESTHESIOLOGY 16550 #495-53-1971 L1982 **AN GP** *020 †05
RAJAGOPAL, Ambil S I. 3216 STATE ST 16508 #495-09-1983 L1994 **GS** *020
RAM, Sant. 2123 W 8TH ST 16505 #495-36-1974 L1981 **PD** *020 †55
RANISH, Deborah A. 145 W 23RD ST, STE 101 16502 #041-02-1981 L1982 **FM** *020 †18
RAY, Christie Jo. 5241 BUFFALO RD 16510 #041-02-1997 L1999 **FM** *020 †18
REICHERT, James Chas. 3330 PEACH ST 16508 #041-14-1992 L1994 **FM OS** *020 †18
REICHTER, Russell E. 5515 PEACH ST, MILLCREEK COMMUNITY HOSP 16509 #016-11-1981 L2004 **DR NM** *020 †80
REILLY, John Charles. 3216 STATE ST 16508 #035-19-1973 L1978 **CRS** *020 †10,85
REITZ, Mary Ellen. 1526 PEACH ST, ASSOCIATED CLINICAL LAB 16501 #035-06-1981 L1986 **ATP CLP** *020 †50
RELAMPAGOS, Jose R V, Jr. 232 W 25TH ST 16544 #748-09-1982 L1998 **AN** *020 †05
REYNOLDS, Sam David. 1202 STATE ST 16501 #041-14-1998 L2000 **FM** *020 †18
RHODES, Virginia Ann. 2500 W 12TH ST, THE REGIONAL CANCER CENTER 16505 #038-40-1988 L2000 **ON** *020 †20
RIEDESEL, Jeremy Martin. ■ 16502 #038-41-2007 L2007 **FP** *012
RIPPLE, Wendy L. 3416 STATE ST 16508 #041-12-1993 L1995 **PD** *020 †55
RIZZONI, Walter E. 120 E 2ND ST 16507 #024-05-1983 L2007 **TS VS** *020 †85,90 ‡
RODRIGUEZ, Shaunda M. ■ 16502 #028-79-2007, ▲ L2007 *012
ROGERS, Vincent Paul. 104 E 2ND ST 16507 #038-41-1968 L1972 **ORS OSM** *020 †40
ROMANO-JANA, Lourdes R. 2931 PEACH ST 16508 #748-01-1962 L1982 **PMM IM** *071 ‡
ROOS, Alfred Thomson. ■ 16511 #065-06-1940 L1941 **FM** *071 †18
ROQUIZ, Eliseo Maniago. 232 W 25TH ST 16544 #748-10-1974 L1979 **AN** *020
ROSENFELD, Anna. 232 W 25TH ST 16544 #038-06-2000 L2005 **AN** *020 †05
ROTHMAN, Jan Mitchell. 2500 W 12TH ST, REGIONAL CANCER CENTER 16505 #917-04-1984 L1995 **ON HEM** *020 †20
ROVNER, Aleksandr. 120 E 2ND ST, 2ND FL 16507 #038-06-1998 L2005 **CD** *020 †20
ROZWADOWSKI, Jack Vincent. 1526 PEACH ST, PATHOLOGY DEPARTMENT 16501 #041-09-1964 L1971 **CLP PTH** *071 †50
RUBIN, Adam Mark. 311 W 24TH ST, STE 402 16502 #041-13-2001 L2001 **NEP** *020 †20
RUSSO, Stephanie Ann. 3910 CAUGHEY RD, STE 170 16506 #041-09-1984 L1991 **PD** *020 †55
SALAMEH, Abdel Aziz. ■ 16507 #875-01-1972 L1975 **EM U** *075
SALMON, James Henry. ■ 16509 #041-09-1957 L1958 **NS** *071 †25
SALMON, James Thomas. 135 E 38TH ST, DEPT OF SURGERY 16504 #041-09-1997 L2000 **GS** *020 †85
SANDSTROM, Paul Hilmer. 201 STATE ST 16550 #041-13-1962 L1965 **R** *071 †80 ‡
SANTOMENNA, Michael A. 238 W 22ND ST 16502 #041-12-1965 L1966 **GS** *020 †85
SANTOSO, Limjadi. 232 W 25TH ST 16544 #506-01-1960 L1971 **IM FM** *071 †20
SARDESAI, Prabhaker G. 104 E 2ND ST, DANGELO CLINIC 16507 #495-23-1961 L1973 **TS CD** *020 †85,90
SAUER, Robert Howard. 3300 BAER BEACH RD 16505 #035-06-1960 L1975 **P** *071 †75
SAVOIA, Anthony L. 252 W 11TH ST 16501 #005-15-1962 L1975 **GP AN** *071
SCHAAF, John Thos. 3580 PEACH ST, CHEST DISEASES OF 16508 #041-12-1965 L1972 **PUD** *071 †20
SCHAEFER, Timothy Francis. 225 W 25TH ST, STE 208 16502 #038-41-1995 L2005 **OBG** *020 †30
SCHELL, Stephen Eugene. 3580 PEACH ST, ENT SPECIALISTS OF 16508 #041-13-1979 L1980 **OTO HNS** *020 †45
SCHENCK, Arthur Cyril. 3939 W RIDGE RD, STE A204 16506 #028-79-1964, ▲ L1965 **FM CD** *020
SCHOBER, Justine Marut. 333 STATE ST, STE 201 16507 #041-09-1982 L1983 **UP U** *020 †95
SCHUCHARDT, William Arthu, Jr. 135 E 38TH ST 16504 #038-06-1974 L1976 **GS TRS** *020 †85
SCHUSTER, James L. 135 E 38TH ST 16504 #038-06-1949 L1950 **ORS** *020 †40
SCHWARTZ, Robert Mark. 300 STATE ST, STE 103 16507 #035-09-1980 L1985 **GE IM** *020 †20
SCIARRINO, Peter Chas. 300 STATE ST, STE 302 16507 #010-02-1977 L2008 **U** *020 †95
SCIBETTA, Mario Peter. 2500 W 12TH ST 16505 #038-06-1958 L1964 **RO ON** *071 †80
SCULLY, Dennis Michael. 3822 SCHAPER AVE 16508 #041-13-1974 L1975 **FM** *020 †18
SCULLY, Michael Sean. ■ 16509 #041-13-2007 *012
SCUTELLA, Micheal Alan. 311 W 24TH ST STE 303 16502 #041-09-1984 L1987 **OBG** *020 †30
SEARS, Mary E. 2301 EDINBORO RD 16509 #035-45-1950 L1951 **ON IM** *071
SEGU, Subramanyam. 2409 STATE ST 16503 #495-62-1970 L1975 **OPH** *020 †35
SEIFERTH, William John. ■ 16505 #041-12-1943 L1944 **IM GP** *071
SEMPLE, Joseph Michael. 3204 STATE ST 16508 #041-13-1959 L1960 **OBG** *020 †30
SEON, Carl Yangil. 300 STATE ST, STE 400A 16507 #035-06-1998 L2000 **ORS** *020
SHAFFER, Kevin Paul. 3822 COLONIAL AVE, STE A 16506 #041-09-1981 L1982 **FM** *020 †18
SHAH, Suresh Shantilal. 2500 W 12TH ST 16505 #495-23-1966 L1999 **ON HO** *020 †20 ‡
SHALABI, Ahmed A.. ■ 16506 #473-04-1994 L2007 **CRS** *012
SHANG, Jingzi. 120 E 2ND ST, FL 2CD 16507 #243-03-1987 L2002 **N** *020 †75
SHARMA, Sukh Dev. 120 E 2ND ST 16507 #495-03-1962 L1973 **CD IM** *020 †20
SHATYNSKI, Todd Stephen. 4950 BUFFALO RD, EAST HARBOR PRIMARY CARE 16510 #051-04-2002 L2002 **FSM** *020 †18
SHEPPECK, Richard Adam. 120 E 2ND ST 16507 #041-12-1985 L1986 **VS** *020 †85
SHIVDE, Pinakini Sudhakar. 1348 S SHORE DR, PEDIATRICS AND NEONATOLOGY 16505 #495-19-1967 L1982 **PD NPM** *020 †55
SHIVERS, Jeffrey Clifford. 232 W 25TH ST, PATHOLOGY DEPARTMENT 16544 #036-07-1978 L1982 **PTH** *020 †50
SHULKOSKY, Mark James. 201 STATE ST 16550 #041-13-1986 L1987 **AN** *020 †05
SILKO, Gary John. 2314 SASSAFRAS ST, STE 200 16502 #041-02-1980 L1981 **FM** *040 †18
SIMONIAN, Thomas Michael. 201 STATE ST, EMERGENCY DEPARTMENT 16550 #041-02-1986 L1987 **EM FM** *020 †18 ‡
SIMORA, Felix S. 2209 W GRANDVIEW BLVD 16506 #748-11-1967 L1974 **P** *020
SINGARAJU, Vamsi Mohan. 201 STATE ST, HAMOT MEDICAL CENTER 16550 #495-73-2002 L2007 **ORS** *012
SINGH, Asim Ranjan. 350 E BAYFRONT PKWY, STE C 16507 #495-54-1983 L1991 **NEP** *020 †20
SINGH, Kripa Shankar. 1330 W 26TH ST, CPFG 16508 #495-05-1954 L1975 **P** *071 †75 ‡

SKOBIERANDA, Kathe R. 3317 LIBERTY ST 16508 #041-14-1993 L1995 **RHU** *072 †20
SLABIC, Peter P. 5215 PEACH ST 16509 #305-01-1982 L1984 **IM** *020
SLABIC, Stan F. 5215 PEACH ST 16509 #654-01-1982 L1984 **IM OS** *020 †20
SNOW, Ross Anthony. 1202 STATE ST 16501 #041-12-1978 L1979 **FM** *020 †18
SPECTOR, Richard Harris. 4619 PEACH ST 16509 #017-20-1981 L1998 **P** *020 †75
SPENCE, Calvin John. 3211 LIBERTY ST, STE 202 16508 #836-01-1951 L1981 **DR** *071
STAMM, Barry Duane. 300 STATE ST STE 200, BAYFRONT PROFESSIONAL BLDG 16507 #041-09-1974 L1978 **OPH** *020
START, Jefrey. 1341 W 26TH ST, STE 200 16508 #041-78-2000, ▲ L2001 **FM** *020 †18
STEFANOVSKI, Nick. 300 STATE ST, STE 400 16507 #041-13-1986 L1987 **ORS** *020 †40
STEINBRINK, William Harry. 3211 LIBERTY ST, STE 103 16508 #041-12-1974 L1978 **OBG GYN** *020 †30
STEINSAPIR, Jaime. 240 W 11TH ST, STE 2 16501 #231-01-1975 L1999 **END** *020 †20
STERLING, Karen Stephanie. 1520 E 10TH ST, ION HEALTH 16511 #048-12-1979 L2001 **PD** *030 †55
STEVENS, Danielle Teresa. ■ 16506 #017-20-1995 L1996 **FM** *020 †18
STEVENS, Scott A. 201 STATE ST 16550 #041-78-1998, ▲ L2002 **AN** *020
STILLER, Sonja Ruth. 232 W 25TH ST, SAINT VINCENT HEALTH CENTE 16544 #041-07-1995 L1997 **EM** *020 †16
STONITSCH, Frank Chas. 201 STATE ST 16550 #035-06-1989 L1989 **EM** *020 †16
STRASSER, David Michael. 120 E 2ND ST, FL 2CD 16507 #041-13-1991 L1995 **CD** *020 †20
STRATTON, Robert David. 300 STATE ST, STE 201 16507 #036-01-1974 L1984 **OPH** *020 †35
STRAZEK, Leslaw M. ■ 16505 #759-10-1960 L1973 **AN** *071
STRONY, Ronald S, Jr. 201 STATE ST 16550 #041-09-1994 L1996 **EM** *020 †16
STRZALKA, Christopher T. 120 E 2ND ST, HAMOT MEDICAL CENTER 16507 #035-15-1989 L1997 **TS VS** *020 †85,90
STUMPF, Rebecca Louise. 4950 BUFFALO RD, EAST HARBOR PRIMARY CARE 16510 #041-14-1980 L1982 **FM IMG** *020 †18
STURDEVANT, Joseph L, III. 201 STATE ST, HAMOT MEDICAL CENTER 16550 #048-15-1998 L2005 **CCM** *100
SU, Sean. 5367 FRAZIER ST, STAIRWAYS BEHAVIORAL HEALT 16510 #041-07-1993 L1995 **P** *020 †75
SUMMERS, David Stewart. 4437 W RIDGE RD 16506 #051-01-1959 L1976 **N** *071
SUPPA, Osvaldo Sergio. 201 STATE ST 16550 #132-01-1968 L1972 **DIA RHU** *020
SURI, Ashok Kumar. 300 STATE ST, STE 302 16507 #495-45-1972 L1977 **U** *020 †95
SUSANN, Philip Wm. ■ 16505 #012-05-1971 L1981 **GS** *071 †85
SYMES, Philip Henry. 2500 W 12TH ST, THE REGIONAL CANCER CENTER 16505 #051-01-1983 L1992 **ON HEM** *020 †20
TAKARA, James Patrick. 232 W 25TH ST, MEDICAL STAFF OFFICE 16544 #021-06-1989 L2005 **TS** *020 †85,90
TAN, Wilfredo S. ■ 16510 #748-01-1965 L1975 **TS** *071 †85,90
TAVANA-POUR-FARD, M. 238 W 22ND ST 16502 #869-04-1957 L1967 **GS TS** *071 †85
TAVARES, Joao M O De M. 1645 W 8TH ST, SHRINERS HOSPITAL FOR CHIL 16505 #770-02-1969 L1973 **ORS OP** *020 †40
THOMAS, Joseph Martin. 2374 VILLAGE COMMON DR, STE 100 16506 #033-05-1981 L1991 **PMM AN** *020 †05
THOMAS, Kenneth Clemens. ■ 16505 #007-02-2005 L2005 **ORS** *012
THOMAS, Kimberly Beth. ■ 16502 #007-02-2005 L2006 **FP** *012
THOMAS, Matthew Howard. 232 W 25TH ST, ST VINCENT HEALTH CENTER 16544 #041-14-1990 L1994 **DR** *020 †80
THOMPSON, Larry Wade. 311 W 24TH ST, STE 303 16502 #041-02-1995 L1997 **OBG** *020 †30
TOLEDANO, Conrado Pineda. 4137 AVENIEL CT 16506 #748-10-1973 L1992 **PM** *020 †60
TOOZE, Frank M. ■ 16506 #035-45-1953 L1969 **PS** *071 †65
TOPERZER, Betty Cline. 104 E 2ND ST 16507 #041-12-1958 L1959 **FM** *020 †18
TOWNSEND, Mark Edward. 215 HOLLAND ST 16507 #041-12-1982 L1983 **OBG** *020 †30 ‡
TRAGESER, Timothy Carey. 120 E 2ND ST 16507 #023-01-1984 L1991 **CD IM** *020 †20
TRAN, Khoa Dinh. 1330 W 26TH ST, 2ND FL 16508 #665-01-1998 L2007 **FM** *020 †18
TRETTER, Christopher P G. 2500 W 12TH ST, THE REGIONAL CANCER CENTER 16505 #067-01-1994 L2006 **HO** *020 †20
TRONETTI, Michael Jos. ■ 16510 #041-77-1984, ▲ L1985 **P** *071
TSENG, Francis Hinyin. 225 W 25TH ST, STE 208 16502 #048-02-1979 L1988 **OBG** *020 †30
TURNER, Thomas Harvey. 7200 PEACH ST, UNIT 420 16509 #041-09-1980 L1981 **FM** *020 †18
ULUS, Mehmet Fuat. 1910 SASSAFRAS 16502 #902-10-1968 L1974 **P** *020 †75 ‡
URQUICO, Cecilia Teresa N. 232 W 25TH ST 16544 #748-10-2001 L2005 **FP** *012
VACALIE, Doina. ■ 16509 #781-01-1987 L1995 **P** *020 †75 ‡
VANHOVE, Shawn Paul. 201 STATE ST 16550 #038-43-1986 L1990 **AN** *020 †05
VATAVUK, Mark Kenneth. 1910 SASSAFRAS ST, THE OCCPTNL HLTH CTR 16502 #041-12-1978 L1978 **FM** *020 †18
VEMULAPALLI, Lakshmi R. 215 HOLLAND ST, LAKE ERIE WOMEN'S CTR 16507 #495-50-1972 L1981 **OBG** *020 †30
VEMULAPALLI, Ramachandra. 201 STATE ST 16550 #495-50-1973 L1979 **AN** *020
VEY, Eric Lee. 140 W 6TH ST, ERIE CNTY CORONERS OFCS 16501 #041-12-1988 L1994 **FOP** *020 †50
VIDMAR, Dennis Alan. 3416 STATE ST 16508 #038-40-1977 L1999 **D DMP** *020 †15
VISCUSI, Donald Jos. 3010 W LAKE RD 16505 #041-13-1984 L1985 **OM EM** *020 †18 ‡
VOORA, Bharathi S. 2005 W 8TH ST, STE 200 16505 #495-50-1976 L1983 **IM** *020 †20
VOORA, Sambasivarao. 311 W 24TH ST STE 302 16502 #495-50-1971 L1983 **NPM PD** *020 †55
WALKER, Brent Edwin. 1827 W 38TH ST 16508 #041-09-1981 L1982 **OPH** *020 †35
WALKER, James Foster. 335 SUPERIOR AVE 16505 #041-12-1950 L1951 **FM** *071
WALLACE, Aaron Jack. 201 STATE ST 16550 #004-01-2003 L2003 **ORS** *012
WALTERS, Lisa Ann. 5094 COVENTRY DR, ERIE VETERANS ADDAIRS MED 16506 #041-14-1996 L1998 **IM** *020 †20
WALTON, Ralph Gerald. 1330 W 26TH ST 16508 #035-15-1967 L2004 **P** *020 †75
WARD, Edgar H. ■ 16506 #041-01-1951 L1952 **IM** *071 †20
WARD, Samuel Robt, Jr. 2315 MYRTLE ST, STE 190 16502 #051-04-1989 L1997 **CD** *020 †20
WARDEN, James Richard. 3211 LIBERTY ST STE 302 16508 #041-02-1965 L1974 **GS** *020 †85 ‡
WARFEL, Martin C. 560 E 3RD ST BOX 6239 16507 #041-01-1942 L1954 **GP** *071
WEBSTER, Michael Lynn. 300 STATE ST 16501 #041-09-1984 L1996 **PD** *020 †55
WEHRER, Julie A. 1700 PEACH ST, STE 200 16501 #041-09-1988 L1991 **FM** *030 †18
WEIBEL, Cynthia Marie. 3580 PEACH ST, STE 100 16508 #041-13-1989 L1991 **PD** *020 †55 ‡
WEIBEL, Timothy Joseph. 3211 LIBERTY ST, STE 103 16508 #041-12-1989 L1993 **OBG** *020 †30
WEISENFLUH, Mark Gerard. 810 E 38TH ST 16504 #041-09-1988 L1990 **FM** *020 †18
WEISSBACH, Nancy Ellen. 2314 SASSAFRAS ST, STE 310 16502 #033-06-1985 L1992 **ID** *020 †20

WELCH, Mark Jos. 120 E 2ND ST, FL 2CD 16507 #041-09-1992 L1996 **DR** *020 †80
WHARTON, Stanley Wm. ■ 16511 #041-13-1955 L1956 **OM** *071
WHEELING, Theresa. 333 STATE ST 16507 #041-02-1990 L1994 **PM** *020 †60
WIBUL-OU-TAI, Boonterm. ■ 16511 #891-03-1965 L1972 **GP GS** *020 †20
WICKRAMSINGHE, Eardly K P. 3535 PINE AVE 16504 #220-01-1970 L1973 **GP** *020
WICZYK, Barbara B. ■ 16505 #759-03-1940 L1978 **GYN** *071
WICZYK, Stanislaw. ■ 16505 #759-03-1939 L1978 **FM IMG** *071 †18
WILCZANSKI, Peter L. 5241 BUFFALO RD 16510 #759-01-1980 L1987 **FM** *020 †18
WILL, Ryan Edward. 201 STATE ST 16550 #038-41-2003 L2003 **ORS** *012
WILLIAMS, Richard Alan. 201 STATE ST 16550 #041-12-1980 L1984 **DR** *020 †80
WILSON, Robert Elden. 1910 SASSAFRAS ST 16502 #035-45-1989 L1994 **P CHP** *020 †75
WITCHELL, Stephen James. 232 W 25TH ST, MEDICAL STAFF OFFICE 16544 #067-01-1977 L1991 **DR** *020 †80
WITTMANN, Thomas A. 3580 PEACH ST, CHEST DISEASES 16508 #041-12-1977 L1982 **PUD IM** *020 †20
WRIGHT, Merja T. 1202 STATE ST, COMMUNITY HEALTH NET 16501 #154-07-1975 L1980 **FPG FM** *020 †18
YOST, Mark Fielding. 201 STATE ST, HAMOT MED CTR 16550 #025-01-1978 L1994 **R** *020 †80
YOUNG, Henry Albert. ■ 16505 #035-08-1941 L1985 **GS** *071 †85
YOUNG, Linda Louise. 145 W 23RD ST STE 101 16502 #041-02-1989 L1991 **FM** *020 †18
ZETO, Shawn Christopher. 2701 EVANSTON AVE, STE 100 16506 #041-14-2000 L2003 **IM** *020 †20 ‡
ZIEGLER, Thomas Richard. 5515 PEACH ST 16509 #038-40-1981 L1987 **PTH DMP** *020 †50
ZIEZIULA, Ronald Frank. ■ 16508 #041-02-1967 L1971 **PD NPM** *020 †55
ZOMCIK, Anne Marie. 4671 W LAKE RD, CHILDRENS HLTH CARE WEST 16505 #041-12-1993 L1995 **PD** *020 †55
ZYCHSKA-DMOCHOW, Hanna. 4500 PINE AVE, GRANDVIEW FAMILY PRACTICE 16504 #759-04-1978 L1994 **FM** *020 †18

ERWINNA – BUCKS

VICTOR, Stephen Jay. 42 EVERBREEZE DR 18920 #036-07-1971 L1991 **N** *050 †75

ETTERS – YORK

AMEIGH, Margretta Johnson. 564 OLD YORK RD, FAIRVIEW FAMILY HEALTH CEN 17319 #041-07-1984 L1985 **FM** *020 †18
EDLA, Surender Reddy. 1790 OLD TRAIL RD 17319 #495-57-1999 L2003 **FM** *020 †18
PEARSON, Michael David. ■ 17319 #041-15-2008 *012
STACHNIAK, Linda Marie. 1790 OLD TRAIL RD STE A 17319 #016-01-1991 L1995 **FM** *020 †18
STOUFFER, Vance R, Jr. 1790 OLD TRAIL RD 17319 #041-02-1967 L1968 **GP** *020 †18

EVANS CITY – BUTLER

METCALF, John Wardell. 135 WOLFE RUN ROAD 16033 #649-33-1986 L1987 **IM** *020 †20

EVERETT – BEDFORD

ALDINGER, Ralph Emmert. 195 MEMORIAL DR, STE 6 15537 #041-77-1976, ▲ L1977 **OBG MFM** *020
BAER, David Grant. 227 HOSPITAL DR 15537 #041-02-1979 L1980 **FM** *020 †18
DE LAS ALAS, Ernesto M. 10455 LINCOLN HWY 15537 #748-01-1965 L1975 **IM IMG** *020
EYLER, Joseph Albert. ■ 15537 #041-13-1944 L1945 **GP** *071
FABER, David Clayton. 283 HOSPITAL DR 15537 #055-01-1996 L1998 **GS VS** *020 †85
FEIST, Fredric Warren. 195 MEMORIAL DR, STE 6 15537 #001-06-1987 L2001 **OBG** *020 †30
FLEMING, Geo Edward, Jr. 10455 LINCOLN HWY, UPMC BEDFORD MEMORIAL 15537 #041-02-1989 L1991 **FM** *020 †18
FOOR, Jeffrey Lee. 14 E 3RD ST 15537 #041-12-1976 L1981 **PD EM** *020 †55
GIRDANY, David Steven. 249 HOSPITAL DR 15537 #041-12-1979 L1981 **ORS** *020 †40
HARTLE, John E. ■ 15537 #041-12-1953 L1954 **FM** *071 †18
HORTON, David James. 10455 LINCOLN HWY 15537 #041-02-1988 L1990 **FM** *020 †18
JACKSON, Raymond W. 10455 LINCOLN HWY, UPMC BEDFORD MEMORIAL 15537 #035-08-1968 L1981 **DR** *071 †80
KERSTETTER, David Lee. 185 HOSPITAL DR STE 1 15537 #041-14-1972 L1977 **PD** *020 †55
KLINE, Michael Steven. 10455 LINCOLN HWY, UPMC BEDFORD MEMORIAL HOSP 15537 #016-42-1990 L1993 **IM** *020 †20
MINO, Frank Allen. 10455 LINCOLN HWY, MEMORIL HSPTL OF BDFRD CNT 15537 #010-02-1985 L1995 **DR GS** *020 †80
PATEL, Sureshchandra A. 10455 LINCOLN HWY 15537 #495-89-1982 L1995 **PTH** *020 †50
RINARD, Graffious Levi. YR R 1 BOX 80 15537 #010-02-1937 L1938 **GP** *072
SCHILLI, Rudolph. 10455 LINCOLN HWY, GASTROINTESTINAL 15537 #016-06-1974 L1979 **GE IM** *020 †20
SULLIVAN, Anne Cecilia. 249 HOSPITAL DR, STE 1 15537 #038-40-1994 L2002 **ORS** *020 †40
TORRES, Flora Macalintal. 220 W MAIN ST 15537 #748-08-1968 L1977 **GP EM** *020
TORRES, Robin Gatchalian. 195 MEMORIAL DR STE 6 15537 #748-08-1966 L1973 **OBG EM** *020
TOUSI, Harjaran Abbas. 195 MEMORIAL DR, STE 6 15537 #517-01-1962 L1984 **OBG** *071
VREELAND, James Hogg. 201 HOSPITAL DR, STE A 15537 #308-03-1981 L1982 **GS** *020
YANOSHAK, Stephen Jerome. 202 MEMORIAL DR STE 2 15537 #041-77-1990, ▲ L1991 **U IM** *020
ZUBAK, George Michael. 300 N SPRING ST 15537 #041-07-1985 L1986 **FM EM** *020 †18

EXPORT – WESTMORELAND

BENZ, George Henry, Jr. 4923 SIMMONS CIR 15632 #041-12-1967 L1968 **GS VS** *020 †85
MAMO, George Elias. ■ 15632 #018-03-1960 L1966 **P** *071 †75
MUTHAPPAN, Palaniappan. 5845B WASHINGTON AVE 15632 #495-42-1974 L1981 **IM** *020 †20
PAULONE, Mary Elizabeth. ■ 15632 #041-12-1967 L1978 **OBG** *020 †30
POLENTA, John Paul. ■ 15632 #041-13-1984 L1985 **IM PD** *020 †20,55
TALABI, Abimbola Iyabo. ■ 15632 #690-01-1970 L1974 **IM** *020 †20

TALAMO, Thomas Salvatore. ■ 15632 #041-02-1978 L1979 **PTH** *020 †50
WALTER, Daniel B. 167 EVANS RD 15632 #041-13-1980 L1981 **AN PME** *020 †05

EXTON – CHESTER

BAHLER, Eileen. 62 SURREY WAY 19341 #041-02-1987 L1989 **FM** *020 †18
BARSKY, Diane Lori. 481 JOHN YOUNG WAY 19341 #035-48-1987 L1990 **PD NTR** *020 †55
BEHMANSHAH, Yasmin. ■ 19341 #495-21-1981 L1993 **AN** *075
BLACKBURN, Michael Glen. 460 CREAMERY WAY, STE 103 19341 #407-10-1965 L1972 **PD** *071 †55
BRAZEROL, William Francis. 119 E UWCHLAN AVE, STE 100 19341 #038-45-1989 L1992 **OBG** *020 †30
CADIEUX, Amy Jane. 400 GORDON DR, STE 701 19341 #032-01-1992 L1995 **OBG** *020 †30 ‡
CAGGIANO, John D, Jr. 460 CREAMERY WAY STE 103 19341 #041-09-1967 L1970 **ORS** *020 †40
CAVE, Sergil Lawson. ■ 19341 #010-03-1947 L1949 **GYN** *071 †30
CHACKO, Lyssa Nicole. 495 THOMAS JONES WAY, STE 200 19341 #056-05-2001 L2007 **GE** *020 †20
CHANG, Won S. 470 JOHN YOUNG WAY, STE 400 19341 #041-13-1995 L2000 **RO** *020 †80
CHUMA, Andrew V. 460 CREAMERY WAY, STE 103 19341 #065-01-1993 L1997 **OTO PDO** *020 †45
COHEN, Fredric Lee. 400 GORDON DR, STE 701 19341 #041-13-1978 L1979 **OBG** *020 †30
CUOZZO, Alfonso. 80 W WELSH POOL RD STE 10 19341 #561-11-1971 L1973 **IM** *020
DAROCHA, Irene B. 495 THOMAS JONES WAY, STE 104 19341 #041-07-1986 L1987 **DR** *075 †80
DAWN, Marianne Edwards. 501 GORDON DR 19341 #036-07-2003 L2007 **D** *020 †15
DESAI, Neha Bharat. 111 ARRANDALE BLVD, CHESTER COUNTY PEDIATRICS 19341 #035-46-2001 L2002 **PD** *100
DORRELL, Sean Green. 860 SPRINGDALE DR STE 10 19341 #033-05-1986 L1988 **NEP IM** *020 †20 ‡
DUNCHESKIE, Robert C. 400 GORDON DR STE 702, ALL STAR PEDIATRICS 19341 #041-13-1998 L2001 **PD** *020 †55
DYER, Bradley J. 400 GORDON DR STE 702 19341 #005-11-1989 L1991 **PD** *020 †55
EDWARDS, Christopher. 904 GRANDVIEW DR 19341 #016-11-1998 L2000 **EM** *020
EFFAT, Mahmoud K. 108 JOHN ROBERT THOMAS DR, ALLERGY & ASTHMA CTR 19341 #915-02-1977 L1984 **AI PD** *020 †55,03
ELLIS, Christina Eileen. 119 E UWCHLAN AVE, STE 100 19341 #041-02-1984 L1985 **OBG** *020 †30
FRANKEL, Andrew Steven. 780 W LINCOLN HWY 19341 #041-01-1986 L1987 **ORS** *020 †40
GILCHRIST, Kim Annette. 625 N POTTSTOWN PIKE 19341 #041-09-1985 L1986 **OM IM** *020 †20
GLESSNER, Carol Ann. 491 JOHN YOUNG WAY, STE 200 19341 #038-40-1987 L1994 **FM** *020 †18
GOLDEN, Gil Adam. 102 PICKERING WAY STE 200, AZUR PHARMA 19341 #041-15-1999 **IM NUP** *050
GOLDSTEIN, Steven Joel. 495 THOMAS JONES WAY, STE 101 19341 #045-01-1975 L1977 **GE** *020 †20
GOTTLIEB, Scott Lawrence. 501 GORDON DR 19341 #035-20-1990 L1994 **D** *020 †15
GREWAL, Manohar Singh. ■ 19341 #495-03-1953 L1978 **IM CD** *020
HETZEL, Jonathan Keppele. 80 W WELSH POOL RD 19341 #063-01-1975 **FM** *020 †18 ‡
HOFFMASTER, Roselle Marga. ■ 19341 #038-06-2004 L2005 **IM** *020
HOLLAND, Ruth S. 119 E UWCHLAN AVE STE 200, CHESTER CNTY INTL MED 19341 #041-07-1992 L1994 **IM** *020 †20 ‡
JAN, Ambereen Mahtab. 860 SPRINGDALE DR, STE 100 19341 #704-09-1982 L1992 **NEP** *020
JOHN, Jessy. 103 ARRANDALE BLVD, HEALTHY STEPS PEDIATRICS 19341 #495-31-1991 L1998 **PD** *020 †55 ‡
JUNCOS, Guillermo Roque. 80 W WELSH POOL RD, MEDICAL ARTS BLDG STE 206 19341 #132-02-1961 L1972 **AI PUD** *020 †03
KALKIEWICZ, Thomas, Jr. 319 N POTTSTOWN PIKE, STE 205 19341 #033-05-1992 L1995 **PD** *020 †55
KENSEY, Kenneth R. 15 E UWCHLAN AVE, STE 414 19341 #038-40-1975 L1988 **IM** *050
KIM, Paul Sung. 460 CREAMERY WAY STE 110 19341 #024-16-1979 L1980 **PS VS** *020 †65
KRANTZ, Ian D. 481 JOHN YOUNG WAY 19341 #550-02-1991 L1994 **PD MG** *050 †55,19
KRCH, Marilyn Beth. 625 N POTTSTOWN PIKE 19341 #035-15-1980 L1993 **EM** *020 †20
KRISHNAN, Raj Kumar. ■ 19341 #016-42-2006 **IM** *012
LA PORTE, Steven Mark. 495 THOMAS JONES WAY, STE 306 19341 #041-13-1973 L1974 **CD IM** *020 †20
LEE, James Hurnjoung. 222 VALLEY CREEK BLVD, STE 300 19341 #016-11-1994 L2007 **IM** *020 †20
LEHOVICH, Alexandra. 400 GORDON DR, STE 702 19341 #038-06-2002 L2002 **PD** *020 †55
LEMERT, Michael Richard. 400 GORDON DR, STE 701 19341 #038-40-1966 L1970 **OBG** *020 †30 ‡
LEVY, Sharon F. 222 VALLEY CREEK BLVD, STE 300 19341 #024-16-1980 L1982 **PUD IM** *050 †20
LYONS, Christopher Jos. 479 THOMAS JONES WAY, STE 300 19341 #041-13-1980 L1985 **ORS** *020 †40
MAGGITTI, Michael John. 460 CREAMERY WAY STE 109 19341 #041-13-1980 L1985 **ORS** *020 †40
MANNA, Louis M. 119 E UWCHLAN AVE, STE 101 19341 #035-08-1993 L1999 **OS FPS** *020
MANTA, John Patrick. 479 THOMAS JONES WAY, STE 300 19341 #041-13-1990 L1992 **ORS** *020 †40
MAY, Daniel Scott. 638 WHARTON BLVD 19341 #051-04-1990 L1998 **PD** *020 †55
MC AFOOS, Louis G, Jr. ■ 19341 #041-09-1943 L1944 **IM IMG** *072
MC GUIRE, Michael Anthony. 432 EXTON CMNS 19341 #010-03-1993 L1995 **FM** *020 †18
MEEHAN, Margarita. 481 JOHN YOUNG WAY, CHOP SPECIALTY CARE AT EXT 19341 #913-69-1988 L1997 **CHN PD** *020 †75,55
MELNYCHUK, Jennifer Olga. 400 GORDON DR, STE 702 19341 #041-01-2003 L2003 **PD** *020 †55
MEYER, Christine. 103 ARRANDALE BLVD 19341 #041-09-1997 L1999 **IM** *020 †20
MEYER, Christopher James. 103 ARRANDALE BLVD 19341 #041-09-1997 L1999 **PD** *020 †55 ‡
MEYERS, Charles Loeb. 501 GORDON DR, DERMATOLOGY & SKIN SURGERY 19341 #035-19-2001 L2005 **D** *020 †15
MICHAEL, Herman J, Jr. 860 SPRINGDALE DR, STE 100 19341 #041-02-1984 L1985 **NEP IM** *020 †20

MILLER, Gladys Marple. ■ 19341 #041-13-1951 L1952 **IM** *071
MOVSOWITZ, Herman David. 495 THOMAS JONES WAY, STE 306 19341 #836-02-1990 L2000 **CD** *020 †20
MUSUNURI, Sailaja. 91 DOWLIN FORGE RD, CHILD & ADOLESCENT PSYCHIA 19341 #496-24-1992 L2000 **CHP** *020 †75
OCHSNER, Gregory John. 470 JOHN YOUNG WAY, STE 400 19341 #021-01-1988 L1995 **RO** *020 †80
O'HARA, John James, Jr. 495 THOMAS JONES WAY, STE 306 19341 #041-09-1976 L1978 **CD IM** *020 †20
OSTROW, Betsy Alison. 491 JOHN YOUNG WAY, BAXTER BLDG OAKLANDS CORP 19341 #038-41-1979 L1981 **PD** *020 †55 ‡
PAHLAWANIAN, Maria Pilar. ■ 19341 #847-04-1963 L1974 **PMM FM** *020
PANDYA, Paresh Gajanand. 425 BOWEN DR 19341 #495-23-1987 L2000 **P** *020
PIERSON, Brian Douglas. 495 THOMAS JONES WAY, STE 202 19341 #051-07-1989 L1993 **OM** *020 †70
PODOLSKY, Leo Alexander. 495 THOMAS JONES WAY, STE 306 19341 #550-02-1985 L1988 **CD IM** *020 †20 ‡
POOMKUDY, Geetha J. 327 PENWYLLT CT 19341 #422-01-1998 L2001 **IM** *030 †20
ROGERS, Jon Morrison. 405 EAGLEVIEW BLVD 19341 #038-41-1978 L1999 **CD** *050 †20
ROITMAN, Susan. 400 GORDON DR, STE 701 19341 #041-07-1987 L1988 **OBG** *020 †30
ROSENBLUM, Jeffrey Lee. 80 W WELSH POOL RD, STE 100 19341 #024-05-1988 L1994 **U** *020 †95
SABADISH, Kimberly Ann. 319 N POTTSTOWN PIKE, STE 102 19341 #041-09-1996 L1999 **IM** *020 †20 ‡
SERKES, Constantine A. 103 ARRANDALE BLVD 19341 #033-06-1987 L1990 **PD** *020 †55
SHINAL, Kevin Edward. 495 THOMAS JONES WAY, STE 306 19341 #041-02-1998 L2000 **CD** *020 †20
SHIRKER, Allison Louise. 400 GORDON DR, STE 701 19341 #041-13-1997 L2000 **OBG** *020 †30
SIGAL, Christine J. 400 GORDON DR, STE 701 19341 #041-09-1996 L2000 **OBG** *020 †30
SILVERBERG, Alan. 400 GORDON DR, STE 701 19341 #041-07-1981 L1982 **OBG** *020 †30
SIMONOWITZ, Beth. 491 JOHN YOUNG WAY, STE 201 19341 #024-07-1976 L1981 **PD** *020 †55
SINGER, David Patrick. 460 CREAMERY WAY STE 10, PLASTIC AND RECONSTRUCTIVE 19341 #048-12-1998 L2006 **PS** *020 †65
SINHA, Anubha. 318 E LINCOLN HWY 19341 #305-01-1998 L2001 **GE** *020 †20
SMITH, Matthew T. 860 SPRINGDALE DR, STE 100 19341 #048-02-1998 L2000 **NEP IM** *020 †20
SPYROPOULOS, Nicholas G. ■ 19341 #418-01-1959 L1971 **PD** *071
STAID, Rashna K. 119 E UWCHLAN AVE, WHITELAND MEDICAL ASSOCIAT 19341 #035-15-1996 L2005 **IM** *020 †20
STEFAN, Michael Mark. 491 JOHN YOUNG WAY, STE 320 19341 #041-07-1985 L1986 **PS DR** *020 †85,65
STEIN, Leon. ■ 19341 #028-79-1954, ▲ L1959 **FM OMM** *072
TODD, Mary Louise. ■ 19341 #024-05-1981 L1983 **OBG** *020
TUCCI, Richard Paul. 495 THOMAS JONES WAY, STE 306 19341 #051-07-1988 L1993 **CD IM** *020 †20
ULICHNEY, Andrew Bernard. 460 CREAMERY WAY STE 104 19341 #041-09-1995 L1997 **IM** *020 †20
WALLIN, Bruce Addington. 700 PENNSYLVANIA DR 19341 #026-04-1976 L1982 **RHU IM** *050 †20
WARD, Susan Bullitt. 666 EXTON CMNS 19341 #041-02-1985 L1986 **RHU IM** *020 †20
WHEELER, Sara Lyn. 495 THOMAS JONES WAY, STE 210 19341 #041-01-1988 L1995 **OBG** *020 †30
WILLIAMS, Andre O. 460 CREAMERY WAY, STE 102 19341 #566-01-1974 L1979 **AN PME** *020 †05
WILNER, Brian Frederic. 495 THOMAS JONES WAY, STE 306 19341 #041-15-2001 L2007 **CD** *020 †20
WILSON, Linda C. 495 THOMAS JONES WAY, STE 210 19341 #041-02-1978 L1981 **OBG** *020 †30
WILSON, Martin Conway. 481 JOHN YOUNG WAY, OAKLANDS CORPORATE CENTER 19341 #041-13-1990 L1994 **OPH** *072 †35
WINGATE, Gary F. 460 CREAMERY WAY STE 110 19341 #016-06-1984 L1989 **PS HS** *020 †65 ‡
WRIGHT, Sean Anthony. 460 CREAMERY WAY, STE 110 19341 #024-01-2000 L2006 **PS** *020 †65 ‡
YOUNG, Patrick Allen. 460 CREAMERY WAY, ANESTHESIA ASSOCIATES OF C 19341 #041-13-2001 L2001 **AN** *020
ZABELL, Arleen S. 225 CANDALWOOD LN 19341 #041-07-1974 L1976 **DR NM** *020
ZAMUCO, Leonara M. ■ 19341 #748-01-1954 L1970 **P OS** *071
ZHUKOVSKIY, Oleg Igorevic. 13 HERITAGE LN 19341 #913-86-1995 L2003 **IM** *020 †20

EYNON – LACKAWANNA

ACHECAR, Rafael. 681 SCRANTON CARBONDAL HWY, EYNON SURGICAL CTR 18403 #308-01-1968 L1981 **AN APM** *020 ‡
CHOWDHURY, Mohammed R. 681 SCRANTON CARBONDAL HWY 18403 #308-07-1982 L1990 **GE** *020 †20
MARTYNIUK, John Wm. 708 3RD ST 18403 #011-02-1987 L1990 **P** *020 †75
SHAH, Nayan Chimanlal. 681 SCRANTON CARBONDAL HWY 18403 #495-23-1979 L1984 **GE** *020 †20
WILLIAMS, Lori Ann. 157 SCRANTON CARBONDAL HWY, PINELINE PLAZA 18403 #041-09-1993 L1995 **IM** *020 †20

FACTORYVILLE – WYOMING

CHILSON, Terrance Scott. PO BOX D, 90 COLLEGE AVE 18419 #005-12-1998 L2002 **IM** *020 †20
WALLINE, Joseph Harold. ■ 18419 #041-15-2006 L2008 **EM** *012

FAIRFIELD – ADAMS

CURLEY, Christine A. ■ 17320 #047-20-1988 L2005 **GP ADM** *020
FARKAS, Andrew A. 4910 FAIRFIELD RD, STE A 17320 #041-02-1981 L1982 **FM EM** *020 †18 ‡
MOORE, David Sadler. 4910 FAIRFIELD RD STE A 17320 #041-01-1985 L1986 **FM** *020 †18

FAIRLESS HILLS – BUCKS

BARASH, Craig Ross. 333 N OXFORD VALLEY RD, STE 402 19030 #035-47-1991 L1994
GE *020 †20
BLUMENTHAL, Jeffrey Ray. 333 N OXFORD VALLEY RD, STE 201 19030 #041-09-1975 L1976
IM *020 †20
BONNER, William Francis. 333 N OXFORD VALLEY RD, STE 102 19030 #539-06-1981 L1983
PM OM *020 †60
CHOY, Suk Saing Cho. ■ 19030 #583-03-1948 L1970 P *071
DUNN, Adelina Manese. 605 S QUEEN ANNE DR 19030 #748-01-1971 L1979 GP GPM *020
DUNN, Lewis Jeffrey. 605 S QUEEN ANNE DR 19030 #038-41-1973 L1974 IM EM *020
IKEZUAGU, Ojiaku Balewa. ■ 19030 #422-01-2005 L2006 GS *100
KALANURIA, Atul Ashok. ■ 19030 #496-44-2002 L2005 IM *012
LAMPROU, Emanuel, Jr. 333 N OXFORD VALLEY RD, STE 510 19030 #748-12-1982 L2003
AN *020 †05
LIEBREICH, Mark E. 333 N OXFORD VALLEY RD, STE 201 19030 #041-02-1987 L1989
FM *020 †18
MODENA, Scott Alan. 333 N OXFORD VALLEY RD, STE 402 19030 #035-15-1999 L2001
GE *020 †20
MOSKAITIS, John Edward. 333 N OXFORD VALLEY RD, STE 107 19030 #010-02-1994 L1996
IM *020
SALOWE, David Ross. 333 N OXFORD VALLEY RD, STE 402 19030 #033-06-1986 L1989
GE IM *020 †20
SALVAGE, Robert Harris. 333 N OXFORD VALLEY RD, STE 510 19030 #422-01-1988 L1992
AN PME *020 †05
SANTOS, Reynaldo Cruz. 333 N OXFORD VALLEY RD, STE 510 19030 #748-10-1976 L1986
IM *020
SHANAHAN, Nancy E Rogers. 333 N OXFORD VALLEY RD, STE 102 19030 #041-07-1957 L1958
PM PRS *020 †60 ‡
SHANKAR, Ram Gouri. US STEEL CORP MED, DEPT CM6 19030 #495-04-1950 L1968
OM OTO *020 †45
TADDONIO, Richard Bruce. 333 N OXFORD VALLEY RD, STE 201 19030 #041-14-1979 L1980
FM *020 †18

FAIRMOUNT CITY – CLARION

NABATCHI, Ahmad. 1323 BROOKVILLE ST, BARRY J SNYDER MD & ASSOC 16224
#517-01-1962 L1974 IM GE *020
SHORE, Roger John. 82 TOWN RUN RD, FAMILY HEALTH CARE 16224 #025-01-1976 L1977
FM *020 †18
SLAGLE, Dennis Carl. ■ 16224 #041-77-2006, ▲ PD *012
SNYDER, Barry J. 1323 BROOKVILLE ST 16224 #041-02-1980 L1981 FM *020 †18

FAIRVIEW – ERIE

BATHRICK, Charles Earlton. 6475 NAEFF RD 16415 #035-15-1978 L1982 DR *020 †80
BATHRICK, Marie Colburn. ■ 16415 #035-15-1977 L1982 OPH *071 †35
BERNHARD, Robert Albert. ■ 16415 #041-13-1958 L1959 R *071 †80
DUGAN, Thomas Martin. 6694 KNOLLWOOD DR 16415 #041-12-1972 L1975 CD *020 †20
HRINDA, John Gregory. 7686 MAIN ST, W COUNTY MEDICAL CENTER 16415
#016-43-1964 L1965 FM *071
KELLOGG, Ronald Alan. ■ 16415 #024-07-1974 L1977 FM *071 †18
LAYDEN, Paul W. ■ 16415 #041-02-1950 L1951 ORS *072 †40
MC CLELLAN, Joseph Robt. ■ 16415 #010-02-1972 L1980 CD IM *020 †20
NACOPOULOS, Katerina Cons. ■ 16415 #041-14-2007 L2007 FP *012
PELLIZZARI, Rinaldo G. ■ 16415 #561-09-1954 L1960 PTH *071 †50
PENMAN, Robert Keith. ■ 16415 #041-12-1945 L1946 ORS *071 †40
VEMULAPALLI, Kutumbarao. 6285 STONEBRIDGE DR 16415 #495-70-1974 L1981 AN *020 †05
WILHELM, Wm Christian. ■ 16415 #041-09-1967 L1968 PD *071 †55

FALLS – WYOMING

SHAH, Evelyn A Moran. RR 1 BOX 301 18615 #748-08-1961 L1986 IM PUD *071

FARMINGTON – FAYETTE

CORRADO, Cataldo F. 6 DEER PATH ST 15437 #010-02-1962 GP EM *020 †18,16
MAENDEL, Anneke S. 101 NEW MEADOW RUN DR, OAK VALLEY MEDICAL & DENTA 15437
#917-07-1994 L1999 FM *020 †18
PERRONE, Frank Felix R. 4176 NATIONAL PIKE 15437 #041-12-1981 L1982 FM *020 †18
ROUND-WYLIE, Francesca. ■ 15437 #041-12-1950 L1951 OS *071
WILHELM, Barbara E. 4176 NATIONAL PIKE 15437 #041-12-1979 L1980 EM FM *020 †16,18

FARRELL – MERCER

CAMARA, Jocelyn F. 350 SHARON NEW CASTLE RD, INSTITUTE 16121 #748-02-1994 L2001
CD *020 †20 ‡
CRANE, Cheryl Ann. 1914 MERCER AVE 16121 #038-44-1990 L1993 PD *020 †55
MC FADDEN, Ronald Dale. 1980 GREEN ST 16121 #041-12-1995 L2000 OS P *020 †20,75
MIDELKA, Andrew, Jr. ■ 16121 #047-07-1966 L1982 PTH FOP *050
MULTARI, Robert D. 2120 LIKENS LN, STE 101 16121 #041-77-1976, ▲ L1977 IM PME *020
MUNDRUCZO, Gyorgy. 2000 GREEN ST 16121 #473-01-1997 L2005 CCM *020 †20
NALUBEGA, Rita. 350 SHARON NEW CASTLE RD, PRIMARY HEALTH NETWORK PAR 16121
#905-01-1997 L2003 FM *020 †18
OTENG-BEDIAKO, Evelyn. 2120 LIKENS LN, UNIVERSITY OF PITTSBURGH M 16121
#412-01-1997 L2007 APM *020 †05
RAZA, Syed Mtr. 2000 GREEN ST 16121 #704-02-1988 L1996 PUD SME *020 †20
TAN, Jocelyn. 2200 MEMORIAL DR 16121 #748-10-1988 L1999 IM ON *020 †20

FAWN GROVE – YORK

OLSON, Janne Robt. 36 WEBB LN 17321 #023-01-1965 L1969 FM *020 †18

FAYETTE CITY – FAYETTE

SOLAN, James Andrew. PO BOX 67, 217 MAIN ST 15438 #041-02-1979 L1981 FM *020 †18

FAYETTEVILLE – FRANKLIN

BAKER, George Wm, Jr. 130 E MAIN ST 17222 #041-13-1965 L1968 GP PUD *020
BARTHEL, Robert A, Jr. ■ 17222 #023-01-1942 L1969 GP *071
BLEWITT, George A. ■ 17222 #041-02-1962 L1963 IM NEP *020 †20
COCHRAN, Bryce Clark. ■ 17222 #041-13-1944 L1945 FM *071
DANIELS, Willard F, Jr. ■ 17222 #051-04-1965 L1965 FM *071 †16
MAGBOJOS, Zenaida Velasco. ■ 17222 #748-02-1960 L1969 AN *071 †05
SEMERARO, Russell John. ■ 17222 #028-03-1971 OPH *071 †35
WEST, Gerard Michael. ■ 17222 #050-02-1964 L1964 CHP P *071 †75

FEASTERVILLE TREVOSE – BUCKS

ANDERSON, Judy Millspaugh. 1829 BUSTLETON PIKE 19053 #654-01-1981 L1983
GP FPG *020
CAVALE, Arvind R. 210 E STREET RD, STE 3E 19053 #496-38-1990 L1994 END IM *020 †20
COHEN, Rona Spector. 1234 BRIDGETOWN PIKE, STE 100 19053 #036-07-1983 L1985
P *020 †75
FREYLIKH, Mikhail. PO BOX 547, MLN REHAB INC 19053 #913-48-1979 L1996 PM *020 †60
GLICKMAN, Peter Louis. 4 NESHAMINY INTERPLEX, STE 209 19053 #024-01-1999 L2005
DR *100 †80 ‡
GRABAR, Joyce Margot. 826 BUSTLETON PIKE, 1ST FL STE 300 19053 #041-13-1979 L1980
OPH *020 †35
KEENE, Robert Jos. ■ 19053 #028-34-1956 L1991 FM *071 †18
KHALUPSKY, Larisa. ■ 19053 #913-07-1979 L1986 IM *020
MUSTEN, Alec Eldar. ■ 19053 #041-15-2003 L2003 CD *012 †20
NERURKAR, Anil Shantaram. 4 ROSE AVE 19053 #496-38-1970 L1978 OBG *020 †30
NERURKAR, Meena Anil. 4 ROSE AVE 19053 #496-38-1971 L1979 OBG *020 †30
NOVOSAD, Eugene Igor. ■ 19053 #154-01-1967 *071
PERTSCHUK, Michael J. 1200 BUSTLETON PIKE, STE 11 19053 #041-01-1972 L1973
P *020 †75
PUNJABI, Priya Haresh. 1629 BRIDGETOWN PIKE 19053 #496-38-1978 L1981 FM *020
SOLANKI, Indukumar M. 4630 E STREET RD, MRI MANAGEMENT 19053 #495-22-1967 L1977
R *020 †80
TERESH, Michelle Ann. ■ 19053 #041-14-2008 *012
TRUITT, Jeffrey Thomas. ■ 19053 #041-15-2006 L2006 AN *012
TU, Jason Manh. ■ 19053 #041-02-2004 L2004 OPH *012

FELTON – YORK

RUBELMANN, Douglas Robt. 14137 GLESSICK SCHOOL RD, YORK HOSPITAL 17322
#023-01-1991 L1993 FM *020 †18

FINLEYVILLE – WASHINGTON

JENKINS, Leonard Eugene. 3516 WASHINGTON AVE 15332 #041-12-2002 L2002 IM *020 †20
JENKINS, Robt Jewett, Jr. 3516 WASHINGTON AVE 15332 #041-12-1970 L1977 IM FM *020

FISHERTOWN – BEDFORD

WEAVERLING, Eric Richard. 2040 QUAKER VALLEY RD 15539 #041-02-1982 L1983
FM EM *020 †18

FLEETWOOD – BERKS

HOLLIMAN, Cecil James. 16 N CHESTNUT ST, FLEETWOOD VOLUNTEER FIRE C 19522
#028-02-1979 L1985 EM *020 †16
KULAGA, Stanley Frank, Jr. 19522 #010-01-1964 L1965 OS OPH *030
KURJANOWICZ, Wadim. 19522 #759-10-1951 L1962 GP *071
NEUMAIER, George Jos. ■ 19522 #010-02-1967 L2001 D *071 †15
OUANO, Romeo Cuizon. ■ 19522 #748-01-1961 L1973 DR NM *071
SELLERS, Robert Walter. 805 N RICHMOND ST 19522 #028-34-1976 L1980 FM *020
TREXLER, Ethan Loraine. ■ 19522 #041-09-1938 L1939 FM *071

FLOURTOWN – MONTGOMERY

BAILEY, Marie Ann. 1811 BETHLEHEM PIKE 19031 #041-07-1996 L1998 GE *020 †20
BECK, William Chris, Jr. ■ 19031 #041-13-1946 L1947 OM GP *071
BECKER, David Jonathan. 1722 BETHLEHEM PIKE 19031 #033-06-1983 L1984 CD IM *020 †20
BELSER, Nancy Lautensack. 1811 BETHLEHEM PIKE, STE A106 19031 #041-07-1988 L1990
PD *020 †55
BERTIGER, Gerald. 1811 BETHLEHEM PIKE 19031 #041-09-1979 L1982 IM *020 †20
BLOOMGARDEN, Raphael. 1722 BETHLEHEM PIKE 19031 #025-07-1981 L1982
CD IM *020 †20
BOYNTON, Robert Francis. 1811 BETHLEHEM PIKE 19031 #041-07-1986 L1987
GE IM *020 †20
BRANIGAN, Alison E. 1722 BETHLEHEM PIKE 19031 #041-07-1987 L1989 CD *020 †20
BROWN, Melissa Moore. 1107 BETHLEHEM PIKE STE 2 19031 #041-02-1986 L1987
OPH *020 †35
CENTENO, Jose Casia. ■ 19031 #748-01-1962 L1967 GS GP *020 †85

CHINN, David Erik. 1722 BETHLEHEM PIKE 19031 #005-02-1993 L2000 **CD** *020 †20
CHOLLAK, William Lewis. 1401 BETHLEHEM PIKE 19031 #041-02-1971 L1972 **ORS** *020 †40
CORCORAN, Sharon Mullin. 1811 BETHLEHEM PIKE BLDG A 19031 #041-13-1988 L1991 **PD** *020 †55
DE FELICE, Peggy L. 1811 BETHLEHEM PIKE, STE A-106 19031 #041-14-1983 L1986 **PD** *020 †55
DI TRAPANI, Tonya Marie. 1811 BETHLEHEM PIKE, STE A101 19031 #048-13-1999 L2003 **N** *020 †75
DOONEIEF, George Harman. 1811 BETHLEHEM PIKE, STE A1 19031 #033-05-1984 L1996 **N** *020 †75 ‡
GEIST, Audrey A. 8509 WIDENER ROAD 19031 #041-07-1978 L1981 **IM D** *030
GORDON, Ram Yosef. 1722 BETHLEHEM PIKE 19031 #041-12-1998 L2000 **CD** *020 †20
GUPTA, Vidhu Bhusan. 1811 BETHLEHEM PIKE, STE A1 19031 #496-03-1987 L1999 **N** *020 †75
HAMMER, William Jos. 1722 BETHLEHEM PIKE 19031 #041-13-1969 L1970 **CD IM** *020 †20
HARRIS, S Miller. ■ 19031 #041-13-1986 L1987 **IM** *020 †20 ‡
HIRSCH, Michael Andrew. 1811 BETHLEHEM PIKE, STE 108 19031 #041-13-1988 L1990 **FM** *020 †18
HYMAN, Daniel. 1811 BETHLEHEM PIKE, # A-112 19031 #035-46-1986 L1987 **PD** *020 †55
ILYAS, Erum Naseem. 1811 BETHLEHEM PIKE, STE A101 19031 #041-15-2001 L2001 **D** *020 †15
KERSON, Lawrence Alan. 1811 BETHLEHEM PIKE, STE A101 19031 #041-01-1968 L1971 **N** *020 †75 ‡
KIMBALL, Ronald W. 1 WINGATE CT 19031 #041-01-1973 L1974 **OPH** *020 †35 ‡
KRON, Kenneth M. 720 BETHLEHEM PIKE 19031 #041-02-1952 L1953 **P RHU** *020
LIMMER, Kathryn Cyr. 1811 BETHLEHEM PIKE, STE A106 19031 #024-07-1985 L1994 **PD** *020 †55
LIN, Bradford Jay. 1722 BETHLEHEM PIKE 19031 #041-09-1985 L1986 **CD IM** *020 †20
MATARAZZO, Stephen Alfred. 1811 BETHLEHEM PIKE 19031 #041-09-1971 L1972 **GE IM** *071 †20
MC HARG, Malcolm Lennox. 1811 BETHLEHEM PIKE, STE A1 19031 #041-09-1984 L1991 **CHN PD** *020 †55,75 ‡
MESSORI, Divo Angelo. 1811 BETHLEHEM PIKE # 300 19031 #041-02-1957 L1958 **GE IM** *020 †20
MILLER, Donald Lawrence. 1811 BETHLEHEM PIKE 19031 #041-07-1987 L1990 **IM** *020 †20
NACK, Steven Lee. 1811 BETHLEHEM PIKE 19031 #041-13-1979 L1982 **GE IM** *020 †20
NAPS, Michelle Stephanie. 1811 BETHLEHEM PIKE, STE 233 19031 #051-04-1991 L1993 **FM** *020 †18
OBBEHAT, Mina Fatimah. 1107 BETHLEHEM PIKE # 210 19031 #038-41-2003 L2007 **FM** *100 †18
POLLACK, Andrew Keith. 1811 BETHLEHEM PIKE, STE 101 19031 #041-07-1978 L1979 **D RHU** *020 †15
REEKIE, Timothy Gale. 1107 BETHLEHEM PIKE, STE 210 19031 #041-09-1978 L1979 **FM** *020 †18
RODGERS, David Martin. 1722 BETHLEHEM PIKE 19031 #041-02-1977 L1978 **CD IM** *020 †20 ‡
RODRIGUEZ, Raymond. 1722 BETHLEHEM PIKE 19031 #010-02-1983 L1984 **CD IM** *020 †20 ‡
ROTHERT, Jude Damian. 110 W WISSAHICKON AVE, SAINT JOSEPH VILLA 19031 #041-07-1976 L1977 **IM** *020
RUBIN, Cindy Joy. 1811 BETHLEHEM PIKE, STE 234 19031 #041-07-1990 L1993 **IM** *020 †20
SCHILLER, Herbert Marvin. 311 HAWS LN 19031 #005-17-1962 L1966 **GP** *020 †18
SCHWARTZ, Laurel Radcliff. ■ 19031 #041-15-2005 L2005 **D** *012
SEDLACK, Jeanianne T. ■ 19031 #041-09-1988 L1990 **AN** *005
SMITH, Laurance Dean. 1811 BETHLEHEM PIKE, STE A1 19031 #041-01-1982 L1987 **N** *020 †75 ‡
SNYDERMAN, Danielle Amy. ■ 19031 #010-03-2003 L2003 **FPG** *020 †18
TATERKA, James Andrew. 1528 BETHLEHEM PIKE, HILLMONT ENDOSCOPY CENTER 19031 #035-01-1985 L1988 **GE IM** *020 †20
WILSON, Robert Merrill. ■ 19031 #035-45-1969 L1977 **IM** *020 †20
ZEIGLER, Katherine Louise. 407 NORFOLK RD 19031 #028-34-2002 L2002 **FM** *020 †18
ZUCKERMAN, Gilbert L. 1722 BETHLEHEM PIKE 19031 #041-09-1970 L1973 **CD IM** *020 †20 ‡

FOGELSVILLE — LEHIGH

MOTSAY, George Jos. 32 PHEASANT RUN 18051 #041-01-1963 L1987 **TS GS** *020 †85
RICHARDSON, David Mark. ■ 18051 #041-02-1992 L1995 **EM** *020 †16
STANTON, Elizabeth Lee. ■ 18051 #847-04-1987 L1991 **FM** *020 †18
STEWARD, J A. 2278 APPLE RD, FOGELSVILLE MEDICAL ASSOCI 18051 #041-13-1985 L1986 **IM OM** *020
WORRILOW, Charles Cobb. ■ 18051 #051-01-1986 L1990 **EM** *020 †16

FOLCROFT — DELAWARE

CORYELL, Lee Arthur. ■ 19032 #041-01-2008 *012
KRECIOCH, Piotr Karol. ■ 19032 #041-15-2007 L2007 **GS** *012

FOLSOM — DELAWARE

BONNER, James Francis. 217 KEDRON AVE 19033 #539-06-1979 L1982 **PM** *020 †60
DONATI, Omero John. 607 MACDADE BLVD 19033 #041-77-1950, ▲ L1958 **FM** *071
FROMAL, Amy Lynne. ■ 19033 #041-02-2004 L2004 **DR** *012
LIBERATI, Maryanne T. 1405 MACDADE BLVD 19033 #654-01-1981 L1983 **IM** *020

FOMBELL — BEAVER

NOUR, Joseph H. ■ 16123 #422-01-1989 L1993 **AN PME** *020
NOUR, Petra S. 171 OMNI ST 16123 #409-20-1987 L1993 **AN** *020 †05

FORCE — ELK

VALIGORSKY, Paul Jos. ■ 15841 #010-02-1943 L1944 **GP AN** *071

FORD CITY — ARMSTRONG

CROSS, Samuel, Jr. ■ 16226 #041-12-1958 L1959 **GS** *071 †85
GELACEK, Philip Andrew. 313 FORD ST STE 2A 16226 #041-12-1977 L1978 **FM** *020 †18
MOORE, Terence Edward. 710 4TH AVE 16226 #041-13-1982 L1983 **FM** *020 †18 ‡
OPALKA, Michele Ann. ■ 16226 #041-02-2004 L2004 **FM** *020
RISHI, Usha Satchidanand. ■ 16226 #495-30-1956 L1971 **DR R** *071 †80
TOOR, Shaista Nasreen. 834 4TH AVE, MALIK MEDICAL ASSOCS 16226 #704-08-1969 L1980 **IM** *020

FOREST CITY — SUSQUEHANNA

GADDIS, Ewa. ■ 18421 #759-07-1981 L2002 **P** *020
PATTON, Howard Rand. ■ 18421 #041-02-1933 L1935 **PTH IM** *100
SORIANO, Carmenciata L B. ■ 18421 #748-01-1972 L1998 **PTH** *020 †50
TOMAZIC, David Robt. 632 MAIN ST 18421 #041-77-1978, ▲ L1979 **FM FPG** *020 †18 ‡

FORKSVILLE — SULLIVAN

MILES, Michael A. RR 1 BOX 1349 18616 #041-09-1971 L1972 **EM** *020 †16

FORT WASHINGTON — MONTGOMERY

AQUILINA, Joseph Wolfgang. 420 DELAWARE DR, MCNEIL PEDIATRICS 19034 #025-12-1985 L2001 **U PA** *050 †95
AU, Angela Kayan. ■ 19034 #041-02-2008 L2008 *012
AU, Arthur K. ■ 19034 #041-13-2008 L2008 *012
BADOLATO, David Jos. 1244 FORT WASHINGTON AVE, STE E 19034 #041-09-1975 L1976 **FM** *020 †18
BAGGISH, Jeffrey Steven. 7050 CAMP HILL RD 19034 #051-04-1989 L1990 **GP** *020
BALASUBRAMANIAN, Easwarn. 220 COMMERCE DR 19034 #495-16-1975 L1979 **ORS** *020 †40
BERKOW, Robert. ■ 19034 #023-01-1953 L1975 **IM OS** *071 †20
BOWEN, Debra. 7050 CAMP HILL RD, MCNEIL CONSUMER HEALTHCARE 19034 #024-01-1978 L2001 **ID EM** *050 †20,03
BRECKENRIDGE, John Wm. 1244 FORT WASHINGTON AVE 19034 #041-02-1970 L1973 **DR** *020 †20
BROBYN, Thomas James. 467 PENNSYLVANIA AVE, STE 203 19034 #041-13-1966 L1967 **PS** *020 †65
BUCK, Ruth Elizabeth. ■ 19034 #041-13-1965 L1966 **R** *071 †80
CAULFIELD, Maureen Siat. ■ 19034 #038-44-1983 L1994 **GE IM** *020 †20,55
CHINITZ, Joel Lloyd. ■ 19034 #035-08-1962 L1965 **PHP IM** *071 †20
CHUNG, Hack R. 7170 LAFAYETTE AVE 19034 #583-01-1965 L1971 **P** *020 †75
COATS, Thomas David. 1244 FORT WASHINGTON AVE, OPHTHAL ASSOC OF FT WSHNGT 19034 #041-02-1992 L1994 **OPH** *020 †35
CRISCI, Kristin Lee. 1244 FORT WASHINGTON AVE 19034 #041-12-1984 L1985 **PDR PD** *020 †80
DAVIS, Nicole. 535 PENNSYLVANIA AVE, STE 100 19034 #041-14-1999 L2001 **FM** *020 †18
DEMP, Neal Brian. 7170 LAFAYETTE AVE, BROOKE GLEN BEHAVIORAL HOS 19034 #041-07-1988 L1990 **CHP** *020 †75
D'ORAZIO, Edward Alfred. ■ 19034 #041-02-1962 L1963 **R OS** *071 †80
FELLHEIMER, Susan L. 260 NEW YORK DR, FORT WASHINGTON PEDIATRICS 19034 #041-07-1979 L1980 **PD** *020 †55
FLEISCHER, Scott Allan. 275 COMMERCE DR STE 323 19034 #041-09-1977 L1978 **P PYG** *020 †75
FRABIZZIO, Jennifer Villa. 1244 FORT WASHINGTON AVE 19034 #041-09-1995 L1997 **RNR DR** *020 †80
GASTEYER, Susan. ■ 19034 #030-05-1969 L1975 **P CHP** *020 †75
GERSTMAN, Ira. 1244 FORT WASHINGTON AVE, FAMILY PRACTICE ASSOCIATES 19034 #033-05-1978 L1981 **FM** *020 †18
GHOSALA, R Reddy. 7170 LAFAYETTE AVE, BEHAVIORAL HOSPITAL 19034 #495-62-1988 L2001 **CHP** *020
HARRISON, Diane Deborah. 420 DELAWARE DR 19034 #041-01-1987 L1988 **OBG PHP** *050 †30
INDIK, Jonathan Howard. 426 PENNSYLVANIA AVE, STE 200 19034 #041-13-1980 L1981 **P FM** *020 †75
JONES, Warren Mead. ■ 19034 #008-01-1961 L1966 **OPH OS** *020 †35
KANE, William Martin. 1244 FORT WASHINGTON AVE 19034 #041-02-1946 L1947 **OBG** *071 †30
KAPLAN, Andrew Laurence. 501 OFFICE CENTER DR, PHILADELPHIA INSTITUTE OF 19034 #036-07-2000 L2006 **D DS** *020 †15 ‡
KELLY, John David, IV. 220 COMMERCE DR 19034 #038-41-1984 L1985 **ORS** *020 †40
KESSELRING, Joseph James. 1244 FORT WASHINGTON AVE 19034 #041-02-1985 L1986 **OPH** *020 †35
KHAN, Ambareen Afshan. ■ 19034 #041-15-2006 L2006 **AN** *012
KNOBLER, Robert Leonard. 520 PINETOWN RD 19034 #035-08-1975 L1984 **N PMM** *020 †75
KOMASZ, Jason Michael. 260 NEW YORK DR, STE 1 19034 #033-06-1998 L2000 **PD** *020 †55
KORTSCH, Daniel Ulrich. 535 PENNSYLVANIA AVE 19034 #051-01-2003 L2003 **FM** *100 †18
KUFFNER, Edwin Karl, Jr. 7050 CAMP HILL RD, ROCKY MOUNTAIN POISON & DR 19034 #035-08-1991 L2007 **EM** *020 †16
KUKLINSKI, Louise Helen. 1244 FORT WASHINGTON AVE, STE E 19034 #041-14-1982 L1985 **FM FPG** *020 †18
LAUDADIO, Charles. 7050 CAMP HILL RD 19034 #020-02-1977 L1991 **PHM PME** *030
LEE, Andrew Wentseng. ■ 19034 #035-20-1997 L1999 **ID** *020 †20
LIM, Philip Shueyin. 1244 FORT WASHINGTON AVE 19034 #023-01-1994 L1999 **DR** *020 †80
LIU, Jinn. 1244 FORT WASHINGTON AVE, STE E 19034 #041-02-2004 L2006 **FM** *020 †18
LOCKMAN, Bruce Evan. 270 COMMERCE DR, STE 250 19034 #033-01-1976 L1978 **PD** *020 †55
LOMAZOFF, Igor. 501 OFFICE CENTER DR, STE 195 19034 #041-15-1999 L2001 **D** *020 †15
LUBELL, Andrew Howard. 270 COMMERCE DR STE 250 19034 #035-47-1995 L1997 **PD** *020 †55
MANILOV, Anna. 501 OFFICE CENTER DR, STE 195 19034 #041-13-2003 L2003 **D** *020 †15 ‡
MASARACHIA, Sam Camie. 1244 FORT WASHINGTON AVE, STE E 19034 #033-05-1985 L1986 **FM** *020 †18

MAUDE, Shannon Leigh. ■ 19034 #041-01-2006 L2006 **PD** *012
MC LAUGHLIN, Jennifer L. 7170 LAFAYETTE AVE, BROOKE GLEN BEHAVIORAL HEA 19034 #041-15-1998 L2001 **CHP** *100 †75
MOORE, Samuel R, Jr. ■ 19034 #041-01-1944 L1945 **OM IM** *072
MORAN, J Roberto. 601 OFFICE CENTER DR 19034 #341-01-1973 L1982 **PD PG** *062 †55
MOYER, Ray Arlan. 220 COMMERCE DR 19034 #041-01-1968 L1972 **ORS OSM** *020 †40
MULLIGAN, Margaret Ann. 1244 FT WASHINGTON AVE, FAMILY PRACTICE ASSOC OF U 19034 #041-07-1979 L1982 **FM** *020 †18
PAN, Jeffrey Charles. 1244 FORT WASHINGTON AVE 19034 #033-05-1994 L2000 **DR** *020 †80
PARMESHWARAN, Chand Jayan. 7170 LAFAYETTE AVE, BROOKE GLEN HOSPITAL 19034 #496-38-1985 L2001 **P** *020 †75
PLOTKIN, Randi Lynn. 7237 HOLLYWOOD RD, FL 2 19034 #041-07-1997 L1999 **P** *020 †75
READ, Paul James. ■ 19034 #041-02-2005 L2005 **DR** *012
REHMAN, Atta-Ur. 2101 PENNSYLVANIA AVE 19034 #704-02-1992 L1999 **CHP** *020 †75
REIMET, Elizabeth Ann. ■ 19034 #041-07-1993 L1996 **IM** *020 †20
RESNICK, Edward J. 220 COMMERCE DR 19034 #041-13-1951 L1952 **ORS** *020 †40
RICE, Sharon Marie. ■ 19034 #041-13-1997 L2000 **OBG** *020 †30
ROGERS, Deborah Krohn. 450 S BETHLEHEM PIKE 19034 #035-03-1973 L1978 **P CHP** *020 †75
SAMUELS, Trudy. ■ 19034 #041-09-1984 L1986 **P** *020
SCHWARTZ, Geoffrey Paul. 1244 FORT WASHINGTON AVE 19034 #041-02-1998 L2000 **OPH** *020 †35
SEELAUS, Jere Francis. 1244 FORT WASHINGTON AVE 19034 #041-02-1975 L1976 **DR** *020 †80
SERRUYA, Delia G. 450 S BETHLEHEM PIKE 19034 #132-01-1967 L1972 **P** *020
SILBER, Steven Alan. 7050 CAMP HILL RD, MCNEIL PHARMACEUTICALS 19034 #023-07-1976 L1978 **IM** *020 †20
STARR, Harriette Lynn. 420 DELAWARE DR, MAILSTOP *951 19034 #041-07-1989 L1992 **PD PHM** *062 †54
TAUPIN, Michel Jean-Chas. 1244 FORT WASHINGTON AVE 19034 #024-05-1981 L1982 **DR** *020 †80
URBAN, Edward Louis. 7170 LAFAYETTE AVE 19034 #041-09-1965 L1966 **P** *020
VAIL, Barbara Lynn. 501 OFFICE CENTER DR, STE 195 19034 #041-15-1999 L2000 **D** *020 †15 ‡
WEISS, Alan Richard. 1244 FORT WASHINGTON AVE 19034 #041-13-1974 L1975 **DR** *020 †80
WEISS, Sharon Nicole. 1244 FORT WASHINGTON AVE 19034 #041-13-1988 L1991 **DR** *020 †80
WOODWARD, Trevor. ■ 19034 #352-07-1957 L1960 **PD ADL** *030 †55
WORONOFF, Alan Joel. 1244 FORT WASHINGTON AVE 19034 #025-07-1994 L1999 **DR** *020 †80
ZAVITSANOS, George Peter. 467 PENNSYLVANIA AVE, STE 203 19034 #041-13-1988 L1990 **PS** *020 †85,65
ZIMMERMAN, Michael R. 401 COMMERCE DR STE 200, SENECA MEDICAL LAB INC 19034 #035-19-1963 L1970 **PTH** *030 †50

FORTY FORT – LUZERNE

BARRAS, David Israel. 190 WELLES ST 18704 #035-46-1973 L1978 **OTO** *020 †45
BOYLE, William Hugh. 1732 WYOMING AVE 18704 #041-13-1971 L1973 **GP** *020 †18
CASTERLINE, Charlotte L. ■ 18704 #028-34-1971 L1977 **A IM** *020 †20,03 ‡
DELLA ROSA, John Jos, Jr. 190 WELLES ST STE 114 18704 #010-02-1980 L1984 **N SME** *020 †75
ENGEL, Robert. 190 WELLES ST 18704 #649-36-1979 L1983 **IM** *020
FREIMAN, Michael Anthony. 190 WELLES ST 18704 #041-14-1998 L2006 **OTO** *020 †45
GALASSO, James W, III. 1169 WYOMING AVE 18704 #028-78-1991, ▲ L1992 **FM** *020 †18
GERNHARDT, Elizabeth A. 920 WYOMING AVE, STE 202 18704 #041-77-1997, ▲ L1998 **FM** *020 †18
HANLON, Thomas Walter. 190 WELLES ST, SURGICAL SPECIALTY CENTER 18704 #041-12-1987 L1991 **PME AN** *020 †05
KOPEN, Dan Francis. 190 WELLES ST, NE SURGICAL SPECIALTY GRP 18704 #041-14-1974 L1982 **OS LM** *020 †85
LEVANDOSKI, Gerald Jos. 1516 WYOMING AVE 18704 #041-09-1984 L1985 **PS GS** *020 †65
PACURARIU, Radu Ioan. 920 WYOMING AVE STE 201 18704 #781-03-1965 L1974 **OPH** *020 †35
SHAH, Nareshkumar R. 190 WELLES ST 18704 #495-22-1974 L1981 **DR** *020 †80
USTYNOSKI, Kenneth Robt. 1732 WYOMING AVE 18704 #041-09-1983 L1984 **CRS GS** *020 †85,10

FOUNTAIN HILL – NORTHAMPTON

ALIA, Christopher Scott. 709 DELAWARE AVE 18015 #035-09-2000 L2006 **PCC** *020
ANDERSON, John Russell. 701 OSTRUM ST STE 603 18015 #041-01-1968 L1969 **U** *020 †95
BACAK, Joseph Francis, III. 701 OSTRUM ST, STE 404 18015 #041-09-1975 L1976 **IM** *020 †20
BECKHARD, Sharon Ann. 821 DELAWARE AVE 18015 #041-02-1987 L1988 **N CN** *075 †75
BELL-SKRINE, Robin Annett. 701 OSTRUM ST STE 602, SURGICAL ASSOC OF BETHLEHE 18015 #041-02-1991 L1991 **OS** *020 †85
BEN-DAVID, Joseph. 701 OSTRUM ST STE 502 18015 #550-01-1980 L2003 *020
BHATT, Bankim Ashok. 800 OSTRUM ST, STE 307 18015 #051-07-1998 L2001 **END** *020 †20
BUSCHI, Marie. 826 DELAWARE AVE 18015 #041-14-1990 L1992 **IM** *020 †20
CAMPBELL, Stephen Edward. 701 OSTRUM ST, STE 403 18015 #028-02-1970 L1988 **ON HEM** *071 †20
COHEN, Martin Arthur. 709 DELAWARE AVE 18015 #035-08-1973 L1974 **ORS** *020 †40
DALE, Hiram Thompson. 618 DELAWARE AVE 18015 #041-01-1973 L1978 **CD IM** *020 †20
DOLL, Robert Benj, Jr. 800 OSTRUM ST, STE 307 18015 #041-02-1977 L1978 **END** *020 †20
DORVILLE, Fabio Lopes. 1130 DELAWARE AVE 18015 #187-58-1974 L1977 **IM IMG** *020 †20
DUHAYLONGSOD, Francis G. 701 OSTRUM ST, STE 201 18015 #047-07-1986 L1989 **TS GS** *020 †85,90
ESTRADA, Fernando Parayno. 701 OSTRUM ST, STE 504 DOCTORS PAVILION 18015 #748-02-1973 L1980 **GS VS** *020 †85
FAROUN, Yacoub Georges. 701 OSTRUM ST, STE 403 18015 #875-01-1989 L2001 **HO** *020 †20
GADBOIS, William F. 701 OSTRUM ST STE 603 18015 #010-02-1970 L1972 **U** *020 †95
GARBER, Todd Ryan. 826 DELAWARE AVE 18015 #051-01-1999 L2003 **CN** *020 †75 ‡
GAYNER, Robert. 701 OSTRUM ST, STE 304 18015 #035-47-1986 L1990 **NEP** *020 †20
GIAMBER, Samuel Ross. 618 DELAWARE AVE 18015 #041-01-1966 L1967 **CD IM** *071 †20
GOULD, Jeffrey David. 701 OSTRUM ST, STE 302 18015 #041-09-1994 L1997 **N** *020 †75
GRUNBERG, Robert W. 800 OSTRUM ST, STE 102 18015 #396-19-1969 L1974 **NEP IM** *020 †20 ‡

HARRISON, Drew Stone. 800 OSTRUM ST, STE 102 18015 #041-13-1985 L1986 **NEP IM** *020 †20 ‡
HART, Alex Dick. 701 OSTRUM ST, STE 602 18015 #566-01-1979 L1982 **AN** *020 †05
HAYTMANEK, Craig Thos. 735 DELAWARE AVE 18015 #041-02-1972 L1978 **OTO** *020 †45
HODDINOTT, Kevin Murcell. 701 OSTRUM ST, STE 504 18015 #063-01-1980 L1995 **VS GS** *020
HRATKO, John Ralph. 934 DELAWARE AVE 18015 #422-01-1983 L1986 **OBG GS** *020 †30
IVARSSON, Bengt Lennart W. 701 OSTRUM ST, STE 601 18015 #024-01-1985 L1996 **VS GS** *020
JACOBS, Joseph Manuel. 701 OSTRUM ST, STE 304 18015 #035-47-1984 L1986 **NEP** *020 †20
KARA, Aoun Basheer. 701 OSTRUM ST STE 503 18015 #875-01-1974 L1977 **CD** *020 †20
KIMMEL, Andrew Scott. 800 OSTRUM ST STE 100 18015 #041-07-1984 L1990 **OPH** *020 †35 ‡
KINTZER, John S, Jr. 709 DELAWARE AVE 18015 #048-02-1973 L1976 **PUD CCM** *020 †20
KOLECKI, Richard Stephen. 701 OSTRUM ST, STE 401 18015 #041-02-1988 L1990 **CD** *020 †20
KRAEFT, Jessica J. ■ 18015 #033-06-2008 L2008 *012
LENNERT, Joseph. 701 OSTRUM ST STE 603 18015 #041-13-1973 L1974 **U** *020 †95
LUKASZCZYK, John James. 701 OSTRUM ST, STE 504 18015 #041-09-1984 L1986 **GS TRS** *020 †85
MC CAUGHAN, James Souder. 701 OSTRUM ST, STE 201 18015 #038-45-1988 L1992 **TS** *020 †85,90
MC CLINTOCK, Marilyn Ruth. ■ 18015 #019-02-2004 L2005 **EM** *012
MC DONALD, Marian Passaro. 800 OSTRUM ST, STE 307 18015 #041-14-1990 L1996 **GS** *020 †85
MC DONALD, Marilyn Ruth. 522 DELAWARE AVE 18015 #065-10-1979 L1986 **OPH N** *020 †35
MC GUIRE, James Jos, Jr. 701 OSTRUM ST STE 402 18015 #041-13-1980 L1981 **OBG** *020 †30
MORROW, Gerald Jos. 701 OSTRUM ST, STE 603 18015 #010-02-1969 L1970 **GS** *020 †85
MORROW, Robert Allen. 800 OSTRUM ST 18015 #041-13-1971 L1972 **NS OS** *020 †25
MOYER, Glenn E. 804 DELAWARE AVE 18015 #041-07-1973 L1975 **OPH** *020
MUNVES, Jonathan Henry. 800 OSTRUM ST 18015 #010-01-1978 L1982 **IM N** *020 †20
NATHANSON, Douglas C. 826 DELAWARE AVE 18015 #033-05-1989 L1993 **N** *020 †25
NGUYEN, Minh Quang. 820 N BISHOPTHORPE ST 18015 #041-13-1984 L1985 **CD IM** *020 †20
NIEWIAROWSKA, Anna A. 800 OSTRUM ST, STE 300 18015 #759-03-1982 L1988 **ON HO** *020 †20
NOVAK, Christopher. 514 DELAWARE AVE 18015 #041-09-1986 L1987 **PD** *075 †55
PANAYOTOVA, Maria L A. 1204 DELAWARE AVE 18015 #198-01-1961 L1970 **OPH** *020 †35 ‡
POTASH, Andrew Saml. 701 OSTRUM ST, STE 202 18015 #041-13-1989 L1992 **CD** *020 †20
PULEO, Peter Robt. 618 DELAWARE AVE 18015 #035-01-1978 L1998 **CD EM** *020 †20
RISHER, William Henry. 701 OSTRUM ST, STE 201 18015 #021-05-1985 L2002 **TS** *020 †85,90
RYAN, John Jos. 709 DELAWARE AVE 18015 #041-09-1964 L1965 **PUD IM** *020 †20
SALGADO, Edward Manuel. 825 DELAWARE AVE 18015 #041-02-1967 L1968 **PS** *020 †85,65
SOMASUNDARAM, Anasuya. 701 OSTRUM ST, STE 203 18015 #495-04-1963 L1973 **OBG** *020 †30
SPURLOCK, John W. 826 DELAWARE AVE 18015 #041-02-1984 L1986 **OBG U** *020 †30
SUN, Yun Lynn. 800 OSTRUM ST, STE 206 18015 #243-69-1984 L2001 **N** *020 †75
THEMAN, Terrill Edward. 701 OSTRUM ST, STE 201 18015 #060-01-1971 L1983 **TS CD** *020 †85,90
TURKI, Mohamed A. 709 DELAWARE AVE 18015 #613-02-1989 L2004 **PCC** *020 †20
VISPERAS, Emiliana P. 934 DELAWARE AVE 18015 #748-01-1956 L1973 **OBG** *071
VOLK, Stephen Alexander. 701 OSTRUM ST, STE 403 18015 #041-02-1972 L1977 **ON HEM** *020 †20
WEBER, Robert C. 522 DELAWARE AVE 18015 #041-02-1989 L2003 **OPH** *020 †35
WILLIS, Johnnie S, Jr. 685 DELAWARE AVE 18015 #018-03-1980 L1981 **OBG** *020 †30

FOUNTAINVILLE – BUCKS

BUCK, Kristen Katya. ■ 18923 #041-14-1999 L2001 **IM** *020 †20
BYER, Harold H. 5045 SWAMP RD STE 101 18923 #041-01-1978 L1979 **OPH** *020 †35
COYNE, Veronica E. 5039 SWAMP RD STE 402 18923 #041-07-1963 L1964 **IM** *020
PURCELL, Susan Marie. 5039 SWAMP RD 18923 #041-02-1995 L1997 **IM** *020 †20
RINALDI, Robert Edward. 5045 SWAMP RD STE 103, FAAP 18923 #041-09-1972 L1987 **PD PDC** *020 †55
SANDER, Susan Fisk. 5039 SWAMP RD 18923 #005-11-1984 L2006 **IM** *020 †20
SHAW, Diana Sutphen. 5039 SWAMP RD STE 402, COYNE MED ASSOC BOX 417 18923 #422-01-1988 L1991 **IM** *020 †20
WRIGHT, James Hayward. 5039 SWAMP RD, STE 406 P O BOX 477 18923 #041-01-1990 L1993 **AN** *020 †05

FRACKVILLE – SCHUYLKILL

MATHUR, Kailash Nath. 14 S LEHIGH AVE 17931 #495-08-1963 L1972 **GP** *071 †80

FRANKLIN – VENANGO

BENDT, Peter Uwe. 464 ALLEGHENY BLVD, STE 2D 16323 #045-01-1983 L1988 **FM IM** *020 †18
BISNETT, Teresa. 464 ALLEGHENY BLVD, PENNWOOD CENTER, SUITE 2A 16323 #035-03-1989 L1992 **CCM** *020 †20
CARTWRIGHT, Scott Robt. 110 N 13TH ST 16323 #041-14-1990 L1992 **PD** *020 †55
CENEDELLA, Stephen Chas. 150 PROSPECT AVE 16323 #051-04-1968 L1972 **IM GE** *020 †18
CONDON, Ian Michael. ■ 16323 #041-14-2007 L2007 **TY** *014
COOKE, Curtis Wendell. 110 N 13TH ST, FRANKLIN PED ASSOC PC 16323 #035-03-1988 L1991 **PD** *020 †55
CORSETTI, Jeffrey Philip. ■ 16323 #041-02-1996 L1998 **EM** *020 †16
CRAWFORD, Pamela Ann. 1029 LIBERTY ST 16323 #041-07-1986 L1992 **OTO GS** *020 †45
DIXON, Garrett Ward. 425 13TH ST 16323 #035-09-1980 L1983 **PM** *020 †60
DONAN, Anderson W. 1 SPRUCE ST 16323 #041-13-1951 L1958 **FM** *072
DRAGUN, Joanne Barone. 1 SPRUCE ST 16323 #041-09-1988 L1990 **RO** *020 †80
DUNAGIN, William Galen. 108 N 13TH ST 16323 #019-02-1975 L1985 **D** *020 †15 ‡
EDWARDS, William Plummer. 464 ALLEGHENY BLVD, STE 2D 16323 #561-01-1978 L1981 **CD IM** *020 †20
EMERSON, John Adams. ■ 16323 #035-09-1956 L1975 **OPH** *071 †35
FACKLER, Eric Gregory. 1310 LIBERTY ST 16323 #041-14-1996 L2000 **OBG** *020 †30
FERRARO, David Nicholas, Jr. ■ 16323 #041-02-1996 L2001 **CRS** *020 †85

FETTEROLF, Michael Lynn. 1310 LIBERTY ST 16323 #041-02-1983 L1984 **OBS FM** *020 †18
FITCH, Kathleen Annette. 1029 LIBERTY ST 16323 #020-02-1984 L2000 **OTO HNS** *020 †45
GLOWACKI, Francis Leonard. 190 GOODWILL RD 16323 #041-13-1959 L1960 **AN OS** *071 †05
HAM, James Walter Mc Lean. 1310 LIBERTY ST 16323 #051-01-1964 L1973 **OBG** *020 †30
HOPE, Alexandra M. 425 13TH ST 16323 #054-04-1988 L1990 **PM** *020
HORAN, Paris Burke. 464 ALLEGHENY BLVD, STE 2D 16323 #035-15-1991 L1994 **CD IM** *020 †20
JANSEN, Bruce Martin, Jr. 1266 LIBERTY ST 16323 #024-16-1989 L1991 **FM** *020 †18
KAHLER, Gerald Wm. 1263 ELK ST 16323 #038-45-1984 L1987 **FM** *020 †18
KAHLER, Roberta Ann. 1263 ELK ST 16323 #038-45-1984 L1987 **IM** *020
KARIAN, John M. 150 PROSPECT AVE, STE 301 16323 #041-13-1978 L1979 **NS** *020 †25
KIRTLAND, Howard H, III. 1339 LIBERTY ST 16323 #035-20-1970 L1979 **ON HEM** *020 †20
KLINGER, Frank Anthony. 150 PROSPECT AVE, STE 12 16323 #041-02-1977 L1982 **GS VS** *020 †85
LEHMAN, Matthew Howard. 150 PROSPECT AVE, FRANKLIN SURGICAL GROUP 16323 #041-02-1981 L1990 **GS** *020 †85
MC AFEE, Roy Donald. 1266 LIBERTY ST 16323 #041-09-1976 L1977 **FM** *020 †18
MC CANDLESS, David Perry. 1228 ELK ST, FRANKLIN MEDICAL GRP 16323 #041-12-1977 L1979 **IM** *020 †20
MC CANDLESS, Warren J. 601 WENDY WAY 16323 #041-13-1946 L1947 **FM IM** *071 †18
MC GRAIL, William Thos. 1310 LIBERTY ST 16323 #041-02-1986 L1994 **OBG** *020 †30
MILLER, Susan Allen. 1 SPRUCE ST 16323 #041-07-1987 L1989 **FM** *020
PADIN, Frederico Alfafara. 150 PROSPECT AVE 16323 #748-10-1962 L1969 **U** *020 †95 ‡
PALERMO, Daniel Peter. 212 PROSPECT AVE, NORTHWEST SURGICAL ASSOC - 16323 #025-12-2000 L2005 **GS** *085 ‡
PIRANIAN, Scott Steven. 150 PROSPECT AVE 16323 #041-12-1984 L1985 **FM** *020 †18
RAMANUJAM, Vijayaprabha. 464 ALLEGHENY BLVD, STE 2D 16323 #495-59-1992 L2000 **IM** *020 †20
SMITH, Donald Bryan. 44 CIRCLE ST 16323 #001-06-1984 L1992 **ORS** *020 †40
SPADARO, Donna Puleio. 1339 LIBERTY ST, VOHA 16323 #041-12-1986 L1987 **ON IM** *020 †20
SRICHAROEN, Nattapong. ■ 16323 #891-03-1991 L2003 **IC** *100 †20
STANLEY, Gerald John. 170 KEITH LN, KEITH LANE 16323 #050-02-1988 L1992 **DR** *020 †80
STEVENS, Jay David. 150 PROSPECT AVE 16323 #041-12-1999 L2002 **IM** *020 †20
STRAUB, William Henry. ■ 16323 #010-02-1964 L1981 **DR OS** *071 †80,28
THOMPSON, Peter John. 150 PROSPECT AVE 16323 #033-05-1970 L1973 **IM** *020
VIRGILE, Roger S. 312 13TH ST 16323 #050-02-1985 L1991 **OPH IM** *020 †35
WALKUP, Shelia Joan. ■ 16323 #055-01-1978 L1983 **IM** *074 †20

FRAZER – CHESTER

BATISH, Rajesh. ■ 19355 #495-29-1990 L1997 **NEP** *075
CABOT, Catherine M Foster. ■ 19355 #035-01-1972 L1979 **CD IM** *050 †20
D'ANDREA, Denise. 41 MOORES RD 19355 #010-02-1987 L1990 **NEP IM** *050 †20 ‡
GLAUSER, Elinor. 641 LANCASTER AVE 19355 #041-07-1957 L1958 **PUD PA** *071
PROCIUK, Peter Jos. 619 LANCASTER AVE, VILLAGE HALL CLINIC 19355 #068-01-1981 L1983 **IM** *020 †20
YOUAKIM, James Maurice. 41 MOORES RD 19355 #048-04-1989 L1993 **P SME** *050 †75

FREDERICK – MONTGOMERY

HUNSBERGER, Joseph Leidy. PO BOX 548 19435 #041-13-1935 L1936 **GP IM** *071
WENDELL, Kathleen E Kirk. ■ 19435 #035-01-1944 L1947 **PD OS** *071 †55

FREDERICKSBURG – LEBANON

MAY, Joseph William. ■ 17026 #041-14-2004 **PD** *100 †55
ROARK, Gary Lee. ■ 17026 #036-05-1989 L1994 **AN PME** *020 †05

FREDERICKTOWN – WASHINGTON

AKHTAR, Riffat. 1070 OLD NATIONAL PIKE, PIKE ROAD 15333 #704-16-1987 L1996 **IM** *020 †20
GLASSER, Stuart Allen. 1070 OLD NATIONAL PIKE 15333 #016-42-1974 L1978 **D** *020 †15
KUNKEL, George A. 1070 OLD NATIONAL PIKE 15333 #041-12-1952 L1953 **IM R** *071 †80
PLUTE, Rebecca Lynn. 1070 OLD NATIONAL PIKE 15333 #041-07-1997 L2001 **FM** *020 †18
SKIFFINGTON, Eugene W. 1070 OLD NATIONAL PIKE 15333 #055-02-1995 L1997 **FM** *020 †18
SUNG, Chun Mo. 1070 OLD NATIONAL PIKE 15333 #583-02-1956 L1977 **OTO GS** *071 †45
TAYLOR, Brian Terry. 1070 OLD NATIONAL PIKE 15333 #030-06-1982 L1988 **FM MDM** *020 †18
TRIPOLI, Charles James. 1070 OLD NATIONAL PIKE 15333 #041-12-1955 L1956 **FM** *071 †18
WHALEN, Thomas Jos. 1070 OLD NATIONAL PIKE 15333 #041-13-1965 L1966 **FM** *020

FREDONIA – MERCER

WELLS, Cynthia Mayquick. ■ 16124 #041-12-2002 L2002 **AN** *100 †05

FREEBURG – SNYDER

YINGLING, William Leonard. ■ 17827 #041-13-1971 L1972 **FM** *020 †18

FREEDOM – BEAVER

EL BARBARY, Aida Mounir. 723 ROOSEVELT BLVD 15042 #915-02-1978 L2003 **AN** *020

FREELAND – LUZERNE

SECHERESIU, Adrian. 415 CENTRE ST, A & E MEDICAL ASSOCIATES P 18224 #781-03-1984 L1990 **IM** *020

FREEPORT – ARMSTRONG

SUWAN, Nipapan. 419 MARKET ST, FREEPORT MED ASSOC 16229 #891-02-1967 L1973 **PD** *020 †55
SUWAN, Sakdidej. 419 MARKET ST 16229 #891-02-1968 L1973 **IM ID** *020 †20

FRENCHVILLE – CLEARFIELD

HICKS, James Thos. PO BOX 177 16836 #004-01-1956 L1957 **CLP** *071 †50

FURLONG – BUCKS

DE ANGELIS, Michael Alex. ■ 18925 #041-02-2001 L2003 **EM** *020 †16
MARDER, Harold Kay. 2100 ELDERBERRY LN 18925 #041-12-1975 L1982 **PN PD** *030 †55
PERATE, Alison Reed. ■ 18925 #041-15-2005 L2005 **AN** *012
PROPHETE, Judith. ■ 18925 #035-08-1978 L1988 **OBG** *020 †30
REAVEY-CANTWELL, Nelson H. PO BOX 258, 3864 SPRING VALLEY RD 18925 #035-01-1959 L1963 **IM END** *071
REYES, Jose Manuel. ■ 18925 #041-13-1978 L1979 **PTH** *020 †50
SUNDERMEYER, Mark Lee. ■ 18925 #028-03-2000 L2001 **HO** *020 †20
WAMIL, Artur Witold. ■ 18925 #759-06-1986 L2001 **N PPN** *020
WOLINSKY, Steven Ira. ■ 18925 #038-06-1980 L1994 **IM OS** *020 †20 ‡

GAINES – TIOGA

BELLER, Martin Leonard. ■ 16921 #035-01-1946 L1952 **ORS** *071 †40

GALETON – POTTER

CALLAHAN, Michael E. 30 RIVER ST 16922 #041-77-1972, ▲ L1973 **FM** *020 †18 ‡

GAP – LANCASTER

HARTLEY, David Walsh. 5275 LINCOLN HWY, COUNTY LINE MEDICAL 17527 #041-13-1986 L1987 **FM** *020 †18
HOGG, Susan M. 5275 LINCOLN HWY, COUNTY LINE MEDICAL 17527 #041-07-1978 L1979 **FM** *020 †18
KOCHEL, Randy L. 5275 LINCOLN HWY, COUNTY LINE MEDICAL 17527 #041-14-1983 L1986 **FM** *020 †18 ‡
SUMMERS, Kermit Leon. 760 WHITE HORSE RD 17527 #041-01-1960 L1961 **EM GP** *071 †16
TINDALL, Janice Clough. 5275 LINCOLN HWY, COUNTY LINE MEDICAL 17527 #041-09-1980 L1981 **FM** *071 †18

GARDNERS – ADAMS

BATT, Diane Marie. ■ 17324 #035-08-1990 L1990 **EM** *020 †16
DANIELS, Michael Owain. 1463 GOODYEAR RD 17324 #041-14-1978 L1986 **FPG AM** *020 †18
MC BETH, Orville G, Jr. 3375 CARLISLE RD, ADAMS CUMBERLAND MEDICAL C 17324 #041-14-1981 L1982 **FM** *020 †18 ‡
WAMPLER, David Lee. 3375 CARLISLE RD, ADAMS/CUMBERLAND FAMILY ME 17324 #051-04-1980 L1981 **FM** *020 †18
WELTMAN, Andre Chas. ■ 17324 #035-08-1990 L1995 **GPM** *062 †70

GARNET VALLEY – DELAWARE

CHIRINOS MEDINA, Julio A. ■ 19061 #737-11-1999 L2007 **CD** *020 †20
COPE, David Arthur. ■ 19061 #023-01-1958 L1959 **OTO PS** *071 †45
ELKIN, Rodney Moshemordec. 1440 CONCHESTER HWY STE 5A 19061 #041-01-1982 L1984 **IM IMG** *020 †20
GIOMETTI, Renee Marie. ■ 19061 #047-06-1990 L2001 **PCC IM** *020 †20
GROARK, James Gregory. 3807 HIGHLAND DR 19061 #035-03-1994 L1996 **IM** *020 †20
HAMILTON, Glenn David. ■ 19061 #041-02-1987 L1988 **FM MDM** *030 †18
KAPUR, Neeraj. ■ 19061 #496-09-1994 L2003 **AN PME** *020 †05 ‡
LIM, Manuel Tan. 1440 CONCHESTER HWY STE 5A, BOOTHWYN MED ASSOCS 19061 #748-01-1968 L1981 **N GP** *020
PARIKH, Shamik J. ■ 19061 #495-17-1995 L2004 **END** *020 †20,55 ‡
POLINSKY, Ronald John. ■ 19061 #023-01-1973 L1977 **N** *050 †75
RAHMAN, Abdul Nabi. ■ 19061 #023-07-1956 L1971 **N IM** *062
SHAH, Sonal Rohit. 1440 CONCHESTER HWY, STE 17C 19061 #041-15-1999 L2000 **FM** *020 †18
SHOR, Lawrence David. 43 CASSIN HILL RD 19061 #041-09-1967 L1968 **N** *071 †75
WOLFE, Katherine E. ■ 19061 #010-02-1994 L1998 **PTH** *100

GETTYSBURG – ADAMS

ACQUAAH, Theresa Yankey. ■ 17325 #039-01-2003 L2003 **OBG** *100
ADAIR, William James. 524 S WASHINGTON ST, GETTYSBURG FAMILY 17325 #041-02-2004 L2004 **FM** *020 †18
BAJAJ, Rajesh. 147 N WASHINGTON ST 17325 #495-45-1978 L1991 **GE** *020 †20
BARANSKI, Edward Jos. 453 S WASHINGTON ST 17325 #041-02-1959 L1960 **GS** *071 †85
BARYEH, Kwadwo Boadi. 450 S WASHINGTON ST, STE B 17325 #041-14-1999 L2003 **OBG** *020 †30
BEVILACQUA, Daniel F. 455 S WASHINGTON ST, STE 24 17325 #041-09-1970 L1971 **OPH** *020 †35
BJERKE, Kari Lynn. ■ 17325 #018-03-2003 L2004 **EM** *012
BLANK, Carol Ann. 11 HUNTERS TRL, GETTYSBURG PEDIATRICS 17325 #023-07-1984 L1999 **PD MG** *020 †55,19
BOBIN, John Jos. 147 GETTYS ST 17325 #041-09-1979 L1980 **CD** *020 †20

BOBONICH, Arlene Skurkis. 37 N 5TH ST 17325 #038-40-1992 L1995 **IM** *020 †20
CHANG, Yu Wen. 147 GETTYS ST 17325 #244-02-1970 L1993 **PTH** *020 †50
COWDERY, Susan Lynn. 423 S WASHINGTON ST 17325 #041-13-1982 L1984 **RHU OM** *020 †20
DAMJANOVIC, Dusan. 147 GETTYS ST, SERVICES 17325 #007-02-2002 L2003 **AN** *100 †05
DICKSON, Harrison Mc Crea. 55 W BROADWAY 17325 #041-01-1958 L1960 **GS GP** *020 †85
DOO, Gerald Kyi-loong. 147 GETTYS ST 17325 #242-09-1942 L1956 **AS IMG** *071
DUFENDACH, John Howard. 147 GETTYS ST 17325 #041-14-1980 L1981 **FM** *020 †18
ELLINGER, Geo Frederick. ■ 17325 #026-04-1935 L1935 **IM PHP** *071 †20
ELLSWORTH, Bettina Marie. 450 S WASHINGTON ST 17325 #051-04-1975 L1982 **OBG** *020 †30
EYER, Douglas Edward. 524 S WASHINGTON ST, GETTYSBURG FAMILY 17325 #041-12-1996 L1998 **FM** *020 †18
FLECKNER, Alan Norman. ■ 17325 #041-02-1960 L1965 **EM OBG** *062 †30,16
GAFFAR, Yousuf Abdul. 40 V-TWIN DR, STE 102 17325 #665-01-1998 L2006 **HO IM** *020 †20
GARAZO, Amy Beth. 147 GETTYS ST, THE GETTYSBURG HOSP 17325 #035-15-1994 L1999 **DR** *020 †80
GRACEY, Jack Gary. 147 GETTYS ST 17325 #041-12-1962 L1963 **CD IM** *071
GREY, Marijka Angelica. 37 N 5TH ST 17325 #023-01-2003 L2003 **IM** *020 †20
HAMMETT, James H. 147 GETTYS ST 17325 #041-13-1952 L1953 **FM** *071 †18
HARBACH, Harrison F. 147 GETTYS ST 17325 #041-13-1943 L1944 **FM AM** *071 †18
HELLER, Kimberly Ann. 450 S WASHINGTON ST, STE B 17325 #024-16-1985 L1989 **MFM** *030 †30
HOCH, Bradley Roy. 147 GETTYS ST 17325 #041-02-1974 L1975 **PD** *020 †55
HOFFMAN, Richard R, Jr. ■ 17325 #041-01-1969 L1970 **DR** *071 †80
HOLLAND, Timothy Wm. 147 GETTYS ST, DEPT EMER MEDCN 17325 #041-02-1979 L1980 **EM GP** *020 †16
IBIKUNLE, Jimmy O. 408 E MIDDLE ST 17325 #690-08-1991 L2001 **P** *020 †75
JAEGER, Scott Matthew. 11 HUNTERS TRL 17325 #023-07-1987 L1989 **PD** *020 †55
JIMENEZ, Marta. 820 CHAMBERSBURG RD 17325 #308-03-1994 L2003 **N** *020
JIVANJEE, Shafiq Qurban. 455 S WASHINGTON ST, STE 24 17325 #024-07-1995 L1999 **OPH** *020 †35
JONES, Joseph Chas. 147 GETTYS ST, GETTYSBURG DIAGNOSTIC 17325 #047-07-1970 L1980 **DR** *020 †80
KAGUYUTAN, Alfredo G. 450 S WASHINGTON ST 17325 #748-01-1958 L1972 **OBG** *071 †30
KAGUYUTAN, Ofelia L D. ■ 17325 #748-08-1959 L1971 **PD** *071 †55
KALLOZ, John Richard. 147 GETTYS ST, GETTYSBURG HOSP 17325 #041-14-1978 L1979 **IM IMG** *020 †20
KAMSLER, David Foster. 423 S WASHINGTON ST 17325 #041-09-1979 L1980 **IM** *020 †20
KARCHNER, Cathyrn Lea. 11 HUNTERS TRL, GETTYSBURG PEDIATRICS 17325 #041-14-2001 L2004 **PD** *020 †55
KRABLIN, Ronald. 423 S WASHINGTON ST 17325 #041-14-1971 L1974 **IM** *020 †20
KRUTER, Flavio Wainberg. 40 V-TWIN DR, STE 102 17325 #187-80-1978 L2003 **IM ON** *020 †20
KRZEMINSKI, Joseph Philip. 40 V-TWIN DR, STE 205 17325 #041-13-1984 L1986 **NS** *020 †25
LITTLE, Thomas Allan. 455 S WASHINGTON ST 17325 #041-14-1996 L1998 **ORS** *020 †40
MACKLE, Edward Jos. 147 GETTYS ST, SERVICES 17325 #041-02-1990 L1994 **AN** *020 †05
MAKKENCHERY, Rajesh. 450 S WASHINGTON ST 17325 #496-23-1995 L2006 **GS** *020
MANNING, James Aloysius. 508 S WASHINGTON ST 17325 #048-15-1984 L1990 **OTO** *020 †45
MARTIN, Horace F, III. 147 GETTYS ST 17325 #041-02-1980 L1981 **FM** *020 †18
MAXWELL, Henry L, Jr. 450 S WASHINGTON ST, STE C 17325 #041-02-1980 L1989 **GS** *071 †85
MC ARDLE, Gilbert Charles. 453 S WASHINGTON ST 17325 #049-01-1962 L1963 **GS** *071 †85
MC ARDLE, M J Tessaro. ■ 17325 #041-07-1961 L1962 **P CHP** *071 †75
MC GLAUGHLIN, Michael Jay. 147 GETTYS ST 17325 #041-02-1979 L1980 **FM** *020 †18
MC KEE, Timothy Russell. 450 S WASHINGTON ST, STE C 17325 #041-13-1986 L1987 **GS** *020 †85
MICHAEL, Dwight Ira. 524 S WASHINGTON ST, GETTYSBURG FAMILY 17325 #041-12-1982 L1983 **FM** *020 †18
MICKELSON, Anthony B. ■ 17325 #654-01-1997 L2000 **P CHP** *020 †75
MILLER, Ivan Leroy, Jr. 455 S WASHINGTON ST 17325 #041-09-1976 L1987 **ORS** *020 †40
MILLER, Kelly Patrick. 423 S WASHINGTON ST 17325 #041-14-1989 L1991 **IM** *020 †20
MILLS, James Douglas. 147 GETTYS ST 17325 #055-01-1991 L1996 **CD** *020 †20
MIRANDA, Hernan Emilio. 147 GETTYS ST, GETTYSBURG HOSPITAL 17325 #737-06-1982 L2006 **IM** *020 †20
MONDEJAR, Magdalena D. ■ 17325 #748-10-1965 L1975 **PTH** *020 †50
NELSON, David Krug. 11 HUNTERS TRL 17325 #041-02-1997 L2000 **PD** *020 †55
NICHOLSON, Walter Jos. 455 S WASHINGTON ST, STE 23 17325 #041-12-1969 L1976 **CD** *020 †20
NICHOLSON, William Jay. 147 GETTYS ST 17325 #041-14-1998 L2006 **IC** *020 †20
PENNINGS, Laura Snyder. 149 HANOVER ST 17325 #023-07-1997 L1999 **FM** *020 †18
PHAM, Chinh Ngoc. 450 S WASHINGTON ST, 3RD FLOOR, SUITE C 17325 #023-01-2001 L2006 **GS** *020
PORTER, Edgar Lee. ■ 17325 #045-01-1939 L1940 **P** *071 †75
QUEEN, George Noyes. 147 GETTYS ST 17325 #041-09-1985 L1986 **AN** *020 †05
RAHMAN, Rukhsana Khatoon. 147 GETTYS ST, GETTYSBURG DIAGNOSTIC 17325 #965-01-1978 L1984 **R** *020 †80
RAST, Robyne Gail. 236 WEST ST, GETTYSBURG AMBULATORY SURG 17325 #048-02-1988 L2007 **AN** *020 †05
REDDY, Uma M. 455 S WASHINGTON ST, STE 22 17325 #043-01-1991 L1997 **OBG** *020 †30
RESCINITI, Mark Alfred. 147 GETTYS ST, SERVICES 17325 #041-09-1985 L1986 **AN** *020 †05
REYBURN, John A, Jr. ■ 17325 #051-01-1968 L1968 **AM IM** *020 †20
RICE, Robert Lamar. 40 V-TWIN DR, STE 102 17325 #041-12-2000 L2006 **HO** *020 †20
ROSENBACH, Stefan Patrick. 147 GETTYS ST, GETTYSBURG HOSPITAL EMERGE 17325 #041-02-2000 L2001 **EM** *020
SALOTTO, Arnold Gennaro. 423 S WASHINGTON ST 17325 #041-13-1988 L1994 **NS** *020 †25
SCHLEGEL, Robert J, Jr. 423 S WASHINGTON ST 17325 #034-01-1982 L1988 **NS** *020 †25
SCHRYVER, Thomas Edward. 147 GETTYS ST 17325 #010-02-1985 L1992 **CD IM** *020 †20
SCHULER, Brian Thomas. 147 GETTYS ST 17325 #038-44-1999 L2006 **CD** *020 †20
SHAH, Johar Ali. 408 E MIDDLE ST 17325 #704-09-1992 L2003 **P** *020
SHAH, Satish Amratlal. 20 EXPEDITION TRL, STE 101 17325 #495-23-1980 L1984 **ON** *020
SIVENDRAN, Tharmalingam. 455 S WASHINGTON ST, STE 24 17325 #220-01-1967 L1979 **OPH** *020 †35
SMITH, Talbot Lee. 455 S WASHINGTON ST, STE 22 17325 #023-01-2002 L2003 **FM** *020 †18
SPAGNOLI, Marie Virginia. 147 GETTYS ST, GETTYSBURG DIAGNOSTIC 17325 #041-02-1980 L1984 **DR** *020 †80
STEINOUR, William Jos. ■ 17325 #041-02-1979 L1981 **EM** *020 †16
STERLING, Robert Laurence. 820 CHAMBERSBURG RD 17325 #051-07-2001 L2005 **CN** *020 †75
SZOKE, Edward Ernest. 11 HUNTERS TRL 17325 #041-14-1978 L1981 **PD** *020 †55
TAUSCHER, Eric Shawn. 105 PALACE DR 17325 #023-01-1994 L2000 **IM** *020 †20
TRIPI, Joseph Ernest. 18 DEATRICK DR 17325 #035-06-1972 L1978 **ORS** *020 †40
TYLER, Allen Eugene. 820 CHAMBERSBURG RD 17325 #041-02-1979 L1980 **N** *020 †75
VAKILI, Bahman Fakhimi. ■ 17325 #517-01-1962 L1968 **U** *071 †95
VIRAMGAMA, Kirankumar. 124 W HIGH ST 17325 #495-22-1990 L1996 **PCC** *020 †20
VISWANATHAN, Byravan. 147 GETTYS ST 17325 #495-34-1962 L1981 **IM HEM** *020 †20
VU, Khanh Hung. 147 GETTYS ST, GETTYSBURG DIAGNOSTIC 17325 #041-07-1993 L1999 **DR** *020 †80
WASSERMAN, Adam Ira. 524 S WASHINGTON ST, GETTYSBURG FAMILY 17325 #051-01-1988 L1990 **FM EM** *020 †18
WEISS, Raymond Butler. 147 GETTYS ST 17325 #026-04-1965 L1967 **ON** *050 †20
WHITLOCK, Duane Michael. 455 S WASHINGTON ST, STE 24 17325 #023-01-1999 L2002 **OPH** *020 †35 ‡
WINER, Joel Warren. 423 S WASHINGTON ST 17325 #021-01-1985 L1986 **NS** *020 †25
WOOD, Elizabeth T. 20 E HIGH ST 17325 #056-05-1967 L1969 **FM** *071 †18
WOOD, Mary Elizabeth W. 20 E HIGH ST 17325 #011-03-1973 L1982 **DR R** *100 †80
WOODS, Lon D. 455 S WASHINGTON ST, STE 16 17325 #005-14-1979 L1984 **ORS** *020
ZESHONSKY, Paul Joseph. 524 S WASHINGTON ST, GETTYSBURG FAMILY 17325 #010-01-1984 L1990 **FM** *020 †18
ZUCKERMAN, Mitchell Evan. 147 GETTYS ST, SERVICES 17325 #035-06-1984 L1990 **AN** *020 †05 ‡

GIBSONIA – ALLEGHENY

BAFNA, Kala. 2170 GRANDEUR DR 15044 #496-01-1985 L1996 **CCM** *020 †20
BALDERSTON, Virginia M. 5318 RANALLI DR, STE 1 15044 #041-12-1989 L1991 **PUD** *020 †20
BASSI, Florence H. ■ 15044 #055-01-1990 L1998 **OPH** *071 †35
BAYLEY, Matthew Douglas. ■ 15044 #041-01-2003 L2004 **IM** *100
BROWN-ABBOTT, Lorna P. ■ 15044 #033-05-1982 L1987 **IM** *020
BRUEHLMAN, Richard Dean. 5548 WILLIAM FLYNN HWY, RENAISSANCE FAMILY PRACTIC 15044 #041-02-1982 L1983 **FM EM** *030 †18
BRUNGO, John Anthony. ■ 15044 #056-06-1962 L1963 **PD** *071 †55
CARIGNAN, Coleen Anne. 5830 MERIDIAN RD 15044 #016-43-1992 L1994 **IM** *020 †20
CAUNA, Dzidra. ■ 15044 #594-01-1943 **OS** *071
CLISTA, Brian Thaddeus. 5321 WILLIAM FLYNN HWY 15044 #041-12-1992 L1994 **PD** *020 †55
CUTLER, Stanley Mark. 5830 MERIDIAN RD 15044 #041-13-1980 L1985 **FM FPG** *020 †18
DEAKIN, Susan Luse. 5375 WILLIAM FLYNN HWY 15044 #041-77-1992, ▲ L1996 **IM** *020 †20
DEMARCO, Andrew Dominic. 5375 WILLIAM FLYNN HWY 15044 #038-45-1989 L1992 **IM** *020 †20
DE SILVA, M B S. 364 OLD BABCOCK TRL 15044 #220-01-1967 L1974 **EM FM** *020 †16
DICENZO, Valentina Elena. 5321 WILLIAM FLYNN HWY, C C P HEALTH QUEST PEDS 15044 #041-12-1992 L1994 **PD** *020 †55
EDWARDS, Rosemary H. ■ 15044 #041-12-1984 L1985 **BBK** *020 †50
FAGHFOORY, Katie Parand. ■ 15044 #010-01-1999 L2001 **GE** *020 †20
FANTASKI, Mark R. 5318 RANALLI DR, STE 1 15044 #041-02-1990 L1993 **IM** *020 †20
GILMOUR, Sara Mendell. 5548 WILLIAM FLYNN HWY 15044 #023-01-1991 L1993 **FM** *020 †18
GRADOWSKI, Joel Francis. ■ 15044 #041-02-2004 L2004 **PTH** *012
GREENE, Robert Francis. ■ 15044 #539-01-1958 L1961 **GS** *071 †85
HANNA, Salah Girgis. ■ 15044 #330-03-1965 L1971 **FM GS** *071 †18
HEIDENREICH, Kelly Rush. 5375 WILLIAM FLYNN HWY 15044 #028-02-1996 L1999 **PD** *020 †55
HELLER, Matthew Thomas. ■ 15044 #041-12-2001 L2001 **IM** *020 †80
HOYSON, Gregory Mitchell. 5375 WILLIAM FLYNN HWY 15044 #041-12-1982 L1983 **PD ADL** *020 †55
IBINSON, James William. ■ 15044 #038-40-2006 L2006 **AN** *012
IQBAL, Zafar. 205 ESSEX CT 15044 #704-09-1978 L1990 **NEP IM** *020 †20
JONES, Shadrach H, IV. 321 IVY DR 15044 #041-14-1985 L1986 **IM** *020 †20
KERN, John M, Jr. ■ 15044 #041-12-1975 L1976 **FM OM** *071 †18
KHALID, Asif. ■ 15044 #704-25-1993 L2001 **GE** *020 †20
KIM, Yong Min. ■ 15044 #583-02-1954 L1984 **IMG** *020
KOLLI, Sireesha. ■ 15044 #041-15-2004 L2004 **CHP** *012
KOWAL, Charles Dale. ■ 15044 #038-40-1976 L1982 **IM** *100
LANGE, Carl K. ■ 15044 #422-01-1983 L1987 **GS** *020 †85
LEVIS, Michael Paul. ■ 15044 #028-34-1958 L1966 **GS** *071 †85
LIDEN, Craig Bradford. 4156 KENNETH DR 15044 #038-40-1972 L1977 **OS PD** *020 †55
LIPPERT, Louis Copeland. ■ 15044 #041-13-1947 L1948 **R NM** *071 †80
LOWERY, Clinton Hershey. ■ 15044 #041-12-1955 L1956 **GS** *030 †85
MANDELL, Gordon Lee. 7000 W GROVE TRCE 15044 #023-01-1981 L1988 **AN OBG** *050 †05
MANN, Geoffrey Stuart. 182 WEDGEWOOD DR 15044 #021-01-1990 L2002 **EM** *020 †16
MANTELLA, Domenic Michael. ■ 15044 #035-09-2007 L2007 **FP** *012
MC KELVY, Maribel. ■ 15044 #041-07-1954 L1955 **PD** *071
MC MAHON, Brenda Lynn. ■ 15044 #010-01-1995 L1998 **PM** *020 †60
MUIGAI, David Mucuha. ■ 15044 #577-01-1994 L2002 **CCM** *100 †20
MUTHUKRISHNAN, Ashok. ■ 15044 #495-61-1995 L2005 **NM** *100
NATHAN, Girija. ■ 15044 #495-16-1970 L1980 **PTH** *020 †50
NEMIROFF, Paul Michael. ■ 15044 #005-14-1981 L1982 **OTO** *071 †45
NUNNA, Nagabhushanam G. ■ 15044 #495-37-1961 L1972 **IM HEM** *071 †20
PAWAR, Surendra Vasantrao. 116 PINEHURST LN, ALLE-KISKI MEDICAL CENTER 15044 #495-23-1973 L1979 **DR NR** *020 †80
PAYAN, Hushang Mofakham. WINDFALL LANE 15044 #517-01-1951 L1985 **PTH CLP** *071 †50
RASZEWSKI, Richard Leo. 620 WARRENDALE RD, TREESDALE MARKET SQUARE 15044 #041-12-1986 L1996 **PS** *020 †65
REICH, Sanford Martin. ■ 15044 #035-03-1965 L1995 **OS** *030 †20
REIGEL, Donald Harry. 5178 POLO FIELDS DR 15044 #056-05-1963 L1973 **NS** *071 †25
RODRIGUES, James Jos. 5375 WILLIAM FLYNN HWY 15044 #010-01-1991 L1994 **PD** *020 †55
SHOBANA, Ganesan. 5830 MERIDIAN RD 15044 #495-16-1987 L1997 **IM** *020 †20
SHOLOSH, Biatta. ■ 15044 #035-08-1999 L2004 **DR** *100 †80 ‡
SILK, David Garett. 5375 WILLIAM FLYNN HWY 15044 #033-06-1998 L2001 **PD** *020 †55
SPRATT, Donna Lee. ■ 15044 #041-13-1998 L2001 **AN** *020
STEIGERWALT, Robert D, Jr. ■ 15044 #561-17-1977 L1979 **OPH** *020 †35

■ = Address Information Privacy Protected

STINE, Ann Menzel. 5321 WM FLYNN HWY, 5321 WM 15044 #023-07-1986 L1989 **PD** *020 †55
SUDOL, Katarzyna Sophie. 5375 WILLIAM FLYNN HWY 15044 #041-14-1996 L1999 **PD** *020 †55
SUMMERS, Susan Kay. ■ 15044 #035-45-1985 L1988 **EM FM** *020 †16
SWANSON, Heidi E. 5321 WILLIAM FLYNN HWY 15044 #025-07-1988 L1991 **PD** *020 †55
SWEENEY, Patrick Edward. ■ 15044 #035-06-2003 **GS** *100
THORNTON, Helen Ruth. 5548 WM FLYNN HWY 15044 #055-02-1985 L1986 **FM** *020 †18
UDEKWU, Catherine Ngozi. 5321 WILLIAM FLYNN HWY, HEALTH QUEST PEDS 15044 #690-04-1988 L1996 **PD** *020 †55
VANDERWEELE, Robert Alan. ■ 15044 #041-15-2007 L2007 **IM** *012
VANEGAS, Maria Eugenia. ■ 15044 #264-13-1985 L2003 **DR** *020 †18
WILSON, Jennifer Jocuns. ■ 15044 #035-45-1995 L1997 **GS** *020
ZACHARIAH, Ann. ■ 15044 #495-37-1995 L2001 **PYG** *020 †75

GILBERTSVILLE — MONTGOMERY

CORSON, Ann F. 1885 SWAMP PIKE, MEDICAL WELLNESS CTR 19525 #041-01-1982 L1983 **FM** *020 †18
KENNEDY, David Shawn. 1885 SWAMP PIKE, STE 108 19525 #041-09-1995 L2000 **PD** *020 †55

GIRARD — ERIE

BISHOP, Deborah Elaine. 5165 IMPERIAL PKWY 16417 #038-44-1993 L1995 **FM** *020 †18
GILMORE, Frederick R. ■ 16417 #024-01-1944 L1947 **DR OS** *071 †80
HILBERT, Wesley A. 5165 IMPERIAL PKWY 16417 #038-44-1985 L1996 **FM** *020 †18
JUANG, Richard C. 318 MAIN ST E 16417 #385-04-1967 L1976 **GS GP** *020
TREUSCH, Lisa A. 5165 IMPERIAL PKWY 16417 #038-44-1992 L1994 **FM** *020 †18

GLADWYNE — MONTGOMERY

ABRAMS, Peggy Lynn. 1221 LAFAYETTE RD 19035 #041-07-1982 L1983 **PM** *020 †60 ‡
ALLISON, Samuel D. ■ 19035 #040-02-1936 L1943 **D** *071 †15
ASCH, David Alan. ■ 19035 #035-20-1984 L1985 **IM** *020 †20
BARNARD, Frank Geo. ■ 19035 #041-09-1934 L1935 **GS** *071
BONAN, A Ferdinand. ■ 19035 #035-09-1950 L1954 **P CHP** *071 †55
BORA, Frank Wm. 1550 MONK RD, GLADWYNE 19035 #035-09-1954 L1962 **HS ORS** *020 †40
BRINSTER, Clayton Joseph. ■ 19035 #041-01-2005 L2005 **GS** *012
BURKEY, Adam Robert. ■ 19035 #010-02-1998 L2002 **APM** *020 †75
BYRNE, Christopher Hilles. ■ 19035 #041-01-2003 L2003 **GS** *012
CHUANG, Emil. 1435 WESLEYS RUN 19035 #143-03-1984 L1994 **GE** *020 †55
DESAI, Mohan Gopalji. ■ 19035 #496-38-1951 L1977 **R** *071 †80
DE VOE, Arthur Gerard. ■ 19035 #035-20-1935 L1948 **OPH** *071 †35
FALLAHNEJAD, Anne C. ■ 19035 #041-09-1972 L1973 **PTH** *020
FRANCISCO-SOLON, Maria E. ■ 19035 #748-01-1989 L1997 **CHP** *040 †75
FRENCH, Pamela Poinier. ■ 19035 #041-07-1986 L1989 **ID IM** *020
GERSH, Richard Neil. ■ 19035 #035-08-1992 L1994 **OBG** *020 †30 ‡
GILBERT, Robert P. ■ 19035 #016-06-1943 L1966 **IM CD** *071 †20
GOLDSCHMIDT, Herbert. ■ 19035 #407-32-1951 L1962 **D** *072 †15
GOLSHAN, Nasrin. ■ 19035 #517-05-1974 L1977 **ID IM** *020
GOYAL, Kavitha Gurijala. ■ 19035 #055-01-1993 L1996 **IM** *020 †20
HAMMOND, N Le Roy, III. ■ 19035 #041-02-1966 L1969 **ORS** *071 †40
HARDER, Debra M Lew. ■ 19035 #038-44-1985 L1986 **D** *012
HEIDARY, Noushin. ■ 19035 #035-19-2005 L2005 **D** *012
HIRSCH, Hildegard. ■ 19035 #561-16-1937 **PD** *071
JOHNSTON, Frank B. ■ 19035 #041-02-1943 L1944 **IM** *071
JOHNSTON, Jean Caton. ■ 19035 #041-13-1951 L1952 **OS IM** *071
JOSEPH, Raymond Edward. ■ 19035 #010-01-1972 L1976 **IM** *020 †20
KATZ, Sheila Moriber. ■ 19035 #036-07-1966 L1972 **PTH** *071 †50
KAYE, Donald. ■ 19035 #035-19-1957 L1969 **IM ID** *030 †20
KNORR, John Keyser, III. ■ 19035 #041-02-1942 L1943 **GYN** *072 †30
KOSOVE, Jason Eric. ■ 19035 #041-15-2003 L2003 **DR** *012
KOWLESSAR, Muriel H C. ■ 19035 #035-01-1951 L1966 **PD** *071 †55
LEVINE, Sanford. ■ 19035 #050-02-1965 L1975 **IM PUD** *020 †20
LEWIS, Daniel Wm. ■ 19035 #041-02-1944 L1944 **CD IM** *071 †20
MENSCHIK, Elliot Dov. ■ 19035 #041-01-2001 *100
MILLER, Matthew Chas. 1133 CLUB HOUSE RD 19035 #041-02-1981 L1982 **IM** *020 †20
MORRISON, Gail. ■ 19035 #041-01-1971 L1974 **NEP IM** *020 †20
MULHOLLAND, John Kevin. ■ 19035 #041-02-2000 L2002 **D DMP** *020 †15
NAGLE, Frank O, Jr. ■ 19035 #041-09-1945 L1946 **OPH** *071 †35
NAST, Philip Robt. ■ 19035 #035-20-1954 L1955 **GE IM** *071 †20
OWEN, Oliver Elon. ■ 19035 #007-02-1962 L1968 **IM END** *071 †20
PARHAD, Irma Malcolm. ■ 19035 #016-43-1973 L1977 **N** *075 †75
PENDERGRASS, Henry P. ■ 19035 #041-01-1952 L1958 **R NM** *071 †28
RENTHAL, A Gerald. ■ 19035 #035-01-1955 L1974 **PHP DR** *071
RUSHING, Susan Elizabeth. ■ 19035 #008-01-2005 L2007 **P** *012
SAFIER, Shannon David. ■ 19035 #033-06-2000 L2001 **OP OSM** *020
SAFIER, Tracie Michelle. ■ 19035 #041-02-2002 L2002 **PD** *020 †55
TOBIAS, Gordon L. ■ 19035 #041-09-1952 L1953 **U** *071 †95
VESSEL, Simin. ■ 19035 #517-05-1971 L1973 **PD PDA** *020
WEXLIN, Donald Jos. ■ 19035 #035-45-1958 L1960 **IM** *071

GLASSPORT — ALLEGHENY

REYES, Vicente Edgardo S. 624 MONONGAHELA AVE 15045 #748-01-1971 L1978 **IM** *020 †20

GLEN MILLS — DELAWARE

ALI, Waheeda F. ■ 19342 #704-20-1987 L1996 **IM** *020 †20
ARNOLD, Ryan Coleman. ■ 19342 #005-12-2004 L2006 **EM** *100
ARREDONDO, Matthew John. 300 EVERGREEN DR, STE 310 19342 #033-06-1998 L2001 **FM** *020 †18

BARTAL, Sharon Ann. ■ 19342 #041-07-1987 **IM** *020 †20
BASH, Evan Karl. 300 EVERGREEN DR, PREMIER ORTHOPAEDIC & 19342 #041-02-1982 L1983 **ORS** *020 †40
BENESKI, Daniel Anthony. ■ 19342 #041-02-1984 L1985 **AN** *020 †05
BERKOWITZ, Scott Darrell. 15 IRIS LN 19342 #041-02-1979 L1980 **HEM PHM** *050 †20
BONILLA, Luis Augusto. 300 EVERGREEN DR 19342 #042-01-2000 L2005 **GS** *020 †85 ‡
BRITT-KIMMINS, Allison H. 300 EVERGREEN DR STE 160 19342 #041-02-1994 L1996 **D** *020 †15
CABRY, Robert Joseph, Jr. 300 EVERGREEN DR, PREMIER ORTHOPAEDIC & 19342 #041-02-1991 L1998 **FSM FM** *020 †18 ‡
CAREY, Sharon Lee. ■ 19342 #025-07-1971 L1988 **P** *020
CELELLO, Thomas Frederic. 300 EVERGREEN DR, STE 150 19342 #035-03-1973 L2005 **IM** *020 †20
CHILES, Kelly Alison. ■ 19342 #041-14-2008 *012
COLLAZZO, Lisa. 300 EVERGREEN DR STE 210, SOUTHEAST MEDICAL IMAGING 19342 #023-01-1993 L1997 **DR** *020 †80
CONROY, Kelly Joseph. ■ 19342 #041-02-1997 L1999 **EM** *020
CRONIN, Dennis Wm. 300 EVERGREEN DR 19342 #041-01-1968 L1969 **GS** *020 †85
DAGOSTINO, Francesco. ■ 19342 #561-17-1949 L1955 **GP** *020
DESANCTIS, Armand N, Jr. 45 CREEK RD 19342 #035-09-1977 L1979 **IM** *020
DREYER, Michael Stephen. 1766 WILMINGTON PIKE, KIDS FIRST CHADDS FORD 19342 #041-13-1990 L1996 **PD** *020 †55
GABROY, Allen Shuart. 300 EVERGREEN DR 19342 #041-09-1971 L1972 **GS CCS** *020 †85
GIAMMATTEI, Frank Presby. 300 EVERGREEN DR, PREMIER ORTHOPAEDIC & 19342 #038-41-1980 L1982 **ORS** *020 †40
GIULIANI, Nicholas A, III. 736 BALTIMORE PIKE, CONCORD COMMONS PROF CNTR 19342 #041-13-1990 L1993 **FM** *020 †18
GOLDBERG, Ronald J. 1788 WILMINGTON PIKE, STE 2200 19342 #025-07-1984 L1986 **PD** *020
GREENBERG, Jared Scott. ■ 19342 #041-01-2004 L2006 **PM** *012
HEANEY, Madeleine E. 300 EVERGREEN DR, STE 150 19342 #035-45-1993 L2006 **IM** *020 †20
HUMMER, Charles D, III. 300 EVERGREEN DR, PREMIER ORTHOPAEDIC & 19342 #041-02-1989 L1991 **ORS OSM** *020 †40
KASPER, Donald John. STONY BANK RD 19342 #041-09-1956 L1957 **R** *020 †80
KIPP, Charles Maurice. ■ 19342 #041-02-1958 L1959 **AN** *020 †40
KUTZ, Bethany Eve. 1766 WILMINGTON PIKE, KIDSFIRST CHADDS FORD 19342 #041-15-2002 L2002 **PD** *020 †55
LAMOREUX, Michele Renee. 24 ANNESLEY DR 19342 #035-19-1994 L1997 **FM** *020 †18
LIBERI, Alfred A. ■ 19342 #041-09-1941 L1946 **DR** *071 †80
LOZANO-CELIS, Maria Consu. ■ 19342 #264-16-1996 **P** *100
LUTZ, R Bruce. 300 EVERGREEN DR, PREMIER ORTHOPAEDIC & 19342 #041-02-1982 L1984 **ORS** *020 †40
MAKI, Junsuke. ■ 19342 #035-08-2004 L2007 **GE** *012 †20
MATSUMURA, Martin E. 272 WILLITS WAY 19342 #038-06-1993 L1995 **CD** *020 †20
MC CANN, Tomi Janette. 736 BALTIMORE PIKE, STE 6 19342 #041-09-1980 L1984 **IM** *020 †20
MC GLYNN, James Thomas. 300 EVERGREEN DR, PREMIER ORTHOPAEDIC & 19342 #010-02-1982 L1991 **ORS** *020 †40 ‡
MELTON, Susan Mc Mullen. 425 FEATHERBED LN 19342 #041-02-1986 L1987 **IM** *071 †20
MENDEL, Kenneth D. 300 EVERGREEN DR, STE 140 19342 #035-47-1978 L1983 **CD IM** *020 †20
MESMER, Roselle Dagostino. 300 EVERGREEN DR, STE 140 19342 #041-09-1993 L1996 **CD** *020 †20
MUETTERTIES, Kurt Andrew. 300 EVERGREEN DR, STE 210 19342 #005-19-1992 L1998 **VIR** *020 †80 ‡
PHAETON, Rebecca. ■ 19342 #055-02-2004 L2005 **OBG** *012
RAMPRASAD, Krishnamurthy. ■ 19342 #495-04-1976 L1978 **DR** *020 †80
RAVISHANKAR, Raman. ■ 19342 #495-61-1988 L1997 *020
RAVISHANKAR, Sudha. ■ 19342 #495-59-1991 L1998 **PD** *020 †55
RENCIC, Adrienne. 1102 BALTIMORE PIKE, STE 202 19342 #041-02-1998 L2003 **D** *020 †15 ‡
ROOKLIN, Anthony Robt. 300 EVERGREEN DR, ASTHMA & ALLERGY 19342 #041-02-1972 L1976 **AI PD** *020 †55,03
SAEED, Sherin Fatima. ■ 19342 #704-09-1997 L2006 **IM** *012
SCHOFFSTALL, John Martz. ■ 19342 #036-01-1984 L1985 **EM** *020 †16
SEGRETI, Francis Matthew. ■ 19342 #023-01-2002 L2005 **PD** *100 †55
STRANSKY, Kristina Louise. ■ 19342 #041-02-2008 *012
SUTTON, Robert Michael. 11102 ELAM DR 19342 #041-12-2002 L2002 **CCP** *012 †55
THOMPSON, Elmer Lee. ■ 19342 #041-09-1956 L1957 **GP OS** *071
TIRO, Allan C. 282 STANTON CT 19342 #748-02-1971 L1980 **NPM GS** *050
WHITNEY, Douglas Alan. ■ 19342 #041-13-1984 L1985 **P** *012 †05
WHITNEY, Leslie Winfield. ■ 19342 #041-13-1944 L1945 **GS** *071 †85
WILF, Theodore Jos. ■ 19342 #041-02-1967 L1975 **P** *020 †75 ‡
WOLFE, Raymond M, Jr. 300 EVERGREEN DR, PREMIER ORTHOPAEDIC & 19342 #010-02-1995 L2000 **ORS** *020 †40
YOW, Michael Vernon. 300 EVERGREEN DR, STE 140 19342 #012-01-1968 L1974 **CD** *020 †20
ZORANSKI, Bernard S. 1788 WILMINGTON PIKE, STE 2400 19342 #041-77-1980, ▲ L1981 **IM NEP** *020
ZURBACH, James Michael. 300 EVERGREEN DR, PREMIER ORTHOPAEDIC & 19342 #041-14-1980 L1989 **ORS** *020 †40
ZUSSMAN, Debra Rutstein. 1766 WILMINGTON PIKE 19342 #041-12-1984 L1985 **PD** *020 †55

GLEN RIDDLE LIMA — DELAWARE

CONTOSTAVLOS, Dimitri L. FAIR ACRES ROUTE 352 19037 #539-03-1961 L1971 **FOP PTH** *062 †50

GLEN ROCK — YORK

ALTLAND, Robert Clarence. 14 WATER ST 17327 #041-09-1958 L1959 **FM** *071
SCHWARTZ, Bradford Benj. ■ 17327 #051-01-1961 L1978 **P** *020 †95,75

GLENMOORE — CHESTER

ANDAL, Andres Hernandez. GUDULUSIA INDIAN RUN RD 19343 #748-01-1958 L1968 **AN** *071 †05

MANGE, Kevin Carl. 1885 FAIRVIEW RD 19343 #041-02-1992 L1996 **IM** *020 †20
MULLIN, Kathleen Mary. ■ 19343 #041-13-1981 L1983 **IM** *020 †20
OLDHAM, Erica Joan. 1230 POTTSTOWN PIKE, STE 1 19343 #041-07-1993 L1996 **IM** *020 †20
REIDELL, John Stewart. ■ 19343 #041-09-1967 L1968 **GS** *020 †85
UHLER, Walter Miller. ■ 19343 #041-02-1943 L1944 **IM GP** *071
WINE LEE, Lara Judith. ■ 19343 #041-01-2007 L2007 **PD** *012

GLENOLDEN — DELAWARE

CALDERON, Maria Monica Ro. ■ 19036 #748-01-2000 L2003 **IM** *100 †20
GREEN, Holly Lynn. 39 S CHESTER PIKE 19036 #033-06-1997 L1999 **FM** *020 †18
HSU, Antony Poyu. ■ 19036 #035-19-2005 L2005 **EM** *012
KESHISHIAN, Michael Arsen. 39 S CHESTER PIKE 19036 #913-38-1973 L1984 **IM CD** *020
MIRANDA, Cesar H. ■ 19036 #649-05-1961 **GYN OBG** *020 †30
VOGEL, Adolph Whitten. 343 S CHESTER PIKE BOX 4 19036 #041-01-1945 L1946 **OPH** *071 †35
ZIEGLER, Elizabeth Sower. 39 S CHESTER PIKE 19036 #043-01-1997 L2000 **FM** *020 †18

GLENSHAW — ALLEGHENY

ARORA, Sandeep. ■ 15116 #495-45-1998 L2003 **CD** *012 †20
AYUYANG, Herminia Quilala. ■ 15116 #748-01-1969 L1975 **GP** *020
BROCKLEHURST, William W. ■ 15116 #038-45-2006 L2006 **EM** *012
BROWN, Stacey Lin. ■ 15116 #038-45-2007 L2007 **FP** *012
CONERMANN, Till Jost. ■ 15116 #041-15-2001 L2001 **APM** *100 †05
DIDOMENICO, Paul Julian. ■ 15116 #041-02-2006 L2006 **OTO** *012
FAGBUYI, Daniel B. ■ 15116 #010-01-1999 L2005 **PEM** *012 †55
GIBSON, William Albert S. ■ 15116 #041-12-1942 L1943 **D** *072 †15
HILL, Justin David. ■ 15116 #026-04-2003 L2004 **DR** *012
HOLTZ, Andrea Susan. ■ 15116 #051-07-2008 *012
HUGHAN, Kara Nicole. ■ 15116 #038-45-2004 L2007 **PDE** *012 †55
JAMIESON, Patrick Wm. ■ 15116 #038-40-1981 L1983 **N** *050 †75
JERABEK, Jay John. ■ 15116 #041-09-1979 L1980 **FM** *020 †18
KOEHLER, E Lucille Morgan. ■ 15116 #041-07-1949 L1950 **GPM GP** *071
MC HUGH, Elmer F. ■ 15116 #051-04-1951 L1954 **CD IM** *020 †20
MEZU, Ure Laura. ■ 15116 #305-01-2003 L2006 **CD** *012 †20
NELLIS, Kurt Jos. ■ 15116 #041-12-1983 L1984 **IM** *020 †20
O'KEEFE, James F, Jr. ■ 15116 #041-12-1953 L1954 **IM** *071
PANDEY, Pragati. ■ 15116 #495-38-2002 L2007 **FP** *012
PARWANI, Anil Vasdev. ■ 15116 #038-06-1999 L2003 **PTH** *020 †50 ‡
PERKS, Valerie Joanne. 3447 HARTS RUN RD 15116 #016-01-1980 L1990 **EM** *020 †20,16
ROMERO, Jennifer Rose. 3394 SAXONBURG BLVD, STE 600 15116 #041-12-2000 L2001 **PD** *020 †55 ‡
SANCHEZ, Gustavo. 920 GARDEN PL 15116 #737-01-1964 L1967 **IM** *075
SEAMAN, Craig Daniel. ■ 15116 #055-02-2008 *012
SERAFY, Michael Mourad. ■ 15116 #330-03-1959 L1971 **GPM GP** *071
SILVAGGIO, Teresa. ■ 15116 #041-12-1986 L1987 **OM** *062 †70
SNYDER, Allen Perry. 3390 SAXONBURG BLVD, STE 250 15116 #021-01-1970 L1974 **GS** *071 †85
TARASI, Paul Glenn, Jr. ■ 15116 #041-12-2008 L2008 *012
THEERAKULSTIT, Virachai. 120 LAMMERT DR 15116 #891-01-1965 L1973 **TS** *020 †85
THOMAS, Danny George. ■ 15116 #016-06-2002 L2002 **PEM** *012 †55
USMAN, Mahmood Ahmed. 1901 LOUISE DR 15116 #035-09-1988 L1990 **N PYG** *020

GLENSIDE — MONTGOMERY

BROWNSTEIN, Elliott. 115 E GLENSIDE AVE, STE 9 19038 #041-13-1979 L1981 **IM** *020 †20
CAPRIOTTI, Kara Dixon. ■ 19038 #041-15-2005 L2005 **D** *012
FERRIS, Allison Hollabaug. ■ 19038 #041-15-2005 L2007 **IM** *012
FILMYER, Edward A, Jr. 2220 MOUNT CARMEL AVE 19038 #041-02-1944 L1944 **PD** *071
FISCHER, Paula Jane K. ■ 19038 #041-07-1974 L1980 **CHP PYA** *020 †75
GOUDA, Mohamed Yasser R. 8601 STENTON AVE 19038 #915-03-1989 L1998 **PM** *020
GREEN, Leland James. 548 WILLOW GROVE AVE 19038 #026-04-1955 L1964 **NTR A** *020 †03
HERMAN, Harold. ■ 19038 #041-13-1956 L1957 **OM OS** *062 †85
HOLMBERG, Donald Elwyn. ■ 19038 #041-13-1964 L1965 **GP** *071
JOHNSON, Stacey Robyn. ■ 19038 #035-01-2004 L2004 **PD** *012
LYMAN, Lewis. ■ 19038 #024-06-1937 **GP OS** *072
LYONS, Michael. 255 N EASTON RD 19038 #041-09-1980 L1981 **FM** *020 †18
MARCUS, Francine Lee. 8200 FLOURTOWN AVE 19038 #041-07-1975 L1976 **P** *020 †75
MOSIER, Donald Edward. ■ 19038 #016-02-1971 L1978 **IG PTH** *050
O'CONNOR, Matthew James. ■ 19038 #051-01-2004 L2005 **PDC** *012 †55
PARK, Jung Hoon. ■ 19038 #041-01-2007 L2007 **ORS** *012
PAUL, Michael Lee. ■ 19038 #010-01-1977 L1978 *020
QUIGLEY, John Thomas. 2418 FAIRHILL AVE, DAIMLER-CHRYSLER CORP. 19038 #041-13-1995 L1998 **GPM** *100
REISS, George Russell, Jr. 2220 MOUNT CARMEL AVE 19038 #041-13-1957 L1958 **PD** *020 †55
ROBERTSON, Katharine Anne. ■ 19038 #035-09-2008 *012
SHU, Winston Weidak. 715 N TYSON AVE 19038 #041-02-2003 L2003 **IM** *100 †20
SILVER, Carlton Ira. 115 E GLENSIDE AVE STE 7 19038 #041-13-1988 L1990 **FM** *020 †18
STERIOUS, Steven Nicholas. ■ 19038 #041-02-2008 *012
SWANLJUNG, Peter Tor. ■ 19038 #041-13-2002 L2002 **P** *100 †75
THEODORSON, David Robert. ■ 19038 #040-02-1993 L1998 **EM** *020 †16
THOME, Jennifer Lynn. 2444 ARDSLEY AVE 19038 #025-01-1997 L1999 **OBG** *020 †30
WHALEN, Edward Wm., Jr. ■ 19038 #041-02-1961 L1962 **U GS** *075

GLENVILLE — YORK

MOORE, Richard Lee. ■ 17329 #023-01-1994 *075
SHARMA, Chintu. ■ 17329 #018-03-2003 L2007 **MPD** *100 †20,55
WEISS, Michael A. ■ 17329 #035-46-1991 L1995 **AN** *020 †05

GORDONVILLE — LANCASTER

MC BRIDE, William Charles. ■ 17529 #041-13-2003 L2003 **IM** *100
STEPHENSON, James Emmett. 3413 HARVEST DR, STE 100 17529 #030-06-1993 L2004 **FM** *020 †18

GRANTHAM — CUMBERLAND

SEID, Arlene. ■ 17027 #023-01-1991 L2002 **GPM PM** *020 †70
THUMA, Philip Eugene. MESSIAH COLLEGE, ENGLE HEALTH CENTER 17027 #041-13-1974 L1990 **GP PD** *020 †55

GREEN LANE — MONTGOMERY

NICHOLS, Warren Wesley. ■ 18054 #041-02-1954 L1955 **OS PD** *071 †55
SOUDER, Francis R. ■ 18054 #041-09-1944 L1945 **FM** *071 †18

GREENCASTLE — FRANKLIN

ACOL, Jose Almazan. 50 EASTERN AVE STE 144, ANTRIM FAMILY MEDICINE 17225 #748-18-1987 L2002 **FM** *020 †18
ARNOULT, Susan Kaufman. 50 EASTERN AVE, GREENCASTLE FAMILY 17225 #023-01-1996 L1999 **FM OBS** *020 †18
ASUNCION, Melissa Marie. 2095 CASTLEGREEN DR 17225 #748-18-1987 L2002 **FM** *020 †18
BUSH, Jon Lee. ■ 17225 #041-15-2003 L2003 **EM** *020 †16
CHASKO, Mary Theresa. ■ 17225 #041-15-2003 L2003 **PMM** *012
ENSMINGER, Chalmers L. ■ 17225 #048-04-1970 L1989 **GYN OS** *071 †30
GEORGE, Robert B. 50 EASTERN AVE, STE 144 17225 #043-01-1977 L1980 **FM** *020 †18
HUDZINSKI, Martin. 50 EASTERN AVE, GREENCASTLE FAMILY 17225 #041-14-1979 L1980 **FM** *020 †18
HUGH, Annmarie Nicole. ■ 17225 #010-03-1998 L2007 **GS** *020 †85
MATRE, Jon. 50 EASTERN AVE, STE 141 17225 #693-03-1984 L2003 *020
MILLER, Lisa Nichole. 50 EASTERN AVE 17225 #023-01-1996 L2002 **OBG** *020 †30
SHALLCROSS, Ann Louise. 50 EASTERN AVE 17225 #033-06-1979 L1980 **FM** *020 †18
SIPES, Duane Eugene. 50 EASTERN AVE, GREENCASTLE FAMILY 17225 #041-14-1987 L1990 **FM** *020 †18
TEJADA, Nelly Adriana. ■ 17225 #264-01-1993 L2001 **PTH** *020
THORNTON, Joseph Keith. 50 EASTERN AVE, GREENCASTLE FAMILY 17225 #041-14-1979 L1980 **FM** *020 †18

GREENSBORO — GREENE

CASTILLO-BARONIA, Vivian. 7 GLASSWORKS RD, CORNERSTONE CARE 15338 #748-10-1984 L2001 **FM** *020 †18
GOPAL, Murali. 7 GLASSWORKS RD, WPIC PHYSICIAN PRACTICE CO 15338 #305-01-1998 L2002 **P** *020 †75 ‡
MILLER, John Harthill. 7 GLASSWORKS RD 15338 #016-06-1969 L2005 **IM** *020 †20

GREENSBURG — WESTMORELAND

ADISEY, James Eugene. 44 S WASHINGTON AVE 15601 #305-01-1986 L1987 **CD** *020 †20
ALMALOUF, Thaer. 530 SOUTH ST, STE 220 15601 #875-02-1993 L1998 **PD** *020 †55
ALRAWI, Mouwafak Muflih M. 433 FRYE FARM RD, CENTRAL MEDICAL ARTS BLDG 15601 #528-01-1978 L1999 **OTO HNS** *020 †45
AMBROSINO, John Jos. 540 SOUTH ST, STE 306 15601 #050-02-1978 L2005 **GS VS** *020 †85
ANDROKITES, Arthur Thos. 540 SOUTH ST, STE 204 15601 #041-02-1985 L1986 **PM** *020 †60
ANTON, Lee Nicholas. 532 W PITTSBURGH ST 15601 #041-12-2000 L2003 **MPD** *020 †55,20
AREVALO, Alfonso S. 105 WESTPOINT DR 15601 #649-14-1977 L1988 **FM** *020
AROUSE, Ayman Molhem. 214 KINGSBROOKE DR, WESTMORELAND PEDIATRICS 15601 #875-03-1988 L1997 **PD** *020 †55
AUSTIN, George Lynn. 562 SHEARER ST, STE 302 15601 #023-01-1970 L1980 **GS VS** *020 †85 ‡
BAHRI, Sanjeev. 200 VILLAGE DR 15601 #012-05-1991 L1995 **RO** *020 †80
BARR, Karen Elizabeth. 532 W PITTSBURGH ST 15601 #051-07-1996 L2000 **CCM** *020 †20
BARUA, Subrata Prasad. 6303 STATE ROUTE 30, WALTON TEA RM RD ROUTE 30 15601 #704-03-1962 **ORS** *020 †40
BASHYAM, Mani. 530 SOUTH ST, STE 300 15601 #495-04-1984 L1999 **IM END** *020 †20
BAUM, Neil Bruce. 532 W PITTSBURGH ST, WESTMORELAND HOSPITAL 15601 #041-02-1983 L1984 **EM FM** *020 †18 ‡
BAYANI, Eladio Yambot, Jr. 532 W PITTSBURGH ST 15601 #748-10-1966 L1977 **U EM** *020 †95
BEAUREGARD, Wesley Christ. ■ 15601 #038-43-2005 L2006 *020
BELAK, Michele Marie. 532 W PITTSBURGH ST, EMERGENCY DEPT 15601 #041-12-1994 L1996 **EM** *020 †16
BEYER, David Wm. 348 DONOHOE RD, LAUREL SURGICAL CENTER 15601 #654-01-1986 L1987 **AN** *020 †05
BEYER, Francis D. ■ 15601 #041-01-1951 L1952 **PTH OS** *071 †50
BISIGNANI, Geoffrey J. 522 W NEWTON ST, G U INC 15601 #041-12-1993 L1995 **U** *020 †95
BISIGNANI, Gregory Alfred. 532 W PITTSBURGH ST 15601 #041-12-1993 L1995 **ORS** *020 †40
BLACKBURN, Lawrence F. 111 W 3RD ST 15601 #041-01-1952 L1953 **IM** *071 †20
BLOOM, Marvin Alan. ■ 15601 #041-12-1971 L1972 **PUD IM** *050 †20
BORTZ, Donald W. 559 SHEARER ST, WESTMORELAND MED PAVILION 15601 #041-02-1939 L1941 **IM** *071 †20
BOYLE, Brian Francis. 207 S MAPLE AVE 15601 #041-02-1985 L1987 **PM** *020 †60
BRADLEY, Bruce A. 443 FRYE FARM RD, STE 200 15601 #041-77-1988, ▲ L1989 **GE HEP** *020 †20
BRAUNSTEIN, Neil Aaron. 562 SHEARER ST STE 103, MEDICAL ARTS BLDG 15601 #041-12-1997 L1999 **RHU** *020 †20
BRICKLEY, Richard Scott. 532 W PITTSBURGH ST 15601 #041-12-1982 L1987 **AN** *020 †05
BROWN, Robert Russell. ■ 15601 #011-02-1991 L1993 **DR** *020 †80
BRUNO, Maria A. 532 W PITTSBURGH ST 15601 #132-01-1961 L1976 **OBG** *020 †30

BRYAN, Frank Saml. 351 HARVEY AVE, DEPT OF LABOR & INDUSTRY 15601 #041-02-1957 L1958 **ORS OS** *071 †40
BUCCI, Lorenzo Anthony. 443 FRYE FARM RD, STE 100 15601 #041-12-1985 L1991 **GS VS** *020 †85
CAPONE, Ralph A. 532 W PITTSBURGH ST, EXCELA HLTH WESTMRELD HOSP 15601 #041-12-1978 L1979 **IM IMG** *030 †20
CARAMANNA, James Francis. 532 W PITTSBURGH ST 15601 #654-01-1981 L1983 **IM** *075
CARETTI, J William. 559 SHEARER ST 15601 #041-13-1961 L1962 **OBG** *071 †30
CATALANO, Louis Wm, Jr. 433 FRYE FARM RD 15601 #041-12-1967 L1969 **N PMM** *020 †75 ‡
CHAHIN, Juan Jorge. 44 S WASHINGTON AVE 15601 #308-02-1985 L1990 **CD** *020 †20
CHILDERS, Henry Erle, IV. 530 SOUTH ST, STE 380 15601 #024-07-1996 L2003 **TS** *020 †85,90
CHILDERS, Maria P. 530 SOUTH ST, STE 220 15601 #033-06-1998 L2001 **PD** *020 †55
CHIN, Suzette Andrea. 532 W PITTSBURGH ST 15601 #023-01-2000 L2001 **PCC** *100 †20
CHIRIGOS, Gregg Geo. 532 W PITTSBURGH ST 15601 #041-12-1979 L1981 **IM** *020 †20
CHRISTLIEB, Jose Ignacio. 532 W PITTSBURGH ST 15601 #041-07-1995 L1998 **IM** *020 †20
CLARK, Daniel Chas. 443 FRYE FARM RD, STE 100 15601 #041-12-1988 L1992 **GS** *020 †85
CLARK, Roy Reynolds. 530 SOUTH ST, STE G20 15601 #035-45-1991 L1995 **OBG** *020 †30
CLARKSON, Michael C. 532 W PITTSBURGH ST 15601 #041-13-1997 L1999 **EM** *020 †16
COBETTO, Bernard H. ■ 15601 #041-12-1947 L1948 **DR** *071
CONTRAFATTO, Daniel S. 44 S WASHINGTON AVE 15601 #041-13-1979 L1986 **CD IM** *020 †20
COOK, Randall Chas. 530 SOUTH ST, STE 360 15601 #041-13-1984 L1985 **IM** *020 †20
COSTA, Marc Lance. 540 SOUTH ST STE 304, MEDICAL COMMONS TWO 15601 #041-01-1993 L1996 **GS** *020 †85
COURTNEY, Wm Burleigh. ■ 15601 #041-13-1957 L1958 **OBG** *071 †30
DALY, Francis Leslie, III. ■ 15601 #008-02-1982 L1983 **P ADP** *020 ‡
DANIELE, Kathleen Brienza. 200 VILLAGE DR, STE C 15601 #008-02-1994 L2004 **FM** *020 †18
DE FRANCESCO, Chas Angelo. 141 AESTHETIC WAY, AESTIQUE MEDICAL CENTER 15601 #041-12-1982 L1983 **AN** *020 †05
DE MEZZA, Angelo. 1275 S MAIN ST, WALWORTH MEDICAL CTR 15601 #041-12-1973 L1974 **IM** *071 †20
DENINO, Lawrence Anthony. 44 S WASHINGTON AVE 15601 #048-14-1986 L1990 **CD IM** *020 †20
DIXIT, Sanjay B. 1275 S MAIN ST, STE 102 15601 #041-12-2003 L2005 **IM** *020 †20
D'ONOFRIO, Matthew A. 1275 S MAIN ST, STE 102 15601 #041-13-1992 L1995 **IM** *020 †20
DULL, James Albert. ■ 15601 #041-01-1948 L1949 **GS ORS** *071 †85
DUTT, Rinku Mitra. RR 17 BOX 9, HEMPFEILD POINTE 15601 #038-06-1985 L1992 **OPH** *020 †35
EISEMAN, Paul C, Jr. ■ 15601 #041-02-1948 L1949 **ORS** *071 †40
EVANS, Terry Lynn. 200 VILLAGE DR 15601 #041-12-1974 L1975 **ON HEM** *020 †20
FEMIANO, Jennifer Ann. ■ 15601 #008-01-1997 L1999 **PD** *020 †55
FERGUSON, Robert Howard. 562 SHEARER ST, STE 104 15601 #041-12-1979 L1984 **IM NEP** *020 †20
FONG, Jake. ■ 15601 #041-12-1953 L1954 **FM EM** *071
FOSTER, Walter Daniel. ■ 15601 #041-12-1957 L1958 **R** *071 †80
FOX, Carol Woolcock. 200 VILLAGE DR, STE C 15601 #041-02-1987 L1989 **FM** *020 †18
FRANZINO, Robert Russel. 501 W OTTERMAN ST 15601 #041-12-1982 L1983 **EM** *020 †16
FREEDBERG, Lawrence E. 522 W NEWTON ST, G U INC 15601 #035-19-1969 L1976 **U** *020 †95
FRUMAN, Dale Bernard. 40 HUFF AVE 15601 #041-12-1966 L1967 **CHP PD** *020
GALL, Joseph A. 562 SHEARER ST 15601 #041-12-1967 L1968 **ON HEM** *020 †20 ‡
GEBROSKY, Norman Paul. 522 W NEWTON ST 15601 #041-12-1990 L1996 **U** *020 †95
GIBSON, Kevin F. 532 W PITTSBURGH ST 15601 #033-06-1980 L1984 **PUD CCM** *050 †20
GOLDSTROHM, Gregg Lincoln. 507 W NEWTON ST STE 1 15601 #041-12-1980 L1981 **ORS HS** *020 †40
GORBY, Robert Si. 530 SOUTH ST 15601 #010-02-1989 L1991 **AI IM** *020 †20,03
GRABIAK, Gregory Dennis. 457 FRYE FARM RD, FRYE FARM RD 15601 #016-43-1965 L1966 **OTO** *071 †45
GREEN, James Matthew. 532 W PITTSBURGH ST 15601 #041-12-1987 L1989 **AN PME** *020 †05 ‡
GUIDICE, Mary Ann. 433 FRYE FARM RD, NEUROLOGICAL INSTITUTE OF 15601 #038-40-1971 L2002 **N** *020 †75
GUMM, Edward A. 540 SOUTH ST, STE 302 15601 #041-13-1980 L1981 **FM** *020 †18
HAFFNER, Daniel Loren. 530 SOUTH ST STE 200 15601 #041-14-1987 L1996 **ORS** *020 †40
HAMATY, Fred Geo. 419 W PITTSBURGH ST, WESTMORELAND DERM ASSOC 15601 #041-14-1992 L1996 **D** *020 †15
HAMMERMAN, Samuel Ira. 532 W PITTSBURGH ST 15601 #045-01-1989 L1991 **PCC** *020 †20
HAPP, Richard Anthony. 1225 S MAIN ST STE 302A 15601 #041-09-1966 L1967 **CRS GS** *020 †85,10
HARTMAN, H King, Jr. 516 PELLIS RD 15601 #041-13-1991 L1993 **OPH** *020 †35 ‡
HARTMAN, Harry King. 516 PELLIS RD 15601 #041-13-1963 L1967 **OPH** *020 †35
HAWKINS, James Gilson, Jr. 532 W PITTSBURGH ST 15601 #041-12-1981 L1982 **EM** *020 †16
HEBRANK, Gregory T. 532 W PITTSBURGH ST 15601 #021-01-1982 L1983 **OBG** *020 †30
HENNESSEY, William James. 120 VILLAGE DR 15601 #041-13-1992 L1996 **PM** *020 †60
ICLI, Nadir. ■ 15601 #902-10-1956 L1970 **AN** *020
JABBOUR, Nabil. 337 HARVEY AVE 15601 #875-01-1975 L1983 **FM** *020 †18
JABBOUR, Victor Fouad. 337A HARVEY AVE 15601 #875-01-1978 L1984 **FM** *020 †18
JABIR, Rizwan. 532 W PITTSBURGH ST 15601 #704-02-1986 L1996 **PD** *020 †55 ‡
JAIN, Bharat. 426 PELLIS RD, DBA WEST MORLAND MEDICINE 15601 #495-21-1987 L1995 **IM PUD** *020 †20
JIN, Yang. 532 W PITTSBURGH ST 15601 #243-47-1992 L2003 **PCC** *020 †20
JOHNS, Rachelle Lynn. 532 W PITTSBURGH ST, EXCELA HEALTH WESTMORELAND 15601 #041-12-2001 L2001 **GE** *100
JOHNSON, Edward Patrick. 530 SOUTH ST, STE 360 15601 #041-12-1995 L1998 **IM** *020 †20
JOSEPH, Geoffrey. 510 PELLIS RD STE 203 15601 #041-12-1983 L1988 **GS CRS** *020 †85
KANAPARTHI, Lalit Kumar. 532 W PITTSBURGH ST 15601 #495-16-1985 L2000 **PUD** *012 †20
KAPOOR, Ajoy. 532 W PITTSBURGH ST 15601 #495-30-1992 L2001 **CCM** *100 †20
KATZ, Jerald Milton. ■ 15601 #396-17-1962 L1965 **U** *071 †95
KENNEDY, George Wm. 532 W PITTSBURGH ST 15601 #041-02-1981 L1993 **EM** *020 †16
KENNEY, David Alan. 433 FRYE FARM RD, STE 10 15601 #041-01-1975 L1976 **VS GS** *020 †85
KETTERING, Joseph Michael. 424 GLENMEADE RD, RADIOLOGIC CONSULTANTS 15601 #041-12-1990 L1995 **DR** *020 †80
KHALIL, Karim. 532 W PITTSBURGH ST 15601 #847-02-1975 L1982 **OBG** *020 †30
KIM, Joann Boyung. 532 W PITTSBURGH ST 15601 #041-02-2000 L2001 **PCC** *100 †20
KLINGENSMITH, Mark R. 522 W NEWTON ST STE 200 15601 #041-14-1981 L1982 **OTO FPS** *020 †45
KLIONS, Douglas Earl. 443 FRYE FARM RD, STE 200 15601 #041-07-1989 L1991 **GE HEP** *020 †20
KOLONICH, John G, Jr. 532 W PITTSBURGH ST, 532 WEST PITTSBURG STREET 15601 #041-14-1987 L1989 **EM** *020 †16
KOWALYK, Stephan. 530 SOUTH ST, STE 300 15601 #033-05-1985 L1994 **END IM** *020 †20
KOZAKIEWICZ, Richard Todd. 120 VILLAGE DR 15601 #041-14-1993 L1997 **PM** *020 †60
KUCERA, Richard Frank. 562 SHEARER ST, STE 203 15601 #041-09-1982 L1983 **PCC** *020 †20
KUMAR, Pradeep. 527 W NEWTON ST 15601 #496-03-1980 L1984 **IM GE** *020 †20
KUMAR, Rama V. 351 HARVEY AVE 15601 #495-50-1970 L1977 **FM** *020 †18
KUMAR, V. 1275 S MAIN ST STE 203 15601 #495-50-1969 L1976 **FM** *020 †18
LAFONTANT, Robert R. 421 ETON DR 15601 #010-02-1963 L1968 **GS** *071 †85
LANG, Karen A. 300 CAMEO LN 15601 #041-02-1987 L1989 **FM** *020 †18
LAPPEN, Justin Ross. ■ 15601 #023-07-2006 L2006 **OBG** *012
LAZZARO, Karen K. 1275 S MAIN ST, STE 101 15601 #041-12-1992 L1995 **IM** *020 †20
LAZZARO, Theodore A. 141 AESTHETIC WAY 15601 #010-02-1974 L1977 **PS** *020 †65
LEE, Jin Sung. 200 VILLAGE DR 15601 #012-01-1997 L1999 **HO** *020 †20 ‡
LEE, Jong Yeoul. 532 W PITTSBURGH ST, WESTMORELAND HOSPITAL ASSO 15601 #583-10-1972 L1978 **AN** *020
LEE, Jong Yoon. ■ 15601 #583-01-1944 **AN** *020
LEIBU, Tatiana. 660 PELLIS RD, STE 201 15601 #781-02-1983 L1996 **IM PHP** *020 †20
LEONE, Guy Robt. 141 AESTHETIC WAY 15601 #032-01-1979 L1980 **AN PD** *020 †05
LEVIN, Matthew Welsh. 259 OLD ROUTE 30, STE C 15601 #041-02-1985 L1986 **FM** *020 †18 ‡
LEWIS, Henry C. 532 W PITTSBURGH ST 15601 #041-12-1953 L1954 **IM** *071
LJUNGMAN, Thomas Nils. 800 MARGUERITE RD 15601 #023-07-1987 L1989 **FM** *020 †18
LUCK-COSTA, Kerry A. 532 W PITTSBURGH ST, DEPT OF ANESTHESIA 15601 #041-09-1993 L1997 **AN** *020 †05
MAC PHAIL, John Adam. 4000 HEMPFLD PLZ BLVD #963 15601 #051-01-1972 L1979 **ORS** *020 †40
MAIDA, Frank V. ■ 15601 #561-17-1963 L1964 **FM IMG** *071
MALEY, Richard Hardy. 530 SOUTH ST, STE 380 15601 #041-09-1988 L1995 **TS** *071 †90,85
MAZOWIECKI, Michael C. 433 FRYE FARM RD 15601 #010-02-1995 L2005 **N** *020 †75
MC HUGH, Regis Wm. 419 W PITTSBURGH ST 15601 #041-12-1978 L1979 **D** *020 †15 ‡
MEHTA, Navdeep Kumar. 562 SHEARER ST, STE 203 MEDICAL ARTS BUILD 15601 #065-09-1990 L1994 **CCM IM** *020 †20
MILLER, Anna. 1 GIBRALTER WAY 15601 #913-15-1985 L1999 **OPH N** *020 †35
MILLER, Thomas Robt. 532 W PITTSBURGH ST 15601 #041-12-1979 L1980 **PTH** *062 †50
MIRANDA, Ralph Adolph. 196 OLD ROUTE 30 15601 #041-14-1976 L1977 **PTX FM** *020 †18 ‡
MISRA, Hari Krishna. 6303 STATE ROUTE 30, WALTON TEA RM ROAD 15601 #495-05-1961 L1972 **IM HEM** *071 †20
MOCKUS, Linas. 532 W PITTSBURGH ST 15601 #913-96-1994 L2001 **CCM** *020 †20
MONSOUR, William John. RR 6 BOX 60K 15601 #649-33-1985 L1994 **IM** *020
MORROW, John Allen, Jr. 532 W PITTSBURGH ST, WESTMORELAND REGIONAL HOSP 15601 #041-07-1993 L1997 **IM** *020 †20
MORROW, Thayer K, Jr. ■ 15601 #021-01-1949 L1963 **CLP PTH** *071 †50
MURCEK, Martin Aristark. 562 SHEARER ST, STE 101 15601 #041-12-1958 L1959 **AI PD** *020 †55,03
MYSLEWSKI, Walter John. 103 ALEXANDER AVE 15601 #010-02-1965 L1966 **GS** *071 †85
NAIDU, Rahul Kalahastri. 4731 STATE ROUTE 30, STE 302 15601 #035-01-1986 L1990 **OTO GS** *020 †45
NAVALGUND, Brinda Kulkarn. 913 CLAYTON ST 15601 #665-01-1999 L2000 **PME PM** *020 †60
NEGRO, Attilio Giulio. 870 WEATHERWOOD LN, STE 1 15601 #064-01-1978 L1980 **GYN FM** *020 †30
NEWMAN, William Thos. 259 OLD STATE ROUTE 30 # C, WILLOWBROOK PROFESSIONAL 15601 #041-13-1985 L1986 **GS** *020 †85
NSEIR, Nawaf Ibrahim. 562 SHEARER ST, MEDICAL ARTS BLDG 15601 #875-01-1971 L1976 **NEP IM** *020 †20
OSKIN, Hilbert Edgar. 1248 MAYWOOD LN 15601 #041-02-1958 L1959 **P** *071 †75
OVERLY, Wylie Lightcap. ■ 15601 #041-01-1961 L1962 **ON HEM** *071 †20
PAL, Subhashish. 44 S WASHINGTON AVE 15601 #035-19-1993 L1996 **CD** *020 †20
PAYHA, Richard Edward, Jr. 510 PELLIS RD, STE 203 15601 #041-12-1988 L1993 **GS** *020 †85
PESKE, Edgar Derek. 125 HARTMAN RD, STE A 15601 #011-02-1969 L1970 **FM** *020 †18
PETERS, Jerome Albert. 330 W PITTSBURGH ST 15601 #041-12-1980 L1981 **OPH** *020 †35
PHILIPKOSKY, Monica Ann. 530 SOUTH ST, STE G20 15601 #041-13-1990 L1992 **OBG** *020 †30
PICA, James Enrico. 916 GREEN ST 15601 #041-13-1982 L1983 **D IM** *020 †20,15 ‡
PIFFERETTI, Thomas Wm. 532 W PITTSBURGH ST 15601 #561-15-1983 L1985 **FM** *020 †18
PISANO, James Jos. 532 W PITTSBURGH ST, DEPT PATHOLOGY WESTMORELND 15601 #041-14-1992 L1995 **PTH** *020 †50
PLUMMER, Lloyd Gordon. 532 W PITTSBURGH ST 15601 #041-02-1958 L1959 **GYN** *071 †30
POLTINNIKOV, Igor Mikh. 200 VILLAGE DR 15601 #023-01-2001 L2002 **RO** *020 †80
PROSPERI, Stephanie Anne. 530 SOUTH ST, STE 380 15601 #055-01-1994 L1997 **FM** *020 †18
PROVANCE, William J. 443 FRYE FARM RD, STE 200 15601 #041-77-1987, ▲ L1989 **GE HEP** *020 †20
PUNUKOLLU, C. 105 COBBLESTONE DR 15601 #495-50-1979 L1990 **GE IM** *020 †20
QUEL, Rebecca Ann. RR 12 BOX 431 15601 #041-12-2002 L2002 **FM** *020 †18
RAGOOR, Vijayalakshmi R. 433 FRYE FARM RD, CENTRAL MEDICAL ARTS BUILD 15601 #495-04-1988 L1997 **IM** *020 †75
RASEFSKE, Jason Paul. 1215 S MAIN ST STE 102, WESTMORELAND INTERNAL MEDI 15601 #041-13-1996 L1998 **FM** *020 †18 ‡
RICHARDS, David Stewart. 530 SOUTH ST, STE 360 15601 #041-12-1990 L1992 **IM** *020 †20
RICO, Philippe. 562 SHEARER ST, STE 203 MEDICAL ARTS BUILD 15601 #067-01-1989 L1993 **CCM IM** *020 †20
RIGGENBACH, Michael. ■ 15601 #038-45-2006 L2006 **ORS** *012
ROSENBLOOM, Alan John. 532 W PITTSBURGH ST 15601 #023-01-1980 L1987 **IM** *020 †20
ROSENBLUM, Earl Irving. ■ 15601 #038-40-1936 L1936 **AS GS** *071
RUTIGLIANO, Michael J. 433 FRYE FARM RD, FRYE FARM ROAD 15601 #041-12-1989 L1991 **NS** *020 †25
SACHAKUL, Chitrinee. 501 W OTTERMAN ST 15601 #891-02-1969 L1976 **OBG** *020 †30
SADEKNI, Marwan Elias. ■ 15601 #847-08-1978 L1984 **FM EM** *020 †18
SALOMON, Michael Anthony. 503 W NEWTON ST, GREENSBURG FAMILY PRACTICE 15601 #935-06-1974 L1987 **FM** *075
SARGENT, Susan Cole. 562 SHEARER ST, STE 203 MEDICAL ARTS BUILD 15601 #041-13-1984 L1986 **IM CCM** *020 †20
SAUER, Dieter. 545 RUGH ST, STE 3000 15601 #132-02-1968 L1971 **U** *071
SAUTER, Michael Keith. 327 W PITTSBURGH ST 15601 #038-40-1987 L1993 **N OS** *020 †75 ‡
SERRA, Paul Chas. 200 VILLAGE DR, STE C 15601 #005-19-1992 L1994 **FM** *020 †18
SHARAN, Rupam. 545 RUGH ST 15601 #422-01-1999 L2001 **GE** *020 †20

■ = Address Information Privacy Protected

SHAULIS, Jennifer Ann. 300 CAMEO LN 15601 #041-12-2001 L2001 **FM** *020 †18
SHOPE, William Benner. ■ 15601 #041-02-1948 L1949 **OS** *071 †55
SIMITHRAARATCHY, C N. 532 W PITTSBURGH ST 15601 #220-01-1968 L1974 **GS** *020
SMITH, Jack Douglas. 532 W PITTSBURGH ST 15601 #041-12-1973 L1974 **ORS** *020 †40
SMITH, Robert Chas. 400 OLD ROUTE 66 15601 #041-09-1986 L1987 **IM** *020 †20
SNOWMAN, Whitney Ross. 522 W NEWTON ST, G U INC 15601 #038-43-1988 L1992 **U** *020 †95
SOTELO, Augusto. 235 HUMPHREY RD STE 6 15601 #264-01-1957 L1970 **OTO** *020 †45
SPEEDY, Harry Wilson. ■ 15601 #041-12-1967 L1968 **IM** *071 †20
SPINO, Pascal Danl. 208 CENTER AVE 15601 #023-01-1947 L1948 **PD PP** *071 †55
STEFFENSEN, David Oass. 530 SOUTH ST STE 140, 140 MEDICAL COMMONS 15601 #051-01-1980 L1982 **ID IM** *020 †20 ‡
STEM, Theodore B, Jr. 562 SHEARER ST, STE 104 15601 #036-05-1981 **NEP** *020 †20
STEVENSON, Peter Thos. 547 OLD STATE ROUTE 66 15601 #561-01-1974 L1976 **EM IM** *030 †16
SULECKI, Matthew Gerard. 2000 VILLAGE DR 15601 #041-09-1984 L1985 **ON HEM** *020 †20
SULLIVAN, Christopher D. 532 W PITTSBURGH ST, EXCELA HEALTH 15601 #041-01-1999 L1999 **GPM MDM** *030 †70 ‡
SUZUKI, Mark Masaru. 540 SOUTH ST, STE 306 15601 #010-01-1986 L1995 **TS CD** *020 †85,90
SWACKHAMMER, Randy Lee. 530 SOUTH ST, STE 360 15601 #041-12-1985 L1986 **IM** *020 †20
TALAMO, James Michael. 529 RUGH ST 15601 #041-12-1980 L1981 **PD** *020 †55
TALAMO SUSANG, Mary Lou. 529 RUGH ST 15601 #041-12-1985 L1986 **IM** *020
TAYLOR, Gary Craig. 518 PELLIS RD 15601 #041-12-1980 L1985 **FM** *020 †18
TEET, Daniel Albert. 1000 TOWER WAY, # 2 15601 #012-01-1974 L1976 **PS GS** *020 †65
TOMCI, Thomas Geo. 539 GREEN ST 15601 #654-01-1986 L1988 **IM** *020
TONEY, David Mitchell. WESTMORELAND HOSPITAL 15601 #041-02-1965 L1966 **R** *071 †80
TORIO, Reynaldo M. 436 LAKEWOOD RD 15601 #748-01-1968 L1975 **ORS** *020
TROUT, John Arthur. ■ 15601 #041-12-1977 L1978 **IM IMG** *071 †20
TYMOCZKO, Robert Gordon. 545 RUGH ST 15601 #041-14-1978 L1979 **IM** *020 †20 ‡
VAN NORMAN, Anthony J. ■ 15601 #055-01-2002 L2007 **D** *020 †15
VASUDEVAN, Gopalan. 44 S WASHINGTON AVE 15601 #495-66-1968 L1975 **CD IM** *020 †20
VIVERETTE, Joseph F, Jr. 200 VILLAGE DR 15601 #051-04-1981 L1982 **ON HO** *020 †20
WALKER, Heather Lynn. 532 W PITTSBURGH ST 15601 #041-12-1999 L2001 **EM** *020 †16
WANG, Barbara Kay. 530 SOUTH ST, STE 360 15601 #023-07-1978 L1979 **IM** *020 †20
WEST, David Michael. 540 SOUTH ST, STE 306 15601 #055-01-2000 L2005 **TS** *020 †85 ‡
WETZEL, Matthew Merle. 425 FRYE FARM RD 15601 #023-07-1998 L2000 **NS** *100
WHIPKEY, Robert Reed, Jr. 532 W PITTSBURGH ST 15601 #041-12-1981 L1982 **EM** *030 †16
WHITTEN, Thomas Lynn. 4893 ROUTE 30, STE 8 15601 #308-11-1984 L1987 **PMM ADM** *020 †18
WILLIAMSON, Edward Lloyd. 426 PELLIS RD 15601 #041-12-1967 L1973 **N** *020 †75 ‡
WILSON, John Stewart, Jr. 545 RUGH ST 15601 #041-02-1963 L1964 **DR** *071 †80
WILSON, Jonathan Mark. 2000 VILLAGE DR 15601 #041-02-1989 L1991 **FM** *020 †18
WISSINGER, Eric Lee. 532 W PITTSBURGH ST 15601 #055-01-1999 L2001 **EM** *020 †16
WODZINSKI, Steven Francis. 532 W PITTSBURGH ST 15601 #011-04-1981 L1984 **IM CCM** *020 †20
WOLFF, Jeffrey M. 419 W PITTSBURGH ST 15601 #041-12-1978 L1979 **D GP** *020 †15
WOOD, Kelly Ann. 532 W PITTSBURGH ST 15601 #035-06-1993 L2000 **PCC** *020 †20
WOODSKE, Matthew Eliot. 532 W PITTSBURGH ST 15601 #041-14-2001 L2001 **PCC** *012
WYSZOMIERSKI, Mary Ellen. 200 VILLAGE DR 15601 #023-07-1979 L1984 **FM EM** *020 †18
YAKULIS, Robert. 532 W PITTSBURGH ST, DEPARTMENT OF PATHOLOGY 15601 #041-12-1979 L1980 **PTH** *020 †50
ZACCAGNINI, Robert M. 38 UNITY SQ 15601 #041-07-1996 L1998 **PUD** *020 †20
ZAYAT, Joseph. 327 W PITTSBURGH ST, WESTMORELAND NEUROLOGY ASS 15601 #875-02-1975 L2006 **N** *020 †20,75
ZORCH, Michael John. 7 HIGH ACRES CIR 15601 #041-02-1982 L1983 **EM** *020 †18

GREENTOWN – PIKE

KLOCK, Brian Earle. PO BOX 63, 191 MARINA WAY 18426 #035-09-1985 L1996 **GS CCS** *020 †85

GREENVILLE – MERCER

ANDERSON, Stuart Douglas. 1 GREENVILLE ORTHOPEDC CTR, GOA 16125 #041-02-1996 L1998 **ORS OTR** *020 †40
BAKER, Robert Hershey. 1 GREENVILLE ORTHOPEDC CTR, STE 1 16125 #041-02-1947 L1948 **ORS OS** *071 †40 ‡
BARKAN, Alexander. 428 S MAIN ST, GREENVILLE SURGICAL ASSOCI 16125 #422-01-1998 L2006 **GS** *020
BECK, Donald Eugene. 90 SHENANGO ST 16125 #041-12-1958 L1959 **GYN** *071 †30
BEE, Matthew Thomas. 110 N MAIN ST 16125 #055-01-1995 L2000 **RNR** *100 †80
BROSSARD, Iris. 428 S MAIN ST, UPMC HORIZON NEUROLOGY 16125 #035-03-1985 L1989 **N** *020 †75
CANO, Francisco Jose. 59 W MAIN ST 16125 #649-02-1969 **CHP PYA** *020 †75
CANO DIAZ, Francisco J D. 59 W MAIN ST 16125 #308-02-1982 L1988 **AI PD** *020 †55,03
COLAIACO, Victor I. 90 SHENANGO ST, GREENVILLE MEDICAL CENTER, 16125 #041-12-1974 L1978 **IM** *020 †20
CONSTANTINIDI, Sanda M. 90 SHENANGO ST, GREENVILLE MEDICAL CENTER, 16125 #781-01-1964 L1976 **PD A** *071 †55 ‡
DOWDELL, Paul James. 90 SHENANGO ST 16125 #041-02-1946 L1947 **IM AI** *071
ESTRADA-QUINTERO, Tulio. 428 S MAIN ST 16125 #264-06-1981 L1994 **CD IM** *020 †20
FERGUSON, Steven W. 308 MERCER RD, COMMUNITY HOSPITALISTS 16125 #028-78-1988, ▲ L1989 **IM** *020 †20
HASSAN, Farooq. 30 CONNEAUT LAKE RD 16125 #704-02-1991 L2001 **IM** *020 †20
JONES, Todd Lane. 90 SHENANGO ST, GREENVILLE MEDICAL CENTER 16125 #038-44-1995 L1998 **IM** *020 †20
JONES, Tom Benj. 110 N MAIN ST # RAD, GREENVILLE REGL HOSPITAL 16125 #041-12-1959 L1960 **DR** *071 †60
JONES, Troy Alan. 90 SHENANGO ST, GREENVILLE MEDICAL CENTER 16125 #038-40-1993 L1997 **IM** *020 †20
KERRY, Roy Eugene. 17 6TH AVE 16125 #041-12-1964 L1965 **OTO AI** *020 †45
KOLENICH, James Jeffrey. 111 N MAIN ST 16125 #016-43-1968 L1975 **GS** *020 †85
KOVOOR, Suvir Philip. 110 N MAIN ST, ST. JOSEPH'S FAMILY MEDICA 16125 #495-20-1980 L2006 **IM AN** *020 †20,05

KRISHNA RAO, Chevuru V. 110 N MAIN ST, 3622 BELMONT AVENUE 16125 #495-50-1965 L1977 **AN** *020
KUMAR, Pradeep. 81 N MAIN ST 16125 #495-36-1972 L1975 **CD IM** *020 †20
LANG, John Andrew. 428 S MAIN ST, HORIZON SURGICAL ASSOCIATE 16125 #041-14-1997 L2000 **CRS** *100 †85
LISZEWSKI, James Leonard. 90 SHENANGO ST, UPMC GREENVILLE MEDICAL CE 16125 #023-01-1995 L1997 **FM** *020 †18
LOB, Edgardo Rodolfo. 103 WOODFIELD DR 16125 #035-48-1984 L1990 **IM ON** *020 †20
MCBEAN, Etwar Hylton. 428 S MAIN ST, DEPARTMENT OF SURGERY 16125 #566-01-1999 L2007 **GS TY** *012 †85
MC ELREE, Frank E, Jr. 110 N MAIN ST 16125 #041-02-1950 L1951 **GS** *071
MC ELREE, James C. 98 CLINTON ST 16125 #041-02-1943 L1944 **OPH OTO** *072 †45
MC FADDEN, David L. 90 SHENANGO ST 16125 #041-02-1989 L1996 **OBG GS** *020 †30
MC WHIRTER, William Robt. ■ 16125 #041-13-1958 L1959 **ORS** *020 †40
MELTSNER, Gilbert. ■ 16125 #041-09-1957 L1961 **R NR** *071 †80
MEYN, Joseph William. 90 SHENANGO ST, GREENVILLE MEDICAL CENTER 16125 #041-15-1999 L2001 **OBG** *020 †30
MIKHAIL, Hosny Bushra. 110 N MAIN ST, EMERGY RM UPMC HORIZON 16125 #915-05-1973 L1983 **EM GP** *030 ‡
MILLER, John Lada. 110 N MAIN ST 16125 #041-13-1969 L1970 **DR OS** *071 †80
MONG, David Glen. ■ 16125 #041-13-1972 L1978 **OBG GP** *020
MORAN, Theodore R. ■ 16125 #041-12-1970 L1972 **ORS** *020 †40
MYEROWITZ, Richard Louis. 110 N MAIN ST 16125 #035-46-1968 L1975 **PTH PCP** *020 †50 ‡
PERRY, James Michael. 110 N MAIN ST 16125 #035-15-1994 L1996 **IM** *020 †20
PERRY, Lina Patel. 110 N MAIN ST, DEPT OF PATH 16125 #038-41-1993 L1996 **PTH PCP** *020 †50
PETRICK, Marcia Lynn. 110 N MAIN ST, UPMC - HORIZON (PATHOLOGY) 16125 #016-01-1992 L2004 **PTH** *020 †50
PETROCHKO, Constantine N. 110 N MAIN ST 16125 #036-06-1990 L1994 **DR** *020 †80
PICKERING, Scott Ford. 24 IMPERIAL DR 16125 #035-03-1981 L1985 **DR** *020 †80
POOLOS, Constantine James. 90 SHENANGO ST 16125 #041-12-1956 L1957 **IM** *071 †20
RAJA, Naseer Mahmood. 110 N MAIN ST, ANESTHESIOLOGY DEPARTMENT 16125 #704-01-1965 L1972 **AN PTH** *020 †05
RAYNAK, Frank Raymond. ■ 16125 #041-13-1947 L1948 **R NM** *071 †80
REASBECK, Jeffrey Lee. 90 SHENANGO ST, GREENVILLE MEDICAL CENTER 16125 #041-09-1983 L1984 **IM** *020 †20
RICHARDS, Richard Stephen. 125 N MAIN ST 16125 #038-43-1996 L1999 **ORS** *071 †40
SCULLIN, John Patrick. 1 GREENVILLE ORTHOPEDC CTR 16125 #028-34-1969 L1976 **ORS OSM** *020 †40 ‡
SE GALL, Janet Elaine. 90 SHENANGO ST, GREENVILLE MEDICAL CENTER 16125 #048-04-1982 L1992 **GYN** *020 †30
SHAMS, Ameer Zakaria. 1 SOUTHPOINT LN 16125 #915-03-1999 L2004 **FM** *020 †18
SILVA, Oscar Recinto. 110 N MAIN ST, GREENVILLE CAMPUS 16125 #748-01-1961 L1971 **IMG** *071
SMITH, Keith Bowman. 408 S MAIN ST 16125 #041-12-1958 L1959 **OPH** *020 †35
SMITH, Kevin Geo. 408 S MAIN ST 16125 #041-12-1986 L1988 **OPH** *020 †35
SOTUS, Peter Chris. 110 N MAIN ST 16125 #012-05-1956 L1981 **PTH GS** *071 †85,50
SPIELVOGLE, William Eric. 8 COLLEGE AVE 16125 #021-06-1998 L2003 **HO** *020 †20
STEELE, John Floyd. 160 MAIN ST 16125 #038-41-1968 L1977 **ORS** *020 †40
STITT, Donald Golder. 341 E JAMESTOWN RD, UNIT 48 16125 #041-13-1943 L1944 **FPG PD** *071
TE, Gabriel Ong. 11 LEECH RD, GREENVILLE OTOLARYNGOLOGY 16125 #748-02-1989 L1996 **OTO** *020
TIAN, Will T H. 90 SHENANGO ST 16125 #660-03-1955 L1966 **U** *071 †95
TOWLE, Murray Albert. 428 S MAIN ST 16125 #024-01-1963 L1979 **GS VS** *071 †85
VALENA, Loe Villapando. 87 N MAIN ST 16125 #748-01-1954 L1973 **EM FM** *071
VALLESTEROS, Federico P. 223 GREENVILLE RD, HORIZON ANESTHESIOLOGIST A 16125 #748-01-1960 L1967 **AN** *020
WITTENAUER, Genevieve F M. ■ 16125 #038-40-1966 L1966 **FM GP** *071
WOLFF, Bruce Robert. 90 SHENANGO ST 16125 #067-01-1962 L1974 **GS GP** *071 †85
WORKS, Kirk Loring. 125 N MAIN ST, STE 102 16125 #030-06-1983 L1990 **GE IM** *020 †20

GRINDSTONE – FAYETTE

BURSTYNOWICZ, Linda Marie. 111B ROBERTS RD 15442 #055-01-1996 L2000 **MPD** *020 †20,55

GROVE CITY – MERCER

AZOUZ, Samer. 647 N BROAD STREET EXT 16127 #875-02-1991 L2000 **CD** *020 †20
BACKSTROM, James Wilbert. 631 N BROAD STREET EXT 16127 #041-12-1984 L2002 **DR** *020 †80
BROWN, William Emson. 631 N BROAD STREET EXT 16127 #041-12-1964 L1965 **OTO A** *020 †45
CAMARA, Armando D. 631 N BROAD STREET EXT 16127 #748-20-1989 L2001 **CD** *020 †20 ‡
COLE, Andrew Koryoun. 631 N BROAD STREET EXT 16127 #054-04-1972 L1973 **FM EM** *020
DILLON, Stephen Vincent. 631 N BROAD STREET EXT, UNITED COMMUNITY HOSP 16127 #010-02-1986 L1987 **EM** *020 †85 ‡
DUNDORE, William Calvin. 647 N BROAD STREET EXT 16127 #041-12-1976 L1977 **OBG** *020 †30
FARAH, Tony Geo. 647 N BROAD STREET EXT 16127 #605-01-1984 L1985 **CD IM** *020 †20
FERGUSON, Daniel. 631 N BROAD STREET EXT 16127 #422-01-1984 L1987 **IM** *020 †20
FRITZ, William Danl. 631 N BROAD STREET EXT 16127 #035-47-1979 L1980 **ORS** *020 †40
GAY, Thomas Clark. 647 N BROAD STREET EXT 16127 #038-40-1968 L1974 **CD IM** *020 †20
GONZALEZ, Lorenzo. PO BOX 1058, 233 GEORGE JUNIOR REPUBLIC 16127 #042-01-1988 L1993 **P CHP** *020 †75
HAJJ ALI, Raef Haidar. 647 N BROAD STREET EXT 16127 #605-01-1993 L2002 **CD** *020 †20
JANCART, Robert. 631 N BROAD STREET EXT 16127 #305-01-1988 L1995 **PTH** *020 †50 ‡
KHALIL, Ramzi Fadel. 647 N BROAD STREET EXT 16127 #605-01-1996 L2001 **IC** *020 †20
KO, Yih-Song. 675 N BROAD STREET EXT, 675 NORTH BROAD ST EXT 16127 #244-05-1968 L1973 **FM** *020
KUMAR, Prem. 631 N BROAD STREET EXT 16127 #495-45-1975 L1984 **CD IM** *020 †55,20 ‡
LABERGE, Anne-Marie. 631 N BROAD STREET EXT 16127 #067-02-1986 L1994 *020

LIMKAKENG, Alexander Du. 631 N BROAD STREET EXT 16127 #748-01-1964 L1973 **U** *020 †95
LYNE, John C. 647 N BROAD STREET EXT, STE 201 16127 #539-04-1989 L1992 **U** *020 †95
MAJCHRZAK, Charles G, Jr. 631 N BROAD STREET EXT 16127 #041-09-1993 L1996 **GS** *020 †85
MAMARIL, Felixberto G, Jr. 631 N BROAD STREET EXT 16127 #748-16-1981 L1993 **FM EM** *020 †18
MASLOV, Marc David. 631 N BROAD STREET EXT 16127 #016-42-1981 L1990 **OTO** *020 †45
MEHTA, Sunil Kumar. 675 N BROAD STREET EXT, PINE MEDICAL CENTER 16127 #495-20-1962 L1973 **IM CD** *020 †20
MENZIES, Wm Cattanach. 420 HILLCREST AVE 16127 #041-13-1954 L1955 **FM** *071 †18
MEYERS, Jeffrey Michael. 200 CAMPUS DR, BOX 1464 16127 #038-43-2006 L2006 **PD** *012
MILLER, Glenn David, II. 647 N BROAD STREET EXT 16127 #041-09-1989 L1991 **CD** *020 †20
MOORE, Martha Jeanne. 631 N BROAD STREET EXT 16127 #041-12-1991 L1996 **FM** *020 †18
NEY, Francis G. RR 1 16127 #041-12-1953 L1954 **R GP** *071 †80
NICHAMIN, Louis David. 217 S BROAD ST 16127 #025-07-1984 L1988 **OPH** *020 †35
PEFFERMAN, Charity Ann. 200 CAMPUS DR, GROVE CITY COLLEGE #1824 16127 #039-01-2006 **MPD** *012
PERSUN, Michelle Lee. 647 N BROAD STREET EXT, STE 201 16127 #041-13-1998 L2001 **U** *020 †95
PICA, Richard Allen, Jr. 631 N BROAD STREET EXT 16127 #038-40-1990 L1993 **DR** *020 †80
PRENATT, William Edward. 631 N BROAD STREET EXT 16127 #041-13-1988 L1990 **FM** *020 †18
ROODE, Philip James. ■ 16127 #038-06-1974 L1975 **EM PD** *020 †16
ROTHMAN, David L. 647 N BROAD STREET EXT 16127 #035-03-1972 L1977 **VS GS** *020 †85
SAWARDEKAR, Arun Sazro. 631 N BROAD STREET EXT 16127 #495-37-1968 L1978 **PD** *020 †55
SAWARDEKAR, Shubhada Arun. 631 N BROAD STREET EXT 16127 #495-01-1971 L1980 **FPG OPH** *020
SCIULLO, Armando Carmine. 631 N BROAD STREET EXT 16127 #041-77-1997, ▲ L1998 *020
SILVIS, David M. 631 N BROAD STREET EXT 16127 #231-01-1983 L1988 **EM IM** *020
SMITH, Edward Geo. 420 HILLCREST AVE, FAMILY HEALTHCARE PARTNERS 16127 #041-01-1980 L1982 **FM** *020 †18
SYBING, Eugenio Aquino. 675 N BROAD STREET EXT, PINE MEDICAL CTR 16127 #041-10-1973 L1982 **ORS** *020 †40
SYBING, Melita Mangubat. PINE MED CTR 16127 #748-10-1974 L1982 **AI PD** *071
TAIWO, Olakunle O. 631 N BROAD STREET EXT 16127 #690-01-1982 L1998 **AN** *020 †05
TAN, Isabel G. 675 N BROAD STREET EXT 16127 #748-01-1962 L1964 **R OS** *071 †80
TILLI, Frank Vincent. 647 N BROAD STREET EXT 16127 #041-01-1989 L1997 **CD IC** *020 †20
TRENT, Craig Cargill. 631 N BROAD STREET EXT 16127 #041-12-1988 L1990 **DR** *020 †80
URBAN, Kimberly Ann. 647 N BROAD STREET EXT 16127 #041-09-1996 L1999 **CD** *020 †20
WEILAND, T Frederick. ■ 16127 #041-02-1944 L1945 **R** *071 †80
WHITE, Betty Jo. ■ 16127 #028-78-1963, ▲ L1965 **GP OS** *071
WHITFORD, Theodore C. 631 N BROAD STREET EXT 16127 #041-13-1990 L1993 **DR** *020 †20,80
WONSETTLER, Donald E. ■ 16127 #041-13-1941 L1942 **GP** *071
YOURD, Raymond A. 631 N BROAD STREET EXT 16127 #041-12-1949 L1950 **OTO** *071 †45
ZABKAR, John H. 631 N BROAD STREET EXT, GROVE CITY MEDICAL CENTER 16127 #041-12-1968 L1969 **PTH** *062 †50

GUYS MILLS — CRAWFORD

HALL, Jack Richard. ■ 16327 #017-20-1941 L1954 **GP** *071

GWYNEDD — MONTGOMERY

DAVIDSON, Jack Dougan. ■ 19436 #035-01-1943 L1946 **ON PA** *071 †28
HAMMOND, Lois Miriam. ■ 19436 #050-02-1940 L1942 **PD** *071 †55
KINLAW, William B. ■ 19436 #041-02-1949 L1955 **CD** *071 †20
PARRY, Henry Frazer. ■ 19436 #041-01-1940 L1945 **PM** *071 †60
RANDALL, Peter. ■ 19436 #023-07-1946 L1949 **PS** *071 †65
RHOADS, Donald Vail. ■ 19436 #041-01-1954 L1955 **IM** *071 †20
SABOKBAR, Nasser. ■ 19436 #869-04-1956 L1961 **AI PDA** *071 †55,03
VOLFOVA, Vladimira. ■ 19436 #409-23-1979 **IM** *074

GWYNEDD VALLEY — MONTGOMERY

DEW, Robert Alan. ■ 19437 #041-12-1961 L1965 **OS IM** *071 †20
FARAG, Samir Youssef F. 1416 FLORENCE DRIVE 19437 #915-04-1973 L1983 **P** *075
LANCE, Louisa. TOWNSHIPLINE RD 19437 #041-07-1973 **P** *020 †75
OLIFF, Allen I. ■ 19437 #035-46-1974 L1986 **ON** *050 †20
PHILIP, George. ■ 19437 #041-02-1985 L1988 **AI IM** *050 †20,03
ROBERTSON, Jayne Carolyn. ■ 19437 #041-07-1991 L1993 **P** *020
TEUTSCH, Steven Michael. ■ 19437 #036-07-1974 L1975 **PHP IM** *030 †20,70

HALIFAX — DAUPHIN

GUTIERREZ, Julian. 36 S RIVER RD 17032 #030-05-1986 L1991 **FM** *020 †18
LITTLE, Robert Glenn, Jr. 36 S RIVER RD UNIT 1, COMMUNITY MEDICAL ASSOCIAT 17032 #041-02-1967 L1968 **FM FPG** *020 †18
POFFENBERGER, Kyle Robert. PO BOX 204 17032 #041-14-2007 L2007 **TY** *012
STAUFFER, Julie Beth. 401 SHEETZ RD 17032 #041-09-1973 L1983 **P D** *020 †75

HAMBURG — BERKS

BLAUSER, Robert Bruce. 700 HAWK RIDGE DR 19526 #041-13-1980 L1981 **FM** *020 †18
CHAUDHRY, Sana Mohsin. 31 INDUSTRIAL DR STE 100 19526 #704-20-1998 L2002 **FM** *020 †18
CLYMER, David Gerald. 700 HAWK RIDGE DR, HAMBURG FAMILY PRACTICE 19526 #041-02-1987 L1989 **FM** *020 †18
D'ANCONA, Sara A. 31 INDUSTRIAL DR 19526 #041-02-1990 L2000 **FM** *020 †18

DAVID, Fernando L. ■ 19526 #748-01-1954 L1962 **GS** *071
KINDT, Jason Haines. 31 INDUSTRIAL DR, STE 100 19526 #041-77-1999, ▲ L2001 **FM** *020
LYONS, Clifford Hayes. 700 HAWK RIDGE DR 19526 #041-13-1983 L1984 **FM OS** *071 †18
MILLER, Margaret Dill. ■ 19526 #041-07-1936 L1937 **OM OS** *071
RACHSHTUT, Ilana Alla. 700 HAWK RIDGE DR 19526 #665-01-1998 L2003 **FM** *020 †18
RIGHTMYER, John Nathan. 122 N 4TH ST 19526 #041-02-1963 L1964 **GP** *071
STAPINSKI, Brian Christop. ■ 19526 #041-14-2005 L2005 *020
VILLANUEVA, Onofre Q. HAMBURG CTR 19526 #748-01-1956 L1970 **GP** *020

HANOVER — YORK

ADAM, David John. 795 CHERRY TREE CT 17331 #042-03-1982 L1985 **GE IM** *075 †20
ADER, Michael Harris. 71 GEORGE ST 17331 #010-02-1978 L1983 **PUD IM** *020 †20
ALANDETE, Alvaro. 217 BROADWAY 17331 #264-02-1960 L1964 **PD** *020 †55
ALEXANDROV, Stefan Kiril. 26 CHARLES ST 17331 #198-02-1963 L1974 **GP** *071
ALLEN, Brian David. 300 HIGHLAND AVE 17331 #041-02-1983 L1984 **FM** *020 †18
BAKER, Leonard Patrick. 300 HIGHLAND AVE, HANOVER DIAGNOSTIC IMAGING 17331 #023-01-1976 L1981 **DR** *071 †80
BAST, William Roy. 100 PENN ST 17331 #041-12-1972 L1974 **U** *020 †95
BERMAN, Ira Jos. 525 MCCOSH ST 17331 #023-01-1974 L1977 **D** *020 †15 ‡
BHARDWAJ, Prem. ■ 17331 #495-36-1961 L1977 **IM CD** *100
BISCHOFF, Robert John. 207 BLOOMING GROVE RD 17331 #021-01-1988 L1994 **ORS** *020 †40 ‡
BITTINGER, Ralph E. 425 WESTMINSTER AVE 17331 #025-01-1943 L1946 **GP AN** *071
BLAIR, Sidney Martin. ■ 17331 #005-02-1958 L1959 **P OTO** *071 †75
BRIDENBAUGH, George Alan. 310 STOCK ST, STE 3 17331 #041-02-1979 L1980 **CD IM** *020 †20 ‡
BUNCH, Nicole Micheal. 217 BROADWAY, HANOVER PEDIATRICS 17331 #048-02-1994 L1997 **PD** *020 †55
BUSLER, Verne Monroe, Jr. 300 HIGHLAND AVE 17331 #041-13-1963 L1964 **FM** *071
CALDER, Terrence Michael. 250 FAME AVE STE 101 17331 #041-09-1987 L1989 **AN PME** *020
CHAN, Joanne. 250 FAME AVE, STE 201 17331 #035-19-1994 L1996 **IM** *020 †20
CORONADO, Edward R. 625 W ELM AVE 17331 #748-08-1976 L1986 **P** *020
CROOKS, David L. 310 STOCK ST STE 8, MEDICAL OFFICE BLDG 17331 #539-06-1989 L1996 **GS SO** *020 †85
D'AGATA, Samuel D. 207 BLOOMING GROVE RD 17331 #024-07-1983 L1989 **ORS OSM** *020 †40
DANIELS, Warren Cornel. 300 HIGHLAND AVE, OCCUPATIONAL HEALTH SERVIC 17331 #041-02-1975 L1976 **OM IM** *020
DE ANGELO, Debra A. 250 FAME AVE, STE 101 17331 #041-77-1992, ▲ L1993 **APM AN** *020 †05
DE PAMPHILIS, Hy J. 795 CHERRY TREE CT 17331 #041-07-1982 L1983 **IM IMG** *071 †20
DIAZ, Danilo Victor, Jr. 795 CHERRY TREE CT, DIGESTIVE DISEASE CENTER 17331 #035-19-1997 L2004 **GE** *020 †20
ELLISON, James Haines. 207 BLOOMING GROVE RD 17331 #041-13-1971 L1974 **ORS** *020 †40
FINK, Albert Hopkins. ■ 17331 #041-01-1954 L1955 **R NM** *071 †80,28
FORTIER, Gregory Alan. 773 CHERRY TREE CT 17331 #051-01-1983 L1987 **RO** *020 †80
FREER, Carol Van Dyke. 300 HIGHLAND AVE 17331 #010-01-1978 L1979 **ID IM** *030 †20
FREER, Lawrence S. 310 STOCK ST, STE 3 17331 #041-14-1981 L1986 **CD IM** *020
GARCIA, Michael John. 3130 GRANDVIEW RD BLDG A 17331 #042-03-1989 L1992 **IM** *020 †20
GARCIA, Theodore Angel. ■ 17331 #041-02-1954 L1955 **OS OPH** *071
GENT, Donald H. ■ 17331 #035-01-1952 L1954 **P** *072 †75
GERLACH, Detlef Horst. 3130 GRANDVIEW RD 17331 #012-05-1975 L1979 **OBG** *020 †30
HAMME, Elmer G. 946 LAUREL WOODS LN 17331 #041-09-1952 L1953 **GP** *071
HARDEN, Wesley R, III. 221 POTOMAC AVE 17331 #041-02-1975 L1977 **GS TS** *020 †85,90
HAUGH, Jeffrey Thos. 250 FAME AVE, STE 206 17331 #041-13-1983 L1987 **AN** *020 †05
HAYWOOD, Thomas Bernard. 310 STOCK ST, STE 3 17331 #023-01-1979 L1987 **CD** *020 †20
HENKE, Robert J, Jr. 848 BROADWAY, HANOVER FAMILY PRACTICE 17331 #023-01-1980 L1981 **FM** *020 †18
HOFMANN, James Walter. 300 HIGHLAND AVE 17331 #010-01-1966 L1975 **GS VS** *071 †85
HOWARD, Thomas Kenneth. ■ 17331 #041-02-1960 L1961 **ORS** *071 †40
HUANG, Gene Jenwei. 195 STOCK ST, STE 306 17331 #048-02-1991 L1993 **P** *020 †75
JANUSZ, Walter Francis. 317 HIGHLAND AVE 17331 #041-13-1967 L1968 **CD IM** *020 †20
JONES, Richard Elliott. 195 STOCK ST, STE D 17331 #051-01-1972 L1974 **U** *020 †95
KHALAFALLAH, Amr A. 625 W ELM AVE 17331 #915-04-1983 L1996 **P** *020 †75
KILKELLY, Francis Xavier. 207 BLOOMING GROVE RD 17331 #010-02-1989 L2001 **ORS** *020 †40
KIM, Kae Jin. 217 BROADWAY, HANOVER PEDIATRIC ASSOC IN 17331 #041-13-1992 L1996 **PHO** *020 †55
KIM, Young Bai. ■ 17331 #583-01-1971 L1976 **DR** *020 †80
KIRBY, Catherine B. 848 BROADWAY 17331 #023-01-1998 L2000 **FM** *020 †18
KNOP, Brian Carl. 310 STOCK ST, STE 4 17331 #035-09-1997 L2000 **FM** *020 †18
LASKOWICH, Monica. 250 E WALNUT ST 17331 #422-01-1981 **FM** *075
LAVALLEE, Melissa P. 217 BROADWAY 17331 #023-01-2001 L2004 **PD** *020 †55
LEIB, Gregory R. ■ 17331 #041-14-1985 **OM PM** *030
LEISTER, Glenn Frederick. 300 HIGHLAND AVE 17331 #041-13-1958 L1959 **GP OBG** *071 †18
LIEB, John Geo. 111 PENN ST 17331 #051-04-1980 L1983 **FM** *020 †18
LIGGON, Cinda Anne. 625 W ELM AVE 17331 #007-02-1990 L1998 **P OS** *020
LOCKARD, Harry G, Jr. PO BOX 483 17331 #051-04-1948 L1948 **IM** *062
LOUBEAU, Jeanmarc. 1201 W ELM AVE, HANOVER ANESTHESIOLOGY FEL 17331 #041-14-1994 L2003 **AN** *100 †05
LUNSFORD, John Wm, Jr. 112 CLOVER LN 17331 #038-40-1980 L1983 **FM** *020 †18
LUNSFORD, Nancy Mayo. 300 HIGHLAND AVE 17331 #056-06-1978 L1983 **OBS AM** *020 †80
MARROCCO, Gregory Lee. ■ 17331 #023-01-1977 L1983 **R NM** *020 †80
MASUCCI, Douglas Jos. 217 BROADWAY 17331 #028-34-1981 L1983 **PD** *020 †55
MATHEWS, Raymond Eric. 795 CHERRY TREE CT, STE 3 17331 #023-01-1985 L1986 **IM** *020 †20
MAURICIO-TAN, Marivi S. 195 STOCK ST, STE 306 17331 #748-01-1989 L1998 **P PYG** *020
MAY, Carl Joseph, Jr. 250 FAME AVE, STE 200 17331 #041-02-1989 L1994 **OPH IM** *020 †35
MC LIN, Leon Norse. 300 HIGHLAND AVE 17331 #023-07-1947 L1949 **GP** *071
MOHAN, Shanthi. 777 CHERRY TREE CT STE 3, BLOOD & CANCER CTR 17331 #495-59-1974 L2001 **HO IM** *020 †20

MONTGOMERY, Matthew Lewis. 100 PENN ST, CORNERSTONE SURGICAL LLC 17331 #041-02-1992 L1994 **GS** *020 †85

MURILLO, Oscar Fredrick. 250 FAME AVE, STE 201 17331 #847-21-1982 L1986 **IM** *020 †20

NALAVANY, Gary W. 300 HIGHLAND AVE, DEPT ANESTHESIA HANOVER 17331 #422-01-1990 L1997 **AN** *020 †05

PALLONE, Michael Nicholas. ■ 17331 #041-14-1993 L1995 **PDP** *020 †55

PHILLIPS, Christine Anne. 795 CHERRY TREE CT STE 1 17331 #041-07-1985 L1987 **RHU IM** *020 †20

PHILLIPS, Robert Wayne. 201 STOCK ST 17331 #023-01-1969 L1973 **IM IMG** *020 †20,16

PHILLIPS, Todd Eugene. 310 STOCK ST STE 10 17331 #041-02-1988 L1990 **FM** *020 †18

PIERRE-LOUIS, Michele. 3130 GRANDVIEW RD 17331 #043-01-1999 L2001 **OBG** *020

PIRRELLO, Anthony, Jr. ■ 17331 #041-13-1962 L1965 **PTH CLP** *062 †50

PISULA, Vincent P., Jr. ■ 17331 #041-02-1953 L1954 **GS** *071 †85

PRESTON, Vernon Harkness. 300 FREDERICK ST 17331 #041-09-1980 L1981 **FM** *020 †18

PRIN, William A. 120 PENN ST 17331 #035-08-1972 L1973 **OBG** *020 †30

RALEY, Thomas John, Jr. 207 BLOOMING GROVE RD, HANOVER ORTHOPAEDIC ASSOC 17331 #017-20-1998 L2005 **OSS** *020 †40

RAPP, Thomas Douglas. 848 BROADWAY 17331 #055-01-1978 L1983 **FM** *020 †18

REIN, Jennifer Ann. 112 CLOVER LN 17331 #041-14-1999 L2003 **FM** *020 †18

RIVERA, Joseph Robt. 300 HIGHLAND AVE 17331 #035-08-1992 L1996 **IM** *020 †20

ROOS, Leon. ■ 17331 #041-02-1937 L1938 **FM** *071

RUDNICK, Howard Lawrence. 300 HIGHLAND AVE 17331 #836-01-1985 L1988 **EM OM** *020 †20 ‡

RUPP, Michael John. ■ 17331 #041-02-1984 L1986 **PCP PTH** *020 †50

SAUERS, Patricia Lynn. 300 HIGHLAND AVE 17331 #041-13-1991 L1998 **RO** *020 †80

SHAH, Amit Bhalchandra. 773 CHERRY TREE CT 17331 #041-13-1991 L1998 **RO** *020 †80

SHAH, Vipul Bhupendra. 3130 GRANDVIEW RD 17331 #495-37-1997 L2007 **IM** *100

SHANK, Jessica Ann. ■ 17331 #041-02-2008 *012

SHIPMAN, Robert Harry. 300 HIGHLAND AVE 17331 #010-03-1972 L1982 **DR GS** *020

SHUTE, Barbara Sue. 460 CLOVER LN, MEADOWVIEW FAMILY PRACTICE 17331 #023-01-1983 L1984 **IM** *020 †20

SIDDIQUI, Khalid. 250 FAME AVE, STE 203 17331 #704-02-1985 L1994 **ON** *020 †20

SINGH, Prashant Kumar. 195 STOCK ST 17331 #496-01-1998 L2006 **IM** *020 †20

SMITH, Beth Bowman. 300 HIGHLAND AVE, HANOVER GENERAL HOSPITAL 17331 #041-12-1978 L2003 **EM PD** *020 †55

SMITH, James W. 3130 GRANDVIEW RD 17331 #041-01-1953 L1954 **OBG** *071 †30

SOCRATES, Jess U. 300 HIGHLAND AVE DEPT PATH 17331 #748-02-1973 L1977 **PTH** *020 †50

SPEARS, Paul Frey. 795 CHERRY TREE CT 17331 #041-01-1979 L1983 **GE IM** *071 †20

SROUR, Zaher. 195 STOCK ST, STE 305 17331 #875-01-1999 L2007 **OTO FPS** *020

STAUB, Perpetua Ann. 300 HIGHLAND AVE 17331 #041-13-1990 L2004 **IM** *020 †20

STEIN, Thomas William, Jr. 1230 HIGH ST 17331 #030-06-1999 L2002 **FM** *020 †18

STONER, John Gillespie. 525 MCCOSH ST 17331 #038-06-1978 L1983 **D** *020 †15 ‡

STURTZ, Cindy L. 300 HIGHLAND AVE, HANOVER HOSP 17331 #041-14-1992 L1996 **PTH** *020 †50

SYED, Zeba Aziz. ■ 17331 #065-09-1993 L1999 **DR** *020 †80

SYLVESTER, Alfred P. 195 STOCK ST, STE 306 17331 #041-13-1993 L1995 **PYG** *020 †75

TAN, Desmond Thoan Yong. 1230 HIGH ST, FAMILY FIRST HEALTH 17331 #064-01-2000 L2001 **IM** *020 †20

TAN, Wilson Sy. ■ 17331 #748-01-1989 L1997 **DR** *020 †80

THOMAS, Charles Edmond. 300 BALTIMORE ST 17331 #028-78-1959, ▲ L1962 **AN PUD** *071

TONER, Thomas Jos. 300 HIGHLAND AVE 17331 #023-01-1972 L1977 **OTO** *071 †45

TULISZEWSKI, Robert. 195 STOCK ST, STE D 17331 #033-05-1976 L1977 **U** *020 †95

UGARTE, Marcos Antonio. 300 HIGHLAND AVE 17331 #023-01-1988 L1994 **GS OS** *020 †85

VALDES-DAPENA, Andres. 217 BROADWAY 17331 #041-13-1980 L1984 **PD** *020 †55

WATSON, Michael Roy. 773 CHERRY TREE CT 17331 #041-14-1984 L1989 **RO** *020 †80

WEINBERG, Harold H. ■ 17331 #023-01-1945 L1945 **OTO OS** *071

WILLIAMS, Jason Armstrong. 250 FAME AVE, STE 200 17331 #033-05-2001 L2002 **OPH** *020 †35

YOON, Kyung Ook. 300 HIGHLAND AVE, HANOVER HOSPITAL 17331 #583-01-1971 L2007 **PM** *020 †20

YOUNES, Mamdouh S. 300 HIGHLAND AVE 17331 #330-04-1956 L1969 **OBG** *071 †30

ZICKAFOOSE, David Elliot. 220 POTOMAC AVE 17331 #011-03-1963 L1969 **IM RHU** *020

ZLOTNICK, Jeffrey Alan. 111 PENN ST 17331 #033-05-1982 L2005 **FM FSM** *020 †18

HANOVER TOWNSHIP – LUZERNE

ANISTRANSKI, Joseph A. 665 CAREY AVE 18706 #041-14-1987 L1988 **FM** *020 †18 ‡

BAROODY, Susan Mary. ■ 18706 #041-77-2007, ▲ L2007 **IM** *012

GASOWSKI, Gary Lee. 25 CHARLES ST, STE 7 18706 #041-14-1972 L1974 **DR OS** *020 †80

HORN, Frank Wm. III. 25 CHARLES ST STE 9 18706 #041-12-1974 L1975 **GS** *020 †85 ‡

LIGHTFOOT, Thomas Gene. ■ 18706 #036-01-1989 L2001 **BBK** *020 †50

MENIO, John Nicholas. 133 OXFORD ST 18706 #041-09-1980 L1981 **FM** *020 †18 ‡

WASNICK, William. 22 LEE PARK AVE 18706 #041-02-1944 L1944 **GP** *071

HARLEYSVILLE – MONTGOMERY

BOLANOWSKI, Deborah Jean. 706 MAIN ST, PENNRIDGE PEDIATRIC 19438 #035-19-1982 L1986 **PD** *020 †55

BUCKWALTER, David R. 484 HARLEYSVILLE PIKE 19438 #041-13-1996 L1999 **FM** *020 †18

BURKE, Jerome M. 270 MAIN ST 19438 #035-09-1984 L1986 **GE IM** *020 †20

CARLIER, Curt Charles. 484 HARLEYSVILLE PIKE 19438 #041-13-1996 L1998 **FM** *020 †18

CASSIDY, Michael John. 270 MAIN ST 19438 #041-13-1991 L1993 **GE IM** *020 †20

CHMIELEWSKI, Michael J. 270 MAIN ST, STONERIDGE OBSTETRICS & 19438 #041-13-1992 L1996 **OBG** *020 †30

COPE, Ernest Earl, III. 270 MAIN ST, STE 2 19438 #041-07-1987 L1990 **ORS** *020 †40

DERSTINE, Ralph Lawrence. ■ 19438 #041-13-1964 L1965 **FM** *071 †18

DIGAMBER, Pramod. ■ 19438 #495-21-1968 L1979 **DR OS** *020

DOLHA, Anuta. ■ 19438 #041-15-2004 L2004 **PD** *100 †55

DUPRE, Jayson M. ■ 19438 #041-77-1999, ▲ L2000 **IM** *100

ESKIN, Evamaria Ursula. 670 WHITTAKER WAY 19438 #041-13-1982 L1987 **OM GPM** *020 †70

FACCENDA, Deborah Rogers. 706 MAIN ST, PENNRIDGE PEDIATRIC 19438 #041-01-1988 L1990 **PD** *020 †55

GRASSE, John M, Jr. ■ 19438 #041-02-1952 L1953 **FM P** *071

HIPP, Thomas John. 706 MAIN ST, PENNRIDGE PEDIATRIC 19438 #045-01-1970 L1971 **PD** *020 †55 ‡

HOMEIER, Barbara Pyle. 270 MAIN ST 19438 #041-02-1995 L1999 **PD** *020 †55

KELBERMAN, Ira Avery. 270 MAIN ST 19438 #033-06-1986 L1989 **IM GE** *020 †20 ‡

KENNEDY, Thomas Ignatius. 706 MAIN ST, PENNRIDGE PEDIATRIC 19438 #010-02-1982 L1983 **PD** *020 †55

KIM, Annette Sunhi. ■ 19438 #024-01-1998 L2004 *100

KUPERSMITH, Stephen J. 270 MAIN ST, STONERIDGE OBSTETRICS & 19438 #024-07-1977 L1978 **OBG** *020 †30

LAMBERTH, Erik Fred. 706 MAIN ST, PENNRIDGE PEDIATRIC 19438 #041-13-1995 L1997 **PD** *020 †55 ‡

LAMPARELLA, Nicholas Edwa. ■ 19438 #041-77-2007, ▲ L2007 **IM** *012

LANDES, Ray P. ■ 19438 #041-01-1949 L1950 **IM** *071 †20

LINDBERG, Nicholas Oscar. 270 MAIN ST, STONERIDGE OBSTETRICS & 19438 #041-01-1986 L1988 **OBG** *020 †30

MOYER, Dennis Lee. ■ 19438 #041-09-1968 L1969 **GS** *020 †85

ORTIZ, Daisy. 270 MAIN ST 19438 #041-13-1992 L1996 **GE** *020 †20

O'TOOLE, William J, Jr. 270 MAIN ST 19438 #041-09-1984 L1985 **GE IM** *020 †20 ‡

PAGAN, Mary Elizabeth. 270 MAIN ST, STONERIDGE OBSTETRICS & 19438 #023-01-1989 L1993 **OBG** *020 †30

PATEL, Shalin S. ■ 19438 #041-01-2007 **TY** *012

PIEROTTI, Richard John. 484 HARLEYSVILLE PIKE, TRIVALLEY PRIMARY CARE 19438 #041-02-1976 L1977 **FM** *020 †18

ROTHSTEIN, Edward Paul. 706 MAIN ST, PENNRIDGE PEDIATRIC 19438 #041-13-1967 L1968 **PD** *020 †55

ULASEWICZ, Joseph Thos. 484 HARLEYSVILLE PIKE 19438 #041-09-1985 L1986 **FM** *020 †18

UNDERWOOD, Susan K. 484 HARLEYSVILLE PIKE 19438 #041-07-1988 L1990 **FM** *020 †18

VERMA, Ajay. ■ 19438 #023-07-1991 L1995 **N** *020 †75

WILLIAMS, Elizabeth A. 345 MAIN ST STE 9 19438 #041-09-1993 **PD** *020 †55

HARMONY – BUTLER

PALANISWAMY, Sundaram. 241 PERRY HWY, ELLWOOD PHYSICIAN GROUP 16037 #495-94-1981 L1996 **HO** *020 †20

WAHL, Dayne Frederick. 835 EDMUND ST 16037 #041-12-1958 L1959 **FM PD** *072

WAHL, Jeffry R. 835 EDMUND ST, WAHL & SON'S FAMILY PRACTI 16037 #422-01-1985 L1987 **FM** *020 †18

HARRISBURG – DAUPHIN

ACHARYA, Falguni Ravi. 4700 UNION DEPOSIT RD, STE 220 17111 #665-01-2000 L2006 **PD** *020 †55

ADAMS, Vallee Michelle. ■ 17110 #018-03-1989 L2005 **IM** *062 †20

ADKINS, Russell Eugene. 1310 GREEN ST 17102 #012-01-1984 L2006 **U** *012

ALAWAD ALJALKI, Samir. POLYCLINIC MED CTR, DEPT MED 17110 #875-01-1992 **IM** *100

ALBERT, Adam Jason. ■ 17111 #041-14-2005 L2008 *012

ALEXANDER, Roland R. 750 E PARK DR 17111 #003-01-1979 L1984 **ON HEM** *020 †20

AL-LAHAM, Ammar. 2601 N 3RD ST 17110 #875-01-1998 L2004 **IM** *020 †20

ALUQUIN, Vincent Protacio. 121 N NYES RD, SUITE D MC HP14 17112 #748-02-1994 L2004 **PDC** *100 †55

ALUR, Radha Inagandla. 1821 FULTON ST 17102 #495-62-1991 L2005 **PD** *020 †55

ALVEAR, Domingo Tolentino. 2600 N 3RD ST 17110 #748-01-1965 L1973 **PDS GS** *020 †85

AMMAR, Katherine Lucille. ■ 17112 #950-01-1964 L1971 **PD** *020 †55

AMUSO, Samuel Jos. 2033 LINGLESTOWN RD # 249 17110 #041-02-1964 L1965 **ORS** *071 †40

ANDERSON, Lyle Fredrick, Jr. 2626 N 3RD ST, CAPITAL AREA SURGICAL 17110 #041-12-1976 L1978 **GS** *020 †85

ANDERSON, Tania Elaine. 1800 LINGLESTOWN RD, STE 200 17110 #041-07-1993 L1995 **IM** *020 †20

ANDREWS, Albert Thomas, III. 4518 UNION DEPOSIT RD 17111 #041-09-1968 L1969 **ON HEM** *020 †20

ANGSTADT, Diane. 2215 FOREST HILLS DR, STE 38 17112 #041-14-1986 L1987 **P** *020 †75

ANUSIONWU, Obiora Frank T. 205 S FRONT ST, PINNACLEHEALTH HOSPITALS 17104 #690-04-2005 L2007 **IM** *012

AQUINO, Edwin Abella. 845 SIR THOMAS CT, STE 10 17109 #748-01-1973 L1982 **PM** *020

AQUINO, Elma Teh. 845 SIR THOMAS CT, STE 10 17109 #748-07-1974 L1982 **PM** *074

ARTHUR, Joseph Anthony. 2601 N 3RD ST 17110 #412-02-2002 **IM** *012

ASUZU, Juliet Jane. 1118 N 3RD ST, STE 100 17102 #041-14-1996 L1998 **IM** *020

AZUBIKE, Elizabeth Nkem. 2601 N 3RD ST, PINNACLEHLTH SYS-POLYCLINI 17110 #690-05-1998 L2005 **IM** *012

BAKARE, Ayodeji O. 1821 FULTON ST 17102 #690-01-1978 L1986 **OBG** *020 †30

BALKIR, Levent. 777 E PARK DR 17111 #902-03-1992 L2003 **IM** *100

BALTZ, Richard David. 111 S FRONT ST 17101 #041-09-1959 L1960 **PD HEM** *071 †55

BANDUCCI, Dennis Ray. 2807 N FRONT ST 17110 #005-19-1980 L1988 **PS HS** *020 †65

BARNES, Alice Joar. 2601 N 3RD ST 17110 #550-03-2005 L2005 **DR** *100

BAU, Jennifer Lynn. 17111 #041-14-2004 L2004 **DR** *012

BAUGHMAN, Paul Joseph. 4605 LOCUST LN 17109 #041-77-1998, ▲ L1999 **FM** *020

BEAUCHEMIN, Suzanne M. 4424 OAKHURST BLVD 17110 #065-09-1985 L1997 *020

BECK, Gunhilde. 3601 N PROGRESS AVE, COMMUNITY MEDICAL 17110 #409-10-1975 L1978 **IM** *020 †20

BEITTEL, Chas Rouss, Jr. 111 S FRONT ST 17101 #041-02-1944 L1945 **OBG** *071 †30

BENNETT, Joshua Henry. 3721 TECPORT DR 17111 #023-07-1978 L1987 **FM EM** *030 †16,18

BENTZ, Michael Scott. 100 S 2ND ST 17101 #041-14-1976 L1977 **PTH** *020 †50 ‡

BENTZEN, Brian Douglas. ■ 17111 #041-14-2007 L2007 **AN** *012

BERGHAUS, Lydia Frances. 111 S FRONT ST 17101 #025-01-1976 L1983 **RO** *020 †20,80

BESSELMAN, David M. 4601 DEVONSHIRE RD 17109 #041-01-1962 L1963 **PD PDA** *020 †55

BEUTLER, William Jos. 805 SIR THOMAS CT 17109 #035-06-1983 L1989 **NS OSS** *020 †25 ‡

BHARDWAJ, Atul. 2601 N 3RD ST, PINNACLEHLTH SYS-POLYCLINI 17110 #495-69-1999 L2005 **IM** *012

BHARDWAJ, Neeti. 205 S FRONT ST, PINNACLEHEALTH HOSPITALS 17104 #495-69-1999 L2007 **IM** *012

BIBOSO, Arcadio Jose. ■ 17110 #030-06-2000 L2003 **FM** *020 †18

BISHAI, Emad Mikhail Tewf. 307 S FRONT ST, PINNACLE HEALTH 17104 #915-02-1997 L2005 **P** *020 †75

BLOOMER, Christopher Marc. ■ 17112 #048-02-2002 L2007 *020
BOGDANOVICH, Tatiana. 111 N FRONT ST, DEPT OF MED EDU 17101 #913-78-1999 L2006 IM *012
BONGIOVANNI, Michael B. ■ 17111 #041-01-1976 L1977 PTH *020 †50
BONNEAU, Amy J. 895 S ARLINGTON AVE 17109 #041-14-1988 L1991 PD *020 †55
BORROR, Megan Joann. 4807 JONESTOWN RD, STE 141 17109 #051-04-1988 L1990 FM *020 †18
BOWEN, Karen Anne. 3105 N 4TH ST 17110 #041-01-1983 L1985 IM AN *020 *020
BOWMAN, Herbert Spencer. 111 S FRONT ST 17101 #041-02-1947 L1948 HEM AI *072 †20
BOYD, William Jos. 131 STATE ST 17101 #041-09-1955 L1956 IM *071
BRASON, Frederick Wells. ■ 17112 #065-01-1944 L1955 GS *071 †50
BRAUN, Max. 825 SIR THOMAS CT, STE B 17109 #041-13-1996 L2001 PM *020 †60
BRENNER, Louis Obrasky. ■ 17110 #041-01-1947 L1949 END IM *071 †20
BRENNER-WILLIAMS, Caryn M. 2501 N 3RD ST, KLINE FAMILY PRACTICE CTR 17110 #023-01-1989 L1991 FM *020 †18
BRETTSCHNEIDER, Paul D. 2501 N 3RD ST, MEMORIAL BLDG. - 3RD FLOOR 17110 #023-07-1993 L1997 P *020 †75 ‡
BRIDGEMAN, Pauline. 7780 ROBIN RD 17111 #048-12-1997 L2001 MPD ID *020 †20,55
BROWN, Terry Tyrone. ■ 17110 #021-01-2000 L2001 DR *100 †80
BUCKINGHAM, Robert C. 2601 N 3RD ST 17110 #035-45-1953 L1954 FM *071 †18
BUDGE, Matthew Daniel. ■ 17111 #041-12-2005 L2005 ORS *012
BUI, Tuong Nguyen. 2310 PATTON RD 17112 #041-14-1987 L1989 FM *020 †18
BUKARI, Abdulai M. 43 KLINE PLZ, KLINE PLAZA MEDICAL CENTER 17104 #412-02-1983 L1996 IM *020 †20
BURNS, William Thos. 111 S FRONT ST 17101 #041-13-1945 L1946 OS GYN *030 †30
BUSH, William Bradley. 5100 LANCASTER ST 17111 #041-12-1971 L1972 IM GP *020
CADIEUX, Roger Jos. 2215 FOREST HILLS DR, STE 38 17112 #041-06-1977 L1978 P PYG *020 †75
CARAWAY, William Aaron. ■ 17102 #048-16-2005 L2005 GS *100
CARDINALE, Joseph Peter. 879 S ARLINGTON AVE 17109 #028-78-1972, ▲ L1977 GS TS *020
CARLISI, Joseph Robert. 111 S FRONT ST 17101 #561-01-1980 L1983 IM *020 †20
CARMAN, Robert. ■ 17111 #041-77-2007, ▲ L2007 *012
CARP, Mason Joshua. 4212 LINGLESTOWN RD 17112 #035-19-1973 L1979 OBG *020 †30
CARTER, Ryalynn Morgan. ■ 17111 #041-14-2008 *012
CARY, Gene Leonard. 2601 N 3RD ST 17110 #035-15-1957 L1971 CHP *071 †75
CASSEL, Ralph Douglas. 4401 FARGREEN RD 17110 #041-09-1961 L1962 GS CRS *020 †85
CASTRINA, Frank Paul, Jr. 777 E PARK DR, KEPRO 17111 #041-13-1968 L1969 IM *071 †20
CHALLA, Laxmi Devi. 2601 N 3RD ST 17110 #495-21-2000 L2003 FM *100
CHAMBERS, Christopher P. 111 S FRONT ST 17101 #023-01-1993 L2001 AN *020 †05
CHANG, Byung Doo. 111 S FRONT ST 17101 #583-01-1974 L1979 PD *020 †55
CHAPMAN-ROLLE, Loretta D. 1821 FULTON ST 17102 #041-09-1992 L1995 PD *020 †55
CHARCZUK, Maciej T. 2151 LINGLESTOWN RD, SARAGOTA CTR STE 240 17110 #759-09-1989 L2002 PM *020 †20
CHENG, Jihua. 205 S FRONT ST, PINNACLEHEALTH HOSPITALS 17104 #243-44-1997 L2007 *012
CHEUNG, Esther. ■ 17111 #048-13-2005 OTO *012
CHIMAHOSKY, Jeffrey. 1199 COLONIAL RD 17112 #041-77-1995, ▲ L1998 IM *020
CHMIL, Steven William. ■ 17103 #017-20-2005 L2005 GS *012
CHOTINER, Bennett. 4100 LINGLESTOWN RD 17112 #041-14-1972 L1973 OPH PO *020 †35
CHOTINER, Erik Alan. 4100 LINGLESTOWN RD 17112 #041-02-2001 L2001 OPH *100 †35
CHUGH, Ranjini. 1310 GREEN ST 17102 #496-38-1985 L2006 PD *020 †55
CIMIKOSKI, William J Jr. ■ 17112 #306-01-1991 L2006 ETX *012
CLAYTON, Richard James. 111 S FRONT ST 17101 #041-01-1975 L1978 OM IM *071
CLAYTON, Samuel Thos, Jr. 3320 RIDGEWAY RD, FAMILY MEDICAL CARE 17109 #041-13-1974 L1975 FM *020 †18
COHEN, Mark Howard. 121 N NYES RD STE D 17112 #165-04-1977 L1988 PDC ICE *020 †55
CONSEVAGE, Mary Potera. 3705 VARTAN WAY 17110 #041-01-1989 L1991 PD *020 †55
CONWAY, Joseph Leo, Jr. 4700 UNION DEPOSIT RD, STE 230 17111 #041-14-1998 L2003 OPH *020 †35
CORONADO, Rizalino H. 1801 N FRONT ST 17102 #748-01-1958 L1963 P *020
CREARY, Paul J. 1821 FULTON ST 17102 #035-20-1978 L1980 GS *020 †85
CREUTZBURG, Gina Marie. ■ 17111 #017-20-2003 L2004 DR *012
CRISPEN, James Franklin. 2645 N 3RD ST STE 390 17110 #041-13-1959 L1960 ON HEM *071
CRISPINO, Richard Dale. 4700 UNION DEPOSIT RD # 14 17111 #041-02-1974 L1975 OBG GYN *020 †30
CUETO, Sylvia Marcela. 4300 LONDONDERRY RD 17109 #051-04-1996 L1999 EM *020 †16
CULLEY, Gregory Allen. 2500 ELMERTON AVE 17177 #008-01-1965 L2000 PD *030 †55
CULNAN, Derek Martin. ■ 17111 #033-05-2005 L2005 GS *012
CUMMINGS, Cary, III. 1617 N FRONT ST 17102 #047-07-1976 L1980 CCM NEP *020
DAILEY, Edward Geiser. 111 S FRONT ST 17101 #041-09-1958 L1959 OPH *071 †35
DAUDJEE, Munib Shabbir. 111 S FRONT ST, DEPT OF MED EDU 17101 #495-48-1993 L2006 IM *012
DAUGHTRY, Glen R. 2850 COMMERCE DR, STE 300 17110 #055-75-1987, ▲ L1989 FM IM *020 †18
DAVID-HUGUES, Michelle D. 111 S FRONT ST, NICU OFFICE, 8TH FLOOR 17101 #055-01-1997 L2000 NPM *020 †55 ‡
DAVIS, Robert Hugh. CAMERON AND MACLAY STS 17105 #041-14-1975 L1976 P PFP *030 †75 ‡
DEA, John Yenlan. 2310 PATTON RD, FAMILY CARE-LOWER PAXTON 17112 #023-01-1989 L1991 FM *020 †18
DE ARMITT, Don Alan. 2310 PATTON RD 17112 #041-12-1986 L1988 FM *020 †18
DEDYO, Tanya. 2645 N 3RD ST, 1ST FL 17110 #035-01-1989 L1995 PD *020 †55
DE LONG, Brian Scott. 1511 N FRONT ST 17102 #041-14-1983 L1984 CRS GS *020 †10,85
DESAI, Sweta Arvind. 668 ANTHONY DR 17111 #495-48-1993 L2000 PCC *012 †20
DESCIAK, Matthew Charles. ■ 17111 #041-12-2006 L2006 AN *012
DHATT, Ravinder Singh. 205 S FRONT ST, PINNACLEHEALTH HOSPITALS 17104 #654-01-2005 L2006 IM *012
DIAMOND, Ivona Pesek. 1821 FULTON ST, HAMILTON HEALTH CENTER 17102 #286-03-1984 L1997 PD *020 †55
DIAMOND, Jonathan Russell. 4700 UNION DEPOSIT RD, STE 240 17111 #035-15-1979 L1989 NEP IM *020 †20
DIAMOND, Stephanie Patric. 2151 LINGLESTOWN RD, STE 210 17110 #041-14-1989 L1993 D *020 †15
DIETZIUS, Harold Paul. ■ 17111 #539-03-2002 L2007 CD *012
DINC, Mert. 2601 N 3RD ST 17110 #902-07-1999 L2002 OBG *020

DIRKSEN, Jesse Lee. ■ 17112 #046-01-2006 L2006 GS *012
DI SANTO, Susan Kurucz. ■ 17111 #041-14-1989 L1992 PTH *020 †50
DITLOW, Richard James, Jr. 775 S ARLINGTON AVE, TREATMENT CENTER 17109 #041-13-1974 L1975 RO *020 †80
DONAHUE, Margaret Louise. 111 S FRONT ST, HARRISBURG HOSPITAL 17101 #041-14-1987 L1995 NPM PD *020 †55
DUARTE GUANEME, Angelica. 111 S FRONT ST, PINNACLEHEALTH HOSPITALS 17101 #264-10-2004 L2006 IM *012
DUDA, Laura Margaret. 1821 FULTON ST 17102 #041-01-1993 L1995 PD *020 †55
DUGGAN, Francis Joseph, Jr. 4310 LONDONDERRY RD, STE 209 17109 #035-20-1966 L1971 U *020 †95
DUNHAM, Eleanor F. 111 S FRONT ST, DEPT OF EMERGENCY MEDICINE 17101 #010-02-1995 L2004 EM *020 †16
EBENEZER, Marjorie R. 7 ST & FORSTER, PA DEPT OF HEALTH H&W BLDG 17120 #495-16-1968 L2002 PHP FM *020
ELNOUR, Mohamed Fadl M. 2601 N 3RD ST 17110 #915-08-1974 L1992 NEP IM *020 †20
ELSNER, Cynthia Ann. 2205 FOREST HILLS DR 17112 #041-07-1989 L1991 PD *020 †55
EMERY, John Scott. ■ 17104 #054-04-2004 L2006 *012
ENDARA, Andres Santiago. 2601 N 3RD ST, PINNACLEHLTH SYS-POLYCLINI 17110 #319-08-2001 L2006 IM *012
ENSLEY, John Timothy. ■ 17112 #035-03-2007 L2007 EM *012
ERNST, Brett Bernard. 2509 N FRONT ST, SCHEIN EYE ASSOCIATES 17110 #025-07-1987 L1993 OPH *020 †35
ESTIME, Edriss. 111 S FRONT ST, DEPT OF MED EDU 17101 #104-01-2006 L2006 IM *012
EUGENE, Pierre Bernard. 4700 UNION DEPOSIT RD, STE 140 17111 #440-01-1986 L2000 OBG *020 †20
EVANS, Richard G, III. 1631 N FRONT ST, MED. ASSOCIATES 17102 #041-77-1987, ▲ L1988 PUD *020 †20
EVERHART, Wilson C. 111 S FRONT ST 17101 #041-01-1939 L1940 GYN *075 †30
FABER, Frederick Saml. 121 NYES RD, UNIVERSITY PHYSICIAN GROUP 17112 #041-14-1973 L1975 FM *020 †18
FACKLER, Emerson Floyd. 2601 N 3RD ST 17110 #035-15-1941 L1944 OBG *071 †30
FANNING, Walter Lee. 1310 GREEN ST 17102 #051-01-1970 L1999 IM ID *020 †20 ‡
FAROOQ, Umar. 2601 N 3RD ST 17110 #704-21-2003 IM *012
FARZIN, Safa. 2601 N 3RD ST 17110 #422-01-1998 L2000 CCM *020 †20
FENCEL, Richard M. 2601 N 3RD ST, TRISTAN ASSOCIATES 17110 #041-01-1960 L1961 R *071 †80
FERMO, Carlos Castillo. 2601 N 3RD ST 17110 #748-20-1999 L2001 IM *100 †20
FIEDLER, Eric Paul. 2708 COMMERCE DR, UNIT 2 17110 #035-06-1991 L1993 REN *020 †30
FISCHMAN, Daniel. 205 S FRONT ST, BMAB-3C 17104 #041-14-1998 L2002 MPD *040 †20,55
FISHER, Justin Robert. 4310 LONDONDERRY RD, STE 202 17109 #041-14-2001 L2001 CN *020 †75
FISHER, Robert A. ■ 17111 #041-09-1952 L1953 P *071
FLORE, Leigh Anne. ■ 17111 #025-12-2007 L2007 PD *012
FORTI, William P. 3705 VARTAN WAY 17110 #041-13-1969 L1970 PD *020 †55
FOSTER, Crispin Barry. 111 S FRONT ST 17101 #836-04-1978 L1987 EM FM *020 †18
FRANKEL, Carl Abbott. 1800 LINGLESTOWN RD # 200 17110 #051-07-1980 L1984 OPH PO *020 †35
FRANKEL, Sharon R. 2501 N 3RD ST, 2ND FLOOR LANDIS BLDG 17110 #035-09-1981 L1984 IM *020 †20
FRESHMAN, John Rodney. 845 SIR THOMAS CT, STE 3 17109 #041-02-1967 L1968 IM *020 †20
FRIEDLANDER, Milton Alan. 4518 UNION DEPOSIT RD 17111 #035-19-1959 L1961 NR R *071 †80,28
FRIEDMAN, Mark. 4760 UNION DEPOSIT RD 17111 #035-46-1971 L1978 GE IM *020 †20
FULLER, Lonnie E, Jr. 1821 FULTON ST 17102 #048-02-1988 L1990 IM *020 †20
GANDY, Vivian Marie. ■ 17102 #035-03-1984 L1989 PM *020 †60
GARCIA-CABRERO, Guillermo. 4700 UNION DEPOSIT RD, STE 220 17111 #649-01-1971 L1974 PD PHP *020 †55
GARDYASZ, Miroslaw David. 895 S ARLINGTON AVE, DAROWISH & ASSOC, PC 17109 #041-14-1985 L1986 PD *020 †55
GAREIS, Margarita R. 4518 UNION DEPOSIT RD 17111 #264-05-1988 L1995 HO *020 †55
GARVIN, Robert Paul. ■ 17112 #041-13-2002 L2002 VS *012 †85
GEDER, Laszlo. CAMERON AND MACLAY STS 17105 #473-04-1958 L1982 N PM *020
GEIB, Ann-Jeannett Helene. 111 S FRONT ST, PINNACLE HEALTH - HARRISBU 17101 #033-06-2000 L2006 ETX *020 †16
GEMBUSIA, Keith A. ■ 17111 #041-77-2007, ▲ L2007 *012
GENTILE, Gwen Phyllis. 2601 N 3RD ST, POLYCLINIC HOSPITAL 17110 #041-13-1962 L1964 OBG *020 †30
GEORGE, Paula Balboni. 111 S FRONT ST 17101 #024-01-1979 L1983 PD OS *020 †55
GERLACH, Charles David, IV. 4700 UNION DEPOSIT RD, STE 120 17111 #308-11-1985 L1987 IM *020
GETTE, Michael Timothy. 2201 FOREST HILLS DR, STE 7 17112 #041-13-1987 L1989 D *020 †15
GIBBIN, Candace Lynn. 100 N 2ND ST, RM 4B 17101 #051-04-1976 L2000 PDC PD *020 †55
GILANI, Syed Aamir Masood. 205 S FRONT ST, PINNACLE HLTH HOSP 17104 #704-22-2002 L2008 *100
GILDEA, James Eugene. 100 CHESTNUT ST 17101 #041-09-1959 L1960 AN *071 †05
GILLMAN, Edwin C. 4310 LONDONDERRY RD STE 1, SUSQUEHANNA VALLEY SURGERY 17109 #041-14-1993 L1995 AN CCA *020 †05
GILROY, Robert Cummings. 1631 N FRONT ST 17102 #041-02-1962 L1963 PUD CCM *020 †20
GOEL, Rajat. 2501 N 3RD ST 17110 #010-01-1997 L2004 PCP *020 †50
GOEL, Vidyottama. CAMRON & MCLAY ST, HARRISBURG STATE HOSP 17105 #495-12-1962 L1980 GP PD *071
GOELTSCH, Robert Eduard. 845 SIR THOMAS CT, OBGYN 17109 #041-02-1972 L1973 OBG *020 †30
GOHEER, Aisha Anjum. ■ 17112 #041-14-2005 L2005 AN *012
GOLDMAN, John Douglas. 205 S FRONT ST 17104 #016-02-1990 L1996 ID IM *040 †20
GOLDMAN, Stanley Ralph. 4700 UNION DEPOSIT RD, STE 120 17111 #041-09-1971 L1972 IM CD *020 †20
GONSORCIK, Vicki. ■ 17111 #055-75-2004, ▲ L2004 PTH *012
GONZALEZ, Roberto. 17105 #042-01-1989 L1991 PUD *020 †20
GOODMAN, Bruce. 4800 LINGLESTOWN RD 17112 #041-02-1955 L1956 ORS *071
GOODMAN, Cynthia Diane. 7TH & FORSTER STS, HLTH & WELFARE BLD RM 925 17120 #048-13-1983 L1988 PHP PM *062 †60
GORDON, Dudley Ross. 8012 BRETZ DR 17112 #041-09-1977 L1979 FM *020 †18
GORDON, Joanne Griffiths. ■ 17112 #041-01-1981 L1982 IM *020 †20

■ = Address Information Privacy Protected

GORDON, Robert Alan. 4519 UNION DEPOSIT RD, STE 201 17111 #041-02-1973 L1974 HO HEM *020 †20

GORDON, William Saml. 6091 LINGLESTOWN RD 17112 #041-09-1960 L1961 FM GP *071 †18

GORTON, Christopher Paul. 1821 FULTON ST 17102 #035-01-1984 L1991 PD MDM *020 †55

GRANDON, Raymond Chas. 131 STATE ST 17101 #041-02-1945 L1946 IM CD *071

GRAY, Robert Jos, Jr. 4400 LEWIS RD, CONCENTRA MEDICAL CENTER 17111 #041-14-1992 L1994 FM *020 †18

GREEN, M Edwin, Jr. 500 FISHING CRK VLY RD # R 17112 #041-13-1948 L1949 IM OS *071

GREM, Judith Louise. ■ 17112 #041-09-1976 L1977 GP *075

GREM, Philip Chas. 241 PEACE LN 17112 #041-02-1976 L1977 IM *020 †20

GRIFF, Leonard Clark. 4518 UNION DEPOSIT RD, TRISTAN ASSOC 17111 #869-04-1960 L1962 R DR *075 †80

GROSH, Paul Roebuck. 65 E EAST WING, MAIN CAPITAL BUILDING 17120 #041-09-1964 L1965 IM *071 †20

GUL, Zonaira. 205 S FRONT ST, PINNACLEHEALTH HOSPITALS 17104 #704-21-2004 L2007 IM *012

HA, Chi Duyquyet. PO BOX 8700, PINNACLEHEALTH HOSPITALS 17105 #041-15-2004 L2004 GS *012

HAFER, Robert K. 213 MARKET ST 17101 #041-77-1953, ▲ L1958 *071

HAGEN, Mary E. 205 S FRONT ST 17104 #041-07-1989 L1992 OBG *020 †30

HAKE, Jean Harris. 111 S FRONT ST 17101 #038-06-1960 L1964 CHP *072

HAKKI, Fawaz Zakai. 1310 GREEN ST 17102 #875-01-1987 L2006 GE HEP *020 †20

HALBERT, David Robt. ■ 17112 #041-01-1965 L1966 OBG *071 †30

HALBERT, Douglas Edward. 4200 PROSPEROUS DR, 2025 TECHNOLOGY PKWY 17112 #023-07-1998 L2002 PD *020 †55

HALIM, Kausar. ■ 17110 #704-02-1986 L1994 GS *100

HALL-NDLOVU, Beverly A. 100 S 2ND ST 4A, WEBER OB/GYN ASSOCIATES 17101 #041-14-1992 L1994 OBG *020 †30

HAMEED, M Ahmad. 2501 N 3RD ST, POLYCLINIC CAMPUS 17110 #704-21-1993 L2006 P *020 †75 ‡

HARRISON, Jill Monique. ■ 17103 #016-01-2002 L2006 P *100

HARTMAN, Justin Garrett. ■ 17110 #041-77-2007, ▲ L2007 IM *012

HARTY, James Ronald. 1609 BUCKINGHAM RD 17112 #051-04-1996 L1998 FM *020 †18

HE, Minghua. 3705 VARTAN WAY, FORTI AND CONSEVAGE PC 17110 #243-52-1983 L2000 PD *020 †55

HENAO OCAMPO, Gloria Leti. 111 S FRONT ST, PINNACLEHEALTH HOSPITALS 17101 #264-06-2002 L2006 IM *012

HENDERSON, Terrance E. PO BOX 8700, PINNACLEHEALTH HOSPITALS 17105 #023-01-2000 L2003 GS *100

HERSPERGER, Webb Sellman. 111 S FRONT ST 17101 #023-01-1956 L1961 OTO *071 †45 ‡

HERZEL, Frank Benton, Jr. 17109 #041-13-1956 L1964 P *071 †75

HESPELL, Jennifer Lee. ■ 17112 #041-14-2007 IM *012

HETTICK, Jamie Lynn. 4319 LONDONDERRY RD 17109 #039-05-1989 L1992 IM *020 †20

HILLWIG GARCIA, Jolene Ma. ■ 17112 #041-14-2005 L2005 CHP *012

HOCHSTETLER, Bradley S. ■ 17112 #038-06-2002 L2007 OPH *012

HOLMAN, Michael Jeffrey. 205 S FRONT ST 17104 #005-15-1979 L1995 GS OBG *020 †85

HOWANITZ, Michael Peter. 2310 PATTON RD 17112 #047-06-1966 L1967 GP *072

HUGHES, Ian Michael. 205 S FRONT ST, PINNACLEHEALTH HOSPITALS 17104 #422-01-2007 IM *012

HUSSAIN, Mohammad Junaid. 2601 N 3RD ST 17110 #704-21-2003 IM *012

IMTIAZ, Aized Ali. 111 S FRONT ST, PINNACLEHEALTH HOSPITALS 17101 #704-21-2004 L2006 IM *012

ISKANDAR, Alaa Gamal. ■ 17111 #305-01-1998 L2001 PUD *020 †20 ‡

JACKSON, Mary Beth K. 121 N NYES RD STE E 17112 #041-13-1989 L1991 FM *020 †18

JEREV, Alexandar Stoilov. 1821 FULTON ST 17102 #198-01-1992 L2000 IM *020 †20

JINDAL, Prabha. CAMERON AND MACLAY STS 17105 #496-07-1965 L1983 PD ON *020

JOBE, Lyle Lester. 4800 LINGLESTOWN RD STE 30 17112 #039-05-1990 L1992 P *020 †75

JOHNSON, Calvin B. 7TH AND FORSTER STREETS 17120 #023-07-1993 L1995 PD *020 †55

JOSHI, Monika. 205 S FRONT ST, PINNACLEHEALTH HOSPITALS 17104 #495-37-2001 L2007 IM *012

JOSHI, Nirmal. 205 S FRONT ST 17104 #495-05-1983 L1989 ID *020 †20

JOSHI, Renu. 205 S FRONT ST 17104 #495-05-1985 L1990 END *020 †20

JOUDEH, Jamal. 2601 N 3RD ST 17110 #913-96-2001 L2004 IM *020 †20

JUDD, Seth Christian. 2601 N 3RD ST 17110 #665-02-2005 L2005 GS *012

KAKARIA, Sandeep Kumar. 4640 HIGH POINTE BLVD, STE 60 17111 #047-05-2004 L2006 OPH *035

KALLU, Preeti. 111 S FRONT ST, DEPT OF MED EDUCATION 17101 #495-21-2001 L2005 IM *012

KANDRA, Joseph John. 1711 N FRONT ST, UNIVERSITY PHYSICIANS GROU 17102 #041-14-1996 L1999 MPD *020 †20,55

KANTNER, Anne Constance. 1711 N FRONT ST, UNIVERSITY PHYSICIANS GROU 17102 #041-14-1996 L1999 MPD *020 †20,55

KANTOR, Robert Jay. 205 S FRONT ST, 6TH FL 17104 #035-03-1972 L1975 IM *030 †20

KAPLAN, Keith Charles. ■ 17112 #035-06-2006 L2006 DR *012

KARLICEK, Martin. 2601 N 3RD ST 17110 #286-07-1998 L2004 PCC *012 †20

KATES, Charity. ■ 17110 #041-14-2008 *012

KAUSHIK, Sridhar. 111 S FRONT ST, PINNACLE HEALTH 17101 #496-09-1985 L2002 NPM PD *020 †55 ‡

KAY, Lawrence Edward. 2404 PARK DR 17110 #010-02-1983 L1984 FM *030 †18 ‡

KEENEY, Galen Eugene. FIRSTCARE, RT 22 & COLONIAL RD 17109 #041-13-1956 L1957 FM *071 †18

KEFFER, Rosemary Martha. 4918 LOCUST LN 17109 #041-14-1992 L1994 P *030 †75

KEHR, Anthony Ryan. 205 S FRONT ST, PINNACLE HLTH HOSPS 17104 #654-01-2007 L2008 *012

KELLEHER, John Paul. ■ 17111 #041-14-2006 L2006 NS *012

KELLEY, David Keith. ■ 17110 #041-12-1985 L1987 IM IMG *020 †20

KELLIS, Dana Sterling. 2501 N 3RD ST, 2ND FLOOR LANDIS BLDG 17110 #028-02-1983 L1988 IM CCM *030 †20

KELLY, Kevin James. 4807 JONESTOWN RD, STE 141 17109 #019-02-1984 L1987 FM *020 †18 ‡

KESLER, Kimberly Michele. ■ 17112 #023-01-2005 L2005 OBG *012

KHAFAGY, Tamer Abdellatif. 2601 N 3RD ST, PINNACLEHLTH SYS-POLYCLINI 17110 #915-02-1998 L2005 IM *012

KHALAK, Rubia. 111 S FRONT ST, PEDIATRIX MED 17101 #035-15-1992 L1999 NPM PD *020 †55

KHAN, Mohammad Khalid. 4417A FARGREEN RD 17110 #704-20-1981 L1996 P PME *020 ‡

KHETARPAL, Suneeta. 2601 N 3RD ST, POLYCLINIC HOSPITAL 17110 #060-01-1989 CHP *020 †75

KLEIN, Arthur Leonard. 111 S FRONT ST, HARRISBURG HOSPITAL 17101 #041-02-1964 L1994 PD *020 †55

KNAUB, Mark Andrew. ■ 17112 #041-12-1997 L2000 OSS *020 †40

KNIGHT, Hugh Thos. ■ 17110 #041-09-1953 L1954 EM OM *071 †85

KOERBER, Walter A, Jr. 2000 LINGLESTOWN RD, STE 205 17110 #023-01-1970 L1982 D *020 †15

KOHLER, Gregory Douglas. 4300 LONDONDERRY RD 17109 #041-77-2006, ▲ L2006 *012

KOLASCH, Craig Donald. 123 CONOY ST 17104 #748-21-2001 L2002 GS *020

KONDA, Sangeetha Reddy. 2601 N 3RD ST 17110 #496-01-2001 L2003 OBG *012

KOSTIN, Raymond Francis. 205 S FRONT ST 17104 #030-06-1969 L1970 TS GS *020 †90,85

KRECKO, Valentins Francis. 2215 FOREST HILLS DR, STE 38 17112 #035-45-1986 L1987 P CHP *075

KREHER, Margaret. 2145 N 3RD ST STE 250, POLYCLINIC MED CTR 17110 #035-15-1986 L1990 IM *020 †20

KREISER, Jos Richard, Jr. 2601 N 3RD ST 17110 #041-02-1976 L1977 FM IM *020

KRISHNAMURTHY, Parul. 111 S FRONT ST 17101 #495-96-1984 L2001 OBG *020 †30

KUDAKKASSERIL, Anup Skari. ■ 17112 #495-63-2000 L2005 PD *012

KUNKEL, George Woodruff. 2405 LINGLESTOWN RD 17110 #041-01-1960 L1961 RHU *071 †20

KURIAN, Binumol. 205 S FRONT ST, BMAB 4TH FLOOR 17104 #495-63-1997 L2003 IM *020 †20

KUTZ, Eric M. 805 SIR THOMAS CT 17109 #022-75-2001, ▲ L2001 *020

KWEE, Him Gan. 100 S 2ND ST, MED SCIENCES BLDG-LAB 17101 #506-02-1964 L1977 PTH CLP *020 †50

LABUSKI, Mark Raymond. 4518 UNION DEPOSIT RD, TRISTAN ASSOCIATES 17111 #041-14-1992 L1998 DR *020 †80

LACEY, Paul Gray. 2626 N 3RD ST STE 3 17110 #041-14-1988 L1991 GE *020 †20

LADIE, Danielle Elizabeth. 205 S FRONT ST, HARRISBURG HOSPITAL 17104 #422-01-2007 L2007 GS *012

LAHR, Joseph Wilson. 205 S FRONT ST 17104 #035-45-1976 L1977 FM *020 †18

LAPSIWALA, Apurva Ashok. 4300 LONDONDERRY RD 17109 #496-42-2002 L2003 IM *020 †20

LASEK, Robert W. 111 S FRONT ST, DEPARTMENT OF EMERGENCY ME 17101 #035-06-1984 L1985 EM *020 †16

LAWSON, Herman, Jr. 3601 N PROGRESS AVE, COMMUNITY MEDICAL 17110 #041-14-1975 L1976 FM *020 †20

LAZAR, John Franklin Leop. 2601 N 3RD ST 17110 #422-01-2006 L2006 GS *012

LEBER, David Clair. 2807 N FRONT ST 17110 #041-13-1967 L1971 PS *020 †65 ‡

LEE, Chul Su. 205 S FRONT ST, PINNACLEHEALTH HOSPITALS 17104 #583-27-2000 L2007 IM *012

LEGASPI, Candelaria G. ■ 17110 #748-08-1963 L1976 IM GP *020 †20

LEVIN, Randy. 111 S FRONT ST 17101 #023-01-1981 L1986 N IM *020 †75

LIMANN, Baba Habuguwie. 1631 N FRONT ST, PULMONARY CRITICAL CARE ME 17102 #902-19-1996 L2005 PCC SME *012

LOGAN, John Beach. STATE HOSP 17105 #041-01-1948 L1949 P N *071 †75

LORD, Jacqueline. ■ 17112 #023-07-1967 L1970 GYN *071 †30

LOWDEN, Max Ricardo. ■ 17111 #308-04-1999 L2005 N *012

LUPO, Katherine Elaine. ■ 17112 #041-14-2007 L2007 OBG *012

LURIE, Perrianne. 7TH & FORSTER STS RM 933, PA DEPT HLTH 17120 #035-09-1986 L1994 GPM PHP *062 †70

LUTHER, Robert Jos. ■ 17111 #016-43-1954 L1955 GP FM *071

MACUT, Sylvester Sava. ■ 17111 #041-13-1956 L1957 GP *071

MAGILL, Richard Martin. 205 S FRONT ST 17104 #041-13-1965 L1966 GP *020

MAHON, Marilyn Sohn. ■ 17112 #041-07-1950 L1951 GP *071

MAINGI, Naresh S. 1433 N 2ND ST 17102 #495-12-1967 L1975 PD *020 †55

MALIK, Aqsa. 2601 N 3RD ST 17110 #704-21-1995 L2002 IM *100

MALIN, Thomas Herbert. 111 S FRONT ST 17101 #041-02-1965 L1966 ORS *071 †40

MANCHENO, Rodrigo Medardo. 205 S FRONT ST, PINNACLEHEALTH HOSPITALS 17104 #319-08-2002 L2007 IM *012

MANDAPATI, Rama Devi. 2601 N 3RD ST 17110 #495-21-2000 L2003 IM *100 †20

MANJON, Jose Manuel. 2416 GREEN ST 17110 #308-03-1982 L1986 GYN *020

MARGARYAN, Susanna. 205 S FRONT ST, PINNACLEHEALTH HOSPITALS 17104 #913-38-1987 L2007 IM *012

MARGOLIS, Bernard Marvin. ■ 17112 #041-09-1957 L1958 PD *071 †55

MARIANO, Gregorio Torres. 777 E PARK DR 17111 #748-02-1962 L1999 IM *071 †20

MARJANOVIC, Milorad. 2601 N 3RD ST, PINNACLEHLTH SYS-POLYCLINI 17110 #654-01-2005 L2005 GS *012

MARQUART, Precious Jewel. 121 N NYES RD, STE F 17112 #048-02-2003 L2003 FM *020 †18

MARQUART, Wesley. 205 S FRONT ST, DEPT. OF GEN. SURGERY 17104 #048-02-2003 L2003 GS *012

MARTINEZ, Francis Jerome. 100 S 2ND ST, STE 4B 17101 #028-78-1990, ▲ L1991 OBG *020

MARTINS, Mary Michele. ■ 17112 #038-43-2006 L2006 OBG *012

MASCARENHAS, Vernon Harol. ■ 17112 #495-48-1993 L2003 CD *012 †20

MATLIN, Emily W. 4300 LONDONDERRY RD 17109 #028-78-1979, ▲ L1986 N *062

MAZZA, Thomas Michael. 1511 N FRONT ST 17102 #063-01-2000 L2001 CRS *020 †85

MC ALLISTER, Meada June. 38C HALL MNR, COMM CHECK-UP CENTER 17104 #045-01-1978 L1989 PD ADL *020

MC BRIDE, William W. ■ 17104 #041-02-1951 L1952 *071

MC CALL, William Michael. 417 TRUDY RD, STE 140 17109 #035-09-1962 L1963 OBG *020 †30

MC GRATH, Joseph Michael. 2101 N FRONT ST, STE 3-301 17110 #041-13-1958 L1959 P *020

MC INROY, Robert Donnal. 2601 N 3RD ST 17110 #041-13-1959 L1960 IM END *020 †20

MC KINNEY-BOURNE, Angeliqu. 2501 N 3RD ST 17110 #012-21-1999 L2001 FM *020 †18

MC LAUGHLIN, John P. 4760 UNION DEPOSIT RD 17111 #041-77-1973, ▲ L1978 GE HEP *020 †20

MEHROK, Sandeep. ■ 17111 #495-48-1994 L2001 IM *100 †20

MEI, Haiping. 2151 LINGLESTOWN RD, STE 240 SARATOGA CENTER SU 17110 #243-16-1988 L1999 PM *020 †60

MEIHOFER, Mary A. 2501 N 3RD ST 17110 #041-02-1989 L1992 PCP BBK *020 †50

MEISLER, William Jay. ■ 17111 #035-01-1978 L1991 DR *020 †80

MENEELY, Alfred Wm. 777 E PARK DR 17111 #035-09-1955 L1957 PD *071 †55

MESAROS, Michael John, Jr. HEALTH & WELFARE BLDG, PA DEPT OF HEALTH RM 932 17120 #041-09-1978 L1979 OM IM *062 †20,70,16

MESSIMER, Julie Marie. ■ 17102 #665-02-2005 L2005 OBG *012

MESSNER, Jean Thorsen. 100 CHESTNUT ST 17101 #041-13-1963 L1964 AN *071 †05

MILLER, Lee C. 2209 FOREST HILLS DR # 1 17112 #041-13-1969 L1970 P PYG *020 †75

MISAS, Jose Enrique. 3901 N FRONT ST 17110 #051-04-1978 L1980 GO OBG *020 †30

MISHRA, Gautam. 2509 N FRONT ST 17110 #041-02-1999 L2006 OPH *020 †35

MOGLIA, Bernadine Ann. 205 S FRONT ST, 10TH FL 17104 #041-14-1987 L1990 NPM PD *020 †55

MOLONEY, Joseph David. 2601 N 3RD ST 17110 #041-13-1965 L1966 **GP** *071
MOMIN, Malik Nurmohamed. 6271 RYECROFT DR 17111 #041-14-1987 L1987
  PMM AN *020 †05
MONSOUR, Roy Everett. 111 S FRONT ST 17101 #023-01-1971 L1974 **EM OM** *020 †16
MONTANER, Jose Luis. 2601 N 3RD ST 17110 #042-02-1986 L1987 **P** *075
MONTISANO, Denise Fellin. 4807 JONESTOWN RD, STE 141 17109 #051-04-1991 L1993
  FM *020 †18
MONTRELLA, Mary J. 4700 UNION DEPOSIT RD, STE 240 17111 #041-13-1984 L1989
  NEP IM *020 †20
MOODY, Jack Holland. 4700 UNION DEPOSIT RD #305-01-1985 L1987 **IM** *020 †20
MORGAN, Nashaat Labib Was. 1310 GREEN ST 17102 #915-09-1990 L2005 **IM** *020 †20
MORGANSTEIN, Steven E. 845 SIR THOMAS CT, STE 7 17109 #041-77-1990, ▲ L1994
  PM *020 †60
MORITZ, Troy Allen. 4300 LONDONDERRY RD 17109 #041-78-2003, ▲ L2003 **GS** *020
MORRIS, Karen Sarena. ■ 17103 #008-01-2007 L2007 **TY** *012
MORRISON, David P, Jr. 92 TUSCARORA ST 17104 #041-13-1961 L1962 **OPH** *020 †35
MORTON, John Chas. 2601 N 3RD ST, TRISTAN ASSOCIATES 17110 #023-01-1960 L1969
  DR *072 †80
MOSCOSO, Aurelio A. CAMERON MCCLAY STS 17105 #748-07-1954 L1962 **P GP** *071
MOULTON, Mary T. 2645 N 3RD ST, UPTOWN PROF. BLDG. 3RD FL 17110 #010-02-1993 L1997
  OBG *020 †30
MOVASSAGHI, John Mehzad. 6645 TERRACE WAY UNIT B 17111 #305-01-2000 L2001
  IM *020 †20
MOY, Kai Hong. 2645 N 3RD ST, CHILDREN'S AND TEEN CENTER 17110 #035-03-1983 L1989
  PD *020 †55 ‡
MOYER, Earl Stanton. 111 S FRONT ST 17101 #041-02-1948 L1949 **IM** *071
MURRAY, Richard C. ■ 17112 #041-02-1942 L1943 **GP FM** *071
MYERS, Collin Lewis. 2626 N 3RD ST, CAPITAL AREA SURGICAL 17110 #041-14-1989 L1991
  GS TRS *020 †85
MYERS, Franklin J, III. 1631 N FRONT ST 17102 #041-01-1970 L1971 **PUD CCM** *020 †20
MYERS, Gordon Dale. 111 S FRONT ST 17101 #040-09-1947 L1948 **GS TS** *072 †85,90
NAVARRO, Norman Fernandez. 2645 N 3RD ST, WOMEN'S OUTPATIENT HEALTH 17110
  #041-14-1993 L1996 **OBG** *020 †30
NDLOVU, Hanford. 100 S 2ND ST 4A, WEBER OB/GYN ASSOCIATES 17101 #041-14-1992 L1994
  OBG *020 †30
NELSON-HORAN, Catherine L. ■ 17110 #041-12-1997 L2000 **EM** *020 †16
NEU, Kristoffer Philip. 2601 N 3RD ST, PINNACLEHLTH SYS-POLYCLINI 17110
  #422-01-2005 L2005 **IM** *012
NEVELING, Ulane. 2501 N 3RD ST 17110 #836-04-1981 L2002 **PTH** *020 †50
NGUYEN, Khanh-Ha Dan. ■ 17110 #041-02-2005 L2005 **OBG** *012
NIKOLAI, Cody Allenrogan. ■ 17111 #056-05-2005 L2005 **ORS** *012
NOZARI, Ala. 777 E PARK DR 17111 #858-03-1992 L2003 **AN** *020
O'BRIEN, Lenore Rice. ■ 17110 #041-01-1923 L1924 **P IM** *100
O'CONNELL, Barbara Ellen. 4310 LONDONDERRY RD, STE 202 17109 #041-14-1980 L1981
  NM N *050 †75
OETTING, Lori Alison. 875 S ARLINGTON AVE, CENTRAL PENN BREAST CARE C 17109
  #041-12-1981 L1982 **GS** *020 †55
OLARTE, Fabio. 2601 N 3RD ST, POLYCLINIC MED CTR 17110 #264-04-1971 L1979
  NPM PD *020 †55
O'LEARY, Amber Catherine. ■ 17112 #041-14-2006 L2006 **OBG** *012
OLMSTEAD, Phillip M. 100 S 2ND ST, DEPT OF PATHOLOGY 17101 #010-01-1968 L1983
  ATP DMP *020 †18,50 ‡
O'MALLEY, Thomas Chas. 2626 N 3RD ST, STE 2A 17110 #041-14-1990 L1993 **OBG** *020 †30
OMOTOSO, Omolola Ajoke. 2601 N 3RD ST, PINNACLEHLTH SYS-POLYCLINI 17110
  #690-02-1999 L2005 **IM** *012
OSWALD, Niccole Mambu. 1310 GREEN ST 17102 #041-02-1999 L2001 **FM** *020 †18
PACZYNSKI, Richard Paul. 4310 LONDONDERRY RD, PINNACLE HEALTH NEUROLOGY 17109
  #026-08-1989 L2001 **N** *020 †75
PAPANDREA, Augustus Jos. 4300 DEVONSHIRE RD 17109 #041-13-1975 L1976 **FM** *020 †18
PARTOVI, Iris. 2601 N 3RD ST, PINNACLEHLTH SYS-POLYCLINI 17110 #286-03-2001 L2005
  IM *012
PASSARIELLO, Christopher. 2601 N 3RD ST 17110 #305-01-2004 L2004 **GS** *012
PASZKOWIAK, Barbara. 1310 GREEN ST 17102 #759-10-1996 L2005 **IM** *020
PATEL, Shashikant B. 4518 UNION DEPOSIT RD 17111 #495-23-1966 L1972 **ON HO** *020 †20
PATEL, Shreya Manubhai. 100 S 2ND ST 4A, MEDICAL SCIENCES BUILDING 17101
  #041-02-1996 L1999 **OBG** *020 †30
PAULIKS, Linda Barbara. 121 N NYES RD, PENN STATE UNIVERSITY PEDI 17112
  #409-33-1991 L2007 **PD PDC** *020 †55
PEISNER, David B. 100 S 2ND ST 4B, MATERNAL FETAL MEDICINE OF 17101
  #025-07-1978 L2008 **MFM OBG** *020 †30 ‡
PENDHARKAR, Ninad Chandra. ■ 17111 #041-14-2007 L2007 **IM** *012
PENDRAK, Robert Francis. ■ 17111 #041-09-1972 L1973 **IM** *030 ‡
PENNYPACKER, Jason Lee. ■ 17111 #041-14-2003 L2003 **DR** *012
PEROUTKA, Kathryn Ann. 4518 UNION DEPOSIT RD 17111 #023-01-1975 L1984
  ON HEM *020 †20
PERROTTI, Andrew. 4700 UNION DEPOSIT RD # 1 17111 #030-06-1996 L2000 **OBG** *020 †30
PETERSEN, Christopher A. 3211 N FRONT ST, STE 102 17110 #012-01-1976 L1996
  CHP P *020 †75
PICCIOTTO, Maurice Ralph. 2201 FOREST HILLS DR 17112 #429-01-1980 L1983 **P** *072
PIERINI OROZCO, Monica Ca. ■ 17112 #935-03-1995 L2006 **IM** *012
PILEK, Eugene John. ■ 17110 #035-20-1971 L1989 **P** *071 †75
PIPER, James Anthony. 2601 N 3RD ST 17110 #016-45-1982 L1986 **PTH** *020 †50
PLAUT, Martin R. 702 SHOWERS ST 17104 #024-05-1956 L1976 **NS** *030 †25
POKORNY, Jeffrey John. 2807 N FRONT ST 17110 #038-44-1996 L2002 **HS** *020 †65
POPAT, Anjana G. 1821 FULTON ST 17102 #495-80-1914 L1978 **PD** *020
POTTER, Lizabeth Ann. 5351C JAYCEE AVE, RR 22 17112 #305-01-1998 L2001 **CHP** *100
POTTS, Jennifer Rae. ■ 17103 #038-44-2007 L2007 **OBG** *012
POWELL, John David, Jr. 205 S FRONT ST, HARRISBURG HOSPITAL 17104 #422-01-2007 L2007
  GS *012
POWERS, Stephen Kent. 4310 LONDONDERRY RD, STE 202 17109 #038-40-1977 L1992
  NS LM *025
PRAKASH, Charu Gupta. 111 S FRONT ST, DEPT OF MED EDU 17101 #495-05-1997 L2006
  IM *012
PRENSNER, Richard W. 2501 N 3RD ST, KLINE FAMILY PRACTICE 17110 #036-05-1990 L1992
  FM OBS *020 †18
PRICE, Shawn Lamar. ■ 17111 #038-40-2005 L2005 **ORS** *012

PRUDENCIO, Jose Naval, Jr. 2151 LINGLESTOWN RD, STE 120 17110 #748-10-1978 L1986
  U *020
PURAYIDOM, Annilyn Sebast. ■ 17112 #495-31-2002 L2006 **PTH** *012
QUESADA VARGAS, Manuel F. 111 S FRONT ST 17101 #649-01-1963 L1970 **GS** *020 †85
QUIRK, Brian Carey. 2151 LINGLESTOWN RD, STE 100 17110 #035-08-1980 L1981 **GP** *020 †18
RAJESH, Chindanoor Venkat. 2601 N 3RD ST, PINNACLEHLTH SYS-POLYCLINI 17110
  #496-35-1993 L2005 **IM** *012
RALEV, Georgi Kolev. 2601 N 3RD ST 17110 #198-02-1994 L2005 **IM** *012
RAY, Subir. 891 S ARLINGTON AVE 17109 #032-01-1985 L1991 **GS** *020 †85
RAYNER, Richard Mark. 121 N NYES RD STE A, UPG NYES ROAD 17112 #041-02-1987 L1991
  FM *020 †18
REDCROSS, Joseph W.. 205 S FRONT ST, BRADY 9 17104 #018-75-2003, ▲ L2003 **GS** *012
REDDY, Patricia Anne. 4217 KIRKWOOD RD 17109 #041-14-1979 L1980 **GYN REN** *020 †30
REILLY, Desmond John. ■ 17110 #539-04-1965 L1971 **AN** *071 †05
RICHARD, David Curtis. 121 N NYES RD 17112 #035-15-1984 L1985 **FM** *020 †18
RICHARDS, Andrew John. 1511 N FRONT ST 17102 #035-20-1986 L1992 **CRS** *020 †85,10 ‡
RIGBERG, Corey Nyles. 111 S FRONT ST, HARRISBURG HOSPITAL 17101 #024-01-1971 L1997
  PYG P *030 †20,75 ‡
RIVEROS, Carlos Alberto. 2601 N 3RD ST, PINNACLEHLTH SYS-POLYCLINI 17110
  #264-19-1991 L2005 **IM** *012
ROBINSON, Bradley Wm. 100 S 2ND ST, RM 4B 17101 #036-01-1986 L1992 **PDC** *020 †55
RODRIGUEZ, Adolfo E. 777 E PARK DR 17111 #041-13-1961 L1962 **GS CRS** *071 †85
ROGERS, John Paul, Jr. 205 S FRONT ST, BRADY HALL FAM PRAC CTR 17104
  #051-04-1989 L1991 **FM** *020 †18
ROHRABAUGH, Chas Merton. 2601 N 3RD ST 17110 #041-01-1956 L1957 **OBG** *071 †30
ROLLE, William Arthur, Jr. 4310 LONDONDERRY RD 17109 #041-09-1990 L1992 **PM** *020 †60
RONDON, Eliseo Josue. 777 E PARK DR 17111 #308-01-1994 L2001 **CCM** *012
ROQUE, Raymond Santos. ■ 17111 #748-01-2002 L2007 **FM** *100 †18
ROSCA, Mihaela Lacramioar. ■ 17111 #781-03-1998 L2005 **IM** *012
ROSE, Joel Eugene. 121 NYES RD 17112 #048-13-1984 L1987 **PD** *020 †55
ROSEN, Kerry Leland. 121 N NYES RD STE D 17112 #011-04-1990 L1993 **PDC** *020 †55
ROSSOTTI, Edgardo Maximo. ■ 17104 #132-02-1968 L1974 **CD** *074 †20
RUBIN, Morton Louis. 111 S FRONT ST 17101 #041-02-1967 L1968 **ORS** *020 †40
RUDY, Frank Raymond. 100 S 2ND ST, MEDICAL SCIENCES BLDG 17101 #041-12-1974 L1975
  PTH *020 †50
RUSSEK, Edward. 1800 LINGLESTOWN RD STE 40 17110 #041-14-1974 L1975 **P** *020 †75 ‡
RUSSELL, Richard L. 111 S FRONT ST 17101 #039-01-1949 L1956 **TS** *071 †85,90
SAACKS, Dennis L. 2310 PATTON RD 17112 #836-02-1969 L1988 **FM** *020 †20
SACHS, Larissa Viktorovna. 2601 N 3RD ST 17110 #913-11-1999 L2004 **RHU** *012 †20
SAKMAR, Katherine A. 205 S FRONT ST, STE 3C 17104 #016-02-1984 L2005 **IM** *020 †20
SALVA, Renato H. CAMERON MCCLAY STS 17105 #748-01-1944 L1962 **P N** *020
SALVAGGIO, Heather Leanne. ■ 17111 #041-14-2007 L2007 **IM** *012
SAMKOFF, Judith Sheila. 777 E PARK DR, KEPRO 17111 #041-07-1985 L1986 **OS PHP** *071
SANTO, Jean Louise. 2501 N 3RD ST 17110 #041-09-1984 L1985 **PME PMM** *020 †05
SARKAR, Monali. 2601 N 3RD ST 17110 #495-09-2000 L2004 **IM** *020 †20
SAUERTIEG, Elliott Abbey. ■ 17110 #041-09-1956 L1957 **OS GYN** *020 †30
SAYE, William Henry, Jr. 2201 FOREST HILLS DR, STE 7 17112 #041-14-1975 L1976 **D** *020 †15
SCHEIN, Alan Lance. 2509 N FRONT ST 17110 #041-02-1969 L1973 **OPH GP** *020 †35
SCHIETROMA, John Jos. 4700 UNION DEPOSIT RD #230 17111 #041-14-1981 L1982
  OPH *035
SEIDLICH, Franklin T. 2416 GREEN ST 17110 #035-03-1969 L1973 **OBG** *020 †30
SEPAHPANAH, Farshad. 205 S FRONT ST, PINNACLEHEALTH HOSPITALS 17104
  #517-08-1995 L2001 **IM** *100 †20
SEWALL, Warren. 2501 N 3RD ST, POLYCLINIC HOSP 17110 #024-01-1967 L1974
  RO *020 †80 ‡
SEWERIN, Barbara. ■ 17101 #041-01-75-2007, ▲ L2007 **MPD** *012
SHAFFER, Carolyn Wine. 2300 FISHING CREEK VALY RD 17112 #017-20-1971 L1975
  TS *020 †85,90
SHAH, Chirag Vijay. 777 E PARK DR 17111 #028-46-2000 L2004 **PCC** *012 †20
SHARMA, Rohini. 2601 N 3RD ST, PINNACLEHLTH SYS-POLYCLINI 17110 #495-55-2001 L2003
  ID *012
SHAW, Lewis Chas, III. 111 S FRONT ST, HARRISBURG HOSP EMER DEPT 17101
  #041-14-1983 L1984 **EM** *020 †16
SHOWALTER, Martha Ferne. ■ 17112 #041-14-2007 L2007 **IM** *012
SHOWELL, Nakiya Naomi. ■ 17112 #033-06-2007 L2007 **PD** *012
SIDOROV, Jaan Erik. 413 VILLAGE WAY, SIDOROV HEALTH SOLUTIONS 17112
  #041-14-1981 L1984 **IM** *020 †20
SIEGELBAUM, Steven Peter. 2626 N 3RD ST, STE 3A 17110 #033-05-1974 L1979
  GE IM *020 †20
SILVER, Lawrence. ■ 17112 #041-02-1966 L1967 **OBG** *071 †30
SIMMONDS, Mary Anne. 4518 UNION DEPOSIT RD 17111 #041-07-1975 L1976
  ON HEM *020 †20
SIMMONS, John Wesley. 1171 S CAMERON ST, PA BUREAU OF DIS DETER 17104
  #041-09-1967 L1969 **GPM AM** *071 †70
SIRAGOWNI, Sowmya. 2601 N 3RD ST 17110 #496-39-2000 L2004 **IM** *020
SIVARAJAH, Surendra. 205 S FRONT ST, BRADY HALL,4TH FLOOR 17104 #041-14-2002 L2002
  END *012
SKARUPA, Steven John. 2501 N 3RD ST 17110 #041-09-1982 L1983 **PTH IM** *020 †20,50
SMALLEY, Aaron David. ■ 17111 #010-01-2004 L2004 **OPH** *012
SMITH, Eric Brandon. 100 S 2ND ST RM 4B 17101 #041-02-2000 L2001 **ORS** *020
SMITH, Michael F, Jr. 111 S FRONT ST 17101 #033-05-1988 L1992 **CD ICE** *020 †20
SOLLENBERGER, Larry Lee. 1511 N FRONT ST, SOLLENBERGER COLON & RETCA 17102
  #041-13-1980 L1981 **CRS** *020 †10,85 ‡
SOLLER, Herbert Isaac. 100 CHESTNUT ST 17101 #041-09-1962 L1963 **NEP IM** *071 †20
SOMMARIPA, Amory Mstislav. ■ 17111 #051-01-1961 L1962 **OS FM** *071 †18
SOUDER, Matthew Glen. 111 S FRONT ST, DEPT OF MED EDU 17101 #422-01-2006 L2006
  GS *012
SOUTHAM, Jodi Dew. ■ 17101 #010-02-2005 L2005 **ORS** *012
SPATZ, Christin Mary. ■ 17111 #041-14-2007 L2007 **PD** *012
SPIEGELMAN, Jay. ■ 17110 #041-13-1940 L1942 **IM OM** *071 †03
SPIGNER, Donald Wayne. 3601 N PROGRESS AVE, COMMUNITY MEDICAL 17110
  #005-02-1966 L1971 **FM PM** *020 †18
SPILK WALL, Samson John. 2601 N 3RD ST 17110 #649-13-2002 L2005 **IM** *012
SRINIVASA, Raghavendra. 2601 N 3RD ST 17110 #496-35-1993 L2001 **CHP** *020 †75
STEINIG, Jeffrey Daniel. ■ 17110 #041-15-2004 L2004 **DR** *012

STEPP, Jason Christopher. ■ 17112 #039-01-2007 L2007 **IM** *012

STERSTE, Andrea M. 2601 N 3RD ST 17110 #041-14-1987 L1989 **FM** *020 †18

STILES, Monica Chadha. 205 S FRONT ST, BRADY MEDICAL ARTS BUILDIN 17104 #056-05-2003 L2003 **END** *012 †20

STOCK, Heather Elizabeth. ■ 17110 #041-14-2006 L2006 **IM** *012

SUMBATIAN, Barbara. 205 S FRONT ST 17104 #913-19-1980 L2001 **CHP** *020

SUNG-SUN, Yuan Mei. CAMERON MACLAY STS POUCH A 17105 #025-01-1946 L1963 **P** *020

SURAPANENI, Rakesh. 777 E PARK DR 17111 #496-24-2001 L2003 **IM** *100 †20

SWALLOW, Nicole Ann. ■ 17111 #041-14-2005 L2005 **IM** *012

SWARTZ, Oliver Henry, Jr. ■ 17112 #041-01-1947 L1948 **OS** *030

TADAVARTHY, Jyothi Pavani. 1100 S CAMERON ST, . 17104 #495-50-1980 L1988 **CHP** *020

TAHERI, Mohammad Reza. 2601 N 3RD ST, PINNACLEHLTH SYS-POLYCLINI 17110 #847-04-1999 L2003 **IM** *100 †20

TAN, Aaron. 777 E PARK DR 17111 #065-06-2004 L2004 **MPD** *012

TAN, Yoke Yee. 4700 UNION DEPOSIT RD, STE 220 17111 #624-01-1969 L1976 **PD ID** *020 †55 ‡

TASWIR, Rahat. 2209 FOREST HILLS DR STE 1 17112 #704-02-1992 L1999 **P** *020 †75

TAYLOR, James Swan, III. 111 S FRONT ST, HARRISBURG HOSPITAL, 17101 #041-14-1971 L1972 **EM OM** *020 †16

TEGENE, Benyam Gessesse. 4918 LOCUST LN, SERVICES 17109 #286-03-1988 L2002 **CHP** *020 †75

THORNSLEY, Susan Lynn. 3300 N 3RD ST 17110 #041-02-1983 L1984 **CHP P** *020 †75

TIYYAGURA, Pavan Kumar. ■ 17111 #495-11-2003 **IM** *012

TKATCH, Lisa Shumaker. 205 S FRONT ST, BRADY HALL 3RD FL 17104 #041-14-1987 L1989 **FM** *020 †18

TOMASELLO, Donald Carl. 777 E PARK DR 17111 #041-02-1996 L1999 **GS** *020 †85

TRAIN, Henry Danl. 1465 OLD COLONIAL RD 17112 #035-08-1974 L1978 **VS OBG** *020 †30

TRAN, Quynh Chi Thuy. 2601 N 3RD ST, PINNACLEHLTH SYS-POLYCLINI 17110 #422-01-2001 L2001 **IM** *020 †20

TRAUTLEIN, Joseph James. PO BOX 67103, 3721 TECPORT DR 17106 #035-09-1966 L1970 **OS A** *071 †20,03

TRESSLER, Terry B. 100 S 2ND ST, RM 4B 17101 #028-78-1981, ▲ L1982 **OBG** *020

ULRICH, Richard Gary. 111 S FRONT ST 17101 #041-13-1959 L1960 **GS CRS** *020 †85

UNAL, Abdurrahman. 775 S ARLINGTON AVE, GREATER HARRISBURG CANCER 17109 #902-05-1974 L1980 **RO** *020 †80

VANNOORD, Brandon Alan. ■ 17110 #005-06-2005 L2006 *100

VARMA, Bhupinder Kumar. 2601 N 3RD ST, PINNACLE HEALTH SYSTEM 17110 #495-36-1964 L1974 **PD IG** *020 †55

VARMA, Neena Paul. 2205 FOREST HILLS DR, STE 12 17112 #495-08-1967 L1984 **PD** *020 †55

VELIUONA, Michael A. 4760 UNION DEPOSIT RD 17111 #143-11-1999 L2001 **GE** *020 †20

VIOLAGO, Eduardo S. 2151 LINGLESTOWN RD, STE 240 SARATOGA CENTER 17110 #748-01-1972 L1978 **PM** *020 †60

VON RAGO, Lawrence Laszlo. 3235 N 3RD ST 17110 #041-14-1992 L1994 **P** *020 †75

WAGNER, Drue Orin. 3940 LOCUST LN, PRIMECARE MEDICAL, INC. 17109 #005-12-1985 L1987 **FM GS** *020 †18

WAIT, Amanda Geraldine. ■ 17111 #028-78-2006, ▲ L2006 **OBG** *012

WAIT, David Aurele. 845 SIR THOMAS CT STE 6 17109 #305-01-1995 L1998 **IM** *020

WALKER, Kimberly Camille. 2030 N 3RD ST, FAMILY CLINIC 17102 #021-01-1987 L1989 **CHP** *020 †75

WALLENDJACK, John C. 3721 TECPORT DR, PO BOX 67103 17111 #010-02-1976 L1977 **IM** *030 †20

WARD, Samuel Porter. 2501 N 3RD ST 17110 #024-01-1968 L1973 **ATP** *071 †50

WARREN, William Stuart. 2601 N 3RD ST 17110 #010-01-1960 L1963 **PD ID** *020 †55

WASKO, Margery Lynn. 1821 FULTON ST 17102 #035-01-1981 L1989 **PD ADL** *020 †55

WATANABE, Miki. 2601 N 3RD ST, PINNACLEHLTH SYS-POLYCLINI 17110 #572-57-1999 L2005 **IM** *012

WATKIN, Walter Brown, Jr. 845 SIR THOMAS CT, STE 3 17109 #041-02-1967 L1968 **IM** *020

WEBB, Desiree Mae William. 4601 DEVONSHIRE RD 17109 #023-07-1994 L2001 **PD** *020 †55

WEBB, Gary Allen. 1310 GREEN ST 17102 #654-01-2002 L2002 **IMG** *020 †18

WEBER, Harry Peter. 111 S FRONT ST 17101 #036-01-1997 L2000 **PD** *020 †55

WEBER, Martin Raymond. 3560 N PROGRESS AVE, # 233 17110 #660-03-1956 L1963 **OPH** *071

WESSNER, Susan Lee. 1199 COLONIAL RD 17112 #041-77-1987, ▲ L1988 **GPM GS** *040

WESTACOTT, Simon. 111 S FRONT ST, DEPT OF RADIOLOGY 17101 #917-21-1980 L1993 **R** *020 †80

WESTRA, Kevin Chas. 2601 N 3RD ST 17110 #041-77-1990, ▲ L1991 **GE** *020 †20

WHEELER, Glen Nelson. 3320 RIDGEWAY RD, FAMILY MEDICAL CARE 17109 #041-09-1970 L1971 **GP PD** *020 †20

WIECKS, Michael James. 2501 N 3RD ST, POLYCLINIC HOSPITAL, 3RD F 17110 #026-04-1982 L1985 **PME AN** *020 †05

WIEGAND, David Alan. 2601 N 3RD ST 17110 #041-14-1981 L1983 **OTO HNS** *020 †45

WILKINSON, Michael John. ■ 17112 #025-07-1986 L2003 **OPH PS** *020 †35

WILLIAMS, Anita. ■ 17106 #021-01-1998 L2000 **FM** *100

WILLIAMS, Arthur L, II. 1821 FULTON ST 17102 #023-01-1991 L1995 **HEM** *020

WILLIAMS, Jessica Ying. 899 S ARLINGTON AVE, ARLINGTON PROFESSIONAL CTR 17109 #243-47-1983 L1997 **PMM OM** *020 †20

WILLIAMS, Paul D. 100 S HOUCKS RD, HOUCKS ROAD FAMILY PRACTIC 17109 #041-77-1986, ▲ L1987 **FM** *020 †18

WILLIAMS, Roy Allen, Jr. 4518 UNION DEPOSIT RD 17111 #055-02-1996 L2006 **HO** *020 †20

WILLIS, Gregory Scott. 3901 N FRONT ST 17110 #048-78-1994, ▲ L1996 **OBG GO** *020

WILSON, Jack Edward. 2626 N 3RD ST, CAPITAL AREA SURGICAL 17110 #041-13-1980 L1981 **GS** *020

WINGARD, Barry A. 3721 TECPORT DR, HEALTH AMERICA 17111 #041-12-1978 L1980 **MDM PHP** *030 †85,10

WISMAN, Craig Burton. 111 S FRONT ST, PINNACLE HEALTH SYS 17101 #041-14-1979 L1980 **MDM** *030 †85,90

WITTE, Eric Henry. ■ 17111 #041-02-1978 L1983 **OS** *075

WOLFE, Lewis Timothy. ■ 17112 #041-09-1984 L1992 **PDC PD** *020 †55

YANG, Harold Chiling. 205 S FRONT ST, BRADY MEDICAL ARTS BUILDIN 17104 #016-02-1980 L1987 **GS OS** *020 †85

YAO, Jing. ■ 17113 #041-14-2003 L2003 **DR** *012

YENCHICK, Albert Thos. ■ 17111 #041-07-1976 L1977 **FM** *030 †18

YORK, Eugene Paul. 4300 LONDONDERRY RD 17109 #308-07-1982 L1982 **IM** *020 †20

ZEIGLER, Maurice L, Jr. 2601 N 3RD ST 17110 #041-02-1960 L1961 **AN OS** *071

ZUCKERMAN, Robert Mark. 2151 LINGLESTOWN RD, STE 160A 17110 #305-01-1983 L1984 **AI PDA** *020 †03,55

HARRISON VALLEY – POTTER

VEERABATHINI, Mukundam. 4309 SR 49 16927 #495-21-1978 L2001 **CHP** *020

HARRISVILLE – VENANGO

FEDEROFF, Susan Theresa. 321 E MERCER ST 16038 #043-01-1987 L1989 **FM** *020 †18

SPRANDO, Christopher. 321 E MERCER ST 16038 #041-12-2003 L2003 **FM** *020 †18

HARWICK – ALLEGHENY

NOVAK, Joseph. ■ 15049 #154-01-1950 L1961 **PM** *071 †60

HASTINGS – CAMBRIA

IGNACIO, Glicerio V, Jr. 189 LAUREL DR 16646 #748-07-1964 L1979 **GP** *071

HATBORO – MONTGOMERY

ATILLASOY, Ercem Sirri. 331 N YORK RD 19040 #008-01-1991 L1994 **D** *050 †15

CHOI, Cheuk Kin. ■ 19040 #308-11-1984 *100

CLARK, Francis J. 331 N YORK RD, OPHTHALMILOGY PHYSICIANS&S 19040 #041-02-1986 L1986 **OPH** *020 †35

CLARK, Frank. 331 N YORK RD 19040 #041-02-1944 L1944 **OPH EM** *020

FINEMAN, Jay Stuart. 2300 DOUGLASS LN 19040 #041-02-1986 L1991 **AN PME** *020 †05

FISHER, Norman J. ■ 19040 #041-02-1949 L1950 **FM** *071 †18

GRAVELEY, Michael John. 345 N YORK RD 19040 #041-13-2000 L2001 **FSM** *020 †18

HORN, William Alan. 331 N YORK RD 19040 #041-01-1982 L1983 **D** *020 †15

MILLER, Thomas Jos. ■ 19040 #035-45-1976 L1993 **DR** *020 †80

MILLER, Thomas Jos. 345 N YORK RD, BOX 606 19040 #041-13-1975 **FM** *020 †18

MONTEFORTE, Joseph S. 358 S WARMINSTER RD 19040 #422-01-1988 L1991 **ID** *020 †20

O'CONNOR, Michael Patrick. ■ 19040 #023-07-1981 **IM** *074 †20

PESCE, Suzanne Jennifer. 331 N YORK RD 19040 #010-01-1996 L2007 **OPH** *020 †35

REDICAN, Lindsay Alison. 345 N YORK RD 19040 #041-13-2005 L2005 **PD** *012

ROGERS, Nadine Elizabeth. 2460 BYBERRY RD 19040 #041-07-1998 L2000 **P** *020

ROSEN, Rachel Eve. 345 N YORK RD 19040 #041-02-1998 L2000 **FM** *020 †18

SNYDER, Harry Dean. ■ 19040 #041-02-1958 L1959 **OPH AM** *071 †35

SOCK, Jennifer Deeney. ■ 19040 #041-15-2006 L2006 **OBG** *012

STEFFENS, Arnold Otto. 345 N YORK RD 19040 #041-02-1964 L1965 **OBG** *020 †30

SWIDER, Deborah Anne. 345 N YORK RD 19040 #041-15-1999 L2001 **FM** *020 †18

ZUCKER, Eli Warren. 345 N YORK RD 19040 #041-09-1966 L1967 **FM** *072 †18

HATFIELD – MONTGOMERY

DY, Caridad Mercado. ■ 19440 #748-01-1958 L1967 **AN** *071 †05 ‡

GOLDBERG, Louis. ■ 19440 #041-02-1939 L1940 **OPH** *071 †35

KARI, Manjula. ■ 19440 #041-15-2006 L2006 **PD** *012

LUPIN, Gordon W. MAIN ST AND OVERBROOK RD 19440 #041-02-1951 L1952 **FM** *071 †18

SEAVY, George N. 115 E BROAD ST 19440 #041-77-2002, ▲ L2002 *020

SESTITO, Maureen A. 115 E BROAD ST 19440 #041-77-2002, ▲ L2002 **IM** *100

SOPKA, Dennis Michael. ■ 19440 #041-15-2008 *012

ZAMANSKY, Gregory. ■ 19440 #913-01-1962 L1988 **GP FM** *071

HAVERFORD – MONTGOMERY

ADLER, Scott Howard. 419 LANCASTER AVE 19041 #023-01-1995 L1999 **NEP** *020 †20

ALEXANDER, Saml Craighead. ■ 19041 #041-01-1955 L1960 **OS AN** *071 †05

ALLEN, Amy Joanne. 600 HAVERFORD RD, STE 100 19041 #041-02-1985 L1987 **PD** *020 †55

ATILLASOY, Suzan Marie. ■ 19041 #035-09-1990 L1993 **PD** *020 †55

BARNETT, Marvin. ■ 19041 #041-09-1947 L1948 **IM GE** *071 †20

BARNHART, Kathleen Shelly. 600 HAVERFORD RD, STE 100 19041 #041-09-1978 L1983 **PD** *020 †55

BERMAN, James Craig. 355 LANCASTER AVE, STE 201 19041 #041-09-1982 L1983 **IM ADM** *020 †20

BHAT, Shazia F. 370 LANCASTER AVE 19041 #041-01-2006 L2006 **PD** *012

BISHOP, Harry Craden. ■ 19041 #024-01-1945 L1955 **PDS** *071 †85

BLOCK, Gilbert Alan. ■ 19041 #038-06-1981 L1988 **N** *074

BOK, John B. ■ 19041 #041-13-1944 L1945 **P AM** *071 †70,75

BOWEN, Thales, Jr. ■ 19041 #041-01-1952 L1954 **AN** *071 †05

BROWN, Sarah Carty. 100 LLANALEW RD, UNIT 3 19041 #041-02-1977 L1978 **OM FM** *020 †18

BULLOCK, Brian Wm. 600 HAVERFORD RD STE 205 19041 #010-02-1984 L1986 **FM** *020 †18 ‡

CALBOT, Cynthia Lynn. 600 HAVERFORD RD, STE G102 19041 #041-07-1982 L1983 **IM** *020 †20

CURTIS, Homer Chipman. ■ 19041 #049-01-1944 L1948 **PYA P** *071 †75

DIXON, James Payson, Jr. ■ 19041 #041-03-1944 L1944 **PHP** *071 †70

FERNANDEZ, Pedro C. ■ 19041 #847-05-1965 L1974 **IM NEP** *020 †20

FLEEGLER, Edward Morton. ■ 19041 #041-12-1977 L1978 **IM** *030 †20

FORSTER, Robert Elder, II. ■ 19041 #041-01-1943 L1951 **OS** *072

GARFIELD, Ruth Sylvia. 355 LANCASTER AVE D 19041 #041-07-1989 L1991 **P PYA** *020 †75

GODDARD, Katharine Evans. ■ 19041 #041-01-1943 L1944 **CHP PD** *071 †55

GOTTLIEB, Ruth Panzer. ■ 19041 #041-01-1954 L1955 **NEP PD** *071 †55

GROWNEY, Steven Rodger. 551 W LANCASTER AVE, STE 205 19041 #041-02-1991 L1996 **FM** *020 †85,18

HANSEN, Mary Larney. 3500 DARBY RD 19041 #041-01-1945 L1946 **P** *071 †75

HERRING, John Alan. 101 CHESWOLD LN, APT 1G 19041 #041-03-1968 L1969 **P** *020 †75

HURTUBISE, C A Wayne, Jr. ■ 19041 #041-01-1957 L1958 **FM IMG** *071

HYMAN, Harold Lee. ■ 19041 #041-13-1940 L1942 **IM** *071

JADALI, Nassrin. ■ 19041 #517-01-1969 L1981 **OBG** *071

JORT, Sharon Buchsbaum. ■ 19041 #041-13-1980 L1981 **FM** *020

JOSON, Raymond Martin. 350 GRAYS LN 19041 #010-02-1954 L1955 **NS** *071 †25
KAPLAN, Rosalind Diane. 551 W LANCASTER AVE, STE 302 19041 #041-01-1987 L1989 **IM** *020 †20
KESZELI, Alexander R. ■ 19041 #473-01-1952 L1961 **AN** *071
KOELLE, Winifred Angenent. ■ 19041 #035-01-1952 L1962 **IM PA** *050 †20
KOHLHAS, Virginia D A. CAMBRIDGE RD 19041 #023-07-1948 L1953 **OS** *074
KOHUTIAK, Vsevolod. 40 TUNBRIDGE RD 19041 #035-15-1964 L1970 **IM CD** *020 †20 ‡
KONKOLY-WOEHLING, Joanne. 600 HAVERFORD RD STE 1 19041 #041-13-1985 L1986 **PD** *020 †55
KORENYI-BOTH, Ildiko. 551 W LANCASTER AVE, STE 205 19041 #473-01-1966 L1979 **IMG GP** *071 ‡
KRAUSS, Audrey Ruth. ■ 19041 #041-09-1958 L1959 **AN** *071 †05
KREB, R J, III. 200 ROSE LN 19041 #041-01-1971 L1977 **PM PMM** *020 †60
LAWRENCE, L Theodore. 3500 DARBY RD 19041 #041-01-1950 L1951 **IM CD** *071 †20
LEBENTHAL, Emanuel. ■ 19041 #550-01-1964 L1990 **GE PD** *050 †55
LEE, Major Kenneth. ■ 19041 #041-01-2006 L2006 **GS** *012
LESSIN, Stuart Robt. 191 CARDIFF LN 19041 #041-13-1982 L1983 **D** *020 †15
LEYDEN, James Jos. 360 GRAYS LN 19041 #041-01-1966 L1967 **D GP** *050 †15
LIGHTY, George Walter, Jr. 551 W LANCASTER AVE, STE 305 19041 #041-07-1976 L1991 **CD IM** *050 †20
MANOGUE, Robert Stephen. 424 MONTGOMERY AVE, # 4C 19041 #035-09-1954 L1955 **GYN** *071 †30
MARGULIES, Milton. ■ 19041 #065-01-1956 L1969 **DR** *071 †80
MATTONE-VOLPE, Francesca. 600 HAVERFORD RD, STE 100 19041 #035-47-1989 L1993 **PD** *020 †55
MC CAUSLAND, Paul Jos. ■ 19041 #041-09-1979 L1980 **FM OM** *020 †18,70 ‡
MC NEAL, Lynnette H. 3500 DARBY RD 19041 #041-07-1961 L1962 **P** *020 †75
MINTZ, Alfred Martin. ■ 19041 #041-02-1947 L1950 **ORS** *071 †40
MYERS, Robert Elliot. ■ 19041 #041-01-1981 L1987 **PHM IM** *050 †20
NUTE, William L, Jr. ■ 19041 #023-07-1943 L1945 **PHP OS** *071
OFFIT, Bonnie. 600 HAVERFORD RD STE 100 19041 #051-01-1987 L1988 **PD** *020 †55
PEREZ, Christian Manuel. ■ 19041 #264-09-1990 L2004 **OBG** *012
PLOTKIN, Robert Frederick. ■ 19041 #041-13-1947 L1948 **PD** *071 †55
POSNER, Joel David. ■ 19041 #396-04-1971 L1975 **IMG PUD** *020 †20
REARDON, Mary R Wester. ■ 19041 #041-13-1952 L1953 **AN** *071 †05
REED, Katherine Marie A. 349 LANCASTER AVE 19041 #041-07-1978 L1979 **P PYA** *020 †75
RICHTER, Howard Anthony. ■ 19041 #023-07-1963 L1972 **NS** *071 †25
RITCHIE, Charles A. ■ 19041 #041-01-1952 L1953 **GYN** *071 †30
ROBBINS, Matthew. 100 GRAYS LN 19041 #035-08-2004 L2005 **N** *012
ROBBINS, William Stanton. ■ 19041 #041-13-1943 L1944 **P PYA** *072 †75
RODGERS, Charles Harold. ■ 19041 #010-03-1967 L1968 **GP** *072
ROSEFSKY, Jonathan B. 251 MONTGOMERY AVE 19041 #024-01-1964 L1969 **PD PHM** *071 †55 ‡
ROSS, Michael Elliot. ■ 19041 #024-01-1970 L1987 **ON PA** *050 †20
RUGART, Karl Frederick. ■ 19041 #041-01-1948 L1950 **OBG OM** *071 †30
SCHIMMEL, Morris Jos. ■ 19041 #028-03-1968 L1970 **P N** *071
SELBY, Stanly T. ■ 19041 #143-03-1954 L1978 **OM** *020
SOKOLL, Steven Marc. ■ 19041 #051-01-1986 L1988 **CHP P** *020 †75
STAKE, Robert Eric. 385 LANCASTER AVE, STE 207 19041 #026-08-1977 L1978 **P** *020 †75
STEIN, Deborah Leigh. ■ 19041 #025-07-2000 L2006 **RNR** *100 †80
STOREY, Patrick B. ■ 19041 #010-02-1947 L1967 **IM PUD** *071 †20
SZUMOWSKI, John David. 370 LANCASTER AVE 19041 #024-01-2007 L2007 **IM** *012
TREAT, Michael Edward. ■ 19041 #041-02-1940 L1942 **IM** *071
UFFNER, Julia Margaret. 551 W LANCASTER AVE, STE 302 19041 #041-01-1985 L1987 **IM GPM** *020 †20
VEGA, Janelle Marie. 370 LANCASTER AVE 19041 #011-03-2006 L2006 **IM** *012
WARHOL, Michael Jos. 135 ALLGATES DR 19041 #041-12-1969 L1974 **PTH** *020 †50
WILLIAMS, Gregory David. 600 HAVERFORD RD, STE G102 19041 #011-03-1973 L1977 **IM DIA** *020 †20 ‡
WOOD, Howard Page. ■ 19041 #041-01-1947 L1949 **P** *071 †75
WOODRUFF, David Stratton. ■ 19041 #041-01-1954 L1955 **FM** *071 †18

HAVERTOWN – DELAWARE

ANNAPOORNA, Varada. 2000 OLD WEST CHESTER PIKE, HAVENFORD ANESTHESIA ASSOC 19083 #495-11-1971 L1979 **AN** *020 †05
ANSON, Jonathan Aaron. ■ 19083 #041-02-2005 L2005 **AN** *012
ARAI, Taro. 1010 W CHESTER PIKE, STE 201 19083 #041-02-1990 L1993 **CRS** *020 †85,10
ARDITO, Joseph Michael. 301 W CHESTER PIKE 19083 #041-13-1976 L1981 **OTO PS** *020 †45
AUNG-BWINT, Cherry. 41 JACALYN DR 19083 #209-01-1957 L1978 **P** *020
BAIO, Michael Vincent. 2010 W CHESTER PIKE, STE 344 19083 #561-12-1983 L1985 **IM** *020 ‡
BASCIANO, Paul Andrew. ■ 19083 #035-01-2005 L2007 **IM** *012
BAUM, Eric David. 1824 BELLEMEAD AVE 19083 #041-01-1999 L2001 **PDO** *100 †45
BEERS, Leanne Constance. ■ 19083 #041-01-1999 L2002 **ID** *020 †20
BEHJAT, Fa-Ezeh. 201 LANSDOWNE RD 19083 #517-01-1966 L1976 **GP PTH** *020
BENSTOCK, Elizabeth C. 21 N EAGLE RD 19083 #008-01-1997 L2000 **D** *020 †15
BLINMAN, Thane Andrew. ■ 19083 #047-05-1994 L2001 **PDS** *020 †85
BOROW, Lawrence Stephen. 2000 OLD WEST CHESTER PIKE 19083 #041-13-1970 L1971 **OBG** *020 †30
BOSWINKEL, Jan Pieter. ■ 19083 #041-01-2001 L2003 **PD** *020 †55
BOUT-TABAKU, Sharon Maria. ■ 19083 #041-02-2003 L2006 **PPR** *012 †55
BRANDT, Bari Michele. 56 W EAGLE RD 19083 #035-47-1986 L1994 **OPH OS** *020 †35
BRENNER, Sophie A. 2000 OLD WEST CHESTER PIKE 19083 #041-07-1945 L1946 **IM PA** *071
BRIGANDI, Mary K. 1401 KINGSLEY RD 19083 #041-77-1999, ▲ L2000 **FM** *020 †18 ‡
CANTOR, Adrianne Levin. 301 W CHESTER PIKE STE 201 19083 #041-02-2002 L2002 **IM** *020 †20
CARLSON, Alfred John, Jr. 420 TOWNSHIP LINE 19083 #041-09-1965 L1966 **PD** *020 †55
CHOI, Eung Ryong. 850 W CHESTER PIKE, STE 104 19083 #583-10-1966 L1973 **PD** *020 †55 ‡
CHOU, Larry Hy. 510 DARBY RD, PREMIER ORTHOPAEDIC & 19083 #041-01-1995 L2000 **PM** *020 †60
COHEN, Julia Harriett. 2010 W CHESTER PIKE, STE 350 19083 #660-04-1988 L1991 **D** *020 †20,15
COLLINS, Ronnie Thomas. ■ 19083 #047-06-2002 L2006 **PDC** *012 †20,55
CONNAUGHTON, Joanne T. ■ 19083 #024-16-1985 L1989 **IM** *020 †20
CONSTABLE, G Robert. 850 W CHESTER PIKE 19083 #041-02-1960 L1961 **IM** *020
COPPOLA, Kathleen. ■ 19083 #041-13-2001 L2004 **IM** *020
DEGENHARDT, Karl. ■ 19083 #035-47-2001 L2004 **PDC** *100 †55
DELP, Richard Ulysses. 625 PADDOCK RD 19083 #041-02-1963 L1964 **GP** *020
DEZOETEN, Edwin Fulco. ■ 19083 #016-11-2001 L2004 **PG** *100 †55
DIAMOND, Joshua Matthew. ■ 19083 #035-45-2004 L2004 **IM** *100 †20
DICKERMAN, Diane Eloise. ■ 19083 #041-09-1983 L1984 **FM EM** *020 †16
DI NUBILE, Nicholas A. 510 DARBY RD, PREMIER ORTHOPAEDIC & 19083 #041-13-1977 L1978 **ORS OSM** *020 †40 ‡
ELIA, Eugene Anthony. 510 DARBY RD, PREMIER ORTHOPAEDIC 19083 #041-13-1983 L1984 **ORS** *020 †40
FERRACUTI, Daniela. 2000 OLD WEST CHESTER PIKE, CHILD GUIDANCE RESOURCE CE 19083 #561-01-1983 L1991 **CHP P** *020
FIRPO, John James, Jr. 510 DARBY RD, FL 2 19083 #030-06-1967 L1973 **NEP IM** *020 †20
FISSIKOUDI, Aspasia. ■ 19083 #418-02-1999 L2005 **NPM** *012 †55
FRIEDMAN, Steven Arthur. 850 W CHESTER PIKE 1ST FL 19083 #041-02-1966 L1970 **PUD IM** *020 †20
FROMELL, Gregg Jos. ■ 19083 #041-13-1983 L1989 **IM** *050 †20
GLATZ, Andrew Charles. ■ 19083 #028-02-2002 L2002 **PDC** *012 †55
GLAZER, Alan Usher. 600 E TOWNSHIP LINE RD, FL 2 19083 #016-42-1984 L1985 **DR** *020
GOLDSTEIN, William Mark. 2010 OLD WEST CHESTER PIKE, STE 330 19083 #051-04-1981 L1982 **AN IM** *020 †20,05
GREEN, Linda Diane. 850 W CHESTER PIKE 19083 #041-02-1976 L1978 **PD AI** *020 †55,03
GROSSMAN, Monte Stuart. 737 W CHESTER PIKE, DOCTOR'S EXPRESS CARE, LLC 19083 #422-01-1980 L1983 **EM** *020
GUARINO, Julius Michael. 1010 W CHESTER PIKE, STE 202 19083 #041-02-1981 L1984 **GE IM** *020 †20
HAMSHER, Carl David. 57 E EAGLE RD 19083 #041-02-1974 L1975 **IM** *020
HARDING, John Damien. ■ 19083 #041-13-2000 L2001 **ICE** *012 †20
HAUSER, Zachary David. 525 W CHESTER PIKE, STE 203 19083 #036-01-2003 L2007 **PM** *020
HERDRICH, Benjamin James. ■ 19083 #056-05-2004 L2004 **GS** *012
HIMEBAUCH, Adam Steven. ■ 19083 #041-12-2005 L2005 **PD** *012
HOLGADO, Roseller V. ■ 19083 #748-01-1985 **PD** *100
HUMBERT, Stephen M. 2510 W TOWNSHIP LINE RD 19083 #041-77-1990, ▲ L1990 **IM** *020 †20
ISAACSON, William Scott. 2010 W CHESTER PIKE, SURGERY CENTER OF PENNSYLV 19083 #041-07-1982 L1983 **AN PMM** *020 †05
JACOBS, Mark. 1010 W CHESTER PIKE, STE 202 19083 #023-01-1973 L1978 **GE** *020 †20
JORGENSEN, Scott Andrew. ■ 19083 #040-02-2004 L2005 **DR** *012
KELBICK, Elaine Haltman. 2010 W CHESTER PIKE # 3, HAVERFORD ANESTHESIA ASSOC 19083 #041-13-1979 L1980 **AN** *020 †05
KEPLER, Walter E, Jr. ■ 19083 #041-09-1948 L1949 **FM PD** *071
KIM, Eugene John. ■ 19083 #025-01-2000 L2007 **EM** *020 †16
KIRWAN, Greg Walter. ■ 19083 #041-77-2007, ▲ L2007 *012
KLICK, Jeffrey Christian. ■ 19083 #012-05-2002 L2002 **PD** *100 †55
KLINE, Matthew Theodore. 218 WICKFORD RD 19083 #051-04-1982 L1983 **PMM OS** *020 †05
LACY, Regina Ann. ■ 19083 #033-05-1997 L2001 **FM** *020 †18
LEE, James Hyunsoo. ■ 19083 #041-13-2007 **GS** *012
LEFTOW, Stewart Ross. 607 BEECHWOOD DR 19083 #035-20-1985 L1992 **AN IM** *020 †20,05
LEHMAN, Robert David, Jr. 31 S EAGLE RD, STE 107 19083 #041-02-1980 L1981 **OPH** *020 †35
LESSER, Raymond Wm. 2010 W CHESTER PIKE 19083 #041-12-1981 L1986 **OTO** *020 †45
LEVIN, Bruce H. 2010 W CHESTER PIKE, STE 330 19083 #035-46-1984 L1988 **APM PMM** *100 †05
LICHTMAN, Jeremy Owen. 420 TOWNSHIP LINE RD 19083 #005-18-1973 L1975 **PD** *020 †55
LIEBMAN, Emil Polis. 2010 W CHESTER PIKE 19083 #041-13-1959 L1960 **OTO** *071 †45
LIPSCHUTZ, Louis B. 525 W CHESTER PIKE, STE 102A 19083 #422-01-1982 L1983 **P** *020 †75
LOTKE, Paul Alexander. 510 DARBY RD 19083 #041-01-1963 L1964 **ORS** *020 †40
LUBIN, Howard S. 100 S EAGLE RD, OSTEOPATHIC PHYS 19083 #041-77-1955, ▲ L1957 **FM OMM** *072
MANGANO, Mark Francis. 420 W TOWNSHIP LINE RD, PEDIATRIC MED ASSOC 19083 #041-01-1982 L1988 **PD** *020 †55
MANSUR, Nasima R. 2010 W CHESTER PIKE 19083 #160-02-1984 L1996 **AN** *020 †05
MASLOFF, Melvin Louis. 2010 W CHESTER PIKE 19083 #041-13-1969 L1971 **OTO** *020 †45
MCCULLEN, Marykate. ■ 19083 #041-02-2004 L2004 **IM** *012 †20
MCKENNA, Thomas John. ■ 19083 #041-13-2004 L2004 **GE** *012 †20
MENTA, Dominic. 420 W TOWNSHIP LINE RD, PEDIATRIC MEDICAL ASSOC 19083 #041-09-1953 L1954 **PD CHN** *071 †55
MILLER, Gerard Augustine. 510 DARBY RD 19083 #041-01-1986 L1987 **IM** *020 †20
MINGLE, A David. ■ 19083 #041-09-1980 L1999 **FM** *020 †18
MINNECI, Peter C. ■ 19083 #035-19-1998 L2007 **CCM** *020 †85
MONTE, Steven Anthony. 220 N ORMOND AVE 19083 #041-02-1982 L1983 **PTH** *020 †50
NARUNSKY, Leslie. ■ 19083 #836-02-1967 L1981 *020
NIKOLIC, Ivana. ■ 19083 #036-07-2006 L2006 **IM** *012
NISSIM, Sahar. ■ 19083 #024-01-2007 L2007 **IM** *012
NUSSBAUM, Steven Joel. 1010 W CHESTER PIKE, STE 202 19083 #035-08-1974 L1979 **GE IM** *020 †20
OLOUGHLIN, Brian John. ■ 19083 #041-15-2007 **TY** *012
O'NEILL, John J. ■ 19083 #041-02-1949 **GP** *071
PALMER, Deborah Stevens. ■ 19083 #041-01-2002 L2002 **PD** *100
PARK, Hyeran. 510 DARBY RD 19083 #041-13-2001 L2001 **NEP** *020 †20
PARK, Kyong Bin. 525 W CHESTER PIKE, STE 102B 19083 #028-34-1993 L1995 **IM** *020 †20
PARSONS, Ronald Fairbairn. ■ 19083 #035-06-2005 L2005 **GS** *012
POPKY, George Lewis. 600 E TOWNSHIP LINE RD, FL 2 19083 #041-13-1960 L1961 **DR** *030 †80
PROKOP, Wieslaw. 600 E TOWNSHIP LINE RD, 1ST FL 19083 #759-11-1988 L2000 **AN** *020
QUARTERMAIN, Michael D. ■ 19083 #036-05-2001 L2001 **PDC** *100 †55
RESSLER, Kristie Margevic. 1010 W CHESTER PIKE 19083 #041-77-2001, ▲ L2001 **CRS** *100 †85
RICCIUTI, Alexander J. 34 BROOKLINE BLVD, HAVERTOWN WELLNESS CENTER 19083 #041-07-1991 L1993 **IMG** *020
RITSEMA, Rita. 1010 W CHESTER PIKE, STE 202 19083 #024-05-1983 L1985 **GE IM** *020 †20
RIZVI, Syed Mehdi M. 525 W CHESTER PIKE, STE 305 19083 #704-16-1992 L2003 **IM** *020 †75
ROBBEN, Norbertus C E M. 2000 OLD WEST CHESTER PIKE, MERCY HAVERFORD HOSP ER 19083 #660-04-1988 L1991 **EM IM** *020 †20
ROBERTS, Christopher C. ■ 19083 #011-75-2005, ▲ L2005 *100
RODZVILLA, John Paul, Jr. 420 TOWNSHIP LANE RD 19083 #041-02-1972 L1973 **PD** *020 †55

■ = Address Information Privacy Protected

RONIS, Max Lee. 2010 W CHESTER PIKE 19083 #041-13-1956 L1957 **OTO** *020 †45
SCHAFFER, Elliott Lee. 301 W CHESTER PIKE, STE 204 19083 #025-01-1972 L1982 **FM** *020 †18
SCHULER, Mary Louise. 850 W CHESTER PIKE, C/T MEDICAL ASSOCIATES 19083 #041-02-1995 L1997 **IM** *020 †20
SCHWABE, Karl Gustav. 301 W CHESTER PIKE, STE 201 19083 #041-02-1984 L1985 **IM IMG** *020 †20
SCOTT, Heather Renee. ■ 19083 #041-02-2006 L2006 **IM** *012
SENGAT, Helene. ■ 19083 #396-24-1991 **ID** *100
SHIAU, Yih-Fu. 21 N EAGLE RD 19083 #385-04-1966 L1973 **GE IM** *020 †20
SHIRODKAR, Manoj Amrut. 1010 W CHESTER PIKE, STE 202 19083 #023-01-1998 L2000 **GE** *020 †20
SHMOKLER, Mitchell Frank. 301 W CHESTER PIKE, STE 204 19083 #041-02-1979 L1980 **FM** *020 †18
SIDOR, Michael Louis. 2010 OLD WEST CHESTER PIKE, STE 344 19083 #041-13-1987 L1991 **ORS OSM** *020 †40 ‡
SILVER, Richard Craig. 301 W CHESTER PIKE, STE 201 19083 #041-02-1981 L1982 **IM IMG** *020 †20
SILVER, Stephen Chaitt. 1010 W CHESTER PIKE # 201 19083 #041-02-1971 L1972 **CRS GS** *020 †85,10
SMITH, Brian Patrick. ■ 19083 #041-13-2005 L2005 **GS** *012
SPEARS, James Louis. 615 COVINGTON RD 19083 #038-06-2002 L2005 **HO** *012 †20
STELLABOTTE, Joseph M. 510 DARBY RD, PREMIER ORTHOPAEDIC & 19083 #041-09-1996 L1998 **ISM** *020 †20
SULLIVAN, Matthew Francis. ■ 19083 #024-07-2006 L2006 **IM** *012
SURKIN, Marc Ivan. 301 W CHESTER PIKE 19083 #041-02-1978 L1983 **OTO** *020 †45
SWAMI, Sanjeev Kumar. ■ 19083 #041-01-2003 L2003 **PD** *020 †55
SYLVESTRE, Vonetta Tamara. ■ 19083 #041-02-2005 L2005 **OBG** *012
THOMAS, Sean Patrick. ■ 19083 #035-48-2003 L2004 **OPH** *020
TODD, Peter Kennedy. ■ 19083 #056-05-2004 L2004 **N** *012
TOOF, Richard Saml. 850 W CHESTER PIKE 19083 #041-02-1980 L1981 **IM** *020 †20 ‡
TUCHMAN, Lisa Kessler. ■ 19083 #021-01-2001 L2004 **ADL** *020 †55
TUCHMAN, Shamir. ■ 19083 #021-01-2001 L2004 **PD** *020 †55
VANKUST, Bianca Denice. ■ 19083 #041-01-2002 L2002 **PD** *020 †55
VELAYADIKOT, Deepa N. 110 W EAGLE RD, STE A 19083 #496-38-1994 L2000 **IM** *020 †20
VORA, Naina H. 2000 OLD WEST CHESTER PIKE, CHILD GUIDANCE RESOURCE 19083 #913-92-1976 L1996 **P** *020 †75
WEIL, Sharon Robyn. 127 W CHESTER PIKE 19083 #016-06-1985 L1986 **PDC NPM** *020 †55
WHITE, Robert Allan. 712 DARBY RD 19083 #041-02-1964 L1967 **OBG** *020 †30
WHITE, Shawn Edwin. ■ 19083 #041-13-2006 L2006 **U** *012
WILLIAMS, Wm Valentine. ■ 19083 #024-07-1980 L1986 **IG RHU** *020 †20
WILSON, Francis Perry, III. ■ 19083 #035-01-2006 L2006 **IM** *012
YUSSEN, Philip Steven. 600 E TOWNSHIP LINE RD, FL 2 19083 #041-07-1983 L1985 **DR** *020 †80

HAWLEY — WAYNE

ANTENUCCI, Joseph. ■ 18428 #561-10-1953 L1961 **OBG** *071 †30
BASU, Samik. ■ 18428 #041-13-2005 *100
BERMAN, Abraham. ■ 18428 #041-12-1960 L1961 **IM** *071 †20
KONIDALA, Ravi Kishore. 750 ROUTE 739, PIKE COUNTY MEDICAL CENTER 18428 #495-50-1997 L2003 **FPG** *020 †18
KUSIAK, Victoria Ann. 1699 ROUTE 6 18428 #041-01-1975 L1976 **CD** *050 †20
MALINOV, David Nathan. 200 CANTERBROOK DRIVE, 2991 HEMLOCK FARMS 18428 #035-06-1963 L1992 **OS FM** *071
MONTES, Sylvia Orda. ■ 18428 #748-01-1962 L1972 **PD EM** *071 †55
MOWATT, Susan Leigh. 221 MAIN AVE STE D, KEYSTONE FAMILY PRACTICE 18428 #041-14-1998 L2000 **FM** *020 †18
NEWMAN, Walter Zeland. 750 ROUTE 739 18428 #035-09-1954 L1955 **EM GP** *020
PARDINE, Marilyn Theresa. 221 MAIN AVE ST E 18428 #041-07-1964 L1965 **GP OS** *071
ZEGLEN, Arthur F J. ■ 18428 #041-09-1949 L1950 **IM FM** *071

HAZLETON — LUZERNE

AMENTLER, John Peter. 1074 FOREST RD 18202 #041-09-1975 L1976 **OM** *020 †18
BARNA, Nicholas Jos. 1060 N CHURCH ST 18202 #041-02-1985 L1987 **OPH FPS** *020 †35 ‡
BITTAR, Bassam Faiz. 1740 E BROAD ST # 103 18201 #875-02-1984 L1995 **PD P** *020 †55
BONO, Michael. 50 MOISEY DR, STE 214 18202 #041-09-1992 L1998 **GS** *020 †85
BROOM, William Bryan. 212 W BROAD ST, 906 NORTHEASTERN BANK BL 18201 #917-30-1956 L1976 **AN** *074
BUTT, Hameed Ahmad. 50 MOISEY DR, STE 214 18202 #704-01-1970 L1973 **GS VS** *020 †85
CAGGIANO, James Francis. 1730 E BROAD ST 18201 #041-14-1977 L1979 **PD ADL** *020 †55
CARRATO, Anthony Michael. 50 MOISEY DR, STE 214 18202 #041-02-1991 L1993 **GS VS** *020 †85
CASTILLO, Jose. 1740 E BROAD ST, ASSOCIATES INC 18201 #649-01-1954 L1970 **PS GS** *020
CASTILLO, Jose. 1740 E BROAD ST 18201 #649-38-1990 L1999 **HO** *020 †20
CHERTOW, Todd Eric. 50 MOISEY DR, STE 210 18202 #055-02-2000 L2007 **ORS** *100
CHIKARMANE, Ajit Mahadev. 20 N LAUREL ST STE 2B, CENTER CITY MEDICAL COMPLE 18201 #495-35-1972 L1982 **N** *020 †75
CHIKARMANE, Kalpana Ajit. 20 N LAUREL ST 18201 #495-98-1976 L1982 **IM** *020 †20
CHILDS, Robert Wm. 1730 E BROAD ST 18201 #036-07-1972 L1973 **PD ADL** *020 †55
CHOI, Edward Moo-Woong. 780 N CHURCH ST 18201 #583-02-1967 L1972 **RO** *020 †80
CHRISTIAN, Brenda. 700 E BROAD ST, HAZLETON GENERAL HOSPITAL- 18201 #042-02-1996 L2006 **DR** *020
CIOTOLA, Augustine A. 687 N CHURCH ST 18201 #041-09-1940 L1941 **FM OBG** *071
CIOTOLA, Joseph Gerard. 687 N CHURCH ST 18201 #041-09-1982 L1983 **DR** *020 †80 ‡
CIOTOLA, Thomas John. 141 N VINE ST 18201 #041-09-1976 L1977 **CD IM** *020 †20
COX, Howard James. 20 N LAUREL ST, STE 1B 18201 #305-01-1980 L1987 **IM** *020
DAVE, Deepak Vinodrai. 78 N CHURCH ST 18201 #495-57-1969 L1986 **OPH** *020 †35 ‡
DAVE, Kailas Deepak. 23 E BROAD ST, MOUNTAIN AREA HEALTHCARE P 18201 #495-48-1968 L1991 **PD** *020 †55
DESAI, Manikant Viveklal. 101 W BROAD ST, STE 508 18201 #495-39-1966 L1976 **P** *020
DITTMAN, Thomas Harry. 20 N LAUREL ST 18201 #041-13-1973 L1974 **PUD IM** *030 †20

DOBBINS, Kendall R B. 126 AIRPORT RD 18202 #067-01-1994 L1997 **OPH** *020 †35
ESTIOKO, Noel Pacleb. 700 E BROAD ST, HAZLETON GENERAL HOSPITAL 18201 #748-16-1986 L1999 **IM** *020 †20
FELLIN, Rudolph Silas. 54 N LOCUST ST 18201 #041-09-1979 L1981 **IM** *020 †20
FURNER, Carl Ludwig. 20 N LAUREL ST 18201 #018-75-1974, ▲ L1976 **IM GE** *071
GANDHI, Harsh. 1740 E BROAD ST 18201 #495-36-1974 L1986 **ON HEM** *020 †20 ‡
GAZEK, Francisco Alberto. 1090 N CHURCH ST, HAZLETON PROFESSIONAL PLAZ 18202 #132-02-1966 L1976 **CD IM** *020 ‡
HABER, Arthur Stephen. 20 N LAUREL ST, CENTER CITY MEDICAL COMPLE 18201 #041-09-1963 L1964 **R** *071 †80
JAIN, Mohan H. 750 E BROAD ST, NORTHEAST COUNSELING SERVI 18201 #495-01-1954 L1970 **P** *020 †20
JAMES, Roy Lewis. 700 E BROAD ST, HAZLETON GENERAL HOSPITAL 18201 #041-13-1984 L1985 **FM** *020 †18
JANG, Jang Huei. 700 E BROAD ST 18201 #244-06-1967 L1976 **OTO** *020 †45 ‡
KAMEL, Hesham Mohamed Ahm. 700 E BROAD ST, HAZLETON GENERAL HOSPITAL 18201 #915-03-2000 L2007 **PD** *100 †55
LABBATE, Victor Anthony. 1710 E BROAD ST 18201 #033-05-1971 L1974 **RHU IM** *020 †20 ‡
LEE, Ki Bum. 1730 E BROAD ST, HAZLETON MEDICAL BLDG 18201 #583-02-1962 L1971 **OBG** *020 †30
LEE, Ohchung. ■ 18201 #041-13-1997 L1998 **OBG** *100
LEESON, Mark David. 687 N CHURCH ST 18201 #023-01-1980 L1996 **DR RNR** *020 †80
LOPEZ, Agapito. 123 W BROAD ST 18201 #042-01-1971 L1990 **OPH** *071
LOSHAKOV, Vadim. 1730 E BROAD ST, STE 4 18201 #913-15-1985 L2002 **OBG** *020 †30
LOVRINIC, Daniel Francis. 687 N CHURCH ST 18201 #041-02-1966 L1972 **ORS** *020 †40
MARTINO, James V. 149 N VINE ST 18201 #041-02-1990 L1992 **PUD IM** *020 †20
MUIR, Scott D. 601 ALTER ST 18201 #028-78-1989, ▲ L1990 **OBG** *020
NASSAR, Fawaz. 1090 N CHURCH ST 18202 #875-01-1988 L2000 **IM** *020 †20
NELSON, James Edward. 67 COUNCIL CREST LN 18202 #041-09-1982 L1984 **OBG** *075
NOTZ, Robert G. 126 AIRPORT RD 18202 #010-02-1973 L1976 **OPH** *020 †35
NULL, Jeffrey Alan. 101 W BROAD ST 18201 #010-03-1974 L1978 **PTH** *020 †50
PATALAM, Sriharsha S. 750 E BROAD ST 18201 #495-01-1972 L1981 **P AM** *020 ‡
PATEL, Dilipkumar J. 851 MCNAIR ST 18201 #495-22-1977 L1990 **IM** *020 †20
PATEL, Minaben Dilipkumar. 851 MCNAIR ST 18201 #495-22-1985 L1997 **IM** *020 †20
PATTEN, Donald Arthur. 20 N LAUREL ST 18201 #035-15-1984 L1986 **DR** *020 †80
PEGUERO, Alberto. 851 MCNAIR ST 18201 #308-01-1961 L1984 **IM** *020 †20
PERLMUTTER, Mark Nicholas. 50 MOISEY DR, STE 202 18202 #041-02-1987 L1988 **HS** *020
PETTERSON, Eric Evan. 1090 N CHURCH ST 18202 #561-20-1981 L1984 **IM** *020 †20
PHILLIPS, Earl Lynn. 50 MOISEY DR STE 210, HAZLETON HEALTH & WELLNESS 18202 #047-06-1978 L2006 **ORS** *071 †55,40
POLIDORA, Frank Chas. 1710 E BROAD ST 18201 #041-01-1975 L1976 **ORS NS** *020 †40
PRAWDZIK, Leocadia T. 1090 N CHURCH ST, INTERNAL MED ASSOC 18202 #759-10-1982 L1984 **IM** *020 ‡
PUSTI, Janine A. ■ 18201 #422-01-1992 L1996 **AN** *020
QADRI, Syed Farasat Ali. 668 N CHURCH ST, STE 103 18201 #704-02-1988 L2006 **SCI** *020
RACHO, George Jerome. 700 E BROAD ST 18201 #041-02-1961 L1962 **OTO** *071 †45
RODA, Paul Ivan. 1740 E BROAD ST 18201 #041-09-1976 L1977 **ON HEM** *020 †20
SARAS, Peter L. 101 S LAUREL ST, INTERNIST ASSOC 18201 #041-09-1949 L1950 **IM DIA** *072
SCHEERS, George Frank. 20 N LAUREL ST 18201 #035-09-1956 L1957 **OBG** *071 †30
SCHLEICHER, Stephen M. 20 N LAUREL ST, DERMDX CENTERS FOR DERMATO 18201 #041-09-1976 L1977 **D** *020 †15
SHEEN, Kwangsup Kane. 687 N CHURCH ST, HAZLETON - ST JOSEPH 18201 #583-15-1986 L1995 **IM EM** *020 †20
SIDARI, Jude Francis. 700 E BROAD ST 18201 #041-13-1985 L1986 **IM** *020
SRINIVASAN, Arvind. 140 N SHERMAN CT, PHOENIX MED BLDG 18201 #033-06-1991 L1993 **U** *020 †95
STISH, Anthony Girard, Jr. 600 PENN CT 18201 #041-13-1947 L1948 **GP OS** *071
TAGGART, George Webster. ■ 18201 #041-01-1952 L1953 **OPH** *072 †35
TEDESCO, Louis Jos. 1000 ALLIANCE DR # 20, 1000 ALLIANCE DRIVE 18202 #041-02-1985 L1986 **FM** *020 †18
TODD, Rhonda Sue. 126 AIRPORT RD, GEISINGER MED GROUP-HAZELT 18202 #045-04-1995 L2003 **IM** *020
VALENTE, Anthony Francis. 700 E BROAD ST 18201 #041-14-1987 L1990 **IM CCM** *020 †20
VEGLIA, Anthony Patrick. 1525 N CHURCH ST 18202 #041-09-1982 L1983 **IM** *020 †20
VEGLIA, Kathleen Stish. 1525 N CHURCH ST 18202 #041-14-1983 L1984 **D** *020 †15
VENIT, Bethany Anne. 881 N CHURCH ST 18201 #041-02-1974 L1975 **PD** *020 †55
VOUTSINAS, Louisa. 1001 ALLIANCE DR # 1, AIRPORT BELTWAY 18202 #418-01-1968 L1976 **OBG** *020 †30
WENNER, Robert Bruce. ■ 18201 #041-13-1954 L1955 **GP GS** *075
WILSON, Thomas Wm. 126 AIRPORT RD 18201 #041-01-1990 L1993 **OPH** *020 †35
WYCHULIS, Adam Robt. ■ 18202 #010-02-1961 L1962 **TS** *071 †85,90
YAMULLA, Robert Stanley. 128 W 14TH ST 18201 #041-09-1983 L1984 **IM GE** *020 †20
YOO, Young Kul. 1500 E 36TH ST 18202 #583-02-1976 L1985 **GE IM** *020 †20
YOON, Myung Sun. 238 W CHESTNUT ST 18201 #583-02-1966 L1986 **CD IM** *020 †20
YU, Sook Hie Han. 700 E BROAD ST 18201 #583-08-1959 L1969 **AN** *071

HEGINS — SCHUYLKILL

MALICK, Donald Vernon. 523 E MAPLE ST 17938 #041-09-1953 L1954 **GP GS** *071
MISHRA, Kamla Kant. 523 E MAPLE ST 17938 #495-15-1986 L1996 **IM** *020 †20

HELLAM — YORK

EICHNER, Gerald Jay. ■ 17406 #041-14-1975 L1977 **ID PD** *050 †55
NICHOLAS, James Le Roy. ■ 17406 #041-13-1954 L1955 **GP** *071

HELLERTOWN — NORTHAMPTON

ALEKSANDROVA, Yulia. 255 FRONT ST 18055 #913-03-1994 L2001 **FM** *020 †18
ALICEA, Ariel Albert. 255 FRONT ST 18055 #041-02-1989 L1992 **FM** *020 †18
BORSHANSKY, Maryana. 255 FRONT ST, SULKEN VALLEY FAMILY PRAC 18055 #913-18-1982 L2000 **FM** *020 †18

BROWN, Jeff S. 1072 MAIN ST 18055 #033-75-1997, ▲ L1998 **FM** *020 †18
FLEMING, Edward Joseph. ■ 18055 #038-43-2006 L2008 *012
HEMMERLY, William Chas. ■ 18055 #041-13-1946 L1947 **GP IM** *071
LODEIRO, Sila Margarita. 2075 CHARLES DR 18055 #935-04-1982 L2003 **OBG** *020 †30
STEINBACH, E V. SPRINGTOWN P.O. BOX R, DRIFTING DRIVE 18055 #041-07-1960 **NM** *071 †28

HERMINIE – WESTMORELAND

BOONE, Edgar Alan. 401 CHURCH ST 15637 #041-12-1981 L1982 **FM EM** *020 †18 ‡
BOONE, Joy Louise. 401 CHURCH ST 15637 #041-12-1983 L1987 **FM** *020 †18 ‡
MONSOUR, Helen. 24 HIGHLAND AVE 15637 #649-33-1983 L1985 **IM IMG** *020 †20
MONSOUR, Howard Paul. 24 HIGHLAND AVE 15637 #041-12-1946 L1950 **GP** *071

HERMITAGE – MERCER

ABDUL-MALAK, Michael E. 875 N HERMITAGE RD, STE 1 16148 #875-01-1978 L1994 **OBG OS** *020 †30
AKRAM, Zahid. 295 N KERRWOOD DR, STE 103 16148 #704-01-1977 L1997 **N** *020 †75
ANGOTT, Allison Ann. 3110 HIGHLAND RD, STE 203 16148 #041-12-1987 L1989 **FM** *020 †18
BANKS, Virginia D N. 875 N HERMITAGE RD, STE 2 16148 #038-06-1974 L1991 **IM ID** *020 †20
BATAILLE, Jacques Albert. ■ 16148 #440-01-1955 L1973 **IM PUD** *071
BENNETT, Jason Andrew. ■ 16148 #055-01-2000 L2006 **PTH** *100
BUISER, Rodolfo Abril. ■ 16148 #748-01-1966 L1975 **EM** *071
CANTELLOPS, Diana. ■ 16148 #308-02-1987 L2007 **IM CD** *020 †20
CARRICK, John Scott. 737 BROOKSHIRE DR 16148 #041-13-1995 L1999 **IM** *020 †20
CHATHA, Iftikhar Ahmed. 2500 HIGHLAND RD STE 10 16148 #704-08-1966 L1976 **FM EM** *020
CLEMENZA, John William. 3041 INNOVATION WAY 16148 #041-07-1994 L1996 **OMF** *020
COLAIACOVO, Lynn Ann. 2501 SHENANGO VALLEY FWY, STE 1 16148 #041-12-1993 L1995 **D** *020 †15 ‡
CRAGO, Harry Robt. 2151 SHENANGO VALLEY FWY 16148 #035-01-1958 L1966 **GS** *030 †85
DALONI, Peter Michael. 2400 HIGHLAND RD 16148 #041-12-1985 L1991 **U** *020 †95
DOUGHERTY, Mary Catherine. 2151 SHENANGO VALLEY FWY 16148 #041-02-1991 L1993 **IM** *020 †20
ESTAFANOUS, Marc George. 3135 HIGHLAND RD, CONSULTANTS INC 16148 #010-02-1997 L2003 **OPH** *020 †35
ETTYREDDY, Mohan Reddy. ■ 16148 #495-65-1985 L2007 **AN** *005
EZIASHI, James Chike. 2501 SHENANGO VALLEY FWY, STE 3 16148 #690-04-1982 L2001 **IM GE** *020 †20
FLAMBERG, Ira Wayne. ■ 16148 #035-19-1942 L1947 **GP** *072 †05
FRAGOLA, Jorge Alberto. 737 BROOKSHIRE DR 16148 #132-04-1974 L1977 **NEP IM** *020 †20 ‡
FRANK, Joseph Rocco. 2425 GARDEN WAY, STE 101 16148 #038-44-2004 L2006 **PD** *020 †55
GARROW, George Capella. 2320 HIGHLAND RD, CANCER CARE CENTER 16148 #041-14-1985 L2000 **ON PLM** *020 †20
GAUNTNER, Wallace Charles. 737 BROOKSHIRE DR 16148 #028-34-1971 L1977 **IM NEP** *020 †20 ‡
GERSMAN, Mark Andrew. 3135 HIGHLAND RD, CONSULTANTS INC 16148 #038-40-1989 L1995 **OPH** *020 †35
GROSS, Marie Midler. ■ 16148 #407-16-1961 L1963 **P CHP** *075 †75
GRYN, Jeffrey Francis. 2320 HIGHLAND RD 16148 #041-07-1982 L1983 **HO ON** *020 †20
HANIGOSKY, Rebecca Marie. 480 N KERRWOOD DR, STE 103 16148 #038-75-1990, ▲ L1995 **OBG** *020 †30
JAMES, Milton. 3135 HIGHLAND RD, CONSULTANTS INC 16148 #041-09-1992 L1999 **OPH** *020 †35
JOSEPH, Alfred John. 2151 SHENANGO VALLEY FWY 16148 #041-09-1975 L1978 **IM** *020 †20 ‡
JOSEPH, Joseph Thos. 1466 N HERMITAGE RD 16148 #422-01-1984 L1985 **IM** *020
KALIK, Joseph Randy. 295 N KERRWOOD DR, STE 101 16148 #018-75-1984, ▲ L1990 **FM** *020
KAUFMAN, Stephen Richard. 3135 HIGHLAND RD, CONSULTANTS INC 16148 #038-06-1985 L1998 **OPH** *020 †35
LAWSON, Glasine Ortenza. 875 N HERMITAGE RD, STE 2 16148 #010-01-1992 L2006 **OBG** *020 †30
LUSTIG, Keith A. 2151 SHENANGO VALLEY FWY 16148 #010-01-1982 L1983 **ORS** *020 †40
MANDELL, Andrew. ■ 16148 #041-13-1965 L1966 **FM EM** *075
MARCELLI, Gene A, Jr. 2425 GARDEN WAY STE 101 16148 #041-02-1980 L1982 **GS** *020 †85
MARX-ARMILE, Theresa. 220 N BUHL FARM DR 16148 #038-44-1995 L2003 **END** *020 †20
MATTHEWS, Michael Kukuvka. 875 N HERMITAGE RD, STE 3 16148 #030-05-1985 L1990 **N** *020 †75
MC KINNEY, Craig Arthur. 2425 GARDEN WAY STE 101 16148 #010-03-1996 L2007 **GS** *100 †85
MESSINA, Michael Peter. 295 N KERRWOOD DR, STE 109 16148 #041-77-1982, ▲ L1982 **PD** *020 †55
MIGNELLA, Ronnie John. 2999 PRESIDENTIAL BLVD, REGIONAL CARDIOLOGY ASSOCI 16148 #038-44-1989 L1992 **CD IM** *020 †20
MILLER, Sharon Lynn. 752 BROOKSHIRE DR, STE E 16148 #018-75-1986, ▲ L1987 **GE IM** *020 †20
NOVERO, Wally Nobleza. 2375 GARDEN WAY, SHARON REGIONAL HEALTH SYS 16148 #748-28-1992 L2000 **CHP P** *020
PANICKER, Harish. ■ 16148 #495-45-1994 L2005 *100 †80 ‡
PATEL, Dilip Chhaganlal. 2999 PRESIDENTIAL BLVD 16148 #495-22-1980 L1989 **CD IM** *020 †20
PISTON, Robert Walter. 3120 HIGHLAND RD, STE 202 16148 #041-13-1985 L1987 **ORS HS** *020 †40
PUCHARICH, Frances Jo. 2151 SHENANGO VALLEY FWY 16148 #055-01-1994 L1996 **IM** *020 †20
RAUCH, Douglas. 2151 SHENANGO VALLEY FWY 16148 #561-01-1970 L1972 **OBG** *020 †30
RICCIUTTI, Vincent. 1655 KIMBERLY ST 16148 #010-02-1954 L1961 **OBG** *071 †30
RIGGALL, Steven O'Neill. 2375 GARDEN WAY 16148 #032-01-1984 L1988 **CHP P** *020 †75
ROGERS, Warren Saml. 2375 GARDEN WAY, SHARON REG HEALTH SYSTEM 16148 #035-06-1981 L2004 **P** *020 †75
RUSSELL, Kimberly Tanis. 710 RICHMOND DR 16148 #654-01-1996 L1999 **FM** *020 †18
RYAN, James Gerard. 2999 PRESIDENTIAL BLVD, REGIONAL CARDIOLOGY ASSOC, 16148 #539-03-1987 L1992 **CD** *020 †20
SACHDEVA, Ravindra Kumar. 2425 GARDEN WAY STE 101 16148 #495-45-1967 L1972 **GS VS** *020 †85

SALCEDO, Roberto O. 295 N KERRWOOD DR, STE 103 16148 #132-02-1977 L1995 **N** *020 †75
SANTIAGO, Jose W. 295 N KERRWOOD DR, STE 108 16148 #042-01-1986 L1996 **P** *020
SANTIAGO-STEVENSON, D. 295 N KERRWOOD DR, STE 108 16148 #051-04-1938 L1987 **CD IM** *071 †20
SHANNON, Brian D. 2151 SHENANGO VALLEY FWY 16148 #010-02-1995 L2002 **OAR** *020 †40 ‡
SHAUGHNESSY, Patrick. 3150 HIGHLAND RD, WILLIAM M TRACHTMAN MD, PC 16148 #035-06-1987 L1994 **PM OM** *020 †60
SILE, Cynthia C. 2320 HIGHLAND RD 16148 #748-01-1989 L2001 **HO** *020 †20
SMITH, John F, Jr. 875 N HERMITAGE RD, GI ASSOCIATES OF HORIZON-U 16148 #041-12-1992 L1994 **GE** *020 †20
STEINFELD, Richard Ira. ■ 16148 #028-34-1974 L1977 **IM** *020
SWAMI, Sri Chandra. 701 N HERMITAGE RD 16148 #220-01-1960 L1973 **GP** *020
SWANSON, Ernest Wm. 2151 SHENANGO VALLEY FWY, STE 2 16148 #041-12-1972 L1978 **ORS** *020 †40
TAYLOR, Matthew. ■ 16148 #041-15-2004 L2004 **IM** *020
TONNIES, David Alan. 1005 CAMPUS CIR 16148 #038-40-1992 L1994 **ORS** *020 †40
ULEWICZ, Dennis Edward. 2320 HIGHLAND RD 16148 #025-07-1989 L1998 **RO** *020 †80
VALLABH, Sagar Vihari. 2501 SHENANGO VALY FWY #AY 16148 #495-73-1975 L1982 **GE IM** *020 †20
VERMEIRE, David Amos. 220 N BUHL FARM DR 16148 #041-12-1954 L1955 **ORS** *020 †40
WENZ, Robert Edward. 3135 HIGHLAND RD, CONSULTANTS INC 16148 #038-06-1987 L1988 **OPH OS** *020 †35
WRIGHT, Eugena Lynn. 875 N HERMITAGE RD, STE 3 16148 #017-20-1993 L1999 **END** *020 †20
YAO, Francisco C. 701 N HERMITAGE RD 16148 #748-01-1956 L1968 **OTO** *020
ZAMAN ALI, Shaffi Deen. 2375 GARDEN WAY, SHARON REGIONAL HEALTH SYS 16148 #220-01-1970 L2003 **P GP** *030 †75

HERNDON – NORTHUMBERLAND

KLINGER, Angela J. RR 1 BOX 1658 17830 #041-77-1999, ▲ L2000 **MPD** *020 †20,55
RISSINGER, Wendy Ann. RR 1 BOX 1658 17830 #041-02-2003 L2003 **FM** *020 †18
SCOTT, Robert David. ■ 17830 #041-12-1992 L1994 **IM** *020 †20

HERSHEY – DAUPHIN

ABADILLA, Arvin Acedo. 500 UNIVERSITY DR, DEPT OF GME 17033 #748-02-2003 L2005 **PD** *012
ABENDROTH, Catherine. DEPT OF PATHOLOGY, HERSHEY MEDICAL CENTER 17033 #023-01-1984 L1985 **ATP** *020 †50
ABENDROTH, Thomas Willets. 500 UNIVERSITY DR 17033 #023-01-1984 L1986 **OS CLP** *030 †50
ABER, Robert Clark. 500 UNIVERSITY DR 17033 #005-11-1970 L1976 **ID IM** *040 †20 ‡
ABOU-ELELLA, Ashraf Ahmed. 500 UNIVERSITY DR, DEPT OF PATHLGY #H179 17033 #915-02-1985 L2001 **HMP** *020 †50
ABT, Arthur Bernard. 500 UNIVERSITY DR, M S HERSHEY MEDICAL CENTER 17033 #010-01-1966 L1973 **PTH** *020 †50
ABUEL-HAIJA, Anan A.. 500 UNIVERSITY DR, DEPT OF GME 17033 #575-01-2004 L2006 **IM** *012
ADAMS, David Richard. 500 UNIVERSITY DR, PENN STATE HERSHEY MEDICAL 17033 #041-14-1997 L2000 **D** *020 †15
ADELMAN, Alan M. 845 FISHBURN RD 17033 #041-13-1975 L1992 **FM FPG** *020 †18
ADIACONITEI, Andreea. PO BOX 850, M S HERSHEY MED CTR 17033 #781-02-1995 L2007 **CHP** *012
AGARWAL, Siddharth. ■ 17033 #024-05-2004 L2007 **GS** *012
AGGARWAL, Richa. PO BOX 850 17033 #495-03-2003 **P** *012
AGUILAR, James Anthony. PO BOX 850 17033 #654-01-2005 L2006 **AN** *012
AHMADPOUR, Nasrollah. ■ 17033 #057-05-1998 L2006 **IM** *012
AHMED, Aiesha. PO BOX 850, M S HERSHEY MED CTR 17033 #704-26-2000 L2007 **CN** *012
AHMED, Faris Abu Sianina. PO BOX 850 17033 #848-01-2002 L2007 **IM** *012
AHMED, Tamer A. 500 UNIVERSITY DR, H159 SURGERY 17033 #048-02-2000 L2001 **GS** *012
AKSU, Errol Michael. 500 UNIVERSITY DR, DEPARTMENT OF PSYCHIATRY 17033 #041-02-1987 L1989 **P** *020 †75
ALAGONA, Peter, Jr. 500 UNIVERSITY DR, H047 PO BOX 850 17033 #016-42-1976 L1977 **CD** *020 †20
ALAM, Shoaib. 500 UNIVERSITY DR, HERSHEY MEDICAL CENTER 17033 #704-01-1995 L2001 **PCC** *020 †20
ALBANO, Shirley Angeles. PO BOX 850, 500 UNIVERSITY DR 17033 #748-02-1994 L2004 **RHU** *020 †20
ALI, Syed Sameer. 500 UNIVERSITY DR H-043, PENN STATE UNIVERSITY 17033 #704-25-2002 L2004 **EM** *012
AL-MONDHIRY, Hamid A B. 500 UNIVERSITY DR, HERSHEY MEDICAL CENTER HEM 17033 #528-01-1961 L1980 **HEM IM** *020 †20
ALSAIDI, Mohammed H. ■ 17033 #041-14-2008 *012
AMBROSE, Anthony. 670 CHERRY DR, HERSHEY MEDICAL CENTER 17033 #041-14-1975 L1979 **MFM OBS** *020 †30
AMINLARI, Ali. 500 UNIVERSITY DR 17033 #517-05-1967 L1975 **OPH IM** *020 †35
AMMIRATI, Christie T. 500 UNIVERSITY DR 17033 #048-02-1992 L2000 **DS D** *020 †15 ‡
ANDERSEN, Lucille Bennett. 30 HOPE DR EC089, BONE & JOINT INSTITUTE 17033 #035-03-1999 L2005 **ORS** *100
ANDERSON, Bryan Erik. 500 UNIVERSITY DR, DEPT OF DERMATOLOGY, HU14 17033 #038-40-1998 L2001 **D** *020 †15
ANDERSON, Gregory Scott. ■ 17033 #041-02-2002 L2002 **GS** *020
ANDERSON, Karla Marie. 500 UNIVERSITY DR, HERSHEY MED CTR DEPT SURG 17033 #011-04-1989 L1991 **VS** *020 †85
ANDERSON, Kesha-Gaye. ■ 17033 #041-14-2007 *012
APPELBAUM, Peter Colin. 500 UNIVERSITY DR, DEPT PATH 17033 #836-03-1968 L1979 **PTH** *020
ARMSTRONG, April Dawn. 30 HOPE DR EC089, BONE & JOINT INSTITUTE 17033 #065-06-1996 L2003 **GS** *020
ATNIP, Robert Geo. 500 UNIVERSITY DR, DEPT SURG 17033 #001-02-1978 L1985 **VS CCS** *020 †85
AU, Katherine. 500 UNIVERSITY DR, MCH 159 17033 #041-14-2003 L2003 **PS** *012

AZAR, Madona Georges. PO BOX 850, M S HERSHEY MED CTR 17033 #605-02-2002 L2007 END *012 †20

AZIZ, Tariq Abdul. PO BOX 850, # H047 17033 #045-01-2003 L2007 CD *012 †20

BACKENSTOSE, Daniel L. ■ 17033 #041-02-1950 L1951 FM PD *071

BAHADORI, Ali. 500 UNIVERSITY DR, MAIL CODE UH-15 17033 #041-14-1996 L1998 IM *020 †20

BAKER, Whitney Taft. ■ 17033 #048-16-2007 L2007 EM *012

BALLARD, James Otis, III. 500 UNIVERSITY DR, MS HERSHEY MEDICAL CENTER 17033 #023-01-1969 L1975 HO IM *020 †20

BALLENTINE, Noel Hudson. 500 UNIVERSITY DR, DGIM STE 4100 HU 15 17033 #036-01-1979 L1980 IM IMG *020 †20

BALOG, Balint. 32 NORTHEAST DR 17033 #041-14-1981 L1982 ORS EM *020 †40 ‡

BANCHS, Javier Eduardo. ■ 17033 #935-01-1997 L2005 ICE *020 †20

BARRETTO, Greg Alcantara. ■ 17033 #748-20-1999 L2005 NPM *012 †55

BARRY-LANE, Patricia Anne. ■ 17033 #048-02-2002 L2002 IM *100 †80

BARTLETT, Glen Sloane. 441 E CHOCOLATE AVE 17033 #005-11-1965 L1975 PD ADL *020 †55

BATES, Mark Andrew. 500 UNIVERSITY DR 17033 #038-06-1984 L1985 GPM IM *020 †20,70,16

BATTISTA, Frank Joseph. 1120 COCOA AVE 17033 #024-05-1977 L1978 FM *020 †18

BAUCHWITZ, Robert P. PO BOX 447 17033 #035-20-1991 *020

BAXTER, Zachery Chad. 500 UNIVERSITY DR, OF UROLOG 17033 #005-12-2003 L2003 U *012

BAYERL, Michael Gerard. 500 UNIVERSITY DR, DEPT OF PATH H179 17033 #025-01-1994 L2001 PTH HMP *020 †50

BECK, Michael James. 500 UNIVERSITY DR, PO BOX 850 17033 #041-02-1997 L2000 MPD IM *020 †20,55

BEITIA, Jose. ■ 17033 #847-10-1953 L1972 R *071 †80

BEKTESHI, Edgar. ■ 17033 #120-01-1997 L2007 PCC *012 †20

BELACHEW, Dina. 500 UNIVERSITY DR, MILTON S HERSHEY MEDICAL C 17033 #366-01-2002 L2006 PD *012

BELL, Karen Sue. 500 UNIVERSITY DR, DEPT IM 17033 #038-40-1994 L1998 IM *020 †20

BERLIN, Cheston Milton. 500 UNIVERSITY DR 17033 #024-01-1962 L1971 PD OS *020 †55

BETHARDS, Deborah M. 500 UNIVERSITY DR, HERSHEY MEDICAL CENTER 17033 #010-01-1983 L1984 GE *020 †20

BETTERMANN, Kerstin. 500 UNIVERSITY DR, MEDICAL CENTER 17033 #409-10-1996 L2007 N *020 †75

BHATTI, Faizah Naheed. PO BOX 850, DEPT OF PEDIATRICS 17033 #704-25-1998 L2004 PD *100 †55

BILLINGSLEY, Elizabeth M. 500 UNIVERSITY DR, HERSHEY MEDICAL CENTER 17033 #041-14-1989 L1992 D *020 †15

BINGHAM, Catherine April. 500 UNIVERSITY DR 17033 #051-01-1998 L2004 PD PPR *020 †55

BIUCKIANS, Adam George. 500 UNIVERSITY DR, DEPT OF PSYCHIATRY 17033 #041-02-2003 L2003 CHP *100

BLACK, Kevin Paul. 500 UNIVERSITY DR BOX 850, DEPT OF ORTHOPAEDIC SURGER 17033 #035-45-1981 L1993 ORS GS *020 †40 ‡

BLACK, Molly Dianne. 500 UNIVERSITY DR, ORTHOPAEDIC SURGERY 17033 #019-02-2001 L2007 OTR *020

BLAIN, Elizabeth A. 500 UNIVERSITY DR 17033 #041-77-2007, ▲ L2007 IM *012

BLOSSER, Sandralee Ann. 500 UNIVERSITY DR, DRIVE MCH186 17033 #050-02-1982 L1990 CCA AN *020 †20,05

BOAL, Richard John. 32 NORTHEAST DR 17033 #041-13-1972 L1974 ORS *020 †40

BOEHMER, John Phillip. 500 UNIVERSITY DR, DR 4047 17033 #041-14-1986 L1992 CD IM *020 †20

BOLLARD, Edward Richard. 670 CHERRY DR 17033 #041-14-1993 L1995 IM *020 †20

BONSALL, Eric Keith. 500 UNIVERSITY DR, DEPT PSYCH 17033 #041-14-1985 L1986 P *020 †75

BOOKER, Corenthian Jerome. ■ 17033 #030-06-2005 L2005 OBG *012

BOSAK, Jodi Lynne. 500 UNIVERSITY DR, PENN STATE HERSHEY MED CTR 17033 #041-14-2006 L2006 AN *012

BOTTI, John Jos. 670 CHERRY DR, HERSHEY MEDICAL CENTER 17033 #035-03-1974 L1975 OBG MFM *020 †30

BOTTIGER, Brandi Anne. ■ 17033 #041-14-2006 L2006 AN *012

BOURGEOIS, Jonathan W. 500 UNIVERSITY DR H187, PENN STATE UNIVERSITY MEDI 17033 #054-04-2003 L2003 AN *100

BOUSTRED, Alistair Mark. 500 UNIVERSITY DR, HMC 071 PLASTIC SURG DEPT 17033 #836-01-1979 L2001 PS CFS *020

BRADY, Jodi Lynn. 500 UNIVERSITY DR, ADOLESCENT MEDICINE 17033 #041-14-1997 L2005 ADL *100 †55

BRANNOCK, Kristina Renee. ■ 17033 #055-02-2003 L2006 PTH *100

BRENNAN, Robert Walter. 500 UNIVERSITY DR, MILTON S HERSHEY MED CTR 17033 #035-20-1962 L1971 N *071 †75

BRIAN, James Michael. 460 E GOVERNOR RD, MILTON HERSHEY SCHOOL HEAL 17033 #041-01-1994 L1996 FM *020 †18

BRIAN, Pamela B. 500 UNIVERSITY DR, RADIOLOGY DEPT 17033 #011-03-1997 L2001 DR *020 †80

BRIDGEMAN, Amy Elizabeth. ■ 17033 #041-14-2005 L2005 PD *012

BRIDGEMAN, Colin Reed. 500 UNIVERSITY DR H085, PENN STATE HERSHEY MED CTR 17033 #041-14-2006 L2006 PD *012

BRIDGEMAN, Jay Thomas. PO BOX 850, 500 UNIVERSITY DR 17033 #030-06-2001 L2001 HSO *012

BRIEN, James Cooper. ■ 17033 #048-16-2004 L2004 GS *100

BRUBAKER, Warren W. ■ 17033 #041-02-1954 L1955 OM *072 †70

BRUNO, Michael Andrew. 500 UNIVERSITY DR #005-15-1987 L1994 MSR NR *040 †80

BRYANT, Darren Patrick. 500 UNIVERSITY DR, HERSHEY MEDICAL CENTER 17033 #041-13-1996 L1998 CCS *100 †85

BRYCE, Chris Daniel. ■ 17033 #003-01-2004 L2004 ORS *012

BUCHSBAUM, Jeffrey C. 500 UNIVERSITY DR HO63, MILTON S HERSHEY MED CTR 17033 #023-07-1997 L2005 RO *020 †80

BURKE, Sean Thomas. ■ 17033 #023-01-2006 L2006 N *012

BURKHART, Christina P. 500 UNIVERSITY DR, HERSHEY MEDICAL CENTER 17033 #041-07-1982 L1990 FM *020 †18

BURLA, Kiran Kumar. MCH088, MILTON S HERSHEY MEDICAL C 17033 #495-73-2005 L2007 PD *012

BUSTILLO, Jorge. 500 UNIVERSITY DR, DEPT OF ORTHOPAEDICS H 089 17033 #047-07-1998 L2003 ORS *100 †40

BUZZELLI, Mark David. 500 UNIVERSITY DR, PENN STATE UNIVERSITY - MI 17033 #024-05-2003 L2003 GS *012

CAMPBELL, David Bruce. 500 UNIVERSITY DR 17033 #017-20-1976 L1979 TS *020 †85,90

CANTORE, William Anthony. 500 UNIVERSITY DR, DEPT OPH 17033 #035-08-1986 L1989 OPH *020 †35

CAPUTO, Gregory Michael. 500 UNIVERSITY DR, H043 17033 #023-01-1980 L1982 IM ID *040 †20

CARNEY, Daniel Edward. 500 UNIVERSITY DR, HERSHEY MEDICAL CENTER, DE 17033 #016-42-1997 L2000 GS *020 †85

CARR, Michele M. 500 UNIVERSITY DR, P O BOX 850 17033 #065-01-1992 L2003 *020

CASTELLANI, William John. 500 UNIVERSITY DR, MC H160 17033 #025-01-1980 L2005 PTH *020 †50

CENEVIVA, Gary D. 500 UNIVERSITY DR, DEPT OF PEDIATRICS 17033 #041-07-1988 L1992 CCP *020 †55

CHAMBERS, Charles Edward. 500 UNIVERSITY DR, MILTON S HERSHEY MEDICAL C 17033 #023-01-1981 L1987 IM CD *040 †20

CHAMBERS, Linda Leier. 500 UNIVERSITY DR 17033 #023-01-1981 L1987 FM *020 †18

CHANG, Ying-Tai. 500 UNIVERSITY DR, PEDIATRIC ENDOCRINOLOGY, H 17033 #244-01-1975 L2007 PDE PD *020 †55

CHASKO, Nancy Hope. 500 UNIVERSITY DR 17033 #422-01-2007 L2007 IM *012

CHEGINI, Soheil Farahani. 500 UNIVERSITY DR HO41, PO BOX 850 17033 #154-07-1993 L2003 MPD AI *020 †20,55,03

CHERIYATH, Pramil. ■ 17033 #495-37-2001 L2006 IM *100 †20

CHERRY, Robert Allen. 500 UNIVERSITY DR, DEPT OF SURGERY MC H075 17033 #035-01-1991 L2002 GS TRS *020 †85

CHERUIYOT, Honey Chemutai. PO BOX 850, HERSHEY M 17033 #010-03-2003 L2003 IM *020

CHERUKURI, Ravi Kiran Anj. PO BOX 850 17033 #495-62-1999 L2006 EM *012

CHI, Jamin Chung. ■ 17033 #041-02-2006 L2006 AN *012

CHIN, Steve Hsukwo. ■ 17033 #306-01-1998 L2005 OS *100

CHOUDHARY, Arabinda Kumar. 500 UNIVERSITY DR, BOX 850 17033 #495-42-1995 L2006 PDR *100

CHUANG, Cynthia Hinkee. 500 UNIVERSITY DR 17033 #035-19-1997 L1999 IM GPM *050 †20,70

CHUN, Yoon Keun. ■ 17033 #583-12-1998 L2005 END *012 †20

CIARDULLO, Joanne Ilene. 441 E CHOCOLATE AVE, HERSHEY PEDIATRIC CENTER 17033 #035-15-1994 L1996 PD *072 †55

CILLEY, Robert Edward. 500 UNIVERSITY DR BOX 8, HERSHEY MC/PED SURG H113 17033 #041-13-1981 L1991 PDS GS *020 †85

CLAPP, Edelveis R M. 500 UNIVERSITY DR H08, MEDICAL CEN 17033 #018-75-2004, ▲ L2004 PD *100

CLARK, Joseph Brian. ■ 17033 #036-01-1997 L2007 TS *020 †85,90

CLARKE, Jennie Thorn. 500 UNIVERSITY DR, M.S. HERSHEY MEDICAL CTR 17033 #041-14-2001 L2001 D *100 †15

CLAWSON, Gary Alan. 500 UNIVERSITY DR, P O BOX 850 17033 #011-02-1983 L1991 ATP *050

CLAXTON, David F. 500 UNIVERSITY DR, H046 17033 #067-01-1978 L2000 ON HEM *020 †20

COCKROFT, Kevin Mark. 500 UNIVERSITY DR 17033 #035-20-1991 L1998 NS *020 †25

COLLIN, Belinda G. 500 UNIVERSITY DR, MILTON S HERSHEY MEDICAL C 17033 #041-14-1995 L1999 DR *020

COMO, James Davis. ■ 17033 #051-04-2005 L2005 IM *012

CONNER, George Henry. 500 UNIVERSITY DR, DEPT OTO 17033 #016-11-1957 L1973 OTO *020 †45

CONTER, Robert Louis, II. 500 UNIVERSITY DR, MILTON S HERSHEY MEDICAL C 17033 #016-01-1981 L1987 GS AS *020 †85

COONEY, Robert Nickerson. 500 UNIVERSITY DR 17033 #050-02-1985 L1992 GS *020 †85

COQUIA, Stephanie Frances. 500 UNIVERSITY DR, MC H066 17033 #010-02-2006 L2007 DR *012

CRAFT, Gregory Lane. PO BOX 850, DEPT OF ANES -H187 17033 #010-03-2004 L2004 AN *012

CRANDALL, Eric B. 500 UNIVERSITY DR, # H043 17033 #048-13-2007 L2007 EM *012

CREAM, Carlos Lester. 500 UNIVERSITY DR, DEPT OF MEDICINE 17033 #032-01-2000 L2000 IM *100

CRIMMEL, Ellen Marie. 500 UNIVERSITY DR 17033 #041-07-1986 L1987 FM *020 †18

CRIST, Henry Spera. 500 UNIVERSITY DR, ANATOMIC PATH H179 17033 #023-01-1966 L1968 PTH *020 †50

CROOK, Tonya Jane. 500 UNIVERSITY DR, DEPARTMENT OF MEDICINE 17033 #917-28-1990 L1999 IM *020 †20

CROWELL, Kathryn R. 500 UNIVERSITY DR, BLVD BOXH085 17033 #010-02-1998 L2000 PD *020 †55

CUTHBERT, David Anthony. 500 UNIVERSITY DR BOX 850, PA STATE UNIV COLL OF MED 17033 #041-14-2006 *012

CZARNECKI, John. 500 UNIVERSITY DR, DEPT OF GME 17033 #759-01-2003 L2005 FM *100

DABAS, Sanjay. ■ 17033 #305-01-2003 L2005 AN *012

DAGATA, Carie Ann. 670 CHERRY DR, HERSHEY MEDICAL CENTER 17033 #041-13-1998 L2001 OBG *020 †30

DAHMUS, Robert Raymond. 32 NORTHEAST DR 17033 #041-14-1980 L1981 ORS *020 †40

DALLING, Jason Glenn. ■ 17033 #054-04-2007 L2007 ORS *012

DANIELS, Douglas Michael. ■ 17033 #038-41-1963 L1969 PD *071 †55

D'ARCANGELO, Margaret R. 500 UNIVERSITY DR 17033 #041-14-1985 L1991 PDE PD *020 †55

DAVIDSON, Wm Reed, Jr. 500 UNIVERSITY DR, CARDIOLOGY 11046 17033 #041-01-1979 L1980 CD *020 †20

DAVIES, Matthew Foley. 500 UNIVERSITY DR, HERSHEY MED CTR H103 17033 #041-14-1989 L1992 OBG *020 †30 ‡

DAVIS, Charles M, III. 500 UNIVERSITY DR 17033 #047-05-1991 L1997 ORS *020 †40

DAVIS, Dwight. 500 UNIVERSITY DR 17033 #035-45-1975 L1981 CD *020 †20

DAVIS, Thomas Stanley. 339 GOVERNER RD 17033 #041-01-1966 L1967 PS *020 †65

DEARMENT, Rena. 500 UNIVERSITY DR, HERSHEY MEDICAL CENTER 17033 #041-14-1996 L1999 END *020 †20

DECTER, Ross Michael. 500 UNIVERSITY DR, MILTON S. HERSHEY MEDICAL 17033 #068-01-1975 L1987 FM *020 †95

DEFLITCH, Christopher J. 500 UNIVERSITY DR, DEPT OF EMERGENCY MEDICINE 17033 #041-14-1994 L1997 EM *020 †12

DE MUTH, William Warren. 32 NORTHEAST DR 17033 #041-14-1981 L1982 ORS *020 †40

DEVER, Maria Teresa. PO BOX 850 17033 #008-02-1993 L1994 DR *100

DHAMODHARAN, Anjani. 500 UNIVERSITY DR, DEPT PSYCHIATRY 17033 #495-04-1998 L2004 P *020

DHAR, Padmani. 500 UNIVERSITY DR, OF ANESTHESIA,H-187 17033 #495-51-1984 L2001 AN *020 †05

DIAS, Mark Steven. 500 UNIVERSITY DR, DIV OF NEUROSURGERY,MCH110 17033 #023-07-1982 L1983 NS *020 †25

DICK, Andre Ainsworth. PO BOX 850, MS HERSHEY MED CTR 17033 #035-06-1999 L2001 GS *100 †85

DILLON, Peter Worden. PO BOX 850, HERSHEY MC/PED SURG 17033 #035-01-1980 L1990 PDS GS *020 †85

DINH, Binh Quang. 500 UNIVERSITY DR 17033 #010-03-2007 L2007 P *012

DO, An Ngocdang. ■ 17033 #041-14-2008 *012

DODSON, William Chas. 670 CHERRY DR, HERSHEY MEDICAL CENTER 17033 #041-13-1980 L1990 OBG REN *020 †30

DONOVAN, Joseph Ward. 500 UNIVERSITY DR, M.S. HERSHEY MEDICAL CENTE 17033 #010-01-1974 EM ETX *020 †16

DOSSETT, John Hamilton. 500 UNIVERSITY DR, MILTON HERSHEY MEDICAL CTR 17033 #001-02-1964 L1971 ID PD *055

DOUGHERTY, David Wesley. 500 UNIVERSITY DR, DEPARTMENT OF 17033 #041-02-2005 L2005 IM *012

DOWNEY, Matthew James. 500 UNIVERSITY DR, H045 17033 #035-15-2002 L2002 GE *012 †20

DRAGO, Denise Ann. ■ 17033 #041-14-2007 L2007 PD *012

DUNKLE, David Bertram. 19 E CHOCOLATE AVE 17033 #041-13-1958 L1959 OM FM *071

DUNN, Jennifer Adele. ■ 17033 #012-01-2003 L2006 PD *020 †55

DURRANI, Faryal. PO BOX 850 17033 #305-01-2003 L2007 NPM *012

DURVESH, Saima. PO BOX 850, MILTON S HERSHEY MED CTR 17033 #704-02-1999 L2007 END *012

DYE, Anthony Joseph. ■ 17033 #030-06-2004 L2004 AN *012

DYE, Robert Eugene. ■ 17033 #051-01-1958 L1970 GE IM *072 †20

DYKES, Thomas Mack. 500 UNIVERSITY DR, BOX 850 17033 #019-02-1984 L2005 DR FM *020 †80

ECCHER, Matthew Alan. 500 UNIVERSITY DR, PENN STATE-HERSHEY MEDI 17033 #038-41-1999 L2005 CN N *020 †20

EGGLI, Douglas F. 500 UNIVERSITY DR, RADIOLOGY H066 17033 #016-02-1976 L1988 NM R *040 †80,28

EGGLI, Kathleen Dunne. 500 UNIVERSITY DR, PENN STATE UNIV HOSP 17033 #016-02-1976 L1988 PDR DR *020 †80

EHMANN, Wm Christopher. DEPT OF MEDICINE, DIV OF HEMATOLOGY 17033 #035-03-1980 L1988 HEM ON *020 †20

ELAMIR, Belal Mohamed. 500 UNIVERSITY DR H164, PENN STATE HERSHEY MED CEN 17033 #915-03-1995 L2005 CHP *020

ENGBRECHT, Brett Wayne. 500 UNIVERSITY DR, PEDIATRIC SURGERY - MCH113 17033 #023-01-1994 L1996 PDS *020 †85

ENGLISH, David Andrew. ■ 17033 #041-14-2008 *012

EPLER, Mark J. 500 UNIVERSITY DR, PENN STATE MILTON S HERSHE 17033 #011-02-2000 L2001 TS *012

ESCOTT, Mark Edward. PO BOX 850 17033 #143-11-2003 L2005 EM *012

ESTES, Stephanie Jean. 500 UNIVERSITY DR, P O BOX 850 17033 #041-14-2000 L2004 REN GYN *020

ETTINGER, Steven M. 500 UNIVERSITY DR, MED CTR 500 UNIVERSITY DRI 17033 #550-02-1986 L1991 CD IM *050 †20

EYSTER, M Elaine. 500 UNIVERSITY DR, HERSHEY MEDICAL CENTER 17033 #036-07-1960 L1970 HEM OS *020 †20

FAGELMAN, Kerry Marc. 500 UNIVERSITY DR MCH061, DEPT SURGERY/PEDIATRIC SUR 17033 #028-34-1974 L1984 PDS *020 †85

FARZIN GOHAR, Shadi. 153A UNIVERSITY MNR E 17033 #858-01-2002 L2007 PHO *012

FAUSNIGHT, Tracy Brooks. 500 UNIVERSITY DR 17033 #041-14-1997 L2000 AI PDA *020 †55,03

FEHR, David Michael. 500 UNIVERSITY DR 17033 #041-14-1982 L1982 AN *020 †05

FERNANDEZ, Michael Louis. 500 UNIVERSITY DR, PENN STATE ORTHO, H089 17033 #041-14-2003 L2003 ORS *012

FERNANDO, Caissa Navarro. 500 UNIVERSITY DR, DEPT OF GME 17033 #748-10-2002 L2005 FP *012

FIELD, John Mc Cabe. 500 UNIVERSITY DR, DEPT CARD 17033 #041-14-1972 L1974 EM CD *020 †20,16

FINKELSTEIN, Jordan W. 500 UNIVERSITY DR 17033 #035-19-1958 L1989 PDE ADL *071 †55

FLEISCHMANN, Melanie Ruth. 1120 COCOA AVE 17033 #035-03-1997 L2006 FM *020 †18

FLEMMING, Jill Kristine. PO BOX 850, PENN ST U HP-M S HERSHEY 17033 #041-14-2005 L2005 PD *012

FOGELBERG, Anneli Christi. 500 UNIVERSITY DR, PA UNIV MS HERSHEY MC 17033 #041-14-2003 L2003 D *020

FOLTS, Deborah Diane Kees. 500 UNIVERSITY DR 17033 #038-40-1984 L1992 PN PD *020 †55

FORNADLEY, John Andrew. 34 NORTHEAST DR 17033 #041-14-1981 L1982 OTO OS *020 †45

FOSNOCHT, Deanne Louise. 441 E CHOCOLATE AVE, 441 EAST CHOCOLATE AVE 17033 #041-14-1995 L1998 PD *020 †55

FOSTER, Patrick Anthony. 500 UNIVERSITY DR, M.S. HERSHEY MEDICAL CENTE 17033 #836-02-1949 L1988 AN PMM *071

FRANKENY, John R, II. 32 NORTHEAST DR 17033 #005-02-1986 L1987 ORS *020 †40

FRAUENHOFFER, Elizabeth E. PO BOX 850, HERSHEY MC-PTH 17033 #041-07-1983 L1984 ATP PCP *020 †50

FREIBERG, Andrew Steven. DEPT OF PEDIATRICS, DIV OF HEMATOLOGY ONCOLOGY 17033 #005-14-1983 L1992 PHO PD *020 †55

FRENCH, Daniel Kevin. 500 UNIVERSITY DR, HERSHEY MEDICAL CENTER 17033 #041-15-2000 L2003 EM *020

FRIEDER, Ryan Dennis. 500 UNIVERSITY DR, PENN STATE HERSHEY MED CTR 17033 #003-75-2002, ▲ L2007 AN *012

GALLAGHER, James Vincent. ■ 17033 #001-02-1990 L1994 PTH *020 †50

GARCIA, Luis Jose. PO BOX 850, DEPT OF SURGERY MC H 159 17033 #041-14-2004 L2004 GS *012

GARCIA, Margret Joy Garci. 500 UNIVERSITY DR, DEPT OF GME 17033 #748-02-2003 L2005 FP *012

GARDNER, Thomas Wright. 500 UNIVERSITY DR, HERSHEY MEDICAL CENTER 17033 #041-02-1979 L1984 OPH *020 †35

GARSA, Aman. MCH088, MILTON S HERSHEY MEDICAL C 17033 #495-69-2003 L2007 IM *012

GASCHO, Joseph Alvin. 500 UNIVERSITY DR, DEPT CARD 17033 #051-01-1973 L1986 CD IM *020 †20

GEETING, Glenn Knoll. 500 UNIVERSITY DR, DEPT OF EMERGENCY MEDICINE 17033 #005-06-1993 L2000 EM *020 †16 ‡

GEORGE, Rosalyn Elizabeth. 500 UNIVERSITY DR, DEPT. OF DERMATOLOGY, HU14 17033 #051-04-2004 D *012

GERARD, Wray Anthony. ■ 17033 #041-14-1984 L1985 EM FM *020 †18

GERSTLE, Justin Theodore. 500 UNIVERSITY DR 17033 #032-01-1988 L1990 GS *100 †85

GHAHRAMANI, Nasrollah. 500 UNIVERSITY DR 17033 #517-09-1984 L2001 NEP *100 †20

GHARAEI, Amir Abbass. PO BOX 850 17033 #517-08-1994 L2003 IM *012

GILCHRIST, Ian Chas. 500 UNIVERSITY DR, BOX 850 17033 #035-01-1982 L1988 CD CCM *020 †20

GILL, David John. 500 UNIVERSITY DR, BOX 850 17033 #011-03-2001 L2007 NUP *020 †75

GINGRICH, Dennis Lynn. 500 UNIVERSITY DR 17033 #041-14-1976 L1977 FM *020 †18

GIRALDO-GOMEZ, Alvaro A. 22 NORTHEAST DR, PSYCHIATRY 17033 #264-04-1967 L2004 P *100 †50

GIRDHARRY, Tyrone Dexter. 500 UNIVERSITY DR, HERSHEY MEDICAL CENTER 17033 #654-01-1993 L2000 CCA *100 †05

GLEESON, Kevin. 500 UNIVERSITY DR, DEPT PUL DIS 17033 #010-02-1977 L1984 PUD IM *020 †20

GNATUK, Carol Lynn. 670 CHERRY DR, HERSHEY MEDICAL CENTER 17033 #041-12-1983 L1991 REN *020 †30

GOLDBERG, Stuart Howard. ■ 17033 #023-01-1983 L1989 OPH *020 †35

GOLDENBERG, David. 500 UNIVERSITY DR H091, OTOLARYNGOLOGY - HEAD AND 17033 #550-04-1996 L2005 *020

GOLDMAN, John Nicholas. 500 UNIVERSITY DR, DEPT ID 17033 #038-41-1964 L1986 IM ID *050

GOLDSTEIN, Jennifer Price. 500 UNIVERSITY DR, HU-15 17033 #041-02-1998 L2000 IM *020 †20

GONZALEZ DE CASTILLA, Fran. 500 UNIVERSITY DR H085, MEDICAL CEN 17033 #649-31-1999 L2003 NPM *012

GOOD, David Chas. 500 UNIVERSITY DR, DEPT OF NEGROLOGY 17033 #056-05-1974 L2005 N PM *030 †75

GOODSPEED, David Clifton. 500 UNIVERSITY DR, PO BOX 850 17033 #056-05-1993 L1999 ORS *020 †40

GORDIN, Vitaly. ■ 17033 #913-16-1978 L1995 AN *020 †05

GORMAN, Richard Edward. 500 UNIVERSITY DR, MCH070 17033 #041-02-1989 L1994 GS *020 †85

GOYAL, Nilufer Raj. 500 UNIVERSITY DR H08, MEDICAL CEN 17033 #495-29-2003 L2004 PD *100

GRAYBILL, Michael John. ■ 17033 #041-14-2008 *012

GREEN, Michael Jay. 500 UNIVERSITY DR, H134, C1743 17033 #016-11-1988 L1996 IM *040 †20

GROH, Brandt Park. 500 UNIVERSITY DR, HERSHEY MEDICAL CENTER 17033 #056-06-1987 L1997 PD *020 †55

GUNN, James Stephen. ■ 17033 #001-06-2007 L2007 GS *012

GUPTA, Sameer. ■ 17033 #496-34-2005 L2006 IM *012

GUSANI, Niraj Jaysukh. 500 UNIVERSITY DR, MCH 149 17033 #041-01-1998 L2005 GS SO *100 †85

GUSIC, Maryellen E. 500 UNIVERSITY DR 17033 #041-01-1990 L1994 PD *040 †55

HAJIAN, Hooman. ■ 17033 #517-01-2000 L2007 IM *012

HALL, Virginia E. 670 CHERRY DR, HERSHEY MEDICAL CENTER 17033 #041-09-1972 L1973 OBG IM *020 †30

HALLOCK, Richard Henry. 32 NORTHEAST DR 17033 #023-01-1978 L1979 ORS *050 †40

HALUCK, Randy Scott. 500 UNIVERSITY DR, MC H149 17033 #041-14-1991 L1993 GS *020 †85

HAMDAN, Isam Mohamed. M S HERSHEY MED CTR, DEPT PSYCH 17033 #913-07-1986 L1994 P *100

HAMID, Subarna. ■ 17033 #041-14-2007 L2007 IM *012

HAMILTON, Robert Wm. 739 FISHBURN RD 17033 #038-40-1963 L1970 IM HO *071 †20

HAMMER, Richard Kyle. 500 UNIVERSITY DR, MILTON S HERSHEY MED CTR 17033 #041-15-2000 L2001 PD *020 †55 ‡

HAMMOND, James Mahoney. 500 UNIVERSITY DR 17033 #028-02-1966 L1973 END IM *020 †20

HAN, David C. 500 UNIVERSITY DR, HERSHEY MEDICAL CENTER 17033 #024-01-1992 L1999 VS *020 †85

HANCEY, Matthew Jason. 500 UNIVERSITY DR, PENN STATE MILTON S HERSHE 17033 #041-14-2004 L2004 PS *012

HANISCH, Benjamin Robert. ■ 17033 #041-14-2008 *012

HANKS, Gregory Allan. 32 NORTHEAST DR 17033 #041-14-1982 L1987 ORS *020 †40

HANSEN, Nathan John. ■ 17033 #041-14-2007 L2007 GS *012

HAOUZI, Philippe Aaron. 500 UNIVERSITY DR, P O BOX 850 17033 #396-05-1987 L2006 *100

HAOUZI-JUDENHERC, Annick. 500 UNIVERSITY DR, P O BOX 850 17033 #396-05-1989 L2006 *100

HARBAUGH, Kimberly Sue. 500 UNIVERSITY DR, DRIVE MCH110 17033 #005-18-1990 L2003 NS *020 †25

HARBAUGH, Robert Eugene. 500 UNIVERSITY DR, NEUROSURGERY 17033 #041-14-1978 L2003 NS OS *020 †25

HARKINS, Gerald Joseph. 670 CHERRY DR, HERSHEY MEDICAL CENTER 17033 #041-14-1996 L2004 OBG *020 †30

HARPSTER, Lewis Edward. 500 UNIVERSITY DR 17033 #041-02-1987 L1989 U GS *020 †95

HARRIS, Matheson Adams. ■ 17033 #041-14-2005 L2005 OPH *012

HARTNETT, Kimberly Lyn. 500 UNIVERSITY DR, PENN STATE MILTON S. HERSH 17033 #036-01-2000 L2007 GS *100

HARVEY, Harold A. 500 UNIVERSITY DR, DEPT IM 17033 #950-01-1970 L1974 ON *040 †20

HASHEMI, Ismaeel Badr. ■ 17033 #704-01-2002 L2007 PD *012

HAUCK, Randy Milton. 500 UNIVERSITY DR, DEPT PLASTIC SURGERY 17033 #041-13-1982 L1983 HS PS *020 †85,65

HAUSER, Jean Mara. FISHBURN RD, HERSHEY OB/GYN ASSOCIATES 17033 #051-01-1990 L1993 OBG *020 †30

HEGARTY, James D. 500 UNIVERSITY DR, DEPT PSYCH # H073 17033 #041-14-1989 L1996 P ADP *020 †75

HEINLY, Mark Nevin. 500 UNIVERSITY DR, DEPT OF PSYCHIATRY 17033 #041-14-1992 L1994 P *020 †75

HELM, Klaus Frederick. 500 UNIVERSITY DR, HERSHEY MED CTR 17033 #035-45-1985 L1991 D DMP *020 †15

HENDERSON, Rugh Alexander. 500 UNIVERSITY DR 17033 #041-02-1963 L1966 FM GPM *020 †70,18

HENNESSY, Jeannie. PO BOX 850 17033 #913-60-1992 L2005 PTH *012

HERMAN, James Martin. 500 UNIVERSITY DR, HERSHEY MED CTR FAM MED 17033 #023-07-1978 L1986 FM *030 †18

HEYDT, Stuart. ■ 17033 #030-05-1972 L1973 HNS *030

HIGH, Kane Michael. 500 UNIVERSITY DR, MILTON S HERSHEY MEDICAL C 17033 #041-14-1982 L1983 AN CCA *020 †05

HILL, Kenneth Lloyd, Jr. 500 UNIVERSITY DR, DEPARTMENT OF NEUROSURGERY 17033 #041-14-2003 L2003 NS *012

HILLS, Everett Carl. 500 UNIVERSITY DR, DEPT ORTHO & REHAB H094 17033 #010-01-1987 L1990 PM OM *020 †60

HILLS, Rebecca Gilbert. 500 UNIVERSITY DR 17033 #041-02-1995 L1998 IM *020 †20
HINKLE, Bruce James. ■ 17033 #041-14-1981 L1982 EM *020 †16
HOLLAR-WILT, Laura Jean. 500 UNIVERSITY DR H085, MEDICAL CEN 17033 #035-03-2002 L2002 P *012
HORWITH, Melvin. 500 UNIVERSITY DR, HERSHEY MED CTR H-0444 17033 #035-03-1951 1986 END IM *020
HOSLER, Matthew Robert. ■ 17033 #033-05-2005 L2006 OPH *012
HOSTETTER, Emmaleigh Susa. ■ 17033 #038-43-2007 L2007 FP *012
HUA, Li. PO BOX 850 17033 #243-52-1985 IM *012
HUBBELL, Jennifer R. 500 UNIVERSITY DR 17033 #035-15-1998 L2000 PD *020 †55
HUERTER, Nancy Crowder. 500 UNIVERSITY DR, DEPT PSYCH 17033 #048-02-1985 L1986 CHP P *020 †75
HUSAIN, Shabeera. PO BOX 850, DEPT OF ANES 17033 #495-42-2002 L2004 AN *012
HUSTON, Zachary Sloan. ■ 17033 #019-02-2006 L2006 IM *012
IANTOSCA, Mark Robt. 500 UNIVERSITY DR 17033 #024-07-1991 L2006 NS *020 †25
IMADOJEMU, Virginia A. 500 UNIVERSITY DR, MILTON S. HERSHEY MED CTR 17033 #690-02-1984 L1994 CCM *020 †20
IOFFREDA, Michael David. 500 UNIVERSITY DR 17033 #041-02-1990 L1996 D DMP *020 †15
IQBAL, Fauzia. PO BOX 850, M S HERSHEY MC DEPT OF PSY 17033 #704-21-2000 CHP *012
JAGLOWSKI, Jeffrey Robert. ■ 17033 #041-14-2008 *012
JANICKI, Piotr Kazimierz. 500 UNIVERSITY DR, HERSHE MED CTR H187 17033 #759-03-1979 L2003 AN *020 †05
JANIGA, Matthew Andrew. 500 UNIVERSITY DR, OF UROLOG 17033 #026-04-2003 L2003 U *020
JAVIER, Maria-Cristina. 500 UNIVERSITY DR, MS HERSHEY MEDICAL CENTER 17033 #748-08-1992 L2002 NPM *020 †55
JEFFRIES, Graham Harry. PO BOX 850, HERSHEY MEDICAL CTR 17033 #671-01-1953 L1969 GE IM *030
JENSEN, Jason Richard. PO BOX 850 17033 #422-01-2005 L2005 AN *012
JHA, Bhawna. PO BOX 850 17033 #495-92-1996 L2006 N *012
JOHNSON, Amanda Lee. 500 UNIVERSITY DR, PENN STATE HERSHEY MED CTR 17033 #041-15-2006 L2007 ORS *012
JOHNSON, Dennis Lee. 500 UNIVERSITY DR BOX 850, CTR-PALLIATIVE CARE H106 17033 #005-15-1971 L1992 PLM NS *020 †25
JOHNSON, Gerald. 500 UNIVERSITY DR, PEDIATRIC CARDIOLOGY 17033 #045-01-1997 L2003 PDC *020 †55
JOHNSON, Mary Claire. ■ 17033 #041-14-2008 *012
JOHNSON, Timothy Shane. 500 UNIVERSITY DR, MC: H071 17033 #041-13-1998 L2000 PS *100 †65
JONES, Dallon Lee. ■ 17033 #041-14-2008 *012
JONES, Lawrence Huben. 670 CHERRY DR 17033 #041-07-1989 L1992 IM *020 †20
JONNAKUTY, Catherine Gina. ■ 17033 #495-37-2001 L2006 END *012 †20
JOSHI, Aditya. PO BOX 850 17033 #495-37-2001 L2007 P *012
JULIAN, Kathleen Glenda. 500 UNIVERSITY DR, BMR BLDG C6833, MAILCODE H 17033 #051-04-1997 L2000 IM *020 †20
KADRY, Zakiyah. 500 UNIVERSITY DR, TRANSPLANT 17033 #539-06-1983 L1987 GS *020 †85
KAISER, Gerard Danl. ■ 17033 #041-09-1958 L1959 FM *074 †18
KALAPOS, Paul. 500 UNIVERSITY DR, HERSHEY MED CTR 17033 #067-01-1982 L2004 DR *020
KALAVAPALLI, Ramprasad Re. MCH088, MILTON S HERSHEY MEDICAL C 17033 #495-62-1998 L2007 P *012
KALENAK, Alexander. 500 UNIVERSITY DR, PENN ST ORTHOPEDICS 17033 #041-09-1961 L1962 ORS *040 †40
KALES, Anthony. 500 UNIVERSITY DR, THE MILTON S HERSHEY MED C 17033 #025-07-1959 L1971 P SME *030 †75
KANCHWALA, Sabiha Fakhrud. 500 UNIVERSITY DR 17033 #759-12-2004 L2005 PD *012
KANEDA, Robert R. 32 NORTHEAST DR 17033 #041-77-1974, ▲ L1975 ORS HS *020
KANG, Jason Humphrey. ■ 17033 #036-08-2005 L2005 PTH *012
KASS, Lawrence Edward. 500 UNIVERSITY DR, DEPT OF EMERGENCY MED H043 17033 #024-05-1987 L1991 OPH OS *020 †20,16
KASS, Rena Beth. 500 UNIVERSITY DR H149, MEDICAL CENTER/DEPT SURGER 17033 #035-03-1995 L2004 GS *020 †20
KATOS, Michael Gregory. PO BOX 850 17033 #305-01-2005 L2005 AN *012
KATZMAN, Michael. 500 UNIVERSITY DR, H036 17033 #035-01-1981 L1989 ID IM *050 †20
KAUFFMAN, Gordon Lee. 500 UNIVERSITY DR, DIV OF GEN SURG-H149/MSHMC 17033 #025-01-1972 L1985 GS CRS *020 †85
KECK, Terrah Marie. PO BOX 850, 500 UNIV DR H085 17033 #041-02-2006 L2006 PD *012
KEMP, John. ■ 17033 #022-75-2002, ▲ L2006 AI *012
KENDIG, James Willis. 500 UNIVERSITY DR, MILTON S HERSHEY MED CTR 17033 #041-02-1970 L1974 NPM *020 †55,18
KHALIL, Hitham Hashem. 500 UNIVERSITY DR, PENNSTATE M S HERSHEY MEDI 17033 #038-43-2000 L2001 NS *020
KHAN, Aimal. PO BOX 850, DEPT OF PSYCHIATRY 17033 #033-05-2003 L2006 CHP *012
KHAN, Bakhtiar. 4 WESTMINISTER 17033 #704-01-1972 L1976 CD IM *020 †20
KHAN, Mahinur Habib. PO BOX 850, HERSHEY M 17033 #160-11-2000 L2002 HO *012 †20
KHAN, Muhammad Sajid. MCH088 17033 #654-01-2003 L2008 *100
KHAN, Osman. PO BOX 850, DEPT OF PEDIATRICS 17033 #704-21-2000 L2004 PD *012
KHAN, Sufana Jawed. ■ 17033 #704-25-2005 L2007 PD *012
KHOV, Steven. ■ 17033 #041-77-2007, ▲ L2007 MPD *012
KIMAK, Mark John. 500 UNIVERSITY DR, MILTON HERSHEY MED CTR 17033 #041-14-1981 L1982 EM IM *020 †20,16
KIMATIAN, Stephen John. 500 UNIVERSITY DR, DEPT OF ANESTH H187 17033 #035-06-1992 L1998 AN *020 †05
KIMCHI, Eric Tzvi. 500 UNIVERSITY DR, HC 70 17033 #041-14-1996 L1996 GS *020 †85
KLINE, Adrienne Wilson. ■ 17033 #041-14-2008 *012
KNOWLES, Jarol Boan. 500 UNIVERSITY DR, MAILCODE HU-15 HERSHEY MED 17033 #068-01-1981 L1985 IM NTR *030 †20
KNUTSON, David Wm. 500 UNIVERSITY DR, BOX 850 17033 #026-04-1967 L1985 NEP IM *050 †20
KOCONIS, Kristen Gledhill. PO BOX 850, MILTON S HERSHEY MED CTR 17033 #043-01-2005 L2005 DR *012
KOH, Joyce Michelle. ■ 17033 #041-14-2008 *012
KOLTUN, Walter Alex. 500 UNIVERSITY DR, COLORECTAL SURGERY - H137 17033 #024-01-1981 L1990 CRS GS *020 †85,10
KOZAK, Mark. PO BOX 850, DIV OF CARDIOLOGY 17033 #023-07-1984 L1993 CD IM *020 †20
KRASSILNIKOVA, Svetlana I. PO BOX 850, M S HERSHEY M 17033 #913-03-1994 L2004 AI *012 †20

KRIEG, Arthur Frederick. 500 UNIVERSITY DR 17033 #024-07-1956 L1968 CLP *071 †50
KRISHNAMOORTHY, T. PO BOX 850 17033 #495-94-1991 RNR *012
KUHLENGEL, Barbara. 928 E CHOCOLATE AVE, HERSHEY PSYCH ASSOC 17033 #018-03-1990 L1990 P *020 †75 ‡
KULIN, Howard Eric. 500 UNIVERSITY DR, HERSHEY MED CTR DEPT PED 17033 #035-20-1963 L1973 PDE *020 †55
KUPERMAN, Ethan Frank. ■ 17033 #041-14-2008 *012
KWON, Osun. 500 UNIVERSITY DR - H040, MEDICAL CENTER 17033 #583-12-1981 L2005 NEP *020 †20
LADDA, Roger Louis. 500 UNIVERSITY DR, M S HERSHEY MEDICAL CENTER 17033 #016-02-1963 L1974 PD *050 †19,55
LAKSHMINARAYANAN, Sonali. ■ 17033 #495-16-1993 L2007 PHO *020 †55
LA PAGLIA, Michael A. 500 UNIVERSITY DR H-043, PENN STATE UNIVERSITY 17033 #016-43-2001 L2004 EM *020
LARACH, Marilyn Green. 500 UNIVERSITY DR, DEPT OF ANESTHESIOLOGY H18 17033 #035-19-1978 L1980 AN PAN *040 †55,05
LATHROP, Mary Ann. 500 UNIVERSITY DR 17033 #041-02-1988 L1995 END OBG *020 †20
LAUER, Eric Lee. ■ 17033 #012-05-2004 L2004 GS *100
LAUER, Katheryn Justine. ■ 17033 #012-05-2004 L2004 FM *020 †18
LAZAR, Michael John. 500 UNIVERSITY DR, MCH165 17033 #033-05-1997 L2003 GS *100 †90
LAZUSKY, Heather Michelle. ■ 17033 #023-01-2007 L2007 PD *012
LE, Tri Huu. 500 UNIVERSITY DR, HERSHEY MED CENTER/GI-HO45 17033 #032-01-1997 L2003 GE *020 †20
LEAMAN, David Martin. 500 UNIVERSITY DR, HERSHEY MEDICAL CENTER 17033 #041-13-1964 L1965 CD *040 †20
LEAMAN, Thomas Leed. ■ 17033 #010-01-1948 L1949 FM *071 †18
LEASER, Joseph Patrick. 500 UNIVERSITY DR 17033 #041-14-1971 L1973 FM IMG *040
LEE, Peter Allen. 500 UNIVERSITY DR, MS HERSHEY MEDICAL CENTER 17033 #025-01-1969 L1981 PDE PD *050 †20
LEE, Rebecca Evayne. ■ 17033 #041-14-2008 *012
LEGRO, Richard Scott. 670 CHERRY DR, HERSHEY MEDICAL CENTER 17033 #035-47-1987 L1989 OBG REN *020 †30
LEIDIG, Suzi R. ■ 17033 #055-01-1989 L2000 P *020 †75
LEIS, Dean Jerry. 1120 COCOA AVE 17033 #041-02-1973 L1974 FM *020 †18
LEONARD, Timothy Orth. 500 UNIVERSITY DR, MILTON S HERSHEY MED CTR 17033 #041-14-1998 L2000 PTH *100 †50
LEONEN, Ryan Paul. PO BOX 850, MILTON S HERSHEY MED CTR 17033 #051-04-2004 L2005 DR *012
LEONG, Shou Ling. 500 UNIVERSITY DR, HERSHEY MEDICAL CENTER 17033 #035-19-1980 L1992 FM *020 †18
LEUENBERGER, Urs Andreas. 500 UNIVERSITY DR BOX 850, PEN ST UNIV/MS HERSHEY MC 17033 #869-02-1977 L1982 CD IM *050 †20
LEVI, Benjamin M. 500 UNIVERSITY DR, HERSHEY MED CTR MC H134 17033 #016-11-1996 L1999 PD *020 †55
LEVINE, Richard Leland. 500 UNIVERSITY DR 17033 #021-01-1983 L1993 PD ADL *040 †55 ‡
LEWIS, Peter Ripley. 500 UNIVERSITY DR H154 17033 #041-02-1993 L1997 FM *020 †18
LI, Baihan. 500 UNIVERSITY DR H187, MS HERSHEY MEDICAL CENTER 17033 #243-52-1982 L2001 AN *020 †05
LIANG, David. 500 UNIVERSITY DR, HU19 17033 #041-07-1997 L2005 OPH *020 †35
LIN, Jason Seitetsu. 500 UNIVERSITY DR, PENN STATE MILTON S HERSHE 17033 #035-47-2004 L2004 ORS *012
LIN, Tom. ■ 17033 #041-14-2008 *012
LINDSAY, Jerome Allen. 500 UNIVERSITY DR H-043, PENN STATE UNIV 17033 #041-14-2005 L2005 EM *012
LIPKE, Rebecca Annesundbe. ■ 17033 #041-14-2008 *012
LIPPE, Ronald Watson. 32 NORTHEAST 17033 #033-06-1984 L1985 ORS *020 †40
LIPSON, Adam Craig. 500 UNIVERSITY DR, MC H110 17033 #024-01-2000 L2006 NS *012
LIPTON, Allan. 500 UNIVERSITY DR 17033 #035-19-1963 L1971 ON IM *050 †20
LISZKA, Edward George, II. 500 UNIVERSITY DR 17033 #041-14-1997 L1999 CD *020 †20
LOBELL, Mark Elliot. 500 UNIVERSITY DR 17033 #041-14-1997 L2001 DR PD *020 †80
LORBERBAUM, Jeffrey P. 500 UNIVERSITY DR, DEPT OF PSYCHIATRY 17033 #011-03-1992 L2005 P *020 †75
LOUGHRAN, Thomas P, Jr. 500 UNIVERSITY DR, H072 17033 #041-09-1979 L1980 ON *050 †20
LUCAS, Kenneth Gerald, Jr. 500 UNIVERSITY DR, PENN STATE CHILDRENS HOSPI 17033 #035-15-1989 L1991 PHO *020 †55
LYNCH, Frank Craig. ■ 17033 #041-14-1991 L1991 VIR *020 †80
LYNCH, Scott Alan. 500 UNIVERSITY DR 17033 #041-12-1991 L1997 OSM *020 †40
LYONS, Robert Patrick. PO BOX 850, 500 UNIVERSITY DR 17033 #041-13-1990 L1992 ORS *020 †40
LYSENKO, Lyudmyla Mykolay. PO BOX 850 17033 #913-10-1997 L2006 EM *012
MACARTHY, Adetokunbo Elus. ■ 17033 #041-14-2005 IM *012
MACK, Julie Aileen. 500 UNIVERSITY DR, HO66 17033 #024-01-1990 L1998 PDR *020 †80
MACKAY, Donald Roy. 500 UNIVERSITY DR, DIV OF PLASTIC SURG, H071 17033 #836-01-1980 L1990 PS CFS *020 †65
MACKNIGHT, Brenda Marie. 500 UNIVERSITY DR BOX 850, PA STATE UNIV COLL OF MED 17033 #041-14-2002 L2002 AN *100 †05
MAC NEILL, Colin. 670 CHERRY DR, HERSHEY MEDICAL CENTER 17033 #041-14-1988 L1988 OBG *020 †30
MAGEE, Trevor Hancock. ■ 17033 #010-01-2004 L2004 ORS *012
MAHMOOD, Qasim. PO BOX 850, DEPT OF PEDIATRICS 17033 #704-01-2002 L2004 PD *100
MAHRAJ, Rickhesvar P M. 500 UNIVERSITY DR, MILTON S HERSHEY MEDICAL C 17033 #917-14-1979 L1980 R IM *020 †20
MAI, Weiyuan. MCH088, MILTON S HERSHEY MEDICAL C 17033 #243-21-1986 L2007 GS *012
MAKI, Matthew Douglas. PO BOX 850, DEPT OF ANESTHES H187 17033 #048-13-2004 L2004 AN *012
MAKKAR, Abhishek. ■ 17033 #495-69-2003 L2007 PD *012
MALLIS, Caitlin Jean. ■ 17033 #041-14-2008 L2008 *012
MANN, Lowell Dean. DEPT OF PSYCHIATRY, HERSHEY MEDICAL DEAN 17033 #041-02-1957 L1959 P GP *071 †75
MANNI, Andrea. 500 UNIVERSITY DR, MSHERSHEY MEDICAL CENTER 17033 #561-06-1970 L1982 EM IM *062 †20
MAPARA, Zohair. ■ 17033 #704-25-2003 L2007 FP *012
MARCHBEIN, Shari Brooke. 500 UNIVERSITY DR, DEPT OF DERMATOLOGY, HU14 17033 #035-15-2004 L2004 D *012
MARKS, James Garfield, Jr. 500 UNIVERSITY DR 17033 #041-13-1971 L1972 D *020 †15
MARKS, Keith H. 500 UNIVERSITY DR, RM 1479 17033 #836-01-1966 L1976 NPM *020 †55

MARRONE, Michael S. 500 UNIVERSITY DR 17033 #041-14-1975 L1977 **FM** *071 †18
MARTIN, Donald Eugene. 500 UNIVERSITY DR 17033 #041-02-1976 L1977 **AN** *020 †05
MARTIN, Jonathan Hamilton. ■ 17033 #041-14-2008 *012
MARU, Yogesh Dhanji. 500 UNIVERSITY DR, LANCASTER GENERAL HOSPITAL 17033 #496-38-1978 L2002 *020
MASON, Heidi Puyrea. PO BOX 850 17033 #654-01-2004 L2005 **AN** *012
MASTERS, Erin Anne. ■ 17033 #051-04-2004 L2004 **EM** *012
MASTERS, Philip Allen. 500 UNIV DR STE UPC 4100, M S HERSHEY MEDICAL CTR 17033 #041-01-1989 L1991 **IM** *020 †20
MATHEW, Abraham. 500 UNIVERSITY DR, DIV OF GASTROENTEROLOGY 17033 #495-63-1994 L1998 **GE** *020 †20
MATIZ, Catalina. ■ 17033 #264-01-2003 L2005 **PD** *012
MATLYUK, Zinaida. ■ 17033 #041-14-2002 L2003 **IM** *100 †80
MATOS, Sergio. ■ 17033 #042-03-1994 L2001 **P IM** *020
MATTHEWS, Mark Aaron. ■ 17033 #041-14-2002 L2005 **CD** *012 †20
MC CABE, Paul Henry. 500 UNIVERSITY DR, DEPT OF NEUROLOGY 17033 #041-02-1987 L1989 **N** *020 †75
MCCAULEY, Robert Andrew. ■ 17033 #041-02-2004 L2004 **MPD** *012
MCCOLLESTER, Sarah M. 500 UNIVERSITY DR, PENN STATE HERSHEY MED CTR 17033 #041-14-2006 L2007 **OBG** *012
MCCREADY, Mariah Beth. PO BOX 850, PENN ST U HP-M S HERSHEY 17033 #041-13-2006 L2006 **PTH** *012
MCCULLOUGH, Paul Brigham. ■ 17033 #028-34-2006 L2006 **AN** *012
MC GARRITY, Thomas Jos. 500 UNIVERSITY DR, DEPT GAST 17033 #051-01-1979 L1981 **GE IM** *050 †20
MC GINN, Johnathan David. 500 UNIVERSITY DR 17033 #041-14-1995 L2001 **OTO** *020 †45
MC INERNEY, James. 500 UNIVERSITY DR, MCH110 17033 #010-02-1993 L2002 **NS** *020 †25
MC KEE, Michael Benj. DEPT OF MED/CARDIOL, HERSHEY MED CTR 17033 #035-20-1969 L1975 **CD IM** *020 †20
MC KENNA, Kevin J. 500 UNIVERSITY DR, DIV OF COLON/RECTAL SURG 17033 #035-08-1988 L1990 **CRS** *020 †85,10
MC MANAWAY, James W, III. 233 W CHOCOLATE AVE, HERSHEY PED OPHTH ASSOC PC 17033 #051-04-1984 L1989 **OPH PO** *020 †35
MC NAMARA, Kevin Patrick. PENN STATE UNIV HOSP, DEPT OF RADIOLOGY 17033 #041-02-1982 L1987 **RNR DR** *020 †80
MEADOR, Steven Arthur. 500 UNIVERSITY DR, HERSHEY MEDICAL CENTER 17033 #028-02-1981 L1984 **EM** *020 †16
MEASEL, Matthew Kelly. ■ 17033 #004-01-2007 L2007 **MPD** *012
MEHDI, Asad. PO BOX 850 17033 #704-16-2000 L2005 **P** *012
MEIER, Andreas H. 500 UNIVERSITY DR, DIV PEDIATRIC SURGERY/MC H 17033 #409-40-1991 L2002 **PDS** *020 †85
MEILSTRUP, Jon W. 500 UNIVERSITY DR, HERSHEY MED CTR DEPT RADI 17033 #049-01-1976 L1988 **DR** *020 †80
MEIRELLES, Katia. MCH088, MILTON S HERSHEY MEDICAL C 17033 #187-72-1995 L2007 **GS** *012
MESSER, Jamie Christopher. ■ 17033 #020-12-2006 L2006 **GS** *012
METS, Berend. 500 UNIVERSITY DR, DEPT ANESTHESIOLOGY H187 17033 #836-04-1980 L2002 **AN** *030 †05
MICHAEL, Eric John. 500 UNIVERSITY DR, PSMHSMC H085 17033 #041-02-1978 L1979 **NPM PD** *020 †55
MIGHTY, Jeannette Antoine. PO BOX 850 17033 #566-01-2001 L2005 **PD** *012
MIKULA, Margaret Irene. 500 UNIVERSITY DR 17033 #025-07-1999 L2001 **MPD** *020 †55
MILKE, Denis Jerome. 500 UNIVERSITY DR 17033 #041-09-1965 L1966 **P OS** *020 †75
MILLER, Debra Quinn. 670 CHERRY DR, HERSHEY INTERNAL MEDICINE 17033 #041-14-1990 L1993 **IM** *020 †20
MILLER, Jeffrey Joseph. 500 UNIVERSITY DR, SECTION OF DERM MCHUI4 17033 #041-02-1993 L1996 **D** *020 †15
MILLER, Ronald Peter. 500 UNIVERSITY DR BOX 850, DIV OF NEPHROLOGY H040 17033 #024-05-1994 L2002 **NEP** *020 †20
MILLWARD, Peter Ashley. 500 UNIVERSITY DR, MC H160 17033 #041-02-1997 L2001 **PTH** *100 †50
MINNICH, Keith Alan. 500 UNIVERSITY DR 17033 #041-14-1987 L1988 **AN** *020 †05 ‡
MOATZ, Bradley William. ■ 17033 #041-14-2008 *012
MOBEEN, Haris. 3 ROSEDALE 17033 #704-20-2000 L2004 **IM** *020 †20
MORADKHAN, Raman. 500 UNIVERSITY DR, H047 CARDIO DEPT 17033 #517-10-1990 L2002 **CD** *012 †20
MORALES, Jeanette. 500 UNIVERSITY DR, DEPT PSYCH 17033 #042-01-1981 L1982 **CHP P** *020 †75
MORTEL, Rodrigue. 500 UNIVERSITY DR, MILTON S HERSHEY MEDICAL C 17033 #440-01-1960 L1965 **GO GYN** *030 †30
MORTIMORE, Glenn E. 500 UNIVERSITY DR 17033 #040-02-1952 L1956 **IM** *100
MOSHER, Timothy John. 500 UNIVERSITY DR, DEPT RADIOLOGY MSHERSHEY M 17033 #041-14-1989 L1994 **DR** *020 †80
MOUZAKI, Marialena Dionys. 500 UNIVERSITY DR, DEPT OF GME 17033 #418-01-2005 L2006 **PD** *012
MOYER, Matthew Timothy. 500 UNIVERSITY DR, DEPT OF GASTROENTEROLOGY 17033 #041-14-2002 L2002 **GE** *012 †20
MUJSCE, Dennis Jimmy. PENN STATE CHILDRENS HOSP 17033 #035-08-1982 L1985 **NPM PD** *020 †55
MULLER, Herbert Arnold. 500 UNIVERSITY DR 17033 #024-01-1955 L1965 **EM IM** *020 †20,16
MUNOZ, Frank J. 201 BRIARCREST SQ 17033 #047-05-1984 L1997 **P** *020 †50,75
MURPHY, Claire. 500 UNIVERSITY DR 17033 #033-05-1998 L2003 **FM** *020 †18
MURRAY, Michael John. 22 NORTHEAST DR 17033 #041-14-1993 L1996 **P** *020 †75
MURRAY, W Bosseau. 500 UNIVERSITY DR, DEPT OF ANESTH H-187 17033 #836-03-1971 L1993 **AN** *020 †05
MYERS, Abigail Kate. ■ 17033 #041-13-2007 L2007 **PD** *012
MYERS, Catherine Freedman. 500 UNIVERSITY DR, H085 17033 #041-15-2000 L2001 **NPM** *020 †55 ‡
MYERS, John Lyerly. PO BOX 850, MCH 165 17033 #017-20-1977 L1978 **TS** *020 †85,90
NACCARELLI, Gerald V. PO BOX 850, MS HERSHEY MEDICAL CENTER 17033 #041-14-1976 L1978 **ICE CD** *020
NAEYE, Richard L. 500 UNIVERSITY DR 17033 #035-01-1955 L1967 **PTH** *050 †50
NAHI, Fatin Talib. ■ 17033 #528-01-1986 L2004 **P** *012
NAIDU, Sanjiv H. PO BOX 850, 500 UNIVERSITY DR MC H089 17033 #041-01-1988 L1992 **ORS** *020 †40
NANDATE, Koichiro. 500 UNIVERSITY DR, PO BOX 850 17033 #572-83-1992 *100

NDEY, Maria Assumpta. MCH088, MILTON S HERSHEY MEDICAL C 17033 #539-02-1996 L2007 **GS** *012
NEELY, John Edward. MS HERSHEY MEDICAL CTR, DEPT OF PEDIATRICS 17033 #041-14-1973 L1985 **IM PD** *020 †55
NEELY, Kimberly Ann. 500 UNIVERSITY DR, DEPT OF OPTHALMOLOGY 17033 #047-05-1984 L1997 **OPH** *020 †35
NEUWIRTH, Charles Alan. 500 UNIVERSITY DR, MILTON S HERSHEY MEDICAL C 17033 #550-03-2000 L2006 **VS** *012
NEVES, Rogerio Izar. 500 UNIVERSITY DR, MC H071 17033 #187-67-1985 L2007 *100
NEWPORT, Kristina Michell. ■ 17033 #041-14-2005 L2005 **IM** *012
NICHTER, Charles Albert. 500 UNIVERSITY DR, PEDIATRIC NEUROLOGY- 6TH 17033 #041-13-1976 L1980 **CHN** *020 †55,75
NICKELS, Michael S. ■ 17033 #045-04-1998 L2000 **AI** *020
NIFONG, Thomas P. 500 UNIVERSITY DR 17033 #035-45-1995 L1999 **CLP** *020 †50
NIKFARJAM, Mehrdad. SURGICAL ONCOLOG, PENN STATE MILTON S HERSHET 17033 #143-08-1997 L2007 **SO** *020
NOORI, Shamimi S. 377 W GOVERNOR RD 17033 #517-01-1969 L1976 **P** *020 †75
NUMMIKOSKI, Miia Maria. PO BOX 850 17033 #422-01-2004 L2004 **AN** *012
NURI, Muhammad A Khalid. 500 UNIVERSITY DR MCH165, PENN STATE M.S.HERSHEY MED 17033 #704-25-1998 L2004 **TS** *100 †85,90
O BRYAN, Thomas Anthony. 500 UNIVERSITY DR, P O BOX 850/HU15 17033 #041-09-1986 L1988 **IM** *020 †20
O'GUREK, Amy Lee. ■ 17033 #041-14-2007 L2007 **MPD** *012
OLT, George Jeffrey. 500 UNIVERSITY DR 17033 #038-41-1984 L1991 **OBG ON** *020 †30
OLYMPIA, Robert Patrick. 500 UNIVERSITY DR, PENN STATE MILTON S HERSHE 17033 #041-02-1996 L2005 **PD** *100 †55
ONCU, Kerim Ibrahim. 500 UNIVERSITY DR, INTERNAL MEDICINE DEPARTME 17033 #041-77-2002, ▲ L2002 **NEP** *012 †20
OSTROV, Barbara Ellen. 500 UNIVERSITY DR 17033 #035-06-1983 L1987 **RHU PPR** *020 †20,55
PAE, Walter Edward. 500 UNIVERSITY DR, MED CENTER 17033 #041-14-1977 L1979 **TS** *020 †85,90
PAJERLA, Sravanthi. PO BOX 850, M S HERSHEY MED CTR 17033 #759-12-2003 L2007 **CHP** *012
PALMER, Charles. DEPT OF PEDIATRICS, MILTON S HERSHEY MED CTRS 17033 #836-02-1974 L1988 **NPM** *030 †55
PAN, Ming. 500 UNIVERSITY DR, DEPT SURGERY/MC H419 17033 #243-21-1986 L2000 **GS** *020 †20
PAPROTA, Joseph Russell. 500 UNIVERSITY DR H-041 17033 #041-13-2003 L2003 **PCC** *012 †20
PARENT, Leslie Joan. ■ 17033 #036-07-1987 L1991 **ID** *050 †20
PASTOR, Danielle Marie. ■ 17033 #035-75-2004, ▲ L2004 **GS** *012
PATEL, Amish Ashwinkumar. 500 UNIVERSITY DR 17033 #422-01-2000 L2001 **PAN** *100 †20,05
PATEL, Parag Pramukh. 500 UNIVERSITY DR, H039 17033 #041-14-2002 L2002 **CD** *012 †20
PATEL, Viral Pramodbhai. MCH088, MILTON S HERSHEY MEDICAL C 17033 #495-76-2002 L2007 **GS** *012
PATRONE, Sabrina. ■ 17033 #051-07-1988 L1994 **DR** *020 †80
PATTISHALL, Evan G, III. 158 HOTEL RD 17033 #038-06-1975 L1983 **PD** *030 †55
PAUL, Ian Michael. PO BOX 850, DEPT OF PEDS H085 17033 #041-14-1998 L2001 **PD** *020 †55
PAZ, Harold Louis. 500 UNIVERSITY DR, PENN STATE MAILCODE H 162 17033 #035-45-1982 L1988 **PUD CCM** *030 †20 ‡
PEES, Richard Conrad. 670 CHERRY DR 17033 #041-09-1977 L1978 **GYN** *020 †30
PERKINS, James Lorenzo, Jr. 65 UNIVERSITY MNR E 17033 #041-14-2008 *012
PETTY, Leonora Kathleen. ■ 17033 #041-01-1973 L1974 **P CHP** *020 †75
PHAM, Thai Hong. 500 UNIVERSITY DR - MCH15, PENN STATE MILTON S HERSHE 17033 #003-01-2002 L2002 **GS** *012
PHAM, Tri Minh. PO BOX 850 17033 #010-01-2000 L2000 **IM** *020
PHELPS, Tiffany Nicole. ■ 17033 #041-14-2008 *012
PHILLIPS, Peter P, Jr. 500 UNIVERSITY DR 17033 #041-14-1989 L1991 **PTH** *020 †50
PIERCE, William Schuler. 500 UNIVERSITY DR # 850, MS HERSHEY MD CTR RM C4608 17033 #041-01-1962 L1963 **TS** *071 †85,90
PO, Wilson Chi. 500 UNIVERSITY DR, ANESTHESIA DEPT H187 17033 #748-18-1988 L2004 **AN** *020 †05
PODCZASKI, Edward S. 500 UNIVERSITY DR, HERSHEY MEDICAL CENTER 17033 #016-02-1977 L1984 **OBG** *020 †30
POLACHECK, William Joseph, Jr. 32 NORTHEAST DR 17033 #041-02-1980 L1981 **ORS HS** *020 †40 ‡
POORAN, Nakechand Rai. 500 UNIVERSITY DR, H045 17033 #422-01-1997 L2005 **GE** *020 †20
POPELIANSKY, Ella Alexand. 400 UNIVERSITY MNR W, PENN STATE HERSHEY MED CTR 17033 #051-01-2006 L2007 **N** *012
POPJES, Eric Drukker. 500 UNIVERSITY DR, RM C5833 17033 #035-01-1995 L1998 **CD** *020 †20
POTOCHNY, John Damian. 500 UNIVERSITY DR, DRIVE, MCH113 17033 #041-02-1993 L1995 **PS** *020 †85,65
POWELL, Aaron Michael. PO BOX 850, M S HERSHEY M C 17033 #035-15-2006 L2007 **DR** *012
POWELL, James R, Jr. 500 UNIVERSITY DR 17033 #041-14-1992 L1994 **PHO** *020 †55
PRADHAN, Anay Dilip. MCH088, MILTON S HERSHEY MEDICAL C 17033 #495-23-2002 L2007 **IM** *012
PRADHAN, Anupam Kumar. ■ 17033 #047-05-2006 L2006 **ORS** *012
PRAMANIK, Sudeep. 825 FISHBURN RD, CENTRAL PENNSYLVANIA EYE I 17033 #048-04-2001 L2006 **OPH** *100 †35
PREMATTA, Michael Joseph. ■ 17033 #041-14-2005 L2005 **IM** *012
PRESTON, Todd William. 500 UNIVERSITY DR, HERSHEY MEDICAL CENTER 17033 #038-43-2001 L2001 **OTO** *100
PRICE, Harper Nichole. 500 UNIVERSITY DR, DEPT OF DERMATOLOGY, HU14 17033 #041-02-2004 L2007 **D** *012
PRYSTOWSKY, Harry. 500 UNIVERSITY DR BX 850 17033 #045-01-1948 L1974 **OBG** *030 †30
QUILLEN, David Andrew. 500 UNIVERSITY DR, HERSHEY MEDICAL CENTER 17033 #041-14-1990 L1994 **OPH** *020 †35
QUIOGUE, Thelma. 500 UNIVERSITY DR 17033 #025-01-1980 L1982 **PDR** *020 †80
QURESHI, Muhammad Azim. 500 UNIVERSITY DR H085, DEPT OF PEDIATRIC GASTROEN 17033 #704-02-1989 L2004 **PD PG** *020 †55
RAFFERTY, Colleen Marie. 500 UNIVERSITY DR, DIVISION OF GENERAL INTERN 17033 #005-18-1999 L2004 **IM** *020 †20
RAJA, Nazia Trannum. ■ 17033 #035-08-2000 L2004 **END** *100 †20
RAJAN, Niraja. PO BOX 850, 500 UNIVERSITY DR 17033 #495-45-1994 L2001 **PAN** *020 †05
RAMER, Jeanette Carol. 500 UNIVERSITY DR 17033 #041-14-1977 L1979 **PD** *020 †55,19

■ = Address Information Privacy Protected

RANASINGHE, Moksha Gandha. 500 UNIVERSITY DR, H110 17033 #032-01-2004 L2004 NS *012

RAPP, Mark Anthony. 500 UNIVERSITY DR, MILTON S HERSHEY MEDICAL C 17033 #033-06-1997 L2007 P *020 †75

RAYCO, Eriberto Roa. 500 UNIVERSITY DR 17033 #748-01-2003 L2007 PD *012

RAZA, Uroos Annie. 500 UNIVERSITY DR H-043, PENN STATE UNIV 17033 #704-25-2003 L2007 EM *012

READ, Selina Nichole. 500 UNIVERSITY DR 17033 #023-01-2007 L2007 AN *012

READENCE, Scott Michael. 32 NORTHEAST DR, STE 102 17033 #038-41-2003 L2003 OBG *020

REBSTOCK, Sarah Elizabeth. 500 UNIVERSITY DR, DEPT OF ANESTHESIOLOGY/ PO 17033 #409-32-2002 L2003 PAN *012

REESE, Carl Thomas. 500 UNIVERSITY DR 17033 #041-14-1997 L1999 U *020 †95

REEVES, William Brian. 500 UNIVERSITY DR, PENN STATE COLLEGE OF MEDI 17033 #041-02-1979 L2000 IM NEP *050 †20

REICHWEIN, Raymond K, III. 500 UNIVERSITY DR, DIV OF NEUROLOGY 17033 #041-14-1991 L1994 N *020 †75

REID, John Spence. 500 UNIVERSITY DR, PENN STATE ORTHO 17033 #041-14-1985 L1987 ORS GS *020 †40

REINKE, Timothy Scott. 500 UNIVERSITY DR H149, MEDICAL CENTER 17033 #025-07-1999 L2004 GS *020 †85

REITER, George Timothy. 500 UNIVERSITY DR, DEPARTMENT OF NEUROSURGERY 17033 #041-09-1995 L1998 NS *020 †25

REPKE, John Thos. 670 CHERRY DR, HERSHEY MEDICAL CENTER 17033 #035-09-1978 L2002 OBG MFM *020 †30 ‡

RIAZ, Shazia. 500 UNIVERSITY DR H085, MEDICAL CEN 17033 #704-06-1998 L2004 PD *012

RIEDY, Dawn Kathleen. B 850 MS HERSY MED CTR-PTH 17033 #035-45-1984 L1989 PTH *062 †50

RILEY, Thomas R, III. 500 UNIVERSITY DR 17033 #038-40-1990 L1995 HEP GE *020 †20

RINKUS, Keith Michael. PO BOX 850, 500 UNIVERSITY DR 17033 #036-05-2002 L2002 ORS *020

RIVAS, Sharon Woodswebb. 500 UNIVERSITY DR, MC H110 17033 #045-04-2002 L2002 NS *012

RIZK, Elias Boulos. PO BOX 850, PENN ST U HP-M S HERSHEY M 17033 #605-01-2003 L2005 NS *012

RODGERS, Daniel Robert. 500 UNIVERSITY DR H043, PENN STATE MSH MEDICAL CEN 17033 #023-01-1993 L2007 EM *020 †16 ‡

RODICHOK, Laurence D. 500 UNIVERSITY DR 17033 #016-43-1972 L1986 N *020 †75

RODRIGUEZ, Daniella. 500 UNIVERSITY DR, DEPT OF GME 17033 #649-52-2004 L2006 PD *012

ROGERS, Ann Marie. 500 UNIVERSITY DR, PENN STATE MILTON S. HERSH 17033 #035-20-1987 L2006 GS OS *020 †85 ‡

ROHNER, Thomas John, Jr. 500 UNIVERSITY DR 17033 #041-01-1961 L1962 U *020 †95

ROHRER, George Victor. 500 UNIVERSITY DR 17033 #039-01-1958 L1971 DR GE *030 †20,80

ROLAND, Lincoln Antonio. ■ 17033 #041-14-2004 GS *012

ROQUE, Nina Josefa Villan. PO BOX 850 17033 #748-01-2003 L2005 PD *012

ROSENWASSER, George O. 825 FISHBURN RD, CENTRAL PA EYE INSTITUTE 17033 #011-02-1983 L1988 OPH *040 †35

ROSS, Jody Michele. 670 CHERRY DR STE 102, UNIVERSITY PEDIATRICS ASSO 17033 #038-45-1994 L1997 PD *050 †55

ROSS, Stephen Curtis. 500 UNIVERSITY DR, P O BOX 850 17033 #038-45-1993 L1997 N *020 †75

ROWE, William A. 1421 FISHBURN RD 17033 #008-02-1986 L1987 GE IM *050 †20

RUBBO, Ernest Robert. 32 NORTHEAST DR 17033 #041-13-1982 L1983 ORS *020 †40

RUFFLE, Joan Madeline. 500 UNIVERSITY DR, DEPT ANES 17033 #041-14-1973 L1979 AN *020 †05

RUNYON, Scott Lawrence. ■ 17033 #041-14-2008 *012

RYAN, Colleen Marie. ■ 17033 #041-14-2002 FM *020 †18

SAFAEE-SEMIROMI, Saeid. 500 UNIVERSITY DR, HERSHEY MEDICAL CENTER 17033 #517-08-1987 L1998 PCC *012 †20

SALMAN, Nadim Henri. 500 UNIVERSITY DR H-043, PENN STATE UNIVERSITY 17033 #045-04-2005 L2005 EM *012

SALNESS, Kym Alan. 1120 COCOA AVE 17033 #041-13-1976 L1993 PUD IM *030 †20,16

SAMSON, Thomas Daniel. 500 UNIVERSITY DR, HERSHEY MED CTR 17033 #030-06-2002 L2007 PS *012

SANCHEZ, Joseph Richard. ■ 17033 #041-14-2004 *100

SANDHU, Sandeep Kaur. 500 UNIVERSITY DR H085, PENN STATE HERSHEY MEDICAL 17033 #759-12-2004 L2005 PD *012

SASSANI, Joseph Wm. ■ 17033 #041-02-1973 L1989 OPH OS *020 †35 ‡

SASSER, John Matthew. PO BOX 850 17033 #422-01-2005 L2005 EM *012

SAUDER, Matthew Alan. 500 UNIVERSITY DR, MILTON S. HERSHEY MEDICAL 17033 #041-14-2005 L2005 IM *012

SCHAFFER, David Nelson. 475 GOVERNOR RD 17033 #041-14-1977 L1979 PD *020 †55

SCHLEGEL, Daniel John. 845 FISHBURN RD 17033 #041-01-2003 L2003 FM *020 †18

SCHOLFIELD, Kimberly Rose. 500 UNIVERSITY DR 17033 #041-02-1993 L2001 EM *020 †16

SCHULLER, Diane Ethel. 500 UNIVERSITY DR, HERSHEY MEDICAL CENTER 17033 #035-08-1970 L1974 AI PD *020 †03,55

SCHWENTKER, Edwards Park. PO BOX 850, PENN STATE-HERSHEY MED CTR 17033 #023-07-1968 L1969 OP PM *040 †40

SCORZA, Leslie Bernard. 500 UNIVERSITY DR H066, RADIOLOGY DEPT/POB 850 17033 #041-02-1986 L1988 DR OS *020 †80,85

SCOTT, Ingrid Ursula. 500 UNIVERSITY DR HU19, PENN STATE COLLEGE OF MED 17033 #023-07-1993 L2005 OPH *020 †35 ‡

SCOTT, Kevin Randall. PO BOX 850 17033 #036-05-1999 L2001 N *100 †75

SEDEEK, Khaled Anwar. 500 UNIVERSITY DR, DEPT OF ANESTHESIOLOGY 17033 #915-02-1993 L2006 *020

SEIDERS, Dawn Elizabeth. ■ 17033 #041-14-2006 L2006 IM *012

SEIDL, Dana Claire. 500 UNIVERSITY DR 17033 #041-14-1980 L1981 AN *040 †05

SHADROU, Shahrouz. ■ 17033 #517-08-2000 L2006 IM *012

SHEEHAN, Jonas Michael. 500 UNIVERSITY DR, DIVISION NEUROSURGERY/MC H 17033 #051-01-1996 L2002 NS *020 †25

SHEIKH, Hassan Shahryar. PO BOX 850 17033 #704-25-2003 L2005 IM *012

SHEIKH, Mahvash Zahra. PO BOX 850 17033 #704-01-2002 L2006 P *012

SHEIKH, Saba Sartajuddin. ■ 17033 #704-25-2005 L2007 PD *012

SHENBERGER, Jeffrey Scott. 500 UNIVERSITY DR, HERSHEY MEDICAL CENTER 17033 #041-14-1989 L2006 NPM PD *050 †55

SHETTY, Sujeeth Kuthyar. 500 UNIVERSITY DR, DEPT OF GME 17033 #496-35-2001 L2006 FP *012

SHI, Guoxiang. ■ 17033 #243-73-1984 L2007 GE *012

SHIREY, Jonathan Edward. ■ 17033 #010-02-2007 L2007 AN *012

SHOPE, Timothy Robert. 500 UNIVERSITY DR, DRIVE/MS H149 17033 #041-09-1997 L2002 GS *020 †85

SILBER, David Henry. 500 UNIVERSITY DR 17033 #041-14-1990 L1993 CD IM *020 †20

SILVIS, Matthew Leroy. ■ 17033 #041-14-2002 L2007 FSM *100 †18

SIMMONS, Zachary. 500 UNIVERSITY DR, DEPT NEUROL H037 17033 #011-03-1982 L1992 N CN *020 †75

SIMMS, George Robt. 500 UNIVERSITY DR 17033 #869-07-1963 L1985 FM P *071 †18

SIMONS, Richard John, Jr. 500 UNIVERSITY DR, MC H176 17033 #041-14-1981 L1984 IM IMG *040 †20

SIMONYANTS, Lusine. ■ 17033 #913-38-1998 L2003 PCC *012 †20

SINDERMAN, Steven C. 22 NORTHEAST DR, BEHAVIORAL HEALTH 17033 #045-01-1986 L1996 P *020 †75

SINGAREDDY, Ravi Kumar R. 500 UNIVERSITY DR, DEPT OF PSYCHIATRY, H073 17033 #495-62-1995 L2004 SME *050 †20,75

SINGH, Gaganvir. 500 UNIVERSITY DR, MILTON S HERSHEY MEDICAL C 17033 #496-01-1999 L2006 P *012

SINGH, Harjit. 500 UNIVERSITY DR, HERSHEY MEDICAL CTR-RADIOL 17033 #035-03-1990 L1995 DR *100 †80

SINGH, Ravi Shankar Jit. MCH088, MILTON S HERSHEY MEDICAL C 17033 #495-29-2000 L2007 IM *012

SINGH, Tejpal Bal. PO BOX 850, HERSHEY M 17033 #051-01-2004 L2004 DR *020

SINOWAY, Lawrence Isaac. 500 UNIVERSITY DR, CARDIOLOGY MCH047 17033 #033-05-1978 L1984 CD IM *020 †20

SINZ, Elizabeth Hylton. 500 UNIVERSITY DR, DEPARTMENT OF ANESTHESIOLO 17033 #051-04-1991 L1993 AN CCA *040 †05

SIVENDRAN, Shanthi. PO BOX 850 17033 #539-04-2004 L2005 IM *012

SMITH, J Stanley, Jr. 500 UNIVERSITY DR, MC H070 MS HERSHEY MED CTR 17033 #041-02-1971 L1972 GS TRS *020 †85

SMITH, Jill Palmer. 500 UNIVERSITY DR, H-045 HERSHEY MEDICAL CENT 17033 #011-03-1980 L1987 GE IM *050 †20

SMITH, Patricia Ann. 500 UNIVERSITY DR - H110, HERSHEY MED CTR-NEUROSURGE 17033 #025-07-1993 L2000 NS *012

SMITH, Ronald Eugene. 500 UNIVERSITY DR 17033 #038-41-1971 L1975 AN *020 †05 ‡

SNIDER, Michael Thos. 500 UNIVERSITY DR 17033 #012-05-1972 L1981 PUD AN *050 †05

SOHRABI, Sohrab. ■ 17033 #038-41-2007 L2007 OTO *012

SOLDANSKA, Magdalena Wiol. ■ 17033 #041-14-2007 *012

SOPHIE, Azka. PO BOX 850 17033 #704-25-2002 L2005 PD *012

SREEDHARAN, Akila. ■ 17033 #017-20-2003 L2005 AI *012 †20

STAGG, Ryan Edward. ■ 17033 #041-14-2008 *012

STAVELEY O'CARROLL, Kevin. 500 UNIVERSITY DR, HERSHEY MEDICAL CENTER 17033 #039-01-1990 L2000 GS SO *020 †85

STEADHAM, Robert Michael. PO BOX 850, PENN STATE COLL OF MED 17033 #045-01-2006 L2006 N *012

STEEL, Christopher Allen, Jr. PO BOX 850 17033 #654-01-2007 L2007 AN *012

STENE, John Kennison, Jr. 500 UNIVERSITY DR H187, DEPT OF ANESTHESIOLOGY 17033 #023-07-1973 L1988 AN CCA *040 †05 ‡

STEPHENSON, Edward Roger. 500 UNIVERSITY DR 17033 #035-06-1993 L1995 GS *020 †85,90

STEVENSON, Robert Thomas. 500 UNIVERSITY DR 17033 #041-15-2000 L2001 ICE *012 ‡

STOUGHTON, Tracy Rachelle. ■ 17033 #041-14-2005 L2005 PD *012

STRIGENZ, Timothy Joseph. 500 UNIVERSITY DR, PENN STATE ORTHO, H089 17033 #040-02-2003 L2004 ORS *100

STURTZ, Kraig Wm. 500 UNIVERSITY DR 17033 #041-14-1990 L1994 PTH *020 †50

SUBRAMANIAN, Thyagarajan. 500 UNIVERSITY DR, DEPT OF NEUROLOGY, H037, 17033 #495-44-1985 L1993 N *050 †75

SULIMAN, Alawia K. 500 UNIVERSITY DR, BOX 850 17033 #848-01-1978 L1993 PD *020 †55

SUNDARAM, Arun Nagarasamp. 500 UNIVERSITY DR, HERSHEY M 17033 #496-35-1997 L2004 N *100

SYED, Syyeda F.. 500 UNIVERSITY DR 17033 #704-16-1990 L2004 P *012

TAMBURRO, Robert Francis. 500 UNIVERSITY DR, HERSHEY MEDICAL CTR DEPT O 17033 #038-44-1986 L2004 PD *020 †55

TAN, Fritza See. M S HERSHEY M C U OF PA, DEPT INT MED 17033 #748-01-1982 L1993 IM *100

TAN, Tjiauw-Ling. 500 UNIVERSITY DR, DEPT PSYCH 17033 #506-01-1961 L1973 P PYG *040 †75

TAPPOUNI, Rafel F. Raphae. 500 UNIVERSITY DR, HERSHEY MED CTR 17033 #539-06-1995 L2005 *100

TASHKO, Gerti. ■ 17033 #023-01-2004 L2005 IM *012

TAY, James Joseph. PO BOX 850, DEPT OF ANESTH H187 17033 #748-20-2001 L2002 AN *012

TENSER, Richard Bruce. 500 UNIVERSITY DR, DEPT NEUR 17033 #403-15-1968 L1976 N *020 †75

TERNDRUP, Thomas Edward. 500 UNIVERSITY DR MCH1234, MILTON S. HERSHEY MED CTR 17033 #041-14-1981 L2006 EM *020 †16

TESTA, Donna Marie. 1120 COCOA AVE, COCOA FAMILY MEDICINE 17033 #041-07-1975 L1977 FM *020 †18

THIBOUTOT, Diane Marie. 500 UNIVERSITY DR 17033 #041-14-1988 L1991 D *020 †15

THIELE, Brian Leslie. 500 UNIVERSITY DR, DEPT SURG 17033 #143-05-1966 L1983 VS *020

THOMAS, Neal James. 500 UNIVERSITY DR 17033 #041-13-1991 L1995 CCP *020 †55

THORNDYKE, Luanne E. 500 UNIVERSITY DR, MILTON S HERSHEY MEDICAL C 17033 #030-05-1983 L1984 IM IMG *075 †20

THORYK, David Tilton. 1120 COCOA AVE 17033 #035-15-1993 L1995 FM *020 †18

THWING, Michael William. ■ 17033 #041-14-2003 L2005 PD *020 †55

TOBLER, Kyle James. ■ 17033 #041-14-2007 *012

TODD, Stephanie Lea. PO BOX 850 17033 #422-01-2004 L2005 IM *012

TOLAN, Jeffrey Robert. 1120 COCOA AVE, COCOA FAMILY MEDICINE 17033 #014-01-1982 L1983 FM EM *020 †18

TONEY, Eugene Asbury. ■ 17033 #017-20-2004 L2005 ORS *012

TORTORA, Matthew John. ■ 17033 #041-14-2004 L2005 PTH *012

TOTH, Jennifer Whitney. 500 UNIVERSITY DR, DEPT OF PULMONARY MEDICINE 17033 #041-15-2000 L2001 PCC *100

TOURTELOT, Ellen Jane. PO BOX 850, DEPT OF OB/GYN 17033 #035-45-1987 L1993 OBG *020 †30

TOWFIGHI, Javad. 500 UNIVERSITY DR 17033 #517-01-1963 L1970 NP PTH *020 †50

TREADWAY, Travis William. 1120 COCOA AVE 17033 #047-06-1997 L2004 FM *020 †18

TRESCHER, William H. 500 UNIVERSITY DR, HERSHEY MED CTR H085 17033 #041-14-1983 L2005 CHN PD *020 †75,55

TROJANOWSKI, Andrzej. 500 UNIVERSITY DR 17033 #759-03-1970 L2003 **AN** *020

TROSTLE, David Chas. 475 W GOVERNOR RD 17033 #041-14-1980 L1983 **RHU IM** *020 †20

TRUSSELL, J C. 500 UNIVERSITY DR, DIV OF UROLOGY POB 850 17033 #041-13-1992 L2001 **U** *020 †95

TULCHINSKY, Mark. 500 UNIVERSITY DR 17033 #913-21-1981 L1989 **NM IM** *020 †20,28

TUREL, Anthony Paul, Jr. 500 UNIVERSITY DR, PENN STATE MILTON HERSHEY 17033 #035-20-1967 L1974 **N IM** *020 †75

UEMURA, Tadahiro. 500 UNIVERSITY DR MCH0, PENN STATE MILTON S HERSHE 17033 #572-09-1994 L2006 *020

UPADHYA, Bharathi. ■ 17033 #495-09-1993 L2007 **CD** *012 †20

URAL, Serdar H. 500 UNIVERSITY DR, STE C3624 DEPT OB/GYN 17033 #902-03-1989 L2000 **OBG** *020 †30

VALENTINE, Danny Lee. 500 UNIVERSITY DR, OF ANESTHESIOLOGY 17033 #041-14-2001 L2001 **AN** *020

VALENTINE, Elizabeth G. 500 UNIVERSITY DR 17033 #041-14-1987 L1990 **EM** *020 †16

VAN HOOK, David Madison. 500 UNIVERSITY DR, DEPT RAD 17033 #028-03-1966 L1988 **DR ORS** *020 †80

VANNUCCI, Robert Chas. 500 UNIVERSITY DR 17033 #041-02-1966 L1974 **CHN** *071 †55,75

VASSAR, Margo Marion. ■ 17033 #023-01-2001 L2004 **CD** *020

VAVAL, Alain Raymond. ■ 17033 #041-14-2007 *012

VEDENIAPIN, Andrei Boriso. PO BOX 850 17033 #913-06-1985 L2005 **P** *012

VESELL, Elliot Saul. 500 UNIVERSITY DR, BX 850 17033 #024-01-1959 L1969 **PA** *050

VGONTZAS, Alexandros N. 500 UNIVERSITY DR 17033 #418-01-1978 L1986 **P** *020

VIGUE, Lisa Ann. ■ 17033 #030-06-2005 L2005 **OBG** *012

VILLANUEVA, Philip A. 500 UNIVERSITY DR, DRIVE, EC110 17033 #011-02-1976 L2007 **NS** *020 †25

VLASIC, Vukmir. 500 UNIVERSITY DR H085, DIVISION OF PEDS PULMONOLO 17033 #957-01-1991 L2005 **PDP** *020 †55

VOCALAN, Leopoldo Merced, Jr. PO BOX 850 17033 #748-10-1996 L2006 **P** *012

VOROBEYCHIK, Yakov. 500 UNIVERSITY DR, PENN ST HERSHEY MED 17033 #913-37-1983 L2001 **APM N** *020 †75

VOZORIS, Socrates Andrew. PO BOX 850, PENN STATE U HOSP 17033 #041-02-2000 **IM** *100

WAGNER, Henry, Jr. 500 UNIVERSITY DR MCH063, PENN STATE CNCR INST/RAD 17033 #024-07-1976 L2003 **RO ON** *020 †80

WALCOTT, Gregory Philip. 500 UNIVERSITY DR 17033 #024-16-1988 L1989 **GS** *020

WALDHAUSEN, John Anton. 500 UNIVERSITY DR, MILTON S HERSHEY MED CTR 17033 #028-34-1954 L1966 **TS GS** *071 †85,90

WALKER, Eric Alfred. 500 UNIVERSITY DR 17033 #041-02-1995 L2000 **DR** *020 †80

WALKER, James Lysle. PO BOX 850, PENN STATE-HERSHEY MED CTR 17033 #036-05-1989 L1991 **CHP** *020 †75

WALLACE, Jennifer Lynn. 500 UNIVERSITY DR 17033 #023-01-1997 L2000 **PD** *020 †55

WALLEN, Beth Anne. 845 FISHBURN RD 17033 #023-07-1991 L1994 **FM** *020 †18

WASICZKO, Trisha Marie. ■ 17033 #005-12-2004 L2005 **U** *012

WASSEF, Fady. ■ 17033 #041-14-2008 *012

WASSERMAN, Sara Dana. ■ 17033 #041-14-2008 *012

WASSNER, Steven Joel. 500 UNIVERSITY DR, HERSHEY MED CTR 17033 #035-19-1972 L1977 **PN PD** *030 †55

WATSON, Theodore David. PO BOX 850 17033 #539-04-2005 L2005 **EM** *012

WATSON, Travis Daniel. ■ 17033 #047-20-2007 L2007 **EM** *012

WAY, Emily Elizabeth. ■ 17033 #041-14-2008 *012

WAYBILL, Peter Nelson. 500 UNIVERSITY DR, PENNSYLVANIA STATE UNI 17033 #051-04-1985 L1989 **VIR IM** *020 †20,80

WEBB, Sheppard Clark. PO BOX 850, MS HERSHEY M C 17033 #035-09-1995 L2007 **TS** *012

WEIDA, Thomas James. 845 FISHBURN RD, PENN STATE COMM HLTH CTR 17033 #041-09-1980 L1981 **FM FPG** *020 †18

WEISE, Shauna Lynn. 500 UNIVERSITY DR 17033 #665-01-2007 L2007 **AN** *012

WEITEKAMP, Michael R. 500 UNIV DR /HU15, M S HERSHEY MEDICAL CTR 17033 #010-02-1977 L1978 **IM ID** *020 †20

WERKMAN, Robert Frank. 1421 FISHBURN RD, GI ASSOC CENTRAL PA PC 17033 #041-02-1980 L2000 **GE IM** *020 †20

WERNER, Michael Ronald. 32 NORTHEAST DR 17033 #041-02-1996 L2004 **ORS** *020 †40

WHITENER, Cynthia Joan. 500 UNIVERSITY DR, C6833 HERSHEY MEDICAL CENT 17033 #055-01-1988 L1991 **ID IM** *020 †20

WICKEY, Gregory Scott. 500 UNIVERSITY DR 17033 #016-06-1984 L1985 **AN** *020 †05 ‡

WIDOME, Mark David. 500 UNIVERSITY DR, MC H0850 17033 #041-02-1973 L1974 **PD PHP** *040 †55

WILLIAMS, Duane Charles. ■ 17033 #041-14-2006 L2006 **PD** *012

WILLIAMS, Ronald Jay. 500 UNIVERSITY DR, DEPT OF PEDIATRICS MC H085 17033 #023-01-1989 L1991 **IM PD** *020 †20,55

WIMPEE-GUNN, Holly J. ■ 17033 #041-06-2007 L2007 **IM** *012

WOJNAR, Margaret Mary. 500 UNIVERSITY DR H041 17033 #041-09-1980 L1997 **PCC CCM** *020 †20

WOLBRETTE, Deborah L. 500 UNIVERSITY DR, HERSHEY MED CTR CARDIO DIV 17033 #048-14-1986 L1995 **ICE CD** *020 †20

WOLF, Steven Brian. 32 NORTHEAST DR 17033 #041-13-1984 L1985 **OSS ORS** *020 †40

WOLFGANG, Christopher Lee. 500 UNIVERSITY DR, DEPARTMENT OF SURGERY-MCH0 17033 #041-13-1998 L2001 **GS** *020 †85

WONG, Hin-Hing. PO BOX 850 17033 #244-04-1973 L2001 **CHP** *100

WORSHAM, Anne E. 500 UNIVERSITY DR, DEPT OF ANESTHESIA, H187 17033 #048-04-1990 L1993 **AN** *020 †05

WRIGHT, Leon D. 500 UNIVERSITY DR, DEPARTMENT OF ANESTHESIA 17033 #023-01-1991 L1999 **CCA AN** *020 †05

YADAVA, Ritu Dev Prakash. 500 UNIVERSITY DR, PENN STATE HMC, DEPT HEMAT 17033 #496-36-2001 L2003 **HO** *012 †20

YAROSLAVSKY, Yury. 22B NORTHEAST DR, UPG BEHAVIORAL HEALTH, 17033 #913-18-1985 L2004 **P** *020

YARWOOD, Robert Lawrence. 670 CHERRY DR 17033 #048-12-1979 L1994 **OBG AM** *020 †30

YASIN, Tareq. ■ 17033 #041-14-2007 L2007 **IM** *012

ZACHARIA, Titty Thomas. ■ 17033 #495-63-1998 L2007 **R RNR** *062

ZAENGLEIN, Andrea Leigh. PO BOX 850, DEPT OF DERM, PENN ST, HU1 17033 #041-14-1996 L1999 **D** *020 †15

ZAINO, Richard John. 500 UNIVERSITY DR, DEPT PATH 17033 #036-07-1975 L1980 **PTH** *020 †50

ZANDER, Dani. 500 UNIVERSITY DR, PENN STATE HERSHEY MED CTR 17033 #011-03-1986 L1993 **PTH** *030 †50

ZANGARDI, Alfonso Joseph. 500 UNIVERSITY DR HO39 17033 #041-13-2004 L2004 **IM** *100 †20

ZELIS, Robert Felix. 500 UNIVERSITY DR, #047 CARD. 17033 #016-02-1964 L1965 **CD** *020 †20

ZHENG, Hong. PO BOX 850 17033 #243-69-1995 L2007 **IM** *012

ZHU, Shaobo. ■ 17033 #243-21-1984 L2001 **PCP** *100

ZUBERI, Shahid Akhtar. PO BOX 850, DEPT PED 17033 #704-02-1982 L1995 **PD** *100

ZURLO, John Jos. 500 UNIVERSITY DR, HERSHEY MEDICAL CENTER 17033 #035-03-1983 L1990 **IM** *020 †20

HIGHSPIRE – DAUPHIN

ALBRIGHT, William Jeffrey. 533 2ND ST 17034 #041-02-1985 L1986 **FM** *020 †18

ALBRIGHT, William John, III. 533 2ND ST 17034 #041-02-1954 L1955 **FM** *020 †18

SZYMANSKI, Alexander Will. ■ 17034 #041-14-2005 L2005 **IM** *012

HOLICONG – BUCKS

RICHIE, A Thos. PO BOX 75, 2310 BYECROFT RD 18928 #041-01-1949 L1951 **GP** *071

HOLLAND – BUCKS

BAK, Yury. ■ 18966 #041-77-2007, ▲ *012

BELL, Larry Prentice. ■ 18966 #048-02-1978 L1978 **NTR IM** *071 †20

BU, Tae-Hyung. ■ 18966 #583-06-1960 L1973 **OBG** *071 †30

CHAWLA, Meera. ■ 18966 #495-30-1971 L1999 **PD** *020

DEVINE, Peter Jos. ■ 18966 #041-02-1963 L1964 **OM** *071 †70

FALKER, John Michael. ■ 18966 #041-02-1973 L1974 **DR** *071 †80 ‡

FELDSTEIN, Brad. 295 BUCK RD STE 106 18966 #041-02-1981 L1983 **PD** *020 †55 ‡

FRIEDMAN, Irwin. 54 NETHERLANDS DR 18966 #041-13-1970 L1971 **OBG** *020 †30

GEORGE, Krissa Jo. ■ 18966 #041-02-2005 L2006 **PD** *012

MALLON, Mary Elizabeth. ■ 18966 #041-02-2007 L2007 **IM** *012

MARRONI, James E. ■ 18966 #561-17-1954 L1963 **P** *020

MENTZER, Brittany Michele. ■ 18966 #041-77-2007, ▲ L2007 **OBG** *012

MEZHERITSKIY, Irina S. ■ 18966 #035-15-2004 L2006 **DR** *012

MOHAN, Chittur R. ■ 18966 #495-53-1979 L1993 **VS** *020 †85

MOLDAVSKY, Sophia. 94 FORREST DR 18966 #041-13-1999 L2002 **NEP** *020 †20

SALTZMAN, Robin Lynn. ■ 18966 #039-01-1979 L1981 **HS IM** *050 †20

SARASWATHY, Sreethy. 20 APPALOOSA TRL 18966 #496-32-2000 L2006 **ID** *100

SHAH, Mubarik Ahmad. 35 STARDUST DR 18966 #704-04-1971 L1979 **GS VS** *020 †85

SHERR, Virginia Truitt. 47 CRESCENT DR 18966 #023-01-1956 L1959 **P** *020 †75 ‡

VINNIKOV, Oleg. ■ 18966 #913-39-1994 L2002 **IM** *020 †20

HOLLIDAYSBURG – BLAIR

AMIRNENI, Satish B. ■ 16648 #495-58-1982 L1994 **PYG** *020

ANDRINA, John James. ■ 16648 #010-02-1937 L1939 **AN** *071 †05

AZAD, Niyaz M. 721 N JUNIATA ST, FL 1 16648 #220-01-1969 L1974 **FM** *020 †18

BENNETT, Kathie Wareham. ■ 16648 #041-14-1981 L1982 **FM EM** *020

BIESINGER, George John. 9 BRUSHMEADE, STE A 16648 #028-34-1966 L1968 **OBG** *020 †30

BLESCIA, Adam John. ■ 16648 #041-02-2003 L2003 **EM** *100

CARTUN, Steven Mark. ■ 16648 #028-46-1981 L1990 **P CLP** *020 †75

CAUGHEY, Robert Jason. ■ 16648 #041-12-2002 L2006 **OTO** *020

CHEUNG, Hoo Joon. 1113 PENN ST, P O BOX 1000 16648 #385-02-1961 L1969 **GP GS** *075

CHOPRA, Rakesh Kedar. ■ 16648 #038-40-2000 L2003 **PD** *020 †55

CORTES-LEVICH, Cecilia. 501 CLEARVIEW DR 16648 #748-02-1972 L1999 **P PYA** *020 †75

DELERME-MARTINEZ, Augusto. RR 4 BOX 344 16648 #042-01-1956 L1957 **HNS OTO** *020 †45

DENNING, Philip Patrick. ■ 16648 #024-05-1933 L1949 **OM** *071

FEES, Arch William, Jr. ■ 16648 #041-13-1962 L1963 **U** *071 †95

FONDER, Cynthia Theresa. ■ 16648 #016-42-1999 L2001 **P** *020

GOLDSCHMIDT, Zvi Herbert. ■ 16648 #396-06-1964 **NEP IM** *071

GONZALEZ CRUZ, Jorge. ■ 16648 #649-52-2000 L2007 **NS** *012

HILSHEY, William Alan. ■ 16648 #024-16-1977 L1979 **CD** *071 †20

HURST, John Witwer. ■ 16648 #041-01-1940 L1941 **R** *071 †80

HUSSAIN, Arif. ■ 16648 #704-09-1999 L2003 **IM** *020 †20

JUAN-MARIANO, Ana V. ■ 16648 #748-01-1962 L1999 **PTH CLP** *075 †50

KHALIL, Basma Mahmoud. ■ 16648 #875-01-1991 L1995 **IM** *020 †20

KURIAN, James. ■ 16648 #495-04-1962 L1972 **GS TS** *020 †85

KURIAN, Santhamma. ■ 16648 #495-63-1970 L1981 **PTH** *020 †50

LONG, Samuel E. ■ 16648 #654-01-1986 L1987 **EM FM** *020 †18

MALLADI, Visalakshi. ■ 16648 #495-57-1974 L1981 **PM** *020 †60

MARTIN, Maryanne. ■ 16648 #308-07-1982 L1985 **P** *071

MARTINELLI, Joseph A. ■ 16648 #041-12-1992 L1995 **AN** *020 †05

MC INNES, Harriet S. ■ 16648 #050-02-1949 L1973 **GPM OS** *071

MEDINA, Rodolpho M. OAK KNL 16648 #748-10-1972 L1982 **P N** *020 †75

MONTERO, Cesar A. ■ 16648 #737-01-1959 L1970 **IM CD** *072

POLMUELLER, Eugene F. ■ 16648 #654-01-1984 L1988 **P** *020

PONTZER, Peter Friery. ■ 16648 #041-13-1965 L1966 **FM** *071 †18

RAJAKONE, Sagayabama. ■ 16648 #220-04-1984 L2006 **IM** *020 †20

RAPOSAS, Cynthia Rainey. RR 2, BOX 242A 16648 #041-13-1990 L1993 **FM** *020 †18

SHEEDY, John Gerald. ■ 16648 #041-12-1958 L1959 **FM IMG** *071 †18

SHUMAKER, Scott Danl. ■ 16648 #041-02-1978 L1979 **FM** *075 †18

SLAT, David F. ■ 16648 #041-13-2006 **IM** *012

SUBBARAO, Aragam R. ■ 16648 #913-92-1969 L1981 **GS GP** *020 †85

SWAIN, Asha Lata. ■ 16648 #495-13-1975 L1981 **FM** *020 †18

SWAIN, Pradip Kumar. ■ 16648 #495-13-1965 L1978 **EM** *020 †16

SWEENEY, Gregory Chas. 5 N JUNIATA ST 16648 #010-02-1984 L1985 **FM** *020 †18

TAN, Edwin Ladja. 1113 PENN ST 16648 #748-02-1912 L1982 **P OS** *020 †75

TAYLOR, Mark Allen. ■ 16648 #023-01-1985 L1990 **ORS** *071 †40

TRYBUS, Adam Geo. ■ 16648 #041-09-1966 L1967 **FM** *071

WATSON, John Ward. 170 ALLISON WAY 16648 #036-05-1984 L2000 **TS GS** *020 †85,90

WATSON, John Ward. 170 ALLISON WAY 16648 #040-02-1976 L1977 **OTO FPS** *020 †45

WILKINS, Paul James. 1890 N JUNIATA ST 16648 #065-05-1995 L1997 **FM** *020 †18

YOUNG, Ray Bin. ■ 16648 #244-04-1974 L1983 **GS** *020 †85

ZAVAHIR, Mohamed Feizal. 2 N JUNIATA ST 16648 #220-01-1969 L1973 **PD A** *020 †55

HOLLSOPPLE – SOMERSET

GRESS, William Walter. ■ 15935 #041-12-1954 L1955 **FM** *071 †18

HOLMES – DELAWARE

LELE, Pramod Sadashiv. 2325 MACDADE BLVD 19043 #496-38-1980 L1983 **NEP IM** *020

HOMER CITY – INDIANA

BARNES, Richard Lee. 40 W LIBERTY ST 15748 #041-12-1982 L1985 **OS** *020 †18
BROWN, Ralph Richard. 321 JACKSONVILLE RD 15748 #041-12-1954 L1955 **FM** *020 †18
FRAZER, Ross L. ■ 15748 #649-33-1983 L1984 **FM** *020 †18

HOMESTEAD – ALLEGHENY

DELIERE, Emil A. 495 WATERFRONT DR E, STE 210 15120 #041-12-1977 L1983 **PUD IM** *020 †20
GESKIN, Gennady. 495 WATERFRONT DR E, STE 200 15120 #913-16-1989 L1994 **CD IC** *020 †20
HANDELSMAN, Oliver. 4121 MAIN ST 15120 #041-12-1950 L1951 **FM** *071
HARTMANN, David Barry. 495 WATERFRONT DR E, STE 220 15120 #024-05-1970 L1974 **ORS** *020 †40
JORDAN, Danette Marie. ■ 15120 #041-12-2008 *012
KAHL, Paul J. 220 E 8TH AVE 15120 #035-19-1981 L1982 **IM** *075 †20
LIM, Elizabeth G. 495 WATERFRONT DR E, STE 200 15120 #748-02-1979 L1984 **CD** *020 †20
MADISON, Jan Wilma. 495 WATERFRONT DR E, STE 210 15120 #041-12-1985 L1989 **IM PUD** *020 †20
MANGIERI, Deanna. ■ 15120 #055-75-2005, ▲ L2005 **IM** *012
NEIMAN, Lee M. 1800 WEST ST 1 FL 15120 #016-42-1964 L1965 **IM** *020 ‡
PESYNA, Edward Harry. ■ 15120 #041-12-1976 L1977 **IM** *075
SHERMAN, Vera Spector. 330 E 8TH AVE 15120 #032-01-1987 L1993 **IM** *020
SILVER, Saul J. 495 WATERFRONT DR E, STE 200 15120 #041-09-1980 L1987 **CD CCM** *020 †20
WAIN, John C. ■ 15120 #041-12-1952 L1953 **GP OS** *020
WEISS, Robert Frederick. 495 WATERFRONT DR E, STE 220 15120 #041-12-1977 L1979 **ORS** *020 †40

HONESDALE – WAYNE

BALLENTINE, Rudolph M. ■ 18431 #036-07-1967 L1978 **P FM** *030
BUSTARD, Brian Reginald. ■ 18431 #065-09-1971 L1997 **PTH** *020
CANDAL, Eva Maria Fodor. ■ 18431 #132-01-1960 L1963 **OPH OS** *020
CAUCCI, David John. 3355 LAKE ARIEL HWY 18431 #035-15-1992 L1998 **ORS** *020 †40
CHOI, Edward Lee. ■ 18431 #041-15-2006 L2006 **IM** *012
CLARE, Everton George. 601 PARK ST 18431 #035-08-2001 L2006 **IM** *100
DE CASTRO, Cesar Augusto. ■ 18431 #308-01-1954 L1964 **D GP** *020
DEMERS, Carrie E. ■ 18431 #038-41-1989 L1995 **IM** *020 †20
DEWAR, William Russell. 1325 MAIN ST 18431 #041-09-1947 L1948 **FM** *075
DIAMOND, Paul Matthew. 1837 FAIR AVE 18431 #035-48-1983 L1984 **PD** *020 †55
DIGGS, John Spencer. ■ 18431 #047-06-1966 L1966 **PM IM** *071
DINU, Catalina. ■ 18431 #781-01-1997 L2004 **OBG** *020
EVEN, Leroy Milton. RR 1 BOX 400, HIMALAYAN INST 18431 #030-06-1962 L1985 **AN** *020 †55,05
GUSTAINIS, George Jude. ■ 18431 #041-02-1973 L1974 **FM** *020 †18
JORDAN, Christopher S. 626 PARK ST 18431 #041-02-2002 L2002 **OPH** *100
KORDAS, Paul J. ■ 18431 #025-01-1950 L1951 **P** *071
KUBER, Matthew Timothy. 310 SUNRISE AVE 18431 #041-13-1977 L1986 **CD IM** *020 †20
KUTCH, James Donald. 1860 FAIR AVE 18431 #033-05-1979 L1985 **GE IM** *020 †20 ‡
LENA, Joseph Emmanuel R. 601 PARK ST 18431 #220-04-1984 L1998 **AN** *020
LEONHARDT, Herbert Albin. RR 2 BOX 1409 18431 #035-06-1955 L1985 **ORS** *071 †40
LIM, Chang-Sein. ■ 18431 #244-02-1977 L1984 **AN** *020
LIU, Philip Go. 650 PARK ST # 2 18431 #035-19-1981 L1986 **OTO** *020 †45
LIU, Rosita O. 650 PARK ST # 2 18431 #748-10-1978 L1986 **ID IM** *075 †20
MARITATO, Gerard John. ■ 18431 #012-05-1986 L1989 **FM** *020 †18
MC GRAW, James Jos. ■ 18431 #041-02-1973 L1974 **FM** *020 †18
MC VEIGH, Sean Kevin. 500 PARK ST 18431 #023-12-1997 L1999 **PUD SME** *100 †20 ‡
MENCIA, Pedro Ramon. 110 PARK ST 18431 #010-01-1981 L1989 **OBG** *020 †30 ‡
MILKS, Carl John. 17 BEECH GROVE RD 18431 #025-01-1973 L1976 **AI PD** *020 †55,03
NEZEZON, Stephen Allen. 601 PARK ST, BEHAVIORAL HEALTH SVCS 18431 #016-11-1985 L1986 **P ADP** *020 †75
O'BOYLE, Julianne J. 500 PARK ST 18431 #041-09-1989 L1993 **N** *020
PEK, Monika Rosemary. 1837 FAIR AVE 18431 #473-01-1994 L2006 **PD** *020
PURVIS, Michele A. 601 PARK ST, DEPT OF EMERGENCY MEDICINE 18431 #041-02-1996 L1998 **EM** *020 †16
REYNOLDS, David De Witt. 1860 FAIR AVE 18431 #041-09-1988 L1990 **GE IM** *020 †20
SAPIENZA, Nicholas Frank. 601 PARK ST, WAYNE MEMORIAL HOSPITAL 18431 #035-09-1979 L2005 **DR** *020 †80
STEMPEL, Meredith Deborah. 1325 MAIN ST 18431 #050-02-1984 L1985 **IM** *020 †20
TIETJEN, George Wm. 507 HIGH ST 18431 #010-01-1969 L1975 **GS GP** *020 †85
TOY, Frederick Kindt. 1325 MAIN ST 18431 #041-13-1980 L1982 **GS VS** *020 †85
TULLY, Vincent Jerome. 1325 MAIN ST 18431 #041-13-1957 L1958 **FM** *071
WALKER, Marcellus Andre. 1855 FAIR AVE, COMMUNITY HEALTH CONCERN 18431 #016-11-1984 L1987 **IM EM** *020
WILLIS, Bernard John. 614 CHURCH ST 18431 #016-43-1946 L1947 **P GP** *071
YOO, Eun Sook. 110 PARK ST 18431 #583-08-1970 L1976 **P** *020 †75
YOO, Hoon. 110 PARK ST 18431 #583-10-1967 L1976 **OBG** *020 †30 ‡

HONEY BROOK – CHESTER

HOCH, Willis Showers. ■ 19344 #041-13-1956 L1957 **PTH** *020 †50
SHANAHAN, John Rush. ■ 19344 #010-02-1948 L1955 **RHU IM** *071 †20
TINDALL, Herbert L, Jr. PO BOX 190 19344 #041-09-1942 L1943 **FM** *071 †18
WOOD, John Christopher. ■ 19344 #041-13-2004 L2004 **FM** *100 †18

HOP BOTTOM – SUSQUEHANNA

CAVENDER, John C. ■ 18824 #041-02-1944 L1944 **GP PD** *071
HAGAN, P John. RR 1 BOX 99 18824 #041-09-1956 L1957 **OTO** *071 †45

HOPWOOD – FAYETTE

BRASUK, John Leo. PO BOX 589, BENNINGTON ROAD 15445 #041-12-1957 L1958 **ORS OS** *071 †40
GLAD, Lawrence Jerome. 1142 NATIONAL PIKE 15445 #041-12-1990 L1992 **OBG** *020 †30
SUNYECZ, John Alexander. 1142 NATIONAL PIKE 15445 #038-40-1992 L1994 **OBG** *020 †30
WILSON, Christine B. 1142 NATIONAL PIKE, LAUREL HIGHLANDS OB/GYN 15445 #055-01-1996 L2000 **OBG** *020 †30

HORSHAM – MONTGOMERY

AHMED, Irfan. ■ 19044 #704-16-2000 L2006 **IM** *012
AU, Daniel Chunsang. ■ 19044 #016-06-1998 *100
BAKHTAR, Maryam. 900 BUSINESS CTR DR 19044 #517-01-1976 L1982 **ATP CLP** *062 †50
BOHNING, James Matthew. ■ 19044 #041-13-2002 L2002 **GE** *012 †20
BUCKWALTER, Phyllis A S. WELSH RD INVERNESS DR 19044 #041-13-1956 L1957 **FM** *020
CASTRO, Nemesia G. ■ 19044 #748-01-1962 L1971 **GP P** *071 †75 ‡
DALAL, Anil Ramdas. ■ 19044 #495-01-1966 L1975 **IM CD** *020
DASILVA, Anthony Abiola. 232 LAKESIDE DR 19044 #690-01-1980 L1985 **EM** *020 †16
DE HORATIUS, Raphael Jos. 800 RIDGEVIEW DR, MS H22 19044 #041-02-1968 L1976 **RHU IG** *040 †20
EDELMAN, Andrew Scott. 800 BUSINESS CENTER DR, QUEST DIAGNOSTICS 19044 #035-19-1986 L1991 **CLP ATP** *020 †50
GAZAK, Stephen Jos. 232 LAKESIDE DR 19044 #041-07-1980 L1981 **EM** *020 †16
GERSTBERGER, Matthew Ryan. ■ 19044 #041-15-2005 L2005 **FP** *012
GEVER, Harold Kenneth. 433 CAREDEAN DR 19044 #043-01-1978 L1979 **IM** *020 †20 ‡
HAIDAR, Aqeel. 800 BUSINESS CENTER DR 19044 #704-01-1984 L2004 **PTH DMP** *020 †50
HURWITZ, Herman Samuel. 800 BUSINESS CENTER DR 19044 #041-13-1962 L1963 **PTH** *030 †50 ‡
KIM, Chung Woo. 224 OAKDALE AVE 19044 #583-06-1968 *074
KLENN, Philip James. 900 BUSINESS CENTER DR 19044 #020-12-1988 L1992 **PTH** *020 †50
KOLLMAR, James Joseph, Jr. 405 CAREDEAN DR, STE J 19044 #041-13-1994 L1996 **PD** *020 †55
KURTZ, James Woodard. 433 CAREDEAN DR, V J SARACINI VA OUTPATIENT 19044 #041-02-1987 L1989 **P ADP** *020 †75
KURUVILLA, Achamma Susan. 232 LAKESIDE DR 19044 #495-63-1977 L1992 *020
LOZANOFF, Freda. 232 LAKESIDE DR 19044 #016-17-1962 L1975 **EM FM** *020 †16
MATTEO, Anthony Jos. 303 HORSHAM RD, STE 1B 19044 #041-14-1982 L1984 **OBG** *020 †30
MC GLUMPHY, Thomas H. 300 WELSH RD, STE 4 19044 #041-13-1959 L1960 **GYN** *071 †30
MEIGS, Amory Hubbard. 300 WELSH RD, HORSHAM BUSINESS CTR BLG 2 19044 #041-12-1998 L2002 **OBG** *020 †30
MEREWITZ, Glenn Steven. 232 LAKESIDE DR, EMCARE 19044 #023-01-1977 L1979 **EM IM** *020 †20,16
NEMZOFF, Sol Leon. 198 PRECISION RD 19044 #660-03-1955 L1956 **P** *071
O'BRIEN, Jennifer A. 405 CAREDEAN DR, STE J 19044 #041-13-1997 L2000 **PD** *020 †55
PANSE, Ramanand Vishnu. 232 LAKESIDE DR 19044 #308-03-1984 L1988 **EM IM** *020
PEREZ, Lina Marie. 620 WITMER RD 19044 #042-03-1997 L2001 **PYG** *020
POWELL, Ericka Lynette. 232 LAKESIDE DR 19044 #041-13-2001 L2004 **EM** *020 †16
QUINN, Kristen Helane. ■ 19044 #041-13-2003 L2004 **OBG** *012
RANKIN, Robert Lawrence, Jr. ■ 19044 #041-13-2007 L2007 **IM** *012
RANUCCI, Denise Anne. 303 HORSHAM RD STE 1B 19044 #033-06-1993 L1995 **OBG** *020 †30
REIT, Yechiel Aaron. 232 LAKESIDE DR, EMCARE 19044 #035-15-1999 L2003 **EM** *100
SCHANTZ, Arthur Stephen. 900 BUSINESS CENTER DR, QUEST DIAGNOSTICS 19044 #024-01-1967 L1973 **PTH** *020 †50 ‡
SHEPHERD, Mary. 800 RIDGEVIEW DR 19044 #016-11-1988 L1989 **D** *020 †15
SHIN, Jung Sik. ■ 19044 #012-01-2000 L2001 **PTH** *100 †50
STANDER, Eric. 232 LAKESIDE DR 19044 #033-06-1992 L1995 **EM** *020 †16
TURNER, Clarice P. ■ 19044 #047-07-1949 L1951 **P** *071
WOODRUFF, Charles Lawrenc. 101 ROCK RD, MOBILEX USA 19044 #041-02-1966 L1972 **R NM** *020 †80,28 ‡

HOUSTON – WASHINGTON

ANTHONY, David Thomas. ■ 15342 #041-13-2003 L2003 **ADP** *012
BARDZIL, Joseph Wayne. 801 W PIKE ST 15342 #041-12-1964 L1965 **FM** *071 †18
REARDON, Paul L, Jr. 22 W PIKE ST 15342 #041-13-1983 L1984 **FM** *020 †18

HOWARD – CENTRE

WILSON, Christopher James. ■ 16841 #041-02-2007 L2007 **EM** *012

HUGHESVILLE – LYCOMING

GROSS, Michael Alan. 246 S MAIN ST 17737 #016-02-1969 L1975 **FM PHP** *020 †18
KIM, Il Gon. 420 S MAIN ST 17737 #583-01-1957 L1962 **GS IM** *071
KIRK, Quinn. 246 S MAIN ST 17737 #041-15-2003 L2003 **FM** *020 †18
STEVENSON, Robert Edward. ■ 17737 #041-13-1957 L1958 **OBG** *072 †30

■ = Address Information Privacy Protected

WETZEL, Allen Anthony. 246 S MAIN ST 17737 #041-14-2003 L2003 **FM** *020 †18

HUMMELSTOWN – DAUPHIN

ADEJOH, Bello Abdullahi. ■ 17036 #690-03-1985 L2007 **CHP** *100
AHMED, Atheer Ja'Afar. ■ 17036 #528-01-2000 L2006 **IM** *012
AITTANIEMI, Mark Haskell. ■ 17036 #654-01-2005 L2007 **AN** *012
ALSOP, Skylar Ted. ■ 17036 #049-01-2005 L2005 **PTH** *012
AREF, Ahmad Amr. ■ 17036 #016-06-2006 L2007 **OPH** *012
ARLOTTI, Anthony Paul, Jr. 590 ELIOT DR 17036 #041-15-2000 L2003 **PD** *020 †55
ASHKER, Lamees. ■ 17036 #010-01-2004 L2005 **OPH** *012
BAKER, Mark Seth. 1215 EDGEWOOD DR 17036 #041-14-1984 L1987 **PD** *020 †55
BAMAN, Neil Sudhaker. ■ 17036 #041-14-2006 L2006 **IM** *012
BANTA, Erin Michelle. ■ 17036 #035-06-2006 L2006 **IM** *012
BARBIERI, Carolyn Ann. ■ 17036 #041-14-2004 L2004 **AN** *012
BAROCHIA, Amitkumar Chand. ■ 17036 #495-22-2003 L2006 **IM** *012
BARTO, Tara Lynn. ■ 17036 #030-06-2004 L2004 **MPD** *012
BELLO, Margarita E. PO BOX 217 17036 #041-14-1985 L1994 **PD** *020 †55
BERRY, Keith Andrew. ■ 17036 #040-02-2006 L2006 **GS** *012
BETANCOURT RAMIREZ, Manuel. ■ 17036 #935-02-2000 L2007 **PCC** *012 †20
BIEBUYCK, Julien Francois. ■ 17036 #836-02-1959 L1977 **OS** *071 †05
BIRKHOLZ, James Herbert. ■ 17036 #041-14-2002 L2002 **IM** *100 †80
BLANKENSHIP, Geo Wm, Jr. 640 OLDE VENTURA FARM RD 17036 #021-01-1966 L1989
    OPH *020 †35
BOOTH, Sarah Elizabeth. ■ 17036 #041-14-2005 L2005 **GS** *012
BOWEN, Jon Barry. ■ 17036 #654-01-2003 L2004 **AN** *012
BRADSHAW, Price, III. ■ 17036 #048-14-2003 L2003 **AN** *020
CAMERON, Michelle Lynn. ■ 17036 #041-14-2008 *012
CHANDY, Mark Josephkoont. ■ 17036 #041-14-2008 *012
CHENG, Keith Chi. ■ 17036 #035-19-1980 L1987 **ATP** *050 †50
CLARDY, Stacey Lynn. ■ 17036 #041-14-2007 L2007 **IM** *012
CLARKE, Loren Emory. ■ 17036 #041-14-2001 L2001 **DMP** *100 †50
COLLINS, Casey Kenneth. ■ 17036 #041-14-2008 *012
COMITO, Melanie Ann. ■ 17036 #018-03-1986 L1999 **PHO** *020 †55
DAILEY, Elena Romero. ■ 17036 #041-14-2004 **FM** *100
DA SILVA, Marcelo Caetano. ■ 17036 #187-45-1990 L1996 **TS** *020 †85
DAVIDSON, Bradley K. 8170 ADAMS DR, STE 100 17036 #035-45-1990 L1997 **IM PD** *020 †20
DE MUTH, Cynthia T. ■ 17036 #041-14-1981 L1983 **PD** *071 †55
DENCH, Christine M. ■ 17036 #041-14-2006 L2006 **PD** *012
DI PIETRO, Amy Elizabeth. ■ 17036 #038-43-2005 L2005 **MPD** *012
DIRESO, Dorothea T. ■ 17036 #041-77-2002, ▲ L2002 **PCC** *012 †20
DULKA, Susan E. ■ 17036 #041-13-2006 L2006 **DR** *012
DURKIN, Michael. ■ 17036 #041-15-2001 L2001 **CD** *012
EAGAN, Margaret Reiss. ■ 17036 #021-05-2006 L2006 **PD** *012
EBAMA, Nyabilondi Huguett. ■ 17036 #041-14-2007 **IM** *012
EHLENBERGER, Charles A. ■ 17036 #051-01-2002 L2003 **DR** *100 †80
ERANKI, Srini P. ■ 17036 #495-11-1987 L1991 **IM** *020 †20
ERDAHL, Lillian Marie. ■ 17036 #041-14-2006 L2006 **GS** *012
EVANS, Juanita Juttapatri. ■ 17036 #036-01-2007 L2007 **PTH** *012
FISHER, Todd Richard. 605 E MAIN ST 17036 #041-14-1985 L1986 **FM** *020 †18
FOSTER, Gregory Alan. ■ 17036 #041-14-2005 L2005 **P** *012
FOSTER, Janette Dawn. ■ 17036 #041-14-1995 L2001 **PCC** *020
FREDRICK, Norman Benjamin. ■ 17036 #041-14-2000 L2001 **FM** *020 †18 ‡
FREESTONE-BERND, Megan Ma. ■ 17036 #049-01-2007 L2007 **AN** *012
GENTILE, Bryon Alfred, II. ■ 17036 #041-14-2008 *012
GHAFFARI, Gisoo. ■ 17036 #517-05-1988 L2003 **AI** *012 †20
GIDVANI, Sandeep Nand. ■ 17036 #035-09-2006 L2006 **ORS** *012
GILBERT, Lisa Michele Laz. ■ 17036 #748-02-2007 L2007 **FP** *012
GLASS, Jaimey Maureen. ■ 17036 #041-14-2004 L2004 **OBG** *012
GOLDSTEIN, Melissa Jill. ■ 17036 #035-20-1999 L2000 **PD** *100 †55
GONZALEZ, Mario Daniel. ■ 17036 #132-04-1974 L2006 **CD** *020 †20
GRAGNOLI, Claudia. ■ 17036 #561-17-1992 L2006 **PD** *100
GREENSMITH, J Eric. ■ 17036 #041-14-1987 L1989 **CCA AN** *020 †05
GRIECO, Carmine Alexander. ■ 17036 #035-06-2004 L2006 **OS** *100
GUPTA, Rakhi S. ■ 17036 #038-40-2007 L2007 **PD** *012
HAIGHT, Krista Nightingal. ■ 17036 #050-02-2005 L2006 **OPH** *012
HAN, Bing. ■ 17036 #243-94-1984 L2006 **PTH** *100 †50
HANDFORD, H Allen. ■ 17036 #018-03-1957 L1959 **CHP P** *071 †75
HARLESS, Amanda Elaine. ■ 17036 #041-14-2004 L2006 **PD** *012
HARTMAN, David Scott. ■ 17036 #005-14-1972 L1991 **DR** *020 †80
HASAN, Syed Waqar. ■ 17036 #704-02-1999 L2007 **ID** *100
HASZ, Richard Donald. ■ 17036 #035-06-1963 L1969 **FM** *071 †18
HEASTON, Daniel Reed. ■ 17036 #038-40-2004 L2005 **ORS** *012
HEFFLEY, William Mailey. 120 W MAIN ST 17036 #041-13-1953 L1954 **IM** *071
HOLDER, Sheldon L. ■ 17036 #005-12-2007 L2007 **IM** *012
HOLES, Kelly Anne. ■ 17036 #035-06-1999 L2006 **P** *012 ‡
HOLMES, Rebecca Kathryn. ■ 17036 #041-02-1994 L1997 **PHO** *020 †20,19,55
HUANG, Karen May. ■ 17036 #005-15-1999 L2001 **DR** *012
HUGHES, Joseph Alden, III. ■ 17036 #051-04-2006 L2007 **DR** *012
ISAACS, Charles Thos. ■ 17036 #041-02-1953 L1954 **AN** *071 †05
JAMES, Benjamin Christoph. ■ 17036 #041-14-2008 *012
JENKINS, David E, Jr. ■ 17036 #038-06-1958 L1970 **BBK HMP** *071 †20
JIANG, Yixing. ■ 17036 #243-16-1990 L2005 **ON** *100 †20
JOHNNIDES, Christopher G. ■ 17036 #051-07-1997 L2001 **VS** *100 †85
JONES, Benjamin Clifford. ■ 17036 #048-14-2006 L2006 **EM** *012
JONES, Christopher Riddel. ■ 17036 #001-06-2004 L2006 **D** *012
JONES, Teresa Marie. ■ 17036 #035-06-2006 L2006 **MPD** *012
KATSAMPES, Ernest Thos. ■ 17036 #649-01-1978 L1980 **AN** *075
KEOUGH, Jonathan Edward. ■ 17036 #041-09-1979 L1980 **DR NR** *071 †80
KHAN, Leila Zeinab. ■ 17036 #023-01-2004 L2004 **IM** *020 †20
KHAN, Zahid Tufail. ■ 17036 #704-09-1988 L1996 **AN** *020 †05
KIM, Brian Takemoto. ■ 17036 #041-14-2008 *012
KLINE, Shannon Marie. ■ 17036 #041-14-2007 L2007 **AN** *012
KNIPPER, Jaimie Lynn. ■ 17036 #041-14-2008 *012

KNOEDLER, John Joseph. ■ 17036 #041-14-2008 *012
KORMAN, Lowell Ross. ■ 17036 #010-02-2006 L2006 **MPD** *012
LAKE, Carol Lee. ■ 17036 #041-07-1970 L1971 **AN MDM** *030 †05 ‡
LALL, Shelly C. ■ 17036 #035-45-2003 L2003 **GS** *012
LAUER, Mark Alan. 605 E MAIN ST 17036 #041-14-1992 L1994 **FM OM** *020 †18
LEWIS, Todd Christopher. ■ 17036 #021-01-1999 L2007 **CD** *012 †20
LIPPINCOTT, Pia V. ■ 17036 #048-13-2005 L2005 **AN** *012
MACKLEY, Christine L. 530 WALTON AVE, BROWNSTONE DERM ASSOC 17036
    #041-14-1999 L2001 **D** *020 †15 ‡
MAISH, David Raymond. ■ 17036 #041-02-1998 L2000 **ORS** *020 †40
MANAHAN, Charito Bulambot. ■ 17036 #748-01-2004 L2007 **FP** *012
MC ALEVY, Mary Elizabeth. ■ 17036 #030-05-2004 L2004 **AN** *012
MC GURRIN, John Francis. ■ 17036 #041-13-1982 L1993 **VS GS** *020 †85,80
MC QUILLAN, Patrick M. ■ 17036 #023-12-1982 L1983 **AN** *020 †05
MEDLOCK, Leia Mercedes. ■ 17036 #035-08-2008 **OBG** *012
MITZNER, Ron. ■ 17036 #035-06-2006 L2006 **OTO** *012
MONTH, Richard Christophe. ■ 17036 #011-02-2006 L2006 **AN** *012
MOOLE, Sumana. ■ 17036 #496-01-1998 L2005 **GE** *012 †20
MORROW, Jill Deanne. ■ 17036 #041-01-1984 L1991 **PD PM** *020 †55
MOSER, Lauren Elaine. ■ 17036 #041-14-2005 L2007 **PTH** *012
MOSHIRI, Sara Tafreshi. ■ 17036 #051-04-2004 L2005 **DR** *012
MUKAI, Yuki. ■ 17036 #033-06-2006 **P** *012
OLIVER, Jaime Jose. 1152 MAE ST, PMB 126 17036 #042-03-1997 L1998 **P** *100
ORT, Stuart Alan. ■ 17036 #041-14-2003 L2003 **OTO** *012
PATTERSON, Connor Albrigh. ■ 17036 #021-05-2006 L2006 **D** *012
PAULI, Eric Mark. ■ 17036 #041-14-2004 L2004 **GS** *012
PILIPOVIC, Milena. ■ 17036 #957-07-1996 L2000 **AN** *100
POST, Jarvis Harold. ■ 17036 #038-06-1948 L1955 **OPH** *071 †35
POTT, Leonardus Meindert. ■ 17036 #836-01-1979 L2006 **P** *100
POULSON, Nathan Andrew. ■ 17036 #021-01-2007 L2007 **AN** *012
RAGHAVAN, Meera. ■ 17036 #035-19-2001 L2007 **IM** *100 †80
RAJU, Vidya. ■ 17036 #024-07-2006 L2006 **MPD** *012
RISBOOD, Milish Prabhakar. ■ 17036 #035-06-2006 L2006 **IM** *012
ROSSI, Malina Marie. ■ 17036 #041-14-2007 **AN** *012
ROSSIGNOL, James Gerald. ■ 17036 #035-06-2005 L2005 **AN** *012
RUGGIERO, Francis Patrick. ■ 17036 #041-12-2001 L2001 **OTO** *030 †45
RUTH, Torre Braun. ■ 17036 #041-14-2005 L2005 **ORS** *012
SAKSE, Andrea Louise. 1120 WALTONVILLE RD 17036 #041-14-1981 L1999 **P CHP** *020 †75
SCHARTMAN, Jerome Paul. ■ 17036 #023-01-2003 L2004 **OPH** *100
SCHLOTFELDT, Katherine Jo. ■ 17036 #041-14-2005 L2005 **PD** *012
SCHREIBMAN, Ian Roy. ■ 17036 #035-19-1999 L2001 **GE** *020 †20
SHARMA, Kusum. ■ 17036 #495-73-1995 L2007 **AI** *012 †20
SHERWOOD, Lisa Lynn. ■ 17036 #041-14-2004 L2004 **IM** *100 †20
SHOWALTER, John Wesley. ■ 17036 #041-14-2005 L2006 **IM** *012
SHRIVASTAVA, Pritika. ■ 17036 #496-23-2002 L2007 **NEP** *012 †20
SHUKLA, Gayatri Harshadra. ■ 17036 #041-14-2007 L2007 **TY** *012
SILVONEK, Steven Scott. ■ 17036 #041-14-2008 L2008 *012
SINGH, Manish Kumar. ■ 17036 #495-67-1995 *100
SIVARAJAH, Rebecca Tauber. ■ 17036 #041-14-2002 L2002 **IM** *100 †80
SMITH, Jennifer Lynn. ■ 17036 #041-14-2003 **PD** *100
SO, Celaine May. ■ 17036 #028-02-2006 L2006 **AN** *012
STAUFF, Michael Paul. ■ 17036 #041-14-2003 L2003 **ORS** *012
STONER, Paul Schaffner. ■ 17036 #041-13-1953 L1954 **GP** *020
SUKERNIK, Mikhail R. 114 SPARROW RD 17036 #913-72-1982 L2003 **AN** *020 †05
SWAMI, Jaya. ■ 17036 #051-04-2007 L2007 **GS** *012
TANAKA, Akane Cristina. ■ 17036 #048-14-2006 L2006 **PD** *012
TAWIL, Tara Michelle. ■ 17036 #051-01-2006 L2006 **IM** *012
TEICHER, Matthew L. ■ 17036 #035-08-2007 L2007 **ORS** *012
TICE, Joshua Gardner. ■ 17036 #041-14-2002 L2007 *020
TIEDEKEN, John James, III. ■ 17036 #041-09-1994 L2001 **GS** *012
VANDER HAVE, Kenneth, Jr. 1150 JILL DR 17036 #033-05-1994 L2003 **EM** *020 †16
VEA, Carissa Jean Ildefon. ■ 17036 #748-10-2003 L2004 **FP** *012
VENBRUX, Nuchanart U. ■ 17036 #049-01-1979 L1991 **P** *020 †75
VENDER, Robert Louis. ■ 17036 #041-09-1979 L1986 **IM PUD** *020 †20
VERMA, Mamta. ■ 17036 #495-43-1998 L2003 **CN** *012
VIDYARTHI, Janak Akshay. ■ 17036 #041-14-2003 L2003 **IM** *012
VIGNESH, Shivakumar. ■ 17036 #495-04-1996 L2002 **GE** *020 †20
VORA, Vagmin Pravin. ■ 17036 #495-17-1993 L2006 **OSS** *100
WAREHIME, Sarah Sun. ■ 17036 #055-01-2005 L2005 **MPD** *012
WEAVER, Aaron Newey. ■ 17036 #041-14-2003 L2006 **CD** *012 †20
WEBER, Douglas Anthony. ■ 17036 #041-04-2007 L2007 **EM** *012
WEIL, Robert Fred. 920 CHOWNING DR 17036 #035-19-1988 L1990 **IM** *020 †20
WEINSTEIN, Joel Merrill. ■ 17036 #035-46-1973 L1980 **OPH** *020 †35
WEITEKAMP, Claudia L. ■ 17036 #041-02-1977 L1978 **EM** *020 †16
WENZEL, Kerri Lane. ■ 17036 #023-01-2006 L2006 **OBG** *012
WILSON, Matthew Scott. ■ 17036 #041-14-2008 *012
WUNDERLICH, Catherine Sue. ■ 17036 #035-19-1988 L1988 **FM** *020
YODER, Krista Michelle. ■ 17036 #041-14-2008 *012
ZALATIMO, Omar Akram. ■ 17036 #041-14-2007 L2007 *012
ZHANG, Zhiyou. ■ 17036 #243-48-1994 **IM** *100
ZILIOLI, Gina Noelle. ■ 17036 #023-01-2004 L2007 **ID** *012 †20

HUNKER – WESTMORELAND

HARMATZ, Lee Jeffrey. 1007 OLD STATE ROUTE 119 15639 #041-13-1990 L1992 **FM** *020 †18

HUNTINGDON – HUNTINGDON

ACKER, Brett Lawrence. 835 WASHINGTON ST 16652 #041-02-1988 L1990 **FM** *020 †18
ARANEDA, Luis Osvaldo. 1100 PIKE ST, S C I HUNTINGDON 16654 #132-04-1960 L1970
    EM PME *020
BERGER, Winfried W M. 1225 WARM SPRINGS AVE 16652 #407-21-1962 L1983 **ORS** *020 †40
BOLINGER, Mark Steven. 1225 WARM SPRINGS AVE 16652 #041-14-1982 L1983 **FM OM** *020

■ = Address Information Privacy Protected

BOLLINGER, Beth A. 900 BRYAN ST STE 2, HUNTINGDON COUNSELING AND 16652 #011-02-1985 L1996 **P** *020

BRESSLER, William Lloyd. 3228 COLD SPRINGS RD 16652 #041-02-1972 L1973 **IM IMG** *020 †18,20

BUNYOR, Agnes Knoll. WARM SPRINGS AVE 16652 #473-01-1951 L1967 **OPH** *071 †35

BUZA, Richard Stanley. 3228 COLD SPRINGS RD 16652 #041-02-1978 L1979 **FM FSM** *020 †16,18

CARTER, Thomas Lloyd. WARM SPRINGS AVE, JC BLAIR MEM HOSPITAL 16652 #041-02-1956 L1957 **R NM** *020 †80,28

COLMENAR, Antonio B. J.C. BLAIR MEM HOSP 16652 #748-10-1964 L1973 **AN** *020

DAHAL, Sheel Kumar. ■ 16652 #160-08-1998 L2007 **IM** *020 †20

DELP, Daniel Lamar. 814 WASHINGTON ST 16652 #041-13-1988 L1990 **EM FM** *020 †18

DI DONATO, Louis Richard. WARM SPRINGS AVE, DEPT RAD 16652 #041-02-1964 L1969 **R** *020 †80

DRASKOCZY, Steven P. 1225 WARM SPRINGS AVE, FL 2 16652 #473-01-1966 L1972 **CD** *020 †20

DUNN, Philip F. ■ 16652 #041-02-1952 L1953 **GP** *071

ETTENGER, Allen Belo. 1227 WARM SPRINGS AVE, STE 301 16652 #051-01-1978 L1985 **PD** *020 †55

ETTENGER, Molly Miller. 1225 WARM SPRINGS AVE, J C BLAIR MEM HOSPITAL 16652 #038-40-1977 L1985 **IM PHP** *020 †20

HAYDEN, James Bernard. 835 WASHINGTON ST 16652 #041-13-1983 L1984 **FM** *020 †18

HILL, Suzanne Marie. ■ 16652 #023-07-1974 L1976 **R** *074

KEENEY, Galen Martin. 1227 WARM SPRINGS AVE, STE 201 16652 #028-34-1990 L1994 **P** *020 †75

LAMEY, Robert Calvin. 412 PENN ST 16652 #041-14-1972 L1973 **IM GP** *020 †20 ‡

LEE, Kenneth K. 1227 WARM SPRINGS AVE, STE 302 16652 #583-02-1956 L1980 **CLP PTH** *071 †50

LEE, Kenneth Kyung Yun. 1227 WARM SPRINGS AVE, STE 302 16652 #583-01-1973 L1978 **OBG** *020 †30

LEE, Kyung Soo. ■ 16652 #583-03-1968 L1976 **AN GS** *020

LIDSTON, Bruce Malcolm. 1227 WARM SPRINGS AVE, STE 301 16652 #035-20-1967 L1969 **PD** *020 †75

LONG, Ronald Andrew. 835 WASHINGTON ST 16652 #041-02-1983 L1984 **FM FPG** *020 †18

LONG, V Spencer. 900 BRYAN ST, STE 4 16652 #054-04-1967 L2005 **U** *020 †95

MILLER, David Steven. 3228 COLD SPRINGS RD 16652 #041-13-1976 L1977 **FM** *020 †18

MINOR, Mark R. 3228 COLD SPRINGS RD 16652 #422-01-1988 L1990 **FM** *020

ONUKOGU, Ngozi Onyemaechi. 1227 WARM SPRINGS AVE, STE 302 16652 #041-14-2002 L2007 **OBG** *020

PATITSAS, Christopher J. 1227 WARM SPRINGS AVE, STE 303 16652 #038-44-1986 L1990 **OPH** *020 †35

REINERS, Charles Robt, Jr. 1225 WARM SPRINGS AVE 16652 #041-01-1947 L1948 **GP ORS** *071 †85

ROSS, Edith Joan. 1225 WARM SPRINGS AVE 16652 #047-07-1981 L1984 **EM OS** *020

ROTH, John David. ■ 16652 #055-02-1990 L1992 **FM** *020 †18

SAVORY, James Eugene. 805 MIFFLIN ST 16652 #025-01-1973 L1980 **IM IMG** *020 †20

SCHALL, James Edward. 790 BRYAN ST 16652 #028-02-1976 L1977 **GS** *020 †20,85

SCHUCKER, Charles Lane. BRYANT HEIGHTS 16652 #041-02-1941 L1942 **OS OBG** *071 †30

SEKULA, Jeffrey John. 3228 COLD SPRINGS RD 16652 #033-05-1996 L2003 **U** *020 †95

SMITH, Burgess A. ■ 16652 #041-02-1949 L1952 **GS GP** *071

SUTTON, Alfred Keith. 9823 WINDY JACK LN, 754 WASHINGTON ST 16652 #041-14-1979 L1980 **FM** *020 †18

THOMAS, Bruce Le Roy. 3228 COLD SPRINGS RD 16652 #056-05-1971 L1977 **IM RHU** *020 †20

THORPE, George Edward. J.C. BLAIR MEM HOSP, EMER DEPT 16652 #041-02-1974 L1975 **IM** *020

WAWROSE, Frederick Eugene. 1225 WARM SPRINGS AVE 16652 #041-01-1954 L1958 **P CHP** *020 †75

WHITSEL, Theodore D. WARM SPRINGS AVE 16652 #041-01-1949 L1950 **IM** *072 †20

WILLIAMS, Glenn Gordon. 1225 WARM SPRINGS AVE, J.C. BLAIR MEMORIAL HOSPIT 16652 #048-02-1993 L1996 **EM** *020 †16

HUNTINGDON VALLEY – MONTGOMERY

ABIR, Mahshid. ■ 19006 #038-41-2004 L2005 **EM** *012

ACHILDI, Olga. ■ 19006 #041-13-2007 L2007 **GS** *012

ACKER, Matthew Carl, III. 821 HUNTINGDON PIKE, HUNTINGDON VALLEY 19006 #041-02-1990 L1995 **AN** *020 †05

ADELMAN, Ronald Wayne. 821 HUNTINGDON PIKE 19006 #041-14-1980 L1982 **DR** *020 †80

AFFATATO-BRADLEY, Lisa. 793 HUNTINGDON PIKE, LAWNDALE INTERNAL MEDICINE 19006 #041-13-1993 L1994 **IM** *020 †20

AKTER, Rashida. ■ 19006 #160-01-1997 L2001 **CHP** *020

ALEXANDER, Edward James. 2600 PHILMONT AVE, STE 118 19006 #035-20-1981 L1986 **IM PM** *020 †60

ALI, Hakim Azfar. ■ 19006 #495-51-2000 L2005 **PCC** *012 †20

ALISUAG, Restituto M. ■ 19006 #748-08-1961 L1973 **AN** *020

AVERBUCH, Ilya M. 143 STEELE WAY 19006 #913-06-1975 L1984 **PME** *020 †05

BALLAY, William Francis. 2651 HUNTINGDON PIKE 19006 #041-13-1972 L1973 **OBG** *020 †30

BANKULLA, Pradeep Reddy. 821 HUNTINGDON PIKE 19006 #496-01-1996 L2003 **R VIR** *020 †80

BARBERA, Lawrence Stewart. 727 WELSH RD, STE 206 19006 #041-09-1960 L1961 **PD** *020 †55

BARNETT, Jordan Biet. 380 RED LION RD, STE 202A 19006 #035-15-1993 L1995 **EM** *020 †16 ‡

BARTOLANZO, Robert Angelo. 727 WELSH RD, STE 201 19006 #035-09-1983 L1984 **PD** *020 †75

BECK, Richard. 821 HUNTINGDON PIKE 19006 #041-13-1999 L2001 **DR** *020 †80

BEHINAEIN, Taraneh. 2284 STAHL RD 19006 #517-01-1977 L1987 **PD** *020 †55

BENEDICT, Catherine Ruth. ■ 19006 #041-02-1993 L1997 **PTH** *020 †50

BENSON, William Edmunds. 727 WELSH RD, STE 201 19006 #035-01-1969 L1975 **OPH** *020 †35

BLOCH, Martin Adam. 1833 BERTRAM RD 19006 #035-18-1995 L1999 **IM** *020 †20

BLUM, Andrew Ross. ■ 19006 #041-13-2002 L2002 **DR** *012

BRAUNSCHWEIG, Ira J. 821 HUNTINGDON PIKE 19006 #035-09-1989 L2000 **DR** *020 †80

BRECHER, William. ■ 19006 #041-13-1929 L1930 **GP** *071

BRUNO, Leonard A. 727 WELSH RD, STE 108 19006 #035-01-1971 L1973 **NS** *020 †25

BUCKLEY, Nancy M. 332 LAMPLIGHTER LN 19006 #041-01-1950 L1951 **CD** *071

CAMIEL, Edwin Peter, Jr. 727 WELSH RD, STE 202 19006 #041-01-1976 L1977 **P** *020

CAMINITO, Salvatore, Jr. 821 HUNTINGDON PIKE 19006 #035-48-1998 L2000 **DR** *100 †80

CARAPELLOTTI, Richard A. 2651 HUNTINGDON PIKE 19006 #041-02-1979 L1980 **OBG** *020 †30

CASSIDY, William J. PO BOX 318 19006 #041-13-1945 L1946 **ORS** *071 †40

CERRA-GILCH, Sonja. 821 HUNTINGDON PIKE 19006 #041-13-1994 L1997 **DR** *020 †80

CHECKOFF, Jaime Louis. 821 HUNTINGDON PIKE 19006 #041-02-1997 L2001 **DR** *020 †80

COHEN, Erwin Aaron. ■ 19006 #041-01-1948 L1950 **VS GS** *071 †85

COOPER, Martin. 1927 NICHOLAS DR 19006 #041-13-1959 L1960 **IM** *020

COREN, Gary Stephen. 821 HUNTINGDON PIKE 19006 #041-02-1969 L1970 **R** *020 †80

CREAMER, Thomas Edward. ■ 19006 #041-09-1962 L1963 **GP** *020

DANG, Khoi Cong. 727 WELSH RD, STE 206 19006 #041-13-1992 L2001 **PD** *020 †55

DASS, Chandra A. ■ 19006 #495-61-1984 L2003 **DR NM** *020 †80,28

DEAROLF, Walter W. 2301 HUNTINGDON PIKE, STE 100 19006 #041-02-1982 L1983 **ORS** *020 †40 ‡

DE LA CRUZ, Rafael Atenza. ■ 19006 #847-03-1949 L1960 **U** *071 †95

DE VINCENT, Henry Geo. 2301 HUNTINGDON PIKE, # 1ST-FL 19006 #041-13-1960 L1961 **ORS** *071 †40

DEVLIN, Jeanine. 821 HUNTINGDON PIKE 19006 #041-12-1998 L2001 **OBG** *020 †30

DI BELLO, Joseph N, Jr. 2361 HUNTINGDON PIKE 19006 #041-02-1989 L1991 **PS** *020 †85,65

DI IENNO, Joseph Anthony. ■ 19006 #041-13-1967 L1968 **P** *020 †75 ‡

DOERING, Andrew Alan. ■ 19006 #041-09-1938 L1939 **GP** *071

DWECK, Eli F. 821 HUNTINGDON PIKE 19006 #028-02-1988 L1992 **DR** *020 †80,28

EHRLICH, Jeffrey N. ■ 19006 #041-09-1978 L1979 **GP** *020

FARRELL, Christopher Paul. ■ 19006 #041-77-2006, ▲ L2006 **IM** *012

FELDMAN, Robert A. 793 HUNTINGDON PIKE, LAWNDALE INTERNAL MEDICINE 19006 #041-13-1988 L1990 **IM** *020 †20

FICKE, John Ronald. ■ 19006 #010-02-1955 L1956 **OM IM** *071

FINEMAN, Debora S. 821 HUNTINGDON PIKE 19006 #041-02-1985 L1986 **DR NM** *020 †28,80

FINKELSTEIN, Stanley P. 1320 WELSH RD 19006 #041-13-1997 L2000 **P** *020 †75

FISHER, Joanna Maria. 2643 HUNTINGDON PIKE 19006 #041-07-1982 L1983 **OPH** *020 †35 ‡

FREEDMAN, Allan Perry. 930 HENRIETTA AVE STE B 19006 #041-02-1970 L1973 **PUD OM** *062 †20

FRITER, Barry Steven. 2301 HUNTINGDON PIKE, STE 202 19006 #041-13-1984 L1984 **D** *020 †15

GAFFIELD, James William. 438 MEADOWBROOK DR 19006 #041-07-1994 L1996 **PS** *020 †65,85

GAGNON, Michael Paul. ■ 19006 #539-06-2004 L2004 **FM** *100 †18

GARBAK, Frank. ■ 19006 #154-01-1965 L1982 **AN** *071 ‡

GATTI, Dominic Louis. ■ 19006 #041-13-1958 L1959 **GP** *071

GELMAN, Liebe Kazan. 106 CLEARVIEW AVE 19006 #041-09-1988 L1990 **P** *020 †75 ‡

GINLEY, Edward Jos. ■ 19006 #041-13-1985 L1986 **AN IM** *020 †05

GOLDMAN, Yevgeniy L. ■ 19006 #913-03-1981 L2000 **IM** *020

GRABER, Martin Alan. 821 HUNTINGDON PIKE 19006 #041-13-1980 L1982 **DR NM** *020 †80

GROUS, Dennis Jos. ■ 19006 #041-07-1976 L1978 **IM CD** *071 †20

GUL, Naveed A. ■ 19006 #041-13-2003 **IM** *100

HARRIS, Kevin Robt. 727 WELSH RD STE 201 19006 #041-02-1979 L1981 **PD** *020 †55

HENNESSEY, Joseph Francis. 2284 STAHL RD 19006 #041-13-1963 **PD** *071

HONG, Yoon Wha. ■ 19006 #583-10-1972 L1977 **OBG PTH** *020

HOROWITZ, Glenn David. ■ 19006 #041-02-1979 L1984 **GS NTR** *020 †85

HUD, Laryssa Maria. ■ 19006 #041-02-2008 L2008 *012

KAHN, Sidney N. ■ 19006 #836-02-1970 L1987 **PHM CLP** *062

KALIAN, Makram Paul A. ■ 19006 #528-01-1974 L1991 **IM** *020

KAPP, Anton, Jr. 2301 HUNTINGDON PIKE # 201 19006 #041-13-1981 L1982 **U** *020 †95

KARAMUZ, Josef E. ■ 19006 #759-03-1963 L1978 **IM EM** *020 †16

KARASICK, Sheldon Roy. 821 HUNTINGDON PIKE 19006 #041-09-1971 L1972 **R** *020 †80

KATES, Michael Brian. 821 HUNTINGDON PIKE 19006 #041-13-1984 L1986 **DR** *020 †80

KELLEY, Laura Mayer. 70 BOUCHER DR 19006 #012-05-1988 L1997 **PD** *020 †55

KIM, Jieun. ■ 19006 #583-12-1988 L2003 **CHP** *012

KOEHLER, William Phillips. 801A HUNTINGDON PIKE 19006 #041-07-1990 L1992 **IM FM** *020 †18

KOHN, Mark I. 821 HUNTINGDON PIKE 19006 #010-01-1983 L1985 **DR** *020 †80

KOLIASKO, Nataliya. ■ 19006 #913-86-1995 L2005 **P** *012

KRAKOVITZ, Mark Richard. 821 HUNTINGDON PIKE 19006 #041-07-1983 L1985 **NM DR** *020 †80,28

KRAMER, Frederick Louis. 821 HUNTINGDON PIKE 19006 #041-02-1973 L1974 **DR** *020 †80

KRAMER, Mark Stephen. 3525 WALSH LN 19006 #041-09-1962 L1964 **NEP IM** *071 †20

KUMAR, Ravi Jonnalagadda. 3630 CHIMNEY SWIFT DR 19006 #495-57-1985 L2005 **GS SO** *100

LEBOWITZ, Daniel John. 821 HUNTINGDON PIKE 19006 #024-05-1997 L2006 **DR** *020 †80

LEHRMAN, Bruce Jay. 821 HUNTINGDON PIKE 19006 #041-02-1985 L1986 **R** *020 †80

LEVIN, Michael David. 821 HUNTINGDON PIKE, STE 204 19006 #041-01-1967 L1968 **PD** *020 †55

LEVINE, Arnold Howard. 821 HUNTINGDON PIKE 19006 #165-04-1958 L1959 **DR** *062 †80

LEVITT, Debra Troy. 3658 CHIMNEY SWIFT DR 19006 #041-07-1986 L1987 **EM** *020 †16

LEXOW, Stacy Lynn. 2651 HUNTINGDON PIKE 19006 #019-02-1994 L1998 **OBG** *020 †30

MAGIDENKO, Leonid. 1904 COUNTY LINE RD, HEALTH SMART MEDICAL CENTE 19006 #913-69-1985 L1995 **IM** *020 †20

MALONEY, Joseph C, III. 2651 HUNTINGDON PIKE, VILLAGE CENTER 19006 #041-13-1982 L1983 **OBG** *020 †30

MANIN, Gordon C. 1800 BYBERRY RD STE 705, WORKNET OUTPATIENT MED 19006 #041-02-1990 L1993 **OM** *030 †70,18

MANSTEIN, Carl Howard. 821 HUNTINGDON PIKE, STE 120 19006 #041-13-1976 L1977 **PS HS** *020 †85,65

MANSTEIN, George. 821 HUNTINGDON PIKE, STE 120 19006 #041-01-1941 L1943 **PS** *071 †85,65

MANSTEIN, Mark Eric. 821 HUNTINGDON PIKE, STE 120 19006 #041-07-1978 L1979 **PS HS** *020 †85,65

MANZIONE, Marc. ■ 19006 #041-13-2006 L2006 **EM** *012

MANZIONE, Marc. 2301 HUNTINGDON PIKE STE 103 19006 #010-02-1977 L1979 **ORS OSM** *020 †40

MARKMANN, William John. 2301 HUNTINGDON PIKE, STE 100 19006 #041-13-1974 L1975 **ORS** *020 †40

MAYER, Jeffrey David. ■ 19006 #041-13-2006 L2006 **EM** *012

MAYER, Natalie Lauren. ■ 19006 #041-13-2000 *100

MC COMBS, Elaine Mattie. ■ 19006 #024-07-1970 L1971 **PD** *071 †55
MC GINNIS, Paul Jonathan. 821 HUNTINGDON PIKE 19006 #051-07-1998 L2006 **DR** *020 †80
MC GREEVEY, John Raymond. ■ 19006 #010-02-1959 L1963 **R** *071 †80
MC GREGOR, Sharon Alice. ■ 19006 #041-14-1981 L1982 **PD PEM** *020 †55
MC LAUGHLIN, Elgie Rose. 821 HUNTINGDON PIKE, STE 204 19006 #041-02-1985 L1987 **PD** *020
MCMICKEN, William H. 2335 HUNTINGDON PIKE 19006 #041-02-1958 L1959 **IM UM** *020
MCNAMARA, J Arch. 727 WELSH RD, STE 201 19006 #063-01-1979 L1983 **OPH** *020 †35
MERMELSTEIN, Alan Mark. ■ 19006 #041-13-1983 L1985 **GE IM** *020 †20
MICHELSON, Robert. 930 HENRIETTA AVE STE B 19006 #035-47-1980 L1982 **PUD CCM** *020 †20
MISTRY, Kavin Dalpat. 821 HUNTINGDON PIKE 19006 #033-06-1999 L2004 **RNR** *100 †80
MOHIUDDIN, Jawaad Mohamme. ■ 19006 #041-13-2007 L2007 **TY** *012
MONTO, Raymond R. 727 WELSH RD, STE 111 19006 #035-19-1986 L1993 **ORS** *020 †40
MOSNY, Aimi Young. ■ 19006 #035-09-1998 L1999 **OPH** *071
NANDAKUMAR, Calathur G. ■ 19006 #495-16-1980 L1995 **AN** *100
NEEMAN, Ziv. 821 HUNTINGDON PIKE 19006 #550-04-1992 L2007 **DR VIR** *020 †80
NEMEROF, Victor Jay. 727 WELSH RD, STE 202 19006 #028-78-1980, ▲ L1983 **P PM** *020 †75,60
NEWMAN, Andrew. 2030 COUNTY LINE RD, PMB 261 19006 #041-13-1963 L1967 **ORS LM** *020 †40 ‡
NGUYEN, Karen Kim. ■ 19006 #041-15-2006 L2006 **PTH** *012
NISSENBAUM, Mark. 1841 HUNTINGDON PIKE 19006 #041-02-1969 L1970 **HS OS** *020 †40
NOONE, James Francis. 821 HUNTINGDON PIKE, HUNTINGDON VALLEY 19006 #028-34-1973 L1976 **AN PME** *020 †05
NOWROOZI, K. 1276 WELSH RD 19006 #517-01-1968 L1978 **OBG** *020 †30 ‡
NTOSO, May-Ange. 821 HUNTINGDON PIKE 19006 #035-46-1979 L1983 **OBG** *020 †30
O'MALLEY, Thomas F, Jr. 2651 HUNTINGDON PIKE 19006 #041-02-1981 L1982 **OBG** *020 †30
ORDENTLICH, Elena. ■ 19006 #781-05-1966 L1976 **CHP P** *071 ‡
OZDEN, Zekeriya S. ■ 19006 #902-10-1990 L1995 **GE** *020 †55,20
PALAZZOLO, Michael James. 821 HUNTINGDON PIKE, STE 205 19006 #041-09-1985 L1986 **IM** *020 †20
PANIS, Roberto P. 2352 PHILMONT AVE 19006 #748-01-1981 L1987 **IM FM** *020 †20
PARDES, Jorge Gustavo. 821 HUNTINGDON PIKE 19006 #132-01-1976 L1993 **DR PD** *020 †80
PARELLADA, Joan Antoni. 821 HUNTINGDON PIKE 19006 #847-01-1989 L2000 **DR** *020 †80
PARSONS, Robert Boyd. 791 HUNTINGDON PIKE 19006 #041-13-1959 L1960 **FM** *071 †18
PHILLIPS, Jason Charles. ■ 19006 #010-02-2005 L2005 **ORS** *012
POLLOCK, Jeffrey Leonard. 2600 PHILMONT AVE STE 309 19006 #041-13-1976 L1977 **D** *020 †15
POZON, Angelina Bolinao. ■ 19006 #748-01-1957 L1970 **IM** *074
PUCCI, Michael Joseph. ■ 19006 #041-02-2007 **GS** *012
QUEBRAL, Agnes V. 2352 PHILMONT AVE 19006 #748-02-1982 L1996 **IM** *020 †20
REGILLO, Carl Dana. 727 WELSH RD, STE 201 19006 #024-01-1988 L1990 **OPH** *020 †35
REINPRECHT, James Todd. 793 HUNTINGDON PIKE, LAWNDALE INTERNAL MEDICINE 19006 #008-01-1982 L1984 **IM GP** *020 †20
REITER, Sean Blake. 821 HUNTINGDON PIKE 19006 #011-03-1993 L1996 **DR** *020 †80 ‡
ROACH, Neil. 821 HUNTINGDON PIKE 19006 #035-01-1987 L1993 **DR** *020 †80
ROSENBERG, Randy Marc. 2600 PHILMONT AVE, STE 203 19006 #041-13-1974 L1975 **N** *020 †75
RUNER, Evelyn Rosario. 929 HUNTINGDON PIKE 19006 #035-47-1995 L1999 **END** *020 †20
RUSH, Jordan Scott. 821 HUNTINGDON PIKE 19006 #041-13-1990 L1993 **OBG** *020 †30
SAFFRAN, Bruce Nathan. 821 HUNTINGDON PIKE 19006 #038-41-1992 L2005 **RNR** *020 †80
SAGALOW, Barry Richard. 821 HUNTINGDON PIKE 19006 #033-05-1981 L1983 **DR** *020 †80
SAGERMAN, Jason Evan. 821 HUNTINGDON PIKE 19006 #422-01-1983 L1991 **DR** *020 †80
SALKIND, Gene Zachary. 727 WELSH RD, STE 108 19006 #041-13-1979 L1981 **NS** *020 †25
SCHLESSEL, Richard Benj. 727 WELSH RD, STE 202 19006 #407-05-1958 L1960 **CHP P** *071
SCHOENBERGER, E Alec. 821 HUNTINGDON PIKE 19006 #038-06-2001 L2007 **RNR** *100 †80
SCHWARCZ, Ricardo Martin. ■ 19006 #132-01-1995 L2001 **PCC** *012 †20
SCHWARTZ, Barbara Harriet. ■ 19006 #041-13-1965 L1967 **PYA P** *020 †75
SCOTT, Kathleen Morris. ■ 19006 #041-01-1953 L1954 **PD** *071
SEAVER, Margaret Eleanor. 521 MOREDON RD 19006 #035-45-2005 **IM** *100
SHAH, Pallav Naresh. 821 HUNTINGDON PIKE 19006 #035-15-1999 L2001 **RNR** *100 †80 ‡
SHAH, Rasila Vinodkumar. 821 HUNTINGDON PIKE, HUNTINGDON VALLEY 19006 #495-17-1967 L1977 **AN** *020 †05
SHEVCHENKO, Yuri O. ■ 19006 #913-04-1986 L1996 **AN** *020 †05
SHILOH, Aaron Opher. 821 HUNTINGDON PIKE 19006 #041-01-1997 L2001 **VIR** *020 †80
SHIN, Hae Won. 821 HUNTINGDON PIKE 19006 #041-02-1994 L1999 **DR** *020 †80
SILVESTRI, Archimede. ■ 19006 #561-11-1951 L1961 **ORS** *071
SINGER, Fred J. 793 HUNTINGDON PIKE, LAWNDALE INTERNAL MEDICINE 19006 #041-13-1986 L1988 **IM** *020 †20
SINGH, Deeptej. ■ 19006 #024-05-2008 *012
SINGH, Navjeet. ■ 19006 #495-03-1975 L1978 **N** *040 †75
SIRKEN, David Howard. 2600 PHILMONT AVE, STE 203 19006 #035-75-1987, ▲ L1989 **N** *020 †75 ‡
SISKIND, Barry Neil. 821 HUNTINGDON PIKE 19006 #035-09-1977 L1993 **DR** *020 †80
SKENDERI, Sonela. ■ 19006 #041-77-2007, ▲ L2007 **IM** *012
SONSINI, Gregg Albert. 727 WELSH RD STE 206 19006 #041-02-1985 L1986 **PD** *020
SOROKORENSKY, Irene. ■ 19006 #041-12-2003 L2003 **CN** *012
SOSIS, Mitchel. 821 HUNTINGDON PIKE, HUNTINGDON VALLEY 19006 #020-12-1978 L1984 **AN** *020 †05
SPIEGEL, Richard Harvey. ■ 19006 #041-02-1985 L1988 **AN** *020
STEIN, Hymen Donald. 106 HILL HOUSE 19006 #041-02-1939 L1941 **OS LM** *071
STEINBERG, Joel S. 1332 WRIGHT DR 19006 #041-13-1976 L1977 **VM IM** *020 ‡
SUTTON, Douglas Craig. 727 WELSH RD, STE 103 19006 #041-02-1989 L1991 **ORS** *020 †40
SWARTZ, Joel David. 3501 MASONS MILL RD, STE 501 19006 #010-01-1975 L1980 **DR** *020 †80
TAN, Elizabeth L. 821 HUNTINGDON PIKE 19006 #035-03-1993 L1998 **DR** *020 †80
TASMAN, William Samuel. 727 WELSH RD, STE 201 19006 #041-13-1955 L1956 **OPH** *020 †35
TERSHAKOVEC, Andrew M. ■ 19006 #011-02-1983 L1987 **NTR PD** *050 †55
TOLAT, Pratima Ramniklal. 1832 MELMAR RD, P O BOX 70 19006 #495-22-1962 L1972 **OPH OS** *071 †35
TREBELEV, Edward A. ■ 19006 #913-15-1957 L1985 **PTH GP** *071
VAHEDI, Houshang. ■ 19006 #517-01-1966 L1973 **IM GP** *020
VAZE, Geeta M. 727 WELSH RD, STE 101 19006 #496-38-1987 L1995 **IM** *020 †20
WALD, Lawrence M. 821 HUNTINGDON PIKE 19006 #035-47-1979 L1983 **R** *020 †80
WATERS, Thaddeus Patrick. ■ 19006 #041-15-2003 L2003 **OBG** *100
WEISS, Edward David. ■ 19006 #041-13-1936 L1938 **CRS** *071 †10
WELSH, Louis Ward. ■ 19006 #041-09-1956 L1957 **OTO** *071 †45
WHITE, Kathlene. ■ 19006 #041-07-1976 L1977 **ORS** *030
WITKIN, Lisa Rochelle. 466 LONG LN 19006 #023-07-2008 *012
WOLKO, Jonathan David. 821 HUNTINGDON PIKE 19006 #033-05-1999 L2004 **DR** *100 †80
WOODWARD, John Paul. 821 HUNTINGDON PIKE # 207 19006 #041-14-1978 L1980 **GP PD** *020
YANG, Steven St. 821 HUNTINGDON PIKE 19006 #035-46-2001 L2006 **DR NR** *020 †80,28
ZACHOR, Ditza Antebi. 390 PIKE RD, UNIT6 19006 #550-03-1980 L1990 **PD** *020 †55
ZALUT, Warren Jay. 727 WELSH RD, STE 202 19006 #041-13-1975 L1976 **P** *020 †75 ‡
ZIBELMAN, Robert Stephen. 2910 FRANKS RD 19006 #041-02-1976 L1979 **P CHP** *020 †75
ZOLFAGHARI, Roknedin. 2643 HUNTINGDON PIKE # 2 19006 #517-01-1956 L1965 **GS** *020 †85

HUNTINGTON MILLS – LUZERNE

STONE, Donald J. PO BOX 46 18622 #041-77-1979, ▲ L1980 **FM** *020 †18

IMPERIAL – ALLEGHENY

DI CLEMENTE, Domenick. 7900 STEUBENVILLE PIKE, PC/ ESSEX W PLAZA STE 39. 15126 #038-43-1974 L1987 **OBG** *075 †30
GOUNDER, Ramakumar N. 180 IMPERIAL PLAZA DR, STE 400 15126 #010-03-1997 L2001 **OPH** *020 †35
MC CASLIN, Todd Allan. 300 PENN LINCOLN DR, W ALLEGHENY HLTH CARE SERV 15126 #041-02-1994 L1996 **FM** *020 †18
RUZICH, Andrew Hinckley. 236 W ALLEGHENY RD 15126 #041-02-1987 L1987 **OPH** *020 †35
SINGLETON, Marlynn. 300 PENN LINCOLN DR 15126 #041-07-1995 L2006 **FM** *020

INDIANA – INDIANA

AHMED, Durre S. 2121 SHELLY DR 15701 #160-02-1979 L1996 **IM** *020 †20
AHMED, Jamil. 2121 SHELLY DR 15701 #160-02-1980 L1993 **IMG** *071 †20
AMBROSE, Joseph E. 850 HOSPITAL RD, STE 1400 15701 #041-77-1981, ▲ L1982 **IM** *020
AMIN, Shirish. 119 PROFESSIONAL CTR, 1265 WAYNE AVENUE, SUITE 3 15701 #495-89-1989 L1993 **GE** *020 †20
BAJWA, Imran Mushtaq. 850 HOSPITAL RD, STE 2400 15701 #704-21-1985 L1994 **PUD** *020 †20
BAJWA, Rabia I. 850 HOSPITAL RD, STE 2400 15701 #704-20-1995 L1999 **IM** *020 †20
BARNICLE, Mary Ann. 15 S 8TH ST 15701 #030-06-1985 L1987 **GE IM** *020 †20
BAUER, James E. 1177 S 6TH ST 15701 #018-03-1950 L1987 **R NM** *020 †80,28
BILLON, Andrew. 841 HOSP RD STE 2300, GEN & VSCLR SURG 15701 #654-01-1984 L1986 **GS** *020 †85
BIZOUSKY, David Thos. 1265 WAYNE AVE, STE 307 15701 #041-09-1984 L1985 **ORS OSM** *020 †40
BORON, Stella Marie. 15 S 8TH ST 15701 #041-12-1976 L1977 **IM** *020 †20
BOYKIW, Mark Emerson. 841 HOSPITAL RD 15701 #041-09-1977 L1979 **GS VS** *020 †85
BRZEZINSKI, Sandra Ann. 875 HOSPITAL RD, STE 301 15701 #654-01-1984 L1985 **FM** *020 †18
BUSH, Bruce A. 1176 GRANT ST, STE 2200 15701 #041-09-1978 L1983 **PUD CCM** *030 †20
BUSH, Stephen Thos. HOSPITAL RD 15701 #010-02-1961 L1972 **PTH** *071 †50
CASADAY, Floyd M, III. 1265 WAYNE AVE 15701 #041-02-1971 L1975 **CD IM** *020 †20 ‡
CASH, Andrew David. 1265 WAYNE AVE STE 207 15701 #028-79-1993, ▲ L1993 **IM** *020
CAVOTO, Michael Jos. 470 BEN FRANKLIN RD S, ORTHOPEDIC SURGERY 15701 #041-02-1961 L1962 **ORS** *071
CAWLEY, John Patrick. HOSP ROAD, INDIANA HOSP 15701 #010-02-1992 L1992 **EM** *020 †16
CHADDAH, Ashok. 841 HOSPITAL RD, STE 3500 15701 #495-73-1974 L1983 **NEP** *020 †20
CLARK, M Dorcas. HOSPITAL RD 15701 #023-01-1945 L1979 **DR IM** *071
CONTI, Joseph Dominic. 1265 WAYNE AVE, STE 103 15701 #041-02-1976 L1977 **U** *020 †95
COPPOLO, Bernard Louis. 15 S 8TH ST 15701 #041-12-1976 L1977 **IM** *020 †20
CSEH, William Michael. 793 OLD ROUTE 119 HWY N, COMMUNITY GUIDANCE CENTER 15701 #025-07-1970 L2001 **P** *020 †75
FEGLEY, Henry William. ■ 15701 #024-05-1970 L2006 **PS** *020
GARG, Vipul. DEPARTMENT OF EMERGENY SVC, INDIANA HOSPITAL 15701 #919-05-1983 L1991 **IM EM** *020 †20
GARRETTSON, James Albert. 805 HOSPITAL RD, CITIZENS AMBULANCE SERV IN 15701 #041-12-1965 L1972 **IM** *071 †20
GATUMU, Sarah Nduta Mbogo. 850 HOSPITAL RD 15701 #577-01-1993 L2002 **CHP** *020
GELFAND, Steven Barry. 850 HOSPITAL RD 15701 #308-07-1983 L1988 **N P** *020 †75
GHATE, Sharad Bhalchandra. 1265 WAYNE AVE STE 104 15701 #495-82-1973 L1976 **OBG** *020 †30
GOEL, Vineet. PO BOX 788, INDIANA HOSP 15701 #496-09-1980 L1993 **EM IM** *020 †20
GREGG, John Stewart. 15 S 8TH ST STE 301 15701 #041-12-1973 L1976 **CD IM** *020 †20
HAN, Shenggao. 1177 S 6TH ST, STE D 15701 #243-38-1983 L2003 **IM** *020 †20 ‡
HATCHER, Kim Alan. 1265 WAYNE AVE STE 107 15701 #051-01-1976 L1979 **FM D** *020 †18
HAUBER, Peter John. 793 OLD ROUTE 119 HWY N 15701 #041-13-1984 L1985 **P** *020 †75
HUGHES, David Chas. 835 HOSPITAL RD 15701 #051-04-1965 L1966 **OTO A** *020
JABIR, Ameena R. 1265 WAYNE AVE, 119 PROFESSIONAL CTR/STE 3 15701 #704-02-1986 L1996 **PD** *020 †55 ‡
JASPER, Ronald L. 835 HOSPITAL RD, DEPT OF ANESTHESIA 15701 #041-77-1989, ▲ L1990 **AN PME** *020 †05
JESICK, Ann Roberts. 15 S 8TH ST STE 301, ROSE MED BLDG 15701 #041-12-1985 L1986 **FM** *020 †18
JUHASZ, Alex Bert. 549 OLD ROUTE 119 HWY N 15701 #041-02-1972 L1973 **GS** *020 †85
KARANJIA, Minoo Dinshawji. ■ 15701 #495-17-1962 L1972 **OTO A** *071
KHAN, Farooq Irfan. 850 HOSPITAL RD 15701 #704-21-1992 L1999 **N** *020 †75
KIRK, Henry Zane. 560 OAK ST 15701 #048-04-1965 L1965 **PD** *020 †55
LAN, Victor Sungshu. 2255 PHILADELPHIA ST 15701 #244-01-1967 L1977 **GP** *020 ‡
LEAR, William Lawrence. 119 PROF BLDG STE 200 15701 #041-13-1977 L1978 **OBG** *020 †30
LEE, Jongwon. 835 HOSPITAL RD 15701 #035-15-1992 L1996 **NR** *020 †80,28
LUBOLD, Chrstina B. 15 S 8TH ST, STE 200 15701 #041-13-1991 L1994 **PD** *020 †55
LUTZ, Harold Edward. ■ 15701 #041-12-1975 L1978 **FM** *020 †18
MACCHIAROLI, Joseph A. 835 HOSPITAL RD, DEPT OF ANESTHESIA 15701 #041-12-1987 L1989 **AN** *020 †05

■ = Address Information Privacy Protected

MACEYKO, Ronald Frank. 835 HOSPITAL RD 15701 #038-40-1988 L1992 **D** *020 †15

MALIVER, Leonard Eric. 841 HOSPITAL RD STE 2400 15701 #041-02-1980 L1985 **U** *020 †95

MARTENS, Jeffrey David. 1177 S 6TH ST, STE B 15701 #041-12-1993 L1999 **IM** *020 †20

MATHUR, Sumeet. 850 HOSPITAL RD, STE 2100 15701 #024-01-1993 L1998 **OTO GS** *020 †45 ‡

MC COY, Thomas D. 841 HOSPITAL RD STE 2600 15701 #041-12-1978 L1979 **OBG** *020 †30

MC DOWELL, Edward Paul. 15 S 8TH ST 15701 #041-12-1977 L1979 **CD** *020 †20

MC KIRGAN, Craig Charles. 1265 WAYNE AVE STE 307, MEDICINE,119 PROFESSIONAL 15701 #018-75-1988, ▲ L1994 **ORS OSM** *020

METZGER, Diana Leigh. 15 S 8TH ST, STE 303 15701 #041-12-1991 L1995 **CD** *020 †20

MIHAESCU, Mihaela Br. 850 HOSPITAL RD 15701 #781-01-1995 L2000 **CN** *020 †75

MILLER, Ralph Jewart. HEALTHERBRAE SQUARE, INDIANA MEDICAL CENTER 15701 #041-12-1952 L1953 **U** *071 †95

MILLS, John W. ■ 15701 #035-09-1953 L1954 **GYN** *071 †30

MIR, Tahir Usman. 7 S 5TH ST 15701 #704-01-1974 L1977 **EM GP** *020 †16

MITCHELL, Henry. ■ 15701 #041-01-1947 L1948 **PD** *072 †55

MOHAMED AHMED, Amira M. 15 S 8TH ST, STE 200 15701 #848-01-1989 L2000 **CCP** *020 †55

MULAC, James Edward. 835 HOSPITAL RD, DEPT OF ANESTHESIA 15701 #041-01-1986 L1987 **AN PME** *020 †05

NAYAK, Ramesh Mukund. 835 HOSPITAL RD, DEPT OF ANESTHESIA 15701 #496-38-1971 L1992 **AN** *020 †05

NEAL, Harry Beecher, Jr. HOSPITAL RD 15701 #035-01-1942 L1943 **GP** *071

NEALE, John M. 935 INDIAN SPRINGS RD 15701 #010-02-1975 L1978 **PD** *020 †55

NESPER, James Alan. 841 HOSPITAL RD 15701 #035-20-1982 L1986 **OPH** *020 †35

NETTLETON, Matthew. 835 HOSPITAL RD 15701 #035-15-2000 L2003 **IM** *020 †20

NOEL, Kenneth Robt. 881 HOSPITAL RD 15701 #005-12-1967 L2004 **AN** *040 †05

ORIFE, Ediri Ann. ■ 15701 #041-12-2003 L2003 **FM** *020

PARK, Chong Min. 1265 WAYNE AVE, STE 207 15701 #583-10-1967 L2006 **ORS HS** *020 †40

PARK, Joseph M. 645 N 6TH ST 15701 #583-02-1958 L1972 **U** *020 †95

PARKER, Robert C. ■ 15701 #050-02-1961 L1962 **OS PD** *071 †55

PATEL, Pravinkumar P. 1265 WAYNE AVE STE 306 15701 #496-38-1973 L1977 *075

PHADKE, Michael S. 1265 WAYNE AVE STE 106 15701 #495-20-1973 L1982 **GS** *020 †85

POLLOCK, Michael S. 841 HOSPITAL RD, STE 2500 15701 #041-12-1978 L1979 **ORS** *020 †40

SANDROWICZ, Richard Robt. 1265 WAYNE AVE, STE 105 15701 #041-02-1980 L1981 **FM** *020 †18

SETTY, P Sadasiva. 112 SADDLEBROOK DR 15701 #495-72-1969 L1973 **AN** *020 †05

SIBOLBORO, Isabelo Zamora. HOSP ROAD, INDIANA HOSP-ANEST DEPT 15701 #748-01-1956 L1970 **AN** *071

SIMPSON, William Lee. ■ 15701 #748-01-1964 L1966 **EM** *071

SINGH, Bijai Bahadur. 1177 S 6TH ST 15701 #495-15-1959 L1974 **IM** *020 †20

STEPHENS, Marilyn I Hart. 502 PRATT DRIVE, INDIANA UNIVERSITY OF PA 15705 #047-07-1963 L1969 **FM** *071 †18

STEVER, Michael R. 1075 INDIAN SPRINGS RD 15701 #041-77-1981, ▲ L1990 **OBG** *020 †30

SULLIVAN, Mark Ford. 1265 WAYNE AVE, STE 103 15701 #010-02-1983 L1987 **TS** *020 †85,90

TAKACH, Stephen J. HOSPITAL RD 15701 #041-01-1949 L1950 **GS GP** *071

TOMACRUZ, Luis P. 835 HOSPITAL RD, INDIANA REGIONAL MEDICAL C 15701 #748-01-1988 L1995 **FM** *020 †18

TREVORROW, Thomas Chas. 1265 WAYNE AVE STE 203 15701 #038-40-1988 L1993 **OPH** *020 †35 ‡

TSAI, Edward Ming-Kang. 1177 S 6TH ST 15701 #244-01-1968 L1973 **IM** *020 †20

TUNIO, Ali Murad. ■ 15701 #704-10-1980 L2003 **RO** *020 †80

TURNBULL, Roberto Esteban. 1177 S 6TH ST 15701 #649-01-1976 L1982 **IM** *020 †20

TWAL, Shafic Y. 15 S 8TH ST 15701 #035-06-1970 L1977 **PD** *020 †55

VAGLIA, Christopher Paul. 15 S 8TH ST, STE 200 15701 #041-13-1998 L2001 **PD** *020 †55

VERNOCY, William Gary. 45 N 7TH ST 15701 #055-01-1968 L1970 **GS** *020 †85

WALDO, Ralph Fordyce. ■ 15701 #041-12-1948 L1949 **CD IM** *071

WILLIAMS, Melvin Clayton. ■ 15701 #010-01-1959 L1960 **NM** *071 †20,28

WILSON, David Blair. 1265 WAYNE AVE STE 307, 119 PROFESSIONAL CENTER 15701 #041-12-1992 L1998 **ORS OSM** *020 †40

WOOLCOCK, Ruth B. 15 S 8TH ST, STE 201 15701 #005-12-1982 L1988 **IM** *020 †20

IRWIN – WESTMORELAND

ACOSTA, Antonio E. 231 MAIN ST, BOX 487 15642 #042-01-1964 L1978 **GE IM** *071 †20

ANAND, Sandeep. 3520 ROUTE 130, STE 1 15642 #495-45-1994 L2006 **PD** *020 †55

BROWN, Donald Clyde. 100 PENNSYLVANIA AVE 15642 #038-06-1961 L1962 **GS VS** *071 †85

CONFORTI, William J. 13370 LINCOLN HWY E 15642 #308-07-1982 L1987 **FM** *020 †18

DE JESUS, Robert. 905 SPRUCE ST 15642 #041-12-1973 L1974 **GE** *020 †20

ELIAS, Farid Jos. 8775 NORWIN AVE 15642 #605-01-1972 L1977 **GS** *020

FILES, Shawn Correll. 9337 ROUTE 30 15642 #038-41-1995 L1997 **FM** *020 †18

GILLESPIE, Harry Keally. ■ 15642 #041-12-1952 L1953 **PD PHP** *071 †55

GOGAL, Helen Mildred. ■ 15642 #041-12-1977 L1993 **PD** *020 †55

GREENE, Stephen Mitchel. 3520 ROUTE 130, STE 1 15642 #050-02-1989 L1991 **PD** *020 †55

HATTOUM, Pittagore. 8700 PENNSYLVANIA AVE 15642 #132-01-1968 L1970 **OBG** *071 †30

JOHNSTON, James Clark, Jr. ■ 15642 #041-12-1971 L1972 **N** *075

KRISHNAPPA, N Boriah. 111 BLACKS HILL RD 15642 #495-09-1966 L1976 **PD** *020 †55

LESLIE, Martha Irene. 9337 ROUTE 30 15642 #041-12-1994 L1996 **FM** *020 †18

LINGARAJU-DURKAC, Sathyava. 111 BLACKS HILL RD 15642 #495-33-1970 L1974 **PHP PD** *030 †55,70

LORA, Juan A. 905 SPRUCE ST 15642 #308-02-1985 L1991 **GE** *020 †20

MOLLURA, Joseph A. 13370 LINCOLN HWY E 15642 #308-07-1982 L1988 **FM** *020 †18

NASSUR, Adnan K. 9173 ROUTE 30 STE 1 15642 #875-01-1972 L1979 **PUD IM** *020 †20

NAVALGUND, Krupa Ashok. ■ 15642 #495-35-1970 L1991 **IM** *071 †20

NIKOULA, Jawdat. 905 SPRUCE ST, STE 201 15642 #305-01-1981 L1984 **FM** *020 †18

PAE, Dong Wan. 606 OAK ST 15642 #583-09-1964 L1972 **FM PTH** *020 ‡

PATTI, Christine Hartnett. 3520 ROUTE 130 15642 #035-08-1986 L1987 **PD** *020 †55

RAHIM, Owais. 905 SPRUCE ST 15642 #704-01-1989 L1998 **GE** *020 †20

SANDERS, Robert Edward. 8981 NORWIN AVE STE 101 15642 #041-12-1977 L1978 **IM** *020 †20

SEIJAS, Gloria Antonia. 3520 ROUTE 130 STE 2 15642 #737-06-1984 **PDE PD** *020 †55

SRODES, Michael Scott. 8775 NORWIN AVE 15642 #041-12-1998 L2005 **OTO** *020 †45

TAYLOR, Jerry Albert. 761 STONEBRIDGE DR 15642 #041-14-1995 L1997 **EM** *020 †16

TORET, Michel Pierre. 8775 NORWIN AVE, STE 107 15642 #396-23-1973 L1977 **FM PTH** *020 †18

UBINGER, Jeffrey Paul. 3520 ROUTE 130, STE 1 15642 #041-12-1987 L1989 **PD ADL** *020 †55

VILLEGAS, Emilio. 100 PENNSYLVANIA AVE 15642 #264-07-1967 L1973 **FM** *020 †18

WHITE, Jill Erin. 3520 ROUTE 130, STE 1 15642 #041-12-1995 L1997 **PD** *020 †55

JAMESTOWN – CRAWFORD

BARDELLA, Betty-Jean S. 402 JACKSON ST, JAMESTOWN HEALTH CENTER 16134 #041-01-1986 L2002 **FM** *020 †18

JAMISON – BUCKS

HEMSLEY, Stanley E, Jr. ■ 18929 #024-01-1985 L1987 **PD** *020 †55

HIGGINS, Edward John. 2370 YORK RD, STE A8 18929 #028-34-1994 L1997 **PD** *020 †55

HUTTON, Lisa Jeanette. 2370 YORK RD, STE A8 18929 #041-13-1988 L1990 **PD** *020 †55

KAGANOVICH, Michael. ■ 18929 #913-09-1973 L1984 **P** *020

KARIS, Paul E. 1705 FAIRWAY DR 18929 #010-02-1981 L1982 **EM** *030 †16

LOPEZ, Nereida Isaura. 2370 YORK RD, STE A8 18929 #035-20-1997 L1999 **PD** *020 †55

PARNES, Curt Ira. 2370 YORK RD, STE A8 18929 #047-05-1982 L1983 **PD** *020 †55

POLLACK, Stuart Neil. 1820 AUGUSTA DR 18929 #041-01-1989 L1994 **VIR RNR** *020 †80

RUDDELL, Millard A. ■ 18929 #041-09-1971 L1974 **EM OM** *020 †16

SANDROCK, Deborah Ann. 2370 YORK RD, STE A8 18929 #041-13-1989 L1991 **PD ADL** *020 †55

SIVITZ, Michael Chas. 2370 YORK RD, STE A8 18929 #041-13-1969 L1970 **PD** *020 †55

STEFURAK, Maria Palasiuk. 2370 YORK RD, STE A8 18929 #041-13-1990 L1992 **PD** *020 †55

STONE, Julie Anne. ■ 18929 #041-13-1982 L1988 **IM** *020 †20

JEANNETTE – WESTMORELAND

ALI, Abu Nasar Muhammad. 610 JEFFERSON AVE 15644 #704-03-1961 L1975 **OTO** *020 †45

ANNAMRAJU, Srinivas. 600 JEFFERSON AVE 15644 #038-44-1988 L1991 **DR** *020 †20,80

AYOUB, Omar Basil. 70 LINCOLN HWY E 15644 #649-01-1962 L1966 **FM EM** *071

BAUTISTA, Primo V. 600 JEFFERSON AVE, MERCY JEANETTE HOSP 15644 #748-01-1972 L1977 **PTH HMP** *020 †50 ‡

BYERS, Joanne Szalkay. 3000 PENNY LN STE 103, PREMIER MEDICAL ASSOCIATES 15644 #041-14-1987 L1989 **FM** *020 †18

CONSTANTINE, Jill M. 601 MICHIGAN AVE 15644 #649-33-1985 L1986 **FM** *020 †18

DZIALOWSKI, Kenneth J. 600 JEFFERSON AVE 15644 #041-12-1984 L1985 **OBG** *020 †30

EL ATTRACHE, Mamdouh F. 70 LINCOLN HWY E 15644 #649-14-1977 L1982 **FM** *020 ‡

EL-HILLAL, Mohammad. 6590 ROUTE 30 15644 #875-01-1972 L1977 **GS** *020 †85

GALLAGHER, Martin Peter. 6402 ROUTE 30 15644 #130-01-2002 L2007 **FM** *020

GERGER, Joseph Paul. 607 MICHIGAN AVE 15644 #041-13-1975 L1976 **FM EM** *020 †16,18

GOHEL, Shyam. 600 JEFFERSON AVE, MERCY JEANETTE HOSPITAL 15644 #495-37-1989 L1996 **DR** *020 †80

HANNA, Antonious Hanna. 70 LINCOLN HWY E 15644 #649-14-1981 L1985 **IM** *020 †20

HARSTER, Gerald Alfred. 600 JEFFERSON AVE 15644 #035-06-1982 L1983 **PTH** *020 †50

HOSSAIN, Ayesha. 1111 LOWRY AVE, STE 6 15644 #160-02-1966 L1979 **FM** *020 †18

HUNTER, George Raymond. 610 JEFFERSON AVE 15644 #041-13-1976 L1977 **IM FPG** *020 †20

JACKSON, Jodi Lea. 520 JEFFERSON AVE, STE 601 15644 #055-01-1999 L2002 **PD** *020 †55

KALASH, Yaser. 70 LINCOLN HWY E, MONSOUR MEDICAL CENTER 15644 #875-02-1978 L1989 **CD IM** *020 †20

KHARMA, Bassam K. 6637 STATE ROUTE 30 15644 #875-01-1978 L1995 **CD** *020 †20

KIM, Dong Heup. 520 JEFFERSON AVE, PHYSICIAN'S BUILDING 15644 #583-06-1959 L1972 **GS** *071 †85

LOWDEN, Patrick Michael. 3000 PENNY LN, STE 103 15644 #041-14-1997 L1999 **FM** *020 †18 ‡

MARIANO, Benedicto P. 600 JEFFERSON AVE, MERCY JEANNETTE MEMORIAL H 15644 #748-01-1958 L1966 **R GP** *020

MC WILLIAMS, Fred D. 6451 STATE ROUTE 30 15644 #041-02-1949 L1950 **IM CD** *071 †20

MONSOUR, Miroya Jean. 1075 HARRISON CTY EXPRT RD, STE 1 15644 #010-02-1988 L1988 **IM** *020 †35

MONSOUR, William James. 70 LINCOLN HWY E 15644 #649-02-1956 L1960 **CD IM** *071

PATHEJA, Jotinder Kaur. 600 JEFFERSON AVE 15644 #496-07-1969 L1980 **RO** *020 †80

PRICENER, Valerie M. 520 JEFFERSON AVE 15644 #041-12-1987 L1989 **IM** *020 †20

RAO, Mandiga V B. 600 JEFFERSON AVE, JDMH ANESTHESIOLOGY 15644 #495-21-1973 L1977 **AN** *020 †05

REDDY, Ragoor Kumaraswamy. 1115 LOWRY AVE 15644 #495-70-1975 L1985 **CD IM** *020 †20

RELIGIOSO, Eloisa Pablo. 520 JEFFERSON AVE, STE 601 15644 #748-01-1961 L1972 **PD** *071 ‡

RELIGIOSO, Erson L. 600 JEFFERSON AVE 15644 #748-01-1961 L1971 **IM** *071 †20

SALARI-LAK, Farhad. 600 JEFFERSON AVE, MERCY JEANNETTE HOSPITAL 15644 #517-03-1968 L1976 **AN EM** *020

SAVAY, Edwin Harold. 600 JEFFERSON AVE, MERCY JEANNETTE HOSPITAL 15644 #035-08-1995 L2002 **EM** *020 †20

SHAH, Ratan S. 174 BEECH VALLEY DR 15644 #495-76-1973 L1976 **DR** *020 †80

SHAIKH, Mohammed Nasir. 600 JEFFERSON AVE 15644 #704-02-1958 L1973 **TS** *020 †85,90

SHAVER, James Alvin, Jr. 520 JEFFERSON AVE, STE 601 15644 #041-12-2001 L2001 **PD** *020 †55

SHETTY, Karunakar S. 600 JEFFERSON AVE 15644 #495-37-1962 L1971 **DR** *020 †80

SHUSTER, Michael J. 600 JEFFERSON AVE, MERCY JEANNETTE HOSPITAL, 15644 #010-02-1975 L2005 **EM IM** *020 †16

WERNER, Joyce. 1117 LOWRY AVE, LOWRY SURGICENTER 15644 #041-12-1983 L1984 **AN CCM** *020

ZAHID, Maliha. 6637 ROUTE 30, ADK CARDIOLOGY 15644 #704-25-1993 L2000 **CD** *020 †20

ZELKOVIC, Mark Alan. 520 JEFFERSON AVE 15644 #041-02-1988 L1991 **GS** *020 †85

ZIADEH, Rana. 520 JEFFERSON AVE, STE 601 15644 #875-02-1988 L1997 **PD** *020 †55

JEFFERSON HILLS – ALLEGHENY

ESSER, Steven Andrew. ■ 15025 #041-02-1997 L1999 **CRS** *100 †85,10

HERBERT, Vicki Lou. 198 MEADOWFIELD LN, SOUTH HILLS MEDICAL BLDG 15025 #041-09-1978 L1979 **END IM** *020 †20

JUREWICZ, Witold Roch. 575 COAL VALLEY RD, STE 209 15025 #759-01-2002 L2003 **FM** *020 †18

KIM, Jae Chil. 575 COAL VALLEY RD, STE 361 15025 #583-06-1967 L1974 **PM** *020 †60
KIM, Wan Jo. 5003 JACKSON DR 15025 #583-04-1971 L1980 **DR** *020 †80
KOREN, Mikhail Semenovich. 575 COAL VALLEY RD, STE 573 15025 #913-32-1998 L2005 **END** *020 †20
LAMAN, Paul David, Jr. 1200 BROOKS LN, STE 130 15025 #041-12-1970 L1971 **PUD IM** *020 †20
MCCANN, Spring Seeman. ■ 15025 #041-12-2005 L2005 **AN** *012
ROCKE, Alice Faye. 575 COAL VALLEY RD STE 575 15025 #056-06-1985 L1986 **GS** *020 †85
SATYAWADI, Reena. 575 COAL VALLEY RD, STE 573, SOUTH HILLS MEDICAL BLDG 15025 #495-01-1993 L2000 **END** *020 †20
SICENICA, Toni. 1200 BROOKS LN, JMA BLDG STE 130 15025 #957-01-1987 L2000 **PUD SME** *020 †20
SIMS, William Robt. 1200 BROOKS LN, STE 160 15025 #055-01-1983 L1989 **PUD IM** *020 †20

JENKINTOWN – MONTGOMERY

ABBOUD, Elias M. 261 OLD YORK RD, THE PAVILION SUITE 325 19046 #165-03-1982 L1986 **AI** *020 †55,03
ADLER, Lee Paul. 261 OLD YORK RD, STE 106 19046 #036-01-1981 L1983 **NR DR** *020 †80,28
ALBERT, Elizabeth Victori. ■ 19046 #041-15-2003 L2003 **PTH** *100
ALBERT, Ross Howard. ■ 19046 #041-15-2005 L2005 **FP** *012
ALLON, Steven Michael. 1648 HUNTINGDON PIKE 19046 #041-12-1983 L1984 **ORS OS** *020
ALPERT, Charles Bailey. 801 OLD YORK RD STE 201 19046 #041-07-1984 L1986 **PM PMM** *020 †60 ‡
ALVAREZ, Orlando. 1648 HUNTINGDON PIKE, HOLY REDEEMER 19046 #035-06-1980 L1988 **DR** *020 †80
ANASTASOPOULOU, Catherine. 100 OLD YORK RD STE 3116 19046 #418-01-1990 L1997 **END** *100 †20
ANNON, Walter Thos, Jr. ■ 19046 #041-13-1948 L1949 **GS** *071 †85
ANTIC, Anica. ■ 19046 #957-02-1991 L2004 **PTH** *012
ANTONIOU, Maria. 314 COTTMAN ST, SUBURBAN CHEST ASSOC 19046 #067-01-1992 L1997 **IM** *020 †20 ‡
AZARI, Amir Akhavan. ■ 19046 #041-15-2007 L2007 **IM** *012
BARBA, William Philip, II. ■ 19046 #041-01-1946 L1947 **OS PD** *071 †55
BARUSEWYCZ, Maria. 710 FOX CHASE RD 19046 #154-02-1949 L1970 **CHP P** *075
BEMIS, Charles Eastman. 1650 HUNTINGDON PIKE, PENNSYLVANIA HEART & 19046 #024-07-1966 L1971 **CD** *020 †20
BERENBAUM, Paul L. 261 OLD YORK RD STE 309, THE PAVILION 19046 #051-04-1972 L1978 **GE HEP** *020 ‡
BERMAN, Jessica Alana. 1648 HUNTINGDON PIKE, STE 1000 19046 #033-05-1997 L2000 **IM** *020 †20
BLOCHER, Nissa Christine. 100 OLD YORK RD, STE 3116 19046 #003-01-2002 L2002 **IM** *100 †20
BLUMSTEIN, Chas Goldman. 261 OLD YORK RD, STE 801 19046 #041-13-1962 L1963 **AI IM** *020 †20,03
BONONI, Paula Ann. 500 OLD YORK RD, RYDAL SQUARE #203 19046 #041-07-1980 L1981 **IM IMG** *020 †20
BRENNER, Angus Lejaren. ■ 19046 #041-02-1944 L1945 **EM OBG** *071 †30
BRUNO, Joseph Michael. 1095 RYDAL RD, STE 100 19046 #041-02-1995 L1997 **GE** *020 †20
BUTLER, Jennifer Ann. 500 OLD YORK RD, STE 108 19046 #041-02-2001 L2001 **FM** *020
CARRIER, Marie Therese. 261 OLD YORK RD, STE 620 19046 #041-07-1997 L1999 **PD** *020 †55
CASCINO, Doris Maria. 1648 HUNTINGDON PIKE 19046 #035-15-1996 L2002 **PD** *020 †55
CASTELBAUM, Arthur Jay. 1650 HUNTINGDON PIKE, STE 154 19046 #028-02-1988 L1990 **OS** *072 †30 ‡
CHATZINOFF, Martin. 1095 RYDAL RD, STE 100 19046 #033-05-1982 L1983 **GE IM** *020 †20
CHERNOFF, Arthur. 100 OLD YORK RD STE 3116 19046 #041-01-1972 L1978 **END IM** *020 †20
CHOE, Eun Sook. ■ 19046 #583-08-1976 L1980 **PTH** *100
CLARK, Mathew Mccoy. 500 OLD YORK RD, STE 108 19046 #008-01-1983 L1986 **FM** *020 †18
CLOUSE, Amy Lynn. 500 OLD YORK RD, STE 108 19046 #041-07-1995 L1998 **FM** *020 †18
COOPERBERG, David B. 1648 HUNTINGDON PIKE 19046 #012-05-1994 L2000 **PD** *020 †55
DABEZIES, Marta Ana. 1095 RYDAL RD, STE 100 19046 #041-01-1979 L1981 **GE IM** *020 †20
DAMSKER, Jason Asher. 1648 HUNTINGDON PIKE, STE 1000 19046 #041-09-1997 L1999 **HO** *020 †20 ‡
DAMSKER, Keith Evan. 500 OLD YORK RD, STE 203 19046 #041-09-1997 L2006 **IM** *020 †20
D'ANGIO, Salvatore John. 523 GIBSON AVE 19046 #041-09-1984 L1985 **FM** *020 †18
DEFRANCISCO, Mary E. 120 HUNTINGDON PIKE 19046 #041-09-1979 L1982 **OPH** *020
DICKSTEIN, Benjamin. ■ 19046 #041-01-1940 L1942 **PD HEM** *071 †55
DIEPOLD, Julia Alexandra. ■ 19046 #041-02-2006 L2006 **FP** *012
DONOVAN, Mary. ■ 19046 #041-07-1994 *100
DOYLE, M France. ■ 19046 #010-02-1974 L2005 **EM CD** *030 †16
DUPUIS, Richard, Jr. 314 COTTMAN ST 19046 #041-07-1984 L1986 **PUD CCM** *020 †20 ‡
ECKER, Michelle Laura. 500 OLD YORK RD, STE 203 19046 #041-01-1992 L1994 **IM** *020 †20
EDELMAN, Meyer. ■ 19046 #041-02-1948 L1949 **AN** *071 †05
EDELSTEIN, Joel K. 101 WASHINGTON LN, STE G-1 COLONNADE MONOR 19046 #041-09-1976 L1977 **P CHP** *020 †75
EDELSTEIN, Merle P Gross. 261 OLD YORK RD STE 501, FOX PAVILION 19046 #041-02-1965 L1966 **PYA P** *020 †75
EL-MANSOURY, Jeylan Ate. 261 OLD YORK RD STE 520 19046 #915-03-1974 L1996 **OPH** *020 †35
EMMONS, Robert Van Buren. ■ 19046 #038-41-1989 L2003 **HEM** *020 †20
EVANS, Joseph Bernard. ■ 19046 #041-09-1944 L1945 **PD** *071
FENSTEMACHER, Pamela Ann. 500 OLD YORK RD, STE 108 19046 #035-19-1986 L1989 **FM FPG** *040 †18
FERRARA, Vincent Louis. 261 OLD YORK RD STE 708 19046 #041-13-1964 L1965 **NS** *020 †25
FINE, Sharon Ruth. 101 GREENWOOD AVE STE 150 19046 #041-09-1997 L1999 **DR** *020 †80
FINKELSTEIN, Emily Anne. 100 WEST AVE, STE 400A 19046 #035-48-1986 L1990 **P** *020 †75
FOGEL, Jeffrey Mitchell. 1077 RYDAL RD, STE 300 19046 #035-15-1980 L1983 **PD** *020 †55
FOX, Robert Douglas. 261 OLD YORK RD, THE PAVILION STE 312 19046 #010-02-1978 L1979 **D FM** *020 †15
FREEMAN, Danl Moshe Avrom. ■ 19046 #065-01-1962 L1973 **CHP PYA** *072
FRISCH, Mark Benj. 201 OLD YORK RD STE 202 19046 #035-08-1980 L1984 **OBG** *020 †30
FUDGE, Melinda Teresa. 261 OLD YORK RD, THE PAVILION SUITE 634 19046 #041-13-1990 L1992 **OBG** *020 †30
GASH, Arnold K. ■ 19046 #041-13-1972 L1973 **CD IM** *020 †20
GAVIN, Barbara Muller. 500 OLD YORK RD STE 203 19046 #041-13-1994 L1996 **IM** *020 †20
GENTER, Bruce Eric. 100 YORK RD, STE 3120 19046 #041-01-1977 L1984 **PS CS** *020 †85,65
GEORGE-LOMAX, Keris Maria. 261 YORK RD, STE 520 19046 #041-02-1994 L1998 **OPH** *071 †35
GHARPURE, Vishwanath S. 1648 HUNTINGDON PIKE, STE 1000 19046 #496-38-1983 L1999 **HO IM** *020 †20
GLASSMAN, Joel Martin. 201 YORK RD, # 205 19046 #041-09-1977 L1979 **IM** *020 †20
GLICKMAN, Murray. ■ 19046 #041-02-1951 L1952 **ORS OS** *071 †40
GOLD, Neil Spencer. 376 BAR HARBOR RD 19046 #041-09-1979 L1981 **FM** *020
GOLDBERG, Melvyn. 1472 GUNPOWDER RD, DEPT SURGICAL ONCOLOGY 19046 #065-01-1965 L1993 *100
GOLDBERG, Melvyn Ralph. 1472 GUNPOWDER RD, DEPT SURGICAL ONCOLOGY 19046 #011-02-1975 L1976 **PD PEM** *020 †55
GOLDSTEIN, Philip David. 1077 RYDAL RD, STE 300 19046 #008-01-1981 L1983 **PD MDM** *020 †55
GOODMAN, Sanford M. ■ 19046 #041-02-1949 L1950 **FM** *071 †18
GREENSPAN, June E. 261 OLD YORK RD, STE 434 19046 #041-07-1959 L1960 **P PYA** *020 ‡
GREWAL, Ritu G. 216 HOLMECREST RD 19046 #495-36-1984 L1993 **PCC CCM** *020 †20
GROHSMAN, Jonathan Murray. 261 OLD YORK RD, SUITE 520 - THE PAVILION 19046 #041-13-1977 L1979 **OPH** *020 †35
GURMAN, Felix G. ■ 19046 #023-01-2008 *012
GUTTMANN, Harvey. 1095 RYDAL RD, STE 100 19046 #035-20-1979 L1984 **GE IM** *020 †20
HAAZ, William Stephen. 1650 HUNTINGDON PIKE, PENNSYLVANIA HEART & 19046 #041-13-1975 L1976 **CD** *020 †20
HAIDER, Agha W. 261 OLD YORK RD, STE 214 19046 #704-16-1984 L2002 **CD** *100 †20
HAND, Roy H. 309 FLORENCE AVE 19046 #041-02-1953 L1954 **GS CRS** *071 †85
HANDAL, John A. 201 OLD YORK RD, STE 202 19046 #041-07-1979 L1981 **ORS** *020 †40
HANSEN, Gerald Joseph. 500 OLD YORK RD, STE 108 19046 #008-02-1983 L1984 **FM FPG** *020 †18
HAYES, Julia M C. 261 OLD YORK RD, STE 732 19046 #041-01-1973 L1975 **CHN PM** *020 †55
HELLER, J June. NOBLE PLZ OLD YORK RD 322 19046 #660-03-1954 L1956 **P** *071
HOGAN, Kimberly Ann. 500 OLD YORK RD STE 1 19046 #056-06-1994 L1996 **FM** *020 †18 ‡
JAYARAJ, Jacintha Lourdu. ■ 19046 #495-66-1995 L2001 **OBG** *020 †30
KALAFER, Marvin. 100 OLD YORK RD, STE L-136 19046 #165-01-1976 L1977 **OBG** *020 †30
KASDIN, Sharon R Lebowitz. ■ 19046 #041-07-1966 L1967 **GP** *050
KATZ, Alan Stephen. 314 COTTMAN ST 19046 #016-42-1969 L1970 **PUD IM** *020 †20 ‡
KAUFMAN, Stephen Edward. 1095 RYDAL RD, STE 100 19046 #026-04-1971 L1977 **GE IM** *020 †20
KEATES, Edwin Utley. 500 OLD YORK RD STE 102 19046 #041-02-1957 L1958 **OPH** *020 †35
KIMBALL, Michael Joseph. ■ 19046 #041-15-2008 *012
KONAKANCHI, Anu R. 261 OLD YORK RD 19046 #308-11-1985 L1995 **IM** *020 †20
KOVATS-ONGRADI, Eniko. 201 OLD YORK RD, STE 202 19046 #473-01-1979 L1993 **PD** *020 †55
KRAMER, Eli G. 500 OLD YORK RD, STE 203, RYDAL SQUARE 19046 #043-01-2000 L2006 **IM** *020 †20 ‡
KRESS, Marc Mitchell. 610 YORK RD, STE 70 19046 #041-02-1981 L1982 **FM IMG** *020 †18
KURIEN, Mary. 343 HOLMECREST RD, TEMPLE UNIVERSITY HOSPITAL 19046 #495-59-1988 L2001 **P** *020
LACKS, Gayle. BENSON EAST 19046 #041-13-1986 L1987 **CHP** *020 †75
LADDEN, John Jos. 1650 HUNTINGDON PIKE, STE 250 HOLY REDEEMER HOSP 19046 #041-07-1976 L1978 **GS** *075
LAM, Sofia. 1 ABINGTON AVE, STE 100 19046 #561-13-1983 L1986 **AN** *020 †05
LEBEAU, Jack. ■ 19046 #038-06-1966 L1967 **CD IM** *071 †20
LEMONOVICH, Tracy Lynn. 500 OLD YORK RD, STE 203 19046 #038-06-2002 L2002 **ID** *012 †20
LEPAR, Felice Hilary. 1648 HUNTINGDON PIKE, STE 1000 19046 #024-01-1997 L2000 **HO** *020 †20
LESKOWITZ, Steven C. 1095 RYDAL RD, STE 100 19046 #422-01-1981 L1983 **GE IM** *020 †20
LIANG, Gwen Joan. 510 WEST AVE 19046 #024-01-1977 L1985 **OPH** *071 †35
LINDSEY, Beth Hanson. 100 OLD YORK RD STE 214B, THE BENSON EAST 19046 #041-02-1979 L1980 **P PYA** *020 †75
LINTGEN, Arthur Benner. 500 OLD YORK RD, RYDAL SQUARE #203 19046 #041-02-1966 L1967 **IM IMG** *020 †20
LITT, David Loren. 1650 HUNTINGDON PIKE, ASSOC, LTD, SUITE 156 19046 #041-02-1993 L1996 **IM** *020 †20
LITVIN, Henry. ■ 19046 #041-01-1948 L1950 **PYG P** *071
LONG, Charles David. 1250 GREENWOOD AVE, STE 14 19046 #041-13-1988 L1990 **PS** *020 †85,65
LOUDIS, Patricia J. 101 WASHINGTON LN, # H230 19046 #041-09-1979 L1981 **N** *020 †20,75
MACKRELL, John Patrick. ■ 19046 #041-13-2003 L2003 **DR** *012
MAHONEY, Maria Marinaro. 261 OLD YORK RD, STE 620 19046 #041-13-1995 L1997 **PD** *020 †55
MAJMUNDAR, Amar Jayprakas. ■ 19046 #041-01-2008 *012
MANNO, Bruno V, Jr. 1650 HUNTINGDON PIKE, PENNSYLVANIA HEART & 19046 #041-09-1978 L1980 **CD** *020 †20
MARINCHAK, Roger Alan. 261 OLD YORK RD, PENNSYLVANIA HEART & 19046 #041-07-1977 L1978 **ICE CD** *020 †20
MATTLEMAN, Nathan. ■ 19046 #041-13-1942 L1943 **GP** *071
MATTLEMAN, Steven Jay. 261 OLD YORK RD, PENNSYLVANIA HEART & 19046 #041-09-1978 L1980 **IM** *020 †20
MAXWELL, Robert Allan. 1648 HUNTINGDON PIKE, STE 1000 19046 #020-02-1958 L1959 **HO ON** *020 †20
MAYE, Thomas J. ■ 19046 #041-13-1941 L1942 **GP OS** *020
MAYRO, Julian. ■ 19046 #041-02-1958 L1959 **IM** *071 †20
MC CLURG, Mark Andrew. 1650 HUNTINGDON PIKE, STE 258 19046 #038-41-1990 L1992 **P PYG** *020 †75 ‡
MCFADDEN, Raymond J. ■ 19046 #041-07-1984 L1986 **GP** *020
MC GLYNN, Charles Thos. ■ 19046 #033-05-1984 L1986 **P** *075
MENICHELLO, Gina Marie. 500 OLD YORK RD, STE 108 19046 #041-77-2006, ▲ L2006 **FP** *012
MEROPOL, Sharon Bloom. ■ 19046 #047-05-1985 L1988 **PD** *040 †55
MIAN, Ibrahim Mohammad. ■ 19046 #036-05-2007 L2007 **FP** *012
MOAVEN, Jubeen. ■ 19046 #041-02-2008 L2008 **CCA** *012
MOHAPATRA, Neelam. 500 OLD YORK RD, STE 203 19046 #495-37-2001 L2003 **IM** *020 †20
MOON, Edmund Kyung. ■ 19046 #023-01-2004 L2004 **PCC** *012 †20
MYERS, Andrew Earl. 205 MATHER RD 19046 #041-13-1994 L1996 **IM** *020 †20
MYHRE, Jennifer Aylestock. 100 WEST AVE STE W960 19046 #023-07-1988 L1988 **PD** *020 †55

MYHRE, Scott David. 100 WEST AVE STE W960 19046 #038-41-1987 L1987 **FM** *020 †18
NAIDS, Richard Eric. 120 HUNTINGDON PIKE 19046 #041-13-1984 L1985 **OPH** *020 †35
NOTTE, Christopher M. 500 OLD YORK RD 19046 #041-15-2003 L2003 **FM** *020 †18
PABLO, Gil Enriquez. ■ 19046 #748-02-1942 L1961 **TS PUD** *071
PICKENS, Peter Vincent. 1648 HUNTINGDON PIKE, STE 1000 19046 #035-47-1978 L1981 **HEM ON** *020 †20
PITKOW, Perry Shalom. ■ 19046 #041-13-1985 L1988 **EM FM** *020 †18
PIZZANO, Joseph Anthony. 500 OLD YORK RD STE 102 19046 #033-05-1972 L1973 **OPH** *020 †35
POTZ, Joseph Louis. 1648 HUNTINGDON PIKE, STE 1000 19046 #024-07-1982 L1993 **ON IM** *020 †20
PYFER, Mark Franklin. 500 OLD YORK RD, STE 102 19046 #041-01-1995 L1997 **OPH** *020 †35
RAINA, Amresh. ■ 19046 #035-01-2003 L2005 **CD** *012 †20
RAYNER, William Jeffery. 100 OLD YORK RD STE L-136, THE CLINICAL TRAIL CENTER 19046 #035-09-1975 L1982 **FM** *050 †18
REME, Jeanette Antoine. ■ 19046 #440-01-1962 L1967 **PD GP** *020
RIGOTTI, Joseph A. 500 OLD YORK RD, RYDAL SQUARE SUITE 203 19046 #041-77-1984, ▲ L1985 **IM** *020 †20
RISEN, Stephen Elkin. 261 YORK RD, # 683 19046 #041-09-1967 L1968 **P CBG** *020 †75
ROSATO, Melissa Anne. 500 OLD YORK RD, STE 108 19046 #041-02-2005 L2005 **FP** *012
ROSEN, Steven Mark. 261 OLD YORK RD 19046 #023-01-1984 L1985 **AN PME** *020 †05
ROSENBAUM, Susan Jane. ■ 19046 #030-05-1987 L1998 **P** *020 †75
ROSS, Ronald Dudley. ■ 19046 #649-33-1980 L1981 **OS OM** *050 †70
RUDIN, Robert Lawrence. 610 YORK RD, STE 70 19046 #041-09-1986 L1989 **IM** *020 †20
RUSSELL, John Joseph. 500 OLD YORK RD, STE 108 19046 #041-14-1990 L1992 **FM** *020 †18
SADOFF, Robert Leslie. 261 OLD YORK RD STE 326, THE PAVILION 19046 #026-04-1959 L1965 **P PFP** *071 †75
SCHNALL, Barry. 1610 THE FAIRWAY STE 111 19046 #041-13-1974 L1975 **PM PMM** *020 †60
SCHUMAN, Edward Peter. 1650 HUNTINGDON PIKE 19046 #024-05-1977 L1980 **PUD CCM** *020 †20
SEARS, Brenda. 500 OLD YORK RD, INTERNAL MEDICAL ASSOCIATE 19046 #024-16-1993 L1996 **FM** *020 †18
SHARP, Ira Robt. 201 OLD YORK RD, STE 205 19046 #041-02-1979 L1980 **IM IMG** *020 †20
SHAW, John L. 1095 RYDAL RD 19046 #035-45-1953 L1955 **U** *072 †95
SHIELDS, John Judd. ■ 19046 #024-01-1935 L1937 **PD** *071 †55
SIEGEL, Bernard. 500 OLD YORK RD, STE 201 19046 #041-09-1938 L1939 **OBG** *071 †30
SILIQUINI, John J. 120 HUNTINGDON PIKE 19046 #033-05-1960 L1961 **OPH** *071 †35 ‡
SILIQUINI, John Joseph, Jr. 120 HUNTINGDON PIKE 19046 #041-02-1994 L1996 **OPH** *020 †35 ‡
SIVITZ, Jay Morton. 100 YORK RD, STE 3108 19046 #041-13-1959 L1960 **OBG** *020 †30
SJOHOLM, Lars Ola Ingvar. ■ 19046 #858-01-1993 L2000 **CCS** *100 †85
SKOLNIK, Neil Saml. 500 OLD YORK RD STE 108, ABINGTON FAMILY MEDICINE 19046 #012-05-1984 L1985 **FM** *040 †18
SKOWRONSKI, Theodore John. 500 OLD YORK RD, RYDAL SQUARE, SUITE 203 19046 #041-02-1968 L1969 **IM** *020 †20
SLOCHOWER, Dennis. 120 HUNTINGDON PIKE 19046 #016-42-1978 L1982 **OPH** *020 †35
SONNEBORN, Duane G. 801 OLD YORK RD, STE 221 19046 #041-01-1937 L1939 **GP IM** *071
SPIELMAN, Scott Ronald. 261 OLD YORK RD, PENNSYLVANIA HEART & 19046 #035-01-1973 L1974 **CD IM** *020 †20
STEIN, Robert Benj. 1095 RYDAL RD, STE 100 19046 #041-13-1991 L1993 **GE** *020 †20
STERNBERGER, Kenneth. 1650 HUNTINGDON PIKE, STE 355 19046 #033-06-1983 L1984 **IM** *020 †20
STERNLIEB, Jonathan M. 1095 RYDAL RD, STE 100 19046 #041-01-1985 L1986 **GE IM** *020 †20 ‡
SWEIGARD, Keith Ward. 500 OLD YORK RD STE 203 19046 #041-09-1980 L1981 **IM IMG** *030 †20
TAUBER, Stanley Abraham. ■ 19046 #041-13-1948 L1949 **IM** *071
THALLNER, Elaine Anne. 616 RODMAN AVE 19046 #041-13-1985 L1995 **EM** *020 †16
TINGO, Jennifer Elizabeth. ■ 19046 #051-07-2007 L2007 *012
TOPKIS-SCHLAFF, Lillian B. ■ 19046 #041-13-1945 L1946 **PHP GPM** *071
TRICHTINGER, Martin Drew. 500 OLD YORK RD, RYDAL SQUARE SUITE 203 19046 #041-02-1980 L1981 **IM NTR** *020
URBAN, Heather Mowrey. 500 OLD YORK RD, STE 203 19046 #051-07-2001 L2001 **IM NTR** *020
WALDSTEIN, David John. 261 OLD YORK RD STE 214 19046 #016-06-1987 L1993 **CD** *020 †20
WALSH-SHAW, Ellen Marie. 1095 RYDAL RD, STE 100 19046 #041-09-1978 L1979 **GE IM** *020 †20
WARD, Stephen De Jour. ■ 19046 #041-13-1964 L1965 **IM** *071 †20
WAX, Amy L. ■ 19046 #024-01-1981 **N IM** *100
WELSH, John Jos. 179 WASHINGTON LN 19046 #041-09-1956 L1957 **OTO** *071 †45
WERTHEIMER, John Harvey. 261 OLD YORK RD, PENNSYLVANIA HEART & 19046 #041-01-1976 L1977 **CD** *020 †20
WETZEL, Jennifer Thuma. 610 YORK RD, STE 70 19046 #041-15-2002 L2003 **FM** *020 †18
WIEDEMANN, Anne T. 500 OLD YORK RD, STE 108 19046 #041-15-2004 L2004 **FM** *020 †18
WILKES, Warren Arthur. 1650 HUNTINGDON PIKE 19046 #065-05-1994 L2004 **PCC** *020 †20
WILLIAMS, John Thos. 201 OLD YORK RD, STE 202 19046 #010-03-1964 L1965 **ORS OS** *040
ZAMORA, Danilo Dominguez. 261 OLD YORK RD STE 414 19046 #748-01-1966 L1973 **U** *020 †95
ZIVANOVIC, Dragan. 524 BENSON EAST 19046 #957-02-1963 *050

JENNERSTOWN – SOMERSET

TIMENS, Lawrence Jos. 327 LAKE SHORE DRIVE 15547 #025-07-1972 L1977 **CHP P** *020 †75

JERMYN – LACKAWANNA

BLOES, Walter Shaffer. ■ 18433 #041-02-1959 L1960 **GP** *071
KOLUCKI, Frank Ralph. ■ 18433 #010-02-1943 L1944 **FM** *071
MIRANDA-MARANON, Jorge. ■ 18433 #176-03-1963 L1973 **U** *071 †95
PAULISHAK, Melody. ■ 18433 #016-76-2000, ▲ L2004 *100

JERSEY SHORE – LYCOMING

ACOSTA, Melanio Dilag, Jr. ■ 17740 #748-01-1959 L1966 **GS AS** *071
BALDWIN, Richard Donald. 1052 CREEKSIDE LN 17740 #035-09-1957 L1980 **NM IM** *071 †20,28
CHAPLA, Pravinchandra G. 116 KERR AVE, STE B 17740 #495-48-1989 L1997 **IM** *020 †20
CORNEL, Reynaldo Navarro. 116 KERR AVE 17740 #748-01-1980 L1998 **IM** *020 †20
EISTER, Ronald N. 1020 THOMPSON ST 17740 #041-02-1980 L1981 **FM** *020 †18 ‡
FORKER, Thomas Stephen. 1020 THOMPSON ST, JERSEY SHORE HOSPITAL 17740 #033-05-1976 L1979 **FM EM** *020 †18
FOULSHAM, Charles Kenneth. 1020 THOMPSON ST 17740 #041-02-1978 L1982 **OTO** *020 †45
HAMOY, George Lestica. 116 KERR AVE 17740 #041-01-1966 L1976 **GS TRS** *071
PATEL, Rajesh Jerambhai. 116 KERR AVE # B2 17740 #495-48-1983 L1991 **IM** *020 †20
RECINTO, Cynthia K. 990 THOMPSON ST 17740 #748-01-1980 L2000 **IM** *020 †20
TUSEK, Zdenek A. 1020 THOMPSON ST, JERSEY SHORE HOSP RAD DEPT 17740 #286-02-1972 L1980 **DR** *020 †80
WILLIAMSON, Neihl J. ■ 17740 #041-01-1943 L1944 *071
WITTHOFF, E Milton. 1020 THOMPSON ST 17740 #041-02-1957 L1961 **FM** *071

JIM THORPE – CARBON

GONZALEZ, Roberta B. 616 NORTH ST, STE 307 18229 #041-07-1964 L1965 **P** *020 †18,75
MANZELLA, Edward Danl. 1353 STATE ROUTE 903 18229 #422-01-1986 L1992 **IM** *020 †20
MANZELLA, John R. 1353 STATE ROUTE 903 18229 #035-75-1995, ▲ L1999 **MPD** *020
MANZELLA, Victor A. 1353 STATE ROUTE 903 18229 #422-01-1992 L1997 **IM** *020
MC GINLEY, Clement Chas. 1104 NORTH ST 18229 #041-14-1976 L1977 **FM** *020 †18
SMITH, Deborah Ann. 1580 CENTER AVE 18229 #041-13-1979 L1980 **FM** *020 †18
VON NEIDA, Anne. 1104 NORTH ST, THORPE 18229 #033-06-1994 L1998 **IM** *020 †20

JOHNSONBURG – ELK

PLATT, Dwayne Larry, Jr. 111 COBB ST 15845 #041-02-1998 L2000 **FM** *020 †18
SLAVIK, Gretchen Marie. 111 COBB ST 15845 #041-13-1998 L2000 **FM** *020
WU, Chau Hsiung. 81 CLARION RD 15845 #244-01-1969 L1973 **FM** *020 †18

JOHNSTOWN – CAMBRIA

ABRAHAMS, Jonathan I. 504 TIOGA ST 15905 #016-42-1974 L1978 **DR** *020 †80
ACKERMANN, Wiebke. 1086 FRANKLIN ST 15905 #408-14-2005 L2006 **TY** *012
ACOSTA, William R. 1159 BOYD AVE 15905 #308-01-1979 L1984 **N** *020
ADESARA, Rashmin Premchan. 1086 FRANKLIN ST 15905 #495-22-1998 L2007 **FP** *012
AFANASENKA, Aksana. 1086 FRANKLIN ST, CONEMAUGH VALLEY MEM HOSP 15905 #912-05-2001 L2005 **IM** *012
AHLSTROM, Brian Patrick. 353 MARKET ST 15901 #165-01-1978 L1987 **N CHN** *020 †55,75
AKHAND, Md. Arifur Rahman. OFFICE E3349, GRADUATE MED ED 15905 #160-04-1992 L2007 **FP** *012
ALBERT, Andrew M. 1086 FRANKLIN ST 15905 #422-01-1992 L2000 **AN** *020 †05
ALI, Mullah Layaque. 1086 FRANKLIN ST, DEPT MED 15905 #496-05-1980 **IM** *100
ALI, Syed Asif. ■ 15905 #704-16-1995 L1999 **IM** *020 †20
ALLAM, Savitha. 1086 FRANKLIN ST 15905 #495-11-2000 L2003 **IM** *020 †20
ALLEN, Herbert Victor. 1086 FRANKLIN ST 15905 #041-02-1957 L1958 **FM GP** *040
AL SOUDI, Mahdi Abdel Mah. 1086 FRANKLIN ST, DEPT OF GME 15905 #575-01-2004 L2006 **IM** *012
AMPER, Geraldine G. 1450 SCALP AVE 15904 #748-01-1989 L1997 **FM** *020 †18
AMPER, Leonardo. 321 MAIN ST, STE 3B 15901 #748-01-1988 L1996 **IM** *020 †20
ANQUILO, Louie Astrera. 1086 FRANKLIN ST, CONEMAUGH VALLEY MEM HOSP 15905 #748-01-1999 L2003 **FM** *020 †18
ANTEMANN, Richard Wm. 337 SOMERSET ST 15901 #035-03-1961 L1966 **RO** *020 †80
ANTICO, Dominic Anthony. 320 MAIN ST, DEPT OF RADIOLOGY 15901 #016-02-1964 L1972 **DR** *020 †80
ARIFUDDIN, Mohammed. 1086 FRANKLIN ST 15905 #495-21-1977 *100
ARISE, Bhagyarekha. 1086 FRANKLIN ST, DEPT OF INTERNAL MED 15905 #495-21-1997 L2004 **IM** *020 †20
ARMSTRONG, David Craig. 348 BUDFIELD ST 15904 #041-07-1984 L1985 **OTO AI** *020 †45
ASHMAN, George S. 120 MAIN ST 15901 #041-12-1966 L1967 **OPH** *020 †35 ‡
ASLAM, Asifa. 1086 FRANKLIN ST, CONEMAUGH VALLEY MEM HOSP 15905 #704-21-1995 L2004 **IM** *100
AZER, Magdi Selim. 88 OSBORNE ST 15905 #330-01-1957 L1969 **TS** *071 †85,90
BABRA, Ramindra Singh. 320 MAIN ST 15901 #495-30-1966 L1976 **EM GP** *020 †16
BABRA, Sudha Talwar. 1086 FRANKLIN ST 15905 #495-30-1968 L1981 **EM** *020
BAJEMA, Robert Jon. ■ 15905 #018-03-1974 L1976 **FM** *020
BANTLY, Victor Saml. 1086 FRANKLIN ST 15905 #041-12-1943 L1944 **GP NM** *071
BARTO, Johnnie Wilson. 241 SCHOOLHOUSE RD 15904 #041-12-1973 L1974 **PD NPM** *020 †55
BAYER, George Thos. 1086 FRANKLIN ST, CONEMAUGH MEMORIAL HOSPITA 15905 #041-12-1989 L1991 **EM** *020 †16
BEATTY, Lawrence Thos. 201A COLLEGE PARK PLZ 15904 #041-02-1975 L1977 **FM** *020 †18
BEERMAN, Curtis A. 15901 #028-34-1940 L1941 **PD** *071 †55
BEGLEY, Christopher James. 271 SCHOOLHOUSE RD 15904 #047-05-1978 L1986 **PUD** *020 †20
BENCIE, David Jos. 1511 SCALP AVE 15904 #041-13-1980 L1981 **IM** *020 †20
BENNETT, John Lawrence. 320 MAIN ST, LEE HOSPITAL 15901 #016-11-1972 L1973 **EM** *020 †16
BERES, Chester John. 335 NEES AVE 15904 #041-12-1982 L1989 **FM** *020 †18
BERGREN, Robert Leonard. 969 EISENHOWER BLVD 15904 #017-20-1987 L1988 **OPH** *020 †35
BEZEK, Joel A. 120 MAIN ST 15901 #041-02-2000 L2004 **OPH** *020 †35 ‡
BHAT, Krishna Mundathaje. 321 MAIN ST, STE 5H 15901 #649-33-1983 L1986 **CD IM** *020 †20
BHATNAGAR, Mukul. 1086 FRANKLIN ST 15905 #495-30-1982 L1994 **CD** *020 †20
BINDAL, Ankur. 1086 FRANKLIN ST, DEPT OF GME 15905 #496-43-2003 L2006 **FM** *100
BOCCARDO, Justin. 1086 FRANKLIN ST 15905 #132-09-2003 L2003 **GS** *012
BORECKY, David C. 1450 SCALP AVE STE 106 15904 #041-12-1953 L1954 **IM NEP** *020

BORKOW, Joel Elliot. 415 NAPOLEON PL 15901 #064-01-1973 L1978 **PS** *020 †65 ‡
BRADLEY, Samuel Milton. ■ 15905 #010-02-1954 L1957 **IM CD** *071
BROWN, Kathleen L. ■ 15905 #035-45-1987 L1993 **FM** *020
BROWN, William J, III. 1086 FRANKLIN ST 15905 #038-41-1982 L1992 **OBG** *071 †30
BROZETTI, John Jos. 120 MAIN ST 15901 #010-01-1987 L1989 **OPH IM** *020 †20,35
CAMPBELL, Robert James. 1086 FRANKLIN ST, CENTER 15905 #041-09-1977 L1984 **GP** *020 †18,16
CARDELLINO, Thomas James. 1020 FRANKLIN ST 15905 #016-43-1963 L1964 **CD** *020 †20
CARNEY, Frank Thos. 1111 FRANKLIN ST, CARNEY WARIKOO & MCMURTRY 15905 #041-02-1958 L1959 **U** *071 †95
CARNEY, William Michael. 1015 FRANKLIN ST, LEVEL C 15905 #041-02-1988 L1991 **GS** *020 †85
CAROFF, Romuald Jos. 1450 SCALP AVE # OO3B 15904 #041-12-1955 L1956 **FM** *071 †18
CARRIER, Judith M. 131 ROCKWOOD LN 15905 #308-07-1982 L1986 **FM** *071 †18
CARRIER, William Willis. 1086 FRANKLIN ST 15905 #308-07-1982 L1985 **EM** *071 †16
CARTWRIGHT, Richard Lee. 320 MAIN ST 15901 #035-06-1981 L1983 **IM** *020 †20
CARUSI, Donato Rocco. 321 MAIN ST, STE 4B 15901 #024-16-1981 L1986 **OPH IM** *020
CASALE, Lawrence F. ■ 15905 #041-02-1947 L1948 **ORS** *071 †40
CASSONE, Richard Amedeo. 110 FRANKLIN ST, 3RD FL 15901 #033-05-1971 L1987 **P PYG** *020 †75 ‡
CATINCHI, Steven. ■ 15904 #042-04-2003 L2004 **PTH** *012
CERIMELE, Nicholas A. 1086 FRANKLIN ST 15905 #010-01-1970 L1974 **GS CRS** *020 †85
CHAN, John Osmund. 1086 FRANKLIN ST, MEMORIAL MEDICAL CENTER 15905 #748-02-1983 L1990 **NPM** *020 †55
CHIKERSAL, Anjali. 1086 FRANKLIN ST 15905 #496-07-1988 L1998 **PTH** *100
CHMEL, Herman. 1086 FRANKLIN ST # MED, CONEMAUGH MEM MED CTR 15905 #041-09-1968 L1999 **ID IM** *030 †20
CHOUDHURY, Shahin Ara Sid. 1086 FRANKLIN ST, DEPT OF GME 15905 #160-11-2000 L2006 **FP** *012
CHOWDHRY, Zafar Iqbal. 1111 FRANKLIN ST, STE 210 15905 #704-01-1968 L1975 **NS GS** *020 †25
CONFER, Elaine Ann. 241 SCHOOLHOUSE RD 15904 #041-07-1977 L1989 **PD** *020 †55
CONTAKOS, Samuel Christos. 305 FRANKLIN ST 15901 #048-04-1960 L1960 **GP OS** *071
COREY, W Theodore, Jr. 935 SAINT CLAIR RD, UPMC LEE REGIONAL MRI CENT 15905 #011-03-1971 L1972 **R** *020 †80
COTTLE, Harold Ranson. 1086 FRANKLIN ST 15905 #035-09-1948 L1970 **FOP ATP** *071 †50
CSIKOS, David Anthony. 1511 SCALP AVE 15904 #041-13-1977 L1979 **IM** *020 †20 ‡
DABHI, Vasant Laljibhai. 1086 FRANKLIN ST 15905 #495-89-1996 L2006 **FP** *012
DAS, Shweta. 1086 FRANKLIN ST, DEPT OF GME 15905 #495-45-2004 L2006 **PTH** *012
DAVIS, Glenn Bryan. 128 WALNUT ST, AND PAIN CARE CENTER 15901 #020-02-1982 L2000 **FM** *020 †18
DAVIS, James Kenneth. ■ 15904 #041-09-1959 L1960 **D** *071 †15
DAVIT, Flavia Evangelista. 1086 FRANKLIN ST, A-300-2 15905 #187-10-1996 L2005 **GS** *012
DE MATOS, Silverio Freire. 1020 FRANKLIN ST, MERCY HOSPITAL 15905 #770-01-1963 L1980 **GYN OBS** *020 †30
DEMAYO, William M. 360 GOUCHER ST, SUMMIT MED REHAB PC 15905 #035-01-1986 L1986 **PM SCI** *020 †60
DEPRIEST, Jack Legrand. 1086 FRANKLIN ST, CONEMOUGH MEMORIAL MEDICAL 15905 #045-01-1986 L1998 **CCM IM** *020 †20
DEVELIN, Edward Dunham. 318 GOUCHER ST 15905 #055-01-1987 L1990 **FM** *020 †18
DEVINENI, Rajsekhar. 1086 FRANKLIN ST 15905 #495-20-1973 L1987 **TS VS** *020
DHARBHAMULLA, Anuradha M. ■ 15905 #496-07-1984 L1999 **PTH PCP** *020 †50
DHARBHAMULLA, Venkata. 110 MAIN ST 15901 #495-45-1988 L1997 **PD** *020 †55
DHAWER, Virender Pal S. 321 MAIN ST, STE 4H 15901 #495-45-1966 L1972 **CD IM** *020
DOERING, Richard Albert. ■ 15904 #041-02-1972 L1991 **GS** *020 †85
DRENNEN-BRANT, Kristin. 348 BUDFIELD ST, ENT ASSOC OF JOHNSTOWN INC 15904 #051-04-1994 L1998 **OTO** *020 †45
DUKE, Bruce Edward, III. 1015 FRANKLIN ST, LEVEL C WESSEL BLDG 15905 #041-13-1968 L1969 **GS** *020 †85
DUKE, Darcy Nicole. 1015 FRANKLIN ST, LEVEL C 15905 #041-13-1997 L2002 **GS** *020 †85
DUMIRE, Russell Dale. 1086 FRANKLIN ST, TRAUMA SERVICES 15905 #023-12-1987 L1997 **GS** *020 †85
DVORCHAK, Matthew John. 1086 FRANKLIN ST 15905 #654-01-1983 L1984 **FM** *020 †18
ELIAS, Sahar. 1086 FRANKLIN ST, CONEMAUGH VALLEY MEM HOSP 15905 #875-02-1997 L2005 **FP** *012
ELLENBERGER, Thomas R, Jr. 321 MAIN ST, STE 5D 15901 #041-02-1975 L1976 **IM** *020 †20
ERGAS, Sanders Stuart. 119 WALNUT ST 15901 #041-02-1976 L1977 **EM FM** *020 †18
FEREZ, Marcio Cesar, Jr. 1086 FRANKLIN ST, CONEMAUGH MEMORIAL MED CEN 15905 #654-01-1995 L1998 *100
FIKRI, Erden. 353 MARKET ST 15901 #550-01-1970 L1973 **GS** *020 †85
FINK, Dorothy Alanna. ■ 15905 #010-02-2007 L2007 **MPD** *012
FINK, William Harmon. 1086 FRANKLIN ST, CONEMAUGH VALLEY MEM HOSP 15905 #748-11-1984 L1985 **IM** *020 †20
FLORIDA, Audie Cailing. 1086 FRANKLIN ST, CONEMAUGH VALLEY MEM HOSP 15905 #748-11-1995 L2004 **FP** *012
FRANCIS, Peter Rhys. ■ 15905 #946-01-1957 L1960 **P** *075
FREM, George Jos. 1086 FRANKLIN ST 15905 #422-01-1986 L1988 **IM NEP** *020 †20 ‡
FRITZ, William Thos. 1086 FRANKLIN ST 15905 #041-09-1986 L1988 **AN PME** *020 †05 ‡
FROESCHLE, Robert Eugene. ■ 15905 #005-12-1959 L1960 **GS FM** *071 †18
FUENTES, Maritess Garcia. OFFICE E3349, GRADUATE MED ED 15905 #748-01-1999 L2007 **FP** *012
FURNARY, James Saml. 1015 FRANKLIN ST 15905 #041-09-1957 L1958 **GS** *071 †85
GANNON, Reynaldo T. 1086 FRANKLIN ST 15905 #748-01-1963 L1970 **AN** *020 †05
GANNU, Rajya Lakshmi. 1086 FRANKLIN ST 15905 #495-57-1999 L2006 **IM** *100
GARBARINO, Andrew A, III. 110 MAIN ST 15901 #422-01-1981 L1983 **PD** *020 †55
GARGUILO, Gerard Anthony. 1111 FRANKLIN ST, STE 30 15905 #035-08-1976 L1996 **CRS** *020 †10,85
GATMAITAN, Patrick Tengco. ■ 15905 #748-01-1999 L2002 **GS** *100 †85
GAVIOLA, Raul Kanen. ■ 15904 #748-09-1974 L1983 **AN** *020
GELLA, Jyothi Kamal. 1086 FRANKLIN ST 15905 #495-70-1991 L1997 **IM** *020 †20
GIAMPOLO, Anthony John. 1086 FRANKLIN ST 15905 #041-12-1987 L1990 **N CN** *020 †75
GISBERT, Celine Regina Da. 1086 FRANKLIN ST, CONEMAUGH VALLEY MEM HOSP 15905 #748-01-1999 L2005 **FP** *012
GLOVER, Dennis Raymond. 318 GOUCHER ST 15905 #041-02-1994 L1996 **FM** *020 †18
GLYNN, Martin Jos. 1086 FRANKLIN ST, MEMORIAL MEDICAL CTR 15905 #023-07-1975 L1977 **RHU IM** *030 †20
GOLDBLATT, Curtis Samuel. 1086 FRANKLIN ST, CONEMAUGH HEALTH SYSTEM 15905 #041-12-1993 L1996 **PTH** *020 †50
GOLDBLATT, Sidney Allan. ■ 15905 #041-13-1959 L1973 **PTH FOP** *020 †50
GORCHESKY, Mark S. PO BOX 5608 15904 #305-01-1985 L1986 **AN** *020 †05
GORE, Alvin Igor. 1086 FRANKLIN ST, BLDG E 15905 #913-96-1995 L2000 **FM** *040 †18
GREEN, Richard Jos. 213 VINE ST 15901 #041-13-1982 L1983 **FM** *020 †18
GRESS, Gordon Albert. 905 MENOHER BLVD 15905 #041-12-1963 L1964 **IM CD** *071 †20
GRINBERG, Roman. 1086 FRANKLIN ST 15905 #913-15-1999 L2005 **GS** *012
GUNNLAUGSON, Brian Earl. 321 MAIN ST 15901 #063-01-1984 L1993 **ORS** *020 †40
GUPTA, Sandeep. 1086 FRANKLIN ST 15905 #495-55-2005 L2007 **IM** *012
GVOZDEN, Phillip. 128 FAIRFIELD AVE 15906 #654-01-1996 L1998 **FM** *020 ‡
GVOZDEN, Robert. 128 FAIRFIELD AVE 15906 #041-12-1956 L1957 **FM** *071
HAFFAR, Abdulkarim Y. 1086 FRANKLIN ST, STE 3301 15905 #038-44-1995 L1998 **CCM** *020 †20
HAMATY, Ronald Michael. 311 WARREN ST, BERKLEY HILLS PROF. BLDG. 15905 #041-12-1964 L1965 **OBG** *071 †30
HAMMUDI, Bassam M. 1086 FRANKLIN ST 15905 #528-01-1985 L2002 **AN** *020
HAQ, Bushra. 1086 FRANKLIN ST, CONEMAUGH VALLEY MEM HOSP 15905 #704-26-1998 L2002 **HO** *012 †20
HAQUE, Ikram Ul. 1111 FRANKLIN ST, STE 210 15905 #704-01-1955 L1987 **NS** *020 †25
HARBART, Allison Ford. 348 BUDFIELD ST 15904 #016-43-1999 L2003 **OTO** *020 †45
HARDY, Richard Irving. 250 WALNUT ST 15901 #041-13-1960 L1961 **GP OS** *075 ‡
HARMON, Claude Alexander. 337 SOMERSET ST 15901 #012-01-1979 L2006 **RO** *020 †20,80 ‡
HARRIGER, Clyde Everett. ■ 15904 #041-02-1954 L1955 **FM** *071 †18
HARTNETT, Robert Wayne. 213 VINE ST 15901 #041-12-1961 L1962 **GP** *071
HAUGER, William Doit. 941 PINEGROVE LN # A 15905 #024-05-1976 L1982 **IM CD** *020 †20
HAYEK, Naji Emile. 1111 FRANKLIN ST STE 130, PLASTIC SURGERY CLINIC 15905 #028-34-1994 L1998 **PS** *020
HE, Chun. 1086 FRANKLIN ST, CONEMAUGH VALLEY MEM HOSP 15905 #243-36-1985 L2004 **PTH** *012
HEGGERE, Manjunath S. ■ 15905 #495-99-1983 L1998 **PTH** *100 †50
HELLING, Thomas Sacher. 1086 FRANKLIN ST, CONEMAUGH MEMORIAL MEDICAL 15905 #019-02-1973 L2005 **GS** *020 †85
HENRIQUES, Errol Dudley. 1086 FRANKLIN ST 15905 #275-01-1951 L1965 **FM** *071
HERSHBERGER, David Glenn. 320 MAIN ST 15901 #041-02-1981 L1982 **EM FM** *020 †18,16
HILL, Edward Brown. 1111 FRANKLIN ST, STE 110 15905 #041-13-1960 L1961 **ORS** *020 †40 ‡
HOLLINGSWORTH, James H. 1086 FRANKLIN ST 15905 #654-01-1986 L1988 **IM** *071 †20
HONG, Yiyan. 321 MAIN ST, STE 5J 15901 #038-06-1988 L1993 **AN PME** *020 †05
HORNER, Barbara Ann. ■ 15905 #041-12-1947 L1948 **FM OS** *075
HOTT, Erin Marie. ■ 15909 #041-15-2004 L2004 **OBG** *012
HOU, Ping. 1086 FRANKLIN ST, CONEMAUGH VALLEY MEM HOSP 15905 #243-44-1990 L2005 **PTH** *012
HU, Jian. ■ 15904 #243-29-1984 L2007 **P** *100
HUANG, Jie. 1086 FRANKLIN ST 15905 #243-16-1987 L2004 **PTH** *012
HUNSBERGER, Charles L, Jr. ■ 15905 #041-13-1952 L1953 **OPH** *071 †35
HUSSAIN, K M Anwar. 1123 FRANKLIN ST 15905 #913-92-1982 L1999 **CD** *020 †20
HUSSIN, Jamal A. ■ 15904 #875-01-1983 L1994 **N** *020
HYMAN, Paul Rubin. ■ 15905 #016-02-1962 L1979 **N** *071 †75
ISKAPALLI, Srinivasa Redd. 1086 FRANKLIN ST, DEPT OF INTERNAL MED 15905 #495-62-2000 L2004 **IM** *020 †20
ISLAMOFF, Igor Ilia. ■ 15905 #041-09-1959 L1966 **GS** *071 †85
JANAKIRAMAN, V. 1086 FRANKLIN ST 15905 #495-61-1973 L1979 **CD IM** *020 †20
JARAMILLO, Victor. 1111 FRANKLIN ST, STE 120 15905 #264-03-1980 L2005 **N** *020
JOFRE, Maria Paula. 1086 FRANKLIN ST 15905 #132-09-2003 L2004 **IM** *100 †20
KAHANE, Gerardo Javier. 1086 FRANKLIN ST, DEPT OF GME 15905 #132-06-2001 L2005 **GS** *012
KANSAGRA, Jasmat N. 1086 FRANKLIN ST 15905 #495-23-1975 L1977 **AN** *020 †05
KASHURBA, Mary T. 727 GOUCHER ST 15905 #041-14-1982 L1985 **PM OM** *020 †60
KASTELIC, Richard Michael. 322 WARREN ST, STE 300 15905 #305-01-1984 L1986 **FM** *020 †18 ‡
KASWAN, Sumesh. 1086 FRANKLIN ST 15905 #495-55-2004 L2005 **GS** *012
KATTER, George Woodrow. ■ 15905 #010-02-1945 L1946 **IM CD** *071
KATZ, Ian. 2 CELESTE DR, WESTERN PA ORTHOPEDICS 15905 #067-01-1984 **ORS** *100 †40
KHALEGHI, Mir-Behnam. 315 LOCUST ST STE 6A 15901 #517-08-1995 L2003 **RHU** *020 †20
KHAN, Ahmad Haroon. 1086 FRANKLIN ST 15905 #704-01-1986 L1995 **IM** *020 †20
KHAN, Kamran Ur-Rahman. 1086 FRANKLIN ST, MEMORIAL MEDICAL CENTER 15905 #704-26-1999 L2002 **IM** *020 †20
KHOSLA, Anil K. ■ 15904 #495-45-1986 L1993 **IM** *100
KHOUZAMI, Adib Najib. 1111 FRANKLIN ST, STE 300 15905 #605-01-1989 L1998 **OBG MFM** *020 †30
KING, Andrew Jordan. 350 SOUTHMONT BLVD 15905 #027-01-1978 L1983 **D** *020 †15
KIVITZ, Alan Jan. 336 BLOOMFIELD ST 15904 #035-03-1977 L1982 **RHU** *020 †20
KOELLER, Royal Robt. 1086 FRANKLIN ST 15905 #047-06-1970 L1976 **FM FPG** *040 †18
KOH, Jeanmarie A. 1940 WILLIAM PENN AVE, PARKHILL MEDICAL CENTER 15909 #748-10-1987 L1993 **FM** *020 †18
KOLEILAT, Bassem Mohamad. 1086 FRANKLIN ST, CONEMAUGH VALLEY MEM HOSP 15905 #308-13-2001 L2004 **IM** *012
KOLLI, Geetha. 1086 FRANKLIN ST 15905 #495-65-2001 L2003 **IM** *100 †20
KONVOLINKA, Carl W, Jr. 1086 FRANKLIN ST 15905 #041-12-1960 L1967 **GS** *072 †85
KOUL, Hira Lal. 970 FRANKLIN ST, CAMBRIA GASTROENTEROLOGY I 15905 #495-51-1969 L1977 **GE** *020 †20
KRELL, Arthur Solomon. 1020 FRANKLIN ST STE 306 15905 #035-09-1978 L1982 **OPH** *020 †35
KRESAK, George Francis. 1086 FRANKLIN ST 15905 #016-43-1963 L1964 **GP** *020
KRISHNA, Nama Mohan. 1086 FRANKLIN ST, LAUREL GROUP ANESTHESIA 15905 #495-53-1975 L1999 **AN** *020 †05
KULKARNI, Pradeep K. 1111 FRANKLIN ST 15905 #496-38-1971 L1976 **OBG** *020 †30
KUPCHELLA, Regina Marie. 110 MAIN ST 15901 #010-02-1988 L1991 **PD** *020 †55
LAMBERT, Beth Yvonne. 241 SCHOOLHOUSE RD, LAUREL PEDIA ASSOCS 15904 #041-14-1985 L1992 **PD** *020 †55 ‡
LAWLESS, David Francis. 320 MAIN ST 15901 #041-09-1976 L1977 **FM** *020 †18
LOWRY, Don Allen. 2 CELESTE DR 15905 #018-03-1979 L1984 **ORS** *020 †40
MACKEY, Terryl Lynn. ■ 15905 #004-01-1979 L2001 **P** *020 †70,16
MAHARAJH, Balkissoon A. 1015 FRANKLIN ST, LEVEL A 15905 #308-10-1985 L1992 **IM IMG** *020 †20

MAJEED, Mahmud. ■ 15904 #704-02-1980 L1994 **IM** *020 †20
MAKHOUL, Nahla Saliem. 1086 FRANKLIN ST, CMMC/ DEPARTMENT OF MEDICI 15905 #875-02-1997 L2002 **IM** *100 †20
MALHIS, Safouh. L086 FRANKLIN STREET 15905 #875-02-1992 L1997 **PUD** *020 †20
MALHOTRA, Vijay K. 78 FAIRFIELD AVE 15906 #495-29-1969 L1977 **IM CD** *020 †20
MALICKI, Mark Mitchell. 322 WARREN ST, STE 300 15905 #041-02-1997 L1999 **FM** *020 †18
MARAVALLI, Camille Jos. 320 MAIN ST 15901 #041-13-1959 L1960 **OPH** *020 †35
MARI-MAYANS, Juan B. 320 MAIN ST, UPMC LEE REGIONAL HOSP 15901 #847-08-1975 L1978 **IM EM** *071
MASCIOTRA, Nicholas James. 321 MAIN ST STE 4C 15901 #041-12-1974 L1975 **OTO** *020 †45
MASSOUD, Samuel M. 1086 FRANKLIN ST 15905 #915-03-1979 L1995 **IM IMG** *020 †20
MASTRINE, Larry Richard. 1086 FRANKLIN ST 15905 #041-12-1979 L1980 **IM FM** *020
MATHUR, Dinesh Prasad. 970 FRANKLIN ST 15905 #495-30-1963 **IM END** *020 †20
MATHUR, Renee Jennifer. 913 MENOHER BLVD 15905 #024-01-1994 L1998 **D** *020 †15 ‡
MAVRIDIS, Savas. 1086 FRANKLIN ST STE A219 15905 #041-09-1995 L1997 **TS GS** *020 †85,90
MAZID, Mohammad Nurul. 1086 FRANKLIN ST, CONEMAUGH VALLEY MEM HOSP 15905 #160-08-1989 L2005 **FP** *012
MC GEE, Dale Leonard. 1086 FRANKLIN ST 15905 #041-12-1990 L1992 **FM** *020 †18
MC KENDREE, James Edward. 322 WARREN ST, STE 300 15905 #041-13-2000 L2001 **FM** *020 †18
MCKINNEY, Christian Mark. 1086 FRANKLIN ST 15905 #759-01-2002 L2005 **GS** *100
MCNIEL, Dawn Marie. 1086 FRANKLIN ST 15905 #305-01-2004 L2005 **AN** *012
MC NIESH, Lawrence M. 1086 FRANKLIN ST 15905 #010-02-1975 L1989 **DR** *020 †80
MC QUILLAN, Bernard P. ■ 15905 #010-02-1960 L1966 **IM CD** *020 ‡
MEENAN, Daniel R. 1086 FRANKLIN ST 15905 #041-09-1988 L1993 **AN** *020 †05
MICHAUD, Joseph Ellery. 1141 FRANKLIN ST 15905 #010-02-1946 L1953 **PD** *071 †55
MIHALY, Csaba. 804 SUNBERRY ST 15904 #473-03-1987 L2002 **GS** *030
MILLER, Stephen Lee. 1086 FRANKLIN ST, BLDG E5 15905 #005-19-1986 L1992 **GS** *020 †85
MILLWARD, James Walter. 214 COLLEGE PARK PLZ 15904 #041-12-1977 L1978 **P** *020 †75 ‡
MITAL, Mohan Swarup. 1123 FRANKLIN ST, 1123 FRANKLIN STREET 15905 #495-05-1963 L1972 **CD IM** *020 †20
MITAL, Nirmal Gupta. 1086 FRANKLIN ST, CAMBRIA SOMERSET RAD 15905 #496-07-1961 L1971 **DR** *020 †80
MITTAL, Neelum. ■ 15904 #041-15-2007 L2007 **TY** *012
MITTAL, Vimal. ■ 15904 #495-30-1979 L1983 **PTH** *020 †50
MODI, Sunil Jashvantlal. ■ 15905 #495-22-2002 L2007 **FP** *012
MOGHARBEL, Asma Mohahmad. 1086 FRANKLIN ST, MEMORIAL MEDICAL CTR 15905 #704-16-1991 L2000 *100
MORGAN, Owen King. 422 MAIN ST 15901 #041-12-1958 L1959 **OPH** *071 †35
MOSES, James Michael. 2 CELESTE DR 15905 #018-03-1970 L1975 **ORS OSM** *020 †40
MOSZKOWICZ, Arie Israel. OFFICE E3349, GRADUATE MED ED 15905 #305-01-2007 L2007 **TY** *012
MOWLA, Muhammad Saiful. OFFICE E3349, GRADUATE MED ED 15905 #704-16-1998 L2007 **FP** *012
MRKICH, Robert. 1397 EISENHOWER BLVD, STE 303 15904 #010-01-1963 L1964 **FM** *020 †18
MUCCIOLA, Robert Nicholas. 1481 EISENHOWER BLVD, STE B 15904 #051-07-1982 L1985 **OBG** *020 †30
MUGERWA, Jude Arnold. 321 MAIN ST, STE 5H 15901 #905-01-1997 L2004 **CD** *020 †20 ‡
MURALIDHARAN, Bhaskaran. 353 MARKET ST STE 109 15901 #495-04-1969 L1975 **GS** *020 †85
MURTHA, Kevin Thos. 1020 FRANKLIN ST, CHI ADMINSTRATION 15905 #041-12-1992 L1994 **FM** *020 †18
MUSSIO, John August. 1111 FRANKLIN ST STE 103 15905 #035-09-1963 L1967 **NS** *071 †25
NADEEM, Rashid. 970 FRANKLIN ST 15905 #704-02-1992 L2002 **PCC** *020 †20
NAIR, Vinay Vasudevan. 1086 FRANKLIN ST, CONEMAUGH VALLEY MEM HOSP 15905 #495-37-2001 L2004 **IM** *012
NANDAGOPAL, Udhay Kumar. 1086 FRANKLIN ST, CONEMAUGH VALLEY MEM HOSP 15905 #496-21-2002 L2004 **IM** *020 †20
NARAHARI, Premnath. 350 SOUTHMONT BLVD, C/O GASTROINTESTINAL CON I 15905 #495-04-1980 L1988 **IM GE** *020 †20
NASSR, Kussay. 1450 SCALP AVE, STE 2100 15904 #875-01-1993 L2001 **N PME** *020 †75
NATHANIEL, Cyril. 1015 FRANKLIN ST, FL D 15905 #495-29-1983 L1996 **CD** *020 †20
NELSON, Robert David. 1086 FRANKLIN ST 15905 #028-03-1967 L1984 **PM** *020 †60
NEVARRE, Daniel Raymond. 415 NAPOLEON PL 15901 #041-07-1994 L1996 **PS** *020 †65
NGINYO, Josphat Allan. 135 OSBORNE ST 15905 #036-05-1977 L1979 **OBG** *020 †30
NOBILETI, John B. ■ 15905 #035-08-1989 L1998 **CLP BBK** *020 †50
NUNE, Udayasree. 1086 FRANKLIN ST 15905 #495-62-1980 L2003 **FM** *020 †18 ‡
O'CONNOR, Leo Edward. 1748 LYTER DR 15905 #041-13-1963 L1964 **FM GP** *020
OLALERE, Adewale A. 970 FRANKLIN ST 15905 #690-01-1991 L2002 **PUD** *020 †20
OPILA, Loretta Ann. 320 MAIN ST 15901 #308-03-1982 L1983 **EM** *020 †20
OSCHWALD, Charles Joseph. 1123 FRANKLIN ST 15905 #308-03-1981 L1983 **CD OS** *020 †20
OVEISI, Shahin. 1086 FRANKLIN ST 15905 #517-01-1999 L2005 **FP** *012
PADHIAR, Ashok Vishram. 1086 FRANKLIN ST, STE M4000 15905 #577-01-1979 L2006 **AN** *020 †05
PAI, Narendra Mangalore. 1086 FRANKLIN ST, DEPT OF ANESTHESIA 15905 #495-37-1978 L1990 **AN** *030 †05
PANEK, Bernard Stephen. 1086 FRANKLIN ST 15905 #041-13-1967 L1968 **FM** *020 †18
PAREDES, Jose Leonel. ■ 15905 #429-02-2001 L2007 **GS** *012
PASCUA, Febenido Villon. 320 MAIN ST 15901 #748-11-1972 L1977 **EM PTH** *020 †16
PATEL, Jagdishchandra D. 905 MENOHER BLVD 15905 #495-05-1966 L1981 **IM** *020 †20
PATEL, Priya Rushang. 1086 FRANKLIN ST, DEPT OF GME 15905 #495-23-2002 L2006 **IM** *012
PATEL, Tejaskumar Babulal. 1086 FRANKLIN ST, CONEMAUCH MEMORIAL MEDICAL 15905 #495-22-1993 L2006 **P** *020 †75
PATIL, Ritesh. 1086 FRANKLIN ST 15905 #495-98-2004 L2006 **IM** *012
PATIL, Trupti. 1086 FRANKLIN ST 15905 #495-98-2004 L2006 **IM** *012
PATIL, Vishwas Bapurao. OFFICE E3349, GRADUATE MED ED 15905 #496-31-1999 L2007 **GS** *012
PATTERSON, Michael David. 1086 FRANKLIN ST 15905 #654-01-2004 L2005 **PM** *012
PECHITTY, Smita Sagar. 1086 FRANKLIN ST 15905 #495-21-2002 L2005 **IM** *012
PENG PHD, Hairong. 1086 FRANKLIN ST 15905 #243-74-1982 L2004 **AN** *012
PHILLIPS, Jane G. 1450 SCALP AVE, MEDWELL EAST HILLS OFFICE 15904 #041-07-1965 L1966 **PM** *071 †60
PICKERILL, Robert Glenn. 1086 FRANKLIN ST 15905 #041-12-1976 L1977 **PUD IM** *020 †20
PLANK, Sharon Marie. 1086 FRANKLIN ST 15905 #654-01-1986 L1990 **FM** *020 †18
PO, Ricardo Patton Uy. OFFICE E3349, GRADUATE MED ED 15905 #748-01-1998 L2007 **GS** *012
POLITICO, Jovencio L. ■ 15901 #748-01-1963 L1973 **AN** *020 †05
POTE, Harry Harvey, Jr. 353 MARKET ST STE 106, JOHNSTOWN INTERNISTS 15901 #041-13-1970 L1972 **IM NEP** *020 †20
POTHINENI, Aravind. OFFICE E3349, GRADUATE MED ED 15905 #495-11-2001 L2007 **IM** *012
POTHURAJU, Aruna Sree. 1086 FRANKLIN ST, CONEMAUGH VALLEY MEM HOSP 15905 #495-50-1995 L2004 **FM** *020 †18
POTHURAJU, Krishna Rao Ve. 1086 FRANKLIN ST, DEPT OF GME 15905 #495-58-1994 L2006 **FP** *012
PRASAD, Shailendra A. 1086 FRANKLIN ST, BLDG 4 15905 #495-34-1983 L1996 **IM** *100 †20
PRICE, Richard Elmer. ■ 15904 #041-12-1960 L1961 **OM IM** *071
PRIMAK, Anatoly N. ■ 15902 #913-06-1957 L1981 **OBG GP** *020
PRUCHNIC, William Foster. 1020 FRANKLIN ST # 202 15905 #041-14-1971 L1975 **IM END** *020 †20
PUEBLITZ, George. 891 MENOHER BLVD 15905 #649-01-1974 L1983 **EM** *020
PUEBLITZ, Manuel. ■ 15905 #649-01-1947 L1986 **P** *071
PUSAPATI, Satyanarayana R. OFFICE E3349, GRADUATE MED ED 15905 #495-11-2003 L2007 **IM** *012
QIAN, Lian. ■ 15905 #243-54-1984 L2006 **PTH** *062 †50
QURESHI, Muhammad Rehan. 1086 FRANKLIN ST, DEPT OF GME 15905 #704-16-2000 L2006 **IM** *012
RAHHAL, Suhail. 1086 FRANKLIN ST, CONEMAUGH MEMORIAL CENTER 15905 #875-01-1988 L2002 **IM** *020 †20
RAPURI, Bhargav Srinivas. 1086 FRANKLIN ST 15905 #495-50-1993 **FP** *012
RATCHFORD, Mark J. 1086 FRANKLIN ST 15905 #041-78-1999, ▲ L2001 **FM** *020 †18
RATH, Pamela Rae. 969 EISENHOWER BLVD 15904 #035-06-1997 L2006 **OPH** *020 †35
RHOADS, Harry M. ■ 15902 #041-09-1949 L1950 **GP** *071
RICHEY, James Elden. 350 SOUTHMONT BLVD 15905 #041-12-1972 L1975 **GE** *071 †20
RIDELLA, Peter James. 1111 FRANKLIN ST, STE 140 15905 #041-12-1975 L1977 **ORS OSS** *020 †40
RINGLER, Harold L, Jr. 1086 FRANKLIN ST, DEPARTMENT OF RADIOLOGY 15905 #005-02-1962 L1982 **R OS** *020 †80
RIZKALLA, Sameh M. 1020 FRANKLIN ST, CONEMAUGH HEALTH INITIATIV 15905 #915-05-1984 L2002 **PM** *020 †60
RIZKALLA, Waheeb M M. 1086 FRANKLIN ST, CONEMAUGH MEM HOSP LAB MED 15905 #915-04-1968 L1986 **PTH ATP** *062 †50
RIZVI, Amir Ali. ■ 15905 #704-08-1991 L1999 **IM** *100 †20
RODRIGUEZ-FEO, Raul. 132 WALNUT ST 15901 #649-01-1978 L1988 **P** *020 ‡
ROGERSON, David R. 348 BUDFIELD ST 15904 #041-07-1974 L1975 **OTO HNS** *020 †45
ROLLINS, Paul Anthony. 315 LOCUST ST, STE 2A 15901 #035-08-1989 L1995 **PS** *020 †85,65
ROSENBERG, Lawrence Seth. 1086 FRANKLIN ST 15905 #035-19-1974 L1975 **PD** *020 †55
ROSENBLATT, Stanley Geo. 1086 FRANKLIN ST, CAMBRIA SOMERSET - RADIOLO 15905 #041-02-1965 L1971 **DR NM** *020 †80
RUDRANGI, Rajani. OFFICE E3349, GRADUATE MED ED 15905 #495-21-2004 L2007 **IM** *012
RUNDORFF, Robert Link. 1020 FRANKLIN ST 15905 #026-04-1984 L1987 **PM** *020 †60
RUSH, Calvin Chas. ■ 15905 #041-12-1944 L1945 **OPH OTO** *071 †35
SABOURI, Abdolnabi Sassan. 1086 FRANKLIN ST, DEPT OF GME 15905 #517-08-1993 L2006 **AN** *012
SALAS, Marty Maria. 1086 FRANKLIN ST 15905 #038-40-1980 L1982 **VS** *020 †85
SALEM, Khaled Yousef. 1086 FRANKLIN ST, CONEMAUGH MEMORIAL MED CTR 15905 #915-04-1989 L1997 **IM** *020 †20
SAMAL, Lipika. ■ 15904 #038-06-2004 L2007 **IM** *100 †20
SANTA CRUZ CHAVEZ, Rosalin. 1086 FRANKLIN ST 15905 #737-06-2002 L2004 **DR** *012
SAVIT, Jan Myron. 422 MAIN ST, STE 202 15901 #035-08-1976 L1993 **N** *020 †75
SBEITAN, Ibrahim H. 1020 FRANKLIN ST 15905 #575-01-1990 L1996 **HEM** *020 †20
SCHAEFER, Thomas J. 1020 FRANKLIN ST 15905 #010-02-1952 L1958 **GS** *071 †85
SCHENFELD, Louis Alan. 1111 FRANKLIN ST 15905 #165-04-1977 L1982 **ID IM** *020 †20
SCUDERI, Anthony Joseph. 1450 SCALP AVE STE 1 15904 #035-20-1986 L1994 **RNR NM** *020 †28,80
SEEBER, John Jos, Jr. 320 MAIN ST 15901 #041-13-1968 L1969 **PM** *020 †60
SEWAK, Michael Edward. 268 MAIN ST 15909 #041-12-1958 L1959 **GP** *071
SHAH, Suryakant M. 1086 FRANKLIN ST, FAMILY MEDICAL CENTER 15905 #495-01-1957 L1982 **FM FPG** *040 †18
SHENOUDA, Maged Asaad. 1086 FRANKLIN ST 15905 #915-07-1986 L2000 **PTH** *020 †50
SHUE, Gongliang. 195 STARDUST DR, LEE HOSPITAL 15904 #243-45-1982 L1999 **AN** *020 †05
SI, Qiusheng. 1086 FRANKLIN ST, CONEMAUGH VALLEY MEM HOSP 15905 #243-18-1986 L2005 **PTH** *012
SIDDAMREDDY, Suman. OFFICE E3349, GRADUATE MED ED 15905 #495-62-2004 L2007 **IM** *012
SIDDIQI, Mohammed Fazil. 1086 FRANKLIN ST 15905 #915-09-1999 L2004 **IM** *012
SIDDIQUI, Yasmin. 1086 FRANKLIN ST 15905 #704-09-1997 **FP** *012
SINGERMAN, Burton. 1086 FRANKLIN ST 15905 #024-01-1973 L1994 **P PHP** *020 †75
SIRSIKAR, Shriram Prabhak. 1086 FRANKLIN ST 15905 #495-37-1995 L2001 **IM** *020
SIVULICH, Michael Jos. ■ 15905 #041-09-1946 L1947 **OPH** *071 †35
SMEAL, William E. 321 MAIN ST 15901 #041-13-1982 L1983 **CD** *020 †20
SNITZER, Lewis Stephen. 2253 SPEAR AVE 15905 #041-07-1973 L1988 **NS** *071 †25
SOBIESKI, Joseph Thos. ■ 15904 #041-12-1975 L1976 **OM IM** *030 †20
SOI, Anuradha. 350 BUDFIELD ST STE A 15904 #496-07-1983 L1992 **PTH** *020 †50
SOI, Sunil K. 350 BUDFIELD ST, # A 15904 #495-08-1983 L1986 **CCM IM** *020 †20
SPENCER, Jeanne Putinas. 1086 FRANKLIN ST, CONEMAUGH VALLEY MEM HOSP 15905 #035-45-1990 L1992 **FM** *040 †18
SRACIC, Michael Kiel. ■ 15904 #023-12-2008 *012
STEFANIK, David Francis. 337 SOMERSET ST 15901 #041-12-1977 L1978 **RO** *020 †80
STEIN, Alan Harvey. 1450 SCALP AVE STE 106 15904 #041-13-1976 L1977 **OM EM** *020 †18,16,70
STEINMAN, Mark Edward. 1086 FRANKLIN ST, DEPT OF EMERGENCY MEDICINE 15905 #041-07-1976 L1984 **GP FM** *030 †16
STENBERG, Robert Gregory. 1123 FRANKLIN ST 15905 #054-04-1982 L1990 **CD IM** *020 †20
STERLIN, Anne-Marie. 1111 FRANKLIN ST, STE 300 15905 #025-01-1994 L2000 **OBG** *020 †30
STEWART, James Andrew. 1086 FRANKLIN ST 15905 #041-09-1983 L1984 **EM** *020 †18
STINE, Karl Frederic. 1086 FRANKLIN ST 15905 #422-01-1983 L1984 **FM PD** *020
STOTLER, Brie Alexandra. ■ 15904 #041-02-2005 L2006 **PTH** *012
STOTLER, Charles Wilbur. 334 BLOOMFIELD ST 15904 #041-02-1974 L1975 **FM** *020 †18
STOVER, Donald Lee. ■ 15904 #041-12-1958 L1959 **EM** *071
STROTHER, George Weldon. 321 MAIN ST, STE 5F 15901 #010-01-1965 L1974 **PUD** *071 †20
STRUNK, Thomas John. ■ 15905 #056-06-1947 L1948 **U** *072 †95

SURAPANENI, Prathima. 404 SUSQUEHANNA ST 15905 #495-50-1995 L2005 **FP** *012
SWANSIGER, Robert John. 1511 SCALP AVE 15904 #041-12-1972 L1973 **FM** *020 †18
SWIHART, Andrew Reed. 1086 FRANKLIN ST, MEDICAL C 15905 #041-12-2006 L2007 **TY** *012
TABIB, Ralph. 1145 1/2 FRANKLIN ST 15905 #875-02-1981 L1996 **RHU** *020 †20
TAN, Francis Richard. 1086 FRANKLIN ST, DEPT OF GME 15905 #748-10-2006 L2006 **GS** *012
TAN, Ramon Ng. ■ 15904 #748-01-1964 L1974 AN *071 †05
TEPPER, Giselly. 1743 GOUCHER ST 15905 #737-01-1991 L1996 **IM** *020 †20
TEWARI, Arpana Gopal. 1086 FRANKLIN ST, DEPT OF GME 15905 #496-17-1991 L2005 **FP** *012
THOMAS, Gary Stephen. 338 BLOOMFIELD ST STE 101 15904 #041-77-1988, ▲ L1989 **FM** *020 †18
THOMAS, Nathan Owen. 1086 FRANKLIN ST 15905 #041-02-1970 L1971 **FM IMG** *020 †18
TOMHAVE, Robert Harold. 132 WALNUT ST 15901 #018-03-1970 L1974 **OBG** *071 †30
TORP, Richard Prescott. ■ 15905 #041-13-1958 L1980 **OS ORS** *071 †40
TURCO, Phillip Jos. 1086 FRANKLIN ST 15905 #561-15-1983 L1984 **IM** *020 †20
UNTRACHT, Steven Harris. 1086 FRANKLIN ST 15905 #016-02-1981 L1994 **GS AS** *020 †85
VENA, Vincent Eugene. 2 CELESTE DR 15905 #041-01-1993 L1997 **ORS** *020 †40
VITTONE, Daniel Christian. 1086 FRANKLIN ST 15905 #041-12-1987 L1989 **OPH** *020 †35
VOLKAR, Judith Keene. 1481 EISENHOWER BLVD 15904 #041-07-1983 L1984 **OBG** *020 †30
VOON, Nyuk Yean. 1086 FRANKLIN ST 15905 #654-01-1988 L1991 **IM** *100
VOYTKO, Richard Edwin. 1020 FRANKLIN ST 15905 #041-12-1961 L1962 **GP EM** *071
WAHL, Terry Edward. 119 WALNUT ST, LEE HOSPITAL EMERGENCY DEP 15901 #041-13-1973 L1988 **EM IM** *020 †20,16
WALL, Rod Alan. 1123 FRANKLIN ST 15905 #041-14-1972 L1975 **IM** *020 †20
WARIKOO, Nanna. 1086 FRANKLIN ST, BLDG E FLR 3 15905 #495-51-1966 L1973 **IM** *020 †20 ‡
WARSHEL, Kelly Dick. 1111 FRANKLIN ST, STE 120 15905 #041-14-1994 L1996 **IM** *020 †20
WEHNER, Daniel Robt. 1086 FRANKLIN ST, CONEMAUGH MMC 15905 #041-02-1981 L2000 **EM** *020 †16
WEHR, Matthew David. 1086 FRANKLIN ST 15905 #041-14-1997 L1999 **FM** *020 †18
WEYGANDT, Paul Luther, Jr. 1086 FRANKLIN ST 15905 #038-41-1979 L1982 **MDM LM** *030 †40
WIECZOREK, Brian Jude. 1086 FRANKLIN ST 15905 #041-14-1996 L1998 **EM** *020 †16
WIECZOREK, Joseph Eric. 320 MAIN ST 15901 #041-13-1981 L1982 **FM FPG** *020 †18
WIN, Khaing Soe. 1086 FRANKLIN ST, DEPT OF GME 15905 #209-01-1998 L2006 **PTH** *012
WINT, Samuel James. 401 BROAD ST 15906 #041-12-1971 L1972 **IMG FM** *020 †18
WIRFEL, Lisa Marie. 1430 SCALP AVE STE 4 15904 #041-09-1998 L2000 **FM** *020 †18
WOLFE, Judith Ann. 1020 FRANKLIN ST, STE 301 15905 #041-07-1975 L1976 **OTO A** *020 †45
WOLFF, Teresa Ann. 1086 FRANKLIN ST 15905 #649-60-2000 L2001 **FM** *020 †18
WOOLLEY, Paul Vincent, III. 88 OSBORNE ST 15905 #025-01-1969 L1992 **ON HEM** *050 †20
WYNERT, William Rodger. 337 SOMERSET ST 15901 #041-13-1970 L1971 **ON HEM** *020 †20
YANG, Huaitao. OFFICE E3349, GRADUATE MED ED 15905 #243-67-1987 L2007 **PTH** *012
YARDLEY, Trevor Wayne. 204 COLLEGE PARK PLZ 15904 #065-01-1974 L1986 **ORS** *020 †40
YARLAGADDA, Sandeep. 1086 FRANKLIN ST 15905 #496-33-2004 L2006 **IM** *012
YATES, William Albert. ■ 15905 #065-05-1954 L1957 **OM** *030 †85
YERGER, John Floyd. 1086 FRANKLIN ST 15905 #041-13-1960 L1961 **PTH** *020 †50
YODER, Delbert Lynn. 1111 FRANKLIN ST 15905 #041-12-1979 L1980 **OBG** *020 †30
ZABAT, Enrico A. ■ 15904 #748-07-1963 L1985 **GP** *020
ZAMAN, S.M. Hasanuz. 1086 FRANKLIN ST, DEPT OF GME 15905 #160-09-1999 L2006 **FP** *012
ZEIDAN, Boutros Moussa. 315 LOCUST ST, STE 5B 15901 #875-01-1991 L1998 **PUD** *020 †20
ZHANG, Shehui. 1086 FRANKLIN ST 15905 #243-38-1983 L2001 **AN** *020 †05 ‡
ZITNAY, Kevin Michael. 1111 FRANKLIN ST, STE 210 15905 #025-01-1991 L2004 **NS** *020 †25

JONES MILLS — WESTMORELAND

VITTONE, Christian M. HC 63, RT 711 S 15646 #041-12-1994 L1997 **FM** *020 †18 ‡

JONESTOWN — LEBANON

HAGGARD, Robert Anthony. 100 E QUEEN ST, FREDERICKSBURG COMMUNITY 17038 #023-12-1983 L1993 **FM** *020 †18
LOVETT, William Jeffrey. 100 E QUEEN ST, FREDERICKSBURG COMMUNITY 17038 #041-02-1980 L1981 **FM** *020 †18
MARGUT, Shelby Lee. 100 E QUEEN ST, FREDERICKSBURG COMMUNITY 17038 #041-02-2004 L2004 **FM** *020 †18
MILLER, Doreen Edith. 100 E QUEEN ST, JONESTOWN HEALTH CENTER 17038 #016-11-1984 L1987 **FM** *020
MUNDA, Patricia Juma. 100 E QUEEN ST, FREDERICKSBURG COMMUNITY 17038 #577-01-1990 L1999 **FM** *020 †18
SEARS, Carol Dianne. 100 E QUEEN ST, FREDERICKSBURG COMMUNITY 17038 #041-12-1981 L1983 **FM** *020 †18
WEANER, Pamela A. 100 E QUEEN ST, JONESTOWN HEALTH CENTER 17038 #035-15-1993 L1996 **FM** *020 †18

JULIAN — CENTRE

DE HART, Scott Michael. 350 MILES HOLLOW RD 16844 #041-02-1974 L1975 **EM** *020 †16

KANE — MCKEAN

ABBASSI, Shahram. ■ 16735 #305-01-1985 L1991 **PME** *020 †20,05
BLEDAY, Raymond M. 4355 ROUTE 6, KCH SPECIATY CLINIC BLGD 16735 #032-01-1993 L1995 **ORS OSM** *020 †40
CZAPLICKI-MARGIOTTI, M. 4372 ROUTE 6 16735 #033-05-1974 L2002 **ORS** *020 †40
HIPOLITO, Emmanuel F, Jr. PO BOX 399, 38 THOMPSON PARK 16735 #748-10-1972 L1977 **IM NEP** *020 ‡
IBANEZ, Melchisedec C. 100 SPRUCE AVE 16735 #748-07-1954 L1963 **GS AS** *071 †85
LANGILLE, Kenneth Ralph. 4372 ROUTE 6 16735 #064-01-1975 L1995 **FM** *020
LE FEBVRE, Flordeliza B D. 4372 ROUTE 6, KANE COMMUNITY HOSPITAL 16735 #748-01-1966 L1971 **AN ADM** *020
OLSON, Dennis Albert. ■ 16735 #041-13-1980 L1981 **FM** *020 †18
PUNZALAN, Catalino Gomez. 2 THOMPSON PARK 16735 #748-08-1972 L1978 **OBG** *020
RETTGER, Linda D. 4372 ROUTE 6 16735 #005-12-1974 L1977 **FM OS** *020 †18
SICHER, Bruno Pio. ■ 16735 #041-09-1957 L1958 **FM** *071 †18

SIMON, Renato Francisco. 2 THOMPSON PARK, SUMMIT PARK MED CTR 16735 #748-08-1970 L2003 **GS** *020 †85
SUDDLE, Mohammad Nawaz. 2 THOMPSON PARK 16735 #704-01-1978 L1999 **IM** *020 †20

KENNETT SQUARE — CHESTER

ALEXANDER, George L. ■ 19348 #067-01-1952 L1965 **P PYA** *071 †75
ANDERSEN, Martin Gregor. ■ 19348 #035-09-1956 L1961 **NS** *072 †25
ARVANITIS, Lisa Ann. ■ 19348 #054-04-1983 L1990 **N P** *020 †75
ASHTON, Wm Aloysius, Jr. ■ 19348 #051-01-1977 L1987 **AN IM** *020 †20,05
ATKINS, William Robt. 404 MCFARLAN RD 19348 #041-01-1978 L1980 **OBG** *020 †30
BEEREPOOT, Lucas Jurgen. PO BOX 1278 19348 #660-01-1998 L2007 **CN** *100
BERNETT, Gary Bruce. 101 E STATE ST 19348 #041-02-1976 L1977 **IM IMG** *020 †20
BIGLER, Brian Charles. 404 MCFARLAN RD 19348 #041-02-2001 L2001 **OPH** *020 †35
BIRZESCU, Maria Mihaela. ■ 19348 #041-13-2004 L2004 **AN** *012
BOYEK, Timothy John. 404 MCFARLAN RD 19348 #041-09-1982 L1983 **IC CD** *020 †20
BROOKS, Joae Graham. ■ 19348 #035-45-1954 L1955 **P CHP** *072 †75
BROWN, Angela Davis. 404 MCFARLAN RD, STE 101 19348 #041-13-1997 L2000 **FM** *020 †18
CASS, Paul Taylor. 101 E STATE ST 19348 #041-09-1971 L1972 **IM IMG** *020 †20
CHAN, Grace Jeanyee. ■ 19348 #024-01-2007 L2007 **PD** *012
COHEN, Ronald Aaron. ■ 19348 #041-02-1960 L1962 **IM** *071
D'ORAZIO, Nicholas Jos. 747 W CYPRESS ST 19348 #041-13-1978 L1979 **GP** *020 †75
DROESCHER, John Jos, Jr. ■ 19348 #010-01-1960 L1963 **IM AM** *071 †70
ERB, Alice Robinson. KENDAL 220 19348 #041-01-1940 L1941 **OS** *071
FABULIAN, Peter. 115 MARSHALL ST 19348 #041-77-1991, ▲ L1992 **FM** *071
FALCONE, Rita Ann. 404 MCFARLAN RD 19348 #041-07-1989 L2002 **CD** *020 †20
GAMBHIR, Anshul Vibhu. 404 MCFARLAN RD 19348 #041-13-1998 L2000 **FM** *020 †18
GOLD, Morrie Geo. 404 MCFARLAN RD 19348 #035-19-1973 L1974 **OBG** *020 †30
GREGORY, Elizabeth A. ■ 19348 #024-05-1942 **PD PDA** *071 †55
GROMADZKI, Louis Edmund. ■ 19348 #041-01-1958 L1959 **N** *071 †75
HALE, Mary Lou Hoover. ■ 19348 #051-04-1954 L1954 **P** *071 †75
HARLER, Marybeth. ■ 19348 #055-02-1993 L1993 **GS** *100
HARVIE, Fred Herbert. ■ 19348 #041-05-1930 L1940 **RD** *071
HNELESKI, Ignatius S, III. 404 MCFARLAN RD 19348 #041-02-1992 L1995 **OPH** *020 †35 ‡
HOOBLER, James Linford. 404 MCFARLAN RD 19348 #041-12-1955 L1956 **GP** *071
HUI, Richard Chiushek. 404 MCFARLAN RD 19348 #024-07-1990 L2004 **CD** *020 †20
JENKINS, Jule, Jr. 747 W CYPRESS ST, NEW GARDEN PLAZA 19348 #033-06-1980 L1988 **OM IM** *020
JOHNSON, Cheryl Ann. 404 MCFARLAN RD, STE 1 19348 #041-07-1989 L1992 **HEM** *020 †20
JUNKER, Margaret E Miller. ■ 19348 #035-01-1947 L1973 **FM** *071
KAUL, Venita. 891 E BALTIMORE PIKE, KIDS FIRST-KENNETT SQUARAE 19348 #012-01-1993 L1998 **PD** *020 †20,55
KENT, Richard Bernard. 404 MCFARLAN RD 19348 #041-01-1959 L1960 **OPH** *072 †35
KHWAJA, Razaullah A. 311 MARLBORO RD 19348 #917-06-1976 L1981 **HS** *020 †85
KINKAID, Stanley Gordon. 701 E BALTIMORE PIKE STE C2 19348 #654-01-1984 L1986 **IM** *020 †20
KNOWLES, Robert Curtis. ■ 19348 #038-06-1964 L1971 **CLP** *071
KUREY, Pamela Henrich. 404 MCFARLAN RD 19348 #041-09-1993 L1995 **OBG** *020 †30
LEVINTHAL, Jeana Davison. ■ 19348 #036-07-1950 L1952 **PD** *071 †55
LINDMAYER, Katalin Komlos. ■ 19348 #913-70-1990 *100
LU, Calvin. 404 MCFARLAN RD, STE 1 19348 #023-07-1978 L1982 **HO HEM** *020 †20
LUGINBUHL, William Emil. 404 MCFARLAN RD, STE 1 19348 #050-02-1987 L1990 **HO** *020 †20
MANCILLA, Sandra. 830 W CYPRESS ST 19348 #649-14-1998 L2007 **FM** *020 †18
MARSH, Carol Lynn. 630 COPE RD 19348 #041-09-1977 L1978 **PD** *020 †55
MAURIELLO, Alfred J, II. 402 MCFARLAN RD, STE 203 19348 #041-02-1969 L1970 **OTO FPS** *020 †45
MC KINSTRY, Robert B. ■ 19348 #041-09-1952 L1953 **FM** *071
MC LAUGHLIN, Raymond S. 701 E BALTIMORE PIKE STE D, LONGWOOD CORPORATE CENTER 19348 #041-02-1980 L1986 **FM** *020 †18 ‡
MEYERS, Faye Portland. ■ 19348 #056-06-1948 L2002 **FM** *020 †18
MOUNTS, Barbara Mc Murry. ■ 19348 #016-11-1942 L1952 **P** *071
MOUTSATSOS, George D. 404 MCFARLAN RD 19348 #041-02-1993 L1999 **CD** *020 †20
NEITHARDT, Gregg Lawrence. 404 MCFARLAN RD 19348 #010-02-1996 L2005 **CD** *020 †20
OCHS, Matthew Edward. 687 UNIONVILLE RD 19348 #041-13-1973 L1998 **IMG IM** *020 †20
PALMER, Clarkson Taylor. ■ 19348 #041-01-1955 L1959 **PHP** *071 †70
PATTERSON, James Mc Kee. 400 MCFARLAN RD, STE 1 19348 #051-07-1994 L1996 **HO** *020 †20
PHELPS, Paulding. ■ 19348 #035-01-1960 L1961 **RHU** *071 †20
PICARIELLO, Michael A. 402 MCFARLAN RD, STE 203 19348 #041-07-1986 L1987 **OTO HNS** *020 †45
QURAISHI, Uzma Anum. 701 E BALTIMORE PIKE STE C 19348 #704-01-1993 L2004 **IM** *020
RABIN, Sidney C. 404 MCFARLAN RD 19348 #041-13-1951 L1952 **GYN OBS** *071 †30
RIPPMANN, Ernst Theodor. ■ 19348 #869-07-1953 L1955 **OBG OS** *020
SANDOR, Victor A. ■ 19348 #067-01-1990 L2000 **IM** *050 †20
SCHAEFFER, Matthew Ward. 404 MCFARLAN RD, CHESTER CTY ORTHOPAEDICS 19348 #041-13-1998 L2004 **PM** *020 †60
SIMMONS, Cheston. 404 MCFARLAN RD, CHESTER CTY ORTHOPAEDICS 19348 #041-02-1987 L1988 **ORS OSM** *020 †40
SIMONSON, Steven Glen. ■ 19348 #056-06-1986 L1989 **EM CCM** *020 †20
SMITH, Joseph Lorenzo, II. 402 MCFARLAN RD, STE 203 19348 #041-02-2001 L2006 **OTO** *020 †45
SOLANET, Pedro Maria. 830 W CYPRESS ST 19348 #132-01-1961 L1995 **FM IM** *020 †18
SORARUF, Louis Peter. 687 UNIONVILLE RD 19348 #041-02-1974 L1976 **FM FPG** *020 †18 ‡
TOWSEN, Adrienne Jeannine. 404 MCFARLAN RD, CHESTER CTY ORTHOPAEDICS 19348 #041-07-1998 L2004 **ORS** *100 †40
VAGANOS, Nicholas A. 404 MCFARLAN RD 19348 #041-09-1978 L1979 **CD IM** *020 †20 ‡
WAHL, Jeffrey M. 404 MCFARLAN RD 19348 #041-09-1984 L1986 **CD** *020 †20
WARD, Maurice John, Jr. 404 MCFARLAN RD, JOHN H BENNER MD 19348 #041-02-1963 L1964 **R** *071 †80
WARD, Rebecca Heaps. 400 MCFARLAN RD, STE 3 19348 #023-01-1992 L1998 **OPH** *020 †35 ‡
WARNICK, William Clay. 404 MCFARLAN RD 19348 #041-09-1989 L1991 **CD** *020 †20
WHITE, Martha Lynn. 402 MCFARLAN RD 19348 #041-02-1996 L1998 **FM** *020 †18 ‡
ZEARFOSS, John E. ■ 19348 #051-01-1944 L1944 **OBG** *071
ZEINER, George Banker. 830 W CYPRESS ST 19348 #035-03-1965 L1991 **OM AM** *020 †70

ZIEGLER, Richard Wm. 404 MCFARLAN RD, CHESTER CTY ORTHOPAEDICS 19348 #041-02-1979 L1980 ORS *020 †40

ZIMMERMAN, Karl Arthur. 127 W STREET RD, STE 101 19348 #041-13-1993 L1995 IM *020 †20

KING OF PRUSSIA – MONTGOMERY

AHONKHAI, Vincent Irivbua. 2301 RENAISSANCE BLVD #510, GLAXO SMITH KLINE 19406 #690-02-1972 L1983 ID PD *062 †55

ALEXANDER, Robert Clifton. 2301 RENAISSANCE BLVD, BOX 61540 19406 #016-02-1984 L1991 P *020 †75

ALTER, Craig Alan. 210 MALL BLVD, FL 2 19406 #024-01-1987 L1990 PD *050 †55

AMSTER, Norman H. ■ 19406 #016-76-1967, ▲ L1970 AN *071

AQUI, Nicole Alyse. ■ 19406 #041-01-2001 L2001 PTH *100

BARON, Arthur Martin. ■ 19406 #041-13-1954 L1955 IMG *071

BEAROFF, Richard Jos. 860 1ST AVE STE 870, MEDICINE LLC 19406 #041-02-1976 L1977 IM *020 †20

BEAUSOLEIL, Janet Leruo. 210 MALL BLVD, FL 2 19406 #008-02-1991 L1995 AI PDA *020 †55,03

BECKER, Frederic Scott. 491 ALLENDALE RD, STE 222 19406 #041-01-1992 L1995 IM *020 †20

BENNETT, John Arthur. 1100 1ST AVE, DEVON HEALTH SERVICES 19406 #041-09-1975 L1976 IM *030 †20

BERGMAN, Garrett Edward. 1020 1ST AVE 19406 #041-02-1969 L1970 PD HEM *040 †55

BERTUCCI, Maria Janel. 625 CLARK AVE, STE 13 19406 #041-15-2004 L2004 FM *020 †18

BILYK, Jurij R. 200 MALL BLVD 19406 #041-02-1987 L1990 OPH FPS *020 †35

BONAGURA, Anthony Francis. 2201 RENAISSANCE BLVD 19406 #035-48-1990 L1992 HEM *020 †20

BROWN, Laurence Wm. 210 MALL BLVD, FL 2 19406 #035-19-1971 L1973 N PD *020 †55,75

BROWN-WHITEHORN, Terri F. 210 MALL BLVD, FL 2 19406 #028-46-1991 L1995 AI PDA *020 †03,55

BUONOCORE, Bonnita Kubiak. 860 1ST AVE 19406 #035-08-1977 L1979 IM *020 †20

BUTLER, Adrian Lee. 700 S HENDERSON RD, STE 200 19406 #017-20-2001 L2001 HS *020

CAMP, Anthony Merrill. 625 CLARK AVE, STE 13 19406 #041-13-1981 L1982 FM *020 †18

CANUSO, Nicholas A. 2000 VALLEY FORGE CIR, APT 1225 19406 #041-09-1939 L1940 AM GYN *071

CASTELLI, Joseph L, Jr. 170 N HENDERSON RD 19406 #018-75-1983, ▲ L1986 OBG *020 †30

CHANG, David Jihoon. 2301 RENAISSANCE BLVD, RN 0410 19406 #035-19-1988 L1997 RHU IM *020 †20

COBITZ, Alexander Ralph. 2301 RENAISSANCE BLVD, MAIL CODE RN-0410 19406 #016-02-1992 L1999 END *050 †20

CONRAD, Margaret V. ■ 19406 #041-07-1952 L1953 CHP P *071 †20,75

DAVIS, Kara Alison. 150 S WARNER RD, STE 160 19406 #047-07-1993 L1998 APM *020 †05

DE BERARDINIS, Thomas. 216 MALL BLVD 19406 #041-01-1982 L1983 IM *020 †20 ‡

DE LA CRUZ, Apolinar. ■ 19406 #748-02-1955 L1963 EM *071

DENG, Hong Bing. ■ 19406 #243-47-1990 L2002 PCP *100 †50

DESAI, Ansuya Mohanlal. 583 SHOEMAKER RD, STE 104 19406 #496-38-1956 L1977 OBG *071 †30

DLUGOS, Dennis Jos. 210 MALL BLVD, FL 2 19406 #035-01-1988 L1994 CHN CN *020 †55,75

DOWELL, Suzy Lee. 491 ALLENDALE RD 19406 #010-01-1997 L2000 PD *020 †55

ECKER, Andrew Michael. 700 S HENDERSON RD, STE 306 19406 #041-14-1981 L1983 IM *020 †20

EDDE, Peter Boutros. 700 S HENDERSON RD, STE 306 19406 #605-01-2000 L2001 FM *020 †18

FOWLER, John Roy, Jr. ■ 19406 #041-13-2007 L2007 ORS *012

FREUDENBERG, Doris T. ■ 19406 #041-07-1960 L1961 PM *071 †60 ‡

FRIEDLANDER, Mark Steven. 1100 1ST AVE, F226 19406 #836-01-1982 L1988 P CHP *062 †75

GARABEDIAN, Joseph Andre. 1012 W 9TH AVE 19406 #875-01-1973 L1976 FM OM *020 ‡

GINSBERG, Jill Phillips. 210 MALL BLVD, FL 2 19406 #035-20-1992 L1995 PHO *020 †20

GINSBERG, Susan Beth. 700 S HENDERSON RD, STE 306A 19406 #041-02-1990 L2002 IM *020 †20

GLEASON, Marie Murphy. 210 MALL BLVD, FL 2 19406 #035-19-1981 L1983 PDC *020 †55

GLUNK, Richard Paul. 216 MALL BLVD, STE 101 19406 #041-07-1982 L1983 PS *020 †65

GOLDFARB, Samuel Brian. 210 MALL BLVD, FL 2 19406 #550-02-1993 L2000 PDP *020 †55 ‡

GOLDSTEIN, Dov Alexander. 455 S GULPH RD, STE 310 19406 #008-01-1995 IM *100

GRAD, Leila Christine. ■ 19406 #041-02-1978 L1980 IM *050 †20

HABIB, Michael Anthony. 414 MONROE BLVD 19406 #041-01-1966 L1967 ON HO *062 †20 ‡

HAKIM, Arafat. ■ 19406 #495-37-2000 L2004 IM *020 †20

HALLUR, Ravindra Chanabas. ■ 19406 #495-72-1996 L2007 IM *100 †20

HIRSHMAN, Philip Gregory. 583 SHOEMAKER RD, STE 104 19406 #035-09-1994 L1997 OBG *020 †30

HITZ, David Leon. 1008 W 8TH AVE 19406 #041-13-1979 L1980 FM *020 †18

HOFFMAN, Susan Denise. 491 ALLENDALE RD, PRACTICE 19406 #041-02-1989 L1991 FM *020 †18

HOLMES, Robert Henry. ■ 19406 #024-01-1967 L1970 GPM *062 †70

HOWE-MISBIN, Barbara J. 2301 RENAISSANCE BLVD, GLAXO SMITH KLINE 19406 #041-02-1986 L1988 ID *050 †20

IZADI, Mohammed Ali. 1000 VALLEY FORGE CIR, UNIT 909 19406 #917-04-1959 L1995 U *020 †95

JOHNSTON, Michael Richard. ■ 19406 #016-11-1972 L1978 TS *050 †85,90

JUBELIRER, Tracey Friedma. 950 PULASKI DR, CHILDRENS HOSPITAL OF PHIL 19406 #011-03-2001 L2001 PHO *100 †55

KALKSTEIN, David. 700 S HENDERSON RD, STE 302B 19406 #011-02-1979 L1980 P *020

KARKALAS, Elias Arthur. 170 N HENDERSON RD, STE 206 19406 #041-13-1980 L1981 FM *020 †18

KATOLIK, Leonid Iwan. 700 S HENDERSON RD, STE 200 19406 #041-09-1998 L2007 HS *020 †40

KATZMAN, Jeffrey Ira. 901 E 8TH AVE, STE 101 19406 #035-09-1972 L1977 OPH *020 †35

KEE, Chandra Angelena. 1100 1ST AVE, STE 200 19406 #033-06-1987 L1989 P *020 †75 ‡

KELLY, Janice Ann. 210 MALL BLVD, FL 2 19406 #010-02-1985 L1987 PG GE *020 †55 ‡

KEYKHAH, Shahnaz Sadri. ■ 19406 #517-06-1969 L1981 PTH OS *062 †50

KOHN, Max Morton. ■ 19406 #041-77-1943, ▲ L1958 OS *071

KOLATKAR, Nikheel S. 2301 RENAISSANCE BLVD, RN0410 19406 #026-04-1999 L2006 END *100 †20 ‡

KOMISAROF, Jerome H. 700 S HENDERSON RD, STE 302B 19406 #041-01-1959 L1960 CHP P *020

KONDRATOWSKI, Richard Z. ■ 19406 #759-03-1957 L1973 OTO *071

KOTIHAL, Deepthi Shivanan. ■ 19406 #041-15-2007 L2007 IM *012

KOTIHAL, Usha Shivanand. 205 STEVEN DR 19406 #495-09-1978 L1997 P *020

KREMER, Frederic Byron. 200 MALL BLVD 19406 #041-02-1976 L1977 OPH *071 †35

KRUGER, Hillary Anne. 210 MALL BLVD, FL 2 19406 #035-19-1990 L2002 PD *020 †55

LEIMER, Elisabeth Barbara. 200 N WARNER RD STE 121, OAK HILL PLAZA 19406 #409-16-1972 L1985 GS D *020

LERMAN, Roy Michael. 700 S HENDERSON RD, STE 308C 19406 #041-13-1983 L1991 PM *020 †60

LIGHTSTONE, Harold. 150 S WARNER RD, WALNUT HILL PLAZA 19406 #041-77-1958, ▲ L1959 AN *071

LIN, Nora Jajin. 234 MALL BLVD, STE 170 19406 #035-09-1998 L2001 AI PD *020 †55,03

LIPSCHITZ, Alan. 2301 RENAISSANCE BLVD, MC RN0410 BLDG 510 19406 #011-02-1977 L1978 P *020 †75

LISS, Donald. 2201 RENAISSANCE BLVD F608, AETNA INC 19406 #041-07-1987 L1989 IM *020 †20

LOOMES, Kathleen Mary. 210 MALL BLVD, FL 2 19406 #048-12-1992 L1996 PG PD *020 †55

LUTCHKOVA, Marina Borisov. ■ 19406 #913-04-1984 *100

MAC VAUGH, Horace. 600 W DEKALB PIKE STE 301, NUHART HAIR SOLUTIONS 19406 #041-01-1955 L1956 PS *020 †90,85

MAGNUSSON, Mark Robt. 210 MALL BLVD, FL 2 19406 #028-02-1985 L1987 PD *020 †55

MENDEZ ROSA, Iliana G. ■ 19406 #264-05-1974 L1980 DR *020

MISKI, Pinar. ■ 19406 #041-13-2006 L2007 P *012

NIAMI, Nersi. 491 ALLENDALE RD, STE 121 19406 #517-08-1982 L1991 PD *020 †55

NISEN, Perry David. 2301 RENAISSANCE BLVD, GLAXOSMITHKLINE 19406 #035-46-1982 L2005 PD HEM *050 †55

NYE, Bonnie Ann. 210 MALL BLVD, FL 2 19406 #041-01-1988 L1991 IM *020 †20

OKADA, Shunichiro Steve. 2301 RENAISSANCE BLVD, RN0320 19406 #048-12-1985 L1987 CD IM *020 †20

OSTERMAN, A Lee. 700 S HENDERSON RD, MERION BLDG STE 200 19406 #041-01-1973 L1974 HS ORS *020 †40 ‡

PADGET, James Wm, III. 491 ALLENDALE RD 19406 #041-13-1971 L1973 D *020 †15

PADGET, Sonia Mary K. 491 ALLENDALE RD 19406 #041-13-1972 L1973 D PD *020 †55,15

PANARO, Rudolph Jos. ■ 19406 #041-13-1956 L1957 GP OM *071

PARIDON, Stephen Michael. 210 MALL BLVD, FL 2 19406 #038-06-1981 L1994 PDC *050 †55

PARISH, Naomi Asnien. ■ 19406 #041-13-1978 L1979 P *020 †75

PATANKAR, Kalpana Uday. 2200 RENAISSANCE BLVD, STE 320 19406 #496-38-1970 L1974 VS PD *020 †55

PAWLOWSKI, Nicholas A. 210 MALL BLVD 2ND FL 19406 #010-02-1976 L1986 PDA AI *020 †55,03

PHILLIPS, Martin Douglas. 1020 1ST AVE, DIR MEDICAL AFFAIRS 19406 #025-07-1982 L1998 ON HEM *020 †20

POLGAR, George. ■ 19406 #473-02-1943 L1974 PUD PD *100

PORTER, Lisa Ellen. 2301 RENAISSANCE BLVD, BLDG 510 19406 #036-07-1989 L1997 END *020 †20

POSNER, Mark Alan. 234 MALL BLVD, STE 170 19406 #033-06-1985 L1990 AI PDA *020 †03,55

RASKIEWICZ, Edward Brian. ■ 19406 #041-13-1981 L1983 AN *075

RHEINGOLD, Susan Robbins. 210 MALL BLVD, FL 2 19406 #041-01-1992 L1995 PD PHO *020 †55

RICCI, Dominick Alexander. ■ 19406 #847-04-1978 L1980 GE IM *075

RICHARD, Michael David. ■ 19406 #011-02-1992 L1995 NM *075

RICHARDSON, Kimberly A. 700 S HENDERSON RD, STE 306 19406 #041-13-1998 L2000 FM *020 †18

RICHARDSON, William Ward. 625 CLARK AVE STE 13, FAMILY PRACTICE ASSOCIATES 19406 #041-13-1975 L1976 CD IM *020 †18

RICHMOND, John Michael. ■ 19406 #041-13-2007 L2007 ORS *012

ROGERS, Denis Patrick. 700 S HENDERSON RD 19406 #041-02-1994 L1997 PM *020 †60

ROSEN, Richard Alan. 2201 RENAISSANCE BLVD, F 604 19406 #028-34-1970 L1997 PD MDM *030 †55

ROWLINGS, Pamela K. ■ 19406 #041-15-2001 FM *100

ROY-GHANTA, Sumita. ■ 19406 #038-44-2001 L2007 AI *100 †20,55

SABO, Susan Joyce. 128 FORGE RD 19406 #038-45-1982 L1988 OM PTX *072 †70

SAPIN, Joyce Irene. 210 MALL BLVD 19406 #033-05-1983 L1984 CHN PD *020 †75,55

SCHULTHEIS, Carl Frank. 491 ALLENDALE RD, STE 121 19406 #041-02-1959 L1960 PD *071 †55 ‡

SHAH, Mehul Navinchandra. 170 N HENDERSON RD, STE 302 19406 #495-23-1981 L1985 IM VM *020 †20

SHARADA, Manjula Jagannat. ■ 19406 #495-37-1996 L2007 IM *020 †20

SHARMA, Madhulika. ■ 19406 #495-45-1994 L2002 NEP *012 †20

SIU, Philip Tao-Sung. 221 TYLER RD 19406 #041-01-1985 L1987 PD *020 †55 ‡

SMITH, Angela Dorman. 210 MALL BLVD 19406 #012-05-1979 L1987 OP OSM *020 †40

SMITH, Michelle Ann. 625 CLARK AVE, STE 13 19406 #041-13-1987 L1989 FM *020 †18

SOLOMON, Dory Matthew. 1020 1ST AVE, PO BOX 61501 19406 #654-01-1994 L1998 PD *020 †55

SPERGEL, Jonathan Michael. 210 MALL BLVD, FL 2 19406 #035-47-1992 L1998 AI *020 †55,03

SPRECHER, Dennis Louis. 709 SWEDELAND RD UW2350 19406 #024-05-1978 L2003 CD OS *050 †20

STAWICKI, Stanislaw. ■ 19406 #020-02-2001 L2001 CCS *012 †85

STERN, Julie Wynne. 950 PULASKI DR, CHILDREN'S HOSP OF PHILA 19406 #016-06-1993 L1995 PHO *020 †55

SUH, Jennifer Jin-Kyung. 491 ALLENDALE RD STE 12 19406 #035-09-2001 L2004 PD *020 †55

TARKA, Elizabeth Ann. 2301 RENAISSANCE BLVD, GLAXOSMITHKLINE RN 0320 19406 #041-01-1992 L1994 CD *020 †20

TILL, Ann Gallagher. 491 ALLENDALE RD, STE 222 19406 #041-13-2003 L2003 IM *100 †20

TOSO, John Franco. 2301 RENAISSANCE BLVD, GLAXOSMITHKLINE 19406 #041-12-1992 L1998 MM *020 †50

VELOSO, Estela Hermogena. ■ 19406 #748-07-1958 L1980 P *020

WACHS, Richard Alan. 491 ALLENDALE RD, STE 201 19406 #033-06-1995 L2001 PD *020 †55,03

WEBER, Barbara Lynn. 2301 RENAISSANCE BLVD, REN 510 19406 #054-04-1982 L1994 ON IM *020 †20

WILLIAMS, Burton Jeffrey. 2200 RENAISSANCE BLVD, STE 320 19406 #041-02-1978 L1979 FM *020 †18

WODELL, Ruthven Adriance. 491 ALLENDALE RD, STE 111 19406 #040-07-1980 L1982 PUD AI *020 †55,03

WOMER, Richard Berry. 210 MALL BLVD, FL 2 19406 #035-45-1978 L1982 PHO *020 †55

WRIGHT, David Curtis. ■ 19406 #041-01-2001 L2001 **EM** *020 †16

YAO, Liping. 170 N HENDERSON RD, STE 310 19406 #243-16-1983 L2000 **PM APM** *020 †60

KINGSTON – LUZERNE

ABRAMOWITZ, Richard Paul. 610 WYOMING AVE 18704 #041-02-1978 L1981 **CD IM** *020 †20 ‡

AICHER, David Craig. 703 RUTTER AVE 18704 #041-09-1955 L1956 **OPH** *071 †35

ALEXANDROV, Maria Todor. 26 CHARLES ST 18704 #198-02-1964 L1974 **GP** *020

ALLEY, Richard Abbes. 440 PIERCE ST 18704 #041-02-1960 L1961 **IM END** *071 †20

AMINI, Rohullah. 610 WYOMING AVE 18704 #118-01-1987 L2000 **CD** *020 †20

AQUILINA, Charles Jos. 571 WYOMING AVE 18704 #041-13-1968 L1969 **AN PUD** *071 †05

AZADFARD, Mohammadreza. 2 SHARPE ST 18704 #517-11-2000 L2007 **FP** *012

BAERWALD, Wolfgang Hans. 42 JAMES ST 18704 #025-07-1978 L1988 **RO** *020 †80

BASNET, Prativa. PRACTICE RESIDENCY, UNITED HLTH HOSP 18704 #672-02-2000 L2008 *100

BAUMAN, Julie Elaine. ■ 18704 #024-07-1999 L2007 **ON** *100 †20

BEDNAREK, Thomas Francis. 517 PIERCE ST, PREMIER RADIOLOGY ASSOC 18704 #041-13-1969 L1973 **DR** *020 †80

BERBANO, Recaredo R. 445 WYOMING AVE 18704 #748-01-1986 L2002 **END** *020 †20

BERMUDEZ, Minda. 451 3RD AVE 18704 #748-02-1978 L1991 **DR** *074

BOST, Ronald Eugene. 440 PIERCE ST 18704 #036-07-1970 L1989 **D** *020 †15

BROWN, Fredric Steven. 440 PIERCE ST 18704 #041-01-1977 L1980 **D** *020 †15

BURAK, William Edward. 470 WYOMING AVE 18704 #041-02-1963 L1964 **U** *020 †95

BURNS, C N, Jr. 423 3RD AVE 18704 #041-02-1976 L1977 **U** *020 †95

BURNS, Charles Nicholas. 423 3RD AVE, STE B 18704 #041-02-1941 L1942 **U OS** *071 †95

CANDAL, Alfredo R L. ■ 18704 #132-01-1960 L1963 **ORS** *020

CHARLTON, William Hopkins. 390 PIERCE ST 18704 #041-02-1995 L1997 **ORS** *020 †40

CHOLLAK, Joseph Paul, Jr. 950 WYOMING AVE 44TH 18704 #041-02-1967 L1970 **FM OS** *020 †18

CITTI, John Gregory. 610 WYOMING AVE 18704 #010-02-1981 L1987 **IM** *020 †20

CLERICO, Dean Michael. 534 WYOMING AVE 18704 #033-05-1987 L1992 **OTO HNS** *020 †45

CORONITI, Lisa Jennifer. 499 WYOMING AVE 18704 #041-13-1986 L1987 **PD** *020 †55

CRAMTON, David Chester. 610 WYOMING AVE 18704 #023-01-1962 L1965 **IM CD** *071

CROUSE, Kevin Michel. 250 PIERCE ST, STE 217 18704 #010-02-1982 L1991 **D** *020 †15

DANIEL, Ronald Otto. 499 WYOMING AVE 18704 #035-09-1977 L2004 **OBG** *020 †30

DE CURTIS, George Matthew. 2 POPLAR ST 18704 #041-02-1958 L1959 **FM** *020 †18 ‡

DELEHANTY, Thomas Jay. 250 PIERCE ST STE 211 18704 #041-02-1977 L1979 **PUD** *020 †20 ‡

DEL GAUDIO, Walter. 470 WYOMING AVE, UROLOGY ASSOCIATES OF KING 18704 #035-08-1959 L1977 **AN IM** *071 †20,05

DEL GAUDIO, Walter R. 470 WYOMING AVE 18704 #041-12-1996 L2001 **U** *020 †95

DE PASQUALE, Sam Cataldo. 540 PIERCE ST 18704 #041-02-1963 L1964 **GS AS** *020 †85 ‡

DE ROSE, David. 190 WELLES ST 18704 #041-09-1992 L1996 **OPH** *020 †35

DOLPHIN, Murray. ■ 18704 #041-02-1946 L1947 **OPH** *075 †35

ENGLISH, Richard Buck. 2 SHARPE ST, WYOMING VALLEY FAMILY 18704 #041-02-1976 L1977 **FM FPG** *040 †18

FAZILI, Fatima Rizwan. ■ 18704 #496-17-1995 L2007 **FP** *012

FELLERMAN, Herbert. ■ 18704 #035-15-1965 L1969 **END IM** *071 †20 ‡

FISCHBEIN, Richard E. 562 WYOMING AVE, NESBITT HOSP 2ND FL 18704 #305-01-1982 L1984 **P IM** *020 †75

FIUME, Thomas Jos. 562 WYOMING AVE, FIRST HOSPITAL OF NESBITT 18704 #649-33-1980 L1984 **P** *020 ‡

FRIED, Martin Barry. 382 PIERCE ST 18704 #035-03-1971 L1978 **GE IM** *020 †20

FRIEDMAN, Robert Chas. PO BOX 1152 18704 #041-02-1964 L1965 **DR RO** *071 †80

GAIA, Juan Dario. 451 3RD AVE 18704 #132-06-1971 L1974 **DR NM** *020 †80

GARG, Sanjeev. 610 WYOMING AVE 18704 #495-19-1997 L2002 **N** *020 †75

GAUDIO, John Carmen. 425 TIOGA AVE 18704 #041-09-1965 L1966 **PD** *020 ‡

GAZOWSKI, Thomas E. ■ 18704 #041-02-1950 L1951 **GP** *071

GERNHARDT, Roy Walter. 2 SHARPE ST 18704 #422-01-2004 L2004 **FM** *020 †18

GIARDINA, Anthony Charles. 178 UNITED PENN PLZ 18704 #561-17-1959 **PTH** *071 †50

GOVINDJI, Trusha Jayanti. ■ 18704 #010-01-2008 *012

GRASSO, David James. ■ 18704 #041-15-2008 *012

GREENWALD, David Wm. 382 PIERCE ST 18704 #041-13-1970 L1971 **ON HO** *020 †20

GRIESMER, Paul Dalton. 425 TIOGA AVE, OB-GYN ASSOCIATES 18704 #041-02-1954 L1955 **GYN** *071 †30

GROSSMAN, Ira C. 470 WYOMING AVE 18704 #035-08-1975 L1976 **U** *020 †95

GUNSTER, Gerald Donald. 425 TIOGA AVE 18704 #041-13-1962 L1963 **OBG** *020 †30

HARRIS, Michael Wm. 425 TIOGA AVE 18704 #021-01-1976 L1979 **PD PDA** *020 †55 ‡

HASAN, Rabia. PRACTICE RESIDENCY, UNITED HLTH & HOSP 18704 #704-01-2000 L2008 *100

HAZLETT, William Henry. ■ 18704 #041-13-1942 L1943 **OBG OS** *071

HOTTENSTEIN, William D. 270 PIERCE ST 18704 #041-09-1988 L1990 **IM** *020 †20

HOWANITZ, Emil P. ■ 18704 #041-02-1944 L1945 **GS TS** *071

IMPERIALE, Salvatore M. 451 3RD AVE 18704 #041-09-1959 L1960 **R** *071 †80

JAMAL, Chaklader Naushad. 499 WYOMING AVE 18704 #160-02-1979 L2004 **NPM** *020 †55

JAMES, Russell Elmer. 700 3RD AVE 18704 #041-01-1955 L1959 **IM PUD** *071

KACHHADIYA, Govindbhai Pa. ■ 18704 #495-89-1995 L2007 **FP** *012

KAFRISSEN, Steven Robt. 562 WYOMING AVE 18704 #041-09-1967 L1968 **P** *020 †75

KCOMT, Juanita Regina. ■ 18704 #737-09-1993 L2007 **END NEP** *020 †20

KELLMEL, Kelly Jean. 2 SHARPE ST, FAMILY PRACTICE 18704 #041-15-2002 L2002 **FM** *100

KHAN, Sabir. 2 SHARPE ST, WYOMING VALLEY FAMILY PRAC 18704 #748-09-2000 **FP** *012

KHAN, Sumaira. 2 SHARPE ST, WYOMING VALLEY FAMILY PRAC 18704 #704-26-1997 **FP** *012

KILE, Jeffery Roman. 425 TIOGA AVE 18704 #041-15-1999 L2003 **PD** *020 †55

KOO, Wook Hun. WYOMING AVE, NESBITT MEMORIAL HOSPITAL 18704 #583-04-1964 L1972 **AN** *020

KOPEN, Pamela Ann. ■ 18704 #041-14-1978 L1979 **DR** *020 †80

KORDEK, Michael Emile. 499 WYOMING AVE 18704 #008-02-1981 L1982 **FM** *020 †18

KOZLEK, Thomas Francis. 534 WYOMING AVE 18704 #041-02-1966 L1968 **OTO** *020 †45

KUMAR, Sanjeev. 2 SHARPE ST 18704 #495-69-1997 L2002 **FM** *100

KURELLO, Phillip John. 562 WYOMING AVE 18704 #422-01-1983 L1984 **FM OS** *020 †18

LADANI, Binalkumar Dhiraj. 2 SHARPE ST, WYOMING VALLEY FAMILY PRAC 18704 #496-54-2002 L2006 **FP** *012

LAFOND, Gisele Marie. 517 PIERCE ST, PREMIER RADIOLOGY ASSOCIAT 18704 #035-03-1992 L1997 **DR** *020 †80

LEE, Dal Soon. 525 WYOMING AVE R 18704 #583-08-1971 L1976 **P** *020

LISKOV, Cynthia Pronko. ■ 18704 #041-02-1981 L1984 **EM** *020 †16

LITCHMAN, Maureen M. 2 SHARPE ST, WYOMING VALLEY FAMILY 18704 #041-09-1978 L1979 **FM** *020 †18

LOBITZ, Stanley Allen. 155 E BENNETT ST 18704 #041-09-1982 L1983 **FM EM** *020 †18

LOMBARD, Michael Francis. 155 E BENNETT ST 18704 #041-09-1982 L1983 **EM FM** *020 †18

LOTTICK, Edward Antrim. 789 WYOMING AVE 18704 #030-05-1968 L1969 **FM IM** *071 †18

MAHAJAN, Monica. 33 HOLIDAY DR 18704 #496-17-1996 L2003 **IMG** *020 †18

MAKHMETOV, Michael. 382 PIERCE ST, MEDICAL ONCOLOGY ASSOCIATE 18704 #035-46-1997 L1998 **HO** *020 †20

MARIEN, Brian James. 540 PIERCE ST 18704 #035-06-1992 L2001 **VS** *020 †85

MATTUCCI, James Michael. 390 PIERCE ST 18704 #041-13-1994 L1999 **ORS** *020 †40

MENDELSSOHN, Saul. 610 WYOMING AVE 18704 #041-02-1961 L1962 **NEP IM** *071

MICHELSTEIN, Richard D. 610 WYOMING AVE 18704 #010-01-1978 L1979 **GE IM** *020 †20

MITCHELL, Arthur Bentley. 141 S MAPLE AVE 18704 #041-09-1983 L1984 **FM** *020 †18

MONACO, Michele Peter. 160 LATHROP ST, HOME 18704 #041-14-1978 L1987 **PDC** *020 †55

MOORE, David Hunkele. 440 PIERCE ST, GASTROENTEROLOGY SPEC INC 18704 #041-02-1975 L1976 **GE** *020 †20

MYERS, Frederick Benham. 610 WYOMING AVE 18704 #041-09-1972 L1973 **IM PUD** *071

NAHAR, Rajesh. 382 PIERCE ST 18704 #495-02-1991 L1999 **HO** *020 †20

NARDELL, Kristie Marie. 562 WYOMING AVE 18704 #041-14-1996 L1998 **P CHP** *020 †75

NARINS, Joseph. 2 SHARPE ST 18704 #025-07-1983 L2006 **OBG** *020 †30

NORK, Edward P. 562 WYOMING AVE 18704 #041-09-1952 L1953 **OPH** *071

O'BRIEN, Frank D, III. 390 PIERCE ST 18704 #041-14-1984 L1985 **ORS** *020 †40

OH, Dong Joon. 562 WYOMING AVE 18704 #583-03-1973 L1982 **AN** *020 †05

PALERMO, Regino Pantig, III. 2 SHARPE ST, WYOMING VALLEY FAMILY PRAC 18704 #748-18-1992 L2005 **FP** *012

PARK, Kie Jung. 562 WYOMING AVE 18704 #583-01-1967 L1972 **P PFP** *020 †75

PARSAEI, Nazanin. ■ 18704 #517-25-2000 L2007 *100

PATEL, Jigneshbhai Mohanb. 2 SHARPE ST 18704 #496-54-2001 L2007 **FP** *012

PENUGONDA, Haragopal S S. 470 WYOMING AVE, UROLOGY ASSOC OF KINGSTON 18704 #495-11-1962 L1973 **U** *020 †95

POLIN, Mark Steven. 445 WYOMING AVE 18704 #041-12-1984 L1988 **GYN OS** *020 †30

RAKLEWICZ, Michael Chas. 390 PIERCE ST 18704 #041-12-1972 L1973 **ORS** *020 †40

RANDHAWA, Rinku. ■ 18704 #495-53-2000 L2004 **FP** *012

RIMPLE, David Fell. 610 WYOMING AVE 18704 #041-09-1959 L1960 **CD IM** *071

RINEHOUSE, Jeanne A. 517 PIERCE ST, STE B 18704 #021-01-1990 L1994 **P** *020 †75

RINEHOUSE, Steven E. 517 PIERCE ST, ASSOCIATES, P.C. 18704 #021-01-1990 L1994 **DR** *020 †80

RITTENBERG, Michael H. 423 3RD AVE 18704 #041-02-1981 L1982 **U** *020 †95

ROBINSON, Joseph. 562 WYOMING AVE 18704 #028-34-1943 L1947 **PD IMG** *071 †55

ROGERS, John P. 425 TIOGA AVE 18704 #041-02-1975 L1976 **PD** *020 †55 ‡

ROGERS, Robert Allen. 562 WYOMING AVE, NESBITT MEMORIAL HOSPITAL 18704 #047-05-1981 L1983 **PTH** *020 †50 ‡

RUMBAUGH, Marshall U. 445 WYOMING AVE 18704 #041-13-1945 L1946 **U** *071 †95

SAIDMAN, Bruce Howard. 382 PIERCE ST 18704 #041-13-1984 L1987 **ON** *020 †20

SAUERWINE, Scott Alan. 517 PIERCE ST 18704 #041-02-1989 L1996 **DR** *020 †80

SCHREDER, Frank Seraph. ■ 18704 #407-20-1944 L1955 **U PA** *071

SCOTT, Durelle Tower. 610 WYOMING AVE 18704 #041-01-1968 L1969 **IM PUD** *020

SHAFER, Edward Alfred. 562 WYOMING AVE 18704 #041-02-1944 L1944 **FM** *071

SHAH, Ramesh M. 354 STANLEY DR 18704 #495-01-1971 L1980 **PUD IM** *040 †20

SHALLER, David Adam. 610 WYOMING AVE 18704 #023-01-1976 L1983 **IM RHU** *020 †20 ‡

SHARKNESS, Catherine M. ■ 18704 #041-07-1979 L1999 **GPM** *071 †70,18

SHARMIN, Mokarroma. 2 SHARPE ST 18704 #160-01-1999 L2007 **FP** *012

SHYNN, Tae Il. 562 WYOMING AVE 18704 #583-10-1971 L1976 **P PYG** *020 †75

SOLOMON, Cynthia Ann. 610 WYOMING AVE 18704 #041-09-1978 L1979 **IM** *020 †20

SPECTOR, Howard Lee. 517 PIERCE ST 18704 #018-75-1975, ▲ L1976 **DR** *020 †80

SPRING, Deborah Ann. 2 SHARPE ST, WYOMING VALLEY FAMILY 18704 #041-09-1978 L1979 **FM FPG** *040 †18

STANISH, Stanley Michael. 675 WYOMING AVE 18704 #308-04-1981 L1985 **OS PD** *020

STEC, Eugene Eric. 423 3RD AVE, ENT SURGICAL GROUP 18704 #041-02-1992 L1994 **OTO** *020 †45

TAGGART, Nina Mithi. 703 RUTTER AVE 18704 #035-20-1988 L1992 **OPH** *030 †35 ‡

TERMINI, Paul Gregory. 562 WYOMING AVE 18704 #041-13-1992 L1994 **CHP P** *020 †75

TSOUTSOPLIDES, George C. 534 WYOMING AVE 18704 #418-01-1962 L1972 **OBG OCC** *020 ‡

USHINSKI, Stanley Carl. 480 PIERCE ST, STE 209 18704 #041-02-1963 L1968 **PDA AI** *071 †55,03

VARHADE, Shakuntala Y. ■ 18704 #495-01-1976 L1996 **PD** *020 †55

VERAZIN, Gary Thos. 540 PIERCE ST 18704 #041-13-1984 L1985 **OS GS** *071 †85

VINSHTOK, Olga. 2 SHARPE ST, FAMILY PRACTICE 18704 #913-02-2000 L2006 **FP** *012

VOHRA, Ira. 2 SHARPE ST, FAMILY PRACTICE 18704 #495-03-2003 L2006 **FP** *012

WHITBECK, Elaine Goodale. ■ 18704 #041-07-1975 L1981 **ON IM** *071 †20

WILKIE, William Louis. 562 WYOMING AVE 18704 #041-13-1961 L1968 **ATP PTH** *071 †50

WORNYO, James Dotse Yaw. 2 SHARPE ST 18704 #412-02-2001 L2007 **FP** *012

YUZ, Michael. 451 3RD AVE 18704 #035-08-1999 L2004 **DR** *020 †80

KINZERS – LANCASTER

JUNG, Haeho. 930 HILLCREST DR 17535 #041-12-1991 L1996 **AN** *020 †05

KIRKWOOD – LANCASTER

VIVIAN, Gail Marie. ■ 17536 #035-15-1974 L1983 **GS** *072 †85 ‡

KITTANNING – ARMSTRONG

ALTMAN, Harold Arthur, Jr. 100 MEDICAL ARTS, STE 170 16201 #041-13-1979 L1981 **PD** *020 †55

BARRETT, Randall K. 1 NOLTE DR 16201 #028-79-1993, ▲ L1996 **AN PME** *020 †05

BETTS, Charles Ross. 1 NOLTE DR, BOX 1001 16201 #025-01-1984 L1990 **NEP** *020 †20

BONO, John. 125 N MCKEAN ST 16201 #041-12-1948 L1949 **OTO OS** *071 †45

BORJA, Rogelio. 1 NOLTE DR 16201 #748-01-1963 L1973 **U** *020

BUCHBARKER, Diane Marie. 1 NOLTE DR, LAUBE CANCER CTR 16201 #016-42-1992 L1995 **HO HEM** *020 †20

7926

■ = Address Information Privacy Protected

BUCK, Keith Kirkwood. ■ 16201 #041-12-1959 L1960 **GP** *071

CHILDS, James Edward. 1 NOLTE DR, PATHOLOGY 16201 #051-01-1974 L1978 **PTH** *020 †50

CORDOBA, Diego R. 100 MEDICAL ARTS BLDG, STE 140 16201 #935-02-1966 L1974 **CD IM** *020 ‡

DAVID, Jeffrey Wayne. 1 NOLTE DR STE 540, 500 MEDICAL ARTS BLDG 16201 #038-41-1975 L1986 **OBG** *020 †30

DOERFLER, Frederick B, Jr. 260 S JEFFERSON ST 16201 #654-01-1982 L1983 **IM** *020 †20

EVANKOVICH, Christine E. 500 MEDICAL ARTS BLDG, STE 510 16201 #001-06-1993 L2001 **GS** *020 †85

FOWLER, Stephen Thomas. 100 MEDICAL ARTS, STE 170 16201 #051-01-1996 L1999 **PD** *020 †55

FREDERICK, Paul Leon. 500 MEDICAL ARTS BLDG, STE 510 16201 #041-12-1960 L1963 **GS CD** *071 †85

GALONSKI, Mary Anne. 300 S JEFFERSON ST 16201 #041-12-1982 L1984 **P** *020 †75

GARCIA, Luis. ■ 16201 #935-02-1966 L1974 **TS GS** *020 †85,90

GARROTT, John Wolcott. 230 MEDICAL ARTS BLDG 16201 #047-05-1969 **OBG FM** *071 †18,30

GENOVESE, Frank Nicholas. 200 MEDICAL ARTS, STE 210 16201 #041-12-1975 L1976 **OPH** *020 †35

GERSTBREIN, Harry Louis. ■ 16201 #041-12-1956 L1957 **PTH** *071 †50

GILBOA, Deborah Ruth. 198 WEST GATE DR, STE 101 16201 #041-12-2000 L2001 **FM** *020 †18 ‡

GROOMES, Roderick Berl. 1 NOLTE DR 16201 #041-02-1976 L1985 **EM IM** *020 †20,16

HAUBER, Louis Kenneth. 200 MEDICAL ARTS, STE 240 16201 #041-13-1980 L1981 **P CHP** *020 †75 ‡

HERRING, Craig Scott. 200 MEDICAL ARTS, STE 230 16201 #305-01-2000 L2004 **OBG** *020

KANNAPADI, Uma Mohan. 700 MEDICAL ARTS BLDG, STE 720 16201 #495-59-1990 L1995 **NEP** *020 †20

KISLOFF, Laura Eileen. 100 MEDICAL ARTS, STE 170 16201 #041-12-1998 L2001 **PD** *020 †55

KOHL, David Harris. 1 NOLTE DR, STE 540 16201 #041-13-1957 L1958 **GS** *071 †85

KUNDA, Gopal D. 1 NOLTE DR 16201 #495-62-1966 L1980 **AN** *020

LEKHWANI, Manoj Suresh. 300 S JEFFERSON ST 16201 #495-19-1986 L2001 **P** *020 †75

LYNCH, Thomas Gerard. 100 MEDICAL ARTS, STE 170 16201 #035-15-1990 L1992 **PD** *020 †55

MAJEWSKI, Jerzy. 1 NOLTE DR 16201 #759-06-1964 L1970 **U GP** *071 ‡

MC NUTT, Frank Hamilton. 1 NOLTE DR 16201 #035-20-1943 L1944 **GP D** *071

MERCURIO, Richard Allen. 300 WESTGATE RD 16201 #041-13-1981 L1984 **FM** *020 †18

MINTEER, Donald W. 1 NOLTE DR, ARMSTRONG CO MEMORIAL HOSP 16201 #041-12-1943 L1944 **GP PM** *071 †80

NICKLEACH, Joann. 100 MEDICAL ARTS, STE 170 16201 #041-12-1990 L1992 **PD** *020 †55

PATERNO, Steven Andrew. 300 MEDICAL ARTS BLDG 16201 #036-01-1997 L1999 **OBG** *020 †30

PATIL, Mahendra L. 300 S JEFFERSON ST 16201 #495-19-1986 L2000 **CHP P** *020

PITTS, William H. 1 NOLTE DR 16201 #041-12-1951 L1952 **GP** *071

REITZ, Suzanne Marie. 100 MEDICAL ARTS, STE 170 16201 #041-12-2000 L2003 **PD** *020 †55

RUSSELL, Maureen Marie. 300 MEDICAL ARTS 16201 #041-09-1992 L1996 **OBG** *020 †30

SANTOS, Ramon De La Cruz. 1 NOLTE DR 16201 #748-01-1968 L1973 **AN** *020

SELVARAJ, Mylappan. 600 MEDICAL ARTS BLDG, STE 670 16201 #495-04-1975 L1983 **CD** *020 †20 ‡

SHAH, Nutan Samir. 1 NOLTE DR 16201 #495-01-1988 L1999 **AN** *020 †05

SHAH, Vinod Hiralal. 1 NOLTE DR, ARMSTRONG COUNTY MEM HOSP. 16201 #495-01-1974 L1985 **RO** *020 †80

SKURA, Douglas Stephen. 400 MEDICAL ARTS, STE 420 16201 #060-01-1984 L1990 **ORS** *020 †40

SOTOS, Lazaros Nicholas. 179 NORTH PARK DR, STE 2 16201 #041-12-1968 L1976 **ORS** *020 †40

SOTOS, Peter Nicholas. 1 NOLTE DR, STE 660 MED ARTS BLDG 16201 #418-01-1976 L1977 **ORS** *020

TOLMAN, Leon M. 600 MEDICAL ARTS BLDG, STE 610 16201 #049-01-1980 L1981 **IM** *020 †20

TURCO, Domenic Angelo. ■ 16201 #010-01-2008 *012

VEGA, Roger E. 1 NOLTE DR, MEDICAL ARTS BLDG SUITE 11 16201 #748-02-1958 L1968 **U** *072 †95

VIGLIOTTI, Donald James. 100 MEDICAL ARTS BLDG, STE 170 16201 #041-14-1985 L1986 **PD** *020 †55

WINGARD, Jeremy Blaine. ■ 16201 #036-07-2007 L2007 **IM** *012

WINGARD, Larry Blaine. 100 MEDICAL ARTS 16201 #041-12-1973 L1974 **IM** *020 †20

YANG, Jae-Taek. 443 BUTLER RD 16201 #583-03-1965 L1972 **GS OBG** *020 †85

ZIMMERMAN, Levi Ken. 1 NOLTE DR 16201 #041-12-2002 L2002 **APM** *020 †05

KULPMONT — NORTHUMBERLAND

FABIAN, Teresa Alina. 1 NEVADA DR 17834 #759-10-1979 L1988 **IM** *020 †20

HOOD, Thomas J. 1 NEVADA DR, PENN STATE GEISINGER KULPM 17834 #041-02-1996 L1998 **FM** *020 †18

ROMANIC, Bruce Mark. 1 NEVADA DR 17834 #041-02-1983 L1984 **FM** *020 †18

TOMEDI, John Robt. 1 NEVADA DR 17834 #041-13-1980 L1981 **FM** *020 †18 ‡

KUNKLETOWN — MONROE

POPE, James Norford. ■ 18058 #051-01-1966 L1966 **GS GP** *071 †85

STROHLEIN, Stephen Sarto. RR 5 BOX 5272 18058 #561-17-1981 L1985 **GE IM** *020 †20

KUTZTOWN – BERKS

ANGELISANTI, Susan Michel. 89 MILL CREEK RD, P O BOX 322 19530 #028-02-1998 L2000 **OBG** *020 †18,30

BERGER, Barry Ivan. 333 NORMAL AVE 19530 #010-01-1992 L1998 **ORS** *020 †40

BOLLU, Ravindra Babu. 45 CONSTITUTION BLVD, FMC DIALYSIS SERVICES KUTZ 19530 #495-11-1988 L1999 **NEP** *020 †20

CAVANAUGH, Barbara C. 333 NORMAL AVE, STE 101 19530 #041-09-1982 L1985 **DR OS** *020 †80

COOPER, Mitchell Edward. 333 NORMAL AVE 19530 #041-13-1993 L1999 **OSM** *020 †40

D'ANGELO, Carl Franz. 333 NORMAL AVE, STE 203 19530 #041-01-1972 L1979 **GE IM** *020 †20

DI BENEDETTO, Thomas D. 333 NORMAL AVE 19530 #033-05-1983 L1987 **ORS** *020 †40

DONOVAN, Robert Sersall. 15050 KUTZTOWN RD 19530 #041-01-1957 L1963 **FM** *020

EMES, William Russell. KUTZTOWN FAM MED CTR 19530 #041-09-1954 L1955 **FM** *071

FAYAZI, Amir Hossain. 333 NORMAL AVE 19530 #028-02-1998 L2001 **OSS ORS** *020 †40

FEDERICO, Dale James. 333 NORMAL AVE 19530 #041-09-1983 L1992 **OSM ORS** *020 †40

FLICKER, Amanda Beth. 333 NORMAL AVE, COLLEGE HEIGHTS OB/GYN 19530 #041-14-2000 L2003 **OBG** *020 †30

FRIEL, Kristin Sinnock. 333 NORMAL AVE, COLLEGE HEIGHTS OB/GYN 19530 #024-01-1995 L1999 **OBG** *020 †30

GRIDER, Natalie Kunsman. 15050 KUTZTOWN RD 19530 #041-07-1994 L1997 **FM** *020 †18

HUTCHINSON, Thomas Andrew. 333 NORMAL AVE, COLLEGE HEIGHTS OB/GYN 19530 #041-02-1978 L1980 **OBG** *020 †30 ‡

IMAM, Tanveer M. 333 NORMAL AVE, STE 203 19530 #704-02-1987 L1994 **GE** *020 †20

KUTZ, Timothy John. 162 TREXLER AVE # A 19530 #041-14-1986 L1988 **FM** *020 †18

LAMBERT, Kenneth P. ■ 19530 #041-01-1943 L1944 **GP OS** *071

LEBBY, Eric Brian. 333 NORMAL AVE 19530 #041-13-1997 L1999 **ORS** *020 †40

PETERS, Molly Samuel. 333 NORMAL AVE, COLLEGE HEIGHTS OB/GYN ASS 19530 #005-12-1984 L1986 **OBG** *020 †30

REITZ, Melvin Lewis. ■ 19530 #041-02-1946 L1947 **GP DR** *071

STANSBURY, Neal Alan. 333 NORMAL AVE 19530 #041-09-1989 L1991 **OSM** *020 †40

VERVERELI, Prodromos A. 333 NORMAL AVE 19530 #041-02-1989 L1991 **OAR OTR** *020 †40

WEISS, Lawrence Edward. 333 NORMAL AVE 19530 #033-06-1993 L1995 **HS ORS** *020 †40

YEAGER, Bradford Allen. 333 NORMAL AVE, STE 101 19530 #041-01-1982 L1983 **DR** *020 †80

KYLERTOWN – CLEARFIELD

REICHARD, James L. ■ 16847 #035-20-1953 L1954 **FM EM** *071

LA PLUME – LACKAWANNA

HARRISON, Cynthia. ■ 18440 #041-13-1972 L1973 **EM** *071 †16

LAFAYETTE HILL – MONTGOMERY

ABRAHAM, Mini G. ■ 19444 #495-31-1990 L2002 **HMP** *020 †50

ADAMSONS, Ingrid A. ■ 19444 #043-01-1984 L1993 **OPH** *020 †35

ALNOAH, Zaid. ■ 19444 #016-42-2008 *012

BATUNKYI, Saw. ■ 19444 #209-01-1961 L1981 **PM** *020 †60

BHUYAN, Prakash Kailash. ■ 19444 #048-12-1998 L2001 **ID** *020 †20

CHU, Andrew. ■ 19444 #048-04-2004 L2007 **PG** *012

CONWAY, Jill Marie. ■ 19444 #016-11-2002 L2002 **N** *100 †75

FRANKEL, David Andrew. 660 THOMAS RD 19444 #041-09-1978 L1979 **P** *020 †75

FREED, Martin I. 2108 BASSWOOD DR 19444 #041-14-1986 L1987 **OS NEP** *050 †20

FRY, June Marie. 443 GERMANTOWN PIKE 19444 #041-07-1977 L1993 **N** *020 †75

GOLDBERG, Michael Ross. ■ 19444 #021-01-1976 L1979 **PA IM** *050 †20

GOODMAN, Doris. 9305 EAGLEVIEW DR 19444 #041-07-1960 L1961 **CD IM** *020 †20

GOULD, Richard Brent. ■ 19444 #041-01-1962 L1963 **P PYA** *071 †75

HE, Michael. ■ 19444 #041-12-2004 L2004 **AN** *012

HUEBNER, Stephen Bradley. ■ 19444 #047-05-2004 L2007 **DR** *012

HUNTER, Sheryl Denette. 9801 GERMANTOWN PIKE, STE 206 19444 #033-06-1992 L1994 **P** *020 †75

KRAUSE, Katherine C. 1022 LINCOLN WOODS 19444 #041-02-1978 L1997 **FM** *040 †18

KUNDEL, Harold Louis. ■ 19444 #035-01-1959 L1960 **DR** *050 †80

LIOUDIS, Adriane Hipp. ■ 19444 #041-14-1996 L2007 **PD** *020 †55

LIOUDIS, Michael D. ■ 19444 #035-06-1999 L2004 **MPD** *100

MERIZALDE, Bernardo A. 600 GERMANTOWN PIKE STE A 19444 #264-10-1980 L1984 **P GP** *020 †75

MILLER, Bernard J. ■ 19444 #041-02-1943 L1944 **TS GS** *071 †85

MINTZER, Fredric M. 555 ANDORRA GLEN CT STE 7 19444 #041-09-1978 L1979 **P** *020 †75

MOSTATAB, Akbar. 833 ANDORRA RD 19444 #517-06-1962 L1982 **PM PME** *020

MOURY, Nelson Frederick. ■ 19444 #041-02-1954 L1955 **IM OS** *071 †20

MOWERY, Robert Francis. 509 GERMANTOWN PIKE 19444 #041-09-1976 L1977 **FM IMG** *020 †18

OBRIEN, Lauren Lynne. 9801 GERMANTOWN PIKE, # 602 19444 #010-02-1994 L2004 **FM** *020 †18

O'CONNELL, Rose Reilly. ■ 19444 #016-43-1943 L1944 **PD** *072

OJEDA, Virginia Lloren. ■ 19444 #748-01-1956 L1967 **AN FM** *071

OYEFULE, Biyi Kayode. 660 THOMAS RD 19444 #308-07-1982 L1985 **P** *020 †75

PANZER, Herman Mayer. ■ 19444 #041-01-1946 L1948 **D** *071 †15

PODSAKOFF, Gregory M. ■ 19444 #005-12-1977 L1978 **IM** *020 †20

POTHEL, Ralph Louis. 9801 GERMANTOWN PIKE, # 907 19444 #035-06-1988 L2005 **FM** *020 †18

RILEY, Pat. 833 ANDORRA RD 19444 #041-07-1994 L1996 **PM OS** *020 †60

ROBERTS, John M. ■ 19444 #008-01-1952 L1953 **GS TS** *071 †85 ‡

RODGERS, Robert A, Jr. ■ 19444 #041-09-1954 L1955 **OBG** *071 †30

ROSEN, Laura Beth. 9801 GERMANTOWN PIKE 19444 #041-04-1997 L1997 **N** *020 †75

ROSEN, Michael Bruce. 509 GERMANTOWN PIKE 19444 #041-09-1987 L1988 **FM** *020 †18

SAAH, Alfred Jos. 4141 JACKSON DR 19444 #023-01-1973 L1997 **ID GPM** *050 †20,70

SHACKLETT, Dorothy E. ■ 19444 #041-13-1942 L1943 **IM OM** *071

SINGH, Pooja. 9319 EAGLEVIEW DR 19444 #495-82-2002 L2003 **NEP** *012 †20

SOMERS, Laurence Alan. ■ 19444 #041-01-1956 L1957 **PDS** *071 †85

SOPRANO, Catherine Marie. ■ 19444 #041-13-2008 L2008 **AN** *012

STEINBERG, Dean Alan. ■ 19444 #041-13-1982 L1983 **AN** *075 †05

SWAMI, Kumar. 750 GERMANTOWN PIKE, LAFAYETTE HIGHWAY 19444 #495-01-1966 L1974 **N** *062 †75

UNINSKY, Eliane. 413 GERMANTOWN PIKE 19444 #021-01-1976 L2002 **OPH OS** *020 †35

WEBER-NEWMAN, Hilary Beth. ■ 19444 #041-07-1989 L1993 **PTH** *020 †50

WEINER, Harold M. ■ 19444 #041-13-1962 L1965 **DR NM** *071 †80

WEISS, Andrew Scott. ■ 19444 #041-09-1987 *030

YANITY, Eugene James. 660 THOMAS RD 19444 #041-12-1956 L1957 **P** *071 †75

YOO, John H. 660 THOMAS RD 19444 #583-03-1963 L1972 **P** *020

ZIBELMAN, Matthew Rion. ■ 19444 #041-13-2007 **IM** *012

■ = Address Information Privacy Protected

LAHASKA – BUCKS

BEERE, Polly Anne. ■ 18931 #016-02-1986 L1990 **CD IM** *020

LAKE ARIEL – WAYNE

BETZ, Amy Houm. 62 INDUSTRIAL PARK RD 18436 #041-12-1997 L2000 **PD** *020 †55
KRISANDA, Joseph Benedict. ■ 18436 #041-02-1946 L1947 **GP** *071 ‡
MAIGUR, William Saml. 1434 MOUNT COBB RD 18436 #495-27-1963 L1970 **FM** *020 †18
MARICI, Frank. ■ 18436 #561-11-1957 L1960 **PUD IM** *071

LAKE COMO – WAYNE

WOODMANSEE, Carly Jean. ■ 18437 #041-02-2005 L2005 **P** *012

LAKE HARMONY – CARBON

GEIS, William Peter. ■ 18624 #016-43-1968 L1996 **GS TRS** *020 †85
GROTZINGER, Paul John G. ■ 18624 #041-09-1943 L1944 **GS ON** *071 †85

LAKE WINOLA – WYOMING

MURRAY, Patrick Michael. RTE 307 18625 #041-12-1985 L1986 **FM EM** *020 †18

LAKEWOOD – WAYNE

DOHNER, Robert P. 18 COMO RD STE 1, LAKEWOOD MED CTR 18439 #022-75-1998, ▲ L2001 **FM** *020 †18
GAY, James R. ■ 18439 #023-07-1939 L1954 **NS N** *071 †75,25

LANCASTER – LANCASTER

ADAMS, William Henry. 555 N DUKE ST 17602 #041-12-1989 L1991 **EM** *020 †16 ‡
ADDIS, Christopher T. 2110 HARRISBURG PIKE, GRP AT MEDICAL ASSOC OF 17601 #041-14-1988 L1990 **IM** *020 †20
ADOLPH, Carl M, Jr. 2104 HARRISBURG PIKE, STE 100 17601 #001-06-1988 L2001 **ORS** *020 †40 ‡
AHN, Chang Won. 90 GOOD DR STE 302 17603 #583-03-1967 L1981 **PM APM** *020 †60 ‡
ALBERTSON, Brian Keith. ■ 17601 #016-01-2005 L2005 **FP** *012
ALEXANDER, Alan Richard. 924 RED ROSE CT, LANCASTER REG MED CTR 17601 #008-02-1981 L1986 **DR RNR** *020 †80
ALLEN, Harold Y. ■ 17602 #041-02-1953 L1958 **OM IMG** *071 †70
ALLEN, John E. ■ 17602 #038-41-1944 L1972 **PD** *071 †55
ALLEYNE, Lisa Anthony. ■ 17602 #051-07-2006 **FP** *012
ALLWARDT, Sylvia Anne. 2301 COLUMBIA AVE 17603 #041-09-1996 L1999 **IM** *020 †20
ALTADONNA, Victor Francis. 2110 HARRISBURG PIKE # 1 17601 #041-02-1982 L1984 **U** *020 †95
ALVAREZ, Victor Enrique. ■ 17601 #737-01-1957 L1966 **PD** *072
AMMONS, Daniel Myles. 250 COLLEGE AVE 17603 #033-06-1998 L2000 **EM** *020 †16
ANDERSEN, Rolf Leon. 217 HARRISBURG AVE, STE 101 17603 #035-01-1983 L1989 **CD IM** *020 †20
ANDERSEN, William Karl. 190 N POINTE BLVD, # 1 17601 #035-01-1987 L1997 **DMP** *020 †50,15 ‡
ANDERSON, Rolf Lyman. 217 HARRISBURG AVE, STE 200 17603 #028-02-1962 L1962 **GE IM** *071 †20
ANDREWS, Robert James. ■ 17602 #038-40-1962 L1962 **GS** *071 †85
ANNESE, Joseph Stephan. 810 PLAZA BLVD 17601 #028-79-1972, ▲ L1976 **OTO** *020
ARGIRES, James Peter. 2150 HARRISBURG PIKE, STE 200 17601 #001-02-1962 L1967 **NS** *020 †25
ARGIRES, Perry James. 2150 HARRISBURG PIKE, STE 200 17601 #001-02-1991 L1997 **NS** *020 †25
ARIYANAYAGAM-BAKSH, S. 555 N DUKE ST 17602 #566-01-1990 L1998 **PTH** *020 †50
ARNOLD, Jame Francis. 2110 HARRISBURG PIKE 17601 #051-07-1993 L1999 **PS** *020 †85,65
ARTHUR, Kenneth Roy. 2110 HARRISBURG PIKE 17601 #041-02-1989 L1990 **PS HS** *020 †85
ARTUSO, James David. 133 E FREDERICK ST 17602 #041-14-1984 L1989 **AN PME** *020 †05 ‡
ASTARITA, Salvatore John. 133 E FREDERICK ST, ANESTHESIA ASSOC OF LANCAS 17602 #033-05-1987 L1991 **AN** *020 †05
AXELROD, Norman M. 996 E ORANGE ST 17602 #041-77-1958, ▲ L1959 **GS** *072
BABAR, Shahid Iqbal. 2110 HARRISBURG PIKE, GRP AT MEDICAL ASSOC OF 17601 #704-01-1996 L2000 **FPG** *100
BACHARACH, Matthew Dennis. 330 N ARCH ST 17603 #051-01-1981 L1987 **GS VS** *020 †85
BAIRD, Edward F. 250 COLLEGE AVE 17603 #024-05-1974 L1982 **AN** *072 †05
BAKKEN, William Ward. 101 ABBEYVILLE RD, GRP AT FAMILY PRACTICE 17603 #041-13-1974 L1975 **FM** *020 †18 ‡
BALEPUR, Shyam Sunder. 2102 HARRISBURG PIKE, GROUP AT HEMATOLOGY 17601 #495-21-1990 L2000 **HO IM** *020 †20
BARBASO-SCHWARTZ, Alma. 3059 COLUMBIA AVE 17603 #748-11-1975 L1983 **PD** *020 †55
BARBIERI, Jennie Maria. 2301 COLUMBIA AVE, GENERAL INTERNAL MEDICINE/ 17603 #041-13-2004 L2004 **IM** *100 †20
BARR, Valry Ward, Jr. ■ 17601 #021-01-1966 L1976 **NS** *071 †25
BASARAB, Robert Mark. 555 N DUKE ST 17602 #041-07-1978 L1983 **NM DR** *020 †80,28
BASHORE, Robert M, Jr. 555 N DUKE ST 17602 #041-02-1952 L1953 **OBG** *071 †30
BASSETT, James G. ■ 17602 #036-07-1946 L1955 **GS** *071 †85
BATOR, Susan Mary. 555 N DUKE ST, DEPT PATH 17602 #033-05-1984 L1988 **BBK** *020 †50
BAYLISS, Philip Martin. 690 GOOD DR, WOMEN & BABIES HOSPITAL 17601 #051-04-1984 L1994 **OBG** *020 †30
BECKER, Carl Eric, II. 609 N CHERRY ST, THE WESTPHAL GROUP 17602 #041-02-1994 L1996 **OAR OSM** *020 †40

BECKER, Hilary J Spence. 2150 NOLL DR, BEITTEL-BECKER PEDIATRIC 17603 #803-03-1968 L1973 **PD NPM** *020 †55
BEEDASSY, Ashok. 2102 HARRISBURG PIKE, GROUP AT HEMATOLOGY 17601 #495-74-1983 L1995 **HO** *020 †20
BEIDLER, Leanne Kay. 1655 CROOKED OAK DR, GRP AT CROOKED OAK FAMILY 17601 #041-13-1994 L1997 **FM** *020 †18
BEISECKER, Kaitlyn Anne. ■ 17602 #051-01-2007 L2007 **FP** *012
BELL, Stephen Thos. 2112 HARRISBURG PIKE 17601 #041-02-1980 L1982 **CD IM** *020 †20
BELSER, Robert Bruce, Jr. 2185 OREGON PIKE, LANCASTER OTOLARYNGOLOGY 17601 #041-01-1991 L1996 **OTO** *020 †45
BENNETT, Thomas Ewald. 2301 COLUMBIA AVE, GENERAL INTERNAL MEDICINE 17603 #036-08-1991 L1994 **IM** *020 †20
BERKENSTOCK, Kenneth G. 2102 HARRISBURG PIKE, LANCASTER GEN HEALTH CAMPU 17601 #041-09-1989 L1993 **RO** *020 †80
BERKOW, Don Alan. 555 N DUKE ST 17602 #023-01-1983 L1986 **EM** *030 †16
BERNABEI, Alvise Fileno. 233 COLLEGE AVE, STE 101 17603 #025-07-1988 L1991 **TS** *020 †90,85
BESECKER, Joseph Albert. 160 N POINTE BLVD, STE 110 17601 #041-02-1959 L1960 **PD** *071 †55
BEYER, Frederick Chas. 2104 HARRISBURG PIKE, STE 200 17601 #036-05-1976 L1981 **GS VS** *020 †85 ‡
BIEBER, Larien Geo. 2301 COLUMBIA AVE 17603 #041-14-1971 L1974 **IM** *020 †20
BILLS, Lyndra J. 802 NEW HOLLAND AVE, GROUP PSYCHIATRIC 17602 #048-13-1988 L1994 **P IM** *020 †75
BISHOP, Nancy V Rider. ■ 17603 #025-01-1944 L1946 **GP** *071
BISHOP, Ronald Clare. ■ 17603 #025-01-1944 L1948 **HEM IM** *071 †20
BOAN, Jarol Lee. ■ 17602 #068-01-1981 L2005 *100
BOBEN, Wm Robt Allen, Jr. 2100 HARRISBURG PIKE, BLDG 2106 17601 #041-02-1964 L1965 **PD AM** *020 †55
BODNER, Daryl Geo. 810 PLAZA BLVD, STE 101 17601 #041-09-1981 L1989 **OTO GS** *020 †45
BODNER, Gail Fedyna. 440 W CHESTNUT ST 17601 #041-09-1981 L1989 **FM EM** *020 †16,18
BOGEN, Janet Titchener. 555 N DUKE ST, LANCASTER GENERAL HOSPITAL 17602 #041-01-2000 L2001 **FM DIA** *100 †18 ‡
BOLEY, Timothy James. 690 GOOD DR, WOMEN AND BABIES HOSPITAL 17601 #012-01-1984 L2005 **OBG** *020 †30
BONCHEK, Lawrence I. 555 N DUKE ST 17602 #035-46-1963 L1983 **TS GS** *030 †85,90
BOWMAN, John Herman. ■ 17602 #041-02-1958 L1959 **OPH** *071 †35
BOYD, Charles E, Jr. 250 COLLEGE AVE 17603 #051-04-1994 L2001 **DR** *020 †80
BRESLIN, Jos Aloysius, Jr. 2106 HARRISBURG PIKE 17601 #041-02-1970 L1978 **U GP** *071 †95
BROD, Bruce Alan. 1650 CROOKED OAK DR, DERMATOLOGY ASSOCIATES OF 17601 #041-01-1987 L1988 **D IM** *020 †15
BROD, Roy David. 2150 HARRISBURG PIKE 17601 #041-13-1983 L1984 **OPH OS** *020 †35
BROSBE, Donna Elaine. 2150 NOLL DR, BEITTEL-BECKER PEDIATRIC 17603 #041-13-1980 L1981 **PD** *020 †55
BROWN, George Lance, Jr. PO BOX 5093 17606 #041-13-1940 L1942 **D** *071 †15
BROWN, Paul Sherman, Jr. 233 COLLEGE AVE, STE 101 17603 #028-34-1986 L1993 **TS GS** *020 †85,90 ‡
BROWN, Robert Edwin. 133 E FREDERICK ST 17602 #041-12-1964 L1965 **AN** *071 †05
BRYSON, Richard L. 555 N DUKE ST 17602 #041-02-1949 L1950 **GP** *071
BURLINGAME, Mark Wayne. 555 N DUKE ST, CARDIOTHORACIC SURGEONS 17602 #030-06-1975 L1983 **TS** *020 †90,85
CALEGA, Virginia C. 280 GRANITE RUN DR 17601 #041-07-1987 L1990 **IM IMG** *020 †20
CALKINS, Joseph L. 202 BUTLER AVE, STE 3 17601 #025-01-1970 L1980 **OPH** *020 †35
CAMPANELLA, Karla. 322 N ARCH ST 17603 #038-06-1992 L1994 **P** *012 †18
CAPPIELLO, Justin Louis. 324 N DUKE ST 17601 #041-01-1969 L1971 **OPH** *020 †35 ‡
CARON, Pierre A. 1655 CROOKED OAK DR, GRP AT CROOKED OAK FAMILY 17601 #067-02-1984 L1997 **FM** *020 †18
CARROLL, Bryan Thomas. ■ 17601 #038-06-2007 L2007 **IM** *012
CARROLL, Paul Francis. 2104 HARRISBURG PIKE, STE 100 17601 #035-09-1992 L1999 **OSM** *020 †40
CARSON, James Hubert. 2104 HARRISBURG PIKE, STE 100 17601 #023-07-1987 L1989 **ORS** *020 †40 ‡
CARTER, William Alvin. 930 RED ROSE CT, STE 301 17601 #035-45-1976 L1977 **FM** *020 †18
CASALE, Paul Nicholas. 217 HARRISBURG AVE, STE 200 17603 #035-20-1982 L1993 **CD IM** *020 †20
CASKEY, William Brewster. 2110 HARRISBURG PIKE, STE 100 17601 #035-01-1965 L1966 **END IM** *020 †20 ‡
CASSEL, Franklin Kulp. BRETHREN VILLAGE NO 5093 17601 #041-09-1939 L1941 **AN GP** *071
CASTLE, Charles Anthony. 694 GOOD DR, STE 201 17601 #051-01-1973 L1980 **OBG GPM** *020 †30 ‡
CAVICCHIA, Candice Michel. ■ 17602 #041-02-2007 L2007 **FP** *012
CHALHOUB, George Yusuf. 217 HARRISBURG AVE, STE 103 17603 #605-01-1984 L1997 **AN** *020 †05
CHARLES, Hyasmine Marie. 2112 HARRISBURG PIKE, STE 3 17601 #041-14-1995 L1998 **IM** *020
CHASKO, Stephen B. 555 N DUKE ST 17602 #010-02-1976 L1981 **PTH** *020 †50
CHATHA, Gurpinder Kaur. 217 HARRISBURG AVE, STE 200 17603 #495-29-1998 L2001 **CD** *020
CHAUDHRY, Bilal Khalid. 202 HEATHERSTONE WAY, STE 1 17601 #035-03-1996 L1998 **PUD** *020 †20
CHEN, Robert Daihwa. 133 E FREDERICK ST, ANESTHESIA ASSOC OF LANCAS 17602 #041-14-1994 L1998 **APM** *020 †05
CHEN, Steve T. 2112 HARRISBURG PIKE, STE 323 17601 #041-02-1984 L1992 **GE IM** *020 †20 ‡
CHIRKOV, Sergei V. 233 COLLEGE AVE 17603 #913-99-1994 L2002 **IM** *020
CHORY, Edward Terence. 2104 HARRISBURG PIKE, STE 200 17601 #033-05-1980 L1985 **GS NTR** *020 †85 ‡
CIUS, Elizabeth Germaine. 555 N DUKE ST, LANCASTER GENERAL HOSPITAL 17602 #010-02-2008 L2008 *012
CLARK, Neil Ross. 217 HARRISBURG AVE, STE 200 17603 #041-09-1985 L1986 **CD IM** *020 †20
COCO, Andrew Steven. 555 N DUKE ST, LANCASTER GENERAL HOSPITAL 17602 #024-16-1986 L1995 **FM OBG** *020 †18
COHEN, Donna. 555 N DUKE ST 17602 #041-02-1999 L2001 **FM** *020 †18
COLDREN, Sean. 802 NEW HOLLAND AVE, GROUP PSYCHIATRIC 17602 #041-13-1989 L1991 **P** *020 †75
COLLURA, Paul T. 250 COLLEGE AVE 17603 #010-02-1971 L1972 **DR** *020 †80 ‡
CONDRON, Brian Philip. 790 NEW HOLLAND AVE 17602 #016-43-1969 L1970 **P ADP** *020 †75
CONNAUGHTON, Patrick Noel. 555 N DUKE ST, DEPT RADOLOGY 17602 #539-04-1968 L1975 **DR RNR** *020 †80

■ = Address Information Privacy Protected

CONSLATO, Paul Michael. 2110 HARRISBURG PIKE, GRP AT MEDICAL ASSOC OF 17601 #041-02-1992 L1995 **IM** *020 †20
CONSLATO, Sharon S. 694 GOOD DR, STE 18 17601 #041-02-1992 L1996 **OBG** *020 †30 ‡
COOKE, Alfred Jos, Jr. 2104 HARRISBURG PIKE, STE 100 17601 #041-02-1964 L1965 **ORS OS** *071 †40
COOKE, Christopher C. 170 N POINTE BLVD, ORTHOPEDIC ASSOC LANCASTER 17601 #041-02-1995 L2001 **OAR** *020 †40
COONEY, Nancy F. ■ 17601 #041-13-1997 L2000 **OS** *062
COOPER, Edgar Leon. ■ 17602 #010-03-1961 L1986 **PD** *030 †55
COOPER, Herbert Kurtz. 3045 MARIETTA AVE 17601 #010-02-1974 L1975 **P** *020 †75
COOPER, Walter Wallace. ■ 17602 #028-02-1955 L1955 **AN** *071 †05
COPE, Denise Noel. 101 ABBEYVILLE RD, FAMILY PRACTICE ASSOCIATES 17603 #038-06-2004 L2004 **FM** *020 †18
COPE, Jeffrey Todd. 555 N DUKE ST, CARDIOTHORACIC SURGEONS 17602 #041-14-1992 L2002 **TS** *020 †85,90
CORALLO, Diane Marie. 558 N DUKE ST, OPHTHALMOLOGICAL ASSOC 17602 #041-09-1987 L1988 **OPH** *020 †35
CORCORAN, John J, Jr. ■ 17602 #026-04-1973 **OBG** *020
CORCORAN, John Jos. ■ 17602 #010-02-1961 L1962 **OBG** *071 †30
COTTER, John Thomas, Jr. 2207 OREGON PIKE, STE 202 17601 #041-14-1993 L1995 **FM** *020 †18
COULTER, Erica Leigh. ■ 17603 #019-02-2005 L2005 **FP** *012
COURSIN, David Baird. ■ 17603 #041-01-1943 L1944 **NTR PD** *050 †55
COVACI, Letitia Alida. 2141 OREGON PIKE, T W PONESSA AND ASSOC 17601 #781-01-1988 L2000 **P** *020 †75
CRILL, Norman C. 701 N DUKE ST, FAMILY CARE OF LANCASTER 17602 #041-02-1953 L1954 **FM** *071
CRUZ, Rizalino Soria. 555 N DUKE ST 17602 #748-01-1970 L1980 **P** *020 †75 ‡
DALEY, Marvin Clifford. ■ 17601 #041-02-1959 L1960 **U** *071 †95
D'ANDREA-SPICA, Marilyn. 555 N DUKE ST 17602 #036-05-1986 L1987 **IM** *020 †20
DAUGHERTY, James Hamilton. 1655 CROOKED OAK DR 17601 #041-13-1990 L1993 **FM** *020 †18
DAVIS, Allan Scott. 231 N SHIPPEN ST 17602 #041-02-1978 L1982 **ON HEM** *020 †20 ‡
DAVIS, James Henry. 133 E FREDERICK ST 17602 #041-01-1982 L1984 **AN IM** *020 †20,05
DAVIS, Jeffrey Allan. 2185 OREGON PIKE 17601 #041-02-1988 L1994 **OTO** *020 †45
DAVIS, Mary Helen. 822 MARIETTA AVE STE 31 17603 #048-02-1975 L1995 **CHP PYA** *020 †75
DECK, Roy, Jr. ■ 17603 #041-02-1949 L1952 **R** *071 †80
DE GREEN, Hyatt Peter. 1858 CHARTER LN, STE 202 17601 #038-40-1972 L1980 **ON HEM** *020 †20
DELONG, Ryan Scott. 2110 HARRISBURG PIKE, STE 300 17601 #041-14-2004 L2004 **FPG** *012 †18
DEL TERZO, Michael A. 2106 HARRISBURG PIKE # 200 17601 #010-02-1988 L2003 **U** *020 †95
DE POE, Craig Kenneth. 133 E FREDERICK ST, LANCASTER LTD 17602 #041-09-1994 L1997 **AN** *020 †05
DERRICO, Anne-Marie. 555 N DUKE ST 17602 #041-02-1999 L2001 **FM** *020 †18
DESHPANDE, Swapna R. 2301 COLUMBIA AVE 17603 #495-56-1989 L1997 **IM** *020 †20
DEUTCHKI, Ian Matthew. 555 N DUKE ST, LANCASTER GENERAL HOSPITAL 17602 #041-14-2007 L2007 **FP** *012
DIAMANTONI, Stephen Gust. 440 W CHESTNUT ST 17603 #041-09-1982 L1983 **FM FPG** *020 †18
DIAZ, Ailyn Diurka. 790 NEW HOLLAND AVE, COMMUNITY SERVICES GROUP 17602 #041-14-2000 L2001 **P** *020 †75
DIAZ, Hector. 802 NEW HOLLAND AVE, GROUP PSYCHIATRIC 17602 #033-06-1983 L1985 **P** *020 †75
DI CAMILLO, Vito James. 555 N DUKE ST 17602 #041-13-1996 L1998 **FM** *020 †18
DIETRICH, C Wallace. 210 WILLOW VALLEY SQ 17602 #041-13-1953 L1954 **GP** *071
DISE, Kirk Robert. 133 E FREDERICK ST, ANES ASSOCS/LANCASTER LTD 17602 #041-09-1997 L2001 **AN** *020 †05
D'ORAZIO, Dominick John. 555 N DUKE ST 17602 #041-14-1971 **AN** *020 †05
DOSHI, Janak Anilkumar. 2110 HARRISBURG PIKE # 302, MED REHAB ASSOC 17601 #038-43-1995 L2000 **PM** *020 †60
DOUGHERTY, Kathleen Clare. 555 N DUKE ST 17602 #041-02-1979 L1990 **P PFP** *020 †75
DUBOIS, Scott Reynold. 250 COLLEGE AVE 17603 #654-01-2000 L2004 **AN** *020 †05
DUGGAL, Anoop. 924 RED ROSE CT, IMAGING CTR OF LANCASTER 17601 #495-45-1986 L1997 **DR NR** *020 †80
DUKE, Lee Monroe, II. 555 N DUKE ST 17602 #051-01-1980 L1991 **PUD IM** *020 †20
DUMASIA, Rupal Pravin. 217 HARRISBURG AVE, STE 200 17603 #033-05-1999 L2006 **CD IC** *020 †20
DUMORNAY, Jean David. 555 N DUKE ST 17602 #440-01-1997 L2006 **FP** *012
EASH-SCOTT, Rachel Anne. 555 NORTH ST, DEPT FAMLY & COMMNTY MED 17602 #041-12-2003 L2004 **FM** *020 †18
EASTMAN, James Turner. 555 N DUKE ST, PATHOLOGY DEPT LANCASTER G 17602 #038-41-1973 L1978 **ATP CLP** *020 †50
EBERSOLE, Irene M. ■ 17601 #041-07-1951 L1952 **PTH** *071
ECKENRODE, Joseph Lewis. ■ 17602 #010-02-1944 L1945 **GP** *071
EDELSON, Simon Stephen. ■ 17601 #041-01-1975 L1976 **AN** *071 †05
EDMONDS, Catherine Joy. 555 N DUKE ST 17602 #051-01-1996 L1999 **FM** *020 †18 ‡
EICHENLAUB, John Jos. 2128 EMBASSY DR 17603 #038-06-1990 L1993 **OBG** *020 †30
EISENHOWER, Edward A. 250 COLLEGE AVE, LANCASTER REGL MED CTR 17603 #045-01-1974 L1977 **PTH** *020 †50
EL-BORNO, Bassam M A. 160 N POINTE BLVD STE 204 17601 #915-02-1980 L1988 **CHP P** *020 ‡
ELIA, Timothea. 205 SOUTHGATE DR 17602 #035-15-1994 L1997 **FM** *020 †18
ELSER, Christopher Scott. 133 E FREDERICK ST 17602 #041-12-1999 L2003 **AN** *020 †05
ENGLISH, John Talbot. ■ 17603 #041-13-1982 L1987 **GS** *020 †85
ESHLEMAN, Jeffrey Scott. 2102 HARRISBURG PIKE 17601 #041-09-1997 L2001 **RO** *020 †80
ESHLEMAN, John David. 555 N DUKE ST, DULMONARY SERVICES 17602 #041-01-1966 L1969 **PUD IM** *020 †20
ESHLEMAN, S Kendrick, III. 317 N DUKE ST 17602 #041-01-1953 L1954 **P** *071 †75
ESSIS, Frank Mike, Jr. 2104 HARRISBURG PIKE, STE 100 17601 #041-14-2002 L2004 **ORS** *020
ETNOYER, John Jos. 694 GOOD DR, STE 112 17601 #041-01-1966 L1977 **OBG** *020 †30
ETTER, Mark Douglas. 217 HARRISBURG AVE, STE 200 17603 #041-14-1995 L2000 **CD** *020 †20
FAHS, Gerald Richard. 555 N DUKE ST 17602 #041-13-1959 L1960 **PTH FOP** *020 †50
FAIZON, Robert Andre. 694 GOOD DR STE 11 17601 #041-12-1995 L2004 **OBG** *040 †30
FALK, Robert Barclay, Jr. 133 E FREDERICK ST 17602 #041-02-1971 L1972 **AN** *020 †05
FANNIN, Mandy Renea. 555 N DUKE ST, LANCASTER GENERAL HOSPITAL 17602 #041-15-2006 L2006 **FP** *012
FEARNOW, Edgar C, III. 555 N DUKE ST, LANCASTER RAD ASSOC LTD 17602 #036-07-1985 L1994 **DR RNR** *020 †80
FEEHAN, Patrick Robt. 1650 CROOKED OAK DR # 200 17601 #025-01-1974 L1978 **D** *020 †15
FEFFERMAN, Mark. 555 N DUKE ST 17602 #005-18-1983 L1985 **PHP FM** *020 †18
FELIX, Todd Matthew. 555 N DUKE ST 17602 #041-14-2005 L2005 **FP** *012
FERNANDO, Maria Corazon G. 231 N SHIPPEN ST # 21B 17602 #748-01-1980 L1984 **P** *020 †75 ‡
FIFE, William Andrew, Jr. 625 S DUKE ST 17602 #035-08-1998 L2000 **FM** *020 †18
FINK, Stacey Marc. 690 GOOD DR, NICU WBH 17601 #020-02-1985 L1999 **NPM PD** *020 †55
FINKELSTEIN, Eric Irving. 1671 CROOKED OAK DR 17601 #035-06-1997 L2001 **PM PME** *020 †60
FISHER, Laura Helen. 2445 MARIETTA AVE, ALLERGY & ASTHMA CENTER 17601 #041-14-2001 L2001 **AI** *100 †20,03
FOHRER, Aviva. 555 N DUKE ST, LANCASTER GENERAL HOSPITAL 17602 #550-04-2003 L2006 **FP** *012
FOUST, Wilson Arbogast. ■ 17601 #041-09-1929 L1930 **GP A** *071
FOX, Christopher Heisey. 701 N DUKE ST 17602 #041-13-1997 L1999 **FM** *020 †18 ‡
FOX, Owen Daniel. 2920 MARIETTA AVE, DAVID SILVERSTEIN ASSOCIAT 17601 #041-78-2002, ▲ L2002 **IMG** *020
FRANCOS, Charles Geo. ■ 17603 #041-02-1948 L1949 **CD GP** *071
FRISCH, Sandford Chas. 2207 OREGON PIKE, STE 102 17601 #035-08-1983 L1988 **OPH** *020 †35 ‡
FRYE, Gladys Mae. 555 N DUKE ST, LANCASTER GENERAL HOSPITAL 17602 #050-02-1993 L1995 **FM** *020 †18
FUCHS, David Earl. 3045 MARIETTA AVE 17601 #041-14-1978 L1979 **FM FPG** *020 †18
FUNK, Wendell L. 230 HARRISBURG AVE 17603 #041-13-1976 L1977 **PS U** *020 †95,65 ‡
GAREIS, John Wm. 555 N DUKE ST, LANCASTER GEN HOSP 17602 #023-01-1967 L1970 **R** *071 †80
GARRIDO, Eddy. 2100 HARRISBURG PIKE, BLDG 2108 17601 #308-01-1969 L1977 **NS** *020 †25 ‡
GARVEY, Edmund Patrick. 133 E FREDERICK ST 17602 #539-04-1970 L1978 **AN** *020 †05
GASTALDO, John Andrew. 2100 HARRISBURG PIKE, BLDG 2108 17601 #041-09-1972 L1973 **NS** *020 †25
GATES, Thomas Jay. 555 N DUKE ST, LGH DEPT FAMILY MEDICINE 17602 #024-01-1980 L1995 **FM PLM** *040 †18
GBADOUWEY, Charles. 233 COLLEGE AVE, STE 300 17603 #610-01-1988 L1997 **PCC** *020 †20 ‡
GEHMAN, Gary Stephen. 101 ABBEYVILLE RD, GRP AT FAMILY PRACTICE 17603 #041-13-1985 L1986 **FM** *020 †18
GENTZLER, Richard D, II. 217 HARRISBURG AVE, STE 200 17603 #036-07-1969 L1972 **IC CD** *071 †20 ‡
GERBERT, Kathleen Holly. 694 GOOD DR, STE 112 17601 #041-09-1984 L1988 **OBG** *020 †30
GERSTEIN, Howard Jay. 440 W CHESTNUT ST 17603 #041-14-1983 L1987 **FM** *020 †18
GIBSON, Joseph Martin. 133 E FREDERICK ST 17602 #041-02-1986 L1987 **AN** *020 †05
GILD, William Morris. 224 N PRESIDENT AVE 17603 #836-02-1972 L1979 **AN** *040 †05
GILLIO, Robert Gene. 2141 WATERFORD DR 17601 #016-01-1980 L1986 **PUD IM** *020 †20
GINDER, Steven Russell. 555 N DUKE ST 17602 #016-42-1994 L1997 **EM** *020 †16
GISH, Jonathan Samuel. 555 N DUKE ST 17602 #041-13-1993 L1996 **EM** *020 †16
GISH, Michael William. 2104 HARRISBURG PIKE, STE 100 17601 #041-01-1994 L1998 **OSM** *020 †40
GIVENS, Kerry T. 2108 HARRISBURG PIKE, STE 200 17601 #036-07-1986 L1987 **OPH** *020 †35
GOHN, Douglas Christopher. 1810 OREGON PIKE, THE HEART GROUP, LTD 17601 #041-09-1984 L1986 **CD IM** *020 †20
GOLDFARB, Lloyd G. 227 GRANITE RUN DR, STE 110 17601 #035-47-1978 L1983 **PUD IM** *020 †20
GOOD, Daniel Chas. 1671 CROOKED OAK DR, LANCASTER NEUROSCIENCE & S 17601 #041-13-1969 L1970 **NS** *071 †25
GOOD, Laura. 694 GOOD DR, STE 201 17601 #041-12-1999 L2003 **OBG** *020 †30
GOTTLIEB, Jerome I. 1030 NEW HOLLAND AVE, BLDG 12A 17601 #010-02-1974 L1984 **P** *020 †75
GOTTLIEB, Robert Jos. 2102 HARRISBURG PIKE, GROUP AT HEMATOLOGY 17601 #035-20-1965 L1971 **ON HEM** *020 †20
GOTTLIEB, Steven Michael. 2108 HARRISBURG PIKE, STE 315 17601 #048-04-1990 L1996 **CHN** *020 †55,75
GRANGER, Bradford Dylan. 2110 HARRISBURG PIKE, GRP AT MEDICAL ASSOC OF 17601 #041-12-1999 L2003 **IM** *020 †20
GRAY, Louis Philip. 1875 LITITZ PIKE 17601 #033-05-1979 L1980 **FM** *020 †18
GREENE, Neil Alan. 2106 HARRISBURG PIKE # 301 17601 #041-07-1977 L1979 **ID IM** *020 †20
GRESS, Robert Eugene. 555 N DUKE ST, LANCASTER RADIOLOGY ASSOC 17602 #041-09-1983 L1988 **DR VIR** *020 †80
GRINER, Jonathan Hersh. 1059 COLUMBIA AVE 17603 #023-01-1999 L2003 **OBG** *020 †30
GROLEAU, George Eudore. 2106 HARRISBURG PIKE 17601 #023-01-1982 L1986 **D** *020 †15
GROVE-MAHONEY, Debra E. 555 N DUKE ST, DEPT OF PATHOLOGY 17602 #038-44-1985 L1990 **PTH PCP** *020 †50
GSCHWEND, Paul, III. 555 N DUKE ST 17602 #041-01-1970 L1971 **GS** *071 †85
GUTIERREZ BOU, Fernando A. 133 E FREDERICK ST 17602 #341-03-1994 L2002 **AN** *020 †05
HAFIZ, Arif. 250 COLLEGE AVE, LAMCASTER REGIONAL MEDICAL 17603 #704-02-1990 L1995 **IM** *020 †20
HALPERN, Barton Lorence. 140 N POINTE BLVD 17601 #035-08-1974 L1979 **OPH** *020 †35
HAMBLIN, Cherise Yolande. ■ 17603 #016-06-2007 **OBG** *012
HAMPTON, Janet Anne. 502 ELIZABETH DR 17601 #041-07-1947 L1948 **FM** *071 †18
HANNA, Sameh. 1650 CROOKED OAK DR, DERMATOLOGY ASSOCIATES OF 17601 #041-14-1996 L2001 **D** *020 †15
HARBERSON, Justin J. 2112 HARRISBURG PIKE, STE 323 17601 #041-13-2002 L2002 **GE** *012 †20
HARDIN, Jeffrey M. 217 HARRISBURG AVE 17603 #023-12-1988 L2007 **CD** *020 †20
HARDY, Viviana Elise. 2110 HARRISBURG PIKE, AT DIABETES AND 17601 #020-02-1997 L2000 **END** *020 †20
HARFORD, Rhondey I. 924 RED ROSE CT 17601 #035-08-1994 L2001 **DR** *020 †80
HARGRAVE, Hugh John. 133 E FREDERICK ST 17602 #061-01-1964 L1972 **AN** *020 †05
HARROLD, Joan K C. 685 GOOD DR, HOSPICE OF LANCASTER COUNT 17601 #051-04-1989 L1997 **PLM IM** *030 †20
HAY, Alan Jay. 2110 HARRISBURG PIKE, STE 21 17601 #056-05-1970 L1994 **OM AM** *030 †18,70

HEBEL, Jeanette Louise. 1650 CROOKED OAK DR, DERMATOLOGY ASSOCIATES OF 17601 #041-12-1993 L2005 **DS D** *020 †15
HEFFERN, James Edward. 555 N DUKE ST 17602 #010-02-1964 L1983 **FM PM** *020 †60
HEINLE, Frederick J, Jr. 2104 HARRISBURG PIKE, STE 200 17601 #041-14-1973 L1974 **GS TS** *020 †85 ‡
HEISE, Andrew Patrick. 190 GOOD DR 17603 #051-04-1994 L1998 **GS** *020
HEISTERKAMP, Charles A. 1949 PINE DR 17601 #041-01-1958 L1960 **GS OS** *071
HELM, John Daniel, Jr. ■ 17601 #041-01-1938 L1940 **IM GE** *071 †20
HERMANSEN, Christian L. 555 N DUKE ST, LANCASTER GENERAL HOSPITAL 17602 #041-02-2000 L2001 **FM** *020 †18 ‡
HERSCHAFT, Richard J. 2106 HARRISBURG PIKE 17601 #051-04-1974 L1975 **D** *020 †15 ‡
HESTER, Paul Stewart. 133 E FREDERICK ST, ANMESTH ASSOC OF LANCASTER 17602 #041-14-1995 L1999 **AN** *020 †05
HINES, Roderick Edward. 1869 CHARTER LN, STE 101 17601 #041-12-1975 L1979 **N** *020 †75
HIRSCH, Irwin Leonard. 1671 OREGON PIKE 17601 #016-42-1957 L1960 **FM** *071 †18
HIRSCH, Lorin Scott. 1671 OREGON PIKE 17601 #041-13-1986 L1987 **FM** *020 †18
HO, Hieu Van. 555 N DUKE ST, DEPT OF FAMILY MED 17602 #306-01-2003 L2005 **FP** *012
HOANG, Duc Kim. ■ 17603 #941-01-1971 L1985 **PM** *020
HOERNER, George Herbert. ■ 17602 #041-09-1939 L1941 **FM** *071
HOREN KAMP, Elizabeth C. 2102 HARRISBURG PIKE, GROUP AT HEMATOLOGY 17601 #041-01-1992 L1995 **HO** *020 †20
HORVAT, Craig Peter. 555 N DUKE ST 17602 #041-09-1995 L1997 **PCC SME** *020 †20
HOWELL, Amy Elizabeth. ■ 17603 #041-14-2007 L2007 **FP** *012
HOWSE, Robert Maurice, Jr. 2110 HARRISBURG PIKE, STE 300 17601 #023-01-1986 L1987 **FM** *040 †18
HUFFNAGLE, Henry W. 555 N DUKE ST 17602 #041-01-1959 L1960 **U** *071 †95
HUGHES, David Plummer. 2104 HARRISBURG PIKE, STE 100 17601 #041-02-1972 L1978 **ORS** *020 †40 ‡
HUTT, Gordon Howard. 2112 HARRISBURG PIKE 17601 #035-09-1980 L1983 **CD IM** *020 †20
IBARRA, Joseluis. 217 HARRISBURG AVE, STE 200 17603 #048-12-1982 L1984 **CD IM** *020 †20
JACKSON, David Wm. ■ 17601 #036-01-1983 L1994 **ID** *020 †20
JANTZI, Philip James. 2301 COLUMBIA AVE 17603 #038-45-1987 L1989 **IM** *020 †20
JAROWENKO, Daleela Getsiv. 2104 HARRISBURG PIKE, STE 200 17601 #035-03-1981 L1987 **GS** *020 †85 ‡
JAROWENKO, Mark Vadim. 2110 HARRISBURG PIKE, STE ONE 17601 #035-03-1978 L1985 **U OS** *020 †95
JAYADEVAN, Rajeev. 2112 HARRISBURG PIKE, STE 202 17601 #495-27-1992 L2003 **GE** *020 †20 ‡
JIANG, Dongsheng. 555 N DUKE ST 17602 #243-32-1986 L2006 **FP** *012
JIRICKO, Milos Jilji. 1301 E KING ST 17602 #286-02-1961 L1975 **AN END** *020 †05
JOHNSON, Bertram Lee, Jr. 1821 OREGON PIKE 17601 #041-02-1970 L1971 **CD IM** *020 †20
JOHNSON, David Lewis. 1120 FRANCES AVE 17601 #041-09-1978 L1979 **P** *030 †75
JOHNSON, Joan Elliott. 2108 HARRISBURG PIKE 17601 #041-02-1983 L1984 **OBG** *071 †30
JOHNSTON, Mark Harold. 2112 HARRISBURG PIKE, STE 202 17601 #041-09-1985 L2004 **GE IM** *020 †20
JONES, David Emlyn. 133 E FREDERICK ST 17602 #041-14-1992 L1995 **AN** *020 †05
JONES, Kara Fitzmaurice. 694 GOOD DR, STE 18 17601 #051-04-1996 L2000 **OBG** *020 †30
JONES, Theodore David. 140 N POINTE BLVD 17601 #041-09-1995 L1997 **OPH** *020 †35
JONES-HENDERSON, Sheryl A. ■ 17601 #023-01-2000 L2004 **IM** *020
JORDAN, Michelle L.. 2110 HARRISBURG PIKE, # 100 17601 #041-77-2003, ▲ L2007 **IM** *100 †20
KAGER, Christopher Dion. 1671 CROOKED OAK DR 17601 #041-01-1994 L2000 **NS** *020 †25
KAGER, Stephanie P. 2100 HARRISBURG PIKE, BLDG 2106 17601 #041-13-1994 L2001 **PD** *020 †55
KANE, Joan D. 1858 CHARTER LN, STE 202 17601 #041-09-1970 L1971 **ON HO** *020 †20 ‡
KAPLAN, Karen Michelle. ■ 17601 #035-15-1979 L1982 **PD** *040 †55
KASALES, Clarence John. ■ 17601 #041-13-1946 L1947 **GP U** *072 †55,95
KEENER, Brian Jay. 231 GRANITE RUN DR, PENN STATE ORTHOPAEDICS, H 17601 #041-14-2002 L2002 **HSO** *012
KEGEL, Daniel Paul. 1059 COLUMBIA AVE, OB-GYN OF LANCASTER, INC 17603 #041-02-1978 L1981 **OBG** *020 †30
KEGEL, Eugene E. ■ 17603 #041-02-1952 L1953 **GYN** *071 †30
KEGEL, Mary Frances. 1650 CROOKED OAK DR, STE 200 17601 #041-02-1982 L1986 **D** *020 †15
KELLY, Marianne Lutz. 501 HARRISBURG AVE, BOX 3003 17603 #041-13-1975 L1979 **IM** *020 †20 ‡
KEMP, Robert Metcalfe. 211 WILLOW VALLEY SQ, D316 17602 #041-13-1956 L1957 **FM** *030 †18
KEMRER, J Donald. ■ 17601 #041-01-1959 L1960 **GP** *071
KENDALL, Leigh Wakefield. 555 N DUKE ST 17602 #050-02-1963 L1969 **GS FSM** *071 †85 ‡
KENNA, Joseph Patrick. ■ 17601 #041-02-1948 L1949 **OM EM** *071
KENT, George M. 555 N DUKE ST 17602 #041-13-1951 L1958 **ORS** *071 †40
KERR, Samuel. 2102 HARRISBURG PIKE, GROUP AT HEMATOLOGY 17601 #041-13-1999 L2001 **IM** *100 †20
KETELS, Erik Francis. 555 N DUKE ST 17602 #041-15-2001 L2001 **FM** *020 †18
KETTL, Paul Andrew. 802 NEW HOLLAND AVE, GROUP PSYCHIATRIC 17602 #041-13-1980 L1986 **PYG** *020 †75
KILBOURN, Cynthia Lynn. 555 N DUKE ST, DEPT FAMILY & COMM MED 17602 #041-01-1987 L1994 **FM OBG** *020 †18
KILLOUGH, Steven F. 2100 HARRISBURG PIKE, BLDG 2106 17601 #041-09-1986 L1987 **PD** *020 †55
KING, Bruce Edwin. ■ 17601 #051-04-1993 L1998 **HMP** *020 †50
KING, John Allen. 2301 COLUMBIA AVE 17603 #045-01-1992 L1994 **IM** *020 †20
KIRCHNER, G Gary. 555 N DUKE ST 17602 #041-09-1959 L1960 **GS** *071 †85
KISTLER, Heidi Tamana. 555 N DUKE ST, LANCASTER GENERAL HOSPITAL 17602 #041-14-2004 L2004 **FM** *020 †18
KLOTZ, Steven Glen. 2461 LITITZ PIKE 17601 #035-47-1992 L2006 **P CHP** *020
KNAUB, Marilyn Bauer. 625 S DUKE ST 17602 #041-07-1979 L1980 **FM** *020 †18
KO, Eugene Chong Hun. 227 GRANITE RUN DR, STE 110 17601 #583-01-1982 L1987 **PUD IM** *020 †20
KOCH, Andrew W. ■ 17601 #041-13-1951 L1955 **DR** *071 †80
KONTRA, Joseph Michael. 2106 HARRISBURG PIKE # 310 17601 #041-12-1982 L1985 **ID IM** *020 †20
KRAMER, John Beryl. 2110 HARRISBURG PIKE, STE 21 17601 #023-01-1971 L1985 **OM IM** *020 †70
KRATZ, Fran Kennel. 555 N DUKE ST, LANCASTER EMERGENCY ASSOCI 17602 #041-12-2001 L2001 **EM** *020 †16
KRAVITZ, Daniel Bruce. 101 GOOD DR 17603 #041-02-1984 L1985 **P** *020 †75
KREBS-JIMENEZ, Jessica D. 120 ROUNDTOP DR 17601 #036-08-1995 L1998 **OBG** *020 †30
KREIDER, John Kuhns. 555 N DUKE ST 17602 #041-02-1958 L1963 **GP OM** *071 †18
KRESPAN, Charles Bentley. 694 GOOD DR, STE 112 17601 #041-02-1982 L1985 **OBG** *020 †30 ‡
KRISSINGER, Robert C. ■ 17601 #041-13-1957 L1958 **GP** *071
KRULEWSKI, Thomas Frank. 810 PLAZA BLVD, STE 103 17601 #035-47-1990 L1994 **OPH** *020 †35 ‡
KRUSEN, David Edward. 1703 OREGON PIKE 17601 #041-09-1947 L1948 **GP** *071
KUMAR, Shakthi Mangesh. 2100 HARRISBURG PIKE, STE 1 2106 MEDICAL OFFICE 17601 #495-04-1986 L2001 **PD** *020 †55
KUSTERA, Stephen John. 2541 MONDAMIN FARM RD 17601 #165-04-1968 L1984 **PM** *020 †60
LA CORTE, Anthony Joseph. 1725 OREGON PIKE, STE 107B 17601 #041-13-1994 L1996 **IM** *020 †20 ‡
LACY, Lucy Goode Garnett. ■ 17603 #051-01-1948 L1950 **P** *071
LANCASTER, Edward Lee, Jr. ■ 17601 #041-02-1948 L1949 **ORS** *071
LANCELOTTA, Charles J, III. 133 E FREDERICK ST, LANCASTER 17602 #023-01-1995 L2000 **AN** *020 †05
LANDA, Israel. 439 N PINE ST 17603 #016-11-2004 L2004 **EM** *020
LANDO, Yaroslav. 555 N DUKE ST 17602 #041-13-1992 L1994 **PCC** *020 †20
LARRABEE, Roland Jos, Jr. 555 N DUKE ST, LANCASTER GENERAL HOSPITAL 17602 #050-02-1980 L1981 **FM** *040 †18
LATSHAW, Robert Frederick. 555 N DUKE ST 17602 #041-14-1973 L1974 **DR** *020 †80
LAUBE, Greta L B. 2150 NOLL DR, BEITTEL-BECKER PEDIATRIC 17603 #038-41-1999 L2002 **PD** *020 †55
LAUTER, O Scott. 2110 HARRISBURG PIKE, GRP AT MEDICAL ASSOC OF 17601 #041-02-1982 L1985 **IM IMG** *020 †20 ‡
LAWSON, Joseph Hamilton. ■ 17602 #048-02-1945 L1945 **DR** *071
LE, Phuoc Hong. 702 EDEN RD, WILLOW SPRING IM 17601 #050-02-1990 L2004 **IM** *020 †20
LEAMAN, Douglas Edward. ■ 17602 #041-09-1997 L2007 **FM** *020 †18
LEAMAN, Ivan Barge. 555 N DUKE ST 17602 #041-09-1958 L1959 **FM** *072 †18
LEAMAN, John Harold, II. ■ 17603 #041-01-2002 *100
LEAPMAN, Herschel Ronald. ■ 17603 #041-12-1963 L1964 **EM** *071
LEA-STOKES, Michele J. 2141 OREGON PIKE, T.W. PONESSA & ASSOC COUNS 17601 #041-14-1982 L1991 **P** *020 †75
LEGERE, John B. 2106 HARRISBURG PIKE 17601 #041-77-1982, ▲ L1991 **D VS** *020
LEHMAN, Harvey L, Jr. ■ 17603 #041-01-1946 L1950 **GP OM** *071
LEISEY, John Richard. 555 N DUKE ST 17602 #041-14-1997 L2003 **EM** *020 †16
LENTZ, Ronald Jay. ■ 17603 #041-02-1961 L1962 **AM FM** *020 †70,18
LESKO, Michael G. 2112 HARRISBURG PIKE 17601 #041-77-1985, ▲ L1987 **CD** *020 †20
LESLIE, Paul Albert. 555 N DUKE ST 17602 #025-07-1984 L1991 **DR N** *030 †80
LESSANS, Kenneth Daniel. 2110 HARRISBURG PIKE 17601 #021-01-1993 L1995 **U** *020 †95
LEVIN, Richard Mark. 1608 LITITZ PIKE 17601 #016-11-1968 L1975 **PS HS** *020 †65
LEVY, Bret Michael. 555 N DUKE ST, LANCASTER GENERAL HOSPITAL 17602 #041-02-1996 L2001 **EM** *020 †16
LEWIS, Maryellen Cathleen. 555 N DUKE ST, LANCASTER GENERAL HOSPITAL 17602 #035-15-2007 L2007 **FP** *012
LINCOLN, Stephen D. 250 COLLEGE AVE 17603 #023-01-1977 L2003 **TS GS** *020 †85,90
LING, David. 2145 NOLL DR 17603 #041-13-1986 L1987 **FM** *020 †18
LONG, Thomas Jeffrey. 133 E FREDERICK ST 17602 #054-04-1979 L1996 **AN PD** *020 †55,05
LORAH, Kevin Neal. 690 GOOD DR, WOMEN & BABIES HOSPITAL 17601 #041-02-1985 L1986 **NPM PD** *020 †55
LOSS, David M. 1810 OREGON PIKE 17601 #041-77-1978, ▲ L1979 **CD IM** *020
LU, Milton Ming-Dei. 614 N DUKE ST 17602 #242-17-1951 L1959 **PS HS** *071
LUCK, Jerry Conrad. 2112 HARRISBURG PIKE, STE 100 - P O BOX 3200 17601 #041-13-1973 L1976 **CD IM** *040 †20
MACKEY, Stephanie Annette. 800 NEW HOLLAND AVE STE A 17602 #041-14-1992 L1995 **D** *020 †15
MADARA, Glenn Stanger. 250 COLLEGE AVE, LANCASTER REGIONAL MED CTR 17603 #041-02-1983 L1988 **AN** *020 †05
MAHAJAN, Anand B. 690 GOOD DR 17601 #496-38-1980 L1984 **NPM PD** *020 †55
MALCYNSKI, John Thomas. 555 N DUKE ST, LANCASTER GENERAL HOSPITAL 17602 #024-07-1991 L1998 **CCS** *020 †85
MALEY, Edward David. 2104 HARRISBURG PIKE, STE 100 17601 #028-02-1966 L1974 **ORS** *020 †40 ‡
MALHOTRA, Preeti. 2145 NOLL DR 17603 #496-07-1994 L2002 **FM** *020 †18
MANDALAKAS, Nicholas John. 2112 HARRISBURG PIKE 17601 #041-02-1985 L1986 **CD IM** *020 †20
MANETTA, Frank. 555 N DUKE ST, LANCASTERN GEN HOSPITAL 17602 #041-07-1994 L2001 **GS** *020 †85,90
MANN, Eric Ashton. 1771 WICKERSHAM LN 17603 #041-07-1988 L1994 **OTO** *020 †45
MANN, Marianne Culkin. 1771 WICKERSHAM LN 17603 #041-07-1986 L1987 **CCM IM** *020 †20
MANNING, Francis Jos. 2158 EMBASSY DR 17603 #041-14-1989 L1991 **OPH** *020 †35 ‡
MARTENS, Wm Stanton, II. 233 COLLEGE AVE, STE 200 17603 #035-03-1974 L1977 **PD** *020 †55
MARTIN, Jeffrey Lee. 2112 HARRISBURG PIKE, STE 312 17601 #041-14-1998 L2000 **NEP IM** *020 †20
MARTIN, Jeffrey Roth. 555 N DUKE ST, COMMUNITY MEDICINE 17602 #007-02-1993 L1996 **FM** *020 †18
MARTIN, Robert Whitney. 645 N PRESIDENT AVE, 645 N. PRESIDENT AVE. 17603 #041-09-1964 L1965 **IM** *020 †20
MARWAHA, Ajay Rai. 217 HARRISBURG AVE 17603 #038-06-1997 L2000 **CD** *020 †20
MAST, Truman Emanuel. 8 N QUEEN ST 17603 #038-06-1961 L1974 **P** *071 †75
MASTROPIETRO, Nunzio A. 2145 NOLL DR 17603 #010-02-1971 L1972 **FM** *020 †18
MATHEWS, Robert Simon. 554 N DUKE ST STE 2 17602 #036-07-1964 L1973 **ORS APM** *020 †40 ‡
MAURIELLO, Anthony J, Jr. 554 N DUKE ST, STE 2 17602 #030-06-1993 L1999 **ORS** *020 †40
MAY, Dorothy Christine. 2128 EMBASSY DR, DRS. EICHENLAUB AND MAY 17603 #041-07-1996 L2000 **OBG** *020 †30
MAY, John Clark. 2100 HARRISBURG PIKE, WOMEN WELLNESS CLINIC 17601 #041-01-1960 L1963 **OBG** *071 †30
MAZZACCO, Stacey Louise. 2104 HARRISBURG PIKE, STE 200 17601 #041-13-1992 L1994 **VS GS** *020 †85 ‡
MC CANN, William Dean. 1866 COLONIAL VILLAGE LN 17601 #041-02-1961 L1962 **OM CD** *071 †20
MC GILLIS, Susan Teri. 230 HARRISBURG AVE 17603 #005-19-1984 L2006 **D OS** *020 †15

■ = Address Information Privacy Protected

MC INTYRE, Daniel Patrick. 555 N DUKE ST 17602 #041-02-2000 L2003 EM *020 †16

MC KERNAN, Melissa Lynn. 217 HARRISBURG AVE, THE HEART GROUP 17603 #041-02-1998 L2001 ICE *020 †20

MC LANE, Christopher G. 1671 OREGON PIKE, FAMILY PRACTICE ASSOCIATES 17601 #038-06-1995 L1997 FM *020 †18

MCMICHAEL, Josette Renee. ■ 17602 #051-01-1994 L1994 FM *020 †18

MC SPARREN, Clark, Jr. 2100 HARRISBURG PIKE, BLDG 2106 17601 #041-01-1959 L1960 PD *071 †55

MEDINA, James Lawrence. 555 N DUKE ST 17602 #023-01-1999 L2003 EM *020 †16

MEGIVERN, Daniel Gary. 113 BUTLER AVE 17601 #041-02-1984 L1985 FM *020 †18

MEHM, Joseph William. 703 LAMPETER RD, ORTHOPEDIC CONSULTANTS 17602 #028-34-1970 L1988 ORS *071 †40 ‡

MELAMED, Brian R. 1371 BEACONFIELD LN 17601 #011-02-1983 L1984 AN *020 †05

MICHEL, Donna Marie. 2112 HARRISBURG PIKE, HYPERTENSION AND KIDNEY 17601 #038-06-1993 L1996 NEP IM *020 †20

MIESZKALSKI, Glenn B. 233 COLLEGE AVE, STE 100 17603 #041-09-1990 L1993 RO *020 †80

MILLER, John William, Jr. 810 PLAZA BLVD, STE 101 17601 #041-02-1962 L1963 OTO *071 †45

MILLER, John Wm. III. 810 PLAZA BLVD 17601 #051-01-1988 L1993 OTO HNS *020 †45

MILLER, Myrna Broun. 802 NEW HOLLAND AVE, GROUP PSYCHIATRIC 17602 #038-06-1965 L1992 P PYG *030 †75

MILLER, Parry John. 924 RED ROSE CT 17601 #041-13-1970 L1971 R *020 †80 ‡

MIZERAK, Nancy J. 2741 LITITZ PIKE 17601 #011-04-1980 L1981 FM *020 †18

MODY, Lena Jaswant. 1858 CHARTER LN, STE 202 17601 #665-01-2000 L2006 HO *020 ‡

MOHLER, J Harold. 817 N CHERRY ST 17602 #041-13-1974 L1979 IM NEP *020 †20 ‡

MONCRIEF, Richard D. 1671 OREGON PIKE 17601 #041-12-1949 L1950 FM *071

MONTEFORTE, Madhavi R. 133 E FREDERICK ST 17602 #041-13-1994 L1996 AN PMM *020 †05

MONTGOMERY, Maxine D. 1671 CROOKED OAK DR 17601 #041-13-1970 L1971 N GP *071 †75

MOORE, Rachel Marie. 734 N FRANKLIN ST 17602 #041-02-1995 L1997 FM *020 †18

MOORE, Robert Glen. 133 E FREDERICK ST 17602 #041-14-1977 L1985 AN *020 †05

MORPHY, Heather Anne. 1725 OREGON PIKE, STE 107B 17601 #035-01-1996 L1998 FM *071 †35 ‡

MOTL, Margaret A. 133 E FREDERICK ST 17602 #056-06-1981 L2002 AN *020 †05

MUELLER, Garry Leland. 3045 MARIETTA AVE 17601 #023-01-1983 L1984 FM *020 †18

MURPHY, Gregory Lee. 3045 MARIETTA AVE 17601 #041-13-1982 L1983 FM *020 †18

MUSSER, David John. 555 N DUKE ST 17602 #041-13-1989 L1994 VS *071 †85

NADKARNY, Uday Ramdas. 690 GOOD DR 17601 #495-01-1975 L1983 NPM PD *020 †55

NEBEL, Kristen Marie. 544 N DUKE ST 17602 #041-77-2003, ▲ L2003 FPG *020 †18

NELSON, Althea Murrie. 555 N DUKE ST, LANCASTER GENERAL HOSPITAL 17602 #041-07-1991 L1993 FM *020 †18

NEPTUNE, Steven Michael. 133 E FREDERICK ST 17602 #041-14-1995 L1999 AN *020 †05 ‡

NEUREUTER, Louis John. 25 E JAMES ST 17602 #041-09-1975 L1976 PUD UM *020 †20

NEWCOMER, David Lee. 217 HARRISBURG AVE, STE 201 17603 #041-13-1973 L1976 GS *020 †85 ‡

NEWMAN, Paul Gerard. 2104 HARRISBURG PIKE, STE 200 17601 #033-05-1992 L1995 CCS TRS *020 †85 ‡

NGUYEN, Don Quang. 555 N DUKE ST 17602 #065-10-1993 L1998 IM *020 †20

NICHOLS, Stephen Frederic. 555 N DUKE ST 17602 #041-13-1984 L1985 AN PME *020 †05

NODINE, John Hazen. PO BOX 3555 17604 #041-01-1947 L1951 FM IM *020 †20

NOJIMA, Kimi. ■ 17602 #025-01-1932 L1935 PUD *071

NOVOSEL, Peter Steven. 446 W CHESTNUT ST 17603 #041-13-1973 L1974 FM *020 †18

OCHENRIDER, Paul David. ■ 17603 #041-13-1943 L1944 GP GS *071

OCKRYMIEK, Douglas Alex. 101 GOOD DR 17603 #041-77-1971, ▲ L1980 P PYG *020 †75,18

O'CONNOR, Elizabeth Anne. ■ 17601 #021-01-2002 L2008 IM *020 †20

O'CONOR, Gregory Thos., Jr. 2102 HARRISBURG PIKE, GROUP AT HEMATOLOGY 17601 #010-02-1978 L1979 HEM ON *020 †20

OLIN, Stephen T. 555 N DUKE ST, LANCASTER GENERAL HOSP 17602 #024-05-1973 L1974 FM *020 †18

O'NEILL, Brendan James. ■ 17602 #041-15-2007 L2007 IM *012

ONGUKA, Stephanie Lynn. ■ 17601 #010-02-2007 L2007 *012

OVERHOLT, Thomas Chas. 2110 HARRISBURG PIKE, STE 100 17601 #041-14-1979 L1989 IM PD *020 †20,55

OYER, Randall A. 609 N CHERRY ST, LANCASTER GENERAL HOSPITAL 17602 #010-02-1980 L1982 ICE *020 †20

OYER, Rosanne Elizabeth. ■ 17603 #010-02-1980 L1982 OBG *071 †30

PACELLI, James Patrick. 2106 HARRISBURG PIKE, GROUP LANCASTER NEUROLOGY 17601 #422-01-2000 L2004 N *020

PAIST, Stanley Scott, III. 2106 HARRISBURG PIKE, STE 10 17601 #041-02-1975 L1978 FM *040 †18

PALLEN, Daniel. 2106 HARRISBURG PIKE, STE 309 17601 #035-06-1970 L1977 OPH *020 †35

PALUMBO, John Anthony. 1525 OREGON PIKE, STE 1201 17601 #561-01-1970 L1972 FM *020 †18

PARAKHOODI M., Hamid. 233 COLLEGE AVE, STE 201 17603 #166-01-1999 L2006 ID *020 †20

PARIKH, Ameet N. 2112 HARRISBURG PIKE, STE 323 17601 #495-76-1991 L1999 GE *020 †20 ‡

PARKER, Steven Leslie. 2104 HARRISBURG PIKE, STE 200 17601 #035-20-1982 L1987 GS VS *020 †85 ‡

PARRISH, William Michael. 2150 NOLL DR, PENN STATE ORTHOPEDICS 17603 #055-01-1986 L1993 OMO ORS *020 †40

PATEL, Harshadkumar B. 555 N DUKE ST 17602 #495-23-1970 L1976 PUD SME *071 †20

PATEL, Sunil Prabhundas. 2112 HARRISBURG PIKE 17601 #495-22-1992 L2002 CD *020 †20

PAVLICA, Michael Robt. 2110 HARRISBURG PIKE, FAMILY EYE GRP 17601 #035-19-1990 L1996 OPH IM *020 †35 ‡

PAWLSON, Brent David. 2100 HARRISBURG PIKE, BUILDING 2106/P O BOX 3200 17601 #051-07-2000 L2001 PD *020 †55

PEARMAN, Trevor James. ■ 17601 #352-01-1958 L1970 P *071

PENA, Rhonda Lynn. 555 NORTH ST, DEPT FAMLY & COMMNTY MED 17602 #422-01-2002 L2002 OBG *012

PENCHANSKY, Barry Howard. 625 S DUKE ST 17602 #041-02-1971 L1972 FM AM *020 †18

PENNELL, Rebecca Grace. 555 N DUKE ST 17602 #041-07-1980 L1982 DR *020 †80

PEREZOUS, Mark Kenneth. 231 GRANITE RUN DR, STE 100 17601 #041-13-1989 L1991 ORS OSM *020 †40

PERLIS, Maria F. 440 W CHESTNUT ST 17603 #035-15-1994 L1996 FM *020 †18

PERLMAN, Marc Brian. 555 N DUKE ST, LANCASTER GENERAL HOSPITAL 17602 #035-03-1979 L2008 NPM PD *020 †55

PETERS, Harold E. 555 N DUKE ST 17602 #041-02-1951 L1952 OM *071

PETERSON, Alan Scott. 555 N DUKE ST 17602 #024-05-1972 L1973 FM FPG *040 †18

PETERSON, Christopher J. 133 E FREDERICK ST 17602 #041-14-1984 L1985 AN *020 †05

PETERSON, Roger Delmar. 555 N DUKE ST, LANCASTER GENERAL HOSP 17602 #011-02-1963 L1971 R NM *071 †80

PFALTZGRAFF, Roy Edward. PO BOX 5093, 3001 LITITZ PIKE 17606 #041-13-1942 L1944 OS *071

PHAN, Hiep Chautuan. 355 W CHESTNUT ST, APT 310 17603 #041-13-1996 L2003 GS *020 †85

PHEASANT-VISCUSI, Holli. 555 N DUKE ST 17602 #041-02-1994 L1997 FM *020 †18

PHILLIPS, Spencer David. 408 CARDINAL CT 17601 #041-13-1982 L1983 FM *020 †18 ‡

PLASTINO, John Edward. 555 N DUKE ST 17602 #041-02-1976 L1979 FM IM *020 †18,16

PLAYFOOT, Donald Edward. 685 GOOD DR BOX 4125, HOSPICE OF LANCASTER CNTY 17601 #041-02-1977 L1981 FM *020 †18

PLOURDE, Paul Victor. 734 N FRANKLIN ST 17602 #050-02-1978 L1979 END IM *050 †20

PLUTNICKI, Ronald Stephen. 549 N LIME ST, C/O MAY-GRANT ASSOC 17602 #033-05-1971 L1977 OBG *020 †30

POHL, Charles Edward. ■ 17603 #041-09-1956 L1957 U *071 †95

POHL, Joanne C. 694 GOOD DR, STE 112 17601 #035-15-1993 L1995 OBG *020 †30

POLIN, David G. 2110 HARRISBURG PIKE 17601 #041-02-1984 L1987 PM *020 †60

PONTIUS, James G. ■ 17601 #041-01-1953 L1954 GS *071 †85

POOLE, Kevin Jan. 701 N DUKE ST 17602 #023-01-2001 L2001 FM *020

POPA, Camelia. ■ 17601 #781-06-1984 L2000 PYG *020 †75

PRAZAK-LERMAN, Beatrice. PO BOX 5093, 3001 LITITZ PIKE 17606 #041-13-1942 L1943 HEM *071

PRICE, Albert Chas. ■ 17603 #041-02-1959 L1960 PD PDC *071 †55

PRICE, Mary Lynne. ■ 17603 #005-12-1983 L1989 PD N *020 †80

PROCOPE, Julian A. 822 MARIETTA AVE, STE 22 17603 #023-07-1990 L1995 OPH *020 †35

PULLIAM, Robert Ward, II. 217 HARRISBURG AVE, THE HEART GROUP 17603 #027-01-1997 L2002 ICE *020 †20

PUNJWANI, Nooruddin S. ■ 17601 #704-25-1996 L2006 DR *020 †80

PURDY, Richard Thos. ■ 17601 #035-09-1957 L1976 VS GS *020 †85

QUINN, Timothy. 1671 OREGON PIKE 17601 #035-15-1990 L1992 FM *020 †18

RAICH, William Alan. 2108 HARRISBURG PIKE, STE 200 17601 #041-01-1967 L1968 OPH *071 †35 ‡

RAO, Akinepally Naveen. ■ 17603 #495-57-1977 L1980 IM *020 †20

RAPP, Terri Lynne. 694 GOOD DR, STE 112 17601 #035-08-1996 L1998 OBG *020 †30

RAST, Mark Lyndon. 555 N DUKE ST, LANCASTER GENERAL HOSPITAL 17602 #041-01-1987 L1994 FM *020 †18

REESE, Kelly Ann. 625 S DUKE ST, SOUTHEAST LANCASTER HEALTH 17602 #041-09-1997 L2007 FM *020 †18

RICE, Samuel Alan. 2301 COLUMBIA AVE 17603 #041-14-1971 L1976 IM ADM *020 †20 ‡

RIDGWAY, William Gerald. ■ 17601 #041-02-1942 L1943 GP *071 †18

RIEBEL, Scott Taylor. 802 NEW HOLLAND AVE, STE 200 17602 #035-15-1994 L1996 IC CD *020 †20 ‡

RIGANO, Rudolph Francis. 230 HARRISBURG AVE 17603 #422-01-1981 L1982 IM *020 †20

RILEY, Daron Paul. 555 N DUKE ST 17602 #024-07-1995 L1998 EM *020 †16

RILEY, Deborah K. 2106 HARRISBURG PIKE, STE 301 17601 #038-40-1988 L1993 ID IM *020 †20

RILEY, Timothy Daniel. 734 N FRANKLIN ST 17602 #035-15-2002 L2002 FM *020 †18

RIPPLE, Paul Harnish. ■ 17602 #041-14-1946 L1947 OPH *071 †35

RIZZO, Karen A. 810 PLAZA BLVD, STE 101 17601 #041-13-1985 L1986 OTO *020 †45

ROBBINS, Warren Jay. 231 GRANITE RUN DR 17601 #041-01-1957 L1967 ORS OSM *071 †40

ROBERTS, Karen Leigh. 694 GOOD DR, MAY GRANT 17601 #038-44-1984 L1996 OBG *020 †30

ROBERTS, William Dotson. 101 ABBEYVILLE RD, FAMILY PRACTICE ASSOC 17603 #036-07-1977 L1978 FM *020 †18

ROCHESTER, James Alfred. 241 ROHRERSTOWN RD, STE 200 17603 #041-13-1995 L1997 FM *020 †18

ROCKWELL, Nicholas Leigh. 555 N DUKE ST 17602 #041-14-1999 L2003 AN *020 †05

RODENBERGER, Charles H. 2112 HARRISBURG PIKE, HYPERTENSION AND KIDNEY 17601 #041-01-1988 L1990 NEP *020 †20

RODGERS, John Chas. 2104 HARRISBURG PIKE, STE 100 17601 #041-02-1989 L1990 ORS OTR *020 †40

ROMBERGER, Charles Frank. 555 N DUKE ST, LANCASTER GENERAL HOSPITAL 17602 #041-13-1986 L2007 PTH *020 †50

ROMITO, Roseann. 1023 WOODS AVE 17603 #010-01-1984 L1987 DR *020 †20,80

ROMMEL, Catherine Thomas. 2128 EMBASSY DR 17603 #041-02-1980 L1981 OPH *020 †35 ‡

ROSCHEL, Robert Lambert. 2106 HARRISBURG PIKE 17601 #041-01-1958 L1959 D *020 †15 ‡

ROSENFELD, David Jon. 233 COLLEGE AVE, STE 202 17603 #035-06-1983 L1984 OTO HNS *020 †45

ROSS, Patricia Eyrich. 555 N DUKE ST 17602 #041-13-1963 L1967 PD *062 †55

ROSSINI, Gregory Joseph. 555 N DUKE ST 17602 #041-09-1994 L1997 PCC *020 †20

ROST, Charles Richard. 2110 HARRISBURG PIKE, AT DIABETES AND 17601 #041-13-1974 L1984 DIA END *020 †20 ‡

ROTHACKER, Gerald W, Jr. 2104 HARRISBURG PIKE # 100 17601 #041-09-1976 L1981 ORS OTR *020 †40 ‡

ROWAN, Paul Jos. 1277 MEADOWBROOK RD 17603 #041-01-1945 L1946 GS CRS *071 †85

RUNG, George Wm. 555 N DUKE ST 17602 #041-14-1982 L1983 AN PME *020 †05 ‡

RUSSELL, Hollyann Emily. ■ 17603 #035-45-2007 L2007 FP *012

RUSSINKO, Paul Joseph. 2106 HARRISBURG PIKE, STE 200 17601 #033-06-1996 L2005 U *020 †95

RUTH, Thomas Kevin. 817 N CHERRY ST 17602 #051-04-1983 L1984 IM *020 †20 ‡

SAAD, Christine Georgine. 2110 HARRISBURG PIKE, STE 215 17601 #041-13-2002 L2002 OPH *100 †35 ‡

SADHUKHAN, Ankur Kumar. 2112 HARRISBURG PIKE 17601 #033-05-1997 L2000 FM *020 †18

SADHUKHAN, Madhumita. 240 W CHESTNUT ST 17603 #041-09-1997 L2000 FM *020 †18

SALAMA, Hany G. 1869 CHARTER LN, STE 101 17601 #915-04-1985 L2004 CN *020 †75

SALLAVANTI, Robert A, Jr. 2207 OREGON PIKE, STE 202 17601 #041-14-1992 L1994 FM *020 †18

SALMONS, Valerie Ann. 133 E FREDERICK ST 17602 #041-14-1995 L2000 AN *020 †05 ‡

SANCHEZ, Carlos Alberto. 817 N CHERRY ST, LANCASTER INTERNAL MEDICAL 17602 #041-14-1997 L2000 IM *020 †20

SANDHAUS, Beatrice W. 250 COLLEGE AVE 17603 #041-07-1938 L1939 GP GYN *071

SAUNDERS, Frederick Carel. 2112 HARRISBURG PIKE, STE 202 17601 #005-12-1966 L1987 GE IM *020 †20 ‡

SAWANT, Sharayu Bipin. 555 N DUKE ST, DEPT OF FAMILY MED 17602 #496-52-1996 L2005 FP *012

SCEPPA, Jennifer Ann. 1650 CROOKED OAK DR, STE 200 17601 #041-01-2001 L2001 D DMP *020 †15

■ = Address Information Privacy Protected

SCHAEFFER, William Andrew. ■ 17603 #024-01-1944 L1950 **IM** *071 †20
SCHANTZ, John Christian. 555 N DUKE ST 17602 #041-09-1971 L1972 **PS** *020 †85,65
SCHMIDT, Winsor Chase. ■ 17601 #024-01-1943 L1946 **ORS** *071 †40
SCHNEIDER, Chester Louis. ■ 17602 #041-02-1947 L1949 **P** *071 †75
SCHWARTZ, Stephen M. 3059 COLUMBIA AVE 17603 #041-02-1980 L1985 **EM FM** *020
SCHWARTZ, Steven Robt. 217 HARRISBURG AVE STE 101 17603 #041-02-1984 L1985 **OPH** *071 †35
SCOTT, Jason Eric. 2110 HARRISBURG PIKE, GRP AT MEDICAL ASSOC OF 17601 #038-43-1996 L2000 **IM** *020 †20 ‡
SCOTT, John Jeffrey. 2301 COLUMBIA AVE 17603 #012-05-1984 L1988 **IM IMG** *020 †20
SCOTT, Susanne Engler. 3045 MARIETTA AVE, OYSTER POINT FAMILY HEALTH 17601 #036-07-1999 L2001 **FM PLM** *020 †18
SCOTT, Thomas Christopher. 3045 MARIETTA AVE 17601 #041-02-1999 L2001 **FM** *020 †18
SHARKEY, Sean Jos, Jr. 555 N DUKE ST 17602 #041-07-1987 L1988 **AN PME** *020 †05
SHARP, John Wm, Jr. 2106 HARRISBURG PIKE, STE 309 17601 #033-06-1984 L1985 **OPH** *020 †35
SHAUB, Howard Geo, Jr. ■ 17603 #041-02-1946 L1948 **CLP PTH** *071 †50
SHIRK, Michael Scott. 2113 MANOR RIDGE DR 17603 #041-13-1996 L1998 **FM** *020 †18
SHLIMOVICH, Mara. 211 WILLOW VALLEY SQ, # D-306 17602 #913-86-1958 L1985 **P** *071
SHULTZ, Margarita. 1300 MILLERSVILLE PIKE 17603 #041-12-1968 L1969 **R** *020 †80 ‡
SHULTZ, Robert Glenn. 900 E KING ST 17602 #041-12-1965 L1966 **IM END** *020 †20
SIEGER, David Douglas. 2104 HARRISBURG PIKE, STE 100 17601 #041-02-1984 L1985 **ORS** *020 †40 ‡
SILBERT, David Irving. 2110 HARRISBURG PIKE 17601 #038-06-1989 L1993 **OPH PO** *020 †35 ‡
SIMMONS, Mark Linwood. 2110 HARRISBURG PIKE, GRP AT MEDICAL ASSOC OF 17601 #041-14-1995 L1997 **IM** *020 †20
SINGH, Surender. 2112 HARRISBURG PIKE 17601 #495-36-1972 L1975 **CD IM** *020 †20
SINGMAN, Eric L. 2110 HARRISBURG PIKE 17601 #035-08-1992 L1997 **N OPH** *020 †35 ‡
SINOR, Bakhti Jehangir. 1858 CHARTER LN, LANCASTER CANCER CENTER LT 17601 #496-38-1971 L1982 **ON HEM** *020 †20 ‡
SISSON, William Hempstead. ■ 17601 #050-02-1945 L1949 **P** *071 †75
SKEEHAN, Thomas Michael. 133 E FREDERICK ST, ANESTHESIA ASSOCIATES OF L 17602 #016-06-1983 L1984 **AN** *020 †05
SLENKER, Kevin F. 133 E FREDERICK ST 17602 #041-02-1983 L1987 **AN** *020 †05
SLJAPIC, Tatjana. 802 NEW HOLLAND AVE, HEART SPECIALISTS OF LANCA 17602 #957-07-1992 L1997 **ICE CD** *020 †20
SLOVAK, John Paul, Jr. 217 HARRISBURG AVE, THE HEART GROUP, LTD 17603 #041-09-1976 L1977 **CD IM** *020 †20
SMALL, Roy Scott. 217 HARRISBURG AVE STE 200 17603 #028-34-1979 L1990 **CD IM** *020 †20
SMITH, Ellen Kathleen. 2135 NOLL DR, STE D 17603 #041-02-1978 L1979 **CD** *020 †20
SMITH, Eugene Chas. 1655 CROOKED OAK DR 17601 #041-13-1960 L1961 **FM** *071 †18
SMITH, Peter Raymond. 250 COLLEGE AVE 17603 #054-04-1978 L1987 **DR** *020 †80 ‡
SNYDER, Scott Gordon. 3045 MARIETTA AVE 17601 #041-14-1993 L1996 **FM** *020 †18
SOHAIL, Neelofer. 2110 HARRISBURG PIKE, STE 300 17601 #496-33-1996 L2001 **FM** *020 †18
SOLOMON, Elias Max. 516 N DUKE ST 17602 #041-01-1934 L1935 **GP** *071
SPICHER, James Everett. 2301 COLUMBIA AVE 17603 #041-14-1986 L1987 **IM** *020 †20
SPRINGER, Robert M, III. 250 COLLEGE AVE 17603 #041-05-1981 L1986 **VIR** *020 †80 ‡
STABLER, Christine K. 555 N DUKE ST, FAMILY & COMM MED 17602 #041-02-1980 L1981 **FM** *040 †18
STEINMAN, Robert Chas. ■ 17601 #035-08-1945 L1972 **PM** *071 †60
STENGEL, Robert Joseph. 3045 MARIETTA AVE, OYSTER PT FAM HLTH CTR 17601 #041-12-1985 L1986 **FM** *020 †18
STENMAN, Nils Gustaf. 1059 COLUMBIA AVE, PENNSYLVANIA HOSPITAL 17603 #041-02-2001 L2001 **OBG** *020
STERENFELD, Elliot B. 555 N DUKE ST 17602 #016-06-1989 L1993 **PM** *020 †60
STEWART, Christi Ann. 555 N DUKE ST 17602 #051-01-2003 L2003 **FPG** *020 †18
STEWART, Peter Jeremy. 555 N DUKE ST, TRAMA DEPT 17602 #056-05-1983 L2005 **TRS CCS** *020 †85
STIEBER, Scott Frederick. 133 E FREDERICK ST 17602 #056-05-1981 L1985 **AN** *020 †05
STILLWELL, Peter Mackey. 924 RED ROSE CT 17601 #041-07-1996 L2001 **DR** *020 †80
ST JOHN, Kelly Marie. 133 E FREDERICK ST, LTD 17602 #041-07-1991 L1994 **AN** *020 †05
STOKKE, Orton Harry. ■ 17602 #056-06-1948 L1949 **IM** *020 †20
STOUT, William John. 555 N DUKE ST 17602 #041-13-1945 L1946 **GP** *071
STUART, Thomas Jos. 555 N DUKE ST 17602 #010-02-1954 L1961 **N** *071 †75
STULL, Mark Warren. 133 E FREDERICK ST 17602 #041-02-1982 L1986 **AN ORS** *020 †05
SULLIVAN, Brian Patrick. 101 ABBEVILLE RD, GRP AT FAMILY PRACTICE 17603 #041-13-2001 L2001 **FM** *020 †18
SUPPLE, Edward Wm. 1810 OREGON PIKE, THE HEART GROUP, LTD 17601 #024-01-1979 L1987 **CD IM** *020 †20
SUSSMAN, Gilbert Barry. 140 N POINTE BLVD 17601 #035-08-1967 L2000 **OPH** *020 †35
SWEENEY, Christine. 233 COLLEGE AVE, STE 200 17603 #041-02-1994 L1996 **PD** *020 †55
SZARKO, Richard James. PO BOX 7111, COLLEGE ANESTHESIA ASSOCS 17604 #041-01-1983 L1984 **AN** *071 †20,05
TACHIBANA, Yukako. 555 N DUKE ST 17602 #572-08-2002 L2006 **FP** *012
TEDESCHI, Kristina Rose. 694 GOOD DR STE 112 17601 #035-04-1990 L2002 **OBG** *020 †30
THOMAS, Margaret Caroline. 555 N DUKE ST, LANCASTER GENERAL HOSPITAL 17602 #041-15-2004 L2004 **FPG** *012 †18
TIEDEKEN, Patrick Thos. 2106 HARRISBURG PIKE, STE 309 17601 #041-01-1980 L1981 **OPH IM** *020 †20,35
TOLLIN, Steven Robt. 2110 HARRISBURG PIKE, STE 100 17601 #041-13-1987 L1989 **IM** *020 †20
TON-THAT, Tony Tung. 1671 CROOKED OAK DR 17601 #041-09-1996 L2002 **IM** *020
TRIANO-RODGERS, Marla. 690 GOOD DR 17601 #041-02-1989 L1991 **NPM PD** *020 †55
TRIBUZIO, Melissa Anne. 233 COLLEGE AVE, STE 200 17603 #051-04-1998 L2003 **PD** *020 †55
TRIBUZIO, Robert A. 2301 COLUMBIA AVE 17603 #051-04-1998 L2003 **IM** *020 †20
TROST, Jeffrey Thos. 440 W CHESTNUT ST 17603 #041-13-1991 L1993 **FM** *020 †18
TURNAMIAN, Richard John. 694 GOOD DR, AND BA 17601 #033-06-1982 L1983 **OBG** *020 †30
TURULA, Jon Basil. 133 E FREDERICK ST 17602 #035-45-1981 L1984 **AN** *020 †05 ‡
TYMON, Timothy Patrick. 555 N DUKE ST 17602 #016-43-1974 L1976 **ORS** *020 †40
TYUS, Ama Asantewaa. 555 N DUKE ST, LANCASTER GENERAL HOSPITAL 17602 #041-15-2001 L2001 **FM** *020
UMIKER, William O. 250 COLLEGE AVE 17603 #035-06-1940 L1960 **ATP** *071 †50
UPADHYA, Savithar. 802 NEW HOLLAND AVE, GROUP PSYCHIATRIC 17602 #495-99-1973 L2002 **P** *020 †75

VAN AULEN, Elizabeth Sue. ■ 17603 #041-14-2007 L2007 **FP** *012
VNENCHAK, Pamela Ann. 694 GOOD DR STE 11, LANCASTER GENERAL FAMILY 17601 #033-05-1990 L1992 **FM** *020 †18
VOYSTOCK, Joseph F, Jr. 2106 HARRISBURG PIKE 17601 #041-09-1988 L1992 **GS** *020 †85
WALLACE, Heather Anne. ■ 17602 #049-01-2005 **FP** *012
WARFEL, Benjamin Seigley. 2106 HARRISBURG PIKE, STE 111 17601 #041-14-1989 L1992 **PM** *020 †60
WARFEL, Joshua Levi. ■ 17603 #041-02-2008 L2008 *012
WARREN, Michael W. 3045 MARIETTA AVE 17601 #035-09-1983 L1984 **FM** *020 †18
WASIEWSKI, Warren Walter. 2051 WATERFORD DR 17601 #035-06-1982 L1987 **CHN** *020 †55,75
WEAVER, W Ronald. 100 ZOOKS LN 17601 #041-13-1960 L1961 **FM** *071 †18
WEBER, Richard Herman. ■ 17601 #041-09-1956 L1957 **FM** *071 †18
WEED, Michael K. 3045 MARIETTA AVE 17601 #041-13-1981 L1982 **FM FPG** *020 †18 ‡
WEHIBE, Stephen Shawle. 101 ABBEVILLE RD, GRP AT FAMILY PRACTICE 17603 #051-01-1996 L1999 **FM** *020 †18 ‡
WEINER, Marc Harris. 2112 HARRISBURG PIKE, HYPERTENSION AND KIDNEY 17601 #041-14-1984 L1985 **NEP IM** *020 †20
WEISMER, Richard Marc. 250 COLLEGE AVE 17603 #041-09-1971 L1972 **R** *020 †80
WEITZEL, Matthew Alan. 555 N DUKE ST, LANCASTER GENERAL HOSPITAL 17602 #032-01-2005 L2005 **FP** *012
WENTZ, Henry S. ■ 17602 #041-02-1944 L1945 **FM** *071 †18
WERT, Daniel David. ■ 17601 #041-77-1977, ▲ L1978 **AN PME** *071
WESTON, David M. 2112 HARRISBURG PIKE, STE 201 17601 #026-04-1966 L1971 **GE** *020 †20 ‡
WESTPHAL, Thomas Russell. 2150 HARRISBURG PIKE, # 200 17601 #041-02-1981 L1983 **ORS** *020 †40 ‡
WEYBRIGHT, Patrick Noel. 1525 VALLEY RD 17603 #024-01-1998 L2006 **RNR** *020 †80
WHITE, Robert Henry, Jr. 160 VALLEY RD 17601 #047-05-1965 L1966 **OPH PO** *020 †35
WILBRAHAM, Steven Charles. 440 W CHESTNUT ST 17603 #041-09-1993 L1996 **FM** *020 †18
WILCOX, Winthrop Peabody. ■ 17601 #035-20-1964 L1965 **AN** *071 †05
WILEY, David E. ■ 17601 #041-77-1958, ▲ L1959 **OBG** *071
WILLENKIN, Matthew Jos. 810 PLAZA BLVD, STE 101 17601 #035-09-1992 L1994 **AN** *020 †20
WILLIAMS, Henry Noyes. ■ 17603 #035-01-1941 L1946 **FM OS** *071
WILLIAMS, Kimberly Kaye. ■ 17602 #019-02-2006 L2006 **FP** *012
WILLS, Michael Hamilton. 133 E FREDERICK ST 17602 #056-06-1981 L1988 **AN** *020 †20,05
WILSKER, Herbert B. 117 PROSPECT ST 17603 #561-01-1969 L1971 **FM** *020
WILSON, Frederick S. 2041 KESTREL CT 17603 #041-02-1953 L1954 **PA FM** *071
WILSON, James Arthur. ■ 17602 #041-12-1966 L1967 **FM PD** *071 †18
WIN, Maung Kyaw. 817 N CHERRY ST 17602 #209-01-1994 L2004 **IM** *020 †20
WINTER, Charles R. 120 RIDER AVE 17603 #407-23-1951 L1961 **ORS PM** *071
WOLF, James Craig. 1671 OREGON PIKE, FAMILY PRACVTICE ASSOCIATE 17601 #041-07-1979 L1980 **FM** *020 †18
WOLGEMUTH, John Musser. 555 N DUKE ST 17602 #041-13-1970 L1971 **FM** *071 †18
WOOD, Ernest. 1059 COLUMBIA AVE 17603 #010-02-1963 L1972 **OBG** *071 †30
WOOD, John Morgan. ■ 17602 #050-02-1947 L1950 **IM** *071
WORATYLA, Steven Phillip. 2110 HARRISBURG PIKE, STE 308 17601 #041-02-1991 L2001 **VS GS** *020 †85
WORLEY, Seth Jos. 217 HARRISBURG AVE, THE HEART GROUP, LTD 17603 #041-13-1978 L1987 **CD IM** *020 †20
YEE, Spage Mingshi. 590 CENTERVILLE RD, STE 13J 17601 #035-46-1996 L2000 **OPH** *020 †35
YELCICK, John Matthew. 555 N DUKE ST 17602 #041-13-1991 L1995 **PTH** *030 †50
YETURU, Mamatha. 623 WYNCROFT LN, APT 7 17603 #495-70-1996 L2005 **FP** *012
YINGLING, Bryan Lynn. 694 GOOD DR, STE 112 17601 #041-02-1983 L1984 **OBG** *020 †30
YOUNG, James Frederic. 217 HARRISBURG AVE, GASTROENTERLOLGY ASSOCS 17603 #008-01-1953 L1954 **GE IM** *071 †20
ZAEPFEL, Joseph Patrick. 555 N DUKE ST 17602 #036-07-1965 L1973 **OTO** *020 †18
ZAKHAROVA, Anzhelika Vlad. 555 N DUKE ST 17602 #913-84-1995 L2005 **FP** *012
ZERVANOS, Nikitas John. 555 N DUKE ST 17602 #041-01-1962 L1963 **FM** *040 †18
ZVARGULIS, Janis E. 250 COLLEGE AVE 17603 #023-07-1969 L1977 **AN PD** *020 †55,05

LANDENBERG – CHESTER

ERICKSON, Laurel Alanna. ■ 19350 #041-15-2007 L2007 *012
GRAZELA, Jocelyn Stanley. ■ 19350 #051-01-2004 L2005 **PD** *012
LYNSKEY, George Emmett, III. ■ 19350 #010-02-2007 L2007 **IM** *012
RIEHL, Evan Danl. ■ 19350 #042-01-1963 L1964 **OM OS** *071
SALTZBERG, Mitchell Todd. ■ 19350 #008-01-1992 L1992 **CD** *020 †20
SHERWOOD, David Johnston. ■ 19350 #041-13-1978 L1979 **FM** *020 †18
SINGH, Ramnik K. 321 BUTTONWOOD RD 19350 #495-03-1991 L2002 **P** *020
STROBER, Ellen R. ■ 19350 #035-08-1964 L1971 **DR** *071 †80
WAGENFUHR, Timm. ■ 19350 #409-33-1970 L1976 **DR** *020

LANDISBURG – PERRY

CHAPPELKA, Alfred Roger. ■ 17040 #035-09-1957 L1977 **OM GE** *071 †20

LANDISVILLE – LANCASTER

ALBRIGHT, Gerald Snyder. ■ 17538 #041-01-1959 L1961 **FM** *071 †18
ESHLEMAN, D Rohrer. ■ 17538 #041-09-1949 L1950 **EM OS** *071
HOFFMAN, Harry H, Jr. 300 STONY BATTERY RD 17538 #041-02-1952 L1953 **FM IMG** *071
KIM, Hack Jung. 3244 HARRISBURG PIKE 17538 #583-04-1951 L1969 **IM R** *071 †80
MC GLAUGHLIN, Victor G. 405 MAIN ST, GRP LANDISVILLE FAMILY 17538 #023-12-1986 L2005 **FM** *020 †18
RAAB, David Bruce. ■ 17538 #041-12-1956 L1957 **GP** *071
RYNIER, Donald Lee. ■ 17538 #041-13-1966 L1967 **P** *020 †75
STOLTZFUS, George Byron. ■ 17538 #041-14-1975 L1976 **GP** *020
WINIARSKI, Genevieve C. 3224 HARRISBURG PIKE 17538 #041-07-1972 L1974 **GS** *020

LANGHORNE – BUCKS

AHMED, Safi Uddin. 1205 LANGHORNE NEWTOWN RD, STE 310 19047 #305-01-1999 L2000 **ICE** *012 †20

■ = Address Information Privacy Protected

AKRUK, Samir Rizk. 1205 LANGHORNE NEWTOWN RD, STE 312 19047 #649-33-1983 L1984 **IM** *020

ALAND, Christopher Martin. 582 MIDDLETOWN BLVD, STE B100 19047 #023-01-1982 L1991 **ORS** *020 †40

ALI, Juan Omar. 380 OXFORD VALLEY RD, ANESTHESIA DEPT. 2-ND FLOO 19047 #528-01-1987 L2000 **AN** *100

ALLEY, Evan Wayne. 240 MIDDLETOWN BLVD, SUITE205 19047 #019-02-1996 L1999 **HO** *020

ANIS, Muhammad. 240 MIDDLETOWN BLVD, STE 200 19047 #704-16-1987 L1994 **NEP** *020 †20

ARIF, Ghulam. 370 MIDDLETOWN BLVD 19047 #654-01-1981 L1984 **IM** *020 †20

ATRI, Srinivas Shankar. 370 MIDDLETOWN BLVD, STE 510 19047 #495-96-1975 L1983 **CD** *020 †20 ‡

BAKSHI, Kalind Ravindra. 400 MIDDLETOWN BLVD, STE 112 19047 #496-38-1969 L1979 **VS GS** *020 †85

BANKOLE, Sunday Olumuyiwa. 1201 LANGHORNE NEWTOWN RD, ST. MARY MEDICAL CENTER 19047 #690-02-1987 L2006 **CCP** *020

BARNES, Denice Marie. 404 MIDDLETOWN BLVD, STE 306 19047 #016-45-1984 L1987 **PD** *020 †55 ‡

BARSKY, Bernard Robt. LANGHORNE-NEWTOWN RD 19047 #041-09-1965 L1966 **A PDA** *020 †55,03

BARTOLOZZI, Maria Ann. 1201 LANGHORNE NEWTOWN RD 19047 #033-06-1988 L1992 **AN** *020 †05

BASI, Puneet Pal Singh. ■ 19047 #495-43-2003 **IM** *012

BEATTY, Albert Cecil. 370 MIDDLETOWN BLVD, OXFORD VALLEY SQ VEIN 19047 #041-09-1958 L1959 **TS GS** *020 †85,90

BELECANECH, George Alec. 404 MIDDLETOWN BLVD, STE 305 19047 #041-07-1987 L1990 **AI IM** *020 †20,03 ‡

BERK, Robert Lawrence. 540 WOODBOURNE RD, STE 1 19047 #041-09-1988 L1991 **OBG** *020 †30

BERKOWITZ, Andrew Mark. ST MARYS OFFICE BUILDING 19047 #041-07-1985 L1986 **IM** *020

BERNARDINO, Evelina A. 1205 LANGHORNE NEWTOWN RD, ST MARY MED BLDG SUITE 215 19047 #748-02-1961 L1974 **D DMP** *020 †15

BLECKER, Alla. ■ 19047 #781-02-1957 L1984 **P** *071

BOE, Brian Scott. 280 MIDDLETOWN BLVD, BARIX CLINICS OF PENNYSLVA 19047 #016-11-1990 L2007 **OS** *020 †85

BOGUSH, Stephen Anthony. 1201 LANGHORNE NEWTOWN RD 19047 #041-14-1994 L1998 **AN** *020 †20

BONNER, John Jos. 508 CORPORATE DR W 19047 #041-02-1980 L1986 **FM** *020 †18

BORAH, Bishnu Charan. 380 MIDDLETOWN BLVD, STE 702 19047 #495-78-1969 L1979 **PD** *020 †55

BOSWORTH, Eric. 1201 LANGHORNE NEWTOWN RD 19047 #008-02-1991 L1996 **R** *020 †80 ‡

BRACKIN, Phillip Snowden. 582 MIDDLETOWN BLVD 19047 #041-09-1970 L1973 **R PHP** *020 †80

BRACKUP, Alan Bart. 1203 LANGHORNE NEWTOWN RD, # 120 19047 #005-11-1984 L1984 **FPS OPH** *020 †35 ‡

BRADER, Alan Hayden. 280 MIDDLETOWN BLVD 19047 #041-12-1982 L1983 **GS** *020 †85

BRESSLER, Lawrence Paul. 183 BRISTOL OXFORD VALY RD 19047 #041-02-1980 L1982 **NEP** *020 †20

BRIGGS, Kenneth Ralph. ■ 19047 #024-01-1954 L1995 **P N** *071 †20,75

BROTMAN, David Neil. 1205 LANGHORNE NEWTOWN RD, STE 304 19047 #041-02-1986 L1993 **GS PHL** *020 †85

BUCHANAN, Kathleen M. 170 MIDDLETOWN BLVD, STE 101 19047 #041-14-1995 L1999 **IM** *020 †20

BUCK, Gary Bruce. 280 MIDDLETOWN BLVD 19047 #033-06-1993 L1999 **AN PME** *020 †05

BURKHOLDER, Janet Filemyr. 380 MIDDLETOWN BLVD, STE 704 19047 #041-13-1989 L1992 **RHU** *020 †20

CAMPBELL, Neil P. 300 MIDDLETOWN BLVD, STE 100 19047 #041-13-1961 L1962 **OBG** *020 †30

CARDINALE, Robert Michael. 1201 LANGHORNE NEWTOWN RD, ST MARY MEDICAL CENTER 19047 #023-01-1991 L2005 **RO** *020 †80

CARESTIA, John Gary. ■ 19053 #308-07-1981 L1984 **AN** *020

CARLIN, Marie Claire. LANGHORNE-NEWTOWN RD 19047 #041-14-1983 L1987 **D** *075 †15

CARVAJAL, Roberto Tan. 240 MIDDLETOWN BLVD, STE 201 19047 #748-11-1970 L1973 **IM CD** *020 ‡

CASTEL, Norman. ■ 19047 #041-01-1971 L1972 **EM FM** *020

CHALAL, Jo Ann. 1201 LANGHORNE NEWTOWN RD 19047 #041-13-1982 L1988 **RO ON** *020 †20,80 ‡

CHOI, Matthew Byong Lyean. 1201 LANGHORNE NEWTOWN RD 19047 #583-03-1965 L1973 **AN** *020

CHON, Brian Hisuk. 1201 LANGHORNE NEWTOWN RD, ST MARY MEDICAL CENTER 19047 #033-06-1997 L2005 **RO** *020 †80

CICCOTELLI, Aldo Anthony. 106 CORPORATE DR E 19047 #308-06-1981 L1987 **FM** *020 †18 ‡

CICCOTELLI, Kristina K. 380 OXFORD VALLEY RD, DEPT OF ANESTHESIA 19047 #033-06-1990 L1993 **AN** *020 †05

COHEN, Daniel J. 1201 LANGHORNE NEWTOWN RD 19047 #048-12-1983 L1983 **DR CD** *020 †80 ‡

COHEN, Fredric Jay. 13 SUMMIT SQUARE CTR, STE 132 19047 #041-14-1990 L2000 **PHM IM** *062 †20

CONNOLLY, Kevin Ryan. ■ 19047 #041-13-2005 L2005 **P** *012

CONNORS, Earl Kenneth, Jr. SAINT MARY HOSP, LANGHORNE-NEWTON RD 19047 #041-09-1960 L1961 **OS FM** *071 †18

CONROY, Jos Vincent, III. 1205 LANGHORNE NEWTOWN RD 19047 #041-02-1980 L1981 **NS** *020 †25

COOK, Traci L. ■ 19053 #041-77-2004, ▲ L2004 **OBG** *012

CORVASCE, Joseph Mauro. 1 CORNERSTONE DR, STE 300 19047 #041-09-1972 L1973 **GE** *020 †20

COSTANTINO, Geo Nicholas. 1205 LANGHORNE NEWTOWN RD, STE 307 19047 #041-13-1977 L1978 **GS** *020 †85 ‡

DANIELEWSKI, George L. 142 N BELLEVUE AVE 19047 #759-03-1967 L1973 **FM** *020

DEFILIPPIS, David John. 1205 LANGHORNE NEWTOWN RD, STE 408 19047 #010-02-1988 L1991 **OBG** *020 †30

DE MARIA, Gail Reedman. 508 CORPORATE DR W, NEWTOWN 19047 #041-02-1984 L1988 **FM** *020 †18

DE SANTOS, Marcelino S. 1205 LANGHORNE NEWTOWN RD, STE 401 19047 #748-02-1973 L1977 **PD PHO** *020 †55

DESHPANDE, Anil Shriram. 1205 LANGHORNE NEWTOWN RD, ASSOC, P C/STE 308 19047 #495-17-1974 L1979 **TS CD** *020 †85,90

DI MOIA, Frank. ■ 19047 #023-07-1958 L1959 **CHP** *071 †55,75

DI MOIA, Margaret M R. ■ 19047 #016-06-1958 L1961 **PD** *020 †55

DOLAN, Kevin Arthur. 1201 LANGHORNE NEWTOWN RD 19047 #024-07-1983 L1999 **APM OM** *020 †05

DUFFIELD, Thomas Edward. 1205 LANGHORNE NEWTOWN RD, STE 406B 19047 #041-09-1987 L1988 **FM** *020 †18 ‡

DUNSKY, Eliot Harold. 404 MIDDLETOWN BLVD, STE 305 19047 #550-01-1971 L1972 **AI PD** *020 †55,03 ‡

EDWARDS, Marc Dana. ■ 19047 #003-75-2006, ▲ L2006 *012

EMPEDRAD, Albert B. 1205 LANGHORNE NEWTOWN RD, STE 302 19047 #748-02-1991 L2006 **END IM** *020 †20

EVERTS, Eric A. 1201 LANGHORNE NEWTOWN RD 19047 #041-02-1979 L1985 **AN PD** *020 †55,05

EZELL, Paul Carter. 1205 LANGHORNE NEWTOWN RD, STE 215 19047 #025-01-1979 L1981 **OPH** *020 †35 ‡

FEDERICI, Valerio J. ■ 19047 #041-02-1948 L1950 **GS AS** *071 †85

FINLEY, John G. LANGHORNE-NEWTOWN RD 19047 #041-02-1949 L1950 **R NM** *071 ‡

FOGLER, Sean Graham. 380 OXFORD VALLEY RD, LIBERTY ANESTHESIA ASSOCIA 19047 #305-01-2000 L2000 **AN** *100

FOOTE, Thomas Joseph. LANGHORNE-NEWTOWN RD 19047 #041-77-1964, ▲ L1965 **FM** *071

FRANKLIN, Irvin Danl. 360 OXFORD VALLEY RD, STE 400 19047 #041-09-1971 L1972 **GS OM** *020

FRIEDBERG, Jay Gary. 172 MIDDLETOWN BLVD # 200 19047 #041-13-1973 L1974 **OPH** *020 †35 ‡

FRIEDMAN, Andrew Chas. 390 MIDDLETOWN BLVD, STE 604 19047 #041-77-1977, ▲ L1978 **CD IM** *020

GABALE, Devdatta R. 1205 LANGHORNE NEWTOWN RD, STE 304A 19047 #495-01-1979 L1994 **U** *020 †95

GABRIEL, Rosalinda V. 1517 DURHAM RD 19047 #748-08-1962 L1971 **P** *020 †75

GALLAGHER, John Timothy. 3 CORNERSTONE DR, CORNERSTONE EXEC STE 703 19047 #041-09-1982 L1983 **OTO** *020 †45

GALLAGHER, Judith Eva. 3 CORNERSTONE DR, STE 703 19047 #033-06-1991 L1994 **OTO** *020 †45

GAUL, James Jos. 1205 LANGHORNE NEWTOWN RD, STE 402 19047 #041-09-1980 L1984 **N** *020 †75

GIBAS, Zenon. ST MARY MED CTR, DEPT OF PATHOLOGY 19047 #759-07-1977 L1985 **PTH CCG** *020 †19,50 ‡

GLASSMAN, Gary. ST MARY HOSPITAL, EMERGENCY DEPARTMENT 19047 #041-09-1986 L1987 **EM** *020 †18

GOLD, Jonathan. 1205 LANGHORNE NEWTOWN RD, STE 204 19047 #011-02-1980 L1984 **CD IM** *020 †20 ‡

GOLDFINE, Michael Aaron. 1205 LANGHORNE NEWTOWN RD 19047 #041-13-1994 L1997 **AN** *020 †20

GOLDSTEIN, Arnold Lewis. 170 MIDDLETOWN BLVD # 101 19047 #041-14-1973 L1978 **IM PUD** *020 †20

GOLDSTEIN, Marc Fred. 404 MIDDLETOWN BLVD, STE 305 19047 #041-01-1979 L1980 **IM AI** *020 †20,03 ‡

GOLDSTEIN, Richard S. 1203 LANGHORNE NEWTOWN RD, STE 130 19047 #023-07-1977 L1984 **CRS PRO** *020 †10,85 ‡

GORDON, Gregory Randal. 380 OXFORD VALLEY RD 19047 #041-02-1984 L1985 **FM OM** *020 †18

GORDON, Nancy Deborah. 404 MIDDLETOWN BLVD, STE 305 19047 #041-13-1995 L1997 **AI** *050 †20,03 ‡

GREENBAUM, Roy Lawrence. 1201 LANGHORNE NEWTOWN RD 19047 #045-01-1981 L1986 **DR OS** *020 †80

GREENBERG, Scott Ross. 680 MIDDLETOWN BLVD, STE 100 19047 #041-09-1996 L1998 **FM** *020 †18

GROSSMAN, Debra Joan. 402 MIDDLETOWN BLVD, STE 21 19047 #008-02-1981 L1992 **D** *020 †15

HALPERN, Janis Susan. 1205 LANGHORNE NEWTOWN RD, STE 108 19047 #035-47-1980 L1982 **PD** *020 †55

HALPERN, Lee Stacy. 1205 LANGHORNE NEWTOWN RD, STE 408 19047 #041-13-1996 L1998 **OBG** *020 †30

HAQ, Imran U. 1205 LANGHORNE NEWTOWN RD, STE 215 19047 #704-21-1985 L2003 **GS** *020

HARALABATOS, Irene C. 404 MIDDLETOWN BLVD, STE 305 19047 #033-06-1992 L1997 **AI** *020 †20,03

HARIDAS, Anand. 1205 LANGHORNE NEWTOWN RD, STE 204 19047 #496-32-1998 L2006 **CD** *020 †20

HARTENBAUM, Natalie P. 152 BATEMAN RD 19047 #041-13-1985 L1986 **IM OM** *020 †20,70

HARVEY, Amy L. 540 WOODBOURNE RD, STE 1 19047 #041-13-1990 L1992 **GYN** *020 †30 ‡

HEINE, Marilyn Joan. 240 MIDDLETOWN BLVD, STE 205 19047 #033-06-1982 L1983 **EM HO** *020

HELLINGS, Terri L Mc Cart. 580 MIDDLETOWN BLVD, STE D-101-C 19047 #047-05-1993 L1995 **N CN** *020 †75

HIRSCH, Stuart Ellis. 360 MIDDLETOWN BLVD, EYE ASSOCIATES OF BUCKS 19047 #038-40-1968 L1970 **OPH** *020 †35 ‡

HOLUB, Edward Jos. LANGHORNE-NEWTOWN RD 19047 #010-02-1977 L1979 **EM** *020 †16

HORNBERGER, Kevin F. 129 RUGBY DR 19047 #041-07-1987 L1988 **CHP** *020 †75

IMMORDINO, Laura Elizabet. ■ 19053 #041-02-2006 L2006 **IM** *012

JACKSON, Mark Chas. LANGHORNE-NEWTOWN ROAD, ST MARY MEDICAL CENTER 19047 #654-01-1986 L1990 **IM** *020 †20

JACOBELLI, Michael Chas. 1205 LANGHORNE NEWTOWN RD, STE 106 19047 #041-14-1979 L1980 **GS** *020 †85

JAFFE, Joel Daniel. 400 MIDDLETOWN BLVD, STE 100 19047 #041-13-1975 L1976 **OTO GP** *020 †45

JAMBRO, Robert Douglas. 172 MIDDLETOWN BLVD, STE 203 19047 #041-02-1971 L1973 **IM** *020 ‡

JASSER, Samar Aisha. ■ 19047 #041-02-2005 L2005 **P** *012

JAVIAN, Thos Abraham, Jr. 376 STATION AVE 19047 #041-09-1970 L1972 **ORS** *020 †40

KAIFER-ZAJDOWICZ, Marie C. 1201 LANGHORNE NEWTOWN RD, ST MARY'S MEDICAL CENTER 19047 #023-01-1991 L2005 **PD** *020 †55

KAKARIA, Darshin Kumar. ■ 19047 #209-02-1966 L1979 **AN** *020

KALAWADIA, Vinodrai D. 200 OXFORD VALLEY RD 19047 #495-97-1975 L1980 **GS** *020

KANEFSKY, Terry Mark. 1205 LANGHORNE NEWTOWN RD, STE 302 ST MARY MED CTR 19047 #041-13-1973 L1974 **END IM** *020 †20 ‡

KANSAL, Nidhi Rajgopal. 1201 LANGHORNE NEWTOWN RD, RR 413 19047 #041-15-2001 L2004 **EM** *020 †16 ‡

■ = Address Information Privacy Protected

KANSUPADA, Bindukumar C. 240 MIDDLETOWN BLVD, STE 201 19047 #495-17-1977 L1983
  CD IM *020 †20

KIM, Hak Ryun. ST MARY HOSP MED BLDG 202 19047 #583-02-1958 L1971 OBG *071

KIM, Young Wook. 1201 LANGHORNE NEWTOWN RD 19047 #583-02-1960 L1970 AN *020

KIRKPATRICK, Christopher. 1201 LANGHORNE NEWTOWN RD 19047 #041-13-2001 L2001
  MSR *020 †80

KLEEMAN, Audrey Karen. 402 MIDDLETOWN BLVD, STE 214 19047 #041-09-1983 L1986
  IM *020 †20

KO, Min-Hsiung. LANGHORNE-NEWTOWN RD 19047 #385-04-1966 L1973 FM IM *020 †50 ‡

KOGANSKI, Valeri. 1205 LANGHORNE NEWTOWN RD, ST MARY MOB, SUITE 411 19047
  #913-81-1986 L1995 IM OS *020 †20

KOKROO, Archana. 370 MIDDLETOWN BLVD, STE 502 19047 #495-51-1987 L2002 IM *020 †20

KOTTIATH, Prince George. ■ 19047 #495-63-1997 L2003 IM *100 †20 ‡

KRAJESKI, R Drew. 1205 LANGHORNE NEWTOWN RD, STE 405 19047 #041-01-1980 L1981
  ORS *020 †40

KRAVETS, Marina. 240 MIDDLETOWN BLVD 19047 #913-16-1977 L1998 IM *020 †20

KU, Tony Wen-Wei. 1201 LANGHORNE NEWTOWN RD 19047 #654-01-1999 L2001
  AN PMM *100

KUHN, Mark Devlin, III. 540 WOODBOURNE RD, STE 1 19047 #033-06-1985 L1986
  OBG *020 †30 ‡

LEDIS, Seymour. 370 MIDDLETOWN BLVD, OXFORD SQUARE SUITE 502 19047
  #041-13-1947 L1948 PD *071 †55

LIBFRAIND, Lester. 582 MIDDLETOWN BLVD 19047 #033-06-1986 L1992 DR *020 †80

LINDENMAYER, A Earle. 280 MIDDLETOWN BLVD 19047 #660-04-1988 L1995 BBK *020 †50

LOEV, Marvin. 360 MIDDLETOWN BLVD, OXFORD SQUARE, SUIT 400 19047 #041-01-1959 L1960
  GYN *020 †30

LOFTUS, Kelly Ann. 1205 LANGHORNE NEWTOWN RD, STE 302 19047 #041-15-2001 L2001
  END *020

MADANY, Bahij Hanna. LANGHORNE-NEWTOWN RD 19047 #028-34-1957 L1963 U *071 †95

MAGNER, Alan Lee. 400 MIDDLETOWN BLVD, PENNS SQUARE STE 107 19047
  #016-43-1970 L1971 IM *020 †20 ‡

MAILMAN, Wendy Robin. 400 MIDDLETOWN BLVD STE 10 19047 #041-02-1985 L1986
  AN *020 †05

MALEN, Michael Jos. ■ 19047 #041-13-1977 L1978 PD *020 †55

MAQUILAN, Jose March E. 1203 LANGHORNE NEWTOWN RD, STE 226 19047
  #748-11-1972 L1977 TS GS *050 †85,90 ‡

MARCOUX, Anne Marie C. 1203 LANGHORNE NEWTOWN RD, STE 130 19047
  #035-45-1983 L1989 CRS *020 †85,10 ‡

MARYMOR, Neil S. 280 MIDDLETOWN BLVD 19047 #041-01-1980 L1982 GS PS *020 †85

MATARESE, Emil Lawrence. 1205 LANGHORNE NEWTOWN RD, STE 201 19047
  #033-05-1982 L1986 N *020 †75

MAZLIN, Steven Eric. 940 TOWN CENTER DR, STE F50 19047 #035-19-1984 L1988
  N CN *020 †75

MCHUGH, Robert. ■ 19047 #022-75-2007, ▲ L2008 *012

MC LAUGHLIN, Carlin. 240 MIDDLETOWN BLVD, STE 205 19047 #041-77-1984, ▲ L1985
  HO HEM *020

MECHANIC, William Scott. 1201 LANGHORNE NEWTOWN RD 19047 #035-06-1986 L1992
  R *020 †80

MESHKOV, Steven Lee. 1201 LANGHORNE NEWTOWN RD 19047 #041-13-1978 L1982
  DR *020 †80

METKUS, Francis Michael. 240 MIDDLETOWN BLVD, STE 203 19047 #041-02-1978 L1981
  IM IMG *020 †20 ‡

MILLER, Lee H. 400 MIDDLETOWN BLVD, STE 100 19047 #041-09-1971 L1973 OTO *020 †45 ‡

MILUNSKY, Cyril. DEPT OF RADIOLOGY, ST MARY HOSPITAL 19047 #836-01-1969 L1979
  DR NR *071 †80

MITRA, Jesmin. 360 MIDDLETOWN BLVD, STE 400 19047 #496-38-1974 L1981 OBG *020 †30

MODAY, Heather Joanna. 404 MIDDLETOWN BLVD, STE 305 19047 #021-01-1998 L2003
  AI *020 †20,03 ‡

MODY, Mahendra Ishwarlal. 1201 LANGHORNE NEWTOWN RD, LUXEMBOURG CORPORATE
  CENTE 19047 #495-76-1971 L1976 IM GP *020

MORTON, Denise Marie. ■ 19053 #041-15-2003 L2003 GS *012

MULLIN, Guy Scott. 409 EXECUTIVE DR 19047 #010-02-1992 L1996 OPH *020 †35 ‡

MULLIN, Hugh Jos, Jr. 330 MIDDLETOWN BLVD 19047 #041-09-1963 L1964 R *071 †80 ‡

NEMETH, Andrew Martin. 940 TOWN CENTER DR 19047 #023-07-1953 L1981 P *071 †75

NEWSOM, John Harlan. LANGHORNE-NEWTOWN RD 19047 #054-04-1971 L1974 FM *020 †18

NIXON, Todd Earl. 1205 LANGHORNE NEWTOWN RD, DELEWARE VALLEY CARDIO SUR 19047
  #041-14-1989 L1998 TS CD *020 †85,90 ‡

NOBLE, Jeyaseelan John. 402 MIDDLETOWN BLVD, STE 204 19047 #495-27-1959 L1973
  DS *020 †85,65

OLINE, Jonathan Paul. 390 MIDDLETOWN BLVD, STE 604 19047 #041-77-1983, ▲ L1984
  CD *020

ORLAND, Steven Mark. 1205 LANGHORNE NEWTOWN RD, STE 104 19047 #035-01-1981 L1982
  U *020 †95 ‡

ORNSTEEN, Richard Paul. ■ 19047 #041-01-1947 L1948 OS *071

OSTROVSKY, Alexander M. 1205 LANGHORNE NEWTOWN RD, STE 407 19047
  #913-69-1984 L2001 HO *020 †20

OTTO, Allison Dawn. 404 MIDDLETOWN BLVD 19047 #035-46-2000 L2003 PD *020 †55

PAUL, Champa. ■ 19047 #496-07-1957 L1973 GP PTH *071 †50

PAULEY, Lois Price. 131 S BELLEVUE AVE, PHILLIP FRIEDMAN MD 19047 #041-13-1955 L1956
  FM ADM *071 †55

PONNAMBALAM, Amrit R. 1201 LANGHORNE NEWTOWN RD, RR 413 19047
  #033-05-1999 L2007 EM *020 †16 ‡

POOLE, Edward Franklin. 360 MIDDLETOWN BLVD, EYE ASSOCIATES OF BUCKS 19047
  #033-05-1971 L1977 OPH EM *020 †35 ‡

PRAGER, Roy Matthew. 1201 LANGHORNE NEWTOWN RD 19047 #035-08-1980 L1983
  R *020 †80 ‡

PUPKOVA, Lyudmila S. 280 MIDDLETOWN BLVD 19047 #913-01-1974 L2006 GS *020 †85 ‡

QUINN, Jennifer Lynn. ■ 19047 #024-07-2002 IM *100

RAJAGOPALAN, Venkataraman. 240 MIDDLETOWN BLVD, STE 205 19047 #495-52-1984 L1988
  HO HEM *020 †20

RAJAN, Ravi R. 310 MIDDLETOWN BLVD STE 2, BUCKS COUNTY UROLOGY PC 19047
  #038-40-1994 L1996 U *020 †95

RANGA RAO, Adiraju V. 370 MIDDLETOWN BLVD, OXFORD SQUARE SUITE 510 19047
  #495-65-1973 L1978 CD IM *050 †20

RATNER, Lawrence Mark. 1201 LANGHORNE NEWTOWN RD 19047 #028-34-1979 L1985
  IM DR *020 †80 ‡

RAYNER, Mark Edward. 240 MIDDLETOWN BLVD, STE 201 19047 #041-02-1975 L1978
  GS VS *020 †85

REDDY, Siddavatam Naveen. ■ 19047 #495-09-1997 L2004 IM *100 †20

RIEDER, Michael Jacob. 1201 LANGHORNE NEWTOWN RD 19047 #041-01-1986 L1987
  DR *020 †80 ‡

RIVERA, Victor Carbonell. 1205 LANGHORNE NEWTOWN RD, STE 108 19047
  #748-02-1966 L1972 PD GE *020 †55 ‡

ROSS, William M. 1201 LANGHORNE NEWTOWN RD 19047 #041-09-1979 L1984
  R IM *020 †20,80 ‡

ROTHBERG, Jay Sean. 1205 LANGHORNE NEWTOWN RD, STE 311 19047 #033-06-1990 L1993
  OBG *020 †30

RUCH, Nathanael Geoffrey. 1201 LANGHORNE NEWTOWN RD, DEPT OF EMERGENCY
  MEDICINE 19047 #041-14-1998 L2006 EM *020 †16

SAHU, Pawan Kumar. 1 CORNERSTONE DR, STE 300 19047 #014-01-1992 L1994
  GE HEP *020 †20

SANTIAGO, Tirza Shanny. ■ 19047 #042-02-2001 L2006 EM *020 †16

SARAF, Asha Arvind. 1201 LANGHORNE NEWTOWN RD 19047 #495-01-1970 L1973
  AN *020 †05

SATTERTHWAITE, Adaline P. ■ 19047 #005-02-1942 L1942 OBG OS *071

SCHORR, Alan Bruce. 380 MIDDLETOWN BLVD 19047 #028-79-1981, ▲ L1982 END IM *020

SCHWARTZ, Milton Arnold. 508 CORPORATE DR W 19047 #041-13-1963 L1964 GP OM *020

SCHWARTZ, Stephanie J. 540 WOODBOURNE RD, STE 1 19047 #035-15-1992 L1996
  OBG *020 †30

SCOGNA, Joseph E. 1205 LANGHORNE NEWTOWN RD, STE 210 19047 #041-13-1975
  NS *020 †25

SEGAL, Leigh G. 380 MIDDLETOWN BLVD, STE 704 19047 #012-05-1991 L1996 RHU *020 †20 ‡

SHAH, Rajnikant S. 240 MIDDLETOWN BLVD, STE 201 19047 #495-23-1969 L1973
  CD IM *020 †20

SHAH, Rakesh Rajnikant. 1205 LANGHORNE NEWTOWN RD, STE 204 19047
  #041-13-1993 L1996 CD *020 †20 ‡

SHAIKH, Shagufta Hassan. ■ 19047 #704-18-1995 L2005 IM *012

SHARIFF, Haji Mohammed. 1203 LANGHORNE NEWTOWN RD, STE 226 19047
  #495-21-1972 L1982 TS CD *020 †85,90 ‡

SHNEIDMAN, Paul Saml. 380 OXFORD VALLEY RD, FRANKFORD BUCKS HOSP-EEG 19047
  #035-46-1980 L1989 OS N *050 †75

SHONBERG, Barbara Hollis. 170 MIDDLETOWN BLVD, STE 101 19047 #041-01-1979 L1982
  IM *020 †20

SHULTZ, Thomas Laurie. 240 MIDDLETOWN BLVD, STE 203 19047 #041-14-1976 L1977
  IM IMG *020 †20

SHUSTERMAN, Denise K. 2 DOUBLEWOODS RD 19047 #041-07-1985 L1986
  DR NM *020 †80 ‡

SILVERMAN, Ira Jay. 100 MEER DR 19053 #016-43-1976 L1978 OBG *020 †30

SIMON, Owen Jeffrey. 1201 LANGHORNE NEWTOWN RD 19047 #041-14-1983 L1984
  AN *020 †05

SINAIKO, Peter Albert. 940 TOWN CENTER DR, STE F100 19047 #016-42-1969 L1974
  U *020 †95

SKLAVENITOU, Vassiliki S. ■ 19047 #418-01-1989 L1994 PD *020

SNYDER, Alan Isa. ST MARY MED BLDG, STE 104 19047 #041-02-1959 L1960 U *020 †95

SNYDER, Jerrold M. 360 MIDDLETOWN BLVD, STE 400 19047 #041-77-1978, ▲ L1979
  OBG GS *020

SPIEGEL, Edward Phillip. 370 MIDDLETOWN BLVD # 506 19047 #041-01-1975 L1980
  PD *020 †55

STEVENSON, Christina E. ■ 19047 #010-01-2002 L2006 GS *012

TALUCCI, Raymond Chas. 1205 LANGHORNE NEWTOWN RD 19047 #023-01-1977 L1988
  TRS CCS *020 †85

THAKUR, Arun Sobti. 1201 LANGHORNE NEWTOWN RD, ST. MARY MEDICAL CENTER 19047
  #495-30-1975 L1981 IM *020 †20

THANKI, Ashokkumar S. 174 LANGHORNE NEWTOWN RD, THE LOFTS C304 19047 #495-22-1975 L1980
  NS *020 †25

THEBPATIPHAT, Nuthida. ■ 19047 #891-01-1999 OPH *100

TING, George Hin Chan. 1201 LANGHORNE NEWTOWN RD 19047 #209-01-1967 L1970
  AN *071

TRIEU, Kevin. 170 MIDDLETOWN BLVD, STE 101 19047 #422-01-2004 L2007 IM *020 †20

TRIVEDI, Atul D. 1205 LANGHORNE NEWTOWN RD, STE 204 19047 #495-01-1981 L1982
  CD *020 †20 ‡

TRIVEDI, Raksha Atul. 580 MIDDLETOWN BLVD, STE D205 19047 #495-66-1982 L1990
  IM *020 †20

TURNER, Richard L. 360 MIDDLETOWN BLVD, STE 400 19047 #041-77-1979, ▲ L1980
  OBG *020

TYERECH, Sangeeta Kamath. 1201 LANGHORNE NEWTOWN RD 19047 #033-06-1992 L1997
  RO *020 †80

VAHEDI, Mohsen. 380 OXFORD VALLEY RD, BUCKS COUNTY CAMPUS 19047
  #517-05-1980 L1993 GS *020 †85

VARKLETT, Vickie Lynne. 1205 LANGHORNE NEWTOWN RD 19047 #036-05-1993 L1997
  APM *020 †05

VERTICELLI, Adeline Maria. ■ 19047 #010-02-1998 L2001 IM *020 †20

VINCENT, Gregory Jos. 402 MIDDLETOWN BLVD, STE 212 19047 #041-13-1977 L1978
  GS *071 †85

WAHRMAN, Julie Hyman. 402 MIDDLETOWN BLVD, STE 210 19047 #041-01-1988 L1991
  D *020 †15

WALKER, Anne Marie. 540 WOODBOURNE RD, STE 1 19047 #041-07-1995 L1997
  OBG *020 †30

WARNER, Wendy. 940 TOWN CENTER DR, STE F90 19047 #047-06-1986 L1987 OBG *020 †30

WEISBERG, Robert Abraham. 508 CORPORATE DR W, LUXEMBOURG MED ASSOCS 19047
  #041-13-1963 L1964 FM OM *071

WEISER, Paul Joel. 1201 LANGHORNE NEWTOWN RD 19047 #035-46-1971 L1975 R *020 †80 ‡

WILTZ, Magdalena. 930 TOWN CENTER DR, STE G40 19047 #041-13-1978 L1979 P *020 †75

WOLFSON, Saul David. 400 N BUCKSTOWN DR, STE 1A 19047 #041-09-1965 L1969
  CHP P *020 †75

WORTZEL, Richard Drew. 402 MIDDLETOWN BLVD, STE 210 19047 #016-02-1985 L1987
  D *020 †15

WORTZEL, Sandra Horlick. 402 MIDDLETOWN BLVD, STE 210 19047 #041-01-1986 L1987
  D *075 †15

WRY, Philip Craig. 1201 LANGHORNE NEWTOWN RD, DEPARTMENT OF TRAUMA 19047
  #038-43-1984 L1988 GS *020 †85

YOUSSEF, John Aziz. 240 MIDDLETOWN BLVD, STE 205 19047 #038-43-2000 L2006
  HO *020 †20

ZABALA-OMBAO, Lourdes A. S-406 ST MARY MED BLDG 19047 #748-01-1955 L1971
OBG *071

ZELINSKY, Joseph John, Jr. 1205 LANGHORNE NEWTOWN RD, SAINT MARY MEDICAL
CENTER 19047 #041-13-1993 L2001 AN *020 †05

ZIMMER, Gary David. 1201 LANGHORNE NEWTOWN RD 19047 #035-20-1997 L2005
EM *020 †16 ‡

ZOLLNER, Gregory Paul. 240 MIDDLETOWN BLVD 19047 #033-06-1988 L1990
NEP IM *020 †20 ‡

LANSDALE – MONTGOMERY

AHMAD, Navid. ■ 19446 #704-02-1996 L2008 HMP *012

ALBIN, Jonathan Blake. 125 MEDICAL CAMPUS DR, STE 101 19446 #035-19-1978 L1983
CD *072 †20

ALPERT, Marc Holman. 1057 S BROAD ST, ASSOCIATES 19446 #041-01-1976 L1984
VS GS *020 †85

ALPERT, Richard Eckhouse. 100 MEDICAL CAMPUS DR 19446 #035-09-1959 L1964
PD *071 †55

ANASTASIA, John Jos. ■ 19446 #024-15-1937 L1941 P PM *071

ANDERSON, Alice Miriam. 1001 S VALLEY FORGE RD, # 1313 19446 #041-07-1946 L1947
GPM GP *071

ANOLIK, Robert. 2031 N BROAD ST, STE 129 19446 #035-06-1978 L1979 PDA AI *020 †55,03

AREVALO, Leonardo B. ■ 19446 #748-08-1969 L1984 P *020

AVARBOCK, Andrew Brian. 1958 MUHLENBERG DR 19446 #041-01-2008 *012

AXELROD, Lawrence Seth. 100 MEDICAL CAMPUS DR 19446 #041-13-1982 L1983
FM *020 †18

BANDYOPADHYAY, Bharati. 2031 N BROAD ST STE 145 19446 #495-15-1979 L1986
PD *075 †55 ‡

BARNETT, Arthur Malcolm. ■ 19446 #035-01-1937 L1964 FM GYN *071 †18

BAYARD, David J. 2031 N BROAD ST, STE 139 19446 #043-01-1986 L1991 N *020 †75 ‡

BECK, Jonathan Edward. 1019 S BROAD ST 19446 #041-77-1972, ▲ L1973 FM *020 †18 ‡

BECKER, Marta Taylor. 108 COWPATH RD, STE 2 19446 #024-01-1998 L2003 OTO *020 †45

BLATT, Jeffrey Mark. 1031 S BROAD ST 19446 #041-13-1971 L1972 OBG *020 †30

BOTHWELL, William Nassau. 2100 N BROAD ST, STE 100 19446 #041-02-1988 L1990
GS *020 †85

BRAUN, Dennis Roy. 125 MEDICAL CAMPUS DR 19446 #035-09-1984 L1990 U *020 †95

BUCKLER, Richard Alan. 100 MEDICAL CAMPUS DR 19446 #041-07-1981 L1988 N *020 †75 ‡

BUTSON, Harry Eugene. ■ 19446 #041-01-1947 L1948 PD *071 †55

CHANG, Amy. ■ 19446 #041-13-2004 L2004 ID *012 †20

CHERAYIL, Marina Joseph. 100 MEDICAL CAMPUS DR, CENTRAL MONTGOMERY
MEDICAL 19446 #496-39-1988 L2003 IM *020 †20

CHRISTIAN, Colleen June. 1000 N BROAD ST, POHTALMIC ASSOCIATES 19446
#038-06-1985 L1989 OPH PD *020 †35 ‡

CHUNG, Chung Y. ■ 19446 #583-13-1977 *100

COZZARELLI, James D. 1057 S BROAD ST 19446 #010-01-1959 L1967 GS *071 †85

CULP, Bruce Richard. 826 N BROAD ST 19446 #041-13-1986 L1987 FM *020 †18

D'ADDARIO, Richard T. 2031 N BROAD ST, STE 139 19446 #041-13-1966 L1967 N *071 †75

DELGIORNO, Thomas Charles. 125 MEDICAL CAMPUS DR, STE 300 19446
#041-02-1997 L1999 IM *020 †20

DESMOND, Robert Edward. 100 W MAIN ST STE 512 19446 #041-14-1980 L1981 P *020 †75

DETWEILER, Robert O'Neill. 1970 N BROAD ST 19446 #041-77-1985, ▲ L1986 FM *020

DORVAL, Jane. 309 COUNTRY CLUB DR 19446 #035-06-1976 L1978 PM IM *030 †60 ‡

DOSHI, Sangita Kiran. 1019 S BROAD ST 19446 #041-02-1999 L2001 FM *020 †18

DRIVER, Albert Gardner. 601 E MAIN ST 19446 #041-14-1978 L1993 PUD AI *020 †20,03

EBBINGHAUS, Scot Wm. 125 KELSEY DR 19446 #028-46-1989 L2007 ON *020 †20

EHRLICH, Clifford Lewis. 125 MEDICAL CAMPUS DR, STE 101 19446 #035-09-1981 L1983
CD CCM *020 †20

ENEANYA, Uche Ogochukwu. ■ 19446 #041-15-2005 L2005 PM *012

EVANS, Judith Kristin. ■ 19446 #041-01-2000 PTH *100

EWING, Lesley Lynne. ■ 19446 #019-02-1981 L1983 PDC *020 †55

FAIRFIELD, James Clarke. 1003 S BROAD ST 19446 #041-14-1975 L1976 D FM *020 †18,15 ‡

FAJARDO, Atanasio Candido. ■ 19446 #275-01-1944 L1969 GP EM *071

FAYE, Robyn Beth. 1031 S BROAD ST 19446 #041-13-1984 L1985 OBG *020 †30

FELDMAN, Jessica Arlene. 2031 N BROAD ST, STE 139 19446 #021-01-2002 L2002 N *020

FILOSA, Robert James. 902 N BROAD ST 19446 #041-13-1968 L1969 OBG *020 †30

FINK, Jack Wm. 2032 N BROAD ST 19446 #041-02-1954 L1955 GYN *071 †30

FRIEDMAN, Richard Allen. 125 MEDICAL CAMPUS DR, STE 300 19446 #041-09-1975 L1982
NEP IM *020 †20

FRY, Emily Christine. ■ 19446 #038-45-2003 L2006 EM *020 †16

GALENA, Edward Chas, IV. 1013 S BROAD ST, LANSDALE PEDIATRICS 19446
#041-09-1992 L1994 PD *020 †55

GEWIRTZ, Eric Carl. 100 MEDICAL CAMPUS DR 19446 #308-07-1983 L1987 AN *020 †05

GIBBONS, Ian Sills E. ■ 19446 #671-01-1957 GE PD *071

GIVEN, Kenneth Marshall. ■ 19446 #041-02-1961 L1962 IM HEM *030 †20

GLADSTONE, Leonard Gary. 1801 N BROAD ST 19446 #041-02-1974 L1975 IM *020 †20

GOLDMAN, William Jos. ■ 19446 #041-09-1976 L1977 IM PA *071 †20

GOODYEAR, James Allan. 2100 N BROAD ST STE 100, NORTH PENN SURGICAL ASSOC 19446
#041-13-1975 L1976 GS AS *020 †85

GREEN, Barry Paul. 826 N BROAD ST 19446 #041-09-1972 L1973 FM *020 ‡

GREENE, Thomas Edward. 635 N BROAD ST 19446 #001-02-1975 L1983 ORS *020 †40

GUICO-PABIA, Christine J. ■ 19446 #748-01-1985 *030

HALL, Donald Thomas. 100 MEDICAL CAMPUS DR 19446 #041-09-1993 L1997 AN *020 †05

HALL, Glennis Rosemarie. 100 MEDICAL CAMPUS DR 19446 #041-02-1991 L1995 AN *020

HALSTEAD, Christina Amy. ■ 19446 #041-15-2005 L2005 PD *012

HARMAN, Scott Myers. 400 N BROAD ST 19446 #051-04-1990 L1992 P *020 †75

HASHEMI, Seyed Mansoor. 100 MEDICAL CAMPUS DR, DEPT RAD 19446 #517-01-1967 L1977
R *020 †80

HENRY, William Jos. 108 COWPATH RD, STE 2 19446 #041-01-1983 L1985 OTO *020 †45

HEYMAN, Sydney. ■ 19446 #836-01-1966 L1979 NM PD *071 †28

HUSTAD, Thomas Joel. ■ 19446 #041-02-2000 *100

IRVIN, John David. ■ 19446 #041-09-1975 PA NS *050

JAKABOVICS, Eva. 2031 N BROAD ST, STE 129 19446 #473-01-1980 L1988 PD AI *020 †03,55

JEYARAJ, Francis. 1013 S BROAD ST 19446 #496-38-1969 L1975 PD *020 †55

JOCHNOWITZ, Michael J. 100 MEDICAL CAMPUS DR 19446 #038-41-1966 L1973
OBG *020 †30

JULES, Arnold Jay. 635 N BROAD ST 19446 #023-01-1963 L1969 ORS *071 †40

KEHINDE, Folasade Ibironk. ■ 19446 #690-01-1991 L2007 NPM *020 †55 ‡

KENNEDY, Susan Heather. 826 N BROAD ST 19446 #041-02-2000 L2003 FM *020 †18 ‡

KENNEDY, William. ■ 19446 #005-11-1992 L2001 PDI *020

KERAWALA, Rubina Noor. 601 E MAIN ST 19446 #704-16-1995 L2005 PCC *020 †20

KIM, Tae-Moon. 100 MEDICAL CAMPUS DR 19446 #583-04-1960 L1972 PTH *020 †50

KLEBACK, Carol. 108 COWPATH RD, STE 1 19446 #041-15-1999 L2001 PD *020 †55

KNEELAND, Malcolm E. ■ 19446 #035-01-1943 L1954 GS *071 †85

KNUDSEN, Sandra Jane. 826 N BROAD ST 19446 #041-15-1999 L2004 FM *020 †18

KOFFLER, Howard Barry. 601 E MAIN ST 19446 #041-13-1971 L1972 IM PUD *020 †20 ‡

KOLECKI, Robert Vincent. 2100 N BROAD ST, STE 100 19446 #041-02-1989 L1992 GS *020 †85

KRAYNAK, Joseph Chas. 125 MEDICAL CAMPUS DR, STE 101 19446 #041-14-1978 L1980
CD IM *020 †20

KRIEBEL, Richard Howard. ■ 19446 #041-13-1955 L1956 AN *071 †05

KWEDER-DE VINE, Jean. 131 BLUEBIRD XING 19446 #041-09-1950 L1951 PD PHP *071

LEE, William Manhon. 826 N BROAD ST 19446 #041-13-1986 L1987 FM *020 †18

LEVIN, Alex Van. 100 MEDICAL CAMPUS DR 19446 #041-02-1982 L1984 OPH PDS *020 †55,35

LEVINE, Robert Todd. ■ 19446 #041-02-1982 L1983 IM *020 †20

LIM, Nicholas Yao. ■ 19446 #748-08-1959 L1970 END IM *030

LORRAINE, Richard Scott. 100 MEDICAL CAMPUS DR 19446 #041-02-1982 L1983
IM *020 †20

LUKBAN, Wilfredo Siy. 100 MEDICAL CAMPUS DR, CENTRAL MONTGOMERY MEDICAL 19446
#748-02-1992 L1997 IM *020 †20

MALIK, Khalil. 1037 S BROAD ST, KM ALLERGY & ASTHMA CTR 19446 #704-02-1976 L1986
Ai IM *020 †20,03

MARX, Marvin Henry. 506 N BROAD ST 19446 #035-01-1958 L1963 U *071 †95

MAZZOLA, Robert Donato. 419 S BROAD ST, LANSDALE INTERNAL MED TVPC 19446
#041-13-1966 L1967 IM *020 †20

MC CORD, James Andrews. ■ 19446 #045-01-1962 L1967 OBG *071 †30

MERGAMAN, Jay M. 100 MEDICAL CAMPUS DR 19446 #305-01-1982 L1983 AN *020

MINEHART, Richard Jacob. 100 MEDICAL CAMPUS DR 19446 #041-13-1983 L1984 GS *020

MINEROFF, Allan David. 1709 N BROAD ST 19446 #035-08-1993 L1997 D *020 †15

MINSTER, William G. ■ 19446 #041-09-1952 L1953 IM P *071

MISTRY, Parul Ramanlal. ■ 19446 #495-96-1992 L1997 IM *020 †20

MOHAMMED, Naheed Ghouse. 100 MEDICAL CAMPUS DR 19446 #495-37-1988 L2001
PAN *020 †05

MONAHAN, George R. ■ 19446 #035-09-1957 L1958 OS *071 †05

MOTLEY, John Francis. ■ 19446 #041-02-1971 L1972 FM *071 †55 ‡

NAIK, Archit A. ■ 19446 #041-15-2004 L2004 GS *012

NALINI, Chakram. 1001 S BROAD ST, STE 1031 19446 #495-45-1983 L1998 CD *020 †20

NIBBELINK, Donald Wilfred. ■ 19446 #018-03-1965 L1975 N *071 †75

O'CONNOR, Thomas James. 1000 N BROAD ST 19446 #024-07-1991 L1995 OPH *020 †35

O'MALLEY, Joseph F. ■ 19446 #041-09-1962 L1963 IM *071

O'MALLEY, Rika Nagakuni. ■ 19446 #572-51-1994 L2003 EM *012

OSIAS, Marc Barry. 125 MEDICAL CAMPUS DR 19446 #008-01-1972 L1980 U *020 †95 ‡

OSKANIAN, Ohanes. 100 MEDICAL CAMPUS DR 19446 #396-04-1959 L1966 U *071 †95 ‡

PARENTI, Dennis Louis. ■ 19446 #028-02-1978 L1980 RHU *020 †20

PARIKH, Prashant Pramod. 419 S BROAD ST 19446 #495-01-1984 L1999 FM *020 †18

PELLEGRINO, Andrea Wisser. ■ 19446 #041-15-2001 L2002 FM *020 †18

PINSKY, William. ■ 19446 #041-15-1962 IM *071 †20

POLLOCK, Denzel Wayne. 125 MEDICAL CAMPUS DR, STE 101 19446 #019-02-1983 L1985
CD IM *020 †20

PORTNER, Jeff Howard. 1019 S BROAD ST 19446 #041-14-1987 L1989 FM *020 †18

PRAVS, Daila Melita. ■ 19446 #038-06-2005 L2005 FP *012

QUINN, Vincent John. 1001 S BROAD ST, STE 1031 19446 #041-09-1985 L1986 CD IM *020 †20

RAI, Rajesh. 100 MEDICAL CAMPUS DR 19446 #495-47-1972 L1979 DR EM *020 †20

RAJPUT, Shilpa V. 100 MEDICAL CAMPUS DR 19446 #495-17-1988 L1994 CCA *020 †05

RAMIC, Dzanan. ■ 19446 #028-03-2004 L2004 IM *100 †20

RAMOS, Andres Armando. 1031 S BROAD ST 19446 #024-05-1983 L1985 OBG *020 †30

RAVETZ, Larry Alan. 2100 N BROAD ST, STE 100 19446 #041-07-1986 L1989 IM *020 †20

RAWSON, Helen H. ■ 19446 #035-15-1951 L1953 PD *071 †55

RHODES, Anthony L. 1011 S BROAD ST 19446 #041-13-1986 L1987 ORS *020 †40

ROSENBERG, Carl Elihu. 108 COWPATH RD, STE 4 19446 #024-04-1977 L2000 N *050 †75

ROSENFELD, Jack Craig. 826 N BROAD ST 19446 #041-13-1984 L1985 FM *020 †18

ROSENTHAL, Brian Jeffrey. 125 MEDICAL CAMPUS DR 19446 #047-05-1984 L1984 U *020 †95

SAG, Jerome Edward. 419 S BROAD ST, LANSDALE IM TVPC 19446 #035-09-1972 L1975
IM *020 †20 ‡

SALOMONE, Ronald Jerry. 100 MEDICAL CAMPUS DR 19446 #035-01-1982 L1983 EM *020 †16

SATASHIA, Bhavesh Dayalbh. 320 ABBEY LN 19446 #495-48-1995 L2003 IM *020 †20

SAWICKI, Rafal Wojciech. 601 E MAIN ST 19446 #759-07-1993 L1998 PCC *020 †20 ‡

SAXENA, Aradhna. 212 READING CIR, ADVANCED DERMATOLOGY ASSOC 19446
#041-02-2002 L2003 D *100 †15

SCHERZINGER, Felix A. 2031 N BROAD ST STE 145 19446 #407-10-1962 L1964 PD *020 †55

SEIDNER, Michael Richard. 826 N BROAD ST 19446 #033-06-1975 L1976 FM OS *020 †18 ‡

SENSENIG, David M. ■ 19446 #024-01-1945 L1962 VS GS *071 †85,90

SHAH, Dipti R. 1000 WALNUT ST, STE 122 19446 #495-01-1987 L1996 OBG *020 †20

SHAHID, Naheed Ahmad. 419 S BROAD ST, LANSDALE INTERNAL MED 19446
#041-15-2001 L2003 IM *020 †20

SHANIS, Bonnie Schildkret. 100 MEDICAL CAMPUS DR 19446 #041-09-1975 L1991
END IM *020

SHANKEN, Williard Jay. 100 MEDICAL CAMPUS DR 19446 #041-09-1967 L1968 P PYA *020 †75

SHIELDS, Thomas John. 902 N BROAD ST 19446 #035-08-1967 L1974 OBG *020 †30

SHISLER, Frederick H. ■ 19446 #041-02-1960 L1961 GP *071

SIDDIQUI, Shehla Sarki. ■ 19446 #704-02-1989 L1995 PD *020 †55

SILVER, Barry Alan. 635 N BROAD ST 19446 #041-02-1967 L1968 ORS *071 †40

SIMCOX, Margaret Mary. 2100 N BROAD ST 19446 #041-09-1976 L1977 IM *020 †20

SIMOES, Antonio J L. 2100 N BROAD ST 19446 #770-01-1953 L1963 GS TS *071 †85,90

SISTER, Igor. ■ 19446 #913-77-1987 L2004 IM *020 †20

SKOBIERANDA, Franck G. 117 BROOKSHYRE WAY 19446 #041-14-1991 L2000 N OM *020 †75

SMITH, Erik Charles. 1031 S BROAD ST 19446 #010-03-1997 L2001 OBG *020 †30

SPELLMAN, William Henry. 1011 S BROAD ST 19446 #028-03-1975 L1981 ORS *020 †40

STEVENSON, Richard Dale. 1013 S BROAD ST, MEDICAL ASSOC 19446 #041-13-1964 L1965
PD *020 ‡

STRUNK, Harold Philip. 100 MEDICAL CAMPUS DR 19446 #010-01-1970 L1973 R *020 †80

TENDLER, Steven Warren. 100 MEDICAL CAMPUS DR 19446 #041-09-1969 L1970
CD IM *071 †20

■ = Address Information Privacy Protected

TOLSCIK, Richard. 100 MEDICAL CAMPUS DR 19446 #759-06-1962 L1971 **AN** *071
TRUSCOTT, William Ray. 419 S BROAD ST, LANSDALE INTERNAL MED TVPC 19446 #041-13-1961 L1963 **FM** *020 †18
TYSON, R Robert. ■ 19446 #041-01-1944 L1948 **CD GS** *071 †85
VARIA, Apurv Kirit. ■ 19446 #041-13-2005 L2005 **IM** *012
WANG, Peter, Jr. 635 N BROAD ST 19446 #035-19-1991 L2000 **ORS** *071 †40
WANG, Qinping. 100 MEDICAL CAMPUS DR 19446 #034-01-1997 L1999 **IMG** *020 †20
WANG, Xin. 2031 N BROAD ST, STE 139 19446 #243-69-1986 L2002 **N** *020 †75
WARD, Stephen Christopher. ■ 19446 #023-01-2003 L2006 **SP** *100 †50
WOO, Zung-Pah. ■ 19446 #242-09-1940 L1959 **PTH** *071 †50
WRIGHT, David Manfred. 100 MEDICAL CAMPUS DR 19446 #041-01-1973 L1974 **PTH** *030 †50
YARNOFF, Lisa Beth. 1013 S BROAD ST, LANSDALE PEDIATRIC & ADOLE 19446 #041-13-1990 L1993 **PD** *020 †55

LANSDOWNE – DELAWARE

ANWAR, Shahgul. ■ 19050 #704-20-1997 L2004 **PTH** *100
CAMBRIDGE, Florinda L. ■ 19050 #010-03-1949 L1952 **OBG P** *020
CONLY, Jeffrey Robert. ■ 19050 #041-13-2004 L2004 **PM** *012
FAN, Minghui. ■ 19050 #024-01-1997 L2006 **PCC** *012
FURTH, John Jacob. ■ 19050 #036-07-1958 L1970 **PTH** *071
GIACCONE, Ann Johanna. ■ 19050 #041-15-2005 L2005 **PD** *012
HARTOG, Maurice. ■ 19050 #660-01-1963 L1987 **GP PTH** *072 †50
HOFELDER, Christian T. ■ 19050 #409-10-1998 L1998 **M** *100
KLOOS, Angelica Louise. ■ 19050 #041-77-2005, ▲ L2005 **P** *012
KOTAKIS, John. 23 N LANSDOWNE AVE 19050 #041-09-1954 L1955 **IM** *071
LEVY, Edwin J. 85 N LANSDOWNE AVE 19050 #041-02-1943 L1944 **D PA** *071 †15
LINK, Michael Gary. ■ 19050 #033-05-2005 L2005 **IM** *012
MARK, Dustin George. ■ 19050 #045-02-2004 L2004 **EM** *012
MOOREVILLE, Michael. 272 N LANSDOWNE AVE 19050 #041-14-1978 L1979 **U** *020 †95 ‡
NOLT, Brendon Robert. ■ 19050 #041-01-2006 L2006 **FM** *012
NWANESHIUDU, Ifeanyi. ■ 19050 #041-13-2006 L2006 **GS** *100
ONUOHA, Onyinye Chiechefu. ■ 19050 #023-07-2007 *012
ONUOHA, Uchechukwu Nkechi. ■ 19050 #041-13-2007 L2007 **IM** *012
PATTERSON, Christopher J. ■ 19050 #917-19-1970 **M** *100 †20
PEARSON, Nathaniel C. ■ 19050 #036-05-2003 L2007 **IM** *100
PENNY-PETERSON, Erica. 101 W BALTIMORE AVE, # 1G1 19050 #041-01-2000 L2001 **ICE** *012 †20
PERCZAK-DUDKOWSKA, B. 281 N LANSDOWNE AVE 19050 #759-06-1975 L1998 **IM** *020 †20
PICCONE, Connie Marie. ■ 19050 #041-15-2003 L2007 **PHO** *012 †55
REDDY, Chandra Shekar K. 433 S LANSDOWNE AVE 19050 #495-72-1986 L2001 **ORS** *020
SACKS, Edmond J. ■ 19050 #035-08-1968 L1976 **PDC** *071 †55
SHAIK, Arif Mohammed. ■ 19050 #496-27-2002 L2005 **IM** *012
SWENSON, David Whitmer. ■ 19050 #041-01-2008 *012
WILSON, Christina Annette. ■ 19050 #041-01-2008 *012
WOJCIECHOWSKI, Brian Stan. ■ 19050 #041-13-2005 L2005 **IM** *012

LATROBE – WESTMORELAND

AHMAD, Saghir. 121 W 2ND AVE 15650 #704-02-1978 L1996 **P** *020 †75
AMADEE, Charles Michael. 121 W 2ND AVE, LATROBE HOSP-ER DEPT 15650 #041-02-1982 L1983 **EM** *020 †18
ARMANIOUS, Adel Wadie. 600 LIGONIER ST 15650 #330-02-1965 L1970 **GS VS** *020 †85
ARULANANTHAM, Gowri. 121 W 2ND AVE 15650 #220-02-1979 L1988 **P** *020 †75
BALLIET, Helen Elizabeth. 121 W 2ND AVE 15650 #005-11-1983 L1987 **AN** *030 †05
BARR, Lisa Marie. 121 W 2ND AVE, ER DEPARTMENT 15650 #012-05-1997 L1999 **EM** *020 †16
BARSOUM, Adib Hanna. 206 WELDON ST 15650 #330-03-1955 L1965 **NS PMM** *020 †25
BARTON, George Robt. ■ 15650 #041-12-1966 L1967 **FM** *020
BASSLER, Arwen Elena. 121 W 2ND AVE 15650 #041-15-2002 L2003 **FM** *020 †18
BERARDI, Ronald Stephen. W 2ND AVE, DEPT PATH 15650 #016-43-1967 L1969 **PTH OS** *071 †50 ‡
BERGQUIST, Erick John. 121 W 2ND AVE, LATROBE AREA HOSPITAL 15650 #041-02-1973 L1974 **ID IM** *020
BRADLEY, James Paul. 300 FRASER PURCHASE RD, ST VINCENT COLLEGE 15650 #041-02-1991 L1993 **PS** *020 †85,65
BRENEMAN, Donald Paul. 121 W 2ND AVE 15650 #041-12-1963 L1964 **P OS** *020 †75
BURES, J Conrad. 121 W 2ND AVE, LATROBE AREA HOSP DEPT PTH 15650 #055-01-1971 L1971 **PTH** *020 †50 ‡
CANTINI, Marco. 121 W 2ND AVE 15650 #561-15-1984 L1993 **AN** *020 †05
CARTER, James Stephen. 121 W 2ND AVE 15650 #055-01-1967 L1968 **P** *020 †75 ‡
CATALANO, Kathleen J F. 210 WELDON ST 15650 #041-07-1964 L1965 **PD** *020 †55
CHAMBERLIN, Amanda Megan. ■ 15650 #041-14-2006 L2006 **FP** *012
CHANG, Juei-Ling. 121 W 2ND AVE 15650 #244-04-1969 L1974 **AN** *020 †05
CHRISTIANSON, Alan David. 121 W 2ND AVE 15650 #041-12-1979 L1980 **FM EM** *020 †18
CLARK, Margaret L. 1 MELLON WAY 15650 #041-12-1989 L1992 **DR** *020 †80
CONTE, Robert Ralph. 121 W 2ND AVE 15650 #041-02-1961 L1962 **GYN** *071 †30
CURRIE, Philip Williams. 1010 LIGONIER ST 15650 #041-01-1958 L1959 **GYN** *071 †30
DANIELE, Anthony G. 121 W 2ND AVE, DEPARTMENT OF RADIOLOGY 15650 #008-02-1996 L2003 **DR** *020 †80
DE FABO, Francis Leonard. 911 LIGONIER ST, STE 205 15650 #041-13-1989 L1992 **GYN** *020 †30
DEMANGONE, Dawn Adele. 4941 STATE ROUTE 982 15650 #041-02-1993 L1995 **EM** *020 †16
D'EMILIO, Terrance A. 330 WELDON ST 15650 #654-01-1982 L1984 **FM** *071 †18
DENNING, Diana Fern. 121 W 2ND AVE 15650 #019-02-1994 L1999 **OBG** *020 †30
DE ST MAURICE, Annabelle. ■ 15650 #035-45-2008 *012
DI COLA, Daniel Bradley. 121 W 2ND AVE 15650 #041-02-1978 L1979 **FM IMG** *020 †18
DINGER, Kenneth Michael. 1 MELLON WAY 15650 #017-20-2005 L2005 **FP** *012
FELL, Bradley Alan. 121 W 2ND AVE 15650 #041-02-1993 L1995 **FM** *020 †18
FLANNAGAN, Samuel Wm. 217 DEPOT ST 15650 #041-12-1968 L1969 **GYN** *020 †30
FLORENDO, Christine Lee. 5927 ROUTE 981 STE 8 15650 #748-16-1981 L1995 **PD** *020 †55
FOX, Diane Mary. 5927 ROUTE 981, STE 8 15650 #016-01-1979 L1991 **FM P** *020 †18
FRANCHINO, Charles Jos. 121 W 2ND AVE 15650 #010-01-1984 L1992 **P** *020 †50,75
GAVIN, George Michael. 555 ROUTE 217 15650 #041-13-1979 L1980 **FM** *020 †18 ‡

GERA, Jerome William. 121 W 2ND AVE, PRACTICE RESIDENCY 15650 #041-02-2000 L2001 **FM** *020 †18
GILLESPIE, Martin J. 911 LIGONIER ST, STE 3 15650 #010-02-1989 L1994 **OSM** *020 †40
GOVI, Joseph Richie. 121 W 2ND AVE, LATROBE AREA HOSPITAL 15650 #041-09-1958 L1959 **FM** *062 †18
GUTTI, Bindu Madhavi. ■ 15650 #038-43-2008 *012
HALL, Laura F. 210 WELDON ST 15650 #011-03-1975 L1977 **PD** *020 †55
HARTER, Scott Coleman. 121 W 2ND AVE, ER DEPARTMENT 15650 #041-12-1993 L1995 **EM** *020 †16
HERSHOCK, Bruce Alan. 1010 JEFFERSON ST 15650 #041-13-1974 L1975 **ORS FM** *020 †18,40
HOFFMAN, William John. 121 W 2ND AVE 15650 #041-12-1965 L1966 **DR GP** *020 †80
HORNE, John P. 121 W 2ND AVE, FAMILY PRACTICE DEPT 15650 #041-12-1992 L1994 **FM** *020 †18
HOSMER, Donna Balewick. 121 W 2ND AVE, ER DEPARTMENT 15650 #035-03-1987 L1999 **FM** *020 †18
HOSSAIN, Mohammad Shakhaw. ■ 15650 #160-07-1996 L2007 **FP** *012
HURTT, Mark R. 911 LIGONIER ST, STE 108 15650 #041-02-1981 L1986 **NP N** *020 †75
JAKUBEK, Donald Jos. 501 WELDON ST 15650 #041-14-1984 L1985 **FM** *020 †20
JENKINS, William Arthur. 121 W 2ND AVE, ER DEPARTMENT 15650 #041-12-1990 L1992 **EM** *020 †18
JETHMALANI, Sanjeev S. 911 LIGONIER ST, STE 204 15650 #495-20-1984 L1992 **CCM** *020 †20
KAR, Dilip S. 121 W 2ND AVE 15650 #496-38-1969 L1976 **OBG** *020 †30
KASSIR, Walid Ahmad. 10 LIBERTY LN, P O BOX 737 15650 #605-01-1998 L2003 **NEP** *100 †20
KAUFFMAN, Lara Michelle. 1 MELLON WAY 15650 #041-14-2005 L2005 **FP** *012
KAUFFMAN, Tate Matthew. 1 MELLON WAY, EXCELA HEALTH LATROBE HOSP 15650 #041-14-2005 L2005 **FP** *012
KHALID, Faiza. ■ 15650 #704-02-1997 L2007 **FP** *012
KINNEY, Mary K Seamon. 121 W 2ND AVE 15650 #016-43-1939 L1939 **GP** *075
KROUSE, John Milton. 121 W 2ND AVE 15650 #041-01-1955 L1956 **VS TS** *071 †85,90
KUMARI, Priyanka. 121 W 2ND AVE, LATROBE AREA HOSPITAL 15650 #104-01-2004 L2006 **FP** *012
LALLY, Patrick Thos. 911 LIGONIER ST 15650 #041-12-1979 L1980 **OPH** *020 †35
LAST, Joel Irwin. 121 W 2ND AVE 15650 #654-01-1986 L1987 **P** *020 †75
LAURO, Gregory Ralph. 5840 STATE ROUTE 981, STE 101 15650 #035-45-1986 L1991 **ORS** *020 †40
LAZARUS, Robert Eric. 121 W 2ND AVE, LATROBE AREA HOSPITAL 15650 #041-07-1989 L1991 **DR** *020 †80
LEONIDA, Efren Bolante. 121 W 2ND AVE, PRACTICE RESIDENCY 15650 #016-42-2000 L2001 **FM** *020 †18 ‡
LINVILLE, Terry Lee. 121 W 2ND AVE, LATROBE AREA HOSPITAL 15650 #038-45-1983 L1984 **FM** *020 †18
LONG, Anne. ■ 15650 #038-40-1996 L1998 **FM** *020 †18
LOPEZ, Florita Cordero. 121 W 2ND AVE, LATROBE AREA HOSP 15650 #748-10-1993 L2006 **FP** *012
MARRERO, Carlos Jose. 324 UNITY PLZ 15650 #042-03-1981 L1990 **N IM** *020 †75
MATTHEWS, Ted A, Jr. 326 MCKINLEY AVE STE 200 15650 #041-09-1984 L1986 **GS** *020 †85
MAXWELL, Beth Ann. 1010 LIGONIER ST, C/O GYNO ASSOCIATES 15650 #041-07-1985 L1989 **OBG** *020 †30 ‡
MAZERO, John Robt. LATROBE AREA HOSPITAL 15650 #010-01-1954 L1955 **IM** *071 †20
MC CLURE, Thomas David. 121 W 2ND AVE 15650 #041-12-1965 L1966 **DR GP** *020 †80
MEMARI, Elias Yousef. 121 W 2ND AVE, PATHOLOGY DEPT 15650 #875-01-1985 L2003 **PTH** *100 †50
MERRINGER, Mickey Roger. 911 LIGONIER ST, STE 108 15650 #056-06-1993 L1997 **FM** *072 †18
MILCHAK, Mark Allen. 1005 LIGONIER ST 15650 #041-14-1983 L1990 **CD** *020 †20
MILLENDORF, Jerold B. 121 W 2ND AVE, LATROBE AREA HOSPITAL 15650 #035-19-1978 L1991 **GS** *020
MILLS, Stephen Chas. 121 W 2ND AVE 15650 #041-13-1985 L1986 **FM** *020 †18
MOHAN, Govindaraj Vijay. 1 MELLON WAY, LATROBE HOSPITAL 15650 #495-94-1974 L1979 **R VIR** *020 †80
MOSS, Joseph Stanley, Jr. 10 LIBERTY LN 15650 #038-40-1984 L1993 **NEP IM** *020 †20
MURRAY, Jill Marie. ■ 15650 #041-02-2006 L2006 **FP** *012
NANJIAH, Sudharani Banga. ■ 15650 #496-39-1990 L2005 **FP** *012
ORR, Randall Scott. 121 W 2ND AVE 15650 #055-01-2001 L2005 **P** *020
PALAIKA, John Stanley. 305 MELLON BANK BLDG 15650 #041-12-1964 L1965 **OPH GP** *071 †35
PARKER, John Sheldon. 121 W 2ND AVE 15650 #035-06-1957 L1961 **IM IMG** *071 †20
PETRICK, Thomas Paul. WEST SECOND AVENUE 15650 #041-01-1960 L1961 **GS** *071 †85
PLUTO, Christine M. 210 BINKEY RD, UPMC BEDFORD HOSPITAL 15650 #041-02-1989 L1991 **FM** *020 †18
PROSPERI, Aldo John. 501 WELDON ST 15650 #041-02-1984 L1985 **FM** *020 †18
RAO, Gutti Parvathi P. 121 W 2ND AVE 15650 #495-11-1969 L1974 **AN** *020 †05
REYNA, Oscar Duran. 328 WELDON ST 15650 #264-04-1968 L1972 **GP** *020
RICE, David John. 121 W 2ND AVE, LATROBE AREA HOSPITAL 15650 #051-04-1982 L1983 **EM** *020 †16
RIVERA-MULERO, Maribel. 121 W 2ND AVE, LATROBE AREA HOSPITAL MENT 15650 #042-01-2001 L2005 **CHP** *100 †75
ROSENTHAL, David Michael. 121 W 2ND AVE 15650 #041-13-1992 L1994 **P** *020 †75
SARVER, Ray Gourley. 1100 LIGONIER ST 15650 #041-01-1954 L1955 **A PD** *071 †55
SCHULTZ, Fred Russell. 121 W 2ND AVE, LATROBE AREA HOSP 15650 #018-03-1973 L1984 **CHP P** *020 †55,75
SEARFOSS, Rodger Carl. 911 LIGONIER ST 15650 #005-11-1970 L1975 **ORS** *020 †40
SEECOF, Richard Mark. 1005 LIGONIER ST 15650 #041-12-1981 L1983 **CD IM** *020 †20
SELIP, Steven Wood. 911 LIGONIER ST, STE 101 15650 #654-01-1981 L1982 **FM** *020 †18
SHAKER, Milad Ishak. ■ 15650 #915-02-1996 L2006 **FP** *012
SHROFF, Vivekkumar Kartik. ■ 15650 #496-41-2001 L2007 **FP** *012
SINGH, Daljit. 911 LIGONIER ST STE 204 15650 #495-20-1965 L1973 **IM PUD** *020 †20
SINGH, Usha. W 2ND AVE, DEPT PATH 15650 #495-20-1965 L1975 **PTH** *020 †50
SONNENBERG, Jill Marie. ■ 15650 #422-01-2006 L2007 **FP** *012
STAFFEN, Robert Nicholas. 1005 LIGONIER ST 15650 #041-02-1988 L1990 **CD IM** *020 †20
STOREY, Amanda Jean. ■ 15650 #041-02-2005 L2005 **FP** *012
SUNG, Lee Hi. 121 W 2ND AVE 15650 #583-02-1958 L1971 **NEP** *020 †75
SUNG, Lee-Hyun. 10 LIBERTY LN, JOSEPH S MOSS MD 15650 #583-01-1972 L1977 **NEP IM** *020 †20
SZABO, Edward Theodore. 1005 LIGONIER ST 15650 #038-40-1985 L1986 **CD IM** *020 †20

■ = Address Information Privacy Protected

TAN, Marie Kwai-Che. 210 WELDON ST 15650 #462-01-1979 L1990 **PD OS** *020 †55
TRESKOVICH, Jacob Anthony. ■ 15650 #041-13-2008 *012
TRIMELONI, Lauren Elizabe. 104 W 2ND AVE 15650 #041-13-2004 L2004 **FM** *100 †18
VITTONE, Michael Andrew. 1010 LIGONIER ST 15650 #041-12-1995 L1998 **OPH** *020 †20,35
VITTONE, Ronald B. 1010 LIGONIER ST 15650 #041-01-1959 L1960 **OPH** *020 †35 ‡
WANG, Hai-Wei. 121 W 2ND AVE 15650 #243-69-1984 L2005 **P** *020 †75
WARD, Thomas David, Jr. 121 W 2ND AVE 15650 #041-12-1980 L1985 **NEP IM** *020 †20
WEINBERG, Michael Gary. 501 WELDON ST 15650 #041-02-1977 L1978 **FM** *020 †18
WIDLAN, Sheldon. 1100 LIGONIER ST 15650 #025-07-1967 L1977 **D** *020 †15
WIGLE, Arnold Roger. 911 LIGONIER ST STE 3 15650 #041-09-1973 L1974 **ORS** *020 †40
WYSZOMIERSKI, David A. 210 WELDON ST 15650 #041-12-1979 L1984 **PD PDP** *020 †55
YELOVICH, Ann-Kathryn. 1060 WHITNEY COURT DR 15650 #041-14-1991 L1995
   CHP P *020 †75
ZELEZNIK, Miroslav. 121 W 2ND AVE 15650 #286-03-1958 L1976 **FM IM** *072 ‡
ZORCH, Paul Martin. 121 W 2ND AVE, ER DEPARTMENT 15650 #041-02-1982 L1983
   FM EM *020 †18

LAUGHLINTOWN – WESTMORELAND

SCHROCK, Laura Jane. ■ 15655 #060-01-1964 L1966 **GS** *071

LAUREL RUN – LUZERNE

D'IORIO, James Patrick. 1100 E NORTHAMPTON ST 18706 #041-01-1970 L1971 **GP IM** *020

LAURELDALE – BERKS

DREAZEN, Jonathan Robt. 3212B KUTZTOWN RD 19605 #035-45-1977 L1983
   OM IMG *020 †18
SANTORO, William. 3212 KUTZTOWN RD 19605 #042-03-1981 L1984 **FM ADM** *020 †18

LAURYS STATION – LEHIGH

BADAWY, Samy B. 5649 WYNNEWOOD DR, STE 202 18059 #041-07-1986 L1989 **GS** *020
HAAS, Susan Ilene. 5649 WYNNEWOOD DR, STE 101 18059 #041-02-1995 L1997 **OBG** *020 †30
HARAKAL, Thomas Paul. 5649 WYNNEWOOD DR STE 202 18059 #041-13-1975 L1976
   FM IMG *020 †18
JEFFERIS, Earl Stein, Jr. 5649 WYNNEWOOD DR, STE 101 18059 #041-09-1964 L1965
   OBG *020 †30
LYNOTT, Paul Jos. 5649 WYNNEWOOD DR, PA 18059 #041-02-1986 L1987 **FM** *020 †18
ROBBINS, Terry Jean. 5649 WYNNEWOOD DR, STE 202 18059 #041-13-1975 L1976 **D** *020 †15
SHAWE, Toby. 5649 WYNNEWOOD DR, STE 202 18059 #396-24-1987 L1991 **D** *020
SHEETS, Kimberly Rae. 5649 WYNNEWOOD DR, STE 203 18059 #041-01-1997 L1999
   FM *020 †18
SHEINBERG, Michael. 5649 WYNNEWOOD DR, STE 101 18059 #016-06-1992 L1996
   OBG *020 †30

LAVEROCK – MONTGOMERY

BOWLING, Chetwynd Edmund. ■ 19038 #010-03-1968 L1970 **IM OS** *020
GOLLUB, Morton Jerome. ■ 19038 #016-42-1954 L1954 **IM** *071 †20
ROSS, Denise A. 7921 DEER RUN RD 19038 #041-01-1980 L1981 **IMG IM** *030 †20
SAGIN, Todd. ■ 19038 #041-12-1978 L1980 **FM FPG** *020 †18
TENER, Trilby Jo. 7700 DOE LN 19038 #041-07-1997 L2000 **OBG** *020 †30 ‡
WESSEL, Isadore Jay. ■ 19038 #041-09-1931 L1932 **DR RO** *071

LAWRENCE – WASHINGTON

DAHL, James Douglas. ■ 15055 #041-12-1992 L1995 **FM** *020 †18

LAWRENCEVILLE – TIOGA

SCOTT, Phyllis B. 32 E LAWRENCE RD, LAUREL HEALTH CENTER 16929 #034-01-1988 L1990
   FM *020 †18

LAWTON – SUSQUEHANNA

FRITZ, Louisa Joan. ■ 18828 #660-03-1962 L1980 **GP** *071

LE RAYSVILLE – BRADFORD

BUSHYAGER, Ross M. ■ 18829 #041-13-1954 L1955 **GP PM** *020

LEBANON – LEBANON

ABELEDA, Guillerma F M. ■ 17042 #041-01-1963 L1976 **IM GP** *020
ABELEDA, Rafael Villas. ■ 17042 #748-08-1966 L1984 **P** *020
ABRISHAMCHIAN, Ahmad Reza. FOURTH & WALNUT ST, 2ND FLOOR 17042
   #422-01-1996 L2006 **TS** *020 †85,90
ACRICH, Ivonne Adriana. 503 CUMBERLAND ST, CATHOLIC CHARITIES 17042
   #041-14-1991 L1993 **P CHP** *020 †75
ADAMS, Tamara Jean. 755 NORMAN DR 17042 #041-15-2000 L2003 **IM** *020 †20
AITKEN, Paul V, Jr. 17042 #035-06-1992 L2005 **GPM** *020 †70,18
ALI, Mahmud. ■ 17042 #160-03-1995 L2005 **FP** *012
ALI, Suhail M. 1700 S LINCOLN AVE, LEBANON VA MED CTR 17042 #704-02-1988 L1997
   HO *020 †20

ALLEN, Denyse Marie. 700 CHESTNUT ST 17042 #035-48-1983 L1984 **FM** *020 †18
ALLEY, Albert Abbas. 1510 CORNWALL RD 17042 #041-13-1964 L1967 **OPH** *020 †35
ANDREOZZI, Robert James. 845 NORMAN DR 17042 #041-09-1968 L1973 **D DMP** *020 †15
ARES, Nilda Evelyn. ■ 17042 #042-03-1980 L1987 **IM NEP** *075
BAASE, Carol Audrey. 4TH & WALNUT STS 17042 #035-45-1985 L1986 **FM** *040 †18
BAER, Michael Thos. 1700 S LINCOLN AVE 17042 #041-14-1984 L1985 **FM** *020 †18
BAGHERI, Saeed A. 1151 CORNWALL RD, STE 5 17042 #517-05-1969 L1988 **GE IM** *020 †20
BAGHERI-DASTGHEIB, Bita A. 845 NORMAN DR, DERMATOLOGY ASSOCIATES 17042
   #041-01-1998 L2003 **D** *020 †15
BALOGH, Robert J, Jr. 956 ISABEL DR, PRIORITY CARE 17042 #041-09-1984 L1985
   EM *020 †16
BAMBERGER, John Alexander. ■ 17042 #041-09-1947 L1948 **OTO** *071
BARBER, Joseph Anthony. ■ 17042 #041-14-1990 L1993 **P** *020 †75
BARTGES, John David. 1023 POPLAR ST 17042 #041-02-1977 L1978 **U** *020 †95
BARTON, Robert Lester. 101 FAIRVIEW CIR 17042 #041-09-1965 L1969 **FM OM** *020 †18
BATRA, Erich Karamvir. 101 FAIRVIEW CIR, GOOD SAMARITAN FAMILY 17042
   #051-01-1994 L1998 **IM PD** *020 †20,55
BAYRAKDAR, Ahmad Khaldoun. 755 NORMAN DR 17042 #875-01-1970 L2007 **GE IM** *020 †20
BAZEWICZ, Robert A. 229 S 4TH ST 17042 #033-06-1983 L1988 **GS PDS** *085 ‡
BELTZ, Michael Scott. 815 NORMAN DR, UROLOGY ASSOC-LEBANON PA 17042
   #017-20-1995 L1997 **U** *020 †95
BERING, Joseph Paul. 618 CORNWALL RD, GOOD SAMARATIN FAM PRAC 17042
   #041-02-1956 L1957 **FM** *071 †18
BLAS BORIA, Juan Carlos. ■ 17042 #042-03-1997 L2001 **DR** *020 †80
BONDUGULA, Vijayamala. ■ 17042 #495-65-1992 L2006 **FP** *012
BOOGAARD, Ronald Geo. 775 NORMAN DR 17042 #010-02-1979 L1984 **CD IM** *020 †20 ‡
BROWN, Spencer Alan. 204 HATHAWAY PARK, PHILHAVEN BEHAVIORAL HEALT 17042
   #019-02-1989 L2000 **CHP** *020 †75
BROWN, Victoria Ann. 4TH AND WILLOW STREETS 17042 #005-14-1987 L1990 **FM** *020 †18
BRUMMETT, Robert Greville. 323 CUMBERLAND ST, ALLCARE FAMILY HEALTH PC 17042
   #041-01-2000 L2000 **FM** *020 †18
BUSH, James Wm. 770 NORMAN DR, LEBANON OPHTHALMIC ASSOC 17042
   #035-01-1983 L1987 **OPH** *020 †35
BUSTAMANTE, Christopher D. ■ 17042 #748-02-1997 L2006 **FP** *012
CAMPBELL, Navneet S. ■ 17042 #023-01-1988 L1990 **IM** *074 †20
CAMPBELL, Robert A. 912 RUSSELL DR 17042 #023-01-1988 L1990 **AN PME** *020 †05
CARHART, Judy Ann. 1700 S LINCOLN AVE, MEDICAL CENTER 17042 #051-04-1975 L1977
   FM *020 †18
CASAS, Angelina Wagas. 1700 S LINCOLN AVE 17042 #748-11-1966 L1973 **PTH CLP** *020 †50
CAUSAK, Rachel Ann. 1700 S LINCOLN AVE, LEBANON VA MED CTR 17042
   #041-14-2000 L2001 **MPD** *020 †55,20
CHAMBERS, Jennifer Anne. 1700 S LINCOLN AVE, LEBANON VA MEDICAL CENTER 17042
   #041-14-1995 L1998 **IM** *020 †20
CHODOS, Andrew P. 775 NORMAN DR 17042 #035-03-1985 L2003 **CD** *020 †20
CHRISTMAN, James C. 300 WILLOW ST, WOMENS HLTH CTR OF LEBANON 17046
   #041-14-1976 L1977 **OBG** *020 †30
CLARK, David Paul. 300 WILLOW ST, WOMEN'S HEALTH CENTER 17046 #041-14-1979 L1984
   OBG *020 †30
CLARK, Joseph Martin. ■ 17042 #035-46-1968 L1973 **DR NM** *071 †80,28
CLEMENS, Thomas Michael. 775 NORMAN DR 17042 #041-02-1973 L1974 **CD IM** *020 †20
COCHRAN, Janet Moorfield. 1700 S LINCOLN AVE, BLDG 23 17042 #047-06-1978 L1999
   PM *020 †60
COLLIER, Herman Edward. 775 NORMAN DR 17042 #041-13-1986 L1988 **CD** *020 †20
COOPEY, Frederick Donald. 1700 S LINCOLN AVE, LEBANON VA MED CTR 17042
   #041-09-1970 L1971 **OTO** *020 †45
CRAWFORD, Donald Gordon. ■ 17042 #041-09-1963 L1964 **FM** *071 †18
CREAM, Leah Von Reyn. 1700 S LINCOLN AVE, LEBANON VA MEDICAL CENTER 17042
   #032-01-2000 L2001 **IM** *020
DA COSTA, Nicolau. 1700 S LINCOLN AVE, LEBANON MED CENTER 17042 #187-43-1986 L1995
   IM END *020 †20
DALL, Anne Virginia. 701 CHESTNUT ST 17042 #041-14-1992 L1994 **P** *020 †75
DARRELL, John Charles. PO BOX 1281, 4TH & WALNUT STREETS 17042 #023-01-1982 L1989
   TS VS *020 †85,90
DAVIDSON, William Ross. 775 NORMAN DR 17042 #051-01-1971 L1978 **CD IM** *020 †20 ‡
DAVIES, Robert H. ■ 17042 #025-01-1941 L1942 **OPH** *071 †35
DEYSHER, David Paul. 755 NORMAN DR 17042 #041-77-1983, ▲ L1984 **GE IM** *020 †20 ‡
DHADUK, Narendrakumar V. ■ 17042 #495-48-1982 L1993 **N GPM** *020 †75
DHATRIKA, Amita Venkatesh. ■ 17042 #495-85-2001 L2004 **FM** *100
DI GIACOMO, Paul Richard. 775 NORMAN DR 17042 #041-09-1969 L1970 **CD IM** *020 †20
DORSCH, Raymond Michael. 4TH & WALNUT STS 17042 #041-01-1956 L1957 **ORS** *071 †40
DY-REYES, Roberto R. 4TH & WALNUT ST, GOOD SAMARITAN HOSP 17042
   #748-01-1965 L1971 **R** *020 †80
EAGLESON, Bruce Kent. 956 ISABEL DR, PRIORITY CARE 17042 #025-07-1976 L1977
   EM OM *020 †70,16,18
ESTERBROOK, Beth Irene. 1700 S LINCOLN AVE, DEPT OF VETERANS AFFAIRS 17042
   #041-13-1999 L2005 **IM** *020 †20
FARALLI, Victor Jos. 912 RUSSELL DR 17042 #041-13-1979 L1980 **ORS** *020 †40
FERRARA, Leonard Peter. 815 NORMAN DR 17042 #748-08-1982 L1987 **U** *020
FIESCHKO, Julie Theresa. ■ 17042 #041-12-1977 L1981 **N** *020 †75
FLOWERS, Peter Boone. ■ 17042 #041-13-1962 L1965 **FM** *071 †18
FOSNOCHT, Brian Joseph. 1700 S LINCOLN AVE, LEBANON VA MEDICAL CENTER 17042
   #041-14-1995 L2002 **IM** *020 †20
FRANK, Patrick Jos. ■ 17042 #041-02-1948 L1949 **GP** *075
GERGIS, Samy Botros. 101 FAIRVIEW CIR, WEST CORNWALL FAMILY PRACT 17042
   #915-09-1986 L1996 **FM** *020 †18
GHADIRI, Guita. 755 NORMAN DR, LEBANON INTERNAL MEDICINE 17042 #517-11-1997 L2005
   NEP IM *020 †20
GIBBS, Stephen Delano. 1700 S LINCOLN AVE, LEBANON VETS HOSP 17042
   #030-06-1970 L1971 **D A** *020 †15
GINGRICH, Kerry Harlan. 618 CORNWALL RD 17042 #041-09-1955 L1956 **GP** *071
GISH, Joel Saml. 618 CORNWALL RD 17042 #041-13-1989 L1991 **EM** *020 †18
GLICK, Mark Richard. 775 NORMAN DR 17042 #041-14-1985 L1986 **CD IM** *020 †20 ‡
GRIFFIN, David Chas. 775 NORMAN DR 17042 #055-02-1990 L1993 **CD IM** *020 †20
GUTIERREZ, Ernesto. 755 NORMAN DR 17042 #028-02-1999 L2006 **RHU IM** *020 †20
HABECKER, Elizabeth T. ■ 17042 #041-02-1974 L1975 **PD** *071 †55
HALLAHAN, William Francis. 775 NORMAN DR 17042 #010-01-1964 L1965 **CD IM** *020 †20

■ = Address Information Privacy Protected

HARTMAN, Samuel A, II. 3RD AND WALNUT 17046 #041-09-1952 L1955 **PD** *071 †55
HARVEY, Benson. 229 S 4TH ST 17042 #047-05-1972 L1985 **GS VS** *020 †85
HAUER, Marlin L. ■ 17042 #041-09-1949 L1950 **GP OM** *071
HAYES, Anne B. 755 NORMAN DR 17042 #041-13-1992 L1994 **IM** *020 †20 ‡
HEBERLING, Thomas Paul. ■ 17042 #041-13-1970 L1973 **EM FM** *020 †16,18
HEISEY, Robert Gordon. 300 WILLOW ST 17046 #041-01-1960 L1961 **GYN** *071 †30
HENDERSON, Ricky Alan. ■ 17042 #036-08-2002 L2005 **CD** *012 †20
HESS, Stacy Lyn. 755 NORMAN DR 17042 #041-14-1996 L1999 **IM** *020 †20
HINE, Roger A. 300 WILLOW ST, WOMENS HLTH CTR OF LEBANON 17046 #048-12-1996 L1998 **OBG** *020 †30
HIRSHBERG, Alan Jeffrey. 1700 S LINCOLN AVE, MAIL CODE 300 17042 #024-07-1990 L1994 **EM PHP** *030 †16 ‡
HUSSAIN, Sajjad. 1700 S LINCOLN AVE, LEBANON VA MED CTR 17042 #704-01-1988 L1995 **END** *020 †20
JONES, Frederick Lewis. 1700 S LINCOLN AVE, LEBANNON VA MED CTR 17042 #024-01-1971 L1979 **ORS** *020 †40
KAKARALA, Renuka. 1700 S LINCOLN AVE 17042 #495-65-1997 L2004 **IM** *020 †20
KASE, Edwin Mark. 755 NORMAN DR 17042 #041-02-1996 L1999 **IM** *020 †20
KEANE, Michelle Fischer. ■ 17046 #041-09-1995 L1998 **EM** *020 †16
KEARNS, Joseph Wm. 956 ISABEL DR, PRIORITY CARE 17042 #041-01-1979 L1980 **EM** *020 †16
KELLER, James Wade. 815 NORMAN DR 17042 #041-12-1977 L1981 **GS EM** *020 †85
KELLERMIER, Gretchen Garn. 17046 #038-44-2006 L2006 **MPD** *012
KILKER, Robin Lynn. ■ 17042 #041-14-2006 L2006 **FP** *012
KIRK, Robert Allen. 1700 S LINCOLN AVE, LEBANON VA MEDICAL CENTER 17042 #039-05-1984 L1989 **P** *020 †75
KLATCHKO, Barbara Ann. 402 S 12TH ST 17042 #035-20-1984 L1989 **GS** *020 †85 ‡
KURBAN, Ramsay Sameer. 845 NORMAN DR 17042 #605-01-1985 L1991 **D DMP** *020 †15
LAICHA, Patricia Ann. ■ 17042 #041-07-1969 L1971 **GP AI** *075
LEE, Najin. 755 NORMAN DR 17042 #035-47-2000 L2006 **NEP** *020 †20
LEISURE, Katherine Murray. 341 CUMBERLAND ST, STE 1 17042 #024-01-1978 L1984 **ID IM** *020 †20
LE PONE, Kenneth. 101 FAIRVIEW CIR 17042 #041-14-1980 L1986 **FM** *020 †18
LIGHT, John J B. 25 N 9TH ST 17046 #041-01-1938 L1940 **IM OPH** *071 †80
LONG, Rebecca Rich. 410 CUMBERLAND ST 17042 #041-02-1995 L1998 **FM** *020 †18
LONG, Theodore K. 327 CUMBERLAND ST 17042 #041-01-1939 L1941 **OPH** *071 †35
LUKAS, Daniel Stanley. ■ 17042 #035-01-1947 L1951 **CD IM** *071 †20
MADDUKURI, Sivaramaiah. 1700 S LINCOLN AVE, LEBANON VA MED CTR 17042 #495-50-1989 L1999 **IM** *020 †20
MAISH, George Orville, Jr. 1700 S LINCOLN AVE 17042 #041-13-1968 L1973 **GS** *020 †85 ‡
MAISH, George Orville, III. 1700 S LINCOLN AVE, LEBANON VA MEDICAL CENTER 17042 #041-02-1994 L1996 **CCS** *020 †85
MARIA, Mark Christopher. 875 NORMAN DR 17042 #010-02-1986 L1987 **OPH** *020 †35
MATLIN, Robert Allen. 1700 S LINCOLN AVE, DEPT OF VETERANS AFFAIRS V 17042 #035-08-1969 L1976 **PUD** *020 †20
MC GARRITY, Susan Jenkins. 1700 S LINCOLN AVE 17042 #051-01-1979 L1981 **AN PME** *020 †05
MC KENNEY, Patrice Ann. 775 NORMAN DR 17042 #025-01-1986 L2003 **IM** *020 †20
MEDZOYAN, Karen Ann. 701 CHESTNUT ST, PENNSYLVANIA COUSELING SVC 17042 #035-48-1999 L2001 **P** *020
MEDZOYAN, Randal Harout. 618 CORNWALL RD, STE 2 17042 #035-48-1999 L2001 **PD** *020 †55
MELLO, Ana Maria. 1700 S LINCOLN AVE 17042 #187-42-1984 L1990 **NM** *030 †28
MELNICK, Howard Berman. 927 RUSSELL DR 17042 #041-07-1982 L1983 **OTO HNS** *020 †45
MESAROS, Glen Jos. 927 RUSSELL DR 17042 #041-12-1992 L1994 **OTO** *020 †45
MIKHAIL, Asser Ibrahim. 1700 S LINCOLN AVE, VAMC 17042 #915-03-1979 L1999 **IM** *020 †20
MOFFITT, John Jos. 927 RUSSELL DR 17042 #041-02-1988 L1990 **OTO HNS** *020 †45
MORALES, Francisco J. ■ 17042 #042-03-1980 L1986 **DR** *020
MORRIS, Wilson Sims. 850 TUCK ST 17042 #041-77-1975, ▲ L1976 **PUD IM** *020 †20 ‡
MYSTAKAS, Fotis George. 912 RUSSELL DR 17042 #418-01-1963 L1973 **ORS** *020 †40
NAZEERI, Musaddiq Nadeem. 302 N 5TH ST 17046 #025-07-1995 L2000 **FM** *020 †18
NETLAND, Eric Edward. ■ 17042 #035-09-2000 L2004 **DR** *012
NGUYEN, Quang Tuan. ■ 17042 #941-01-1969 L1981 **IM NEP** *020 †20
NOVICK, Marsha Beth. ■ 17042 #016-01-1995 L1997 **FM OS** *020 †20
OH, Chang Wha. 618 CORNWALL RD 17042 #583-01-1972 L1983 **OBG** *020 †30
OKAMOTO, Jeffrey Akira. 204 HATHAWAY PARK, PHILHAVEN/LEBANON 17042 #041-14-1980 L1986 **P** *020 †75
OTTO, Eugene P, III. 1570 CORNWALL RD 17042 #010-02-1972 L1977 **PD** *020 †55
OVERHOLT, David John. 912 RUSSELL DR 17042 #041-13-1983 L1988 **ORS** *020 †40
PATEL, Madhukar R. 840 NORMAN DR 17042 #495-76-1972 L1981 **U** *020 †95
PATERNITI, Samuel Frank. 300 WILLOW ST, WOMEN'S HEALTH CENTER 17046 #035-06-1964 **GYN** *020 †30
PEREZ, Ruben. 4TH & WILLOW ST, HYMAN CAPLAN PAVILLION 17042 #042-01-1981 L1985 **ON IM** *020 †20
PICHARDO-LOWDEN, Ariana R. 1700 S LINCOLN AVE, LEBANON VA MEDICAL CTR 17042 #308-04-1999 L2005 **IM** *020 †20
PILKINGTON, Bryan Geo. 618 CORNWALL RD 17042 #035-08-1983 L1988 **GS** *071 †85
PITYK, Peter E, Jr. 254 TROON WAY, CENTRAL PA ANESTHESIA PART 17042 #041-12-1984 L1985 **AN** *020 †05
POTASH, George Cyril. ■ 17042 #041-12-1967 L1968 **OPH** *071 †35
POTTER, Donald Mark. 755 NORMAN DR 17042 #041-14-1971 L1982 **NEP END** *020 †20
PROVENCIO, Florencio P. ■ 17042 #847-04-1961 L1974 **PTH** *071 †50
RAND, Seymour. 1700 S LINCOLN AVE, VETERANS HOSPITAL 17042 #051-04-1975 L1976 **D** *020 †15
RUIZ, Marilyn. ■ 17042 #042-01-2005 L2005 **FP** *012
RUSLI, Michael. 4TH AND WALNUT ST, THE GOOD SAMARITAN HOSP 17042 #016-02-1979 L1980 **EM** *020 †16 ‡
SARAIYA, Rakesh B. 775 NORMAN DR 17042 #035-08-1996 L1999 **CD** *020 †20 ‡
SAWYER, Rita Ann. FOURTH & WALNUT, LEBANON ANESTHESIA ASSOC 17042 #041-07-1982 L1983 **AN** *020 ‡
SAYSON, Jose N Redulla. 4TH & WALNUT STS 17042 #748-01-1962 L1973 **IM CD** *071 †20
SCHAEFFER, William E, Jr. 755 NORMAN DR 17042 #041-13-1955 L1956 **IM IMG** *020 †20 ‡
SCHREIBER, Richard D. 801 WALNUT ST 17042 #041-01-1938 L1938 **GP** *072
SCOGNO, Charles Alfred. 1700 S LINCOLN AVE, PRIMARY CARE N400 17042 #041-14-1995 L1998 **FM** *020 †18 ‡

SEE, Hilario. ■ 17042 #065-01-1997 L2001 **FM** *100 †18
SEES, Jack Nevin, Jr. 4TH & WALNUT STS 17042 #041-13-1986 L1987 **PTH** *020 †50
SHAH, Hemant Hasmukhbhai. ■ 17042 #495-20-1983 L2004 **P** *012
SHEFFIELD, John Coventry. ■ 17042 #051-04-1993 L1995 **FM** *020 †18
SIMOYAN, Olapeju Modupeol. ■ 17042 #041-14-2006 L2006 **FPP** *012
SLAGLE, Richard Bryan. 912 RUSSELL DR 17042 #041-13-1990 L1992 **ORS** *020 †40
SLAVINSKI, Anthony Jos. 1700 S LINCOLN AVE, LEBANON VAMC 17042 #041-13-1984 L1986 **IM** *020 †20
SOBHANI, Hossein C. 1700 S LINCOLN AVE 17042 #010-01-1961 L1971 **R** *020 †80,28
SPARROW, Francis David. 283 BUTLER RD 17042 #041-14-1980 L1982 **CHP P** *020 †75
SPOTTS, Ricke Lyle. 717 S 8TH ST 17042 #041-02-1976 L1977 **FM** *020 †18
STAUFFER, James David. 4TH & WALNUT STS 17042 #041-13-1985 L1986 **FM FPG** *020 †18
STIEG, Philip Dennison. ■ 17042 #023-07-1970 L1986 **DR** *020 †80
SURAPANENI, Padma. 1700 S LINCOLN AVE, VA MEDICAL CENTER 17042 #495-50-1978 L1984 **PM** *020 †60
SZYDLOWSKI, Thaddeus R. 755 NORMAN DR 17042 #041-02-1972 L1973 **GE HEP** *020 †20
TEIKEN, Paul Jason. 830 TUCK ST, LEBANON ANESTHESIA ASSOCIA 17042 #026-04-1989 L2000 **AN CCA** *020 †05
THOMAS, James. ■ 17042 #495-17-1973 L2007 **FM** *020 †18
TIBBITTS, James A. ■ 17042 #056-05-1953 L1966 **GP** *077
TIEU, Huy. 1700 S LINCOLN AVE 17042 #041-15-2001 L2001 **AN** *100 †05
TUCKER, Leonard. VA MEDICAL CENTER, WARD 23A 17042 #035-08-1944 L1978 **IM** *100
UHRICH, Kathryn M Harbach. ■ 17046 #041-07-1947 L1949 **GP** *071
UHRICH, Robert Walter. ■ 17046 #041-09-1946 L1949 *071
VANGALA, Venkatarami R. 1700 S LINCOLN AVE, VAMC 17042 #306-01-1983 L1989 **P** *020
WALTERS, Jeremy Alistair. ■ 17042 #033-06-2000 L2004 **P** *020 †75
WERT, Roy Eugene. ■ 17042 #041-01-1966 L1967 **ORS** *071 †40
WILLIAM, Punitha S. 618 CORNWALL RD 17042 #495-27-1981 L1994 **FM** *020 †18
WILLIAMS, Beth Pantuso. 300 WILLOW ST, WOMENS HEALTH CENTER OF LE 17046 #041-15-1999 L2003 **OBG** *020 †30
WORRILOW, Suzanne Hayward. 419 CUMBERLAND ST 17042 #051-01-1947 L1948 **FM IM** *071
YANNEY, Rodolph Marcus. ■ 17042 #330-02-1952 L1992 **IM** *071 †20
YARUS, Lance Owen. 410 CUMBERLAND ST, PO BOX 629 17042 #018-75-1981, ▲ L1982 **ORS** *020
YUN, Won Khill. 618 CORNWALL RD 17042 #583-02-1965 L1973 **OBG** *020 †30
ZAVADAK, Daniel Greg. 702 S 12TH ST, CORNERSTONE DERM 17042 #041-12-1991 L1995 **D** *020 †15
ZINSSER, Kendall Roy. 4TH WALNUT DEP PTH 17042 #038-06-1977 L1978 **PTH** *020 †50

LEECHBURG — ARMSTRONG

HACH, Shannon Suzanne. 62 GREENBRIAR DR 15656 #010-01-1999 L2002 **FM** *020 †18
MC FADDEN, Debra Ruth. 62 GREENBRIAR DR, STE ONE 15656 #041-12-1984 L1985 **FM** *020 †18
SCHUMAKER, Donald Haines. ■ 15656 #038-06-1941 L1948 **GS GP** *072
WILLIAMS, Gayle Ann. 62 GREENBRIAR DR 15656 #038-40-1991 L1993 **FM** *020 †18 ‡

LEESPORT — BERKS

EVANS, George Edward Chas. ■ 19533 #018-75-1956, ▲ L1963 **P ADM** *071
LONGENECKER, Roger Neil. ■ 19533 #041-13-1964 L1965 **FM** *071 †18
LORD, Kenneth John. 111 ROBBY DR 19533 #041-13-1980 L1981 **FM** *020 †18
STEFANIC, Richard Anthony. 1010 CATHY DR 19533 #021-01-1987 L1990 **U** *020
TUKE, Gregory Chas. CENTRE AND WALL STREETS 19533 #038-43-1979 L1983 **FM EM** *020 †18

LEETSDALE — ALLEGHENY

ANTALIS, George James. 12 QUAKER VILLAG SHPNG CTR, OHIO RIVER BOULEVARD 15056 #038-40-1992 L1996 **CD** *020 †20
LALLY, Francis Leonard. 12 QUAKER VILLAG SHPNG CTR, SWEWICKLEY VALLEY MED GRP 15056 #041-09-1976 L1977 **CD IM** *020 †20
MALKOWSKI, Michael Jos. 12 QUAKER VILLAG SHPNG CTR, OHIO RIVER BOULEVARD 15056 #033-06-1988 L1990 **CD IM** *020 †20
NITZBERG, Robert Scott. 12 QUAKER VILLAG SHPNG CTR, # 2A 15056 #041-13-1974 L1976 **CD IM** *020 †20
SANDHU, J S. 12 QUAKER VILLAG SHPNG CTR, OHIO RIVER BOULEVARD 15056 #539-06-1980 L1986 **CD IM** *020 †20
TAYLOR, Craig Allan. ■ 15056 #038-06-1986 L1987 **P** *020 †75
TUNICK, Stephen Eric. 12 QUAKER VILLAG SHPNG CTR, # 2A 15056 #035-19-1979 L1980 **CD EM** *020 †20

LEHIGH VALLEY — NORTHAMPTON

HECKMAN, Harold Klein. PO BOX 21447 18002 #041-13-1964 L1965 **P CHP** *020 †75
HOOSHMAND, M Mathew. PO BOX 20007 18002 #517-01-1965 L1971 **PM** *071 †60
LEONARD, Marcia V W. 17 S COMMERCE WAY, STE 20872 18002 #043-01-1975 L1986 **CHN** *020

LEHIGHTON — CARBON

AFZAL, Sheikh M. 701 BRIDGE ST, STE 204 18235 #704-02-1990 L1997 **P PYM** *020 †75
AMBANI, Narendra Vrajlal. 990 BLAKESLEE BOULVRD DR E 18235 #495-23-1974 L1979 **PD** *020
ANTHONY, Alfred. 281 N 12TH ST 18235 #495-15-1967 L1985 *075 †55
BERGER, Harry. 281 N 12TH ST, STE B 18235 #033-06-1977 L1978 **IM** *020 †20
BYRNE, James Evert. 1080 BLAKESLEE BOLVRD DR E 18235 #016-06-1974 L1975 **OS** *071
CONNERTON, George Edward. 211 N 12TH ST, GNADEN HEUTTEN-MENTAL HELT 18235 #041-02-1977 L1978 **PTH** *062 †50
DAIT, Jose E. ■ 18235 #748-01-1958 L1968 **U** *071
DIAZ, Floriel P. 211 N 12TH ST 18235 #748-01-1953 L1961 **GS** *020

DIZON, Gaudencio Sia. ■ 18235 #748-01-1954 L1968 **GP** *071
FEINBERG, Kalmen Alex. 211 N 12TH ST, GNADEN HEUTTEN-MENTAL HELT 18235 #035-09-1964 L1971 **PTH** *020 †50
GAJULA, Lakshminarayana. 281 N 12TH ST, STE E 18235 #495-21-1971 L1979 **PD** *020 †55
GEDEON, Maxime. 1638 BLAKESLEE BOLVRD DR E 18235 #035-08-1991 L1996 **APM** *020 †05
GOUW, Christopher B H. ■ 18235 #506-01-1961 L1972 **DR R** *071 †80
HANLEY, Patrick J. 211 N 12TH ST 18235 #041-77-1989, ▲ L1990 **IM EM** *020 †20
HASAN, Abne. 800 MAHONING ST 18235 #704-02-1972 L1986 **RO NM** *020
HOCHHAUSER, David M. 211 N 12TH ST, HOSPITAL/DEPT OF EMERG MED 18235 #033-06-1984 L2002 **EM IM** *020 †55,20
HOFFMAN, William Wayne. 38 MAHONING DR E 18235 #041-13-1960 L1961 **GP** *071
KADEWARI, Ramesh Prasad. 281 N 12TH ST, BUILDING 18235 #495-21-1984 L1999 **PD** *020 †55
KADEWARI, Sarada. 438 CYPRESS ST 18235 #495-21-1994 L2002 **PD** *020 †55
KO, Yih-Shyong. 211 N 12TH ST, GNADEN HEUTTEN-MENTAL HELT 18235 #243-50-1966 L1976 **AN** *020
KUNKLE, Herbert L. 246 N 6TH ST 18235 #041-09-1979 L1980 **ORS GP** *020 †40
LA ROCK, Michael Jos. 1001 MAHONING ST, UNIT 1 18235 #051-07-1991 L1993 **IM** *020 †20
LISENBEY, Edward Alan. ■ 18235 #040-02-2006 L2006 **EM** *012
MAKHIJA, Kailash Ramchand. 281 N 12TH ST STE F 18235 #495-01-1975 L1978 **OBG** *020 †30
MARTINEZ, Michael F. 281 N 12TH ST, STE D 18235 #041-09-1995 L1997 **GS** *020 †85
MC GINLEY, Joseph Michael. ■ 18235 #035-09-1944 L1971 **PD** *071
MILLER, Edward Jos. 204 STATE RD 18235 #654-01-1983 L1985 **IM EM** *020 †20
MILLER, Richard Clayton. 281 N 12TH ST, STE A 18235 #041-01-1972 L1974 **OBG** *020 †30
MOTRONI, Alexsandra K. 1001 MAHONING ST 18235 #001-02-1981 L1983 **IM** *020 †20
MUSER, Daniel Edward. 246 N 6TH ST 18235 #033-05-1983 L1991 **ORS** *020 †40
PENATER, Frank R. 211 N 12TH ST 18235 #041-02-1975 L1976 **EM FM** *020 †18
RAZA SYED, Hyder. 211 N 12TH ST 18235 #704-08-1963 L1976 **GS TS** *020 †85
SNYDER, Marvin C G. 211 N 12TH ST 18235 #041-02-1953 L1954 **GP** *071
TAYLOR, James Alan. 211 N 12TH ST, GNADEN HEUTTEN-MENTAL HELT 18235 #041-09-1966 L1967 **P N** *075 †75
VISPERAS, Mario F. 2ND AND SOUTH STS 18235 #748-01-1956 L1973 **GS** *020 †16
WESNER, Neil. 400 S 9TH ST 18235 #035-09-1975 L1979 **GE IM** *020 †20

LEMONT – CENTRE

HIGGINS, Elizabeth Mary. ■ 16851 #919-03-1961 L1982 **RO** *071 †80
PARKS, Lytle R, Jr. ■ 16851 #041-02-1945 L1947 **GP** *071

LEMONT FURNACE – FAYETTE

CHALFANT, John C. 106 COMMONWEALTH DR 15456 #038-45-1984 L1985 **FM** *020 †18 ‡
KARSCHNER, Janet Kimberly. 48 NICKMAN PLZ 15456 #654-01-1987 L1990 **IM** *020 †20
LARKIN, William Aristead. ■ 15456 #010-02-1944 L1945 **GS** *071 †85

LEMOYNE – CUMBERLAND

ABRAMOVA, Victoriya K. 108 LOWTHER ST 17043 #913-99-1993 L2000 **IM** *020 †20
ACHARYA, Shubha Ramdas. 108 LOWTHER ST 17043 #495-37-1979 L1996 **IM** *020 †20
ADAMS, Donald Leslie. 1 LEMOYNE SQ, STE 201 17043 #041-02-1967 L1968 **OBG** *020 †30
BOAL, Danielle K Bird. 802 MICHIGAN AVE 17043 #041-13-1972 L1974 **PDR DR** *020 †80,55
BRENT, Shawna K. 20 ERFORD RD, STE 101 17043 #041-13-1993 L1998 **CHP GP** *020 †75
BRIER, Peter Martin. 108 LOWTHER ST, HARRISVIEW PROFESSIONAL CE 17043 #041-14-1974 L1975 **IM** *020 †20
CADIZ, Jennifer Laura. 50 N 12TH ST, UPPER LEVEL 17043 #035-06-1987 L1997 **ON HEM** *020 †20
CARR, William Francis. ■ 17043 #023-01-1946 L1952 **OBG** *071 †30
COHICK, Bruce Sheaffer. 3 WALNUT ST, STE 100 17043 #041-02-1982 L1983 **FM** *020 †18
CONROY, John D, Jr. 50 N 12TH ST, CENTRAL PA HEMATOLOGY & 17043 #041-77-1981, ▲ L1982 **IM HO** *020
CONTI, Paul Anthony. 20 ERFORD RD STE 101 17043 #035-08-1973 L1981 **CHP P** *020 †75
DE MICHELE, Michael A. 108 LOWTHER ST, HARRISVIEW PROF CENTER 17043 #041-09-1991 L1996 **ID** *020 †20
DENTE, Carla Jean. 108 LOWTHER ST, INTERNISTS OF CENTRAL PA 17043 #422-01-1996 L1999 **IM** *020 †20
DO, Si Van. 4 LEMOYNE DR STE 200 17043 #041-14-1988 L1992 **PM** *020 †60
FAIRCLOTH, Vivian Clouser. 110 LOWTHER ST 17043 #041-14-1996 L2000 **N** *020 †75
FELDMAN, Sherrie B. 3 WALNUT ST, STE 100 17043 #041-14-1984 L1985 **D** *020 †15
FINN, Jeffrey Wallace. 550 N 12TH ST, STE 140 17043 #038-43-1999 L2004 **PM** *020 †60
FONTE, Richard James. 20 ERFORD RD STE 204 17043 #035-03-1975 L1983 **P GP** *020 †75
FULTZ, Craig Warren. 550 N 12TH ST, STE 140 17043 #041-14-1983 L1984 **ORS** *020 †40
GALLIA, Francis Joseph. 53 SOUTH TER 17043 #041-01-1962 L1963 **DR** *020 †80
GLUCK, Michael Louis. 108 LOWTHER ST, HARRISVIEW PROF CENTER 17043 #041-14-1974 L1975 **IM IMG** *020 †20
GOEDECKE, John Barnes. 1 LEMOYNE SQ, STE 201 17043 #041-09-1960 L1961 **GYN OBG** *020 †30
GREENHOE, Joshua Marks. 108 LOWTHER ST 17043 #035-45-1996 L2003 **IM** *020 †20
GROTZINGER, Margaret L. 1 LEMOYNE SQ, STE 201 17043 #041-14-1985 L1987 **GYN** *020 †30
HARRISON, Charles Scott. 701 BOSLER AVE 17043 #041-12-1963 L1970 **ORS** *071 †40
HECK, Albert W. 110 LOWTHER ST 17043 #047-06-1984 L1990 **N IM** *020 †75
JANTON, Francis Joseph. 110 LOWTHER ST 17043 #051-07-1988 L1992 **N** *020 †75
KACHEL, Thomas Alan. 645 N 12TH ST 17043 #036-05-1982 L1984 **U** *020 †95
KAPOOR, Veena Martha. 108 LOWTHER ST, HARRISVIEW PROF CENTER 17043 #495-16-1988 L2001 **IM** *020 †20
KONKLIN, Sharon. ■ 17043 #041-09-1998 L2001 **FM** *100 †18 ‡
LAZA, Liana Ioana. 110 LOWTHER ST 17043 #781-03-1993 L1999 **N** *020 †75
LEAL, Alfred Raul. 3 WALNUT ST, STE 204 17043 #041-09-1988 L1990 **HO** *020 †20
LIU, Limin. 50 N 12TH ST, CENTRAL PA HEMATOLOGY & 17043 #243-21-1982 L2000 **HO** *020 †20
MAURER, Robert J, Jr. 550 N 12TH ST, STE 140 17043 #041-13-1982 L1983 **HS ORS** *020 †40
PACKMAN, Ira Joel. 108 LOWTHER ST, HARRISVIEW PROF CENTER 17043 #041-14-1975 L1976 **IM** *020 †20

PATTERSON, Richard Jos. ■ 17043 #041-13-1958 L1959 **ORS** *071 †40
PICCHIO, Luciano Paul. 20 ERFORD RD, STE 202 17043 #041-14-1983 L1987 **P** *020 †75
PRATHEESH, Viswanathan. 108 LOWTHER ST 17043 #495-04-1995 L2004 **IM** *020
RATNASAMY, Patrick. 108 LOWTHER ST 17043 #495-04-1988 L1998 **IM** *020 †20
RYCHAK, John Saml. 550 N 12TH ST, STE 140 17043 #041-12-1971 L1972 **ORS** *020 †40
SAHI, Harry S. 108 LOWTHER ST 17043 #041-02-2004 L2006 **IM** *020 †20
SCHAENEN, Wendy. 108 LOWTHER ST, INTERNISTS OF CENTRAL PA 17043 #035-20-1983 L1989 **IM** *020 †20
SCHREIBER, Richard. 108 LOWTHER ST, HARRISVIEW PROF CENTER 17043 #035-03-1979 L1984 **IM IMG** *020 †20 ‡
SMELTZER, Kenneth Louis. ■ 17043 #041-13-1964 L1965 **NEP IM** *071 †20
SMITH, Ellen George. 3 WALNUT ST STE 205, HERITAGE FAMILY MEDICINE 17043 #041-14-1984 L1985 **FM** *020 †18 ‡
STROCKBINE, Melvin Fisher. ■ 17043 #041-13-1955 L1956 **RO** *071 †80
SWEENEY, Alan J.. 108 LOWTHER ST 17043 #305-01-1998 L2000 **IM** *020 †20
TYNDALL, James Alan. 108 LOWTHER ST 17043 #041-12-1976 L1977 **IM** *020 †20
VARGAS CASTILLO, Elsa Rox. 108 LOWTHER ST 17043 #649-14-1993 L2004 **IM** *100
ZIMMERMAN, Lawrence B, Jr. 108 LOWTHER ST 17043 #041-14-1978 L1980 **IMG IM** *020 †20
ZUMOFF, Bertram. ■ 17043 #010-01-1960 L1961 **A** *071 †20,03

LENHARTSVILLE – BERKS

JOZETICK, Jennifer Lynn. ■ 19534 #041-77-2007, ▲ *012

LEOLA – LANCASTER

GOOD, Robert Luke. 15 ZIMMERMAN RD 17540 #039-01-1985 L1986 **OM FM** *020 †18
HURST, Kenneth Landis. 146 E MAIN ST 17540 #041-01-1975 L1976 **FM NTR** *020 †18
KNEPPER, Joseph Ausherman. 11 HOLLY DR 17540 #024-07-1958 L1959 **FM PD** *071 †18
MARTELL, Stephen Paul. 146 E MAIN ST 17540 #041-02-1974 L1975 **FM** *020 †18
NGUYEN, Vu Thanh. 146 E MAIN ST 17540 #041-14-2000 L2003 **FM** *020 †18 ‡
NIEMEYER, Richard Howard. 146 E MAIN ST 17540 #041-02-1972 L1973 **FM** *020 †18
QUIMBY, Dean Louis. 218C W MAIN ST, FAMILY PRACTICE 17540 #047-05-1985 L1986 **FM** *020 †18
SAMITT, Joel Leslie. 337 W MAIN ST, STE 100 17540 #041-77-1964, ▲ L1965 **GP** *071
STAUFFER, Harold Edwin. 146 E MAIN ST 17540 #041-01-1937 L1938 **IMG** *072
VAFEAS, Joyce Ann. 218C W MAIN ST, STEPHEN G. DIAMANTONI 17540 #041-13-1988 L1990 **FM** *020 †18

LESTER – DELAWARE

FALCO, Frank Gabriel. 100 DIPLMAT DR 19029 #005-06-1956 L1964 **IM OM** *071

LEVITTOWN – BUCKS

BONNER, Dennis James. 1854 VETERANS HWY 19056 #041-02-1976 L1977 **PM OS** *020 †60
BOSCH, Ursula Felicitas. 1530 WOODBOURNE RD 19057 #041-02-1998 L2001 **IM** *020 †20
CAUFFMAN, William J. 1530 WOODBOURNE RD 19057 #041-13-1953 L1954 **FM IM** *071 †18
CHEN, Wei. ■ 19054 #243-72-1998 **IM** *012
DE, Nirmal K. ■ 19057 #495-39-1960 L1972 **IM CD** *071
DE SANTIS, Luigi. 50 SERPENTINE LN, STONYBROOK MEDICAL CENTER 19055 #561-26-1983 L1985 **IM** *020
FERRY, Nicholas Joseph. 238 WILLOW DR 19054 #041-13-1962 L1963 **GP** *071
FLACCO, Albert Jos. ■ 19056 #041-02-1948 L1949 **PD** *071 †55
GLODEK, John Francis. 20 LAKESIDE DR 19054 #041-09-1959 L1960 **OPH** *020 †35
GOLDSTEIN, Robert Carl. 1339 WOODBOURNE RD, STE B101 19057 #041-09-1969 L1970 **GE** *020 †20
GUTTMAN, Michael. 1400 VETERANS HWY, STE 105-106 19056 #041-09-1978 L1979 **ON HEM** *020 †20
JANNELLI, Angela Frances. 1609 WOODBOURNE RD, STE 302B 19057 #041-13-1973 L1974 **RHU IM** *020 †20
KANE, Jill R. 2 QUINCY DR 19057 #041-77-1994, ▲ L1995 **FM** *020
KHAN, Zafar Ali. 1609 WOODBOURNE RD, STE 212B 19057 #305-01-1997 L2000 **IM** *020 †20
KLINGE, Sarah Marie. ■ 19056 #041-77-2007, ▲ L2007 *012
LAMBROS, John E. 1568 WOODBOURNE RD 19057 #418-01-1958 L1963 **OPH** *020
LAVRICH, Judith Barbara. 1568 WOODBOURNE RD 19057 #038-41-1986 L1990 **OPH** *020 †35 ‡
LIU, Chengyu. ■ 19054 #243-72-1998 L2007 **IM** *100 †20
LUSCOMBE, Herbert Jude. 1400 NEW RODGERS RD # 107 19056 #041-02-1968 L1969 **FM** *020
MALLOY, Christine Ann. ■ 19056 #041-13-2003 L2003 **PD** *100 †55
MIRANI, Gayatri. ■ 19056 #035-08-2005 L2008 **PD** *012
MOTIWALA, Muhammad J. ■ 19054 #704-02-1989 L1994 **ID IM** *020 †20
MUDDASSIR, Salman Muazzam. ■ 19056 #704-22-1998 L2006 **IM** *020 †20
NADAL, Ramon B. 1723 WOODBOURNE RD, MEDICAL ARTS PC 19057 #748-08-1962 L1970 **IM** *071
NAPLES, Jerry Francis. 2222 TRENTON RD 19056 #041-13-1956 L1957 **OBG** *071 †30
OH, Sang Baik. ■ 19057 #583-01-1954 L1979 **GP** *071
OSCOVITCH, Richard John. ■ 19057 #041-07-1991 **PD** *020
RAO, Adiraju Sadhana. 238 WILLOW DR 19054 #495-65-1973 L1979 **GP** *071 †50
SARDI, Vincent Frederick. 1568 WOODBOURNE RD 19057 #041-13-1984 L1984 **OPH** *020 †35
SAVINO, Yoko. ■ 19056 #035-75-2004, ▲ L2006 **IM** *012
SILVER, Bernice Snyderman. ■ 19057 #041-07-1953 L1954 **GP IMG** *071
SIMON, Joshua Scott. 7405 NEW FALLS RD, LEVITTOWN-FAIRLESS HILLS R 19055 #035-15-1999 L2001 **EM** *020 †16
SLIWINSKI, Stanley John. 1339 WOODBOURNE RD, WOODBOURNE PROFESSIONAL PA 19057 #056-06-1975 L1976 **OBG** *020 †30
SNYDER, Barry Jay. 1609 WOODBOURNE RD, STE 301 19057 #028-03-1974 L1975 **ORS LM** *020 †40
SPEERS, Herbert K. 1339 WOODBOURNE RD 19057 #038-40-1949 L1950 **GYN** *075 †30
TAHIR, Pshtiwan Abdulqade. ■ 19054 #528-02-1993 **IM** *012

TRUMAN, Lori Ann. 2346 TRENTON RD 19056 #041-77-1997, ▲ L1998 **FM** *020
VASSALLUZZO, Julio Emil. 152 HARMONY RD, JE VASSALLUZZO MD 19056 #041-02-1963 L1964 **FM OS** *071
VERGIS, James Geo. 1723 WOODBOURNE RD 19057 #041-13-1961 L1962 **NEP IM** *071 †20
VLESSING, Eva Wulf. 1568 WOODBOURNE RD, WOODBOURNE EYE CTR 19057 #869-05-1952 L1964 **OPH** *071
ZANKMAN, Nathan. 1310 FROSTY HOLLOW RD 19056 #041-02-1961 L1962 **PD** *020 †55

LEWISBERRY – YORK

BINKLEY, Mark David. ■ 17339 #041-02-2008 *012
CRAWFORD, George Andrew. 629D LOWTHER RD 17339 #023-01-1969 L1978 **DR** *020 †80
GIULIAN, Bertrand Bruce. 629D LOWTHER RD 17339 #041-09-1967 L1968 **DR NM** *020 †80
HETRICK, Gurney Eugene. ■ 17339 #041-13-1941 L1942 **P** *071
JACKSON, Cynthia Lynn. 629 LOWTHER RD 17339 #016-06-1994 L1999 **DR** *020 †80
LAUCKS, Stanley P. 629D LOWTHER RD 17339 #041-01-1946 L1947 **P** *071 †75
LEVY, Allen Jeffrey. 629D LOWTHER RD 17339 #024-07-1991 L1996 **DR** *020 †80
LICATA, Paul. 629D LOWTHER RD, QUANTUM IMAGING 17339 #035-19-1996 L2001 **VIR** *020 †80
MILLER, William Dean. 629D LOWTHER RD 17339 #041-02-1978 L1979 **IM** *020 †20
SIDER, Roger Claude. ■ 17339 #065-01-1966 L1999 **P** *030 †75
STEPHENSON, Jonathan D. 629D LOWTHER RD 17339 #051-07-2001 L2002 *100 †80
TAGGART, Richard Eugene. ■ 17339 #041-12-1977 L1980 **EM FM** *020 †16,18
TRIANO, Gene J. 629D LOWTHER RD 17339 #041-01-1950 L1951 **R** *071 †80

LEWISBURG – UNION

ALABAKOFF, Jason. ■ 17837 #041-02-2007 **OMF** *020
AMACHER, A Loren. 1 HOSPITAL DR 17837 #065-06-1962 L1987 **NS PD** *020
ARBOGAST, John W, Jr. 3 HOSPITAL DR 17837 #041-13-1951 L1952 **GYN** *071 †30
BETZ, Louis Henry. 3 HOSPITAL DR 17837 #041-01-1966 L1967 **OPH** *020 †35
BHANGDIA, Darshan Kumar. 3 HOSPITAL DR, MID-PENN UROLOGIC ASSOC PC 17837 #041-09-1993 L1998 **U** *020 †95
BLAKESLEE, Mark A. 3 HOSPITAL DR, STE 204 17837 #041-77-1992, ▲ L1992 **N SME** *020 †75
BOTHE, Albert Edward, Jr. ■ 17837 #024-01-1971 L2005 **GS NTR** *030 †85
BOWES, Donald Earl. ■ 17837 #065-05-1950 L1975 **OS CD** *071 †85,90
BROWN, Michael David. 98 REITZ BLVD, BROOKPARK FAMILY PRACTICE 17837 #038-41-1981 L1984 **FM FPG** *020 †18
BRUCE, William Beall. 80 MEDICAL PARK DR 17837 #011-02-1976 L1980 **OTO** *020 †45
CALDERON, Amador G A. EVANGELICAL COMMUNITY HOSP 17837 #748-08-1961 L1973 **EM GP** *020
CASTELLAN, David Matthew. 55 MEDICAL PARK DR 17837 #023-12-1988 L1999 **PD** *020 †55
CASTELLAN, Sue Ellen T. ■ 17837 #056-06-1989 L1990 **OBG** *020 †30
CHAPPEN, Margaret Wetmore. 250 REITZ BLVD, GEISINGER MEDICAL GROUP 17837 #016-02-1983 L1992 **PD IM** *040 †20,55
CHUDOW, Sterling Kenneth. ■ 17837 #035-46-1976 L2007 **OBG IM** *020 †30
DARER, Jonathan David. ■ 17837 #008-02-1996 L2007 **IM** *020 †20
DOUGLAS, Donald Dean. ■ 17837 #023-01-1970 L1976 **GE IM** *071 †20 ‡
DUPREE, William Brion. ■ 17837 #050-02-1976 L1989 **PTH** *020 †50
FAIRWEATHER, Jack Lee. 1 HOSPITAL DR 17837 #064-01-1956 L1964 **OBG** *071 †30
FARLEY, Traci Louise. 1 HOSPITAL DR, EVANGELICAL COMMUNITY HOSP 17837 #041-12-1996 L2004 **EM** *020 †16
FASANO, Nicholas Charles. 1 HOSPITAL DR 17837 #041-01-2001 L2006 **DR** *020 †80
FELDMANN, Daniel David. 250 REITZ BLVD 17837 #041-02-1996 L1998 **OSM** *020 †40
FELLIN, Chris Wm. 1 HOSPITAL DR 17837 #041-09-1986 L1987 **IM** *020 †20 ‡
FULLANA-JORNET, Maria E. 3 HOSPITAL DR, STE 312 17837 #132-01-1988 L2004 **OBG** *020 †30
FURTADO, Francisco De A. 129 BETH ELLEN DR, SUNBURY COMMUNITY HOSPITAL 17837 #187-16-1979 L1990 **AN** *020
GALLAGHER, Joseph B. 90 MEDICAL PARK DR 17837 #041-14-1987 L1990 **GE** *020 †20
GESSNER, Harlen Wilford. 1 HOSPITAL DR 17837 #041-02-1983 L1984 **EM** *020 †16
GINSBURG, John Lawrence. 1 HOSPITAL DR 17837 #041-13-1971 L1972 **FM OS** *020 †18
GRANATH, Linda Lee. 3 HOSPITAL DR, STE 214 17837 #048-12-1983 L1984 **FM** *020 †18 ‡
GRAY, David Warren. 1 HOSPITAL DR 17837 #047-05-1958 L1966 **GS** *071 †85
GRINDLINGER, Jonathan L. 11 REITZ BLVD STE 202 17837 #041-02-1984 L1985 **P** *020 †75
HAHN, Jonathan Frederick. 1 HOSPITAL DR 17837 #041-09-1970 L1972 **ORS** *071 †40
HARTZELL, Judith Meritz. ■ 17837 #041-09-1990 L1992 **OPH** *072 †20
HARTZELL, Scott Macbain. 137 JPM RD 17837 #041-09-1991 L1993 **OPH** *020 †35
HEID, Charles Eugene. 131 JPM RD 17837 #041-12-1969 L1970 **CD** *020 †20
HILLIKER, Jan Kenneth. 137 JPM RD 17837 #056-05-1974 L1975 **OPH OS** *020 †35
HUNTINGTON, Ayn Carroll. ■ 17837 #041-13-2008 *012
IRWIN, Abby Melissa. ■ 17837 #041-13-2000 L2002 **P** *100
KANT, Naval. 1 HOSPITAL DR 17837 #209-01-1962 L1973 **DR NM** *020 †80 ‡
KANT, Nila Naval. ■ 17837 #495-22-1971 L1981 **DR CD** *075
KELLY, Thomas F. ■ 17837 #023-07-1996 L2001 **MPD** *020 †20,55
KISVARDAY, Susannah Marsh. ■ 17837 #021-05-2005 L2007 **EM** *012
LAMPARTER, Robert W. 1 HOSPITAL DR, EANGELICAL COMM HOSP 17837 #041-02-1976 L1977 **PTH IM** *020 †50
LAPP, Frederick Carlton. 1 HOSPITAL DR, EVANELICAL COMMUNITY HOSP 17837 #035-15-1986 L1987 **EM** *020 †18
LEE, Christopher Joseph. 45 FORESTWOOD DR 17837 #041-13-2003 L2003 **FM** *100 †18
LEE, Eileen May. ■ 17837 #035-08-2000 **P** *100
LEIPOLD, Robert Weirich. ■ 17837 #005-02-1948 L1949 **FM** *072 †18
LEWIS, Janet Marie. 250 REITZ BLVD 17837 #041-14-1984 L1985 **IM PD** *020 †20,55
LONG, Robert Dale. 3 HOSPITAL DR 17837 #041-13-1974 L1975 **D IM** *020 †20,15
MALCOLM, John Albert, Jr. 1 HOSPITAL DR 17837 #041-02-1959 L1960 **PTH** *071 †50
MARTIN, Jack Thomas. 1 HOSPITAL DR 17837 #041-14-1995 L1997 **R** *020 †80
MAUR, Eric Evan. ■ 17837 #041-15-2001 L2006 **EM** *012
MC LEOD, Randi James. 1 HOSPITAL DR, EMERGENCY DEPT 17837 #050-02-1993 L1995 **EM** *020 †16
MILITZER, Emily Louise. 75 MEDICAL PARK DR 17837 #028-03-1975 L2005 **RO** *020 †80
MILLER, George C, II. 3 HOSPITAL DR STE 216 17837 #035-03-1972 L1978 **OBG** *020 †30
MOREAU, Joan Martin. 3 HOSPITAL DR, STE 308 17837 #041-09-1975 L1977 **P CHP** *020 †75 ‡
MORGAN, James Wm, Jr. 135 JPM RD 17837 #041-09-1972 L1973 **GS VS** *020 †85 ‡
MOTTO, Christopher John. 135 JPM RD 17837 #041-09-1998 L2000 **GS** *020 †85
MOYER, Brad Keller. 1 HOSPITAL DR, EVANGELICAL HOSP 17837 #041-13-1997 L1999 **EM** *020 †16
MUCCIOLO, Joseph Matthew. 135 JPM RD 17837 #010-02-1996 L1998 **GS** *020 †85
NEWTON, Sonia Yvette. 1 HOSPITAL DR, EVANGELICAL COMM HOSP 17837 #051-07-1990 L1994 **PTH** *020 †50
NICKLES, Nancy D'Amico. ■ 17837 #048-04-1985 L2004 **PD** *020 †55
NISSLEY, Jay Marlin. 55 MEDICAL PARK DR 17837 #041-13-1968 L1969 **PD** *020 †55
NORMINGTON, Ernest Young. 210 JPM RD, STE 200 17837 #041-09-1988 L1990 **HS** *020 †85,65
O'BRIEN, James Sean. 1 HOSPITAL DR 17837 #008-02-1982 L1984 **DR** *020 †80
ORBISON, James Lowell. ■ 17837 #016-06-1944 **PTH** *071 †50
PANOV, Fedor Eugene. ■ 17837 #041-02-2007 **GS** *012
PARDUS, Jessica Lynn. ■ 17837 #041-02-2007 L2007 **GS** *012
PATEL, Mayur Amrut. 75 MEDICAL PARK DR 17837 #010-03-1996 L1999 *020 †20
PATEL, Rasila P. 1 HOSPITAL DR 17837 #495-48-1971 L1979 **DR** *020 †80 ‡
PATTERSON, James Robert. 3 HOSPITAL DR 17837 #055-02-1998 L2000 **FM** *020 †18
PERLE, James Edward. 1 HOSPITAL DR, EMSF HOSPITALIST GROUP 17837 #041-14-1994 L1997 **MPD PD** *020 †20,55
PERLE, Kristine E. 1 HOSPITAL DR 17837 #041-14-1994 L1997 **FM** *020 †18
PERSING, John Hartman. 1 HOSPITAL DR 17837 #035-03-1967 L1968 **IM** *020 †20
PETORAK, Vladimir, Jr. 111 MEDICAL PARK DR 17837 #041-09-1988 L1991 **GE** *020 †20
PIGOS, Kevin Leonard. ■ 17837 #035-06-2001 L2003 **FM** *020
REDCAY, Julia E. 3 HOSPITAL DR, STE 312 17837 #035-75-1991, ▲ L1992 **OBG** *020 †30
REED, Roseline Rodney. 64 ANDREWS CT 17837 #041-13-1991 L1998 **IM** *020 †20
REISH, Matthew William. 900 BUFFALO RD 17837 #041-13-2001 L2001 **OSM** *020
RICE, John Edward, III. 3 HOSPITAL DR, STE 318 17837 #041-14-1981 L1982 **N CN** *020 †75
ROTHERMEL, Lori Kaye. 1 HOSPITAL DR, EVANGELICAL COMMUNITY HOSP 17837 #041-02-1996 L2001 **EM** *020 †16
RUKSTALIS, Margaret Ruyle. ■ 17837 #032-01-1987 L1995 **P** *020 †75
RUSSIN, Mary Simionevna. 1 HOSPITAL DR, EVANGELICAL COMMUNITY 17837 #041-07-1969 L1970 **DR** *071 †80
RUTKOSKI, Pamela H. 1 HOSPITAL DR 17837 #041-02-1984 L1985 **FM** *020 †18
SALAM, Ahmed Samir Abdel. 116 CAMBRIDGE LN 17837 #330-02-1963 L2000 **GP** *020
SATYAM, Bhagyalakshmi D. 1 HOSPITAL DR 17837 #495-62-1974 L1984 **GP PM** *020 †60
SCHRECKENGAUST, Robt Hill. 3 HOSPITAL DR 17837 #041-01-1970 L1971 **OBG** *020 †30
SCHWINDINGER, Wm Francis. ■ 17837 #035-46-1987 L1990 **END** *050 †20
SMITH, Dennis Randall. 131 JPM RD 17837 #056-06-1981 L1982 **CD IM** *020 †20
SMITH, Thomas Chandler. 1 HOSPITAL DR 17837 #041-02-1985 L1986 **IM IMG** *020 †20
SPEAKE, Mark Robt. 250 REITZ BLVD 17837 #023-01-1984 L1985 **IM PD** *020 †20,55
SPOTTS, Douglas Alan. 45 FORESTWOOD DR, FAMILY MED CARE PC 17837 #041-14-1993 L1996 **FM FPG** *020 †18 ‡
STACKOWSKI, Maryjane. 1 HOSPITAL DR 17837 #041-13-1961 L1962 **R** *071 †80
STANKIEWICZ, Russell J. 3 HOSPITAL DR, STE 312 17837 #305-01-1984 L1988 **OBG AM** *020 †30 ‡
STECHSCHULTE, Donald, Jr. ZIEGLER HLTH CTR BUCKNELL 17837 #308-03-1978 L1981 **FM ADL** *020 †18
STECKEL, Donald Clyde. 1 HOSPITAL DR 17837 #041-01-1967 L1968 **IM** *072 †20
STEFAN, Todd M. 135 JPM RD 17837 #041-09-1992 L1999 **VS** *020 †85 ‡
STOLTZFUS, Elam R. 55 MEDICAL PARK DR 17837 #051-04-1968 L1969 **PD** *020 †55
STONER, Debra I. 1 HOSPITAL DR, EVANGELICAL HOSPITAL 17837 #055-02-1990 L1992 **EM** *020 †16
TEICHMAN, Fred. 111 MEDICAL PARK DR 17837 #041-02-1978 L1982 **OBG** *020 †30 ‡
TURNER, John Floyd, III. 135 JPM RD 17837 #051-07-1984 L1985 **GS VS** *020 †85 ‡
VELAYO, Dante Padiernos. 3 HOSPITAL DR 17837 #748-08-1963 L1971 **GS** *071 †85
WEIBEL, David Clinton. 3 HOSPITAL DR 17837 #041-02-1957 L1958 **U** *020 †95
WESTON, John Michael. 3 HOSPITAL DR 17837 #039-05-1985 L1986 **IM** *020 †20
WILLIAMS, Irving. 1 HOSPITAL DR 17837 #035-06-1959 L1962 **AN PS** *071
WILSON, Nicholas James. 1 HOSPITAL DR, EVANGELICAL COMMUNITY HOSP 17837 #038-43-2001 L2001 **DR** *020 †80
WOLVERTON, Kevin Charles. 3 HOSPITAL DR, STE 312 17837 #031-01-2000 L2004 **OBG** *020
ZALESKI, Chas Edward, Jr. 3 HOSPITAL DR, STE 306 17837 #041-12-1987 L1993 **U** *020 †95
ZALESKI, Linda Kay. 1 BUFFALO RD 17837 #011-02-1989 L1993 **AN** *020 †05
ZELECHOSKI, David Mark. 3 HOSPITAL DR 17837 #041-09-1986 L1987 **IM** *020 †20
ZUG, Paul Ronald. 3 HOSPITAL DR, STE 206 17837 #041-13-1970 L1973 **IM PUD** *020 †20 ‡

LEWISTOWN – MIFFLIN

ACOSTA, Jose Ramon. 27 SANDY LN STE 140 17044 #308-01-1973 L1981 **PUD CCM** *020 †20
ANTONESCU, Oana. 4 WINDING WAY 17044 #781-01-1977 L2000 **IM FM** *020 †20
BASOM, Donald Eugene. 400 HIGHLAND AVE 17044 #041-13-1956 L1957 **EM** *071
BEREGOVSKY, Olga. 21 GEISINGER LN 17044 #913-41-1986 L2000 **IM** *020 †20
BHIMASANI, Hemanth Kumar. 400 HIGHLAND AVE, 2ND FL 17044 #495-21-1991 L2004 **ADP** *020
BRAHMAKULAM, Paul Mathew. 130 HIGHLAND AVE 17044 #495-52-1972 L1980 **PD ADL** *020 †55
BROWN, Jos Sherlock, Jr. 400 HIGHLAND AVE 17044 #041-02-1945 L1946 **IM CD** *071 †20 ‡
BZIK, Edward Paul. 400 HIGHLAND AVE 17044 #041-09-1980 L1996 **EM IM** *020 †20,16
CREIGHTON, Danl Kirk, Jr. ■ 17044 #035-15-1965 L1967 **FM** *071 †18
CUSTER, Christopher C L. 300 HIGHLAND AVE, GEISINGER 17044 #041-13-1982 L1984 **OBG** *075 †30
DALTON, Charles Munford. 16 W MARKET ST 17044 #051-07-1987 L1993 **U** *020 †95
DEININGER, Arthur G, Jr. 400 HIGHLAND AVE 17044 #165-04-1961 L1963 **EM FM** *020 †18
DE VITA, Dennis Michael. 305 4TH ST, PLEASANT ACRES 17044 #041-13-1975 L1977 **ORS** *020 †40
DILCHER, Harry Edward, Jr. 400 HIGHLAND AVE 17044 #041-09-1978 L1980 **IM** *020 †20
DREIBELBIS, Charles Leroy. 27 SANDY LN, STE 270 17044 #041-02-1998 L2000 **FM** *020 †18 ‡
EVERHART, Charles Wm. 310 ELECTRIC AVE STE 100 17044 #041-09-1973 L1977 **GE IM** *020 †20
FENICHEL, Robert. 24 N MAIN ST 17044 #041-01-1959 L1971 **P** *071
FLEISHMAN, Martin Jerold. 27 SANDY LN 17044 #041-02-1972 L1973 **GS** *020 †85
GALVIN, Sharon H. 21 GEISINGER LN 17044 #038-45-1998 L2000 **FM** *020 †18
GARDNER, Harry Waddell. ■ 17044 #041-12-1957 L1958 **FM PUD** *020 †18

■ = Address Information Privacy Protected

GEHMAN, John Wayne. 27 SANDY LN, STE 250 17044 #041-13-1981 L1982 **EM** *020 †18
GORDON, Alan David. 27 SANDY LN 17044 #033-05-1974 L1977 **OPH EM** *020 †35
GRILL, Frank A. 400 HIGHLAND AVE 17044 #028-78-1980, ▲ L1982 **OBG** *020
GUADAGNO, Robert Chas. 27 SANDY LN, STE 207 17044 #035-03-1991 L1993 **FM** *020 †18
GUSHUE, Maryann Teresa. 21 GEISINGER LN 17044 #041-14-1978 L1980 **FM** *020 †18
HAIGHT, Joel Bruce. 310 ELECTRIC AVE, STE 100 17044 #051-04-1982 L1987 **GE** *020 †20
HARMANCI, Mehmet Cem. 611 ELECTRIC AVE 17044 #902-10-1967 L1981 **NEP IM** *020 †20
HOPKINS, Deborah Sue. 400 HIGHLAND AVE 17044 #023-01-1994 L2001 **EM** *020 †16
HUNT, Clyde Mccoy. 400 HIGHLAND AVE 17044 #036-05-1973 L1998 **AN PAN** *071 †05
KOLONICH, Kimberly A. 27 SANDY LN, STE 207 17044 #041-13-1989 L1992 **FM** *020 †18
LAMB, Terance Lamonte. 21 GEISINGER LN 17044 #036-01-1985 L1988 **IM** *020 †20
LEOPOLD, Albert Reid, Jr. 300 HIGHLAND AVE 17044 #041-12-1957 L1958 **GP** *071
LEVIN, Robert M. 400 HIGHLAND AVE, DEPT OF RADIOLOGY 17044 #041-12-1977 L1985
  DR *020 †80
MALHOTRA, Rajeshwar P. 18 N MAIN ST 17044 #495-03-1971 L1974 **OBG** *020 †30
MALHOTRA, Shashpal Kaur. 18 N MAIN ST 17044 #495-03-1970 L1976 **OBG GP** *020
MANGANARO, Kimberly Joan. 21 GEISINGER LN 17044 #041-07-1982 L1985 **FM** *020 †18 ‡
MARTHOUSE, Stephen J. ■ 17044 #041-02-1942 L1943 **IMG** *071
NANCOLLAS, Paul Harvey. 21 GEISINGER LN 17044 #035-06-1985 L1986 **OPH** *020 †35
NUNGESSER, Raymond F. 21 GEISINGER LN 17044 #041-02-1980 L1981 **FM** *020 †18
OLSZOWSKA, Agata K. ■ 17044 #035-08-1998 L2000 **FM** *020 †18
OSELINSKY, David. 16 W MARKET ST 17044 #041-13-1984 L2000 **U GS** *020 †95
PAREKH, Mitesh Himatlal. 21 GEISINGER LN 17044 #011-04-1994 L2002 **OBG** *020 †30
PHELAN, Elna Therene. 21 GEISINGER LN 17044 #028-02-1971 L1988 **PD PHO** *020 †55
RAJASEKHARAIAH, Anitha. 21 GEISINGER LN 17044 #495-09-1994 L2005 **IM** *020 †20
REAMS, Jean Marie. 16 N BROWN ST 17044 #041-77-1991, ▲ L1991 **GP** *020
RECALDE, Carlos Marcelo. 307 4TH ST, PLEASANT ACRES 17044 #319-01-1974 L1985
  OTO FPS *020
REIFSNYDER, Daniel S. 400 HIGHLAND AVE 17044 #041-13-1981 L1983 **FM** *020 †18
RIDEN, Jay Mc Cartney. ■ 17044 #041-13-1955 L1956 **ORS** *071 †40
ROGERS, Bernard Rousseau. 400 HIGHLAND AVE 17044 #047-07-1971 L1991 **RO** *020 †80
ROGUSKY, Edwin John. 12 N DORCAS ST 17044 #041-09-1985 L1992 **ORS** *020 †40
SHETH, Nitin Vasantrai. 400 HIGHLAND AVE 17044 #495-01-1980 L1986 **CHP** *020
SILVERMAN, Harold. 24 N BROWN ST 17044 #062-01-1979 L2000 **TS** *100
SLOANE, Yancey Alvin, Jr. 400 HIGHLAND AVE 17044 #010-03-1999 L2006 **IM** *020 †20
SMOOKE, Mark. ■ 17044 #308-03-1981 L1981 **PTH** *020 †50
SOLOMON, Stephen Umberto. 21 GEISINGER LN 17044 #033-05-1988 L1992 **OBG** *020
SZULAWSKI, Ireneusz. 21 GEISINGER LN 17044 #759-03-1990 L1995 **IM** *020 †20
TAM, Perlita Kwan. 27 SANDY LN, STE 250 17044 #748-01-1983 L1997 **PD** *020 †55
TRIVEDI, Gopalkrishna M. 400 HIGHLAND AVE DEPT PATH 17044 #495-01-1971 L1980
  PTH *020 †50
VAKHARIA, Pratibha Vijay. 400 HIGHLAND AVE 17044 #495-98-1981 L1988 **PD AI** *020 †03,55
VALDIVIA, Duilio E. 27 SANDY LN 17044 #737-05-1968 L1979 **ON IM** *020 †20
WIMSATT, Michael Hughes. 27 SANDY LN, LEMED BUILDING 17044 #035-45-1971 L1978
  GS EM *085
WOOTEN, Sally Ann. 27 SANDY LN, STE 170 17044 #001-02-1981 L1987 **PUD IM** *020 †20

LIBERTY – TIOGA

MONTAGUE, James Wm. ■ 16930 #041-02-1958 L1959 **FM FPG** *071 †18

LIGONIER – WESTMORELAND

ANTO, David Pierre. 221 W LOYALHANNA ST 15658 #041-02-1991 L1993 **FM** *020 †18
BRALLIER, Hugh Wallace. 221 W LOYALHANNA ST, CRPC LIGONIER DIVISION 15658
  #041-13-1974 L1975 **FM** *020 †18
COMAS, Sharon Goff. 202 WESTVIEW DR 15658 #654-01-1986 L1990 **IM** *020
COX, Carla Lynn. 117 JUNIPER LN 15658 #041-14-1985 L1987 **CHP P** *020 †75
CRIBBS, Richard Madison. 210 W CHURCH ST 15658 #649-22-1978 L1980 **IM** *020
DE COSMO, Vincent J. 221 W LOYALHANNA ST 15658 #010-02-1981 L1982 **FM** *020 †18
GORDON, Harold E. 117 S SAINT CLAIR ST 15658 #041-12-1949 L1950 **PTH OS** *071 †50
KELLY, Tiffany Brock. 15658 #051-04-2008 L2008 †012
LONGPHRE, Frederick V. ■ 15658 #041-12-1939 L1940 **GP** *020
MONSOUR, Robert Gilbert. PO BOX 348 15658 #041-12-1943 L1944 **GP** *072
NOVAK, Joseph Francis. ■ 15658 #041-12-1938 L1939 **OPH** *035
SHUTTER, Walter David. ■ 15658 #041-12-1942 L1943 **FM** *071
TALBOT, George Tracy. 210 W CHURCH ST 15658 #042-03-1992 L1994 **FM** *020 †18 ‡
WHITE, William James. 262 ANGELA LN, HEMLOCK SQUARE 15658 #010-02-1941 L1942
  FM GP *071

LIMA – DELAWARE

YANKOPOLUS, Konstantine G. PO BOX 73, 209 HUNTER ST 19037 #024-05-1942 **GS** *071 †85

LIMERICK – MONTGOMERY

AKINKUNMI, Lanre Tajudeen. 296 W RIDGE PIKE 19468 #690-01-1988 L2003 **FM** *020 †18
BRUDER, Danielle Campisi. 649 N LEWIS RD STE 130, CHES-MONT MEDICAL GROUP, P 19468
  #041-02-1994 L1996 **IM** *020
BRUDER, John B, III. 649 N LEWIS RD STE 130, CHES-MONT MEDICAL GROUP, P 19468
  #041-02-1994 L1996 **FM** *020
CARTER, Marlo Lee. 420 W LINFIELD TRAPPE RD, STE 3300 19468 #012-22-2003 L2007
  OBG *020
MC WILLIAMS, Cathryn A. 420 W LINFIELD TRAPPE RD, STE 1000A 19468 #041-13-1993 L1996
  PD *020 †55
RODRIGUEZ, Guillermo L. 296 W RIDGE PIKE, LIMERICK FAMILY CARE 19468
  #042-02-1990 L1996 **FM** *020 †18 ‡
SIEGEL, Amy Lynn. 420 W LINFIELD TRAPPE RD, STE 1000A 19468 #041-09-1986 L1989
  PD *020 †55
STITT, Susan Elizabeth. 420 W LINFIELD TRAPPE RD, STE 2000 19468 #033-06-1997 L1999
  FM *020 †18

SUMNER, Janice Lynn. 420 W LINFIELD TRAPPE RD, STE 2000 19468 #056-06-1995 L1999
  FM *020 †18
TSOI, Pochau Anne. 420 W LINFIELD TRAPPE RD, STE 1000A 19468 #035-48-2001 L2004
  PD *020 †55
WILKERSON, Ashley E. 420 W LINFIELD TRAPPE RD, STE 3300 19468 #047-05-2000 L2006
  OBG *020 ‡

LINCOLN UNIVERSITY – CHESTER

THRESHER, Oliver S. ■ 19352 #041-01-1952 L1953 **OBG** *071 †30

LINESVILLE – CRAWFORD

COOK, Stephen Baldwin. ■ 16424 #035-09-1972 L1978 **GP PD** *020 †55
DEES-PORCH, Frances. ■ 16424 #024-05-1938 L1940 **OBG** *071 †30
RAMIREZ, Renato Pacheco. 226 W ERIE ST, P O BOX 843 16424 #748-01-1965 L1973 **IM** *020

LINWOOD – DELAWARE

STANKIEWICZ, Edward R. 1579 CHICHESTER AVE 19061 #759-10-1983 L1984 **IM** *075 ‡
TEANO, Dan Abellon. 1541 CHICHESTER AVE 19061 #748-08-1978 L1986 **IM NEP** *020

LITITZ – LANCASTER

ACUNA, Joann Gega. 51 PETERS RD 17543 #011-04-2001 L2001 **OBG** *020 †30
AMMONS, Jennifer Sue. 51 PETERS RD, GROUP AT ROSEVILLE 17543 #033-06-1998 L2001
  PD *020 †55
ANDERSEN, Leon Ove. ■ 17543 #035-01-1957 **CD IM** *020
ANDERSEN, Thomas Wade. 562 W 2ND AVE, GRP AT LITITZ FAMILY 17543 #041-13-1984 L1985
  FM *020 †18
BADE, Steven Carl. 2320 ROTHSVILLE RD, ROTHSVILLE MED CTR 17543 #041-02-1989 L1991
  FM *020 †18
BOWERS, David Walden. 562 W 2ND AVE 17543 #024-07-1978 L1979 **FM** *020 †18
BUSKO, Carlton Walter. 1810 ROTHSVILLE RD 17543 #041-09-1979 L1980 **GP** *020
CAMPANELLA, Cary Lee. 6 W NEWPORT RD 17543 #041-13-1988 L1991 **FM** *020 †18
CONWELL, John Eric. 2320 ROTHSVILLE RD, STE 200 17543 #041-14-2003 L2003 **FM** *020 †18
COURTER, Monte Harold. ■ 17543 #025-01-1963 L1964 **D IM** *020 †15
DE LA VERGNE, Tanya. 679 GOOSE NECK DR 17543 #021-05-1990 L2002 **PD** *020 †55
ESHELMAN, Guy R, Jr. 6 W NEWPORT RD 17543 #035-45-1987 L1988 **FM** *020 †18
ESHELMAN, J Lester. 1001 E OREGON RD 17543 #041-09-1949 L1950 **U** *020 †95
FREDERICK, David Wm. ■ 17543 #004-01-1971 L1972 **FM** *071 †18 ‡
FROMUTH, Thomas Edward. 51 PETERS RD 17543 #041-02-1985 L1988 **OBG** *020 †30
GANGOLI, Amit Harsh. 212 BUCKFIELD DR 17543 #495-73-1995 L1999 **ID** *020 †20
GAROFOLA, John Howard. 51 PETERS RD 17543 #041-13-1979 L1982 **DR** *020 †80 ‡
GERARD, Jeffrey Raymond. 6 W NEWPORT RD, CORNERSTONE FAMILY HEALTH 17543
  #041-14-1999 L2003 **MPD** *020 †20,55
GODDARD, James Edward. ■ 17543 #041-12-1958 L1959 **AN** *071 †05
GOLDBERG, Jacqueline M. 1575 HIGHLANDS DR, STE 101 17543 #041-09-1994 L1996
  OBG *020 †30
GOODENOW, Willis G. ■ 17543 #041-13-1951 L1952 **P CHP** *072
GROSH, William Kilgore. ■ 17543 #041-09-1954 L1955 **FM** *071
GUERTLER, Vera Natalie. 2320 ROTHSVILLE RD, STE 200 17543 #016-45-1990 L1999
  FM *020 †18
HANNA, Christine Mary. 51 PETERS RD, GROUP AT ROSEVILLE 17543 #036-05-1999 L2002
  PD *020 †55
HAUGHT, William Michael. 51 PETERS RD, GROUP AT ROSEVILLE 17543 #055-01-1997 L2000
  PD *020 †55
HERR, Dwight Alvin. ■ 17543 #041-01-1977 L1978 **FM** *020 †18
HESS, Paul Good. ■ 17543 #041-09-1943 L1944 **FM** *071
HOLDER, Arthur James. 722 FURNACE HILLS PIKE, UNITED ZION HOME 17543
  #041-13-1955 L1956 **FM** *072 †18
HORNICK, John Fred. ■ 17543 #051-04-2007 L2007 **FP** *012
HOSHAUER, Cathy Joan. 51 PETERS RD, GROUP AT ROSEVILLE 17543 #041-09-1984 L1985
  PD *020 †55
HOUSMAN, John Harold. 1001 E OREGON RD 17543 #041-02-1956 L1957 **OPH** *071 †35
IVY, Mary E. 562 W 2ND AVE, GRP AT LITITZ FAMILY 17543 #836-01-1982 L1986 **FM** *020 †18
KAUR, Manjeet. 1011 BLUESTONE DR 17543 #495-45-1973 L1980 **NPM** *020 †55 ‡
KNOUSE, Albert Bauer. ■ 17543 #041-09-1958 L1959 **FM** *071
KOBB, Mark Everett. 100 HIGHLANDS DR STE 20 17543 #308-07-1981 L1987 **PD** *020 †55
KOCH, Pamela Jane. 51 PETERS RD 17543 #041-14-1983 L1984 **DR** *062 †80
KRAK, Ronald Vincent. 51 PETERS RD, GROUP AT ROSEVILLE 17543 #041-14-1984 L1987
  PD *020 †55
KRONENWETTER, Lois Ann. 51 PETERS RD 17543 #012-05-1984 L1988 **OBG** *020 †30
KUMAR, Ramesh. ■ 17543 #495-16-1992 L2005 **N** *020
LEE, John Chung-Lam. ■ 17543 #065-01-1961 L2000 **ON HEM** *071 †85
LEONARD, Raymond L. ■ 17543 #016-43-1991 L1995 **AN** *020 †05
LLOYD, Mark. ■ 17543 #041-77-2004, ▲ L2007 **FM** *020 †18
MANGESHKUMAR, Venkatachala. 640 E OREGON RD, NEUROLOGY AND STROKE
  ASSOC 17543 #495-04-1978 L1997 **N** *020 †75
MARRIE, Stacie Micheel. 100 HIGHLANDS DR, STE 204 17543 #041-14-1992 L1994
  PD *020 †55
MARTINI, Enrico Edoardo T. 51 PETERS RD 17543 #008-02-1974 L1978 **OBG** *020 †30
MC GEARY, James Edward. 6 W NEWPORT RD, CORNERSTONE FAMILY HEALTH 17543
  #041-02-1975 L1976 **FM** *020 †18
MERSHON, Charles Richard. 6 W NEWPORT RD, CORNERSTONE FAMILY HEALTH 17543
  #039-05-1984 L1985 **FM** *020 †18 ‡
MEYER, Jennifer Ann. 51 PETERS RD, GROUP AT ROSEVILLE 17543 #035-06-1997 L2000
  PD *020 †55
MONTEFORTE, Mark Joseph. ■ 17543 #041-13-1993 L1996 **PTH** *100
MORRISSEY, Douglas Robert. 6 W NEWPORT RD, CORNERSTONE FAMILY HEALTH 17543
  #048-02-1998 L2000 **FM** *020 †18

MORROW, Dorcas Leah. 1001 E OREGON RD 17543 #041-07-1960 L1961 **P FM** *071

MUSSER, Jeffrey B. ■ 17543 #041-77-1998, ▲ L1999 **AN** *020 †05

NERNOFF, John, III. 1500 HIGHLANDS DRS 17543 #024-07-1963 L1982 **ATP CLP** *020 †50

NGUYEN, Van Huy. ■ 17543 #051-04-2001 L2001 **P** *020 †75

O'CONOR, Gregory Thos. ■ 17543 #035-20-1948 L1951 **ON PTH** *071 †50

PARIDA, Saroj. ■ 17543 #495-53-1982 L1997 **NPM** *020 †55

PERSON, Theodore C. ■ 17543 #017-20-1950 L1950 **GP** *071

RAO, Nagbhushan S. 640 E OREGON RD, NEUROLOGY AND STROKE ASSOC 17543 #495-29-1960 L2000 **N** *040 †75

REGAN, Mark Christopher. 1500 HIGHLANDS DR 17543 #023-01-1983 L1984 **PTH EM** *020 †50

REILLY, Anne Kathleen. 51 PETERS RD, GROUP AT ROSEVILLE 17543 #035-45-1990 L1999 **PD** *020 †55

RIDEN, Alice Elizabeth. 6 W NEWPORT RD, CORNERSTONE FAMILY HEALTH 17543 #041-07-1984 L1985 **FM** *020 †18

ROZANS, Mark H. 1575 HIGHLANDS DR, STE 201 17543 #010-01-1986 L1990 **IM PUD** *020 †20

RUSSO, Marc Steven. 562 W 2ND AVE, GRP AT LITITZ FAMILY 17543 #041-02-1988 L1990 **FM** *020 †18

SAILER, Dale Wm. 562 W 2ND AVE, GRP AT LITITZ FAMILY 17543 #041-02-1983 L1984 **FM** *020 †18

SANCHEZ, Kimberly W. 51 PETERS RD, GROUP AT ROSEVILLE 17543 #041-14-2002 L2002 **PD** *020 †55

SCALAMOGNA, Philip A. 1500 HIGHLANDS DR 17543 #041-12-1987 L1991 **PTH** *020 †50

SCHULZ, August Jos. 281 BLOOMFIELD DR 17543 #041-01-1958 L1959 **P** *020 †75

SCIBAL, Gary John. 562 W 2ND AVE, GRP AT LITITZ FAMILY 17543 #051-01-1976 L1977 **FM** *020 †18

SHERIDAN, Kathleen. 51 PETERS RD 17543 #041-14-2002 L2002 **OBG** *020

SINGAPURI, Kishor. 51 PETERS RD 17543 #063-01-1978 L1988 **DR ON** *020 †80

STEFFY, Harry L. ■ 17543 #041-77-1952, ▲ L1960 **GP OS** *071

SUPERDOCK, David Thos. 562 W 2ND AVE, GRP AT LITITZ FAMILY 17543 #041-14-1987 L1990 **FM** *020 †18 ‡

TALBERT, Madonna Lynn. 51 PETERS RD 17543 #016-02-1980 L1984 **GYN** *020 †30 ‡

TIFFT, Stephen Woodward. 51 PETERS RD, GROUP AT ROSEVILLE 17543 #035-45-1976 L1977 **PD** *020 †55 ‡

TODD, William Upton. ■ 17543 #041-13-2005 L2005 **PTH** *012

UTSINGER, Peter Devlin. 116 W AIRPORT RD STE B 17543 #010-02-1969 L1977 **RHU** *020 †20

VASSIL, Paul Edward. 2320 ROTHSVILLE RD STE 2 17543 #041-12-1992 L1994 **FM** *020 †18

WALIA, Anurag. 640 E OREGON RD, NEUROLOGY AND STROKE ASSOC 17543 #495-05-1994 L2003 **N** *020

WALLS, Theresa Ann. 1500 HIGHLANDS DR 17543 #041-77-1975, ▲ L1976 **P** *020 †75

WASMUHT-PERROUD, Vivian. 1575 HIGHLANDS DR, STE 106 17543 #869-04-1992 L1997 **OMF** *020

WEAVER, Michael Allen. 1575 HIGHLANDS DR STE 200B 17543 #041-07-1989 L1994 **AN PME** *020 †05

WIGGINS, Matthew Clayton. ■ 17543 #047-05-2000 L2006 **DR** *100 †80

WILLIAMS, Richard Bruce. 153 E MAIN ST 17543 #143-02-1972 L1996 **END IM** *062 †20

WINNER, Louis Scott. 51 PETERS RD 17543 #048-12-1992 L1998 **DR** *020 †80,28

YOUNG, John Michael. 1500 HIGHLANDS DR 17543 #004-01-1978 L1984 **PTH** *020 †50

ZEHR, Bonnie M. 51 PETERS RD, GROUP AT ROSEVILLE 17543 #041-13-1991 L1993 **PD** *020 †55

ZIMMERMAN, Mark David. 6 W NEWPORT RD, CORNERSTONE FAMILY HEALTH 17543 #016-06-1994 L2005 **FM** *020 †18

LITTLESTOWN – ADAMS

ARUMUGARAJAH, K. 10 W KING ST 17340 #220-01-1966 L1980 **FM PD** *020

CAPOSTAGNO, Vincent Jos. 41 S COLUMBUS AVE 17340 #010-02-1971 L2006 **RO PHO** *020 †80

CARSON, John Nevin, III. 43 S COLUMBUS AVE, STE 101 17340 #041-02-1972 L1974 **NEP IM** *020 †20

GEORGE, Christopher James. 300 W KING ST STE C 17340 #023-01-2001 L2001 **FM** *020

LIVERPOOL – PERRY

DODDS, Lawrence Edwin. ■ 17045 #005-06-1963 L1994 **PHP FM** *072 †70

LOCK HAVEN – CLINTON

ADROJA, Bharat Girdharlal. 930 BELLEFONTE AVE STE 105, LOCK HAVEN MED CTR INC 17745 #495-22-1993 L2001 **IM GP** *020 †20

ALTMAN, Brian Roy. 24 CREE DR, HAVEN ORTHOPEDIC AND SPORT 17745 #035-09-1976 L2005 **ORS EM** *020 †40

ARMSTRONG, Mark Eugene. 955 BELLEFONTE AVE 17745 #041-13-1988 L1991 **GS** *020 †85

BALDINO, William Anthony. 24 CREE DR, STE A 17745 #041-13-1973 L1976 **TS GS** *020 †85,90

BHATT, Prafulchandra U. 72 E CHURCH ST 17745 #495-23-1973 L1981 **PD EM** *020 †55

BLAZINA, Stacey Lynn. ■ 17745 #041-77-2007, ▲ *012

BOTEK, Alison Ann. 930 BELLEFONTE AVE 17745 #041-14-1992 L1998 **D** *020 †15

BOYLE, Jenny Lee. 225 OAK HOLLOW RD 17745 #041-13-1979 L1983 **PCP** *100 †16,50

BRANDT, John Philip. 947 BELLEFONTE AVE BOX 9 17745 #041-12-1943 L1944 **OPH** *071 †35

DALY, Francis Thos, Jr. 24 CREE DR 17745 #023-01-1986 L1987 **P** *020 †20

DI CUCCIO, Nicholas Wm. ■ 17745 #041-02-1968 L1969 **GS GP** *071 †85 ‡

DIETRICH, Henry Thornton. 955 BELLEFONTE AVE 17745 #051-01-1982 L1990 **FM** *020 †18

DOLAN, James Jos, III. 955 BELLEFONTE AVE 17745 #010-02-1969 L1971 **FM** *071 †18

ELLIS, Jerome Keefer. 24 CREE DR, HAVEN HOSPITALIST PROFESSI 17745 #024-07-1995 L1999 **MPD** *020 †20,55

GABINSKIY, Boris. 955 BELLEFONTE AVE, GEISINGER MEDICAL GROUP 17745 #913-21-1983 L1998 **FM** *020 †18

KAPOOR, Sarla. 214 HIGH ST 17745 #495-15-1968 L1977 **OBG** *020

KAPOOR, Shailendra Nath. 214 HIGH ST 17745 #495-15-1958 L1971 **U** *020 †95

KEPHART, Dale Chester. 955 BELLEFONTE AVE 17745 #041-12-1976 L2001 **D** *020 †20,15

LONG, William C, Jr. 53 W MAIN ST 17745 #041-01-1942 L1943 **GP** *071

LYTLE, Larry Hunter. ■ 17745 #041-13-1962 L1965 **GS OS** *071 †85

MEYER, Carl Andrew, Jr. ■ 17745 #041-02-1960 L1961 **AN** *020 †05

MISHRA, Randhir. ■ 17745 #495-15-1960 L1981 **IM CD** *071 †20

MIZES, David Saml. 24 CREE DR 17745 #005-14-1965 L1999 **GP** *020 †18

PECHT, Karl Richard. 24 CREE DR 17745 #041-13-1979 L1982 **FM** *020 †18

PETROSKI, Rayford Andrew. 24 CREE DR, LOCK HAVEN HOSPITAL 17745 #010-02-1994 L1999 **U** *020 †95

PIERGALLINI, Mary E. 208 E CHURCH ST, STE 100 17745 #041-14-1991 L2003 **FM** *020 †18 ‡

RIEDHAMMER, Marcus M. 208 E CHURCH ST, STE 200 17745 #011-04-2000 L2002 **FM** *020 †18 ‡

SPINNEY, Carmen Estacion. 24 CREE DR 17745 #748-02-1965 L1973 **IM PUD** *020

TALREJA, Ramesh P. 24 CREE DR 17745 #495-01-1980 L2004 **AN** *020 †05

TURNER, Thane Nolan. ■ 17745 #041-02-1993 L1996 **FM** *020 †18

VIYUOH, Nicholas G. 24 CREE DR, HAVEN HEALTHCARE FOR WOMEN 17745 #001-06-1994 L2007 **OBG** *020 †30

VOSK, Arno David. 24 CREE DR, EMER DEPT LOCK HAVEN HOSP 17745 #035-47-1974 L1985 **EM** *071 †16

WINNER, Forney Drew. PO BOX 926, 201 E MAIN ST APT 4 17745 #041-09-1940 L1941 **OS** *071

YOUNG, James Forrest. 955 BELLEFONTE AVE 17745 #003-01-1977 L1995 **OBG** *020 †30

LORDS VALLEY – WAYNE

NADAL, Luis Lorenzo. 2930 HEMLOCK FARMS 18428 #308-13-1995 L2005 **VIR** *100 †80

LOWER BURRELL – WESTMORELAND

ASHE, Charles Patton. ■ 15068 #041-12-1959 L1960 **PD** *071 †55 ‡

BALACKO, John Andrew. 2781 LEECHBURG RD 15068 #041-12-1984 L1986 **CD** *020 †20

BRUNO, Anthony Jos. ■ 15068 #041-12-1955 L1956 **U** *020

BRUNO, Jacomina. 2900 LEECHBURG RD 15068 #660-04-1961 L1965 **OPH** *071 ‡

CLOHECY, Robert Jasper. ■ 15068 #041-13-1948 L1950 **GP** *071

DEORAS, Kiran Sunil. 2663 LEECHBURG RD 15068 #495-01-1983 L1995 **P** *020 †75

DUNN, Robert Thomas. 1600 WILDLIFE LODGE RD 15068 #041-13-1996 L1996 **FM** *020 †18

HEPPNER, Bradley Todd. 2781 LEECHBURG RD 15068 #026-04-1983 L1992 **CD IM** *020 †20

KAMBHAMPATI, Radha K. 2663 LEECHBURG RD, PENNPSYCARE 15068 #495-65-1979 L1987 **P PYG** *020 †75

LUTHRA, Damyanti. 3058 LEECHBURG RD 15068 #495-20-1960 L1974 **OBG** *071

LUTHRA, Manmohan Singh. 3058 LEECHBURG RD 15068 #495-29-1958 L1971 **IM GE** *074

PORKOLAB, Frederick Lewis. 2781 LEECHBURG RD, TRI-COUNTY CARDIOLOGY 15068 #041-01-1972 L1975 **ICE CD** *020 †20

SANDHU, Rajinder Singh. 2663 LEECHBURG RD 15068 #905-01-1972 L1976 **P** *020 †75

SRINIVASAN, Venkatraman. 2781 LEECHBURG RD 15068 #495-61-1975 L1978 **CD IC** *020 †20

LOWER GWYNEDD – MONTGOMERY

BONNER, Eileen Marita. ■ 19002 #041-13-1981 L1983 **IM IMG** *020 †20,70

EL-DAIEF, Samir Fahim. 900 WHARTON CIR, LOWER GWYNEDD 19002 #330-02-1955 L1970 **GS CD** *020 †85

HARUN, Joseph Stanley. 1241 ROSSETT CT 19002 #041-02-1955 L1956 **D** *071 †15

MAMBU, Joseph Fred. 714 N BETHLEHEM PIKE, STE 101 19002 #041-02-1973 L1976 **FM** *020 †18

MUDE, Deepali Avinash. ■ 19002 #041-02-2008 *012

SCARPA, Harry Chas. ■ 19002 #041-09-1943 L1944 **GP** *071

WHITE, Cheryl Jo. ■ 19002 #048-04-1979 L1987 **ID IM** *030 †20

LOYSVILLE – PERRY

BISBING, Richard Grover. 1104 MONTOUR RD 17047 #041-13-1990 L1993 **FM** *020 †18

CREPS, Steven Roy. 1100 MONTOUR RD, WEST PERRY FP 17047 #041-12-1990 L1993 **FM** *020 †18

MATUNIS, Joseph John. ■ 17047 #041-09-1957 L1958 **FM FPG** *071 †18

LUZERNE – LUZERNE

COSLETT, Douglas Scott. 24 MAIN ST, VALLEY GYN SPECIALISTS 18709 #041-02-1989 L1991 **GYN** *020 †30

GRATTAN, James P. ■ 18709 #036-07-1949 L1950 **IM** *020

PLUCKNETT, Barbara Lynn. 24 MAIN ST 18709 #041-14-1991 L1996 **OBG** *040 †30

LYKENS – DAUPHIN

BOWER, James H. 614 MAIN ST 17048 #041-09-1975 L1977 **IM** *020

LYNDORA – BUTLER

BROWN, Timothy Alden. 6 CHESAPEAKE ST STE 205 16045 #055-01-1975 L1981 **D** *020 †15

MACUNGIE – LEHIGH

BANZHOF, Rebecca Anne. ■ 18062 #654-01-2002 L2006 **FP** *012

BURMEISTER, David B. ■ 18062 #041-77-1996, ▲ L1997 **EM** *020 †16

CAMPION, Paul Izak. 1840 HARVEST LN 18062 #035-19-2008 *012

CLIFFORD, James Richard. ■ 18062 #041-13-1956 L1957 **FM** *071 †18

DODSON, Steven Ray. 2480 FRESH MEADOW DR 18062 #041-14-1987 L1989 **AN** *020 †05

HARTZELL, George W. ■ 18062 #041-01-1959 L1962 **GS** *071 †85

JACKSON, Olga Elizabeth. ■ 18062 #024-05-2007 L2007 **OBG** *012

JONES, Maria L. 4 W MAIN ST 18062 #308-03-1988 L1997 **FM** *020 †18

KAR, Anuradha Reema. ■ 18062 #041-14-2008 *012

LEE, Yayu D. ■ 18062 #035-15-2001 L2006 **END** *020

MALLON, Joseph Leo, Jr. ■ 18062 #041-01-1989 L1992 **IM** *020 †20

MANGANO, Andrew Peter. ■ 18062 #041-77-2007, ▲ L2007 IM *012
MAZZACCARO, Richard John. ■ 18062 #035-46-2001 L2003 PD *020 †55
MCCONVILLE, Karin Minjung. ■ 18062 #026-04-2006 L2006 GS *012
MILLER, Robert Walker. 1950 MILL CREEK RD 18062 #041-13-1978 L1988 PDP PD *020 †55
PATEL, Sunil Kamal. 2750 ROLLING GREEN PL 18062 #495-28-1994 L2002 GS *100 †85
RAMMOHAN, Guhan. ■ 18062 #038-43-2004 L2004 EM *100
SCHNEIDER, Vanessa Jo. ■ 18062 #041-77-2006, ▲ L2006 FP *012
SHAH, Ankit M. ■ 18062 #041-15-2005 L2005 EM *012
TIEN, Elizabeth Chernling. ■ 18062 #041-02-2006 L2006 P *012
TUGBIYELE, Folusho Akin. ■ 18062 #035-19-2000 L2007 OBG *020
WALLS, Cedric Absalaam. ■ 18062 #035-08-2006 L2007 OBG *012

MAHANOY CITY – SCHUYLKILL

GRAF, Thomas Ross. 31 S MAIN ST 17948 #025-01-1992 L2004 FM *020 †18
KESSLER, Kendell. ■ 17948 #041-15-2004 L2004 PM *012
KIM, Sunchoong. 136 W MARKET ST 17948 #583-06-1960 L1973 GP EM *071
LANGON, James Patrick. 31 S MAIN ST 17948 #041-14-1979 L1980 FM *020 †18
LEWIS, Ivor Fenton. 31 S MAIN ST 17948 #041-02-1976 L1977 FM OBS *020 †18
SINGH, Gursharan. 323 E CENTRE ST 17948 #495-03-1973 L1984 FM *020

MALVERN – CHESTER

ALFANO, Jose Angel. PO BOX 275, 655 SUGARTOWN RD BLDG 15 19355 #132-01-1961 L2006 P *020 †75
ALLEN, Robert Roy. ■ 19355 #024-07-1985 L1987 N *020
ALLEVA, Annette M. 1017 REES RD, CONCENTRA MEDICAL CENTER P 19355 #041-14-1997 L2002 GS *020
AMPARO, Adonis Carrillo. 153 CHURCH ST 19355 #748-01-1964 L1975 P *020 †75
ANZALONE, Deborah Ann. ■ 19355 #041-09-1984 L1986 NEP IM *020
AVADHANI, Anjali Narayan. ■ 19355 #041-01-2001 L2004 HO *020
BAKER, Daniel Geo. 200 GREAT VALLEY PKWY, CENTOCOR INC 19355 #041-01-1976 L1978 IM RHU *020 †20
BARENBERG, Paul A. ■ 19355 #035-08-1947 L1959 P CHP *072 †75
BECKMAN, Robert A. 200 GREAT VALLEY PKWY, CANCER INC 19355 #024-01-1983 L1988 PHO PD *050 †55 ‡
BELLANCA, Joseph John. 63 LINE RD 19355 #010-02-1966 L1986 OM GPM *071 †70
BEUTLER, Anna. 200 GREAT VALLEY PKWY 19355 #759-04-1984 L1998 IM *020 †20
BICHEFSKY, Helise B. 32 RAFFAELA DR 19355 #041-77-1994, ▲ L1996 IM OS *020 ‡
BOSCIA, Jerome A. 200 GREAT VALLEY PKWY 19355 #041-13-1977 L1979 ID IM *050 †20
BRANDT, Samuel I. ■ 19355 #051-07-1981 L1999 FM *020 †18
BUDIKE, Alexandra B. 4 SOUTHWINDS LN 19355 #041-09-1993 L1996 AN *020 †05
BURGOON, Carroll F, Jr. 266 LANCASTER AVE STE 304 19355 #041-13-1943 L1944 D *071 †15
BYRNES, William James. 11 GREAT VALLEY PKWY 19355 #041-07-1994 L1998 N PHM *050 †75
CAMPBELL, Twining Forrest. 21 ALMY DR 19355 #041-01-1957 L1958 AN *071 †05
CHIDESTER, John Henry, IV. 254 LANCASTER AVE, STE 2 19355 #041-01-1970 L1977 ORS *020 †40
CHRUSCH, Adam Terrence. ■ 19355 #041-13-2004 L2004 FP *012
CROWLEY, Kurt Richard. 266 LANCASTER AVE, BARR BLDG SUITE 301 19355 #041-02-1993 L1996 IM *020 †20
DE MARCO, James Chas. ■ 19355 #041-13-1977 L1979 PD *071 †55
DEMITRACK, Mark Andrew. 1 GREAT VALLEY PKWY, STE 2 19355 #033-06-1983 L2003 P *050 †75
DEWIS, Lester Stevens. 414 PAOLI PIKE 19355 #024-05-1961 L1982 PM *072 †60
DOYLE, Mittie Kelleher. 200 GREAT VALLEY PKWY, CENTER FOR RESEARCH AND DE 19355 #008-01-1990 L2005 RHU *020 †20
EISENBERG, Floyd Plotnick. 51 VALLEY STREAM PKWY, SIEMENS MED SLTNS HLTH SER 19355 #041-14-1977 L1978 ID IM *030 †20 ‡
ELFMAN-BANNER, Karen Sue. 414 PAOLI PIKE 19355 #041-02-1990 L1992 P *020 †75
FAKIYESI, Olutope Olusiji. 655 SUGARTOWN RD 19355 #690-08-1987 L1997 CHP P *020 †75
FAUST, Herbert A. RR 2 19355 #041-09-1952 L1954 N *074
FAYSSOUX, Reginald Scott. ■ 19355 #041-15-2004 L2004 ORS *012
FERRONI, Joseph Salvatore. 462 E KING ST 19355 #041-02-1973 L1974 OBG *020 †30
FRIEDMAN, Jeffrey. 414 PAOLI PIKE 19355 #035-03-1992 L1994 PM *020 †60
FRIEDMAN, Jeffrey Michael. 414 PAOLI PIKE, BRYN MAUR REHABILITATION 19355 #035-03-1977 PM *020 †20
FUNG, Shirley Manwah. ■ 19355 #011-04-1999 L2002 AI *020 †20,03 ‡
GHATTAS, Nasrat Gabra. 414 PAOLI PIKE 19355 #915-04-1974 L2001 PM *020 †60
GODDARD, Gisele. 63 LINCOLN HWY, C/O VISHAY INC 19355 #550-01-1984 L1998 *100
GOLDSTEIN, Neil Howard. 5 GREAT VALLEY PKWY, STE 283 19355 #024-16-1979 L1984 IM ID *050 †20
GROSS, Ellen Ann. ■ 19355 #041-09-1983 L1985 IM *020 †20
HAGINO, Owen Rinzo. 9 GREAT VALLEY PKWY 19355 #014-01-1988 L1998 PD *020 †55,75
HAMPE, Warren Wilson, Jr. 324 LANCASTER AVE 19355 #041-01-1946 L1947 P *071 †75
HEYMAN, Julius Scott. 1086 W KING RD, ACT K-212 19355 #041-02-1995 L1997 AN *020 †05
HORWICH, David Norman. 414 PAOLI PIKE, MAIN LINE, P.C. 19355 #041-09-1991 L1994 IM *020 †20
JACOBS, Benjamin Richard. 1880 CHAUTAUQUA TRL 19355 #036-05-1985 L1991 AN *020 †05
JOHNSON, Joanna R. 721 S WARREN AVE 19355 #041-02-1973 L1975 PDA PD *050 †55,03
KEENAN, Gregory Foster. 200 GREAT VALLEY PKWY, CENTOCOR INC 19355 #035-03-1986 L1990 RHU PPR *040 †20,55
KIM, Sanghoon. 414 PAOLI PIKE 19355 #041-02-1990 L1996 PM *020 †60
KIM, Seung Hee Lee. 2234 GEORGETOWN DR 19355 #583-08-1967 L1973 P *020 †75
KRAUS, John Jos. 414 PAOLI PIKE 19355 #041-12-1974 L1975 PM SCI *020 †60 ‡
LANGAN, Erin Courtney. ■ 19355 #041-02-1999 L2003 OBG *012
LASOTA, Jeanne Marie. 414 PAOLI PIKE 19355 #041-02-1994 L1997 IM *020 †20
LEE, Michael Soonchul. 266 LANCASTER AVE, STE 200 19355 #024-07-1998 L1998 PMM PM *020 †60
LEWIS, Rebecca Elizabeth. 17 MILL RD, GOLDEN PONY RANCH INC 19355 #020-12-1985 L1986 P *020
LONG, David Fullerton. 414 PAOLI PIKE 19355 #041-09-1978 L1983 N *020 †75
LUTSKY, Kevin Feldman. ■ 19355 #041-15-2001 L2007 HS *020

MARK, William Steven. ■ 19355 #041-09-1969 L1970 IM *071 †20
MAZUR, Donald Wm. 266 LANCASTER AVE STE 200, RUGGIERO ORTHPAEDIC ASSOCI 19355 #041-02-1992 L1996 ORS *020 †40
MCCANDLESS, Laura Elizabe. ■ 19355 #041-02-2007 L2007 EM *012
MENDELSOHN, Alan Marc. 200 GREAT VALLEY PKWY, CENTOCOR 19355 #035-08-1987 L2000 PDC *020 †55
MEZZANOTTE, William S. ■ 19355 #041-01-1984 L1985 PUD IM *020 †20
MILLER, Lloyd F. ■ 19355 #030-05-1943 PA GPM *071 †70
MILLER, Stanley Jos, Jr. ■ 19355 #041-01-1957 L1958 P *071
MOELLER, Douglas James. 5 COUNTRY VIEW RD 19355 #017-20-1979 L1979 IM *071 †20
NEEFE, D Lynne I. ■ 19355 #041-01-1969 L1991 ID IM *020 †20
NEEFE, John Robt, Jr. ■ 19355 #041-01-1969 L1994 IM *020 †20
NEMETH, Nicole Angelina. ■ 19355 #041-01-2000 L2002 PD *020 †55
ODGERS, Charles Justine. 266 LANCASTER AVE, STE 200 19355 #041-13-1992 L1994 ORS *020 †40
PADHYE, Rajendra Sudhakar. 414 PAOLI PIKE 19355 #496-38-1991 L1999 PM *020 †60
PALMISANO, Joanne Joyce. ■ 19355 #035-01-1979 L1981 IM DIA *020 †20
PATEL, Shital R. 414 PAOLI PIKE 19355 #495-17-1992 L1997 END *020 †20
PATEL, Shital Rasik. 414 PAOLI PIKE 19355 #033-05-1999 L2001 PM *020 †60 ‡
PATTON, James Philip. ■ 19355 #041-07-1982 L1986 IM *020 †20
PAULSON, Daniel Mark. 9 GREAT VALLEY PKWY 19355 #051-04-1992 L2005 IM *020 †20
PENROD, Mary. ■ 19355 #041-02-1992 L1995 PD *020 †55
PITT, Leldon Ponder. 8067 GOSHEN RD, R D 2 19355 #035-01-1945 L1955 EM TS *020 †85
PITT, Pearl Stewart. PAPER HILL FARMS GOSHEN RD 19355 #035-01-1947 L1956 PHP PDA *030 †55
PUGLIESE, Maria A. 940 W KING RD, MALVERN INSTITUTE 19355 #041-01-1974 L1975 P ADP *020 †75
RAHMAN, Mahboob Ur. 200 GREAT VALLEY PKWY 19355 #160-02-1982 L1994 RHU *020 †20
RAJWAR, Ritu. ■ 19355 #495-23-1995 L2001 DR *100 †80
RICH, Dean Chas. ■ 19355 #040-02-1965 L1970 NS *071 †25
RUGGIERO, Robert A, Jr. ■ 19355 #041-02-1992 L1995 ORS *020 †40,20
RUGGIERO, Robert Anthony. 266 LANCASTER AVE STE 200 19355 #041-09-1967 L1968 ORS *020 †40
SANDERS, Martin Estle. 200 GREAT VALLEY PKWY 19355 #016-02-1979 L1992 RHU A *020 †20,03
SAPPERSTEIN, Scott Brian. 414 PAOLI PIKE 19355 #041-09-1997 L1999 IM *020 †20
SCHLEMAN, Margo. ■ 19355 #035-19-1970 L1976 PA PDC *071 †55
SCHULER, Shelley Sue. 266 LANCASTER AVE, STE 304 19355 #016-01-1977 L1979 D GP *020 †15
SEKHON, Kulwinder Kaur. ■ 19355 #028-34-2004 L2004 FM *020 †18
STEWART, William Grove. 2045 UNION HILL RD 19355 #041-01-1959 L1968 ORS *020 †40
STRAUBE, Richard Conrad. 244 GREAT VALLEY PKWY 19355 #016-02-1977 L1978 ID PD *050 †55
STROZ, Margaret Magdalene. 9 GREAT VALLEY PKWY, SANOFI-AVENTIS MEDICAL 19355 #041-02-1984 L1985 FM *040 †18
SUVARNAMANI, Chanes. ■ 19355 #891-02-1983 L1987 OPH *020 †35
SWAMINATH, Ramadevi K. 414 PAOLI PIKE 19355 #495-61-1992 L2000 PM *020 †60
TAWDE, Darshana Prafullar. ■ 19355 #496-26-2000 L2005 IM *020
TEEPLE, Leslie Ann. ■ 19355 #041-13-1985 L1986 RHU IM *020 †20
TEJURA, Bindu Ramniklal. ■ 19355 #917-18-1992 L1999 IM *020 †20
THAKARAR, Pushpa Tejura. ■ 19355 #495-01-1971 L1975 PM *020 †60
TORNA, Patricia Ann. ■ 19355 #041-02-1990 P *100
TUMOLA, John Jos. 414 PAOLI PIKE, MAIN LINE BHVRL HLTH AFFLT 19355 #041-09-1971 L1972 IM *020 †20
UDVARHELYI, Ian Steven. 2185 WYNDTREE LN 19355 #023-07-1983 L2000 IM *030 †20
WARREN, William L. ■ 19355 #041-13-1950 L1953 D *071 †15
WILSON, Brenda Ann. ■ 19355 #041-15-2002 L2002 PD *100
YOUNG, Clarence L, III. 30 SPRING MILL DR 19355 #024-01-1981 L1986 IM ID *050 †20
ZIEGRA, Sumner Root. ■ 19355 #008-01-1947 L1960 PD *071 †55
ZISELMAN, Ethel Marsha. ■ 19355 #041-07-1978 L1979 DMP ATP *020 †50

MANAYUNK – PHILADELPHIA

NADLER, Chad Jeremy. ■ 19127 #035-15-2004 L2004 GS *012

MANCHESTER – YORK

BAMFORD, Jennifer B. 212 ROSEDALE DR 17345 #023-01-1997 L2000 FM *020 †18
LUCKENBAUGH, Jessica Mari. ■ 17345 #041-14-2008 L2008 *012
PATER, David Russell. 212 ROSEDALE DR 17345 #041-12-1986 L1988 FM *020 †18
RINTOUL, James Neil F. ■ 17345 #654-01-1984 L1987 IM *020 †20
ST JOHN, Kevin Brian. 212 ROSEDALE DR 17345 #023-01-1979 L1986 FM *020 †18
SURRY, John Howard. 212 ROSEDALE DR 17345 #028-34-1974 L1975 FM *020 †18

MANHEIM – LANCASTER

CRUTCHLEY, Carolynn Adele. 6 N PENRYN RD 17545 #055-01-1977 L1981 P LM *020 †75
ELNAGGAR, Kathleen Lewis. ■ 17545 #051-01-1989 L1994 P *020 †75
ENGLE, Eugene Kenneth. 76 DOE RUN RD, BARON FAMILY PRACTICE 17545 #041-14-1976 L1977 FM *020 †18
EVANS, Matthew Stephen. ■ 17545 #041-14-2007 L2007 IM *012
HESS, Joseph Brubaker. ■ 17545 #041-02-1957 L1958 GP *071
HOPKINS, Robert Gary. 130 S PENN ST, GRP AT MANHEIM FAMILY 17545 #041-09-1979 L1980 FM *020 †18
HUNT, William D L. 130 S PENN ST, GRP AT MANHEIM FAMILY 17545 #041-13-1976 L1977 FM FPG *020 †18
JAMIL, Qazi Akhtar. ■ 17545 #160-02-1968 L1975 IM *020 †20
JONES, Terrence Howard. 130 S PENN ST, GRP AT MANHEIM FAMILY 17545 #033-06-1976 L1977 FM *020 †18
KAMBOJ, Sukhjeet Kaur. ■ 17545 #495-29-1995 L2007 FP *012
KANTOR, Thomas Victor. 107 W END DR 17545 #035-15-1985 L1986 RHU IM *020 †20 ‡
LAIRD, Kenneth Wm. ■ 17545 #025-07-1975 L1978 EM FM *020 †18,16

LANGMUIR, Holly Marie. ■ 17545 #036-05-2008 *012
MESSNER, Kenneth Harold. ■ 17545 #041-13-1963 L1972 **OPH** *071 †35
MOLL, Maria Elizabeth. ■ 17545 #036-07-1979 L1990 **OS IM** *050 †20
RYAN, Gayle B. ■ 17545 #024-05-1997 L1998 *020 †85
SEMENUK, Janna G. 130 S PENN ST, GRP AT MANHEIM FAMILY 17545 #913-05-1986 L2001
   FM *020 †18 ‡
SIMONS, William Miller. ■ 17545 #041-01-1943 L1944 **OPH OTO** *071
STEKERT, Ruth. ■ 17545 #041-13-1949 L1950 **PD** *071
WALDEN, Joseph Jude. 76 DOE RUN RD 17545 #035-03-1996 L2004 **FM** *020 †18

MANSFIELD — TIOGA

CETTON, Gregory Allen. 63 S MAIN ST, GUTHRIE CLINIC 16933 #005-12-1997 L1999
   FM *020 †18
CRUZ, Maria L. 40 W WELLSBORO ST 16933 #063-01-1981 L1983 **GP** *020
DY, George Reyes. 40 W WELLSBORO ST 16933 #748-10-1982 L1986 **IM NEP** *020 †20,55 ‡

MAPLE GLEN — MONTGOMERY

CHANNICK, Steven Andrew. 710 LIMEKILN PIKE 19002 #041-13-1985 L1988 **IM** *020 †20
CHEN, Mao-Hsiung. ■ 19002 #244-01-1967 L1999 **AN** *020
CHRISTOPHER, Theodore A. 1698 PEMBROOK RD 19002 #035-47-1981 L1983
   EM IM *030 †20,16
JACOBSON, Kenneth Leonard. 701 LIMEKILN PIKE 19002 #041-13-1987 L1989 **FM** *020 †18
KANG, Nancy Nina. ■ 19002 #041-13-2006 L2006 **DR** *012
KESACK, Andrea Fellerman. ■ 19002 #041-14-1993 L1997 **PTH** *071 †50
LEVIN, Lissa Beth. ■ 19002 #041-13-2005 L2005 **IM** *012
LITTMAN, Susan Joy. ■ 19002 #035-03-1989 L2006 **HO** *020
MC HUGH, Michelle Marie. ■ 19002 #041-07-1997 L2000 **EM** *020 †16
MURTHY, Lakshmi. 1261 APPALACHIN RD, LIBERTY ANESTHESIA ASSOCIA 19002
   #495-39-1981 L1991 **AN** *05
NJO, Soen Hien. ■ 19002 #506-01-1952 L1971 **GP** *071
NJO-INJO, Tjoei Eng. ■ 19002 #506-01-1952 L1971 **GP PTH** *071
PATEL, Tejas Navin. ■ 19002 #041-13-2006 L2006 **DR** *012
PETKUN, William Mark. ■ 19002 #035-19-1982 L1985 **IM** *040 †20
SAGREIYA, Usha. ■ 19002 #495-30-1983 L1996 **P** *020
SANDER, Laura Dawn. ■ 19002 #041-01-2008 *012
STEPHENSON, Wendy Panzer. ■ 19002 #041-13-1979 L1988 **GPM** *071 †70
STILWELL, Gary James. ■ 19002 #041-13-2000 L2000 **FM** *100
TANG, Wanzhu. 858 E WELSH RD STE 10, PRIMARY CARE GROUP PC 19002
   #243-48-1987 L2000 **IM** *020 †20 ‡

MARCUS HOOK — DELAWARE

BAGCHI, Sonali. 1541 CHICHESTER AVE, PENN DEL MEDICAL ASSOC, IN 19061
   #495-02-1987 L1998 **IM** *020 †20
WILSON, Roma A. ■ 19061 #671-01-1960 L1978 **ATP** *071 †50

MARIETTA — LANCASTER

BREWER, Robert Harold. 1159 RIVER RD, GRP AT SUSQUEHANNA FAMILY 17547
   #051-04-1976 L1977 **FM** *020 †18
HERR, James Danl. 1159 RIVER RD, GRP AT SUSQUEHANNA FAMILY 17547
   #023-01-1983 L1984 **FM** *020 †18
HERR, Jill Marita. 1159 RIVER RD 17547 #041-13-1998 L2001 **FM** *020 †18
JHAVERI, Mona Madhu. 1159 RIVER RD, GRP AT SUSQUEHANNA FAMILY 17547
   #035-03-1995 L2001 **MPD** *020 †20,55
JONES, Brian Arthur. 1159 RIVER RD, GRP AT SUSQUEHANNA FAMILY 17547
   #010-02-1991 L1993 **FM** *020 †18
LEHMAN, Nelson Richard. 1159 RIVER RD, GRP AT SUSQUEHANNA FAMILY 17547
   #023-01-1976 L1979 **FM** *020 †18
MILLER, Gerald Erb. 1159 RIVER RD, GRP AT SUSQUEHANNA FAMILY 17547
   #041-09-1976 L1977 **FM FPG** *020 †18

MARS — BUTLER

ABRAHAM, William David. 6998 CRIDER RD, ASSOCIATES 16046 #041-12-1984 L1985
   ORS *020 †40
AGNEW, Daniel K. 6998 CRIDER RD, ASSOCIATES 16046 #055-01-1989 L1994 **ORS** *020 †40
BAUMGARTEL, Ira Everett. 1571 THREE DEGREE RD 16046 #041-12-1977 L1978 **IM** *020 †20
BAUMGARTEL, Jennifer Mari. ■ 16046 #041-14-2005 L2005 **IM** *012
BIELO, Ruth Raupp. ■ 16046 #041-12-1954 L1955 **P** *071
BRABENDER, Rebecca R. 825 FOX RIDGE CT 16046 #041-12-1990 L1992 **IM EM** *020 †20,16
CHUNG, Chin-Yong. ■ 16046 #583-01-1957 L1971 **PD A** *071 †55
COLOVOS, Nick Edward. 6998 CRIDER RD, STE 100 16046 #011-02-1993 L1998 **EM** *020 †16
DHIR, Rajiv. ■ 16046 #495-36-1984 L1997 **PTH** *020 †50
GAUSE, Trenton Michael. 6998 CRIDER RD, ASSOCIATES 16046 #041-14-1986 L1987
   ORS *020 †40
GOLD, Kathryn Ann. ■ 16046 #028-02-2005 L2005 **IM** *012
HANNA, Abeer Emile. ■ 16046 #915-07-1994 L1997 **IM** *020 †20
HYDER, Syed S. PO BOX 848, 123 GRAND 16046 #704-21-1986 L1994 **IM ID** *020 †20
KIM, Chong Hwan. ■ 16046 #041-13-2004 L2004 **PM** *012
LIENESCH, Douglas Wm. ■ 16046 #023-01-1989 L2005 **RHU** *020 †20
MANTINE, Laura Marie. ■ 16046 #041-13-2005 L2005 **IM** *012
MUZZONIGRO, Thomas S. 6998 CRIDER RD, ASSOCIATES 16046 #035-46-1995 L1999
   ORS *020 †40
ONDECKO, Kristin Marie. ■ 16046 #051-04-2007 L2008 **IM** *012
PALMER, Bradley Alexander. ■ 16046 #016-42-2006 L2006 **ORS** *012
PFAEFFLE, Hugo James. 6998 CRIDER RD, ASSOCIATES 16046 #041-12-2000 L2001 **HS** *100
PU, Cunfeng. ■ 16046 #243-49-1984 L2003 **PTH** *020 †50

RIPEPI SANGIMINO, Ursula. ■ 16046 #041-02-1990 L2000 **GP IM** *020
RUMPF, Regis Paul. ■ 16046 #023-01-2005 L2005 **IM** *100
SZABO, Scott Joshua. 6998 CRIDER RD, ASSOCIATES 16046 #041-09-1998 L2000
   ORS *020 †40
TRISAL, Vijay Kumar. ■ 16046 #495-51-1979 L1991 **ON** *020
WALTRIP, Robert Lee. 6998 CRIDER RD, ASSOCIATES 16046 #023-07-1996 L1998
   OSM *020 †40
WEISS, Michael Wm. 6998 CRIDER RD, ASSOCIATES 16046 #033-06-1979 L1984 **ORS** *020 †40

MARSHALLS CREEK — MONROE

HOLMBERG, Anders Axel. PO BOX 180 18335 #654-01-1981 L1985 **PM GP** *030

MARTINSBURG — BLAIR

AKE, Burton K. ■ 16662 #041-12-1978 L1980 **OBG** *075 †30
BULGER, Richard H. 430 S MARKET ST, # 315 16662 #041-12-1941 L1942 **GP** *072
MOCK, Gregory Darley. RR 2 BOX 140 16662 #041-02-1984 L1986 **FM** *020 †18
WEAVER, Lunda E. 300 OAKDALE RD 16662 #041-14-1981 L1982 **FM** *020 †18

MARYSVILLE — PERRY

DAVIS, Kendra Marie. 506 S STATE RD 17053 #041-13-1996 L1999 **FM** *020 †18

MASONTOWN — FAYETTE

CHO, Jong Soo. 200 N REDWOOD ST 15461 #583-04-1958 L1972 **GP P** *071
SONTHEIMER, Gary Gene. 101 S MAIN ST # 103 15461 #407-10-1969 L1979 **FM** *020 †18

MATAMORAS — PIKE

ALAM, Mehjabeen. 906 PENNSYLVANIA AVE 18336 #704-16-1983 L2000 **IM** *020 †20 ‡

MAYPORT — JEFFERSON

YEANEY, Gabrielle Anna. ■ 16240 #041-14-2002 L2006 **NP** *012 †50

MC ALISTERVILLE — JUNIATA

ALDINGER, David L, II. RR 1 BOX 400 17049 #041-09-1974 L1975 **FM** *020 †18

MC CONNELLSBURG — FULTON

BRADY, Joanna. 525 FULTON DR 17233 #041-14-1997 L1999 **FM** *020 †18
COHEN, Steven Sam. 292 BUCHANAN TRL 17233 #306-01-1983 L1985 **GP FM** *020 ‡
HAQ, Tehmina. 525 FULTON DR 17233 #704-06-1986 L2007 **IM** *020 †20
HOFFMAN, Howard Lee. 216 S 1ST ST 17233 #041-13-1954 L1955 **PTH** *072 †50
IGUCHI, Albert Keiyu. 216 S 1ST ST, FULTON COUNTY MEDICAL CENT 17233
   #649-14-1979 L1985 **IM** *020
MILROTH, William Lynn. 318 N 1ST ST, BOX 721 17233 #041-02-1964 L1965 **GP** *020
ORNDORF, Thomas Patrick. 182 BUCHANAN TRL, STE 148 17233 #041-02-1985 L1986
   OBG *020 †30
WILLIAMS, Meredith M. 525 FULTON DR 17233 #054-04-1980 L1986 **PD** *075 †55

MC DONALD — WASHINGTON

BENTREM, George C. ■ 15057 #041-01-1965 L1966 **GYN** *071 †30
HSU, Shien Shong. 303 W LINCOLN AVE 15057 #244-02-1970 L1974 **FM EM** *020 †18
HUGHEY, James Richard. ■ 15057 #041-12-1944 L1945 **GP** *071
RESTINO, Elizabeth Reitz. 8050 NOBLESTOWN RD, STE 102 15057 #041-12-2001 L2001
   FM *020 †18

MC MURRAY — WASHINGTON

ALCANTARA, Vicente A. ■ 15317 #748-10-1963 L1972 **R** *020 †80 ‡
ARGENTINE, Robt Phillip, Jr. 159 WATERDAM RD 15317 #041-14-1976 L1977 **PD** *020 †55 ‡
BANYAS, Jeffrey Brian. 3001 WATERDAM PLAZA DR, STE 280 15317 #041-02-1982 L1983
   OTO AI *020 †45
BROWN, Stephanie Shaw. ■ 15317 #020-02-1995 L2003 **OBG** *020 †30
BULSECO, Patricia. 4000 WATERDAM PLAZA DR, STE 180 15317 #748-01-1960 L1969
   OBG *020 †30
BURKEY, David James. 4000 WATERDAM PLAZA DR, STE 280 15317 #041-12-1982 L1983
   CD IM *020 †20
BURNETT, Thomas Joseph. ■ 15317 #038-43-2007 L2007 **TY** *012
CAVASINA, Mary M. 157 WATERDAM RD, STE 120 15317 #041-07-1952 L1953 **FM GS** *071 †85
COHEN, Jeffrey Kirk. 4141 WASHINGTON RD 15317 #035-15-1979 L1985 **U GS** *020 †95
COLODNY, Stephanie. 5000 WATERDAM PLAZA DR, STE 120 15317 #035-09-1980 L1986
   IM *020 †20
DAINESI, Edward Geo. 1000 WATERDAM PLAZA DR, STE 220 15317 #035-09-1989 L1991
   IM *020 †20
DATTILO, Colleen M. 159 WATERDAM RD, STE 220 15317 #041-12-1979 L1980 **PD** *020 †55
DI CAMILLO, Tonja Jeanine. 6000 WATERDAM PLAZA DR, STE 280 15317 #041-13-2000 L2002
   PD *020 ‡
DI MAURO, Cynthia Lynne. 6000 WATERDAM PLAZA DR, STE 260 15317 #654-01-1982 L1986
   PM OS *020 †60
D'ORAZIO, Thomas James. 4160 WASHINGTON RD 15317 #048-12-2001 L2005 **OPH** *020 †35

■ = Address Information Privacy Protected

FOLB, Henry Allen. 2001 WATERDAM PLAZA DR, STE 208 15317 #016-06-1980 L1992 IM *020 †20

GABRIEL, Danl Edmund, Jr. 3944 WASHINGTON RD 15317 #055-01-1974 L1975 GP OS *020 †20

GAGLIARDI, Lisa Gabrielle. ■ 15317 #305-01-1983 L1985 FM GS *020 †18

GIBBONS, John Martin. 5000 WATERDAM PLAZA DR, ORTHOPEDIC ASSOCIATION 15317 #035-01-1992 L2000 OP *020 †40

GOTKIEWICZ, Dawn-Marie. 159 WATERDAM RD, STE 220 15317 #023-07-1994 L1996 PD *020 †55

GRETZ, Jeffrey. 157 WATERDAM RD, STE 120 15317 #018-75-1993, ▲ L1994 IM *020 †20 ‡

HALLER, Jordan D. ■ 15317 #017-20-1957 L1985 TS *071 †85,90

HAMMELL, Eugene John. 242 E MCMURRAY RD, STE 280 15317 #041-02-1983 L1984 GS *020 †85

HAPPEL, John Lindsay. 3035 WASHINGTON RD 15317 #041-09-1979 L1980 PHL VS *020 †85

HEISE, Michael Jerome. 1000 WATERDAM PLAZA DR, STE 220 15317 #055-02-1988 L1990 IM *020 †20

HERDMAN, Jeanine. ■ 15317 #016-42-2006 L2006 P *012

HESLOP, Robert Chas, Jr. 3515 WASHINGTON RD, STE 558 15317 #041-12-1970 PD *020

HIRSH, Steven Lawrence. ■ 15317 #041-13-1966 L1967 R *071

HRABOVSKY, Sharon Lynn. 2001 WATERDAM PLAZA DR, STE 101 15317 #041-12-1989 L1997 D *020 †15

KARPEN, Jay Leonard. 3402 WASHINGTON RD, CENTER FOR PAIN RELIEF PC 15317 #305-01-1984 L1988 IM *020

KING, Kurt William. 375 VALLEY BROOK RD, STE 101 15317 #041-02-1997 L2000 FM *020 †18

KUMAR, Shashi L. 3515 WASHINGTON RD, STE 508 15317 #495-33-1962 L1973 PDS *020 †85 ‡

LENART, Deborah Ann. 4000 WATERDAM PLAZ DR #180 15317 #038-45-1989 L1996 OBG *020 †30

LESNOCK, Robert Grube. 2001 WATERDAM PLAZA DR, STE 208 15317 #055-01-1966 L1967 IM IMG *020 †20,18 ‡

MACHIKO, Gregory Geo. 2001 WATERDAM PLZ DR, STE 205 15317 #041-02-1985 L1986 GE IM *020 †20

MACKAY, Douglas Henninger. 4000 WATERDAM PLAZA DR, STE 180 15317 #038-40-1992 L1995 OBG *020 †30 ‡

MAGRENI, Gregory Stephen. ■ 15317 #041-12-1982 L1984 EM *020 †16

MC CULLOCH, Patrick T. 5000 WATERDAM PLAZA DR, STE 240 15317 #055-01-2001 L2003 HS *020

MC CUNE, Ann Brossard. 2001 WATERDAM PLAZA DR, WATERDAM MED PLACE STE 202 15317 #007-02-1986 L1987 D *020 †15

MC MASTER, Gilbert B. ■ 15317 #041-12-1939 L1940 AN *071 †05

MITTELL, David Chas. 5000 WATERDAM PLAZA DR, STE 180 15317 #041-13-1978 L1979 FM *020 †18

MORECI, James Anthony. 5000 WATERDAM PLAZA DR, STE 120 15317 #041-12-1982 L1987 IM *020 †20 ‡

ORTENZO, Carole Ann. ■ 15317 #023-12-1982 L1983 GS *071 †85

OSOWSKI, Thad. 103 APPLE CT 15317 #654-01-1982 L1984 AN PME *020

PASCUAL, Generoso S. ■ 15317 #748-01-1966 L1975 DR *020

PAUTLER, Simona V. 3311 WASHINGTON RD, STE 200 15317 #035-01-1995 L2000 PS *020 †65

SANJEEVI, Arunkumar. 4000 WATERDAM PLAZA DR, STE 240 15317 #495-04-1988 L2005 HO *020 †20

SERALY, Mark Patrick. 222 E MCMURRAY RD 15317 #041-02-1990 L1993 D *020 †15

SIMPSON, David M. 225 VICTORIA LN 15317 #041-12-1953 L1954 IM *071

SINCLAIR, Catherine P. ■ 15317 #016-11-1962 L1971 GP *071

SLONE, Harold W. 105 ROBINHOOD LN 15317 #041-12-1955 L1956 FM *071

STEINMAN, Arnold M. 3001 WATERDAM PLAZA DR 15317 #041-12-1952 L1953 PD *071 †55

TARWATER, Doyle Le Roy. 103 SHERBORNE DR 15317 #026-04-1981 L1983 OS *020

TERNULLO, Damian Lee. 2001 WATERDAM PLAZA DR, STE 105 15317 #041-12-2001 L2007 PD *020 †55

TETRICK, Elbert L. ■ 15317 #017-20-1949 L1978 OM IM *071

THEIS, Steven Wm. 2000 WATERDAM PLAZA DR, STE 140 15317 #041-12-1969 L1971 ORS *020 †40

URREA, Oscar. 110 HIDDEN VALLEY RD 15317 #264-06-1967 L1972 P SME *020 †75

WEYRICH, Timothy Paul. 2000 WATERDAM PLAZA DR, STE 120 15317 #055-01-1984 L1987 U GS *020 †95

ZINOBILE, Anthony Jos. 4017 WASHINGTON RD, PMB 162 15317 #038-06-1984 L1985 EM FM *020 †18 ‡

MC SHERRYSTOWN – ADAMS

DICKSON, Ralph Wm. 70 ACADEMY ST, MCSHERRYSTOWN FAMILY PRACT 17344 #041-13-1989 L1991 FM *020 †18

SCHMEYER, Jon Eric. ■ 17344 #035-09-1981 L1985 OPH *071 †35

MCKEES ROCKS – ALLEGHENY

ALI, Syed Tahir. 710 THOMPSON AVE, STO ROX FAM HLTH CTR 15136 #704-21-1983 L1996 IM *020 †20

BASHORE, Roberta Lynn. 1800 PINE HOLLOW RD, DRS SAUER & LEIBENSPERGER 15136 #025-12-1996 L1998 FM *020 †18 ‡

BATTISTELLA, Gene M. 27 HECKEL RD, STE 207 15136 #041-77-1992, ▲ L1994 IM *020 †20

BELL, William Gene. 25 HECKEL RD, OHIO VALLEY GENERAL HOSP E 15136 #055-01-1984 L1985 EM FM *020 †18

BLAUGRUND, James Ean. 133 CHURCH HILL RD 15136 #008-01-1992 L1998 OTO *020 †45

BRESLIN, Janet Marie. 5676 STEUBENVILLE PIKE, STE C & D 15136 #041-12-1984 L1985 PD *020 †55

BUBENHEIM, Daniel Martin. 1800 PINE HOLLOW RD 1, KENNEDY MEDICAL ARTS BLDG. 15136 #041-02-1985 L1986 FM *020 †18

BURGO, Alfred John. 1800 PINE HOLLOW RD, STE 2C 15136 #024-05-1988 L1990 IM *020 †20 ‡

CATALANE, David Baines. 1800 PINE HOLLOW RD, STE 4A 15136 #041-12-1984 L1985 GS VS *020 †85

CHEN, Anne. 6000 STEUBENVILLE PIKE #10 15136 #654-01-1981 L1983 PD *055

CHRISTY, Patrick Thomas. 6000 STEUBENVILLE PIKE, STE 105 15136 #041-02-1994 L1996 OBG *020 †30

CLEMENTS, Harry Michael. HECKEL RD 15136 #041-02-1967 L1970 GP EM *075

COOPERSTEIN, Lawrence A. 25 HECKEL RD 15136 #035-45-1979 L1980 DR *020 †80 ‡

CROSKEY, Ralph Smith, III. 25 HECKEL RD 15136 #051-07-1977 L1978 EM *020 †16

DATTA, Bhupinder Singh. 25 HECKEL RD 15136 #495-73-1975 L1980 EM IM *020

DEJONCKHEERE, Joseph Paul. 27 HECKEL RD 15136 #025-07-1997 L2002 NEP *020 †20

DIEZ, Charles Michael. 1764 PINE HOLLOW RD, O J LEE MD 15136 #041-09-1961 L1962 OBG OS *071 †30

GANDHI-KULKARNI, Rina. 27 HECKEL RD, STE 103 15136 #495-17-1991 L1995 CD *020 †20

GEORGEVICH, Philip George. 1800 PINE HOLLOW RD, STE 4A 15136 #041-12-1981 L1982 GS VS *020 †85

GIGNAC, Marc Rene. 25 HECKEL RD, STE 201 15136 #048-15-1989 L1995 U *020 †95

GINSBURG, Michael Jed. 10 HECKEL RD 15136 #016-02-1971 L1983 EM *020 †16

HOOVER, Walter Weaver. 25 HECKEL RD, BUSINESSFIT 15136 #041-09-1978 L1979 OM IM *020 †20,70

HURH, Ryon. 25 HECKEL RD 15136 #583-04-1967 L1976 PM *020 †60

KAZIENKO, Brian Thomas. 6 CASTLE VIEW DR 15136 #055-01-1999 L2002 CD *020 †20

KROKONKO, Vera Ann. 25 HECKEL RD 15136 #041-12-1961 L1962 PD ADL *071

KUNSMAN, William Edward. 27 HECKEL RD STE 200, PGH HEART MED OFF BLDG 15136 #041-02-1973 L1975 CD IM *020 †20

LADANI, Chhaganlal D. 27 HECKEL RD, STE 101 15136 #495-23-1972 L1979 CD IM *020 †20

LEE, Kwan Il. 75 HECKEL RD 15136 #583-06-1967 L1973 AN *020 †05

LEIBENSPERGER, Stephen N. 1800 PINE HOLLOW RD, DRS SAUER & LEIBENSPERGER 15136 #041-14-1986 L1987 FM FPG *020 †18

LEMONICK, David Morris. 10 HECKEL RD, OHIO VLY GENERAL HOSPITAL 15136 #035-09-1981 L1992 EM GS *020 †85,90

MAHAJAN, Madhuri V. 827 BROADWAY AVE 15136 #496-38-1991 L1997 IM *020 †20

NOTTE, Michael Angelo. 27 HECKEL RD, STE 207 15136 #041-09-1993 L1995 IM *020 †20

NUNEZ, Hermes. 756 CHARTIERS AVE 15136 #935-01-1954 L1963 GS GP *020

PALMIER, Danny. 1800 PINE HOLLOW RD, STE 2C 15136 #035-47-1995 L1999 IM *020 †20

PARTEZANA, Janette Sue. 710 THOMPSON AVE 15136 #038-40-1990 L1992 FM *020 †18

PATEL, Kaushik P. 27 HECKEL RD, STE 101 15136 #495-23-1995 L2000 IM *020 †20

POUTOUS, George Wm. 6200 STEUBENVILLE PIKE 15136 #041-12-1973 L1974 OBG *020 †30

RANGE, Linda Ellen. 5676 STEUBENVILLE PIKE, PEDIATRICS SOUTH 15136 #035-03-1987 L1990 PD *020 †55

ROOKER, Gina Marie. 25 HECKEL RD, STE 201 15136 #039-01-1988 L1995 U *020 †95

SAUER, Gary Gale. 1800 PINE HOLLOW RD, DRS SAUER & LEIBENSPERGER 15136 #035-15-1985 L1988 FM FPG *020 †18

SCHEINMAN, Harold Zalick. 25 HECKEL RD, OHIO VALLEY GEN HOSP 15136 #016-42-1960 L1982 PTH NM *062 †50,28

SHETE, Leena Prakash. 25 HECKEL RD, OHIO VALLEY HOSPITAL 15136 #496-38-1973 L1976 AN *020 †05

SHETTY, Supritha A. 27 HECKEL RD, STE 101 15136 #495-37-1994 L1997 IM *020 †20

SINGH, Daljit. 827 BROADWAY AVE 15136 #495-03-1978 L1981 IM *020 †20

STARENCHAK, Scott Michael. 133 CHURCH HILL RD, ROBINSON MEDICAL CENTER / 15136 #041-12-2002 L2002 FM *020 †18

STEPT, Larry L. 25 HECKEL RD 15136 #041-09-1983 L1989 TS *020 †90,85

STEVENS, Stephen Andrew. 25 HECKEL RD 15136 #041-12-1958 L1959 GP *071

THOMAS, Bijo Jos. 25 HECKEL RD 15136 #010-03-2002 L2003 AN *020

URFFER, Jonathan Morrow. 500 PINE HOLLOW RD 15136 #041-12-1994 L1996 IM *020 †20

VINARSKI, Irina E. 5855 STEUBENVILLE PIKE, STE 200 15136 #913-69-1989 L1997 IM *020 †20

WATERS, Mark H. 25 HECKEL RD 15136 #041-12-1989 L1991 IM EM *020 †20

WOLKIN, Sharon Beth. 5676 STEUBENVILLE PIKE, STE C & D 15136 #041-12-1985 L1986 PD *020 †55

YELLENIK, Robert Francis. 27 HECKEL RD STE 103 15136 #422-01-1983 L1984 FM *020 †18 ‡

YOUNG, Adrienne Michele. 27 HECKEL RD, STE 204 15136 #011-02-1979 L1988 IM IMG *020 †20

YOUNGUE, Eugene L, III. 25 HECKEL RD 15136 #041-14-1981 L1982 FM *020 †18

ZUBRITZKY, Paul Myron. 6000 STEUBENVILLE PIKE, STE 105 15136 #041-13-1977 L1978 OBG *020 †30 ‡

MCKEESPORT – ALLEGHENY

ABBAS, Ghulam. 1500 5TH AVE 15132 #704-25-1994 L2004 TS *020 †85,90

ABDEL MASSIEH, Nader Faiz. 1801 LINCOLN WAY, STE 2 15131 #915-05-1985 L1999 APM *020 †60

AGSTER, Bruce Edward. 1432 LINCOLN WAY, CARDIOVASCULAR ASSOCIATES 15131 #041-13-1969 L1970 TS *020 †85,90

AHMAD, Usman. 500 HOSPITAL WAY STE 7 15132 #704-01-1968 L1974 IM END *040 †20

AKINFOLARIN, Akinwande Ak. 1500 FIFTH AVE, INTERNAL MED RESDNCY 15132 #690-01-2001 L2008 *100

ALAM, Md Khairul. 331 SHAW AVE, INC. 15132 #160-04-1974 L1997 P *020 †75

ALVI, Mumtaz. 1220 LINCOLN WAY STE 100 15131 #704-01-1980 L1987 GS *020 †85

AMBRAD, Antonio J. 1500 5TH AVE 15132 #264-02-1964 L1973 RO NM *020 †80

AMIN, Kamal. 1303 LINCOLN WAY, STE B 15131 #704-20-1987 L2004 ID *020 †20

ANDEMESKEL, Tesfamariam. 1500 5TH AVE # MED 15132 #408-09-1984 L1994 IM *020 †20

ANTONCIC, Rudolph A, Jr. 5301 WALNUT ST 15132 #422-01-1981 L1982 IM *020 †20

ANTONCIC, Rudolph A Iii. 5301 WALNUT ST 15132 #422-01-1998 IM *100 †20

ARISUMI, David Nobuo. 2001 LINCOLN WAY, OAK PRK MALL 15131 #023-01-1983 L1984 IM *020 †20

ASSAF, Wassim Wadie. 1500 FIFTH AVE, INTERNAL MED RESDNCY 15132 #875-03-2004 L2008 *100

AURE, Horacio Suelto. 1433 FAWCETT AVE 15131 #748-01-1970 L1977 CD IM *020

AWAN, Ihsan H. 1500 5TH AVE 15132 #704-08-1973 L1976 CD IM *020 †20

AYAD, Ingy Nabih. ■ 15131 #915-03-2002 L2006 FP *012

BACANI, Oswaldo Cruz. 1500 5TH AVE 15132 #748-10-1970 L1975 GS GP *020

BALLA, Ashfaq Shafi. 1303 LINCOLN WAY, STE B 15131 #495-51-1994 L2003 NEP *012 †20

BALUR MANJUNATH, Meghana. 1500 FIFTH AVE, INTERNAL MED RESDNCY 15132 #496-59-1999 L2008 *100

BARNABEI, Robert Anthony. 2347 5TH AVE 15132 #055-02-1994 L1996 FM *020 †18

BECK, Paul Walter. 1500 FIFTH AVE 15132 #041-14-1996 L1999 EM *020 †16

BEDI, Harsimran. 1500 5TH AVE, UPMC MCKEESPORT 15132 #495-03-2002 L2006 IM *012

BHATIA, Mudita. 1500 5TH AVE, DEPT OF INTERNAL MED 15132 #496-59-2003 L2006 IM *012

BHUTTA, Omar Iqbal. 331 SHAW AVE 15132 #704-04-1968 L1974 P *020 †75 ‡

BIANCULLI, Paul Domenic. 1500 5TH AVE 15132 #561-01-1978 L1985 GS *020

BICKET, Daphne. 2347 FIFTH AVE, LATTERMAN FAMILY HEALTH CE 15132 #036-05-1987 L1996 FM *020 †18

BOEN, Bradley Nelson. ■ 15135 #038-40-1962 L1969 P *071 †75

BONDI, Richard Paul. 1500 FIFTH AVE 15132 #041-12-1969 L1971 GS TS *020 †85

BOWSER, Stephen Allen. 1500 5TH AVE 15132 #041-12-1992 L1994 CD *020 †20

BROWN, Wynne R E. 1966 LINCOLN WAY 15131 #041-12-1981 L1983 OBG *020 †30

BRUNSKILL, Dennis Everett. 500 HOSPITAL WAY, 4TH FLOOR PAINTER BUILDING 15132 #038-40-1972 L1973 ON HO *020 †20

BUCK, Rudolph Leonard. 1433 FAWCETT AVE 15131 #041-12-1952 L1953 CD IM *071 †20

CANADY, Jerome John. 600 HOSPITAL WAY 15132 #041-13-1981 L1983 GS *020 †85

CASTRO, Arturo F. 1500 FIFTH AVE, 2831 JACKS RUN ROAD 15132 #748-10-1968 L1974 DR *020 †80

CHALIKONDA, Sri Charan. 1500 5TH AVE 15132 #495-37-1997 L2003 GS *020 †85

CHAMBERLIN, Eric C. 1321 FIFTH AVE 15132 #041-12-1997 L2003 ORS *020 †40

CHAUDHRY, Mehboob Khurram. 1321 5TH AVE 15132 #704-05-1980 L1984 PUD IM *020 †20

CHAUDHRY, Rahat Mahmood. 1321 5TH AVE 15132 #704-01-1968 L1975 PUD IM *020 †20

CHAUDHRY, Rauf A. 1500 5TH AVE # 306, KELLY BLDG 15132 #704-15-1979 L1992 IM *020 †20

CHITTA, Venkat Lakshmi De. 1500 5TH AVE, DEPT OF INTERNAL MED 15132 #496-59-2005 L2007 IM *012

CHOUGH, Simon H. 1500 5TH AVE 15132 #041-09-1988 L1991 CD *020 †20

CHOUGH, Vincent Hyunsuk. 2001 LINCOLN WAY, MONROEVILLE MEDICAL ASSOC. 15131 #041-12-1994 L1997 IM *020 †20

CHREKY, Emile Haim. 1500 5TH AVE 15132 #308-07-1982 L1989 EM IM *020 †20

COHEN, Cathy Sue. 1433 FAWCETT AVE 15131 #041-07-1977 L1979 DR *020 †80

CONKLIN, William Todd. 600 HOSPITAL WAY, KELLY BLDG 2ND FL 15132 #041-12-1978 L1979 PS HS *020 †65

CONTI, Tracey Denise. 2347 FIFTH AVE, FAMILY MEDICINE RESIDENCY 15132 #041-13-1997 L2001 FM *020 †18

CREAVEN, Fidelma Mary A. ■ 15131 #539-05-1975 *100

CRICHLOW, Amril G. 4706 WALNUT ST 15132 #010-03-1974 L1977 IM *020

DAVIS, Peter L. 2001 LINCOLN WAY, IRG STE 19 15131 #005-14-1976 L1986 DR IM *020 †80

DEAN, Lori Lynn. 1500 FIFTH AVE, UPMC MCKEESPORT HOSPITAL 15132 #003-01-2001 L2001 PM *020 †60

DEMIAN, Essam Magdy A. 2347 FIFTH AVE 15132 #915-04-1981 L1999 FM OBG *020 †18

DILL, James Newcomer, Jr. 1500 5TH AVE 15132 #041-13-1944 L1946 GYN *071

DI TOPPA, Louis August. 1978 LINCOLN WAY, DITOPPA MEDICAL CENTER 15131 #041-77-1983, ▲ L1984 FM *020 †18 ‡

DOMMALAPATI, Kiranmaayi. 1500 5TH AVE, DEPT OF INTERNAL MED 15132 #496-32-2004 L2007 IM *012

DONLEY, Chas Marquis, Jr. 1433 FAWCETT AVE 15131 #165-06-1981 L1982 R *020 †80

EDELSTEIN, Norman L. 1605 LINCOLN WAY 15131 #041-12-1968 L1971 OPH *020 †35

EL EZZEDDINE EL DANDACHI, . 1500 5TH AVE, DEPT OF INTERNAL MED 15132 #605-01-2002 L2005 IM *012

ERGINA, Francis Lee. 1500 5TH AVE 15132 #038-44-1990 L1992 CD IM *020 †20

FARKAS, Barry L. 1432 LINCOLN WAY 15131 #041-12-1977 L1979 FM FPG *071 †18

FARKAS, Farial Rawji. 1432 LINCOLN WAY, STE 101 15131 #905-01-1973 L1975 FM FPG *020 †18

FONASH, Catherine Ann. 1214 CALIFORNIA AVE 15131 #041-07-1986 L1988 GS *020 †85

FONTANA, Armand Leonard. 1500 5TH AVE 15132 #041-12-1943 L1944 GYN *071 †30

FULCINITI, Rocco Anton. 1966 LINCOLN WAY # 100 15131 #041-12-1972 L1975 OBG *020

GARA, Nedal. 1500 5TH AVE, DEPT OF INTERNAL MED 15132 #661-02-2007 L2007 IM *012

GARZARELLI, David Michael. 2347 FIFTH AVE 15132 #654-01-1981 L1982 FM *020 †18

GHOBRIAL, Ibrahim Isaac. 1500 FIFTH AVE, UPMC MCKEESPORT HOSPITAL 15132 #915-02-1979 L1995 IM OM *020 †20

GILLIS, Victoria Ann. 1500 5TH AVE 15132 #041-02-1974 L1977 IM EM *030 †20,16

GJONI HYSA, Lauresha Petr. 1500 FIFTH AVE 15132 #120-01-1997 L2002 IM *020 †20

GONZALEZ-ABOLA, Evelyn. 1500 5TH AVE 15132 #748-01-1970 L1976 AN *020 †05

GUINTO, Jose Cruz. 1500 FIFTH AVE 15132 #748-02-1966 L1973 R *020 †20

HAN, Dalsoo. 1500 5TH AVE, DEPT RAD 15132 #583-02-1959 L1970 DR *020 †80

HANLON, James Thos. ■ 15135 #041-12-1973 L1974 GS *071 †85

HARINSTEIN, David Alan. 1048 LINCOLN WAY 15132 #308-07-1982 L1985 IM IMG *020 †20

HASKETT, Roger F. 1500 FIFTH AVE 15132 #143-02-1968 L1992 P *020 †75

HERRING EDWARDS, Mary D. 1220 LINCOLN WAY, STE 201 15131 #036-01-1970 L1974 PD PHP *071 †55

HILBERG, Robert Wm. 500 HOSPITAL WAY, 4TH FLOOR PAINTER BLDG 15132 #041-12-1967 L1968 ON HEM *071 †20

HOCH, Carl Wm. ■ 15135 #041-12-1943 L1944 OTO *071 †45

HODGSON, John Pearce. 1500 5TH AVE, DEPT CARDIOLOGY MH-UPMC 15132 #041-12-1956 L1957 IM CD *072 †20

HUNG, Gregory Liu. 2001 LINCOLN WAY 15131 #024-01-1991 L1993 ORS OSM *020 †40

HUSSAIN, Humaira. 1500 5TH AVE 15132 #495-51-1999 L2002 RHU *100 †20

IDREES, Muhammad. 1949 LINCOLN WAY 15131 #704-04-1967 L1978 IM ID *020 †20

INKLAB, Mahakit. 1500 5TH AVE, UPMC MCKEESPORT 15132 #891-01-2005 L2006 IM *012

IQBAL, Fatima. 1500 FIFTH AVE, INTERNAL MED RESDNCY 15132 #704-25-2006 *012

ISLAM, Nadeem Ul. 1048 LINCOLN WAY 15132 #704-20-1991 L1998 IM *020 †20

JACOBS, David. 1050 LINCOLN WAY 15132 #041-12-1962 L1963 U *020 †95

JENKINS, Lauracinnie D. 2347 FIFTH AVE 15132 #035-06-1982 L2003 FM *020 †18

JOHNSON, James Robt. 332 5TH AVE STE 301 15132 #010-03-1961 L1962 GP EM *020

KAPPAKAS, Geo Stamatios. 1321 FIFTH AVE 15132 #041-12-1974 L1975 ORS *020 †40

KASTLER, Senta Elizabeth. 1500 5TH AVE, UPMC MCKEESPORT 15132 #154-08-2005 L2006 IM *012

KHAIRY, Raniah Sherif. 1500 5TH AVE 15132 #915-03-1998 L2002 OBG *012 †18

KHANNA, Vineesh. 1500 5TH AVE, MC KEESPORT HOSP/UPMC 15132 #495-49-1999 IM *100

KHWAJA, Rahila Sehr. 2001 LINCOLN WAY, PRIMARY CARE EAST LLC 15131 #704-01-1984 L1991 IM *020 †20

KIM, Eugene Yoonchoul. ■ 15131 #583-01-1962 L1971 DR NM *020 †80,28

KLEIN, Albert. 1949 LINCOLN WAY, WHITE OAK MEDICAL CENTER L 15131 #781-03-1975 L1986 IM *020 †20

KLIMOWICZ, Kinga. 1500 5TH AVE, DEPT OF INTERNAL MED 15132 #759-06-2003 L2007 IM *012

KOCHENBACH, Katherine. 1432 LINCOLN WAY STE 101 15131 #041-12-1997 L1999 FM *020 †20

KUMMANT, Eileen Marie. 3025 JACKS RUN RD 15131 #041-12-1983 L1984 FM *020 †18

LAKSHMINARAYANA, Pradeep. 1500 FIFTH AVE, INTERNAL MED RESDNCY 15132 #496-22-1998 L2008 *100

LARKINS-PETTIGREW, M. 1500 5TH AVE 15132 #041-12-1994 L1996 OBG *020 †30

LEE, Ji-Yang. 1500 5TH AVE, MC KEESPORT HOSP/UPMC 15132 #583-01-1997 L2001 NEP *100 †20

LEZEK, Vincent Jos, Jr. 1500 5TH AVE 15132 #041-09-1948 L1949 PD *071 †55

LOTRICH, Francis Everett. 1500 5TH AVE 15132 #040-02-1998 L2001 P *050 †75

LUTKA-FEDOR, Teresa Lynn. 331 SHAW AVE 3RD FL, MYCS 15132 #038-44-2001 L2001 P *020 †75

MANAHAN, Margarita Bulamb. 1500 FIFTH AVE 15132 #748-01-2003 L2005 IM *012

MANN, Richard M. ■ 15131 #041-12-1951 L1952 GYN *071 †20

MARKLE, William Howard. 1500 5TH AVE 15132 #041-14-1973 L1994 FM *040 †18

MC AVOY, William Bernard. ■ 15131 #010-01-1947 L1952 R *071 †80

MEHTA, Rohiat. 1500 5TH AVE, DEPT OF INTERNAL MED 15132 #661-02-2006 IM *012

META, Louis David. 500 HOSPITAL WAY, STE 4 15132 #041-12-1967 L1969 ON HEM *020 †20

MIKLOS, Bernard Geo. 1604 HILL ST 15131 #041-12-1956 L1957 IM OS *072

MONDIK, Barbara Lynn. 600 HOSPITAL WAY 15132 #041-12-1987 L1992 GS *020 †85

MOSKOWITZ, Barry David. 1533 LINCOLN WAY 15131 #041-12-1972 L1974 OPH *020 †35

MUKHOPADHYAY, Sukanta K. 1500 5TH AVE 15132 #495-24-1964 L1972 FM *020

MUKHTAR, Muhammad A. 1801 LINCOLN WAY 15131 #704-01-1986 L1996 IM *020 †20

NAIK, Rohan Dilipbhai. 1500 FIFTH AVE, INTERNAL MED RESDNCY 15132 #748-08-2008 *100

NARLA, Sudhir K. 1320 5TH AVE STE A 15132 #495-65-1975 L1978 GE IM *020 †20

NARLA, Sunil Kumar. 1500 5TH AVE, UPMC MCKEESPORT 15132 #496-33-2001 L2006 IM *012

NAVEED, Sajid Mohammad Yo. 1500 5TH AVE, DEPT OF INTERNAL MED 15132 #704-01-1998 L2007 IM *012

NAVID, Forozan. 1500 5TH AVE 15132 #051-01-1988 L1995 GS *020 †85,90

NIYAMUDDIN, Anthony. 1500 5TH AVE, DEPT OF INTERNAL MED 15132 #661-02-2007 L2007 IM *012

NOLAN, Mary Bridget. MC KEESPORT HOSP PATH DEPT 15132 #539-05-1966 L1973 PTH BBK *020 †50

NOTHMANN, Bruce Jos. 1320 5TH AVE STE A 15132 #035-19-1968 L1974 GE IM *072 †20

NUNEZ, Joanne Lynn Ponce. 1500 5TH AVE, UPMC MCKEESPORT 15132 #748-02-2004 L2006 IM *012

ORIBELLO, Adrian Mark Pel. ■ 15132 #748-02-2001 L2005 IM *012

OSUNKUNLE, Kehinde Bukola. 1500 5TH AVE, UPMC MCKEESPORT 15132 #690-01-2002 L2006 IM *012

OSUNKUNLE, Taiwo Ibukunol. 1500 5TH AVE, UPMC MCKEESPORT 15132 #690-01-2002 L2006 IM *012

OYENUGA, Olusegun Adewole. 1500 5TH AVE, UPMC MCKEESPORT 15132 #690-01-2002 L2006 IM *012

PAAT, Florante P. 1500 5TH AVE 15132 #748-08-1966 L1972 PTH *020 †50

PALEPU, Showri. 1801 LINCOLN WAY 15131 #495-70-1968 L1976 GS *020 †85 ‡

PANDYA, Kamlesh N. 1220 LINCOLN WAY 15131 #495-23-1968 L1975 PD EM *020 †55

PARRY, John Scott. 1500 FIFTH AVE, DEPT OF MEDICINE 15132 #041-09-1980 L1981 IM IMG *020 †20

PATEL, Mamta D. 2347 FIFTH AVE 15132 #495-89-2004 FP *012

PAVLAK, Robert James. 1500 FIFTH AVE, 3RD FLOOR KELLY BUILDING 15132 #041-14-1982 L1983 IM *020 †20

PELEKANOS, Michael James. 1220 LINCOLN WAY 15131 #041-01-1980 L1981 OBG *020 †30

PERRIN, Ronald Louis. 1433 FAWCETT AVE 15131 #041-12-1966 L1967 DR *020 †80

PETKOV, Milen Petkov. 1500 FIFTH AVE, UPMC MCKEEPSOORT ANESTH 15132 #198-01-1996 L2005 AN *020 †05 ‡

PIGOZZI, William Norman. 909 ZIMMER LN 15135 #041-09-1944 L1945 FM *071

POMIECKO, Jan. 1668 LINCOLN WAY, SECOND FLOOR 15131 #759-07-1997 L2000 FM *020 †18

PRABHAKARAN, Prasanth. 1500 FIFTH AVE, INTERNAL MED RESDNCY 15132 #495-31-2002 *100

PRIZANT, Tracy Lynn. 1220 LINCOLN WAY STE 101 15131 #041-12-1992 L1995 D *020 †15

PUTTING, Benedicte J. 1500 5TH AVE 15132 #660-01-1982 L1985 GS *100

RADKOWSKI, Christopher A. 1321 5TH AVE 15132 #036-07-2000 L2005 OSM *100

RAIN, Kristi Lynn. ■ 15131 #041-02-2008 *012

RAKFAL, Susan M. 1500 FIFTH AVE, DEPT OF RADIATION ONCOLOGY 15132 #033-06-1981 L1994 RO *020 †80

RANDHAWA, Anwaar Hassan. 1500 5TH AVE, UPMC MCKEESPORT 15132 #704-21-1997 L2002 IM *020 †20

RAO, Leelavathi K. 1500 FIFTH AVE, UPMC MCKEESPORT 15132 #495-70-1968 L1978 RO GP *020

RASHID, Shaik A. 1500 FIFTH AVE, RADIOLOGY DEPT. 15132 #495-50-1969 L1980 DR R *050 †80

RAZA, Hashim. 1303 LINCOLN WAY, STE B 15131 #704-21-1985 L1992 NEP IM *020 †20

RAZA, Naeem. 1500 5TH AVE, INTERNAL MEDICINE 15132 #704-01-1996 L2000 IM *020 †20

RITCHIE, Laurence Thos. 1430 LINCOLN WAY 15131 #041-13-1955 L1956 GP *020

RIZK, Magued. ■ 15131 #915-03-2002 L2007 FP *012

SABEH, George. 1048 LINCOLN WAY, BONESSI SABEH MEDICAL ASSN 15132 #018-03-1960 L1962 IM DIA *071

SALEH, Neam H. 1500 5TH AVE 15132 #575-01-1996 L2000 IM *020 †20

SARADAR, Raja. 1220 LINCOLN WAY 15131 #875-01-1979 L1985 PD *020 †55

SCHNURER, Charles Irwin. 1220 LINCOLN WAY 15131 #041-12-1948 L1949 GP *071 †85

SECOSKY, Joseph John. 1433 FAWCETT AVE 15131 #041-12-1985 L1986 CD *020 †20

SELEDNIK, Leonard J. 1220 LINCOLN WAY 15131 #041-12-1978 L1979 OBG *020 †30

SETH, Prabhat. 1500 5TH AVE 15132 #495-45-1973 IM *020 †20

SHAPIRO, Lester F. 1501 LINCOLN WAY 15131 #020-02-1966 L1967 OTO *020 †45

SHARMA, Jashwant K. 1500 5TH AVE 15132 #495-34-1969 L1974 IM *020 †20

SILBERMAN, Leslie Jay. 1220 LINCOLN WAY STE 201 15131 #041-12-1973 L1974 PD *020 †55

SINHA, Milind Kumar. 1500 FIFTH AVE, INTERNAL MED RESDNCY 15132 #495-02-1996 L2008 *100

SMITH, Robert Wm. 1500 5TH AVE 15132 #005-15-1977 L1984 FM MDM *050 †18

SOUTH-PAUL, Jeannette E. 1500 5TH AVE 15132 #041-12-1979 L2001 FM *020 †18

STEELE-BUCK, Ann Louise. 1433 FAWCETT AVE 15131 #041-07-1956 L1957 R *071 †80

STOKAR, Lawrence Mitchell. 1220 LINCOLN WAY, STE 101 15131 #016-42-1981 L1982 D IM *020 †20,15

TARHINI, Ahmad Ali. 1500 5TH AVE 15132 #913-96-1999 L2003 HO *100 †20 ‡

THOMPSON, Robert Leon. 1500 5TH AVE 15132 #041-12-1973 L1974 OBG *020 †30

TRANOVICH, Michael A. 1321 FIFTH AVE 15132 #038-40-1974 L1975 ORS *020 †40

TRUXAL, Blair David. 604 EVANS AVE 15132 #305-01-1983 L1984 OM *020 †20

TRZCIENIECKA, Anna Agata. 2347 5TH AVE 15132 #759-10-1996 L2001 FM *020 †18

UPPALAPATI, Aditya. 1500 5TH AVE, UPMC MCKEESPORT 15132 #496-22-2005 L2006 **IM** *012
USYK, John. ■ 15132 #041-12-1948 L1949 **OS GP** *020
VIOLAGO, Martin Alejandro, Jr. 2347 FIFTH AVE, LATTERMAN FAM HLTH CENT 15132 #748-01-2001 L2007 **FP** *012
VISWANATHAN, Perinkulam V. 1500 5TH AVE 15132 #495-31-1992 L2001 **CD** *020 †20
WECHT, Daniel Alan. 500 HOSPITAL WAY, STE 6 15132 #041-01-1989 L1998 **NS** *020 †25
WEERASINGHE, Dinesha Thil. ■ 15131 #220-01-1997 L2005 **FP** *012
WELDON, Patrick O. 500 HOSPITAL WAY, STE 5 15132 #028-78-1993, ▲ L1994 **AN PME** *020
WHITE, T Michael. 1500 5TH AVE, UPMC MCKEESPORT 15132 #035-03-1974 L1988 **IM** *040 †20
ZAFAR, Rakhshinda. ■ 15131 #704-06-1978 L1989 **IM** *020 †20
ZIONCHECK, Roger Jan. 1318 5TH AVE, HEALTHFIRST MEDICAL ASSOC 15132 #759-01-1986 L1991 **IMG** *020 †20
ZUBRITZKY, Desiderius I. 1500 5TH AVE 15132 #041-12-1945 L1946 **GE IM** *020 †20

MCKNIGHT — ALLEGHENY

MCFARLANE, Daniel James. ■ 15237 #038-41-2006 L2006 **MPD** *012

MEADOWBROOK — MONTGOMERY

ADAMS, William Liden. 1648 HUNTINGDON PIKE 19046 #041-13-1964 L1965 **GP** *020
ARMENTO, Donald Francis. 1650 HUNTINGDON PIKE, STE 221 19046 #010-02-1957 L1963 **U** *075 †95
BAND, Philip T. ■ 19046 #010-01-1949 L1956 **CHP P** *072
BECKER, Theresa Creneti. 1650 HUNTINGDON PIKE, STE 320 19046 #041-13-1996 L1998 **PD** *020 †55 ‡
BESDEN, Jodi Ellen. 1648 HUNTINGDON PIKE 19046 #041-13-1998 **OBG** *020
BUCKWALTER, Richard Alan. 1648 HUNTINGDON PIKE 19046 #041-13-1956 L1957 **FM** *020
BUTTERWICK, Laura Ann. 1650 HUNTINGDON PIKE, STE 156 19046 #041-07-1995 L1997 **IM** *020 †20
CHORNEY, Stephanie Kim. 1648 HUNTINGDON PIKE, HOLY REDEEMER HOSPITAL - P 19046 #041-13-1995 L1997 **PD** *020 †55 ‡
CIPRIANI, Debra Ann. 1648 HUNTINGDON PIKE, MEDICAL CENTER 19046 #033-06-1985 L1986 **NPM** *020 †55 ‡
CLEARY, Stephen Patrick. 1650 HUNTINGDON PIKE, STE 118 19046 #035-08-1980 L1981 **OBG** *020 †30
COOPER, Gregory William. 1650 HUNTINGDON PIKE, STE 258 19046 #035-03-1983 L1988 **N** *020 †75
CRIVARO, Michael Anthony. 1650 HUNTINGDON PIKE, STE350 19046 #041-09-1981 L1982 **GS VS** *020 †85
DE LARATO, Nicole Helene. 1650 HUNTINGDON PIKE, STE 357 19046 #033-06-1995 L1998 **OPH** *020 †85
DHAND, Sandeep. 1650 HUNTINGDON PIKE, SUITE 305 M O B 19046 #495-36-1972 L1973 **PUD CCM** *020 †20
ELLIS, Paul S. 1648 HUNTINGDON PIKE 19046 #041-02-1979 L1980 **DR** *020 †80
ETTER, Jonathan Rand. ■ 19046 #041-02-2005 L2005 **OPH** *012
FABIUS, Barry Michael. 1648 HUNTINGDON PIKE 19046 #041-13-1984 L1986 **IM IMG** *030 †20
FARANO, Peter Jos. 1648 HUNTINGDON PIKE, HOLY REDEEMER HOSP & MC 19046 #041-09-1983 L1984 **PTH CLP** *020 †50
FARR, Nasser Askari. ■ 19046 #517-05-1963 L1971 **GP** *030
FISHER, Joseph Saul. 1650 HUNTINGDN PIKE #S-317 19046 #041-02-1970 L1971 **END** *020 †20 ‡
FREEDMAN, Martin Frederic. 1650 HUNTINGDON PIKE, STE 154 19046 #025-07-1977 L1981 **REN** *020 †30
FRUMIN, Vera Lynne. 1650 HUNTINGDON PIKE STE 3 19046 #041-13-1981 L1983 **PD** *020 †55 ‡
GALAPO, Simon. 1650 HUNTINGDON PIKE, STE 357 19046 #035-08-1998 L2001 **APM** *020 †05
GALLUZZO, Dominick Albert. ■ 19046 #041-15-2001 L2001 **IM** *020
GHAHRAMANI, Mahmood. ■ 19046 #517-01-1959 L1973 **P GP** *020 †75
GHALILI, Kourosh. 1650 HUNTINGDON PIKE, STE 208 19046 #024-16-1987 L2006 **TS** *020 †90,85
GIBBONS, William James. 1650 HUNTINGDON PIKE, STE 156 19046 #041-02-1974 L1975 **IM CD** *020 †20
GODFREY, Elizabeth G. 1648 HUNTINGDON PIKE 19046 #041-02-2000 L2001 **PD** *020 †55 ‡
GOLD, Allan. 1650 HUNTINGDON PIKE, STE 214 19046 #041-02-1962 L1963 **OTO OS** *020 †45
GOLDSTEIN, Irwin Stuart. 1650 HUNTINGDON PIKE, STE 221 19046 #041-02-1975 L1976 **U** *020 †95
GOROVITS, Lilia. 1648 HUNTINGDON PIKE 19046 #913-05-1983 L1997 **IM ADM** *020 †20
GUNDY, Deirdre J. 1650 HUNTINGDON PIKE, STE 118 19046 #041-09-1992 L1995 **OBG** *020 †30 ‡
GUTIERREZ-ABELLA, E. 1648 HUNTINGDON PIKE, DPT PM 19046 #748-02-1966 L1973 **PM IM** *020 †20,60
HAGAN, Eugene Patrick. 1650 HUNTINGDON PIKE, STE 250 19046 #041-13-1958 L1959 **OBG OS** *020 †30
HERZOG, Keith Douglas. 1648 HUNTINGDON PIKE 19046 #036-01-1984 L1987 **PD ID** *020 †55
HOSTELLEY, Richard Thos. 1648 HUNTINGDON PIKE 19046 #041-13-1969 L1970 **EM** *020 †16
IANNARONE, Lorenz N. 1650 HUNTINGDON PIKE, STE 318 19046 #041-13-1979 L1980 **GS VS** *020 †85
KARNIK, Subhash Shridhar. 1648 HUNTINGDON PIKE 19046 #495-28-1963 L1973 **GS OS** *020 †85
KESSLER, Howard Beryl. 1648 HUNTINGDON PIKE, RAD DEPT 19046 #038-40-1980 L1982 **DR** *020 †80
KHOURY, Joshua Bernard. 1650 HUNTINGDON PIKE, STE 258 19046 #654-01-1999 L2001 **N** *020 †75
KIESEL, Harry Alexander. 1650 HUNTINGDON PIKE, MED OFFICE BLDG/SUITE 355 19046 #041-09-1975 L1976 **IM** *020 †20
KOLLER, Harold Paul. 1650 HUNTINGDON PIKE, STE 150 19046 #021-01-1964 L1968 **OPH PD** *020 †35 ‡
KOLLMER, Joseph John, III. 1648 HUNTINGDON PIKE 19046 #041-13-1959 L1960 **FM FPG** *020 †18
KOWALYSHYN, Michael John. 1648 HUNTINGDON PIKE, HOLY REDEEMER HOSP-PATH 19046 #023-01-1979 L1981 **PTH** *020 †50

KRUPNICK, Jason Garrett. 1648 HUNTINGDON PIKE 19046 #041-02-1999 L2002 **PD** *020 †55
LA PAT, Richard C. 1648 HUNTINGDON PIKE 19046 #035-09-1962 L1963 **PD PDA** *071 †55
LAX, Kevin Gordon. 1650 HUNTINGDON PIKE 19046 #035-47-1990 L1997 **CD IM** *020 †20
LEHMAN, Mary Elizabeth. ■ 19046 #041-07-1928 L1929 **OS** *071
LEHMAN, Roy Jacob. 1650 HUNTINGDON PIKE, STE-107 19046 #041-13-1973 L1974 **FM IMG** *020 †18
LICHTENSTEIN, Israel H. 1648 HUNTINGDON PIKE 19046 #041-01-1975 L1976 **ID IM** *020 †20
LOSBEN, Stephen Jay. 1650 HUNTINGDON PIKE # 315 19046 #041-09-1972 L1973 **D** *020 ‡
LUCCA, Michael. 1648 HUNTINGDON PIKE, MEDICAL CENTER 19046 #035-09-1984 L1985 **EM ESM** *020 †16
LUSCHINI, David John. 1650 HUNTINGDON PIKE, STE 224 19046 #041-09-1973 L1975 **IM IMG** *020 †20 ‡
MANZ, Donald Jos. 1648 HUNTINGDON PIKE 19046 #041-02-1955 L1956 **PTH OS** *071 †50
MARCUCCI, Ruth Addis. 1648 HUNTINGDON PIKE 19046 #041-07-1955 L1956 **PD** *071 †55
MC DEVITT, James Jos. 1648 HUNTINGDON PIKE 19046 #041-13-1957 L1958 **FM** *071 †18
MC ELWAIN, Guy Edward. 1650 HUNTINGDON PIKE, STE 156 19046 #041-02-1976 L1977 **IM IG** *020 †20
MC GUCKIN, Joseph Michael. 1648 HUNTINGDON PIKE 19046 #041-13-1970 L1971 **ORS** *075 †40
MC PEAK, Vincent J, Jr. 1648 HUNTINGDON PIKE, HOLY REDEEMER HOSP 19046 #041-02-1951 L1952 **OS** *071 †30
MEEHAN, John Jos. 1650 HUNTINGDON PIKE 19046 #041-02-1947 L1948 **CD IM** *071 †20
METHIKALAM, Blessy. 1648 HUNTINGDON PIKE 19046 #010-03-2000 L2003 **PD** *020
MILLS, Don Allan. 1648 HUNTINGDON PIKE 19046 #010-02-1958 L1960 **OS GP** *020 †18
MONTANEZ, Jaime A. ■ 19046 #869-04-1961 L1972 **GS TS** *071
MULLER, Alfons Jos. ■ 19046 #041-09-1948 L1949 **PM LM** *071
MUSTIN, Andrew Jay. 1650 HUNTINGDON PIKE, STE 256 19046 #041-02-1988 L1990 **CD** *020 †20
NATTER, Howard Michael. 1650 HUNTINGDON PIKE, STE 258 19046 #041-09-1986 L1987 **N** *020 †75
NGAYAN, Julia Palalay. 1648 HUNTINGDON PIKE, HOLY REDEEMAR HOSP 19046 #748-08-1964 L1984 **OBG** *020
OO, Nwe G. ■ 19046 #209-03-1984 L1998 **PYG** *020 †75
PEDICINO, Alexander Robt. 1650 HUNTINGDON PIKE, STE 301 19046 #041-02-1975 L1976 **FM** *020 †18
PELLECCHIA, Patrick E. 1650 HUNTINGDON PIKE, STE 350 19046 #041-13-1974 L1976 **VS** *020 †85
RACHSHTUT, Michael. 1648 HUNTINGDON PIKE 19046 #305-01-2002 L2002 **HO** *012 †20
REINACH, Alan Joseph. 1648 HUNTINGDON PIKE 19046 #041-02-1993 L1995 **PCC IM** *020 †20
RICKETTS, Robyn Denise. 1650 HUNTINGDON PIKE, STE 313 19046 #040-02-2000 L2001 **AN** *100
ROBINSON, James Jos, Jr. 1648 HUNTINGDON PIKE 19046 #041-09-1942 L1943 **FM** *071
ROBINSON, Randy C. 1650 HUNTINGDON PIKE, STE 357 19046 #038-41-1999 L2001 **AN** *100 †05
ROITMAN, Leonore Berman. 1650 HUNTINGDON PIKE, STE 101 19046 #041-07-1955 L1957 **AN** *071
RUBENSTEIN, Michael Neil. 1650 HUNTINGDON PIKE, HOLY REDEEMER MED OFF BLDG 19046 #055-01-1985 L1988 **N** *020 †75
SALDIVAR, Eliseo V. 1648 HUNTINGDON PIKE 19046 #748-01-1966 L1973 **EM FM** *020 †16
SANTILLI, Thomas F. 1648 HUNTINGDON PIKE 19046 #035-09-1949 L1955 **CD PUD** *071 †20
SANTILLI, Thomas Michael. 1650 HUNTINGDON PIKE, STE 252 19046 #035-09-1980 L1982 **CD** *020 †20
SASTRY, Dasika M. 1650 HUNTINGDON PIKE, STE 311 19046 #495-50-1965 L1973 **TS VS** *071 †85,90
SAULL, Sondra Carol. 1650 HUNTINGDON PIKE, STE 214 19046 #041-01-1980 L1981 **OTO** *020 †45
SCHNEIDER, Henry C, Jr. 1650 HUNTINGDON PIKE, STE 221 19046 #036-07-1967 L1968 **U** *020 †95
SHAFTEL, Peter Adam. 1650 HUNTINGDON PIKE # 252 19046 #035-20-1986 L1987 **IC CD** *020 †20
SHPIGEL, Yelena. 1650 HUNTINGDON PIKE, STE 258 19046 #913-94-1982 L2002 **N** *020
SMITH, Connor William. ■ 19046 #041-02-1994 L1999 **IM** *020
SMITH, Morgan Teddy, Jr. 1691 PAPER MILL RD 19046 #041-13-1969 L1970 **OBG** *071 †30
SMITH, Richard Norris. 1650 HUNTINGDON PIKE, ALLERGY & ASTHMA CARE 19046 #041-02-1957 L1958 **CHP P** *072
SOERGEL, David Griffith. 1420 STOCKTON RD 19046 #035-20-1996 L2003 **PDC** *020 †55
STEINBERG, William J. ■ 19046 #041-02-1977 L1978 **EM** *020
SUANLARM, Chintana. 1648 HUNTINGDON PIKE, HOLY REDEEMER HOSPITAL 19046 #891-03-1971 L1975 **IM GP** *020
SZEREMETA, Wasyl. 1077 RYDAL RD, STE 201 19046 #041-02-1989 L1994 **OTO** *020 †45
TAI, Victoria Chihchuang. 1648 HUNTINGDON PIKE, HEALTH CARE DELIVERY OFFIC 19046 #051-04-2001 L2001 **OBG** *020
TAUSCH, Gilbert Speed. 1650 HUNTINGDON PIKE, STE 258 19046 #048-04-1981 L1989 **N** *020 †75
THORNTON, Richard Scott. 1650 HUNTINGDON PIKE, STE 250 19046 #041-01-1979 L1981 **GYN** *020 †30
TOLAND, Joseph C. ■ 19046 #041-09-1963 L1964 **OPH** *020 †35 ‡
TOLL, Joshua Adam. ■ 19046 #041-13-2008 *012
TOMEO, Michael A. 1650 HUNTINGDON PIKE, STE 354 19046 #041-13-1983 L1984 **D** *020 †15
UNGER, Henry David. 1648 HUNTINGDON PIKE, HOLY REDEEMER HOSPITAL 19046 #021-01-1983 L1984 **EM** *020 †16
VAZE, Milind Mahaded. 1650 HUNTINGDON PIKE 19046 #496-38-1982 L1991 **GE** *020 †20
VIGDERMAN, Anne Miriam. 1650 HUNTINGDON PIKE, STE 258 19046 #041-02-1993 L1996 **N** *020
WAGNER, Charles Irving. 1648 HUNTINGDON PIKE, HOLY REDEEMER HEALTH SYS 19046 #041-01-1967 L1968 **GE IM** *030 †20
WURTELE, Lester H, Jr. 1648 HUNTINGDON PIKE, DEPT R 19046 #050-02-1964 L1965 **R** *020 †80
YETIMYAN, Vahe. 1648 HUNTINGDON PIKE 19046 #902-10-1970 L1980 **GP** *020

MEADVILLE — CRAWFORD

ALEXANDER, Rebecca Kate. ■ 16335 #038-40-2007 L2007 **IM** *012
ARIDA, Edward J. 277 JEFFERSON ST 16335 #033-06-1990 L1998 **DR** *020
ARNO, John Thos. 751 LIBERTY ST 16335 #035-06-1978 L1983 **CD** *020 †20

BAILEY, John H., III. 901 WATER ST 16335 #041-77-1981, ▲ L1982 IM IMG *020 †20
BAILEY, Robin Lynn. 461 PINE ST 16335 #041-01-1985 L1986 P *020 †75
BOLLARD, Glenn Alden. 751 LIBERTY ST 16335 #038-44-1983 L1995 U *020
BROWN, Jason Wayne. 751 LIBERTY ST 16335 #041-15-2001 L2001 HO *020
BROWN, Regina Grimm. ■ 16335 #041-15-2001 L2004 FM *020 †18
BURKHOLDER, James Henry. 1012 WATER ST 16335 #038-06-1975 L1978 FM *020 †18
BUTTERS, David Ernest. 505 POPLAR ST, STE G03 16335 #065-09-1979 L2001 *020
CALDWELL, Jeffrey Alan. 765 LIBERTY ST, STE 307 16335 #055-02-1994 L1996 FM *020 †18
CHADALAWADA, Durga Rani. 1009 WATER ST, WATER STREET URGENT CARE 16335 #495-11-2000 L2005 FM *020 †18
CHALLENER, Jacquelyn L S. ■ 16335 #041-12-1961 L1969 PTH *074 †50
CHALLENER, Kenneth Robt. 765 LIBERTY ST, STE 301 16335 #038-06-1988 L1991 IM *020 †20
COLANTONIO, Anthony James. 1034 GROVE ST 16335 #010-02-1998 L2003 APM *020 †05
COUTO, Ana Cristina. 1034 GROVE ST 16335 #654-01-1998 L2002 AN *020
DEAN, Vernon Entwistle. 751 LIBERTY ST 16335 #917-21-1952 L1977 GP EM *020 †18
DE KRUIF, Hendrik. ■ 16335 #008-01-1942 L1958 IM *071 †20
DHALIWAL, Ranjit S. 1245 PARK AVE 16335 #495-08-1971 L1979 RO *020 †80
DORTA, Humberto Ramon. ■ 16335 #033-05-2000 L2005 PYG *020
DOWNING, Timothy Marion. 765 LIBERTY ST, STE 111 16335 #041-12-1980 L1981 PD *020 †55
ENCARNACION, Carol Felisa. 751 LIBERTY ST 16335 #748-01-1982 L2002 ID IM *020 †20
FERGUSON, Brenda J. 751 LIBERTY ST, STE 202 16335 #041-78-1997, ▲ L1999 OBG *020
FERNANDEZ, Roderick Romo. 1034 GROVE ST, MEADVILLE MEDICAL CENTER 16335 #048-02-1990 L1994 AN *020 †05
FINE, Edward Michael. 1012 WATER ST 16335 #024-05-1972 L1973 FM *071 †18
FORERO, Manuel Francisco. 287 NORTH ST 16335 #264-11-1980 L1993 CD *020 †20
GALEY, Stephanie Marie. 640 ALDEN ST, ORTHOPEDIC ASSOCIATES OF M 16335 #041-09-1996 L1998 OFA ORS *020 †40
GODFREY, Craig Robt. 765 LIBERTY ST, STE 301 16335 #041-77-1980, ▲ L1981 IM *020 †20
GOMEZ, Luis L. 505 POPLAR ST 16335 #737-01-1972 L1977 FM EM *020
GUANZON, Danilo Lacson. 764 KENNEDY 16335 #748-01-1963 L1971 U *020 ‡
HEANEY, Steven John. 765 LIBERTY ST STE 207 16335 #035-15-1982 L1984 PS GS *020 †85,65
HEFLIN, John Christopher. 765 LIBERTY ST, STE 209 16335 #041-13-1991 L1993 FM *020 †18
JOHNSON, Denise Andrey. 765 LIBERTY ST, STE 202 16335 #010-02-1992 L1996 OBG *020 †30
KING, Sidney Kwok-Yin. 765 LIBERTY ST, STE 202 16335 #065-01-1975 L1992 *020
KIRCHNER, Lucille Kendall. 505 POPLAR ST, STE 111 16335 #055-01-1978 L1979 IM *020 †20
KIRKPATRICK, David D, Jr. 765 LIBERTY ST 16335 #041-01-1947 L1948 IM *072
KUCHNIO, Andrzej. 1034 GROVE ST 16335 #759-08-1988 L2002 AN *020
LASHBROOK, Rebecca D. 730 ALDEN ST 16335 #017-20-1996 L2000 FM *020 †18
LAUB, Curtis Henry. 640 ALDEN ST 16335 #038-06-1979 L1984 ORS *071 †40
LEE, Seung Chan. 1034 GROVE ST 16335 #583-10-1962 L1977 AN *071
LEUNG, Raymond Kwong Wah. 765 LIBERTY ST STE 111 16335 #462-01-1982 L1995 PD *020 †55
LITTLE, Harry. 751 LIBERTY ST, CITY HOSPITAL 16335 #062-01-1951 L1961 P *072 †75
LORAN, David Brett. 751 LIBERTY ST, MEADVILLE MEDICAL CENTER 16335 #048-16-1998 L2006 TS *020 †85
MACIELAK, James Rudolph. 640 ALDEN ST, ORTHOPEDIC ASSOCIATES OF 16335 #041-12-1981 L1982 ORS GS *020 †40
MALHOTRA, Narinder K. 1116 PARK AVE, THE REGIONAL CANCER CTR 16335 #495-73-1973 L1976 HO IM *020 †20
MAXFIELD, Jodi Powlus. 765 LIBERTY ST, STE 202 16335 #041-09-1998 L2001 OBG *020 †30
MC DERMOTT, Frederic Thos. 751 LIBERTY ST, MEADVILLE MEDICAL CENTER 16335 #038-41-1989 L1993 DR *020
MC GINN, Anna Lisa. ■ 16335 #422-01-1999 L2007 RO *020 †80
MC GUINNESS, John Paul. ■ 16335 #016-43-1976 L1993 FM AN *020 †05,18
MC LAMB, James Richard. 640 ALDEN ST 16335 #041-13-1960 L1961 ORS *030 †40
MC NAMARA, David Edward. 751 LIBERTY ST 16335 #008-02-1982 L1995 FM *020 †18
MITCHELL, Thomas James. 20446 COCHRANTON RD, P O BOX 1166 16335 #030-06-1994 L1997 FM *020 †18
MOAKEH, Mohamed. 751 LIBERTY ST 16335 #875-01-1972 L1975 U *020 †95
MORRIS, Matilda Jane. ■ 16335 #041-77-1946, ▲ L1957 FM *020
MORRIS, William James. 961 S MAIN ST 16335 #041-12-1974 L1975 OBG *020 †30
MOUSSA, Samir Milad. ■ 16335 #915-02-1976 L1983 GP PTH *020 †50 ‡
MOWERY, David Charles. 765 LIBERTY ST, STE 111 16335 #041-14-1994 L1996 PD *020 †55
MUCKINHOUPT, Frederick H. ■ 16335 #041-13-1936 L1938 GP GS *072
NESBITT, John Beecher. 751 LIBERTY ST, STE 307 16335 #038-06-1966 L1971 IM GP *020 †20
NEWHOOK, G Lawrence A. 505 POPLAR ST, STE 207 16335 #065-10-1983 L1993 GS TS *020 †85
NIKIFOROUK, Vladimir. 765 LIBERTY ST, STE 202 16335 #913-42-1992 L2006 OBG *020
OYLER, Paul Francis. 765 LIBERTY ST, STE 307 16335 #041-01-1991 L1994 IM *020 †20
PACZKOSKIE, Amy Jo. 1034 GROVE ST 16335 #041-09-1993 L1997 AN *020 †05
PACZKOSKIE, Vincent John, Jr. 640 ALDEN ST, ORTHOPEDIC ASSOCIATES OF 16335 #041-09-1994 L1998 ORS OSM *020 †40
PEIRSEL, Paul Everett. 751 LIBERTY ST, MEADVILLE MEDICAL CENTER 16335 #025-01-1973 L1975 FM CCM *020
PLESS, Peter Robt. 505 POPLAR ST 16335 #035-08-1981 L1989 D *020 †20,15
POUX, Paul T. ■ 16335 #041-01-1949 L1951 GP *020
PULITO, John Michael. 390 LINDEN ST 16335 #035-08-1980 L1989 OPH *020 †35
REZEK, Donald Lee. 505 POPLAR ST 16335 #056-05-1981 L1986 N *020 †75
RICHARDS, Gregory Lee. 464 PINE ST, BETHESDA COMMUNITY CARE 16335 #021-01-1980 L1992 P *020 †75
ROSS, Peter K. 1034 GROVE ST, MEADVILLE MEDICAL CENTER 16335 #067-06-1992 L1999 P *020
RUST, David Gary. 20 FOREST AVE, 1034 GROVE STREET 16335 #055-01-1990 L1994 AN *020 †05
SAAVEDRA, Diogenes A. 664 HIGHLAND AVE 16335 #737-01-1956 L1962 GS TS *071 †85,90
SANTORA, Donald Cellini. 390 LINDEN ST 16335 #041-14-1991 L1993 OPH *020 †35
SANTORA, Robert Alan. 390 LINDEN ST 16335 #561-01-1965 L1967 OPH *020 †35
SCHROECKENSTEIN, Richard. 751 LIBERTY ST, MEADVILLE MEDICAL CTR 16335 #038-41-1973 L1986 PTH *020 †50 ‡
SMART, Lawson Charles. 640 ALDEN ST, ORTHOPEDIC ASSOCIATES OF 16335 #041-12-1970 L1979 ORS *020 †40
SUDAN, Nimit. 765 LIBERTY ST STE 203, COMPREHENSIVE CANCER CARE 16335 #025-07-2000 L2003 HO *020
SULLIVAN, William Donald. 751 LIBERTY ST 16335 #024-16-1976 L1982 PUD PCC *020

SUPRYS, Marianne Jean. 751 LIBERTY ST 16335 #041-07-1987 L1988 FM *020 †18
TAYLOR, John Ogden, Jr. 751 LIBERTY ST 16335 #041-02-1965 L1966 GS OS *020 †85
TEMPLIN, Kristin Kaye. 765 LIBERTY ST, STE 307 16335 #041-14-1998 L2000 IM *020 †20
THAKUR, Gautam Chandra. 751 LIBERTY ST, DEPT OF RADIOLOGY 16335 #060-01-1993 L1997 RNR *075
THOMAS, Christopher Wm. 765 LIBERTY ST STE 307 16335 #041-09-1972 L1975 IM *020 †20
VANBEBER, Monty James. 747 TERRACE ST 16335 #665-02-2001 L2006 FM *020
VUKMER, George J. 1058 S MAIN ST 16335 #041-14-1986 L1987 OPH *020 †35
WAGAMON, Charlotte Bowen. 751 LIBERTY ST, MEADVILLE MED CTR 16335 #038-44-1988 L1991 IM EM *020 †20
WEIBEL, Christopher J. 765 LIBERTY ST, STE 311 16335 #041-13-1992 L1994 GS *020 †85
WEISS, Alfred David. ■ 16335 #017-20-1954 L1954 N OS *071
WHITE, Peter Francis. 505 POPLAR ST 16335 #065-01-1985 L1992 OTO GS *020 †45
WHITNEY, Mark Bryan. 1034 GROVE ST 16335 #051-07-1986 L1988 AN *020 †05
WILLIAMS, David Albert. 1015 GROVE ST 16335 #041-78-2003, ▲ L2003 FM *020 †18
ZEHNER, Luther Roland. 918 DIAMOND PARK 16335 #041-09-1948 L1949 GP *071

MECHANICSBURG – CUMBERLAND

ABDALLAH, Heba Yousif. 5 E MAIN ST 17055 #575-01-1997 L2000 SP *100 †50
ADAMS, Samuel Bruce, Jr. ■ 17050 #041-02-2004 L2008 ORS *012
ADLESTEIN, Lee Barry. 2025 TECHNOLOGY PKWY, STE G08 17050 #041-14-1985 L1994 AN *020 †05
ALVEAR, Veneranda G. 2025 TECHNOLOGY PKWY, STE G08 17050 #748-01-1964 L1973 AN *020 †05
ALVIN, Robert Stephen. 5 E MAIN ST 17055 #041-12-1982 L1983 FM *020 †18
ANSWINE, Joseph Frederick. 4999 LOUISE DR, STE 105 17055 #041-14-1989 L1992 AN *020 †05
ARLOTTI, Stephanie. 890 CENTURY DR, KILMORE EYE ASSOC 17055 #041-15-2000 L2000 OPH *020
ARMESTO, David Michael. 2025 TECHNOLOGY PKWY # 103 17050 #035-15-1981 L1992 OPH *020 †35 ‡
ARNOLD, Karen Jayne. ■ 17050 #028-02-1968 L1968 GS *071 †85
ARONOFF, Robert David. 856 CENTURY DR, STE A 17055 #035-03-1980 L1986 CD IC *020 †20
ASUNI, Bolanle Rasheedat. ■ 17050 #035-09-2003 IM *100
AUSTIN, Chas Baldrey, Jr. 4665 E TRINDLE RD 17050 #041-02-1978 L1979 DR EM *020 †16,80
AZZAM, Helen Carol. 5 E MAIN ST 17055 #035-20-2003 L2003 ID *012 †20
BAGARIA, Surendra Kumar. 5 E MAIN ST 17055 #496-14-1979 L1993 CD *020 †20
BAILEY, Laurel Petras. 310 LAMBS GAP RD 17050 #041-14-1986 L1987 FM OS *020 †18
BARNES, Kevin Scott. 2106 ASPEN DR 17055 #039-05-1988 L1992 PD OS *020 †55
BASHIR, Rifaat Mustafa. 2025 TECHNOLOGY PKWY, STE 201 17050 #605-01-1974 L2005 N *020 †75
BEBE, Rommel Bayot. ■ 17055 #748-20-1991 L2007 PCC *020 †20
BENACK, Carl Anthony. 5 E MAIN ST 17055 #041-12-1955 L1956 FM P *071
BHARUCHA, Shernavaz. 4999 LOUISE DR, STE 105 17055 #496-38-1970 L1974 AN *020 †05
BIKLE, Harry Dwight. 120 S FILBERT ST 17055 #041-13-1956 L1957 AN GP *071
BIRKNES, John Kurt. 5 E MAIN ST 17055 #041-02-2001 L2001 NS *100
BOGDAN, Ann Marie. 3 FLOWERS DR 17050 #051-04-1987 L1989 FM *020 †18
BOHONYI, William Anthony. 9 FLOWERS DR 17050 #041-09-1982 L1983 OBG *020 †30
BOLINE, Geo Bernard, Jr. 200 CUMBERLAND PKWY 17055 #041-12-1987 L1989 U *020 †95
BOSAK, Michael Dennis. 856 CENTURY DR, STE A 17055 #041-13-1992 L1995 CD *020 †20
BOWLES, Alfred Perry, Jr. 5 E MAIN ST 17055 #005-02-1983 L2005 NS *020 †25
BRONFMAN, Howard Joel. 2015 TECHNOLOGY PKWY 17050 #035-08-1971 L1976 DR NR *020 †80,28
BROWN, Amanda Kathleen. 5 E MAIN ST 17055 #026-08-2001 L2005 PAN *100 †05
BROWN, Richard Bennett. 2025 TECHNOLOGY PKWY, STE 211 17050 #024-07-1957 L1966 N IM *020 †20,75
BRYAN, William Thos. ■ 17050 #038-41-1954 L1956 PD *020
BUCHER, Robert Walter, Jr. 9 FLOWERS DR 17050 #308-03-1981 L1985 OBG *020 †30
BUCS, Roger Geo. 4999 LOUISE DR STE 105 17055 #041-09-1968 L1971 AN *020 †05
BUXTON, Donald Riddle, Jr. 4665 E TRINDLE RD 17050 #041-09-1967 L1968 DR *020 †20
CALCAGNO, David. 2025 TECHNOLOGY PKWY, STE 304 17050 #036-07-1981 L1992 VS *020 †85
CAMPBELL, Karen Ann. 2140 FISHER RD, SHEPHERDSTOWN FAMILY PRACT 17055 #051-04-1979 L1984 FM *020 †18
CANNON, Christopher Scott. 2025 TECHNOLOGY PKWY # 209 17050 #041-09-1987 L1990 PM *020 †60
CARDINAL, Peter Anthony. 525 LUCINDA LN, GETTYSBURG HOSPITAL- 17050 #023-12-1984 L2001 FM *030 †18
CEDENO, Loris Frances. ■ 17055 #041-14-1995 L2006 RNR *100 †80
CHANG, Steven L. ■ 17050 #035-01-2002 L2003 U *012
CHEN, Jeffrey Kuan-Chao. 4999 LOUISE DR STE 105 17055 #041-12-1994 L1997 AN *020 †05
CINCOTTA, Janet. 2140 FISHER RD 17055 #035-15-1974 L1976 FM *020 †18
CINCOTTA, Joseph Anthony. 2140 FISHER RD 17055 #035-15-1975 L1976 FM *020 †18
CLARK, Timothy Allen. 5 WILLOW MILL PARK RD 17050 #422-01-1995 L1998 PCC *020 †20
COHEN, Howard Roy. 4713 E TRINDLE RD 17050 #041-14-1972 L1974 IM EM *020
COLDREN, Robert Louis. 2025 TECHNOLOGY PKWY 17050 #041-13-1969 L1970 PD *020 †55
COTTON, Joy L. 856 CENTURY DR, STE A 17055 #041-14-1987 L1990 CD *020 †20
CRITES, Dana L. ■ 17055 #023-01-1985 L1987 CHP P *020 †75
CRONIN, Arthur John. 4999 LOUISE DR, STE 105 17055 #051-01-1989 L1991 AN *020 †05
CROTEAU, J Russell. 4665 E TRINDLE RD 17050 #025-07-1958 L1964 DR *071 †80
CYRAN, Stephen Edward. 5 E MAIN ST 17055 #010-01-1981 L1982 PDC *020 †20
DAMICO, Frank Chas. 200 CUMBERLAND PKWY 17055 #041-12-1988 L1990 U *020 †95
DAVE, Rajesh M. 856 CENTURY DR, STE A 17055 #495-48-1988 L1997 IC IM *020 †20
DEES, Terence Dale. 4999 LOUISE DR STE 105 17055 #033-05-1989 L1993 AN *020 †05
DE LA FUENTE, Carlos. 6 MARKET PLAZA WAY 17055 #847-04-1971 L1978 IM *020
DERAMON, Richard Andrew. 2025 TECHNOLOGY PKWY, STE 303 17050 #041-02-1991 L2000 PS CS *020 †85,65
DESTEFANO, Dennis Michael. 4999 LOUISE DR STE 105 17055 #033-06-1988 L1992 AN *020 †05
DOMBROWSKI, Dennis James, Jr. ■ 17050 #041-14-2007 L2007 P *012
DOUGHERTY, John E, III. 122 S FILBERT ST 17055 #041-77-1971, ▲ L1972 GP *071
DOWNEY, Mark P. 4999 LOUISE DR, STE 105 17050 #041-02-1982 L1988 AN *020 †05
DURBECK, Donald Carl. 856 CENTURY DR STE A 17055 #035-03-1965 L1972 CD IM *020 †20

■ = Address Information Privacy Protected

DURISEK, George Stephen. 4665 E TRINDLE RD 17050 #050-02-1970 L1973 **DR** *020 †80
ENGLE, Harold Hoffman. 925 MECHANICS VILLAGE 17055 #041-13-1943 L1944 **FM IM** *072 †18
ERKI, Lenke. 856 CENTURY DR, STE A 17055 #041-09-1994 L1997 **CD** *020 †20
FAHNESTOCK, Julienne Ruth. 122 S FILBERT ST 17055 #051-07-1992 L1997 **FM** *020 †18
FAIRBROTHER, Maureen Enid. 4999 LOUISE DR, STE 105 17055 #041-14-1983 L1985 **AN** *020 †05
FAJARDO, Amy Marlinda. 409 DARLA RD 17055 #017-20-2000 L2002 **EM** *020 †16
FARRELL, Deborah Maschner. 2025 TECHNOLOGY PKWY 17050 #041-14-1983 L1985 **PD** *020 †55
FARRELL, Leo Danl. 2025 TECHNOLOGY PKWY 17050 #041-14-1983 L1984 **PS GS** *020 †85,65
FARRELL, Timothy Patrick. 2015 TECHNOLOGY PKWY 17050 #041-14-1979 L1981 **DR** *020 †80
FELDMAN, Nathan Irwin. 5275 E TRINDLE RD STE 201, LACKAWANNA MOBILE DIAG SVC 17050 #041-07-1981 L1984 **R NM** *020
FLAIG, Ronald Chas. ■ 17050 #041-13-1964 L2001 **PD** *030 †55
FLEMING, Kenneth David. 5 E MAIN ST 17055 #041-13-1980 L1981 **PD ADL** *020 †55
FLURKEY, Emerson Cook. ■ 17055 #047-06-1957 L1962 **OBG** *071
FOOS, Colleen Cooke. 5 E MAIN ST 17055 #041-01-1990 L1998 **OBG** *020 †30 ‡
FRANK, David Philip. 6108 CARLISLE PIKE 17050 #422-01-1987 L1992 **FM FSM** *020 †18
FRITSCH, Matthew Curran. ■ 17050 #041-13-2005 L2005 **AN** *012
FRY, Chloe Oneita. ■ 17050 #041-07-1927 L1928 **GYN PM** *062 †30
FUZZELL, Jameso. ■ 17055 #028-34-1950 L1950 **OBG** *071
GARDNER, Shyrelle. 5 E MAIN ST 17055 #041-13-1978 L1983 **IM FM** *020
GASSIS, Safwat Albert. 856 CENTURY DR, STE A 17055 #010-02-1999 L2006 **ICE** *100 †20
GAYNER, Scott Matthew. 2025 TECHNOLOGY PKWY, STE 309 17050 #051-04-1993 L1999 **OTO FPS** *020 †45
GEDULDIG, Michael Marc. ■ 17050 #035-19-1955 L1963 **GE IM** *020 †20
GENS, Robert D. ■ 17055 #035-20-1953 L1970 **PDS** *071 †55
GHALI, Hani Adli. 5 E MAIN ST 17055 #915-02-1998 L2005 **IM** *020 †20
GILROY, Robert Cummings. 4665 E TRINDLE RD 17050 #041-02-1997 L2002 **DR** *020 †80
GRADZKA, Agnieszka. 2025 TECHNOLOGY PKWY, STE 108 17050 #759-03-1997 L2002 **PD** *020 †55
GRIFF, Roberta Evans. 5124 E TRINDLE RD 17050 #035-08-1964 L1967 **PM** *020
GROFF, Margaret Yoder. 310 N SALEM CHURCH RD, SILVER CREEK FAMILY HEALTH 17050 #038-44-1982 L1985 **FM** *020 †18
GULLOTTI, Michael John. 5 E MAIN ST 17055 #041-02-1974 L1976 **CD IM** *071 †20
HAIDET, Keith Richard. 4665 E TRINDLE RD 17050 #041-14-1983 L1985 **DR OS** *020 †80 ‡
HARKER, Richard Craig. 6375 MERCURY DR, STE 200 17050 #041-14-1991 L1993 **FM** *020 †18
HARTER, Andrew Jason. 4999 LOUISE DR, STE 105 17055 #041-14-2001 L2001 **AN** *020 †05
HARTZELL, Kimberly Marie. ■ 17050 #041-13-2006 L2006 **TY** *012
HAWN, Margaret Merriam. 2025 TECHNOLOGY PKWY, STE 212 17050 #035-03-1979 L1981 **OBG** *020 †30
HEIMERT, Tamra Lynne. 4665 E TRINDLE RD 17050 #143-11-2000 L2001 **IM** *020 †80
HEPLER, Kevin Michael. 6005 CHARLTON WAY 17050 #036-07-1979 L1983 **FM** *030 †18
HEROLD, Creston Chas, Jr. 6375 MERCURY DR, STE 200 17050 #041-02-1979 L1980 **FM EM** *020 †18
HLAVAC, Cheryl Ann. 5 E MAIN ST 17055 #041-02-1984 L1985 **FM** *020 †18 ‡
HOERNER, Oscar G. 120 S FILBERT ST 17055 #041-02-1952 L1953 **GP** *071
HOLDING, Michele Yvette. 5 E MAIN ST 17055 #041-09-1990 L1994 **PM** *071 †60
HOWE, Francis Robt Carter. 4999 LOUISE DR, STE 105 17055 #041-14-1980 L1980 **AN** *071 †05
HUANG, Alina Minli. ■ 17050 #041-12-2008 *012
INNERS, Charles Robt. ■ 17050 #023-07-1974 L1978 **IM** *020 †20
IYER, Viswanathan Sankara. ■ 17050 #495-31-1990 L2007 **NEP** *020
JAGANNATH, Anand S. 4665 E TRINDLE RD 17050 #035-20-1983 L1989 **DR VIR** *020 †80
JAMES, Geoffrey. 1 KACEY CT, STE 101 17055 #041-01-1978 L1979 **FM** *020 †18
JINDAL, Ramesh Kumar. ■ 17050 #495-03-1967 L1987 **P** *020
JONES, Jeffry Lynn. 4999 LOUISE DR, STE 105 17055 #005-12-1987 L1991 **AN PD** *020 †05
KANG, Se-Boo. ■ 17050 #583-02-1961 L1972 **AN** *071
KANNANGARA, Saman. 5 E MAIN ST 17055 #041-15-2000 L2003 **ID IM** *020 †20 ‡
KAPADIA, Kiranchandra M. 4665 E TRINDLE RD 17050 #495-01-1974 L1998 **DR** *020 †80
KEYSER, Glenn Curt. 2015 TECHNOLOGY PKWY, WEST SHORE SURGERY CENTER 17050 #041-14-1983 L1984 **AN** *020 †05
KILMORE, Vance Eugene. 890 CENTURY DR 17055 #041-13-1973 L1977 **OPH** *020 †35 ‡
KIM, Sang. 856 CENTURY DR, STE A 17055 #041-02-1995 L2000 **CD** *020 †20
KLEMOW, Sherri Lynn. 5 E MAIN ST 17055 #041-13-1985 L1987 **FM** *020 †18 ‡
KNIGHT, Emerson L, Jr. 200 CUMBERLAND PKWY 17055 #055-01-1973 L1974 **U** *020 †95
KRATZ, Ronald Dean. 4999 LOUISE DR, STE 105 17055 #051-04-1991 L1994 **AN MDM** *020 †05
KUNDU, Sambhu Nath. 6343 STEPHENS XING, CENTRAL PA OB-GYN INC 17050 #495-38-1958 L1974 **GYN** *020 †30 ‡
KURA, Raghuveer Reddy. 5 E MAIN ST 17055 #495-73-1997 L2003 **NEP** *012
LARSON, Jeanne N. 1 KACEY CT, STE 101 17055 #005-19-1976 L2005 **FM** *020 †18
LEE, Sonya. 5 E MAIN ST 17055 #025-01-1996 L1998 **OBG** *020 †30
LIFTON, Lester J. 5 TRUFFLE GLEN RD 17050 #035-06-1972 L1975 **GE IM** *020 †20
LONGENDERFER, Roger Lynn. ■ 17050 #041-09-1979 L1980 **FM** *020 †18
LORENZO, Frederick Vetus. 2025 TECHNOLOGY PKWY, PINNACLE HLTH WOUND CTR 17050 #035-47-1972 L1974 **GS TS** *020 †85
LUPINACCI, Michael F. 175 LANCASTER BLVD 17055 #010-02-1981 L1988 **PM** *020 †60
LUTNESS, Mark Philip. 175 LANCASTER BLVD 17055 #037-01-1983 L1986 **PM** *071 †60
LUTTERMOSER, Gary Kenneth. 1506 COUNTRY DR 17055 #038-43-1978 L1982 **OBG FPG** *040 †18
MACALUSO, Russell Anthony. 2025 TECHNOLOGY PKWY, STE G03 17050 #041-12-1984 L1985 **OTO HNS** *020 †45
MALINIAK, Keith Kimmel. 4999 LOUISE DR, STE G08 17055 #010-01-1975 L2004 **AN** *020 †05
MAN, David Chungtin. 856 CENTURY DR, STE A 17055 #035-46-1990 L1993 **CD** *020 †20
MANI, Anne Elizabeth. ■ 17050 #023-07-2005 L2008 **IM** *012
MANIGLIA, Rosario. ■ 17055 #041-09-1946 L1952 **PTH** *071 †50
MARCUS, Michael Steven. 4999 LOUISE DR STE 105 17055 #023-01-1990 L1993 **AN PME** *020 †05
MARSHALL, Wayne Keith. 4999 LOUISE DR STE 105, RIVERSIDE ANESTH ASSOC 17055 #051-04-1974 L1980 **AN PME** *020 †05 ‡
MAY, Kenneth James. 856 CENTURY DR, STE A 17055 #422-01-1982 L1986 **CD IM** *020 †20
MC MILLEN, James Irving. 1001 S MARKET ST, STE D 17055 #041-09-1970 L1971 **RHU IM** *020
MILES, Ronald Durrant. 4641 WESTPORT DR, US MILITARY ENT PROC STAT 17055 #010-03-1974 L1998 **OBG** *020
MILITO, Stephen Jos. 880 CENTURY DR 17055 #011-02-1990 L1992 **RO** *020 †80
MILSTEEN, Scott Alan. 4999 LOUISE DR, STE G08 17055 #023-01-1986 L1989 **AN OBG** *020 †05
MIN, Liliane. 5 E MAIN ST 17055 #035-19-2000 L2002 **RHU** *100 †20
MOORE, Barry Brooks. 920 CENTURY DR 17055 #041-13-1967 L1972 **NS** *020 †25
MORCOS, Ehab F. 5 E MAIN ST 17055 #915-09-1985 L1993 **IC CD** *020 †20
MOSHER, James Elliott. 2025 TECHNOLOGY PKWY, STE 108 17050 #041-14-2000 L2001 **PD** *020 †55
MOSTOFA, Golam. ■ 17055 #160-01-1990 L2004 **IM** *020 †20
MOUSSAVIAN, Bahar. 5 E MAIN ST 17055 #654-01-2000 L2002 **DR** *100 †80
MUDAN, Pushpa R. 1415 SILVER CREEK DR 17050 #495-09-1972 L1994 **GS EM** *020 †85,16
MUELLER, Scott Douglas. 2025 TECHNOLOGY PKWY, STE 207 17050 #041-14-1983 L1984 **FM PME** *020 †18
MUFTI, Sadia. 5 E MAIN ST 17055 #704-02-2000 L2003 **PD** *020
MURAIKA, R Scott. 4999 LOUISE DR, STE 105 17055 #041-12-1993 L1996 **AN PME** *020 †05
MURPHY, Shawn C. 4999 LOUISE DR, STE 105 17055 #041-77-2004, ▲ L2004 **AN** *012
MURRAY, William Massie. 5020 RITTER RD, STE 211 17055 #041-02-1970 L1972 **ORS** *071 †40
NASSAR, Jay Paul. 4999 LOUISE DR STE 105 17055 #035-06-1989 L1993 **AN** *020 †05
NIKIFOROV, Sergei I. 4999 LOUISE DR, STE 105 17055 #913-01-1988 L2000 **AN** *020 †05
NIKIFOROVA, Tamara V. 4999 LOUISE DR, STE 105 17055 #913-01-1988 L2001 **AN** *020 †05
OKEN, Kenneth Jeffrey. 2025 TECHNOLOGY PKWY, STE 212 17050 #023-01-1990 L1993 **OBG** *020 †30
OSTDAHL, Roger Harold. 920 CENTURY DR 17055 #036-07-1973 L1979 **NS** *020 †25
PACKER, Leslie Alan. 2025 TECHNOLOGY PKWY, STE G08 17050 #021-05-1987 L1991 **AN** *020 †05
PALADE, Adelina Lidia. 5 E MAIN ST 17055 #781-01-1993 L2002 **FM** *020 †18
PARIKH, Ankur Mukul. ■ 17050 #041-13-2007 L2007 **GS** *012
PARIKH, Mukul Lalit. 4999 LOUISE DR, STE 105 17055 #495-21-1978 L1984 **AN PME** *020 †05
PINK, Stuart Bruce. 856 CENTURY DR, STE A 17055 #035-20-1980 L1988 **CD IM** *020 †20
POLICARE, Christine Marie. ■ 17050 #041-14-2005 L2005 **DR** *012
POPAT, Vrajlal Hirjibhai. ■ 17050 #495-01-1976 L1982 **IM** *020
POTTER, Jeffrey Neal. 2140 FISHER RD 17055 #041-02-1979 L1980 **FM** *020 †18
PROBOLUS, James Andrew. 5 E MAIN ST 17055 #422-01-2002 L2006 **FM** *100 †18
QAZIZADEH, Salim. 2025 TECHNOLOGY PKWY, STE 201 17050 #473-03-1996 L2001 **CN** *020 †75
REDCLIFT, Matthew Scott. 4999 LOUISE DR, STE 105 17055 #051-04-1995 L1998 **CCA AN** *020 †05
RUPP, Kathleen Nicole. 3 BADEN POWELL LN STE 4 17050 #041-14-1997 L2000 **OPH** *020
RYDER, Christopher Stuart. 2106 ASPEN DR 17055 #836-01-1971 L1986 **PD** *020 †55
SACKMAN, Ira. 856 CENTURY DR, STE A 17055 #024-07-1976 L1977 **CD IM** *020 †20
SAHA, Banani. 2140 FISHER RD, SHEPHERDSTOWN FAMILY PRACT 17055 #160-04-1993 L2001 **IMG** *020 †18
SAHI, Rajinder Kaur. ■ 17050 #748-08-2000 L2006 **IM** *012
SANGHVI, Kavita B. 4665 E TRINDLE RD 17050 #495-01-1993 L2001 **DR** *100 †80
SAXENA, Narendra Mohan. ■ 17050 #495-34-1956 L1996 **IM PUD** *020
SCANDARIATO, Giovanna M. ■ 17055 #035-08-1985 L1990 **PUD IM** *020
SCHER, David Lee. 856 CENTURY DR, STE A 17055 #561-01-1984 L1988 **CD IM** *020 †20
SCHERZER, Wendy Jane. 5 E MAIN ST 17055 #033-05-1986 L1989 **OBG** *020 †30
SCHUMACHER, Harold Robt. ■ 17055 #038-41-1955 L1962 **HEM PTH** *071 †20
SCHWARTZ, Gary Marc. 2140 FISHER RD 17055 #041-14-1986 L1987 **FM** *020 †18
SEMPELES, Kathleen R. 3 FLOWERS DR, SILVER SPRING FAMILY PRACT 17050 #041-02-1984 L1985 **FM** *020 †18
SETZER, Dana Anstine. 2025 TECHNOLOGY PKWY, STE 180 17050 #051-01-1994 L1997 **PD** *020 †55
SETZER, William Scott. 1 KACEY CT, STE 101 17055 #051-01-1994 L1997 **FM** *020 †18
SHAHINIAN, George Kevork. 1521 WOODCREEK DR 17055 #422-01-1996 L1999 **PCC** *020 †20
SHAMBAUGH, Corey Dean. ■ 17050 #041-14-2006 L2006 **PD** *012
SHENAI, Pundalik Ganguli. 4999 LOUISE DR STE 105 17055 #495-37-1975 L1979 **AN PME** *020 †05
SINHA, Janardan Prasad. ■ 17050 #495-15-1965 L1980 **PUD IM** *020 †20
SIVICK, Edward Michael. ■ 17055 #041-13-1943 L1944 **GP IM** *071
SKURCENSKI, Alison Hayes. 1965 FISHER RD 17055 #035-15-1996 L1999 **FM** *020 †18
SKURCENSKI, Craig Alan. ■ 17055 #035-15-1996 L1999 **EM** *020 †16
SOBOTA, Bret Theodore. ■ 17055 #041-14-1994 L1997 **OTO** *020 †45
SOISSON, Ferdinand Louis. ■ 17055 #010-02-1955 L1963 **GYN** *071 †30
SOTO-HAMLIN, Angela M. 880 CENTURY DR 17055 #041-01-1980 L1985 **GS** *020 †85
STAGG, Richard Donald. 120 S FILBERT ST 17055 #038-40-1965 L1992 **EM OM** *030 †70
STERLING, Nancy Isaacs. 4999 LOUISE DR STE 105 17055 #041-07-1980 L1981 **AN** *020 †05
STEWART, Jonathan Drew. 5 E MAIN ST 17055 #051-01-2003 L2003 **FM** *020 †18
STONE, Kerry Buschman. 5 E MAIN ST 17055 #041-12-2001 L2001 **RHU** *020
STONER, John Clinton. ■ 17050 #041-09-1963 L1964 **GP** *071
STRATIS, John Peter. 2025 TECHNOLOGY PKWY, STE 309 17050 #041-01-1982 L1984 **PS** *020 †65,85
STROCK, Bradford Kent. ■ 17055 #041-09-1947 L1948 **OS ADM** *071 †18
SULLIVAN, John Michael. 1001 S MARKET ST, STE B 17055 #038-41-1975 L1976 **FM A** *020 †18
THOMPSON, James Sharon. 910 CENTURY DR, STE 150 17055 #041-09-1992 L1994 **FM** *020 †18
THUMA, Alvan E. PO BOX 2015 17055 #041-09-1947 L1947 **GP** *071
TUCKER, Peter Joseph. 200 CUMBERLAND PKWY 17055 #041-14-1993 L1995 **U** *020 †95
TYNDALL, Ann W. ■ 17050 #041-14-1977 L1979 **IM** *040 †20
UNIACKE, Brian Michael. 2025 TECHNOLOGY PKWY, STE 306 17050 #041-02-1982 L1983 **FM** *020 †18
VENABLE, J Clark. 4999 LOUISE DR, STE 105 17055 #005-18-1992 L1999 **AN** *020 †05
VONAH, Savitha. 4999 LOUISE DR, STE 105 17055 #041-02-1995 L1998 **AN** *020 †05
WALDNER, Joseph Francis. 4999 LOUISE DR, STE 105 17055 #041-09-1994 L1998 **AN** *020 †05
WALI, Andreas U. 856 CENTURY DR, STE A 17055 #690-01-1987 L1999 **CD** *020 †20
WALKER, Andrzej R. 4910 RITTER RD 17055 #759-01-1990 L2001 **IM** *020 †20
WEIGEL, Jesse Allen. ■ 17050 #041-12-1960 L1961 **EM FM** *071
WILLIAMS, Virginia M. ■ 17055 #041-13-1949 L1950 **PD** *072
WILT, Faith Michelle. 2025 TECHNOLOGY PKWY, STE 108 17050 #035-03-2002 L2002 **PD** *100 †55
WORMAN, Robert K. ■ 17055 #041-02-1950 L1988 **GS** *071 †85
WRIGHT, Scott Christian. ■ 17050 #023-12-1994 L2007 **DR** *020 †80

■ = Address Information Privacy Protected

YEAGER, James Paul. ■ 17055 #041-09-1957 L1958 **GP** *071

YODFAT, Uriel A. 2025 TECHNOLOGY PKWY # G08, RIVERSIDE ANESTHESIA ASSOC 17050 #550-02-1986 L1994 **AN** *020 †05

ZAMBARANO, Thomas John. ■ 17055 #010-02-1964 L1971 **DR** *071 †80

ZAMPOGNA, Jennifer C. 950 WOODLAND ST, ADV DERM SKIN SURG 17055 #010-02-1998 L2001 **D DS** *020 †15

ZHU, Jie. 5 E MAIN ST 17055 #243-69-1986 L2002 **PM** *020 †60

ZIMMERMAN, David Seebold. 6 MARKET PLAZA WAY 17055 #041-01-1958 L1959 **FM** *020 †18

MEDIA – DELAWARE

ADESMAN, Michael B. 1088 W BALTIMORE PIKE, STE 2403 19063 #043-01-1982 L1983 **CD IC** *020 †20

ALTMAN, Jamie Frederick. 1088 W BALTIMORE PIKE, STE 2506 19063 #041-13-1996 L2003 **D** *020 †15

ANDERSON, Ronald Bernhard. 1098 W BALTIMORE PIKE, STE 3408 19063 #017-20-1979 L1980 **RHU IM** *020 †20

ANTONELLO, Anthony, Jr. 1098 W BALTIMORE PIKE, STE 3302 19063 #041-07-1985 L1985 **OPH** *020 †35

APPLEGATE, Russel C, III. 1098 W BALTIMORE PIKE, RIDDLE OUTPT PAV STE 3403 19063 #041-09-1977 L1978 **PD** *020 †55

AYERS, William Harry, Jr. 1088 W BALTIMORE PIKE, HCC II STE 2507 19063 #041-07-1978 L1979 **GS** *020 †85

BABUSHOK, Daria Valeri. ■ 19063 #041-01-2008 *012

BACANI, Ofelia Agustin. 1068 W BALTIMORE PIKE 19063 #748-08-1967 L1976 **IM N** *020

BADORF, Michelle Christin. ■ 19063 #041-77-2007, ▲ L2007 *012

BALIN, Arthur Kirsner. 110 CHESLEY DR 19063 #041-01-1974 L1977 **D DMP** *020 †20,15 ‡

BANSBACH, Jean M Ceccoli. ■ 19063 #041-09-1951 L1952 **D** *071 †15

BARPUJARI, Vikram. 1088 W BALTIMORE PIKE, STE 2407 19063 #495-04-1980 L1997 **GE** *020 †20

BATIPPS, Percy O, Jr. ■ 19063 #010-03-1944 L1946 **GP** *071

BATTA, Satish Kumar. ■ 19063 #649-33-1981 L1982 **FM PME** *071 †05

BEHBEHANIAN, Mahin Dokht. 1088 W BALTIMOR PIKE #2203, HECTT RIDDLE MEDM HOSP 19063 #041-07-1965 L1972 **GS SO** *020 †85

BELL, James Buchanan, Jr. 605 W STATE ST 19063 #051-01-1961 L1970 **IM ID** *071

BEPLER, Charles Robt. 1098 W BALTIMORE PIKE, STE 3408 19063 #041-13-1948 L1949 **RHU** *020 †20

BERCZ, Peter Andras. ■ 19063 #473-03-1998 L2004 **IM** *020 †20

BETHEL, Courtney Ann. 142 E KNOWLTON RD 19063 #021-01-1983 L1988 **EM OM** *016

BHULLAR, Navneet. ■ 19063 #495-03-1995 L1998 **IM** *020 †20

BOGUCKI, Edwin I. 1223 N PROVIDENCE RD 19063 #028-34-1972 L1974 **PD** *071 †55

BOOR, John Wm. 1068 W BALTIMORE PIKE 19063 #041-14-1973 L1974 **N** *020 †75

BOSACCO, David Nicholas. 1088 W BALTIMORE PIKE 19063 #041-09-1960 L1961 **ORS OSS** *020 †40 ‡

BOYD, Kenneth John. 1088 W BALTIMORE PIKE, STE 2101 19063 #056-06-1980 L1986 **CRS GS** *020 †10,85 ‡

BRASLOW, Norman Harris. 1098 W BALTIMORE PIKE, STE 3402 19063 #041-02-1973 L1978 **PUD CCM** *020 †20

BROD, Robert Colton. 1098 W BALTIMORE PIKE, STE 3311 19063 #035-08-1956 L1958 **FPG CD** *072 †20

BROOKS, John. ■ 19063 #035-08-1950 L1975 **OBG** *071 †30

BRUNSINK, Kimberly Renee. ■ 19063 #033-06-1993 L2006 **FM** *020 †18

BURKE, Marie T E. ■ 19063 #041-07-1952 L1953 **OS** *071 †30

BURSTEIN, Stephen Robt. 4 STATE RD, # 510 19063 #016-02-1973 L2001 **PD** *020 †55

CABRERA, Linda Schaller. ■ 19063 #021-05-1990 L2001 **IM** *020 †20

CALEB, Mae Helen. 1068 W BALTIMORE PIKE 19063 #041-01-1975 L1977 **IM AI** *020

CAMERON, Donald Drews. ■ 19063 #048-04-1968 L1969 **R** *020 †80

CARLUCCI, Ronald Jos. 720 SUMMER ST 19063 #030-06-1960 L1961 **FM** *072 †85

CELLINI, Lucetti Luke. 176 S NEW MIDDLETOWN RD, CENTER FOR FAMILY HEALTH 19063 #561-17-1967 L1968 **FM FSM** *012

CHALFIN, Richard F. ■ 19063 #308-07-1982 L1985 **IM IMG** *020 †20

CHAN, Edward Fung. 101 CHESLEY DR 19063 #024-01-1994 L1999 **D** *020 †15

CHANG, Andrew J. ■ 19063 #041-13-2006 L2006 **GS** *012

CHANG, Eugene Eng-June. 41 CEDAR HILL LN 19063 #385-03-1964 L1973 **IM PTH** *071 †50

CHANG, Susan Soojin. 109 COVE LN, 801 OSTRUM STREET 19063 #041-13-1997 L2004 **GS** *020 †85

CHAVEZ, Hector. ■ 19063 #649-04-1951 L1964 **GS AN** *071

CHEN, Tse-Ping. ■ 19063 #242-26-1944 L1961 **AN** *071

CHEN, Wei-Fan. ■ 19063 #244-02-1960 L1974 **FM EM** *071

CIANCIULLI, Francis Danl. 1068 W BALTIMORE PIKE 19063 #041-09-1965 L1966 **PUD IM** *071 †20

COLOMBO, James Laurence. 1088 W BALTIMORE PIKE, STE 2405 19063 #561-17-1964 L1966 **PS** *020 †65

CONNER, J Hubert. 411 N MIDDLETOWN RD, # D202 19063 #041-02-1955 L1957 **OS** *071 †40

CONSTANTINE, Jay. 100 W 6TH ST, STE 5 19063 #041-09-1980 L1981 **END IM** *020 †20

COWNIE, Douglas Heron. 411 N MIDDLETOWN RD # D 19063 #067-01-1944 L1957 **P** *071

CZUBAROFF, Valentine B. 1098 W BALTIMORE PIKE 19063 #024-07-1969 L1970 **P** *020

DALLARA, Charles Allen. 1068 W BALTIMORE PIKE, # 2507 19063 #041-02-1988 L1992 **GS** *020 †85

DARBY, Janine Massa. 1068 W BALTIMORE PIKE 19063 #041-13-2004 L2004 **FM** *100

DE CAESTECKER, Jacques E. 1098 W BALTIMORE PIKE, STE 3415 19063 #165-02-1963 L1967 **U** *020 †95

DEIRMENGIAN, Gregory Krik. ■ 19063 #041-01-2004 L2004 **ORS** *012

DE LONE, Francis Xavier, Jr. 1088 W BALTIMORE PIKE, STE 2405 HEALTHCARE CTR II 19063 #041-02-1977 L1978 **PS HS** *020

DENNY, Sharon Therese. ■ 19063 #041-13-1970 L1971 **PM** *020 †60

DER KRIKORIAN, Hagop L. 1098 W BALTIMORE PIKE, STE 3306 19063 #605-01-1975 L1978 **NS** *020

DI MAGGIO, Olivia T. 100 GRANITE DR, STE 200 19063 #041-09-1976 L1977 **PD** *020 †55

DI NICOLA, Michelle Maria. 1068 W BALTIMORE PIKE 19063 #041-02-1995 L1998 **EM** *020 †16

DIVINCENZO, Joseph John. 100 YEARSLEY MILL RD 19063 #041-01-1992 L1994 **P** *020 †75

DIWAN, Kanta. 211 N MONROE ST 19063 #495-54-1967 L1976 **GP** *020

DIWAN, Satyendra Kumar. 211 N MONROE ST 19063 #495-54-1966 L1974 **P PYG** *020 ‡

DIXIT, Ujwala. 200 N MONROE ST 19063 #495-21-1979 L1997 **CHP** *020 †75

DONNENFELD, Alan Erwin. 1068 W BALTIMORE PIKE 19063 #032-01-1981 L1982 **CG OBG** *020 †19,30 ‡

DRUCKER, John Jos. 1343 W BALTIMORE PIKE, APT E218 19063 #035-20-1943 **PD** *071 †55

EBERLY, David Eugene. 605 W STATE ST 19063 #035-03-1976 L1977 **IM** *020 †20

EGAN, Christine Lynn. 101 CHESLEY DR, THE GEORGETOWN BLDG SUITE 19063 #041-09-1992 L1995 **D** *020 †15

EISENHOWER-TURNER, E S. 1078 W BALTIMORE PIKE, HEALTH CARE CTR I STE 206 19063 #041-02-1977 L1978 **P PYG** *075

ELCOCK-MESSAM, June E. 920 N PROVIDENCE RD, 1ST FL 19063 #041-07-1997 L2000 **PD** *020 †55

FAGAN, Matthew John. 1098 W BALTIMORE PIKE, OUTPATIENT PAVILION SUITE 19063 #041-02-1999 L2006 **OBG** *020 †30

FEEHERY, John Michael. 1098 W BALTIMORE PIKE, STE 3406 19063 #041-02-1996 L1999 **OTO** *020 †45

FELSHER, Jonathan Caleb. 1088 W BALTIMORE PIKE, STE 2403 19063 #035-06-1980 L1985 **CD** *020 †20

FERNANDES, Carolyn Rodney. ■ 19063 #496-44-2002 L2007 **IM** *012

FINK, Albert H, Jr. 605 W STATE ST 19063 #041-09-1981 L1982 **IM** *020 †20

FISCHER, Steven William. 1098 W BALTIMORE PIKE, STE 3406 19063 #041-02-1967 L1968 **OTO A** *020 †45

FOAD, Fazl Ahmad. ■ 19063 #118-01-1962 L1973 **EM HEM** *020 †20,16 ‡

FREIDUS-KATZ, Lauren Sue. 107 CHESLEY DR, CARE 19063 #041-09-1982 L1983 **P PYA** *020 †75

GALIB, Emile Hanna. 1088 W BALTIMORE PIKE, RMH HCC II STE 2306 19063 #035-15-1975 L1976 **OTO HNS** *020 †45

GARTHWAITE, Thos Leonard. ■ 19063 #041-13-1973 L1974 **END IM** *020 †20

GARTNER, William Sawyer, Jr. 1098 W BALTIMORE PIKE, STE 3406 19063 #041-13-1963 L1964 **OTO** *071 †45

GATTER, Robert Ashley. 1098 W BALTIMORE PIKE, STE 3408 19063 #041-12-1957 L1958 **RHU IM** *071 †20

GAUDET, Alison Derow. 100 GRANITE DR, STE 200 19063 #041-12-2000 L2001 **PD** *020 †55 ‡

GERSON, Andrew Gerald. 1068 W BALTIMORE PIKE 19063 #041-13-1980 L1981 **MFM OBG** *020 †30 ‡

GESSEL, Arnold Hadley. ROYLENCROFT LN 19065 #041-01-1958 L1959 **P** *071

GIBBONS, Jacquelyn Hayes. 100 GRANITE DR STE 200 19063 #041-13-1961 L1962 **PD GP** *020

GOODKIN, Michael Bruce. 1088 W BALTIMORE PIKE, STE 2403 19063 #033-05-1975 **CD IM** *020 †20

GOPALAKRISHNAN, Raman Nur. 101 FAWN HILL LN, ST. JONES CENTER FOR BEHAV 19063 #495-01-1994 L2002 **P** *020

GOSTIGIAN, John John. 1068 W BALTIMORE PIKE 19063 #041-02-1956 L1957 **GS GE** *020 †85

GRAUDUSIUS, Ruta Terese. ■ 19063 #033-06-1979 L1980 **RHU IM** *020

GUERZON, Roque P. 1068 W BALTIMORE PIKE, RIDDLE MEMORIAL HOSPITAL 19063 #748-07-1968 L1978 **GS N** *020

GURIJALA, Lalitha. 1078 W BALTIMORE PIKE, HEALTH CARE CENTER I SUITE 19063 #495-58-1971 L1977 **P** *020 †75

GURNANEY, Harshad Govindr. ■ 19063 #496-38-1997 L2001 **AN** *100 †05 ‡

HAGG, Beena J. 1068 W BALTIMORE PIKE 19063 #041-09-1993 L1998 **DR** *020 †80

HALENDA, J Ronald. 1098 W BALTIMORE PIKE, STE 3401 19063 #041-02-1957 L1958 **PD ID** *020 †55

HALLAHAN, John Dallas. ■ 19063 #041-13-1944 L1945 **IM** *071 †20

HALOSKIE, Jessica Lindsey. ■ 19063 #041-02-2005 L2005 **FP** *012

HARDY, Willie Lee, Jr. 20 CARNOUSTIE WAY 19063 #033-05-1983 L1986 **AN** *020 †05

HATTI, Shivkumar Shivappa. 107 CHESLEY DR, CARE 19063 #496-38-1974 L1978 **P PYA** *020

HAUGHEY, Robt Emmett, Jr. 1068 W BALTIMORE PIKE, RIDDLE MEMORIAL HOSP 19063 #041-13-1977 L1978 **AN EM** *020 †05,16

HAUSER, Martin. 1068 W BALTIMORE PIKE, RIDDLE MEMORIAL HOSP 19063 #041-13-1965 L1969 **R** *020

HAYES, Timothy Jos. 1098 W BALTIMORE PIKE, OP PAVILION STE 3304 19063 #041-13-1985 L1986 **GS** *020

HECKSHER, Rudolph H. ■ 19063 #041-02-1943 L1948 **GS** *071 †85

HENDERSON, Vicki Lynn. 1400 N PROVIDENCE RD SU, ROSE TREE CENTER 19063 #003-01-1994 L2006 **FM** *020 †18

HOLFORD, Fred De Witt. ■ 19063 #050-02-1956 L1974 **CD IM** *071 †20

HUSTED, Evan Edmund. ■ 19063 #010-01-2007 *012

INGERSOLL-WENG, E. 1068 W BALTIMORE PIKE 19063 #005-18-1999 L2005 **IM** *020 †05

INYAMA, Beatrice Chukumba. 1400 N PROVIDENCE RD, STE 1025 19063 #041-07-1998 L2006 **FM IM** *020 †18

JACOB, Thomas Charles. 1088 W BALTIMORE PIKE, STE 2405 HEALTHCARE CTR II 19063 #041-02-1985 L1987 **PS** *020 †85,65

JAEGER, Edward Abbott. 1098 W BALTIMORE PIKE, STE 3302 19063 #041-12-1957 L1958 **OPH** *020 †35

JAHNLE, Richard Lawrence. 1068 W BALTIMORE PIKE 19063 #041-02-1982 L1983 **OPH** *020 †35 ‡

JALALI, Aman. ■ 19063 #041-13-2007 L2007 *012

JAMALI, Anmar Ali. 1098 W BALTIMORE PIKE 19063 #528-01-1969 L1973 **IM** *020

JOHNSON, Jaime Brynne. ■ 19063 #041-02-2008 L2008 *012

JOHNSON, Jennifer Maria. ■ 19063 #041-12-2008 *012

JOHNSTON, Robert Henry. ■ 19063 #041-01-1941 L1942 **GP PUD** *071

JONES, Ancil Arthur. 1088 W BALTIMORE PIKE, STE 2403 19063 #008-01-1974 L1981 **CD** *020 †20

JOSEPH, Samuel I. ■ 19063 #025-07-1947 L1951 **AN** *071 †05

KANCHWALA, Rashida N. 1068 W BALTIMORE PIKE, OPP STE 3304 19063 #495-74-1974 L1983 **OBG** *020 †30

KANEHANN, Lisa Basheda. 1068 W BALTIMORE PIKE 19063 #041-13-1986 L1988 **DR** *020 †80

KAPLAN, Jennifer Harris. ■ 19063 #048-12-1998 L2001 **NPM** *020 †55

KASARDA, Lynnanne. 176 S NEW MIDDLETOWN RD, CENTER FOR FAMILY HEALTH 19063 #041-02-1987 L1988 **FM** *020 †18

KAUR, Sukhjinder. ■ 19063 #495-37-2002 L2006 **IM** *012

KENT, Patricia. 101 CHESLEY DR, GEORGETOWN BLDG 201 19063 #048-13-1985 L1994 **P** *020 †75 ‡

KESSLER-CONSTANTINE, G. 100 W SIXTH ST, STE 5 19063 #041-13-1981 L1982 **RHU** *020 †20

KHELLA, Lewis. 1068 W BALTIMORE PIKE 19063 #330-02-1940 L1968 **PM** *071 †60

KHUZEMA, Abdulla K. ■ 19063 #495-20-1974 L1986 *020

KIM, Bonnie B. 1088 W BALTIMORE PIKE, HEALTH CTR 2 STE 2206 19063 #583-03-1970 L1977 **OBG** *020

■ = Address Information Privacy Protected

KIM, Eun Ae. ■ 19063 #051-04-2005 L2005 **FP** *012
KLEIMAN, David Steven. 176 S NEW MIDDLETOWN RD 19063 #041-01-1995 L1997 **PD** *020 †55 ‡
KLEIN, Thomas Edward. 1088 W BALTIMORE PIKE 19063 #035-03-1980 L1983 **AI PD** *020 †55,03
KNAPP, Richard Dominick. 600 N JACKSON ST 19063 #035-45-1958 L1965 **P PYA** *071 †75
KOLY, Diep Ngoc. ■ 19063 #028-46-1996 L1997 **IM** *100
KOSTAL, Michael John. ■ 19063 #033-06-2002 L2006 **CD** *012 †20
KOZIN, William. 112 COVE LN, STE 21 19063 #041-13-1960 L1961 **FM OBG** *020 †18
KRACKOW, Joel Arnold. 1088 W BALTIMORE PIKE, STE 2403 19063 #023-01-1966 L1970 **CD** *020 †20
KUNZ, Robert Allison. 1068 W BALTIMORE PIKE 19063 #041-13-1987 L1989 **EM** *020 †16
KWAPIEN, Frederic Jos. 1048 W BALTIMORE PIKE, # J-306 19063 #024-07-1954 L1956 **P** *071 †75
LABORDA, Oscar Enrique. 1088 W BALTIMORE PIKE, STE 2407 19063 #132-01-1965 L1975 **GE** *020 †20
LASKAS, John J. 605 E BALTIMORE PIKE, STE 205 19063 #041-01-1945 L1946 **D** *072 †15
LASKAS, John Jos, Jr. 101 CHESLEY DR STE 100 19063 #041-02-1972 L1973 **D** *020 †15 ‡
LAWSON, Ericka G. ■ 19063 #041-15-1999 L2001 **END** *100 †20
LEE, Tigerlily Justine. 176 S NEW MIDDLETOWN RD 19063 #023-07-1996 L1998 **PD** *020 †55
LEHMICKE, Albert John. 1098 W BALTIMORE PIKE, STE 3403 19063 #038-40-1973 L1976 **PD** *020 †55
LEUNISSEN, Reinhard L A. 1078 W BALTIMORE PIKE, RIDDLE HEALTH CARE CENTER 19063 #660-06-1957 L1971 **IM CD** *020
LEVIN, Alicia Anne. ■ 19063 #041-01-2007 L2007 **TY** *012
LEVIN, Norman Paul. 1068 W BALTIMORE PIKE, RIDDLE MEM HOSP 19063 #041-02-1976 L1977 **PTH** *050
LEWIS, Walter Edwin. 1088 W BALTIMORE PIKE, STE 2208 19063 #041-02-1993 L1995 **FM** *020 †18
LI, Weiye. 311 E BALTIMORE PIKE 19063 #243-69-1969 L1995 **OPH OS** *020 ‡
LINDENBAUM, Connie Ruth. ■ 19063 #041-13-1982 L1983 **OBG** *020 †30
LINDHOLM, Robert Norman. 1098 W BALTIMORE PIKE, STE 3307 19063 #026-04-1963 L1986 **OTO AI** *020 †45,03 ‡
LIPCIUS, Frank. ■ 19063 #041-09-1943 L1944 **FM OM** *071 †18
LITTMAN, Jeffrey Jay. 401 HIGHLAND AVE, 401 HIGHLAND AVENUE 19063 #035-46-1978 L1981 **AN CCM** *020 †05
LIU, Evan Young. ■ 19063 #041-02-1984 L1987 **FM** *062 †18
LOURIE, Eli Matthew. ■ 19063 #038-06-1995 L1998 **PD** *020 †55
LUCENA, Ernesto Erice. 1068 W BALTIMORE PIKE, RIDDLE MEMORIAL HOSPITAL 19063 #748-01-1962 L1970 **R** *020 †80
LUDWIG, Noelle Christiane. 1088 W BALTIMORE PIKE, STE 2303 19063 #041-09-1993 L1997 **OBG** *020 †30
MATTHEWS, Herbert H, Jr. 1068 W BALTIMORE PIKE 19063 #008-02-1973 L1974 **EM IM** *020 †20,16
MATTILA-EVENDEN, Marja El. ■ 19063 #374-01-1996 L2004 **P** *012
MC CARTHY, Michael John. 2978 N PROVIDENCE RD 19063 #041-01-1976 L1977 **P PYA** *020 †75
MCCURDY, Richard R, Jr. ■ 19063 #041-02-2002 L2002 **CD** *012 †20
MC CURDY, Richard Ross. 1088 W BALTIMORE PIKE, STE 2500 19063 #041-02-1972 L1973 **CD IM** *020 †20
MC FARLAND, Joseph Peter. 1078 W BALTIMORE PIKE, STE 204 19063 #016-43-1973 L1974 **D** *020 †15 ‡
MC KEE, Thomas V. RMH HEALTH CARE CENTER 19063 #041-01-1953 L1954 **OBG** *071 †30
MCLAUGHLIN, Joseph Franci. ■ 19063 #041-02-2008 L2008 *012
MC NAMARA, Cathryn Anne. 605 W STATE ST, DELAWARE COUNTY 19063 #035-45-2002 L2007 **IM** *020 †20
MCNEILL, Maria Palatucci. 1098 W BALTIMORE PIKE, STE 3302 19063 #041-02-2003 L2003 **OPH** *012
MIELCAREK, Leon M, Jr. 319 W STATE ST 19063 #041-02-1962 L1963 **OPH** *020 †35
MILLER, Susan Kravitz. 176 S NEW MIDDLETOWN RD 19063 #041-01-1987 L1989 **PD** *020 †55 ‡
MISHALOVE, Robert David. 1088 W BALTIMORE PIKE, STE 2403 19063 #041-01-1966 L1967 **CD** *020 †20
MONTE, D Marie. ■ 19063 #041-07-1964 L1965 **GP** *071
MORROW, Jannette Alethea. 1098 W BALTIMORE PIKE, STE 3101 19063 #038-41-1984 L2006 **IMG IM** *020 †20
MUDGIL, Shikha. 1068 W BALTIMORE PIKE 19063 #041-13-1994 L2002 **DR** *020 †80
MULVANEY, Denise Ann. 176 S NEW MIDDLETOWN RD 19063 #041-09-1988 L1991 **FM** *020 †18
NARDELLA, Guy Michael, Jr. 1088 W BALTIMORE PIKE, STE 2405 HEALTHCARE CTR II 19063 #041-02-1974 L1975 **PS HS** *020 †85,65
NEGREY, John Nicholas. 1068 W BALTIMORE PIKE 19063 #041-13-1968 L1969 **OPH** *020 †35
NONACK, Peter Borger. 605 W STATE ST, PETER B NONACK MD 19063 #041-09-1985 L1986 **IM** *020 †20
OBERFIELD, William Jay. 19 E SECOND ST 19063 #024-07-1971 L1972 **P** *020 †75
O'FLYNN, Richard Paul. 1068 W BALTIMORE PIKE 19063 #041-09-1987 L1989 **AN PME** *020 †05 ‡
PALENA, Peter Vincent. 1098 W BALTIMORE PIKE, OUTPATIENT PAVILION, STE 3 19063 #041-02-1963 L1964 **OPH** *030 †35 ‡
PARIKH, Samir N. 1088 W BALTIMORE PIKE, STE 2101 19063 #035-03-1994 L1996 **CRS** *020 †85,10 ‡
PARK, Lauren Rae. ■ 19063 #041-02-2006 L2006 **PTH** *012
PATEL, Prakash C. ■ 19063 #917-08-1983 L1986 **CD CCM** *020 †20
PERLOFF, Joel Robert. 1098 W BALTIMORE PIKE, STE 3406 19063 #041-01-1999 L2001 **OTO** *020 †45
PETRIDES, Anastasia B. 3 CHESLEY DR 19063 #041-07-1960 L1963 **PD CHN** *020 †55
PFEIFFER, Michael Paul. ■ 19063 #041-02-2006 L2006 **IM** *012
PIRAINO, Anthony Jos. 172 DAM VIEW RD, ASTRAZENECA PHARMACEUTICAL 19063 #041-09-1984 L1986 **AN** *020
POLLACK, David Mark. 176 S NEW MIDDLETOWN RD 19063 #035-01-1979 L1983 **PD** *020 †55 ‡
PONTELL, Jonathan. 101 CHESLEY DR, GEORGETOWN BLDG 19063 #041-02-1989 L1999 **FPS** *020 †45
PRATT, Loretta. 110 CHESLEY DR 19063 #035-47-1982 L1988 **D IM** *020 †20,15 ‡
PRESTIFILIPPO, Rita Elyse. ■ 19063 #041-02-1992 L1995 **PD** *020 †55
RA, Hong Shik. 1068 W BALTIMORE PIKE, RIDDLE MEM HOSP 19063 #033-05-2002 L2002 **CD** *012 †20

RACE, Betsy Godfrey. 100 GRANITE DR, STE 200 19063 #041-13-1995 L1997 **PD** *020 †55
RAO, Srikantha Lakshminar. 340 MEDIA STATION RD 19063 #496-39-1994 L2001 **AN** *020 †05
RAO, Vara Sukhavasi. 1098 W BALTIMORE PIKE, STE 3403 19063 #495-96-1993 L1999 **PD** *020 †55
RECH, Frank Morton. 1098 W BALTIMORE PIKE, STE 3406 19063 #041-13-1960 L1964 **OBG** *071 †30
RENDIN, Larry James. ■ 19063 #041-09-1943 L1944 **GP** *071
RHOOD, Samuel Geo. 1831 KIMBERWICK RD, ROSE TREE 19063 #041-13-1958 L1959 **AN** *071 †05
RIGGS, Karen Pearce. 101 CHESLEY DR, STE 100 19063 #023-01-2004 L2004 **D** *012
RINGIEWICZ, Paul Anthony. 1223 N PROVIDENCE RD, STE 301 19063 #422-01-1981 L1984 **PD** *020
RIVERA, Aida Navidad. ■ 19063 #748-07-1976 **P** *100
ROAT, Melvin Israel. 319 W STATE ST 19063 #065-01-1981 L1985 **OPH OS** *020 †35
ROBERTS, Nancy S. 1068 W BALTIMORE PIKE 19063 #041-02-1976 L1977 **MFM OBG** *020 †30
ROOTENBERG, Pamela. 35 INDIAN SPRING RD 19063 #836-01-1984 L1992 **P CHP** *020 †75
ROTH, Christopher Geordie. 1068 W BALTIMORE PIKE, RIDDLE MEMORIAL HOSPITAL 19063 #051-04-1997 L2002 **DR** *020 †80
RUBIO, Emir. 5130 PENNELL RD 19063 #737-03-1967 L1973 **FM** *020 †18
RUSSELL, Eric Marc. ■ 19063 #041-77-2007, ▲ L2007 **IM** *012
RUSSELL, Kamal Bowan. 1068 W BALTIMORE PIKE 19063 #041-07-1979 L1981 **DR OS** *020 †80
SAFI, Abdul-R. 1068 W BALTIMORE PIKE 19063 #875-01-1972 L1979 **GS GP** *020
SALAND, David K. 411 MANCHESTER AVE, MADISON STE 310 19063 #035-01-1966 L1967 **ORS LM** *020
SALKIND, Gary David. 1400 N PROVIDENCE RD, ROSE TREE CORP CTR 2 19063 #041-13-1980 L1982 **FM FPG** *020 †18
SAMMARITANO, Renee Maria. 176 S NEW MIDDLETOWN RD 19063 #035-20-1989 L1991 **PD** *020 †55
SCHOTT, C Richard. 1088 W BALTIMORE PIKE, STE 2403 19063 #041-09-1970 L1971 **CD IM** *020 †20
SCHUBERT, Mary. 415 N PROVIDENCE RD, PROVIDENCE MEDICAL CENTER 19063 #041-09-1990 L1993 **IM** *020 †20
SEENEY, Sueny Maria. 1098 W BALTIMORE PIKE, STE 3106 19063 #041-13-1990 L1993 **OBG** *020 †30
SESTOKAS, Onile Vaitkus. 15 CHRISTINE LN, NEUROMONITORING MED SV LLC 19063 #024-05-1979 L1995 **IM** *020 †20 ‡
SHAFTO, Carl Richard. 211 N MONROE ST 19063 #041-09-1974 L1975 **P** *020 †75
SHANK, Laura Quarello. ■ 19063 #041-14-2005 L2005 **PD** *012
SHARMA, Madhu. 20 HIGHLAND DR, RIDDLE MEMORIAL HOSPITAL 19063 #495-67-1968 L1977 **P** *020
SHIM, Wan Sup. 1068 W BALTIMORE PIKE 19063 #583-02-1973 L1981 **DR** *020 †80
SHOWELL, Regina M. ■ 19063 #041-01-1973 L1979 **P** *020 †75
SIBINGA, Maarten S. ■ 19063 #660-03-1958 L1960 **GE PD** *071 †55
SIMON, Douglas Seth. ■ 19063 #041-13-1992 L1995 **AN** *020 †05
SINCAVAGE, Joseph Thos. 200 E STATE ST, STE 106 19063 #041-09-1983 L1984 **OBG** *020 †30
SINCLAIR, Stephen Hayward. 311 E BALTIMORE PIKE, 1ST FL 19063 #024-01-1973 L1979 **OPH** *020 †35
SIRIANNI, Archie Jos. 1068 W BALTIMORE PIKE 19063 #041-09-1987 L1999 **AN** *020 †05
SMITH, William Davy. 1068 W BALTIMORE PIKE, STE 2101 19063 #065-01-1946 L1965 **CRS** *071 †85,10
SOCH, Jason Fredrich. 1068 W BALTIMORE PIKE 19063 #026-04-1997 L2004 **AN** *020 †18
SOFFER, Daniel Eric. 605 W STATE ST 19063 #041-01-1994 L1996 **IM** *020 †20
SOLAN, Merrill Joan. 1078 W BALTIMORE PIKE, JEFF RAD ONC AT RIDDLE 19063 #035-03-1975 L1980 **RO PD** *020 †55,80 ‡
SON, Chang Bae. 101 CHESLEY DR STE 100, DERMATOLOGY LTD 19063 #067-01-2001 L2005 **D** *020 †15
SORICELLI, Rhonda Lesley. ■ 19063 #143-03-1971 L1987 **OS IM** *071
SORICELLI, Richard R. 310 CRUM CREEK RD 19063 #041-02-1960 L1961 **NEP IM** *071 †20 ‡
STEIN, Donald B, Jr. 1068 W BALTIMORE PIKE 19063 #041-02-1958 L1960 **PTH NM** *071 †50
STORM, Charles Theodore H. ■ 19063 #041-02-1955 L1956 **AN** *071 †05
STROWHOUER, William Jos. 100 GRANITE DR, STE 207 19063 #041-77-1984, ▲ L1984 **FM NTR** *020
STURMAN, Martin F. ■ 19063 #035-15-1952 L1957 **NM IM** *071 †20,28
SULLIVAN, Edward M. 1078 W BALTIMORE PIKE, STE 207 19063 #041-13-1952 L1973 **GYN** *071 †30
TAUSEEF, Muhammad Asif. ■ 19063 #704-25-2001 L2006 **PD** *012
TEACHEY, Rochelle C. 176 S NEW MIDDLETOWN RD 19063 #035-06-1992 L1995 **PD** *020 †55 ‡
THOMAS, James Anthony, Jr. 1088 W BALTIMORE PIKE, ORTHOPAEDIC ASSOCIATES LTD 19063 #041-02-1960 L1961 **ORS OS** *071 †40
THOMAS, Steven Abbe. ■ 19063 #025-01-1991 *100
THOMAS-PATTERSON, Denne M. 176 S NEW MIDDLETOWN RD, STE 100 19063 #036-08-1998 L2000 **FM** *020 †18
THURMAN, John Neal. 605 W STATE ST 19063 #041-01-1967 L1968 **IM END** *020 †20 ‡
TIRADO, Doris Elsa. 1098 W BALTIMORE PIKE #3106 19063 #649-14-1973 L1994 **OBG** *020 †30
TOBIA, Enio Wm. ■ 19063 #041-02-1946 L1947 **GP** *072
TOGLIA, Marc Richard. 1098 W BALTIMORE PIKE, OUTPATIENT PAVILION 19063 #047-05-1989 L1996 **GYN OS** *020 †30
TOMLINSON, John Wesley. 411 N MIDDLETOWN RD 19063 #041-02-1927 L1929 **OPH** *071 †35
TRABULSI, L Richard. 1088 W BALTIMORE PIKE 19063 #041-02-1964 L1965 **ORS** *020 †40 ‡
TREBELEV, Alexander E. ■ 19063 #041-02-2000 L2001 **VIR** *100 †80
TREMBLAY, Ernest Arthur. 1088 W BALTIMORE PIKE, HCCII STE 2202 19063 #041-13-1956 L1957 **FM GP** *020 †20
TREMBLAY, Geoffrey Peter. 1088 W BALTIMORE PIKE, HCC II STE 2500 19063 #041-13-1983 L1984 **CD IM** *020 †20
VAKIL, Hassan C. 1098 W BALTIMORE PIKE, STE 3411 19063 #517-01-1958 L1969 **GS TS** *020 †85,90
VELOSO, Kathleen. 1068 W BALTIMORE PIKE 19063 #041-13-1987 L1992 **PME AN** *020 †05
VICTORIA, Nenita V. RTE 1 BALTIMORE AVE, RIDDLE MEMORIAL HOSP 19063 #748-01-1967 L1973 **IM HOS** *020
VILLASIS, Henry Arsena. 1068 W BALTIMORE PIKE 19063 #748-01-1972 L1978 **AN** *020
VIOLA, Annette M. 100 GRANITE DR, STE 207 19063 #041-09-1983 L1984 **RO** *071 †80
WALICHUCK, John G. ■ 19063 #041-09-1950 L1951 **OS OM** *071
WANG, Lynn Yiling. 1098 W BALTIMORE PIKE, RIDDLE MEMORIAL HOSPITAL 19063 #041-02-1998 L2000 **OBG** *020 †30
WANG, Tsailing. 1068 W BALTIMORE PIKE, RIDDLE MEM HOSP/LAB 19063 #055-02-1991 L1995 **PTH** *020 †50

WARE, Christopher John. 1068 W BALTIMORE PIKE 19063 #041-15-2000 L2002 **EM** *020
WEAN, Lawrence. 1098 W BALTIMORE PIKE, STE 3304 19063 #041-07-1980 L1981
  IM EM *020 †20 ‡
WEINBERG, Richard Allen. ■ 19063 #016-02-1958 L1962 **D** *071 †15
WERTHEIMER, Marc Joel. 605 W STATE ST 19063 #041-02-1975 L1976 **IM** *020 †20
WHITE, Frank Jos. 1088 W BALTIMORE PIKE, STE 2303 19063 #041-07-1987 L1988
  OBG *020 †20,30 ‡
WICOFF, David Norris. ■ 19063 #035-09-1954 L1956 **P** *071
WOLFE, Kenneth Howard. 100 W SIXTH ST, STE 5 19063 #035-19-1988 L1990 **RHU** *020 †20
WOLFSON, Helen Anne. 1088 W BALTIMOR PIKE #2202, RIDDLE MEMORIAL HOSP HCCII 19063
  #035-15-1991 L1994 **IM** *071 †20
WOOLF, Nancy S Slater. 101 CHESLEY DR, STE 201 19063 #035-19-1968 L1999
  P CHP *020 †75
WRIGHT, William C. ■ 19063 #041-13-1951 L1954 **GS TS** *071 †85
YANEZ, Daria. 1088 W BALTIMORE PIKE, STE 2303 19063 #041-02-1989 L1992 **OBG** *020 †30
YARON, Noemi Susana. 1068 W BALTIMORE PIKE 19063 #132-04-1972 L1980 **PTH** *020 †50
YUM, Sabrini Si Wai. ■ 19063 #243-77-1983 L1996 **CHN** *020 †55,75
ZIEGENFUS, William David. 1088 W BALTIMORE PIKE, STE 2105 19063 #041-02-1961 L1962
  U UP *020

MELROSE PARK – MONTGOMERY

BASS, Amira Munas. ■ 19027 #041-02-2008 *012
COOPERMAN, Michael T. 921 W CHELTENHAM AVE 19027 #035-03-1970 L1976
  IM END *020 †20 ‡
DOUGLASS, Edwin C. ■ 19027 #016-02-1974 L1992 **PHO PD** *020 †55
GOLD, Estelle Melman R. ■ 19027 #041-13-1943 L1944 **PD D** *071 †55
GRAVES, Salina Dunbar. ■ 19027 #041-13-1983 L1984 **FM** *020 †20
ROSEN, Rhoda. 1011 VALLEY RD 19027 #041-01-1958 L1959 **OBG** *071 †30
SIEGLER, Alvin. ■ 19027 #041-09-1944 L1945 **OBG** *020 †30
STUPNIKER, Sonia. ■ 19027 #041-13-1934 L1936 **AI GP** *071 †03

MENDENHALL – CHESTER

COGGINS, Eugene John. GRENNWOOD ROAD 19357 #041-13-1960 L1961 **PD OS** *020 †55

MERCER – MERCER

AOUN, Kamal Habib. 16137 #605-02-1954 L1967 **FM** *071 †18
CERTO, Salvatore A. 868 LATONKA DR 16137 #016-43-1950 L1951 **GS** *071
MINSHULL, James Barton. 23 W CAPE HORN RD 16137 #305-01-1985 L1986 **IM EM** *020 †20

MERCERSBURG – FRANKLIN

GEORGE, Elizabeth A R. 2 KEEFER DR 17236 #043-01-1976 L1980 **FM** *020 †18

MERION STATION – MONTGOMERY

AGOSTI, Yasmeen Mele. ■ 19066 #041-15-2008 *012
BAE, Hannah Yeonsoo. ■ 19066 #041-12-2002 L2002 **NR** *012 †80
BARTOW, Anna Elaine. ■ 19066 #041-01-2002 *100
BEN-MAIMON, Carol S. ■ 19066 #041-02-1985 L1987 **NEP IM** *030 †20
BENSTON, Susan Lee. ■ 19066 #008-01-1979 L1985 **IM** *075
BERMAN, Ellen Jane. ■ 19066 #011-03-1967 L1971 **P** *020 †75
BERMAN, Perry Allen. ■ 19066 #011-03-1964 L1967 **P** *020 †75
BLOOM, Roy Dennis. ■ 19066 #836-01-1983 L1989 **IM NEP** *020 †20
BLYN, Charlotte Lilly. ■ 19066 #041-07-1965 L1968 **P PYA** *071
BRANELLA, Tonino F. ■ 19066 #561-17-1940 L1949 **IM GP** *071
BRIGHTMAN, Signe A. ■ 19066 #041-07-1961 L1969 **ATP** *040 †50
BUCKSTEIN, Michael Hal. ■ 19066 #041-01-2008 *012
CAHILL, Patrick John. ■ 19066 #016-11-2001 L2007 **OSS** *020
CAMARDO, Joseph Saml, Jr. ■ 19066 #041-01-1979 L1987 **IM** *050 †20
COLLINS, Marjeanne. ■ 19066 #041-01-1961 L1962 **ADL** *071 †55
CORN, Benjamin Wm. 335 SYCAMORE AVE, HABER HOME 19066 #024-05-1986 L1987
  RO IM *020 †80
EICHMAN, Mary C Redner. 310 LINDEN LN 19066 #041-01-1945 L1946 **P CHP** *075 †75
EL HABRE, Wassim Gergi. ■ 19066 #913-07-1994 L2004 **GS** *100
ENRIQUEZ, Kristin Eck. ■ 19066 #021-01-2003 L2007 **AN** *020
FIKS, Alexander G. ■ 19066 #024-01-1997 L1999 **PD** *020 †55
FISCHER, Bruce Stuart. ■ 19066 #035-46-2000 L2004 **PHO** *100 †55 ‡
FLAXENBURG, Gary Michael. ■ 19066 #041-09-1978 L1979 **P** *020
FLYNN, John Patrick. ■ 19066 #041-15-2008 *012
FRIEDMAN, Judith Gordon. ■ 19066 #041-07-1982 L1983 **PTH** *020 †50
GARFIELD, Robert Michael. 508 WALDRON TER 19066 #016-06-1971 L1974 **N P** *020 †75
GARTY, Ben Zion. ■ 19066 #561-01-1975 L1986 **AI PUD** *020 †05
GENDZEL, Leonardo. ■ 19066 #187-78-1998 L2003 **PAN** *020 †05
GRANT, Susan Pitt. ■ 19066 #024-05-1973 L1975 **P** *075 †75
HAMMOUDEH, Ziyad Shawkat. ■ 19066 #041-13-2008 *012
HOROWITZ, Janice Abbott. ■ 19066 #041-07-1978 L1980 **P** *075 †75
HUSSEIN, Wiam Ibrahim. ■ 19066 #797-01-1990 L1995 **END IM** *020 †20
KELZ, Max Benjamin. ■ 19066 #008-01-2000 L2004 **AN** *100 †05
KIRSH, David. ■ 19066 #041-01-1940 L1973 **R** *071 †80
KOSTEVA, John Andrew. 510 MONROE RD 19066 #041-13-2002 L2002 **HO** *012 †20
KOTSIS, Eugenia. ■ 19066 #035-46-1982 L1984 **P** *020 †75
LEIBMAN, Joseph Bradley. ■ 19066 #035-46-1986 L1987 **EM GP** *075
LEIBOWITZ, Jason Martin. ■ 19066 #035-19-2005 L2005 **OTO** *012
LISAN, Philip. 468 MERION RD 19066 #041-09-1951 L1952 **CD IM** *071 †20
MAGGE, Sheela Natesh. ■ 19066 #008-01-1998 L2001 **PDE** *100 †55
MAGUIRE, Henry Clinton. 409 N LATCHES LN 19066 #016-02-1983 L1988 **N** *020 †55,75
MAQSOOD, Tahir. 210 MEETING HOUSE LN 19066 #704-05-1985 L1997 **P** *020 †75

MARGOLIN, Gregory. ■ 19066 #041-15-2004 L2004 **OBG** *012
MIANI, Mark Anthony. ■ 19066 #035-03-1980 L2001 **IM EM** *020 †20
MILLER, Laurence Brent. 304 OLD LANCASTER RD, AMBER COUNSELING ASSOC. 19066
  #047-07-1972 L1973 **P CHP** *020 †75
MYERSON, Ralph Mayer. ■ 19066 #024-07-1942 L1953 **GE IM** *062 †20
NELIGAN, Patrick Joseph. ■ 19066 #539-04-1991 L2002 *020
NEWMAN, Andrew Geoffrey. 513 MERCER RD 19066 #305-01-1997 L2001 **AN** *020 †05 ‡
NEWMARK, Jordan Lee. ■ 19066 #041-13-2007 L2007 **IM** *012
OLUGBADEOSEYEMI, Cecilia. ■ 19066 #041-13-2005 L2005 **IM** *100
POSNER, Howard Paul. 728 BEDFORD PL 19066 #035-08-1965 L1977 **IM NTR** *020
RAMOS-TARAMPI, Lourdeline. ■ 19066 #748-01-1969 L1977 **AN OBS** *020 ‡
RAPPAPORT, Elizabeth B. ■ 19066 #024-01-1973 L1990 **PDE PD** *050 †55
RIFKIN, Daniel Scott. ■ 19066 #041-02-1994 L1997 **PDP** *020 †55
RIGG, L Isobel. ■ 19066 #065-01-1943 L1959 **P** *072 †75
ROMAN, Laurian. ■ 19066 #781-01-1948 L1966 **IM CD** *071 †20
ROSS, S Michael. ■ 19066 #010-01-1983 L2001 **PD** *030 †55
ROTH, David Alan. 412 ANDREW RD 19066 #035-08-1985 L1988 **NEP** *020 †20
SCHOTLAND, John Carl. ■ 19066 #041-01-1997 *100
SCHWAB, Charles. ■ 19066 #041-01-2001 L2004 **U** *020
SCHWAB, Sandra Hervey. ■ 19066 #038-45-2000 L2001 **PEM** *020 †55
SCHWARTZ, Leon Eleazer. ■ 19066 #041-09-1985 L1987 **IM** *020 †20
SHEAR, Leroy. ■ 19066 #023-01-1957 L1969 **NEP IM** *071 †20
SIRKEN, Carol Rivie. ■ 19066 #041-01-1967 L1971 **DR** *020 †80
SLOTNICK, Victor Bernard. ■ 19066 #041-02-1965 L1966 **PA FM** *062 †18
SOKIL, Alexis Bohdan. 456 ROCKLAND RD 19066 #023-01-1978 L1983 **CD IM** *020 †20
STOLLMAN, Nachum Burt. ■ 19066 #035-46-2004 L2006 **PD** *100
TAKEDA, Misao. ■ 19066 #572-32-1957 L1970 **PCP ATP** *071 †20
THORNE, Marc Christian. ■ 19066 #028-02-2001 L2006 **PDO** *012 †45
TIRUMALAREDDY, Srinivasa. 225 MEETING HOUSE LN 19066 #495-62-1997 L2002 **IM** *020 †20
VARKI, Roslyn T. ■ 19066 #041-02-1999 L2004 **D** *012 †55
WASSERMAN, Robert. ■ 19066 #023-07-1984 L1986 **PHO PD** *050 †55
WEINRIEB, Robert Murry. ■ 19066 #035-06-1987 L1991 **P** *020 †75
WEISS, Leon Paul. ■ 19066 #035-08-1948 **HEM IG** *050
ZAGER, Ruth P. 237 HAMILTON RD 19066 #048-02-1953 L1956 **CHP P** *020 †55,75
ZASLOFF, Eva Stechel. ■ 19066 #041-01-2006 *012
ZASLOFF, Michael Alan. ■ 19066 #035-19-1973 L1990 **PD** *050 †55,19
ZEBROWITZ, Joseph Robert. ■ 19066 #041-13-1994 L1997 **OBG** *020

MERTZTOWN – BERKS

SHAH, Chandrakant C. 506 WOODSIDE AVE 19539 #495-48-1972 L1981 **EM** *020 †20

MEYERSDALE – SOMERSET

ATWELL, Grant E. 200 HOSPITAL DR 15552 #028-79-1941, ▲ L1958 **GP** *072
DIAZ, Carlos A. 202 BEACHLEY ST, FAMILY HEALTH CARE 15552 #308-05-1986 L1993
  IM *020 †20
POLITO, Joseph R. 200 HOSPITAL DR 15552 #041-09-1983 L1984 **OPH** *020 †35 ‡
ROCK, Leonard L. ■ 15552 #041-12-1950 L1951 **GP** *071

MIDDLEBURG – SNYDER

CRIM, Ryan Charles. 7 DOCK HILL RD, FAMILY PRACTICE CENTER 17842 #010-02-1997 L2000
  FM *071 †18 ‡
GUISER, Lynn Gerald. 7 DOCK HILL RD, FAMILY PRACTICE CENTER, PC 17842
  #041-13-1967 L1968 **GP PHP** *020 ‡
INDERBITZIN, Lawrence Ben. ■ 17842 #025-01-1964 L2001 **P PYA** *071 †75
KREBS, Thomas Allen. 412 W MARKET ST 17842 #041-02-1986 L1988 **FM** *020 †18
ROSARIO, Brenda. 7 DOCK HILL RD, FAMILY PRACTICE CENTER PC 17842 #042-01-2000 L2004
  FM *020 †18

MIDDLETOWN – DAUPHIN

BARNOSKI, John Francis. 1022 N UNION ST 17057 #041-13-1973 L1974 **FM** *020 †18
BERICH, Bridget. 4000 VINE ST, WOODWARD AND ASSOCIATES, P 17057 #041-77-1990,
  ▲ L1991 **OBG** *020 †30
BURD, Mark Douglas. 3100 SCHOOLHOUSE RD, PENN STATE UNIV PHYSICS 17057
  #033-06-1983 L1986 **FM AM** *020 †18
CONROY, Joseph Andrew. ■ 17057 #055-02-2005 L2005 **AN** *012
CURRY, Gwendolyn Zillig. 3100 SCHOOLHOUSE RD 17057 #041-14-1983 L1995
  FM EM *020 †18
CURRY, William Jon. 3100 SCHOOLHOUSE RD, PENN STATE FAMILY HEALTH 17057
  #041-14-1983 L1995 **FM** *020 †18
GRUNDEN, Richard Larry. ■ 17057 #041-14-2008 L2008 *012
HALLIWELL, Brooke. ■ 17057 #022-75-2007, ▲ L2007 **OBG** *012
HAVERSTICK, Charles David. 1022 N UNION ST 17057 #041-14-1987 L1989 **FM OM** *071 †18
HENRY, Cathy Renee. ■ 17057 #041-14-2007 L2007 **GS** *012
LEVINE, Martha Peaslee. 118 AUTUMNWOOD DR 17057 #021-01-1984 L2005 **P** *030 †75
LUPCHO, Christopher. ■ 17057 #041-14-2008 L2008 *012
MAGUIRE, Phillip Hugh. ■ 17057 #035-20-1972 L1974 **FM** *020 †18,16
MANTIONE, John Richard, Jr. 4000 VINE ST, WOODWARD ASSOCIATES 17057
  #041-02-1997 L2000 **OBG** *020 †30
MANWAR, Simone Bilkis. ■ 17057 #041-14-2006 L2006 **OBG** *012
MASTERS, Rebecca Bloyer. 3100 SCHOOLHOUSE RD 17057 #010-01-1991 L1995 **IM** *020 †20
REID, Donald. ■ 17057 #041-13-1956 L1957 **IM PUD** *030
REYNOLDS, Brandon Quayle. ■ 17057 #018-03-2006 L2006 **GS** *012
RIGILAND, John C. 3100 SCHOOLHOUSE RD, MIDDLETOWN OFFICE 17057
  #033-06-1980 L1989 **FM AM** *020 †18
SEGRAVE-DALY, Stephen L. 4000 VINE ST 17057 #041-07-1984 L1986 **OBG** *020 †30
UNGAR, David Rodney. ■ 17057 #051-04-1986 L1993 **PHO** *020 †55
WITMYER, Rachel A. 999 W HARRISBURG PIKE, # 310-T 17057 #041-77-1933, ▲ L1959
  LM *071

■ = Address Information Privacy Protected

WOODWARD, Edward Gerald. 4000 VINE ST, WOODWARD & ASSOC PC 17057 #028-03-1975 L1979 **OBG** *020 †30

MIDLAND – BEAVER

PURTELL, Marcela. 21 7TH ST 15059 #286-13-1996 L2001 **FM** *020 †18

MIFFLIN – JUNIATA

COX, Laurie Ann. HC 67 BOX 6A 17058 #041-07-1987 L1988 **FM** *020 †18
FUOCO, John Jos. HC 67 BOX 6A, JUNIATA FAMILY HELTH CENTE 17058 #041-07-1982 L1985 **FM** *020 †18 ‡
GENC, Salim. ■ 17058 #902-10-1954 L1964 **ORS** *071

MIFFLINBURG – UNION

CHO, Danny Hyun. 137 FOREST HILL RD 17844 #041-13-1994 L1997 **IM** *020 †20
MC GLAUGHLIN, Shawn P. 101 MEADOW GREEN DR 17844 #041-02-1993 L1995 **FM** *020 †18
MUSSER, William Thos. ■ 17844 #041-13-1955 L1956 **GP PUD** *071
PASSI, Vikas. 137 FOREST HILL RD 17844 #033-06-1996 L1999 **FM** *020 †18
WARD, Harold Richard. 101 MEADOW GREEN DR 17844 #041-09-1962 L1963 **GP** *071
WARD, Richard Harold. 101 MEADOW GREEN DR 17844 #038-40-1962 L1962 **OTO** *071 †45

MIFFLINTOWN – JUNIATA

GOSLIN, J Pepper. ■ 17059 #041-77-2001, ▲ L2002 **FM** *020 †18
SHANBAKY, Isis M. HC 63 BOX 48C 17059 #041-13-2002 L2002 **FM** *020 †18

MIFFLINVILLE – COLUMBIA

PATRICK, Thomas Eugene. 210 E MAIN ST 18631 #041-02-1946 L1947 **FM** *071

MILAN – BRADFORD

RANCK, Sidney Graydon, Jr. ■ 18831 #041-12-1969 L1970 **OBG** *071 †30

MILFORD – PIKE

BESSER, Mitchell Jay. 510 ROUTE 6 AND 209 18337 #024-01-1981 L2001 **OBG** *020 †30
BLEWETT, Charles Howell. ■ 18337 #041-09-1968 L1969 **IM** *020
BROOKS, Jane Frances. 510 ROUTE 6 AND 209, STE 2 & 4 18337 #041-07-1970 L1982 **ON HO** *020 †20
BUCKLEY, Marina. 303 W HARFORD ST, FAMILY MEDICINE & DERMATAL 18337 #308-07-1982 L1986 **FM GP** *020
BUCKLEY, Richard E. 303 W HARFORD ST 18337 #422-01-1982 L1986 **IM D** *020
BYADGI, Shalini Chetan. 10 BUIST RD, STE 202 18337 #496-33-1993 L2005 **IM** *020 †20
DROEGE, Gerard Francis. 200 3RD ST 18337 #028-02-1984 L1998 **OBG** *020 †30
EMAMI, Reza. 111 E CATHERINE ST, MILFORD URGENT CARE 18337 #033-06-1991 L2005 **EM FM** *020 †18
GARRISON, David Michael. 111 E CATHERINE ST, STE 2300 18337 #024-05-1989 L1996 **IM** *020 †20
GORRELL, Robert Jos, Jr. 396 ROUTE 6 AND 209, STE 2B 18337 #041-09-1977 L1978 **GS VS** *020 †85
HAINES, Edward Toy. ■ 18337 #016-02-1966 L1968 **FM GS** *071 †85,18
IRIZA, Ecaterina. 405 BROAD ST 18337 #781-01-1991 L1999 **PD** *020 †55
JOHNSON, Robert Alan. 510 ROUTE 6 AND 209, STE 4 18337 #041-09-1991 L1996 **PCC IM** *020 †20 ‡
LA FRANCO, Theresa Ann. 396 ROUTE 6, STE 1A 18337 #033-06-1987 L1988 **PD** *020 †55 ‡
LIMARZI, Joseph A. 111 E CATHERINE ST, MILFORD URGENT CARE CENTER 18337 #561-17-1984 L1996 **EM** *020 †20 ‡
LO, Kathy Kaiyee. 113 POCONO DR, UPPER DELAWARE VALLEY CANC 18337 #041-02-2002 L2007 **RO** *020
MELZER, Patricia Sue. ■ 18337 #041-14-1984 L1991 **PD** *071 †55
MESKIN, Inna. 111 E CATHERINE ST, STE 140 18337 #913-99-1990 L1997 **PD** *020 †55
O'NEILL, Michael Bernard. 111 E CATHERINE ST, STE 140 18337 #033-05-1969 L1991 **PD N** *020 †55
PALYDOWYCZ, Severin B. 510 ROUTE 6 AND 209 STE 67 18337 #033-05-1989 L1993 **OPH** *020 †35
PEGHER, Matthew D. 111 E CATHERINE ST, STE 130 18337 #011-75-1992, ▲ L1994 **EM IM** *020
PINO Y TORRES, Jose Luis. 113 POCONO DR 18337 #847-04-1967 L2005 **RO ON** *020 †20,80
RIVKIN, Matthew Gerald. 111 E CATHERINE ST, MILFORD URGENT CARE 18337 #051-04-1962 L2007 **FM** *020 †18
SCHOLL-GERSON, Catherine. 510 ROUTE 6 AND 209, STE 8 18337 #041-02-1979 L1980 **FM** *020 †18
SEQUEIRA, Ricardo. 111 E CATHERINE ST, P O BOX 1614 18337 #308-03-1981 L2000 **GP** *020 †20
SHISHAK, Aryo A. ■ 18337 #495-45-1966 L1978 **GP** *071
SINGARAVELU, Nila. 200 3RD ST, COMMUNITY MEDICAL CARE 18337 #495-59-1983 L2007 **OBG** *020
SOMMER, Diane Rita Marie. ■ 18337 #035-15-1987 L1989 **FM** *020 †18
VERGARA, Jesus Roberto. 111 E CATHERINE ST, STE 110 18337 #748-02-1981 L1987 **IM** *020 †20
WALDMAN, Albert Louis. 104 W HIGH ST 18337 #038-40-1966 L1991 **P** *020

MILL HALL – CLINTON

DANSKY, Larry Stephen. 7133 NITTANY VALLEY DR 17751 #011-02-1973 L1992 **FM** *020 †18

GREENBERG, Michael R. 7133 NITTANY VALLEY DR, P O BOX 157 17751 #010-01-1969 L1970 **FM MDM** *020 †18
HERBERG, James Peter. 7133 NITTANY VALLEY DR 17751 #026-04-1959 L1960 **EM GP** *020 ‡
MICKENS, Clifford Nolan. ■ 17751 #041-13-1973 L1974 **FM** *020
SIMPSON, Paul Kerry. 7133 NITTANY VALLEY DR 17751 #048-13-1979 L2000 **IM** *020 †20
THOMAS, David Wesley, Jr. PO BOX 157, 7133 NITTANY VALLEY DR 17751 #041-02-1948 L1949 **GS** *071

MILLERSBURG – DAUPHIN

ELLIS, David W. 192 W CENTER ST 17061 #024-16-1980 L1982 **IM** *020
ETTLINGER, Robert Alan. 1000 EVELYN DR, PINNACLE HLTH FAMILY CARE 17061 #033-06-1981 L1982 **FM EM** *020 †18
EVANS, Hilary. 415 WALNUT ST 17061 #048-04-1962 L1976 **PTH** *071 †50
HOTTENSTEIN, Rahn L. ■ 17061 #041-01-1942 L1943 **GP** *071
JORDAN, Herbert V, Jr. 1000 MEDICAL RD, FREDERICK HLTH CTR 17061 #041-02-1946 L1947 **GYN FPG** *071 †30
LONGABAUGH, Edward Espey. 1000 EVELYN DR 17061 #041-12-1947 L1948 **GS** *071 †85
MENDE, William Richard. 1000 EVELYN DR 17061 #016-11-1976 L1977 **GPM NTR** *020 †16
SEIDEL, Frederick James. 1000 EVELYN DR 17061 #035-08-1979 L1980 **IM** *020 †20

MILLERSTOWN – PERRY

ROCHMAN, Alan Jos. 705 E SUNBURY ST 17062 #041-01-1967 L1968 **GP R** *020

MILLERSVILLE – LANCASTER

ALTIMARE, Peter Jos, Jr. 16A MANOR AVE, MANOR FAMILY HEALTH CTR LT 17551 #041-09-1974 L1975 **FM** *020 †18
BAIRD, Robert James. 16A MANOR AVE 17551 #041-13-1973 L1974 **FM** *020 †18
CATANIA, Clifford Phillip. 138 W FREDERICK ST 17551 #041-01-1981 L1982 **EM** *020 †16
EMMERT, David Howard. 16A MANOR AVE 17551 #051-01-1996 L1998 **FM** *020 †18 ‡
GAYESKI, Richard John. 16A MANOR AVE 17551 #051-01-1975 L1976 **FM** *020 †18
ICHTER, Jon Robt. 16A MANOR AVE 17551 #041-13-1981 L1982 **FM** *020 †18
JONES, Julie Lynn. 16A MANOR AVE 17551 #041-14-1983 L1984 **FM** *030 †18
MARKOWITZ, Philip I. 283 LETORT RD 17551 #035-08-1975 L1986 **P** *020 †55
SCHROCK, Jon Harvey. 16A MANOR AVE 17551 #051-01-1979 L1980 **FM** *071 †18
SHERMAN, Christopher John. ■ 17551 #038-44-1986 L1986 **AN** *020

MILLVALE – ALLEGHENY

FRAZER NAGRANT, Erin Cath. ■ 15209 #025-07-2003 L2003 **MPD** *100 †20
HARRIS, Malcolm Stuart. 1099 NORTH AVE 15209 #041-01-1976 L1977 **FM** *020 †18 ‡

MILLVILLE – COLUMBIA

DUBARTELL, Michael L. 515 JERSEYTOWN RD 17846 #035-06-1993 L1995 **FM** *020 †18
WINSKI, Leonard Andrew. PO BOX 10 17846 #041-09-1957 L1958 **FM IMG** *020 †18

MILTON – NORTHUMBERLAND

CHOW, Danquing. 155 S ARCH ST, STE B 17847 #243-45-1990 L2000 **IM** *020 †20
DIX, Robert Clough, Jr. 17847 #041-02-1944 L1945 **FM** *071
FOLLMER, Kristy Denise. ■ 17847 #041-14-2005 L2005 **EM** *012
GRAMMES, Charles F. ■ 17847 #041-13-1957 L1958 **DIA END** *071 †20
MATURANI, Larry Joe. 550 MAHONING ST 17847 #422-01-1997 L2002 **IM** *020 †20
ROHRER, George Redsecker. 155 S ARCH ST 17847 #041-02-1982 L1983 **FM EM** *020 †18
SNOVER, Seth Wm. 155 S ARCH ST, STE B 17847 #010-01-1972 L1973 **OM IM** *071 †20,16,70
THEIN, Win. 155 S ARCH ST, GEISINGER HEALTH GROUP-MIL 17847 #209-01-1987 L1994 **FM** *020 †18
TRESSLER, Sandra Beall. 155 S ARCH ST, STE B 17847 #027-01-1977 L1986 **PD** *020 †55

MINERAL POINT – CAMBRIA

RAGER, Allison R. ■ 15942 #036-07-2007 **IM** *012

MINERSVILLE – SCHUYLKILL

DI NICOLA, Arthur N. 28 SUNBURY ST 17954 #041-02-1957 L1958 **GP** *071
TAVARIA, Soli Feradoon. 105 N DELAWARE AVE 17954 #495-96-1970 L1974 **IM CD** *020 †20 ‡

MOHNTON – BERKS

HOROWITZ, Jeffrey A. ■ 19540 #035-48-1997 L2000 **GS** *020
JONES, Rebecca Keene. ■ 19540 #041-01-1991 L1993 **OBG** *020 †30
KENNEDY, Edward Richard. ■ 19540 #041-09-1969 L1982 **IM ORS** *020 †16
REED, Ronald Wm. ■ 19540 #041-13-1972 L1973 **EM IM** *020
ROBEL, David Kawika. 226 E WYOMISSING AVE, MIFFLIN AREA MEDICAL CENTE 19540 #023-01-2000 L2001 **FM** *020 †18

MOHRSVILLE – BERKS

GILLIS, Tiffany Anne. ■ 19541 #041-02-2003 L2007 **EM** *020
STELTZ, Michael David. ■ 19541 #033-06-1985 L1986 **R** *020 †80 ‡
YOUNGBERG, Russell E. ■ 19541 #005-12-1949 L1960 **PM** *071

■ = Address Information Privacy Protected

MONACA – BEAVER

ALTMAN, Kevin Chas. 3452 BRODHEAD RD 15061 #017-20-1985 L1989 **N** *020 †75
ANDERSON, Garland. ■ 15061 #041-13-1960 L1967 **OM** *071
ASHFAQ, Sarmad. ■ 15061 #704-20-1998 L2005 **FP** *012
BOWERS, Richard Allen. 95 GOLFVIEW DR, STE A 15061 #041-09-1986 L1987 **OPH** *020 †35
CAREY, John Timothy. 3452 BRODHEAD RD 15061 #041-12-1971 L1972 **N P** *020 †75
COLPO, Jennifer Lyn. ■ 15061 #041-77-2004, ▲ L2004 **FM** *020 †18
COOMBS, Matthew Britt. 3950 BRODHEAD RD, STE 200 15061 #143-05-1996 L2000 **FM** *020 †18
KASI, Nagamani K. 3542 BRODHEAD RD 15061 #495-33-1978 L1982 **PD** *020 †55
KRISHNA KUMAR, Kasi A. 3542 BRODHEAD RD 15061 #496-01-1973 L1981 **PD END** *020 †55
KRUCZEK, Michael W. 90 WAGNER RD, VETERANS ADMINISTRATION CL 15061 #024-16-1990 L1992 **FM EM** *020 †18
LEW, Chung Moo. 1414 PENNSYLVANIA AVE 15061 #583-01-1947 L1974 **GP EM** *072
MONYAK, John G. ■ 15061 #010-01-1952 L1957 **GP GS** *071
WHARTON, Keith Hamilton. 3572 BRODHEAD RD, STE 301 15061 #055-02-1981 L1985 **OBG** *020 †30
WILCOX, Simmon. 3428 BRODHEAD RD 15061 #035-48-1982 L1985 **FM** *020 †18

MONESSEN – WESTMORELAND

FAIRCHILD, Su. EASTGATE 8, PRIMARY CARE CENTER 15062 #041-07-1997 L1999 **FM** *020 †18
LEMENTOWSKI, Michael. 1295 GRAND BLVD 15062 #759-03-1968 L1979 **GS GP** *020 †85
MC CRACKEN-FLAHERT, Dawn. 8 EASTGATE, # 300 15062 #041-12-1993 **PD** *020 †55
NATHANSON, Michael Steven. 1295 GRAND BLVD 15062 #043-01-1984 L1992 **CD IM** *020 †20
PALUSO, Arthur Kendrick. MON VALLEY HTL CTR EGATE, RM 8 15062 #041-02-1959 L1960 **GP** *071
QURESHI, Amer. 301 E DONNER AVE, MON YOUGH MENTAL HEALTH SE 15062 #704-01-1987 L2000 **P** *020 †75
RIPEPI, Jennifer K. EASTGATE 8, MON VALLEY COMM HLTH SVC 15062 #041-12-1986 L1989 **PD** *020 †55
WEISS, Malcolm Stuart. 1295 GRAND BLVD 15062 #041-02-1968 L1969 **FM GPM** *020 †18
WEISS, Paul Irving. 8 EASTGATE 15062 #041-13-1978 L1979 **P IMG** *020 †75

MONONGAHELA – WASHINGTON

ANEJA, Surinder. 1163 COUNTRY CLUB RD 15063 #495-69-1975 L1978 **PUD CCM** *020 †20
BOONVISUDHI, Thumrong. 1163 COUNTRY CLUB RD 15063 #891-02-1966 L1978 **PD** *020 †55
BROUGHER, David Eugene. 1163 COUNTRY CLUB RD 15063 #041-12-1956 L1957 **GYN** *071 †20
CERVONE, Paul Nicholas. 1163 COUNTRY CLUB RD, LOMBARDI CENTER STE 101 15063 #041-12-1987 L1989 **OBG** *020 †30 ‡
CHIU, Robert Jen. 100 STOOPS DR 15063 #035-46-2000 L2001 **OTO** *100 †45
COSTA, Eugene Ernest. 1163 COUNTRY CLUB RD 15063 #041-02-1945 L1946 **GP** *020
COX, Walter Robt. 1163 COUNTRY CLUB RD 15063 #041-02-1986 L1987 **OBG** *020 †30
CUNNINGHAM, Wm Louis, Jr. 1163 COUNTRY CLUB RD 15063 #041-12-1957 L1958 **GS** *071 †85
DANOFF, Mike. 1290 CHESS ST 15063 #041-12-1966 L1967 **CD IM** *020 †20
FARACI, Marie. MON VALLEY HOSP, STE 101 15063 #041-07-1965 L1967 **GYN** *020 †30
FONTANA, Frank Leonard. 100 STOOPS DR, STE 230 15063 #041-12-1954 L1955 **GS** *071 †85
FRANCIS, Elie L. 1163 COUNTRY CLUB RD 15063 #605-01-1999 L2003 **IM** *020 †20
GEORGE, Robert Alexander. 447 W MAIN ST 15063 #020-12-1978 L1979 **GS** *020 †85
HAUSER, John R. 1025 COUNTRY CLUB RD 15063 #561-01-1974 L1976 **GE IM** *020 †20
HERTZOG, Francis Jerome. 1163 COUNTRY CLUB RD, MONONGAHELA HOSP 15063 #041-02-1960 L1961 **EM GS** *020 †85
HOLETS, Henry Ernest, Jr. 1290 CHESS ST 15063 #041-12-1975 L1976 **FM** *020 †18
HOLETS, John Alan. 447 W MAIN ST 15063 #041-13-1982 L1983 **FM** *020 †18
JAIN, Ashok Kumar. 1163 COUNTRY CLUB RD 15063 #495-30-1980 L1988 **IM ID** *020 †20
KILPATRICK, William Ford. 1025 COUNTRY CLUB RD 15063 #041-09-1976 L1978 **IM** *020 †20
KLETKE, Richard Rudolph. 610 PARK AVE 15063 #062-01-1956 L1966 **GP** *020
KOMEN, Supote S. 1025 COUNTRY CLUB RD 15063 #891-04-1973 L1977 **CD IM** *020 †20
KOTWAL, Nirmal Deepak. RT 88 COUNTRY CLUB RD, MONONGAHELA VALLEY HOSP. 15063 #496-38-1973 L1976 **PTH** *020 †50
KRISHNAN, R G. 1025 COUNTRY CLUB RD 15063 #495-04-1971 L1976 **CD IM** *020 †20
LEMIS, Peter M. 1163 COUNTRY CLUB RD 15063 #035-09-1977 L1988 **CD IM** *020 †20 ‡
LIM, Dawson. 1163 COUNTRY CLUB RD, SWEENEY MELENYZER PAVILION 15063 #025-01-1976 L1977 **HEM** *020
LOZANO, Ramon Garcia. 1163 COUNTRY CLUB RD 15063 #748-01-1971 L1977 **NEP IM** *020 †20
MALEPATI, Vasu. 1163 COUNTRY CLUB RD, MONONGAHELA HOSP 15063 #495-70-1974 L1986 **OTO** *020 †45
MATEYA, Dennis Jos. 1163 COUNTRY CLUB RD 15063 #041-12-1987 L1989 **PM OS** *020 †60 ‡
MATHUR, Ajay Kumar. 1029 COUNTRY CLUB RD, STE 203 15063 #495-30-1979 L1984 **RHU IM** *020 †20
NEMANI, Pandharinath. 1163 COUNTRY CLUB RD 15063 #495-21-1961 L1970 **ORS** *071
NICOLO, Enrico. 100 STOOPS DR 15063 #561-17-1972 L1980 **GS** *020 †85
PARENT, Fernand Noel, Jr. 1163 COUNTRY CLUB RD 15063 #041-02-1957 L1958 **GS** *020 †85
RACH, Joel Francis. 900 W MAIN ST 15063 #041-02-1983 L1985 **U** *020 †95
RUSCHAK, Paul Jos. 100 STOOPS DR, STE 220 15063 #041-02-1975 L1976 **D IM** *020 †15
SHROFF, Sanatkumar. 1163 COUNTRY CLUB RD 15063 #495-76-1984 L1993 **IM** *020 †20
SIRRI, Carlo. ■ 15063 #041-01-1949 L1963 **P** *071
SPERGEL, Andrew Laurence. 1163 COUNTRY CLUB RD, STE 101 15063 #035-09-1996 L2000 **OBG** *020 †30
VAZQUEZ, Jorge Luis. 1163 COUNTRY CLUB RD, MONONGAHELA HOSP 15063 #308-03-1981 L1982 **AN** *020 †05
WEBSTER, Corey A. 15063 #055-01-2008 *012
WELDON, John Francis. ■ 15063 #041-12-1957 L1958 **AN GP** *020 †05
WILSON, Douglas Gray. 1163 COUNTRY CLUB RD, MONONGAHELA VALLEY HOSPITA 15063 #011-02-1981 L1988 **NM** *020 †28,80
YOVANOF, Silvana. 420 W MAIN ST 15063 #654-01-1985 L1992 **IM END** *020 †20
ZAHALSKY, Andrew J. 1163 COUNTRY CLUB RD 15063 #043-01-1996 L2001 **HO** *020 †20

MONROEVILLE – ALLEGHENY

AGUILAR, Estuardo. 1105 EAGLES NEST LN 15146 #429-01-1985 L1996 **END** *020 †20
ALMOUKAMAL, Salah Aldin. 1000 INFINITY DR, STE 100 15146 #875-01-1998 L2002 **FM** *020 †18
ALTOP, Haluk. 2570 HAYMAKER RD, FORBES REGIONAL HEALTH CTR 15146 #902-03-1963 L1972 **AN OS** *020 †05
ANOLIK, Steven Lee. 2600 HAYMAKER RD, INTERCOMMUNITY CANCER CENT 15146 #028-02-1986 L1991 **RO** *020 †80
APEL, Amy Louise. 2790 MOSSIDE BLVD, STE 700 15146 #041-07-1984 L1991 **PD** *020 †55
ARIFF, Kabir. 3824 NORTHERN PIKE, STE 500 15146 #495-04-1984 L1998 **IM** *020 †20
ARORA, Anju. 2550 MOSSIDE BLVD, MONROEVILLE MED ASSOC 15146 #495-45-1994 L2004 **IM** *020 †20
ASHTA, Raman. 2570 HAYMAKER RD 15146 #495-03-2003 L2006 **FP** *012
ASMAN, Barry Jay. 2550 MOSSIDE BLVD, STE 202 15146 #001-06-1983 L1986 **AI PD** *020 †55 ‡
AZAR, Michael Jos. 2571 MOSSIDE BLVD 15146 #041-12-1990 L1993 **OPH** *020 †35 ‡
AZIZ, Abdul Rab. 125 DAUGHERTY DR, STE 301 15146 #118-01-1977 L1980 **CD IC** *062 †20
BAILEY, Stephen Ross. 2566 HAYMAKER RD, FORBES REGIONAL HLTH CENTE 15146 #035-08-1972 L1976 **ORS** *020 †40
BALEST, Arcangela Lattari. 2570 HAYMAKER RD, FORBES REGIONAL HEALTH CTR 15146 #041-12-1986 L1987 **NPM PD** *020 †55
BARAN, James John. 2566 HAYMAKER RD STE 206 15146 #041-02-1985 L1986 **CRS GS** *020 †85,10
BEDETTI, Carlos David. 2570 HAYMAKER RD, WESTERN PA HOSP FORBES REG 15146 #132-01-1969 L1976 **PTH ATP** *020 †50 ‡
BERKOWITZ, Fred. 2566 HAYMAKER RD, STE 203 15146 #035-01-1971 L1972 **GS** *071 †85
BIDULA, Maureen Mc Nulty. 2570 HAYMAKER RD 15146 #041-13-1979 L1980 **DR** *020 †80
BISHOP, Kristina Dawn. 3824 NORTHERN PIKE, ONE MONROEVILLE CENTER, #8 15146 #041-15-2002 L2006 **OBG** *020
BRANCEL, Jennifer Anne. 2550 MOSSIDE BLVD 15146 #038-41-1998 L2001 **IM** *020 †20
BRENT, Bradley Harvey. ■ 15146 #041-12-1985 L1988 **PD** *071 †55
BRETHAUER, Edward A, Jr. 2589 MOSSIDE BLVD, # 322 15146 #041-12-1940 L1941 **IM CD** *071 †20
BRINK, Earl James. 4232 NORTHERN PIKE, 204 COMERCE BLDG 15146 #041-12-1962 L1964 **P** *071 †75
BROADHEAD, Richard. 2570 HAYMAKER RD 15146 #041-12-1974 L1975 **IM IMG** *020 †20
BROSTOFF, Leon Michael. 2790 MOSSIDE BLVD, STE 700 15146 #041-01-1979 L1983 **PD** *020 †55
BROUDY, Arnold S. 2550 MOSSIDE BLVD, STE 405 15146 #023-07-1971 L1978 **ORS HS** *020 †40
BUTLER, Christopher L. 1000 INFINITY DR, STE 100 15146 #024-16-1981 L1983 **FM** *020 †18
BYERS, Gerald Thos, III. 1000 INFINITY DR, STE 100 15146 #041-14-1987 L1989 **FM** *020 †18
CAMINOS, Oliverio W. 2490 MOSSIDE BLVD 15146 #132-03-1967 L1975 **CD IM** *020 †20
CARTER, Daniel Jerome. 4318 NORTHERN PIKE, STE 103 15146 #422-01-1982 L1984 **FM** *020 †20
CHAUDHARY, Zahida. ■ 15146 #704-04-1984 *100
CHAUDRY, Jawad U.. ■ 15146 #704-20-1998 *100
CHAUKIYAL, Pooja. ■ 15146 #495-28-1999 L2007 **IM** *020 †20
CHOUGH, Andrew C. ■ 15146 #583-01-1961 L1971 **CD IM** *071 †20
CHRISTIAN, Robert. 600 OXFORD DR, PRIMARY CARE CENTER 15146 #041-12-1978 L1979 **IM** *020 †20
CHUNG, Ki Young. 2570 HAYMAKER RD 15146 #583-08-1978 L1982 **IM** *020 †20
CIGNETTI, Franklin Eugene. 2571 MOSSIDE BLVD 15146 #041-12-1964 L1965 **OPH** *020 †35 ‡
COHEN, Larry Kenneth. 339 OLD HAYMAKER RD, PARKWAY BLDG, SUITE 201 15146 #035-46-1974 L1978 **D** *020 †15
COLANGELO, Francis R. 3824 NORTHERN PIKE, PREMIER MEDICAL ASSOCIATES 15146 #041-02-1984 L1985 **IM** *020 †20
CONTENTO, Anna Marie. 4099 WILLIAM PENN HWY, STE 200 15146 #055-01-1985 L1986 **PTH** *020 †50
COSTA, Frank Jos. 125 DAUGHERTY DR, STE 400 15146 #041-12-1980 L1981 **U** *020 †95 ‡
COSTLOW, James S. 3824 NORTHERN PIKE, STE 500 15146 #041-12-1978 L1979 **IM** *020 †20
CROWELL, Janet Patricia. ■ 15146 #422-01-2005 L2007 **FP** *012
D'ALTORIO, Ronald Anthony. 2570 HAYMAKER RD 15146 #010-01-1963 L1966 **R** *020 †80
DAWSON, Erin Michelle. 2566 HAYMAKER RD 15146 #056-06-2003 L2003 **FM** *100 †18
DE BIASSE, Timothy Albert. 2566 HAYMAKER RD, EAST SUBURBAN PEDIATRICS 15146 #041-02-1977 L1978 **PD** *020 †55
DELANEY, John Francis, Jr. 2570 HAYMAKER RD 15146 #041-12-1964 L1966 **PYG N** *020 †75 ‡
DE LONG, Stephen Richard. 2570 HAYMAKER RD, RADIOLOGY DEPT 15146 #038-41-1972 L1979 **NM** *020 †28 ‡
DHOBALE, Sudhir Dattatray. 2566 HAYMAKER RD 15146 #495-28-1997 L2007 **FP** *012
DI CAPRIO, Michael John. 2570 HAYMAKER RD, DEPT OF EMERGENCY MEDICINE 15146 #041-12-2000 L2003 **EM** *020 †16
DINGESS, Yolanda Edith. 2566 HAYMAKER RD, EAST SUBURBAN PEDIATRICS 15146 #041-07-1988 L1990 **PD** *020 †55
DUA, Aashish. 3824 NORTHERN PIKE, STE 525 15146 #495-45-1994 L1997 **IC CD** *020 †20
DUGGAN, James Hubert. 2580 HAYMAKER RD, STE 200 15146 #041-12-1980 L1981 **OBG** *020 †30
ENGLISH, Dennis Howard. 4075 MONROEVILLE BLVD 15146 #041-12-1976 L1977 **OBG** *020 †30
EVANS, Cynthia Kay. 2580 HAYMAKER RD STE 404, PROFESSIONAL BLDG 2 15146 #020-12-1987 L1988 **ON HEM** *020 †20
FAKHRI, Abid Ali. ■ 15146 #041-15-2007 L2007 **IM** *010
FANDEL, Christa Marie. 2570 HAYMAKER RD, STE 106 15146 #047-05-1983 L1989 **PD** *020 †55
FANG, Charlie Weichin. 1000 INFINITY DR, STE 310 15146 #036-01-1998 L2000 **FM** *020 †18
FISCH, John Morrison. 3824 NORTHERN PIKE, 1 MMONROEVILLE CTR STE 800 15146 #035-06-1984 L1985 **OBG** *020 †30
FISHER, Matthew Charles. 2566 HAYMAKER RD, STE 311 15146 #041-12-2001 L2001 **FSM** *020 †18
FORSTATE, William Jacob. 3824 NORTHERN PIKE, STE 525 15146 #028-02-1979 L1982 **CD** *020 †20
FOWLER, David Paul. 600 OXFORD DR, STE 200 15146 #041-12-1981 L1983 **ORS** *020 †40
FRISCH, Lauren S. 2570 HAYMAKER RD # 1, PEDIATRIC SPECIALTY CENTER 15146 #043-01-1985 L1991 **PDE PD** *020 †55
GALLA-ELIZEUS, Kathy L. 4225 NORTHERN PIKE 15146 #041-07-1995 L1997 **OBG** *020 †30
GANJAM, Satishkumar Muddu. 2570 HAYMAKER RD 15146 #495-99-1998 L2005 **FP** *012

■ = Address Information Privacy Protected

GARFINKEL, Michael David. 2570 HAYMAKER RD, EMERGENCY DEPT. 15146 #041-07-1997 L1999 **EM** *020 †16
GELB, Elaine Sarah. 2566 HAYMAKER RD STE 304 15146 #017-20-1981 L1986 **EM** *020 †16
GOLDBERG, Lisa Ann. 339 OLD HAYMAKER RD, PARKWAY BUILDING, SUITE 20 15146 #041-07-1978 L1981 **D DS** *020 †15
GOWDA, Bhavna Raghavendra. 2566 HAYMAKER RD 15146 #496-21-2002 L2007 **FP** *012
GOWDA, Jeevan Chaythan. ■ 15146 #496-22-2001 L2004 **IM** *100
GUHANAND, Nithya. 2566 HAYMAKER RD 15146 #496-32-1992 L2007 **FP** *012
HABIB, Morcos Wahballa Fa. ■ 15146 #915-04-2000 L2005 **FP** *012
HADEED, Veniece A. 2580 HAYMAKER RD, STE 106 15146 #875-01-1986 L1993 **ON** *020 †20
HANSEN, Michael Morris. 2570 HAYMAKER RD 15146 #010-01-1984 L1988 **IM** *020 †20
HARIKA, Jopinder Pal. ■ 15146 #495-73-1981 L1983 **P** *020
HEJAMADI TATI, Vasudev. ■ 15146 #495-37-2004 L2006 **IM** *012
HENDRICKSON, Ernest S. 2570 HAYMAKER RD 15146 #041-12-1970 L1972 **P GP** *075
HICKMAN, Renee Booker. 2566 HAYMAKER RD 15146 #041-12-1998 L2000 **FM** *020 †18
HO, Lawrence Yih. ■ 15146 #041-12-2004 L2004 *100
HOCA, Renata Dora. 4075 MONROEVILLE BLVD, STE 222 15146 #035-06-1986 L1987 **OBG** *020 †30
HOFFMAN, Rebeccah Alice. 1000 INFINITY DR, STE 100 15146 #036-01-1998 L2000 **FM** *020 †18
HOU, Jing-Zhou. 2571 MOSSIDE BLVD, STE 3 15146 #243-38-1986 L2006 **HEM** *020 †20
HOYT, John Wm. 2570 HAYMAKER RD 15146 #038-41-1971 L1974 **CCA AN** *020 †05 ‡
HRACH, Charles James. 2571 MOSSIDE BLVD 15146 #025-01-1996 L2000 **OPH** *020 †35 ‡
HSU, Gin-Ming. 2380 MCGINLEY RD, STE 01455711 15146 #051-04-1994 L1998 **PM PME** *020 †60
HU, Lin Aung (A) Rex. 2570 HAYMAKER RD 15146 #209-03-2000 L2005 **FP** *012
HUGO, Maryanne. 4075 MONROEVILLE BLVD, STE 222 15146 #041-12-1988 L1990 **OBG** *020 †30
HUSSEIN, Steven Jay. 3824 NORTHERN PIKE, STE 525 15146 #305-01-1998 L2006 **CD** *100 †20
HYNES, Maryann. 3824 NORTHERN PIKE, STE 500 15146 #041-12-1985 L1986 **IM** *020 †20
ISMAIL, Hamza. ■ 15146 #496-26-2003 L2005 **IM** *012
ISSAC, Veronica Elisabeth. ■ 15146 #010-01-2008 *012
JAMBUSARIA, Anokhi Harsha. ■ 15146 #041-13-2006 *012
JETTI, Vamseen. ■ 15146 #041-02-2003 L2003 **AN** *020
JOHNS, Francis Regis. 1 MONROEVILLE MALL STE 100 15146 #041-12-1995 L1997 **PS** *020 †65
JOHNSON, Franklin P. 2570 HAYMAKER RD 15146 #041-12-1952 L1953 **GP** *071
JOSEPH, Elaine Riemer. 4075 MONROEVILLE BLVD, STE 125 15146 #041-12-1977 L1979 **PD** *020 †55
KANAKAMEDALA, Usha. ■ 15146 #035-08-1992 L1997 **DR** *020 †80
KANDASAMY, Usha. 2570 HAYMAKER RD 15146 #495-16-2002 L2006 **FP** *012
KARAJALA SUBRAMANYAM, Vija. ■ 15146 #495-36-2000 L2003 **IM** *020 †20
KELCHAK, Joseph Andrew. ■ 15146 #020-12-1986 L1987 **FM** *020 †18
KELLER, Matthew Adam. 2566 HAYMAKER RD, EAST SUBURBAN PEDIATRICS 15146 #041-13-2000 L2003 **PD** *020 †55
KELLERMAN, Andrew David. 1 MONROEVILLE CTR, STE 800 15146 #041-12-1984 L1985 **OBG** *020 †30
KELLY, Amy Lou. 4075 MONROEVILLE BLVD, BLDG TWO 15146 #041-14-1983 L1984 **P CHP** *020 †75
KENKRE, Sricrishna B. 2570 HAYMAKER RD 15146 #495-01-1957 L1972 **OBG** *020 †30
KENNAH, Adam Edwin. 2570 HAYMAKER RD 15146 #041-12-2003 L2007 **EM** *020 †16
KHAN, Arshad Ali. 3824 NORTHERN PIKE, STE 500 15146 #495-16-1988 L1997 **IM** *020 †20
KHAN, Mehernosh Pheroze. 4328 NORTHERN PIKE, STE 103 15146 #495-01-1977 L1979 **FM FPG** *020 †18
KHAN, Mohammad Mussadiq. ■ 15146 #704-09-1974 L1977 **GS TRS** *020
KIRIMLI, Bulent I. ■ 15146 #902-01-1956 L1962 **AN CCM** *071 †05
KLEIST, Paul Charles. 3824 NORTHERN PIKE, STE 525 15146 #056-06-1981 L1984 **CD** *020 †20
KNEPP, Elizabeth Esther. 2580 HAYMAKER RD STE 201, EAST SUBURBAN OB/GYN ASSOC 15146 #038-45-1983 L1984 **OBG** *020 †30
KODURI, Beaula Vijaya. 2580 HAYMAKER RD, STE 404 15146 #495-21-1993 L2001 **HO** *020 †20
KRUPNIK, Yelena V. 2566 HAYMAKER RD, FORBES REGIONAL HOSPITAL 15146 #913-36-1988 L2005 **FP** *012
KUMAR, Rani Kiran. 400 SECO RD 15146 #495-03-1976 L1982 **EM P** *020 †55,16
KUNSCHNER, Albert John. ■ 15146 #026-04-1931 L1935 **GP** *071
LEIBOWITZ, Leonard D. 2570 HAYMAKER RD 15146 #024-05-1957 L1962 **PD** *071 †55
LEVINE, Michael. 2550 MOSSIDE BLVD STE 405, ORTHOPAEDIC ASSOC OF PITTS 15146 #041-14-1982 L1987 **ORS** *020 †40
LEVINSON, Bradley Alan. 2566 HAYMAKER RD STE 206 15146 #035-06-1978 L1984 **CRS** *020 †10,85 ‡
LIANG, David Youthy. 4318 NORTHERN PIKE, STE 204A 15146 #244-04-1967 L1973 **GS** *020 ‡
LICHTENSTEIN, Seth Howard. 2566 HAYMAKER RD, PROF BLDG 1, STE 101 15146 #041-12-1994 L1999 **N CN** *020 †75
LIN, Ming Shek. 4099 WILLIAM PENN HWY, STE 805 15146 #385-02-1964 L1972 **AI PD** *020 †55,03
LIN, Shiow-Bih. ■ 15146 #244-01-1976 L1981 **PD** *020
LISS, Robert Gary. 2550 MOSSIDE BLVD, STE 405 15146 #041-13-1984 L1990 **ORS OSS** *020 †40
LU, Xuong Cam. 2570 HAYMAKER RD 15146 #041-13-2005 L2005 **IM** *012
LUBINGA, Esther Serwadda. 2570 HAYMAKER RD 15146 #905-01-1994 **FP** *012
LYNN, Jerry. 4099 WILLIAM PENN HWY, JONNET BUILDING/SUITE 805 15146 #041-12-1996 L2000 **AI** *020 †20,03
MAC DONALD, Douglas A. 3835 NORTHERN PIKE 15146 #041-12-1967 L1968 **OBG** *020 †30
MAHMOUD, Nevine Nayer. 2566 HAYMAKER RD, STE 216 15146 #915-02-1993 L2007 **FP** *012
MAHMUD, Rashida Parveen. 4227 NORTHERN PIKE 15146 #704-15-1980 L1993 **IM** *020 †20
MAJMUDAR, Harshit P. 2570 HAYMAKER RD 15146 #495-48-1968 L1982 **EM** *020
MANGES, Christine Cook. 1 MONROEVILLE CTR, STE 800 15146 #041-07-1992 L1995 **OBG** *020 †30
MARGOLIS, Andrew Lewis. 3824 NORTHERN PIKE, STE 250 15146 #041-12-1987 L1988 **IM** *020 †20
MC CARTHY, Thomas Edward. 4318 NORTHERN PIKE 15146 #041-12-1955 L1961 **OBG** *071 †30
MC CLURE, Thomas Arthur. 2550 MOSSIDE BLVD, MONROEVILLE MEDICAL ASSOC 15146 #041-12-1988 L1991 **IM MDM** *020 †20
MC QUIGG, Richard Neal. 3824 NORTHERN PIKE, STE 250 15146 #654-01-1984 L1985 **IM** *020 †20
MENON, Anil S. 2580 HAYMAKER RD 15146 #495-01-1982 L1990 **IM PUD** *020 †20 ‡
MILLER, Jennifer Lee. ■ 15146 #041-12-2007 L2007 **PTH** *012
MILLER, Roberta Neal. 2566 HAYMAKER RD 15146 #041-12-1999 L2001 **FM** *020 †18
MIRZABEIGI, Nematollah. 2570 HAYMAKER RD, FORBES REGIONAL HOSPITAL 15146 #517-01-1967 L1977 **PTH** *020 †50 ‡
MOHAN, Niraj. 2570 HAYMAKER RD, WPH/FORBES REGIONAL CAMPUS 15146 #038-40-1994 L1997 **IM** *020 †20
MONTALBO, Serafin A. ■ 15146 #748-01-1956 L1973 **GP EM** *071
MOODEY, Rachel Komala. 136 MOUNT VERNON DR 15146 #495-50-1989 L2001 **PUD** *012 †20
MORANGANTI, Amitha Reddy. ■ 15146 #495-37-2002 L2005 **IM** *012
MOUKAMAL, Ezz-Eldin. 2570 HAYMAKER RD 15146 #875-02-1995 L2001 **IM** *020 †20
MOY, Elizabeth Ann. 2570 HAYMAKER RD, FORBES REG HOSP-EMERG DEPT 15146 #041-12-1997 L1999 **EM** *020 †16
MUNIRJI, Antoin Elias. 2550 MOSSIDE BLVD, STE 214 15146 #875-01-1987 L1993 **N** *020 †75
MUPPARAPU, Santosh Kumar. ■ 15146 #495-21-2002 L2005 **IM** *012
MUSSELMAN, Kirk Frederick. 2550 MOSSIDE BLVD, STE 208 15146 #041-09-1982 L1983 **IM CD** *020 †20
MUVVALA, Kalyan Chakravar. 3824 NORTHERN PIKE 15146 #495-37-2001 L2004 **IM** *020 †20
NAMAN, Peter Sami. 2566 HAYMAKER RD, STE 103 15146 #605-01-1989 L1993 **GS** *020 †85
NASEEM, Mohammad. 2570 HAYMAKER RD, RADIOLOGY DEPT 15146 #704-01-1962 L1971 **R PM** *020 †80
NASEEM, Shawn Omar. 2550 MOSSIDE BLVD, FL 5 15146 #422-01-1998 L2001 **IM** *020 †20
NASEER, Samina. 2570 HAYMAKER RD 15146 #704-06-1989 L2005 **FP** *012
NATALI, David Geo. 2570 HAYMAKER RD 15146 #041-12-1980 L1982 **EM** *020 †16
NEMEC, John Edward. 2570 HAYMAKER RD 15146 #041-12-1970 L1971 **FM** *040 †18
NEUSCHWANDER, David C. 2550 MOSSIDE BLVD, STE 405 15146 #041-12-1984 L1990 **ORS** *020 †40
NGUYEN, Diem Khue. 2580 HAYMAKER RD 15146 #041-12-2000 L2001 **OBG** *100
NOLAN, Teresa Ann. 2580 HAYMAKER RD, STE-106 15146 #023-07-1977 L1978 **ON HEM** *020 †20
ODDI, Frederick John. 125 DAUGHERTY DR 15146 #041-09-1964 L1965 **FM** *020 †18
OGAGAN, P Dafe. ■ 15146 #041-12-2007 L2007 *012
ONG, Jimmy J. 2571 MOSSIDE BLVD STE 4 15146 #748-10-1972 L1979 **N** *020 †75
PARANDHAM, Koduri. ■ 15146 #495-21-1960 L1973 **EM FM** *071 †18,16
PARANJPE, Mohan Kashinath. 2570 HAYMAKER RD 15146 #495-01-1967 L1978 **OBG OS** *020 †30
PERRONE, Frank M. 2570 HAYMAKER RD 15146 #041-12-1976 L1977 **R** *020 †80
PETICCA, Benjamin Bernard. 2580 HAYMAKER RD, STE 201 15146 #041-12-1980 L1981 **OBG OS** *020 †30
PINCUS, Jack Howard. ■ 15146 #041-12-1954 L1955 **GP** *020
PLETZ, Gregory Johnathan. 2570 HAYMAKER RD 15146 #041-09-1991 L1993 **EM** *020 †16
PLOWEY, Kenneth C. 2550 MOSSIDE BLVD, 5TH FL 15146 #041-77-2003, ▲ L2003 **IM** *020 †20
POTNIS, Asha Vishwanath. 2550 MOSSIDE BLVD 15146 #495-01-1967 L1978 **PHO PD** *020 †55
PRASAD, Mahalingiah. 424 ARDEN DR, TORRANCE ROAD, 15146 #495-09-1979 L1992 **P** *020
RAGOOR, Balakrishna R. 4217 NORTHERN PIKE 15146 #495-70-1980 L1990 **FM** *020 †18
RAINA, Gunjan. 2566 HAYMAKER RD 15146 #495-37-2004 L2007 **FP** *012
RAIZMAN, Richard Eric. 125 DAUGHERTY DR 15146 #041-12-1971 L1972 **GE IM** *020 †20
RAJASHEKAR, Kalpana. EMP OF ALLEGHENY COUNTY, FORBES REGIONAL HOSP 15146 #495-33-1985 L1995 **EM IM** *020 †20
RAJUPET, Kamala Alla. 2580 HAYMAKER RD, STE 201 15146 #495-65-1990 L1997 **END** *020 †20
RATHFON, Grace Yunkyung. ■ 15146 #041-12-2001 L2001 **DR** *020 †80
RATHGEB, Michelle Anne. ■ 15146 #041-01-1994 L1997 **IM** *020 †20
RAVANO, Edwin Quietson. 2550 MOSSIDE BLVD, STE 500 15146 #748-10-1996 L2001 **IM** *020 †20
RAVULAPATI, Janakiram. ■ 15146 #496-01-2003 L2005 **IM** *012
REDDY, Sugandhi. 2550 MOSSIDE BLVD, STE 111 15146 #495-65-1982 L1987 **PD** *020 †55
REID, Elsie Logan. 4099 WM PENN HWY 15146 #041-12-1946 L1947 **P EM** *071
ROSENDALE, Brian Edward. 2570 HAYMAKER RD 15146 #041-14-1990 L1994 **PTH** *020 †50
ROSENFELD, Leonardo. 125 DAUGHERTY DR, MONROEVILLE SPECIALISTS CL 15146 #187-09-1969 L1977 **AN** *020 †05
ROSENTHAL, Richard Harold. 600 OXFORD DR, PREMIER MEDICAL ASSOCIATES 15146 #041-07-1978 L1979 **IM IMG** *020 †20
RUBIANO, Remigio C. 1330 KNOLLWOOD DR 15146 #748-08-1967 L1977 **AN GP** *071
RUBINO, Mark Anthony. 2580 HAYMAKER RD, STE 201 15146 #041-01-1983 L1984 **OBG** *020 †30
RUDMAN, Richard. 4487 BROADWAY BLVD 15146 #035-19-1984 L1987 **FM** *020 †18
RYGG, Sandra G. 1 MONROEVILLE CTR, STE 800 15146 #041-12-1989 L1991 **OBG** *020 †30
SAMPSON, Arnold. ■ 15146 #041-12-1944 L1945 **GS OS** *071 †85
SANNER, Edgar Geo, Jr. ■ 15146 #041-13-1958 L1959 **U** *071
SARWER, Wafia. 2566 HAYMAKER RD 15146 #704-29-2004 L2007 **FP** *012
SCHLOSSBERG, Michael A. 3824 NORTHERN PIKE, STE 500 15146 #035-09-1975 **IM** *020 †20
SCHOTT, Stewart Gustav. 4075 MONROEVILLE BLVD, STE 125 15146 #041-12-1989 L1991 **PD** *020 †55
SEIAVITCH, Samuel Alvin. 4075 MONROEVILLE BLVD, STE 330 15146 #041-12-1977 L1978 **OBG** *020 †30
SEIDERS, Elizabeth P. 4075 MONROEVILLE BLVD, STE 320 15146 #038-44-1986 L1990 **OBG** *020 †30
SHAH GILANI, Syed Rahat A. ■ 15146 #704-20-2001 L2005 **IM** *012
SHARMA, Parminder Kumar. 2550 MOSSIDE BLVD, STE 208 15146 #495-03-1978 L1983 **IM CD** *020 †20
SHIBLI, Urooj Basit. 2570 HAYMAKER RD 15146 #704-29-2004 L2006 **FP** *012
SHINN, Lowell Carroll. 2580 HAYMAKER RD, STE 106 15146 #055-02-1985 L2004 **HO** *020 †20
SHRISHRIMAL, Shripal Chan. ■ 15146 #495-28-2000 L2003 **PUD** *012 †20
SHYMANSKY, Laura Marie. 2380 MCGINLEY RD, EAST SUBURBAN REHAB ASSOC 15146 #051-01-1986 L1990 **PM** *020 †60
SINGH, Vikramjit. ■ 15146 #495-03-2001 L2004 **IM** *100 †20
SKEZAS, Marion. 4321 NORTHERN PIKE, MEDICAL WEIGHT LOSS 15146 #041-09-1954 L1955 **GS TS** *071 †85
SNODGRASS, W Homer, Jr. ■ 15146 #041-09-1961 L1963 **PD** *071 †55
SOTOS, Steven N. 2580 HAYMAKER RD 15146 #418-01-1971 **PUD IM** *020 †20
STANGER, Robert Henry. 120 DAUGHERTY DR 15146 #012-05-1964 L1965 **P** *071
STURM, Charles Fredrick. 2570 HAYMAKER RD 15146 #035-46-1984 L1985 **FM** *040 †18
SUSANG-TALAMO, Barbara A. 2570 HAYMAKER RD 15146 #041-01-1979 L1980 **OBG** *020 †30
SWANSON, Michael D. 4075 MONROEVILLE BLVD, STE 330 15146 #010-02-1975 L1976 **OBG** *020 †30

■ = Address Information Privacy Protected

SWIDWA, Denise Mary. 2580 HAYMAKER RD 15146 #041-09-1977 L1978 **PUD IM** *020 †20

TAL, Alexander. 2580 HAYMAKER RD, STE 201 15146 #550-02-1982 L2000 **IM END** *020 †20

TAN, Hai-Sing Anthony. 2566 HAYMAKER RD, STE 103 15146 #462-01-1979 L1982 **GS** *020 †85

TELLAKULA, Kavitha Ramamu. 2570 HAYMAKER RD 15146 #496-21-2000 L2005 **FP** *012

TRAINER, Paul J. 2566 HAYMAKER RD, EAST SUBURBAN PEDIATRICS 15146 #035-06-1980 L1985 **PD** *020 †55

TRONZO, Robert David. 2570 HAYMAKER RD, DEPT PATH 15146 #041-13-1978 L1979 **PTH OS** *020 †50

TURNER, Joseph. 2580 HAYMAKER RD, STE 105 15146 #038-40-1975 L1976 **OTO** *020 †45

ULTMANN, Michelle Claire. 2790 MOSSIDE BLVD, STE 700 15146 #038-06-1982 L1985 **PD PDE** *020 †55

URBANDT, Jorge Eduardo. 2566 HAYMAKER RD, STE 304 15146 #132-01-1984 L2004 *020

VALKO, Annemarie P S. 2380 MCGINLEY RD 15146 #041-12-1969 L1970 **PM PD** *071 †55,60

VARGA, Arthur B. ■ 15146 #041-12-1952 L1953 **AN PUD** *071 †05

VARLEY, William Anthony. 4075 MONROEVILLE BLVD, STE 125 15146 #041-01-1989 L1991 **PD** *020 †55

VELPARI, Sudarshan. ■ 15146 #041-15-2008 *012

VERMA, Karan. 2520 KING LEAR DR, APT 3 15146 #496-43-2003 L2005 **FP** *012

WADHAR, Harshad. 2570 HAYMAKER RD 15146 #495-23-1979 L1995 **FM EM** *020 †18

WAHAL, George Anthony. 3824 NORTHERN PIKE, STE 500 15146 #041-12-1979 L1980 **IM** *020 †20

WALTER, William James. 4225 NORTHERN PIKE 15146 #041-12-1954 L1955 **OBG** *071 †30

WARD, Sheila Marie. 300 OXFORD DR 15146 #054-04-1981 L1985 **MFM OBG** *040 †30

WEAVER, Jeffrey G. 2790 MOSSIDE BLVD STE 105 15146 #041-77-1978, ▲ L1979 **D DS** *020

WEINSTOCK, Elliott. 125 DAUGHERTY DR 15146 #041-14-1977 L1978 **AN** *020 †05 ‡

WEISBERG, Edward Saul. 2545 MOSSIDE BLVD 15146 #055-01-1963 L1965 **OTO OS** *020 †45

WEISS, James. 2566 HAYMAKER RD, STE 201 15146 #018-03-1979 L1981 **NEP IM** *020 †20

WERNER, Kathleen Thomas. 2566 HAYMAKER RD, STE 306 15146 #041-12-1988 L1990 **FM** *020 †18

WETTON, Rita. 2550 MOSSIDE BLVD, STE 204 15146 #041-07-1958 L1959 **CHP P** *071 †55,75

WHITESIDE, Deborah Ann. 4075 MONROEVILLE BLVD 15146 #041-12-1995 L1997 **OBG** *020 †30

WINCKO, Jeffrey Todd. 2571 MOSSIDE BLVD 15146 #041-12-2003 L2007 **OPH** *020

WOJCIK, Traci L. 2580 HAYMAKER RD, STE 201 15146 #041-12-1992 L1996 **OBG** *020 †30

WYNN, Juliet Elizabeth. ■ 15146 #035-06-1979 L2001 **PTH** *020

YADAV, Rashmi Mansingh. ■ 15146 #495-28-2003 L2004 **IM** *100 †20

YAO, Michael Jos. 2570 HAYMAKER RD 15146 #041-02-1987 L1989 **FM** *020 †18

YOON, Donald D. 108 WHITEHEAD LN 15146 #583-04-1971 L1976 **GP** *020

YOUNG, Cheng Dong. 1000 INFINITY DR, STE 310 15146 #244-03-1963 L1977 **GP IM** *020

YU, Hong. 2570 HAYMAKER RD 15146 #243-55-1993 **FM** *100

ZARANDONA, Jose Manuel. ■ 15146 #049-01-2003 L2003 **PTH** *100 †50

ZIDO, Albert John. 4318 NORTHERN PIKE, POLIDORA BUILDING STE 204 15146 #041-09-1955 L1956 **FM** *071 †18

MONT CLARE — MONTGOMERY

GOPLERUD, Jan Marie. ■ 19453 #051-04-1980 L1983 **NPM** *040 †55

MONTGOMERYVILLE — MONTGOMERY

BERNSTEIN, Mark Henry. 593 BETHLEHEM PIKE, STE 4B 18936 #041-01-1972 L1974 **P** *020 †75 ‡

MONTOURSVILLE — LYCOMING

AUSMANAS, Militza. ■ 17754 #047-07-2007 L2007 **FP** *012

BOHR, Angela Dorothy. ■ 17754 #041-14-2007 L2007 **OBG** *012

COFFMAN, Kaohlin M. ■ 17754 #023-01-1951 L1952 **EM GP** *071

DURRWACHTER, Robert James. ■ 17754 #041-13-1961 L1964 **GP** *020

ESSEL, Adwoa Serwaa. ■ 17754 #412-01-1988 L2007 **NM** *020 †20,28

FERNANDEZ, Eduardo Inamac. 269 MADDEN RD 17754 #748-01-1958 L1971 **AN** *072

FINN, Martha Jane B. 1660 SYCAMORE RD, STE C 17754 #041-07-1972 L1973 **NEP IM** *020 †20

GANDY, Daniel Ross. 1660 SYCAMORE RD STE C 17754 #018-75-1969, ▲ L1976 **NEP IM** *020 †20 ‡

HAUSSMANN, Andrew Nelson. 1500 BROAD ST 17754 #041-14-1999 L2001 **FM** *020 †18

HINDI, Musa A. 1601 SYCAMORE RD STE 2A 17754 #330-04-1968 L1987 **OPH OS** *020 †35 ‡

LONGENBACH, Eric Warren. 1500 BROAD ST 17754 #041-02-1981 L1982 **FM** *020 †18

LUBBE, Wilhelm Johannes. ■ 17754 #041-02-2007 **TY** *012

LUKAS, Raymond A. ■ 17754 #030-06-1969 L1972 **AN** *074

MICHAEL, Sharon Rosalia. 780 BROAD ST 17754 #005-12-1999 L2001 **FM** *020 †18

MINASSIAN, Vatche Arakel. 780 BROAD ST, STE 4 17754 #605-01-1994 L2004 **OBG** *020 †30

NAIDU, Jai Prakash. 780 BROAD ST, STE 4 17754 #495-21-1971 L1977 **PD** *071 †55

NIX, Collier Bussey. 999 N LOYALSOCK AVE, STE B 17754 #001-06-1981 L1982 **FM** *020 †18

PFEIL, Russell Wm. ■ 17754 #041-01-1946 L1947 **GP** *071

SINGH ELANGBAM, Dilip K. 780 BROAD ST, STE 4 17754 #495-02-1986 L1997 **IM** *074 †20

STEA, Sam Faris. 1660 SYCAMORE RD STE C 17754 #035-09-1989 L1997 **NEP IM** *020 †20 ‡

STORY, Nancy Susan. 2140 WARRENSVILLE RD 17754 #041-12-1978 L1979 **FM FPG** *020 †18 ‡

WRIGHT, Michael Forrest. 1500 BROAD ST 17754 #038-41-1999 L2001 **FM** *020 †18

YASUI, Robert Shu. ■ 17754 #041-13-1947 L1948 **GS** *071 †85

MONTROSE — SUSQUEHANNA

BENNETT, Raymond Leslie. 1 GROW AVE 18801 #041-13-1946 L1947 **GP** *071

BERTSCH, Albert Monroe. ■ 18801 #041-02-1944 L1944 **GS** *071 †85

BIELECKI, William. PO BOX 285, 61 CHURCH ST 18801 #407-16-1958 L1981 **CHP** *071

DANA, Ihab. 3 GROW AVE, MONTROSE MEDICAL ARTS CLIN 18801 #605-01-1988 L1993 **IM EM** *020 †30

GLADDING, Samuel Watson. ■ 18801 #041-13-1945 L1948 **PD OS** *071

HOMILY, Blessing. ■ 18801 #495-27-1954 L1973 **GS** *071

KERR, Paul B. 1 GROW AVE 18801 #016-06-1950 L1950 **FM AN** *071 †18

KHALIL, Hassan Younes. 3 GROW AVE 18801 #875-01-1991 L1997 **GE IMG** *020 †20

LATTIMORE, Kenneth Robt. RR 7 BOX 7117, LAKE PLAZA 2 RTE 706 EAST 18801 #008-02-1982 L1986 **P** *020 †75

NAZAR, Jose Enrique. 3 GROW AVE, ENDLESS MOUNTAIN HEALTH SY 18801 #649-01-1975 L1986 **ORS** *020 ‡

RUCKER, Ellis Donell. 13 GROW AVE 18801 #041-02-1980 L1983 **IM** *020

MOON TOWNSHIP — ALLEGHENY

ASH, Richard David. 1600 CORAOPOLIS HEIGHTS RD 15108 #041-01-1977 L1980 **PD ADL** *020 †55

BALABAN, Edward P. 1600 CORAOPOLIS HEIGHTS RD, STE F 15108 #041-77-1977, ▲ L1979 **IM** *020 †20

CHEW, Brandon George. ■ 15108 #041-12-2008 *012

CIRUCCI, Christina Ann. 1009 BEAVER GRADE RD, STE 200 15108 #041-02-1994 L1998 **OBG** *020 †30

CROMO, Sandra Ann. 1600 CORAOPOLIS HEIGHTS RD 15108 #041-02-1987 L1990 **GPM** *040 †18

DANKO, Eugene Thos. 890 BEAVER GRADE RD 15108 #041-12-1963 L1964 **DR NR** *071 †80

DOLENCE, Danielle. 993 BROADHEAD RD, STE 200 15108 #561-26-1981 L1986 **FM** *020 †18

DOYLE, Alfred Pirnie. 1600 CORAOPOLIS HEIGHTS RD, STE F 15108 #041-01-1954 L1964 **ON HEM** *020 †20

FILOTAS-MARWAHA, Hedwig. 960 BEAVER GRADE RD, LOWER LEVEL 15108 #067-01-1970 L1974 **PD** *020 †55

FLANNAGAN, Renee Barbas. 725 CHERRINGTON PKWY SU 15108 #041-07-1998 L2000 **GE** *020 †20

FUSCO, Robert Donald. 725 CHERRINGTON PKWY, STE 101 15108 #041-12-1973 **GE IM** *020 †20

HOTTENSTEIN, Jonathan E. 725 CHERRINGTON PKWY 15108 #041-13-1973 L1974 **ORS** *020 †40

JEWELL-MAHLER, Victoria K. 1600 CORAOPOLIS HEIGHTS RD, STE E 15108 #025-01-2001 L2001 **PD** *020 †55

KIM, Frank. 725 CHERRINGTON PKWY, STE 101 15108 #023-01-1984 L2001 **GE IM** *020 †20

KIM, Richard. 725 CHERRINGTON PKWY, STE 101 15108 #051-04-1987 L1989 **GE** *020 †20 ‡

KONDAVEETI, Rajani. 1474 CORAOPOLIS HEIGHTS RD 15108 #422-01-2000 L2004 **IM** *020

KUBIK, Nicholas Joseph. 725 CHERRINGTON PKWY, STE 200 15108 #041-12-1997 L1999 **ORS OSM** *020 †40

LAMBROU, Peter James. 1600 CORAOPOLIS HEIGHTS RD, UNIVERSITY OF PITTSBURGH M 15108 #041-09-1978 L1979 **EM** *020

MILLER, Patricia S. 1600 CORAOPOLIS HEIGHTS RD, STE E 15108 #041-14-1980 L1982 **PD** *020 †55

MORACA, John Idolo. 1009 BEAVER GRADE RD, STE 200 15108 #041-12-1959 L1960 **GYN** *020 †30

NEELY, Eileen Purcell. 935 THORN RUN RD, STE 204 15108 #051-04-1986 L1989 **IM** *020 †20

OSMANSKI, Stephen John. 935 THORN RUN RD, STE 204 15108 #041-12-1981 L1983 **IM** *020 †20

PRICE, Tamara L W. 400 ROUSER RD, BLDGE 2 STE 102 15108 #011-02-1989 L1992 **IM OS** *020 †20

SADYKOVA, Oksana R. 220 THORNWOOD CT, ALLEGHENY GENERAL HOSPITAL 15108 #913-36-1992 L2001 **P** *020 †75

SANTERINI, Kristine Rae. 1009 BEAVER GRADE RD, STE 200 15108 #041-12-1990 L1998 **OBG** *020 †30

SCHOEMER, Pamela Lynn. 1600 CORAOPOLIS HEIGHTS RD, STE E 15108 #041-12-1993 L1995 **PD** *020 †55

SCICUTELLA, Carol J. 1600 CORAOPOLIS HEIGHTS RD, STE C 15108 #033-75-1983, ▲ L1988 **RO** *020 †80 ‡

SHERRY, Michael Mc Clain. 1600 CORAOPOLIS HEIGHTS RD, STE F 15108 #041-12-1980 L1981 **ON IM** *020 †20

SINGH, Surinder Kaur. 110 GATEHOUSE DR 15108 #495-03-1971 L1981 **P** *020

SMITH, James Kevin. 1009 BEAVER GRADE RD, STE 100 15108 #055-01-1981 L1983 **PS** *020 †65 ‡

STANLEY, Ernest Joseph. 725 CHERRINGTON PKWY, STE 100 15108 #063-01-1986 L1995 **GE** *020 †20 ‡

STINE, Lester Edward, Jr. 725 CHERRINGTON PKWY, STE 100 15108 #023-07-1986 L1989 **GE HEP** *020 †20 ‡

THOMAS, Derek James. 725 CHERRINGTON PKWY, STE 200 15108 #051-04-1999 L2005 **ORS** *100 †40

MOOSIC — LACKAWANNA

BELARDI, Albert Adam, Jr. 202 SALINGER CLOSE 18507 #041-02-1988 L1991 **AN OS** *020 †05

BERGER, Matthew Adam. 340 MONTAGE MOUNTAIN RD 18507 #308-03-1983 L1988 **P** *020

CAMPANELLA, Jos Anthony. 500 MAIN ST 18507 #041-02-1960 L1961 **GP OS** *020

DE SOTO, Danilo A. 340 MONTAGE MOUNTAIN RD 18507 #308-03-1986 L1990 **P PYG** *020 †75

DOUGHERTY, Edward A. ■ 18507 #030-06-1949 L1950 **EM OBG** *071 †30

ESWAR, Bharati. ■ 18507 #496-39-1989 L2003 **AN** *100

NOURIAN, Ali Akbar. 41 STEINBECK DR 18507 #517-01-1964 L1973 **P CHP** *020 †75

PATEL, Suman Ambalal. 12 FITZGERALD DR 18507 #495-23-1976 L1986 **R** *020 †80

WESSEL, Andrea. 4004 BIRNEY AVE 18507 #409-10-1990 L2001 **FM** *100 †18

MORGANTOWN — BERKS

D'URSO, Angela. ■ 19543 #654-01-1989 L1996 **AI RHU** *020 †20,03

FOX, Edward J. 10 MORGAN SPRING DR 19543 #035-45-1995 L2003 **ORS SO** *020 †40 ‡

RHAUDA, Patricia P. ■ 19543 #041-09-1996 L1998 **IM** *020

MORRISVILLE — BUCKS

BEREAU, Anca. 401 FLORAL VALE BLVD 19067 #781-01-1981 L1988 **N** *020

CAUTILLI, David Allen. 115 FLORAL VALE BLVD, STE C 19067 #041-02-1988 L1990 **ORS HS** *020 †40

CAUTILLI, Richard A, Jr. 115 FLORAL VALE BLVD STE C 19067 #041-02-1985 L1986 ORS OSM *020 †40

DRAGANOSKY, Eugene A. 105 FLORAL VALE BLVD 19067 #041-13-1965 L1966 OBG *020 †30

DRUCKER, David Wayne. 407 FLORAL VALE BLVD 19067 #028-02-1990 L1999 CD *020 †20

HEYRICH, George Patrick. 407 FLORAL VALE BLVD, MERCER BUCKS CARDIOLOGY 19067 #010-02-1989 L1991 CD *020 †20

HIRSCH, William Steven. 407 FLORAL VALE BLVD, MERCER BUCKS CARDIOLOGY 19067 #041-77-1991, ▲ L1992 CD IM *020 †20

HYMAN, Richard Louis. 407 FLORAL VALE BLVD, MERCER BUCKS CARDIOLOGY 19067 #041-13-1989 L1992 CD IM *020 †20 ‡

KASTURI, Avinash. ■ 19067 #496-35-2005 GS *012

KHAN, Yusuf Mujtaba. 423 N PENNSYLVANIA AVE 19067 #654-01-1981 L1983 IM *020 †20

KIM, In Soon. 801 W TRENTON AVE 19067 #583-02-1974 L1978 GP HEM *020 †20

KIM, In Soon. 801 W TRENTON AVE 19067 #583-08-1968 L1981 GP OS *020

MECHANIC, Leslie Dana. ■ 19067 #035-06-1987 L1992 PTH *020 †50

PARABOSCHI, Charles Frank. 407 FLORAL VALE BLVD, MERCER BUCKS CARDIOLOGY 19067 #041-12-1988 L1990 CD *020 †20

SAMAD, Fasih Us. 78 N PENNSYLVANIA AVE, STE 4 19067 #704-01-1967 L1972 IM HEM *020 †20

SCHREMMER, Bruno Laurent. 423 N PENNSYLVANIA AVE, PULM CRCTL CARE SLEEP MED 19067 #396-41-1991 L2005 PCC *050 †20

SETH, Paula S. 407 FLORAL VALE BLVD 19067 #041-07-1998 L2006 CD *020 †20

VELOSO, Manuel Javier. ■ 19067 #748-01-1956 L1964 FM EM *020

WEISS, David. 201 WOOLSTON DR STE 2B 19067 #041-77-1973, ▲ L1974 FM *020 †18 ‡

MORTON — DELAWARE

BALL, Thomas William. ■ 19070 #041-13-2004 L2007 EM *100

BRADBURY, Nicholas Coren. ■ 19070 #041-02-2008 *012

CARO, Jose C. ■ 19070 #748-01-1959 L1972 IM PUD *071

DEL ROSARIO-CARO, A. ■ 19070 #748-01-1959 L1977 PTH *071

GOBENCIONG-VARONA, Raida. ■ 19070 #041-01-1970 L1976 OBG *100

JENKINS, Timothy Francis. 1803 FRANKLIN AVE 19070 #041-09-1976 L1977 FM *020

JOHNSON, Howard John. 8 OLDE BEECHTREE VILLAGE 19070 #041-13-1973 L1975 ORS *020

MCMULLEN, Jamie Lynn. ■ 19070 #041-02-2008 L2008 *012

MELLON, Lawrence Jos. ■ 19070 #041-02-1959 L1960 OM FM *071 †70 ‡

MOSCOW — LACKAWANNA

ALUNNI, Michael Albert. ■ 18444 #041-02-2005 L2005 *100

DE WARREN, Eric Christian. 103 NP 502 PLZ 18444 #422-01-2000 L2003 FM *020 †18

HARASYM, Eugene Daniel. RR 6 BOX 6239 18444 #041-13-1977 L1978 FM *020 †18

KAUSMEYER, Dana Theresa. ■ 18444 #041-14-2006 L2007 PTH *020

SHADEROWFSKY, Paul Daniel. 117 CONSTITUTION DR 18444 #033-05-1996 L1999 DR *020 ‡

WAIBEL, David Alan. RR 9, BOX 9444 18444 #041-13-1983 L1985 IM *020 †20

MOUNT BETHEL — NORTHAMPTON

RASO, Jon Antony. 10 MOUNT BETHEL PLZ, MT BETHEL MEDICAL CENTER 18343 #041-07-1992 L1994 IM *020 †20

MOUNT CARMEL — NORTHUMBERLAND

ABDUL-AL, Houssam. 93 W STATE ROUTE 61 17851 #875-01-1988 L1993 IM *020 †20

FRANTZ, Dolores B. ■ 17851 #041-02-1981 L1983 *020

KHOUDEIR, Yasser. 50 N MAPLE ST 17851 #875-02-1991 L1997 IM *020 †20

MCNEIL, Peter Edward. 240 S HICKORY ST 17851 #035-45-1980 L1981 FM EM *020 †18

NEWTON, Andrew O. 129 E 5TH ST, MT CARMEL MNTL HLTH ASSOC 17851 #690-05-1988 L1998 P *020 †75 ‡

MOUNT GRETNA — LEBANON

BOWMAN, Scott Wm. PO BOX 564 17064 #041-02-1976 L1981 A RHU *020 †20,03

CARVELL, Michael Chas. 283 SOUTH BUTLER ROAD 17064 #041-14-1977 L1978 P *020 †75

ELLENBERGER, Carl, Jr. ■ 17064 #008-01-1965 L1973 RNR OPH *071 †75

FENSTERMACHER, Thomas L. PO BOX 550, PHILHAVEN HOSP 17064 #041-14-1986 L1987 P *020 †75

FUEYO, Michael Anthony. 283 SOUTH BUTLER ROAD, PHILHAVEN HOSPITAL 17064 #041-14-1984 L1999 CHP P *020 †75

JESKE-JANICKA, Magdalena. PO BOX 550, 283 S BUTLER RD 17064 #759-03-1979 L2003 CHP P *020 †75

NGUYEN, Nhien Duc. 283 S BUTLER ROAD 17064 #941-01-1974 L1982 P ADP *020 †75

OLULEYE, Olaniyi I. PO BOX 550, 283 S BUTLER RD 17064 #690-05-1982 L2002 CHP *020 †75

PAKOLA, Richard S. 283 S BUTLER RD 17064 #041-13-1970 L1972 P GP *020 †75

SAMII, Akbar Mehraban. ■ 17064 #041-13-1960 L1972 GS *071 †85

MOUNT HOLLY SPRINGS — CUMBERLAND

DAVIS, Harry R. 303 N BALTIMORE AVE 17065 #041-01-1953 L1954 FM IMG *071 †18

DELL, David Alan. 303 N BALTIMORE AVE 17065 #041-14-1984 L1985 FM *020 †18

MOUNT JOY — LANCASTER

ANTHONY, Christopher H. 667 HAWTHORNE LN 17552 #041-02-1975 L1976 PTH *020 †50

HUSSAR, Terra Lee. ■ 17552 #001-06-2003 L2003 N *100

MURPHY, Maria Linnell. ■ 17552 #024-07-2005 L2005 FP *012

MYERS, Herbert Ezra, Jr. ■ 17552 #041-13-1970 L1971 P FM *020 †75,18

NAVALKOWSKY, Peter J. 410 S ANGLE ST, DONEGAL PROF CTR 17552 #060-01-1975 L1983 IM *020 †20

SCHLOSSER, David Eugene. ■ 17552 #041-02-1943 L1944 GP *071

STULTZ, Esther Edith. ■ 17552 #041-14-2007 L2007 FP *012

YEAKEL, Allen E. ■ 17552 #041-01-1951 L1952 AN *071 †05 ‡

MOUNT LEBANON — ALLEGHENY

ANTYPAS, Philip Geo. ■ 15228 #605-01-1948 L1977 HS *072 †85,65

DIVEN, Judith Carter. 520 WASHINGTON RD, STE 203 15228 #041-12-1975 L1976 P CHP *020 †75

JANICIJEVIC, Nenad. 1691 WASHINGTON RD 15228 #957-02-1971 L1978 EM FM *020 †16

MACIAS, Carlos Aitor. ■ 15228 #132-01-1999 L2005 GS *012

MOATS, Anthony W. 1537 WASHINGTON RD, INDEPENDENCE MANOR 15228 #041-13-1945 L1946 OS GP *030

SULLIVAN, Richard P. ■ 15228 #016-45-1991 L1993 EM *020 †16

MOUNT MORRIS — GREENE

ALMASY, William Michael. ■ 15349 #055-01-1986 L1988 DR NR *072 †80

MOUNT PLEASANT — WESTMORELAND

ABOOSI, Ali Jawad. 599 N CHURCH ST 15666 #528-01-1960 L1972 PD PDC *020 †55

ABUL-FADL, Yahya. 599 N CHURCH ST 15666 #605-01-1962 L1970 IM ON *062

AL-MALLAH, Shadiya. ■ 15666 #902-01-1954 L1969 OBG *071 †30

ALPONAT, Orhan Sevki. ■ 15666 #902-10-1955 L1971 OBG *020

ASSEFA, Aster. 508 S CHURCH ST 15666 #408-09-1984 L1997 FM *020 †18

BALCITA, Angel B. 1027 W MAIN ST 15666 #748-07-1965 L1983 IM *020

BANKACI, Murat. 609 N CHURCH ST, STE 1 15666 #902-10-1971 L1974 OTO *020 †45 ‡

BOSCHA, Kenneth William. 1 BRADDOCK ROAD AVE 15666 #422-01-1981 L1984 CD IM *020 †20

BRADLEY, William Lawrence. 315 TURNPIKE RD 15666 #305-01-1982 L1984 AN IM *020 †20,05

BURSALI, Selahattin. 609 N CHURCH ST 15666 #902-01-1949 L1971 IM *071

CAWOG, Antoine Francis. 508 S CHURCH ST 15666 #875-01-1973 L1977 FM PTH *020 †18

CENIZAL, Jesus Salonga. 508 S CHURCH ST, FRICK COMMUNITY HEALTH CTR 15666 #748-01-1971 L1988 R *020 †80

CHANDRASEKARAN, Sannasie. 828 W MAIN ST, STE 1 15666 #495-04-1969 L1974 GE IM *020 †20

DASCANI, Paul. 508 S CHURCH ST 15666 #847-06-1980 L1986 FM *020 †18

DAVIS, Helen Ann Patricia. 741 N CHURCH ST 15666 #024-07-1978 L1987 OPH *020 †35

DESAI, Bharati P. 1 BRADDOCK ROAD AVE 15666 #496-38-1970 L1978 PD *020 †55

DESAI, Praful Vasantlal. 1 BRADDOCK ROAD AVE 15666 #495-20-1966 L1973 U GS *020 †95

DOMIT, John. 220 BESSEMER RD, EXEC BLDG STE 202 15666 #649-13-1985 L1987 GS *020 †85

EL ATTRACHE, Selim. 606 S CHURCH ST 15666 #605-02-1956 L1963 ORS OFA *020 †40

GEMMELL, Tracy Jo. 220 BESSEMER RD, STE 208 15666 #055-02-1994 L1996 OBG *020 †30

GUNTUR, Sivarama Krishna. 1027 W MAIN ST, STE 4 15666 #495-62-1971 L1985 FM EM *020 †18 ‡

HAUS, Mary Margaret. 508 S CHURCH ST 15666 #035-03-1980 L1981 OTR *020 †40

KAMINSKI, Thomas Nick. 1 BRADDOCK ROAD AVE, LYNN TKAMINSKI MED ASSOC 15666 #561-01-1975 L1977 IM *020 †20

KETTERING, Donald Louis. 508 S CHURCH ST, FRICK HOSP 15666 #041-12-1959 L1960 PUD IM *071 †20

KIM, Hyoung Dal. 220 BESSEMER RD, STE 102 15666 #583-02-1970 L1977 HO HEM *020 †20

KIM, Yong-Il. 508 S CHURCH ST, FRICK COMMUNITY HLTH CTR 15666 #583-01-1962 L1973 AN *020

LEONIDA, Efren Labay. 1 BRADDOCK ROAD AVE, # A 15666 #748-01-1970 L1973 FM *020

LEVINSON, William Danl. ■ 15666 #041-23-1945 L1946 GP *071 †20

LIM, Felixberto Diao. 220 BESSEMER RD, STE 210 15666 #748-11-1979 L1986 ON HEM *071 †20

LIM, Young Kyu. 605 N CHURCH ST 15666 #583-01-1970 L1975 PD *020 †55

LYNN, Richard Eugene. 1 BRADDOCK ROAD AVE 15666 #041-09-1974 L1975 IM *020 †20

MORCOS, John Peter. 220 BESSEMER RD, STE 102 15666 #036-07-2001 L2004 HO *020 †20

NAVARRO, Emilio Ramon. 599 N CHURCH ST, LEVELB 15666 #308-07-1982 L1991 EM PME *020

NICOLETTE, Anthony J, Jr. 508 S CHURCH ST, FRICK HOSP EXCELA HLTH 15666 #010-01-1968 L1969 DR *020 †80 ‡

PATEL, Ramesh Premji. 508 S CHURCH ST 15666 #495-97-1975 L1983 IM *020 †20

RAMACHANDRAN, Mooriath. 508 S CHURCH ST, FRICK HOSPITAL 15666 #495-44-1968 L1985 AN PME *020 †05

RASHEED, Mamoon A. 828 W MAIN ST 15666 #198-02-1987 L1995 IM *020 †20

REILLY, Philip Jerome, Jr. 508 S CHURCH ST 15666 #041-12-1962 L1963 GP *020

RYAN, William Chas. 601 S CHURCH ST 15666 #010-02-1957 L1960 P N *071 †75

SALOOM, Albert Timothy. 6533 STATE ROUTE 819 15666 #041-02-1998 L2000 FM *020 †18 ‡

SANTAMARIA, Frank R. ■ 15666 #748-01-1953 L1964 GS GYN *020

SLEZAK, Joseph Adrian. 603 N CHURCH ST 15666 #041-02-1963 L1964 OBG *071 †30

VEMULAPALLI, Syama S. 1027 W MAIN ST 15666 #495-50-1990 L2002 GE IM *020 †20

WEISEL, William Mark. 220 BESSEMER RD STE 208, WEISEL FAMILY PRACTICE 15666 #041-02-1976 L1977 FM FPG *020 †18

WILLIAMS, Norman Saml. 508 S CHURCH ST 15666 #024-07-1955 L1956 RO *071 †80

ZAITOON, Mohammad Munir. 1027 W MAIN ST 15666 #875-01-1972 L1979 U *020 †95

MOUNT PLEASANT MILLS — SNYDER

SLAVENS, Timothy Earl. 9627 ROUTE 35 STE 10 17853 #041-02-1988 L2000 FM *020 †18

MOUNT POCONO — MONROE

BLOOM, Frederick J, Jr. 21 COMMERCE CIR 18344 #041-09-1983 L1984 FM FPG *020 †18

BROWN, Timothy Michael. 21 COMMERCE CIR 18344 #016-06-1993 L1995 FM *020 †18

CARL, David Alfred. 21 COMMERCE CIR 18344 #032-01-1982 L1983 **OPH** *020
CUSH, Gerard John, Jr. 21 COMMERCE CIR 18344 #041-09-1982 L2000 **ORS** *020 †40
FISHER, Seth Ward. 21 COMMERCE CIR 18344 #041-09-1982 L1983 **CD IM** *020 †20
FOX, Michael Jonathon. 21 COMMERCE CIR 18344 #041-09-1988 L1990 **IM** *020 †20
GLICINI, Robert Leno. 21 COMMERCE CIR 18344 #033-06-1984 L1989 **GS VS** *020 †85
IMBER, Christopher Dean. 21 COMMERCE CIR 18344 #041-13-1995 L2003 **FM** *020 †18
KAMENAR, Elizabeth. 21 COMMERCE CIR 18344 #038-40-1975 L2000 **N NP** *020 †50,75
KAWAMURA, Akiko. 21 COMMERCE CIR 18344 #035-47-1993 L2003 **PD** *020 †55
OLSEN, Hans Peter, IV. 21 COMMERCE CIR 18344 #043-01-1999 L2005 **OSM** *020 †40
PULLEN, Harvey Test. PO BOX 171 18344 #041-09-1943 L1949 **IM PUD** *071 †50
SOMMA, Richard Martin. 21 COMMERCE CIR 18344 #033-05-1968 L1970 **OS N** *030 †20,75
VALENTA, George F. 21 COMMERCE CIR 18344 #048-14-1983 L1988 **OBG** *020 †30

MOUNT UNION — HUNTINGDON

DEPP-HUTCHINSON, Wm Scott. 100 S PARK ST 17066 #041-12-1988 L1990 **FM** *020 †18

MOUNT WASHINGTON — ALLEGHENY

JAMES, Jessica Kamalini. ■ 15211 #020-02-2005 L2006 **IM** *012
KOBBEMAN, Amy Elizabeth. ■ 15211 #038-43-2003 L2004 **DR** *012
KORKHOV, Vadim. ■ 15211 #305-01-2000 L2007 **CCM** *020 †20 ‡

MOUNTAIN TOP — LUZERNE

AHMED, Bina. ■ 18707 #704-16-1986 L2001 **IM** *020
ALI, Mirza. ■ 18707 #495-65-1983 L2001 **ID** *020 †20
ASCENCIO, Janice Krystal. ■ 18707 #051-01-1998 L2007 **OBG** *020 †30
BRAUNSTEIN, Larry. ■ 18707 #041-09-1993 L1995 **VIR** *020 †80
BUCKEY, Joseph Thos. 10 BIRCH ST, FAIRVIEW HEIGHTS 18707 #041-09-1941 L1942 **GP** *072
BUTTERFIELD, Jeanne. ■ 18707 #030-06-1957 L1959 **GS OS** *071
CHOONG, Shung Sen. ■ 18707 #244-01-1971 L1976 **GP** *075
DUA, Chetna. ■ 18707 #495-03-2002 L2008 **PD** *100
DUA, Punkaj Kumar. ■ 18707 #305-01-1999 L2008 **IM** *100 ‡
FISHER, Seth Myles. ■ 18707 #041-09-1948 L1949 **AN** *071 †05
GEORGIYEVSKIY, Sergey. 56 N MOUNTAIN BLVD, ANESTHESIA CARE CONSULTANT 18707 #913-04-1982 L2000 **AN** *071 †05
GILHOOLEY, Nancy. 12 KIRBY AVE 18707 #041-07-1991 L1993 **FM** *030 †18
HUANG, Albert. ■ 18707 #041-13-2007 L2008 **EM** *012
HUSSAINEE, Tasneem. 10 1/2 S MOUNTAIN BLVD 18707 #704-16-1989 L1998 **P CHP** *020 †75
KHAN, Iqbal. 10 1/2 S MOUNTAIN BLVD 18707 #704-02-1985 L1994 **N SME** *020 †75
LUCAS, Irene Diane. 62 N MOUNTAIN BLVD 18707 #041-09-1984 L1985 **FM** *020 †18 ‡
PANIKER, Kamala Devi. ■ 18707 #495-31-1964 L1975 **PTH GP** *062 †50
PANIKER, Vasudera N. ■ 18707 #654-01-1992 **FM** *100
POPIELARSKI, Edmund Paul. ■ 18707 #041-13-1973 L1974 **GP** *030 ‡
PUNEKAR, Rafi Ahmed A. ■ 18707 #495-72-1976 L1998 **AN** *020 †05
QULI, Syed Hossain. ■ 18707 #495-15-1959 L1980 **GS TS** *040 †85
RAHMAN, Shafiq-Ur. ■ 18707 #704-16-1981 L1994 **P** *020
RAJAMANICKAM, Natarajan. 56 N MOUNTAIN BLVD, ANESTHESIA CARE CONSULTANT 18707 #495-04-1987 L2000 **AN** *020
SHEEHY, James Michael. ■ 18707 #050-02-1985 L1992 **GS** *020
SHONK, John J, Jr. ■ 18707 #007-02-1984 L1986 **PM** *020 †60
SMITH, Henry Francis. ■ 18707 #041-02-1963 L1964 **FM** *020 †18
STACHOWIAK, Edward Jos. 140 N MOUNTAIN BLVD 18707 #654-01-1987 L1991 **FM** *020 †18
TEITELBAUM, Carl. ■ 18707 #016-42-1957 L1961 **OS GP** *071
TORRES, Albert Larino. ■ 18707 #649-14-1979 L1985 **AN** *020
VILLACRUSIS, Lucia T. ■ 18707 #748-02-1957 L1973 **FM IM** *071 †18
WANDER, Sharon Anita. ■ 18707 #308-07-1982 L1988 **PD FM** *062
YUM, Sun Young. ■ 18707 #583-02-2002 L2006 **P** *020

MOUNTVILLE — LANCASTER

BERNHEISEL, James Arthur. 2 COLLEGE AVE 17554 #041-13-1986 L1987 **FM** *020 †18
PARKE, James Wm. 2 COLLEGE AVE 17554 #035-45-1977 L1978 **FM** *020 †18
WESTGATE, Randy Ralph. 2 COLLEGE AVE 17554 #041-02-1980 L1981 **FM** *020 †18

MUNCY — LYCOMING

BELENKO, Michael Ira. 215 E WATER ST 17756 #035-09-1979 L1987 **PTH PCP** *020 †20,50 ‡
BORYS, David Joseph. 215 E WATER ST 17756 #041-09-1993 L1995 **HMP** *020 †50
DILLMAN, Nicholas Jos. 215 E WATER ST 17756 #041-13-1986 L1987 **PTH** *020 †50
GOODENOW, Elizabeth Lee. 9 S MAIN ST 17756 #041-13-1964 L1965 **GYN** *072
HILL, Daniel Edward. 215 E WATER ST 17756 #026-04-1969 L1974 **PTH BBK** *020 †50
LEATHERS, Donald Joel. 215 E WATER ST 17756 #041-14-1982 L1983 **PTH** *020 †50
LEBER, Paul Edward. 215 E WATER ST, MUNCY VALLEY HOSPITAL 17756 #041-12-1972 L1975 **EM FM** *020 †20 ‡
LEXON, Joseph J. 215 E WATER ST, MUNCY VALLEY HOSPITAL ED 17756 #041-02-1991 L1993 **FM** *020 †18
LUBBE, Willem J. 215 E WATER ST 17756 #836-02-1971 L1978 **OS** *020 †50
NAGPAL, Naresh Chandra. 10 SHADY LN, BOX 89 17756 #495-45-1974 L1981 **GS** *020 †85
PETERMAN, Heather Rae. 17756 #041-15-2001 L2001 **PTH** *100 †50
REDDY, Rajidimadan. 10 SHADY LN 17756 #495-57-1969 L1976 **CD IM** *020 †20
SCHWARTZ, Sheldon Miles. 215 E WATER ST 17756 #041-01-1977 L1981 **PTH** *020 †50 ‡
TREVOULEDES, Peter Basil. 10 SHADY LN STE 202 17756 #041-09-1989 L1997 **GS** *020 †85
YORDY, Steven Edward. 10 SHADY LN STE 103 17756 #038-40-1995 L1997 **FM** *020 †18

MUNHALL — ALLEGHENY

ARAVENA, Ernesto Baudilio. ■ 15120 #231-01-1965 L1974 **GS GE** *072

BHIMRAJ, Adarsh. ■ 15120 #495-65-1999 L2003 **ID** *012 †20
HANDELSMAN, Gordon Louis. 3212 MAIN ST 15120 #041-12-1983 L1986 **FM IMG** *020 †18
HASSAN, Rabih Hassan. ■ 15120 #605-01-2002 L2005 **IM** *012
MALINOWSKI, John Albin. 2000 WEST ST 15120 #041-13-1959 L1960 **OBG OS** *071 †30
SRINIVASAGAM, Narasimman. 1803 WEST ST 15120 #495-16-1960 L1970 **GP AN** *020 †18
THIELEMANN, Daniel George. ■ 15120 #027-01-2006 L2006 **IM** *012
WOLFSON, Brian Max. 600 E 12TH AVE 15120 #041-15-2002 L2002 **EM** *100 †16
YANG, Jennifer M J. ■ 15120 #748-02-1999 L2002 **SCI** *100 †60
ZELNIK, John Albert, Jr. ■ 15120 #041-12-1948 L1949 **OS GP** *072

MURRYSVILLE — WESTMORELAND

AHMED, Shema. ■ 15668 #704-02-1989 L2005 **IM** *020 †20
BIGLAN, Albert W. 4750 OLD WILLIAM PENN HWY, OLD WILLIAM PENN PROF BLDG 15668 #035-06-1968 L1969 **OPH PD** *071 †35 ‡
BLAND, Mary M. 4614 WILLIAM PENN HWY, FRANKLIN PLAZA 15668 #055-01-1994 L1997 **FM** *020 †60
BONFIGLIO, Richard Paul. 4125 OLD WILLIAM PENN HWY 15668 #025-01-1978 L1981 **PM** *020 †60
CHUNG, Kwang Ho. ■ 15668 #583-01-1979 L1981 **EM** *020 †16
DAVIS, John Scott. 4750 OLD WILLIAM PENN HWY 15668 #036-07-1981 L1993 **OPH PO** *020 †35
FERENCE, Lisa B. 4614 WILLIAM PENN HWY 15668 #047-05-1989 L1991 **FM** *020 †18
FLAHERTY, Kathleen Christ. ■ 15668 #023-12-2006 **FP** *012
GAMWO, Elsa Kuetiam. ■ 15668 #217-01-1990 L2004 **IM** *100
GOLDSTEIN, Jerome Eric. 3200 CAMBRIDGE CT 15668 #561-01-1981 L1985 **IM LM** *020 †20
GONZALEZ, Stephanie Marie. 3405 LASHAN DR 15668 #025-07-1994 L2002 **EM** *020 †16
GOWDA, Krishne N. ■ 15668 #495-37-1960 L1976 **GS** *071
HAGAN, James Lewis. ■ 15668 #041-12-1968 L1969 **R FM** *020 †80
HUGHES, Jane. 4750 OLD WILLIAM PENN HWY 15668 #041-02-1993 L1998 **PO** *020 †35 ‡
LOUGHMAN, Linda Kay. 4614 WILLIAM PENN HWY 15668 #041-09-1982 L1983 **FM** *020 †18
MANLEY, Mollie O. ■ 15668 #038-06-2007 L2007 **ORS** *012
MANTELL, Donald J. 3495 GREENSBURG RD 15668 #165-01-1978 L1980 **GP** *020
MC GARVEY, Richard N. ■ 15668 #041-12-1948 L1949 **OS** *030 †30
PAVIGLIANITI, Joseph C. 4750 OLD WILLIAM PENN HWY 15668 #011-04-1995 L2004 **OPH PO** *020 †35 ‡
PEIRSOL, Betty Louise. ■ 15668 #041-12-1955 L1956 **EM GS** *071
RAGHU, Usha Kalathur. ■ 15668 #495-16-1982 †074
RAY, Sourav. ■ 15668 #035-03-2002 L2002 **PTH** *100 †50
ROPERTI, Karen Ann. 3005 WEDGEWOOD CT, GREATER PITTSBURGH OB/GYN 15668 #041-02-1990 L1992 **OBG** *020 †18
ROSENBERG, Lisa Joy. 5032 IMPALA DR 15668 #045-01-1996 L1998 **IMG** *020 †20
SAHOTA, Sandeep. ■ 15668 #495-29-1985 L1999 **IM** *020 †20
SHETTY, Ashok K. 4212 OLD WILLIAM PENN HWY 15668 #495-09-1970 L1977 **IM IMG** *020 †20
TURNER, Carla Juanita. ■ 15668 #020-02-1982 L1983 **EM** *020 †18
VERY, Ronald Mark. 4948 ASHBAUGH RD 15668 #041-14-1986 L1987 **FM** *020 †18
WITT, Erik Kurt. ■ 15668 #041-12-1997 **PUD** *100

MYERSTOWN — LEBANON

COURTNEY, Drew E. 431 W LINCOLN AVE 17067 #041-02-1950 L1951 **FM** *071 †18
JOHNSON, Ellen Anne. 6 PERRI AVE 17067 #035-19-1986 L1987 **FM** *020 †18
KOVARIKOVA, Daria. 6 PERRI AVE, ELCO FAMILY HEALTH CENTER 17067 #286-05-1980 L1997 **FM** *020 †18
SHERPA, Tshering Wangdi. 431 W LINCOLN AVE 17067 #017-20-1993 L1998 **FM** *020 †18
YEAGER, Joel Eugene. 7 W PARK AVE, STONERIDGE FAMILY MEDICINE 17067 #905-02-2002 L2003 **FM** *020 †18
YEAGER, Luanne. 7 W PARK AVE 17067 #905-02-2002 L2002 **FM** *100 †18
YEAMANS, Bruce Edward. 431 W LINCOLN AVE BOX 217, FAMILY PRACTICE ASSOC PC 17067 #030-06-1974 L1977 **FM FPG** *020 †18 ‡
YODER, John Byard. 6 PERRI AVE 17067 #051-04-1980 L1983 **FM** *020 †18
ZIMMERMAN, Franklin D, Jr. ■ 17067 #041-02-1943 L1944 **GP** *071

NANTICOKE — LUZERNE

BRENNAN, John Patrick. ■ 18634 #041-02-1960 L1961 **CD IM** *020 †20
GAJULA, Rajendra Prasad. 130 W WASHINGTON ST 18634 #495-65-1980 L1992 **P** *020 †75
GRABOWSKI, Marie Hanish. 128 W WASHINGTON ST 18634 #041-07-1966 L1967 **PD** *020 †55
HUANG, Jung Tsung. 128 W WASHINGTON ST 18634 #244-04-1974 L1985 **FM** *020 †18
JOHN, Samuel H, Jr. 451 S HANOVER ST 18634 #041-09-1949 **IM FM** *074
KOTCH, Michael John. 40 N MARKET ST 18634 #041-09-1955 L1956 **GP OS** *071
PILAREK, Valentine Frank. 128 W WASHINGTON ST 18634 #041-13-1967 L1968 **GP** *020
ROSPIGLIOSI, Kelly Lynn. ■ 18634 #041-14-2006 L2006 **AN** *012
SCOTT, Alvin J. 128 W WASHINGTON ST 18634 #010-02-1950 L1951 **GP** *072
SHARMA, Rakesh K. 130 W WASHINGTON ST 18634 #495-84-1980 L1988 **P** *020 †75
SLAVOSKI, Linda A. 128 W WASHINGTON ST 18634 #041-07-1990 L1992 **ID IM** *020 †20
UDOSHI, Geeta M. NANTICOKE STATE HOSPITAL 18634 #495-35-1970 L1981 **IM** *020
WOLANIN, Janusz Ferdynano. 233 S PROSPECT ST 18634 #759-04-1979 L1982 **FM** *020 †18

NANTY GLO — CAMBRIA

JOHNSON, Daniel Wesley. 1060 LLOYD ST 15943 #038-45-1988 L1990 **FM** *020 †18
LEONARD, Daniel James, III. ■ 15943 #041-02-1990 L1992 **IM** *020 †20
TATARKO, Michael. 1060 LLOYD ST 15943 #041-02-1989 L1991 **FM** *020 †18

NARBERTH — MONTGOMERY

BENNETT, Ian Moore. 507 HOMEWOOD AVE 19072 #041-02-1998 L2000 **FM** *050 †18
BRAUN, Sarah Jane. 117 FORREST AVE, STE 101 19072 #005-02-1987 L1990 **P CHP** *020 †75
BRAVERMAN, Ron Alexander. 130 CONWAY AVE, PHYSICIAN MEDICINE DIVISIO 19072 #041-13-1986 L1989 **FM OM** *020 †18

BRUNNER, Richard A. ■ 19072 #041-01-1942 L1948 **P PYA** *072 †75
BUROCK, Marc Alexander. ■ 19072 #041-01-2003 L2007 **P** *100
CHAIN, William Thos. 327 WINDSOR AVE 19072 #041-02-1973 L1974 **IM ADM** *020 ‡
COFFIN, Laurence Haines. ■ 19072 #038-06-1959 L1959 **TS** *040 †85,90
COFFIN, Roberta R. ■ 19072 #038-06-1959 L1959 **PHP** *030 †55
DI SILVESTRO, John M A. ■ 19072 #561-17-1936 L1939 **IM GE** *071
FAICH, Gerald Alan. ■ 19072 #056-05-1968 L1991 **IM PA** *020 †20,70
FLOR, Armando W. ■ 19072 #319-01-1993 L2003 **PDE** *020 ‡
FREY, Noelle Virginia. ■ 19072 #035-01-2001 L2001 **HO** *020
GOLDENBERG, Paula C. ■ 19072 #040-02-2003 L2007 **MG** *012 †19,55
HOOVER, Todd Alan. 822 MONTGOMERY AVE, STE 306 19072 #041-02-1984 L1986 **FM OM** *018
JORDAN, Hugh Anthony. ■ 19072 #539-04-1972 L1985 **DR** *020
KELLY, Jeane Neskodny. ■ 19072 #036-07-1971 L1972 **IM RHU** *020
KELLY, John Thomas. ■ 19072 #024-01-1979 L1994 **OS EM** *030
KUDRJAVCEV, Tatiana. 425 GROVE PL, PEDIATRIC NEUROLOGIST 19072 #005-06-1969 L1989 **CHN PD** *071 †55
LYTTON, Margaret Steane. 145 N NARBERTH AVE 19072 #041-07-1979 L1993 **FM** *020 †18
MADY, Mackenzie A. ■ 19072 #041-77-2007, ▲ L2007 *012
MOREIN-FRENCH, Heather Ly. ■ 19072 #005-18-2002 L2002 **NPM** *012 †55
PASTERNAK, Rona Eve. 438 ANTHWYN RD, PASTERNAK, LLC 19072 #028-03-1987 L1989 **P** *020 †75
PORTER, Huntington. ■ 19072 #024-01-1944 L1948 **N** *071
RAMSEY, Matthew Reuling. 206 PRICE AVE 2ND FL 19072 #422-01-2006 L2006 **TY** *012
REED, Amy J. ■ 19072 #041-01-2005 L2006 **AN** *012
RUETER, Jens. ■ 19072 #408-30-2000 L2007 **HO** *012 †20
SCHULZ, Kevin Jeffrey. ■ 19072 #041-15-2008 *012
SOLOMON, Alyson Jill. ■ 19072 #041-01-2000 **PTH** *100
STALLKAMP, Christine Ciel. 145 N NARBERTH AVE, LOWER MERION FAMILY PRACTI 19072 #041-02-2000 L2004 **FM** *020
SWANN, Leah Joy. ■ 19072 #041-02-2007 L2007 **FP** *012
VAN TASSEL, Pamela. ■ 19072 #012-01-1979 L2004 **DR OS** *020 †80
WASILEWSKI, Christine L. ■ 19072 #021-01-2001 L2005 **HO** *012
YANG, Kalen. ■ 19072 #023-01-2000 L2005 **IM** *100
YEO, Charles John. ■ 19072 #023-07-1979 L2005 **GS SO** *020 †85

NATRONA HEIGHTS – ALLEGHENY

AGGARWAL, Avinash. 2865 FREEPORT RD 15065 #495-30-1985 L1993 **N** *020 †75
AHUJA, Suman. 805 JEFFERSON AVE 15065 #495-18-1971 L1980 **P** *020 †75
BALASH, William Richard. 1623 UNION AVE 15065 #010-02-1956 L1957 **IM END** *020 ‡
BARNES, Arthur Edward, II. 1604 BURTNER RD, STE 2100 15065 #041-13-1953 L1954 **IM ON** *071 †20
BAUER, James Earl. 1300 CARLISLE ST 15065 #041-12-1960 L1970 **R** *071 †80
BOBBETT, Cameron Mitchell. 1301 CARLISLE ST, ALLE-KISKE MEDICAL CENTER 15065 #045-01-2001 L2004 **EM** *020 †16
BORGIA, Frank Anthony. 1629 UNION AVE, MEDICAL ARTS BUILDING 15065 #041-02-1973 L1978 **GS** *020 †85
BOYLE, Mary Catherine. 1600 PACIFIC AVE, CCP- NATRONA HEIGHTS 15065 #041-12-1993 L1995 **PD** *020 †55
BREGAR, Frank Wm. 1301 CARLISLE ST, ALLEGHENY VALLEY HOSP 15065 #041-12-1980 L1981 **EM GS** *020 ‡
CHAMBERS, Carolyn Ann. 3063 FREEPORT RD 15065 #038-40-1989 L1993 **OBG** *020 †30
CHESEK, Lorraine M. 1600 PACIFIC AVE, C C P NATRONA HEIGHTS 15065 #033-06-1982 L1988 **PD** *020 †55
DALY, Peter Francis, Jr. 1600 PACIFIC AVE, CCP-NATRONA HEIGHTS 15065 #033-06-1981 L1988 **PD** *020 †55
DIVELBISS, Karen L. 1301 CARLISLE ST, ALLKSKI MDCL CTR RDTN 15065 #018-03-1991 L1996 **DR** *020 †80
DVORAK, Mary Dolores. ■ 15065 #041-02-1988 L1990 **IM PD** *020 †20,55
EAGON, Catherine Louise. 1719 UNION AVE 15065 #041-12-1997 L1999 **IM** *020 †20
FALCON, Jos Richard, Jr. 2913 FREEPORT RD 15065 #041-09-1977 L1978 **PS HS** *020 †65 ‡
FETCHKO, Alexander M. 1301 CARLISLE ST 15065 #028-34-1948 L1950 **OBG** *071
FETCHKO, Joseph Paul. ■ 15065 #041-12-1993 L1997 **CHP** *020 †75
FINLEY, Gene Grant. 1301 CARLISLE ST, ALLE-KISKI MEDICAL CENTER- 15065 #041-12-1981 L1983 **HO IM** *020 †20
FRIEDMAN, Bart Jeffrey. 1301 CARLISLE ST, DEPT OF RADIOLOGY 15065 #041-09-1976 L1981 **DR** *040 †80
GIBSON, Alice S. 1600 PACIFIC AVE, CCP-NATRONA HEIGHTS 15065 #041-12-1980 L1981 **PD** *020 †55
GOLIO, Anthony Geo. 3063 FREEPORT RD STE A 15065 #035-06-1982 L1988 **U** *020 †95
GORDON, Thomas John. 2853 FREEPORT RD 15065 #038-40-1974 L1977 **OPH EM** *020 †35 ‡
HANZLIK, Heather M. 1719 UNION AVE STE A 15065 #041-13-1997 L2000 **IM** *020 †20
HARTNER, Miriam Sturgeon. 1301 CARLISLE ST 15065 #041-12-1962 L1963 **P CHP** *020
HOWER, Robert David. 1629 UNION AVE, MEDICAL ARTS BLDG 15065 #041-13-1972 L1973 **GS** *020 †85 ‡
HUSAINI, Syed Nayeemullah. 1624 PACIFIC AVE 15065 #495-61-1975 L1983 **CD IM** *020 †20
JONES, Heather Angellaann. 1604 BURTNER RD, RADIATION ONCO UPMC 1ST FL 15065 #010-03-1998 L2001 **RO** *020 †80
KALINOWSKI, Denise T. 2801 FREEPORT RD, RADIOLOGICAL IMAGING ASSOC 15065 #055-01-1977 L1978 **R NM** *020 †80
KAUSE, Suzanne Marie. 1301 CARLISLE ST 15065 #016-11-1992 L1995 **EM** *020 †16
KIM, Wha Sun. 1301 CARLISLE ST, ALLEGHENY VALLEY HOSPITAL 15065 #583-01-1968 L1975 **PTH** *071 †50 ‡
KIM, Yong Deok. 1301 CARLISLE ST, ALLKSKI MDCL CTR RDTN 15065 #583-02-1959 L1972 **R RO** *071 †80
KRASINSKY, Walter Greg. 1627 UNION AVE, STE 1 15065 #041-15-2000 L2002 **OPH** *100 †35
KUMAR, Rakesh. 1629 UNION AVE, STE 2 15065 #496-03-1977 L1985 **IM FM** *020
LEIGH, Rewng. 1629 UNION AVE, MEDICAL ARTS BLDG 15065 #583-02-1966 L1972 **GS** *020 †85
LICHTER, James Gross. 1621 UNION AVE STE C 15065 #035-03-1973 L1975 **HO IM** *020 †20
MALLOY, Edward Leo. 1604 BURTNER RD 15065 #041-12-1973 L1975 **ON HEM** *020 †20
MEHTA, Ravindra Kumar. 1301 CARLISLE ST 15065 #495-30-1980 L1986 **IM P** *020 †75
MIECKOWSKI, Gregory C. 1301 CARLISLE ST, ALLEGHENY VALLY HOSP 15065 #041-12-1980 L1982 **DR** *020 †80

MILLER, Calvin Jos. 1301 CARLISLE ST, ALLE-KISKI MEDICAL CENTER 15065 #041-13-1980 L1981 **EM** *020 †16
MUCHLADO, Felix J. ■ 15065 #041-09-1943 L1944 **OPH GP** *071
NADDOUR, Murhaf. 3063 FREEPORT RD, STE C 15065 #875-01-1985 L1999 **OBG** *020 †30 ‡
NATH, Manju Eswarappa. 1301 CARLISLE ST, ALLEGHENY VALLEY HSOPITAL 15065 #495-99-1980 L1987 **PTH** *020 †50
NAYAK, Satish R. 1600 PACIFIC AVE STE 4 15065 #495-37-1972 L1978 **OBG** *020 †30
NGUYEN, Nghi Van. 1301 CARLISLE ST, DEPT ANES 15065 #941-01-1967 L1979 **AN OS** *071 †05
OEHRLE, John Scott. 1301 CARLISLE ST 15065 #041-12-1963 L1968 **PTH HMP** *020 †50
OSTLUND, Warren Francis. 1301 CARLISLE ST, DEPT OF RADIOLOGY 15065 #026-04-1968 L1983 **DR FM** *020 †80
PACEK, Robert Francis. ■ 15065 #041-12-1963 L1964 **GP PD** *071 †18
PORTNOY, Scott Laurence. 2853 FREEPORT RD 15065 #021-01-1985 L1989 **OPH** *020 †35
RAGHEB, Youssef Shafik. 591 SUGAR LOAF LN, MEDICAL ARTS BUILDING 15065 #915-04-1967 L1978 **OBG** *071 ‡
ROPPOLO, Helen M Nowicki. 2801 FREEPORT RD, R I A 15065 #025-01-1969 L1971 **DR RNR** *020 †80 ‡
SCHEID, Edward Randolph. 1301 CARLISLE ST, DEPT OF RADIOLOGY 15065 #038-06-1984 L1985 **DR** *020 †80
SCOTT, Elaine Barbara. 1301 CARLISLE ST, AKMC ALLEGHENY VLY HOSP 15065 #041-12-1980 L1981 **PM FPG** *020 †18,60 ‡
SIGAL, Michael B. 2853 FREEPORT RD 15065 #041-13-1983 L1987 **OPH PO** *020 †35
SINGH, Datar. 1709 UNION AVE 15065 #495-03-1971 L1975 **OBG** *020 †30
SMITH, Ryan Patrick. 1604 BURTNER RD 15065 #041-13-1999 L2001 **RO** *020 †80
SONG, Kyo Chul. 1301 CARLISLE ST 15065 #583-15-1983 L1993 **PTH** *020 †50
SUWAN, Sarun. 1629 UNION AVE 15065 #041-13-1997 L2000 **GS** *020 †85
SZYMKOWIAK, Vidya. 1604 BURTNER RD, STE 2100 15065 #041-12-1999 L2002 **IM** *020 †20
TANG, Denny. 1629 UNION AVE 15065 #041-13-1998 L2001 **CRS** *020 †85,10
WALLEY, Robert Emmett, III. 1301 CARLISLE ST, PENNA ANES PROVIDERS INC 15065 #041-13-1966 L1969 **AN** *071 †05
WENIGER, Frederick Chas. 1301 CARLISLE ST, AKMC ANESTHESIA 15065 #041-12-1971 L1972 **AN** *020 ‡
WIENEKE, Karl, III. 1301 CARLISLE ST, PAP ALLE KISKI MED CTR 15065 #010-02-1989 L1993 **AN** *020 †05
WILSON, Richard Alvin. ALLEGHENY UNIV HOSP, REHABILITATION SERVICES 15065 #041-12-1957 L1958 **PM** *071 †60,18
ZOVE, Daniel Craig. 1600 PACIFIC AVE, CCP-NATRONA HEIGHTS 15065 #035-46-1988 L1990 **PD** *020 †55 ‡

NAZARETH – NORTHAMPTON

AMRICK, Christopher J. ■ 18064 #041-02-1992 L1996 **EM** *020 †16
AZCONA, Oscar C. ■ 18064 #748-08-1960 L1982 **GP** *071
ECKHARDT, Linda Decker. 111 S SPRUCE ST 18064 #033-05-1992 L2000 **FM** *100 †18
GURUNATHAN, Sanjay. ■ 18064 #496-09-1989 L1994 **ID** *020 †20
HOCH, John Junior. ■ 18064 #041-02-1955 L1956 **FM DIA** *071 †18
KAUR, Simrat. 305 W NORTH ST 18064 #495-29-1996 L2004 **IM** *020 †20
KINDT, Willard F. ■ 18064 #023-01-1951 L1952 **GP** *071
KUCHARSKI, Andrzej. 305 W NORTH ST 18064 #759-06-1986 L2000 **FM** *020 †18
LIAO, Xiang. ■ 18064 #242-17-1987 **IG MM** *050
MARTIN, James Jos. 305 W NORTH ST 18064 #041-02-1984 L1985 **FM** *020 †18
OOMMEN, Shobin. ■ 18064 #894-01-2001 L2007 **P** *100
POGODZINSKI, Christopher. 25 S BROAD ST, STE 104 18064 #024-16-1992 L1998 **FM** *020 †18
PRESTIFILIPPO, Orazio. ■ 18064 #561-15-1960 L1966 **FM** *071
SNYDER, Robert Lucas. ■ 18064 #041-09-1957 L1958 **FM AM** *071
SPADONI, Joseph Lawrence. 4537 FOXTAIL DR 18064 #041-09-1976 L1979 **EM IM** *020 †20,16 ‡
STEINSIECK, Robert T. ■ 18064 #035-01-1944 L1969 **GS** *071 †85
WASSON, James Christopher. 534 S MAIN ST 18064 #041-02-1993 L1995 **IM** *020 †20 ‡

NEW BETHLEHEM – CLARION

DRUMMOND, Jack Newton. ■ 16242 #036-05-1957 L1957 **OS FM** *030 †18
SHAFFER, Chad Ryan. 3615 STATE ROUTE 28 AND 66 16242 #041-14-2001 L2001 **MPD** *020 †20,55

NEW BLOOMFIELD – PERRY

BELMONT, Frank Albert. ■ 17068 #010-02-1945 L1948 **OBG GP** *071

NEW BRIGHTON – BEAVER

BOOK, Morris Maynard. 1520 3RD AVE, ASSOCIATION OF SPECIALTY 15066 #005-15-1973 L1980 **GS VS** *020 †85
BURKE, Marshall Lynn. 1520 3RD AVE, ASSOCIATION OF SPECIALTY 15066 #055-01-1975 L1987 **GS** *020 †85
FUNKHOUSER, Jay Lewis. 721 5TH AVE 15066 #041-12-1961 L1962 **FM OBG** *020 †18
KIM, Kyung Hwa. 1520 3RD AVE, ASSOCIATION OF SPECIALTY 15066 #005-14-1994 L1999 **GS** *020 †85
NADIGA, Chandrasekharappa. 910 3RD AVE 15066 #495-37-1961 L1979 **OM** *020
SHETTY, Ratnakar S. 1307 6TH AVE 15066 #495-01-1962 L1973 **IM PUD** *020

NEW BRITAIN – BUCKS

GOLDSTEIN, Scott M. 352 E BUTLER AVE 18901 #024-05-1996 L1998 **OPH FPS** *020 †35
LONDON, Debra Sue. ■ 18901 #056-06-1984 L1985 **P** *020 †75
MENACKER, Sheryl Jablon. 352 E BUTLER AVE 18901 #041-07-1982 L1983 **PO OS** *020 †35 ‡
MILLER, David Harry. 352 E BUTLER AVE 18901 #041-02-1967 L1968 **OPH** *020 †35 ‡

■ = Address Information Privacy Protected

NEW CASTLE – LAWRENCE

ABUL-ELA, Ahmad E. ■ 16105 #330-02-1961 L1973 **GS VS** *071 †85

ABUL-ELA, Mohamad. 212 ENCLAVE DR 16105 #915-04-1972 L1983 **IM** *020

ACOSTA, Elbert R, II. 3128 WILMINGTON RD 16105 #305-01-1983 L1985 **IM** *020

AHMED, Wasim. 29 E NORTH ST, STE 203 16101 #704-16-1989 L2000 **NEP IM** *020 †20

ALI, Mohammad Irshad. 217 N JEFFERSON ST 16105 #495-20-1966 L1974 **PUD IM** *020 †20

AMEDIA, Chester A, Jr. 178 ENCLAVE DR, STE 200 16105 #038-40-1973 L1985 **NEP IM** *030 †20

AMINA, Suresh Prakash. 2623 WILMINGTON RD, STE B 16105 #495-21-1970 L1979 **U** *020 †95

ANDERSON, David Stewart. 1211 WILMINGTON AVE 16105 #038-43-1991 L1997 **EM** *020 †16

ANTONESCU, Doina. 3121 WILMINGTON RD 16105 #781-03-1983 L1997 **PD** *020

ANTONESCU, George. 2655 ELLWOOD RD 16101 #781-03-1976 L1995 **PD** *020 †55

AROMATORIO, George John. 145 ENCLAVE DR 16105 #041-12-1980 L1981 **CD IC** *020 †20

BAINS, Anup S. 143 ENCLAVE DR 16105 #495-29-1986 L1997 **NEP** *020 †20

BASSALY, Rifaat Roshdy. 1 W WASHINGTON ST, OLDE POST OFFICE COMPLEX 16101 #330-02-1965 L1971 **OBG** *020 †30

BELVEDERE, David Anthony. 145 ENCLAVE DR 16105 #041-12-1979 L1980 **CD IM** *020 †20

BENDONI, Roberto. 1112 S MILL ST 16101 #561-02-1986 L1999 **IM** *020 †20

BIWOJNO, Christopher S. 1211 WILMINGTON AVE, JAMESON MEMORIAL HOSPITAL 16105 #759-04-1979 L1985 **IM PTH** *020 †20

BOWER, James Norman. 3349 WILMINGTON RD 16105 #041-12-1960 L1961 **FPG** *030 †18

BURICK, Sheila Marie. 1112 S MILL ST, NEW CASTLE PRIMARY CARE 16101 #041-09-1988 L1990 **IM PD** *020 †20,55

CALLAGHAN, Daniel Jos, Jr. 3126 WILMINGTON RD 16105 #010-02-1980 L1982 **OTO** *020 †45

CAROLIPIO, Raynaldo R. 1211 WILMINGTON AVE, JAMESON MEMORIAL HOSPITAL 16105 #748-08-1971 L1975 **GP EM** *020

COOK, Albert James. 1211 WILMINGTON AVE, RADIOLOGY DEPARTMENT 16105 #038-06-1966 L2004 **R RNR** *020 †80

COOK, Albert James, II. 1211 WILMINGTON AVE 16105 #038-44-1990 L2004 **RNR VIR** *020 †80

CORBETT, John Michael. 2602 WILMINGTON RD 16105 #041-09-1964 L1971 **ORS** *071 †40

DE JESUS, Michael Yman. 2602 WILMINGTON RD, ASSOCIATES 16105 #748-10-1999 L2001 **GE** *020 †20

DHEEN, Mohamed Husaiwul R. 168 ENCLAVE DR 16105 #220-01-1968 L1975 **IM CD** *020 †20

DOE, Nathaniel S. 143 ENCLAVE DR 16105 #410-01-1983 L1995 **NEP IM** *020 †20

DUANGNET, Chatree. 2602 WILMINGTON RD, MEDICAL ARTS BLDG 16105 #891-01-1970 L1976 **PD OS** *020 †55

ENRIQUEZ, Joel Suarez. 122 GLOVER RD 16105 #748-08-1972 L1984 **AN** *075

FADDEN, Robert Jos. 2602 WILMINGTON RD, ASSOCIATES 16105 #023-01-1982 L1985 **GE** *020 †20

FALLON, L Fleming, Jr. ■ 16101 #422-01-1984 **PHP OM** *040

FAZIOLI, Lawrence A. 2520 WILMINGTON RD 16105 #654-01-1987 L1990 **FM** *020 †18

FENNER, Henry Edgar. 1000 S MERCER ST 16101 #041-13-1958 L1959 **PTH** *071 †50 ‡

FITZSIMONS, John Peter. 1211 WILMINGTON AVE 16105 #016-06-1989 L2006 **VIR** *020 †80

FLANNERY, Wilbur Eugene. 131 N COLUMBUS INTERBELT, MEDICAL DIRECTOR 16101 #024-01-1935 L1936 **IM** *072

FLORES, Carlos Isidro. 11 SHENANGO RD, STE 2 16105 #649-02-1974 L1976 **PD AI** *020 †55

GABRIEL, Larry Chas. 29 E NORTH ST 16101 #023-07-1980 L1984 **OPH** *020 †35

GABRIEL, Steven Alexander. 29 E NORTH ST, STE 100 16101 #649-36-1979 L1981 **IM** *020

GARDNER, James Larimer. 804 N JEFFERSON ST 16105 #041-02-1972 L1973 **GS VS** *020

GARDNER, Stuart Alexander. 401 N JEFFERSON ST 16101 #041-02-1979 L1984 **ORS** *020 †40

GILLELAND, William N, Jr. 804 N JEFFERSON ST, GENERAL & VASCULAR SURGEON 16101 #041-12-1989 L1992 **GS** *020 †85

GRAHAM, Timothy Smith. 3120 WILMINGTON RD 16105 #021-01-1982 L1983 **ORS** *020 †40

GREGORY, James Gordon. 3131 WILMINGTON RD 16105 #649-02-1992 L1998 **FM** *020 †18

GROSSMAN, Louis Ward, Jr. 25 N MILL ST, FIRST FEDERAL PLAZA 16101 #023-01-1947 L1948 **IM CD** *071

GUERRERO, Purisima T. 1211 WILMINGTON AVE 16105 #748-11-1972 L1983 **AN** *020

HENDERSON, Robert Earl. ■ 16105 #041-01-1952 L1953 **GS** *071

HOUSTON, Robert Ross, Jr. 145 ENCLAVE DR 16105 #041-02-1975 L1976 **CD IM** *020 †20

INGLESE, Roberto. 2602 WILMINGTON RD, ASSOCIATES 16105 #561-17-1980 L1991 **GE** *020 †20

ISIDRO, Eugenio Gonzales. ■ 16105 #748-01-1956 L1963 **CLP PTH** *071 †50

JEROME-ZAPADKA, Karen M. 2602 WILMINGTON RD, ASSOCIATES 16105 #041-12-1988 L1991 **GE IM** *020 †20

KARASHIN, Elizabeth Seed. 1211 WILMINGTON AVE, RADIOLOGY DEPARTMENT 16105 #048-78-1998, ▲ L2000 **DR** *020 †80

KIM, Je Hong. 177 ENCLAVE DR 16105 #583-02-1971 L1976 **PM** *020 †60

KOSTUREK, Anna Barbara. 130 W NORTH ST, HSC 16101 #759-06-1979 L2002 **P** *020 †75

LAMANCUSA, Nancy Cecelia. 117 ANGELA LN 16101 #041-07-1957 L1973 **GP OBG** *020

LAMB, Joann Helen. 188 ENCLAVE DR 16105 #041-14-1996 L1998 **FM** *020 †18

LAN, David D Y. 1211 WILMINGTON AVE, RADIOLOGY DEPARTMENT 16105 #244-06-1968 L1976 **R** *020

LANDSBERG, Marc Alan. 1000 S MERCER ST 16101 #041-13-1975 L1976 **OBG** *020 †30

LARKIN, Michael James. 2602 WILMINGTON RD 16105 #041-13-1977 L1978 **ORS** *020 †40

LIEDKE, Richard David. 104 PLAZA ST S 16101 #041-09-1975 L1976 **OM IM** *020 †20,16

LINGANNA, Avinash. 3450 CARMELA DR 16105 #041-15-2003 L2003 **CD** *012 †20

LINGANNA, Bhattarahally Y. 1232 S MILL ST 16101 #495-09-1964 L1978 **IM** *020 †20

MAGDA, Jerzy K. 125 ENCLAVE DR, # 1 16105 #759-01-1987 L1993 **IM** *020

MALVAR, Maritoni Cynthia. 178 ENCLAVE DR 16105 #748-10-1996 L2002 **FM** *100 †18

MALVAR, Thomas Joseph. 178 ENCLAVE DR 16105 #748-10-1997 L2002 **FM** *020 †18

MALVAR, Thomas Q. 178 ENCLAVE DR 16105 #748-01-1953 L1963 **GP** *020

MAMARIL, Amelita. 3315 WILMINGTON RD 16105 #748-16-1981 L1993 **PD** *020

MANCINO, Peter Jos. ■ 16105 #041-02-1958 L1960 **IM** *020

MARCELLA, Lawrence Chas. ■ 16105 #010-01-1955 L1956 **OBG** *071 †30

MASTRIAN, Anthony Saml. RR 5 16105 #041-13-1959 L1960 **GS** *071

MATTA-ARMANIOUS, Shoukry. 130 W NORTH ST, HUMAN SERVICES CENTER 16101 #915-04-1958 L1971 **P CHP** *020 †75

MC CLURE, Jonathan Knight. 2602 WILMINGTON RD, ASSOCIATES 16105 #041-12-1977 L1979 **GE** *020 †20

MC CONAHY, John Glass. ■ 16103 #024-01-1945 L1946 **D** *071 †15

MEDRANO-COLEMAN, Silvia E. 125 ENCLAVE DR 16105 #270-02-1989 L1994 **IM** *020 †20

MENDEL, Isadore. ■ 16105 #038-40-1957 L1985 **R** *071 †80

MIRRA, Theodore Robt. 1211 WILMINGTON AVE, JAMESON MEMORIAL HOSPITAL 16105 #012-05-1989 L1995 **R VIR** *020 †80

MOSKOVITZ, Morry. 2602 WILMINGTON RD, ASSOCIATES 16105 #041-13-1973 L1974 **GE IM** *020 †20

NAGY, Christine Lynn. 1 W WASHINGTON ST 16101 #041-09-1991 L1994 **OBG** *020 †30

NEWMARK, Abe Arthur. ■ 16105 #041-02-1934 L1935 **PD** *071

NORD, Roland Eugene. 1211 WILMINGTON AVE 16105 #041-12-1955 L1956 **GP** *020

ONG, Bienvenido Sarao. 1211 WILMINGTON AVE 16105 #041-07-1965 L1973 **PTH** *020 †50

PADGITT, Kathleen Slavin. 143 ENCLAVE DR 16105 #038-44-1989 L1993 **NEP** *020 †20

PALUMBO, Kelly Ann. 1906 WILMINGTON RD 16105 #041-13-1995 L1999 **OBG** *020 †30

PANELLA, Michael Jos. ■ 16105 #041-07-1989 L1994 **FOP** *100 †50

PARAS, Nora Flores. 3413 WILMINGTON RD 16105 #748-08-1991 L2002 **IMG** *020 †20

PATEL, Kanchanlal S. 415 HIGHLAND AVE 16101 #495-48-1971 L1980 **GP** *020

PENKROT, Ronald Jos. 2019 PENNSYLVANIA AVE 16101 #041-12-1977 L1978 **DR GP** *020 †80

PHILLIPS, Howard Troy, III. 1211 WILMINGTON AVE 16105 #055-01-1971 L1976 **ORS AM** *071 †40

PICCIONE, Elizabeth Ann. 2602 WILMINGTON RD, STE 200 16105 #041-12-1997 L2000 **CD** *020 †20

POMMERSHEIM, William John. 217 N JEFFERSON ST, UROLOGIC ASSOCIATES 16101 #041-12-1958 L1959 **U** *071 †95

PROCTOR, Julian Warrilow. 2602 WILMINGTON RD, STE 104 16105 #917-24-1967 L1979 **RO** *020 †80

RANIERI, Thomas Anthony. ■ 16101 #020-12-1982 L1987 **AN** *020 †05

REDOVAN, Edward Gregory. 708 N JEFFERSON ST 16101 #041-13-1982 L1984 **OPH GS** *020 †35

REZK, Hany S. 1750 NEW BUTLER RD 16101 #915-02-1975 L1996 **IM** *020 †20

RICHARDSON, W Randolph. 26 NESBITT RD, STE 110 16105 #012-05-1987 L1990 **P** *020 †75

SABLE, Jeremiah Henry. ■ 16105 #038-06-1983 L1986 **FM** *020 †18

SCOTT, Van Edward. 214 ENCLAVE DR 16105 #025-01-1980 L1998 **PMM** *020

SHAER, Andrea Jill. 143 ENCLAVE DR 16105 #041-02-1993 L2002 **NEP** *020 †20

SHAFFER, Terry Deane. 130 ENCLAVE DR 16105 #041-07-1983 L1984 **DR** *020 †80 ‡

SIMON, Sheryl Randy. 2602 WILMINGTON RD STE 101 16105 #016-02-1978 L1985 **ON HO** *020 †20

SIRIPONG, Silpachai. 29 E NORTH ST 16101 #891-01-1970 L1985 **GS** *020 †85

SOLIMAN, Sherif Awad. 143 ENCLAVE DR 16105 #915-05-1989 L2001 **NEP IM** *020 †20

SOMMERFELD, James P. 3121 WILMINGTON RD, STE 3 16105 #041-09-1951 L1954 **PD OS** *071 †55

SRIPAN, Teerasit. 29 E NORTH ST STE 200 16101 #891-01-1970 L1973 **PS GS** *020 †85,65

STARR, Robert, Jr. 2024 E WASHINGTON ST, RICHARD A PAPA DO FAAP 16101 #055-01-1989 L1991 **P** *075 †75

STONER, J Fred. 218 W MOODY AVE 16101 #231-05-1984 L1991 **PTH OS** *020 †50

SUNG, Paul. 1612 W STATE ST 16101 #583-03-1969 L1975 **FM** *020

TATA, Ramachandra Rao. 2602 WILMINGTON RD, MED ARTS BLDG STE 103 16105 #495-11-1976 L1994 **N** *020 †75

TEH, Pek Chiew. 3121 WILMINGTON RD 16105 #244-04-1972 L1979 **OBG** *020 †30

TEJPAR, Mohamed Kassamali. 2602 WILMINGTON RD STE 208 16105 #905-01-1972 L1975 **IM** *020 †20

TOCA, Angel R, Jr. 1211 WILMINGTON AVE, DEPT LAB 16105 #308-01-1987 L1993 **PTH** *020 †50 ‡

TRAGO, Durell Vincent, Jr. 1211 WILMINGTON AVE 16105 #038-45-1987 L2004 **DR** *020 †80

TURNER, Harry Leland, Jr. 1211 WILMINGTON AVE 16105 #027-01-1976 L2001 **DR** *020 †80

ULHAQ, Ata. 3548 ELLWOOD RD, MID WAY MEDICAL CLINIC 16101 #517-05-1979 L1980 **FM OM** *020 †50,16

VASSILAROS, Leonidas Geor. 143 ENCLAVE DR 16105 #418-01-1982 L1985 **NEP IM** *020 †20

VIRAY, Nick. 3413 WILMINGTON RD 16105 #748-20-1984 L1992 **IM** *020 ‡

WADHWA, Kamal Prasad. 2602 WILMINGTON RD 16105 #495-36-1964 L1972 **CD IM** *020 †20

WANG, Jenny J Y. 3121 WILMINGTON RD 16105 #243-47-1970 L1995 **OBG** *020 †30

WAWRZYNSKI, Paul Eugene. 2602 WILMINGTON RD, STE 200 16105 #041-12-1990 L1996 **CD** *020 †20

WILLIAMS, Lynn Ryan. 3105 WILMINGTON RD 16105 #041-02-1988 L1990 **D** *020 †15 ‡

WRIGHT, William Russell. 2 CASCADE GALLERIA 16101 #041-12-1954 L1955 **OBG** *071 †30

WRIGHTSON, John David. 3212 WILMINGTON RD STE 20 16105 #035-15-1989 L1996 **EM PME** *020 †60

YACOUB, Basem A. 1211 WILMINGTON AVE 16105 #915-03-1979 L2006 **DR** *020 †80,28

YAKOOB, Shahid. 217 N JEFFERSON ST, STE C 16101 #704-16-1995 L2004 **IM PCC** *100 †20

YUMANG, Norberto Yamat. 2539 WILMINGTON RD 16105 #748-07-1961 L1974 **EM GP** *020

ZIMMER, Wayne Michael. 3126 WILMINGTON RD 16105 #035-06-1989 L1991 **OTO FPS** *020 †45

NEW CUMBERLAND – CUMBERLAND

ANDERSON, Darryl Putney. ■ 17070 #023-01-2001 L2001 **NEP** *012 †20

CICCARELLI, Clem Anthony. 503 BRIDGE ST, GREEN PROF BLDG 17070 #036-05-1980 L1981 **FM OBS** *020 †18 ‡

CUSHNER, Courtney Catheri. ■ 17070 #036-05-2008 *012

EDWARDS, George E. 1900 BRIDGE ST 17070 #041-12-1952 L1953 **GP** *071

GEBERT, Harry Falck. ■ 17070 #041-02-1980 L1981 **FM GS** *075 †18

GEBERT, Janice Williams. ■ 17070 #041-07-1980 L1981 **FM** *074 †18

JONES, James Edward. ■ 17070 #041-01-1959 L1960 **PD OS** *071 †55

LITTLE, George Robt. 1900 BRIDGE ST 17070 #041-09-1963 L1964 **GP** *020

POTTER, Donald Edward. ■ 17070 #561-11-1978 L1987 **GPM OM** *020

REZA, Robert Joel. ■ 17070 #035-01-1969 L1973 **PUD IM** *075 †20

RHODES, Joshua Thomas. 834 RUDYTOWN RD 17070 #041-14-2000 L2004 **AN** *100 †05

ROSAMILIA, Lorraine Larse. ■ 17070 #041-14-2005 L2005 **D** *012

SCHAFFER, Sonja. 1515 BRIDGE ST, SMITH RADIOLOGY INC 17070 #429-01-1978 L1981 **DR** *020 †80

VARMA, Seema. ■ 17070 #495-56-1964 L1979 **OBG** *020

NEW EAGLE – WASHINGTON

MICHAEL, Joseph Thos. 433 MAIN ST 15067 #041-12-1981 L1983 **IM FM** *020 †20

SCIALDONE, Anthony M. 314 7TH AVE 15067 #023-01-1979 L1980 **EM** *020 †16

NEW FLORENCE – INDIANA

COOK, Anne Houston Rush. ■ 15944 #010-01-1946 L1948 **DR** *071

KUNKLE, Richard Francis. 241 GROSS RD, HIGH TURR FARM 15944 #041-12-1971 L1976 EM AM *071 †16

WOZNIAK, Richard Stephen. 138 N VIEW HTS 15944 #041-09-1984 L1985 FM FPG *040 †18

NEW FREEDOM – YORK

BORTNER, Donald Leroy. 40 S BROAD ST 17349 #041-02-1958 L1960 FM *071

BRANGO, Carl Wm. 13515 WOLFE RD, STE C 17349 #055-01-1992 L1994 FM *020 †18

CUTTI, Eric Moore. 13515 WOLFE RD, STE C 17349 #033-06-1996 L1999 FM *020 †18

GRIM, Tracey Pamela. 13515 WOLFE RD 17349 #041-13-1987 L1989 OBG *020 †30

HENRIKSEN, Susan A. 13515 WOLFE RD 17349 #041-07-1990 L1992 FM *040 †18

HILMAS, Corey John. ■ 17349 #023-01-2004 *100

MILLER, Marcia Susan. 13515 WOLFE RD STE C, SPRING VALLEY FAMILY MEDIC 17349 #023-01-2001 L2001 FM *020

MUNESES, Todd Ildefonso. 781 FAR HILLS DR STE 600 17349 #021-01-1989 L2000 P *020 †75

PRINCE, Douglas Herbert. 13515 WOLFE RD, STE C 17349 #033-06-1991 L1993 FM *020 †18

ROBINSON, Richard F. ■ 17349 #041-02-1953 L1954 GP *071

RUSSO, Michael Paul. 13515 WOLFE RD, STE D 17349 #041-02-1978 L1980 OBG *020 †30

SCHLOSSER, Michelle L. 13515 WOLFE RD, STE C 17349 #051-07-1998 L2001 FM *020 †18

WOLFE, C Anthony, Jr. 13515 WOLFE RD, STE C 17349 #041-02-1992 L2001 FM *020 †18

YOUNG, Henry Albert. ■ 17349 #035-01-1978 L1982 NS *075 †25

NEW GALILEE – LAWRENCE

TRITSCHLER, Joseph P. PO BOX 413 16141 #041-13-1954 L1956 GP *071

NEW HOLLAND – LANCASTER

BACON, Richard Warren. 676 E MAIN ST, GRP AT NEW HOLLAND FAMILY 17557 #035-15-1974 L1976 FM *020 †18

CHESKY, Joseph Frank. 435 S KINZER AVE, WORK PLACE PARTNERS 17557 #023-12-1989 L2005 OM UCM *100 †70

IAKOMI, Vladimir V. 1065 W MAIN ST 17557 #913-50-1982 L2002 FM *020

JOHNSON, Robert Philip. 676 E MAIN ST, GRP AT NEW HOLLAND FAMILY 17557 #041-02-1970 L1971 FM *020 †18

KIMBER, Roger Girard, Jr. 435 S KINZER AVE, STE 6 17557 #028-34-1977 L1989 FM OM *020 †18

KOHL, Traci M. 435 S KINZER AVE, STE 7 17557 #041-12-1999 L2001 IM *020 †20

KREIDER, Kathleen Anne. 301 E MAIN ST 17557 #041-02-1978 L1981 FM *020 †20

MALLOZZI, Mariano D. 435 S KINZER AVE, STE 2 17557 #781-01-1985 L1995 IM *020

MC GEE, Michael James. 676 E MAIN ST, GRP AT NEW HOLLAND FAMILY 17557 #041-02-1984 L1985 FM *020 †18

MELLINGER, Richard Walter. 435 S KINZER AVE, STE 7 17557 #041-13-1970 L1974 IM GP *020

ORNELAS, Victor Gamez. 1065 W MAIN ST, PAROCHIAL MEDICAL CENTER 17557 #003-01-1979 L2003 FM *020 †18

SCHRANTZ, William Francis. 574 E JACKSON ST 17557 #051-04-1970 L1999 ORS OP *020 †40

STRITTMATTER, John M. 676 E MAIN ST, GRP AT NEW HOLLAND FAMILY 17557 #041-02-1982 L1983 FM *020 †18

TAYLOR, Fred R. 676 E MAIN ST, GRP AT NEW HOLLAND FAMILY 17557 #041-09-1976 L1977 FM *020 †18

WOLFE, Dwight Douglas. 676 E MAIN ST, GRP AT NEW HOLLAND FAMILY 17557 #041-02-1977 L1978 FM *020 †18

NEW HOPE – BUCKS

AMUTHASAKARAN, Aravindan. ■ 18938 #306-01-2000 L2004 FM *020

BORKOWSKI, Bernard B. 3363 WINDY BUSH RD 18938 #041-02-1954 L1955 EM CD *071 †85

BRADLEY, Edward Campney. ■ 18938 #024-01-1975 L1991 IM ON *020 †20

BRIDGE, Thomas Peter. 1846 AQUETONG RD 18938 #051-04-1971 L2003 P *050 †75

DE GUZMAN, Denise. ■ 18938 #305-01-1998 L2002 P *020 ‡

DEHNKAMP, Wade A. ■ 18938 #041-13-2006 L2006 EM *012

DEPP, Oren Richard. ■ 18938 #016-11-1983 L1983 AN *020 †05

DI PIETRO, David Edward. 6542 LOWER YORK RD 18938 #041-13-1985 L1986 FM *020 †18

GILLESPIE, William M, Jr. ■ 18938 #028-02-1952 L1952 FM *071 †18

GODEK, Brent Walter. 6542 LOWER YORK RD 18938 #041-02-2001 L2001 FM *020 †18

GOODKIND, M Jay. ■ 18938 #035-01-1983 L1964 CD IM *071 †20

HO, Leah. ■ 18938 #035-09-2008 *012

HOLAHAN, Gordon Vincent. 10 HILLSIDE LN 18938 #010-02-1987 L1988 GS *020

KAPLAN, Barry Stephen. 128A N MAIN ST 18938 #041-09-1963 L1964 P OS *020 †75

KEATES, Richard Harry. 99 N MAIN ST 18938 #041-02-1957 L1958 OPH *050 †35

LEE, Robert Earl. 9 OLD WINDY BUSH RD 18938 #035-20-1952 L1992 IM GE *071 †20

LEVIN, Barry Kenneth. ■ 18938 #869-07-1952 L1954 OM IM *030 †70 ‡

MAAS, Margaret E. 257 DEERFIELD CT 18938 #041-13-1985 L1990 P *020 †75

MAGRAN, Irene Cynthia. ■ 18938 #041-09-1983 L1988 OBG *020 †30

MARINO, Louis Charles. 6542 LOWER YORK RD 18938 #041-02-1995 L1997 FM *020 †18

MARSH, Claire C. ■ 18938 #041-07-1971 L1973 P *020 †75

MILLS, William L. ■ 18938 #041-02-1944 R *071

MOHR, Brian Dudley. ■ 18938 #025-01-1968 L1969 CD IM *071 †20

MORRISON, Alan L. 5151 LOWER MOUNTAIN RD 18938 #041-02-1995 P *100

NEIL, Garry Arthur. ■ 18938 #041-02-1994 IM GE *050

NETTLES, Richard Edward. ■ 18938 #036-07-1998 L2005 ID *020 †20

NEWBOLD, Richard Claxton. 7142 UPPER YORK RD 18938 #041-07-1979 PTH *030

OH, Charles Jay. ■ 18938 #028-02-1997 L2002 IM *020 †20

PADGET, Edward Saul. ■ 18938 #041-01-1956 L1957 AN *020 †05

PETRAUSKI, Gary Thos. ■ 18938 #041-13-1976 L1980 DR NM *074

PLAKINS, Harold Gregory. ■ 18938 #869-07-1952 L1954 FM *071 †18

RIGNEY, James Herbert, Jr. 8 VILLAGE SQ 18938 #010-12-1969 L1980 IM NEP *071

RODRIGUEZ, Ana Isabel. ■ 18938 #649-14-1974 L1981 FM *020 †18

SALAK, Wasyl Wm. ■ 18938 #407-16-1954 L1956 GS AS *071

SALZMAN, Alan Scott. 7076 ELY RD 18938 #035-46-1987 L1989 END *020 †20

SANTANELLO, Nancy C. ■ 18938 #010-03-1982 L1985 GPM *050 †70

SCANNAPIECO, Michelle Ann. ■ 18938 #305-01-1998 L2001 IMG *020 †20

SHAFFER, Horace Melvin. ■ 18938 #035-01-1946 L1952 IM *071 †20

SHAPIRO, Bennett M. ■ 18938 #041-02-1962 L1992 OS *050

SHERROD, John Hudson. ■ 18938 #041-02-1965 L1966 EM *020 †18,16

SHRAGER, Joseph D. 5M MARKET PL, STE 50 18938 #041-01-1960 L1961 D *020 †15 ‡

SHULMAN, Alfred J. ■ 18938 #065-01-1945 L1971 P *072 †75

SPIRO, Paul David. 9 VILLAGE SQ, LOGAN SQUARE STE 9 18938 #041-01-1984 L1985 FM *020 †18

WALLER, Louis Clinton. ■ 18938 #005-12-1944 L1946 FM *071

WANG, Andreus. ■ 18938 #385-01-1962 L1973 CD IM *020 †20

WEINER, Jeffery Richard. ■ 18938 #041-09-1966 FM OS *030 †18

NEW KENSINGTON – WESTMORELAND

ALLMAN, John Harry. 251 7TH ST 15068 #041-12-1956 L1957 OM GP *072

ANTOON, Saleem J, Jr. 251 7TH ST STE C202 15068 #041-12-1949 L1950 U *020 †95

ARETZ, Thomas Edward. 651 4TH AVE, DEPT OF RADIOLOGY 15068 #041-07-1976 L1977 R *020 †80

BAJWA, Surinder Singh. 305 7TH ST 15068 #495-43-1972 L1977 IM PUD *020 †20

BALCITA, Amelia Guevara. 635 5TH AVE 15068 #748-08-1965 PTH *075

BALCITA, Arthur Lete. 635 5TH AVE 15068 #748-01-1965 L1973 OBG *020 †30

BASTIAENS, Leo Jan. 310 CENTRAL CITY PLZ 15068 #165-04-1984 L1990 CHP P *020 †75

BERKOBEN, Ilona Horti. ■ 15068 #957-02-1988 FM *100

BONATTI, William De Ray. FELDARELLI SAUARE STE6 15068 #041-02-1959 L1960 OPH *071 †35

BRADY, Douglas F. 7 FELDARELLI SQ 15068 #041-02-1951 L1952 GS *071 †85

BRADY, James Steven. 651 4TH AVE, AKMC-CITIZENS AMBULATORY C 15068 #041-12-1983 L1984 EM *020 †20

BRAYER, Paul Jos. 1600 WILDLIFE LODGE RD, STE 300 15068 #041-12-1981 L1982 FM *020 †18

CASPER, Daniel Ralph. 305 7TH ST 15068 #041-12-1977 L1978 IM *020 †20

COLELLA, Mark Samuel. 651 4TH AVE, DEPT OF RADIOLOGY 15068 #041-12-1989 L1991 DR *020 †80

DAJANI, T A. 8 FELDARELLI SQ 15068 #605-01-1953 L1969 GS TS *020 †85,90

ELIGATOR, Julian. 1260 MARTIN AVE, RUSSELLTON MEDICAL GROUP 15068 #024-07-1959 L1966 IM *071 †20

FINE, Daniel. 651 4TH AVE 15068 #008-01-1950 L1957 IM NEP *071 †20

FIROZ, Hadi Abdul. 305 7TH ST 15068 #035-08-1997 L1999 IM *020 †20

GUPTA, Krishna Gopal. 251 7TH ST, STE C202 15068 #495-20-1972 L1978 U *020 †95

HAN, Jonathan Kyungho. 301 11TH ST, NEW KENSINGTON FAM HLTH 15068 #016-06-1988 L1997 FM *020 †18

HANNA, Reem Salah. SUITE 6 FELDARELLI SQUARE 15068 #041-12-1994 L1994 OPH *020 †35

HOUSTON, James Lee. PROFESSIONAL ARTS BLDG 15068 #041-12-1962 L1963 GYN *071 †30

IYENGAR, Purushothama M S. 2663 LEECHBURG RD 15068 #495-33-1980 L1990 P *020 †75

KAUR, Prakash. 311 7TH ST 15068 #496-07-1973 L1985 AI PD *020 †55

KICHLER, Joel Michael. 1 KENSINGTON SQ 15068 #038-43-1976 L1977 GE IM *020 †20 ‡

KOSTER, Lee Harry. 634 FOURTH AVE 15068 #041-12-1972 L1973 U *020 †95

LEYDIG, Richard Allen. FREEPORT ROAD, SUITE 14 FELDARELLI SQUARE 15068 #041-13-1954 L1955 GP *071

MC CLUNG, Larry Stewart. 651 4TH AVE 15068 #041-13-1955 L1956 FM EM *071 †18

MORRISSEY, Mark Wm. 1600 WILDLIFE LODGE RD, STE 300 15068 #041-12-1984 L1985 FM *020 †18

O'NEIL, Kenneth Stuart. ■ 15068 #035-03-1974 L1978 PS HS *020 †65

PARKER, Gerald A. 356 FREEPORT ST 15068 #308-11-1985 L1986 IM IMG *020 †20

PETURSSON, Sigurdur R. 651 FOURTH AVE 2ND FL, CITIZENS AMBULATORY CARE C 15068 #035-45-1974 L1975 ON HEM *020 †20

RAVANO, Jose Fabricante. ■ 15068 #748-02-1962 L1974 GS CRS *020 †85

RAVANO, Paraluman Q. ■ 15068 #748-02-1962 L1974 PTH GP *020 †50

REILLY, Paul A. 344 FREEPORT ST 15068 #748-07-1981 L1983 CD IM *020 †20

RICHLESS, Lloyd Keith. 251 SEVENTH ST, STE 201B 15068 #050-02-1981 L1982 FM OM *020 †18

SAGHAFI, Darius. 251 7TH ST, STE C 15068 #517-03-1967 L1974 NEP IM *020 †20

SALATKA, Karl Wm. 638 4TH AVE 15068 #041-12-1972 L1973 GS CRS *020 †85

SCHOWALTER, Donald Ralph. 356 FREEPORT ST 15068 #041-09-1976 L1977 IM IMG *020 †20

SHERGILL, Kultar. 2300 FREEPORT RD, #12 FELDARELLI SQ 15068 #130-01-1993 L1998 PD ID *020 †55

SWIERCZEWSKI, Edward V. 504 GREENRIDGE RD 15068 #649-33-1981 L1986 FM *071 †18 ‡

TABAS, Janet Helene. 651 4TH AVE, DEPT OF RADIOLOGY 15068 #041-02-1984 L1986 R DR *020 †80

TOMASELLI, David Lee. 1600 WILDLIFE LODGE RD, STE 300 15068 #305-01-1982 L1986 FM *020 †18

VEMULAPALLI, Harikrishna. 2663 LEECHBURG RD 15068 #496-24-1993 L2001 P *020 †75

VICHARE, Kawita. ■ 15068 #012-01-2002 L2002 FPG *020 †18

WEINSTEIN, David Paul. 651 FOURTH AVE, AV MEDICAL IMAGING 15068 #041-13-1968 L1969 DR *020 †80

WEISKOPF, Jay R. 301 7TH ST 15068 #035-19-1979 L1981 OPH *020 †35

WITTIG, Lorayn Kay. 1600 WILDLIFE LODGE RD, STE 300 15068 #051-04-1997 L1999 FM *020 †18

YANCHUS, Robert Michael. ■ 15068 #041-12-1950 L1951 ORS *071 †40

ZUCK, Walter Nelson. CITZENS GENERAL HOSPITAL 15068 #041-12-1959 L1960 R *071 †80

NEW OXFORD – ADAMS

COLE, Suzanne Rachel. 5615 YORK RD, NEW OXFORD MEDICAL CENTER 17350 #035-48-1999 L2006 FM *020 †18

FLORY, Ray Herbert. ■ 17350 #041-02-1944 L1945 AN *071 †05

GANDIONCO, John Rizarri. 2900 CARLISLE PIKE 17350 #035-08-1992 L2005 IM *020 †20

HOOVER, Dean Stayer. ■ 17350 #041-09-1948 L1949 FM *071

RUBENSTEIN, Morton Jerome. 2900 CARLISLE PIKE 17350 #028-02-1971 L1972 PUD CCM *020 †20

SHIBLEY, Phillip Rowell. ■ 17350 #005-12-1991 L2006 AN *020 †05

VIDAL, Carlos Javier. 5615 YORK RD 17350 #737-01-1991 L2002 IM *020 †20

WETZEL, Chris Tobin. ■ 17350 #041-14-2006 L2006 FP *012

NEW PARIS – BEDFORD

JOHNSTON, Lynn Catherine. 4186 CORTLAND DR 15554 #041-14-1994 L1996 **FM** *020 †18 ‡
SHOENTHAL, Henry Wm. 4186 CORTLAND DR, BOX 367 15554 #041-12-1972 L1973
  FM *020 †18 ‡

NEW PHILADELPHIA – SCHUYLKILL

MOYLAN, David John. 15 ALLIANCE ST, SIMON KRAMER INST 17959 #010-02-1977 L1978
  RO IM *020 †80
MOYLAN, Jacqueline Denise. 15 ALLIANCE ST, SIMON KRAMER INSTITUTE 17959
  #041-13-1973 L1974 **PUD IM** *020 †20

NEW PROVIDENCE – LANCASTER

GAGLIANO, Allene. ■ 17560 #051-01-2003 L2003 **FP** *012
MADISON, Shirley A. ■ 17560 #041-14-1979 L1984 **PS** *075

NEW RINGGOLD – SCHUYLKILL

HART, Patrick Edward. ■ 17960 #051-07-1997 L2003 **IM** *020 †20

NEW STANTON – WESTMORELAND

GIANNI, Pamela Irene. 111 S CENTER AVE, STANTON HOUSE - STE ONE 15672
  #041-07-1992 L1995 **FM OM** *020 †18 ‡
JABBOUR, Muna Nassar. 512 S CENTER AVE, NEW STANTON PRIMARY CARE 15672
  #875-01-1990 L1997 **IM** *020 †20

NEW TRIPOLI – LEHIGH

BLAISDELL, Colborn T. ■ 18066 #041-01-1959 L1960 **AN OS** *071 †05
CUTITTA, Christopher J. ■ 18066 #041-77-2005, ▲ L2005 **IM** *012
FLOYD, Jan. 7096 DECATUR ST 18066 #038-45-1997 L2005 **PD** *020 †55
FOLLWEILER, Barry Roger. 7096 DECATUR ST 18066 #041-14-1980 L1981 **IM FM** *020 †20
LIBONATI, Margaret Mary A. ■ 18066 #041-02-1965 L1966 **AN OS** *071 †05
VAUGHN, Lisa Baker. 8360 HOLBENS VALLEY RD 18066 #041-13-1983 L1984 **OBG** *020 †30

NEW WILMINGTON – LAWRENCE

BARSZCZOWSKI, Peter J, Jr. 141 S MARKET ST 16142 #308-07-1983 L1986 **FM** *020 †18
GARDNER, James Larimer. 150 N NEW CASTLE ST, LAWRENCE COUNTY INC 16142
  #041-02-2002 L2005 **FM** *100 †18
GARROW, Diane Celecki. 217 DAR DR 16142 #041-14-1985 L2002 **OBG** *020 †30
HART, George R. ■ 16142 #041-01-1952 L1953 **OTO A** *071 †45
MANSELL, John Lawson. 150 N NEW CASTLE ST 16142 #041-01-1958 L1959 **FM** *020 †18
SCHNEIDER, Timothy Edward. 142 N MARKET ST 16142 #016-43-1995 L1999 **P** *020 †75
TANYEL, Mary C Mahlon. 150 N NEW CASTLE ST, WILMINGTON 16142 #041-13-1993 L1995
  FM *020 †18
UBERTI, Anthony Frederick. 565 W NESHANNOCK AVE 16142 #041-14-1991 L1993
  FM *020 †18

NEWMANSTOWN – LEBANON

KLINE, Robert Mann. ■ 17073 #041-02-1955 L1956 **GP** *071

NEWPORT – PERRY

BRENIZER, Michelle L. 46 RED HILL CT 17074 #041-14-1995 L1997 **FM** *020 †18
KNOUSE, Albert Bauer, Jr. 46 RED HILL CT 17074 #041-09-1988 L1991 **FM** *020 †18
KNOUSE, Kathleen Jennifer. 46 RED HILL CT, HERITAGE MEDICAL GROUP 17074
  #041-09-1988 L1991 **PD** *020 †55
MENON, Madhu. 28 W SHORTCUT RD 17074 #495-65-1979 L1997 **FM** *020 †18
RUMBAUGH, James Orville. RED HILL RD, COWLEY MEDICAL ASSOCIATES 17074
  #041-02-1954 L1955 **FM** *071 †18
THIEBLEMONT, Michael A. 46 RED HILL CT 17074 #041-14-1993 L1995 **FM** *020 †18

NEWPORTVILLE – BUCKS

MUFSON, Richard Alan. ■ 19056 #041-09-1968 L1971 **P PD** *020 †75

NEWTOWN – BUCKS

AIELLO, Stephen Anthony. PENNSWOOD VILLAGE RETIRE C 18940 #041-13-1978 L1979
  IMG IM *020 †20
ALDEN, James Cooper. ■ 18940 #041-09-1960 L1961 **IM DIA** *071 †20,18 ‡
BARTLETT, Frederick H, III. 11 FRIENDS LN, STE 101 18940 #041-02-1981 L1985 **OBG** *020 †30
BRECKENRIDGE, Bruce M. ■ 18940 #035-45-1956 L1961 **OS** *071
BRISTER, Randy. 4 TERRY DR, THE ATRIUM SUITE 1 18940 #041-13-1979 L1981 **PD** *020 †55
BROWN, William Chas, Jr. 638 NEWTOWN YARDLEY RD, STE 1D 18940 #041-12-1979 L1981
  OPH *020 †35
BURKE, Scott Walter. 2700 S EAGLE RD, STE 200 18940 #041-02-1998 L2005 **CD** *020 †20
CHAGANTI, R Krishna. ■ 18940 #041-13-1999 L2002 **RHU** *100 †20
COLEMAN, William Henry. ■ 18940 #041-13-1945 L1946 **IMG OS** *071
COLEMAN-MILLER, Beverly. ■ 18940 #041-13-1981 L1982 **IM** *074
DAVIES, Richard O. ■ 18940 #065-01-1962 **CD PA** *071

DAVIS, Barbara Karen. 638 NEWTOWN YARDLEY RD, STE 1H 18940 #039-01-1993 L2002
  P *020
DUGAN, Theresa Ann. 11 FRIENDS LN, STE 101 18940 #041-07-1986 L1987 **OBG** *020 †30
ELLIS-BENNETT, Melissa P. ■ 18940 #041-14-1997 L1999 **PD** *062 †55
EPSTEIN, Martin. ■ 18940 #038-06-1944 L1948 **IM** *071
FAST, Willis Burton. ■ 18940 #041-01-1947 L1953 **GS** *071
FEIBUSCH, Evan Lawrence. 2865 S EAGLE RD 18940 #033-06-1993 L2003 **PFP** *020 †75
FISCHER, Michael B. 2950 S EAGLE RD 18940 #041-77-1999, ▲ L2000 **FM** *020
FRANGIPANE, William Leo. 11 FRIENDS LN, STE 101 18940 #041-14-1982 L1983
  OBG *020 †30 ‡
FRANKEL, Leslie Berman. 11 FRIENDS LN, STE 101 18940 #041-13-1978 L1979 **OBG** *020 †30
GARNER, Blaine R. 50 S CONGRESS ST, STE 3 18940 #041-02-1939 L1941 **FM** *071
GEER-YAN, Lisa Margaret. 11 FRIENDS LN, STE 101 18940 #035-15-2001 L2001 **OBG** *020 †30
GOLDHAMMER, Jordan Evan. ■ 18940 #041-02-2008 *012
GOODMAN, Bruce Alan. 790 NEWTOWN YARDLEY RD, STE 420 18940 #041-09-1986 L1987
  IM *020 †20
GREGERSEN, James Orman. ■ 18940 #041-02-1952 L1953 **R** *071
HARTMAN, Denise Lynn. 11 FRIENDS LN, STE 101 18940 #041-13-1982 L1983 **OBG** *020 †30
HERMANS, Michel Hans Edua. ■ 18940 #660-02-1981 *100
HOFFMAN-STEEGER, Vicki N. ■ 18940 #041-07-1983 L1984 **IM** *020 †20
HUSSAIN, Sadaf Hashim. ■ 18940 #041-02-2008 *012
JACOBSON, Zev. 638 NEWTOWN YARDLEY RD, STE 1E 18940 #035-46-1996 L1998
  PDC *020 †55
JARMAN, Martha Lindsay. ■ 18940 #041-01-1958 L1959 **GP** *071
JOSHI, Preeti. ■ 18940 #495-73-1997 L2004 **AN** *100
KARDOS, Julie Elizabeth. 6 PENNS TRL STE 105, KIDS FIRST NEWTOWN 18940
  #038-06-1994 L1996 **PD** *020 †55
KATZ, Amir. 503 WASHINGTON AVE, STE 2D 18940 #550-02-1987 L1991 **PM** *020 †60
KEEN, Allison. 11 FRIENDS LN, STE 101 18940 #041-15-2003 L2003 **OBG** *020
KIM, Ellen Hwang. 2324 2ND STREET PIKE 18940 #041-15-2004 L2004 **FM** *020 †18
KIM, Joseph C. 54 FRIENDS LN, STE 125 18940 #004-01-2002 L2002 **HO IM** *020
KIPP, Joseph. 11 FRIENDS LN, # 102 18940 #041-13-1982 L1983 **FM** *020 †18
KITCHEN, Jennifer Lee. ■ 18940 #023-01-2003 L2003 **IM** *020 †20
KOLANDER, Scott A. 444 S STATE ST, STE A1 18940 #041-09-1982 L1983 **IM** *020 †20 ‡
KORENBLIT, Jason Alan. ■ 18940 #041-02-2007 L2007 **IM** *012
KRICHEVSKY, Rita Anna M. 12 PENNS TRL, MS 323 18940 #041-07-1994 L1996 **FM** *020 †18
KURZ, George Harper. ■ 18940 #041-01-1954 L1955 **OPH** *071 †35
LEICHNER, John Philip. ■ 18940 #010-01-1975 L1980 **GS** *020
LERNER, Mary Fenyes. ■ 18940 #396-06-1936 L1942 **A** *071
LEWIN, Sara. ■ 18940 #561-17-1954 L1957 **P** *071
LIPSON, M Barry. 505 WASHINGTON AVE 18940 #041-13-1965 L1966 **ORS** *020
LIU, Jung-Ching. ■ 18940 #385-02-1951 L1968 **OTO** *020 †45
LIU, Shaojun. ■ 18940 #243-16-1984 L2001 **PTH** *020 †50
LOEWY, Gabriel. ■ 18940 #308-11-1986 L1993 **HEM ON** *020 †20
MAGARGAL, Helga L Olsen. 1382 NEWTOWN LANGHORNE RD, PENNSWOOD VILLAGE 18940
  #041-13-1969 **OPH** *020 †35
MARKOW, Harry Gregory. 4 TERRY DR, THE ATRIUM SUITE 2 18940 #041-13-1972 L1973
  P CHP *020 †75
MEINERT, Lawrence Andrew. ■ 18940 #041-07-1982 L1983 **PHP** *030 †70
MICHAELSON, Robert I. 11 FRIENDS LN, STE 101 18940 #041-02-1976 L1977 **OBG** *020 †30
MOREY, Victoria Ann. 11 FRIENDS LN, STE 101 18940 #041-01-1993 L1996 **OBG** *020 †30
MURPHY, Joseph James, III. 11 FRIENDS LN, STE 101 18940 #041-02-1996 L1999
  OBG *020 †30
NARULA, Shilpi. 4 TERRY DR STE 10A, THE ATRIUM 18940 #035-03-2000 L2003
  AI *020 †20,03 ‡
NEWAY, William Edward, III. ■ 18940 #041-77-2007, ▲ *012
NUSSBAUM, Lawrence Lee. ■ 18940 #020-02-1977 L1987 **CD IM** *074 †20
OLSHIN, Irving Joel. GEORGE SCHOOL 18940 #041-01-1954 L1957 **PD** *072 †55
OPPENHEIM, Barry. 842 DURHAM RD, STE 7-8 18940 #023-01-1989 L1995 **OPH PO** *020 †35 ‡
ORTIZ, Neftali. 660 NEWTOWN YARDLEY RD, STE 101 18940 #042-01-1982 L1983
  CHP P *020 †75
PATHALAPATI, Radhika. 60 BLACKSMITH RD 18940 #495-70-1994 L2006 **NEP** *020 †20
PRICE, Elizabeth. ■ 18940 #010-01-1951 L1994 **PHP OM** *071 †70
RINGOLD, Murray H. ■ 18940 #041-13-1950 L1951 **GP** *071
ROSENBAUM, Joel Norman. ■ 18940 #035-19-1988 L1990 **PM IM** *020 †60
ROSENBERG, Ruth. 4 TERRY DR, THE ATRIUM, SUITE 6 18940 #035-19-1988 L1990
  CHP P *020 †75
ROSENGARTEN, Herbert H. 2700 S EAGLE RD, STE 200 18940 #035-08-1980 L1985
  IM PD *020 †20,55
ROUSE, Paul Vincent. ■ 18940 #041-02-1943 L1944 **U** *072 †95
RUIZ, Jimmy Joseph. 11 FRIENDS LN, STE 101 18940 #041-09-1998 L2001 **OBG** *020
RUSNAK, James Michael. 604 PINEVILLE RD 18940 #041-12-1997 L2000 **IM** *020 †20
SASSON, Robert. 6 PENNS TRL, STE 105 18940 #035-08-1974 L1975 **RO** *020 †55
SILVERSTEIN, Keith E. 219 N SYCAMORE ST 18940 #041-01-1994 L2002 *020
SITAPARA, Ashish Jamnadas. 780 NEWTOWN YARDLEY RD, STE 314A 18940
  #166-03-2000 L2006 **IM IMG** *020
SKAGGS, James Wm, Jr. ■ 18940 #023-01-1956 L1966 **OS PHP** *075
SLOAN, Sheldon. ■ 18940 #016-01-1983 L1984 **GE** *020 †20
SOANS, Rohit Sydney. ■ 18940 #041-14-2007 *012
SODOWICK, Bradford Charin. 2700 S EAGLE RD, STE 200 18940 #041-02-1991 L1993
  CD *020 †20
STEIN, Harmon Chas. 451 S STATE ST 18940 #035-09-1979 L1980 **OPH** *020 †35
STEVENSON, Ruth Anne. ■ 18940 #917-33-1999 L2004 **IM** *020
THLICK, Aien Chu. 444 S STATE ST 18940 #051-01-2004 L2004 **IM** *020 †20
THUR, Mara Stolber. 11 FRIENDS LN, STE 101 18940 #041-13-2002 L2002 **OBG** *020
VENKATESULU, Sunder. 2700 S EAGLE RD, STE 200 18940 #041-02-1989 L1991
  CD IM *020 †20
VITTI, Richard Albert. 124 S ELM AVE 18940 #041-09-1980 L1981 **NM DR** *020 †28 ‡
WALDER, Mary Ellen. 6 PENNS TRL STE 105, KIDS FIRST NEWTOWN 18940
  #051-04-1986 L1989 **PD** *020 †55
WARNER, Michael Alan. 100 CAMPUS DR 18940 #041-13-1988 L1990 **FM** *020 †18
WHITE, Aruby Odom. 105 TERRY DR, STE 103 18940 #041-07-1985 L1989 **P** *020 †75
WINGATE, Barbara Jean. ■ 18940 #041-13-1987 L1990 **P** *020 †75
WOLF, Robert Allen. ■ 18940 #024-01-1980 L1981 **CD IM** *020 †20
WOOD, John C. ■ 18940 #035-01-1949 L1951 **CD IM** *071 †20

■ = Address Information Privacy Protected

YI, Lusia Sangsuk. ■ 18940 #041-77-2007, ▲ L2007 *012
ZEGA, Edward L. ■ 18940 #035-01-1946 L1969 **GS** *071 †85

NEWTOWN SQUARE – DELAWARE

AFABLE, Richard F. 3805 W CHESTER PIKE, # 100 19073 #016-43-1978 L2000 **IM IMG** *030 †20
AHN, Kyung Jun. ■ 19073 #583-09-1964 L1972 **P** *020 †75
ANBARI, Rachad. 17 BISHOP HOLLOW RD 19073 #875-01-1952 L1983 **PD PHO** *071 †55
BARALDI, Raymond L, Jr. 43 LLANGOLLEN LN 19073 #041-02-1976 L1977 **DR** *020 †20,80 ‡
BARKER, Richard Gleim. ■ 19073 #024-01-1939 L1942 **IM GM** *071 †20
BINNION, Peter Fletcher. 3475 W CHESTER PIKE # 200, SUBURBAN PRIMARY CARE 19073 #917-09-1956 L2007 **IM GP** *020
BOERNER, Thomas Frederick. ■ 19073 #041-02-1986 L1987 **AN** *020 †05
CARROLL, William Luke. 5048 W CHESTER PIKE 19073 #041-02-1989 L1992 **FM** *020 †18
COLASANTE, David Anthony. ■ 19073 #041-13-1980 L1981 **PA** *050
COOKE, Lynn Adele. 3475 WEST CHESTER PIKE, STE 200 19073 #041-07-1991 L1993 **FM** *020 †18
COOPER, Donna Laure. ■ 19073 #041-02-1969 L1970 **GPM OBG** *075 †70
CORRATO, Robert Ricardo. 15 CAMPUS BLVD 19073 #041-07-1992 L1995 **IM MDM** *020 †20
DECKER, Mark Jeffrey. 15 CAMPUS BLVD, STE 200 19073 #010-02-1975 L2007 **FM** *062 †18
DE RIVAS, Carmela F. 3500 W CHESTER PIKE, DUNWOODY VLG CH 112 19073 #041-07-1946 L1947 **P** *071 †75
DE STEFANO, Louis Michael. 23 BISHOP HOLLOW RD 19073 #422-01-1984 L1985 **FM** *020 †18
DHARGALKAR, Aneesha K. ■ 19073 #041-02-2006 L2006 **EM** *012
DZWONCZYK, John. ■ 19073 #041-09-1954 L1955 **GS** *071 †85
EPSTEIN, Solomon. 231 JEFFREY LN, DOYLESTOWN HOSPITAL 19073 #836-02-1966 L1986 **END** *020
ESCOBAR, Francisco S, III. ■ 19073 #043-01-1984 L1985 **TTS GS** *020 †85
FABIUS, Raymond Jay. ■ 19073 #041-09-1977 L1980 **OS PD** *071 †55
FAZELI, Abolfath. ■ 19073 #407-32-1958 L1987 **GP** *071
FAZELI, Pouneh Khadejeh. ■ 19073 #041-01-2002 L2003 **END** *012 †20
FITTI, Regina M. ■ 19073 #041-09-1949 L1950 **CHP P** *071
FLEMING, Nancy Ann. ■ 19073 #033-05-1995 **FM** *071
FLICK, John Albert. ■ 19073 #024-01-1943 L1944 **OS** *071
FLORES, Alberto C. ■ 19073 #041-01-1951 L1963 **IM OS** *071 †85
FORT, John G. 3409 WEST CHESTER PIKE, STE 202 19073 #847-08-1980 L1984 **RHU IM** *050 †20
GAVIN, Mary Louise. 3855 W CHESTER PIKE, STE 280 19073 #035-45-1989 L2001 **PD** *020 †55
GILLIS, Angus Thos. 5 MARTINS RD, 5 MARTINS RD 19073 #041-02-1985 L1987 **AN** *020 †05
GORAL, Mehmet Ihsan. ■ 19073 #902-10-1984 L2002 **PTH** *050
GORDON, Linda Diane. 3240 SAINT DAVIDS RD 19073 #035-19-1980 L1982 **CHP P** *020 †55,75
GRUBB, Gary Sondermann. ■ 19073 #038-06-1979 L1981 **PHP** *050 †70
HARKINS, James P, Jr. 3217 W CHESTER PIKE 19073 #041-01-1981 L1983 **IM** *020 †20
HASSAN, Zamir U. ■ 19073 #704-04-1976 L1993 **IM** *020 †20
HELFRICH, Harry M, Jr. ■ 19073 #035-20-1950 L1981 **IM CD** *071
HESS-HARDY, Sophy. ■ 19073 #041-07-1945 L1946 **OM** *071
HITCHNER, Lewis C. ■ 19073 #041-09-1943 L1944 **AN** *071 †05
HOLLAND, Denise Edgecombe. 235 EXCALIBUR DR 19073 #010-03-1976 L2003 **P** *030 †75
HORNER, George John. 3500 WEST CHESTER PIKE, DUNWOODY VILLAGE CH18 19073 #143-03-1961 L1969 **PUD PA** *071
HOUSE, Diane B Peters. ■ 19073 #041-07-1973 L1974 **IM FM** *020 †20
JACQUES, Gary James. ■ 19073 #005-18-1982 L1985 **IM** *040 †20
JENAB-WOLCOTT, Jenia. ■ 19073 #024-07-2003 L2007 **HO** *012 †20
JURNOVOY, Joel Bruce. ■ 19073 #041-02-1967 L1968 **D** *071 †15 ‡
KIM, Phillip Bok-Soo. ■ 19073 #583-01-1957 L1971 **PTH CLP** *050
KOTYO, John Albert. ■ 19073 #561-01-1976 L1980 **FM** *020 †18 ‡
KUBEK, Kimberly Anne. 3475 W CHESTER PIKE, STE 240 19073 #038-41-1982 L1983 **DR** *020 †80
LAZARIDIS, Nikolaos. ■ 19073 #418-02-1992 *100
LIEBERMAN, Jamie Shawn. ■ 19073 #041-13-1990 L1993 **PCC** *020 †20
LINDER, Lisa Jayne. 3501 WEST CHESTER PIKE, STE 202 19073 #035-47-1979 L1984 **OPH** *020 †35
MACDONALD, Brian Richard. ■ 19073 #917-10-1987 L1993 *020
MARGERUM, Bryan Swain. 15 CAMPUS BLVD STE 200 19073 #041-13-1994 L1997 **IM** *062 †20
MARINO, Daniel Jos. ■ 19073 #041-07-1942 L1947 **CD IM** *071 †20
MAYER, Lawrence James. 617 ANDOVER RD 19073 #041-01-1968 L1969 **GS** *020 †85
MILLER, Lawrence S. 3740 WEST CHESTER PIKE 19073 #041-02-1979 L1980 **ORS OSM** *020 †40
MINEO, Cyrus Louis. 50 LONGVIEW LN 19073 #041-02-1962 L1963 **OPH** *071 †35
MOHAGEB, Salah M O. 15 CAMPUS BLVD, CLINICAL STAFFING SOLUTION 19073 #125-03-1990 L2004 **IM** *020
MONTGOMERY, Patricia A. 23 BISHOP HOLLOW RD 19073 #041-01-1979 L1980 **FM FPG** *020 †18
MORGAN, Jonathan Asher. ■ 19073 #035-06-1997 L2001 **RNR** *020 †80
MYERS, J Martin. ■ 19073 #023-07-1943 L1951 **P** *071 †75
NEWTON, Corinne Vahlstrom. ■ 19073 #041-07-1954 L1958 **GP** *071
O'DOWD, Liza Carina. 50 DREAM VALLEY DR 19073 #041-01-1992 L1994 **PCC AI** *050 †03,20
PARK, Eunice Young. ■ 19073 #035-19-2008 *012
PARRY, Peter Vaughan. ■ 19073 #035-01-1962 L1963 **IM END** *071 †20
PECHER, Stefana Marina. 3855 W CHESTER PIKE, STE 300 19073 #286-13-1999 L2003 **FM** *020 †18
PERRONE, Jeanmarie. ■ 19073 #023-01-1990 L1995 **EM** *020 †16
PETCHETTI, Lavanya Rao. 15 CAMPUS BLVD STE 200, NEWTON SQUARE 19073 #495-11-1999 L2006 **IM** *100 †20 ‡
PETERS, Barbara Dawn. ■ 19073 #041-02-1988 L1993 **DR** *020 †80
PINSK, Jeffrey Howard. 3475 WEST CHESTER PIKE, STE 120 19073 #041-09-1984 L1985 **IM FM** *020 †20
POLLACK, Evan Jay. 15 CAMPUS BLVD, STE 200 19073 #038-41-1984 L2005 **IM** *062 †20
POOLE, Robert. ■ 19073 #041-02-1953 L1954 **FM** *071 †18
POWELL, Mary Martin. ■ 19073 #041-07-1949 L1959 **ORS** *020 †40
PRUKSANANONDA, Prasong. ■ 19073 #891-01-1978 L1985 **ID PD** *020 †55
RAYMOND, Fred Douglas. ■ 19073 #041-01-1954 L1955 **RHU** *071 †20
REITANO, Joseph Francis. 3475 W CHESTER PIKE, STE 200 19073 #041-13-1970 L1972 **IM END** *020 ‡

ROBINSON, Elliott S, Jr. 3500 W CHESTER PIKE, # 162 19073 #024-01-1947 L1955 **OS OBG** *071 †30
RODER, Sanam Claudia. ■ 19073 #041-01-2006 L2006 **FP** *012
ROSENBERG, Lauren. ■ 19073 #041-13-2002 L2005 **CD** *012 †20
RUFFINI, John Anthony. 535 GRADYVILLE RD, WHITEHORSE VILLAGE S126 19073 #041-02-1958 L1959 **GP** *071
SALVO, John Paul. 3740 WEST CHESTER PIKE 19073 #041-02-1994 L1997 **OSM** *020 †40
SCHACHTER, Molly Jean. ■ 19073 #024-01-2000 L2003 **HO** *020 †20
SHAHINFAR, Shahnaz. ■ 19073 #517-04-1975 L1981 **PD PN** *030 †55
SHEAFFER, Harold Clement. 3475 W CHESTER PIKE, STE 200 19073 #041-02-1961 **IM** *071 †20
SHRAGER, Morton Wm. 845 HUNT RD 19073 #041-01-1956 L1957 **IM CD** *071 †20
SHROM, Stanley H. 3553 WEST CHESTER PIKE, # 331 19073 #041-02-1974 L1975 **U** *020 †95
SMITH, Jennifer D. ■ 19073 #048-02-1998 L2000 **DR PDR** *020 †80
SMITH, Sally Ann. ■ 19073 #041-09-1959 L1965 **OS R** *074
WEBSTER, Gordon Woodhall. 841 GALER DR 19073 #041-01-1958 L1962 **IM CD** *071
WINTER, James. ■ 19073 #041-02-1969 L1994 **DR** *075 †80
WINTER, Rebecca Cooper. ■ 19073 #041-02-2008 L2008 *012
ZUBIETA, Juan Carlos. 15 CAMPUS BLVD, STE 200 19073 #935-05-1995 L2002 **CCM** *020 †20

NEWVILLE – CUMBERLAND

GREENWALD, Earl Franklin. 161 BEETEM HOLLOW RD 17241 #033-05-1965 L1975 **GO OBG** *071 †30
HARRIS, Jeffrey Hamilton. 100 S HIGH ST 17241 #041-09-1996 L1998 **FM** *020 †18
HAZLETT, Jane. ■ 17241 #041-07-1948 L1949 **OBG OS** *071 †30
KONHAUS, Carol Henry. ■ 17241 #041-02-1944 L1945 **GS** *071 †85
KOWALSKI, Richard Jos. ■ 17241 #010-02-1964 L1997 **P** *071
TOWNSEND, Jay Anthony. 100 S HIGH ST 17241 #041-02-1968 L1969 **FM** *020

NORRISTOWN – MONTGOMERY

ALCANTARA, Consolacion A. 1301 POWELL ST 19401 #748-01-1969 L1977 **P** *020
ALEXANDRE, Journel. 901 SANDY ST 19401 #495-01-1960 L1967 **GP GS** *071 †85
AMIN, Bipin Ramanlal. 1301 POWELL ST 19401 #495-22-1969 L1980 **FM IM** *020 ‡
AMOAH, Daniel. 1301 POWELL ST 19401 #412-02-2002 L2004 **FM** *020
ANDERSON, Arlo Conrad. 1308 DEKALB ST 19401 #041-01-1960 L1962 **ORS** *071 †40
ANDINO GUARDERAS, Jose Fe. 1330 POWELL ST, MONTGOMERY HOSPITAL 19401 #319-08-2002 L2007 **FP** *012
ANGSTADT, Paul Norman, Jr. 1301 POWELL ST 19401 #041-02-1960 L1961 **R OS** *071 †80
ASGAONKER, Lisa. ■ 19401 #035-03-2005 **DR** *012
AVANCENA, Edgardo P. ■ 19401 #748-08-1957 L1969 **GP OM** *072
AVENIROV, Alexander G. 1001 STERIGERE ST 19401 #913-01-1968 L1986 **P** *020 ‡
AYYASWAMY, Vatsala. 1001 STERIGERE ST, BLDG 10 19401 #495-04-1972 L1984 **P** *020 ‡
BARD, Joseph Lewis. 2701 DEKALB PIKE 19401 #041-02-1956 L1957 **FM GP** *071
BARNETT, Ronald Bruce. 1330 POWELL ST, STE 508 19401 #012-05-1983 L1984 **PUD IM** *020 †20 ‡
BARRY, Theodore Jos. 1001 STERIGERE ST 19401 #041-13-1954 L1955 **P** *020
BAUTISTA, Fidel Dale Mend. 1301 POWELL ST 19401 #654-01-2003 L2005 **FP** *012
BAYLEY, John Frederick. 1001 STERIGERE ST 19401 #047-06-1954 L1961 **PD** *071 †55
BECKER, Andrea Joyce. 2705 DEKALB PIKE, STE 305 19401 #041-02-1980 L1981 **CD** *020 †20 ‡
BECKER, Michael A. 530 CHURCH ST, 2ND FL 19401 #041-77-1987, ▲ L1988 **FM OS** *040
BEHJAT, Shahla. 1001 STERIGERE ST 19401 #517-01-1975 L1988 **P** *020
BELSER, Paul Harper. 1300 POWELL ST 19401 #041-14-1984 L1985 **PTH** *020 †50
BENDER, Joseph. 1544 DEKALB ST 19401 #067-01-1953 L1954 **IM GE** *071 †20
BENNETT, Mark Alan. 2701 DEKALB PIKE, SUBURBAN GENERAL HOSPITAL 19401 #041-14-1990 L1993 **AN** *020 †05
BERNABEI, Joanne Yvonne. 1001 STERIGERE ST 19401 #041-13-1976 L1977 **P** *020 †75
BISH, Roman V. ■ 19401 #041-02-2008 L2008 *012
BLANK, Ira Burkhardt. 1301 POWELL ST 19401 #024-07-1958 L1959 **AN** *020 †05
BLUESTEIN, Hazel Marian. 1330 POWELL ST, STE 409 19401 #041-07-1981 L1982 **FM** *020 †18
BOLTON, Gregory Cornel. 1330 POWELL ST, STE 507 19401 #041-01-1972 L1974 **OBG** *020 †30
BRAJER, Jason. 1301 POWELL ST 19401 #041-09-1980 L1981 **AN PME** *020 †05
BRAY, Joshua Carter. 1301 POWELL ST 19401 #035-19-1948 L1951 **FM AM** *071
BUONOCORE, Edward R. 342 W GERMANTOWN PIKE, STE 1 19403 #035-08-1976 L1979 **CD IM** *020 ‡
BYRNE, Robert James. 1308 DEKALB ST 19401 #023-01-1956 L1961 **ORS** *020 †40
CARGAN, Jonathan Seth. ■ 19401 #041-14-1988 L1989 **OS** *074
CARLIN, Bernard H. 342 W GERMANTOWN PIKE, STE 200 19403 #041-09-1981 L1982 **FM** *020 †20
CARLSON, Robert E. ■ 19401 #035-01-1952 L1959 **GS** *071 †85
CELEBRE, Joan Adele. 2705 DEKALB PIKE 19401 #041-07-1960 L1961 **OBG OBS** *071 †30
CERINO, Michael A, II. ■ 19401 #041-77-2007, ▲ L2007 *012
CHELEHMALZADEH, Mohammad. 1301 POWELL ST 19401 #166-01-2001 L2006 **FP** *012
CHERISME-THEOPHILE, E. 15 W WOOD ST, FAMILY OB/GYN AT MONTGOMER 19401 #041-14-1999 L2000 **OBG** *020 ‡
CHOI, Tohshik. 1001 STERIGERE ST 19401 #583-04-1960 L1972 **GP IM** *071
CLANEY, Jonathan Holt. 15 W WOOD ST 19401 #041-09-1955 L1956 **P CHP** *075 †75
COHEN, Samuel Folk. 1301 POWELL ST 19401 #041-13-1953 L1936 **GP IMG** *071
CRUZ GUTIERREZ, L D. 1001 STERIGERE ST 19401 #748-02-1960 L1970 **P** *020
CUTLER, Charles. 1411 POWELL ST 19401 #041-13-1974 L1975 **IM** *020 †20
DADVAND, Mahmood. 1201 DEKALB ST 19401 #517-06-1973 L1983 **P** *020
DANIELS, Richard John. 342 W GERMANTOWN PIKE, STE 310 19403 #041-02-1993 L1995 **VIR** *020 †80
DE CASTRO, Nieves V. 2701 DEKALB PIKE, MERCY SUBURBAN HOSP 19401 #748-01-1970 L1975 **AN** *020 †05
DHAR, Gargi. 1301 POWELL ST 19401 #495-32-1995 L2006 **FP** *012
DI GIACOMO, Philip J, Jr. 1330 POWELL ST, STE 310 19401 #041-02-1972 L1973 **GE IM** *020 †20
DRIZIN, Gary Steven. 1330 POWELL ST, STE 508 19401 #041-13-1977 L1978 **PUD IM** *020 †20 ‡

■ = Address Information Privacy Protected

7963

DUKLE, Vijaya Sagar. 2701 DEKALB PIKE, SUBURBAN GENERAL HOSPITAL 19401 #495-17-1994 L2001 **AN** *020 †05
DUMAGSA-MCGOWAN, Leila Cl. 1301 POWELL ST 19401 #748-09-1991 L2006 **FP** *012
EDMAN, Richard Lee. 1330 POWELL ST STE 409 19401 #041-12-1984 L1989 **FM** *020 †18
ELDAIEF, Daisy Shams. 1340 DEKALB ST, DEKALB PEDS STE 4 19401 #330-02-1960 L1970 **PD ADL** *020 †55 ‡
ERSNER, Arthur R. 1411 POWELL ST 19401 #041-13-1974 L1975 **IM** *020 †20
EVANS, Susanna Grace. 1330 POWELL ST, STE 409 19401 #041-14-1995 L2001 **FM** *020 †18
FARB, Stanley Norman. 306 W LOGAN ST 19401 #023-01-1958 L1962 **OTO** *071 †45
FITZGERALD, John J, III. 1437 DEKALB ST, STE 101 19401 #041-77-1982, ▲ L1983 **OBG** *020 †30 ‡
FLANAGAN, John J, Jr. 1330 POWELL ST, STE 100 19401 #041-07-1985 L1991 **VS GS** *020 †85
FORMAN, Kenneth Jay. 1301 POWELL ST 19401 #010-01-1969 L1970 **IM CD** *020 †20
FOX, David Stuart. 1330 POWELL ST, STE 409 19401 #041-02-1992 L1994 **FM** *040 †18
FRIEDMAN, Ronald Harry. 1001 STERIGERE ST, NORRISTOWN STATE HOSP 19401 #041-13-1959 L1960 **IM CD** *020 †20
FROST, A Gerald. 1330 POWELL ST, STE 100 19401 #041-09-1976 L1982 **CRS GS** *020 †85,10
FUNARO, Anthony Harry. 102 W GERMANTOWN PIKE, STE C 19401 #041-09-1973 L1974 **R** *020 †80
GALLO, Amelia N. ■ 19401 #041-09-1950 L1952 **OM GP** *071
GANIME, Peter David. 363 W JOHNSON HWY, STE 1 19401 #021-01-1966 L1967 **P CHP** *020 †75
GEORGE, Daniel A. 15 W WOOD ST 19401 #496-21-1992 L1999 **NEP** *020 †20
GEORGE, Romani Susan. 1100 POWELL ST, CENTRAL MH/MR CENTER 19401 #495-27-1986 L1994 **P** *020 †75
GINN, Eric Roy. 1330 POWELL ST, MONTGOMERY HOSPITAL 19401 #665-02-2005 L2007 **FP** *012
GOLDEN, Mano Robt. 1313 DEKALB ST 19401 #041-01-1945 L1946 **U** *071 †95
GOLDSTEIN, Philip Robt. 2705 DEKALB PIKE, STE 305 19401 #035-09-1983 L1986 **CD IM** *020 †20
GOMEZ, Pedro Felix. 1001 STERIGERE ST 19401 #275-01-1946 L1966 **P OS** *071
GOMEZ, Pedro I. 1001 STERIGERE ST 19401 #275-01-1945 **GP OS** *020
GOREN, Lawrence Jay. 160 W GERMANTOWN PIKE, STE D4 19401 #041-09-1978 L1980 **TS** *020
GRAEFFE, Estella Phylis. 1330 POWELL ST, MONTGOMERY CANCER CENTER 19401 #041-07-1978 L1979 **RO** *020 †80
GULATI, Roshi. 1330 POWELL ST STE 409, PRACTICE PRO 19401 #495-74-2002 L2004 **FP** *012
HALE, Robert G. 1301 POWELL ST 19401 #041-02-1951 L1952 **FM** *071 †18
HARVEY, Christopher D. 1330 POWELL ST, STE 507 19401 #027-01-2003 L2007 **OBG** *100
HAYES, Arthur Commons. 1330 POWELL ST, STE 510 19401 #041-02-1975 L1976 **EM IM** *020 †20,16
HAYES, Joseph T. 1330 POWELL ST, STE 200 19401 #305-01-1980 L1981 **PM OM** *020 †70
HENIEN, Samia Raouf. 2701 DEKALB PIKE, MERCY SUBURBAN HOSP 19401 #915-02-1977 L1991 **PTH** *020 †50 ‡
HORWITZ, Brett Robt. 1401 DEKALB ST 19401 #041-13-1984 L1985 **ORS OSM** *020 †40
HRIC, Jerome J. 2701 DEKALB PIKE, MEDICAL AFFAIRS 19401 #041-09-1981 L2003 **PD NPM** *020 †55
HUDOCK, Emanuel B, Jr. 1301 POWELL ST 19401 #041-13-1960 L1961 **IM** *071
JACKSON, Althea Judith. 1330 POWELL ST, STE 507 19401 #041-09-1986 L1987 **OBG** *020 †30
JOHNSTON, Sjanna. 15 W WOOD ST 19401 #041-02-1978 L1979 **FM GYN** *020
JOSSELSON, Alan Stuart. 1330 POWELL ST, STE 508 19401 #041-02-1973 L1975 **PUD IM** *020 †20 ‡
JULIAN, Josephine Dwintar. 1301 POWELL ST, MONTGOMERY HOSPITAL 19401 #506-03-1993 L2006 **FP** *012
KARKANIAS, Cherolyn. 1330 POWELL ST STE 409 19401 #041-13-1989 L1991 **FM** *020 †18
KASSIS, Spiro Yacoub. 40 W GERMANTOWN PIKE 19401 #528-01-1983 L1997 **ADP** *020
KIRSCHNER, Ronald Allen. 2701 DEKALB PIKE 19401 #041-77-1966, ▲ L1970 **OTO FPS** *020
KOFSKY, Phillip Mark. 1330 POWELL ST, STE 100 19401 #041-13-1984 L1985 **CRS GS** *020 †85,10
KONECKE, Lee Louis. 2705 DEKALB PIKE, STE 305 19401 #041-09-1967 L1968 **CD IM** *020 †20 ‡
KOUYOUMDJIAN, Michael. 530 CHURCH ST 19401 #041-77-2001, ▲ L2001 **IM FPG** *020
KOVALSKY, Evan Scott. 1308 DEKALB ST 19401 #041-07-1984 L1985 **ORS** *020 †40
KUDES, Diana Barnett. 530 CHURCH ST 2ND FL, MERCY SUBURBAN FAMILY PRAC 19401 #041-13-2001 L2007 **PD** *020 †55
KULLAR, Rupinder Kaur. ■ 19403 #033-05-2008 L2008 *012
LANDIN, Kenneth John Neil. 1330 POWELL ST, STE 409 19401 #060-01-1974 L1996 **FM** *020 †18
LEAHY, Joann Marie. 1541 POWELL ST, NRCC 19401 #041-07-1981 L1982 **RO** *020 †80
LESCHAK, Stephen Andrew. 342 W GERMANTOWN PIKE, STE 310 19403 #041-09-1990 L1995 **VIR** *020 †80
LI, Weiguo. 1301 POWELL ST, DEPT OF FAMILY PRAC 19401 #243-03-1995 L2004 **FM** *020 †18
LININGER, John Richard. 1301 POWELL ST 19401 #025-01-1978 L1983 **PTH** *062 †50
LIPSHUTZ, Hugh. 2705 DEKALB PIKE, STE 305 19401 #041-07-1982 L1983 **CD IM** *020 †20 ‡
LIU, Xia. 1301 POWELL ST 19401 #243-77-1983 L2005 **FP** *012
LUGO-MARTINEZ, Victor M. ■ 19401 #042-03-1997 L2007 **GS** *020
MAGARGEE, Edward M. 1330 POWELL ST, STE 301 19401 #041-02-1964 L1965 **PTH** *020 †50
MALEBRANCHE, Josy M. 1001 STERIGERE ST 19401 #440-01-1961 L1972 **FM** *071
MANDELL, Delaine Madeline. 1301 POWELL ST 19401 #041-07-1983 L1984 **DR** *020 †80 ‡
MARGOLIS, Nora Marta. 1100 POWELL ST 19401 #041-07-1991 L1993 **P CHP** *020 †75
MARRONE, Ralph Thos. ■ 19403 #041-09-1961 L1962 **CHP GPM** *020 ‡
MARTIN, Jacqueline Selma. 1330 POWELL ST 19401 #041-13-2002 L2005 **FM** *100 †18
MASH, Michael John. 1301 POWELL ST 19401 #561-17-1980 L1982 **IM** *020 †20
MATHEWS, Sheelu. 1330 POWELL ST, MONTGOMERY HOSPITAL 19401 #495-37-2004 L2007 **FP** *012
MC CUSKER, Francis Xavier. 15 W WOOD ST 19401 #041-07-1981 L1983 **NEP IM** *020 †20 ‡
MC DONOUGH, Patrick Jos. 363 W JOHNSON HWY, STE 1 19401 #041-13-1958 L1959 **P** *020
MC LAUGHLIN, Geo Edward. 1330 POWELL ST STE 603 19401 #041-13-1959 L1960 **RHU IM** *071 †20
MEIER, Louis Alois. 1301 POWELL ST 19401 #067-01-1963 L1966 **GS** *071 †85
MELNICK, Scott Allen. 1301 POWELL ST 19401 #041-13-1974 L1975 **FM** *020 †18
MENA, Lilia Fe Deconich F. ■ 19401 #275-01-1946 L1968 **P PD** *072
MENKOWITZ, Bruce Jay. 1401 DEKALB ST 19401 #041-13-1972 L1973 **ORS** *030 †40
MERVINE, Charles King, III. 1301 POWELL ST 19401 #041-02-1956 L1957 **FM A** *071 †18
MOHSENIAN, Javad. 1001 STERIGERE ST 19401 #517-05-1964 L1971 **CHP** *020
MOLLICK, James Andrew. 1437 DEKALB ST STE 101 19401 #041-13-1956 L1957 **GYN** *071 †30
MOLLICK, James Louis. 1437 DEKALB ST, STE 101 19401 #041-13-1986 L1987 **OBG** *020 †30
MORGAN, Corinne. 15 W WOOD ST 19401 #041-13-1977 L1979 **NEP IM** *020 †20
MORIARTY, Madeline T. 133 W MAIN ST 19401 #016-43-1992 L2005 **MPD PD** *020 †55,20 ‡
MUKERJEE, Venu. 1100 POWELL ST 19401 #495-21-1960 L1978 **P** *020
MUSTHAQ, Fathima Farhana. 1201 DEKALB ST, CENTRAL MONTGOMERY MHMR 19401 #220-02-1987 L1999 **CHP P** *020 †75
NELL-BADRA, Rocio E. 50 BEECH DR 19403 #847-02-1971 L1974 **P** *030 †75
NESBIT, David G. 1001 STERIGERE ST RM 48 19401 #422-01-1988 L1995 **PYG** *020
NEVULIS, John James. 1308 DEKALB ST 19401 #041-02-1976 L1977 **ORS OSM** *020 †40
NGUYEN, Dai Le. ■ 19401 #166-03-2003 L2005 **FP** *012
NUTT, James Norwell, III. 1308 DEKALB ST 19401 #041-02-1970 L1972 **ORS HS** *020 †40 ‡
O'BRIEN, James Jos. 1330 POWELL ST STE 301, CARDIOLOGY CONSULT PHILA 19401 #041-02-1960 L1961 **CD IM** *071 †20
O'NEIL, Annette Denise. 133 W MAIN ST, NORRISTOWN REGIONAL HEALTH 19401 #041-09-1986 L1987 **IM** *020 ‡
PAN, Weilan. 1301 POWELL ST, MONTGOMERY HOSPITAL 19401 #243-16-1992 L2006 **FM** *100
PANEQUE, Grato. 1001 STERIGERE ST 19401 #308-03-1981 L1993 **P** *020
PARAMBIL, Joseph Rajan. 1301 POWELL ST, STE 123 19401 #305-01-2001 L2004 **IM** *020 †20
PARKER, John Felix. 1001 STERIGERE ST, DEPT OF PSYCHIATRY 19401 #041-09-1954 L1955 **P FM** *071 ‡
PATEL, Hiral. 1330 POWELL ST, STE 508 19401 #033-05-2007 **IM** *012
PATRONE, Richard Anthony. ■ 19401 #041-09-1985 L1986 **AN** *020 †05
PEIKES, Irwin L. 1301 POWELL ST 19401 #065-01-1941 L1942 **OBG** *071 †30
PERCH, Robert Bernard. 1313 DEKALB ST 19401 #041-02-1955 L1956 **U** *071 †95
PEROSIO, Patricia Mary. 1301 POWELL ST, MONTGOMERY HOSPITAL 19401 #041-01-1988 L2001 **PTH** *020 †50
POLISH, Bernardine Mary. 2705 DEKALB PIKE, STE 202B 19401 #041-13-1985 L1987 **PM** *020 †60
POLSKY, Harry Steven. 1330 POWELL ST, STE 100 19401 #041-02-1970 L1971 **GS VS** *020 †85
PRITT, Pauline. ■ 19401 #041-07-1951 L1952 **OS** *071
PULEO, Samuel Michael. 1401 DEKALB ST 19401 #041-02-1978 L1979 **ORS** *020 †40
PUTNAM, Samuel Grady, III. 342 W GERMANTOWN PIKE, STE 310 19403 #041-02-1986 L1988 **DR AM** *020 †80
QAZI, Abdul Sami. 1330 POWELL ST STE 409, MONTGOMERY FAMILY PRACTICE 19401 #704-09-1999 L2003 **FPG** *020 †18
RAFFENSPERGER, Charlotte. 1100 POWELL ST, CENTRAL MONTGOMERY MENTAL 19401 #041-07-1954 L1955 **P** *071 †75
REEDER, Tilden Berk. 1211 DEKALB ST 19401 #038-41-1972 L1998 **CHP P** *020 †75
RIM, Sun Mi. 1001 STERIGERE ST, NORRISTOWN STATE HOSP 19401 #583-08-1972 L1976 **P CHP** *020
RIVERA, Jennifer Nerves. 1330 POWELL ST, MONTGOMERY HOSPITAL 19401 #748-11-1998 L2007 **FP** *012
RODGERS, Wm Henry, III. 1330 POWELL ST, STE 409 19401 #041-13-1959 L1960 **FM** *020 †18 ‡
ROSE, Gina Lynn. 1330 POWELL ST, STE 409 19401 #041-13-1998 L2000 **FM** *020 †18
ROSENTHAL, David. 2705 DEKALB PIKE 19401 #041-77-1960, ▲ L1961 **PM** *071
RUDERMAN, Richard M. 1301 POWELL ST, MONTGOMERY HOSPITAL MEDICA 19401 #041-09-1982 L1986 **DR VIR** *020 †80
SARKER, Shila. 1001 STERIGERE ST, DEPT OF PSYCHIATRY 19401 #160-04-1972 L1976 **P** *020 †75
SCHMIDT, H Wm. 1301 POWELL ST 19401 #041-02-1950 L1951 **PTH FOP** *071 †50
SCHNEIDER, Jill. 1330 POWELL ST, STE 610 19401 #041-07-1981 L1982 **OPH** *020 †35
SCHWARTZ, Gary Richard. 342 W GERMANTOWN PIKE, STE 1 19403 #038-40-1978 L1983 **CD** *020 †20
SENEKO, Patricia Lynn. ■ 19401 #041-15-2000 L2001 **TS** *012
SHAFI, Sabeena. 1330 POWELL ST STE 409, PRACTICE PRO 19401 #613-02-1996 L2001 **FM** *100
SHAH, Navin P. 1301 POWELL ST 19401 #495-57-1967 L1980 **GS** *020
SHAKIR, Adil. 1301 POWELL ST 19401 #496-40-1997 L2004 **FP** *012
SHAMSI, Muhammad Nadeem. 2701 DEKALB PIKE 19401 #704-16-1990 L1997 **P** *020 †75
SHARMA, Amita. 1330 POWELL ST 19401 #495-12-1989 L2001 **FM** *020 †18
SHARMA, Harinder. 342 W GERMANTOWN PIKE, STE 1 19403 #495-45-1994 L2001 **CD** *020 †20
SIMONSON, Gloria A. 1330 POWELL ST, STE 409 19401 #041-13-1997 L1999 **FM** *020 †18
SINGARAM, Thenmozhi. 1330 POWELL ST, MONTGOMERY HOSPITAL 19401 #495-16-2000 L2007 **FP** *012
SINGER, Barry Lester. 1544 DEKALB ST 19401 #023-07-1967 L1968 **ON IM** *020 †20
SOLOMON, Robert Asher. 1330 POWELL ST, STE 409 19401 #041-02-1986 L1987 **FM** *020 †18
SPITZER, Laurence John. 1301 POWELL ST 19401 #041-09-1992 L1995 **DR** *020 †80
SRINIVASAN, Mahalakshmi. 1330 POWELL ST STE 409, MONTGOMERY FAMILY PRACTICE 19401 #495-66-1991 L2002 **FM** *020 †18
STOKES, Sudhir. 1001 STERIGERE ST 19401 #495-45-1971 L1976 **P** *020 †75
STOLTZ, William C. 1201 DEKALB ST 19401 #305-01-1985 L1988 **P** *020 †75
SURH, Yvonne Suk. POWELL & FORNANCE STREETS, MONTGOMERY HOSPITAL 19401 #008-02-1985 L1990 **EM OM** *020 †16
TAIT, Edwin Copp. 15 W WOOD ST 19401 #025-01-1948 L1949 **OPH** *071 †35
TAMAKI, Hitoshi Thomas. 1301 POWELL ST 19401 #024-05-1943 L1945 **PTH** *071 †50
TANG, Xiaowen. 1301 POWELL ST 19401 #041-15-2000 L2002 **EM** *020 †16
THOMAS, Garry Joseph. 2500 DEKALB PIKE, STE 301 19401 #055-01-1985 L1987 **OPH OS** *020 †35
THOMPSON, Eric D, Jr. 1301 POWELL ST, MONTGOMERY HOSPITAL 19401 #041-13-1992 L1995 **PD** *020 †55
THOMPSON, Patreece May. ■ 19401 #023-07-1980 L1982 **P IM** *020 †75
TROUTMAN, Michele Renee. ■ 19401 #041-13-1998 **P** *100
TRUMBORE, David John. 15 W WOOD ST 19401 #041-02-1979 L1981 **ID** *020 †20
UMAR, Kenan. RR 1 BOX 2, CREST TERRACE 19403 #902-01-1954 L1963 **P N** *071
VERGHESE, Cherian. 1401 DEKALB ST, STE 201 19401 #495-01-1984 L1992 **P** *020 †75
VILLAS, Peter Angelo. 1330 POWELL ST, STE 510 19401 #041-02-1996 L1998 **VIR** *020 †80
VLHA, Janet Dolores. 2701 DEKALB PIKE 19401 #041-12-1977 L1979 **IMG** *020 †20
VOLOKHONSKY, Helen. 342 W GERMANTOWN PIKE, STE 200 19403 #913-41-1991 L2000 **IMG** *020 †18 ‡
WARREN, Sara Ann. 1001 STERIGERE ST 19401 #041-02-1966 L1967 **P PFP** *071 †75
WEINER, Bruce. 1330 POWELL ST, STE 100 19401 #033-06-1981 L1986 **GS** *020 †85
WEISS, George Henry. 3023 DEKALB BLVD 19401 #407-16-1958 L1959 **FM** *020 †18 ‡

WIDZER, Helen. 1330 POWELL ST, STE 507 19401 #041-07-1978 L1979 **OBG** *020 †30
WILLIAMS, Patricia Janine. 1301 POWELL ST 19401 #024-05-1989 L1992 **OBG** *020 †30
WILLIAMS, R Hallock. 1301 POWELL ST 19401 #067-01-1961 L1962 **P** *071 †75
WILLIAMS, Stephen Kerr. 1301 POWELL ST 19401 #041-02-1956 L1957 **GP** *071
WILSON, Kyle Ericsson. 2705 DEKALB PIKE, STE 205 19401 #038-40-1989 L1996 **PD** *020 †55
WISGO, Christopher John. 2701 DEKALB PIKE, MERCY SUBURBAN HOSP ED 19401 #041-02-1993 L1995 **EM** *020 †16
WOLF-SCHATZ, Ann Marie C. 1211 DEKALB ST 19401 #041-07-1978 L1979 **CHP** *020 †75
WOO, Ok-Kyoung. 1001 STERIGERE ST 19401 #583-08-1971 L1976 **PM** *020
YOUNG, In Min. 3209 PATRICIA CIR 19401 #583-01-1948 L1979 **FM** *071
ZAJICK, Donald Charles, Jr. ■ 19401 #041-02-2002 L2007 **MSR** *012 †80
ZELJKO, Tomislav. 1330 POWELL ST STE 409, PRACTICE PRO 19401 #957-01-1998 L2004 **FM** *020 †18
ZLOTOWSKI, David Mark. 1301 POWELL ST 19401 #041-15-1999 L2001 **EM** *020 †18

NORTH APOLLO – ARMSTRONG

HALL, Dennis Alan. ■ 15673 #041-01-1969 L1970 **IM NEP** *020 †20
VELEZ, Fidel E. PO BOX 87 15673 #042-01-1983 L1988 **FM** *020 †18
WARBY, Terry John. ■ 15673 #654-01-1987 L1991 **IM** *020 †20

NORTH EAST – ERIE

CARSI, Belen. ■ 16428 #847-04-1991 L1999 **OMO** *020
DAVIE, James Robert. ■ 16428 #048-12-1998 L2002 **DMP** *020 †50
GODFREY, Benjamin Robert. ■ 16428 #022-75-2007, ▲ L2007 *012
GOURGOUTIS, Geo Demetrios. ■ 16428 #418-02-1953 L1969 **GE IM** *071 †20
MAC LACHLAN, Margaret A. ■ 16428 #065-06-1948 L1953 **AN** *071 †05
MC GEEHAN, Paul Anthony. 11487 SCOTLAND AVE 16428 #041-02-1982 L1984 **R** *020
MILLER, Jonathan Taylor. 5595 WILLIAMS RD 16428 #041-15-2003 L2006 **EM** *100 †16
SHANLEY, Margaret H. 2060 N PEARL ST 16428 #008-02-1993 L1997 **FM** *020 †18

NORTH HUNTINGDON – WESTMORELAND

BAUM, Alicia. 8700 PENNSYLVANIA AVE 15642 #132-01-1968 L1977 **D** *020 †15 ‡
GARIN, Amalia. ■ 15642 #561-17-1938 L1967 **R** *071 †80
JETTI, Krishna Prasad. 12279 ROUTE 30 15642 #495-70-1975 L1978 **CRS** *020 †85 ‡
KERR, Clark M, Jr. 12279 ROUTE 30, NORWIN FAMILY MED 15642 #041-12-1979 L1980 **FM FPG** *020 †18
LIPINSKI, Joseph Leo. 8775 NORWIN AVE 15642 #041-01-1990 L1992 **IM** *020 †20
MERCEA, Radu. 40 LINCOLN WAY, STE 310 15642 #781-01-1986 L1998 **FM** *020 †18 ‡
SHETTY, Balu B. 8775 NORWIN AVE 15642 #495-37-1981 L1984 **IM** *020

NORTH VERSAILLES – ALLEGHENY

OTTONELLO, Domingo G. 500 NAYSMITH RD 15137 #132-05-1967 L1977 **RHU IM** *020 †20

NORTH WALES – MONTGOMERY

AMCHIN, Jess David. ■ 19454 #035-01-1982 L1986 **PHM P** *062 †75
ARSEVER, Christiane L. 351 N SUMNEYTOWN PIKE, PO BOX 1241 19454 #025-01-1979 L2000 **RHU IM** *030 †20
AVERBUCH, Steven D. ■ 19454 #016-11-1979 L1996 **ON PA** *020 †20
BANTLEY, David S, Jr. ■ 19454 #041-01-1952 L1953 **R** *071 †80
BERG, Jodi Liebman. 1010 HORSHAM RD, NORTH WILLOW GROVE 19454 #041-13-2001 L2003 **PD** *020 †55 ‡
BLACKMAN, Samuel Charles. 351 N SUMNEYTOWN PIKE, (MSUG4D-34 19454 #016-11-2001 2008 **PHO** *012 †55
BLANZACO, Andre Chas. ■ 19454 #041-01-1959 L1960 **OBG** *071 †30
BROZENA, Susan Celia. ■ 19454 #041-13-1981 L1983 **CD** *020 †20
CHEN, Janine Junying. ■ 19454 #041-13-2005 L2005 **OBG** *012
CIROTTI, Joseph James. 1010 HORSHAM RD, NORTH WILLOW GROVE 19454 #041-02-1961 L1962 **PD** *020 †55 ‡
FREEDMAN, Steven David. 351 N SUMNEYTOWN PIKE, P O BOX 1000 19454 #008-02-1986 L1988 **GE IM** *020 †20
GOLDBERG, Allan Irving. ■ 19454 #016-42-1977 L1990 **IM NEP** *050 †20
GORDON, Robert Harris. 1425 HORSHAM RD 19454 #041-02-1975 L1978 **IMG RHU** *020 †20
GULATI, Usha. ■ 19454 #495-08-1959 L1988 **PM** *071
HALBE, Kevin John. ■ 19454 #041-02-2005 L2005 **AN** *012
HARTENBAUM, David. 351 N SUMNYTWN U643-30, MSP MANAGED CARE 19454 #041-01-1985 L1985 **OPH** *071 †35
HOFFMANN, Ron. 212 N MAIN ST 19454 #041-13-1988 L1991 **OBG** *020 †30
JACKEL, Roy Allen. 124 DEKALB PIKE 19454 #041-12-1981 L1985 **N** *020 †75 ‡
JOHN, Alin Annie. ■ 19454 #041-15-2008 *012
JOHNSON, Lisa Renee. 351 N SUMNEYTOWN PIKE, U63A-053 19454 #010-03-1989 L1992 **IM** *020 †20
KALAWADIA, Nina Vinodrai. ■ 19454 #041-13-2008 *012
KARSON, Craig Neal. 351 N SUMNEYTOWN PIKE, UG2A-047 19454 #025-01-1975 L1981 **P** *050 †75
KASLOW, David Cutler. 351 N SUMNEYTOWN PIKE, # UG3C-48 19454 #005-02-1983 L2000 **IM** *050
KUHNERT, Paul Melvin. ■ 19454 #038-06-1988 **OS** *062 ‡
LEARY, Kathleen Elizabeth. 1010 HORSHAM RD STE 101 19454 #041-15-2001 L2003 **FM** *020 †18
LEWIS, Courtney Bain. ■ 19454 #036-01-2002 L2003 **RO** *020
LUBINIECKI, Gregory M. 351 N SUMNEYTOWN PIKE, UG4D-72 19454 #023-07-1998 L2001 **HO** *020 †20
MAC DONALD, Laurie J. ■ 19454 #041-01-1990 L1993 **IM** *020 †20
MAHMUD, Mariam Rahman. ■ 19454 #041-15-2004 L2004 **PD** *100
MANTELL, Geraldine. ■ 19454 #041-13-1963 L1965 **OBG** *100

MARINCHAK, Pamela Anne. ■ 19454 #041-07-1978 L1980 **CHP P** *030 †75
MC MASTER, John D. ■ 19454 #041-13-1951 L1952 **IM RHU** *071 †20
NAPOLETANO, Mario Oscar. 1010 HORSHAM RD, STE 101 19454 #041-02-1995 L1997 **FM** *020 †18
O'NEILL, Bryan James. 124 DEKALB PIKE 19454 #035-48-1992 L1996 **PM PMM** *020 †60
PARKER, Kathryn Alayne. ■ 19454 #041-02-2005 L2006 **EM** *012
PATEL, Ketankumar V. ■ 19454 #495-22-1986 L1994 **P** *020 †75
QI, Yan. 124 DEKALB PIKE 19454 #243-21-1982 L2000 **N** *020 †75 ‡
ROSENBLOOM, Michael Henry. ■ 19454 #035-01-2004 L2005 **IM** *100
SARGENT, Chala Ao. ■ 19454 #048-14-1988 L1990 **P** *020 †75
SASSON, Marvin. 311 N SUMNEYTOWN PIKE, STE 1E 19454 #035-19-1993 L1997 **D** *020 †15
SHAFER, Frank Edward. ■ 19454 #030-06-1983 L1994 **PHO PD** *020 †55 ‡
SHAH, Hansa K. ■ 19454 #495-22-1964 L1976 **P CHP** *020 †75
SHIN, Grace H. ■ 19454 #041-13-2008 *012
SKUBICK, Daniel Lewis. 124 DEKALB PIKE 19454 #025-01-1972 L1976 **N** *020 †75 ‡
SOHN, William J. 1010 HORSHAM RD, NORTH WILLOW GROVE 19454 #050-02-1951 L1952 **PD** *020 †55 ‡
SOLOMON, Howard Michael. ■ 19454 #028-03-1983 L1983 **PTH** *050 †50
STIERSTORFER, Michael B. 311 N SUMNEYTOWN PIKE # 1E, STE 1E 19454 #041-13-1985 L1988 **D** *020 †15
SUN, Lu Amy. 351 N SUMNEYTOWN PIKE, UG4D-34 19454 #243-71-1982 L2007 **IM PA** *020 †20
TAYLOR, George Thomas, IV. 4702 CONGRESS CT 19454 #041-02-1997 L1999 **FM** *020 †18
TRAVALINE, John Michael. ■ 19454 #041-02-1988 L1991 **PUD CCM** *020 †20
VENEZIA, Mary Ann. 126 SWEDESFORD RD 19454 #033-06-1981 L1983 **P** *020 †75
VISWANATH, Sathyamurthy. 405 GEORGES CT 19454 #496-39-1991 L2002 **IM** *100
WALLACE, Donald W, Jr. ■ 19454 #041-13-1981 L1984 **PA** *030
WALSH, Louisa Marcy. 212 CHURCH RD 19454 #045-01-1986 L1991 **PA** *020
WETTER, Marvin S. 212 CHURCH RD, ICON CLINICAL RESEARCH 19454 #041-02-1966 L1999 **U** *030
WLODARCZYK, Marcin J. 212 CHURCH RD 19454 #759-03-1990 *020

NORTH WARREN – WARREN

BUTT, Frank Henry. ■ 16365 #041-02-1944 L1944 **FM** *071
DRESZER, George L. 33 MAIN DR 16365 #759-10-1963 L1972 **CHP P** *020
FRITZ, Karl John, Jr. ■ 16365 #041-12-1945 L1946 **R** *071 †80
HO, Shou-Chao. ■ 16365 #244-01-1969 L1972 **AN** *100
NIERRAS, Leo. 33 MAIN DR 16365 #748-01-1955 L1972 **P** *075 †75
PATHAK, Hridayesh Kumar. 33 MAIN DR 16365 #843-01-1978 L1982 **P** *020
PUESAN, Reynaldo. 33 MAIN DR 16365 #308-07-1982 L1987 **P** *020 †75
SAQUIN, Raineldo Cortes. 33 MAIN DR 16365 #748-01-1969 L1974 **GP PTH** *020 †50
SOOD, Arun Kumar. ■ 16365 #495-08-1972 L1978 **P** *020 †75
SOOD, Promila. 33 MAIN DR 16365 #495-43-1970 L1981 **P** *020
VERVILLE, Edward Geo. 19 WEATHERBEE ST 16365 #011-02-1964 L1965 **GP** *020

NORTHAMPTON – NORTHAMPTON

COUTINHO-HAAS, Sunita P. 93 W 26TH ST 18067 #496-15-1992 L2003 **PD** *020 †55
DESHPANDE, Smita Vilas. 602B E 21ST ST 18067 #495-17-1979 L1982 **FM** *020 †18
EDWARDS, Judith K. ■ 18067 #019-02-1975 L1976 **OBG** *074
GONZALEZ-PRADO, Angeles. 602B E 21ST ST 18067 #847-13-1980 L1997 **IM** *020 †20
KUCHARCZUK, John B. 1357 MAIN ST 18067 #041-01-1951 L1952 **GYN** *020 †30
SONI, Shweta. ■ 18067 #495-74-2001 L2006 **FP** *012
SPATZ, Daniel Michael, Jr. 602B E 21ST ST, STE 400 18067 #041-13-1979 L1980 **FM** *030 †18

NORTHERN CAMBRIA – CAMBRIA

FOULK, Brian Richard. 4210 CRAWFORD AVE, NORTHERN CAMBRIA FAMILY ME 15714 #041-12-2003 L2003 **FM** *020 †18
SCHETTINI-PRASKO, Debra. 917 PHILADELPHIA AVE 15714 #041-77-1993, ▲ L1994 **FM** *020 †18

NORVELT – WESTMORELAND

PATERSON, Alexander G. NORVELT FAM PRAC 15674 #041-02-1975 L1976 **FM FPG** *020 †18

NORWOOD – DELAWARE

WIDDOWSON, Harold Ray. ■ 19074 #041-02-1945 L1946 **AN** *071

NOXEN – WYOMING

GALASSO, Gwendolyn Marie. RR 1 BOX 174, MONROE-NOXEN HEALTH CENTER 18636 #308-08-1983 L1988 **FM** *020 †18

OAK RIDGE – ARMSTRONG

KUENNEN, Rebecca Ann. ■ 16245 #041-15-2003 L2003 **OPH** *100

OAKDALE – ALLEGHENY

BENEDUM, Karen J. 3000 MONTOUR CHURCH RD, STE 100 15071 #041-12-1982 L1983 **PD** *020 †55
ESTRIN, Edward Harris. 7777 STEUBENVILLE PIKE, BRIGHT RADIOLOGY 15071 #550-02-1984 L1989 **DR** *020 †80
FIORINI, Cynthia M. 3000 MONTOUR CHURCH RD, STE 100 15071 #539-06-1988 L1990 **PD** *020 †55

■ = Address Information Privacy Protected

GABRIELE, Michael W. 7777 STEUBENVILLE PIKE, BRIGHT RADIOLOGY 15071 #055-01-1990 L1995 **VIR** *020 †80

GREENLER, Daniel Philip. 7777 STEUBENVILLE PIKE, BRIGHT RADIOLOGY 15071 #024-07-1984 L1985 **DR IM** *020 †80

GRIFFIN, Dayle Bonnielynn. 3000 MONTOUR CHURCH RD, STE 100 15071 #010-03-1991 L1993 **PD** *020 †55

HONG, Sung Hak. 7777 STEUBENVILLE PIKE, BRIGHT RADIOLOGY 15071 #583-10-1966 L1974 **DR R** *020 †80

IQBAL, Nadeem. 7777 STEUBENVILLE PIKE, BRIGHT RADIOLOGY 15071 #016-02-1984 L1991 **DR RNR** *020 †80

KAMENSKI, Robert Scott. 7777 STEUBENVILLE PIKE, BRIGHT RADIOLOGY 15071 #041-12-2000 L2000 **DR** *020 †80

KAVIC, Thomas Adam. 7777 STEUBENVILLE PIKE, BRIGHT RADIOLOGY 15071 #041-12-1977 L1978 **DR** *020 †80 ‡

MATHEO, Loreta Myra. 3000 MONTOUR CHURCH RD, STE 100 15071 #035-19-1983 L1992 **PD** *020 †55

MC CONNELL, Harry Waldron. 7777 STEUBENVILLE PIKE 15071 #038-40-1982 L1992 **N P** *020 †75

PATEL, Nimish Harshad. 7777 STEUBENVILLE PIKE, BRIGHT RADIOLOGY 15071 #033-05-1999 L2001 **VIR** *100 †80

PRESTON, Jack Michael. 7777 STEUBENVILLE PIKE, BRIGHT RADIOLOGY 15071 #016-02-1976 L1982 **DR GP** *020 †80

PROVENZANO, David Anthony. ■ 15071 #035-45-1999 L2000 **APM** *100 †05

ROS, Emil John. 8020 STEUBENVILLE PIKE 15071 #649-14-1983 L1985 **GP OM** *020

ROSS, Lisa. 7777 STEUBENVILLE PIKE, BRIGHT RADIOLOGY 15071 #041-13-1987 L1989 **DR** *020 †80

SCHNURER, Mark Alexander. 7777 STEUBENVILLE PIKE, BRIGHT RADIOLOGY 15071 #041-12-1985 L1990 **DR** *020 †80

SESHADRI, Vijaya Ganesh. 3000 MONTOUR CHURCH RD, STE 100 15071 #495-09-1983 L1993 **PD PDC** *020 †55

SEVCIK, Matthew F A. 7777 STEUBENVILLE PIKE, BRIGHT RADIOLOGY 15071 #051-07-1990 L1993 **VIR** *020 †80

TRECHA, Gregory Todd. 7777 STEUBENVILLE PIKE, BRIGHT RADIOLOGY 15071 #025-07-1987 L1989 **DR VIR** *020 †80

VARGO, Jeffrey Paul. 7777 STEUBENVILLE PIKE, BRIGHT RADIOLOGY 15071 #041-02-2001 L2001 **DR** *020 †80

OAKLAND — ALLEGHENY

ABADI, Babak. 1001 QUEEN ST WEST, C A M H GERIATRIC RM 2061 15213 #061-01-1993 L1998 **PYG** *100

HUNT, Susan Candace. 200 LOTHROP ST, STE 900 15213 #054-04-1979 L1981 **IMG** *040 †20

MOORE, Robert Clifton. 33 HALKET ST, MAGEE WOMENS HOSPITAL 15213 #021-06-2002 L2006 **OBG** *100

OAKMONT — ALLEGHENY

BAHL, Mohinder Mohan. ■ 15139 #495-28-1963 L1974 **FM CD** *071 †18

BONIFACE, Dolores Jean. 640 5TH ST 15139 #561-01-1966 L1968 **OPH OS** *071

DESIMONE, Marisa Elizabet. ■ 15139 #035-15-2005 L2005 **IM** *012

FIROIU, Denisa. ■ 15139 #781-01-1989 L2002 **FM** *020 †18

KAWANAMI, Takashi. ■ 15139 #572-12-1972 L1981 **DR** *020 †80

KOLARCZYK, Lavinia Maria. ■ 15139 #041-12-2006 L2006 **AN** *012

MANSOOR, Mohammad. ■ 15139 #517-01-1963 L1973 **DR CD** *020

RICKETTS, Mary Hansberry. ■ 15139 #041-12-1945 L1946 **GP** *071

ROMES, Jean-Paul. 890 15TH ST 15139 #048-14-1999 L2002 **EM** *020 †18

ROTTSCHAEFER, Bernard L. 530 DELAWARE AVE 15139 #041-12-1971 L1972 **IM EM** *071

SCHIFF, Melvin M. ■ 15139 #016-42-1954 L1954 **IM** *071

STEINER, Daniel Richard. 333 ALLEGHENY AVE, STE 200 15139 #041-09-1983 L1984 **IM IMG** *020 †20

SUDILOVSKY, Abraham. ■ 15139 #132-01-1964 **P PA** *050

TROMBLEY, Michael Travis. 222 ALLEGHENY RIVER BLVD 15139 #038-41-2003 L2003 **FM** *020 †18

WALKER, Mary Agnes. 222 ALLEGHENY RIVER BLVD 15139 #041-14-1991 L1993 **FM** *020 †18 ‡

OIL CITY — VENANGO

ANDERSON, Donna. 204 CENTRAL AVE 16301 #035-03-1996 L2000 **IM PD** *020 †20,55

BOYER, Walter E, Jr. ■ 16301 #041-02-1949 L1950 **FM** *071

DILKS, Allison M. 1 MEMORIAL DR 16301 #041-15-2001 L2004 **IM** *020

DRYE, Robert C. ■ 16301 #035-19-1951 L1987 **P PYA** *075 †75

EMMOLO, Alfonse Anthony. ■ 16301 #561-01-1969 **IM CD** *071

ESPARRAGUERA, Francisco. 9 GLENVIEW AVE, GLENVIEW PROFESSIONAL BLDG 16301 #847-04-1950 L1960 **U** *071

GOLD, Arnold Z. 122 W 1ST ST 16301 #035-06-1967 L1971 **IM** *075

HEBDA, William Bernard. 155 E BISSELL AVE 16301 #039-05-1984 L1988 **FM** *020 †18

HUSTON, Chas Clover, III. 116 CENTRAL AVE 16301 #041-13-1976 L1981 **GS** *020 †85

JENSON, Martha Kay. 217 SYCAMORE ST, THE SALVATION ARMY 16301 #025-12-1981 L1995 **FM** *020 †18

LANDOLT, Dolores Martinez. 9 GLENVIEW AVE, GLENVIEW PROFESSIONAL BLDG 16301 #649-02-1952 L1963 **PD OS** *071

LASTER, Rodney Jos. 174 E BISSELL AVE 16301 #010-01-1988 L1991 **AN IM** *020 †05

LA VERDE, Philip S. ■ 16301 #041-09-1962 L1965 **GS CD** *071 †85

LOVESTRAND, Daniel J. 155 E BISSELL AVE 16301 #748-01-1985 L1988 **CCM** *020 †18

MAKNOON, Ali Akbar. 222 PARK AVE 16301 #517-06-1961 L1971 **ORS HS** *071 †40

MAURER, Carol Nellis. ■ 16301 #041-13-1960 L1961 **P** *020

PILEWSKI, Robert Martin. 174 E BISSELL AVE 16301 #041-02-1965 L1966 **IM** *071 †20

POPESCU, Cristian Liviu. 9 GLENVIEW AVE STE 206 16301 #781-03-1998 L2004 **IM** *020 †20

RIGHTOR, John Thorburn. 204 CENTRAL AVE 16301 #041-02-1958 L1959 **GP OS** *071

ROMERO, Charles Jeffrey. 406 W 1ST ST 16301 #034-01-1987 L1997 **P** *020 †75

SHAPIRO, Stuart Gary. 1 MEMORIAL DR 16301 #041-12-1978 L1979 **IM IMG** *020 †20

SNIDER, Erica Gwendolyn. ■ 16301 #305-01-2002 L2007 **FM** *020 †18

THAMMAVONG, Roulay. ■ 16301 #305-01-2002 L2007 **IM** *020 †20

WALTER, David Leland. 180 E BISSELL AVE 16301 #038-40-1971 L1977 **D DMP** *071 †15

OLD FORGE — LACKAWANNA

BOYER, Darren Michael. ■ 18518 #654-01-2004 L2007 **FP** *012

BUFALINO, Russell Saml. 102 N MAIN ST, COMPREHENSIVE MEDICAL NETW 18518 #041-13-1965 L1966 **ORS** *020 †40

CHARABATI, Jihad. 315 S MAIN ST 18518 #913-06-1981 L1986 **FM** *030 †18 ‡

CHIAVACCI, Eugene John. 730 S MAIN ST 18518 #041-13-1981 L1982 **ORS** *020 †40

GIACOMETTI, Joseph Neil. ■ 18518 #041-02-2008 *012

PAGNOTTI, Joseph Paul. ■ 18518 #041-14-1982 L1984 **IM** *020

WONG, Grace Ichia. ■ 18518 #654-01-2004 L2007 **IM** *020 †20

OLEY — BERKS

BEYER, John Chas. ■ 19547 #041-02-1986 L1989 **EM** *020 †16

CAPPA, Robert James. 2866 W PHILADELPHIA AVE, FAMILY PRACTICE 19547 #035-47-1971 L1977 **FM** *071 †18

HORNICKLE, David Joseph. 346 MAIN ST 19547 #041-12-2001 L2001 **FM** *020 †18

HOULE, Robert Evan. DUTTERER ROAD 19547 #041-13-1977 L1979 **EM FM** *020 †18,16

SZARKO, Frank Jos. ■ 19547 #041-02-1966 **RO R** *071 †80

OLIVEBURG — JEFFERSON

GRIFFIN, Steven Patrick. 2838 ROUTE 36 15764 #041-13-1968 L1970 **PTH** *020 †50

OLYPHANT — LACKAWANNA

CUTILLO, Douglas Peter. 110 TERRACE DR, STE 102 18447 #033-05-1984 L1993 **DR VIR** *020 †80

DEDHIA, Champak Maganlal. 110 TERRACE DR, STE 102 18447 #496-38-1974 L1982 **DR** *020

DETRICK, Earl Patrick. 110 TERRACE DR, STE 102 18447 #041-09-1956 L1957 **R** *020 †80

GAZMEN, Candonino C. 117 SUSQUEHANNA AVE 18447 #748-02-1966 L1975 **GS GP** *075

HOU, Timothy Chie. 110 TERRACE DR, STE 102 18447 #035-06-1989 L1995 **DR VIR** *020 †80

MULLOTH, Rajan. 109 TERRACE DR 18447 #495-45-1983 L1996 **IM PUD** *020 †20 ‡

REEDY, Gary Lee. 109 TERRACE DR 18447 #047-06-1982 L1988 **OBG** *020 †30

STROBBE, Richard Dean. PO BOX 249, 1500 MAIN ST 18447 #308-11-1985 L1989 **IM** *075

THEK, Joseph Chas. 204 GRANT ST 18447 #033-06-1979 L1980 **EM** *020 †16

ONEIDA — SCHUYLKILL

YURICK, Natalie Ann. PO BOX 55, 158 1ST ST 18242 #041-13-1965 L1966 **IM EM** *020

ORANGEVILLE — COLUMBIA

DE HOFF, John Newcomer. ■ 17859 #035-19-1937 L1984 **PD** *071 †55

OREFIELD — LEHIGH

AHMED, Imran. ■ 18069 #160-07-1993 L2007 **IM** *020 ‡

BHATTI, Anjam N. ■ 18069 #047-07-1981 L1984 **IM** *020 †20

BROWN, Sheila. 5213 HIGH VISTA DR, 18069 #041-13-1970 L1971 **AN** *020 †05

CARBONE, Gary Michael S. 5270 CREEKVIEW DR 18069 #305-01-1990 L1991 **NEP IM** *020 †20

CHALEBY, Kutaiba Salem. 5300 KIDSPEACE DR 18069 #041-15-1970 L1992 **CHP P** *020 †75

DUMONT, Larry Edward. 5300 KIDSPEACE DR 18069 #016-06-1980 L1992 **CHP P** *020 †75

FELTINGOFF, Melissa Lee. ■ 18069 #035-47-1992 L1998 **DR** *100

GONG, Li. ■ 18069 #243-16-1984 **PTH** *100

KWAN, Bhe Hong. 5266 CREEKVIEW DR 18069 #506-16-1972 L1976 **DR** *020 †80

LAYNE, George Stark. 5300 KIDSPEACE DR 18069 #025-01-1970 L1973 **P** *020 †75

LE BOEUF, William L. ■ 18069 #041-03-1991 L1993 **CHP** *020 †75

MANDELL, Herbert Elliott. 5300 KIDSPEACE DR, KIDSPEACE CHILDREN'S HOSPI 18069 #041-02-1975 L1976 **CHP P** *020 †75

MARTIN, Jeffrey Allen. 5300 KIDSPEACE DR 18069 #012-01-1991 L1993 **AN APM** *020 †05

MISENHIMER, Martin David. 5300 KIDSPEACE DR 18069 #041-09-1959 L1960 **PD** *071 †55

PEPEN, Lazaro. 5731 RICKY RIDGE TRL 18069 #308-03-1986 L1997 **FM** *020 †18

SCHWARTZ, Lynnae. 5300 KIDSPEACE DR 18069 #024-07-1977 L2008 **PD AN** *050 †55,05

SINHA, Ranjana. 1790 APPLEWOOD DR, ST LUKE'S HOSPITAL, BETHLE 18069 #166-01-1999 L2006 **CN** *100

SMITH, Charles Franklin. 5300 KIDSPEACE DR, KIDSPEACE HOSP 18069 #041-01-1964 L1965 **PD** *020 †55 ‡

SPATZ, Deneen Marie. ■ 18069 #041-13-2007 L2007 **IM** *012

YOUNG, John V, Jr. 4668 YORK DR 18069 #024-16-1974 L2007 **GS VS** *020 †85

ZAWAWI, Adnan Bakr. 5300 KIDSPEACE DR 18069 #797-01-1976 L1983 **N** *020 †75

ORELAND — MONTGOMERY

BUXTON, Douglas Hunter. ■ 19075 #041-15-1999 L2005 **PM** *012

PALMER, Aslene Elaine. ■ 19075 #010-03-1984 L1992 **IM** *020 †20

PARENTE, Thomas Jos. ■ 19075 #041-09-1970 L1971 **LM** *030

SWEHLA, Brian Paul. ■ 19075 #041-13-2007 L2007 **IM** *012

SZPERKA, Christina Lynch. ■ 19075 #008-01-2005 L2005 **CHN** *012

ORWIGSBURG — SCHUYLKILL

BARCLAY, Clayton Carson. ■ 17961 #041-09-1943 L1945 **R** *071 †80

■ = Address Information Privacy Protected

BOHNENBLUST, Walter R. ■ 17961 #019-02-1945 L1948 **R** *071 †80
DARHUN, Benjamin. 200 PINE BROOK PL, STE 5 17961 #041-09-1987 L1989 **FM** *020 †18
ELBERFELD, Jeanne B. ■ 17961 #041-09-1987 L1988 **FM** *020 †18
HARKINS, Robert Steve. 209 E MARKET ST 17961 #041-13-1984 L1985 **FM** *020 †18
LADO, Michael David. 1828 RIDGEWOOD RD, LADO PLASTIC SURGERY 17961 #041-13-1987 L1998 **PS HS** *020 †85,65
LIGHT, Beng Cheah. 46 WALNUT DR 17961 #041-13-1978 L1979 **DR** *020 †80
LUO, Caesar Kyle. ■ 17961 #035-45-2006 L2006 **OPH** *012
PUZZI, Kelly R. 2006 RIDGEVIEW DR 17961 #035-47-1994 L1997 **PD** *020
QUDDUS, Adeeba. ■ 17961 #704-06-1970 L1983 **PD** *020 †55
SHAH, Raza Murtaza. ■ 17961 #041-15-2008 †012
SHAW, Ralph Arthur. ■ 17961 #016-06-1962 L1964 **IM** *030
SHOLEVAR, Bahman. 340 S LIBERTY ST, ACCESS OUTPATIENT SERV 17961 #041-09-1976 L1977 **P** *020 †75
SLIMMER, Samuel John. ■ 17961 #041-13-2007 L2007 **EM** *012
TENNEY, Barbara Lea. 200 PINE BROOK PL, STE 5 17961 #041-02-1971 L1997 **PD** *040 †55
YARCZOWER, Bret Steven. 200 PINE BROOK PL, STE 5 17961 #041-07-1984 L1988 **PD** *020 †55

OTTSVILLE — BUCKS

KRINSKY, Sam Irwin. ■ 18942 #011-02-1976 L1982 **NM DR** *030 †28
WARREN, Judith A Sheldon. ■ 18942 #035-15-1969 **A** *020 †55,03

OXFORD — CHESTER

ALEXANDER, Charles Edward. ■ 19363 #041-01-1955 L1956 **GPM** *071 †70
BARLOW, John Christopher. 303 N 3RD ST, OXFORD PROF CTR 19363 #051-04-1983 L1986 **IM** *020 †20
BEATTIE, Amanda Lynn. ■ 19363 #041-13-2006 L2006 **GS** *012
DAGHIR, John Nejm. 57 N 4TH ST 19363 #041-02-1986 L1987 **FM** *020 †18
DOYLE, Faye Robinson. 133 E LOCUST ST 19363 #041-13-1954 L1955 **FM** *071
EVERETT, Linda Gillespie. 2217 BALTIMORE PIKE 19363 #041-02-1999 L2004 **IM** *020 †20
HOLCOMBE, Guy Truman, Jr. ■ 19363 #041-01-1954 L1956 **GP** *071
KLEIN, Joseph Felix. 7 E LOCUST ST 19363 #869-05-1972 L1975 **IMG GP** *071
KNOX, James David, Jr. 57 N 4TH ST 19363 #041-02-1986 L1987 **FM FSM** *020 †18
MANFIELD, Laura Jean. ▲ 19363 #041-77-2006, ▲ L2006 **FP** *012
MEHTA, Ketki Dhaval. ■ 19363 #495-48-1995 L2003 **IM** *020 †20
NEWILL, Vaun Archie. ■ 19363 #041-12-1947 L1948 **OM PHP** *071
RAO, Brinda Erraballi. 305 N 3RD ST 19363 #495-62-1979 L1984 **PD** *020 †55
ROONEY, David G. 57 N 4TH ST 19363 #041-02-1987 L1988 **FM** *020 †18
WARD, Michael Jos. 133 E LOCUST ST, 152709344 19363 #010-02-1989 L1998 **OTO** *020 †45

PALMER — NORTHAMPTON

FRIEDMAN, Jerald Nathan. 2531 NORTHAMPTON ST 18045 #024-07-1966 L1967 **GS GYN** *020 †85

PALMERTON — CARBON

ASO, Orlando Anoos. 135 LAFAYETTE AVE 18071 #748-01-1961 L1973 **GS** *020 †85
BOHRI, James David. 135 LAFAYETTE AVE 18071 #033-05-1982 L1987 **DR NM** *020 †80
BOSCHI, Alessandro S. 135 LAFAYETTE AVE 18071 #035-01-1984 L1988 **OBG** *020 †30
CHANG, Che-Yi. 135 LAFAYETTE AVE 18071 #244-03-1963 L1984 **AN GP** *020 ‡
COPE, E Stanley P. ■ 18071 #041-01-1946 L1947 **IM** *071
DANCHA, Andrew J. 218 DELAWARE AVE, STE A 18071 #041-77-1989, ▲ L1990 **NEP IM** *020 †20
DEVANI, Shyamsunder H. 135 LAFAYETTE AVE, MEDICAL CENTER FOR WOMEN 18071 #495-01-1975 L1984 **OBG** *020 †30
GOPLERUD, Elizabeth J. ■ 18071 #018-03-1944 L1948 **OBG** *071 †30
HASAN, Ahmed M. 135 LAFAYETTE AVE 18071 #704-16-1982 L1995 **IM GE** *020 †20
HOLENDER, Eric Scott. 217 FRANKLIN AVE, STE 5 18071 #041-77-1994, ▲ L1995 **OTO** *020
KENNEDY, Arthur R, III. 135 LAFAYETTE AVE 18071 #429-01-1980 L1984 **GS** *020 †30
KHAN, Shahzad Ahmad. 185 DELAWARE AVE STE A, U MO HOSPITAL & CLINICS 18071 #704-02-1989 L2007 **N CN** *020 †75
KHAN, Shaukat Hayat. 135 LAFAYETTE AVE 18071 #704-04-1969 L1979 **IM GP** *020 †20
KRAMER, James William, Jr. 135 LAFAYETTE AVE 18071 #051-04-1994 L1996 **GS** *020 †85
LESHOCK, Leon Eugene. PALMERTON HOSPITAL 18071 #016-43-1954 L1961 **IM** *071 †20
LIPSON, Cheryl Sandra. 218A DELAWARE AVE 18071 #308-07-1982 L1986 **IM NEP** *020 †20
MONTES, Manuel Yusay. THE PALMERTON HOSP 18071 #748-07-1961 L1971 **GP PD** *020
SHAHID, Mian Mehboob A. 135 LAFAYETTE AVE 18071 #704-04-1969 L1990 **IM NEP** *020 †20
SLIZOVSKY, Mira. 217 FRANKLIN AVE, PALMERTON PEDS 18071 #913-48-1979 L1998 **PD** *020 †55
TOGHANIAN, Mehran. 135 LAFAYETTE AVE, PALMERTON HOSP 18071 #517-08-1993 L2001 **IM** *020
WAKSTEIN, Andrew. 217 FRANKLIN AVE STE 5 18071 #011-75-1993, ▲ L1994 **OTO** *020
ZHOU, Joe Shuangwen. 135 LAFAYETTE AVE 18071 #243-44-1978 L1998 **IM** *020 †20

PALMYRA — LEBANON

ADDISON, Stephanie Rochel. ■ 17078 #023-01-2007 L2007 **PD** *012
BAUER, Robert Louis. ■ 17078 #041-13-1946 L1947 **FM A** *071
BIEVER, John Albert. 801 S FORGE RD 17078 #041-14-1979 L1980 **CHP P** *020 †75
CORSON, Jane. 941 PARK DR 17078 #041-02-1986 L1987 **FM** *020 †18
CORTES, Jamie Danielle. ■ 17078 #035-48-2007 L2007 **IM** *012
CURANZY, Raymond R. ■ 17078 #023-01-1951 L1952 **FM** *071 †18
DUNN, Thomas Mason. ■ 17078 #041-14-2006 L2006 **AN** *012
ELLIOTT, Vanessa Leigh. ■ 17078 #041-14-2006 L2006 **U** *012
FASSERO, Daniel J. 136 MACINTOSH DR 17078 #030-06-2001 L2002 **OPH** *020
GALVAN, Dan A. ■ 17078 #048-02-1986 L2005 **CCS** *100 †85

GIAMPETRO, David Matthew. ■ 17078 #041-14-2001 L2005 **APM** *100 †75
GRAFF, Gavin Richard. ■ 17078 #041-13-1991 L2002 **PDP** *020 †55
GRAVES, Nancy Sarah. ■ 17078 #041-14-2006 L2006 **FP** *012
HACKMAN, Nicole Marie. ■ 17078 #041-14-2007 L2007 **PD** *012
HAZADI, Danielle Verlee. ■ 17078 #041-14-2004 L2004 **OBG** *012
HAZARD, Sprague William, III. ■ 17078 #041-14-2006 L2006 **GS** *012
HENNING, George Frederick. 941 PARK DR 17078 #041-13-1984 L1986 **FM** *020 †18 ‡
HOHENWARTER, Adrian John. ■ 17078 #041-14-1989 L1992 **FM** *074
HORNER, Kyle Leland. ■ 17078 #054-04-2005 L2007 **D** *012
IRVINE, Olive A Young. ■ 17078 #040-02-1949 L1952 **P** *071 †75
KEITER, James Marcus. ■ 17078 #041-01-1946 L1947 **EM** *071
KELLER, David Alan. 1400 S FORGE RD STE 1, LEBANON VLY FAM MED 17078 #041-14-1992 L1994 **FM** *020 †18
KHALID, Ayesha Naz. ■ 17078 #041-14-2003 L2003 **OTO** *012
KLEPEISS, Stacy Egert. ■ 17078 #041-14-2005 L2005 **D** *012
KREIDER, John Wesley. ■ 17078 #041-01-1963 L1965 **PTH ON** *050
KULP, David W. ■ 17078 #041-02-1953 L1954 **CHP P** *071 †75
LANE, Aaron Brice. ■ 17078 #010-01-2002 L2002 **FM** *100 †18
LAUBACH, George B. ■ 17078 #041-09-1943 L1944 **FM** *072
LEE, Jenny Sue. 1400 S FORGE RD, STE 2 17078 #041-12-1998 L2000 **FM** *020 †18
LINE, Christian Hathaway. ■ 17078 #035-03-2006 L2006 **AN** *012
LINTON, Latoya Natasha. ■ 17078 #041-14-2002 L2005 **CD** *012 †20
MC LAUGHLIN, Maryanne T. 701 LEON AVE 17078 #041-12-1993 L1995 **OBG** *020 †30
MESSMER, John Jos, III. 941 PARK DR, UNIVERSITY PHYSICIAN GROUP 17078 #041-14-1977 L1978 **FM FPG** *020 †18
MILLER, Robyn Renee. ■ 17078 #023-01-2007 L2007 **PD** *012
MONTAGNESE, Elizabeth Ann. 801 S FORGE RD 17078 #025-07-1993 L1998 **CHP P** *020 †75
NATOLI, Noel Blythe. ■ 17078 #035-15-2005 L2005 **PS** *012
NGUYEN, John Duc. ■ 17078 #041-13-2003 L2003 **DR** *012
NIKOLOFF, Matthew Andon. ■ 17078 #041-14-2005 L2005 **IM** *012
ONDIK, Michael Paul. ■ 17078 #016-11-2005 L2005 **OTO** *012
PAGANO, Marlo Marie. ■ 17078 #051-07-2004 L2006 **DR** *012
PAHL, Michelle Theresa. ■ 17078 #050-02-2005 L2005 **MPD** *012
PLUMMER, Samuel Herbert. ■ 17078 #041-77-2007, ▲ L2007 **AN** *012
QURAISHI, Sadeq Ali. ■ 17078 #041-14-2004 L2004 **AN** *012
RAHAM, David Chas. ■ 17078 #065-06-1962 L1970 **FM** *071 †18
RASHID, Samuel F. 1400 S FORGE RD STE 1 17078 #915-04-1978 L1992 **FM** *020 †18
ROLLO, Daniel P. 701 LEON AVE 17078 #035-06-1978 L1979 **OBG** *020 †30 ‡
SANTROCK, Dale Alan. ■ 17078 #055-01-2004 L2004 **AN** *012
SCHMIDOVA, Karin. ■ 17078 #054-04-2003 L2003 **GS** *012
SHAVER, Robert Davis. 701 LEON AVE 17078 #051-04-1989 L1991 **OBG** *020 †30
SHEREEF, Serene. ■ 17078 #041-14-2005 L2005 **GS** *012
STEVENSON, Julia Catherin. ■ 17078 #041-14-2007 L2007 **GS** *012
STONEBACK, Raymond Delano. ■ 17078 #041-09-1959 L1960 **AN** *071 †05
STORCH, Jennifer Lisa. ■ 17078 #016-06-2004 L2004 **P** *012
THEN, Matthew Thomas. ■ 17078 #041-14-2007 L2007 **PTH** *012
TRUONG, Thanh Hue. ■ 17078 #005-15-2004 L2004 **OBG** *012
WAGNER, J Kent Lynwood. 1400 S FORGE RD, STE 1 17078 #041-02-1986 L1987 **FM** *020 †18
WIEGAND, Laurel. 2460 S FORGE RD 17078 #041-14-1981 L1984 **PUD IM** *020 †20
WOLFF, Brynn Sigal. ■ 17078 #051-04-2003 L2003 **GS** *012
WOO, Alice. ■ 17078 #041-14-2007 **GS** *012
YEAGER, Michael John. 701 LEON AVE 17078 #041-14-2002 L2002 **OBG** *020
YEASTED, Nathan Joseph. ■ 17078 #041-14-2007 L2007 **IM** *012

PAOLI — CHESTER

ADAMS, Raymond Davies. 255 W LANCASTER AVE 19301 #041-13-1977 L1979 **AN** *020 †05
ADELMAN, Philip A. 21 INDUSTRIAL BLVD, STE 205 19301 #016-01-1983 L1988 **N** *020 †75
AINSWORTH, Ann S Minehan. 255 W LANCASTER AVE, FL 1 19301 #028-02-1969 L1972 **ATP PCP** *071 †50 ‡
ANDERSON, Kenneth F. ■ 19301 #024-01-1953 L1957 **OM IM** *071
ANTHOPOULOS, Alexander P. 255 W LANCASTER AVE, STE 227 19301 #041-14-1988 L1990 **OBG** *020 †30
ARMSTRONG, Jennifer L. 209 W LANCASTER AVE, STE 100 19301 #041-01-1998 L2004 **HO** *020 †20
ASPEN, Nelson P. 255 W LANCASTER AVE 19301 #041-02-1952 L1953 **ORS PM** *071
AYERLE, Robert S. ■ 19301 #041-01-1951 L1952 **OM** *071
BABINECZ, John Michael. 255 W LANCASTER AVE, STE 330 19301 #048-12-1981 L1984 **PD** *020 †55
BAINBRIDGE, William Jos. 250 W LANCASTER AVE, STE 120 19301 #041-02-1970 L1971 **GP** *020
BANNER, Richard Neil. 255 W LANCASTER AVE 19301 #035-06-1984 L1987 **AN** *020 †05
BANVI, Shaila. 255 W LANCASTER AVE 19301 #495-35-1993 L2001 **AN** *020 †05
BATTAFARANO, Nicholas C. 255 W LANCASTER AVE 19301 #041-09-1949 L1950 **IM GP** *020
BECKER, Sandra Jean. ■ 19301 #048-12-1978 L1983 **PD** *020 †55
BELDEN, R Michael. 11 INDUSTRIAL BLVD, STE 203 19301 #041-07-1994 L1996 **OBG** *020 †30
BENNETT, Joseph Smith, IV. ■ 19301 #041-01-1954 L1955 **IM** *071 †20
BILELLO, Philip. 1 INDUSTRIAL BLVD, PAOLI SURG CTR 19301 #035-09-1989 L1993 **AN** *020 †05
BLACK, Lisa P. 255 W LANCASTER AVE 19301 #023-07-1984 L1996 **IM** *020 †20
BOLLINGER, James Richard. 209 W LANCASTER AVE, STE 200 19301 #041-13-1972 L1973 **U GS** *020 †95 ‡
BOWMAN, Andrew Rael. 328 PAOLI MEDICAL BLDG, STE 328 19301 #836-02-1992 L2001 **CD** *020 †20
BRAY, Joseph Beyer. 250 W LANCASTER AVE, STE 240 19301 #041-13-1961 L1963 **OTO PS** *071 †45
BRILLIANT, Stuart Aaron. 255 W LANCASTER AVE, MAIN LINE EMERGENCY 19301 #035-15-1997 L2000 **EM** *020 †16
BROD, Jennifer Suzanne. 11 INDUSTRIAL BLVD, STE 2 19301 #041-01-1987 L1988 **PD** *020 †55
BROWN, Charles Gerard. ■ 19301 #010-02-1978 L1979 **EM** *050 †16
BROWN, Fraser Huntington. 255 W LANCASTER AVE, RADIOLOGY ASSOCIATES OF TH 19301 #041-15-1999 L2001 **RNR** *012 †80
BUCKLAND, Lawrence Scott. 250 W LANCASTER AVE 19301 #041-02-1995 L2000 **FM** *020 †18

BURGET, Dean Edwin, Jr. 1410 RUSSELL RD, STE 205 19301 #008-01-1962 L1966 PS FPS *020 †65 ‡

BURKE, Meghan Deirdre. ■ 19301 #041-15-2005 L2005 PD *012

BUSSARD, Anne Louise. 255 W LANCASTER AVE, STE 227 19301 #041-02-2001 L2001 OBG *020 †30

CABRAL, Michael Eric. 255 W LANCASTER AVE 19301 #055-01-1995 L1999 *020 †05

CEDRONE, Francine Anne. 17 INDUSTRIAL BLVD # B 19301 #041-01-1976 L1978 PS *020 †65

CHAMCHAD, Dmitri. 255 W LANCASTER AVE 19301 #913-15-1992 L2001 AN *020 †05

CHASTENEY, Edward A. 250 W LANCASTER AVE, STE 150 19301 #041-13-1956 L1997 OBG *020 †30

CLARE, Henry Emmanuel. 209 W LANCASTER AVE, STE 101 19301 #041-01-1959 L1960 P ADM *071 †75

COLDREN, Carol Lynne. 255 W LANCASTER AVE 19301 #041-01-1988 L1990 OBG *020 †30

COMPENDIO, Roel De Mesa. 15 INDUSTRIAL BLVD, STE 203 19301 #748-10-1990 L1997 P *020 †75

CONNELL, Janet T. 325 W CENTRAL AVE, STE 102 19301 #041-09-1971 L1972 P *020 †75

COOPERMAN, Jay Stratford. 250 W LANCASTER AVE, STE 180 19301 #005-14-1981 L1982 IM *020 †20

CURRAN, Marilyn Rohrer. 255 W LANCASTER AVE 19301 #041-01-1954 L1955 P CHP *020 ‡

CURRY, Heather Anne. 255 W LANCASTER AVE, CANCER CTR PAOLI MEM HOSPI 19301 #041-13-1995 L2001 RO *020 †80

CUTLER, Robert S. 255 W LANCASTER AVE, STE 100 19301 #041-02-1966 L1968 OPH *071 †35

DAMPIER, Mary Frances. 255 W LANCASTER AVE, MAIN LINE EMERGENCY 19301 #016-43-1980 L1989 IM HEM *020 †20

DAMSTRA, Ingeborg K. 171 W LANCASTER AVE, COUNCIL FOR RELATIONSHIPS 19301 #010-01-1985 L1994 P CHP *020 †75

DAVIS, Caroline Kamper. 255 W LANCASTER AVE 19301 #041-14-1990 L1994 AN *020 †05

DAY, Nancy Scott. 255 W LANCASTER AVE 19301 #041-13-1977 L1979 AN *020 †05

DAY, Robert Eugene, Jr. 255 W LANCASTER AVE 19301 #041-07-1980 L1984 AN *020 †05

DE COLLI, Joseph Albert. 255 W LANCASTER AVE 19301 #041-09-1966 L1967 PTH *071 †50

DEEVAKONDA, Vaijayanthi. 255 W LANCASTER AVE, PAOLI HOSPITAL, MOB I, SUI 19301 #495-65-1997 L2004 IM *020 †20

DELLEVIGNE, Wm Michael. 255 W LANCASTER AVE, ROBERT W WHITE LIBRARY 19301 #041-02-1967 L1968 GS CD *020 †85

DENOVAN, Richard Edward. 255 W LANCASTER AVE 19301 #041-13-1990 L1994 APM *020 †05

DEUTSCH, E Thomas, Jr. 255 W LANCASTER AVE 19301 #041-13-1962 L1963 FM *071 †18 ‡

DEVON, Michael. 11 INDUSTRIAL BLVD, STE 2 PAOLI MEDICAL BLDG 19301 #041-01-1998 L2000 PD *020 †55

DILLOWAY, Mary A Gillett. 255 W LANCASTER AVE, STE 101 19301 #041-07-1971 PD *020 †55

DOHERTY, James Laurence. 255 W LANCASTER AVE 19301 #028-34-1989 L1992 AN *020 †05

DONNELLY, Dennis Wm. 255 W LANCASTER AVE, STE 224 PAOLI MMB 19301 #041-09-1968 L1969 P PYA *020 †75

DRAKE, Mitchell Scott. 255 W LANCASTER AVE, MAIN LINE EMERGENCY 19301 #041-07-1997 L1999 EM *020 †16

DUCKETT, James Edward. 255 W LANCASTER AVE 19301 #041-14-1976 L1977 AN *020 †05 ‡

DYCKMAN, Sharon. 255 W LANCASTER AVE 19301 #035-47-1981 L1987 OPH *020 †35

ETEZADY, M Hossein. 325 W CENTRAL AVE, STE 102 19301 #517-06-1962 L1971 P *020 †75

FERNANDES, Zereen. 1440 RUSSELL RD, LIFE COUNSELING SERVICES 19301 #495-33-1974 L1983 P *020

FINNEGAN, Mark Owen. 11 INDUSTRIAL BLVD, STE 203 19301 #041-02-1987 L1988 OBG *071 †30

FIRST, Howard E. 255 W LANCASTER AVE, STE 208 MEDICAL OFFICE BUI 19301 #041-01-1950 L1951 OBG *071 †30

FORSTED, David Henry. 255 W LANCASTER AVE 19301 #016-42-1970 L1971 DR *020 †80 ‡

FOX, Stephen C. 21 INDUSTRIAL BLVD STE 204 19301 #024-05-1974 L1977 ON IM *020 †20

FOX, Timothy Trudeau. 102 INDUSTRIAL BLVD, PAOLI POINTE 19301 #033-05-1982 L1983 GS CRS *020 †85

FREEBERG, John Russell. 255 W LANCASTER AVE 19301 #056-06-1979 L1981 AN *020 †05 ‡

FRIED, Robert Carey. 11 INDUSTRIAL BLVD, STE 102 19301 #028-02-1980 L1982 GS VS *020 †85

FRIEDMAN, Meira Malka. 11 INDUSTRIAL BLVD, STE 2 19301 #041-02-2000 L2003 PD *020 †55

GALIB, Samuel H. 17 INDUSTRIAL BLVD 19301 #605-01-1966 L1974 OPH OS *020 †35

GALLAGHER, Terence J. 255 W LANCASTER AVE 19301 #041-02-1990 L1993 AN *020 †05

GAMBURG, Steven J. 255 W LANCASTER AVE, MAIN LINE EMERGENCY 19301 #041-02-1981 L1985 EM *020 †16

GEIGER, Leonard Robt. 250 W LANCASTER AVE, STE 250 19301 #035-03-1966 L1967 N *020 †75

GELMAN, Kenneth Jay. 250 W LANCASTER AVE, STE 340 19301 #041-07-1994 L1996 PD *020 †55

GERBER, Elliot Mark. 15 INDUSTRIAL BLVD, STE 103 19301 #035-09-1980 L1987 CD EM *020 †20

GILLAN, Ernest Francis. 250 W LANCASTER AVE 19301 #041-02-1984 L1985 FM IMG *020 †18

GODSHALL, Duane Kenneth. 255 W LANCASTER AVE, MAIN LINE EMERGENCY 19301 #041-09-1998 L2001 EM *020 †16

GONZALES, Jerry Michael. 255 W LANCASTER AVE 19301 #005-02-1984 L1985 AN *020 †05

GRAHAM, Thomas Hild. 11 INDUSTRIAL BLVD, STE 204 19301 #041-14-1978 L1979 N CN *020 †75

GRECO-HUNT, Valerie T. 255 W LANCASTER AVE #RADIO, PAOLI MEMORIAL HOSPITAL 19301 #041-02-1986 L1987 DR *020 †80

GREER, William Robson. 21 INDUSTRIAL BLVD, STE 200 19301 #041-01-1993 L1995 IM *020 †20

GROFE, Jerrold Gilbert. ■ 19301 #041-01-1955 L1956 CHP P *071

GROVES, Roger Leonard. 250 W LANCASTER AVE, STE 215 19301 #869-05-1971 L1972 IM FM *020 †18

GUPTA, Atul. 255 W LANCASTER AVE, PAOLI HOSPITAL RADIOLOGY 19301 #035-03-1994 L1998 DR VIR *020 †80

HACKMAN, Barbara Boyle. 30 S VALLEY RD, STE 205 19301 #041-02-1998 L2000 FM *020 †18

HANACHE, Jeanne Anne. 255 W LANCASTER AVE, STE 233 PAOLI MEM HOSP MD 19301 #010-01-1962 L1965 P CHP *072 †75 ‡

HANHAUSEN, Edward H, Jr. 91 CHESTNUT RD 19301 #041-01-1950 L1951 OPH PTH *071 †35

HARIHARAN, Lakshmi. 250 W LANCASTER AVE # 340, KIDS FIRST PAOLI 19301 #143-03-1987 L1998 PD *020 †55

HARKNESS, Michael Jos. 255 W LANCASTER AVE, STE 330 19301 #041-12-1981 L1986

HAUPT, Richard Michael. 255 W LANCASTER AVE, ST. 331 PAOLI MED. BLDG II 19301 #024-01-1983 L1985 PD *020 †55

HAVILDAR, Sapna G.. 255 W LANCASTER AVE 19301 #495-37-1994 L2002 AN *020

HAYMAN, Harris Robt. 21 INDUSTRIAL BLVD, STE 203 19301 #041-09-1968 L1969 FM *020 †18 ‡

HE, Ningning. ■ 19301 #243-92-1997 L2007 PMM *012

HERVADA, Arturo R. ■ 19301 #847-10-1953 L1962 PD NTR *071 †55

HILLYER, Peter Norman. 255 W LANCASTER AVE, STE 124 PAOLI MEM. HOSP. M 19301 #035-45-1958 L1963 IM NEP *071 †20

HOESSLY, Michel. 209 W LANCASTER AVE 19301 #869-01-1980 L1985 HO IM *020 †20

HOPPER, Bruce Donald. 255 W LANCASTER AVE, BLDG III 19301 #041-02-1965 L1966 GYN *071 †18,30

HORAN, Kevin Francis. 255 W LANCASTER AVE 19301 #035-47-1988 L1993 AN *020 †05

HORSTMANN, Joseph Patrick. 255 W LANCASTER AVE, MAIN LINE PATHOLOGY ASSOC 19301 #041-02-1972 L1973 PTH PCP *020 †50

JONES, Raymond Richard. 255 W LANCASTER AVE, STE 100 19301 #041-02-1978 L1983 OPH *020 †35

KAKARLA, Radhika Prasad. 255 W LANCASTER AVE, ASSOCIATES 19301 #021-06-1997 L2006 OBG *020 †30

KARBINER, Helmut L. 255 W LANCASTER AVE, STE 230 19301 #409-10-1970 L1976 GYN *020 †30

KATIN, Lawrence Ira. 255 W LANCASTER AVE STE 22, MOB II 224 19301 #041-07-1986 L1987 OTO *020 †45

KELLY, Brian Kevin. 21 INDUSTRIAL BLVD, STE 205 19301 #041-09-1989 L1994 N CN *020 †75

KIENZLE, G Edward. 17 INDUSTRIAL BLVD, PAOLI W PROFESSIONAL PARK 19301 #041-02-1962 L1964 PD PDA *071 †55

KIENZLE, Rand Edward. 17 INDUSTRIAL BLVD, PAOLI WEST PROFESSIONAL PA 19301 #041-02-1992 L1995 PD *020 †55

KIM, Young Shik. 255 W LANCASTER AVE, MOB II STE 124 19301 #008-01-1986 L1999 ID IM *020 †20

KOEHLER, Melanie Ann. 11 INDUSTRIAL BLVD, STE 2 19301 #041-13-1993 L1995 PD *020 †55

KOLTER, James Stephen. 255 W LANCASTER AVE, ASSOCIATES 19301 #041-01-1976 L1978 OBG *020 †30 ‡

KRAUSER, Ronald Eric. 11 INDUSTRIAL BLVD STE 201, PAOLI POINTE MED BLDG 19301 #036-05-1969 L1970 RHU IM *020 †20

KRELL, Stephen Paul. 255 W LANCASTER AVE, ASSOCIATES 19301 #041-09-1978 L1979 OBG *020 †30

KRIPKE, Elana Nudel. 11 INDUSTRIAL BLVD STE 101, MAIN LINE INTERNAL MED 19301 #041-01-1989 L1992 IM *020 †20

KRIPKE, Scott Alden. 11 INDUSTRIAL BLVD, STE 102 19301 #041-01-1983 L1985 GS *020 †85

KROUSE, Laurel Helen Heim. 255 W LANCASTER AVE, MAIN LINE EMERGENCY 19301 #035-20-1996 L1998 EM *020 †16

KRULL, James Christopher. 250 W LANCASTER AVE 19301 #010-02-1998 L2000 FM *020 †18

KULP-HUGUES, Deborah A. 255 W LANCASTER AVE 19301 #041-02-1988 L1991 U *020 †95

KWAN-MORLEY, Jennifer Gra. 11 INDUSTRIAL BLVD STE 201, RONALD E KRAUSER, MD, PC 19301 #016-06-2001 L2005 IM *020 †20

LANGRALL, Harrison M. ■ 19301 #023-01-1953 L1987 PA IM *071

LANZA, Ralph Andrew. 255 W LANCASTER AVE, STE 120 19301 #035-45-1986 L1987 IM *020 †20 ‡

LASKIN, Keith J. 332 W LANCASTER AVE, PAOLI MEMORIAL MEDICAL BLD 19301 #035-19-1984 L1985 GE *020 †20

LETWIN, Lee Barry. 255 W LANCASTER AVE 19301 #035-15-1973 L1974 AN *020 †05

LEVY, Mark Alan. 255 W LANCASTER AVE 19301 #041-07-1975 L1976 IM *020 †20

LILIAN, Michael Lee. 255 W LANCASTER AVE 19301 #041-13-1980 L1981 AN *020 †05

LINDVIG, Kirk Philip. 255 W LANCASTER AVE 19301 #038-40-1980 L1981 AN *020 †05

LIVINGSTON, Julie Zrubek. ■ 19301 #023-07-1986 L1995 CD IM *020 †20

LOTITO, Patricia Hannigan. 250 W LANCASTER AVE 19301 #041-07-1987 L1989 FM *020 †18

LOVE, Russ Lawrence. 225 W LANCASTER AVE, MAIN LINE 19301 #041-09-1994 L1997 DR *020 †80

LUCAS, Christopher A. 255 W LANCASTER AVE, STE 120 BLDG #2 19301 #022-75-1998, ▲ L2005 IM *020 †20

LUSTINE, Howard Todd. 255 W LANCASTER AVE, BLDG 2 19301 #010-02-1992 L1995 PCC *020 †20

MALIT, Lee Arnall. 255 W LANCASTER AVE 19301 #041-02-1969 L1970 AN *020 †05

MANSER, Jeanne Ireland. 255 W LANCASTER AVE 19301 #041-02-1975 L1977 NPM PD *020 †55,05

MANSMANN, Kevin Alexander. 250 W LANCASTER AVE, STE 310 19301 #041-02-1981 L1989 ORS *020 †40

MARTIN, Christopher M. ■ 19301 #024-01-1953 L1971 ID IM *030

MARTIN, Christopher Walsh. 255 W LANCASTER AVE 19301 #041-02-1995 L1997 IM *020 †20

MATTSON, Ronald Jos. 11 INDUSTRIAL BLVD, STE 102 19301 #041-13-1971 L1972 GS VS *020 †85

MC CONNELL, Patricia H. 11 INDUSTRIAL BLVD, STE 203 19301 #012-01-1986 L1988 OBG *020 †30

MC GONIGLE, Edward James. 1440 RUSSELL RD 19301 #041-13-1998 L2003 P *020 †75

MC LAUGHLIN, Mary Janet. 255 W LANCASTER AVE 19301 #041-13-1977 L1978 AN *020 †05

MC MAHON, Patrick Chas. 11 INDUSTRIAL BLVD, STE 2 19301 #041-13-1966 L1967 PD *071 †55

MC MICHAEL, Harrison. ■ 19301 #041-01-1956 L1958 PTH *071

MEGERIAN, Garo. 255 W LANCASTER AVE 19301 #041-09-1988 L1990 MFM OBG *020 †30

MEHTA, Nirav Nikhilesh. 328 PAOLI MEDICAL BLDG, STE 328 19301 #041-03-1997 L2000 CD *020 †20

MILLER, Harris Paul. 255 W LANCASTER AVE, DEPT RADIOLOGY 19301 #041-01-1970 L1971 DR NM *020 †80

MOREWOOD, Gordon Henry. 255 W LANCASTER AVE 19301 #065-05-1992 L1998 AN *020 †05

MULL, Thomas Dissinger. 255 W LANCASTER AVE 19301 #041-01-1965 L1967 AN *020 †05

NIRANJAN, Sumitra. STATION SQUARE 3 204 19301 #496-22-1991 L1993 PTH *100 †50

OBERKIRCHER, Paul Edward. 255 W LANCASTER AVE 19301 #035-06-1959 L1969 R *020 †80

O'BRIEN, Margaret Mary. 255 W LANCASTER AVE 19301 #035-47-1990 L1993 AN *020 †05

O'FLYNN, Teresa Hayes. 255 W LANCASTER AVE 19301 #041-09-1992 L1994 AN *020 †05

ORRIS, John Joseph. 11 INDUSTRIAL BLVD, STE 100 19301 #041-77-1995, ▲ L1996 OBG *020 †30

PANZER, Dale Eric. 43 LEOPARD RD, STE 101 19301 #041-09-1990 L1993 P *020 †75

PARSONS, Kimberly Voight. 250 W LANCASTER AVE, STE 340 19301 #035-06-2005 L2005 PD *012

PEKAR, Aleksandr. 255 W LANCASTER AVE 19301 #913-43-1988 L2005 AN *020 †05

PETERSON, Ila Marie. 255 W LANCASTER AVE, MAIN LINE PATHOLOGY ASSOC 19301 #045-01-1975 L1999 PTH GP *062 †50

PETROCELLI, Ronald D. ■ 19301 #016-42-1968 L2002 **R NM** *071 †28,80

PINSK, Robert. 255 W LANCASTER AVE, PAOLI HOSPITAL 19301 #041-01-1986 L1991 **DR** *020 †80

PODELL, Ross Douglas. 250 W LANCASTER AVE, STE 200 19301 #041-09-1993 L1998 **IM** *020 †20

POTTAGE, John Cooper. ■ 19301 #028-34-1978 L1979 **ID IM** *050 †20

RACHMAN, Ray Arthur. ■ 19301 #041-13-1958 L1959 **PTH** *071 †50

ROBINSON, David M, II. 255 W LANCASTER AVE 19301 #041-02-1980 L1982 **AN** *020 †05

ROGALSKI, Cynthia. 255 W LANCASTER AVE 19301 #041-02-1984 L1986 **AN IM** *020 †20

ROME, Lauren Ann. 255 W LANCASTER AVE 19301 #836-01-1991 L1998 **PUD IM** *020 †20

ROSATO, Anne Veronica. 250 W LANCASTER AVE, STE 340 19301 #041-02-1997 L2001 **PD** *020 †55

ROSE, Matthew Howard. ■ 19301 #003-75-2005, ▲ L2007 **FM** *100

ROSENBERG, Eric Jay. 255 W LANCASTER AVE 19301 #035-47-1993 L2001 **AN** *020 †05

ROXBY, John Byers, Jr. ■ 19301 #041-13-1941 L1942 **OS D** *071 †15

RUBENSTEIN, Elyse Shari. 255 W LANCASTER AVE 19301 #033-06-1984 L1985 **P** *020 †75

RUDO, Todd Jonathan. 15 INDUSTRIAL BLVD, STE 103 19301 #041-02-2000 L2001 **ICE** *020 †20

RUSSINO, Joseph Louis. 255 W LANCASTER AVE, STE 227 19301 #041-13-1981 L1982 **OBG** *030 †30

RYAN, Sean Vincent. 11 INDUSTRIAL BLVD, STE 102 19301 #041-02-1997 L2000 **GS** *020 †85

RYAN, Stephen Gregory. ■ 19301 #036-07-1980 L1983 **N PD** *020 †55,75

SAMBASIVAN, Arathi. 255 W LANCASTER AVE 19301 #496-20-1991 L2004 **AN** *020 †05

SAMUELSON, Donald Glenn. 255 W LANCASTER AVE, DEPT OF RADIOLOGY 19301 #041-13-1987 L1988 **DR** *020 †80

SAUTER, John Geo. 255 W LANCASTER AVE 19301 #041-13-1984 L1985 **AN** *020 †05

SCHADE, Alicia Jannette. 255 W LANCASTER AVE 19301 #048-04-2000 L2002 **AN** *020 †05

SCHETMAN, Anna. 250 W LANCASTER AVE, STE 340 19301 #033-05-1986 L1987 **PD** *020 †55

SCHUSTER, Robert T. 255 W LANCASTER AVE, STE 120 19301 #041-14-1976 L1980 **IM** *020 †20

SCHWARTZ, Robert Roger. 321 S VALLEY RD 19301 #041-02-1956 L1957 **ON IM** *020

SCOVILL, Curtis Neal. 202 PAOLI MEDICAL BLDG 19301 #024-07-1967 **END IM** *020 †20

SEBRING, Heatly Dulles. 255 W LANCASTER AVE, STE 209 19301 #041-01-1966 L1973 **A PD** *020 †55,03

SEHGAL, Poonam. 255 W LANCASTER AVE 19301 #035-47-1987 L1998 **AN** *020 †05

SENZON, Shari Leigh. 255 W LANCASTER AVE, ASSOCIATES 19301 #041-01-1994 L1996 **OBG** *020 †30

SHEN, Huaqiong. ■ 19301 #243-71-1983 L2006 **P** *020 †75

SHEPARD, Wm Rutherford. 255 W LANCASTER AVE 19301 #041-13-1981 L1983 **AN** *075 †05

SHRESTHA, Mahesh. 255 W LANCASTER AVE, MAIN LINE EMERGENCY 19301 #008-01-1986 L1994 **IM EM** *020 †20,16

SIMONE, Alyssa Lynne. 255 W LANCASTER AVE 19301 #041-77-2001, ▲ L2001 **AN** *020 †05

SIMONYAN, Garen M. 255 W LANCASTER AVE 19301 #913-38-1994 L2001 **AN** *020 †20,05

SKOP, Neal Franklin. 328 PAOLI MEDICAL BLDG, STE 328 19301 #011-03-1994 L1997 **CD** *020 †20

SOFFER, Joseph. 255 W LANCASTER AVE, STE 328 PAOLI MEMORIAL MED 19301 #016-02-1977 L1979 **CD IM** *020 †20

SOMERS, Joseph V. 255 W LANCASTER AVE 19301 #041-13-1985 L1987 **AN GS** *020 †05

SPECK, Sally Goodman. 255 W LANCASTER AVE, MAIN LINE EMERGENCY 19301 #041-07-1998 L2000 **EM** *020 †16

STADLEN, Sallie G. 15 INDUSTRIAL BLVD, STE A102 19301 #550-02-1988 L1992 **IM** *020 †20

STRASSMAN, Ira Howard. ■ 19301 #041-13-1988 L1990 **PD** *020 †55

SULPIZI, Antoinette Marie. 255 W LANCASTER AVE # 328, PAOLI MEM MED BLDG 2 19301 #033-05-1981 L1982 **CD** *020 †20

SZARKA, Christine Esther. 255 W LANCASTER AVE, CANCER CENTER PAOLI HOSP 19301 #041-07-1986 L1989 **ON HEM** *020 †20

TERZIAN, Raffi Vahan. 11 INDUSTRIAL BLVD, STE 103 19301 #010-01-1993 L1998 **EM** *040 †16

THAL, Ira Mervyn. 255 W LANCASTER AVE, STE 202 19301 #011-02-1989 L1991 **IM** *020 †20

THOMAS, John Jayakaran. 1440 RUSSELL RD, LIFE COUNSELING SERVICES 19301 #495-16-1963 L1995 **P CHP** *020 †75

THOMPSON, Gregory Mark. 255 W LANCASTER AVE, PAOLI MEM MED BLDG 3 #333 19301 #030-05-1983 L1989 **U** *020 †95 ‡

TIRER, Samuel. 255 W LANCASTER AVE 19301 #067-01-1976 L1980 **AN** *020 †05

TOLIN, Richard Dean. 255 W LANCASTER AVE, MED BLDG 3 STE 332 19301 #024-07-1972 L1975 **GE IM** *020 †20

TOWNEND, Stephen Coughlin. 330 PAOLI MEDICL BLDG #330 19301 #041-02-1975 L1976 **PD** *020 †55

VISNAPUU, L A. ■ 19301 #038-44-1983 L2004 **PTH** *030 †50

WALKER, Amy Santeusanio. 250 W LANCASTER AVE 19301 #041-14-1994 L1997 **FM** *020 †18

WALLACE, Daniel. 255 W LANCASTER AVE 19301 #847-01-1969 L1972 **P** *020 †75

WEINBLATT, Fred Martin. 250 W LANCASTER AVE, STE 250 19301 #023-07-1976 L1978 **N IM** *020 †20,75

WEISS, Marisa Carey. 250 W LANCASTER AVE 19301 #041-01-1984 L1985 **RO IM** *020 †80

WHITE, Jack Carlton. PAOLI MEMORIAL HOSPITAL, DIRECTOR OF MEDICAL AFFAIR 19301 #050-02-1952 L1953 **GS** *071 †85

WILLIAMS, Gregory Stuart. 255 W LANCASTER AVE, BLDG 2 19301 #038-40-1975 L1979 **PUD IM** *020 †20

WILLIAMS, Melissa Jane. 255 W LANCASTER AVE, MAIN LINE HEALTHCARE HEMAT 19301 #056-05-2001 L2001 **HO** *012

WOLFSON, Michael Benjamin. 255 W LANCASTER AVE # 332, MAIN LINO GASTRENTOLOGY 19301 #041-15-1999 L2001 **GE** *020 †20 ‡

WU, Yonggang. ■ 19301 #243-70-1984 **GS** *100

YELOVICH, Maureen L. 250 W LANCASTER AVE 19301 #041-02-1981 L1982 **FM** *020 †18

YELOVICH, Richard Matthew. 250 W LANCASTER AVE, STE 100 19301 #041-02-1981 L1982 **RO IM** *030 †20,80

YI, Jean Kyong. 255 W LANCASTER AVE, RADIOLOGY ASSOCIATES OF MA 19301 #041-14-1995 L1997 **DR** *020 †80

YOUSEF-ZAHRA, Dina Monzer. 255 W LANCASTER AVE, RADIOLOGY ASSOCIATES OF TH 19301 #018-03-1999 L2006 **RNR** *100 †80

ZAPPACOSTA, Anthony R. 255 W LANCASTER AVE 19301 #041-09-1969 L1970 **NEP IM** *020 †20

PARADISE – LANCASTER

INDIRA, Thiruvalam P. 3320 LINCOLN HWY E 17562 #495-04-1983 L1995 **IM** *020 †20

PARKER – CLARION

KAPLON, Charlotte Anne. 855 ROUTE 58, STE 1 16049 #038-40-1982 L1984 **FM** *020 †18

PARKESBURG – CHESTER

BARKAN, Craig Adam. 4229 W LINCOLN HWY 19365 #025-01-2000 L2005 **PD** *020 †55

BRAZELTON, Jill. 4229 W LINCOLN HWY 19365 #005-11-1999 L2005 **PD** *020 †55

COOPER, David John. 4229 W LINCOLN HWY 19365 #011-02-1978 L1979 **PD GP** *020

FABER, Mark Robert. 4229 W LINCOLN HWY 19365 #041-01-1984 L1985 **PD** *020 †55 ‡

PAROYA, Nadeem Ashiq. 406 W 1ST AVE 19365 #305-01-1998 L2003 **FM GS** *020 †18

SCHWAB, Thomas Chas. 351 W 1ST AVE 19365 #041-09-1979 L1980 **IM** *020 †20

SHRAGER, Jennifer Lynn. 4229 W LINCOLN HWY 19365 #041-09-1993 L1998 **PD** *020 †55

WARNER, Norman Max. PO BOX 39 19365 #041-09-1941 L1942 **FM AM** *071

PATTON – CAMBRIA

HASABNIS, Suhas P. 1101 5TH AVE 16668 #495-01-1959 L1972 **OBG** *072 †30

MILLER, Russell Paul. 121 BEECH AVE 16668 #041-14-1994 L1996 **FM** *020 †18

SABO, Joseph Robt. 503 RAILROAD AVE STE 4 16668 #041-09-1974 L1975 **FM** *020 †18

PEACH BOTTOM – LANCASTER

DE AUGUSTINE, Vincent P. ■ 17563 #041-02-1950 L1951 **FM A** *071

PECKVILLE – LACKAWANNA

BESEN, Lee Terry. 1329 MAIN ST 18452 #041-09-1979 L1980 **FM EM** *020 †16

BRUNDAGE, Robert Pierce. 1400 MAIN ST 18452 #041-01-1947 L1948 **GP** *020

SU, Lang-Pao. 1418 MAIN ST, STE 207 18452 #244-01-1960 L1973 **AN GP** *020 †05

WILLIAMS, Kevin Geo. 320 KEYSTONE AVE 18452 #041-13-1985 L1987 **IM** *020 †20

PEN ARGYL – NORTHAMPTON

SHUSTIK, Miriam. 14 N ROBINSON AVE 18072 #187-03-1989 L1997 **FM** *020

TURTZO, Douglas Franklin. 101 S SCHANCK AVE 18072 #041-13-1968 L1969 **IM PUD** *020 †20

PENLLYN – MONTGOMERY

ELIA, Josephine. 527 PENLLYN PIKE 19422 #041-07-1982 L1983 **CHP P** *020 †75

GREEN, Nicole Adelaide. ■ 19422 #041-02-2005 L2005 **PD** *012

PENN HILLS – ALLEGHENY

JORDAN, Becky Theresa. 7175 SALTSBURG RD, PEN PLUM FAMILY MED 15235 #041-12-2000 L2001 **FM** *020 †18

MAYERNIK, David Gregory. 1000 INTEGRITY DR, STE 210 15235 #041-13-1977 L1978 **ON HEM** *020 †20

SABEH, Raif Kamel. 7125 SALTSBURG RD 15235 #605-01-1955 L1958 **OTO** *020 †45

SPRITZER, Albert A. ■ 15235 #035-03-1952 L1959 **IM OM** *071

SPRITZER, Susan Mc Fadyen. ■ 15235 #036-07-1951 L1958 **GYN** *071 †30

PENN VALLEY – MONTGOMERY

AMBARDEKAR, Aditee Parag. ■ 19072 #023-01-2004 L2005 **AN** *012

ARONSON, Susan R Shane. ■ 19072 #038-06-1965 L1971 **PD PHP** *030 †55

BALABAN, Donald Jay. 853 MONTGOMERY AVE 19072 #041-13-1968 L1975 **MDM IM** *071 †70

BECK, Katherine Graham. ■ 19072 #010-02-1998 L2005 **FSM** *012 †18

BEN-RAFAEL, Zion. ■ 19072 #550-02-1976 L1987 *100 †30

BIEMULLER, Martha Lydia. ■ 19072 #041-07-1956 L1957 **OBG** *071 †30

BRAHMAKULAM, Lana Elizabe. 1637 OAKWOOD DR 19072 #041-77-2005, ▲ L2005 **OTO** *012

BROSNAN, William Jos. ■ 19072 #035-09-1965 L1971 **IM** *020 †05,20

BUNYA, Vatinee Yam. ■ 19072 #041-01-2001 L2002 **OPH** *100 †35

BUNYA, Vichai. ■ 19072 #891-01-1963 L1973 **FM** *071 †55

CAREL, Warren David. 1479 FLAT ROCK RD, PENN VALLEY 19072 #836-01-1973 L1978 **AN** *020 †55

CHAIT, Arnold. ■ 19072 #660-04-1957 L1967 **R** *071 †80

CHAPLIN, Stanley Saul. ■ 19072 #041-02-1965 L1966 **OBG MDM** *071 †30

COHEN, Michael Saul. ■ 19072 #035-19-2004 L2004 **OTO** *012

COOK, Philip Ira. ■ 19072 #041-02-1986 L1989 **PD** *020 †55

COOPER, Mark W. 816 CHAUNCEY RD 19072 #041-02-1977 L1978 **DR** *062 †80 ‡

CORSON, Stephen Louis. ■ 19072 #041-01-1964 L1965 **GYN REN** *071 †30

DALONZO, Henry A. ■ 19072 #041-77-1951, ▲ L1955 *071

ESCALANTE, Ovidio Duarte. ■ 19072 #341-01-1961 **N NS** *100

ESCOLL, Philip J. ■ 19072 #041-02-1951 L1952 **P PYA** *071 †75

FABIANI, Joseph Albert. ■ 19072 #561-17-1955 L1960 **ORS** *071 †40

FINK, Gordon Bernard. ■ 19072 #041-13-1956 L1957 **CLP PTH** *071 †50

HANSEN, A Victor, Jr. ■ 19072 #041-13-1945 L1946 **P** *071 †75

HOFFMAN, Alisa Hope. ■ 19072 #010-01-1993 L1995 **PD** *020 †55

HORWITZ, Milton Roy. ■ 19072 #041-13-1966 L1967 **OTO PS** *020 †45

HSU, Karl Yuanyi. ■ 19072 #041-01-1995 L2005 **IM** *020 †20

JACOBSON, Louise. ■ 19072 #041-07-1966 L1967 **P CHP** *071

JOHNSON, L Audrey. ■ 19072 #017-20-1956 L1960 **IM OS** *040

KAPUR, Rahul. ■ 19072 #051-01-2003 L2003 **FSM** *100 †18

KARTSONIS, Nicholas Athan. ■ 19072 #012-05-1994 L2000 **ID** *020 †20

KATZ, Merwin Richard. ■ 19072 #028-02-1955 L1968 **NS** *071 †25

KIM, Esther Marie. ■ 19072 #041-09-1990 L1993 **NM** *020 †80,28

LANSMAN, Gregary Paul. 1409 CENTENNIAL RD 19072 #041-07-1983 L1985 **DR** *020 †80
LERNER, Lori Anne. ■ 19072 #041-02-1984 L1985 **P PD** *075 †75
MAGILL, Ian David. 1654 OAKWOOD DR, OAKHILL CONDOS #309N 19072 #041-02-1984 L1986 **P** *020 †75
MAHESHWARI, Sunita. ■ 19072 #495-21-1992 L1995 **PD PDC** *020 †55
MALSCH, Eva Marie K. ■ 19072 #407-05-1964 L1972 **AN** *071 †05
MASON, Jeannette C. 911 BRYN MAWR AVE 19072 #041-09-1950 L1951 **PD CHN** *071 †55
MILLS, Steven La Roi. ■ 19072 #047-07-1967 L1990 **PD** *020
MOLINARO, Thomas Anthony. 1655 OAKWOOD DR, N411 19072 #033-05-2002 L2002 **OBG** *100 †30
MORESCHI, Michelle Ann. 1640 OAKWOOD DR, W314 19072 #041-07-1990 L1992 **PCC** *020 †20
OREN, Arie. ■ 19072 #913-16-1971 L1986 **NEP GPM** *075
PENIAZEK, Ziszko. ■ 19072 #924-01-1959 L1977 **P** *071 †75
PORAT, Manny David. ■ 19072 #041-13-2005 L2005 **ORS** *012
SARVET-HABER, Nancy D. ■ 19072 #035-19-1986 L1993 **AN** *020 †05
SEVIN, Elizabeth Guttman. ■ 19072 #041-13-1969 L1970 **EM** *030 †16
SHANKAR, Venkatramanan. ■ 19072 #495-36-1986 L1995 **CCP** *020 †55
SINGER, Melvin. ■ 19072 #041-09-1962 L1963 **P** *020 †75
SOLOMON, Brian Andrew. 1431 HAGYS FORD RD 19072 #041-01-1992 L1998 **VIR** *020 †80
SPECTER, Janet Sue. 623 RIGHTERS MILL RD 19072 #041-09-1976 L1977 **IM IMG** *020 †20
SUBRAMANIAN-KHURANA, D. ■ 19072 #495-36-1989 L1998 **CHN** *020 †55,75
SUMMERS, Lauren Michelle. ■ 19072 #041-07-1997 L2000 **IM** *100 †20
WEISS, Yoram Georges. ■ 19072 #550-03-1989 L1998 **IM** *100
WILLIAMSON, Clarke Edward. 813 LARKSPUR LN 19072 #041-01-1979 L1981 **GS VS** *020 †85
WINEGRAD, Saul. ■ 19072 #041-01-1956 L1957 **OS** *100
YEH, Sze-Ya. ■ 19072 #385-02-1961 L1975 **OBG MFM** *040 †30
ZAFAR, Sarosh Naz. ■ 19072 #041-15-2007 L2008 **GS** *012
ZAVODNICK, Jacquelyn M. 1655 OAKWOOD DR 19072 #041-02-1970 L1974 **CHP P** *020 †75

PENNDEL – BUCKS

BIUCKIANS, Edward. 1517 DURHAM RD 19047 #517-01-1964 L1972 **P** *020 †75
BRAVERMAN, Eric Randall. 142 BELLEVUE AVE 19047 #035-19-1983 L1990 **GP P** *020 ‡
DI RIENZO, Enrico James. 833 DURHAM RD 19047 #041-13-1965 L1966 **FM** *020 †18
FRIEDMAN, Phillip. 833 DURHAM RD 19047 #869-02-1957 L1959 **FM** *020 †18
FUCANAN, Vilma. 1517 DURHAM RD 19047 #748-09-1978 L1986 **P IM** *020
HIDALGO, Horacio A. 833 DURHAM RD, DURHAM PHYSICIANS PC 19047 #649-01-1955 L1963 **FM** *071 †18
LANE, John Dennis. 833 DURHAM RD 19047 #041-02-1958 L1959 **FM** *020 †18
WHEATON, Marianne Lee. ■ 19047 #041-13-2005 L2005 **EM** *012

PENNSBURG – MONTGOMERY

BENNER, Priscilla Matson. 2781 GERYVILLE PIKE 18073 #041-07-1975 L1976 **IM FM** *020 †20
BERDINI, John Andrew. 570 MAIN ST 18073 #033-05-1988 L1991 **FM** *020 †18
BLUE, Elaine Stefo. 101 W 7TH ST, STE 2C 18073 #041-13-1999 L2001 **FM** *020 †18
CIANFRANI, Peter Michael. 925 MAIN ST, STE 100 18073 #041-02-1973 L1975 **FM** *020 †18 ‡
KISTLER, Priscilla Jane. 101 W 7TH ST, STE 2C 18073 #041-02-1973 L1976 **GP IM** *020 †20
KURIAN, Linda Poykayil. 925 MAIN ST, STE 100 18073 #305-01-1999 L2007 **FM** *020 †18
LESKA, Norbert Walter. 101 W 7TH ST STE 2C 18073 #041-09-1976 L1978 **IM** *020 †20 ‡
MYERS, Tina M. 925 MAIN ST, STE 100 18073 #041-78-1999, ▲ L2000 **FM** *020 ‡
SHUHLER, Phyllis Marie. 101 W 7TH ST STE 2C, TRI-VALLEY PRIMARY CARE U. 18073 #025-12-1976 L1981 **FM GS** *020 †18

PENNSDALE – LYCOMING

BARTLOW, William Paul. 151 JOHN BRADY DR, STE 4 17756 #041-02-1984 L1985 **FM** *020 †18
MAYS, Richard Ray. ■ 17756 #041-02-1960 L1961 **P** *071
PICCUTA, Michael James. ■ 17756 #041-09-1969 L1970 **D** *020

PENNSYLVANIA FURNACE – CENTRE

GUILLARD, Peter M. ■ 16865 #041-02-1951 L1952 **FM** *020 †18
KLINGLER, Robert Chas. 110 TIMOTHY LN, BOX 28C 16865 #004-01-1981 L1982 **EM IM** *020 †20,16

PEQUEA – LANCASTER

HASSEL, C Walter, Jr. ■ 17565 #041-02-1954 L1955 **D** *071 †15

PERKASIE – BUCKS

BEEM, John Raymond. 18944 #051-04-1945 L1953 **CD IM** *020
BROWN V, Thomas Wistar. ■ 18944 #041-13-1967 L1968 **GS** *071 †85
CLAY-ADAMSON, Anngela Daw. ■ 18944 #041-15-2004 L2004 **EM** *012
CONRAD, James Leroy. ■ 18944 #041-13-1965 L1966 **FM** *071
CORRADO, Michael Louis. ■ 18944 #047-07-1973 L1981 **ID PHM** *050
DECARDONA, Greg John. ■ 18944 #041-77-2005, ▲ L2005 **AN** *012
DIVEN, Liany T. ■ 18944 #048-12-2006 L2006 **OBG** *012
DIVEN, Thomas Andrew. ■ 18944 #048-12-2006 L2006 **GS** *012
FELLING, Ryan Jordan. ■ 18944 #041-14-2007 L2007 **PD** *012
FORMAN, David. ■ 18944 #130-01-2001 L1001 **P** *012
KUNST, Linda F. ■ 18944 #041-13-1968 L1981 **P PD** *020 †75
LYONS, Wilbert Abram. 333 S 3RD ST 18944 #041-13-1948 L1949 **P** *020 †75
MOLL, David Conrad. 1301 N 5TH ST 18944 #041-13-1974 L1975 **FM** *020 †18
NAUNCZEK, Michael John. 1301 N 5TH ST 18944 #041-02-1995 L1997 **FM** *020 †18
ONEILL, Craig Alan. ■ 18944 #051-07-2008 L2008 **EM** *012
POOR, Alexander Edward. ■ 18944 #041-02-2007 L2007 **GS** *012

THOMAS, Howard P, Jr. ■ 18944 #041-01-1944 L1945 **PD** *071 †55

PHILADELPHIA – DELAWARE

CHODOFF, William Geo. 200 STEVENS DR 19113 #041-02-1969 L1972 **PD** *020 †55
GUERRA-GARCIA, Humberto. 200 STEVENS DR 19113 #737-06-1987 L1999 **IMG IM** *020 †20
INCHAUSTEGUI, Hector J. 200 STEVENS DR 19113 #308-01-1962 L2004 **MPD** *030
RAHMAN, Fazlu. 200 STEVENS DR 19113 #016-11-1982 L2004 **IM** *030 †20
WERTHER, Norman M. 100 DIPLOMAT DR 19113 #041-09-1966 **FM** *020 †18

PHILADELPHIA – PHILADELPHIA

AARON, John. ■ 19131 #308-07-1982 L1991 **IMG** *020
AARON, Todd David. 33 E CHESTNUT HILL AVE, STE 204 19118 #308-11-1985 L1988 **IM** *020 †20
AARONSON, Gary Alan. 6404 ROOSEVELT BLVD STE 1D 19149 #041-77-1983, ▲ L1984 **PUD IM** *020
ABADILLA, Maria Emilia Ac. 5501 OLD YORK RD, ALBERT EINSTEIN MEDICAL CE 19141 #748-01-2003 L2006 **OBG** *012
ABALOS, Rosario M. ■ 19115 #748-01-1969 L1981 **P GP** *020
ABANYIE, Francisca. ■ 19135 #033-06-2006 L2006 **PD** *012
ABBAS, Muhammad Ali. ■ 19107 #704-04-1999 L2007 **P** *100
ABBAS, Saleha. 27 E MOUNT AIRY AVE 19119 #704-02-1991 L1997 **PYG** *020 ‡
ABBASI, Adeel Ahmed. 3400 SPRUCE ST, OF PENNSYLVANIA 19104 #035-45-2007 L2007 **EM** *012
ABBASI, Soraya. 800 SPRUCE ST, FL 2 19107 #517-05-1975 L1979 **NPM PD** *020 †55
ABBATEMATTEO, David. ■ 19128 #041-15-2008 *012
ABBOUD, Joseph Albert. 800 SPRUCE ST, 8TH FLOOR PRESTON BUILDING 19107 #010-02-1998 L2000 **OAR** *020 †40
ABBUHL, Stephanie Bryant. 3400 SPRUCE ST 19104 #035-45-1980 L1982 **EM IM** *020 †20,16
ABDELMALEK, Mark A. 219 N BROAD ST, FL 4 19107 #041-15-2002 L2002 **D DS** *020 †15
ABDELNUR, Beatriz M. M.S.300 BROAD VINE 19102 #770-02-1990 **PD** *100
ABDOLLAHI, Hamid. ■ 19107 #041-02-2005 L2005 **GS** *012
ABDOLLAHIAN, Javad. 1411 HARRISON ST 19124 #517-04-1955 L1966 **CD IM** *020
ABDULALLY, Adam. ■ 19128 #041-15-2008 L2008 *012
ABDULHADI, Mike Abdurraih. ■ 19104 #041-01-2006 L2006 **DR** *012
ABDUL-HADI, Omar. 1015 WALNUT ST, THOMAS JEFFERSON UNIV HOSP 19107 #875-01-2000 L2006 **OAR** *020
ABDUL-RAHMAN, Sharan. 1015 CHESTNUT ST STE 313 19107 #008-01-1984 L1985 **OBG** *020 †30
ABE, Margherita C. 5501 OLD YORK RD, DEPT OF ANESTHESIA 19141 #010-02-1974 L1991 **AN P** *020 †75,05
ABED, Thair Mohamed. 3509 N BROAD ST, DEPARTMENT OF PEDIATRICS 19140 #528-01-1981 L1998 **PD** *020 †55
ABEL, Mark D. 3620 HAMILTON WALK, UNIV OF PA SCH OF MED 19104 #041-01-2006 L2006 *012
ABELLA, Benjamin S. 3400 SPRUCE ST, GROUND RAVDIN 19104 #023-07-1998 L2006 **EM** *050 †20,16
ABELLA, Romeo Suarez. 915 E CAYUGA ST 19124 #748-01-1959 L1972 **IM NEP** *020
ABEND, Nicholas Scott. ■ 19146 #041-02-2002 L2004 **CHN** *020
ABERRA, Faten Nureddin. 3400 SPRUCE ST, HOSP OF THE UNIV OF PA 19104 #032-01-1997 L1999 **GE** *020 †20
ABKAR, Kevork Bedros. YORK & TABOR RD DEPT CD, A EINSTEIN MED CTR 19141 #875-01-1972 L1974 **CD IM** *050
ABLAZA, Sariel Gerardo G. 5401 OLD YORK RD 19141 #748-02-1951 L1967 **TS** *071 †85,90
ABOUASALEH, Raghan Salim. 5501 OLD YORK RD, ALBERT EINSTEIN HOSPITAL 19141 #875-01-1998 L2004 **IM** *020
ABOUNA, George M. BROAD & VINE STS 19102 #352-04-1961 L1991 **TTS GS** *071
ABRAHAM, Andrew Jacob. 3401 N BROAD ST, DEPT MED # 8PP 19140 #030-05-2006 L2007 **IM** *012
ABRAHAM, Barry Benj. 9501 ROOSEVELT BLVD, STE 508 19114 #041-02-1973 L1974 **D DMP** *020 †15
ABRAHAM, Binny. ■ 19152 #056-06-2005 **IM** *012
ABRAHAM, Sheeja K. 9880 BUSTLETON AVE, STE 309 19115 #035-08-1990 L1996 **PD PG** *020 †55
ABRAHAMY, Michael Alan. ■ 19107 #550-02-2007 L2007 **OBG** *012
ABRAMS, Charles Saml. 3401 N BROAD ST 19140 #008-01-1984 L1985 **HEM ON** *020 †20
ABRAMS, David Joel. 2615 W SOMERSET ST 19132 #041-77-1959, ▲ L1960 **GP** *071
ABRAMS, Henry. ■ 19103 #041-13-1937 L1938 **OPH** *071 †35
ABRAMS, Jeffrey Alan. 132 S 10TH ST 19107 #035-15-1989 L1991 **GE** *020 †20
ABRAMS, Tara Jeanne. ■ 19103 #041-01-2006 L2006 **IM** *012
ABRUZZO, John Louis. 1015 WALNUT ST 19107 #010-02-1957 L1967 **RHU IM** *020 †20
ABT, Peter Lawrence. 3400 SPRUCE ST, FL 4 19104 #032-01-1994 L2001 **GS** *020 †85
ACCARDO, Jennifer Anne. ■ 19143 #028-34-2000 L2006 **PD** *020 †55
ACHENBACH, Alexi E. ■ 19147 #041-02-2007 L2007 **OBG** *012
ACIKGOZ, Gunsel. 3400 SPRUCE ST, DONNER BLG 110 19104 #902-03-1989 L2002 **NM** *100 †28
ACKER, Michael A. 3400 SPRUCE ST, FL 6 19104 #043-01-1981 L1982 **TS** *020 †90,85
ACKERMAN, Stacey Lynn. 2610 E ALLEGHENY AVE 19134 #035-06-1981 L1984 **OPH** *020 †35
ACQUAVELLA, Anthony Peter. ERIE AVE AT FRONT ST, ST CHRISTOPHER HOSP 19134 #010-02-1983 L1998 **IM PD** *020 †55
ACRI, Trisha Lynn. 3322 N BROAD ST 19140 #041-13-2000 L2003 **FM** *020 †18 ‡
ACZON, Ferdinand Bulusan. 2724 N 5TH ST 19133 #748-01-1972 L1981 **FM** *020 †18
ADAMO, Robert Deciucis. ■ 19107 #035-08-2006 L2006 **GS** *012
ADAMS, Cynthia Marie. ■ 19104 #041-01-2008 *012
ADAMS, Judith Anne. ■ 19130 #041-07-1979 L1982 **IM** *020
ADAMS, Julie Elizabeth. 834 CHESTNUT ST, STE G114 19107 #001-02-2001 L2007 **HSO** *012
ADAMS, Sarah Foster. ■ 19143 #016-02-2001 L2006 **OBG** *100
ADAMS, Tiy Leilani. ■ 19151 #010-03-2008 *012
ADAMSKI, Jill. ■ 19130 #001-02-2006 L2006 **PTH** *012
ADAMSON, Peter Chas. 324 S 34TH ST 19104 #035-20-1984 L1986 **PD PHO** *020 †55
ADEBAMIRO, Adedotun. ■ 19138 #041-12-2008 *012
ADEFISAN, Olujimi Ayodele. 2900 W QUEEN LN 19129 #690-05-1995 L2005 **P** *012

■ = Address Information Privacy Protected

ADEGBOLA, Onikepe Adetoun. ■ 19104 #690-02-1995 L2005 **NM** *100 †28

ADELEKAN, Tahira Gittens. ■ 19151 #048-13-1999 L2003 **PD** *020 †55

ADENAIKE, Michael Babatun. ■ 19139 #041-13-2006 L2006 **IM** *012

ADENIYI-JONES, Susan C. 1025 WALNUT ST, STE 700 19107 #917-01-1977 L1990 **NPM** *020 †55

ADES, Anne Molly. 324 S 34TH ST 19104 #024-07-1995 L2001 **NPM** *020 †55

ADESEUN, Gbemisola Adekem. ■ 19131 #023-07-2005 L2005 **IM** *012

ADETUNJI, Babatunde Abayo. 1616 WALNUT ST STE 816, MHM CORRECTIONAL SERVICES 19103 #690-05-1987 L2002 **PFP** *012 †75

ADJOVU, Adelaide Adede. ■ 19128 #041-15-2008 *012

ADKINSON, Joshua Michael. ■ 19107 #041-02-2006 L2007 **GS** *012

ADLER, Alan Gary. 1901 MARKET ST 19103 #024-07-1975 L1976 **IM IMG** *030 †20

ADLER, Herbert Morris. 1015 CHESTNUT ST 19107 #041-09-1955 L1956 **P** *020 †75

ADLER, Joan Florence. 3509 N BROAD ST, TU CMC 19140 #038-41-1970 L1972 **ADL PD** *020 †55

ADLER, Matthew Israel. ■ 19147 #011-03-2007 L2007 **FP** *012

ADLIN, E Victor. 3401 N BROAD ST 19140 #041-13-1956 L1957 **END IM** *020 †20

ADOM, Akuete Edwin. 255 S 17TH ST, SUITE 2704 MEDICAL TOWER B 19103 #047-07-1968 L1970 **P** *020 †75

ADUNBARIN, Kayode Omoshol. 3401 N BROAD ST 19140 #690-01-1985 L2004 **P** *100

ADUNUTHULA, Hema. 601 WALNUT ST, CURTIS CENTER, STE 925 EAS 19106 #495-65-1997 L2003 **OBG** *100

ADVANI, Anisha B. 403 S 40TH ST, 3RD FL 19104 #035-01-2006 L2007 **OPH** *012

ADZICK, Nick Scott. 324 S 34TH ST, CHILDRENS HSPTL OF PHLDLPH 19104 #041-07-1979 L1995 **PDS** *020 †85

AGARWAL, Arvind. 2900 W QUEEN LN, MCP HAHNEMANN UNIV 19129 #495-46-1996 *100

AGARWAL, Ashish Madanlal. 5501 OLD YORK RD, DEPT OF CARDIOLOGY 19141 #495-22-1998 L2003 **CD** *012 †20

AGARWAL, Rajan. ■ 19103 #041-01-2004 L2004 **DR** *012

AGBAHIWE, Harold Chinedu. ■ 19106 #036-07-2006 L2006 **IM** *012

AGERSON, Ashley Nicole. 3401 N BROAD ST, DEPT OF ANESTHESIOLOGY 19140 #025-01-2005 L2005 **AN** *012

AGGARWAL, Nisha. ■ 19107 #041-01-2008 *012

AGGARWAL, Piyush. 3400 SPRUCE ST 19104 #496-59-2005 L2007 **GS** *012

AGGARWAL, Sandeep. 2900 W QUEEN LN 19129 #495-69-2003 L2005 **IM** *012

AGNANT, Joanne Michele. ■ 19130 #033-05-2006 L2006 **PD** *012

AGOSTINELLI, Nicole Ryann. ■ 19147 #010-03-2006 **GS** *012

AGRAMA, Susan Dina. 3401 N BROAD ST, 8TH FL 19140 #011-02-2000 L2001 **IM** *020

AGRONS, Geoffrey Ansel. 800 SPRUCE ST, PENNSYLVANIA HOSPITAL 19107 #033-05-1986 L1987 **PDR** *020 †80

AGUILAR, Barbara Carolina. 5501 OLD YORK RD 19141 #935-01-2000 L2007 **GS** *012

AGUILAR, Lielanie Mae Lio. 5501 OLD YORK RD, ALBERT EINSTEIN MED CTR 19141 #748-02-1999 L2004 **P** *012

AGUIRRE, Geoffrey Karl. 3400 SPRUCE ST 19104 #041-01-2000 L2001 **N** *020 †75

AGUIRRE, Melanio D. 5735 RIDGE AVE STE 2 19128 #748-02-1966 L1970 **IM** *020

AGUMADU, Charles Osita. ■ 19120 #690-06-1991 **P** *100

AGUS, Zalman Stephen. 423 GUARDIAN DR, 333 BLOCKLEY HALL 19104 #023-01-1965 L1975 **NEP IM** *020 †20

AHIMA, Rexford S. 415 CURIE BLVD, RESEARCH BUILDING 19104 #412-01-1986 L1999 **IM** *020 †20

AHMAD, Akif. 245 N 15TH ST, DEPT OF GME 19102 #704-02-2003 L2006 **FP** *012

AHMAD, Asyia Shareen. 219 N BROAD ST, FL 5 19107 #422-01-1998 L2001 **GE** *020 †20

AHMAD, Fawzia Faiyaz. ■ 19149 #042-21-1982 L2001 **IM** *100

AHMAD, Harris. ■ 19101 #041-15-2004 L2004 **DR** *100

AHMAD, Jamal. 925 CHESTNUT ST, FIFTH FLOOR 19107 #016-11-2000 L2005 **ORS** *100 ‡

AHMAD, Mian Ayyaz. 230 N BROAD ST 19102 #704-01-1984 L2001 **AN** *020

AHMAD, Mushtaq. 500 E GODFREY AVE 19120 #704-05-1982 L1996 **IM** *020 †20

AHMAD, Nuzhat A. 3400 SPRUCE ST, RAVDIN 3/DIVISION OF GASTR 19104 #704-02-1990 L1997 **GE** *020 †20

AHMAD, Sajjad. 700 SPRUCE ST STE 304 19106 #704-09-1991 L2003 **PCC** *012 †20

AHMADI, Tahamtan. ■ 19103 #409-22-2001 L2007 **HO** *012

AHMADPOUR, Oliver Abbas. 1800 LOMBARD ST, GRADUATE HOSPITAL /DEPT IM 19146 #858-04-1990 L2000 **CHP** *012

AHMADY, Hamid Reza. 2900 W QUEEN LN 19129 #517-01-1991 L2006 **IM** *100

AHMED, Intekhab. 211 S 9TH ST 19107 #704-21-1987 L2002 **END** *020 †20

AHMED, Irfan Haroon. 3401 N BROAD ST, TEMPLE UNIV HOSP 19140 #704-02-2001 L2004 **ORS** *012

AHMED, Murtuza Mohammed. 3600 SPRUCE ST, 844 WEST GATES BUILDING 19104 #055-01-2000 L2004 **PCC** *012 †20 ‡

AHMED, Mustafa Mohammed. ■ 19107 #055-01-2005 L2005 **IM** *012

AHMED, Shahzad. 2900 W QUEEN LN 19129 #704-21-2003 **IM** *012

AHMED, Zianddin. 3300 HENRY AVE 19129 #160-02-1976 L1982 **NEP IM** *020 †20

AHN, Jaimo. 3400 SPRUCE ST, 2 SILVERSTEIN 19104 #041-01-2003 L2003 **ORS** *012

AHN, Yoon J. 3400 SPRUCE ST, DIVISION OF RENAL-ELCTRLYT 19104 #041-13-1991 L1997 **NEP** *020

AHN, Yvonne Jean. ■ 19107 #041-02-2008 *012

AHRENSFIELD, Debra C. 1317 WOLF ST 19148 #041-02-1991 L1993 **CD** *020 †20

AHTARIDIS, George S. 1800 LOMBARD ST, STE 100 PEPPER PAVILION 19146 #418-02-1968 L1975 **GE** *020 †20

AHYA, Vivek Narendra. 2900 W QUEEN LN 19130 #495-05-1994 L2000 **PCC** *020 †20

AILAWADI, Monica. ■ 19146 #035-19-2000 **OBG** *100

AIMINO, Barbara Jo. 2601 HOLME AVE 19152 #041-09-1992 L1994 **IM** *020

AIRAN, Subha Lakshmi. ■ 19148 #023-01-2004 L2004 **IM** *100 †20

AIZENBERG, David Jacob. ■ 19128 #035-19-2007 L2007 **IM** *012

AJAYI, Olayinka Morenike. 8001 STATE RD, PHILADELPHIA PRISONS SYSTE 19136 #690-05-1989 L2004 **CHP** *012

AJIT, Challa. 5401 OLD YORK RD, DIV OF GASTROENTEROLOGY 19141 #495-57-1992 L2000 **GE** *020 †20

AKAI, Yasuhiro. 3400 SPRUCE ST 19104 #572-55-1989 L1999 **NEP** *100 †20

AKANBI, Adebola Oyeronke. 834 CHESTNUT ST STE 400, BENJAMIN FRANKLIN HOUSE 19107 #038-06-2003 L2007 **OBG** *100

AKERS, Scott Robert. ■ 19104 #041-12-2000 L2001 **DR** *100 †80

AKHBARATI, Hengameh Laila. 4641 ROOSEVELT BLVD 19124 #858-05-1995 L2006 **P** *020

AKHTAR, Salman. 833 CHESTNUT ST, STE 210C 19107 #495-77-1969 L1979 **P** *020 †75

AKINYEMI, Tolulope Kofi. 3401 N BROAD ST, OF S 19140 #010-03-2005 L2005 **GS** *012

AKIYAMA, Hideki. 3401 N BROAD ST 19140 #572-35-1977 L1984 **HO ON** *020 †20

AKKARA VEETIL, Bharath Ma. 800 SPRUCE ST, PENNSYLVANIA HOSPITAL 19107 #496-45-2003 L2006 *100

AKPAN, Imo. ■ 19143 #041-01-2008 *012

AKROUT, Hafedh. 3996 RED LION RD 19114 #396-06-1972 L1977 **PM** *020 †60

AKVAN, Shahab. ■ 19129 #041-15-2008 *012

ALABI, Titilayo Oluseyi. ■ 19147 #041-02-2005 L2005 **FP** *012

ALADE, Folashade Olajoke. ■ 19135 #041-15-2004 L2007 **RHU** *012 †20

AL-ALAO, Bashar. 245 N 15TH ST MS 437, DREXEL UNIV COLL OF MED 19104 #875-01-2001 L2007 **NEP** *012 †20

ALAM, Syeda Naureen. 800 SPRUCE ST 19107 #051-04-2003 L2003 **OBG** *020

AL-ANI, Firas Raouf R. 245 N 15TH ST, MS 470 19102 #528-04-1993 L2002 **IC** *100 †20

ALAO, Kamardeen O. 3401 N BROAD ST, DEPT OF ANESTHESIOLOGY 19140 #690-02-1991 L2003 **CCA** *020 †05

ALARCON, Anthony James. 3401 N BROAD ST, TEMPLE UNIV HOSP 19140 #010-01-2006 L2007 **AN** *012

ALAVI, Abass. 3400 SPRUCE ST # RAD, DIV NUCLEAR MEDICINE 19104 #517-01-1964 L1972 **NM IM** *020 †20,28

ALAVI, Jane Bradley. 3400 SPRUCE ST, 16 PENN TOWER 19104 #024-01-1966 L1971 **ON HEM** *020 †20

ALAVI, Mosen. 100 E LEHIGH AVE, MAB 204 19125 #517-01-1968 L1974 **CD IM** *020 †20 ‡

ALAVI, Rowshan Ziaie. 5619 VINE ST 19139 #517-01-1968 L1974 **PD PUD** *020 †55

AL-BACHA HJAZI, Izat Khal. ■ 19125 #957-01-1988 L2003 **FM** *100 †18

ALBALA, Maurizio Z. 51 N 39TH ST 19104 #561-03-1978 L2002 **APM AN** *100 †05 ‡

AL-BATAINEH, Mohammad A. 219 N BROAD ST, FL 6 19107 #575-02-1992 L2001 **CD** *020 †20

ALBELDA, Steven Mark. 3600 SPRUCE ST 19104 #041-01-1979 L1981 **PUD** *050 †20

ALBERT, Lawrence. 7600 CENTRAL AVE, JEANES HOSP EMGY DEPT 19111 #041-13-1973 L1974 **EM IM** *020 †20,16 ‡

ALCANTARA, Manuel B. ONE GRADUATE PLZ 19146 #308-02-1986 L1993 **CD** *100 †20

ALDAY, Edgardo S. 111 S 11TH ST # G-A270 19107 #748-01-1957 L1977 **GS** *020 †85

ALDEN, Mark Edward. 216 N BROAD ST MS 200, DEPT ONC HAHNEMANN HOS 19102 #041-02-1988 L1990 **RO HNS** *020 †80

ALEEM, Sadia. 3400 SPRUCE ST 19104 #704-05-1997 **DMP** *012

ALEGARBES, Marina R. ■ 19140 #748-01-1961 **P** *100

ALEMO-HAMMAD, Saeid. FRONT & LEHIGH AV 19133 #517-01-1974 L1978 **NS** *072 †25

ALESSANDRINI, Evaline A. 324 S 34TH ST 19104 #423-08-1988 L1992 **PEM PD** *050 †55

ALESSI, Thomas Vincent. 2821 ISLAND AVE, MERCY WORKCARE 19153 #308-07-1983 L1988 **IM** *020

ALEXANDER, Christian M. 51 N 39TH ST 19104 #036-07-1979 L1982 **AN** *020 †05

ALEXANDER, George A. ■ 19129 #010-03-1977 L1984 **RO ON** *020

ALEXANDER, Lawrence R. ■ 19111 #016-42-1959 L1960 **GP** *075

ALEXIS, Rhonda A. 3400 SPRUCE ST 19104 #566-01-1986 L1996 **PAN PD** *020 †05,55

ALEYAS, Sajive. 834 WALNUT ST, STE 650 19107 #473-04-2000 L2005 **PCC** *012 †20

ALFANDRE, Joanne Hallie. ERIE AVE AT FRONT ST 19133 #003-01-1992 L1994 **PD** *020 †55

ALGAZY, Kenneth Mark. 3400 SPRUCE ST, HOSP OF THE UNIV OF PENN 19104 #041-13-1969 L1970 **HEM ON** *020 †20

ALGEO, Suzanne Barndt. 8835 GERMANTOWN AVE 19118 #041-07-1982 L1985 **RHU** *020 †20

ALGUIRE, Patrick Craig. WEST, 190 NORTH INDEPENDECE MALL 19106 #025-12-1975 L1998 **IM** *020 †20

AL HAJ, Rany Samir. ■ 19107 #605-02-1999 L2003 **IM** *020

ALHOMSI, Motaz. 27 E MOUNT AIRY AVE 19119 #875-01-1986 L1997 **P** *020

ALI, Ahmed Naser. 3400 SPRUCE ST, 2 DONNER 19104 #041-01-2006 L2006 **RO** *012

ALI, Freddy Mohamed Ismai. 5501 OLD YORK RD, ALBERT EINSTEIN MED CTR 19141 #915-02-2000 L2003 **P** *020

ALI, Nadia Kabiruddin. 800 SPRUCE ST, PENNSYLVANIA HOSPITAL 19107 #704-25-2001 L2004 **IM** *020 †20

ALI, Sayed Muhammad. 3401 N BROAD ST 19140 #566-01-1988 L2002 *020 †80

ALIM, Salman Raza. 2900 W QUEEN LN 19129 #704-25-2003 L2005 **IM** *012

ALIZAI, Adeela Masood. 3401 N BROAD ST, DEPT OPH 19140 #704-25-1995 L2007 **OPH** *012 †75

ALJUMAILY, Raid Maki Dawo. 245 N 15TH ST, DEPT OF GME 19102 #528-01-1993 L2005 *100

ALKASEM, Rima. 3401 N BROAD ST, DEPT OF GME 19140 #875-01-2003 L2006 *100

ALKHOULI, Mohamad Adnan. 3401 N BROAD ST, DEPT OF MED - 8PP 19140 #875-01-2006 L2007 **IM** *012

ALLAN, David A. 39TH & MARKET ST, STE 107 MAB 19104 #041-02-1976 L1977 **RHU OM** *020 †20

ALLAN, Mark Douglas. 2301 S BROAD ST, DEPT OF RADIOLOGY 19148 #035-01-1992 L1998 **DR** *020 †80

ALLARD, Eloise Nadine. 2900 W QUEEN LN 19129 #422-01-2003 L2007 **IM** *012

ALLAREDDY, Mrudula Reddy. 2900 W QUEEN LN 19129 #495-70-2002 L2005 **IM** *012

ALLEN, April Estelle. ■ 19143 #024-05-2002 L2002 **GS** *012

ALLEN, Arleen Adinavivia. ■ 19107 #023-01-2007 L2007 **EM** *012

ALLEN, Carol Hope. 3401 N BROAD ST, TEMPLE UNIV HOSPITAL 19140 #035-06-1979 L1981 **N** *020

ALLEN, Erica Monique. ■ 19102 #025-12-2008 *012

ALLEN, Herbert Brockton. 219 N BROAD ST, FL 4 19107 #023-07-1970 L1974 **D DMP** *020 †15 ‡

ALLEN, Julian Lewis. 324 S 34TH ST 19104 #035-01-1978 L1986 **PDP PD** *020 †55

ALLEN, Mark Downing. 1601 WALNUT ST STE 5 19102 #041-13-1978 L1980 **ORS** *020

ALLEN, Shannon Leslie. 2900 W QUEEN LN, DREXEL COLLEGE OF MEDICINE 19129 #041-15-2007 L2007 **GS** *012

ALLEVI, Angela Michelle. 833 CHESTNUT ST STE 300, JEFFERSON DUPONT CHILDS HL 19107 #041-02-1997 L2004 **PD** *020 †55

ALLEY, Cynthia Lee. 3401 N BROAD ST, DEPT OF OPHTHALMOLOGY 19140 #041-13-2000 L2001 **OPH** *020 †35

ALLEYNE, Gregg David. 245 N 15TH ST, 16TH FL 19102 #010-03-1994 L1996 **OBG** *020 †30 ‡

ALLI, Oluseun Olukayode. 5501 OLD YORK RD, ALBERT EINSTEIN MED CTR 19141 #690-02-2001 L2004 **CD** *012 †20

ALLMAN, Richard Lawrence. 5501 OLD YORK RD 19141 #041-02-1969 L1970 **IM RHU** *020 †20

ALLMENDINGER, Nikki. ■ 19128 #008-02-2001 L2007 **PD** *100

ALLUKIAN, Myron. ■ 19146 #043-01-2006 L2006 **IM** *020

ALMALIKY, Muhamed Hassan. ■ 19103 #436-01-1998 L2001 **IM** *020 †20

ALMENDRALA, Jennifer Cabu. 5501 OLD YORK RD, ALBERT EINSTEIN MEDICAL CE 19141 #748-10-1998 L2006 **P** *012

ALMONTE, Licette. ■ 19129 #041-15-2008 L2008 *012

ALNOUNOU, Mustafa. 333 COTTMAN AVE, FOX CHASE CANCER CENTER 19111 #875-01-1992 L2005 **GE** *020 †20

ALOI, Joseph Michael. ■ 19147 #041-02-2004 L2004 **AN** *012

AL-OKAILI, Riyadh Nassir. 3400 SPRUCE ST, DEPT OF RADIOLOGY 19104 #797-01-1996 L2003 **RNR** *100

ALPAS, Abe Passuguiron. ■ 19145 #748-10-1974 L1980 *071

ALPERN, Elizabeth Rachel. 324 S 34TH ST 19104 #025-01-1992 L1994 **PD PEM** *020 †55

ALPERT, N Paul. 1800 LOMBARD ST 19146 #165-08-1982 **IM** *020

AL-SALEEM, Essel Asaad. 245 N 15TH ST, DREXEL UNIV COLL MED/HAHNE 19102 #528-01-1998 L2005 **PTH** *012

AL-SALEEM, Tahseen Isa. 333 COTTMAN AVE 19111 #528-01-1961 L1992 **PTH** *020 †50

AL-SHEIKH, Afaf Abdulaziz. 3600 SPRUCE ST, HUP - DERMATOLOGY 19104 #797-01-1994 L2000 **D** *100 †15

ALSIBAI, Ahmad. 3401 N BROAD ST, DEPT OF MED- 8PP 19140 #875-01-2005 L2007 **IM** *012

AL-TAHER, Ossama M. ■ 19119 #041-15-2007 L2007 **IM** *012

ALTER, Todd Matthew. ■ 19128 #041-15-2008 *012

ALTMAN, Howard Glen. 1342 COTTMAN AVE 19111 #035-20-1983 L1985 **U** *020 †95

ALTMAN, Linda S. 1616 WALNUT ST, STE 2114 19103 #035-20-1980 L1982 **P** *020 †75

ALTMANN, James William. ■ 19107 #422-01-2002 L2006 **AN** *012

ALTSCHULER, Stanley L. 9501 ROOSEVELT BLVD, STE 208 19114 #035-15-1964 L1970 **PUD IM** *020 †20

ALTSCHULER, Steven Mark. 324 S 34TH ST, THE CHILDRENS HOSP PATH 19104 #038-06-1979 L1982 **PG** *020 †55

ALTSHULER, Marc Jay. 833 CHESTNUT ST, STE 301 19107 #041-02-2001 L2001 **FM** *020 †18

AL-TURKI, Abdullah. CHILDRENS HOSP PHILADLPHIA, DEPT ANEST CRTCL CR 19104 #797-01-1988 L1996 **CCP** *020 †55

ALUR, Ram Sanjeev. 4TH FLOOR - S TOWER MAIL, DREXEL UNIVERSITY COLLEGE 19102 #495-62-1999 L2007 **IM** *012

ALVANDI, Firoozeh. 800 SPRUCE ST, DEPT OF PATHOLOGY 19107 #010-01-1996 L1997 **PTH** *100 †50

ALVAREZ, Daniel Fernando. 1427 VINE ST, 3RD FL 19102 #737-06-1991 L1997 **IM** *020 †20

AMANULLAH, Aman Md. 5501 OLD YORK RD, HAKENBURG BLDG 3RD FL 19141 #781-01-1979 L1997 **CD IM** *020 †20

AMARAVADI, Ravi Kumar. 3400 SPRUCE ST, 15 PENN TOWER 19104 #023-07-2000 L2003 **HO** *100 †20

AMARO MORA, Mario. ■ 19130 #649-20-1962 L1972 **CCM EM** *020

AMBATI, Sreekanth Reddy. 5501 OLD YORK RD 19141 #496-27-2004 L2006 **MPD** *012

AMBRAD BECHARA, Jaime. ■ 19128 #264-01-1965 L1974 **TS GS** *020 †85

AMBROSINI, Paul John. 3200 HENRY AVE, DREXEL UNIVERSITY COLL OF 19129 #036-05-1976 L1988 **CHP P** *050 †75

AMENTA, Peter Sebastian. ■ 19107 #041-02-2006 L2006 **NS** *012

AMERI, Vahideh Tourzani. 245 N 15TH ST, MAIL STOP 495 19102 #422-01-2000 L2001 **OBG** *012

AMEXO, Kwaku. 501 S 54TH ST, MERCY PHILADELPHIA 19143 #913-18-1987 L1995 **IM** *020 †20

AMIN, Mehul Bipin. 1800 LOMBARD ST, TENET HEALTHSYSTEM GRADUAT 19146 #654-01-2006 L2006 **IM** *012

AMIN, Neha Pradip. ■ 19103 #041-01-2007 L2007 **IM** *012

AMIN, Nirav. ■ 19103 #041-15-2008 *012

AMMAR, Tamer. 245 N 15TH ST, DREXEL UNIV COLL OF MED 19102 #895-01-2004 L2006 **N** *012

AMORES, Rebecca M. 100 E LEHIGH AVE, STE 206 MED ARTS 19125 #748-02-1968 L1973 **OBG** *020

AMOROSA, Valerianna Klara. 822 PINE ST STE 3A 19107 #028-02-1998 L2000 **ID** *020 †20

AMROM, George Jerry. ■ 19107 #041-09-1972 L1976 **GS** *020 †85

AMRUTIA, Shirish Shantila. 2900 W QUEEN LN 19129 #495-22-2002 L2006 **IM** *012

AMSTEL, David Jeremy. 3401 N BROAD ST 19140 #035-08-2005 L2005 **IM** *012

AMSTER, Melanie Ina. 1216 ARCH ST, STE 3B 19107 #041-09-1991 L1997 **U** *020 †95

AMSTERDAM, Jay David. 3535 MARKET ST, DEPRESSION RESEARCH 3RD FL 19104 #041-02-1974 L1975 **P PA** *050 †75

AMUNDSON, Russell Henry. 5501 OLD YORK RD, KLEIN STE 501 19141 #035-08-1982 L2006 **NS** *020 †25

ANACIUS, Elisabeth. ■ 19107 #041-02-2008 *012

ANAGNOSTOPOULOS, Annemarie. ■ 19103 #041-01-2004 L2004 **IM** *012

ANAKWENZE, Okechukwu Amad. ■ 19102 #026-08-2007 L2007 **ORS** *012

ANAND, Girish. 5401 OLD YORK RD STE 363 19141 #495-27-2000 L2001 **GE** *012 †20

ANAND, Rahul. ■ 19106 #495-45-2004 L2004 **ID** *012 †20

ANANDANADESAN, Rathai. ■ 19107 #041-02-2007 *012

ANDAY, Endla P. 4150 CITY AVE, HOSPITAL LOBBY 19131 #041-07-1973 **NPM PD** *020 †55

ANDERSON, Brett Romeo. ■ 19103 #041-01-2007 L2007 **PD** *012

ANDERSON, David Thomas. ■ 19107 #041-02-2007 L2007 **ORS** *012

ANDERSON, James Paul. ■ 19107 #051-01-2008 *012

ANDERSON, Juliette Coche. ■ 19103 #041-01-2004 L2004 **P** *012

ANDERSON, Laura Min Hae. ■ 19106 #014-01-2001 L2007 **FM** *020 †18

ANDERSON, Penny Rawdin. 333 COTTMAN AVE 19111 #041-13-1994 L1996 **RO** *020 †80

ANDERSON, Renee T. 301 S 8TH ST, STE 3D 19106 #041-77-2003, ▲ L2003 **OBG** *012

ANDERSON, William A, III. 925 CHESTNUT ST, FIFTH FLOOR 19107 #025-01-2002 L2003 **PM** *020 †60

ANDEWELT, Alexa Sara. 833 CHESTNUT ST, STE 210 19107 #010-01-2005 L2005 **P** *012

ANDREADIS, Charalambos. 3400 SPRUCE ST, 16 PENN TOWER 19104 #035-01-1998 L2001 **HO** *020 †20

ANDREWS, David Wallace. 909 WALNUT ST, 2ND FL 19107 #007-02-1983 L1989 **NS** *020 †25

ANDREWS, E Jeanne. ■ 19103 #041-07-1946 L1949 **PM PD** *071 †55

ANDREWS, Genevieve Ambros. ■ 19128 #041-13-2003 **OTO** *012

ANDREWS, Wade Justin. ■ 19128 #041-13-2003 L2003 **ORS** *012

ANG, Dexter Ong. 5501 OLD YORK RD 19141 #748-20-2002 L2005 **PD** *012

ANG, Gina Charlene. ■ 19104 #041-01-2002 L2002 **PRD** *020 †15

ANGA, Altaf Gulamhusain. ■ 19116 #041-13-2006 L2006 **FP** *012

ANGEL, Brett Graeme. 5401 OLD YORK RD, KLEIN 363 19141 #836-01-2001 L2007 **IM** *012

ANGELES, Anne Marie C. 1440 MCKEAN ST 19145 #010-03-1981 L1983 **D ID** *020 †15

ANGELINI, Renata. 245 N 15TH ST, DREXEL UNIV COLL OF MED 19102 #661-02-2006 L2006 **P** *012

ANGELL, Karen Patrice. 101 E OLNEY AVE, STE C5 19120 #035-45-1999 **PD** *020 †55

ANGELO, Mark Anthony. 2 PENN BLVD STE 111 19144 #041-13-1998 L2000 **EM** *020 †20

ANGELOV, Angel Stoyanov. 1020 SANSOM ST, 1652 THOMPSON BUILDING, RM 19107 #198-01-1997 L2001 **P** *020 †75 ‡

ANIL KUMAR, Mysore S. 216 N BROAD ST, FL 5 19102 #495-09-1972 L1992 **OS VS** *020

ANIM-APPIAH, Desmond Y. 3401 N BROAD ST, JONES HALL BLDG., RM 812 19140 #412-01-1987 L1998 **RHU** *020 †20

ANJUM, Waqas. 1800 LOMBARD ST 19146 #704-15-1999 L2005 **GS** *100

ANKAM, Nethra Sridhara. ■ 19107 #041-02-2003 L2003 **IM** *100

ANNE, Pramila Rani. 111 S 11TH ST 19107 #051-01-1990 L1995 **RO** *020 †80

ANNESLEY, William H, Jr. 840 WALNUT ST 19107 #041-02-1948 L1949 **OPH** *071 †35

ANNOPOLSKY, Elena. 9150 MARSHALL ST, STE 17 19114 #913-01-1982 L1999 **IM** *020 †20

ANO, Antonio Cruz. 111 S 11TH ST, STE 6460 19107 #748-01-1956 L1967 **AM** *071

ANOLIK, Miriam Olga. 2085 N 63RD ST, PHA PEDIATRICS PC 19151 #035-08-1974 L1977 **PD** *020 †55 ‡

ANOLIK, Mitchell Arthur. 3400 SPRUCE ST, 2 RHOADS PAVILION 19104 #035-08-1972 L1974 **D IM** *020 †20,15

ANREDDY, Sandeep Reddy. 111 S 11TH ST 19107 #495-65-2003 L2005 **IM** *012

ANSARI, Husamuddin. 51 N 39TH ST, UNIV OF PENNSYLVANIA 19104 #035-01-2002 L2002 **OPH** *100 †35

ANSARI, Ramin. 3401 N BROAD ST, DEPT OF MED - 8PP 19140 #517-06-1992 L2007 **IM** *012

ANTHONY, James Alvin. 255 S 17TH ST 19103 #047-07-1967 L1978 **ORS OTR** *020 †40

ANTIA, Smita Xerxes. 8220 CASTOR AVE 19152 #495-01-1988 L2002 **CHP** *100 †75

ANTONIUK, Robert. ■ 19144 #041-13-2004 L2004 **EM** *100

ANTONYRAJ, Kavitha Joseph. ■ 19130 #010-02-2004 L2004 **PEM** *012 †55

ANTUNES, Marcelo Barros. 3400 SPRUCE ST, UNIVERSITY OF PENNSYLVANIA 19104 #187-80-2001 L2007 **OTO** *012

ANYADIKE, Nnaemeka Uchend. ■ 19107 #051-01-2007 L2007 **IM** *012

AOUTHMANY, Asma Moustafa. 5501 OLD YORK RD, ALBERT EINSTEIN MED CTR 19141 #038-44-2003 L2006 **CD** *012

APARICIO, Hugo Javier. ■ 19146 #041-01-2008 *012

APENTENG, Tawia Ahwirema. ■ 19146 #041-01-2005 L2005 **PD** *012

APLENC, Richard. 3615 CIVIC CENTER BLVD, 916G ARC 19104 #051-01-1994 L1997 **PHO** *020 †55

APOSTOLOPOULOU, Sotiria C. 324 S 34TH ST, CHILDRENS HOSP DEPT PED 19104 #418-01-1988 L1995 **PDC** *100 †55

APPIAH, Grace. 2201 MOUNT VERNON ST 19130 #051-01-2008 *012

APPLEGATE, John Richard. 255 S 17TH ST STE 1708 19103 #033-06-2001 L2001 **P** *020 †75

APPOO, Jehangir Jamshed. 8 REX AVE, APT 4 19118 #067-01-1997 L2004 *100

APTER, Andrea Joan. 3400 SPRUCE ST, 829 GATES 19104 #041-01-1984 L1998 **AI IM** *050 †20,03

ARAFAT, Yaser. 1800 LOMBARD ST, GRADUATE HOSP (TENET HLTH 19146 #704-21-2001 L2004 **IM** *100 †20

ARAI, Kazuhiko. 1 GRADUATE PLZ, GRADUATE HOSP DEPT PATH 19146 #572-20-1952 **CLP IG** *050

ARANGUENA SHARPE, Guadalup. 5501 OLD YORK RD, ALBERT EINSTEIN MED CTR 19141 #649-13-2001 L2003 **P** *100

ARANO, Leonardo Villamar. 1628 JOHN F KENNEDY BLVD, STE 950 19103 #748-01-1958 L1970 **IM** *071 †20

ARASU, Gopinath. 3400 SPRUCE ST, ONE FOUNDERS PAVILION 19104 #495-59-1993 L2007 **IM** *020 †20

ARAUJO, Luis Ignacio. 3400 SPRUCE ST, RM 110 DONNER BLDG 19104 #132-01-1977 L1992 **NM CD** *020 †28

ARAYA, Victor Rene. 5401 OLD YORK RD, STE 204 19141 #010-01-1989 L1991 **GE IM** *020 †20

ARBETER, Allan Morris. 5501 OLD YORK RD 19141 #041-02-1967 L1973 **PD PHP** *020 †55

ARCE, Maria L Saenz Bazan. ■ 19152 #737-06-1969 L1973 **IM** *020

ARCHER, John Hoffman, Jr. 3400 SPRUCE ST 19104 #005-11-1986 L2001 **AN** *020 †05

ARENSON, Christine Ann B. 1015 WALNUT ST STE 401 19107 #041-02-1990 L1993 **FM FPG** *020 †18

ARFAI, Naisohn S. ■ 19147 #048-13-2003 L2005 **EM** *012

ARGER, Peter Harry. 3400 SPRUCE ST, DEPT OF RAD 19104 #016-11-1961 L1962 **R** *050 †80

ARGUELLO GUERRA, Vivian. 19114 #308-02-2002 L2004 **PTH** *012

ARIA, Robert Jadali. ■ 19147 #041-13-2006 L2006 **DR** *012

ARIATHURAI, Priya Shanthi. ■ 19107 #041-15-2007 L2007 *012

ARIF, Sabreena. 3901 CONSHOHOCKEN AVE, ABINGTON MEMORIAL HOSPITAL 19131 #704-25-2000 L2006 **IM** *020 †20

ARKADER, Alexandre. 1 CHILDRENS CTR 19104 #187-78-1998 L2005 **OP** *100

ARKOOSH, Valerie Ann. 3400 SPRUCE ST, HOSPITAL OF THE UNIV. OF P 19104 #030-05-1986 L1987 **AN** *030 †05

ARM, Edward Solomon. 561 FAIRTHORNE AVE 19128 #913-01-1962 L1985 **P** *071

ARMBRECHT, Kimberley Tart. 3401 N BROAD ST, TEMPLE UNIV HOSP 19140 #041-13-2006 L2006 **AN** *012

ARMENTI, Vincent Thos. 3401 N BROAD ST, PARKINSON PAV 19140 #041-02-1982 L1988 **GS** *020 †85

ARMSON, Kris Karl. 230 N BROAD ST 19102 #041-15-2002 L2002 **AN** *100

ARMSTEAD, Valerie E. 111 S 11TH ST, 8TH FLOOR GIBBON BLDG 19107 #028-02-1981 L1992 **AN PD** *020 †05

ARMSTRONG, Anna Elina. 24 E GRAVERS LN 19118 #374-01-1993 L1998 **HEM IM** *050 †20

ARMSTRONG, Benjamin David. ■ 19147 #008-02-2006 L2007 **EM** *012

ARMSTRONG, Katrina Alison. 51 N 39TH ST, UPHS/PRESBYTRN INTRNL MDCN 19104 #023-07-1991 L1996 **IM** *020 †20

ARNO, Irvin C. 5501 OLD YORK RD 19141 #041-01-1951 L1952 **OBG** *020 †30

ARNOLD, Steven Edward. 415 CURIE BLVD, 547 CLINICAL RESEARCH BLDG 19104 #024-05-1983 L1990 **N P** *050 †75

ARNOLD, William Vincent. 925 CHESTNUT ST, FIFTH FLOOR 19107 #041-02-1998 L2000 **ORS** *012 †40

ARONCHICK, Craig Alan. 230 W WASHINGTON SQ 19106 #041-13-1978 L1979 **GE** *020 †20

ARONCHICK, Judith Marsha. HOSP UNIV OF PA, DEPT RADIOLOGY 19104 #041-01-1978 L1980 **DR** *020 †80

ARONOFF, Stephen Carl. 3509 N BROAD ST, TEMPLE UN. CHILDREN'S MED 19140 #041-12-1976 L1999 **PD** *020 †55

ARONOWITZ, Robert Alan. 51 N 39TH ST, PRESBYTERIAN MEDICAL CTR 19104 #008-01-1985 L1986 **IM** *020 †20

ARONSON, Jerold Michael. 231 N BROAD ST, FEINSTEIN BLDG. 2ND FLOOR 19107 #038-06-1965 L1971 **PD** *071 †55

ARONSON, Paul L. ■ 19103 #035-19-2005 L2005 **PD** *012

ARORA, Alka. 111 S 11TH ST, # 4290 19107 #539-03-1993 L1998 **NEP** *020 †20

AROSARENA, Oneida Albania. 3400 N BROAD ST, STE 102 19140 #023-07-1993 L2006 **OTO FPS** *020 †45

ARRIEN, Mauricio Daniel. 2900 W QUEEN LN 19129 #649-14-2003 L2005 **IM** *012

■ = Address Information Privacy Protected

ARSCOTT-MILLS, Tonya K. 3156 KENSINGTON AVE 19134 #036-05-2001 L2001 PD *020 †55
ARTAMONOV, Mikhail J. 3401 N BROAD ST 19140 #913-06-1994 L2000 APM *020 †60
ARTZ, Gregory James. 925 CHESTNUT ST, FL 6 19107 #025-07-2001 L2001 NO *012 †45
ARYA, Lily Agarwal. 3400 SPRUCE ST, DEPT OB/GYN - 5 DULLES 19104 #495-02-1987 L2000 OBG *020 †30
ARZANIPOUR, Dan. ■ 19128 #005-14-2004 L2005 PM *012
ASAKURA, Toshio. 324 S 34TH ST, CHILDRENS HOSPITAL 19104 #572-13-1960 HEM PD *050
ASAM, Bruce Alan. 111 S 11TH ST, STE 8490 19107 #041-13-1985 L1987 AN IM *020 †20,05
ASAR, Mariam Hasanali. 100 E LEHIGH AVE, DEPT OF PSYCHIATRY 19125 #704-02-1980 L1994 CHP *012 †55
ASBEL, Lenore Elsberg. 3300 HENRY AVE, RM 211 19129 #041-07-1991 L1994 IM *020 †20
ASBELL, Sucha Order. 9908 ROOSEVELT BLVD, MNAP 19115 #041-07-1966 L1967 RO *020 †80 ‡
ASBURY, Arthur Knight. UNIV PENN HOSP, DEPT NEURO 19104 #038-41-1958 L1974 N NP *030 †75
ASEEM, Sultan Mohammad. ■ 19131 #041-13-2007 *012
ASEMOTA, Obehi Alexandria. 245 N 15TH ST MS 49, OF M 19102 #041-15-2007 L2007 OBG *012
ASHBEY, Dwight R, Jr. ■ 19118 #041-02-1946 L1947 CHP PD *071 †55
ASHBURN, Michael Alan. 1840 SOUTH ST, 2ND FL TUTTLEMAN CENTER 19146 #001-06-1984 L2007 AN PMM *062 †05
ASHER, Janice B. 3400 SPRUCE ST FL 5, HOSP OF THE UNIV OF PENN 19104 #016-01-1977 L1988 GYN *020 †30
ASHIKIAN, Nazely. ■ 19131 #041-15-2008 *012
ASHKENAZI, Abraham Avi. 111 S 11TH ST STE 8130 19107 #550-01-1993 L2003 *100
ASHOK, John Dhanasekaran. ■ 19149 #495-27-1981 L2004 GS *012
ASHWORTH, Rene Eleanor. ■ 19150 #041-13-2008 *012
ASKARI, Hossein Ali. 2100 W GIRARD AVE, BLDG 3 19130 #517-01-1961 L1992 PD END *020 †55
ASNANI, Bharti. ■ 19131 #496-22-2000 L2003 ID *012 †20
ASPER, Ronald Frank. 2301 S BROAD ST 19148 #041-13-1972 L1973 ID IM *020 †20
ASSIS, David Nilson. ■ 19103 #041-02-2005 L2005 IM *012
ATKINS, Joshua Henry. 3400 SPRUCE ST, 6 DULLES BLDG 19104 #035-01-2003 L2003 AN *100
ATKINS, Paul Chas. 3400 SPRUCE ST STE G, SILVERSTEIN PAVILLION 3RD 19104 #035-09-1967 L1974 A IM *020 †20,03
ATLURI, Pavan. 3400 SPRUCE ST 19104 #035-03-2001 L2001 GS *012
ATOGHO, Ata. 245 N 15TH ST, OF M 19102 #010-03-2003 L2004 OBG *012
ATRI, Gouri S. 2010 LEVICK ST, CONCENTRA MEDICAL CENTER 19149 #495-15-1980 L1983 OM GP *020 †70
ATTARI, Mehrunnisa. 2623 E ALLEGHENY AVE 19134 #495-44-1969 L1990 PD *020 †55
ATTIYEH, Edward Fathi. ■ 19130 #035-46-1999 L2002 PHO *100 †55
AU, Clement Chichung. 911 ARCH ST, STE 101 19107 #041-13-1982 L1983 FM *020 †18
AU, Francis Chi-Sun. 3400 N BROAD ST STE 429, TEMPLE UNIV HOSP DEPT SUR 19140 #041-13-1971 L1973 GS OS *020 †85
AUDU, Paul B. 111 S 11TH ST STE G6460, THOMAS JEFFERSON UNIV HOSP 19107 #690-03-1987 L1994 AN *020 †05
AUER, Jennifer Ann. 3615 CIVIC CENTER BLVD, RM 802 19104 #011-03-2002 L2002 PDE *012
AUERBACH, Arthur H. 67 HAMILTON CIR 19130 #041-02-1951 L1952 P *072 †75
AUERBACH, Joshua David. 3400 SPRUCE ST, DEPT OF ORTHOPAEDIC SURGER 19104 #035-47-2002 L2002 ORS *012
AUERBACH, Robert Stephen. 7604 CENTRAL AVE, STE 101 19111 #041-77-1972, ▲ L1973 OBG *020 †30
AUGOUSTIDES, John G T. 3400 SPRUCE ST, HOSPITAL OF THE UNIV OF PA 19104 #836-02-1990 L1998 AN *020 †05 ‡
AUGUSTHY, Roy K. 5735 RIDGE AVE, STE 210 19128 #495-31-1967 L1981 P PYG *020 †75
AUGUSTIN, Gerda. 251 E BRINGHURST ST 19144 #305-01-2000 L2005 PD *100
AUKBURG, Stanley Jay. 3400 SPRUCE ST 19104 #041-01-1968 L1969 AN *020 †05
AURE, Shaun Frederick Mag. 5501 OLD YORK RD 19141 #748-01-2001 L2003 NEP *012 †20
AURIACOMBE, Marc. 3900 CHESTNUT ST 19104 #396-01-1985 L1992 P *050
AURIACOMBE, Sophie. ■ 19106 #396-01-1984 L1992 N *012
AURITT, William Allen. 40 W EVERGREEN AVE, STE 112 19118 #041-02-1975 L1976 A *020 ‡
AUSTIN, Frances Schencksn. ■ 19129 #041-15-2007 L2007 GS *012
AUSTIN, Luke Stanford. 1015 CHESTNUT ST, THOMAS JEFFERSON UNIV 19107 #041-02-2004 L2004 ORS *012
AUSTRIA, David. 5429 GERMANTOWN AVE 19144 #748-10-1976 L1985 P *020
AUSTRIA, Jocelyn M. 2601 HOLME AVE 19152 #748-10-1980 L1984 NPM PD *020 †55
AVDIC, Aida. ■ 19103 #035-45-2006 L2006 IM *012
AVELINO, Rossana Isabel. 3440 MARKET ST, DEPT OF CHILD ASOLESCENT 19104 #924-01-1992 L2001 CHP *020 †75
AVERSA, Zefferino A, Jr. 2301 S BROAD ST 19148 #561-17-1953 L1958 OTO PUD *071
AVERY, Caudrean Latiste. ■ 19148 #010-03-2004 L2004 OBG *012
AVETA, Jacquelyn Marie. 225 S COBBS CREEK PKWY, CHOP PRIMARY CARE CENTER 19139 #033-06-1996 L1998 PD *020 †55
AWADALLA, Farah C. ■ 19102 #041-15-2008 *012
AWOPETU, Oluwakemi Temita. ■ 19119 #033-05-2008 *012
AWSARE, Bharat Kumar. 834 WALNUT ST STE 650, PULMONARY/CRITICAL CARE ME 19107 #036-05-1996 L1999 PCC *020 †20
AXEL, Leon. 3400 SPRUCE ST 19104 #005-02-1976 L1981 DR *050 †80
AXELROD, David Joseph. 833 CHESTNUT ST, STE 701 19107 #041-12-2000 L2003 IM *020 †20
AXELROD, Peter. 3401 N BROAD ST 19140 #008-01-1980 L1982 ID IM *040 †20
AXELROD, Rita Susan. 111 S 11TH ST, 4240 GIBBON BLDG 19107 #035-19-1970 L1974 HO IM *020 †20
AXELSEN, Paul Hagen. 3620 HAMILTON WALK 19104 #026-08-1982 L1993 ID IM *020 †20
AXILROD, Andrew Chas. 3400 SPRUCE ST, 9 PENN TOWERS 19104 #038-06-1982 L1984 U *020 †95
AYACHE, Saleh. 111 S 11TH ST, GIBBON BLDG RM 8220 19107 #875-01-1988 L2006 PTH *100 †50
AYE, Khin Moe. 245 N 15TH ST, DREXEL UNIV COLL OF MED 19102 #209-01-1999 L2006 PTH *012
AYEHU, Gashu Haileyesus. ■ 19103 #048-02-2003 L2007 IM *100
AYZEN, Marsha. ■ 19103 #005-02-2006 L2006 PD *012
AZAM, Adeel Hasan. 132 S 10TH ST, UNIVERSITY HO 19107 #041-14-2005 L2005 DR *012
AZAR, Eid Elias. ■ 19102 #605-02-2000 ID *100
AZEEZ, Saleem Abdul. 2540 N FRONT ST 19133 #308-07-1982 L1986 GP EM *020 †20
AZFAR, Rahat Syed. ■ 19103 #033-05-2004 L2005 D *012

AZIZ, Peter Fekri. ■ 19103 #038-40-2004 L2007 PDC *012 †55
AZIZI, Aimel. 4TH FLOOR - S TOWER MAIL, DREXEL UNIVERSITY COLLEGE 19102 #422-01-2007 L2007 IM *012
AZIZI, Sayed Ausim. 3401 N BROAD ST STE C525, PARKINSON PAVILION 19140 #048-12-1990 L1994 N *020 †75
AZRILEVICH, Mikhail Iosif. 9331 OLD BUSTLETON AVE 19115 #913-54-1979 L1997 IM *020 †20
BAANG, Ji Hoon. 3401 N BROAD ST, TEMPLE UNIVERSITY HOSPITAL 19140 #583-01-2002 L2005 IM *012
BABALOLA, Adeniyi C. 3401 N BROAD ST, TEMPLE UNIVERSITY HOSPITAL 19140 #016-42-2001 L2006 IM *020
BABARIA, Ashokkumar R. 3509 N BROAD ST, 2ND FL 19140 #495-22-1976 L1983 DR RNR *020 ‡
BABARIA, Usha Ashok. 245 N 15TH ST 19102 #495-23-1971 L1977 RO *020 †80 ‡
BACCASH, Patricia Denise. 230 N BROAD ST 19102 #041-07-1978 L1979 IM EM *020 †20,16
BACHARACH, Benjamin. 1025 WALNUT ST # 116, JEFFERSON MEDICAL COLLEGE 19107 #041-02-1956 L1957 TS GS *071 †85
BACHHUBER, Marcus Alexand. ■ 19146 #041-01-2008 *012
BACHMAN, Sara Beth. ■ 19129 #025-07-2004 L2004 IM *100
BACKUP, Clifford Eliott. 4641 ROOSEVELT BLVD 19124 #050-02-1945 L1958 P *075 †75
BADAKI, Oluwakemi Bukola. ■ 19131 #067-01-2002 L2005 PEM *012 †55
BADALA, Federico. 840 WALNUT ST, WILLS EYE HOSPITAL 19107 #561-04-2000 L2005 *100
BADAR, Asma. 1200 W TABOR RD, ALBERT EINSTEIN MED CTR 19141 #704-16-1992 L2002 PYG *012 †75
BADAWY, Amr Hassan Mohamm. 2900 W QUEEN LN, MCP HAHNEMANN UNIV 19129 #915-02-1989 L2000 APM *100 †05
BADER, Stephen Oliver. 111 S 11TH ST, DEPT OF ANESTHESIOLOGY 19107 #041-02-2002 L2002 AN *100 †05
BADER, Thomas James. 3400 SPRUCE ST 19104 #010-02-1989 L1991 OBG *050 †30
BADGIO, Daphne M. 5803 KINGSESSING AVE, HEALTH ANX FRNCS MYRS RCRT 19143 #041-15-1999 L2002 FM *020 †18
BADKERHANIAN, Henrick. 27 E MT AIRY AVE 19119 #517-05-1977 L1987 P *020 †75
BAEK, Jennie Hyojin. ■ 19106 #032-01-2007 L2007 GS *012
BAER, Alisa Judith. ■ 19103 #035-19-2006 L2006 PD *012
BAER, Harry Max. 2701 HOLME AVE, STE 101 19152 #041-13-1984 L1985 GS *020 †95
BAER, Heidi Alexandra. 3300 HENRY AVE, OF HLTH SCI 19129 #041-15-2007 L2007 EM *012
BAER, Jesse Duncan. 2900 W QUEEN LN, MCP HAHNEMAN SCH OF MED P 19129 #041-15-2004 EM *012
BAEZ-ESCUDERO, Jose Luis. 3401 N BROAD ST, TEMPLE UNIV HOSP 19140 #319-07-2001 L2002 CD *012 †20
BAEZ SOCORRO, Virginia Ma. 5501 OLD YORK RD 19141 #935-01-2003 L2006 PD *012
BAGAMERI, Gabor. ■ 19127 #473-01-1999 L2003 GS *012
BAGHERI, Baharak. 2900 W QUEEN LN 19129 #517-01-1987 L2001 DR *100 †80
BAGHIAN, Sepideh. 3400 SPRUCE ST, HOSPITAL OF UNIVERSITY OF 19104 #021-05-2000 L2001 HS *100
BAGLA, Ritu. ■ 19147 #422-01-2002 L2002 CN *012
BAGLEY, Demetrius H, Jr. 1025 WALNUT ST, DEPT OF UROLOGY RM 1115 19107 #023-07-1970 L1983 U *020 †95 ‡
BAGLEY, Linda Jane. 3400 SPRUCE ST 19104 #041-01-1990 L1993 DR *020 †80
BAGSHAW, Roger James. 3400 SPRUCE ST 19104 #917-19-1963 L1969 AN *050 †05
BAHIRWANI, Ranjeeta Rames. ■ 19104 #016-06-2005 L2005 IM *012
BAHNA, Heidi. ■ 19102 #035-09-2004 L2004 GS *012
BAHREMAND, Manijeh. 2840 W DAUPHIN ST, STRAWBERRY MANSION HEALTH 19132 #517-01-1979 L1993 IM *012 †20
BAI, Jean Young. 8220 CASTOR AVE 19152 #905-02-2001 L2003 CHP *020
BAILEY, Edward David. 3401 N BROAD ST, 10TH FL 19140 #023-01-1995 L1998 EM *020 †16
BAILEY, Heatherlee. 230 N BROAD ST 19102 #033-05-1994 L1996 EM *020 †16
BAILEY, L Charles. 1 CHILDRENS CTR 19104 #041-01-1998 L2001 PHO *012
BAILEY, Patricia M. 8815 GERMANTOWN AVE STE 20 19118 #024-16-1980 L1982 GS *020 †85
BAIME, Michael Jay. 423 GUARDIAN DR, 1138 BLOCKLEY HALL 19104 #041-01-1981 L1982 IM IMG *020 †20
BAIME, Regina V. 3701 MARKET ST 7TH FL, PENN FACULTY PRACTICE 19104 #041-01-1989 L1992 IM *020 †20
BAIRD, Marilyn Angeli. ■ 19118 #033-05-2007 L2007 PTH *012
BAIRD, Matthew Bruce. ■ 19151 #032-01-2006 L2006 EM *012
BAIR-MERRITT, Megan Hayes. 3535 MARKET ST, RM 1540 19104 #036-01-2000 L2001 PD *100 †55
BAKAYA, Priya. 2900 W QUEEN LN 19129 #495-45-2005 L2006 IM *100
BAKER, Chandra Mia. 3400 SPRUCE ST, DEPT RAD 19104 #010-02-2002 L2007 VIR *012 †80
BAKER, Howard Scott. 1420 WALNUT ST STE 1412 19102 #056-05-1965 L1967 P *020 †75
BAKER, Jaclyn Aileen. 3401 N BROAD ST, TEMPLE UNIV HOSP 19140 #041-13-2003 L2006 ID *012 †20
BAKER, Katherine Rotondo. ■ 19123 #041-15-2008 *012
BAKER, Lauren E. ■ 19128 #041-77-2007, ▲ IM *012
BAKER, Lester. 324 S 34TH ST 19104 #035-01-1959 L1960 DIA PDE *071 †55
BAKER, Paul Scott. 840 WALNUT ST, WILLS EYE HOSP 19107 #035-20-2005 L2006 OPH *012
BAKER, Richard Arthur. 1025 WALNUT ST # 310 19107 #049-01-1956 L1979 OBG *040 †30
BAKHRU, Prashant Thakur. ■ 19144 #041-15-2008 *012
BAKHRU, Vikram Deepak. ■ 19107 #010-01-2005 L2005 GS *012
BAKHSHI, Manavendra. 100 E LEHIGH AVE 19125 #041-15-1976 L1994 CD IM *020 †20
BAKHSH TEHRANI, Fereidoun. 6521 FRANKFORD AVE 19135 #517-01-1976 L1981 FM FPG *020 †18 ‡
BAKOVIC, Vjera Maritza. 32 W BELLS MILL RD 19118 #231-03-1964 L1998 IM END *020
BAKSHI, Kinnari Kalind. 7601 CASTOR AVE, STE 204 19152 #496-38-1969 L1980 OPH EM *020
BALA, Rupa. 3400 SPRUCE ST 19104 #010-02-1998 L2001 ICE *100 †20
BALABAN, Joan. ■ 19119 #016-42-1977 L1987 PD *020
BALAICUIS, John Martin. ■ 19118 #041-02-2002 L2002 SME P *100
BALAMUTH, Frances B. ■ 19104 #008-01-2005 L2005 PD *012
BALAMUTH, Naomi Jill. ■ 19104 #008-01-2002 L2002 PHO *012 †55
BALANDRA, Arturo. ■ 19147 #041-01-2006 L2006 U *012
BALASUNDARAM, Anusuya. 908 SPRUCE ST 19107 #033-06-2001 L2005 P *020
BALAZICH, Elizabeth Ellen. ■ 19147 #035-15-2007 L2007 EM *012
BALBUS, Theodore G. 12000 BUSTLETON AVE 19116 #041-09-1950 L1952 R *071
BALCER, Laura J. 3400 SPRUCE ST 19104 #023-07-1991 L1993 N *020 †75
BALCHANDANI, Rajkumari. 3401 N BROAD ST 19140 #748-02-1972 L1975 DR *020
BALDASSANO, Claudia F. 3535 MARKET ST FL 2 19104 #041-14-1991 L1991 P N *020 †75

BALDASSARRE, James S. 3300 HENRY AVE 19129 #035-08-1986 L1987 **IM ID** *050 †20

BALES, Christina B. ■ 19104 #041-01-2002 L2002 **PG** *012

BALESTRA, Ricardo Ramon. 5401 OLD YORK RD, KLEIN 363 19141 #132-01-2004 L2007 **IM** *012

BALIN, Benjamin R. 19106 #041-02-1944 L1944 **GP** *072

BALITAAN, Emerito B. ■ 19152 #748-01-1955 L1977 **GP IM** *071

BALL, William Austin. 3400 SPRUCE ST, CLINICAL PRACTICES UNIV PA 19104 #041-01-1983 L1984 **P** *020 †75

BALLANTINE, Allison. 324.S 34TH ST 19104 #041-14-1998 L2000 **PD** *020 †55

BALLARD, Elise C. ■ 19129 #041-15-2008 *012

BALLAS, Christos Angelos. 3535 MARKET ST, FL 2 19104 #041-02-1996 L1999 **P** *020

BALLAS, Paul Angelos. ■ 19131 #041-77-2004, ▲ L2004 **CHP** *012

BALLAS, Samir Khamis. 1015 WALNUT ST, CARDEZA FOUNDATION 19107 #605-01-1967 L1975 **IM HEM** *050 †20 ‡

BALLESTEROS, Juan R. ■ 19130 #715-01-1987 L1995 **NPM** *020 †55

BALLS, Kent Franke. ■ 19151 #035-20-1947 L1949 **END IM** *071 †20

BALLWEG, Jean Ann. ■ 19128 #056-06-1998 L2004 **PDC** *100 †55

BALOCH, Zubair. 3400 SPRUCE ST, DEPT OF PATHOLGY & LB MDCN 19104 #704-08-1985 L1994 **PTH** *050 †50

BALOGUN, Evelyn Kemi. 3401 N BROAD ST 19140 #041-02-1999 L2003 **GPM** *020 †20,70

BALSARA, Gulnar Rohinton. 3300 HENRY AVE, DEPT OF PATHOLOGY 19129 #495-04-1971 L1974 **PTH** *020 †50

BALTAROWICH, Oksana H. 111 S 11TH ST, 3350 GIBBON BLDG 19107 #025-07-1976 L1980 **DR OS** *040 †80 ‡

BALTUCH, Gordon Hirsh. 3400 SPRUCE ST, 5TH FLR SILVERSTEIN BLDG 19104 #067-01-1986 L1996 **NS** *020 †25

BALTZELL, William H. 19118 #041-02-1946 L1949 **OTO** *071 †45

BALUARTE GUEVARA, Jorge H. 324 S 34TH ST, CHILDRENS HOSP 19104 #737-01-1965 L1973 **NEP PD** *040 †55

BALZER, Naomi Susanne. 333 COTTMAN AVE, FOXCHASE CANCER CTR 19111 #038-44-1985 L1986 **HEM ON** *020 †20

BAMBA, Vaneeta. 324 S 34TH ST 19104 #021-05-2000 L2003 **PD** *020 †55

BAMFORD, Laura Phillips. 3400 SPRUCE ST STE E, HOSP OF UNIV OF PENNSYLVAN 19104 #041-02-2002 L2005 **IM ID** *050 †20

BANAN, Gity H. 3333 N BROAD ST #517-05-1959 L1971 **PD FOP** *071 †55

BANCROFT, Ursula Faye. 3996 RED LION RD #041-07-1982 L1984 **IM** *020 †20

BAND, Richard Louis. ■ 19106 #035-08-1971 L1980 **ORS** *020

BAND, Roger Allen. 3400 SPRUCE ST, EMERGENCY MED/GROUND RAVDI 19104 #041-02-2001 L2001 **EM** *100 †16

BANDI, Gaurav. 111 S 11TH ST STE 1200, UROLOGY 19107 #495-20-2000 L2007 **U** *100

BANDI, Subramanya Someswa. 245 N 15TH ST, DREXEL UNIV COLL MED/HAHNE 19102 #495-11-1997 L2006 **AN** *012

BANDINI, Paul Jos. 3401 N BROAD ST, 8TH FL 19104 #041-09-1975 L1976 **GE IM** *020 †20

BANERJEE, Arnob. 3400 SPRUCE ST, PENN TOWER 16 19104 #035-01-2002 L2002 **HO** *012 †20

BANGA, Amit. 245 N 15TH ST, DREXEL UNIV COLL MED/HAHNE 19102 #495-34-1997 L2005 **IM** *100

BANINO, Robyn B. ■ 19138 #033-05-2005 L2005 **OBG** *012

BANK, William J. 3400 SPRUCE ST, HOSP V OF PA 19104 #005-02-1960 L1968 **N** *020

BANKA, Reena. 2101 BRIGHTON ST, NEUROLOGY & EMG 19149 #495-03-1967 L1975 **N** *020

BANKA, Sahil Sagar. ■ 19128 #010-03-2003 L2007 **OBG** *012

BANKA, Vidya Sagar. 301 S 8TH ST, STE 2B 19106 #495-03-1965 L1973 **CD IM** *020 †20

BANKOV, Aleksandr B. ■ 19154 #913-81-1984 L2001 **AN** *020 †05 ‡

BANKOWITZ, Richard A. ■ 19104 #016-02-1983 L1984 **OS IM** *050 †20

BANKS, Caroline Amber. ■ 19103 #041-01-2008 *012

BANKS, Michael C. 3400 SPRUCE ST, HUP/ DEPT OF ANESTHESIA 19104 #041-12-1997 L2005 **AN** *020 †05

BANNAN, Amr Talal. ■ 19103 #797-02-1999 L2007 **CD** *012

BANNER, David Warren. 3550 MARKET ST, FL 4 19104 #035-46-1995 L2002 **PD** *020 †55

BANNER, Marc Perry. 3400 SPRUCE ST, HOSP OF THE UNIV OF PA 19104 #041-02-1971 L1972 **DR** *040 †80

BANNER, Ronald Stuart. 2050 WELSH RD 19115 #041-01-1967 L1969 **IM P** *020 †20

BANNETT, Aaron David. 5401 OLD YORK RD, KLEIN BLDG STE 505 19141 #041-02-1946 L1947 **TS GS** *071 †85

BANNON, Erin. 833 CHESTNUT ST, STE 300 19107 #041-02-2000 L2003 **PD** *020 †55

BANOV, David Wm. ■ 19119 #016-11-1976 L1978 **AN** *020 †05

BANSAL, Saurabh. ■ 19107 #038-06-2005 L2005 **IM** *012

BANTOM, Walter E, III. 5615 W GIRARD AVE 19131 #041-13-1981 L1989 **IM OS** *020

BAPTISTE, Justina Wavle. 3400 SPRUCE ST, DEPT OF ANESTHESIA 19104 #041-07-1996 L1999 **AN** *020

BAPTISTE, Vanessa. ■ 19107 #041-02-2008 *012

BAR, Allen Herbert. 301 S 8TH ST, STE 4A 19106 #024-07-1967 L1968 **GS** *020 †85

BARAHIMI, Behin. 5501 OLD YORK RD, A WINSTEIN MED CTR 19141 #047-05-2007 L2007 **TY** *012

BARAN, Ernest Michael. 2601 HOLME AVE 19152 #041-13-1967 L1969 **PM OS** *020 †60

BARANOV, Dimitry Y. 3400 SPRUCE ST 19104 #913-02-1984 L1998 **GS** *012

BARASH, Joshua Hershel. 833 CHESTNUT ST, STE 301 19107 #038-06-1996 L1998 **FM** *020 †18

BARATZ, Burton. KNIGHT & RED LION RD 19114 #041-09-1954 L1955 **OBG** *071 †30

BARATZ, Michael D. ■ 19107 #041-02-2008 *012

BARBE, Maria E. 100 E LEHIGH AVE, FL 3 19125 #035-03-1994 L1999 **OPH PO** *020 †35

BARBER, Lee A. 3300 HENRY AVE, MEDICAL COLLGE OF PNNSYLVN 19129 #041-07-1977 L1978 **IM** *020 †20

BARBETTA, Stephanie. 3401 N BROAD ST, DEPT OF EMERG MED 19140 #041-15-1999 L2000 **FM EM** *020 †18

BARBOUR, Joseph Pius, Jr. 3400 SPRUCE ST 19104 #047-07-1946 L1947 **GP P** *075

BARCHI, Robert Lawrence. 1020 WALNUT ST RM 641, OFFICE OF THE PRESIDENT 19107 #041-01-1973 L1974 **N** *050 †75

BARCLAY, David Moore, III. 3400 N BROAD ST, 2ND FLR CANCER CTR 19140 #021-01-1988 L1997 **FM** *020 †18

BARDEN-MAJA, Yvonne A. 3400 SPRUCE ST 19104 #008-01-1993 L1997 **IM** *020 †20

BAREN, Jill Marjorie. 324 S 34TH ST 19104 #041-12-1989 L1997 **EM PEM** *020 †16

BARG, Ronald Bruce. 3400 SPRUCE ST 19104 #041-01-1980 L1981 **MDM IM** *030 †20

BARGE, Rosa Isabel. 3401 N BROAD ST, DEPT OF ANESTHESIOLOGY 19140 #033-06-1979 L1986 **AN IM** *020 †20,05

BARHAM, Kalleen Stacy-Ann. 5501 OLD YORK RD, DEPT MED KLEIN 3 19141 #566-01-1999 L2003 **END** *012 †20,55

BARI, Merle Mindy. 3400 SPRUCE ST, 2 RHOADS PAVILION 19104 #041-07-1986 L1987 **D** *020 †15

BARILE, David Robert. 3300 HENRY AVE, MEDICAL COLLEGE OF PENNA 19129 #051-07-1995 L2001 **IMG** *020 †20

BARKER, Clyde Frederick. 3400 SPRUCE ST, FL 4 19104 #035-20-1958 L1964 **VS** *030 †85

BARLOW, Robert A, Jr. 800 W MONTGOMERY AVE, 1ST FL 19122 #050-02-1982 L1983 **OM** *020

BARMACH, Kenneth Robt. 211 S 9TH ST, STE 401 19107 #041-02-1973 L1974 **IM IMG** *020 †20

BARNABY, Arthur Jos, Jr. 2701 HOLME AVE, STE 104 19152 #561-01-1977 L1980 **GS VS** *020 †85

BARNATHAN, Elliot Stephen. 34TH & CIVIC CENTER BLVD 19104 #041-01-1981 L1982 **CD IM** *050 †20

BARNES, Anne Utley. 3996 RED LION RD 19114 #047-05-1955 L1964 **GS** *071 †85

BARNES, James Utley. 5000 FRANKFORD AVE 19104 #041-15-2000 L2001 **IM** *020 †20

BARNES, Michael Thomas. 3401 N BROAD ST, OF SURGE 19140 #005-06-2007 L2007 **GS** *012

BARNETT, Frederic J. 51 N 39TH ST, PRESBYTERIAN HOSPITAL 19104 #035-46-1961 L1984 **DR LM** *020 †20

BARNETT, Kara Michelle. ■ 19102 #028-02-2005 L2005 **AN** *012

BARNETT, Rebecca Ann. 3400 SPRUCE ST 19104 #775-01-1987 L1999 **AN** *020 †05

BARNETTE, Rodger Edward. 3400 N BROAD ST, DEPT AN 19140 #041-13-1979 L1980 **AN CCA** *020 †20,05

BARNEY, Romano. 5043 N 5TH ST 19120 #264-01-1946 L1969 **GP FM** *075

BARNHART, Kurt Thos. 3701 MARKET ST, 8TH FL 19104 #035-47-1988 L1991 **OBG** *020 †30

BARODKA, Viachaslau Mikal. ■ 19107 #913-32-2000 L2005 **AN** *012

BARON, David A. 100 E LEHIGH AVE, MAB STE 305 19125 #041-77-1978, ▲ L1979 **P CHP** *030 †75

BARON, Richard James. 345 E MT AIRY AVE 19119 #008-01-1978 L1984 **IM IMG** *020 †20

BARONE, Amy Kathleen. ■ 19107 #038-41-2007 L2007 **PD** *012

BAROUH, Adam Daniel. 245 N 15TH ST, HANNEMANN 19102 #041-15-2003 L2003 **PE** *012 †55

BARR, Frederic Glenn. 3400 SPRUCE ST, 6 FOUNDERS/PATH 19104 #028-02-1987 L1989 **PTH** *050 †50

BARR, Harry Jos. 3400 N BROAD ST, DEPT OF RADIO TEMPLE UNIV 19140 #010-02-1961 L1965 **R NM** *040 †80,28 ‡

BARRETT, David Maxwell. ■ 19146 #051-04-2004 L2004 **PHO** *012 †55

BARRETT, Jeffrey Scott. 3401 N BROAD ST, TEMPLE UNI HOSP 19140 #033-06-1999 L2001 **EM** *020 †16

BARRETT, Patrick Michael. ■ 19103 #010-02-2007 L2007 **EM** *012

BARRETT, Robyn Lerner. 5501 OLD YORK RD 19141 #041-07-1985 L1986 **DR** *020 †80

BARRINGER, Lydia C R. 111 S 11TH ST, ANES DEPT TJU-FRC STE 6460 19107 #748-01-1962 L1971 **AN** *020

BARRIOCANAL, Jose Alberto. 3401 N BROAD ST, DEPT RAD 19140 #041-13-2006 L2006 **DR** *012

BARROS, Suzanna Isabelle. 3400 SPRUCE ST, DEPT OF EMERG MED/GROUND R 19104 #033-05-2003 L2003 **EM** *020

BARRY, Thomas Bernard. 3401 N BROAD ST, EMERGENCY DEPT 19140 #748-08-1981 L2003 **EM** *020 †16

BARRY, William Eugene. 3401 N BROAD ST 19140 #035-09-1954 L1961 **HEM IM** *071 †20

BARRY-THURMOND, Carlita D. NICHOLS HOUSE RM 11-6 19104 #035-19-1977 **GS P** *100

BARSOTTI, Benjamin Bruno. 111 S 11TH ST, JEFFERSON UNIVERSITY 19107 #041-02-2006 L2006 **PD** *012

BARTHOLOMAE, Julie Lynn. 4401 OLD YORK ROAD, DEPT OF PSYCH 19140 #041-77-2006, ▲ L2006 **P** *012

BARTKOWSKI, Richard Robt. 111 S 11TH ST, ANESTHESIA DEPT 19107 #011-02-1974 L1975 **AN** *020 †05

BARTLETT, Edmund King. ■ 19104 #041-01-2008 *012

BARTLETT, Scott Paul. 3400 SPRUCE ST, 10TH FL 19104 #028-02-1975 L1985 **PS** *020 †85,65

BARTOLOZZI, Arthur R, III. 800 SPRUCE ST, PENNSYLVANIA HOSPITAL 19107 #005-18-1981 L1983 **ORS** *050 †40

BARTON, Christopher David. ■ 19128 #041-13-2007 L2007 **OBG** *012

BARTON, Joel Wells. ■ 19128 #041-13-2007 L2007 **TY** *012

BARTON, Jonathan Miles. ■ 19106 #041-15-2008 *012

BARTON, Todd Daniel. 3400 SPRUCE ST, FL 3 19104 #035-45-1997 L2000 **ID** *020 †20

BARTUSKA, Doris Gorka. P3300 HENRY AVE 19129 #041-07-1954 L1955 **END IM** *071 †20

BASCARA, Daniel Cruz. 33 S 9TH ST, STE 210-C 19107 #748-16-1994 L2001 **CHP** *020 †20

BASERGA, Renato Luigi. 3401 N BROAD ST 19140 #561-03-1949 L1965 **PTH** *050 †50

BASHA, Samer Shamsi. 2301 E ALLEGHENY AVE, NORTHEASTERN HOSP 19134 #875-01-1992 L2001 **CD** *020 †20

BASIL, Biju. 4641 ROOSEVELT BLVD 19124 #495-52-1995 L2002 **P** *020

BASILE, Ellen. 2900 W QUEEN LN 19129 #041-77-2005, ▲ L2005 **AN** *012

BASSALY, Renee Marie. ■ 19128 #041-77-2003, ▲ L2003 **OBG** *012

BASTEK, Jamie Ann. 3400 SPRUCE ST, GYNECOLOGY, D 19104 #010-02-2005 L2005 **OBG** *012

BASTL, Christine Phyllis. 3400 N BROAD ST, RM 3401 19140 #038-06-1970 L1974 **NEP IM** *020 †20

BASU, Devraj. ■ 19104 #028-02-2001 L2006 **OTO** *100 †45

BATISTE, Corey Gregory. 840 WALNUT ST, STE 1140 19107 #025-07-2002 L2006 **OPH** *100 †35

BATRA, Kiran. 245 N 15TH ST, DREXEL UNIV COLL MED/HAHNE 19102 #496-07-1997 L2004 **DR** *012

BATRA, Preet Mohini. 2268 E CLEARFIELD ST 19134 #495-12-1964 L1973 **FM** *071 †18

BATTAFARANO, Leonard A. ■ 19151 #041-09-1942 L1943 **GP** *071

BATTERTON, Thomas Davies. 1900 JFK BLVD, PENN CENTER HOUSET 19103 #017-20-1957 L1963 **IM** *071 †20 ‡

BATTLE, William Michael. 1403 RHAWN ST 19111 #041-01-1972 L1973 **IM** *020 †20 ‡

BATY, Darric Edward. BROAD-ONTARIO STS 19140 #017-20-2002 L2002 **NS** *012

BAUGH, Wilfreta. 5519 GERMANTOWN AVE 19144 #041-02-1979 L1981 **IM** *020 †20

BAUM, Stanley. 3400 SPRUCE ST DEPT RAD 19104 #660-04-1957 L1963 **DR** *071 †80

BAUMAN, Joel Alter. 3400 SPRUCE ST, 3RD FLOOR SILVERSTEIN PAV 19104 #035-19-2005 L2005 **NS** *012

BAUMANN, Donald Otto. ■ 19104 #661-02-2005 L2006 **AN** *012

BAUMGARDNER, James Edward. 3400 SPRUCE ST 19104 #041-01-1984 L1986 **AN** *040 †05

BAURER, Frederic Martin. 11 N 49TH ST 19139 #041-13-1984 L1985 **P ADP** *030 †75

BAUTISTA, Brigid Bonsato. 403 S 13TH ST 19147 #748-16-1985 L2000 **P** *020

BAUTISTA, Odezza Agustin. 5501 OLD YORK RD, ALBERT EINSTEIN MED CTR 19141 #748-20-2000 L2004 **P** *012

BAUTISTA OTANEZ, Felipe S. ALUMNI AFFAIRS, ALBERT EINSTEIN MC 19141 #319-07-2007 L2008 *012

BAVARIA, Joseph Edward. 3400 SPRUCE ST, FL 6 19104 #021-01-1983 L1985 **TS** *020 †85,90

BAVENDAM, Tamara Gholson. 3300 HENRY AVE, MCP HOSPITAL 19129 #018-03-1981 L1997 U *020 †95

BAXT, William Gordon. 3400 SPRUCE ST 19104 #008-01-1967 L1994 EM IM *020 †20,16

BAXTER, Eugene Earl. ■ 19141 #010-03-1956 L1961 IM OS *020

BAXTER, Jason Kizer. 834 CHESTNUT ST, STE 400 19107 #048-02-1998 L2001 MFM OBG *020 †30

BAYLIS, Linell. 6100 W JEFFERSON ST, 1ST FL 19151 #041-13-1976 L1978 GS *020

BAYRLEE, Ahmad. 3401 N BROAD ST, DEPT OF INTERNAL MED 19140 #875-01-2001 L2005 N *012

BAYSAL, Ali Ihsan. 3400 N BROAD ST, DPT NEUROL 19140 #902-05-1970 N *100

BAYYA, Vijaya Veena. 1800 LOMBARD ST, TENET HEALTHSYSTEM GRADUAT 19146 #495-58-1997 L2005 IM *012

BAZARGANI, Tawoos. 2471 N 54TH ST, STE 203 19131 #517-01-1967 L1978 P *020

BAZELON, Eileen A Ferrin. 3900 CITY AVE STE 120 19131 #041-07-1970 L1972 P CHP *020 †75

BEAL, Ryan Rossi. ■ 19104 #041-01-2000 *100

BEAMS, Maggie. ■ 19107 #035-03-2005 L2005 EM *012

BEARN, Alexander Gordon. ■ 19106 #352-07-1946 L2000 IM OS *071

BEASLEY, Elizabeth Susan. ■ 19104 #041-13-1995 L1998 OBG *100

BEATIE, William Edward. 2301 E ALLEGHENY AVE, NORTHEASTERN HOSPITAL 19134 #028-02-1979 L2007 ORS *020 †40

BEATTIE, Philip. 3401 N BROAD ST, TEMPLE UNIVERSITY HOSPITAL 19140 #033-06-1997 L1999 EM *020 †16

BEATTY, Gregory Lawrence. ■ 19106 #041-01-2004 L2004 HO *012 †20

BEAVER, Andrew Bradley. 5501 OLD YORK RD 19141 #041-02-2004 L2005 ORS *012

BEAVER, Kathleen Mae. 1800 LOMBARD ST 19146 #041-07-1982 L1983 IM *020 †20

BECK, Agustus Alexander. 245 N 15TH ST, MAILSTOP 470 19102 #038-06-2003 L2005 CD *012 †20

BECKER, Alyssa Sue. 132 S 10TH ST, DIV OF CLINICAL PHARMACOLO 19107 #041-02-1995 L1997 IM PA *050 †20

BECKER, Daniel Grant. 272 S 2ND ST 19106 #051-01-1990 L1996 GS *020 †45

BECKER, Daniel Martin. 3400 SPRUCE ST 19104 #005-11-1987 L1987 P *100

BECKER, Julia Beth. ■ 19106 #025-01-2005 L2005 IM *012

BECKER, Lance Bart. 3400 SPRUCE ST, HUP / DEPARTMENT OF EMERGE 19104 #016-11-1980 L2006 EM IM *020 †20,16

BECKER, Madeleine Anne. 272 S 2ND ST 19106 #041-02-2002 L2002 P *020

BECKER, William Clark. 1601 KATER ST 19146 #041-13-2001 L2002 IM *020

BECKETT, Sibyl Beatrice. 2 PENN BLVD STE 112 19144 #041-07-1963 L1964 FM IM *072

BECKFORD, Tamara Shakari. 111 S 11TH ST, DEPT EM 19107 #033-05-2007 L2007 EM *012

BECKMANN, Charles R B. 5501 OLD YORK RD, ALBERT EINSTEIN MEDICAL CE 19141 #028-03-1975 L2001 OBG OS *040 †30

BECKWITH, Joan C Travis. 131 E CHELTEN AVE, HEALTH 19144 #041-13-1976 L1977 HEM IM *050 †20

BEDI, Sarabjit Singh. 501 S 54TH ST, DEPT OF ANESTHESIOLOGY 19143 #496-09-1997 L2004 AN *100 †105

BEDRICK, Edward Lawrence. 7500 CENTRAL AVE, STE 104 19111 #024-05-1979 L1981 IM *020 †20

BEDRICK, Jeffrey David. 255 S 17TH ST STE 1905 19103 #041-01-1986 L1992 P ADP *020 †75

BEDROSIAN, Jeffrey Carnig. ■ 19129 #041-01-2006 L2006 OTO *012

BEG, Mirza M A. 39TH & MARKET ST 19104 #704-02-1955 L1974 IM CD *071 ‡

BEGUM, Khurshid Ara. 245 N 15TH ST, MCP HAHNEMANN UNIV 19102 #160-02-1976 L2004 P *100

BEHAN, Katherine Anne. 255 S 17TH ST 19103 #041-15-2001 L2001 IM *020

BEHAR, Robert David. 1703 S BROAD ST, PHILADELPHIA EYE ASSOCIATE 19148 #041-01-1978 L1979 OPH *020 †35

BEHLING, Eric Max. 111 S 11TH ST, SUITE 301 PAVILLION BLDG 19107 #041-02-2000 L2001 HMP ATP *040 †50

BEHLING, Kathryn Celenza. ■ 19107 #041-01-2004 L2007 PTH *012

BEHRMAN, Amy Jane. 3400 SPRUCE ST, OCCUPATIONAL MEDICINE 19104 #041-01-1984 L1986 IM OM *030 †20

BEIGHT, John Lawton. 7500 CENTRAL AVE, STE 108 19111 #010-02-1986 L1987 ORS *020 †40

BEKERIS, Leonas Gediminas. 3400 SPRUCE ST, 7.018 FOUNDERS PAVILION 19104 #264-04-1972 L1996 CLP PTH *020 †50

BELASCO, Jennifer Lerner. 225 S 18TH ST 19103 #048-13-2003 L2003 PPR *012 †55

BELAY, Jeannie Alexandra. 225 S COBBS CREEK PKWY 19139 #035-47-2000 L2005 PD *020 †55

BELAZI, Misa Taher. ■ 19106 #024-05-2005 L2005 OBG *012

BELDEN, Katherine C. 111 S 11TH ST, STE G4250 19107 #041-02-1997 L1999 ID *020 †20

BELL, George Stuart. 5501 OLD YORK RD, DEPARTMENT OF PSYCHIATRY 19141 #041-02-1968 L1969 P *020 †75 ‡

BELL, Jason. 3300 HENRY AVE, ALLEGHENY UNIV OF HLTH SCI 19129 #041-15-2002 L2002 EM *100 †16

BELL, Joanna Danni. 1427 VINE ST 5TH FL 19102 #041-15-2001 L2005 MPD *012

BELL, John Craig. 3300 HENRY AVE, MEDICAL COLLGE OF PNNSYLVN 19129 #041-01-1967 L1968 N IM *020

BELL, Louis M, Jr. 324 S 34TH ST 19104 #023-01-1980 L1981 PD PDI *020 †55

BELL, Richard Henry, Jr. 1617 JFK BLVD STE 860, AMERICAN BOARD OF SURGERY 19103 #016-06-1971 L1975 GS *030 †85

BELL, Rodney Donald. 1025 WALNUT ST, STE 310 19107 #040-02-1972 L1985 N IM *040 †20,75

BELL, Steven Dean. 111 S 11TH ST, STE 8490 19107 #039-01-1975 L1984 AN OS *020 †05

BELLAH, Richard David. 324 S 34TH ST, CHILDRENS HOSP PA DEPT RAD 19104 #045-01-1979 L1988 PDR *020 †80,55

BELL-CHEDDAR, Yolandee Re. 5501 OLD YORK RD 19141 #566-01-1997 L2006 PD *012

BELL-HIBBS, Anna Kerlin. ■ 19104 #041-15-2007 L2007 OBG *012

BELLIN, Harvey Jay. 2301 S BROAD ST, DEPT PATH 19148 #041-02-1965 L1967 PTH PCP *020 †50

BELLINI, Lisa Maria. 3400 SPRUCE ST, 100 CENTREX 19104 #001-02-1990 L1992 PCC *020 †20

BELLOWS, Jillan Marie. ■ 19147 #041-77-2007, ▲ L2007 IM *012

BELMONT, Jonathan Bruce. 840 WALNUT ST, STE 1020 19107 #041-02-1976 L1978 OPH OS *020 †35

BELSKY, Andrei. ■ 19154 #913-04-1990 L2000 AN *020 †05

BELTINGER, Christian P. CHILDS HOSP PF PA 19104 #409-16-1985 L1993 ON *020

BELTON, Erica Monet. 4329 LANCASTER AVE 19104 #041-13-1992 L1995 IM *020 †20

BELTRAN, Luis Saura. ■ 19106 #035-09-2004 L2005 DR *012

BENACK, Andrea. 5501 OLD YORK RD 19141 #035-47-1981 L1982 AN *020 †05 ‡

BENALT, Wendi Allison. ■ 19103 #005-14-2007 L2007 *012

BENDESKY, Brad Steven. 501 S 54TH ST 19143 #033-06-1997 L1999 EM *020 †16

BENDITT, Philip L. 1717 ARCH ST, STE 2910 19103 #041-07-1978 L1979 IM MDM *030 †20

BENEDETTO, Paul Xavier. ■ 19107 #041-02-2008 *012

BENEDICT, Karl T, III. 2301 S BROAD ST, MOB #205 19148 #024-07-1994 L1996 IM *020 †20

BENFIELD, Thomas Chas. 10015 CHESTNUT ST, STE 1013 19107 #041-02-1977 L1978 P PYA *020 †75 ‡

BENITO-HERRERO, Maria I. 415 CURIE BLVD, 778 CRB 19104 #847-16-1993 L2000 END IM *071 †20

BENJACOB, Talia Kate. ■ 19107 #050-02-2007 GS *012

BENJAMIN, Alex Navarro. 245 N 15TH ST, DEPT ID 19102 #010-01-2004 L2004 ID *012

BENJAMIN, Ivor. 1515 LOCUST ST, 8TH FL 19102 #035-01-1987 L2009 GO OBG *020 †30

BENJAMIN, Joe. 3401 N BROAD ST, 6TH FL PARKINSON PAVLN 19140 #495-20-1973 L1980 NEP IM *020 †20

BENJAMIN, Mark. 9501 ROOSEVELT BLVD, STE 208 19114 #056-06-1977 L1982 PUD IM *020 †20

BENNETT, Amanda Erin. 111 S 11TH ST, JEFFERSON UNIVERSITY 19107 #055-02-2002 L2002 DBP *012 †55

BENNETT, Andrea Lynn. ■ 19103 #028-02-2005 L2005 PD *012

BENNETT, Joel Steven. 421 CURIE BLVD, 914 19104 #025-01-1967 L1968 HEM ON *050 †20

BENNETT, Richard H. 5401 OLD YORK RD, KLEIN BLDG STE 405 19141 #041-02-1975 L1976 N *020 †75

BENNETT, William Wilson. ■ 19119 #056-06-1975 L1976 PM *020

BENNOV, Benjamin. 10125 VERREE RD STE 101, VERREE RD PROF BLVD 19116 #913-19-1974 L1987 IM *020 †20

BENO, Suzanne Marie. 324 S 34TH ST 19104 #068-01-1999 L2001 PEM *100 †55

BENSON, Esther. 7439 FRANKFORD AVE 19136 #033-06-1996 L1999 FM *020 †18

BENTON, Tami Dianne. 3440 MARKET ST 2ND FL, CHOP BEHAVIORAL HEALTH CTR 19104 #038-40-1989 L1998 P *020 †55,75

BENZAQUEN WAHNICH, Sadia. 5401 OLD YORK RD, KLEIN 363 19141 #935-01-1998 L2003 PCC *012 †20

BERBA, Regina P. ■ 19129 #748-02-1987 L1993 IM *020 †20

BERD, David Allen. 1015 WALNUT ST STE 1024, THOMAS JEFFERSON UNIV 19107 #041-02-1968 L1969 IM *020 †20

BERDICHEVSKAYA, Violetta. 2614 WOODWARD ST 19152 #913-08-1988 L2001 IM *020 †20

BEREDJIKLIAN, Pedro K. 3400 SPRUCE ST, 2 SILVERSTEIN PAVILION 19104 #035-01-1992 L1994 HS *020 †40

BERENSON, Zoya. 10890 BUSTLETON AVE, STE 103 19116 #913-94-1976 L1995 IM *020 †20

BERG, Alan Paul. 1 PENN BLVD, HOME VISIT DOCTORS #3026 19144 #041-07-1980 L1982 IMG *020 †20

BERG, Dale Daniel. 125 S 9TH ST, STE 502 19107 #056-06-1986 L2001 IM *020 †20

BERG, David Adam. 3401 N BROAD ST, TEMPLE UNIV HOSP 19140 #024-07-2001 L2001 GS *012

BERG, Laura Christine. 3400 SPRUCE ST, UNIV OF PENNSYLVANIA 19104 #032-01-2004 GE *012

BERG, Sigrid Eva. 3400 SPRUCE ST, 510 MALONEY BUILDING 19104 #036-07-2002 L2005 HO *012

BERGANT, Jennifer Marie. ■ 19146 #020-02-2004 L2005 ORS *012

BERGELSON, Jeffrey M. 3400 SPRUCE ST 19104 #041-01-1981 L1997 ID PD *050 †55

BERGELSON, Victor D. 2301 E ALLEGHENY AVE 19134 #041-09-1950 L1951 R *071 †80

BERGER, Adam Craig. 1100 WALNUT ST, MOB SUITE 500 19107 #035-19-1995 L2002 GS *020 †85

BERGER, Andrea Angelique. 255 S 17TH ST, STE 1700 19103 #035-45-1998 L2000 CD *100 †20

BERGER, Bruce Alan. 1335 W TABOR RD, STE 206 19141 #041-02-1970 L1971 OBG *020 †30

BERGER, Carl. 822 PINE ST, STE 4B 19107 #041-01-1962 L1964 P *020 †75

BERGER, Eric David. 3998 RED LION RD, STE 215 19114 #047-05-1994 L1998 PD *020 †55

BERGER, Henry Grant. 2401 PENNSYLVANIA AVE, STE 1A4 19130 #041-01-1969 L1970 CHP P †75

BERGER, Mark David. 230 W WASHINGTON SQ, FL 3 19106 #011-02-1983 L1984 CD *020 †20

BERGER, Mark Stanley. 3400 SPRUCE ST 19104 #051-01-1980 L1981 ON HEM *050 †20

BERGER, Simon Melvin. 1 PENN BLVD, GERMANTON HOSP & MED CTR 19144 #041-02-1938 L1949 DR *071 †80

BERGER, Stanley Randolph. 5249 CEDAR AVE 19143 #041-01-1988 L1990 CD IM *020 †20

BERGEY, Philip David. 422 CURIE BLVD, B1 STELLAR-CHANCE LABS 19104 #041-01-1983 L1989 DR *020 †80 ‡

BERGHELLA, Vincenzo. 834 CHESTNUT ST STE 400 19107 #041-02-1990 L1994 OBG MFM *020 †30 ‡

BERGHER, Daniel. ■ 19149 #041-13-1988 *100

BERGHER, Moises. ■ 19149 #935-01-1950 L1966 CHP P *071

BERGIN, Diane. 111 S 11TH ST, 3350 GIBBON BLDG 19107 #539-04-1993 L2001 *020

BERGMAN, Erik William. ■ 19104 #023-12-1994 L2007 RNR *012 †80

BERGMAN, Herbert Morris. 8410 ROOSEVELT BLVD 19152 #041-09-1970 L1971 IM IMG *020

BERGQVIST, Christina A. 324 S 34TH ST 19104 #041-13-1992 L1995 CHN *020 †75

BERKO, Barbara Ann. 925 CHESTNUT ST, JEFFERSON HEART INST 19107 #024-07-1977 L1985 CD IM *020 †20

BERKOWITZ, Arnold. 668 PARLIN ST 19116 #041-01-1979 L1980 NM *100 †28

BERKOWITZ, Henry David. 5401 OLD YORK RD, KLEIN BUILDING SUITE 206 19141 #041-01-1963 L1965 VS GS *020 †85

BERKOWITZ, Karen M. 3400 SPRUCE ST, GENERAL OBSTETRICS/GYNECLG 19104 #035-46-1993 L1997 OBG *020 †30

BERKOWITZ, Robert Ira. 3535 MARKET ST STE 3026, UNIV OF PENNSYLVANIA 19104 #008-02-1973 L1990 CHP P *020 †75

BERKWITS, Michael. 190 N INDEPENDENCE MALL W 19106 #016-11-1990 L1993 IM *062 †20

BERLIN, Christopher Jack. ■ 19147 #016-06-2005 L2005 IM *012

BERLINERBLAU, Michele M. 325 CHESTNUT ST, STE 905 19106 #305-01-1986 L1987 P *020 †75

BERLINGER, William G, III. 2126 FAIRMOUNT AVE, PRIMARY CARE ADULT -MCP 19130 #041-01-1979 L1998 IMG IM *020 †20

BERMAN, David Benjamin. 800 SPRUCE ST, SOCIETY HILL ANESTHESIA CO 19107 #035-03-2001 L2005 AN *020 †20

BERMAN, Micah Avner. ■ 19146 #041-01-2008 *012

BERMAN, Natalya. ■ 19103 #033-06-2006 L2007 DR *012

BERMAN, Peter Henry. 1 CHILDRENS CTR, CHILDREN'S HOSPITAL 19104 #035-19-1957 L1969 CHN *020 †55,75

BERMAN, Richard Alan. 111 S 11TH ST 19107 #041-12-1970 L1985 IM AN *020 †20,05

BERMAN, Tara Jill. 237 N BREAD ST, APT 2 19106 #041-02-2000 L2003 PD *020 †55 ‡

BERMUDEZ, Dustin Miguel. 3400 SPRUCE ST, OF PENNSYLVAN 19104 #005-11-2005 L2005 GS *012

BERMUDEZ WAGNER, Karla Ma. 3401 N BROAD ST, TEMPLE UNIVERSITY HOSPITAL 19140 #935-01-1996 L2005 OBG *012

BERNAL, William Enrique. ■ 19146 #016-06-2004 L2007 PD *100 †55

BERNARD, David Barnett. 201 S 18TH ST 19103 #836-01-1965 L1995 NEP IM *040 †20

BERNARDIN, Ronald. 3600 SPRUCE ST, HUP DERMATOLOGY 19104 #041-15-2002 D *012

BERNAS, Carlallen Diestro. ■ 19129 #041-15-2008 *012

BERNAT, Richard Alan. 925 CHESTNUT ST, FL 6 19107 #041-13-2000 L2001 OTO *45

BERNBAUM, Judy C. 3400 SPRUCE ST 19104 #041-13-1975 L1976 PD NPM *020 †55

BERNEY, Steven Nathan. 3401 N BROAD ST 19140 #035-15-1962 L1971 RHU IM *020 †20

BERNS, Jeffrey Scott. PEPPER PAVILION, STE 703 19146 #038-06-1981 L1989 NEP PN *071 †20

BERNSTEIN, David Adam. 2900 W QUEEN LN 19129 #305-01-2007 IM *012

BERNSTEIN, Deborah. 210 W RITTENHOUSE SQ 4 19103 #035-46-1991 L1997 P *020 ‡

BERNSTEIN, Joseph. 501 S 54TH ST, MERCY ORTHOPEDICS STE G-28 19143 #035-20-1990 L1992 OSM *020 †40

BERNSTEIN, S Todd. 1513 RACE ST 19102 #041-13-1984 L1985 PM IM *020 †60

BERRETTINI, Wade H. 415 CURIE BLVD DEPT PSYCH, 1 CLNC RESEARCH BLDG 19104 #041-02-1977 L1978 P *050 †75

BERRY, Gerard Thos. 1025 WALNUT ST, STE 102 19107 #041-02-1975 L1976 MG PDE *050 †55,19

BERTELSEN, Irmgard K A. 2322 SPRUCE ST 19103 #409-12-1984 L1990 P *020 †75

BESA, Emmanuel C. 125 S 9TH ST, 801 SHERIDAN BLDG. 19107 #748-02-1967 L1974 HEM ON *020

BESHARA, Mathew Nabeeh. 5 PENN CENTER PLZ, 3400 SPRUCE STREET 19103 #025-07-1997 L2000 OBG *020 †30

BESLOW, Lauren Allegra. ■ 19104 #005-11-2003 L2003 CHN *012

BEST, Kimberly R. 5501 OLD YORK RD 19141 #041-02-1978 L1980 P PYM *030 †75

BEST, Lauren Paige. 5501 OLD YORK RD 19141 #305-01-2006 L2007 EM *012

BETESH, Joel Sam. 801 SPRUCE ST 19107 #041-09-1977 L1978 IM IMG *020 †20 ‡

BETHALA, Hannah M. ■ 19126 #465-65-1974 L1989 P *012

BETTIGOLE, Cheryl Anne. 321 W GIRARD AVE, CITY HEALTH CENTER, #6 19123 #041-02-1996 L1998 FM *020 †18

BETTIKER, Robert Lloyd. 3401 N BROAD ST, TEMPLE UNIVERSITY HOSPITAL 19140 #010-02-1997 L1999 ID *020 †20

BETZ, Randal R. 3551 N BROAD ST 19140 #041-13-1977 L1978 ORS *040

BEUMONT, Maria Gloria. 1015 CHESTNUT ST, STE 610 19107 #132-01-1986 L1992 ID *020 †20

BEVERLY, Avery Walker. 5029 WOODLAND AVE 19143 #010-03-1955 L1962 R OS *071

BEWLEY, Arnaud Fassett. 3400 SPRUCE ST, DEPT OTO 19104 #035-01-2007 L2008 OTO *012

BHAGAT, Pradeep Kumar. 5800 RIDGE AVE, DEPT LAB MEDICINE 19128 #496-04-1983 L1987 PTH *020 †50

BHAMBHANI, Sumita. 3401 N BROAD ST, TEMPLE UNIVERSITY HOSPITAL 19140 #495-49-1989 L2001 AN *100 †05

BHANDARE, Prashant Shreek. ■ 19104 #047-05-2004 L2004 AN *012

BHANUSHALI, Ashok Bhanji. ■ 19131 #496-36-1997 L2006 VIR *100

BHARADWAJ, Amitabh Kant. 840 WALNUT ST, WILLS EYE HOSP RETINA SERV 19107 #024-01-2001 L2005 OPH *100

BHARADWAJ, Swati Suresh. 51 N 39TH ST, PHI 2B 19104 #496-44-1998 L2001 RHU *100

BHARGAVA, Hema Prasad. 324 S 34TH ST 19104 #495-33-1981 L1985 PDC *020 †55

BHARUCHA, Diana Xerxes. 3741 WALNUT ST, # 219 19104 #041-15-2007 L2007 PD *012

BHAT, Rekha Ramachandra. 2900 W QUEEN LN 19129 #495-01-1997 L2006 PTH *012

BHAT, Yasser Maqbool. 3400 SPRUCE ST 19104 #495-37-1998 L2003 GE *100 †20

BHATI, Mahendra Takashi. 800 SPRUCE ST 19107 #021-06-2001 L2001 P *050 †75

BHATT, Amar Bharat. ■ 19144 #041-15-2007 L2007 IM *012

BHATTACHARYA, Sangeeta. 324 S 34TH ST 19104 #023-07-1999 L1999 MPD *020 †20,55

BHATTI, Jamil Masih. 27 E MOUNT AIRY AVE 19119 #704-04-1979 L2000 P *100

BHATTI, Sarwat Ara. 5619 VINE ST 19139 #704-06-1963 L1995 OBG *020 †30

BHATTI, Tricia Renee. ■ 19106 #012-01-2002 L2005 PTH *100 †50

BHOGAL, Pamneit. ■ 19144 #041-13-2005 L2005 FP *012

BHOWMICK, Deb Ashish. 3400 SPRUCE ST, 3RD FLOOR SILVERSTEIN PAV 19104 #048-04-2004 L2004 NS *012

BIAFORA, Sam John. 19107 #016-42-2002 L2007 HSO *012

BIANCHI, Shannon Lynn. ■ 19147 #038-06-2005 L2005 IM *012

BIANROSA, John Jos. 51 N 39TH ST, PENN PRESBYTERIAL MEDICAL 19104 #035-15-1975 L1976 AN *020 †05

BIBBO, Marluce. 132 S 10TH ST, STE 285K 19107 #187-11-1964 L1992 PCP *040

BIELER, Bert Michael. ■ 19130 #041-13-2002 L2005 FM *020 †20

BIEN-AIME, Michel J. 4510 FRANKFORD AVE, SECOND FLOOR 19124 #440-01-1979 L1993 CHP P *020 †75

BIERHOFF, Mark Lester. 7901 BUSTLETON AVE STE 307 19152 #033-05-1980 L1981 GE IM *020 †20

BIERMANN, William Albert. 111 S 11TH ST STE 8214 19107 #041-02-1975 L1976 ON IM *020 †20

BIEWENGA, Eric Donald. ■ 19128 #041-15-2008 *012

BIGELOW, Douglas Chas. 3400 SPRUCE ST 19104 #026-04-1985 L1991 OTO NO *020 †45

BIGGANS, Robert Paul. 6449 RISING SUN AVE 19111 #041-13-1969 L1970 IM CD *020 †20

BIGGS, Lisa Marie. 3550 MARKET ST, FL 5 19104 #038-41-1991 L1993 PD *020 †55

BILANIUK, Larissa T. 324 S 34TH ST, CHILD HOSP OF PHIL 19104 #025-07-1965 L1967 DR RNR *040 †80

BILBOW, Alexis. ■ 19148 #041-15-2004 L2004 AN *012

BILINSKI, Slavomir Andrew. 2330 MARGARET ST 19137 #041-02-2004 L2004 FM *100

BILLER, Christina Gabriel. ■ 19127 #041-13-2004 L2005 GS *100

BILSKY, Alan Charles. 5501 OLD YORK RD 19141 #047-35-1981 L1982 IM IMG *020 †20

BINDER, David. 9807 BUSTLETON AVE 19115 #041-09-1979 L1981 OBG *020 †30

BINENBAUM, Gil. ■ 19146 #041-01-2002 L2002 OPH *100 †35

BING, Zhanyong. 3400 SPRUCE ST, DEPT OF PATH & LAB MED 19104 #243-13-1983 L2004 PTH *012

BINIAURISHVILI, Raoul G. 11685 BUSTLETON AVE # C 19116 #913-06-1972 L1993 N *020 †75

BINKLEY, Emily Elizabeth. 19147 #047-05-2006 L2006 OBG *012

BIRARDI, Theresa S. ■ 19130 #041-77-2007, ▲ L2007 *100

BIRBE, Ruth Carolina. ■ 19106 #935-01-1995 L2001 PCP *100 †50

BIRD, Geoffrey Langton. 625 W SEDGWICK ST 19119 #010-02-1994 L1996 CCP *020 †55

BIRD, Luis Jesus. 100 W LEHIGH AV 19133 #005-15-1977 L1978 P *020 †75 ‡

BIRD, Shawn Jos. 3400 SPRUCE ST 19104 #023-07-1983 L1987 N *020 †75

BIRDSALL, Thomas Morrison. 51 N 39TH ST, STE 205 19104 #041-01-1948 L1950 U *071 †95

BIRKHOFF, Michael John. ■ 19128 #033-06-2004 L2005 DR *012

BIRNBAUM, Belinda K. 1316 W ONTARIO ST, TEMPLE UNIVERSITY 19140 #035-45-2000 L2005 RHU *100 †20

BIRNBAUM, Julia Ann. 3400 SPRUCE ST, DEPT RADIOLOGY 19104 #005-14-1992 L1998 DR *020 †80

BISCHOFF, Lindsay Ann. ■ 19107 #041-02-2007 L2007 IM *012

BISCOVEANU, Mihaela. 9501 ROOSEVELT BLVD, ASSOCIATES 19114 #781-01-1990 L1998 END *020 †20

BISHAI, David Makram. UNIVERSITY & WOODLAND AVES 19104 #005-18-1987 L1991 PHP IM *050 †20,55

BISHOP, Douglas Scott. ■ 19147 #033-06-2007 L2007 FP *012

BISHOP, Gene B. 700 SPRUCE ST 19106 #035-48-1976 L1979 IM IMG *020 †20

BISHOW, Heidi Ann. 834 CHESTNUT ST, STE 400 19107 #023-01-2002 L2002 END *012

BISKER, Esther Rose. ■ 19103 #041-01-2008 L2008 P *012

BISSON, Gregory Paul. 3400 SPRUCE ST, DEPT INFECTIOUS DISEASE 19104 #026-04-1997 L2001 ID *020 †20

BISWAS, Debashis. 1514 WOLF ST 19145 #495-38-1989 L1999 N CD *020

BISWAS, Navaneel. 3400 SPRUCE ST, DEPT OF GME 19104 #495-78-2002 L2006 GS *012

BITTNER, Doerte. 800 SPRUCE ST, PENNSYLVANIA HOSPITAL 19107 #409-36-2001 L2002 IM *100 †20

BIX, Barbara Caron. 7500 CENTRAL AVE, STE 104 19111 #026-04-1986 L1987 IM *020 †20

BJORNSON, Jon. 111 S 11TH ST 19107 #035-15-1958 L1968 P PFP *071 †75

BLACK, Daniel O. ■ 19118 #024-05-1991 L1993 OPH *020 †35

BLACK, Iain Fletcher S. 3601 A ST, ST CHRISTOPHERS HOSP CHLD 19134 #803-05-1957 L1965 PD PDC *071 †55

BLACK, Jennifer. 3401 N BROAD ST, 8PP 19140 #035-01-1998 L2001 IM *020 †20

BLACK, Martin. 3401 N BROAD ST 2ND FL 19140 #917-29-1961 L1989 HEP GE *020

BLACK, Perry. 245 N 15TH ST STOP 40, NEUROSURGERY DREXEL UNI OF 19102 #067-01-1956 L1979 NS *030 †25

BLACKBURN, Lisa. 3801 MARKET ST, STE 201 19104 #051-01-2000 L2006 P *020 †20

BLACKSTONE, Mercedes M. ■ 19103 #035-19-2002 L2002 PEM *012 †55

BLACKWELL, Boon-Nam. 3300 HENRY AVE, MEDICAL COL OF PA 19129 #891-02-1949 L1973 PTH *071 †50

BLACKWOOD, Mary Anne. 3400 SPRUCE ST, HOSPITAL OF PA HEM-ONC DEP 19104 #035-01-1988 L1994 HEM *020 †20

BLADE, Kent Alan. 900 WALNUT ST, RETINA WILLS EYE 19107 #023-12-1990 L2001 OPH *020 †35

BLAIR, Frank W. 5800 RIDGE AVE 19128 #041-02-1944 L1945 OPH *071 †35

BLAKE, Emily J. 6015 WAYNE AVE 19144 #035-01-1989 L1992 OBG *020 †30

BLAKELY, Collin Michael. ■ 19103 #041-01-2007 L2007 IM *012

BLAKER, Martin Abraham. FRANKFORD AV & PALMER 19125 #041-13-1937 L1939 ORS *071 †40

BLANCHARD, Edward Joseph. ■ 19107 #041-01-2004 L2004 ID *012 †20

BLASCO, Luis. 3701 MARKET ST, 8TH FL 19104 #847-08-1963 L1964 OBG *071 †30

BLEBEA, John. 3401 N BROAD ST, PARKINSON PAVILION ROOM 44 19140 #038-06-1982 L1997 VS GS *040 †85

BLEBEA, Judy Sanna. 3400 SPRUCE ST, HOSP UNIV OF PA 19104 #035-08-1983 L1997 DR *020 †80

BLEICHER, Melissa B. 3400 SPRUCE ST, HOSPITAL OF THE UNIVERSITY 19104 #035-08-2003 L2006 IM *100 †20

BLEICHER, Richard Joel. 333 COTTMAN AVE, FOX CHASE CANCE CENTER 19111 #041-13-1994 L1997 SO GS *020 †85

BLEVINS, Annette Danielle. ■ 19107 #038-40-2005 L2005 OBG *012

BLIDNER, Elizabeth Nolan. ■ 19107 #041-02-2008 *012

BLINKOFF, Barry A. 2230 COTTMAN AVE # 10, PHILA MUNICIPAL MED CLNC 19149 #041-13-1963 L1964 IM *012

BLOEDON, Esa Alohilani. ■ 19146 #041-02-2003 L2003 OTO *012

BLONDHEIM, David Simeon. 5501 OLD YORK RD 19141 #550-01-1980 L1989 CD *100

BLOOM, Benjamin Harris. 913 WALNUT 19107 #024-07-1974 L1980 OPH *020 †35

BLOOM, Eric Jeffrey. 5501 OLD YORK RD, ALBERT EINSTEIN MED CTR 19141 #041-13-1984 L1986 IM *020 †20

BLOOM, Jason David. ■ 19102 #925-01-2005 L2005 OTO *012

BLOOM, Lawrence Howard. 525 JAMESTOWN ST, STE 207 19128 #035-03-1976 L1977 OPH IM *020 †35

BLOOM, Sandra L Treen. 4641 ROOSEVELT BLVD 19124 #041-13-1975 L1977 P *030 †75

BLOOMGARDEN, Eve Dana. ■ 19103 #035-19-2007 L2007 IM *012

BLOSCH, Annette Kristina. 5401 OLD YORK RD, KLEIN 363 19141 #409-19-2007 L2007 IM *020 †20

BLOUGH, Herbert Allen. 3400 SPRUCE ST 19104 #016-42-1955 L1959 MM IM *071

BLOY, Dorothy Sara. ■ 19119 #041-13-2005 L2006 EM *012

BLUEMLE, Lewis Wm, Jr. 11TH AND WALNUT ST 19107 #023-07-1946 L1950 OS IM *071 †20

BLUM, Lawrence David. 2400 CHESTNUT ST, APT 2810 19103 #041-01-1981 L1982 P PYA *020 †75

BLUM, Lorna. 800 SPRUCE ST 19107 #041-07-1983 L1984 DR *020 †80

BLUM, Marissa Anne. 3400 SPRUCE ST, 504 MALONEY 19104 #023-07-2004 L2007 RHU *012 †20

BLUM, Matthew David. 3400 N BROAD ST, STE 102 19140 #010-01-1969 OTO *020 †45

BLUM, Nathan Jon. 3405 CIVIC CENTER BLVD, CHILDREN'S SEASHORE HOUSE 19104 #023-07-1988 L1990 PD *020 †20

BLUMBERG, Baruch. 7701 BURHOLME AVE 19111 #035-01-1951 L1964 OS *071

BLUMBERG, Emily A. 3400 SPRUCE ST, 3 SILVERSTEIN SUITE E 19104 #035-19-1981 L1987 ID IM *020 †20

BLUMBERG, Myron Lee. ■ 19103 #041-09-1960 L1964 R *071 †80

BLUME, Joshua Adam. ■ 19104 #041-02-2006 L2006 P *012

BLUMNER, Kate Hanna. 3535 MARKET ST, FL 2 19104 #041-01-2005 L2005 P *012

BOATENG, Percy. 230 N BROAD ST MS 111, HAHNEMANN UNIVERSITY HOSPI 19102 #023-01-1998 L2003 TS *020 †85

BOCHENEK, Wieslaw Janusz. P3300 HENRY AVE 19129 #759-10-1962 L1989 GE NTR *074 †20

BODACK, Jeffrey Mark. 7600 CENTRAL AVE 19111 #041-01-1974 L1975 IM *020 †20

BODE, Udo. 324 S 34TH ST 19104 #409-15-1971 PD *100

BODEN, Gunther. 3400 N BROAD ST, TEMPLE MEDICAL SCHOOL 19140 #407-16-1959 L1970 DIA IM *050 †20

BODIN, Nathan Daniel. ■ 19146 #041-15-2007 L2007 ORS *012

BODZIN, Adam Seth. 111 S 11TH ST, THOS JEFFERSON UNIV HOSP 19107 #024-05-2007 L2007 GS *012

BOEHM, Rosemarie. 925 CHESTNUT ST, FIFTH FLOOR 19107 #041-13-1993 L1997 FSM *020 †18

■ = Address Information Privacy Protected

BOFINGER, Jason Joseph. 3401 N BROAD ST, DEPT OF ID/5TH FL/PARK PAV 19140 #041-01-2001 L2001 **ID** *012
BOGAR, Linda Jean. 1025 WALNUT ST STE 607 19107 #041-13-1993 L1995 **TS** *020 †85,90
BOGEN, Craig Alan. 7602 CENTRAL AVE STE 203 19111 #035-01-1980 L1982 **N IM** *020 †75
BOGEN, Daniel Kent. ■ 19104 #024-01-1979 **OS** *050
BOGHOSIAN, Garen. ■ 19107 #035-08-2003 L2004 **DR** *012
BOGNER, Hillary Rohn. 3400 SPRUCE ST, DEPT OF FAMILY PRACTICE 19104 #041-01-1996 L1998 **FM** *020 †18
BOGUCKI, Alfred Robt. 3998 RED LION RD STE 1 19114 #041-07-1987 L1988 **GS TRS** *020 †85
BOHM, Matthew Eric. 3401 N BROAD ST, DEPT MED 19140 #041-77-2007, ▲ L2007 **IM** *012
BOIGON, Margot Inez. 3401 N BROAD ST, TEMPLE ANESTHESIA ASSOCIAT 19140 #041-07-1990 L1992 **IM** *020 †20
BOLAND, Torrey Ann. ■ 19107 #041-02-2007 L2007 **IM** *012
BOLINGER, Bryan David. ■ 19131 #041-77-2007, ▲ L2007 **TY** *012
BOLISETTI, Sreedevi. 2301 E ALLEGHENY AVE 19134 #495-62-1997 L2004 **IM** *020
BOLNO, Paul Benjamin. 8434 SHAWNEE ST 19118 #041-15-2000 L2001 **GS** *100 ‡
BOLOGNESE, Ronald Jos. 834 CHESTNUT ST, STE 300 19107 #041-01-1963 L1964 **MFM OBG** *020 †30
BOLTON, Jeffrey Brian. ■ 19146 #020-02-2006 L2006 **PD** *012
BOMALASKI, John Stephen. 800 SPRUCE ST 19107 #028-34-1978 L1982 **IM RHU** *062 †20
BOMAN, Bruce Millring. 1100 WALNUT ST, STE 400 19107 #026-04-1976 L1998 **ON MG** *020 †20
BOMBONATI, Alessandro. ■ 19107 #561-32-2001 L2004 **PTH** *012
BONAFIDE, Christopher Pet. ■ 19103 #041-14-2004 L2004 **PD** *012 †55
BONAKDAR-POUR, Akbar. 3400 N BROAD ST, DEPT OF RADIOLOGY 19140 #517-01-1953 L1963 **DR** *020 †80
BONANNO, Donn E. ■ 19115 #041-09-1949 L1954 **PD OS** *020
BONAVITA, John Anthony. 3400 SPRUCE ST, DEPT RADIOLOGY 19104 #041-01-1973 L1974 **R IM** *020 †80
BOND, Andrew Richard. ■ 19104 #041-01-2008 *012
BONDI, Edward Edge. 3400 SPRUCE ST, 2 RHOADS PAVILION 19104 #041-09-1974 L1975 **D** *020 †15
BONGIORNO, Charles Philip. 5501 OLD YORK RD, EINSTEIN GASTRO ASSOCIATES 19141 #038-43-1979 L1981 **GE IM** *020 †20
BONILLA, Mabel Monserrate. 9002 BUTTONWOOD PL 19128 #042-02-1998 L2000 **OM** *020
BONITA, Raphael Edward. ■ 19119 #041-15-2003 L2003 **CD** *012 †20
BONNEMANN, Carsten G. 324 S 34TH ST 19104 #409-05-1989 L2004 **CHN** *020
BONNER, Lara Prashanti. 3400 SPRUCE ST, DEPT MED 19104 #023-01-2007 L2007 **IM** *012
BONNER, Robert Louis, Jr. 3601 A ST, AMBULATORY PEDS 19134 #016-11-1989 L1991 **PD** *040 †55
BOOKER, Michael Rashad. ■ 19150 #028-02-2006 L2006 **ORS** *012
BOOKER, Timberly Esther. ■ 19107 #023-01-2006 L2006 **EM** *012
BOOKMAN, Michael Arnold. 333 COTTMAN AVE, FOX CHASE CANCER CENTER 19111 #024-01-1980 L1988 **ON IM** *050 †20
BOON, Maurits Steven. 925 CHESTNUT ST, FL 6 19107 #035-06-1995 L1998 **OTO** *020 †45
BOONN, William Wiroon. ■ 19146 #035-47-2002 L2002 **DR** *100 †80
BORAAS, Marcia Christine. 3400 SPRUCE ST, FL 4 19104 #041-01-1977 L1979 **SO** *020 †85
BORATE, Uma Madhav. 5501 OLD YORK RD, ALBERT EINSTEIN MED CTR 19141 #495-28-2003 L2004 **IM** *012 †20
BORDE-PERRY, William Ches. 5501 OLD YORK RD, ALBERT EINSTEIN MC 19141 #041-02-2004 L2004 **EM** *012
BORENSTEIN, Julius. 1416 W ALLEGHENY AVE 19132 #041-01-1950 L1951 **OBG** *072
BORGE, Prabhakar Dayanand. 7720C STENTON AVE APT 210 19118 #041-01-2004 L2004 **PTH** *012
BORGIA, Victoria Marie. 1415 N BROAD ST, BROAD STREET HEALTH CENTER 19122 #035-08-1998 L2005 **FM** *020 †18
BORGMAN, Jody Brian. 5501 OLD YORK RD, ALBERT EINSTEIN MED CTR 19141 #038-06-1989 L1991 **IM OS** *040 †20
BORGMANN-WINTER, Karin E. 125 S 31ST ST, 549 CLINICAL RES BLDG 19104 #041-07-1996 L2000 **CHP** *020 †75
BORKOWSKI, Winslow Jos. 9880 BUSTLETON AVE, STE 309 19115 #041-02-1975 L1997 **CHN N** *020 †75,55
BORKSON, Joseph L. 1530 LOCUST ST, # L 19102 #308-12-1984 L1987 **IM GPM** *020
BORNAK, Arash. 1800 LOMBARD ST 19146 #869-05-2002 L2003 **GS** *012
BORNSTEIN, Judith Aviva. ■ 19123 #041-14-2005 L2005 **IM** *012
BOROFSKI, Annmarie. 3400 SPRUCE ST 19104 #041-09-1988 L1990 **RO** *020 †80
BOROFSKY, David Mark. 230 N BROAD ST DEPT RPSYCH 19102 #041-09-1984 L1985 **P** *020
BOROWSKY, Larry Mason. 1811 S BROAD ST 19148 #041-09-1980 L1981 **GE** *020 †20
BORREGO, John Paul. ■ 19104 #035-20-2004 L2005 **AN** *012
BOSACCO, Stephen John. 245 N 15TH ST MS 420 19102 #041-09-1966 L1967 **ORS OSS** *030 †40 ‡
BOSANAC, Amy Michelle. 1025 WALNUT ST, THOMAS JEFFERSON UNIV HOSP 19107 #041-02-2003 L2003 **IM** *100 †20
BOSE, Brent Jerrod. ■ 19144 #041-15-2007 L2007 **TY** *012
BOSELLI, Joseph Mark. 205 N BROAD ST, FL 1 19107 #041-09-1982 L1984 **IM** *020 †20 ‡
BOSELLI, Karen June. 3400 SPRUCE ST, HOSPITAL OF THE UNIVERSITY 19104 #010-02-2004 L2004 **ORS** *012
BOSSARD, Valerie Janet. 8001 ROOSEVELT BLVD, STE 500 19152 #041-01-1978 L1979 **OBG** *020 †30
BOSSBALY, Jose Antonio. 1741 FRANKFORD AVE 19125 #308-07-1982 L1986 **EM IM** *020 †20
BOSZORMENYI-NAGY, Ivan. BROAD & VINE STS 19102 #473-01-1944 L1959 **P OS** *071 †75
BOTERO, Andres. 5501 OLD YORK RD, PALEY #4 GERIATRIC DIVISIO 19141 #264-16-1991 L2002 **IMG** *020 †20
BOTVINICK, Matthew M. 23 W GRAVERS LN 19118 #035-20-1994 L1998 **P** *020 †75
BOUCHER, Robert Manuel. ■ 19147 #016-11-1987 L1988 **OTO** *020 †45
BOUDEN, Evelyn Sydnor. ■ 19106 #041-07-1955 L1957 **PD PHP** *071 †55
BOUKMAN, Imhotep Leroy. 3401 N BROAD ST, TEMPLE UNIVERSITY HOSPITAL 19140 #047-07-1998 L2000 **IM** *020 †20
BOURDEU, Kathrin Ingrid J. ■ 19146 #409-22-2004 L2007 **AN** *012
BOVE, Alfred Anthony. 3401 N BROAD ST 19140 #041-13-1966 L1967 **CD** *050 †20
BOVE, Mary Elizabeth. 833 CHESTNUT ST, STE 300 19107 #041-02-2006 L2006 **PD** *012
BOVE, Richard Lawrence. 1901 MARKET ST, INDEPENDENCE BLUE CROSS 19103 #041-13-1974 L1975 **GS CRS** *020 †10,85
BOW, Jennifer Katherine. 1015 WALNUT ST 19107 #065-06-2002 L2007 **OAR** *012
BOWE, Whitney Paige. 5501 OLD YORK RD, A EINSTEIN MED CTR 19141 #041-01-2007 L2007 **TY** *012
BOWEN, Sarah Elizabeth. 2900 W QUEEN LN 19129 #143-02-2000 L2006 **D** *012
BOWER, Raymond Paul F. 3400 SPRUCE ST, 2 GATES BUILDING 19104 #060-01-1992 L2000 **FM** *020 †18
BOWER, Robert. 230 N BROAD ST 19102 #024-01-1950 L1952 **GS** *071 †85
BOWERING, Amy Robbins. ■ 19147 #024-07-2003 L2003 **OBG** *020
BOWERS, Andrea Legath. 3400 SPRUCE ST, 2 SILVERSTEIN - ORTHOPAEDI 19104 #047-05-2004 L2004 **ORS** *012
BOWERS, Geoffrey David. 834 CHESTNUT ST, LBBY 3 19107 #041-02-2005 L2005 **OBG** *012
BOWERS, Jacqueline N. 5501 OLD YORK RD, ALBERT EINSTEIN MEDICAL CT 19141 #010-03-1998 L2000 **IM** *020 †20
BOWERS, Rory Austin. ■ 19107 #041-02-2006 L2006 **IM** *012
BOWLES, Karen Elaine. 3701 MARKET ST, STE 741 19104 #041-12-1991 L1993 **IM** *020 †20
BOWMAN, Kevin L. ■ 19102 #041-02-2006 L2007 **DR** *012
BOWMAN, Marjorie A. 3400 SPRUCE ST, DEPT FAMILY PRACTICE 19104 #041-02-1976 L1996 **FM GPM** *020 †70,18
BOWMAN, Sallyann Margaret. 399 S 34TH ST 19104 #041-14-1976 L1977 **IM RHU** *020 †20
BOYD, Robert Livingston. 3400 N BROAD ST, TEMPLE MEDICAL SCHOOL 19140 #041-02-1976 L1977 **P** *100 †20 ‡
BOYD, Thompson H, III. ■ 19130 #051-01-1979 L1980 **IM CD** *020 †20 ‡
BOYKO, Orest Bohdan. 3401 N BROAD ST, DEPT DIAGNOSTIC IMAGING 19140 #017-20-1982 L1994 **NP PTH** *020 †80
BOYLE, Krystene I. 834 CHESTNUT ST STE 400, BENJAMIN FRANKLIN HOUSE 19107 #033-05-2003 L2004 **OBG** *100
BOYLE, Monica Rose. 219 N BROAD ST, FL 4 19107 #041-15-2006 L2006 **D** *012
BOYLE, Suzanne Marie. ■ 19123 #033-06-2007 L2007 **IM** *012
BOZORGNIA, Babak. ■ 19128 #041-13-2002 L2002 **CD** *012 †20
BOZORGNIA, Behnam. ■ 19128 #041-13-2002 L2002 **CD** *012 †20
BRABENDER, Robert Colin. ■ 19144 #041-15-2008 L2008 *012
BRACHFELD, Jonas. ■ 19106 #041-01-1952 L1953 **CD IM** *071 †20
BRACKBILL, Andrew John. ■ 19107 #041-02-2006 L2007 **IM** *012
BRADEN, Geoffrey Lee. 3998 RED LION RD 19114 #038-40-1975 L1980 **GE IM** *020 †20 ‡
BRADFORD, George Werner. 1100 WALNUT ST, STE 303 19107 #033-05-1968 L1969 **FM** *020 †18
BRADFORD, Marilyn Ross. 239 E THOMPSON ST, 1020 SANSOM ST. 19125 #010-02-1974 L1975 **FM PD** *020 †18
BRADLEY, Edward Chas. 950 WALNUT ST, APT 607 19107 #041-02-1955 L1956 **IM CD** *071
BRADLEY, Kevin Michael. ■ 19106 #041-13-1996 L1998 **CCS** *020 †85
BRADY, John Paul. 3400 SPRUCE ST 19104 #024-05-1955 L1963 **P** *071 †75
BRADY, Kathleen A. 301 S 8TH ST, STE 1B 19106 #024-05-1992 L1995 **ID** *020 †20
BRADY, Luther Weldon, Jr. 230 N BROAD ST 19102 #010-01-1948 L1956 **RO ON** *071 †80 ‡
BRADY, Paul Scott. 5501 OLD YORK RD, DEPT INTERVENTIONAL RADIOL 19141 #539-06-1995 L2002 **VIR ESN** *020 †80
BRADY, William Martin. ■ 19119 #024-07-1992 L1994 **IM** *020 †20
BRAFFMAN, Michael Neil. 1 PINE PL W, 800 SPRUCE STREET 19115 #041-01-1980 L1982 **ID IM** *020 †20
BRAHMAKULAM, Francis Geor. 245 N 15TH ST, HAHNEMANN UNIV HOSP 19102 #496-22-2001 L2004 **PCC** *012 †20
BRAHMBHATT, Khyati Jitend. 5501 OLD YORK RD 19141 #495-01-2003 L2005 **P** *012
BRAINARD, Jason Conrad. ■ 19104 #028-34-2004 L2004 **AN** *012
BRANDENBURG, Jennifer Ann. 800 SPRUCE ST, FL 6TH FL 19107 #041-12-1998 L2000 **OBG** *020
BRANDMAN, Ita Shulman. ■ 19130 #041-07-1966 L1967 **IM PUD** *071 †20
BRANDT, Justin Samuel. ■ 19107 #041-02-2008 *012
BRANDWEIN, Warren Mark. ■ 19104 #016-42-2007 **TY** *012
BRANNON, Ryan K. 245 N 15TH ST, OF M 19102 #041-12-2007 L2007 **OBG** *012
BRANT, Shane Eugene. 1903 WALNUT ST, APT 160 19103 #041-13-2000 **FM** *100
BRASLOW, Benjamin. 3440 MARKET ST 1ST FL, TRAUMA 19104 #041-02-1996 L1998 **CCS** *100 †85
BRASS, Lawrence Fisher. 421 CURIE BLVD, BRB II, RM 915 19104 #038-06-1977 L1980 **HEM ON** *050 †20
BRAUN, David Timothy. ■ 19129 #041-13-2007 L2007 **ORS** *012
BRAUNER, Jason Saul. ■ 19103 #041-01-2003 *100
BRAUNSTEIN, Inbal. ■ 19103 #041-01-2008 *012
BRAUNSTEIN, Seth Neal. 3400 SPRUCE ST, HOSPITAL OF UNIV OF PA 19104 #035-19-1972 L1973 **IM DIA** *020 †20
BRAVERMAN, Debra Lynne. 700 COTTMAN AVE, BLD B-LL 19111 #035-20-1992 L1996 **PM OS** *020 †60
BRAVETTE, Barry Alan. 1317 WOLF ST, STE 19 19148 #033-06-1985 L1986 **CD IM** *020 †20
BRAY, Eric Wesley. ■ 19119 #041-13-1978 L1979 **FM** *020
BRAY, Paul Francis. 1015 WALNUT ST, RM 705 19107 #049-01-1977 L2006 **IM** *020 †20
BRAY, Susan H. 219 N BROAD ST, FL 5 19107 #041-07-1970 L1973 **NEP IM** *020 †20
BREAKSTONE, Nina Joelle. ■ 19130 #041-15-2008 *012
BREAM, Kent Douglas W. 51 N 39TH ST, FL 7 19104 #023-01-1994 L1996 **FM** *020 †18
BREAULT, Steven Robert. ■ 19127 #041-15-2007 L2007 **TY** *012
BREAUX, Elizabeth J. ■ 19102 #041-07-1977 **R** *075
BREECKER, Steven Wm. 111 S 11TH ST, STE 4280 19107 #024-07-1982 L1986 **CD IM** *020 †20
BREEN, Gregory. 8815 GERMANTOWN AVE STE 12, PENN JERSEY PULMONARY ASSO 19118 #041-07-1994 L1994 **PCC** *020 †20
BREHM, Anthony. 5401 OLD YORK RD, KLEIN 363 19141 #836-01-2004 L2007 **IM** *012
BREISH, Charles Fletcher. ■ 19130 #041-13-2007 L2007 **IM** *012
BREISH, Russell Stewart. 8815 GERMANTOWN AVE, FL 5 19118 #041-02-1982 L1983 **FM** *020 †18
BREITE, Herbert Jack. 1518 WALNUT ST, STE 1210 19102 #407-10-1969 L1973 **EM** *072
BRENDEL, Erica Marie. 111 N 49TH ST 19139 #041-01-1976 L1977 **P** *020 †75 ‡
BRENMAN, Arnold King. 8350 ROOSEVELT BLVD 19152 #016-02-1955 L1958 **NO OS** *071 †45
BRENMAN, Scott Alan. 800 SPRUCE ST, 10TH FLOOR SPRUCE BUILD IN 19107 #041-02-1981 L1983 **PS HS** *020 †85,65 ‡
BRENNAN, Kathleen Jane. 340 N BROAD ST FL 7, PARKINSON PAVILION 19102 #038-43-1988 L1991 **PUD CCM** *050 †20
BRENNAN, Patrick Jos. 399 S 34TH ST, UNIV PA HLTH SYS 19104 #041-13-1982 L1984 **IM** *030 †20
BRENNER, Sidney. ■ 19149 #041-01-1943 L1944 **GP** *071
BRENNER, Stacey Rayelle. ■ 19104 #041-01-2008 *012
BRENT, Lawrence Harry. 9880 BUSTLETON AVE, STE 220 19115 #041-02-1979 L1980 **RHU** *020 †20
BRESCH, David. 5700 RIDGE AVE, STE 100A 19128 #035-08-1997 L2000 **P** *020 †75 ‡

BRESNICK, George Henry. ■ 19107 #035-19-1963 L1970 **OPH PHP** *071 †35

BRESNITZ, Eddy A. 1505 RACE ST MS 644, MCP HAHNEMANN SCHOOL OF ME 19102 #067-01-1974 L1981 **OM PUD** *040 †20,70

BRESS, Jonathan Wade. 3400 SPRUCE ST, HUP - 210 WHITE BLDG. 19104 #035-20-2002 L2005 **IM** *100 †20

BRESSI, Thomas E, Jr. 8835 GERMANTOWN AVE 19118 #041-09-1951 L1952 **ORS CRS** *062 †85

BREST, Albert N. 925 CHESTNUT ST, MEZZ LEVEL 19107 #041-13-1953 L1954 **CD IM** *030 †20

BRIBRIESCO, Alejandro Can. ■ 19104 #041-01-2008 *012

BRICENO, Pedro Jose. 5501 OLD YORK RD, ALBERT EINSTEIN MED CTR 19141 #935-07-2000 L2002 **GS** *020

BRIDGER, Wagner H. 3200 HENRY AVE, MEDICAL COLLEGE OF PENNSYL 19129 #035-19-1950 L1982 **P CHP** *050 †75

BRIDGES, Charles R. 230 W WASHINGTON SQ, CARDIO THORACIC SURGERY 19106 #024-01-1981 L1984 **TS IM** *020 †85,90

BRIGHAM, Marie Hinman. 525 JAMESTOWN ST, STE 105 19128 #024-16-1987 L1989 **OPH** *075 †35

BRIGHAM, Mark Prince. 525 JAMESTOWN ST, PREMIER ORTHOPAEDIC & 19128 #041-13-1983 L1984 **ORS** *020 †40

BRIGHTON, Carl Theodore. 3400 SPRUCE ST 19104 #041-01-1957 L1958 **ORS** *071 †40

BRIGNOLA, Michael Peter. 1900 S BROAD ST 19145 #041-09-1945 L1946 **IM PUD** *071 †20

BRISBON, Nancy Elizabeth. 833 CHESTNUT ST, STE 301 19107 #041-13-2001 L2001 **FM** *020 †18

BRISLIN, Brian Thomas. 7500 CENTRAL AVE, STE 108 19111 #041-02-2000 L2001 **OSM** *020

BRISTER, Neil W. 3401 N BROAD ST 19140 #041-13-1983 L1984 **AN CCM** *020 †05

BRITTO LEON, Clemente Jos. 5501 OLD YORK RD, ALBERT EINSTEIN MED CTR 19141 #935-01-2002 L2004 **IM** *012 †20

BROAD, Louis T. 1015 CHESTNUT ST, STE 916 19107 #041-02-1974 L1975 **GE IM** *020 †20

BROBECK, John R. 3400 SPRUCE ST, RM G3 19104 #008-01-1943 **OS** *071

BROCK, Charlene D'Alessio. 8500 HENRY AVE, TPI HENRY AVE PEDIATRICS 19128 #041-07-1978 L1979 **PD** *020 †55

BROCK, David Geoffrey. 900 WALNUT ST, STE 200 19107 #035-06-1988 L1996 **N** *020 †75

BRODER, George Jerry. 8305 RIDGE AVE 19128 #041-01-1962 L1963 **DR NM** *020 †80 ‡

BRODEUR, Garrett Michael. 3615 CIVIC CENTER BLVD, RM 902D 19104 #028-02-1975 L1994 **PHO PD** *050 †55

BRODIE, Donald Edward. 5458 RIDGE AVE, ROXBOROUGH FAM PRAC 19128 #041-02-1962 L1964 **FM** *020 †18

BRODKIN, Edward Stuart. 125 S 31ST ST RM 2220, U PENN SCH OF MED TRL BLDG 19104 #024-01-1992 L1999 **P** *050 †75

BRODOVSKY, Harvey Selig. 111 S 11TH ST 19107 #062-01-1955 L1960 **IM ON** *071 †20

BRODSKY, Isadore. 230 N BROAD ST, 15TH FL 19102 #041-03-1955 L1956 **ON HEM** *020 †20

BRODSKY, Jeffrey Tobin. 3998 RED LION RD 19114 #041-01-1984 L1990 **GS SO** *020 †85

BRODY, Jerome I. 3300 HENRY AVE, MED COLLEGE OF PENNSYLVANI 19129 #041-02-1952 L1953 **HEM IM** *020 †20

BRODY, Julia B. 1726 S BROAD ST, STE 103 19145 #035-46-1977 L1982 **PUD IM** *020 †20 ‡

BRODY, Marion Beth. 5501 OLD YORK RD, ALBERT EINSTEIN MEDICAL CE 19141 #041-02-1991 L1993 **DR** *012 †20

BROENNLE, Albert Michael. 1 CHILDRENS CTR, CHILDRENS HOSP OF PHILADEL 19104 #038-40-1967 L1973 **AN** *020 †05

BROKER, Brian Jeffrey. 5735 RIDGE AVE, STE 208 19128 #041-02-1991 L1994 **OTO FPS** *020 †45

BROMBERG, Kenneth. 5800 RIDGE AVE 19128 #035-06-1975 L1976 **PD ID** *030 †55

BROMBERG, Michael. 333 COTTMAN AVE 19111 #041-13-1988 L1990 **HEM ON** *020 †20

BRON, Kerry Allison. 3400 SPRUCE ST 19104 #035-47-1992 L1994 **PDR** *012 †55,80

BRONSTEIN, Howard David. 7500 CENTRAL AVE, STE 104 19111 #041-14-1974 L1975 **IM** *020 †20

BRONSTEIN, Judy Bob. 5753 WAYNE AVE 19144 #041-07-1976 L1978 **FM** *020

BRONSTEIN, Robert Marc. 2301 S BROAD ST, FL 2CD 19148 #041-09-1972 L1973 **R DR** *020 †80,28 ‡

BROOKS, Adam John. 3440 MARKET ST, 1ST FL 19104 #917-10-1992 L2004 **CCS** *100

BROOKS, Allan. BLDG, OLD YORK & TABOR RD-KLEIN 19141 #041-09-1957 L1958 **CHP PYA** *071

BROOKS, Ari David. 219 N BROAD ST, STE 8 19107 #041-09-1992 L2001 **SO GS** *020 †85

BROOKS, David Michael. ■ 19106 #035-06-2008 *012

BROOKS, Dennis Lee. 2 PENN BLVD, STE 110 19144 #038-40-1967 L1974 **OPH** *020 †35

BROOKS, Robert. 7600 WOODBINE AVE 19151 #041-13-1944 L1945 **GP** *071

BROOKS, Ronald Jay. 1901 MARKET ST, FL 27 19103 #041-09-1977 L1978 **IM** *020 †20

BROOKS-KAYAL, Amy R. 324 S 34TH ST 19104 #023-07-1988 L1990 **CHN** *020 †55,75

BROSE, Marcia Simpson. 415 CURIE BLVD, CLINICAL RESEARCH BUILDING 19104 #035-20-1995 L1997 **IM HO** *020

BROTZ, Corey S. 132 S 10TH ST, STE 480 MAIN BLDG 19107 #035-15-2002 L2005 **GE** *012 †20

BROUDO, Samuel F. 6800 CASTOR AVE STE A 19149 #330-04-1955 L1963 **ORS** *071 †40

BROWN, Andrea Elaine. 3401 N BROAD ST 19140 #041-13-1984 L1988 **PM** *020 †60

BROWN, Andrew Keone. 1015 WALNUT ST, THOMAS JEFFERSON UNIV 19107 #041-02-2004 L2006 **ORS** *012

BROWN, Avrom S. 9150 MARSHALL ST, STE 15 DBA KESSLER REHAB 19114 #041-77-1974, ▲ L1975 **FM DMP** *071

BROWN, Daniel Bennett. 111 S 11TH ST, SUITE 4200 GIBBON BUILDING 19107 #041-09-1993 L1998 **VIR** *020 †80

BROWN, Danielle Lasharniq. 3620 HAMILTON WALK, UNIV OF PA SCH OF MED 19104 #041-01-2006 **FP** *012

BROWN, Donna Lynn. ■ 19128 #041-15-2007 L2007 **OBG** *012

BROWN, Earl Ray. 1335 W TABOR RD, STE 110 19141 #041-13-1977 L1978 **FM** *020 †18 ‡

BROWN, James Oliver. 5301 CEDAR AVE, MISERICORDIA PAVILION 19143 #047-07-1948 L1950 **GP R** *071

BROWN, Jayne Henderson. 2501 W LEHIGH AVE, 2501 W LEHIGH AVE 19132 #041-07-1985 L1989 **IM** *020

BROWN, Jodi Hara. 325 CHESTNUT ST, STE 1308 19106 #012-05-1990 L1993 **CHP** *020 †75

BROWN, Kenneth Robt. ■ 19118 #041-01-1961 L1962 **ID IM** *050 †20

BROWN, Kevin Walker. 1000 WALNUT ST, APT 1000 19107 #041-02-2002 L2002 **DR** *100 †80

BROWN, Leonard Reid. ■ 19107 #035-08-1976 L1977 **GP** *075

BROWN, Louis Alfred, Jr. 6326 RISING SUN AVE 19111 #041-01-1981 L1984 **D** *020

BROWN, Mark Jeffrey. 3400 SPRUCE ST 19104 #023-01-1966 L1974 **N** *020 †75

BROWN, Mary Allyson. 7028 GREENE AVE 19119 #012-05-1994 L1999 **OBG** *020 †30

BROWN, Melandee Dawn. ■ 19102 #035-01-2002 L2005 **NS** *100

BROWN, Meredith Ann. 3400 SPRUCE ST, DEPT MED 19104 #041-01-2007 L2007 **IM** *012

BROWN, Meshagay Melanie. ■ 19104 #041-01-2008 *012

BROWN, Michael Allen. 3401 N BROAD ST, TEMPLE UNIVERSITY HOSPITAL 19140 #010-02-1999 L2008 **IC** *012 †20

BROWN, Michael D. 1810 LIACOURAS WALK, 4TH FL 19122 #043-01-1988 L1988 **FM** *020 †18

BROWN, Michael Mc Daniel. 2301 E ALLEGHENY AVE, NORTHEASTERN HOSPITAL 19134 #008-01-1990 L1997 **AN** *020

BROWN, Naomi Judith. ■ 19147 #024-07-2006 L2006 **PD** *012

BROWN, Ouida Lynna. ■ 19107 #036-01-2002 L2007 **GS** *100

BROWN, Raymond David. 7100 GERMANTOWN AVE 19119 #041-13-1979 L1980 **OBG** *020 †30

BROWN, Rebecca Allison. ■ 19104 #041-01-2008 *012

BROWN, Roderick Eugene. 4900 FRANKFORD AVE, FRANKFORD HOSPITALRDLGY DP 19124 #056-05-1995 L1998 **AN** *020 †05

BROWN, Ronald Stephen. 300 N 52ND ST 19139 #041-13-1979 L1984 **ID PUD** *075

BROWN, Scot Andrew. ■ 19129 #041-15-2008 *012

BROWN, Scott Wesley. ■ 19128 #051-07-2006 L2006 **EM** *012

BROWN, Steven Jeffrey. 1901 MARKET ST, INDEPENDENCE BLUE CROSS 19103 #041-07-1985 L1986 **IM** *020 †20,08

BROWN, Valerie Inez. 3615 CIVIC CENTER BLVD, ARC 902F 19104 #041-01-1996 L1998 **PHO** *020 †55

BROWNE, Barbara Jo. 6 FRANKLIN PLZ, MAGEE REHABILITATION HOSPITA 19102 #041-07-1986 L1991 **PM IM** *020 †20,60

BROWNE, Laurence T. 3900 CITY LINE AVE # D125, PRESIDENTIAL MED CTR 19131 #041-01-1951 L1952 **IM GPM** *020 †20

BROWNE, Thomas Monroe. ■ 19116 #041-13-1984 L1986 **IM** *020 †20

BROWNE, Timothy Lloyd. ■ 19146 #041-01-2008 *012

BROWNGOEHL, Laurie A. 1 GRADUATE PLZ DEPT PM 19146 #010-01-1982 L1985 **PM** *020 †60

BROWNSTEIN, Bernard Alan. 30 S 18TH ST, 9TH FL 19103 #041-09-1973 L1976 **FM** *020 †18

BROWNSTEIN, Bruce Keith. STE 102 19144 #041-13-1977 L1978 **OPH** *020 †35

BROWNSTEIN, Phillip K. 833 CHESTNUT ST 6250 19107 #041-09-1970 L1972 **U** *020 †95 ‡

BROYER, Zach. 925 CHESTNUT ST, FL 5 19107 #033-05-1997 L2001 **APM** *020 †60

BRUCE, Kristine Jessica. ■ 19103 #035-48-2006 L2006 **PD** *012

BRUCKER, Alexander Jay. 39TH & MARKET 19104 #035-09-1972 L1977 **OPH OS** *020 †35

BRUCKER, Benjamin Michael. ■ 19102 #041-01-2005 L2005 **U** *012

BRUCKER, Paul Chas. 1015 WALNUT ST RM 303 19107 #041-01-1957 L1958 **FM** *040 †18

BRUMBERGER, Kenneth Eric. 8305 RIDGE AVE 19128 #035-01-1992 L1997 **DR PTH** *020 †80

BRUN, Francisco Antonio. ■ 19147 #038-45-1998 L2003 **CCM IM** *020 †20 ‡

BRUNELLI, Steven Michael. 3400 SPRUCE ST, WHITE BLDG, STE 210 19104 #041-01-2000 L2001 **NEP** *100 †20

BRUNK, Samuel Frederick. 1331 E WYOMING AVE 19124 #051-01-1959 L1994 **ON IM** *020 †20

BRUNNER, Jaclyn Renee. ■ 19130 #033-06-2008 *012

BRUNO, Christopher Joseph. 1427 VINE ST 5TH FL, MAIL STOP 959 19102 #035-01-2001 L2001 **IM** *020

BRYAN, Robert Nick. 3400 SPRUCE ST, DEPT RADIO 19104 #048-02-1969 L1999 **DR RNR** *050 †80

BRYANSMITH, Dale. 3998 RED LION RD, STE 130 19114 #038-41-1976 L1978 **ON HEM** *020 †20

BUB, Barry. ■ 19119 #836-02-1969 L1973 **FM** *071 †18

BUBNAJ, Radavon. 3400 SPRUCE ST 19104 #957-01-1973 L1983 **R** *020 †80

BUCH, David L. 822 PINE ST, STE 1A 19107 #047-05-1977 L1984 **P PYG** *020 †75 ‡

BUCHANAN, Edward Michael. 833 CHESTNUT ST, STE 401 19107 #041-01-1992 L2001 **FM** *020 †30,18

BUCHHEIT, Wm Anderson. 1015 CHESTNUT ST 19107 #041-13-1960 L1961 **NS OS** *071 †25

BUCKINGHAM, Suzanne W. 7996 OXFORD AVE 19111 #041-07-1984 L1987 **OBG** *020

BUCKLEY, Roland M, Jr. 800 SPRUCE ST # 1-PINE-W 19107 #008-01-1972 L1975 **ID IM** *030 †20

BUCKMAN, Robert Francis. 3333 N BROAD ST, RM 343 19140 #036-07-1972 L1987 **GS** *020 †85

BUCKS, Colin M. 3401 N BROAD ST, TEMPLE UNIVERSITY HOSPITAL 19140 #041-13-2003 L2003 **EM** *100

BUCKY, Louis Philip. 230 W WASHINGTON SQ 19106 #024-01-1986 L1995 **PS GS** *020 †85,65

BUCOLO, Frank. 530 S 2ND ST 19147 #308-11-1988 L1996 **IM IMG** *020

BUCURESCU, Gabriel. 3900 WOODLAND AVE, NEUROLOGY SVCS 19104 #660-02-1991 L1996 **N** *020 †75

BUDAC, Stefan. ■ 19103 #038-40-2000 L2007 **PAN** *012 †05

BUDHARAJU, Venkata Govind. 800 SPRUCE ST, PENNSYLVANIA HOSPITAL 19107 #495-21-1997 L2006 *100

BUEHLER, Greg Bennett. ■ 19107 #047-05-2004 L2004 **EM** *012

BUHL, Keith Jos. 7500 CENTRAL AVE STE 209, FOX CHASE GASTROENTEROLOGY 19111 #041-09-1985 L1987 **GE IM** *020 †20 ‡

BUI, Bao Thai. ■ 19107 #041-14-2007 L2007 **IM** *012

BUI, Quang Tan. 3400 SPRUCE ST, DIV OF CARDIOLOGY - 9 FOUN 19104 #043-01-2003 L2003 **CD** *012 †20

BUKHARI, Khatija Nazir. 230 N BROAD ST, DEPT OF PSYCHIATRY 19102 #704-02-1989 L1994 **P** *100

BULLINGA, John Richard. 51 N 39TH ST, PENN CARDIOLOGY AT PRESBYT 19104 #018-03-1998 L2006 **ICE** *020 †20

BULLUCK, David Ernest, Jr. INDEPENDENCE SQ P M INS CO 19172 #023-01-1953 L1960 **OM IM** *030

BUNIN, Nancy Jane. 324 S 34TH ST 19104 #038-41-1980 L1987 **PHO** *020 †55

BUNUAN, Hernando D. ■ 19141 #748-10-1967 L1973 **IM NEP** *100 †20

BUNYA, Vathana O. 2415 N 33RD ST 19132 #891-01-1970 L1974 **FM** *020

BURAK, Joshua Michael. 245 N 15TH ST, DEPT OF GME 19102 #422-01-2006 L2006 **IM** *012

BURCH, William. 2425 N BROAD ST 19132 #041-01-1971 L1972 **ORS** *075 †40

BURD, Irina. 834 CHESTNUT ST STE 400, BENJAMIN FRANKLIN HOUSE 19107 #033-06-2003 L2003 **OBG** *100

BURDEN, Theodore. 6711 OLD YORK RD, BURDEN-NEWTON MEDICAL ASSO 19126 #041-09-1977 L1978 **IM** *020

BURDETTE, Hillary Louella. 324 S 34TH ST 19104 #047-06-1997 L1999 **PD** *020 †55

BURDICK, William Paul. ■ 19119 #035-20-1979 L1982 **EM IM** *020,16

BURGESS, David Bruce. 3405 CIVIC CENTER BLVD, CHILDRENS SEASHORE HOUSE 19104 #056-05-1973 L1997 **OS PD** *020 †55

BURGESS, Judith Elmore. 5070 PARKSIDE AVE, STE 5100 19131 #041-13-1992 L1994 **FM** *020 †18

BURIGATTO, Renata Marie. ■ 19107 #041-13-2006 L2006 **FP** *012

BURKA, Edward Richard. 39TH & MARKET 19104 #035-01-1956 L1966 **HEM IM** *075

BURKE, James Francis. 111 S 11TH ST STE 4290, JEFFERSON HOSP/GIBBON BLDG 19107 #041-02-1966 L1967 **NEP IM** *020 †20

■ = Address Information Privacy Protected

BURKE, Kathleen Ann. 8TH & SPRUCE STS 19107 #041-01-1987 L1990 **OBG** *020 †30
BURKE, Margaret Ann. ■ 19119 #041-13-1980 L1981 **IM** *020 †20
BURKE, Sarah Hyland. ■ 19146 #051-01-2005 L2005 **PD** *012
BURKE, William Francis. 245 N 15TH ST, DREXEL UNIV COLLEGE 19102 #041-14-2003 L2004 **DR** *012
BURKEY, Brooke Alissa. ■ 19103 #041-01-2001 L2007 **PS** *020
BURKEY, Dell Robt. 3400 SPRUCE ST 19104 #041-13-1977 L1978 **AN PMM** *020 †05 ‡
BURKHARD, Edward John. 1913 N BROAD ST 19122 #010-02-1958 L1959 **PTH DMP** *071 †50
BURKHART, Keith Karl. 1650 ARCH ST 3HS00, ATSDR 19103 #041-07-1982 L1990 **EM ETX** *062 †16
BURKHOLDER, Bryn Melissa. ■ 19104 #041-01-2007 L2007 **TY** *012
BURKINS, John Andrew. 561 FAIRTHORNE AVE 19128 #041-13-1975 L1976 **P AM** *030 †75
BURKLAND, Danielle Lea. 3400 SPRUCE ST, DEPARTMENT OF OB/GYN, DULL 19104 #033-05-2002 L2002 **OBG** *012
BURLINGAME, Todd A. 3401 N BROAD ST, DEPT OF ANESTHESIOLOGY 19140 #022-75-2000, ▲ L2001 **AN** *020 †05
BURNETT, Mark Gordon. 3400 SPRUCE ST, OF PENNSY 19104 #023-01-1998 L2000 **NS** *100
BURNETTA, Edward C. 2601 HOLME AVE 19152 #539-06-1990 L1995 **PM** *020 †60
BURNHAM, Jon Michael, Jr. 3405 CIVIC CENTR BLVD #236, CHILDREN'S HOSPITAL OF 19104 #041-01-1997 L1999 **PD** *020 †55
BURNS, Anthony Scott. 132 S 10TH ST, 375 MAIN BLVD 19107 #008-01-1994 L2000 **PM SCI** *050 †20,60
BURNS, David Russell. 1601 WALNUT ST STE 1109, MEDICAL ARTS BUILDING 19102 #041-09-1966 L1967 **P** *020 †75
BURNS, Michael C. 800 SPRUCE ST 19107 #050-02-1997 L2000 **AN** *020 †05
BURNSED, Jennifer Christi. ■ 19128 #041-15-2008 *012
BURSHTEYN, Mark. 3401 N BROAD ST, DEPT RAD 19140 #033-06-2006 L2007 **DR** *012
BURSTEIN, Frank. 2601 HOLME AVE 19152 #041-09-1953 L1954 **FM IM** *071 †18
BURSTEIN, William Harris. ■19115 #041-09-1985 L1986 **FM** *020 †20
BURT, Francis Xavier. ■ 19129 #041-04-1986 L2006 **IM** *012
BURTNESS, Barbara Ann. 333 COTTMAN AVE, DEPARTMENT OF MEDICAL ONCO 19111 #035-48-1986 L2005 **ON IM** *050 †20
BURTON, Juanita Sharon. ■ 19151 #041-02-1977 L1993 **OBG** *020 †30
BUSCHIAZZO, Horacio Jorge. 4955 FRANKFORD AVE 19124 #132-01-1968 L1973 **IMG IM** *020 ‡
BUSILLO, Nicholas Anthony. 2821 ISLAND AVE STE 226 19153 #041-02-1978 L1979 **IM** *020
BUSIS, Sarah Beck. ■ 19103 #041-01-2008 *012
BUTLER, Brenda J. 2900 W QUEEN LN RM 221H 19129 #396-02-1989 L1993 **CHP** *020 †75
BUTLER, John Morris. 8014 BURHOLME AVE 19111 #041-02-1993 L1995 **IM** *020 †20
BUTTS, Samantha Florenz. 3701 MARKET ST 8TH FL, PENN FERTLY CARE U OF PA 19104 #024-01-1998 L2001 **END** *012
BUXBAUM, Laurence Umberto. 3900 WOODLAND AVE, RESEARCH 151 (A505) 19104 #023-07-1995 L1997 **ID** *020 †20
BUYSKE, Jo. 1617 JOHN F KENNEDY BLVD, STE 860 19103 #035-01-1987 L1996 **GS** *020 †85
BUYYOUNOUSKI, Mark K. 7701 BURHOLME AVE 19111 #033-05-2000 L2001 **RO** *100 †80
BYERS, James Wm, III. 5501 OLD YORK RD, LIFTER BLDG RM 1604 19141 #032-01-1982 L1984 **MFM OBG** *020 †30 ‡
BYLER, Leonard Edwin. 6024 WAYNE AVE, CARRIAGE HOUSE REAR 19144 #041-13-1967 L2003 **FM** *020 †18
BYREM, William C. 3400 SPRUCE ST 19104 #422-01-1994 L1996 **AN CCA** *050
BYRNE, Kevin Jos. 8835 GERMANTOWN AVE, CHESTNUT HILL HOSP 19118 #010-02-1979 L1981 **IM** *020 †80
BYUN, Sharon Young. 3400 SPRUCE ST, 5 PENN TOWER 19104 #041-13-2000 L2001 **OBG** *020
CABAS VARGAS, Jenny Marga. 5401 OLD YORK RD, KLEIN 363 19141 #264-04-2004 L2007 **IM** *012
CABILING, David Shannon. ■ 19106 #041-01-2007 L2007 **PS** *012
CACCIAMANI, John Donald. 3401 N BROAD ST, TEMPLE UNIVERSITY HOSPITAL 19140 #041-01-1996 L1998 **IM** *020 †20
CADAR, Andreea. ALUMNI AFFAIRS, ALBERT EINSTEIN MEDICAL CE 19141 #781-04-2004 L2007 **OBG** *012
CADAVID SEPULVEDA, Juan C. 5501 OLD YORK RD, ALBERT EINSTEIN MED CTR 19141 #264-04-1998 L2004 **PCC** *012 †20
CADE, Ena Marietta. 432 N 6TH ST, GPHA INC 19123 #041-01-1998 L2001 **PD** *020 †55
CADUNGOG, Mark Gregory. ■ 19106 #041-13-2001 L2005 **OBG** *100
CADY, Herbert Mills, Jr. 7056 GERMANTOWN AVE 19119 #041-13-1971 **PD** *020 †55
CAHILL, Anne Marie. 19104 #539-05-1990 L1999 **PDR** *020 †80
CAJULES, Arthur Bohadilla. 230 N BROAD ST, DEPT ANESTHESIOLOGY 19102 #748-07-1969 **AN** *100
CALABRIA, Andrew Charles. 111 S 11TH ST, JEFFERSON UNIVERSITY 19107 #033-06-2005 L2005 **PD** *012
CALABRO, Salvatore Peter. 2401 PENNSYLVANIA AVE, #1A5 THE PHILADELPHIAN 19130 #561-01-1971 L1973 **GS** *020
CALANDRI, Cesare. 100 E LEHIGH AVE 19125 #561-17-1983 L1985 **HEM IM** *020 †20
CALCANO PEREZ, Julio A. U OF PA CEREB MED CTR 429 19104 #042-01-1970 L1987 **NM N** *020
CALHOUN, Joseph Harlan. 840 WALNUT ST, WILLS EYE HOSP 19107 #041-01-1962 L1966 **OPH** *020 †35
CALIMANO, Nilda Margarita. 5501 OLD YORK RD, A EINSTEIN MED CTR 19141 #042-02-2003 L2004 **IMG** *012 †20
CALLAGHAN, Brian Christop. 3400 SPRUCE ST, 2ND FLOOR, RAVDIN BUILDING 19104 #041-01-2004 L2004 **N** *012
CALLAGHAN, Marian P. 3440 MARKET ST STE 200, DEPT OF CHILD AND ADOLESCE 19104 #041-13-1983 L1985 **CHP P** *040 †75
CALLAHAN, Clara Ann. 1015 WALNUT ST STE 110 19107 #041-07-1977 L1979 **PD** *030 †55
CALLAHAN, Ryan Michael. ■ 19144 #041-15-2008 *012
CALLANAN, Vincent Patrick. 3400 N BROAD ST, STE 102 19140 #539-02-1987 L2003 **P** *020
CALLANS, David John. 3400 SPRUCE ST 19104 #023-07-1986 L1987 **ICE CD** *020 †20
CALLEGARI, Peter Edward. 3400 SPRUCE ST, DIVISION OF RHEUMATOLOGY 19104 #035-19-1982 L1984 **RHU IM** *020 †20
CALLIGARO, Keith Don. 700 SPRUCE ST STE 101 19106 #033-06-1982 L1989 **VS** *020 †85
CALVERT, Paula Mary. 7701 BURHOLME AVE, MEDICAL ONCOLOGY/SUITE C30 19111 #539-04-1990 L1997 **HO** *100
CALVO, Carmela Valentina. 3509 N BROAD ST 9TH FL, DEPT OF PEDIATRIC EMERGENC 19140 #035-09-1994 L1999 **PD** *020 †55
CALVO, Felipe Angel. ■ 19106 #847-13-1978 L1992 *100
CAMACHO, Cheri Ann. ■ 19146 #035-45-2006 L2007 **AN** *012

CAMACHO GONZALEZ, Andres. 5501 OLD YORK RD 19141 #264-10-2001 L2005 **PD** *012
CAMARENA, Ruby Joy. 1412 FAIRMOUNT AVE, STE 2098 19130 #041-13-1987 L1988 **EM IM** *020
CAMERON, Robert A. 5800 RIDGE AVE, ROXBOROUGH MEM HOSP EMERGY 19128 #035-03-1982 L1984 **EM OM** *020 †16 ‡
CAMP, Nicole L. ■ 19131 #041-15-2008 *012
CAMPBELL, Cabrina. 116A, PVAMC INPATIENT PSYCHIATRY 19104 #004-01-1989 L1992 **P** *020 †75
CAMPBELL, Carla Cay. 324 S 34TH ST, CHILDRENS HSPTL OF PHLDLPH 19104 #020-12-1985 L1991 **PD** *020 †55
CAMPBELL, Kathryn Aimee. ■19146 #036-01-2005 L2005 **OBG** *012
CAMPBELL, Kimberly Lynn. 111 S 11TH ST, MEZZANINE LEVEL 19107 #041-02-2004 L2005 **CD** *012 †20
CAMPBELL, Peter Gravel. ■ 19107 #021-06-2005 L2005 **NS** *012
CAMPBELL, Robert Edwin. 800 SPRUCE ST 19107 #041-01-1957 L1958 **DR RO** *071 †80
CAMPBELL, Scott Alan. ■ 19148 #041-01-2006 L2006 **P** *012
CAMPEN, Cynthia Jane. 5015 CATHARINE ST # 2 19143 #005-02-2004 L2006 **CHN** *012
CAMPHOR, Sonia Ezra. ■ 19107 #704-09-1990 L2006 **NEP** *100
CAMPION, Michael John. 1 GRADUATE PLAZA #805 19146 #917-18-1978 **GO GYN** *020
CAMPLING, Barbara G. 3400 SPRUCE ST 19104 #065-06-1975 L2000 **ON IM** *020 †20
CANADA, Robin Elizabeth. 332 W MT AIRY AVE 19119 #041-02-2002 L2002 **IM** *100 †20
CANALS, Joaquin. 112 N BROAD ST, JFK MH/MR CLC 19102 #275-01-1948 L1967 **P** *020
CANCRO, Jennifer. 2301 E ALLEGHENY AVE, NORTHEASTERN HOSPITAL 19134 #041-15-1998 L2000 **IM** *030 †20
CANE, Martin. 5501 OLD YORK RD 19141 #041-13-1978 L1979 **IM** *020 †20
CANGELLO, David Laurence. ■ 19103 #035-15-2002 L2007 **GS** *100
CANINO, Michael Justin. 19102 #041-02-2008 L2008 *012
CANNING, Douglas Arthur. 324 S 34TH ST 19104 #032-01-1982 L1992 **UP** *020 †95
CANNON, Ayana Georleen. 19102 #035-09-2007 **IM** *012
CANTAGALLO, Val R. 2601 HOLME AVE 19152 #041-09-1975 L1978 **FM** *020 †18
CANTER, Daniel James. 19130 #010-01-2004 L2004 **U** *012
CANTER, Donald. ■ 19149 #041-09-1942 L1943 **FM OTO** *020
CANTER, Lauren Michelle. ■ 19146 #041-01-2005 L2006 **DR** *012
CANTERA, John Andrew. ■ 19147 #041-02-1996 *100
CANTOR, Charles Rodman. 330 S 9TH ST 19107 #024-16-1986 L1987 **N SME** *020 †75
CANTOR, Joshua Philip. 111 S 11TH ST, DEPT SURGERY/605 COLLEGE B 19107 #041-02-2000 L2001 **PTH** *012
CANTOR, Ronald Israel. 111 S 11TH ST STE G4100 19107 #041-13-1968 L1969 **ON** *020 †20
CAOILE, Benjamin Geo. HOUSE OF CORRECTIONS, 8001 STATE ROAD MOD II 19136 #748-01-1976 L1989 **PTH** *020
CAPECE, Danielle Marie. ■ 19103 #035-06-2006 L2006 **GS** *012
CAPITANIO, Marie A. 3333 N BROAD ST 19140 #041-07-1959 L1960 **PDR** *071 †80
CAPIZZI, Robert L. ■ 19103 #041-09-1964 L1965 **IM ON** *040 †20
CAPKIN, Mark Jeffrey. 5501 OLD YORK RD STE 331 19141 #041-13-1980 L1982 **IM** *020 †20
CAPLAN, Howard Saul. 601 WALNUT ST, STE 506E THE CURTIS CTR 19106 #023-01-1969 L1970 **PS HS** *020 †85,65
CAPLAN, Murray Saml. 4641 ROOSEVELT BLVD 19124 #041-02-1959 L1960 **P** *071 †75
CAPLIN, Neil James. ■ 19143 #143-06-1992 L2002 **PDE** *100
CAPONE, Gaetano Jos. 2701 HOLME AVE 19152 #041-02-1979 L1980 **CD IM** *020 †20
CAPORUSSO, Frank Donald. 1843 S BROAD ST 19148 #010-02-1978 L1979 **PUD IM** *020 †20
CAPPOLA, Anne R. 415 CURIE BLVD, 764 CRB 19104 #041-01-1994 L2002 **END** *020 †20
CAPPOLA, Thomas Peter. 3400 SPRUCE ST, HOSP. UNIV. PENNSYLVANIA 19104 #024-01-1995 L2002 **CD** *020 †20
CAPUTO, Larry Anthony. 2301 S BROAD ST, DEPT OF RADIOLOGY 19148 #041-02-1974 L1975 **DR R** *020 †80
CARABALLO, Victor. 1901 MARKET ST, FL 30 19103 #043-01-1991 L1994 **EM** *020 †16
CARABASI, Matthew Henry. 125 S 9TH ST, STE 801 19107 #041-02-1980 L1982 **ON HEM** *050 †20
CARABASI, Ralph Anthony. 111 S 11TH ST, STE 6350 GIBBON NLDG 19107 #041-02-1977 L1979 **VS GS** *020 †85
CARABELLI, Ronald Jos. 230 W WASHINGTON SQ 19106 #010-02-1979 L1982 **CD OS** *020 †20 ‡
CARAZO, Elizabeth. 101 E OLNEY AVE STE C5 19120 #042-02-1989 L1994 **IM** *020 †20
CARDAMONE, S Joseph. 3400 SPRUCE ST 19104 #561-17-1960 L1961 **P PYG** *020
CARDENAS GOICOECHEA, Segun. 800 SPRUCE ST, PENNSYLVANIA HOSPITAL 19107 #737-01-2000 L2002 **OBG** *012
CARDI, Gaetano. 3300 HENRY AVE, MEDICAL COLLGE OF PNNSYLVN 19129 #561-17-1981 L1994 **HO** *020 †20
CARDILLO, Serena. 3400 SPRUCE ST, 4 PENN TOWER 19104 #041-01-2001 L2001 **END** *100
CAREAGA, Eduardo. ■ 19130 #033-06-2002 L2006 **GS** *012
CAREY, Ann Marie. 3401 N BROAD ST, DEPT OF ANESTHESIOLOGY 19140 #010-02-1983 L1989 **AN** *020 †05
CAREY, William Bacon. 324 S 34TH ST 19104 #024-01-1954 L1955 **PD** *040 †55
CARLSON, Eric Jon. 1601 MARKET ST, STE 2410 19103 #028-03-1975 L1978 **OTO DS** *020 †45 ‡
CARLSSON, Christer. 3401 N BROAD ST 19140 #858-01-1970 L1986 **AN** *020
CARMELI, Yehuda. ■ 19111 #550-04-1989 L1995 **ID** *100
CARMI, Lemore. 3300 HENRY AVE, ALLEGHENY UNIV OF HLTH SCI 19129 #041-15-2003 L2003 **DR** *012
CARNABUCI, Guy. 1612 S BROAD ST 19145 #041-02-1958 L1959 **D** *072 †15 ‡
CARNEY, Edward A, Jr. ■ 19115 #308-07-1981 L1994 **FM** *075
CARNEY, Jessica Teresa. ■ 19106 #016-02-2004 L2004 **PD** *012 †55
CARO, Pilar. 111 S 11TH ST, THOMAS JEFFERSON UNIV HSPT 19107 #231-01-1970 L1981 **OS PD** *020 †80
CAROFF, Stanley Nathan. UNIVERSITY AVE, VA MED CTR-116A 19104 #035-47-1975 L1979 **P** *020 †75
CAROLINE, Dina Finck. 3401 N BROAD ST 19140 #041-07-1977 L1978 **R** *020 †80
CARPENTER, Eileen Kelly. 1800 LOMBARD ST 19146 #016-02-1984 L1987 **IM** *020 †20
CARPENTER, Elise Audrey. ■ 19104 #041-01-2008 *012
CARPENTER, Gary Grant. 833 CHESTNUT ST, STE 300 19107 #041-02-1960 L1961 **PDE PD** *040 †55
CARPENTER, Jeffrey Palmer. 3400 SPRUCE ST, FL 4 19104 #008-01-1986 L1987 **VS** *020 †85
CARPENTER, Judith T. 3400 SPRUCE ST 19104 #041-01-1988 L1990 **IM** *020 †20
CARPINIELLO, Victor L. 299 S 8TH ST 19106 #035-03-1971 L1975 **U** *020 †95
CARR, Anna-Marie. 5501 OLD YORK RD, ALBERT EINSTEIN MEDICAL CE 19141 #048-02-1989 L1999 **PD** *020 †55

CARR, Brendan Gerard. 3400 SPRUCE ST, DEP OF EMERGENCY MEDICINE 19104 #041-13-2001 L2001 **EM** *100 †16

CARR, Robert Wm. 1 FRANKLIN PLZ RM FP1805, SMITHKLINE BEECHAM 19102 #011-02-1981 L1989 **GPM PHP** *030 †70

CARRASCO, Jacqueline Rene. 840 WALNUT ST, STE 102 19107 #011-02-1999 L2001 **OPH PS** *020 †35

CARRASQUILLO, Jose R. 230 W WASHINGTON SQ FL 4T 19106 #042-01-1995 L1998 **GE** *020 †20

CARRIGAN, Paul Thos. ■ 19111 #041-02-1945 L1946 **PTH** *072 †50

CARROLL, Fred. 6608 CASTOR AVE 19149 #041-02-1983 L1989 **PD** *020 †55

CARROLL, Martin Peter. 421 CURIE BLVD, RM 708 19104 #032-01-1988 L1998 **HO** *020 †20

CARROLL, Phillip Ross. 7600 CENTRAL AVE 19111 #038-41-2002 L2003 **AN** *020 †05

CARROLL, Stanton Franklin. 101 E OLNEY AVE, STE 400 19120 #041-13-1971 L1972 **GS TS** *071 †85

CARROLL, Tannon Dajuan. ■ 19130 #041-01-2005 L2005 **IM** *012

CARRUTH, Stephanie Elizab. ■ 19130 #047-06-2005 L2006 **DR** *012

CARSON, John Manning. ■ 19147 #041-02-2008 L2008 *012

CARSON, Lesley Sloan. 3615 CHESTNUT ST 19104 #024-01-1977 L1983 **IMG** *020 †20

CARSTENS, Russ Paul. 380 S UNIVERSITY AVE, 411 HILL PAVILION 19104 #008-01-1990 L2000 **NEP** *020 †20

CARTER, Christopher David. ■ 19146 #051-04-2002 L2006 **PDC** *012 †20,55 ‡

CARTER, Merle Andrea. 5501 OLD YORK RD, DEPT OF EMERGENCY 19141 #008-01-1998 L1998 **EM** *020 †16

CARUSO, John Wm. 1025 WALNUT ST, STE 801 19107 #041-02-1991 L1994 **IM** *020 †20

CARVALHO, Carla Marie. ■ 19147 #016-01-2005 L2007 **GS** *012

CARVALHO, Karen Souza. ■ 19106 #187-14-1996 L2007 **CN** *020 †75

CARVER, Joseph Robt. 3400 SPRUCE ST, GROUND RHODES PAVILLION 19104 #041-09-1972 L1973 **CD IM** *030 †20

CASALE, Louis John. 5619 VINE ST # 25, SPECTRUM HEALTH SVCS 19139 #041-13-1962 L1965 **PD** *071 †55

CASALE, Pasquale. 111 S 11TH ST, DEPARTMENT OF UROLOGY 19107 #035-46-1996 L1998 **UP** *100 †95

CASANOVA, Bruno Francisco. ■ 19146 #737-06-2000 L2003 **OBG** *012

CASARETT, David Jonathan. 510 BAILEY BUILDING, 36TH & SPRUCE STREETS 19107 #038-06-1993 L1998 **IM** *020 †20

CASAS, Adela Teresa. 833 CHESTNUT ST, 3RD FL 19107 #012-01-1991 L1997 **PDS TTS** *020 †85

CASE, Warren Geo, Jr. 2400 CHESTNUT ST 19103 #035-09-1961 L1963 **P** *071

CASEY, Michael Paul. 700 SPRUCE ST, STE 500 19106 #035-08-1971 L1975 **ORS** *020 †20

CASH, Dione Jaimee. 3509 N BROAD ST, TUCMC, 5TH FLOOR, TPC 19140 #038-41-1998 L2003 **PD** *020 †55

CASHER, Danielle. 6001 RIDGE AVE, ROXBOROUGH PEDIATRICS 19128 #005-02-1993 L1995 **PD** *020 †55

CASIANO, Delane Ericker. 3535 MARKET ST, FL 2 19104 #012-21-2003 L2003 **P** *020

CASSEL, Christine Karen. 510 WALNUT ST STE 1700, AMERICAN BOARD OF INTERNAL 19106 #024-16-1976 L2004 **IM IMG** *030 †20

CASSELLI, Helene J. 170 LEVERING ST, PHILADELPHIA 19127 #041-13-1978 L1979 **IM RHU** *020 ‡

CASTA, Aurora Margarita. 33 S 36TH ST 2ND FL 19104 #042-01-1982 L1983 **P CHP** *020 †75

CASTELLANOS, Andres E. 219 N BROAD ST, STE 8 19107 #935-03-1990 L2000 **GS** *020 †85

CASTELO-SOCCIO, Leslie An. ■ 19104 #035-20-2005 L2005 **D** *012

CASTILLA, Ruby Cecilia. ■ 19147 #264-09-1989 **P EP** *050 ‡

CASTILLO, Christian Eber. ■ 19103 #035-45-2005 L2005 **IM** *012

CASTRO, Fidel Edmundo. ■ 19125 #005-18-2007 L2007 **EM** *012

CASWELL, Horace T. ■ 19140 #041-13-1939 L1941 **GS** *071 †85

CATALANO, Patricia M S. 111 S 11TH ST, STE 4240 19107 #035-03-1971 L1975 **HEM IM** *050 †20

CATO, Robert Keith. MAB SUITE 102, 39TH & MARKET STREETS 19104 #035-20-1993 L1995 **IM** *020 †20

CATTELL, Douglas Andrew. ■ 19104 #010-02-1998 L2000 **EM** *100

CAULK, Alyn Robinson. 800 SPRUCE ST 19107 #041-02-1987 L1988 **FM** *020 †18

CAVALLAZZI, Rodrigo Silva. 111 S 11TH ST, THOS JEFFERSON UNIV HOSP 19107 #187-17-2001 L2007 **PCC** *012 †20

CAVANAUGH, Michael F. 8815 GERMANTOWN AVE, STE 22 19118 #041-13-1983 L1984 **ORS** *020 †40

CAVOTO, Francis Vincent. 1616 WALNUT ST LOWR LEVEL 19103 #041-07-1976 L1977 **PM PME** *020

CAYA, James G. 3401 N BROAD ST, TEMPLE ANESTHESIA ASSOCIAT 19140 #056-06-1978 L1993 **PTH PCP** *020 †50 ‡

CAYCO, Ruby. 3509 N BROAD ST, ATTN: SYLVIA REYNOLDS 6TH 19140 #748-02-1990 L2000 **PD** *020 †55

CECIL, Henry S. 3405 CIVIC CENTER BLVD 19104 #047-05-1950 L1953 **PD OS** *071 †55

CEDERSTROM, Janice Joy. 834 CHESTNUT ST, STE T140 19107 #041-09-1980 L1981 **P IM** *020 †20,75

CELIO, Lee Anthony. 2701 HOLME AVE STE 206 19152 #041-09-1982 L1983 **IM IMG** *020 †20

CENSITS, David Michael. 1616 WALNUT ST, STE 312 19103 #041-02-2000 L2001 **P SME** *020 †75

CENTRONE, Anthony L. 1900 S BROAD ST, DEPT OBG 19145 #041-02-1957 L1958 **OBG** *030 †30

CEREDA, Maurizio Franco. ■ 19130 #561-03-1991 L2003 **AN** *100 †05 ‡

CEREFICE, Mark Leonard. 111 S 11TH ST 19107 #422-01-2005 L2005 **IM** *012

CERNETICH, John Alan, Jr. ■ 19119 #041-13-2006 L2006 **EM** *012

CERTA, Kenneth Michael. 833 CHESTNUT ST, STE 210 19107 #041-02-1979 L1980 **P** *040 †75

CERZA, Dante. ■ 19104 #008-02-2003 L2003 **PAN** *012

CEVALLOS, Salvador Leo To. ■ 19131 #748-10-1999 L2003 **CHP** *012

CHA, Susan Hayejean. 132 S 10TH ST, UNIVERSITY HO 19107 #041-14-2005 L2005 **DR** *012

CHACHKIN, Samuel Lloyd. 3400 SPRUCE ST, HOSPITAL OF THE UNIVERSITY 19104 #010-01-2002 L2002 **D** *012 †55

CHACKO, Sonia Mary. 5501 OLD YORK RD, KORMAN B6 19141 #539-03-2002 L2006 **EM** *100 †16

CHACON, Daria Arnold. 3400 SPRUCE ST, HEALTH SYST 19104 #041-13-2007 L2007 **MPD** *012

CHAGIN, Karen Deborah. ■ 19146 #041-13-2002 L2006 **PHO** *012 †55

CHAHROUDI, Ann Marjorie. ■ 19143 #012-05-2006 L2007 **PD** *012

CHAITAS, Paula Andrea. 5501 OLD YORK RD, ALBERT EINSTEIN MEDICAL CE 19141 #132-01-1999 L2006 **IM** *012

CHAITOWITZ, Mark Hillel. 111 S 11TH ST, GIBBON 4240 19107 #836-01-1997 L2001 **HO** *100 †20

CHAKKARAVARTHI, Venkat P. 100 E LEHIGH AVE, STE 105 19125 #041-02-2003 L2004 **P** *012

CHAKRABARTI, Indranil. 4641 ROOSEVELT BLVD, DEPT OF PSY 19124 #495-02-1995 L2002 **PYG** *020

CHALAL, Gerald S. 2428 BROWN ST 19130 #041-13-1951 L1952 **FM** *020 †18 ‡

CHALIAN, Ara Asadour. 3400 SPRUCE ST, OLOLARYNGLY HEAD/NECK SURG 19104 #017-20-1988 L1993 **OTO** *020 †45

CHALIAN, Raffi Ara. 3400 SPRUCE ST 19104 #917-33-2000 L2003 **OBG** *100

CHAMBERS, Bryan Patrick. 230 N BROAD ST 19102 #033-06-1987 L1988 **AN OTO** *075 †05

CHAMBERS, Christopher V. 1015 WALNUT ST STE 401 19107 #036-07-1980 L1981 **FM ADL** *040 †18

CHAMBERS, Richard Alfred. 1025 WALNUT ST, JEFFERSON MEDICAL COLLEGE 19107 #352-09-1947 L1967 **N** *072

CHAMBLISS, Robert Bryan. 245 N 15TH ST 19102 #047-05-1992 L1997 **P** *020 †75

CHAMP, Colin Eamon. ■ 19106 #041-02-2008 *012

CHAMROONRAT, Wichana. 3400 SPRUCE ST, UNIV OF PA HLTH SYS 19104 #891-04-2000 L2007 **NM** *012

CHAN, Anne Khu. 840 WALNUT ST, 11TH FLOOR,S-1120 19107 #748-01-1953 L1966 **OPH** *020 †35

CHAN, Guy Hugh, Jr. 3401 N BROAD ST 19140 #065-09-1957 L1969 **OPH** *071 †35

CHAN, Jennifer Emi. ■ 19104 #035-19-2006 L2007 **EM** *012

CHAN, Kang G. 245 N 15TH ST, DEPT OF OB/GYN 19102 #165-01-1978 L1980 **OM IM** *020 †20,70

CHAN, Karen Rita. 3400 SPRUCE ST 19104 #010-02-1993 L1996 **AN** *020 †05

CHAN, Kathryn Ruste. 111 S 11TH ST, & ONCOLOGY 19107 #748-01-2000 L2002 **HO** *012 †20

CHAN, Steve Shekting. ■ 19107 #041-15-2003 L2003 **DR** *012

CHANDELA, Sweta. 245 N 15TH ST, MAILSTOP 427 19102 #041-15-2003 L2003 **CD** *012

CHANDER, Avantika. ■ 19146 #041-01-2006 L2006 **IM** *012

CHANDLER, Bronell Elbert. 51 N 39TH ST 19104 #047-07-1990 L1992 **IM** *020

CHANDLER, Justin David. 245 N 15TH ST, MAIL STOP 413 19102 #041-02-2003 L2003 **GS** *012

CHANDLER, Leon Makesi. 3401 N BROAD ST, DEPT PM&R 19140 #035-08-2004 L2005 **PM** *012

CHANDRA, Avinash. 1025 WALNUT ST 19107 #495-21-2001 L2007 *100

CHANDRAN, Manoj. 5501 OLD YORK RD, ALBERT EINSTEIN MED CTR 19141 #117-01-1999 L2004 **CHP** *012

CHANDRASEKARAN, Shivanandh. 1316 W ONTARIO ST, JONES HALL 19140 #025-01-2001 L2004 **IM** *100

CHANDRASEKARAN, Sruti. 5401 OLD YORK RD, KLEIN 363 19141 #495-59-2006 L2007 **IM** *012

CHANDRASEKHARAN, Kotakat. ■ 19131 #495-16-1957 L1977 **P** *071

CHANDRIKA PARAMESWARAN, An. 5501 OLD YORK RD, ALBERT EINSTEIN MED CTR 19141 #495-31-1999 L2005 **CD** *012 †20

CHANG, Alice Gin. 3535 MARKET ST, FL 2 19104 #041-13-2000 L2001 **CHP** *100 †75

CHANG, Andy Yuhow. ■ 19103 #005-06-1998 L2004 **UP** *100

CHANG, Anna Marie Chia-Yu. ■ 19104 #016-06-2006 L2006 **EM** *012

CHANG, Benjamin. 3400 SPRUCE ST, 10TH FL 19104 #024-01-1986 L1992 **HS PS** *020 †85,65 ‡

CHANG, Howard Yao. ■ 19107 #051-01-2005 L2005 **EM** *012

CHANG, Joanne Meejin. ■ 19107 #033-05-2008 L2008 *012

CHANG, John Tzuyu. 3400 SPRUCE ST FL 3, RAVDIN BLDG 19104 #041-13-2001 L2001 **GE** *020

CHANG, Kenneth. 211 S 9TH ST, # 300 19107 #041-02-1994 L1997 **IM** *020 †20

CHANG, Kyong-Mi. 3400 SPRUCE ST 19104 #041-07-1987 L1990 **GE GS** *050 †20

CHANG, Lan. 5501 OLD YORK RD, DEPT MED 19141 #025-01-2007 L2007 **IM** *012

CHANG, Margaret Katherine. 3400 SPRUCE ST 19104 #065-01-1994 L2000 **RNR** *100 †80

CHANG, Patrick Hsichih. 833 CHESTNUT ST, STE 701 19107 #041-02-1996 L1998 **IM** *020

CHANG, Virginia W. 423 GUARDIAN DR, 1233 BLOCKLEY HALL-U OF PA 19104 #025-01-1994 L2002 **IM** *050 †20

CHANNICK, Bertram J. 3401 N BROAD ST 19140 #024-05-1949 L1953 **END IM** *071 †20

CHANOINE, Pierre Patrick. 922 PINE ST SIDE 3R 19107 #023-07-2001 L2001 **PD** *100 †55

CHAO, David. ■ 19107 #041-01-2004 L2006 **PD** *012

CHAO, Michael Chungyaw. ■ 19106 #005-15-2002 L2007 **OTO** *100

CHAO, Simon. ■ 19140 #041-13-2004 L2004 **ORS** *012

CHAO, Wen. 230 W WASHINGTON SQ, FL 5 19106 #041-02-1990 L1992 **ORS** *020 †40

CHAPMAN, Andrew Edward. 1328 W RITNER ST 19148 #028-78-1987, ▲ L1988 **ON HEM** *020 †20

CHAPMAN, Joseph L. 1900 S BROAD ST 19145 #041-13-1959 L1960 **GS** *020

CHAPMAN, Kimberly Ann. ■ 19123 #030-05-2002 L2002 **MG** *012 †20,55

CHAPMAN, Peter Ralph. HOSP-UNIV OF PA DEPT/RAD 19104 #143-03-1980 L1988 **NM** *020

CHAPOVSKY, Felix. ■ 19115 #041-13-2005 L2005 **PM** *012

CHAPPELL, James Edward. 3322 N BROAD ST 3RD FL, TEMPLE UNIVERSITY HOSP 19140 #051-07-1992 L1996 **PS** *020 †65

CHARALAMPOUS, Frixos C. 3400 SPRUCE ST 19104 #418-01-1946 **OS** *050

CHARKES, N David. 3401 N BROAD ST 19140 #028-02-1955 L1962 **NM IM** *071 †28,20

CHARKOUDIAN, Leon David. 51 N 39TH ST, SCHEIE EYE INST 19104 #023-07-2005 L2005 **OPH** *012

CHARLES, Jeremy. 3400 SPRUCE ST, UNIV OF PA HLTH SYS 19104 #035-08-2007 L2007 **PM** *012

CHASKY, Moshe Chaim. 3322 N BROAD ST, MEDICAL ONCOLOGY 19140 #550-02-2002 L2005 **HO** *012 †20

CHAT, Emanuel. ■ 19116 #041-13-1936 **P** *071 †75

CHATFIELD, Kathryn Collie. ■ 19103 #032-01-2006 L2006 **PMG** *012

CHATILLA, Wissam M. 3401 N BROAD ST, TUH 763 PP 19140 #605-01-1990 L1995 **PCC SME** *020 †20

CHATTEN, Jane. 324 S 34TH ST, CHILDRENS HOSP PATHOLOGY 19104 #067-01-1957 L1962 **ATP** *071 †50

CHATTERGOON, Michael Anan. ■ 19146 #041-01-2005 L2005 **IM** *012

CHATTERJEE, Anjan Kumar. 3400 SPRUCE ST, HOSP OF THE UNIV OF PENN 19104 #041-01-1985 L1985 **N** *020 †75

CHATTERJEE, Pia. 3400 SPRUCE ST, OF PENNSYLVAN 19104 #041-15-2005 L2005 **EM** *012

CHATWANI, Ansuya Ashvin. 3401 N BROAD ST DEPT ANES 19140 #495-17-1973 L1977 **AN** *020 †05

CHATWANI, Ashwin Jamnadas. 3400 N BROAD ST, DEPT OBGYN 19140 #495-17-1973 L1978 **OBG** *020 †30

CHAU, Andrew Francis. 5501 OLD YORK RD, DEPT OF OB/GYN 19141 #021-05-1990 L1996 **OBG** *020 †30

CHAUDHRI, Asma Sana. ■ 19144 #704-21-1990 L1994 **IM** *020 †20

CHAUDHRI, Muhammad S. ■ 19104 #704-20-1990 L2006 **DR** *100 †80

CHAUDHRI, Munawar Sultana. 2827 N 5TH ST 19133 #704-06-1958 L1975 **GP PTH** *071 †50
CHAUDHRI, Yasmin. ■ 19107 #033-05-2003 L2004 **DR** *012
CHAUDHRY, Aziz Ur Rehman. 4000 N MARSHALL ST 19140 #308-07-1981 L1986 *020
CHAUDHRY, Kunal. ■ 19107 #051-07-2007 L2007 **IM** *012
CHAUDHRY, Sohail Sharif. 111 S 11TH ST 19107 #010-03-2003 L2003 **RO** *100
CHAUHAN, Veeraish. 2900 W QUEEN LN 19129 #496-43-2004 L2007 **IM** *012
CHAVARRIA, Kevin Anthony. 19119 #041-13-1983 L1985 **AN IM** *075
CHAVEZ, Alejandro. ■ 19104 #041-01-2008 *012
CHAVKIN, Diana Elana. ■ 19103 #035-19-2005 L2005 **OBG** *012
CHAWICH, Salwa B. 3509 N BROAD ST, MEDICAL CENTER/PED ER 19140 #875-02-1984 L2003 **PD** *020 †55
CHAWLA, Harbhajan Singh. 231 N BROAD ST 19107 #209-01-1964 L1977 **PD NPM** *020 †55 ‡
CHAWLA, Rashmi. ■ 19107 #495-37-2000 L2006 **PCC** *012 †20
CHAYAPRUKS, Thomas Y. 950 WALNUT ST, APT 315 19107 #041-02-2001 L2001 **RNR** *100 †80
CHAYEN, Benjamine. 1025 WALNUT ST RM 310 19107 #550-02-1978 L1985 **OBS GYN** *020 †30
CHE, Wesley Yenru. 3401 N BROAD ST, DEPT OF MEDICINE 8-PP 19140 #035-09-2006 L2006 **IM** *012
CHEEK, Theodore Glenn. 4141 TIMBER LN 19129 #005-12-1974 L1982 **AN** *040 †05
CHEESEMAN, Leslie Ann. ■ 19118 #041-13-1996 L1999 **IM** *020 †20
CHELLAPPA, David Ananthan. 1600 VINE ST MC, GLAXOSMITH KLINE 19102 #495-27-1972 L1998 **PHM** *030 †55
CHEN, Alexander. 3401 N BROAD ST, OF SURGE 19140 #024-07-2007 L2007 **GS** *012
CHEN, Alice S. ■ 19103 #041-15-2004 L2005 **DR** *012
CHEN, Chijen. MEDICAL SCIENCE BLDG 19151 #385-02-1958 L1969 **GS** *072 †85
CHEN, Daniel Lo. ■ 19107 #041-02-2008 *012
CHEN, David Yentang. 333 COTTMAN AVE, DEPT OF SURGICAL ONCOLOGY 19111 #035-20-1997 L2004 **U SO** *020 †95
CHEN, Dona W. 3300 HENRY AVE, PEDIATRICS 19129 #041-02-1997 L1999 **PD** *020 †55
CHEN, Elbert Tse-Fu. ■ 19144 #041-15-2008 *012
CHEN, Emily Jia. ■ 19107 #038-40-2006 L2006 **EM** *012
CHEN, Emmie I M. 3440 MARKET ST STE 200, ADOLESCENT PSYCHIATRY 19104 #041-02-2002 L2006 **CHP** *012
CHEN, Esther Hunghwa. 3400 SPRUCE ST, DEPT OF EMERGENCY MEDICINE 19104 #035-48-1998 L2000 **EM** *020 †16
CHEN, Han-Chiao Isaac. ■ 19146 #041-01-2007 L2007 **GS** *012
CHEN, James Yen-Yu. 3400 SPRUCE ST, DEPT RAD 19104 #043-01-2002 L2007 **RNR** *012 †80
CHEN, Jane. 1 PENN BLVD, STE 1026 19144 #028-02-1993 L1996 **ICE CD** *020 †20
CHEN, Janet Showe. ERIE AVE AT FRONT ST, DEPT OF INFECTIOUS DISEASE 19134 #033-06-1995 L1997 **PDI** *020 †55
CHEN, Jodi N. ■ 19103 #041-02-2002 L2005 **PDC** *012 †55
CHEN, Jung Fu. 7324 CHESTNUT AV 19126 #244-02-1956 L1976 **OBG** *072
CHEN, Kathleen Jeanne. 19148 #035-47-1993 L1996 **PD** *020 †55
CHEN, Kevin Yeekai. ■ 19107 #041-02-2008 *012
CHEN, Lan X. 3701 MARKET ST, STE 741 19104 #243-16-1987 L1999 **RHU** *020 †20
CHEN, Linda. 3400 SPRUCE ST 19104 #043-01-1979 L1982 **AN** *020 †05 ‡
CHEN, Lingyi. 19131 #004-01-2002 L2002 **HO** *012 †20
CHEN, Loren. ■ 19107 #051-04-2006 L2006 **IM** *012
CHEN, Maria Fangchun. ■ 19146 #041-02-2007 **IM** *012
CHEN, Michael Wayne. 5501 OLD YORK RD, ALBERT EINSTEIN MED CTR 19141 #041-02-2006 L2006 **DR** *012
CHEN, Mike K. 3509 N BROAD ST, TEMPLE CHILDREN'S UNIV MED 19140 #048-14-1987 L1996 **PDS GS** *020 †85
CHEN, Peter Jenchih. 3400 SPRUCE ST 19104 #041-09-1996 L1998 **OBG** *020 †30
CHEN, Shiuyi Emily. 19103 #036-05-2003 L2007 **PAN** *012
CHEN, Sing-Tsung. 1015 CHESTNUT ST, STE 902 19107 #244-04-1980 L1991 **HMP PTH** *020 †50
CHEN, Stephen Samfong. ■ 19144 #041-15-2008 *012
CHEN, Susan Minhui. 51 N 39TH ST 19104 #025-01-1995 L1997 **EM** *020 †16
CHEN, Xiaoli. 1800 LOMBARD ST 19146 #041-13-1988 **PTH PCP** *020 †50
CHEN, Yuh Teh. 6 FRANKLIN PLZ, MAGEE REHABILITATIONHOSPIT 19102 #244-02-1970 L1975 **PM** *071 †60
CHENEY, Maryalice. 1100 WALNUT ST 19107 #016-42-1980 L1981 **CRS** *020 †85,10 ‡
CHENG, Cynthia. 833 CHESTNUT ST STE 301, JEFFERSON FAM MED ASSOC 19107 #041-02-1994 L1996 **FM** *020 †18
CHENG, Gang. 3400 SPRUCE ST, UNIV OF PA HLTH SYS 19104 #243-16-1987 L2007 **NM** *012
CHENG, Jiun-Chen. 5450 WISSAHICKON AVE 19144 #244-05-1978 *100
CHENG, Jocelyn Y. ■ 19102 #041-02-2006 L2006 **N** *012
CHENG, Jonathan Dean. 333 COTTMAN AVE, FOX CHASE CANCER CTR 19111 #026-04-1992 L1998 **ON** *020 †20
CHENG, Shih C. ■ 19131 #041-01-1997 L1999 *100
CHENG, Siulai. 1025 WALNUT ST, THOMAS JEFFERSON UNIV HOSP 19107 #041-15-2004 L2004 **IM** *100
CHENG, Sonia Songyee. 1900 S BROAD ST, PRIMARY CARE CTR SO PHIL 19145 #041-02-1997 L2003 **PD** *020 †55
CHENG, Tsung-Yuen. 3400 SPRUCE ST 19104 #244-01-1977 L1988 **N** *020
CHENITZ, Kara Beth. ■ 19107 #033-05-2007 L2007 **IM** *012
CHENNAPATNA MANJUNATH, Nay. ALUMNI AFFAIRS, ALBERT EINSTEIN MEDICAL CE 19141 #496-21-2005 L2007 **OBG** *012
CHENNUPATI, Sri Kiran. 3400 SPRUCE ST, DEPARTMENT OF ORL HHS 19104 #048-04-2004 L2004 **OTO** *012
CHEN-PLOTKIN, Alice S. 330 S 9TH ST 3RD, FLOOR NEUROLOG 19107 #024-01-2003 L2003 **IM** *100
CHERIAN, Dinu. ■ 19107 #041-02-2008 *012
CHERIAN, Julie Sosa. 1720 S BROAD ST, HEALTH CARE CENTER #2 19145 #496-32-1999 L2002 **IM** *020
CHERKASSKY, Marina. 8102 LANGDON ST 19152 #913-99-1980 L1991 **FM** *020 †18
CHERNAK, Esther Debra. 500 S BROAD ST, DEPT PUBLIC HLTH 19146 #033-06-1986 L1989 **ID IM** *030 †20
CHERNOFF, Jonathan D. 7701 BURHOLME AVE, RM W428 19111 #035-47-1984 L1985 **IM ON** *050 †20
CHERNUKHA, Konstantin V. 5501 OLD YORK RD 19141 #913-99-1984 L2002 **RNR** *020 †80
CHERNYAK, Natalya. 2900 W QUEEN LN 19129 #422-01-2005 L2005 **P** *012
CHESKIS, Ellina. ■ 19107 #041-02-2005 L2005 **IM** *012
CHESNICK, Richard Martin. 221 N BROAD ST 19107 #041-07-1981 L1983 **DR** *020 †80
CHESTER, Allan. 255 S 17TH ST 19103 #869-04-1954 L1960 **OBG** *071 †30

CHESTNUT, Wendell L. ■ 19132 #010-03-1965 L1966 **GP** *071
CHEUNG, Albert Tinwai. 3400 SPRUCE ST, DEPT OF ANESTHESIA DULLES 19104 #005-18-1985 L1990 **AN** *020 †05
CHEUNG, Dorothy Szewing. 1015 CHESTNUT ST, STE 1300 19107 #048-12-2000 L2006 **AI** *020 †20,03 ‡
CHEUNG, Joseph Yat-Sing. 833 CHESTNUT ST STE 700, DIV NEPHROLOGY/JEFFERSON 19107 #036-07-1978 L1986 **NEP IM** *050 †20
CHEUNG, Nina Lam. 5819 WAYNE AVE 19144 #041-15-2006 L2006 **IM** *012
CHEUNG, Raynard J. 3998 RED LION RD 19114 #041-01-1992 L1994 **GE** *020 †20 ‡
CHEUNG, Vivian. 3516 CIVIC CENTER BLVD, RM 516G/ABRAMSON RESEARCH 19104 #024-07-1993 L1997 **CHN PD** *020
CHHABRA, Avneesh. ■ 19130 #495-45-1996 L2003 **MSR MSR** *012 †80
CHHIBBER, Geeta. 1427 VINE ST, FL 7 19102 #495-08-1974 L1978 **MFM OBG** *020 †30
CHI, Anthony Weishine. ■ 19146 #041-01-2008 *012
CHI, John Jeonhwan. ■ 19104 #035-08-2007 L2007 **OTO** *012
CHI, Kai-Zu. ■ 19103 #041-02-2006 L2006 **GS** *012
CHI, Luqi. ■ 19116 #243-20-1984 L2006 **IM** *100 †20
CHI, Nung-Ja. 9501 ROOSEVELT BLVD, STE 404 19114 #583-03-1969 L1973 **OBG GP** *020 ‡
CHIANG, Jenny Shihjen. ■ 19103 #041-13-2008 *012
CHIANG, Mark Yatfung. 3400 SPRUCE ST 19104 #041-01-2001 L2001 **HO** *012
CHIB, Vineet Kiran. ■ 19140 #041-13-2003 L2003 **DR** *012
CHIDEKEL, Aaron S. 833 CHESTNUT ST, STE 300 19107 #043-01-1990 L1996 **PDP PD** *020 †55
CHIKWENDU, Nnaemeka Gus. 2 PENN BLVD, STE 112 19144 #690-04-1997 L2007 **IM NEP** *020 †20
CHILDS, John Norris, III. 432 W WALNUT LN 19144 #023-07-1974 L1980 **GS** *020 †85
CHILDS, Usha Mathew. 536 WALNUT LN REAR 19128 #495-17-1963 L1980 **PD OS** *020 †55
CHIN, Alvin Juilin. 324 S 34TH ST 19104 #005-11-1977 L1984 **PDC** *020 †55 ‡
CHIN, Bianca Celeste. 3400 SPRUCE ST, UNIVERSITY OF PENNSYLVANIA 19104 #566-01-2003 L2006 **GS** *012
CHIN, Jaime Marie. 1025 WALNUT ST, THOMAS JEFFERSON UNIV HOSP 19107 #035-48-2002 L2002 **IM** *100 †20
CHINITZ, Jason Samuel. ■ 19102 #041-01-2007 **IM** *012
CHIRLA, Sujala. 2900 W QUEEN LN 19129 #495-11-2001 L2003 **GE** *012 †20
CHISM, Keira Leona. ■ 19104 #041-12-2002 L2003 **IM** *100
CHISUM, Melvin J. ■ 19129 #041-01-1952 L1953 **OM IM** *071 †20
CHITALE, Rohan Vidyadhar. ■ 19107 #041-02-2007 L2007 **GS** *012
CHITI-BATELLI, Sandro. ■ 19119 #561-06-1993 L1995 **IM** *100
CHIU, Alexander Guangyu. 3400 SPRUCE ST, 5 REVLON BLDG 19104 #035-03-1997 L2003 **OTO** *020
CHIVUKULA, Aruna. 3401 N BROAD ST, TEMPLE ANESTHESIA ASSOCIAT 19140 #495-65-1972 L1985 **AN** *020 †05
CHIVUKULA, Ravi Shankar V. 245 N 15TH ST, DREXEL UNIV COLL 19102 #496-49-1998 L2005 **P** *012
CHIZEA, Chineze. ■ 19132 #041-13-1977 *100
CHIZEADENNAR, Chuchu N. ■ 19126 #041-13-2001 **MPD** *020 †20,55
CHMARA, Edward Stephan. 3300 HENRY AVE - HAHNEM, OF M 19129 #033-06-1999 L2000 **PTH** *100
CHNG, Seo Yi. 1 CHILDRENS CTR 19104 #825-01-1998 L2006 *100
CHO, Hyun Bok. ■ 19130 #041-15-2004 **ORS** *012
CHO, Jang Eun. ■ 19107 #010-02-2007 L2007 **GS** *012
CHO, Jay Che-Bom. 5046 SPRUCE ST 19139 #583-03-1966 L1973 **GP EM** *020
CHODOFF, Peter. 1015 WALNUT ST, STE 115 19107 #041-02-1951 L1952 **OS PHP** *030 †05
CHODOSH, Lewis Alan. 421 CURIE BLVD, 612 BRB II/III 19104 #024-01-1989 L1994 **END** *020 †20
CHOE, Hana. 3401 N BROAD ST, DEPT MED # 8PP 19140 #035-06-2002 L2003 **IM** *012
CHOI, Cyndia Sun. MENTAL HEALTH CLINIC, PHILADELPHIA VA. HOSPITAL 19104 #033-06-1985 L1987 **P** *020 †75
CHOI, Daniel Kyuyoung. ■ 19107 #041-15-2008 *012
CHOI, Edward Won. ■ 19104 #041-13-2005 L2007 **EM** *012
CHOI, Eugene Jinkyu. ■ 19103 #041-02-2003 L2003 **HO** *012
CHOI, Jiyon Jane. ■ 19103 #033-06-2003 L2003 **HO** *012 †20
CHOI, John Kim. 3400 SPRUCE ST 19104 #041-01-1991 L1994 **HMP** *050 †50
CHOI, Michelle Yoonyoung. ■ 19107 #035-08-2006 L2006 **IM** *012
CHOI, Youngsook. 3300 HENRY AVE, MEDICAL COLLGE OF PNNSYLVN 19129 #035-46-1985 L1997 **IM PHP** *062 †20
CHOKSHI, Reena Vijay. ■ 19103 #048-13-2006 L2006 **IM** *012
CHOKSI, Radhika Bipin. ■ 19103 #051-04-2005 L2005 **PD** *012
CHON, Joanna. 833 CHESTNUT ST STE 70 19107 #010-01-1994 L2001 **U** *020 †95
CHONG, William Hsuanhua. ■ 19107 #041-13-2005 L2005 **IM** *012
CHOU, Carol M. 3701 MARKET ST STE 741 19104 #035-01-1992 L1995 **IM** *020 †20
CHOU, Doris. 3400 SPRUCE ST, DEPT OF OB/GYN 19104 #033-06-1998 L2000 **MFM** *050
CHOU, Edgar Youchei. 1427 VINE ST, FL 6 19102 #035-09-2000 L2001 **IM** *020 †20
CHOU, Hubert Shihhan. 51 N 39TH ST, SMITHKLINE BEECHAM CLINIC 19104 #028-02-1988 L1999 **END** *020 †20
CHOU, Joli C. ■ 19106 #041-01-2004 L2004 **GS** *100
CHOU, Stella Ting. 3615 CIVIC CENTER BLVD, ARC 310C 19104 #035-09-2000 L2001 **PHO** *040 †55
CHOUDHARY, Ilmia S Bano. 1800 LOMBARD ST 19146 #704-06-1963 L1973 **EM PTH** *020 †16
CHOUDHRY, Modassir Saeed. ■ 19154 #043-01-1998 L1999 **TS** *100 †85
CHOUDHRY, Netan. 51 N 39TH ST, SCHEIE EYE INST 19104 #010-02-2005 L2005 **OPH** *012
CHOUDRY, Rabia Bano. 9880 BUSTLETON AVE, NEUROLOGY ASSOCIATES 19115 #041-15-2000 L2001 **N** *020 †75
CHOUDRY, Rashad Ghafoor. 3401 N BROAD ST 19140 #041-14-1999 L2001 **VS** *100 †85
CHOWDHURY, Mashiul Haq. 219 N BROAD ST, FL 5 19107 #160-02-1987 L1998 **ID** *020 †20
CHRIST, Lori Ann. ■ 19107 #041-12-2007 L2007 **PD** *012
CHRISTENSEN, Anne Mette. 324 S 34TH ST 19104 #297-01-1987 L2000 **PN** *020 †55
CHRISTENSEN, Marcy Marie. ■ 19149 #041-15-2008 *012
CHRISTENSON, Thomas Eliot. 925 CHESTNUT ST, FL 6 19107 #026-04-2004 L2004 **OTO** *020
CHRISTIAN, Cindy W. 324 S 34TH ST 19104 #035-03-1985 L1987 **PD OS** *020 †55
CHRISTIANSON, Matthew S. ■ 19141 #010-02-2003 L2003 **EM** *012
CHRISTIE, Jason Douglas. 3400 SPRUCE ST, PULMONARY & CC, 836 W GATE 19104 #035-01-1993 L1995 **PCC** *020 †20
CHRISTOPHE, Kathleen Mary. 1999 W HUNTING PARK AVE 19140 #041-07-1997 L1998 **OBG** *020 †30
CHU, Christina Shuwai. 3400 SPRUCE ST, DEPT OF OB/GYN 19104 #041-01-1995 L1998 **GO GYN** *020 †30

CHU, Emily Yukuang. ■ 19103 #041-01-2006 L2007 **D** *012
CHU, Jennifer. 3401 MARKET ST, STE 135 19104 #209-03-1972 L1979 **PM** *020 †60
CHUA, Eduardo Alvarez. 5501 OLD YORK RD, ALBERT EINSTEIN MED CTR 19141 #748-02-2002 L2004 **IM** *100 †20
CHUA, Winona Dy. 3405 CIVIC CENTER BLVD, CHOP 19104 #748-02-1984 L1997 **PD** *020 †55
CHUANG, Michael Jia. ■ 19144 #041-15-2008 *012
CHUBE, Ramona. ■ 19119 #041-07-1986 L1990 **FM** *020 †18
CHUDNOFSKY, Carl. 5501 OLD YORK RD, DEPT OF EMERGENCY MEDICINE 19141 #010-01-1985 L2000 **EM** *030 †16
CHUMSRI, Saranya. 5501 OLD YORK RD, ALBERT EINSTEIN MED CTR 19141 #891-01-1999 L2002 **HO** *012 †20
CHUN, Sae Il. 1900 S BROAD ST 19145 #583-01-1961 L1972 **PM** *020 †60
CHUNG, Chan Yong. ■ 19130 #041-13-2003 L2003 **GE** *012 †20
CHUNG, Christina Lee. 219 N BROAD ST, FL 4 19107 #041-13-2002 L2002 **D** *020 †15
CHUNG, Edward K. JEFF U HOSP STE 5611C 19107 #583-02-1957 **CD IM** *020
CHUNG, Esther Kyunghi. 833 CHESTNUT ST, STE 300 19107 #035-01-1991 L1993 **PD PHP** *020 †55
CHUNG, Hannah Koh. ■ 19131 #041-13-2006 L2006 **IM** *012
CHUNG, Jooyeun. 1015 WALNUT ST, COLLEGE 511 19107 #041-14-2002 L2002 **GS** *012
CHUNG, Peter. ■ 19131 #041-13-2006 L2006 **IM** *012
CHUNG, Whan Soon. 2320 E ALLEGHENY AVE 19134 #583-01-1966 L1972 **OBG GO** *071 †30
CHUNG, William Lee. ■ 19118 #041-13-2003 *100
CHUNHAMANEEWAT, Narathip. 5501 OLD YORK RD, ALBERT EINSTEIN MEDICAL CE 19141 #891-02-2003 L2006 **IM** *012
CHVALA, Robert Paul. 245 N BROAD ST, STE 110 19107 #033-06-1976 L1980 **NEP IM** *020 †20
CHWISTEK, Marcin A. 333 COTTMAN AVE, DEPARTMENT OF MEDICAL ONCO 19111 #759-01-1993 L2005 **IM PMM** *020 †20
CIANCI, Luigi Anthony. 2801 ISLAND AVE, STE 5 19153 #035-08-1974 L1975 **IM** *020 †20 ‡
CIANFARRA, Vincenzo. ■ 19104 #561-10-1950 L1959 **N** *071
CICCOLELLA, David Eugene. 3401 N BROAD ST, TEMPLE UNIVERSITY HOSPITAL 19140 #035-06-1981 L1994 **PCC IM** *020 †20
CIMINIELLO, Frank A. 3400 SPRUCE ST, BLOCKLEY HALL OFFICE 1218 19104 #035-19-2002 L2002 **IM** *100 †20
CIMINIELLO, Michael E. 1015 WALNUT ST, THOMAS JEFFERSON UNIV 19107 #041-02-2002 L2004 **ORS** *012
CINES, Douglas Brock. 3400 SPRUCE ST 19104 #035-19-1972 L1975 **HEM ON** *050 †20
CINES, Pamela Hope. ■ 19130 #041-13-2004 L2005 **IM** *100
CIPOLLA, James. 3440 MARKET ST, FIRST FLOOR 19104 #041-07-1995 L1996 **GS AN** *020 †85
CIRIGLIANO, Michael D. 3701 MARKET ST, 7TH FLOOR SUITE 741 19104 #041-01-1990 L1992 **IM** *020 †20
CIVAN, Jesse Michael. ■ 19104 #041-01-2006 L2006 **IM** *012
CIVAN, Mortimer Mordecai. 3700 HAMILTON WALK, A303 RICHARDS BLD 19104 #035-01-1959 L1964 **NEP IM** *050 †20
CIVIC, Brian Kendall. ■ 19129 #041-13-2007 L2007 **IM** *012
CIZMAN, Borut. 415 CURIE BLVD, 700 CRB RENAL DIVISION 19104 #957-03-1979 L1997 **IM NEP** *020 †20
CLAIR, Henry Stephen. 7602 CENTRAL AVE STE 201 19111 #041-02-1958 L1959 **GP OS** *071
CLAIR, Michael R. 8305 RIDGE AVE 19128 #016-06-1977 L1979 **DR** *020 †80
CLANCY, Michael. 3333 N BROAD ST, RM 343 19140 #041-02-1970 L1971 **ORS** *020 †40
CLANCY, Patricia Ann. 3401 N BROAD ST 19140 #041-15-1999 L2001 **IM** *020 †20
CLANCY, Robert Ryan, Jr. 324 S 34TH ST, CHILDERN'S HOSP OF PHILA 19104 #023-07-1975 L1981 **N PD** *020 †55,75
CLARK, Christopher M. 3615 CHESTNUT ST, PENN-RALSTON CTR 19104 #041-02-1973 L1977 **N** *020 †75
CLARK, Douglas Paul. 3400 SPRUCE ST, MEDICAL AFFAIRS OFFICE 19104 #023-07-1989 L1992 **ATP PCP** *050 †50
CLARK, James Michael. 3400 SPRUCE ST 19104 #041-01-1963 L1964 **OS** *020
CLARK, Linda Pat. 7604 CENTRAL AVE STE 104, FRIENDS HALL PHYS BLDG 19111 #048-12-1976 L1996 **IM IMG** *020 †20
CLARK, Tamika Danielle. ■ 19150 #035-19-2003 L2003 **EM** *020
CLARKE, Deborah Anne. 1999 W HUNTING PARK AVE, HUNTING PARK HLTH CTR 19140 #041-07-1995 L2006 **FM** *020 †18
CLARKE, Leon Edison. 501 S 54TH ST, STE 530 19143 #010-01-1975 L1976 **GS ON** *020 †85
CLARKE, Sylvan Eugene. 5501 OLD YORK RD WCB4, ALBERT EINSTEIN MEDICAL CE 19141 #041-01-2004 L2004 **ORS** *012
CLAUSS, Heather Ellen. 3401 N BROAD ST, OF MED 19140 #041-15-2002 L2002 **ID** *012 †20
CLAY, Stephen Nathaniel. ■ 19139 #016-45-1989 L1992 **IM** *020
CLEARFIELD, Harris R. 219 N BROAD ST FL 5 19107 #041-02-1959 L1960 **GE IM** *020 †20
CLEMMER, Jill Alison. 2400 CHESTNUT ST 19103 #041-01-2003 L2003 **IM** *100 †20
CLIMACO, Antonette Badua. 5501 OLD YORK RD 19141 #748-01-2003 L2006 **IM** *012
CLOSE, Jeremy David. ■ 19147 #041-02-2006 L2006 **FP** *012
CLOUGH, Jeffrey David. ■ 19107 #041-02-2008 *012
CLOUSE, Roy Gilman. ■ 19102 #038-40-1961 L1962 **P** *075
CLOVIS, William Leroy. 2052 SANSOM ST 19103 #041-01-1957 L1958 **P** *020 †75 ‡
CLYMAN, Stephen Gary. 3930 CHESTNUT ST 19104 #041-02-1982 L1987 **OS** *030
COASSOLO, Kara. 3400 SPRUCE ST 19104 #041-13-1999 L2001 **OBG MFM** *020 †30
COBBS, Walter Herbert, III. 3400 SPRUCE ST 19104 #036-07-1971 L1974 **N** *050 †75
COBERT, Howard Stephen. 2236 E ALLEGHENY AVE 19134 #041-02-1977 L1979 **CD** *020 †20
COBURN, Ronald Franklin. 3400 SPRUCE ST 19104 #016-06-1967 L1971 **PUD OS** *050 †20
CODARIO, Ronald Anthony. 2511 S BROAD ST 19148 #041-09-1973 L1974 **IM CD** *020 †20
CODELLA, Mark Stephen. 1403 RHAWN ST 19111 #041-09-1984 L1985 **GE IM** *020 †20 ‡
CODISPOTI, Joseph Raymond. 800 SPRUCE ST 19107 #041-02-1980 L1981 **IM** *020 †20
CODOLOSA, Jose Nicolas. 5401 OLD YORK RD, KLEIN 363 19141 #132-01-2003 L2007 **IM** *012
COFFIN, Susan Elizabeth. 324 S 34TH ST 19104 #050-02-1987 L1992 **PD ID** *050 †55
COGEN, Frederick Chas. 10125 VERREE RD, STE 106 19116 #041-01-1970 L1973 **AI IM** *020 †20,03
COHEN, Adam David. ■ 19146 #041-01-1999 L2001 **HO** *100 †20
COHEN, Alan Richard. 3400 CIVIC CENTER BLVD, RM 9555 19104 #041-01-1972 L2002 **PD HEM** *050 †55
COHEN, Alana Elise. ■ 19104 #041-01-2005 L2007 **IM** *012
COHEN, Arnold Wm. 5501 OLD YORK RD, ALBERT EINSTEIN MED CTR 19141 #035-20-1971 L1972 **OBG MFM** *040 †20
COHEN, David Elliott. 3400 SPRUCE ST 19104 #023-01-1978 L1981 **AN PME** *020 †05,55
COHEN, David Jan. ■ 19103 #041-01-1937 L1938 **GP CD** *071
COHEN, Debbie Louise. 3400 SPRUCE ST, UNIV OF PA-210 WHITE BLDG 19104 #836-01-1990 L1998 **NEP** *020 †20

COHEN, Elisabeth Jane. 840 WALNUT ST STE 920 19107 #024-01-1975 L1976 **OPH** *020 †35
COHEN, Faith Hartman. 2200 BEN FRANKLIN PKWY 19130 #041-09-1965 L1967 **PYA P** *020 †75
COHEN, Gary Meir. 7131 RIDGE AVE 19128 #041-13-1990 L1993 **FM** *020 †18
COHEN, Gary Scott. 3401 N BROAD ST, DIAGNOSTIC IMAGING DEPT T. 19140 #035-47-1988 L1990 **DR** *020 †80
COHEN, Herbert E. 111 S 11TH ST STE G4280, GIBBON BLDG 19107 #041-09-1961 L1963 **CD IM** *020 †20
COHEN, Ian Jos. 324 S 34TH ST, DEPT OF ONCOLOGY 19104 #917-06-1968 **ON** *050
COHEN, Ira. 925 CHESTNUT ST, JEFFERSON HEART INSTITUTE 19107 #035-46-1967 L2001 **CD IM** *020 †20
COHEN, Jack Burton. 230 N BROAD ST 19102 #041-12-1990 L1995 **AN** *020 †05
COHEN, Jill Barrie. 3300 HENRY AVE 19129 #041-77-1992, ▲ L1994 **IM** *020 †20
COHEN, Jodi Melissa. 324 S 34TH ST, CHILDRENS HSPTL OF PHLDLPH 19104 #028-02-1991 L1993 **PD** *020 †55
COHEN, Kenneth D. 4200 MONUMENT RD 19131 #016-42-1954 L1954 **P PYA** *020 †75 ‡
COHEN, Larry Warren. 14425 BUSTLETON AVE 19116 #041-09-1980 L1982 **FM** *020 †18
COHEN, Leonard Harvey. 7500 CENTRAL AVE, STE 204 19111 #041-09-1972 L1973 **VS GS** *020 †20
COHEN, Lisa Joanne. 3400 SPRUCE ST, 100 CENTREX 19104 #036-01-2005 L2005 **IM** *012
COHEN, Marc Andrew. ■ 19102 #041-01-2005 L2005 **OTO** *012
COHEN, Martin Herbert. 101 E OLNEY AVE, STE 400 19120 #035-19-1964 L1990 **ON IM** *020 †20
COHEN, Matthew Seth. 132 S 10TH ST, STE 480 MAIN BLDG 19107 #041-02-2000 L2003 **GE** *020 †20
COHEN, Michael Bernard. ■ 19146 #041-01-2008 *012
COHEN, Michael Brandon. 1025 WALNUT ST, THOMAS JEFFERSON UNIV HOSP 19107 #011-02-2004 L2004 **IM** *100
COHEN, Mitchell Jos. 833 CHESTNUT ST STE 210, PSYCHIATRY/HUMAN BEHAVIOR 19107 #041-07-1984 L1994 **P** *020 †75
COHEN, Murray Jay. 1100 WALNUT ST STE 501 19107 #041-13-1981 L1983 **TRS CCS** *020 †85
COHEN, Noam Aryeh. 3400 SPRUCE ST, 5 RAVDIN 19104 #023-07-1998 L2000 **OTO** *020
COHEN, Patti Lynn. 3401 N BROAD ST, TEMPLE ANESTHESIA ASSOCIAT 19140 #041-01-1990 L1995 **HMP** *020 †50
COHEN, Paul A G. 801 SPRUCE ST 19107 #041-01-1969 L1970 **IM IMG** *020 †20
COHEN, Philip Lawrence. 3322 N BROAD ST, MEDICAL OFFICE BUILDING 19140 #008-01-1972 L1999 **IM RHU** *050 †20
COHEN, Raphael Meyer. 19TH & LOMBARD, STE 701 19146 #024-01-1977 L1981 **NEP** *020 †20
COHEN, Richard Howard. 102 BETH DR 19115 #041-09-1986 L1988 *020
COHEN, Richard Wayne. 2401 PENN AVE 1 A 7 19130 #041-13-1977 L1978 **P** *020 †75
COHEN, Robert M. ■ 19102 #041-02-1965 L1973 **NS** *071
COHEN, Roger Bryan. 333 COTTMAN AVE 19111 #024-01-1980 L2001 **ON IM** *020 †20
COHEN, Sarle Hirst. 321 N 18TH ST 19103 #041-01-1955 L1956 **IM IMG** *071 †20
COHEN, Sidney. 132 S 10TH ST 19107 #035-08-1964 L1969 **GE IM** *020 †20
COHEN, Stanley N. 111 S 11TH ST 19107 #051-04-1952 L1959 **END IM** *071
COHEN, Steven Brad. 925 CHESTNUT ST, FL 5 19107 #033-06-1999 L2005 **OSM** *100
COHEN, Steven Jonathan. 333 COTTMAN AVE, RM C307 19111 #035-48-1996 L1998 **HO** *020 †20
COHEN, Theodore B. 111 S 11TH ST 19107 #041-01-1951 L1952 **PYA P** *071 †75
COHEN-KOGAN, Jennifer R. 3701 MARKET ST, EDWARD S COOPER PRACTICE I 19104 #041-01-1995 L1998 **IM** *020 †20
COHN, Herbert Edward. 1025 WALNUT ST STE 607 19107 #041-02-1955 L1957 **GS TS** *020 †85,90
COHN, Jeffrey Brait. 5501 OLD YORK RD 19141 #041-02-1980 L1982 **ON HEM** *030 †20
COHN, Jennifer Elizabeth. ■ 19104 #041-01-2004 L2004 **ID** *012 †20
COHN, John Robt. 1015 CHESTNUT ST, STE 1300 19107 #041-02-1976 L1977 **AI PUD** *020 †20,03
COHN, Lillian Esther. 211 S 9TH ST, NINTH STREET INTERNAL 19107 #024-05-1978 L1979 **IM IMG** *020 †20
COHN, Robert Merrill. 34TH ST AND CIVIC CENTER B 19104 #008-01-1965 L1986 **PCH PD** *030 †55
COKER, Adam David. ■ 19128 #041-15-2008 L2008 *012
COLANCECCO, Michael R. ■ 19130 #041-77-2007, ▲ *012
COLAVITA, Anthony. 6334 ELMWOOD AVE 19142 #561-01-1970 L1972 **FM** *020 ‡
COLBERG, James Edward. 1025 WALNUT ST, JEFFERSON MEDICAL COLLEGE 19107 #024-01-1959 L1972 **GS** *071 †85
COLCHER, Amy. 330 S 9TH ST, FL 3 19107 #041-02-1989 L1989 **N** *020 †75
COLE, K Niki. 2375 WOODWARD ST 19115 #041-07-1972 L1973 **OBG** *020
COLEMAN, Beverly C. 3400 SPRUCE ST, UNIV OF PA HOSP 19104 #024-01-1974 L1991 **DR** *020 †80
COLEMAN, Colleen Marie. 10160 BUSTLETON AVE, STE F 19116 #025-07-2000 L2005 **OPH** *020 †35
COLEMAN, Jenell Sheree. 3400 SPRUCE ST, DEPT OB/GYN 5TH FL DULLES 19104 #041-01-1999 L2006 **OBG** *020 †20
COLEMAN, Lee T. 3600 CHESTNUT ST 19104 #671-01-1979 L1993 **PDR** *100
COLEMAN, Marcia Jeanne. BROAD AND VINE STREETS 19102 #041-01-1974 L1979 **OBG OS** *030
COLEMAN, Raymond L. 501 S 54TH ST, PAVILLION 19143 #041-02-1976 L1977 **IM** *020
COLL, Milton Emanuel. 3998 RED LION RD, STE 305 19114 #041-07-1981 L1983 **U GS** *020 †95
COLLAZO, Edgar Rafael. 452 W ALLEGHENY AVE 19133 #041-13-1997 L1999 **PD** *020 †55
COLLEY, Alfred Leroy. ■ 19115 #041-13-1944 L1945 **GS** *071 †85
COLLIER, Andrew Jos, Jr. 2410 S BROAD ST, STE 200 19145 #033-06-1980 L1981 **ORS** *020 †40 ‡
COLLIER, Annelise. ■ 19107 #041-15-2004 L2004 **FM** *020 †18
COLLIER, Sherita Latimore. 2501 W LEHIGH AVE, QCHC 19132 #012-21-1996 L1998 **IM** *020 †20
COLLIER, Wesley. 784 S 2ND ST 19147 #041-09-1978 L1980 **IM** *075
COLLMAN, Ronald Gary. 3400 SPRUCE ST, MALONEY 872 19104 #024-05-1981 L1983 **IM** *020 †20
COLMAN, Robert Wolf. 3400 N BROAD ST 19140 #024-01-1960 L1974 **HEM IM** *050 †20
COLONNA-ROMANO, Pietro. 800 SPRUCE ST, 9TH FL 19107 #561-12-1976 L1985 **AN** *020 †05
COMEAU, Jason Albert. ■ 19104 #041-02-2006 L2006 **GS** *012
COMIS, Robert Leo. 1818 MARKET ST STE 1100 19103 #035-15-1971 L1984 **ON** *030 †20 ‡
COMPONOVO, Roger Massa. ■ 19103 #041-02-2002 L2007 **OAR** *012
CONAHAN, Thomas Jos, III. 3400 SPRUCE ST, DEPT OF ANESTHESIA 19104 #041-01-1967 L1968 **AN** *020 †05 ‡

■ = Address Information Privacy Protected

CONANT, Emily Randall. 3400 SPRUCE ST DEPT RADIO, HOSPITAL UNIV OF PENN 19104 #041-01-1984 L1989 **DR** *020 †80

CONRAD, Katrina Anne. ■ 19104 #041-01-1979 L1980 **PTH** *020 †50

CONCORS, Edwin Robt. 6404 ROOSEVELT BLVD, STE 1B 19149 #041-02-1958 L1959 **PD** *071

CONILL, Alicia Maria. 3535 MARKET ST, STE 4045 19104 #010-02-1983 L1987 **IM ON** *020 †20

CONLIFFE, Theodore David. 2630 HOLME AVE, STE 200 19152 #041-09-1993 L1998 **PM** *072 †60

CONN, Mitchell Irvin. 132 S 10TH ST, 480 MAIN BUILDING 19107 #035-19-1980 L1983 **GE HEP** *020 †20

CONN, Rex Boland. 1015 CHESTNUT ST, STE 902 19107 #008-01-1953 L1987 **CLP** *071 †50

CONN, Victoria Ann. 3965 CONSHOHOCKEN AVE, CENTER FOR AUTISTIC CHILD 19131 #033-06-1979 L1996 **CHP PYA** *020 †75

CONNELL, Joanne Elizabeth. 205 N BROAD ST, FL 1 19107 #041-15-2002 L2002 **IM** *020 †20

CONNELLY, Felicia Marie. 2 PENN BLVD, MEDICAL OFFICE BLDG #110 19144 #033-06-1995 L1999 **PD** *020 †55

CONNOLLY, Patrick Joseph. 3400 SPRUCE ST, HOSP OF THE UNIV OF PA, SI 19104 #023-01-1998 L2006 **NS** *012

CONNOR, Robert Walter. 840 WALNUT ST 19107 #041-02-1960 L1961 **OPH** *020 †35

CONRAD, Rebecca Smith. 2230 COTTMAN AVE 19149 #041-07-1973 L1974 **OBG** *020 †30

CONSOLINI, Deborah Marie. 833 CHESTNUT ST, 3RD FL 19107 #008-02-1993 L1995 **PD** *020 †55

CONSTANT, Elizabeth R. ■ 19104 #041-07-1938 L1939 **D** *074

CONSTANTINESCU, Cristian. ■ 19147 #024-05-1988 L1991 **N** *020 †75

CONSTANTINESCU, Serban. 3401 N BROAD ST, RM B150 19140 #041-02-2000 L2002 *020

CONSTANTOPOULOS, Stavros. 5501 OLD YORK RD, DEPT OF PULMONARY DISEASES 19141 #418-01-1968 L1975 **PUD** *020

CONTRAFATTO, Igino. 3401 N BROAD ST STE 345, PARKINSON PAVILION 19140 #561-01-1981 L2002 **ICE** *020

CONVENTO, Celia R. ■ 19147 #748-08-1969 **PTH** *100

CONWAY, Daniel Henry. FRONT & ERIE AVE, ST CHRISTOPHERS HOSP 19134 #041-13-1994 L1997 **NPM** *020 †55

CONWAY, Edward Walter. ■ 19134 #041-09-1929 L1930 **GP OS** *072

CONWAY, Raymond Francis. ■ 19104 #041-02-2003 L2003 **DR** *012

CONWELL, Maria Perone. 3509 N BROAD ST, 6TH FLOOR EAST TUCMC 19140 #041-07-1990 L1994 **PD** *020 †55

COOK, David Gershon. 800 SPRUCE ST, DEPT OF NEUROLOGY 19107 #041-01-1968 L1970 **N** *071 †75

COOK, Jonathan Christian. ■ 19107 #011-02-2006 L2006 **OBG** *012

COOK, Noah Michael. ■ 19103 #041-01-2000 L2003 **PD** *100 †55

COOK, Rachel Jenkins. ■ 19104 #016-43-2002 L2006 **HO** *012 †20

COOK, Rosemary Ann. 211 S 9TH ST, NINTH STREET INTERNAL 19107 #051-04-1987 L1988 **IM** *020 †20

COOK, Tessa A. ■ 19103 #041-01-2007 L2007 *012

COOKE, Cynthia Wentworth. 3400 SPRUCE ST 19104 #056-05-1967 L1968 **GYN** *020 †30

COOKE, Nancy Evelyn. 415 CURIE BLVD, 752B C.R.B., UNIV OF PA 19104 #038-06-1974 L1982 **END IM** *050 †20

COOKE-CHEN, Ayanna Najuma. 3440 MARKET ST, STE 200 19104 #041-01-2003 L2003 **CHP** *012

COOLER, Stewart. 1331 E WYOMING AVE, STE 3100 19124 #041-09-1974 L1976 **PD** *020 ‡

COOLEY-RONAN, Jeanine. 1233 LOCUST ST, STE 400 19107 #035-06-1998 L2000 **PD** *020 †55

COON, Julius Mosher. 1025 WALNUT ST 19107 #016-11-1945 **PA** *071

COOPER, Adam Michael. ■ 19103 #422-01-2003 L2003 **EM** *020

COOPER, David Young, III. UNV OF PENN, DEPT SURG 19104 #041-01-1948 L1956 **GS OS** *085

COOPER, Edward Clissold. 3400 SPRUCE ST 19104 #008-01-1990 L2002 **N** *020 †75

COOPER, Edward Irvin. HAVERFORD & WOODBINE AV 19151 #041-02-1957 L1958 **GP OS** *071

COOPER, Edward S. ■ 19119 #047-07-1949 L1952 **IM** *071 †20 ‡

COOPER, Glenn Scott. 1339 W PORTER ST 19148 #041-02-1988 L1990 **CD** *020 †20

COOPER, Harry S. 333 COTTMAN AVE, FOX CHASE CANCER CENTER 19111 #041-02-1972 L1974 **PTH CLP** *020 †50

COOPER, Joshua Morrey. 3624 MARKET ST, STE 560W 19104 #028-02-1996 L2003 **CD** *020 †20

COOPER, Lisette Triana. 3401 N BROAD ST 19140 #041-09-1986 L1987 **IM** *020 †20

COOPER, Richard Alan. 3641 LOCUST WALK, LEONARD DAVIS INST 19104 #028-02-1961 L1971 **HEM** *050 †20

COOPERMAN, Lee Herschel. ■ 19103 #028-02-1960 L1961 **AN** *071 †05

COOPERSTONE, Brenda Gail. 324 S 34TH ST 19104 #067-01-1988 L1991 **PN** *020 †55

COPE, Constantin. 3400 SPRUCE ST, HOSP UNIV PA, RADIOLOGY 19104 #035-09-1951 L1964 **VIR CD** *071 †20

COPELAND, Adrian Dennis. 1420 WALNUT ST, STE 1412 19102 #869-04-1957 L1958 **P OS** *030 †75

COPELAND, Nathaniel H. BROAD & VINE STS 19102 #010-03-1945 L1946 **IM FM** *030 †18

COPIT, Steven Eric. 210 W RITTENHOUSE SQ 19103 #041-02-1988 L1990 **PS** *020 †85,65

COPLON, Michael Carl. HILL TOWER APTS 19118 #041-02-1966 L1967 **P** *020 †75 ‡

COPPELLI, Francesca Marie. ■ 19143 #041-12-2005 L2005 **IM** *012

COPTY, Tarek Victor. 2900 W QUEEN LN 19129 #539-06-2003 L2004 **GS** *012

CORBIN, Theodore James, Jr. 1020 SANSOM ST, "THOMPSON BLDG, STE 239" 19107 #041-07-1997 L2001 **EM** *020 †16

CORBOY, Margaretma Ellen. 3400 SPRUCE ST 19104 #041-02-1983 L1988 **IM** *020 †20

CORCINO, Ana Josefina. 9TH & WALNUT STS, WILLS EYE HOSPITAL 19106 #035-45-1989 L1993 **AN** *020 †05

CORCORAN, Amy Margaret. 3615 CHESTNUT ST, RALSTON HOUSE CLINIC 19104 #654-01-2003 L2006 **IMG** *100 †20

CORCORAN, Thomas Anthony. 3110 GRANT AVE 19114 #035-19-1989 L1992 **ORS OSM** *020 †40

CORDERA, Fernando. 333 COTTMAN AVE, FOX CHASE CANCER CTR 19111 #649-13-1998 L2005 **GS SO** *012

CORDOVA, Francis Chan. 3401 N BROAD ST, 785 PARKINSON PAVILION 19140 #748-01-1986 L1993 **PCC** *020

CORNELIUS, Kathy Camille. ■ 19131 #038-45-2006 L2006 **FP** *012

CORNFIELD, Richard Borek. 1830 RITTENHOUSE SQ # 1 19103 #041-01-1968 L1970 **P** *030 †75

CORNISH, James W. 3535 MARKET ST, 4TH FL CTR STUDIES ADDICT 19104 #041-02-1974 L1975 **P ADM** *050 †75

CORON, Roger Nathaniel. ■ 19107 #033-05-2006 L2006 **IM** *012

CORSON, Joseph Kirby. 33 E CHESTNUT HILL AVE 19118 #041-01-1947 L1948 **D** *071 †15

COSEO, Jennifer M.. ■ 19106 #035-06-2006 L2006 **PD** *012

COSGROVE, Donna Ann. 561 FAIRTHORNE AVE 19128 #041-02-1988 L1990 **PYG P** *020 †75

COSGROVE, Douglas Schenck. ■ 19103 #041-07-1989 L1991 **P** *020 †75

COSLETT, Harry Branch. 2003 WALLACE ST 19130 #041-01-1977 L1983 **N** *050 †75

COSSA, John Paul. 1900 S BROAD ST 19145 #041-09-1958 L1959 **GS** *030 †85

COSTANTINO, David Alan. 3400 SPRUCE ST, DEPT RAD 19104 #025-01-2005 L2007 **DR** *012

COSTANTINO, Thomas Guy, Jr. 3401 N BROAD ST, DEPT OF EMERGENCY MEDICINE 19140 #025-01-1996 L1998 **EM** *020 †16

COSTELLO, Michael Robert. 3401 N BROAD ST, STE AO-F300 19140 #041-14-2004 L2004 **IM** *020 †20

COTE, Mary Louise. 3333 N BROAD ST, RM 343 19140 #041-07-1959 L1960 **PD PN** *020 †55

COTE, Sean Arie. ■ 19107 #041-77-2002, ▲ L2002 **PTH** *012

COTLER, Jerome M. 1025 WALNUT ST # G-4, JEFFERSON MED COL 19107 #041-02-1952 L1953 **ORS OSS** *071 †40

COTROPIA, Joseph Paul. 3400 SPRUCE ST 19104 #048-12-1973 L1987 **IG IM** *050

COTSARELIS, George. 3401 SPRUCE ST, HOSPITAL OF UNIV OF PA. 19104 #041-01-1987 L1990 **D** *050 †15

COTTLER, Ilene. 111 N 49TH ST 19139 #041-07-1981 L1982 **P PYA** *071 †75

COTTRELL, Daniel Michael. ■ 19104 #010-01-2006 L2006 **OBG** *012

COTZEN, Donna Joyce. 325 CHESTNUT ST, STE 905 19106 #041-07-1975 L1976 **P** *020 †75

COUKOS, George. 3400 SPRUCE ST, OB/GYN DEPT 1000 COURTYARD 19104 #561-09-1987 L1996 **OBG** *020 †30

COUPLAND, Robert W. 3401 N BROAD ST 19140 #060-01-1979 L1993 **PTH** *071 †50

COUSIN, Molly Kristine. ■ 19103 #056-06-2008 *012

COUSINS, James Lee, Jr. 8011 NAVAJO ST, CHESTNUT HILL 19118 #011-02-1987 L1988 **EM MPD** *020 ‡

COUTIFARIS, Christos O. 3701 MARKET ST, 8TH FL 19104 #041-01-1982 L1984 **REN OBG** *050 †30

COUTURIE, Michael John. ■ 19147 #041-02-2004 L2004 **IM** *100 †20

COVALESKY, Veronica Ann. 1703 S BROAD ST, STE 300 19148 #041-09-1983 L1985 **CD IM** *020 †20

COVELLO, Seana Patrice F. 621 PINE ST 19106 #041-09-1994 L1999 **D** *020 †15

COWAN, Andrew Thomas. ■ 19143 #041-02-2002 *012

COWAN, Scott William. 51 N 39TH ST, STE 2D 19104 #041-02-1997 L1999 **TS** *100 †85

COWCHOCK, F Susan. 7125 SPRAGUE ST 19119 #041-02-1968 L1969 **MG END** *020 †20,19

COWELL, Vincent Swindell. 3401 N BROAD ST, 3RD FLOOR OUTPATIENT BUILD 19140 #041-07-1990 L1992 **AN** *020 †05

COX, James L. 111 N 49TH ST 19139 #041-01-1953 L1957 **P** *020 †75

COX, Jennifer Leigh. 3401 N BROAD ST 19140 #051-07-2005 L2005 **OBG** *012

COX, Jonathan Michael. 10752 BUSTLETON AVE, STE G 19116 #041-02-1980 L1981 **CD** *020 †20

COX, Karen Monica. 3400 SPRUCE ST 19104 #035-47-1999 L2001 **AN** *020 †05

COYLE, John Jos. 840 WALNUT ST 19107 #041-02-1960 L1961 **OPH** *071 †35

COYLE, Patrick Jos. 5450 WISSAHICKON AVE, STE 1-4 19144 #539-04-1956 L1966 **IM** *071

COYTE, Thomas Daniel, Jr. 10151 BUSTLETON AVE 19116 #033-06-1994 L1997 **PD** *020 †55

CRABBE, Deborah Lynn. 3401 N BROAD ST 19140 #010-03-1988 L1995 **CD** *020 †20

CRANE, Gregory James. ■ 19107 #035-06-2007 L2007 **PD** *012

CRAWFORD, Christie Daniel. ■ 19107 #041-02-2007 L2007 **IM** *012

CRAWFORD, Eileen Aidan. ■ 19129 #041-01-2007 *012

CRAWFORD, Glen Howard. 801 SPRUCE ST, FL 10 19107 #035-19-1996 L2001 **D** *020 †15

CREECH, Richard Hearne. 7500 CENTRAL AVE STE 203 19111 #041-01-1965 L1966 **ON HEM** *071 †20 ‡

CREELAN, Benjamin C. ■ 19107 #041-02-2007 L2007 **IM** *012

CRESPO-GOMEZ, Efrain J. 1412 FAIRMOUNT AVE 22, FAIRMOUNT PRIMARY CARE CTR 19130 #847-05-1977 L1993 **PD** *020 †55

CRESSWELL, Adrienne J. ERIE AVE AT FRONT ST, ST CHRISTOPHER HOSP 19134 #041-07-1987 L1989 **PS** *020

CREVAR, Ember Lee. 111 S 11TH ST, JEFFERSON UNIVERSITY 19107 #041-13-2006 L2006 **PD** *012

CRIMM, Allan Lawrence. 211 S 9TH ST, NINTH STREET INTERNAL 19107 #036-07-1980 L1982 **IM IMG** *012

CRINER, Gerard Jos. 3401 N BROAD ST 19140 #041-13-1979 L1980 **PUD** *040 †20

CRINO, Janet Asprelli. 3400 SPRUCE ST 19104 #024-05-1987 L1991 **PD** *020 †55

CRINO, Peter Benj. 3400 SPRUCE ST 19104 #008-01-1990 L1992 **N** *020 †75

CRISTANCHO, Ana Gabriela. ■ 19130 #041-01-2008 *012

CRISTANCHO PIMIENTO, Lucia. 3400 SPRUCE ST, DEPT OF PSYCH 19104 #264-09-2000 L2004 **P** *012

CRISTOL, Allan Herbert. 3400 N BROAD ST 19140 #041-01-1959 L1960 **P** *020 †75

CRISTOL, James L. 4900 FRANKFORD AVE 19124 #041-01-1970 L1971 **OPH EM** *020 †35 ‡

CRITCHELL, C Dana. 111 S 11TH ST, UNIVERSITY HOSPITAL 19107 #035-01-2005 L2005 **IM** *012

CRITIDES, Samuel D, Jr. 5501 OLD YORK RD, DIVISION OF NEUROSURGERY 19141 #033-05-1994 L2000 **NS** *020

CROFT, Damien Jamal. 216 N BROAD ST, FL 4 19102 #035-15-2000 L2001 **OBG** *020 †30

CRONHOLM, Peter Foster. 51 N 39TH ST 19104 #041-13-1998 L2001 **FM** *020 †18

CRONIN, Brian Colum. 8001 ROOSEVELT BLVD, STE 502 19152 #035-45-1997 L2000 **NEP** *020 †20 ‡

CRONKHITE, Alison Jan. ■ 19104 #028-34-2004 L2004 **AN** *012

CRONLEY, Shea Ann. 1233 LOCUST ST, STE 400 19107 #038-45-1982 L1985 **PD** *020 †55

CROOKS, Gary Walter. 3400 SPRUCE ST, PENN TOWER 11TH FLOOR 19104 #024-01-1981 L1983 **IM EM** *040 †20

CROOKS, Steven David. ■ 19146 #041-01-2006 L2006 **AN** *012

CROOKSHANK, Aaron David. ■ 19127 #041-13-2003 L2003 **PCC** *012

CROOP, Robert Stephen. 3400 SPRUCE ST 19104 #041-01-1981 L1983 **N** *020 †75

CROPSEY, John Mark. 19145 #025-01-2005 L2005 **OPH** *012

CROSBY, Dana Lynn. ■ 19144 #041-15-2008 *012

CROSS, Robert Charles. 3401 N BROAD ST, TEMPLE UNIVERSITY HOSPITAL 19140 #422-01-2001 L2001 **CD** *012

CROSS, Stephanie Alexis. ■ 19104 #041-01-2008 *012

CROUL, Sidney Edward. 3300 HENRY AVE, DEPT PATHOLOGY 19129 #041-01-1977 L1978 **NP N** *020 †75

CROWLEY, Moira Aileen. ■ 19130 #024-16-2004 L2004 **NPM** *012 †55

CROZIER, Kelley Sue. 111 S 11TH ST 19107 #041-09-1985 L1986 **PM** *020 †60

CRUDU, Vitalie. 5501 OLD YORK RD, ALBERT EINSTEIN MED CTR 19141 #913-50-2003 L2005 **IM** *012

CRUM, Dana Darlene. ■ 19146 #033-06-2008 *012

CRUMLISH, Colleen Marie. 3400 SPRUCE ST, PENN TOWER STE 2009 19104 #041-02-2000 L2001 **IM** *020 †20

CRUTCHLOW, Michael F. 1025 WALNUT ST, JEFFERSON MED COLL 19107 #041-02-1998 L2001 **END** *100 †20

CRUZ, Carlos Oscar. ■ 19146 #041-01-2008 *012

CRUZ, Ernesto S. 3401 N BROAD ST 19140 #748-01-1983 L1994 **IM PM** *020 †60,20

CRUZ, Mario. ■ 19146 #035-03-2004 L2004 **PD** *012 †55

CRUZ-ALVAREZ, Rebeca A. 3400 SPRUCE ST 19104 #042-01-1971 L1977 **IM END** *020

CUASO, Charles Co. 34TH CIVIC CTR BLVD PDC 19146 #748-01-1971 L1975 **PDC** *030

CUCCHIARA, Brett Lee. 3400 SPRUCE ST 19104 #021-01-1996 L1999 **N** *020 †75

CUCCHIARO, Giovanni. 3400 SPRUCE ST 19104 #561-03-1983 L1997 **AN** *020 †05

CUCINOTTA, Salvatore. 2301 S BROAD ST 19148 #041-09-1936 L1937 **GYN** *071

CUELLAR, Ada. ■ 19127 #048-02-2006 L2006 **EM** *012

CUHACI, Bulent. 245 N 15TH ST, MAIL STOP 437 19102 #902-10-1985 L1997 **NEP CCM** *020 †20

CUI, Jie. 111 S 11TH ST 19107 #243-03-2007 L2008 *012

CUKER, Adam Charles. 3400 SPRUCE ST, 15 PENN TOWER 19104 #008-01-2003 L2006 **HO** *012 †20

CUKRAS, Catherine Ann. 51 N 39TH ST, SCHEIE EYE INST 19104 #028-02-2003 L2003 **OPH** *100

CULTON, Harold Hugh, Jr. 6611 FRANKFORD AVE 19135 #041-09-1960 L1961 **GP D** *072

CUMANI, Blendi S. 1800 LOMBARD ST, DEPT OF MEDICAL EDUCATION 19146 #661-02-2005 L2005 **GS** *012

CUMMINGS, Curtis E. 245 N 15TH ST MS 660, DREXEL UNIV SCHL OF PUB HL 19102 #041-02-1977 L2003 **PHP** *071 †20,70

CUMMINGS, Daniel Bruce. ■ 19147 #035-45-2006 L2006 **EM** *012

CUMMINGS, Marissa. ■ 19129 #005-12-2002 L2005 **CHP** *100 †75

CUNNANE, Mary Ferry. 132 S 10TH ST, STE 285 MAIN BLDG 19107 #041-07-1964 L1967 **PTH SP** *020 †50

CUNNINGHAM, Brooke Ayoka. ■ 19139 #041-01-2007 **IM** *012

CUNNINGHAM, Erin Lucinda. ■ 19147 #041-02-2008 *012

CUNNINGHAM, Lea Christine. 34 ST CIVIC CTR BLVD, CHILDRENS HOSP 19104 #041-02-2004 L2004 **PHO** *012 †55

CUNNINGHAM, Susan Louise. ■ 19154 #041-13-1982 L1987 **GS** *020 †85

CUPINO, Andrew Christophe. ■ 19125 #041-02-2007 L2007 **TY** *012

CURCILLO, Paul G. 219 N BROAD ST, FL 10 19107 #041-01-1989 L1993 **GS NTR** *020 †85

CURRY, Joseph Mathias. 925 CHESTNUT ST FL 6 19107 #010-02-2004 L2004 **GS** *100

CURTIS, Jacque Major. 2501 REED ST 19146 #041-13-1991 L1995 **MPD** *020 †20

CURTIS, Mark Thos. 132 S 10TH ST, STE 285K 19107 #041-13-1989 L1992 **PTH NP** *020 †50

CURTIS-COHEN, Marjorie. 800 SPRUCE ST, FL 2 19107 #035-46-1979 L1981 **NPM PD** *020 †55

CUSACK, Carrie Ann R. 219 N BROAD ST, FL 4 19107 #041-02-1999 L1999 **D DMP** *020 †15

CUSTODIO, Hipolito Mance. 5501 OLD YORK RD, OFFICE OF ACADEMIC 19141 #748-02-2001 L2005 **OBG** *012

CUTHBERTSON, Rita Patrici. 3400 SPRUCE ST, HEALTH SYST 19104 #045-01-2005 L2006 **MPD** *012

CUTILLI, Bruce Jos. 3401 N BROAD ST 19140 #041-07-1989 L1989 **HNS OTO** *071

CUTLER, Irvin. 6600 ROOSEVELT BLVD 19149 #041-01-1944 L1945 **IM GP** *071

CUTLER, Neil Chas. 2116 CHESTNUT ST, 2ND FL 19103 #041-02-1967 L1968 **FM** *020 †80

CWIK, Jason Chas. 800 SPRUCE ST 19107 #041-02-1988 L1992 **AN** *020 †05

CZARNECKI, Casimir. 9412 ACADEMY RD 19114 #041-09-1962 L1963 **OPH** *020 †35

CZARNECKI, Dorothy G. 9412 ACADEMY RD 19114 #041-07-1961 L1962 **OBG** *020 †30

CZARNECKI, Nancy Sonia S. 9410 ACADEMY RD 19114 #041-02-1965 L1966 **FM OM** *030 †18

CZERNIECKI, Brian Jos. 3400 SPRUCE ST, FL 4 19104 #033-06-1988 L1995 **GS** *020 †85

CZMUS, Akim F. 1125 WALNUT ST 19107 #043-01-1977 L1984 **OPH GP** *075

CZULEWICZ, Andrew Jos. 7600 CENTRAL AVE, DEPT PATH JEANES HOSP 19111 #024-01-1974 L1986 **PTH BBK** *020 †50

DABIR, Faranak. 4500 FRANKFORD AVE, ARIZONA GRAND MEDICAL CENT 19124 #517-11-1998 L2004 **IM** *020 †20

DABNEY, Kirk Wesley. 833 CHESTNUT ST, 3RD FL 19107 #041-02-1984 L1984 **OP ORS** *020 †40

DABRAL, Sanjay. 501 S 54TH ST, MERCY HOSPITAL OF PHILADEL 19143 #495-03-1988 L2001 **IM** *020 †20

DACKIS, Charles Andrew. 51 N 39TH ST 19104 #036-07-1977 L1994 **P ADP** *020 †75

DACOSTA, Annamaria Monica. 5003 UMBRIA ST, KIDS FIRST-ROXBOROUGH 19128 #041-01-1988 L1990 **PD** *020 †55

DACOSTA, Deline Maria. 7600 CENTRAL AVE 19111 #496-15-1993 L2006 **PTH** *100 †50

DADABHAI, Alia Simjee. 3401 N BROAD ST, TEMPLE UNIV HOSP 19140 #041-15-2004 L2007 **GE** *012

D'ADDESI, Leonard Lucio. 834 CHESTNUT ST, STE G114 19107 #041-13-2002 L2002 **HSO** *012

DADOURIAN, Daniel Gregory. 230 N BROAD ST, FL 7 19102 #035-19-1985 L1993 **CD IM** *020 †20

DADPARVAR, Simin Dokht. 3400 SPRUCE ST, HOSP OF UNIV OF PENN 19104 #517-05-1974 L1980 **NM DR** *040 †28

DAFFNER, Scott Daniel. 1015 CHESTNUT ST, STE 719 19107 #041-02-2001 L2002 **ORS** *020

DAHLEM, Stephen Thos. ■ 19118 #028-03-1982 L1985 **END** *020 †55

DAHLKE, Miriam Brehmeyer. AMERICAN RED CROSS 19103 #041-07-1955 L1956 **BBK HEM** *071 †20

DAHODWALA, Nabila Abbas. 423 GUARDIAN DR, 13TH FL BLOCKLEY HALL 19104 #035-01-2002 L2002 **N** *100 †75

DAILY, Madeline S. ■ 19111 #041-09-1980 L1981 **PD** *020

DAINTY, Erin Elizabeth. ■ 19129 #051-01-2005 L2006 **OBG** *012

DAKAKNI, Tarek. 3401 N BROAD ST, TEMPLE UNIVERSITY HOSPITAL 19140 #418-01-1972 L2007 **IM** *100

DALAKAS, Marinos. 900 WALNUT ST STE 200, DEPT. OF NEUROLOGY 19107 #418-01-1972 L2007 **N** *020 †75

DALAL, Kamini Jagat. 5501 OLD YORK RD 19141 #495-22-1968 **PTH** *100

DALAL, Shamsher Singh. 3708 N 5TH ST, DEPT OF OMA/GME 19140 #495-69-2000 L2005 **RNR** *012

DALEY, Desrene Debbieann. 3400 N BROAD ST, TEMPLE UNIV SCH OF MED 19140 #041-13-2000 **IM** *100

DALFINO, John Charles, Jr. ■ 19107 #041-02-2003 **NS** *012

DALINKA, Murray Kenneth. 3400 SPRUCE ST, DEPT RAD 19104 #025-01-1964 L1971 **R** *020 †80

DALLAL, Ramsey Michael. 5501 OLD YORK RD, KLEIN STE 510 19141 #051-04-1996 L1998 **GS** *020

DALLER, John Alfons. 3322 N BROAD ST, MOB STE 132 19140 #035-08-1987 L1996 **GS TTS** *020 †85

DALLMEIER ROJAS, Dhayana. 800 SPRUCE ST 19107 #409-10-2000 L2005 **IM** *012

DALMAU, Jose Obrador. 3400 SPRUCE ST, 3 W GATES/HUP 19104 #847-17-1978 L2002 *020

D'ALONZO, Walter A. 1439 E PASSYUNK AVE, SOUTH PHILA HEALTH GRP 19147 #041-13-1939 L1940 **GP** *071 †85 ‡

DALOPE, Rosauro. 231 N BROAD ST, FEINSTEIN BLDG. 2ND FLOOR 19107 #748-02-1990 L1993 **PD** *020 †55

DALSANIA, Henry Jivan. ■ 19128 #028-34-2003 L2004 **DR** *012

DALTON, John Russell. 1015 CHESTNUT ST, STE 910 19107 #917-30-1955 L1975 **U** *071 †95

DALTON, Nicole Marie. ■ 19146 #041-01-2008 *012

DALWADI, Bela Hasmukhbhai. 245 N 15TH ST, DREXEL UNIV COLL MED/HAHNE 19102 #495-23-2001 L2004 **PTH** *012

DALY, John Michael. 3420 N BROAD ST, DEANS OFFICE 19140 #041-13-1973 L1985 **AN** *020 †85

DALY, Mary Beryl. 333 COTTMAN AVE 19111 #036-01-1978 L1989 **ON HEM** *050 †20

DALY, Sean Francis Xavier. 834 CHESTNUT ST, STE 400 19107 #539-03-1988 L1996 **OBG** *100

D'AMANDA, Christopher. 7921 GERMANTOWN AVE 19118 #035-06-1962 L1974 **PM PHP** *030

D'AMATO, Gabriel Alexis P. ■ 19107 #035-01-1947 **CHP P** *071 †75

DAMATO, Thomas Andrew. 1025 WALNUT ST STE 607, DIVISION OF CARDIOTHORACIC 19107 #041-02-1990 L1995 **TS** *020 †90,85

D'AMBROSIO, David. ■ 19128 #035-48-2003 L2004 **RO** *012

DAMILANO, Cecilia Paola. ALUMNI AFFAIRS, ALBERT EINSTEIN MEDICAL CE 19141 #132-01-2002 L2007 **PD** *012

DAMJANOV, Nevena. 3322 N BROAD ST 19140 #041-09-1989 L1991 **IM HO** *020 †20

DAMM, Christopher John. 3400 SPRUCE ST 19104 #035-01-1986 L1992 **CD** *062 †20

DANCEL-VILLASIS, Cynthia. 1025 WALNUT ST STE 700, MEDICAL COLLEGE 19107 #748-01-1972 L1976 **NPM PD** *020 †55

DANCIS, Andrew B. 421 CURIE BLVD, 709 BRBII/III 19104 #035-19-1978 L1996 **HEM ON** *020 †20

DANDOLU, Bhaktavathsala R. 230 W WASHINGTON SQ, FARM JOURNAL BLDG 19106 #495-36-1985 L1997 **TS** *020 †85,90

DANDOLU, Vani. 3401 N BROAD ST 19140 #495-70-1988 L1995 **OBG** *020 †30

DANG, Christine Mai. ■ 19107 #041-02-2005 L2005 **EM** *012

D'ANGIO, Giulio John. 3400 SPRUCE ST HSP UN PA 19104 #024-01-1945 L1976 **RO** *072 †80

DANIEL, Brian Peter. ■ 19106 #035-75-2006, ▲ L2006 **AN** *012

DANIEL, Vijendra. 51 N 39TH ST 19104 #422-01-1991 L1993 **IM** *100

DANIELE, Maria T Fincza. ■ 19130 #041-09-1969 L1970 **CHP P** *020 †75

DANIELS, Kelli Elaine. 1403 W MOYAMENSING AVE 19145 #038-41-2002 L2002 **OBG** *020

DANIELS, Maurice Nigel. 1408 S BROAD ST 19146 #035-15-1983 L1984 **PD** *020 †55

DANIELS, Michael Adrian. 2 PENN BLVD, STE 206 19144 #041-13-1982 L1984 **U** *020 †95

DANIELS, Roger Bruce. 1100 WALNUT ST # 601 19107 #041-01-1960 L1966 **IM** *020 †20

DANIELSON, Shane Darren. 4200 MONUMENT RD, BELMONT CENTER 19131 #041-14-2002 L2002 **CHP** *020 †75

DANIERO, James Joseph. 111 S 11TH ST, THOMAS JEFFERSON UNIVERSIT 19107 #051-07-2008 L2008 *012

DANILA, Dan Marian. 5501 OLD YORK RD, KLEIN 363 19141 #781-04-2004 L2006 **IM** *012

DANILEWITZ, Mervyn D. ■ 19106 #836-03-1974 L1997 **GE IM** *020 †20

DANOFF, Theodore Marc. 3400 SPRUCE ST 19104 #016-02-1987 L1989 **NEP** *020 †20

DANTE, Lee Gerard. 4200 MONUMENT RD 19131 #041-01-1972 L1973 **P** *020

DANTE, Stephen Jos. 909 WALNUT ST, 2ND FL 19107 #008-02-1983 L1984 **NS** *020 †25

D'ANTONIO, Joseph. 8835 GERMANTOWN AVE 19118 #035-15-1976 L1978 **P PYG** *020 †75

D'ANTUONO, Justin Michael. 111 S 11TH ST, THOMAS JEFFERSON UNIV 19107 #033-05-2007 L2007 *012

DANZIG, Jennifer A. ■ 19103 #025-01-2006 L2006 **PD** *012

D'AQUILANTE, Debra Ann. 8001 STATE RD, PHS INC MOD II-HOC 19136 #041-13-1985 L1986 **ID IM** *020 †20

D'AQUILI, Eugene Guy. 2400 CHESTNUT ST 19103 #041-01-1966 L1968 **P** *100 †75

DARBOUZE, Pierre. 6613 CHEW AVE 19119 #649-01-1965 L1972 **FM PTH** *020 †50

DARBY, Neil Leon. 2601 HOLME AVE, HOLME AVENUE EMGY PHYS 19152 #047-05-1980 L1985 **EM** *020 †16

DARDAINE, Halcyeane Theod. 3401 N BROAD ST, DEPT EM 19140 #024-01-2007 L2007 **EM** *012

DARZE, Eduardo Sahade. 3400 SPRUCE ST, HOSPITAL OF THE UNIV OF PE 19104 #187-01-1993 L1997 **CD** *020 †20

DAS, Srikant. 5501 OLD YORK RD, ALBERT EINSTEIN MED CTR 19141 #495-36-1999 L2004 **PD** *100 †55

DASENT, James G, Jr. 1411 E WASHINGTON LN 19138 #010-03-1945 L1952 **GP OS** *075

DASGUPTA, Indranil. 925 CHESTNUT ST, JEFFERSON HEART INST 19107 #422-01-1994 L1998 **CD** *020 †20

DASGUPTA, Sunavo. ■ 19104 #056-06-2004 L2005 **AN** *012

DASKAL, Ierachmiel. 5501 OLD YORK RD 19141 #649-33-1982 L1983 **OS** *020 †50

DASS, Kapil Gupta. ■ 19107 #041-77-2007, ▲ *012

DATKO, Farrah Mikhail. ■ 19107 #008-01-2007 L2007 **IM** *012

DATNER, Elizabeth Mellon. 3400 SPRUCE ST 19104 #041-14-1991 L1995 **EM** *020 †16

DATTA, Tejwant Singh. 5501 OLD YORK RD, ALBERT EINSTEIN MED CTR 19141 #041-13-2004 L2004 **GS** *012

DATTO, Catherine J. 3535 MARKET ST, RM 3055 19104 #033-06-1994 L1996 **PYG** *020 †75

DATTO, George Anthony, III. 833 CHESTNUT ST, STE 300 19107 #033-06-1994 L1996 **PD** *020 †55

DAUBON, Horacio Fernando. ■ 19128 #042-01-2004 L2004 **N** *012

DAUBON, Vasco Jose, Jr. ■ 19107 #042-02-2003 L2003 **CHP** *012

DAUMERIE, Geraldine Jacqu. ■ 19130 #048-04-2005 L2005 **AN** *012

DAVE, Nisha Krishnan. 840 WALNUT ST STE 12, DEPT PEDIATRIC OPTOMOLOGY 19107 #056-05-1985 L2003 **OPH PD** *020 †35

DAVID, Martine. 5401 OLD YORK RD, KLEIN 363 19141 #836-02-1998 L2007 **IM** *012

DAVID, Mitchell. 2095 BAINBRIDGE ST 19146 #041-09-1954 L1955 **P** *020 †75

DAVIDOFF, Scott Jared. ■ 19130 #041-13-2004 L2004 **PM** *012

DAVIDSON, Alexander. 3509 N BROAD ST, TEMPLE UNIV CHILDRENS MED 19140 #165-04-1980 L1988 **CD PD** *020 †55 ‡

DAVIDSON, Chadd Paul. ■ 19104 #041-01-2006 L2007 *012

DAVIDSON, Marson Tunde. 333 COTTMAN AVE, DEPARTMENT OF SURGICAL ONC 19111 #010-01-1999 L2006 **GS** *100 †85

DAVIDSON, Richard S. 324 S 34TH ST 19104 #035-19-1976 L1982 **ORS OP** *020 †40

DAVIDSON, Robert. 1907 S BROAD ST 19148 #041-02-1965 L1969 **EM** *020

DAVIES, Robert Jos. 2301 E ALLEGHENY AVE 19134 #041-09-1984 L1986 **IM** *020 †20
DAVIRATANASILPA, Svastijay. ■ 19146 #891-01-2001 L2004 **NEP** *012 †20
DAVIS, Carl Walton. ■ 19103 #041-01-2008 *012
DAVIS, Cheryl Luise. 717 CORNELIA PL 19118 #050-02-1978 L2001 **NPM PD** *020 †55
DAVIS, Gary Randolph, Jr. 321 W GIRARD AVE, HEALTH CENTER 6 19123 #032-01-1996 L2000 **FM** *020 †20
DAVIS, George Anthony. 230 N BROAD ST, FL 7 19102 #041-09-1984 L1985 **CD IM** *020 †20
DAVIS, Glenn Craig. 1835 MARKET ST STE 2000 19103 #036-07-1972 L1972 **P** *030 †75
DAVIS, James Edward, Jr. 833 CHESTNUT ST, STE 701 19107 #041-13-2001 L2001 **IM** *020 †20
DAVIS, Jason E. ■ 19103 #041-15-2008 *012
DAVIS, Julie Ann. ■ 19146 #008-01-2000 L2003 **PD PDC** *100 †55
DAVIS, Kathryn A. ■ 19146 #008-01-2004 L2004 **N** *012
DAVIS, Kelly Diane. 3400 SPRUCE ST, STE J PENN TOWERS 9TH FLOO 19104 #019-02-1984 L1986 **END IM** *020 †20
DAVIS, Mitzieann Tamika. ■ 19151 #041-13-2007 **OBG** *012
DAVIS, Richard A. 3400 SPRUCE ST 19104 #016-06-1951 L1959 **NS** *020 †25
DAVIS, Sheila Joyce. ■ 19144 #041-01-1995 *100
DAVIS, Thomas Walter. ■ 19149 #041-15-2008 L2008 *012
DAVITCH, Leonard Saml. ■ 19103 #041-02-1943 L1944 **GP** *071
DAVITT, Ana Maria. ■ 19147 #041-01-2004 L2007 **EM** *012
DAVNE, Sanford Harry. 1911 ARCH ST 19103 #041-13-1976 L1977 **ORS OSS** *020 †40
DAVOLIO, Danielle Jeanett. ■ 19106 #041-15-2008 L2008 *012
DAVOUDI, Ramin Riaz. ■ 19106 #035-09-1999 L2006 **ICE** *020 †20
DAWSON, Martin Scott. 230 N BROAD ST 19102 #041-09-1993 L1997 **CD IM** *020 †20
DAY, Susan C. 3701 MARKET ST STE 760, PENN CARE INTERNAL MEDICIN 19104 #041-01-1977 L1981 **IM** *020 †20
DAYMONT, Carrie Bess. ■ 19103 #028-02-2003 L2003 **PD** *100 †55
DAYNO, Jeffrey Marc. 1025 WALNUT ST, STE 8439 19107 #041-13-1988 L1990 **N** *020 †75
DAYTON, Andrew Imbrie. 3400 SPRUCE ST 19104 #041-01-1977 *100
DEAL, Jane Elizabeth. 324 S 34TH ST 19104 #917-07-1978 L1984 **PD** *020
DEAN, Anthony John. 3400 SPRUCE ST, DEPARTMENT OF EMERGENCY ME 19104 #041-13-1984 L1984 **EM** *020 †16
DEAN, James Leo. ■ 19107 #041-07-1988 L1991 **ID** *020 †20 ‡
DE ANGELIS, Michael A. 525 JAMESTOWN ST, STE 107 19128 #041-09-1986 L1987 **CD** *020 †20
DEANS, Katherine J. 34TH-CIVIC CTR BLVD, CHILDRENS HOSP 19104 #032-01-1998 L2007 **PDS** *012 †85
DEARDORFF, Matthew A. ■ 19130 #041-21-2001 L2001 **OS** *100 †55,19
DEATON, Justin Granville. 111 S 11TH ST, DEPT EM 19107 #047-06-2007 L2007 **EM** *012
DEBENEDICTIS, Caroline N. ■ 19106 #041-02-2008 L2008 *012
DEBLANK, Peter Matthewken. ■ 19146 #005-02-2005 L2005 **PD** *012
DEBOO, Anahita Farrokh. 245 N 15TH ST, STOP 423 19102 #041-12-1997 L1999 **N** *020 †75
DEBRADY, Akili Hammond. 33 E CHESTNUT HILL AVE, STE 203 19118 #041-13-2004 L2006 **FM** *020 †18
DECARLO, Emily Angel. 840 WALNUT ST, WILLS EYE HOSP 19107 #041-01-2005 L2005 **OPH** *012
DE CARLO, John Peter. 7904 BUSTLETON AVE 19152 #654-01-1981 L1982 *020
DE CARO, Matthew V, Jr. 925 CHESTNUT ST, JEFFERSON HEART INST 19107 #041-02-1980 L1981 **CD IM** *020 †20
DE CASTRO, Miguel Amora. 1006 W LEHIGH AVE 19133 #748-01-1970 L1982 **FM** *020
DE CHADAREVIAN, Jean-P E. ST CHRISTOPHER CHILD HOSP, SELECTIVE PATHOLOGY 19134 #605-02-1968 L1986 **PTH PP** *020 †50
DECHERT, Martha Payson. 1025 WALNUT ST STE 726, THOMAS JEFFERSON UNIVERSIT 19107 #041-15-1999 L2005 **PDE** *100 †55
DECKER, John Paul. ■ 19103 #041-02-1946 L1949 **PTH** *071 †50
DE CLEMENT, Frederick A. 3401 N BROAD ST 19140 #033-05-1964 L1968 **GS** *071 †85
DECOONS, Ryan Michael. ■ 19102 #033-06-2006 L2006 **ORS** *012
DEDEOGLU, Ismail Ozhan. 601 N FRONT ST 19123 #902-10-1983 L1998 **PD PN** *020 †55
DEELY, Diane Marie. 111 S 11TH ST, G3390 19107 #041-12-1986 L1991 **DR** *020 †80
DEENEY, Gerard Magella. 100 W LEHIGH AVE 19133 #041-13-1994 L1996 **CHP** *020
DEENEY, John Jos. 3998 RED LION RD STE 230 19114 #041-07-1979 L1980 **OBG** *020 †30
DEES, Adina Marie. ■ 19107 #041-13-2005 L2005 **FP** *012
DEE TIN, Aurora. 2840 W DAUPHIN ST, 555 SOUHT 43RD STREET 19132 #748-01-1965 L1972 **PD** *020 †55 ‡
DEFELICE, Magee Lindinger. ■ 19107 #041-02-2006 L2006 **PD** *012
DEFRANCESCH, Giuliana I. 3401 N BROAD ST 19140 #737-06-1991 L1995 **IM** *020 †20
DEGEN, Jeffrey William. ■ 19130 #041-15-2005 L2005 **PM** *012
DEGER, Florin Titus. 3401 N BROAD ST 19140 #781-06-1987 L1997 **ICE** *020 †20
DEGLIN, Edward Alan. 2465 GRANT AVE 19114 #041-02-1968 L1973 **OPH** *020 †35
DEGNAN, Tina Hoynash. ■ 19130 #041-15-2005 L2005 **FP** *012
DE HORATIUS, Raphael F. 255 S 17TH ST 19103 #041-01-1944 L1945 **CD IM** *071 †20
DEIRMENGIAN, Carl Arsen. 800 SPRUCE ST, 8TH FL PRESTON BUILDING 19107 #024-01-2000 L2001 **ORS** *100
DEIRMENGIAN, Jennifer. 834 CHESTNUT ST STE 400, BENJAMIN FRANKLIN HOUSE 19107 #041-01-2004 L2004 **OBG** *012
DEITCH, Bernard. 4400 HAVERFORD AVE, PHILADELPHIA DEPT. OF PUBL 19104 #016-42-1955 L1961 **IM** *020 †20
DE JESUS, Joseph Ocampo. ■ 19147 #047-07-2002 L2003 **DR** *100 †80
DE JESUS, Melissa Yahaira. 3535 MARKET ST FL 2, PENN BEHAVIORAL HEALTH 19104 #041-01-2005 L2007 **PD** *012
DE JOSEPH, Daniel. ■ 19147 #041-02-2005 L2005 **FP** *012
DELACRUZ, Maria Syl. ■ 19128 #041-15-2008 *012
DE LA CRUZ, Nestor Enriqu. 2900 W QUEEN LN 19129 #748-08-1981 L2003 **PTH** *012
DE LA CRUZ-CASTRO, A. 3400 SPRUCE ST 19104 #748-02-1967 L1973 **AN** *040 †05
DE LA MOTA PEYNADO, Jose. 3401 N BROAD ST 19140 #308-05-2003 L2006 **OBG** *012
DELANEY, Mary Anne. 4641 ROOSEVELT BLVD 19124 #041-09-1977 L1978 **CHP P** *030 †75
DELANTY, Norman. 3400 SPRUCE ST, 3 WEST GATES 19104 #539-02-1988 L1997 **N** *020 †75
DELAPLANE, James Michael. 4641 ROOSEVELT BLVD 19124 #041-02-1964 L1966 **P** *020 †75
DEL BORGO, Laura Nancy. 833 CHESTNUT ST, STE 740 19107 #041-15-2004 L2004 **D** *012
DELBRUNE, Jean. 5501 OLD YORK RD, DEPT OF RADIOLOGY 19141 #035-09-1999 L2007 **VIR** *100 †80
DEL BUSTO, Elena. ■ 19128 #041-15-2005 L2005 **P** *012
DE LEON, Diva. 3615 CIVIC CENTER BLVD, CHILDS HOSP OF PHILA 19104 #715-01-1992 L1999 **PDE** *050 †55
DE LEON, Erlinda M. 2230 COTTMAN AVE 19149 #748-01-1957 L1967 **IM PUD** *020

DELGADO, Jose A. 5401 OLD YORK RD, KLEIN 363 19141 #408-30-1993 L2003 **PCC** *020 †20
DELIS, Spiros Georgion. 1420 LOCUST ST, ACADEMY HOUSE 19102 #418-01-1990 L1994 **GS** *020
DELISSER, Horace Michael. 3400 SPRUCE ST, DEPT MED 19104 #041-01-1985 L1987 **PUD** *020 †20
DE LISSER, Lawton Oswald. 10551 DECATUR RD STE 200 19154 #041-07-1996 L1999 **FM** *020 †18
DELIVORIA-PAPADOPOULOS, M. 3400 SPRUCE ST 19104 #418-01-1957 L1968 **PD** *040 †55
DELLA VECCHIA, Michael A. 900 WALNUT ST STE 1, WILLS EYE HOSP ER 19107 #041-13-1976 L1978 **OPH PTH** *020 †35
DELLWEG, Dominic. 5501 OLD YORK RD 19141 #409-22-1997 L2001 **IM** *100 †20
DE LOS ANGELES, Antonio F. 2601 HOLME AVE 19152 #748-10-1975 L1982 **NEP** *020
DELOWERY, Mark. 150 S INDEPENDENCE MALL W, STE 368 19106 #041-77-1983, ▲ L1984 **OM FM** *030
DELPORT, Anton Grant. 132 S 10TH ST, THOMAS JEFFERSON UNIV HOSP 19107 #041-15-2006 L2007 **DR** *012
DEL PRIORE, Joseph. ■ 19130 #041-77-2007, ▲ L2007 *012
DE LUCA, Francesco. 1900 S 10TH ST 19148 #561-23-1983 L2001 **PDE** *020 †55
DELVECCHIO, Michael T. 3509 N BROAD ST, TEMPLE UNIV CHILDREN MED C 19140 #047-05-1987 L1991 **PD** *020 †55 ‡
DE MARCO, Joseph F, Jr. 7996 OXFORD AVE 19111 #561-17-1957 L1959 **OBG OS** *071 †30
DE MARIA, Peter A, Jr. 1810 LIACOURAS WALK, 5TH FL 19122 #041-02-1984 L1985 **P ADM** *020 †75
DEMAURO, Sara Bonamo. ■ 19103-06-2004 L2004 **NPM** *012 †15
DEMEDIO, William Jos. 1100 WALNUT ST STE 602 19107 #041-13-1987 L1988 **FM GP** *020 †18
DE MICHELE, Angela Marie. 3400 SPRUCE ST, UNIV OF PA/14 PENN TOWER 19104 #028-02-1991 L1993 **HO ON** *020 †20
DE MICHELE, Joseph. 1332 W RITNER ST 19148 #041-09-1958 L1959 **GS** *071 †85
DEMICHELE, Sarah Gelbach. 3535 MARKET ST, FL 2 19104 #041-09-1993 L1995 **P** *020 †75
DE MORAES, Eduardo Dias. 111 S 11TH ST STE 4240, ONCOLOGY CLINIC 19107 #187-01-1992 L1997 **HO** *020 †20
DE MOURA, Jamilo Barbosa. 5501 OLD YORK RD 19141 #187-06-1964 L1969 **ORS** *071
DEMPSEY, Anthony Francis. ■ 19147 #041-02-2008 *012
DEMPSEY, Daniel Thomas. 3401 N BROAD ST, DEPT OF SURGERY 19140 #035-45-1979 L1981 **GS** *020 †85
DEMPSEY, Glenn Bryant. 9892 BUSTLETON AVE, STE 204 19115 #033-05-1975 L1996 **D IM** *020 †20,15
DEMPSEY, Maryfrances. ■ 19146 #041-13-2006 L2006 **GS** *012
DENBO, Nancy J. 561 FAIRTHORNE AVE 19128 #035-09-1974 L1981 **P CHP** *020 †75
DENDI, Udaya Sena Reddy. 2900 W QUEEN LN 19129 #496-31-2005 L2007 **IM** *012
DENE, Barbara Anne. 3401 N BROAD ST, DEPT OF MEDICINE -8PP 19140 #017-20-2006 L2006 **IM** *012
DENG, Xiaoying. 1800 LOMBARD ST 19146 #243-70-1985 L2005 **IM** *012
DENIS, Reginald Jacques. ■ 19147 #033-06-2001 L2005 **RNR** *100 †80
DENIZARD, Carl Etienne. 2915 N 5TH ST 19133 #440-01-1963 L1971 **PD PHP** *071
DENLINGER, Crystal S. 333 COTTMAN AVE, DEPARTMENT OF 19111 #033-05-2001 L2004 **HO** *100
DENNERY, Phyllis Armelle. 324 S 34TH ST 19104 #010-03-1984 L2003 **NPM PD** *020 †55
DENNEY, Jeffrey Morgan. ■ 19130 #012-01-2004 L2004 **OBG** *012
DENNIS, Dean Rice. 51 N 39TH ST DEPT ROTAT 19104 #041-02-1995 L1998 **IM** *020 †20
DENNIS, William John. 3823 J ST 19124 #041-02-1968 L1969 **PD** *020 †55
DEPALMA, Anthony Peter. 19131 #041-77-2007, ▲ **IM** *012
DEPAPP, Anne Emoke. 211 S 9TH ST, STE 601 19107 #032-01-1988 L1993 **END** *020 †20
DEPIETRO, Michael Rocco. 840 WALNUT ST, STE 930 19107 #041-09-1986 L1987 **PCC IM** *020 †20
DEPMAN, Stanley T. 9501 STATE RD, RIVER'S EDGE NURSING HOME 19114 #041-02-1982 L1985 **GPM FPG** *020 †18
DEPPERT, Eric Jon. 51 N 39TH ST, MEDICAL OFFICE STE 220 19104 #041-09-1990 L1992 **IM** *020 †20 ‡
DERALEAU, Erika Lynn. ■ 19129 #041-15-2008 *012
DEREN, Julius Jay. 1800 LOMBARD ST, STE 100 19146 #035-08-1958 L1969 **GE IM** *020 †20
DEREVYANNY, Vicki Diana. ■ 19102 #041-15-2007 L2007 **EM** *012
DERIMANOV, Geo Stoyanov. 3400 SPRUCE ST, FL 8 19104 #198-04-1988 L1999 **RHU** *020 †20
DERK, Chris Terry. 1015 WALNUT ST, 613 CURTIS BLDG 19107 #041-02-1994 L1996 **RHU** *020 †20
DERMISH, Amna I. 800 SPRUCE ST, DEPT OF OB/GYN 19107 #007-02-2006 L2006 **OBG** *012
DEROOS, Francis Jerome. 3400 SPRUCE ST, HOSPITAL OF THE UNIVERSITY 19104 #005-14-1990 L1995 **EM** *020 †16
DERSHAW, Bruce Bernard. 2630 HOLME AVE, INSTITUTE FOR RESPIRATORY 19152 #041-13-1976 L1977 **PUD IM** *020 †20
DE RUSSO, Greg. 3996 RED LION RD 19114 #041-09-1990 L1997 **IM** *020 †20
DESAI, Ajit Manibhai. 5501 OLD YORK RD, STE 1 19141 #495-23-1967 L1973 **HO HEM** *020 †20
DESAI, Bimal Ramesh. 324 S 34TH ST 19104 #028-02-2000 L2001 **PD** *020 †55
DESAI, Dhaval Ghansyam. ■ 19147 #041-02-1998 L2007 **IM** *012
DESAI, Hemant J. 1025 WALNUT ST, STE 709C 19107 #495-23-1970 L1975 **PD NPM** *040 †55
DESAI, Melissa Nitin. ■ 19103 #036-07-2007 L2007 **PD** *012
DESAI, Nirav Kishor. ■ 19130 #033-06-2005 L2005 **PD** *012
DESAI, Nita Ajit. 2900 W QUEEN LN 19129 #305-01-2004 L2004 **OBG** *012
DESAI, Parag B.. ■ 19130 #033-05-2005 L2005 **IM** *012
DESAI, Ravi Veeranagouda. 245 N 15TH ST MS 437, DREXEL UNIV COLL OF MED 19102 #495-35-1997 L2007 **NEP** *012
DESAI, Rohit Mahendrabhai. 7500 CENTRAL AVE STE 202 19111 #495-23-1971 L1975 **IM** *020 †20
DESAI, Shauna Manikant. ■ 19107 #041-15-2005 L2005 **P** *012
DESAI, Shital Sureshchand. ■ 19131 #023-01-2005 L2005 **FP** *012
DESAI, Shivraj Jagdish. 1726 S BROAD ST STE 3 19145 #495-01-1982 L1984 **PUD** *020 †20 ‡
DESAI, Shobhana D. 1025 WALNUT ST 19107 #495-22-1969 L1974 **NPM PD** *020 †55
DESAI, Usha B. 2301 E ALLEGHENY AVE 19134 #495-23-1970 L1978 **FM PD** *020
DE SANTOLA, Joseph Robt. 230 W WASHINGTON SQ, FL 3 19106 #028-02-1981 L1985 **CD** *020 †20
DESA VENKATANARAYANA, Thir. 800 SPRUCE ST 19107 #496-22-2002 L2006 **IM** *100
DESHMUKH, Sandeep Prakash. ■ 19146 #041-15-2000 L2001 **DR** *100 †40
DESIDERIO, Vincent C. 2901 ISLAND AVE, BUSINESS MED/MED COLLEGE O 19153 #041-09-1953 L1954 **IM PTH** *071
DE SILVERIO, Robt Vincent. 1700 BENJAMIN FRANKLN PKWY, THE WINDSOR STE 2109 19103 #041-09-1959 L1960 **P** *020 †75 ‡

DE SIMONE, Joseph Andrew. 125 S 9TH ST, STE 403 19107 #041-09-1994 L1997 **ID** *020 †20

DESIMONE, Kristin Lengle. 1015 WALNUT ST, STE 401 19107 #041-02-1996 L1998 **FM** *020 †18

DESIPIO, Joshua Peter. ■ 19123 #041-02-2000 L2001 **GE** *020 †20

DESMOND, Mark. 3110 GRANT AVE 19114 #010-02-1997 L2002 **ORS GS** *020 †40

DESNOYERS, Rodwige J. 8835 GERMANTOWN AVE 19118 #036-05-1994 L1996 **HEM** *020 †20

DESOUSA, Eduardo A. 900 WALNUT ST, STE 200 19107 #187-01-1997 L2001 **N CN** *100 †75

DESOUSA, Ricardo Avelino. ■ 19107 #042-16-2005 L2006 **AN** *012

DESROCHERS, Colette Rose. 225 S COBBS CREEK PKWY, CHOP PRIMARY CARE CENTER 19139 #024-16-1994 L1996 **PD** *020 †55

DETRE, John Alan. 3400 SPRUCE ST 19104 #008-01-1986 L1987 **N** *050 †75

DEU, Rajwinder Singh. 833 CHESTNUT ST, STE 301 19107 #023-01-2001 L2003 **FSM** *020 †18

DEUTSCH, Lawrence S. 3998 RED LION RD, STE 215 19114 #035-09-1971 L1972 **PD** *020 †55

DEUTSCHMAN, Clifford S. 3400 SPRUCE ST, DEPT OF ANES DULLES 781A/ 19104 #035-09-1980 L1993 **AN CCA** *050 †05

DEVARAKONDA, Veena Srinat. 2900 W QUEEN LN, DEPT OF INTERNAL MED 19129 #496-38-2000 L2003 **PCC** *012 †20

DE VAUGHN, Gerald Lane. 5249 CEDAR AVE 19143 #041-09-1979 L1980 **CD IM** *020 †20

DEVAUGHN, Pamela Huffman. 105 W SCHOOL HOUSE LN 19144 #047-07-1980 L1984 **PD ADL** *020 †55 ‡

DEVECIOGLU, Sabri. 3400 N BROAD ST 19140 #902-03-1959 **CRS** *020 †10

DEVGAN, Sue. 2900 W QUEEN LN, DREXEL UNIV COLL OF MED 19129 #005-06-2006 *012

DEVGON, Pitamber, Jr. ■ 19103 #051-07-2005 L2005 **IM** *012

DE VILLE, Curtiland. 3400 SPRUCE ST, DEPT OF RAD ONCOLOGY 19104 #043-01-2005 L2006 **RO** *012

DEVINE, Shubhangini C. 3300 HENRY AVE RM 220H, INTERNAL MEDICINE OFFICE 19129 #665-01-1999 L2001 **IM** *020 †20

DE VITO, Nicholas Michael. ■ 19107 #041-12-2007 L2007 **IM** *012

DEVLIN, John Gerard, Jr. 333 COTTMAN AVE, MEDICAL ONCOLOGY 19111 #041-13-2001 L2001 **HO** *020

DEVON, Octavia Nanagas. 19107 #041-15-2005 L2005 **GS** *012

DEVOTO-CANESSA, Luigi P. 3400 SPRUCE ST DEPT OB 19104 #231-01-1971 **OBG** *100

DEWAN, Sanjiv. 100 E LEHIGH AVE 19125 #495-29-1973 L1985 **GS VS** *020 ‡

DE WOLF, William F. ■ 19129 #041-15-2004 L2004 **P** *012

DEWYNGAERT, Susan T Keon. 1100 WALNUT ST, BSMT 19107 #041-01-1992 L1999 **DR** *020 †80

DHALIWAL, Savreet. 3401 N BROAD ST, TEMPLE UNIV HOSP 19140 #041-07-1997 L1999 **GE** *020 †20

DHAND, Mary Frances. 3300 HENRY AVE, PRIMARY CARE UNIT 19129 #041-13-1977 L1978 **PD** *075 †55

DHEER, Sachin. 132 S 10TH ST, UNIVERSITY HO 19107 #041-01-2001 L2002 **MSR** *100 †80

DHILLON, Ravinder Singh. ■ 19107 #016-06-2002 L2002 **GE** *012 †20

DHIR, Gauri. ■ 19131 #495-29-1998 L2006 **IM** *100 †20

DHOLAKIA, Madhuri Anil. 925 CHESTNUT ST, FL 5 19107 #041-15-2002 L2002 *100 †60

DHOND, Abhay Jagannath. 245 N 15TH ST STOP 42, RM 6209 19102 #495-36-1983 L2001 **IM** *020 †70,20

DHOPESH, Vasant. UNIVERSITY & WOODLAND AVE, VA MEDICAL CTR 116A 19104 #495-19-1961 L1970 **P ADP** *020 †75

DHRUVAKUMAR, Sandhya. ■ 19147 #024-16-2000 L2006 **ICE** *012 †20

DIABO, Jennifer Dana. 2318 E ALLEGHENY AVE 19134 #041-13-1999 L2001 **PD** *020 †55

DIAMOND, Gary Richard. 216 N BROAD ST MS 20 19102 #023-07-1974 L1979 **OPH** *040 †35 ‡

DIAMOND, Robert Harrison. 1720 LOMBARD ST 19146 #035-19-1986 L1989 **GE IM** *020 †20

DIARRA, Cheickna. ■ 19106 #036-05-2004 L2007 **GS** *012

DIAZ, Gloria Janet. 2301 E ALLEGHENY AVE, 4TH FL 19134 #041-13-1992 L1994 **OBG** *020 †30

DIAZ, Laura K. 3400 CIVIC CENTER BLVD, 9TH FL MAIN BLDG DEPT ANES 19104 #021-01-1985 L1988 **AN PD** *020 †05

DIAZ, Victor A. 833 CHESTNUT ST, STE 301 19107 #308-04-1986 L1995 **FM** *020 †18

DIAZ ABAD, Montserrat. 3401 N BROAD ST, TEMPLE UNIV HOSPITAL 19140 #308-05-1997 L2001 **PCC** *100

DIAZ-GARCIA, Rafael Jose. ■ 19147 #041-01-2007 L2007 **PS** *012

DIAZ QUINONES, Juan Jose. 3401 N BROAD ST 19140 #308-05-2002 L2005 **OBG** *012

DI BELLO, Angelo Mario. 8201 CRAIG ST 19136 #041-09-1954 L1955 **GP** *020 †18

DICHTER, Howard Neal. 5501 OLD YORK RD, DEPT OF PSYCHIATRY 19141 #026-04-1977 L1983 **OS P** *020 †75

DICHTER, Marc Allen. 3400 SPRUCE ST, HUP/NEUROLOGY/3 W GATES 19104 #035-19-1969 L1969 **N** *050 †75

DICKENS, Timothy. 1617 JOHN F KENNEDY BLVD, STE 1500 19103 #917-25-1970 L1976 **P** *030 †75

DICKER, Adam Paul. 111 S 11TH ST, DEPT OF RADIATION ONCOLOGY 19107 #035-20-1992 L1996 **RO** *020 †80

DI CUCCIO, Michael N. 111 S 11TH ST # DR, THOMAS JEFFERSON UNIV HOSP 19107 #036-07-1996 L1998 **DR** *100

DIECIDUE, Robert J. 909 WALNUT ST STE 300 19107 #041-02-1997 L2006 *040

DIEGO, Emilia Josefa Borr. 5501 OLD YORK RD 19141 #748-02-2004 L2005 **GS** *012

DIEHL, James Thos. 1025 WALNUT ST, STE 607 19107 #035-46-1978 L1992 **GS TS** *020 †85,90

DIEMER, Gretchen Ann. 833 CHESTNUT ST, STE 701 19107 #051-01-2001 L2001 **IM** *020

DIERKING, Elizabeth Linda. ■ 19143 #041-01-2005 L2008 **OBG** *012

DIETZ, Nicole Alyssaemma. ■ 19143 #010-02-2006 L2006 **N** *012

DIETZEN, Diane Louise. 3300 HENRY AVE, MEDICAL COLLGE OF PNNSYLVN 19129 #041-13-1987 L1989 **IM** *020 †20

DI GEORGE, Angelo Mario. 3401 N BROAD ST, TEMPLE ANESTHESIA ASSOCIAT 19140 #041-13-1946 L1947 **PDE PD** *072 †55

DI GEORGE, Anthony M. ■ #041-13-1979 L1982 **PDE PSM** *020 †55

DIGIACOMO, Joseph N. 3400 SPRUCE ST 19104 #025-07-1957 L1967 **P** *020 †75 ‡

DILLER, Kathleen Convery. ■ 19143 #041-13-2005 L2005 **P** *012

DIMANLIG, Zenaida D. 2301 S BROAD ST 19148 #748-01-1964 L1975 *100

DIMARCO, Jack Peter. 604-36 S WASHINGTON SQ 19106 #028-02-1979 L1980 **PM** *020 †60

DI MARINO, Anthony J, Jr. 132 S 10TH ST, THOMAS JEFFERSON UNIVERSIT 19107 #041-09-1968 L1969 **GE IM** *020 †20 ‡

DIMEO, Christopher A. ■ 19146 #041-01-2000 L2002 *020 †05

DIMUZIO, Paul Jos. 111 S 11TH ST STE G6350 19107 #041-01-1989 L1991 **VS** *020 †85

DINARDO, Andrew Russo. ■ 19146 #025-07-2007 L2007 **IM** *012

DI NARDO, Courtney Denton. ■ 19146 #025-01-2006 L2006 **IM** *012

DINE, Constance Jessica. 3400 SPRUCE ST, UNIVERSITY OF PENNSYLVANIA 19104 #041-01-2002 L2002 **PCC** *012 †20

DING, William. ■ 19122 #041-15-2007 L2007 **IM** *012

DINICOLA, Christina Ilse. 701 S 2ND ST 19147 #033-06-2003 L2003 **PD** *020 †55

DINOME, Jessie W. 111 S 11TH ST 19107 #036-01-1983 L1997 **ON** *020 †80

DIOGUARDI, Phyllisann K. 132 S 10TH ST, THOMAS JEFFERSON UNIV HOSP 19107 #041-02-2002 L2002 **DR** *012

DI PALMA, Joan Solowey. 9880 BUSTLETON AVE, STE 309 19115 #041-02-1979 L1998 **PD GE** *020 †55

DIPAOLA, Matthew James. 113 N BREAD ST, 3F3 19106 #035-20-2003 L2003 **ORS** *012

DIRIENZO, Rosalinda Ann. 3300 HENRY AVE 19129 #041-07-1988 L1990 **IM** *020 †20 ‡

DISALVO, Carmelo. 245 N 15TH ST, DEPT OF GME 19102 #654-01-2004 L2005 **FP** *012

DISANDRO, Daniel Gustave. 5401 CEDAR AVE, DEPT OF EMERG MED 19143 #041-13-1993 L1995 **EM** *020 †16

DISSANAYAKE, Imara R. 5501 OLD YORK RD, 5 LEVY BUILDING 19141 #836-01-1991 L2000 **NEP** *020 †20

DISSIN, Jonathan. 9880 BUSTLETON AVE, NEUROLOGY ASSOCIATES AT 19115 #422-01-1982 L1983 **N OS** *020

DITRE, Cherie Marie. 3400 SPRUCE ST, 2 RHOADS PAVILION 19104 #041-01-1983 L1985 **D** *020 †15

DITUNNO, John Francis. 132 S 10TH ST, STE 375 19107 #041-09-1958 L1959 **PM IM** *072 †60

DIVAKER, Shashi Raj. 2840 W DAUPHIN ST 19132 #496-20-1990 L1997 **IM** *020 †20

DIVGI, Chaitanya. 3400 SPRUCE ST, NUCLEAR MEDICINE/RADIOLOGY 19104 #495-52-1976 L2006 **IG IM** *020 †28

DIVI, Venu. ■ 19103 #038-44-2001 L2006 **OTO** *020 †45

DJERASSI, Isaac. 54TH ST & CEDAR AVE, MISERICORDIA HOSP RM 196 19143 #550-01-1952 L1961 **ON IM** *020

DLIN, Barney Martin. 230 W ALLENS LN 19119 #060-01-1949 L1958 **P OS** *072

DLUTOWSKI, Bernard Jos. ■ 19114 #041-09-1961 L1962 **GP** *071

DOAN, Huynh Trieu. 221 N BROAD ST 19107 #941-01-1972 L1980 **R GS** *020

DOANE, Stephen Matthew. 3401 N BROAD ST, OF SURGE 19140 #005-14-2007 L2007 *012

DOBERCZAK, Linda J S. 2601 HOLME AVE, NAZARETH HOSP ANES DEPT 19152 #041-13-1980 L1981 **AN** *020 †05

DOBOS, Nora. 3400 SPRUCE ST, DEPT OF RADIOLOGY 19104 #040-02-1998 L2001 **DR** *020 †80

DODDA, Venkata Ranganadh. 1800 LOMBARD ST, TENET HEALTHSYSTEM GRADUAT 19146 #495-11-2002 L2005 **IM** *012

DODDS, H Thos. 840 WALNUT ST 19107 #035-03-1964 L1965 **OPH** *020 †35 ‡

DOGHRAMJI, Karl. 211 S 9TH ST, STE 500 19107 #041-02-1980 L1981 **P SME** *020 †75

DOGIN, Judith Wynn Young. 1735 MARKET ST STE A 19103 #038-06-1976 L1997 **CHP P** *020 †75

DOHERTY, Emily Aliber. 3400 SPRUCE ST, 5 PENN TOWER 19104 #051-01-2000 L2007 **MG PD** *020 †55,19

DOHERTY, Jeanne Gallagher. 6 FRANKLIN PLZ, MAGEE REHABILITATION HOSPI 19102 #010-02-1995 L1999 **PM** *020 †60

DOHERTY, John U. 925 CHESTNUT ST, JEFFERSON HEART INSTITUTE 19107 #010-02-1976 L1978 **CD IM** *020 †20

DOHERTY, Timothy James. 4TH FLOOR - S TOWER MAIL, DREXEL UNIVERSITY COLLEGE 19102 #422-01-2007 L2007 **IM** *012

DOKTOR, Katherine Leigh. ■ 19103 #033-06-2008 *012

DOLD, Frederick George. 3998 RED LION RD, STE 130 19114 #041-09-1997 L1999 **HO IM** *020 †20

DOLINSKAS, Carol Anne. 800 SPRUCE ST, DEPT OF RADLGY-PA HOSPITAL 19107 #041-02-1971 L1972 **DR NM** *020 †80,28

DOLLARD, Denis James. 501 S 54TH ST, MERCY HOSPITAL/PHILADELPHI 19143 #041-13-1996 L1998 **EM** *020 †16

DOLVANE, Rubina M. 5501 OLD YORK RD 19141 #665-01-2005 L2005 **PD** *012

DOMA, Siva Prasad. 3401 N BROAD ST, TEMPLE UNIV HOSP 19140 #495-50-1997 L2005 **GE** *012 †20

DOMANSKI, Robert Edward. 5800 RIDGE AVE 19128 #041-07-1974 L1975 **DR NR** *020 †80 ‡

DOMBROSKI, Derek George. 834 SOUTH ST 19147 #048-13-2005 L2005 **ORS** *012

DOMCHEK, Susan Mary. 3400 SPRUCE ST, PENN TOWER 14 UNIV OF PA 19104 #024-01-1995 L2001 **HO** *020

DOMERACKI, Gary Francis. 3401 N BROAD ST, DEPT OF OPHTHALMOLOGY 19140 #041-02-1995 L1997 **OPH** *020 †35

DOMINGUEZ, Troy E. 3400 SPRUCE ST 19104 #048-12-1992 L1997 **CCP** *020 †55

DOMINGUEZ SANTAMARIA, Dolo. 1800 LOMBARD ST, DEPT OF MED EDU 19146 #847-05-2003 L2006 *100

DOMINIQUE, Devanand A. 3401 N BROAD ST # C-540 19140 #539-04-1992 L1998 **NS** *020 ‡

DOMS, Robert W. 3400 SPRUCE ST, DEPT OF PATHOLGY & LB MDCN 19104 #008-01-1988 L1991 **PTH** *020 †50

DONAIRE, Melissa Catherin. 3400 N BROAD ST, DEPT OF PSYCHIATRY 19140 #041-13-2006 L2006 **P** *012

DONATO, Robert Anthony. 39TH MARKET PRES HOSP 19104 #041-09-1948 L1949 **PTH HEM** *071 †50

DONEGAN, Derek James. ■ 19104 #041-02-2006 L2006 **ORS** *012

DONLON, Stacy Lynn. ■ 19107 #035-09-2008 *012

DONNELLY, Eric Donald. ■ 19143 #028-34-2006 L2007 **IM** *012

DONOGHUE, Aaron Jeremiah. 324 S 34TH 19104 #033-06-1997 L1999 **PEM** *020 †55

DONOSO, Larry A. 840 WALNUT ST 19107 #049-01-1973 L1978 **OPH** *050 †35

DONOVAN, Colleen Mary. ■ 19130 #033-05-2007 L2007 **EM** *012

DORATOTAJ, Behzad. 245 N 15TH ST, DREXEL UNIV COLL MED/HAHNE 19102 #517-01-2002 L2005 **IM** *012

D'ORAZIO, Joseph Louis. 878 N TAYLOR ST 19130 #041-15-2004 L2004 **ETX** *012

DORCE, Jackie Patricia. ■ 19128 #012-21-2007 L2007 **PD** *012

DORE, Carlos. 452 W ALLEGHENY AVE 19133 #042-01-1973 L1988 **PD** *020 †55

DORFMAN, Aaron Todd. ■ 19103 #041-01-2004 L2004 **PDC** *012 †55

DORFMAN, Alan Mark. 840 WALNUT ST 19107 #041-13-1976 L1977 **OPH** *020 †35

DORIA, Cataldo. 111 S 11TH ST 19107 #561-15-1990 L1997 *020 ‡

DORMANS, John Paul. 3405 CIVIC CENTER BLVD, 2ND FLOOR, WOOD BLDG 19104 #017-20-1983 L1991 **ORS PD** *020 †40

DOROTAN, Jose G. 3401 N BROAD ST, DEPARTMENT OF ANESTHESIA 19140 #748-03-1998 L1998 **AN** *020 †05

DOROZYNSKY, Leo Geo. UNIVERSITY & WOODLAND AVES 19104 #016-06-1976 L1979 **P** *020 †75

DORSEY, Alfred Thos, Jr. ERIE AVE AT FRONT ST 19133 #041-09-1981 L1990 **AN CCA** *020 †05,55

■ = Address Information Privacy Protected

DORSEY, Jay Fitzgerald. ■ 19130 #011-04-2003 L2004 **RO** *012

DORSHIMER, Gary Wm. 3601 S BROAD ST, WACHOVIA CENTER SPORTS COM 19148 #041-01-1981 L1982 **IM** *020 †20

DOSHI, Arpi. ■ 19102 #025-01-2006 **RO** *012

DOSHI, Kirti K D. 111 S 11TH ST, STE 8490 19107 #495-17-1966 L1973 **AN** *020 †05

DOSHI, Manish. 245 N 15TH ST, DEPT OF GME 19102 #422-01-2006 L2006 **IM** *012

DOTSON, Kathleen. ■ 19147 #041-07-1996 **IM** *100

DOUGHERTY, Matthew Jos. 700 SPRUCE ST STE 101 19106 #024-01-1984 L1992 **VS** *020 †85

DOUGHERTY, Rebecca Harper. ■ 19118 #041-13-2005 **IM** *012

DOUGLAS, Steven Danl. 324 S 34TH ST 19104 #035-20-1963 L1980 **IG PDA** *050

DOVI, S Frank, Jr. 2001 MARKET ST, 2 COMMERCE SQ STE 4000 19103 #010-02-1966 L1988 **IM CD** *030

DOVNARSKY, James Howard. 1726 S BROAD ST, STE 103 19145 #041-02-1970 L1973 **PUD IM** *020 †20 ‡

DOWINSKY, Steven Kenneth. 230 W WASHINGTON SQ, FL 3 19106 #409-23-1979 L1987 **CD IM** *020 †20

DOWNES, John Jos. ■ 19103 #016-43-1956 L1961 **CCP PAN** *071 †05

DOWNES, Kevin James. ■ 19103 #041-01-2008 *012

DOWNIE, Robert Wahl. 25 S 9TH ST 19107 #041-01-1964 L1976 **PM IM** *020 †20,60

DOWNING, Kristopher Lee. ■ 19104 #005-14-2004 L2005 **ORS** *012

DOYCH, Yelena. 219 N BROAD ST FL 3, OPHTHALMOLOGY DEPARTMENT 19107 #041-15-2001 L2001 **OPH** *020 †35

DOYLE, Aiden John M. 111 S 11TH ST 19107 #539-06-1969 L2005 **NS N** *050 †25

DOYLE, Alden Michael. 415 CURIE BLVD, 700 CLINICAL RESEARCH BLDG 19104 #021-01-1994 L1999 **NEP** *012

DOYLE, Harry A. 230 S 22ND ST 19103 #041-02-1971 L1972 **P PFP** *020 †75

DOZOR, Richard Jon. ■ 19106 #041-13-1981 L1982 **IM** *020

DRACH, George Wisse. 3400 SPRUCE ST, 9 PENN TOWERS 19104 #038-06-1961 L1998 **U ID** *071 †95

DRAGOMIR, Dan. 1316 W ONTARIO ST, 9TH FL 19140 #781-01-1997 L2006 **IM** *020 †20

DRAGOUN, Jennifer Marie. 33 E CHESTNUT HILL AVE, STE 203 19118 #041-02-1998 L2000 **FM** *020 †18

DRAIN, Randall Terence. 1914 N 63RD ST 19151 #041-13-1983 L1984 **PD ADL** *020

DRAKE, Thomas Philip. 3405 CIVIC CENTER BLVD, RM 231 19104 #041-02-1998 L2001 **RPM** *020 †55,60

DRAPER, Jennie Elizabeth. ■ 19130 #051-04-2007 **OBG** *012

DRAPER, Kari Anne. CHOP PRIMARY CARE, 39TH AND CHESTNUT STREET 19104 #026-04-1993 L1995 **PD** *020 †55

DRATCH, Michael Benjamin. 5401 OLD YORK RD, STE 201 19141 #041-09-1967 L1968 **CD** *020 †20 ‡

DRATMAN, Mary A Bagan. 3300 HENRY AVE 19129 #041-07-1945 L1946 **IM** *050

DREBIN, Jeffrey Adam. 3400 SPRUCE ST, FL 4 19104 #024-01-1987 L2004 **GS SO** *020 †85

DRELICH, Douglass Alan. ■ 19107 #033-05-2003 L2003 **HO** *012 †20

DRESZER, Roni E. 2900 W QUEEN LN, DREXEL UNIV COLL OF MED 19129 #041-15-2004 L2004 **GS** *100

DREYFUS, Robert M. 1315 WALNUT STE 1700 19107 #061-01-1963 L1965 **P** *020 †75 ‡

DRISCOLL, Deborah Anne. 800 SPRUCE ST, FL 8 19107 #035-19-1983 L1985 **OBG CG** *030 †19,30

DRIVER, Paul John. 10160 BUSTLETON AVE, STE F 19116 #041-13-1990 L1990 **OPH** *020 †35

DROBA, Marian Patricia. 135 S 19TH ST, STE 230 19103 #038-40-1981 L1984 **P** *020 †75

DROWER, Christine Marie. ■ 19130 #041-15-2008 *012

DRUMM, Christopher. ■ 19130 #041-15-2006 L2006 **FP** *012

DRUMMOND, Denis Sise. 34TH ST & CIVIC CTR BLVD, DEPT ORTHOPEDIC SURG 19104 #067-01-1962 L1985 **OP ORS** *071 †40

D'SOUZA, Benjamin Anthony. ■ 19128 #041-02-2007 L2007 **MPD** *012

D'SOUZA, Genevieve. 111 S 11TH ST, THOS JEFFERSON UNIV HOSP 19107 #495-06-1999 L2004 **AN** *020

DU, Christine W. ■ 19129 #041-15-2008 L2008 *012

DU, Kevin Lee. ■ 19106 #041-01-2006 L2006 **RO** *012

DUA, Rita. 111 S 11TH ST, THOMAS JEFFERSON UNIV HSPT 19107 #495-83-1981 L1991 **AN** *020

DUBB, Abraham Samuel. ■ 19130 #041-13-1998 L2001 **IM** *020 †20

DUBB, Jeffrey Wolfe. 39TH & MARKET ST 19104 #016-02-1968 L1972 **NEP** *020 †20

DUBE, Benoit. 3535 MARKET ST FL 4, DEPT OF PSYCHIATRY 19104 #067-02-1997 L1999 **P PYM** *040 †75

DUBIN, Gary. 3400 SPRUCE ST, DIVISION OF INFECTIOUS DSS 19104 #041-01-1983 L1987 **IM** *020 †20

DUBIN, William Robt. 100 E LEHIGH AVE STE 305, MEDICAL ARTS BLDG 19125 #045-01-1974 L1975 **P PYG** *030 †75

DUBNER, Sarah Elizabeth. ■ 19143 #041-01-2008 *012

DU BREUIL, Anne Lemaigre. 1015 WALNUT ST STE 401, DEPT OF FAMILY MEDICINE 19107 #041-01-1977 L1978 **FM** *020 †18

DUBROFF, Jacob Gershon. ■ 19102 #035-15-2006 L2006 *012

DUBYANSKITE, Anna. 7600 CENTRAL AVE 19111 #913-49-1973 L1984 **NEP IM** *020 †20 ‡

DUCKETT, Christopher Pace. 3401 N BROAD ST, 2ND FL 19104 #035-03-2002 L2002 **CHP** *012

DUCKETT, Joyce Agatha. 5301 CEDAR AVE STE 26, MERCY HOSP OF PHILADELPHIA 19143 #041-13-1979 L1980 **IM** *020

DUCKETT, Serge. 1025 WALNUT ST 19107 #396-06-1958 L1970 **OS** *040

DUCKLES, Benjamin Jeffrey. ■ 19104 #041-01-2006 L2006 **AN** *012

DUCKWORTH, Karen Melissa. 131 E CHELTEN AVE 19144 #041-07-1996 L2001 **FM** *020 †18

DUDA, John Eric. 3900 WOODLAND AVE MS 127, PHILADELPHIA VA HOSP 19104 #041-02-1994 L1997 **N** *050 †75

DUDDA SUBRAMANYA, Raghunan. 2900 W QUEEN LN 19129 #496-21-2000 L2003 **CD** *012 †20

DUDNICK, Robert Stuart. 5401 OLD YORK RD, KLEIN BUILDING STE 363 19141 #033-05-1986 L1990 **GE** *020 †20

DUESLER, Bernice Giordano. 3401 N BROAD ST, TEMPLE UNIVERSITY HOSPITAL 19140 #041-07-1991 L1993 **NPM** *020 †20

DUFFALO, Chad Jeremy. ■ 19144 #041-13-2005 L2005 **IM** *012

DUFFY, Danielle. 925 CHESTNUT ST, MEZZANINE LEVEL 19107 #041-01-2002 L2002 **CD** *012 †20

DUFFY, Karen Ann. 7701 BURHOLME AVE, FOX CHASE CANCER CENTER 19111 #539-04-1993 L1998 **RO** *100

DUFFY, Kevin James, Jr. 3400 SPRUCE ST 19104 #041-01-2000 L2001 **CD** *100 †20

DUFFY, Ryan Killian. ■ 19130 #041-15-2008 *012

DUFFY, William Neal. 727 DELANCEY ST, DELANCEY MEDICAL ASSOC. 19106 #010-02-1993 L1995 **IM** *020 †20

DUFRAYNE, Francis Jos. 230 W WASHINGTON SQ, FL 4 19106 #041-13-1986 L1987 **GE IM** *020 †20

DUGGER, Ida Wagner. ■ 19144 #035-08-2005 L2005 **GS** *012

DUGGIRALA, Chandra Sekhar. 3300 HENRY AVE, DEPT OF GME 19129 #495-58-2002 L2005 **IM** *012

DUGGIRALA, Chandrudu. 561 FAIRTHORNE AVE 19128 #495-11-1972 L1999 **P** *020 †75

DUKE, Pamela M. 219 N BROAD ST, STE 8 19107 #008-02-1991 L1998 **IM** *040 †20

DUKER, Nahum Johanan. 3401 N BROAD ST 19140 #016-11-1966 L1978 **PTH** *050 †50

DUMAS, Mario Eddy. ■ 19131 #440-01-1983 L2000 **PD** *020 †55 ‡

DUMON, Kristoffel Dirk. 3400 SPRUCE ST, FL 4 19104 #165-04-1990 L2001 **GS** *020

DUMONT, Charles Antoine. ■ 19103 #041-01-2005 L2005 **IM** *012

DUN, Erica Candice. 3400 SPRUCE ST, 5TH FLOOR DULLES BLDG 19104 #036-05-2004 L2006 **OBG** *012

DUNAIEF, Joshua Lawrence. 51 N 39TH ST, SCHEIE EYE INSTITUTE 19104 #035-01-1996 L2000 **OPH** *020 †35

DUNBAR, Jeffrey Kim. 1415 N BROAD ST, SECOND FLOOR 19122 #041-07-1993 L2003 **IM** *020 †20

DUNBAR, Richard Louis. 51 N 39TH ST, PHI BLDG STE 351 19104 #051-04-1997 L2003 **IM CD** *050 †20 ‡

DUNCAN, Gwienevere. ■ 19146 #041-02-2000 L2003 **NPM** *020

DUNCAN, Ian Charles. 3401 N BROAD ST 19140 #016-42-2006 L2006 **ORS** *012

DUNCAN, Theodore Garfield. 829 SPRUCE ST, STE 302 19107 #041-02-1955 L1957 **IM DIA** *071 †20

DUNFEY, Maura. 833 CHESTNUT ST, STE 210 19107 #041-77-2007, ▲ L2007 **P** *012

DUNKMAN, William Bruce. 3900 WOODLAND AVE # 111C, VETERANS ADMINISTRATION 19104 #024-01-1965 L1974 **CD IM** *020 †20

DUNLOP, Lance Russell. 8001 STATE RD, MOD II 19136 #041-01-2004 L2004 **P** *100

DUNN, Jeffrey Marc. 3333 N BROAD ST 19140 #035-03-1970 L1978 **TS** *030 †90

DUNN, Lara Ann. ■ 19103 #041-01-2008 *012

DUNN, Linda Kloote. 3400 SPRUCE ST 19104 #025-01-1972 L1978 **MFM CG** *020 †30,19

DUNN, Tricia Leigh. ■ 19130 #041-02-2006 L2006 **EM** *012

DUNNE, Christopher John. ■ 19131 #041-15-2007 L2007 *012

DUNZIK, Scott Dennis. 561 FAIRTHORNE AVE, FAIRMOUNT BEHAVIORAL HEALT 19128 #041-13-1992 L1994 **P** *020 †75

DUPREE, Kendall Towana. 2900 W QUEEN LN 19129 #016-01-2000 L2001 **P** *012

DURAN, Maria Angelica. 4126 WALNUT ST 19104 #231-01-1972 L1998 **IM** *020

DURAN MORA, Ricardo Mauri. 727 DELANCEY ST 19106 #264-19-1995 L2007 **ISM** *012 †20

DURBIN, Dennis Robt. 324 S 34TH ST 19104 #016-06-1987 L1989 **PD EM** *050 †55

DURHAM, Davis Godfrey. 840 WALNUT ST 19107 #041-02-1943 L1944 **OPH** *071 †35

DURING, Matthew J. 1025 WALNUT ST, STE 511 19107 #671-02-1982 L2000 **END NTR** *050

DUROCHER, John Raymond. 800 SPRUCE ST 19107 #041-01-1967 L1968 **IM HEM** *020 †20

DUSEJA, Reena. 3400 SPRUCE ST, GROUND RAVDIN 19104 #010-01-2002 L2005 **EM** *020 †16

DUTKA, Michael Vincent. ■ 19106 #008-01-2002 L2003 **DR** *100 †80

DUTTA, Pinaki Rana. 3400 SPRUCE ST, 2 DONNER BLDG HOSPITAL OF 19104 #023-01-2004 L2005 **RO** *012

DUTTA, Utpal Kanti. 2900 W QUEEN LN 19129 #160-02-1999 L2005 **IM** *012

DUVALL, Monica Elise. 908 RHAWN ST 19111 #041-13-2001 L2001 **FM** *020 †18

DUVVURI, Umamaheswar. ■ 19104 #041-01-2002 L2002 **OTO** *100

DUWE, Beau Vance. 3400 SPRUCE ST, HOSPITAL OF UNIVERSITY OF 19104 #041-01-2003 L2003 **PCC** *012

DWORET, Jessica Heidi. 3624 MARKET ST 560, UPHS/PRESBYTERIAN MEDICAL 19104 #041-01-2007 L2007 **TY** *012

DWYER, Erica Christine. ■ 19139 #041-01-2008 *012

DWYER-JOYCE, Lisa E. 111 S INDEPENDENCE MALL E, STE 968 THE BOURSE BLDG. 19106 #539-06-1990 L1998 **PCP** *012

DY, Rochelle Coleen Tan. 5501 OLD YORK RD, ALBERT EINSTEIN MED CTR 19141 #748-01-2001 L2003 **PPM** *012 †55

DYER, Chad Christopher. 3400 N BROAD ST, TEMPLE UNIV SCH OF MED 19140 #041-13-2000 **AN** *100

DYER-GOODE, Pamela T. 2425 N BROAD ST 19132 #041-13-1977 L1978 **GYN FM** *030

DYKYJ, Roman. 8151 REVERE ST 19152 #407-16-1958 L1965 **IM GP** *071 ‡

DYSART, Kevin Charles. 111 S 11TH ST 19107 #041-09-1998 L2001 **NPM** *020 †55

DYUTIN, Oleg. 111 S 11TH ST 19103 #913-17-1984 L2006 **P** *100

DZIALO, Kelly Ann. ■ 19128 #051-04-2007 L2007 *012

DZIEWIT, John Andrew. ■ 19104 #041-13-2007 L2007 **TY** *012

DZUBOW, Leonard Mark. 3400 SPRUCE ST 19104 #041-01-1975 L1977 **D IM** *020 †20,15

EADE, Thomas. 333 COTTMAN AVE, MEDICAL STAFF OFFICE 19111 #671-01-1994 L2006 *100

EAGLE, Ralph Conrad, Jr. 840 WALNUT ST, WILLS EYE INSTITUTE 19107 #041-01-1970 L1971 **OPH OS** *040 †35

EARLE, Ginneh Olisa. ■ 19106 #041-13-2000 *100

EARLE, Joyleen Elaine. 1 PENN BLVD 2ND FL 19144 #035-19-1979 L1988 **CD** *020 †20

EARLE, Linda Ann. 1100 WALNUT ST 19107 #041-02-1986 L1988 **PUD CCM** *020 †20

EASLER, Jeffrey James. ■ 19103 #036-05-2007 L2007 **IM** *012

EASTMOND, Cyrilene Anna. 131 E CHELTEN AVE, HEALTH CTR # 9 19144 #041-02-1991 L1993 **IM** *020 †20

EBCIOGLU, Zeynep Ayse. ■ 19107 #035-06-2000 L2001 **NEP** *100 †20

EBEDE, Kenechi Kingsley. ■ 19107 #913-48-2004 L2006 **GS** *012

EBIZADEH, Payam. ■ 19107 #305-01-1999 L2001 **DR** *100

EBURUOH, Rita Ngozi. 1900 N 20TH ST 19121 #690-04-1992 L2003 **FM** *020 †18

ECKENHOFF, Roderic Geo. 3400 SPRUCE ST, HOSP OF THE UNIV PA 19104 #016-06-1978 L1986 **AN OS** *050 †05

ECKER, Malcolm Lewis. ■ 19103 #041-13-1961 L1962 **ORS** *020 †40

ECKLUND, James Michael. 5401 OLD YORK RD, STE 501 19141 #023-12-1987 L1991 **NS** *020 †25

ECKMANN, David Matthew. 3400 SPRUCE ST, DEPT OF ANESTHESIA-HUP 19104 #016-06-1990 L1996 **AN** *050 †05

ECONOMEDES, Demetri Manue. ■ 19128 #041-77-2007, ▲ L2007 *012

EDELIST, Darrin D. 1015 WALNUT ST 19107 #065-06-1999 L2002 **FSM** *100 †18

EDELMAN, Bret Robert. ■ 19103 #041-01-2002 L2003 **GS** *012

EDELMAN, Jonathan Mark. 3400 SPRUCE ST, # 3 RAVDIN BLDG STE F PULM 19104 #035-47-1983 L1988 **PUD IM** *050 †20

EDELSOHN, Gail A. 1101 MARKET ST FL 8, MENTAL RETARDATION SERVICE 19107 #041-13-1978 L1992 **CHP P** *062 †75

EDELSTEIN, Paul Herbert. 3400 SPRUCE ST, DEPT PATH 19104 #005-14-1973 L1986 **ID IM** *050 †20

EDIE, Richard Newbery. 1025 WALNUT ST, STE 607 19107 #035-01-1965 L1979 TS GS *071 †85,90

EDMONDS, Pamela Ruth. 1020 LOCUST ST, STE 244 19107 #028-02-1980 L1983 **PTH** *020 †50

EDMONSTON, Tina B. 125 S 11TH ST RM 421A, MOLECULAR DIAGNOSTICS 19107 #409-16-1994 L2001 PTH *020 †50

EDMUNDS, L Henry, Jr. 3400 SPRUCE ST 19104 #024-01-1956 L1973 TS *020 †85,90

EDMUNDS, Kristin Wolcott. 2301 S BROAD ST, DEPT OF RADIOLOGY 19148 #041-13-1998 L2001 **AR** *020 †20

EDWARDS, Mc Iver W, Jr. PHILA VA MED CTR 19104 #041-01-1962 L1964 **AN** *040 †05

EDWARDS, Robin C. 3400 SPRUCE ST, DEPT OF PATHOLGY & LB MDCN 19104 #038-06-1989 L1992 **PTH** *020 †50

EDWARDS, Scott E. 3400 SPRUCE ST, DEPT OF OB/GYN 19104 #008-01-1991 L1995 **OBG** *020 †30

EFFINGER-KASSOW, Ellin. ■ 19106 #038-43-1974 L1975 **OPH IM** *020 †35

EGGER, Andrew David. ■ 19144 #025-12-2005 L2007 **PM** *012

EGLICK, Paul Geo. 10151 BUSTLETON AVE 19116 #041-01-1942 L1943 **PD** *071 †55

EHLERS, Justis Potter. 840 WALNUT ST, WILLS EYE HOSPITAL 19107 #028-02-2004 L2005 **OPH** *012

EHRLICH, Alexander Evan. 1900 RITTENHOUSE SQ 19103 #041-02-1972 L1973 **D** *020 †15

EHRLICH, Dion Ralph. 840 WALNUT 19107 #010-01-1973 L1974 **OPH** *035

EHRLICH, George Edward. ■ 19106 #016-42-1953 L1964 **RHU IM** *071 †20

EHRLICH, Lauren Jamie. ■ 19146 #041-01-2005 L2005 **DR** *012

EHRLICH, Michael Stuart. ■ 19146 #041-02-2005 L2005 **OPH** *012

EHYA, Hormoz. 333 COTTMAN AVE, FOX CHASE CANDER CTR 19111 #517-01-1974 L1983 **ATP PCP** *050

EICHENBAUM, Matthew Dan. 1015 CHESTNUT ST, THOMAS JEFFERSON UNIV 19107 #041-02-2003 L2004 **ORS** *012

EICHHORN, Patricia Lynn. 5501 OLD YORK RD, DEPT OF MED EDU 19141 #422-01-2006 L2006 **GS** *012

EID, Hala Milad. 245 N 15TH ST, MCP HAHNEMANN 19102 #605-02-1991 L2001 **IM RHU** *020 †20

EIGER, Glenn. 5501 OLD YORK RD, ALBERT EINSTEIN MED CENTER 19141 #035-06-1987 L1990 **PUD CCM** *020 †20

EINHORN, Kim. 834 CHESTNUT ST STE 400, BENJAMIN FRANKLIN HOUSE 19107 #550-02-2003 L2003 **OBG** *020

EISEN, Andrea Frances. 3400 SPRUCE ST, 16 PENN TOWER 19104 #065-01-1992 L1998 **ON** *100 †20

EISEN, Howard Joel. 245 N 15TH ST, MAIL STOP#1012 19102 #041-01-1981 L1982 **CD IM** *020 †20

EISEN, Teddi F. 600 ARCH ST, RMS 4306-4310 19106 #041-07-1983 L1993 **OM EM** *062 †16,70

EISENBERG, Daniel Alan. 9880 BUSTLETON AVE, CENTER ONE 19115 #041-01-1992 L1997 **NM NR** *072 †80,28

EISENBERG, Judith Michele. 5501 OLD YORK RD, DEPT OF EMERGENCY MEDICINE 19141 #041-09-1998 L2001 **ETX** *062 †16 ‡

EISENBERG, Robert Alan. 3600 SPRUCE ST, 504 MALONEY BLDG 19104 #005-11-1971 L1995 **RHU IM** *050 †20

EISENBERG, Ted S. 2375 WOODWARD ST, STE 102 19115 #041-77-1976, ▲ L1978 **GP** *020

EISENHOWER, Michelle M. 2301 S BROAD ST, # 201 19148 #041-02-2000 L2001 **FM** *020 †18

EISNER, Henry. 6300 GREENE ST # SW407 19144 #041-01-1955 L1956 **PYA CHP** *071 †55,75

EISON, Theodore Matthew. 1025 WALNUT ST, STE 700 19107 #045-01-2000 L2003 **PD** *020 †55

EISZNER, James Richard, III. ■ 19107 #041-02-2007 L2007 *012

EKBERG, Olle. 3900 WOODLAND AVE, VETERANS ADMINISTRATION 19104 #858-01-1972 *100

EKBLADH, Lamar Eric V. 245 N 15TH ST, MAIL STOP 495- OB/GYN 19102 #008-01-1968 L1987 **OBG** *030 †30

ELAHI, Mohammed Mehboob. ■ 19103 #065-06-1993 L2002 **PS** *020

EL-AHWANY, Mohamed Dorry. ■ 19136 #915-02-1960 **ORS** *071

ELAMIN, Lisa Catherine. 5501 OLD YORK RD STE 3, DEPT OF MED A E MED CTR 19141 #041-01-2002 L2002 **DR** *100 †80

ELCOCK, Claudius A R. 5301 CEDAR AVE 19143 #010-03-1959 L1969 **IM** *071

ELCOCK, Julia Angela. 555 S 43RD ST, HEALTH CENTER #3 19104 #041-13-1987 L1997 **FM** *100 †18

ELDAKAR-HEIN, Shaden Tons. 3401 N BROAD ST, DEPT MED 19140 #041-13-2007 L2007 **IM** *012

EL-DEIRY, Wafik S. 415 CURIE BLVD, SCHOOL OF MEDICINE 19104 #011-02-1987 L1994 **ON** *020

ELDEN, Lisa Melinda. 1601 WALNUT 19102 #067-01-1988 L2001 **OTO** *020 †45

ELDER, David Eric. 3400 SPRUCE ST, DEPT ANATOMIC/CLIN PATH 19104 #671-01-1970 L1979 **PTH** *050

ELDER, Justin Lee. ■ 19127 #041-77-2007, ▲ *012

ELEFANT, Howard Lawrence. 3996 RED LION RD 19114 #041-13-1973 L1975 **IM** *075 †20

ELENITSAS, Rosalie. 3400 SPRUCE ST, 2 RHOADS PAVILION 19104 #041-12-1985 L1987 **D DMP** *020 †15

ELFATAH, Mahmoud Ahmed. 2900 W QUEEN LN 19129 #915-04-1996 L2006 **P** *012

ELGABALAWI, Fayez Kamel Z. 3401 N BROAD ST 19140 #915-02-1975 L1985 **P** *020 †75

ELGART, Richard Lee. 111 S 11TH ST, STE 8490 19107 #041-02-1988 L1991 **AN** *020 †05

ELGOHARY, Bassem Galal. 1025 WALNUT ST, THOMAS JEFFERSON UNIV HOSP 19107 #056-05-2002 L2002 **IM** *100 †20

ELIA, Elia Shamoun. 111 S 11TH ST, STE 8940 19107 #875-02-1988 L2000 **AN** *020

ELIAS, Sara Beth. 625 BAINBRIDGE ST, # 6 19147 #033-06-2002 L2002 **OBG** *020 †30

ELIGULASHVILI, Victoria. ■ 19130 #041-15-2005 L2005 **EM** *012

ELIJOVICH, Matias. ■ 19128 #033-05-2006 L2006 **EM** *012

ELISON, Inessa. 11685 BUSTLETON AVE C, HENDRIX CENTER 19116 #913-01-1975 L1997 **IM** *100 †20

EL-JACK, Amr Kamal. 2751 PENNSYLVANIA AVE, B-205 19130 #024-05-2001 L2002 **DR** *100 †80

ELKEEB, Ahmed A. Mohamed. 3401 N BROAD ST, DEPT OF INTERNAL MED 19140 #613-01-2005 L2005 **IM** *012

EL KHATIB, Fateh Ahmad Ri. 2900 W QUEEN LN 19129 #875-01-2002 L2003 **IM** *100 †20

ELKINS, William L. 324 S 34TH ST, CHILDRENS HOSPITAL RM 9093 19104 #024-01-1958 L1960 **IG PTH** *050

ELLICK, Bertram J. 4000 N 9TH ST, DBA KESSLER REHAB CTRS 19140 #041-77-1958, ▲ L1959 *071

ELLIOTT, Elizabeth Meyer. 3550 N 5TH ST, MARKET STREE 19140 #023-07-1977 L1997 **PD EM** *020 †50

ELLIOTT, River Mckenzie. ■ 19104 #041-01-2007 L2007 **PS** *012

ELLIS, David Melech. 800 SPRUCE ST 19107 #041-13-1960 L1961 **CHP P** *020 †75 ‡

ELLIS, H Lenwood. ■ 19131 #010-03-1955 L1957 **IM GP** *071

ELLIS, Leander Theodore. 2746 BELMONT AVE 19131 #010-03-1954 L1960 **P** *020 †75

ELLMAN, Jared Keith. 1601 WALNUT ST STE 1516 19102 #041-01-1998 L2000 **P** *020 †75

ELMAN, Lauren. 3400 SPRUCE ST 19104 #035-20-1998 L2000 **N** *020

ELNEKAVE, Eldad. 5501 OLD YORK RD, DEPT RAD 19141 #024-07-2006 L2006 **DR** *012

ELOVITZ, Michal Aviva. 3400 SPRUCE ST 19104 #035-46-1994 L2001 **OBG** *020 †30

ELSTROM, Rebecca Linnea. 3400 SPRUCE ST, HOSPITAL OF UNIV OF PA 19104 #041-01-1996 L1999 **HO** *020 †20

ELVEY, Sharon Marie. 2129 W OREGON AVE FL R, PED & ADOLESCENT MED GRP 19145 #041-07-1978 L1981 **PD A** *020 †55

EMAMI, Djaafar Abarghoui. ■ 19140 #517-06-1966 L1975 **RO** *100 †80

EMAMI, Kawouss. 9807 BUSTLETON AVE, H.R. MILLENNIUM OB/GYN 19115 #517-03-1971 L1976 **OBG** *020 †30

EMANUEL, Raymond Jos. 4641 ROOSEVELT BLVD 19124 #010-01-1986 L1991 **P CHP** *020 †75

EMERSON, Stephen Gould. 3600 SPRUCE ST, MALONEY 510 19104 #008-01-1980 L1994 **HEM** *050 †20

EMERY, Christopher Lloyd. 230 N BROAD ST 19102 #038-44-1992 L1999 **MM** *020 †50

EMMETT, Edward Anthony. 3400 SPRUCE ST, SILVERSTEIN PAV 19104 #143-03-1964 L1996 **OM D** *020 †70

EMMETT, Gary Allen. 833 CHESTNUT ST, STE 301 19107 #041-02-1976 L1977 **PD** *020 †55

ENDE, Jack. 39TH & MARKET STREETS, PRESBYTERIAN MED CTR 19104 #051-04-1973 L1989 **IM** *020 †20

ENDE, Kevin Howard. 625 BAINBRIDGE ST, # 6 19147 #033-06-2002 L2002 **OTO** *100

ENDERS, Gregory Hay. 3400 SPRUCE ST, FL 3 19104 #041-02-1979 L1985 **RHU IM** *020 †20 ‡

ENEANYA, Dennis Ilozulike. 16 W GIRARD AVE 19123 #028-03-1987 L1990 **NEP** *020 †20

ENER, Rasih A. 3401 N BROAD ST 9PP, TEMPLE UNIV SCH OF MED 19140 #902-07-1991 L1996 **IC HO** *040 †20 ‡

ENG, Joann. ■ 19129 #041-15-2008 *012

ENGDAHL, Ryan Kent. 1735 MARKET ST, STE A198 19103 #041-13-2004 L2004 **GS** *012

ENGEL, Andrew Jesse. 3400 SPRUCE ST 19104 #035-20-2002 L2003 **AN** *100 †05

ENGELAGE, Elysia Marie. ■ 19144 #041-15-2008 *012

ENGELS, Friederike H C. 3400 SPRUCE ST 19104 #409-23-1995 L2002 **HMP** *100 †50

ENGLAND, James Morris. 245 N 15TH ST 19102 #028-02-1982 L1983 **PTH** *050 †50

ENGLANDER, Brian Samuel. 111 S 11TH ST, THOMAS JEFFERSON UNIV HOSP 19107 #041-02-1998 L2001 **DR** *100 †80

ENGSTROM, Paul Frederick. 333 COTTMAN AVE 19111 #026-04-1962 L1963 **ON IM** *050 †20

ENIS, David Richard. 3600 SPRUCE ST, HUP DERMATOLOGY 19104 #008-01-2006 L2007 **D** *012 †20

ENRIQUEZ, Miriam Lynn. ■ 19104 #041-01-2006 L2006 **PTH** *012

ENTINE, Joseph H. 9892 BUSTLETON AVE, STE 206 MOSS PLAZA 19115 #041-09-1949 L1950 **GS** *071 †85

ENTWISTLE, John W, III. 230 N BROAD 19102 #036-01-1990 L1999 **TS** *020 †85,90

ENYINNA, Chinonyerem Vero. ■ 19107 #033-06-2004 L2007 **IM** *100 †20

EPELBOIM FELDMAN, Joyce. 5501 OLD YORK RD 19141 #935-01-1993 L2006 **IM** *012

EPPES, Stephen Cole. 111 S 11TH ST 19107 #011-04-1979 L1987 **PD PDI** *020 †55

EPSTEIN, Alan L. 822 PINE ST, STE 1C 19107 #024-07-1979 L1985 **RHU IM** *020 †20 ‡

EPSTEIN, Alan Neil. 326 LEIDY LABORATORY, RM G7 19104 #023-07-1958 L1958 **OS** *075

EPSTEIN, Richard Howard. 111 S 11TH ST STE 5480G, THOMAS JEFFERSON UNIVERSIT 19107 #041-01-1978 L1981 **AN PD** *020 †55,05

ERGAS, Heath Brian. ■ 19107 #041-02-2007 L2007 **TY** *012

ERIKSSON, Lars Ingvar. 3400 N BROAD ST 19140 #858-06-1982 *100

ERINLE, Ayodele Olumide. 1205 LEVICK ST, UNIVERSITY OF PITTSBURGH M 19111 #690-02-1996 L2005 **NEP** *012 †20

ERKES, Neal. 9501 ROOSEVELT BLVD, STE 506 19114 #038-40-1982 L1983 **IM** *020 †20

ERNST, Linda Marie. ■ 19147 #028-02-1999 L2003 **PTH** *100

ERRO, Roger I. 2147 N 6TH ST 19122 #308-03-1982 L1984 **P** *020 ‡

ERSLEV, Allan J. 1015 WALNUT ST 19107 #297-01-1945 L1960 **HEM IM** *071 †20

ERTEL, Nathan W. 800 SPRUCE ST, PENNSYLVANIA HOSP 19107 #017-20-2006 L2007 **DR** *012

ESANGBEDO, Issy Claire. 1000 WALNUT ST 19107 #690-02-2001 L2002 **PD** *100 †55

ESCARCEGA ALARCON, Ricardo. 3401 N BROAD ST, DEPT OF HOSP ADMINISTRATIO 19140 #649-18-2003 L2007 **IM** *012

ESCARTE, Felicitas Hizon. ■ 19116 #748-01-1947 L1963 **P** *020

ESCHELMAN, David John. 111 S 11TH ST, CVIR/SUITE 4200 GIBBON 19107 #041-02-1986 L1990 **VIR** *020 †80

ESKENAZI, Marko M. 8140 VERREE RD 19111 #902-10-1952 L1963 **FM** *071

ESKIN, Bernard Abraham. 4190 CITY AVE, STE 418 19131 #035-03-1955 L1956 **GYN REN** *071 †30 ‡

ESKUCHEN, Julia Beth. ■ 19128 #023-01-2006 L2006 **PD** *012

ESLAMPOUR, Aidin. 111 S 11TH ST, DEPT OF MED EDU 19107 #517-10-2004 L2006 **ORS** *012

ESSIEN-LEWIS, Ime Bassey. 800 SPRUCE ST, PA HOPSITAL 19107 #033-75-2006, ▲ L2006 **OBG** *012

ESTACIO, Restituto N. LANGDON & CHELTENHAM AVES 19124 #748-07-1959 L1971 **AM PD** *020

ETEMAD, Bijan J. 3535 MARKET ST STE 670, UNIV OF PENNA 19104 #517-05-1961 L1972 **IMG P** *050 †75

ETORMA, Rodolfo Palomares. ■ 19116 #748-01-1960 *075

ETTINGER, Jeffrey B. 7500 CENTRAL AVE STE 205 19111 #041-09-1975 L1976 **PD** *020 †55

EUBANKS, Chenia Yvonne. ■ 19141 #041-01-1997 L1999 **PD** *020 †55

EVAGELIOU, Nicholas F. 1214 LOCUST ST, # 3 19107 #008-02-2002 L2002 **PHO** *012 †55

EVANGELISTA, Christine Lo. 5501 OLD YORK RD, ALBERT EINSTEIN MED CTR 19141 #748-01-1995 L2003 **P** *100

EVANGELISTA, Evaristo U. 2329 E ALLEGHENY AVE 19134 #748-07-1966 L1980 **OM EM** *020 †18

EVANGELISTO, Amy Marie. 3400 SPRUCE ST 19104 #041-13-1997 L1999 **RHU** *100 †20

EVANS, Adele Karen. 3400 CIVIC CENTER BLVD, WOOD 1 19104 #012-05-2000 L2005 **PDO** *100 †45

EVANS, Audrey Elizabeth. 324 S 34TH ST, ARB902 19104 #803-09-1950 L1969 **PHO** *050 †20

EVANS, Barry J. 3509 N BROAD ST, FLOOR 5 BOYER PAVILLION 19140 #041-09-1976 L1977 **PD PDP** *020 †55

EVANS, Dwight Landis. 423 SERVICE DR, 305 BLOCKLEY HALL 19104 #041-13-1976 L1997 **P** *020 †75

EVANS, James John. 909 WALNUT ST, 2ND FL 19107 #024-16-1995 L2003 **NS** *020 †25

EVANS, Katherine Laura. ■ 19146 #041-01-2007 L2007 *012

EVANS, Lisa Remage. 304 LOMBARD ST, REAR 1 19147 #065-05-2002 L2002 **EM** *100 †16

■ = Address Information Privacy Protected

EVANS, Mark Ira. 245 N 15TH ST, MS495 19102 #035-08-1978 L2000 **OBG MG** *020 †19,30

EVANS, Tracey Lynn. 3400 SPRUCE ST, 510 MALONEY BLDG 19104 #041-01-1996 L2002 **HO** *020 †20

EVCIMEN, Harun. ■ 19144 #902-01-1999 L2004 **P** *012

EVERITT, Daniel Eric. 39TH & MARKET ST 19104 #024-01-1979 L1991 **IMG IM** *050 †20

EVERLY, Eileen M. 3550 MARKET ST FL 5, PRIM CARE CTR-CHLDRNS HOSP 19104 #041-12-1999 L2001 **PD** *020 †55

EVERS, Kathryn A. 7701 BURHOLME AVE 19111 #035-19-1975 L1976 **DR** *020 †80

EWALD, Denise Elaine. 3300 HENRY AVE, MEDICAL COLLGE OF PNNSYLVN 19129 #041-09-1983 L1984 **N** *020 †75

EWIDA, Ashrafe Saad M. 245 N 15TH ST, MCP-HAHNEMANN UNIV 19102 #915-06-1992 L2001 **AN** *020

EWING, Madeleine Quail. 700 SPRUCE ST STE 100 19106 #041-01-1973 L1974 **OPH** *020 †35

EWING, Stanford Graham. 800 SPRUCE ST, FL 2 19107 #038-41-1976 L1995 **PDC PD** *020 †55

EWING, Stephanie Holter. 601 WALNUT ST STE 92 19106 #038-41-1991 L1994 **OBG** *020 †30

EZE, Nnamdi Ifeanyi. ALUMNI AFFAIRS, ALBERT EINSTEIN MC 19141 #690-04-2003 L2008 *100

EZUGHA, Herbert Osita. ERIE AVE AT FRONT, ST CHRISTOPHERS HOSP 19134 #690-03-1998 L2007 **CHN** *012

EZZAT, Waleed Hazem. 925 CHESTNUT ST FL 6, AND N 19107 #025-07-2005 L2005 **OTO** *012

FABENS, Elizabeth Lawrie. 8835 GERMANTOWN AVE 19118 #024-16-1985 L1987 **IM** *020 †20

FABI, Mark Bernard. 834 CHESTNUT, STE 427 19107 #041-02-1985 L1986 **P** *020 †75

FABIO, Mary Beth. 39TH & CHESTNUT STE 110, CHOP PRIMARY CARE 19104 #035-46-1993 L1995 **PD** *020 †55

FABISZEWSKA, Ewa. 7927 FAIRFIELD ST 19152 #759-10-1981 L1993 **IM** *020

FABRIZIO, Raymond Michael. ■ 19114 #041-13-2002 L2002 **VIR** *012 †80

FADALE, Daniel Justin. ■ 19107 #011-03-2007 L2007 **EM** *012

FADOJU, Doris Olukemi. ■ 19111 #033-06-2005 L2005 **PD** *012

FAERBER, Eric Norman. ERIE AVE AT FRONT ST 19134 #836-01-1966 L1980 **PDR** *020 †80 ‡

FAGER, Samuel Shaw. 324 S 34TH ST, CHILDRENS HSPTL OF PHLDLPH 19104 #041-09-1973 L1975 **IM PD** *020 †55

FAIRMAN, Ronald Marc. 3400 SPRUCE ST, FL 4 19104 #041-02-1977 L1978 **VS GS** *020 †85

FAISAL, Manthodi Kulangar. 800 SPRUCE ST, PA HOSPITAL-UPHS 19107 #495-44-1995 L2004 **IM** *100 †20

FAJARDO, Mildred Therese. 5501 OLD YORK RD, ALBERT EINSTEIN MED CTR 19141 #748-02-2003 L2005 **P** *012

FAKHARZADEH, Steven S. 3400 SPRUCE ST, 2 RHOADS PAVILION 19104 #041-01-1991 L1995 **D** *020 †15

FAKHRAEE, Michael S. 7500 CENTRAL AVE, STE 101 19111 #517-05-1972 L1976 **PS GS** *020

FALK, Mark Bradley. 3400 SPRUCE ST, GROUND RAVDIN 19104 #023-01-2000 L2001 **EM** *020 †16

FALK, Marni Joy. 3615 CIVIC CENTER BLVD, ARC 1002C 19104 #010-01-2000 L2006 **OS** *100 †55,19

FALK, Scott Austin. 2220 WALNUT ST # PH6 19103 #010-01-2000 L2006 **CCA** *020 †05

FALKNER, Bonita E F. 833 CHESTNUT, STE 700 19107 #026-04-1967 L1968 **NEP PD** *050 †55

FALKOWITZ, Dianna Carol. 2821 ISLAND AVE, STE 131 19153 #041-13-1992 L1995 **NEP** *020 †20

FALLON, Theodore J, Jr. 3200 HENRY AVE, AUH MCP RM 333 APH 19129 #041-14-1981 L1983 **CHP P** *020 †20,75

FAMADOR, Mark Benjamin Fl. ■ 19128 #748-10-1999 L2004 **P** *012

FAMORCA, Florentino P. 5606 GERMANTOWN AVE 19144 #748-01-1962 L1973 **FM OS** *075

FARABAUGH, Dana Castafero. 245 N 15TH ST, STOP 495 19102 #041-15-2003 L2008 **OBG** *100

FARAH, Mirna M. 324 S 34TH ST 19104 #605-02-1988 L1995 **PD PEM** *020 †55

FARBER, Abigail First. 324 S 34TH ST 19104 #041-01-1963 L1966 **PD** *020 †20

FARBER, Barry Mitchell. 730 WESTVIEW ST 19119 #041-09-1969 L1971 **P** *020 †75

FARBER, Harold F. 9892 BUSTLETON AVE, 204 MOSS PLZ 19115 #035-03-1983 L1984 **D** *020 †15 ‡

FARBER, John Lewis. 132 S 10TH ST, STE 285K 19107 #005-02-1966 L1972 **PTH** *050 †50

FARIS, David Gordon. 500 S BROAD ST 19146 #035-01-1954 L1984 **PHP** *030

FARMER, Nicole Marie. 1025 WALNUT ST, THOMAS JEFFERSON UNIV HOSP 19107 #010-03-2004 L2004 **IM** *100

FARMER, Steven Alan. 3400 SPRUCE ST, DEPARTMENT OF MEDICINE 19104 #008-01-2003 L2003 **CD** *012 †20

FARNSWORTH, Pauline E. 3401 N BROAD ST 19140 #041-13-2003 L2003 **EM** *100 †16

FARO, Scott Hunter. 3401 N BROAD ST, DEPT OF RADIOLOGY 19140 #033-06-1986 L1992 **RNR DR** *020 †80

FARQUHAR, John Denney. 335 E WYOMING AVE 19120 #041-01-1944 L1945 **PD** *020 †55

FARRAR, John Timothy. 423 GUARDIAN DR, RM 816 19104 #035-45-1981 L1991 **N PMM** *050 †75

FARRELL, Colleen C. 3998 RED LION RD STE 215 19114 #033-05-2001 L2001 **PD** *100 †55

FARRIS, Zachary. 3300 HENRY AVE, ALLEGHENY UNIV OF HLTH SCI 19129 #041-15-2002 L2002 **GS** *012

FARUQI, Saima. 100 E LEHIGH AVE, SUITE 105, MEDICAL ARTS BU 19125 #704-16-1991 L2007 **P** *012

FASAN, Omotayo Olusola. 245 N 15TH ST, DREXEL UNIV COLL MED/HAHNE 19102 #690-02-1995 L2004 **IM** *012

FASIHUDDIN, Quadeer Moham. 4TH FLOOR - S TOWER MAIL, DREXEL UNIVERSITY COLLEGE 19102 #422-01-2007 L2007 **IM** *012

FASIUDDIN, Airaj Fatima. ■ 19130 #033-06-2003 L2003 **OPH** *100

FATEMA, Ahmed. 4400 HAVERFORD AVE, FAMILY MEDICAL CARE 19104 #160-02-1976 L1987 **IM** *020 ‡

FAUST, Thomas Wilson. 3400 SPRUCE ST 19104 #047-06-1983 L2002 **GE HEP** *020 †20

FAYEK, Sameh Adel. ■ 19131 #915-02-1992 L2006 **GS** *100

FAYNBERG, Nora. 9150 MARSHALL, STE 17 19114 #913-04-1952 L1981 **FM** *020 ‡

FAYOCK, Kristopher Scott. ■ 19147 #041-02-2008 L2008 *012

FEBO-SAN MIGUEL, Carmen. 3401 N BROAD ST 19140 #042-01-1973 L1974 **FM** *020 †18

FEDCHIN, Brian David. 1339 W PORTER ST 19148 #010-02-1998 L2000 **CD** *020 †20

FEE, Maureen A. FRONT ST & ERIE AVE, ST CHRISTOPHER'S HOSPITAL 19134 #041-07-1978 L1980 **PD PM** *030 †55

FEEMSTER, Kristen Allysn. ■ 19146 #035-01-2002 L2002 **PD** *100 †55

FEETHAM, Megan Chen. ■ 19128 #041-15-2008 #012

FEIGENBERG, Steven Joel. 333 COTTMAN AVE, FOX CHASE CANCER CENTER 19111 #041-09-1997 L1997 **RO** *020 †80

FEIN, Joel Allen. 324 S 34TH ST 19104 #035-19-1988 L1990 **PEM EM** *050 †55

FEINBERG, Daniel Marc. 330 S 9TH ST, DEPT NEURO 19107 #041-14-1992 L1992 **N** *020 †75

FEINBERG, Mark Bennett. ■ 19119 #005-11-1987 L1992 **IM** *020 †20

FEINER, Jeffrey Michael. ■ 19104 #035-06-2005 L2007 **PS** *012

FEINSMITH, Norman. 51 N 39TH ST, PHILADELPHIA HEART INST ST 19104 #035-47-1978 L1982 **CD IM** *020 †20

FEINSTEIN, Michael Allen. 2314 S 3RD ST 19148 #041-02-1973 L1974 **OBG** *020 †30

FEINSTEIN, Steven Aaron. 2821 ISLAND AVE, MERCY WELLNESS CENTERSTE D 19153 #028-02-1983 L1984 **IM** *020 †20

FEIT, Helen. 3300 HENRY AVE 19129 #035-06-1980 L1984 **IMG END** *020 †20

FEKETE, Thomas. 3400 N BROAD ST 19140 #024-07-1978 L1984 **ID IM** *050 †20

FELD, Ellen Dove. 245 N 15TH ST MS 504, DREXEL UNIV PA PROGRAM 19102 #038-41-1984 L1985 **IM OM** *040 †20

FELD, Ricky Ian. 132 S 10TH ST, DIV OF DIAGNOSTIC ULTRASOU 19107 #035-47-1981 L1987 **DR IM** *020 †20,80

FELDMAN, Arthur Michael. 1025 WALNUT ST, RM 822 19107 #021-06-1981 L1994 **CD IM** *030 †20

FELDMAN, Arthur Myron. 3998 RED LION RD, STE 130 19114 #041-01-1973 L1974 **ON HEM** *020 †20

FELDMAN, Elad. ■ 19107 #035-48-2003 L2007 **OPH** *012

FELDMAN, Harold Ira. 923 BLOCKLEY HALL, UNIV PA SCHOOL MED 19104 #024-05-1982 L1985 **NEP IM** *050 †20

FELDMAN, Jeffrey Mark. 3300 HENRY AVE, ANESTH MCP HOSP 19129 #035-03-1983 L1992 **AN** *020 †05

FELDMAN, Julian David. 604 S WASHINGTON SQ, APT 2802 19106 #041-02-1958 L1959 **OBG** *062

FELDMAN, Michael David. 3400 SPRUCE ST, DEPT OF PATHOLGY & LB MDCN 19104 #033-05-1992 L1997 **PTH** *020 †50

FELDMAN, Michael S. 230 W WASHINGTON SQ, FARM JOURNAL BLDG. 3RD FLO 19106 #041-09-1967 L1968 **CD IM** *020 †20

FELICIANO, Melvyn Anthony. 3400 SPRUCE ST 19104 #035-01-1990 L1996 **RNR** *020 †80

FELIX, Carolyn Ann. 3615 CIVIC CENTER BLVD, ABRAMSON RESEARCH BLDG RM 19104 #024-05-1981 L1982 **OS** *050 †55

FELLIN, Frederick Michael. 111 S 11TH ST, STE G4100 19107 #041-02-1979 L1981 **ON HO** *020 †20

FELLOWS, Lesley Kathleen. ■ 19104 #067-01-1996 L2001 *100

FELSENSTEIN, Chad Harold. 51 N 39TH ST, EMERGENCY DEPARTMENT 19104 #041-07-1998 L2000 **EM** *020 †16

FENKEL, Jonathan Mark. ■ 19147 #041-02-2004 L2007 **GE** *012 †20

FENLIN, John Major, Jr. 925 CHESTNUT ST, FIFTH FLOOR 19107 #041-02-1963 L1964 **ORS** *020 †40

FENNING, Robert Scott. ■ 19146 #041-01-2008 L2008 *012

FENTON, Gregory Lucien. 840 WALNUT ST, WILLS EYE HOSP 19107 #025-01-2004 L2005 **OPH** *012

FEO AGUIRRE, Leandro Javi. 5501 OLD YORK RD 19141 #935-05-2002 L2006 **GS** *012

FERBER, Andres Sasson. 1015 WALNUT ST, RM 804 19107 #924-01-1988 L1999 **HO IM** *020 †20

FERGUSON, Monica Odetta. 3701 MARKET ST STE 640 19104 #041-12-1995 L1998 **IM** *020 †20

FERGUSON, Toby Arlo. 3400 SPRUCE ST, OF NEUROLOGY 19104 #011-03-2001 L2002 **N** *100

FERNANDES, Doris E. 4400 HAVERFORD AVE, DISTRICT HEALTH CTR NUMBER 19104 #495-05-1955 **PD** †55

FERNANDES, Eugene Agnelo. 840 WALNUT ST 19107 #917-01-1969 L1978 **OPH IM** *020 †35

FERNANDES, Violet Maria. ■ 19129 #041-15-2008 L2008 *012

FERNANDEZ, Alexander. ■ 19107 #003-01-2007 L2007 **EM** *012

FERNANDEZ, Forrest Bryan. 3440 MARKET ST, FIRST FLOOR 19104 #025-01-1989 L2006 **GS** *020 †85

FERNANDEZ, Victor M. ■ 19116 #308-07-1984 *075

FERNANDO, Antonio T, III. 3600 MARKET ST 19104 #748-17-1991 L1996 **P** *100 †75

FERNANDO, Dayantha Manila. ■ 19103 #010-02-2004 L2006 **DR** *012

FERRAGUT MARTI, Juan. 2600 N LAWRENCE ST 19133 #847-11-1967 **PD** *100 †55

FERRAN, Claudia Margarita. 3819 CHESTNUT ST 33, ST. LEONARD'S CT STE 120 19104 #041-13-1995 L2003 **PD** *020 †55

FERRARA, Lynn Ann. 9122 FRANKFORD AVE 19114 #041-13-1996 L1998 **PD** *020 †55 ‡

FERRARI, Victor Alfred. 3400 SPRUCE ST, # 9014E GATES PAV 19104 #041-01-1986 L1987 **CD IM** *050 †20

FERRARIS, Nina Elizabeth. ■ 19103 #041-15-2008 *012

FERREIRA, Arturo Jose. 4955 FRANKFORD AVE 19124 #132-09-1969 L1973 **IM RHU** *020 ‡

FERRI, Lara Rita. ■ 19130 #010-02-1994 L1996 **PE** *020 †55

FERRIER, Moira Catherine. 131 N 4TH ST 2R 19106 #305-01-2005 **DR** *012

FEUDTNER, John C. 324 S 34TH ST, CHILDRENS HOSP 19104 #041-01-1995 L2002 **PD PHP** *020 †55

FEULNER, Lara Michele. 3400 N BROAD ST, TEMPLE UNIV SCH OF MED 19140 #041-13-2008 *012

FEUSSNER, James Walter. 2401 PENNSYLVANIA AVE 19130 #041-13-1973 L1974 **CHP P** *020 †75 ‡

FEYGIN, Tamara. ■ 19152 #913-01-1983 L2001 **PDR** *100 †80

FIEL, Stanley Bruce. 3333 N BROAD ST 19140 #041-07-1973 L1974 **PUD IM** *040 †20

FIELD, Howard Lawrence. 1020 SANSOM ST, STE 1652 19107 #041-02-1954 L1955 **P** *071 †75

FIELDS, Jason Matthew. ■ 19146 #024-05-2005 L2005 **EM** *012

FIELDSTON, Evan Scott. ■ 19104 #041-01-2003 L2003 **PD** *100 †55

FIGICIOGLU, Can Huseyin. ■ 19103 #902-07-1985 L2003 **PD** *020 †19,55

FIGUEREDO, Vincent M. 5501 OLD YORK RD, LEVY 3 19141 #035-01-1987 L2005 **IM** *020 †20

FIGUEROA, Peter Ricalde. 100 E LEHIGH AVE, DEPT SURG 19125 #748-01-1967 L1979 **TS** *020 †85,90

FIGUEROA DUGARTE, Rafael. 3401 N BROAD ST, OF S 19140 #935-01-2001 L2008 **GS** *012

FILANTE, Mary M Scott. ■ 19128 #026-04-1951 L1952 **PM** *072 †60

FILICE, Ross Warren. ■ 19104 #026-04-2004 L2007 **DR** *012

FILICKO, Joanne Elizabeth. 130 S 9TH ST, 125 SOUTH 9TH ST 19107 #041-09-1992 L1995 **HO** *050 †20

FILIPPONE, Edward John. 2228 S BROAD ST 19145 #035-47-1978 L1980 **NEP IM** *020 †20

FILMER, Robert Bruce. 833 CHESTNUT ST, STE 300 19107 #143-03-1963 L1974 **U** *020 †95

FILMYER, William Geo. FRANKFORD HOSPITAL, DEPT OF ANESTHESIA 19114 #028-02-1988 L1992 **AN** *020 †20

FINALLE, Rodney Randel. 225 S COBBS CREEK PKWY, PRIMARY CARE CTR 19139 #041-01-1993 L1995 **PD** *020 †55

FINDEISEN, Kurt Otto. 1937 PEMBERTON ST, HEALTH CENER #4 19146 #041-01-1975 L1976 **IM** *020 †20

FINE, Alexander Semyon. 6404 ROOSEVELT BLVD, STE 1D 19149 #913-21-1976 L1999 IM *020 †20

FINE, Eric Wm. 1200 WALNUT ST, STE 2 19107 #917-18-1959 L1972 **P** *030 †75

FINE, Lauren Cortell. ■ 19103 #041-01-2008 *012

FINE, Richard Howard. 5501 OLD YORK RD 19141 #035-09-1984 L1992 **AN GS** *020 †05

FINE, Stuart Lee. 51 N 39TH ST 19104 #023-01-1966 L1991 **OPH** *020 †35

FINEGOLD, Amanda. 3400 SPRUCE ST 19104 #035-47-2002 L2002 **FM** *100 †18

FINEMAN, Mitchell Scott. 840 WALNUT ST, STE 1020 19107 #012-05-1993 L1995 **OPH** *020 †35

FINESTONE, Albert J. 3223 N BROAD ST, RM 228 19140 #041-13-1945 L1946 **IM IMG** *030 †20

FINK, David Lee. 135 S 18TH ST, ONE RITTENHOUSE, SUITE 701 19103 #041-02-1985 L1986 **P** *020 †75

FINK, James Allen. 833 CHESTNUT ST, STE 701 19107 #143-05-2000 L2004 **IM** *020

FINKEL, David M. 51 N 39TH ST, MOB SUITE 280 19104 #041-13-1977 L1979 END IM *050 †20 ‡

FINKEL, Leif Hari. 220 S 33RD ST 19104 #041-01-1981 **N** *050

FINKEL, Richard Sanford. 3400 CIVIC CENTER BLVD, CHILDREN'S HOSP OF PHILA 19104 #028-02-1978 L1999 **N CHN** *020 †55,75

FINKEL, Terri H. 3615 CIVIC CENTER BLVD, 1102 ABRAMSON RESEARCH CEN 19104 #005-11-1982 L1999 **PD** *020 †55

FINKELSTEIN, Amy Hope. 2230 COTTMAN AVE 19149 #041-01-1980 L1982 **IM IMG** *020 †20

FINKELSTEIN, Jeffrey Mark. 3998 RED LION RD STE 204 19114 #041-07-1985 L1990 OTO HNS *020 †45

FINKELSTEIN, Richard M. 309 S 13TH ST 19107 #035-19-1972 L1973 **IM IMG** *020 †20 ‡

FINKENSTADT, Eric V. 8815 GERMANTOWN AVE, STE 12 19118 #041-09-1978 L1979 PUD CCM *020 †20 ‡

FINLAY, Esme Elizabeth. ■ 19146 #035-06-2003 L2003 **HO** *012

FINN, Erin Elizabeth. ■ 19103 #041-77-2007, ▲ L2007 *012

FINSTEIN, Joseph Louis. ■ 19107 #041-21-2005 L2006 **ORS** *012

FINTELMANN, Robert Eyck. 840 WALNUT ST, WILLS EYE HOSP 19107 #409-41-2005 L2006 OPH *020

FIOL-SILVA, Zoraida. 910 WALNUT ST 19107 #042-01-1978 L1979 **OPH OS** *020

FION, Gladys Lorena. 3401 N BROAD ST 19140 #429-01-1988 L1999 **ID** *020 †20 ‡

FIORITO, Michael John. 3401 N BROAD ST, DEPT OF EMERGENCY MEDICINE 19140 #041-13-2003 L2003 **EM** *100 †16

FIRDU, Tikikil. ■ 19128 #041-15-2008 *012

FISCHEL, Jason Adam. ■ 19131 #422-01-2007 L2007 **EM** *012

FISCHER, David Hadwin. 840 WALNUT ST, STE 102 19107 #041-13-1974 L1979 **OPH** *020 †35

FISCHER, Grace M. ■ 19118 #041-13-1953 L1954 **CD OS** *071

FISCHER, John Richard. 222 CHURCH ST, APT 6C 19106 #018-75-2004, ▲ L2005 **EM** *100

FISCHER, Lauren Jane. 1100 WALNUT ST 19107 #033-05-2002 L2002 **GS** *012

FISCHER, Robert Allen. 5401 OLD YORK RD, KLEIN BUILDING STE 363 19141 #024-01-1977 L1982 **ID IM** *020 †20

FISCHER, Sandra L Eppley. 2601 HOLME AVE 19152 #041-13-1971 L1972 **PTH** *071 †50 ‡

FISCHMAN, David Lee. 925 CHESTNUT ST 19107 #035-09-1984 L1988 **CD IM** *020 †20

FISH, David Jonathan. 333 COTTMAN AVE 19111 #041-13-1978 L1979 **AN CCA** *020 †20,05

FISH, James Edmund. 1025 WALNUT ST, STE 8439 19107 #016-06-1971 L1985 PUD IM *050 †20

FISH, Stephanie Anne. 3400 SPRUCE ST DEPT MED 19104 #035-19-1997 L1999 **END** *020 †20

FISHBEIN, Gary Eric. 1740 SOUTH ST, STE 306 19146 #041-02-1985 L1991 **IM** *020 †20

FISHER, Aron Baer. 3400 SPRUCE ST 19104 #041-01-1960 L1965 **PUD IM** *050 †20

FISHER, Cynthia Elaine. 3400 SPRUCE ST, DEPT IM 19104 #023-07-2007 L2007 **IM** *012

FISHER, Frederick. 2400 CHESTNUT ST 19103 #041-13-1964 L1965 **P PYA** *020 †75

FISHER, George Edward. 1018 W LEHIGH AVE 19133 #041-02-1994 L1997 **IM** *020 †20

FISHER, Jon Scott. 2543 S BROAD ST 19148 #041-77-1986, ▲ L1987 **FM** *020

FISHER, Kyle William. 925 CHESTNUT ST, FL 6 19107 #041-02-2005 L2005 **OTO** *012

FISHER, Michael Jay. 324 S 34TH ST 19104 #024-01-1994 L1997 **PHO** *020 †55

FISHER, Robert Stephen. 3401 N BROAD ST, DEPT GASTRO 19140 #041-01-1964 L1965 GE IM *020 †20 ‡

FISHER, Sarah Margaret. 530 S 2ND ST, STE 108 19147 #023-01-1985 L1989 **AN GP** *020 †05

FISHKIN, Lana P. 111 S 11TH ST 19107 #041-09-1970 L1971 **P OTO** *020 †75

FISHMAN, Alfred Paul. 423 GUARDIAN DR, 316 BLOCKLEY HALL OFC PROG 19104 #020-02-1943 L1969 **PUD IM** *020 †20

FISHMAN, Herman Chas. PO BOX 40158 19106 #056-06-1972 L1973 **CHP P** *075 †75

FISHMAN, Michael Kalman. ■ 19131 #041-13-2005 L2005 **GS** *012

FISHMAN, Peter Eric. 3400 SPRUCE ST, UNIVERSITY OF PENNSYLVANIA 19104 #041-01-2005 L2007 **EM** *012

FISMAN, David Norman. 1505 RACE ST, 11TH FL 19102 #065-06-1994 L2003 **ID** *020 †20

FISS, David Matthew. 3401 N BROAD ST, TEMPLE UNIVERSITY HOSPITAL 19140 #041-15-2000 L2001 **IC** *012

FITZGERALD, David Patrick. 4503 SPRUCE ST 19139 #036-01-2000 L2001 **ID** *012

FITZGERALD, Garret Adare. 422 CURIE BLVD, BRB 1 RM 909 19104 #539-04-1974 L1994 PA CD *050

FITZGERALD, Roy G. 1518 WALNUT ST, STE 1110 JEFFERSON MED COL 19102 #038-06-1964 L1970 **P** *020 †75

FITZPATRICK, Denise F. 7700 GERMANTOWN AVE, FL 2 19118 #041-13-1991 L1993 PD *020 †55

FITZPATRICK, James Thos. 3401 N BROAD ST, STE 320 PARKINSON PAVILION 19140 #041-02-1991 L1994 **CD** *020 †20

FITZPATRICK, Jane Moira. 227 N BROAD ST, FL 2 19107 #422-01-1985 L1991 **CD IM** *020 †20

FITZPATRICK, Janet H. 219 N BROAD ST, STE 8 19107 #041-09-1995 L1998 **IM** *020 †20 ‡

FITZSIMMONS, John Michael. 216 N BROAD ST, FL 4 19102 #041-09-1975 L1976 OBG *020 †30

FLAGG, Alice Helen Wentz. ■ 19150 #041-13-1959 L1960 **OS** *071

FLAGG, Stephanie Diane. 219 N BROAD ST 19107 #041-01-1998 L2001 **RHU** *020 †20

FLAHERTY, Devon Margaret. ■ 19130 #041-13-2008 L2008 *012

FLAHERTY, James Francis. 333 COTTMAN AVE, C308 19111 #010-02-1990 L2006 GS SO *020 †85

FLAHERTY, John Thos. ■ 19103 #036-07-1967 L1994 **CD** *062 †20

FLAHERTY, Keith Thomas. 51 N 39TH ST 19104 #023-07-1997 L2000 **HO** *020 †20

FLAHERTY, Lois Talbot. ■ 19103 #036-07-1968 L1993 **CHP P** *071 †75

FLAKE, Alan Wayne. 34TH ST & CIVIC CTR BLVD, DEPT OF SURGERY 19104 #004-01-1981 L1996 **PDS GS** *020 †85

FLAMMA, John C. 51 N 39TH ST, DEPT OF EMERGENCY MEDICINE 19104 #422-01-1988 L1991 EM IM *040 †20

FLANAGAN, Joseph Chas. 840 WALNUT ST, STE 102 19107 #041-02-1963 L1964 PS OPH *020 †35

FLANAGAN, Melina Bree. ■ 19104 #021-01-2002 L2002 **PCP** *012

FLANDERS, Adam Eugene. 111 S 11TH ST, 3350 GIBBON BLDG 19107 #016-01-1983 L1987 RNR R *020 †80

FLECKSER, Adam Myles. 3401 N BROAD ST, DEPARTMENT OF ANESTHESIOLO 19140 #041-13-2004 L2004 **AN** *012

FLEECE, David Michael. 3509 N BROAD ST, 5TH FL 19140 #024-07-1993 L1995 **PD** *020 †55

FLEEGLE, Stephenie Rebecc. ■ 19107 #023-01-2008 L2008 *012

FLEGEANCE, Tanya Marie. 5501 OLD YORK RD, ALBERT EINSTEIN MED CTR 19141 #665-01-2004 L2004 **P** *012

FLEISHER, Lee Alan. 3400 SPRUCE ST, DULLES 6 19104 #035-48-1986 L2004 **AN GS** *030 †05

FLEMING, Burton Ailes. 8835 GERMANTOWN AVE 19118 #041-13-1953 L1957 **P** *072 †75

FLESCH, Judd David. ■ 19104 #041-01-2006 L2006 **IM** *012

FLESZLER, Frederick. 2821 ISLAND AVE, STE 131 19153 #935-01-1999 L2001 **NEP** *020 †20

FLEURANT, Marshall. ■ 19148 #035-46-2006 L2006 **IM** *012

FLIEDER, Douglas B. 333 COTTMAN AVE, DEPT OF PATHOLOGY 19111 #035-45-1992 L2004 PTH *020 †50

FLINKMAN, Leonard. 5735 RIDGE AVE 19128 #041-09-1944 L1945 **GP** *071

FLIPSE, Dylan Scott. ■ 19107 #041-13-2008 *012

FLOMENBERG, Neal. 1025 WALNUT ST, THOMAS JEFFERSON UNIVERSIT 19107 #041-02-1976 L1994 **ON HEM** *050 †20

FLOMENBERG, Phyllis R. 1020 LOCUST ST, 326 JEFFERSON ALUMNI HALL 19107 #035-46-1980 L1994 **IB** *050 †20

FLOOD, Jeremy James. 211 S 9TH ST STE 600 19107 #035-06-2001 L2001 **END** *100

FLOOD, William Augustus. 2 LOGAN SQ, STE 820 19103 #041-13-1990 L1997 **ON** *020 †20

FLORENCE, Kim Camille. 2301 E ALLEGHENY AVE, HELENE FULD BLDG 4TH FL 19134 #024-05-2001 L2001 **OBG** *020

FLORES, Ana Isabel. ■ 19104 #041-01-2008 L2008 *012

FLORES, Maria Luisa P. ■ 19106 #748-01-1966 L1969 **AN** *020 †05

FLORES, Roberto. 245 N 15TH ST MS 310, OF M 19102 #041-15-2002 **AN** *020

FLORO, Claro Noriega. 3401 N BROAD ST 70PD, TEMPLE OB-GYN 19140 #748-01-1965 L1973 OBG *020 †30

FLORY, James Howard. ■ 19103 #041-01-2008 *012

FLOYD, Latoya Anyika. ■ 19128 #041-15-2007 L2007 **P** *012

FLOYD, Thomas Frederick. 3400 SPRUCE ST 19104 #041-01-1986 L1996 **AN GS** *020 †05

FLYNN, Anthony Michael. ■ 19147 #041-02-2005 L2005 **IM** *012

FLYNN, Colleen Mary. ■ 19107 #041-02-2006 L2006 **IM** *012

FLYNN, Edward Thos. 3400 SPRUCE ST 19104 #041-01-1967 L1971 **OS** *050 †05

FLYNN, John Matthew. 34TH & CIVIC CENTER BLVD 19104 #041-12-1989 L1996 **OP** *020 †40

FOBIA, John Bisong. 501 S 54TH ST, # 537 19143 #041-01-1977 L1978 **GS VS** *020 †85

FOGATA, Maria Lourdes. 5501 OLD YORK RD, 5 LEVY BUILDING 19141 #748-10-1983 L1994 IMG *020 †20

FOGEL, Mark Alan. 324 S 34TH ST 19104 #035-15-1985 L1989 **PDC PD** *050 †55

FOGEL, Sari Nussbaum. 135 S 18TH ST, UNIT 301 19103 #041-01-1983 L1985 **P** *020 †75

FOGELSANGER, Lester Neil. 1810 LIACOURAS WALK, 5TH FL 19122 #041-13-2003 L2003 P *020

FOGG, Matthew Isaac. 702 S WASHINGTON SQ 19106 #035-19-1999 L2001 **PD** *020 †55,03

FOGG, Ryan Noelle. ■ 19147 #039-01-2006 L2006 **GS** *012

FOGH, Shannon Elizabeth. ■ 19107 #024-05-2005 L2006 **RO** *012

FOGLIA, Elizabeth Ellen. ■ 19146 #028-02-2006 L2006 **PD** *012

FOGT, Franz. 3400 SPRUCE ST, DEPT OF PATHOLOGY & LB MDCN 19104 #409-16-1988 L1997 PTH *020 †50

FOJTIK, Dorothy. 833 CHESTNUT ST, STE 301 19107 #035-06-2000 L2001 **FM** *020 †18 ‡

FOJTIK, John Philip. 245 N 15TH ST 19102 #035-06-1999 L2001 **EM** *020 †16

FOK, Kum Chung. 800 SPRUCE ST 19107 #143-02-2002 L2005 **IM** *100

FOLCIK, Renee Maria. 111 S 11TH ST, JEFFERSON UNIVERSITY 19107 #033-06-2005 L2005 PD *012

FOLEY, Catherine Mary. 3333 N BROAD ST, RM 343 19140 #041-01-1974 L1976 **PD** *020 †55,75

FOLEY, Paul Joseph, III. ■ 19146 #041-01-2002 L2004 **GS** *012

FOLEY, Reghan. ■ 19103 #010-02-2003 L2005 **CHN** *012

FOLEY, Thomas. 100 E LEHIGH AVE 19125 #422-01-2005 L2005 **P** *012

FOLSOM, Michelle Antoinet. ■ 19107 #023-01-2005 L2005 **FP** *012

FONT, Zuleika Coralee. 211 S 9TH ST, NINTH STREET INTERNAL 19107 #004-01-1995 L1997 IM *020 †20

FONTAINE, John. 245 N 15TH ST 19102 #033-06-1979 L1990 **ICE CD** *020 †20

FONTANILLA, Johnrodolf Go. ■ 19107 #035-05-2006 L2006 **IM** *012

FONTANILLA, Nenita C G. 1900 N 20TH ST 19121 #748-01-1968 L1979 **FM** *020 †18

FONTANILLA, Rodolfo C. 703 CECIL B MOORE AVE 19122 #748-08-1966 L1973 **GP** *020

FOO, Russell. 1025 WALNUT ST, JEFFERSON MED COLL-THOS JE 19107 #041-02-2003 L2003 P *012

FOOTE, Joseph W. 3900 MARKET ST 19104 #041-07-1985 L1985 **OS** *020

FORCE, Thomas Lee. 1025 WALNUT ST STE 316, JEFFERSON MEDICAL COLLEGE 19107 #024-01-1978 L1984 **CD IM** *020 †20

FORCIEA, Mary Ann. 3615 CHESTNUT ST 19104 #036-07-1975 L1981 **IMG END** *020 †20

FORD, Ashley Elizabeth. ■ 19104 #036-05-2008 *012

FORD, D Patrick. ■ 19147 #041-01-1983 L1989 **OM PHP** *071 †70

FORD, Patricia Ann. 230 W WASHINGTON SQ, FL 2 19106 #011-02-1987 L1988 ON HEM *020 †20

FORD, William Thomas, Jr. 3401 N BROAD ST, COGENT HEALTHCARE OF PA, I 19140 #041-15-2000 L2004 **IM** *100 †20

FORDE, David Laurence. 8815 GERMANTOWN AVE, STE 12 19118 #041-02-1963 L1964 PUD IM *020 †20

FORFIA, Paul Robert. 3400 SPRUCE ST, HEART FAILURE/TRANSPLANTAT 19104 #035-09-2000 L2006 **CD** *100 †20

FORMAL, Christopher S. 1513 RACE ST 19102 #023-01-1979 L1981 **PM** *020 †60

FORMAN, Alan Robt. 840 WALNUT ST STE 1250, WILLS EYE HOSPITAL-CPEC 19107 #024-07-1971 L1978 **OPH** *020 †35 ‡

FORMAN, Harvey Richard. 2236 E ALLEGHENY AVE 19134 #041-13-1973 L1974 **IM CD** *020

FORMAN, Lanny Philip. 2116 CHESTNUT ST, 2ND FL 19103 #041-13-1968 L1976 **FM** *020

FORMAN, Marc Allan. 1101 MARKET ST STE 7 19107 #041-01-1959 L1960 **CHP P** *071 †75

FORMAN, Mark Stuart. 422 CURIE BLVD, 605B STELLAR CHANGE 19104 #036-07-1995 L1998 NP *050 †50

FORMAN, Wendy Lynn. 9501 ROOSEVELT BLVD, STE 208 19114 #041-01-1989 L1992 IM ID *020 †20

FORNALIK, Hubert. 5501 OLD YORK RD 19141 #759-03-2000 L2003 **OBG** *100

FOROOHAR, Abtin Abby. 3401 N BROAD ST, TEMPLE UNIV HOSP 19140 #041-15-2004 L2004 ORS *012

FOROUZAN-GANDASHMIN, Iraj. 245 N 15TH ST, MS 495 DEBPT OBGYN MCP 19102 #517-05-1976 L1979 **OBS MFM** *020 †30 ‡
FORREST, Christopher B. 100 PENN SQ E, CHILDRENS HOSP PHILADELPHI 19107 #024-05-1986 L1987 **PD** *050 †55
FORRESTER, Anique Kerryan. ■ 19153 #010-03-2007 L2007 **P** *012
FORSBERG, Martin Mischa. 3535 MARKET ST, 3RD FLOOR # 3049 19104 #041-15-2001 L2001 **P** *020 †75
FORSTATER, Alan Thos. 1020 SANSOM ST, T239 19107 #041-13-1974 L1975 **EM** *020 †20,16
FORSYTH, Thomas. ■ 19119 #041-02-1974 L1976 **GS** *020 †16
FORTH, Darlene Louise. 1800 LOMBARD ST, PEPPER PAVILION STE 803 19146 #041-02-1995 L1998 **PM** *020 †60
FORTINA, Paolo. 324 S 34TH ST, CHOP WOOD BLDG RM 4385 19104 #561-20-1984 **HEM MG** *050
FORTNA, Ryan Robert. ■ 19104 #041-01-2006 L2006 **PTH** *012
FORTUNA, Kristine Lynn. 3401 N BROAD ST, 6TH OPB 19140 #041-13-1995 L1997 **ORS** *020 †40
FORZLEY, Paul E. 800 SPRUCE ST, PENNSYLVANIA HOSPITAL 19107 #010-02-1981 L2000 **AN** *020 †05
FOSNOT, Joshua. ■ 19119 #041-01-2003 L2003 **GS** *012
FOSTER, Bethany Joy. ■ 19104 #065-09-1994 L2001 *100 †55
FOSTER, Cherie Deon. 3400 SPRUCE ST 19104 #047-05-1993 L1996 **NPM** *020 †55
FOSTER, Jill Ann. ERIE AVE AT FRONT ST, ST CHRISTOPHERS HOSP 19134 #041-07-1990 L1990 **PDI IG** *020 †55
FOSTER, Jody Jane. 245 S 8TH ST, PENN HOSP 19106 #041-07-1989 L1991 **P** *020 †75
FOSTER, Mark Raymond. 5501 OLD YORK RD, DEPT OF MED EDU 19141 #422-01-2006 L2006 **EM** *012
FOSTER, Sarah Semple. ■ 19130 #041-15-2008 *012
FOSTER, Taliba Malika. ■ 19151 #033-06-2004 L2007 **CHP** *012
FOWLER, Ashley Jahnine. ■ 19107 #010-02-2001 L2004 **D** *020 †15
FOX, Alyson Nicole. ■ 19104 #035-47-2004 L2007 **GE** *012 †20
FOX, Donald. 2801 ISLAND AVE STE 10 19153 #041-09-1954 L1955 **IM GP** *020
FOX, James W, IV. 210 W RITTENHOUSE SQ 19103 #041-02-1970 L1971 **PS** *020 †65
FOX, Kevin Reitnauer. 3400 SPRUCE ST, HEMATOLOGY/ONCOLOGY SECTIO 19104 #023-07-1981 L1984 **HEM ON** *020 †20
FOX, Rosanne Marie. 2401 PENNSYLVANIA AVE 19130 #041-07-1993 L1998 **P** *020 †75
FOX, Stacey Garfield. ■ 19147 #041-01-2004 L2004 **PD** *020 †55
FOX, William Willis. 3400 SPRUCE ST 19104 #036-07-1966 L1973 **PD** *020 †55
FOY, Andrew James, Jr. ■ 19107 #041-02-2008 L2008 *012
FOY, Reginald Darnell. 520 S 19TH ST STE 1B 19146 #041-15-1999 L2001 **AN** *020 †05
FRAGA, Maria Victoria. 5501 OLD YORK RD 19141 #132-01-2000 L2005 **PD** *012
FRAGA, Polly Dane. 3401 N BROAD ST 19140 #041-01-1995 L1997 **IM** *071 †20
FRAGOS, George. 136 S 11TH ST 19107 #418-01-1959 L1971 **GS OBG** *100
FRAGOSO, Jose Manuel. ■ 19102 #042-02-2005 L2007 **DR** *012
FRAGOSO, Ruben Corral. 111 S 11TH ST, UNIVERSITY HO 19107 #024-01-2004 L2005 **RO** *012
FRAKER, Douglas Leon. 3400 SPRUCE ST, FL 4 19104 #041-01-1983 L1995 **SO END** *020 †85
FRAME, Lawrence Henry. 3900 WOODLAND AVE 111C, VAMC CARDIOLOGY 19104 #024-01-1975 L1983 **CD IM** *050 †20
FRANCO, Tatiana Carolina. 5501 OLD YORK RD, ALBERT EINSTEIN MED CTR 19141 #935-07-1998 L2005 **IM** *100
FRANCONI, Giovanna M. 1 GRADUATE PLZ, DEPT IM 19146 #561-17-1983 L1992 **IM** *100
FRANK, Adam Mathias. 1025 WALNUT ST, STE 605 19107 #041-01-1995 L1998 **GS** *020 †85
FRANK, Arthur Leonard. 245 N 15TH ST MS 660, DREXEL UNIV SCH PUB HLTH 19102 #035-47-1972 L2002 **OM IM** *040 †20,70
FRANK, Barbara Balis D. 219 N BROAD ST, FL 5 19107 #041-01-1962 L1963 **GE IM** *071 †20
FRANK, Dale Michael. 3400 SPRUCE ST 19104 #035-01-1992 L2004 **ATP HMP** *020 †50
FRANK, Ian. 3400 SPRUCE ST 19104 #032-01-1980 L1981 **ID IM** *050 †20
FRANK, John Lewis. 5500 WISSAHICKON AVE, ALDEN PARK MANOR 19144 #041-12-1966 L1968 **CHP PYA** *020 †75
FRANK, Kenneth David. 3900 WOODLAND AVE, PRIMARY CARE CTR 111GM 19104 #024-01-1972 L1975 **IM** *020 †20
FRANK, Leonard Arnold. 833 CHESTNUT ST, STE 703 19107 #041-09-1961 L1962 **U** *072 †95
FRANK, Lori Claudia. 925 CHESTNUT ST, MEZZANINE LEVEL 19107 #041-02-1998 L2000 **CD** *020 †20
FRANK, Ruth Felice. ■ 19107 #035-46-1981 L1998 **P** *012 †55
FRANKEL, David Simon. 3400 SPRUCE ST, 8 EAST GATES PAVILION 19104 #041-01-2004 L2007 **CD** *012 †20
FRANKEL, Harry A. 2028 SPRING GARDEN ST 19130 #041-02-1978 L1979 **FM** *020 †18
FRANKEL, Matthew Chas. 135 S 19TH ST 19103 #035-09-1978 L1983 **IM NEP** *020 †20 ‡
FRANKEL, Robert. 5501 OLD YORK RD 19141 #422-01-2002 L2002 **EM** *020 †16
FRANKL, William Stewart. 2100 SPRING GARDEN ST, THE PHILA CNTY MEDL SCTY 19130 #041-13-1955 L1956 **CD IM** *071 †20
FRANKLIN, B Benj. 7715 CASTOR AVE 19152 #005-12-1973 L1975 **IM** *020
FRANKLIN, Deborah Julie. ■ 19107 #041-01-1996 L1999 **PM** *020 †60
FRANKLIN, Howard Jay. 9892 BUSTLETON AVE, SURGICAL SERVICES LIMITED 19115 #041-07-1988 L1994 **GS** *020 †85
FRANKLIN, Urmila James. 7715 CASTOR AVE 19152 #495-21-1961 L1971 **GYN** *020 †30
FRANS, Ebenezer Edward Ab. ■ 19114 #275-01-1995 L2006 **IM** *020 †20
FRANTON, Barry. ■ 19103 #041-02-1976 L1979 **CD IM** *020 †20
FRANTZ, Katherine B. 4641 ROOSEVELT BLVD 19124 #050-02-1984 L1985 **P PYA** *020 †75 ‡
FRANZE, Vincent P. 111 S 11TH ST 19107 #033-75-2001, ▲ L2002 **AN** *100 †05
FRANZI, Joseph John. 8846 FRANKFORD AVE 19136 #041-13-1989 L1989 **FM** *020 †18 ‡
FRAYER, William Cornelius. 39TH & MARKET ST 19104 #025-01-1945 L1951 **OPH** *071 †35
FREDERIC, Myron Wayne. 51 N 39TH ST 19104 #038-40-1957 L1959 **N IM** *020 †20,75
FREDERICK, John Richards. ■ 19146 #048-14-2004 L2004 **GS** *012
FREDERICK, Robert Winston. 925 CHESTNUT ST, FL 5 19107 #016-01-1985 L1999 **ORS OSM** *020 †40
FREDERICKS, Claudine N. 7604 CENTRAL AVE 19111 #654-01-1998 L2002 **IM** *020 †20
FREDERICKS, Duane Alistan. 100 E LEHIGH AVE 19125 #041-13-1996 L2000 **GS** *100
FREDETTE, Jenna Marie. ■ 19104 #035-06-2006 L2006 **EM** *012
FREDIAN, Lisa N. 1025 WALNUT ST, THOS JEFFERSON 19107 #041-02-2008 *012
FREDRICKS, Karla Marie. ■ 19103 #028-02-2006 L2006 **PD** *012
FREEDMAN, Abraham. 111 S 11TH ST 19107 #041-13-1939 L1940 **P PYA** *071 †75
FREEDMAN, Alan Reinald. 2085 N 63RD ST 19151 #041-02-1962 L1963 **PD OS** *020 †55 ‡
FREEDMAN, Gary Mitchel. 333 COTTMAN AVE, FOX CHASE CANCER CENTER 19111 #041-13-1993 L1995 **RO** *020 †80
FREEDMAN, Lawrence Tollin. 7604 CENTRAL AVE, STE 101 19111 #041-01-1955 L1956 **OBG OS** *071 †30
FREEHILL, Nicole Elizabet. 834 CHESTNUT ST, LBBY 3 19107 #021-01-2005 L2005 **OBG** *012
FREEMAN, Andrew Myles. ■ 19128 #035-06-2003 L2006 **CD** *012 †20
FREEMAN, Jeffrey S. 4190 CITY AVE, STE 324 19131 #917-05-1968 *100
FREEMAN, Leo Colton. ■ 19130 #869-07-1953 L1955 **P PYA** *071 †75
FREEMAN, Susan Lynn. 3401 N BROAD ST, TEMPLE UNIVERSITY HOSPITAL 19140 #025-12-1984 L2006 **END IM** *030 †20
FREID, Jeffrey D. 3300 HENRY AVE 19129 #041-13-1979 L1981 **CD IM** *020 †20
FREIDL, Michael Conrad. ■ 19130 #041-15-2006 L2006 **ORS** *012
FREILICH, Howard Stanley. 9501 ROOSEVELT BLVD, STE 103 19114 #041-13-1980 L1982 **GE** *020 †20
FREIMAN, David B. 3400 SPRUCE ST, DEPT RAD 1 SILVERSTEIN 19104 #041-01-1973 L1973 **VIR CD** *020 †80
FREIRE, Jorge E. 216 N BROAD ST MS 200, HAHNEMANN UNIV. HOSPITAL 19102 #319-01-1972 L1983 **RO** *020
FREISINGER, Francis Alexa. ■ 19118 #041-15-2007 L2007 **IM** *012
FREIWALD, Milton Jos. 5501 OLD YORK RD 19141 #035-19-1943 L1944 **OPH FM** *071 †35
FREMPONG, Tamiesha A. 51 N 39TH ST, SHEIE EYE INST 19104 #008-01-2004 L2005 **OPH** *012
FREUNDLICH, Bruce. 1800 LOMBARD ST STE 501 19146 #035-47-1977 L1981 **RHU IM** *020 †20
FREY, Ala Stanford. 3509 N BROAD ST, TEMPLE UNIV CHILDRENS MED 19140 #041-14-1997 L2002 **PDS** *100 †85
FREYER, Jessica Erin. ■ 19121 #041-15-2007 L2007 **IM** *012
FREYNE, Patricia Ann. BROAD AND VINE STS, HAHNEMANN MED COLL 19102 #041-09-1997 L1998 *100
FRIDMAN, Guenrietta. 11749A BUSTLETON AVE 19116 #913-96-1990 L2002 **IM** *020 †20
FRIDMAN, Vera. ■ 19103 #024-07-2006 L2006 **N** *012
FRIED, Guy Wm. 1513 RACE ST 19102 #008-01-1985 L1987 **PM** *020 †60
FRIED, Rebecca Abgott. ■ 19102 #010-02-1979 L2006 **FM** *075 †18 ‡
FRIED, Richard Gregg. 3400 SPRUCE ST, 2 RHOADS PAVILION 19104 #035-08-1990 L1993 **D P** *020 †15
FRIEDBERG, Joseph Stewart. 51 N 39TH ST, STE 2D 19104 #024-01-1986 L1996 **TS** *020 †90,85
FRIEDE, Rotem. 501 S 54TH ST, CRITICAL CARE 19143 #033-05-1997 L2003 **CCM** *020 †20,16
FRIEDENBERG, Frank Karpf. 3401 N BROAD ST, # 8PP 19140 #041-13-1989 L1991 **GE** *020 †20
FRIEDENBERG, Zachary B. 51 N 39TH ST, PRESBYTERIAN HOSPITAL 19104 #035-01-1939 L1948 **ORS** *071 †40
FRIEDLAENDER, Eron Yael. 324 S 34TH ST 19104 #025-01-1997 L1999 **PD** *020 †55
FRIEDMAN, Alan Lee. 5501 OLD YORK RD, STE 1 19141 #041-09-1975 L1976 **HO ON** *020 †20
FRIEDMAN, David Paul. 132 S 10TH ST, STE 1072 MAIN BLDG 19107 #035-01-1983 L1990 **DR RNR** *020 †80
FRIEDMAN, David Steven. 111 S 11TH ST, DEPARTMENT OF RADIOLOGY 19107 #024-01-1992 L1994 **OPH** *050 †35
FRIEDMAN, Donald M. ■ 19146 #041-01-1970 L1971 **RHU IM** *071 †20
FRIEDMAN, Eliot Bruno. 3600 SPRUCE ST, 975 MALONEY BLDG 19104 #935-01-1999 L2003 **PCC** *100 †20
FRIEDMAN, Gina Y. KNIGHT AND RED LION RD, FRANKFORD HOSP 19114 #041-78-2005, ▲ L2005 **AN** *012
FRIEDMAN, Harvey Michael. 536 JOHNSON PAVILION, UNIV PENN 19104 #067-01-1969 L1973 **ID IM** *050 †20
FRIEDMAN, L Adele Kynette. 200 SPRUCE ST 19106 #041-01-1950 L1951 **DR** *071 †80
FRIEDMAN, Oren Leonard. 2701 HOLME AVE, STE 304 19152 #016-01-1980 L1984 **CD** *020 †20
FRIEDMAN, Susan Ann. 324 S 34TH ST 19104 #041-01-1982 L1984 **PD** *020 †55
FRIEMAN, Barbara Grugan. 2630 HOLME AVE, STE 200 19152 #041-02-1980 L1981 **ORS OTR** *020 †40
FRISCH, Daniel R. 925 CHESTNUT ST, MEZZANINE LEVEL 19107 #035-19-2000 L2007 **ICE** *100 †20
FRISCH, Eric Victor. 3400 SPRUCE ST 19104 #035-19-1976 L1981 **AN IM** *040 †20,05
FRISCIA, Michael Edward. 739 S DARIEN ST 19147 #041-01-2002 L2002 **GS** *012
FRISHBERG, Yaacov. 324 S 34TH ST 19104 #550-01-1983 L1991 **PN** *100
FRISS, Helena Ellen. 3333 N BROAD ST 19140 #035-08-1981 L1986 **NPM PD** *020 †55
FRITTS, Aaron Haskell. ■ 19107 #021-01-2007 L2007 **IM** *012
FROMM, Laurentine R. 800 SPRUCE ST 19107 #041-07-1979 L1981 **CHP P** *020 †75
FROST, Barbara Diane. ■ 19118 #041-09-1985 L1987 **P CHP** *020
FROST, Michael Patrick. 6100 CITY AVE 19131 #654-01-2000 L2000 **ADM IM** *020 †20 ‡
FRUCHTERMAN, Todd. ■ 19103 #041-01-1998 *100
FRUMIN, Abraham Maurice. 1900 S BROAD ST 19145 #041-13-1942 L1943 **HEM ON** *071 †20
FRUNCILLO, Richard John. 1300 WOLF ST 19148 #041-09-1979 L1980 **IM PA** *020 †20
FRY, Robert Dean. 700 SPRUCE ST, STE 305 19106 #028-02-1972 L1994 **CRS** *020 †10,85
FUCHS, Amy Chernoff. 219 N BROAD ST, FL 5 19107 #041-01-1988 L1995 **ID** *020 †20
FUCHS, Barry David. 216 N BROAD ST 19102 #035-46-1985 L1987 **CCM PUD** *020 †20
FUCHS, Lynn Marie. ■ 19106 #041-14-2006 L2006 **PD** *012
FUGARO, Anthony Joseph. 2601 HOLME AVE 19152 #041-77-1966, ▲ L1967 **AN** *072 †05
FULD, Alexander David. 3400 SPRUCE ST, PENN HOSPITAL CARE PHYSICI 19104 #041-02-2002 L2002 **IM** *100 †20
FULLER, Brian Matthew. ■ 19146 #001-02-2003 L2003 **CCM** *012
FULLER, Stephanie M. 1025 WALNUT ST 6TH FL, THOMAS JEFF UNIV 19107 #051-07-1999 L2001 **TS** *100 †85
FUMO, Peter Francis, Jr. 2 PENN BLVD, STE 112 19144 #035-19-1987 L1989 **NEP** *020 †20
FUNCH, Ross Simpson. ■ 19118 #041-02-1947 L1948 **AN** *071 †05
FURIA, Frances Kathleen. 3400 SPRUCE ST 19104 #041-02-2002 L2002 **EM** *100
FURIA, Samantha Lee. ■ 19148 #041-15-2007 L2007 **EM** *012
FURIE, Gregg Lawrence. ■ 19103 #024-01-2007 L2007 **IM** *012
FURMAN, Roy Evans, II. 3400 SPRUCE ST 19104 #041-01-1974 L1976 **N** *050 †75
FURTH, Emma Elizabeth. 3400 SPRUCE ST, DEPT OF PATHOLGY & LB MDCN 19104 #016-02-1984 L1986 **PTH** *020 †50
FURUKAWA, Satoshi. 3401 N BROAD ST, TEMPLE UNIV HOSPITAL 19140 #041-01-1984 L1985 **TS** *020 †85,90 ‡
FURUYA, Emily Yoko. 3400 SPRUCE ST, 100 CENTREX 19104 #041-01-1999 L2001 **ID** *100 †20
GAARY, Alvin Edward V. 3401 N BROAD ST, TEMPLE ANESTHESIA ASSOCIAT 19140 #041-09-1947 L1948 **AN** *071 †05
GABLE, Carl Chris, III. ■ 19104 #047-20-2002 L2007 **PTH** *100
GABOS, Peter B. 833 CHESTNUT ST, STE 300 19107 #035-19-1991 L1996 **OP** *020 †40

■ = Address Information Privacy Protected

GABRIEL, Peter Edward. 102 W PENN ST, 39TH & FILBERT, MAB 19144 #028-02-2003 L2003 IM *100 †20

GABRIEL, Veronica. 33 E CHESTNUT HILL AVE, STE 201 19118 #024-05-1981 L1982 FM *020 †18

GABRIELE, Elizabeth. ■ 19107 #041-02-2006 L2006 PD *012

GADDAM, Santhosh Reddy. ■ 19104 #495-57-1999 IM *100

GADDIPATI, Hima Bindu. ■ 19130 #495-11-1998 L2003 MG *012

GADDIPATI, Kishore Venkat. 3401 N BROAD ST 19140 #496-24-1996 L2002 GE *020 †20

GADEGBEKU, Annette Bridge. 833 CHESTNUT ST, STE 301 19107 #041-13-2004 L2004 FM *018

GAGLIARDI, Gregg Stephen. 132 S 10TH ST, 480 MAIN BUILDING 19107 #033-06-2001 L2004 GE *000

GAIESKI, David Foster. 3400 SPRUCE ST, GROUND SILVERSTEIN 19104 #041-01-1994 L1996 EM *020 †20,16

GAIN, Thomas B. 1420 RACE ST 19102 #041-09-1967 L1968 GS *020 †85

GAISER, Robert Raymond. 3400 SPRUCE 19104 #035-01-1988 L1992 AN *020 †05

GAITENS-ARAMINI, Tanis J. 3905 FORD RD 19131 #060-02-1989 L1997 CHP *020 †75 ‡

GAJARY, Zia Louise. ■ 19119 #041-01-1992 L1995 PD *020 †55

GAJRAJ SINGH SACHAN, Reena. ■ 19145 #495-04-2002 L2007 FP *012

GALANIS, Taki. 269 S 9TH ST, APT 604 19107 #041-02-2004 L2004 IM *100 †20

GALANTE, Lisa Marie. 9501 ROOSEVELT BLVD 19114 #041-01-1982 L1982 IM IMG *020 †20

GALBRAITH, Robert Michael. 3750 MARKET ST 19104 #917-19-1971 L1996 CRS IM *050 †20

GALETTA, Steven Louis. 3400 SPRUCE ST 19104 #035-20-1983 L1984 N *020 †75

GALIOTE, John Paul. ■ 19129 #041-15-2006 L2006 PD *012

GALKIN, Yelena M. 321 W GIRARD AVE 19123 #913-97-1990 L2001 IM *020 †20

GALLAGHER, Anna Marie. ■ 19147 #041-13-2003 L2003 PD *100 †55

GALLAGHER, Mary. ■ 19147 #041-13-2000 L2000 APM *100 ‡

GALLAGHER, Rachel Anne. ■ 19130 #035-20-2005 L2005 PD *012

GALLAGHER, Rollin M, III. 1800 LOMBARD ST, PAIN CENTER 1ST FLOOR 19146 #024-05-1970 L1997 OS P *030 †75

GALLAGHER-ORTIZ, James J. ■ 19147 #042-01-1999 DR *100 †80

GALLER, Avi Sternstein. ■ 19147 #041-02-2006 L2006 GE *012

GALLI, Kristin Kain. 7701 BURHOLME AVE, FOX CHASE CANCER CENTER 19111 #041-02-1994 L1996 AN *020 †05

GALLO, Giampaolo. 4641 ROOSEVELT BLVD, FRIENDS HOSP 19124 #561-17-1993 L2000 P *020 †75

GALLO, Joseph John. 3400 SPRUCE ST, U OF PA/FM/2 GATES 19104 #041-14-1982 L1999 FM FPG *020 †18

GALLO, Ralph C. 10551 DECATUR RD, STE 200 19154 #041-13-1974 L1975 SME PD *020 †55

GALPERIN, Mura. ■ 19116 #913-24-1957 L1986 DR *071

GALPERIN, Zhanna V. 1822 BENTON ST 19152 #913-01-1963 L1986 IMG FM *020 ‡

GALVAO, Carla Patricia. 1000 WALNUT ST, ORLOWITZ/704 19107 #041-02-2005 L2005 PD *012

GALVEZ, Juan Pablo. ■ 19107 #041-02-2007 L2007 IM *012

GAMBESCIA, Richard Alan. 219 N BROAD ST, STE 8 19107 #041-09-1971 L1972 GE IM *020

GAMSE, Adam Jonathan. 501 S 54TH ST, MERCY HEALTH SYSTEM EMERGE 19143 #048-15-2005 L2005 EM *020

GAN, Juan Jose. 5501 OLD YORK RD, DEPT OF PSYCHIATRY 19141 #422-01-2004 L2005 P *012

GAN, Walter Stanley. ■ 19152 #041-09-1943 L1944 OPH *071 †35

GAN, Yuebo. 245 N 15TH ST, DEPT OF GME 19102 #243-43-1982 L2006 PTH *012

GANATRA, Nautam Bhailalbh. 3400 SPRUCE ST, UNIVERSITY OF PENNSYLVANIA 19104 #495-22-2002 L2007 GS *012

GANDHI, Arpita. ■ 19115 #033-05-2004 L2004 EM *012

GANDHI, Kishor. ■ 19107 #033-06-2004 L2004 AN *012

GANDHI, Neil Ashok. ■ 19106 #041-02-2005 L2005 EM *012

GANDIKOTA, Praveena. 5501 OLD YORK RD, ALBERT EINSTEIN MED CTR 19141 #495-21-2003 L2003 IM *012

GANESANA, Naga Madhuri. 2900 W QUEEN LN 19129 #495-11-2000 L2003 GE *012 †20

GANESH, Arjunan. 111 S 11TH ST, DEPT OF ANESTHESIOLOGY 19107 #495-59-1988 L2000 PAN *020 †05

GANESH, Jaya. 324 S 34TH ST 19104 #495-59-1990 L2001 OS *020 †55,19

GANNE, Jayanthi. 2900 W QUEEN LN, DREXEL UNIV COLL OF MED 19129 #041-15-2006 L2006 H *012

GANSHEROFF, Neal. 2475 NAPFLE ST 19152 #056-05-1967 L1969 P *020 †75

GARBER, Bruce B. 8815 GERMANTOWN AVE, STE 34 19118 #041-01-1980 L1981 U *020 †95 ‡

GARBRECHT, Frederick Carl. ■ 19119 #017-20-1980 L1995 PD *020 †55

GARCHA, Jasjot Kaur. 2900 W QUEEN LN, DEPT OF INTERNAL MED 19129 #495-03-2002 L2004 NEP *012 †20

GARCHA, Puneet Singh. 245 N 15TH ST, 6TH FLOOR, DEPT OF MEDICIN 19102 #495-37-2001 L2005 IM *020

GARCIA, Fermin Carlos. 9501 ROOSEVELT BLVD, STE 305 19114 #935-07-1996 L2001 ICE *100 †20

GARCIA, Fernando Uriel. 245 N 15TH ST 19102 #737-06-1981 L1995 PTH *020 †50

GARCIA, Gabriel. ■ 19107 #031-01-2005 L2006 AN *012

GARCIA, Gretchen Marie. ■ 19118 #042-03-2005 L2005 P *012

GARCIA, Laureano. ■ 19120 #041-13-1996 L1998 FM *020 †18

GARCIA, Patricia Adriana. ■ 19104 #025-01-2008 L2008 *012

GARDECKI, Michelle Lynn. ■ 19107 #041-02-2008 *012

GARDEN, Jack. 1339 W PORTER ST 19148 #035-47-1983 L1987 CD IM *020 †20

GARDEN, Marc David. 2610 E ALLEGHENY AVE, PHILADELPHIA EYE ASSOCIATE 19134 #041-12-1980 L1982 OPH *020 †35 ‡

GARDINER, Geoffrey A, Jr. 111 S 11TH ST, DEPT OF RADIOLOGY 19107 #005-12-1973 L1986 VIR CD *020 †80

GARDINER, George Clarke. 1315 WINDRIM AVE 19141 #024-07-1961 L1964 P IM *040 †20,75

GARDINER, Margarita H. 2116 CHESTNUT ST 19103 #041-07-1985 L1987 RHU IM *020 †20

GARDNER, Beth C. 1811 S BROAD ST, PHILADELPHIA GASTROENTEROL 19148 #041-09-1983 L1985 GE *020 †20 ‡

GARDNER, Jennifer Michell. ■ 19146 #028-02-2006 L2006 IM *012

GARDNER, Vincent E. ■ 19118 #005-12-1944 L1972 GPM *071

GARES, Kathie Ann. 1234 MARKET ST, SEPTA MEDICAL DEPT 19107 #041-07-1977 L1979 IM GM *020 ‡

GARFIELD, Jamie Lee. 111 S 11TH ST 19107 #422-01-2004 L2004 PCC *012 †20

GARFIELD, Samuel J. 3998 RED LION RD 19114 #041-13-1941 L1947 OBG *020

GARFINKLE, William B. 5501 OLD YORK RD, DEPT OF RADIOLOGY 19141 #041-01-1964 L1965 R RNR *020 †80

GARG, Manish. ■ 19131 #025-07-2001 L2004 EM *020 †16

GARG, Nick Sonu. 133 S 36TH ST LBBY 2, CAPS 19104 #056-05-1996 L2002 CHP *020 †75

GARG, Shalini. ■ 19104 #041-01-2008 *012

GARG, Urmilesh Kumari. 5501 OLD YORK RD, DEPT OF PATHOLOGY 19141 #495-12-1973 L1979 PTH *100

GARGIULO, Andrew Michael, Jr. BROAD-ONTARIO STS, DEPT OF DIAG RAD 19140 #041-14-2006 L2007 DR *012

GARIBIAN, Garo S. 700 COTTMAN AVE, BLDG A 19111 #041-01-1978 L1979 CD IM *020 †20

GARIEPY, Aileen Maray. 834 CHESTNUT ST STE 400, BENJAMIN FRANKLIN HOUSE 19107 #041-15-2001 L2001 OBG *020

GARINO, Jonathan Peter. 3400 SPRUCE ST FL 2, SILVERSTEIN PAVLN DPT ORTH 19104 #010-02-1988 L1993 ORS OTR *020 †40

GAROFALO, Cara Angela. ■ 19103 #033-05-1999 L2007 CCP *100 †55

GARRAS, David N. ■ 19111 #036-07-2007 L2007 ORS *012

GARRELTS, Katie Elizabeth. ■ 19130 #038-40-2006 L2006 OBG *012

GARRETTO, Diana Janet. ■ 19129 #041-15-2008 *012

GARTLAND, John J. 1020 WALNUT ST, 615 SCOTT BLDG 19107 #041-02-1944 L1946 ORS *071 †40

GARVER, Jennie Vantress. ■ 19146 #041-01-2008 *012

GARY, Gerald Lamarr. 833 CHESTNUT ST, STE 300 19107 #041-02-1978 L1979 PD *020 †55

GARZA, Luis Andres. 415 CURIE BLVD, RM 202CRB 19104 #041-01-2001 L2001 D *020 †15

GASH, Richard Martin. 1901 MARKET ST 19103 #041-12-1961 L1962 GS OS *030 †85

GASINK, Christopher R. 3400 SPRUCE ST, DIV OF GASTRO/3 RAVDIN 19104 #051-01-1998 L2001 GE *020 †20

GASKINS, Albert Lee, Jr. 4947 PARKSIDE AVENUE 19131 #010-03-1948 L1950 PD PHP *071 †55

GASPAR, Stephen Ross. 3401 N BROAD ST 19140 #048-12-1978 L1986 IM PM *020 †20,60

GASSMAYR, Susanne. ■ 19107 #154-02-1990 L2006 AN *012

GASTFRIEND, Robert Jay. 7600 CENTRAL AVE 19111 #041-13-1982 L1984 GS *020 †85 ‡

GATES, Jane Elizabeth. 8400 PINE RD 19111 #010-02-1955 L1956 GP *071

GATHIUNI, Raymond Wahome. 3401 N BROAD ST, DEPT OF ANESTHESIOLOGY 19140 #010-03-2002 L2002 AN *012

GAUSAS, Roberta Elizabeth. 51 N 39TH ST 19104 #016-06-1989 L1996 OPH *020 †35

GAUTHIER-DELAPLANE, Mary. ■ 19104 #024-05-2003 L2004 FP *012

GAUWERKY, Charlotte E. ■ 19103 #409-21-1972 L1987 *020

GAVIN, Laurence Jos. 51 N 39TH ST, EMERGENCY DEPARTMENT 19104 #035-20-1978 L1984 EM IM *020 †20,16

GAVINI, Gopikrishna. FRONT AND ERIE AVE, ST CHRISTOPHERS HOSP 19134 #495-50-1986 L1997 NPM *020 †55

GAVRIN, Jonathan Robt. 3400 SPRUCE ST, DEPT OF ANESTHESIA 19104 #032-01-1978 L1989 AN IM *020 †20,05

GAWTHROP, Sarah Miller. ■ 19146 #041-02-2004 L2004 PD *100 †55

GAY, Roy Neil. 2116 CHESTNUT ST 19103 #038-43-1976 L1978 HEM IM *040 †20

GAYESKI, David Richard. 245 N 15TH ST, MS 310 19102 #041-15-2003 L2003 AN *020

GAYNOR, James Wm. 34TH & CIVIC STS, CHOP CARDIO SURG 19104 #045-01-1982 L1995 TS IM *020 †85,90

GE, Tong. 8835 GERMANTOWN AVE, DEPARTMENT OF RADIOLOGY 19118 #243-78-1984 L2003 DR *020 †80

GEARHART, Peter Allen. 601 WALNUT ST, STE 925 19106 #041-14-1998 L2001 OBG *020 †30

GEBRESELASSIE, Millen W. 2230 COTTMAN AVE, CITY HEALTH DISTRICT # 10 19149 #041-15-2001 L2001 FM *020 †18

GEE, Albert Ooguen. ■ 19146 #028-02-2005 L2005 ORS *012

GEE, Rebekah Elizabeth. ■ 19130 #035-20-2002 L2006 OBG *100 †30

GEFTER, Warren Bruce. 3400 SPRUCE ST, HOSPITAL OF THE UNIV. OF P 19104 #041-01-1974 L1975 DR *020 †80

GEHRING, James Morley. 205 N BROAD ST 19107 #046-01-2002 L2002 IM *020 †20

GEIFMAN-HOLTZMAN, Osnat. 3401 N BROAD ST, TEMPLE UNIV. HOSP. 19140 #550-02-1988 L2002 OBG MFM *020 †19,30

GEIGER, Geoffrey Alan. 3400 SPRUCE ST 19104 #041-01-2007 L2007 IM *012

GEIRSSON, Arnar. 3400 SPRUCE ST, CARDIOTHORACIC SURGERY 19104 #484-01-1997 L2005 TS *100

GEJER, Wendymarie. 501 S 54TH ST, MERCY HOSPITAL OF PHILADEL 19143 #041-15-2003 L2003 EM *100 †16

GELAW, Bethlehem. ■ 19104 #024-07-2001 L2002 AR *012 †80

GELBER, Jeremy Winthrop. 801 SPRUCE ST, PENNSYLVANIA HOSPITAL 19107 #041-02-2003 L2003 IM *100 †20

GELFAND, Joel Mitchell. 3600 SPRUCE ST, 2 MALONEY BUILDING 19104 #024-01-1998 L2000 D *020 †15

GELFAND, Jonathan L. 9501 ROOSEVELT BLVD, STE 208 19114 #035-46-1975 L1981 PUD IM *020 †20

GELLER, Evan. ■ 19129 #024-05-1984 L1989 PDR *020 †80

GELMAN, Beth P. ERIE AVE AT FRONT ST PED 19134 #035-46-1991 L1992 PHO *020 †55

GELMAN, Bruce Paul. 700 COTTMAN AVE, STE 201 19111 #023-07-1980 L1982 GE *020 †20

GENCORELLI, Frank Jason. ■ 19102 #011-02-2008 *012

GENERETTE, Pasha Michelle. 2 PENN BLVD, STE 112 19144 #023-01-1993 L1996 FM *020 †16

GENG, Qingdi. 1800 LOMBARD ST 19146 #243-47-1993 L2006 IM *012

GENTILE, Nina Teresa. 3401 N BROAD ST, DEPT OF EMERGENCY MEDICINE 19140 #041-07-1986 L1997 EM *020 †16

GENTZLER, Ryan David. ■ 19147 #041-13-2008 *012

GEORGAKIS, Alexander. 833 CHESTNUT ST, STE 710 19107 #024-05-2002 L2005 CD *012 †20

GEORGE, Bassem Ragheb. 4TH FLOOR - S TOWER MAIL, DREXEL UNIVERSITY COLLEGE 19102 #915-02-1995 L2007 GS *012

GEORGE, Brian Philip. 3401 N BROAD ST, TEMPLE UNIVERSITY HOSPITAL 19140 #041-15-2006 L2006 ORS *012

GEORGE, Jeffrey Stephen. 8835 GERMANTOWN AVE, DEPT OF EMERGENCY MEDICINE 19118 #041-15-2000 L2000 EM *020 †16

GEORGE, Sabu Jacob. 245 N 15TH ST, MS 470 19102 #690-07-1990 L2000 IC *012 †20

GEORGE, Simeon John. ■ 19147 #041-02-2006 L2007 *012

GEORGE, Vinu Michael. 5501 OLD YORK RD, ALBERT EINSTEIN MED CTR 19141 #495-52-1998 L2004 P *012

GERBER, Jeffrey Stephen. ■ 19147 #041-13-2003 L2003 PDI *012 †55

GERBER, Walter Le Roy. 5401 OLD YORK RD STE 502 19141 #035-46-1970 L1985 U *020 †95 ‡

GERDES, Jeffrey Scott. 800 SPRUCE ST, FL 2 19107 #032-01-1977 L1982 NPM PD *020 †55

GERHARDT, Robert Edward. 230 W WASHINGTON SQ, STE 100 19106 #041-01-1970 L1971 NEP IM *071 †20 ‡

GERMAN, Terry Manuel. 5501 OLD YORK RD 19141 #041-02-1960 L1961 **GYN OBG** *071 †30

GERNER, Edward Wm. 1015 CHESTNUT ST STE 1125 19107 #035-19-1965 L1970 **OPH N** *020 †75,35 ‡

GERNERD, Mark D. 1 CRESCENT DR STE 100, NAVY YARD CORPORATE CENTER 19112 #041-02-1976 L1978 **EM** *020 †16

GERSHKOFF, Arthur Maurice. 1200 W TABOR RD, MOSS REHAB MEDICINE 19141 #008-01-1978 L1980 **PM** *020 †60

GERSHMAN, Boris. ■ 19103 #041-01-2008 *012

GERSON, Benjamin. 10551 DECATUR RD, STE 200 19154 #041-02-1973 L1989 **IG CLP** *020 †50

GERSTEIN, Laurie P. 834 CHESTNUT ST STE T171 19107 #016-42-1998 L2001 **OBG** *020 †30

GERSTENFELD, Edward Paul. 3400 SPRUCE ST 19104 #016-06-1993 L2000 **ICE CD** *020 †20

GERTZ, Zachary Martin. ■ 19146 #041-01-2005 L2005 **IM** *012

GESSER, Richard Martin. 324 S 34TH ST, CHILDRENS HSPTL OF PHLDLPH 19104 #035-20-1986 L1987 **PD ID** *050 †55

GESSMAN, Laura Michelle. 111 S 11TH ST, JEFFERSON UNIVERSITY 19107 #033-06-2005 L2005 **PD** *012

GESSNER, Victoria. 5501 OLD YORK RD 19141 #041-13-1983 L1984 **GP OS** *020

GETSY, Joanne. 10 SHURS LN, STE 205 19127 #024-07-1983 L1985 **SME** *020 †20

GETTES, Nancy Jane. 345 E MOUNT AIRY AVE 19119 #041-13-1971 L1972 **IM FM** *020 †20,18

GETZ, Charles Lonnie. 925 CHESTNUT ST, FIFTH FLOOR 19107 #033-06-1998 L2000 **ORS** *100 †40

GETZEWICH, Kathryn Anne. ■ 19103 #033-06-2003 L2003 **EM** *100

GEVORKYAN, Rafael Yuriyov. 1800 LOMBARD ST 19146 #913-04-1995 L2006 **GS** *012

GEWIRTZ, Alan Michael. 421 CURIE BLVD, 716 BRB 2 3 19104 #035-06-1976 L1983 **HEM ON** *040 †20

GEYFMAN, Vitaly. 2900 W QUEEN LN 19129 #022-75-2000, ▲ L2001 **ICE** *020 †20

GHALI, Sherin R. 5000 WOODLAND AVE 19143 #915-02-1981 L1996 **IM IMG** *020 †20

GHANEM, Elie Semaan. ■ 19107 #605-01-2005 L2007 **ORS** *012

GHANEM, Helen Jean. 100 PARKER AVE UNIT 27 19128 #041-12-2003 L2003 **PD** *100 †55

GHANEM, Louis Roland. ■ 19128 #041-12-2007 L2007 **PD** *012

GHATGE, Aditi Prakash. ■ 19146 #041-15-2002 L2002 **PCC** *012 †20

GHAURI, Baber. 2900 W QUEEN LN 19129 #305-01-2001 L2001 **IM** *100 †20

GHAVAM, Sarvin. 111 S 11TH ST, JEFFERSON UNIVERSITY 19107 #023-01-2006 L2006 **PD** *012

GHIAM-FOTOOHI, Gholamreza. ■ 19129 #517-05-1970 L1975 **GS HNS** *050 †85

GHIASIAN, Vahid. 51 N 39TH ST, PRESBY MED CTR-PHILADELPHI 19104 #517-05-1981 L1996 **N** *020 †75

GHOHESTANI, Reza. 233 S 10TH ST, BLSB ROOM 412 19107 #517-28-1993 L2002 **D** *100

GHOROGHCHIAN, Peter Paima. ■ 19104 #041-01-2008 *012

GHOSH, Suresh Chandra. 2230 E ALLEGHENY AVE 19134 #495-02-1960 L1971 **TS** *020 †85,90

GIAMPETRO, Anthony M. 1411 WOLF ST 19145 #041-02-1962 L1963 **IM PUD** *020 †20

GIANELLA, Gonzalo E. 5401 OLD YORK RD, KLEIN 363 19141 #737-06-1996 L2002 **PCC** *100 †20

GIANNAKOUPOLOS, Helen. 3900 MARKET ST 19104 #041-15-1999 L2000 *020

GIANTONIO, Bruce Jos. 51 N 39TH ST, 103 MEDICAL ARTS BLDG/STE 19104 #010-02-1987 L1990 **ON** *020 †20

GIBBONS, Wayne Leroy. 813 ADAMS AVE STE A 19124 #041-07-1979 L1980 **FM** *020

GIBNEY, Sandra Mcgowan. 1800 LOMBARD ST 19146 #041-02-1994 L2001 **IM EM** *020 †20

GIBSON, Eric. 1025 WALNUT ST STE 700/DEP, PEDIATRICS/DIV NEONATOLOGY 19107 #010-01-1983 L1984 **PD** *020 †55

GIBSON, Ericka Camille. ■ 19143 #041-01-2008 L2008 *012

GIBSON, Lisa Kay. ■ 19129 #041-01-2008 *012

GILARDINO, Miroslav S. 1 CHILDRENS CTR, CHILDREN'S HOPSITAL 19104 #067-01-2001 L2007 **PS** *100

GILBERT, Elissa Susan. ■ 19146 #035-45-2006 **PD** *012

GILCHRIST, Amber Michelle. 111 S 11TH ST, JEFFERSON UNIVERSITY 19107 #041-12-2003 L2003 **PD** *100

GILDEN, Adam Howard. 3535 MARKET ST FL 3, WEIGHT AND EATING DISORDER 19104 #041-01-1999 L2001 **IM** *050 †20

GILFOR, Jeffrey Marc. 5501 OLD YORK RD 19141 #041-02-1998 L2001 **AN** *020 †05

GILL, Denis G. 324 S 34TH ST, DEPT NEOU 19104 #539-04-1968 **N** *050

GILL, Donald Joseph. 111 N 49TH ST 19139 #024-01-1962 L1963 **P ADP** *075 †75

GILL, Gurpreet. 2900 W QUEEN LN 19129 #913-07-2002 **GS** *012

GILL, Karanbir Singh. 5501 OLD YORK RD, ALBERT EINSTEIN MEDICAL CE 19141 #025-07-2004 L2007 **PD** *100

GILL, Robert Jos. 715 SPRUCE ST 19106 #035-45-1948 L1950 **IM CD** *020 †20

GILLESBY, Robert Jos. 8835 GERMANTOWN AVE 19118 #038-40-1970 L1970 **IM** *030 †20

GILLESPIE, Avrum. ■ 19127 #035-08-2004 L2004 **NEP** *012 †20

GILLESPIE, Colin Thomas. 3400 SPRUCE ST, 8 GATES 19104 #016-42-2000 L2001 **PCC** *100 †20

GILLESPIE, Heather Marie. 833 CHESTNUT ST, STE 301 19107 #036-07-2003 L2003 **FSM** *100 †18

GILLESPIE, Thomas Arthur. ■ 19107 #001-02-1972 L1973 **CD IM** *071 †20

GILMAN, Gary Richard. 2701 HOLME AVE, STE 203 19152 #041-02-1985 L1986 **IM** *020 †20

GILMAN, Susan C. 5700 RIDGE AVE, STE 100A 19128 #035-46-1974 L1980 **P PYG** *020 †75 ‡

GILMORE, Kimberly Kaye. 111 S 11TH ST, # G-6460 19107 #025-07-1991 L1995 **AN** *020 †05

GILOT, Bryant Joseph. 3400 SPRUCE ST, MED CTR 19104 #067-01-1994 L1996 **TS** *012 †85

GILOTRA, Mohit Neeru. ■ 19107 #041-02-2007 **ORS** *012

GINDHARDT, Robert J. 2637 E ALLEGHENY AVE 19134 #042-03-1981 L1984 **PM** *020

GINGRICH, Kevin Allen. 245 N 15TH ST, MS 420 19102 #041-09-1986 L1987 **ORS** *020 †40

GINLEY, Thomas Henry. 3905 FORD RD 19131 #010-02-1948 L1950 **U** *071 †95

GINSBERG, David Kellner. 2221 S BROAD ST 19148 #010-01-1954 L1958 **IM GE** *071 †20

GINSBERG, Gregory Gerard. 3400 SPRUCE ST, DIVISION GASTROENTEROLOGY 19104 #041-02-1987 L1989 **GE** *040 †20

GINSBURG, Edio. 3401 N BROAD ST, TEMPLE ANESTHESIA ASSOCIAT 19140 #550-02-1989 L1997 **AN** *020 †05

GINSBURG, Kenneth R. 3550 MARKET ST, FL 4 19104 #035-46-1987 L1988 **PD ADL** *020 †55

GINWALLA, Rashna Farhad. 3401 N BROAD ST, OF S 19140 #005-06-2004 L2004 **GS** *012

GIORDANO, Augustin Thos. 34TH ST AND CIVIC CENTER B 19104 #041-01-1943 L1944 **PD** *071

GIRALDO ISAZA, Maria Adel. 5501 OLD YORK RD, DEPT OF OB/GYN 19141 #264-16-2000 L2005 **OBG** *012

GIRANDA, Vincent Louis. ■ 19111 #041-13-1987 *074

GIRARDO, Salvatore Paul. 1317 WOLF ST, STE 19 19148 #041-02-1969 L1970 **CD IM** *020 †20

GIRI, Jay S. ■ 19130 #016-06-2004 L2007 *012

GIROIS, Susan Brown. 3400 SPRUCE ST, HOSPITAL OF THE UNIV OF PA 19104 #041-14-1997 L1999 **IM** *020 †20

GIRONE, Joseph Anthony C. 5501 OLD YORK RD 19141 #041-02-1966 L1967 **PD OS** *071 †55 ‡

GIST-WATSON, Patricia L. 6643 CHEW AVE, KIDCARE PEDIATRICS 19119 #041-13-1990 L1993 **PD** *055

GITLIN, Joshua Marc. ■ 19103 #025-07-2002 L2005 **ORS** *100

GITTENS, Paul Reginald, Jr. 19147 #041-15-2003 L2003 **U** *012

GIULIAN, Karl Anthony. 100 E LEHIGH AVE 19125 #041-09-1962 L1989 **OBG** *030 †30

GIUNTOLI, Robert Lawrence. 233 S 6TH ST # B 19106 #028-34-1966 L1973 **GO OBG** *071 †20

GIVENS, Jane L. 260 S 24TH ST 19103 #005-02-1997 L2000 **IMG** *012 †20

GLANZMAN, Marianne M. 3405 CIVIC CENTER BLVD, CHILDREN'S SEASHORE HOUSE 19104 #041-01-1983 L1985 **PD** *050 †55

GLASER, David Louis. 3400 SPRUCE ST, HOSP UNIV OF PA 19104 #035-20-1994 L1999 **ORS** *020 †40

GLASER, Ruchira. 3400 SPRUCE ST 19104 #035-20-1996 L1999 **IC** *020 †20

GLASKIN, Carol Lynne. 3 PENN BLVD, AEMC LTSR/GERMANTWN CAMPUS 19144 #041-09-1978 L1979 **P** *020 †75

GLASOFER, Adam Kramer. ■ 19147 #041-02-2005 L2005 **PD** *012

GLASS, Jon. 333 COTTMAN AVE, FOX CHASE CANCER CENTER 19111 #035-08-1986 L1992 **N** *020 †75 ‡

GLASS, Steven J. 111 N 49TH ST 19139 #041-02-1976 L1977 **P** *050 †75 ‡

GLASSBERG, Helene Leslie. 3401 N BROAD ST, 9TH FL 19140 #041-13-1993 L2000 **CD** *020 †20

GLASSBURN, John R, Jr. 800 SPRUCE ST 19107 #041-09-1966 L1967 **RO** *020 †80

GLASSER, Steven Alan. 800 SPRUCE ST 19107 #041-01-1978 L1980 **AN** *020 †05

GLASSMAN, David Jacob. ■ 19102 #024-15-1945 L1947 **IM CD** *071

GLASSMAN, Deborah Tova. 1025 WALNUT ST, STE 1100 19107 #035-19-1995 L2002 **U** *020 †95

GLASSMAN, Solomon. 2615 W SOMERSET 19132 #016-42-1957 L1958 **FM GE** *071

GLAT, Paul Mitchell. 9501 ROOSEVELT BLVD, STE 101 19114 #035-19-1988 L1996 **PS** *020 †85,65

GLATSTEIN, Eli Jack. 3400 SPRUCE ST, 2 DONNER BLDG-DEPT OF RAD 19104 #005-11-1964 L1996 **RO** *020 †80

GLEASON, Jonathan Lee. ■ 19104 #012-01-2005 L2005 **OBG** *012

GLENNEL, Minda Avasa. 245 N 15TH ST, DEPT OF OB/GYN 19102 #041-15-2005 L2005 **OBG** *012

GLENNON, Susan Elaine. 727 DELANCEY ST 19106 #038-45-2001 L2001 **IM** *020

GLEW, Catherine Mary. 3300 HENRY AVE 19129 #917-12-1982 L1991 **IMG** *020 †20

GLIATTO, Michael Francis. 3900 WOODLAND AVE, 7TH FL 19104 #028-34-1985 L1987 **P IM** *020 †20,75

GLICK, John Harrison. 3400 SPRUCE ST 19104 #035-01-1969 L1974 **IM ON** *020 †20

GLICK, Seth Nathaniel. 230 N BROAD ST DEPT DR 19102 #041-13-1975 L1976 **DR** *020 †80

GLICKMAN, Joel David. 230 W WASHINGTON SQ, PENNSYLVANIA NEPHROLOGY AS 19106 #035-08-1982 L1986 **NEP IM** *020 †20

GLIEBUS, Gediminas. ■ 19147 #913-49-2003 L2005 **N** *012

GLIKMAN, Nadezhda. 9150 MARSHALL ST 19114 #913-73-1954 L1984 **GP IM** *071

GLITZA, Isabella Claudia. 5401 OLD YORK RD, KLEIN 363 19141 #409-10-2004 L2007 **IM** *012

GLOVER, Donna J. 2 FRANKLIN TOWN BLVD # 100, ONCOLOGY CARE LLC 19103 #041-01-1977 L1979 **ON HEM** *020 †20

GLOYER, Kathryn Leigh. ■ 19147 #023-01-2007 L2007 **FP** *012

GLUCKMAN, Stephen John. 536 JOHNSON PAVILLION, INFECT DIS CLIN SER 19104 #035-01-1971 L1972 **ID IM** *062 †20

GLUSKIN, Jill Stacey. ■ 19103 #024-07-2007 L2007 **TY** *012

GLUZMAN, Ellen. ■ 19102 #048-12-2007 L2007 **P** *012

GLYNN, Simon Malcolm. 3400 SPRUCE ST, 3 WEST GATES 19104 #010-02-2000 L2005 **CN** *020 †75

GO, Efren C. 555 S 43RD ST, HC 3 19104 #748-01-1976 L1992 **PD** *020 †55

GO, Ruby Tan. ■ 19107 #748-02-1978 L1985 **END IM** *020 †20

GOCIAL, Benjamin. 1015 CHESTNUT ST, STE 1500 19107 #041-13-1978 L1979 **REN GYN** *012

GODINEZ, Rodolfo Ignacio. 324 S 34TH ST, DEPT OF ANESTHESIOLOGY 19104 #028-34-1974 L1977 **PAN CCP** *020 †05

GODLEY, Joanne. ■ 19143 #008-01-1977 L1982 **IM PHP** *020 †20

GOEL, Inder Prakash. 205 N BROAD ST 19107 #495-49-1961 L1977 **TS TRS** *071 †85,90

GOEL, Nishant Rajiv. 3401 N BROAD ST, DEPT MED 19140 #033-06-2007 L2007 **IM** *012

GOEL, Rajat. 4900 WYALUSING AVE, HEALTH ND MENTAL RETARDATI 19131 #495-36-1991 L1997 **P** *020

GOETT, Harry Joseph. ■ 19130 #041-15-2007 L2007 **EM** *012

GOGIA, Mandeep Kaur. 833 CHESTNUT ST, THOMAS JEFFERSON UNIV HOSP 19107 #016-42-2007 L2007 **P** *012

GOGINENI, Keerthi. 3400 SPRUCE ST, UNIV OF PA 19104 #023-01-2004 L2004 **HO** *012 †20

GOHAR, Kathy. 5501 OLD YORK RD, ALBERT EINSTEIN MED CTR 19141 #016-42-2000 L2005 **GS** *100 ‡

GOHEL, Mira Manhar. ■ 19147 #041-02-1990 L1992 **FM** *020 †18

GOJKOVIC, Olivera. ■ 19111 #041-15-2007 L2007 **IM** *012

GOKHALE, Janaki Ajit. 111 S 11TH ST, JEFFERSON UNIVERSITY 19107 #041-12-2006 L2006 **PD** *012

GOLD, Barbara Wyler. 9501 ROOSEVELT BLVD, STE 410 19114 #041-02-1978 L1979 **PD** *020 †55

GOLD, Julia. ■ 19115 #041-13-2004 L2004 **EM** *100

GOLD, Marla Jean. 245 N 15TH ST, MS 660 19102 #033-05-1985 L1987 **ID** *020 †20

GOLD, Michael Jonah. 132 S 10TH ST, UNIVERSITY HO 19107 #035-08-2005 L2006 **DR** *012

GOLDBACHER, Arleen Joy. 2301 E ALLEGHENY AVE 19134 #041-07-1985 L1988 **DR** *020 ‡

GOLDBERG, Allison Faith. ■ 19107 #035-46-2007 L2007 **GS** *012

GOLDBERG, Amy Joy. 3401 N BROAD ST, TEMPLE UNIVERSITY HOSPITAL 19140 #035-47-1987 L1989 **TRS CCS** *012

GOLDBERG, Ari David. ■ 19103 #041-01-2004 L2004 **DR** *012

GOLDBERG, Barry Benson. 132 S 10TH ST, JEFFERSON HOSP ULTRASOUND 19107 #041-01-1963 L1964 **R** *020 †80

GOLDBERG, David Jacob. ■ 19119 #033-06-2001 L2005 **PDC** *012 †55

GOLDBERG, E Marshall. 1015 CHESTNUT ST, STE 313 19107 #024-07-1956 L1989 **IM END** *071 †20

GOLDBERG, Harry. DEPT OF CARDIOLOGY, ALBERT EINSTEIN MED CENTER 19141 #035-08-1944 L1951 **CD** *071 †20

GOLDBERG, Herbert Irwin. 3400 SPRUCE ST 19104 #050-02-1956 L1964 **DR NS** *020 †80

GOLDBERG, James Brian. ■ 19127 #041-15-2000 L2001 **EM** *020 †16

GOLDBERG, Jared Brian. ■ 19147 #035-19-2005 L2005 **EM** *012

GOLDBERG, Jay David. 834 CHESTNUT ST STE 400 19107 #041-01-1993 L1995 **OBG** *020 †30
GOLDBERG, Larry Howard. ■ 19130 #041-09-1976 L1977 **IM** *071 †20
GOLDBERG, Lee Richard. 3400 SPRUCE ST 19104 #024-05-1992 L1994 **CD IM** *100 †20
GOLDBERG, Marc Bruce. 900 WALNUT ST, 5TH FLOOR ANESTHESIA 19107
 #041-02-1979 L1980 **AN** *020 †05 ‡
GOLDBERG, Martin. 571 PARKINSON PAVILION, TEMPLE UNIV HOSP 19140
 #041-13-1955 L1957 **IM NEP** *030 †20
GOLDBERG, Michael Falk. ■ 19104 #023-07-2003 L2003 **DR** *012
GOLDBERG, Richard Earl. 900 WALNUT ST 19107 #041-02-1962 L1963 **OPH** *071 †35
GOLDBERG, Sheldon. 230 N BROAD ST, FL 7 19102 #041-01-1971 L1973 **CD** *020 †20
GOLDBERG, Shmuel. ■ 19151 #051-01-1988 L1994 **PDP** *100
GOLDBERG, Steven K. 5501 OLD YORK RD, DEPT OF PULMONARY DISEASES 19141
 #010-02-1968 L1980 **PUD CCM** *020 †20
GOLDBERG, Tamara S. 1208 PINE ST 19107 #008-02-2005 L2005 **IM** *012
GOLDE, Todd E. 3400 SPRUCE ST DEPT PATHOL 19104 #038-06-1994 L1996 **PTH** *100
GOLDEN, Gerald Saml. 3405 CIVIC CENTER BLVD 19104 #035-01-1961 L1992
 CHN PD *071 †75,55
GOLDEN, Michael Arthur. 51 N 39TH ST, STE 2D 19104 #041-01-1981 L1990 **VS GS** *020 †85
GOLDENBERG, Gennifer Erin. ■ 19102 #011-02-2001 L2005 **EM** *100 †16
GOLDENBERG, Nancy J J. 1619 GRANT AVE, FOX CHASE MEDICAL CENTER 19115
 #035-46-1973 L1980 **DR** *020 †80
GOLDFARB, Alvin Frank. 1015 CHESTNUT ST, STE 1225 19107 #047-05-1947 L1958
 GYN REN *072 †30
GOLDFARB, Stanley. 3400 SPRUCE ST, U PA HLTH SYS #100 CENTREX 19104
 #035-45-1969 L1970 **IM NEP** *050 †20
GOLDFINGER, Michael Paul. 5401 OLD YORK RD 19141 #041-07-1989 L1992 **IM** *020 †20
GOLDING, Daphine Gay. 7700A STENTON AVE, MEDICAL CENTER 19118 #041-01-1990 L1994
 PM *020 †60
GOLDMAN, Arthur. ■ 19103 #041-01-1948 L1949 **IM CD** *071
GOLDMAN, Bruce Ian. 3400 N BROAD ST 19140 #041-06-1980 L1987 **PTH** *020 †50
GOLDMAN, Jason Daniel. 245 N 15TH ST, FL NCB 19102 #035-15-2005 **EM** *012
GOLDMAN, Jason David. ■ 19143 #041-01-2008 *012
GOLDMAN, Jesse Mark. 3401 N BROAD ST, TEMPLE UNIVERSITY HOSPITAL 19140
 #035-09-1987 L1992 **NEP EP** *020 †20
GOLDMAN, Robert J. 527 W SEDGWICK ST, WOUND CARE AND REHAB MEDIC 19119
 #048-02-1987 L1988 **PM VM** *020 †60 ‡
GOLDMAN, Stephen Marc. 700 SPRUCE ST STE 100 19106 #041-07-1985 L1986 **OPH** *020 †35
GOLDMAN, Yale Edward. 3400 SPRUCE ST, DEPT PHYS 19104 #041-01-1975 **OS** *050
GOLDMANN, Rachel Elisabet. ■ 19106 #024-01-2004 L2005 **N** *012
GOLDMUNTZ, Elizabeth. 3615 CIVIC CENTER BLVD 19104 #041-01-1987 L1989 **PDC** *050 †55
GOLDSMITH, Jeffrey F. ■ 19146 #041-02-2000 L2001 **AN** *100
GOLDSMITH, Joyce. 300 SPRING GARDEN ST, 2ND FLOOR EAST 19123 #847-01-1976 L1986
 GP PD *020 †55
GOLDSMITH, Kelly C. 904F ARCH ST, 3615 CIVIC CENTER BLVD 19107 #001-02-1999 L2001
 PHO *100 †55
GOLDSMITH, Michelle Dana. 3535 MARKET ST, OUTPATIENT CLINIC 19104
 #041-15-2004 L2004 **P** *012
GOLDSTEIN, Allan. 800 SPRUCE ST, PENNSYLVANIA HOSPITAL 19107 #143-11-1988 L1993
 AN PME *020 †05
GOLDSTEIN, Barry Jay. 1015 WALNUT ST, RM 320 19107 #035-45-1982 L1992
 END DIA *020 †20
GOLDSTEIN, Bernard. 5501 OLD YORK RD 19141 #065-01-1945 L1949 **AN** *071 †05
GOLDSTEIN, Daniel Todd. ■ 19107 #041-02-2008 *012
GOLDSTEIN, Franz. 132 S 10TH ST, M-480 JEFFERSON UNIV HOSP 19107 #041-02-1953 L1954
 GE IM *071 †20
GOLDSTEIN, Jacob. 700 COTTMAN AVE, BLDG A 19111 #275-01-1957 L1966 **CD IM** *071 †20
GOLDSTEIN, Jeremiah. 1415 N BROAD ST, FL 2 19122 #041-13-1992 L1994 **PD** *020 †55
GOLDSTEIN, Karen Elizabet. ■ 19130 #036-07-2004 L2004 **IM** *100 †20
GOLDSTEIN, Lori Ann. ■ 19103 #041-02-2005 L2005 **P** *012
GOLDSTEIN, Lori Jill. 333 COTTMAN AVE, FOX CHASE CANCER CENTER 19111
 #035-15-1982 L1983 **ON IM** *020 †20
GOLDSTEIN, Mitchell J. 5501 OLD YORK RD, STE 1 19141 #041-12-1998 L2001 **IM** *020 †20
GOLDSTEIN, Scott. 4124A TERRACE ST, 2ND FL 19128 #035-75-2002, ▲ L2002 **EM** *100 †16
GOLDSTEIN, Scott D. 1100 WALNUT ST, STE 702 19107 #006-06-1978 L1984 **CRS** *020 †10,85
GOLDSTEIN, Stephen Andrew. 811 SPRUCE ST 19107 #035-15-1996 L1999 **OTO FPS** *020 †45
GOLDSTEIN, Stephen J. 5501 OLD YORK RD, EINSTEIN MEDICAL CENTER 19141
 #056-06-1978 L1979 **NEP** *062 †20
GOLDSTEIN, Steven Craig. 3400 SPRUCE ST, 16 PENN TOWER 19104 #041-12-1985 L1990
 IM *020 †20
GOLDSTEIN, Steven Howard. 2308 E ALLEGHENY AVE 19134 #041-77-1984, ▲ L1985 **CD** *020
GOLDWEIN, Joel Wise. 3400 SPRUCE ST 19104 #041-01-1983 L1984 **RO** *020 †80
GOLDWEIN, Marlene Fox. 6001 RIDGE AVE 19128 #041-01-1985 L1987 **IM** *020 †20
GOLESORKHI, Negar. ■ 19107 #051-04-2002 L2002 **GS** *012
GOLUB, Michael Stuart. 229 S 18TH ST FL 2 19103 #041-01-1983 L1984 **IM EM** *062 †20
GOLUB, Robert M. 3998 RED LION RD 19114 #550-02-1987 L1991 **GS** *020 †85
GOMBERG, Jonathan David. 1809 S BROAD ST STE 300, CARDIOLOGY CONSULTANTS
 OF 19148 #041-07-1982 L1983 **CD IM** *020 †20
GOMBINER, Ross Aaron. UNIVERSITY & WOODLAND AVES 19104 #016-02-1994 L1997
 IM *020 †20
GOMBOS, Zoltan. 5501 OLD YORK RD, ALBERT EINSTEIN MEDICAL CE 19141
 #286-03-1992 L2004 **PTH** *100 †50 ‡
GOMELLA, Leonard Gabriel. 833 CHESTNUT ST, STE 703 19107 #020-12-1980 L1988
 U *040 †95
GOMEZ, Geraldine V. 3400 N BROAD ST, DEPT ANES 19140 #748-02-1971 L1974 **AN** *020
GOMEZ, Laura. 111 S 11TH ST, JEFFERSON UNIVERSITY 19107 #010-02-2001 L2001
 PD *020 †55
GOMEZ, Oscar Hernandez. ■ 19153 #748-01-1971 L1976 **EM** *020
GOMEZ-ABRAHAM, Jesus A. 245 N 15TH ST STOP 111, DEPT OF CARDIOTHORACIC
 SUR 19102 #935-02-1990 L1999 **TS GS** *012
GOMORI, John. 3400 SPRUCE ST 19104 #040-02-1976 L1984 **R** *020 †80
GONATAS, Nicholas K. 3400 SPRUCE ST 19104 #418-02-1952 L1976 **NP PTH** *062 †50
GONEN, Boas. 111 S 11TH ST 19107 #550-01-1971 L1988 **END IM** *071 †20
GONICK, Paul. 227 N BROAD ST 19107 #008-01-1955 L1969 **U** *071 †95
GONNELLA, Joseph Salvator. 1025 WALNUT ST, JEFFERSON MEDICAL COLLEGE 19107
 #024-01-1959 L1966 **IM ID** *030
GONSALVES, Anitha Samir. 132 S 10TH ST, STE 1072 19107 #495-01-1999 L2003
 RNR *012 †80

GONSALVES, Carin Frances. 111 S 11TH ST, GIBBON BLDG, SUITE 4200 19107
 #041-09-1993 L1998 **VIR** *020 †80
GONZALEZ, Carlos F. 3300 HENRY AVE 19129 #264-01-1960 L1970 **R** *020 †80
GONZALEZ, Juan Miguel. UNIV OF PENNSYLVANIA 19104
 #042-01-2001 L2002 **OBG MFM** *100
GONZALEZ, Madelyn. ■ 19128 #422-01-2006 L2006 **OBG** *012
GONZALEZ, Maria Cecilia. 5501 OLD YORK RD 19141 #132-01-2000 **PD** *100
GONZALEZ PANTALEON, Adalbe. 219 N BROAD ST FL 9 19107 #308-13-2001 L2003
 END *012 †20
GONZALEZ-SCARANO, F A. 3400 SPRUCE ST 19104 #016-06-1975 L1976 **N** *020 †75
GOOD, Linda. 760 CARPENTER LN 19119 #041-07-1985 L1987 **FM** *020 †18
GOODE, Penelope Anne. ■ 19128 #051-01-2002 L2007 **EM** *012
GOODKIN, Margot Lilly. 51 N 39TH ST, SCHEIE EYE INST 19104 #035-47-2004 L2004 **OPH** *012
GOODMAN, Andrew Ward. 3400 SPRUCE ST, DEPT FM 19104 #025-07-2007 L2007 **FP** *012
GOODRICH, Edward O. 16TH ST & GIRARD AVE 19130 #035-09-1949 L1984 **PM GP** *071 †85
GOODWIN, Edward Howard. ■ 19118 #041-02-2001 *100
GOODWIN, Emily Fry. ■ 19146 #045-04-2003 L2007 **PHO** *012 †55
GOODWIN, Peter Lloyd. ■ 19146 #045-04-2003 L2008 **OPH** *012
GOODY, Howard Edward. 1015 CHESTNUT ST 19107 #041-02-1975 L1976 **D DS** *020 †15
GOODYEAR, Sarah Ruth. 333 COTTMAN AVE, CENTER BUILDING, RM 307 19111
 #041-13-2003 L2003 **IM** *100 †20
GOONERATNE, Nalaka S. 3615 CHESTNUT ST, RALSTON HOUSE 19104 #016-06-1993 L1995
 PCC *020 †20
GOOREVICH, Erica C. 833 CHESTNUT ST STE 210 19107 #010-01-2002 L2002 **P** *100
GOPALAN, Anjali. ■ 19103 #028-02-2008 L2008 *012
GOPALANI, Rohan. 100 E LEHIGH AVE, MAB, SUITE 105 19125 #041-13-2004 L2004 **CHP** *012
GORADIA, Ami Dinesh. ■ 19130 #024-01-2003 L2003 **PTH** *100 †50
GORAL, Simin. 3400 SPRUCE ST 19104 #902-07-1984 L2001 **IM NEP** *020 †20
GORALCZYK, Malgorzata Edy. ■ 19107 #759-07-2000 L2005 **DR** *012
GORAYA, Jatinder Singh. ERIE AVE AT FRONT ST, DEPT OF PEDIATRICS 19134 #495-43-1992
 CHN *012
GORDIAN, Maria Ann. 3615 CHESTNUT ST, 3 WEST 19104 #024-07-1988 L1993 **DR** *020 †80
GORDIN, Eli. ■ 19106 #041-02-2008 L2008 *012
GORDON, Arthur Erwin. 9331 OLD BUSTLETON AVE, STE 201 19115 #041-13-1956 L1957
 GYN *071 †30
GORDON, Jeffrey. 900 WALNUT ST, WILLS EYE HOSPITAL 19107 #035-01-1988 L1996
 AN *020 †05 ‡
GORDON, Stacy. 324 S 34TH ST 19104 #016-06-1983 L2000 **PD EM** *020 †55
GOREN, Eric Neal. ■ 19130 #016-02-2005 L2005 **IM** *012
GOREN, Louis. ■ 19124 #041-09-1950 L1951 **GP** *071
GOREN, Ronald Claude. 9501 ROOSEVELT BLVD, STE 208 19114 #041-13-1973 L1979
 ID IM *020 †20
GORMAN, Joseph Hevey, III. 3400 SPRUCE ST, FL 6 19104 #033-06-1991 L1993 **TS** *020 †85,90
GORMAN, Robert Chas. 3400 SPRUCE ST, FL 6 19104 #033-06-1989 L1992 **TS** *050 †85,90
GORMAN, Sean James. 8835 GERMANTOWN AVE 19118 #041-13-1993 L1995 **EM** *020 †16
GORNIAK, Richard Joseph. ■ 19102 #035-19-1998 L2005 **RNR** *100 †80
GORODIN, Paulina. 821B KATER ST 19147 #422-01-2000 L2001 **CD** *100 †20
GORRY, Thomasine G. 51 N 39TH ST, SCHEIC EYE INST 19104 #041-15-2001 L2001
 OPH *020 †35
GORSTEIN, Fred. 1020 LOCUST ST, DEPT OF PATH 19107 #035-19-1955 L1995 **PTH** *030 †50
GORTI, Subbarao. 1139 E LUZERNE ST 19124 #495-37-1987 L1992 **PD** *100 †18
GORTON, Gregg Emmanuel. UNIVERSITY & WOODLANDS AVE, VAMC, MS 116 19104
 #024-07-1981 L1986 **P** *020 †75
GOSFIELD, Edward, Jr. 2113 SPRUCE ST 19103 #041-01-1944 L1945 **CD IM** *020 †20
GOSNELL, Kermit Barron. 3801 LANCASTER AVE 19104 #041-02-1966 L1967 **FM GYN** *020
GOTTAM, Nithin Reddy. ■ 19107 #041-02-2008 *012
GOTTLIEB, Diane Beth. 3401 N BROAD ST 19140 #041-07-1988 L1997 **P** *020 †75
GOTTLIEB, Neil Bruce. 9500 ROOSEVELT BLVD 19115 #041-02-1998 L2000 **PS** *100 †85,65
GOTTSCHALK, Allan. 3400 SPRUCE ST, DEPT ANES 19104 #041-01-1984 L1986 **AN** *020 †05
GOTZ-PRUCKMAYR, Gertrude. 3400 N BROAD ST, DEPT AN 19140 #154-07-1960 **AN** *040 †05
GOUGOUTAS, Alexander Jaco. 19147 #041-01-2006 L2006 **GS** *012
GOULD, Bruce Jay. ■ 19130 #041-01-1958 L1959 **CD IM** *071 †20
GOULD, David Samuel. 1025 WALNUT ST, JEFFERSON MED COLL 19107 #041-02-1998 *100
GOULD, Jane Marie. 324 S 34TH ST 19104 #035-03-1989 L1992 **PD PDI** *040 †55
GOULD, Milena Andrea. 3400 SPRUCE ST, 3 RAVDIN GASTROENTEROLOGY 19104
 #035-06-2001 L2004 **GE** *012
GOULD, Stuart Dennis. 1025 WALNUT ST, THOMAS JEFFERSON UNIV HOSP 19107
 #050-02-2003 L2003 **CD** *012 †20
GOURINENI, Venu. 800 SPRUCE ST, PENNSYLVANIA HOSPITAL 19107 #495-21-2003 L2006 *100
GOVIL, Anita. 5501 OLD YORK RD, 353 KLEIN BLDG 19141 #495-34-1984 L2001 **IM** *020 †20
GOVIL, Yogesh Kumar. 5401 OLD YORK RD, STE 202 19141 #495-77-1980 L1997
 GE IM *020 †20
GOWDA, Archana. 245 N 15TH ST, DREXEL UNIV COLL MED/HAHNE 19102 #496-22-2000 L2004
 IM *012 †20
GOYAL, Gagandeep. 2900 W QUEEN LN 19129 #496-43-2001 L2006 **AN** *012
GOYAL, Monika Kumari. 19147 #041-01-2004 L2004 **PEM** *012 †55
GOYAL, Munish. 3400 SPRUCE ST, GROUND RAVDIN 19104 #051-04-2000 L2004
 EM CCS *020 †16
GOYAL, Neera K. ■ 19103 #048-12-2005 L2005 **PD** *012
GOYAL, Nitin. 1015 WALNUT ST, THOMAS JEFFERSON UNIV 19107 #041-02-2005 L2005
 ORS *012 †20
GOZUM, Marvin Vincent E. 1025 WALNUT ST RM 119 19107 #748-21-1984 L1987
 IMG UM *012 ‡
GRABO, Daniel Eric. 1015 WALNUT ST, CURTIS BLDG. SUITE 620 19107 #010-02-2003 L2003
 GS *012
GRABOYES LEOPOLD, Nancy L. 219 N BROAD ST, STE 8 19107 #041-13-1988 L1990
 GE *020 †20
GRACIA, Clarisa Raquel. 3701 MARKET ST, 8TH FL 19104 #035-06-1997 L2000 **OBG** *020 †30
GRACIA, Judith Nadine. 3535 MARKET ST FL 1, OF PHILADELPHIA 19104 #041-12-2002 L2002
 PD *012 †55
GRACIAS, Vicente Herman. 3440 MARKET ST, 1ST FL 19104 #049-01-1991 L1997
 CCS *020 †85
GRADY, Michael Sean. 3400 SPRUCE ST, DEPT NEUROSURGERY 19104 #010-02-1981 L1999
 NS *020 †25
GRAFF, Harold Allen. 4641 ROOSEVELT BLVD, FRIENDS HOSPITAL 19124 #041-01-1958 L1959
 P PYA *020 †75

■ = Address Information Privacy Protected

GRAHAM, Joseph Daniel. ■ 19130 #041-01-2003 L2003 **FM** *100 †18
GRAHAM, Mark Gerard. 2301 S BROAD ST, STE 205 19148 #008-02-1978 L1979
  IM OM *020 †20,70 ‡
GRAHAM-MAAR, Rose. 34TH & CIVIC CENTER BLVD, CHILDRENS HOSP 19104
  #035-06-2000 L2001 **PG** *020 †55
GRANDE, David Thomas. ■ 19146 #038-40-1999 L2001 **IM** *020 †20
GRANQUIST, Eric J. ■ 19103 #041-01-2007 L2007 *012
GRANT, Matthew Harris. ■ 19107 #041-15-2006 L2006 **IM** *012
GRANT, Richard J. 5401 OLD YORK RD, PALEY 4TH FL. STE4320 19141 #024-05-1974 L1991
  IMG IM *020 †20
GRATCH, David M. 111 S 11TH ST, STE 8490 19107 #048-78-1985, ▲ L1988 **AN CCA** *020 †05
GRAU, Jillian Rachel. ■ 19127 #041-15-2003 L2003 **PTH** *100
GRAU, Justo Honorio. ■ 19128 #726-01-1964 L1974 **U** *100
GRAVES, Beverly, Jr. 1006 W LEHIGH AVE 19133 #010-03-1945 L1947 **IM OS** *071
GRAVES, Jennifer Sharon. ■ 19103 #048-12-2006 L2007 **N** *012
GRAVES, Laurel Ann. 3535 MARKET ST, 2ND FLOOR / DEPT OF PSYCHI 19104
  #041-01-2003 L2003 **CHP** *012
GRAVES, Vaughan Channing. 601 WALNUT ST 19106 #041-13-1977 L1982 **D** *020
GRAY, Chancellor Folsom. ■ 19147 #041-02-2008 *012
GRAY, Charles Roland. 100 W LEHIGH AVE 19133 #035-06-1993 L1996 **PYG P** *020
GRAY, Daniel Paul. ■ 19128 #051-01-2007 L2007 **FP** *012
GRAY, Florette Kimberly. ■ 19148 #010-02-2002 L2004 **PTH** *100 †50
GRAY, Laurie Beth. ■ 19104 #041-01-2008 *012
GRAY, Stacy Elizabeth. 3620 WALNUT ST RM 405, ANNENBERG SCHOOL, CECCR 19104
  #016-02-1999 L2005 **HO** *100 †20
GRAYBEAL, Laura Susan. 329 SOUTH ST, # 2 19147 #041-14-2003 L2007 *100
GRAZIANI, Corina. 2305 FAIRMOUNT AVE 19130 #041-02-1992 L1994 **FM** *020 †18
GRAZIANI, Leonard Jos. 1025 WALNUT ST 19107 #041-02-1955 L1956 **CHN N** *040 †55,75
GRECO, Joseph Francis, III. 219 N BROAD ST FL 4 19107 #041-01-2002 L2002 **D** *100 †15
GREELEY, Philip H. 4413 PINE ST, STE 6 19104 #004-01-1970 L2001 **OBG** *071 †30
GREELEY, William Jos, Jr. 34TH ST & CIVIC CTR BLVD, CHILDRENS HOSP DEPT AN 19104
  #048-14-1976 L1982 **AN** *020 †55,05
GREEN, Carol Harriet. 3600 CONSHOHOCKEN AVE, RIVER PARK HOUSE STE 3600 19131
  #041-09-1977 L1980 **P** *071
GREEN, Joshua Steven. 833 CHESTNUT ST, STE 210 19107 #035-46-1997 L2004 **P** *012
GREEN, Judith Rose. 3400 SPRUCE ST, OCCUPATIONAL MED GROUND FL 19104
  #008-01-1987 L1997 **GPM** *020 †20,70
GREEN, Michael Brian. 700 SPRUCE ST, STE 304 SPRUCE INTERNL MDC 19106
  #041-01-1994 L1996 **IM** *020 †20
GREEN, Phillip Aaron. 3400 SPRUCE ST, # 3 SILVERSTEIN BLDG STE D 19104
  #041-02-1987 L1998 **ID IM** *020 †55,20
GREEN, Steven Aaron. ■ 19102 #041-12-1973 L1975 **PD** *030 †55
GREENACRE, Judith K F. ■ 19103 #024-01-1968 L1984 **IM PUD** *071 †20
GREENBAUM, Linda Ellen. 3400 SPRUCE ST 19104 #035-01-1984 L1993 **IM** *020 †20
GREENBAUM, Steven Samuel. 1528 WALNUT ST STE 1101 19102 #021-01-1983 L1988
  D OS *020 †15
GREENBERG, Adena Beth. 1900 S BROAD ST 2ND FL 19145 #035-20-1996 L2000 **PD** *020 †55
GREENBERG, Howard Ellis. 132 S 10TH ST, 1170 MAIN BLDG - TJV 19107 #041-02-1992 L1994
  PA IM *050 †20
GREENBERG, Jack Oscar. 5090 SUMMERDALE AVE 19124 #041-12-1959 L1966 **N OS** *071 †75
GREENBERG, Judah Norman. ■ 19104 #041-01-2008 *012
GREENBERG, Kenneth Peter. ■ 19103 #041-01-2003 L2006 *100
GREENBERG, Michael Ira. 230 N BROAD ST 19102 #041-13-1976 L1977 **EM** *020 †70,16 ‡
GREENBERG, Richard Harris. 5401 OLD YORK RD, KLEIN OFFICE BUILDING STE 19141
  #041-02-1979 L1980 **CRS GS** *020 †10,85
GREENBERG, Richard Mark. 3401 N BROAD ST, 960 PARKINSON PAVILION 19140
  #024-05-1976 L1981 **ICE CD** *020 †20 ‡
GREENBLATT, Dana Bruce. 4623 SPRUCE ST 19139 #041-02-1989 L1991 **FM** *020 †18
GREENBLATT, Eric Paul. 3400 SPRUCE ST, HOSP OF THE UNIV OF PA 19104
  #035-01-1986 L1988 **AN** *020 †05
GREENE, Gary Stuart. 800 SPRUCE ST, PENNSYLVANIA HOSP-RADIOL 19107
  #041-13-1979 L1981 **DR NM** *040 †80
GREENE, Mark Irwin. 3400 SPRUCE ST 19104 #062-01-1972 L1985 *020
GREENE, Richard Anthony. 834 CHESTNUT ST STE 400, BEN FRANKLIN HOUSE 19107
  #539-03-1991 L1999 **OBG** *100
GREENFELD, Alan. 5501 OLD YORK RD, STE 3 19141 #035-15-1976 L1977 **AN** *020 †05
GREENFIELD, Steven Mark. 132 S 10TH ST 19107 #016-42-1976 L1979 **GE IM** *020 †20
GREENHOPKINS, Israel. ■ 19128 #041-15-2008 *012
GREENHOW, Donald E F. 3400 SPRUCE ST, HOSP OF UNIV OF PENN 19104
  #065-01-1956 L1969 **AN** *071 †05
GREENSPAN, Allan M. 5501 OLD YORK RD STE 3, EPS OFFICE AEMC 19141
  #041-01-1973 L1976 **CD IM** *020 †20
GREENSPAN, Gail Sandra. 255 S 17TH ST, STE 2900 19103 #041-02-1980 L1981
  P PYA *020 †75
GREENSPAN, Kathleen N. 800 SPRUCE ST, 2 CATHCART 19107 #038-06-1983 L1984
  EM IM *020 †20
GREENSPAN, Stephen Saxe. 255 S 17TH ST, STE 2001 19103 #041-02-1987 L1993 **IM** *020 †20
GREENSPON, Arnold Jack. 925 CHESTNUT ST, JEFFERSON HEART INSTITUTE 19107
  #041-01-1975 L1980 **ICE CD** *020 †20
GREENSTEIN, Jeffrey Ian. 1740 SOUTH ST, STE 401 19146 #836-02-1971 L1983 **N IG** *050 †75
GREENSTEIN, Robert Alan. 3400 SPRUCE ST 19104 #041-02-1966 L1970 **P** *020 †75
GREENSTEIN, Susan Beth. 3400 SPRUCE ST, UNIV PEN HOSPITAL 19104 #041-01-1984 L1984
  DR *020 †80
GREENWALD, Phyllis Louise. 1901 MARKET ST, FL 30 19103 #023-01-1978 L1996 **P** *020 †75
GREER, Brendan Miles. 4025 CHESTNUT ST FL 1 19104 #035-20-1992 L1994 **P** *020 †75
GREGOR, Frank Andrew. 2601 HOLME AVE 19152 #041-13-1961 L1962 **R** *071 †80
GREGORY, James Matthew. ■ 19146 #041-01-2008 *012
GRESCHNER, Dimitri. ■ 19130 #035-48-2001 L2004 **IC** *012 †20
GRESSEN, Eric Lance. 111 S 11TH ST 19107 #041-09-1994 L1999 **RO** *020 †80
GREWAL, Harsh. 3509 N BROAD ST, PEDIATRIC SRGY TUCMC 5 E 19140 #495-36-1984 L2001
  PDS GS *020 †85
GREWAL, Navneet Kaur. 245 N 15TH ST MS 310 19102 #495-01-1996 L2006 **AN** *020
GREWAL, Rasveg Singh. 2301 S BROAD ST, METHODIST HOSPITAL 19148 #422-01-2002 L2002
  CD *020 †20
GREYWOODE, Jewel Dunamis. 925 CHESTNUT ST, JEFFERSON OTOLARYNGOLOGY 19107
  #011-03-2006 L2006 **OTO** *012

GRIECO, William Michael. 2601 HOLME AVE 19152 #041-02-1988 L1991 **AN PME** *020 †05
GRIFFITH, John Richard. 1025 WALNUT ST, STE 8439 19107 #041-02-1946 L1947 **CD IM** *071
GRIMBERG, Adda. 3615 CIVIC CENTER BLVD, ABRAMSON RSCH CTR RM 802 19104
  #035-20-1993 L1995 **PDE PD** *050 †55
GRINDLE, Christopher Robe. 925 CHESTNUT ST, JEFFERSON OTOLARYNGOLOGY 19107
  #056-05-2005 L2005 **OTO** *012
GRISAFI, Joseph Leo. 5501 OLD YORK RD 19141 #041-13-2003 L2003 **GS** *012
GRISKA, Joel Adam. 51 N 39TH ST # 212 19104 #041-01-1971 L1972 **IM** *020 †20
GRISSO, Jeanne-Ann. 3400 SPRUCE ST, # 3 SILVERSTEIN BLDG STE D 19104
  #036-01-1978 L1979 **IM** *040 †20
GRISWOLD, Sharon Kay. 245 N 15TH ST, DUCOM DEPT OF EM, NCB RM 2 19102
  #041-02-1993 L1995 **EM** *020 †16
GRIVAS, Petros. 4TH FLOOR - S TOWER MAIL, DREXEL UNIVERSITY COLLEGE 19102
  #418-03-2005 L2007 **IM** *012
GRIZOS, William Thos. 8835 GERMANTOWN AVE, PENN RADIATION ONCOLOGY AT 19118
  #041-01-2004 **RO GE** *020 †20
GRODECKI, Wlodzimierz. 111 S 11TH ST STE G-8490, DEPT OF ANESTHESIOLOGY 19107
  #759-09-1981 L1994 **AN** *020 †05
GROENEVELD, Peter William. 423 GUARDIAN DR, 1229 BLOCKLEY HALL 19104
  #024-07-1995 L2003 **IM** *050 †20
GROFT, Caroline Margaret. ■ 19104 #035-20-2006 L2007 **D** *012
GROMES, Susanne Natalie. 5501 OLD YORK RD 19141 #409-20-1999 L2002 **P** *100 †75
GRONICH, Joseph Howard. 8001 ROOSEVELT BLVD, STE 502 19152 #550-02-1982 L1992
  IM *020 †20 ‡
GROOKETT, Thomas Wister. 3401 N BROAD ST, TEMPLE UNIVERSITY HOSPITAL 19140
  #051-04-2003 L2003 **PCC** *012 †20
GROSH, Julieta D. BROAD & ONTARIO STS, TEMPLE UNIV HOSP DEPT SURG 19140
  #023-01-1969 L1970 **VS GS** *020 †85
GROSHEK, Frank Joseph. ■ 19128 #041-13-2008 L2008 *012
GROSS, Brion Guy. 800 SPRUCE ST 19107 #005-11-1983 L1985 **AN** *020 †05
GROSS, Craig Farrell. 900 WALNUT ST, 5TH FLOOR ANESTHESIA 19107 #041-09-1991 L1998
  AN *020 †05
GROSS, Harriet Sharon. 3905 FORD RD, WORDSWORTH ACAD 19131 #041-07-1983 L1984
  CHP P *020 †75
GROSS, Paul Robert. 220 S 8TH ST 19107 #041-01-1962 L1963 **D DMP** *020 †15
GROSS, Robert. 423 GUARDIAN DR, RM: 804 BLOCKLEY HALL 19104 #035-20-1991 L1993
  ID *020 †20
GROSSMAN, Eric Laurence. ■ 19147 #041-02-2003 L2003 **ORS** *012
GROSSMAN, Gilbert. 700 COTTMAN AVE, BLDG A 19111 #041-13-1957 L1958 **IM CD** *020 †20
GROSSMAN, Marvin. 1800 LOMBARD ST, ATTN:DENISE ISLAM MED STAF 19146
  #041-02-1961 L1962 **CD** *020 †20
GROSSMAN, Murray. 3400 SPRUCE ST 19104 #067-01-1985 L1987 **N** *020 †75
GROSSMAN, Robert A. 3400 SPRUCE ST # 210 19104 #035-01-1967 L1968 **NEP IM** *020 †20
GROTKOWSKI, Carolyn Ernst. 3300 HENRY AVE, DEPT OF PATHOLOGY 19129
  #038-41-1976 L1978 **PTH** *071 †50
GROVER, Alison Hayley. ■ 19103 #041-01-2008 *012
GROVER, Evangeline. 316 ROCHELLE AVE 19128 #033-05-1993 L1997 **PD** *020 †55
GROVES, Ashley Mcallister. ■ 19103 #917-04-1993 L1995 **IM** *100
GRUBER, Stacey Marie. ■ 19146 #041-15-2005 L2005 **N** *012
GRULLON, Luis R. 230 N BROAD ST 19102 #308-01-1970 **AN** *100
GRUNDMEIER, Robert Wayne. 1900 S BROAD ST 2ND FL, CHOP PRIMARY CARE CTR 19145
  #041-01-1997 L1999 **PD** *020 †55
GRUNDY, Richard Guy. 324 S 34TH ST, DEPT PED 19104 #917-01-1986 L1990 **PD** *100
GRUNSTEIN, Michael M. 324 S 34TH ST 19104 #067-01-1977 L1987 **PD** *050 †55
GRUNT, Richard Frank. 800 SPRUCE ST 19107 #041-02-1969 L1970 **IM GE** *071 †20
GRUNWALD, Juan. 5 N 39TH ST, SCHEIE EYE INSTITUTE 19104 #550-02-1976 L1984
  OPH *050 †35 ‡
GRUNWALD, Lili. ■ 19146 #041-01-2006 L2006 **OPH** *012
GRUNWALD, Zvi. 111 S 11TH ST, STE G-8490 19107 #550-01-1982 L1987 **AN PAN** *020 †20
GRUPP, Stephan Alkmar. 324 S 34TH ST 19104 #038-41-1987 L1996 **PHO** *050 †55
GRZYWACZ, Kelly. ■ 19103 #067-02-2007 L2007 *012
GU, Yuejie. 3401 N BROAD ST 19140 #243-46-1987 L2004 **N** *012
GUARDABASCIO, Lisa Marie. 111 S 11TH ST, JEFFERSON UNIVERSITY 19107
  #023-07-2006 L2006 **PD** *012
GUDIS, David Adam. ■ 19103 #041-01-2008 *012
GUENDELMANN, Rafael A. 111 S 11TH ST, SUITE 4042/GIBBON BLDG 19107
  #187-12-1995 L2001 **IM** *020 †20
GUEORGUIEVSKAIA, Elena Yu. ■ 19154 #913-06-1983 L2002 **FM** *100 †18
GUERETTE, Nathan Leslie. 801 SPRUCE ST, 7TH FL 19107 #035-48-1997 L2005
  OBG *020 †18,30
GUERRA, Carmen Estela. 3701 MARKET ST, STE 760 19104 #035-45-1993 L1995 **IM** *050 †20
GUERRATY, Albert Jose. 1800 LOMBARD ST, GRADUATE HOSPITAL 19146 #231-01-1972 L1998
  TS GS *020
GUERRERO SUBERO, Larissa. 3401 N BROAD ST, DEPT OF HOSP ADMINISTRATIO 19140
  #308-05-2005 L2007 **OBG** *012
GUERRIERI, Patrizia M N. ■ 19107 #561-23-1984 L1995 **RO** *020
GUERRY, Dupont, IV. 3400 SPRUCE ST 19104 #051-01-1968 L1975 **HO HEM** *050 †20
GUESON, Emerita Torres. 3336 ALDINE ST 19104 #041-01-1967, ▲ L2007 **EM** *012
GUEST, Rebecca Schwager. ■ 19106 #035-20-2000 L2001 **EM** *016
GUEST ROSSO, Megan Elizab. ■ 19118 #041-77-2007, ▲ L2007 **EM** *012
GUEVARA, James Patrick. 3550 MARKET ST FL 3 19104 #016-06-1990 L2000 **PD** *020 †55
GUGLIELMO, Flavius F. 132 S 10TH ST 1087, MAIN BLDG. 19107 #033-05-1985 L1986
  DR OS *020 †80
GUHAROY, Rajeeb Kumar. 1025 WALNUT ST, JEFFERSON MED COLL 19107
  #041-02-2001 L2001 **EM** *100 †16
GUIDO, Laurance Jacobius. ■ 19106 #035-01-1969 L1970 **NS** *071 †25
GUIDOTTI, Janice Lindel. ■ 19103 #041-09-1986 L1987 **P** *020
GUIHA, Nabil H. 3300 HENRY AVE BX 100 19129 #915-04-1960 L1974 **CD PA** *050
GUILFOIL, Daniel Scott. 216 N BROAD ST, FL 4 19102 #041-07-1991 L1994 **OBG** *020 †30
GUILLEN, Ursula. ■ 19129 #036-01-2004 L2007 **NPM** *012 †55
GUILLERMO-LOPEZ, Aisa. 5800 RIDGE AVE 19128 #748-01-1957 L1978 **PM PD** *020
GUJRAL, Vishal. ■ 19128 #021-05-2004 L2004 **CD** *012 †20
GUJRATHI, Urmila N. 100 E LEHIGH AVE, PIZZICA HEALTH SYSTEM 19125 #495-34-1965 L1972
  PD *020 †55
GULATI, Rakesh. 833 CHESTNUT ST, STE 700 19107 #495-20-1984 L1997 **NEP IM** *020 †20
GUMEINER, Steven Chas. 1 PENN BLVD 19144 #048-02-1980 L1982 **AN** *020 †05

■ = Address Information Privacy Protected

GUMMADI, Vedam. 2301 E ALLEGHENY AVE, NORTHEASTERN HOSPITAL 19134 #495-58-1988 L1998 ID *020 †20
GUNDU RAO, Nagashree. 5501 OLD YORK RD 19141 #496-59-2004 L2006 MPD *012
GUNN, Pamela Renita. 8125 STENTON AVE, NW MEDICAL CENTER 19150 #041-02-1988 L1990 PD *020 †20
GUNTER, Heather Elspeth. ■ 19146 #024-01-2005 L2005 N *012
GUNTHER, Edward Joseph. 3400 SPRUCE ST, DEPT MED 19104 #008-01-1993 L1995 HO *020 †20
GUNTON, Kammi B. 840 WALNUT ST, WILLS EYE INST PED OPHTH 19107 #005-02-1995 L1999 OPH *020 †35
GUNTUR, Rakesh Kumar. 1800 LOMBARD ST 19146 #495-21-2000 L2006 IM *012
GUO, Jinping. 1316 W ONTARIO ST, SAMARITAN PROGRAM/JOHNS HA 19140 #243-39-1985 L2001 AI *020 †20,03 ‡
GUPTA, Mala Rani. 255 S 17TH ST, STE 2710 19103 #495-43-1987 L1990 CHP P *020 †75
GUPTA, Narainder Kumar. 111 S 11TH ST 19107 #496-09-1982 L2002 *100 †80
GUPTA, Naveen. ■ 19144 #041-15-2002 L2005 NEP *100 †20
GUPTA, Neil. ■ 19146 #041-01-2007 L2007 MPD *012
GUPTA, Omesh Parkash. 840 WALNUT ST, WILLS EYE HOSPITAL 19107 #035-45-2003 L2004 OPH *020 †20
GUPTA, Prabodh Kumar. 3400 SPRUCE ST, RM 6037 FOUNDERS PAVILION 19104 #495-03-1960 L1988 PCP ATP *020 †50
GUPTA, Rishi Nath. ■ 19128 #047-06-2006 TY *012
GUPTA, Santosh. 452 W ALLEGHENY AVE, MARIA DE LOS SANTOS HLTH 19133 #495-34-1959 L1971 OBG *020 †30
GUPTA, Sarita Ashish. 1800 LOMBARD ST 19146 #495-19-1990 L2005 GS *012
GUPTA, Shuchita. 5401 OLD YORK RD, KLEIN 363 19141 #495-45-2002 L2007 IM *012
GUPTA, Shweta. 5501 OLD YORK RD, ALBERT EINSTEIN MED CTR 19141 #495-45-2005 L2006 IM *012
GUPTA, Ved Prakash. 2137 WELSH RD STE 2E 19115 #495-34-1966 L1973 RHU *020 †20
GUPTA-BALA, Santosh. 255 S 17TH ST, STE 1700 19103 #041-07-1987 L1988 CD *020 †20
GUR, Raquel E. 3400 SPRUCE ST, # 10 GATES HUP 19104 #041-01-1980 L1982 P N *050
GURGENASHVILI, Khatuna. 245 N 15TH ST, DREXEL U COLL OF MED 19102 #912-02-2004 L2006 N *012
GURKAYNAK, Necmi. 5501 OLD YORK RD 19141 #902-01-1951 L1963 CD IM *020
GURMU, Samson. PO BOX 45358, 4641 ROOSEVELT BLVD 19124 #366-03-2002 L2007 P *012
GURUBHAGAVATULA, Indira. 3600 SPRUCE ST, PULMONARY & CRITICAL CARE 19104 #023-07-1990 L1994 PUD *020 †20
GURUPRASAD, Hemalatha. 3501 N BROAD ST 19140 #496-06-1984 L1997 PD *020 †55
GUSIC, Blaze Robt. 3550 MARKET ST, FL 5 19104 #041-01-1991 L1997 PD *020 †55
GUSTAFSON, Karen Sue. 3400 SPRUCE ST 19104 #026-04-1998 L2001 PTH *100 †50
GUSTAFSON, Timothy B. ■ 19103 #041-01-2004 P *100
GUTHRIE, Michael Andrew. ■ 19130 #422-01-1992 L1997 PM *020
GUTIERREZ, Camilo Alejand. ■ 19107 #042-02-2005 L2005 N *012
GUTIERREZ FORERO, Maria J. ■ 19130 #264-01-1999 L2006 PD *100
GUTMANN, Jacqueline Nina. 1015 CHESTNUT ST, STE 1015 19107 #008-01-1985 L1992 OBG REN *020 †30
GUTOWICZ, Lorraine F. 1717 ARCH ST FL 45, COMP SERV INC MED DIR 19103 #041-07-1978 L1979 OM FM *030 †18
GUTSCHE, Brett Bruce. 3400 SPRUCE ST, DEPT OF ANESTH HUP 19104 #035-45-1961 L1969 AN *020 †05
GUTSCHE, Jacob Thomas. 3400 SPRUCE ST 19104 #041-01-2001 L2001 AN *020 †05
GUTT, Poonam Lata. 230 N BROAD ST, MEHARRY MEDICAL COLLEGE 19102 #023-01-1999 L2007 IM *020 †20
GUTTENBERG, Marta Ellen. 34TH ST AND CIVIC CENTER B 19104 #005-06-1974 L1989 PP *020 †55,50
GUTTENTAG, Adam Richard. 101 E OLNEY AVE, STE 400 19120 #041-01-1985 L1993 DR *020 †80
GUTTENTAG, Susan Hall. 3400 SPRUCE ST 19104 #041-07-1985 L1993 NPM PD *020 †55
GUTTERMAN, Brett. ■ 19114 #035-48-2008 *012
GUTTERMAN, Paul. ■ 19106 #041-09-1963 L1964 NS *020 †25
GUTTMANN, Marlane Casper. 7701 BURHOLME AVE 19111 #035-09-1983 L1984 DR *020 †80
GUVAKOV, Dmitri Vladimiro. 3400 SPRUCE ST, 5TH FLOOR DULLES BLDNG 19104 #913-72-1986 L2002 AN *100
GUY, Edward Blair. 8201 STATE RD 19136 #051-04-1948 L1948 P *030
GUYNN, Kevin Craig. 800 SPRUCE ST 19107 #041-13-1983 L1984 AN *020 †20,05
GUZZO, Cynthia Ann. 36TH AND SPRUCE 19104 #041-12-1982 L1984 D *020 †15
GUZZO, Mark Andrew. 3400 SPRUCE ST, HOSP OF UNIV OF PENNA 19104 #035-01-2002 L2002 EM *020 †16
GUZZO, Thomas Joseph. 3400 SPRUCE ST, 9TH FLOOR, PENN TOWER 19104 #041-13-2002 L2002 U *020
GYI, Aung. 5501 OLD YORK RD 19141 #209-01-1981 L1996 AN *020 †05
GYULAI, Laszlo. 3535 MARKET ST STE 670, UNIV OF PENN MED CTR 6TH F 19104 #473-01-1973 L2002 P *050 †75
GZESH, Dan Jonathan. 219 N BROAD ST, FL 7 19107 #041-02-1985 L1986 N *020 †75
HA, Alice Soojung. ■ 19103 #041-01-2003 L2003 DR *012
HAAR, Peter Jacob. ■ 19103 #051-04-2006 L2007 DR *012
HAAS, Allen B. 800 SPRUCE ST 19107 #035-19-1975 L1976 AN *071 †35,05 ‡
HAAS, Andrew Robert. 834 WALNUT ST STE 650, PULMONARY MEDICINE 19107 #041-02-1999 L2001 PCC *020 †20
HAAS, Janet F. 1200 W TABOR RD 19141 #041-09-1977 L1978 PM *020 †60
HAASE, Gunter Roland. 800 SPRUCE ST 19107 #407-16-1949 L1964 N *071 †75
HAASE, Volker H. 415 CURIE BLVD, 700 CRB. 19104 #409-23-1987 L2001 IM NEP *020 †20
HABBOUSHE, C M Parhad. 4534 RICHMOND ST 19137 #528-01-1964 L1973 PD PUD *020 ‡
HABBOUSHE, Fawzi Petros. 1 GRADUATE PLZ 1003 19146 #528-01-1961 L1973 GS EM *020 †85,90,16
HABBOUSHE, Reem Ann. 4900 FRANKFORD AVE, FRANKFORD HOSPITAL - FRANK 19124 #041-13-1996 L1999 IM *020 †20
HABER, Alan David. 19TH AND LOMBARD STS, PEPPER PAV STE 607 19146 #024-05-1984 L1993 PCC SME *012
HABER, Barbara Anne. 324 S 34TH ST 19104 #035-19-1983 L1990 GE PD *020 †55
HABER, Howard L. 230 W WASHINGTON SQ, FL 3 19106 #035-19-1986 L1993 CD IC *020 †20 ‡
HABER, Marian M. 1800 LOMBARD ST 19146 #035-01-1987 L1993 PTH *020 †50
HABER, Scott Alan. 5501 OLD YORK RD 19141 #035-48-1987 L1997 R NM *020 †80
HACHEN, Rachel Kaufman. 324 S 34TH ST 19104 #041-01-1989 L1994 PD *020 †55
HACHMANN, Lauren Barbara. ■ 19106 #035-48-2002 N *100
HACKMAN, Anne Nason. ■ 19107 #041-02-2007 L2007 FP *012

HACKNEY, Janel Elizabeth. 3400 SPRUCE ST, HOSPITAL OF UNIVERSITY OF 19104 #008-01-1997 L2004 PCC *100
HAECKER, Trude Anna. 3550 MARKET ST, 5TH FLR MAIN BLDG PEDIAT 19104 #041-07-1980 L1984 PD *020 †55
HAEGELE, Linda Anne. 2601 HOLME AVE 19152 #041-13-1973 L1975 ON HEM *020 †20 ‡
HAFEZ KHAYYATA, Said. 3400 SPRUCE ST, U PA MED CTR 19104 #875-02-2000 L2007 PCP *012 †50
HAGER, Margaret H. 441 LYCEUM AVE 19128 #041-13-1985 L1986 FM *020 †18
HAGERDAL, Magnus N. 3400 SPRUCE ST DEPT ANES 19104 #858-01-1969 AN *050
HAGGERTY, David Allan. ■ 19144 #041-15-2005 L2005 EM *012
HAGHBIN, Mahroo. 216 N BROAD ST, MAIL STOP 200 19102 #517-01-1958 L1978 RO *020 †55,80
HAHN, Chang-Gyu. 415 CURIE BLVD, 547A CLINICAL RESEARCH BLD 19104 #583-02-1981 L1990 P *020 †75
HAHN, David. 475 SPRING LN 19128 #041-07-1993 L1996 P *020 †75
HAHN, Miah. 8400 ROOSEVELT BLVD 19152 #065-01-1988 L1994 OP *020
HAHN, Paul. ■ 19104 #041-01-2006 L2006 OPH *012
HAHN, Stephen M. 3400 SPRUCE ST, UNIV PA DEPT RAD 19104 #041-13-1984 L1996 RO IM *020 †20,80
HAILS, Kevin Chas. 1200 W TABOR RD 19141 #041-09-1976 L1977 P *040 †75
HAILU, Tesfu Lisanework. 245 N 15TH ST, DREXEL UNIV COLL MED 19102 #366-02-1994 L2004 PTH *012
HAINES, Christopher A. 833 CHESTNUT ST, 3RD FL 19107 #041-02-1999 L2001 FPG *020 †18
HAINES, Philip Gustav. 3400 SPRUCE ST, UNIVERSITY OF PENNSYLVANIA 19104 #917-09-2004 L2007 IM *012
HAKIMIAN, Roozbeh H. 3910 N POWELTON AVE 19104 #306-01-1992 AN *100
HAKMA, Zakaria. 2900 W QUEEN LN 19129 #875-01-2001 L2003 NS *012
HAKONARSON, Hakon. 324 S 34TH ST, CHILDRENS HSPTL OF PHLDLPH 19104 #484-01-1986 L1993 PDP *050 †55
HALDEMAN-ENGLERT, Chad Ro. ■ 19128 #041-14-2002 L2006 MG *012 †20,55
HALE, Benjamin Patrick. 19107 #041-02-2007 L2007 IM *012
HALE, Paula Marie. ERIE AVE AT FRONT ST 19134 #056-06-1981 L1990 PDE PD *020 †55
HALEEM, Kamran. ■ 19128 #041-15-2004 L2005 IM *012
HALEGOUA-DE MARZIO, Dina. ■ 19148 #041-13-2007 L2007 IM *012
HALL, Clifton Everett. 3996 RED LION RD 19114 #041-01-1983 L1985 AN IM *020 †20,05
HALL, Eugene Kevin. ■ 19103 #539-03-2003 L2006 PDC *012 †55
HALL, Jennifer Krendel. 51 N 39TH ST, SCHEIE EYE INSTITUTE 19104 #041-01-2001 L2001 OPH *100
HALL, Neal Edward, Jr. ■ 19119 #025-12-1982 L1987 OPH *020
HALL, Robert Harry. 1225 VINE ST FL 3 19107 #041-09-1992 L1994 P *020
HALL, Ronald Vincent, Jr. 239 E THOMPSON ST, 1020 SANSOM ST. 19125 #033-05-2000 L2001 EM *020 †16
HALLER, Daniel Geo. 3400 SPRUCE ST 19104 #041-12-1973 L1980 ON *020 †20
HALLER, Julia A. 840 WALNUT ST, STE 1510 19107 #041-02-1980 L1985 OPH *020 †35
HALLERBACH, Marco. 5501 OLD YORK RD 19141 #409-10-2005 L2006 IM *012
HALLIGAN, Gregory Emmett. 2600 N LAWRENCE ST 19133 #165-01-1977 L1979 PHO PD *020 †55
HALLOCK, James Anthony. 3624 MARKET ST, ECFMG 4TH FL 19104 #010-02-1967 L1968 PD *030 †55
HALLORAN, Owen Joseph. ■ 19146 #035-45-2005 L2006 AN *012
HALLOWELL, Michael John. 245 N 15TH ST, MS206 DREXEL RAD ASSOC 19102 #023-01-1985 L1987 DR *020 †80
HALLUSKA, Maria Lin. 5501 OLD YORK RD, KORMAN STE B-14 19141 #041-15-2000 L2001 EM *100 †16
HALPERN, Marcia Lynn. 7602 CENTRAL AVE STE 203 19111 #041-01-1980 L1981 N *020 †75
HALPERN, Scott David. ■ 19146 #041-01-2003 L2003 PCC *012 †20
HALPHEN LASSO, Giselle Ma. 3401 N BROAD ST, TEMPLE UNIVERSITY HOSPITAL 19140 #715-01-1998 L2003 IM *020 †20
HALPIN, Christopher Gene. ■ 19136 #041-13-2005 L2005 IM *012
HALSTEAD, Eric Scott. ■ 19129 #041-15-2004 L2005 PD *012
HALSTEAD, Jeffrey Edward. 3300 HENRY AVE, MCP HAHNEMANN UNIVERSITY 19129 #041-07-1998 L2004 L2005 PD *012
HALUSZKA, Oleh. 333 COTTMAN AVE STE C307, FOX CHASE CANCER CTR 19111 #023-12-1982 L2002 GE IM *020 †20
HAMAD, Eman Ahmad. 925 CHESTNUT ST, TRANSPLANT CENTER AT THE J 19107 #305-01-2003 L2006 IM *100 †20
HAMED, Fadi Ahmad Azzam M. 5501 OLD YORK RD, ALBERT EINSTEIN MEDICAL CE 19141 #575-01-2004 L2006 IM *012
HAMEL, Marianne. 1000 WALNUT ST, ORLOWITZ APT # 1913 19107 #041-02-2004 L2004 PTH *012
HAMID, Sammy. 7300 CITY LINE AVE, RM 203 19151 #047-07-2001 L2004 IM *020
HAMILTON, Aaron Charles. ■ 19146 #016-02-2007 L2007 IM *012
HAMILTON, Hamish Elliot C. ■ 19103 #775-01-1983 L1987 GS *020 †85
HAMILTON, Ralph W. 3400 SPRUCE ST 19104 #041-01-1959 L1960 PS *071 †85,65
HAMILTON, Richard Jos. 230 N BROAD ST 19102 #041-09-1987 L1989 EM ETX *020 †16
HAMILTON, Roy Hoshi. 3400 SPRUCE ST, OF PENN. 19104 #024-01-2001 L2002 N *100 †75
HAMILTON, Thanuja Kumari. 4TH FLOOR - S TOWER MAIL, DREXEL UNIVERSITY COLLEGE 19102 #422-01-2006 L2007 IM *012
HAMILTON, William Craig. 7500 CENTRAL AVE 19111 #041-02-1971 L1973 ORS GP *020 †40
HAMILTON, William Lenhard. 100 S BROAD ST, STE 2226 19110 #041-01-1954 L1955 D ID *071 †15
HAMMERMAN, Seth Brian. 3535 MARKET ST, PENN BEHAVIORAL HEALTH 19104 #050-02-2004 L2004 CHP *012
HAMMERSMITH, Kristin M. 840 WALNUT ST STE 920, WILLS EYE HOSPITAL 19107 #055-01-1998 L2002 OPH *020 †35
HAN, Dale. ■ 19130 #035-48-2003 L2003 GS *012
HAN, Joyce H. 3542 WELSH RD 19136 #043-01-1997 L1999 FM *020 †18
HAN, Nancy Elizabeth. ■ 19149 #035-47-2005 L2007 PD *012
HAN, Sangwoo. ■ 19104 #041-15-2005 L2005 IM *100
HAN, Soo Sung. 800 SPRUCE ST, PENNSYLVANIA HOSPITAL 19107 #583-03-1968 L1978 DR *020 †80
HAN, Steven Sanguk. 111 S 11TH ST, STE 4290 19107 #035-47-1999 L2001 NEP *020 †20
HAN, William Yunsup. 3401 N BROAD ST DEPT M, 8TH FLR/PARKINSON PAVILION 19140 #023-01-1998 L2000 PCC *020 †20
HAN, Won Kook. 833 CHESTNUT ST STE 700, JEFFERSON MEDICAL COLLEGE 19107 #041-13-1994 L2007 NEP *050 †20

HAN, Yusheng. 800 SPRUCE ST 19107 #243-71-1988 L2006 **PTH** *012

HANAU, Cheryl A. 245 N 15TH ST 19102 #041-02-1989 L1992 **PTH PCP** *040 †50

HANCOCK, Amy Colleen. ■ 19107 #041-02-2008 L2008 *012

HANDA, Dipti. 5501 OLD YORK RD 19141 #496-21-2004 L2005 **IM** *100

HANDLER, Jay Joel. 2137 WELSH RD STE 2C-2D 19115 #041-12-1968 L1969 **U GP** *020 †95

HANDLY, Neal Bruce. 245 N 15TH ST, DEPT OF EMERGENCY MEDICINE 19102 #005-15-1997 L1999 **EM** *020 †16

HANEEF, Zulfi. ■ 19131 #495-63-1999 L2004 **N** *012

HANKIN, Abigail Dorit. 3400 SPRUCE ST, OF PENNSYLVAN 19104 #005-02-2003 L2006 **EM** *012

HANKINS, Althea Vernice. 5801 GERMANTOWN AVE 19144 #025-12-1981 L1984 **IM ADL** *020 †20

HANKINS, Shelley Ronnell. 230 N BROAD ST, FL 7 19102 #041-01-1993 L1996 **CD IM** *020 †20

HANLEY, Colleen Marie. ■ 19130 #041-13-2007 L2007 **IM** *012

HANN, Hie Won L. 132 S 10TH ST 19107 #583-02-1961 L1971 **HEP** *020 †55

HANNA, Amgad Saddik. ■ 19154 #915-02-1990 L2002 **NS** *012

HANNA, Brian D. 3509 N BROAD ST 19140 #067-01-1983 L1998 **PD PDC** *020 †55

HANNA, George M. ■ 19146 #041-01-2008 *012

HANNA, Josef. 2900 W QUEEN LN 19129 #875-01-1999 L2003 **IM** *100

HANNAH, Brian Alexander. 5000 FRANKFORD AVE, WAKELING BLDG 19124 #041-01-1984 L1987 **IM** *020 †20

HANNAN, Hashibul. 245 N 15TH ST, NEW COLLEGE BUILDING, ROOM 19102 #035-48-2002 L2007 **EM** *100

HANNAWAY, Barbara Ann. 5753 WAYNE AVE 19144 #917-04-1977 L1984 **FM** *020

HANN-DESCHAINE, Jason B. 111 S 11TH ST, JEFFERSON UNIVERSITY 19107 #043-01-2000 L2001 **PD** *020 †55

HANNO, Philip Mark. 3400 SPRUCE ST, 9 PENN TOWERS 19104 #048-04-1973 L1975 **U** *020 †95

HANSELL, John Royer. UNIVERSITY & WOODLAND AVES 19104 #041-02-1957 L1958 **NM PTH** *071 †50,28

HANSEN, Christopher L. 925 CHESTNUT 19107 #041-13-1981 L1987 **CD IM** *020 †20

HANSEN-FLASCHEN, John H. 3400 SPRUCE ST, 873 MALONEY BLDG 19104 #035-19-1976 L1977 **PUD CCM** *030 †20

HANSON, Clarence Wm. 3400 SPRUCE ST 19104 #041-01-1983 L1989 **IM** *020 †20,05

HANSON, Matthew Russell. 219 N BROAD ST, FL 4 19107 #041-15-2005 L2005 **D** *012

HANSPAL, Era Kaur. 19107 #035-15-2005 L2006 **N** *012

HANUSCHAK, Lee Nicholas. 829 SPRUCE ST 19107 #038-06-1977 L1978 **IM DIA** *020 ‡

HAQ, Omar Anwar. 2900 W QUEEN LN 19129 #704-01-2001 L2005 **IM** *012

HAQUE, Besma Muneer. 1811 S BROAD ST, GROUP PC 19148 #035-08-1998 L2004 **GE** *100 †20

HAQUE, Mohammed A. 7901 STATE RD 19136 #496-05-1977 L1993 **IM** *020 †20

HARADA, Shuko. 2900 W QUEEN LN 19129 #572-03-1985 L2004 **PTH** *012

HARBISON, Sean Patrick. 1800 LOMBARD ST RM 1101 19146 #041-13-1986 L1987 **GS OS** *020 †85 ‡

HARDEN, Miriam Reon. 8815 GERMANTOWN AVE STE 40 19118 #026-04-1993 L1995 **OBG** *020 †30

HARDING, John Jos. 3401 N BROAD ST, TEMPLE HOSPITAL 19140 #041-13-1973 L1974 **P** *020 †75

HARDY, Kevin Ross. 3400 SPRUCE ST 19104 #041-02-1984 L1988 **EM UM** *020 †16

HARGROVE, Amanda George. ■ 19153 #041-15-2007 L2007 **TY** *012

HARGROVE, Walter C. 51 N 39TH ST, STE 2D 19104 #036-05-1973 L1974 **TS** *020 †85,90

HARIDAS, Arun. 2900 W QUEEN LN 19129 #495-37-2000 L2007 **P** *012

HARKANYI, Zoltan. 1025 WALNUT ST, MAIN 10 DEPT RADIOLOGY 19107 #473-01-1974 **R** *040

HARKAVY, Sandra Eglick. 501 S 54TH ST 19143 #041-07-1977 L1978 **PTH** *062 †50 ‡

HARKAWAY, Richard Corey. 5501 OLD YORK RD, KLEIN 500 19141 #041-01-1989 L1991 **U** *020 †95

HARLAN, Carmen. 1611 GREEN ST, # B 19130 #038-40-1993 L1995 **CHP** *020 †75

HARMATZ, Alexander Jerome. 3998 RED LION RD 19114 #041-01-1984 L1991 **GE** *020 †20 ‡

HARMON, Robert David. ■ 19151 #016-06-1989 *100

HARNER, Richard Neal. 3901 NETHERFIELD RD 19129 #026-04-1959 L1965 **N** *020 †55

HAROZ, Rachel Burshtein. 2900 W QUEEN LN 19129 #024-07-2000 L2000 **ETX** *100 ‡

HARPER, Deirdre Wood. 6810 CASTOR AVE 19149 #041-07-1996 L2000 **D** *020

HARRELL, Cynthia Loretta. 2 PENN BLVD, STE 220 19144 #036-01-1979 L2000 **GP** *020

HARRIGAN, Richard Allen. 3401 N BROAD ST, EMER DEPT TX UNIV HOSP 19140 #028-34-1987 L1991 **EM IM** *020 †20,16

HARRIS, Brian C. 3620 HAMILTON WALK, UNIV OF PA SCH OF MED 19104 #041-01-2006 L2006 *012

HARRIS, David Michael. 1000 WALNUT ST 19107 #041-02-2005 L2005 **IM** *012

HARRIS, Eleanor C. 2 DONNER, 3400 SPRUCE STREET 19104 #020-02-1992 L1995 **RO** *020 †80

HARRIS, Eric Brent. ■ 19107 #023-12-1999 L2007 **ORS** *012

HARRIS, Holly Carmelita. 19104 #010-03-2004 L2004 **FP** *012

HARRIS, Jennifer Hope. 3401 N BROAD ST, DEPT OF EMERGENCY MEDICINE 19140 #041-13-2003 L2003 **EM** *020 †16

HARRIS, Julian Joseph. 19104 #041-01-2008 *012

HARRIS, Kathleen Anne. ■ 19103 #422-01-2005 L2005 **AN** *012

HARRIS, Kristen M. ■ 19104 #041-01-2008 *012

HARRIS, Lisa Jane. ■ 19102 #035-08-2005 L2005 **GS** *012

HARRIS, Louis Cecil. 3333 N BROAD ST, RM 343 19140 #023-07-1959 L1966 **P PHP** *020 †75

HARRIS, Martin Edward. 3400 SPRUCE ST, PENN TOWERS 9TH FLOOR 19104 #035-08-1961 L1972 **DR** *020 †80

HARRIS, Mary Catherine. 3400 SPRUCE 19104 #032-01-1976 L1979 **NPM PD** *050 †55

HARRIS, Matthew Aaron. ■ 19103 #016-11-1997 L2000 **PDC** *012

HARRIS, Merleen. 6323 VINE ST 19139 #041-13-1984 L1985 **IM** *071 †20

HARRIS, Walter P, Jr. 255 S 17TH ST, STE 1002 19103 #041-02-1983 L1983 **OPH** *020 †35

HARRISON, Bernard M. 500 S BROAD ST STE 360, DEPT. OF PUBLIC HEALTH - A 19146 #041-07-1982 L1984 **FM** *020 †18

HARRISON, Mark Allan. 3400 SPRUCE ST, 100 CENTREX 19104 #035-47-2005 L2005 **IM** *012

HARROP, James Shields, Jr. 909 WALNUT ST, 2ND FL 19107 #041-02-1995 L2000 **NS** *020 †25

HARRYHILL, Joseph Francis. 299 S 8TH ST 19106 #038-40-1986 L1988 **U** *020 †95

HART, Bruce. 1020 SANSOM ST, THOMPSON BLDG, STE 239 19107 #041-02-1981 L1982 **EM IM** *020 †20,16

HART, Carol. 501 S 54TH ST, MERCY HOSPITAL OF PHILADEL 19143 #041-02-1989 L1991 **EM** *020 †16

HART, Jessica Sarah. ■ 19146 #041-01-2007 L2007 **PD** *012

HART, Michael Anthony. ■ 19129 #041-77-2007, ▲ L2007 *012

HARTIS, Jason Noel. ■ 19147 #045-04-2008 *012

HARTKE, Amy Kristine. ■ 19147 #041-02-2008 L2008 *012

HARTMAN, John D. ■ 19141 #038-06-1946 L1963 **ATP** *062 †50

HARTNER, Lee Peter. 230 W WASHINGTON SQ, FL 2 19106 #024-07-1994 L2004 **HO IM** *020 †20

HARTZ, William Harry. 5800 RIDGE AVE 19128 #041-09-1978 L1979 **DR** *020 †80

HARTZELL, Dwight Jeffery. 727 DELANCEY ST, DELANCEY MED ASSOC 19106 #041-01-1966 L1967 **IM** *071 †20

HARVEY, Arthur James. 111 S 11TH ST 19107 #041-07-1983 L1984 **RO** *020 †80

HARVIE, Heidi Sharp. ■ 19130 #041-01-2002 L2002 **OBG** *100

HARWOOD, Marc Ira. 2630 HOLME AVE, STE 200 19152 #041-13-1997 L1999 **FSM** *020 †18

HASAN, Rani Khalil. ■ 19146 #023-07-2006 L2006 **IM** *012

HASAN, Tajamul. 245 N 15TH ST, DREXEL UNIV COLL MED/HAHNE 19102 #495-21-2002 L2005 **IM** *012

HASBANI, Daphne Maya. ■ 19103 #028-02-2007 L2007 **PD** *012

HASBROUCK, Edith Douw. 5501 OLD YORK RD 19141 #041-13-1982 L1984 **PD IM** *075 †20,55

HASBROUCK, Nicole Cherie. 1600 S BROAD ST, # 6A 19145 #016-02-2002 L2005 **PHO** *012

HASHEMI, Seyed Mohammad. 1600 W GIRARD AVE 19130 #517-06-1997 L2001 **IM** *020 ‡

HASKIN, Pamela Herr. 8835 GERMANTOWN AVE 19118 #041-09-1978 L1979 **DR** *020 †80

HASNI, Syed Farhan Ahmed. 1427 VINE ST, FL 6 19102 #704-02-1998 L2002 **IM** *020 †20

HASSAN, Chaudhry Muhammad. 1220 N 64TH ST 19151 #308-10-1985 L1999 **N SME** *020

HASSAN, Tahmina. 1800 LOMBARD ST, GRADUATE HOSP (TENET HLTH 19146 #160-02-1995 L2004 **IMG** *012 †20

HASSANI, Cameron. ■ 19102 #041-15-2006 L2006 **DR** *012

HASSLACHER, Elisabeth A. 800 SPRUCE ST 19107 #041-13-1989 L1992 **P** *020 †75

HASTON, Rhonda Lynn. 5501 OLD YORK RD, ALBERT EINSTEIN 19141 #023-01-1993 L1995 **IM** *020 †20

HAUG, Richard Patrick. ■ 19146 #041-13-2006 L2006 **FP** *012

HAUPT, Alicia Lynn. ■ 19146 #041-12-2006 L2006 **PD** *012

HAUPT, Helen Miller. 218 SPRUCE ST 19106 #023-07-1981 L1989 **PTH** *020 †50

HAUPTMAN, Stephen Phillip. 2000 HAMILTON ST, STE 303 19130 #018-75-1968, ▲ L1969 **IG HEM** *020 †20

HAUPTMAN, William. 1801 MARKET ST STE 200 19103 #041-01-1988 L1993 **GE IM** *020 †20

HAURANI, Farid I. 1025 WALNUT ST, JEFFERSON MEDICAL COLLEGE 19107 #605-01-1953 L1958 **HEM OS** *071 †20

HAUSMAN, Cheryl Lynn. 709 W MT AIRY AVE, 709 WEST MT AIRY AVE 19119 #035-19-1982 L1986 **PD** *040 †55

HAUT, Michael Joel. 230 W WASHINGTON SQ 19106 #041-01-1967 L1968 **HEM ON** *020 †20

HAVA, Milos. ■ 19147 #286-02-1952 **PA** *071

HAVES, Valorie Sloan. 1 PENN BLVD, 3RD FL 19144 #308-07-1983 L1987 **P** *020 †75

HAWKINS, Richard Eric. 3750 MARKET ST 19104 #041-02-1982 L2002 **ID IM** *030 †20

HAWTHORNE, Katie Marie. ■ 19125 #041-02-2008 *012

HAYASHIDA, Motoi. UNIVERSITY & WOODLAND AVES, PHILADELPHIA VA MED CTR 19104 #572-20-1958 L1973 **P** *020 †75

HAYES, Ada Dorothy. 324 S 34TH ST, CHILDRENS HSPTL OF PHLDLPH 19104 #036-01-1969 L1977 **PD PM** *020 †55

HAYES, George Thos. 3720 N SYDENHAM ST 19140 #041-12-1975 L1977 **IM** *020

HAYES, Margaret Chiquita. ■ 19141 #041-13-1984 *100

HAYNES, Jeffrey Caleb. 3400 SPRUCE ST, 2ND FL OF THE DONNER BLDG 19104 #041-01-2004 L2004 **RO** *012

HAYNES-LAING, Arleen G. 800 SPRUCE ST, FL 2 19104 #566-01-1984 L1991 **NPM** *020 †55

HAYON, Ronni. ■ 19130 #041-15-2008 *012

HAYTMANEK, Craig Thomas, II. ■ 19107 #041-02-2008 *012

HE, Ming. 3401 N BROAD ST, TEMPLE UNIV HOSP 19140 #243-45-1989 L2006 **N** *012

HEADLEY, Peter Abraham. ■ 19129 #041-15-2008 *012

HEATH, Candice Rachelle. 932 PINE ST, SOCIETY HILL DERMATOLOGY 19107 #051-01-2004 L2007 **PD** *100

HEBELA, Nader Mohamed. 3400 SPRUCE ST, ORTHOPAEDIC ASSOCIATES 19104 #041-01-2000 L2001 **ORS** *020

HECHT, Todd Emanuel. 3400 SPRUCE ST, PENN TOWER STE 2009 19104 #041-01-1995 L1997 **HOS** *020 †20

HECKER, James Gordon, III. 3620 HAMILTON WALK, MORGAN 305 DEPT OF ANESTH 19104 #051-01-1989 L1992 **AN OS** *050 †05

HECKER, William P. 3401 N BROAD ST, TEMPLE UNIV HOSP 19140 #041-13-1990 L1992 **GS TTS** *020 †85

HECKERT, Kimberly Gail. ■ 19107 #041-02-2003 L2003 *100

HEDGES, Thomas R. 301 S 8TH ST, STE 1A 19106 #035-20-1947 L1954 **OPH** *071 †35

HEERSINK, Sebastian B. ■ 19147 #041-02-2008 L2008 **TY** *012

HEESE, Curt Jan. 245 N 15TH ST, HAHNEMANN HOSP MAIL STOP 2 19102 #010-02-2002 L2003 **RO** *100

HEFFELFINGER, Ryan Neil. 925 CHESTNUT ST, FL 6 19107 #041-02-2000 L2001 **OTO** *100 †45 ‡

HEFFLER, Karen Frankel. 219 N BROAD ST, FL 3 19107 #041-01-1986 L1987 **OPH** *020 †35

HEFFRON, Sean Patrick. ■ 19146 #036-07-2008 *012

HEGAZY, Jihan. 5401 OLD YORK RD, STE 503 19141 #038-44-1995 L2004 **GS** *020

HEGDE, Sanjay Ramesh. ■ 19107 #024-07-2001 L2003 **GE** *012

HEGEDUS, Dalma. 5501 OLD YORK RD, ALBERT EINSTEIN MED CTR 19141 #473-01-2001 L2002 **IMG** *020 †20

HEHIR, David A. ■ 19146 #035-15-2000 L2001 **CCP** *012 †55

HEIMAN, Donald F. 1 PENN BLVD 19144 #041-01-1953 L1954 **CD** *071 †20

HEIMANN, David M. 333 COTTMAN AVE, FOX CHASE CANCER CENTER 19111 #035-15-1998 L2006 **GS** *100

HEIMAN-PATTERSON, Terry D. 245 N 15TH ST, NEW COLLEGE BUILDING 19102 #035-03-1975 L1978 **N** *050 †75

HEINTZELMAN, Rebecca Carr. 245 N 15TH ST, HAHNEMANN HOSPITAL 19102 #041-15-2006 L2006 **PTH** *012

HEINZEL, Randolph Pike. ■ 19130 #016-45-2003 L2003 **OBG** *020

HEISER, Mark Sandor. 3405 CIVIC CENTER BLVD 19104 #041-02-1974 L1975 **AN** *020 †05

HEIT, Jeffrey. 7133 ROOSEVELT BLVD 19149 #035-19-1993 L1995 **IM** *020 †20

HEITNER, Stephen Barri. 5501 OLD YORK RD, ALBERT EINSTEIN MED CTR 19141 #836-01-1999 L2004 **IM** *012 †20

HEITZ, James Walter. 111 S 11TH ST, GIBBONS BUILDING, STE 8490 19107 #023-01-1989 L1991 **AN IM** *020 †05,20

HELD, David Avishai. 2601 HOLME AVE 19152 #035-47-1991 L2002 **EM** *020

HELLER, Arthur. LANGDON & CHELTENHAM AVES 19124 #041-01-1953 L1954 **GP OS** *071

HELLER, Joshua E. 3401 N BROAD ST, STE C540 19140 #041-13-2003 L2003 **NS** *012

HELLER, Melvin Saml. 3401 N BROAD ST 19140 #024-07-1948 L1955 **P LM** *030 †75

HELLINGER, Jeffrey Craig. ■ 19103 #011-02-1996 L2006 **DR** *020 †80

HELLMAN, Michelle Suzanne. ■ 19107 #041-02-2008 *012

HELLWIG, Gregg Edward. 239 E THOMPSON ST, 1020 SANSOM STREET 19125 #028-34-2004 L2004 **EM** *020

HELM, Denina Adele. 1602 E WADSWORTH AVE 19150 #010-03-1994 L1997 **FM** *020 †18

HELZNER, Richard Charles. 9908 ROOSEVELT BLVD 19115 #041-13-1969 L1970 **R** *020 †80 ‡

HEMACHANDRA, Sonali. 800 SPRUCE ST 19107 #422-01-2004 L2004 **ID** *012 †20

HEMAN-ACKAH, Yolanda D. 219 N BROAD, STE FL10 19107 #016-06-1995 L2000 **OTO PDO** *020 †45

HENDERSON, Polly Ann. 219 N BROAD ST FL 3, DEPT OF OPHTHALMOLOGY 19107 #016-02-2000 L2005 **OPH** *020 †35

HENDJE, Abayomi. ■ 19138 #010-03-2005 L2005 **FP** *012

HENDRICKS, Dorothy Helen. ■ 19118 #035-06-2003 L2004 **OPH** *100

HENLE, Gertrude. 324 S 34TH ST 19104 #407-10-1936 **IG MM** *050

HENNAWY, Randa Philip. 2601 HOLME AVE, NAZARETH HOSP 19152 #915-02-1987 L1998 **PTH** *020

HENNE, Terence Eric. 2301 S BROAD ST, ""THOMPSON BLDG, STE 239"" 19148 #041-09-1992 L1994 **EM** *020

HENRETIG, Frederick M. 3400 CIVIC CENTER BLVD, CHILDREN'S HOSPITAL OF PHI 19104 #008-01-1973 L1976 **PD EM** *040 †55

HENRIKSSON, Jan. 2400 CHESTNUT ST 19103 #858-02-1973 L2005 *100

HENRY, Adaora Chikwendu. 7332 BROOKHAVEN RD 19151 #041-13-1999 L2001 **PD** *020 †55

HENRY, Camille Angela Nic. 4317 BALTIMORE AVE 19104 #041-01-2006 L2006 **MPD** *012

HENRY, Jessica Athalia. 3401 N BROAD ST, TEMPLE UNIV HOSPITAL 19140 #005-12-2003 L2003 **OBG** *020

HENRY, Jimmy Mike. ■ 19147 #046-11-2005 L2006 **PM** *012

HENRY, Lana Pikus. ■ 19145 #041-01-2005 L2005 **DR** *012

HENSELL, Daniel O. 3401 N BROAD ST, 8TH FL ATPT BLDG 19140 #041-09-1973 L1984 **GS OS** *020 †85

HENSKE, Elizabeth Petri. 333 COTTMAN AVE 19111 #024-01-1985 L1996 **IM ON** *020 †20

HEPPENSTALL, R Bruce. 3400 SPRUCE ST 19104 #062-01-1966 L1973 **ORS** *020 †40

HERBISON, Gerald Joseph. 25 S 9TH ST, THOMAS JEFFERSON UNIV 19107 #016-43-1962 L1968 **PM** *071 †60 ‡

HERLING, Irving Marc. 3400 SPRUCE ST 19104 #041-01-1974 L1975 **CD IM** *020 †20

HERLINGER, Hans. 3400 SPRUCE ST 19104 #154-01-1947 **DR** *071

HERMAN, Carl David. 1200 W TABOR RD 19141 #035-06-1957 L1958 **P PYG** *020 †75

HERMAN, Ira Neil. 407 S 10TH ST 19147 #041-01-1974 L1981 **P** *020

HERMAN, Jay Howard. 111 S 11TH ST, ROOM 8220 GIBBON BUILDING 19107 #024-01-1977 L1986 **BBK PHO** *020 †55

HERMAN, Jerry Hale. 9331 OLD BUSTLETON AVE 19115 #041-13-1955 L1956 **OBG** *020 †30

HERMAN, Marianne. 5325 OLD YORK RD, # 15 19141 #396-06-1972 L1976 **IM** *020 †20

HERMAN, Samantha Leslie. ■ 19107 #011-03-2008 *012

HERMAN, Susan Therese. 3400 SPRUCE ST 19104 #035-01-1993 L2001 **N CN** *020 †75

HERMAN, Walter M. 111 S 11TH ST, HERMAN GRDN & NIERENBERG 19107 #041-01-1959 L1960 **CD** *071 †20

HERMANN, George Arthur. PRESBYTERIAN HOSP 19104 #024-05-1958 L1959 **NM PTH** *020 †50,28

HERNANDEZ, Enrique. 3401 N BROAD ST, TEMPLE UNIVERSITY HOSP 19140 #042-01-1977 L1986 **GO GYN** *020 †30 ‡

HERNANDEZ, Michelle Rebec. ■ 19103 #041-01-2004 L2004 **IM** *020 †20

HERNANDEZ, Zaida. 2301 E ALLEGHENY AVE, NORTHEASTERN HOSPITAL 19134 #024-01-1983 L1986 **EM IM** *020 †20 ‡

HERNANDEZ ANGUERA, Maria. 245 N 15TH ST, DEPT OF GME 19102 #308-13-2004 L2006 **P** *012

HERNANDEZ PAMPALONI, Jose. ■ 19104 #847-04-1991 L2006 **NM** *012

HEROLD, Sanford Lawrence. 3400 SPRUCE ST 19104 #041-01-1969 L1970 **GE IM** *020 †20

HERRAN DE ESTEVEZ, Onilda. TEMPLE UNIV HOSP, BROAD-ONTARIO STS 19140 #275-02-1981 L2006 **P** *100

HERRELL, Kristine Ann. 3550 MARKET ST FL 4, FACULTY PRACTICE 19104 #010-02-2004 L2006 **PD** *020 †55

HERRERA, Jesus. 801 W GIRARD AVE, PSYCH OUTPATIENT 19122 #275-02-1990 L2005 **P** *020

HERRERA, Larry. 3509 N BROAD ST, 5TH FLOOR EAST 19140 #048-16-1991 L2005 **PHO** *020 †55

HERRINE, Gail Margaret. 2301 E ALLEGHENY AVE, WOMEN CARE AT NORTHEASTERN 19134 #041-02-1987 L1988 **OBG** *020 †30

HERRINE, Steven Kenneth. 132 S 10TH ST 19107 #041-02-1990 L1992 **GE** *020 †20

HERRING, William. 5501 OLD YORK RD, ALBERT EINSTEIN MED CTR 19141 #041-13-1970 L1971 **R** *040 †80

HERRMANN, Howard Craig. 3400 SPRUCE ST, 9 FOUNDERS PAVILION 19104 #024-01-1981 L1987 **IC CD** *020 †20

HERSH, Lauren Rachel. ■ 19107 #041-13-2007 L2007 **FP** *012

HERSHEY, Beverly Louise. 3401 N BROAD ST 19140 #041-02-1980 L1981 **R RNR** *020 †80 ‡

HERSHOCK, Diane Marie. 3400 SPRUCE ST 19104 #041-02-1993 L1995 **HO** *020 †20

HERSKOVITS, Edward Harry. 3400 SPRUCE ST 19104 #005-14-1986 L2002 **RNR** *020 †80

HERTZOG, David Ray. 5501 OLD YORK RD, GROUND FLOO 19141 #041-07-1981 L1982 **GS** *020 †85 ‡

HERZ, Amy Lynn. ■ 19147 #041-02-2006 L2006 **DR** *012

HESLER, Jennifer Jane. ■ 19107 #041-02-2007 L2007 *012

HESS, Bryan Davidbrown. ■ 19107 #041-02-2006 L2006 **IM** *012

HESS, Jay Lowell. 422 CURIE BLVD, 413B STELLAR CHANCE 19104 #023-07-1989 L1999 **PTH** *050

HESS, Steven Gordon. 9501 ROOSEVELT BLVD, PENNSYLVANIA HEART & 19114 #020-02-1976 L1984 **CD IM** *020 †20

HESSEN, Scott Edward. 230 N BROAD ST, FL 7 19102 #041-02-1982 L1983 **ICE CD** *020 †20

HESTER, Gloria Evans. 3998 RED LION RD STE 215 19114 #539-03-1966 L1973 **PD FM** *071 †55

HETZNECKER, James Michael. 561 FAIRTHORNE AVE 19128 #041-13-1998 L2000 **CHP** *020 †75

HEUER, Gregory George. 3400 SPRUCE ST, 3RD FLOOR SILVERSTEIN PAV. 19104 #041-01-2003 L2003 **NS** *012

HEWITT, Amma Nzinga. ■ 19103 #041-01-2008 *012

HEXNER, Elizabeth Olson. 3400 SPRUCE ST, 15 PENN TOWER 19104 #035-01-1999 L2002 **HO** *100 †20

HEYBOER, Marvin, III. 3620 HAMILTON WALK, INSTITUTE FOR ENVIRONMENTA 19104 #038-06-2000 L2007 **EM** *020 †16

HEYDT, David Miller. 1025 WALNUT ST, JEFFERSON MED COLL 19107 #041-02-1999 L1999 **PTH** *012

HEYNS, Laura Frances. ■ 19104 #025-01-2005 L2005 **IM** *012

HICKS, Albert James, III. ■ 19147 #041-13-2007 L2007 **IM** *012

HICKS, Edward Livingston. 1616 WALNUT ST STE 2116 19103 #010-02-1969 L1970 **P PYA** *071

HICKS, Richard Elberson. 111 N 49TH ST 19139 #041-02-1955 L1956 **P** *020 †75 ‡

HICKS, Sarah B. 255 S 17TH ST, STE 1606 19103 #041-01-1997 L1999 **P** *020 †75

HIESINGER, William Matthi. ■ 19103 #041-01-2007 L2007 **GS** *012

HIGGINS, Ying Loo. 833 CHESTNUT, STE 300 19107 #041-09-1990 L1992 **PD** *020 †55

HIGH, Katherine A. 302 ARCH ST, 3615 CIVIC CENTER BLVD 19106 #036-01-1978 L1992 **HEM IM** *050 †20

HILIBRAND, Alan Sander. 925 CHESTNUT ST, THE ROTHMAN GRP/5TH FL 19107 #008-01-1990 L1998 **OSS ORS** *020 †40

HILL, Christine Elizabeth. 3400 SPRUCE ST, DEPT OF RAD ONCOLOGY 19104 #041-01-2005 L2005 **RO** *012

HILL, Cynthia Ann. 1233 LOCUST ST, STE 400 19107 #041-02-1987 L1989 **PD** *020 †55

HILL, Gideon D, III. 1901 MARKET ST 19103 #041-02-1983 L1987 **FM** *030 †18

HILL, Lauren M. ■ 19103 #041-01-2008 *012

HILLS, Carver Aurelius. 2524 N BROAD ST 19132 #038-06-1993 L1995 **IM** *020

HILLS, Jessica Lynn. 3550 MARKET ST, FL 4 19104 #035-08-2000 L2001 **PD** *100 †55

HILLSON, Christina Marie. ■ 19107 #041-15-2006 L2006 **FP** *012

HILTON, Susan. 3400 SPRUCE ST, DEPT OF RAD HOSP UNIV PA 19104 #041-07-1975 L2002 **DR** *020 †80

HINES, Janet Mariner. 3400 SPRUCE ST 19104 #001-02-1990 L1993 **ID** *020 †20

HINES, Patrick Charles. ■ 19147 #036-01-2004 L2004 **CCP** *012

HINGORANI, Shivam L. ■ 19130 #495-48-1984 L1999 **PYG** *020 †75

HINSON, John Travis. PO BOX 171, 3820 LOCUST WALK 19105 #024-01-2007 L2007 **IM** *012

HIRANI, Amyn. ■ 19107 #496-27-2002 L2005 **PCC** *012 †20

HIROSE, Hitoshi. 3400 SPRUCE ST 19104 #572-08-1990 L2004 **CD VS** *040 ‡

HIRSCH, Irvin Harold. 833 CHESTNUT ST, STE 703 19107 #035-47-1979 L1985 **U** *020 †95

HIRSCH, Michele Linne. 2979 W SCHOOL HOUSE LN 19144 #041-13-2004 L2004 **IM** *012

HIRSCH, Randal Scott. 3156 KENSINGTON AVE 19134 #005-14-1983 L2005 **FM** *020 †18

HIRSH, Laurie Ellen. 5501 OLD YORK RD, DEPT OF ORTHOPEDICS 19141 #035-46-1997 L2002 **HS** *020 †40 ‡

HIRSHFELD, John W, Jr. 3400 SPRUCE ST, 9.119 FOUNDERS BLDG 19104 #035-20-1969 L1974 **IC CD** *020 †20

HLAVAC, Julieanne Marie. 10 SHURS LN, STE 203 19127 #041-02-1995 L2002 **FM** *020 †18

HNELESKI, Ignatius S, Jr. 840 WALNUT ST 19107 #041-02-1964 L1965 **OPH OS** *020 †35 ‡

HO, Allen C. 840 WALNUT ST, STE 1020 19107 #035-01-1988 L1990 **OPH** *020 †35

HO, Magdalene Yuen Yee. 7500 CENTRAL AVE STE 109 19111 #041-01-1977 L1978 **D** *020 †15

HO, Ming-Jung. ■ 19104 #041-01-1999 *100

HO, Reginald Thomas. 925 CHESTNUT ST, MEZZANINE LEVEL 19107 #041-01-1993 L1995 **CD** *040 †20

HOAG, Jeffrey Brian. 219 N BROAD ST FL 9, DIVISION OF PULMONARY AND 19107 #051-04-2001 L2007 **IM** *100

HOANG, Chuong Dinh. 3400 SPRUCE ST, MED CTR 19104 #026-04-1998 L2006 **TS** *012

HOANG, Gil. 5501 OLD YORK RD, ALBERT EINSTEIN MED CTR 19141 #038-06-2001 L2001 **VIR** *100 †80

HOANG, Khoa Dang. 2900 W QUEEN LN, DEPT OF INTERNAL MED 19129 #305-01-2004 L2004 **IM** *100

HOANG, Teresa Loan. 10 SHURS LN 19127 #305-01-2004 L2004 **FM** *100 †18

HOANG, Tuan Anh. 909 S 8TH ST 19147 #941-02-1972 L1984 **GP** *020

HOBBIB, George Charles. 3900 RED LION RD, FRANKFORD HSPTLTRRSDLE CMP 19114 #041-13-1998 L2001 **EM** *020 †16

HOBBS, Janice Elizabeth. ■ 19129 #041-13-2008 *012

HOCHBERG, Abby Madeline. ■ 19103 #008-01-2008 *012

HOCHBERG, Hilary Michele. ■ 19102 #035-20-2002 L2003 **DR** *020 †80

HODARA FRIEDMANN, Roberto. ■ 19141 #924-01-2002 L2005 **IM** *012

HODAS, Gordon Richard. ■ 19118 #041-01-1973 L1975 **CHP P** *020 †75

HODGDON, Susan Elizabeth. ■ 19103 #051-07-2002 L2002 **PD** *020 †55

HOEH, Nicholas. 3400 SPRUCE ST, HOSP OF UNIV OF PA-PSYCH 19104 #033-06-1998 L2000 **PYG** *100

HOELLEIN, Deborah E. 131 E CHELTEN AVE 19144 #041-02-1978 L1980 **PD** *020 †55

HOELLEIN, Kenneth Donald. 101 E OLNEY AVE, STE C5 19120 #041-02-1978 L1979 **IM** *020 †20

HOELSCHER, Lindsay Judett. 3401 N BROAD ST, TEMPLE UNIV HOSP 19140 #035-06-2006 L2007 **AN** *012

HOEY, Courtney Leigh. 5501 OLD YORK RD, A EINSTEIN MED CTR 19141 #041-02-2007 L2007 **TY** *012

HOFF, Kolin Kristinn. 3400 SPRUCE ST, UNIV OF PENNSYLVANIA 19104 #041-09-1998 L2004 **END** *100 †20

HOFF, William Scott. 3400 SPRUCE ST, UNIV PA HOSP DIV TRAUMA 19104 #041-02-1986 L1988 **TRS GS** *020 †85

HOFFER, Zachary Scott. ■ 19129 #041-15-2008 *012

HOFFMAN, Brenda Barber. 834 WALNUT ST, JEFFERSON DIALYSIS UNIT 19107 #041-01-1989 L1991 **IM NEP** *020 †20

HOFFMAN, Bruce Ira. 7908 BUSTLETON AVE 19152 #041-13-1974 L1975 **RHU IM** *020 †20

HOFFMAN, Carl Jos. ■ 19149 #010-01-1945 L1946 **P NEP** *071 †75

HOFFMAN, Ian Patrick. ■ 19143 #033-06-2006 L2007 **FP** *012

HOFFMAN, Jean Heather. 1025 WALNUT ST, THOMAS JEFFERSON UNIV HOSP 19107 #041-02-2002 L2002 **HO** *012 †20

HOFFMAN, Joel David. 2050 LOCUST ST 19103 #041-02-1956 L1957 **ORS** *071 †40

HOFFMAN, John Parker. 333 COTTMAN AVE, FOX CHASE CANCER CENTER 19111 #038-06-1970 L1986 **SO CRS** *020 †85

HOFFMAN, Mark Alan. 1525 LOCUST ST, FL 19 19102 #035-01-1977 L1991 **PDS ON** *062 †85

HOFFMAN, Roy. 321 W GIRARD AVE, PHILADELPHIA HEALTH CARE C 19123 #035-48-1999 L2003 **GPM** *020 †55,70

HOFFMAN, Scott Jeremy. ■ 19118 #041-15-2008 L2008 *012

HOFFMANN, Marc Steven. ■ 19130 #041-01-2008 L2008 *012

HO FUNG, Victor Manuel. 800 SPRUCE ST, PENNSYLVANIA HOSP 19107 #042-01-2003 L2005 **DR** *012

HOGAN, Annique Kozak. ■ 19130 #038-43-2004 L2004 **PD** *100 †55

HOGAN, Jonathan James. 3620 HAMILTON WALK, UNIV OF PA SCH OF MED 19104 #041-01-2007 L2007 **IM** *012

HOGAN, Joseph Michael. 1726 S BROAD ST 19145 #041-09-1959 L1960 **RHU IM** *020 †20

HOGARTY, Michael David. 3615 CIVIC CENTER BLVD, 9 NORTH ARC 902C 19104 #035-01-1990 L1994 **PHO PD** *050 †55

HOLE, Richard W, Jr. 1601 WALNUT ST, STE 110T 19102 #041-01-1975 **P** *020 †75

HOLLANDER, Judd Eric. 3400 SPRUCE ST, HOSPITAL UNIV OF PA 19104 #035-19-1986 L1996 **EM IM** *050 †20,16

HOLLANDER, Sheri Lynn. ■ 19103 #041-13-2004 L2004 **P** *012

HOLLERAN, Daniel Kevin. 833 CHESTNUT, STE 701 19107 #041-09-1986 L1987 **IM** *020 †20

HOLLING, Herbert Edward. 3400 SPRUCE ST, HOSP OF UNIV OF PA 19104 #352-10-1932 L1959 **CD** *071

HOLLINGER, Bryan Robt. 3156 KENSINGTON AVE 19134 #041-14-1988 L1993 **GPM PD** *020 †20,55

HOLMES, Lillias Christine. ■ 19103 #041-01-2008 *012

HOLMES, Seth Mcelwee. 3400 SPRUCE ST, UNIV OF PA HLTH SYS 19104 #005-02-2007 L2007 **IM** *012

HOLMES, William Chas. 423 GUARDIAN DR, OF MEDICINE 733 BLOCKLEY H 19104 #041-01-1990 L1993 **IM** *020 †20

HOLSCLAW, Douglas S, Jr. 39TH & MARKET STS STE 441, PHI - PULMONARY 19104 #035-01-1960 L1967 **PUD PD** *020 †55 ‡

HOLTZMAN, David Lee. ■ 19104 #041-01-2008 L2008 *012

HOLZER, Cordula Thekla M. 120 S 30TH ST, HORIZON HOUSE 19104 #409-22-1986 L1992 **P** *030 †75

HOMAN, Richard Van Ness. 245 N 15TH ST, MS400 - 19TH FLOOR 19102 #035-06-1982 L1983 **FM FPG** *030 †18

HONDA, Miwako. ■ 19107 #572-23-1993 L2000 **IMG** *100

HONG, Eugene Sukpyo. 10 SHURS LN, STE 203 19127 #041-24-1994 L1999 **FM FSM** *020 †18

HONG, Joe. ■ 19107 #022-75-2007, ▲ *012

HONG, Keumsoon. ■ 19118 #583-08-1967 L1973 **OBG** *071 †30

HONG, Lina Chang. ■ 19121 #016-42-2004 L2004 **EM** *100

HONG, Seung Hee. 1840 SOUTH ST 19146 #041-13-2001 L2004 **FM** *100 †18

HONG, Tom. ■ 19106 #041-15-2008 *012

HONIGMAN, Frederic H. 1 PENN BLVD 19144 #041-13-1959 L1960 **PTH** *071 †50

HONISH, Robert Louis. 801 SPRUCE ST STE 3E 19107 #024-07-1965 L1968 **IM IMG** *020

HONKER, Nancy Ann. ■ 19104 #041-01-1963 L1964 **ATP** *071 †50

HONTZ, Blair Elizabeth. ■ 19128 #041-77-2007, ▲ L2007 **EM** *012

HOOD, Ian Clark. 321 UNIV AVE MED EXAM OFF 19104 #671-02-1977 L1989 **FOP** *020 †50

HOOK, Karen Marie. ■ 19104 #008-02-2005 L2005 **IM** *012

HOOPS, Timothy Calvin. 3400 SPRUCE ST 19104 #016-11-1981 L1991 **GE IM** *020 †20

HOPKINS, John N. 245 N 15TH ST, MAIL STOP 1011 19102 #011-75-2007, ▲ L2007 **EM** *012

HOPKINS, Richard Snowden. 19147 #041-01-1974 L1975 **PHP IM** *030 †20,70

HOPKINS, Tim Brian. 51 N 39TH ST, SCHEIE EYE INSTITUTE- RETI 19104 #041-09-1994 L1999 **OPH OS** *020 †35

HOPPER, Bruce Donald, Jr. 925 CHESTNUT ST, FIFTH FLOOR 19107 #041-02-2000 L2001 **FM FSM** *020 †18 ‡

HOQUE, Mohammad Ziaul. ■ 19114 #160-02-1998 L2007 **IM** *020 †20

HORAK, Jiri George. 3400 SPRUCE ST, OF PENNSYLVANIA 19104 #286-04-1988 L1999 **CCA** *020 †05

HORAN, Colleen M. 834 CHESTNUT ST STE 400, BENJAMIN FRANKLIN HOUSE 19107 #035-15-2001 L2001 **OBG** *020

HORENSTEIN, Paul Aaron. 525 JAMESTOWN ST, PREMIER ORTHOPAEDIC & 19128 #041-02-1991 L1993 **ORS** *020 †40

HORGAN, Kevin James. ■ 19118 #539-02-1982 L1990 **GE IG** *020 †20

HORGAN, Timothy John Noel. 840 WALNUT ST, STE 1440 19107 #539-03-1996 L2005 **OPH** *020

HORN, Amanda. ■ 19128 #041-13-2006 L2006 **EM** *012

HORN, Bernard David, Jr. 34TH & CIVIC CTR BLVD, ORTHOPAEDIC SURGERGY 19104 #038-43-1986 L1992 **OP** *020 †40

HORN, David Linneus. 211 S 9TH ST, STE 210 19107 #035-09-1983 L1994 **ID** *020 †20

HORN, Philip J, Jr. 2 PENN BLVD, STE 108 19144 #041-01-1983 L1985 **OBG** *020 †30

HORNE, Marion Morgan. P3300 HENRY AVE 19129 #041-07-1977 L1978 **CLP** *071 †50 ‡

HORNER, Melissa Lynn. 101 E OLNEY AVE 19120 #041-13-1999 L2001 **FM** *020 †18

HORNSTEIN, Jonathan Brad. 5501 OLD YORK RD, EMERGENCY DEPT 19141 #422-01-2002 L2002 **EM** *020 †16

HOROWITZ, Allison Rachel. ■ 19103 #041-15-2008 L2008 *012

HOROWITZ, David Allan. 3400 SPRUCE ST # MED, MEDICAL AFFAIRS OFFICE 19104 #041-01-1989 L1991 **IM** *040 †20

HOROWITZ, Gary R. 9880 BUSTLETON AVE, NEUROLOGY ASSOCIATES AT 19115 #016-76-1971, ▲ L1972 **N** *020 †75 ‡

HOROWITZ, Jerome Howard. 3998 RED LION RD STE 21 19114 #041-09-1963 L1964 **PD** *020 †55

HOROWITZ, Kari Michele. ■ 19107 #041-02-2008 *012

HOROWITZ, Ronald Jay. 3998 RED LION RD, STE 211 19114 #041-09-1994 L1997 **PD** *020 †55

HOROWITZ, Steven Craig. ■ 19104 #035-08-2004 L2004 **PM** *012

HORROW, Jay Charles. 230 N BROAD ST 19102 #041-01-1977 L1979 **AN PA** *030 †05

HORROW, Mindy Meislich. 5501 OLD YORK RD 19141 #041-07-1980 L1982 **R OS** *020 †80

HORSTMANN, Helen M. 245 N 15TH ST 19102 #041-07-1972 L1973 **ORS OFA** *020 †40

HORT, Shoshana. 321 W GIRARD AVE, HEALTH CTR #6 19123 #035-19-2002 L2002 **IM** *020 †20

HORTON, April Carol. ■ 19104 #036-07-2006 L2007 **AN** *012

HORVAT, John Franklin. 5000 PARKSIDE AVE, PARKSIDE RECOVERY 19131 #041-09-1978 L1979 **IM** *075 †20

HORVATH, Jessica Erin. ■ 19107 #041-02-2003 L2003 **FM** *020 †18

HORVATH, Kedron Nicole. ■ 19107 #041-02-2004 L2007 **FP** *012

HORWITZ, Brenda Lapinski. 3401 N BROAD ST, 8 PARKINSON PAVILION 19140 #041-02-1987 L1989 **GE IM** *020 †20

HORWITZ, Eric Mark. 333 COTTMAN AVE, FOX CHASE CANCER CENTER 19111 #035-03-1992 L1997 **RO** *020 †80

HOSALKAR, Harish Sadanand. 3400 SPRUCE ST, TWO SILVERSTEIN 19104 #496-38-1995 L2004 **ORS** *012

HOSKINS, Eliza Niles. ■ 19147 #010-01-2004 L2004 **OPH** *012

HOSSAIN, Azm Ashraf. 5116 N BROAD RD 19141 #160-03-1997 L2007 **IM** *020 †20

HOSSAIN, Shabbir Majid. 2900 W QUEEN LN 19129 #422-01-2005 L2005 **IM** *012

HOSSEINI, Nima. 2900 W QUEEN LN, DREXEL UNIV COLL OF MED 19129 #041-15-2006 **AN** *012

HOU, Jun. 245 N 15TH ST 19102 #243-67-1982 L1997 **PCP** *020 †50

HOUGEIR, Serge Ammar. 19147 #003-01-2006 L2006 **EM** *012

HOUGH, Jeffrey Lewis. 2411 MANNING ST 6 19103 #041-07-1977 L1979 **DR** *020 †80

HOUSEMAN, Daniel Edward. ■ 19103 #041-01-2008 *012

HOUSSOCK, Carrie Ann. ■ 19147 #041-02-2008 *012

HOWARD, Joseph R. 3620 HAMILTON WALK, UNIV OF PA SCH OF MED 19104 #041-01-2005 L2005 *100

HOWARD, Justin Reinhardt. ■ 19107 #041-02-2007 L2007 **IM** *012

HOWARD, Robert David. 1800 LOMBARD ST 19146 #041-09-1995 L1997 **EM** *020 †16

HOWE, Nathan Read. 3400 SPRUCE ST 19104 #048-02-1985 L1991 **D DS** *020 †15 ‡

HOWELL, Jevere Akim. ■ 19128 #041-01-2005 L2005 **AN** *012

HOWER, Lindsey Markell. ■ 19107 #038-06-2006 L2006 **OBG** *012

HOWLETT, Paul John. 3300 HENRY AVE 19129 #836-01-1978 L1988 **PTH** *020 †50

HOXIE, James Albert. 421 CURIE BLVD, RM 356-BRB 19104 #041-01-1976 L1980 **ON** *050 †20

HOYER, John Richard. 324 S 34TH ST, CHILDRENS HOSPITAL 19104 #024-01-1964 L1983 **NEP PD** *050 †55

HOYER, Paul J. 321 S UNIVERSITY AVE 19104 #041-02-1976 L1977 **FOP PTH** *062 †50

HOYME, James Balfour. 210 W RITTENHOUSE SQ, STE 405 19103 #036-05-1959 L1983 **P** *030 †75

HOZACK, William James. 925 CHESTNUT ST, ROTHMAN INSTITUTE 19107 #067-01-1981 L1982 **ORS** *020 †40

HRIBAR, Laura Ann. 833 CHESTNUT ST, STE 301 19107 #041-15-2003 L2003 **FM** *020 †18

HSIA, Elizabeth Chunching. 3400 SPRUCE ST, DEPT OF RHEUM 8 PENN TOWER 19104 #008-01-1996 L1998 **RHU** *020 †20

HSIA, Henry Hsuheng. 3400 SPRUCE ST, HOSP OF UNIV OF PA 19104 #024-07-1984 L1992 **ICE CD** *020 †20

HSIEH, Christine. 111 S 11TH ST DEPT FAM 19107 #051-04-1996 L1999 **FPG** *020 †18

HSIEH, Dennis Shu-Wei. 1901 MARKET ST, 30TH FLOOR MAILROOM 19103 #041-02-1993 L1995 **IM IMG** *020 †20

HSIEH, Kuang-Chun Jim. ■ 19129 #041-13-2008 *012

HSIN, Ken. ■ 19129 #041-13-2008 *012

HSIUNG, Sherry Hsinhua. ■ 19146 #041-01-2000 L2001 **D** *020 †15

HSU, Benjamin Liping. 51 N 39TH ST, MYRIN 2 19104 #028-02-1995 L1998 **RHU** *020 †20

HSU, George Chiahung. 111 S 11TH ST, STE #4140 GIBBON 19107 #051-01-2004 L2004 **AN** *012

HSU, Jason. ■ 19146 #016-06-2007 **ORS** *012

HSU, Vivian Minhweu. ■ 19103 #041-01-2008 *012

HSU, Wei Teresa. 10 SHURS LN, STE 203 19127 #041-09-1987 L1989 **D** *020 †15

HSU, Yeouching. 3615 CIVIC CENTER BLVD, RM 802 19104 #035-09-2004 L2007 **PDE** *012 †55

HTAY, Soe. 700 SPRUCE ST, STE 304 19106 #209-01-1987 L2001 **IM** *020 †20

HU, Carol Tajou. ■ 19107 #041-02-2008 L2008 *012

HU, Michelle Frances. 3701 MARKET ST, STE 760 19104 #035-47-1995 L2001 **IM** *020 †20

HUA, Yi. 245 N 15TH ST MS 310, DREXEL UNIV COLL OF MED 19102 #243-72-1997 L2004 **AN** *012

HUAN, Yonghong. 833 CHESTNUT ST STE 700 19107 #035-01-2002 L2005 **IM** *100 †20

HUANG, Elena Ting. 3819 CHESTNUT ST, STE 120 19104 #024-01-2000 L2006 **PD** *020 †55

HUANG, Kevin. 4000 PRESIDENTIAL BLVD 19131 #748-10-1984 L2000 **CHP** *020 †75

HUANG, Min. 333 COTTMAN AVE, DEPT OF PATHOLOGY 19111 #243-16-1995 L2000 **ATP PCP** *020 †50

HUANG, Nancy Wei-Ling. ■ 19130 #051-01-2007 L2007 **OBG** *012

HUANG, Shirley Hseueyee. 3535 MARKET ST RM 1577, CHILDRENS HOSPITAL OF PHIL 19104 #035-06-2000 L2003 **PD NTR** *050 †55 ‡

HUANG, Tzuchuan Jane. ■ 19106 #012-01-2004 L2007 **IM** *100 †20

HUANG, Yajue K. 3401 N BROAD ST, TEMPLE UNIV HOSP/DEPT PATH 19140 #243-45-1992 L2001 **PTH** *100 †50

HUANG, Yihua. ■ 19143 #028-02-2004 L2007 **IM** *100 †20

HUBERT, Darrin Michael. 853 N 28TH ST A 19130 #041-01-2001 L2001 **PS** *020

HUBERT, Jennifer Marie. ■ 19130 #041-02-2003 L2003 **DR** *012

HUDA, Nazmul. 1025 WALNUT ST, THOMAS JEFFERSON UNIV HOSP 19107 #035-48-2003 L2003 **IM** *100 †20

HUDES, Debra Lynn. 3400 SPRUCE ST 19104 #041-01-1982 L1983 **IM** *020 †20

HUDES, Gary Robt. 333 COTTMAN AVE 19111 #035-08-1979 L1980 **ON IM** *020 †20

HUDOCK, Kristin Mara. ■ 19139 #010-02-2003 L2007 **PCC** *012 †20

HUDSON, Frank Parker, III. ■ 19104 #041-01-2008 *012

HUEGE, Steven Fredrick. 3615 CHESTNUT ST, UNIVERSITY OF PENNSYLVANIA 19104 #048-12-2002 L2002 **PYG** *020 †75

HUERTAS, Roberto. 3401 N BROAD ST 19140 #042-01-1989 L1992 **AN** *020 †05

HUFFNAGLE, H Jane. 111 S 11TH ST, STE 8490 19107 #041-77-1987, ▲ L1988 **AN** *020 †05

HUFFNAGLE, Suzanne. 111 S 11TH ST, STE 8490 19107 #041-77-1987, ▲ L1988 **AN** *020 †05

HUGHES, Deurward Lyeman. 3300 HENRY AVE, MEDICAL COLLGE OF PNNSYLVN 19129 #047-07-1956 L1958 **OBG** *071 †30

HUGHES, Eugene Patrick. 8815 GERMANTOWN AVE STE 20 19118 #041-02-1975 L1979 **GS** *020 †10,85

HUGHES, Lesley Ann. 245 N 15TH ST MS 200 19102 #041-09-1998 L2001 **RO** *020 †80

HUGHES, Max Madoc. 2044 PINE ST 19103 #041-09-1955 L1956 **P OS** *020 †75

HUGHES, Samuel Lee. 9908 ROOSEVELT BLVD, MNAP MEDICAL SOLUTIONS 19115 #028-03-1996 L1998 **RO** *020 †80

HUGHES, Susan Marie. 1800 LOMBARD ST, ONE GRADUATE PLAZA 19146 #010-01-1975 L1982 **FPS CS** *020 †35

HUGHES, Tiffany Ann. ■ 19107 #041-02-1996 L2000 **P** *020 †75

HUGHES, William Boyd. 2222 S BROAD ST 19145 #041-13-1992 L1994 **GS** *020 †85

HUH, Jimmy Wook. 3400 SPRUCE ST 19104 #035-15-1992 L1997 **CCP** *020 †55

HUMMELER, Klaus. 324 S 34TH ST 19104 #407-21-1949 **PTH PD** *050

HUMPHREY, Lisa Michelle. ■ 19143 #038-06-2004 L2004 **PD** *012 †55

HUMPHREYS, Tatyana R. 833 CHESTNUT ST, STE 740 19107 #041-01-1990 L1992 **D** *020 †15

HUNENKO, Oksana A. ■ 19130 #041-01-2001 L2008 **PS** *100

HUNG, Emily Wailin. ■ 19104 #048-04-2006 L2006 **IM** *012

HUNT, Patrick Jos. 111 S 11TH ST, DEPT OF ANESTH 8490 BLDG 19107 #041-12-1982 L1984 **AN** *020 †05

HUNTER, Frances Carroll. 5116 N BROAD ST 19141 #041-07-1981 L1983 **IM** *020

HUNTER, James M. 834 CHESTNUT ST 19107 #041-02-1953 L1954 **HS ORS** *071 †40

HUNTER, William Curley. 3400 SPRUCE ST, SUITEA 19104 #041-01-1993 L1996 **IM** *020

HUPPERT, Arthur S. 230 N BROAD ST 19102 #035-46-1978 L1981 **RHU IM** *020 †20

HUREWITZ, Sylvan Jay. 51 N 39TH ST, ANDREW MUTCH BLDG 1ST FL 19104 #041-13-1971 L1972 **IM HEM** *062 †20

HURIE, Justin Brothwell. ■ 19104 #016-43-2004 L2004 **GS** *012

HURLEY, Catherine Eileen. ■ 19147 #041-02-2008 *012

HURLOCK, Joan Emma. 5735 RIDGE AVE, STE 105 19128 #041-07-1970 L1971 **FM** *072 †18

HURST, Robert Wayne. 3400 SPRUCE ST, HOSPITAL OF THE UNIV OF PA 19104 #048-14-1981 L1990 **DR N** *020 †75,80

■ = Address Information Privacy Protected

HURT, Hallam. 3535 MARKET ST, RM 1509 19104 #051-01-1971 L1981 **NPM PD** *020 †55
HURTIG, Howard Irving. 1 GRADUATE PLAZA, GRADUATE HOSPITAL 19146 #021-01-1966 L1966 **N IM** *012
HURWITZ, Alisheba Tai. 3400 SPRUCE ST, OF PENNSYLVAN 19104 #048-04-2005 L2005 **EM** *012
HUSAIN, Abbas. 2900 W QUEEN LN, MCP HAHNEMANN SCH OF MED 19129 #041-15-2005 L2005 **EM** *012
HUSAIN, Abid. UNIVERSITY & WOODLAND AVES 19104 #704-08-1982 L1988 **PM IM** *020
HUSAIN, Kamran. 245 N 15TH ST MS 310, DREXEL UNIV COLL OF MED 19102 #704-02-1998 L2007 **AN** *012
HUSAIN, Mansoor Ulhaque. 5501 OLD YORK RD 19141 #016-02-1988 L1993 **AN IM** *020 †05
HUSE, Jason Thomas. 3400 SPRUCE ST, 6 FOUNDERS 19104 #041-01-2003 L2003 **PTH** *100 †50
HUSEVA, Katsiaryna Serhee. DEPT OF MEDICAL EDUCATION, FRANKFORD HOSPITAL 19114 #913-32-2003 L2007 **TY** *012
HUSSAIN, Asif Iftikhar. 2422 S BROAD ST 19145 #016-06-1996 L1999 **CD** *020 †20
HUSSEN, Sophia Ahmed. 3400 SPRUCE ST, HEALTH SYST 19104 #041-01-2006 L2006 **MPD** *012
HUSSON, Michael A. 800 SPRUCE ST, DEPT PATH 19107 #024-05-1980 L1981 **PTH** *020,50
HUTCHINS, Diana L Hadley. 3960 WOODLAND AVE, PHILADELPHIA VETERANS ADM 19104 #010-03-1969 L1971 **IM** *071 †20
HUTCHINS, Francis L, Jr. ■ 19144 #010-03-1969 L1970 **GYN OBG** *020 †30
HUTCHINSON, Claudine L. 5501 OLD YORK RD, ALBERT EINSTEIN MEDICAL CE 19141 #010-03-1996 L1999 **IMG** *020 †20
HUTCHINSON, Howard G. THOMAS JEFFERSON HOSP, DEPT OF CARDIOLOGY 19107 #041-02-1987 L1988 **CD** *020 †20
HUTCHINSON, Mathew David. ■ 19146 #028-34-2000 L2003 **ICE** *100 ‡
HUTT, Howard Chas. 7600 CENTRAL AVE, RADIOLOGY DEPT 19111 #858-05-1982 L1987 **N DR** *020 †80
HWAN, Warden Huawin. 7600 CENTRAL AVE 19111 #041-13-1998 L2000 **AI PDA** *020 †55,03
HWANG, Austin F. ■ 19107 #035-15-2006 L2006 **IM** *012
HWANG, Catherine Jeeyoung. 51 N 39TH ST 19104 #041-01-2003 L2003 **OPH** *100
HWANG, Lisa Hsini. ■ 19144 #041-15-2008 L2008 *012
HYATT, Lynnae Diane. ■ 19107 #041-13-2005 L2005 **IM** *012
HYDE, Patrice Marie. 833 CHESTNUT ST, STE 740 19107 #041-02-1980 L1986 **PD** *020 †55,15
HYDER, Jennifer Jackson. 19129 #051-01-2002 L2004 **RO** *012
HYLTON, Casimer C. 509 S 52ND ST 19143 #010-03-1958 L1961 **GP OS** *020
HYMAN, Elizabeth Carol. ■ 19106 #035-10-2003 L2004 **RO** *100
HYUN, Bong Hak. 111 S 11TH ST, THOS JEFFERSON U HOSP 19107 #583-01-1945 L1988 **CLP PTH** *020 †50
IAGOUNOVA, Anna. 2900 W QUEEN LN 19129 #913-01-1996 L2003 **IM** *100
IAIA, Bartolomeo D. ■ 19145 #016-42-1945 L1958 **TS** *071
IANNONE, Robert. 324 S 34TH ST 19104 #008-01-1994 L2001 **PHO** *020 †55
IAROCCI, Thomas P. 1101 MARKET ST, 14TH FL 19107 #023-01-2001 L2001 *100
IBRAHIM, Mahmoud Ahmed. ■ 19135 #848-01-1981 L2005 **NPM** *100
IBRAHIM, Sulfikar Fahd. 230 N BROAD ST, DREXEL U COLLEGE OF MED 19102 #023-01-2004 L2004 **HO** *012 †20
ICE, Susan Margaret. 475 SPRING LN 19128 #023-07-1972 L1982 **P** *030 †75
ICHORD, Rebecca Nuti. 324 S 34TH ST 19104 #010-01-1979 L2001 **CHN** *020 †55,75
IDDENDEN, David Antony. 2301 S BROAD ST STE 102, METHODIST HOSP 19148 #917-08-1975 L1980 **GYN** *020 †30
IFFT, Fred Nicholas. 621 CHRISTIAN ST, 1233 LOCUST ST STE 500 19147 #041-02-1969 L1970 **P** *020
IGBOKIDI, Victor Jideofor. 1900 N 20TH ST, DISTRICT HEALTH CENTER #5 19121 #690-08-1988 L2000 **PD** *020 †55
IGBRE, Ann Okemena. 5501 OLD YORK RD, DEPT MED 19141 #041-13-2007 L2007 **IM** *012
IGIDBASHIAN, Vartan N. 2601 HOLME AVE, NAZARETH HOSPITAL 19152 #041-77-1983, ▲ L1984 **DR** *020
IGLESIAS, Stephanie Marie. ■ 19130 #040-02-2004 L2004 **PD** *100
IHEAGWARA, Kelechi Nneoma. ■ 19128 #035-19-2000 L2005 **CCP** *012 †55
IJELU, Gordon Kolawole O. 6329 N BROAD ST 19141 #690-06-1978 L1989 **IM NEP** *020
ILIVITSKY, Valentin Benja. 51 N 39TH ST 19104 #422-01-1999 L2001 **AN** *100
ILSON, Bernard E. 30 S 15TH ST, 15TH FL 19102 #035-19-1981 L1984 **PA NEP** *050 †20 ‡
ILYAS, Asif Mohammad. 3401 N BROAD ST, OUT PT BLDG-5TH FL 19140 #041-15-2001 L2001 **HS** *012
IM, Eun Kyung. 5501 OLD YORK RD 19141 #583-10-2003 L2005 **IM** *012
IMAI, Yumi. 415 CURIE BLVD, CRB 778 19104 #572-10-1986 L2002 **END IM** *020 †20
IMONITIE, Victor E. 4811 FLORENCE AVE 19143 #690-02-1983 L1992 **IM** *100
IMPERIALE, S Michael, Jr. 1315 WALNUT ST, HAHNEMANN HOSPITAL 19107 #041-09-1987 L1987 **IM** *012
IMRAN, Muhammad Naser. 800 SPRUCE ST 19107 #704-02-1994 L2002 **CD** *012
INAMPUDI, Radha. 3400 SPRUCE ST, DEPT RAD 19104 #016-06-2002 L2007 **RNR** *012 †80
INCE, Elif Evrim. ■ 19103 #041-01-2005 L2005 **PD** *012
INFANTOLINO, Anthony. 132 S 10TH ST, DIV OF GASTRO AND HEPATOLO 19107 #033-06-1985 L1986 **GE IM** *020 †20
INGERSOLL, Wendy Bodie. 7700 GERMANTOWN AVE, FL 2 19118 #041-13-1987 L1988 **PD** *020 †55
INGRAM, Sharyn Annabel. ■ 19147 #016-01-1999 L2004 **DR** *020 †80
INGUI, John. 1800 LOMBARD ST 19146 #041-01-1982 L1982 **P** *020 †75
INKLES, Randy Alan. 3200 HENRY AVE, EASTERN PA PSYCHIATRIC INS 19129 #308-07-1983 L1987 **CHP** *020
INNIS, Bruce Lamont. 22 E SEDGWICK ST 19119 #008-01-1977 L2002 **ID** *075 †20
INNISS, Raquel Arlene. 1999 W HUNTING PARK AVE 19140 #010-03-1998 L2001 **IM PD** *020 †20,55
INNISS, Susan Antoinette. 2301 E ALLEGHENY AVE 19134 #033-06-1986 L1995 **SP** *020 †18,50
INSELMAN, Laura Sue. 833 CHESTNUT ST STE 300, HEALTH PROGRAM 19107 #041-07-1970 L1992 **PD PDP** *020 †55
INTEMANN, Peter Michael. ■ 19130 #041-13-2004 L2004 **EM** *100
INTENZO, Charles Michael. 111 S 11TH ST, 3350 GIBBON BLDG 19107 #041-09-1980 L1981 **NM IM** *020 †28
INTROCASO, Camille Elizab. ■ 19146 #041-01-2005 L2005 **D** *012
INVER, Marc Robt. 829 SPRUCE ST STE 302 19107 #041-13-1984 L1985 **P PYA** *020 †75
IOZZO, Renato Vincenzo. 132 S 10TH ST, STE 285K 19107 #561-06-1975 L1982 **PTH** *020 †50
IQBAL, Jabed. 245 N 15TH ST, DREXEL UNIV COL MED 19102 #160-02-1986 L2007 **HMP** *012 †50
IQBAL, Nayyar. 3400 SPRUCE ST, 1 MALONEY-ENDOCRINE 19104 #704-25-1990 L1997 **IM END** *050 †20

IQBAL, Sarwat Azma. 4104 N 5TH ST, SIAL MEDICAL AND DENTAL CE 19140 #704-06-1974 L1984 **PD FM** *020 †55
IQBAL, Zafar. 2900 W QUEEN LN 19129 #704-09-2002 **IM** *012
IRELAND, Patricia. 51 N 39TH ST 19104 #041-12-1967 L1974 **IM GE** *075
IRIGOYEN, Matilde M. 5501 OLD YORK RD, ALBERT EINSTEIN MEDICAL CE 19141 #132-01-1972 L2006 **PD** *012
IRIGOYEN, Oscar Horacio. 1015 WALNUT ST, STE 613 19107 #132-01-1972 L2006 **RHU IM** *020 †20
IRO-NWOKEUKWU, Obioma C. 6613 CHEW AVE, JEFFERSON UNIVERSITY HOSPI 19119 #030-06-1995 L1997 **APM** *020 †05
IRVIN, James Milton. 3900 WOODLAND AVE, VETERANS ADMINISTRATION 19104 #041-13-1967 L1968 **IM** *020 †20
IRWIN, Sibyl Rickard. ■ 19107 #041-02-2005 L2005 **PTH** *012
ISAACS, Jennifer Nehama. 834 CHESTNUT ST, STE 400 19107 #041-12-2002 L2002 **OBG** *100
ISAACS, Stuart Neal. 3400 SPRUCE ST 19104 #008-01-1985 L1986 **ID IM** *050 †20
ISAACSON, Cindy Saltz. 111 S 11TH ST 3G, THOMAS JEFFERSON UNIV HOSP 19107 #041-01-1984 L1985 **DR** *020 †80
ISAACSON, Glenn Chas. 3401 N BROAD ST 19140 #041-01-1982 L1984 **OTO PD** *020 †45
ISAWI, Hanny. ■ 19130 #041-12-2007 L2007 **TY** *012
ISDANER, Neil Lewis. 7602 CENTRAL AVE STE 103, JEANES HOSP STAPLEY BLDG 19111 #041-09-1975 L1976 **GYN PHP** *020 †30 ‡
ISEMAN, Christine Marie. ■ 19128 #035-09-2008 *012
ISENBERG, Derek Lawrence. 245 N 15TH ST, MAIL STOP 1011 19102 #021-01-2005 L2005 **EM** *012
ISENBERG, Gerald Alan. 1100 WALNUT ST STE 500 19107 #035-47-1982 L1987 **CRS GS** *020 †85,10 ‡
ISHAC, Roger George. 5501 OLD YORK RD 19141 #605-03-2002 L2006 **IM** *100 †20
ISHIGAMI, Shigenobu. C/O KRUSEN RESEARCH CENTER 19141 #572-35-1966 **PM** *062
ISIADINSO, Ijeoma. 19151 #041-15-2003 L2003 **CD** *012 †20
ISIK, Ebru Fusun. 3401 N BROAD ST, 7TH FLOOR OPB OB-GYN DEPT 19140 #902-10-1998 L2002 **OBG** *020 ‡
ISLAM, M. Nazrul. 2900 W QUEEN LN, MCP HAHNEMANN UNIV 19129 #160-01-1989 L2001 **CHP** *020
ISMAT, Fraz Ahmed. 3400 SPRUCE ST 19104 #035-03-1995 L1999 **PDC MPD** *050 †20,55
ISRANI, Rubeen Kanayo. 415 CURIE BLVD 19104 #024-05-1999 L2003 **NEP** *050 †20
ITALIA, Kathryn Elizabeth. 111 S 11TH ST, JEFFERSON UNIVERSITY 19107 #041-02-2005 L2005 **PD** *012
ITKIN, Maxim. 3400 SPRUCE ST, RADIO DEPT 1 SILVERSTEIN 19104 #913-99-1992 L2001 **VIR DR** *020 †80
ITOE, Roselyn Makane. ■ 19107 #033-05-2008 L2008 *012
ITRI, Jason Neil. 3400 SPRUCE ST, DEPT RAD 19104 #005-14-2006 L2007 **DR** *012
ITSKOV, Boris S. ■ 19107 #913-86-1990 L1998 **P** *020 †15
IVES, Elizabeth Payne. 1015 WALNUT ST 11TH FL, DEPT OF UROLOGY 19107 #023-01-2001 L2001 **DR** *012
IVILL, Dennis W. 925 CHESTNUT ST, ROTHMAN INST 19107 #041-13-1988 L1990 **PM** *020 †60
IWASHYNA, Theodore John. ■ 19130 #016-02-2002 L2002 **PCC** *012 †20
IYER, Harish Venkatachala. 5501 OLD YORK RD, ALBERT EINSTEIN MEDICAL CE 19141 #496-38-2003 L2006 **IM** *012
IYER, Sanjay. ■ 19103 #041-01-2008 *012
IYER, Sujit Srinivasan. ■ 19106 #048-04-2002 L2006 **PEM** *012 †55
IZANEC, James Louis. ■ 19146 #035-20-2001 L2001 **GE** *020 †20
IZZO, Kenneth Louis. 2318 S BROAD ST, STE 221 19145 #016-43-1971 L1975 **PM R** *020 †60
JABBOUR, Pascal Marcel. 909 WALNUT ST, 3RD FL 19107 #605-02-1998 L2004 **NS** *012
JABBOUR, Serge Alfred. 211 S 9TH ST FL 6, SUITE 600 19107 #605-02-1993 L1997 **END** *020 †20
JABLON, Lisa Karen. 5501 OLD YORK RD 19141 #041-13-1985 L1987 **GS SO** *020 †85
JABLON, Norman Chas. 4900 WYALUSING AVE 19131 #041-02-1959 L1960 **P** *020 †75
JABLONER, Judith Lee. 3400 SPRUCE ST 19104 #035-19-1960 L1965 **ADL PDC** *020 †55
JACKINS, Paul David, Jr. ■ 19130 #023-01-1993 L2003 **P** *100
JACKSON, Benjamin Materi. 789 N PENNOCK ST 19130 #041-01-2000 L2001 **VS** *012 †85
JACKSON, Darryl Brett. 1340 E BARRINGER ST 19119 #041-02-1988 L1991 **IM** *020 †20
JACKSON, Eric Michael. 3400 SPRUCE ST, 3 SILVERSTEIN 19104 #025-01-2002 L2002 **NS** *012
JACKSON, Gavin. ■ 19147 #041-02-2008 *012
JACKSON, Jennifer Ellis. ■ 19106 #041-13-2004 L2004 **EM** *100
JACKSON, Laird Gray. 245 N 15TH ST MS 495, DEPT OB/GYN/16TH FLOOR 19102 #038-41-1955 L1960 **CG IM** *071 †20,19
JACKSON, Melvin Langston. 5501 GREENE ST 19144 #041-09-1976 L1980 **IM** *071
JACOB, Arun T. 3400 SPRUCE ST, DEPT OF NEURO SCI 19104 #495-31-2000 L2005 **NS** *012
JACOB, Jensy Pulikamalil. ■ 19128 #041-13-2008 *012
JACOB, Jerry. ■ 19104 #041-01-2008 *012
JACOB, Regina Acama. ■ 19102 #010-01-2007 L2007 **IM** *012
JACOB, Ron Mathew. 3300 HENRY AVE, MCP HAHNEMANN UNIVERSITY 19129 #495-37-1992 L2001 **CD** *100 †20
JACOB, Varghese V. ■ 19116 #495-31-1976 L1997 **IM** *100
JACOBI, Athole Mc Neil. P3300 HENRY AVE 19129 #803-03-1954 L1967 **AN** *020
JACOBS, Dina Allyson. 3400 SPRUCE ST 19104 #041-01-1996 L1998 **N** *020 †75
JACOBS, E Gardner. ■ 19144 #041-01-1952 L1953 **P PYA** *020 †75
JACOBS, Jill Eileen. 3400 SPRUCE ST 19104 #041-02-1985 L1990 **R** *020 †20
JACOBS, Joseph. 19TH & LOMBARD ST, GRADUATE HOSP STE 601 19146 #041-02-1973 L1974 **U** *020 †95
JACOBS, Lewis Meyer. 1512 W GIRARD AVE 19130 #869-07-1965 L1967 **GP** *020 ‡
JACOBS, Stanley Robt. 25 S 9TH ST 19107 #041-02-1972 L1973 **PM** *020 †60
JACOBS-KOSMIN, Dana Beth. 5501 OLD YORK RD 19141 #033-06-2000 L2001 **RHU** *020 †20
JACOBSON, Irwin R. 4000 N 9TH ST 19140 #024-15-1945 L1950 **FM** *071
JACOBSON, Jeffrey Martin. 1427 VINE ST, FL 3 19102 #035-20-1977 L2006 **IM ID** *020 †20
JACOBSON, Mercedes Paula. 3401 N BROAD ST STE 558, DEPT OF NEUROLOGY 19140 #035-01-1987 L1989 **N** *020 †75
JACOBSON, Samuel Gregory. 51 N 39TH ST, SCHEIE EYE INSTITUTE 19104 #016-11-1970 L1995 **OPH** *050 ‡
JACOBSTEIN, Cynthia Ruth. 324 S 34TH ST 19104 #041-01-1993 L1995 **PEM** *020 †55
JACOBY, Sidney Mark. 1015 WALNUT ST, STE 801, CURTIS BUILDING 19107 #041-02-2003 L2003 **ORS** *012
JADICO, Suzanne Kay. 840 WALNUT ST, WILLS EYE INSTIT 19107 #041-01-2006 L2006 **OPH** *012
JAEGER, Jeffrey Robt. 3701 MARKET ST, STE 760 19104 #024-07-1992 L1994 **IM** *020 †20

JAEGER, Scott Herbert. 325 CHESTNUT ST, STE 719 19106 #041-02-1972 L1973 HS ORS *020 †40

JAFAR, Mohammed Ali. 68 W CHELTENHAM AVE 19120 #704-03-1969 L1977 IM *020

JAFFARI, Mohammed. 100 E LEHIGH AVE, EPISCOPAL HOSPITAL 19125 #517-01-1948 L1970 PM RHU *071 †60

JAFFE, David. 3400 SPRUCE ST 19104 #041-02-1950 L1982 PYA P *020

JAFFE, Jane. ■ 19147 #041-77-2007, ▲ 2007 IM *012

JAFFE, Rebecca Caroline. ■ 19104 #041-01-2008 2008 *012

JAFFE, Richard Louis. 4200 MONUMENT RD 19131 #041-02-1974 L1975 P *020 †75

JAFFE, Stephen Chas. 221 N BROAD ST 19107 #041-13-1980 L1982 R RNR *020 †80

JAFFE, William Ira. 3401 N BROAD ST, STE 350 19140 #041-01-1999 L2001 U *020 †95

JAGADEESH, Jyothi. 3401 N BROAD ST, TEMPLE UNIV HOSP 19140 #496-24-2002 L2007 IMG *012

JAGARLAMUDI, Rajasekhar. 800 SPRUCE ST, PENNSYLVANIA HOSPITAL 19107 #495-09-1999 L2006 *100

JAHAN, Sarwat. 5402 W GIRARD AVE 19131 #160-02-1983 L1999 IM *020 †20

JAIN, Diwakar. 219 N BROAD ST, FL 6 19107 #495-69-1977 L2001 CD *040 †20

JAIN, Mukesh. 3900 WOODLAND AVE, VA MEDICAL CENTER, ROOM A1 19104 #495-36-1981 L1989 IM *020 †18

JAIRAJ, Sudha. ROOSEVELT BLVD AND ADAMS, NE COMM MENTAL HLTH CTR 19124 #495-28-1972 L1978 P *020

JAIRAJ, Suryanarayan. 1633 W GIRARD AVE 19130 #495-53-1971 L1974 GS VS *020 †85

JALLO, Jack Issa. 3401 N BROAD ST, STE C540 19140 #010-01-1990 L1992 NS CCS *020 †25

JAMES, Abike Thelma. 3400 SPRUCE ST, 5 PENN TOWER-DEPT OF OB/GY 19104 #008-01-1997 L1999 OBG *020 †30

JAMES, Frank Stanley. 1 PENN BLVD 3RD FL, CENTER TOWER BLDG 19144 #041-01-1973 L1974 CD *020 †20

JAMES, Holly Anne. ■ 19103 #041-07-1979 L1982 EM *020 †16

JAMES, Lesley Ann. 833 CHESTNUT ST, STE 301 19107 #041-02-1997 L2001 OBG *020 †18

JAMES, Stephanie Dereath. 225 S COBBS CREEK PKWY, PRIMARY CARE CENTER 19139 #035-01-1991 L1996 PD *020 †55

JAMES, William Danl. 3400 SPRUCE ST STE F, MALONEY BLDG 19104 #017-20-1977 L1995 D *020 †15

JAMIESON, Brooke Greaney. ■ 19104 #051-04-1943 OS *075

JAMME, Elizabeth Ann. 3400 SPRUCE ST 19104 #041-13-2000 L2001 PD HOS *020 †55

JAMULLAMUDI, Joseph Saday. 1800 LOMBARD ST, TENET HEALTHSYSTEM GRADUAT 19146 #495-27-1998 L2004 IM *100 †20

JAN, Arif Mustafa. 4TH FLOOR - S TOWER MAIL, DREXEL UNIVERSITY COLLEGE 19102 #495-51-1999 L2007 IM *012

JAN, Rehana Amin. 111 S 11TH ST, STE 8460 19107 #704-09-1971 L1977 AN *020 †05

JANCOSKO, Jason Joseph. ■ 19128 #041-77-2007, ▲ 2007 *012

JANDALI, Shareef. ■ 19146 #035-15-2005 L2005 PS *012

JANECZKO, Michael John. 111 S 11TH ST, JEFFERSON UNIVERSITY 19107 #033-05-2001 2001 NPM *100 †55

JANG, Anna Sun. 1011 CHESTNUT ST, # 701 19107 #036-08-2004 L2004 OBG *012

JANI, Shraddha Devendra. ■ 19102 #041-13-2008 *012

JANSEN, Michele Marie. 1025 WALNUT ST, JEFFERSON MED COLL 19107 #041-02-1998 *100

JANTZEN, Ellen Coleman. 3400 SPRUCE ST 19104 #024-01-1977 L1982 AN PD *020 †55,05

JARAMILLO, Diego. ■ 19118 #264-04-1981 L2004 DR *020 †80

JARBRINK, Ellionore Maria. ■ 19146 #649-14-2002 L2008 GE *012

JARDINES, Lori Anna. 5501 OLD YORK RD 19141 #011-03-1982 L1989 GS *020 †85

JARETT, Leonard. 3400 SPRUCE ST 19104 #028-02-1962 L1980 CLP END *050 †50

JAROSH, Samara Louise. 1400 LOMBARD ST, HEALTH CTR NO ONE 19146 #034-01-1990 L1993 IM *020 †20

JARRA, Hadijatou Joyce. 111 S 11TH ST, HOUSE STAFF OFFICE 19107 #036-01-2003 L2003 FPG *020 †18

JASLOW, David Scott. 5501 OLD YORK RD, DEPARTMENT OF EMERGENCY ME 19141 #041-02-1992 L1997 EM *020 †16

JASLOW, Rebecca Jo. 5501 OLD YORK RD, STE 1 19141 #035-47-1996 L2002 HO *020 †20

JASPER, Edward. 1020 SANSOM ST, "THOMPSON BLDG, STE 239" 19107 #041-02-1980 L1982 EM IM *020 †20,16

JASSAR, Arminder Singh. 3400 SPRUCE ST 19104 #495-36-2002 L2005 GS *012

JASWAL, Suman. 255 S 17TH ST, STE 1700 19103 #422-01-1998 L2001 ICE *100 †20

JAVIA, Luv Ram. 3400 SPRUCE ST FL 5, DEPT OF OTORHINOLARYNGOLOG 19104 #036-01-2003 L2003 OTO *012

JAWORSKI, Michael Joseph. 3401 N BROAD ST, TEMPLE UNIVERSITY HOSPITAL 19140 #041-13-2003 L2003 RHU *012

JAYALAKSHMI, Pannathpur. 6366 SHERWOOD RD 19151 #495-09-1961 L1973 GP PD *071 †55

JAYANT, Deepak Anthony. ■ 19111 #041-77-2007, ▲ L2007 *012

JAYASANKAR, Vasant. 3400 SPRUCE ST, SURGERY EDUC/4 SILVERSTEIN 19104 #035-03-1998 L2001 TS *100 †85 ‡

JEAN, Stephanie. ■ 19146 #035-48-2007 OBG *012

JEAN-GILLES, Marc-Andre. TEMPLE UNIV HOSP, DEPT OBG 19140 #035-75-2005, ▲ L2005 OBG *012

JEANLOUIS, Florence. 245 N 15TH ST STOP 49, MCP HAHNEMANN UNIVERSITY 19102 #035-15-2002 L2002 OBG *100

JEFFERS, Adam Bredahl. ■ 19103 #056-06-2007 L2007 TY *012

JEFFERS, John Baker. 900 WALNUT ST, WILLS EYE HOSPITAL 19107 #041-13-1967 L1968 OPH *071 †35

JEFFREY, Mary Elizabeth. 5800 RIDGE AVE, ROXBOROUGH MEM HOSP RADIO 19128 #041-07-1965 L1966 DR NM *012

JELEN, Joseph Anthony, Jr. 2701 HOLME AVE STE 301 19152 #041-09-1978 L1979 ORS *020 †40

JEMMOTT, Ngina Afi. ■ 19139 #023-01-2003 IM *100

JENKINS, Matthew Patrick. ■ 19118 #041-13-2008 *012

JENKINS, Peter Clifton. 2621 CATHERINE ST 19146 #041-01-2005 L2005 GS *012

JENNINGS, Bridget Lashley. 132 S 10TH ST, OF G 19107 #035-03-2003 GE *012

JENOFF, Jay S. 3400 SPRUCE ST, TRAUMA CTR AT PENN 19104 #041-02-1999 L2001 CCS *020 †85

JENQ, Katherine Ying. 3400 SPRUCE ST, DEPT OF EMERGENCY GROUND R 19104 #043-01-2004 L2004 EM *012

JENSEN, Halden Fitzgerald. ■ 19146 #035-01-2004 L2004 PEM *012 †55

JENSEN, Scott Edmund. 1025 WALNUT ST, JEFFERSON MED COLL 19107 #041-02-1999 L2000 EM *020

JENSSEN, Sigmund G. 1331 E WYOMING AVE, STE 1100 19124 #847-13-1991 L2001 N *020 †75

JERE, Charles Shingirai. 245 N 15TH ST MS 437, DREXEL UNIV COLL OF MED 19102 #622-01-1995 L2006 NEP *012

JERE, Grace Mayamiko. 2100 W GIRARD AVE, PNH 19130 #622-01-1995 L2006 IM *100 †20

JEROME, Yves Jos. ■ 19141 #440-01-1955 L1964 GS *071

JERONIS, Stacey Lynne. 3401 N BROAD ST, DEPT OB 19140 #035-03-2000 L2001 OBG *020

JERPBAK, Christine Marie. 833 CHESTNUT ST, JEFFERSON FAMILY MED ASSOC 19107 #026-04-1984 L1998 FM *040 †18

JERUD, Elliot Sigmund. ■ 19104 #035-46-2007 L2007 IM *012

JESPERSEN, Marsha Renee. ■ 19143 #021-01-1998 L2006 PS *012 †85

JESSUP, Mariell L. 3333 N BROAD ST, RM 343 19140 #041-09-1976 L1978 CD *020 †20

JETHVA, Reen Natwarlal. ■ 19103 #038-06-2003 L2003 MG *012 †55

JEWELL, Melanie. 1843 S BROAD ST 19148 #041-09-1982 L1983 IM IMG *020 †20

JHA, Saurabh. 2101 CHESTNUT ST 19103 #917-36-1997 L2002 *100 †80

JIAN, Bo. 2900 W QUEEN LN 19129 #243-16-1990 L2002 PCP *100 †50

JIANG, Kanli. ■ 19143 #041-01-2005 2005 OBG *012

JICHICI, Draga. 3300 HENRY AVE, MEDICAL COLLGE OF PNNSYLVN 19129 #065-10-1989 L1996 P *020 †75

JIH, Debra Minming. 801 SPRUCE ST, FL 10 19107 #041-01-1999 L1999 D *020 †15 ‡

JILANI, Aysha Ambreen. 1800 LOMBARD ST, TENET HEALTHSYSTEM GRADUAT 19146 #704-16-2003 L2005 IM *012

JIMENEZ, Robert Anthony. ■ 19147 #038-40-2005 GS *012

JIMENEZ, Sergio A. 233 S 10TH ST RM 509 19107 #737-01-1966 L1973 RHU IM *050 †20

JIMENEZ-SERRANO, Manuel J. 3401 N BROAD ST, DEPARTMENT OF INTERNAL ME 19140 #715-01-1999 L2003 IM *020 †20

JINDAL, Gaurav. ■ 19103 #010-01-2003 L2005 DR *012

JINIVIZIAN, Hasmig Barkev. 245 N 15TH ST, MAIL STOP 1011 19102 #033-05-2007 L2007 EM *012

JOBE, Ann Connor. 3624 MARKET ST, 2ND FLR W 19104 #031-01-1986 L2007 FM *030 †18

JOFFE, Mark Danl. 324 S 34TH ST 19104 #035-01-1983 L1985 PD EM *040 †55

JOHANNES, James Robert. ■ 19147 #041-02-2005 L2005 GS *100

JOHANNSON, Joshua B. ■ 19139 #025-01-2001 L2001 OBG *100 †30

JOHANSSON, Jonas Stig. 3400 SPRUCE ST, DEPT OF ANESTHESIOLOGY 19104 #011-02-1990 L1992 AN *020 †05

JOHN, Anitha Sara. ■ 19146 #041-15-2001 L2006 PDC *012 †20,55

JOHN, Denny. 9880 BUSTLETON AVE, NEUROLOGY ASSOCIATES AT 19115 #495-37-1991 L1999 N *012

JOHN, Sheryl Mary. 1 CHILDRENS CTR, OFFICE OF MED AFFAIRS 19104 #495-37-2004 L2005 PD *012

JOHN, Thomas Karoor. ■ 19111 #033-05-2007 L2007 ORS *012

JOHNS, Spurgeon S, Jr. 1 PENN BLVD 19144 #041-09-1961 L1963 IM OS *071

JOHNSON, Ahashta Tameka. ■ 19126 #041-02-2005 L2005 MPD *012

JOHNSON, Ann Michelle. ■ 19143 #025-01-1997 L2002 PDR *020 †80

JOHNSON, Bernett Logan. 3600 SPRUCE ST, 1 HUP 19104 #047-07-1957 L1979 D DMP *071 †15 ‡

JOHNSON, Brandon B. ■ 19146 #041-01-2008 *012

JOHNSON, Claude Rembert. ■ 19131 #047-07-1948 L1950 R *071 †80

JOHNSON, Eric M. 2900 W QUEEN LN, DREXEL UNIV COLL OF MED 19129 #041-15-2005 L2007 ORS *012

JOHNSON, F B. 3400 SPRUCE ST, DEPT OF PATHOLGY & LB MDCN 19104 #005-11-1995 L2001 PTH *020 †50

JOHNSON, Jennifer Hilliar. ■ 19118 #041-13-2006 L2006 FP *012

JOHNSON, Jerry Calvin. 51 N 39TH ST 19104 #038-06-1974 L1977 IM *020 †20

JOHNSON, Margaret Elizabe. ■ 19103 #041-02-2005 L2005 FP *012

JOHNSON, Mark Paul. 3400 SPRUCE ST 19104 #026-04-1984 L1998 OBG MG *050 †19,30

JOHNSON, Melvin Louis. 1018 W LEHIGH AVE, TEN EIGHTEEN MEDICAL GROUP 19133 #165-04-1955 L1960 GP PD *020

JOHNSON, Millisaun. 1025 WALNUT ST, THOMAS JEFFERSON UNIV HOSP 19107 #033-06-2001 L2001 IM *100 †20

JOHNSON, Robert Jos. 3400 SPRUCE ST, RM 248 19104 #018-03-1943 L1987 OS *040

JOHNSON, Shaneek Donnette. 3401 N BROAD ST, MED ARTS BLDG STE 015 19140 #041-13-2005 L2005 P *012

JOHNSON, Tarani. PO BOX 13143 19101 #041-13-2006 *012

JOHNSON, Todd Riley. ■ 19104 #041-01-2002 *100

JOHNSON, Turner C. ■ 19140 #010-03-1949 L1950 IM *075

JOHNSON, Valerie Elaine. ■ 19147 #041-02-2004 N *012

JOHNSON, Walton R. ■ 19129 #010-03-1949 L1951 GP *071

JOHNSON-HAMERMAN, L. 800 SPRUCE ST 19107 #035-45-1952 L1963 NPM PD *071 †55

JOHNSTON, Douglas Robert. 925 CHESTNUT ST, JEFFERSON OTOLARYNGOLOGY 19107 #041-13-2005 L2005 OTO *012

JOHNSTON, Lindsay Callaha. ■ 19102 #041-12-2003 L2003 NPM *012 †55

JOHNSTON, Patricia Camody. 1015 CHESTNUT ST STE 405 19107 #041-09-1971 L1972 PD *020 †55

JOHNSTON, Timothy David. 1331 E WYOMING AVE, JUNIATA MEDICAL OFFICE SUI 19124 #017-20-1996 L2006 MPD *020,20,55

JOINES, Ronald W. 1 FRANKLIN PLZ, MAIL CODE FP1605 19102 #036-07-1989 L1993 OM PHP *030 †70

JOLAPARA, Panna Kolyanji. 4641 ROOSEVELT BLVD 19124 #495-76-1984 L1997 P *020 †75

JONES, Akhnuwkh. ■ 19124 #041-13-2006 L2006 IM *012

JONES, Amanda Lauren. ■ 19128 #035-19-2007 L2007 PD *012

JONES, Aribelle Dethrea. 561 FAIRTHORNE AVE 19128 #041-09-1982 L1984 IM *020

JONES, Christopher Scott. ■ 19107 #041-15-2007 L2007 TY *012

JONES, Daniel Arthur. 5615 W GIRARD AVE 19131 #041-07-1985 L1987 IM *020 †20

JONES, Deborah Tilford. ■ 19146 #041-01-2008 *012

JONES, Edward Raymond. 1 PENN BLVD STE 2240 19144 #045-01-1973 L1975 NEP IM *020 †20

JONES, Joshua Adam. ■ 19128 #035-19-2007 L2007 IM *012

JONES, Kimberly Toland. 4200 MONUMENT RD, BELMONT CTR 19131 #041-02-1993 L1995 P ADM *020 †20

JONES, Lisa P. 3400 SPRUCE ST, RADIOLOGY HUP 19104 #023-07-2000 L2001 DR *020 †80

JONES, Matthew Steven. ■ 19107 #041-15-2007 L2007 EM *012

JONES, Michael Richard. 840 WALNUT ST, WILLS EYE SURGICAL CENTER 19107 #010-01-1970 L1971 AN *020 †05

JONES, Nathan Patrick. ■ 19107 #023-07-2004 L2004 D *012

JONES, Nicholas Isaac. 5501 OLD YORK RD, DEPT. OF SURGERY 19141 #021-05-2004 L2004 GS *012

JONES, Niya Armentha. ■ 19104 #008-01-2005 L2005 IM *012

JONES, Noble Sidney. 1408 S BROAD ST 19146 #010-01-1976 L1978 IM *020 †20

JONES, Patricia Hughes. 5235 WALNUT ST 19139 #041-09-1984 L1988 OBG *020 †30

JONES, Robert Erwin. 702 S WASHINGTON SQ 19106 #041-01-1957 L1958 P *020 †75

JONES, Tracey. 325 CHESTNUT ST, STE 1308 19106 #025-12-1995 L1997 CHP P *020

JONES, Vaughnette M. 105 W SCHOOL HOUSE LN, MEDICINE CENTER FOR PA , P 19144 #047-07-1994 L1998 PD *020

JONES, William Lee. 701 N 42ND ST 19104 #047-07-1958 L1960 GP OS *071

JONES, William Virgil. ■ 19131 #010-03-1954 L1956 GP IM *071

JOO, Jin Hui. ■ 19119 #041-12-2004 L2004 P *012

JORDAN, Andrea Grace. 111 S 11TH ST, RM 405PAV 19107 #041-02-1981 L1986 OS ATP *020 †50

JORDAN, Carrie. 5000 WOODLAND AVE, WOODLAND AVENUE HEALTH CEN 19143 #041-14-1998 L2001 IM *020

JORDAN, Pamela Murray. ■ 19144 #035-08-1979 L1980 IM *020 †20

JORGENSEN, Valerie. 700 SPRUCE ST STE 30, SUITE 305 19106 #054-04-1966 L1967 OBG P *020 †30

JOSE, Tessey. ■ 19107 #035-15-2007 L2007 IM *012

JOSEPH, Natalie Evadne. 333 COTTMAN AVE, FOX CHASE CANCER CENTER 19111 #041-13-1993 L2000 GS *85

JOSEPH, Robert J. 4641 ROOSEVELT BLVD 19124 #035-08-1951 L1953 P PYA *072 †75

JOSEPH, Rosaline Resnick. 3300 HENRY AVE 19129 #041-07-1953 L1954 IM HEM *071 †20

JOSEPH, Sasha Oommen. 3401 N BROAD ST, DEPT OF MEDICINE 8-PP 19140 #041-13-2006 L2006 IM *012

JOSEPHSON, David Michael. ■ 19146 #035-09-2001 L2008 FSM OS *100

JOSHI, Harendra V. 4900 FRANKFORD AVE 19124 #495-22-1961 L1973 GS VS *020 †85

JOSHI, Hari Prakash. 245 N 15TH ST MS 470, HAHNEMANN UNIVERSITY HOSPI 19102 #495-28-1999 L2001 ICE *012 †20

JOSHI, Kundabala Suresh. 20TH & BERKS, FAMILY MEDICAL CARE CENTER 19121 #496-38-1967 L1974 PD *020 †20

JOSLIN, Jenny Michelle. 225 S COBBS CREEK PKWY, CHOP-PRIMARY CARE CENTE 19139 #033-06-1996 L1999 PD *020 †20

JOUBERT, Berta H. ■ 19143 #847-02-1976 L1981 P *050

JOUKOVA, Irina Mikhailovn. ■ 19102 #913-06-1981 L2000 CD *020

JOY, Javed Ahmed. 100 E LEHIGH AVE, MAB 305 19125 #160-01-1987 L2001 P *020 †75

JOY, Parijat Saurav. BROAD AND VINE ST, DEPT OF GME 19102 #495-36-2000 L2006 IM *012

JOYNER, Makesha Ann. ■ 19142 #041-15-2006 P *012

JUAREZ, Rolando. 100 E LEHIGH AVE, EPISCIPAL HOSP ED DEPT 19125 #649-14-1968 L1974 EM GP *020 †16

JUCOVY, Peter Michael. 3900 WOODLAND AVE, VETERANS ADMINISTRATION 19104 #035-19-1971 L1977 OS PTH *030

JUDGE, Sheila. 3400 SPRUCE ST 19104 #041-07-1984 L1985 P PYA *020 †75

JUDY, Kevin David. 3400 SPRUCE ST, DEPT NEUROSURGERY HUP 19104 #041-12-1984 L1985 NS *040 †25

JULIAN, Maryjane Anne. ■ 19152 #041-14-1985 L1986 FM *075

JUN, John Young. ■ 19107 #041-02-2006 L2006 AN *012

JUNCO, Ricardo Jorge. 1601 WALNUT ST STE 11, MEDICAL ARTS BLDG. 19102 #042-02-1986 L1987 P *020 †75

JUNDI, Majd M. 3300 HENRY AVE, DEPARTMENT OF PATHOLOGY MC 19129 #875-03-1993 L2002 PTH *020 †50

JUNE, Carl Howard. 421 CURIE BLVD, CANCER CENTER/554 BRB II/I 19104 #048-04-1979 L2000 IM ON *050 †20

JUNE, Rayford Robel. ■ 19129 #041-13-2008 *012

JUNEJA, Damyanti. 1335 W TABOR RD, STE 303 19141 #495-29-1968 L1974 IM GYN *071

JUNG, Leszek Janusz. TEMPLE UNIV HOSP, DEPT SURG 19140 #759-03-1977 L1995 GS *020

JUNG, Mary Lois. 8400 PINE RD 19111 #041-07-1958 L1959 GS GP *071 †85

JUNGREIS, Charles Andrew. 3401 N BROAD ST, TUH DEPT OF RADIOLOGY 19140 #035-08-1980 L1986 RNR ESN *030 †80

JUNKINS-HOPKINS, J M. 3600 SPRUCE ST # DERM, HOSP OF U OF PA 2 MALONEY 19104 #023-07-1987 L1995 D IM *020 †20,15

JUSTMAN, Judith Irene. 1020 SANSOM ST, "THOMPSON BLDG, STE 239" 19107 #035-08-1978 L1984 GS *020 †16

JYONOUCHI, Soma Chung. ■ 19130 #056-06-2004 L2007 AI *012 †55

KADAKIA, Anish Anil. 51 N 39TH ST, UNIVERSITY OF PENNSYLVANIA 19104 #005-06-1999 L2007 OPH *020 †35

KADKHODA, Mohamad. 2701 N BROAD ST 19132 #517-01-1966 L1973 PD *020

KAGAN, David Benjamin. ■ 19104 #016-01-2006 L2008 MPD *012

KAHANOVITZ, Neil. 245 N 15TH ST 19102 #023-01-1975 L2002 ORS *020 †40

KAHLE, Eden Joy. ■ 19130 #043-01-2007 L2007 PD *012

KAHLER, Allan Curtis. 3509 N BROAD ST, TEMPLE UNIV CHILDREN'S MED 19140 #041-13-1997 L1998 CCP *020 †55

KAHN, Donald Lee. 5401 OLD YORK RD, STE 401 KLEIN PROFESSIONAL 19141 #041-09-1967 L1968 CD IM *020 †20

KAHN, Jeremy Michael. ■ 19104 #051-01-1999 L2006 PCC *100 †20

KAHN, Mark B. 5501 OLD YORK RD, HACKENBURG BLDG. 3RD FLOO 19141 #041-02-1983 L1984 VS GS *020

KAHN, Sandra Joyce. 800 SPRUCE ST, PENNSYLVANIA HOSPITAL 19107 #035-20-1984 L1985 AN PME *020 †05

KAHNG, Kim U. 3300 HENRY AVE, MEDICAL COLLEGE OF PA 19129 #041-02-1979 L1992 GS *030 †85

KAIRYS, John Chas. 1025 WALNUT ST, ROOM 107 COLLEGE BLDG 19107 #041-02-1988 L1990 GS TRS *020 †85

KAISER, Larry Robt. 3400 SPRUCE ST, FL 4 19104 #021-01-1977 L1991 TS *020 †85,90

KAISER, Richard Scott. 840 WALNUT ST, STE 1020 19107 #035-19-1995 L1998 OPH *020 †35

KAJANI, Mehdi Khan. 5501 OLD YORK RD 19141 #517-06-1957 L1970 HEM *020

KAK, Sunayna. ■ 19104 #495-01-1996 L2003 DR *100

KAKALIA, Spenta J. ■ 19126 #704-02-1998 L2001 MPD *020 †55

KAKARLA, Madhavi. 245 N 15TH ST, MCP HAHNEMANN UNIV 19102 #495-58-1994 L2004 EM GP *020 †16

KALA, Savita. ■ 19131 #496-07-1992 L2007 PAN *020 †05

KALACHE, Fares. 800 SPRUCE ST, PA HOSPITAL-UPHS 19107 #422-01-2005 L2005 IM *012

KALAGATE, Rajni Suresh. 5501 OLD YORK RD, ALBERT EINSTEIN MEDICAL CE 19141 #495-98-2003 L2006 MPD *012

KALATHIL, Eapen Varghese. ■ 19104 #041-13-2000 L2001 GS *100

KALAVATHI, Narayan. 3400 SPRUCE ST, HOSP UNIV OF PA DEPT RAD 19104 #495-04-1944 L1969 R *020 †80

KALB, Robert Gordon. 401 S 3RD ST 19147 #035-20-1982 L2002 N *050 †75

KALIA, Madhu Prasad. 1020 WALNUT ST, STE B-6-A SCOTT BLDG 19107 #496-07-1964 N AN *030

KALIKIRI, Pramood Chakrav. 245 N 15TH ST MS 310, DREXEL UNIV COLL OF MED 19102 #495-04-2001 L2005 AN *012

KALISH, Robert Wm. 8835 GERMANTOWN AVE 19118 #041-02-1964 L1966 P *020

KALRA, Amit Deep. ■ 19107 #016-11-2004 L2004 IM *100 †20

KALRA, Tamanna H. 1025 WALNUT ST, THOMAS JEFFERSON UNIV HOSP 19107 #033-05-2002 L2002 NEP *100 †20

KALSI, Mandip Singh. ■ 19107 #041-01-2007 L2007 IM *012

KALU, Eke Ndubisi. 8001 STATE RD, HOC - MOD 2 19136 #690-04-1989 L2005 IM *030 †20

KALWANI, Hemlata Mansinh. 899 ANCHOR ST 19124 #495-35-1974 L1977 IM *020 †20

KALYOUSSEF, Sabah. 1 CHILDRENS CTR, DEPT OF MED AFFAIRS 19104 #033-75-2005, ▲ L2005 PD *012

KAMAL, Sawsan M. 1020 SANSOM ST RM 1652-G, TJU HOSPITAL 19107 #155-01-1995 L1998 P *100

KAMAT, Manisha Salil. 1427 VINE ST, FL 8 19102 #496-38-1995 L2003 P *100

KAMATH, Atul Frederick. ■ 19102 #024-01-2007 L2007 ORS *012

KAMATH PATEL, Binita Maya. ■ 19103 #917-03-1995 L2001 PD *100 †55

KAMBAYASHI, Taku. ■ 19104 #012-05-2004 L2004 BBK *012

KAMBIN, Parviz. 3400 SPRUCE ST 19104 #517-01-1956 L1964 ORS *071 †40

KAMEL, Ihab Raouf. 3401 N BROAD ST, 3RD FLOOR OUTPATIENT 19140 #915-04-1995 L2001 AN *020 †05

KAMHOLZ, Sandra Harriet. ■ 19130 #035-19-2008 L2008 *012

KAMINENI, Uma. 2510 N FRONT ST 19133 #495-11-1961 L1982 PD FM *020

KAMPLAIN, Trey Lee. 8835 GERMANTOWN AVE, CHESTNUT HILL HOSP-RAD 19118 #001-02-1998 L2004 RNR *100 †20

KAMPMAN, Kyle Matthew. 3900 CHESTNUT ST, TREATMENT RESEARCH CENTER 19104 #021-01-1985 L1990 P OS *020 †75

KANAGARAJAN, Nandhakumar. 2900 W QUEEN LN 19129 #495-04-2000 L2003 GE *012 †20

KANAMALLA, Uday Shankar. 2301 E ALLEGHENY AVE 19134 #496-39-1991 L2001 NM *020 †28,80

KANCHWALA, Suhail Khuzema. ■ 19146 #041-01-2002 L2003 PS *012

KANDADAI, Padmasini. 834 CHESTNUT ST STE 400, BENJAMIN FRANKLIN HOUSE 19107 #035-15-2004 L2004 OBG *012

KANDIAH, Sheetal Choudhri. ■ 19107 #894-01-1999 L2005 ID *100

KANDIYIL, Purple Navesh N. ■ 19118 #496-51-2000 L2004 GS *100

KANDPAL, Saurabh Basu. 3401 N BROAD ST, 812 PARKINSON PAVAILLION 19140 #496-38-2003 L2006 IM *012

KANDULA, Praveena. 5501 OLD YORK RD, A EINSTEIN MED CTR 19141 #041-01-2007 L2007 TY *012

KANE, Bart J. 1 CHILDRENS CTR, CHILDREN'S HOSP 19104 #024-01-2000 L2007 PDS *012

KANE, Elliot C. 2626 E ALLEGHENY AVE 19134 #005-15-1962 L1975 EM *071

KANE, Gregory Chas. 834 WALNUT ST, STE 650 19107 #041-02-1987 L1988 PUD IM *020 †20

KANE, Saul Solomon. 3401 N BROAD ST, DEPT MED 19140 #035-46-2007 L2007 IM *012

KANEFF, Scott Robt. 3200 HENRY AVE 19129 #041-07-1980 L1981 P *071 †80

KANES, Stephen Jay. 3600 SPRUCE ST, 10TH FL/GATES BLDG 19104 #035-48-1995 L1999 P *050 †75

KANESHIRO, Brandy Heidi. ■ 19102 #041-15-2004 L2004 IM *100 †20

KANG, Hyun Seon. 5501 OLD YORK RD, ALBERT EINSTEIN MEDICAL CE 19141 #583-02-1998 L2006 DR *012

KANG, Jane Sunmi. 3400 SPRUCE ST, 504 MALONEY 19104 #035-46-2004 L2007 RHU *012 †20

KANG, Melissa Dohyun. ■ 19107 #035-09-2001 L2002 RNR *100 †80

KANG, Tammy Inyoung. 859 N 22ND ST 19130 #007-02-1995 L1999 PHO *020 †20

KANG, Yoo Goo. 111 S 11TH ST, DEPT OF ANESTHESIOLOGY 19107 #583-02-1971 L1976 AN TTS *020 †05

KANGOTRA, Vijay. ■ 19131 #496-17-1989 L2006 AN *100

KANGOVI, Shreya. 3400 SPRUCE ST, HEALTH SYST 19104 #024-01-2006 L2006 MPD *012

KANJWAL, Mohammad Khalil. 245 N 15TH ST, DREXEL UNIV COLL MED/HAHNE 19102 #495-51-1998 L2004 IM *100 †20

KANSAGRA, Kavita Bhagawan. ■ 19128 #759-12-2003 L2003 IM *100

KANSAGRA, Nilesh Vallabh. ■ 19103 #033-05-2004 L2004 EM *100

KANSAL, Suleena. ■ 19119 #035-03-1999 L2004 OBG *020 †30

KAO, Gary Dazzan. 3400 SPRUCE ST, UNIV OF PA DEPT RAD ONC 19104 #023-07-1988 L1990 RO *020 †80

KAPADIA, Ami Dilip. ■ 19106 #041-02-2005 L2005 FP *012

KAPADIA, Chirag Rushi. ■ 19128 #035-19-2002 L2005 PDE *012 †55

KAPINYA, Krisztian. 5501 OLD YORK RD, DEPT OF CARDIO DIS 19141 #473-01-1999 L2003 CD *012 †20

KAPITSINOU, Pinelopi Pana. ■ 19106 #418-01-2000 L2006 IM *100 †20

KAPLAN, Bernard Sidney. 324 S 34TH ST 19104 #836-01-1964 L1987 PD *020 †55

KAPLAN, Carol Irene. 3400 SPRUCE ST 19104 #028-02-2001 L2001 HO *020

KAPLAN, David Edward. 3400 SPRUCE ST FL 3, RAVDIN BLDG/GASTROENTEROLO 19104 #048-12-1997 L2001 GE *020 †20 ‡

KAPLAN, David Jarret. 3401 N BROAD ST, STE 330 19140 #035-06-2005 L2005 U *100

KAPLAN, Frederick Saml. UNIV OF PENN HOSPITAL 19104 #023-07-1976 L1978 ORS *020

KAPLAN, J Martin. ■ 19130 #035-19-1966 L1973 PD ID *071

KAPLAN, Javier David. 1 FRANKLIN TOWN BLVD 19103 #132-04-2000 L2006 AN *100

KAPLAN, Justin. 5501 OLD YORK RD 19141 #033-05-1980 L1986 EM *062 †16

KAPLAN, Lawrence Ira. 1316 W ONTARIO ST, JONES HALL 1ST FL 19140 #041-13-1986 L1988 IM *020 †20

KAPLAN, Mark Jay. 5401 OLD YORK RD STE 20 19141 #041-13-1981 L1983 GS CCS *020 †85

KAPLAN, Paige Berman. 3405 CIVIC CENTER BLVD, CHILDS HOSP OF PHILADELPHI 19104 #836-01-1965 L1988 CBG PD *020 †55

KAPLAN, Richard Harlan. 1015 CHESTNUT ST STE 1205 19107 #041-09-1973 L1974 PM PMM *020 †60

KAPLAN, Summer. ■ 19147 #041-01-2008 *012

KAPLAN, Susan Gordon. 230 N BROAD ST 19102 #041-02-1980 L1981 AN DR *020 †80,05

KAPLAN, Susan Sufka. 1427 VINE ST, 3RD FL 19102 #036-07-2002 L2006 IM *062 †20

KAPO, Jennifer Marie. 3615 CHESTNUT ST, RALSTON HOUSE GERIATRICS 19104 #041-01-1997 L2001 IMG *020

KAPOOR, Dharmesh Sohanlal. 5501 OLD YORK RD, ALBERT EINSTEIN MED CTR 19141 #495-17-1991 *100

KAPOOR, Tarun Kumar. 1010 RACE ST, # 7H-7 19107 #033-06-2000 L2004 IM *020 †20

KAPUR, Asha. ■ 19103 #036-05-2007 L2007 IM *012

■ = Address Information Privacy Protected

KARAFIN, Lester. 3400 N BROAD ST RM 350, TEMPLE U DEPT UROLOGY 19140 #041-13-1949 L1950 **U** *020 †95

KARAKOUSIS, Giorgos C. ■ 19106 #041-01-2001 L2001 **GS** *012

KARALAKULASINGAM, Chrishan. ■ 19103 #041-01-2004 L2005 **PD** *012

KARALIS, Dean Geo. 230 N BROAD ST, FL 7 19102 #035-03-1984 L1987 **CD** *020 †20

KARAM, Joseph Anthony, Jr. 2020 WALNUT ST, NUMBER 18B 19103 #041-02-1987 L1989 **TRS CCS** *020 †85

KARAMITOPOULOS, Mara Sele. ■ 19103 #041-02-2005 L2005 **ORS** *012

KARANTH, Nithin Sripathi. ■ 19102 #035-03-2003 L2006 **GE** *012 †20

KARASICK, David. 111 S 11TH ST, G3440N 19107 #041-02-1974 L1975 **R** *020 †80

KARASICK, Stephen. 1025 WALNUT ST, STE 8439 19107 #041-02-1974 L1975 **DR** *040 †80

KARAYANNIS, Basil. 7600 CENTRAL AVE 19111 #422-01-1984 L1985 **AN PME** *020 †05

KARCHEVSKY, Michael. ■ 19106 #041-02-2003 L2003 **DR** *012

KARETAS, Alexandra Irene. 3401 N BROAD ST, DEPT OF ANESTHESIOLOGY 19140 #041-13-1964 L1965 **AN** *020 †05

KARETI, Aparna Lakshmi. 3401 N BROAD ST, TEMPLE UNIV HOSPITAL 19140 #495-70-1991 L2003 **OBG** *100

KARGUL, George John. ■ 19130 #025-07-2005 L2005 **IM** *012

KARIA, Darshak H. 5501 OLD YORK RD, LEVY 3 EAST SUITE 3207 19141 #495-23-1996 L1998 **CD** *100 †20

KARIM, Shahana Nasreen. 1740 SOUTH ST STE 300, PHILADELPHIA HEALTH ASSOCI 19146 #160-04-1983 L1998 **IM** *020

KARK, John Alexander. 111 S 11TH ST, STE 4225 19107 #024-01-1969 L2007 **IM** *050 †20

KARLAWISH, Jason Healy. 3615 CHESTNUT ST 19104 #016-06-1991 L1997 **IMG** *020 †20

KARMAZIN, Nelly. ■ 19115 #913-50-1991 L1994 **ATP** *040 †50

KARNIK, Ankur Ashok. ■ 19118 #035-48-2005 L2005 **IM** *012

KARP, Joshua Myer. 5501 OLD YORK RD, DEPT OF MEDICINE 19141 #051-04-2006 L2006 **IM** *012

KARPIN, Max. 2130 S 16TH ST 19145 #187-03-1954 L1969 **NS N** *072

KARRAS, David John. 3401 N BROAD ST, TEMPLE UNIV SCH OF MED 19140 #035-19-1987 L1989 **EM** *020 †20,16

KARTHA, Swapna Seetha. 1721 PINE ST 19103 #020-02-2002 L2007 **OTO** *020

KARTHIKEYAN, Lakshmiprabha. 1800 LOMBARD ST 19146 #495-42-1997 L2005 **IM** *012

KARUTHU, Shamila. ACADEMIC AFFAIRS OFFICE, PENNSYLVANIA HOSP 19107 #917-10-2002 L2008 *100

KARZOVA, Elena Yurievna. 6722 BUSTLETON AVE 19149 #913-69-1985 L2002 **P** *020

KASE, Gail Yvonne. 1722 PINE ST 19103 #041-14-1994 L1996 **P** *020 †75

KASHEF, Kiana. ■ 19102 #041-15-2008 *012

KASNER, Margaret Kan. ■ 19103 #041-01-2001 L2001 **HO** *020

KASNER, Scott Eric. 3400 SPRUCE ST 19104 #008-01-1992 L1994 **N** *020 †75 ‡

KASPER, Jamie Ann. 3998 RED LION RD 19114 #041-07-1991 L1993 **GE HEP** *020 †20 ‡

KASPER, Kevin Jos. 230 N BROAD ST, FL 7 19102 #041-09-1987 L1988 **CD IM** *020

KASSAROV, Luka B. ■ 19106 #198-01-1954 **HEM** *071

KASTENBERG, Judith S. 255 S 17TH ST STE 2810 19103 #024-07-1994 L1996 **P** *020 †75

KATALAN, Maurice M. 2601 S BOUVIER ST 19145 #396-06-1962 L1970 **FM IM** *071 †18

KATARI, Ajoy. ■ 19115 #496-01-1996 L2001 **AN** *020 †05

KATARI, Sunita. ■ 19115 #495-58-1996 L2002 **OBG** *050 †30

KATARIA, Neelam. ■ 19107 #495-20-2002 L2006 **AN** *020

KATCHMAN, Stacy Dee. 833 CHESTNUT ST 19107 #041-02-1991 L1996 **D** *020 †15

KATEL, Sarah Friedland. 2900 W QUEEN LN, DREXEL UNIV COLL OF MED 19129 #041-15-2006 L2008 **OBG** *012

KATES, Malcolm. ■ 19106 #041-02-1959 L1960 **IM** *071 †20

KATHURIA, Richa. 5501 OLD YORK RD, A EINSTEIN MED CTR-EM MED 19141 #033-05-2000 L2001 **EM** *020 †16

KATOWITZ, James Andrew. 3400 SPRUCE ST 19104 #041-01-1963 L1964 **OPH** *020 †35

KATOWITZ, William R. 51 N 39TH ST, SCHEIE EYE INST 19104 #041-01-2001 L2001 **OPH** *100

KATSETOS, Christos D. ■ 19130 #422-01-1983 L1996 **NP IG** *050

KATSEV, Svetlana. 3998 RED LION RD, TORRESDALE CAMPUS MEDICAL 19114 #041-12-2000 L2006 **CD** *020 †20

KATSNELSON, Marina. 834 CHESTNUT ST STE 400, BENJAMIN FRANKLIN HOUSE 19107 #041-02-2005 L2005 **OBG** *012

KATSNELSON, Michael J. ■ 19128 #041-15-2005 L2005 **N** *012

KATSUFRAKIS, Peter Jos. 3750 MARKET ST, NATIONAL BOARD OF MEDICAL 19104 #005-18-1985 L2007 **FM** *040 †18

KATTAL, Namita. 5501 OLD YORK RD, ALBERT EINSTEIN MED CTR 19141 #495-36-2002 L2004 **OBG** *012

KATZ, Amy Beth. ■ 19107 #041-02-2007 L2007 **IM** *012

KATZ, David Foa. ■ 19103 #035-45-2006 L2006 **IM** *012

KATZ, Elana Beth. ■ 19147 #041-01-2008 *012

KATZ, Ira R. 3535 MARKET ST, RM 3055 19104 #035-46-1973 L1982 **PYG P** *050 †75

KATZ, Jeffrey Alan. ■ 19143 #041-01-2008 *012

KATZ, Jonathan Peter. 3400 SPRUCE ST 19104 #016-02-1993 L1995 **GE IM** *050 †20

KATZ, Julian. 3300 HENRY AVE 19129 #016-02-1962 L1969 **GE IM** *071 †20

KATZ, Laurie B K. 111 S 11TH ST, PAV BLDG RM 405 19107 #008-01-1982 L1984 **PTH** *020 †50

KATZ, Leo Chas. 132 S 10TH ST STE 480 19107 #035-15-1988 L1990 **GE HEP** *020

KATZ, Leslie Jay. 840 WALNUT ST STE 1110, WILLS EYE HOSPITAL 19107 #008-01-1979 L1984 **OPH** *020 †35

KATZ, Lucia Cecilia. 1 INDEPENDENCE PL 19106 #781-05-1982 L1998 **CHP P** *020 †75

KATZ, Miriam Green. 225 S COBBS CREEK PKWY, PRIMARY CARE CTR OF CHOP 19139 #041-01-1986 L1988 **PD** *020 †55

KATZ, Olga Anatolievna. 1015 CHESTNUT ST, STE 810 19107 #913-50-1984 L2001 **N** *020 †75 ‡

KATZ, Philip Owen. 5401 OLD YORK RD STE 363, ALBERT EINSTEIN MEDICAL CE 19141 #036-05-1978 L1996 **IM** *040 †20

KATZ, Richard I. 5401 OLD YORK RD, KLEIN BLDG STE 405 19141 #036-07-1965 L1972 **N** *020 †75

KATZ, Robert Irwin. PRESBY MED OFFICE BLDG 19104 #010-03-1963 L1973 **CD IM** *020 †20

KATZ, Youval. 3401 N BROAD ST, DEPT OF MED -8PP 19140 #041-15-2005 L2005 **IM** *012

KATZEN, Caroline Sidona. ■ 19144 #041-13-2007 L2008 *012

KATZKA, David A. 3400 SPRUCE ST, 3 RAVDIN BLDG, HOSP UNIV P 19104 #035-47-1980 L1985 **IM** *020 †20

KAUFFMAN, Kerry Rachel. ALUMNI AFFAIRS, ALBERT EINSTEIN MEDICAL CE 19141 #305-01-2006 L2007 **PD** *012

KAUFFMAN, Leon A. 1900 S BROAD ST 19145 #041-13-1961 L1962 **PUD CCM** *020 †20

KAUFFMAN, Stuart Alan. ■ 19115 #005-02-1968 L1975 **PMM** *020

KAUFMAN, Adam Bryan. ■ 19107 #041-02-2006 L2006 **IM** *012

KAUFMAN, Beth Dawn. 3400 CIVIC CENTER BLVD, STE 2165, 2ND FLOOR MAIN 19104 #035-20-1996 L2004 **PD** *020 †55

KAUFMAN, Edward Andrew. 200 N 16TH ST, ONE FRANKLIN PLAZA 19102 #024-05-1972 L1984 **PTH** *030 †50

KAUFMAN, Richard Ellis. 5501 OLD YORK RD 19141 #041-13-1982 L1983 **PUD IM** *020 †20 ‡

KAUFMANN, Michael Ryan. ■ 19104 #012-01-2008 L2008 *012

KAUH, Eunkyung Ann. 3400 SPRUCE ST, 4 PENN TOWER 19104 #041-02-1996 L2001 **END** *012

KAUH, Young Chai. 833 CHESTNUT ST, STE 740 19107 #583-01-1961 L1971 **D DMP** *040 †15

KAUL, Shailja. ■ 19131 #496-04-1996 L2003 **IM** *100 †20

KAULBACK, Kris Robert. 1100 WALNUT ST, 5TH FL 19107 #041-09-1994 L1996 **GS** *020 †85

KAULBACK, Kurt Wm. 230 N BROAD ST 19102 #041-09-1988 L1990 **CD IM** *020 †20

KAUR, Ikjot. 5401 OLD YORK RD, KLEIN 363 19141 #496-43-2005 L2007 **IM** *012

KAUR, Primal Pal. 3401 N BROAD ST 8PP, DEPT OF MEDICINE 19140 #495-29-1996 L2002 **RHU** *020 †20

KAUR, Tashveen. ■ 19107 #035-45-2002 L2004 **PD** *020 †55

KAUSHAL, Aradhana. 111 S 11TH ST, BODINE CENTER 19107 #024-05-2002 L2003 **RO** *100

KAUTZKY, Mira. 211 S 9TH ST, NINTH STREET INTERNAL 19107 #041-02-1997 L2000 **IM** *020 †20

KAVANAUGH, Bryan C. 132 S 10TH ST, OF G 19107 #010-02-2003 L2003 **GE** *012 †20

KAVEH, Houshang. 115 E LEHIGH AVE 19125 #517-01-1961 L1970 **GS** *020 †85

KAVESH, William Nathan. UNIV & WOODLAND 19104 #035-46-1969 L1990 **IM IMG** *020 †20

KAVOKIN, Aleksandr Alekse. ■ 19148 #913-15-1994 L2004 **GS** *100

KAVOUSSI, Richard James. 3200 HENRY AVE, MCP/EPPI PSYCHIATRY 19129 #035-09-1981 L1991 **P** *020 †75 ‡

KAWUT, Steven Mark. 3600 SPRUCE ST, DEPT PUL & CRITICAL CARE 19104 #008-01-1995 L1997 **PCC** *020 †20

KAY, Abigail Louise. 833 CHESTNUT ST STE 210, DEPT OF PSYCHIATRY 19107 #033-06-2001 L2001 **P** *100 †75

KAY, Gordon Morris. KNIGHTS RED LION ROADS 19114 #803-03-1956 L1967 **PTH CLP** *071 †50

KAY, Julie Kim. ■ 19107 #041-02-2002 L2008 *100

KAY, Michael Leon. 601 WALNUT ST, STE L30 19106 #041-01-1968 L1971 **OPH** *020 †35

KAY, Robert. 451 S UNIVERSITY AVE, WEST PHILADELPHIA MENTAL H 19104 #024-07-1957 L1965 **CHP P** *071

KAYE, Adam Jonathan. 3400 SPRUCE ST, 4TH FLOOR MALONEY 19104 #035-08-2002 L2002 **GS** *012

KAYED, Deeb Maxwell. ■ 19127 #422-01-1990 L1995 **N** *020 †75

KAYSER, Joshua. ■ 19147 #021-01-2002 L2006 **PCC** *012 †20

KAZEMINEZHAD, Zhabiz. ■ 19131 #041-15-2002 L2002 **P** *100

KEAFER, Sarah Lynn. NORTH FRONT ST & ERIE AVE, ST CHRISTOPHERS HOSPITAL 19134 #041-02-2006 L2006 **PD** *012

KEANE, Martin Gerard. 3401 N BROAD ST, STE C540 19140 #035-19-1989 L1994 **CD IM** *050 †20

KEANE, William Martin. 925 CHESTNUT ST FL 6 19107 #024-01-1970 L1975 **OTO HNS** *020 †45

KEARNEY, James John. 800 SPRUCE ST 19107 #041-02-1990 L1992 **OTO** *020 †45

KEARNEY, Rosemary Ann. 727 DELANCEY ST 19106 #041-02-1990 L1993 **IM** *020 †20

KEARNS, Kenneth Aaron. 1015 WALNUT ST, THOMAS JEFFERSON UNIV 19107 #038-43-2006 L2006 **ORS** *012

KECHLI, Amer M. 146 N 3RD ST, # B 19106 #605-01-1991 L2004 **PD PHO** *020 †55

KEDIKA, Ramalinga. ■ 19107 #041-02-2008 *012

KEEFE, Stephen Michael. 3400 SPRUCE ST, HOSPITAL OF THE UNIV OF PE 19104 #016-02-2003 L2003 **HO** *012 †20

KEEGAN, Joan Alicia. 1538 SOUTH ST, # 3 19146 #041-77-2006, ▲ L2006 **OBG** *012

KEELE, Linda. ■ 19128 #041-15-2008 *012

KEELEY, Francis X, Jr. 111 S 11TH ST 19107 #028-02-1990 L1995 **U** *100 †95

KEENAN, Mary Ann. 3400 SPRUCE ST, TWO SILVERSTEIN 19104 #041-07-1976 L1977 **ORS** *020 †40

KEENE, Sarah Dunn. ■ 19130 #012-05-2002 L2002 **NPM** *012 †55

KEFALIDES, Nicholas A. 3701 MARKET ST, # 468 19104 #016-11-1956 L1957 **IM** *071

KEFER, Jodi Michele. 1400 S 5TH ST, SOUTH PHILADELPHIA PEDIATR 19147 #035-45-1994 L1997 **PD** *012

KEIM, Brooke Kathryn. ■ 19147 #041-13-2007 L2007 **IM** *012

KEISER, Jessica Lee. ■ 19107 #041-02-2007 L2007 **IM** *012

KEISMAN, Robert A. ■ 19130 #041-01-1950 L1951 **CD IM** *030 †20

KELEKAR, Gauri Dilip. ■ 19103 #041-15-2008 *012

KELEPOURIS, Ellie. 3401 N BROAD ST, TEMPLE UNIV HOSPITAL 19140 #418-01-1975 L1979 **NEP IM** *050 †20

KELLER, Alan Seth. 3400 SPRUCE ST 19104 #041-01-1976 **P** *020 †75 ‡

KELLER, Deborah Susan. ■ 19106 #033-05-2007 L2007 **GS** *012

KELLER, Stephanie Diane. ■ 19127 #041-15-2008 *012

KELLEY, Maura Ann. 200 S BROAD ST STE 400 19102 #035-45-1989 L1992 **ID** *020 †20

KELLEY, William Nimmons. 3400 SPRUCE ST 19104 #012-05-1963 L1990 **IM RHU** *030 †20

KELLOGG, Cynthia Kent. 800 SPRUCE ST, FL 2 19107 #051-07-1985 L1991 **NPM PD** *020 †55

KELLOGG, William Thos. 100 E LEHIGH AVE, FL 3 19125 #041-01-1972 L1973 **OPH** *020 †18

KELLUM, Wendell Everett. 3156 KENSINGTON AVE 19134 #001-02-2001 L2001 **FM** *020 †18

KELLY, Andrea. 324 S 34TH ST 19104 #041-02-1995 L1997 **PDE** *020 †55

KELLY, Anton G. ■ 19119 #041-15-2008 L2008 *012

KELLY, Barbara Ann. 5501 OLD YORK RD 19141 #024-07-1977 L1983 **PD** *075 †55

KELLY, Deborah Simon. 700 SPRUCE ST STE 100 19106 #035-01-1995 L1999 **OPH** *020 †35

KELLY, Habib Rajai. 6112 TORRESDALE AVE 19135 #605-02-1967 L1973 **U FM** *020 ‡

KELLY, Jeanne Ann. 2623 E ALLEGHENY AVE 19134 #035-09-2003 L2003 **PD** *020 †55

KELLY, Kara Maureen. 324 S 34TH ST 19104 #035-06-1989 L1991 **PHO PD** *020 †55

KELLY, Maureen Patricia. 3701 MARKET ST, STE 800 19104 #041-09-1983 L1992 **REN** *020 †30

KELLY, Shareen Fay. ERIE AVE AT FRONT ST PED 19134 #036-01-1991 L1993 **PD** *040 †55

KELSEN, Judith Rachel. 5501 OLD YORK RD 19141 #035-20-2001 L2001 **PG** *012

KELSEN, Steven. 3400 N BROAD ST 19140 #041-09-1968 L1971 **IM** *050 †20

KELZ, Rachel. 3400 SPRUCE ST, FL 4 19104 #008-01-1997 L2000 **GS** *020 †85

KEMPEN, John Harold. 51 N 39TH ST, SCHEIE EYE INSTITUTE 19104 #005-18-1992 L2005 **OPH** *050 †35

KEMPF, Francis C, Jr. 700 SPRUCE ST, STE 403 19106 #041-07-1979 L1981 **CD ICE** *020 †20

KENDALL, A Richard. 3401 N BROAD ST 19140 #041-13-1956 L1957 **U** *071 †95

KENDALL, Benjamin. 601 WALNUT ST STE 504, INDEPENDENCE SQUARE WEST 19106 #041-13-1955 L1956 **OBG** *071 †30

KENDALL, Norman. 2401 PENNSYLVANIA AVE, STE 20 19130 #041-13-1936 L1938 **PD** *071 †55
KENEPP, Nancy B. 3401 N BROAD ST 19140 #035-08-1968 **AN** *040 †05
KENNEDY, David William. 3400 SPRUCE ST, 5TH FL RAVOLIN BLDG 19104 #539-06-1972 L1990 **OTO** *020 †45
KENNEDY, Eugene Paul. 1025 WALNUT ST, THOS JEFFERON UNIV 19107 #051-04-1996 L2005 **GS** *020 †85
KENNEDY, Michael Arthur. 501 S 54TH ST, MERCY WORKCARE/MERCY HOSPI 19143 #016-11-1987 L1996 **OM PHP** *020 †70
KENNEDY, Richard Dennis. 3120 W SCHOOL HOUS LN #A11 19144 #041-07-1992 L1993 **GS** *075
KENNEDY, Sean Kevin. 3400 SPRUCE ST, HOSPITAL UNIV OF PENNSYLVA 19104 #024-01-1973 L1988 **AN IM** *020 †20,05
KENYON, Lawrence Chas. 111 S 11TH ST 19107 #035-19-1991 L1994 **ATP NP** *020 †50
KEOBOUNNAM, Manivanh Na. ■ 19104 #018-03-2005 L2005 **AN** *012
KEOGH, John Howard. 3400 SPRUCE ST, DEPT OF ANESTHESIA 19104 #030-05-1997 L1998 **AN** *100 †05
KEOHANE, Richard Blair. 800 SPRUCE ST, DEPT RADY 19107 #041-02-1967 L1968 **DR** *020 †80
KEOSATHIT, Narong. 1600 W GIRARD AVE, DEPT OF SURGERY 19130 #891-01-1965 L1973 **GS TS** *020
KEREN, Ron. 3535 MARKET ST, RM 1524 19104 #035-19-1994 L2001 **PD** *020 †55
KERESZTURY, Michael F. 3401 N BROAD ST 19140 #033-05-1990 L1993 **AN** *020 †05
KERNAGIS, Lily Yvonne. ■ 19104 #041-01-2002 L2002 **DR** *100
KERNER, Caroline Lesley. ■ 19102 #036-05-2004 L2008 **IM** *100 †20
KERRIGAN, Martin Hurley. ■ 19107 #041-02-2005 L2005 **IM** *012
KERSCHBAUM, Wesley Edward. 4224 N FRONT ST, PATH PROGRAM AT CEP 19140 #041-02-1975 L1977 **CHP P** *020
KERSE, Ngaire Margaret. 3615 CHESTNUT ST 19104 #671-01-1984 L1988 **FM IMG** *020 †18
KERSHBAUM, Kenneth Lowell. 801 SPRUCE ST 19107 #041-02-1967 L1968 **CD IM** *020 †20
KERSTEN, Hans Bruno. ■ 19130 #041-13-1994 L1996 **PD** *020 †55
KERSUN, Leslie Segal. 324 S 34TH ST 19104 #035-03-1996 L1998 **PHO** *020 †55
KESSEL, Julie Beth. 2222 WALLACE ST, STE 750 19130 #011-02-1987 L1990 **P** *020 †75
KESSEL, Lawrence Jay. 8200 HENRY AVE STE G1 19128 #041-01-1980 L1981 **IM IMG** *020 †20
KESSLER, Arnold S. 9807 BUSTLETON AVE 19115 #041-13-1953 **OBG** *071 †30
KESSLER, Mark Alexander. ■ 19128 #041-01-1980 L1982 **PTH** *100
KESSLER, Stephen Louis. 9807 BUSTLETON AVE 19115 #041-07-1986 L1990 **OBG** *020 †30
KESSLER, Steven Marc. 3400 SPRUCE ST 19104 #035-05-1986 L1988 **P** *020 †75
KESTNER, Christopher Jose. 3401 N BROAD ST, TEMPLE UNIVERSITY HOSPITAL 19140 #041-02-2006 L2006 **ORS** *012
KEVORKIAN, Gaby George. 5501 OLD YORK RD 19141 #913-38-1975 **OS** *020
KEYES, Michael Joseph. 3401 N BROAD ST, OF S 19140 #021-01-2004 L2004 **EM** *012
KEYHANI, Ali Reza. 111 S 11TH ST, STE 6460 19107 #517-01-1961 L1983 **AN** *020 †05
KEYKHAH, Mohammad. DEPT OF ANESTHESIOLOGY, MS310 245 N 15TH ST 19102 #517-01-1963 L1974 **AN OS** *040 †05
KHADILKAR, Rashmi V. ■ 19128 #041-13-2003 L2003 **RHU** *012 †20
KHADR, Hisham A F. 2301 E ALLEGHENY AVE, C/O EMERGENCY ROOM DEPARTM 19134 #915-02-1983 L1988 **IM** *020 †20
KHALEEQ, Ghulam. 2900 W QUEEN LN 19129 #704-09-1999 L2003 **PCC** *012 †20
KHALID-KHAN, Sarosh. 3535 MARKET ST STE 670 19104 #704-02-1989 L1998 **CHP** *050 †75
KHALIL, Ahlam N. 31 N COLUMBUS BLVD, NUMBER 318 19106 #915-02-1979 L1992 **OBG** *020 †30
KHAN, Amir Saif. ■ 19130 #004-01-2004 L2007 **N** *012
KHAN, Azad. 6320 ELMWOOD AVE 19142 #654-01-1982 L1984 **IM** *020
KHAN, Khudsiya. 500 S BROAD ST # 360 19146 #495-33-1984 L1988 **PD** *020 †55
KHAN, M Farrukh Ali. 501 S 54TH ST, SURGERY 19143 #704-01-1975 L1983 **GS TTS** *020 †85
KHAN, Muhammad Akram. 3440 MARKET ST, STE 200 19104 #704-16-1992 L2001 **CHP** *020
KHAN, Muhammad Asad. ■ 19131 #704-02-2005 *100
KHAN, Nabila Farhat. 2900 W QUEEN LN, MCP HAHNEMANN UNIV 19129 #917-08-1997 L2000 **IM** *020 †20
KHAN, Qadar. 702 W GIRARD AVE 19123 #704-01-1964 L1972 **IM CD** *020 ‡
KHAN, Saba. ■ 19146 #917-35-2001 L2004 **IM** *100
KHAN, Shahid Mushtaq. 4TH FLOOR - S TOWER MAIL, DREXEL UNIVERSITY COLLEGE 19102 #704-21-2001 L2007 **GS** *012
KHAN-BARONE, Francesca M. 2514 N BROAD ST 19132 #561-01-1965 L1974 **CHP P** *020
KHANDAKAR, Saema Homaira. 3901 LOCUST WALK, BOX 704 19104 #035-48-2007 **PD** *012
KHANDAVALLI, Sarat Chandr. 5500 WISSAHICKON AVE, M 708 B 19144 #496-23-2004 L2004 **PTH** *012
KHANNA, Monika. ■ 19106 #041-02-2002 L2004 **END** *012 †20
KHELLA, Sami. 51 N 39TH ST 19104 #041-01-1984 L1985 **N** *020 †75
KHEMASUWAN, Danai. 5501 OLD YORK RD 19141 #891-01-2004 L2006 **IM** *012
KHLYAVICH, Eve Jacqueline. 2900 W QUEEN LN, DREXEL UNIV COLL OF MED 19129 #041-15-2006 **P** *012
KHOJASTEH, Artemis. ■ 19147 #041-02-2008 *012
KHOURY, Dennis James. 4900 FRANKFORD AVE 19124 #016-43-1969 L1977 **OPH** *020 †35
KHOURY, John Safa. ■ 19107 #041-02-2006 L2006 **N** *012
KHOURY, Philip B. 1182 S 11TH ST 19147 #041-13-1981 L1982 **IM** *020
KHURANA, Jasvir S. 3400 SPRUCE ST, DEPT OF PATHOLGY & LB MDCN 19104 #495-36-1982 L1998 **PTH** *020 †50
KHURANA, Vikas. 1800 LOMBARD ST, SUITE 100, PEPPER PAVILION 19146 #495-45-1993 L2006 **GE** *020 †20
KHUSID, Rudolf. 2630 HOLME AVE, INSTITUTE FOR RESPIRATORY 19152 #913-50-1988 L1998 **PCC** *020 †20
KIDDOO, Darcie A. ■ 19104 #060-01-1998 L2003 **UP** *100
KIDWAI, Mohammed Shoaib J. 2900 W QUEEN LN, DEPT OF INTERNAL MED 19129 #496-27-2000 L2004 **IM** *100 †20
KIEFNER, Frederick Jos. 1 PENN BLVD 19144 #041-01-1967 L1968 **R** *071 †80 ‡
KIEL, Richard George. ■ 19144 #041-15-2008 *012
KILBAUGH, Todd Justen. ■ 19147 #045-01-1999 L2002 **CCP** *100 †05
KILLION, Matthew Joseph. 1015 CHESTNUT ST # 1506, STE 1506 19107 #041-02-1993 L1996 **IM** *020 †20
KILMARTIN, Elaine C. 2152 E NORRIS ST 19125 #041-02-2001 L2001 **AN** *100 †05 ‡
KILPATRICK, Michaux R. ■ 19103 #036-01-2001 L2007 **NS** *100
KIM, Aimee Geeyoung. ■ 19103 #041-01-2008 *012
KIM, Amy. 3440 MARKET ST, 2ND FL 19104 #035-19-1999 L2001 **CHP** *100 †55,75
KIM, Ann Keongju. ■ 19103 #051-01-2001 L2006 **RNR** *012 †80

KIM, Bo Soo. 1025 WALNUT ST 19107 #041-02-2002 L2002 **PCC** *012 †20
KIM, Cadence Amy. 2137 WELSH RD, UROLOGICAL ASSOC, PC 19115 #035-45-1989 L1996 **U** *020 †95
KIM, Caroline Sunwha. 3910 POWELTON AVE, PRESBYTERIAN MULTISPECIALT 19104 #017-20-1992 L2006 **IM PD** *020 †55,20 ‡
KIM, Catherine Sunjoo. 111 S 11TH ST 19107 #041-02-2002 L2003 **RO** *100
KIM, Cheung Kook. 834 CHESTNUT ST STE 400, MEDICAL SPECIALTIES 19107 #035-08-1994 L2003 **OBG** *020 †30
KIM, Chong Hwan. 9880 BUSTLETON AVE 19115 #726-01-1995 L2001 **PYG** *100
KIM, Chong Tae. 3405 CIVIC CENTER BLVD, RM 233 19104 #583-01-1982 L2001 **PM SCI** *020 †60
KIM, Dae Hyun. 111 S 11TH ST 19107 #583-01-2001 L2005 **IM** *012
KIM, Daniel Foonchul. 6725 CASTOR AVE 19149 #041-13-2006 L2006 **GS** *012
KIM, Darlene. ■ 19130 #035-47-2004 L2004 **IM** *100 †20
KIM, David Youngjin. 3401 N BROAD ST, TEMPLE UNIVERSITY HOSPITAL 19140 #041-12-1994 L1997 **AN** *020 †05
KIM, Deborah Rubin. 3535 MARKET ST, FL 2 19104 #041-12-1998 L2000 **P** *020 †75
KIM, Denis J. ■ 19131 #025-07-2005 L2005 **EM** *012
KIM, Eileen H. 501 S 54TH ST, THE INTENSIVIST GROUP 19143 #035-20-2000 L2005 **CCM** *100
KIM, Elizabeth Mikyoung. 1630 SOUTH ST 19146 #041-01-2003 L2003 **PS** *012
KIM, Ellen J. 3400 SPRUCE ST, DEPT OF DERM-UNIV OF PENNS 19104 #041-01-1996 L1998 **D** *020 †15
KIM, Eugene Jongho. ■ 19144 #041-15-2008 *012
KIM, Haewon C. 324 S 34TH ST 19104 #583-08-1968 L1974 **BBK PHO** *020 †55
KIM, Hi Sook. 5438 N LAWRENCE ST 19120 #583-06-1970 L1975 **PD** *020 †55
KIM, Hyung Min. ■ 19144 #041-15-2008 *012
KIM, Ikjin. 2230 COTTMAN AVE, DEPT. 19149 #583-02-1960 L1979 **IM** *020 †20
KIM, Jee Hyun. ■ 19131 #041-15-2002 L2002 **P** *012
KIM, Jennifer Hyunsook. 3624 MARKET ST 560, UPHS/PRESBYTERIAN MEDICAL 19104 #041-01-2006 L2006 **OPH** *012
KIM, Ji Hyun. ■ 19107 #041-15-2008 *012
KIM, Joanne J. ■ 19107 #041-13-2007 L2007 **IM** *012
KIM, Judith Chinhui. 132 S 10TH ST, STE 285K 19107 #035-06-1998 L2001 **DMP** *020 †50
KIM, Jung-Hoon. 5401 OLD YORK RD, DEPT OF MEDICINE 19141 #583-02-1999 L2004 **IMG** *012 †20
KIM, Kwan Eun. 219 N BROAD ST, FL 5 19107 #583-01-1959 L1969 **NEP IM** *050 †20
KIM, Kyong-Ja. 3996 RED LION RD 19114 #583-08-1961 L1975 **GP** *020
KIM, Marc Jason. 245 N 15TH ST, MAIL STOP 427 19102 #305-01-2007 L2007 **IM** *012
KIM, Matthew Ian. 3400 SPRUCE ST DEPT MED 19104 #028-02-1996 L1998 **END** *020 †20
KIM, Nancy Mookyeong. ■ 19103 #041-12-1996 L2006 **IM** *020 †20
KIM, Patrick K. 3440 MARKET ST, TRAUMA CENTER AT PENN 19104 #036-07-1995 L1998 **CCS** *020 †85
KIM, Paul Koung. ■ 19111 #041-13-2005 L2005 **IM** *012
KIM, Peter Y. 19107 #048-16-2004 L2007 **CD** *012
KIM, Philip Y. 101 E OLNEY AVE, STE 400 19120 #583-02-1957 L1968 **ATP CLP** *071 †50
KIM, Richard Kyungho. ■ 19130 #033-06-2007 L2007 **GS** *012
KIM, Richard Wookyum. ■ 19146 #035-19-2004 **TS** *100 †90
KIM, Samuel Suk. 3400 SPRUCE ST, SILVERSTEIN 4 19104 #024-07-2002 L2005 **GS** *012
KIM, Sang Boum. 1 PENN BLVD 19144 #583-04-1958 L1972 **GS TS** *020
KIM, Seo Young. 3600 SPRUCE ST - 504, UNIV OF PA - RHEUMATOLOGY 19104 #583-13-2000 L2006 **RHU** *012 †20
KIM, Soo Yoon. 3401 N BROAD ST 19140 #041-13-1997 L2000 **CRS** *020 †85,10
KIM, Stephen. 3400 SPRUCE ST, DEPT MED 19104 #024-07-2007 **IM** *012
KIM, Steve Soohong. 34TH-CIVIC CTR BLVD, CHILDRENS HOSP 19104 #035-20-2001 L2007 **UP** *012
KIM, Sue Yeon. ■ 19104 #035-19-2002 L2005 **DR OS** *100
KIM, Sun Ju. 245 N 15TH ST, DREXEL UNIV COLL MED/HAHNE 19102 #583-08-1988 L2005 **PDR** *012
KIM, Sung Moon. 132 S 10TH ST, THOMAS JEFFERSON UNIV HOSP 19107 #583-01-1979 L1985 **NM** *020 †28 ‡
KIM, Victor. 3401 N BROAD ST, 785 PARKINSON PAVILION 19140 #041-12-1998 L2000 **PCC** *100 †20
KIM, Won Myung. 6705 OLD YORK RD, JAISOHN MED CTR 19126 #583-08-1968 L1972 **IM** *020 †20
KIM, Wonhee. 6816 CASTOR AVE 19149 #035-06-1999 L2003 **IM PD** *020 †20,55
KIM, Woojin. 5501 OLD YORK RD 19141 #041-01-2001 L2001 **DR** *100 †80
KIM, Yong Kook. 100 E LEHIGH AVE RM 318, MEDICAL ARTS BUILDING 19125 #583-02-1964 L1972 **P CHP** *020 †75
KIM, Young Nam. 5401 OLD YORK RD, STE 331 19141 #583-02-1968 L1974 **IM END** *020 †20
KIM, Yu Sung. ■ 19147 #051-01-2006 L2006 **IM** *012
KIMBIRIS, Demetrios G. BROAD & VINE STS 19102 #418-01-1956 L1967 **CD IM** *071
KIMCHI, Eitan Zeev. ■ 19107 #041-02-2008 *012
KIMMEL, Murray Harris. 16TH ST & GIRARD AVE 19130 #041-13-1954 L1955 **U** *071 †95
KIMMEL, Stephen Edward. 423 GUARDIAN DR, BLOCKLEY HALL RM 717 19104 #035-19-1988 L1991 **CD IM** *020 †20
KINCEL, David Nathaniel. ■ 19106 #041-78-2007, ▲ L2007 **EM** *012
KINDER, Kimberly Joy. ■ 19146 #041-01-2008 *012
KINDWALL, Kathryn E. 3401 N BROAD ST 19140 #035-20-1980 L1982 **CD IM** *040 †20
KING, Conrad Kirklyn. 7125 FRANKFORD AVE 19135 #041-01-1978 L1979 **PME** *020
KING, Earl Dwayne. 333 COTTMAN AVE, FOX CHASE CANCER CENTER. 19111 #041-14-1986 L1987 **PUD** *020
KING, Emmanuel Suchi. 3400 SPRUCE ST, PENN TOWER STE 2009 19104 #033-06-2001 L2001 **IM** *020 †20
KING, Joseph John, III. ■ 19129 #041-15-2006 L2007 **ORS** *012
KING, Kathleen Shelly. 170 S INDEPENDENCE MALL W, STE 640S 19106 #041-13-1994 L1997 **IM** *020 †20
KING, Lorraine Carole. 834 CHESTNUT ST, STE M207 19107 #041-07-1971 L1972 **END OBG** *020 †30
KING, Rebecca Leigh. ■ 19103 #041-01-2007 L2007 **PTH** *012
KING, Stephanie Angela. 230 N BROAD ST, STE 1536 19102 #041-01-1983 L1985 **OBG** *020 †30
KING, William Frank, Jr. 105 W SCHOOL HOUSE LN, PAMCOP 19144 #008-01-1993 L1995 **PD** *020 †55 ‡
KINI, Vinay Ullal. ■ 19107 #041-13-2007 L2007 **IM** *012
KINNIRY, Paul A. 700 SPRUCE ST, STE 500 19106 #041-01-1997 L2000 **PCC** *100 †20

■ = Address Information Privacy Protected

KINOSIAN, Bruce Paul. ■ 19146 #005-02-1981 L1985 **IMG** *020 †20
KINSMAN, Sara Brett. 3550 MARKET ST FL 4 19104 #041-01-1990 L1993 **PD** *020 †55
KIPNES, Joanna Ruth. 1025 WALNUT ST, THOMAS JEFFERSON UNIV HOSP 19107 #041-02-2004 L2004 **IM** *012
KIRBY, Cheryl Lipowitz. 5501 OLD YORK RD DEPT RAD, ALBERT EINSTEIN MED CTR 19141 #041-01-1987 L1988 **DR** *020 †80
KIRBY, Simon David. 2 LOGAN SQ STE 1815, 18TH & ARCH STREETS 19103 #063-01-1993 L1997 **OTO** *020 †45
KIRI, Ajay Narendra. 8835 GERMANTOWN AVE, DEPT FM 19118 #033-06-2002 L2007 **FP** *012
KIRIAKIDOU, Marianthi. 3400 SPRUCE ST, FL 8 19104 #418-02-1992 L2001 **RHU** *100 †20
KIRICHENKO, Alexander Vla. 333 COTTMAN AVE, FOX CHASE CANCER CENTER 19111 #913-05-1981 L2005 **RO** *100 †80
KIRK, Jean H. 8400 PINE RD 19111 #033-05-1985 L1990 **DR** *020 †80
KIRKLAND, Matt Lockwood. 700 SPRUCE ST, STE 507 19106 #041-21-1983 L1984 **GS** *020 †85
KIRKPATRICK, James Neal. 3400 SPRUCE ST, 9 GATES 19104 #005-12-1998 L2006 **CD** *100 †20
KIRKSEY, Duane Erron. 1125 BLOCKLEY HALL, 423 GUARDIAN DRIVE 19131 #028-02-2002 L2005 **IMG** *020 †20
KIRKSEY, Levester, Jr. 51 N 39TH ST, 805 PEPPER PAVILTON 19104 #038-40-1993 L1998 **VS** *020 †85
KIRSCH, Peter Emanuel. ■ 19107 #836-01-1961 L1980 *072
KIRSCHNER, Caren E. 7500 CENTRAL AVE STE 205 19111 #041-13-1996 L1998 **PD** *020 †55
KIRSCHNER, Emily R. ■ 19106 #033-06-2003 **OBG** *012
KIRTZ, Jeremy Fechter. 3401 N BROAD ST, TEMPLE UNIVERSITY HOSPITAL 19140 #045-01-2005 L2005 **EM** *012
KISLER, Tanya. ■ 19148 #041-12-2002 L2002 **DR** *100 †80
KISSICK, William Lee. 3615 CHESTNUT ST, 221-222 RALSTON PENN CTR 19104 #008-01-1957 L1969 **GPM** *040 †70 ‡
KISTENMACHER, Mildred L. ERIE AVE AT FRONT ST 19133 #024-05-1950 L1951 **OS PD** *071 †55,19
KISTLER, Jonathan Austin. 4641 ROOSEVELT BLVD, FRIEND'S HOSPITAL 19124 #041-15-1999 L2004 **CHP** *020
KITAZONO, Mary Tsuta. 3400 SPRUCE ST, DEPT RAD 19104 #005-06-2006 L2006 **DR** *012
KITCHEN, Jason Michael. 501 N 54TH ST, DEPT OF EMERGENCY MEDICINE 19143 #041-02-2002 L2002 **EM** *100 †16
KITEI, Milton Norman. 2243 S 9TH ST 19148 #041-02-1944 L1945 **GP IM** *071 ‡
KITNER, Isidor. ■ 19116 #781-04-1954 L1968 **P** *020
KLANAMAN, Elena M.. 2900 W QUEEN LN 19129 #913-15-1997 L2003 **IM** *100 †20
KLASS, Daniel Jacob. 3750 MARKET ST, NATIONAL BOARD OF MED EXAM 19104 #067-01-1967 L1990 **IM PUD** *062
KLATT, Brian Andrew. 1015 WALNUT ST, RM. 324, CURTIS BLDG. 19107 #041-12-1997 L1999 **OAR** *020 †40
KLAUSMAN, Kenneth Barry. 1800 LOMBARD ST, EMERGENCY RM 19146 #308-03-1981 L1983 **IM EM** *020 †20,70
KLAUSMEIER, Jessica Hope. ■ 19144 #041-15-2008 *012
KLEBANOFF, David Bruce. 9331 OLD BUSTLETON AVE, STE 201 19115 #041-13-1981 L1982 **OBG** *020 †20
KLEEMAN, Christopher S. 219 N BROAD ST, FL 5 19107 #024-07-2002 L2005 **GE** *012 †20
KLEIMANN, Alexander Avrah. ■ 19107 #035-06-2007 L2007 **EM** *012
KLEIN, Brad Craig. 111 S 11TH ST STE 8130, THOM JEFFERSON HOSP 19107 #041-02-2003 L2003 **N** *020 ‡
KLEIN, Eitan Moshe. ■ 19104 #035-47-2004 L2004 **IM** *100 †20
KLEIN, Howard Simon. 5301 OLD YORK RD, TEMPLE CONTINUING CARE CEN 19141 #041-02-1978 L1979 **PUD IMG** *020 †20
KLEIN, Joseph Robert. ■ 19102 #016-06-2005 L2006 **AN** *012
KLEIN, Melissa Ilene. ■ 19107 #041-02-2008 L2008 *012
KLEIN, Michael Elihu. 111 S 11TH ST 19107 #008-01-1972 L1983 **HEM ON** *020 †20
KLEIN, Peter Steven. 415 CURIE BLVD, UNIV OF PA SCHOOL OF MED 19104 #023-07-1988 L1995 **HO** *100 †20
KLEIN, Sheldon. 7901 BUSTLETON AVE, STE 303 19152 #041-02-1966 L1967 **GP** *071 †04
KLEIN, Thomas Alexander. 111 S 11TH ST 19107 #035-45-1966 L1993 **OBG REN** *040 †30
KLEIN, Wendy Pamela. 3400 SPRUCE ST 19104 #016-42-1993 L1998 **DR** *020 †80
KLEINER, Matthew T. ■ 19107 #041-13-2008 *012
KLEINER, Robert Charles. 840 WALNUT ST, STE 1020 19107 #023-07-1981 L1983 **OPH** *020 †35
KLEINER-FISMAN, Galit. 3900 WOODLAND AVE MS 127, PADRECC PHILA VA HOSP 19104 #067-01-1996 L2003 **N IM** *020 †75
KLEINMAN, David Samuel. 230 N BROAD ST, FL 7 19102 #035-19-1990 L1992 **ICE** *020 †20
KLEIN-SZANTO, Andres J P. 7701 BURHOLME AVE 19111 #132-01-1965 **PTH DMP** *050
KLENK, Lisa G. 2206 DELANCEY PL 19103 #035-06-1988 L1992 **P PYA** *020 †75
KLEOPA, Kleopas. 3400 SPRUCE ST, NEUROLOGY ASSOC. 2 RAVDIN 19104 #409-20-1994 L1999 **CN** *020 †75
KLEPPEL, Judy Beth. 2601 HOLME AVE 19152 #016-42-1983 L1988 **PM** *020 †60
KLIGMAN, Albert M. 415 CURIE BLVD, 226 CRB 19104 #041-01-1947 L1949 **D** *071 †15
KLIGMAN, Douglas E. 8815 GERMANTOWN AVE, STE 30 19118 #011-02-1990 L1993 **D** *020 †15
KLIMAS, Enoch Geo, Jr. ■ 19134 #041-13-1943 L1944 **PHP** *071
KLIMKE, Anne Elizabeth. ■ 19128 #010-02-2005 L2005 **EM** *012
KLINE, Benjamin Matthew. 111 S 11TH ST, STE 6460 19107 #041-02-1993 L1995 **AN** *020 †05
KLINE, Jason Andrew. ■ 19107 #041-02-2002 L2002 **IM NEP** *012 †20
KLINE, Mary Josephine. 7700 GERMANTOWN AVE, FL 2 19118 #041-15-2000 L2001 **PD** *020 †55
KLINEBERG, Peter Lindsay. 3400 SPRUCE ST DEPT ANES 19104 #143-03-1969 L1975 **AN PUD** *020
KLING, Scott Richard. ■ 19130 #041-01-2008 *012
KLINGHOFFER, Leonard. 1800 LOMBARD ST 19146 #041-02-1953 L1954 **ORS** *071 †40
KLINMAN, Norman Ralph. 3400 SPRUCE ST, DEPT PATH 19104 #041-02-1962 **OS** *050
KLINMAN, Steven W. 7600 CENTRAL AVE 19111 #041-02-1971 L1972 **IM IMG** *020
KLISCH, Wolodemer. ■ 19129 #043-04-1952 L1961 **OM GP** *071
KLOCK, Barbara Louise. 5003 UMBRIA ST 19128 #008-01-1996 L1999 **PD** *020 †55 ‡
KLUMP, William Jefferis. 333 COTTMAN AVE, FOX CHASE CANCER CTR PATH 19111 #041-13-1999 L2001 **PTH** *100
KLUMPP, Thomas Russell. 7604 CENTRAL AVE, FOX CHASE-TEMPLE BMT PROG 19111 #041-01-1982 L1990 **HO HEM** *020 †20
KLYASHTORNY, Boris N. 4900 WYALUSING AVE, COMM COUNCIL MM/MR INC 19131 #913-05-1964 L1985 **P** *020

KNIBB, Charles Bernard. ■ 19101 #041-13-1987 **GS** *020
KNIGHT, Andrea M. ■ 19151 #035-01-2004 L2004 **PD** *100 †55
KNIGHT, Barbara Suzanne. 833 CHESTNUT ST, STE 701 19107 #041-13-1990 L1992 **IM** *020 †20
KNIGHT, Michelle Robin. ■ 19107 #041-02-2006 L2006 **OBG** *012
KNISELY, Alexander Saml. 324 S 34TH ST, CHILDRENS HOSP DEPT PATH 19104 #024-01-1981 L1988 **HEM ON** *020 †50
KNOX, David E. N BROAD ST 26 19141 #041-14-1976 L1977 **IM CD** *020 †20
KNUDSON, Alfred Geo, Jr. 7701 BURHOLME AVE 19111 #035-01-1947 L1950 **ON** *071 †55
KO, Anita Genny. 219 N BROAD ST, STE 8 19107 #041-15-1999 L2001 **PCC** *020 †20
KO, Janet Jinyoung. 5501 OLD YORK RD, ALBERT EINSTEIN MEDICAL CE 19141 #063-01-2002 L2002 **OBG** *100
KO, Kichul. ■ 19130 #016-01-2007 L2007 **IM** *012
KO, Paul. ■ 19144 #024-05-2002 L2002 **EM** *100 †16
KOBB, Harold Jay. 3550 MARKET ST 19104 #041-02-1960 L1961 **IM CD** *071 †20
KOBLENZER, Peter Johann. ■ 19103 #352-07-1951 L1962 **D OS** *020 †55,15 ‡
KOBRIN, Sidney Michael. 3400 SPRUCE ST, RENAL DIVISION 1 FOUNDERS 19104 #836-01-1978 L1988 **NEP IM** *020 †20
KOCH, Charles Richard. 800 SPRUCE ST 19107 #041-01-1960 L1961 **CHP P** *071
KOCH, Penelope Ann G. 410B ALDEN PARK MANOR 19144 #041-13-1969 L1973 **PD ON** *100 †20
KOCHAN, Jeffrey Philip. 3401 N BROAD ST, INTERVENTL NEURORADIOLOGY 19140 #649-14-1980 L1987 **RNR NRN** *020 †80
KOCHAN, Polly Shriver. 3401 N BROAD ST, DIAGNOSTIC IMAGING 19140 #649-14-1980 L2001 **DR** *020 †20
KOCHAR, Minisha. ■ 19154 #041-13-2004 L2004 **CD** *012 †20
KOCHER, William Douglas. 132 S 10TH ST, STE 285K 19107 #041-02-1981 L1983 **PTH** *020 †50
KOCHMAN, Michael Lee. 3400 SPRUCE ST, HUP GI DIV 3 RAVDIN 19104 #016-11-1986 L1993 **GE HEP** *040 †20
KOCHMAN, Sidney. ■ 19111 #041-77-1944, ▲ L1957 *071
KOELLE, George B. 3400 SPRUCE ST, U PA SCH MED DEPT PHARM 19104 #023-07-1950 L1970 *072
KOENIGSBERG, Bess A. 111 S 11TH 19107 #033-05-1984 L1986 **IM** *020 †20
KOENIGSBERG, Joanna Beth. ■ 19107 #041-02-2007 L2007 **TY** *012
KOEPSELL, Don Geo. 840 WALNUT ST 19107 #056-05-1978 L1980 **OPH** *020 †35
KOERS, Donald Terry. ■ 19102 #017-20-2003 L2003 **AN** *012
KOFKE, William A. 3400 SPRUCE ST, DULLES BUILDING/HUP 19104 #041-12-1978 L1979 **AN CCA** *020
KOFOD, Lauren Marie. 3400 SPRUCE ST, UNIV OF PA HLTH SYS 19104 #041-01-2004 L2004 **P** *012
KOFSKY, Stanton. 5800 RIDGE AVE 19128 #041-13-1988 L1990 **DR** *020 †80
KOGAN, Mikhail R. 3300 HENRY AVE, ALLEGHENY UNIV OF HLTH SCI 19129 #041-15-2004 L2007 **IM** *100 †20
KOHL, Benjamin Adam. 3400 SPRUCE ST, DULLES BUILDING, STE 604 19104 #041-01-1998 L2001 **AN** *100 †05
KOHLER, Christian Gudo. 1434 BAINBRIDGE ST 19146 #154-02-1985 L1994 **P** *020 †75
KOHUT, Andrew Roman. 245 N 15TH ST, DEPT OF INTERNAL MEDICINE 19102 #041-15-2002 L2002 **CD** *012 †20
KOIRALA, Rajendra Prasad. 4641 ROOSEVELT BLVD, FRIENDS HOSPITAL, P.O. BOX 19124 #672-01-2001 L2004 **P** *012
KOIWAI, Eichi Karl. 16TH ST & GIRARD AVE 19130 #041-09-1947 L1948 **PTH** *072 †50
KOKA, Anish Ravindra. 3401 N BROAD 19140 #041-13-2003 L2003 **CD** *012 †20
KOKROO, Tej Krishen. 100 E LEHIGH AVE, STE 109 19125 #495-51-1989 L2000 **IM** *020 †20 ‡
KOLANSKY, Ana S. 3400 SPRUCE ST, DEPT RADLGY HOSP UNIV PA 19104 #008-01-1984 L1992 **DR** *020 †80
KOLANSKY, Daniel M. 3400 SPRUCE ST, 9 FOUNDERS 19104 #008-01-1984 L1992 **IC CD** *020 †20
KOLASKY, Rebecca Irene. ■ 19146 #038-06-2002 L2005 **N** *100
KOLECKI, Jennifer T. 601 WALNUT ST, STE 504 19106 #041-18-2000 L2001 **OBG** *020 ‡
KOLECKI, Paul Francis. 1020 SANSOM ST, EMERGENCY MEDICINE 19107 #041-02-1992 L1998 **EM** *020 †16
KOLETH, John. 100 W LEHIGH AVE 19133 #496-01-1989 L2007 **ADP** *100
KOLOGINCZAK, Rachel Marie. 245 N 15TH ST, MAIL STOP 1011 19102 #012-01-2007 L2007 **EM** *012
KOLSKY, Rebecca Denise. ■ 19143 #041-01-2008 *012
KOLSON, Dennis Larry. 3400 SPRUCE ST 19104 #041-12-1985 L1990 **N** *050 †75
KOLSUN, Kathleen Ann. 8815 GERMANTOWN AVE FL 5 19118 #041-13-2000 L2001 **FM** *020 †18
KOLTES, John Albert, Jr. 5800 RIDGE AVE 19128 #041-02-1947 L1948 **P PYA** *071 †75
KOMARNICKY-KOCHER, Lydia. 216 N BROAD ST, FL 1 19102 #041-07-1981 L1983 **RO PTH** *020 †80
KONERU, Himabindu. ERIE AVE AT FRONT ST 19133 #495-50-1989 L2001 **CHP** *020 †75
KONG, Jane Borneen. 1000 WALNUT ST APT 1403 19107 #041-02-2003 L2003 **FM** *020 †18
KONKIMALLA, Sridevi. 800 SPRUCE ST 19107 #495-21-1998 L2005 **IM** *012
KONKLE, Barbara Ann. 111 S 11TH ST, THOS JEFFERSON U HOSP 19107 #047-05-1979 L1988 **HEM IM** *020 †20
KONNO, Fumiko. ■ 19103 #041-15-2008 *012
KONOPKA, Kristine Elizabe. ■ 19102 #041-13-2008 *012
KONSKI, Andre A. 7701 BURHOLME AVE, DEPT OF RADIATION/ONCOLOGY 19111 #035-09-1984 L2002 **RO** *020 †80
KOOHDARY, Sara Fatemeh. ■ 19147 #041-02-2005 L2005 **PD** *012
KOOLVISOOT, Ajchara. 3600 SPRUCE ST, 5 MALONEY/STE 504 19104 #891-04-1987 L1997 **RHU** *100
KOPPEL, Alexander Joshua. ■ 19128 #035-01-2008 *012
KOPPEL, Max Monroe. 833 CHESTNUT ST STE 703 19107 #041-02-1957 L1958 **U** *020 †95
KOPROWSKI, Hilary. 1020 LOCUST ST, STE M85-JAH 19107 #759-03-1940 L1961 **PD GYN** *062
KORBA, Vladimir Demetrius. PO BOX 8299 19101 #041-09-1960 L1964 **OBG** *030 †30
KORDE, Neha Sanat. ■ 19106 #033-06-2005 L2005 **IM** *012
KORDEK, Jan A. ■ 19111 #759-01-1981 *100
KOREN, Dorit. ■ 19102 #038-06-2003 L2003 **PDE** *012 †55
KOREN, Garrett Leigh. ■ 19103 #033-05-2001 L2006 **P** *020
KORENTZWITT, Edith. 6901 OLD YORK RD 19126 #041-07-1939 L1940 **IM** *071
KORENYI-BOTH, Andras L. 2116 CHESTNUT ST 19103 #473-02-1962 L1979 **ATP GP** *020 †50
KORETZKY, Gary Alan. 421 CURIE BLVD, 415 BRB II 19104 #041-01-1984 L1999 **RHU IM** *020 †20
KORIN, Laura. ■ 19107 #035-46-2007 L2007 **FP** *012

KORMAN, Charles H. 120 E HUNTINGDON ST, STE 100 19125 #041-77-2003, ▲ L2003 IM *020

KORNHAUSER, Michael S. 111 S 11TH ST, STE 4260 19107 #041-02-1980 L1982 NPM PD *020 †55

KORUS, Gary B. 51 N 39TH ST, STE 2D 19104 #038-06-1989 L1994 GS *020 †85

KORYTNAYA, Evgenia Efimov. 5501 OLD YORK RD #913-72-2001 L2006 IM *012

KOSHKAREVA, Yekaterina Al. ■ 19116 #041-13-2006 L2007 GS *012

KOSMIN, Aaron Rushfield. 5401 OLD YORK RD, DEPT. OF MEDICINE 19141 #033-06-2000 L2001 ID IM *012

KOSS, Seth Jeremy. 3131 WALNUT 19104 #041-01-1996 L1998 FM *020 †18

KOSTIANOVSKY, Deborah J. 245 S 8TH 19106 #041-02-1988 L1991 P *020 †75

KOSTIANOVSKY, Jorge E. ■ 19103 #132-04-1959 L1972 P CHP *072 ‡

KOSTIANOVSKY, Mery. 205 EDISON BUILDING 19107 #132-04-1958 L1975 PTH CLP *020 †50

KOSTINSKY, Spencer Jay. 800 SPRUCE ST, HALL MERCER CMHC 19107 #041-14-2000 L2001 P *020

KOSTMAN, Jay Robt. 3401 N BROAD 19140 #008-01-1984 L1986 ID *020 †20

KOTAGIRI, Sunanda. 5501 OLD YORK RD 19141 #449-50-1997 L2006 PD *012

KOTAPKA, Mark Joel. 5401 OLD YORK RD, KLEIN PROF BLDG STE 501 19141 #023-01-1985 L1988 NS *020 †25

KOTHARI, Neha A. 3400 SPRUCE ST 19104 #033-05-1993 L2000 PDR *020,80

KOTIAH, Sandy Diana. 111 S 11TH ST, DEPT OF HEMO/ONC 19107 #035-06-2004 L2004 HO *012 †20

KOTLER, Morris Nathan. 5501 OLD YORK RD 19141 #836-01-1959 L1973 CD IM *020 †20

KOTLER, Ronald Lee. 700 SPRUCE ST, STE 500 19106 #041-01-1982 L1983 IM *020 †20

KOTLOFF, Robert Mark. 3400 SPRUCE ST 19104 #008-01-1983 L1984 PUD CCM *020 †20

KOTOH, Samuel Y. 5000 WOODLAND AVE, WOODLAND AVENUE HEALTH CEN 19143 #412-02-1989 L2001 IM *020 †20

KOTSKO, Jude David. ■ 19107 #055-01-2006 L2006 EM *012

KOTSKO, Raegan Nichole. ■ 19106 #055-01-2003 L2006 OBG *020

KOTTON, Ryan. 3401 N BROAD ST, TEMPLE UNIV HOSP 19140 #550-02-2004 L2004 PPM *012

KOTWAL, Neville Homi. 561 FAIRTHORNE AVE 19128 #041-14-1989 L1991 CHP *020 †75

KOU CHOW, Annie. ■ 19114 #270-01-2002 L2007 FP *012

KOUTCHER, Martin Edward. 2221 S BROAD 19148 #041-02-1967 L1968 RHU IM *020 †20

KOVAR, Leo. ■ 19131 #035-03-1950 L1953 P *071 †75

KOVARIK, Carrie Lynn. 3600 SPRUCE ST, 2 MALONEY BLDG 19104 #048-04-2001 L2006 D *100 †15

KOVATICH, Audrey M. 230 N BROAD ST DEPT PED 19102 #041-02-1979 L1979 PD *020

KOVEN, Norman Lee. 10125 VERREE RD, STE 106 19116 #035-19-1978 L1980 AI PD *020 †55,03

KOWAL, Lionel. WILLIS EYE HOSP/PED OPH 19107 #143-02-1974 L1987 PD OPH *100

KOWALCZYK, Monika. 3401 N BROAD ST, DEPT OF MEDICINE 8-PP 19140 #021-01-2006 L2006 IM *012

KOWALSKI, Christopher. 3401 N BROAD ST, STE 400/PARKINSON PAVILION 19140 #041-13-1997 L2002 GS *020 †85

KOWALSKI, Thomas Edward. 132 S 10TH ST 19107 #035-06-1988 L1991 GE HEP *020 †20

KOWLESSAR, O Dhodanand. 1025 WALNUT 19107 #035-45-1955 GE IM *050

KOZERA, Richard John. 3420 N BROAD ST, 107 MED RESEARCH BLDG 19140 #008-01-1965 L1987 IM END *030 †20

KOZIN, Scott Hal. 3551 N BROAD ST, SHRINERS HOSPITAL CHILDREN 19140 #041-09-1986 L1987 HS ORS *020 †40

KOZINSKI, Andrzej W. 3400 SPRUCE ST 19104 #759-03-1953 IM OS *050

KOZLOVSKAYA, Svetlana. ■ 19116 #913-01-1992 L1998 IM *075

KOZUCH, Patricia Lorraine. ■ 19107 #035-20-1999 L2006 GE *100 †20

KOZYAK, Benjamin Wesley. ■ 19104 #041-01-2008 *012

KRAEMER, Francis Wickham, III. ■ 19119 #051-07-2001 L2001 PAN *100 †05

KRAEMER, Mary Suchenski. 3401 N BROAD ST, INTERNAL MEDICINE 19140 #051-07-2001 L2001 IM *020

KRAFT, Walter Karl, Jr. 132 S 10TH ST, 1170 MAIN BUILDING 19107 #041-12-1995 L1997 PA IM *050 †20

KRAIN, Samuel. 3300 HENRY AVE, MEDICAL COLLGE OF PNNSYLVN 19129 #041-02-1961 L1962 R *020 †80,28 ‡

KRAINES-HOFFMAN, Seth A. ■ 19118 #041-01-2000 L2003 PCC *012 †20

KRAINSKY, Samuel M. 100 E LEHIGH AVE 19125 #913-18-1974 L1982 IM *020 †20

KRAJEKIAN, Joseph I. 2900 W QUEEN LN, DREXEL UNIV COLL OF MED 19129 #041-15-2006 L2006 *012

KRAMAN, David Jonathan. 2137 WELSH RD STE 2D, UROLOGICAL ASSOC PC 19115 #041-01-1987 L1989 U *020 †95

KRAMER, Alanna Meredith. 9501 ROOSEVELT BLVD, STE 410 19114 #041-13-1995 L1997 PD *020 †55

KRAMER, Jan Lloyd. 5501 OLD YORK RD 19141 #023-07-1978 L1992 AN GS *020 †05

KRAMER, Nora M. 8220 CASTOR AVE, STE 1 19152 #132-02-1984 L1991 P *020 †75

KRAMER, Sandra Sue Kynett. 3400 SPRUCE ST 19104 #020-02-1968 L1988 R IM *020 †80

KRANE, Marvin Allan. BROAD & VINE STS 19102 #051-04-1956 L1962 OBG GO *071 †30

KRANTZ, Kathryn Elizabeth. 9331 OLD BUSTLETON AVE 19115 #008-02-1979 L1981 OBG *020 †30

KRASNER, Matthew A. ■ 19131 #048-13-2002 L2002 DR *100 †80

KRATHEN, Michael Scott. ■ 19104 #041-01-2007 L2007 IM *012

KRAUSE, Robert L. 3996 RED LION RD 19114 #041-01-1962 L1963 CD IM *030 †20

KRAUSS, Jack. 2301 S BROAD 19148 #041-02-1961 L1962 P *071 †75

KRAUSS, Richard K. 3998 RED LION RD STE 106 19114 #041-09-1977 L1979 OBG *020 †30

KRAUSZ, Daniela. 5501 OLD YORK RD, DEPT. OF PSYCHIATRY 19141 #781-01-1995 L2001 P *100

KRAVITZ, Joel. 5501 OLD YORK RD, KORMAN BLG B14 19141 #067-01-1996 L2003 EM *020 †16

KRAYCHIK, Eduard A. 3998 RED LION RD, STE 125 19114 #913-18-1997 L2005 P *020 †75

KRECZ, Joseph Gregory. ■ 19144 #033-06-2008 *012

KREIBICH, Thomas Alfred. ■ 19130 #041-01-2007 L2007 IM *012

KREIDER, Edward Eugene. 3400 SPRUCE ST 19104 #041-09-1983 L1984 AN *020 †05

KREIDER, Maryelizabeth. 3400 SPRUCE ST 19104 #041-01-1997 L2000 PCC *020 †20

KREIGER, Portia Ann. 324 S 34TH ST RM 5203, DIV OF ANATOMIC PATH 19104 #041-01-2002 L2002 ATP PP *062

KREIN, Howard David. 925 CHESTNUT ST, OF OTOLARYNGOLOGY 19107 #041-02-2000 L2001 OTO *020 †45

KREKUN, Susan. 3400 SPRUCE ST, 2009 PENN TOWER 19104 #035-08-1994 L1998 IM *020 †20

KREMENS, Daniel Erik. 900 WALNUT ST, STE 200 19107 #041-02-2000 L2001 N *020 †75

KREMER, Felix. 230 N BROAD ST 19102 #913-50-1973 L1997 AN *020 †05

KRENITSKY, Kevin Francis. 1010 ARCH ST, UNIT 604 19107 #041-02-1997 L1999 FM *020 †18

KRESHAK, Allyson Ann. 239 E THOMPSON ST, 1020 SANSOM ST. 19125 #041-02-2002 L2002 EM *100 †16

KRETSCHMAN, Dana Marie. ■ 19107 #041-13-2007 L2007 IM *012

KREVSKY, Benjamin. 3401 N BROAD ST, TEMPLE HOSP DEPT GE 19140 #038-41-1979 L1982 GE IM *020 †20 ‡

KRICUN, Morrie E. 3400 SPRUCE ST, DEPT RADIOLOGY 19104 #041-02-1963 L1964 DR *071 †80

KRIEGER, Benson. ■ 19130 #041-02-1945 L1946 FM *072

KRISCH, Robert Earle. 5301 CEDAR AVE, DEPT OF RADIATION ONCOLOGY 19143 #041-13-1960 L1980 RO ON *071 †80

KRISHAN, Rachna. ■ 19102 #041-15-2008 *012

KRISHNAN, Sriyesh. 3400 SPRUCE ST, DEPT RAD 19104 #036-07-2006 L2007 DR *012

KRIVITSKY, Leonard. 1745 N 4TH ST, ACHIEVEMENT THROUGH COUNSE 19122 #913-27-1975 L1981 IM GP *020

KROL, Roman. 2900 W QUEEN LN, MCP HAHNEMANN UNIV 19129 #305-01-2000 L2001 PCC *020 †20

KRON, Reuben Eliahu. 3400 SPRUCE ST, FOUNDERS 11TH FLOOR 19104 #035-08-1954 L1959 P N *050 †75

KROOP, Howard Samuel. 132 S 10TH ST, 480 MAIN BUILDING 19107 #036-01-1972 L1973 GE IM *020 †20 ‡

KROSER, Albert S. 2855 WELSH RD 19152 #041-77-1958, ▲ L1959 FM *071

KROSER, Joyann Allison. 219 N BROAD ST, 5TH FL MAILSTOP 913 19107 #041-07-1990 L1992 GE IM *020 †20

KROUSE, Theodore B. 100 E LEHIGH AVE, DEPT PATH 19125 #041-01-1948 L1949 PTH IM *071 †50 ‡

KRUSE, Lakota Klaas. 34TH ST AND CIVIC CENTER B 19104 #041-01-1990 L1992 GPM *030 †70,55

KRUSE, Laurel Farnham. 3550 MARKET ST, FL 4 19104 #033-06-1986 L1987 PD *020 †55

KRUSZEWSKI, Patrice Genev. 111 S 11TH ST, THOMAS JEFFERSON UNIV 19107 #041-77-2006, ▲ L2006 *012

KRYNETSKIY, Evgeny E. ■ 19107 #041-15-2006 L2006 ORS *012

KRYSS, Meri Lvovna. 11054 RENNARD ST, # 11054 19116 #913-01-1981 L1998 IM *020 †20

KUBACKI, Joseph John. 3401 N BROAD ST, TEMPLE OPTHAL DEPT 19140 #041-13-1975 L1976 OPH PO *020 †20

KUCER, Brian Thomas. ■ 19130 #041-02-2004 L2004 PM *012

KUCERA, Tomas. ■ 19144 #286-13-1981 NSP *020

KUCHACULLA, Vishal R... ■ 19103 #166-03-2001 L2004 IM *012

KUCHARCZUK, John C. 3400 SPRUCE ST, FL 6 19104 #041-01-1992 L1994 TS *020 †85,90

KUCHARCZUK, Kristen L. 3550 MARKET ST FL 5, CHOP PRIMARY CARE CENTER 19104 #041-01-1998 L2000 PD *030 †55

KUCZINSKI, Kim Marie. 3401 N BROAD 19140 #041-77-2004, ▲ L2004 IM *020 †20

KUDSI, Hussam. 5501 OLD YORK RD, ALBERT EINSTEIN MED CTR 19141 #308-13-1999 L2001 GS *020

KUEPPERS, Friedrich. 3400 N BROAD 19140 #407-25-1961 L1973 OS PUD *020

KUHNEN, Ann Elizabeth. 1 FRANKLIN PLZ 19102 #024-05-1988 L1995 OM FM *030 †70,18

KUKAFKA, Jeremy David. ■ 19147 #033-06-2003 L2003 AN *100

KULANDAIVEL, Kandan. ■ 19144 #495-04-2003 L2005 N *012

KULASEKARAN, Yeshwant. ■ 19146 #038-41-2004 L2004 PD *100 †55

KULKARNI, Kedar. 2601 HOLME AVE 19152 #496-15-1989 L2004 R RNR *062 †80

KULKARNI, Prakash Vinayak. 111 S 11TH ST, STE 8490 19107 #495-28-1974 L2000 AN *020

KULKARNI, Prashant Prakas. ■ 19107 #041-02-2006 L2007 AN *012

KULKARNI, Shubha. 5501 OLD YORK RD 19141 #495-98-2000 L2005 P *012

KULKARNI, Snehankita Guru. 4TH FLOOR - S TOWER MAIL, DREXEL UNIVERSITY COLLEGE 19102 #496-42-2003 L2007 GS *012

KUMAR, Anjali Gupta. 3400 SPRUCE ST, HOSPITAL OF THE UNIV OF PA 19104 #017-20-1992 L1997 RO *020 †20

KUMAR, Anoop. 5501 OLD YORK RD 19141 #661-02-2007 L2007 EM *012

KUMAR, Gajal. ■ 19107 #041-02-2008 *012

KUMAR, Karthik Chiranjeev. ■ 19128 #041-15-2008 L2008 *012

KUMAR, Monisha Anjali. ■ 19103 #041-15-2000 L2001 N *020 †75

KUMAR, Pallavi. ■ 19103 #036-07-2007 *012

KUMAR, Ritu. 3400 SPRUCE ST, OF PENNSYLVANIA 19104 #041-15-2007 L2007 EM *012

KUMAR, Rohini J. ■ 19107 #041-02-2007 L2007 IM *012

KUMAR, Rohit. 1800 LOMBARD ST, ONE GRADUATE PLAZA 19146 #496-09-2001 L2003 PCC *012 †20

KUMAR, Veerandra. ■ 19126 #495-03-1955 L1968 IM PD *071

KUMARAIAH, Deepa. ■ 19104 #041-01-2008 *012

KUNA, Samuel Thos. UNIV & WOODLAND AVENUE, VAMC (111)-SLEEP SECTION 19104 #035-01-1974 L1975 PUD *050 †20

KUNDAVARAM, Chandan Reddy. 111 S 11TH ST, THOS JEFFERSON UNIV HOSP 19107 #003-01-2007 L2007 GS *012

KUNDU, Mondira. ■ 19104 #041-02-1999 L2008 *100 †50

KUNDU, Sudeshna. 800 SPRUCE ST 19107 #496-12-1999 L2003 IM *100 †20

KUNG, Brian Chunsu. 925 CHESTNUT ST, FL 6 19107 #041-02-2001 L2001 OTO *100 †45

KUNG, Shiang-Cheng. 5501 OLD YORK RD, NEPHROLOGY DIVISION 19141 #836-01-1992 L2000 NEP *020 †20

KUNG, Shiang-Ju. ■ 19104 #836-01-1995 L2001 MPD AI *100 †20,55,03

KUNIS, Richard L. 440 S BROAD ST, UNIT 1401 19146 #035-19-1979 L2008 CD IM *020 †20

KUNKEL, Elisabeth J S. 1020 SANSOM ST, THOMAS JEFFERSON UNIV 19107 #067-01-1983 L1989 P PYM *030 †75

KUNZ, Richard Daniel. ■ 19122 #051-04-2005 L2006 PM *012

KUO, Cindy P. 2230 COTTMAN AVE 19149 #041-02-1990 L1990 FM *020 †18

KUO, Grace. 3550 MARKET ST, CHILDREN'S HOSPITAL OF PHI 19104 #043-01-1994 L1997 PD *020 †55 ‡

KUO, Maryanne May. ■ 19107 #041-02-2007 L2007 *012

KUPERMAN, Julio Luis. 1900 S BROAD ST 19145 #132-01-1968 L1973 N *020 †75

KUPFER, Joel M. 5501 OLD YORK RD, DEPT OF CARDIOLOGY 19141 #035-47-1985 L2004 CD IM *020 †20

KUPFER, Katie Jean. 1028 IRVING ST 19107 #041-02-2008 L2008 *012

KUPFER, Mendel. 1513 RACE ST 19102 #550-02-2002 L2003 PM *020 †60

KURD, Mark Faisal. ■ 19127 #041-02-2007 L2007 ORS *012

KURIAN, Ashwin Antony. 2900 W QUEEN LN 19129 #496-39-2002 L2006 IM *012

KURIEN, Karimpumanil M. 111 S 11TH ST, STE 8490 19107 #496-09-1985 L1997 AN *020 †05

■ = Address Information Privacy Protected

KURITZKY, Nicolas Keith. ■ 19107 #041-01-2001 L2003 **RO** *100 †80
KURNIK, Brenda Chinn. 245 N 15TH ST, MAILSTOP 437 19102 #028-02-1978 L1987
 NEP IM *020 †20 ‡
KURTZ, Alfred Bernard. 132 S 10TH ST, 763 C MAIN BLDG ULTRASOUND 19107
 #005-11-1972 L1977 **DR OS** *020 †80
KURYAN, Ranita Elizebeth. 111 S 11TH ST, THOMAS JEFFERSON UNIV 19107
 #041-15-2007 L2007 *012
KUSHEN, Medina Calli. ■ 19130 #026-04-2005 L2007 **NM** *012
KUSHNER, Jake Alden. 3615 CIVIC CENTER BLVD, DIV ENDOCRINOLOGY/ARC802C 19104
 #035-03-1994 L2003 **PDE** *020 †55
KUSHON, Donald John, Jr. 1427 VINE ST, FL 8 19102 #041-09-1986 L1988 **P** *050 †75
KUSIAK, Joseph Francis. 7701 BURHOLME AVE, FOX CHASE CANCER CENTER 19111
 #041-01-1975 L1976 **PS HNS** *020 †65,85
KUSSMAUL, William Guy, III. 230 N BROAD ST, FL 7 19102 #041-01-1976 L1978
 IC CD *020 †20
KUTALEK, Steven P. 245 N 15TH ST 19102 #035-19-1979 L1981 **ICE CD** *020 †20
KUZMA, Mary Ann. 2126 FAIRMOUNT AVE 19130 #041-01-1984 L1985 **IM** *020 †20
KWAH, Joann Aekyung. ■ 19144 #041-15-2006 L2006 **IM** *012
KWAK, Andrew. 3400 SPRUCE ST 19104 #041-02-1996 L2001 **VIR** *020 †80
KWAKWA, Helena Akua. 500 S BROAD ST 19146 #008-01-1992 L1996 **IM** *020 †20
KWAN, Matthew David. 3401 N BROAD ST, OF S 19140 #023-01-2002 L2002 **GS** *012
KWAN, Tina C. ■ 19103 #048-14-2001 L2005 **PD** *020 †55
KWASNIAK, Diane Teresa. 3551 N BROAD ST 19140 #041-13-1981 L1983 **AN** *075 †05
KWIATKOWSKI, Janet Lucy. 324 S 34TH ST 19104 #035-01-1992 L1995 **PHO** *020 †55
KWON, Soohyun. ■ 19107 #041-02-2008 L2008 *012
KY, Betty. ■ 19146 #016-02-2006 L2006 **IM** *012
KY, Bonnie. ■ 19103 #041-01-2001 L2001 **CD** *100
KYLE, George Clayton. 3400 SPRUCE ST 19104 #041-01-1947 L1948 **DIA IM** *071 †20
KYLE, Thomas Rogers, III. 333 COTTMAN AVE 19111 #041-01-1979 L1983 **IM** *020 †20
KYRILLOS, Janine Viviane. 833 CHESTNUT ST, STE 701 19107 #033-06-1999 L2001
 IM *020 †20
LABIK, Jeanna Ane. ■ 19107 #041-15-2007 L2007 *012
LABORDE, Andrea Totin. 1200 W TABOR RD 19141 #041-07-1987 L1990 **PM** *020 †60
LABOWSKIE, Richard Jos. ■ 19143 #010-02-1967 L1969 **OM PD** *020
LACKMAN, Richard Danl. 1015 CHESTNUT ST 19107 #041-01-1977 L1978 **ORS** *075 †40
LACKNER, David Michael. 326 TREE ST 19148 #035-46-1983 L1984 **IM RO** *020 †20
LADAVAC, April Suzanne. 3401 N BROAD ST STE 105, DEPT OF PSYCHIATRY 19140
 #041-13-2005 L2005 **P** *012
LADD, Christopher Dean. 5800 RIDGE AVE 19128 #038-43-1991 L1995 **DR** *020 †80
LADENHEIM, Miles Chas. 561 FAIRTHORNE AVE 19128 #035-08-1987 L1988 **P** *020 †75
LADENHEIM, Steven Elliot. 1920 CHESTNUT ST, STE 200 19103 #041-07-1978 L1982
 OTO A *020 †45
LAFAIR, Joel Sidney. 7500 CENTRAL AVE STE 100 19111 #869-07-1963 L1964 **PUD** *020
LAFER, Edmund Lawrence. 7604 CENTRAL AVE, FRIENDS HALL SUITE 100 19111
 #550-02-1987 L1988 **IM** *020 †20
LAFLEUR, Ricardo. 1025 WALNUT ST, COLLEGE BUILDING ROOM 801 19107
 #035-03-2004 L2004 **IM** *020 †20
LA FOLLETTE, Paul S, Jr. ■ 19119 #041-13-1974 L1975 **EM OS** *050
LAFONTANT, Gilbert. 5501 OLD YORK RD, 5 LEVY BUILDING 19141 #440-01-1985 L1987
 PM *020 †60
LAGER, Eric. BROAD & VINE STS 19102 #035-08-1958 L1962 **P PYA** *020 †75
LAGUERRE, Roberta Linda. 131 E CHELTEN AVE, ERIE AVE AT FRONT ST 19144
 #035-08-1999 L2001 **PD** *020 †55
LAHERI, Aasha Narendra. ■ 19128 #041-15-2006 L2006 **PD** *012
LAHMANN, Brian Michael. ■ 19104 #041-13-2006 L2008 **EM** *012
LAI, Emily W. ■ 19128 #043-01-2003 L2003 *012
LAIBSON, Peter R. 840 WALNUT ST, STE 920 19107 #035-08-1959 L1965 **OPH** *071 †35
LAIGHOLD, Saaron Levy. 1025 WALNUT ST, THOMAS JEFFERSON UNIV HOSP 19107
 #035-20-2003 L2003 **CD** *012 †20
LAIGON, Eugene Edward, Jr. 1101 MARKET ST, FL 10 19107 #010-01-1977 L1978
 PHP MDM *030 †70
LAINE, Christine Anne. 190 N INDEPENDENCE MALL W, ANNALS OF INTERNAL MED 19106
 #035-48-1987 L1992 **IM** *050 †20
LAJE, Pablo. 1 CHILDRENS CTR, CHILDREN'S HOSPITAL OF PHI 19104 #132-01-2000 L2005
 PDS *100
LAKHANI, Paras C. ■ 19106 #041-01-2005 L2005 **DR** *012
LAKIN, Gregory Ethan. ■ 19103 #042-02-2004 L2007 **GS** *020
LAKSHMAN, Thiru Venkat. ■ 19107 #020-12-2002 L2002 **GS** *012
LALLAS, Costas Dean. 1025 WALNUT ST STE 1100, DEPT OF UROLOGY 19107
 #041-02-1998 L2005 **U** *020 †95
LALLY, Brian Edward. 333 COTTMAN AVE, RADIATION ONCOLOGY 19111 #041-02-2000 L2003
 RO *100 †80
LALLY, Sara Elizabeth. 840 WALNUT ST, STE 1440 19107 #041-02-2001 L2001 **OPH** *020 †35
LALOR, Michael John. 1900 W OLNEY AVE, HEALTH CENTER 19141 #033-05-1995 L1997
 IM *020 †20
LALWANI, Tarik. ■ 19107 #041-02-2003 L2006 **IM** *100
LAM, Andrew. 840 WALNUT ST 1020 19107 #041-01-2002 L2003 **OPH** *012 †35
LAM, Christopher. 3440 MARKET ST 4TH FL, ADOLESCENT PSYCHIATRY 19104
 #048-13-1990 L2004 **P** *020 †75
LAM, Louis Wai-Kei. 2801 ISLAND AVE, STE 8 19153 #041-07-1989 L1991 **IM** *020
LAMBERT, Erica Hope. 950 WALNUT ST, APT 707 19107 #041-02-2003 L2005 **U** *020
LAMBERT, Maciej. 2643 ORTHODOX ST 19137 #759-08-1975 L1986 **IM** *020
LAMBERT, Michele P. 3400 CIVIC CENTER BLVD, DIV HEM #033-05-1999 L2001
 PHO *050 †55
LAMBERTSEN, Christian J. 3620 HAMILTON WALK 19104 #041-01-1943 L1944 **PA AM** *050
LAMBRIGHT, Warren Dean. 8835 GERMANTOWN AVE 19118 #041-02-1966 L1971
 IM FM *030 †20,18
LAMBSON, David L. 2301 S BROAD ST 19148 #011-02-1985 L1986 **AN** *020 †05
LAMDAN, Ruth. 100 E LEHIGH AVE, MAB 305 19125 #041-14-1975 L1976 **P PYG** *040 †75 ‡
LAMMI, Matthew Robert. 3401 N BROAD ST 19140 #041-13-2005 L2005 **IM** *012
LANCASTER, Eric. 2429 LOCUST ST 19107 #023-01-2003 L2003 **CN** *012
LANDRY, Angie Marie. 34TH-CIVIC CTR BLVD, DEPT OF PEDS 19104 #021-05-2002 **PDR** *012
LANDRY, Jonathan Philip. ■ 19130 #041-12-2006 L2006 **EM** *012
LANDSBURG, Daniel Jeffrey. ■ 19147 ...
LANE, Andrew Peter. 3400 SPRUCE ST, DEPT OF OTORHINLARYNGOLOGY 19104
 #041-01-1994 L2000 **OTO** *020 †45

LANE, J Lindsey. 833 CHESTNUT ST, STE 300 19107 #917-09-1978 L1981 **PD** *040 †55
LANE, Katherine Ann. ■ 19106 #035-01-2003 L2004 **OPH** *100
LANE, Meghan Brooks. ■ 19143 #008-01-2006 L2006 **AN** *012
LANE, Sally Dimschultz. 5735 RIDGE AVE STE 103 19128 #041-01-1974 L1975
 ON HEM *020 †20
LANFRANCO, Anthony Reed. ■ 19128 #041-15-2003 L2003 **IM** *012
LANG, Nikki. 634 PINE ST 19106 #041-07-1978 L1979 **FM EM** *020 †18
LANG, Shihshan. ■ 19104 #011-03-2007 L2007 **GS** *012
LANGAN, Nicholas Early. 1 PENN BLVD # 3RDFLTWR 19144 #550-02-1986 L1989
 CD IM *020 †20
LANGE, Beverly Jane. 324 S 34TH ST 19104 #041-13-1971 **PHO** *050 †55
LANGE, Nancy Elizabeth. 3600 SPRUCE ST, HOSP OF THE UNIV OF PA 19104
 #035-20-2003 L2007 **PCC** *012 †20
LANGER, Corey Jay. 333 COTTMAN AVE, FCCC DEPT MED ONCOLOGY 19111
 #024-05-1981 L1982 **HEM ON** *020 †20
LANGER, David Jonathan. 3400 SPRUCE ST 19104 #041-01-1991 L1993 **NS** *020 †25
LANGER, Dennis H. 2005 MARKET ST, PHOENIX IP VENTURES #2030 19103
 #010-02-1975 L1992 **CHP LM** *030 †75 ‡
LANGER, Jill Eve. 3400 SPRUCE ST, HOSP UNIV OF PA RAD DEPT 19104 #041-01-1986 L1987
 DR *020 †80
LANGLEBEN, Daniel D. 3900 CHESTNUT ST, TREATMENT RESEARCH CENTER 19104
 #550-01-1988 L1990 **NM P** *020 †75
LANGLOIS, Read T. ■ 19104 #041-01-2008 *012
LANGLOTZ, Curtis Philip. 3400 SPRUCE ST 19104 #005-11-1989 L1993 **DR** *050 †80
LANGMAN, Jessica Paige. ■ 19107 #041-14-2008 L2008 *012
LANGMAN, Marc Jay. 4641 ROOSEVELT BLVD 19124 #041-09-1974 L1976 **CHP PYA** *020
LANGO, Miriam Natasa. 333 COTTMAN AVE, DEPT OF SURGICAL ONCOLOGY 19111
 #035-19-1996 L2003 **OTO** *020 †45
LANKEN, Paul Nicolas. 3400 SPRUCE ST, 8.43 W GATES 19104 #024-01-1970 L1975
 CCM PUD *040 †20
LANKFORD, Edward B. 925 CHESTNUT ST 19107 #023-01-1984 L1990 **CD** *050 †20
LANKIN, Kenneth Michael. 4898 S BROAD ST, BLDG 615 19112 #023-12-1991 L1992
 OM FM *020 †18,70
LA NOCE, Louis F. 5817 HENRY AVE 19128 #041-02-1946 L1947 **FM P** *071
LANSMEN, Amy Kaneff. 1 PENN BLVD 19144 #041-07-1982 L1983 **DR** *020 †80
LANTIERI, Robert Louis. 2601 HOLME AVE 19152 #041-09-1975 L1976 **DR NM** *020 †80,28
LAPAYOWKER, Marc S. ■ 19103 #041-13-1954 L1956 **R** *071 †20
LAREEF, Mohamed Thaha Moh. 1800 LOMBARD ST, GRADUATE HOSP (TENET HLTH 19146
 #913-65-1992 L2004 **IM** *012
LARGOZA, Naciancenco T, Sr. 1800 LOMBARD ST 19146 #748-01-1955 L1971 **IM FM** *071 †18
LARICCIA, Patrick James. 51 N 39TH ST 19104 #165-02-1978 L1982 **IM** *020 †20
LARKIN, Jacob Charles. ■ 19107 #041-12-2004 L2004 **OBG** *012
LARNED, Paul Alan. 230 N BROAD ST, HAHNEMANN HOSP 19102 #025-07-1969 L1971
 GPM FM *020
LA ROSSA, Donato D. 3400 SPRUCE ST, 10TH FL 19104 #010-02-1967 L1968 **PS** *020 †85,65
LARRAURI REYES, Delia Mer. 5501 OLD YORK RD 19141 #935-05-2002 L2006 **OBG** *012
LARRIEU, Alberto J. 2301 E ALLEGHENY AVE, NORTHEASTERN HOSPITAL ER 19134
 #042-01-1973 L1981 **GS TS** *020 †85,90
LARSON, Robert Anthony. 111 S 11TH ST, STE 6350 19107 #041-01-1993 L1997 **VS** *020 †85
LARSON, Sigrid Anne. 2601 HOLME AVE 19152 #041-01-2000 L2001 **FM** *020 †18 ‡
LARSON, Steven Craig. 3400 SPRUCE ST, EMERGENCY DEPT 19104 #041-01-1988 L1990
 EM IM *020 †20
LARYNGAKIS, Nicholas Aris. 1420 LOCUST ST, APT 14P 19102 #011-03-2007 L2007 **GS** *012
LASA, Javier Jorge. ■ 19128 #023-07-2005 L2005 **PD** *012
LA SALVIA, Lucy A. 3001 W QUEEN LN 19129 #041-09-1945 L1946 **GYN OBG** *071 †30
LASKE, Douglas Walter. 3401 N BROAD ST STE 580, TEMPLE UNIV HOSP NEUROSURG 19140
 #035-01-1985 L1995 **NS** *020 †25
LASKIN, Leona P Cohen. ■ 19103 #035-15-1949 L1981 **AN** *071 †05
LASOTA, George Leslaus. 4641 ROOSEVELT BLVD 19124 #041-02-1962 L1963 **P** *020 †75 ‡
LASSMANN, Jenny. 1 CHILDRENS CTR, OFFICE OF MEDICAL AFFAIR 19104
 #408-30-2000 L2005 *100
LATCHMAN, Robert R. 51 N 39TH ST, PRESBY MED CTR-PHILADELPHI 19104 #661-01-1990
 IM *100
LATIES, Alan Malev. 51 N 39TH ST, SCHETE EYE INSTITUTE 19104 #048-04-1959 L1960
 OPH *050 †35
LATIF, Sherif Medhat. ■ 19104 #041-01-2007 **IM** *012
LATIF, Shuaib Aziz. ■ 19106 #028-02-1999 L2007 **ICE** *012 †20
LATTE, Shelly. ALUMNI AFFAIRS, ALBERT EINSTEIN MC 19141 #409-46-2005 L2008 *100
LAU, Dian C. 520 S 19TH ST, STE 1B 19146 #041-01-1991 L1994 **AN** *105 ‡
LAU, Jason Matthew. 3400 SPRUCE ST, OF PENNSYLVAN 19104 #041-13-2002 L2002
 EM *020 †16
LAU, Wayne Bond. 239 E THOMPSON ST, 1020 SANSOM ST. 19125 #041-02-2004 L2004
 EM *100
LAUCIUS, Joseph Frederick. 1015 CHESTNUT ST STE 306 19107 #041-02-1967 L1970
 ON IM *020 †20 ‡
LAUFER, Dagna Skoog. 34TH ST AND CIVIC CENTER B 19104 #035-09-1985 L1987 **PD ID** *020
LAUFER, Igor. HOAP-UNIV OF PA, DEPT RADIO 19104 #065-01-1967 L1976 **DR GE** *020 †80
LAUFER-CAHANA, Ayala. 34TH & CIVIC CENTER BLVD, CHILDREN'S HOSP OF PHIL 19104
 #550-01-1991 L1998 **MG** *020
LAUGHINGWELL, Raeph. ■ 19123 #033-05-2004 L2004 **OBG** *012
LAUGHLIN, Mark Allan. 1025 WALNUT ST 19107 #016-01-1983 L1986 **IM ID** *020
LAURENCE, Brett Ryan. ■ 19147 #041-13-2006 L2006 **IM** *012
LAURY, William L. 1 PENN BLVD 19144 #041-02-1974 L1975 **IM GP** *020
LAUTENBACH, Ebbing. 423 GUARDIAN DR, 825 BLOCKLEY HALL 19104 #035-01-1993 L1995
 ID *020 †20
LAUTENBACH, Gillian Ladd. 3701 MARKET ST, STE 760 19104 #035-01-1993 L1995
 IM *020 †20
LA VAN, Donald Wolf. 1420 LOCUST ST 19102 #041-01-1959 L1960 **CD IM** *020 †20
LAVASANI, Leela Sanamme. 925 CHESTNUT ST, JEFFERSON OTOLARYNGOLOGY 19107
 #010-01-2006 L2006 **OTO** *012
LAVELLE, Jane Marie. 324 S 34TH ST 19104 #010-02-1984 L1986 **PEM** *020 †55
LAVI, Ehud. 449 JOHNSON PAVILION, DIV/NEURO UNIV/PA MED CTR 19104 #550-03-1978 L1990
 PTH NP *020 †50
LAVIGNE, Keri Marie. 7600 CENTRAL AVE, JEANE HOSP EMG DEPT 19111 #035-15-1990 L1996
 PM *020 †60 ‡
LAVINE, Marc Adam. 2137 WELSH RD, STE 2C 19115 #041-13-1995 L2000 **U** *020 †95

LAVOIE, Aubert. 34TH & CIVIC CENTER STS, CHILDRENS HOSP OF PHILA 19104 #067-03-1980 L1986 **AI IM** *020 †03
LAVOIE, Megan Elizabeth. ■ 19103 #024-07-2004 L2004 **PD** *100 †55
LAVU, Navin. 2900 W QUEEN LN 19129 #003-75-2005, ▲ L2006 **AN** *012
LAWRENCE, David Ansley. ■ 19128 #041-15-2008 *012
LAWRENCE, James Patrick. ■ 19106 #008-02-2002 L2007 **ORS** *100
LAWRENCE, Tonya Nicole. 4TH FLOOR - S TOWER MAIL, DREXEL UNIVERSITY COLLEGE 19102 #305-01-2007 L2007 **P** *012
LAWSON, George Benedict. 241 S 6TH ST 19106 #041-01-1955 L1956 **P PYA** *062 †75
LAWTON, Angela P. 9501 ROOSEVELT BLVD # 208, INFECTION DISEASES ASSOC 19114 #041-02-1996 L1999 **ID** *020 †20
LAWTON, Angela Suzanne. 9501 ROOSEVELT BLVD, STE 208 19114 #054-04-1990 L1990 **FM** *020 †18
LAWTON, Thomas Jos. 3400 SPRUCE ST, HOSPITAL OF UNIV OF PA 19104 #025-01-1990 L1992 **PTH** *020 †50
LAX-KAMENICKA, Helena. 6 FRANKLIN PLZ, MAGEE REHAB HOSPITAL 19102 #286-07-1979 L2000 **PM** *020 †60
LAYER, Laura Lynn. 3156 KENSINGTON AVE 19134 #047-05-1987 L1989 **PD** *020 †55
LAZAAR, Aili Linnea. 51 N MARKET ST, 1ST FL 19104 #035-19-1986 L1991 **PUD** *020 †20
LAZAR, Alina. ■ 19103 #781-01-1999 L2003 **PAN** *012
LAZAR, Melissa Ann. ■ 19107 #041-02-2006 L2006 **GS** *012
LAZAR, Mitchell Avery. 415 CURIE BLVD, 611 CLINICAL RESEARCH BLDG 19104 #005-11-1982 L1989 **END IM** *050 †20
LAZARCIUC, Mirela Shoh Ni. 3400 SPRUCE ST, DEPT EMER MED 19104 #021-01-2007 L2007 **EM** *012
LAZARUS, Mark David. 925 CHESTNUT ST, FL 5 19107 #033-05-1988 L1990 **ORS** *020 †40
LAZARUS, Sydney S. ■ 19129 #016-42-1945 L1945 **PTH** *075 †50
LAZATIN, Bien De Ocampo, Jr. ■ 19107 #041-02-2004 L2004 **EM** *012
LAZATIN, Jovin Ocampo. 111 S 11TH ST 19107 #041-02-2004 L2004 **AN** *012
LAZOFF, Marjorie. 769 S 2ND ST, STE A 19147 #038-41-1987 L1988 **EM IM** *040 †20
LE, Hoang Uyen. 3401 N BROAD ST, DEPT OF OB/GYN 19140 #305-01-2006 L2006 **OBG** *012
LE, Liza Do. ■ 19103 #051-01-2004 L2004 **EM** *100
LE, Phuc Van. ■ 19146 #041-01-2007 L2007 *012
LE, Tina Thanh. 8835 GERMANTOWN AVE, DEPT FP 19118 #041-13-2007 L2007 **FP** *012
LE, Tuong Kim. PO BOX 99, TEMPLE U MED SCH 19140 #041-13-1993 **FM** *100
LEACH, David Mark. 2301 E NORRIS ST 19125 #038-40-1986 L1987 **AN** *020
LEAFE, Morgan Elizabeth. ■ 19127 #041-02-2006 L2006 **PD** *012
LEAHEY, Ann Marie. 324 S 34TH ST 19104 #043-01-1987 L1990 **PD** *020 †55
LEAHY, John Jos. 9TH & WALNUT STS 19107 #020-02-1947 L1954 **AN** *071 †05
LEAMAN, Timothy Jon. 2940 N 5TH ST 19133 #041-13-1998 L2000 **FM** *020 †18
LEAR, Walter Jay. ■ 19104 #035-08-1946 L1965 **OS PHP** *062 †70
LEATH-JONES, Susan Venida. 760 CARPENTER LN 19119 #041-07-1983 L1984 **FM** *020 †18
LEBED, Brett Daniel. 3401 N BROAD ST, DEPT OF UROLOGY 19140 #041-13-2002 L2004 **U** *012
LEBENTHAL, Abraham. 333 COTTMAN AVE, FOX CHASE CANCER CENTER 19111 #550-01-1993 L2008 **TS GS** *020
LEBER, Ernest Howard. 201 N BROAD ST, EMERGENCY MEDICINE 19107 #041-09-1998 L2000 **EM** *020 †16
LEBOVITCH, Steve. ■ 19147 #035-08-2003 L2003 **U** *012
LEDDY, Cheryl Lea. 2701 HOLME AVE, STE 105 19152 #041-07-1973 L1983 **CD IM** *020 †20
LEDERER, Philip Albert. ■ 19143 #041-01-2008 *012
LEDLEY, Gary Stewart. 245 N 15TH ST MS 470, DREXEL UNIV CLGE OF MED 19102 #010-02-1982 L1990 **CD IC** *020 †20
LEE, Aaron William. ■ 19106 #030-05-2004 L2004 **U** *012
LEE, Albert. 833 CHESTNUT ST, STE 701 19107 #035-47-2003 L2007 **IM** *020 †20
LEE, Alex T. 1000 WALNUT ST, 2003 ORLOWITZ BLDG 19107 #041-02-2006 **AN** *012
LEE, Andrew N. ■ 19107 #035-19-2006 L2006 **IM** *012
LEE, Anita C. 1800 LOMBARD ST 19146 #016-02-1995 L1997 **IM** *020 †20
LEE, Argon. KEARSLEY HOUSE NO 315 19143 #242-10-1951 **NP PM** *020
LEE, Bong Shik. 1810 RITTENHOUSE SQ, STE B2 19103 #583-01-1964 L1971 **ORS HS** *020 †40
LEE, Charles Trumbull, Jr. ■ 19128 #041-01-1947 L1948 **IM DIA** *071 †20
LEE, Chong. ■ 19130 #005-18-1995 L2003 **VS** *100 †85
LEE, Christopher Sohnpio. 34TH-CIVIC CTR BLVD, CHILDRENS HOSP 19104 #041-02-2000 L2003 **PAN** *012 †05
LEE, Cynthia Elizabeth. ■ 19103 #041-02-2008 *012
LEE, Daniel J. ■ 19106 #041-15-2003 L2003 **ORS** *012
LEE, Dong Heun. 2900 W QUEEN LN 19129 #583-13-2000 L2004 **ID** *012 †20
LEE, Edward B. 3400 SPRUCE ST, 6 FOUNDERS 19104 #041-01-2005 **NP** *012
LEE, Elizabeth Leilani. ■ 19130 #041-15-2007 L2007 **IM** *012
LEE, Esther Youngju. ■ 19107 #051-04-2006 L2006 **IM** *012
LEE, Ga Yi. ■ 19103 #035-03-2007 L2007 **OBG** *012
LEE, Grace Eunhay. ■ 19147 #016-06-2005 L2005 **PD** *012
LEE, Gwo-Chin. 245 N 15TH ST, MS #420 19102 #048-04-1998 L2004 **OAR OSM** *020 †40
LEE, Hae-Rhi. 324 S 34TH ST 19104 #660-01-1991 L1997 **PDC** *020 †55
LEE, Hang Jae. UNIV & WOODLAND AVENUES 19104 #583-03-1965 L1977 **PM** *020 †60
LEE, Howard Jay. 2630 HOLME AVE, INSTITUTE FOR RESPIRATORY 19152 #033-06-1980 L1986 **PUD CCM** *020 †20
LEE, Hyun-Joo. 5401 OLD YORK RD 19141 #041-01-1993 L1995 **OBG** *020 †30
LEE, In Kook. 5401 OLD YORK RD, ALBERT EINSTEIN MED CENTER 19141 #583-01-1969 L2003 **OBG** *020 †30
LEE, Ingi. ■ 19103 #008-01-2002 L2002 **IM** *100 †20
LEE, Iris Jungwon. ■ 19147 #041-09-1998 L2001 **NEP** *020 †20
LEE, James Chihmeng. 3400 SPRUCE ST, 826 GATES BUILDING 19104 #041-01-2001 L2004 **PCC** *012 †20
LEE, Jason Bok. 833 CHESTNUT ST 19107 #041-02-1993 L1995 **D** *020 †15
LEE, Jason Hesung. 111 S 11TH ST 19107 #033-05-2000 L2001 **PM** *020 †60
LEE, Jean. 3322 N BROAD ST, TEMPLE U SCHOOL OF MEDICIN 19140 #033-05-1981 L1982 **NEP IM** *020 †20
LEE, Jean D. 245 N 15TH ST, MAIL STOP 427 19102 #041-15-2003 L2003 **IM** *100 †20
LEE, Joanne Sunah. 5501 OLD YORK RD, DEPT RAD 19141 #041-15-2006 L2006 **DR** *012
LEE, John Chienchiang. 900 WALNUT ST 19107 #024-05-1995 L1999 **AN** *020 †05
LEE, John Jangwhan. 2818 COTTMAN AVE 19149 #035-03-1997 L2000 **OPH** *020 †35
LEE, John Mingyi. 3400 SPRUCE ST, OF PENNSYLVAN 19104 #041-13-2005 L2005 **EM** *012
LEE, John S. 421 CURIE BLVD, 950 BRB II/III 19104 #024-05-1999 L2001 **CD** *100 †20
LEE, Jonathan Myungsoo. ■ 19103 #041-01-2008 *012
LEE, Julia Anne. ■ 19104 #024-07-2005 L2005 **ORS** *012
LEE, Juliane H. ■ 19103 #041-14-2006 L2006 **PD** *012
LEE, Karen C.. 2900 W QUEEN LN 19129 #422-01-2001 L2001 **IM** *020
LEE, Karen Lilia. ■ 19144 #041-15-2008 *012
LEE, Kenneth Jacque. 800 SPRUCE ST 19107 #005-02-1957 L1973 **AN** *020 †05
LEE, Kwang Won. 3400 SPRUCE ST 19104 #583-01-1960 L1972 **AN** *020 †05
LEE, Kwanwoo Jos. 1311 SOUTH ST, JEFFERSON COMM HEALTHCARE 19147 #583-04-1962 L1971 **PD** *071 †55
LEE, Lai Fong M. ■ 19114 #462-01-1989 L1997 **IM** *100 †20
LEE, Mina Kim. 8815 GERMANTOWN AVE, FL 5 19118 #041-09-1996 L1999 **FM** *020 †18
LEE, Paul Alfred. ■ 19104 #028-34-2004 L2004 **EM** *012
LEE, Ray Souy. ■ 19129 #041-15-2007 **TY** *012
LEE, Regina Chiwon. ■ 19147 #033-06-2006 L2006 **IM** *012
LEE, Robert Ankuo. 801 SPRUCE ST, FL 10 19107 #005-14-2003 L2004 **D** *100 †15
LEE, Ronald T. ■ 19130 #041-15-2007 L2007 *012
LEE, Ryan Karlsun. 3400 SPRUCE ST 19104 #041-15-2000 L2000 **RNR** *100 †80
LEE, Sang Hyung. 1800 LOMBARD ST 19146 #583-18-2001 L2006 **GS** *012
LEE, Sang Mi. ■ 19107 #041-02-2005 **AN** *012
LEE, Sueyun. 5501 OLD YORK RD, DEPARTMENT OF ORTHOPAEDICS 19141 #041-13-1998 L2001 **HS** *020 †40
LEE, Sun Tack. 5245 N 5TH ST 19120 #583-02-1974 L1981 **FM OS** *020
LEE, William May. ■ 19106 #041-15-2008 *012
LEE, William Ming Fu. 421 CURIE BLVD, UNIVERSITY OF PENNSYLVANIA 19104 #016-02-1975 L1976 **IM HEM** *050 †20
LEE, Yien Hwei. 3300 HENRY AVE 19129 #244-02-1963 L1985 **FM IM** *020
LEECH, Stephen Harry. 3401 N BROAD ST, TEMPLE UNIV HOSP PATH DEPT 19140 #803-03-1965 L1993 **IG ON** *020 †03
LEFEVER, Gerald Stephen. 51 N 39TH ST 19104 #016-11-1974 L1976 **AN CD** *020 †05
LEFRAK, Shayna Nicole. ■ 19147 #051-01-2004 L2004 **GS** *012
LEFTON, Harvey Bennett. 3998 RED LION RD 19114 #041-02-1970 L1976 **GE IM** *020 †20 ‡
LEGA, Bradley Charles. ■ 19146 #048-04-2006 L2006 **NS** *012
LEGIDO, Agustin. ERZE AVE AT FRONT ST, ST CHRISTOPHERS HOSP NEUR 19134 #847-06-1980 L1986 **CHN PD** *050 †75,55
LEHMAN, Sharon Skibber. 111 S 11TH ST, STE 4260 19107 #041-02-1985 L1986 **OPH** *020 †35
LEHMANN, David Chas. 2701 HOLME AVE STE 207 19152 #041-02-1983 L1984 **CD IM** *020 †20
LEIBOWITZ, Helen Ann. 501 S 54TH ST 19143 #041-02-1972 L1973 **DR** *020 †80 ‡
LEIBOWITZ, Karen Louise. ■ 19103 #050-02-2002 L2004 **PG** *012 †55
LEICHNER, Thomas Jos. 2347 E ALLEGHENY AVE 19134 #041-02-1965 L1966 **GS** *075 †85
LEICHT, Martin Lawrence. 7604 CENTRAL AVE STE 104 19111 #056-06-1979 L1980 **IM IMG** *020 †20
LEIGHTON, Barbara M. 3998 RED LION RD, STE 250 19114 #041-02-1990 L1992 **PCC** *020 †20
LEIGHTON, John Chas, Jr. 5501 OLD YORK RD, STE 1 19141 #041-13-1989 L1992 **HO** *020 †20
LEINER, Seymour. 8869 ROOSEVELT BLVD 19152 #869-01-1966 L1971 **ORS** *020
LEINWEBER, Bruce K. 5501 OLD YORK RD 19141 #041-02-1963 L1964 **OBG** *071 †30 ‡
LEISER, Jonathon Bruce. 1 PENN BLVD, EMERG DEPT GERMANTOWN 19144 #041-13-1992 L1994 **EM** *020 †16
LEIST, Thomas Paul. 900 WALNUT ST, STE 200 19107 #011-02-1993 L2000 **NRN N** *020 †75
LEKKHAM, Rapeepat. ALUMNI AFFAIRS, ALBERT EINSTEIN MC 19141 #891-01-2005 L2008 *100
LELAND, J Martin, III. ■ 19107 #041-02-2002 L2007 **OSM** *012
LEMA, Gareth Mark. ■ 19102 #035-06-2007 L2007 **TY** *012
LEMAN, William W. ■ 19103 #041-09-1941 L1942 **GP GS** *071
LEMBERT TEZANOS, Larissa. 245 N 15TH ST, HAHNEMANN HOSP 19102 #308-13-2001 L2003 **PCP** *012
LEMEN, Tiffani Dawn. ■ 19128 #055-01-2007 L2007 **FP** *012
LENAHAN, R Sean. 1316 W ONTARIO ST, STE 1001 19140 #041-13-1998 L2001 **EM** *020 †16
LENAHEN, Patrick Jos. 5735 RIDGE AVE, STE 206 19128 #041-07-1983 L1985 **U** *020 †95
LENHART, Aaron Galun. ■ 19128 #041-77-2007, ▲ L2007 *012
LENNOX, Tricia Lynn. 2818 COTTMAN AVE 19149 #041-02-1999 L2003 **OPH** *020 †35 ‡
LENOW, Jeffrey Lewis. 833 CHESTNUT ST, THIRD FLOOR 19107 #041-09-1978 L1979 **FM OBG** *020 †18 ‡
LENROW, David Ames. 3400 SPRUCE ST 19104 #035-08-1985 L1987 **PM** *020 †60
LEONARD, Cassie Elaine. ■ 19129 #055-01-2007 L2007 **OBG** *012
LEONARD, Edward C, Jr. 4641 ROOSEVELT BLVD 19124 #041-02-1964 L1965 **P** *071 †75
LEONARD, Mary Beth. 3535 MARKET ST, RM 1564 19104 #005-11-1989 L1991 **NEP PD** *020 †55
LEONE, Francesco Thos. 834 WALNUT ST, STE 650 19107 #041-12-1990 L1992 **PCC** *020 †20
LEONE, Nicholas Thomas. 1015 CHESTNUT ST, 39TH & MARKET STS 19107 #041-02-2003 L2003 **U** *012
LEONG, Jackie. 3401 N BROAD ST, RADIOLOGY DEPT 19140 #035-46-1986 L1992 **DR** *020
LEOPOLD, Gretta. 111 N 49TH ST 19139 #041-07-1977 L1978 **P PYA** *020 †75
LEOPOLD, Lance Howard. BROAD & VINE STS 19102 #041-13-1987 L1989 **HEM ON** *020 †20
LEPORE, John Joseph. 421 CURIE BLVD RM 951, CARDIO DIV UNIV PA BRB 2/3 19104 #024-01-1993 L2001 **IM CD** *020 †20
LEPRE, Scott John. ■ 19127 #010-02-2004 L2004 **PM** *012
LERMAN, Melissa Ann. ■ 19146 #041-01-2005 L2005 **PD** *012
LERNER, Andres. 1800 LOMBARD ST 19146 #132-10-1999 L2003 **GS** *012
LERNER, Arthur Mark. 21 N 52ND ST 19139 #654-01-1981 L1983 **NEP IM** *020
LERNER, Harvey Jack. 907 PINE ST 19107 #041-13-1958 L1959 **SO GS** *020 †85
LERNER, Helen Barbara. 1500 LOCUST ST STE 4, SUITE 4007 19102 #041-02-1981 L1983 **PS GS** *020
LERNER, Keren. 245 N 15TH ST STOP 49, OF M 19102 #041-15-2007 L2007 **OBG** *012
LERNER, Leonid Edward. 51 N 39TH ST, SCHEIE EYE INSTITUTE 19104 #913-99-1989 L2004 **OPH** *020 †35
LERNER, Yevgeny. 7600 CENTRAL AVE 19111 #913-06-1969 L1997 **AN** *020 †05
LE ROUX, Peter D. 330 S 9TH ST, 4TH FL 19107 #836-02-1983 L2000 **NS** *020 †25
LESHINSKY, Irene. ■ 19116 #041-77-2007, ▲ L2007 **IM** *012
LESHNOWER, Bradley Graham. ■ 19106 #048-12-2001 L2001 **GS** *012
LESNESKI, Matthew James. ■ 19104 #033-06-2008 L2008 *012
LESSARD, Daniel Jos. 1811 CHESTNUT ST 19103 #067-02-1970 L1976 **FM EM** *020
LESTINI, Brian. ■ 19128 #038-06-2003 L2006 **PHO** *012 †55
LETO, Francesco. 1419 S BROAD ST 19147 #561-10-1953 L1958 **IM FM** *020
LEUCCI, Gino. ■ 19134 #561-21-1957 L1962 **U** *020 †95
LEUNG, Daniel Haobin. ■ 19103 #048-13-2003 L2006 **PG** *012 †55
LEUNG, Dolan Carl. ■ 19107 #041-02-2008 L2008 *012

■ = Address Information Privacy Protected

LEUNG, Lucinda Phoenin. 324 S 34TH ST 19104 #005-06-2000 L2003 **PD** *020 †55 ‡
LEUNG, Tyrone Sai Gee. WILLS EYE HOSP, DEPT ANES 19130 #572-53-1963 L1975 **AN** *020
LEUNG, Yuenpok. 3400 SPRUCE ST, 2 SILVERSTEIN 19104 #041-01-1998 L2000 **ORS** *100
LEV, Amiram. 3400 N BROAD ST 19140 #550-01-1973 L1988 **PUD** *020
LEVEEN, Emily Ann. ■ 19146 #041-01-2008 *012
LEVENE, Howard Benjamin. 3401 N BROAD ST, DEPT NEUROSURGERY 19140 #033-06-2001 L2001 **NS** *012
LEVENSON, Amy Elizabeth. ■ 19128 #041-15-2008 *012
LEVENTHAL, Douglas Drew. 925 CHESTNUT ST FL 6, DEPARTMENT OF OTOLARYNGOLO 19107 #033-06-2004 L2004 **GS OTO** *100
LEVENTHAL, Lawrence Jay. 219 N BROAD ST, FL 9 19107 #041-09-1984 L1985 **RHU IM** *020 †20 ‡
LEVICK, Leonard J. 5501 OLD YORK RD 19141 #041-02-1946 L1947 **IM ON** *071
LEVICK, Stephen Eric. 800 SPRUCE ST 19107 #038-06-1977 L1987 **P** *020 †75
LEVICOFF, Eric Alan. 1000 WALNUT ST, APT 1903 19107 #041-02-2003 L2003 **ORS** *012
LEVIN, Alan Jay. 7131 FRANKFORD AVE, # 7139 19135 #041-09-1977 L1980 **FM** *020 †18
LEVIN, David Carl. 111 S 11TH ST, DEPT OF RADIOLOGY 19107 #023-07-1964 L1986 **R** *071 †80
LEVIN, Dayna. 111 S 11TH ST, 10TH FLR MAIN 19107 #041-02-2001 L2001 **DR** *020 †80
LEVIN, Harvey Marvin. 420 BAINBRIDGE ST, STE 1 19147 #041-02-1960 L1961 **NTR GYN** *020 †30
LEVIN, Howard Alan. 227 S 6TH ST, APT 3NW 19106 #035-19-1966 L1988 **RHU IM** *062 †20
LEVIN, I Howard. 2407 E ALLEGHENY AVE 19134 #041-09-1977 L1989 **N ON** *020 †75
LEVIN, John M. 100 E LEHIGH AVE, DEPT OF SURGERY 19125 #010-02-1970 L1971 **GS** *020 †85
LEVIN, Joseph F. 7604 CENTRAL AVE, STE 100 19111 #041-13-1952 L1953 **IM** *071
LEVIN, Lawrence Mark. 3400 SPRUCE ST, 5TH FLOOR WHITE BUILDING 19104 #041-07-1989 L1989 **OMF** *020
LEVIN, Moisey. 2301 E ALLEGHENY AVE 19134 #913-06-1961 L1985 **N** *020
LEVIN, Stephen Alan. 1602 E WADSWORTH AVE 19150 #051-04-1979 L1981 **PD** *020 †55
LEVINE, Amy Beth. 245 N 15TH ST, FL 16 19102 #035-20-1985 L1993 **OBG** *020 †30 ‡
LEVINE, Bruce David. 3509 N BROAD ST, DEPT ANESTHESIA 6TH FL 19140 #041-12-1989 L1993 **PAN** *020 †05
LEVINE, Charles M. ■ 19131 #035-19-2008 *012
LEVINE, Jeffrey Gregg. 3401 N BROAD ST 19140 #035-09-1984 L1997 **GE IM** *040 †20
LEVINE, Joshua Mark. 3400 SPRUCE ST 19104 #024-01-1998 L2001 **N** *020 †75
LEVINE, Marc Solomon. 3400 SPRUCE ST, DEPT RADLGY HOSP UNIV PA 19104 #025-01-1978 L1980 **DR** *020 †80
LEVINSON, Arnold Irving. 3400 SPRUCE ST, ALLERGY CLIMIC 19104 #023-01-1969 L1978 **AI IM** *050 †20,03
LEVINSON, Brett Adam. 840 WALNUT ST, STE 920 19107 #023-01-2002 L2006 **OPH** *100 †35
LEVINSON, Stuart L. 8220 CASTOR AVE 19152 #041-09-1987 L1988 **P** *020 †75 ‡
LEVISON, Matthew Edmund. 3300 HENRY AVE, RM 211 19129 #035-08-1962 L1970 **ID IM** *071 †20
LEVISON, Sandra J Peltz. 245 N 15TH ST, MAIL STOP 437 19102 #035-19-1965 L1970 **NEP IM** *040 †20
LEVISTE, Adoracion L. 1726 S BROAD ST, STE 102 19145 #748-01-1966 L1976 **PD** *020
LEVITAN, Bennett Simeon. ■ 19151 #041-01-1995 *100
LEVITAN, Richard Mark. 5501 OLD YORK RD, EMERGENCY MEDICINE DEPT. 19141 #035-19-1990 L1996 **EM** *020 †16
LEVITSKY, Carl Murray. 601 WALNUT ST, STE 640 19106 #041-09-1972 L1973 **IM** *020 †20
LEVITT, Jerry David. 230 N BROAD ST 19102 #041-01-1966 L1967 **AN PME** *020 †05 ‡
LEVITT, Mark Lester. ■ 19115 #041-13-1978 L1982 **IM ON** *050 †20
LEVITT-KATZ, Lorraine E. 324 S 34TH ST 19104 #008-02-1989 L1996 **PD** *020 †55
LEV-TOAFF, Anna S. 111 S 11TH ST, 3350 GIBBON BLDG 19107 #035-19-1979 L1981 **DR OS** *020 †80
LEVY, Adam Hilly. ■ 19107 #011-02-2003 L2003 **GE** *012 †20
LEVY, Carolyn D. ■ 19147 #043-01-2007 L2007 *012
LEVY, Elizabeth Helen. 1616 WALNUT ST, STE 2106 19103 #025-01-1954 L1981 **P** *020 †75 ‡
LEVY, Howard A. 1800 LOMBARD ST 19146 #035-08-1950 L1954 **NM** *050 †20,28
LEVY, Jeffrey Scott. 1845 WALNUT ST, FL 12 19103 #028-03-1984 L1991 **OBG** *020 †30
LEVY, Margaret. 7604 CENTRAL AVE 19111 #016-42-1976 L1988 **GS** *020 †85
LEVY, Michael Herbert. 333 COTTMAN AVE, FOX CHASE CANCER CENTER 19111 #041-02-1976 L1978 **PLM ON** *020 †20
LEVY, Richard Jonathan. 313 N 3RD ST, # 1B 19106 #035-09-1995 L1997 **CCP** *020 †05,55
LEVY, Robert Jules. 3516 CIVIC CENTER BLVD, ABRAMSON 702 19104 #023-07-1970 L1997 **PDC PD** *050 †55
LEVY, Sara Josephine. 3401 N BROAD ST 19140 #021-01-2005 L2005 **EM** *012
LEVY, Warren J. 3400 SPRUCE ST, 680 DULLES 19104 #041-01-1974 L1975 **AN** *020 †05
LEVY, William. ■ 19146 #035-15-1948 L1950 **P** *020 †75
LEWIS, Allan Andrew. 800 SPRUCE ST, SOCIETY HILL ANEST CONSULT 19107 #041-09-1990 L1993 **AN** *020 †05
LEWIS, David William. 760 CARPENTER LN 19119 #025-07-1998 L2000 **IM** *020 †18
LEWIS, Dawnette Annmarie. 834 CHESTNUT ST, STE 400 19107 #038-43-1996 L2001 **OBG** *020 †30
LEWIS, Felicia M. 500 S BROAD ST, SECOND FLOOR 19146 #035-19-1998 L2006 **ID** *020 †20
LEWIS, Frank Russell, Jr. 1617 JFK BLVD STE 860, AMERICAN BOARD OF SURGERY 19103 #023-01-1965 L1966 **GS TRS** *030 †85
LEWIS, Howard Steven. 100 E LEHIGH AVE, EPISCOPAL HOSPITAL 19125 #035-08-1974 L1978 **RO PDR** *020 †80
LEWIS, James David. 3400 SPRUCE ST, GI DIVISION HUP 3 DULLES 19104 #041-01-1991 L1995 **GE** *050 †20
LEWIS, James Wm. 7601B GERMANTOWN AVE 19119 #033-05-1973 L1978 **IM** *020
LEWIS, Nancy Lynn. 333 COTTMAN AVE, FOX CHASE CANCER CENTER 19111 #041-13-1994 L1997 **HO** *020 †20
LEWIS, Paul Le Roy. 2301 S BROAD ST 19148 #035-15-1953 L1954 **PTH** *072 †50
LEWIS, Robert Taylor. ■ 19146 #041-01-2005 L2005 **GS** *012
LEWITT, Michael Herman. 8835 GERMANTOWN AVE 19118 #041-02-1974 L1975 **EM OM** *020 †70,18,16 ‡
LEWULLIS, Gabriel Edward. ■ 19130 #041-15-2005 L2005 **ORS** *012
LEX, Joseph Rohan, Jr. 8835 GERMANTOWN AVE, CHESTNUT HILL HOSP 19118 #048-13-1986 L1987 **EM** *020 †16
LEXA, Frank James. 7600 CENTRAL AVE 19111 #005-11-1985 L1989 **RNR DR** *020 †80 ‡
LEYPOLD, Bradley Georges. 132 S 10TH ST, UNIVERSITY HO 19107 #035-01-2002 L2002 **DR** *100 †80
LEYZIN, Mara. 8025 CASTOR AVE 19152 #913-87-1962 L1984 **FM IM** *020 †18 ‡
LI, Diane Xiaomeng. 3400 SPRUCE ST, DEPT RAD 19104 #041-01-2006 L2006 **DR** *012
LI, Doris Sophia. ■ 19144 #041-15-2007 **GS** *012
LI, Geming. ■ 19104 #243-92-1986 L2004 **NM** *012
LI, Helen K. 840 WALNUT ST STE 1 19107 #048-14-1986 L2007 **OPH** *040 †35
LI, Hongyan. 9880 BUSTLETON AVE, NEUROLOGY ASSOCIATES AT 19115 #243-32-1984 L2003 **N CN** *020 †75
LI, James Edward. 2301 E ALLEGHENY AVE, DEPT OF ANESTHESIA, 2ND FL 19134 #005-14-1991 L1994 **AN** *020 †05
LI, Jongming. 1015 WALNUT ST, STE 1024 CURTIS BLDG 19107 #033-06-1999 L2005 **HEM** *100 †20
LI, Kehua. 833 CHESTNUT ST STE 740 19107 #243-46-1986 L2001 **D DMP** *100 †15
LI, Sophia S. ■ 19128 #041-13-2007 L2007 **IM** *012
LI, Yong-Tong. 800 SPRUCE ST, HALL-MERCER 19107 #243-47-1986 L2000 **P** *040 †75
LIACOURAS, Chris A. 3400 CIVIC CENTER BLVD 19104 #024-01-1985 L1987 **GE PD** *040 †55
LIANG, Hongyan. 1800 LOMBARD ST, TENET HEALTHSYSTEM GRADUAT 19146 #243-03-1997 L2005 **IM** *012
LIANG, Lijun. ■ 19131 #243-14-1985 L2000 **IM** *020 †20
LIANG, Michael Daniel. ■ 19146 #024-05-2007 L2007 **IM** *012
LIANG, Tsao-Wei. 900 WALNUT ST STE 200, JEFFERSON HOSP FOR NEURO S 19107 #035-19-1999 L2001 **N** *020 †75
LIAO, John Ben. ■ 19147 #010-01-1998 L2007 **OBG** *020
LIAO, Margaret K. ■ 19130 #043-01-1988 L1990 **P** *075
LIAO, Sophie Daisy. 5501 OLD YORK RD, DEPT MED 19141 #025-01-2007 L2007 **IM** *012
LIAW, Phillip. 10160 BUSTLETON AVE, STE A 19116 #041-02-1998 L2001 **IM** *020 †20
LIAW, Wen-Haw. 2301 E ALLEGHENY AVE 19134 #244-06-1968 L1976 **EM** *020 †16
LIAW, Yischon. ■ 19107 #041-02-1993 L1995 **FM** *020 †18
LI BASSI, Mark Jos. 3996 RED LION RD 19114 #041-07-1987 L1988 **GS TRS** *020 †85
LIBERMAN, Shari Rachel. ■ 19115 #041-13-2006 **ORS** *012
LIBORO, Regina Kaluag. 3400 SPRUCE ST 19104 #748-02-1978 L1983 **NEP IM** *020 †20
LIBSON, Eugene. 111 S 11TH ST, DEPT RAD 19107 #913-06-1972 **DR** *020
LICATA, Lauren Audrey. ■ 19107 #035-09-2005 **GS** *012
LICHT, Harvey Michael. 3401 N BROAD ST, TEMPLE UNIVERSITY HOSPITAL 19140 #035-46-1975 L1980 **GE IM** *020 †20
LICHTENSTEIN, Gary Roth. 3400 SPRUCE ST, 3 RAVDIN BLDG 19104 #035-47-1984 L1986 **GE IM** *020 †20
LICHTMAN, Craig Victor. 2031 LOCUST ST 19103 #038-06-1982 L1983 **P PYA** *020 ‡
LICHTMAN, Joe Michael. 514 S 4TH ST 19147 #041-13-1971 L1972 **GP** *020
LIEB, Michael. 9622 BUSTLETON AVE, STE 2 19115 #308-07-1983 L1986 **GE** *020 †20
LIEBEN, Jan. ■ 19130 #352-06-1943 L1954 **OM PHP** *040 †70
LIEBENBERG, Robert Eric. 5501 OLD YORK RD WBC4, DEPT OF ORTHOPED 19141 #010-02-1974 L1978 **ORS** *020 †40
LIEBERMAN, Alexis S. 5501 OLD YORK RD, ALBERT EINSTEIN MED CTR 19141 #041-07-1993 L1996 **PD** *040 †55
LIEBERMAN, Daniel. 833 CHESTNUT ST STE 210 19107 #005-02-1946 L1968 **P** *071
LIEBERMAN, Edwin. ■ 19114 #422-01-1983 L1988 **FOP** *020
LIEBERMAN, Frederick S. 255 S 17TH ST, FL 5 19103 #041-07-1975 L1976 **ORS** *020 †40
LIEBERMAN, Scott Matthew. ■ 19146 #035-46-2005 L2005 **PD** *100
LIEBHABER, Stephen Aaron. 415 CURIE BLVD, RM 428 C.R.B. 19104 #008-01-1972 L1982 **HEM IM** *050 †20
LIEBMAN, Jared Jason. 5501 OLD YORK RD, ALBERT EINSTEIN MED CTR 19141 #041-02-2005 L2005 **GS** *012
LIEBMAN, Kenneth Michael. 909 WALNUT ST, 2ND FL 19107 #041-13-1991 L1996 **NS** *020 †25
LIEBMAN, Paul Arno. 143 ANAT CHEM BLDG UNIV MC, DEPT OF NEU UNIV OF PA 19104 #023-07-1958 L1970 **OPH OS** *050
LIECHTY, Kenneth Wayne. ■ 19118 #049-01-1994 L1996 **PDS** *020 †85
LIEF, Bruce Alexander. 2701 HOLME AVE 19152 #021-01-1966 L1972 **P** *020 †75
LIEM, Marina Dewi. 3900 RED LION RD, FRANKFORD HOSPITAL, RADIOL 19114 #024-05-1986 L1988 **R RNR** *020 †80
LIEN, Rey-In. 3400 SPRUCE ST 19104 #244-04-1981 L1990 **PD** *020 †55
LIGAS, Adam Anthony. 804 S 48TH ST, FL 3 19143 #033-05-2006 **P** *012
LIGHT, Karen Lee. 125 S 9TH ST STE 600, MENTOR NETWORK 19107 #036-05-1991 L1993 **P CHP** *020 †75
LIGHTS, Vernether M. 400 E CHELTEN AVE, LIGHTS MEDICAL CENTER 19144 #041-01-1978 L1980 **IM** *075
LIGHVANI, Andre Arash. ■ 19104 #036-07-2002 L2003 **MSR** *012 †80
LILLY, Scott Matthew. ■ 19103 #038-43-2006 L2006 **IM** *012
LIM, Diane Chungyeon. 245 N 15TH ST, MAIL STOP 107 19102 #005-12-1995 L2003 **PCC** *020 †20
LIM, M Blanche. 205 N BROAD ST, STE 600 19107 #748-11-1972 L1977 **IM NEP** *020 †20
LIM, Mario Rosario. 1766 FRANKFORD AVE 19125 #748-01-1956 L1962 **FM** *072
LIM, Mary Ann Chong. ■ 19104 #748-02-2002 L2007 **IM** *100 †20
LIM, Nyok Kheng. 1415 N BROAD ST, FL 2 19122 #041-02-1980 L1982 **IM IMG** *020 †20
LIMBERAKIS, Anthony John. 9601 BUSTLETON AVE, BUSTLETON RADIOLOGY ASSOC 19115 #036-07-1978 L1980 **DR** *020 †80
LIMOGES, Richard F. 822 PINE ST, STE 1B 19107 #041-13-1964 L1965 **ADP PFP** *020 †75
LIMOUZE, John Sanford. ■ 19146 #041-01-2008 *012
LIN, David. 3400 SPRUCE ST, 9 FOUNDERS-CARDIO 19104 #035-09-1995 L2001 **ICE CD** *020 †20
LIN, Ines Chiying. 3400 SPRUCE ST, OF PENNSYLVAN 19104 #041-01-2004 L2004 **PS** *012
LIN, Jennifer Chwenyin. ■ 19102 #036-07-2007 L2007 **IM** *012
LIN, Joseph. ■ 19104 #038-06-2001 L2002 **DR** *100
LIN, Julie Hsiao-Wen. 3600 SPRUCE ST, # 2 MALONEY 19104 #067-01-2002 L2005 **D** *012
LIN, Karen. 1316 W ONTARIO ST, JONES HALL, 1ST FLOOR 19140 #033-06-2001 L2001 **IM** *020
LIN, Kathleen. 3701 MARKET ST, STE 810 19104 #035-46-1999 L2003 **OBG** *020 †30
LIN, Lilie Leming. 3400 SPRUCE ST FL 2, DONNER BLDG 19104 #028-02-2001 L2006 **RO** *100 †80
LIN, Ming Valerie. 800 SPRUCE ST 19107 #836-05-2004 L2007 *012
LIN, Richard John. 34TH ST & CIVIC CIR BLVD 19104 #041-01-1993 L1995 **CCP** *050 †55
LIN, Shann Bin. 100 E LEHIGH AVE, FL 3 19125 #033-05-1994 L1999 **OPH** *020 †35 ‡
LIN, Sunson. ■ 19144 #041-15-2005 L2005 **EM** *012
LIN, Timothy J. ■ 19107 #035-15-2002 L2005 **PCC** *012 †20
LINCOSKI, Christopher J. 834 CHESTNUT ST, STE G114 19107 #041-13-1999 L1999 **HSO** *012
LINDEN, Robert Andor. 111 S 11TH ST, STE 2170 19107 #041-02-2004 L2004 **U** *012
LINDQUIST, John Norman. 111 S 11TH ST 19107 #041-02-1943 L1944 **IM IMG** *071
LINDSAY, Beverly L Archer. 1 FRANKLINTOWN BLVD 19103 #010-02-1989 L2007 **PEM** *020 †55

LINDSAY, Henry Hill. ■ 19122 #047-07-1957 L1962 **PTH OS** *075
LINEK, Julie Ann. ■ 19107 #041-02-2008 *012
LINES, John Farrell. 1409 LOMBARD ST, CATCH, INC 19146 #034-01-2002 L2002 **P** *100 †75
LINEVSKY, Joanne Karen. 3400 SPRUCE ST 19104 #041-12-1987 L1998 **GE IM** *020 †20
LING, Stephen E. 3401 N BROAD ST, TEMPLE UNIVERSITY HEALTH S 19140 #035-19-1996 L2002 **DR** *020 †80
LINGANATHAN, Karthik Kilp. 245 N 15TH ST MS 470, DEPT OF CARDIOLOGY HAHNEMA 19102 #495-04-1998 L2002 **CD** *012 †20
LINGARAJU, Nagaraj. 230 N BROAD ST 19102 #495-33-1974 L1985 **AN** *020 †05
LINKER, Martha Katherine. 3400 SPRUCE ST, OF PENNSYLVAN 19104 #047-05-2000 L2006 **EM** *012 †55
LINKIN, Darren Robert. 3900 WOODLAND AVE, PHIL VA MED CTR OFF 8A-801 19104 #016-02-1997 L2000 **ID IM** *050 †20
LINNEMANN, Roger Edward. 3019 DARNELL RD 19154 #026-04-1956 L1969 **R NM** *030 †80,28
LINSKY, Amy Michelle. ■ 19103 #033-06-2005 L2005 **IM** *012
LINTON, Julie Michelle. ■ 19103 #041-01-2007 L2007 **PD** *012
LIOY, Janet Makris. 324 S 34TH ST 19104 #033-06-1988 L1990 **PD** *020 †55
LIPKIN, David Ernest. 5325 OLD YORK RD, # 15 19141 #010-03-1969 L1970 **IM GP** *020 †20 ‡
LIPORACE, Joyce Diane. 111 S 11TH ST, STE 4150 19107 #023-07-1988 L1990 **N** *020 †75
LIPORACI LUCENA, Jorge Lu. 2900 W QUEEN LN 19129 #935-05-2002 L2006 **GS** *012
LIPPA, Andrew Moss. ■ 19104 #041-01-2008 *012
LIPPA, Carol Frances. 245 N 15TH ST, RM 7102 19102 #024-16-1983 L1995 **N** *020 †75
LIPPMAN, Deborah Steele. 800 SPRUCE ST 19107 #041-09-1990 L1994 **AN** *020 †05 ‡
LIPPMANN, Michael L. 5401 OLD YORK RD, KLEIN BLDG 363 19141 #035-06-1970 L1971 **PUD CCM** *020 †20
LIPPO, Frank Louis. 2301 S BROAD ST 19148 #561-17-1957 L1960 **GYN** *071 †30
LIPSCHIK, Gregg Yuri. 39TH & MARKET ST, PRESBYTERIAN U PA MED CTR 19104 #035-08-1980 L1985 **CCM** *040 †20
LIPSCHUTZ, Joshua Henry. 380 S UNIVERSITY AVE, HILL PAVILION, ROOM 480 19104 #017-20-1988 L2001 **IM** *020 †20
LIPSCHUTZ, Marc Harris. 2200 BENJAMIN FRANKLN PKWY, E109 19130 #025-01-1974 L1975 **P PYA** *020 †75
LIPSCHUTZ, Steven Michael. 170 W OLNEY AVE 19120 #041-09-1977 L1978 **FM** *071 †18
LIPSHUTZ, Laurel Sprung. 601 WALNUT ST, CURTIS CENTER STE 960W 19106 #035-03-1972 L1975 **P** *020 †75
LIPSHUTZ, William Herman. 230 W WASHINGTON SQ 19106 #041-01-1967 L1968 **GE** *020 †20
LIPSITZ, Emily Gustava. ■ 19103 #028-34-2004 L2007 **PHO** *012 †55
LIPSON, David Andrew. 8 WEST GATES, 3400 SPRUCE STREET 19104 #041-02-1994 L1998 **PCC** *020 †20
LIPTON, Steven Elliott. 2375 WOODWARD ST 19115 #041-13-1976 L1977 **OBG** *020 †30
LIRIO, Stephanie Katz. 3535 MARKET ST, FL 2 19104 #035-09-2001 L2001 **CHP** *100 †75
LISANTI, Michael Phillip. ■ 19147 #041-15-2008 *100
LISBY, Deeann Shlease. 3405 W QUEEN LN, DEPARTMENT OF NEONATOLOGY 19129 #041-09-1991 L1994 **NPM** *020 †55
LISCHNER, Harold W. 3333 N BROAD ST, RM 343 19140 #016-02-1952 L1954 **IM PD** *030 †55
LISHANSKY, Izolda. 7600 CENTRAL AVE, JEANES HOSP EMERGENCY ROOM 19111 #913-01-1976 L1986 **FM** *020
LISI, Louise Marie. 131 E CHELTEN AVE 19144 #041-09-1970 L1986 **PD PHP** *020 †55
LISKER, Sheldon Alan. 1840 SOUTH ST 19146 #041-01-1958 L1959 **ON HEM** *072 †20 ‡
LISS, Deborah R. 277 SHAWMONT AVE 19128 #041-07-1983 L1984 **AN CCM** *071 †05
LISTA, William Anthony. 525 JAMESTOWN ST STE 101 19128 #041-02-1955 L1956 **CD IM** *071 †20
LISTERUD, John Morris. 3535 MARKET ST, 2ND FLOOR, PSCYH 19104 #054-04-1987 L1999 **ADP** *100 †75
LITAN, Michael Morris. 5501 OLD YORK RD 19141 #019-02-1980 L1989 **PYG P** *075 †75
LITKA, Paul Andrew. 39TH & MARKET ST 19104 #033-05-1975 L1982 **IM** *050 †20
LITMAN, Ronald S. 34TH ST, DEPT ANESTH CRIT CARE 19104 #035-75-1985, ▲ L2001 **AN PD** *020 †05,55
LITT, Brian. 3400 SPRUCE ST 19104 #023-07-1986 L1999 **N CN** *020 †75
LITT, Harold Ira. 3400 SPRUCE ST, 1 SILVERSTEIN 19104 #035-06-1996 L2000 **DR** *020
LITTLE, Brian Woods. 245 N 15TH ST 19102 #050-02-1973 L1987 **NP CLP** *040 †50
LITTMAN, Louis. 1420 WALNUT ST, STE 902 19102 #041-01-1999 L2001 **P** *020
LITTMAN, Mario. 7300 CITY LINE AVE, RM 203 19151 #781-01-1983 L1985 **IM** *020 †20
LITTMAN, Solomon I. 4200 MONUMENT RD, BLMNT CTR FR CMPRHNSVE 19131 #781-01-1948 L1966 **P CHP** *071 †75
LITTY, Cathy Ann. ERIE AVE AT FRONT ST, DEPT PATH & LAB MEDICINE 19134 #035-15-1986 L1991 **BBK CLP** *030 †50
LITWACK, Andrew Jay. 3400 SPRUCE ST, 8 PENN TOWER 19104 #033-06-1990 L2004 **CD** *020 †20
LITWIN, Jeffrey S. 30 S 17TH ST FL 8, E RESEARCH TECHNOLOGY 19103 #047-07-1981 L1988 **CD PHM** *030 †20
LITZKY, Leslie Anne. 3400 SPRUCE ST, DEPT OF PATHOLGY & LB MDCN 19104 #010-01-1987 L1989 **PTH** *050 †50
LIU, Beiqing. 3300 HENRY AVE, DEPT OF PATHOLOGY 19129 #243-52-1982 L2001 **PTH** *020 †50
LIU, Christine Kee. 3400 N BROAD ST, TEMPLE UNIV SCH OF MED 19140 #041-13-2005 L2005 **IM** *012
LIU, Christopher F. ■ 19103 #035-01-2001 L2004 **ICE** *012
LIU, Frank Fu Son. ■ 19149 #243-46-1960 L1984 **PM** *020
LIU, Grant T. 3400 SPRUCE ST 19104 #035-01-1988 L1992 **N OPH** *020 †75
LIU, Jesse Kueyu. ■ 19130 #051-01-2004 L2007 **GE** *012 †20
LIU, Jun. 132 S 10TH ST 19107 #243-16-1991 L2001 **SP** *020 †50
LIU, Peter Shoucheng. 3400 SPRUCE ST 19104 #038-06-2002 L2003 **DR** *100 †80
LIU, Ping. 1800 LOMBARD ST 19146 #243-52-1992 L2006 **IM** *012
LIU, Stephen. 3400 SPRUCE ST, 100 CENTREX 19104 #023-01-2005 L2005 **IM** *012
LIU, Te Hua. 3401 N BROAD ST 19140 #041-13-2005 L2005 **RNR** *072 †80
LIU, Winston Tak-Ho. 3996 RED LION RD 19114 #242-03-1959 L1980 **IM** *071
LIU, Xiaolong Shawn. ■ 19107 #016-06-2008 L2008 *012
LI VOLSI, Virginia Anne. 3400 SPRUCE ST DEPT PATH 19104 #035-01-1969 L1982 **ATP** *020 †50 ‡
LLADO, Roald Jon. ■ 19103 #041-15-2007 L2007 **ORS** *012
LLERA, Wallace. 452 W ALLEGHENY AVE 19133 #042-01-1977 L1979 **FM** *020 †18
LLOYD, Jessica Ellen. ■ 19104 #005-14-2006 **PD** *012
LLOYD, Joshua Matthew. 950 WALNUT ST, BARRINGER BLDG #608 19107 #041-02-2004 L2004 **PTH** *012

LO, Adrian King Man. 301 S 8TH ST, DUNCAN BLDG, SUITE 3H 19106 #065-06-1985 L1991 **PS** *020 †65
LO, David Yiuwah. 111 S 11TH ST, DEPT OF ANESTHESIOLOGY 849 19107 #035-08-2003 L2007 **AN** *020
LO, Francis. 2115 SOUTH ST, 2ND FL 19146 #041-13-1990 L1992 **IM** *020 †20
LO, Helen Grant. 3400 SPRUCE ST, OF PENNSYLVANIA 19104 #035-19-2007 L2007 **EM** *012
LOBIANCO, Anthony D. 1225 S 8TH ST 19147 #041-77-1960, ▲ L1961 **FM** *071
LOC, Kiet Minh. ■ 19107 #041-14-2006 L2006 **GS** *100
LOCH, Alexander. 800 SPRUCE ST 19107 #408-11-2001 **IM** *012
LOCKARD, Erin Rae. 3401 N BROAD ST, TEMPLE UNIVERSITY HOSPITAL 19140 #035-09-2003 L2003 **IM** *100 †12
LOCKETT, Lawrence Mark. ■ 19131 #041-12-2003 L2003 **PD** *020 †55
LODISE, Raymond Jos. 1420 LOCUST ST STE 100 19102 #041-02-1959 L1960 **IM CD** *071
LOEB, Eva Gomez. 135 S 19TH ST, THE WELLINGTON 19103 #041-07-1979 L1980 **P PYA** *020 †75
LOEVNER, Laurie Anne. 3400 SPRUCE ST 19104 #041-01-1988 L1993 **RNR** *020 †80
LOEW, Clifford Kenneth. 8835 GERMANTOWN AVE, CHESTNUT HILL HOSPITAL 19118 #050-02-1954 L1960 **CD** *071 †20
LOEWEN, Jonathan Mark. ■ 19128 #036-05-2000 L2002 **DR** *020 †80
LOEWENBERG, Leopold Saml. 111 S 11TH ST 19107 #041-02-1956 L1957 **OBG** *071 †30
LOFTUS, Christopher M. 3401 N BROAD ST, STE-540 PARKINSON 19140 #035-08-1979 L1993 **NS** *020 †25
LOGAN, Sabrina Julia. 3400 SPRUCE ST 19104 #610-01-1985 L2001 **CCP** *020 †55
LOGANI, Sachin. ■ 19144 #041-15-2008 L2008 *012
LOGUE, Christopher J. 3620 HAMILTON WALK, ONE JOHN MORGAN BUILDING 19104 #035-06-2002 L2008 **EM** *100 †16
LOGUE, James G, Jr. 2 PENN BLVD 19144 #041-01-1941 L1942 **OBG** *071 †30
LOHOFF, Falk-Wilhelm. 125 S 31ST ST, RM 2210 19104 #408-30-2002 L2002 **P** *020 †75
LOKEY, Patricia Annette. 800 SPRUCE ST, 6TH FL 19107 #041-09-1985 L1989 **OBG** *020 †30
LOMBANA MARTINEZ, Clara I. 245 N 15TH ST, DREXEL UNIV COLL OF MED 19102 #264-04-1999 L2006 **FM** *100
LOMBARDI, Joseph Vincent. 111 S 11TH ST, STE 6350, GIBBON BUILDING 19107 #041-02-1996 L1999 **VS** *020 †85
LOMBARDO, Gary Gaspare. 3440 MARKET ST, 1ST FL 19104 #305-01-2001 L2006 **CCS** *012
LONDON, William Thos. 333 COTTMAN AVE 19111 #035-20-1957 L1966 **IM EP** *030 †20
LONERGAN, Terence Patrick. ■ 19102 #033-05-1993 L1995 **CCM** *012 †20
LONG, Christopher Joseph. 3401 N BROAD ST, OF S 19140 #033-05-2006 L2006 **GS** *012
LONG, Judith Ariadne. 423 GUARDIAN DR, 1201 BLOCKLEY HALL 19104 #035-46-1993 L1996 **IM** *050 †20
LONG, M Sarah Sundborg. 3601 A ST STE 1112, ST CHRISTOPHERS HOSPITAL 19134 #041-02-1970 L1971 **PD PDI** *020
LONG, Suzanne Sundborg. 712 ADDISON ST 19147 #041-02-2002 L2002 **DR** *012 †20
LONG, William Barstow. 3400 SPRUCE ST, DIVISION OF GASTROENTEROLG 19104 #041-01-1963 L1967 **GE IM** *020 †20
LONGENECKER, Joseph Craig. ■ 19104 #023-07-1990 L1993 **IM** *020 †20
LONGO, Michael David. 833 CHESTNUT ST, STE 701 19107 #041-02-1997 L1999 **IMG** *020 †20
LONGO, Stephen Ralph. 3400 SPRUCE ST 19104 #033-05-1989 L1992 **AN** *020 †05
LONNER, Jess Hanley. 800 SPRUCE ST, 3B ORTHOPAEDICS 19107 #024-05-1991 L1997 **ORS** *020 †40
LOPEZ, Andrew Mark. 11082 KNIGHTS RD 19154 #033-05-1999 L2001 **P** *100 †75
LOPEZ, Annette Meliza. ■ 19128 #041-15-2008 *012
LOPEZ, Bernard Luis. 1020 SANSOM ST, "THOMPSON BLDG, STE 239" 19107 #041-02-1986 L1987 **EM** *030 †16
LOPEZ, Christian Sullano. ■ 19128 #041-13-2003 L2006 **CD** *012
LOPEZ, Francis Joseph. 19102 #422-01-2002 L2002 **PM** *100
LOPEZ PAJARES, Nuria. 4231 N 5TH ST, TEMPLE COMM MED CTR 19140 #847-04-1993 L1999 **GP GPM** *020 †70
LOPINTO, Carla Francesca. ■ 19107 #035-19-2006 L2006 **N** *012
LORBER, Bennett. 3401 N BROAD ST, PARKINSON PAVILION ROOM 50 19140 #041-01-1968 L1969 **ID IM** *040 †20
LORCH, Scott Andrew. 3535 MARKET ST STE 1029 19104 #016-06-1996 L1999 **NPM** *050 †55
LO RE, Vincent, III. 532 JOHNSON HALL, UNIV OF PENN 19104 #041-01-1997 L2000 **ID** *050 †20
LORELL, Dennis Lewis. 834 CHESTNUT ST STE 400, DEPT OB/GYN 19107 #035-15-1970 L1987 **OBG** *020 †30
LOREN, Alison Wakoff. 3400 SPRUCE ST DEPT MED 19104 #028-02-1996 L1998 **HO** *020 †20
LOREN, David Ethan. 132 S 10TH ST 19107 #028-02-1996 L1998 **GE** *020 †20
LORICO, Abagael Norada. 7604 CENTRAL AVE, STE 101 19111 #748-02-1968 L1973 **OBG** *020 †30
LOTFI, Mohamed A. ■ 19107 #915-02-1985 L1993 **U** *020
LOTT, Kristen. ■ 19145 #036-07-2004 L2005 **DR** *012
LOU, Julia Eemai. ■ 19147 #041-02-2007 L2007 **FP** *012
LOUIS, Marie Edwige. 2501 W LEHIGH AVE 19132 #041-15-2001 L2001 **FM** *020 †18
LOUIS-CHARLES, Roy. 5501 OLD YORK RD 19141 #440-01-1956 L1962 **PD** *071 †55
LOUNDES, Donna Dolores. 1015 CHESTNUT ST, STE 1300 19107 #067-01-1990 L2000 **PUD IM** *020 †20
LOVE, Carol Anne. 5501 OLD YORK RD 19141 #041-02-1978 L1979 **FM** *020 †18
LOVE, Margaret Mary. ■ 19147 #041-13-2005 L2005 **PD** *012
LOVE, Michael Barry. 800 SPRUCE ST, PA HOSP DEPT OF RADIOLOGY 19107 #041-13-1970 L1971 **DR** *020 †80 ‡
LOVELAND, Mary Weisbach. 5735 RIDGE AVE STE 202 19128 #041-07-1962 L1963 **GYN** *030
LOVELANDJONES, Catherine. ■ 19103 #041-01-2005 L2005 *100
LOVITT, Ann Louise. 7600 CENTRAL AVE 19111 #021-01-1973 L1986 **AN** *020 †05
LOW, David Wei-Wen. 3400 SPRUCE ST, 10TH FL 19104 #024-01-1980 L1982 **PS** *020 †85,65
LOW, Li Shien. ■ 19147 #041-02-2008 L2008 *012
LOWE, David Arnold. 3333 N BROAD ST 19140 #041-01-1975 L1976 **AN PD** *020 †55,05
LOWE, Michael Charles. ■ 19151 #010-02-2007 **GS** *012
LOWRY, Louis Dale. 925 CHESTNUT ST, NECK SURGERY 6TH FLOOR 19107 #028-03-1962 L1973 **OTO** *071 †45
LOZARES, Eleanore. ■ 19119 #041-15-2008 *012
LU, Jason Jonathan. 245 N 15TH ST, HAHNEMANN UNIV HOSP 19102 #422-01-2003 L2006 **PCC** *012 †20
LU, Ta Shung. 2301 E ALLEGHENY AVE 19134 #244-06-1969 L1977 **AN** *071 †05 ‡
LU, Weiquan. 1800 LOMBARD ST 19146 #243-03-1997 L2005 **IM** *012

LU, Yang. 2900 W QUEEN LN 19129 #243-58-1995 **GS** *012
LUBARR, Naomi Judith. ■ 19104 #041-01-2000 L2001 **CHN** *100 †75
LUBERTI, Anthony Albert. 3535 MARKET ST, STE 1024 19104 #041-01-1984 L1986 **PD** *030 †55
LUBIN, Joseph D. ■ 19103 #660-01-1957 L1959 **AN PMM** *071 †05
LUBIN, Thomas Ira. ■ 19131 #041-02-2002 L2006 **FM** *020 †18
LUCAN, Sean Christian. 51 N 39TH ST, MUTCH BUILDING, 6TH FLOOR 19104
#008-01-2004 L2004 **FM** *100 †18
LUCAS, Richard Morris. 111 S 11TH ST 19107 #035-46-1984 L1985 **EM** *020 †16
LUCAS, Robert Mark. 10431 ACADEMY RD 19114 #305-01-1982 L1984 **PTH RO** *020 †50
LUCAS, Shannon Hart. 3400 SPRUCE ST, DPT OF EM. ME. 19104 #032-01-2005 L2005 **EM** *012
LUCAS-FEHM, Lynn Michele. 1100 WALNUT ST, BREAST IMAGING CTR 19107
#038-41-1982 L1983 **DR NR** *020 †80 ‡
LUCEY, Denis John. ■ 19118 #041-13-1968 L1970 **PHP OBG** *100
LUCHI, Monica Elizabeth. 3701 MARKET ST STE 741, PENN RHEMATOLOGY ASSOCIATE 19104
#038-44-1987 L1992 **IM** *020 †20
LUCK, Lori Renee. ■ 19106 #051-01-1995 L2004 **PHO** *020 †55
LUCK, Michael Donaldson. 3400 SPRUCE ST, UNIV OF PA HLTH SYS 19104
#024-05-2002 L2003 **MSR** *012 †80
LUCK, Raemma Paredes. 3401 N BROAD ST 9TH FL, DEPT PEDS EMERGENCY MED 19140
#748-08-1988 L1997 **PD** *020 †55
LUDMIR, Jack. 800 SPRUCE ST, FL 8 19107 #041-13-1981 L1982 **MFM OBG** *020 †30
LUDOLPH, Carol Ann. 5049 OXFORD AVE 19124 #041-07-1976 L1985 **NS** *020
LUDOMIRSKY, Abraham. 3401 N BROAD ST 19140 #550-02-1977 L1994 **OBG NPM** *020
LUDVIGSSON, Petur. 3400 N BROAD 19140 #484-01-1973 L1981 **CHN PD** *050 †55,75
LUDWIG, Stephen. 3550 MARKET ST, FL 4 19104 #041-13-1971 L1974 **PD EM** *040 †55 ‡
LUDWIN, Steven Michael. 19107 #021-01-2007 L2007 **IM** *012
LUEBBERT, James Francis. 3905 FORD RD 19131 #030-05-1985 L1986 **CHP P** *020 †75
LUFADEJU, Adedamola. 5501 OLD YORK RD, ALBERT EINSTEIN MED CTR 19141
#690-01-1998 L2003 **GE** *012 †20
LUGANO, Eugene Michael. 700 SPRUCE ST, STE 500 19106 #041-01-1975 L1976
IM IG *050 †20
LUGER, Selina M. 3400 SPRUCE ST FL 6, UNIV PENNSYLVANIA MED CTR 19104
#067-01-1987 L1990 **HEM** *020 †20
LUGINBUHL, Adam John. ■ 19107 #008-02-2007 L2007 **OTO** *012
LUISTRO, Anthony Uriante. 2520 SNYDER AVE, GREATER PHILADELPHIA HEALT 19145
#004-01-2003 L2003 **FM** *100 †18
LUISTRO, Patria De Castro. 2301 S BROAD ST 19148 #748-01-1957 L1968 **FOP OS** *071
LUIZAGA COCA, Ever. ■ 19128 #176-04-2002 L2004 **PCC** *012
LUKENS, John Nicholas. ■ 19146 #041-01-2008 L2008 *012
LUNA-REYES, Ofelia B. PO BOX 7618 19101 #748-01-1965 L1985 **PM** *100 †60
LUND, Mark Edwin. 1331 E WYOMING AVE 19124 #041-02-1997 L1999 **PCC OS** *020 †20
LUNING PRAK, Eline T. 3400 SPRUCE ST 19104 #041-01-1996 L1998 **PTH** *020 †50
LUO, Betsy Peichi. ■ 19106 #041-13-2006 L2006 **OPH** *012
LUO, Jin-Jun. 3401 N BROAD ST C525 19140 #243-21-1983 L2001 **N OS** *020 †75 ‡
LUO, Solomon Chihwei. 100 E LEHIGH AVE, FL 3 19125 #048-02-1982 L1983
OPH IM *020 †35 ‡
LUO, Stella Linda. ■ 19103 #041-13-2007 L2007 **TY** *012
LUSTIG, Robert Allan. 3400 SPRUCE ST, 2 DONNER DEPT RAD-ONCOL 19104
#041-02-1969 L1973 **RO** *020 †80 ‡
LUTZ, Ronald Anthony, Jr. 3300 HENRY AVE DEPT EM 19129 #041-12-1996 L1998 **EM** *020 †16
LYBRAND, Janice Ann. 8835 GERMANTOWN AVE 19118 #004-01-1988 L1990 **P** *020 †75
LYEN, Yuen Chin. PRESBY UNIV PA MED CTR/PUD 19104 #917-28-1976 L1982 **PUD** *100
LYNCH, David Robinson. 3400 SPRUCE ST 19104 #023-07-1988 L1990 **N** *020 †75
LYNCH, John Patrick. 3400 SPRUCE ST 19104 #008-02-1994 L1997 **GE** *020 †20
LYNCH, Katherine Eladore. ■ 19103 #041-01-2008 *012
LYNCH, Malcolm Alexander. ■ 19103 #028-02-1963 L1965 **GP** *071
LYNN, David John. 1020 SANSOM ST 19107 #041-01-1974 L1993 **P** *020 †75
LYNN, Deidre Kathleen. ■ 19131 #041-77-2007, ▲ *012
LYNN, Gelsey Paul. ■ 19106 #041-13-2006 L2006 **IM** *012
LYNN, Lorna Anne. 510 WALNUT ST, STE 1700 19106 #041-01-1986 L1987 **IM** *062 †20
LYNN, Richard Brian. 132 S 10TH ST, 480 MAIN BLDG 19107 #035-01-1982 L1986 **GE** *062 †20
LYON, Sarah M.. 3400 SPRUCE ST, DEPARTMENT OF INTERNAL MED 19104
#035-04-2004 L2004 **IM** *100 †20
LYON, Thomas Felton. 760 CARPENTER LN, MT AIRY FAMILY PRACTICE 19119
#041-13-1985 L1987 **FM** *020 †18
LYONS, Amy Kathleen. ■ 19107 #041-13-2007 L2007 **OBG** *012
LYONS, Daniel Coombs. 1901 MARKET ST, FL 33 19103 #041-13-1976 L1977 **FM IMG** *020 †18
LYONS, Karen Marie. 219 N BRANDYWINE ST, FL 10 19107 #041-01-1979 L1981 **OTO HNS** *020 †45
LYONS, Patricia Jane. 245 N BROAD ST, STE 110 19107 #041-09-1968 L1973 **NEP P** *030 †20
LYONS, Paul Eric. 3400 N BROAD ST, TEMPLE UNIV MED SCHOOL 19140 #038-40-1991 L1998
FM *020 †18
LYREN, Kate Elizabeth. 3400 N BROAD ST, OF PENNSYLVANIA 19104 #038-06-2007 L2007
EM *012
LYSIAK, Anne Catherine. 8400 BUSTLETON AVE, STE 101 19152 #759-01-1973 L1980
IM *020 †20
LYU, Byong-Sook. ■ 19122 #583-03-1955 L1968 **AN OS** *071
MA, Julie Phuong. ■ 19107 #041-13-2005 L2005 **AN** *012
MA, Marek. 3400 SPRUCE ST, DEPARTMENT OF EMERGENCY ME 19104 #025-01-2000 L2004
EM *050 †16
MA, Xiaoli. 201 N 9TH ST STE A, 1800 LOMBARD STREET STE 10 19107 #243-69-1983 L1998
GE *020 †20
MA, Yitao. 3401 N BROAD ST, TEMPLE UNIVERSITY HOSPITAL 19140 #243-69-1995 L2006 *100
MA, Yuxiang. 2900 W QUEEN LN 19129 #243-83-1986 L2006 **PTH** *012
MAANY, Iradj. PHILA VA MED CTR NO 116E 19104 #517-01-1967 L1973 **P ADP** *020 †75 ‡
MABINE, Bruce Junious. 3401 N BROAD ST, TEMPLE UNIV HOSPITAL 19140
#041-13-1977 L1980 **OBG** *020 †30
MACALUSO, Christopher R. 3401 N BROAD ST, TEMPLE UNIVERSITY HOSPITAL 19140
#041-13-2004 L2004 **EM** *012
MACATANGAY, Evangeline. 2601 HOLME AVE 19152 #748-01-1972 L1975 **GP** *020
MACCHIAVELLI, Anthony J. 2301 S BROAD ST, STE 205 19148 #041-13-1996 L1998
IM *020 †20
MAC EVILLY, Myles Patrick. 324 S 34TH ST, DEPT ANES 19104 #539-05-1966 **AN** *050
MAC EWEN, G Dean. 3551 N BROAD ST, SHRINERS HOSPITAL 19140 #065-05-1951 L1988
ORS *071 †40
MACFADDEN, Wayne. UNIVERSITY & WOODLAND AVES 19104 #035-06-1986 L1986 **P** *020 †75

MAC GREGOR, Rob Roy, III. 536 JOHNSON PAVILION, UNIV PA DEPT ID 19104
#024-01-1964 L1971 **ID IM** *020 †20
MACHADO, Carlos Andres. 3401 N BROAD ST, DEPT MED 19140 #033-05-2007 L2007 **IM** *012
MACHADO, Rodolfo Rozindo. 5501 OLD YORK RD, ALBERT EINSTEIN MEDICAL CE 19141
#187-14-2004 L2006 **IM** *012
MACHARE DELGADO, Nestor E. ■ 19107 #132-03-1998 L2008 **PCC** *012
MACHOVEC, Kelly Ann. 3401 N BROAD ST, OF S 19140 #036-01-2006 L2006 **GS** *012
MACHTAY, Mitchell. 3400 SPRUCE ST, 2 DONNER MED AFFAIRS OFF 19104
#035-19-1989 L1991 **RO** *020 †80
MACINTYRE, Neil Ross. 3401 N BROAD ST, TEMPLE UNIVERSITY HOSPITAL 19140
#041-13-2004 L2004 **ORS** *012
MACKARONIS, Anthony C. ■ 19130 #033-06-2002 L2002 **OBG** *020
MACKELAITE, Lina. 2900 W QUEEN LN, DEPT OF INTERNAL MED 19129 #913-49-2003 L2004
NEP *012 †20
MACKENZIE, Amy Rodd. ■ 19128 #041-15-2005 L2006 **IM** *012
MACKENZIE, Larami Gaetano. ■ 19128 #041-15-2002 L2002 **N** *012
MACKLER, Scott Andrew. 38 WOODLAND SEC OF GEN MED, VAMC 19104 #041-01-1986 L1990
IM *050 †20
MACKNIN, Jonathan Benjami. ■ 19146 #041-01-2008 *012
MACKOWIAK, Lisa. 501 S 54TH ST 19143 #041-02-1999 L2002 **EM** *020 †16
MAC MILLAN, Robert M, Jr. 2701 HOLME AVE STE 207, GREATER PHILADELPHIA CARDI 19152
#041-02-1969 L1970 **CD IM** *020 †20 ‡
MAC MORAN, Jay W. 3401 N BROAD ST 19140 #041-02-1950 L1951 **R** *040 †80
MACOLINO, Marcie E. 7056 GERMANTOWN AVE, MT AIRY PEDIATRICS, LLP 19119
#041-13-1993 L1995 **PD** *020 †55
MACONES, Alexander Jos. ■ 19103 #041-02-1984 L1986 **DR** *020
MACVEY, Marilyn Joan. 2650 E SOMERSET ST 19134 #061-01-1964 L1987 **EM CCM** *020 †16
MACY, Charles Thos. 1628 JOHN F KENNEDY BLVD, STE 950 19103 #036-01-1958 L1965
IM *071 †20
MADABHUSHI, Aditi Ramaswa. 3401 N BROAD ST, OF S 19140 #495-96-2001 L2003 **GS** *012
MADAIO, Michael Peter. 3401 N BROAD ST STE 658, PARKINSON & TUSM 19140
#035-03-1974 L1990 **NEP** *050 †20
MADAN, Ichchha. BROAD-ONTARIO STS, DEPT OF OB/GYN 19140 #495-45-2003 L2004
OBG *012
MADANI, Reza. ■ 19130 #041-15-2008 *012
MADDEN, James Jos. 1628 JOHN F KENNEDY BLVD, STE 950 19103 #016-02-1973 L1975
IM *020 †20
MADIANOS, Michael. 2614 WOODWARD ST 19152 #035-06-1961 L1962 **IM END** *071
MADJAROV, Bojidar D. 51 N 39TH ST, SCHEIE EYE INSTITUTE 19104 #198-03-1984 L2005
OPH *012
MADOW, Leo. 2401 PENNSYLVANIA AVE 19130 #038-06-1942 L1943 **P N** *020 †75
MADRIGAL, Vanessa Nicole. ■ 19103 #038-45-2004 L2007 **CCP** *012 †55
MADRINAN, Nestor O. 452 W ALLEGHENY AVE 19133 #748-01-1968 L1983 **FM** *020
MADU, Chika Ngozi. ■ 19136 #025-01-2003 L2003 **RO** *012
MADUKA-EZEH, Awele Nwamal. 5501 OLD YORK RD, ALBERT EINSTEIN MEDICAL CE 19141
#690-01-2000 L2006 **IM** *012
MAENPAA, Garath Alan. 727 DELANCEY ST 19106 #917-10-1992 L2001 **IM ISM** *020 †20
MAGARGAL, Larry Elliot. 840 WALNUT ST, STE 1020 19107 #041-13-1969 L1970 **OPH** *071 †35
MAGEE, John G, Jr. 7700 GERMANTOWN AVE, FL 2 19118 #041-13-1979 L1981 **PD** *020 †55
MAGGE, Suresh Natesh. 3400 SPRUCE ST, OF PENNSY 19104 #024-01-2001 L2001 **NS** *012
MAGILNER, Arthur David. 333 COTTMAN AVE 19111 #041-02-1963 L1964 **DR** *020 †80
MAGLIOCCO, Anthony Martin. 7701 BURHOLME AVE, FOX CHASE CANCER CTR 19111
#060-01-1987 L1991 **PTH** *020 †50
MAGNANI, Gretchen E. 4641 ROOSEVELT BLVD 19124 #034-01-1994 L2001 **P** *020 †75
MAGO, Rajnish. 833 CHESTNUT ST, STE 210E 19107 #495-05-1988 L1998 **P** *020 †75
MAGRAN, Leonardo. ■ 19130 #132-01-1948 L1963 **CHP P** *071
MAGUIRE, Albert Mahler. 51 N 39TH ST, SCHEIE EYE INSTITUTE 19104 #024-01-1986 L1992
OPH *035
MAGUIRE, David Patrick. 111 S 11TH ST, G-8490 19107 #041-02-1982 L1984 **AN** *020 †05
MAGUIRE, Henry Clinton. 111 S 11TH ST, THOMAS JEFFERSON UNIV HSPT 19107
#016-02-1954 L1957 **D ON** *050 †15
MAGUNDAYAO, Minda B. 6701 N BROAD ST, WEDGE MEDICAL CENTER 19126
#748-08-1971 L1985 **P** *020
MAHADEVIAH, Ann Sheila. 800 SPRUCE ST 19107 #038-44-1989 L1992 **AN** *020 †05 ‡
MAHAN, John Paul. 2630 HOLME AVE, INSTITUTE FOR RESPIRATORY 19152
#010-02-1974 L1979 **PUD SME** *020 †20
MAHANIAH, Wakengo. ■ 19118 #041-13-2003 L2003 **FP** *012
MAHBOUBI, Soroosh. 3400 SPRUCE ST 19104 #041-01-1966 L1974 **PDR** *020 †80
MAHER, Ian Atticus. ■ 19102 #055-02-2005 L2005 **D** *012
MAHER, Mary Brooke. ■ 19102 #055-02-2004 L2005 **PTH** *100
MAHLAB, Ron David. ■ 19106 #041-12-1996 L1998 **P** *012 ‡
MAHMOOD, Abdul Aziz. 111 S 11TH ST 19107 #704-01-1997 L2001 **GS** *100
MAHMOOD, Iram. 245 N 15TH ST MS 437, DREXEL UNIV COLL OF MED 19102
#704-06-1998 L2006 **NEP** *012
MAHMOODI, Mandana. 2900 W QUEEN LN 19129 #517-01-1999 L2002 **DMP** *100 †50
MAHMOUD, Najjia Nora. 700 SPRUCE ST, STE 305 19106 #035-20-1993 L2001 **GS** *020 †85,10
MAHMUD, Jamal. 1427 VINE ST, FL 8 19102 #704-01-1987 L2002 **P** *100
MAHMUD, Semhar. ■ 19129 #041-15-2008 *012
MAHNKE, Lisa Ann. ■ 19146 #056-05-2000 L2006 **ID** *050 †20
MAHONEY, Nicholas Adam. ■ 19107 #041-02-2008 *012
MAHR, Tamara Alisa. ■ 19106 #033-06-2004 L2004 **PCC** *012 †20
MAHRER, Arie Emil. 1 SILVERSTEIN, 3400 SPRUCE STREET 19104 #550-03-2000 L2007
VIR *012
MAI, John Michael. ■ 19106 #030-05-2004 L2004 **U** *012
MAIATICO, Marc A. 1 PENN BLVD 19144 #033-05-1976 L1977 **PM** *020 †60 ‡
MAIDA, Jennifer Marie. 3401 N BROAD ST, 6TH FLOOR PP 19140 #041-13-2004 L2004
OPH *012
MAILA, Kamishele. 800 SPRUCE ST, DEPT OF GME 19107 #965-01-1996 L2006 **IM** *012
MAILLARD, Ivan Patrick. 3400 SPRUCE ST, 16TH PENN TOWER 19104 #869-05-1993 L2001
HO IM *050
MAINIGI, Sumeet Kumar. 5501 OLD YORK RD HB3 19141 #035-19-2000 L2001 **ICE** *100 †20
MAISTROW, Marla Gayle. 800 SPRUCE ST 19107 #035-47-1987 L1990 **AN** *020 †05
MAITIN, Ellen C. 7500 CENTRAL AVE, STE 108 19111 #035-48-1978 L1980 **HS ORS** *020 †40 ‡
MAITIN, Ian Bruce. 3401 N BROAD ST, TEMPLE UNIV HOSP-PMR 19140 #041-02-1989 L1993
PM *020 †60

MAJID, Nasira Yasmin. 445 W GIRARD AVE 19123 #704-06-1966 L1974 **FM PD** *020 †55 ‡
MAJMUNDAR, Sureshchandra. ■ 19152 #496-01-1980 **PCH PTH** *100
MAJOR, David Alan. 211 S 9TH ST, NINTH STREET INTERNAL 19107 #041-09-1964 L1965 **IM** *020 †20
MAKAR, Mary S. 840 WALNUT ST, WILLS EYE HOSPITAL 19107 #024-01-2000 L2001 **OPH** *020 ‡
MAKARY, Rafik Zaky. ■ 19103 #330-04-1957 L1971 **P** *020
MAKDA, Junaid. 1015 WALNUT ST, THOMAS JEFFERSON UNIV 19107 #016-01-2006 L2006 **ORS** *012
MAKIPOUR, Kian. ■ 19130 #051-07-2006 L2006 **IM** *012
MAKKUNI, Premraj. 5501 OLD YORK RD, DEPT OF CARDIO DIS 19141 #143-04-2001 L2003 **CD** *012 †20
MAKLER, Paul T. ■ 19106 #041-01-1943 L1944 **IM** *020 †20
MAKOUS, Norman. 829 SPRUCE ST STE 304 19107 #056-05-1947 L1959 **CD IM** *071 †20
MALAKOOTI, Marcelo Ramin. ■ 19144 #041-15-2008 *012
MALAMUT, Leonard Lee. 5219 N BROAD ST 19141 #041-01-1943 L1944 **IM** *072 †20
MALATACK, James Jeffrey. 833 CHESTNUT ST, DEPARTMENT OF PEDIATRICS 19107 #041-07-1976 L1977 **PD PHO** *020 †55
MALAYAMAN, Saninuj Nini. ■ 19147 #041-15-2005 L2005 **AN** *012
MALCOLMSON, Chas Herbert. 324 S 34TH ST, CHILDRENS HOSPITAL 19104 #065-05-1958 L1985 **PD** *020
MALDONADO, Lisa Margarita. 26 S 40TH ST 19104 #042-02-1985 L1986 **P CHP** *020 †75
MALDONADO, Michael A. 3400 SPRUCE ST, FL 8 19104 #042-01-1988 L1990 **RHU IM** *020 †20
MALEK, Kamoun. 3400 SPRUCE ST 19104 #396-06-1975 L1983 **PTH CLP** *020 †50
MALEKI, Kataneh Farsani. 1703 S BROAD ST, STE 300 19148 #517-06-1992 L2002 **CD** *020 †20
MALESON, Franklin Geo. 1015 CHESTNUT ST 19107 #041-02-1965 L1966 **P** *020 †75 ‡
MALETA, Viviana Maria. 1900 S BROAD ST, 2ND FL 19145 #041-09-1994 L1996 **PD** *020 †55
MALGORZATA, Maria. 1000 WALNUT ST, APT 502 19107 #759-07-1975 L1984 *100
MALHOTRA, Anita Kumari. ■ 19130 #041-13-2003 L2005 **AN** *012
MALHOTRA, Gaurav. ■ 19103 #041-01-2008 *012
MALHOTRA, Neil Rainer. 3400 SPRUCE ST, OF PENNSY 19104 #051-01-2002 L2002 **NS** *012
MALHOTRA, Prashant Solank. 925 CHESTNUT ST, DEPARTMENT OF OTOLARYNGOLO 19107 #038-06-2004 L2004 **GS** *100
MALIK, Abdul. 7909 OXFORD AVE 19111 #913-89-1983 L1998 **IM** *020 †20
MALIK, Afshan. MCP HAHNEMANN UNIV, DEPT FAM PRAC 19102 #704-01-1981 L2001 **FM** *100
MALIK, Nasreen. 432 N 6TH ST, ACTION INC. 19123 #050-02-1997 L2000 **FM** *020 †18
MALIN, Murray Jay. ■ 19102 #038-43-1984 L1986 **AN** *020 †05
MALISOFF, Vera. 3300 HENRY AVE 19129 #041-07-1951 L1952 **PD PDA** *071
MALKIN, Alan Gary. 6404 ROOSEVELT BLVD, STE 1A 19149 #041-09-1978 L1980 **IM EM** *020 ‡
MALKIN, Richard Ira. 3996 RED LION RD 19114 #041-01-1974 L1978 **PD** *020 †55 ‡
MALKOWICZ, Stanley Bruce. 3400 SPRUCE ST, DEPT UROLOGY 19104 #041-01-1981 L1982 **U** *020 †95
MALLER, Eric Steven. 324 S 34TH ST 19104 #024-01-1980 L1984 **GE PD** *020 †55
MALLO, Gregory Charles. ■ 19107 #041-02-2005 **ORS** *012
MALLOW, Eric Bardon. 800 SPRUCE ST, FL 2 19107 #033-05-1986 L1988 **NPM** *020 †55
MALLOY, Kelly Michele. 299 S 8TH ST 19106 #041-02-2002 L2002 **OTO** *020
MALLOY, Terrence Reed. 299 S 8TH ST 19106 #041-01-1963 L1964 **U** *020 †95
MALLULA, Kiran Kumar. ALUMNI AFFAIRS, ALBERT EINSTEIN MEDICAL CE 19141 #495-21-2001 L2007 **PD** *012
MALLYA, Giridhar G. 833 CHESTNUT ST, STE 301 19107 #043-01-2003 L2003 **FM** *050 †18
MALLYA, Raghuram G. 1025 WALNUT ST, THOMAS JEFFERSON UNIV HOSP 19107 #033-05-2001 L2001 **CD** *012
MALMKVIST, Gunnar. 3400 SPRUCE ST DEPT AN 19104 #858-01-1975 **AN** *020
MALODIYA, Amratash. 3400 SPRUCE ST, U OF PA HOSP 19104 #495-37-2001 L2008 *100
MALONE, Richard P, Jr. 4641 ROOSEVELT BLVD 19124 #041-09-1983 L1984 **CHP P** *040 †75
MALTZMAN, Jonathan Scott. 415 CURIE BLVD, 105 CLINICAL RESEARCH BUIL 19104 #041-01-1997 L2000 **NEP** *100 †20
MALVAR, Potenciano R. 1619 WALNUT ST 19103 #748-07-1964 **CRS** *020
MAMA, Saifuddin Taiyeb. 700 SPRUCE ST, STE 305 19106 #041-02-1993 L1996 **OBG** *020 †30
MAMARY, Albert James. 3401 N BROAD ST, TEMPLE UNIVERSITY HOSPITAL 19140 #041-13-1999 L2001 **PCC** *100 †20
MAMBALAM, Pramod Kumar. ■ 19107 #041-15-2007 L2007 **IM** *012
MAMELAK, Joshua D. ■ 19107 #065-01-1996 L2003 **DR** *100 †80 ‡
MAMENISKIS, Algird R. 255 S 17TH ST, STE 2200 19103 #041-13-1986 L1988 **PS** *020 †85,65
MAMMEN, Ajit Chandy. ■ 19103 #495-27-2000 L2007 **CCP** *012 †55
MAMULA, Petar. 324 S 34TH ST 19104 #957-01-1991 L1998 **PG PD** *020 †55
MAN, Matthew. 3401 N BROAD ST, DEPT MED 19140 #041-15-2007 L2007 **IM** *012
MANABAT, Eileen Rose Figu. ■ 19107 #748-02-2004 L2006 **AN** *012
MANAKER, Scott. 3400 SPRUCE ST, 100 CENTREX 19104 #041-01-1985 L1987 **PCC CCM** *020 †20
MANALO, George Quesada. 2028 N 22ND ST 19121 #748-01-1974 L1981 **FM** *020 †18
MANCALL, Elliott Lee. 900 WALNUT ST STE 200, JEFFERSON HOSPITAL FOR NE 19107 #041-01-1952 L1959 **N NP** *040 †75
MANCHANDIA, Ajay Mahesh. ■ 19130 #041-15-2008 L2008 *012
MANCINI, Deslyn M. 5501 OLD YORK RD, KLEIN 410 19141 #041-07-1993 L1997 **OBG** *020 †30 ‡
MANCUSO, Mark William. 3401 N BROAD ST, TEMPLE UNIV HOSP 19140 #041-02-1997 L2007 **AN** *012 †18
MANDAL, Sanat Kumar. 829 SPRUCE ST, STE 105 19107 #495-38-1964 L1973 **CD** *020 †20
MANDAL, Sanchita. 829 SPRUCE ST, STE 105 19107 #041-07-1992 L1998 **CD** *020 †20
MANDARINO, Michael James. 2832 BELMONT AVE 19131 #041-09-1972 L1973 **ORS** *020 †40
MANDEL, Dale Mason. 1901 MARKET ST, FL 27 19103 #561-01-1978 L2004 **GS** *030 †85 ‡
MANDEL, Jeff E. 3400 SPRUCE ST, HUP 19104 #048-13-1980 L1981 **AN** *020 †05
MANDEL, Steven. 1015 CHESTNUT ST STE 810 19107 #035-46-1975 L1980 **N CN** *020 †75 ‡
MANDEL, Susan Jennifer. 3400 SPRUCE ST, 1 MALONEY UNIV PA ENDOCRIN 19104 #035-01-1986 L1997 **END IM** *020 †20
MANDELL, Morton Stanley. 5401 OLD YORK RD, KLEIN PROF BLDGS STE 401 19141 #041-01-1959 L1960 **CD IM** *020 †20
MANDODY, Zarina. ■ 19104 #704-06-1953 L1984 *071
MANEK, Neil R. 3401 N BROAD ST, DEPT MED 19140 #048-02-2007 L2007 **IM** *012
MANGALICK, Vip. 5501 OLD YORK RD 19141 #422-01-2007 L2007 **GS** *012
MANGAN, Kenneth Francis. 7604 CENTRAL AVE LOWR LEV, FRIENDS HALL PHYS BLDG 19111 #010-01-1973 L1981 **GE IM** *020 †20
MANGEL, Joseph. 111 S 11TH ST 19107 #041-77-1991, ▲ L1992 **IM FM** *020
MANGIN, Teresa Marie. ■ 19146 #041-01-2004 L2004 **N** *012
MANGINO, Jennifer Lyn. ■ 19146 #038-40-2004 L2008 **PD** *100 †55
MANGINO, William, II. 313 S 12TH ST 19107 #847-06-1977 L1978 **PME PMM** *020
MANGIONE, Antoinette. 5501 OLD YORK RD 19141 #035-06-1983 L1985 **IM EM** *020 †20,16
MANGIONE, Salvatore. 834 WALNUT ST, STE 650 19107 #561-23-1980 L1982 **PUD IM** *020 †20
MANI, Ashwin Kumar. 1025 WALNUT ST, 805 COLLEGE BLDG 19107 #495-59-1998 L2002 **PCC** *100 †20
MANI, Shobha. 501 S 54TH ST 19143 #495-08-1971 L1977 **AN** *020 †05
MANIA, Irakli I.. 2900 W QUEEN LN, DEPT OF PSYCHIATRY 19129 #912-02-2000 L2004 **P** *012
MANIAR, Gayatri Chaitan. 3401 N BROAD ST, TEMPLE UNIVERSITY HOSPITAL 19140 #495-17-2001 L2004 **OBG** *012
MANIAR, Tapan Nitin. 3400 SPRUCE ST, 100 CENTREX BUILDING 19104 #041-01-2004 L2004 **HO** *012 †20
MANIGLIA, Richard Jos. 39TH & MARKET STS 19104 #041-09-1988 L1991 **ID** *020 †20
MANIN, Beth Ilene. 6001 RIDGE AVE, ROXBOROUGH PLZ INTERNL MED 19128 #041-07-1991 L1994 **IM** *020 †20
MANIS, Robert E. 7600 CENTRAL AVE 19111 #165-01-1975 L1976 **P EM** *100
MANIU, Cristina Magdalena. ■ 19107 #041-02-2008 *012
MANKIN, Eric Robt. 9331 OLD BUSTLETON AVE, STE 201 19115 #041-13-1987 L1994 **FM** *020 †18
MANN, Stephanie Elise. ■ 19104 #010-01-1989 L2006 **OBG** *020 †30
MANNAN, Sonia. ■ 19103 #051-07-2006 L2006 **IM** *012
MANNING, Eddie Ward. ■ 19139 #041-13-2004 **GS** *012
MANNING, Francis Patrick. 2601 HOLME AVE 19152 #041-13-1962 L1963 **R** *020 †80
MANNO, Catherine Scott. 324 S 34TH ST 19104 #041-09-1978 L1980 **PHO** *040 †55
MANOFF, Susan Beth. 324 S 34TH ST, DEPT PED 19104 #008-01-1981 L1983 **PD** *020 †55
MANOLAS, Michael Charles. 1025 WALNUT ST, THOMAS JEFFERSON UNIV HOSP 19107 #041-02-2004 L2004 **IM** *100 †20
MANON, Ramon. 1015 CHESTNUT ST STE 810 19107 #042-01-1980 L1989 **N CN** *020 †75 ‡
MANSMANN, Herbert C, Jr. 1020 LOCUST ST # 543, JEFFERSON ALUMNI HALL 19107 #041-02-1951 L1952 **AI PD** *071 †55,03
MANSOUR, Tamer. 51 N 39TH ST, SPCHEIE EYE INST 19104 #010-03-2001 L2005 **OPH FPS** *100
MANSUKANI, Sharad Sunder. 200 LOCUST ST, CONDO 25-C 19106 #041-07-1993 L1997 **OPH MDM** *030
MANTELL, Mark Philip. 1800 LOMBARD ST, SET 805 PEPPER PAVILION 19146 #041-01-1989 L1992 **VS GS** *020 †85
MANTRAVADI, Anand Venkat. 840 WALNUT ST STE 1130, WILLS EYE HOSPITAL/JEFFERS 19107 #017-20-2003 L2007 **OPH** *020
MANZARBEITIA, Cosme. 5401 OLD YORK RD, LIVER TRANSPLANT 19141 #847-13-1982 L1995 **GS OS** *020 †85
MAO, Jun. 3400 SPRUCE ST, 2 GATES BUILDING 19104 #016-11-2000 L2003 **FM** *020 †18
MAQBOOL, Asim. 3535 MARKET ST, RM 1572 19104 #010-01-1997 L2004 **PG** *020 †55
MARAIS, Jake Ralph. ■ 19128 #041-15-2005 L2008 **IM** *012
MARAJ, Suraj. 5501 OLD YORK RD, ALBERT EINSTEIN MED CTR 19141 #539-06-1999 L2003 **CD** *012 †20
MARANOFF, Richard Bruce. 2601 HOLME AVE 19152 #041-09-1961 L1964 **PTH** *020 †50
MARATHE, Pallavi Ravindra. 245 N 15TH ST, MS 412 19102 #422-01-2000 L2001 **HO** *020
MARCANTUONO, Nicole Maria. ■ 19130 #041-15-2007 L2007 *012
MARCHAN, Eduardo Miguel. ■ 19107 #008-01-2004 **GS** *012
MARCHAN, Jennifer Stephan. ■ 19129 #041-15-2008 *012
MARCHIANO, Dominic Adam. 800 SPRUCE ST, FL 8 19107 #035-19-1994 L1999 **OBG** *020 †30
MARCHILDON, Michael Bert. 833 CHESTNUT ST, 3RD FL 19107 #005-11-1968 L1986 **PDS** *020 †85
MARCIANO, Juliet Anne. 7700 GERMANTOWN AVE 19118 #041-07-1989 L1991 **PD** *020 †55
MARCOS, Cecilia Salting. 1900 N 20TH ST 19121 #748-01-1961 L1972 **PD** *071
MARCOTTE, Paul John. 3400 SPRUCE ST, FL 5 19104 #065-09-1984 L1992 **NS** *020 †25
MARCUCCI, Michael Chas. 219 N BROAD ST, STE 8 19107 #041-09-1982 L1985 **GS VS** *020 †85
MARCUS, Carole Lesley. 324 S 34TH ST 19104 #836-01-1982 L2003 **PDP PD** *020 †55
MARCUS, Donald Keith. 9501 ROOSEVELT BLVD, STE 208 19114 #024-05-1983 L1984 **ID** *020 †20
MARDINI, Issam A. 3400 SPRUCE ST, UNIVERSITY OF PENNSYLVANIA 19104 #875-01-1978 L1996 **AN PMM** *020 †05
MAREINEFRON, Gabriela. ■ 19103 #041-01-2008 L2008 *012
MARENBERG, Marjorie Ellen. 1845 WALNUT ST, FL 12 19103 #008-01-1996 L1999 **IMG** *020 †20
MARESCA, Michelle Marie. 111 S 11TH ST, THOMAS JEFFERSON UNIV 19107 #033-06-2007 L2007 *012
MARGIOTTI, Gerard A, Jr. 3996 RED LION RD 19114 #041-09-1982 L1983 **PD** *020 †55 ‡
MARGO, Geoffrey Myles. 210 W WASHINGTON SQ, MEZZANINE LEVEL 19106 #836-01-1970 L1994 **P** *020 †75
MARGO, Katherine L. 51 N 39TH ST 7TH FL, PENN FAMILY CARE 19104 #035-15-1978 L1994 **FM** *040 †18
MARGOLIS, David Joel. 3400 SPRUCE ST, 2 RHOADS PAVILION 19104 #016-02-1985 L1986 **D** *020 †20,15
MARGOSHES, Barton Gray. 1601 CHESTNUT ST, SIGNA 19192 #165-06-1978 L2007 **IM** *030 †20
MARGOSSIAN, Hagop. 700 COTTMAN AVE, BLDG A 19111 #875-03-1984 L1997 **CD** *020 †20
MARGULIES, Kenneth Ber. 422 CURIE BLVD, 709 STELLAR CHANCE 19104 #041-02-1986 L1993 **CD IM** *020 †20
MARIANI, Chiara. 3400 SPRUCE ST, UNIVERSITY OF PENNSYLVANIA 19104 #561-03-1999 L2007 **PM** *012
MARIANO, Joseph. ■ 19130 #041-13-1978 L1979 **OS GP** *050
MARIK, Paul Ellis. 1015 CHESTNUT ST, STE 650 19107 #836-01-1981 L2000 **CCM** *020 †20
MARIN, Jennifer Rebecca. ■ 19104 #011-02-2001 L2006 **PEM** *012 †55
MARINO, Ignazio Roberto. 1025 WALNUT ST, STE 605 COLLEGE BLDG 19107 #561-23-1979 L1991 **GS TTS** *062
MARINO, Michael Howell. ■ 19147 #041-13-2007 L2007 **IM** *012
MARINO, Ralph James. 132 S 10TH ST, STE 375 MAIN BLDG 19107 #041-02-1982 L1986 **PM SCI** *020 †60 ‡
MARIS, John Matthew. 3615 CIVIC CENTER BLVD, STE 902 19104 #041-01-1989 L1991 **PHO** *020 †55
MARK, Beth Zimet. 133 S 36TH ST LBBY 2, COUNSELING & PSYCHOLOGICAL 19104 #041-13-1988 L1990 **P** *020 †75
MARK, Mina Edith. 1428 W PORTER ST 19145 #041-09-1987 L1990 **RHU** *020
MARKHAM, Fred Wm. 833 CHESTNUT ST, STE 301 19107 #032-01-1976 L1977 **FM** *040 †18

8012 ■ = Address Information Privacy Protected

MARKOFF, Joseph Ira. 2610 E ALLEGHENY AVE 19134 #026-04-1974 L1975 **OPH** *020 †35

MARKOV, Dimitri. 1020 SANSOM ST, DEPARTMENT OF PSYCHIATRY 19107 #041-15-1999 L2001 **P** *020 †75

MARKOVITZ, Bruce Jay. 10160 BUSTLETON AVE, STE F 19116 #041-02-1991 L1993 **OPH** *020 †35

MARKOWITZ, Clyde Edward. 3400 SPRUCE ST 19104 #035-01-1990 L1998 **N** *020 †75

MARKOWITZ, Richard Ira. 34TH ST & CIVIC CTR BVLD 19104 #035-15-1969 L1970 **PDR** *020 †80

MARKOWITZ, Scott David. 34TH & CIVIC CENTER BLVD, DEPT ANES 19104 #028-02-1993 L2001 **PAN AN** *020 †05

MARKS, Allan David. 3401 N BROAD ST, TEMPLE HOSPITAL 19140 #041-13-1962 L1963 **IM END** *071 †20

MARKS, Joshua Aaron. ■ 19107 #041-02-2007 L2007 **GS** *012

MARKUS DE MOGUILLANSKY, Na. 5501 OLD YORK RD, OFFICE OF ACADEMIC 19141 #132-01-2004 L2005 **IM** *012

MARMURA, Michael James. ■ 19102 #051-04-2002 L2006 **IM** *100

MAROHN, Kimberly Lynn. 111 S 11TH ST, THOMAS JEFFERSON UNIV 19107 #041-15-2007 L2007 *012

MAROKO, Deborah L. 833 CHESTNUT ST, DUPONT AT JEFFERSON 19107 #024-07-1995 L1998 **PD** *050 †55

MARON, David James. 51 N 39TH ST, STE 2D 19104 #010-02-1997 L1999 **GS** *020 †85,10

MARONE, Phillip Jos. 130 S 9TH ST 19107 #041-02-1957 L1958 **ORS OSM** *071 †40

MARQUARDT, Kristen Marie. ■ 19102 #035-03-2001 L2004 **PM** *100

MARQUETAND, Ralph A. 3400 SPRUCE ST 19104 #041-01-1994 L1997 **OS** *020

MARQUEZ, Manuel Saturnino. 4553 N 5TH ST 19140 #132-01-2951 L1964 **PD PDC** *075

MARSELAS, Sharon Louise. ■ 19104 #023-01-1972 L1973 **NS** *020

MARSENIC-DJORDJEVIC, Olive. ■ 19121 #957-02-1993 L2006 **PN** *012 †55

MARSH, Eric David. 3400 CIVIC CENTER BLVD, 6TH FL WOOD BLDG 19104 #035-19-1998 L2001 **CHN PD** *050 †75,55

MARSH, Evelyn Bricklin. 3400 SPRUCE ST, HOSPITAL OF THE UNIVERSITY 19104 #024-07-2005 L2005 **OBG** *012

MARSH, Julian Bunsick. 2900 W QUEEN LN, DEPT BIOCHEMISTRY 19129 #041-01-1947 L1949 **OS** *050

MARSHALL, Benton H. ■ 19130 #020-02-1951 L1953 **P** *072 †75

MARTE, Jennifer Laura. 1025 WALNUT ST, JEFFERSON MED COLL 19107 #041-02-1999 *100

MARTEN, Paul. ■ 19130 #035-46-2001 L2006 **DR** *020 †80

MARTENS, Timothy Paul. ■ 19147 #035-19-2001 L2001 **GS** *100

MARTIN, Clarence Havard, Jr. 8815 GERMANTOWN AVE, STE 35 19118 #010-03-1976 L1979 **IM NEP** *071

MARTIN, Donald Beckwith. U HOSP PA MAHONEY BLDG 19104 #024-01-1954 L1979 **IM** *040 †20

MARTIN, Elaine Marie. 302 S 13TH ST 19107 #016-11-2004 L2004 **P** *012

MARTIN, Janelle Marie. ■ 19107 #023-01-2005 L2005 **EM** *012

MARTIN, Lainie. 333 COTTMAN AVE, FOX CHASE CANCER CENTER 19111 #041-13-1999 L2003 **HO** *100 †20

MARTIN, Laura Margaret. 51 N 39TH ST, PENN FAMILY CARE 19104 #004-01-1982 L2006 **FM FPG** *020 †18

MARTIN, Linda Diane. 1408 S BROAD ST, 2ND FL 19146 #041-01-1978 L1980 **PD** *020 †55

MARTIN, Mary Ellen. 7604 CENTRAL AVE, GROUND FLOOR 19111 #035-08-1996 L1999 **HO** *020 †20

MARTIN, Melanie Cowan. 840 WALNUT ST 19107 #041-13-1981 L1983 **OPH** *020 †35

MARTIN, Niels Douglas. 111 S 11TH ST 19107 #033-06-2000 L2001 **CCS** *012 ‡

MARTIN, Richard Eliot. 8835 GERMANTOWN AVE 19118 #041-02-1970 L1974 **EM** *020 †16

MARTIN, Ronald Christophe. ■ 19107 #023-01-2005 L2005 **IM** *012

MARTIN, Seth Shay. ■ 19146 #041-01-2008 *012

MARTIN, Ubaldo Jose. 3401 N BROAD ST, 9PP 19140 #429-02-1994 L1998 **PCC** *020 †20

MARTIN, Veronica. ■ 19118 #041-01-2007 L2007 **P** *012

MARTIN, Vicki Lynn. 4641 ROOSEVELT BLVD, FRIEND HOSPITAL 19124 #012-01-1990 L1992 **CHP** *020 †75

MARTINEZ, Edgar Alfredo. 8201 STATE RD 19136 #042-02-2002 L2002 **P** *075

MARTINEZ, Irisaida. 216 N BROAD ST 19102 #041-13-1982 L1984 **PD** *020 †55

MARTINEZ, Jasmine. 111 S 11TH ST, DEPT OF HOUSE STAFF 19107 #041-77-2004, ▲ L2005 **PM** *012

MARTINEZ, Maritza. 2028 SPRING GARDEN ST, # 3F 19130 #035-48-2005 L2005 **PD** *012

MARTINEZ CANTARIN, Maria. 111 S 11TH ST, THOS JEFFERSON UNIV HOSP 19107 #847-04-2003 L2004 **NEP** *012 †20

MARTINEZ-LAGE ALVAREZ, Mar. 3400 SPRUCE ST, UNIV OF PA HOSP 19104 #847-20-2001 L2008 *100

MARTINEZ-LOPEZ, Jose. 1015 WALNUT ST STE 804, CARDEZA FOUNDATION 19107 #847-04-1957 L1969 **IM** *071 †20

MARTINEZ OUTSCHOORN, Ubald. 1025 WALNUT ST, THOMAS JEFFERSON UNIV HOSP 19107 #847-04-2002 L2003 **HO** *012 †20

MARTINEZ-SANCHEZ, Oscar M. 5501 OLD YORK RD, ALBERT EINSTEIN MED CTR 19141 #649-02-1995 L2003 **GS** *100

MARTINEZ VILLAR, Carmen S. 2900 W QUEEN LN 19129 #308-05-2004 **P** *100

MARTIN-ROSS, Amber. 245 N 15TH ST MS 310, DREXEL UNIV COLL OF MED 19102 #422-01-2005 L2007 **AN** *012

MARTUCCI, Albert A, Jr. 3300 HENRY AVE 19129 #041-13-1957 L1958 **FM** *071 †18

MARTYAK, Gregg Gabriel. 532 S 15TH ST # 2 19146 #041-02-2002 L2002 **HSO** *012

MARTYN, Lois Jeanette. 3509 N BROAD ST 19140 #041-13-1962 L1963 **OPH PO** *071 †35

MARVA, Donald Jos. 1900 JOHN F KENNEDY BLVD 19103 #041-02-1960 L1961 **IM GP** *071

MARZAN, Yolanda. ■ 19104 #035-45-2006 L2007 **AN** *012

MASANGKAY, Neil Mendoza. ■ 19103 #041-01-2008 L2008 *012

MASCARENHAS, Maria R. 324 S 34TH ST, CHILDRENS HOSPITAL 19104 #495-52-1982 L1986 **PG NTR** *020 †55

MASCHHOFF, Kathryn Lynn. 3400 SPRUCE ST 19104 #048-12-1993 L1999 **PD** *020 †55

MASHAYEKHI, Arman. 840 WALNUT ST, 14TH FLOOR, STE 1440 19107 #517-05-1988 L2007 *100

MASLACK, Mark Michael. 800 SPRUCE ST 19107 #050-02-1977 L1979 **NM DR** *020 †80

MASLANKOWSKI, Lisa Ann. 3535 MARKET ST, STE 4051 19104 #041-13-1992 L1994 **IM** *020 †20

MASLIN, Stuart J. 7000 HOLSTEIN AVE 19153 #041-02-1983 L1984 **FM OM** *020 †18

MASLOW, Joel Neal. 3400 SPRUCE ST, UNIVERSITY OF PENNSYLVANIA 19104 #041-02-1984 L1985 **ID IM** *050 †20

MASON, Bernard Arthur. 230 W WASHINGTON SQ 19106 #041-01-1972 L1973 **ON HEM** *020 †20

MASON, Christopher James. 3400 N BROAD ST, TEMPLE UNIV SCH OF MED 19140 #041-13-2006 **AN** *012

MASON, Daniel. 227 N BROAD ST, STE 200 19107 #041-09-1944 L1947 **CD IM** *020 †20

MASON, Jeffrey Todd. 3400 SPRUCE ST, OF PENNSYLVAN 19104 #023-01-2006 L2006 **EM** *012

MASON, Thornton B A, II. 324 S 34TH ST 19104 #051-04-1990 L2000 **CHN** *050 †55,75

MASS, Burton. 6129 PALMETTO ST 19111 #041-02-1966 L1967 **PUD IM** *020 †‡

MASSARI, Ferdinand Edward. 3400 SPRUCE ST 19104 #041-02-1983 L1985 **AI IM** *050 †20,03

MASSARO, Matthew Gurion. 3401 N BROAD ST 19140 #041-77-2003, ▲ L2003 **IM** *020

MASSEY, Daron Clive. 3400 SPRUCE ST 19104 #836-01-1995 L2006 **P** *012

MASSEY, Julie S. 1000 W TABOR RD 19141 #035-47-1992 L1994 **PD** *020 †55 ‡

MASSEY, Patrick Allen. ■ 19107 #041-02-2008 *012

MASSO, Cynthia Lynn. 1 QUEEN ST UNIT 15A 19147 #033-05-1998 L2000 **PD** *020 †55

MASSONE, Richard Joseph. 3400 SPRUCE ST, GROUND RAVDIN 19104 #033-05-2004 L2004 **EM** *012

MAST, Kristie Lynne. 3156 KENSINGTON AVE 19134 #041-07-1996 L1999 **FM** *020 †18

MASTER, Christina Lin. 324 S 34TH ST 19104 #035-06-1993 L1995 **PD** *020 †55

MASTER, Susan Elizabeth. 840 WALNUT ST, WILLS EYE HOSP 19107 #041-02-2004 L2004 **OPH** *012

MASTRANGELO, Michael Jos. 111 S 11TH ST STE 4240 19107 #023-07-1964 L1965 **ON IM** *050 †20 ‡

MASTROGIANNIS, Dimitrios. 3401 N BROAD ST, DEPT. OB/GYN ZONE B 19140 #418-03-1983 L1988 **OBG MFM** *020 †30

MASTROIANNI, Luigi, Jr. 3701 MARKET ST, STE 800 19104 #024-05-1950 L1965 **OBG REN** *020 †30

MATALON, Terence A S. 5501 OLD YORK RD, DEPT RAD 19141 #024-05-1977 L2003 **DR** *040 †80

MATEO, Jose Manuel. ■ 19103 #042-01-1979 L1987 **P** *020 †75 ‡

MATHER, Paul J. 925 CHESTNUT ST 19107 #041-13-1988 L1990 **CD IM** *020 †20

MATHER, Susan. 211 S 9TH ST, WALNUT TOWERS BLDG 19107 #041-13-1997 L1999 **IM** *020 †20

MATHEUS, Tonantzin. ■ 19141 #935-07-2000 L2001 **GE** *100

MATHEUS, Virgilio. 5501 OLD YORK RD, ALBERT EINSTEIN MED CTR 19141 #935-07-2003 L2005 **GS** *100

MATHEW, Mathew. 51 N 39TH ST 19104 #495-31-1982 L1993 **IM** *020 †20

MATHEW, Paul George. 3401 N BROAD ST 19140 #422-01-2005 L2005 **N** *012

MATHEW, Rex George. 239 E THOMPSON ST, 1020 SANSOM STREET 19125 #010-01-2001 L2001 **EM** *100 †16

MATHEW, Suja. 3300 HENRY AVE 19129 #495-37-1987 L1992 **CHP P** *020 †75

MATHEWS, Jeffery John. 132 S 10TH ST, THOMAS JEFFERSON UNIV HOSP 19107 #033-06-2005 L2005 **DR** *012

MATHEWS, Maju. 230 N BROAD ST 19102 #495-72-1996 L2002 **P** *020 †75

MATHUR, Mayank. ■ 19107 #033-05-2005 L2005 **N** *012

MATIN, Ayaz. 245 N 15TH ST, MCP HAHNEMANN UNIV 19102 #704-25-2002 L2004 **IM** *100 †20

MATLACK, Eileen O'Hara. 111 S 11TH ST STE G8490, THOMAS JEFFERSON UNIVERSIT 19107 #041-09-1980 L1982 **AN CD** *020 †05

MATO, Anthony R. ■ 19130 #035-06-2002 L2002 **HO** *012 †20

MATOZZO, Marc Anthony. 1028 W OREGON AVE 19148 #041-77-1996, ▲ L1997 **FM** *020

MATRO, Jennifer Madeline. ■ 19103 #041-01-2008 *012

MATSKO, Christopher Micha. ■ 19102 #041-13-2007 *012

MATSKO, Janine Ann. 250 PHILIP PL 19106 #041-02-1975 L1977 **OPH** *020 †35

MATSUMOTO, Shigeyo. 3400 SPRUCE ST 19104 #572-47-1969 L1980 **DR** *050

MATSUMOTO, Teruo. BROAD & VINE STS 19102 #572-12-1953 L1969 **GS VS** *071 †85

MATTESON, Sarah Kathleen. ■ 19103 #012-01-2005 L2006 **N** *012

MATTHEW, Dwight Marvin. 4TH FLOOR - S TOWER MAIL, DREXEL UNIVERSITY COLLEGE 19102 #422-01-2003 L2007 **IM** *012

MATTHEWS, Andrew Thomas. ■ 19107 #041-02-2008 *012

MATTHEWS, John Francis. 2601 HOLME AVE 19152 #010-02-1986 L1991 **RNR** *020 †80,28

MATTHEWS, Patrick Jeffers. ■ 19107 #041-02-2003 L2003 **EM** *100 †16

MATTHEWS, Randolph P. ■ 19147 #054-04-1998 L2000 **PD** *020 †55

MATULEWICZ, Theodore Jos. 1800 LOMBARD ST, ALLEGHENY UNIV HOSP 19146 #041-09-1970 L1971 **PTH** *020 †50

MATZON, Jonas Leif. 3400 SPRUCE ST, SILVERSTEIN TWO 19104 #016-02-2004 L2004 **ORS** *012

MAULITZ, Russell Chas. 10 SHURS LN, STE 203 19127 #036-07-1973 L1975 **IM** *020 †20

MAURER, Alan Harvey. 3401 N BROAD ST, TEMPLE UNIV HOSP 19140 #041-13-1975 L1976 **IM NM** *020 †20,28

MAURER, Mary Ann. ■ 19128 #041-77-2007, ▲ L2007 **FP** *012

MAURER, Philip Mitchel. 800 SPRUCE ST, STE 800 19107 #041-02-1983 L1984 **PME** *020 †05

MAURY, Rebecca Marie. 833 CHESTNUT ST STE 701, JIMA 19107 #034-01-2002 L2002 **IM** *020 †20

MAUST, Donovan Todd. ■ 19104 #023-07-2007 L2007 **P** *012

MAXWELL, Emilie L. 1513 RACE ST 19102 #041-07-1934 L1935 **PM** *071

MAXWELL, Lynne N Gerson. 744 LOMBARD ST, # 3 19147 #023-07-1973 L2002 **AN PD** *020 †55,05

MAXWELL, Pinckney J, IV. 1100 WALNUT ST STE 702, DIVISION OF COLON AND RECT 19107 #045-01-2000 L2007 **CRS** *012

MAXWELL, Wheeler Thomas. ■ 19129 #041-15-2007 L2007 **FP** *012

MAY, Kim Weems. 2701 N BROAD ST, TEMPLE PHYSICIANS INC 19132 #041-13-1995 L1998 **IM** *020 †20

MAY, Nathalie Saget. 219 N BROAD ST, STE 8 19107 #041-01-1997 L1999 **IM** *020 †20 ‡

MAY, Robert Elliot. 8815 GERMANTOWN AVE, STE 21 19118 #016-02-1957 L1958 **U** *071 †95

MAYER, Eugene Marc. 7901 BUSTLETON AVE STE 307 19152 #041-13-1972 L1973 **GE IM** *020 †20

MAYER, Wesley Adam. ■ 19130 #048-04-2005 L2005 **U** *012

MAYERS, Chester T, Jr. 3001 WALNUT ST, JFK MEDICAL CENTER SOUTHWE 19104 #047-07-1974 L1991 **AM** *020

MAYOR, Geraldine F R. 5501 OLD YORK RD, DEPT OF PSYCHIATRY 19141 #748-02-1994 L1998 **P** *020 †75

MAYRO, Gregory. 5401 OLD YORK RD, ALBERT EINSTEIN MEDICAL CT 19141 #041-02-2001 L2001 **ID** *100

MAYRO, Jeffrey Scott. 1025 WALNUT ST, JEFFERSON MED COLL 19107 #041-02-1997 L2001 **IM** *020 †80

MAYRO, Leslie Barbara. 4000 GYPSY LN UNIT 301 19129 #041-12-1983 L1984 **IM** *020 †20

MAYSON, Sarah Emily. ■ 19107 #041-02-2007 L2007 **IM** *012

MAZAR, Rebecca Michelle. ■ 19146 #041-01-2003 L2003 **OBG** *100

MAZAREK, Anthony Pasco. ■ 19130 #056-05-1967 L1971 **P** *100

MAZER, Maryann. ■ 19114 #041-13-2006 L2006 **EM** *012
MAZUR, Justin David. 245 N 15TH ST, FL NCB 19102 #041-13-2004 L2004 **EM** *020
MAZZARELLI, Joanne K. 3400 SPRUCE ST, 100 CENTREX 19104 #033-06-2005 L2005 **IM** *012
MAZZEO, Anthony Santo. 501 S 54TH ST, EMERGENCY MEDICINE 19143 #041-12-2002 L2002 **EM** *020 †16 ‡
MBAH, Ngozi Nwamaka. 5501 OLD YORK RD 19141 #690-07-1994 L2006 **OBG** *012
MCBRIDE, Brenda L.. ■ 19147 #539-06-2001 L2004 **PD** *020 †55
MC CABE, Edward S. 39TH & MARKET ST 19104 #041-01-1942 L1943 **END CD** *071 †20
MC CAFFERTY, John Michael. 5501 OLD YORK RD, ALBERT EINSTEIN MEDICAL CE 19141 #038-43-1993 L1995 **P PYG** *071 †75 ‡
MC CALLY, Michael. ■ 19106 #038-06-1960 L1960 **PHP** *030
MCCAMANT, Colleen Allison. ■ 19129 #041-13-2004 L2004 **PD** *100 †55
MCCANN, Georgia Anne. ■ 19123 #041-02-2006 L2006 **OBG** *012
MCCAREY, Yvonne Lorraine. ■ 19147 #051-07-2005 L2005 **IM** *012
MCCARTHY, Angela Denine. ■ 19144 #041-77-2005, ▲ L2005 **P** *012
MC CARTHY, David Murray. 3400 SPRUCE ST, 800 PENN TOWER 19104 #035-01-1971 L1979 **CD IM** *020 †20
MC CLOSKEY, Sister Ann M.. ■ 19148 #041-02-1977 L1978 **PTH PCP** *071 †50
MCCLUNG, Heather Ann. 3400 SPRUCE ST, UNIVERSITY OF PENNSYLVANIA 19104 #023-07-2003 L2003 **PAN** *012
MC CLURE, Kristen E.. ■ 19128 #024-05-2004 L2004 **DR** *012
MC CLURKEN, James B. 3401 N BROAD ST, TEMPLE UNIV HOSP STE 300 19140 #041-13-1976 L1977 **TS** *020 †85,90 ‡
MC COLGAN, Maria. ERIE AVE 19114 #041-13-2000 L2001 **PD** *020 †55 ‡
MC COLLUM, Richard George. 3401 N BROAD ST 10TH, FL JONES 19140 #041-13-2002 L2002 **EM** *100
MC COMBS, Peter Reist. 3900 WOODLAND AVE 19104 #024-07-1970 L1971 **VS GS** *020 †85
MCCOOK, Michelle Annmarie. ■ 19128 #035-06-2007 *012
MCCORMICK, Jacob Cattell. ■ 19144 #041-15-2006 L2006 **EM** *012
MC CORMICK, John Francis. 1900 S BROAD ST 19145 #041-02-1970 L1972 **PTH** *020 †50 ‡
MC CORMICK, Marianne P. 800 SPRUCE ST, 2 CATHCART 19107 #041-14-1990 L1992 **IM** *020 †20
MCCOY, Chrishonda Curry. 840 WALNUT ST, WILLIS EYE HOSPITAL 19107 #023-07-2003 L2003 **OPH** *100
MC COY, Michael Ronald, Jr. 5555 GERMANTOWN AVE 19144 #041-13-1996 L1998 **FM** *020 †18
MC CREA, Leon, II. ■ 19119 #041-12-2006 L2007 **FP** *012
MC CROSSON, Stacy Ann. 834 CHESTNUT ST, STE 400 19107 #041-15-2002 L2002 **OBG** *020
MC CUE, Peter Allan. 132 S 10TH ST, JEFFERSON UNIV HOSP 19107 #035-47-1977 L1988 **ATP** *020 †50
MC CULLEN, Kristen Michel. 834 CHESTNUT ST STE 400, BENJAMIN FRANKLIN HOUSE 19107 #041-02-2005 L2005 **OBG** *012
MC CUNE, Wallace G. 2 PENN BLVD, STE 111 19144 #016-02-1943 L1944 **IM** *071 †20
MC DERMOTT, Lawrence, III. 3300 HENRY AVE, MCP HOSPITAL 19129 #041-02-1992 L1994 **PCC** *020 †20
MC DONALD, David William. ■ 19104 #038-44-2002 L2004 **PDR** *012 †80
MCDONALD, Devin Rugawah. 245 N 15TH ST, M 19102 #033-05-2006 L2006 **EM** *012
MC DONALD, Margarita Elen. ■ 19150 #024-07-2005 L2005 **OBG** *012
MCDONALD, Matthew Basil, III. ■ 19111 #041-13-2006 L2006 **PD** *012
MC DONOUGH, Michael Thoma. 3400 N BROAD ST 19140 #010-02-1954 L1960 **CD IM** *072
MC EVILLY, James P J. ■ 19154 #041-02-1941 L1942 **P** *072
MC FADDEN, Robert Francis. 833 CHESTNUT ST STE 210 19107 #033-06-2001 L2001 **P** *100
MCFARLANE, Nadia Anne. 3400 SPRUCE ST, UNIV OF PA 19104 #035-06-2007 L2007 **P** *012
MC GARVEY, Jane Mary. 800 SPRUCE ST, PENNSYLVANIA HOSPITAL 19107 #041-15-2003 L2003 **EM** *020
MC GARVEY, Michael Lee. 3400 SPRUCE ST 19104 #010-02-1995 L1997 **N** *020 †75
MC GEARY, Andrea. 225 S COBBS CREEK PKWY, PRIMARY CARE CENTER 19139 #008-02-1993 L1995 **PD** *020 †55
MC GEHEE, Edward H. 1015 WALNUT ST RM 401 19107 #041-02-1945 L1951 **FM IM** *071 †20,18
MCGETTIGAN, Brian Francis. ■ 19147 #041-02-2007 L2007 **OTO** *012
MC GINLEY, Edward Jos. 2701 HOLME AVE STE 304 19152 #041-12-1973 L1974 **CD IM** *020 †20
MC GINLEY, Mary Rodgers. 3333 N BROAD ST 19140 #041-14-1982 L1983 **IM** *020 †20
MCGINLEY, Mollie. ■ 19103 #041-15-2005 L2005 **DR** *012
MC GOVERN, Mark Edward. ■ 19125 #050-02-1980 L1987 **CD IM** *050 †20
MC GOVERN, Paul C. 3400 SPRUCE ST 19104 #016-06-1996 L1998 **ID** *020 †20
MCGOWAN, Christina Anne. ■ 19107 #041-02-2008 *012
MC GOWAN, Jane. 3400 SPRUCE ST, NEONATAL PERINATAL MED 19104 #041-01-1983 L1985 **NPM PD** *050 †55
MC GOWAN, Tracy Ann. 833 CHESTNUT ST, STE 700 19107 #041-02-1992 L1995 **NEP** *020 †20
MC GRATH, Thomas Jos. ■ 19107 #041-13-1992 L1996 **AN** *020
MC GRUDER, Sandra Waldine. 6031 MORTON ST 19144 #041-07-1977 L1979 **IM** *020
MC GUIGAN, Kelly Lorraine. 833 CHESTNUT ST, DEPT OF DERMATOLOGY 7TH FL 19107 #041-02-2004 L2004 **D** *012
MC GUIRE, Jennifer Lara. ■ 19146 #032-01-2005 L2007 **CHN** *012
MC HALE, Teresa. 3400 SPRUCE ST, HOSP UNIV PA 19104 #539-05-1993 L2001 **PCP** *100 †50
MC HUGH, Jennifer L. 2742 CLAYTON ST 19152 #041-14-1999 L2001 **PD** *020 †55 ‡
MC HUGH, Mary Kathryn. 3400 SPRUCE ST, DEPT OF ANESTHESIA 19104 #041-12-1997 L2001 **AN** *100
MC KAY, Charles Philip. 833 CHESTNUT ST 3RD FL, DUPONT AT JEFFERSON 19107 #021-05-1980 L1996 **PN PD** *020 †55
MC KEARN, Thomas Jos. 3400 SPRUCE ST 19104 #041-02-1976 L1979 **CLP PTH** *030
MC KENNA, Marc Walsh. 8835 GERMANTOWN AVE 19118 #010-02-1977 L1980 **FM FSM** *040 †18
MC KENNA, William Gillies. 3400 SPRUCE ST OFC 2, DEPT OF RADIATION ONCOLOGY 19104 #035-46-1981 L1987 **RO ON** *050 †80
MC KENZIE, Steven Edward. 324 S 34TH ST, DEPT PED 19104 #041-01-1985 L1986 **PHO PD** *020 †55
MCKERNAN, Erica Steinhous. 7600 CENTRAL AVE, JEANES HOSPITAL 19111 #041-13-2002 L2002 **EM** *100 †16
MCKEY, Jesse Bryant. 840 WALNUT ST, WILLS EYE HOSP 19107 #025-01-2005 L2006 **OPH** *012
MCKINNEY, Kibwei Alessand. ■ 19104 #041-01-2008 *012
MC KINNEY, Laurence T. 7514 FRANKFORD AVE 19136 #041-09-1980 L1981 **OBG** *020 †30

MCLAIN, Nicholas Warren. 245 N 15TH ST, FL NCB 19102 #048-15-2005 L2005 **EM** *012
MC LAUGHLIN, Carol Ann. 3400 SPRUCE ST, SILVERSTEIN / 3RD FLOOR / 19104 #023-07-2000 L2004 **ID** *020 †20,55
MCLAUGHLIN, Richard. 834 CHESTNUT ST, APT PH105 19107 #041-02-1996 L1998 **EM** *020 †16
MC LAULIN, John Bryce. 801 MARKET ST STE 7, SUITE 500 19107 #045-01-1977 L1997 **P** *030 †75
MCLEAN, Alexandra B. 3535 MARKET ST, FL 2 19104 #396-06-1981 L1995 **P** *020 †75
MC LEAN, Matthew. 3110 GRANT AVE, NORTHEAST ORTHOPAEDICS SPE 19114 #028-02-1998 L2004 **ORS** *020 †40
MCLEAN, Philip Hopkins. 2900 W QUEEN LN, MCP HAHNEMANN UNIV 19129 #654-01-2000 L2000 **AN** *105
MC LEER, Susan Virginia. 4641 ROOSEVELT BLVD 19124 #041-07-1970 L1971 **P CHP** *030 †75 ‡
MCMACKIN, Paul Patrick. ■ 19128 #041-13-2005 **IM** *012
MC MAHON, Damian John. 3400 SPRUCE ST 19104 #143-08-1984 L1996 **CCS** *100
MC MAHON, Patrick James. ■ 19103 #035-48-2005 L2005 **PD** *012
MC MANUS, Maura. 833 CHESTNUT ST 3RD FL, DUPONT AT JEFFERSON 19107 #010-02-1991 L1996 **OS** *020 †55,60
MC MANUS, Ronald Patrick. 833 CHESTNUT ST, STE 301 19107 #045-01-1991 L1993 **FM** *020 †18
MCNALLY, Paul. 3400 CIVIC CENTER BLVD, CHILDRENS HOSP OF PHILA 19104 #539-04-1998 L2007 **PDP** *012
MCNALLY, Paul G. ■ 19147 #539-04-1998 L2008 **PDP** *012
MC NAMARA, Robert Michael. 3401 N BROAD ST, TEMPLE U HOSP DEPT EMER 19140 #041-02-1982 L1983 **EM** *040 †16
MCNEIL, Robert Percival. ■ 19103 #010-03-2007 L2007 **IM** *012
MC NELLIS, Keith Michael. 3401 N BROAD ST, DEPARTMENT OF HOSPITAL MED 19140 #041-13-2000 L2001 **IM HOS** *020 †20
MC NESBY, Francis Xavier. 1331 E WYOMING AVE, PARKVIEW HOSPITAL 19124 #041-02-1993 L1995 **PD** *020 †55
MC NETT, William Garth. 833 CHESTNUT ST 3RD FL, THOMAS JEFFERSON UNIVERSIT 19107 #041-14-1984 L1986 **PD** *020 †55
MC NICHOLAS, Laura F. 3900 WOODLAND AVE, PHILADELPHIA VAMC BEH HLTH 19104 #020-12-1988 L1990 **P ADM** *040 †75
MC NULTY, Stephen Edward. 111 S 11TH ST, STE 8490 19107 #041-77-1981, ▲ L1982 **AN** *050 †05
MC QUAY, Nathaniel, Jr. 3440 MARKET ST, 1ST FL 19104 #051-04-1996 L2003 **CCS** *020 †85
MCRAE, Karen M. 3400 SPRUCE ST 19104 #067-01-1987 L1992 **AN** *020 †05
MC SORLEY, Maryann Bidi. 1233 LOCUST ST, STE 400 19107 #041-01-1983 L1984 **PD** *020 †55
MC VEY, Angela. ■ 19134 #781-01-1949 L1973 **OBG** *074 †30
MCWILLIAMS, Andrew Scott. ■ 19144 #041-13-2005 L2005 **EM** *012
MEAD, Philip Sidney. 245 N 15TH ST, DEPARTMENT OF EMERGENCY ME 19102 #041-02-1996 L1998 **EM** *020 †16
MEADOWS, Adam Christopher. ■ 19119 #028-02-2008 *012
MEADOWS, Anna Taback. 3400 SPRUCE ST 19104 #041-07-1969 L1970 **PHO PD** *030 †55
MEAGHER, Emma Anne. 3400 SPRUCE ST, 164 DULLES 19104 #539-06-1987 L1999 *020
MEANEY, Peter Andrew. ■ 19146 #051-04-1998 L2007 **CCP MPD** *020 †55
MEASLEY, Robert E, Jr. 834 WALNUT ST STE 650 19107 #024-16-1984 L1985 **ID IM** *020 †20
MEBANE, Wm Nelson, III. 8815 GERMANTOWN AVE 19118 #041-01-1954 L1957 **FM PD** *040 †55,18
MECHANIC, Steven Anthony. 3401 N BROAD ST, TEMPLE UNIVERSITY HOSPITAL 19140 #035-08-1990 L1999 **BBK** *020 †50
MECHEM, C Crawford. 115 W LUZERNE ST, PHILADELPHIA FIRE DEPARTME 19140 #041-02-1988 L1994 **EM** *020 †16
MECHOULAM, Hadas. 422 CURIE BLVD, 304 STELLER CHANCE LABS 19104 #550-01-1998 **OPH** *100
MEDINA, Michael Victorino. ■ 19143 #748-02-1995 L2005 **OTO** *012
MEDINILLA, Sandra Patrici. ■ 19118 #041-13-2006 L2006 **GS** *012
MEDURI, Kalyani Rao. 2900 W QUEEN LN, DEPT OF INTERNAL MED 19129 #495-21-2001 L2004 **IM** *012
MEE, Caroline Mapuana. ■ 19118 #041-02-2006 L2006 **FP** *012
MEESALA, Mrinalini. 245 N 15TH ST, MCP HAHNEMANN UNIV 19102 #495-21-2002 L2004 **CD** *012 †20
MEGILL, Matthew Drummond. ■ 19146 #041-13-2005 L2005 **IM** *012
MEGLATHERY, Sharon Beth. 729 S HUTCHINSON ST, EPPI 19147 #040-02-1996 L1999 **P IM** *020 †20,75 ‡
MEHENDIRATTA, Vaibhav. 111 S 11TH ST 19107 #495-45-2005 L2006 **IM** *012
MEHRA, Ranee. 333 COTTMAN AVE, FOX CHASE CANCER CENTER 19111 #035-19-1999 L2006 **ON** *100 †20
MEHROTRA, Deepak. 5501 OLD YORK RD, DEPT OF ANESTHESIOLOGY 19141 #495-67-1976 L1989 **AN PME** *012
MEHTA, Chirag Pankaj. ■ 19107 #041-02-2008 *012
MEHTA, Gaurav. ■ 19131 #496-44-2001 L2002 **GE** *012 †20
MEHTA, Jay. 3405 CIVIC CENTER BLVD, CSH 2ND FLOOR RHEUMATOLOGY 19104 #031-01-2003 L2006 **PPR** *012 †55
MEHTA, Neerav Rajnikant. 3400 SPRUCE ST, 219 DULLES BLDG 19104 #024-05-2000 L2005 **DR** *100 †80
MEHTA, Nehal Nikhilesh. 3400 SPRUCE ST DEPT CARD 19104 #010-01-2001 L2001 **CD** *012
MEHTA, Neil Jagdish. ■ 19104 #005-02-2006 L2006 **IM** *012
MEHTA, Nidhi. ■ 19146 #041-12-2008 L2008 *012
MEHTA, Pallav. 333 COTTMAN AVE 19111 #041-02-2001 L2001 **HO** *020
MEHTA, Prashant Jagdish. 245 N 15TH ST, DEPT MED 19102 #305-01-2006 L2007 **IM** *012
MEHTA, Rajen Anil. ■ 19131 #041-77-2007, ▲ L2007 **IM** *012
MEHTA, Rashi Ishwar. 132 S 10TH ST, UNIVERSITY HO 19107 #041-02-2003 L2003 **DR** *012
MEHTA, Rima Arun. 601 WALNUT ST STE 925EA, THE CURTIS CENTER 19106 #001-06-2002 L2002 **OBG** *100 †30
MEHTA, Sahil. 5501 OLD YORK RD, ALBERT EINSTEIN MED CTR 19141 #495-45-2001 L2005 **IM** *012
MEHTA, Samir. 3400 SPRUCE ST, 2 SILVERSTEIN 19104 #041-13-2000 L2001 **ORS** *020
MEHTA, Saurin Mrugank. ■ 19102 #041-13-2003 L2006 **RHU** *012 †20
MEHTA, Shilpi Snehlata. ■ 19103 #041-15-2004 L2005 **OBG** *012
MEHTA, Shobha. 501 S 54TH ST 19143 #495-77-1967 L1979 **GP** *020
MEHTA, Smita M. 1720 S BROAD ST, HEALTH CENTER #2 19145 #495-22-1968 L1979 **PD** *020 ‡
MEHTA, Sonul. ■ 19129 #041-15-2007 L2007 **TY** *012

■ = Address Information Privacy Protected

MEHTA, Vinay. 5501 OLD YORK RD, ALBERT EINSTEIN MED CTR 19141 #496-43-2000 L2004 IM *012

MEILAHN, John Edward. BROAD & ONTARIO STS, TEMPLE UNIV HOSP DEPT SURG 19140 #041-01-1984 L1991 GS SO *020 †85

MEISEL, Zachary Franklin. 3400 SPRUCE ST, DEPT OF EMERGENCY MEDICINE 19104 #023-07-1999 L2001 EM *020

MEISTER, Steven Gerard. 525 JAMESTOWN ST, STE 107 19128 #024-07-1962 L1970 CD IM *020 †20

MEJIA GARCIA, Alex Vladim. 1100 WALNUT ST, 8TH FLOOR, WALDMAN 19107 #308-02-2001 L2007 IM *020 †20

MELANCON, Douglas Louis. PO BOX 90, 36 AND HAMILTON WALK 19105 #041-01-1994 *100

MELCON, Gisela. 5501 OLD YORK RD, ALBERT EINSTEIN MED CTR 19141 #132-08-2000 L2005 IM *012

MELE, Frank Edward. 1927 S BROAD ST 19148 #041-02-1956 L1957 GS *020 †85

MELE, Michele M. 800 SPRUCE ST 6TH FL, WOMEN FIRST 19107 #041-02-1998 L2000 OBG *020 †30

MELHEM, Elias Rafic. 340 SPRUCE ST 19106 #001-06-1988 L2001 RNR *020 †80

MELICK, Judith Ellen. 6609 RISING SUN AVE 19111 #024-01-1981 L1982 OPH *075 †35

MELIN, Jeffrey Marc. FRONT & LEHIGH AVE, EPISCOPAL HOSP 19125 #041-07-1981 L1983 AI RHU *020 †20,03

MELISIOTIS, Athanasios Ol. ■ 19119 #041-15-2007 L2007 EM *012

MELLA, Maria Teresa. ■ 19107 #041-02-2008 L2008 *012

MELLEN, Arthur Wm. IV. 301 S 8TH ST STE 3D 19106 #041-02-1980 L1982 OBG *020 †30

MELLENCAMP, Eric Joel. 2601 HOLME AVE, NAZARETH HOSPITAL 19152 #056-06-1976 L1987 DR *020 †80

MELLER, Menachem Mendel. 5301 CEDAR AVE 19143 #016-01-1987 L1988 ORS OM *020 †40

MELLER, Steven. 9150 MARSHALL ST, STE 11 19114 #041-12-1983 L1984 U *020 †95

MELNICK, Donald Edward. 3750 MARKET ST 19104 #005-12-1974 L1983 IM PA *030 †20

MELTZER, Alan Jay. 5501 OLD YORK RD 19141 #041-09-1973 L1974 GS *020 †85

MELTZER, David. ■ 19103 #041-09-1940 L1941 IMG GP *072

MELTZER, Lawrence Edward. 39TH & MARKET ST 19104 #020-02-1953 L1955 CD *050

MELTZER, Michele. 1800 LOMBARD ST 19146 #041-09-1975 L1976 RHU IM *020 †20

MELVILLE, David Michael. 5501 OLD YORK RD, DEPT MED 19141 #048-12-2007 L2007 IM *012

MELVIN, James Stuart. ■ 19130 #036-01-2005 L2005 ORS *012

MELVIN, John Lewis. 25 S 9TH ST, JEFFERSON MEDICAL COLLEGE 19107 #038-40-1960 L1991 PM CN *040 †60 ‡

MENAJOVSKY, Leon Bernardo. 833 CHESTNUT ST 19107 #737-01-1984 L1997 IM *040 †20

MENAJOVSKY CHAVES, Jose A. 3401 N BROAD ST, TEMPLE UNIVERSITY HOSPITAL 19140 #737-01-2004 L2006 IM *012

MENAPACE, James Francis. 1800 LOMBARD ST 19146 #041-13-1980 L1981 IM EM *020 †20,16

MENASHE, Sarah Joy. ■ 19102 #041-02-2007 L2007 IM *012

MENDELSON, Kim Gabrielle. ■ 19128 #024-07-1998 L2007 GS *020 †85

MENDEZ, Maria. 205 N BROAD ST, STE-600 19107 #041-08-1984 L1984 NEP IM *020 †20

MENDEZ-TADEL, Mariana. 4025 CHESTNUT AV FL 1, COUNCIL FOR RELTNSHIPS 19104 #041-01-2001 L2001 P *020 †75

MENDOZA, Ivan Jose. 5501 OLD YORK RD, ALBERT EINSTEIN MED CTR 19141 #935-01-2000 L2005 IM *012

MENDOZA, Vinia Madonna Ca. 111 S 11TH ST 19107 #748-02-2004 L2005 IM *012

MENDOZA BALLESTEROS, Fabia. ■ 19123 #737-01-1999 L2003 RHU *012 †20

MENG, Xianmin. 8TH AND SPRUCE STREETS 19107 #243-55-1989 L2007 PTH *012

MENIN, Richard Alan. 9880 BUSTLETON AVE, STE 308 19115 #041-13-1971 L1976 GE IM *012

MENNUTI, Michael T. 3400 SPRUCE ST 19104 #010-02-1968 L1970 OBG OS *030 †19,30

MENON, Rukmini. 1800 LOMBARD ST, ONE GRADUATE PLAZA 19146 #495-66-2001 L2003 N *100

MENON, Sindhu Chandrasekh. 3400 SPRUCE ST, UNIV OF PA HLTH SYS 19104 #048-14-2000 CN *100

MENY, Geralyn M. 700 SPRING GARDEN ST, MUSSER BLOOD CTR 19123 #048-12-1990 L2000 PTH BBK *020 †50

MENZ, Volker. PHILA HEART INST/PRESBY, 39TH & MARKET STREETS 19104 #409-22-1991 CD *100

MERCADER, Virginia. 3401 N BROAD ST 19140 #042-01-1988 L1990 DR *020 †80

MERCADO, Diana Iniguez. 5501 OLD YORK RD, DEPT MED 19141 #748-02-2002 L2004 MPD *012

MERCADO, Jorge Manuel. ■ 19123 #132-01-2002 L2003 PCC *012 †20

MERCADO, Juan Francisco. ■ 19123 #132-11-2004 L2006 IM *012

MERCADO, Max E. 1331 E WYOMING AVE # 3090 19124 #042-03-1998 L2001 IM IMG *020

MERCADO MEDINA, Margarita. 5501 OLD YORK RD, OFFICE OF ACADEMI AFFAIRS 19141 #308-05-2003 L2006 OBG *100

MERIANOS, Demetri J. ■ 19103 #033-05-2004 L2004 GS *012

MERIDEN, Zina. ■ 19104 #041-01-2008 *012

MERIKHI, Afkhamossadat. 219 N BROAD ST, FL 5 19107 #517-12-2001 L2004 GE *012 †20

MERLI, Geno Jos. 833 CHESTNUT ST 19107 #041-02-1975 L1976 IM VM *020 †20

MERLIN, Jessica Sarah. 3400 SPRUCE ST 19104 #041-01-2005 L2005 IM *012

MEROPOL, Neal Jay. 333 COTTMAN AVE, FOX CHASE CANCER CENTER 19111 #047-05-1985 L1988 ON HEM *050 †20

MERRIAM, William Griffin. 1025 WALNUT ST, DEPT OF UROLOGY, STE 1112 19107 #041-15-2001 L2004 U *020

MERRIMAN, Jennifer B. 3400 SPRUCE ST, HOSP OF THE UNIV OF PENN 19104 #036-01-2001 L2001 OBG MFM *100

MERRITT, Christopher R B. 111 S 11TH ST 19107 #021-01-1967 L1999 DR *020 †80 ‡

MERRYMAN, Carmen F. 1025 WALNUT ST, DEPT OF ORTHOPEDIC SURGERY 19107 #275-01-1954 OS *040

MERWOOD, Michelle Anne. ■ 19146 #016-43-2005 L2005 PD *012

MESHKOV, Arnold Bruce. 3401 N BROAD ST 19140 #041-01-1975 L1976 CD IM *020 †20

MESSE, Steven Russell. 3400 SPRUCE ST 19104 #025-01-1998 L2001 N *020

MESSEDER, Octavio H. 3300 HENRY AVE, MEDICAL COLLGE OF PNNSYLVN 19129 #187-01-1973 PUD IM *020

MESSICK, Sarah Elizabeth. 1000 WALNUT ST, ORLOWITZ #702 19107 #041-02-2003 L2003 IM *020 †20

METRO, Michael John. 5401 OLD YORK RD, STE 500 19141 #041-12-1996 L1998 U *020 †95

METZ, David Colin. 3400 SPRUCE ST FL R, HOSPITAL UNIVERSITY OF PEN 19104 #836-01-1982 L1987 GE IM *020 †20

MEURSING, Diederik F. 5501 OLD YORK RD, STE 510 19141 #305-01-2000 L2001 TS *012

MEYAPPAN, Janaki Deepa. ■ 19130 #035-08-2005 L2006 AN *012

MEYER, Angela Adele. ■ 19123 #051-04-2007 L2007 EM *012

MEYER, Brian John. 1316 W ONTARIO ST, FIRST FLOOR, JONES HALL 19140 #041-13-2002 L2002 IM *020 †20

MEYER, Monique Anne. ■ 19144 #008-02-2007 L2007 TY *012

MEYER, Peter Jacob. 3333 N BROAD ST, RM 343 19140 #038-06-1973 L1979 P *020 †75

MEYER, Steven Rhodes. 7323 HIOLA RD 19128 #061-01-1998 L2007 *100

MEYERS, Catherine M. 3400 SPRUCE ST, STE J PENN TOWERS 9TH FLOO 19104 #016-11-1984 L1987 NEP IM *020 †20

MEYERS, Stuart Jay. 5501 OLD YORK RD, DEPT OF EMERG MED 19141 #038-41-2001 L2001 EM *100 †16

MEYERS, William Clark. 245 N 15TH ST RM 7150, DEPT OF SURG 19102 #035-01-1975 L2001 AS *020 †85

MIAN, Ahmad Shafi. 245 N 15TH ST MS 437, DREXEL UNIV COLL OF MED 19102 #305-01-2002 L2002 NEP *100 †20

MIAN, Shabbir Ahmad. ■ 19104 #704-20-1983 *020

MIAZZO, Pietro. 1428 WOLF ST, PIETRO MIAZZO MD 19145 #561-17-1983 L1986 P PFP *020 †75

MICAILY, Bizhan. 3401 N BROAD ST, TEMPLE UNIV HOSP 19140 #517-05-1973 L1977 RO *020 †80

MICHAELS, Mike. 6334 ELMWOOD AVE 19142 #517-01-1956 L1964 FM PTH *020 †50

MICHAELSON, Carolyn Z. 8623 GERMANTOWN AVE 19118 #041-01-1971 L1973 GP ADM *074

MICHAELSON, Thomas Erik. 9501 ROOSEVELT BLVD, STE 208 19114 #035-45-1994 L1996 ID *020 †20

MICHALS, Timothy John. 125 S 9TH ST, STE 1003 19107 #041-02-1966 L1967 P PFP *020 †75

MICHEL, David Pierreabra. ■ 19131 #041-02-2007 IM *012

MICHEL, Jeremy Joseph. ■ 19129 #041-15-2008 L2008 *012

MICHELETTI, Robert Gil. ■ 19107 #036-07-2008 *012

MICHELSON, Eric Lee. BROAD & VINE STS 19102 #035-01-1973 L1974 CD ICE *030 †20 ‡

MICKLER, Thos Robert Jr. 51 N 39TH ST 19104 #051-01-1981 L1987 AN MDM *020 †05

MICOZZI, Marc Steven. 111 S 11TH ST STE 6215, T JEFFERSON UNIV HOS 19107 #041-01-1980 L1981 FOP PHP *062

MIDDLETON, Melissa Kristi. ■ 19106 #041-01-2008 *012

MIDWOOD, Faith. ■ 19106 #041-13-1965 L1966 P PYG *020 †75

MIES, Carolyn. 3400 SPRUCE ST, DEPT OF PATHOLGY & LB MDCN 19104 #016-01-1980 L1986 PTH *020 †20

MIGALY, John. ■ 19107 #035-19-1996 L2000 GS *100 †85,10

MIGNANO, Pasquale A. 2 PENN BLVD STE 103 19144 #041-77-1994, ▲ L1996 PD *020 †55 ‡

MIGNOTT, Harold Ludlow. 3400 SPRUCE ST, STE A 19104 #041-01-1987 L1988 IM *020 †20

MIHALAKIS, Michael James. 3401 N BROAD ST, TEMPLE UNIVERSITY HOSPITAL 19140 #041-12-2002 L2002 EM *100 †16

MIKAELIAN, Diran O. 925 CHESTNUT ST FL 6 19107 #605-01-1954 L1970 OTO *071 †45

MIKES, Beverly Ann. 834 CHESTNUT ST, BEN FRANKLIN BLDG/ROOM 400 19107 #032-01-1993 L1997 OBG *020 †30

MIKKELSEN, Mark Evin. 3400 SPRUCE ST, 839 WEST GATES 19104 #051-01-2002 L2002 PCC *012 †20

MIKOL, Michelle. 324 S 34TH ST 19104 #033-06-1999 L2002 PD *020 †55

MIKUTA, John Jos. 3400 SPRUCE ST, HOSP AT UNIV OF PENN 19104 #041-01-1948 L1949 GO GYN *071 †30

MILAS, Bonnie Lee. 3400 SPRUCE ST, 1105 PENN TOWER 19104 #010-01-1991 L1995 AN *020 †05

MILCU, Maria. 9150 MARSHALL ST 19114 #781-01-1971 L1991 GP PTH *020 †50

MILDENBERG, Budd Jay. 509 VINE ST, APT D2 19106 #016-42-1979 L1980 GS VS *020 †85

MILES, Joseph Shawn. 230 W WASHINGTON SQ, FL 3 19106 #036-07-1997 L2002 CD *020 †20

MILES, O'Connell Douglas. 1315 WINDRIM AVE 19141 #010-03-1963 L1964 P N *020

MILES-MCDONALD, Elena O. 2361 E SUSQUEHANNA AVE, PIZZICA HEALTH SYSTEM P.C. 19125 #041-14-2000 L2003 PD *100

MILESTONE, Barton Neil. 333 COTTMAN AVE 19111 #008-01-1981 L1982 DR IM *020 †80

MILEWSKI, Rita Carrie. 3400 SPRUCE ST, DIVISION OF ORGAN TRANSPLN 19104 #016-06-1984 L1993 TS *020 †85,90

MILGROM, Charles E. PO BOX 2966 19141 #035-08-1975 L1976 ORS *020 †40

MILICIA, Anthony Peter. 9331 OLD BUSTLETON AVE, STE 202 19115 #041-13-1980 L1981 OBG *020 †30

MILLENSON, Michael Mark. 333 COTTMAN AVE 19111 #041-13-1984 L1985 HEM ON *020 †20

MILLER, Andrew Levi. 2301 S BROAD ST 19148 #024-07-1995 L2002 IM *020 †20

MILLER, Bjorn Peter. 1020 SANSOM ST 239, THOMPSON BLDG. 19107 #041-02-2001 L2001 EM *020 †16

MILLER, Christopher James. 3600 SPRUCE ST, DEPT OF DERMATOLOGY 19104 #041-02-2000 L2000 D *020 †15

MILLER, Cynthia Lee. 2301 S BROAD ST, DEPARTMENT OF RADIOLOGY 19148 #041-07-1979 L1980 DR *020 †80 ‡

MILLER, David Seth. 1901 WALNUT ST, # 3A 19103 #035-48-1986 L1990 P *020 †75

MILLER, Elizabeth P. 833 CHESTNUT ST, STE 210C 19107 #041-02-2000 L2001 P *100

MILLER, Eric Darren. ■ 19103 #422-01-2005 L2005 IM *012

MILLER, Eydie Germaine. 51 N 39TH ST, SCHEIE EYE INST UNIV PA 19104 #041-12-1985 L2001 OPH *020 †35

MILLER, Francine Judith P. 5800 RIDGE AVE 19128 #041-07-1968 L1969 FM CCM *020

MILLER, Francis Lee. 51 N 39TH ST 19104 #054-04-1979 L1982 AN *020 †05

MILLER, Frederick Chapman. 5501 OLD YORK RD 19141 #025-01-1971 P PYA *020 †75

MILLER, Glenn. 1849 S 15TH ST 19145 #308-03-1983 L1985 AN PMM *020 †05 ‡

MILLER, Harry. ■ 19147 #869-05-1941 L1942 FM *071 †18

MILLER, Howard Alan. 205 N BROAD ST, FL 1 19107 #041-09-1974 L1975 IM *020 †20 ‡

MILLER, Jacqueline Marie. 324 S 34TH ST 19104 #016-06-1997 L1999 PN *020 †55

MILLER, Jean Carla. 327 BOYER ST 19119 #041-02-1995 L1997 IM *020 †20

MILLER, Jeffrey Lynn. 211 S 9TH ST, 6TH FLOOR, SUITE 600 19107 #836-01-1974 L1984 END IM *040 †20

MILLER, Jeffrey Robert. 3400 SPRUCE ST 19104 #035-47-2005 L2005 MPD *012

MILLER, Larry Sherwin. 3401 N BROAD ST DEPT GI 19140 #016-42-1981 L1983 IM *020 †20

MILLER, Michael David. 255 S 17TH ST, STE 1410 19103 #041-01-1986 L1987 P *020 †75

MILLER, Robert Matthew. ■ 19147 #041-13-1968 L1969 PTH IM *062 †50

MILLER, Robert Victor. 840 WALNUT ST 19107 #041-02-1965 L1968 OPH *020 †35

MILLER, Robin Jeanne. 6315 WOODLAND AVE 19142 #041-07-1986 L1987 FM *020 †18

MILLER, Russell Stuart, Jr. 245 N 15TH ST MS 310, DREXEL UNIV COLL OF MED 19102 #041-77-2001, ▲ L2006 AN *012

MILLER, Tamara Porter. ■ 19103 #008-01-2008 *012

MILLER, Wallace Thos. 3400 SPRUCE ST, DEPT OF RADIOLOGY, HUP 19104 #041-02-1956 L1957 **R** *020 †80

MILLER, Wallace Thos, Jr. 3400 SPRUCE ST, DEPT OF RAD 1 SILVERSTEIN 19104 #041-01-1986 L1987 **DR** *020 †80

MILLER, Wayne Henry. ■ 19107 #041-15-2005 L2005 **IM** *012

MILLETT, Christian Richar. ■ 19107 #041-02-2007 **IM** *012

MILLI, Marina. 3401 N BROAD ST 19140 #132-01-2000 L2004 **OBG** *012

MILLIAN, Bradd Russell. ■ 19103 #033-05-2002 L2007 **RNR** *012 †80

MILLOS, Alberto. GIRARD AVE AT 8TH ST 19122 #924-01-1968 L1979 **PTH** *020 †50

MILLS, Angela M. 3400 SPRUCE ST, HOSP UNIV PA 3400 SPRUCE 19104 #041-13-1997 L2001 **EM** *020

MILLS, Geoffrey David. ■ 19139 #041-13-2006 L2006 **FP** *012

MILLS, Monte Dean. 34TH CIVIC CTR BLVD, DIR OPHTHALMOLOGY 19104 #048-04-1988 L2000 **OPH** *020 †35 ‡

MILOSAVLJEVIC, Natasa. ALUMNI AFFAIRS, ALBERT EINSTEIN MEDICAL CE 19141 #957-02-1993 L2007 **PD** *012

MIN, Patricia Lee. 3701 MARKET ST, STE 640 19104 #035-19-1994 L1996 **IM** *020 †20

MINARD, William Douglas. 1628 JOHN F KENNEDY BLVD, STE 950 19103 #010-01-1955 L1959 **OBG** *071 †30

MINASSIAN, Shahab Sahag. 216 N BROAD ST, FL 4 19102 #041-02-1980 L1981 **OBG REN** *020 †30

MINCZAK, Bohdan Myroslav. 239 E THOMPSON ST, 1020 SANSOM ST. 19125 #041-13-1995 L1997 **EM** *020 †16

MINEHART, Margaret Ann. 1101 MARKET ST STE 7, DEPT OF BEHAVIORAL HLTH 19107 #041-13-1976 L1978 **P** *030 †75

MINERVA, Pierre. 1015 WALNUT ST # 613 19107 #539-06-1994 L1998 **RHU** *020 †20

MING, Jeffrey Eugene. 3615 CIVIC CENTER BLVD, CHILDRENS HOSP OF PHIL 19104 #035-20-1992 L1995 **MG** *020 †19,55

MING, Michael E. 3600 SPRUCE ST, 2 MALONEY BLDG 19104 #024-01-1993 L2000 **D DMP** *020 †15

MING, Pen-Ming Lee. 3401 N BROAD ST 19140 #242-26-1952 L1971 **ATP CCG** *071 †50,19

MING, Si-Chun. 3401 N BROAD ST, TEMPLE ANESTHESIA ASSOCIAT 19140 #242-26-1947 L1971 **ATP** *071 †50

MINGIONI, Nina. 5401 OLD YORK RD, KLEIN BLDG STE 363 19141 #035-19-2002 L2002 **IM** *100 †20 ‡

MINGOS, Mark Allen. ■ 19107 #041-02-2005 L2006 **DR** *012

MINION, Steven Lawrence. 5501 OLD YORK RD 19141 #016-42-1985 L1991 **AN** *05

MINTO, Natalie. ERIE AVE AT FRONT ST, NELSON PAVILION 19134 #033-06-2002 L2002 **PD** *020

MINTURN, Jane Elizabeth. 3615 CIVC CNTR BLVD ARC902, CHILDRENS HOSP OF PHILADEL 19104 #008-01-1996 L1999 **PHO** *020 †55

MINTZ, Akiva. ■ 19104 #041-14-2004 L2004 **NM** *012

MINTZ, Randy Theodore. 230 N BROAD ST, ASSOCIATED CARDIOVASCULAR 19102 #033-06-1985 L1988 **CD IC** *020 †20

MINTZER, David Michael. 230 W WASHINGTON SQ FL 2 19106 #041-02-1977 L1978 **HO IM** *020 †20

MINTZER, Scott Evan. 900 WALNUT ST, STE 200 19107 #016-02-1995 L2005 **N** *020 †75

MINUTILLO, Joseph Patrick. 5500 WISSAHICKON AVE, 806C ALDEN PK MANOR 19144 #539-06-1985 L1999 **P** *100

MIR, Samy Sidney. 220 W WASHINGTON SQ, FARM JOURNAL BUILDING, 3RD 19106 #023-01-2002 L2005 **CD** *012 †20

MIRAKHUR, Beloo. 8815 GERMANTOWN AVE FL 5, PRACTICE 19118 #041-13-2001 L2001 **FM** *100

MIRKOVICH, Christina J. ■ 19104 #035-46-1977 L1978 **IM** *020 †20

MIRMANESH, S Michael. 1800 LOMBARD ST 19146 #305-01-1994 L1999 **IM** *020 †20 ‡

MIROWSKI, Doris. 1528 WALNUT ST 19102 #012-05-1989 L1991 **P** *020

MIRSON, Sofiya. 3500 VISTA ST 19136 #913-06-1993 L2002 **IM** *020 †20

MIRZA, Naureen Azamali. 51 N 39TH ST, SCHEIE EYE INSTITUTE 19104 #041-01-2004 L2004 **OPH** *012

MISHKIN, Mark M. ■ 19103 #035-08-1953 L1960 **DR RNR** *071 †80

MITAL, Praveen Kumar. 245 N 15TH ST, FL NCB 19102 #041-15-2004 L2004 **EM** *020

MITAS, John Albert, II. 190 N INDEPENDENCE MALL W 19106 #012-01-1973 L1974 **IM NEP** *030 †20

MITCHELL, Donald Gordon. 111 S 11TH ST, 3350 GIBBON BLDG 19107 #035-08-1981 L1985 **DR** *020 †80

MITCHELL, Edith Peterson. 233 S 10TH ST, STE 502 19107 #051-04-1974 L1995 **ON IM** *020 †20

MITCHELL, John Broadus. 3535 MARKET ST, FL 2 19104 #041-02-2004 L2004 **P** *012

MITRA, Amitabha. 205 N BROAD ST, TPS IV OF PA, LLC 19107 #495-39-1968 L1980 **PS HS** *020 †85,65

MITSANI, Dimitra. 3601 N 5TH ST, 3A FALK MEDICAL BLDG 19140 #418-02-1999 L2007 **ID** *012

MITTA, Srikanth. 800 SPRUCE ST 19107 #496-35-2000 L2006 **IM** *100

MITTAL, Amit. 111 S 11TH ST 19107 #047-07-2002 L2002 **CD** *012 †20

MIURA, Karen K. ■ 19103 #041-09-1972 L1973 **P GP** *020 †75

MIYAMOTO, Curtis T. 3401 N BROAD ST, RADIATION ONCOLOGY 19140 #847-11-1986 L1988 **RO** *020 †80

MIYANO, Satoshi. ■ 19128 #572-15-1967 L1974 **PM** *020

MIZRAHI LEHRER, Eddy. 5501 OLD YORK RD, OFFICE ACADEMIC AFFAIRS 19141 #935-01-2003 L2006 **IM** *012

MIZRAHI LEHRER, Flor. 5501 OLD YORK RD, OFFICE OF ACADEMIC AFFAIRS 19141 #935-01-2001 L2006 **IM** *012

MMEJE, Okeoma Onyekachi. ■ 19128 #025-01-2006 L2006 **OBG** *012

MO, Gyi Phone. 700 SPRUCE ST, STE 301 19106 #209-01-1987 L2002 **IM** *100

MOBLEY, Derrick K. 144 W ABBOTTSFORD AVE 19144 #041-07-1986 L1987 **GP** *075

MOCHON, Manuel. 100 E ERIE AVE 19134 #649-01-1984 L1989 **PD** *020 †55

MOCK, John E. ■ 19107 #016-06-1947 L1951 **P** *071 †75

MODI, Amy. 132 S 10TH ST, UNIVERSITY HO 19107 #033-06-2004 L2005 **OPH** *100

MOFFITT, Harry Jos. 2401 PENROSE AVE, 2ND FL 19145 #041-13-1968 L1970 **P** *020

MOGHADAM, Eileen M S. 4400 HAVERFORD AVE 19104 #008-01-1963 L1967 **PD** *020 †55 ‡

MOGHANAKI, Drew. 3400 SPRUCE ST, 2 DONNER 19104 #047-05-2002 L2003 **RO** *012

MOGHBELI, Nazanin. ■ 19130 #023-07-2001 L2005 **CD** *012

MOGIL, Neil Sheldon. ■ 19111 #041-09-1976 L1986 **EM OM** *075

MOHAMMADPOUR-DEHKORDI, M. ■ 19129 #517-05-1970 **PM** *020 †60

MOHAMMADZADEH SARABI, Mahz. ■ 19141 #858-03-1999 L2001 **CD** *100 *012

MOHAN, Rajeev Chandra. ■ 19102 #041-15-2008 L2008 *012

MOHANKA, Manish Rajendrap. 245 N 15TH ST, DREXEL UNIV COLL MED/HAHNE 19102 #495-83-2001 L2005 **IM** *012

MOHANRAJ, Bernardine Regi. 111 S 11TH ST, STE 2170 19107 #008-02-2007 L2007 **IM** *012

MOHANTY, Arun Kumar. 3401 N BROAD ST 19140 #496-05-1971 L1979 **IM** *020 †20

MOHATA, Manoj Kumar. 1409 LOMBARD ST, CATCH INC 19146 #496-09-1986 L2000 **P** *020

MOHESS, Denise Trudy-Ann. ■ 19114 #894-01-2001 L2005 **IMG** *012 †20

MOHIUDDIN, Manzoor N. 8110 BUSTLETON AVE 19152 #495-21-1977 L1983 **PM** *020 †60

MOHLER, Emile Riggs, III. 3400 SPRUCE ST, 4TH FLOOR PENN TOWER 19104 #010-02-1988 L1996 **CD** *050 †20

MOHSEN, Nancy Ahmed. BROAD & VINE 19120 #041-07-1995 L2000 **DR** *020 †80

MOJICA, Ronald Dial. ■ 19106 #041-13-2006 L2006 **AN** *012

MOKGETHI, Bianca Matilda. 431 FULTON ST 19147 #041-07-1996 L1998 **IM** *020 †20

MOKRYNSKI, Gregory. 2603 S BROAD ST 19148 #041-02-1986 L1987 **IM OM** *020 †20

MOLDOFSKY, Philip Jay. 8305 RIDGE AVE 19128 #041-01-1976 L1977 **DR NM** *020 †80,28 ‡

MOLDOVAN, Raul. 5501 OLD YORK RD 19141 #781-04-2002 L2006 **IM** *012

MOLESKI, Stephanie Mcconn. ■ 19147 #041-02-2005 L2005 **IM** *012

MOLINA, Ezequiel Jesus. 3401 N BROAD ST, OF S 19140 #132-01-1999 L2001 **GS** *012

MOLINOFF, Perry Brown. 3400 SPRUCE ST, DEPT MED 19104 #024-01-1967 L1990 **OS** *050

MOLLEN, Cynthia Johnson. 324 S 34TH ST 19104 #035-20-1995 L1997 **PEM** *020 †55

MOLLEN, Thomas J. 800 SPRUCE ST, NEWBORN PEDIATRICS 19107 #035-03-1996 L1998 **NPM** *020 †55

MOLLOY, Patricia Taylor. 324 S 34TH ST, CHILDRENS HSPTL OF PHLDLPH 19104 #041-01-1987 L1988 **CHN** *020 †75

MOMONT, Anna Christine. ■ 19147 #056-05-2007 L2007 **TY** *012

MONACO, Meredith Lauren. ■ 19130 #035-08-2006 L2006 **PD** *012

MONDELLO, Melissa. ■ 19130 #051-04-2007 L2007 **PD** *012

MONDSCHEIN, Jeffrey Ian. 3400 SPRUCE ST, DEPT OF RADIOLOGY 19104 #035-19-1995 L2000 **DR** *020 †80

MONDUL, Tracey Elena. 51 N 39TH ST 19104 #035-09-1994 L1997 **EM** *020 †16

MONGELLUZZO, Jillian. ■ 19104 #041-01-2008 *012

MONHEIT, Richard S. 5501 OLD YORK RD 19141 #041-09-1943 L1944 **CD IM** *020 †20

MONIS, Kanishka. 4TH FLOOR - S TOWER MAIL, DREXEL UNIVERSITY COLLEGE 19102 #422-01-2007 L2007 **GS** *012

MONTEALEGRE SANCHEZ, Gina. 5501 OLD YORK RD 19141 #264-04-2001 L2005 **PD** *012

MONTELEONE, Paul N, Jr. 324 S 34TH ST 19104 #038-40-1963 L1963 **PTH** *071 †50

MONTELLA, Joseph Michael. 834 CHESTNUT ST, STE 300 19107 #041-02-1984 L1985 **OBG** *020 †30

MONTENEGRO, Lisa Marie. 3400 SPRUCE ST 19104 #033-05-1989 L1994 **AN** *020 †05

MONTESANO, Angelica T. 5501 OLD YORK RD, DEPT RADIATION ONCOLOGY 19141 #924-01-1973 L1979 **RO** *020 †80 ‡

MONTGOMERY, Kyle David. 4641 ROOSEVELT BLVD 19124 #041-02-1995 L1998 **FM** *020 †18

MONTGOMERY, Owen C. 255 S 17TH ST, FL 9 19103 #041-09-1981 L1983 **OBG** *020 †30 ‡

MONTI, Daniel Alexander. 1020 SANSOM ST, STE 1652 19107 #035-06-1992 L1994 **P** *020 †75 ‡

MONTONE, Kathleen Theresa. 800 SPRUCE ST 19107 #041-14-1989 L1991 **ATP** *020 †50

MONTOZZI, Richard Lynn. 3300 HENRY AVE 19129 #041-09-1977 L1979 **IM** *020

MOOAR, Pekka Antero. 2116 CHESTNUT ST, 2ND FL 19103 #038-41-1979 L1981 **ORS** *020 †40

MOOCK, Paul Cassel, Jr. 8835 GERMANTOWN AVE 19118 #041-09-1959 L1960 **GP CD** *071

MOOKERJEE, Bijoyesh P. 125 S 9TH ST, 801 SHERIDAN 19107 #495-73-1987 L2001 **HO IM** *020 †20

MOOLTEN, David Nadal. 700 SPRING GARDEN ST 19123 #041-01-1987 L1991 **BBK PTH** *020 †50

MOOMJIAN, Lauren Nicole. ■ 19107 #041-02-2007 L2007 **TY** *012

MOON, Alfred Oh. ■ 19103 #035-03-2005 L2005 **IM** *012

MOONBLATT, Steven David. 4900 FRANKFORD AVE, FRANKFORD HOSP-EM DEPT 19124 #041-13-2002 L2002 **EM** *012

MOORE, Derek Edd. ■ 19118 #047-05-1999 L2006 **GS** *020

MOORE, Edward Michael. 561 FAIRTHORNE AVE 19128 #041-09-1990 L1992 **CHP P** *020 †75

MOORE, John Harlan, Jr. 840 WALNUT ST 15TH FL 19107 #051-01-1979 L1980 **PS** *020 †85,65

MOORE, Michael Mc Glenen. 1331 E WYOMING AVE, PARKVIEW HOSPITAL M.O.B. - 19124 #056-05-1984 L1986 **OS** *020 †18

MOORE, Michael Mitchell. 111 S 11TH ST, JEFFERSON UNIVERSITY 19107 #041-12-2001 L2001 **DR** *012 †55

MOORE, Ryan Edward. ■ 19146 #041-01-2007 L2007 **ORS** *012

MOOYOUNG, Jaime Leigh. ■ 19143 #041-01-2008 *012

MORALES, Ahmed. 1100 S BROAD ST, UNIT 407A 19146 #042-02-2002 L2005 **GE** *012 †20

MORALES, Christian R. ■ 19130 #041-13-2005 L2005 **IM** *100

MORALES-CEBALLOS, Diego. 1200 W TABOR RD 19141 #308-01-1969 L1973 **PM** *071 †60

MORALES-MATELUNA, Carlos. ■ 19147 #270-02-1992 L2001 **AI PD** *020 †55,03

MORAN, Mary Margaret. 231 N BROAD ST, ST. CHRISCARE 19102 #041-12-1989 L1992 **PD** *020 †55

MORANTWADE, Yusef Omariwi. ■ 19103 #047-07-2006 L2007 **OBG** *012

MORAVIA, Lucie V. ■ 19144 #051-75-2007, ▲ **OBG** *012

MORELLO, Jennifer Anne. ■ 19145 #041-13-2000 L2004 **IM** *020

MORENO, Carlos. 3900 WOODLAND AVE, VETERANS ADMINISTRATION 19104 #264-01-1941 L1971 **PTH** *100 †50

MORENO, Gustavo Adolfo. 36TH & HAMILTON WALK 19130 #319-01-1958 **OPH OS** *020 †35

MORENO, Ismael Perez. ■ 19143 #005-14-2004 L2004 **DR** *012

MORENO, Mary Ellen. 2311 SOUTH ST APT 301 19146 #004-01-1991 L1993 **P** *020 †75

MOREYRA, Carlos Esteban. 3401 N BROAD ST, OUTPT BLDG, 6TH FLOOR 19140 #041-13-1997 L2004 **ORS** *012

MORGAN, Earl A. 1421 ARCH ST, NUMBER 475 19102 #047-07-1949 L1949 **GP OM** *074

MORGAN, John Marshall. 1025 WALNUT ST, STE 8439 19107 #041-13-1978 L1980 **IM PA** *050 †20

MORGAN, Mark Aloysius. 3400 SPRUCE ST 19104 #035-08-1982 L1984 **GO OBG** *020 †30

MORGAN, Peter Benjamin. 333 COTTMAN AVE, FOX CHASE CANCER CENTER 19111 #048-02-2004 L2005 **RO** *012

MORGANROTH, Joel. 1800 LOMBARD ST 19146 #025-01-1970 L1974 **CD IM** *050 †20

MORGANS, Alicia Katherine. ■ 19106 #041-01-2006 L2006 **IM** *012

MORGENLANDER, Lynn Ellen. 333 COTTMAN AVE 19111 #035-19-1982 L1984 **AN IM** *020 †20

MORGENSTERN, Diana M. 219 N BROAD ST, FL 6 19107 #041-07-1988 L1990 **IM** *062 †20

MORGENSTERN, Ricardo. 219 N BROAD ST, FL 5 19107 #176-03-1981 L2003 **GE** *020

MORIARTY, Gael Ann. 230 N BROAD ST DEPT PED 19102 #041-13-1981 L1981 **PD** *020

MORITZ, Michael Jay. 216 N BROAD ST, MAIL STOP 1001 19102 #023-01-1980 L1982 **TTS GS** *020 †85

MORLEY, James Francis. ■ 19104 #016-06-2005 L2005 **N** *012

MORREALE, Joseph Michael. 3401 N BROAD ST, 6TH FLOOR OUTPATIENT BLDG 19140 #041-02-2003 L2003 **ORS** *012

MORRIS, Christina Sigrid. ■ 19127 #041-15-2001 L2004 **FM** *100

MORRIS, Dennis Lynn. 5501 OLD YORK RD, CARDIOLOGY DIVISION AEMC 19141 #045-01-1978 L1985 **CD IM** *020 †20

MORRIS, Jon Benj. 3400 SPRUCE ST, FL 4 19104 #010-02-1983 L1990 **GS** *020 †85

MORRIS, Rachel Lynn. ■ 19129 #041-15-2008 *012

MORRIS, Rohinton J. 51 N 39TH ST, STE 2D 19104 #041-09-1984 L1986 **TS** *020 †85,90

MORRISON, Elizabeth Mary. ■ 19146 #041-02-2005 L2005 **ORS** *012

MORRISON, Martin J, III. ■ 19128 #041-15-2007 L2007 **ORS** *012

MORRISON, Mary Frances. 3600 MARKET ST, STE 704 19104 #038-06-1985 L1986 **P** *020 †20,75

MORRISON, Tara. 245 N 15TH ST, MAILSTOP 423 19102 #065-09-1995 L2004 **N** *020 †75

MORRISON, William Brian. 111 S 11TH ST, 3350 GIBBON BLDG 19107 #041-02-1990 L1993 **DR** *020 †80

MORRISON, Wynne Ellen. 100 N 20TH ST, STE 200 19103 #047-05-1994 L2005 **CCP** *020 †55

MORRISSETTE, Erin Louise. ■ 19104 #041-02-2006 L2006 **IM** *012

MORRONE, Charles C. 7432 TORRESDALE AVE 19136 #041-77-1974, ▲ L1975 **FM** *011 †18

MORROW, Neil E. 900 WALNUT ST, 5TH FLOOR ANESTHESIA 19107 #660-02-1991 L1998 **AN** *020 †05 ‡

MORSE, Aida Alixandra. ■ 19104 #041-01-2008 *012

MORSE, Michelle Evelyn. ■ 19104 #041-01-2008 *012

MORY, Laura Mcelrone. 3401 N BROAD ST 19140 #041-13-2005 L2005 **EM** *012

MOSCOW, Daniel Mark. 5619 VINE ST 19139 #038-41-1993 L1996 **FM** *020 †18

MOSES, Melvin Lloyd. 2301 S BROAD ST, STE 201 19148 #041-02-1962 L1963 **GS TS** *020 †85,90

MOSHANG, Thomas, Jr. 324 S 34TH ST 19104 #023-01-1962 L1968 **END PD** *050 †55

MOSHER, Kathryn. 111 S 11TH ST, JEFFERSON UNIVERSITY 19107 #026-04-2001 L2001 **PM** *020

MOSKOWITZ, Eric Jason. ■ 19103 #041-02-2008 *012

MOSLEY, Diahann Frances. ■ 19129 #041-07-1996 L1998 **IM** *020 †20 ‡

MOSS, Edward R. 6268 ALGARD ST 19135 #041-13-1950 L1951 **GP PD** *071

MOSS, Joshua David. ■ 19146 #024-01-2003 L2006 **CD** *012 †20

MOSS, Ronald B. 324 S 34TH ST 19104 #016-42-1987 L2003 **AI** *030 †55,03

MOSSABEB, Roschanak. ■ 19146 #154-07-1999 L2006 **NPM** *100 †20

MOSSE, Yael. 324 S 34TH ST 19104 #550-02-1997 L2000 **PHO** *020 †55

MOSTER, Mark Leslie. 5501 OLD YORK RD, DEPT OF NEUROSENSORY SCIS 19141 #035-15-1979 L1980 **N** *020 †75

MOSTER, Marlene. 840 WALNUT ST STE 1120, WILLS EYE INSTITUTE 19107 #035-15-1979 L1980 **OPH OS** *020 †35 ‡

MOSTOFI, Reza Nasser. 245 N 15TH ST, MCP HAHNEMANN UNIV 19102 #422-01-2003 L2003 **HO** *012 †20

MOSTOUFI MOAB, Sogol. 324 S 34TH ST 19104 #041-14-2000 L2001 **PHO** *012 †55

MOTIL, Jennifer Lynn. 219 N BROAD ST, FLOOR4 19107 #051-07-2005 L2005 **D** *012

MOUDGILL, Neil. ■ 19102 #041-02-2004 L2004 **GS** *012

MOULDER, Peter Vincent, IV. ■ 19106 #021-01-2008 *012

MOULDING, Hugh David. 909 WALNUT ST, 3RD FL 19107 #010-02-2002 L2002 **NS** *012

MOULISWAR, Mysore Papanna. 4900 FRANKFORD AVE, FRANKFORD HOSPITAL - FRANK 19124 #495-37-1981 L1994 **IMG** *020

MOURELATOS, Zissimos. 422 CURIE BLVD, 605A STELLAR-CHANCE LABS 19104 #418-02-1991 L1999 **NP** *050 †50

MOUSSOUTTAS, Michael M. 900 WALNUT ST STE 200, CENTER DEPT OF NEUROLOGY 19107 #035-15-1994 L2007 **N** *020 †75

MOWES, Anja Karolin. 5501 OLD YORK RD 19141 #409-15-2000 L2005 **PD** *012

MOY, Gregory John. ■ 19103 #048-12-2007 L2007 **AN** *012

MOYA, Mario. 1815 COTTMAN AVE, AMERICAN ACCESS CARE OF PE 19111 #649-02-1988 L1993 **P VIR** *020 †80

MOYER, Darilyn Valenta. 3401 N BROAD ST, SECT OF GEN INT MED 8PP 19140 #041-13-1985 L1986 **IM** *020 †20

MOYER, Susan Marie. 8556 BUSTLETON AVE 19152 #051-04-1980 L1981 **IM** *020 †20

MRAOVIC, Boris. 111 S 11TH ST, STE G-8490 19107 #957-05-1987 L2005 **AN** *020 †05

MROZ, Barbara Jean. ■ 19131 #021-01-1989 L1991 **PCC** *020 †20

MROZ, Lynne A. 5501 OLD YORK RD 19141 #041-02-1987 L1992 **AN** *020 †05

MSCISZ, Donna Marie. 1227 TASKER ST # 3 19148 #041-02-2004 L2004 **IM** *100 †20

MUCCINO, David Richard. 1025 WALNUT ST, THOMAS JEFFERSON UNIV HOSP 19107 #033-05-2003 L2003 **PCC** *100 †20

MUCKSAVAGE, Phillip. ■ 19146 #035-01-2004 L2004 **U** *012

MUDAKHA, Shikata Almaria. 245 N 15TH ST, DEPT ID 19102 #041-15-2004 L2004 **ID** *012 †20

MUEKSCH, Josef Nile. 230 N BROAD ST 19102 #041-15-2001 L2002 **AN** *020 †05

MUELLER, Darryl Thomas. 3400 N BROAD ST, DEPT OF OTOLARYNGOLOGY 19140 #001-06-1999 L2003 **OTO** *100

MUFDI, Leila Katherine. ■ 19128 #016-76-2004, ▲ L2004 **EM** *012

MUHAMMAD, Aqiyla. ■ 19131 #041-14-2005 L2005 **FP** *012

MUI, Alan Yuk Lan. ■ 19107 #041-13-2003 L2003 **DR** *012

MUI, Mariko Lindsay. ■ 19103 #010-01-2007 L2007 **PD** *012

MUKERJEE, Robin. ■ 19130 #305-01-2004 L2004 **AN** *020

MUKERJEE, Romita. ■ 19107 #041-02-2007 **IM** *012

MUKHERJEE, Monica. ■ 19107 #010-01-2006 L2006 **IM** *012

MUKHERJEE, Prashanta K. 5301 CEDAR AVE, DEPT OF MEDICINE 19143 #495-38-1960 **GS OS** *100

MUKHTAR, Berjees. 5401 OLD YORK RD, KLEIN 363 19141 #495-51-2004 L2007 **IM** *012

MULDERINK, Todd Anthony. ■ 19123 #016-06-2002 L2003 **RNR** *012 †80

MULHERN, Charles B, Jr. 3333 N BROAD ST 19141 #041-13-1971 L1972 **R PD** *020 †80

MULHOLLAND, S Grant. 1025 WALNUT ST, THOMAS JEFFERSON UNIVERSIT 19107 #041-13-1962 L1970 **U** *030 †95 ‡

MULL, Nikhil Kiran. ■ 19129 #041-15-2008 *012

MULLEN, James Leo, Jr. 3400 SPRUCE ST, FL 4 19104 #041-01-1967 L1968 **CCS NTR** *030 †85

MULLEN, Mark Jay. 10160 BUSTLETON AVE, STE A 19116 #041-02-1987 L1988 **IM IMG** *020 †20

MULLEN, Michael Thomas. ■ 19104 #041-01-2005 L2005 **N** *012

MULLESSERILL, Bijoy T. 3401 N BROAD ST 70PB, TEMPLE UNIVERSITY, SCHOOF 19140 #495-23-1996 L1999 **OBG** *020

MULLIN, Daniel Karl. 245 N 15TH ST, EMERGENCY MED 19102 #005-06-2002 L2002 **EM** *020 †16

MULLOY, William Patrick. 255 S 17TH ST 19103 #869-05-1958 L1960 **GP OS** *072 †50 ‡

MUMFORD, James Grant. 100 PENN SQ E, THE WANAMAKER BLDG 8TH FLO 19107 #049-01-1972 L1988 **PD** *020 †55

MUNDATHAJE, Udayashankara. 5401 OLD YORK RD 19141 #495-99-1999 L2002 **PCC** *012 †20

MUNILLA, Eduardo A. 412 W LEHIGH AVE 22 19133 #231-01-1972 L1976 **GP MDM** *020

MUNOZ, Martin. 4231 N 5TH ST 19140 #264-01-1953 L1972 **GP AN** *071

MUNOZ, Santiago Jose. 5401 OLD YORK RD, KLEIN BLDG STE 509 19141 #231-05-1979 L1984 **OS GE** *020 †20

MUNOZ-ALLEN, Maria E. 201 N 8TH ST, UNIT 903 19106 #264-01-1988 L1994 **AN** *020 †05

MUNOZ JIMENEZ, Melissa Ma. 2900 W QUEEN LN 19129 #270-02-2001 L2004 **PTH** *012

MUNOZ MENDOZA, Jair. 5501 OLD YORK RD 19141 #737-01-2001 L2005 **IM** *012

MUNOZ-QUIEN, Ramcel B. 100 E LEHIGH AVE, CHC-1 19125 #748-01-1988 L1993 **PD PN** *020 †55

MUNSHI, Raj Prakash. ■ 19128 #033-05-2005 L2005 **PD** *012

MUNSON, David Allen. 324 S 34TH ST 19104 #041-01-1998 L2000 **NPM** *100 †55

MUNSON, Jeffrey Clark. 3600 SPRUCE ST 836, W GATES 19104 #024-01-2001 L2005 **PCC** *012 †20

MUNZER, Steven Jos. 6129 PALMETTO ST 19111 #041-02-1963 L1964 **R** *020 †80

MUPPIDI, Srikanth. 111 S 11TH ST 19107 #495-21-2000 L2005 **N** *012

MURAD, Waheed. 4TH FLOOR - S TOWER MAIL, DREXEL UNIVERSITY COLLEGE 19102 #704-09-1999 L2007 **IM** *012

MURALI, Ganesan. 5401 OLD YORK RD, KLEIN 331 19141 #495-04-1986 L1995 **PUD SME** *020 †20

MURALI, Vijayalakshmi. 1337 COTTMAN AVE 19111 #495-65-1982 L1989 **PD** *020 †55

MURASHIMA, Miho. 3400 SPRUCE ST, REN ELECTY & HYPERTSN DIV 19104 #572-01-2000 L2003 **IM** *100 †20

MURAVCHICK, Stanley. 3400 SPRUCE ST, DULLES SUITE 680 19104 #035-19-1973 L1981 **AN** *020 †05

MURPHY, Barbara Jean. 1800 LOMBARD ST 19146 #041-07-1974 L1976 **EM** *020 †16

MURPHY, Frank Lloyd, Jr. 3400 SPRUCE ST, DEPT ANES 19104 #024-01-1969 L1971 **AN GS** *100 †05

MURPHY, George F, Jr. 1020 LOCUST ST, STE 244 19107 #050-02-1976 L1987 **DMP** *040 †50

MURPHY, Jerry. 7700 STENTON AVE 19118 #024-05-1979 L1979 **EM GP** *062

MURPHY, John Jos. UNIVERSITY & WOODLAND AVES 19104 #016-06-1982 L1982 **IM GPM** *030 †20

MURPHY, Michael Brian. ■ 19107 #033-06-2008 *012

MURPHY, Thomas Wm. 100 W LEHIGH AVE 19133 #018-03-1958 L1970 **P OS** *020

MURRAY, Austin Paul. 840 WALNUT ST 19107 #041-02-1958 L1959 **OPH** *020 †35

MURRAY, Gina Madriene. 3401 N BROAD ST, OF S 19140 #036-08-2005 L2005 **PTH** *012

MURRAY, Melissa Annette. ■ 19128 #038-40-2002 L2006 **NPM** *012 †55

MURRAY, Paula Christine. ■ 19140 #041-13-2008 *012

MURRAY, Richard K. ■ 19119 #010-03-1981 L1983 **IM PUD** *030 †20

MURRAY, Ryan. 925 CHESTNUT ST, JEFFERSON OTOLARYNGOLOGY 19107 #018-03-2007 L2007 **OTO** *012

MURTAZA, Mohammed. 5401 OLD YORK RD, KLEIN 363 19141 #704-01-1996 L2007 **IC** *012 †20

MURTHY, M S Jayashekara. 8815 GERMANTOWN AVE, STE 15 19118 #495-09-1954 L1968 **IM CD** *071

MURUGAPPAN, Swaminathan M. 245 N 15TH ST, DREXEL UNIV COLL OF MED 19102 #495-04-1999 L2006 **IM** *012

MUSA, Duduzile Likwa. 5630 CHESTNUT ST, MERCY HEALTH ASSOC 19139 #422-01-2002 L2002 **IM** *020 †20

MUSCHEL, Ruth J. 3620 HAMILTON WALK, RM 269A JOHN MORGAN 19104 #035-46-1978 L1987 **PTH OS** *050 †50

MUSHTAQ, Saiqa. 2900 W QUEEN LN 19129 #704-20-1994 L2006 **P** *012

MUSTHAFA, Russal. 245 N 15TH ST, DREXEL UNIV COLL OF MED 19102 #495-44-1997 L2006 **FP** *012

MUSTHAQ, Mohamado Sahidu. 520 N DELAWARE AVE, STE 4D 19123 #220-01-1990 L1996 **P** *020 †75

MUTHUSAMY, Preetha. 245 N 15TH ST 19102 #495-16-2003 L2005 **N** *012

MUTHUVELU, Manoharan. 111 S 11TH ST, HOUSE STAFF OFFICE 19107 #495-16-1987 L2006 **IM** *100

MUVVALA, Srinivas Babu. 2900 W QUEEN LN 19129 #495-11-2002 L2005 **P** *012

MUZAFFAR, Saeher A. ■ 19103 #008-01-2003 L2007 **PCC** *012 †20

MWANGI, Vincent. ■ 19104 #041-01-2001 *100

MYDLO, Jack Henry. 3401 N BROAD ST, DEPT OF UROLOGY 19140 #038-08-1981 L2000 **U GS** *020 †95

MYERS, Allen Richard. 3420 N BROAD ST, TEMPLE UNIV SCHOOL OF MED 19140 #023-01-1960 L1969 **RHU IM** *040 †20

MYERS, Jennifer. 3400 SPRUCE ST, GENERAL INTERNAL MED/STE 2 19104 #041-09-1998 L2001 **IM** *020 †20

MYERS, John R. 5501 OLD YORK RD, ALBERT EINSTEIN MEDICAL CE 19141 #041-77-1999, ▲ L2001 **OBG** *020

MYERS, Jonathan Steven. 840 WALNUT ST STE 1110 19107 #041-01-1992 L1994 **OPH** *020 †35

MYERS, Margaret Anne. 34TH ST AND CIVIC CENTER B 19104 #036-07-1985 L1996 **PD NPM** *020 †55

MYERS, Scott Elliot. 219 N BROAD ST, STE 8 19107 #041-09-1982 L1983 **GE IM** *020 †20

MYINT, Zaw. 11082 KNIGHTS RD 19154 #209-01-1978 L1998 **P** *020

MYUNG, Peggy Suejin. 3400 SPRUCE ST, PENNSYLVANIA MED 19104 #041-01-2003 L2003 **OTO** *100

NABHA, Anil. 2120 WALNUT ST 19103 #041-13-2003 L2004 **NEP** *012 †20

NACE, David Kent. 100 E PENN SQ STE 400 19107 #041-12-1985 L1986 **P ADM** *020 †75

NACHMIAS, Vivianne T. 3400 SPRUCE ST, RM G3 19104 #035-45-1957 *050

NACKE, Elliot Anthony. ■ 19103 #041-01-2008 *012

NADEAU, Pascale. ■ 19107 #041-02-2008 *012

NADEL, Frances M. 324 S 34TH ST 19104 #041-01-1992 L1995 **PD** *020 †55

NADEL, Marcell-Bernhard J. ■ 19151 #781-02-1940 L1963 **FM CD** *071 †18

NADER, Wendy Beth. ■ 19131 #016-06-1984 L1987 *100

NADKARNI, Rajani. 8835 GERMANTOWN AVE, DEPT PATH 19118 #495-17-1968 L1971 **PTH** *020 †50 ‡

NADKARNI, Vinay Moreshwar. 34TH ST AND CIVIC CTR BLVD, 6TH FL ANES CCM 19104 #023-01-1984 L1993 **CCP** *012

NADOLSKI, Gregory Jon. ■ 19103 #017-20-2007 L2007 **DR** *012

NAEEM, Ambreen. 3440 MARKET ST 2ND FL, SUITE 200 19104 #704-06-1997 L2005 **CHP** *100 †75

NAFSI, Tabassum Yusuf. ■ 19107 #704-26-2001 L2007 *012
NAGAHAMA, Masahiko. 800 SPRUCE ST, PA HOSPITAL-UPHS 19107 #572-38-1999 L2004 IM *100 †20
NAGAHAWATTE, Natalie Tany. ■ 19143 #041-15-2008 *012
NAGARAJ, Gayathri. 245 N 15TH ST, DREXEL UNIV COLL MED/HAHNE 19102 #496-39-2002 L2005 IM *012
NAGHASHPOUR, Mojdeh. ■ 19145 #011-02-2004 L2004 PTH *100
NAGLE, Deborah. 1800 LOMBARD ST, STE 1100 19146 #041-01-1988 L1991 CRS GS *020 †85,10
NAGORSKY, Matthew Joel. 205 N BROAD ST, STE 401 19107 #051-01-1983 L1989 OTO *020 †45
NAHAS, Stephanie Jane. ■ 19119 #016-01-2001 L2002 N *100 †75
NAHMIAS, Nissin Capon. 5501 OLD YORK RD, ALBERT EINSTEIN MED CTR 19141 #649-13-2001 L2002 GS *012
NAIDE, William. ■ 19103 #041-02-1965 L1967 GP IM *020 †20
NAIDOFF, Michael Allen. 1100 WALNUT ST 6TH FL 19107 #041-01-1966 L1967 OPH *020 †35
NAIK, Chetan Ashok. 245 N 15TH ST, DREXEL UNIV COLL MED/HAHNE 19102 #495-98-2003 L2005 IM *012
NAIK, Vaishali Dileep. 5501 OLD YORK RD 19141 #495-28-1973 L1981 AN *020 †05
NAIKEN, Veerasamy Samy. ■ 19103 #352-05-1955 L1968 PTH *071 †50
NAIM, Maryam Yasmin. ■ 19130 #704-25-1999 L2004 CCP *100 †55
NAIMA, Niloufar. ■ 19144 #005-06-2008 *012
NAIR, Kappiareth Gopal. 36TH & HAMILTON WALK 19130 #496-38-1953 L1967 IM *050
NAIR, Meera Mohan. ■ 19103 #041-01-2007 L2007 IM *012
NAIR, Nandini. 3300 HENRY AVE, DEPT OF INTERNAL MEDICINE 19129 #422-01-2000 L2001 CD *100 †20
NAIR, Shailaja. 219 N BROAD ST FL 6, DREXEL UNIV CTR FOR WOMENS 19107 #495-44-1993 L2003 IM *020 †20
NAIR, Sridhar Gopalakrish. 3322 N BROAD ST STE 2, DEPT OF NEPHROLOGY 19140 #041-13-2002 L2002 NEP *012 †20
NAJI, Ali. 3400 SPRUCE ST, FL 4 19104 #517-05-1970 L1974 IG *020 †85
NAJJAR, Dany Michel. ■ 19107 #605-01-1998 L2002 OPH *012
NAJJAR, Denise Deriane. 101 E OLNEY AVE, STE 400 19120 #605-01-1977 L1984 PTH OS *020 †50
NAJM, Pierre. 211 S 9TH ST, STE 601 WALNUT TOWER 19107 #010-02-1992 L1995 END *020 †20
NAKANISHI, Mariko. 3405 CIVIC CENTER BLVD, RM 27 19104 #572-16-1996 L2006 DBP *012 †55
NAKASHIMA, Megan Okumoto. 3400 SPRUCE ST, UNIV OF PA HLTH SYS 19104 #028-02-2007 L2007 PTH *012
NAKHGEVANY, Karim B. 4900 FRANKFORD AVE STE 19124 #517-01-1963 L1974 GS *020 †85
NALBANTIAN, Michel S. 9551 BUSTLETON AVE, 9601 BUSTLETON AVE 19115 #330-03-1965 L1971 DR NM *020 †80,28
NALL, Juel R. 265 E LEHIGH AVE, NORTHWESTERN HUMAN SERVICE 19125 #043-01-1996 L2000 CHP *020
NALLA, Sumithra. ONE GRADUATE PLAZA 19146 #495-11-1998 L2003 IM *100 †20
NALLAMSHETTY, Hema Shaila. ■ 19102 #041-02-2006 L2006 DR *012
NALLASAMY, Sudha. ■ 19103 #041-01-2005 L2005 OPH *012
NALLURI, Sowmya Lakshmi. 1800 LOMBARD ST 19146 #496-24-2004 IM *012
NAM, Jonghyun. 2900 W QUEEN LN 19129 #041-09-1998 L2002 GE *020 †20
NAMDARI, Surena. ■ 19131 #043-01-2007 L2007 ORS *012
NAMJOSHI, Shashikala D. 5501 OLD YORK RD 19141 #495-17-1973 L1984 AN *020
NANCE, Michael Lewis. 34TH CIVIC CENTER BLVD 19104 #021-05-1988 L1990 PDS *020 †85
NANDI, Lisa Sharan. 2900 W QUEEN LN 19129 #422-01-2005 L2005 EM *012
NANDI, Neilanjan. ■ 19107 #016-06-2005 L2005 IM *012
NANNAPANENI, Jyothi Chowd. 5501 OLD YORK RD, ALBERT EINSTEIN MED CTR 19141 #495-65-2001 L2004 OBG *012
NAPALINGA, Katherine Muno. 5501 OLD YORK RD, ALBERT EINSTEIN MED CTR 19141 #748-02-2001 L2003 CHP *012
NAPIER, Laura Dougherty. ■ 19130 #041-15-2008 *012
NAPPI, Dominic Francis. 1849 S 15TH ST 19145 #041-02-1958 L1959 ORS GS *020
NAQVI, Zafar Nafis. 245 N 15TH ST, DEPT OF GME 19102 #704-02-1994 L2006 P *012
NARAN, Ketan Nalin. 132 S 10TH ST, UNIVERSITY HO 19107 #051-01-2003 L2004 DR *012
NARAYANAN, Sujata. 5401 OLD YORK RD, KLEIN BLDG STE 363 19141 #496-59-2004 L2007 MPD *012
NARGUND, Veda Narayan. 333 COTTMAN AVE 19111 #041-02-1997 L2004 HO *020 †20
NARRA, Kalyani. 2900 W QUEEN LN 19129 #495-53-2002 L2003 HO *012 †20
NASCA, Thomas Jos. 1025 WALNUT ST # 100, JEFFERSON MEDICAL COLLEGE 19107 #041-02-1975 L1976 IM NEP *030 †20
NASH, David Bret. 1015 WALNUT ST, STE 115 19107 #035-45-1981 L1982 IM *030 †20
NASH, Esther J Rolnick. 1901 MARKET ST, FL 32 19103 #043-01-1981 L1982 IM MDM *030 †20
NASO, Francis. 111 S 11TH ST STE 9605 19107 #041-13-1958 L1959 PM *020 †20,60
NASRALLAH, Ilya Michael. ■ 19143 #041-01-2005 L2005 DR *012
NASTA, Sunita Dwivedy. 3400 SPRUCE ST, 16 PENN TOWER 19104 #051-04-1995 L2001 ON *020 †20
NASTO, Kristen N. 1900 S BROAD ST, CHOP PRIMARY CARE 19145 #023-07-2002 L2002 PD *020
NASUTI, Floyd Thomas. 2129 W OREGON AVE, 1ST FLOOR REAR 19145 #041-09-1961 L1962 PD *020 †55
NATAN, Shaw Robert. ■ 19103 #041-13-2001 L2001 ICE *012
NATH, Pramath. 3509 N BROAD ST 19140 #495-12-1987 L2004 PD *020 †55
NATHAN, Aruna Thirumoola. 3400 CIVIC CENTER BLVD, THE CHILDREN'S HOSPITAL OF 19104 #495-04-1991 L2003 PAN *100
NATHAN, Derek Phillip. ■ 19146 #041-01-2006 L2006 GS *012
NATHAN, Meera V. 2 PENN BLVD STE 103 19144 #495-09-1966 L1971 PD ADL *020 †55 ‡
NATHANSON, Donald L. 255 S 17TH ST 19103 #035-15-1960 L1961 P IM *020 †75 ‡
NATHANSON, Katherine Leah. 3400 SPRUCE ST, 5 MALONEY 19104 #041-01-1993 L1996 IM *020 †20,19
NATHANSON, Neal. 3400 SPRUCE ST, DEPT MICROB 19104 #024-01-1953 ID *050
NATIVI NICOLAU, Jose Napo. 2900 W QUEEN LN, DEPT OF INTERNAL MED 19129 #715-01-2001 L2005 IM *012
NAVAL-BLYDEN, Pamela. 10151 BUSTLETON AVE 19116 #748-10-1994 L1999 PD *020 †55
NAVARRO, Judith Tan. 210 W WASHINGTON SQ, MEZZANINE FLOOR 19106 #748-22-1987 L1998 P *020 †75
NAVARRO, Victor Jos. 132 S 10TH ST, SUITE 480 MAIN BUILDING 19107 #041-14-1988 L1990 GE *020 †20

NAWAB, Ursula Seemi. 1025 WALNUT ST, STE 700 19107 #011-04-1999 L2001 NPM *100 †55
NAWAZ, Asad. ■ 19104 #041-01-2008 *012
NAWROCKA, Joanna. THOS JEFFERSON UNIV HOSP, DEPT SURG 19107 #759-04-1977 L2000 AN *100 ‡
NAYAK, Renuka Rajendra. ■ 19103 #041-01-2008 *012
NAYYAR, Gaurav. 2900 W QUEEN LN, DEPT OF INTERNAL MED 19129 #495-03-2002 L2004 IM *100 †20
NAZARIAN, David Geo. 800 SPRUCE ST, 8TH FL PRESTON BUILDING 19107 #035-01-1991 L1996 ORS *020 †40
NAZARIAN, Levon Nazar. 132 S 10TH ST, THOMAS JEFF UNIV HOSP 19107 #035-20-1986 L1992 DR *020 †80
NDICU, Susan Gacheri. ■ 19107 #041-02-2007 L2007 IM *012
NDUAGUBA, Constance O. 51 N 39TH ST, SCHEIE EYE INSTITUTE 19104 #008-01-2000 L2005 OPH *050 †35
NEAVYN, Mark John. ■ 19146 #041-02-2006 L2006 EM *012
NEE, Michael. ■ 19107 #041-02-2003 AN *012
NEEDLEMAN, Laurence. 111 S 11TH ST, 3350 GIBBON BLDG 19107 #035-09-1977 L1982 R AR *020 †80
NEELI, Hemanth Babu Gopal. ■ 19145 #496-45-2000 L2006 IM *020 †20
NEELI, Surekha. ■ 19145 #495-21-2004 L2007 IM *012
NEFF, Pamela Mitra. 3400 SPRUCE ST, HUP - 5 DULLES 19104 #051-04-2003 L2003 OBG *020
NEGENDANK, William George, III. 3400 SPRUCE ST, DEPT MEDICINE 19104 #041-02-1969 L1970 IM *012 †20
NEGIN, Benjamin Paul. 333 COTTMAN AVE 19111 #008-01-2004 L2007 HO *012 †20
NEGOIANU, Dan. ■ 19146 #008-01-2001 L2005 IM *100 †20
NEGRON, John Carlos. ■ 19106 #649-14-1979 L1982 *020
NEI, Maromi. 900 WALNUT ST, STE 200 19107 #048-13-1993 L1995 N *020 †75
NEIGH, John Lowry. 51 N 39TH ST 19104 #041-01-1959 L1960 AN *071 †05
NEIL, William Patrick. ■ 19107 #035-03-2006 L2006 N *012
NEILL, Richard Alan. 51 N 39TH ST, PENN PRESBYTERIAN PENN FAM 19104 #020-12-1986 L1987 FM *040 †18
NEILSON, Neilon. PRESIDENTIAL APTS STE D119 19131 #047-06-1954 L1961 RHU IM *071 †20
NEIMARK, Geoffrey B. 245 S 8TH ST 19106 #035-08-2002 L2002 P *020
NEIPRIS, Louis Eliezer. ■ 19107 #035-08-1993 L1999 IM *100
NELSON, Aisha Tahira. ■ 19141 #041-01-2001 *100
NELSON, Charles Lenwood. 3400 SPRUCE ST FL 2, 39TH AND MARKET STREETS 19104 #041-01-1992 L1994 ORS *020 †40
NELSON, Corey Keola. 111 S 11TH ST, THOS JEFFERSON U HOSP 19107 #041-02-2006 L2006 AN *012
NELSON, Eric Donald. 1025 WALNUT ST, 1112 COLLEGE BLDG 19107 #024-07-2003 L2003 U *012
NELSON, Fredric Paul. 5000 WOODLAND AVE, WOODLAND AVE HLTH CTR 19143 #026-04-1969 L1979 PD *020 †55 ‡
NELSON, Gregory Alan. 6315 STENTON AVE 17 19138 #024-05-1978 L1981 IM *020
NELSON, James Dallas. ■ 19119 #010-03-1947 L1949 N P *020 †75
NELSON, Kyle Arthur. ■ 19146 #056-06-1997 L2006 PEM *020 †55
NELSON, Leonard Bruce. 2818 COTTMAN AVE 19149 #024-01-1976 L1981 OPH *020 †35
NEMANI, Deepika. ■ 19103 #041-01-2008 *012
NEMETH, Alexander Martin. 3400 SPRUCE ST, RADIOLOGY DEPT 19104 #041-01-2000 L2000 DR *020 †80
NEMEZ, Albert. 7001 KINDRED ST 19149 #041-01-1948 L1949 GP *071
NEMEZ, Jack Saml. 7001 KINDRED ST 19149 #041-13-1980 L1982 IM *020 †20 ‡
NEMIROFF, Richard Lloyd. 301 S 8TH ST STE 3D 19106 #041-02-1970 L1971 OBG *020 †30
NEMIROVSKY, Boris. 3996 RED LION RD 19114 #913-50-1972 L1984 PM PME *020
NEMIROVSKY, Natan I. 11500 BUSTLETON AVE 19116 #913-50-1976 L1988 P *020
NEOFYTOS, Dionissios Tria. ■ 19107 #418-01-1997 L2004 ID *100
NERY, Nomilinne Mallare. 5501 OLD YORK RD, ALBERT EINSTEIN MED CTR 19141 #748-01-2001 L2005 MPD *012
NESTICO, Pasquale F. 1809 W OREGON AVE, STE 13 19145 #041-13-1980 L1981 CD IM *020 †20
NETTLETON, James W. 123 S BROAD ST FL 22 19109 #026-04-1972 L1981 OS PD *030 ‡
NEUMAN, Brian James. ■ 19107 #041-02-2007 L2007 ORS *012
NEUMAN, Jennifer Ilana. ■ 19106 #041-02-2008 *012
NEUMAN, William Richey. 51 N 39TH ST STE 102, PENN CTR FOR PRIM CARE 19104 #041-07-1991 L1997 IM ISM *040 †20
NEUMAR, Robert Wm. 3400 SPRUCE ST, DEPT OF EMERGENCY MEDICINE 19104 #041-12-1990 L1992 EM *020 †16
NEUWELT, Melissa Deanne. ■ 19103 #005-02-2006 L2007 OPH *012
NEVILE, Sameer. ■ 19125 #026-04-2006 L2007 DR *012
NEVIN, Daniel Thomas. ■ 19107 #001-06-2003 L2004 PTH *012
NEVO, Igal. 5501 YORK TABOR RDS, A EINSTEIN MED CTR-ANES 19141 #550-02-1987 AN *020
NEVYAS, Herbert Julian. 2465 GRANT AVE 19114 #041-01-1959 L1961 OPH *020 †35
NEVYAS-WALLACE, Anita S. 2465 GRANT AVE 19114 #041-01-1983 L1984 OPH *020 †35
NEWBERG, Andrew Bernard. 3400 SPRUCE ST, 110 DONNER BLDG 19104 #041-01-1993 L1995 NM *020 †28,20 ‡
NEWHALL, Patricia Nelson. 111 N 49TH ST 19139 #041-07-1962 L1963 P PYA *071
NEWMAN, Andrew Sterling. ■ 19146 #051-01-2004 L2004 GS *012
NEWMAN, Benjamin Eugene. 5800 RIDGE AVE 19128 #036-05-1956 L1962 CD IM *071 †20
NEWMAN, George Chas. 9880 BUSTLETON AVE, NEUROLOGY ASSOCIATES AT 19115 #051-01-1976 L2005 N *020 †75
NEWMAN, Henry Evans. ■ 19150 #041-02-1966 L1967 CD IM *020 †20
NEWMAN, Jason Gabriel. 811 SPRUCE ST, DEPT OF OTOLARYNGOLOGY 19107 #041-02-1997 L1997 OTO HNS *020 ‡
NEWMAN, Marc Colin. 6 E WILLOW GROVE AVE, PERSONAL FAMILY CARE 19118 #038-44-1987 L1993 FM *020 †18
NEWMAN, Suzanne. 3900 WOODLAND AVE, 7TH FL 19104 #041-01-1999 L2000 P *020
NEWMAN, Victor. 1331 E WYOMING AVE 19124 #308-07-1982 L1985 EM IM *020
NEWMARK, Arthur Richard. 1700 SANSOM ST, STE400 19103 #035-08-1989 L1992 EM IM *020
NEWMARK, Thomas Stefan. 6100 CITY AVE # PH217 19131 #041-09-1970 L1972 P *020 †75
NEWSOME, Nakia Alexander. ■ 19134 #010-03-2004 L2004 CD *012 †20
NEWTON, Gene Raymond. 2100 W GIRARD AVE 19130 #041-01-1977 L1978 IM *020
NEY, Joshua John. ■ 19103 #041-01-2008 *012
NEYMAN, Freyda. 5501 OLD YORK RD, DEPT OF PEDS PALEYONE 19141 #041-07-1991 L1993 PD *020 †55

NG, Andrew Ti Su. ■ 19107 #041-02-2007 L2007 **IM** *012
NG, Dennis Ti Ee. 5501 OLD YORK RD 19141 #143-03-2001 L2005 **IM** *012
NG, Jeremy Tuckwoh. ■ 19130 #024-05-2006 L2007 **EM** *012
NG, Moyna Hoosze. 3401 N BROAD ST, DEPT OF MED TEMPLE UNIV 19140 #033-06-2002 L2002 **IM** *100 †20
NGARMCHAMNANRITH, Gataree. 5501 OLD YORK RD, DEPT MED 19141 #891-01-2002 L2005 **IM** *012
NGUYEN, Bach Van. 828 SNYDER AVE 19148 #942-02-1972 L1982 **IMG** *020
NGUYEN, Bao Dinh. 1720 S BROAD ST 19145 #941-01-1974 L1986 **GP** *020 †20
NGUYEN, Giang Truong. 3400 SPRUCE ST, 2 GATES, HUP 19104 #033-06-2000 L2001 **FM** *020 †18 ‡
NGUYEN, Jennifer Van. ■ 19103 #041-01-2007 L2007 *012
NGUYEN, Joan D. ■ 19152 #050-02-2008 *012
NGUYEN, Josephine Camvan. ■ 19147 #005-11-2003 L2007 **D** *012
NGUYEN, Michael Dung. ■ 19107 #035-45-2004 L2007 **PD** *100 †55
NGUYEN, Minhhuyen Thi. 333 COTTMAN AVE, STE C307 19111 #024-01-1987 L1993 **GE HEP** *020 †20
NGUYEN, Quang. 1800 LOMBARD ST 19146 #041-77-2004, ▲ L2004 **IM** *100 †20
NGUYEN, Son Xuan. 909 S 11TH ST # 3 19147 #041-13-2003 L2004 **GS** *012
NGUYEN, Thuan T. 1020 SANSOM ST # 239 19107 #050-02-2002 L2002 **EM** *100
NGUYEN, Tuduy. 2921 W QUEEN LN, # L 19129 #041-15-2004 L2004 *100
NGUYEN, Van Thanh. 1400 S 5TH ST 19147 #056-06-2004 L2007 **PD** *020 †55
NGUYEN, Vietdung Ho. 2900 W QUEEN LN 19129 #305-01-2004 L2004 **IM** *100 †20
NICHINI, Franco Maria. 1800 LOMBARD ST 19146 #917-22-1956 L1967 **RO** *071 ‡
NICHOLAS, Brian Daniel. ■ 19147 #035-15-2006 L2006 **OTO** *012
NICHOLS, Charles Warren. 3400 SPRUCE ST DEPT OPH 19104 #041-02-1964 L1965 **OPH** *020 †35
NICHOLS, Karen Joyce. 51 N 39TH ST 19104 #041-13-1988 L1990 **IM** *020 †20
NICHOLS, Kim Erika. 324 S 34TH ST 19104 #036-07-1989 L1999 **PHO PD** *020 †55
NICHOLS, Kristie Beth. ■ 19103 #035-15-2006 L2006 **FP** *012
NICHOLSON, James Anthony. 3918 CHESTNUT ST 19104 #041-01-1981 L1997 **FM** *020 †18
NICKLIN, David Evan. 51 N 39TH ST, FL 7 19104 #041-01-1981 L1982 **FM EM** *020 †16,18
NICOLAOU, Nicos. 333 COTTMAN AVE, DEPT RAD ONC FCCC 19111 #836-02-1984 L1994 **RO** *020 †80
NICOLO, Danielle Michelle. ■ 19115 #041-13-2006 L2006 **IM** *012
NICOLSON, Susan Craig. 324 S 34TH ST, DEPT ANES 19104 #041-01-1976 L1980 **AN PD** *020 †05
NIEDERMAYER, Geo Huntas. 711 SPRUCE ST 19106 #051-04-1961 L1963 **IM A** *071
NIELSEN, Kristin Echols. ■ 19104 #041-01-2006 L2006 **PD** *012
NIEMAND, Noelle Rose. ■ 19129 #041-15-2008 *012
NIERENBERG, Steven Jay. 1339 W PORTER ST 19148 #035-06-1982 L1985 **CD** *020 †20 ‡
NIERMAN, Eliot Hillel. 3701 MARKET ST, STE 760 19104 #024-01-1976 L1978 **IM** *020 †20
NIEVES, Melissa. 1331 E WYOMING AVE 19124 #033-05-1990 L1992 **FM** *020 †18
NIEWIAROWSKI, Stefan. 3400 N BROAD ST, TEMPLE MEDICAL SCHOOL 19140 #759-03-1950 L1976 *050
NIJJAR, Prabhjot Singh. 5501 OLD YORK RD 19141 #495-36-2004 L2005 **IM** *012
NIKHINSON, Ilia. 3200 HENRY AVE, MCP/HAHNEMANN HOSPITAL 19129 #913-73-1983 L2001 **P** *020 †75
NIKITIN, Dmitriy Anatoyle. 2900 W QUEEN LN 19129 #913-73-1993 L2001 **GS** *100 †85
NIKNAM, Rachel Miriam. 601 WALNUT ST, CURTIS CENTER STE L-30 19106 #041-02-2002 L2002 **OPH** *100 †35
NIKNEJAD, Ghassem. ■ 19128 #517-01-1961 L1969 **VS GS** *071 †85
NIKOLAIDIS, Lazaros A. 3401 N BROAD ST STE C-918, 9 FL-PARKINSON PAV-918 19140 #418-01-1989 L1995 **CD IM** *050 †20
NIKOLAIDIS, Stavroula I. 3401 N BROAD ST, DEPT OF ANESTHESIOLOGY 19140 #418-01-1990 L1995 **AN** *020 †05
NIKOO, Hooshang Alizade. 9807 BUSTLETON AVE 19115 #517-03-1971 L1975 **OBG** *020 †30
NIKPOOR, Borzoo. 2900 W QUEEN LN 19129 #517-01-2000 L2002 **CD** *012 †20
NILES, Deborah Althea. 2 PENN BLVD STE 112 19144 #041-09-1991 L2000 **FM** *020 †18
NILLAS, Romeo T. 5501 OLD YORK RD 19141 #748-01-1986 L1997 **IMG** *020 †20
NILSSON, Ulf Ragnar. 3400 SPRUCE ST, DEPT PATH 19104 #858-01-1967 **OS AI** *050
NIMAN, Dmitry. 3401 N BROAD ST, TEMPLE ANESTHESIA ASSOCIAT 19140 #041-07-1995 L1998 **DR** *020 †80
NIMOITYN, Philip. 1128 WALNUT ST, STE 401 19107 #041-02-1976 L1977 **CD IM** *020 †20
NING, Autumn. TEMPLE UNIV HOSP, BROAD-ONTARIO STS 19140 #422-01-2001 L2001 **P** *020
NINO BARRERA, Gustavo Rod. ■ 19130 #264-01-1999 L2006 **PDP** *012 †55
NISENBAUM, Harvey Leonard. 3400 SPRUCE ST 19104 #024-07-1970 L1974 **DR** *020 †80
NISHISAKI, Akira. ■ 19103 #572-58-1995 L2003 **CCP** *100 †55
NISSMAN, Steven Andrew. 10160 BUSTLETON AVE, STE F 19116 #041-15-2002 L2002 **OPH** *100 †35
NITSKANSKY, Lea. ■ 19115 #913-50-1950 L1982 **PM** *020
NITUICA, Cristina Magdale. 1800 LOMBARD ST 19146 #781-01-1997 L2003 **GS** *012
NIZEN, Jennifer Sue. 601 WALNUT ST, STE 640 19106 #041-09-1989 L1991 **IM** *020 †20
NJAGE, Yvonne Ellen Atien. ■ 19143 #024-01-2006 L2006 **IM** *012
NJOROGE, Wanjiku Felicia. ■ 19107 #048-04-1999 L2001 **CHP** *100
NJUGUNA, Njogu John. ■ 19128 #035-03-2004 L2004 **DR** *012
NKONDE, Chileshe. 245 N 15TH ST, DREXEL UNIV COLL OF MED 19102 #917-34-2003 L2006 **IM** *012
NNEWIHE, Charles Obinna. 3401 N BROAD ST, DEPT INTERNAL MEDICINE 19140 #038-06-2003 L2003 **NEP** *012 †20
NOBEL, Golda Rodley. ■ 19103 #041-07-1931 L1932 **CHP P** *071
NOBLE, Lori Michele. ■ 19103 #041-01-2007 L2007 **IM** *012
NOBLE, Paul Herbert. 111 S 11TH ST, STE 6217 19107 #016-42-1965 L1966 **TS GS** *020 †85,90
NOBLEZA-SANTOS, Salud U. ■ 19120 #748-08-1961 *075
NOCCHI, David Martin. 4417 MAIN ST, 3RD FL 19127 #041-13-1997 L1999 **EM** *020 †16
NOEL-LATOUR, Marie G. 800 SPRUCE ST 19107 #440-01-1964 L1970 **DR** *040 †80
NOGUEIRA, Jose Carlos. ■ 19129 #187-11-1969 L1974 **CHP P** *020
NOLAN, Ellen Patricia. 3401 N BROAD ST 19140 #010-02-1988 L2002 **IM** *020 †20
NOLL, Robert Keefe. 833 CHESTNUT ST, STE 300 19107 #041-02-1998 L2007 **PD** *020 †55
NOOR, Fazle Ali. 245 N 15TH ST MS 437, DREXEL UNIV COLL OF MED 19102 #160-09-1999 L2004 **NEP** *012 †20
NORBURY, John William, III. ■ 19107 #038-06-2006 L2007 **PM** *012
NORDLINGER, Melanie J. 241 S 6TH ST 19106 #041-13-2000 L2007 **IM** *100 †20
NORDQUIST, Valerie J. 3535 MARKET ST, FL 2 19104 #041-02-2003 L2003 **P** *020
NORMAN, Candice Alanna. 15 S BANK ST 19106 #011-03-2003 L2004 **PE** *012
NORONHA, Bosco Edric. 219 N BROAD ST FL 10, HEAD & NECK SURGERY 19107 #495-52-1986 L2001 **OTO HNS** *020
NORRIS, Anne H. 3400 SPRUCE ST 19104 #041-13-1990 L1993 **ID** *020 †20
NORRIS, Charles Morgan. ■ 19128 #041-13-1939 L1941 **PUD OTO** *071 †45
NORRIS, Charles W. 2020 PENNSYLVANIA AVE 19130 #041-09-1978 L1984 **FM** *030
NORRIS, Cynthia. 111 S 11TH ST, STE 4240 19107 #033-05-1989 L1991 **PHO PD** *020 †55
NORRIS, Robert Bruce. 230 W WASHINGTON SQ 19106 #035-19-1984 L1987 **CD IM** *020 †20
NORRIS, Robin Elizabeth. ■ 19146 #041-01-2001 L2005 **PHO** *012 †55
NORTH, Adrienne Hope. ■ 19107 #041-15-2008 *012
NORTHINGTON, Gina M. ■ 19144 #033-06-2000 L2004 **OBG** *100
NORTHROP, John Kent, Jr. ■ 19143 #041-01-2008 *012
NOSHENY, Stanley Zalman. 8021A CASTOR AVE 19152 #041-02-1966 L1967 **RHU** *020 †20
NOTO, Khristian Alfredo. 5501 OLD YORK RD, A EINSTEIN MC-KLEIN 510 19141 #935-07-1999 L2004 **GS** *012
NOTT, Rhoda Lynne. 100 E LEHIGH AVE 19125 #024-16-1995 L1999 **PS** *020
NOTZ, Gregory Matthew. ■ 19131 #041-77-2007, ▲ **IM** *012
NOUH, Amer Badreden. 3401 N BROAD ST 19140 #875-01-1997 L2002 **N** *012
NOVACK, Dennis Howard. 2126 FAIRMOUNT AVE 19130 #041-09-1972 L1973 **IM P** *040 †20
NOVAK, Matthew Ryan. ■ 19104 #024-07-2007 L2007 **TY** *012
NOVI, Joseph M. 51 N 39TH ST 19104 #041-77-1990, ▲ L1991 **OBG** *020 †30
NOVICK, Dorothy Ruth. 1900 S BROAD ST, OF PHILA 19145 #008-01-1995 L1997 **PD** *020 †55
NOVITSKY, Mark Anthony. 111 N 49TH ST, STE 119 19139 #036-05-1982 L1983 **P PYG** *020 †75
NOWELL, Peter C. 3400 SPRUCE ST DPT PATH 19104 #041-01-1952 L1953 **PTH OS** *050
NOWINSKI, Thaddeus S. 840 WALNUT ST 19107 #041-02-1980 L1981 **OPH PS** *020 †35 ‡
NOZNITSKY, Jennifer. ■ 19107 #023-01-2006 L2007 **DR** *012
NTABA, Dziwe Willard. 3300 HENRY AVE, MCP HAHNEMANN SCH OF MED 19129 #040-02-2001 L2002 **EM** *020
NTOSO, Kwabena A. 230 W WASHINGTON SQ, STE 100 19106 #035-46-1979 L1983 **NEP IM** *020 †20
NUCIFORA, Paolo. ■ 19123 #016-02-2001 L2002 **DR** *100 †80
NUMEIR, Malek Georges. 245 N 15TH ST, MAIL STOP 427 19102 #875-01-1996 L2003 **IM** *100 †20
NUNES, Frederick Anthony. 230 W WASHINGTON SQ FL 4 19106 #035-20-1988 L1991 **GE IM** *020 †20
NUNEZ, Ana Elizabeth. 219 N BROAD ST, STE 8 19107 #041-09-1986 L1987 **IM** *020 †20
NUNEZ, Eusebio Ramos. 1216 E HUNTING PARK AVE 19124 #748-01-1974 L1987 **PM** *020 †60
NUNEZ, Luis Enrique. 516 W ERIE AVE, LISETTE T COOPER MD 19140 #737-01-1952 L1965 **TS GS** *020
NURENBERG, Mark. LANCASTER CITY LINE, DEPT PATH 19151 #913-04-1953 L1983 **PTH** *020
NUSBAUM, Moreye. 1800 LOMBARD ST 19146 #035-08-1955 L1956 **GS CRS** *071 †85,90
NUSSBAUM, David Abraham. ■ 19102 #023-07-2004 L2005 **DR** *012
NWANERI, Adankem Angela. 833 CHESTNUT ST, STE 301 19107 #008-01-2004 L2004 **FM** *020
NWOKO, Okechukwu Emeka. ■ 19130 #041-13-2005 **ORS** *012
NWOKO, Rosemary Ebozue. ■ 19123 #036-05-2006 L2006 **IM** *012
NYIRJESY, Paul. 216 N BROAD ST, FL 4 19102 #010-02-1985 L1986 **OBG ID** *020 †30 ‡
OAKS, Wilbur Wilson, Jr. 255 S 17TH ST 19103 #041-09-1955 L1956 **IM** *020 †20
OATES, Angela Jasmine. ■ 19107 #030-06-2005 L2005 **IM** *012
OBI, Cynthia. 111 S 11TH ST, DEPT EM 19107 #033-05-2007 L2007 **EM** *012
O'BRIAN, Jeffrey Joseph. 111 S 11TH ST, THOS JEFFERSON UNIV HOSP 19107 #041-02-2006 L2007 **AN** *012
O'BRIEN, Chas Phillip, Jr. 3900 CHESTNUT ST, TREATMENT RESEARCH CTR 19104 #021-01-1964 L1964 **P N** *030 †75
O'BRIEN, Christopher D. 3400 SPRUCE ST 19104 #008-02-1991 L1993 **PCC** *020 †20
O'BRIEN, John S, II. 3905 FORD RD 19131 #041-02-1979 L1986 **P LM** *020 †75
O'BRIEN, Matthew J. ■ 19143 #043-01-2004 L2004 **IM** *100 †20
O'BRIEN, Meghan Mary. ■ 19146 #024-16-2006 L2006 **D** *012
O'BRIEN, William R. 111 N 49TH ST 19139 #041-02-1943 L1944 **P** *020 †75
O'BYRNE, Michael Liam. ■ 19103 #035-01-2007 L2007 *012
OCHROCH, Edward Andrew. 3400 SPRUCE ST 19104 #041-01-1992 L1992 **AN** *020 †05
OCHS, Rachel Catherine. ■ 19147 #041-01-2008 *012
OCHS, Richard Hagedorn. 3400 SPRUCE ST 19104 #041-01-1973 L1974 **PTH** *040 †50 ‡
O'CONNELL, Wm Francis. 2623 E ALLEGHENY AVE, ALLEGHANY AVE PED CTR 19134 #043-01-1982 L1985 **PD** *020 †55
O'CONNOR, Ellen Maura. 111 S 11TH ST, STE 6230 19107 #012-05-1987 L1988 **IM** *020 †20
O'CONNOR, Erin Elizabeth. 3401 N BROAD ST, DEPARTMENT OF RADIOLOGY/1S 19140 #035-15-1999 L2005 **RNR** *100 †80
O'CONNOR, Julie Marie. 5501 OLD YORK RD 19141 #041-02-2003 L2007 **EM** *100 †16
O'CONNOR, Maureen E. 111 S 11TH ST, STE 8490 19107 #028-03-1966 L1971 **AN OS** *020 †05
O'CONNOR, Michael John. 1015 CHESTNUT ST, STE 1518 19107 #041-01-1967 L1968 **NS** *020 †25
O'CONNOR, Nina Ross. 8815 GERMANTOWN AVE, FL 5 19118 #051-01-2003 L2007 **FM** *020 †18
OCONNOR, Patrick. ■ 19122 #041-15-2005 L2005 **AN** *012
O'CONNOR, Patrick Michael. 2900 W QUEEN LN 19129 #550-04-2003 L2005 **GPM** *012
OCONNOR, Timothy Patrick. ■ 19107 #035-45-2006 L2006 **EM** *012
O'CONNOR, William Henry. 39TH & MARKET STS DEPT CD, PRESBYTERIAN MED CTR 19104 #043-01-1978 L1986 **CD** *020 †20
O'CONNOR, William Michael. 900 WALNUT ST, STE 200 19107 #041-02-2000 L2000 **CN** *020 †75
ODENIGBO, Vincent Uchenna. 230 N BROAD ST 19102 #690-04-1992 L2001 **AN** *020 †05 ‡
O'DOHERTY, Una Teresa. 3400 SPRUCE ST 6.077, FOUNDERS PAVILLION 19104 #035-20-1995 L1998 **PTH** *020 †50
O'DONNELL, Judith Anne. 3300 HENRY AVE, MCP HOSPITAL 19129 #041-13-1989 L1992 **ID** *020 †20
O'DONNELL, Margot Raedigg. ■ 19104 #041-02-2006 L2006 **P** *012
O'DONNELL, Patrick Joseph. ■ 19146 #016-06-2005 L2005 **OTO** *012
O'DWYER, Peter James John. 1025 WALNUT ST, STE 63 19107 #539-03-1975 L1986 **ON IM** *030 †20,55
OFFER, Ryan Elizabeth. 245 N 15TH ST, OF M 19102 #033-05-2004 L2004 **OBG** *012
OFFIT, Paul Allan. 324 S 34TH ST 19104 #023-01-1977 L1978 **ID PD** *050 †55
OGBARA, Jeffrey. ■ 19103 #043-01-2006 L2006 **IM** *012
OGDIE, Alexis Renae. ■ 19104 #010-02-2006 L2006 **IM** *012
OGILBY, John David. 925 CHESTNUT ST, MEZZANINE LEVEL 19107 #024-05-1979 L1986 **CD** *020 †20

■ = Address Information Privacy Protected

OGILVIE, Christian Mckay. 3400 SPRUCE ST, 2 SILVERSTEIN 19104 #026-04-1996 L2003 ORS *020 †40

OGOREK, Carrie Pauline. 3900 WOODLAND AVE, P.V.A MEDICAL CENTER 19104 #035-06-1981 L1983 IM GE *020 †20

OGUNDIPE, Kehinde Abiola. 3401 N BROAD ST, DREXEL UNIV 19140 #690-02-1999 L2005 P *012

OGUNLEYE, Ayodele Omojola. ■ 19144 #690-01-1971 L1974 GS *020

OH, Catherine Hyun. 2361 E SUSQUEHANNA AVE 19125 #041-15-2003 L2003 PD *020 †55

OH, John Chung. ■ 19104 #041-01-2007 L2007 TY *012

OH, Pikai. ■ 19129 #041-13-2003 L2003 PM *100

OH, Sung Kyu. 1820 S BROAD ST 19145 #583-01-1961 L1972 GYN *020 †30

OH, Sung-Hee. 324 S 34TH ST 19143 #583-02-1976 L1985 ID PD *020 †55

OH, Vanessa Sy. 2900 W QUEEN LN 19129 #748-02-1999 L2001 IM *100

OHANISSIAN, Hanrik G. 501 S 54TH ST 19143 #154-07-1967 L1975 ON IM *020 †20

O'HARA, Brian Jerome. 132 S 10TH ST, STE 285K 19107 #041-02-1988 L1991 BBK *020 †20

O'HARE, Peter Gregory, III. 245 N 15TH ST STOP 49, OF M 19102 #665-02-2006 L2007 OBG *012

OHENE-FREMPONG, Kwaku. 324 S 34TH ST 19104 #008-01-1975 L1979 PHO PD *020 †55

OHNSMAN, Christina Celli. 840 WALNUT ST 19107 #033-05-1989 L1994 PO VS *020 †35

OHSIE, Linda Haeeun. 840 WALNUT ST, # 800 19107 #041-02-2006 L2006 OPH *012

OJELABI, Michael Olayiwol. 5501 OLD YORK RD 19141 #690-01-2000 L2005 IM *012

OKAFOR, Chukwuka Chinedum. 1015 WALNUT ST, THOMAS JEFFERSON UNIV 19107 #024-05-2004 L2004 ORS *012

OKAI, Annette F. ■ 19151 #041-15-2002 L2002 N *100

O'KANE, Patrick Louis. 132 S 10TH ST, 7 FL MAIN BLDG 19107 #041-02-1993 L1995 DR *020 †80

OKEN, Donald. 800 SPRUCE ST 19107 #024-01-1949 L1983 P *071 †75

O'KICKI, Letitia Ann. 301 S 8TH ST, STE 1D 19106 #041-13-1982 L1984 FM *020 †18

OKIN, Elihu Michael. 9140 ACADEMY RD, STE A 19114 #025-01-1966 L1973 ORS *020 †40

OKOBI, Adaobi Chibuzo. ■ 19131 #035-45-2007 L2007 *012

OKOLIE-THOMPSON, Patience. 800 SPRUCE ST 19107 #041-13-1993 L1997 AN *020 †05

OKOLO, Emmanuel Chukwudi. 3401 N BROAD ST - 8PP, DEPT OF MEDICINE 19140 #690-04-1992 L2005 IMG *100 †20

OKUM, Gary Steven. 230 N BROAD ST 19102 #041-09-1985 L1986 AN *020 †05

OLAH, Matthew Neill. 3401 N BROAD ST, DEPT OF MED -8PP 19140 #041-02-2005 L2005 IM *012

OLEAGA, Juan Alfonso. 5501 OLD YORK RD, ALBERT EINSTEIN MEDICAL CT 19141 #308-01-1967 L1974 DR *020 †80 ‡

OLEX, Stephen Todd. 111 S 11TH ST 19107 #041-02-2004 L2004 IM *100 †20

OLIGINO, Eric Joseph. ■ 19104 #008-02-2007 L2007 IM *012

OLIM, Dave B. 3401 N BROAD ST 19140 #035-06-1961 L1964 D *020 †15

OLIN, Rebecca Leah. ■ 19103 #041-01-2003 L2003 HO *012 †20

OLINER, Craig Marshall. 5401 OLD YORK RD 19141 #041-07-1980 L1981 CD IM *020 †20

OLIVIERI, Suzanne P. 3550 MARKET ST, FL 4 19104 #041-02-1988 L1990 PD *020 †55

OLSEN, Abby Lauren. ■ 19147 #041-01-2008 *012

OLSHAN, Arthur Robert. 205 N BROAD ST STE 600 19107 #036-07-1975 L1979 NEP IM *020 †20

OLSHESKI, Michelle Elizab. ■ 19130 #041-13-2007 L2007 TY *012

OLTHOFF, Kim M. 3400 SPRUCE ST, FL 4 19104 #016-02-1986 L1995 GS *020 †85

OLUFADE, Oluseun Afolabi. ■ 19107 #030-06-2007 L2007 TY *012

OLUGBESAN, Olufunmilay. 5501 OLD YORK RD, DEPT OF MED 19141 #038-40-2005 L2005 IM *012

OLUWABUSI, Bimbo Olumide. 4TH FLOOR - S TOWER MAIL, DREXEL UNIVERSITY COLLEGE 19102 #690-05-1997 L2007 P *012

OMAIYE, Benjamin Achigili. BROAD-ONTARIO STS 19140 #305-01-2002 L2003 P *100

O'MALLEY, Erin Ann. 525 JAMESTOWN ST, STE 107 19128 #041-09-1993 L1996 CD *020 †20

OMALLEY, Robert Martin. ■ 19103 #041-15-2008 *012

OMALLEY, Susan Anne. 3400 SPRUCE ST, DEPT EMERG MED/GROUND RAVD 19104 #035-48-1999 L2001 EM *020

OMDAL, Charles Arthur. 3601 A ST 19134 #041-13-1961 L1964 PD *071 †55

O'MEARA, Kay Hack. ■ 19146 #035-09-2007 IM *012

OMERT, Laurel Ann. 5401 OLD YORK RD, ALBERT EINSTEIN MEDICAL CE 19141 #016-43-1982 L1995 GS TRS *020 †85

OMINSKY, Alan Jay. ■ 19106 #041-01-1962 L1964 LM AN *071 †05,75

OMOLE, Lawrence Adeboye. 5501 OLD YORK RD, DEPT OF GME 19141 #690-01-2001 L2006 IM *012

O'MURCHU, Brian. 3401 N BROAD ST 19140 #539-04-1984 L2000 CD IC *020 †20

ONDERDONK, John A, Jr. 8835 GERMANTOWN AVE 19118 #041-01-1964 L1965 CD *075 †20

O'NEILL, Anna Marie. 834 CHESTNUT ST STE 400, BENJAMIN FRANKLIN HOUSE 19107 #033-06-2000 L2001 OBG *100 †30

O'NEILL, Hilary Lyons. 111 S 11TH ST, THOMAS JEFFERSON UNIVERSIT 19107 #041-02-2003 L2003 P *020

O'NEILL, Hugh. 226 PINE ST 19106 #041-01-1954 L1955 P *020 †75

ONESTI, Gaddo. 230 N BROAD ST 19102 #561-16-1958 L1964 NEP *050

ONG, Alvin Chua. 925 CHESTNUT ST, FIFTH FLOOR 19107 #035-48-1994 L1997 OTR ORS *020 †20

ONG, Dominador Siayngco. ■ 19114 #748-11-1972 L1975 IM CD *020

ONG, Flaviano S. ■ 19153 #748-01-1961 L1973 TS *020 †85,90

ONG KIAN KOC, Jean Bernad. ALUMNI AFFAIRS 19141 #748-02-2006 L2008 *012

ONLEY, Elvin Otis. ■ 19104 #010-03-1962 L1975 P *050

ONUOHA, Ngozi Victoria. 2501 W LEHIGH AVE 19132 #690-02-1990 L2001 IM IMG *020 †20

OOMMEN, George. 1216 N BROAD ST 19121 #495-04-1972 L1982 IM GP *020 †20

OPENSHAW, John James. ■ 19103 #041-01-2008 *012

OPOTOWSKY, Alexander R. 3400 SPRUCE ST, 9 GATES PAVILION, CARDIOLO 19104 #035-01-2003 L2006 CD *012 †20

OPPENHEIM, Laura. ■ 19107 #041-02-2006 L2006 FP *012

ORA, Carmen Salgado. ■ 19144 #748-01-1942 L1976 DIA END *030

ORANGE, Jordan S. 324 S 34TH ST 19104 #043-01-1997 L1999 AI *020 †03,55 ‡

O'REARDON, John Patrick. 3535 MARKET ST, STE 4005 19104 #539-02-1984 L1996 P *020 †75

OREN, Ahuva. 1413 W MOYAMENSING AVE 19145 #550-02-1978 L1985 FM *020

ORENDAIN, Nancy Rose. 5346 CEDEN AVE 19143 #024-01-1987 L1994 OBG *020 †30

ORIENTE, Michael Anthony. 1900 S BROAD ST 19148 #041-02-1957 L1958 FM *020

O'RIORDAN, Anna C Connor. 3601 A ST 19134 #041-09-1957 L1958 PDC PD *020 †55

ORLIN, Stephen Ellis. 51 N 39TH ST 19104 #836-02-1977 L1983 OPH *020 †35

ORLOVA, Ksenia A. ■ 19103 #041-01-2008 *012

ORMONT, Marian Amanda. 3200 HENRY AVE, AUH MCP RM 333 APH 19129 #041-13-1988 L1996 P *072 †75

OROSE, Richard Emery. ■ 19145 #041-09-1974 L1975 IM *071 †20

O'ROURKE, Donald M. 3400 SPRUCE ST, HOSP OF THE UNIV OF PA 19104 #041-01-1987 L1988 NS *020 †25

O'ROURKE, Maureen M. 34TH ST & CIVIC CTR BLVD 19104 #035-47-1988 L1990 CCP *020 †55

ORR, Nicole Marie. 1025 WALNUT ST, THOMAS JEFFERSON UNIV HOSP 19107 #041-15-2004 L2004 IM *100 †20

ORTEGA, Erik Lillegraven. 900 WALNUT ST, STE 200 19107 #041-01-2003 L2007 IM *100

ORTEGA, Guillermo. 34TH & CIVIC CTR BLVD 19104 #429-01-1956 L1979 PDR *020

ORTIZ, Joseph Manuel. 2465 GRANT AVE 19114 #035-09-1976 L1980 OPH *020 †35 ‡

ORTIZ, Madai. ■ 19107 #042-02-2005 L2007 IM *100

ORTIZ TORRENT, Natalia. 1316 W ONTARIO ST, TEMPLE UNIV HOSP 19140 #042-02-2001 L2001 P OS *020 †20

ORTMAN, Matthew Louis. 925 CHESTNUT ST, MEZZANINE LEVEL 19107 #023-01-2003 L2003 CD *012 †20

ORTOLANO, Susan Ninfa. 34TH CIVIC CTR BLVD PED 19104 #023-07-1996 L1998 PD *020 †55

ORUGANTI, Vishnu Vandhana. 3401 N BROAD ST, DEPT MED 19140 #035-06-2007 L2007 IM *012

ORZECHOWSKI, Joseph Chest. ■ 19128 #023-01-2005 L2005 EM *100

OSBAKKEN, Mary D O Holmes. 3400 SPRUCE ST, DEPT CARDIOL 19104 #041-13-1975 L1976 CD IM *020

OSBAND, Adena Joan. 5501 OLD YORK RD, ALBERT EINSTEIN MED CTR 19141 #033-05-1999 L2005 GS *100 †85

OSBORNE, Christopher Mich. 3401 N BROAD ST, CHILDREN'S HOSP PHILADELPH 19140 #055-01-2006 L2006 PD *012

OSBOURNE, Marlon Stclair. ■ 19154 #033-05-2004 L2004 PTH *012

OSENI, Salewa Tawakalitu. ■ 19104 #038-06-2001 L2007 *020 †85

O'SHEA, Barbara Marie. 245 N 15TH ST 19102 #041-07-1978 L1979 OBG *020 †30

OSHEROFF, Jerome Alan. SIXTH ST AT RACE, AMER COLL OF PHYSICIAN 19106 #010-01-1986 L1987 IM OS *040 †20

OSLICK, Theodore. 7600 CENTRAL AVE 19111 #041-09-1962 L1963 PUD CCM *071 †20

OSLIN, David Wayne. 3535 MARKET ST, RM 3002 UNIV OF PA 19104 #051-01-1989 L1994 P PYG *050 †75

OSMAN, Brian M. ■ 19144 #041-15-2008 *012

OSTERHOUDT, Kevin Chas. 34 S 34TH ST 19104 #035-06-1991 L1993 PD PDT *020 †55

OSTERMAN, Mark Tomislav. 3400 SPRUCE ST 19104 #024-01-1999 L2002 GE *100 †20

OSTERMAN, Meredith Nita. ■ 19107 #041-02-2008 L2008 *012

OSTERTAG, Eric Michael. ■ 19107 #041-01-2002 L2002 PTH *100 †50

OSTICK, Brian John. ■ 19107 #041-02-2008 *012

OSTROW, Vlady. ■ 19130 #041-77-2003, ▲ L2004 PDE *012

OSTRUM, Bernard Jos. 5501 OLD YORK RD 19141 #041-01-1956 L1957 R *071 †80

OSTRUM, Donald Stuart. 2601 HOLME AVE, NAZARETH HOSPITAL 19152 #041-13-1982 L1983 DR *020 †80

O'SULLIVAN, Martin James. 333 COTTMAN AVE 19111 #539-02-1995 L2006 *100

OTERO, Guillermo Roberto. 5501 OLD YORK RD, AEMC DEPARTMENT OF PSYCHIA 19141 #042-01-2002 L2002 P *100

O'TOOLE, Thomas F. ■ 19128 #041-02-1952 GP *020

OTT, Carol Eleanor. 1900 S BROAD ST, CHOP PRIMARY CARE 2ND FL 19145 #041-09-1971 L1973 PD *020 †55

OTTENBERG, B Perry. 601 WALNUT ST, CURTIS BLDG 960W 19106 #024-01-1952 L1953 P PYA *020 †75

OUYANG, Ann. 3400 SPRUCE ST 19104 #917-23-1974 L1976 GE IM *020 †20

OVEREND, Barbara Carol. ■ 19146 #012-05-2007 L2007 PD *012

OVIEDO, Alcides. ■ 19128 #726-01-1964 L1973 U *020

OVIEDO, Nimidia. 2145 N 6TH ST 19122 #726-01-1966 L1979 EM PTH *074

OWEN, Alyson Nina. 925 CHESTNUT ST 19107 #041-01-1982 L1984 CD *020 †20

OWENS, Gary Mitchell. 1901 MARKET ST FL 31 19103 #041-02-1975 L1976 FM *030 †18

OWENS, Judy Kay. ■ 19128 #041-15-2008 *012

OWENS, Keith Jay. 3300 HENRY AVE, MED COLL OF PA DEPT OBG 19129 #011-03-1983 L1989 OBG *020 †30

OWENS, Laura Lee. ■ 19146 #038-41-2008 L2008 *012

OWNBEY, Robert Thomas. 245 N 15TH ST 19102 #051-07-1993 L2001 PTH *020 †50

OWOLABI, Adekunle Mojeed. 800 SPRUCE ST, DEPT OF GME 19107 #690-01-1998 L2006 IM *012

OWUSUANTWI, Jacqueline Y. 324 S 34TH ST 19104 #024-01-1999 L2002 PD *020 †55

OXMAN, Reed Sterling. 226 W RITTENHOUSE SQ # 911 19103 #005-14-1986 L1987 EM PME *020 †16

OZOLS, Robert Felix. 333 COTTMAN AVE, FOX CHASE CANCER CTR 19111 #035-45-1974 L1988 ON IM *050 †20

PACE, William Camp. ■ 19125 #041-13-2005 L2005 IM *012

PACHIKA, Ajay. 2900 W QUEEN LN 19129 #495-57-1998 L2003 IM *100 †20

PACHIKARA, Abraham Stephe. ■ 19146 #041-01-2008 *012

PACHINBURAVAN, Monvasi. 5501 OLD YORK RD 19141 #891-01-1998 L2004 PCC *012 †20

PACHO, Arelyne Bustrillos. 7600 CENTRAL AVE 19111 #748-02-1976 L1981 PM *020 †60

PACK, Allan I. UNIV OF PA HOSP 19104 #919-05-1967 L1979 *020

PACK, Michael Alan. 3400 SPRUCE ST 19104 #028-02-1984 L1985 GE IM *020 †20

PACK, Winifred. 412 WINTON ST, WINIFRED PACK MD FACP 19148 #041-07-1970 L1972 MM NPM *020 †20

PACKER, Susan Beth. 7500 CENTRAL AVE 19111 #041-02-1980 L1981 FM *020 †18

PACKMAN, Barry Ellis. 9880 BUSTLETON AVE 19115 #041-02-1978 L1979 IM *020 †20

PADDER, Farooq Ahmad. 230 N BROAD ST 19102 #495-51-1981 L1999 ICE CD *020 †20

PADHA, Reetika Kumar. 833 CHESTNUT ST 19107 #041-45-2000 L2006 IM *100 †20

PADMALINGAM, My G. 2900 W QUEEN LN 19129 #539-06-2005 L2005 IM *012

PADMANABHUNI, Amitha. 1800 LOMBARD ST 19146 #495-11-2002 L2006 IM *012

PADNES, Stephen Chas. 1800 LOMBARD ST 19146 #041-02-1966 L1967 PMM P *020 †75

PADULA, Anthony Michael. ■ 19118 #041-02-1967 L1968 GS *071 †85

PADULA, Michael Anderson. ■ 19144 #041-02-2000 L2001 PD *100 †55

PAEZ, Eduardo Javier. ■ 19107 #264-01-1965 L1973 GP *071

PAGALILAUAN, Manuel A. 4000 N MARSHALL ST 19140 #748-10-1969 L1975 PTH *020 †50

PAGANELLI, Galia. 1015 WALNUT ST STE 4, THOMAS JEFFERSON UNIV HOSP 19107 #132-01-1998 L2002 IM *012

PAGE, Kathleen Raquel. 1 PINE PL W, 800 SPRUCE STREET 19115 #028-02-1998 L2000 ID *100 †20

PAGNANI, Christopher Just. ■ 19107 #041-02-2008 *012

■ = Address Information Privacy Protected

PAHL, Michael Anton. 1015 WALNUT ST, THOMAS JEFFERSON UNIV 19107 #041-02-2004 L2005 **ORS** *012

PAHYS, Joshua Matthew. 5501 OLD YORK RD, ALBERT EINSTEIN MEDICAL CE 19141 #041-02-2004 L2004 **ORS** *012

PAI, Sheela Surendra. 3401 N BROAD ST, OUTPATIENT BLDG, STE 300 19140 #495-01-1996 L2001 **AN** *020 †05

PAING, Wynn Wynn. 2900 W QUEEN LN 19129 #209-01-1981 L2001 **CHP** *100 †75

PAK, Kevin Ikyo. ■ 19147 #035-08-2004 L2004 **PM** *012

PAK, Raymond Wei. ■ 19107 #033-05-2002 L2007 **U** *100

PAKALNIS, Regina. 3400 SPRUCE ST, DEPT AN 19104 #038-43-1988 L1990 **AN** *020 †05

PALAZZO, Francesco. 1015 WALNUT ST, DEPT OF SURGERY- SUITE 602 19107 #561-04-1997 L2002 **GS** *100 †85

PALAZZO, Irma E. 7600 CENTRAL AVE, JEANES HOSPITAL 19111 #132-02-1982 L1996 **PTH** *020 †50

PALERMO, Brandon John. 3401 N BROAD ST, INFECTIOUS DISEASES 19140 #033-06-2001 L2002 **ID** *100 †20

PALEVSKY, Harold Ingram. 51 N 39TH ST, GROUND FLOOR REAR, PHI BUI 19104 #051-04-1978 L1979 **PCC IM** *020 †20

PALIOU, Maria. 2400 CHESTNUT ST LBBY 2 19103 #418-01-1997 L2005 **END** *020 †20

PALLADINO, Andrew Anthony. ■ 19144 #041-15-2003 L2003 **PDE** *012 †55

PALLEY, Alexis Rachel. ■ 19122 #041-15-2003 L2006 **EM** *100

PALLICKAL, Leejoe Kuruvil. 245 N 15TH ST, DEPT OF GME 19102 #305-01-2006 L2006 **IM** *012

PALMER, James Nathan. 3400 SPRUCE ST, DEPT ORL HNS 5 RANDIN 19104 #038-40-1995 L2001 **OTO** *020 †45

PALMIERI, Ronald John. 4200 MONUMENT RD, BLMNT CTR FR CMPRHNSVE 19131 #041-02-1970 L1971 **P IM** *020 †75

PALUZZI, Richard Glenn. 219 N BROAD ST, STE 8 19107 #035-19-1984 L1986 **IM** *020 †20

PAN, Fushih. ■ 19102 #016-02-1989 L1994 **PS** *020 †65

PAN, Jonathan Zhiyong. ■ 19104 #243-16-1996 L2007 **TY** *012

PANARO, Joseph Nicholas. ■ 19130 #041-13-2007 L2007 **GS** *012

PANCOAST, Maclean Marie. ■ 19143 #041-01-2008 *012

PANDE, Rajendra C. 3300 HENRY AVE 19129 #495-73-1983 L1994 *100

PANDE, Saurabh Anil. 5501 OLD YORK RD, ALBERT EINSTEIN MEDICAL CE 19141 #496-38-2004 L2006 **IM** *012

PANDEY, Aditya Swaroop. 909 WALNUT ST 3RD FL, DEPT NEUROSURGERY 19107 #038-06-2001 L2001 **NS** *020

PANDIT, Inez M. 10 SHURS LN, STE 203 19127 #409-25-1989 L1998 **FM** *020 †18

PANDYA, Nirav Kiritkumar. ■ 19103 #016-02-2005 L2005 **ORS** *012

PANEBIANCO, Nova Leda. 3400 SPRUCE ST, DEPARTMENT OF EMERGENCY ME 19104 #035-48-2004 L2007 **EM** *100

PANETTA, Nicholas Louis. 3401 N BROAD ST 19140 #041-13-2005 L2005 **IM** *012

PANETTIERI, Reynold, Jr. 51 N 39TH ST, HEART INST BLDG 1ST FL 19104 #041-01-1983 L1984 **PUD IM** *020 †20

PANETTIERI, Reynold A. 830 SOLLY AVE 19111 #041-13-1958 L1959 **FM** *020 †18

PANIDIS, Ioannis. 3401 N BROAD ST, TEMPLE UNIV HOSP-PAVILIONB 19140 #418-01-1975 L1981 **CD IM** *020 †20

PANIKKAR, Rajiv Prasanna. 333 COTTMAN AVE, DEPT OF MEDICAL ONCOLOGY 19111 #041-12-2001 L2003 **HO** *012

PANITCH, Howard Barry. 3550 MARKET ST, FL 4 19104 #041-12-1982 L1983 **PDP PD** *020 †55

PANTELYAT, Alexander Yury. ■ 19115 #041-13-2008 L2008 *012

PANTELYAT, Susanna Ilyini. 2601 HOLME AVE 19152 #913-05-1982 L2001 **N** *020 ‡

PANZER, Jeffrey Michael. 111 S 11TH ST, DEPT FM 19107 #041-13-2006 L2006 **FP** *012

PANZER, Jessica Anne. ■ 19104 #041-01-2006 L2006 **PD** *012

PANZETTA, Anthony F. 3401 N BROAD ST 19140 #016-43-1960 L1966 **P** *030 †75

PAO, Kristina Yihwa. ■ 19107 #041-02-2008 *012

PAPANICOLAOU, Nicholas. 3400 SPRUCE ST, PENNSYLVANIA/1 SILVERSTEIN 19104 #418-01-1974 L2002 **DR NM** *020 †80,28

PAPAZAFIRATOU, Chris. ■ 19141 #418-01-1972 L1976 **PD NPM** *020 †55

PAPOUTSIS, Dean V. 2701 HOLME AVE, STE 105 19152 #041-09-1989 L1992 **CD** *020 †20

PAPPAS, Charles Engelos. 8835 GERMANTOWN AVE 19118 #041-13-1972 **PS LM** *071 †65

PAPPAS, Nicholas Demitri, III. ■ 19103 #047-05-2006 L2006 **ORS** *012

PAPPERMAN, Thomas W. 2301 E ALLEGHENY AVE, HELENE FULD BLDG 4TH FL 19134 #035-03-1984 L1987 **OBG** *020 †30

PAPPU, Ramesh. 245 N 15TH ST, ALBERT EINSTEIN MED CTR 19102 #495-21-1981 L1991 **RHU IM** *020 †20 ‡

PARADA, Andrea N. 3400 SPRUCE ST, DEPT OF DIAG RAD 19104 #043-01-2006 L2007 **DR** *012

PARADKAR, Shilpa. ■ 19104 #495-45-2001 L2005 **IM** *020

PARAKKAL, Deepak. 3400 SPRUCE ST, UNIVERSITY OF PENNSYLVANIA 19104 #495-53-2004 L2007 **GS** *012

PARALKAR, Vikram Ravindra. 3401 N BROAD ST, DEPT OF INTERNAL MED 19140 #496-38-2004 L2005 **IM** *012

PARAMESH, Poornima. 2601 HOLME AVE, DEPT-ANESTH NAZARETH HSOP 19152 #496-39-1985 L2000 **AN** *020 †05

PARAMESWARAN, Lalitha. 3401 N BROAD ST, DEPT OF MED - 8PP 19140 #496-21-2004 **IM** *012

PARAMESWARAN, R. 5401 OLD YORK RD, STE 201 19141 #495-31-1958 L1972 **CD IM** *020 †20

PARANG, Pirouz. ■ 19103 #023-01-1999 L2001 **CD** *020 †20

PARANJAPE, Anuradha S. 1316 W ONTARIO ST, TEMPLE UNIVERSITY 19140 #495-28-1991 L2006 **IM** *020 †20

PARCHURI, Ramesh. 161 E LEHIGH AVE 19125 #495-57-1975 L1985 **GP** *020

PARE, Emmanuelle. 3400 SPRUCE ST 19104 #067-04-1994 L1999 **OBG** *020 †30

PAREKH, Amit Anant. 2900 W QUEEN LN 19129 #496-38-2000 L2001 **CD** *012

PARGOLA, Eileen Ford. ■ 19128 #041-14-2007 L2007 **IM** *012

PARIKH, Kavita Hasmukh. ■ 19103 #035-20-2004 L2004 **PD** *020 †55

PARIKH, Sefali Dinesh. ■ 19103 #001-02-2006 L2006 **IM** *012

PARISH, Jennifer Leigh. 1760 MARKET ST, STE 301 19103 #041-02-1998 L2002 **D** *020 †15

PARISH, Landi Marie. ■ 19146 #041-01-2008 *012

PARISH, Lawrence Chas. 1760 MARKET ST, STE 301 19103 #024-07-1963 L1964 **D** *020 †15

PARK, Audrey Youngmi. ■ 19103 #041-01-2003 L2003 **AI** *012 †55

PARK, Chan Hee. 111 S 11TH ST, THOMAS JEFFERSON UNIV HSPT 19107 #583-01-1964 L1971 **NM DR** *062 †80,28

PARK, Chong Ho. 5401 OLD YORK RD, KLEIN PROF BLDG STE 503 19141 #583-01-1961 L1971 **GE IM** *020 †20

PARK, Daniel Jiyong. ■ 19107 #035-48-2008 *012

PARK, Hee-Ok. 111 S 11TH ST 19107 #583-02-1967 L1972 **OBG** *020 †30

PARK, Hyung Kyoun. 8815 GERMANTOWN AVE, CHESTNUT HILL HOSPITAL 19118 #583-10-1965 L1972 **AN** *020

PARK, Jason Young. ■ 19102 #041-02-2003 L2003 **PTH** *012 †50

PARK, Joon Hong. ■ 19103 #051-01-2006 L2006 **IM** *012

PARK, Mee Soon. 3535 MARKET ST, FL 2 19104 #035-08-2005 L2005 **P** *012

PARK, Myoung Je. 2601 HOLME AVE 19152 #583-03-1962 L1978 **GP** *020

PARK, Sangdo. 3400 SPRUCE ST, 2 SILVERSTEIN / DEPT ORTHO 19104 #035-01-2004 L2004 **ORS** *012

PARK, Seung-Eun. TEMPLE UNIV HOSP-ANES, BROAD-ONTARIO STS 19140 #572-66-1983 L2000 **AN** *100

PARK, Sunny Sunwoo. ■ 19107 #041-02-2004 L2004 **OTO** *012

PARKER, Artist Lesley. ■ 19147 #041-09-1976 L1982 **OBG** *020

PARKER, Candace Yvonne. ■ 19137 #036-05-2006 L2006 **OBG** *012

PARKER, Janet Alene. 1 PENN BLVD 19144 #041-07-1958 L1960 **RO NM** *071 †80,28

PARKER, Jeffrey Clarke. 3601 A ST, ST CHRISTOPHER HOSP CHILDN 19134 #016-11-1989 L1992 **NPM** *020 †55

PARKER, Nancy. 3509 N BROAD ST, TEMPLE UNIV CHILD MED CTR 19140 #041-07-1998 L2000 **PD** *020 †55

PARKMAN, Henry Paul. 3401 N BROAD ST, TEMPLE UNIV HOSP 19140 #038-06-1982 L1985 **GE IM** *050 †20

PARKS, Adria Lee. 245 N 15TH ST MS 310, MCP HAHNEMANN UNIV 19102 #041-15-2001 L2002 **AN** *020 †05

PARKS, Donald Bruce. 2305 N BROAD ST 19132 #041-02-1978 L1979 **IM** *020

PARKS, Susan Mockus. 1015 WALNUT ST STE 401 19107 #033-05-1994 L1996 **FPG** *020 †18

PARMACEK, Michael Scott. 3400 SPRUCE ST, CARDIOVASCULAR DIVISION 19104 #016-06-1981 L1998 **IM** *020 †20

PARMET, Jonathan Louis. 800 SPRUCE ST, SCHIEDT BLDG 19107 #041-09-1985 L1989 **AN** *040 †05

PARR, Justin Ludger. 422 CURIE BLVD, 609 STELLAR CHANCE BLDG 19104 #056-05-1958 L1970 **ADM NP** *071 †50

PARRILLO, Douglas Warren. 1512 SPRUCE ST, APT 2601 19102 #010-02-1968 L1971 **R NM** *020 †80

PARRIS, Kristin Helaine. 1316 W ONTARIO ST 19140 #041-13-1990 L1992 **IM** *020 †20

PARRIS, Ted Michael. 230 N BROAD ST, FL 7 19102 #041-02-1976 L1981 **IM** *020 †20

PARRISH, Beth. ERIE AVE AT FRONT ST, ST CHRISTOPHERS HSP CHLDRN 19134 #041-07-1987 L1990 **PD OS** *020 †55

PARRISH, Erin Gale. ■ 19103 #036-08-2002 L2006 **CCP** *012

PARRISH, Saml Kossie, Jr. 2900 W QUEEN LN, STUDENT AFFAIRS 19129 #045-01-1979 L1984 **PD ADL** *020 †55

PARRON, John Keckhut. 3401 N BROAD ST, TEMPLE UNIV HOSP 19140 #033-06-2005 L2005 **ORS** *012

PARROTT, Lilbourn Leo. 601 WALNUT ST STE 504E 19106 #041-01-1968 L1975 **OBG** *020 †30

PARROTT, Louis Anthony, Jr. 245 S 8TH ST, RM 338 19106 #038-06-2001 L2001 **P** *020 †75

PARRY, Samuel Isaiah. 3400 SPRUCE ST, HOSP OF UNIV OF PA 19104 #035-01-1990 L1994 **OBG MFM** *020 †30

PARSHAD, Shiroo. 5501 OLD YORK RD 19141 #495-36-2003 L2005 **IM** *012

PARSONS, Rosaleen B. 333 COTTMAN AVE 19111 #041-07-1986 L1987 **DR** *020 †80

PARTHASARATHY, Sriranjani. ■ 19130 #035-45-2008 *012

PARTHIPAN, Loganathan. 5501 OLD YORK RD 19141 #495-04-1986 L1995 **AN** *020 †05

PARVIZI, Javad. 925 CHESTNUT ST, FL 5 19107 #917-10-1991 L2002 **ORS** *020 †40 ‡

PARZIALE, Nicholas James. ■ 19129 #041-15-2007 L2007 **IM** *012

PASCASIO, Judy Mae C. ERIE AT FRONT ST, ST CHRISTOPHERS HOSP CHILD 19134 #748-02-1990 L1998 **PTH PP** *020 †50

PASCUAL, Jose. 3400 SPRUCE ST 19104 #065-09-1996 L2005 **CCS** *100 †85

PASCUAL-RAMIREZ, Javier. 51 N 39TH ST 19104 #847-04-1984 L1996 **AN** *020 †05

PASHMAN, David Roy. 5401 OLD YORK RD, STE 200 19141 #041-02-1970 L1971 **ORS** *020 †40

PASIRSTEIN, Michael Jason. 245 N 15TH ST, MAIL STOP 1011 19102 #041-15-2007 L2007 **EM** *012

PASKIN, David Louis. 1025 WALNUT ST, DEAN'S OFFICE SUITE 108 19107 #041-02-1964 L1965 **GS** *030 †85

PASQUALI, Sara Kate. 2104 MOUNT VERNON ST, 3RD FL 19130 #036-07-2002 L2002 **PDC** *012 †55

PASQUALIN, Denise D C. 132 S 10TH ST 19107 #187-12-1997 L2001 **PTH** *020

PASQUARIELLO, Patrick, Jr. 324 S 34TH ST 19104 #041-02-1956 **PD** *020 †55

PASTERNAK, Jared Adam. ■ 19107 #035-09-2006 L2006 **PD** *012

PASZCZUK, Anna. 3400 SPRUCE ST, HUP CARDIOVASCULAR DIV 19104 #008-01-2001 L2004 **CD** *020 †20

PATCHEFSKY, Arthur. 333 COTTMAN AVE 19111 #041-09-1963 L1967 **ATP** *020 †50

PATEL, Aalpen Ashokkumar. 3400 SPRUCE ST, 1 SILVERSTEIN 19104 #033-06-1995 L1999 **DR** *020 †80

PATEL, Akash R. ■ 19103 #024-05-2004 L2004 **PDC** *012 †55

PATEL, Ami Mahendra. ■ 19103 #001-06-2005 L2005 **IM** *012

PATEL, Amit Rasikbhai. ■ 19104 #051-01-2006 L2006 **ORS** *012

PATEL, Anita Rakesh. ■ 19128 #495-22-1995 **FM** *020

PATEL, Anita Rambhai. ■ 19128 #041-14-2006 L2006 *012 †18

PATEL, Ashok Vithalbhai. PO BOX 572, FED DETENSION CTR 19105 #495-17-1983 L1985 **IM DIA** *020

PATEL, Avni Hans. ■ 19107 #041-12-2005 L2006 **OPH** *012

PATEL, Badrish Jayanti. 3401 N BROAD ST, TEMPLE UNIV HOSPITAL 19140 #051-04-2001 L2004 **PCC** *020 †20

PATEL, Chirag R. 3620 HAMILTON WALK, UNIV OF PA SCH OF MED 19104 #041-01-2006 L2006 *012

PATEL, Darshan V. 1025 WALNUT ST 19107 #041-02-2001 L2004 **CD** *012

PATEL, Deepan Nitin. ■ 19107 #041-02-2008 *012

PATEL, Dilipkumar K. 3401 N BROAD ST, DEPT OF ANESTHESIOLOGY 19140 #495-48-1990 L1999 **AN** *020 †05

PATEL, Dinesh Nagarbhai. 1331 E WYOMING AVE, REGIONAL MEDICAL CENTER 19124 #495-23-1972 L1976 **ON IM** *020 †20

PATEL, Dipakkumar Dahtabh. 5401 OLD YORK RD, KLEIN BLDG STE 363 19141 #495-23-1990 **MPD** *012

PATEL, Harshad Kantilal. 501 S 54TH ST 19143 #496-38-1969 L1978 **DR** *020 †80

PATEL, Himisha Jayant. ■ 19106 #035-09-2004 L2004 **IM** *100 †20

PATEL, Jashvant. ■ 19103 #407-25-1962 L1974 **TS** *020

PATEL, Jasmine K. 3998 RED LION RD, STE 211 19114 #035-47-1992 L1994 **PD** *020 †55

PATEL, Jitesh Vinod. ■ 19128 #041-13-2005 L2005 **U GS** *012

PATEL, Kartik Kanu. ■ 19147 #041-12-2006 L2006 **IM** *012

PATEL, Manubhai R. 2601 HOLME AVE 19152 #495-23-1964 L1972 **IM** *071
PATEL, Mihir Kantilal. ■ 19107 #012-01-2005 L2006 **IM** *012
PATEL, Monali Chandrakant. 3401 N BROAD ST, TEMPLE UNIV HOSP 19140 #016-42-2007 L2007 **N** *012
PATEL, Namrata Bakulesh. 3401 N BROAD ST 7P, TEMPLE LUNG CENTER 19140 #023-01-1998 L2000 **PCC** *020 †20
PATEL, Nilesh. 3300 HENRY AVE, ALLEGHENY UNIV OF HLTH SCI 19129 #415-15-2002 L2002 *100
PATEL, Nimesh Babubhai. ■ 19123 #033-06-1995 L1998 **IM** *020 †20
PATEL, Nirav. 132 S 10TH ST, UNIVERSITY HO 19107 #035-46-2004 L2006 **DR** *012
PATEL, Nirav Pravinbhai. 3400 SPRUCE ST, DEPT PULMONARY MED 19104 #917-35-1999 L2001 **PCC** *012
PATEL, Nirlep Ashok. 4TH FLOOR - S TOWER MAIL, DREXEL UNIVERSITY COLLEGE 19102 #422-01-2007 L2007 **IM** *012
PATEL, Pankaj Harji. 254 S 9TH ST 19107 #041-02-1991 L1996 **GS TRS** *020 †85
PATEL, Parin Jagdish. ■ 19103 #424-01-2008 *012
PATEL, Parul. ■ 19130 #035-08-1999 L2001 **CD** *020 †20
PATEL, Parul Bhagvan. 111 S 11TH ST 5320G, THOMAS JEFFERSON UNIV HOSP 19107 #422-01-2003 L2003 **PEM** *100 †55
PATEL, Parul Rajiv. 3401 N BROAD ST, TEMPLE ANESTHESIA ASSOCIAT 19140 #495-89-1991 L2001 **AN** *020 †05
PATEL, Prakash Arun. ■ 19114 #041-02-2006 L2006 **AN** *012
PATEL, Preeti R. 34TH-CIVIC CTR BLVD, CHILDRENS HOSP 19104 #035-15-2002 L2005 **NPM** *012 †55
PATEL, Raj Ramabhai. ■ 19107 #041-15-2007 L2007 **IM** *012
PATEL, Rajiv Jayendra. 3401 N BROAD ST, TEMPLE ANESTHESIA ASSOCIAT 19140 #495-22-1988 L1999 **AN** *020 †05
PATEL, Rakesh Dasharath. 245 N 15TH ST, MAIL STOP 1011 19102 #023-01-2007 L2007 **EM** *012
PATEL, Rakesh Pravin. ■ 19128 #495-22-1995 L2003 **U** *012
PATEL, Rakhee Vinu. 700 N PENNOCK ST, UNIT C-201 19130 #010-02-2003 L2003 **PD** *100 †55
PATEL, Riti. 525 JAMESTOWN ST, STE 107 19128 #024-05-1995 L1999 **CD** *020 †20
PATEL, Rohit Amratlal. 3401 N BROAD ST, OF S 19140 #496-23-2001 L2001 **GS** *100
PATEL, Roshani Raman. 333 COTTMAN AVE, FOX CHASE CANCER CENTER 19111 #038-41-2001 L2006 **GS** *050
PATEL, Sameer Anilkumar. 333 COTTMAN AVE, MEDICAL STAFF OFFICE 19111 #033-05-1998 L2007 **PS** *100 †85
PATEL, Sarjan Hemant. 3401 N BROAD ST, OF SURGE 19140 #016-42-2007 L2007 **GS** *012
PATEL, Shital Jayant. ■ 19107 #495-01-2001 L2007 **RNR** *012 †80
PATEL, Shrita Mittal. ■ 19146 #051-04-2001 L2003 **END** *020
PATEL, Sonal Jayant. 245 N 15TH ST, DEPT MED 19102 #422-01-2007 L2007 **IM** *012
PATEL, Tapan Harshad. ■ 19128 #033-05-2006 L2006 **IM** *012
PATEL, Ushama Pravin. 5501 OLD YORK RD, ALBERT EINSTEIN MED CTR 19141 #495-01-2001 L2003 **CHP** *012
PATEL, Utpalkumar Jashbha. ■ 19129 #041-13-2008 L2008 *012
PATEL, Vickas Vithalbhai. 3400 SPRUCE ST, HOSPITAL UNIVERSITY OF PEN 19104 #007-02-1995 L1997 **CD** *020 †20
PATEL, Vikram Manilal. 2301 E ALLEGHENY AVE, NORTH EASTERN HOSPITAL 19134 #495-22-1970 L1977 **OBG** *020
PATHAK, Abhijit Sadashiv. 3401 N BROAD ST, TEMPLE UNIVERSITY HOSPITAL 19140 #041-13-1991 L1996 **CCS** *020 †85
PATHAK, Rameshwar. 201 S CAMAC ST 19107 #495-15-1974 L1983 **CD** *075
PATHARKAR, Milind Dinkar. 3800 HENRY AVE, MCP-HAHNEMANN UNIV HOSP 19129 #305-01-2000 L2001 **APM** *020
PATHIKONDA, Muralidhar. 5501 OLD YORK RD 19141 #496-21-2000 L2005 **IM** *012
PATI, Susmita. 324 S 34TH ST 19104 #008-02-1996 L2002 **PD** *020 †55
PATIL, Madhavi Hari. ■ 19103 #495-82-1996 L2006 **PTH** *100 †50
PATIL, Malini Atul. 233 S 10TH ST, RM 412 19107 #496-38-1999 *100
PATIL, Sarita Ulhas. ■ 19131 #036-07-2006 L2006 **IM** *012
PATNAIK, Ramprasad. 5432 TORRESDALE AVE 19124 #495-13-1965 L1977 **GS EM** *020 †85
PATNAIK, Sudharani. 5432 TORRESDALE AVE 19124 #495-13-1967 L1980 **GP OBG** *020 ‡
PATRASCU, Carmen. 230 W WASHINGTON SQ, STE 100 19106 #781-04-1995 L2005 **NEP** *100 †20
PATRI, Mallika. 3401 N BROAD ST 19140 #496-35-2001 L2004 **P** *100
PATRICK, Herbert. 219 N BROAD ST, STE 8 19107 #041-02-1977 L1978 **PUD CCM** *020 †20
PATRICK, Kathleen E. 2314 S 3RD ST 19148 #008-02-1982 L1983 **OBG** *020 †30
PATRICK, Kenneth Philip. 8815 GERMANTOWN AVE, CHESTNUT HILL MEDICAL PC 19118 #041-01-1978 L1979 **FM OS** *020 †18
PATTERSON, John Robt. 1015 CHESTNUT ST, STE 322 19107 #041-02-1954 L1955 **RHU IM** *072 †20
PATTERSON, Mary Elizabeth. ■ 19107 #654-01-2005 L2005 **PD** *012
PATTERSON, Raymond Kevin. 245 N 15TH ST MS 310, OF M 19102 #041-14-2003 L2003 **AN** *020
PATTISHALL, Amy Elizabeth. ■ 19103 #041-14-2004 L2004 **PD** *012 †55
PATTON, Alison Journey. 3400 SPRUCE ST, HEALTH SYST 19104 #041-01-2007 L2007 **MPD** *012
PATTUGALAN, Theresa De Je. ALUMNI AFFAIRS, ALBERT EINSTEIN MEDICAL CE 19141 #748-02-1999 L2007 **PD** *012
PAUL, Stephen Robt. 3509 N BROAD ST, TEMPLE UNIV CHILD MED CTR 19140 #041-13-1984 L1995 **ON PD** *020
PAULSON, David P. ■ 19128 #048-13-2005 L2005 **GS** *100
PAULSON, Emily Carter. 3400 SPRUCE ST, DEPT OF SURGICAL EDUCATION 19104 #041-01-2003 L2003 **GS** *012
PAVLIDES, Constantinos A. 245 N BROAD ST STE 400 19107 #418-01-1967 L1975 **GS VS** *020 †85 ‡
PAVRI, Behzad Berzelius. 925 CHESTNUT ST 19107 #496-38-1986 L1994 **CD ICE** *020 †20
PAWEL, Barbara. 3400 CIVIC CENTER BLVD 19104 #033-05-1984 L1993 **PEM PTH** *020 †55 ‡
PAWEL, Bruce Robt. 34TH ST AND CIVIC CENTER B 19104 #033-05-1984 L1993 **PP** *020 †50
PAYAWAL-DELA ROSA, Aurora. 1200 W TABOR RD 19141 #748-01-1973 L1981 **PM** *020 †60
PAYENSON, Alon. ■ 19144 #041-15-2008 *012
PAYNE, Aimee Sue. 3600 SPRUCE ST, 2 RHOADS PAVILION 19104 #028-02-2001 L2001 **D** *050 †15 ‡
PAZIANAS, Michael. 3615 CHESTNUT ST 19104 #418-02-1975 L2003 *020
PE, Mark-Rally Lao. 1025 WALNUT ST, STE 1112 COLLEGE BUILDING 19107 #041-02-2004 L2004 **U** *012
PEAR, Warren Scott. ■ 19130 #035-45-1989 L1996 **PTH** *020 †50

PEARSON, Philip Yarnall. ■ 19118 #051-01-1997 L1999 **CRS** *100 †85,10
PEARSON, S. 1316 W ONTARIO ST, JONES HALL 1ST FLOOR 19140 #041-01-1987 L1989 **IM** *020 †20
PEARSON, Vincent. 1901 MARKET ST 19103 #041-14-1976 L1979 **FM** *020 †20
PEBDANI, Parmis. ■ 19128 #041-77-2007, ▲ L2007 *012
PECHET, Taine Tayardvale. 51 N 39TH ST, STE 2D 19104 #024-01-1992 L2001 **TS** *020 †85,90
PECHULIS, Rita Margaret. 3401 N BROAD ST, TEMPLE UNIV HOSPITAL 19140 #041-02-2002 L2002 **PCC** *012 †20
PECK, Jeremy Walter. ■ 19128 #041-15-2007 L2007 **TY** *012
PEDEN, Gerald Wm. 1901 MARKET ST, FL 32 19103 #051-07-1992 L1994 **MDM GS** *030
PEEK, Reginald Demetrius. ■ 19119 #012-21-2004 L2004 **OBG** *100
PEER, Meeta Devendra. 9701 BUSTLETON AVE 19115 #495-22-1967 L1978 **PM** *020 †60
PEET, Alisa. 3401 N BROAD ST, DEPT OF MEDICINE/8 PP 19140 #041-13-2000 L2001 **IM** *100 †85
PEET, Jon Allan. ■ 19103 #041-13-2007 L2007 *012
PEFF, Thomas Costo. 8407 BUSTLETON AVE 19152 #051-01-1975 L1981 **ORS OS** *020 †18,40
PEFKAROS, Nicholas A. 840 WALNUT ST, WILLS EYE HOSPITAL 19107 #041-02-2001 L2001 **OPH** *020
PEIGHTEL, James Allan. 3401 N BROAD ST, TEMPLE ANESTHESIA ASSOCIAT 19140 #041-13-1988 L1990 **P** *020 †75
PEITZMAN, Steven J. 2900 W QUEEN LN RM 221 19129 #041-13-1971 L1973 **NEP IM** *040 †20
PEKALA, Raymond Thos. 840 WALNUT ST 19107 #041-02-1978 L1980 **OPH** *020 †35 ‡
PEKAREV, Maxim. 245 N 15TH ST, MAIL STOP 413 RM 7608 NCB 19102 #033-05-2003 L2003 **GS** *012
PELCHAT, Rodney James. 900 WALNUT ST, 8TH FL 19107 #035-46-1984 L1989 **P** *020 †75
PENA, Antonio Jose. 3400 SPRUCE ST, DEPT RAD 19104 #264-21-2003 L2007 **DR** *012
PENA RICARDO, Carolina. 5501 OLD YORK RD, ALBERT EINSTEIN MEDICAL CE 19141 #264-07-2000 L2006 **PD** *012
PENAVERDE, Pura Encina. 5211 N BROAD ST 19141 #748-01-1961 L1983 *100
PENDER, Niamey Susannah. ■ 19104 #035-01-2006 L2006 **GS** *012
PENDLEY, Valerie Prete. 8815 GERMANTOWN AVE, FL 5 19118 #038-40-1977 L1985 **FM** *040 †18
PENN, Melinda C. 3615 CIVIC CENTER BLVD, RM 802 19104 #051-07-2004 L2007 **PDE** *012 †55
PENNE, Robert Berg. 840 WALNUT ST, STE 102 19107 #026-04-1984 L1985 **OPH PS** *020 †35
PENNEYS, Edith Torgan. 301 S 8TH ST 19106 #041-01-1943 L1944 **P** *071
PENROD, Dale Stewart. ■ 19107 #041-01-1960 L1961 **PS** *020
PENTZ, William Haley. 230 W WASHINGTON SQ FL 3, PENNSYLVANIA CARDIO ASSOC 19106 #041-02-1991 L1999 **CD** *020 †20
PEPE, Matthew David. 925 CHESTNUT ST, FIFTH FLOOR 19107 #010-02-1994 L1996 **ORS** *020 †40
PERCEC, Ivona. ■ 19103 #041-01-2004 L2004 **PS** *012
PEREIRA-RICO, Alvaro. 111 S 11TH ST, GIBBON BLDG. STE 4240 19107 #847-04-1992 L2001 **HO** *020 †20
PERELSHTEYN, Vladimir. 10172 VERREE RD 19116 #913-03-1974 L1984 **PD** *020
PERETZ, Jeffrey Isaac. ■ 19102 #033-05-2005 L2005 **ORS** *012
PEREZ, Elmar O. 3400 N BROAD ST, DEPT ANES 19140 #748-02-1971 L1977 **AN** *100
PEREZ BARRIOS, Julian And. 5501 OLD YORK RD 19141 #935-01-1996 L2005 **IM** *012
PEREZ-ROCHA, Luz Marina. 100 E LEHIGH AVE, MAB 305 19125 #649-14-1979 L1987 **P** *020 †75
PERINI, Rodolfo Fleury. ■ 19145 #187-32-2001 L2006 **NM** *012
PERKEL, Robert Louis. 1015 WALNUT ST 1ST FL 19107 #035-46-1978 L1980 **FM FPG** *040 †18
PERKINS, Julia Jane. 333 COTTMAN AVE, MEDICAL ONCOLOGY 19111 #051-07-2004 L2004 **HO** *012
PERKINS, Rosina Serene. 1015 WALNUT ST 19107 #016-42-2000 L2002 **GS** *100 †85
PERL, Alexander Edward. 3400 SPRUCE ST, 16 PENN TOWER 19104 #035-47-1997 L2003 **ON** *020 †20
PERLIS, Clifford Scott. 333 COTTMAN AVE, DEPT OF DERMATOLOGY 19111 #041-01-2000 L2000 **D** *020 †15
PERLMAN, Morton Henry. 230 N BROAD ST 19102 #041-13-1956 L1965 **OM EM** *071 †85
PERMAN, Sarah Muirhead. ■ 19146 #041-13-2007 L2007 **EM** *012
PERMUT, Irene Quiambao. ■ 19130 #035-47-2004 L2004 **IM** *100 †20
PERMUT, Stephen Robt. 3322 N BROAD ST RM 203 19140 #041-13-1972 L1996 **FM IM** *040 †20,18
PERRE, Anthony. 1331 E WYOMING AVE, CANCER TREATMENT CENTERS O 19124 #041-07-1994 L1996 **IM** *020 †20
PERRIE, Christopher S. 3620 HAMILTON WALK, UNIV OF PA SCH OF MED 19104 #041-01-2005 L2005 *100
PERRINS, Leighton Seaton. 1525 W DUNCANNON AVE 19141 #032-01-1985 L1989 **AN PME** *020 †05
PERROTTE, Nicole Tahira. 2900 W QUEEN LN 19129 #422-01-2001 L2001 **IM** *020
PERROTTO, Santle Louis. 3839 CHALFONT DR 19154 #041-09-1958 L1959 **FM** *020 †20
PERRY, James Jos. 3998 RED LION RD, STE 130 19114 #041-09-1981 L1991 **IM** *020 †20
PERRY, Robin Lynn. ■ 19103 #005-02-2002 L2006 **PHO** *012
PERRY, Ruth Earlene. 100 N INDEPENDENCE MALL W 19106 #041-13-1982 L1983 **IM EM** *020 †20,16
PERRY, Sarah Beth. 111 S 11TH ST, JEFFERSON UNIVERSITY 19107 #041-02-2005 L2005 **PD** *012
PERSHMAN, Karima Rafael. ■ 19146 #041-15-2004 **EM** *020
PERUTO, Christina Marie. ■ 19102 #010-02-2006 L2006 **ORS** *012
PESHEK, Andrew Donald. 1616 WALNUT ST STE 814 19103 #038-06-2000 L2001 **P** *020 †75
PESSLER, Frank Christian. 3405 CIVIC CENTER BLVD, DIR OF RHEUMATOLOGY 19104 #035-48-1998 L2003 **PD RHU** *050 †55
PESTELL, Richard George. 233 S 10TH ST, THOMAS JEFF UNIV HOSP BLSB 19107 #143-06-1982 L2006 *020
PETE, Erin Alexandra. 3400 CIVIC CENTER BLVD, CHILDREN'S HOSP 19104 #041-15-2006 L2006 **PD** *012
PETER, Nadja Gabrielle. 324 S 34TH ST 19104 #035-01-1994 L1996 **ADL IM** *020 †20
PETERS, Candice Annette. 3400 SPRUCE ST, UNIV OF PA HLTH SYS 19104 #010-03-2006 L2007 **IM** *012
PETERSEN, Robert Ole. 1015 CHESTNUT ST, STE 902 19107 #016-06-1967 L1971 **PTH** *020 †50
PETERSEN, Tara Lyn. ■ 19103 #056-05-2006 L2006 **PD** *012
PETERSIDE, Iyalla Elvis. 3400 SPRUCE ST 19104 #690-01-1985 L1999 **NPM** *020 †55
PETERSMEYER, Nancy Quayle. 15 W HIGHLAND AVE STE 2 19118 #024-01-1980 L1991 **P PYA** *020 †75
PETERSON, Arthur Leo. 111 N 49TH ST 19139 #035-09-1945 L1949 **P OS** *020 †75

■ = Address Information Privacy Protected

PETERSON, Jed Russell. ■ 19150 #035-03-2006 L2006 **DR** *012
PETERSON, Kandace Kayanne. ■ 19146 #051-07-2002 **GS** *012
PETIT, Christopher John. 3400 CIVIC CENTER BLVD, DIV OF CARDIOLOGY 19104 #047-05-1999 L2003 **PD** *020 †55
PETRIE, Matthew Shane. 833 CHESTNUT ST, STE 740 19107 #036-05-2006 L2007 **D** *012
PETRINI, Joyce Ann. 7600 CENTRAL AVE, JEANES HOSP EMERG DEPT 19111 #041-07-1980 L1981 **EM** *020 †16
PETRINI, Maria Eugenia. 111 S 11TH ST 19107 #132-07-1996 L2003 **PD** *020 †55
PETROF, Basil John. 3400 SPRUCE ST, # 3 RAVDIN BLDG STE F PULM 19104 #067-04-1983 L1989 **PUD** *020 †20
PETRONE, Louis Ralph. 2305 FAIRMOUNT AVE, JEFFERSON MEDICAL CARE 19130 #041-02-1987 L1988 **FM** *020 †18
PETRONGOLO, Terri Mcfiilli. 3918 CHESTNUT ST 19104 #041-77-1998, ▲ L1999 **FM** *020 †18 ‡
PETROVIC, Marija. 3300 HENRY AVE, MCP HAHNEMANN UNIV 19129 #408-14-2000 L2002 **P** *020
PETRUCELLI, Robert Paul. 1000 WALNUT ST, APT 402 19107 #041-02-2002 L2008 **PM** *012
PETRUZZI, Nicholas Joseph. ■ 19127 #041-02-2008 *012
PFAFF, William Lenox, III. 3401 N BROAD ST, TEMPLE UNIVERSITY HOSPITAL 19140 #041-02-2003 L2003 **ORS** *012
PFANZELTER, Nicklas Rober. ■ 19103 #016-02-2007 L2007 **IM** *012
PFEFFER, Scott Hal. 9501 ROOSEVELT BLVD, PENNSYLVANIA HEART & 19114 #041-77-1986, ▲ L1987 **CD** *020
PFEIFER, Samantha Mae. 3701 MARKET ST STE 8, UNIV OF PENNSYLVANIA 19104 #041-01-1986 L1988 **REN OBG** *020 †30
PHAM, Alexander Darwin Vu. ■ 19103 #041-15-2008 *012
PHAM, Christine K. ■ 19107 #028-46-2004 L2004 **OBG** *012
PHAM, Tuong Do. 1738 W CHELTENHAM AVE 19126 #941-01-1962 L1976 **FM GS** *020 †18
PHAM-THOMAS, Nancy Nguyen. ■ 19123 #036-05-2006 L2006 **OBG** *012
PHAN, Ngoc An. 909 S 11TH ST 19147 #561-14-1978 L1981 **IM IMG** *020 †20 ‡
PHELAN, Gerald Richard. 39 E CHESTNUT HILL AVE 19118 #041-07-1975 L1976 **IMG FM** *020 †18
PHILIP, Shaji Mathew. ■ 19115 #041-02-2008 *012
PHILIP, Shibu. 2900 W QUEEN LN 19129 #035-31-1998 L2003 **IM** *020
PHILIPONIS, Vincent Wm. TEMPLE UNIV ANES 19140 #649-33-1997 **AN** *100
PHILLIPS, Carolyn Ann. 3400 SPRUCE ST, OF PENNSYLVAN 19104 #033-05-2003 L2003 **EM** *100
PHILLIPS, Carolyn Cambor. 3400 SPRUCE ST, UNIV OF PENN HUP MC4283 19104 #048-04-1983 L1994 **PTH** *040 †20,50
PHILLIPS, Gordon Reed, III. 3400 SPRUCE ST, DEPT TRAUMATOLOGY, UPMC 19104 #041-02-1986 L1991 **TRS** *020 †85
PHILLIPS, Peter Clayton. 100 N 20TH ST, STE 301 19103 #008-02-1978 L1991 **N CHN** *020 †55,75
PHILLIPS, Stanley Michael. 3400 SPRUCE ST, DPT MED 19104 #056-05-1966 L1975 **AI IM** *020 †20,03
PHILLIPS, Steven Jones. 3401 N BROAD ST 19140 #041-09-1960 L1963 **OS** *050
PHILP, Matthew Miller. 3401 N BROAD ST, OF S 19140 #041-13-2005 L2005 **GS** *012
PHON, Hla. 2900 W QUEEN LN 19129 #209-01-2003 AN *100
PHUNG, Jennifer Thuy. 2900 W QUEEN LN 19129 #305-01-2005 L2005 **OBG** *012
PIATT, Joseph Howard, Jr. ERIE AVENUE AT FRONT ST, ST CHRISTOPHERS HOSP 19134 #041-01-1979 L1979 **NSP NS** *020 †25
PICCOLI, David A. 324 S 34TH ST 19104 #024-01-1979 L1983 **GE PD** *020 †55
PICCONE, Michele Renee. 100 E LEHIGH AVE, FL 3 19125 #035-03-1984 L1985 **OPH** *030 †35
PICKERING, Nancy Jean. 3939 CONSHOHOCKEN AVE 19131 #041-07-1976 L1980 **CD IM** *020 †20
PICKERING, Sean Pierre. ■ 19130 #023-07-1995 L2000 **IM** *020
PIEN, Grace Weiwei. 3437 MIDVALE AVE 19129 #035-01-1994 L1999 **PCC** *020 †20
PIERCE, Eric A. 422 CURIE BLVD, 305A STELLAR-CHANCE LABS 19104 #024-01-1990 L1999 **OPH** *020 †35
PIERCE, Gregory Harold. 417 N 8TH ST, STE 503 19123 #041-09-1981 L1982 **GS** *020
PIERCE, Harold Ernest, Jr. 4190 CITY AVE STE 522 19131 #010-03-1946 L1948 **D AM** *072
PIERI, Danielle. ■ 19130 #041-77-2004, ▲ L2007 **OBG** *012
PIERI, Paola Giulia. ■ 19106 #025-07-2000 L2001 **CCS** *020
PIERRE-LOUIS, Alain. ■ 19103 #035-08-2006 L2007 **PM** *012
PIERSON, Tyler Mark. ■ 19144 #048-04-2001 L2002 **CHN** *100
PIGGOTT, Caroline Dianesa. 111 S 11TH ST, THOMAS JEFFERSON UNIV 19107 #047-05-2007 L2007 *012
PIGNOLO, Robert John. 3615 CHESTNUT ST, RALSTON-PENN CENTER 19104 #041-07-1998 L2001 **IMG** *020 †20
PIKE, Anne Hollingsworth. 5735 RIDGE AVE STE 104 19128 #041-07-1946 L1947 **OBG** *071 †30
PILANIA, Pramod. 2927 N 5TH ST 19133 #913-14-1997 L2002 **CHP** *012 †75
PILAPITIYA, Leshitha Nuwa. 245 N 15TH ST, DREXEL UNIV COLL OF MED 19102 #422-01-2004 L2006 **FP** *012
PILATIS, Nectarios D. 5501 OLD YORK RD, DEPT OF MED DIV OF CARDIOL 19141 #418-01-1990 L1996 **CD** *100 †20
PILCHMAN, Jeffrey Michael. 3998 RED LION RD 19114 #033-05-1982 L1983 **GE** *020 †20 ‡
PILGRIM, Catherine Angela. 834 CHESTNUT ST, STE 300 19107 #041-01-1994 L2001 **OBG** *020 †30
PILL, Stephan Geoffrey. 3400 SPRUCE ST FL 2, SILVERSTEIN BUILDI 19104 #041-01-2005 L2005 **ORS** *012
PILLAI, Jyoti A. 245 N 15TH ST, HAHNEMANN UNIVERSITY HOSPI 19102 #495-17-1989 L2001 **CN** *020 †75
PILLAI, Prasad. 800 SPRUCE ST 19107 #495-94-1998 L2005 **IM** *012
PILLITTERI, Rian John. 245 N 15TH ST, MAIL STOP 1011 19102 #033-05-2007 L2007 **EM** *012
PIMPALWAR, Ashwin Praful. 1 CHILDRENS CTR, CHILDREN'S HOSPITAL OF PHI 19104 #495-83-1991 L2005 *100
PIMPALWAR, Sheena Ashwin. 1 CHILDRENS CTR, CHILDREN'S HOSPITAL OF PHI 19104 #496-38-1996 L2006 *100
PINEDA, Danielle Marie. ■ 19107 #041-02-2008 L2008 *012
PINEDA, Maria Carissa C. 900 WALNUT ST, STE 200 19107 #748-02-1995 L2001 **N** *020 †75
PINES, Jesse Mireth. 3400 SPRUCE ST, EMERGENCY MEDICINE 19104 #010-02-2001 L2004 **EM** *020 †16
PINNEY, Sara Elizabeth. ■ 19143 #038-41-2002 L2005 **PDE** *012 †55
PINNIX, Chelsea Camille. ■ 19104 #041-01-2007 **IM** *012
PINSKI, Gabriel. 4900 WYALUSING AVE 19131 #649-33-1982 L1983 **P** *020 †75
PINTO, Shailesh Christoph. 5501 OLD YORK RD 19141 #496-44-2001 L2003 **IM** *100 †20
PIRASTEHFAR, Mohammad Hos. 2900 W QUEEN LN 19129 #517-05-2000 L2005 **IM** *012

PIROLLI, Timothy John. ■ 19104 #041-01-2008 *012
PIROUZKAR, Pirouz Peter. ■ 19129 #041-07-1996 L1996 **IM GPM** *074
PIRWANI, Nabeel. 1201 CHESTNUT ST, STE 1502 19107 #704-16-1991 L1996 **CHP** *100 †75
PIRZADEH, Afsaneh. ■ 19103 #036-01-2003 L2006 **CCP** *012
PISANO, Daniel Jos. 9908 ROOSEVELT BLVD 19115 #010-02-1954 L1961 **R NM** *020 †80
PITT, Allyson Sara. ■ 19107 #041-12-2004 L2004 **IM** *100 †20
PITTENGER, Sara Rose. ■ 19104 #048-04-2007 L2007 **OBG** *012
PITTMAN, Kai Ayana. ■ 19143 #035-06-2006 L2006 **FP** *012
PIZZINI, Markalan Dominic. 333 COTTMAN AVE 19111 #041-14-1994 L1997 **AN** *020 †05
PIZZUTILLO, Peter Darrell. ERIE AVE AT FRONT ST, ST CHRISTOPHER HOSP CHLDRN 19134 #041-02-1970 L1970 **OP** *020 †40
PLASTARAS, John Peter. 3400 SPRUCE ST, 2 DONNER BLDG 19104 #047-05-2002 L2003 **RO** *100
PLATT, Alec Bennet. 1630 LATIMER ST 19103 #035-19-2001 L2001 **PCC** *012
PLOTNICK, Michael I. 3400 SPRUCE ST, MALONEY BLDG 8TH FL 19104 #035-19-1986 L1991 **PUD IM** *020 †20
PLUMB, James David. 1015 WALNUT ST, FL 400 19107 #041-02-1974 L1975 **FM** *020 †18
PLUTZER, Martin David. 4641 ROOSEVELT BLVD, FRIEND HOSPITAL 19124 #041-12-1968 L1971 **P PYA** *020 †75
PLZAK, Louis Frank. 1800 LOMBARD ST 19146 #016-02-1958 L1971 **TS PDS** *020 †85,90
POBLETE, Honesto Madjus. 2900 W QUEEN LN 19129 #748-01-1999 L2001 **GS** *020 †85
POCHETTINO, Alberto. 3400 SPRUCE ST, FL 6 19104 #016-06-1987 L1994 **TS** *020 †90,85
PODARALLA, Srikanth. 5501 OLD YORK RD, DEPT OF PEDIATRICS 19141 #495-21-1998 L2002 **PDC** *012
PODOLSKY, Michael Lee. 1403 W MOYAMENSING AVE 19145 #041-02-1974 L1975 **OBG** *020 †30 ‡
POGOZELSKI, Andrew Robert. ■ 19103 #036-07-2008 *012
POHL, Charles Andrew. 833 CHESTNUT ST STE 301, JEFFERSON PEDIATRICS 19107 #041-02-1987 L1989 **PD** *020 †55
POKAL, Shatabdi L. ■ 19107 #305-01-2007 L2007 *100
POLANCO, Alfonso. ■ 19140 #264-01-1964 L1971 **EM** *030
POLASANI, Rajeev Sai. 3400 SPRUCE ST, NEURORADIOLOGY 19104 #016-42-2001 L2002 **RNR** *012 †80
POLICASTRO, Dennis C. 700 SPRUCE ST, STE 304 19106 #035-15-1981 L1982 **IM EM** *040 †20,16
POLIN, Glenn. 3400 SPRUCE ST 19104 #041-01-2000 L2001 **CD** *012 †20
POLINSKY, Martin Sander. ■ 19128 #033-05-1974 L1979 **PN PD** *020 †55
POLISE, Pamela Ann. 800 SPRUCE ST 9TH FL, ANESTHESIOLOGY/SCHIEDT BLD 19107 #041-02-1993 L1993 **AN** *020 †05
POLITI, Roman Cg. ■ 19107 #041-02-2007 L2007 **GS** *012
POLK, Lewis D. 226 W RITTENHOUSE SQ 19103 #041-01-1953 L1954 **PHP PD** *071 †55,70
POLL, David Stanley. 909 WALNUT ST, STE G20 19107 #041-01-1979 L1982 **CD ICE** *020 †20
POLLACCHI, Hernan Luis. 3400 SPRUCE ST, UNIV OF PA HLTH SYSTEM 19104 #132-01-2004 L2006 **GS** *100
POLLACK, Alan. 333 COTTMAN AVE, FOX CHASE CANCER CENTER 19111 #011-02-1987 L1991 **RO** *020 †80
POLLACK, Chas Victor, Jr. 800 SPRUCE ST, EMERGENCY MEDICINE, PENNSY 19107 #021-01-1984 L2001 **EM** *020 †16
POLLACK, Craig Evan. ■ 19130 #005-02-2004 L2006 **IM** *100
POLLACK, Emily S. 324 S 34TH ST 19104 #027-01-1981 L2002 **PD OS** *020 †55
POLLACK, Pia Susman. 925 CHESTNUT ST 19107 #024-01-1981 L1986 **CD IM** *050 †20
POLLAK, Eleanor Susan. 3615 CIVIC CENTER BLVD 19104 #008-01-1991 L1997 **CLP HMP** *020 †20
POLLARD, John Robert. 3400 SPRUCE ST 19104 #041-01-1999 L2001 **N** *020 †75
POLYAK, Paul. ■ 19114 #033-06-2005 L2005 **GS** *012
POMERANTZ, Joel David. 7300 GERMANTOWN AVE 19119 #035-46-1984 L1985 **IM IMG** *020 †20 ‡
POMIDOR, Mary Martha. 8815 GERMANTOWN AVE FL 5, CHESTNUT HILL FAMILY PRACT 19118 #041-02-2000 L2001 **FM** *020 †18
PONAMGI, Vinita Ahuja. 10160 BUSTLETON AVE, STE A 19116 #036-07-1998 L2001 **IM** *020
PONCZ, Mortimer. 3615 CIVIC CENTER BLVD, ARC RM 317 19104 #041-01-1976 L1977 **HEM PD** *050 †55
PONDOK, Theresa Elizabeth. 1025 WALNUT ST, THOMAS JEFFERSON UNIV HOSP 19107 #041-02-2001 L2001 **CD** *012
PONNAMANENI, Abhilasha Ra. KNIGHTS AND RED LION RDS, FRANKFORD HOSPITALS 19114 #496-31-2001 L2007 **TY** *012
PONTARI, Michel Arthur. 3401 N BROAD ST, STE 350 19140 #041-14-1986 L1992 **U SCI** *095
POPESCU, Adrian. 3400 SPRUCE ST 19104 #781-01-2000 **PM** *012
POPESCU, Andra Mirela. ■ 19107 #781-01-2000 L2004 **IM** *012
POPII, Marius Dan. 3440 MARKET ST STE 200 19104 #781-02-1998 L2006 **CHP** *012
POPII, Violeta Botea. 501 S 54TH ST, PHYSICIAN SERVICES 19143 #781-01-1996 L2005 **END** *020 †20
POPNIKOLOV, Nikolay K. 1800 LOMBARD ST 19146 #198-01-1988 L2002 **PTH** *020 †50
POPORAD, George Alexander. 9501 ROOSEVELT BLVD, STE 208 19114 #041-07-1975 L1977 **ID IM** *020 †20
PORADOWSKI, Yolanda Danut. 100 E LEHIGH AVE, COMPREHENSIVE HEALTH CENTE 19125 #759-04-2000 L2006 **IM** *020 †20
PORAT, Rachel. 5501 OLD YORK RD, ALBERT ELDSTEIN MEDICAL CE 19141 #550-02-1975 L1977 **PD** *020 †55
PORCELLI, Steven Anthony. ■ 19119 #008-01-1984 L1985 **RHU IM** *020 †20
PORGES, Stefanie Beth. 3400 SPRUCE ST 19104 #041-09-1988 L1990 **FM** *020 †20
PORRETT, Paige Marie. ■ 19103 #016-06-2001 L2001 **GS** *012
PORTALE, Joseph Victor. ■ 19147 #041-02-2008 L2008 *012
PORTER, Brenda Elaine. 324 S 34TH ST 19104 #028-02-1995 L1998 **CHN** *020 †75,55
PORTER, David Louis. 3400 SPRUCE ST, 16 PENN TOWER 19104 #043-01-1987 L1995 **HEM** *020 †20
PORTILLO, Guillermo, Jr. 3401 N BROAD ST, TEMPLE UNIV HOSP 19140 #041-13-2007 L2007 **P** *012
PORTNOY, Jane Zuger. 51 N 39TH ST, SCHEIE EYE INST 19104 #020-02-1977 L1994 **OPH** *020 †35 ‡
PORTNOY, Joel David. 3535 MARKET ST STE 1029 19104 #025-01-1994 L1998 **CCP** *050 †55
POSATKO, Robert John. ■ 19128 #041-02-1957 L1958 **OBG** *020 †30
POSNER, Jill C. 324 S 34TH ST 19104 #051-04-1993 L1995 **PD** *020 †55
POSNER, Kari Robyn. ■ 19102 #035-46-2005 L2008 **PD** *012

POSNER, Michael Glenn. 2314 E YORK ST, KEYSTONE EYE ASSOCIATES 19125 #051-04-1991 L1996 **OPH** *020 †35

POST, Charles Jos. 1331 E WYOMING AVE 19124 #561-01-1961 L1963 **P FM** *071 †75

POST, Zachary Douglas. ■ 19103 #028-34-2002 L2007 **OAR** *012

POSTLE, Corinne Katrina. ■ 19104 #035-15-2008 *012

POTHARLANKA, Prathibha. 2900 W QUEEN LN, MCP HAHNEMANN UNIV 19129 #305-01-1999 L2001 **IM** *020 †20

POTLURI, Sunitha. ■ 19140 #495-50-1995 L2002 **IM** *100 †20

POTO, Antonio. 245 N 15TH ST MS 310, DREXEL UNIV COLL OF MED 19102 #033-75-2004, ▲ L2005 **AN** *012

POTSIC, William Paul. 3400 CIVIC CENTER BLVD 19104 #012-05-1969 L1974 **OTO** *020 †45

POTTASH, Ruben Robt. 111 N 49TH ST 19139 #041-02-1939 L1940 **P PYA** *071 †75

POTTER, Kirk David. 4190 CITY AVE, GENERAL SURGERY DEPT 19131 #028-78-2001, ▲ L2001 **GS** *012

POTTI, Sushma. 3401 N BROAD ST, TEMPLE UNIVERSITY HOSPITAL 19140 #495-27-2000 L2006 **OBG** *012

POUNCEY, Claire Louise. 100 E LEHIGH AVE, DEPT OF PSYCH STE 305 19125 #041-01-2001 L2004 **P** *020 †75 ‡

POWELL, Alvin Pierce. 3001 WALNUT ST 19104 #041-12-1982 L1984 **PTH GP** *062 †50 ‡

POWELL, Jonathan L. 5445 HOUGHTON PL 19128 #048-12-1998 L2000 **PHO** *020 †55

POWELL, Karlyn Jean. ■ 19147 #041-15-2005 L2005 **AN** *012

POWELL, Robin Dale. 3930 CHESTNUT ST 19104 #016-02-1957 L1988 **IM** *030 †20

POWELL, Wendy Soyini. 4190 CITY AVE, STE 315 19131 #035-15-1980 L1985 **OBG** *020 †30

POWERS, Rachel Marian. ■ 19128 #011-03-2005 L2005 **P** *012

POWLIS, William Davenport. 3400 SPRUCE ST 19104 #035-01-1973 L1982 **RO ON** *040 †80

PRADHAN, Basant Kumar. ALUMNI AFFAIRS, ALBERT EINSTEIN MEDICAL CE 19141 #495-13-1999 L2007 **P** *012

PRADHAN, Madhavi S. 111 S 11TH ST, STE 8490 19107 #495-17-1988 L2002 **AN** *020

PRASAD, Anita Gunturu. 840 WALNUT ST, STE 1020 19107 #016-06-2002 L2007 **OPH** *100 †35

PRASAD, Anjana Rajendra. 19103 #010-01-2004 L2008 **OPH** *012

PRASAD, Meeta. ■ 19102 #047-05-2001 L2006 **PCC** *012 †20

PRASAD, Sashank. ■ 19146 #041-01-2004 L2004 **N** *012

PRAVETZ, Michael Joseph. ■ 19129 #836-01-1982 L1986 **P** *075

PRAWAK, Oksana Tatiana. 1901 MARKET ST, FL 30 19103 #035-06-1991 L1994 **PM** *020 †60

PREMPEH, Maxwell Agyemang. ■ 19129 #036-07-2003 L2006 **CD** *012 †20

PRENTICE, Nikkisha. ■ 19119 #041-12-2006 L2006 **IM** *012

PRESS, Matthew J. ■ 19102 #043-01-2005 L2005 **IM** *012

PRESS, Richard A, Jr. 1234 MARKET ST, SEPTA MEDICAL DEPT 19107 #041-09-1967 L1968 **OM FM** *030

PRESSMAN, Gregg Shein. 1 PENN BLVD, ASSOCIATES 2ND FLOOR 19144 #041-13-1981 L1982 **CD** *020 †20 ‡

PRESTCOE, Flora R. 3300 HENRY AVE, MED COLLEGE PENN HOSP 19129 #041-13-1989 L1993 **PTH** *100

PRESTON, Bennett Gordon. 321 S UNIVERSITY AVE 19104 #025-07-1981 L1988 **FOP PTH** *020

PREVIDI, Bianca Michelle. ■ 19107 #041-02-2008 *012

PREWITT, Rajalla Elika. 4641 ROOSEVELT BLVD 19124 #038-40-1997 L2002 **CHP** *020 †75

PRIBITKIN, Edmund A, II. 925 CHESTNUT ST FL 6 19107 #041-01-1986 L1987 **OTO FPS** *020 †45

PRICE, Christina. ■ 19147 #041-15-2005 L2005 **EM** *012

PRICE, Jos Washington, IV. 514 E SEDGWICK ST 19119 #041-13-1970 L1971 **FM OS** *020 †18

PRICE, Raphael I M. 7219 RISING SUN AVE 19111 #041-02-1962 L1963 **PS** *071 †65

PRIESTLEY, Margaret Ann. 3400 SPRUCE ST 19104 #041-01-1992 L1994 **CCP** *020 †55

PRINGLE, Peyre Gaillard. ■ 19103 #045-01-1986 *020

PRIOLEAU, Yvonne Denise. 301 S 8TH ST STE 2A 19106 #041-01-1994 L1996 **OBG** *020 †30

PRI-PAZ, Shai Moshe. 5501 OLD YORK RD 19141 #550-02-2001 L2004 **OBG** *012

PROCACCI, Pat Michael, Jr. 255 S 17TH ST, STE 1700 19103 #041-09-1969 L1970 **CD** *020 †20

PROCKOP, Darwin Johnson. 245 N 15TH ST, MSC 421 CTR GENE THRPY 19102 #041-01-1956 L1964 **OS** *050

PROCTOR, Janet Cameron. ■ 19130 #023-01-2006 **PD** *012

PROFETA, Bernadette Carol. 1100 WALNUT ST, STE 500 19107 #041-02-1997 L1999 **GS** *020 †85

PROOTHI, Vanita. 1025 WALNUT ST, THOMAS JEFFERSON UNIV HOSP 19107 #041-15-2002 L2002 **END** *100 †20

PROUT, Elizabeth P. ■ 19144 #024-07-1999 L2007 **PD** *020 †55

PROWLER, Matthew L. ■ 19103 #041-02-2006 L2006 **P** *012

PRUCKMAYR, Gregory Thomas. 3400 SPRUCE ST, DEPT OF ANESTHESIA 19104 #041-13-2001 L2001 **AN** *100 †05

PRUITT, Amy Ann. 3400 SPRUCE ST 19104 #024-01-1974 L1991 **N** *020 †20,75

PRYOR, John. 3440 MARKET ST 1ST FL, TRAUMA CENTER AT PENN 19104 #035-06-1994 L1999 **CCS** *020 †85

PSHYTYCKY, Amir. ■ 19104 #550-02-1993 L2007 **CHN** *012

PUGH, Brian Franklin. ■ 19147 #041-02-2006 L2006 **EM** *012

PUGH, Meredith Evans. 3400 SPRUCE ST, 100 CENTREX, HOSPITAL OF T 19104 #051-04-2004 L2004 **IM** *100 †20

PUGLIESE, Steve Casey. ■ 19129 #041-15-2008 *012

PUGLISI, Anthony Stephen. 9880 BUSTLETON AVE, STE 22 19115 #041-09-1965 L1966 **ORS** *020 †40

PUJOLS-MC KEE, Ana Luisa. 51 N 39TH ST, PRESBYTERIAN MEDICAL CENTE 19104 #041-09-1979 L1981 **IM** *020

PULEO, Frances Joanne. ■ 19144 #041-15-2005 L2005 **GS** *012

PULVER, Sydney E. 1714 LOCUST ST STE 2 19103 #041-01-1953 L1954 **PYA P** *020 †75

PUMPHREY, Benjamin Griffi. ■ 19146 #051-01-2005 L2005 **P** *012

PUNJABI, Haresh Mohanlal. 2250 E ALLEGHENY AVE 19134 #495-01-1975 L1979 **FM FPG** *020 †18

PUNJABI, Kusum Arjun. 245 N 15TH ST, FL NCB 19102 #033-06-2005 L2005 **EM** *012

PUREWAL, Miteswar Singh. 51 N 39TH ST, PRESBYTERIAN MEDICAL CENTE 19104 #665-01-2001 L2001 **AN** *100

PUREWAL, Uplekh Singh. 51 N 39TH ST, PRESBYTERIAN MEDICAL CENTE 19104 #665-01-2001 L2001 **AN** *100 †05

PURI, Nitin. ■ 19145 #654-01-2003 L2006 **CCM** *012 †20

PURI, Rajan. 3400 SPRUCE ST, UNIVERSITY OF PENNSYLVANIA 19104 #539-03-2001 L2005 **GS** *012

PURI, Rajeev Naresh. ■ 19130 #033-05-2006 L2006 **GS** *012

PURUSHOTTAM, Bhaskar. 5501 OLD YORK RD 19141 #496-39-2001 L2006 **IM** *012

PUTCHA, Nirupama. ■ 19104 #001-02-2007 L2007 **IM** *012

PUTONG, Paul Bautista. 3401 N BROAD ST DEPT PTH 19140 #748-02-1949 L1973 **PTH** *020 †50

PUTTANNIAH, Suraj Vishakh. 3400 SPRUCE ST, OF PENNSYLVAN 19104 #041-15-2006 L2006 **EM** *012

PYERITZ, Reed Edwin. 3400 SPRUCE ST 19104 #024-01-1975 L1993 **MG IM** *030 †20,19

QAEMI, Roya. ■ 19128 #041-13-2005 L2005 **IM** *012

QAISAR, Muzammil M. KNIGHTS AND RED LION ROAD, DEPT OF ANESTHESIA 19154 #035-75-2002, ▲ L2004 **AN** *020

QASEEM, Amir. 190 N INDEPENDENCE MALL W 19106 #704-20-1994 **IM** *071

QASIM, Atif Nazier. ■ 19103 #023-07-2003 L2003 **CD** *012 †20

QATTASH, Ismail Musa Isma. 245 N 15TH ST MS 437, DREXEL UNIV COLL OF MED 19102 #575-01-2001 L2003 **NEP** *012 †20

QUADDOURA, Amer. 5501 OLD YORK RD 19141 #875-01-1993 L1996 **CCA** *020 †05

QUAN, Christopher Hing. 1000 WALNUT ST APT 1802 19107 #041-02-2006 L2007 **FP** *012

QUANG, Lan Ngoc. ■ 19144 #041-15-2007 L2007 **IM** *012

QUASHIE, Carlene Enez. 5501 OLD YORK RD 19141 #035-15-1984 L1986 **MFM OBG** *020 †30

QUEENAN, Maria Brescia. ■ 19103 #041-15-2007 L2007 **PTH** *012

QUIEN, Emmanuel. 2301 E ALLEGHENY AVE, 3RD FL 19134 #748-01-1988 L1993 **HO IM** *020 †20

QUIGLEY, Heather Forrest. ■ 19106 #012-01-2007 L2007 **IM** *012

QUIGLEY, Robert Lawrence. 3998 RED LION RD, STE 214 MED OFFICE BLDG 19114 #065-01-1982 L1995 **TS CCS** *020 †85,90

QUILL, Caroline Mayberry. ■ 19103 #035-45-2006 L2006 **IM** *012

QUILON, Augusto Mayor. 5501 OLD YORK RD, ALBERT EINSTEIN MED CTR 19141 #748-01-2001 L2004 **IM** *100 †20

QUINLAN, Jack Francis, Jr. 245 N 15TH ST, MAIL STOP 427 19102 #033-05-2002 L2002 **CD** *012 †20

QUINLAN, Patricia A. 111 S 11TH ST, DEPT OF INTERNAL MEDICINE 19107 #048-13-2006 L2006 **IM** *012

QUINN, Colin Christopher. 3400 SPRUCE ST, DEPT IM 19104 #051-01-2007 L2007 **IM** *012

QUINN, Dianne M. 1 PENN BLVD 19144 #036-07-1973 L1976 **PTH** *020 †50

QUINN, Graham Earl. 1 CHILDRENS CTR, 34TH ST AND CIVIC CENTER B 19104 #036-07-1973 L1976 **OPH** *050 †35

QUINN, Peter Dennis. 3400 SPRUCE ST, FL 5 19104 #041-07-1981 L1981 **FPS** *020

QUINTANA, Eileen C. 230 N BROAD ST 19102 #041-13-1995 L1998 **PEM** *020 †16

QUINTERO ARIAS, Christian. 3401 N BROAD ST, OUTPATIENT - OB/GYN 19140 #264-04-1997 L2002 **OBG** *100 †30

QUIROLGICO, Benjamin P. 136 DIAMOND ST 19122 #748-01-1955 L1985 **PTH** *071 †50

QUIROS, Emily Mathis. ST CHRISTOPHER'S HOSP, DEPT OF ANESTHESIA 19134 #048-14-1998 L2005 **PAN** *020

QUON, Harry. 3400 SPRUCE ST, 2 DONNER 19104 #065-01-1993 L2002 *020 †80

QURAISHI, Tariq Ahmed. 111 S 11TH ST, THOMAS JEFFERSON UNIV HOSP 19107 #033-06-1998 L2001 **DR** *100 †80

QURESHI, Azra I. 1602 E WADSWORTH AVE, EINTEIN COMMUNITY HEALTH A 19150 #704-06-1985 L1996 **IM** *020 †20

RA, Jin Hee. ■ 19130 #020-02-2002 L2002 **GS** *012

RAAF, Stephanie. ■ 19107 #409-16-1990 L1998 **N** *100 †75

RABER, Irving Melvin. 2818 COTTMAN AVE 19149 #062-01-1971 L1979 **OPH OS** *020 †35

RABINOVICH, Harris. 5501 OLD YORK RD 19141 #023-01-1969 L1988 **CHP P** *062 †75

RABINOVITCH, Hyman H. ERIE AVE AT FRONT ST UROL 19134 #065-01-1959 L2004 **U UP** *071

RABINOWITZ, Howard K. 833 CHESTNUT ST 19107 #041-12-1971 L1974 **FM PD** *050 †55,18

RABINOWITZ, Marc Scott. 9880 BUSTLETON AVE, STE 301 19115 #041-13-1986 L1987 **IM OBG** *020 †20

RABINOWITZ, Michael Paul. 5501 OLD YORK RD, A EINSTEIN MED CTR 19141 #041-01-2007 L2007 **TY** *012

RABSON, Moses. 5501 OLD YORK RD 19141 #041-13-1941 L1942 **ORS** *071 †40

RAD, Marzban. 132 S 10TH ST, UNIVERSITY HO 19101 #035-10-2005 L2005 **DR** *012

RADER, Daniel James. 39TH & MARKET ST STE 2A, UPHS/PMC CAMPUS PHI BLDG 19104 #041-07-1984 L1993 **IM** *020 †20

RADFORD, Shawn Christophe. ■ 19128 #016-42-2005 L2005 **EM** *012

RADZIEVKA, Ludmila A. 6722 BUSTLETON AVE 19149 #913-05-1981 L2003 **PYG** *020

RAFEEK, Jasmine. 245 N 15TH ST, DEPT OF GME 19102 #496-23-2005 L2006 **IM** *012

RAFFENSPERGER, Bruce W. 717 BETHLEHEM PKE 19118 #041-02-1951 L2005 **GYN** *071 †30

RAFFENSPERGER, Edward C. 3400 SPRUCE ST 19104 #041-01-1940 L1942 **GE** *020 †20

RAFFINI, Leslie Jane. 324 S 34TH ST 19104 #056-05-1996 L1999 **PHO** *020 †55

RAFIQUE, Zubaid Reza. ■ 19106 #026-04-2007 L2007 **EM** *012

RAGHAV, Kanwal Pratap Sin. 5501 OLD YORK RD, DEPT OF MED EDU 19141 #496-09-2004 L2006 **IM** *012

RAGHU, Madhavi. ■ 19106 #035-06-2003 L2004 **DR** *012

RAGLAND, Phillip Sherman. ■ 19131 #010-03-1999 L2006 **GS** *100

RAHIMI NAINI, Sohrab. 2900 W QUEEN LN 19129 #517-01-2000 L2006 **IM** *012

RAI, Manish. ■ 19130 #041-77-2005, ▲ L2005 **IM** *012

RAIBLE, Donald Geo. 216 N BROAD ST 19102 #008-02-1981 L1988 **PUD IM** *050 †20

RAICHLEN, Joel Stuart. 1025 WALNUT ST, STE 8439 19107 #041-01-1977 L1979 **CD IM** *020 †20

RAINA, Shiban. 700 COTTMAN AVE 19111 #495-51-1968 L1995 **IM** *020 †20

RAINES, Jonathan Mark. 800 SPRUCE ST 19107 #041-13-1982 L1983 **PYA P** *020 †75 ‡

RAINIER, Paul Charles, Jr. 1015 CHESTNUT ST, THOMAS JEFFERSON UNIV 19107 #033-05-2003 L2004 **ORS** *012

RAIT, Robin Michele. 6921 FRANKFORD AVE, STE A 19135 #035-08-1988 L1992 **OBG** *020 †30

RAITHATHA, Roheen. ■ 19104 #024-07-2007 **OTO** *012

RAIZEN, David Menassah. 3400 SPRUCE ST, DEPT OF NEUROLOGY 3 GATES 19104 #048-12-1997 L2000 **N** *020 †75

RAJA, Rasib. 5501 OLD YORK RD, C/O AEMC 19141 #704-01-1965 L1971 **NEP IM** *020 †20

RAJANALA, Susnita. 245 N 15TH ST, HAHNEMANN U HOSP 19102 #495-21-1995 L2007 **PCC** *012

RAJARATNAM, Emma Packiam. 2230 COTTMAN AVE, DEPARTMENT OF HEALTH - CTR 19149 #495-42-1970 L1973 **PD OS** *012 ‡

RAJENDRAN, Ramji. 19127 #016-11-2005 L2005 **RO** *012

RAJI, Rhoda Abisola. ■ 19144 #024-07-2008 *012

RAJMANE, Kiran C. ■ 19106 #041-02-2003 L2007 **DR** *012

RAJU, G Praveen. ■ 19104 #041-01-2001 L2006 **CHN** *100 †75

RAKEL, Birgit. 111 S 11TH ST STE 6215, CTR FOR INTEGRATIVE MEDICI 19107 #409-33-1988 L2001 **FM** *020 †18

RAKOCEVIC, Goran. 900 WALNUT ST, STE 200 19107 #957-08-1986 L2007 **N** *020

■ = Address Information Privacy Protected

RALPH, Pamela Joann. 1235 PINE ST 19107 #047-07-1990 L1992 **CHP P** *020

RAM, Nand. 1641 W GIRARD AVE, CORNER 17TH ST 19130 #649-33-1982 L1985 **IM** *020 †20

RAMAKRISHNA, Aneeta. 2900 W QUEEN LN 19129 #496-59-2001 L2004 **IM** *020 †20

RAMAKRISHNAN, Meenakshi. ■ 19103 #024-01-1999 L2004 **GPM** *020 †55,70

RAMAN, Jayalaxmi. 900 RONNIE CIR, STRAWBERRY MANSION HEALTH 19128 #495-77-1970 L1976 **PD GP** *020 †55

RAMAN, Tuhina. 1227 TASKER ST 19148 #495-27-1997 L2004 **PCC** *100

RAMANATHAN, Supriya. 3550 MARKET ST, FL 5 19104 #495-96-1991 L2006 **PD** *020 †55

RAMASUNDER, Shalini. ■ 19130 #033-06-2003 L2003 **ORS** *012

RAMASWAMY, Madhusudanan S. 1800 LOMBARD ST, GRADUATE HOSP (TENET HLTH 19146 #496-20-2000 L2004 **IM** *100 †20

RAMBARAN, Madan G. 100 E LEHIGH AVE, DEPT SURG 19125 #496-38-1978 L1992 **GS** *020

RAMCHANDANI, Dilip. 4641 ROOSEVELT BLVD 19124 #495-45-1975 L1979 **P** *020 †75

RAMCHANDANI, Parvati. 3400 SPRUCE ST, RADIOLOY DEPT UNIV OF PA 19104 #495-45-1975 L1979 **DR** *020 †80

RAMESH, Subhashree. 5501 OLD YORK RD, DEPT OF ACADEMIC 19141 #495-04-1996 L2004 **P** *012

RAMEY, John Robert. 1025 WALNUT ST, STE 1100 19107 #023-01-2001 L2001 **GS** *100

RAMINANI, Lokadri N. 2840 W DAUPHIN ST, STRAWBERRY MANSION HLTH CT 19132 #649-33-1982 L1984 **IM** *020

RAMIREZ, Carlo Gerardo B. 1025 WALNUT ST, THOMAS JEFFERSON UNIV HOSP 19107 #748-02-1985 L1996 **TTS GS** *020

RAMIREZ, Michael Jimie. 1328 W RITNER ST 19148 #041-13-1991 L1993 **HO** *020 †20

RAMOS, Gladys Amely. ■ 19103 #042-01-2002 L2007 **ORS** *100

RAMOS, Sarah Elizabeth. 833 CHESTNUT ST, STE 210 19107 #047-05-2004 L2006 **P** *012

RAMOSKA, Edward A. 245 N 15TH ST, MAIL STOP 1011 19102 #041-09-1981 L1982 **EM** *030 †16

RAMPURE, Ritesh Janardhan. 4TH FLOOR - S TOWER MAIL, DREXEL UNIVERSITY COLLEGE 19102 #495-09-1999 L2007 **IM** *012

RAMSEY, Kevin Paul. ■ 19118 #045-01-2004 L2004 **FM** *100 †18

RAMSEY, Matthew Lee. 925 CHESTNUT ST, FIFTH FLOOR 19107 #035-08-1990 L1992 **ORS** *020 †40

RAMSEY, Ramtin Thomas. 5501 OLD YORK RD 19141 #836-01-2001 L2006 **IM** *012

RANA, Mandeep. 1 CHILDRENS CTR, OFFICE OF MED AFFAIRS 19104 #495-55-1998 L2006 **CHN** *012

RANA, Sameera. ■ 19107 #041-02-2008 *012

RANADE, Ashish Sharadchan. ■ 19128 #495-28-1996 L2006 *100

RANALLI, Nathan Joseph. ■ 19146 #041-01-2004 L2004 **NS** *012

RANCHOD, Tushar Mahendra. ■ 19103 #005-02-2004 L2005 **OPH** *012

RAND, Elizabeth B. 324 S 34TH ST 19104 #016-02-1987 L1993 **PD** *020 †55

RANDALL, Terri Lamarr. 3440 MARKET ST, STE 200 19104 #010-01-2001 L2005 **ADP** *012 †75

RANDALL, Thomas C. 801 SPRUCE ST 7TH FL, DEPT OF OB/GYN PENN HOSPIT 19107 #023-07-1991 L1996 **OBG** *020 †30

RANDAZZO, Bruce Paul. 3400 SPRUCE ST, FL 2 19104 #035-48-1988 L1992 **D** *020 †15

RANDAZZO, Ciro Giuseppe. 909 WALNUT ST, THOMAS JEFFERSON UNIVERSIT 19107 #033-06-2003 L2003 **NS** *012

RANDO, Mary Josephine. 34TH ST AND CIVIC CENTER B 19104 #041-07-1956 L1957 **PD** *071

RANDOLPH, Frederick T. 1020 SANSOM ST, ALBERT EINSTEIN MEDICAL CE 19107 #043-01-2000 L2001 **EM** *020 †16

RANGANNA, Karthik Mudukut. 219 N BROAD ST, FL 5 19107 #495-09-1991 L1999 **NEP** *020 †20

RANI, Beema. 501 S 54TH ST, STE 196 19143 #496-11-1995 L2000 **IM** *020 †20

RANSOM, Evan Rogers. ■ 19146 #035-01-2006 L2006 **OTO** *012

RAO, Angara Koneti. 3400 N BROAD ST, TEMPLE UNIV SCH OF MEDICIN 19140 #495-36-1974 L1975 **IM HEM** *050 †20

RAO, Atul Sadashiv. 1015 WALNUT ST 620, CURTIS BLDG 19107 #033-05-2001 L2001 **GS** *012

RAO, Neeta K. 132 S 10TH ST, UNIVERSITY HO 19107 #033-06-2003 L2004 **DR** *012

RAO, Shilpa Bhaskar. ■ 19128 #047-06-2003 L2003 **IM** *100

RAO, Supriya. ■ 19107 #036-07-2008 *012

RAO, Venkatesh Ragothamar. 800 SPRUCE ST 19107 #495-35-1995 L2003 **IM** *100 †20

RAO, Vijay Madan. 111 S 11TH ST 19107 #495-36-1974 L1975 **DR RNR** *020 †80

RAPER, Steven Eugene. 3400 SPRUCE ST, FL 4 19104 #016-11-1980 L1993 **GS** *050 †85

RAPHAEL, James Stuart. 9880 BUSTLETON AVE, STE 22 19115 #035-15-1988 L1993 **HS** *020 †40

RAPP, Clyde Edward, Jr. ALBERT EINSTEIN MED CTR, PED RESIDENCY PROGRAM 19141 #038-06-1965 L1966 **IM GE** *020 †20

RAPSON, Alicia Kaye. ■ 19107 #041-02-2007 L2007 *012

RAPTIS, Derrick Nicholas. 2900 W QUEEN LN 19129 #422-01-2005 L2005 **IM** *012

RAPUANO, Christopher J. 840 WALNUT ST STE 920 19107 #035-01-1986 L1988 **OPH** *020 †35

RAPURI, Venkat Raghav. 1015 WALNUT ST, THOMAS JEFFERSON UNIV 19107 #495-50-1994 L2000 **ORS** *012

RASCOE, Philip Andrew. ■ 19103 #021-06-2000 L2007 **TS** *012 †85

RASER, Jonathan Matthew. 3400 SPRUCE ST, DEPT IM 19104 #005-02-2007 L2007 **IM** *012

RASHKIS, Harold A. ■ 19106 #041-01-1953 L1954 **P AN** *071 †75

RASHKIS, Shirley Reider. 111 N 49TH ST 19139 #041-07-1962 L1964 **P CHP** *071 †75

RASSADI, Siamak. 245 N 15TH ST, DREXEL UNIV COLL MED/HAHNE 19102 #517-01-2000 L2005 **IM** *012

RASTETTER, Rebecca C. ■ 19103 #038-45-1999 L2007 **PD** *020 †55

RATHNAKUMAR, Swaminathan. 31 N COLUMBUS BLVD 19106 #495-16-1974 L1980 **GS** *020

RATLIFF, John Kevin. 909 WALNUT ST, 2ND FL 19107 #021-01-1995 L2005 **NS** *020 †25

RATNER, Eric Rolf. 6200 FRANKFORD AVE, FIRST FLOOR 19135 #041-14-1989 L1991 **AN PME** *020 †05

RATTNER, Susan Lee. 1025 WALNUT ST, COLLEGE BLDG. 19107 #035-01-1978 L1983 **IM** *030 †20

RAUSCH, Mary Elizabeth. 3701 MARKET ST STE 800, UNIVERSITY OF PENNSYLVANIA 19104 #035-01-2003 L2007 **OBG** *020

RAVANDOOST, Parvaneh. 251 E BRINGHURST ST 19144 #517-01-1971 L1986 **FM ATP** *020 †50,18

RAVETZ, Robert Saml. 4641 ROOSEVELT BLVD, DEPT PSYCH 19124 #041-77-1957, ▲ L1958 **P OS** *071 †75

RAVIKUMAR, Rajan. 10125 VERREE RD, STE 106 19116 #033-05-2000 L2006 **AI** *020 †20,03

RAVIOLA, Carol Ann. 800 SPRUCE ST 19107 #035-01-1970 L1986 **GS** *071 †85

RAVISHANKAR, Chitra. 324 S 34TH ST 19104 #496-38-1994 L2004 **PDC** *020 †55

RAWDIN, David Eric. 3400 SPRUCE ST 19104 #041-13-1994 L2001 **PD** *071

RAWSON, Arnold J. 3400 SPRUCE ST 19104 #035-01-1940 L1948 **PTH** *040 †50

RAY, Firoza. ■ 19124 #495-32-1969 L1983 *030

RAY, Partha S. 3300 HENRY AVE, ALLEGHENY UNIV OF HLTH SCI 19129 #041-15-2002 **GS** *012

RAY, Pulak. ■ 19103 #023-01-2005 L2006 **NS** *012

RAY, Tarun Kumar. 3401 N BROAD ST, TEMPLE UNIVERSITY HOSPITAL 19140 #495-02-1968 L1978 **IM END** *020 †20

RAZA, Muhammad. 245 N 15TH ST 19102 #704-05-2000 L2003 **CD** *012

RAZEK, Tarek S. 3400 SPRUCE ST, DIV OF TRAUMA & SURG CRIT 19104 #067-01-1993 L1998 **CCS** *020 †85

RAZIANO, Donna Brady. 1210 N 12TH ST, STE 202 19122 #030-06-1996 L1998 **IMG** *030 †20 ‡

READE, Clifton Coleman. 3400 SPRUCE ST, OFFICE OF SURGERY EDUCATIO 19104 #051-01-2000 L2005 **TS** *012

REAL, Lawrence Alan. 4200 MONUMENT RD, BELMONT CTR COMP TREATMENT 19131 #041-01-1978 L1980 **P** *020 †75

REALE, Douglas Otto. 1020 LOCUST ST, STE 244 19107 #041-02-2000 L2001 **PTH** *020 †50

REBELE, Erin Catherine. ■ 19103 #033-05-2006 L2006 **OBG** *012

REBER, Mark. 230 N BROAD ST DEPT PSYCH 19102 #041-01-1978 L1979 **P PD** *020 †55,75

REDA, Thomas John, II. 399 S 34TH ST, LOWER LEVEL 19104 #041-13-2000 L2001 **FM** *020 †18 ‡

REDDY, Arpitha Muddasani. 2701 HOLME AVE STE 20 19152 #028-34-1997 L2007 **NEP IM** *020 †20

REDDY, Arthi Chenna. ■ 19107 #016-42-2006 L2007 **IM** *012

REDDY, Deepthi Shankara. 2701 HOLME AVE 19152 #056-05-2004 L2006 **FM** *020 †18

REDDY, K Rajender. 3400 SPRUCE ST, DIV OF GASTROENTEROLOGY 19104 #495-21-1973 L1980 **GE IM** *050 †20

REDDY, Karthik. 3400 SPRUCE ST, HOSPITAL UNIVESITY OF PA 19104 #496-01-1999 L2001 **IC** *012

REDDY, Kusuma Kumari E. 51 N 39TH ST 19104 #495-50-1969 L1986 **IM HEM** *020 †20,16

REDDY, Sridhar Kadumpalli. ■ 19107 #056-05-2007 L2007 **IM** *012

REDDY, Subash Chander. 7600 CENTRAL AVE 19111 #495-57-1974 L1984 **AN** *020 †05

REDDY, Sudha. 5401 OLD YORK RD, ALBERT EINSTEIN MED CTR 19141 #495-09-1996 L2001 **CD** *012

REDDY, Sudheer C. 3400 SPRUCE ST, 2 SILVERSTEIN PAVILION 19104 #035-03-2002 L2002 **ORS** *012

RED HAWK, Patricia Lynn. 510 BAINBRIDGE ST 19147 #041-13-2007 L2008 *012

REDNOR, Ronald Philip. 7503 BROUS AVE 19152 #305-01-1981 L1985 **IMG IM** *020 †20

REED, Charles Richard. ERIE AVE AT FRONT ST SCH 19134 #041-13-1966 L1967 **PD** *040 †55

REED, Elaine Louise. 4623 SPRUCE ST, UNIVERSITY CITY FAMILY MED 19139 #016-11-1984 L1986 **FM** *020 †18

REES, Christopher John. 800 SPRUCE ST, EMERGENCY DEPT 19107 #033-06-1989 L1991 **IM EM** *020 †20

REESE, James Jay. 111 S 11TH ST, JEFFERSON UNIVERSITY 19107 #021-01-2005 L2005 **PD** *012

REESE, Jennifer Michele. 3400 SPRUCE ST, UNIV OF PA HLTH SYS 19104 #023-01-2007 L2007 **PTH** *012

REESE, Peter P. 415 CURIE BLVD, RENAL ELECTROLYTE AND HYPE 19104 #023-07-1999 L2005 **NEP** *100 †20

REEVES, Kathleen Ann. 3509 N BROAD ST, TEMPLE CHILDRENS HOSPITAL 19140 #041-02-1991 L1994 **PD** *020 †55

REEVES, Phillip Roy. 111 S 11TH ST, THOMAS JEFFERSON UNIV HOSP 19107 #041-02-1999 L2001 **P** *020

REGAN, Carmen Louise. 3400 SPRUCE 19104 #539-05-1985 L1996 *100

REGAN, Raymond Francis. 239 E THOMPSON ST, UNIV HOSPITAL, 1020 SANSOM 19125 #035-01-1981 L1993 **EM IM** *020 †20,16

REGINA, Meredith Jan. 51 N 39TH ST, SCHEIE EYE INST 19104 #035-06-2005 L2005 **OPH** *012

REHMAN, Mohamed A. 3400 CIVIC CENTER BLVD, CHILDRENS HOSP 19104 #495-09-1986 L1993 **CCA PD** *020 †05,55

REHMAN, Saqib. 3401 N BROAD ST, DEPT. OF ORTHOPAEDIC SURGE 19140 #035-15-1999 L2004 **ORS** *100 †40

REICH, Alice. 225 S COBBS CREEK PKWY, COBBS CREEK 19139 #041-02-1990 L1996 **PD** *012

REICH, David J. 5401 OLD YORK RD, EINSTEIN MED CTR TRANSPLT 19141 #067-01-1989 L1991 **GS TTS** *020 †85

REICH, Jeffrey David. 2701 HOLME AVE, STE 101 19152 #012-05-1992 L1994 **U** *020 †95

REICHEK, Jennifer Laura. ■ 19147 #041-15-2002 L2002 **PHO** *012 †55

REIFE, Carol Marcia. 833 CHESTNUT ST, STE 701 19107 #028-34-1979 L1990 **IM** *020 †20

REILLY, Anne F. 324 S 34TH ST 19104 #041-02-1987 L1990 **PD** *020 †55

REILLY, John Patrick, III. ■ 19104 #035-19-2007 **IM** *012

REILLY, Muredach Patrick. 3400 SPRUCE ST, HOSP OF UNIV OF PENNSYLVAN 19104 #539-04-1988 L1997 **CD** *020 †20

REILLY, Patrick M. 3400 SPRUCE ST, 10TH FLOOR RAVDIN BUILDING 19104 #041-02-1987 L1993 **GS** *020 †85

REILLY, Theresa K. 2301 E ALLEGHENY AVE 19134 #041-02-1977 L1978 **OPH** *020 †35

REIN, Vanessa. ■ 19103 #035-47-2000 L2006 **END** *020 †20 ‡

REINECKE, Robert Dale. 840 WALNUT ST STE 1450 19107 #019-02-1959 L1981 **PO PD** *020 †35

REINER, Steven Leonard. 3400 SPRUCE ST, DEPT OF MEDICINE/1 GIBSON 19104 #036-07-1985 L1999 **IM** *020 †20

REINERT, Kristy Lynn. ■ 19103 #041-01-2008 *012

REINHARD, Joaopedro Alexa. ■ 19128 #041-15-2008 *012

REINHART, Raymond B, Jr. 4641 ROOSEVELT BLVD 19124 #041-13-1945 L1946 **P** *071 †75

REINHOLD, Caroline. 301 S 8TH ST, STE 4A 19106 #067-01-1984 L1990 **DR** *020 †80

REINUS, William R. 3401 N BROAD ST, TEMPLE UNIVERSITY HOSPITAL 19140 #035-19-1979 L2004 **DR** *020 †80

REIS, Edward. 4631 BALTIMORE AVE, MCKEE, SHEPARD & GRISKA ME 19143 #748-07-1989 L1993 **PUD** *020 †20

REISNER, Russell Mark. 1331 E WYOMING AVE 19124 #035-19-1989 L2007 **SO GS** *020 †85

REITER, David. 925 CHESTNUT ST, FL 6 19107 #041-09-1974 L1975 **FPS HNS** *071 †45 ‡

REITER, Michael Patrick. ■ 19119 #016-01-2002 *100

REIVICH, Martin. 3600 HAMILTON WALK, CVRC RM 415 STEMMLER BLDG 19104 #041-01-1958 L1959 **N** *050

REKANT, Mark Spencer. 834 CHESTNUT ST, STE G114 19107 #033-05-1994 L1999 **HS ORS** *020 †40

RELLES, Daniel Max. ■ 19103 #041-02-2008 *012

RELLOSA, Neil Gilbert. ■ 19106 #041-13-2006 L2006 **PD** *012

REMAKUS, Christopher Jam. 19111 #041-13-2004 L2006 **PCC** *012 †20

REME, Gerard Julien. 3333 N BROAD ST, RM 343 19140 #440-01-1960 L1967 **OBG END** *020 †30

RENDULICH, Karen Wirth. 321 W GIRARD AVE 19123 #041-01-2003 L2003 **PD** *020 †55

RENEDO, Dina E T. 3550 MARKET ST FL 5, PRIMARY CARE CENTER ON MAR 19104 #231-02-1974 L1987 **PD** *020 †55

RENGA, Rajan Natalayil K. 2751 COMLY RD, NORTHEAST WOMEN'S CENTER 19154 #495-38-1956 L1969 **OBG OS** *020 †30

RENGAN, Ramesh. 3400 SPRUCE ST OFC 2, HUP-RADIATION ONCOLOGY 19104 #025-01-2001 L2006 **RO** *100 †80

RENZI, Vincent Anthony. 1900 S BROAD ST, GROUND FLOOR 19145 #654-01-1985 L1990 **IM PD** *020 †20

RESHEF, Ran. 3400 SPRUCE ST, UNIVERSITY OF PENNSYLVANIA 19104 #550-02-1998 L2007 **HO** *012

RESNICK, Andrew Scott. 3400 SPRUCE ST, FL 4 19104 #008-01-2000 L2001 **GS** *100 †85

RESNICK, Matthew Jason. ■ 19107 #041-01-2006 L2006 **U** *012

RESNIK, Alan Michael. 1015 CHESTNUT ST STE 601 19107 #041-02-1973 L1974 **CRS** *071 †85,10

RESTREPO-ORMJBY, Adriana. 3509 N BROAD ST, TEMPLE UNIV HOSP 19140 #264-13-1989 L1995 **PD NPM** *020 †

RESURRECCION, Rosario. 5501 OLD YORK RD, STE 3 19141 #748-01-1958 L1971 **AN** *071

RETAMERO, Carolina Ines. 5501 OLD YORK RD, ALBERT EINSTEIN MED CTR 19141 #935-01-2002 L2004 **P** *012

RETHNAM, Rajesh. 8849 LISTER ST 19152 #495-63-1998 L2003 **PUD** *012

RETIRADO, Vincent Paul. 3400 SPRUCE ST, OF PENNSYLVAN 19104 #010-02-2003 L2003 **EM** *020

RETTIG, Jordan Sage. 3400 CIVIC CENTER BLVD, CHILDREN'S HOSP OF PHILA 19104 #008-02-2006 L2006 **PD** *012

REUMANN, Marko. 3401 N BROAD ST, TEMPLE UNIV HOSPITAL 19140 #154-07-1998 L2001 **N** *100 †75

REVOL-NUNEZ, Rafael J. 100 E LEHIGH AVE, MAB 305 19125 #132-02-1969 L1977 **PD N** *020 †55,75

REYES, Iris Maria. 51 N 39TH ST 19104 #035-47-1986 L1987 **IM** *020 †20,16

REYES, John Carlos. 5501 OLD YORK RD STE 1, ALBERT EINSTEIN MED CTRE 19141 #030-05-1996 L2007 **OBG** *020 ‡

REYES, Jose Manuel, Jr. ■ 19129 #041-13-2007 L2007 **GS** *012

REYES, Melanie Rose. ■ 19103 #041-15-2008 *012

REYES, Tyrone M. PO BOX 7618 19101 #748-01-1965 L1985 **PM** *100

REYES, Vincent Edgar, Jr. ■ 19107 #038-41-2002 L2002 **HO** *012 †20

REYNOLDS, Gary I. 700 ARCH ST, FED DETENTION CTR 19106 #010-03-1981 L1982 **PM IM** *020 †60

REYNOLDS, James Chas. 219 N BROAD ST, FL 5 19107 #011-03-1977 L1980 **GE IM** *030 †20

REYNOLDS, James Webster. 3550 MARKET ST, FL 4 19104 #041-01-1979 L1981 **PD** *020 †55 ‡

REYNOLDS, Patrice Webster. 9501 ROOSEVELT BLVD, FHCS PEDIATRICS 19114 #023-07-1999 L2004 **PD** *020 †55

REZAC, Mark Allen. 900 WALNUT ST, WILLS EYE HOSP 19107 #041-02-2000 L2001 **OPH** *020 †35

REZET, Beth Ellen. 39TH & CHESTNUTS ST #110, CHOP PRIMARY CARE CTR 19104 #041-13-1983 L1984 **PD** *020 †55

REZNAK, Stephen Edward. 1514 WOLF ST 19145 #030-06-1965 L1968 **N** *020 †75

REZVAN, Amir. 2900 W QUEEN LN 19129 #517-11-1999 L2005 **IM** *012

REZVANI, Iraj. 3509 N BROAD ST, TEMPLE UNIV CHILDREN MED 19140 #517-01-1964 L1972 **PDE PD** *012 ‡

RHEE, David Younghan. 840 WALNUT ST STE 1 19107 #035-09-1996 L2000 **MSR** *020 †80

RHEE, David Youngil. ■ 19107 #005-18-2003 L2007 **OPH** *100

RHEE, Soungok. ■ 19123 #583-08-1962 L1972 **CLP PTH** *071

RHIM, Andrew D. ■ 19103 #041-01-2004 L2004 **GE** *012

RHIM, Eugene S. 925 CHESTNUT ST, JEFFERSON HEART INSTITUTE 19107 #023-01-2000 L2001 **ICE** *020 †20

RHO, David Samsun. 10160 BUSTLETON AVE, STE F 19116 #035-01-1989 L2002 **OPH** *020 †35 ‡

RHOA, Matthew Finnerty. 3400 SPRUCE ST, HOSP OF THE UNIV OF PA 19104 #038-45-1989 L1992 **OBG** *020 †30

RHODES, Karin Verlaine. 3400 SPRUCE ST, HUP / DEPT OF EMERGENCY ME 19104 #016-11-1983 L2006 **EM PHP** *020 †16

RHODES, Larry Alan. 3400 CIVIC CENTER BLVD, CHILDRENS CARDIOLOGY HLTH 19104 #055-01-1984 L1995 **PD** *020 †55

RHODES, Robert Sander. 1617 JOHN F KENNEDY BLVD, STE 860 19103 #035-15-1967 L1997 **VS TRS** *030 †85

RIBEIRO, Rodrigo O L. 3300 HENRY AVE 19129 #187-19-1985 **IM** *075

RICCHETTI, Eric Thomas. ■ 19147 #041-01-2003 L2003 **ORS** *012

RICCI, Emily Kathleen. ■ 19107 #041-02-2006 L2006 **OBG** *012

RICCO, Ernest John. 800 SPRUCE ST 19107 #041-07-1984 L1986 **AN** *020 †05

RICE, George Edgar. 111 S INDEPENDENCE MALL E, THE BOURSE STE 968 19106 #051-04-1980 L1990 **PTH** *020 †50

RICE, Justin Lalor. ■ 19130 #051-01-2004 L2004 **EM** *012

RICH, Annasophie. ■ 19103 #041-01-2008 *012

RICHARDS, Nathan George. ■ 19107 #049-01-2006 L2006 **GS** *012

RICHARDSON, Paul Anthony. 221 N BROAD ST 19107 #917-22-1970 L1978 **DR** *040 †80

RICHERTS, Joseph Lester. 9501 ROOSEVELT BLVD, PENNSYLVANIA HEART & 19114 #024-07-1985 L1991 **CD IM** *020 †20

RICHMAN, Jesse. ■ 19107 #041-02-2007 L2007 **TY** *012

RICHMAN, Kenneth Allen. 3400 SPRUCE ST 19104 #041-01-1974 L1975 **AN** *020 †05 ‡

RICHTER, Joel Edward. 3401 N BROAD ST 8PP, DEPT MED-TEMPLE UNIV SCH 19140 #048-12-1975 L2004 **GE** *030 †20

RICKELS, Karl. 3535 MARKET ST STE 670 19104 #407-24-1951 L1959 **P PA** *050

RIDGE, John Andrew. 7701 BURHOLME AVE, SURG ONC 19111 #005-11-1981 L1991 **OTO GS** *020 †85

RIED, Stephanie Renee. 3551 N BROAD ST 19140 #025-01-1986 L1992 **PM PD** *020 †55,60

RIEDER, Evan Andrew. ■ 19103 #041-01-2008 *012

RIEGER, Wolfram. 3400 SPRUCE ST 19104 #407-05-1959 L1969 **P** *020 †75

RIEKE, Eowyn. 432 N 6TH ST 19123 #043-01-1999 L2007 **FM** *020 †18

RIERA LOSADA, Andres Rica. 5501 OLD YORK RD, DEPT OF GME 19141 #935-07-2004 L2005 **GS** *100

RIES, Rose Marie. 230 N BROAD ST 19102 #041-09-1981 L1982 **P** *075 †75

RIFE, Charles J. 840 WALNUT ST, STE 1020 19107 #024-01-1943 L1944 **OPH** *071 †35

RIGDON, Wilson Oliver, Jr. 1936 SPRUCE ST 19103 #067-01-1960 L1961 **U** *071 †95

RIGGIO, Jeffrey Mark. 833 CHESTNUT ST, STE 701 19107 #035-15-1997 L1999 **IM** *020 †20

RIGOGLIOSO, Camille Marie. 800 SPRUCE ST 19107 #033-05-1986 L1987 **IM FM** *020 †20

RIHN, Jeffrey Allen. 925 CHESTNUT ST, FIFTH FLOOR 19107 #041-01-2002 L2002 **ORS** *100

RILEY, Michael Patrick. ■ 19118 #041-01-2000 L2001 **ICE** *100 †20

RINALDI, Katherine Nicole. ■ 19129 #041-13-2008 *012

RINGE, Burckhardt. 216 N BROAD ST 5T, (MS 1001 19102 #409-38-1974 L2002 *020

RINTOUL, Natalie Ellen. 324 S 34TH ST 19104 #065-05-1995 L1998 **NPM** *020 †55

RISHEL, Megan Elizabeth. 245 N 15TH ST, EMERGENCY MED MS 1011 19102 #041-13-2006 L2006 **EM** *012

RITCH, Thaddeus David. ■ 19107 #041-02-2008 *012

RITCHIE, Wallace P, Jr. 1617 JOHN F KENNEDY BLVD, STE 860 19103 #023-07-1961 L1961 **GS** *020 †85

RITCHIE, Wm Galloway M. 3400 SPRUCE ST, DULLES BLDG RADIOLOGY DEPT 19104 #919-03-1964 L1976 **DR** *071 †80

RITTER, Deborah E. 111 S 11TH ST STE 8490G, THOS JEFFERSON UNIV HOSPIT 19107 #041-07-1973 L1974 **AN** *020 †05

RITTERMAN, Melissa Jan. ■ 19129 #041-13-2005 **EM** *012

RIVAS, David Aureliano. 833 CHESTNUT ST, STE 703 19107 #041-02-1984 L1985 **U PHM** *050 †95 ‡

RIVAS TORRES, Maria Teres. 1800 LOMBARD ST 19146 #649-01-1985 L2006 **P** *012

RIVERA, Alejandro. 3401 N BROAD ST, DEPT MED 19140 #042-01-2007 L2007 **IM** *012

RIVERA, Jaime Hernan. 340 N 12TH ST, ELDER HEALTH INC 19107 #024-01-1976 L1991 **PG PD** *071 †55

RIVERA, Veronica. ■ 19107 #041-02-2007 **FP** *012

RIVERA-COLON, Jorge Alber. 5501 OLD YORK RD, ALBERT EINSTEIN MED CTR 19141 #042-03-2004 L2004 **P** *012

RIVERO, Andres Jose. 5501 OLD YORK RD, STE 4 19141 #935-01-2000 L2003 **ID** *012 †20

RIVERO, Mariel. ■ 19106 #041-01-2006 **GS** *012

RIVIELLO, Ralph James. 1020 SANSOM ST, ROOM 239/THOMPSON BUILDING 19107 #041-09-1994 L1996 **EM** *020 †16

RIZZO, Ruth Louise. 1900 S BROAD ST 19145 #041-09-1977 L1979 **GS** *020 †85

RIZZO, Thomas Albert, Jr. 3996 RED LION RD 19114 #041-02-1969 L1970 **PTH** *020 †50

RO, Eric Youngkyoo. ■ 19131 #028-34-2003 L2003 **OTO** *012

ROBBINS, Elizabeth Leigh. 1233 LOCUST ST, STE 400 19107 #051-04-1988 L1990 **PD** *020 †55

ROBBINS, Susan Wenger. ■ 19151 #041-13-1975 L1979 **PD PHP** *030 †55

ROBERTS, Andrew Bayard. 3401 N BROAD ST, PARKINSON PAV - 4TH FL 19140 #026-04-1975 L1984 **VS GS** *020 †85

ROBERTS, James Robt. 501 S 54TH ST 19143 #041-02-1972 L1973 **EM** *020 †16

ROBERTS, Joan Mary. ■ 19118 #041-07-1946 L1947 **OBG** *071 †30

ROBERTS, Leigh Suzanne. 9622 BUSTLETON AVE STE 1 19115 #041-02-1995 L1997 **PD** *020 †55

ROBERTS, Richard Howard. 1100 ORTHODOX ST, MUTUAL PHARMACEUTICAL CO 19124 #041-01-1987 **IM** *030

ROBERTS, Robert Earl. 3401 N BROAD ST, TEMPLE UNIVERSITY HOSPITAL 19140 #041-13-2004 L2004 **PM** *012

ROBERTS, Steven Andrew. 9501 ROOSEVELT BLVD, STE 206 19114 #035-45-1986 L1990 **CD IM** *020 †20

ROBERTSON, Crystal Roxann. PO BOX 820933 19182 #041-09-1989 L1991 **IM** *020

ROBERTSON, John Frederick, Jr. ■ 19146 #033-06-2006 L2006 **FP** *012

ROBINS, Barbara G. 5800 RIDGE AVE, XRAY DEPT 19128 #041-07-1980 L1981 **DR NM** *020 †80 ‡

ROBINSON, Barbara Lynn. ■ 19106 #023-01-2005 L2005 **OBG** *012

ROBINSON, Claire Ebanks. 5401 OLD YORK RD, KLEIN 410 19141 #041-01-1979 L1981 **OBG** *020 †30

ROBINSON, Cynthia Brouse. 3400 SPRUCE ST DEPT PUD 19104 #041-02-1982 L1984 **PUD IM** *020 †20

ROBINSON, Jennifer Acton. ■ 19130 #021-01-2006 L2006 **OBG** *012

ROBINSON, Keith Michael. 801 SPRUCE ST, 3RD FL 19107 #041-01-1981 L1989 **AN** *020 †20,60

ROBINSON, Kevin Geo. 700 COTTMAN AVE, BLDG A 19111 #041-02-1977 L1981 **CD IM** *020 †20

ROBINSON, Kyle William. ■ 19128 #041-13-2006 L2006 **IM** *012

ROBINSON, Leon Reed. ■ 19119 #010-03-1955 L1956 **P** *071

ROBINSON, Martin Herman. ■ 19119 #023-01-1937 L1938 **IM P** *071 †75

ROBINSON, Nathaniel M. 5229 SPRUCE ST 19139 #056-06-1954 L1955 **IMG IM** *071

ROBINSON, Peter Nicholas. ■ 19104 #041-01-1991 L1993 *100

ROBINSON, Thomas Anthony. 1801 CHRISTIAN ST 19146 #041-02-1979 L1980 **FM** *020

ROBINSON, Tracy James. ■ 19128 #049-01-2004 L2007 **DR** *012

ROBY, David Stafford. 3401 N BROAD ST, STE 558 19140 #041-13-1976 L1978 **N IM** *020 †75

ROCCO, Martin James. 3800 SPRUCE ST 19104 #041-13-1982 L1983 **AN** *020 †05

ROCKEY, John Henry. 51 N 39TH ST 19104 #056-01-1955 L1975 **OS IG** *050

RODGERS, Gail Lesley. ■ 19129 #041-13-1989 L1991 **PD** *020 †55

RODGERS, John Martin. 2701 HOLME AVE, STE 101 19152 #041-01-1997 L1999 **U** *020 †95

RODGERS, Shuchi Kiri. 7413 GERMANTOWN AVE 19119 #033-06-1998 L2000 **DR** *100 †80

RODRIGUES, Eduardo Buchel. 840 WALNUT ST FL 14 19107 #187-17-1998 **OPH** *100

RODRIGUES, Joseph Venus. 5501 OLD YORK RD 19141 #495-52-1979 L1995 **AN** *020 †05

RODRIGUES, Neesha Ann. 19123 #008-01-2002 L2003 **IM** *012

RODRIGUEZ, Alexander. ■ 19104 #041-01-1995 *100

RODRIGUEZ, Carlos Rodolfo. 5735 RIDGE AVE, STE 105 19128 #737-01-1969 L1974 **OBG** *020 †30

RODRIGUEZ, Daisy Ann. 841 E ALLEGHENY AVE 19134 #041-01-1987 L1990 **AN** *020 †20 ‡

RODRIGUEZ, Estelamari. ■ 19103 #035-08-2002 L2005 **HO** *012 †20

RODRIGUEZ, George L. 841 E ALLEGHENY AVE 19134 #041-01-1985 L1986 **PM PME** *020 †60

RODRIGUEZ, Hope. 2920 W QUEEN LN # 452 19129 #041-15-2002 L2002 **GS** *100

RODRIGUEZ, Joseph A P. ■ 19104 #748-10-1994 L2004 **GS** *012

RODRIGUEZ, Maria Alexandr. ■ 19104 #030-06-2004 L2007 **CD** *012 †20

RODRIGUEZ, Maria Lourdes. 245 N 15TH ST, MCP HAHNEMANN UNIV 19102 #748-02-1996 L2004 **FPG** *012 †18

RODRIGUEZ, Oscar Manuel. ALUMNI AFFAIRS, ALBERT EINSTEIN MEDICAL CE 19141 #429-02-2006 L2007 **PD** *012

RODRIGUEZ, Samuel Thomas. ■ 19104 #041-01-2008 *012

RODRIGUEZ-JIMENEZ, Liza M. 5401 OLD YORK RD STE 401, KLEN MED BUILD 19141 #308-05-1999 L2001 *020

RODRIGUEZ-PAEZ, Alejandra. 5501 OLD YORK RD 19141 #264-01-2001 L2004 **RHU** *012 †20

RODRIGUEZ ZOPPI, Eduardo. 3400 SPRUCE ST 19104 #935-01-2004 **GS** *012

ROEDDER, Susan Louise. 5800 RIDGE AVE 19128 #041-13-1977 L1978 **IM** *020 †20,16

ROELOFFS, Susan Ann. 2129 W OREGON AVE 19145 #033-06-1984 L1985 **PD DS** *020 †55

■ = Address Information Privacy Protected

ROESER, Mindi Meltzer. 800 SPRUCE ST, EMERGENCY DEPARTMENT 19107 #023-01-1990 L1992 **IM** *020 †20

ROGALSKI, Matthew Joseph. 634 PINE ST, # 3 19106 #036-05-2005 L2005 **OBG** *012

ROGERS, Brenda Donaldson. 1999 W HUNTING PARK AVE 19140 #041-07-1986 L1988 **IM** *030 †20

ROGERS, Joseph Chas. ■ 19147 #010-03-1970 L1971 **P** *071

ROGERS, Marisa Ani. 5619 VINE ST 19139 #012-05-1999 L2003 **IM** *020 †20

ROGERS, R Claude. 3400 SPRUCE ST 19104 #781-01-1949 L1967 **PM** *071 †60

ROGINSKI, Raymond S F. 3620 HAMILTON WALK, 336 JOHN MORGAN BLDG 19104 #035-46-1985 L2002 **AN** *020 †05

ROITMAN, Harry B. 800 SPRUCE ST 19107 #041-01-1953 L1954 **GYN** *071 †30

ROJAN, Adam A. ■ 19103 #043-01-2007 L2007 **IM** *012

ROJAS, Job F. 6001 RIDGE AVE 19128 #176-03-1960 L1972 **PD** *020

ROJAS DELGADO, Francia He. 5501 OLD YORK RD, ALBERT EINSTEIN MEDICAL CE 19141 #264-01-2001 L2006 **IM** *012

ROJER, Charles Louis. 8815 GERMANTOWN AVE STE 16, CHESTNUT HILL HOSP MED OFF 19118 #041-09-1960 L1961 **OTO FPS** *071 †45

ROJO, Rodolfo Mancilla. 4711 WELLINGTON ST 19135 #649-31-1981 L1989 **GS** *020

ROLNICK, Barbara Susan. 5003 UMBRIA ST 19128 #041-01-1987 L1988 **PD** *020 †55 ‡

ROLOFF, Christopher G. 5501 OLD YORK RD 19141 #422-01-1999 L2001 **EM** *020 †16

ROMANO, Gary Jos. 219 N BROAD ST, FL 7 19107 #023-07-1992 L1995 **N** *020 †75

ROMANO, Janet Elizabeth. 1101 MARKET ST FL 9 19107 #041-07-1988 L1990 **OBG** *030 †30

ROMANO, Teresa Marie. ■ 19128 #041-15-2005 **PD PE** *012

ROMAYANANDA, Nongnart. ■ 19106 #891-02-1959 L1972 **OPH PTH** *071 †35

ROMBEAU, John Lee. 3401 N BROAD ST, TEMPLE UNIVERSITY HOSPITAL 19140 #005-12-1967 L1979 **GS NTR** *062 †10,85

ROME, Jonathan Jack. 100 N 20TH ST, STE 301 19103 #005-11-1982 L1994 **PD PDC** *020 †55

ROMERO, Lizeth Jovanna. 3401 N BROAD ST, DEPT OF MEDICINE -8PP 19140 #041-13-2006 L2006 **IM** *012

ROMINGER, C Jules. 501 S 54TH ST, MERCY HOSP OF PHILADELPHIA 19143 #041-02-1948 L1949 **RO NM** *020 †80,28

ROMMEL, Alan Jack. ■ 19103 #409-19-1969 L1977 **PA** *050

RONDON, Luisangel Alberto. 1800 LOMBARD ST, OFFICE OF MED EDU 19146 #935-01-2000 L2006 **GS** *012

RONIS, Tova. ■ 19106 #067-01-2006 L2006 **PD** *012

RONK, Virginia Suhrie. 5501 OLD YORK RD 19141 #067-01-1948 L1954 **IMG GP** *071

RONNER, Wanda. 800 SPRUCE ST, PINE BLDG 19104 #041-13-1984 L1988 **GYN OBS** *020 †30

ROOK, Alain Henry. 3400 SPRUCE ST, UNIV PENN HOSP DEPT DERM 19104 #025-01-1975 L1986 **D IM** *050 †20,15

ROPIAK, Raymond Russell. ■ 19147 #041-02-2004 L2004 **ORS** *012

RORKE-ADAMS, Lucy B. 324 S 34TH ST, CHILDRENS HOSP DEPT PATH 19104 #026-04-1957 L1961 **NP FOP** *062 †50 ‡

ROSA, Luis Antonio. 3400 SPRUCE ST 19104 #305-01-2007 **GS** *012

ROSALES, Gabriel Borbon. 100 E LEHIGH AVE, INDUSTRIAL HEALTH SERVICE 19125 #748-01-1962 L1976 **GS OM** *020 †85

ROSALES, Gerry Aguinaldo. 8835 GERMANTOWN AVE, CHESTNUT HILL HOSP 19118 #748-01-1988 L2003 **FP** *020

ROSALES, Noel Benitez. 3819 CHESTNUT ST STE 33, PRIMARY CARE CTR/ST LEONAR 19104 #005-19-1992 L2001 **PD** *020 †55

ROSAS, Sylvia. 415 CURIE BLVD, 111 CRB 19104 #264-10-1990 L1996 **IM NEP** *050 †20

ROSATO, Ernest Francis. 3400 SPRUCE ST, FL 4 19104 #041-01-1962 L1963 **GS GE** *020 †85

ROSATO, Ernest Lancelot. 1100 WALNUT ST, 5TH FL 19107 #041-02-1990 L1993 **GS** *020 †85

ROSCHER, Christopher Rene. ■ 19104 #041-01-2007 L2007 **TY** *012

ROSE, Andrew Baldwin. 1025 WALNUT ST, THOMAS JEFFERSON UNIV HOSP 19107 #035-01-2004 L2004 **IM** *012 †20

ROSE, Gilbert M. PO BOX 8299, WYETH LABS 19101 #035-08-1973 L1986 **PN** *020 †55

ROSE, Leslie Ira. 230 N BROAD ST 19102 #010-01-1964 L1975 **END DIA** *071 †20

ROSE, Lewis Jay. 1328 W RITNER ST 19148 #024-01-1978 L1979 **ON HEM** *020 †20

ROSE, Louis Frank. 100 S BROAD ST STE 2020 19110 #041-07-1972 **OS** *062

ROSE, Margaret Patricia. 3401 N BROAD ST, DEPT OF MED-8PP 19140 #045-01-2005 L2005 **IM** *012

ROSE, Marisa Zoe. ■ 19118 #041-01-2000 L2001 **OBG** *020

ROSE, Tokunboh Tinuola. ■ 19106 #051-01-2005 L2006 **P** *012

ROSE-GREEN, Gail Sue-Ann. ALUMNI AFFAIRS, ALBERT EINSTEIN MEDICAL CE 19141 #566-01-2004 L2007 **PD** *012

ROSELLI, Anthony Joseph. ■ 19147 #035-06-2006 L2006 **IM** *012

ROSEN, David. 2375 WOODWARD ST STE 112N 19115 #041-09-1962 L1963 **IM** *071

ROSEN, David I. 925 CHESTNUT ST, DEPT OF OTOLARYNGOLOGY 6TH 19107 #035-15-1991 L1997 **OTO HNS** *020 †45

ROSEN, David S. ■ 19106 #035-45-1996 L1998 **EM** *020 †16

ROSEN, David Scott. 3300 HENRY AVE, ALLEGHENY UNIV HLTH SCIENC 19129 #025-01-1984 L1998 **ADL PD** *040 †20,55

ROSEN, Eric Paul. PO BOX 3608 19125 #041-09-1970 L1971 **IM GE** *075 †20

ROSEN, Glenn David. 515 W CHELTEN AVE 19144 #041-02-1999 L2001 **FM** *020 †18

ROSEN, Harvey Mark. 301 S 8TH ST, STE 1D 19106 #041-01-1973 L1980 **PS** *020 †85,65

ROSEN, Howard Bernard. 4200 MONUMENT RD 19131 #041-01-1963 L1964 **P ADP** *020 †75

ROSEN, Ilene Michele. 3624 MARKET ST 19104 #041-01-1993 L1995 **SME PCC** *020 †20

ROSEN, Marc Robt. 925 CHESTNUT ST, NECK SURGERY 6TH FLOOR 19107 #035-15-1983 L1998 **OTO HNS** *040 †45 ‡

ROSEN, Marvin. 9331 OLD BUSTLETON AVE, SHGS JEANES TEMPLE MED CTR 19115 #041-09-1948 L1949 **GYN OS** *020 †30

ROSEN, Sally. 3420 N BROAD ST, TUSM DEANS OFF MRB 107 19140 #035-46-1976 L1979 **PTH** *030 †50

ROSEN, Sarah Janice. 834 CHESTNUT ST STE 400, BEN FRANKLIN HOUSE 19107 #033-06-2003 L2003 **OBG** *100

ROSENBACH, Misha Aaron. ■ 19103 #035-20-2004 L2004 **IMD** *012

ROSENBAUM, Carl Alan. 10160 BUSTLETON AVE STE A 19116 #041-07-1980 L1981 **IMG** *020 †20

ROSENBERG, Aaron Seth. ■ 19125 #035-47-2006 L2006 **IM** *012

ROSENBERG, Daniel Evan. 211 S 9TH ST, STE 600 19107 #041-14-2000 L2001 **END** *020 †20

ROSENBERG, Kenneth Carey. 1128 WALNUT ST # 401 19107 #041-02-1978 L1979 **CD GP** *020 †20

ROSENBERG, Lauren Sue. 525 JAMESTOWN ST STE 201, BAIOCCHI/ROSENBERG 19128 #041-02-1993 L1995 **FM** *020 †18

ROSENBERG, Philip. 7131 FRANKFORD AVE 19135 #041-09-1946 L1947 **PD PDA** *071 †55

ROSENBERG, Robin Eric. 9892 BUSTLETON AVE STE 206 19115 #041-13-1977 L1978 **CRS GS** *020 †10,85 ‡

ROSENBERG, Sara Gobst. 475 SPRING LN, THE RENFREW CENTER 19128 #041-07-1993 L1996 **P** *020 †75

ROSENBERG, Scott Bennett. 8815 GERMANTOWN AVE STE 12, PENN JERSEY PULM ASSOCS 19118 #041-13-1985 L1987 **PUD CCM** *020 †20

ROSENBLOOM, Joel. U PA DENTAL ANATOMY HIST 19104 #041-01-1962 **OS** *050

ROSENBLUM, Norman Glenn. 111 S 11TH ST # 6200, DIV OF GYN-ONC DEPT OB-GYN 19107 #041-02-1978 L1979 **GO GYN** *020 †30 ‡

ROSENFELD, Myrna R. 3400 SPRUCE ST 19104 #016-06-1985 L2002 **N** *020 †75

ROSENSTEIN, Kenneth I. 9880 BUSTLETON AVE, STE 218 19115 #041-13-1979 L1980 **P FM** *020 †75

ROSENSTOCK, Jeffrey G. 800 SPRUCE ST, PENNSYLVANIA HOSP 19107 #023-01-1968 L1972 **RO PHO** *020 †55,80 ‡

ROSENTHAL, Elan Howard. 3401 N BROAD ST, DEPT OF DIANOSTIC RADIO 19140 #041-02-2004 L2005 **DR** *012

ROSENTHAL, Herbert A. 5501 OLD YORK RD 19141 #041-02-1956 L1957 **IM PUD** *020

ROSENTHAL, Lisa Joan. 245 S 8TH ST, 2ND FL 19106 #016-01-2003 L2003 **P** *100

ROSENTHAL, Michael Peter. 1100 WALNUT ST, FIFTH FLOOR 19107 #035-03-1980 L1982 **OS** *020 †18

ROSENWASSER, Robt Hillel. 909 WALNUT ST, 3RD FL 19107 #021-06-1979 L1980 **RNR NS** *020 †25

ROSENWINKEL, Eric Todd. 5500 WISSAHICKON AVE M90AC 19144 #038-06-2001 L2001 **CD** *012

ROSENZWEIG, Andrew Brad. 3615 CHESTNUT ST, RALSTON PENN CENTER 19104 #041-13-2003 L2006 **IMG** *100 †20

ROSENZWEIG, Joshua Simon. 1810 LIACOURAS WALK, 4TH FL 19122 #035-08-2002 L2007 **OM** *020 †20,70

ROSENZWEIG, Martin H. 601 WALNUT ST, STE 960W 19106 #836-01-1985 L1990 **P** *030 †75

ROSENZWEIG, Steven. 111 S 11TH ST, STE 6215 19107 #041-01-1986 L1987 **EM** *020 †16

ROSER-JONES, Christopher. ■ 19104 #041-01-2007 **IM** *012

ROSES, Robert Edward. 3400 SPRUCE ST, MALONEY 4 19104 #024-07-2003 L2003 **GS** *012

ROSETT, Jeffrey Sylvan. 2601 HOLME AVE 19152 #041-13-1974 L1975 **FM FPG** *020 †18

ROSNER, Mara. ■ 19103 #021-01-2003 L2007 **OBG** *100

ROSNER, Michael Jeffrey. 4242 COTTMAN AVE 19135 #041-09-1978 L1979 **GE IM** *020 †20

ROSS, Ellen Irene. 833 CHESTNUT ST, STE 300 19107 #041-02-1984 L1985 **PD** *020 †55

ROSS, Judith L. 1025 WALNUT ST STE 726, DEPT OF PEDIATRICS 19107 #016-02-1977 L1979 **PD** *020 †55

ROSS, R Douglas. ■ 19103 #041-09-1974 L1975 **OBS GYN** *020 †30

ROSS, Richard Jay. UNIVERSITY & WOODLAND AVES 19104 #035-46-1975 L1983 **P** *050 †75

ROSS, Wendy Joy. 5501 OLD YORK RD, LEVY 2 19141 #035-47-1997 L2006 **PD** *020 †55

ROSSI, Adriana Cristina. ■ 19102 #010-01-2007 L2007 **IM** *012

ROSSI, Simona. 132 S 10TH ST, THOMAS JEFFERSON HOSPITAL 19107 #010-02-1998 L2001 **GE** *020 †20

ROSSMAN, Milton David. 3400 SPRUCE ST, 834 GATES BLDG 19104 #041-02-1970 L1975 **IM PUD** *050 †20

ROSSMAN, Ronald Eugene. 1800 LOMBARD ST 19146 #041-01-1965 L1966 **HEM ON** *020

ROSTAIN, Anthony Leon. 3535 MARKET ST FL 2, UNIVERSITY OF PENNSYLVANIA 19104 #035-19-1980 L1982 **CHP P** *020 †55,75

ROSTAMI, Abdolmohammad. 900 WALNUT ST STE 200, THOMAS JEFFERSON UNIV HOSP 19107 #517-05-1974 **OS N** *050 †75

ROTEM, Eran. 4TH FLOOR - S TOWER MAIL, DREXEL UNIVERSITY COLLEGE 19102 #550-01-2001 L2007 **DR** *012

ROTH, Ashley Ann. ALUMNI AFFAIRS, ALBERT EINSTEIN MEDICAL CE 19141 #422-01-2007 L2007 **EM** *012

ROTH, Howard Lee. ■ 19107 #041-02-2008 *012

ROTH, James Eric. ■ 19129 #041-15-2008 L2008 *012

ROTH, Jonathan Victor. 5501 OLD YORK RD 19141 #035-08-1981 L1985 **AN CCM** *020 †05

ROTH, Maurice K. 9150 MARSHALL ST, STE 4 19114 #016-06-1985 L1994 **OTO** *020 †45

ROTH, Serena Lauren. ■ 19143 #035-19-2007 L2007 **IM** *012

ROTHENBERG, Paul Louis. 3400 SPRUCE ST DPT PATH 19104 #028-02-1984 L1989 **ATP** *050 †50

ROTHKOPF, Brad Michael. 6231 OLD YORK RD 19141 #041-13-1971 L1972 **CD IM** *020 †20

ROTHKOPF, Henry. 5501 OLD YORK RD 19141 #023-01-1938 L1940 **IM AM** *071

ROTHKOPF, Jay Evan. 3401 N BROAD ST, TEMPLE DEPT OF ANES 19140 #041-13-2003 L2003 **IM** *012

ROTHMAN, Gerson Barry. ■ 19106 #041-02-1966 L1993 **R** *071 †80

ROTHSTEIN, Kenneth Dean. 5401 OLD YORK RD, STE 509 19141 #012-05-1986 L1989 **HEP GE** *020 †20

ROTHSTEIN, Robin Debra. 230 W WASHINGTON SQ, FL 4 19106 #041-07-1981 L1984 **IM GE** *020 †20

ROTMENSCH, Heschi Henjek. 1187 MOREFIELD RD 19115 #550-02-1974 **CD** *050

ROTTE, Masashi James. ■ 19147 #041-13-2008 *012

ROTTENBERG, Louis. 9300 FRANKFORD AVE 19114 #041-77-1966, ▲ L1967 **GP** *071

ROTTMAN, Steven Joel. HAHNEMANN UNIV HOSP, BROAD & VINE 19102 #422-01-2003 L2005 **GS HNS** *012

ROUGH, James Paul. ■ 19140 #041-13-2004 L2007 **GS** *012

ROULLET, Michele Renee. ■ 19130 #051-07-2003 L2003 **PTH** *100 †50

ROUMIANTSEV, Serguei Livo. 2900 W QUEEN LN 19129 #913-03-1980 L2001 **NM** *020 †28

ROUSTA, Sepideh Tara. 51 N 39TH ST, SCHEIE EYE INSTITUTE 19104 #035-48-1993 L1997 **OPH** *020 †35

ROVELSTAD, Susan Jennifer. 5501 OLD YORK RD, ALBERT EINSTEIN MED CTR 19141 #028-02-2005 L2006 **GS** *012

ROVERA, Giovanni. WISTAR INST 19104 #561-20-1964 L1974 **ATP** *050 †50

ROVNER, Barry Wm. 900 WALNUT ST, JEFFERSON HOSP FOR NEUROSC 19107 #041-02-1980 L1980 **P PYG** *020 †75

ROWE, Lee Dickinson. 2340 E ALLEGHENY AVE 19134 #041-01-1974 L1975 **OTO FPS** *020 †45

ROWE, Paul Alexander. ■ 19104 #836-01-1994 L1997 **GS** *100

ROWLING, Susan Elise. 3400 SPRUCE ST, UNIV OF PENN DEPT RAD/SILV 19104 #041-09-1987 L1989 **DR AR** *020 †80

ROY, Darshan. 3400 SPRUCE ST, UNIV OF PA HLTH SYS 19104 #035-03-2007 L2007 **PTH** *012

ROY, Dipanwita. 8556 BUSTLETON AVE 19152 #495-32-1985 L1993 **PD** *020 †55

ROZENFELD, Michal Rebeka. 5501 OLD YORK RD, ALBERT EINSTEIN MED CTR 19141 #550-02-2004 L2004 **PD** *100

RUBBERT-SLAWEK, Kerstin A. 3400 SPRUCE ST, UNIV PA MED CTR DEPT RAD 19104 #409-25-1992 L1998 **RNR** *020 †80

RUBEL, Martin. 135 S 19TH ST, STE 230 19103 #041-02-1959 L1960 **P PYA** *020 †75

RUBENFELD, Ira Geo. 1015 CHESTNUT ST 19107 #035-08-1980 L1981 **IM** *020 †20 ‡

■ = Address Information Privacy Protected

RUBENSTEIN, Arthur Harold. 3620 HAMILTON WALK, 295 JOHN MORGAN BLDG. 19104 #836-01-1960 L2002 **IM END** *030 †20
RUBENSTEIN, Craig Allen. 925 CHESTNUT ST, FL 5 19107 #041-13-2000 L2001 **EM** *020 †16
RUBENSTEIN, Ronald Craig. 324 S 34TH ST 19104 #048-12-1991 L1993 **PDP** *050 †55
RUBENZIK, Marc Kevin. ■ 19107 #003-01-2006 L2007 **D** *012
RUBERU, Monique Sarana. 245 N 15TH ST, OF M 19102 #048-02-2002 L2004 **OBG** *012
RUBESIN, Stephen Eli. 3400 SPRUCE ST, DEPT OF RADIO 19104 #023-07-1978 L1981 **DR PTH** *040 †80
RUBIN, Adam Ian. 3600 SPRUCE ST, UPHS DEPT OF DERMTLGY 19104 #035-01-2001 L2005 **DMP** *012 †15
RUBIN, Alan. 1905 SPRUCE ST 19103 #041-01-1947 L1948 **GYN** *071 †30
RUBIN, Alexander. 221 S 12TH ST 408S 19107 #550-03-2000 L2003 **CD** *012
RUBIN, Bruce David. 9807 BUSTLETON AVE 19115 #041-09-1998 L2000 **EM** *020 †16
RUBIN, David Michael. 3550 MARKET ST, FL 4 19104 #005-02-1996 L1998 **PD** *020 †55
RUBIN, Emanuel. 1020 LOCUST ST 19107 #024-01-1954 L1977 **PTH** *071 †50
RUBIN, Harvey. ■ 19118 #035-01-1976 L1983 **IM** *020 †20
RUBIN, Helen Metz. 1905 SPRUCE ST 19103 #041-07-1942 L1946 **AN** *071
RUBIN, Jonathan David. 230 N BROAD ST 19102 #041-09-1981 L1982 **DR NM** *020 †28,80
RUBIN, Joyce R. 801 SPRUCE ST 19107 #035-19-1981 L1982 **IM** *020 †20 ‡
RUBIN, Rachel Nicole. 3401 N BROAD ST, DEPT MED 19140 #035-45-2007 L2007 **IM** *012
RUBIN, Raphael. 132 S 10TH ST, STE 285K 19107 #024-05-1979 L1983 **PTH IM** *050 †50
RUBIN, Ronald Neal. 3401 N BROAD ST, TEMPLE UNIVERSITY HOSPITAL 19140 #041-13-1972 L1973 **HEM ON** *020 †20
RUBIN, S Bruce. 9807 BUSTLETON AVE 19115 #041-02-1964 **OBG** *020 †30
RUBIN, Sharon. 925 CHESTNUT ST, MEZZANINE LEVEL 19107 #041-13-1990 L1993 **CD** *020 †20
RUBIN, Stephen Curtis. 3400 SPRUCE ST, DEPT OB 19104 #041-01-1976 L1977 **GO GYN** *020 †30
RUBINO, Matthew Scott. 245 N 15TH ST, # 16TH-495 19102 #041-02-2007 L2007 **GS** *012
RUBINOW, Katya Bronwyn. ■ 19103 #008-01-2006 L2006 **IM** *012
RUBY, Marianne. 834 CHESTNUT ST STE M207 19107 #012-05-1975 L1976 **GYN REN** *020 †30
RUCHELLI, Eduardo D. 3400 SPRUCE ST, DEPT OF PATHOLGY & LB MDCN 19104 #132-01-1980 L1984 **PP** *020 †50
RUCKENSTEIN, Michael Jay. 3400 SPRUCE ST, UNIV OF PA HLTH SYSTEM 19104 #067-01-1986 L1998 **OTO** *020 †45
RUCKER, Donald Walter. 51 N 39TH ST 19104 #041-01-1981 L2000 **EM IM** *020 †20,16
RUDDOCK, Heather Ann. 432 N 6TH ST 19123 #041-13-1993 L1995 **PD** *020 †55
RUDENSTEIN, Robert Steven. 601 WALNUT ST, STE 640 19106 #041-12-1973 L1974 **END** *050 †20
RUDICK, Briana Jennifer. ■ 19103 #035-19-2004 L2004 **OBG** *012
RUDLEY, Lloyd Dave. 111 N 49TH ST 19139 #041-09-1981 L1982 **P** *020 †75
RUDNICK, Andrew Glenn. 9501 ROOSEVELT BLVD, PENNSYLVANIA HEART & 19114 #041-15-1999 L2001 **ICE CD** *020
RUDNICK, Michael Roger. 1800 LOMBARD ST 19146 #041-09-1972 L1973 **NEP IM** *020 †20
RUDNITSKY, Gail Susan. 3300 HENRY AVE 19129 #041-07-1982 L1983 **EM MPD** *040 †20,55,16
RUDOLER, Shari Beth. 111 S 11TH ST 19107 #041-01-1991 L1993 **RO** *020 †80
RUDY, Bret Jeffrey. 3550 MARKET ST, STE 1517 19104 #041-12-1985 L1987 **PD** *020 †55
RUFF, George E, Jr. 3615 CHESTNUT ST 19104 #041-01-1952 L1954 **P** *072 †75
RUFFIN, John Wesley. 3509 N BROAD ST 19140 #028-46-1993 L2003 **EM** *012 †55
RUFFNER, Nichole Denee. ■ 19129 #041-15-2008 *012
RUGGIERO, Francesca M. 3401 N BROAD ST, TEMPLE ANESTHESIA ASSOCIAT 19140 #008-02-1980 L1986 **PTH GE** *020 †50
RUGGIERO, Robert Paul. 2230 E ALLEGHENY AVE 19134 #016-43-1971 L1979 **GS NTR** *020 †85
RUIZ, Jose Manuel. ■ 19154 #847-08-1983 L1992 **END** *020 †20
RUMM, Peter Dennis. 1505 S 15TH ST, SCHOOL OF PUBLIC HEALTH 19102 #012-01-1986 L2004 **GPM PD** *030 †55,70
RUNK, Lorenzo Geo, III. 1514 WOLF ST 19145 #041-01-1963 L1965 **N** *071 †75
RUPANI, Harish. 230 N BROAD ST DEPT SURG 19102 #496-38-1970 **GS** *100
RUPPE, Michael David. 3509 N BROAD ST 19140 #038-43-2002 L2006 **CCP** *012 †55,20
RUSIA, Malini. 245 N 15TH ST, DREXEL UNIV COLL OF MED 19102 #495-77-1999 L2005 **RHU** *012 †20
RUSK, Matthew Harrison. 370 MARKET ST, STE 760 19106 #041-01-1992 L1994 **IM** *020 †20
RUSNACK, Susan Lauren. 950 WALNUT ST, APT 307 19107 #041-02-2002 L2005 **GS** *100
RUSSELL, Cathryn Louise. 8133 GERMANTOWN AVE 3RD FL 19118 #010-01-2003 L2005 **FP** *012
RUSSELL, James Eric. 3400 SPRUCE ST, 16 PENN TOWER 19104 #005-11-1984 L1986 **HEM ON** *020 †20
RUSSELL, Steven Ray. 1800 LOMBARD ST, OFFICE OF MED EDUCATION 19146 #033-06-1992 L1996 **PUD** *020 †20
RUSSO, Christopher John. ■ 19146 #033-06-1997 L2000 **PE** *100 †55 ‡
RUSSO, Gregory Adam. 111 S 11TH ST, CANCER TREATMENT 19107 #033-06-2003 L2004 **RO** *012
RUSSO, Irma Haydee. 333 COTTMAN AVE RM C439, BREAST CANCER RESRCH LAB 19111 #132-06-1970 L1991 **PTH OS** *020 †50
RUSSO, Jose. 7701 BURHOLME AVE 19111 #132-06-1968 L1991 **ATP OS** *050 †50
RUSSO, Pierre Anthony. 324 S 34TH ST 19104 #067-01-1978 L1984 **PD PTH** *020 †50
RUSTGI, Anil Kumar. 415 CURIE BLVD, UNIV OF PENNSYLVANIA 19104 #036-07-1984 L1998 **IM GE** *020 †20
RUTENBERG, Harold Louis. 230 W WASHINGTON SQ, FL 3 19106 #041-13-1960 L1961 **CD IM** *020 †20
RUTH, Corey Kades. 227 N BROAD ST, STE 300 19107 #041-02-1981 L1982 **ORS** *020
RUTHERFORD, Robert Howard. ■ 19118 #041-15-2007 L2007 **EM** *012
RUTKOWSKI, Paul M. ■ 19131 #041-77-2006, ▲ L2006 **IM** *012
RUTTENBERG, Bertram A. 3965 CONSHOHOCKEN AVE, CENTER FOR AUTISTIC CHILD 19131 #041-01-1946 L1950 **CHP P** *020 †75
RUUTIAINEN, Alexander Tuu. ■ 19104 #041-01-2008 *012
RUZINOVA, Marianna B. ■ 19115 #035-20-2005 L2005 **PTH** *012
RYAN, Julia Disabatino. 111 S 11TH ST, THOMAS JEFFERSON UNIV 19107 #041-13-2007 L2007 *012
RYAN, Kathleen Frances. 219 N BROAD ST, STE 8 19107 #041-09-1991 L1993 **IM** *020 †20
RYCHIK, Jacob. 324 S 34TH ST 19104 #035-08-1985 L1988 **PDC** *020 †55
RYNN, Moira Ann. 3535 MARKET ST, STE 670 19104 #033-05-1991 L1993 **CHP** *050 †75
RYNNING, Ralph Erik. 1015 WALNUT ST, STE 719 19107 #041-02-2002 L2002 **ORS** *020

SAAD, Ismail Rady. 333 COTTMAN AVE, MEDICAL STAFF OFFICE 19111 #915-02-1998 L2006 *100
SAADAH, Sarah Ellis. 321 W GIRARD AVE, HEALTH CTR #6 19123 #041-01-1995 L1998 **FM PHP** *012 †18
SABA, Sam Charles. 245 N 15TH ST, DEPT OF GENERAL SURGERY 19102 #033-05-2003 **GS** *012
SABERI, Poune. 8815 GERMANTOWN AVE, FL 5 19118 #024-07-1999 L2001 **FM** *020 †18
SABIR, Sajjad Ahmed. ■ 19104 #041-13-2005 L2005 **IM** *012
SABOGAL, Juan Carlos. 834 CHESTNUT ST STE 400, BENJAMIN FRANKLIN HOUSE 19107 #264-01-1993 L2007 **OBG** *020
SABOL, Mary Elizabeth. 3400 SPRUCE ST, UPHS - CARDO GRND RHDS PVL 19104 #041-02-1991 L1996 **CD IM** *020 †20
SABOL, Phyllis Jane. 3401 N BROAD ST, TEMPLE ANESTHESIA ASSOCIAT 19140 #041-07-1977 L1979 **ON** *020 †20
SABUGO, Evelyn Frances. 450 W DAUPHIN ST 19133 #748-01-1959 L1973 **PD FM** *020
SACHAIS, Bruce Steven. 3400 SPRUCE ST, HOSP UNIVERSITY OF PENN 19104 #028-02-1996 L1999 **BBK** *050 †50
SACHDEVA, Priyanka. 800 SPRUCE ST, DEPT OF MEDICINE 19107 #495-37-2001 L2006 *100
SACHS, David Morton. 255 S 17TH ST 19103 #041-01-1955 L1956 **PYA** *020 †75
SACHS, Marvin L. 3400 SPRUCE ST 19104 #024-01-1950 L1953 **IM OS** *020 †20
SACK, Martha Jane. 3400 SPRUCE ST, DEPT OF PATHOLOGY & LB MDCN 19104 #035-46-1986 L1988 **PTH** *020 †50
SACK, Stephen Zohar. 3400 SPRUCE ST, 2 DONNER 19104 #035-46-2002 L2003 **RO** *020
SACKETT, Daniel Dean. ■ 19147 #041-02-2007 L2007 **GS** *012
SACKS, Ellis Howard. UNIVERSITY OF PA, STUDENT HLTH SERV 19104 #041-09-1968 L1969 **PD ADL** *020
SADAPHAL, Elijah. ■ 19107 #041-15-2005 L2005 **EM** *012
SADEGHI, Homa Khomami. ■ 19144 #517-01-1971 L1978 **N** *050
SADEGHIAN, Mohamad Reza. 111 S 11TH ST, DEPT OF RHEUMATOLOGY 19107 #517-01-1971 L1976 **RHU** *100
SADEJ, Piotr. ■ 19123 #035-15-2006 L2006 **DR** *012
SADEL, Keith Eric. 9880 BUSTLETON AVE, STE 301 19115 #041-13-1997 L1999 **IM** *020 †20
SAEED, Amjad. 800 SPRUCE ST 19107 #704-08-1971 L2000 **GS** *100
SAEED, Muhammad Irfan. 245 N 15TH ST, DEPT OF GME 19102 #704-21-2001 L2005 **GS** *012
SAELENS, Alyssa Nicole. ■ 19130 #041-15-2006 L2006 **AN** *012
SAE-TIA, Sutthichai. ■ 19103 #891-04-1999 L2003 **ID** *012 †20
SAETZLER, Rainer K E. ■ 19130 #409-10-1993 L2001 **GS** *020
SAFAI-NILI, Firouzeh. 6122 RIDGE AVE, COMMUNITY COUNCIL 19128 #396-32-1992 L1997 **P** *020 †75
SAGALYN, Emily Blanche. 3400 SPRUCE ST, OF PENNSYLVAN 19104 #024-16-2006 L2006 **EM** *012
SAGAN, Michelle Lee. 34TH-CIVIC CTR BLVD, CHILDRENS HOSP 19104 #025-01-2002 L2007 **OP** *012
SAGAR, Utpal Navin. 834 CHESTNUT ST STE 61 19107 #033-06-2005 L2005 **IM** *012
SAGER, Jeffrey Seymour. 3400 SPRUCE ST, MED CTR/828 WEST GATES BLD 19104 #836-01-1995 L2001 **PCC** *100 †20
SAGREIYA, Siddharth. 8301 STATE RD, PHILADELPHIA INDUSTRIAL CO 19136 #495-47-1981 L1993 **IM** *020 †20
SAHA, Paban. ■ 19103 #028-02-2006 L2006 **IM** *012
SAHNI, Vaibhav. 245 N 15TH ST, DEREXEL UNIV COLL OF MED 19102 #495-45-2001 L2006 **IM** *012
SAHOO, Dipali. ■ 19127 #041-77-2007, ▲ L2007 **IM** *012
SAHU, Joya. 833 CHESTNUT ST, STE 740 19107 #041-02-2006 L2006 **D** *012
SAID, Yazan S. 909 WALNUT ST, STE 240 19107 #575-01-1991 L1996 **PDP** *100 †55,03
SAID SIRAJ, Elias. 3401 N BROAD ST 8PP, ENDOCRINE ASSOCIATES 19140 #366-02-1988 L2006 **IM** *020 †20
SAIGAL, Kapil. 925 CHESTNUT ST, FL 6 19107 #011-02-2002 L2003 **OTO** *012
SAILAM, Vivek Vardha. 1 FRANKLINTOWN BLVD STE 1 19103 #305-01-2001 L2001 **CD** *012
SAING, Minn Htut. 5501 OLD YORK RD, ALBERT EINSTEIN MEDICAL CE 19141 #041-15-2003 L2003 **ORS** *012
SAIR, Haris Iqbal. ■ 19131 #036-07-2003 L2004 **DR** *012
SAITTA, Sulagna. 3615 CIVIC CENTER BLVD, ARC1002 19104 #041-02-1994 L1997 **MG** *020 †19,55
SAJADI JAHROMI, Seyed Sae. 2900 W QUEEN LN 19129 #517-05-1999 L2002 **CD** *012 †20
SAKAMAKI, Misako. 1000 WALNUT ST, ORLOWITZ 1405 19107 #035-48-2005 L2005 **AN** *012
SAKS, Mark Ari. 245 N 15TH ST, MAIL STOP 1011 19102 #033-06-2002 L2002 **EM** *020 †16
SALAAM, Karriem Lateef. 833 CHESTNUT ST STE 210D, DEPT OF PSYCHIATRY 19107 #033-06-2000 L2001 **P** *020 †75
SALAHI, Ryan Arian. 245 N 15TH ST MS 310, DREXEL UNIV COLL OF MED 19102 #422-01-2004 L2006 **AN** *100
SALAHUDDIN, Zohra Gulnar. 111 S 11TH ST - 2170, OFFICE OF MEDICAL AFFAIRS 19107 #704-02-1982 L2005 **PAN** *100 †05
SALAND, Steven Benjamin. 1903 WALNUT ST, # 275 19103 #041-01-2003 L2003 **AN** *100
SALANON, Paul. 6326 RISING SUN AVE 19111 #005-17-1962 L1966 **FM** *020
SALAS, Sussan Janett. ■ 19106 #033-05-2007 L2007 **GS** *012
SALAZAR, Carlos. 136 DIAMOND ST 19122 #041-13-1956 L1986 **GS GP** *071 †85
SALCIDO, Richard. 3400 SPRUCE ST, 5 W GATES 19104 #649-33-1985 L1998 **PM** *020 †60 ‡
SALDANHA, Vilas. ■ 19144 #041-15-2007 L2007 **ORS** *012
SALDIVAR, Madelaine Ramos. 1427 VINE ST, FL 6 19102 #041-02-1995 L2005 **IM** *020 †20
SALERNO, Daniel Alejandro. 5501 OLD YORK RD, ALBERT EINSTEIN MED CTR 19141 #935-01-1997 L2007 **PCC** *100 †20
SALERNO, Denise Ann. 3509 N BROAD ST 5, DEPARTMENT OF PEDIATRICS 19140 #016-06-1993 L1995 **PD** *020 †55
SALESE, Leonardo. ■ 19107 #033-06-2005 L2005 **IM** *012
SALKO, Philip Anthony. ■ 19107 #041-02-2008 L2008 *012
SALMAN, Salam S. Ebrahim. ■ 19136 #797-03-1996 L2006 **PCC** *012
SALMON, Patricia Marie. ■ 19104 #041-01-2008 *012
SALT, Jessica. 833 CHESTNUT ST STE 70 19107 #051-04-2003 L2006 **IM** *100 †20
SALTZMAN, Erin Alyse. 9501 ROOSEVELT BLVD, STE 314 19114 #033-06-2001 L2006 **END** *020 †20
SALTZMAN, Leslie A. 1632 PINE ST 19103 #041-77-2004, ▲ L2006 **IM** *020
SALUDADES, John T. 3401 N BROAD ST, TEMPLE CHILDRENS EMERGENCY 19140 #748-02-1989 L1995 **PD** *020 †55
SALUJA, Guneesh. ■ 19131 #495-49-1998 L2005 **EM** *012
SALVA, Catherine Rose. 3400 SPRUCE ST, 5 PENN TOWER / DEPT OBGYN 19104 #035-01-1999 L2006 **OBG** *020 †30

SALVADOR, Agnes Simbul. 5501 OLD YORK RD, DIV NEONATALOGY 2ND FL 19141 #748-01-1978 L1987 **PD NPM** *020 †55 ‡

SALVADOR, Albert Simbul. 4507 N 5TH ST 19140 #748-08-1971 L1979 **GP** *020

SALVAGGIO, Christy Ann. ERIE AVE AT FRONT ST 19133 #041-02-1994 L1998 **PE** *020 †55

SALYARD, Lann Biddle. 245 S 8TH ST, HALL MERCER CMHC 19106 #041-01-1984 L1985 **P** *020 †75

SALZMAN, Brooke Ellen. 1015 WALNUT ST 19107 #041-02-2001 L2001 **FPG** *100

SALZMAN, Gary R. 5238 CHESTER AVE #028-78-1987, ▲ L1988 **GP** *020

SALZMAN, Matthew Scott. 5501 OLD YORK RD, KORMAN BUILDING B-6 19141 #041-02-2001 L2001 **ETX** *100 †16

SAMADANI, Uzma. 3400 SPRUCE ST, DEPT OF NEUROSURGERY 19104 #016-11-1999 L2001 **NS** *100

SAMADI, Faraz. ■ 19118 #041-01-2008 L2008 *012

SAMAHA, Frederick Ferris. PHILADELPHIA VA MED CTR, CARDIOLOGY SECTION 111-C 19104 #038-41-1987 L1995 **CD IM** *020 †20

SAMDANI, Amer F. 3551 N BROAD ST, SHRINER'S HOSPITAL FOR CHI 19140 #023-07-1997 L2004 **NS** *020

SAMHOURI, Farouq Ali M. 2137 WELSH RD, STE 1C 19115 #915-02-1970 L1987 **GS VS** *020 †85 ‡

SAMIMI, Farokh. 1800 LOMBARD ST, 1100 PEPPER PAV 19146 #517-05-1975 L1979 **GS VS** *020 †85

SAMINDLA, Kiran. 5501 OLD YORK RD 19141 #495-21-2001 L2003 **NEP** *012 †20

SAMLIN, Barry. 9122 OLD NEWTOWN RD # 44 19115 #041-09-1987 L1987 *020

SAMMARITANO, Donna Marie. 3550 MARKET ST FL 5, CHILDREN'S HOSP PRIMARY CA 19104 #041-01-1980 L1982 **PD** *040 †35

SAMPATH, Krishna. 1337 COTTMAN AVE 19111 #495-04-1970 L1979 **PD** *020 †55

SAMPATHACHAR, Kakkadasam. 6366 SHERWOOD RD 19151 #495-37-1960 L1973 **AN** *071 †05

SAMPATHU, Deepak M. ■ 19146 #041-01-2007 L2007 **TY** *012

SAMPAYO, Esther Maria. 324 S 34TH ST 19104 #035-46-1999 L2003 **PEM** *100 †55

SAMTER, Todd Alexander. 3300 HENRY AVE, ALLEGHENY UNIV OF HLTH SCI 19129 #041-15-2004 L2006 **AN** *012

SAMUEL, Michael Abraham. 840 WALNUT ST, STE 1020 19107 #047-07-1999 L2005 **OPH** *020 †35

SAMUEL, Rafik. 3401 N BROAD ST, TEMPLE HOSPITAL 19140 #041-13-1995 L1999 **ID** *020 †20

SAMUELS, Eyda R. 5501 OLD YORK RD, DEPT OF PEDIATRICS 19141 #715-01-1978 L1995 **PD** *020 †55

SAMUELS, Fania. 10752 BUSTLETON AVE, STE G 19116 #041-09-1987 L1988 **CD IM** *020 †20

SAMUELS, Leonard Edward. 230 N BROAD ST 19102 #038-06-1983 L1994 **EM** *020 †16

SAMUELS, Lleras Armando. 3409 GERMANTOWN AVE 11 19140 #715-01-1978 L1993 **NEP** *020 †20

SAMUELS, Marvin S. 135 S 10TH ST 19107 #048-04-1956 L1958 **OS FM** *071

SAMUELSON, Christian Gene. ■ 19115 #041-13-2007 *012

SAMUELSON, Marta C. 3401 N BROAD ST, 1ST FLOOR OPB 19140 #041-07-1965 L1971 **R OS** *020 †80,28

SANANMAN, Peter David. 5501 OLD YORK RD, DEPARTMENT OF 19141 #041-13-2000 L2001 **EM** *020 †16

SANBORN, Matthew Robert. ■ 19146 #010-02-2006 L2006 **NS** *012

SANCHEZ, Benjamin Jr. 3401 N BROAD ST 19140 #033-05-1995 L1998 **CD** *020 †20

SANCHEZ, Daniel. ■ 19144 #041-15-2008 *012

SANCHEZ, Mark F. 3401 N BROAD ST, OF S 19140 #035-45-2003 L2003 **GS** *012

SANDA, Marie. PO BOX 8299 19101 #286-02-1965 *050

SANDEL, Kristen Michele. 245 N 15TH ST OFC 2, MAILSTOP 1011 19102 #041-12-2002 L2002 **EM** *020 †16

SANDERS, Jaime Allison. ■ 19107 #041-02-2008 *012

SANDERS, Joseph A. ■ 19104 #041-15-2008 *012

SANDIFORD, Patricia Carol. 8733 FRANKFORD AVE, FRANKFORD AVE PEDS 19136 #010-03-1975 L1998 **PD OS** *020 †55

SANDILYA, Vijay Krishna. 2900 W QUEEN LN, DEPT OF INTERNAL MED 19129 #496-09-2003 L2004 **HO** *012 †12

SANDORFI, Nora. 1015 WALNUT ST, STE 613 19107 #473-01-1989 L1998 **RHU IM** *020 †20

SANDROW, Francine C. 1800 LOMBARD ST 19146 #041-02-1998 L2000 **EM** *020 †16

SANFILIPPO, James Arthur. 1015 CHESTNUT ST, THOMAS JEFFERSON UNIV 19107 #033-05-2003 L2003 **ORS** *012

SANFORD, Britt Edward. 111 S 11TH ST, DEPT SURGERY 19107 #041-02-1994 L1996 **DR** *100

SANFORD, Stewart Oliver. ■ 19130 #047-05-2006 L2006 **EM** *012

SANGUINETI, Vincenzo R. 1015 CHESTNUT ST STE 825 19107 #561-03-1965 L1988 **P** *072 †75

SANKAR, Prithvi S. 51 N 39TH ST 19104 #051-01-1996 L2000 **OPH** *020 †35

SANKOORIKAL, Binu-John Va. ■ 19128 #038-06-2007 L2007 *012

SAN PEDRO, Floro D. ■ 19153 #748-01-1965 L1974 **IM CD** *020

SANTAMARINA, Leo. 9126 BLUE GRASS RD 19114 #033-06-1988 L1990 **OPH OS** *020 †35

SANTANA, Leonardo Alexand. ■ 19128 #041-15-2008 *012

SANTIAGO, Reynaldo Lacson. ■ 19115 #748-13-1980 L1983 **P** *075

SANTIAGO, Stanley. 100 E LEHIGH AVE, CHC-2 19125 #042-01-1993 L1997 **OBG** *020 †30

SANTILLANO, Eugene C. 8815 GERMANTOWN AVE, FL 5 19118 #041-15-2003 L2004 **FM OBS** *040 †18

SANTILLANO, Jessica Stace. 3401 N BROAD ST, OF S 19140 #041-13-2005 L2005 **GS** *012

SANTORA, Thomas Anthony. 3300 HENRY AVE 19129 #038-41-1984 L1990 **GS CCM** *020 †85

SANTORE, Matthew Thomas. 3400 SPRUCE ST, DEPARTMENT OF SURGERY- 4 M 19104 #016-02-2005 L2005 **GS** *012

SANTOS, Nelson R. 833 CHESTNUT ST STE 300, PEDIATRICS 19107 #308-04-1988 L1998 **PD** *020 †55

SANTOS, Zorina P Lavares. 3340 S BROAD ST, STADIUM CAMPUS 19145 #748-08-1962 L1973 **AN** *020 †05

SANUCK, Neil Michael. 3401 N BROAD ST, MED ARTS BLDG STE 105 19140 #041-13-2006 L2006 **P** *012

SAPANARA, Nancy Lauren. 2900 W QUEEN LN 19129 #051-04-1996 L2000 **PTH** *100 †50

SAPIENZA, Anthony. 313 BAINBRIDGE ST 19147 #041-15-2005 L2005 **ORS** *012

SAPIRA, Valdi. 2601 HOLME AVE, NAZARETH HOSPITAL-ER 19152 #781-01-1987 L1995 **IM EM** *020

SAPONARA, Fiorella Karina. ■ 19146 #041-01-2008 *012

SAPRA, Ravi Kant. 5735 RIDGE AVE #495-05-1962 L1971 **N P** *020

SAPUTRA, Budi Jayadi. 501 S 54TH ST 19143 #506-01-1999 L2001 **AN** *020 †05

SARANI, Babak. 3440 MARKET ST, FIRST FLOOR 19104 #010-01-1997 L2004 **CCS** *100 †85

SARDI, Alejandro Humberto. 5501 OLD YORK RD 19141 #935-02-1998 L2004 **PCC** *012 †20

SARDI, Gabriel Luis. 5501 OLD YORK RD 19141 #935-02-1997 L2004 **IM** *100 †20

SAREEN, Amit. 3400 SPRUCE ST, OF PENNSYLVAN 19104 #035-46-2003 L2003 **EM** *100

SARELI, Aharon Eliezer. 5501 OLD YORK RD, ALBERT EINSTEIN MED CTR 19141 #836-01-1997 L2001 **PCC** *012

SARGEANT, Delwyn Henson. 5753 WAYNE AVE 19144 #041-13-1991 L1993 **IM** *020 †20

SARIYA, Dinesh Rajmal. ■ 19111 #495-83-1992 L2003 **PTH** *100 †50

SARKAR, Monika Anne. ■ 19104 #005-02-2006 L2006 **IM** *012

SARKAR, Priyankar Pankaj. 5501 OLD YORK RD, OFFICE OF ACADEMIC 19141 #495-01-2004 L2006 **P** *012

SARKAR, Sameer Prasanna. MED COLL PA AFFIL HOSPS, DEPT-PSYCH 19129 #495-02-1987 L1998 **P** *020 †75

SARKIS, Mikhael Hanna. 111 S 11TH ST, G8490 19107 #605-03-1998 L2001 **AN** *020 †05

SARMA, Akkaraju V N. 5656 CHEW AVE, 2135 EAST CHELTEN AVE 19138 #649-33-1980 L1982 **IM FM** *020

SARMA, Deba. 950 WALNUT ST APT 707 19107 #041-02-2004 **GS** *100

SAROHA, Sunil. 1800 LOMBARD ST, GRADUATE HOSP (TENET HLTH 19146 #495-36-2002 L2004 **IM** *100 †20

SARRELL, E Michael. 1015 CHESTNUT ST STE 4 19107 #308-03-1980 L1983 **PD PDA** *020 †55

SARWAR, Ahmad Bilal. 245 N 15TH ST, DEPT OF GME 19102 #704-01-2004 L2006 **IM** *012

SARWAR, Ch Muhammad Shahb. 3400 SPRUCE ST 19104 #704-25-2004 L2006 **GS** *012

SASKEN, Harvey Franklin. ■ 19103 #041-02-1971 L2001 **PTH** *020

SASS, David Alan. 216 N BROAD ST, FEINSTEIN 504 19102 #836-02-1992 L1999 **GE** *020 †20

SATALOFF, Dahlia Mishell. 700 SPRUCE ST STE B03 19106 #025-01-1978 L1979 **GS** *020 †85 ‡

SATALOFF, Joseph. 1721 PINE ST 19103 #041-09-1943 L1944 **OTO LM** *030 †45

SATALOFF, Robert T. 219 N BROAD ST, STE FL10 19107 #041-02-1975 L1976 **OTO NO** *020 †45

SATANARAYANA, Venkata V. ■ 19104 #495-11-1958 L2006 **U** *100

SATO, Takami. 1015 WALNUT ST STE 1024 19107 #572-72-1980 L1992 **ON PHO** *050

SATTEL, Lisa Ellen. 3340 S BROAD ST, WILLS SURGERY CTR 19145 #025-12-1987 L1992 **AN** *020 †05

SATTEN, Neal Richard. 5700 RIDGE AVE, STE 100A 19128 #024-01-1975 L1976 **P** *020 †75 ‡

SATTENBERG, Ronald Jay. 5501 OLD YORK RD, DEPT OF RADIOLOGY 19141 #035-46-1993 L2002 **RNR** *020 †80

SATTI, Sudhakar Reddy. ■ 19146 #041-15-2002 L2002 **RNR** *012 †80

SATZ, Wayne Allen. 3401 N BROAD ST FL JH, TEMPLE UNIVERSITY HOSPITAL 19140 #041-13-1992 L1994 **EM** *020 †16

SAUCO, Conchita Tiongson. ANDORRA SHOPPING CENTER 19128 #748-01-1957 L1967 **OBG** *071 †30

SAUKSCHUBERT, Calies Desi. ■ 19103 #041-01-2005 L2005 **PD** *012

SAUL, Albert. 1900 S BROAD ST 19145 #041-13-1979 L1980 **CD IM** *020 †20

SAUL, Richard Bertrand. 1601 WALNUT ST 19102 #035-09-1960 L1962 **P** *020 †75

SAUNDERS, Alishia Ann. 5630 CHESTNUT ST 19139 #041-02-2002 L2002 **IM** *020 †20

SAVAGE, Michael P. 925 CHESTNUT ST, JEFFERSON HEART INSTITUTE 19107 #041-02-1980 L1983 **CD IC** *020 †20

SAVAR, Louis. ■ 19104 #005-02-2007 L2007 **TY** *012

SAVARESE, Vincent William. ■ 19147 #041-02-2004 L2004 **END** *012 †20

SAVINO, Joseph Silio. 3400 SPRUCE ST 19104 #024-01-1984 L1986 **AN** *020 †05

SAVINO, Peter Joseph. 8025 ROOSEVELT BLVD 19152 #561-01-1968 L1970 **OPH** *020 †35

SAVIO, Peter James. 245 N 15TH ST, OF M 19102 #041-15-2005 L2005 **EM** *012

SAVITZ, Ariel Austryn. ■ 19129 #041-15-2008 *012

SAVITZ, Jodi Michelle. 3400 SPRUCE ST, 2009 PENN TOWER 19104 #024-01-2001 L2001 **IM** *100

SAXENA, Anurag. HOSP OF THE UNIV PA, DEPT PATH 19104 #496-09-1982 L1994 **HMP ATP** *075 †50

SAXENA, Archana. 3401 N BROAD ST, PARKINSON PAVILLION 19140 #041-02-2002 L2005 **CD** *012 †20

SAYDAM, Tippi Cicek. ■ 19104 #005-11-1997 L1999 **PDS** *100

SAYER, Gabriel Tal. ■ 19103 #041-01-2004 L2005 **IM** *100 †20

SAYLES, Erik M. 2900 W QUEEN LN, DREXEL UNIV COLL OF MED 19129 #041-15-2006 L2006 **GS** *012

SBAR, Wingkan Winnie. ■ 19104 #041-02-2006 L2006 **OBG** *012

SBARBARO, James Andrew, Jr. ■ 19104 #041-01-2004 L2004 *100

SCACHERI, Jennifer Elaine. 111D N 11TH ST, DEPT MED 19107 #036-05-1993 L1994 **IM** *100

SCALIA, Roy Francis. ■ 19154 #539-05-1972 L1983 **GS GP** *020

SCARAZZINI, Linda Jean. 1800 LOMBARD ST, SUITE 505 PEPPER PAVILION 19146 #041-13-1994 L1997 **IM** *050 †20

SCARFONE, Richard J. 324 S 34TH ST 19104 #035-06-1987 L1989 **PD** *020 †55

SCARIATO, Albert F. 5501 OLD YORK RD 19141 #041-02-1980 L1982 **RO** *075 †80

SCHACHT, Edward Lewis. 111 S 11TH ST 19107 #051-01-1982 L1983 **CHP** *020 †75

SCHACHTER, Bonnie Kempner. 9880 BUSTLETON AVE STE 214 19115 #041-01-1994 L1997 **FM** *020 †18

SCHACHTNER, Susan Kay. 3516 CIVIC CENTER BLVD, PHILADELPHIA, CARDIOLOGY 19104 #018-03-1989 L1995 **PDC** *050 †55

SCHAEFER, Paul Martin. 4900 WYALUSING AVE, CHILD PSYCHIATRY 19131 #041-13-1985 L1986 **P** *020 †75

SCHAEFFER, Reena C. ■ 19106 #041-13-2005 L2005 **PTH** *100

SCHAEFFER, Susan Alice. 1316 W ONTARIO ST 19140 #035-46-1992 L1995 **IM** *020 †20

SCHAEFFNER, Elke Susanne. ■ 19140 #409-05-1997 *050

SCHAFER, Charles Henry. 2701 HOLME AVE, STE 104 19152 #033-06-1982 L1984 **GS** *020 †85

SCHAFFER, Alyssa Anne. ■ 19139 #041-13-2003 L2004 **ORS** *012

SCHAFFER, Andras. ■ 19130 #473-03-1993 L2004 **DMP** *012 †12

SCHAFFER, David Bernard. 1 CHILDRENS CTR, 34TH & CIVIC CTR BLVD 19104 #041-01-1963 L1964 **OPH PO** *071 †35

SCHAFFER, David Wm. 2701 HOLME AVE 19152 #041-13-1958 L1959 **AN PUD** *071 †05

SCHAMBRON-COOPER, Denise. 3400 SPRUCE ST, HOSP UNIV OF PA 19104 #041-13-1991 L1995 **AN** *020 †05

SCHAPIRO, Gregory David. 3998 RED LION RD, STE 240/207 19114 #041-02-1990 L1993 **GE** *020 †20 ‡

SCHARF, Joshua Lee. 3401 N BROAD ST, KRESGE BLDG, STE 102 19140 #041-15-2001 L2001 **OTO** *020

SCHATANOFF, Joseph. ■ 19106 #041-13-1959 L1960 **DIA IM** *071 †20

SCHECKER, Neil Howard. 111 N 49TH ST 19139 #041-01-1987 L1988 **P** *020 †75

SCHEIB, Stacey Ann. ■ 19128 #041-15-2004 L2004 **OBG** *012

SCHERE, Daniel Ignacio. ■ 19107 #132-01-2001 L2004 **N** *100

SCHERER, Peter Wm. 3400 SPRUCE ST, DEPT BIOENGINEER 19104 #008-01-1973 L1977 **PTH** *050

SCHERER, Steven Simon. 3400 SPRUCE ST 19104 #025-01-1985 L1986 **N** *050 †75

SCHERR, Stuart Allen. 8020 CASTOR AVE 19152 #041-02-1971 L1973 **OTO** *020 †45

SCHERZER, Leah. ERIE AVE AT FRONT, ST CHRISTOPHERS HOSP 19134 #043-01-2006 L2006 **PD** *012

SCHICK, Paul Kenneth. 1015 WALNUT ST 19107 #024-05-1961 L1965 **HEM ON** *050 †20

SCHIFFMAN, Melissa Gail. 345 E MOUNT AIRY AVE 19119 #012-05-1997 L1999 **IM** *020 †20

SCHIFFMAN, Raymond Jack. 1325 MAIN ST STE 263 MAIN, SEC SURG PATHOLOGY 19107 #041-02-1959 L1960 **ATP OS** *071 †50

SCHILDER, Russell J. 333 COTTMAN AVE 19111 #011-02-1983 L1984 **IM ON** *020 †20

SCHILLINGER, Kurt Jacob. ■ 19104 #048-04-2006 L2006 **IM** *012

SCHIMMER, Barry Michael. 822 PINE ST STE 1C, RHEUMATOLOGY ASSOC PC 19107 #035-46-1970 L1971 **RHU** *020 †20 ‡

SCHINA, Michael J, Jr. 3401 N BROAD ST 19140 #041-12-1983 L1986 **VS TRS** *020 †85

SCHINDLER, Alan Michael. 5501 OLD YORK RD, ALBERT EINSTEIN MED CTR 19141 #041-07-1977 L1979 **PD END** *020 †55

SCHINDLER, Barbara Ann. 4700 WISSAHICKON AVE, STE 102 19144 #041-07-1970 L1971 **P PYM** *040 †75

SCHLAEPFER, William Wirth. 3400 SPRUCE ST, DEPT OF PATHOLGY & LB MDCN 19104 #008-01-1958 L1979 **PTH** *020 †50

SCHLAGER, Franz Michael. 324 S 34TH ST 19104 #409-05-1971 L1981 **P CHP** *020 †55,75

SCHLECHT, Hans Peter. 245 N 15TH ST, MAILSTOP 461 19102 #033-05-2000 L2007 **ID** *100 †20

SCHLEELEIN, Laura. ■ 19127 #035-45-2003 L2003 **PAN** *012

SCHLESINGER, Eric. ■ 19107 #041-15-2008 *012

SCHLESINGER, Robert Barry. 9501 ROOSEVELT BLVD, PENNSYLVANIA HEART & 19114 #041-02-1982 L1983 **CD IM** *020 †20

SCHLESS, Guy Lacy. 700 SPRUCE ST, 304 DUNCAN BLDG 19106 #041-02-1955 L1956 **DIA END** *020 ‡

SCHLICHTER, Rolf A. 3400 SPRUCE ST, DEPT OF ANESTHESIA 19104 #036-01-2001 L2001 **AN** *100 †05

SCHLICHTING, Christine M. 3333 N BROAD ST 19140 #040-02-1978 L1981 **AN CCP** *020 †05

SCHLOSSBERG, David. 100 E LEHIGH AVE 19125 #024-07-1970 L1977 **ID** *020 †20 ‡

SCHMAIER, Alec Andrew. ■ 19146 #041-01-2008 *012

SCHMIDT, Erwin R, Jr. 3400 SPRUCE ST, SILVERSTEIN PAVILION 2ND F 19104 #056-05-1952 L1957 **ORS** *071 †40

SCHMIDT, Kathryn Elizabet. ■ 19146 #041-01-2008 *012

SCHMIEDER, Frank Arnold. 118 S 11TH ST, JEFFERSON HLTH SYS/1ST FLO 19107 #028-02-1991 L1998 **VS** *020 †85

SCHMITT, Albrecht. P3300 HENRY AVE 19129 #407-15-1946 L1963 **GYN** *071 †30

SCHMITT, Sarah Elizabeth. 3400 SPRUCE ST, 3 WEST GATES BUILDING 19104 #028-02-2003 L2003 **N** *100

SCHNABEL, Truman G. 3400 SPRUCE ST 19104 #041-01-1943 L1944 **IM CD** *072 †20

SCHNALL, Bruce Michael. 840 WALNUT ST 19107 #041-13-1983 L1983 **OPH** *020 †35

SCHNALL, Nathan. 7310 CASTOR AVE 19152 #041-13-1947 L1948 **OBG** *071 †30

SCHNAUFER, Louise. 34TH & CIVIC CENTER BLVD 19104 #041-07-1951 L1971 **PDS** *071 †85

SCHNECK, Carson D. 3400 N BROAD ST, ANATOMY & CELL BIO DEPT TU 19140 #041-13-1959 L1960 **OS** *040

SCHNEEBERG, Arthur Levine. ■ 19103 #041-09-1947 L1948 **U** *071 †95

SCHNEEBERG, Norman G. ■ 19130 #041-13-1939 L1941 **END IM** *071 †20

SCHNEIDER, Adele Sandra. 111 S 11TH ST 19107 #836-01-1973 L1978 **CG PD** *020 †55,19

SCHNEIDER, Barbara A K. ■ 19147 #041-07-1968 L1971 **PTH** *075 †50

SCHNEIDER, Bernard. 1726 S BROAD ST, STE 101 19145 #021-01-1959 L1964 **OPH** *020 †35

SCHNEIDER, Lawrence H. 834 CHESTNUT ST STE G114, PHILADELPHIA HAND CENTER 19107 #035-08-1958 L1969 **HS ORS** *071 †40

SCHNEIDER, Stacie Leigh. 3401 N BROAD ST, OF S 19140 #051-04-2006 L2006 **GS** *012

SCHNEPP, Robert Walter. ■ 19146 #041-01-2007 L2007 **PD** *012

SCHOCKETT, Erica R. ■ 19103 #043-01-2005 L2005 **IM** *012

SCHOENBERG, Mark Philip. 3400 SPRUCE ST 19104 #048-14-1986 L1986 **U** *020 †95

SCHOTLAND, Donald Lewis. 3400 SPRUCE ST, UNIV PA SCH MED 19104 #024-01-1957 L1967 **N** *071 †75

SCHOTT, Clifford E, Jr. 501 S 54TH ST, MERCY HOSP OF PHILA CARDIO 19143 #041-09-1960 L1961 **CD IM** *020 †20

SCHRACK, Katie Evelyn. ■ 19102 #041-02-2007 L2007 **TY** *012

SCHRAEDER, Paul Louis. ■ 19106 #041-02-1966 L1967 **N** *071 †75

SCHRAGER, Deborah Ann. 3998 RED LION RD, STE 106 19114 #041-01-1983 L1985 **OBG** *020 †30

SCHRAM, Justin Adam. ■ 19107 #041-01-2008 *012

SCHREIBER, Alan D. 421 CURIE BLVD 19104 #035-46-1967 L1974 **IM** *020 †20

SCHREIBER, Courtney Anne. 3400 SPRUCE ST, HOSP UNIV OF PA 19104 #035-19-1999 L2001 **OBG** *020 †30

SCHREINER, Mark Steven. 3535 MARKET ST, STE 1200 19104 #028-34-1978 L1980 **AN PD** *050 †55,05 ‡

SCHRIMSHER, John Patrick. ■ 19107 #041-02-2008 *012

SCHROEDER, Harry William, III. ■ 19146 #041-01-2008 *012

SCHUCHTER, Lynn Mara. 3400 SPRUCE ST, 6 PENN TOWER 19104 #016-42-1982 L1989 **ON IM** *020 †20

SCHULMAN, Edward S. 219 N BROAD ST, FL 5 19107 #041-02-1975 L1983 **PCC AI** *020 †20

SCHULMAN, Gerri Anne. 3322 N BROAD ST STE 201, MEDICAL OFFICE BUILDING 19140 #008-01-1980 L1983 **NEP IM** *020 †20

SCHULTE, Michaela. 5501 OLD YORK RD, KLEIN BLDG STE 363 19141 #409-10-2000 L2003 **ID** *012 †20

SCHULZ, Jacob Foster. ■ 19130 #041-12-2006 L2006 **ORS** *012

SCHULZ, Steffan Walter. ■ 19106 #041-13-2003 L2003 **RHU** *012 †20

SCHUMACHER, H Ralph. 3400 SPRUCE ST, FL 8 19104 #041-01-1959 L1967 **RHU IM** *050 †20

SCHURICHT, Alan Leslie. 800 SPRUCE ST, DEPT SURG PENN HOSP 19107 #045-04-1985 L1987 **GS** *020 †85

SCHURMANN, Paul Antonio. 5501 OLD YORK RD 19141 #935-01-2004 L2006 **IM** *012

SCHUSTER, Albert H. 16TH ST & GIRARD AVE 19130 #041-09-1961 L1962 **U** *020 †95

SCHUSTER, James Mark. 3400 SPRUCE ST, 3 RD FLOOR SILVER STINE BU 19104 #036-07-1993 L2001 **NS** *020 †25

SCHUSTER, Michael Charles. 3600 SPRUCE ST, HUP RHEUMATOLOGY 19104 #056-05-2002 L2002 **RHU** *012 †20

SCHUSTER, Mindy Gail. 536 JOHNSON PAVILION 19104 #008-01-1987 L1990 **IM** *020 †20

SCHUSTER, Stephen John. 3400 SPRUCE ST, 16 PENN TOWER 19104 #041-02-1981 L1982 **HEM IM** *050 †20

SCHUT, Ewout Sander. 111 S 11TH ST 19107 #660-02-1996 L2001 **N** *100

SCHUT, Luis. 324 S 34TH ST, CHILDRENS HSPTL OF PHLDLPH 19104 #132-01-1954 L1964 **NSP NS** *020 †25

SCHUT, Lydia T Mainero. 100 W LEHIGH AVE 19133 #132-01-1954 L1964 **P LM** *071

SCHUTTA, Mark Henry. ■ 19106 #041-02-1993 L1996 **IM END** *020 †20

SCHUTTE-RODIN, Sharon. 3400 SPRUCE ST 19104 #041-07-1980 L1983 **SME OS** *020 ‡

SCHUTZMAN, David Louis. 5501 OLD YORK RD 19141 #041-02-1978 L1980 **NPM PD** *020 †55

SCHWAB, Charles Wm. 3440 MARKET ST, TRAUMA UNIT 19104 #035-15-1972 L1987 **TRS GS** *030 †85

SCHWAB, Edna Pasirstein. 3615 CHESTNUT ST 19104 #041-13-1985 L1986 **IM** *020 †20

SCHWAB, Richard John. 3624 MARKET ST, STE 205 19104 #041-01-1983 L1984 **PUD IM** *020 †20

SCHWALB, Allen Jay. 51 N 39TH ST STE W223, DEPT OF ANESTHESIOLOGY 19104 #041-01-1975 L1976 **AN** *020 †05

SCHWALB, Neil Stanford. 4641 ROOSEVELT BLVD, FRIENDS HOSP 19124 #041-02-1969 L1970 **P** *020 †75 ‡

SCHWARTING, Roland. 132 S 10TH ST, STE 285K 19107 #409-12-1981 L1990 **ATP** *020 †50

SCHWARTZ, Allan Bernard. 219 N BROAD ST, FL 5 19107 #041-09-1964 L1965 **IM NEP** *040 †20

SCHWARTZ, Beth Ilyssa. ■ 19106 #035-45-2008 *012

SCHWARTZ, Elias. 1025 WALNUT ST, DEPT OF PEDS STE 700 19107 #035-01-1960 L1962 **PHO PD** *071 †55

SCHWARTZ, Emanuel E. 1800 LOMBARD ST 19146 #035-08-1950 L1958 **DR** *071 †80

SCHWARTZ, Erin Simon. 324 S 34TH ST, DEPT OF RADIOLOGY 19104 #051-04-1993 L2000 **RNR** *020 †80

SCHWARTZ, Gordon Francis. 1015 CHESTNUT ST STE 510 19104 #024-01-1960 L1968 **SO GS** *030 †85

SCHWARTZ, Harvey Joel. 200 W WASHINGTON SQ, STE 110 19106 #041-09-1976 L1977 **P PYA** *020 †75

SCHWARTZ, Ira. 3400 SPRUCE ST, DEPT UROLOGY 19104 #041-02-1974 L1978 **U PA** *071 †95

SCHWARTZ, Irving R. 5501 OLD YORK RD, DEPT OF HEMATOLOGY 19141 #035-08-1951 L1957 **HEM** *071 †20

SCHWARTZ, J Sanford. 423 GUARDIAN DR RM 1120 19104 #041-01-1974 L1976 **IM** *050 †20

SCHWARTZ, Linden Matthew. 1200 W TABOR RD 19141 #033-05-1987 L1988 **PM** *020 †60

SCHWARTZ, Louis. 1900 S BROAD ST 19145 #154-07-1937 L1939 **GP** *071

SCHWARTZ, Louis Winn. 840 WALNUT ST 19107 #041-02-1967 L1968 **OPH OS** *020 †35 ‡

SCHWARTZ, M Wm. 250 S 3RD ST 19106 #041-01-1961 L1963 **PD NEP** *071 †55

SCHWARTZ, Marc Lee. 111 S 11TH ST, STE 4280 19107 #041-13-1978 L1979 **CD IM** *020 †20 ‡

SCHWARTZ, Marinda Kelley. ■ 19106 #023-07-1963 L1969 **PD** *071 †55

SCHWARTZ, Nadine. 4641 ROOSEVELT BLVD 19124 #041-13-1997 L2004 **PD CHP** *020 †55,75 ‡

SCHWARTZ, Raymond. 5401 OLD YORK RD, STE 201 19141 #041-13-1963 L1964 **CD IM** *020 †20

SCHWARTZ, Robert Paul. 2 PENN BLVD STE 203 19144 #041-13-1974 L1975 **OBG** *020 †30

SCHWARTZ, Roy Eric. ERIE AVE AT FRONT ST, DEPT ANESTHESIA & CRITITIC 19134 #035-03-1979 L1984 **AN CCA** *020 †55,05

SCHWARTZ, Staci Jill. ■ 19106 #041-02-1990 L1993 **PM OS** *020 †60

SCHWARTZ, Stanley Steven. 3400 SPRUCE ST, UNIV OF PA DEPT OF MED 19104 #016-02-1973 L1974 **DIA IM** *020 †20

SCHWARTZ, Stephen Leonard. 833 CHESTNUT ST STE 210 19107 #041-13-1961 L1962 **P** *020 †75

SCHWARTZ, Steven Barnet. 301 S 8TH ST STE 4B, SIMEONE CTR FOR NEUROSURGE 19106 #836-03-1990 L1999 **NS** *020

SCHWARTZMAN, Robert Jay. 245 N 15TH ST, DREXEL U COL OF MED 19102 #041-01-1965 L1967 **N** *020 †20,75

SCHWARZ, Benjamin Alfred. ■ 19146 #041-01-2008 *012

SCHWARZ, Donald Furstman. 1101 MARKET ST, FL 8 19107 #023-07-1982 L1985 **PD ADL** *030 †55

SCHWARZ, Naomi Sarah. ■ 19146 #041-13-2005 L2007 **TY** *012

SCHWEDLER-KERSTEIN, Margar. 111 S 11TH ST, GIBBON 8TH FLR/ANESTHESIOL 19107 #297-01-1975 L1990 **AN** *040 †05

SCHWED LUSTGARTEN, Daniel. 5501 OLD YORK RD, ALBERT EINSTEIN MED CTR 19141 #935-01-2002 L2004 **IM** *012 †20

SCHWEITZER, Karl Martin, Jr. ■ 19107 #041-02-2008 *012

SCHWEITZER, Mark Eliot. 132 S 10TH ST STE 1096A, OF RADIOLO 19107 #035-06-1986 L1991 **DR** *020 †80

SCHWEIZER, Edward E, Jr. 3600 MARKET ST 19104 #016-02-1979 L1980 **P** *050

SCIACCA, Joslyn Renee. ■ 19103 #051-01-2004 L2008 **D** *012

SCIAMANNA, Christopher N. 1015 WALNUT ST STE 115, DEPARTMENT OF HEALTH POLIC 19107 #041-02-1992 L2004 **IM** *020 †20

SCIPIONE, Charles Richard. 3400 SPRUCE ST 19104 #041-09-1972 L1973 **FPS OTO** *020 †45

SCIVOLETTI, Nicole Anne. 4190 CITY AVE STE 205, GRADUATE MED EDUCATION 19131 #041-77-2007, ▲ L2007 *012

SCOLARO, John Alan. ■ 19102 #024-05-2007 L2007 **ORS** *012

SCOLES, Paul. 1800 LOMBARD ST 19146 #033-06-1979 L1985 **ORS** *020 †40

SCOLES, Peter Vincent. 3750 MARKET ST 19104 #041-02-1970 L1975 **ORS** *040 †40

SCOLL, Benjamin Jacob. 3401 N BROAD ST, DEPT OF UROLOGY, ZONE C, # 19140 #041-13-2004 L2004 **U** *012

SCOTT, Benjamin Kiger. 3400 SPRUCE ST, OF PENNSYLVAN 19104 #035-01-2004 L2004 **AN** *012

SCOTT, Craig Hilbert. 3400 SPRUCE ST, 9 FOUNDERS BLDG 19104 #041-12-1989 L1995 **CD** *020 †20

SCOTT, Emma Catherine. 5501 OLD YORK RD 19141 #836-01-2000 L2004 **IM** *012

SCOTT, Kevin Charles. ■ 19106 #041-02-2006 L2006 **FP** *012

SCOTT, Ralph Hyler. 5501 OLD YORK RD - PATHLGY, ALBERT EINSTEIN MED CTR 19141 #041-01-1961 L1962 **PTH CLP** *020 †50 ‡

SCOTT, Rita Elizabeth. 3300 HENRY AVE # PED, MEDICAL COL PA PA 19129 #041-07-1939 L1940 **PD** *071 †55

SCOTT, S David. 8835 GERMANTOWN AVE 19118 #041-02-1977 L1979 **PUD IM** *020 †20

SCOTT, Sean Fenton. 400 HAVERFORD AVE, HEALTH CARE CENTER #4 19104 #033-06-2002 L2002 **PD** *020 †55

SCOTT, Thomas F M. ■ 19103 #352-11-1927 L1938 **PD** *071 †55

SCOTT, Thomas Hyde. ■ 19146 #041-01-2005 L2006 **IM** *012

SCOTT, Walter Jos. 333 COTTMAN AVE 19111 #016-02-1981 L2001 **TS** *020 †85,90

SEA, Stephanie Ann. ■ 19130 #016-45-2008 *012

SEABROOK, Ruth Barron. ■ 19103 #028-02-2005 L2005 **PD** *012

SEAMON, Mark John. 3400 SPRUCE ST, TRAUMA CENTER AT PENN 19104 #041-12-2001 L2001 **CCS** *100

SEBERT, Michael Evan. 324 S 34TH ST 19104 #005-11-1995 L1997 **PDI** *020 †55

SEDRAKYAN, Gevorg. 4TH FLOOR - S TOWER MAIL, DREXEL UNIVERSITY COLLEGE 19102 #913-38-2004 L2007 **IM** *012

SEEBER, Beata Eva. 3701 MARKET ST 8TH FL, DIVISION OF REPRODUCTIVE M 19104 #043-01-1999 L2001 **OBG** *100 †30

SEELAGAN, Davindra Junior. 2601 HOLME AVE 19152 #035-06-2001 L2007 **MSR** *020 †80

SEETAI, Sandimae Vivienne. ERIE AVE AT FRONT ST, ST CHRISTOPHERS HOSP 19134 #024-07-1995 L1997 **PN** *020 †55

SEETHARAMAN, Mythili. 9880 BUSTLETON AVE, STE 220 19115 #495-04-1993 L2000 **RHU** *020 †20

SEGAL, Bernard Louis. 925 CHESTNUT ST 19107 #067-01-1955 L1961 **CD** *020 †20

SEGAL, Shana Amy. ■ 19146 #041-01-2007 L2007 **PD** *012

SEGAL, Stanton. 3550 MARKET ST, FL 4 19104 #024-01-1952 L1966 **IM PD** *071 †20

SEGAL, Stanton Lewis. KNIGHTS AND RED LION RDS 19114 #041-07-1982 L1985 **PUD CCM** *020 †20

SEGAWA, Hiromu. 3400 SPRUCE ST 19104 #572-03-1967 **NS** *020

SEGIN, Robert Stanley. ■ 19105 #041-09-1957 L1958 **CD IM** *020

SEHDEV, Harish Mohan. 800 SPRUCE ST, FL 8 19107 #041-01-1991 L1994 **OBG** *020 †30

SEHGAL, Shailen Shivam. ■ 19103 #035-20-2007 L2007 **GS** *012

SEIBEL, Jolene Susanne. 834 CHESTNUT ST, STE 400 19107 #041-12-2002 L2002 **OBG** *012 †30

SEIBERT, Henry Edward. 1020 SANSOM ST, STE 239 THOMPSON BUILDING 19107 #010-02-1999 L2003 **EM** *020 †16

SEIDEN, Michael Van. 333 COTTMAN AVE 19111 #028-02-1986 L2007 **IM** *020 †20

SEIF, Alix Eden. ■ 19107 #040-02-2002 L2002 **PHO** *012 †55

SEIGEL, George Bernard. 6410A RISING SUN AVE 19111 #660-01-1958 L1960 **P** *020

SEIJO, Luis Miguel. 3400 SPRUCE ST 19104 #041-01-1995 L2000 **PCC** *012

SEINIGE, Ursula L. 1800 LOMBARD ST, PEPPER PAVILION STE 901 19146 #041-07-1978 L1979 **GS** *071 †85

SEITCHIK, Scott Howard. 800 SPRUCE ST 19107 #041-09-1988 L1990 **AN PMM** *020 †05

SEITZ, Horace M, Jr. 3400 SPRUCE ST 19104 #041-01-1952 L1953 **OBG IM** *071 †30

SEKHARAN, Shakuntala C. ■ 19131 #495-16-1958 L1978 **P** *071 †75

SEKIGUCHI, Debora Rosa. 3400 SPRUCE ST, DEPT CLINICAL PATH 19104 #132-01-1991 L2004 **PTH** *012

SELARNICK, Hope Susan. 2301 S BROAD ST 19148 #041-07-1985 L1986 **P** *040 †75

SELBER, Jesse C. ■ 19123 #035-45-2002 L2004 **PS** *012

SELBST, Alison Claire. 101 E OLNEY AVE 19120 #041-07-1981 L1984 **PD** *020 †55

SELIEM, Mohamed Abdel H. 324 S 34TH ST 19104 #915-02-1978 L1989 **PDC PD** *020 †55

SELIG, Daniel Scott. 8945 RIDGE AVE, STE 3 19128 #041-13-2005 L2005 **PD** *012

SELIG, Robert Mark. 8945 RIDGE AVE, STE 3,4,5 19128 #041-13-1976 L1977 **PD DIA** *020 †55

SELIGMAN, Neil Stuart. ■ 19147 #035-15-2004 L2004 **OBG** *012

SELL, Bevin Lashley. ■ 19102 #023-01-2003 L2003 **ID** *012 †20

SELLAKUMAR, Jennifer V. 239 E THOMPSON ST, 1020 SANSOM ST. 19125 #035-15-1997 L2004 **EM** *020 †16

SELLERS, Alfred M. 3400 SPRUCE ST, HOSP UNIV PA 19104 #036-07-1951 L1952 **CD IM** *071 †20

SELTZER, Charles Weinfeld. ■ 19103 #041-02-2004 L2006 **IM** *012

SELTZER, Joseph Louis. 1025 WALNUT ST, THOMAS JEFFERSON UNIVERSIT 19107 #041-02-1971 L1972 **AN** *030 †05

SELZER, Michael Edgar. 3400 SPRUCE ST 19104 #035-19-1968 L1971 **N PM** *050 †75

SEMEAO, Edisio Jose. 324 S 34TH ST 19104 #008-02-1991 L1994 **PG** *020 †55

SEN, Sarbattama. ■ 19106 #041-02-2002 L2002 **NPM** *012

SENGUPTA, Anita Louise. ■ 19104 #038-41-2004 L2004 **PTH** *012

SENNETT, Brian Jeffrey. 235 S 33RD ST, STE 1 19104 #041-01-1988 L1991 **HS** *020 †40

SENNETT, Cary Scott. 510 WALNUT ST STE 510 19106 #008-01-1982 L2005 **IM** *030 †20

SEPE, Dana Marie. ■ 19103 #033-06-2004 L2004 **PHO** *012 †55

SERCHUCK, Leslie Karen. ■ 19103 #024-05-1990 L1993 **PD** *020 †55

SERGOTT, Robert Chas. 8025 ROOSEVELT BLVD 19152 #023-07-1975 L1981 **OPH** *040 †35

SERLETTI, Joseph Michael. 3400 SPRUCE ST, 10TH FL 19104 #035-45-1982 L2005 **PS CFS** *020 †65

SEROTA, Ronald David. 1025 WALNUT ST, STE 8439 19107 #041-02-1968 L1970 **P** *020 †20,75

SERPER, Marina. ■ 19107 #041-02-2006 L2006 **IM** *012

SERRUYA, Gail Marion. 3535 MARKET ST 19104 #016-01-2003 L2007 **P** *100

SERVAES, Sabahenoor. ■ 19103 #024-05-1998 L2004 **PDR** *020 †80

SESOK-PIZZINI, Deborah A. 3300 HENRY AVE, MEDICAL COLLGE OF PNNSYLVN 19129 #041-14-1994 L1997 **PTH** *020 †50

SETH, Rajendra N. 5901 SUMMERDALE AVE 19149 #495-05-1962 L1973 **CD IM** *072 †20

SETH, Rishi. 2900 W QUEEN LN, DREXEL UNIV COLL OF MED 19129 #041-15-2006 L2006 **DR** *012

SETHBHAKDI, Pranee. PHILADELPHIA GERIATRIC CTR 19141 #891-02-1960 L1974 **CD IM** *020

SETHI, Surinder Singh. 2601 HOLME AVE, MEDICAL STAFF OFFICE 19152 #495-51-1977 L1984 **GS** *020

SEUFERT, Lisa. 255 S 17TH ST STE 2810 19103 #041-01-2001 L2001 **P** *020 †75

SEVIN, Bradley Harvey. 829 SPRUCE ST STE 302 19107 #041-13-1969 L1970 **PYA P** *020 †75 ‡

SEVY, Roger Warren. 3400 N BROAD ST 19140 #016-11-1954 **OS** *071

SEWARDS, Patrick Milo. 3401 N BROAD ST 19140 #041-13-1980 L1981 **ORS** *075 †40

SEWELL, Matthew David. 925 CHESTNUT ST, JEFFERSON HEART INSTITUTE 19107 #051-01-2002 L2002 **CD** *012 †20

SEWELL, Myron Lyle. 1408 S BROAD ST 19146 #041-02-1981 L1984 **IM** *020 †20

SEY, Mark John. 6608 CASTOR AVE 19149 #041-13-1968 L1970 **PD** *020 †55

SEYKORA, John Thomas. 3600 SPRUCE ST, UNIV OF PENNSYLVANIA MED C 19104 #035-20-1993 L1997 **DMP PTH** *050 †50

SEYMOUR, Parker Mc Lean. 8835 GERMANTOWN AVE 19118 #041-02-1970 L1973 **EM** *020 †16

SEYMOUR, Peter Edmund. ■ 19107 #035-03-2003 L2003 **OTO** *012

SFEDU, Emil. 716 N 24TH ST 19130 #041-02-1981 L1983 **IM** *020 †20

SHABAZZ, Safiyya Shaheida. 51 N 39TH ST, 6TH FL 19104 #041-01-2002 L2004 **FM** *020 †18

SHABER, Gary Stuart. 111 S 11TH ST, THOMAS JEFFERSON UNIV HSPT 19107 #038-40-1959 L1962 **R DR** *020 †80

SHACK, Jonathan G. 100 E LEHIGH AVE, MAB 305 19125 #041-14-1989 L1991 **IM** *020 †75

SHAER, Andrew Howard. 5800 RIDGE AVE 19128 #035-15-1985 L1990 **DR** *020 †80

SHAFFER, Brian Thomas. ■ 19130 #035-20-2005 L2005 **OTO** *012

SHAFFER, Gene Whittaker. 5501 OLD YORK RD, STE 4 19141 #041-01-1994 L1996 **ORS** *020 †40

SHAFFER, John Francis R. 225 S 18TH ST, RITT RGCY # 1206 19103 #041-02-1940 L1941 **OTO OS** *071 †45

SHAFIA, Hass. 100 E LEHIGH AVE, CHC-1 19125 #517-01-1961 L1968 **IM CD** *020 †20

SHAH, Anjan Rajni. ■ 19123 #024-05-2002 L2002 **ORS** *012

SHAH, Ankur G. 1025 WALNUT ST, THOMAS JEFFERSON UNIV HOSP 19107 #033-05-2002 L2007 **IM** *012

SHAH, Arti. 3300 HENRY AVE 19129 #654-01-1997 L2000 **ICE** *100

SHAH, Arti D. ■ 19104 #041-01-2008 *012

SHAH, Asha Jayendrakum. ■ 19104 #041-01-2008 *012

SHAH, Ashish Mukesh. ■ 19104 #041-01-2007 **IM** *012

SHAH, Chaitali Kantilal. 245 N 15TH ST, DEPT OF GME 19102 #496-44-1998 L2006 **DR** *012

SHAH, Chirag Pradip. 840 WALNUT ST, WILLS EYE HOSP 19107 #035-45-2004 L2005 **OPH** *012

SHAH, Gopi Bipin. 925 CHESTNUT ST, JEFFERSON OTOLARYNGOLOGY 19107 #021-01-2007 L2007 **OTO** *012

SHAH, Gunjan Lalitchandr. ■ 19107 #041-13-2008 *012

SHAH, Hansa Mukund. 5501 OLD YORK RD, DEPT OF PATHOLOGY 19141 #495-76-1971 L1980 **PTH** *020

SHAH, Inayat Ali. 2900 W QUEEN LN 19129 #704-09-1992 L2003 **P** *012

SHAH, Kantilal J. 3905 FORD RD 19131 #495-22-1964 L1975 **FM GS** *020 †18

SHAH, Lina Jitendra. 7600 CENTRAL AVE 19111 #495-01-1971 L1976 **AN** *020 †05

SHAH, Mahendra C. 6715 OGONTZ AVE 19126 #495-48-1972 L1982 **MPD** *020

SHAH, Maully J. 324 S 34TH ST 19104 #495-76-1987 L1993 **PDC ICE** *020 †55

SHAH, Mona Bhatt. ■ 19123 #024-05-2002 L2002 **IM** *100

SHAH, Neil Pravin. 5501 OLD YORK RD, A EINSTEIN MED CTR 19141 #035-20-2007 **TY** *012

SHAH, Nilika Bakulesh. ■ 19103 #048-14-2007 L2007 **PD** *012

SHAH, Niranjana J. 136 DIAMOND ST 19122 #495-17-1971 L1981 **PD** *020

SHAH, Nirav Kishor. 1025 WALNUT ST, JEFFERSON MED COLL 19107 #041-02-1999 L2005 **NS** *012

SHAH, Nishant Satish. ■ 19103 #033-05-2002 L2002 **EM** *020 †16

SHAH, Parina Ashwin. ■ 19103 #012-05-2007 L2007 **IM** *012

SHAH, Payal Deepak. ■ 19103 #041-01-2008 *012

SHAH, Rachana Dinesh. 3615 CIVIC CENTER BLVD, RM 802 19104 #048-04-2002 L2006 **PDE** *012 †20,55

SHAH, Rajiv Janardan. ■ 19103 #041-01-2002 *010

SHAH, Roshan Pradip. ■ 19147 #008-01-2007 L2007 **ORS** *012

SHAH, Rupa Naresh. 3401 N BROAD ST, TEMPLE UNIVERSITY HOSPITAL 19140 #024-05-1999 L2001 **GE** *100 †20

SHAH, Samantha Rao. 9321 OLD BUSTLETON AVE 19115 #025-01-1997 L2004 **IM** *020 †20

SHAH, Samir Suresh. ■ 19104 #008-01-1998 L2000 **PDI** *100 †55

SHAH, Sapna Sanjay. ■ 19128 #041-15-2008 *012

SHAH, Shaan Hemant. 19107 #041-02-2007 L2007 **IM** *012

SHAH, Suken Ashvin. 833 CHESTNUT ST, STE 300 19107 #041-02-1994 L1996 **ORS** *020 †40 ‡

SHAH, Suken Harikrishna. 111 S 11TH ST, THOS JEFFERSON UNIV HOSP 19107 #041-02-2000 L2001 **VIR** *100 †80

SHAH, Susie Shirish. 8835 GERMANTOWN AVE 19118 #041-09-1993 L1996 **DR** *020 †80

SHAH, Tina Pravin. 5501 OLD YORK RD, OFFICE OF ACADEMIC 19141 #495-37-2003 L2005 **IM** *012

SHAH, Tina Rashmi. ■ 19107 #041-02-2008 L2008 *012

SHAHABADI, Shabnam. 833 CHESTNUT ST, STE 740 19107 #010-01-2003 L2007 **D** *100 †15

SHAHID, Nauman. 245 N 15TH ST, DREXEL UNIV COLL MED/HAHNE 19102 #704-21-2004 L2006 **IM** *012

SHAHID, Shabana. 3401 N BROAD ST, TEMPLE UNIVERSITY HOSPITAL 19140 #422-01-2005 L2006 **IM** *012

SHAHSAMAND, Zabi Zaky K. 245 N 15TH ST, DEPT OF GME 19102 #422-01-2006 L2006 **AN** *012

SHAIKH, Faisal. ■ 19107 #051-04-2006 L2006 **IM** *012

SHAKED, Abraham A. 3400 SPRUCE ST, FL 4 19104 #550-01-1981 L1995 **GS** *020 †85

SHAKLEE, Julia. ■ 19106 #047-05-2006 L2006 **PD** *012

SHAMAYEV, Mikhail Mirkhey. 3401 N BROAD ST, TEMPLE UNIV HOSPITAL 19140 #913-79-1983 L2002 **N** *100

SHAMES, Jason Paul. ■ 19103 #041-15-2007 L2007 **IM** *012

SHAMIMI-NOORI, Saum Ali. ■ 19107 #041-02-2005 L2005 **IM** *012

SHAMIR, Raanan. 324 S 34TH ST, DEPT GI 19104 #550-01-1987 L1993 **PD OS** *020

SHAN, Yang. 4641 ROOSEVELT BLVD 19124 #243-44-1982 L2001 **P** *020

SHANBHAG, Manishachandraka. ■ 19103 #036-07-2004 L2004 **MPD** *012

SHANBHAG, Satish Pramod. 333 COTTMAN AVE, FOX CHASE CANCER CENTER 19111 #496-39-2002 L2007 **HO** *012 †20

SHANG, Sherry Shujing. 111 S 11TH ST, DEPT OF RADIOLOGY 19107 #243-38-1991 L2001 **AR** *100 †80

SHANG, Xiaozhou. 2900 W QUEEN LN 19129 #243-44-1985 L2006 **P** *012

SHANGOLD, Mona Marlynn. 1601 WALNUT ST, STE 1200 19102 #036-07-1972 L1989 **GYN REN** *020 †30

SHANMUGAM, Sucharitha. 5501 OLD YORK RD, A EINSTEIN MED CTR 19141 #495-04-2000 L2002 **RHU** *012 †20

SHAO, John Han. 3400 N BROAD ST, TEMPLE UNIV SCH OF MED 19140 #041-13-2001 L2004 **IC** *012

SHAO, Theresa Hua. 3600 CHESTNUT ST, BOX 761 19104 #041-01-2004 L2005 **HO** *012 †20

SHAPIRO, Amiram. 1528 WALNUT ST, STE 1501 19102 #550-01-1973 L1984 **OPH** *020 †35

SHAPIRO, Barbara S. 34TH ST AND CIVIC CENTER B 19104 #023-01-1982 L1984 **PYA PYM** *020 †55

SHAPIRO, Bernard. YORK & TABOR RD, EINSTEIN MED CENTER ND 19141 #041-01-1951 L1952 **NM** *072 †28

SHAPIRO, Jeffrey Lee. 900 WALNUT ST, 5TH FL 19107 #041-15-2003 L2006 **AN** *020

SHAPIRO, Jon Andrew. 1740 SOUTH ST, STE 300 19146 #041-01-1982 L1983 **GE IM** *020 †20

SHAPIRO, Sandor Solomon. 1025 WALNUT ST, STE 8439 19107 #024-01-1957 L1964 **HEM IM** *040

SHAPIRO, Stanley Herbert. 255 S 17TH ST STE 1801 19103 #035-19-1954 L1956 **PYA P** *020

SHARAN, Ashwini Dayal. 909 WALNUT ST 2ND FL, DEPT OF NEUROSURGERY 19107 #033-05-1995 L2000 **NS** *020 †25

SHARIF, Mohammed Umar. 800 SPRUCE ST 19107 #665-02-2004 L2005 **IM** *012

SHARIFI-AZAD, Said. 111 S 11TH ST STE 524MAI, DEPT OF ANESTHESIOLOGY 19107 #517-01-1967 L1974 **AN** *020 †05

SHARKEY, Peter Francis. 925 CHESTNUT ST, THOMAS JEFFERSON U/ROTHMAN 19107 #035-15-1984 L1985 **ORS OAR** *020 †40

SHARMA, Ajay Kumar. 833 CHESTNUT ST, STE 210 19107 #495-45-1995 L2007 **CHP** *012

SHARMA, Dinesh Kumar. 111 S 11TH ST, 10 MAIN BLDG 19107 #495-30-1981 L1998 DR RNR *020 †80

SHARMA, Garima Vishwanath. 3401 N BROAD ST, DEPT OF INTERNAL MED 19140 #495-96-2003 L2005 IM *012

SHARMA, Jagdish Kumar. 230 N BROAD ST DEPT NEUR 19102 #495-05-1963 NS *100

SHARMA, Kumar. 833 CHESTNUT ST, STE 700 19107 #035-46-1985 L1991 NEP *020 †20

SHARMA, Puneet. 2900 W QUEEN LN, DEPT OF INTERNAL MED 19129 #495-69-1996 L2004 IM *100 †20

SHARMA, Raj Kumar. 800 SPRUCE ST, FL 2 19107 #495-67-1968 L1979 NPM PD *020 †55

SHARMA, Saloni. ■ 19107 #041-14-2004 L2004 PM *012

SHARPS, Stephanie Kamila. 3400 SPRUCE ST, 700 CRB HOSP OF U OF PENN 19104 #036-07-2002 L2005 NEP *050 †20

SHARRAR, Karen E M. 7600 CENTRAL AVE 19111 #012-05-1970 L1973 EM *020 †18,16 ‡

SHARRON, Melissa Ann. 230 N BROAD ST #035-19-1990 L1995 AN *020 †05

SHASHATY, Michael George. ■ 19139 #047-05-2003 L2003 PCC *012 †20

SHATS, Daniel. ■ 19102 #305-01-2006 IM *012

SHAUGHNESSY, Rita Ann. 1427 VINE ST MS 950 19102 #016-11-1989 L1995 P *020 †75

SHAW, Christiana Marie. 333 COTTMAN AVE, FOX CHASE CANCER CENTER AT 19111 #011-02-2003 L2008 GS *100

SHAW, Kathy Nunn. 324 S 34TH ST 19104 #035-47-1982 L1984 PD EM *020 †55

SHAW, Wallace M. ■ 19103 #035-19-1943 L1971 AN *071 †05

SHAWALUK, Paul Dmitri. 5001 FRANKFORD AVE 19124 #041-02-1968 L1969 OPH *020 †35

SHAWHUGHES, Laura Graham. ■ 19146 #033-05-2004 L2004 IM *100 †20

SHAWL, Timothy Fred. 2314 S 3RD ST 19148 #041-09-1985 L1986 OBG *020 †30

SHAYEGAN, Mustapha. 4900 FRANKFORD AVE 19124 #517-01-1973 L1975 OPH *020 †35 ‡

SHECHTER, Ronen. 111 S 11TH ST 19107 #550-01-1999 L2006 AN *012

SHEETS, Everett Osborne. 2601 HOLME AVE 19152 #041-09-1947 L1948 FM *072 †18

SHEIBLEY, Daniel Joseph. ■ 19107 #041-02-2008 †012

SHEIKH, Ednan Salahuddin. ■ 19107 #041-02-2005 L2006 AN *012

SHEIKH, Hina Aziz. ■ 19103 #704-25-1998 L2001 MGP *020 †50

SHEIKH, Roomana Maqsood. 3200 HENRY AVE, EPPI 19129 #704-06-1985 L1996 CHP *020 †75

SHEKDAR, Karuna Vithal. 1 CHILDRENS CTR, 34TH AND CIVIC CTR 19104 #496-38-1992 L2003 *100

SHELAT, S. 324 S 34TH ST 19104 #041-01-1999 L2001 PTH *100 †50

SHELLHAAS, Jason Scott. 399 S 34TH ST, PENN TOWER-LOWER LEVEL 19104 #025-01-2001 L2001 FSM *100 †20

SHELSTA, Heather Nicole. ■ 19147 #008-01-2004 L2005 OPH *012

SHELTON, Barbara. 1 INDEPENDENCE PL APT 1006 19106 #041-07-1981 L1982 N ORS *071 †60

SHEMANSIK, Carmella Rose. ■ 19128 #041-14-2005 L2005 AN *012

SHEMESH, Eyal. ■ 19146 #550-01-1989 L2007 OS *020

SHEMS, Estherina. 4900 WYALUSING AVE, COMMUNITY COUNCIL MH/MR IN 19131 #041-07-1958 L1962 CHP P *071

SHEN, Colette Joan. ■ 19107 #041-01-2008 †012

SHEN, Jessica Chunhan. ■ 19103 #025-01-2007 L2007 OTO *012

SHEN, Rhuna. 3741 WALNUT ST, # 211 19104 #033-06-2000 L2004 IC *012 †20

SHENOT, Patrick John. 833 CHESTNUT ST, STE 703 19107 #035-48-1991 L1993 U *020 †95 ‡

SHENOY, Kartik Vasudeva. ■ 19131 #038-44-2005 L2005 IM *012

SHEPARD, Harvey Earl. 1100 WALNUT ST 19107 #041-02-1988 L1990 EM *020 †16

SHEPARD, James Wm. 51 N 39TH ST 19104 #041-13-1976 L1977 IM *020 †20

SHEPHERD, Jessica A. 2900 W QUEEN LN 19129 #305-01-2005 L2005 OBG *012

SHEPHERD, Suzanne Moore. 3400 SPRUCE ST, U HOSP PA DEPT EM 19104 #010-02-1980 L1995 EM OS *040 †16

SHEPPARD, Edith. 3400 SPRUCE ST 19104 #035-19-1944 L1946 P PYA *071

SHER, Daniel Jay. 700 COTTMAN AVE, STE 201 19111 #038-06-1990 L1993 GE IM *020 †20 ‡

SHER, Kathleen. ■ 19107 #041-02-2008 †012

SHER, Liane. 2301 S BROAD ST 19148 #055-01-1982 L1984 PM *020 †60

SHERER, Ilana Michelle. ■ 19143 #041-01-2008 †012

SHERESHEVSKY, Alexey. 2900 W QUEEN LN 19129 #913-01-1994 L2003 FP *012

SHERESHEVSKY, Tatyana. 245 N 15TH ST, MCP HAHNEMANN UNIV 19102 #913-01-1993 L2004 OBG *012

SHERIF, Katherine Devine. 219 N BROAD ST, FL 6 19107 #041-07-1991 L1993 IM GYN *020 †20

SHERK, Henry Huber. 245 N 15TH ST, MS 420 19102 #041-02-1956 L1957 ORS *020 †40

SHERKAT, Abolhassan. GRADUATE HOSP 19146 #517-01-1956 L1961 DR *020 †80

SHERLEY, James Louis. 7701 BURHOLME AVE, FOX CHASE CANCER CTR 19111 #023-07-1988 OS *050

SHERMAN, Eric Jeffrey. 333 COTTMAN AVE 19111 #035-01-1993 L2000 HO *020 †20

SHERMAN, Glenn S. 2301 W ALLEGHENY AVE, NORTHEASTERN OB/GYN 19132 #035-03-1991 L1996 OBG *020 †20

SHERMAN, Michael Steven. 216 N BROAD ST MS 107, UNIVERSITY HOSPITAL 19102 #035-46-1981 L1988 PUD CCM *040 †20

SHERRY, David Dan. 3405 CIVIC CENTER BLVD, RHEUMATOLOGY-2ND FL/CSH 19104 #048-15-1977 L2002 PPR *020 †55

SHESOL, Barry Frederick. ■ 19128 #038-40-1970 L1973 PS GS *020 †85,65

SHETH, Harshal. 3400 N BROAD ST, TEMPLE UNIV SCH OF MED 19140 #041-13-2006 L2006 IM *012

SHETH, Mukund. 5335 CASTOR AVE 19124 #495-23-1972 L1978 IM CD *020 †20 ‡

SHETH, Neerav G. ■ 19107 #038-44-2007 L2007 IM *012

SHETH, Neil Perry. ■ 19103 #035-03-2003 L2003 ORS *012

SHETH, Sunita B. 3400 N BROAD ST, THROMBOSIS RESEARCH CTR 19140 #043-01-1986 L1990 ON HEM *020 †20

SHETTLE, Thos Albert, III. ■ 19143 #008-02-1981 L1982 P *020

SHETTY, Ashwin Jayaprakas. ■ 19107 #024-05-2005 L2006 DR *012

SHETTY, Nagalakshmi Ashok. 1800 LOMBARD ST, TENET HEALTHSYSTEM GRADUAT 19146 #496-39-1997 L2006 IM *012

SHEVADE, Vikas Anand. ■ 19130 #033-06-2002 L2002 DR *100 †80

SHHADEH, Akram. 3303 N PARK AVE, 2ND FL, REAR 19140 #875-01-1999 L2002 N *100 †75 ‡

SHI, Yuquan. 800 SPRUCE ST 19107 #243-39-1984 L2007 PTH *012

SHIEH, Charles Fun-Yang. ■ 19131 #047-05-2002 L2006 GS *100

SHIELDS, Carol Lally. 840 WALNUT ST, STE 1440 19107 #041-12-1983 L1984 OPH ON *020 †35

SHIENBAUM, Gary. ■ 19103 #041-02-2007 L2007 TY *012

SHIH, Henry Hsuanhung. ■ 19104 #021-01-2003 L2004 AN *020

SHIH, Michael H. ■ 19103 #041-13-2005 L2005 GS *012

SHIH, Samuel. 3400 SPRUCE ST, UNIV OF PA HLTH SYSTEM 19104 #539-06-2003 GS *012

SHILEY, Kevin Thomas. ■ 19103 #035-06-2005 L2005 IM *012

SHILLER, David Phillip. 1420 LOCUST ST STE 230 19102 #008-02-1989 L1991 EM *020 †16

SHILLING, Jack Watkins. 5501 OLD YORK RD, WILLOWCREST BLDG 4TH FLOOR 19141 #041-09-1994 L1999 ORS *020 †40

SHILLINGFORD, Amanda Joy. ■ 19146 #035-01-2000 L2001 PD *100 †55

SHIN, David Sullivan. 51 N 39TH ST 19104 #041-01-1997 L1999 OPH *020

SHIN, Myung Hyo. 2301 E ALLEGHENY AVE, WOMENS CARE 19134 #583-03-1967 L1972 GYN *020 †30 ‡

SHIN, Nara Chi Sun. 1020 SANSOM ST 239T, DEPT OF EMERGENCY MEDICINE 19107 #008-01-2002 L2007 EM *020 †16

SHIN, Yeoyang. ■ 19118 #001-02-1997 L2002 DR *020 †80

SHINDLER, Kenneth Scott. 51 N 39TH ST, SCHEIE EYE INST 19104 #028-02-1999 L2001 OPH *020 †35

SHINOHARA, Eric Tatsuo. ■ 19103 #047-05-2003 L2005 RO *012

SHIPON, David Matthew. 1339 W PORTER ST 19148 #041-02-1996 L1998 CD *100 †20

SHIRLEY, Kathryn K Woods. ■ 19106 #020-12-2004 L2004 PD *012

SHIRLEY, Lawrence Andrew. ■ 19106 #020-12-2004 L2004 GS *012

SHIROFF, Adam Michael. 3440 MARKET ST, 1ST FL 19104 #041-02-2002 L2003 CCS *012 †85

SHISHODIA, Himani Singh. 1316 W ONTARIO ST, JONES HALL 1ST FLOOR 19140 #035-48-1999 L2003 IM *020 †20

SHIVELY, Susan. 255 S 17TH ST STE 2710 19103 #041-01-1976 L1977 P PYA *020 †75

SHKLAR, David Lewis. 2301 S BROAD ST, # 205 19148 #035-46-1998 L2001 IM IMG *020 †20

SHLANSKY-GOLDBERG, Richard. 3400 SPRUCE ST, DEPT OF RADIOLOGY 19104 #035-45-1984 L1986 DR *020 †80

SHLOMCHIK, Seymour. 1911 ARCH ST 19103 #041-02-1960 L1961 ORS *072 †40

SHOCHAT, Stephen Jay. 324 S 34TH ST, CHILDRENS HSPTL OF PHLDLPH 19104 #051-04-1963 L1974 PDS TS *020 †85,90

SHOCKMAN, Arlyne Taub. 3400 SPRUCE ST 19104 #041-07-1953 L1954 DR *071 †80

SHOEMAKER, Richard Carl. 8835 GERMANTOWN AVE, CHESTNUT HILL HOSPITAL 19118 #041-13-2003 L2003 EM *020 †16 ‡

SHOFF, William Hudson. 3400 SPRUCE ST 19104 #041-14-1973 L1974 EM IM *040 †20,16

SHOLEVAR, Ellen Harris. 100 E LEHIGH AVE, EPISCOPAL CAMPUS, STE 105 19125 #054-04-1966 L1967 CHP P *040 †75

SHONG, Yimin. 3900 WOODLAND AVE # 117, VA MEDICAL CTR 19104 #243-45-1983 L1999 PM *020 †60

SHOPPER, Glenn Kenneth. 5501 OLD YORK RD 19141 #028-02-1988 L1999 AN *020 †05

SHORE, Robert Alan. 9880 BUSTLETON AVE, STE 301 19115 #041-13-1981 L1982 IM *020 †20

SHORT, Scott Simonson. ■ 19119 #041-13-2008 *012

SHORT, William Rodney. 211 S 9TH ST, STE 210 19107 #041-09-1997 L1999 ID *020 †20

SHORTRIDGE, Beth Ann. 143 W GRAVERS LN 19118 #036-07-1984 L1987 PD *020 †55

SHORTT, Conor Patrick. 111 S 11TH ST, DEPT RAD 19107 #539-04-1999 L2007 MSR *012

SHOURAIE, Zarrin. 930 WASHINGTON AVE, SOUTHEAST HLTH CTR 19147 #517-01-1969 L1973 PD NPM *020 L55

SHOWALTER, Timothy Norman. 111 S 11TH ST, BODINE CANCER CENTER 19107 #051-01-2004 L2004 RO *012

SHOWAN, Ann Maria. 3400 SPRUCE ST 19104 #041-07-1977 L1978 AN *020 †05

SHPANER, Alla. 2375 WOODWARD ST 19115 #913-50-1974 L1998 IM *020 ‡

SHPIGEL, Aleksandr. 833 CHESTNUT ST STE 701 19107 #913-01-1980 L1999 IM *020 †20

SHRAGER, Joseph Ben. 3400 SPRUCE ST, HOSPITAL OF THE UNIV OF PA 19104 #024-01-1988 L1990 TS *020 †85,90

SHROPSHIRE, Diane M. 800 SPRUCE ST, 9TH SCHIEDT BLDG 19107 #005-14-1987 L1988 AN *020 †05

SHROTRIYA, Ritu. 3401 N BROAD ST, DEPT OF MED-8PP 19140 #035-08-2005 L2005 IM *012

SHUBERT, Matthew Alan. 3401 N BROAD ST, ER MED JONES HALL 10TH 19140 #041-02-2005 L2005 EM *012

SHULEMOVICH, Korina. 9501 ROOSEVELT BLVD, ASSOCIATES 19114 #023-07-1987 L1994 END *020 †20

SHULKIN, Mark Weiss. 4200 MONUMENT RD 19131 #056-05-1954 L1957 P *020 †75

SHULMAN, John Fingles. 205 N BROAD ST, 6TH FL 19107 #041-09-1981 L1983 IM NEP *020 †20

SHULMAN, Michael David. 3401 N BROAD ST 19140 #041-01-1983 L1984 NEP *020 †20

SHUM, Patrick Parkchuen. ■ 19107 #041-02-2007 L2007 TY *012

SHUM, Wesley Houchueh. ■ 19107 #033-05-1995 L1998 ORS *071

SHUMAN, Charles Ross. 3401 N BROAD ST STE 281, TEMPLE UNIV HOSP-SECT A 19140 #041-13-1943 L1944 DIA IM *020 †20

SHUMAN, Sandra J. 39TH MARKET STS, STE 120 19104 #041-12-1976 L1980 N *071 †75

SHURMAN, Daniel Louis. 1200 LOCUST ST STE 1, DERMATOLOGY SURGICAL CENTE 19107 #041-13-2002 L2002 D *012

SHUSTER, Eugene. 2601 HOLME AVE 19152 #041-02-1961 L1962 OBG *071 †30

SHUSTERMAN, Richard David. 2630 HOLME AVE, INSTITUTE FOR RESPIRATORY 19152 #041-07-1983 L1984 PUD CCM *020 †20

SIDDIQ, Farhan. ■ 19107 #704-20-2000 L2004 GS *012

SIDDIQI, Omar Khalid. ■ 19103 #028-02-2007 L2007 IM *012

SIDDIQUE, Mahmood Khan. 7600 CENTRAL AVE 19111 #495-65-1978 L1995 AN *020 †05

SIDDIQUI, Huma Sarah. 111 S 11TH ST, JEFFERSON UNIVERSITY 19107 #041-15-2006 L2006 PD *012

SIDDIQUI, Mahrukh. 5501 OLD YORK RD, ALBERT EINSTEIN MEDICAL CE 19141 #704-06-1987 L2001 PYG *020

SIDEROWF, Andrew David. 330 S 9TH ST, FL 3 19107 #036-07-1992 L1994 N *020 †75

SIDHOM, Victor El-Shahat. 245 N 15TH ST, MCP HAHNEMANN UNIV 19102 #915-04-1991 L2002 IM *020

SIDLOW, Stuart Frank. 3400 SPRUCE ST, HOSP OF THE UNIV OF PEN 19104 #041-15-2001 L2001 AN CCA *020 †05

SIEGEL, Donald. 3400 SPRUCE ST 19104 #041-01-1987 L1989 PTH *050 †50

SIEGEL, Eugene H. 6410A RISING SUN AVE 19111 #231-01-1957 L1963 IM ON *071

SIEGEL, Jamie Ellen. 1015 WALNUT ST, RM 904 19107 #041-07-1982 L1983 ON IM *020 †20

SIEGEL, Paul David. 219 N BROAD ST, FL 5 19107 #041-13-1955 L1956 PUD IM *071 †20

SIEGEL, Seymour. 709 S 5TH ST 19147 #041-13-1945 L1946 IM DIA *071 †20

SIEGEL, Steven Joseph. 3400 SPRUCE ST, 10TH FLOOR GATES BUILDING 19104 #035-47-1996 L1998 P *020 †75

SIEGEL, Todd Jeffrey. 1025 WALNUT ST, JEFFERSON MED COLL 19107 #041-02-1998 *100

SIEGELMAN, Evan Spencer. 3400 SPRUCE ST DEPT RAD, 1ST FLOOR FOUNDERS MRI 19104 #023-07-1988 L1991 R DR *040 †80

SIEGLE, Robert Louis. 245 N 15TH ST, DEPT OF RADIOLOGY 19102 #041-01-1967 L1968 DR PDR *020 †80

SIERRA, Karelis. 5501 OLD YORK RD, ALBERT EINSTEIN MED CTR 19141 #042-03-2006 L2006 P *012

SIEVERT, Angela Jae. ■ 19130 #021-01-2003 L2003 **PHO** *012 †55
SIFRI, Randa Dina. 1015 WALNUT ST, STE 401 19107 #038-41-1989 L1991 **FM** *020 †18
SIGEL, Bernard. 3300 HENRY AVE, THE MEDICAL COLLEGE OF PA 19129 #048-02-1953 L1960 **OS** *030 †85
SIGLER, Allison Joan. 1427 VINE ST, FL 3 19102 #041-02-1987 L1988 **ID** *020 †20
SIGURDSON, Elin Ruth. 333 COTTMAN AVE, FOX CHASE CANCER CENTER 19111 #065-01-1980 L1992 **GS SO** *020 †85
SILBER, Cynthia G. 1025 WALNUT ST, RM 107 19107 #035-46-1984 L1988 **OBG** *020 †30
SILBER, Jeffrey Howard. 324 S 34TH ST 19104 #023-07-1980 L1982 **PHO PD** *050 †55
SILBERBERG, Donald H. 3400 SPRUCE ST, DEPT NEURO 19104 #025-01-1958 L1963 **N** *020 †75 ‡
SILBERG, Debra Gail. 415 CURIE BLVD, STE 600CRB 19104 #035-46-1989 L1991 **IM** *020 †20
SILBERMAN, Ira. 3401 N BROAD ST, 1ST FLOOR OPB 19140 #165-04-1967 L1969 **R** *020 †80
SILBERSTEIN, Marsha J M. ■ 19106 #041-01-1971 L1972 **OS AN** *062 †05
SILBERSTEIN, Stephen D. 111 S 11TH ST, STE 8130 GIBBON BUILDING 19107 #041-01-1967 L1968 **N** *020 †75 ‡
SILER, Janet Naidl. 2701 HOLME AVE, STE 201 19152 #041-07-1966 L1969 **AN** *020 †05 ‡
SILFEE, Allen. 245 N 15TH ST, MAIL STOP 1011 19102 #023-01-2007 L2007 **EM** *012
SILIBOVSKY, Randi Sue. 111 S 11TH ST, STE G4250 19107 #035-46-1985 L1991 **ID IM** *020 †20
SILK, Raymond E. 1701 WALNUT ST, EIGHTH FLOOR 19103 #041-02-1948 L1949 **GS TRS** *020 †85 ‡
SILKOFF, Philip Emanuel. 219 N BROAD ST, STE 8 19107 #917-30-1978 L2004 *020 †20
SILPASUVAN, Artit Art. ■ 19146 #010-02-2004 L2007 **END** *012 †20
SILPASUVAN, Dollie D. ■ 19146 #010-02-2003 L2003 **AN** *100
SILVA, Patricio. 3401 N BROAD ST, TEMPLE UNIV HOSP 19140 #231-03-1964 L1997 **NEP IM** *020
SILVER, Michael Allan. 34TH ST AND CIVIC CENTER B 19104 #023-07-1974 L1975 **CHP P** *030 †75
SILVERMAN, Michael Lee. 51 N 39TH ST 19104 #041-13-1980 L1983 **ID IM** *020 †20
SILVERMAN, Morton Lewis. 1616 WALNUT ST 19103 #041-13-1973 L1974 **PM IM** *020 †20
SILVERSTEIN, Julie Harris. 51 N 39TH ST 19104 #035-19-1985 L1989 **IM** *020 †20
SILVERSTEIN, Phillip. 1800 LOMBARD ST 19146 #035-15-1974 L1977 **IM N** *020 †20
SILVERSTEIN, Scot Mark. 3141 CHESTNUT ST BLDG RUSH, DREXEL UNIV CLGE OF INFO 19104 #024-05-1981 L1983 **IM OS** *050
SILVESTRI, Guido. ■ 19143 #561-27-1987 L2000 **CLP** *020 †50
SILVESTRY, Scott C. 1025 WALNUT ST, STE 607 19107 #041-01-1991 L2000 **TS VS** *020 †85,90
SILVIERA, Matthew Leon. 3401 N BROAD ST, OF S 19104 #041-13-2005 L2005 **GS** *012
SIM, Bich-Thuy Thi. ■ 19104 #048-13-2007 L2007 **IM** *012
SIMEONE, Frederick A. 6825 NORWITCH DR 19153 #041-13-1960 L1966 **NS** *020 †25
SIMERMAN, Lee Paul. 800 SPRUCE ST, DEPT OF RADIOLOGY 19107 #035-46-1981 L1982 **DR** *020 †80 ‡
SIMHAN, Jay. 3401 N BROAD ST, OF SURGE 19140 #036-01-2007 L2007 **GS** *012
SIMMONS, Agnes H. 6201 CHESTNUT ST 19139 #041-02-1977 L1978 *020
SIMMONS, Becky Anne. 421 CURIE BLVD RM 1308, U OF PA BRB II/III 19104 #003-01-1983 L1996 **NPM PD** *050 †55
SIMMONS, Jennifer Chalfin. 3998 RED LION RD STE 235 19114 #041-02-1998 L1999 **GS** *020 †85
SIMMONS, Salmi. 501 S 54TH ST 19143 #041-07-1992 L2000 **VIR DR** *020 †80
SIMMONS-BURGESS, Mary E. 1913 N BROAD ST 19122 #041-07-1998 L2001 **FM** *020 †18
SIMMS, Harry Hank. 5501 OLD YORK RD, SURG/KLEIN BLDG - STE 510 19141 #010-01-1979 L2005 **GS** *020 †85
SIMON, Barbara. 245 N BROAD ST MS 437, STE 6109 6TH FLOOR NCB 19107 #041-15-2000 L2001 **END** *100 †20
SIMON, Erica Joyce. ■ 19107 #041-02-2004 L2004 **OBG** *012
SIMON, Frank Alan. 3624 MARKET ST 19104 #035-19-1968 L1971 **PD** *030 †55
SIMON, Jeremy Ian. 925 CHESTNUT ST, FIFTH FLOOR 19107 #041-02-2001 L2001 **PMM** *020 †60
SIMON, Marc Alan. 3998 RED LION RD, STE 230 19114 #041-14-1987 L1988 **OBG** *020 †30
SIMON, Matthew Spector. 4041 WALNUT ST 19104 #035-46-2006 L2007 **IM** *012
SIMON, William Herson. 1800 LOMBARD ST 19146 #041-01-1963 L1964 **ORS** *020 †40
SIMONCINI, Gina Maria. ■ 19147 #041-13-2006 L2006 **IM** *012
SIMONSON, Stephanie M. ■ 19103 #041-02-2002 L2004 **GS** *100
SIMPAO, Allan Frederick. ■ 19107 #041-02-2007 L2007 **IM** *012
SIMPKINS, Henry. 3401 N BROAD ST 19140 #011-02-1975 L1992 **PTH** *020 †50
SIMPKINS, Nicole Alyce. 900 WALNUT ST STE 2 19107 #048-04-2004 L2004 **CN** *012
SIMPSON, Alyson Beth. 111 S 11TH ST, JEFFERSON UNIVERSITY 19107 #016-06-2004 L2004 **PD** *020 †55
SIMPSON, Holly Clare. ■ 19107 #041-02-2008 *012
SIMPSON, Joan Witherspoon. ■ 19119 #041-02-1975 L1976 **OBG** *100
SIMPSON, Sergeemile. 245 N 15TH ST, DUCOM/EMERGENCY MEDICINE 19102 #041-01-2003 L2003 **ETX** *012 †16
SIMS, Carrie Adelia. 3440 MARKET ST 1ST FL, TRAUMA CENTER AT PENN 19104 #005-02-1995 L2004 **CCS** *100 †85
SIMS, Michael William. 51 N 39TH ST, PEN PRESB MED CTR 4TH FL 19104 #041-01-1998 L2001 **PCC** *100 †20
SIMSON, Michael Byron. HSP UNV OF PA 19104 #024-01-1970 L1971 **CD IM** *050 †20
SINCLAIR, Rebecca Ogur. 3401 N BROAD ST 8PP, INTERNAL MEDICINE 19140 #051-04-1998 L2001 **IM** *020 †20
SINDALL, Celina Czeslawa. 111 S 11TH ST, JEFFERSON UNIVERSITY 19107 #023-01-2006 L2006 **PD** *012
SINER, Jonathan Meiss. 3400 SPRUCE ST, 3 SILVERSTEIN/STE E 19104 #041-12-1998 L2000 **PCC** *100 †20
SINGER, Edward Samuel. 5401 OLD YORK RD, STE 201 19141 #041-13-1968 L1969 **CD IM** *020 †20 ‡
SINGER, Maurice. 4517 N BROAD ST 19140 #041-77-1974, ▲ L1975 **FM** *020
SINGH, Basant Kumar. 4900 WYALUSING AVE 19131 #495-67-1985 L1995 **P** *020 †75
SINGH, Dhssraj. ■ 19104 #539-07-2007 *100
SINGH, Gurcharan. 3996 RED LION RD 19114 #495-03-1970 L1976 **PM** *020 †60
SINGH, Harminder. 909 WALNUT ST, 3RD FL 19107 #024-07-2004 L2004 **NS** *012
SINGH, Kamalpreet Kaur. 900 W QUEEN LN 19129 #305-01-2005 L2006 **IM** *012
SINGH, Kuldeep. 2900 W QUEEN LN 19129 #305-01-2003 L2003 **GS** *020
SINGH, Neena Kaur. ■ 19102 #041-13-2007 **GS** *012
SINGH, Nisha. 5243 GROVE AVE 19124 #495-69-1971 L1977 **GP** *020 †20
SINGH, Priya C. 1015 WALNUT ST, UNIVERSITY HO 19107 #033-05-2002 L2004 **HO** *012 †20
SINGH, Rajiv. ■ 19107 #035-01-2002 L2006 **CD** *012 †20

SINGH, Savita. 2137 WELSH RD, STE 2E 19115 #495-59-1990 L2001 **RHU** *100 †20
SINGH, Shashank Shishir. ■ 19130 #496-22-2001 L2002 **PAN** *100
SINGH, Vishwas Anand. ■ 19103 #041-15-2005 L2007 **IM** *012
SINGHAL, Ajay. 51 N 39TH ST 19104 #495-45-1980 L1994 **EM CCM** *020 †85
SINGLA, Smit. 3400 SPRUCE ST, UNIVERSITY OF PENNSYLVANIA 19104 #495-29-2002 L2006 **GS** *012
SINHA, Ashish Chandra. 3400 SPRUCE ST, 6 DULLES BLDG 19104 #496-21-1987 L2005 **AN** *020 †05
SINHA, Manisha. 3509 N BROAD ST, TUMC 19140 #496-01-2000 L2006 **PD** *020 †55
SINK, James David. 3300 HENRY AVE 8TH FL 19129 #036-05-1974 L1989 **CD TS** *071 †85,90
SINKER, Dale Victor. 1335 W TABOR RD, STE 306 19141 #041-13-1971 L1972 **IM OS** *020
SINKIWICZ, Melissa Ann. ■ 19128 #041-77-2007, ▲ L2008 **IM** *012
SINMAYANANDAN, Pranavan. 4TH FLOOR - S TOWER MAIL, DREXEL UNIVERSITY COLLEGE 19102 #654-01-2006 L2007 **IM** *012
SINNAR, Shamim Abbas. 245 N 15TH ST, MAIL STOP 495 19102 #036-07-2001 L2001 **OBG** *100
SIOW, Hua-Chiang. 111 S 11TH ST, STE 8130 19107 #539-06-1995 L2000 **N** *020 †75
SIRAGAVARAPU, Raghavendra. 2900 W QUEEN LN 19129 #495-21-2000 L2006 **P** *012
SIREN, Karen Anne. 3401 N BROAD ST, DEPT EM 19140 #041-13-2007 **EM** *012
SIRI, Matthew A. 3400 SPRUCE ST, HOSP OF U OF PENN 19104 #033-06-2003 L2004 **AN** *020
SIRIPONG, Arida. ■ 19144 #041-15-2008 *012
SIRNA, Sara Jeanne. ■ 19103 #035-08-1980 L1994 **CD IM** *020 †20
SITKOFF, Malcolm. 10201 BUSTLETON AVE, A16 19116 #041-02-1956 L1957 **PD IMG** *020 †55
SITTENFIELD, Stephen Lee. 4200 MONUMENT RD 19131 #041-09-1978 L1979 **P** *020 †75 ‡
SIVA, Shivi Sivananthi. ■ 19103 #305-01-1996 L2001 **GE** *020 †20
SIVADASAN, Nina. ■ 19107 #033-06-2008 *012
SIVAK, Helene Fran. ■ 19103 #035-09-1979 L1980 **IM** *100
SIVAK, Steven Larry. 5401 OLD YORK RD, STE 363 DEPT OF MEDICINE 19141 #035-09-1976 L2001 **IM** *020 †20
SIVAKANTHA, Sivagnanalin. 100 W LEHIGH AVE 19133 #495-44-1991 L1999 **P** *020
SIVAKUMAR, Mahalingam. 3401 N BROAD ST, VASCULAR SURGERY DEPARTMEN 19140 #495-66-1983 L2000 **GS** *020 †85
SIVALINGAM, Eliyathamby. 9TH & WALNUT STREET 19107 #220-01-1955 L1975 **OPH** *071 †35
SIVAMURTHY, Krupa Mathada. 5501 OLD YORK RD, ALBERT EINSTEIN MED CTR 19141 #496-35-1996 L2003 **PHO** *012 †55
SIVAN, Eyal. ■ 19130 #550-04-1983 L1996 *020
SIVARAAMAN, Kartik. 3401 N BROAD ST, TEMPLE UNIVERSITY HOSPITAL 19140 #495-61-2001 L2006 **IM** *100
SIVARAJAN, Venkatesan B. 3400 CIVIC CENTER BLVD 19104 #065-02-1998 L2002 **PDC** *100 †55
SIVASANKAR, Chitra. 245 N 15TH ST, DEPT OF GME 19102 #495-31-1997 L2006 **AN** *012
SIVICK, Donald A, Jr. 736 CORNELIA PL, FOUNDATION SURGERY CENTER 19118 #041-13-1985 L1987 **AN** *020 †05 ‡
SIVITZ, Marta E Brand. 1726 S BROAD ST, STE 101 19145 #041-13-1969 L1970 **OPH A** *020 †35
SIWINSKI, Denise E. 2925 E THOMPSON ST, NORTHEAST MEDICAL PRACTICE 19134 #041-14-1996 L2002 **FM** *020 †18
SKALAK, Genevieve Marie. ■ 19128 #041-77-2006, ▲ L2006 *012
SKAROFF, Richard Mark. 8001 ROOSEVELT BLVD, # 209 19152 #041-09-1981 L1981 **IM** *020
SKIDMORE, Christopher T. 900 WALNUT ST, STE 200 19107 #028-34-1999 L2005 **CN** *020 †75
SKLAR, Peter Andrew. 1427 VINE ST, FL 3 19102 #010-01-1996 L2003 **IM** *012 †20
SKLIROS, Dimitrios S. 7901 STATE RD, CORRECTIONAL FACILITY 19136 #418-01-1980 L1994 **CD** *020 †20
SKOLNIK, Jeffrey Marc. 3615 CIVIC CENTER BLVD, ABRAMSON RESEARCH CENTER 9 19104 #035-19-1999 L2002 **PHO** *020 †55
SKRZYPCZAK, Jan L. ■ 19107 #041-02-2008 *012
SKVARKA, Christopher Bria. 219 N BROAD ST, FL 4 19107 #041-02-2004 L2004 **D** *012
SLANINA, Michael Stephen. 1331 E WYOMING AVE, STE 3100 19124 #041-09-1976 L1978 **PD** *020
SLAP, Joseph W. 1601 WALNUT ST STE 1312 19102 #041-09-1952 L1953 **P PYA** *020 †75
SLEEPER, Joshua Pierce. ■ 19107 #041-02-2007 *012
SLEMP, Alison Elaine. ■ 19143 #041-01-2002 L2002 **PS** *012
SLENKER, Nicholas Robert. ■ 19107 #041-02-2007 L2007 **ORS** *012
SLEVIN, Kieran Anthony. ■ 19106 #539-04-1998 L2001 **AN** *020 †05
SLIPMAN, Curtis. 3400 SPRUCE ST, REHAB MED 19104 #048-04-1983 L1991 **PM** *020 †60
SLIWINSKI, Christopher St. 3401 N BROAD ST, TEMPLE UNIV HOSP 19140 #305-01-2004 L2004 **OBG** *012
SLOANE, Bruce Bordman. 1216 ARCH ST, STE 3B 19107 #035-15-1984 L1991 **U** *020 †95
SLONE, Jenifer Gross. 5501 OLD YORK RD, ALBERT EINSTEIN MEDICAL CE 19141 #041-13-2000 L2005 **RNR R** *100 †80
SLOTCAVAGE, Rachel Lynne. ■ 19104 #041-01-2008 *012
SLOTOROFF, Craig Brook. 1025 WALNUT ST, STE 1112 19107 #041-02-2002 L2002 **U** *012
SLOVITER, Henry A. 313 STEMMLER HALL, UNIVERSITY OF PENNSYLVANIA 19104 #041-01-1949 L1950 **N HEM** *050
SMALL, Calvin Jos. ■ 19130 #007-02-1988 L2005 **IM** *020 †20
SMALS, Laura Elizabeth. ERIE AVE AT FRONT ST 19133 #046-11-1994 L1996 **PD** *040 †55
SMARTT, James Madison. ■ 19147 #041-01-2005 L2005 **PS** *012
SMERGEL, Eleanor Maloney. 3601 A ST 19134 #010-02-1979 L1981 **PDR** *020 †80 ‡
SMITH, Allan Mitchell. 5401 OLD YORK RD, STE 201 19141 #041-09-1967 L1968 **CD IM** *020 †20 ‡
SMITH, Arthur Elliott. 211 S 9TH ST, NINTH STREET INTERNAL 19107 #035-03-1960 L1964 **IM CD** *020 †20
SMITH, Arthur K. 800 SPRUCE ST 19107 #041-02-1971 L1972 **IM FM** *020 †18
SMITH, Christina Topley. 399 S 34TH ST LOWR LEVE, PENN TOW 19104 #041-02-2002 L2002 **FM FSM** *020 †18
SMITH, Courtney Ann. 3400 SPRUCE ST, UNIV PA HLTH SYS 19104 #033-05-2004 L2004 **HO** *012 †20
SMITH, David Jos. 840 WALNUT ST 19107 #056-06-1971 L1974 **OPH** *020 †35
SMITH, David Roy. 33 E CHESTNUT HILL AVE, STE 201 19118 #041-14-1988 L1990 **FM** *020 †18 ‡
SMITH, David Stuart. 3400 SPRUCE ST, DEPT OF ANESTHESIOLOGY 19104 #056-06-1975 L1976 **AN** *020 †05
SMITH, Douglas A. 2016 BAINBRIDGE ST, FIRST FLOOR 19146 #048-12-2004 L2004 **P** *012
SMITH, Emmanuel Ademola. 3998 RED LION RD, SUITE 306 - TC MOB 19114 #036-05-1991 L1998 **GS** *012
SMITH, Harvey Edward. 1015 WALNUT ST, THOMAS JEFFERSON UNIV 19107 #041-14-2002 L2002 **ORS** *020

SMITH, Howard Bradley. 111 N 49TH ST 19139 #041-02-1943 L1944 P *071 †75
SMITH, Jackson Bruce. DEPT OF MEDICINE, JEFFERSON MED COLLEGE 19107 #036-05-1965 L1966 IM OS *050 †20
SMITH, Jordana Margaret. ■ 19107 #041-02-2007 L2007 GS *012
SMITH, Kelly Nicole. ■ 19106 #041-15-2008 *012
SMITH, Kimberly Gail. ■ 19106 #016-02-2007 L2007 OBG *012
SMITH, Lauren Dorothy. ■ 19107 #041-02-2008 *012
SMITH, Lisa Kim. ■ 19123 #041-15-2008 *012
SMITH, Marna Recene. 6826 CRITTENDEN ST 19119 #028-02-2000 L2001 AN *012
SMITH, Megan Emily. ■ 19103 #033-06-2006 L2006 IM *012
SMITH, Michael Louis. 3400 SPRUCE ST, 5 SILVERSTEIN 19107 #051-01-2000 L2001 NS *100
SMITH, Mitchell Reed. 333 COTTMAN AVE, FOX CHASE CANCER CTR 19111 #038-06-1979 L1993 ON HEM *020 †20
SMITH, Ralph Wm, Jr. 8001 STATE RD 19136 #041-13-1975 L1977 FM *050
SMITH, Rebecca Gwendolyn. ■ 19118 #422-01-1995 L1999 PM *020 †60
SMITH, Robert Allan. 1420 LOCUST ST STE 200 19102 #041-02-1957 L1958 FM PME *071 †18
SMITH, Robert Terence. 501 S 54TH ST 19143 #041-09-1992 L1996 DR *020 †80
SMITH, Robert Vincent. 8835 GERMANTOWN AVE 19118 #041-14-1975 L1976 FM IMG *040 †18
SMITH, Ryan. ■ 19107 #041-14-2003 L2003 DR *012
SMITH, Sabrina Elan. ■ 19103 #035-19-1999 L2001 CHN *020 †55,75
SMITH, Steven. 10125 VERREE RD, STE 106 19116 #550-02-1989 L1994 AI *020 †55,03
SMITH, Susan Annette. ■ 19130 #041-01-2007 L2007 *012
SMITH, Timothy Craig. 4641 ROOSEVELT BLVD, FRIENDS HOSPITAL 19124 #041-02-1989 L1991 P PYG *020 †75
SMITH-WHITLEY, Kim Marie. 324 S 34TH ST 19104 #010-01-1989 L1992 PHO PD *020 †55
SMOAK, Benjamin Ryan. 3535 MARKET ST, 2ND FL, DEPT OF PSYCHIATRY 19104 #036-05-2003 L2003 P *020
SMOGER-RIOS, Danah Eve. 1900 S BROAD ST, CHOP PRIMARY CARE CENTER 19145 #041-01-2003 L2003 PD *020 †55
SMOLIK, Sarah Beth. ■ 19106 #054-04-2002 L2002 AN *100 †05
SMOLINSKI, Kara Noelle. 3400 SPRUCE ST, DEPT OF DERMATOLOGY 19104 #023-01-2000 L2003 D *100 †55,15
SMUD, Jorge D. ■ 19146 #132-01-1970 L1975 OBG *075 †30
SMULLEN, Melvyn J. 1001 CITY LINE AVE, STE ED 212 19151 #919-05-1970 L1981 PTH *020
SMYLES, John M, II. 2601 HOLME AVE, NAZARETH HOSP 19152 #010-03-1982 L1982 RO *020 †80
SNEAD, Kenneth. ■ 19147 #047-07-1959 L1960 P CHP *071
SNOW, Jennifer Lucille. 3400 SPRUCE 19104 #041-14-2000 L2001 PCC *100 †20
SNOW, Vincenza Theresa. 190 N INDEPENDENCE MALL W 19106 #231-01-1994 L1998 IM *040 †20
SNOWDEN, Philip Lee. ■ 19140 #047-07-1964 L1987 GP OBG *020
SNYDER, Howard M, III. CHILDRENS HOSP 3RD WOODBLD, DIV OF PED UROLOGY 19104 #024-01-1969 L1971 UP PDS *020 †85,95
SNYDER, Joel Mark. 7401 RHOADS ST 19151 #041-09-1965 L1966 GP IM *020
SNYDER, Laura Ann. ■ 19107 #041-02-2008 *012
SNYDER, Lois K. 8835 GERMANTOWN AVE 19118 #041-07-1983 L1984 FM *020 †18
SNYDER, Maryann. ■ 19146 #041-02-2004 L2004 PD *100
SNYDER, Peter Joseph. 415 CURIE BLVD, 778 CLINICAL RESEARH BLDG. 19104 #024-01-1965 L1971 END *050 †20
SNYDER, Quinn Matthew. 245 N 15TH ST, MAIL STOP 1011 19102 #003-01-2007 L2007 EM *012
SNYDER, Richard Lamar. 1901 MARKET ST FL 30, RICHARD L SYNDER MD 19103 #041-07-1982 L1983 FM *030 †18 ‡
SNYDER, Stuart. 219 N BROAD ST, FL 6 19107 #041-01-1967 L1968 CD IM *020 †20 ‡
SNYDER, Thoburn R, Jr. 1409 LOMBARD ST, CATCH COMM MENT HLTH REHAB 19146 #036-07-1945 L1946 P *062
SNYDERMAN, Deborah Alice. 1616 WALNUT ST, STE 2310 19103 #041-02-1986 L1987 P *020 †75
SNYDERMAN, Nancy Lynn. 3400 SPRUCE ST OFC 5, UNIVERSITY OF PENNSYLVANIA 19104 #030-05-1977 L1978 OTO *020 †45
SNYDMAN, Leonard. 1650 ARCH ST, FL 22 19103 #041-13-1938 L1939 GP IM *071
SO, Andrew Lao. 8835 GERMANTOWN AVE, CHESTNUT HILL HOSPITAL 19118 #748-10-1979 L1988 PTH HMP *020 †50
SOBEL, Adam Craig. 1015 CHESTNUT ST, STE 1500 19107 #041-02-1992 L1994 IM *020 †20
SOBEL, Rachel Kim. ■ 19147 #005-02-2006 L2007 OPH *012
SOBEL, Richard Murray. 1518 WALNUT ST STE 1110 19102 #041-14-1981 L1986 P PMM *020 †75 ‡
SOBER, Stephanie Paula. ■ 19147 #041-01-2007 L2007 OBG *012
SOCCIO, Raymond Edward. ■ 19104 #035-20-2005 L2005 END *012
SODERMAN, Jeffrey Tyler. 3401 N BROAD ST, TEMPLE UNIV HOSP 19140 #024-16-2004 L2007 EM *012
SOHN, Andrew Min. ■ 19131 #041-02-2008 *012
SOHN, Min. 1800 LOMBARD ST, STE 400 19146 #583-06-1959 L1971 PTH *020 †50
SOHN, Richard L. 2137 WELSH RD STE 1C, NORTHEAST PHILA VASCULAR 19115 #035-48-1995 L2004 VS *020 †85
SOKOL-HESSNER, Lauge. ■ 19104 #041-01-2007 L2007 IM *012
SOKOLOFF, Neil M. BROAD & VINE STS 19102 #041-01-1978 L1980 CD *050 †20
SOKUNBI, Gbolabo Olabiyi. 3401 N BROAD ST, TEMPLE UNIVERSITY HOSPITAL 19140 #033-06-2006 L2006 ORS *012
SOL, Lech. ■ 19134 #759-03-1980 PM *075
SOLARI, Paola Regina. 5501 OLD YORK RD, ALBERT EINSTEIN MED CTR 19141 #935-07-1999 L2002 ID *100 †20
SOLARIN, Kolawole O. 1025 WALNUT ST, STE 700 19107 #690-01-1982 L1993 NPM *020 †55
SOLI, Soleiman M. 6043 GERMANTOWN AVE 19144 #517-05-1958 L1967 OBG *071 †30
SOLIMAN, Ahmed Mohamed. 3400 N BROAD ST 19140 #023-07-1991 L1997 OTO *020 †45
SOLIN, Lawrence Jay. 3400 SPRUCE ST DEPT RO 19104 #043-01-1978 L1979 RO *020 †80
SOLIT, Robert Wolf. 5401 OLD YORK RD, STE 203 19141 #041-02-1961 L1962 TS GS *020 †85,90
SOLITRO, Tamara Stolz. ■ 19106 #008-02-2006 L2006 IM *012
SOLL, Adam. ■ 19107 #010-03-2003 L2007 PM *020
SOLL, David Benj. 10160 BUSTLETON AVE, STE F 19116 #016-42-1955 L1959 OPH PS *071 †35
SOLL, Stephen M. 5001 FRANKFORD AVE, SOLL EYE PC OF PA 19124 #016-42-1988 L1993 OPH PS *020 †35
SOLNICK, Paul Bernard. 1900 S BROAD ST 19145 #041-13-1958 L1959 PUD IM *071 †20

SOLOMON, Jack Lee. 111 N 49TH ST 19139 #041-09-1962 L1963 PYA P *020
SOLOMON, Jeffrey Adam. 3400 SPRUCE ST 19104 #041-01-1994 L1999 DR *020 †80
SOLOMON, Missale. 2900 W QUEEN LN 19129 #366-03-2004 L2006 IM *012
SOLON, Victor Ricardo A. 9150 MARSHALL ST, STE 20 19114 #748-01-1989 L1996 IM *020 †20
SOLOW, Edward Allen. 7133 ROOSEVELT BLVD 19149 #041-02-1973 L1974 CD IM *071 †20
SOLTANI, Banafsheh. 3401 N BROAD ST, DEPT MED 19140 #045-01-2007 L2007 IM *012
SOLZHENITSYN, Carolyn O. 3535 MARKET ST FL 2, PENN BEHAVIORAL HEALTH 19104 #041-01-1999 L2000 P *012
SOMA, Siva Kumar Reddy. 2900 W QUEEN LN 19129 #495-73-2003 L2006 IM *012
SOMERS, Debra Lynn. 5401 OLD YORK RD STE 501 19141 #041-02-1989 L1991 DR *020 †80
SOMERS, Debra Lynne. 9331 OLD BUSTLETON AVE, STE 201 19115 #041-02-1989 L1991 OBG *020 †30
SOMERS, Herbert J. 7604 CENTRAL AVE, STE 101 19111 #041-02-1959 L1960 OBG *020 †30
SOMERS, Judy A. 800 SPRUCE ST, EMERGENCY DEPT. 19107 #048-15-1996 L1999 MPD *020 †20
SOMERS, Liza. 8835 GERMANTOWN AVE 19118 #041-01-1993 L1995 EM *020 †16
SOMERS, Robert Glenn. 5501 OLD YORK RD, KLEIN 510 19141 #041-02-1958 L1959 GS CD *020 †85
SOMMER, Julius John Geo. ■ 19144 #041-09-1945 L1948 IM OS *020
SONDHEIMER, Neal John. ■ 19130 #016-02-2002 L2002 OS *100 †55,19
SONDHEIMER, Steven Jos. 3701 MARKET ST, 8TH FL 19104 #041-01-1974 L1975 GYN REN *020 †30
SONEJI, Maulin Surendra. ■ 19115 #028-34-2006 L2006 MPD *012
SONG, Frederick Suh. 5501 OLD YORK RD, WCB-4TH FLOOR, AEMC 19141 #041-02-2003 L2003 ORS *012
SONG, Yung-Doo. 6816 CASTOR AVE 19149 #583-02-1962 L1971 IM *020
SONI, Adarsh Kumar. 100 E LEHIGH AVE, DEPT MED 19125 #495-29-1972 L1975 IM EM *020 †16
SONIS, William Allen. 4641 ROOSEVELT BLVD, MEDICINE/P O BOX 45358 19124 #041-12-1974 L1977 CHP P *050 †55,75
SONMEZOCAK, Levent N. ■ 19103 #902-10-1989 L1998 N *100
SOOD, Shobana. 3400 SPRUCE ST, 2 MALONEY BUILDING 19104 #033-06-1993 L1997 D *020 †15
SOOD, Suman Lata. ■ 19147 #023-07-2001 L2004 HO *012
SORENSEN, Mark Christian. PO BOX 15010, 802 N BROAD ST 19130 #049-01-1978 L1986 EM *020
SORIANO, Humberto Eduardo. 3601 A ST, DEPT OF GASTROENTEROLOGY 19134 #231-03-1984 L2002 PG HEP *050 †55
SORIANO, Ramon Zaratan. ■ 19141 #748-01-1956 PTH ORS *071
SOROKIN, Rachel Bernice. 800 SPRUCE ST 19107 #028-02-1980 L1982 IM RHU *030 †20 ‡
SORRENTINO, David F. ERIE AVE AT FRONT ST 19133 #041-07-1997 L2000 NPM *020 †55
SOSNOVSKY, Isabella. 8220 CASTOR AVE 19152 #913-01-1981 L1997 P *020 †75
SOTO, Andres Felipe. 800 SPRUCE ST, PA HOSPITAL-UPHS 19107 #264-05-1997 L2005 IM *012
SOTO, David Rodolfo. ■ 19130 #035-08-2003 L2006 DR *100
SOUAYAH, Nizar. 3401 N BROAD ST, 5TH FL 19140 #895-01-1990 L2001 N *020 †75
SOUDER, Jeremy Kent. ■ 19131 #041-01-2005 L2005 IM *012
SOULELES, Alexis Maria. 111 S 11TH ST, JEFFERSON UNIVERSITY 19107 #041-77-2004, ▲ L2004 PD *012
SOULEN, Michael C. 3400 SPRUCE ST, HOSP OF THE UNIV OF PA 19104 #041-01-1984 L1990 VIR *020 †80
SOUNDARARAJAN, K. 3401 N BROAD ST 4TH FL, TEMPLE UNIV HOSP 19140 #495-04-1988 L1998 VS GS *020 †85
SOUNDARARAJAN, Suganthi. 1800 LOMBARD ST 19146 #495-04-1988 L1997 PCP *020 †50
SOUSSAN, Elie Ramon. 245 N 15TH ST, DEPT OF GME 19102 #550-02-2006 L2006 OBG *012
SOUTENDIJK, Christine V. 219 N BROAD ST, FL 6 19107 #017-20-1994 L1997 IM *020 †20 ‡
SPAETH, George L. 840 WALNUT ST 19107 #024-01-1959 L1961 OPH *030 †35
SPANDORFER, John M. 833 CHESTNUT ST, STE 701 19107 #041-02-1991 L1991 IM *020 †20
SPARACINO, Barbara. 100 E LEHIGH AVE, SUITE 105, MEDICAL ARTS BU 19125 #308-13-2004 L2007 P *012
SPEAR, Barbara A. 561 FAIRTHORNE AVE, BEHAVIORAL HEALTH SYSTEMS 19128 #041-09-1960 L1961 P *020 †75
SPEARS, Julia Ann. 205 N BROAD ST, STE 200 19107 #041-07-1996 L1999 PS *020 †65
SPECKHALS, Lori Ann. ■ 19103 #038-43-2008 *012
SPECTOR, Barry Marc. 1020 SANSOM ST, THOMPSON BLDG, STE 239 19107 #041-14-1979 L1984 EM PE *020 †16,55
SPECTOR, Nancy Dollase. ERIC AVE AT FRONT ST, ST CHRISTOPHERS HSP-CHLDRN 19134 #024-16-1990 L1993 PD *040 †55
SPELLMAN, Jessica Leia. 1000 WALNUT ST APT 1410 19107 #041-02-2004 L2006 AN *012
SPENCE, Abraham Mead. ■ 19146 #041-01-2008 *012
SPENCER, Ariel Uzziah. ■ 19141 #035-01-2001 L2006 GS *020
SPENCER, Charles L. ■ 19118 #016-06-1977 L1995 IM EM *020 †20
SPENCER, Geoffrey Scott. 3400 SPRUCE ST 19104 #051-07-2000 L2001 GE *100 †20
SPENCER, John Anthony. 132 S 10TH ST 19107 #917-03-1983 R *040
SPENCER, Steven Edward. 4544 TEESDALE ST 19136 #043-01-2003 L2005 IM *100 †20
SPERLING, Brian L. 5501 OLD YORK RD, SUITE 510 KLEIN BUILDING 19141 #041-77-2004, ▲ L2005 GS *020
SPERLING, Michael Robt. 900 WALNUT ST, STE 200 19107 #041-13-1978 L1985 N CN *020 †75
SPETTEL, Sara Elise. ■ 19129 #041-15-2008 *012
SPIEGEL, David Andrew. ■ 19106 #036-07-1990 L1996 OP *020 †40
SPIEGEL, Joseph Richard. 925 CHESTNUT ST FL 6 19107 #041-02-1979 L1985 OTO HNS *020 †45
SPILIOPOULOS, Michail. 3401 N BROAD ST 19140 #418-01-2003 L2005 OBG *012
SPINA, Joseph, Jr. 840 WALNUT ST 19107 #041-01-1966 L1967 OPH *020 †35
SPIRN, Marc Jason. 840 WALNUT ST, STE 1020 19107 #033-06-2002 L2006 OPH *100 †35
SPITALNIK, Steven Leonard. 51 N 39TH ST 19104 #016-02-1978 L1985 PTH *050 †50
SPITZ, Francis Robt. 3400 SPRUCE ST, FL 4 19104 #008-02-1989 L1992 GS *020 †85
SPITZ, Lawrence Kenneth. 1801 MARKET ST STE 200 19103 #041-01-1972 L1973 IM OM *020 †20
SPITZER, Stanley. 700 COTTMAN AVE, BLDG A 19111 #041-09-1962 L1963 CD IM *020 †20
SPIVACK, Daniel Ehud. 3401 N BROAD ST, OF S 19140 #143-11-2001 L2003 GS *012
SPIVACK, Talya Ruth. ■ 19107 #041-02-2007 L2007 IM *012
SPODIK, Maya. ■ 19116 #041-15-2004 L2004 GE *012 †20
SPRATT, Robert Hugh. ■ 19119 #041-13-1964 L1967 OM *071
SPRAY, Thomas Laton. 34TH & CIVIC CENTER BLVD, CHILDRENS SURGICAL ASSOC 19104 #036-07-1974 L1994 TS GS *020 †85,90

SPROCH, Amy Lee. 1400 REED ST 19146 #041-02-1998 L2000 **P** *020 †75
SQUIRES, Kathleen Elaine. 211 S 9TH ST STE 210, WALNUT TOWERS 19107 #041-07-1981 L1983 **ID IM** *030 †20
SRINIVAS, Sindhu. ■ 19146 #033-05-2000 L2001 **OBG** *100
SRINIVASAN, Kuruchi. 1922 COTTMAN AVE 19111 #495-04-1975 L2000 **IM** *020 †20
SRINIVASAN, Sivakumar. ■ 19107 #496-23-1995 L2003 **CD** *012 †20
SRINIVASAN, Swetha Kannam. ■ 19107 #041-02-2007 **GS** *012
SRINIVASAN, Vijay. ■ 19104 #495-36-1995 L2001 **CCP** *020 †55
SROUJI, Nadine Samir. 3400 SPRUCE ST 19104 #041-01-1996 L1998 **IM** *020 †20
STAAB, Jeffrey Paul. 3400 SPRUCE ST - FOUNDERS, HOSP OF UNIV OF PA F11.015 19104 #041-12-1988 L1998 **P ADM** *050 †75
STAAS, William E, Jr. 1513 RACE ST, MAGEE REHAB 19102 #041-02-1962 L1963 **PM** *071 †60
STABLE, Joaquin Jose. 662 PARLIN ST 19116 #308-10-1985 L2007 **PYG** *100
STACK, William T. 900 E WESTMORELAND ST 19134 #041-02-1952 L1953 **GP** *072
STADTMAUER, Edward Allen. 3400 SPRUCE ST, 16 PENN TOWER 19104 #041-01-1983 L1985 **HEM ON** *020 †20
STAFEEVA, Ksenia A. ■ 19130 #041-15-2008 *012
STALLINGS, Virginia Anne. 3535 MARKET ST, RM 1558 19104 #001-02-1979 L1985 **PD NTR** *050 †55
STAMATAKI, Sofia. ■ 19107 #418-01-1996 L2002 **GS** *100
STAMBOLIAN, Dwight Edward. 51 N 39TH ST 19104 #035-08-1976 L1980 **OPH** *050 †35
STAMPAS, Argyrios. 3400 SPRUCE ST, 5 WEST GATES 19104 #035-15-2005 L2005 **PM** *012
STANDIFORD, Steven Brooks. 1331 E WYOMING AVE, CANCER TREATMENT CENTERS O 19124 #033-05-1981 L1982 **SO HNS** *020 †85
STANEK, Marjorie Ann S. 5501 OLD YORK RD 19141 #041-07-1972 L1974 **CD IM** *020 †20
STANGER, Ben. 3400 SPRUCE ST 19104 #024-01-1997 L2006 **GE** *020 †20
STANILLA, Joseph Kipp. 4200 MONUMENT RD 19131 #041-02-1981 L1982 **P OS** *020 †75
STANITSKI, Kate Elizabeth. ■ 19130 #041-12-2003 L2004 **DR** *012
STANKIEWICZ, Corrie Ann. ■ 19146 #041-01-2008 *012
STANKO, Christine Sue. 219 N BROAD ST, FL 4 19107 #030-05-2000 L2001 **D** *020 †15 ‡
STANLEY, Charles Alfred. 802D ARCH ST, 34TH & CIVIC CENTER BLVD 19107 #051-01-1970 L1972 **PDE DIA** *050 †55
STANLEY, John Roger. 415 CURIE BLVD, 211 CRB 19104 #024-01-1974 L1994 **D** *050 †15
STANLEY, Nigel Noel. PENN U HOSP CARD VASC PUL 19104 #917-21-1963 L1973 **PUD** *050
STANSELL, Laura Gale. ■ 19146 #048-15-2006 L2007 **U** *012
STANTON, Robert Wm J. 1601 WALNUT ST STE 1009 19104 #065-09-1960 L1962 **P** *020
STARK, Joanne Nicole. ■ 19146 #041-01-2002 L2002 **PD** *100
STARLING, Amaal Jilani. ■ 19129 #041-15-2008 *012
STARLINGRONEY, Rameen Sha. ■ 19119 #010-03-2005 L2005 **PTH** *012
STAROSCIK, Rudolf N. 3400 SPRUCE ST, DIVISION OF ORGAN TRANSPLN 19104 #041-01-1965 L1966 **GS TS** *020 †85
STARR, Stuart Eliot. 324 S 34TH ST 19104 #024-01-1968 L1977 **PD** *071 †55
STARRELS, Joanna Lynn. 423 GUARDIAN DR, 1303-B BLOCKLEY HALL 19104 #041-02-2002 L2005 **IM** *100 †20
STASSI, John. 5501 OLD YORK RD 19141 #041-01-1981 L1982 **DR** *020 †80
STAUB, Alice Wolferd. ■ 19128 #041-13-1949 L1951 **IM** *071
STAVROPOULOS, Dimitri G. 5501 OLD YORK RD 19141 #418-01-1993 L2001 **IM** *100 †20
STAVROPOULOS, S William. 3400 SPRUCE ST, DEPT OF RADIOLOGY 19104 #016-43-1994 L2000 **VIR** *020 †80
STECHEL, Jaime Nicole. 3401 N BROAD ST, DEPT OF MED -8PP 19140 #041-13-2005 L2005 **IM** *012
STEDMAN, Wm Hansell Hall. 421 CURIE BLVD, UNIV OF PENN 19104 #024-01-1984 L1986 **GS** *020 †85
STEEL, Howard Haldeman. 3551 N BROAD ST 19140 #041-13-1945 L1948 **ORS OS** *071 †40
STEELE, Suzanne Laura. 10551 DECATUR RD 19154 #041-09-1993 L1995 **FM OM** *030 †18
STEENHOFF, Andrew Pierre. ■ 19104 #836-01-1994 L2002 **PDI** *100 †55
STEERE, Joanna. ■ 19129 #051-01-2003 L2003 **PTH** *100 †50
STEERMAN, Paul Harvey. 5401 OLD YORK RD, STE 503 19141 #041-13-1975 L1976 **GS** *020 †85
STEFANESCU-STURZ, Raluca. ■ 19130 #781-01-1997 L2005 **P** *012
STEFANYSZYN, Mary A. 840 WALNUT ST, STE 912 19107 #024-01-1978 L1979 **OPH** *020 †35
STEGNER, Melissa Robyn. ■ 19131 #041-15-2003 L2004 **GS** *020
STEIN, Adam David. ■ 19127 #917-01-2003 **IM** *012
STEIN, Alan Robt. 7600 CENTRAL AVE 19111 #033-06-1989 L1991 **IM** *020 †20
STEIN, David E. 219 N BROAD ST, STE 8 19107 #035-08-1997 L1999 **GS** *020 †85,10
STEIN, Elisa Anne. ■ 19130 #010-01-2003 L2003 **GS** *012
STEIN, Ellen Meredith. ■ 19130 #010-01-2004 L2007 **GE** *012 †20
STEIN, Franklin Milton. 8846 FRANKFORD AVE 19136 #005-17-1962 L1965 **FM** *020 †18
STEIN, Harold. 8001 ROOSEVELT BLVD, STE 502 19152 #035-08-1976 L1983 **NEP IM** *020 †20 ‡
STEIN, Herbert. 9140 ACADEMY RD, STE A 19114 #041-12-1961 L1962 **ORS** *020 †40
STEIN, Jack M. 1735 MARKET ST, FL 14 19103 #041-77-1977, ▲ L1979 **OM IM** *030 †20,70
STEIN, Joel Michael. 3400 SPRUCE ST, UNIV OF PA HLTH SYS 19104 #041-01-2007 L2007 **IM** *012
STEIN, John Robert. 133 S 36TH ST LBBY 2, COUNSELING & PSYCHOLOGIC 19104 #041-01-1995 L2004 **P** *020 †75
STEIN, Louis Henry, Jr. ■ 19107 #041-02-2008 *012
STEIN, Meryl Yvonne. 3400 SPRUCE ST 19104 #033-06-1999 L2003 **PM** *020 †60
STEIN, Mitchell Evan. 2465 GRANT AVE 19114 #041-13-1988 L1988 **OPH** *020 †35
STEIN, Peter Gore. 4508 CHESTNUT ST 19139 #033-06-1983 L2003 **IMG** *020 †18
STEIN, Richard B. ■ 19118 #649-35-1987 L1993 **OS** *100
STEIN, Sherman Chas. ■ 19106 #035-01-1967 L1968 **NS** *071 †25
STEIN, Sophie Deborah. ■ 19103 #033-06-2003 L2003 **HO** *012 †20
STEIN, Tamara Elena. ■ 19102 #021-01-1998 L2005 **PD** *020
STEINBACH, Alan. 2301 E ALLEGHENY AVE 19134 #035-47-1984 L1985 **PUD CCM** *020 †20
STEINBERG, Annie Goldie. 324 S 34TH ST, CHILDRENS HSPTL OF PHLDLPH 19104 #024-05-1982 L1987 **P PD** *020 †55,75
STEINBERG, Daniel Israel. 3400 SPRUCE ST, UNIVERSITY OF 19104 #035-46-1998 L2002 **IM** *020 †20
STEINBERG, David Richard. 39TH & MARKETS ST, PENN ORTHO # 1 CUPP PAV 19104 #041-01-1984 L1985 **HS OTR** *020 †40
STEINBERG, Joshua Andrew. 399 S 34TH ST, PENN TOWER (LOWER LEVEL) 19104 #024-07-2002 L2007 **IM** *020 †20
STEINBERG, Marvin Edward. 3400 SPRUCE ST 19104 #041-01-1958 L1960 **ORS** *071 †40
STEINBERG, Stanford Mark. 255 S 17TH ST STE 2301 19103 #041-02-1962 L1963 **P IM** *020 †20,75

STEINER, Ann Lorie. 3400 SPRUCE ST 19104 #038-06-1978 L1997 **OBG** *020 †30
STEINER, Robert Morris. 800 SPRUCE ST 19107 #041-02-1964 L1965 **DR R** *040 †80
STEINFELD, Jonathan. ERIE & FRONT ST 19134 #041-07-1998 L2001 **PDP** *020 †55
STEINFIELD, Paul Howard. 3110 GRANT AVE 19114 #041-09-1982 L1987 **ORS HS** *020 †40
STEINGARD, Joseph J. 2601 S 12TH ST 19148 #649-14-1972 L1973 **FM** *020
STEINHOFF, Stephanie Alis. ■ 19106 #041-12-2006 L2006 **AN** *012
STEINHOUSE, Natawadee S. 719 RHAWN ST 19111 #891-02-1966 L1971 **PDA PUD** *075
STEINHOUSE, Roy. 100 E LEHIGH AVE, DEPT PSYCH 19125 #041-13-1968 L1969 **P GP** *020 †75
STEIXNER, Brian Lawrence. ■ 19107 #041-13-2005 L2005 **U** *012
STEPHEN, Michael John, Jr. 19103 #024-05-2001 L2005 **PCC** *012
STEPPACHER, Lester G, Jr. ■ 19104 #035-19-1995 L1995 *035 †85
STEPPACHER, Robert Clarke. UNIVERSITY & WOODLAND AVES 19104 #041-09-1963 L1964 **P** *020 †75
STERENSON, Erin Lindsie. ■ 19129 #041-15-2008 L2008 *012
STERLING, Francis Henry. 3900 WOODLAND AVE, VETERANS ADMINISTRATION 19104 #041-02-1960 L1961 **IM END** *020 †20
STERLING, Kevin Adrian. 3400 SPRUCE ST, 1 FOUNDERS PAVILION 19104 #028-02-2001 L2005 **IM** *100 †20
STERMAN, Daniel Howard. 3600 SPRUCE ST DEPT PUD 19104 #035-20-1989 L1991 **PUD** *020 †20
STERN, Aaron Huppert. ■ 19130 #048-02-2005 L2005 **EM** *012
STERN, David Harry. 51 N 39TH ST, PRESBYTERIAN MULTSPCLTY GR 19104 #041-01-1996 L1999 **IM** *020 †20
STERN, John J. 301 S 8TH ST, STE 1B 19106 #035-19-1979 L1988 **ID IM** *020 †20
STERN, Lillian R Hirsch. 2301 S BROAD ST, DEPT OF RADIOLOGY 19148 #041-13-1967 L1968 **DR NM** *020 †80
STERN, Linda. 3300 HENRY AVE, MEDICAL COLLGE OF PNNSYLVN 19129 #041-07-1988 L1991 **IM** *020
STERN, Matthew Bruce. 1800 LOMBARD ST STE 900 19146 #036-07-1978 L1979 **N** *020 †75
STERN, Robert Gary. 3401 N BROAD ST, TEMPLE ANESTHESIA ASSOCIAT 19140 #035-01-1977 L1983 **DR PUD** *020 †80
STERN, Roy. 3333 N BROAD ST, RM 343 19140 #035-09-1960 L1962 **P** *020
STERNBACH, Marna R. 10 SHURS LN, STE 203 19127 #024-07-1975 L1982 **FM** *020 †18
STERNER, Dorrit H. 3340 N BROAD ST 19140 #041-13-1979 L1980 **IM IMG** *020 †20
STERNER, Todd M. 6608 CASTOR AVE 19149 #041-13-1979 L1981 **PD** *020 †55
STETTLER, Nicolas Auguste. 324 S 34TH ST 19104 #869-05-1988 L1998 **PG** *012
STEVEN, James Mac Laren. 324 S 34TH ST, CHILDRENS HOSP OF PHILA 19104 #038-41-1981 L1983 **PAN CCP** *030 †55,05
STEVENS, Jeffrey L. ■ 19128 #041-15-2006 L2007 **IM** *012
STEVENS, Scott Michael. ■ 19143 #035-03-2000 L2006 **P** *020 †75
STEWART, Alexander Leo. ■ 19146 #038-44-2007 L2007 **TY** *012
STEWART, Emily Ann. 111 S 11TH ST 19107 #041-02-2007 L2007 **IM** *012
STEWART, Jeffrey Ivan. ■ 19130 #041-15-2007 L2007 **IM** *012
STEWART, John Robert. ■ 19107 #041-01-2007 L2007 **IM** *012
STIEFEL, Michael Fred. 3400 SPRUCE ST, DEPARTMENT OF NEUROSURGERY 19104 #051-04-2000 L2001 **NS** *100
STIFFEL, Arthur. 5501 OLD YORK RD 19141 #041-13-1944 L1945 **HS TRS** *071
STILLMAN, Alfred Edward. 1 PENN BLVD, STE 4423 19144 #035-19-1963 L1995 **IM IMG** *020 †20
STINEMAN, Margaret Grace. 3615 CHESTNUT ST, RM 101 RALSTON PENN CTR 19104 #041-09-1983 L1985 **PM** *050 †60
STINNETT, James Le Baron. 3400 SPRUCE ST, HOSPITAL OF THE UNIVERSITY 19104 #041-01-1965 L1966 **P** *020 †75
STIRPARO, Joseph James. 5501 OLD YORK RD, ALBERT EINSTEIN MED CTR 19141 #041-02-2005 L2005 **GS** *012
STITELMAN, David Hugo. ■ 19103 #041-01-2004 L2004 **GS** *012
STITZENBERG, Karen Beth. 333 COTTMAN AVE, ATTN: MEDICAL STAFF OFFICE 19111 #036-01-2000 L2007 **GS** *100 †85
STIVERS, Jon Scott. ■ 19143 #041-13-1998 L1998 **FM** *100
STOCKTON, Kevin Lee. 4641 ROOSEVELT BLVD 19124 #308-07-1983 L1985 **P** *020 †75
STODDARD, Frederick Rhode. ■ 19128 #041-13-2002 L2002 **GS** *100
STOFFERS, Doris Adelheid. 3400 SPRUCE ST, STE J PENN TOWERS 9TH FLOO 19104 #023-07-1991 L1998 **END IM** *050 †20
STOFKO, Douglas Lee. ■ 19131 #041-77-2007, ▲ L2007 **TY** *012
STOHL, Sheldon M. ■ 19104 #041-01-2003 L2003 **AN** *012 †55
STOKES, Arthur Lee. 7812 KNOX RD 19118 #041-09-1976 L1976 **FM** *050
STOKES, Francis De Sales. ■ 19118 #041-13-1926 L1927 **ORS** *071
STOKES, Ranjan. 2601 HOLME AVE 19152 #495-45-1972 L1978 **R DR** *020 †80
STOLTZFUS, Glenn Luke. 2142 MT VERNON 19130 #034-01-1979 L1979 **IM** *020 †20
STOLYAROV, Polina. 6722 BUSTLETON AVE 19149 #913-04-1975 L2001 *020
STOLZ, Ruth Ida. 1025 WALNUT ST STE 403, DIVISION OF CARDIOLOGY 19107 #035-46-1981 L1992 **CD IM** *020 †20
STONE, Andrew Michael. 3900 CITY AVE, STE D-108 19131 #041-09-1980 L1983 **P** *020 †75
STONE, Marielle Kathryn. ■ 19107 #041-02-2007 **GS** *012
STONE, Richard Alan. 51 N 39TH ST 19104 #035-01-1972 L1976 **OPH** *050 †35 ‡
STONEHOUSE, Amber Rae. ■ 19103 #041-02-2005 L2005 **FP** *012
STONER, Daryl Elizabeth. ■ 19118 #041-12-1986 L1990 **OBG** *020 †30
STOPYRA, Gary Andrew. CEDARCREST & I78 19105 #041-07-1996 L1998 **PTH OS** *020 †50
STORER, Joan Nancy. 840 WALNUT ST 19107 #041-02-1977 L1981 **OPH** *075 †35
STOREY, Thomas Patrick. 500 S BROAD ST 19147 #041-01-1985 L1989 **IM** *020 ‡
STOVER, Mark Conrad. 800 SPRUCE ST, PENNSYLVANIA HOSPITAL 19107 #028-02-2003 L2003 **EM** *100
STRAHLE GLASER, Gretchen. ■ 19146 #041-15-2006 **OBG** *012
STRAIN, Jay James. 5401 OLD YORK RD, STE 503 19141 #036-07-1990 L2006 **CCS TRS** *020 †85
STRATTON, Stephanie Benay. ■ 19145 #041-14-2008 *012
STRAUB, Renee Danielle. ■ 19130 #041-13-2007 L2007 **TY** *012
STRAUSS, Jerome Frank, III. 421 CURIE BLVD, 1354 BRB II 19104 #041-01-1975 L1976 **GYN** *050
STRAUSS, Louis Samuel. ■ 19119 #021-01-2006 L2006 **FP** *012
STRAYER, David Sheldon. 1020 LOCUST ST, RM 251, DEPT OF PATHOLOGY 19107 #016-02-1976 L1992 **PTH** *050 †50
STREIM, Joel Edward. 100 W LEHIGH AVE 19133 #035-45-1978 L1988 **PYG IM** *050 †75
STRELETZ, Leopold Johann. 834 CHESTNUT ST, STE 420 19107 #041-13-1969 L1971 **N** *020 †75

STRICKLAN, David Keith. 5201 WYNNEFIELD AVE 19131 #041-09-1990 L1993 **IM** *020

STRING, Andreas Sebastian. 1015 WALNUT ST, 620 CURTIS BUILDING 19107 #408-30-1997 L2002 **GS** *100 †85

STROBL, Frank Joseph. 3400 SPRUCE ST, DEPT OF PATHOLGY & LB MDCN 19104 #051-01-1994 L1998 **PTH** *100 †50

STROM, Brian Leslie. 423 GUARDIAN DR, SUITE 823 BLOCKLEY HALL 19104 #023-07-1975 L1980 **IM EP** *050 †20

STRONG, Michael David. 230 N BROAD ST 19102 #041-02-1966 L1967 **TS** *020 †85,90

STRONG, Michelle Lynne. 3440 MARKET ST STE 101, DEPT OF SURGERY/DIV OF TRA 19104 #017-20-2002 L2007 **CCS** *012 †85

STUART, Marie. 1025 WALNUT ST STE 700, THOMAS JEFFERSON UNIV HOSP 19107 #495-04-1966 L1987 **PHO PD** *050 †55

STUBBS, George Winston. 840 WALNUT ST 19107 #010-03-1968 L1975 **OPH** *020 †35

STUCKERT MURPHY, Erika. 111 S 11TH ST, THOS JEFFERSON UNIV HOSP 19107 #409-33-2003 L2004 **N** *012

STUDDIFORD, James S, III. 833 CHESTNUT ST, STE 301 19107 #010-02-1969 L1972 **IM** *020 †20

STUEVE, Jacob Saunders. 1015 WALNUT ST, THOMAS JEFFERSON UNIV 19107 #028-03-2003 L2003 **ORS** *012

STUMACHER, Russell Jean. 1800 LOMBARD ST 19146 #041-02-1968 L1975 **ID IM** *020 †20

STUNKARD, Albert J. 3535 MARKET ST FL 3 19104 #035-01-1945 L1957 **P PHP** *050 †75

STURDIVANT, Erica Lynn. ■ 19150 #024-07-2007 *012

STURM, Eron Robert. ■ 19146 #047-05-2004 L2004 **CD** *012

STUTMAN, Fred A. 3501 NEWBERRY RD 19154 #041-13-1962 L1963 **FM GP** *020 ‡

STYLER, Michael Jay. 230 N BROAD ST, 15TH FL 19102 #056-06-1984 L1986 **HO HEM** *020 †20

STYLES, Terry Jean. 3400 SPRUCE ST 19104 #012-05-1993 L2003 **RO** *020 †80

SU, Chinyu. 3400 SPRUCE ST, DIVISION OF GASTROENTEROLG 19104 #035-46-1994 L1997 **GE** *020 †20

SU, Felice. ■ 19146 #016-06-2000 L2003 **CCP** *020 †55

SU, Huichun Irene. ■ 19146 #035-46-2001 L2001 **OBG** *100

SU, Lillian. 19104 #041-13-2000 L2004 **CCP** *100 †55

SU, Yongquan Simon. 213 N 9TH ST 19107 #243-21-1984 L1998 **IM** *020 †20

SUAREZ, Elizabeth A. ■ 19123 #748-10-1988 L2001 **PDE** *020 †55

SUAREZ, Erik Eddie. ■ 19103 #048-12-2001 L2005 **GS** *012

SUAREZ, Marian G. 3300 HENRY AVE, RM 226H GERIATRIC MEDICINE 19129 #748-10-1981 L1992 **IMG IM** *020 †20

SUBBIAH, Shanthi. 1427 VINE ST 19102 #038-40-1995 L1997 **IM** *020 †20

SUBBIAH, Varadarajan. ■ 19130 #033-05-2006 L2006 **IM** *012

SUBONG, Maria Sophia Libe. 245 N 15TH ST, DEPT OF MED EDU 19102 #748-02-2004 L2006 **GS** *012

SUBRAMANIAN, Hariharan. ■ 19130 #495-59-2002 L2004 **IM** *100 †20

SUBRAMANIAN, Srinivas. 135 E LEHIGH AVE 19125 #495-16-1999 L2001 **NEP** *012 †20

SUBRAMANYA, Deepthi. 4TH FLOOR - S TOWER MAIL, DREXEL UNIVERSITY COLLEGE 19102 #496-20-2005 L2007 **IM** *012

SUBZPOSH, Afreen. ■ 19144 #041-15-2004 L2004 **PD** *012

SUCHE, Kara Judith. ■ 19147 #041-15-2003 L2003 **PM** *020

SUCHIN, Karen Rebecca. 1528 WALNUT ST, STE 1101 19102 #041-01-1997 L1999 **DS D** *020 †15 ‡

SUDAK, Donna Marie. 401 S 2ND ST STE 402 19147 #041-07-1980 L1994 **P** *040 †75

SUDAK, Howard Stanley. 401 S 2ND ST, STE 402 19147 #038-06-1958 L1992 **P** *020 †75

SUDANO, Dominick George. ■ 19129 #041-15-2008 L2012 **IM** *012

SUDSANG, Thanwa. ■ 19104 #891-04-1995 L2004 **IM** *100

SUERO, Rene Oscar. 39TH & MARKET ST 19104 #308-01-1960 L1984 **GS VS** *020

SUGARMAN, Samuel. ■ 19130 #041-13-1939 L1940 **IM PUD** *071

SUGIURA, Henry T. PRESBY/UNIV PA MED CTR 19104 #041-13-1949 L1950 **PTH OS** *030 †50

SUH, Byungse. 7701 BURHOLME AVE 19111 #011-02-1973 L1978 **ID IM** *020 †20 ‡

SUH, David Byunghyun. 1302 WOLF ST 19148 #041-12-1992 L1996 **RO** *020 †80

SUKHAN, Sabrina N. 3400 SPRUCE ST, HOSPITAL OF THE UNIVERSITY 19104 #035-19-2004 L2004 **OBG** *012

SUKONTHAMAN, Yod. 3400 N BROAD ST 19140 #891-01-1964 **CRS** *100 †10,85

SULEIMAN, Nasir Musa. 2301 S BROAD ST, DEPT OF ANESTHESIA 19148 #038-40-1988 L2001 **AN IM** *020 †05,20

SULEWSKI, Michael Edmund. 51 N 39TH ST, SCHEIE EYE INSTITUTE, VAMC 19104 #041-01-1985 L1991 **OPH** *020 †20

SULIT, Benigno M. A EINSTEIN MED CTR/SO DIV 19147 #748-02-1956 **AN** *100 †05

SULLIVAN, Gail Theresa. 216 N BROAD ST, FL 4 19102 #041-07-1991 L1994 **OBG** *020 †30

SULLIVAN, Jennifer Lynn. 111 S 11TH ST, THOMAS JEFFERSON UNIVERSIT 19107 #023-01-2005 L2005 **GS** *012

SULLIVAN, Joseph Edgar. ■ 19119 #035-03-1998 L2002 **N** *100 †55,75

SULLIVAN, Kathleen Elaine. 324 S 34TH ST 19104 #005-02-1988 L1993 **IG RHU** *050 †55

SULLIVAN, Sara Remick. 324 S 34TH ST 19104 #016-06-1998 L2002 **PD** *020 †55

SULTANA, Carmen J. 834 CHESTNUT ST STE 400, DEPT OF OB/GYN 19107 #035-19-1986 L1987 **OBG** *040 †20

SUMERSON, Doris M. INDEPENDENCE PL NO 1611 19106 #041-13-1958 L1959 **GP EM** *020

SUMMERS, Alan Lee. 111 N 49TH ST, KIRKBRIDE CENTER 19139 #041-02-1971 L1972 **P** *020 †75

SUMMERS, Eric Frederick. ■ 19103 #035-46-1989 L1991 **ID** *020 †20

SUMMERS, Richard Fredric. 3535 MARKET ST FL 2, OFFICE OF EDUCATION 19104 #041-01-1984 L1985 **P PYA** *020 †75

SUMMERTON, Susan Lynn. 5501 OLD YORK RD, DEPT OF RADIOLOGY 19141 #041-13-1988 L1990 **DR** *020 †80

SUMMEY, Brett Taylor. ■ 19127 #047-20-2004 L2005 **D** *012

SUN, Alan C. 4301 N BROAD ST, DEPT MED 19140 #041-13-2007 L2007 **IM** *012

SUN, Jianzhong. 111 S 11TH ST, SUITE G8490/GIBBON 19107 #243-95-1985 L2000 **AN** *020 †05

SUN, Weijing. 3400 SPRUCE ST, 16 PENN TOWER 19104 #243-16-1982 L1998 **HO** *020 †20

SUN, William Z. 840 WALNUT ST 19107 #041-09-1976 L1977 **OPH** *020 †35

SUNDARARAJAN, Venkatesh. 834 CHESTNUT ST, T-150 19107 #038-41-2002 L2003 **APM** *020 †05

SUNDT, Linda Marie C. 111 S 11TH ST, STE 8490 19107 #041-02-1974 L1975 **AN** *020 †05

SUNG, Janice Sinae. ■ 19102 #035-06-2003 L2004 **DR** *012

SUNN, Gabriel Hernandez. 19107 #041-02-2006 L2006 **PM** *012

SUNNY, Joseph Kadathalaku, Jr. ■ 19107 #041-02-2008 *012

SURINDRAN, Sheena. 4TH FLOOR - S TOWER MAIL, DREXEL UNIVERSITY COLLEGE 19102 #496-63-2000 L2007 **IM** *012

SURKIS, William David. 4307 MITCHELL ST 19128 #041-15-2002 L2002 **IM** *020 †20

SURREY, Leslie Percy M. 1 PENN BLVD 19144 #010-03-1956 L1958 **IM** *020

SURYAVANSHI, Dilip Singh. 5501 OLD YORK RD 19141 #495-49-1991 L2007 **GS** *012

SUSI, Aita Kai. 3509 N BROAD ST 19140 #041-13-1992 L1994 **PD** *020 †55 ‡

SUSKIN, Murray. 333 COTTMAN AVE 19111 #023-01-1981 L1985 **AN** *012

SUSLOV, Kathryn. 2900 W QUEEN LN, DREXEL UNIV COLL OF MED 19129 #041-15-2006 L2008 **P** *100

SUSOTT, Emily Elizabeth. ■ 19104 #025-01-2006 L2007 **AN** *012

SUSTENTO-REODICA, Nedjema. 1 FRANKLIN TOWN BLVD STE 1 19103 #748-08-1976 L2004 **PTH** *020 †50

SUTARWALA, Anjum Abbas. 5401 OLD YORK RD STE 363, DEPT MED KLEIN BLDG 19141 #495-96-2001 L2001 **ID** *100

SUTHERLAND, Sharon Bonita. ■ 19131 #033-05-2003 L2003 **PD** *012

SUTNICK, Alton Ivan. 2135 SAINT JAMES ST, SUTNICK ASSOC 19103 #041-01-1954 L1955 **OS** *071 †20

SUTTON, Martin G St John. 3400 SPRUCE ST, UNIV OF PA MED CTR 19104 #917-23-1970 L1979 **CD** *020

SUZUKI, Hiroshi. RITTENHOUSE SQUARE, RITTENHOUSE CLARIDGE 517 19103 #572-41-1956 L1973 **GP PTH** *075

SVERSTIUK, Andrij Eugene. 245 N 15TH ST 19102 #913-05-1982 L1996 **BBK** *020 †50

SWABY, Ramona Faith. 333 COTTMAN AVE, STE 307R 19111 #023-01-1996 L1999 **ON** *020 †20

SWAINE, Charles Ritchie. 5233 LAURENS ST 19144 #041-07-1974 L1976 **AN** *100

SWAMI, Vanlila K. 245 N 15TH ST, MS 435, HAHNEMANN HOSPITAL 19102 #495-01-1966 L1974 **PTH** *020 †50

SWAN, Laura Lee. ■ 19106 #050-02-2002 L2005 **PD** *062 †55

SWANSON, Christopher E. ■ 19102 #033-06-2007 L2007 **ORS** *012

SWANSON, Jamie A. ■ 19107 #041-78-2007, ▲ L2007 **IM** *012

SWANSON, Paul Brian. 5735 RIDGE AVE, STE 208 19128 #041-01-1994 L2000 **OTO** *020 †45

SWARTZ, Charles David. 245 N 15TH ST 19102 #035-08-1958 L1962 **NEP IM** *071 †20

SWARTZ, Kristine. ■ 19107 #041-02-2006 L2006 **FP** *012

SWARTZ, Morris Alan. 39TH & MARKET STS, PHI BLDG STE 441 19104 #035-45-1975 L1976 **PUD IM** *020 †20

SWAVELY, Karen A. ■ 19147 #041-02-2007 L2007 **IM** *012

SWEENY, Joseph Michael. 3400 SPRUCE ST, DEPT OF MED, 100 CENTREX 19104 #010-02-2001 L2001 **CD** *012

SWEET, Jason Douglas. 3400 SPRUCE ST 19104 #038-06-2000 L2005 **DR** *012

SWENSON, Robert Melville. 3400 N BROAD ST, TEMPLE UNIV SCHOOL OF MED 19140 #028-02-1963 L1969 **IM ID** *075 †20

SWIERCZEWSKI, Magdalena E. 1800 LOMBARD ST 19146 #422-01-2005 L2005 **IM** *012

SWIERZBINSKI, Matthew Jos. ■ 19107 #041-02-2008 *012

SWIFT, Alexander Edward. ■ 19119 #041-13-2002 L2002 **PCC** *012 †20

SWIFT, Douglas Albert. 265 S 25TH ST, 265 SOUTH 25TH ST 19103 #041-01-1980 L1981 **AN** *020 †05

SWIFT, Sarah Elizabeth. 3400 SPRUCE ST, 3 SILVERSTEIN BL 19104 #041-01-1992 L1994 **IM** *020 †20

SWISHER, Loice A. 501 S 54TH ST 19143 #041-13-1989 L1991 **EM** *020 †16

SWISHER MCCLURE, Samuel D. 3400 SPRUCE ST, DEPT MED 19104 #055-01-2007 L2007 **IM** *012

SYAL, Renu. 3401 N BROAD ST, TEMPLE UNIVERSITY HOSPITAL 19140 #041-15-2001 L2001 **EM** *020 †16

SYAMALA, Jiji. ■ 19116 #495-31-2000 L2004 **IM** *020 †20

SYED, Tahniat Sultana. 231 N BROAD ST 19107 #041-07-1996 L1999 **PD** *020 †55

SYRE, Peter Paul, III. ■ 19104 #041-12-2008 *012

SYROPOULOS, Heidi. 5630 CHESTNUT ST 19139 #026-04-1984 L1988 **IM IMG** *020 †20 ‡

SZALDA, Dava Elizabeth. 3400 SPRUCE ST, HEALTH SYST 19104 #035-48-2007 L2007 **MPD** *012

SZAPARY, Philippe Olivier. 3701 MARKET ST, STE 760 19104 #016-02-1994 L1997 **IM** *050 †20

SZAYNA, Stanley. 2601 HOLME AVE 19152 #759-10-1954 L1971 **IM** *020

SZCZEPANSKI, Karen A. 800 SPRUCE ST, PENNSYLVANIA HOSPITAL CHOP 19107 #041-77-2000, ▲ L2001 **NPM** *100 †55

SZEELEY, Pamela Jeanne. 602 S WASHINGTON SQ, S-1805 19106 #041-12-1983 L1984 **P** *020 †75

SZEP, Zsofia. 3401 N BROAD ST, DEPT OF MEDICINE 19140 #041-02-2002 L2002 **ID** *012 †20

SZETO, Wilson Yuchun. 51 N 39TH ST, STE 2D 19104 #051-04-1996 L1999 **TS** *100 †85,90

SZUBA, Martin Peter. 3400 SPRUCE ST, 2 GIBSON BLDG 19104 #025-01-1984 L1993 **P** *020 †75

SZYLD, Demian. ■ 19106 #035-47-2005 L2005 **EM** *012

TABAS, Janine Gayle. 601 WALNUT ST L30, GALIANI OPTHALMOLOGY 19106 #051-04-1989 L1992 **OPH** *020 †35

TABATABAI, Mahmood. ■ 19130 #517-05-1962 L1983 **AN** *020 †05

TABBARAH, Khalid Zuhayr. ■ 19147 #605-01-2000 L2007 **N** *100 †75

TABBUTT, Sarah. 324 S 34TH ST 19104 #005-18-1990 L1998 **CCP PD** *020 †55

TABBY, Sara Marks. 1331 E WYOMING AVE, STE 1100 19124 #035-45-1980 L1984 **PM** *075 †60 ‡

TABCHI, Rehab. ■ 19131 #041-77-2007, ▲ **FP** *012

TABERSKI, Matthew. 3400 SPRUCE ST DEPT MED 19104 #035-06-1997 L1999 **EM** *020

TABOADA, Luis Angel. ■ 19107 #035-48-2007 L2007 **IM** *012

TACHDJIAN, Vahaken. 39TH & MARKET ST 19104 #605-01-1944 L1960 **IM GE** *071

TACHEV, Stefan Tachev. 245 N 15TH ST, STE 110 19107 #198-01-1995 L2000 **IM NEP** *020 †20

TADA, Hiroomi. 3401 N BROAD ST, TEMPLE UNIVERSITY HOSPITAL 19140 #041-02-1994 L1997 **GS** *020 †85

TAGLE, Raymundo T. 8201 STATE RD, DETENTION CENTER 19136 #748-08-1975 L1992 **IM** *020 †20

TAGOE, Udele Joyce. 245 N 15TH ST STOP 49, MCP HAHNEMANN UNIVERSITY 19102 #033-05-2002 L2002 **OBG** *100

TAHA, Firas Abdallah. 1 CHILDRENS CTR, DEPT OF MEDICAL AFFAIRS 19104 #305-01-2005 L2005 **PD** *012

TAHMOUSH, Albert Jos. 5800 RIDGE AVE, ROXBOROUGH MEMORIAL HOSPIT 19128 #024-07-1967 L1983 **N** *020 †75 ‡

TAHMOUSH, Michelle Emilin. ■ 19104 #041-15-2008 *012

TAICHMAN, Darren Bradley. 3900 MARKET ST 19104 #041-01-1993 L1996 **PCC** *020 †20

TAILOR, Dharmesh Ratilal. ■ 19104 #005-14-2005 L2005 **DR** *012

TAKACH, Patricia Ann. 51 N 39TH ST, UNIVERSITY OF PENN 19104 #024-05-1999 L2000 **AI** *020 †20,03

TAKAHASHI, Osahiro. 230 N BROAD ST, DEPT OF PEDIATRICS 19102 #572-05-1970 L1976 **PDC** *020

TAKAHASHI, Tomohide. 5501 OLD YORK RD 19141 #572-81-1985 L1998 **GS** *100

TAKAKUWA, Kevin Mark. 1020 SANSOM ST RM 239, THOMPSON BLDG 19107 #005-19-1999 L2000 **EM** *100 †16

TAKAO, Maura Noriko. ■ 19146 #016-06-2005 L2005 **PD** *012

TALAIE, Saied. 141 E LEHIGH AVE 19125 #517-01-1974 L1981 **PS** *020 †65

TALANGBAYAN, Francis V. 2244 N FRONT ST 19133 #748-10-1968 L1973 **IM CD** *020 †20

TALAREK, Chad Garrett. ■ 19107 #041-02-2008 *012

TALBOT, Sheryl Flaschen. 800 SPRUCE ST 19107 #035-19-1979 L1980 **AI** *020 †20,03

TALBOTT, Vanessa Armet. 111 S 11TH ST, THOS JEFFERSON UNIV HOSP 19107 #010-01-2007 L2007 **GS** *012

TALERMAN, Aleksander. 1025 WALNUT ST, STE 8439 19107 #352-10-1957 L1990 **PTH** *050

TALKOWSKI, Thomas S. 1800 LOMBARD ST 19146 #041-09-1985 L1988 **EM FM** *020 †18

TALLY, Toby Cohen. 7500 CENTRAL AVE STE 204, JEANES PHYSICIAN OFFICE BL 19111 #036-05-1998 L2003 **GS** *020 †85

TAMASE, Taciano Villano. 8001 STATE RD, HOC MOD II 19136 #748-07-1955 L1965 **GP** *030

TAMBURRINO, Joseph F. ■ 19148 #041-02-2003 L2003 **GS** *012

TAMHANKAR, Madhura Anand. 3900 WOODLAND AVE 19104 #495-96-1993 L2002 **OPH** *100

TAM TAM, Hima Bindu. 8200 HENRY AVE 19128 #894-01-2000 L2002 **OBG** *100

TAN, Josephine Chiu. 9246 JAMISON AVE B 19115 #748-01-1957 L1973 **AN** *071

TAN, Myrna M. 100 E LEHIGH AVE 19125 #748-01-1968 L1973 **AN** *020

TANCK, Allison Rae. ■ 19131 #056-05-2007 L2007 **GS** *012

TANG, Chik Kwun. 3401 N BROAD ST, TEMPLE UNIVERSITY SCHOOL O 19140 #385-03-1967 L1983 **ATP** *071 †50

TANG, Jie. 5501 OLD YORK RD 19141 #243-74-1996 L2006 **OBG** *100

TANG, Lin. 245 N 15TH ST MS 310, OF M 19102 #041-15-2002 L2003 **AN** *012

TANGDHANAKANOND, Kawin. ALUMNI AFFAIRS, ALBERT EINSTEIN MEDICAL CE 19141 #891-01-2004 L2007 **IM** *012

TANGOREN, Musa Ali. ■ 19143 #902-19-1993 L1999 **AN GS** *020

TANIGUCHI, Jennifer. ■ 19146 #028-02-2000 L2005 **ORS** *020 ‡

TANK, Niti. 132 S 10TH ST, THOMAS JEFFERSON UNIV HOSP 19107 #033-05-2006 L2007 **DR** *012

TANNA, Mala. ■ 19144 #041-15-2008 *012

TANNEN, Richard Laurence. 3600 HAMILTON WALK, 295 JOHN MORGAN BLDG 19104 #047-06-1960 L1995 **NEP IM** *050 †20

TANNENBAUM, Alan Harris. 9150 MARSHALL ST, NE MEDICAL CENTER STE 17 19114 #041-13-1984 L1986 **PD** *071 †55

TANNER, Jonathan Wm. 3400 SPRUCE ST, DEPT OF ANESTH 19104 #041-01-1992 L1996 **AN** *020 †05

TANNIRANDORN, Poj. ■ 19128 #891-02-1993 L1999 **END** *020 †20

TANNOURY, Chadi Akl. 111 S 11TH ST, THOMAS JEFFERSON UNIVERSIT 19107 #605-03-2004 L2006 **ORS** *012

TAPIA TAPIA, Ignacio Este. ■ 19147 #231-02-1993 L2004 **PDP** *100

TAPINO, Paul James. 51 N 39TH ST, SCHEIE EYE INST 19104 #041-02-1999 L2001 **OPH** *020 †35

TAPNIO-VITAL, Filipinas O. 2820 W DAUPHIN ST 19132 #748-08-1957 L1980 **GYN FM** *020

TAPPER, Theodore Saml. 3400 SPRUCE ST 19104 #024-01-1964 L1970 **PD** *020 †55

TAQUI, Bizath Syeda. 1316 W ONTARIO ST, MEDICINE 19140 #033-06-1997 L1999 **IM** *020 †20

TARAS, John Stanley. 834 CHESTNUT ST STE G114 19107 #025-01-1982 L1990 **HS ORS** *020 †40

TARATUTA, Elena Gregory. 3400 SPRUCE ST 19104 #024-01-1990 L1996 **DR** *020 †80

TAREEN, Kamran. 2821 ISLAND AVE, SECOND FLOOR 19153 #704-02-1983 L1993 **IM** *020 †20

TAROLA, Nicholas Albert. 950 WALNUT ST, BARRINGER BLDG APT 907 19107 #041-02-2003 L2003 **GS** *012

TARTAGLINO, Lisa Marie. 111 S 11TH ST, 3350 GIBBON BLDG 19107 #011-02-1983 L1991 **RNR R** *020 †80

TATAR, Emiliano Amir. ■ 19144 #041-15-2004 L2004 **PDP** *012 †55

TATEMATSU, Mitsuyoshi. ■ 19107 #572-01-1991 L2000 **IM** *012

TAUB, Daniel Ian. 909 WALNUT ST, STE 300 19107 #041-02-2004 L2006 *100

TAUB, Katherine Susan. 34TH-CIVIC CTR BLVD, CHILDRENS HOSP 19104 #010-02-2005 L2007 **CHN** *012

TAUB, Sarah Mattea. ■ 19119 #041-15-2005 L2005 **PD** *012

TAUBMAN, Bruce M. 324 S 34TH ST 19104 #035-46-1972 L1973 **PD GE** *020 †55

TAULANE, Joan. 800 SPRUCE ST, FL 2 19107 #041-09-1991 L1993 **NPM** *020 †55

TAUS, Lynne Frances. 2601 HOLME AVE 19152 #016-43-1984 L1991 **R** *020 †80

TAVAKOLI, Donald Neema. 123 KALOS ST, PHILADELPHIA 19128 #035-19-2005 L2005 **P** *012

TAVAKOLI, Zahra. 2900 W QUEEN LN, MCP HAHNEMANN UNIV 19129 #305-01-2001 L2001 **FM** *020 †18

TAYLOR, Colette Devona. ■ 19135 #041-77-2007, ▲ *012

TAYLOR, Elmer J, Jr. 600 S 43RD ST 19104 #041-02-1952 L1953 **IM FM** *040 *020

TAYLOR, James Edward. 111 N 49TH ST 19139 #021-01-1945 L1950 **P** *071 †75

TAYLOR, Joseph Paul. 3400 SPRUCE ST 19104 #041-02-1991 L1998 **IM** *020 †75

TAYLOR, Marianne Swan. ■ 19104 #035-45-2007 **MPD** *012

TAYLOR, Megan Beth. 10125 VERREE RD, STE 106 19116 #028-02-1983 L1985 **AI IM** *020 †20,03

TAYLOR, Nyali Elizabeth. ■ 19119 #041-15-2003 L2003 **GS** *012

TAYLOR, Philip Calvert. 3615 CHESTNUT ST 19104 #041-13-1978 L1980 **IMG IM** *020 †20

TAYLOR, Sarah Elizabeth. 3400 SPRUCE ST, OF PENNSYLVANIA 19104 #011-03-2007 L2007 **EM** *012

TAYLOR, Trusanda Elaine. 561 FAIRTHORNE AVE 19128 #041-09-1981 L1982 **ADM IM** *020

TAYLOR, W J Russell. ■ 19103 #062-01-1956 L1967 **PA IM** *020

TCHONG, Leo, Jr. ■ 19147 #024-07-2003 L2003 **END** *012 †20

TCHOU, Julia Chu. 3400 SPRUCE ST, FL 4 19104 #035-48-1995 L2003 **GS** *020 †85

TEBAS MEDRANO, Pablo. 3624 MARKET ST, STE 560W 19104 #847-13-1985 L2003 **ID** *020 †20

TECCE, Marc Anthony. 925 CHESTNUT ST, JEFFERSON HEART INSTITUTE 19107 #041-09-1987 L1989 **CD** *020

TEDALDI, Ellen Marie. 1316 W ONTARIO ST 19140 #035-06-1980 L1986 **IM** *020 †20

TEIXEIRA, Joao Pedro. 3820 LOCUST WALK, BOX 875 19104 #032-01-2008 *012

TELIVALA, Bijoy Pankaj. 333 COTTMAN AVE, STE C307 19111 #495-96-2002 L2004 **HO** *012 †20

TELLECHEA, Cristina M. ■ 19107 #041-02-2008 *012

TELLER, Lynn Ellen. 2307 DELANCEY ST 19103 #024-01-1980 L1982 **PD** *020 †55,05

TELLSCHOW, Steven Robt. 1800 LOMBARD ST 19146 #007-02-1990 L1995 **PCP** *020 †50

TEMPLETON, Abigail Paxton. ■ 19107 #041-02-2007 L2007 **FP** *012

TEMPLETON, Bryce. 4641 ROOSEVELT BLVD 19124 #038-06-1957 L1963 **P** *072 †75

TEMPLETON, John Marks, Jr. 324 S 34TH ST, CHILDRENS HSPTL OF PHLDLPH 19104 #024-01-1968 L1973 **PDS GS** *071 †85 ‡

TEMPLETON, Josephine Joan. 34TH ST & CIVIC CTR BLVD 19104 #561-17-1967 L1976 **AN PD** *071 †05 ‡

TENAGLIA, Nicholas C, Jr. ■ 19107 #041-02-2003 L2003 **EM** *020

TENG, Li-Min. 111 S 11TH ST, DEPT OF INTERNAL MEDICINE 19107 #008-02-2006 L2006 **IM** *012

TENNEY, Jessica Lee. ■ 19128 #041-15-2008 *012

TEPEROV, Elizabeth Gloria. 833 CHESTNUT ST, STE 701 19107 #041-02-1997 L2005 **IM** *020 †20

TEPPER, Richard Edward. 9501 ROOSEVELT BLVD, STE 208 19114 #041-14-1981 L1982 **ID IM** *020 †20

TER, Suat-Eng. 2601 HOLME AVE 19152 #143-05-1987 L1993 **DR NM** *020 †80,28

TERRAZAS, Miguel L. 245 N 15TH ST, MAIL STOP 1011 19102 #048-12-2007 L2007 **EM** *012

TERRIS, Despina. 3300 HENRY AVE 19129 #396-24-1983 L1984 **RO** *020 †80

TERRY, Colette Denise. ■ 19144 #041-13-2005 L2005 **PTH** *012

TERRY, Natalie Anne. ■ 19119 #041-01-2006 L2006 **PD** *012

TERZIAN, Allen Eugene L. 3998 RED LION RD STE 130 19114 #041-09-1982 L1983 **HEM ON** *020 †20

TERZIAN, Christian. ■ 19114 #875-02-1994 L2002 **IMG** *020 †20

TESFAYE-KEDJELA, Aida. ■ 19107 #041-02-2004 L2004 **AN** *020

TESSING, Stephanie Lynn. ■ 19128 #041-13-2008 *012

TESSLER, Alan Ralph. 2900 W QUEEN LN, DEPT OF NEUROBIOLOGY & ANA 19129 #035-19-1969 L1970 **N** *020 †75

TESTER, William John. 5501 OLD YORK RD, ALBERT EINSTEIN CANCER CEN 19141 #041-09-1977 L1979 **ON HEM** *020 †20

TETZLAFF, Michael Thomas. ■ 19104 #048-04-2005 L2005 **PTH** *012

TEWARI, Shruti. ■ 19106 #051-07-2006 L2006 **P** *012

THACHET, Cyriac Thos. 2576 E LEHIGH AVE 19125 #016-01-1989 L1991 **IM** *020 †20

THACKER, Jeffrey Dean. ■ 19131 #010-02-1992 L1999 **GS** *020

THADWAL, Baljeet Singh. 3401 N BROAD ST, DEPT OF ANESTHESIOLOGY 19140 #917-08-1999 L2003 **AN** *012

THAI, Kiet Vi. 251 E BRINGHURST ST 19144 #165-03-1980 L1987 **PD** *020

THAIN, Oung. 699 MAYFAIR ST, TABOR - ADAMS INTERNAL MED 19120 #209-01-1981 L1996 **IM** *020 †20

THAKKAR, Sonal Mahendra. ■ 19103 #038-06-1999 L2001 **PDC** *100 †55

THAKOR, Raju. 245 N 15TH ST, FL NCB 19102 #305-01-2002 L2002 **PCC** *012 †20

THAKUR, Anand Chandra. 5800 RIDGE AVE 19128 #422-01-1995 L2000 **APM** *020 †05

THAKUR, Indra Mohan. BROAD AND VINE STS, HAHNEMANN UNIV HOSP 19101 #495-75-1977 L1994 *100

THAL, Gary David. 3400 SPRUCE ST, 4 DULLES BLDG 19104 #035-01-1987 L2000 **AN** *071 †15,20

THALAYASINGHAM, B. CHRISTOPHERS HOSP, DEPT PED 19133 #917-04-1960 **PD** *050

THALER, Erica Robb. 3400 SPRUCE ST, DEPT OF ORL 5 SILVERSTEIN 19104 #024-01-1990 L1992 **OTO** *020 †45

THAMES, Marc David. 3401 N BROAD ST 19140 #051-04-1970 L1999 **CD IM** *050 †20

THAPLIYAL, Anshi. 5630 CHESTNUT ST 19139 #495-05-1998 L2004 **IM** *020 †20

THARAKAN, Marsha Thomas. 3400 SPRUCE ST, UNIV OF PA HLTH SYS 19104 #035-01-2001 L2001 **IM** *100

THASE, Michael Edward. 3535 MARKET ST, STE 670 19104 #038-40-1979 L1980 **P** *050 †75

THAWERANI, Hasina N. 324 S 34TH ST, CHILDRENS HOSP DEPT PATH 19104 #704-02-1968 L1979 **PTH DMP** *020 †50

THE, Andrew Hongsiang. 374 SHURS LN, APT 201 19128 #033-06-2005 L2005 **IM** *012

THEILING, Brent Jason. ■ 19147 #045-04-2006 L2006 **EM** *012

THEODOROPOULOS, Ioannis. 245 N 15TH ST, DEPT OF GME 19102 #409-15-2003 L2005 **GS** *012

THERIEN, Zsuzsanna Papp. 1100 WALNUT ST, JEFFERSON UNIV BREAST IMAG 19107 #473-01-1986 L2001 **DR** *020 †80

THIEU, Minh Pham. 700 SPRUCE ST STE 304, PENNSYLVANIA HOSPITAL 19106 #041-02-2001 L2001 **D** *020 †15

THISTLETHWAITE, Alan J. ■ 19119 #041-02-1982 *100

THODER, Joseph J, Jr. 3401 N BROAD ST, STE 350 19140 #041-13-1982 L1983 **ORS** *020 †40

THOM, Stephen Raymond. 3620 HAMILTON WALK, U PA INST ENVIRON MED 19104 #035-45-1981 L1987 **OS EM** *050 †16

THOMAS, Becky Ann. 324 S 34TH ST 19104 #041-02-2000 L2001 **PD** *020 †55

THOMAS, Brooke Burkart. ■ 19128 #051-07-2004 L2004 **EM** *012

THOMAS, Djahna. ■ 19104 #010-03-2001 L2007 **IM** *012

THOMAS, Harry L. 5555 WISSAHICKON AVE 19144 #010-03-1946 L1955 **GS** *072 †85

THOMAS, Lynda Theresa. 8815 GERMANTOWN AVE STE 40, HILL 19118 #041-13-1981 L1982 **OBG** *020 †30

THOMAS, Matthew Paulus. ■ 19128 #041-13-2007 L2007 **GS** *012

THOMAS, Michael Joseph. 3401 N BROAD ST, JONES HALL/10TH FLOOR 19140 #041-15-2001 L2001 **EM** *020 †16

THOMAS, Niku Kizuri. 423 GUARDIAN DR, 12TH FL 19104 #024-01-1997 L2000 **CD** *012 †20

THOMAS, Rebecca Meera. 3401 N BROAD ST, TEMPLE ANESTHESIA ASSOCIAT 19140 #495-27-1982 L1993 **PTH PCP** *020 †50

THOMLINSON, Robyn Renee. 3400 N BROAD ST, TEMPLE UNIV SCH OF MED 19140 #041-13-2006 **PD** *012

THOMPSON, Craig Bernie. 421 CURIE BLVD, 451 BRB II/II 19104 #041-01-1977 L1999 **ON IM** *020 †20

THOMPSON, James Edwin, IV. 3900 WOODLAND AVE, C/O VAMC 19104 #035-01-1997 L2000 **HO** *020 †20

THOMPSON, Lara Beth. ■ 19143 #041-13-2007 L2007 **FP** *012

THOMPSON, Leslie E. 3400 SPRUCE ST BOX 745, PENN TOWER HOTEL/LOWER LEV 19104 #065-09-1985 L1986 **IM HEM** *020 †20

THOMPSON, Troy Leon, II. 833 CHESTNUT ST, STE 1001 19107 #012-05-1973 L1987 **P PYA** *030 †75

THOMPSON, Virgil. 4750 FRANKFORD AVE 19124 #041-07-1979 L1983 **FM** *075 †18

THONET, Marcel Armile. 2308 E ALLEGHENY AVE 19134 #165-04-1949 L1962 **GS AS** *071

THORARENSEN, Olafur. 324 S 34TH ST 19104 #484-01-1990 L1995 **PD** *020 †55,75

THORNBURG, Bartley Garver. ■ 19107 #041-02-2008 *012

THORNTON, Eliza Ervin Ful. ■ 19153 #024-04-2006 L2006 **FP** *012

THORON, Louisa. 834 WALNUT ST, STE 650 19107 #035-01-1983 L1994 **ON HEM** *020 †20

THORVALDSSON, Sigurdur E. 1811 CHESTNUT ST 19103 #484-01-1964 L1972 **PS GS** *020

THORWARTH, William T. 8835 GERMANTOWN AVE 19118 #010-02-1951 L1958 **R** *071 †80

THOTA, Gopikiran. 2900 W QUEEN LN, DREXEL UNIV COLL OF MED 19129 #041-15-2006 L2006 *012

THOTTUNGAL, Jacob Paul. ■ 19122 #495-37-1963 L1985 **FM** *020

THRELFALL, Alexander Will. ■ 19130 #048-15-2006 L2006 **P** *012

THURAISINGHAM, Dhilan And. 3400 SPRUCE ST, UNIVERSITY OF PENNSYLVANIA 19104 #539-06-2007 L2007 **GS** *012

THURSTON, Laurel Ashlin. 245 N 15TH ST, DEPT OF EMERGENCY-MS 1011 19102 #051-07-2006 L2006 **EM** *012

TIEN, Wendy Chernwan. 800 SPRUCE ST, PA HOSP 19107 #041-02-2000 L2001 **DR** *100 †80

TIGGETT, Tarika Shareen. ■ 19139 #041-15-2004 **FM** *100 †18

TIKU, Anjali Priya. 3400 SPRUCE ST, DEPT OF MEDICINE 19104 #036-07-2003 L2003 **CD** *012 †20

TILLEKERATNE, Gayani. ■ 19102 #036-07-2007 L2007 **IM** *012

TILTON, John Christian. ■ 19103 #008-01-2001 *100

TIMMAPURI, Shaheen J. 111 S 11TH ST 19107 #033-05-2000 L2001 **PDS** *012

TIN, Lancelot Kwok-Leung. ■ 19107 #041-01-1983 L1984 **GS** *020 †85

TING, Jennifer C. BROAD-ONTARIO STS 19140 #041-14-2000 L2004 **CD** *100 †20

TINO, Gregory. 3600 SPRUCE ST, 826 GATES 19104 #035-47-1986 L1987 **PUD IM** *020 †20

TISNOWER, Herbert. 1837 S 65TH ST 19142 #654-01-1980 L1983 **FM** *020 †18 ‡

TIWANA, Humma Ishaq. BROAD AND ONTARIO ST 19140 #704-21-1998 L2003 **OBG** *100

TIWANA, Mansoor Ishaq. ■ 19114 #704-05-2001 L2004 **IM** *100 †20

TIYYAGURA, Satish. 5800 RIDGE AVE 19128 #041-02-1999 L2001 **ICE** *012 †20

TJIA, Jennifer. 260 S 24TH ST 19103 #024-05-1994 L2000 **IMG** *020 †20

TJOA, Christopher Wilkins. ■ 19103 #035-06-2007 L2007 **P** *012

TJOA, Ping-An. 7600 CENTRAL AVE 19111 #165-04-1974 L1980 **IM PTH** *020 ‡

TJOUMAKARIS, Stavropoula. ■ 19106 #041-02-2003 L2003 **NS** *012

TOBEY, Jennifer Dana. 111 S 11TH ST, THOMAS JEFFERSON UNIV HOSP 19107 #041-01-1996 L2000 **DR** *020 †80

TOBIAS, Terrence Patrick. ■ 19102 #038-34-2002 L2007 **VIR** *012 †80

TOBON, Alejandro. ONE GRADUATE PLAZA 19146 #264-10-1997 L2003 **N** *020

TOBOROWSKY, Robert Mark. 8TH & LOCUST ST, 319 HALL MERCER 19107 #041-01-1964 L1965 **P** *062 †75

TOCA, Forrest Michael. ■ 19104 #038-06-1999 L2003 **ICE** *020 †20

TOCHNER, Zelig. 3400 SPRUCE ST, HOSP OF THE UNIV OF PA 19104 #550-01-1975 L1990 **RO** *020 †80

TODMAN, Michele Suzanne. ■ 19106 #041-14-2007 L2007 **TY** *012

TODOROVSKA, Zagorka. 5301 CEDAR AVE 19143 #957-02-1963 L1982 **FM ADL** *071

TOENNES, Bjoern Erik. 3401 N BROAD ST, TEMPLE UNIVERSITY HOSPITAL 19140 #409-16-2004 L2006 **IM** *012

TOH, Sue-Anne Ee Shiow. 3401 N BROAD ST, DEPT OF INTERNAL MED 19140 #917-03-2003 L2004 **END** *012

TOHAMY, Aley El-Din Moham. 1800 LOMBARD ST 19146 #915-03-1998 L2001 **GS** *020

TOKAR, Jeffrey Lewis. 333 COTTMAN AVE, GASTROENTEROLOGY DIVISION 19111 #035-15-1997 L2000 **GE** *100 †20

TOLEDO, Francisco Leonel. 617 E ALLEGHENY AVE 19134 #429-01-1972 L1975 **GE IM** *020 †20

TOLEDO, Leonel Eduardo. 617 E ALLEGHENY AVE 19134 #033-06-1998 L2000 **PD** *020 †55

TOLL, Adam David. ■ 19115 #041-02-2007 L2007 **PTH** *012

TOM, Carol Mei Lin. 111 S 11TH ST, STE 8490 19107 #041-09-1981 L1984 **AN** *040 †05

TOM, Lawrence Wah-Chan. 324 S 34TH ST, DEPT OF OTOLARYNGOLOGY 19104 #021-01-1975 L1976 **OTO PDO** *020 †45

TOMAKA, Frank L. ■ 19118 #396-24-1988 L1991 **IM** *020 †20

TOMASULO, Lisa Ann. ■ 19107 #035-15-2007 L2007 **OBG** *012

TOMASZEWSKI, John Edward. 3400 SPRUCE ST, 6 FLR 19104 #041-01-1977 L1978 **PTH** *071 †50

TOMESCU, Oana. ■ 19147 #041-01-2004 L2004 **ADL** *012 †20

TOMIE, Hisashi. 3400 MARKET ST STE 350 19104 #572-13-1981 L1996 **AN** *020 †05

TOMKO, Linda Paige. 600 E CATHEDRAL RD 19128 #041-02-1992 L1994 **FPG** *020 †18

TOMOV, Vesselin T. 3400 SPRUCE ST, DEPT IM 19104 #024-01-2007 L2007 **IM** *012

TOMSON, Todd Travis. ■ 19103 #023-07-2007 L2007 **IM** *012

TONGUE, Tracy Ruth. ■ 19154 #041-07-1991 L1996 **PTH** *020 †50

TONSEY, Habib. 2450 W HUNTING PARK AVE 19129 #495-11-1956 L1969 **PME OM** *071

TOOKER, John. 190 N INDEPENDENCE MALL W, AMER COLLEGE OF PHYS 19106 #007-02-1970 L1996 **IM PCC** *030 †20

TOORKEY, Behnaz Cyrus. RED LION & KNIGHTS RD, FRANKFORD HOSP 19114 #495-01-1981 L1993 **PTH ATP** *012

TOPACIO, June. ■ 19103 #748-01-1990 L1998 **P** *020 †75

TOPHAM, Neal Stoddard. 333 COTTMAN AVE STE C 19111 #038-06-1994 L2002 **GS** *020 †65

TOPIWALA, Tasnim. 245 N 15TH ST, DREXEL UNIV COLL MED/HAHNE 19102 #495-66-2002 L2005 **IM** *012

TOPOL, Howard Ira. 201 S 25TH ST APT 428 19103 #033-05-2006 L2006 **PD** *012

TOPOLSKY, David Lane. 230 N BROAD ST, MS 412 19102 #041-09-1982 L1984 **HO** *020 †20

TORBERT, Jesse Taylor. 19144 #038-06-2004 L2005 **ORS** *012

TORCATO, Brian Russell. 699 MAYFAIR ST 19120 #495-17-1990 L1995 **PD** *020 †55

TOREN, Peter Chas. 5735 RIDGE AVE 19128 #025-01-1966 L1967 **FM FPG** *020 †18

TORG, Joseph Steven. 3401 N BROAD ST, DEPT ORTHOPEDIC SURGERY 19140 #041-13-1961 L1965 **ORS** *020 †40 ‡

TORIGIAN, Drew Avedis. 3400 SPRUCE ST, HOSP OF THE UNIVERSITY OF 19104 #035-19-1996 L2001 **DR** *020 †80

TOROTROCHE, Maribel. 4231 N 5TH ST, TEMPLE COMM MED CTR 19140 #041-13-1995 L1998 **PD** *020 †55

TORPIE, Barbara Ann Pilik. ■ 19119 #041-09-1966 L1967 **P** *071 †75

TORRES, Elio Argimiro. 5501 OLD YORK RD, ALBERT EINSTEIN MEDICAL CE 19141 #935-07-2000 L2006 **IM** *012

TORRES, Jorge M. 4900 GRISCOM ST, FRANKFORD HOSP 19124 #176-01-1988 L1993 **AN** *100

TORRES, Jose Luis. 3401 N BROAD ST, DEPT OF MED - 8PP 19140 #319-02-2003 **IM** *012

TORRES, Margarita. 1200 W TABOR RD 19141 #042-01-1981 L1983 **PM** *030 †60

TORRES, Philipp Lopez. 1020 SANSOM ST, STE 1651 THOMPSON BUILDING 19107 #041-13-2004 L2004 **EM** *020

TORRES, Victor Liberato. 125 E LEHIGH AVE 19125 #726-01-1958 L1967 **U** *020 †95

TORRETI, Maryellen Agnes. ■ 19120 #041-07-1989 L1994 **PTH** *020 †50

TOTO, Julia Marie. ■ 19103 #041-01-2004 L2004 **GS** *012

TOUB, David. 1401 WALNUT ST FL 12, MED CASES INC 19102 #016-02-1987 L1990 **OBG GYN** *040 †30

TOUFIK-SCALLY, Loubna. ■ 19115 #820-01-1986 L2000 **RO** *100

TOURE, Joahd Malik. ■ 19103 #008-01-2003 L2006 **IM** *100 †20

TOURTELLOTTE, Charles Dee. 3400 N BROAD ST 19140 #041-13-1957 L1958 **RHU IM** *071 †20

TOUSSAINT, Princess E. ■ 19126 #041-15-2002 **MPD** *100

TOWNSEND, Raymond Roland. 3400 SPRUCE ST, UNIV OF PA 210 WHITE BLDG 19104 #041-09-1979 L1981 **NEP IM** *020 †20

TRABULSI, Edouard John. 1025 WALNUT ST, STE 1100 19107 #035-06-1995 L1997 **U** *020 †95

TRABULSI, Karen May. 2230 COTTMAN AVE # 10, CITY OF PHIL DEPT HLTH 19149 #035-06-1995 L1998 **PD** *020 †55

TRAISAK, Pamela. ■ 19144 #051-04-2005 L2005 **IM** *012

TRAN, Bryan John. ■ 19104 #033-05-2006 L2006 **EM** *012

TRAN, Huyen Dinh. 5501 OLD YORK RD, DEPT RADIOLOGY 19141 #051-01-1980 L1989 **NM DR** *020 †80,28

TRAN, Jordan Le. ■ 19102 #041-15-2007 L2007 **TY** *012

TRAN, Judith Thuha. 501 S 54TH ST, MERCY HOSPITAL OF PHILADEL 19143 #041-13-1994 L1997 **P** *012

TRAN, Nghia Neil. 7600 CENTRAL AVE 19111 #396-04-1971 L1975 **NPM PD** *020 †55 ‡

TRAN, Phong. 5945 LANSDOWNE AVE 19151 #942-01-1980 L1996 **IM** *020

TRAUM, Marcy Kim. ■ 19103 #041-01-2008 *012

TRAVERSO, Carlo Enrico. 19107 #561-07-1979 L1981 **OPH** *012

TRAVOR, Scott. 3401 N BROAD ST, TEMPLE ANESTHESIA ASSOCIAT 19140 #041-09-1991 L1997 **PD** *020 †20

TRAYER, Troy William. ■ 19128 #041-77-2007, ▲ L2007 *012

TRAYES, Kathryn Pool. ■ 19107 #041-02-2006 L2006 **FP** *012

TREHAN, Gaurav. 3401 N BROAD ST 19140 #041-13-2002 L2002 **AN** *100 †05

TREROTOLA, Scott Oakley. 3400 SPRUCE ST, DEPT RIELOGY SILVERSTEIN 19104 #041-01-1986 L2001 **DR** *020 †80

TREVLYN, Dean Wm. 525 JAMESTOWN ST, PREMIER ORTHOPAEDIC & 19128 #041-01-1987 L1989 **ORS** *020 †40 ‡

TRIBIT, Charles B, Jr. ■ 19136 #041-02-1952 L1953 **FM** *071 †18

TRIEN, Leslie Rolstad. 5501 OLD YORK RD 19141 #035-15-2002 L2007 **DR** *100 †80

TRIESTER, Arthur Norris. 833 CHESTNUT ST, STE 701 19107 #041-02-1965 L1966 **IM** *071 †20

TRIGG, Michael Edward. 111 S 11TH ST 19107 #010-01-1975 L1998 **PD PHO** *020 †55

TRIMBA, Lyudmila. 100 E LEHIGH AVE # MAB21 19125 #913-22-1985 L1999 **PM** *020

TRINH, Chuong Van. 5920 N 5TH ST 19120 #941-01-1973 L1985 **NEP IM** *020 †20

TRINH, Phuong Ngoc. 5008 OLD YORK RD 19141 #941-01-1975 L1985 **GP** *020

TRIPATHY, Neeraj. 1630 W GIRARD AVE, SAINT JOSEPH HOSPTIAL 19130 #495-05-1986 L1995 **IM** *020 †20

TRIPP, Lee Anthony. 1144 LOCUST ST 19107 #041-13-1981 L1986 **OBG** *020

TRIVEDI, Mitesh. 5501 OLD YORK RD, DEPT MED 19141 #024-05-2007 L2007 **IM** *012

TROICKI, Filip Tomasz. ■ 19144 #041-01-2008 *012

TROJANOWSKI, John Quinn. 3600 SPRUCE ST, 3RD FL MALHEY BLDG 19104 #024-07-1976 L1979 **PTH IM** *050 †50

TROOSKIN, Stacey Beth. ■ 19144 #033-06-2007 L2007 **IM** *012

TROUPIN, Rosalind Hilsen. 3400 SPRUCE ST 19104 #035-01-1960 L1978 **DR** *020 †80

TROUTMAN, Douglas Alan. ■ 19144 #041-77-2007, ▲ L2007 *012

TROYAN, Beatrice P. ■ 19130 #041-09-1944 L1945 **OM** *071 †30

TRUONG, Nghiep Hoang. 133 E LEHIGH AVE 19125 #941-01-1975 L1985 **IM** *020

TRUONG, Trang Minh. 2301 E ALLEGHENY AVE 19134 #041-15-2005 L2005 **EM** *012

TSAI, Alice Fu-Yi. 19111 #016-02-2002 L2005 **RO** *100

TSAI, Donald Edward. 3400 SPRUCE ST, MEDICINE/HEMATOLOGY-ONCOLO 19104 #036-07-1994 L1996 **HO** *020 †20

TSAI, James Chienjiun. ■ 19107 #051-07-2007 L2007 **IM** *012

TSAI, Jean Chingyi. ■ 19139 #041-01-2003 L2003 **SME** *012

TSAI, Steve Chunhung. 1025 WALNUT ST, THOMAS JEFFERSON UNIV HOSP 19107 #033-05-2002 L2007 **CD** *012

TSALTAS, Margaret E Owen. 111 S 11TH ST 19107 #035-19-1949 L1958 **CHP P** *071 †75

TSANG, Rocky. ■ 19145 #004-01-2008 L2008 *012

TSAROUHAS, Nicholas. 324 S 34TH ST 19104 #041-09-1989 L1991 **PEM PD** *020 †55

TSE, Ka Ming. 3400 SPRUCE ST 19104 #462-01-1988 L1994 **NM** *020 †28

TSENG, Julie. 800 SPRUCE ST, 2 CATHCART 19107 #033-05-2000 L2003 **EM** *020 †16

TSICHLIS, Philip Nicolaos. ■ 19111 #418-01-1968 L1984 **HEM** *050 †20

TSOU, Amy. ■ 19103 #041-01-2005 L2005 **N** *012

TSOU, Amy Menghsuan. ■ 19103 #041-01-2008 *012

TSOU, Walter H. ■ 19119 #041-01-1978 L1979 **PHP IM** *062 †20

TSYSINA, Maya. 11749A BUSTLETON AVE 19116 #913-15-1972 L1996 **IM** *020 †20

TUAN, Bao Kuen. 931 ARCH ST, 2ND FL 19107 #243-46-1955 L1984 **GS GP** *020

TUBB, Erev Emmanuel. 1015 WALNUT ST RM 820, CURTIS BUILDING 19107 #041-02-2002 L2002 **HO** *012 †20

TUCKER, John Anwyl. 219 N BROAD ST, STE FL10 19107 #023-07-1957 L1958 **OTO OS** *020 †45

TUCKER, John David. ■ 19103 #041-13-2002 L2006 **VIR** *012 †80

TUCKER, Robertson Buell. 1315 WINDRIM AVE, WES HEALTH CENTERS 19141 #041-01-1995 L1997 **CHP** *100

TUCKMAN, Terri. 111 S 11TH ST, 3350 GIBBON BLDG 19107 #041-01-1983 L1989 **R** *020 †80

TUITE, Catherine Mary. 3400 SPRUCE ST, GROUND FLOOR DULLES 19104 #035-47-1993 L1998 **VIR** *020 †80

TULUCA, Alexandra. 3401 N BROAD ST, OF S 19140 #033-06-2006 L2006 **GS** *012

TUMA, Gary Alan. 840 WALNUT ST, 15TH FL 19107 #041-02-1996 L1998 **PS CS** *020 †85,65

TUN, Shwe Zin. TEMPLE UNIV HOSPITAL, NEUROLOGY DEPT 19140 #209-01-1979 L1990 **N** *020 †75

TUNG, John Y. 111 S 11TH ST, 4260 GIBBON BUILDING 19107 #917-23-1987 L1994 **PG** *020 †55

TUOHY, Christopher John. ■ 19118 #036-05-2001 L2001 **ORS** *012

TURECK, Richard Walter. 3701 MARKET ST, 8TH FL 19104 #035-20-1975 L1979 **OS OBG** *020 †30

TURKA, Laurence Allan. 422 CURIE BLVD, 700 CLINICAL RESEARCH BLVD 19104 #008-01-1982 L1994 **NEP IM** *020 †20

TURKELTAUB, Peter Ethan. ■ 19143 #010-02-2005 L2006 **N** *012

TURNER, Barbara Jean. 423 GUARDIAN DR, 1123 BLOCKLEY HALL 6021 19104 #041-01-1978 L1979 **IM** *050 †20

TURNER, Bruce Craig. 111 S 11TH ST, DEPT OF RADIATION ONCOLOGY 19107 #041-01-1992 L1998 **RO** *100

TURNER, Clinton Adlai. 1412 FAIRMOUNT AVE 19130 #051-04-1980 L1982 **OBG** *020 †30

TUROW, Judith Anne. 833 CHESTNUT ST, STE 300 19107 #035-09-1976 L1987 **PD** *020 †55

TUVESON, David Arthur. 421 CURIE BLVD, 512 BRB 213 19104 #023-07-1994 L2003 **HO** *020 †20

TUZOVIC, Lea. 3401 N BROAD ST, TEMPLE UNIVERSITY HOSPITAL 19140 #957-01-2000 L2006 **OBG** *012

TWEDDALE, Brian Adair. 612 W NAOMI ST 19144 #041-13-2001 L2001 **DR** *012

TWER, Alan Jeffrey. 7900 BUSTLETON AVE 19152 #041-07-1986 L1987 **OPH** *020 †20,35

TYKOCINSKI, Mark L. 3400 SPRUCE ST, HOSP OF UNIV PA 19104 #035-19-1978 L1998 **PTH IG** *020

TYLER, Donald Chas. 34TH ST & CIVIC CTR BLVD, CHLDRNS HOSP DEPT OPER RM 19104 #041-01-1970 L1998 **AN PD** *020 †55,05

TYRALA, Eileen. 4150 CITY AVE, HOSPITAL LOBBY 19131 #041-12-1971 L1977 **PD** *020 †55

TZANIS, George Loucas. ■ 19147 #041-14-1995 L1997 **IM** *072 †20

TZENG, Diana Lee. 1025 WALNUT ST, THOMAS JEFFERSON UNIV HOSP 19107 #010-02-2004 L2004 **IM** *012

TZOU, Wendy Shin-In. ■ 19143 #023-07-2001 L2005 **CD** *012

U., Khin Cho. 800 SPRUCE ST, PENNSYLVANIA HOSPITAL 19107 #209-01-1990 L2001 **IM** *020 †20

UBERTI-BENZ, Marie O. 3400 SPRUCE ST 19104 #041-02-1978 L1980 **D** *020 †15 ‡

UDDOH, C Nnaemeka. 136 DIAMOND ST 19122 #041-13-1978 L1982 **OBG** *020 †30

UDELL, James. 7908B BUSTLETON AVE 19152 #041-07-1979 L1982 **RHU** *020 †20 ‡

UDOETUK, Joshua Desmond. ■ 19104 #041-01-2008 *012

UENO, Fumiaki. 1811 CHESTNUT ST 19103 #572-20-1973 **IM** *020 †20

UFBERG, David Daniel. 4150 CITY AVE, STE 3D 19106 #041-13-1995 L1997 **OBG** *020 †30

UFBERG, Jacob Wilf. 3401 N BROAD ST, TEMPLE UNIVERSITY HOSP. 19140 #041-13-1996 L1998 **EM** *020 †16

UFFNER, William Martin. 4641 ROOSEVELT BLVD 19124 #041-09-1973 L1975 **P PYG** *020 †75

UGHWANOGHO, Ejovi. ■ 19104 #035-08-2006 L2006 **ORS** *012

UHLER, Tara Arden. 840 WALNUT ST, STE 800 19107 #024-01-1997 L2001 **OPH** *020 †35

UITTO, Jouni Jorma. 833 CHESTNUT ST, STE 740 19107 #374-01-1970 L1986 **D** *050 †15

UJJANI, Chaitra Shankar. 19103 #001-02-2005 L2005 **IM** *012

UKLONSKY, Galina. 10125 VERREE RD STE 101 19116 #913-97-1985 L1994 **IM** *020 †20

UKNIS, Audrey Blythe. 3400 N BROAD ST, MEDICINE 19140 #041-13-1987 L1990 **RHU** *050 †20

UKOMADU, Uzoma. ■ 19147 #043-01-2006 L2007 **ORS** *012

ULITSKY, Mark. 7600 CENTRAL AVE, JEANES HOSP 19111 #913-71-1978 L1995 **IM EM** *020 †20

ULRICHS, Jason George. ■ 19128 #041-15-2008 L2008 *012

ULUS, Ahmet. ■ 19116 #902-10-1950 L1968 **P EM** *071

UM, Scott Saehun. ■ 19103 #035-03-2006 L2006 **GS** *012

UMALI, Juan Mandanas. ■ 19151 #748-07-1953 **GP AN** *071

UMEH, Onuorah Ikechukwu. ■ 19104 #654-01-1981 L1981 **GP** *020

UMOH, Uduak Effiong. ■ 19104 #245-02-2007 L2007 **OBG** *012

UMSCHEID, Craig Alfred. 3400 SPRUCE ST, CEQI/CEP STE 1 FOUNDERS HU 19104 #010-02-2001 L2004 **IM EP** *030

UN, Hyong. 4641 ROOSEVELT BLVD 19124 #041-01-1981 L1982 **P** *030 †75

UNGER, Lisa Donna. 3400 SPRUCE ST, FL 4 19104 #035-19-1986 L1987 **PUD** *020 †20

UNGER, Michael. 333 COTTMAN AVE 19111 #396-01-1971 L1976 **PCC IM** *020 †20

UNIS, Karen Judith. ■ 19147 #016-26-2005 L2005 **P** *012

UNISZKIEWICZ, Robert Nola. ■ 19128 #041-15-2008 *012

UNTEREKER, William Jos. 39TH & MARKET STS, CARDIOLOGY DIVISION 19104 #035-01-1973 L1979 **CD IM** *020 †20

UNWALA, Ashfaque Ali. 230 N BROAD ST 19102 #016-01-1983 L1984 **CD IM** *020 †20

UPPAL, Shitanshu. 3400 SPRUCE ST, DEPT OF GME 19104 #495-36-2004 L2006 **OBG** *012

UPPU, Santosh Chakraverth. 5501 OLD YORK RD, INT MED PEDS 19141 #495-11-2001 L2005 **MPD** *012

URBANSKI, Norbert Krzyszt. 245 N 15TH ST, MS 470 19102 #759-03-1992 L2006 **IC** *100 †20

URBANSKI, Raymond William. 1726 S BROAD ST, STE 200 19145 #033-05-1992 L1995 **IM** *020 †20

URBINE, Jacqueline Ann. ■ 19129 #041-13-2005 L2005 **DR** *012

URI, Antonia Kiss. 324 S 34TH ST 19104 #473-04-1952 L1976 **ATP** *071 †50

URICCHIO, Francis John. 9501 ROOSEVELT BLVD, PENNSYLVANIA HEART & 19114 #024-07-1983 L1985 **CD** *020 †20

URSINO, Gregory Robt. 1700 BENJAMIN FRANKLN PKWY, OFC 3 19103 #041-14-1989 L1993 **OBG** *020 †30

URTECHO, Jacqueline Sue. ■ 19131 #041-13-2005 L2005 **N** *012

URTISHAK, Sandra Lynn. 333 COTTMAN AVE, FOX CHASE CANCER CENTER 19111 #041-01-2003 L2003 **HO** *012 †20

USSAI, Kathryn Eagen. 3900 FORD RD, PH A 19131 #041-02-1996 L1999 **IM** *020 †20

UTAH, Chinedum N S Udenze. 5000 WOODLAND AVE 19143 #690-06-1986 L1993 **PD** *020 †55

UTHAYASHANKAR, Arun Shank. 245 N 15TH ST, DEPT OF GME 19102 #495-94-2001 L2006 **AN** *012

UZZO, Robert Guy. 333 COTTMAN AVE, FOX CHASE CANCER CENTER 19111 #035-20-1991 L2000 **U** *020 †95

VACCARO, Alexander R, III. 925 CHESTNUT ST, FL 5 19107 #010-02-1987 L1988 **ORS SCI** *020 †40

VACCARO, V Michael. 3300 HENRY AVE 19129 #041-02-1958 L1959 **P** *072

VACHANI, Anil. 3400 SPRUCE ST, HOSPITAL/UNIV OF PENNSYLVA 19104 #005-02-1996 L1998 **PCC** *020 †20

VACHARAT, Nibondh. 840 WALNUT ST 19107 #891-02-1963 L1972 **OPH** *071 †35

VACHHANI, Neil Purshottam. 800 SPRUCE ST, PENNSYLVANIA HOSP 19107 #051-07-2003 L2004 **DR** *012

VACLAVIK, Peter Svatopluk. 34TH-CIVIC CTR BLVD, CHILDRENS HOSP 19104 #033-06-2002 L2007 **PAN** *012

VADAKARA, Joseph Joe Luko. 245 N 15TH ST, DREXEL UNIV COLL OF MED 19102 #495-31-2004 L2006 **IM** *012

VADAKETH, Leena. 321 W GIRARD AVE, DEPT OF PUBLIC HEALTH 19123 #495-37-1990 L2005 **IM** *020 †20

VADAPARAMPIL, Justin. ■ 19107 #033-05-2005 L2005 **IM** *012

VAIDYA, Anjali Arun. ■ 19146 #024-05-2005 L2005 **IM** *012

VAIDYA, Kalpana Arun. 321 W GIRARD AVE, PHILADELPHIA DEPT OF PUBLI 19123 #496-38-1969 L1972 **HEM IM** *020 †20 ‡

VAIDYANATHAN, Surya. ■ 19107 #033-06-2003 L2003 **DR** *012

VAKIL, Jeffrey Jahan. ■ 19147 #041-02-2003 L2003 **ORS** *012

VAKILI, Shahla. ■ 19102 #517-01-1971 L1989 **N** *020

VAKOC, Christopher Ryan. ■ 19146 #041-01-2007 *012

VALENCIA, Ignacio. ERIE AVE AT FRONT ST, ST. CHRIS HOSP-DEPT NEUR 19134 #264-10-1994 L2001 **CHN** *020 †75

VALENTINE, Elizabeth Ann. ■ 19103 #041-14-2007 L2007 *012

VALENTINE, Jennifer Cathe. ■ 19107 #033-05-2005 L2005 **IM** *012

VALENTINO, Dominic John, III. 8815 GERMANTOWN AVE, STE 12 19118 #041-77-2001, ▲ L2001 **PCC SME** *020

VALERIO, Holly Janelle. ■ 19103 #011-03-2007 L2007 **P** *012

VALERIO, Jose Amaury. 1800 LOMBARD ST, DEPT OF MED EDU 19146 #308-05-2004 L2006 **GS** *100

VALETTAS, Nicholas. 9 FOUNDERS PAVILLION, UNIV OF PA HOSP-CARD 19104 #065-01-1993 L1999 **IC** *020 †20

VALICENTI, Richard K. 111 S 11TH ST 19107 #041-09-1990 L1990 **RO** *020 †80

VALKO, George Paul. 833 CHESTNUT ST, STE 301 19107 #041-02-1986 L1987 **FM** *020 †18

VALLE, Edgar Orencia. 9150 MARSHALL ST, STE 8 19114 #748-10-1969 L1979 **GS OS** *020 ‡

VALLOW, Morton Jos. 2256 E ALLEGHENY AVE 19134 #041-02-1955 L1956 **OBG** *071 †30

VALSECCHI, Matias Emanuel. 5401 OLD YORK RD, KLEIN 363 19141 #132-01-2002 L2007 **IM** *012

VAN ARSDALE, Cindy Marie. 3400 SPRUCE ST, DEPT OF PATHOLOGY & LB MDCN 19104 #041-01-1994 L1997 **PCP PTH** *020 †50

VAN ARSDALEN, Keith N. 3400 SPRUCE ST, DIV OF UROLOGY 9TH FLOOR 19104 #051-04-1977 L1982 **U UP** *020 †95

VANBEMMELEN, Schalom P. 3401 N BROAD ST, DEPT OF SURGERY 19140 #660-03-1978 L2004 **VS** *020

VANBOSSE, Harold J. 3551 N BROAD ST, SHRINERS HOSPITAL FOR CHIL 19140 #016-11-1989 L1989 **ORS OP** *020 †40

VAN DECKER, Wm Arthur. 3401 N BROAD ST 19140 #010-02-1983 L1988 **CD IM** *040 †20

VAN DEERLIN, Vivianna M. 3400 SPRUCE ST, DEPT OF PATHOLGY & LB MDCN 19104 #041-02-1994 L1997 **PTH** *020 †50

VANDENBERG-WOLF, Mary G. 1316 W ONTARIO ST, JONES HALL 19140 #041-02-1979 L1981 **IM OS** *020 †20

VAN DERHEI, Kathryn E. 3300 HENRY AVE, PRIMARY CARE UNIT 19129 #016-43-1980 L1981 **PD** *020 †55

VAN DER LINDEN, Chris. P3300 HENRY AVE 19129 #660-03-1982 L1988 **N** *020

VAN DERSLICE, Robt Banes. 417 N 8TH ST, STE 501 19123 #041-13-1976 L1977 **R** *020 †80

VANDUZER, Stephanie Krist. 2230 COTTMAN AVE, HEALTH CENTER TEN 19149 #051-01-2002 L2002 **FM** *020 †18

VANETT, Bruce B. 3401 N BROAD ST, OUT-PATIENT/5TH FLOOR 19140 #041-02-1974 L1975 **ORS** *020 †40

VANGA, Shilpa. 1800 LOMBARD ST, TENET HEALTHSYSTEM GRADUAT 19146 #495-57-2002 L2006 **IM** *012

VANGORE, Surya Kumari. 431 W ROOSEVELT BLVD 19120 #495-21-1963 L1981 **GP** *020 ‡

VANGURI, Swathi. ■ 19106 #033-06-2003 L2003 **OBG** *020

VAN HOEVEN, Karen H. 1015 CHESTNUT ST, STE 902 19107 #041-09-1985 L1992 **ATP HO** *040 †50

VAN-HORNE, Simone Soyini. 800 SPRUCE ST, PENNSYLVANIA HOSPITAL 19107 #894-01-1999 L2003 **IM** *012

VANIA, Shamin. ■ 19111 #041-15-2005 L2005 **IM** *012

VANKLEUNEN, Jonathan Paul. ■ 19147 #041-01-2002 L2004 **ORS** *012

VANPELT, Merritt Joan. 1020 SANSOM ST, EMERGENCY MEDICINE / 239 T 19107 #041-02-2001 L2001 **EM** *012 †16

VANSCOY, Michael Paul. ■ 19102 #041-15-2005 L2005 **IM** *012

VANTE, Chantale. ■ 19123 #035-06-2003 L2007 **IM** *012 †20

VANTERPOOL, Kisha. 3401 N BROAD ST 19140 #010-03-2003 L2006 **IM** *100 †20

VAN VOORHEES, Abby Susan. 3600 SPRUCE ST # 2M44, U PA MED SCH MALONEY BLDG 19104 #008-01-1983 L1983 **D** *020 †15

VAN ZANT, Kristin Maria. 120 S 30TH ST, HORIZON HOUSE 19104 #041-01-1987 L1988 **IM** *020 †75 ‡

VAPIWALA, Neha. 3400 SPRUCE ST, OF PA 19104 #041-01-2001 L2001 **RO** *100 †80

VARADA, Koteswar Rao. ■ 19125 #495-21-1978 L1990 **NPM** *020 †55

VARADI, Gabor. 111 S 11TH ST, T JEFFERSON UNIV DEPT MED 19107 #473-01-1983 L2003 **HO** *012 †20

VARANASI, Ajay. 800 SPRUCE ST, PENNSYLVANIA HOSPITAL 19107 #495-21-2001 L2006 **IM** *012

VARDARO, Lina G. 7500 CENTRAL AVE, STE 208 19111 #041-09-1950 L1951 **GYN** *071 †30

VARELA, Carly Rachel. ■ 19119 #035-01-2002 L2006 **PHO** *012 †55

VARGAS, Marcelo Paul. ■ 19144 #033-05-2007 L2007 *012

VARGHESE, Joby. ■ 19115 #041-77-2003, ▲ L2004 **MPD EM** *012

VARJAVAND, Nielufar. 245 N 15TH ST MS 427, DEPARTMENT OF MEDICINE 19102 #010-01-1995 L1997 **IM** *020 †20

VARUPUTOOR, Madhavi. 2900 W QUEEN LN 19129 #495-65-2001 L2005 **IM** *012

VASDEV, Priya. 44 S 3RD ST 19106 #305-01-1997 L2000 **IMG** *020 †20

VASSALL, Mariah E Wilson. 2 PENN BLVD STE 112 19144 #041-07-1966 L1967 **IM A** *071 †03,20

VASSALLO, Ralph Robt, Jr. 700 SPRING GARDEN ST, PENN-JERSEY REGION 19123 #041-01-1987 L1988 **HEM** *062 †20

VASSALLO, Richard Wm. 2701 HOLME AVE, STE 105 19152 #041-09-1968 L1969 **CD IM** *020 †20

VASSALLUZZO, Pasquale D. 4006 ASHBURNER ST 19136 #561-17-1971 L1976 **FM** *020

VASSALOTTI, Stephen Belgo. 7026 FRANKFORD AVE # 1ST 19135 #041-02-1948 L1949 **OBG** *071 †30

VASSY, Jason Lyell. 3400 SPRUCE ST, DEPT IM 19104 #028-02-2007 L2007 **IM** *012

VASU, Tajender Singh. ■ 19107 #495-45-1999 L2007 **PCC** *012 †20

VATANNIA, Shamsi Moluk. 834 CHESTNUT ST STE 400, BENJAMIN FRANKLIN HOUSE 19107 #422-01-2002 L2004 **OBG** *100

VATANPARAST, Rodina. 2900 W QUEEN LN 19129 #422-01-2004 L2004 **IM** *012

YATES, Christopher Charle. ■ 19125 #041-01-2005 L2005 **EM** *012

VAUGHN, Byron Philip. ■ 19130 #041-15-2008 *012

VAUGHN, David Arthur. 1800 LOMBARD ST, TENET HEALTHSYSTEM GRADUAT 19146 #041-02-2005 L2005 **GS** *012

VAUGHN, David Jos. 3400 SPRUCE ST, 16 PENN TOWER 19104 #024-01-1987 L1990 **ON HEM** *020 †20

VAUGHNCOOKE, Anika Dore. 1020 SANSOM ST, 1652 THOMPSON BUILDING, RM 19107 #041-13-2001 L2001 **P** *100 †75

VAZQUEZ, Zael. 4TH FLOOR - S TOWER MAIL, DREXEL UNIVERSITY COLLEGE 19102 #305-01-2006 L2007 **IM** *012

VAZQUEZ MARCH, Jacobo Ale. 5501 OLD YORK RD, ALBERT EINSTEIN MED CTR 19141 #935-01-2000 L2002 **CD** *012 †20

VAZUKA, Jean Tierney. ■ 19103 #041-13-1962 L1965 **P CHP** *071

VEARRIER, David James. 245 N 15TH ST 2ND FL, OF M 19102 #005-18-2005 L2005 **EM** *012

VEASEY, Sigrid Carlen. 3600 SPRUCE ST, HUP 985A MALONEY BLDG 19104 #051-01-1985 L1987 **PCC SME** *050 †20

VEDI, Charanjit Reddy. 3220 BIRCH RD 19154 #495-57-1999 L2006 **IM** *040

VEDULA, Satyanarayana Swa. 3400 SPRUCE ST, UNIV OF PA HLTH SYSTEM 19104 #495-58-2002 **GS** *100

VEGARI, David N. ■ 19127 #041-15-2007 L2007 **ORS** *012

VEGA SANCHEZ, Maria Elena. 3401 N BROAD ST, DEPT OF INTERNAL MED 19140 #319-08-2003 L2005 **IM** *012

VELAGAPUDI, Vijaya L. 561 FAIRTHORNE AVE, FAIRMOUNT BEHAVIORAL HEALT 19128 #495-50-1986 L1994 **CHP** *020

VELDMAN, Peter Bernard. ■ 19103 #041-01-2008 *012

VELEZ, Alfredo Joel. ■ 19140 #041-13-2004 L2007 **P** *012

VELEZ, Isa. 301 S 8TH ST STE 2L, JUST FOR US 19104 #041-09-1978 L1980 **OBG** *020 †30

VELLA, Vijaya Lakshmi. 3401 N BROAD ST, 7TH FLOOR, ZONE B 19140 #495-58-1987 L2003 **OBG** *100

VELMURUGU, Parvati. 5501 OLD YORK RD 19141 #496-28-1992 L2000 **IM** *020

VELOSKI, Colleen Dolores. 1316 W ONTARIO ST, 1ST FL JONES HALL 19140 #041-07-1994 L1996 **END** *100 †20

VELOSO, Virgilio J. ■ 19107 #748-07-1952 L1967 **AN** *071

VELOUDIOS, Alice. 230 N BROAD ST, DEPT RAD 19102 #035-19-1986 L1987 **DR** *020 †80

VEMULA, William Carey. 3401 N BROAD ST, MERCY HOSPITAL OF PHILADEL 19140 #495-21-1998 L2003 **IM** *020 †20

VEMURI, Santhi. ■ 19107 #010-01-2005 L2005 **IM** *012

VENDERVELDT, Garig Michae. ■ 19147 #041-02-2004 L2004 **EM** *100

VENDRAME, Martina. 3401 N BROAD ST, TEMPLE UNIV HOSP 19140 #561-11-2001 L2004 **N** *012

VENEGAS, Cynthia R. 4400 HAVERFORD AVE 19104 #748-08-1988 L1991 **IM** *020 †20

VENKATACHALAPATHY, Shashik. 4641 ROOSEVELT BLVD, BOX 45358 19124 #495-72-1994 L2002 **P** *100

VENKATARAMANA, Panduranga. 501 S 54TH ST, MERCY HOSP OF PHILA 19143 #495-04-1986 L2007 **P** *020 †75

VENKATESH, Vugranam C. 324 S 34TH ST 19104 #495-08-1980 L1991 **NPM** *020 †55

VENNETI, Sriram. 3400 SPRUCE ST, UNIVERSITY OF PENNSYLVANIA 19104 #496-39-1998 L2007 **PTH** *012

VERA, Luis Francio. 12601 CHILTON RD, PARKWOOD MANOR 19154 #319-03-1956 L1964 **GS GP** *020

VERDELL, Clarence Ricardo. 8001 STATE RD, MHM PHILADELPHIA PRISON SY 19136 #041-09-1986 L1989 **P** *020

VERDETTI, Fortunata. 1025 WALNUT ST, THOMAS JEFFERSON UNIV HOSP 19107 #041-13-2004 L2004 **IM** *012

VERDI, Carol Ann. 12401 ACADEMY RD STE 203 19154 #041-14-1982 L1983 **FM** *020 ‡

VERDINO, Ralph Jos. 3400 SPRUCE ST STE F, UNIV OF PENNSYLVANIA HOSP 19104 #035-48-1988 L1999 **ICE CD** *100

VERDUN, Aubrey Vincent, Jr. 2751 PENNSYLVANIA AVE, B104 19130 #025-07-2002 L2006 **PMM** *012

VERGARE, Michael John. 833 CHESTNUT ST STE 210, DEPT OF PSYCHIATRY-TJU 19107 #041-09-1971 L1973 **P IMG** *030 †75

VERGARI, John Anthony, Jr. 230 N BROAD ST 19102 #035-09-1980 L1985 **CD IM** *020 †20

VERMA, Akshra. ■ 19140 #495-20-2002 L2006 **IM** *012

VERMA, Ritu. 324 S 34TH ST 19104 #965-01-1981 L1989 **PG** *020 †55

VERMA, Sunil. 230 N BROAD ST 19102 #495-75-1983 L1999 **P** *020 †75

VERNICK, Jerome Jay. 1800 LOMBARD ST, STE 1100 PEPPER PAVILION 19146 #041-02-1962 L1963 **GS** *020 †85

VERNICK, William Jonathan. 3400 SPRUCE ST, DEPT OF ANESTHESIA 19104 #041-02-2000 L2001 **AN** *100 †05

VERNON, Thomas Martin, Jr. ■ 19103 #024-01-1964 L1991 **PHP IM** *030 †20

VERNOSE, Gerard Vincent. 1841 S BROAD ST 19148 #041-09-1973 L1974 **OTO** *020 †45

VERONESE, Maria Luisa. 3400 SPRUCE ST, ONCOLOGY DIV/15 PENN TOWER 19104 #561-11-1988 L2001 **HO** *100 †20

VERSTANDIG, Anthony Geo. 3400 SPRUCE ST 19104 #917-30-1977 L1984 **DR** *020 †80

VESGA, Renato. ■ 19128 #041-15-2002 L2002 **PMM** *012

VETTER, Victoria Lee. 324 S 34TH ST 19104 #020-12-1972 L1976 **PDC PD** *020 †55

VETTORI, David John. ■ 19131 #041-77-2007, ▲ L2007 **TY** *012

VEZNEDAROGLU, Erol. 909 WALNUT ST, 2ND FL 19107 #035-06-1996 L1998 **NS** *020 †25

VIALIZ, Julio E, Jr. 245 N 15TH ST, MAIL STOP 1011 19102 #016-11-1993 L2001 **PE** *020 †20

VICTOR, Mark Ford. 255 S 17TH ST, STE 1700 19103 #041-09-1976 L1977 **CD IM** *020 †20

VICTORIA, Daniel F.P.. 5501 OLD YORK RD 19141 #396-09-1996 L2003 **OBG** *100

VICTORIA, Teresa. ■ 19147 #041-02-2001 L2001 **DR** *020 †80

VIGILANTE, Gary John. 51 N 39TH ST, MEDICAL CENTER 19104 #033-05-1981 L1984 **CD** *020 †20

VIGLIONE, Joseph Philip. 220 LOCUST ST # 19FS 19106 #041-09-1953 L1954 **FM RHU** *071

VIGORITO, Carlo. 324 S 34TH ST, DEPT OF CARDIO DISEASES 19104 #561-10-1971 **CD** *020

VIJE, Christopher D. ■ 19103 #048-12-2005 L2006 **AN** *012

VILE, Daniel Joseph. 9501 ROOSEVELT BLVD, STE 400 19114 #041-77-1986, ▲ L1987 **CD IM** *020

VILLANO, Stephen Alan. ■ 19147 #023-07-1992 L1995 **ID** *020 †20

VILLARE, Anthony Wm. 1240 W RITNER ST 19148 #308-07-1982 L1983 **FM OS** *020 †18

VILLARIN, L Albert, Jr. 5501 OLD YORK RD, ALBERT EINSTEIN MEDICAL CT 19141 #041-02-1993 L1995 **EM** *020 †16

VINCA, Nancy Maureen. 3400 SPRUCE ST, DEPT OF ANESTHESIA, DRIPPS 19104 #035-01-2001 L2001 **AN** *012 †16

VINCENT, Gregory Andrew. ■ 19128 #041-13-2006 L2006 **PTH** *012

VINES, Eugenio Vazquez. 2 DONNER, 3400 SPRUCE ST 19104 #231-03-1993 L1998 **RO** *100 †80

VINING, Daniel Kanju. 3400 SPRUCE ST, OF PENNSYLVAN 19104 #041-01-2003 L2003 **EM** *020

VINJIRAYER, Elango Packir. 245 N 15TH ST, DEPT OF GME 19102 #496-28-2001 L2006 **IM** *012

VINOCUR, Charles David. ST CHRISTOPHERS HOSPITAL, DEPT OF PED SURGERY 19134 #025-01-1973 L1980 **PDS** *030 †85

VINOGRADOV, Sophia S. 9150 MARSHALL ST, STE 17 19114 #913-05-1962 L1985 **GP** *020

VIRA, Manish Arvind. 3400 SPRUCE ST, DIV UROLOGY 19104 #035-20-2000 L2001 **U** *100

VIRUTAMASEN, Pramual. 3400 SPRUCE ST 19104 #891-01-1963 **OBG OS** *100

VISCO, David Paul. 245 N 15TH ST, MAIL STOP 107 19102 #305-01-2001 L2001 **PCC** *012

VISCUSI, Eugene Robt. 111 S 11TH ST, STE 8490 19104 #041-02-1981 L1982 **AN PME** *020 †05

VISWANATHAN, Prabha. ■ 19130 #019-02-2003 L2003 **PD** *100 †55

VITANZO, Peter Charles, Jr. 925 CHESTNUT ST 19107 #041-13-1996 L1999 **FSM** *020 †18

VITERBO, Rosalia. 333 COTTMAN AVE, CITY OF HOPE, NATIONAL MED 19111 #035-06-2000 L2001 **U** *020

VITERI, Shirley Delosange. 3400 CIVIC CENTER BLVD, PEDIATRIC RESIDENT PROGRAM 19104 #041-01-2006 L2006 **PD** *012

VITTOR, Amy Yomiko. 3400 SPRUCE ST, DEPT MED 19104 #005-11-2007 L2007 **IM** *012

VITTORIO, Carmela C. 3600 SPRUCE ST, DEPT DERM UNIV OF PENN 19104 #041-01-1989 L1999 **D** *020 †15

VITTORIO, Nino. 1720 S BROAD ST, HEALTH DISTRICT 2 19145 #038-41-1985 L1986 **IM** *020 †20

VIVEK, Kumar. 3400 SPRUCE ST, UNIVERSITY OF PENNSYLVANIA 19104 #495-36-2005 L2007 **GS** *012

VIVINO, Frederick B. 51 N 39TH ST, STE 2B 19104 #041-13-1983 L1985 **RHU IM** *020 †20

VLAD, Tudor Jon. 1800 LOMBARD ST 19146 #781-01-2001 L2003 **IM** *100 †20

VODELA, Ravindhar. 800 SPRUCE ST, PA HOSPITAL-UPHS 19107 #495-21-2001 L2004 **IM** *100 †20

VOGL, Dan Toby. 3400 SPRUCE ST, 16 PENN TOWER 19104 #035-20-2000 L2003 **HO** *100 †20

VOGT, Jutta. 3965 CONSHOHOCKEN AVE, THE CENTER FOR AUTISTIC 19131 #409-05-1993 L2000 **P CHP** *020 †75

VOINER, Jonathan L. 3620 HAMILTON WALK, UNIV OF PA SCH OF MED 19104 #041-01-2005 L2005 *100

VOLCHONOK, Oleg. 10890 BUSTLETON AVE, STE 201 19116 #913-15-1986 L1995 **GE IM** *020 †20

VOLIN, Jan Judith. 800 SPRUCE ST, FL 2 19107 #041-09-1979 L1981 **NPM** *020 †55 ‡

VOLPE, Nicholas Jos. 51 N 39TH ST 19104 #035-08-1987 L1993 **OPH N** *020 †35

VOLPICELLI, Joseph Robt. 40 W EVERGREEN AVE, STE 106 19118 #041-01-1981 L1982 **ADM P** *050 †75

VOLPP, Kevin Gerhardming. 423 GUARDIAN DR, 1232 BLOCKLEY HALL 19104 #041-01-1998 L2001 **IM** *050 †20

VOLTAGGIO, Lysandra. 111 S 11TH ST, UNIV HOSPITAL 19107 #042-01-2003 L2003 **PCP** *012 †50

VONBESSER, Kiera Linda. ■ 19102 #016-02-2007 L2007 **OBG** *012

VONDERHEIDE, Robert H. 421 CURIE BLVD, 551 BRB 2-3 19104 #024-01-1993 L2001 **HO IM** *020 †20

VON FELDT, Joan Marie. 3400 SPRUCE ST, FL 8 19104 #041-07-1981 L1984 **RHU IM** *020 †20

VONMEHREN, Margaret. 333 COTTMAN AVE 19111 #035-03-1989 L1992 **ON** *020 †20

VORA, Milan Vasant. ■ 19103 #041-15-2008 *012

VORA, Sudhir Raju. 132 S 10TH ST, UNIVERSITY HO 19107 #024-01-2003 L2003 **DR** *012

VORASINGHA, Thongchai. 627 W RITNER ST 19148 #891-02-1961 L1986 **FM** *020

VOROVICH, Esther Elizabet. ■ 19104 #041-01-2007 L2007 **IM** *012

VOSKANIAN, Pogos Hagop. 3300 HENRY AVE 19129 #024-16-1992 L1997 **PFP P** *030 †75

VOSKERIDJIAN, Armen C. 5501 OLD YORK RD 19141 #035-08-1993 L2003 **AN** *020 †20,05

VOSSOUGH-MODARRESS, A. 324 S 34TH ST 19104 #517-11-1994 L2001 **R RNR** *020 †80 ‡

VRABIE, Raluca. ■ 19104 #035-47-2003 L2007 **GE** *012 †20

VRANIC, Francisco Rodolfo. 111 S 11TH ST, THOMAS JEFFERSON UNIVERSIT 19107 #132-01-1995 L2006 **PD** *012

VRECENAK, Jesse Daya. ■ 19146 #041-01-2007 L2007 **GS** *012

VROOMAN, Samuel Craig. 801 SPRUCE ST 19107 #041-09-1981 L1983 **IM** *020 †20 ‡

VUCKOVIC, Dejan. 111 S 11TH ST STE 8490G, THOMAS JEFFERSON UNIVERSIT 19107 #957-06-1988 L2001 **AN** *020 †05

VUONG, Cuong Tri. 5501 OLD YORK RD, DEPT RAD 19141 #041-14-2005 L2006 **DR** *012

VUPPALAPATI, Anitha. 321 W GIRARD AVE, HEALTH CENTER SIX 19123 #495-70-1991 L1996 **IM** *020 †20

VUYYURU, Srinivasareddy. 2900 W QUEEN LN 19129 #496-65-2003 L2005 **IM** *012

VYAKARANAM, Sudhir Bharga. 245 N 15TH ST, DREXEL UNIV COLL OF MED 19102 #495-65-2003 L2006 **IM** *012

WABLE, Sumathi. 5501 OLD YORK RD, DEPT OF RADIOLOGY 19141 #495-33-1978 L1996 **DR** *020 †28,80

WABLE, Suresh Govindrao. 4900 FRANKFORD AVE, FRANKFORD HOSPITALRDLGY DP 19124 #495-22-1974 L1995 **IM EM** *062 †16

WACIEGA, Mark. 111 S 11TH ST 19107 #041-02-1983 L1985 **FM** *020 †05,18

WADE, Kelly Cant. 800 SPRUCE ST 19107 #008-01-1997 L2001 **NPM** *020 †55

WADHWA, Neha. 5501 OLD YORK RD, ALBERT EINSTEIN MED CTR 19141 #496-07-2003 L2004 **GE** *012 †20

WAGNER, David Keith. 230 N BROAD ST 19102 #028-34-1956 L1964 **EM PDS** *040 †85,16

WAGNER, Jason Erik. ■ 19104 #005-02-2006 L2006 **IM** *012

WAGNER, John Lyle. 1015 WALNUT ST, STE 1024 19107 #041-13-1989 L1999 **HO HEM** *020 †20

WAGNER, Michael John. ■ 19111 #041-02-2006 L2006 **PTH** *012

WAGNER, Seymour. 250 S 18TH ST APT 702 19103 #041-09-1954 L1955 **P OTO** *071 †45,75

WAHBA, Peter Rafik. ■ 19147 #010-01-2003 L2004 **DR** *020

WAHEED, Ayesha. 4641 ROOSEVELT BLVD, DUCOM-FRIEND'S HOSPITAL 19124 #704-01-1998 L2001 **CHP** *020 †20

WAHRMAN, Aron. 8815 GERMANTOWN AVE, STE 36 19118 #008-01-1984 L1986 **ORS** *020 †65

WAINRIGHT, Sharon Anne. ■ 19118 #048-04-1975 L1979 **P OS** *020 †75

WALDMAN, Ilan. 834 CHESTNUT ST 19107 #010-01-2002 L2002 **U** *012

WALDMAN, Scott Arthur. 132 S 10TH ST, 1170 MAIN 19107 #005-11-1987 L1991 **PA** *050 †20

WALIGORA, Grzegorz Karol. 2200 BENJAMIN FRANKLN PKWY, APT N801 19130 #759-10-1996 L2006 **IM** *012

WALINSKY, Paul. 925 CHESTNUT ST 19107 #041-01-1965 L1966 **CD IM** *020

WALKENSTEIN, Michael D. ALBERT EINSTEIN MED CTR 19141 #024-07-1977 L1982 **IM PUD** *020 †20

WALKER, Barry Richard. 3400 SPRUCE ST 19104 #035-01-1962 L1963 **NEP PA** *071 †20

WALKER, Dilys Margaret. ■ 19147 #005-18-1987 L1989 **OBG** *020 †30

WALKER, Linda Kyle. 3400 SPRUCE ST 19104 #027-01-1982 L1998 **CCP PD** *020 †55

WALKER, Manuel Lorenzo. 4401 HAVERFORD AVE, ST IGNATIUS NURSING HOME 19104 #010-03-1955 L1958 **FM** *020 †18 ‡

WALKOVICH, Kelly Jo. ■ 19104 #041-02-2005 L2005 **PD** *012

WALLACE, Richard Paul. 302 S 19TH ST 19103 #041-02-1974 L1976 **IM** *020 †20

WALLENSTEIN, Lisa B. ■ 19118 #041-01-1979 L1981 **IM** *020 †20

WALLIS, Elizabeth Mary. ■ 19130 #032-01-2007 L2007 **PD** *012

WALOFF, Ronald Ira. 5401 OLD YORK RD STE 202 19141 #041-13-1976 L1978 **IM GE** *050 †20

WALSH, Megan Catherine. 5501 OLD YORK RD, DEPT RAD 19141 #041-15-2006 L2006 **DR** *012

WALSH, Peter Newton. 3400 N BROAD ST 19140 #028-02-1961 L1961 **IM** *030 †20

WALTER, Andrew Wm. 833 CHESTNUT ST, THIRD FLOOR 19107 #035-45-1986 L1988 **PHO PMM** *020 †55

WALTERS, Heather Lynne. ■ 19128 #041-02-2005 L2005 **IM** *012

WALTERS, Michele Ingre. 833 CHESTNUT ST, STE 210 19107 #035-08-1993 L1995 **P** *100 †55,75

WANG, Alan Hualee. 1025 WALNUT ST, THOMAS JEFFERSON UNIV HOSP 19107 #025-07-2002 L2002 **GE** *012 †20

WANG, Annie T A H. 3001 WALNUT ST, JOHN F KENNEDY MEDICAL CEN 19104 #041-07-1963 L1966 **PD ON** *020 †55

WANG, Chun. 132 S 10TH ST, UNIVERSITY HO 19107 #035-19-2004 L2005 **DR** *012

WANG, Dajie. 834 CHESTNUT ST, T150 19107 #243-92-1989 L2001 **APM AN** *020 †05

WANG, Eileen. 5501 OLD YORK RD, A EINSTEIN MED CTR 19141 #041-02-2007 L2007 **TY** *012

WANG, Eileen Yee. ■ 19102 #025-01-1991 L2007 **OBG** *020 †30

WANG, Fengwei. 3400 N BROAD ST, TEMPLE UNIVERSITY HOSPITAL 19140 #243-46-1987 L2007 **PTH** *012

WANG, Horn Wen. ■ 19128 #244-04-1970 L1989 **OBG U** *020 †30

WANG, Jenny Yijeng. 833 CHESTNUT ST, STE 701 19107 #041-02-2000 L2001 **IM** *020 †20 ‡

WANG, John Chaw Chian. 3401 N BROAD ST, OF S 19140 #539-06-1997 L2001 **VS** *012 †85

WANG, Julie Ann. 19130 #035-46-2005 L2005 **IM** *012

WANG, Leo David. 19130 #016-02-2005 L2005 **PD** *012

WANG, Mei-Lun. 324 S 34TH ST 19104 #041-01-1995 L2000 **PD** *020 †55

WANG, Melissa. ■ 19144 #035-45-2003 L2003 **N** *100

WANG, Qian. 5501 OLD YORK RD, A EINSTEIN MED CTR 19141 #243-39-1997 L2007 **IMG** *012 †20

WANG, Rebecca Y. 5501 OLD YORK RD 19141 #462-01-1973 L1987 **CD IM** *020 †20

WANG, Theresa Yeuhui. ■ 19104 #023-07-2006 L2006 **PS** *012

WANG, Wei. HAHNEMAN UNIV-PATH 19129 #243-46-1982 L1994 **PTH** *100

WANG, Wenjing. 800 SPRUCE ST 19107 #243-79-1993 L2002 **PD** *100 †50

WANG, Yanhua. 2900 W QUEEN LN 19129 #243-67-1985 L2004 **PTH** *012

WANG, Yen. 3900 WOODLAND AVE, VETERANS ADMINISTRATION 19104 #385-02-1954 L1963 **R NM** *020 †80,28

WANG, Yize. 3401 N BROAD ST, TEMPLE UNIVERSITY HOSPITAL 19140 #243-03-1995 L2006 **IM** *012

WANG, Yue Lynn. 3400 SPRUCE ST, HOSP-UNIV OF PA/DEPT-PATH 19104 #243-47-1988 L2001 **PTH** *020 †50

WANGLEE, P Asvanitchya. FRONT ST & ERIE AVE 19134 #891-01-1957 L1967 **PA OS** *020 †55

WANI, Arshad Ahmad. 5401 OLD YORK RD, ALBERT EINSTEIN MEDICAL CE 19141 #495-51-1997 L2001 **PCC** *020 †20

WAPLES, Charles Henry, Jr. 5801 SPRUCE ST 19139 #041-02-1976 L1978 **IM** *020 †20

WAPNER, Keith Leslie. 230 W WASHINGTON SQ FL 5 19106 #041-13-1980 L1982 **ORS** *020 †40

WARBURTON, Karen Marie. 3400 SPRUCE ST, 1 FOUNDERS, RENAL DIVISION 19104 #036-01-1999 L2001 **NEP** *020 †20

WARD, Kristine Marie. 230 N BROAD ST, 15TH FL 19102 #041-02-1991 L1993 **HO** *012

WARD, Lawrence David. 3401 N BROAD ST, 4TH FL 19140 #041-02-1999 L2001 **IM** *020 †20

WARD, Stephanie Annette. ■ 19137 #041-14-1980 L1982 **CHP P** *075

WARD, Stephanie Hurley. 1316 W ONTARIO ST, JONES HALL, 1ST FLOOR 19140 #041-02-2001 L2001 **IM** *020 †20

WARDLAW, Delana Octavia. 6827 GERMANTOWN AVE 31, BLAKE GI ASSOCIATES 19119 #041-14-2000 L2003 **FM** *020 †18

WARNER, Howard Frank. 3401 N BROAD ST 19140 #041-13-1953 L1954 **CD IM** *071 †20

WARNER, Matthew James. 3401 N BROAD ST, DEPT OF EMERGENCY MEDICINE 19140 #033-06-2003 L2003 **EM** *100 †16

WARREN, Cynthia Collier. 231 N BROAD ST, SCPA CHILD & ADOLESCENT PR 19107 #035-45-1992 L1994 **PD** *020 †55

WARREN, Daniel Mark. ■ 19104 #041-01-1993 *100

WARREN, Leonard. WISTAR INST, DEPT MED 19104 #065-01-1951 **OS** *050

WARREN, Robert Stuart. 100 E LEHIGH AVE 19125 #041-13-1996 L1998 **IMG FM** *020 †18

WARREN, Wilbert Roy. 1740 SOUTH ST STE 300, PHA-ADULT MEDICINE, PC 19146 #035-45-1993 L1995 **IM** *020 †20

WARREN, William Jos. 2601 HOLME AVE 19152 #041-02-1958 L1959 **PTH** *020 †50

WARTER, Oren Alan. 3400 SPRUCE ST, DEPARTMENT OF ANESTHS 19104 #035-08-1995 L1997 **AN** *020 †05

WASFI, Yasmine Sadiq. ■ 19106 #041-01-1995 L1998 **PCC** *100 †20

WASIK, Mariusz. 3400 SPRUCE ST, DEPT OF PATHOLGY & LB MDCN 19104 #759-10-1979 L1993 **HMP** *020 †20

WASSERMAN, Barry Neil. 840 WALNUT ST, STE 1230 19107 #033-05-1992 L1997 **OPH PO** *020 †35

WASSERMAN, Kenneth E. 1817 S BROAD ST 19148 #041-09-1983 L1984 **D** *020 †15

WASSERMAN, Theodore Wolf. 1345 S 4TH ST 19147 #041-02-1961 L1962 **P N** *020 †75

WASSERSTEIN, Alan Geo. 3400 SPRUCE ST, DEPT NEPH 19104 #035-46-1973 L1974 **NEP IM** *020 †20

WATANABE, Meguru. 111 S 11TH ST, THOMAS JEFFERSON UNIV 19104 #572-29-1988 L2005 **VIR** *100

WATERHOUSE, Marie Rogers. ■ 19130 #028-02-2005 L2005 **PD** *012

WATERS, Glenn. 3300 HENRY AVE, ALLEGHENY UNIV OF HLTH SCI 19129 #041-15-2002 *100

WATKINS, Milton David. 3901 MARKET ST 19104 #041-13-1979 L1981 **GS** *075

WATSON, Annette Cacioppo. 5003 UMBRIA ST, KIDS FIRST ROXBOROUGH 19128 #021-05-1993 L1997 **PD** *020 †55

WATSON, Clarence, Jr. 833 CHESTNUT ST, DEPT OF PSYCHIATRY 19107 #041-02-2001 L2001 **PFP** *020 †75

WATSON, Daryl Carl. 6315 WOODLAND AVE 19142 #041-13-1990 L1993 **IM** *020 †20

WATSON, Elizabeth Jeanine. ■ 19102 #051-01-2006 L2008 **AN** *100

WATSON, James. 333 COTTMAN AVE 19111 #048-12-1991 L1997 **GS** *020 †85 ‡

WATTERSON, Robert Brandon. ■ 19130 #038-41-1998 L2001 **MPD** *020 †20,55

WATTS, Lisa Sharee. ■ 19144 #041-15-2005 L2006 **MP** *012

WEASEN, Steven R. 2146 S BROAD ST 19145 #038-40-1980 L1985 **D** *020 †15 ‡

WEAVER, Brian Shanklin. 3400 SPRUCE ST, DEPARTMENT OF ANESTHESIOLO 19104 #051-07-2004 L2005 **AN** *012

WEAVER, Michael William. 3401 N BROAD ST, STE 540 19140 #041-13-1998 L2001 **NS** *020

WEBB, Elizabeth Stabinski. 5501 OLD YORK RD 19141 #041-02-1969 L1970 **P CHP** *020 †75 ‡

WEBB, Gary D. 3400 SPRUCE ST, 6 PENN TOWER 19104 #067-01-1967 L2004 *100

WEBER, Annemarie. 3400 SPRUCE ST, DEPT BIOCHEM 19104 #407-19-1950 **OS CD** *050

WEBER, Dana Mark. 7600 CENTRAL AVE, JEANES HOSP 19111 #041-07-1980 L1981 **EM** *020 †16

WEBER, Lawrence Willard. ■ 19106 #035-20-2001 L2007 **ORS** *100

WEBNER, David. 51 N 39TH ST, 6TH FLOOR MOTCH BLDG 19104 #550-02-1997 L2001 **FSM** *020 †18

WEBSTER, Guy Frederick. 211 S 9TH ST 19107 #041-01-1985 L1986 **D** *020 †15

WEBSTER, Isabella M M. 8400 PINE RD 19111 #041-07-1947 L1948 **OS** *074

WEBSTER, Maryanne Ildiko. 3300 HENRY AVE, DEPT MED 19129 #041-07-1993 L1998 **DR** *075 †80

WECHSLER, Andrew Stephen. 230 N BROAD ST 19102 #035-08-1964 L1998 **TS GS** *020 †85,90

WECHSLER, Richard Joel. 111 S 11TH ST, 3350 GIBBON BLDG 19107 #025-01-1973 L1980 **DR** *071 †80

WEDDINGTON, Wayne P, Jr. 5501 OLD YORK RD, 2ND FLR PALEY BLDG ENT DEP 19141 #010-03-1963 L1968 **OTO** *020 †45

WEED, Samantha. ■ 19107 #041-01-2008 L2008 *012

WEGENER, William A. 3400 SPRUCE ST 19104 #011-02-1987 L1990 **DR IM** *020 †28

WEI, Huafeng. 3400 SPRUCE ST, UNIV OF PENNSYLVANIA HOSPI 19104 #243-52-1988 L2001 *020 †05

WEI, Wenxin. ■ 19102 #041-14-2006 L2006 **OPH** *012

WEIBEL, Robert Eugene. 150 S INDEPENDENCE MALL W, DHHS/SPB ROOM 421 19106 #041-01-1955 L1956 **PD ID** *062 †55

WEIBEL, Sandra Beth. 834 WALNUT ST, STE 650 19107 #041-12-1986 L1988 **PCC** *020 †20

WEICHEL, Eric David. 890 WALNUT ST STE 10, WILLS EYE HOSPITAL 19107 #038-44-1996 L2003 **IM** *020 †35

WEIDNER, Zachary David. ■ 19146 #041-01-2008 *012

WEIGELE, John Burdette. 3400 SPRUCE ST, GROUND FLR/FOUNDERS, H U P 19104 #041-01-1982 L1983 **DR** *020 †80

WEIKERT, Blair Christian. 230 N BROAD ST 19102 #041-13-2003 L2006 **ID** *012 †20

WEIL, Daniel Peter. ■ 19147 #041-01-2003 L2004 **AN** *020

WEIL, Susan Caroline. 111 S 11TH ST 19107 #024-01-1974 L1984 **HEM IM** *050 †20

WEIN, Alan Jerome. 9 PENN CTR, DIVISION OF UROLOGY 19103 #041-01-1966 L1967 **U** *020 ‡

WEINBERG, David Seth. 333 COTTMAN AVE, P3047 19111 #035-20-1989 L1992 **IM** *020 †20

WEINBERG, Sheri Dawn. ■ 19106 #024-07-2006 L2006 **IM** *012

WEINBERGER, Lauren Noel. ■ 19104 #041-12-2006 L2006 **EM** *012

WEINBERGER, Steven Elliot. 190 N INDEPENDENCE MALL W 19106 #024-01-1973 L2004 **PCC IM** *040 †20

WEINBLATT, Howard Alan. 4110 COTTMAN AVE 19135 #041-07-1977 L1977 **OBG** *020 †30

WEINER, Evan Jonathan. ■ 19106 #033-06-2001 L2001 **PD** *020 †55

WEINER, Leon J. 9873 BUSTLETON AVE # A 19115 #649-01-1955 L1959 **IM RHU** *071

WEINER, Mark Gordon. 3701 MARKET ST 6TH FL, EDWARD COOPER MED PRACTICE 19104 #041-01-1992 L1994 **IM** *050 †20

WEINER, Monica Beth. ■ 19106 #035-46-2001 L2004 **PD** *100 †55

WEINER, Oscar R. PARK TOWNE PL W # 108 19130 #041-09-1951 L1952 **P** *020

WEINER, Stuart. 834 CHESTNUT ST STE 400, GYNECOLOGY BEN FRANKLIN BL 19107 #041-01-1972 L1973 **MFM GYN** *020 †30 ‡

WEINFURTNER, Robert Jared. ■ 19128 #038-06-2006 L2006 **N** *012

WEINGARTEN, Michael S. 219 N BROAD ST, STE 8 19107 #041-01-1974 L1982 **GS VS** *020 †85

WEINMAN, Jason Perry. ■ 19125 #007-02-2002 L2007 **PDR** *012 †80

WEINRYB, Joan. 3400 SPRUCE ST 19104 #035-46-1983 L1984 **IM IMG** *020 †20

WEINSTEIN, Edward Alan. ■ 19106 #041-02-2006 L2006 **IM** *012

WEINSTEIN, Gregory S. 3400 SPRUCE ST, HEAD AND NECK SURGERY 19104 #035-09-1985 L1991 **OTO** *020 †45 ‡

WEINSTEIN, Jack H. 111 N 49TH ST 19139 #041-02-1949 L1952 **P** *071 †75

WEINSTEIN, Jeffrey Louis. ■ 19106 #041-02-2006 L2006 **DR** *012

WEINSTEIN, Judith K. 1800 LOMBARD ST, GRADUATE HOSP DEPT RAD 19146 #396-24-1983 L1984 **DR OS** *040 †80

WEINSTEIN, Lara Carson. 833 CHESTNUT ST, DEPT OF FAMILY MEDICINE 19107 #041-02-1995 L1997 **FM** *020 †18

WEINSTEIN, Louis. 834 CHESTNUT ST STE 400, THOMAS JEFFERSON UNIV 19107 #036-05-1972 L2003 **OBG MFM** *030 †30

WEINSTEIN, Michael Scott. 1100 WALNUT ST, 5TH FL 19107 #041-02-1994 L1996 **CCS** *020 †85 ‡

WEINSTEIN, Robert Seidel. 1521 LOCUST ST # 10-FL 19102 #041-01-1971 L1972 **GYN** *020 †30

WEINSTOCK, Robert Michael. 515 W CHELTEN AVE 19144 #041-09-1964 L1965 **GP OS** *020

WEINTRAUB, Ari Yehuda. ■ 19111 #023-01-2000 L2004 **PAN** *012 †55

WEINTRAUB, Daniel. 3615 CHESTNUT ST RM 330, SECTION GERIATRIC PSYCHIAT 19104 #023-01-1991 L2001 **P** *020 †75

WEISBERG, Arthur Barry. ■ 19149 #026-04-1974 L1975 **P** *020

WEISBERG, Louis Ivan. 5501 OLD YORK RD, AEMC LIFTER 2 19141 #005-06-1981 L2006 **NPM PD** *020 †55

WEISBERG, Martin. 111 S 11TH ST 19107 #041-02-1972 L1973 **GYN PHM** *071 †30

WEISBERG, Paul Benj. 3998 RED LION RD 19114 #041-13-1971 L1972 **GE IM** *020 †20 ‡

WEISER, Jeffrey Neal. 324 S 34TH ST, DEPT INFECTIOUS DISEASES 19104 #024-01-1984 L1992 **PD ID** *050 †55

WEISER, Jessica Ann. ■ 19104 #035-46-2007 **IM** *012

WEISMAN, David. ■ 19104 #035-47-2004 L2007 **CD** *012 †20

WEISS, Albert Aaron. 3401 N BROAD ST, 6TH FL 19140 #041-13-1973 L1974 **ORS HS** *020 †40 ‡

WEISS, Barbara Jean. 8835 GERMANTOWN AVE 19118 #041-07-1993 L1995 **FM** *020 †18

WEISS, Burton Saul. 1601 WALNUT ST STE 1422 19102 #041-13-1973 L1974 **P PYG** *020 †75

WEISS, Jared Marc. 19103 #008-01-2004 L2007 **HO** *012 †20

WEISS, Marc David. 717 S CHRISTPHR CLMBS BLVD 19147 #550-02-2003 L2003 **P** *020

WEISS, Mitchell J. 3615 CIVIC CENTER BLVD 19104 #041-01-1989 L2000 **PHO PD** *020 †55

WEISS, Pamela F. ■ 19130 #035-46-2002 L2002 **PPR** *012 †55

WEISS, Roberta Alice. 3400 SPRUCE ST 19104 #041-01-1986 L1987 **IM NEP** *020 †20

WEISS, Roger Eliot. 829 SPRUCE ST, STE 302 19107 #033-05-1973 L1975 **P** *020 †75 ‡

WEISS, Stuart Joel. 3400 SPRUCE ST, 680 DULLES BLG, DEPT. ANES 19104 #041-13-1986 L1990 **AN** *020 †05

WEISSMAN, Drew. ■ 19104 #024-05-1987 L1997 **AI** *020 †20,03

WEISSMAN, Joel Marvin. 7500 CENTRAL AVE STE 107 19111 #035-08-1970 L1973 **U** *020

WEISSMANN, Lauren Erica. ■ 19146 #041-01-2007 L2007 **OBG** *012

WEISZ, Keith Michael. ■ 19103 #035-48-2006 L2006 **PD** *012

WEITZ, Howard Hy. 925 CHESTNUT ST 19107 #041-02-1978 L1979 **CD** *020 †20

WEITZMAN, Adam M. ■ 19103 #035-20-2006 L2006 **OBG** *012

WELCH, Kevin Christian. ■ 19104 #041-15-2002 L2007 **OTO** *020 †20

WELCH, Tamara Lynn. 1015 WALNUT ST, STE 401 19107 #041-02-2004 L2004 **FM** *020 †18

WELCH, William Chas. 330 S 9TH ST 4TH FL, DEPT OF NEUROSURGERY 19107 #035-08-1985 L1990 **NS ORS** *020 †25

WELDEMICHAEL, Sebelewengel. 5501 OLD YORK RD 19141 #366-01-1990 *100

WELLEN, Shari Lynn. ■ 19103 #011-03-2005 L2005 **PD** *012

WELLENBACH, Burton L. 111 S 11TH ST STE 8102 19107 #041-02-1944 L1944 **GYN** *071 †30

WELLER, Elizabeth B. 3440 MARKET ST, # 2 CHILDRENS CTR 19104 #605-01-1975 L1997 **P CHP** *030 †75

WELLER, Kenneth Russell. 111 N 49TH ST 19139 #041-09-1975 L1976 **P** *020 †75

WELLER, Ronald Alan. 3535 MARKET ST FL 2 19104 #028-02-1974 L1997 **P** *050 †75

WELLS, Courtney. 2301 S BROAD ST, TJUH 19148 #041-01-1995 L1998 **AN** *020

WELLS, Rebecca Gray. 3400 SPRUCE ST 19104 #023-07-1987 L2002 **NEP** *020 †20

WEN, Jessica Weiyun. ■ 19103 #048-04-2004 L2007 **PG** *012 †55

WENDER, Richard Chas. 1015 WALNUT ST, STE 401 19107 #041-01-1979 L1980 **FM** *030 †18

WENDLING, Woodrow Wm. 3401 N BROAD ST, TEMPLE UNIVERSITY HOSPITAL 19140 #041-13-1978 L1983 **AN IM** *020 †05

WENGER, Lisa A. 2840 W DAUPHIN ST 19132 #016-43-1990 L1992 **IM** *020 †20

WERNER, Rachel Michele. 423 GUARDIAN DR, 1230 BLOCKLEY HALL 19104 #041-01-1998 L2001 **IM** *050 †20

WERNER-WASIK, Maria. 111 S 11TH ST, BODINE CTR. 19107 #759-10-1979 L1993 **RO** *020 †20,80

WERNICKE, A Gabriella. 111 S 11TH ST, CANCER TREATMEN 19107 #422-01-1999 L2001 **RO** *100 †80

WERNOVSKY, Gil. 324 S 34TH ST 19104 #041-14-1982 L1994 **PD** *050 †55

WERNSING, David Scott. 700 SPRUCE ST, STE 507 19106 #033-06-1995 L1998 **GS OS** *020 †85

WERTH, Victoria Patricia. 3400 SPRUCE ST, 2 RHOADS PAVILION 19104 #023-07-1980 L1989 **D IM** *040 †20,15

WERTHAN, Merylee E. 5049 OXFORD AVE 19124 #041-13-1961 L1962 **NS** *020 †25

WERTHEIM, Gerald B. ■ 19147 #041-01-2005 L2005 **PTH** *020

WESSELL, Rosalie Winter. 4726 OXFORD AVE 19124 #041-02-1977 L1979 **OBG D** *020 †30

WEST, David John. ■ 19103 #011-03-2007 L2007 **TY** *012

WEST, Franklin Howard. 111 N 49TH ST 19139 #041-01-1945 L1948 **P** *071 †75

WEST, James William. 3400 SPRUCE ST, DEPT MED 19104 #041-01-1962 L1963 **IM OS** *071

WEST, Rebecca Lynne. 3440 MARKET ST STE 200, DIVISION OF MENTAL HYGIENE 19104 #035-15-2004 L2007 **CHP** *012

WEST, Susan Elizabeth. 833 CHESTNUT ST, STE 220 19107 #035-15-1985 L1986 **IM** *020 †20

WEST, Therese Belli. 34TH ST AND CIVIC CENTER B 19104 #048-02-1986 L1989 **PHO PD** *020 †55

WETZEL, Franklin Todd. 3401 N BROAD ST, 5TH FLOOR/OPB 19140 #041-01-1981 L1988 **OSS PMM** *020 †40

WEX, Katherine Nicole. 5501 OLD YORK RD, DEPT OF ANESTHESIOLOGY 19141 #023-01-2000 L2007 **AN** *020 †05

WEXLER, Harry. ■ 19154 #041-01-1928 L1930 **R** *071

WEYLER, Richard Thomas. ■ 19145 #041-02-2004 L2004 **AN** *100

WHEEL, Kathryn Lynn. 5501 OLD YORK RD, ALBERT EINSTEIN MED CTR 19141 #035-06-2006 L2006 **GS** *012

WHEELER, James English. UNIV PA HOSP, DEPT PATH 19104 #023-07-1962 L1971 **PTH** *040 †50

WHEELER, Jenette M Harvey. 3400 SPRUCE ST 19104 #012-05-1968 L1971 **FM** *020 †18

WHEELOCK, Earle F. 230 N BROAD ST, RM 435 19102 #035-01-1955 L1963 **IG** *050

WHELAN, Gerald Patrick. 3624 MARKET ST 19104 #035-08-1970 L1997 **EM** *030 †16

WHELIHAN, Kristen Marie. 111 S 11TH ST, JEFFERSON UNIVERSITY 19107 #041-02-2005 L2005 **PD** *012

WHELLAN, David Joshua. 925 CHESTNUT ST, RM 135 19107 #028-02-1994 L1997 **CD** *020 †20

WHEREAT, Arthur F. 3400 SPRUCE ST 19104 #041-01-1951 L1952 **CD** *020 †20

WHITAKER, Linton Andin. 3400 SPRUCE ST, 10TH FL 19104 #021-01-1962 L1969 **PS GS** *020 †85,65 ‡

WHITAKER, Robert Carroll. 3223 N BROAD ST, STE 175 19140 #023-07-1987 L2007 **PD PHP** *040 †55

WHITE, Danette. 1999 W HUNTING PARK AVE 19140 #041-07-1986 L1989 **IM** *020

WHITE, Deborah Anne. 7700 GERMANTOWN AVE, FL 2 19118 #041-13-1978 L1980 **PD** *020 †55 ‡

WHITE, Herbert Leon. 378 E UPSAL ST 19119 #010-03-1952 L1954 **FM GP** *020

WHITE, Jennifer Denise. ■ 19104 #041-13-2005 L2005 **GS** *020

WHITE, Jilian Marie. ■ 19107 #010-01-2006 L2006 **OBG** *012

WHITE, Kelley Jean. 251 E BRINGHURST ST, COVENANT HOUST HEALTH SERV 19144 #024-01-1980 L1982 **PD** *020 †55

WHITE, Laura. 5501 OLD YORK RD, ALBERT EINSTEIN MED CTR 19141 #041-15-2001 L2006 **P** *012

WHITE, Linda Denise. 221 N BROAD ST 19107 #024-01-1989 L1989 **DR** *020 †80

WHITE, Sarah Beth. ■ 19147 #033-05-2005 L2005 **DR** *012

WHITLEY, Kari Alicia. ■ 19107 #033-06-2007 L2007 **OBG** *012

WHITLEY, Karl Vincent. 3400 N BROAD ST, 1ST FL 19140 #010-01-1990 L1993 **OTO** *020 †45

WHITMAN, Glenn Jos Robt. 1025 WALNUT ST, STE 605 19107 #041-01-1979 L1981 **TS** *030 †90,85

WHITMAN, Randal Loring. 7201 RISING SUN AVE 19111 #041-13-1979 L1980 **PD** *020 †55

WHITMAN, Sarah Marie. 8627 GERMANTOWN AVE 19118 #035-45-1987 L1991 **PPN P** *020 †75

WHITMORE, Kristene E. 207 N BROAD ST 19107 #041-09-1979 L1986 **U** *020 †95

WHITMORE, Robert Gray. ■ 19146 #041-01-2006 L2006 **NS** *012

WHITNEY, Christa L. ■ 19106 #035-15-2002 L2005 **PTH** *100 †50

WHITNEY, Theodore R. 5301 CEDAR AVE 19143 #041-09-1957 L1958 **PD PDA** *020 †55,03

WHITON, Michal Anne. 614 S 8TH ST 19147 #054-04-2005 L2006 **RO** *012

WHITTEN, Joseph Anthony. 3400 N BROAD ST, TEMPLE UNIV SCH OF MED 19140 #041-13-2006 L2006 **PTH** *012

WHYTE, John. 1200 W TABOR RD 19141 #041-01-1978 L1989 **PM OS** *050 †60

WICKS, Charles David. ■ 19125 #032-01-2005 L2005 **IM** *012

WICKSTROM, Maj Lee. 324 S 34TH ST, CHILDRENS HSPTL OF PHLDLPH 19104 #016-06-1993 L1998 **PDR** *020 †80

WIDELITZ, Martin Marvin. ■ 19128 #869-05-1957 L1958 **IM END** *050

WIECKOWSKI, Kathryn. ■ 19130 #041-15-2008 *012

WIEGAND, Laura Conant. ■ 19103 #041-12-2007 L2007 **ORS** *012

WIEGERS, Susan Elizabeth. 3400 SPRUCE ST, CARDIO DIV 9 GATES 19104 #035-45-1981 L1992 **IM EM** *020 †20

WIENER, David Hillel. 925 CHESTNUT ST, MEZZANINE 19107 #035-46-1979 L1982 **CD IM** *020 †20

WIENER, Evelyn Barbara. 399 S 34TH ST, PENN TWR LOWER LVL 19104 #041-13-1977 L1979 **IM** *030 †20

WIENER, Jacob Saml. 604 WASHINGTON SQ S 19106 #041-02-1938 L1939 **IM** *071 †20

WILDEN, Jessica Anne. 3400 SPRUCE ST, 3RD FLOOR SILVERSTEIN PAV 19104 #026-08-2005 L2005 **NS** *012

WILDERMAN, Michael J. 3400 SPRUCE ST, SURGERY/4 SILVERSTEIN 19104 #041-01-2001 L2001 **VS** *012 †85

WILE, Margery Blahd. ■ 19103 #016-02-1937 L1965 **P** *020

WILENSKY, Robert L. 3400 SPRUCE ST, HOSPITALL OF UNIVERSITY 19104 #660-01-1984 L1996 **CD IM** *050 †20

WILFRED, Eliza Nyla. 4641 ROOSEVELT BLVD, 4641 ROOSEVELT BLVD. 19124 #496-20-1988 L1998 **P** *020 †16

WILKERSON, Carlos. 111 S 11TH ST, STE 8490 19107 #042-01-1986 L1988 **AN** *020 †05

WILKES, Annina Nicholas. 111 S 11TH ST, 3350 GIBBON BLDG 19107 #041-13-1983 L1987 **DR OBG** *020

WILKES, Jennifer Jill. ■ 19103 #041-01-2007 L2007 **PD** *012

WILL, Daniel Vincent, Jr. 51 N 39TH ST 19104 #010-02-1998 L2004 **OPH** *020 †35

WILLCOX, Thomas O, Jr. 925 CHESTNUT ST, FL 6 19107 #041-01-1987 L1988 **OTO NO** *020 †45

WILLI, Steven Matthew. 324 S 34TH ST 19104 #023-07-1985 L1988 **PDE PD** *050 †55

WILLIAMS, Christopher A. 840 WALNUT ST 19107 #018-03-1988 L1990 **OPH** *020 †20

WILLIAMS, Deandre Ramon. 8835 GERMANTOWN AVE, CHESTNUT HILL HOSP/EMERG D 19118 #016-42-2000 L2003 **EM** *020 †16 ‡

WILLIAMS, Edwin Rae. 5501 OLD YORK RD, DEPT OF EMERGENCY MED 19141 #036-05-1989 L1997 **EM** *020 †20,16

WILLIAMS, Eric Anthony. 9880 BUSTLETON AVE, STE 22 19115 #041-13-1996 L1996 **ORS** *020

WILLIAMS, F Marian. 2 PENN BLVD, STE 210 19144 #035-15-1932 **OBG OS** *020 †30

WILLIAMS, Gerald R, Jr. 3400 SPRUCE ST DEPT ORS 19104 #041-13-1984 L1990 **ORS** *020 †20

WILLIAMS, Glenn Leroy. 1 PENN BLVD 19144 #041-02-1939 L1941 **OBG** *072

WILLIAMS, James Robt. 814 S 4TH ST 19147 #047-07-1955 L1956 **PTH CLP** *071 †50

WILLIAMS, Jay James. 51 N 39TH ST - W223, DEPARTMENT OF ANESTHESIA 19104 #041-01-1976 L1977 **AN** *020 †05

WILLIAMS, Jessica Nancy. ■ 19150 #055-01-2008 *012

WILLIAMS, John Thomas, Jr. 9880 BUSTLETON AVE, STE 22 19115 #010-03-1994 L2000 **ORS** *020 †40

WILLIAMS, Joseph James. 5301 CEDAR AVE, STE 634 19143 #008-02-1975 L1980 **U** *020

WILLIAMS, Joseph Torrence. 5401 OLD YORK RD, STE 403 19141 #041-12-1986 L1988 **IM** *020 †20

WILLIAMS, Joyce Monica. 2449 GOLF RD, STE 11 19131 #041-07-1990 L1996 **IM** *020

WILLIAMS, Katy Michelle. ■ 19130 #041-77-2007, ▲ **IM** *012

WILLIAMS, Kendal Passoth. 19146 #041-01-1995 L1998 **IM** *020 †20

WILLIAMS, Kevin Jon. 1020 LOCUST ST STE 348, CRINOLOGY 19107 #023-07-1980 L1989 **OS END** *050 †20

WILLIAMS, Leigh J. 3400 SPRUCE ST, DEPT OF PATHOLGY & LB MDCN 19104 #001-02-1979 L1986 **PTH** *020 †50

WILLIAMS, Michael Jon. 111 S 11TH ST, STE 524 19107 #028-02-1981 L1992 **AN** *020 †05

WILLIAMS, Noel Norman. 3400 SPRUCE ST, FL 4 19104 #539-06-1981 L2000 **GS** *020

WILLIAMS, Sankey V. 423 GUARDIAN DR, 1220 BLOCKLEY HALL 19104 #024-01-1970 L1971 **IM** *030 †20

WILLIAMS, Sasha Anne. ■ 19107 #035-15-2005 L2005 **AN** *012

WILLIAMS, Sonya Marie. ■ 19119 #041-15-2006 L2006 **OBG** *012

WILLIAMS, Timothy Keith. 1000 WALNUT ST APT 703 19107 #041-02-2004 L2004 **GS** *012

WILLIAMSON, Michael Rober. ■ 19106 #028-03-2005 L2005 **ORS** *012

WILLIAMSON, Owen W. 121 E LEHIGH AVE 19125 #041-13-1976 L1978 **IM** *020

WILLIS, Alliric Isaac. 3998 RED LION RD STE 2 19114 #041-01-1996 L2004 **GS** *020 †85

WILLIS, Carrie Anne. ■ 19136 #041-15-2006 L2006 **IM** *012

WILLIS, Garth John. 840 WALNUT ST, WILLS EYE HOSP 19107 #039-01-2005 L2005 **OPH** *012

WILLIS, Rudolph E. 1331 E WYOMING AVE, CANCER TREATMENT CENTER OF 19124 #028-02-1977 L2005 **ON HEM** *012 †20

WILLMAN, Kelly Marie. ■ 19123 #035-15-2005 L2005 **GS** *012

WILSON, Audrey M Radomsky. 1815 COTTMAN AVE 19111 #005-12-1964 L1966 **OS** *020 †80

WILSON, Deborah F. 2301 E ALLEGHENY AVE, TEMPLE SPORTS ORTHOPEDICS 19134 #041-13-1977 L1979 **AN PD** *020

WILSON, Edward Peter. 324 S 34TH ST 19104 #143-01-1951 L1965 **PD LM** *030 †55

WILSON, George Matthews. 5800 RIDGE AVE, ROXBOROUGH MEM HOSP 19128 #041-02-1957 L1958 **GS** *030

WILSON, James Merton. 125 S 31ST ST, TRL, SUITE 2000 19104 #025-01-1984 L1993 **IM** *020 †20

WILSON, Janet L. 1144 LOCUST ST 19107 #030-06-1977 L1979 **GYN P** *020 †18

WILSON, Justin Nathaniel. ■ 19119 #041-13-2003 L2003 **DR** *012

WILSON, Lisa Marie. ■ 19128 #051-07-2006 L2006 **EM** *012

WILSON, Lorri Beth. ■ 19104 #041-01-2006 L2006 **OPH** *012

WILSON, Melissa Ann. ■ 19130 #041-02-2008 *012

WILSON, Michele Diane. 225 S COBBS CREEK PKWY, COBBS CREEK PRIMARY CARE C 19139 #041-12-1980 L1997 **ADL PD** *020 †55

WILSON, Robert Bruce. 3400 SPRUCE ST, MEDICAL AFFAIRS OFFICE 19104 #041-01-1989 L1991 **BBK** *020 †50

WILSON, Robert Douglas. 3400 SPRUCE ST 19104 #061-01-1977 L2001 **OBS MG** *020

WILSON, Rodgers Mc Kinley. 4641 ROOSEVELT BLVD 19124 #047-07-1985 L2004 **P** *020 †75

WILSON, Vasthi Christense. 302 S 13TH ST 19107 #041-01-2003 L2003 **RO** *012

WILTSHIRE, David Grant. 2001 HAMILTON ST, OFC 1 19130 #065-01-1968 **ORS** *050 †40

WIMMER, Neil Jason. ■ 19143 #041-01-2006 L2006 **IM** *012

WIN, Cho Myamon. 800 SPRUCE ST 19107 #209-01-1998 L2008 **IM** *020 †20

WINGERTER, Sarah Luise. ■ 19107 #041-15-2000 L2007 **PDI** *020 †55

WINKELMAN, Arnold Chas. 1331 E WYOMING AVE, STE 1100 19124 #025-07-1962 L1968 **N PTH** *020 †75

WINOKUR, Ronald Scott. ■ 19103 #041-02-2006 L2007 **IM** *012

WINSTON, Flaura Koplin. 324 S 34TH ST 19104 #041-01-1990 L1993 **PD** *020 †55

WINT, Roger M. 9501 ROOSEVELT BLVD, PENNSYLVANIA HEART & 19114 #035-46-1978 L1981 **IM CD** *020 †20

WINTERS, Sarah Emily. ■ 19130 #041-13-2002 L2002 **PD** *100 †55

WINYARD, Paul Julian D. CHILDRENS HOSP, DEPT PED 19104 #917-09-1986 L1991 **PD** *020

WIRTS, Steven Bayliss. 1331 E WYOMING AVE, PARKVIEW HOSPITAL 19124 #041-02-1974 L1976 **OBG** *020 †30

WISE, Robert I. JEFFERSON MED COLLEGE, DEPT INTERNAL MED 19107 #048-02-1950 L1955 **IM ID** *071 †20

WISNER, Douglas Matthew. ■ 19148 #041-14-2008 *012

WITEK, James. 1427 VINE ST, 5TH FL 19102 #038-43-1988 L1990 **IM** *020 †20

WITHINGTON, Amelia M. 8220 CASTOR AVE 19152 #048-12-1991 L1993 **P** *020 †75

WITKIEWICZ, Agnieszka K. 132 S 10TH ST, STE 285K 19107 #759-10-1996 L2005 **DMP** *100 †50

WITKOWSKI, Joseph Albin. 3501 RYAN AVE 19136 #041-09-1953 L1954 **D** *071 †15 ‡

■ = Address Information Privacy Protected

WITKOWSKI, Thomas Anthony. 111 S 11TH ST, STE 8490 19107 #041-09-1984 L1986
AN *020 †05

WITMER, George Robert, III. 111 S 11TH ST STE 2170, THOMAS JEFFERSON UNIV HOSP 19107
#035-45-2000 L2001 IM *020 †20

WITT, Deborah Kay. 833 CHESTNUT ST STE 301 19107 #041-09-1993 L1996 FM *020 †18

WITTINK, Marsha Nicole. 51 N 39TH ST, FL 7 19104 #041-02-1999 L2001 FM *020 †18

WITZKE, Christian Federic. 5501 OLD YORK RD, ALBERT EISNTEIN MEDICAL CE 19141
#935-07-2000 L2002 CD *012 †20

WIVEL, Nelson Auburn. 125 S 31ST ST STE 2000, TRANSLATIONAL RESCH LABS 19104
#005-11-1961 L1997 PTH MG *050

WIXTED, Thomas Andrew. 3400 SPRUCE ST, 4 MALONEY 19104 #041-02-2002 L2002 GS *012

WLADIS, Edward J. ■ 19102 #035-15-2001 L2001 OPH *020

WLADYSLAWSKI, Colleen M. 3300 HENRY AVE, MCP HAHNEMANN UNIVERSITY 19129
#041-15-1999 L2001 EM *020 †16

WOHLREICH, George M. 19 S 22ND ST 19103 #041-01-1979 L1980 P PYA *020 †75

WOJNARSKI, Mariusz. ■ 19134 #041-14-2007 *012

WOJTOWYCH, Mykola. 5104 N BROAD ST 19141 #407-04-1949 L1961 GP *072

WOLDOW, Adam Bernard. ■ 19107 #041-02-2006 L2006 D *012

WOLDOW, Andrew Bennett. 8200 HENRY AVE, STE G1 19128 #041-13-1980 L1982
CD IM *030 †20

WOLF, Abigail. 834 CHESTNUT ST STE 300, DEPARTMENT OF OB/GYN 19107
#041-13-1995 L1998 OBG *020 †30

WOLF, Bryan Albert. 34TH ST AND CIVIC CTR BLVD, RM 5135 MAIN BLDG 19104
#396-12-1984 L1991 PTH *020 †50

WOLF, Charles Jos, III. 230 W WASHINGTON SQ, STE 100 19106 #041-01-1969 L1970
IM U *020 †20

WOLF, Daniel Herman. 3400 SPRUCE ST, 10TH FLOOR GATES BLDG 19104
#008-01-2001 L2001 P *050

WOLF, Erica. 345 E MT AIRY AVE 19119 #041-13-1995 L1998 IM *020 †20

WOLF, Gunter B. 4104 SPRUCE ST 19104 #409-23-1987 NEP *020

WOLF, Judith Ellen. 219 N BROAD ST, FL 5 19107 #035-20-1981 L1982 ID IM *050 †20

WOLF, Michael Jacob. ■ 19103 #041-01-2007 L2007 PD *012

WOLF, Michael Jason. 132 S 10TH ST, THOMAS JEFFERSON UNVI HOSP 19107
#012-05-1995 L2004 DR RNR *020 †80

WOLF, Nelson Marc. 3300 HENRY AVE 19129 #041-13-1968 L1969 CD IM *020 †20

WOLF, Ronald Lee. 3400 SPRUCE ST 19104 #026-08-1994 L1998 RNR *020 †80

WOLF, Sandra Matthews. 1427 VINE ST, FL 7 19102 #041-02-1977 L1978 OBG *020 †30 ‡

WOLFE, Barbara Blumenberg. 19106 #035-08-1957 L1966 P PYA *012

WOLFE, Robert C. 229 ARCH ST, CENTER/PHILADELPHIA 19106 #035-09-1949 L1952 IM *071

WOLFE, Stuart. 255 S 17TH ST STE 1602, MEDICAL TOWER BUILDING 19103
#035-08-1957 L1959 P PYA *020 †75

WOLFSON, Philip. 833 CHESTNUT ST, 3RD FL 19107 #035-47-1974 L1982 PDS GS *020 †85

WOLFSON, Robert Jos. 219 N BROAD ST FL 10, OF OTOLARYNGOLOGY 19107
#041-09-1957 L1958 OTO *020 †45 ‡

WOLGIN, William. 220 W RITTENHOUSE SQ, APT 21A 19103 #041-09-1947 L1948 U *072 †95

WOLK, Larry Allen. 1201 N 8TH ST, ADC BUILDING - FIRST FLOOR 19122 #041-09-1976 L1977
TS EM *020 †85,90

WOLKOVE, Norman. 3400 SPRUCE ST 19104 #067-01-1971 L1974 PUD *020 †20

WOLMAN, Thomas Scofield. 1201 CHESTNUT ST 19107 #041-14-1971 L1972 P *020 †75

WOLOSHIN, Jeffrey. 2514 N BROAD ST, WARREN E SMITH CMHC 19132 #041-02-1987 L1990
P *020 †75 ‡

WOLRAICH, David Abraham. ■ 19104 #035-46-2006 L2006 OTO *012

WONG, Albert James. ■ 19102 #023-07-1983 L1983 PD *100

WONG, Alex Guon. ■ 19107 #041-02-2002 L2002 GS *100

WONG, Brian Szelik. 5501 OLD YORK RD, ALBERT EINSTEIN MED CTR 19141
#041-13-2006 L2006 P *012

WONG, Bryan Yau-Vei. 3400 N BROAD ST, TEMPLE UNIV SCH OF MED 19140
#041-13-1998 L2001 HO *100 †20

WONG, Chih-An. ■ 19102 #041-06-2007 PTH *012

WONG, Elliot H. 5501 OLD YORK RD, DEPT EMERGENCY MEDICINE 19141 #041-13-2001 L2001
EM *020

WONG, Kar Lai. 230 W WASHINGTON SQ, FL 3 19106 #041-01-1992 L1994 ICE CD *020 †20

WONG, Patricia. 3400 SPRUCE ST, DIVISION OF GASTROENTEROLO 19104 #005-11-2001 L2001
GE *012

WONG, Robert William. 51 N 39TH ST, SCHEIE EYE INSTITUTE 19104 #041-01-2003 L2003
OPH *100

WONG, Stephen. 3400 SPRUCE ST, HUP, 2 RAVDIN 19104 #036-07-2000 L2001 N *020 †75

WONG, Stephen Willis. 3333 N BROAD ST 19140 #041-02-1972 L1976 OPH *020 †35

WONG, Wai Thong. 51 N 39TH ST, SCHEIE EYE INST 19104 #028-02-2001 L2001 *100 †35

WONG, Yuning. ■ 19107 #033-06-1999 L2001 HO *100 †20

WOO, Edward Yiming. 3400 SPRUCE ST, FL 4 19104 #041-01-1996 L1999 VS *020 †85

WOO, John H. 3400 SPRUCE ST, HUP DEPT NEURORADIOLOGY 19104 #035-01-1997 L1997
RNR *020 †80

WOO, Y Joseph. 3400 SPRUCE ST, FL 6 19104 #041-01-1992 L1995 TS *020 †85,90

WOOD, Craig Alan. BROAD & VINE ST MS 461, DIV INFECTIOUS DISEASES 19102
#005-06-1980 L1988 IM *020 †20

WOOD, Kamillah Natisse. 3400 CIVIC CENTER BLVD, DEPT OF PEDS 19104
#010-01-2006 L2006 PD *012

WOOD, Kelly Natasha. 800 SPRUCE ST 19107 #162-01-2004 L2006 IM *100

WOOD, Margaret Diana. 3401 N BROAD ST 19140 #041-07-1987 L1988 CD *020 †20

WOOD, Moira Dorothy. 132 S 10TH ST, STE 260A 19107 #041-07-1991 L1995
PTH PCP *020 †50

WOOD, Richard Kevin, Jr. ■ 19104 #035-47-2002 L2006 GE *012 †20

WOOD, Sarah. ■ 19130 #041-15-2008 L2008 *012

WOODS, Jennifer Elizabeth. ■ 19128 #041-15-2008 *012

WOODSON, Robert H. 230 N BROAD ST 19102 #051-04-1978 L1979 OS *020 †16

WOODWORTH, Bradford Alan. ■ 19103 #021-01-2001 L2006 OTO *100 †45

WOODY, George Edward. 600 PUBLIC LEDGER, TREATMENT RES INST 19106
#041-13-1964 L1966 ADP P *050 †75

WOOLF, Allen Richard. 1601 CHESTNUT ST, TL07B 19192 #024-01-1981 L2000 PD *030 †55

WORK, Brian David. 3400 SPRUCE ST, DEPT OF IM/100 CENTREX 19104 #005-19-2001 L2001
HO *100

WORLY, Brett Lawrence. ■ 19104 #025-12-2005 L2005 OBG *012

WORTHINGTON-KIRSCH, Robt. 5735 RIDGE AVE STE 106 19128 #024-16-1986 L1987
DR VIR *020 †80

WORTMAN, Bethany. ■ 19107 #041-13-2007 L2007 OBG *012

WORTMANN, Wil Karl-Heinz. 3400 SPRUCE ST 19104 #407-15-1969 END OBG *050

WORZALA, Katherine Teresa. 125 S 9TH ST, STE 502 19107 #056-06-1994 L2001
GPM *020 †20

WRABETZ, Lawrence Gerard. 3400 SPRUCE ST, RADIOLOGY ASSOCIATES 19104
#016-02-1984 L1986 N *020 †75

WRAY, Lisa Michelle. ■ 19130 #041-13-2006 L2006 PD *012

WRENN, Glenda Louise. 3535 MARKET ST FL 2, PENN BEHAVORIAL HEALTH 19104
#041-02-2004 L2004 P *012

WRENN, Walter F, III. ■ 19139 #041-02-1974 L1975 IM *020

WRIGHT, Bonnie Louise. 800 SPRUCE ST, HALL MERCER BUILDING 19107 #041-02-1992 L1994
P *020 †75

WRIGHT, Charles Duncan. ■ 19146 #008-01-1982 L2007 P *020 †75

WRIGHT, Erin Armstead. 111 S 11TH ST, JEFFERSON UNIVERSITY 19107 #041-15-2005 L2005
PD *012

WRIGHT, Erin Daniel. 3400 SPRUCE ST # 5-RAVDIN, UNIV OF PENN 19104 #067-01-1993 L1997
OTO *020 †20

WRIGHT, Fay Devine. 601 WALNUT ST, STE 640 19106 #041-07-1987 L1990 OBG *020 †30

WRIGHT, Lance S. 111 N 49TH ST 19139 #047-06-1946 L1954 P CHP *071 †75

WRIGHT, Laura Susanne. ■ 19119 #041-02-2002 L2005 FM *020 †18 ‡

WRIGHT, Scott Howell. 230 W WASHINGTON SQ, FL 4 19106 #041-01-1970 L1973
GE IM *071 †20

WRIGHT, Tracey B. 3405 CIVIC CENTER BLVD, CHILD HOSP DIV OF RHEUM 19104
#041-15-2001 L2001 PPR PPR *012 †55

WU, Andrew Szeyuan. ■ 19107 #016-06-2005 L2005 GS *012

WU, Chadwick. ■ 19107 #047-05-2005 L2005 GS *012

WU, Christine. 834 CHESTNUT ST, STE T171 19107 #041-07-1987 L1988 GYN *020 †30

WU, Chung-Hsiu. 1025 WALNUT ST # 310, JEFFERSON MED COLLEGE OBG 19107
#385-02-1961 L1972 END OBG *020 †30

WU, David Dar-Jiun. 111 S 11TH ST, THOS JEFFERSON UNIV HOSP 19107 #422-01-2006 L2007
AN *012

WU, Gary Dean. 51 N 39TH ST, UPHS/PRESBYTRN INTRNL MDCN 19104 #016-01-1986 L1992
GE *020 †20

WU, Gregory Frederick. 3400 SPRUCE ST, 3 WEST GATES/ HUP 19104 #018-03-2001 L2002
N *020 †75

WU, Henry Mingyow. 245 N 15TH ST MS 461, DIVISION OF INFECTIOUS DIS 19102
#024-01-1997 L1999 ID *020 †20

WU, Hong. 333 COTTMAN AVE, DEPT OF PATH 19111 #243-03-1987 L1997 D *020 †50

WU, Jennifer Nanwah. ■ 19104 #041-01-2006 L2006 PD *012

WU, Jie. ■ 19146 #048-12-2007 L2007 IM *012

WU, Mei Lene. 245 N 15TH ST MS 310, DREXEL UNIV COLL OF MED 19102 #041-15-2004 L2004
AN *012

WU, Sam Wei-Lung. ■ 19104 #047-05-2004 L2007 IM *100 †20

WU, Serena. ■ 19128 #041-15-2008 *012

WU, Shyh-Shiun. 3400 SPRUCE ST 19104 #035-19-1992 L1994 APM *020 †05

WU, Willis Yulin. 19129 #041-15-2007 L2007 IM *012

WU, Yuhsin. 3400 SPRUCE ST, S PENN TOWER 19104 #033-05-1997 L2000 OBG *020 †30

WUHL, Jeffrey Adam. ■ 19128 #051-01-2002 L2002 CD *012 †20

WURCEL, Alysse Gail. ■ 19146 #041-01-2008 *012

WURZEL, Edward Milton. ■ 19147 #035-09-1941 L1975 OS *030 †70

WURZEL, John Martin. 3401 N BROAD ST, DEPT OF PATH 700MRB 19140 #041-01-1978 L1979
ATP *062 †50

WUSTHOFF, Courtney Jane. 34TH & CIVIC CENTER BLVD, 6 WOOD BLDG 19104
#005-02-2004 L2006 CHN *012

WYCKOFF, Tygh Gifford. ■ 19102 #041-02-2007 L2007 TY *012

WYLONIS, Lauren Jean. 2101 PINE ST, 2ND FL 19103 #041-13-1994 L1996 PFP *020 †75

WYNN, Daisy Tan. ■ 19107 #033-06-2005 L2005 FP *012

WYNNE, Brian Richard. ■ 19147 #038-43-1987 L1996 ID *020 †20

WYNNE, Craig S. 3701 MARKET ST 6TH FL 19104 #035-46-1990 L1992 IM *020 †20

WYNNE, Megan Cathleen. 1020 SANSOM ST, 1652 THOMPSON BUILDING, RM 19107
#041-15-2001 L2001 PYM *100 †76

WYNNE-BAKER, Denise E. 8125 STENTON AVE, NW MEDICAL CENTER 19150
#041-13-1988 L1989 PD *020 †55

WYSE, Katrina Anita. 4655 FERNHILL RD 19144 #038-06-2001 L2001 OBG *020 †30

XAVIER, Cherian P. 3905 FORD RD 19131 #495-02-1966 L1980 IM *020

XAVIER, Marin Feldman. ■ 19130 #041-01-2002 L2005 HO *012 †20

XU, Miaohou. ■ 19107 #243-46-1986 L2006 OBG *012

XU, Xiaowei. 3400 SPRUCE ST, HOSP U OF PEN-PATH DEPT 19104 #243-46-1992 L2000
DMP *020 †50

YACHMENYOVA, Yelena. 2375 WOODWARD ST, STE 115 19115 #913-09-1975 L1997
IM *020 †20

YADLA, Sanjay. ■ 19107 #035-19-2005 L2005 NS *012

YAFAI, Faahud Afeef. 3401 N BROAD ST, TEMPLE UNIVERSITY HOSPITAL 19140
#041-13-2003 L2003 NEP *012 †20

YAGANTI, Vamsee Mohan. ■ 19131 #495-01-2003 L2005 IM *012

YAGNIK, Gautam Pratap. 100 N 21ST ST B 19104 #041-12-2003 L2003 ORS *012

YAGNIK, Pratap Mohanlal. 3900 WOODLAND AVE, VETERANS ADMINISTRATION 19104
#495-01-1966 L1973 N CN *020 †75 ‡

YAMASHIRO, Darrell J. 324 S 34TH ST, DEPT PED 19104 #035-19-1989 L1991
PHO PD *050 †55 ‡

YAN, Albert C. 324 S 34TH ST, CHOP DERMATOLOGY 19104 #041-01-1993 L1996
D PD *020 †15,55

YAN, Xiao. 245 N 15TH ST, DREXEL UNIV COLL 19102 #243-36-1983 L2003 PCP *012

YANAGIDA, Roh. ■ 19144 #572-14-1996 L2005 GS *012

YANG, Dorothy Chuan-Ying. ■ 19103 #242-09-1945 L1963 CHN PD *071 †55

YANG, Joyce. ■ 19103 #024-05-2005 L2005 PD *012

YANG, Michele. ■ 19103 #041-12-1999 L2001 CHN *100 †55,75

YANG, Relin Nmn. ■ 19147 #011-02-2005 L2005 GS *012

YANG, Shuin-Lin. 5401 OLD YORK RD STE 505, KLEIN BLDG 19141 #244-04-1974 L1982
AS GS *020 †85

YANG, Tony. 2900 W QUEEN LN, DREXEL UNIV COLL OF MED 19129 #041-15-2005 L2005 *100

YANG, Yuxiao. 3400 SPRUCE ST DEPT MED 19104 #035-19-1996 L2001 GE *020 †20

YANKELEVICH, Raul. 1500 WALNUT ST 19102 #132-01-1967 L1970 GP *071

YANOFF, Myron. 219 N BROAD ST, FL 3 19107 #041-01-1961 L1962 OPH PTH *020 †50,35

YANOVSKI, A Vivian. 5501 GREENE ST 19144 #869-04-1954 L1956 IM *071

YANOVSKI, Alexander G. 3400 SPRUCE ST 19104 #869-04-1953 L1956 P *071

YANTES, Herbert Arthur. 8355 LORETTO AVE, STEVEN W KLINMAN MD 19152
#041-02-1950 L1951 IM OS *071 †20

YARMOHAMMADI, Hooman. 3400 SPRUCE ST, UNIVERSITY OF PENNSYLVANIA 19104 #517-05-1996 L2007 **GS** *012

YAU, James Minhsun. ■ 19102 #033-05-2004 L2007 **CD** *012 †20

YAWMAN, Anne Marie. 1316 W ONTARIO ST 8TH FL, TEMPLE UNIV HOSP 19140 #041-15-1999 L2000 **IMG** *020 †20

YAZDIPOUR, Mariam. 4TH FLOOR - S TOWER MAIL, DREXEL UNIVERSITY COLLEGE 19102 #305-01-2007 L2007 **AN** *012

YEAGER, Robert Craig. 245 N 15TH ST, OF M 19102 #036-08-2006 L2006 **EM** *012

YEE, Kimberly Corrine. 34TH-CIVIC CTR BLVD, CHILDRENS HOSP 19104 #025-01-2002 L2007 **PDC** *012

YEE, Nelson Shusang. ■ 19104 #035-20-1995 L1997 **HO IM** *050 †20

YEGER, Meira Ziva. 3400 SPRUCE ST, 2 SILVERSTEIN PAVILION 19104 #033-05-2004 L2004 **ORS** *012

YEGYA-RAMAN, Vijayalaks. 3550 MARKET ST, FL 4 19104 #495-04-1979 L1988 **PD** *020 †55

YEH, Alexander Kuoshi. 3353 COTTMAN AVE 19149 #649-33-1981 L1983 **IM** *020

YEH, Ernest Lester. 100 E LEHIGH AVE, TEAM INC 19125 #041-13-1997 L1999 **EM** *020 †16

YEH, Heidi. 3400 SPRUCE ST, 4TH FL SILVERSTEIN BLDG 19104 #041-01-1997 L2001 **GS** *100 †85

YEN, Andrew Dawei. ■ 19107 #033-06-2002 L2002 **CD** *012 †20

YENAL, Kem. 2400 E CUMBERLAND ST 19125 #051-07-1991 L1994 **FM** *020 †18

YENCHA, Erika Maria. 1025 WALNUT ST, DIVISION OF NEONATOLOGY 19107 #665-02-2001 L2004 **NPM** *020 †55

YEO, Hyung Yong. 3200 HENRY AVE 19129 #583-02-1994 L2003 **CHP** *012

YEROUSHALMI, Parviz K. 561 FAIRTHORNE AVE 19128 #517-05-1977 L1982 **P CHP** *020 †75

YESENOSKY, George Alan. 700 COTTMAN AVE, BLDG A 19111 #041-07-1998 L2000 **CD** *020 †20

YI, Ju Mi. ■ 19148 #012-01-2007 L2007 *012

YIN, Andrew. ■ 19107 #035-08-2006 **IM** *012

YIN, Dongfang. 833 CHESTNUT ST, STE 701 19107 #243-47-1987 L1997 **IM** *020 †20

YINGLING, Christopher Tho. ■ 19107 #041-02-2008 *012

YLAGAN, Horacio Alberto. 1630 W GIRARD AVE, ST JOSEPHS HOSP DEPT PTH 19130 #748-02-1947 L1974 **CLP PTH** *020 †50

YONG, Pierre L. ■ 19147 #043-01-2003 L2006 **AI** *012 †20

YONKER, Marcy Ellen. 833 CHESTNUT ST STE 300, DUPONT AT JEFFERSON 19107 #041-12-1990 L1992 **CHN N** *020 †55,75

YOO, Edward Young. 245 N 15TH ST, MAIL STOP 413 19102 #041-15-2003 L2003 **GS** *012

YOO, Sook Hee Lee. 4200 MONUMENT RD, BELMONT CENTER 19131 #583-03-1963 L1972 **P** *020 †75

YOO, Stanley Kwansoo. ■ 19118 #024-07-2006 L2007 **PM** *012

YOON, Russell. 501 S 54TH ST, MERCY HOSPITAL 19143 #033-06-1994 L1996 **EM** *020 †20,16

YOUDELMAN, Benjamin A. 1025 WALNUT ST, OF CARDIOTHORA 19107 #028-34-1999 L2004 **TS** *100 †85

YOUNAN, Zyad. 2900 W QUEEN LN, MCP HAHNEMANN UNIV 19129 #422-01-2000 L2001 **ICE** *020 †20

YOUNG, Allison Paige. 840 WALNUT ST, WILLS EYE HOSP 19107 #048-12-2004 L2005 **OPH** *012

YOUNG, Barbara R Naiman. 2401 PENNSYLVANIA AVE, STE 1C52 19130 #041-07-1966 L1967 **PYA P** *020

YOUNG, Christal Marie. ■ 19102 #041-15-2008 *012

YOUNG, Donald Stirling. 3400 SPRUCE ST # G1 19104 #803-01-1957 L1990 **CLP** *062

YOUNG, James Arthur. 100 E LEHIGH AVE 19125 #041-09-1976 L1977 **GYN** *020

YOUNG, Janet Elizabeth. 4510 FRANKFORD AVE, FRANKFORD AVENUE HEALTH CE 19124 #024-01-1982 L1984 **IM** *030 †20

YOUNG, Laura Anne. ■ 19148 #038-41-2003 L2006 **END** *012 †20

YOUNG, Marie L. 800 SPRUCE ST 19107 #010-03-1979 L1981 **AN** *020 †05

YOUNG, Matthew J. ■ 19123 #041-77-2004, ▲ L2004 **EM** *012

YOUNG, Nancy Anne. 333 COTTMAN AVE 19111 #041-07-1983 L1988 **PTH** *040 †50 ‡

YOUNG, Robert Crabill. 333 COTTMAN AVE 19111 #035-20-1965 L1988 **ON IM** *030 †20

YOUNG, Vincent Kevin. 5401 OLD YORK RD, STE 205 19141 #041-13-1983 L1984 **OPH** *020 †35

YOUNG, William Boyd, Jr. 111 S 11TH ST, STE 8130 19107 #041-14-1985 L1989 **N** *050 †75 ‡

YOUNG, Willie Edward. ■ 19126 #010-03-1955 L1956 **OTO** *075

YOUSEM, David Mark. 3400 SPRUCE ST 19104 #025-01-1983 L1988 **DR HNS** *020 †80

YOUSSEF, Mariam Ezzat. 111 S 11TH ST, JEFFERSON UNIVERSITY 19107 #035-15-2005 L2005 **PD** *012

YOUSSEF, Omaya Hussein. 840 WALNUT ST, WILLS EYE HOSPITAL 19107 #023-12-1999 L2001 **OPH** *020 †35 ‡

YU, Anthony Francis. ■ 19103 #024-01-2007 L2007 **IM** *012

YU, David K. ■ 19107 #041-02-2008 *012

YU, Gordon Hi. 3400 SPRUCE ST, DEPT OF PATHOLOGY 19104 #016-06-1989 L1992 **PCP** *020 †50

YU, Helena Alexandra. 3400 SPRUCE ST, DEPT IM 19104 #025-01-2007 L2007 **IM** *012

YU, Jennifer. 5501 OLD YORK RD 19141 #748-10-1987 L1995 **PD** *020 †50

YU, Jian Qin. 333 COTTMAN AVE, DIAGNOSTIC IMAGING 19111 #243-47-1987 L2000 **NM NC** *020 †28 ‡

YU, Kenneth Homing. 3400 SPRUCE ST, 100 CENTREX 19104 #023-07-1999 L2001 **HO** *020 †20

YU, Marie Majelle Ong. 6129 COLGATE ST 19111 #748-02-1994 L1997 **IM** *020 †20

YU, Tao. 1800 LOMBARD ST, TENET HLTH SYSTEM GRADUAT 19146 #243-46-1995 L2006 **IM** *012

YU, Zheya Jenny. 3440 MARKET ST 2ND FL, DEPT CHILD & ADOL PSY CHOP 19104 #243-52-1986 L2002 **CHP** *100 †75

YUAN, Ian. 3400 N BROAD ST, TEMPLE UNIV SCH OF MED 19140 #041-12-2008 L2008 *012

YUCHA, David Thomas. 3401 N BROAD ST 19140 #041-13-2002 L2002 **OSM** *012

YUDELL, Richard Lawrence. 4641 ROOSEVELT BLVD, OFF OF MEDICAL CMHC 19124 #561-01-1975 L1979 **P** *020 †75

YUDKOFF, Marc. 324 S 34TH ST 19104 #035-09-1972 L1975 **IM PD** *050 †55,19

YUEN, Thomas Chungwah. 647 BAINBRIDGE ST 19147 #033-06-2001 L2001 **FM** *100 †18

YUN, Blenda. 607 S 11TH ST # 2 19147 #056-05-2003 L2003 **OBG** *020

YUSKEVICH, Brian. 3996 RED LION RD 19114 #748-18-1988 L1993 **AN PAN** *020 †05

ZABALETA, Ruben. 5800 RIDGE AVE 19128 #308-03-1981 L1983 **OM FM** *020

ZACHAR, Benjamin S. ■ 19118 #011-75-2004, ▲ L2004 **EM** *012

ZACHARIAS, Leo. 5301 CEDAR AVE 19143 #422-01-1989 L1993 **IM** *020 †20

ZACHARY, Dalila Ananda. ■ 19150 #023-07-2005 L2005 **IM** *012

ZACHIAN, Victor Aaron. 700 SPRUCE ST STE 508 19106 #041-02-1978 L1980 **OBG** *020 †30

ZAERI, Nayere S. 5501 OLD YORK RD, A EINSTEIN MED CTR DPT PTH 19141 #517-01-1971 L1981 **PTH PP** *020 †50

ZAFAR, Hanna Maryam. 3400 SPRUCE ST, DEPT OF RADIOLOGY, SILVERS 19104 #041-02-2002 L2002 **DR** *100 †80

ZAGER, Eric Louis. 3400 SPRUCE ST, DEPARATMENT OF NEUROSURGER 19104 #005-11-1982 L1989 **NS** *020 †25

ZAGHLOUL, Kareem Amir. 3400 SPRUCE ST, HOSP OF UNIV OF PENNSYLVAN 19104 #041-01-2003 L2003 **NS** *012

ZAGREBELSKY, Ellen N. 8556 BUSTLETON AVE 19152 #913-90-1976 L2001 **IMG** *020 †20

ZAGREBELSKY, Vladimir. 5501 OLD YORK RD, ALBERT EINSTEIN MED CTR 19141 #913-90-1977 L2001 **IM IMG** *020 †20 ‡

ZAIDI, Ali Akbar. 51 N 39TH ST, SCHEIE EYE INST 19104 #005-02-2005 L2006 **OPH** *012

ZAIDI, Mone. 3400 SPRUCE ST, STE J PENN TOWERS 9TH FLOO 19104 #495-05-1983 L1997 *020

ZAKEOSIAN, Garabet M. 3996 RED LION RD 19114 #041-14-1977 L1978 **AN GP** *020 †05

ZAKI, Hani Shaker. 4641 ROOSEVELT BLVD, FRIENDS HOSPITAL 19124 #915-02-1982 L1998 **P** *020 †75

ZAKI, Radi Farook. 5501 OLD YORK RD, KLEIN/STE 505 19141 #915-02-1992 L1999 **GS** *020 †85

ZAKS, Tal Zvi. 3400 SPRUCE ST, 15 PENN TOWER 19104 #550-04-1996 L2001 **HO** *020 †20

ZALAZNICK, Hillary. ■ 19104 #011-03-2006 L2006 **PTH** *012

ZALEWSKI, Andrezej Pawel. 1025 WALNUT ST, DIV OF CARD/410 COLLEGE BL 19107 #759-03-1975 L1984 **CD** *020 †20

ZALEWSKI, Margaret. 7602 CENTRAL AVE, STE 203 19111 #759-03-1975 L1987 **N** *020 †75

ZALL, Harry. 111 N 49TH ST 19139 #041-09-1965 L1966 **P** *020 †75

ZAMFIRESCU, Isabelle. ■ 19107 #035-15-2005 L2005 **IM** *012

ZAMORA BARROS, Guillermo. 34TH AND CIVIC CENTER BLVD 19104 #231-01-1994 *100

ZAMPIELLO, Frank Albert. ■ 19106 #023-01-1962 L1962 **OM FM** *030

ZANDOMENI, Gabriela Monik. ■ 19128 #132-01-2004 L2007 **OBG** *012

ZANGALADZE, Andro. 900 WALNUT ST, STE 200 19107 #913-23-1987 L2001 **N CN** *020 †75

ZANGRILLI, James Garfield. 1606 CHESTNUT ST 19103 #041-02-1988 L1992 **IM** *050 †20

ZAOUTIS, Lisa B. 324 S 34TH ST 19104 #035-03-1983 L1997 **PD EM** *020 †16,55

ZAOUTIS, Theoklis Elias. 3535 MARKET ST STE 1527, CHILDRENS HOSP PA CHOP NOR 19104 #041-02-1996 L1998 **PDI** *050 †55

ZARATE CACERES, Hernan Al. 5501 OLD YORK RD 19141 #737-06-1999 L2006 **IM** *012

ZARNOW, Deborah Michelle. 324 S 34TH ST, DEPT OF RADIO CHILDS HOSP 19104 #019-02-1998 L2001 **RNR** *020 †80

ZARRO, Suzanne Cohen. ■ 19148 #041-09-1978 L1979 **IM** *030

ZARRO, Vincent Joseph. 219 N BROAD ST, STE 8 19107 #041-09-1962 L1963 **IM ADM** *030 †20

ZAVALA, Stacey Rene. ■ 19144 #016-11-2003 L2003 **GE** *012 †20

ZAVODNICK, Steven. 210 W WASHINGTON SQ 19106 #041-02-1973 L1974 **P** *020 †75

ZAWOLOKA, Alex, Jr. 4TH FLOOR - S TOWER MAIL, DREXEL UNIVERSITY COLLEGE 19102 #422-01-2007 L2007 **IM** *012

ZAWORA, Michele Quintrell. 1015 WALNUT ST, STE 401 19107 #041-12-2003 L2003 **FPG** *100 †18

ZDERIC, Stephen Anthony. 3400 SPRUCE ST DEPT UROL 19104 #005-14-1983 L1985 **UP** *020 †95

ZEBROWER, Marcus Jeremy. 230 N BROAD ST 19102 #654-01-1999 L2001 **AN** *020 †05

ZEESHAN, Ahmad. ■ 19104 #704-20-1997 L2005 **GS** *012

ZEESHAN, Atif. 3401 N BROAD ST, JONES HALL 622/623 19140 #704-02-1995 L2001 **PCC** *020 †20

ZEGEL, Harry Gershon. 3300 HENRY AVE, MEDICAL COLLGE OF PNNSYLVN 19129 #041-02-1975 L1976 **DR** *020 †80

ZEITZER, Kenneth Lee. 5501 OLD YORK RD, DEPT OF RADIATION ONCOLOGY 19141 #041-02-1988 L1992 **RO** *020 †80

ZEKAVAT, Pouran. P3300 HENRY AVE 19129 #517-04-1959 L1969 **R** *071 †80

ZELTSER, Galina. 4900 FRANKFORD AVE, FRANKFORD HOSPITALRDLGY DP 19124 #913-19-1975 L1998 **PM** *020 †60

ZELUCK, Martin. 2301 S BROAD ST 19148 #035-08-1957 L1961 **GYN** *020 †30

ZEMBLE, Herbert. 10101 ACADEMY RD 19114 #041-77-1964, ▲ L1965 **FM** *020

ZEMBLE, Robert Marc. ■ 19130 #041-13-2004 L2007 **AI** *012 †20

ZENG, Fanyi. ■ 19104 #041-01-2005 *100

ZENG, Xiangxing. 3401 N BROAD ST, DEPT OF ANESTH, TEMPLE UNI 19140 #243-52-1986 L2001 **AN** *020 †05

ZERN, Mark Allen. 1025 WALNUT ST, DEPT. OF MEDICINE 19107 #024-01-1975 L1992 **GE IM** *020 †20

ZESERSON, Eli Morgan. 3400 SPRUCE ST, GROUND RAVDIN 19104 #041-02-2003 L2003 **EM** *100

ZHANG, Clare Ying. ■ 19106 #038-06-2005 L2005 **DR** *012

ZHANG, Meijuan. 1800 LOMBARD ST, GRADUATE HOSP (TENET HLTH 19146 #243-03-1999 L2000 **END** *100 †20

ZHANG, Sherri X. 4641 ROOSEVELT BLVD, FRIENDS HOSPITAL 19124 #243-74-1984 L2001 **P** *020

ZHANG, Wei. 3400 SPRUCE ST 19104 #243-16-1993 L2006 **PCP** *100

ZHANG, Yan. 9880 BUSTLETON AVE, NEUROLOGY ASSOCIATES AT 19115 #243-16-1987 L2000 **N** *020 †75

ZHANG, Yejia. 25 S 9TH ST 19107 #243-58-1989 L2005 **PM PME** *050 †60

ZHENG, Peishu. 911 ARCH ST, STE 301 19107 #243-16-1957 L1994 **FM DMP** *020 †50

ZHOU, Linqiu. 111 S 11TH ST, THOMAS JEFFERSON UNIVERSIT 19107 #243-08-1984 L2001 **PM** *100 †60

ZHU, Zhi-Gang. 2301 E ALLEGHENY AVE, C/O NORTHEASTERN HOSPITAL 19134 #243-16-1994 L2004 **AN** *020

ZHUANG, Hongming. 3400 SPRUCE ST, 110 DONNER, HUP 19104 #243-47-1986 L2000 **NM** *020 †20

ZIBELLI, Allison Maria. 1015 CHESTNUT ST STE 13 19107 #010-01-1995 L1998 **HO HEM** *020 †20

ZIEGLER, Kathryn Anne. 111 S 11TH ST, THOMAS JEFFERSON UNIV 19107 #041-77-2007, ▲ L2007 *012

ZIHLIF, Mamoon Awwad. ■ 19114 #575-01-1996 L2004 **PUD** *100 †20

ZILBERING, Polina. 100 E LEHIGH AVE, MAB 305 19125 #913-50-1981 L2001 **P** *020

ZIMMER, Ross Randall. PHI/4, 39TH & MARKET STREET 19104 #041-13-1989 L1992 **CD** *020 †20

ZIMMERMAN, Jessica Lynn. 1201 CHESTNUT ST, STE 1400-C 19107 #025-07-1996 L2000 **CHP** *075

ZIMMERMAN, Marc S. 2410 S BROAD ST, STE 200 19145 #041-07-1975 L1976 **ORS** *020 †40

ZIMMERMAN, Robert Allan. 34ST & CIVIC CTR BLVD 19104 #010-02-1964 L1965 **RNR PDR** *020 †80 ‡

ZIMMERMAN, Robert Lyman. 132 S 10TH ST, RM 260A MAIN BLDG 19107 #041-12-1991 L1996 **PTH** *020 †50

■ = Address Information Privacy Protected

ZIMMERMAN, Stefan Loy. ■ 19103 #041-01-2004 L2004 **DR** *012
ZINGERMAN, Zena M. 8355 LORETTO AVE, STE 102 19152 #913-99-1975 L1997 **PM** *020 †60
ZINK, Jerome Raymond. 1025 WALNUT ST, OF UROLOGY 19107 #008-01-1997 L1999 **U** *020 †95
ZINK, Thomas Keith. 1600 VINE ST # 3F0820, THREE FRANKLIN PLZ 19102 #028-46-1980 L1982 **EM GPM** *071 †16
ZINN, Steven L. 10 SHURS LN, STE 3 19127 #035-06-1975 L1976 **IM IMG** *020 †20
ZINSENHEIM, Joyce Renee. 3400 SPRUCE ST, UNIV OF PA MED CTR 19104 #305-01-1983 L1988 **P SME** *020 †75
ZIRING, Barry S. 833 CHESTNUT ST STE 701 19107 #035-03-1985 L1986 **IM** *020 †20
ZIRING, Deborah Jean. 1427 VINE ST, MS 966 19102 #033-05-1985 L1986 **IM** *020 †20
ZIRLINGER, Andres. 5501 OLD YORK RD, ALBERT EINSTEIN MED CTR 19141 #132-01-2005 L2005 **IM** *012
ZISSELMAN, Marc Howard. 5501 OLD YORK RD 7TH FL, DEPT PSYCHIATRY/TOWER BLDG 19141 #035-09-1987 L1991 **P** *020 †75
ZIV, Barbara Ellen. ■ 19118 #016-06-1987 L1994 **P IM** *020 †75
ZIYADEH, Fuad Nemetallah. 415 CURIE BLVD, 700 CRB- RENAL DIVSION 19104 #605-01-1980 L1987 **NEP** *050 †20
ZOGA, Adam. 111 S 11TH ST, 3350 GIBBON BLDG 19107 #010-02-1994 L1994 **DR** *020 †80
ZOLA, Joseph Charles, Jr. ■ 19107 #051-04-2006 L2006 **GS** *012
ZOLLI, Christine Lyde H. 840 WALNUT ST, WILLS EYE HOSPITAL 19107 #035-08-1970 L1981 **OPH PS** *020 †35
ZOLTICK, Philip Wayne. 3615 CIVIC CENTER BLVD, 1116 ARC DEPT OF SURG 19104 #035-45-1975 L1977 **NP PTH** *062 †50
ZONFRILLO, Mark R. ■ 19119 #043-01-2003 L2007 **PEM** *012 †55
ZONSHAYN, Alexander. 230 N BROAD ST 19102 #913-15-1983 L1995 **AN** *020 †05
ZOOK, Matthew Brent. ■ 19129 #041-02-2005 L2005 **D** *012
ZORATTI, Maria Teresa. 100 W LEHIGH AVE 19133 #561-01-1993 L2003 **CHP** *100
ZORC, Catherine Shea. 111 S 11TH ST, THOMAS JEFFERSON UNIV 19107 #023-01-2007 L2007 *012
ZORC, Joseph John. 324 S 34TH ST 19104 #035-01-1992 L1998 **PE PD** *050 †55
ZSOLWAY, Kathleen M. 3550 MARKET ST, FL 4 19104 #022-75-1989, ▲ L1990 **PD** *020 †55 ‡
ZUBKOFF, Gerald Norman. 7500 CENTRAL AVE STE 205 19111 #023-01-1979 L1980 **PD** *020 †55
ZUBROW, Alan Bruce. FRONT ST AT ERIE AVE, ST CHRISTOPHER HOSPITAL 19104 #041-01-1976 L1978 **NPM PD** *020 †55
ZUBROW, Sidney N. ■ 19103 #041-09-1938 L1939 **IM** *071 †20
ZUCHNER, Mikko Boris. 3400 SPRUCE ST, 680 DULLES BLDG 19104 #409-05-1996 L2004 **CCA** *020 †05
ZUCKER, Amy Harriet. 800 SPRUCE ST, FL 2 19107 #041-13-1982 L1984 **PD NPM** *020 †55
ZUCKERMAN, Jerry Marc. 5501 YORK RD, KLEIN BLG DEPT MED 331 19141 #035-20-1987 L1989 **ID IM** *020 †20
ZUPPA, Athena Francesca. 34TH CIVIC CTR BLVD PED 19104 #035-48-1996 L1998 **CCP** *020 †55
ZWANGER, Mark L. 239 E THOMPSON ST, 10TH AND WALNUT ST 19125 #041-02-1982 L1988 **EM** *020 †16
ZWAS, Donna Rose. 925 CHESTNUT ST, MEZZANIE LEVEL 19107 #024-01-1990 L2000 **CD IM** *074 †20
ZWEIMAN, Burton. 3400 SPRUCE ST 19104 #041-01-1956 L1958 **A IM** *071 †20,03
ZWEIZIG, Helen Z. 5800 RIDGE AVE 19128 #041-07-1961 L1962 **PD** *020 †55 ‡
ZWILLENBERG, David Alan. ERIE AVE AT FRONT STREET, 2ND FLOOR SUITE 2205 19134 #038-43-1976 L1978 **OTO** *020 †45

PHILIPSBURG – CENTRE

ADAMS, Lawrence Glen. 601 N FRONT ST 16866 #010-02-1986 L1987 **IM** *020
AGRA, Conrado F. ■ 16866 #748-08-1968 L1976 **GP GS** *020
BEYER, H Jeanne. 330 ENTERPRISE DR STE B, GUIDED CARE, P.C. 16866 #041-14-1975 L1976 **IM FM** *020 †20
BLAISURE, Beverly Ann. 208 MEDICAL CENTER DR 16866 #041-13-1977 L1978 **FM** *030 †18
BOUCHARD, Roger. 210 MEDICAL CENTER DR 16866 #067-03-1977 L1984 **OBG** *020 †30
BRECH, Kilian Hilmar, II. 210 MEDICAL CENTER DR 16866 #041-13-1989 L2001 **PD** *020 †55
CORCINO, Baltazar L, Jr. 1049 N FRONT ST 16866 #748-01-1963 L1970 **IM** *020
DATTA, Manabendra. 210 MEDICAL CENTER DR 16866 #160-02-1986 L1998 **IM** *020 †20
KOLBE, Timothy Ed. ■ 16866 #041-09-1998 **FM** *100
KOLLMAN, Kevin James. 210 MEDICAL CENTER DR 16866 #305-01-1984 L1985 **IM** *020 †20
MATHIS, James Sylvester. 330 ENTERPRISE DR 16866 #041-14-1976 L1978 **EM IM** *020
NARTATEZ, Pedro C Diaz. 210 MEDICAL CENTER DR 16866 #748-08-1957 L1963 **GS** *071
PATEL, Manisha Nileshkuma. 210 MEDICAL CENTER DR 16866 #495-23-1995 L2005 *020
PATEL, Nilesh Arvindbhai. 210 MEDICAL CENTER DR 16866 #495-23-1991 L2005 **HO** *020 †20
PILGRAM, Philip Alan. 210 MEDICAL CENTER DR 16866 #041-12-1976 L1977 **FM** *020 †18
ROGERS, Kenneth Jacob, Jr. 210 MEDICAL CENTER DR 16866 #041-14-1977 L1978 **DR NM** *020 †80
SAWARDEKAR, Satish Murari. 210 MEDICAL CENTER DR, 210 MEDICAL CENTER DRIVE 16866 #495-17-1970 L1995 **PD** *020 †55
SCHAEFER, Kathleen Ann. 210 MEDICAL CENTER DR 16866 #035-08-1988 L1993 **N** *020 †75
STEWARD, Robert Excel, Jr. 1049 N FRONT ST, MOSHANNON VALLEY SURG CLIN 16866 #041-02-1972 L1973 **GS** *020 †85 ‡
TROUT, Anne Carla. 210 MEDICAL CENTER DR, GEISINGER 16866 #028-02-1979 L1993 **IM** *020 †20
WESTRICK, Diann Marie. 210 MEDICAL CENTER DR, PHILIPSBURG 16866 #041-14-1978 L1979 **IM IMG** *020 †20

PHOENIXVILLE – CHESTER

ACTOR, Carol F. 824 MAIN ST STE 201, BROKER, CRAMER, SWANSON AN 19460 #041-13-1984 L2007 **PDA PD** *020 †55,03
ADAMS, P Evans. ■ 19460 #041-01-1951 L1953 **P** *071 †75
ADAMTHWAITE, Myra E. ■ 19460 #041-13-1969 L1973 **IM** *100
AGARWAL, Anupam. ■ 19460 #495-41-1984 L2006 **CD** *020 †20
BABINCHAK, Timothy John. 190 PEMBROOKE CIR, STE I 19460 #038-44-1984 L1985 **ID IM** *020 †20
BASKIN, Andrew Jay. 8 HANNA LN 19460 #041-13-1978 L1980 **IM** *020 †20
BELIN, Laurence Justin. ■ 19460 #041-02-2008 *012
BELL, Gerald. 206 GAY ST 19460 #041-13-1964 L1965 **FPS A** *020 †45
BELL, Karen Sue. ■ 19460 #041-13-1994 L1999 **DR** *020 †80
BRACKETT, Laura Ellen. ■ 19460 #041-14-1988 L1996 **IM** *020 †20
CABUHAT, Joycelyn Rallos. ■ 19460 #005-15-2008 *012
CANTOR, Ira Scott. 1220 VALLEY FORGE RD, RD #35/36 19460 #035-09-1979 L1984 **IM** *020 †20
CATTON, Raymond Manuel. 45 RIDGE RD 19460 #021-05-1958 L1966 **P** *020 †75
CERCEGA, Mircea. 140 NUTT RD 19460 #781-04-1989 L2000 **AN** *020 †05 ‡
CHEN, Et-Tsu. 824 MAIN ST STE 101, PENN RADIATION ONCOLOGY 19460 #016-06-1989 L1992 **RO** *020 †80
CHEN, Harry Haitak. 140 NUTT RD, PHOENIXVILLE HOSPITAL 19460 #041-01-1984 L1998 **DR VIR** *020 †80
CHILDS, Marion Crawley. 500 GAY ST 19460 #041-07-1977 L1981 **IM** *020 †20
D ACCURZIO, Albert D, Jr. 720 MAIN ST 19460 #035-45-1975 L1978 **IM** *030 †20
DIBLASIO, Jacqueline. 824 MAIN ST, STE 100 19460 #041-09-1992 L1998 **IM** *020 †20
EISNER, Joel William. 824 MAIN ST, STE 100 19460 #035-46-1963 L1964 **IM AI** *020 †03,20 ‡
FEINER, Larry Alan. 206 GAY ST 19460 #041-02-1978 L1983 **OTO** *020 †45
FERRIZZI, Liza Perez. ■ 19460 #041-01-1995 L1998 **PTH** *020 †50
FISCHER, Herbert. 824 MAIN ST STE 100 19460 #407-23-1968 L1975 **CD IM** *020 †20
FLOOD, Jean. 1220 VALLEY FORGE RD, STE 35/36 19460 #016-01-1979 L1995 **GP** *020
FRIED, Richard Grant. 140 NUTT RD 19460 #041-14-1976 L1977 **FM** *020 †18
GIANNOPOULOS, Peter Harry. ■ 19460 #041-13-1959 L1960 **GP** *071
GOLDBERG, Joshua E. 824 MAIN ST STE 201 19460 #041-77-1996, ▲ L1997 **OTO FPS** *020
GOLDSTEIN, Norman Arnold. ■ 19460 #041-02-1962 L1966 **OTO** *071 †45
GORMAN, Johanna H. 45 RIDGE RD 19460 #407-07-1958 L1975 **P CHP** *020 †75
GRAMP, Jeffrey Michael. 140 NUTT RD 19460 #041-15-2001 L2001 **DR** *020 †80
GUPTA, Arti. 710 MAIN ST, MEDICINE 19460 #496-09-1990 L1996 **FM** *020 †18
HANAWAY, Andrea J S. 140 NUTT RD, PHOENIXVILLE U OF PA HOSPI 19460 #041-07-1973 L1974 **EM OM** *020 †16
HAUPT, Hans Michael. 750 MAIN ST, STE 302 19460 #041-02-1986 L1988 **CD GS** *020 †85,90
HOLMBOE, Eric Stephen. 143 CHURCH ST 19460 #035-45-1985 L1986 **IM** *020 †20
HOLROYDE, Christopher P. 824 MAIN ST, PHOENIXVILLE HOSPITAL 19460 #917-26-1965 L1970 **ON HEM** *020 †20
HORNSTEIN, Lucy Spencer. 710 MAIN ST 19460 #041-07-1985 L1986 **FM** *020 †18
IRFAN, Muhammad Anjum. 1039 W BRIDGE ST # 41 19460 #704-04-1981 L1992 **P** *020 †75
KALRA, Pankaj. 824 MAIN ST, STE 301 19460 #051-04-1998 L2004 **U** *020 †95
KEHINDE, Oladoye Oludotun. 824 MAIN ST, STE 100 19460 #690-02-1990 L2007 **IM** *020 †20
KENDERDINE, Su C. ■ 19460 #041-09-1970 L1972 **FM** *071 †18
KOVALOVICH, Asha. 119 S WHITEHORSE RD 19460 #041-02-1992 L1998 **RNR** *020 †80 ‡
KOVALSKI, Raymond John. 824 MAIN ST, STE 100 19460 #041-01-1982 L1983 **PUD IM** *020 †20
LEE, Howard G. ■ 19460 #041-13-1951 L1952 **EM GP** *071
LEECH, John E, Jr. 850 MAIN ST, STE 301 19460 #041-13-1988 L1990 **U** *020 †95
LISS, Gilbert A. ■ 19460 #041-13-1961 L1962 **OBG** *072 †30
MADIANOS, Evan Francis. 140 NUTT RD, PHOENIXVILLE HOSPITAL 19460 #041-13-1990 L1992 **DR** *020 †80
MAGNESS, Kathleen Elena. 824 MAIN ST, STE 100 19460 #041-14-1985 L1986 **CD IM** *020 †20
MALAMED, David Harry. 140 NUTT RD, PHOENIXVILLE HOSPITAL 19460 #035-45-1988 L1990 **DR** *020 †80 ‡
MALINOSKI, Frank Jos. 115 VALLEY PARK RD 19460 #035-03-1985 L2005 **GP** *030
MAYA, Juan Francisco. ■ 19460 #264-05-1988 L1997 **IM** *020 †20
MICHAELSON, Thos Chester. 140 NUTT RD 19460 #041-13-1966 L1967 **IM ID** *020 †20
MILLER, Amy Rebecca. ■ 19460 #041-02-2003 L2007 **IM** *100
MILLER, Charles F. ■ 19460 #050-02-1950 L1954 **GS GYN** *071 †85
MONHEIT, A David, III. ■ 19460 #041-09-1974 L1975 **P** *040 †75
MORENO, Jose Gallegos. 850 MAIN ST, STE 301 19460 #005-06-1987 L1991 **U** *020 †95
MOTEL, Peter John. 1260 VALLEY FORGE RD, STE 101 19460 #041-09-1985 L1987 **D IM** *020 †20,15
NELSON, Eleanor C. 29 FOXCROFT LN 19460 #035-09-1949 L1955 **AN OS** *071 †05
O'CONNELL, Robt Lawrence. 103 STEWARTS CT 19460 #028-34-1955 L1956 **FM OM** *071 †18
OSCARSON, Stephanie J. ■ 19460 #041-02-1993 **LM** *100
OSKANIAN, Peter Ohanes. 824 MAIN ST STE 203 19460 #041-07-1993 L1997 **U** *020 †95
OTERO-MALLON, Suzanne I. 116 WINDY HOLLOW DR 19460 #024-07-1989 L1993 **AN** *020 †05
PLAYER, Mark Russell. ■ 19460 #045-01-1986 **PA OS** *050
PROUTY, Susan Howe. ■ 19460 #023-01-1978 L2000 **IM** *020 †20
REED, Lola Stuart. ■ 19460 #041-01-1942 L1943 **PD** *071
REIS, Gregg Jay. 824 MAIN ST, STE 100 19460 #035-20-1983 L1991 **CD** *020 †20
ROBERTS, Richmond Craig. 400 MAIN ST 19460 #036-01-1965 L1973 **ORS OS** *071 †40
ROCK, Elizabeth Dale. 824 MAIN ST, STE 100 19460 #041-07-1975 L1976 **GE IM** *020 †20
ROGERS, Paul Leeds, Jr. 824 MAIN ST, STE 100 19460 #004-01-1982 L1987 **AN IM** *020 †20
ROSE, Robert Meryl. 824 MAIN ST STE 301 19460 #041-02-1979 L1985 **U** *020 †95
ROSENFELD, Karl. 100 1ST AVE 19460 #010-03-1968 L1969 **ORS** *020 †40
ROTHENBERGER, Rodger F. 824 MAIN ST, STE 100 19460 #041-02-1986 L1987 **FM** *020 †18
ROWLEY, Richard S. 720 MAIN ST 19460 #035-06-1971 L1976 **OPH** *020 †35
ROZWAT, Maurice Stephen. 824 MAIN ST, STE 100A 19460 #041-09-1983 L1985 **PD** *020 †55
SAFINA, Thomas Edward. 1200 BLACK POWDER DR 19460 #041-77-1991, ▲ L1992 **AN** *020 †05
SAPORTAS, Yaneth. ■ 19460 #264-05-1989 L1997 **PD** *020 †55
SCHEURICH, Charles James. 824 MAIN ST, STE 100 19460 #054-04-1987 L1998 **IM** *020 †20
SCHILLER, Debbie Fishbein. 824 MAIN ST, STE 100 19460 #041-01-1987 L1988 **GE IM** *020 †20
SCHWARTZ, Charles Isaac. 824 MAIN ST STE 100A, PENNCARE FOR KIDS 19460 #045-01-1995 L1998 **PD** *020 †55
SHECHTER, Jamine Lee. 140 NUTT RD 19460 #041-01-1988 L1990 **OPH** *020 †35
SHIBE, William John, III. 244 SPRING HOLLOW RD 19460 #035-47-1978 L1979 **EM** *020 †20,16
SMITH, Peter David. 824 MAIN ST, STE 100A 19460 #041-12-1995 L1997 **PD** *020 †55 ‡
SPECTOR, Gus. 824 MAIN ST STE 203 19460 #041-13-1969 L1970 **U** *020 †95
STUART, Lorna Bennett. 143 CHURCH ST, THE CLINIC AT ST PETERS 19460 #061-01-1979 L1980 **FM** *020
TEBERIAN, Garabet Awanes. 26 PLUM CIR 19460 #528-01-1965 L1988 **EM** *020 †16
TEUFEL, Severin. 20 HORSESHOE PT 19460 #041-01-1960 L1963 **CLP BBK** *020 †50 ‡
URBAN, Clifford H. 140 NUTT RD 19460 #035-20-1953 L1958 **PTH PCP** *071 †50
VAUGHN, David Wesley. ■ 19460 #028-34-1983 L1985 **PD** *030 †55
WEBER, Frederic J. 824 MAIN ST, STE 100 19460 #035-06-1980 L1982 **CD IM** *020 †20
WESSON, Laurence G, Jr. RR 2 19460 #024-01-1942 L1963 **NEP** *071 †20

WESTON, Heidi Z. 701 MAIN ST, CCA PHOENIXVILLE AREA FAMI 19460 #041-02-2000 L2001 FM *020 †18

YOXTHEIMER, Robert Lavern. 858 E PHILIP DR 19460 #041-13-1964 L1965 GS *071 †85 ‡

ZAMARIN, Richard Iric. 100 1ST AVE 19460 #041-09-1987 L1989 ORS *020 †40

ZELLER, Donald John. 824 MAIN ST STE 307, FRENCH CREEK FAMILY MEDICI 19460 #041-02-1983 L1984 FM *020 †18

PICTURE ROCKS – LYCOMING

KUHNS, David Benjamin. ■ 17762 #041-14-2005 L2005 FP *012

PINE GROVE – SCHUYLKILL

MOHAN, Francis Patrick. 8 OAK GROVE RD, STE 1 17963 #041-02-1981 L1987 FM *020 †18

POMPELLA, William Paul. 121 N TULPEHOCKEN ST 17963 #028-78-1993, ▲ L1994 IM *020

RISMILLER, Ross Wm. 121 N TULPEHOCKEN ST 17963 #041-13-1964 L1965 IM HEM *071

WATSON, Thomas Geo. 8 OAK GROVE RD, STE 1 17963 #041-13-1985 L1989 FM *020 †18

PINEVILLE – BUCKS

LASSER, Robert Alfonso. 853 DURHAM RD 18946 #024-05-1993 L2007 P *020 †75

PIPERSVILLE – BUCKS

BLORE, James Paul, Jr. 5612 EASTON RD, PLUMSTEADVILLE FAMILY 18947 #041-02-1972 L1977 FM IMG *020 †18

BLORE, Scott Michael. 5612 EASTON RD, PLUMSTEADVILLE FAMILY 18947 #041-02-1999 L2004 FPG *020 †18

BURMEISTER, Charles Willi. 5612 EASTON RD, PLUMSTEADVILLE FAMILY 18947 #038-06-1958 L1959 GP *020 †18

FERRARA, Joseph Dominic. 5612 EASTON RD, PLUMSTEADVILLE FAMILY 18947 #041-14-1984 L1987 FM *020 †18

MC KENNA, Elizabeth. 5612 EASTON RD, PLUMSTEADVILLE FAMILY 18947 #041-14-1996 L1998 FM *020 †18

RANDALL, Daniel Carl. ■ 18947 #035-45-1992 L1999 IM *020 †20 ‡

SAVADOVE, Thomas Sze. ■ 18947 #021-01-2005 L2005 PM *012

PITTSBURGH – ALLEGHENY

AARONS, Jerome Hernan. 300 HALKET ST 15213 #041-12-1954 L1955 IM DIA *071

ABALLAY, Ariel Mariano. 4800 FRIENDSHIP AVE - N4, WEST PENN HOSPITAL 15224 #132-02-1999 L2001 TRS GS *020

ABALOS, Joseph Michael. 15234 #055-02-2004 L2005 IM *012

ABBAS, Ume Lubna. 3601 5TH AVE, FALK MEDICAL BLDG, SUITE 3 15213 #704-01-1990 L2000 ID *020 †20

ABD AL AZIZ, Khaled Moham. ■ 15212 #915-04-1988 L2006 NS *100

ABDELHADI, Raed Husam. 200 LOTHROP ST, UPMC / S-559 SCAIFE HALL 15213 #575-01-1998 L2004 CD *020

ABDEL-HAMID, Hoda Zakaria. 3705 5TH AVE 15213 #915-02-1997 L2002 CHN *020 †55,75

ABDUL-BAKI, Heitham Aref. 200 LOTHROP ST, STE 503 15213 #605-01-2004 L2007 IM *012

ABDULHAQ, Haifaa. 4800 FRIENDSHIP AVE, WESTERN PENNSYLVANIA HOSP 15224 #875-01-1998 L2002 HO *012 †20

ABDULKADIR, Tolani Fausat. 300 HALKET ST, STE 4750 15213 #690-03-1991 L2005 OBG *020 †30

ABDULLAH, Raed Said. 200 LOTHROP ST, SCAIFE HALL A-1301 ANES DP 15213 #528-01-1976 L1999 AN PME *020 †05

ABELEDA, Aris Rodel Oliqu. 121 MEYRAN AVE 15213 #748-10-1999 L2007 FP *012

ABELL, Debra Tanner. 603 STANWIX ST STE 1310 15222 #005-02-1979 L1983 D *020 †15

ABELL, Edward. 5001 CENTRE AVE, FL 3 15213 #917-20-1964 L1980 DMP D *020 †15

ABESAMIS, Michael Gary. 230 MCKEE PL STE 500, OF PITTSBURGH 15213 #025-07-2006 L2006 EM *012

ABHISHEK, None. 4800 FRIENDSHIP AVE 15224 #495-45-2002 IM *012

ABI ANTOUN, Tania Elia. OF PI, HOSPS OF UNIV HEALTH CTR 15261 #605-01-2002 L2007 NEP *012 †20

ABIKOFF, Cory Michelle. ■ 15219 #041-12-2006 L2006 PD *012

ABISSE, Saddam S. ■ 15226 #035-06-2008 *012

ABLA, Adnan A. 200 LOTHROP ST # 5C, UPMC PRESBYN HOSP 15213 #605-01-1978 L1986 NS *020 †25 ‡

ABO, Steven Robt. 200 LOTHROP ST, UPMC-PRESBYTERIAN HOSPITAL 15213 #035-46-1990 L1997 GE *020 †20

ABOSAMRA, Wassim. 121 MEYRAN AVE 15213 #875-01-1998 L2005 FP *012

ABRAHAM, Lisa P. ■ 15229 #035-15-2003 L2005 CHN *012

ABRAHAM, Sunil. ■ 15229 #035-15-2005 L2005 IM *012

ABRAMIAN, Emil. 320 E NORTH AVE, DEPT OF MED EDU 15212 #422-01-2006 L2006 IM *012

ABRAMS, Gordon Scott. 300 HALKET ST, MAGEE-WOMENS HOSPITAL 15213 #008-02-1995 L2000 DR *020 †80

ABRAMS, Pamela Beth. ■ 15206 #041-13-2006 L2006 PD *012

ABRAMS, Ya'Agov. 5608 WILKINS AVE 15217 #024-05-1985 L1995 FM *020 †18

ABRAMSON, Norman S. 1400 LOCUST ST 15219 #035-19-1969 L1977 EM CCM *050 †16

ABU-ELMAGD, Kareem M. 3459 5TH AVE, MUH 7 SOUTH 15213 #915-06-1977 L1993 GS TTS *020 †85

ABUID, Juan. ■ 15220 #737-06-1970 L1974 P *100

ABULLEIL, Medhat Mahmoud. 200 LOTHROP ST, C-WING 15213 #915-02-1972 L1999 AN *020 †05

ABUNTO, Ruben Alzaga. 242 YARDLEY WAY 15206 #748-10-1997 L2002 IM *100 †20

ABU-OBEID, Amer Nayef. 4727 FRIENDSHIP AVE, STE 240 15224 #913-97-1984 L2002 AN *020 †20

ABURANO, Akio. 1400 LOCUST ST 15219 #025-01-1953 L1959 PTH OS *071 †50

ACARTURK, Tahsin Oguz. 3550 TERRACE ST, 677 SCAIFE HALL 15213 #902-05-1995 L2001 PS *100

ACERRA, John Robert. 320 E NORTH AVE, OF EMERGENCY 15212 #038-40-2004 L2004 EM *100

ACEVEDO, Jorge Luis. 5200 CENTRE AVE STE 617 15232 #042-01-1975 L1989 NS *020 †25

ACHCAR, Rosane De Oliveir. 15232 #187-33-1985 L2007 PTH *020

ACHILLEOS, Andreas Nikou. 4800 FRIENDSHIP AVE 15224 #418-01-1996 L2001 IM *020 †20

ACHILLES, Sharon Lynelle. 300 HALKET ST, DEPARTMENT OF OB/GYN, MAGE 15213 #041-12-2004 L2005 OBG *012

ACHIM, Marilena. 320 E NORTH AVE 15212 #781-03-1996 L2007 P *012

ACHKAR, Antonio Amin. 3500 5TH AVE 4TH FL, ARTHRITIS & INTERNAL MEDIC 15213 #038-06-1988 L1994 RHU IM *020 †20

ACKERMAN, Kurt David. 3811 OHARA ST, AND CLINIC 15213 #035-45-1991 L1994 P *020 †75

ACON LAWS, Malcolm. 320 E NORTH AVE, ALLEGHENY GENERAL HOSPITA 15212 #270-02-1999 L2005 PTH *012

ACOSTA, Thalia A. 3811 OHARA ST 15213 #041-15-2003 L2006 P *100

ACUFF, James Harvey. 4815 LIBERTY AVE # GR25 15224 #047-06-1985 L1986 AN *020 †05

ADADA, Haytham Faruq. 1400 LOCUST ST, MERCY HOSPITAL 15219 #605-04-2002 L2006 IM *020

ADAMS, Andrew Curtis. 4800 FRIENDSHIP AVE 15224 #041-13-2004 L2004 IM *100 †20

ADAMS, Anne Stephenson. ■ 15217 #041-07-1937 L1938 GP GYN *071

ADATEPE, Mustafa Hayati. 320 E NORTH AVE 15212 #902-03-1955 L1973 NM IM *071 †28

ADEBAJO, Feyisitan A. 5215 CENTRE AVE 15232 #690-02-1989 L2001 FM *020 †18

ADELSHEIMER, Marc Jeffrey. 107 GAMMA DR 15238 #041-07-1991 L1996 PM *020 †60

ADELSON, Philip David. 3705 5TH AVE 15213 #035-01-1986 L1994 NS NSP *020 †25

ADELSTEIN, Evan Cary. 200 LOTHROP ST, PUH B535 15213 #010-02-1999 L2001 ICE *100 †20

ADEYEYE, Oluwatobi Adetut. ■ 15228 #041-12-2004 L2004 PD *100 †55

ADIBI, Siamak A. 200 LOTHROP ST, CLIN NUTRITION/SCAIFE HALL 15213 #041-02-1959 L1963 IM NTR *050

ADKINS, John Crawford. 3705 5TH AVE 15213 #023-07-1965 L1966 PDS *071 †85

ADLER, Lauri Jo. 200 LOTHROP ST, ANES/SCAIFE HALL 15213 #055-01-1989 L1991 AN *020 †05

ADLER, Lawrence Nathan. 21 YOST BLVD, STE 217 15221 #041-12-1957 L1958 CD IM *020 †20

ADLER, Peter H. 230 MCKEE PL STE 500, OF PITTSBURGH 15213 #036-01-2006 L2006 EM *012

ADLER, Sheldon. 3550 TERRACE ST, #A909 SCAIFE HALL 15213 #035-08-1959 L1967 NEP IM *030 †20

ADUBA, Osita. 230 LOTHROP ST # PATH, PRESBYTERIAN HOSPITAL 15213 #690-01-1963 L1974 PTH *100 †50

ADURTY, Rajashekar. 490 E NORTH AVE, STE 300 15212 #495-65-1994 L2001 PUD *020 †20

AEBA, Ryo. ■ 15213 #572-20-1982 TS *100

AERNI, Giselle Andrea. ■ 15213 #041-12-2008 *012

AFROOZ, Paul Nader. ■ 15222 #016-42-2007 *012

AGARWAL, Surabhi. S 716 BIOMED SCIENCE TOWER, 3500 TERRACE STREET 15261 #495-45-2003 L2007 RHU *012 †20

AGARWAL, Surbhi Moolchand. ■ 15232 #495-06-2002 FP *012

AGARWAL, Vikas. ■ 15206 #024-05-2003 DR *012

AGARWALA, Meena. 5230 CENTRE AVE # 305 15232 #496-38-1984 L1993 IM *020 †18

AGBEDE, Betty O. 3500 5TH AVE, STE 305 15213 #690-04-1980 L1988 FM *020 †18

AGGARWAL, Lovedhi. 1400 LOCUST ST, MERCY HOSPITAL 15219 #496-68-2004 L2006 FP *012

AGGARWAL, Nidhi. 121 MEYRAN AVE 15213 #496-07-2001 PTH *012

AGGARWAL, Shushma Goel. DESOTO AT OHARA STS 15213 #495-05-1972 L1979 AN *020 †05

AGHA, Mounzer Ezzat. 5115 CENTRE AVE, FL 3 15213 #875-02-1983 L1987 ON HEM *050 †20

AGHA-MOHAMMADI, Siamak. 3550 TERRACE STREET, 677 SCAIFE HALL 15261 #917-03-1997 L2000 PS *100 †65

AGNESI, Joseph Nicholas. 4800 FRIENDSHIP AVE, THE WESTERN PENNSYLVANIA H 15224 #038-44-1992 L1996 DR *020 †80

AGRAWAL, Radheshyam M. 1307 FEDERAL ST STE 301 15212 #495-20-1965 L1973 GE IM *020 †20

AGRAWAL, Ritwick. 552 CHATHAM PARK DR 15220 #495-05-2002 L2004 CCM *012 †20

AGUILAR, Pedro J. 200 LOTHROP ST 15213 #048-14-2000 L2003 NS *100

AHEARN, Joseph Michael. 200 LOTHROP ST, E1152 BIOMEDICAL SCIENCE 15213 #023-07-1981 L1996 RHU *050

AHMAD, Ferhaan. 200 LOTHROP ST 15213 #067-01-1991 L2004 CD *020 †20

AHMAD, Iftikhar. 5910 KIRKWOOD ST 15206 #704-09-1985 L1999 DR RNR *020 †80

AHMAD, Jawad. 200 LOTHROP ST 15213 #917-28-1992 L1998 GE *020

AHMAD, Naeem. ■ 15237 #704-21-1999 L2007 FP *012

AHMAD, Sarfraz. 4815 LIBERTY AVE, STE 459 15224 #704-01-1977 L1996 GE *020 †20

AHMAD OBAID, Shakil. 200 LOTHROP ST 15219 #704-01-1979 L1995 IM *020

AHMED, Adiba. 2101 GREENTREE RD STE A103 15220 #704-06-1961 L1976 IM *020 †20

AHMED, Aftab. 320 E NORTH AVE 15212 #704-08-2003 L2006 IM *100

AHMED, Fariha. 320 E NORTH AVE, ALLEGHENY GEN HOSP 15212 #422-01-2003 L2003 PCC *012 †20

AHMED, Nadeem. 1200 REEDSDALE ST 15233 #704-02-1991 L2003 OS P *020 †20,75

AHMED, Quzi Moslehuddin. 200 LOTHROP ST 15213 #704-03-1956 L1968 OPH *071 †35

AHMED, Saleem. 200 LOTHROP ST, S 559 SCAIFE HALL 15213 #038-40-1998 L2000 IC *100 †20

AHMED, Salman. 1400 LOCUST ST, MERCY HOSP-PITTSBURGH 15219 #704-16-2002 IM *012

AHMED, Waseem. ■ 15228 #308-10-1986 L1994 N CD *074

AHRENDT, Gretchen M. 300 HALKET ST 15213 #023-07-1990 L2005 SO *020 †85

AHRENDT, Steven Arthur. 9100 BABCOCK BLVD 15237 #016-02-1987 L2005 GS *020 †85

AHUJA, Jaspreet Singh. 320 E NORTH AVE, DEPT OF MED EDU 15212 #198-04-2003 L2006 IM *012

AHUJA, Namita Satyendra. 5200 CENTRE AVE, STE 405 15232 #496-38-1995 L2005 IMG *100 †20

AHUJA, Subash Chander. 713 RIDGE AVE 15212 #209-02-1967 L1977 PTH PCP *020 †50 ‡

AIKEN, Lucille Boccato. 950 2ND AVE 15219 #561-11-1974 L1978 IM END *020 †20

AIYER, Aryan Narayan. ■ 15206 #035-46-1998 L2000 CD *100 †20

AIZENSTEIN, Howard Joy. 3811 OHARA ST, WPIC 15213 #016-11-1995 L1998 PYG P *020 †75

AIZOOKY, Khattar. 301 CASTLE SHANNON BLVD 15234 #875-01-1992 L1999 CD *020 †20

AKANBI, Fadeke Beatrice. ■ 15237 #041-15-2002 L2002 MPD *100 †20

AKBARI, Amgelene A Cruz. ■ 15232 #041-14-1997 L2000 PD *020 †55

AKBARI-NASAB, Ardalan. ■ 15203 #665-01-2006 L2006 IM *012

AKBARPOURANBADR, Aref. 200 LOTHROP ST, UPP RADIOLOGY - RM 395 15213 #517-15-1992 L2006 NM *012 †28

AKERS, Adam Scott. 200 LOTHROP ST, UPMC 15213 #041-12-1992 L1994 IM *020 †20

AKERS, Aletha Yvette. ■ 15217 #023-07-2000 L2006 OBG *100

AKHRASS, Amer. 1049 UNITY CENTER RD 15239 #875-01-1986 L1994 **IM** *020 †20

AKHTAR, Jawaid. 200 LOTHROP ST 15213 #704-02-1986 L1994 **PD EM** *020

AKHTAR, Ubaid Ahmad. 3705 5TH AVE, STE 3950 15213 #041-13-1996 L2001 **DR** *020 †80

AKINDELE, Raucheline. 9100 BABCOCK BLVD 15237 #035-15-1994 L1998 **DR** *020 †80

AKINMERESE, Olawale Opeye. ■ 15213 #690-01-2004 L2007 **FP** *012

AKKINENI, Madhavi. 320 E NORTH AVE 15212 #449-50-2000 L2007 **IM** *012

AKWAYENA, Raymond K. 200 LOTHROP ST, RM 3950 MAIN TOWER 15213 #412-01-1990 L2005 **DR** *020 †80

ALAGAR, Ravikumar. 1350 LOCUST ST, STE 400 15219 #067-01-1989 L1997 **PUD CCM** *020 †20

ALAGIOZIAN-ANGELOVA, Victo. 121 MEYRAN AVE, RM E733 15213 #198-02-1993 L2007 **SP** *012 †20

ALAGUGURUSAMY, Sankar Sur. 1307 FEDERAL ST, STE 301 15212 #495-37-1998 L2005 **GE** *012 †20

AL-ALI, Mohammad. ■ 15237 #875-01-1998 L2007 **CCM** *012 †20

ALAM, Mansoor. ■ 15206 #496-27-1997 L2005 **IM** *012

ALAM, Zulfaqar. 3550 TERR ST, ANESTHESIOLOGY 15261 #704-16-1990 L1998 **AN** *020 †05

ALARAKHIA, Anika. 320 E NORTH AVE 15212 #422-01-2005 L2005 **IM** *012

ALARCON, Falcon Humberto. 15237 #737-01-1963 **GS IM** *071

ALARCON, Joseph Humberto. ■ 15237 #041-14-2000 **P** *100

ALARCON, Louis Humberto. 646A SCAIFE HALL, 3550 TERRACE ST 15261 #041-12-1992 L1994 **CCS TRS** *020 †85

ALAYLI, Ghassan A. 200 DELAFIELD RD 15215 #605-01-1987 L1993 **RHU IM** *020 †20

ALBA, Jose C. ■ 15213 #748-01-1958 L1971 **GS GP** *071

ALBA, Violeta V. ■ 15213 #748-01-1960 L1972 **GP OBG** *020

ALBERT, Judith Louise. 665 RODI RD, FL 2 15235 #038-41-1982 L1983 **REN GYN** *020 †30

ALBINO RODRIGUEZ, Juan. ■ 15212 #042-01-2003 L2007 **PMM** *012

ALBO, Vincent Chas. 3705 5TH AVE, STE 385 15213 #041-12-1955 L1956 **PHO** *071 †55

ALCINDOR, Dunbar. ■ 15214 #056-06-2006 L2006 **NS** *012

ALCOFF, Joel Michael. ■ 15217 #041-12-1976 L1982 **FM** *020 †18

ALEF, Matthew Jeremy. 200 LOTHROP STREET 15261 #016-01-2005 L2005 **GS** *012

ALEONG, Ryan Gerrard. 200 LOTHROP ST, CARDIOVASCULAR INSTITUTE 15213 #041-12-1999 L2002 **ICE** *100 †20

ALEXANDER, Cynthia Denise. 120 LYTTON AVE, STE 300 15213 #041-12-2000 L2001 **IM** *020 †20

ALEXANDER, Jacob Michael. 3705 5TH AVE, CHP MT3950 15213 #041-12-2002 L2002 **DR** *012

ALGAIER, Robert John. 180 FORT COUCH RD, STE 304 15241 #649-35-1984 L1986 **CHP P** *020

AL-GHOUL, Ahmed Rustom. 203 LOTHROP ST STE 823, UPMC EYE CENTER 15213 #068-01-2001 L2006 *100

AL HADDAD, Omar Salah Edd. SUITE 503 MEDICAL ARTS BLD 15213 #575-02-2004 L2008 *100

AL-HAIL, Layla Nasser. 320 E NORTH AVE 15212 #875-01-1989 L1999 **IM** *100

AL HASHASH, Jana. 121 MEYRAN AVE 15213 #605-01-2006 L2007 **IM** *012

AL-HINDI, Hindi N. ■ 15220 #797-01-1989 L1997 **PTH** *100 †50

ALI, Mohamad Arif. 320 E NORTH AVE 15212 #605-01-2002 L2004 **IM** *100

ALI, Robbie A. 2 HOT METAL ST 2ND FL, QUANTUM ONE 15203 #035-01-1988 L2003 *100 †70

ALI, Sheikh Asim. 121 MEYRAN AVE #704-25-1998 L2002 **HO** *020 †20

ALISSA, Feras T. 3705 5TH AVE 15213 #575-01-1995 L2003 **PG** *020 †55

AL-KHAFAJI, Ali Hussain. 6F SCAIFE HALL, 3550 TERRACE ST 15261 #528-04-1993 L1998 **CCM** *020 †20

AL-KHOURY, Georges Elie. ■ 15217 #605-03-2001 L2007 **VS** *012 †85

ALKHUDARI, Feras. 300 HALKET ST, MAGEE WOMENS HOSP 15213 #875-01-2001 L2003 **NPM** *012 †55

ALLADA, Vivekanand. 3705 5TH AVE, CHILDRENS HOSP OF PITTSBUR 15213 #025-01-1986 L2006 **PD PDC** *050 †55

ALLAIRE, Robert Basil. ■ 15221 #041-01-2004 L2004 **ORS** *012

ALLAM, Bala Sudhakar Redd. 320 E NORTH AVE 15212 #495-11-2002 **IM** *012

ALLANKI, Sailaja P. 275 CURRY HOLLOW RD, STE 205 15236 #495-58-1984 L1996 **CHP** *020 †75

ALLEN, Chris Max. 580 S AIKEN AVE 15232 #041-12-1975 **IM IMG** *020 †20

ALLEN, Christopher C. 4800 FRIENDSHIP AVE 15224 #566-01-1982 L1995 **CD** *020 †20

ALLEN, James Edgar. 1501 LOCUST ST, STE 1080 MD MEDICAL BLDG 15219 #041-02-1984 L1986 **U** *020 †95

ALLEN, Kathleen Ann. 875 GREENTREE RD 15220 #038-44-1990 L2000 **CLP GP** *020 †50

ALLEN, Thomas Elmer. 933 LIBERTY AVE, HEALTH SERVICE OF W PA INC 15222 #041-12-1943 L1944 **OBG** *071 †30

ALMAHAYNI, Muhamad Hitham. 1400 LOCUST ST 15219 #875-02-1997 L2001 **IM** *100

AL MAKKI, Nazar Elnour Mo. OF PITTSBURGH, UNIV HLTH CTR 15261 #848-01-1999 L2007 **CCM** *012 †20

ALMARIO, Vidacecilia A. 200 LOTHROP ST, RM N713 15213 #055-01-2002 L2002 **HO** *012 †20

ALMASRI, Eyad. 5131 LIBERTY AVE 15224 #875-01-1996 L2001 **PUD** *020 †20 ‡

ALMUSA, Omar. 3705 5TH AVE, CHP MT3950 15213 #025-12-1998 L2000 **DR** *020 †80

ALONSO, Laura Cristina. 200 LOTHROP ST, BST E1140, UNIVERSITY OF PITTSBURGH S 15261 #041-01-1998 L2005 **END** *050 †20

ALPER, Cuneyt Metin. 3705 5TH AVE, DEPT OF PEFD ENT CHILDS HS 15213 #902-05-1982 L1997 **OTO PDO** *020 †45

ALPER, Gulay. 203 LOTHROP ST 15213 #902-05-1982 L2001 **PD** *020

ALPERIN, Mariann. ■ 15217 #028-34-2001 L2001 **OBG** *020

ALPERT, Barry Leonard. 4815 LIBERTY AVE, STE 336 15224 #041-01-1971 L1974 **ICE CD** *020 †20

AL SHAKIR, Abdulruzzak M. 542 4TH AVE, ALLEGHENY CTY CORONERS OFF 15219 #528-01-1965 L1985 **FOP PTH** *050 †50

ALSHARI, Mohammed Ghyath. 4800 FRIENDSHIP AVE, MEDICINE DEPARTMENT 15224 #875-01-2001 L2003 **PUD** *012 †20

ALTAMIMI, Sadiq Lafta. 320 E NORTH AVE 15212 #422-01-2004 L2004 **N** *012

ALTMAN, Daniel T. 1501 FEDERAL ST STE 2 15212 #041-13-1991 L1995 **OSS OTR** *020 †40

ALTMAN, Gregory Theodore. 1307 FEDERAL ST, STE 2 15212 #041-13-1991 L1994 **ORS** *020 †40

ALTMAN, Sharon Anita. ■ 15217 #041-12-2004 L2004 **P** *012

ALTMAN, Wanda Teresa. ■ 15241 #759-03-1954 L1974 **GP** *071

ALTSCHULER, Eric Matthew. 1501 LOCUST ST STE 224 15219 #003-01-1984 L1986 **NS** *020 †25

ALTUG, Turgut M. HIGHLAND DR 15206 #902-03-1946 L1969 **ID IM** *020

ALURI, Kalyan Chakravarth. ■ 15219 #496-01-1996 L2005 **FP** *012

ALVARADO, Ganya Eugenia. 300 HALKET ST, STE 1338 15213 #035-01-1999 L2005 **OBG** *020 †30

ALVELO, Miguel F. 200 LOTHROP ST 15213 #042-01-1992 L1998 **GS** *020 †85,90

AMARANATHA, Lakya Anantha. 121 MEYRAN AVE, UNIV HLTH CTR OF PITTSBURG 15213 #495-99-1988 L2001 **IM** *100

AMAYO, Jose G. ■ 15213 #737-03-1966 L1973 **PM CN** *071 †60

AMBROSE, J Lee. 5230 CENTRE AVE, UPMC SHADYSIDE RADIOLOGY 15232 #035-15-1969 L2003 **R NM** *020 †80,28

AMBROSINO, Richard. UNIVERSITY DR C 15240 #035-19-1986 L1987 **IM** *020 †20

AMENTA, Joseph Salvo. 300 HALBIT ST, DEPT OF PATHOLOGY HOSPITAL 15213 #008-01-1957 L1964 **PTH** *072 †50

AMES, Jennifer Taylor. 200 LOTHROP ST, UPMC-PUH 15213 #041-12-2004 L2004 **DR** *012

AMESUR, Nikhil B. 200 LOTHROP ST 15213 #024-07-1991 L1996 **VIR R** *020 †20

AMICO, Janet Ann. 3501 TERRACE ST, UNIV PITTSBURG 15261 #041-07-1975 L1976 **END** *050 †20

AMIDI, Morteza. 0 UNIVERSITY DRIVE C, CARDIOLOGY 15240 #517-01-1962 L1982 **CD IM** *030 †20

AMIN, Devin Vikram. 15214 #041-12-2003 L2003 **NS** *012

AMIN, Priti Kirit. ■ 15213 #001-02-2007 L2007 **IM** *012

AMIN, Rajnikant. 9100 BABCOCK BLVD, DEPT OF LAB UPMC PARMNT 15237 #495-23-1980 L1986 **PTH** *020 †50

AMIRNAZMI, Solmaz. ■ 15206 #041-02-2006 L2007 **DR** *012

AMMAR, Galal Mohamed A. 300 HALKET ST 15213 #915-02-1953 L1973 **AN OBG** *020

AMMER, John Louis. 4815 LIBERTY AVE, MELLON PAVILION 15224 #041-12-1959 L1960 **OBG** *071 †30

AMORES, Alfonso Ycong. 2 ALLEGHENY CTR, STE 530 15212 #748-11-1971 L1989 **PS VS** *020 †85,65

AMORTEGUI, Antonio Jose. 300 HALKET ST, MAGEE WOMENS HOSP 15213 #264-01-1958 L1969 **ATP PCP** *020 †50

AMR, Hesham. 200 LOTHROP ST, RADIOLOGY DEPT 15213 #915-09-1990 L2000 **DR** *020 †80

AMSHEL, Albert L. ■ 15213 #041-02-1952 L1953 **CRS** *071 †10

ANALO, Helen Ifeyinwa. 4727 FRIENDSHIP AVE, STE 340 15224 #690-02-1984 L1998 **HO** *020 †20

ANAND, Archana. 4800 FRIENDSHIP AVE, STE N221 15224 #496-21-2004 L2007 **FP** *012

ANAND, Rahul Jagdish. 200 LOTHROP ST, RM F1281 15213 #025-01-2002 L2002 **GS** *012

ANANTHARAMAN, Ambale S. 4815 LIBERTY AVE, MELLON PAVILION G31 15224 #495-09-1973 L1977 **PUD CCM** *040 †20

ANDERSON, Gregory C. 7171 CHURCHLAND ST 15206 #041-13-2000 L2002 **PD** *020 †55

ANDERSON, J Carolyn H. 114 WOODSHIRE RD 15215 #004-01-1965 L1970 **RHU PD** *071 †55

ANDERSON, Janice Marilyn. 901 WEST ST, STE B 15221 #041-12-1984 L1986 **FM** *040 †18

ANDERSON, William Deaton. 200 LOTHROP ST, A333 15213 #036-07-1988 L1999 **CD** *020 †20

ANDREESCU, Carmen. 3811 OHARA ST, DEPT OF PSYCHIATRY 15213 #781-01-1991 L2002 **PYG** *100 †75

ANDREW-JAJA, Carey D. 300 HALKET ST, STE 1338 15213 #690-01-1973 L1978 **OBG** *020 †30

ANDREWS, Bernard Andrew. 490 E NORTH AVE, STE 200 15212 #041-12-1986 L1988 **IM** *020 †20

ANDREWS, Christine Louise. 117 N NEGLEY AVE, EAST END COMMUNITY HEALTH 15206 #038-06-1992 L1997 **FM** *020 †18

ANDREWS, Gabriel John. 103 GAMMA DR STE 120 15238 #008-02-1989 L1991 **FM** *020 †18

ANEJA, Rajesh Kumar. 3705 5TH AVE 15213 #495-08-1990 L2004 **CCP** *020 †55

ANGUS, Derek Calder. 3550 TERRACE ST, 614 SCAIFE HALL CRIT CARE 15213 #919-05-1984 L1991 **CCM** *020 †20

ANISH, Eric Jonathan. 5200 CENTRE AVE, STE 211 15232 #041-12-1994 L1998 **IM ISM** *020 †20

ANISINGARAJU, Lakshmi. ■ 15239 #496-24-1997 L2003 **IMG** *100

ANIXTER, Miriam Beth. 3705 5TH AVE, DEPT OF ANESTHESIOLOGY 15213 #041-12-2000 L2001 **AN** *020 †05 ‡

ANNE, Samantha. ■ 15213 #025-07-2002 L2007 **PDO** *012

ANSARI, Amir Houshang. 510 S AIKEN AVE, STE 312 15232 #517-01-1956 L1986 **REN GYN** *071 †30

ANTAKI, George Michael. 200 LOTHROP ST, UPP, UNIV RADIOLOGISTS 15213 #035-01-1994 L2000 **DR** *020 †20

ANTALIK, Paul Edwin. 7125 SALTSBURG RD 15235 #038-41-1967 L1972 **OTO OS** *020 †55,45

ANTANAVICIENE, Kristina. 4800 FRIENDSHIP AVE, PENNSYLVANIA HOSPI 15224 #913-49-1995 L2003 **PAN** *012

ANTHIKAD, Fenny. ■ 15215 #495-52-1989 L2005 **AN** *100

ANTI, Alvise. ■ 15217 #561-11-1978 L1983 **IM** *020

ANTOS, Thomas Jos. 13 WOODBROOK DR 15215 #041-09-1969 **IM IMG** *020 †20

AOUN, Elie Samir. 121 MEYRAN AVE, UNIV HLTH CTR OF PITTSBURG 15213 #605-01-2003 L2004 **GE** *012 †20

APAGA, Elmer Lacuata. 1500 5TH AVE, DEPT OF INTERNAL MED 15219 #748-08-1995 L2007 **IM** *012

APOSTOL, Mary Anne Libuna. ■ 15232 #748-01-2002 L2005 **FP** *012

APPASAMY, Ragunath. 2100 JANE ST STE 602 15203 #495-33-1983 L1988 **GE IM** *020 †20

APPLEMAN, Leonard Joseph. 5150 CENTRE AVE 5TH FL, UPMC CANCER PAVILION 15232 #035-19-1995 L2006 **HO** *020 †20

ARAI, Yoshio. 200 LOTHROP ST 15213 #572-29-1978 L1987 **RO DR** *020 †80

ARAKALI, Sheela V. 105 GAMMA DR STE 300 15238 #047-05-1998 L2000 **PD** *020 †55

AREBI, Sameh Miloud. 1307 FEDERAL ST STE 2, ALLEGHENY GENERAL HOSPITAL 15212 #613-02-1990 L2007 **ORS** *020

AREVALO, Bibiana K. ■ 15243 #041-15-2002 L2002 **DR** *100 †80

ARGIRIS, Athanassios. 5150 CENTRE AVE, STE 500 15232 #418-01-1990 L2005 **IM ON** *050 †20

ARGYROPOULOS, Christos P. 121 MEYRAN AVE 15213 #418-03-1997 L2006 **NEP** *012 †20

ARIAS HOWARD, Guillermo J. 3708 5TH AVE, DEPT OF MED EDUCATION 15213 #264-02-1995 L2006 **IM** *012

ARILLOTTA, Clyde. 320 E NORTH AVE, DEPT OF ANESTHESIOLOGY 15212 #041-09-1985 L1985 **AN** *020 †05 ‡

ARKACHAISRI, Thaschawee. 3705 5TH AVE 15213 #891-02-1991 L2003 **PPR** *020 †03,55

ARMAH, Henry. 3708 5TH AVE, UNIVERSITY HEALTH CENTER 15213 #412-01-1998 L2006 **PTH** *012

ARMFIELD, Derek Raphael. 200 LOTHROP ST 15213 #041-12-1997 L2001 **DR** *020 †80

ARNALDEZ, Fernanda Irene. 121 MEYRAN AVE 15213 #132-01-1999 L2005 **PD** *012

ARNHEIM, Falk K. 1050 BOWER HILL RD 15243 #041-12-1943 L1944 **U** *071 †95

ARNOLD, George Louis. 5200 CENTRE AVE, STE 506 15232 #024-07-1974 L1978 **GE IM** *020 †20

ARNOLD, Kali Danielle. 320 E NORTH AVE 15212 #047-07-2003 L2003 **ORS** *012

ARNOLD, Laura Schwartz. 2400 ARDMORE BLVD, STE 301 15221 #041-12-1988 L1990 **IM FM** *020 †18

ARNOLD, Robert Mark. 200 LOTHROP ST, STE 933W 15213 #028-46-1983 L1986 **PLM** *050 †20

ARORA, Gaurav. 3705 5TH AVE 15213 #048-04-1997 L2001 **PDC** *020 †20,55

ARORA, Rangolee Shrawan. ■ 15238 #495-83-2005 L2007 **IM** *012

ARORA, Rupinder Kaur. 4800 FRIENDSHIP AVE 15224 #496-43-1998 L2001 **IM** *100 †20

ARORA, Vikram. 815 FREEPORT RD 15215 #495-45-2000 L2001 **FM** *020

ARRIAGA, Moises A. 420 E NORTH AVE STE 402 15212 #043-01-1985 L1987 **NO OTO** *020 †45

ARRIETA, Omar Steven. ■ 15203 #048-02-2003 L2006 **CCP** *012

ARSHOUN, Youssef M. 320 E NORTH AVE, ALLEGHENEY GEN 15212 #915-04-1987 L1996 **RO** *020 †80 ‡

ARTIS, Cathy Jean. ■ 15243 #041-07-1974 L1976 **GS OM** *020 †85

ARVON, Regina Lisa. 300 HALKET ST, STE 1651 15213 #041-13-1998 L2002 **MG** *020

ARYA, Mukul. 320 E NORTH AVE, ALLEGHENY GENERAL HOSPITAL 15212 #422-01-1999 L2002 **GE** *100 †20

ASAAD, Iyad Hanna. OF PITTSBURGH, UNIV HLTH CTR 15261 #875-01-1996 L2007 **CCM** *012 †20

ASANTE, Sheila. 1709 BLVD OF THE ALLIES, UPTOWN PEDIATRICS 15219 #412-01-1990 L2000 **PD** *020 †55

ASATO, Miya Rei. 3705 5TH AVE, DIV OF CHILD NEUROLOGY 15213 #041-02-1995 L1997 **CHN** *050 †75,55

ASCHERMAN, Dana Preis. 3500 TERRANCE ST BST S707, UNIV OF PITTSBURGH 15261 #005-11-1992 L1998 **RHU IM** *020 †20

ASCHERMAN, Toby Diane. ■ 15217 #005-11-1992 L1998 **PD** *020 †55

ASHER, Andrew David. 320 E NORTH AVE, ALLEGHENY GENERAL HOSPITAL 15212 #041-13-2005 L2005 **EM** *012

ASHOK, Puducheri Sankaran. 9000 PERRY HWY, STE 210 15237 #495-04-1976 L1983 **GE IM** *020 †20

ASIF, Nouman. 121 MEYRAN AVE, UNIVERSITY HEALTH CENTER 15213 #704-20-1998 L2005 **IM** *012

ASIM, Muhammad. 320 E NORTH AVE, ALLEGHENY GEN HOSP 15212 #704-01-2001 L2004 **IM** *100

ASLAM, Nabeel. 3260 5TH AVE 15213 #704-01-1993 L1999 **NEP** *020 †20

ASSANASEN, Benja V. 2585 FREEPORT RD, STE 203 15238 #051-04-1964 L1971 **PD PDA** *020 †55,03

ASTOR, William Matthew. 1400 LOCUST ST, OF PITTSBURGH 15219 #035-15-2006 L2006 **DR** *012

ATASOY DEDE, Ajlan. 121 MEYRAN AVE, DEPT OF INTERNAL MED 15213 #902-05-2001 L2004 **IM** *012 †20

ATHANI, Vijay Satappa. 1400 LOCUST ST, STE 5110 15219 #495-96-1970 L1977 **U** *020 †95

ATILES, Roberto A. 3705 5TH AVE, CHILDRENS HOSPITAL OF PITT 15213 #042-01-1992 L1997 **AN PAN** *020 †05 ‡

ATKINS, Melany Beth. 200 LOTHROP ST, CHP/MT 3950 15213 #055-01-2006 L2007 **DR** *012

ATKINSON, Don Paul. 420 E NORTH AVE, SIOTE 304 15212 #019-02-1972 L1973 **GS SO** *020 †85

ATKINSON, Suzanne M. 2 HOT METAL ST 2ND FL, QUANTUM ONE BUILDING 15203 #041-12-2002 L2002 **EM** *020 †16

ATTEBERRY, Dave Shelton. 200 LOTHROP ST STE B-400, DEPT OF NEUROLOGICAL SURGE 15213 #041-12-2001 L2001 **NS** *012

ATWELL, Robert Burton. 5750 CENTRE AVE STE 370 15206 #041-12-1954 L1955 **GS CRS** *071 †85,10

ATWOOD, Charles Wadsworth. 3459 5TH AVE 15213 #001-02-1988 L1992 **PUD** *020 †20

AU, Alicia K. ■ 15232 #041-02-2004 L2007 **CCP** *012

AUCHENBACH, Ralph Chas. 7180 HIGHLAND DR 15206 #023-07-1968 L1969 **IM GP** *020 †20

AUJLA, Shean J. ■ 15206 #045-01-2000 L2004 **PDP** *012 †20

AUNG, Aye Thiri. 3811 OHARA ST, DEPT OF CHILD AND ADOLESCE 15213 #539-03-2000 L2002 *100

AURE, Isabel Remigio. 300 HALKET ST 15213 #748-01-1970 L1978 **PD** *020 †55

AUSTIN, Edward Michael. 110 FORT COUCH RD 15241 #050-02-1962 L1971 **OBG** *020 †30

AUSTIN, Robert Marshall. ■ 15238 #036-07-1977 L2005 **PTH** *020 †50

AVERCH, Timothy David. 3471 5TH AVE STE 700, KAUFMANN BLDG 15213 #041-12-1989 L2000 **U** *020 †95

AVETTA, Laila Rebeka. ■ 15238 #041-13-1985 L1987 **GS EM** *020

AVRAM, Zheni. 121 MEYRAN AVE 15213 #781-03-2000 L2005 **IM** *012

AVRAMUT, Mihaela. 3708 5TH AVE, UNIVERSITY HEALTH CENTER 15213 #781-02-1995 L2006 **PTH** *012

AWAN, Kanwal Shahzadi. ■ 15232 #704-02-2001 L2005 **IM** *012

AXELSON, Alan Arthur. 969 GREENTREE RD, STE 107 15220 #041-12-1966 L1967 **CHP P** *030 †75 ‡

AXELSON, David Alan. 2000 MARY ST 15203 #036-07-1992 L1996 **CHP** *050 †75

AYALA, Juanbosco J. ■ 15220 #649-43-2003 L2007 **PCC** *012 †20

AYARS, Barbara Lynn. 415 NEPTUNE ST, WEST END HEALTH CENTER 15220 #041-12-1986 L1990 **PD** *020 †55

AYASSO, M Samir. 1000 INTEGRITY DR, ASSOCIATES INC 15235 #875-01-1978 L1985 **GE** *040 †20 ‡

AYYASH, Maher Omar. 3811 OHARA ST, WESTERN PSYCHIATRIC INSTIT 15213 #915-03-1981 L1997 **P** *020 †75

AZAR, Carol Higham. 3436 WILLIAM PENN HWY, STE 166 15235 #038-40-1990 L1993 **IM** *020 †20

AZARI, Kodi K. 3705 5TH AVE 15213 #036-08-1997 L1999 **PS HS** *020 †65

AZKUL, Bassem. 5230 CENTRE AVE 15232 #875-01-1999 L2004 **FM** *020

AZMI, Farrukh Hameed. 5001 CENTRE AVE, FL 3 15213 #704-01-1979 L2005 **PTH** *020 †50

AZURIN, Arturo C. 1501 LOCUST ST 15219 #748-01-1953 L1963 **GS** *071

AZZAM, Pierre Nabil. ■ 15217 #048-04-2005 L2005 **P** *012

AZZUQA, Abeer Aref. 121 MEYRAN AVE 15213 #575-02-1997 L2003 **NPM** *012

BAADE, Eileen. 3000 BROWNSVILLE RD, STE 1 15227 #039-01-1975 L1976 **IMG IM** *020 †20

BABICH, Michael Matthew. 1307 FEDERAL ST STE 301 15212 #024-05-1991 L1993 **GE HEP** *020 †20

BABU, Vallabhaneni S. 1400 LOCUST ST 15219 #496-01-1971 L1976 **DR VIR** *020 †80

BACA, Diana T. ■ 15237 #038-44-2004 L2004 **OBG** *012

BACHA, Fida Farouk. 3705 5TH AVE 15213 #605-01-1995 L2001 **PDE** *050 †55 ‡

BADER, William. 2101 GREENTREE RD, STE B101 15220 #041-02-1975 L1976 **IM EM** *020 †20

BADLANI, Neil Mahesh. 15261 #041-12-2005 L2006 **ORS** *012

BADODARIYA, Lalitkumar Ja. 320 E NORTH AVE 15212 #495-22-2001 L2005 **IM** *012

BAE, Kyongtae. 200 LOTHROP ST 15213 #016-02-1992 L2006 **DR** *020 †80

BAFFONI, Albert D, Jr. 430 E NORTH AVE 15212 #043-01-1979 L1988 **GS CCS** *020 †85

BAGHAI, Parviz. 420 E NORTH AVE, STE 302 15212 #517-01-1974 L1979 **NS** *020 †25

BAHARY, Nathan. 200 LOTHROP ST, E1240 BSTWR 15261 #035-20-1989 L2002 **HO** *040 †20

BAHL, Sachin. 10922 FRANKSTOWN RD 15235 #422-01-1997 L2001 **END** *020 †20

BAHL, Vijay Kumar. 10922 FRANKSTOWN RD 15235 #905-01-1971 L1974 **END IM** *020 †20

BAHNDORF, Fred Robt F. ■ 15209 #041-09-1948 L1949 **GP** *020

BAIDOO, Leonard Kweku. 200 LOTHROP ST, ST,C-WING,MEZZ LEVEL 15213 #412-01-1983 L2001 **GE** *020 †20

BAIG, Rubina Naheed. 200 LOTHROP ST, STE 503 15213 #496-27-1997 L2007 **IM** *012

BAILEY, Mary P Lynch. ■ 15227 #041-12-1944 L1945 **PTH** *071

BAILEY, Stephen Hugh. 320 E NORTH AVE, CARDIOVASCULAR SURGERY CEN 15212 #047-05-1997 L2006 **TS** *100 †85,90

BAILEY, William Ryland, Jr. 1400 LOCUST ST 15219 #051-04-1942 L1946 **CD** *071 †20

BAJAJ, Neeraj. ■ 15213 #041-02-2003 L2006 **CD** *012 †20

BAJWA, Jagdeep K. 7180 HIGHLAND DR 15206 #495-08-1974 L1976 **P PTH** *020 †50,75

BAJWA, Meera. 5140 LIBERTY AVE 15224 #025-01-2001 L2004 **NEP** *020

BAJWA, Neil Singh. 320 E NORTH AVE 15212 #661-02-2007 L2007 **IM** *012

BAJWA, Omer. 490 E NORTH AVE, STE 303 15212 #704-01-1996 L2001 **PUD** *020 †20

BAKER, Carol Clare. FORESTHILLS PLAZA 15221 #041-12-1977 L1979 **IM** *020 †20

BAKER, Christopher Earl. ■ 15238 #011-03-2005 L2005 **ORS** *012

BAKER, David Joel. 2020 ARDMORE BLVD, STE 105 15221 #025-01-1986 L1987 **OPH** *020 †35

BAKER, John Robert. 1501 LOCUST ST, STE 224 15219 #024-01-1997 L2004 **ESN VN** *020 †75

BAKER, Karin Walke. 3705 5TH AVE 15213 #012-01-2002 L2002 **PM** *012 †60

BAKER, Walter Jos. 713 WASHINGTON RD 15228 #041-12-1965 L1966 **OPH** *071 †35

BAKKILA, Henry Allan. 111 SHERIDAN ST 15209 #041-12-1981 L1982 **FM** *020 †18

BAKONDY, Thomas Joseph. ■ 15229 #038-44-2003 L2004 **DR** *012

BALAAN, Marvin Relato. 490 E NORTH AVE 15212 #748-02-1979 L1997 **PUD CCM** *020 †20

BALACHANDRAN, Anita. 121 MEYRAN AVE, UNIV HLTH CTR OF PITTSBURG 15213 #495-59-2002 L2005 **FP** *012

BALASSANIAN, Ronald. 5230 CENTRE AVE, UPMC SHADYSIDE PATH WG 02 15232 #050-02-1996 L2004 **PTH** *020 †50

BALCOM, Joel Eric. ■ 15202 #038-44-2005 L2006 **EM** *012

BALDISSERI, Marie R T. 200 LOTHROP ST 15213 #847-11-1982 L1985 **CCM IM** *020 †20

BALESTRINO, Diane P. 7171 CHURCHLAND ST, LINCOLN LEMINGTON FAM HLTH 15206 #028-46-1979 L1980 **FM** *020 †18

BALHAN, Sukhraj Singh. 320 E NORTH AVE, ALLEGHENY GENERAL HOSPITAL 15212 #495-29-1999 L2007 **IM** *012

BALICHETTY, Aparna. 121 MEYRAN AVE, DEPT OF FAM MED 15213 #496-20-2003 L2006 **FP** *012

BALK, Judith Lyn. 300 HALKET ST, MAGEE WOMENS HOSPITAL 15213 #041-01-1990 L1992 **OBG** *020 †30

BALK, Phillip. 5230 CENTRE AVE, 312 SON BLDG 15232 #041-12-1959 L1960 **RHU IM** *071 †20

BALOUCH, Nazir Ahmed. 1400 LOCUST ST, MERCY HOSPITAL 15219 #704-17-2002 L2005 **IM** *012

BANDARANAYAKE, Piching. 5750 CENTRE AVE STE 270 15206 #220-01-1969 L1973 **A IM** *020 †20

BANDI, Rupal. 200 LOTHROP ST, UPP RADIOLOGY 15213 #495-20-1993 L1997 **VIR** *020 †80

BANEGURA, Allen Tibagaywa. ■ 15213 #021-03-2000 L2004 **GE** *020 †30

BANFIELD, Anne Louise. ■ 15206 #055-01-2005 L2005 **OBG** *012

BANG, Hardy Rok. 5664 NORTHUMBERLAND ST 15217 #041-13-2000 L2001 **GPM** *020 †70

BANGALORE, Srihari Sriniv. 1150 GREENFIELD AVE # 2 15217 #496-39-1999 L2005 **P** *020 †75

BANKS, Louise Yvonne. 320 E NORTH AVE 15212 #041-12-1990 L1992 **GPM** *020 †70,20

BANNA, Moustafa. ■ 15217 #038-41-2005 L2005 **IM** *012

BANSAL, Aditya. 121 MEYRAN AVE, STE C700 15213 #495-23-2000 L2007 **TS** *012

BANSAL, Sanjay Kumar. 3705 5TH AVE, OF PITTSBU 15213 #422-01-2002 L2006 **PDE** *012

BANSAL, Shimul. 5124 LIBERTY AVE, PENNSYLVANIA HOSPI 15224 #038-44-2002 L2002 **APM** *100

BARAD, Roxana Francisca. 4424 PENN AVE STE 103 15224 #035-03-1980 L1982 **OPH PS** *020 †35

BARAFF, Robert. 4815 LIBERTY AVE, STE 432 15224 #041-12-1971 L1973 **N** *020 †75 ‡

BARATZ, Arlene Brown. 320 E NORTH AVE 15212 #041-12-1984 L1985 **DR OBG** *020 †80

BARATZ, Mark Everett. 1307 FEDERAL ST 15212 #041-12-1984 L1985 **ORS HS** *020 †40

BARBER, John Clay. 4815 LIBERTY AVE 15224 #028-02-1965 L1991 **OPH** *071 †35

BARIL, Donald Toru. ■ 15206 #038-40-2001 L2007 **VS** *012 †85

BAR-JOSEPH, Gad. ■ 15217 #550-03-1974 L1980 **OS** *020 †55

BARKEY, Karen Jean. 9100 BABCOCK BLVD, UPMC PASSAVANT 15237 #041-12-1989 L1994 **R NM** *020 †80 ‡

BARKSDALE, Edward M, Jr. 3705 5TH AVE 4A-485, DEPT OF PEDIATRIC SURGERY 15213 #024-01-1984 L1994 **PDS** *020 †85

BARMADA, Mamdouha Ahdab. ■ 15238 #605-02-1968 L1975 **N NPM** *071 †50

BARMAR, Babak. 5230 CENTRE AVE, SON 215 15232 #409-39-2001 L2002 **NEP** *012 †20

BARNATO, Amber Elizabeth. 200 MEYRAN AVE STE 200 15213 #024-01-1994 L2001 **PHP** *050 †70

BARNES, Barbara E Fisher. 200 LOTHROP ST, STE 10055-A 15213 #041-14-1973 L1974 **IM** *040 †20

BARNES, Elvis Leon. 200 LOTHROP ST, PRESBYTERIAN HOSPITAL 15213 #004-01-1966 L1967 **PTH** *040 †50

BARNES, William J. ■ 15216 #041-12-1953 L1954 **OPH** *071 †35

BARNETT, Alan Jos. 2627 MURRAY AVE 15217 #033-06-1976 L1977 **IM** *020 †20

BARNETT, Alison Karen. ■ 15235 #041-09-1986 L1987 **P** *071

BARNETT, E Michael. ■ 15218 #041-12-1978 L1980 **OBG** *020

BARNETT, Marjorie Lee. 3414 5TH AVE, CHOP 3RD FLOOR GAP 15213 #025-12-1979 L2005 **PD** *020 †55

BARON, John. 4815 LIBERTY AVE, MELLON PAVILION 15224 #035-46-1962 L1963 **FM PD** *071 †55,18

BARON, Scott Lincoln. 1145 BOWER HILL RD, STE 301 15243 #010-02-1977 L1983 **ORS** *020 †40

BARRANGER, John Arthur. E1651 BIOMEDICAL SCI TOWER, UNIVERSITY OF PITTSBURGH 15261 #005-06-1974 L1990 **PD** *020

BARRETTE, Roger Robt. 1400 LOCUST ST 15219 #056-05-1979 L1982 **GS TRS** *020 †85

BARRINGTON, William W. 200 LOTHROP ST 15213 #038-40-1983 L1984 **CD IM** *020 †20

BARSOUK, Alexander. 4727 FRIENDSHIP AVE, STE 340 15224 #913-06-1993 L2000 **HO** *020 †20

BARTELS, Christopher J. 200 LOTHROP ST 15213 #051-01-1990 L1998 **GS SO** *020 †85

BARTLETT, David Lawrence. 5150 CENTRE AVE RM 415, UPMC CANCER PAVILION 15232 #048-14-1987 L1989 **GS ON** *020 †85

BARTOLETTI, Stefano Carlo. 3705 5TH AVE 15213 #561-01-1970 L1972 **DR PDR** *020 †80 ‡

BARTON, Kristin Patricia. 3705 5TH AVE, DEPT OF PED CARDLGY 15213 #041-13-2002 L2002 **PDC** *012 †55

BARTOS, Sylvia Ann. ■ 15236 #041-07-1961 L1969 **GP N** *071 †55

BARTYNSKI, Walter Steven. 200 LOTHROP ST RM D-132, MED CENTER/DEPT OF RADIOLO 15213 #041-01-1980 L1981 **DR OS** *020 †80

BARVE, Amit Anil. 1400 LOCUST ST, MERCY HOSPITAL 15219 #495-28-2002 L2006 **IM** *012

BARWELL, Michelle Marie. 3811 OHARA ST, & CLINIC 15213 #041-12-1997 L1999 **P** *040 †75

BASARAB, Jennifer Rose. ■ 15213 #041-12-2008 *012

BASAVA, Veena. 4800 FRIENDSHIP AVE, WESTERN PENNSYLVANIA HOSPI 15224 #495-50-2003 L2004 **AN** *012

BASER, Susan Mary. 420 E NORTH AVE, STE 206 15212 #016-43-1983 L1986 **N** *020 †75

BASHIR, Muhammad Hisham. ■ 15213 #704-01-2003 L2007 **IM** *012

BASKIN, Kevin Marin. 3705 5TH AVE 15213 #030-06-1991 L2003 **DR** *030 †80

BASS, Noah Saml. 3500 5TH AVE, 4TH FL 15213 #012-05-1975 L1977 **RHU IM** *020 †20

BASTACKY, Sheldon Ira. 200 LOTHROP ST 15213 #038-06-1987 L1994 **PTH** *020 †50

BASU, Amit. 3459 5TH AVE, STARZL TRANSPLANT INSTITUT 15213 #495-27-1982 L2000 **GS** *020 †85

BASU, Ranita. 3501 FORBES AVE, 3RD FL 15213 #495-02-1989 L2000 **PYG** *020 †75

BATAC, Ma. Charmaine Rapa. 5230 CENTRE AVE, UPMC SHADYSIDE 15232 #748-01-2002 L2007 **FP** *012

BATAL, Ibrahim. 121 MEYRAN AVE 15213 #875-01-2003 L2005 **PTH** *012

BATTAT, Lisa Rose. 400 PENN CENTER BLVD, BLDG 4 15235 #035-20-1992 L2000 **OPH** *012

BAUER, Frank L. ■ 15219 #018-03-1939 L1963 **IM** *071 †20,70

BAUER, Myriam F. 88 FORT COUCH RD, STE 100 15241 #036-01-2000 L2005 **PD** *020 †55

BAUM, Jeffrey Alan. 200 DELAFIELD RD, STE 1040 15215 #051-01-1980 L1982 **ORS OSS** *020 †40

BAUMBACH, Jennifer Lynn. 300 HALKET ST DEPT OB, MAGEE-WOMENS HOSPITAL 15213 #003-01-2004 L2006 **OBG** *012

BAYIR, Huyla. 3705 5TH AVE 15213 #902-05-1995 L1999 **CCP** *020 †55

BAZAZ, Raveen Raj. 200 LOTHROP ST 15213 #495-01-1994 L2001 **CD** *020 †20

BAZAZ, Vitasta. 2100 JANE ST STE 210 15203 #495-51-1967 L1974 **CHP P** *020

BAZMI, Hassan. 9104 BABCOCK RD, STE 6110 15237 #517-05-1966 L1976 **AS CRS** *071

BEACHLEY, Michael Chas. 5230 CENTRE AVE 15232 #024-01-1965 L1987 **DR** *020 †80 ‡

BEADLES, Barbara Ann. 3811 OHARA ST, UT SOUTHWESTERN MEDICAL CE 15213 #039-01-1998 L2007 **PFP** *020

BEAMAN, Antoinette Alonzo. 4615 FORBES AVE, GRAPHIC ARTS BUILDING 15213 #035-06-2002 L2002 **PD** *100 †55

BEAMAN, Shawn T. 200 LOTHROP ST, MONTEFIORE UNIVERSITY HOSP 15213 #035-06-2002 L2002 **AN** *020 †05

BEASLEY, Harley Scott. 4800 FRIENDSHIP AVE 15224 #017-20-1993 L1998 **DR** *020 †80

BEATTY, Randall Lee. 203 LOTHROP ST 15213 #035-03-1984 L1986 **OPH** *020 †35

BEAUDREAU, David Geo. 1 ALLEGHENY CTR STE 240 15212 #035-46-1978 L1979 **AN FM** *020 †18,05

BEAULIEU, Keith Allen. ■ 15203 #041-02-2003 L2003 **PCC** *012 †20

BEAULIEU, Yanick. ■ 15232 #067-01-1996 L2002 **CCM** *020

BECICH, Michael John. 200 LOTHROP ST, PATH/BIOMEDICAL SCIENCE 15213 #016-06-1984 L1991 **ATP GE** *020 †50

BECKER, Dorothy Joan. 3705 5TH AVE 15213 #836-01-1964 L1976 **PD PDE** *050 †55

BECKETT, Michael Patrick. ■ 15209 #035-03-2005 L2005 **ORS** *012

BECKNER, Marie Elaine. ■ 15238 #001-02-1980 L2000 **MGP** *012 †50

BEDAIR, Hany Salah. 3471 5TH AVE, STE 1011 15213 #008-01-2002 L2002 **ORS** *100

BEDEIR, Ahmed Saleh. 121 MEYRAN AVE 15213 #915-02-1997 L2003 **PTH** *100 †50

BEDELL, Alan Nichols. 530 MARSHALL AVE, PRESSLEY RIDGE 15214 #041-12-1981 L1982 **CHP P** *020 †75

BEERMAN, Lee Bankin. 3705 5TH AVE, CARDIOLOGY CHILDRENS HOSPI 15213 #041-12-1974 L1975 **PDC** *020 †55

BEGLIOMINI, Bruno. ■ 15213 #561-01-1984 L1989 **AN** *020

BEGUM, Dilwara. 100 S JACKSON AVE, EMERGENCY DEPARTMENT 15202 #160-03-1972 L1975 **EM OS** *071 †16

BEHARI, Jaideep. 200 LOTHROP ST, M2, C-WING, PUH 15213 #495-30-1992 L2002 **GE** *100 †20

BEHL, Ashish. 121 MEYRAN AVE, UNIV HLTH CTR OF PITTSBURG 15213 #496-43-2000 L2004 **IM** *100 †20

BEHM, John L. 9100 BABCOCK BLVD 15237 #422-01-1989 L1995 **FM** *020 †18 ‡

BEHRENDT, Richard P. ■ 15235 #038-41-1960 L1964 **OBG AN** *071 †05,30

BEIGI, Richard Hassan. 300 HALKET ST, DEPT. OF OB/GYN/RS 15213 #041-09-1997 L2001 **OBG** *020 †30

BEJJANI, Ghassan K. 200 LOTHROP ST, 9019 FORBES TOWER 15213 #605-02-1991 L1998 **NS** *072 †25

BEKOE, Seth. 400 HOLIDAY DR, STE 101 15220 #561-01-1965 L1974 **TS** *071 †85,90

BELANI, Chandra Prakash. 5150 CENTRE AVE STE 552, UPMC CANCER PAVILLION 15232 #495-30-1977 L1988 **HO HEM** *020 †20

BELDEN, William Arthur. 320 E NORTH AVE, ALLEGHENY GENERAL HOSPITAL 15212 #038-06-1999 L2001 **ICE** *020 †20

BELENKY, Sergei Naum. 320 E NORTH AVE, DEPT OF ALLERGY 15212 #913-99-1978 L1997 **AI** *020 †20

BELL, Michael James. 3705 5TH AVE, 6TH FLOOR MAIN TOWER, PEDI 15213 #035-08-1991 L1993 **CCP** *020 †20

BELLIN, Marvin Leonard. ■ 15217 #038-40-1956 L1964 **P** *062

BELLINGER, Mark Frederick. 128 N CRAIG ST 15213 #035-15-1974 L1979 **U PDS** *020 †95

BELLOT, Peter A. ■ 15235 #950-01-1970 L1977 **PTH** *020 †50

BELLOTTE, Jonathan B. 420 E NORTH AVE STE 302 15212 #055-01-1999 L2001 **NS** *020

BELLO VINCENTELLI, Gustavo. 4800 FRIENDSHIP AVE, DEPT OF SURGERY 15224 #935-01-2003 L2005 **GS** *012

BELMONT, Michael John. 3705 5TH AVE, DEPT OF PEDIATRIC OTOLARNO 15213 #035-08-1995 L1999 **PDO** *020 †45

BEMM, Charles William. 6023 HARVARD SQ 15206 #016-02-1995 L1998 **PD** *020 †55

BENCKART, Danl Harrington. 490 E NORTH AVE, STE 302 15212 #010-02-1977 L1984 **CD GS** *020 †85,90

BEN-DAVID, Bruce. 5230 CENTRE AVE, SHADYSIDE HOSPITAL 15232 #056-06-1980 L1981 **AN** *020 †05

BENDER, Charles Vincent. 300 HALKET ST, MAGEE WOMENS HOSP 15213 #038-40-1974 L1990 **NPM PD** *020 †55

BENDER, Filitsa H. 3504 5TH AVE STE 200, UNIVERSITY OF PITTSBURGH 15213 #418-02-1981 L1986 **NEP IM** *020 †20

BENDER, Helene Lynn. 3285 BABCOCK BLVD 15237 #016-06-1976 L1977 **GE IM** *020 †20

BENDER, Jennifer Ann. ■ 15241 #010-01-1982 L1991 **DR** *020 †80 ‡

BENDER, Thomas Martin. ■ 15217 #041-02-1964 L1966 **PD R** *071 †80

BENEDEK, Thomas Gerth. 3550 TERRACE ST, 7S 15261 #016-02-1952 L1957 **IM RHU** *040 †20 ‡

BEN-ELIEZER, Carmel. 3424 WILLIAM PENN HWY, STE 215 15235 #035-46-1975 L1977 **FM** *020 †18

BENHAYON, David. 3811 OHARA ST, & CLI 15213 #047-06-2005 L2005 **CPP** *012

BENJAMINSSON, Eirikur. 4200 5TH AVE, DEPT ANES 15261 #484-01-1974 L1979 **AN OS** *020 †05

BENKO, Kip Reese. 1501 LOCUST ST, STE 403 15219 #010-02-1989 L1991 **EM** *016

BENNETT, Beth Samantha. ■ 15232 #041-14-2008 *012

BENNETT, Michael Robt. 1400 LOCUST ST, M P O BOX 104 15219 #422-01-1981 L1983 **PUD PCC** *012

BENNETT, Nathan L. 275 CURRY HOLLOW RD, FL 1 15236 #041-02-1990 L1992 **FM** *020 †18

BENNETT, Robert Daniel. 5200 CENTRE AVE, STE 211 15232 #033-06-1981 L1992 **TS GS** *020 †20

BENOIT, Ronald Martin, Jr. 5200 CENTRE AVE, STE 211 15232 #041-12-1990 L1996 **U** *020 †95

BENSY, Joseph John. 1000 BOWER HILL RD 15243 #041-12-1970 L1973 **DR** *020 †80

BENT, George, III. 580 S AIKEN AVE STE 320 15232 #035-01-1972 L1974 **IM** *020 †20

BENYEHUDA, Johane. ■ 15229 #041-14-2006 L2006 **FP** *012

BENZA, Raymond L. 320 E NORTH AVE, 16TH FL SOUTH TOWER 15212 #011-03-1989 L2008 **CD** *020 †20

BENZO, Roberto Pablo. 3471 5TH AVE, STE 1211 15213 #132-04-1986 L2005 **PCC** *020 †20

BERENHOLTZ, Roy. ■ 15206 #422-01-2003 L2007 **PAN** *012

BEREZ, Franne Racelle. 5801 BEACON ST 15217 #649-26-1981 L1986 **FM** *020 †18

BERG, Alan Mark. 200 DELAFIELD RD 15215 #024-05-1985 L1987 **RHU IM** *020 †20

BERG, George. 625 STANWIX ST, STE 1209 1209 ALLEGHENY TO 15222 #041-12-1955 L1956 **U** *071 †95

BERG, Saul R. 1350 OLD FREEPORT RD 15238 #055-01-1965 L1966 **GYN** *020 †30

BERGER, Rachel P. 3705 5TH AVE, RM G321 15213 #041-01-1996 L1998 **PD** *020 †55

BERGMAN, Ira. 3705 5TH AVE 15213 #016-02-1974 L1979 **N PD** *050 †75,55

BERIWAL, Sushil. 300 HALKET ST 15213 #495-38-1994 L2002 **RO** *020 †80

BERK, David A. 8601 OLD PERRY HWY 15237 #041-12-1978 L1980 **OPH** *071 †35

BERKEBILE, Paul Ernest. 1 ALLEGHENY CTR STE 240 15212 #041-02-1958 L1959 **AN** *071 †05

BERKMAN, Ronald Osher. 5701 CENTRE AVE, L3 15206 #041-12-1960 L1961 **OPH** *072 †35

BERKOWITZ, Peter Joel. 532 S AIKEN AVE, STE 520 15232 #067-01-1975 L1980 **OPH** *020 †35 ‡

BERLACHER, Kathryn Lynn. 200 LOTHROP ST, MONTEFIORE N-713 15213 #038-40-2005 L2005 **IM** *012

BERLIN, Charles S. 4615 5TH AVE STE 100 15213 #041-12-1973 L1974 **P PFP** *020 †75

BERMAN, Howard J. ■ 15213 #041-12-1949 L1950 **PTH** *071 †50

BERMAN, Michael Anthony. JEFFERSON HOSP 15236 #041-12-1983 L1985 **PTH** *020 †50 ‡

BERMAN, Sarah Beth. 3471 5TH AVE, STE 810 15213 #041-12-2000 L2000 **N** *100 †75

BERMUDEZ, Christian Andre. 200 LOTHROP ST 15213 #231-02-1994 L2005 **VS** *020

BERNE, Ellen Sue. 5140 LIBERTY AVE 15224 #041-12-1986 L1987 **IM** *020 †20

BERNSTEIN, Cheryl Denise. 5750 CENTRE AVE, STE 400 15206 #035-45-1994 L2001 **APM** *020 †75

BERNSTEIN, Edward D. 4815 LIBERTY AVE, MELLON PAVILION 15224 #869-01-1965 L1967 **OBG** *071 †30

BERNSTEIN, Lawson F, Jr. 128 AYLESBORO LN 15217 #035-20-1987 L1991 **P PFP** *020 †75

BERNSTEIN, Marc Louis. 9100 BABCOCK BLVD, UPMC PASSAVANT DEPT MED IM 15237 #041-02-1973 L1977 **DR** *020 †80

BERNSTEIN, Robert Wm. 3471 5TH AVE, STE 402 15213 #561-01-1978 L1983 **IM** *020 †20

BERSCHLING, Chester M. 232 N CRAIG ST 15213 #035-46-1959 L1960 **P CHP** *071 †75

BERTOCCHI, Cristiana M. 320 E NORTH AVE 15212 #041-12-2001 L2001 **GS** *100 †20

BERTOCCHI, David Alan. 320 E NORTH AVE, DEPT PED 15212 #041-12-1981 L1984 **PD IM** *020 †55,20

BERTY, Rozlyn Maria. 320 E NORTH AVE, ALLEGHENY GENERAL HOSPITAL 15212 #041-12-1983 L1984 **NEP IM** *020 †20

BERWICK, Evelyn Sue. 1524 TRETTER DR 15227 #041-09-1977 L1978 **IM GP** *020 †20

BERWITH, Geneva Diane. ■ 15219 #041-14-2007 L2007 **AN** *012

BERYOZKIN, Gennady. ■ 15241 #913-69-1982 L1997 **CHP** *020 †75

BERZON, Ellis Jay. 5230 CENTRE AVE 15232 #051-04-1989 L1997 **AN PME** *020 †05

BESEKA, Felicia Tongo. 1400 LOCUST ST, MERCY HOSP-PITTSBURGH 15219 #422-01-1995 L2004 **FP** *012

BETANCOURT, Sergio Edward. 4725 MCKNIGHT RD 15237 #035-20-1961 L1977 **GS** *020 †85

BETLER, James A. 320 E NORTH AVE, ALLEGHENY GENERAL HOSPITAL 15212 #041-78-2002, ▲ L2002 **RO** *012 †20

BETTINGER, Robert. 4727 FRIENDSHIP AVE, STE 240 15224 #051-04-1973 L1983 **AN PME** *020 †05 ‡

BHAGWANANI, Drupadi D. 4782 LIBERTY AVE 15224 #495-30-1956 L1969 **DR PDR** *071 †80

BHAMA, Jay Kumar. ■ 15217 #048-04-1998 L2006 **TS** *020 †85,90

BHANDARI, Arun. 200 LOTHROP ST, C-WING PUH 15213 #496-09-1992 L2000 **AN PME** *020

BHARGAVA, Amit. ■ 15217 #056-05-1999 L2002 **GS** *100

BHARGAVA, Manoj. ■ 15213 #649-14-1987 **P** *100

BHARGAVA, Rohit. 3 15213 #495-30-1997 L2004 **SP** *100 †50

BHARGAVA, Ruby. ■ 15206 #495-45-1997 L2004 **PDP** *100 †55

BHARILL, Parth. 1501 LOCUST ST, STE 301 15219 #495-30-1982 L1990 **GE IM** *020 †20

BHARUCHA, Ashok J. ■ 15206 #041-14-1992 L2000 **PYG** *020 †75

BHASHYAM, Siva Kumar. 320 E NORTH AVE 8TH FL, SOUTH TOWER 15212 #496-35-1991 L2003 **IM** *100 †20

BHAT, Samidha Shreyas. ARTS BUILDIN, STE 503 MEDICAL 15213 #496-46-2003 L2007 **FP** *012

BHAT, Shobha Neerkaje. 2920 W LIBERTY AVE 15216 #495-09-1995 L2003 **FM** *020 †18

BHAT, Sunil Vithalray. ■ 15206 #038-43-2001 L2001 **ID** *020

BHAT, Tricia Labuda. 6023 HARVARD SQ 15206 #038-43-2001 L2001 **FM** *020 †18

BHATIA, Sangeeta Rani. ■ 15218 #038-43-2003 L2003 **NPM** *012 †55

BHATIA, Sanjay. 320 E NORTH AVE, ALLEGHENY GENERAL HOSPITAL 15212 #495-45-1987 L2003 **NS** *012 †05

BHATIA, Swati. 320 E NORTH AVE, ALLEGHENY GENERAL HOSPITAL 15212 #495-76-2005 L2006 **IM** *012

BHATKI, Amol Madhav. 200 LOTHROP ST, EYE AND EAR INSTITUTE, SUI 15213 #024-05-2002 L2008 **OTO** *100

BHATNAGAR, Nikhil Kumar. ■ 15232 #041-13-2007 L2007 **AN** *012

BHATNAGAR, Sonika. 8890 WILLOUGHBY RD 15237 #041-15-1999 L2002 **PD** *020 †55

BHATTACHARYA, Rajib Kumar. 3471 5TH AVE, 1110 KAUFMANN BUILDING 15213 #033-05-1999 L2001 **END** *020 †20

BHATTACHARYA, Sanjoy. ■ 15227 #032-01-2003 L2005 **CD** *012 †20
BHATTARAI, Paras Mani. ■ 15232 #672-01-1997 L2007 **PD** *012
BHENDE, Mananda Shailesh. 3705 5TH AVE, PEDIATRIC EMERGENCY MED 15213 #496-38-1976 L1986 **PD EM** *020 †55,16
BIAL, Erica Joy. ■ 15232 #024-05-2002 L2008 **IM** *020 †20 ‡
BICKEL, Jonathan Peter. 3705 5TH AVE 15213 #041-12-2004 L2004 **PD** *020 †55
BICKEL, Kathleen Elizabet. ■ 15212 #033-06-2004 L2004 **IM** *020 †20
BICKEL, Rebecca L. 88 FORT COUCH RD, STE 100 15241 #041-12-1974 L1975 **PD** *020 †55
BIEDERMAN, Robert Wallace. 320 E NORTH AVE, 2ND FL SOUTH TOWERS 15212 #045-01-1993 L1995 **CD** *020 †20
BIEDRZYCKI, Mark Robert. 100 DELAFIELD RD STE 313 15215 #041-12-1995 L1997 **FM** *020 †18
BIELEFELDT, Klaus. 200 LOTHROP ST 15213 #409-39-1986 L2003 **GE** *020 †20
BIELSKA, Wiktoria Barbara. ■ 15232 #041-12-2008 *012
BIERENBAUM, Jason M. ■ 15229 #051-07-2004 L2004 **IM** *100 †20
BIGDELI, Ghazaleh. 1400 LOCUST ST, DEPT OF MEDICINE 15219 #517-12-1999 L2001 **PCC** *012
BIGGS, Jason Matthew. ■ 15221 #041-02-2006 L2006 **EM** *012
BILBAO, Angel. 400 45TH ST # AM&R, ST FRANCIS MED CTR 15201 #847-11-1965 L1973 **PM** *020 †60
BILDER, Milton. 5200 CENTRE AVE STE 304 15232 #041-12-1944 L1945 **IM** *020 †20
BILLER, Aimee Beth. 240 MOUNT LEBANON BLVD 15234 #041-12-1985 L1986 **PD** *020 †55
BILLIAR, Timothy Robt. 200 LOTHROP ST, SUITE F1281 UPMC PRESBYTER 15213 #016-02-1983 L1988 **GS** *020 †85
BILLOCK, Jos Godfrey, III. ■ 15235 #005-12-1969 L1970 **GP** *020
BINAKONSKY, Harry S. ■ 15236 #041-12-1949 L1950 **OS IM** *071 †20
BINDLISH, Rajiv. 420 E NORTH AVE, STE 116 E WING OFFICE BLDG 15212 #065-01-1994 L1999 **OPH** *020 †35
BINGLER, Michael Abraham. ■ 15206 #041-12-2002 L2002 **PDC** *012 †55
BINSTOCK, Harold. ■ 15213 #041-12-1950 L1951 **IM OM** *072
BIRCHER, Nicholas Gregory. 3434 5TH AVE FL 2 15213 #041-12-1981 L1982 **CCM AN** *020 †05
BIRDAS, Thomas John. 4815 LIBERTY AVE STE 160, WEST PENN HOSPITAL LUNG CE 15224 #418-01-1995 L2001 **TS** *100 †85,90
BIRK, Catherine M. 2585 FREEPORT RD, STE 105 15238 #041-12-1984 L1985 **PM** *020 †60
BIRMAHER, Boris. ■ 15243 #264-05-1977 L1987 **CHP P** *020 †75
BIRRELL, Donald Geo. 300 HALKET ST 15213 #041-02-1948 L1949 **OBG** *071 †30
BISKIN, Lawrence Cecil. 100 DELAFIELD RD, STE 213 15215 #308-07-1983 L1987 **GS** *020 †85
BISTA, Bipin Raj. 1400 LOCUST ST, MERCY HOSPITAL 15219 #160-11-2002 L2006 **IM** *012
BITAR, Karim Wafic. 200 LOTHROP ST, STE 503 15213 #605-01-2004 L2007 **IM** *012
BJERKE, Richard J. 3550 TERRACE ST, A-1305 SCAIFE HALL 15261 #048-04-1982 L1983 **AN** *020 †05
BLACK, Judith E S. 815 FREEPORT RD 15215 #041-12-1974 L1975 **IM** *020 †20
BLACK, Milton Henry. ■ 15238 #041-12-1963 L1964 **OM AN** *071 †05,70
BLACKRICK, Lisa Rose. ■ 15206 #038-06-2004 L2004 **ORS** *012
BLAIR, Harry Colbert. DESOTO AND TERRACE STS, UNIVERSITY OF PITTSBURGH 15261 #028-02-1980 L2000 **PTH** *020 †50
BLAIR, Louis. 200 LOTHROP ST, PRESBYTERIAN HOSP 15213 #067-02-1987 L1991 **CCM** *020 †20
BLAKE, Karl Edwin. 405 E NORTH AVE, STE 405 15212 #041-12-1948 L1949 **CRS** *071 †85,10
BLAKOWSKI, Sandra Ann. 0 UNIVERSITY DRIVE C, ONCOLOGY/VA HOSP 15240 #035-06-1977 L1988 **HEM ON** *020 †20
BLANDINO, David A. 5215 CENTRE AVE 15232 #041-12-1978 L1979 **FM** *040 †18
BLASIOLE, Brian. ■ 15218 #041-14-2007 L2007 **AN** *012
BLASTOS, Paul. 400 45TH ST 15201 #016-06-1954 L1956 **PYA P** *020 ‡
BLATTER, Joshua Andrew. ■ 15211 #041-12-2008 *012
BLATTER, Mark Melvin. 1580 MCLAUGHLIN RUN RD, PEDIATRIC ALLIANCE 15241 #051-04-1972 L1973 **PD** *020 †55
BLAZEK-O'NEILL, Betsy W. 1307 FEDERAL ST, STE 3 15212 #056-06-1987 L1991 **PM** *020 †60
BLEICHER, Andrew Gabriel. 200 LOTHROP ST, RM 132 15213 #035-08-2000 L2005 **RNR** *100 †80
BLEVINS, Jonathan William. ■ 15232 #010-02-2006 L2006 **DR** *012
BLIGH, Brendan Jeremy. ■ 15217 #035-09-2002 L2006 **FM** *100 †18
BLISARD, Deanna Marie. ■ 15213 #041-02-1997 L1999 **CCS** *100 †85
BLITSTEIN, Alan. ■ 15217 #165-04-1970 L1971 **PD GP** *020 †55 ‡
BLOBNER, Charles G. ■ 15224 #041-12-1952 L1953 **CD** *020
BLOCK, Bruce. 5215 CENTRE AVE 15232 #008-01-1971 **FM** *030 †18
BLOCK, Dale Jos. 651 HOLIDAY DR, FOSTER PLAZA BLDG #5 15220 #038-43-1987 L1995 **FM MDM** *020 †18
BLOCK, Geoffrey Douglas. 385 WILLIAM PITT WAY, BLOCK MEDICAL ASSOCIATES 15238 #036-05-1984 L1988 **OS GE** *050 †20
BLOCK, Marian R Heimer. 4800 FRIENDSHIP AVE 15224 #008-01-1971 L1995 **FM** *030 †18
BLOCK, Robert Carl. ■ 15238 #041-12-1958 L1959 **PTH** *071 †50
BLOCKINGER, Amanda Kathry. ■ 15221 #010-01-2005 L2005 **PD** *012
BLOCKSTEIN, Robert S. 815 FREEPORT RD 15215 #041-12-1956 L1957 **GYN** *071 †30
BLODGETT, Todd Michael. ■ 15208 #041-12-2000 L2001 **DR** *100 †80
BLOOM, Elana J. 5200 CENTRE AVE, STE 606 15232 #035-19-1981 L1988 **ON HEM** *040 †20
BLOOM, Jonathan David. 1400 LOCUST ST, OF PITTSBURGH 15219 #041-12-2005 L2005 **AN** *012
BLOOMENTHAL, Robert Avram. 815 FREEPORT RD 15215 #050-02-1972 L1994 **FM** *020 †18
BLOUGH, Leland S. 958 PERRY HWY 15237 #041-12-1951 L1952 **ORS** *071 †40
BLUESTEIN, David Danl. ■ 15243 #035-15-1956 L1962 **PD ADL** *071 †55
BLUESTONE, Charles David. 3705 5TH AVE 15213 #041-12-1958 L1959 **PDO** *020 †45
BLUM, Ellen S. ■ 15232 #035-45-1991 L1993 **PD** *020 †55
BLUMBERG, David. UNIV. PITTSBURG MED CENTER, 497 SCAIFE HALL 15261 #035-08-1988 L1990 **CRS** *020 †85,10
BLUME, Robert Paul. 1501 LOCUST ST 15219 #041-13-1956 L1957 **N OS** *071
BLUMENKOPF, Bennett. 420 E NORTH AVE STE 302, DEPT OF NEUROSURGERY 15212 #024-05-1976 L2005 **NS** *020 †25
BOARDMAN, John Fisher. ■ 15221 #035-09-1995 L1995 **RNR** *020 †80
BOCHAROV, Maxim Valeryevi. 1400 LOCUST ST, DEPT OF INTERNAL MED 15219 #913-69-1994 L2004 **IM** *100 †20
BODEA-CRISAN, Nicoleta Ca. ■ 15201 #781-01-1980 L2001 **P** *100
BODEA CRISAN, Tiberiu. 1011 BINGHAM ST, 1ST FL 15203 #781-01-1987 L2001 **P** *020 †75
BODEK, Alvin Mayer. ■ 15213 #041-12-1954 L1955 **FM** *072 †18
BODEK, Kenneth Edward. 490 E NORTH AVE, STE 400 15212 #016-02-1986 L1992 **CD IM** *020 †20
BOETTCHER, Anna. 180 FORT COUCH RD, STE 304 15241 #035-09-1995 L1997 **P** *020 †75
BOGEN, Debra Louise. 3705 5TH AVE 15213 #007-02-1992 L1998 **PD** *020 †55
BOGGS, Dane Ruffner. UNIV OF PITTS MED SCH 15261 #051-01-1956 L1956 **HEM ON** *050 †20
BOGGS, Marcellus Alvin. 7227 HAMILTON AVE 15208 #041-01-1979 L1980 **FM** *075 †18
BOHM-VELEZ, Marcela. 5500 CORPORATE DR, STE 100 15237 #041-07-1981 L1982 **R** *020 †80
BOKHARI, Malak. 490 E NORTH AVE, STE 106 15212 #539-06-1989 L1997 **GS CRS** *020 †85,10
BOLANOVICH, Lester J. 4416 PENN AVE 15224 #041-12-1951 L1952 **P PYA** *071
BOLES, Mark G. 200 FLEET ST, STE 701 15220 #654-01-1983 L1988 **PD** *020 †55
BOLLAND, Monica Alice. 2000 MARY ST, UPMC SOUTH SIDE - ANESTHES 15203 #041-12-2002 L2002 **AN** *100
BOLON, Shannon Keely. 3937 BUTLER ST, LAWRENCEVILLE FAMILY HEALT 15201 #025-07-2003 L2006 **FM** *020 †18
BOLSER, Benjamin Scott. 3705 5TH AVE 15213 #038-44-2000 L2007 **PD** *020 †55
BOLUKOGLU, Hakki. 490 E NORTH AVE, STE 307 15212 #902-04-1985 L1999 **IM** *020 †20
BOMELI, Steven Richard. ■ 15218 #051-01-2006 L2006 **OTO** *012
BONACORSI, Thomas F. 1528 BEECHVIEW AVE 15216 #308-10-1985 L1988 **IM** *020 †20
BONAROTI, Carrie Nogueira. 1608 MAIN ST 15215 #011-04-1989 L1991 **FM** *020 †18
BONAROTI, Eugene Anthony. 5200 CENTRE AVE, STE 612 15232 #041-12-1991 L1993 **NS** *020 †25
BONAVENTURA, Marguerite. 300 HALKET ST 15213 #055-01-1982 L1984 **GS CCM** *020 †85
BOND, Geoffrey James. 3705 5TH AVE 15213 #143-03-1989 L2000 *020
BONFIELD, Christopher Mic. ■ 15229 #041-12-2007 L2007 *012
BONHOMME, Gabrielle R. 203 LOTHROP ST 15213 #041-01-2000 L2001 **OPH** *020 †35
BONIDIE, Marianne. 993 GREENTREE RD, STE 1030 15220 #051-04-1993 L1998 **OBG** *020 †30
BONIDIE, Michael John. 4815 LIBERTY AVE, STE 321 15224 #041-12-1992 L1998 **OBG** *020 †30
BONINGER, Michael Lee. 7180 HIGHLAND DR, HE RSCH LAB 151R-1 15206 #038-40-1989 L1993 **PM** *020 †60
BONINO, Paula. 120 5TH AVE # P5101 15222 #038-06-1979 L1989 **IMG IM** *030 †20
BONNEMA, Rachel Ann. ■ 15232 #046-01-2003 L2003 **IM** *100 †20
BONNET, Christopher A. 320 E NORTH AVE, SECTION OF EP 15212 #041-12-1982 L1983 **ICE CD** *020 †20
BONONI, Patricia Lynn. 5140 LIBERTY AVE 15224 #041-12-1985 L1986 **END IM** *020 †20
BONOW, Alison Lee. ■ 15221 #026-04-2006 L2007 **MPD** *012
BONTEMPO, Franklin A. 3636 BLVD OF THE ALLIES 15213 #041-09-1976 L1978 **HEM ON** *020 †20
BOOKWALTER, John Wm. 5200 CENTRE AVE, STE 612 15232 #016-43-1976 L1980 **NS EM** *020 †25
BOONE, Darrell Craig. ■ 15232 #063-01-1985 L1992 **CCS** *020 †85
BORDEAU, Kevin Patrick. 1050 BOWER HILL RD 15243 #024-07-2000 L2005 **U** *020 †95
BOREK, Rachel Catherine. ■ 15218 #041-13-2003 L2003 **HO** *012
BOREN, Mary Nannette. 1200 REEDSDALE ST, MERCY BEHAVIORAL HEALTH 15233 #041-07-1986 L1987 **P** *020 †75
BORETSKY, Harry. 100 S JACKSON AVE 15202 #041-02-1951 L1952 **AN** *071 †05
BORETSKY, Robert H. 5601 DUNMOYLE AVE 15217 #041-02-1982 L1983 **AN IM** *020 †05
BORGE, Manjula Prakash. 4 ALLEGHENY CTR, 8TH FL 15212 #305-01-2000 L2002 **CHP** *100
BORLAND, Lawrence Michael. 3705 5TH AVE, CHILDREN'S HOSP OF PITTS 15213 #041-01-1971 L1974 **AN PD** *020 †55,05
BORLE, Andre Bernard. UNIV PITTSBURGH SCH MED 15261 #869-04-1955 **OS IM** *040
BOROCHOVITZ, Dennis. 1401 FORBES AVE 15219 #836-01-1966 L1977 **PTH** *020 †50
BORRERO, Camilo Guillermo. ■ 15238 #038-06-2002 L2002 **DR** *100 †80
BORRERO, Sonya Bhutta. 230 MCKEE PL, STE 600 15213 #038-06-2001 L2001 **IM** *100
BORSARI, Thomas Edward. 3471 5TH AVE STE 910, UPMC DEPT OF ANESTH 15213 #010-02-2006 L2006 **AN** *012
BORSETT-KANTER, Leslie. 3705 5TH AVE, GENERAL ACADEMIC PEDIATRIC 15213 #011-03-1983 L1990 **PD OS** *020 †55
BORTINGER, Jonathan Zev. ■ 15232 #041-12-2008 *012
BORTON, Diana Denise. 3705 5TH AVE, RM 4B 15213 #036-01-2003 L2003 **D** *012 †55
BOSSE, Milton Dietrick. ■ 15217 #019-02-1938 L1939 **IM PTH** *017 †50
BOSWORTH, Donna Elizabeth. 320 E NORTH AVE 15212 #041-01-1975 L1978 **PD ID** *020 †55
BOTNARU, Andrei. 320 E NORTH AVE, ALLEGHENY GEN HOSP 15212 #781-03-1996 L2005 **GS** *100
BOUCEK, Charles David. 200 LOTHROP ST, 9019 FORBES TOWER 15213 #041-13-1978 L1979 **AN** *020 †20,05
BOUJOUKOS, Arthur John. 200 LOTHROP ST 15213 #024-07-1986 L1992 **CCM** *020 †20
BOUNDS, Richard Brandon. 230 MCKEE PL STE 500 15213 #023-01-2004 L2004 **EM** *100
BOURDAKOS, Nicolas G. 400 45TH ST 15201 #418-01-1947 L1961 **IM NEP** *071
BOURNE, Ryan Nolan. ■ 15222 #035-06-2001 L2007 **IC** *012
BOU-SAMRA, Georges R. 1350 LOCUST ST, STE 100 15219 #605-02-1990 L1999 **CD** *020 †20
BOUVIER, Marianne. 6000 BABCOCK BLVD 15237 #154-01-1955 L1961 **OPH** *020 †35
BOUWERS, Shawna Teresa. ■ 15217 #041-12-2008 L2008 *012
BOWEN, A'Delbert, III. 3705 5TH AVE 15213 #012-01-1971 L1975 **PDR DR** *020 †80
BOWLES, Stephen Arnold. 1400 LOCUST ST, MERCY HOSPITAL OF PITTSBUR 15219 #041-12-1982 L1987 **CCM** *050 †20
BOYD, Anne Susan. 3937 BUTLER ST 15201 #038-06-1994 L2003 **FM** *020 †18
BOYER, Jessica Beierle. ■ 15206 #041-12-2006 L2006 **EM** *012
BOYIADZIS, Michael M. ■ 15217 #473-04-1995 L2004 **IM** *020 †20
BOYLE, Annelee Crunchy. ■ 15217 #036-05-2007 L2007 **OBG** *012
BOYLE, Eileen Marie. 7171 CHURCHLAND ST, EAST LIBERTY FAMILY HEALTH 15206 #041-09-1983 L1986 **IM** *020 †20
BOYLE, James Wm. 9104 BABCOCK BLVD, STE 1106 15237 #041-09-1983 L1986 **IM IMG** *020 †20
BOYLE, Karen Melissa. 5608 WILKINS AVE 1ST FL 15217 #041-12-2001 L2001 **FM** *020
BOZIK, Elizabeth Anne. ■ 15237 #041-12-1985 L1986 **P** *020 †75
BOZIK, Michael Edward. 200 LOTHROP ST 15213 #041-12-1987 L1989 **N** *020 †75
BRADER, Eric Wm. 1501 LOCUST ST, STE 403 15219 #041-12-1983 L1984 **EM** *020 †16
BRADLEY, Betty Herbert. ■ 15241 #041-12-1941 L1942 **PD** *071
BRADLEY, James Philip. 200 DELAFIELD RD, STE 4010 15215 #010-02-1982 L1984 **ORS OSM** *020 †40 ‡
BRADSHAW, Kalonda Kateece. 3811 OHARA ST, AND C 15213 #010-03-2006 L2006 **P** *012
BRAGDON, Robert Whipple. 4815 LIBERTY AVE STE 235 15224 #041-12-1973 L1974 **PS HS** *020 †65
BRAGG, Elizabeth Alexis. ■ 15232 #055-01-2007 L2007 **PD** *012
BRAHOS, Anthony Geo. ■ 15238 #308-07-1982 L1985 **FM GS** *020
BRAHOS, Nicholas Geo. ■ 15238 #418-01-1934 L1957 **GS** *075
BRAMOWITZ, Alan David. ■ 15236 #016-11-1968 L1975 **CD IM** *020 †20

■ = Address Information Privacy Protected

BRANCH, Robert Anthony. 200 LOTHROP ST 15213 #917-02-1965 L1991 **PA IM** *050
BRANCOLINI, Scott Anthony. 200 LOTHROP ST, STE NE570 15213 #041-14-2002 L2002 **APM** *020 †05
BRAND, Randall Elliot. 5200 CENTRE AVE STE 409, SHADYSIDE MEDICAL BUILDING 15232 #025-01-1987 L2007 **GE** *020 †20
BRANDOM, Barbara W. 200 LOTHROP ST 15213 #041-01-1976 L1977 **AN PAN** *020 †05
BRANDON, John Mitchell. ■ 15241 #041-12-1956 L1957 **PTH HEM** *071 †50,20
BRANDSTETTER, Louis H, Jr. 1699 WASHINGTON RD, STE 403 15228 #055-01-1969 L1972 **U** *020 †95 ‡
BRANDY, Dominic Anthony. 806 S AIKEN AVE 15232 #041-09-1979 L1979 **FPS GP** *020 †16
BRANDYS, Ewa Beata. 1405 SHADY AVE, MED STAFF DEPT 15217 #759-01-1986 L2002 **PM RPM** *020 †60
BRANSTETTER, Barton F, IV. 200 LOTHROP ST RM D-132 15213 #005-18-1995 L2000 **RNR OTO** *020 †80
BRASUK, Virginia May. 230 LOTHROP ST 15213 #041-12-1960 L1961 **OPH** *071 †35
BRAXTON, Ernest Earl. ■ 15233 #041-01-2001 L2003 **NS** *012
BREIT, Robert Newell. 363 VANADIUM RD, STE 104 15243 #045-01-1980 L1983 **PD NPM** *020 †55 ‡
BREITFELD, Volker. 9100 BABCOCK BLVD, UPMC PASSAVANT 15237 #041-12-1967 L1968 **PTH** *071 †50
BRENES, Gilbert. 3471 5TH AVE, STE 201 15213 #270-01-1970 L1975 **PM SCI** *020 †60 ‡
BRENNEN, Peter Michael. ■ 15238 #041-12-2006 L2006 **IM** *012
BRENNER, Richard P. 3601 5TH AVE, RM 653 15213 #020-02-1968 L1982 **N P** *020 †75
BRENT, David Alan. 3811 OHARA ST, WESTERN PSYCHIATRIC INST 15213 #041-02-1974 L1978 **CHP PD** *030 †55,75
BRENT, Nancy B. 4070 BEECHWOOD BLVD, PEDIATRIC ALLIANCE 15217 #024-05-1979 L1980 **PD CHP** *040 †55 ‡
BRESS, Alan Norman. 1400 LOCUST ST # G103 15219 #041-12-1959 L1960 **ON IM** *020
BRESS, James Coleman. 2100 JANE ST, STE 802 15203 #041-12-1962 L1965 **ON OS** *020
BRICE, Judith Alexander. 128 N CRAIG ST 15213 #024-01-1971 L1975 **P CHP** *020 †75
BRIDENSTINE, James B. 3601 5TH AVE, STE 5A 15213 #007-02-1969 L1991 **DS A** *020 †15
BRILLER, Stanley Arthur. 320 E NORTH AVE 15212 #035-19-1947 L1957 **CD IM** *030
BRILLMAN, David Allen. 4815 LIBERTY AVE G-25 15224 #041-02-1978 L1979 **IM IMG** *020 †20
BRILLMAN, Jon. 420 E NORTH AVE, STE 206 15212 #041-12-1967 L1968 **N** *020 †75 ‡
BRINDIS, Charles. ■ 15208 #041-01-1974 L1975 **AN** *071 †05
BRINKMEIER, Matthew Arthu. ■ 15206 #038-40-2007 L2007 **IM** *012
BRINKMEYER, Scott D. ■ 15238 #018-75-1974, ▲ L1978 **AN** *020 †05
BRITTON, Cynthia Ann. 200 LOTHROP ST 15213 #041-14-1983 L1984 **DR** *020 †80
BROACH, Amy Nicole. 300 HALKET ST 15213 #036-08-2003 L2003 **OBG** *020
BROADMAN, Lynn M. 3705 5TH AVE 15213 #038-43-1974 L1998 **AN PMM** *020 †05
BRODE, Susan Elizabeth. 200 LOTHROP ST, 9019 FORBES TOWER 15213 #035-19-1989 L1992 **CD** *020 †20
BRODLAND, David Gene. 5200 CENTRE AVE, STE 303 15232 #016-45-1985 L1989 **D DS** *020 †15
BRODMERKEL, Geo Jos, Jr. 1307 FEDERAL ST STE 301 15212 #016-43-1960 L1969 **GE IM** *020 †20
BROKL, David Anthony. ■ 15217 #051-01-2003 L2003 **IM** *020 †20
BRON, Klaus Michael. 100 S JACKSON AVE, SUBURBAN GENERAL HOSPITAL 15202 #035-19-1955 L1956 **DR** *071 †80
BROOKFIELD, Laura Suzanne. 169 THOUSAND OAKS DR 15241 #038-43-1994 L2000 **EM** *020 †16
BROOKS, John C. ■ 15206 #048-14-1990 L1993 **CHP** *020
BROOKS, Robert Carson. 4 UNIVERSITY DRIVE C, PITTSBURGH VA HEALTHCARE S 15240 #036-01-1991 L1995 **IM** *020 †20
BROSTOFF, Philip. 220 MEYRAN AVE 15213 #041-01-1949 L1950 **IM CD** *071 †20
BROUSSARD, Elsie R. 3811 OHARA ST 15213 #021-05-1944 L1965 **CHP PHP** *071 †70,75 ‡
BROWN, Aaron Michael. 230 MCKEE PL STE 500, OF PITTSBURGH 15213 #041-01-2007 L2007 **EM** *012
BROWN, Alissa Renee. ■ 15222 #023-07-2006 L2006 **PD** *012
BROWN, Amy Lou. ■ 15208 #026-04-2006 L2006 **PD** *012
BROWN, Charles K. 5115 CENTRE AVE, STE 2.32D 15232 #011-03-1992 L1995 **GS** *020 †85
BROWN, Charles Michael. 320 E NORTH AVE, ALLEGHENY GENERAL HOSPITAL 15212 #020-02-1995 L2003 **IC** *020 †20,55
BROWN, Daniel Joseph. ■ 15201 #041-12-2006 L2006 **IM** *012
BROWN, Frank Halstead, III. 532 S AIKEN AVE, AIKEN PROF BLDG. SUITE 300 15232 #041-01-1976 L1978 **IM** *020 †20
BROWN, Jody A. ■ 15213 #038-06-2007 **P** *012
BROWN, Joel Dean. 2400 ARDMORE BLVD, STE 200 15221 #041-12-1990 L1991 **OPH** *020 †35
BROWN, Jolene A. OF PITTSBURGH, UNIV HLTH CTR 15261 #011-03-1999 L2006 **END** *012 †20
BROWN, Mary Ellen. 3414 5TH AVE 1ST FL, PHYSICIANS, PEDI 15213 #041-13-2003 L2005 **PD** *100
BROWN, Robert B. ■ 15243 #041-12-1951 L1952 **R NM** *020 †80,28
BROWN, Shervondalo R. 3471 5TH AVE, STE 1010 15213 #035-45-1999 L2001 **HS** *020 ‡
BROWNING, Jim Robt. 400 PENN CENTER BLVD 15235 #041-02-1964 L1969 **OPH** *020 †35
BROZANSKI, Beverly S. 3705 5TH AVE 6TH FL, CHILDS HOSP OF PITTSBURG 15213 #041-12-1982 L1984 **NPM** *020 †55
BROZOVICH, Marc Edward. 9104 BABCOCK BLVD, STE 4110 15237 #041-13-2002 L2002 **CRS** *012
BRUCE, Ronald Craig. ■ 15229 #035-45-1962 L1966 **ORS** *071 †40
BRUFSKY, Adam Matthew. 300 HALKET ST 15213 #008-02-1990 L1996 **ON IM** *020 †20
BRULA, Joseph Martin. 1000 BOWER HILL RD, DEPT OF ANESTHESIA 15243 #055-01-1997 L1997 **AN PME** *020 †05
BRUMBERG, Howard Andrew. ■ 15217 #422-01-2004 L2004 **IM** *100
BRUNGO, James John. ■ 15237 #016-43-1945 L1946 **OM FM** *071
BRUNGO, John Dominic. 120 5TH AVE, HIGHMARK 15222 #056-06-1969 L1971 **IM MDM** *030 †20
BRUNO, Stephen C. ■ 15237 #041-12-1951 L1952 **R** *071 †80
BRUNS, Frank John. 3550 TERRACE ST 15213 #035-15-1964 L1966 **NEP IM** *040 †20
BUCCI, Arthur John. 1400 LOCUST ST, BLDG D 15219 #016-11-1987 L1988 **END IM** *020 †20
BUCCI, Kimberly Scott. 4727 FRIENDSHIP AVE # 240, WESTERN PA ANESTH ASSC LTD 15224 #025-07-1985 L1991 **AN** *020 †05
BUCHANAN, Edwin Bayley. 1400 LOCUST ST 15219 #041-12-1947 L1948 **GS OS** *071 †85
BUCHDAHL, Alice J. 401 SHADY AVE STE D105 15206 #023-01-1970 L1971 **P CHP** *020 †75
BUCHINSKY, Farrel Joel. 320 E NORTH AVE, SOUTH TOWER 7TH FL 15212 #836-02-1988 L1997 **PDO OTO** *020 †45
BUCK, David George. 1524 S NEGLEY AVE 15217 #041-12-1995 L1999 **VIR** *020 †80
BUCKLEW, Lawrence A, Jr. 200 DELAFIELD RD 15215 #038-40-1969 L1978 **CD IM** *020 †20
BUCKNER, Robert Edward, II. 320 E NORTH AVE 15212 #055-01-2003 L2003 **EM** *100 †16
BUCKTHAL-MCCUIN, Jill. ■ 15217 #012-01-2003 L2007 **DMP** *012 †15
BUDWAY, Raye J. 4800 FRIENDSHIP AVE, 4600N 15224 #041-09-1988 L1990 **GS CCS** *020 †85
BUERGER, Daniel Eugene. 3471 5TH AVE, STE 1115 15213 #028-02-1993 L1996 **OPH** *020 †35 ‡
BUERGER, David George. 3471 5TH AVE 15213 #028-02-1991 L1993 **OPH** *020 †35
BUERGER, George F, Jr. ■ 15221 #010-01-1962 L1963 **OPH OS** *071 †35
BUFFER, Sam A, Jr. 5230 CENTRE AVE 15232 #041-12-1988 L1990 **CD** *020 †20
BUFFINGTON, Charles Wm. SCAIFE HALL, UNIV OF PITTSBURGH SCH OF 15261 #055-01-1973 L1988 **AN** *020 †05
BUI, Diemthuy Duc. 200 LOTHROP ST STE933W, DIV OF GEN INTERNAL MED 15213 #028-02-1991 L1997 **IM** *040 †20
BUI, The Bao. 4800 FRIENDSHIP AVE, WESTERN PENNSYLVANIA HOSP 15224 #067-04-1985 **VIR** *100
BUI, Viet Ngoc. 203 LOTHROP ST, STE 800 15213 #011-03-2002 L2007 **OPH** *100
BUKHARI, Lubna. 3811 OHARA ST 15213 #704-09-1985 L2004 **CHP** *020 †75
BUKSTEIN, Oscar Gary. 3811 OHARA ST, WPIC 15213 #048-02-1983 L1984 **CHP ADP** *050 †75
BULAKHTINA, Elena Alexand. 320 E NORTH AVE 15212 #913-06-1997 L2006 **PTH** *012
BULLARO, Francesca Maria. ■ 15232 #035-06-2002 L2002 **PEM** *012 †55
BULOVA, Peter Daniel. 200 LOTHROP ST 15213 #041-12-1996 L1999 **IM** *020 †20
BUMMER, Michael Anthony. ■ 15209 #035-09-2005 L2005 **OBG** *012
BUMP, Gregory Matthew. ■ 15217 #041-12-2000 L2006 **IM** *020 †20
BUNGE, Katherine Embry. 300 HALKET ST, C/O DEPT OF OB/.GYN 15213 #023-07-2002 L2006 **OBG** *100 †30
BUNKER, Mark Lincoln. 4800 FRIENDSHIP AVE, WESTERN PENNSYLVANIA HOSP 15224 #918-01-1983 L1985 **PTH** *020 †50
BURANOSKY, Raquel A. 200 LOTHROP ST, # 9W20 15213 #036-07-1994 L1997 **IM** *020 †20
BURD, Lawrence Todd. 5900 PENN AVE, NOVUM PHARMACEUTICAL RESEA 15206 #041-14-1996 L1998 **GPM** *020 †70
BURDA, Marianne Louise. 1 BIGELOW SQ, STE 729 15219 #041-07-1985 L1986 **OBG OS** *062 †30
BURGER, Julia Marie. ■ 15232 #041-13-2005 L2005 **PD** *012
BURGESS, James Edward. 420 E NORTH AVE, STE 202 15212 #055-01-1980 L1981 **NS** *020 †25
BURGUERA, Bart G. BST-E1140 LOTHRUP STREET 15261 #847-05-1986 L2000 **END** *020 †20
BURKE, Charles Jos, III. 200 DELAFIELD RD STE 4010, BURKE & BRADLEY ORTHOPEDIC 15215 #038-41-1981 L1983 **ORS OSM** *020 †40
BURKE, Donald Scott. ■ 15217 #024-01-1971 L1974 **ID** *050 †20
BURKE, Lorrianne Francene. ■ 15232 #041-12-2008 *012
BURKET, Jeffrey Scott. 101 DRAKE RD, STE C 15241 #041-13-1992 L1999 **IM** *020 †20
BURKETT, Donald E. ■ 15217 #041-02-1945 L1946 **FM** *071 †18
BURKEY, Matthew David. ■ 15217 #023-07-2007 L2007 **FPP** *012
BURKHOLDER, John Alden. 490 E NORTH AVE STE 302 15212 #023-07-1966 L1967 **CD TS** *020 †85,90
BURNS, David Andrew. 5230 CENTRE AVE, UPMC SHADYSIDE HOSPITAL 15232 #038-40-2002 L2002 **AN** *100
BURNS, Emily Susan. 120 LYTTON AVE 15213 #038-06-1985 L1993 **IM** *020 †20
BURNS, Harumi Uchida. 1910 COCHRAN RD, MANOR OAK II, STE 490 15220 #041-12-1992 L1994 **IM** *020 †20
BURNS, Karen Elizabeth A. 3550 TERRACEAVE/440 SCAIFE, ALLERGY & CRITICAL CARE 15261 #065-06-1994 L2000 **PUD** *020 †20
BURNS, Robert Cartland. 3705 5TH AVE 15213 #028-46-1988 L2006 **PDS** *020 †85
BURSICK, Daniel Myron. 1501 LOCUST ST, STE 224 15219 #041-14-1976 L1977 **NS** *020 †25
BURSTEIN, Stuart Saml. 1050 BOWER HILL RD STE 207 15243 #016-11-1961 L1985 **P PFP** *020 †75 ‡
BURTON, Edward Alan. 3471 5TH AVE, DEPT OF NEUROLOGY 15213 #917-01-1991 L2005 **N** *100
BURTON, Elan Chanel. ■ 15222 #012-21-2005 L2005 **GS** *012
BURTON, Steven Alan. 5230 CENTRE AVE 15232 #050-02-1986 L1987 **RO** *020 †20,80
BUSHATI, Besa. 1400 LOCUST ST 15219 #120-01-1997 L2005 **IM** *012
BUSHKOFF, Stanley H. ■ 15206 #041-09-1957 L1958 **ORS** *071 †40
BUSHMAN, Karl Edward. 200 LOTHROP ST 15213 #035-46-1990 L1992 **IM** *020 †20 ‡
BUSIS, Neil Amdur. 532 S AIKEN AVE, STE 507 15232 #041-01-1977 L1985 **N CN** *020 †75
BUSIS, Sidney N. ■ 15208 #041-12-1945 L1946 **OTO NO** *071 †45 ‡
BUSSELBERG, Peter Donald. 121 MEYRAN AVE, DEPT RAD 15213 #056-06-2006 L2006 **DR** *012
BUTLER, Lawrence James. 4221 PENN AVE, FL 4 15224 #041-12-1990 L1992 **PD** *020 †55
BUTT, Adeel Ajwad. 3601 5TH AVE STE 3A 15213 #704-25-1990 L2002 **ID IM** *050 †20
BUTTRAM, Sandra D. 3705 5TH AVE 15213 #025-07-1999 L2001 **CCP** *100 †55
BUYSSE, Daniel Jos. 3811 OHARA ST RM E-1127 15213 #025-01-1983 L1984 **P SME** *020 †75
BUZZELLI, Philip B. 1004 ARCH ST, MPH - THIRD FLOOR 15212 #561-01-1969 L1971 **OPH** *020
BYERS, James F. 559 TRUMBULL DR 15205 #041-14-1974 L1975 **ADM OBG** *020
BYERS, John Agnew. ■ 15237 #041-12-1948 L1949 **GS** *071 †85
BYERS, Karin Elizabeth. 3601 5TH AVE STE 3A 15213 #041-13-1991 L1993 **ID** *040 †20
BYLER DANN, Rebecca Jane. 300 HALKET ST, DEPT OB 15213 #041-12-2002 L2006 **OBG** *100
BYNUM, Sonia Valeria. ■ 15217 #048-02-2007 L2007 **IM** *012
BYRNE, Kathleen Anne. ■ 15201 #041-14-2005 L2005 **FP** *012
CABACUNGAN, Clarissa B. 230 N CRAIG ST 15213 #748-02-1991 L1998 **CHP** *020
CABACUNGAN, Leonard. 2000 MARY ST 15203 #748-02-1991 L1997 **PM** *020 †60
CABALLE, Jose Baxarias. 572 NEW TEXAS RD 15239 #847-01-1974 L1979 **IM GP** *020 †20
CABATUANDO, Dante Abes. PENN AVE & WEST ST, COLUMBIA HOSP 15221 #748-07-1963 L1972 **DR** *020 †80
CABRAL, Carol Lynn. 3705 5TH AVE, DIAGNOSTIC REFERRAL 15213 #041-15-2001 L2001 **PD** *020 †55
CACCIARELLI, Thomas V. 3601 5TH AVE 4TH FL, CENTER, FOLK CLINIC 15213 #035-08-1982 L1997 **GS OTO** *071 †85
CACERES SERRANO, Manuel. 4800 FRIENDSHIP AVE, DEPT OF SURGERY 15224 #429-02-2001 L2003 **GS** *012
CADARET, Linda Marie. 200 LOTHROP ST 15213 #025-07-1994 L2003 **CD** *020 †20
CADOGAN, David Anthony. ■ 15219 #047-07-2007 L2007 **GS** *012
CAGLAR, Derin. 121 MEYRAN AVE 15213 #902-21-1993 L2005 **PCP** *100
CAHAN, Benjamin D. ■ 15211 #041-15-2007 L2007 **TY** *012
CAI, Wayne Yun-Cai. 1401 FORBES AVE 15219 #243-45-1985 L2000 **PTH** *020 †50
CAIN, Brent Ernest. 5230 CENTRE AVE M205 15232 #041-12-1990 L2000 **AN** *020 †05

■ = Address Information Privacy Protected

CAIN, James Gordon. 3705 5TH AVE 15213 #041-12-1992 L1998 **AN CCA** *020 †05

CAINE, Mark Evan. 4800 FRIENDSHIP AVE, WEST TOWER 15224 #041-13-1979 L1981 **MFM** *020 †30

CAINES, Myrven Jos. VET ADMIN HOSP 15240 #950-01-1963 L1975 **PTH** *020 †50

CAJIAO-PULIDO, Isabela. 121 MEYRAN AVE, UNIV HLTH CTR OF PITTSBURG 15213 #264-04-1999 L2004 **PD** *020 †55

CALABRESE, Jamie. 6301 NORTHUMBERLAND ST 15217 #041-12-1991 L1993 **PD** *030 †55

CALDWELL, John Christian. 2749 MOUNT ROYAL RD 15217 #041-12-1990 L1994 **AN** *020 †05

CALDWELL, Matthew W. 200 LOTHROP ST 15213 #050-02-1986 L1990 **AN** *020 †05

CALIGUIRI, Lawrence A. 3801 MCKNIGHT EAST DR, ALLERGIC DISEASE & ASTHMA 15237 #016-43-1958 L1959 **AI PD** *072 †55,03

CALLAHAN, Lawrence E. ■ 15215 #561-01-1978 L1981 **EM IM** *020 †20,16

CALLAWAY, Clifton Watson. 230 MCKEE PL 15213 #005-18-1993 L1995 **EM** *050 †16

CALVELO, Manuel Gawaran. 1515 LOCUST ST, 5TH FL STE 1080 15219 #748-02-1964 L1971 **CD IM** *020 †20

CAMBIER, Linda Silk. 5230 CENTRE AVE, DEPT OF RADIATION ONCOLOGY 15232 #018-03-1985 L1991 **DR** *020 †80

CAMERON, Robert Douglas A. HOLT ST 15203 #068-01-1970 **GS** *050

CAMERON, William James. ■ 15211 #055-01-2005 L2005 **AN** *012

CAMP, Geoffrey Roberts. 815 FREEPORT RD, DEPT OF MEDICAL EDUCATION 15215 #041-12-2002 L2002 **FM** *020 †18

CAMP, William Leonard, Jr. 190 LOTHROP ST, STE 145 15213 #001-02-2002 L2007 **D** *012 †20

CAMPBELL, Highland R. 3258 KENNETT SQ 15213 #047-07-2000 L2004 **EM** *020 †05

CAMPBELL, Kristen Kay. 4800 FRIENDSHIP AVE, WEST PENN ANESTHESIA ASSOC 15224 #041-77-2001, ▲ L2001 **AN** *020 †05

CAMPBELL, Micha Christoph. ■ 15232 #034-01-2007 L2007 **EM** *012

CAMPBELL, Neal Frederick. ■ 15217 #026-04-2003 L2006 **AN** *012 †55

CAMPBELL, Thomas Patrick. 4800 FRIENDSHIP AVE, EMERGENCY ADMIN 15224 #041-13-1983 L1984 **EM OM** *020 †16

CAMPBELL, Timothy Michael. 1400 LOCUST ST, STE 5109 15219 #055-01-1986 L1987 **IM** *020 †20

CAMPBELL, William Lowell. 200 LOTHROP ST, UNIV PITTSBURGH MC 15213 #035-20-1964 L1975 **DR** *020 †80

CAMPFIELD, Brian Thomas. ■ 15235 #041-12-2006 L2006 **PD** *012

CAMPOPIANO, Melinda Marie. 3811 OHARA ST, WESTERN PSYCHIATRIC INSTIT 15213 #041-12-1999 L2001 **FM** *020 †18

CAMPSEY, David Michael. 320 E NORTH AVE 15212 #041-14-1994 L1996 **CD IC** *020 †20

CANCILLA, Anthony. ■ 15220 #561-12-1957 L1965 **P AN** *020

CANDELARIA, Josefina M. 303 GRANT AVE 15209 #748-08-1966 L1970 **GYN** *020

CANDIDO, Cristina Santos. 3705 5TH AVE, OF PITTSBU 15213 #748-10-2000 L2006 **PDE** *012 †55

CANFIELD, Patricia Hogan. ■ 15217 #041-12-1989 L1991 **PM** *074 †60

CANKURTARAN, Ceylan Zeyne. 200 LOTHROP ST, UPMC-PUH 15213 #902-05-2002 L2006 **DR** *012

CANNON, Eliot Howard. 230 MCKEE PL, STE 500 15213 #036-05-2005 L2005 **EM** *012

CANO, Elmer Raul. 200 LOTHROP ST 15213 #737-03-1972 L1984 **RO** *020 †80

CANTEES, Kimberly Knight. 4727 FRIENDSHIP AVE, STE 240 15224 #041-07-1985 L1987 **AN PME** *020 †05 ‡

CAPDEVILLE, Anne Regina. 37 MCMURRAY RD 15241 #941-01-1972 L1979 **PYG P** *020 †75

CAPERELL, Kerry Scott. ■ 15218 #041-15-2005 L2005 **PD** *012

CAPITANO, Marc Alan. 100 S JACKSON AVE, FL 3 15202 #422-01-1999 L2001 **IM** *020 †20

CAPLAN, Paul Simon. 3500 5TH AVE, STE 401 15213 #041-12-1936 L1937 **IM RHU** *020 †20

CAPOBRES, Rudolfo M, Jr. 3550 TERRACE ST, A-1305 SCAIFE HALL 15261 #748-07-1963 L1973 **AN** *020 †05 ‡

CAPONE, R A, Jr. 5727 CENTRE AVE 15206 #010-02-1977 L1981 **PS HS** *020 †65

CAPUTO, Brian John. ■ 15238 #041-12-1989 L1991 **OPH** *020 †35

CARABELLO, Andrea M. 2740 SMALLMAN ST, STE 300 15222 #396-24-1992 L1997 **GPM GS** *020 †70

CARAIMAN, Myron. ■ 15206 #781-01-1940 L1965 **FM** *072

CARCILLO, Joseph A. 3705 5TH AVE 15213 #010-01-1982 L1992 **PD** *020 †55

CARDONA, Pedro J. 600 GRANT ST, US STEEL TOWER/FLOOR 41 15219 #042-01-1985 L2002 **IM** *030 †20

CARDONE, Anita Louise. 10700 FRANKSTOWN RD, STE 101 15235 #041-07-1985 L1986 **FM** *020 †18

CAREY, Kristen Anne. 1004 ARCH ST 15212 #041-15-2000 L2002 **EM** *020 †16

CARIC-SICENICA, Damira. 320 E NORTH AVE, ALLEGHENY GEN HOSP 15212 #957-01-1988 L2004 **CHP** *012

CARITIS, Steve N. 300 HALKET ST, RM 2229 15213 #055-01-1969 L1970 **MFM OS** *020 †30

CARLIN, Beatrice A. 1004 ARCH ST 15212 #041-12-1979 L1981 **DR** *020 †80

CARLIN, Brian Wintrode. 490 E NORTH AVE STE 300, PULMONARY ASSOCIATE 15212 #041-14-1981 L1982 **IM** *050 †20

CARLOS, Casey Anderson. ■ 15224 #041-12-2007 L2007 **TY** *012

CARLOS, Timothy Martin. 200 LOTHROP ST, HEMATOLOGY/SCAIFE HALL 15213 #010-02-1978 L1980 **IM HEM** *020 †20

CARLSON, Jestin. ■ 15261 #035-06-2007 L2007 **EM** *012

CARLTON, Chad Joseph. 320 E NORTH AVE, ALLEGHENY GENERAL HOSPITAL 15212 #048-02-2004 L2004 **GS** *012

CARNEGIE, Edward John. 4101 BROWNSVILLE RD 15227 #041-12-1957 L1958 **D OM** *071 †15

CARNEIRO FILHO, Benedito. ■ 15237 #187-10-2000 L2007 **IM** *100 †20

CARNIVALE, Scott Paul. 3028 BROWNSVILLE RD, BRENTWOOD MEDICAL GROUP 15227 #023-07-1986 L1993 **IM** *020 †20

CARPATHIOS, Michael Peter. 1039 BROOKLINE BLVD 15226 #038-44-1993 L1995 **IM** *020 †20

CARPENTER, Barbara Jo. ■ 15217 #025-07-1975 L1981 **NEP** *020 †20

CARPENTER, Linda Fay. ■ 15237 #047-06-1991 L1993 **EM** *020 †16

CARPENTER, Nancy Ann. ■ 15206 #041-12-1982 L1982 **GS** *074

CARR, Brian Irving. 200 LOTHROP ST, FALK CLINIC 15213 #917-29-1967 L1989 **GS** *071

CARR, Steven J. 320 E NORTH AVE 15212 #028-34-2004 L2004 **IM** *100 †20

CARRASCO, Mary Margaret. 1709 BLVD OF THE ALLIES, UPTOWN PEDIATRIC ASSOC 15219 #495-96-1972 L1977 **PD PHP** *030 †55

CARRAU, Ricardo Luis. 203 LOTHROP ST 15213 #042-01-1981 L1987 **OTO HNS** *020 †45

CARRELL, Robert Lee. 111 SHERIDAN ST 15209 #011-03-1975 L1976 **FM** *020 †18

CARREON, Myra Drew. ■ 15217 #011-04-2005 L2005 **IM** *012

CARROLL, Joan Barbara. 300 HALKET ST, DEPT. OF ANESTHESIOLOGY-MA 15213 #035-15-1979 L1983 **AN** *020 †05 ‡

CARROLL, Kathleen Anne. 300 HALKET ST 15213 #041-12-2004 L2004 **OBG** *012

CARROLL, Nancy Elizabeth. 4725 MCKNIGHT RD 15237 #041-07-1978 L1979 **IM** *020 †20

CARROLL, Robert John. 9100 BABCOCK BLVD 15237 #041-12-1947 L1948 **IM** *071

CARSON, Donald Grove. 1330 OLD FREEPORT RD, STE 1A 15238 #041-12-1977 L1978 **OBG** *020 †30

CARSON, Paul Allen. 1400 LOCUST ST 15219 #038-43-1993 L1995 **IM** *020 †20

CARTER, Howard Alfred. ■ 15213 #023-07-1970 L1979 **AN** *020 †05

CARTER, Russell H. 320 E NORTH AVE STE 248, ALLEGHENY GENERAL HOSPTIAL 15212 #422-01-2000 L2001 **APM PMM** *020 †60

CARTY, Sally Elizabeth. 3550 TERRACE ST, 497 SCAIFE HALL UNIV OF PI 15261 #041-14-1984 L1986 **GS** *020 †85

CARUPPANNAN, Ketheswaram. 320 E NORTH AVE, ALLEGHENY GEN HOSP 15212 #495-59-2000 L2004 **IM** *020

CARVELLI, Albert Joseph. 800 FAIRVIEW RD, PAIN MEDICINE 15238 #041-07-1998 L2001 **APM** *020 †05

CASAVILLA, Fernando A. ■ 15213 #132-01-1980 L1991 **GS** *020

CASERIO, Rebecca Joann. 815 FREEPORT RD 15215 #041-12-1975 L1977 **D** *020 †20,15 ‡

CASES-CRISTOBAL, Victoria. ■ 15213 #748-01-1975 **AN** *100

CASEY, Francis Leo, III. ■ 15224 #038-06-2007 L2007 **PD** *012

CASEY, Michael Patrick. 5820 CENTRE AVE, ASSOCIATES 15206 #041-12-1978 L1981 **ORS** *020 †40

CASLOW, Susan Amanda. ■ 15217 #041-13-2005 L2005 **EM** *012

CASSADY, Thomas Daniel. 1400 LOCUST ST, DEPARTMENT OF RADIOLOGY 15219 #038-40-2004 L2006 **DR** *012

CASSARA, Antonio. 4800 FRIENDSHIP AVE 15224 #561-12-1985 L2003 **PAN** *012

CASSELBRANT, Margaretha L. 3705 5TH AVE 15213 #858-01-1973 L1994 **OTO** *020 †45

CASSIDY, Elaine Ann. ■ 15208 #038-44-2004 L2007 **PPR** *012 †55

CASSIDY, James Jos. 400 45TH ST 15201 #041-12-1958 L1960 **GP** *071

CASTA, Alfonso. 3705 5TH AVE, DEPT OF ANESTHESIOLOGY 15213 #042-01-1975 L1978 **AN PD** *020 †55,05

CASTELLI, Dario Dante. 9104 BABCOCK BLVD, STE 1113 15237 #041-13-1969 L1976 **PS** *020

CASTILLA, Suzanne Lorrain. ■ 15219 #041-12-2003 L2003 **GS** *100

CASTILLO, Manuel M. 3101 BROWNSVILLE RD 15227 #847-04-1970 L1973 **GS** *020 †85

CASTILLO, William M. 1004 ARCH ST 15212 #847-04-1977 L1983 **GS** *020 ‡

CASTRO, Robert. ■ 15238 #042-02-1987 L2007 **PMM** *012 †05

CASTRO OTERO, Jorge Humbe. 3708 5TH AVE, DEPT OF MED EDU 15213 #264-02-1995 L2006 *100

CATULLO, Victor John. 300 HALKET ST, RADIOLOGY DEPT 15213 #023-12-1985 L1992 **GPM** *020 †80,70

CAUNA, Nikolajs. U PITT SCH MED ANAT CELL 15261 #594-01-1942 **OS** *071

CAUSHAJ, Philip. 4800 FRIENDSHIP AVE, 4600N 15224 #023-07-1979 L1996 **CRS GS** *020 †10,85

CAVANAUGH, Francis J, Jr. 4506 PENN AVE 15224 #041-09-1980 L1981 **IM EM** *020 †20

CAVANAUGH, Lillian O. 4506 PENN AVE 15224 #748-09-1977 L1981 **IM** *020

CELEBREZZE, James Patrick. 320 E NORTH AVE 15224 #038-44-1994 L2000 **CRS** *020 †85,10

CELEBREZZE, Jennifer U. 320 E NORTH AVE, ALLEGHENY GENERAL HOSPTITA 15212 #038-44-1992 L2000 **OBG** *020 †30

CELECHOVSKY, Chris. ■ 15214 #041-12-2004 L2004 **AN** *012

CELINSKI, Scott Alan. 5150 CENTRE AVE, RM 414 15232 #048-04-2002 L2008 **GS** *012

CELKO, David Al. 1050 BOWER HILL RD, STE 306 15243 #041-09-1975 L1976 **PUD IM** *020 †20

CERNY, Bryan George. ■ 15214 #041-13-2006 L2006 **P** *012

CERRI, Hugo Jose Maria. 1501 LOCUST ST STE 1010 15219 #024-05-1978 L1985 **OPH** *020 †35

CERTO, Louis Michael. 1384 OLD FREEPORT RD, STE 1A 15238 #561-17-1982 L1984 **GS** *020 †85

CERUL, Maurice Saml. 401 SHADY AVE STE B104 15206 #041-12-1964 L1965 **P ADP** *020 †75

CHABLANI, Vinod Nanik. 1400 LOCUST ST, THE MERCY HOSPITAL OF PGH 15219 #496-38-1980 L1987 **VIR DR** *020 †80

CHAE, Soo Jung. ■ 15213 #583-08-1968 L1973 **DIA IM** *020 †20

CHAER, Rabih. 5200 CENTRE AVE, STE 211 15232 #605-01-1998 L2006 **VS** *020 †85

CHAFIN, Sherri H. 1000 BOWER HILL RD 15243 #041-14-1995 L1997 **DR** *020 †80

CHAI, Raymond Liu. ■ 15232 #041-12-2008 *012

CHAKRAVARTHY, Mithun. 4800 FRIENDSHIP AVE 15224 #495-65-1999 L2004 **CD** *012 †20

CHAKRAVORTY, Sangeeta S. 3705 5TH AVE 15213 #495-17-1987 L2000 **N** *020 †75

CHAKRAVORTY, Sudeep S. 3811 OHARA ST, WPIC 15213 #495-17-1982 L2000 **P** *020 †75

CHALASANI, Geetha. ■ 15238 #495-72-1996 L2006 **NEP** *100 †20

CHALLINOR, Samuel B, Jr. 1000 BOWER HILL RD 15243 #041-12-1952 L1953 **FM** *071

CHALLINOR, Sue Marion. 3601 5TH AVE, FALK RM 580 15213 #041-12-1981 L1982 **END IM** *020 †20

CHALUVADI, Siresha. 320 E NORTH AVE 15212 #305-01-2006 L2007 **IM** *012

CHAMOVITZ, Robert. 160 N CRAIG ST, STE 117 15213 #023-01-1948 L1950 **GE** *071 †20

CHAMPAGNE, Emily G M. 400 45TH ST 15201 #024-05-1962 L1968 **P** *020

CHAN, Asteria Caces. ■ 15221 #748-07-1954 L1968 **PD OS** *071

CHAN, Chun Wai. 5230 CENTRE AVE 15232 #060-02-2004 L2004 **FM** *020 †18

CHAN, Lisa Yilee. ■ 15224 #023-01-2006 L2006 **AN** *012

CHAN, Yvonne Ruohlei. 3459 5TH AVE NW628, DEPT PULMONARY/ALLERGY/ CC 15213 #024-01-2001 L2004 **PCC** *100

CHANCELLOR, Michael B. 200 LOTHROP ST, SURGERY UROLOGY 15213 #056-06-1983 L1990 **GS U** *020 †95

CHANDHOK, Sheetal. 200 LOTHROP ST, SCAIFE HALL S559 15213 #041-07-1998 L2000 **ICE** *100 †20

CHANDRA, Ram Iyer. 2840 LIBERTY AVE, STE 201 15222 #495-66-1971 **PG** *020 †55

CHANDRA, Ramesh Chandra. 21 YOST BLVD STE 216 15221 #495-15-1962 **CD IM** *020

CHANDRASENA, Amanthi Lour. 4800 FRIENDSHIP AVE, DEPT FM 15224 #759-06-2004 L2005 **FP** *012

CHANG, Alexander C. 2101 GREENTREE RD # 105 15220 #038-06-1976 L1977 **OPH** *020 †35

CHANG, Diane Tsingwen. ■ 15206 #041-12-2008 *012

CHANG, Edward Jinki. 1835 FORBES ST 15219 #036-05-1991 L1994 **OPH** *020 †35

CHANG, Judy Chiachi. 300 HALKET ST, DEPT OESTE GYNECOLOGY 15213 #048-04-1995 L2001 **OBG** *020 †30

CHANG, Thomas S. 5500 CORPORATE DR, STE 100 15237 #028-02-1985 L1986 **DR R** *020 †80

CHANG, Yuan. 5117 CENTRE AVE STE 1.8, HILLMAN CANCER CENTER RSH 15213 #049-01-1987 L2002 **PTH** *020 †85

CHANNAMALAPPA, Umapathy. 3811 OHARA ST, DIV OF GERIATRICS/NEUROPSY 15213 #495-98-1988 L1998 **PYG P** *020 †75

CHANNARASAPPA, Anupama S. 2585 FREEPORT RD, STE 201 15238 #495-37-1984 L1995 **IM** *020 †20

CHANTZ, Daniel James. 815 FREEPORT RD 15215 #041-12-1986 L1987 **FM** *020 †18

CHAPMAN, Meredith Rene. 3811 OHARA ST 15213 #020-02-2003 L2003 **CPP** *012

CHARLEY, John Andrew. 1340 OLD FREEPORT RD # 1A 15238 #041-12-1983 L1984 **OPH** *035

CHARLEY, Michael Robt. ■ 15238 #041-13-1976 L1987 **D IM** *071 †20,15

CHARLSON, Dori Ann. 5130 WESTMINSTER PL, APT 2 15232 #035-46-1994 L1997 **EM** *020 †20,16

CHARLSON, Murray Thos. 401 SHADY AVE 15206 #041-12-1961 L1962 **P PYA** *020 †75

CHARRON, Martin. 3705 5TH AVE 15213 #067-06-1983 L1990 **R PD** *020 †28

CHARUKAMNOETKANOK, Puwat. 203 LOTHROP ST 15213 #035-45-1998 L2004 **OPH** *020 †35

CHASLER, Charles Nicholas. ■ 15213 #041-12-1941 L1942 **DR** *075

CHATER, Kamal. 3550 TERRACE ST, UPMC, DEPARTMENT OF CCM 15261 #655-01-1999 L2002 **CCM** *012

CHATHA, Aiysha Iftikhar. 1400 LOCUST ST, MERCY HOSP-PITTSBURGH 15219 #704-24-1999 L2002 **IM** *020 †20

CHATTA, Gurkamal Singh. 5150 CENTRE AVE RM 564, UPMC CANCER PAVILION 15232 #496-09-1997 L2001 **HEM IM** *020 †20

CHAUDHARI, Sunita N. 6343 PENN AVE, # 201 15206 #041-14-1989 L1991 **PD** *020 †55

CHAUDHRY, Preet M. 5117 CENTRE AVE STE 1-19A, HILLMAN CANCER CENTER 15213 #495-45-1988 L2004 **ON HEM** *050 †20

CHAUDHRY, Asif. 200 DELAFIELD RD, PAIN MEDICIN 15215 #045-04-2003 L2007 **PMM** *012

CHAUDHRY, Haider Saleem. 1500 5TH AVE 15219 #704-05-1998 L2001 **N** *012 †20

CHAUDRY, Abdul Sattar. 425 6TH AVE STE 250 15219 #704-04-1965 L1987 **DR** *020 †80

CHAUHAN, Chirag Ambaram. ■ 15213 #041-12-2008 *012

CHAVES GNECCO, Diego Gabr. 3708 5TH AVE, STE 503 15213 #264-04-1994 L2002 **PD** *100

CHAWLA, Shivani. ■ 15212 #422-01-2005 L2007 **OBG** *012

CHEEMA, Ayesha Faisal. 121 MEYRAN AVE 15213 #704-21-2002 L2006 **IM** *012

CHEISTWER, Marta Esther Z. ■ 15217 #132-01-1965 **GP OS** *020

CHELEN, William Eugene. ■ 15236 #041-13-1979 L1997 **OM** *071 †70

CHELLURI, Lakshmipathi. 200 LOTHROP ST, PRESBYTERIAN HOSP 15213 #495-11-1976 L1980 **OS IM** *050 †20

CHELLY, Jacques Elie. A-1305 SCAIFE HALL, 3550 TERRACE ST 15261 #396-12-1976 L2001 **AN ORS** *020

CHEMAITILLY, Wassim. ■ 15208 #396-02-1999 L2007 **PD** *012

CHEN, Alan Hsaiofeng. 3550 TERRACE ST, 683 SCAIFFE HALL 15261 #035-46-1997 L2000 **HS** *012

CHEN, Alexander Sou. 9100 BABCOCK BLVD 15237 #041-02-1999 L2002 **IM** *020 †20

CHEN, Beatrice Allis. 300 HALKET ST, MAGEE-WOMENS HOSPITAL RM 2 15213 #025-01-2002 L2002 **OBG** *100

CHEN, Clifford. 2020 ARDMORE BLVD, STE 300 15221 #056-06-1993 L1995 **FM** *020 †18 ‡

CHEN, Douglas Austin. 3500 5TH AVE, STE 404 15213 #038-40-1980 L1981 **OTO NO** *020 †45

CHEN, Joy Shanfong. ■ 15212 #041-02-2006 L2006 **IM** *012

CHEN, Liu Lin Lu. 8035 MCKNIGHT RD, STE 304 15237 #187-31-1979 L1993 **P** *020 †75

CHEN, Ming Lam. ■ 15232 #041-12-2005 L2005 **U** *012

CHEN, Robert Fu-Chean. 532 S AIKEN AVE, STE 501 SURGEONS PC 15232 #244-04-1972 L1981 **TS GS** *020 †85,90

CHEN, Shu-Jei. 9100 BABCOCK BLVD, PASSAVANT HOSP RAD ONC 15237 #187-67-1976 L1990 **RO** *020 †80

CHEN, William X. 320 E NORTH AVE 15212 #243-21-1983 L1994 **AN** *020 †05

CHENG, Chun-Pin. 599 THORNCLIFFE DR 15205 #244-04-1972 L1980 **AN** *020 †05

CHENGAPPA, Kadiamada N. 3811 OHARA ST, WESTERN PSYCH INST UPMC 15213 #495-37-1982 L1989 **P PYG** *020 †75

CHENGAPPA, Nirmala. 7180 HIGHLAND DR 15206 #495-98-1974 L1982 **FM** *020 †20

CHENGAPPA, Palecanda P. 2100 JANE ST, STE 801 15203 #495-33-1973 L1982 **CD IM** *020 †20

CHEONG, Alice Puiiok. ■ 15207 #023-01-2007 L2007 **IM** *012

CHERMANSKY, Christopher J. 3471 5TH AVE, KAUFMANN BUILDING - SUITE 15213 #010-02-1990 L2003 **U** *020 †95

CHERNEW, Irwin Marcus. 1000 BOWER HILL RD 15243 #041-12-1961 L1962 **PTH** *020 †50

CHERNUS, Steven Andrew. 1000 BOWER HILL RD 15243 #033-06-1977 L1978 **AN LM** *020 †05

CHERPES, Gregory Louis. 1405 SHADY AVE, THE CHILDREN'S INSTITUTE 15217 #056-06-1991 L1994 **CHP** *020 †75 ‡

CHERPES, Tom Louis. ■ 15237 #036-05-1998 L2001 **ID** *100 †20

CHERUP, E David. ■ 15241 #041-12-1951 L1952 **GP** *071

CHESIN, Carole Kennedy. 300 HALKET ST, STE 1338 15213 #041-01-1978 L1979 **OBG** *020 †30

CHESS, Bart Alan. 320 E NORTH AVE, CARDIOVASCULAR SURGERY CEN 15212 #038-40-1996 L2006 **GS** *020 †85

CHETLIN, Sherwood Michael. 3500 5TH AVE 15213 #041-12-1972 L1973 **RHU IM** *020 †20

CHEUNG, Anson Wai-Chung. 200 LOTHROP ST, UPP-DEPT OF SURGERY-PH C70 15213 #062-01-1992 L1999 *100

CHEUNG, Ka Wai. 3708 5TH AVE, DEPT OF MED EDUCATION 15213 #061-01-2003 L2006 *100

CHEUNG, Sunny Chifung. ■ 15261 #041-12-2004 L2005 **ORS** *012

CHHABRA, Mohan Lal. 9104 BABCOCK BLVD, DOCTORS OFFICE BLDG 15237 #495-20-1963 L1973 **CD IM** *020 †20

CHHAPARWAL, Dhiraj Bharat. 1400 LOCUST ST 15219 #495-20-1990 L2003 **PD** *100

CHI, David Hyunjoon. 3705 5TH AVE 15213 #025-01-1997 L2002 **PDO** *020

CHIA, Stephanie M. 1400 LOCUST ST, OF PITTSBURGH 15219 #024-07-2006 L2006 **AN** *012

CHIA, Yvonne Hungyuan. 5700 CORPORATE DR, STE 700 15237 #041-15-2000 L2001 **FM** *020 †18

CHIANESE, Jennifer Marie. 3705 5TH AVE, GAP 15213 #035-19-1999 L2003 **PD** *020 †55

CHIAO, Wenting Jeffrey. ■ 15213 #041-12-2008 *012

CHIBISOV, Irina Pushkar. 3636 BLVD OF THE ALLIES 15213 #913-57-1994 L2001 **IM** *020 †20,50

CHILAKAPATI, Padmaja. 320 E NORTH AVE, ALLEGHENY GEN HOSP 15212 #495-09-1999 L2004 **CHP** *012

CHILDRESS-HAZEN, Laura Z. 1400 LOCUST ST 15219 #020-02-1990 L1998 **P** *020

CHIMONIDES, Andreas N. 2 ALLEGHENY CTR, STE 530 15212 #035-03-1992 L1999 **PS** *020

CHIOSEA, Simion Ion. RM 707 SCAIFE HALL, UNIV OF PITTSBURGH DEPT OF 15261 #913-50-2000 L2004 **SP** *012 †50

CHIOSSI, Giuseppe. 320 E NORTH AVE, DEPT OF OB-GYN 15212 #561-09-2001 L2003 **OBG** *012

CHIRINOS, Rodolfo Eduardo. ■ 15206 #042-03-2003 L2006 **D** *050

CHISHOLM, Janice Darlene. 3708 5TH AVE, UNIVERSITY HEALTH CENTER 15213 #064-01-2000 L2006 **CCA** *100

CHISHTI, Aftab S. 1709 BLVD OF THE ALLIES, UPTOWN PEDIATRIC ASSOCIATE 15219 #704-25-1990 L1997 **PN** *100 †55

CHISM, Larissa Marie. ■ 15206 #041-13-2002 L2003 **PFP** *012

CHIU, Lolita E. 5750 CENTRE AVE, STE 510 15206 #748-10-1990 L2002 **ID** *020 †20

CHLUDZINSKI, Ronald W. 400 PENN CENTER BLVD, STE 100 15235 #041-13-1967 L1968 **PD** *020 †55

CHO, Jae-Sung. 5200 CENTRE AVE, STE 211 15232 #005-15-1990 L2001 **VS** *020 †85

CHO, Patrick. 320 E NORTH AVE 15212 #041-13-2000 L2001 **PTH** *100

CHO, Raymond Young-Jin. 3811 OHARA ST, WESTERN PSYCH INST & CLNS 15213 #065-01-1993 L2007 **P** *020 †75

CHO, Su Min. 121 MEYRAN AVE 15213 #917-34-2000 L2005 **IM** *012

CHO, Sung Won. 121 MEYRAN AVE 15213 #917-34-2002 L2005 **GS** *100

CHOCKALINGAM, Usharani. 1060 FOX CHAPEL RD, 1060 FOX CHAPEL ROAD 15238 #495-04-1977 L1988 **IM** *020 †20

CHOI, Lisa Eunju. 121 MEYRAN AVE, DEPT OF OTHRO SUR STE 1010 15213 #024-05-2006 L2006 **ORS** *012

CHOI, Sylvia Seungyun. 3705 5TH AVE 15213 #024-05-1994 L1996 **PD** *020 †55

CHOKSI, Rushir. ■ 15209 #036-05-2006 L2006 **IM** *012

CHOLAPRANEE, Rewat. 135 CUMBERLAND RD STE 204 15237 #891-04-1974 L1979 **CD IM** *020 †20

CHONG, Tae Woon. ■ 15228 #051-01-2000 L2007 **GS** *100

CHOO, Phillip Hyunchul. 3471 5TH AVE STE 1115 15213 #035-01-1992 L1994 **OPH** *020 †35

CHOPRA, Kapil Brijmohan. 5200 CENTRE AVE, STE 211 15232 #495-01-1988 L1999 **GE HEP** *020 †20

CHOPRA, Liza Puja. 2349 RAILROAD ST, # 2224 15222 #035-06-2002 L2007 **EM** *100

CHOPRA, Monica I. 815 FREEPORT RD 15215 #038-45-2003 L2003 **FM** *020 †18

CHOU, Franklin Hsiencher. 121 MEYRAN AVE, DEP OF ORTHOPAEDIC SURGERY 15213 #035-01-2005 L2005 **ORS** *012

CHOUGH, Denise Kushner. 300 HALKET ST, DEPARTMENT OF RADIOLOGY 15213 #041-12-1989 L1992 **DR** *020 †80

CHOWDAWARAPU, Sharath Cha. 300 HALKET ST, MAGEE WOMENS HOSP 15213 #496-35-2001 L2007 **NPM** *012

CHOWDHURY, Salim. 1 CHATHAM CTR, STE 700 15219 #160-02-1983 L1996 **P** *020 †75

CHRISTIANSEN, Gregory B. 180 FORT COUCH RD 15241 #041-02-1993 L1998 **ORS** *020 †40

CHRISTIE, Neil Alexander. 5200 CENTRE AVE, STE 211 15232 #065-01-1987 L1998 **GS** *020 †85,90

CHRISTLIEB, Ignacio Y. ■ 15215 #649-01-1952 **TS** *071

CHRISTOFORETTI, John J. 300 CHAPEL HARBOR DR, STE 300 15238 #010-02-2001 L2007 **ORS** *020

CHRISTOFORETTI, Russell J. 3550 TERRACE ST, A-1305 SCAIFE HALL 15261 #041-12-1975 L1976 **AN** *071 †05

CHRISTOPHERSEN, E Bull. ■ 15206 #045-01-1955 L1966 **GS AM** *050

CHRISTOPHERSON, Wayne A. 1400 LOCUST ST, STE 3121 15219 #018-03-1978 L1985 **OBG GO** *020 †30

CHRISTOPOULOS, Alexandros. 4800 FRIENDSHIP AVE 15224 #418-05-1999 L2003 **GS** *100

CHRISTOPOULOS, Vasiliki A. 203 LOTHROP ST 15213 #038-43-1992 L2005 **OPH** *020 †35

CHRISTOU, Antonios. 320 E NORTH AVE 5TH FL, CANCER CENTER 15212 #418-01-1986 L2007 **HO IM** *020 †20 ‡

CHRISTY, Carla Jo. 320 E NORTH AVE, ALLEGHENY GENERAL HOSPITAL 15212 #041-12-2002 L2002 **GS** *100

CHRONISTER, Drew Raymond. ■ 15208 #041-12-2005 L2005 **IM** *100

CHRYSOCHOOU, Georgios. ■ 15220 #473-04-2000 L2005 **PCC** *012 †20

CHRYSOSTOMOU, Constantino. 3705 5TH AVE 15213 #473-04-1996 L2003 **PDC** *020 †55

CHU, Alan Weikai. 2000 MARY ST 15203 #038-40-1993 L2000 **IM PM** *020 †20,60

CHU, Charleen Tanching. 200 LOTHROP ST, UPPPTHLGY - BMDCL SCNCE TW 15213 #036-07-1994 L1998 **NP ATP** *020 †50

CHU, Constance Rentien. 3471 5TH AVE, STE 911 15213 #024-01-1992 L1999 **ORS** *020 †40

CHU, Gorden. 3705 5TH AVE, RADIOLOGY/RM 3950 15213 #041-01-1997 L2001 **VIR** *020 †80

CHUENSUMRAN, Ongart. 9102 BABCOCK BLVD, STE 101 15237 #891-02-1970 L1974 **PUD IM** *020 ‡

CHUENSUMRAN, Rajani S. 9100 BABCOCK BLVD 15237 #891-02-1969 L1974 **AN PME** *020 †05

CHUGHTAI, Arshad Iqbal. 4815 LIBERTY AVE STE 154, MELLON PAVILION 15224 #704-01-1967 L1973 **IM IMG** *020 †18,20

CHUIRAZZI, David Michael. 320 E NORTH AVE 15212 #038-44-1990 L1992 **EM** *020 †16

CHUN, Benjamin Byung. 3471 5TH AVE STE 102, CATARACT & LASER INSTITUTE 15213 #043-01-1993 L2006 **OPH EM** *020 †35

CHUN, Yuri. ■ 15222 #041-07-2007 L2007 **ORS** *012

CHUNG, Marion Ruth. 4800 FRIENDSHIP AVE 15224 #036-05-1982 L1988 **AN** *020

CICCARELLI, Harold Edward. ■ 15241 #041-12-1954 L1955 **AN** *020 †05

CICCO, Robert Carmel. 4800 FRIENDSHIP AVE 3WT, PEDIATRIC & NEONATAL ASSOC 15224 #038-06-1976 L1977 **NPM PD** *020 †55

CICHON, Philip Jerome. 4301 BUTLER ST 15201 #561-01-1977 L1980 **IM IMG** *020 †20

CID, Monica. 4424 PENN AVE, STE 103 15224 #056-06-1993 L1999 **OPH** *020 †35

CIESIELKA, Kenneth. 5173 LIBERTY AVE 15224 #041-01-1980 L1982 **FM PG** *020 †18

CIGANIC, Ratimir. S JACKSON AVE 15202 #957-01-1964 L1976 **DR** *020 †80

CIMBALUK, David John. ■ 15222 #016-43-2003 L2007 **PTH** *100 †50

CINEMRE, Hakan. ■ 15201 #902-07-1992 L2001 **IM** *100 †20

CIPRIANI, Alphonse Joseph. 20 CEDAR BLVD, STE 410 15228 #010-02-1962 L1963 **GP** *020

CITRONE, Peter John. 4815 LIBERTY AVE 15224 #028-34-1957 L1959 **GS** *071 †85

CIVITARESE, Louis Robt. 15220 #041-02-1948 L1949 **GS OS** *020

CLADIS, Franklyn Paul. ■ 15232 #035-45-1995 L2003 **AN PAN** *020 †20,05

CLAIR, Pamela J. 9000 PERRY HWY STE 120, ARCADIA DIVISION 15237 #016-01-1982 L1987 **PD** *020 †55

CLANCY, Cornelius Jos. ■ 15203 #028-02-1991 L2003 **ID** *020 †20

CLARK, Barbara A. 320 E NORTH AVE, ALLEGHENY GENERAL HOSPITAL 15212 #055-01-1982 L1996 **NEP IM** *020 †20

CLARK, Brent. 9816 FRANKSTOWN RD 15235 #010-03-1988 L1990 **FM** *020 †18

CLARK, Duncan Barnes. 3811 OHARA ST, WESTERN PSYCHIATRIC INST 15213 #024-01-1985 L1989 **P** *050 †75

CLARK, Kenneth Howard. OF PAT, UNIV OF PITTSBURGH DEPT 15261 #041-12-2003 L2003 **PTH** *012

CLARK, Lisa. ■ 15211 #035-09-2002 L2002 **EM** *100 †16

CLARK, Melissa Piron. 3459 5TH AVE, UPMC MONTEFIORE NW 628 15213 #001-06-1986 L2002 **PCC** *020 †20

CLARK, Richard E. 320 E NORTH AVE 15212 #035-20-1960 L1990 **TS OS** *071 †85,90

CLARK, Robert Scottbeppu. 3705 5TH AVE 15213 #056-06-1989 L1992 **CCP** *020 †55

CLARKE, Martha Randolph. 5727 CENTRE AVE, PATH STAR 15206 #010-02-1977 L1981 **PTH OAR** *020 †50

CLARKE, Robert Henderson. 4815 LIBERTY AVE, MELLON PAVILION 15224 #041-12-1947 L1948 AN *071 †05

CLARY, Candace Alanna. 300 HALKET ST, STE 4750 15213 #027-01-2002 L2006 **OBG** *020

CLAVELL, Maria Ines. 3705 5TH AVE 15213 #042-01-1992 L2000 **PG** *020 †55

CLAVIJO ALVAREZ, Julio Al. 121 MEYRAN AVE 15213 #264-19-1995 L2005 **PS** *012

CLEARFIELD, Ronald Jay. 308 OXBRIDGE CT 15238 #041-09-1958 L1959 **R** *071 †80

CLEMENS, Paula Ruth. 200 LOTHROP ST 15213 #041-07-1984 L1995 **N** *050 †75

CLERMONT, Gilles. 3550 TERRACE SCAIFE 606B, UNIV OF PITTSBURGH MEDICAL 15261 #067-01-1983 L1994 **CCM IM** *050 †20

CLEVENGER, Robert Wm. ■ 15211 #010-01-1960 L1963 **OTO** *071 †45

CLOUGH, Douglas Frank. 9104 BABCOCK BLVD STE 1113 15237 #038-40-1974 L1975 **IM IMG** *020 †20

CLUTE, Stephen Paynehill. 5200 CENTRE AVE, STE 610 15232 #041-02-1997 L2000 **PCC** *020 †20

COAX, Warren Alan. 0 UNIVERSITY DRIVE C, GEN MED/933 W MONTEFIORE 15240 #041-12-1970 L1972 **IM** *020 †20

COBB, Charles Franklin. 420 E NORTH AVE, STE 304 15212 #016-02-1974 L1975 **GS** *020 †85 ‡

COBLENTZ, Robert H. 4800 FRIENDSHIP AVE # 002, WPH 15224 #041-02-1979 L1980 **CD IM** *020 †20

COELLO, Michael Christian. 200 LOTHROP ST, RM F675PUH 15213 #025-01-1999 L2001 **TS** *012 †85

COFFMAN, Keith Alain. 3705 5TH AVE, RM 2935 15213 #041-14-2001 L2001 **PD** *100 †55

COGNETTI, David Michael. 203 LOTHROP ST, SUITE 500, EYE & EAR BUILD 15213 #041-12-2002 L2002 **OTO** *020

COGNETTI, Melissa Reimel. 200 LOTHROP ST, STE 933W 15213 #041-12-2002 L2002 **IM** *020 †20

COHEN, Claire Ma Chere. 373 BURROWS ST, MATILDA THEISS CTR 15213 #041-09-1980 L1984 **CHP** *020 †75

COHEN, David Benjamin. 420 E NORTH AVE STE 302 15212 #035-03-2000 L2001 **NS** *020

COHEN, Debra Ellenberger. 3705 5TH AVE 15213 #041-12-1997 L2001 **PHO** *020 †55

COHEN, Jeffrey Stewart. 200 DELAFIELD RD 15215 #041-01-1994 L1996 **CD** *020 †20

COHEN, Judith. 4 ALLEGHENY CTR, RM 864 15212 #041-12-1978 L1979 **CHP P** *020 †75 ‡

COHEN, Martin. 1401 FORBES AVE 15219 #005-17-1962 L1965 **PTH CLP** *030 †50

COHEN, Norman Lee. 4411 STILLEY RD 15227 #041-13-1984 L1990 **PD ADM** *050 †55

COHEN, Peter Zelig. 106 UNIVERSITY DRIVE C, 112-OU 15240 #041-12-1963 L1964 **ORS** *071 †40

COHEN, Richard Lawrence. 3811 OHARA ST 15213 #041-01-1947 L1948 **CHP** *071 †75

COHEN, William Ira. 3705 5TH AVE, ONE CHILDRENS PL 15213 #035-06-1975 L1976 **PD CHP** *020 †55

COHLAN, Barbara A. 300 HALKET ST, DEPT OF PEDIATRICS 15213 #035-19-1978 L1980 **PD** *020 †55

COLAIACO, Paul Arthur. 1200 REEDSDALE ST 15233 #041-12-1982 L1984 **P** *020 †75

COLAIZZI, Ivan Vladimir. 300 HALKET ST 15213 #041-12-2004 L2004 **AN** *012

COLATRELLA, Anthony M. 1350 LOCUST ST, STE 406 15219 #041-02-1973 L1974 **GE IM** *020 †20

COLBURN, Marion Joyce. 320 E NORTH AVE, ALLEGHENY GENERAL HOSPITAL 15212 #051-04-2004 L2004 **EM** *012

COLE, Charles Edward. 4721 MCKNIGHT RD 15237 #041-02-1956 L1957 **FM** *071 †18

COLE, Christopher Daniel. 230 MCKEE PL, STE 500 15213 #041-12-2004 L2004 **EM** *020

COLE, John Stephen. 200 LOTHROP ST 15213 #041-01-1993 L1996 **EM** *020 †16

COLEMAN, Craig Steven. 3811 OHARA ST 15213 #041-14-1983 L1984 **CHP** *020

COLEMAN, Donald Jos. ■ 15235 #028-34-1955 L1962 **P PYA** *071 †75

COLEMAN, Samuel R. 200 LOTHROP ST, SCAIFE HALL B 571.3 15213 #010-01-2001 L2001 **CD** *012

COLEMAN CRADDOCK, Shallon. ■ 15219 #007-02-2006 L2006 **PD** *012

COLLIGAN, Robert J. ■ 15243 #041-12-1978 L1979 **DR** *020 †80

COLLINSON, Karen E. ■ 15227 #033-05-2002 L2006 **GE** *012 †20

COLLURA, Jacquelyn Marie. ■ 15224 #010-01-2008 L2008 *012

COLODNY, Stephen Michael. 101 DRAKE RD, STE C 15241 #035-09-1981 L1986 **ID IM** *020 †20

COLONIAS, Athanasios. 320 E NORTH AVE, ALLEGHANY GEN HOSP-RAD/ONC 15212 #038-44-1996 L1999 **RO** *020 †80 ‡

COLUCCI, Maria Josefa. ■ 15201 #275-01-1949 L1957 **P GP** *071

COMERCI, John Thos. 300 HALKET ST, MAGEE-WOMENS HOSPITAL 15213 #041-13-1955 L1956 **OBG** *020 †30

COMERCI, Susan Carol. 3705 5TH AVE, PITTSBURGH 15213 #041-13-1989 L1999 **PDR** *020 †80

COMPARE, Ezio Giulio. 1400 LOCUST ST DEPT PTH 15219 #561-11-1960 L1970 **PTH** *071 †50,28

CONCILIUS, Frank. 1050 BOWER HILL RD STE 308 15243 #023-01-1942 L1943 **CD IM** *071 †20

CONCILUS, Robert Ronald. ■ 15217 #041-07-1980 L1982 **AN** *020 †05

CONDAX, George. 1151 FREEPORT RD, STE 351 15238 #550-02-1999 L2006 **OPH** *020

CONDON, Garry Pascal. 420 E NORTH AVE, STE 116 15213 #063-01-1981 L1987 **OPH** *020 †35

CONFINO, Jason L. 200 DELAFIELD RD 15215 #035-15-2001 L2001 **CD** *100

CONGEDO, Carol H Zinn. ■ 15235 #041-12-1976 L1977 **OTO A** *071 †45

CONLON, Thomas William. ■ 15217 #041-12-2006 L2006 **MPD** *012

CONNOLLY, David Paul. 200 LOTHROP ST 15213 #016-43-1961 L1964 **GS OS** *071 †85

CONNOLLY, Geoffrey Thomas. 2 HOT METAL ST 2ND FL, QUANTUM ONE 15203 #041-01-1996 L1999 **EM** *020 †16

CONNORS, Megan. ■ 15261 #041-12-2007 **EM** *012

CONRAD, Shawn Michael. 320 E NORTH AVE 15212 #041-13-2003 L2003 **EM** *100 †16

CONROY, Margaret Baldwin. 230 MCKEE PL, STE 600 15213 #041-01-1999 L2004 **IM** *020 †20

CONRY, Curt Patrick. 1501 LOCUST ST 15219 #036-06-1998 L2001 **NS** *020 †25

CONSTANTINO, Abraham, Jr. 405 ROSS AVE 15221 #748-08-1965 L1972 **PM GS** *020

CONSTANTINO, Angelo. 4815 LIBERTY AVE, STE 122/MELLON PAV 15224 #035-06-1986 L1988 **IM PHP** *020 †20,20

CONTI, Christopher Tracy. 3433 WILLIAM PENN HWY, MED EXPRESS URGENT CARE CE 15235 #023-01-1997 L2001 **EM** *020

CONTI, Stephen Francis. 1307 FEDERAL ST, STE 2 15212 #033-05-1986 L1992 **ORS OFA** *020 †40

CONTIS-GEORGIADES, Lydia. 200 LOTHROP ST 15213 #418-01-1980 L1981 **HEM PTH** *020 †50

CONTRACTOR, Farhad M. 320 E NORTH AVE, ALLEGHENY RADIOLOGY 15212 #495-23-1968 L1973 **DR** *020 †80 ‡

CONTRACTOR, Laila F M. 3811 OHARA ST 15213 #041-15-2004 L2004 **CHP** *012

COOK, David Ryan. 3705 5TH AVE, ANESTHESIOLOGY/ONE CHILDRE 15213 #041-12-1966 L1967 **AN** *020 †05

COOK, Erin Foster. 121 MEYRAN AVE, DEPT OF OB/GYN 15213 #001-02-2006 L2006 **OBG** *012

COOK, Jeffrey Tona. ■ 15212 #012-05-2008 **EM** *012

COOK, Jennifer. ■ 15241 #055-02-1993 L2007 **FM** *020 †18 ‡

COOK, Lori A. 1400 LOCUST ST, MERCY HOSPITAL OF PITTSBUR 15219 #017-20-1989 L1992 **NPM PD** *040 †55

COOK, Peter Christopher. 3471 5TH AVE 15213 #063-01-1986 L1994 **OP ORS** *012

COOK, Richard Allen. 2101 GREENTREE RD, STE B101 15220 #041-02-1981 L1982 **FM** *020 †18

COOKSEY, Stephen Harper. 5140 LIBERTY AVE 15224 #055-01-1979 L1986 **NEP CCM** *030 †20

COONEY, Robert Raymond. 320 E NORTH AVE, ALLEGHENY GENERAL HOSPITAL 15212 #041-02-2005 L2005 **EM** *012

COOPER, Amanda. 5200 CENTRE AVE, STE 211 15232 #016-11-2000 L2003 **IM** *020

COOPER, David Kempton C. ■ 15211 #917-23-1963 L1986 *020

COOPER, Gregory Floyd. 200 LOTHROP ST, FORBES TOWER/STE 8084 15213 #005-11-1986 *020

COOPER, James David. ■ 15206 #008-02-2003 L2006 **PHO** *012 †55

COOPER, Jeanne Audrey. ■ 15238 #041-09-1947 L1948 **PTH** *071 †50

COOPER, Kristen Marie. ■ 15218 #041-02-2005 L2005 **PD** *012

COOPER, Scott Thomas. ■ 15238 #041-01-2001 L2001 **GE** *012 †20

COPE, Doris Kathleen. 200 DELAFIELD RD 15215 #012-01-1982 L1997 **AN PMM** *020 †05

COPELAND, Charles Edward. 1400 LOCUST ST 15219 #041-12-1958 L1959 **GS** *040 †85

COPLEY-WOODS, Noedahn. 300 HALKET ST 15213 #041-13-2001 L2007 **OBG** *100 †30

COPPA, Christopher P. ■ 15222 #035-15-2002 L2007 **DR** *100 †80

COPPOLA, Carmela. 1400 LOCUST ST 15219 #422-01-1984 L1988 **NPM PD** *020 †55

COPPOLA, Matthew J, III. 2010 KINVARA DR 15237 #422-01-1984 L1991 **IM IMG** *020

COPPULA, William Fiore. 9000 PERRY HWY, STE 120 15237 #055-01-1980 L1981 **PD** *020 †55 ‡

CORCORAN, Anthony Thomas. ■ 15203 #035-00-2005 L2005 **U** *012

CORCOS, Alan Chas. 1400 LOCUST ST 15219 #040-02-1991 L1999 **TRS CCS** *020 †85

COREY, Stephen Hamilton. 300 HALKET ST, STE 1338 15213 #048-04-1973 L1974 **OBG** *020 †30

CORMACK, Graham Michael. ■ 15217 #422-01-2004 L2007 **CCM** *012 †20

CORNELIUS, Jack Randall. 3811 OHARA ST 15213 #016-02-1981 L1982 **P ADP** *050 †75

CORNES, Cleon Leroy. 3811 OHARA ST 15213 #041-12-1959 L1960 **P PYA** *012 †75

CORNETT, Benjamin Lee. 230 MCKEE PL STE 500, OF PITTSBURGH 15213 #035-03-2004 L2004 **EM** *100

CORPUZ, Marcelo B, Jr. 2018 E CARSON ST, STE 1 15203 #748-02-1968 L1973 **IM CD** *020 †20

CORSELLO, Guy Robt. 1350 LOCUST ST STE 402 15219 #041-12-1966 L1968 **N** *071 †75

CORTAZZO, Megan Helen. 2060 MARY ST 15203 #041-12-2001 L2001 **PM** *020 †60

CORTES, Vicente. 320 E NORTH AVE RM 595, ALLEGHENY GEN HOSPITAL 15212 #264-01-1980 L2004 **GS CCM** *020 †85

COSGROVE, James Lovett. 9104 BABCOCK BLVD, STE 2120 15237 #010-01-1983 L1984 **PM** *020 †60

COSTA, Guilherme. ■ 15217 #187-06-1992 L2001 *100 †85

COSTA, Melanie Elizabeth. 4800 FRIENDSHIP AVE 15224 #041-12-1990 L1993 **D** *020 †15

COSTA FILHO, Rubens Barro. 320 E NORTH AVE, ALLEGHENY GEN HOSP 15212 #187-21-2002 L2004 **HO** *012 †20

COSTA-GRECO, Maria A. 100 DELAFIELD RD STE 312, UROLOGY & ULTRASOUND ASSOC 15215 #041-12-1980 L1981 **R** *020 †80

COSTELLO, Bernard J, III. 3471 5TH AVE, STE 1112 15213 #041-01-1997 L1999 **CFS** *020

COSTELLO, Joanna Michele. ■ 15232 #041-07-1985 L1988 **DR** *020 †18,80

COTOMAN, Genica. 320 E NORTH AVE, ALLEGHENY GEN HOSP 15212 #781-05-1997 **GE** *012

COTULBEA, Elena-Ruxandra. 3708 5TH AVE, UNIVERSITY HEALTH CENTER 15213 #781-06-2002 L2006 **FP** *012

COUCE, Marta Emma. 200 LOTHROP ST, UPMC PRESBYTERIAN, A516 15213 #847-05-1986 L2000 **NP** *020 †50

COUGHTRY, Brendon Michael. ■ 15222 #012-01-2003 L2007 **PMM** *012

COUNIHAN, Katherine A. ■ 15238 #041-12-1986 L1987 **PTH** *100

COUNIHAN, Peter James. 200 DELAFIELD RD 15215 #539-06-1983 L1992 **CD OS** *020

COURCOULAS, Anita Pauline. 3380 BOULEVARD, OF THE ALLIES 15213 #024-05-1988 L1990 **GS** *020 †85

COURTNEY-BROOKS, Madeline. ■ 15217 #028-02-2006 L2006 **OBG** *012

COUTINHO, Barry V. 5215 CENTRE AVE, DEPT MED EDUCATION 15232 #917-23-1987 L1995 **FM** *020 †18

COUVRETTE, Carol. 105 BRAUNLICH DR, MERCY FAMILY HEALTH CENTER 15237 #065-05-1987 L1989 **FM** *020 †18

COVATTO, Roseann Horen. 4800 FRIENDSHIP AVE 15224 #041-13-1992 L1995 **OBG** *020 †30

COWDEN, Sharon Norrine. 4923 CENTRE AVE 15213 #041-12-1990 L1992 **PD** *020 †55 ‡

COWHER, Michael Simon. 320 E NORTH AVE, GENERAL SURGERY 15212 #038-44-2004 L2004 **GS** *012

COX, Amy Elizabeth. ■ 15232 #041-14-2005 L2005 **IM** *012

COX, Catherine Jean. 200 LOTHROP ST, FALK CLINIC 15213 #035-08-1980 L1995 **CLP** *020 †50

COYLE, Patricia Gallagher. 120 LYTTON AVE, FIRST FLOOR 15213 #041-13-1986 L1987 **IM IMG** *020 †20

COYLE, Richard Jos. 3550 TERRACE ST, A-1305 SCAIFE HALL 15261 #041-13-1983 L1984 **AN** *020 †05

COYLE, Robert Mc Chesney. 1050 BOWER HILL RD, STE 308 15243 #041-12-1945 L1946 **IM CD** *072 †20

COYNE, Bonnie Ann. 300 HALKET ST, MAGEE WOMENS HOSPITAL 15213 #041-12-1983 L1985 **OBG** *020 †30

COYNE, Christopher. 3601 5TH AVE, FALK MEDICAL BUILDING, SUI 15213 #005-14-1997 L2007 **END** *020

COYNE, Ruth Kane. 400 45TH ST 15201 #041-12-1953 **CHP PYA** *071 †75

CRAIG, Fiona Elizabeth. 200 LOTHROP ST, UPMC PRESBY HOSP RM 604 15213 #917-20-1985 L2001 **PTH HMP** *020 †50

CRAIN, Richard Henry. 7180 HIGHLAND DR 15206 #041-13-1958 L1959 **DR OM** *020 †70,80 ‡

CRANE, Scott Anthony. ■ 15222 #026-04-2002 L2006 **EM** *020

CRANSTON, Ross Douglas. 3601 5TH AVE, FALK MEDICAL BUILDING, SUI 15213 #919-03-1990 L2007 *100

CRATTY, Michael Scott. 320 E NORTH AVE 15212 #055-01-1998 L2000 **MPD** *020 †20,55

CREEL, Michael Eric. ■ 15221 #036-08-2004 L2004 **GPM** *012

CREININ, Mitchell David. 300 HALKET ST 15213 #016-06-1988 L1994 **OBG** *050 †30

CRESPO, Maria M. 200 LOTHROP ST, UPMC MONTEFIORE 15213 #847-20-1983 L2003 **PUD CCM** *020 †20

CRESPO, Sergio Manuel. ■ 15232 #040-02-2005 L2005 **IM** *012

CRICHLOW, Philmore Hamil. 1501 LOCUST ST STE 1000 15219 #010-03-1956 L1965 **IM** *020

■ = Address Information Privacy Protected

CRIPPEN, David Wayne. 3550 TERRACE ST, MEDICAL CENTER/616 SCAIFE 15261 #012-01-1976 L1985 **CCM EM** *020 †16

CRISANTI, Maria Cecilia. 4800 FRIENDSHIP AVE, STE 4600N 15224 #132-01-2002 L2004 **GS** *100

CRISPINO, Charles Michael. 5750 CENTRE AVE, CENTRE COMMONS, SUITE 510 15206 #035-19-1976 L1981 **CD IM** *020 †20

CROCK, Frederick Wm. 200 LOTHROP ST, # S562 15213 #041-13-1978 L1979 **CD IM** *020 †20 ‡

CROCK, Richard. 239 4TH AVE, 211 INVESTMENT BLDG 15222 #041-12-1975 **OPH** *020 †35

CRONIN, Tara Helen. 203 LOTHROP ST, STE 821 15213 #041-12-2004 L2004 *100

CROSSETT, Lawrence Scott. 5200 CENTRE AVE, STE 211 15232 #041-13-1981 L1983 **ORS OS** *020 †40

CROUCH, Ray Dee. 4815 LIBERTY AVE, STE 4126 15224 #041-09-1989 L1997 **TS** *020 †90,85

CRUMRINE, Patricia Kay. 3705 5TH AVE 15213 #041-07-1968 L1975 **N** *020 †55,75

CRUZ, Ma. Veronica Casem. 1405 SHADY AVE 15217 #748-10-1986 L2001 **PM** *100

CRUZ, Mario. 100 N BELLEFIELD AVE, STE 772 15213 #024-07-1983 L2002 **P** *050 †75

CRUZ, Stella Marie Cruz. 1000 BOWER HILL RD, MED.AFFAIRS,ST. CLAIR HOSP 15243 #748-01-1985 L2006 **PD** *100

CRUZ JUNIOR, Ruy Jorge. 3708 5TH AVE, UNIVERSITY HEALTH CENTER 15213 #187-62-1994 L2006 *100

CUDDEBACK, Thomas J, Jr. ■ 15226 #041-12-1950 L1951 **FM** *071 †18

CULIG, Michael Herman. 4815 LIBERTY AVE, STE 156 15224 #024-01-1982 L1984 **TS** *020 †85,90

CULLEN, Elizabeth Anne. ■ 15212 #041-15-2001 L2007 **PTH** *012

CULO, Sandi Ann. 5237 5TH AVE, APT A4 15232 #060-01-2000 L2005 **PYG** *100

CUMMINGS, Lenise Andrea. ■ 15217 #028-34-2005 L2006 **IM** *012

CUNNANE, Megan Shields. 200 LOTHROP ST, UPMC MONTEFIORE 933W 15213 #041-12-1999 L2001 **IM** *020 †20

CURREN, Michael Joseph, Jr. ■ 15229 #041-15-2007 L2007 **IM** *012

CURRY, Scott Robert. ■ 15221 #045-01-2001 L2001 **ID** *012 †20

CURTISS, Edward Ira. 230 LOTHROP ST, PREWSBYTERIAN HOSP RM 748 15213 #035-19-1964 L1969 **CD IM** *040 †20

CYMERMAN, Frank Robert. 3471 5TH AVE, STE 1111 15213 #041-09-1980 L1981 **IM IMG** *020 †20

CZAJKA-GIERMASZ, Anna Ter. 2135 WIGHTMAN ST 15217 #759-03-2000 L2002 **CD** *012 †20

CZERNOBILSKY, Helen. 4200 5TH AVE, DEPT ENDO 15261 #869-05-1953 **IM HEM** *050

DABBS, David Jos. 300 HALKET ST, PATHOLOGY DEPT 15213 #038-43-1980 L1992 **CLP** *020 †50

DACAL, Kirsten. ■ 15237 #041-12-2006 L2006 **FP** *012

DACIC, Sanja. 121 MEYRAN AVE, UNIV HLTH CTR PITTSBURGH 15213 #957-01-1990 L2001 **PTH** *020 †50

DAFFNER, Richard Howard. 320 E NORTH AVE, ALLEGHENY RADIOLOGY 15212 #035-06-1967 L1983 **DR** *020 †20

DAFTARY, Ashi Rasik. 300 HALKET ST 15213 #028-02-1986 L1989 **OBG MFM** *020 †30

DAHL, Ronald Ernest. 3811 OHARA ST, RME-724 15213 #041-12-1984 L1987 **SME CHP** *050 †16

DALAL, Leena Bharat Kumar. 320 E NORTH AVE 15212 #495-22-1968 L1974 **PD** *020 †55

DALBY, Patricia Lorraine. 300 HALKET ST, MAGEE WOMENS HOSPITAL 15213 #041-12-1983 L1984 **AN PME** *020 †20

DALLAPIAZZA, Michelle Lyn. ■ 15243 #041-12-2006 L2006 **IM** *012

DALOPE, Kristin Aguilar. ■ 15213 #035-03-2006 L2006 **CPP** *012

DALTNER, Carl Jos. 4727 FRIENDSHIP AVE, STE 240 15224 #036-05-1986 L1988 **AN** *020 †05

DALY, Christopher J. 1002 MCKNIGHT PARK DR 15237 #010-02-1967 L1977 **GS AS** *040 †85

DALY, Ivonne M. 526 ELLSWORTH AVE 15213 #042-01-1994 L2001 **CCS** *100 †85

DALY, Michael Jos. 105 BRAUNLICH DR, STE 450 15237 #010-02-1983 L1984 **PD** *020 †55

D'AMICO, Adrian Anthony. 100 S JACKSON AVE, SUBURBAN GENERAL HOSPITAL 15202 #038-40-1980 L1981 **EM** *020 †16

DANAEE, Nosratollah. 20 BAILEY AVE 15211 #517-04-1965 L1982 **FM FPG** *020 ‡

DANES, Peter Michael. 1900 BABCOCK BLVD, UPMC PASSAVANT 15209 #038-41-1972 L1983 **R** *020 †20

DANIEL, Ethelyn Dyar. 2000 MARY ST 15203 #035-46-1980 L1990 **AN IM** *020 †20,05

DANIELS, Brook Marie. ■ 15232 #056-06-2008 *012

DANTONIO, James Daniel. 200 LOTHROP ST, SCAIFE HALL, STE B571.3 15213 #040-02-2002 L2005 **CD** *012 †20

DAPOS, John Chas. 4800 FRIENDSHIP AVE 15224 #041-13-1992 L1995 **AN** *020 †05

DARBY, Joseph Michael. 200 LOTHROP ST 15213 #016-11-1981 L1984 **CCM IM** *020 †20

DARDING, David D. ■ 15213 #038-75-2007, ▲ L2007 *012

DARGIN, James M. ■ 15204 #025-04-2004 L2008 **EM** *012

DAROSKI, Marilyn Sabina. 615 WASHINGTON RD, STE TL4 15228 #038-44-1988 L1990 **IM** *020 †20

DARVILLE, Lee Antoinette. 3705 5TH AVE, ARKANSAS CHILDREN'S HOSPIT 15213 #004-01-1987 L2007 **PD** *020 †55

DAS, Niladri. ■ 15201 #041-02-2005 L2005 **FP** *012

DAS, Phani Bhushan. ■ 15241 #495-24-1955 L1987 **TS** *040 †85,90

DASARI, Nageshwara Vijaya. 3708 5TH AVE, DEPT OF GME 15213 #495-65-2002 L2005 **IM** *012

DASH, Nilma. 320 E NORTH AVE, ALLEGHENY RADIOLOGY 15212 #495-79-1968 L1978 **R OS** *020 †80 ‡

DASKIVICH, Timothy John. ■ 15237 #024-01-2006 **GS** *012

DASTUR, Khurshed Jehangir. 1400 LOCUST ST 15219 #917-04-1968 L1973 **R RNR** *020 †80

DATO, Virginia Marie. 300 LIBERTY AVE STE 514, S DISTRICT OFFICE PADOH 15222 #041-12-1983 L1996 **PHP PD** *062 †55,70

DATTILO, James Thos. ■ 15241 #041-12-1943 L1944 **OBG** *071 †30

DAUBER, James Henry. 200 LOTHROP ST, UNIV OF PITTSBURGH MEDICAL 15213 #035-20-1969 L1972 **PUD CCM** *020 †20

DAVARYA, Shekar Ligia. 121 MEYRAN AVE, DEPT OBG 15213 #008-01-2007 L2007 **OBG** *012

DAVID, Arthur. 1517 FORBES AVE 15219 #305-01-1985 L1986 **FM** *020 †18

DAVIDES, Kyriakos. 1402 LINCOLN AVE 15206 #418-02-1965 L1972 **U** *020 †95

DAVIDSON, Eric Lowell. 4800 FRIENDSHIP AVE, PENNSYLVANIA HOSPI 15224 #019-02-1998 L2004 **CCA** *012

DAVIDSON, Harold Carter. 121 MEYRAN AVE 15213 #041-15-2006 L2006 **OTO** *012

DAVIES, Benjamin John. 3471 5TH AVE STE 70, UROLOGY DEPT 15213 #035-47-2000 L2001 **GS** *020

DAVIES, Brian Peter. 3705 5TH AVE, DEPARTMENT OF 15213 #041-12-2004 L2004 **PD** *020 †55

DAVIES, Erin Dawn. 1000 INTEGRITY DR, STE 200 15235 #041-02-2003 L2003 **PD** *020

DAVIES, Sarah D. 3471 5TH AVE, STE 1112 KAUFMANN BUILDING 15213 #041-12-2004 L2004 *100

DAVIS, Amy W. ■ 15222 #048-15-2001 L2001 **PP** *100 †50

DAVIS, Derek Jean. 300 HALKET ST, MAGEE WOMEN'S HOSPITAL 15213 #056-05-1985 L1986 **AN** *020 †05

DAVIS, Holly Wilson. 3705 5TH AVE, PEDS/ONE CHILDRENS PL 15213 #036-07-1971 **PD PEM** *030 †55

DAVIS, Lydia Jenelle. ■ 15215 #041-12-2007 L2007 **IM** *012

DAVIS, Peter Jonathan. 3705 5TH AVE 15213 #035-46-1977 L1983 **PAN AN** *020 †55,05

DAVIS, Rachel Elaine. ■ 15217 #041-13-2008 *012

DAVITT, Mary Cecilia. 5608 WILKINS AVE, STE 202 15217 #035-06-1988 L1990 **NPM** *020 †55

DAVLIAKOS, George Paul. 400 HOLIDAY DR, STE 101 15220 #041-12-1986 L1988 **TS VS** *020 †90

DAVLIN, Martha Louise. 105 GAMMA DR, STE 300 15238 #038-06-1978 L1979 **PD** *020 †55

DAWSON, Damien Omari. ■ 15224 #016-02-2005 L2005 **DR** *012

DAY, Hollis Dorsett. 3459 5TH AVE 15213 #051-04-1994 L1996 **IMG** *020 †20

DAYALAN, Ashim Kumar. 3601 MCKNIGHT EAST DR 15237 #495-33-1989 L1996 **IM** *020 †20

D'CRUZ, Brian Joseph. 230 MCKEE PL STE 500, OF PITTSBURGH 15213 #041-12-2004 L2004 **EM** *020

DEALY, Robert Sumner. 3811 OHARA ST, WESTERN PSYCH INST & CLN 15213 #067-01-1975 L1981 **P** *020 †75

DEAN, David Andrew. 490 E NORTH AVE STE 302, CARDIOVASCULAR 15212 #033-06-1992 L2004 **TS GS** *020 †85,90

DEANTONIS, Kathleen Owens. 1400 LOCUST ST 15219 #055-01-1996 L1998 **PD** *020 †55

DECKER, Michael James. 4800 FRIENDSHIP AVE 15224 #026-04-1991 L1993 **PD PE** *020 †55

DEENEY, Vincent Francis. 3705 5TH AVE 15213 #041-02-1976 L1999 **ORS OP** *020 †40

DEFOE, Gillianne Sarahgen. ■ 15232 #041-12-2006 **RO** *012

DE FRANCES, Marie Colette. 200 LOTHROP ST 15213 #041-12-1997 L2000 **PTH** *020 †50

DEGIOVANNI, Lesley. 717 WASHINGTON RD 15228 #041-09-1986 L1988 **IM** *020 †20

DE GREGORIO, Nicholas. 120 MCCONNELLS MILL LN 15228 #038-41-1977 L1978 **IM** *020 †20

DEGROFF, Curt Gerald. 3705 5TH AVE 15213 #035-08-1989 L2005 **PDC PD** *020 †55

DE HART, David Allen. 735 WILLIAM PITT WAY 15238 #055-01-1974 L1981 **EM GP** *030 †16

DE HOYOS, Alberto L. 200 LOTHROP ST, PUH C800 15213 #649-02-1982 L2003 **TS** *020 †85,90 ‡

DEIBLE, Christopher Ross. 200 LOTHROP ST, MEDICAL CENTER 15213 #041-12-1999 L2001 **DR** *020 †80

DEITRICK, Richard Eugene. 180 FORT COUCH RD, STE 450 15241 #041-12-1959 **OBG OS** *030 †30 ‡

DE KOSKY, Steven Trent. 3471 5TH AVE STE 811, UNIVERSITY OF PITTSBURGH 15213 #011-03-1974 L1990 **N** *050 †75

DE LA CRUZ, Carolyn. ■ 15232 #051-07-1994 L2004 **PS** *100 †65

DELA CRUZ, Victor Jocson. 4200 5TH AVE 15261 #748-01-1973 **OTO** *020

DELAPENA, Nicolas. 5750 CENTRE AVE STE 510, ASSOCIATES IN INFECTIOUS D 15206 #748-02-1989 L2001 **IM** *020 †20

DE LA VEGA, Sofronio B. 300 HALKET ST, DEPT OF ANESTHESIOLOGY 15213 #748-10-1965 L1973 **AN** *020 †05

DEL BIANCO, Paul Raymond. 8075 SALTSBURG RD 15239 #654-01-1983 L1985 **IM** *020

DELEYIANNIS, Frederic W. 3705 5TH AVE 15213 #008-01-1992 L2000 **PS** *020 †45,65

DELFYETT, William Throm. 200 LOTHROP ST, DEPARTMENT OF RADIOLOGY 15213 #041-01-2001 L2007 **RNR** *020 †80

DELGADO, Gregorio. 4815 LIBERTY AVE STE 321, MULTISPECIALISTS PC 15224 #737-03-1967 L1997 **ON GYN** *020 †30

DELGADO, Kristian. ■ 15217 #048-14-2006 L2007 **AN** *012

DELIOS, Anna Maria. 121 MEYRAN AVE, UNIV HLTH CTR 15213 #187-78-2003 L2007 **N** *012

DELO, Daniel Lee. ■ 15241 #055-01-2004 L2007 **RHU** *012 †20

DELPOSEN, Margaret. 1400 LOCUST ST 15219 #041-02-1995 L1997 **PD** *020 †18

DEL RIO MUNOZ, Jose Mauri. ■ 15206 #264-01-1994 L2005 **AN** *012

DELSERONE, Eugene Walter. 1400 LOCUST ST STE 2375 15219 #041-12-1956 L1957 **AN** *071 †05

DE LUCA, Christopher. 1000 BOWER HILL RD, ST CLAIR HOSPITAL 15243 #041-09-1994 L1996 **EM** *020 †16

DE LUCA, Kerry Gill. 3471 5TH AVE STE 201, UNIVERSITY OF PITTSBURGH M 15213 #016-06-1991 L2009 **PD** *020 †60

DE MARINO, Georgine B. 2403 SIDNEY ST STE 220 15203 #041-14-1981 L1987 **DR** *020 †80 ‡

DEMAS, Peter Nicholas. 532 S AIKEN AVE, STE 311 15232 #041-12-1985 L1987 *020

DE MEO, Patrick Jos. 1307 FEDERAL ST, STE 2 15212 #025-07-1986 L1993 **ORS OSM** *020 †40

DEMETRIS, Anthony Jacob. 200 LOTHROP ST 15213 #041-12-1982 L1984 **PTH** *020 †50

DEMIDOVICH, Mark Allen. 3811 OHARA ST, # 153 15213 #045-01-2003 L2003 **CHP** *012

DEMIRCI, Cem Sinan. 3705 5TH AVE, OF PITTSBU 15213 #902-07-1991 L2006 **PDE** *012 †55

DEMOS, John Emery. 121 1/2 SPRINGHOUSE LN 15238 #041-01-1974 L1979 **PS** *020 †65

DENAULT, Andre Y. ■ 15217 #067-02-1987 L1991 **CCM** *100 †20

DENG, Jau-Shyong. 190 LOTHROP ST, STE 145 15213 #244-02-1968 L1986 **D IG** *020 †15

DENKO, Timothey Charles. 3811 OHARA ST, BELLFIELD TOWERS 8TH FLOOR 15213 #038-41-1998 L2000 **P** *020

DENNING, David Alan, II. 9350 TIMBER TRL 15237 #055-02-2002 L2003 **AN** *100

DENNING, Krista Lynn. ■ 15237 #055-02-2004 L2004 **PTH** *012

DENNIS, Alia M. 3705 5TH AVE, 6TH FLOOR, MAIN TOWER 15213 #028-46-2000 L2004 **CCP** *100 †55

DENNIS, William Winston. 3705 5TH AVE DEPT PED 15213 #067-01-1968 **GS** *100

DE PIETRO, Frank Robert. 1498 STURDY OAK DR 15220 #041-12-1997 L2001 **P** *020 †75

DE POVEDA, Gladys M S. ■ 15216 #264-01-1967 L1983 **DR** *020

DERENZO, Joseph Santo. 300 HALKET ST, RM 3510 15213 #041-14-2001 L2001 **AN** *100 †05

DE RISO, Barbara Mary. 4815 LIBERTY AVE # GR25 15224 #024-07-1978 L1982 **AN CCM** *020 †20,05

DE RUBERTIS, F R, Jr. 200 LOTHROP ST, E1140 BST 15261 #041-12-1965 L1966 **IM END** *030 †20

DESAI, Ami Tushar. ■ 15208 #005-15-2007 L2007 **PD** *012

DESAI, Balaji. 1400 LOCUST ST, MERCY HOSPITAL 15219 #495-04-2001 L2006 **IM** *012

DESAI, Neha A. 1400 LOCUST ST, DEPT RAD 15219 #041-15-2006 L2006 **DR** *012

DESAI, Neha Suresh. ■ 15229 #495-37-2001 L2007 **IMG** *012

DE SILVA, Kumudini Damita. 525 MOUNT PLEASANT RD 15214 #220-01-1969 L1974 **FM** *020 †18

DE TOLEDO, Frederico G S. 121 MEYRAN AVE, DEPT OF ENDOCRINOLOGY 15213 #187-03-1996 L2002 **END** *020 †20

DETRE, Kath M Drechsler. GSPH UNIV PITTSBURGH EPID 15261 #065-05-1952 L1974 **GPM IM** *050

DETRE, Thomas Paul. 3811 OHARA ST 15213 #561-17-1952 L1973 **P** *071 †75

DEUTSCH, Melvin. 200 LOTHROP ST, RAD ONC/3RD FL PUH 15213 #035-19-1964 L1968 RO *020 †80 ‡

DE VERA, Michael Eleazar. 3459 5TH AVE, UPMC MONTEFIORE 7SOUTH 15213 #005-14-1991 L1994 GS *020 †85

DEVERE, David Alan. 5230 CENTRE AVE, UPMC SHADYSIDE HOSPITAL 15232 #033-05-1979 L1981 AN *020 †16,05

DEVINE, Joan Marie. 3471 5TH AVE, STE 1111 15213 #041-12-1980 L1982 IM *020 †20

DE VITA, Michael A. 200 LOTHROP ST 15213 #010-02-1981 L1988 IM *020 †20

DEVOOGD, Kelly Michele. ■ 15217 #041-77-2005, ▲ L2005 OBG *012

DEVULAPALLY, Pavan. 1500 5TH AVE, INTERNAL MED RESDNCY 15219 #495-65-2000 L2008 *100

DHAIRYAM, Maya Thersa. 1400 LOCUST ST, STE 5120 15219 #496-07-1979 L1995 IM *020 †20

DHALIWAL, Deepinder K. 203 LOTHROP ST STE 800 15213 #016-06-1990 L1993 OPH *020 †35

DHALIWAL, Rajinder Singh. ■ 15232 #422-01-2005 L2007 FP *012

DHANISETTY, Shilpa. ■ 15213 #041-12-2007 L2007 *012

DHARAN, Vanita Bhavana. 300 HALKET ST, DEPT OF OB/GYN 15213 #041-15-2003 L2003 OBG *020

DHAWAN, Manish K. 1307 FEDERAL ST, STE 301 15212 #495-45-1992 L1996 GE *020 †20

DHUPAR, Rajeev. ■ 15203 #033-06-2004 L2004 GS *012

DIAMOND, Herbert Stephen. 4815 LIBERTY AVE, STE GR-30 15224 #035-08-1962 L1989 RHU IM *020 †20

DIAMOND, Joel Nelson. 2585 FREEPORT RD, STE 202 15238 #035-15-1988 L1990 FM *020 †18

DIANZUMBA, Sinda B. 320 E NORTH AVE, ALLEGHENY GEN HOSP DIVSN 15212 #016-06-1971 L1976 CD IM *020

DIAS PERERA, Anton Surath. 4800 FRIENDSHIP AVE 15224 #220-01-1996 L2003 GS *012

DICIANNO, Brad Edward. 2000 MARY ST 15203 #041-12-2001 L2001 PM *020 †60

DICKMAN, Morris Sanford. 5750 CENTRE AVE, STE 100 15206 #041-12-1973 L1988 N *075 †75

DI CROCE, Joseph Nicholas. 5438 CENTRE AVE 15232 #041-13-1983 L1984 IM *040 †20

DIEGEL, Joan Ellen. ■ 15217 #010-01-1984 L1992 IM *020 †20

DIENERT, Danielle Nicole. ■ 15232 #021-01-2001 L2001 UP *012

DIETLY, Robin Lynn. 111 MILLSTONE LN 15238 #041-12-1981 L1982 IM *020 †20 ‡

DI GIACOMO, Patrick John. 320 E NORTH AVE, MEDICAL AMBULATORY CLINIC 15212 #041-13-1995 L1995 CCM *012 †20

DIGIOIA, Anthony M, III. 300 HALKET ST, STE 1601 15213 #024-01-1986 L1987 ORS GS *020 †40

DI GIOVANNA, Brett M. 3811 OHARA ST 15213 #035-01-2003 L2003 CHP *012

DIKKALA, Sudharani. 320 E NORTH AVE 15212 #495-58-2002 L2005 IM *012

DILANGALEN, Datukan G. S 20TH ST & JANE ST, SOUTHSIDE HOSPITAL 15203 #748-08-1968 L1973 GS *020 †16

DILANGALEN, Lina F. ■ 15241 #748-08-1969 L1979 EM OBG *020

DILER, Rasim Somer. 3811 OHARA ST, WPIC / THOMAS DETER HALL 15213 #902-10-1994 L2000 CHP *012 ‡

DILIP, Madathil Prabhakar. 1400 LOCUST ST, MERCY HOSP-PITTSBURGH 15219 #495-44-1996 L2002 IM *020 †20

DILLAVOU, Ellen Deanne. 1500 FERNLEAF ST 15210 #003-01-1996 L1998 VS *020 †85

DILLINGER, Ellen Marie. 5608 WILKINS AVE, PRIMARY MEDICAL ASSOC 15217 #023-07-1975 L1975 IM *020 †20

DI LORENZO, Carlo. 3705 5TH AVE, BURG 15213 #561-10-1984 L1996 PD *020 †55

DIMARCO, Ross F, Jr. 400 HOLIDAY DR, STE 101 15220 #041-02-1973 L1974 TS *020 †90,85

DIMARTINI, Andrea F. 3811 OHARA ST, SCAIFE RM 537 15213 #016-02-1987 L1989 P *020 †75

DIMITRIOU, George Andrew. 420 E NORTH AVE STE 401 15212 #038-44-1998 L2000 IM *020 †20

DING, Yaoxian. 2000 MARY ST, DEPT OF PATHOLOGY 15203 #243-52-1983 L2006 PTH *100 †50

DIPLACIDO, Amy Jo. ■ 15201 #041-13-2007 L2007 FP *012

DI PRIMIO, Joseph Vincent. ■ 15215 #010-02-1955 L1956 RO NM *020 †80

DIRICO, Domenick Ernest. 320 E NORTH AVE, DEPT OF ANESTHESIOLOGY 15212 #041-09-1987 L1988 AN PME *020 †05

DIRKS, Susan Jeanne. 200 JHF DR, SQUIRREL HILL HEALTH CENTE 15217 #005-06-1989 L1989 FM *020 †18

DISCHMAN, Elaine Cronauer. 525 MOUNT PLEASANT RD, NORTHVIEW HEIGHTS 15214 #041-13-1988 L1990 FM *020 †18

DISHART, Michael Kenneth. 320 E NORTH AVE, ALLEGHENY HOSP 15212 #012-05-1989 L1993 AN CCA *020 †05

DIVENANZO, Debbie Ann. 500 LEWIS RUN RD, SWASC 15122 #055-01-1989 L1992 AN *020 †05

DIXON, Bruce Wayne. 200 LOTHROP ST, GEN MED/933 W MONTEFIORE 15213 #041-12-1965 L1966 IM HEM *020 †20

DIZON-KATZ, Maria Regina. 612 SCAIFE HALL 15261 #917-25-1980 AN *100

DOAN, Richard Jos. 3811 OHARA ST 15213 #008-01-1982 L1983 CHP P *020 †75

DOBKIN, Larry Alan. 250 MT LEBANON BLVD, STE 306 15234 #041-12-1980 L1981 IM IMG *020 †20

DOBLER, Lee Colburn. 9335 MCKNIGHT RD, PRIMARY CARE CENTER 15237 #041-12-1963 L1966 FM *071 †18

DOBSON, Andre. 2275 SWALLOW HILL RD, STE 300 15220 #041-12-1982 L1984 AN PME *020

DOCIMO, Anne Boland. 112 WASHINGTON PL, STE 800 15219 #023-07-1984 L2000 EM *020 †16

DOCIMO, Steven Gerard. 3705 5TH AVE 15213 #023-07-1984 L2000 U GS *020 †95

DOFT, Bernard Harvey. 3501 FORBES AVE, STE 500 15213 #035-19-1971 L1979 OPH IM *020 †20,35

DOHAR, Joseph Edward. 3705 5TH AVE 15213 #038-40-1987 L1992 PDO *020 †45

DOI, Yohei. 3601 5TH AVE, STE 3A 15213 #572-58-1998 L2005 ID *012 †20

DOMAT, Imad. 5200 CENTRE AVE, STE 703 15232 #875-01-1978 L1981 CD IM *020 †20

DOMBROVSKI, Alexandre Yur. 3811 OHARA ST, DEPT OF PSYCHIATRY 15213 #913-06-1999 L2002 PYG *100 †75

DOMBROWSKI, Marianne. 651 HOLIDAY DR, FOSTER PLAZA BUILDING #5 15220 #041-77-1995, ▲ L1996 IM *020 †20 ‡

DOMFEH, Akosua Benefah. 121 MEYRAN AVE 15213 #412-01-1998 L2003 SP *012 †50

DOMSIC, Robyn Therese. 3500 TERRACE ST, BSTWR S727 15213 #018-03-2001 L2004 RHU *100

DONAHOE, Michael Patrick. 3459 5TH AVE, 628 NW MONTEFIORE HOSP 15213 #041-09-1983 L1984 CCM PUD *020 †20

DONALDSON, David H, Jr. ■ 15241 #041-12-1944 L1945 GP *071

DONALDSON, William F, III. 3471 5TH AVE STE 1010 15213 #016-01-1980 L1990 ORS OSS *020 †40

DONATELLI, John Michael. 9000 PERRY HWY, STE 300 15237 #041-12-1985 L1986 FM *020 †18

DONG, Xiang Da. 5150 CENTRE AVE RM 414 15232 #036-07-1999 L2001 GS *020 †85

DONNELLAN, Nicole Michell. ■ 15243 #041-12-2006 L2006 OBG *012

DONNELLY, Brian. 9104 BABCOCK BLVD, STE 2111 15237 #035-15-1986 L1992 PD *020 †55

DONNELLY, Edward Joseph. 510 S LINDEN AVE 15208 #019-02-1974 L1977 IM IMG *020 †20

DONOHUE, Bryan Curry. 4800 FRIENDSHIP AVE 15224 #010-02-1980 L1989 CD ICE *020 †20

DONOVAN, Francis Connor. 1082 BOWER HILL RD STE 19 15243 #010-02-1958 L1959 P CHP *020 †20

DONTCHOS, Brian Nicholas. ■ 15206 #041-12-2008 L2008 *012

DORAISWAMY, Vijay Arun. 4800 FRIENDSHIP AVE, DEPT MED 15224 #495-04-2003 L2005 IM *012

DORFSMAN, Michele Lee. 200 LOTHROP ST 15213 #041-01-1997 L1999 EM *016

DORNENBURG, James R. ■ 15227 #041-12-1940 L1941 GS *071 †85

DORRA, Helen Hyde. ■ 15235 #041-12-2004 L2004 IM *020 †20

DORRITIE, Kathleen Anne. ■ 15222 #035-15-2007 L2007 IM *012

DOSHI, Ankur Ashok. 4800 FRIENDSHIP AVE, TOWER BASEMENT 15224 #041-12-2000 L2001 EM *020

DOSHI, Bhavank. 1400 CENTRE AVE # 225 15219 #495-76-1989 L1997 IM *075 †20

DOSHI, Nalini. WEST PENN HOSP PATH DEPT 15224 #496-38-1966 L1973 PTH PCP *071 †50

DOSHI, Narendra S. 4815 LIBERTY AVE # 435 15224 #496-38-1961 L1972 OBG END *020 †30

DOSIOS, Theodosios J. ■ 15209 #418-02-1963 L1974 TS *020

DOUAIHY, Antoine. 3811 OHARA ST # 1059, DEPT OF PSYCHIATRY 15213 #605-02-1990 L1997 P *020 †75

DOUDS, Howard Nesbit. 733 WASHINGTON RD 15228 #041-01-1943 L1944 IM *020 ‡

DOUGHERTY, Geo Gehr, Jr. 7180 HIGHLAND DR, 151R VA MEDICAL CENTER 15206 #005-11-1976 L1985 P *050 †75

DOUGLAS, Susan Stanton. 3811 OHARA ST, WPIC 15213 #041-12-2004 L2004 CHP *012

DOVEC, Elizabeth Anne. 4800 FRIENDSHIP AVE, WESTERN PA HOSP 15224 #055-02-2007 L2007 GS *012

DOVER, Roman David. ■ 15235 #024-05-2002 L2002 GS *100

DOWLING, John Nelson. 968 SCAIFE HALL 15261 #016-11-1966 L1968 ID IM *040 †20

DOWNEY, David Patrick. 320 E NORTH AVE 15212 #539-03-2005 L2007 IM *012

DOYLE, John Jos. 3471 5TH AVE, STE 811LKB 15213 #041-12-1974 L1975 N *020 †75

DOYLE, Tara Laverne. ■ 15222 #038-41-2007 L2007 GS *012

DOYLE, Thomas James. 200 LOTHROP ST 15213 #041-09-1997 L2000 EM *020 †16

DRABEK, Tomas. 3434 5TH AVE, SAFAR CENTER FOR RESUSCITA 15213 #286-13-1991 L2006 *100

DRANT, Stacey Elizabeth. 3705 5TH AVE, CHILD HOSP OF PITTSBURGH 15213 #043-01-1988 L2006 PDC *020 †55

DRAPER, Randall Richard. 9104 BABCOCK BLVD, STE 4110 15237 #041-02-1990 L1993 GS *020 †85

DRASH, Allan Lee. 3705 5TH AVE, DIV PEDIATRIC ENDOCRINOLOG 15213 #051-01-1957 L1966 PD DIA *030 †55

DRESSER, Michael Chas. 124 UNIVERSITY DRIVE C 15240 #035-03-1985 L1986 IM EM *020 †20

DRICKMAN, Johanna Lynn. 3705 5TH AVE 15213 #016-42-1984 L1990 PDC *050 †55

DRISCOLL, Henry C. ■ 15206 #041-12-2008 *012

DRNOVSEK, Valerie. 15236 #957-01-1987 L2004 DR RNR *020 †80

DUA, Molly. ■ 15238 #495-98-1978 L1981 AN *075

DUA, Monica Pathak. 4815 LIBERTY AVE, STE GR-30 15224 #495-45-1994 L1998 IM *020 †20

DUA, Rup Kumar. 4800 FRIENDSHIP AVE 15224 #495-74-1973 L1997 AN CCA *020 †05 ‡

DUARTE, Cynthia Ann. 3550 TERRACE ST, A-1305 SCAIFE HALL 15261 #024-07-1982 L1991 AN IM *020 †05

DUBIN, Patricia Jean. 3705 5TH AVE 15213 #035-45-1997 L2000 PDP *050 †55

DUBROVSKY, Olga. 0 UNIVERSITY DRIVE C, VAMC 15240 #913-47-1971 L1986 PM R *071 †60

DUCA, Mark Anthony. 339 6TH AVE FL 5, HEINZ 57 CENTER 15222 #041-07-1994 L1996 IM ISM *020 †20

DUERKSEN, Roger Lee. 4800 FRIENDSHIP AVE 15224 #041-13-1963 L1964 OTO HNS *071 †45

DUERR, Richard Hamilton. 200 LOTHROP ST 15213 #026-04-1983 L1991 GE IM *020 †20

DUFRESNE, Scott Dennis. ■ 15232 #024-12-2004 L2007 HMP *012 †50

DUGAN, Maria Procopio. 5889 FORBES AVE 2ND FL 15217 #041-77-1987, ▲ L1988 FM *040

DUGAR, Anand Raj. ■ 15213 #041-02-2004 L2004 AN *012

DUGGAL, Priyanka. 1039 BROOKLINE BLVD 15226 #495-30-1996 L2003 IM *100 †20

DUGGAL ANAND, Mona D. 300 HALKET ST STE 5 15213 #495-45-1994 L2006 IM *020 †20

DUHL, Adam Jon. 1400 LOCUST ST, STE 5108MAC 15219 #008-02-1993 L1995 OBG MFM *020 †30

DUKER, Daniel Gregory. 9100 BABCOCK BLVD 15237 #041-12-1958 L1959 AN *020 †05

DULAI, Harjot Singh. ■ 15205 #051-01-2002 L2007 RNR *012 †80

DULDULAO, Edmundo Fidel B. 5230 CENTRE AVE 15232 #748-10-1999 L2005 FP *012

DUMOUCHEL, Justin Peter. ■ 15232 #041-12-2003 L2006 IM *012

DUNAI, Judit. 121 MEYRAN AVE, UPMC MONTEFIORE N-713 15213 #051-04-2006 L2006 IM *012

DUNBAR, Rebecca Charlotte. 7180 HIGHLAND DR, VETERANS ADM MED CTR 15206 #051-01-1982 L1983 IM *020

DUNCAN, Steven Ray. 3459 5TH AVE, ALLERGY & CRITICAL/NW 628, 15213 #054-04-1981 L1984 IM *050 †20

DUNCAN-GLOSTER, Carol V. 7227 HAMILTON AVE, ALMA ILLERY MEDICAL CENTER 15208 #041-12-1992 L1995 PD *020

DUNKLEBARGER, Joshua Lynn. ■ 15218 #041-12-2006 L2006 OTO *012

DUNMIRE, Lester Addison. 4815 LIBERTY AVE 15224 #041-12-1948 L1949 GS *071 †85

DUNMIRE, Susan Mitchell. 200 LOTHROP ST 15213 #041-12-1985 L1986 EM *020 †16

DUNN, Jeanette Coblentz. 5230 CENTRE AVE, DEPT OF RADIATION ONCOLOGY 15232 #041-02-1979 L1987 PTH MM *020 †50

DUONG, Phuong-Anh Thi. 200 LOTHROP ST, CHPMT 3950 15213 #041-01-1999 L2001 DR *020 †80

DURGAMPUDI, Chandra Sekha. 1500 5TH AVE, DEPT OF INTERNAL MED 15219 #496-24-2000 L2007 IM *012

DURICK, Janet Elaine. 200 LOTHROP ST, RADIOLOGY, SUITE E-177, FI 15213 #038-40-1989 L1995 DR *020 †80

DURNING, Robert Peter. 215 CRIDERS LN 15237 #055-01-1973 L1980 ORS *020 †40

DVERGSTEN, Suzanne E. 3705 5TH AVE, CHOB STE 301 15213 #026-04-1990 L2007 PD *020 †55

DYER, Richard Kerry. 180 FORT COUCH RD 15241 #030-05-1978 L1989 P *020 †75 ‡

EASLER, Richard Eugene. ■ 15238 #041-02-1957 L1958 PTH *071 †50

EASTMAN, Laura Bair. 102 OLD CLAIRTON RD 15236 #041-07-1948 L1950 GP *072

EATON, Debbie Anderson. 4815 LIBERTY AVE, STE 443 15224 #041-12-1997 L2003 OTO *020 †45

■ = Address Information Privacy Protected

EBBERT, Colleen Kennedy. 619 MT ROYAL BLVD, RENAISSANCE FAMILY PRACTIC 15223 #041-12-1993 L1995 **FM** *020 †18

EBERZ, Dennis Ambrose. 1501 LOCUST ST, STE 1070 15219 #041-12-1973 L1974 **CD IM** *020 †20 ‡

ECK, Jeffrey Raymond. 200 DELAFIELD RD, STE 2070 15215 #041-12-2001 L2002 **APM** *020

EDELMANN, Christine A. 300 HALKET ST, MAGEE WOMENS HOSPITAL 15213 #033-05-1977 L1983 **AN PD** *020 †05

EDELSTONE, Daniel Israel. 300 HALKET ST, DEPT OF OB/GYN & WOMENS HE 15213 #005-06-1972 L1973 **OBS MFM** *040 †30

EDINGTON, Howard David J. 300 HALKET ST 15213 #041-13-1981 L1982 **PS GS** *020 †65,85

EDMONDS, Rebecca Denise. ■ 15218 #041-15-2004 L2004 **GS** *012

EDMUNDOWICZ, Daniel. 120 LYTTON AVE STE 302 15213 #041-09-1990 L1992 **CD** *020 †20

EDWARDS, Anita. 2027 LEBANON CHURCH RD, CENTURY III MED ASSOC 15122 #010-03-1985 L1986 **IM** *020 †20

EDWARDS, Robert Gordon. ■ 15224 #041-12-1975 L1976 **FM OBG** *020

EDWARDS, Robert Page. 300 HALKET ST, STE 2130 15213 #041-12-1984 L1985 **OBG GO** *020 †30

EDWARDS, Terry Lynn. A-1305 SCAIFE HALL, ANESTHESIOLOGY & CRITICAL 15261 #041-02-1984 L1999 **DR** *020 †20

EELKEMA, Elizabeth Anne. 1000 BOWER HILL RD 15243 #026-08-1981 L1986 **DR RNR** *080

EGAN, Richard J, Jr. 300 FLEET ST, STE 100 15220 #041-02-1984 L1985 **FM** *020 †18

EGORIN, Merrill Jon. 200 LOTHROP ST, UPP-IM-HEM/ONC 15213 #023-07-1973 L1998 **ON PA** *050 †20

EHLER, Joan Gertrude. 3811 OHARA ST 15213 #041-12-1958 L1959 **P** *020 †75

EIBLING, David Edward. 2000 MARY ST 15203 #038-40-1973 L1985 **OTO HNS** *020 †45

EICHMILLER, John Paul. 200 MARY ST, SOUTH SIDE HOSP 15203 #047-06-1959 L1962 **AN** *071 †05

EID, George Michel. 300 HALKET ST, STE 5500 15213 #605-01-1996 L2001 **GS** *020 †85

EIDSON, Kasey Michelle. ■ 15213 #041-12-2008 *012

EINHORN, Jerzy. 200 LOTHROP ST 15213 #759-04-1951 L1971 **IM END** *071

EINHORN, Robert K. ■ 15213 #649-35-1984 **GS FM** *020

EINWOHNER, Rebecca Susan. 1400 LOCUST ST, M P O BOX 104 15219 #033-05-1997 L1999 **NEP** *040 †20 ‡

EISENBERG, David Paul. ■ 15217 #035-19-2000 L2007 **GS** *100 †85

EISENSTEIN, Eli Michael. 4037 LUDWICK ST 15217 #056-05-1986 L1987 **PD** *020 †03,55

EISNER, Jennifer Lauren. ■ 15214 #023-07-2007 L2007 **EM** *012

EKECHUKU, Chinyere Iheoma. 5230 CENTRE AVE, UPMC SHADYSIDE HOSPITAL 15232 #690-02-1992 L1999 **IMG IM** *020 †20

EKKA, Shweta. 1400 LOCUST ST 15219 #495-53-2001 L2005 **IM** *012

ELAPAVALURU, Subbarao. 3550 TERRACE ST, UPMC PRESBYTERIAN HOSP 15261 #495-70-1991 L2006 **CCM** *012 †20

EL-ATTAR, Anas Amin. ■ 15243 #330-02-1957 L1969 **OM GPM** *071 †70

EL AYASS, Walid Issam. 3708 5TH AVE, DEPT OF MED EDU 15213 #605-01-2001 L2006 **IM** *012

ELBAGHDADI, Mariam Mahdi. ■ 15222 #021-01-2006 L2006 **AN** *012

EL BAYADI, George Sherif. ■ 15237 #041-15-2007 **TY** *012

ELDER, Robert William. ■ 15216 #008-02-2005 L2005 **MPD** *012

ELFORD, Brian R. ■ 15235 #041-77-1999, ▲ L2000 **OTO** *020

EL-HACHEM, Sandra Michel. ■ 15217 #605-01-2003 L2007 **GE** *012 †20

EL HAJJ, Ihab Ibrahim. 200 LOTHROP ST, STE 503 15213 #895-03-2001 L2007 **IM** *012

ELIAS, Garth Abraham. 9104 BABCOCK BLVD, STE 4110 15237 #041-09-1989 L1991 **GS** *020 †85

ELIAS, Stanton Bernard. 1018 W VIEW PARK DR 15229 #041-12-1957 L1958 **OPH** *071 †35

ELIGATOR, Nancy Ruth. 300 HALKET ST, MAGEE WOMENS HOSPITAL 15213 #038-06-1992 L1997 **OBG** *020 †30

ELISHAEV, Esther. ■ 15217 #473-04-1995 L2004 **SP** *100 †50

EL-KADI, Hikmat Abbas. 9100 BABCOCK BLVD STE 2096, UPMC PASSAVANT 2 MAIN 15237 #913-15-1983 L1997 **NS** *020 †25

ELLER, Andrew William. 203 LOTHROP ST, THE EYE & EAR INSTITUTE 15213 #041-09-1979 L1980 **OPH** *020 †20

ELLERMEYER, John Chas. ■ 15237 #033-05-1960 L1961 **EM** *071

ELLIOTT, Jennifer Rae. 3500 TERRACE ST, BSTWR S716 15213 #030-05-2001 L2004 **RHU** *100

ELLIS, Carolyn Denese. 532 S AIKEN AVE 15232 #041-12-1992 L1994 **IM** *020

ELLIS, Demetrius. 125 DESOTO ST, CHILDREN'S HOSP OF PITTSBU 15213 #035-06-1973 L1974 **PN PD** *050 †55

ELLIS, Kris Louis. 1000 BOWER HILL RD 15243 #041-12-1983 L1985 **DR** *020 †80

ELLIS, Lawrence Dobson. 3471 5TH AVE, STE 1111 15213 #041-12-1958 L1959 **IM HEM** *020 †20 ‡

ELLIS, Peter Gerard. 200 DELAFIELD RD, STE 3050 15215 #041-12-1985 L1986 **ON HEM** *020 †20

ELLIS, Ramsey Ann. ■ 15217 #028-02-2000 L2007 **HSP** *012

ELLISON, Patricia H. ■ 15213 #041-12-1970 L1971 **N CHN** *071 †55,75

EL-MAGBRI, Awad Ali. 5140 LIBERTY AVE, RENAL-ENDOCRINE ASSOCIATE 15224 #613-01-1981 L2006 **NEP** *020 †20

ELMER, Edward Marx. 532 S AIKEN AVE 15232 #021-01-1970 L1972 **OTO** *071 †45

ELNICKI, David Michael. 5200 CENTRE AVE, STE 211 15232 #041-12-1983 L2000 **IM** *020 †20

EL TOM, Bassem Mohamad Na. ARTS BUILDIN, STE 503 MEDICAL 15213 #605-04-2003 L2007 **FP** *012

ELWOOD, Hillary Rose. ■ 15217 #041-12-2008 *012

EMEJUAIWE, Nkechinyere. S 716 BST, 3500 TERRACE STREET 15261 #286-13-2000 L2006 **RHU** *012 †20

EMERY, Stephen Paul. 300 HALKET ST RM 2, DEPT OF OB/GYN - RS 15213 #001-02-1991 L2006 **OBG** *020 †30

EMLET, Lillian Liang. 721 BEAR RUN DR 15237 #041-02-2001 L2001 **EM** *100 †16

ENAMA, Joseph Lawrence. ARTHRITIS I, UNIV OF PITTSBURGH 15261 #041-14-2002 L2004 **RHU** *012 †20

ENDRES, Melanie Marie. 121 MEYRAN AVE, UNIV HLTH CTR OF PITTSBURGH 15213 #033-06-2005 L2005 **OBG** *012

ENERSON, Daniel Milton. 4800 FRIENDSHIP AVE 15224 #016-02-1946 L1962 **TS** *071 †85,90

ENGH, Johnathan Anderson. 200 LOTHROP ST, UNIVERSITY OF PITTSBURGH 15213 #051-01-2001 L2001 **NS** *012

ENGLAND, Michael Vincent. 300 HALKET ST, STE 1338 15213 #041-14-1988 L1991 **OBG** *020 †30

ENGLE, David John. 1501 LOCUST ST, STE 224 15219 #041-12-1983 L1984 **NS** *020 †30

ENGLE, Jamison Joel. ■ 15212 #018-03-2007 L2007 **IM** *012

ENGLISH, Joseph C, III. 190 LOTHROP ST, STE 145 15213 #041-14-1991 L2003 **D** *020 †15

ENNIS, Michael Francis. 1000 INTEGRITY DR, ASSOCIATES INC 15235 #041-12-1973 L1974 **GE IM** *020 †20 ‡

ENNIS, Willis Ashton. ■ 15205 #051-07-2006 L2007 **PTH** *012

ENRIQUEZ, Danilo L. 1726 E CARSON ST 15203 #748-02-1971 L1976 **PM PME** *020 †60

ENTABI, Fateh. ■ 15232 #875-01-2003 L2006 **GS** *100

EPPINGER, Mary Ann. 2644 BANKSVILLE RD, FAMILY LINKS 15216 #041-12-1971 L1972 **CHP P** *020 †75 ‡

EPSTEIN, David Michael. 4800 FRIENDSHIP AVE 15224 #041-09-1974 L1975 **DR** *020 †20,80

ERB, Kathleen Marie. 320 E NORTH AVE, ALLEGHENY CANCER CENTER 15212 #041-14-1977 L1978 **GS VS** *020 †85

ERDOS, Jennifer Ann. 1307 FEDERAL ST, ALLEGHENY GENERAL HOSPITAL 15212 #041-02-2002 L2002 **ORS** *020

ERICKSON, Lee Kim. 5889 FORBES AVE, 2ND FL 15217 #038-06-1993 L2001 **FM** *020 †18

ERKAN, Elif. 3705 5TH AVE 15213 #902-03-1990 L2005 **PD** *020 †55

ERSOZ, Namik. 600 GRANT ST STE 3280 15219 #902-03-1956 L1965 **AN** *071 †05

ERTEL, James Michael. 320 E NORTH AVE 15212 #041-12-1987 L1990 **AN** *020 †05

ESCOBAR, Oscar. 3705 5TH AVE 15213 #264-05-1986 L2000 **PDE** *020 †55

ESCOTT, Edward Joel. 200 LOTHROP ST D-132, DETP OF RADIO UPMC PRESBVY 15213 #035-03-1989 L2004 **DR** *020 †80

ESMAN, Judith Hannah. 9104 BABCOCK BLVD, STE 2120 15237 #035-20-1984 L1985 **PM IM** *020 †20,60

ESPEJO, Maria Magnolia So. 5230 CENTRE AVE 15232 #748-01-2000 L2005 **FP** *012

ESPER, Stephen Andrew. ■ 15213 #041-12-2007 L2007 **AN** *012

ESPIRITU, Michael T. 3471 5TH AVE STE 1011 15213 #048-04-2002 L2002 **ORS** *100

ESPOSITO, Francis Anthony. 5230 CENTRE AVE 15232 #041-12-1959 L1960 **PD** *071 †55

ESPOSITO, Nicole Nicosia. ■ 15232 #011-04-2003 L2003 **SP** *012 †50

ESSIG, Michael J. 309 SMITHFIELD ST STE 200, SMITHFIELD MEDICAL 15222 #041-12-1978 L1987 **FM** *020 †18

ESTEVE, Flavia Ramos. 5150 CENTRE AVE, UPMC CANCER PAVILLION 15232 #187-46-2002 L2002 **HO** *012 †20

ESTEVEZ, Miguel. 3471 5TH AVE, STE 810 LILLIAN KAUFMANN B 15213 #028-03-1997 L2000 **N** *020 †75

ESTRADA, Juan Martinez. 815 FREEPORT RD 15215 #649-03-1978 L1985 **CD IM** *020 †20

ETZEL, Kathleen Diane. ■ 15241 #041-12-1988 L1988 **DR** *020 †80

EVANS, Carol. 5115 CENTRE AVE, FL 3 15232 #041-12-1981 L1984 **ON HEM** *020 †20

EVANS, Eric Todd. 107 GAMMA DR, STE 107 15238 #041-12-1992 L1992 **ORS** *020 †40

EVANS, Leonard Elliot. 5200 CENTRE AVE, STE 211 15232 #041-12-1976 L1977 **GS** *020 †20

EVANS, Robert Brendon Jam. 121 MEYRAN AVE, UNIV HLTH CTR OF PITTSBURG 15213 #836-02-1999 L2004 **GE** *012 †20

EVANS, Steven. 5200 CENTRE AVE, STE 211 15232 #010-01-1985 L1986 **PDS ON** *020 †85

EVANS, Thomas Milton. ■ 15243 #041-12-1943 L1944 **OPH** *071 †35

EVERETT, Genevieve Lynn. ■ 15217 #041-02-2004 L2004 **GD** *012 †20

EVRON, Wayne A. 5140 LIBERTY AVE, RENAL-ENDOCRINE ASSOCIATES 15224 #041-01-1980 L1982 **IM END** *020 †20

EZARU, Catalin. 3550 TERRACE ST, A-1305 SCAIFE HALL 15261 #781-01-1995 L2001 **AN** *020 †05

FABER, Christopher Neal. 3601 5TH AVE, COMPREHENSIVE LUNG CENTER 15213 #041-12-1984 L1985 **IM** *020 †20

FABER, Debra Marlene. 1580 MCLAUGHLIN RUN RD, STE 208 15241 #041-12-1995 L1998 **PD** *020 †55

FABER, Scott H. 1405 SHADY AVE, CHILDRENS INSTITUTE OF PIT 15217 #041-12-1984 L1998 **PD** *020 †55

FABREGA, Horacio, Jr. 3501 FORBES AVE RM 353 15213 #035-01-1960 L1978 **P** *020 †75

FACKLER, Andrew C. 815 FREEPORT RD 15215 #051-01-1999 L2001 **FM** *020 †18 ‡

FACKOVEC, Michael. 309 SMITHFIELD ST, STE 200 15222 #305-01-1981 L1986 **FM GS** *020 †18

FAGER, Joseph Shearer. ■ 15238 #041-01-1942 L1943 **P** *071 †75

FAGIOLINI, Andrea. 3811 OHARA ST 15213 #561-16-1993 L2001 **P** *050

FAIX, Laura Elaine. 300 HALKET ST 15213 #055-01-2000 L2001 **DR** *012 †80

FAJT, Merritt Lynn. ■ 15238 #041-13-2004 L2004 **AI** *012 †20

FAKHRAN, Saeed. ■ 15213 #051-01-2004 L2005 **DR** *012

FALBO, Ralph Augustus, III. 1000 BOWER HILL RD 15243 #041-12-1998 L2001 **EM** *020 †16

FALCONE, John Lawrence. 15221 #041-12-2006 L2006 **GS** *012

FALLERT, Michael Anthony. 1 MELLON BANK CTR, STE 2210 15219 #041-01-1986 L1987 **CD IC** *020 †20

FALO, Louis D, Jr. 200 LOTHROP ST 15213 #024-01-1988 L1993 **D** *050

FAM, Ezz Elarab. ■ 15217 #915-02-1986 L2001 **CCM** *020 †20

FAMADOR, Ma. Liza Ann Flo. 121 MEYRAN AVE 15213 #748-10-2003 L2006 **FP** *012

FAN, Katherine Weichen. 3811 OHARA AVE, E502 15213 #001-02-2003 L2003 **CPP** *012

FARAHI, Narges. ■ 15261 #041-12-2007 **FP** *012

FARCHIONE, Tiffany Rose. 3811 OHARA ST, RM 215 LOEFFLER BLDG 15213 #025-07-2002 L2002 **CHP** *020 †75

FARGIANO, Antonio A. ■ 15222 #035-15-2007 L2007 **TY** *012

FARHI, Parisa. 203 LOTHROP ST, EYE AND EAR 8TH FLOOR 15213 #041-12-2003 L2003 **OPH** *020

FARKAS, Linda M. 5150 CENTRE AVE 4TH FL, UPMC CANCER PAVILION 15232 #016-43-1989 L1995 **CRS GS** *020 †85,10

FARMER, Lenore. 1000 BOWER HILL RD 15243 #041-12-1970 L1971 **P PYG** *020 †75

FAROOQ, Umar. 121 MEYRAN AVE 15213 #704-01-2001 L2005 **IM** *012

FARR, Russell Mark. 3811 OHARA ST, AND CLINIC ROOM 672 15213 #016-02-1981 L1982 **P** *020 †75 ‡

FARRELL, Edward L. ■ 15241 #041-12-1951 L1952 **FPG FM** *072

FARRELL, Kristin Marie. 320 E NORTH AVE, 6TH FLOOR, SOUTH TOWER 15212 #024-16-2003 L2006 **PD** *020 †55

FARRELL, Michael Joseph. 880 BUTLER ST 15223 #041-12-1993 L1995 **IM** *020 †20

FARRIS, Joan Stalzer. 5200 CENTRE AVE, STE 211 15232 #051-01-1995 L2006 **IM** *020 †20

FARRIS, R Wesley, II. 3501 5TH AVE, BST3-7019 15213 #051-01-1996 L2006 **N** *020 †75

FASANELLA, Kenneth Edward. 200 LOTHROP ST, MEZZANINE LEVEL 2, C-WING 15213 #051-01-2001 L2004 **GE** *100

FASIUDDIN, Orooj Fatima. 3705 5TH AVE 15213 #023-01-2002 L2005 **PD** *020 †55

FASIUDDIN, Rashida B. ■ 15206 #495-65-1975 L1990 **PD** *020

FATIGATI, Mario Jay. 615 WASHINGTON RD, STE TL4 15228 #561-17-1982 L1984 **IM** *020 †20

FATO, Michelina. 4815 LIBERTY AVE, STE GR-30 15224 #041-12-1986 L1987 **IM** *020 †20

FAUL, Clare Mary. 300 HALKET ST, MAGEE WOMENS HOSPITAL 15213 #539-04-1986 L1996 *020

FEDEN, Jeffrey Preston. 230 MCKEE PL, STE 500 15213 #051-04-2004 L2004 **FSM** *012

FEDERLE, Michael Peter. 200 LOTHROP ST, RAD/CHP MAIN TOWER 15213
#010-02-1974 L1989 **R AR** *020 †80

FEDUSKA, Richard Geo. 4800 FRIENDSHIP AVE, WESTERN PA HOSP 15224
#041-02-1981 L1982 **AN CD** *020 †05 ‡

FEDYSHIN, Peter Joseph. 9100 BABCOCK BLVD 15237 #041-14-1976 L1985 **DR** *020 †80

FEINGOLD, Brian David. 3705 5TH AVE 15213 #041-12-1999 L2002 **PDC** *020 †55

FEINSTEIN, Trevor Mayer. 5150 CENTRE AVE 461 15232 #016-11-2003 L2003 **HO** *012 †20

FEIST, John H. PRESBY UNIVERSITY HOSPT, RADIOLOGY DEPT 15213 #041-13-1950 L1951
DR *072 †80

FELDER, Herman. 3447 FORBES AVE 15213 #041-12-1958 L1959 **OTO** *071 †45

FELDER, Jill D. 532 S AIKEN AVE, STE 509 15232 #035-47-1989 L1991 **END IM** *020 †20

FELDER, Louis Steven. 969 GREENTREE RD 15220 #035-09-1989 L1993 **OTO** *020 †45

FELDMAN, Myra Kay. 4800 FRIENDSHIP AVE, DEPT OF RADIOLOGY 15224 #035-06-2004 L2005
DR *012

FELGAR, Raymond. 200 LOTHROP ST, RM A351.1 15213 #041-12-1992 L1994
HMP PTH *020 †50 ‡

FELIZ, Alexander. ■ 15206 #035-47-1997 L2004 **PDS** *012 †85

FELMET, Kathryn Allison. 3705 5TH AVE 15213 #040-02-1997 L2000 **CCP** *030 †55

FENSTER, Martin M. ■ 15238 #041-02-1972 L1973 **IM** *071 †20

FERGUSON, Albert B, Jr. ■ 15238 #024-01-1943 L1953 **ORS** *071 †40

FERGUSON, Berrylin J. 200 LOTHROP ST, STE 234 15213 #036-07-1980 L1992 **OTO A** *020 †45

FERGUSON, David Michael. 7171 CHURCHLAND ST 15206 #041-01-1996 L1998 **FM** *020 †18

FERGUSON, Laura Hays. ■ 15221 #036-01-2005 L2005 **AN** *012

FERGUSON, Roger John. 5900 CORPORATE DR STE 200 15237 #035-06-1969 L1972
ORS *071 †40

FERIMER, Howard Norman. 1400 LOCUST ST, MERCY HOSP OF PITTSBURGH 15219
#055-01-1987 L1989 **CCP** *020 †55

FERNAIN, Khaled Elias. 121 MEYRAN AVE, UNIV HLTH CTR 15213 #605-01-2002 L2007
PCC *012 †20

FERNAU, James Lawrence. 1000 CLIFFMINE RD, PARK WEST ONE, SUITE 120 15275
#049-01-1986 L1973 **PS OTO** *020 †45,65 ‡

FERRANTE, James Angelo. 619 MOUNT ROYAL BLVD 15223 #041-12-1965 L1966 **FM** *030 †18

FERRARO, Francis Thos. 5000 MCKNIGHT RD STE 202 15237 #041-13-1981 L1987
NS GS *020 †25

FERRERA, Marisa Huliganga. ■ 15206 #051-04-2005 L2005 **AN** *012

FERRIS, James Vincent. 200 LOTHROP ST 15213 #023-01-1988 L1993 **DR** *020 †80

FERRIS, Joseph Michael. 600 GRANT ST, RM 481 15219 #041-09-1981 L1982
OM FM *020 †18,70

FERRIS, Laura Korb. 190 LOTHROP ST, 145 LOTHROP HALL 15213 #023-01-2002 L2002
D *100 †15

FERRIS, Robert Louis. 203 LOTHROP ST 15213 #023-07-1995 L2001 **OTO** *020 †45

FERRONE, Marco Luigi. ■ 15217 #010-01-2003 L2008 *100

FERSON, Peter Fleming. 200 LOTHROP ST 15213 #041-12-1973 L1974 **TS** *040 †85,90

FERTIG, Alexis Marianna. ■ 15203 #021-01-2004 L2004 **CPP** *012

FIDELER, Richard Ward P. 414 S CRAIG ST 15213 #038-06-1971 L1977 **NS** *020

FIDLER, Christian Joseph. ■ 15206 #041-14-2006 L2006 **IM** *012

FIEDOR, Melinda Lee. 3705 5TH AVE 15213 #030-06-1996 L1999 **CCP** *030 †55

FIELD, Richard A. 1400 LOCUST ST, DEPT OF ANESTHESIOLOGY 15219 #005-76-2002, ▲ L2003
AN *020

FIGGINS, Margaret M. ■ 15222 #918-01-1954 **PHP** *071

FIGURA, Judith A Haschak. 4800 FRIENDSHIP AVE, ASSOCIATION 15224 #041-07-1969 L1970
RO DR *020 †80

FILIPEK, Steele William. 1330 OLD FREEPORT RD, STE 1A 15238 #041-12-1977 L1978
GYN *030

FILIPINK, Robyn Ann. 3705 5TH AVE, CHILDREN'S HOSPITAL OF PIT 15213 #035-06-2002 L2002
NDN *012 †55

FINDER, Jonathan Danl. 3705 5TH AVE, PULMONOLOGY 15213 #035-03-1986 L1993
PDP *020 †55

FINE, Joseph. ■ 15213 #132-03-1958 L1966 **FM AN** *020 †05 ‡

FINE, Michael Jonah. UNIVERSITY DRIVE C MB 28, STE 1A102 15240 #041-09-1983 L1985
IM *020 †20

FINEGOLD, David Neal. 3705 5TH AVE 15213 #041-12-1972 L1974 **PDE** *050 †55,19

FINEGOLD, Helene. 4800 FRIENDSHIP AVE # 451 15224 #010-01-1992 L1996 **AN** *020 †05

FINGERET, Abbey Leigh. ■ 15215 #041-15-2008 *012

FINIKIOTIS, Michael W. 6301 FORBES AVE, STE 301 15217 #041-12-1989 L1991 **IM** *020 †20

FINK, Ericka Linn. 3705 5TH AVE, CRITICAL CARE (PEDIATRIC) 15213 #041-02-1999 L2001
PD CCP *020 †55

FINKELSTEIN, Alan Lewis. 5230 CENTRE AVE, UPMC-SHADYSIDE FAMILY HLTH 15232
#041-12-1993 L2000 **FM** *020 †18

FINKELSTEIN, Sydney David. 200 LOTHROP ST, UPPPTHLGYPRSBYTRN UNV HSPT 15213
#067-01-1977 L1984 **ATP NP** *020 †50

FINLAY, James William. 400 PENN CENTER BLVD, BLDG 4 15235 #041-12-1955 L1956
OPH *020 †35

FINO, Gregory John. 1000 BOWER HILL RD, STE 211 15243 #041-12-1976 L1977 **PUD** *020 †20

FINO, Marsha J. 1789 S BRADDOCK AVE 15218 #038-44-1992 L1994 **IM** *020 †20

FIORILLO, Anthony B, Jr. 120 LYTTON AVE, SUITE 100A, UNIVERSITY CEN 15213
#038-41-1982 L1984 **ATP NP** *020 †55,03

FIREMAN, Philip. 3705 5TH AVE, CHILDRENS HOSP 15213 #016-02-1957 L1958 **AI** *020 †55,03

FIRESTONE, Leonard Lewis. 200 LOTHROP ST, ANES/SCAIFE HALL 15213 #008-01-1976 L1987
AN *050 †05

FISCH, Laura Naomi. ■ 15217 #065-09-1998 L2000 *100

FISCHBACH, Marnin Eli. 1702 WIGHTMAN ST 15217 #035-19-1970 L2000 **P** *020 †75

FISCHER, Donald R. 120 5TH AVE, STE 748 15222 #016-11-1977 L1978 **PDC PD** *020 †55

FISCHER, Gary S. 200 LOTHROP ST, MUH 920W 15213 #024-01-1990 L1993 **IM** *040 †20

FISCHER, Ryan Thomas. 3705 5TH AVE 15213 #030-05-2002 L2005 **PG** *012 †55

FISCHL, Edwin Chester. 120 5TH AVE, STE 2015 15222 #041-01-1970 L1972 **GS CRS** *020 †85

FISHER, Alfred Leo. 3471 5TH AVE STE 300, UNIV OF PITT DIV GER MED 15213
#035-20-1999 L2005 **IMG** *050 †20

FISHER, Andrew S. ■ 15228 #041-12-2008 *012

FISHER, Barry Wm. 7180 HIGHLAND DR, VAMC PITTS HIGHLAND DR DIV 15206
#017-20-1986 L1987 **P ADP** *020 †75

FISHER, Bernard. 200 LOTHROP ST, STE 7098 15213 #041-12-1943 L1944 **GS** *062 †85

FISHER, Christine. UNIVERSITY OF PITTSBURGH, 3550 TERRACE STREET 15261
#048-02-2006 L2006 **PS** *012

FISHER, Curtis Kinnear. 490 NORTH AVE STE 301 15212 #041-12-1976 L1977 **CD IM** *071 †20

FISHER, Don L. 320 E NORTH AVE 15212 #028-02-1943 L1952 **CD** *020 †20

FISHER, Edwin Ralph. 320 E NORTH AVE, ALLEGHENY GENERAL HOSPITAL 15212
#041-12-1947 L1948 **PTH** *050 †50

FISHER, Gail Ann. 490 E NORTH AVE STE 402, ALLEGHENY RHEUMATOLOGY 15212
#041-07-1971 L1977 **RHU IM** *020 †20

FISHER, Stephen Neal. ■ 15217 #016-11-1966 L1971 **R GP** *071 †80

FISK, Jesse Alan. ■ 15232 #041-12-2008 *012

FITTING, Geo Matthew, Jr. 1400 LOCUST ST STE 2375 15219 #041-12-1964 L1965 **AN** *071 †05

FITZ, Charles Raymond. 3705 5TH AVE 15213 #025-01-1962 L1968 **RNR OS** *020 †80

FITZGERALD-MALONE, M. 3811 OHARA ST 15213 #539-06-1984 **P** *020

FITZPATRICK, Meghan Eilee. 121 MEYRAN AVE, UPMC MONTEFIORE N-713 15213
#041-13-2006 L2006 **IM** *012

FLAHERTY, Morgan. 4815 LIBERTY AVE STE 125 15224 #041-12-1979 L1980 **AI IM** *020 †20,03

FLANDERS, Sarah Elizabeth. 330 S 9TH ST, MERCY BEHAVORIAL HEALTH 15203
#041-13-1992 L1998 **P** *020 †75

FLANIGAN, Robert Earl. 1050 BOWER HILL RD, STE 305 15243 #041-12-1980 L1981
GE IM *020 †20

FLANNAGAN, Patrick Philip. 420 E NORTH AVE, STE 302 15212 #041-07-1992 L1994
NS *020 †25

FLANNERY, Ryan Garrett. ■ 15203 #041-13-2007 L2007 **GS** *012

FLATI, Veronica Rueda. 320 E NORTH AVE, DEPT OF PATHOLOGY 15212 #143-11-2001 L2005
PTH *100

FLEISCHER, Jessica Beth. 121 MEYRAN AVE DEPT MED 15213 #035-48-1997 L2000
END *020 †20

FLEISHMAN, Martin. ■ 15217 #041-12-1968 L1969 **LM** *075 †75

FLEISSNER, Christopher G. ■ 15229 #041-78-2006, ▲ L2006 **FP** *012

FLEMING, Arthur Wm, Jr. 2020 ARDMORE BLVD, STE 105 15221 #016-43-1965 L1969
OPH *020 †35 ‡

FLEMING, Cynthia Anne. 3705 5TH AVE, RADIOLOGY 15213 #035-46-1984 L2002
RNR GS *020 †80

FLETCHER, Derek Ryan Duan. UNIV OF PITTSBURGH, 3550 TERRACE STREET 15261
#054-04-2007 L2007 **PS** *012

FLICKINGER, John Chas. 200 LOTHROP ST, RAD ONC/3RD FL PUH 15213 #016-02-1981 L1985
RO OS *020 †80

FLINK, Carl Clifford. 320 E NORTH AVE, DEPT RAD 15212 #038-41-2006 L2007 **DR** *012

FLOM, David Milton. 3457 WARD ST 15213 #041-12-1942 L1943 **GP** *072

FLOM, Lynda Lorraine. 3705 5TH AVE 15213 #041-13-1981 L1982 **PDR DR** *020 †80

FLOOD, Hugh Declan. 3471 5TH AVE 15213 #539-04-1979 **U** *020

FLORES, Luis Rene. 5001 CENTRE AVE, FL 3 15213 #649-26-1985 L2004 **PTH DMP** *020

FLORES, Stephanie Diane. ■ 15213 #034-01-2006 L2006 **IM** *012

FLORIAN, Frederick M. 525 MOUNT PLEASANT RD, NORTHVIEW HEIGHTS 15214
#045-01-1981 L1985 **FM** *020 †18

FLUHME, Derrick Joseph. 363 VANADIUM RD, SURGERY ASSOCIATES PC 15243
#010-02-1999 L2001 **OSM** *020 †40

FOGOROS, Richard Nick. 200 LOTHROP ST 15213 #038-40-1975 L1976 **CD IM** *020 †20

FOLEY, Thomas Preston, Jr. 1160 FOX CHAPEL RD, UNIVERSITY OF PITTSBURGH 15238
#051-01-1963 L1971 **END PD** *050 †55

FOLLANSBEE, Wm Phillips. 200 LOTHROP ST 15213 #041-01-1974 L1975 **CD OS** *020 †20

FONTES, Paulo A C. 3459 5TH AVE, UPMC/MUH/N725 15213 #187-04-1985 L1998 **OS GS** *020

FOON, Kenneth Alan. 5115 CENTRE AVE, FL 3 15232 #025-07-1972 L2003 **HEM ON** *050 †20

FORBES, John Dexter. MOBAY RD, MILES INC 15205 #041-13-1964 L1987 **OM** *030 †70

FORBES, Thomas Wm. ■ 15238 #038-40-1968 L1972 **DR NR** *071 †80

FORD, Maisha Omari. ■ 15219 #038-04-2007 L2007 **EM** *012

FORD, Robert W. 9104 BABCOCK BLVD, PASSAVANT PROF BLDG S-6107 15237
#041-13-1963 L1967 **OBG** *071 †30

FORMAN, Steven David. 7180 HIGHLAND DR 15206 #035-47-1988 L1990 **P ADP** *020 †75

FORREST, Paige Elizabeth. ■ 15206 #041-12-2006 L2006 **FPP** *012

FORSTER, Janice Louise. 615 WASHINGTON RD STE 107 15228 #041-12-1977 L1979
CHP P *020 †75

FORTE, Patrick J. A-1305 SCAIFE HALL, DEPT OF ANESTHESIOLOGY 15261
#055-01-1982 L1996 **AN** *020 †20

FORTUNATO, James Junior. 4414 PENN AVE 15224 #561-10-1964 L1966 **OM EM** *071

FORTUNATO, Richard Alfons. 4800 FRIENDSHIP AVE 15224 #041-78-2004, ▲ **GS** *012

FOSS, David Edgar. 1700 GRANDVIEW AVE, 1004 GRANDVIEW TOWERS 15211
#025-01-1954 L1958 **ORS** *071 †40

FOSTER, Howard Kennedy. 401 SHADY AVE STE C202 15206 #041-01-1971 L1972
P PYA *020 †75

FOSTER, Mark Robt. 425 FIRST AVE AT CHRRY WAY 15219 #035-15-1979 L1980
ORS OSS *020 †40

FOSTER, Richard G, Jr. 4800 FRIENDSHIP AVE 15224 #035-15-1986 L1988 **DR** *020 †80

FOTIADIS, Ion G. 7180 HIGHLAND DR 15206 #418-01-1956 L1969 **IM GP** *071

FOUST, Katherine Marie. ■ 15224 #041-13-2006 L2006 **IM** *012

FOX, Andrea Rose. 200 JHF DR, SQUIRREL HILL HEALTH CENTE 15217 #024-05-1982 L1991
IMG IM *020 †20

FOX, Ira J. 3705 5TH AVE STE 4A492, CHILDREN'S HOSPITAL OF PIT 15213 #035-01-1976 L1984
OS GS *020 †85

FOX, Karl Richard. ■ 15228 #018-03-1967 L1984 **PTH HMP** *071 †50

FRAC, Michael John. 88 FORT COUCH RD, STE 100 15241 #010-02-1984 L1990 **PD** *020 †55

FRALEY, Donald Symons, Jr. 3550 TERRACE ST 15213 #041-12-1968 L1970
CCM NEP *020 †20

FRANCIS, Earlie Hill, III. 815 FREEPORT RD, UPMC ST. MARGARET HOSPITAL 15215
#051-01-1991 L1993 **IM EM** *020 †16

FRANCIS, Fadi F. 200 LOTHROP ST, C-WING 15213 #605-03-1992 L1997 **GE IM** *020 †20

FRANCIS, George James. 4727 FRIENDSHIP AVE 15224 #561-01-1971 L1982 **D IM** *020 †15

FRANGISKAKIS, John M. 200 LOTHROP ST, S553 SCAIFE HALL 15213 #025-01-2002 L2002
CD *100 †20

FRANGISKAKIS, Susan Marie. 3705 5TH AVE 15213 #049-01-1998 L2002 **PD** *020 †55

FRANK, Darren Andrew. 320 E NORTH AVE 15212 #041-15-2001 L2001 **OSM** *100

FRANK, Joshua Lee. 3811 OHARA ST 15213 #041-12-2004 L2004 **P** *012

FRANK, Leslie Aubrey. 446 LINCOLN AVE 15202 #008-02-1989 L1992 **PD** *020 †55

FRANK, Robert Larry, Jr. 13 PRIDE ST, EMAP 15219 #051-04-1997 L1994 **EM** *020 †16

FRANKEL, Eric Adam. 619 MT ROYAL BLVD 15223 #041-12-2002 L2002 **FM** *020 †18

FRANKLE, William Gordon. 3811 OHARA ST, WPIC 15213 #035-09-1996 L2006 **P** *020 †75

FRANKLIN, John William B. 815 FREEPORT RD 15215 #917-23-1965 L1970 **DR** *071 †80

FRANKMAN, Elizabeth Anne. 300 HALKET ST, MAGEE WOMENS HOSPITAL 15213
#026-04-2003 L2003 **OBG** *020

FRANKO, Jan. 5150 CENTRE AVE RM 414, DIVISION OF SURGICAL ONCOL 15232
#286-06-1996 L2002 **SO GS** *020

FRANKO, John James. ■ 15237 #056-06-1958 L1959 **GP OS** *071

FRANZ, John. 1050 BOWER HILL RD STE 101 15243 #010-02-1968 L1981 **U** *020 †95

FRANZ, Thomas Allen. 2585 FREEPORT RD, STE 105 15238 #017-20-1987 L1989 **PM** *020 †60

FREDERICK, Irene Beth. 300 HALKET ST 15213 #041-14-1976 L1990 **OBG** *020 †30

FREDERICK, Kristin Lynn. 4411 STILLEY RD 15227 #041-12-1991 L1993 **PD** *020 †55

FREEDMAN, Bethany Dawn. ■ 15206 #016-06-2006 L2006 **PD** *012

FREEDMAN, Steven Alan. 130 N BELLEFIELD AVE 15213 #024-01-1973 L1979 **P** *020 †75

FREEMAN, Brenda Kaye. 412 E COMMONS 15213 #016-45-1990 L1993 **P** *020 †20,75

FREEMAN, David Ross. 901 WEST ST, STE B 15221 #038-40-1990 L1992 **FM** *020 †18

FREEMAN, Michael Aloysius. ■ 15239 #035-03-2008 *012

FREEMAN, Robert Roger. DESOTO & OHARA ST, RAD DEPT 15213 #143-01-1962 **R** *020

FREIBERG, Matthew Scott. 230 MCKEE PL, STE 200 15213 #040-02-1995 L2005 **IM** *020 †20

FREIJE IBANEZ, Mercedes. ■ 15219 #847-11-2004 L2007 **IM** *012

FRENCH, Russell Edward. 320 E NORTH AVE, DEPT OF MED EDU 15212 #422-01-2006 L2006 **IM** *012

FREYVOGEL, Nancy Carol. 320 E NORTH AVE, ALLEGHENY GENERAL HOSPITAL 15212 #041-09-1994 L1997 **IM** *020 †20

FRIBERG, Thomas Richard. 203 LOTHROP ST 15213 #026-04-1973 L1985 **OPH** *020 †35

FRIDAY, Gilbert Anthony. 180 FORT COUCH RD 15241 #041-13-1956 L1957 **PD AI** *071 †55,03

FRIDAY, Rupert Hermes. 1400 LOCUST ST 15219 #041-12-1938 **GYN** *071 †30

FRIED, Linda Faith. 0 UNIVERSITY DRIVE C, RENAL/VA HOSP 15240 #035-47-1990 L1993 **NEP IM** *050 †20

FRIEDEL, Jeffrey Mark. 1050 BOWER HILL RD, STE 380 15243 #041-14-1997 L1999 **CD IC** *020 †20

FRIEDLAND, David Michael. 5115 CENTRE AVE, FL 3 15232 #023-01-1989 L1991 **HEM** *020 †20

FRIEDLANDER, Eric Jason. 88 FORT COUCH RD, STE 100 15241 #041-12-2000 L2001 **PD** *020 †55 ‡

FRIEDMAN, Abe W. 5845 CENTRE AVE, CARDIOLOGY OFFICE 15206 #016-42-1974 L1979 **CD IM** *020 †20

FRIEDMAN, Catherine Ruth. 3811 OHARA ST, 1ST FL 15213 #024-01-2001 L2005 **P** *012

FRIEDMAN, Edward Stuart. 3811 OHARA ST 15213 #041-12-1985 L1987 **P** *050 †75

FRIEHLING, Erika Dawn. ■ 15206 #051-01-2006 L2006 **PD** *012

FRIEHLING, Mati Simon. ■ 15206 #051-01-2005 L2005 **IM** *012

FRIEND, Kevin David. 2000 MARY ST, UPMC SOUTH SIDE 15203 #035-19-1996 L1998 **EM** *020 †16

FROMKIN, Janet Beth. 320 E NORTH AVE 15212 #010-01-1983 L1984 **PD** *020 †55

FRUTIGER, Adrian. 4200 5TH AVE, DEPT ANES 15261 #869-02-1973 L1977 **AN GS** *050

FRYE, Roy Alan. 729 SCAIFE HALL, DEPT OF PATHOLOGY U PITT 15261 #025-01-1985 L1992 **PTH** *020 †50

FU, Ho-Keung Fred. 3471 5TH AVE, STE 1011 15213 #041-12-1977 L1978 **OSM** *020 †40

FUCHS, Julie Robin. 3705 5TH AVE 15213 #028-02-1997 L2006 **PDS** *020 †55

FUGE, La Donna Helaine. 300 PENN CENTER BLVD, STE 702 15235 #041-09-1985 L1986 **FM** *020 †18

FUHRER, Russell Stuart. 320 E NORTH AVE 15212 #035-06-1987 L1989 **RO** *020 †80 ‡

FUHRMAN, Carl Robt. 200 LOTHROP ST 15213 #041-12-1979 L1980 **R** *020 †80

FUJII, Hiroaki. FAIRFAX APARTMENTS 15213 #572-29-1985 L1993 **PTH** *100 †50

FUJIOKA, Mutsuhisa. 125 DE SOTO ST 15213 #572-38-1966 L1976 **PDR** *020 †80

FUJIOKA, Yosuke. 5215 CENTRE AVE 15232 #572-30-1989 L2003 **FM** *100 †18

FUKUI, Melanie B. 200 LOTHROP ST, RAD/CHP MAIN TOWER 15213 #041-12-1987 L1987 **RNR R** *020 †80 ‡

FULCHER-HAWKINS, Kara Bre. ■ 15243 #051-04-2003 L2006 **END** *012 †20

FULTON, David John. 211 N WHITFIELD ST, FAMILYLINKS 15206 #038-44-1990 L2007 **P CHP** *020 †75

FULTON, John Frederick. ■ 15232 #041-12-1955 L1956 **OBG** *071 †30

FUNARI, Bryan Joseph. 3705 5TH AVE, CHILDREN'S HOSPITAL PITTSB 15213 #055-01-2001 L2004 **PDC** *100

FUNT, Loren Scott. 660 WASHINGTON RD, STE 201 15228 #010-01-1973 L1977 **D** *020 †15

FURGIUELE, Natalie. 110 FORT COUCH RD 15241 #041-01-1979 L1980 **GS** *020 †85

FURMAN, Joseph M. 200 LOTHROP ST 15213 #041-01-1977 L1984 **N** *020 †75

FURUKAWA, Hiroyuki. 3601 5TH AVE, 4 WEST 15213 #572-30-1980 L1992 **GS** *040

FUSIA, Joseph Francis. 815 FREEPORT RD 15215 #041-12-1954 L1955 **FM** *071

FUTRELL, James Wm. 300 HALKET ST STE 4430, MAGEE-WOMEN'S HOSPITAL 15213 #036-07-1967 L1979 **PS** *020 †85,65

FYE, Mark Alan. 1307 FEDERAL ST, STE 2 15212 #041-09-1991 L1997 **ORS** *020 †40

GABOS, Dennis Kevin. 4721 MCKNIGHT RD, STE 208 15237 #041-14-1982 L1983 **CD IM** *020 †20

GABOS, Paul. 4815 LIBERTY AVE 15224 #041-12-1959 L1960 **REN OBG** *071 †30

GABRIEL, Jesse Vincent. 15224 #041-12-2007 L2007 **IM** *012

GABRIEL, Luz Galang. ■ 15213 #748-02-1954 L1972 **P CHP** *071

GABRIELE, Orlando F. ■ 15238 #008-01-1954 L1988 **R** *071 †80,28

GABRYEL-GRUDZIAK, A. 969 GREENTREE RD STE 100, GREENTREE DIVISION 15220 #759-04-1981 L1997 **PD** *020

GAFFNEY, Michael Brown. 107 GAMMA DR, STE 107 15238 #041-12-1986 L1987 **ORS GS** *020 †40

GAGE, Deborah Marie. 7332 PRINCETON PL 15218 #041-12-1998 L2000 **PD** *020 †55

GAGE, Kenneth Leslie. ■ 15218 #041-12-2007 L2007 **TY** *012

GAGLIA, Michael Angelo, Jr. 200 LOTHROP ST, MUH-W933 15213 #041-12-2001 L2005 **CD** *012 †20

GAGNE, Daniel John. 4800 FRIENDSHIP AVE, THE WESTERN PENNSYLVANIA H 15224 #024-16-1992 L1997 **GS** *020 †85

GAINES, Anna Katherine. ■ 15206 #041-12-2008 *012

GAINES, Barbara Anne. 3705 5TH AVE STE 4A48, DEPT PEDIATRIC SURGERY 15213 #051-01-1990 L1993 **PDS** *020 †85

GAISFORD, John C. 300 FOX CHAPEL RD, APT 403 15238 #010-02-1942 L1943 **PS** *071 †85,65

GAJENDRAN, Mahesh. 1400 LOCUST ST, MERCY HOSPITAL 15219 #495-16-2005 L2007 **IM** *012

GAKHAR, Bhavna. 320 E NORTH AVE, ALLEGHENY GEN HOSP 15212 #495-28-2004 L2005 **IM** *012

GALAMBOS, Csaba. 3705 5TH AVE 15213 #473-03-1992 L2003 **PP** *020 †50

GALLAGHER, Ann Marie. ■ 15218 #539-03-2006 L2006 **PD** *012

GALLAGHER, Denise Sophia. 203 LOTHROP ST, STE 800 15213 #035-46-2003 L2007 **OPH** *020

GALLI, Sharon Anne. 4815 LIBERTY AVE 15224 #041-14-1983 L1988 **NPM** *020 †55

GALLION, Holly Skaggs. 2516 JANE ST, PRECISION THERAPEUTICS 15203 #020-12-1979 L2001 **GO** *020 †30

GALLON, Raymond Michael. 100 S JACKSON AVE, FL 3 15202 #422-01-1999 L2001 **IM** *020 †20

GALVEZ PADILLA, Christian. ■ 15202 #429-02-1999 L2006 **TS** *012 †85 ‡

GAMBLIN, Thomas Clark. 3459 5TH AVE 7, UPMC MONTEFIORE HOSPITAL 15213 #027-01-1998 L2003 **GS** *020 †85

GANDARA, Luis A. 1400 LOCUST ST, MERCY HOSP 15219 #665-02-2005 L2007 **PM** *012

GANDOTRA, Gaurav. 3811 OHARA ST, DEPT OF PSYCHIATRY 15213 #496-17-1998 L2001 **P** *100 †75

GANESH, Swaytha. 200 LOTHROP ST, DEPT OF MEDICINE 15213 #496-32-1998 L2002 **IM** *020 †20

GANGULI, Mary. 3811 OHARA ST 15213 #495-27-1974 L1978 **P PYG** *050 †75

GANGULI, Rohan. 203 LOTHROP ST 15213 #495-27-1974 L1978 **P IG** *050 †75

GANJOO, Jessie. 200 LOTHROP ST # N713, UNIV HLTH CTR PITTS 15213 #495-51-1988 L2002 **NEP** *012 †20

GANLY, Ian. 200 LOTHROP ST STE 500, OF PITTSBURGH EYE AND EAR 15213 #919-05-1989 L2001 **100**

GANNON, Jessica Michelle. 3811 OHARA ST, AND C 15213 #019-02-2007 L2007 **P** *012

GANNON, Robert Paul. 535 SMITHFIELD ST STE 2320 15222 #056-06-1959 L1960 **OBG** *071 †30

GANOTT, Marie Adele. 300 HALKET ST, FL 3 15213 #035-15-1978 L1983 **DR** *020 †80

GANZ, Leonard I. 320 E NORTH AVE, ALLEGHENY GEN HOSP DPT CD 15212 #024-01-1989 L1997 **ICE** *020 †20

GARBER, H Jordan. 1004 ARCH ST, STE 5500 15212 #016-43-1982 L1990 **P** *020 †75

GARBER, Mandy. ■ 15206 #035-01-1995 L2002 **IM** *062 †20

GARBUTT, Ronald G. 3501 FORBES AVE, MERCY BEHAVIORAL HEALTH 15213 #060-01-1990 L1996 **P** *020 †75

GARCIA, Angela Marie. ■ 15206 #025-07-2006 L2006 **PD** *012

GARCIA, Christine Frances. 200 LOTHROP ST, UPMC-PUH G304 15213 #048-04-2001 L2007 **HMP** *100 †50

GARCIA, Elba. 7175 HIGHLAND DR, PITT JOB CORPS WELLNESS CT 15206 #042-03-1981 L1987 **IM NTR** *020

GARCIA, Lisardo. 200 LOTHROP ST, STE C800 15213 #649-63-1997 L2001 **TS** *012 †85 ‡

GARCIA, Ray Jay Espana. ARTS BUILDIN, STE 503 MEDICAL 15213 #748-10-2003 L2007 **FP** *012

GARDENER, Ralph. 401 SHADY AVE STE D108 15206 #038-40-1965 L1969 **P PYA** *020 †75

GARDNER, Eric Michael. ■ 15206 #038-40-2004 L2004 **MPD** *012

GARDNER, Kara Lisa. 1580 MCLAUGHLIN RUN RD, STE 208 15241 #041-12-2001 L2001 **NPM** *100 †55

GARDNER, Kathy. 3500 TERRACE ST, S-514 BIOMEDICAL SCIENCE 15213 #049-01-1989 L1996 **N** *050 †75

GARDNER, Paul Andrew. 200 LOTHROP ST STE B40, UPMC DEPT OF NEUROSURGERY 15213 #041-12-2001 L2001 **NS** *012

GARFINKEL, Marc Edward. 401 SHADY AVE STE C106 15206 #047-06-1972 L1973 **CHP P** *020 †75

GARIBALDI, Luigi Roberto. 3705 5TH AVE 15213 #561-07-1973 L1979 **PDE PD** *020 †55

GARNER, William J. 1000 INTEGRITY DR STE 100 15235 #041-12-1951 L1952 **FM** *071 †18

GAROFOLI, Caesar Augustus. ■ 15228 #561-17-1955 L1959 **FM** *072 †18

GARRETT, Brianna Lynne. ■ 15206 #041-01-2006 L2006 **EM** *012

GARRETT, Kevin Owen. 100 DELAFIELD RD 15215 #041-12-1987 L1989 **GS** *020 †85

GARRETT, Rebecca A Vick. 3471 5TH AVE, KAUFMANN BLDG/SUITE 201 15213 #005-14-1973 L2003 **PM RHU** *020 †20,60

GARRETT, William Starling. 200 LOTHROP ST 15213 #024-01-1955 L1966 **PS HNS** *071 †85,65

GARSA, Adam Arebi. ■ 15217 #041-12-2008 L2008 *012

GARVER, James Jos. 320 E NORTH AVE, DEPT OB/GYN 7TH FL STH TWR 15212 #847-12-1985 L1986 **OBG** *020 †30

GARVER, Kenneth L. 4800 FRIENDSHIP AVE 15224 #041-12-1946 L1947 **MG PD** *071 †55,19

GARVER-LAMB, Kathleen M. 4721 MCKNIGHT RD STE 209N 15237 #041-12-1979 L1980 **PD** *020 †55

GARVEY, Matthew Lane. ■ 15212 #038-43-2007 L2007 **TY** *012

GASIOR, Thomas Adalbert. 4778 LIBERTY AVE, WPAA, LTD 2ND FLOOR 15224 #041-12-1982 L1983 **AN** *070 †05

GASTINEAU, Robert M. ■ 15241 #039-01-1950 L1975 **OM** *071 †70

GATES, Charley B. 121 MEYRAN AVE, KAUFMANN BLDG STE 1000 15213 #041-12-2004 L2004 **ORS** *012

GATES, Robert Edward. 1004 ARCH ST 15212 #041-12-1974 L1975 **R DR** *020 †80

GATES, Robert Paul. ■ 15221 #041-12-1945 L1946 **IM CD** *071

GAUDER, Stephanie Marie. ■ 15212 #035-06-2008 *012

GAUDIO, Ralph, Jr. 9102 BABCOCK BLVD STE LL1 15237 #041-12-1964 L1966 **PUD CCM** *071 †20

GAUR, Lasya. ■ 15232 #056-05-2007 L2007 **PD** *012

GAUTAM, Shovendra. ■ 15224 #495-02-2005 L2007 **IM** *012

GAUTHIER-CHOUINARD, Marie. 4200 5TH AVE 15261 #067-03-1974 **AN** *020

GAVULA, Cindy Louise. 1400 LOCUST ST 15219 #041-12-1984 L1985 **PD** *020 †55

GAYED, Bishoy Awni. ■ 15232 #028-46-2006 L2007 **GS** *100

GAYLE, Sanya Elizabeth. ■ 15224 #566-01-2005 L2007 **IM** *012

GAYOWSKI, Timothy John. 3601 5TH AVE 15213 #065-10-1984 L1989 **GS TTS** *020 †85

GEDEKOH, Robert Henry. 300 HALKET ST, STE 0610 15213 #041-12-1977 L1978 **OBG** *020 †30

GEDELA, Satyanarayana. 3705 5TH AVE 15213 #495-11-1988 L2003 **CHN** *020 †55,75

GEDIA, Bhavik Lakhabhai. 320 E NORTH AVE, ALLEGHENY GENERAL HOSPITAL 15212 #665-21-2005 L2006 **IM** *100

GEE, Michael Alan. ■ 15237 #012-05-2008 *012

GEHL, Leonard Gerald. 363 VANADIUM RD, US HEART & VASCULAR PC 15243 #033-05-1976 L1977 **CD** *020 †20

GEHL, Raymond H. ■ 15243 #025-01-1940 L1990 **PYA** *071 †75 ‡

GEHL, Richard Stanley. 1350 LOCUST ST 15219 #041-12-1970 L1976 **ORS GS** *020 †40

GEHR, Lynne Connolly. 3705 5TH AVE, OF PITTSBURGH 15213 #055-01-1981 L2007 **PAN** *012 †05,55

GEHRUNG, Carlos Eugenio. PRESBYTERIAN HOSPITAL 15213 #231-01-1964 L1974 **NEP** *020

GEISER, Bernard Thos. 132 WINGATE DR 15205 #041-12-1986 L1987 **FM EM** *020 †18

GEISLER, Susan Christina. ■ 15206 #035-15-2006 L2006 **PD** *012

GELLER, David Adam. 9100 BABCOCK BLVD 15237 #016-06-1988 L1990 **GS** *020 †85

GELLER, Mark Joshua. 4815 LIBERTY AVE STE 234 15224 #035-46-1977 L1983 **CD IM** *020 †20

GELRUD, Andres. 5200 CENTRE AVE, SHADYSIDE MEDICAL BUILDING 15232 #935-01-1994 L2008 **GE** *012

GELZINIS, Theresa Anne. 200 LOTHROP ST, DEPT OF ANESTHESIOLOGY 15213 #043-01-1993 L1997 **AN** *020 †05

GENC, Ayse Fidan. 3550 TERRACE ST, DEPARTMENT OF ANESTHESIOLO 15261 #902-03-1985 L1998 **PAN** *020 †05

GENDELMAN, Marla Susan. 1000 BOWER HILL RD 15243 #025-01-1986 L1990 **AN** *020 †05

GENDY, Mary Salwa. ■ 15237 #038-45-2004 L2007 **ESM** *012

GENERALOVICH, Thomas. 1501 LOCUST ST 15219 #041-01-1976 L1980 **CD IM** *020 †20

GENERETT, William Osborne. 5937 BROAD STRET MALL #222 15206 #041-12-1975 L1976 **OBG FM** *020

GENNARI, Amelia Sargia. 5200 CENTRE AVE, STE 211 15232 #051-01-1992 L1998 **IMG** *020 †20

GENNAULA, Charles Paul. 67 OLD CLAIRTON RD 15236 #041-12-1963 L1964 **FM** *020 †18 ‡

GENTILCORE, Thomas B. 4778 LIBERTY AVE 2ND FL 15224 #041-12-1993 L1996 **AN** *020 †05

GENTILE, Deborah Ann. 320 E NORTH AVE, ALLEGHENY GENERAL HOSPITAL 15212 #041-12-1994 L1996 **AI** *020 †55,03

GEORGE, John Jos. ■ 15241 #041-12-1959 L1960 **AN OS** *071

GEORGE, John Michael. 100 DELAFIELD RD, STE 303 15215 #422-01-1986 L1987 **CD GE** *020 †20 ‡

GEORGE, Marjorie Patricia. 3459 5TH AVE, UPMC - PACCM/628NW MONTEFI 15213 #023-07-2001 L2004 **IM** *020

GEORGE, Robert Nicholas. 1307 FEDERAL ST, STE 300 15212 #016-43-1958 L1963 **U** *071 †95

GEORGE, Thekkekara Varkey. 1400 LOCUST ST DEPT UROLO 15219 #495-33-1960 **U** *100

GEORGIADES, Athan. 5200 CENTRE AVE, STE 614 15232 #418-01-1980 L1982 **GS SO** *020 †85

GEORGIADIS, Mark Sarris. 200 DELAFIELD RD, STE 3050 15215 #041-01-1987 L1997 **HEM ON** *020 †20

GERARD, Joseph A. 9365 MCKNIGHT RD STE 700, CARDIOVASCULAR INSTITUTE 15237 #041-02-1977 L1978 **CD IM** *020

GERBER, Lawrence David. 7180 HIGHLAND DR 15206 #035-19-1993 L1995 **IM** *020

GERBER, Michael James. ■ 15208 #026-04-2007 **EM** *012

GERGES, Magdy Adly Habib. 100 BEECHMAN DR 15230 #915-02-1983 L1996 *062

GERMANWALA, Anand Vasant. ■ 15220 #041-02-1999 L2000 **NS** *100

GERNETH, George J. ■ 15208 #041-12-1953 L1954 **OPH OS** *071 †35

GERSCHULTZ, Kelly Lynn. ■ 15232 #041-12-2007 L2007 **OBG** *012

GERSHON, Samuel. 3811 OHARA ST, UNIVERSITY OF PITTSBURGH 15213 #143-03-1950 L1987 **P** *062

GERSZTEN, Kristina. 300 HALKET ST 15213 #035-45-1988 L1992 **RO** *020 †80

GERSZTEN, Peter C. 200 LOTHROP ST 15213 #023-07-1992 L1994 **NS** *020 †25

GERTZEN, Caroline Hanna. 121 MEYRAN AVE, DEPT OF INTERNAL MED 15213 #759-01-2003 **IM** *100

GERWEL, Stephen J. 120 MARION ST 15219 #759-10-1972 L1985 **CRS GS** *020 ‡

GESKIN, Larisa. 3601 5TH AVE 15213 #041-12-1998 L2001 **D** *020 †15

GEYER, Charles Edward, Jr. 320 E NORTH AVE, ALLEGHENY CANCER CENTER 15212 #048-15-1980 L2002 **ON** *020 †20

GEYER, Stanley James. ■ 15238 #041-02-1974 L1976 **PTH** *030 †50

GEYNISMAN, Daniel M. ■ 15213 #041-12-2006 L2006 **IM** *012

GHANOONI, Sion. 200 LOTHROP ST 15213 #517-05-1958 L1972 **AN** *020 †05

GHARIB, Suzanne Lee. S 716 BST, 3500 TERRACE ST 15261 #055-01-2003 L2006 **RHU** *012 †20

GHEARING, Gena Rebekah. 3471 5TH AVE STE 810, DEPT. OF NEUROLOGY KAUFMAN 15213 #035-09-2001 L2007 **N** *100 †75

GHETTI, Chiara. 300 HALKET ST, MAGEE-WOMENS HOSPITAL; DEP 15213 #017-20-1997 L2004 **OBG** *020

GHORBANI, Tahereh. ■ 15206 #051-01-2007 L2007 **IM** *012

GHOSHHAJRA, Brian Burns. 4800 FRIENDSHIP AVE, RADIOLOGY DEPARTMENT 15224 #038-06-2003 L2003 **DR** *012

GHOSHHAJRA, Kalyanmay. 516 COLQUITT DR, 2801 FREEPORT ROAD 15238 #495-32-1964 L1971 **DR** *020 †80

GHOSHHAJRA, Monica Gogate. ■ 15213 #038-44-2003 L2003 **AI** *012 †20

GHUMMAN, Ambrish Singh. 320 E NORTH AVE, ALLEGHENY GEN HOSP 15212 #495-43-2003 L2004 **GE** *012

GIAP, Hai Phuc. 7180 HIGHLAND DR, VAMC 15206 #941-01-1973 L1984 **P** *020

GIBBONS, Erin Patricia. ■ 15217 #023-01-2002 L2002 **U** *012

GIBSON, Marguerite Irene. ■ 15218 #005-18-1983 L2006 **PD** *020 †55

GIBSON, Michael Kevin. 5150 CENTRE AVE, UPMC CANCER PAVILION, 5TH 15232 #023-07-1996 L2007 **ON** *020 †20

GIERMASZ, Adam. 121 MEYRAN AVE, UNIVERSITY HEALTH CENTER 15213 #759-03-1998 L2005 **IM** *012

GIFFIN, James R. 3200 S WATER ST 15203 #064-01-1994 L1999 **OSM** *100

GILBERT, Andrew Robert. 1011 BINGHAM ST 15203 #025-07-1999 L2001 **P** *100

GILBERT, Christopher Mich. ■ 15217 #041-12-2007 L2007 **PTH** *012

GILBERT, Sebastien. 2000 MARY ST 15203 #067-01-1996 L2001 **TS GS** *020 †85,90

GILBERTI, Frank Francis. ■ 15235 #561-01-1966 L1968 **IM OS** *071

GILBOA, Noam Chaim. ■ 15217 #041-13-2003 L2003 **EM** *012

GILDENGERS, Ariel Gerard. 3811 OHARA ST 15213 #033-05-1997 L1999 **P** *020 †75

GILES, Harlan R. 100 FLEET ST 15220 #036-07-1969 L1996 **MFM OBG** *020 †30

GILL, Roop. 200 LOTHROP ST, F-674 PUH 15213 #917-14-1995 L2005 **GS** *012

GILL, Simrun Kaur. 320 E NORTH AVE, ALLEGHENY GEN HOSP 15212 #495-43-2001 L2004 **IM** *100

GILL, Stephanie Ann. 15232 #041-02-2007 L2007 **FP** *012

GILLESPIE, Amanda Lynn. ■ 15243 #051-04-2007 L2007 **IM** *012

GILLESPIE, Thomas Lee. ■ 15229 #041-12-1996 L2004 **P** *020 †75

GILLMAN, Grant S. 5200 CENTRE AVE, STE 211 15232 #062-01-1987 L1996 **OTO FPS** *020 †45

GILLMAN, Jason Wesley. ■ 15206 #041-12-2008 L2012 *012

GILMORE, George Hogg. 815 FREEPORT RD 15215 #041-12-1952 L1953 **ORS** *071 †40

GILMORE, Nathan Thomas. ■ 15221 #049-01-2007 L2007 **EM** *012

GILMOUR, Carol Huntress. 320 E NORTH AVE, AGH PEDIATRICS 15212 #041-14-1986 L1987 **NPM PD** *050 †55

GIMBEL, Alison Morris. ■ 15217 #036-07-1995 L2001 **PCC** *020 †20

GIMBEL, Mike Lawrence. 5750 CENTRE AVE STE 180 15206 #036-07-1995 L2001 **PS** *100 †65

GINCHEREAU, Eugene Hugh. ■ 15238 #041-12-1972 L1975 **IM OM** *030 †20,70,16

GINGO, Matthew Ray. 121 MEYRAN AVE, UNIV HLTH CTR 15213 #038-43-2004 L2007 **PCC** *012

GINGRICH, Jeffrey Rae. 5200 CENTRE AVE, STE 211 15232 #025-01-1987 L2003 **U GS** *020 †95

GIRDHAR, Rabindra. 5750 CENTRE AVE, STE 510 15206 #539-06-1987 L1990 **CD IM** *020 †20

GIROD, John P. ■ 15228 #041-77-2000, ▲ L2000 **CD** *020

GITTES, Elissa Baker. 3705 5TH AVE, ADOLESCENT MEDICINE 15213 #024-01-1987 L2005 **ADL PD** *020 †55

GITTES, George Kingsley. 3705 5TH AVE 15213 #024-01-1987 L2005 **PDS** *020 †85

GIUSEPPUCCI, Pablo Gabrie. 4800 FRIENDSHIP AVE 15224 #132-01-1994 L2006 **GS** *012

GIVELBER, Rachael Joy. 3459 5TH AVE 15213 #035-01-1990 L1997 **PCC** *020 †20

GIZIENSKI, Terriann. 9100 BABCOCK BLVD, UPMC PASSAVANT 15237 #041-14-1994 L1999 **DR** *020 †80

GLEASON, James Andrew. 5230 CENTRE AVE 15232 #041-12-1976 L1977 **IM D** *020 †20

GLEASON, Thomas Gillette. 200 LOTHROP ST, UPMC PRESBYTERIAN, SUITE C 15213 #016-01-1993 L2000 **TS** *020 †85,90

GLEESON, George Henry, III. 532 S AIKEN AVE, STE 201 15232 #041-09-1975 L1976 **IM IMG** *020 †20

GLICK, Harold Martin. 6343 PENN AVE, STE 201 15206 #016-42-1965 L1968 **PD** *020 †55

GLICK, Israel. ■ 15237 #041-12-1943 L1944 **P** *071 †75

GLICK, Ronald Martin. 580 S AIKEN AVE, STE 310 15232 #016-11-1979 L1981 **PM P** *020 †75,60

GLICKEN, Stephan Ronald. 320 E NORTH AVE, ALLEGHENY GENERAL HOSPITAL 15212 #041-09-1974 L2008 **PD** *020 †55

GLOD, Susan Anne. ■ 15229 #041-14-2005 L2005 **IM** *012

GLORIOSO, David Vaughn. 1350 LOCUST ST, STE 406 15219 #041-02-1990 L1993 **GE IM** *075 †20

GLOSTER, Jerome Ernest. 7227 HAMILTON AVE 15208 #041-12-1992 L1994 **PD** *020

GLUCK, Melissa Lynne. ■ 15221 #041-12-2008 *012

GLUHANICK, Michael Willia. ■ 15201 #041-13-2006 L2006 **IM** *012

GMARIAM, Ewnetu W. 4800 FRIENDSHIP AVE 15224 #366-01-1983 **IM** *100

GO, Michael Roland. ■ 15217 #038-41-2000 L2006 **VS** *012

GOBAO, Richard Allen. 393 VANADIUM RD, STE 307 15243 #041-13-1985 L1986 **IM** *020 †20

GODAY, Swapna. 4800 FRIENDSHIP AVE 15224 #495-21-2003 L2006 **IM** *012

GODLA, Gregory John. 5230 CENTRE AVE 15232 #041-12-1980 L1982 **AN** *020 †05

GODSE, Ravindra Shrikant. 16 TEAL DR 15238 #496-38-1992 L1997 **IM** *020 †20

GOEL, Shiv Kumar. 3471 5TH AVE, 910 LSK 15213 #496-38-1995 L2002 **AN** *100 †05

GOESSLER, Mary Charlotte. 300 HALKET ST 15213 #041-12-1977 L1981 **PD PDC** *020 †55

GOETZ, Danielle Marie. 342 S HIGHLAND AVE 15206 #035-06-2003 L2003 **PDP** *012 †55

GOETZ, Katharine M. 1330 OLD FREEPORT RD, STE 1A 15238 #021-01-1983 L1984 **OBG** *020 †30

GOETZ, Kenneth Lawrence. 105 BRAUNLICH DR, MCKNIGHT BLDG STE 480 15237 #023-07-1983 L1984 **P** *020 †75 ‡

GOFF, Herbert Kenneth. 5230 CENTRE AVE 15232 #041-09-1940 L1941 **IM** *071

GOHEL, Nita Rai. 5750 CENTRE AVE, STE 230 15206 #495-37-1988 L1996 **IM** *020 †20

GOITEIN, David. ■ 15217 #550-01-1995 L2004 **GS** *020

GOITEIN, Kalman J. ■ 15235 #501-01-1969 L1976 **EM PD** *075

GOITZ, Robert Jos. 3705 5TH AVE 15213 #023-07-1992 L1995 **ORS HS** *020 †40

GOLANI, Umesh Anandram. 4815 LIBERTY AVE STE 120 15224 #495-96-1975 L1984 **IM IMG** *020 †20 ‡

GOLD, Kenneth Norman. 3500 5TH AVE 4TH FL, ARTHRITIS AND INTERNAL-UPM 15213 #035-46-1987 L1994 **RHU IM** *020 †20

GOLDBERG, Elliot Bruce. 4800 FRIENDSHIP AVE, WESTERN PA HOSP DPT OF MED 15224 #021-01-1973 L1989 **RHU IM** *030 †20

GOLDBERG, Gary. 1350 LOCUST ST STE 409 15219 #065-10-1977 L1979 **PM CN** *020 †60

GOLDBERG, Jay Arthur. ■ 15217 #041-12-1982 L1983 **PS GS** *020 †85,65

GOLDBERG, Laura Rachel. ■ 15217 #041-12-2005 L2005 **IM** *012

GOLDE, Steven Herbert. 320 E NORTH AVE 5TH FL, DIVISION OF MATERNAL-FETAL 15212 #035-09-1972 L2003 **MFM OBG** *020 †30

GOLDEN, Catherine Lee. 121 MEYRAN AVE, DEPT OBG 15213 #017-20-2004 L2007 **OBG** *012

GOLDEN, Peter, Jr. ■ 15217 #038-06-2002 L2002 **CHP** *100

GOLDFARB, I Wm. 4815 LIBERTY AVE, STE 338 15224 #016-42-1973 L1974 **TRS GS** *020 †85

GOLDING, Irvin Michael. 540 N NEVILLE ST 15213 #041-12-1954 L1955 **P** *071 †75

GOLDMAN, Meidad Baruch. 230 MCKEE PL STE 500, OF PITTSBURGH 15213 #011-02-2006 L2006 **EM** *012

GOLDSTEIN, Amy Cheryl. 1811 BOULEVARD OF THE ALLS 15219 #041-12-1996 L2001 **CHN PD** *020 †75,55

GOLDSTEIN, Elliott J. 230 N CRAIG ST 15213 #035-15-1959 L1960 **P** *020 †75

GOLDSTEIN, Morton L. 5200 CENTRE AVE 15232 #041-12-1957 L1958 **GE IM** *071 †20

GOLDSTEIN, Sharon Lynne. 100 DELAFIELD RD 15215 #035-46-1995 L2001 **GS** *020 †85

GOLDWASSER, Brian Edward. 320 E NORTH AVE, DEPT OF INTERNAL MEDICINE 15212 #041-02-2006 L2006 **IM** *012

GOLEMBIEWSKI, Richard S. 1000 BOWER HILL RD, DEPT PATH 15243 #056-06-1964 L1971 **PTH** *020 †50

GOLESTANEH, Nasser. 1400 LOCUST ST 15219 #517-01-1966 L1973 **PD** *020 †55

GOLLA, Chandra Sekhar. 5000 MCKNIGHT RD, STE 406 15237 #496-01-1971 L1980 **FM** *020

GOLLA, Dinahar. 200 LOTHROP ST, PLASTIC SURGERY 15213 #024-05-1999 **PS** *020 †65

GOLLA, Saraswathi K. 2000 MARY ST 15203 #495-50-1974 L1980 **R** *020 †80

GOLLA, Suman. 2000 MARY ST 15203 #023-01-1995 L1998 **OTO** *020 †45

GOLLATZ, John Wm. 15 HIGHMEADOW RD 15215 #035-15-1971 L1979 **U** *020 †95

GONGLOFF, Richard Kevin. 3436 WILLIAM PENN HWY, STE 166 15235 #035-09-1997 L1999 **IM** *020 †20

GONTHIER, Dolores Marie. 320 E NORTH AVE 15212 #041-12-1988 L1990 **IM** *071 †20

GONZAGA, Alda Maria Ribei. 200 LOTHROP ST, STE 933W 15213 #041-12-2000 L2001 **MPD** *100

GONZALEZ, Alejandro R. 5140 LIBERTY AVE 15224 #847-05-1965 L1971 **END NEP** *020 †20

GONZALEZ, Augusto S. ■ 15238 #264-04-1965 L1973 **EM GS** *020

GONZALEZ, Hiram Alexis. ■ 15219 #042-02-2006 L2006 **GS** *012

GONZALEZ, Ivan Alberto. 3705 5TH AVE, PEDIATRIC INFECTIOUS DISEA 15213 #033-05-2002 L2005 **PDI** *012 †55

GONZALEZ, Rene A. 580 S AIKEN AVE STE 320 15232 #649-01-1963 L1966 **FM** *071 †18

GONZALEZ-ANGULO, Amador. 300 HALKET ST, DEPT PATH 15213 #649-01-1958 **PTH** *050 †50

GOO, Jeanna Sarah. ■ 15213 #041-12-2008 *012

GOOD, Candace. 3811 OHARA ST, CTR FOR CHILD & FAMILIES 15213 #041-14-1999 L2001 **P CHP** *020 ‡

GOOD, Chester Bernell. ■ 15218 #010-01-1983 L1984 **IM** *020 †20

GOOD, Misty Lynn. ■ 15238 #654-01-2005 L2008 **PD** *012

GOODMAN, Brian M. 320 E NORTH AVE, ALLEGHENY GENERAL HOSPITAL 15212 #050-02-2003 L2003 **GS** *012

GOODMAN, Kevin David. 320 E NORTH AVE, DEPT OF MED EDU 15212 #422-01-2006 L2006 **GS** *012

GOODMAN, Mark Alvin. 5200 CENTRE AVE, STE 211 15232 #035-08-1974 L1975 **ORS SO** *020 †40

GOODMAN, Richard Alan. 1699 WASHINGTON RD, STE 400 15228 #041-12-1979 L1980 **AN PME** *020 †05
GOODNIGHT, Todd Anthony. ■ 15217 #051-04-2003 L2004 **DR PD** *012
GOODWORTH, John Halerd. 4800 FRIENDSHIP AVE, STE 4600N 15224 #041-12-1964 L1969 **GS** *020 †85
GOPAL, Indira. ■ 15241 #495-50-1960 L1980 **GP** *071 †50
GOPAL, Rajesh. 92 BRADFORD AVE 15205 #041-09-1998 L2000 **IM** *020 †20 ‡
GOPAL, Rao. 532 S AIKEN AVE STE 411 15232 #495-09-1961 L1970 **TS** *071
GOPALAKRISHNAN, R. 4200 5TH AVE, DEPT ANG 15260 #495-16-1964 L1980 **R** *100
GOPALAN, Priya Raja. 3811 OHARA ST, AND C 15213 #051-01-2007 L2007 **P** *012
GORCSAN, John, III. 200 LOTHROP ST 15213 #041-14-1983 L1984 **CD** *050 †20
GORDON, Adam Joseph. 130U UNIVERSITY DRIVE C, VA PITTSBURGH HLTH CARE 15240 #041-12-1995 L1997 **IM ADM** *020 †20
GORDON, Jerold S. 203 LOTHROP ST, EYE & EAR INSTITUTE PITTSB 15213 #024-01-1969 L1972 **OPH** *020 †35
GORDON, Kimberly. 105 GAMMA DR, STE 300 15238 #035-01-1979 L1980 **PD** *020 †55
GORDON, Murray Bruce. 420 E NORTH AVE, STE 205 15212 #035-03-1977 L1978 **END IM** *020 †20 ‡
GORDON, Rodney Graeme. 5230 CENTRE AVE 15232 #671-01-1979 L1990 **ORS** *020
GORDON, Sanford A. 1004 ARCH ST 15212 #041-77-1960, ▲ L1961 **DR GP** *071 †80 ‡
GORHAM, Laura Melanie. ■ 15217 #038-41-2003 L2003 **MPD** *100 †20,55
GORMLEY, Robert Pershing. ■ 15238 #035-46-2001 L2007 **PTH** *100
GORRILL, Timothy Scott. ■ 15218 #041-13-2007 L2007 **PTH** *012
GORRY, Eileen. 230 N CRAIG ST 15213 #035-01-1996 L1998 **CHP** *020 †75
GOSALIA, Ankur Rajnikant. ■ 15227 #041-15-2002 L2003 **AN** *100 †05
GOSLING, Amy Allen. 1400 LOCUST ST 15219 #035-45-1979 L1980 **PD** *020 †55 ‡
GOSMAN, Gabriella Gray. 300 HALKET ST, DEPT OB 15213 #008-01-1994 L1997 **OBG** *020 †30
GOTH, Joseph H, III. 305 MT LEBANON BLVD, STE 300 15234 #041-12-1983 L1983 **OS** *020
GOTKIEWICZ, Edward M. 603 WASHINGTON RD, STE 300 15228 #041-14-1992 L1994 **PD** *020 †55
GOTTLIEB, Michael Alan. 200 LOTHROP ST 15213 #041-13-1986 L1988 **OTO** *020 †45
GOUBERT, Debrin Packer. 4 ALLEGHENY CTR, DEPT PSYCH 15212 #051-07-1989 L1991 **P** *020 †75
GOURASH, Linda M. 6301 NORTHUMBERLAND ST, THE CHILDRENS INST 15217 #010-02-1976 L1977 **PD** *020 †55
GOVI, Michael Joseph. 200 DELAFIELD RD, STE 2030 15215 #041-12-1993 L1995 **FM** *020 †18
GOVINDARAJULU, Madan Moha. 1400 LOCUST ST, MERCY HOSPITAL 15219 #496-34-2001 L2006 **IM** *012
GOWDA, Anuradha K. 11618 FRANKSTOWN RD 15235 #495-33-1986 L1995 **IM** *020 †20
GOYAL, Alka. 3705 5TH AVE 15213 #496-07-1983 L1998 **PG** *020 †55
GOYAL, Rakesh K. 3705 5TH AVE 15213 #496-07-1987 L1998 **PHO PD** *020 †55
GOYAL, Richa. 4800 FRIENDSHIP AVE, DEPT FM 15224 #495-37-2004 L2006 **FP** *012
GRABLE, Benjamin Rumans. ■ 15226 #041-12-2007 L2007 **TY** *012
GRADMAN, Alan Howard. 4800 FRIENDSHIP AVE, STE 3411 15224 #028-02-1972 L1989 **CD IM** *040 †20
GRAHAM, Steven Hunt. 3500 TERRACE ST, DEPT OF NEUROLOGY S-517 BS 15213 #048-14-1984 L1994 **N** *050 †75
GRAHAM, Toby Jo Orem. 200 LOTHROP ST 15213 #041-13-1969 L1971 **GE IM** *020 †20
GRAMI, Vahid. ■ 15213 #026-04-2001 L2005 **AN** *012
GRANATO, Jerome Ernest. 320 E NORTH AVE, STE 229 15212 #023-07-1979 L1985 **CD** *020 †20 ‡
GRANDE, Elmer Jason Ocamp. ■ 15232 #748-02-2001 L2005 **FP** *012
GRANDE, Robert David. 121 MEYRAN AVE, UNIV HLTH CTR 15213 #038-43-2004 L2007 **CD** *012 †20
GRANDHIGE, Anjali Parmar. 200 MEYRAN AVE, STE 318 15213 #001-02-2004 L2007 **IM** *100
GRANDIS, Jennifer Rubin. 200 LOTHROP ST STE 300, EYE & EAR INST 15213 #041-12-1987 L1989 **OTO PHM** *020 †45
GRANIERI, Rosanne. 200 LOTHROP ST, GEN MED/933 W MONTEFIORE 15213 #016-06-1981 L1989 **IM GP** *040 †20
GRANOWITZ, Samuel Phillip. 3471 5TH AVE, KAUFMAN BLDG, STE 1010 15213 #041-12-1958 L1959 **ORS** *071 †40
GRANT, William Gerard. ■ 15212 #051-01-2008 *012
GRANTCHAROV, Teodor Pantc. 4800 FRIENDSHIP AVE 15224 #198-02-1996 *100
GRAVES, James Anthony. 3705 5TH AVE 15213 #023-07-2002 L2002 **PHO** *012 †55
GRAY, George Hersman, Jr. ■ 15241 #041-12-1946 L1947 **NS** *071 †25
GRAY, Nicola Susan. 320 E NORTH AVE 15212 #041-12-2000 L2001 **P** *100 †75
GRAYBILL, John Christophe. ■ 15228 #038-06-2005 L2006 *100
GREALLY, Peter Gerard. UNIV PITTSBURGH SCH MED, DEPT PED 15261 #539-04-1984 **PD** *040
GREBENYUK, Liliya Anatoli. 320 E NORTH AVE, ALLEGHENY GEN HOSP 15212 #913-29-1992 L2004 **NEP** *012 †20
GRECO, Frank D. 100 DELAFIELD RD STE 312 15215 #041-12-1978 L1979 **U** *020 †95
GREELEY, Parmatma Singh. OF PITTSBURGH, UNIV HEALTH CTR 15261 #041-12-2002 L2002 **END** *020 †20
GREEN, Michael David. 3705 5TH AVE, CHILDREN'S HOSP. OF PITTBU 15213 #016-11-1983 L1984 **PD ID** *020 †55
GREEN, Richard Lee. 320 FORT DUQUESN BLVD #380 15222 #036-07-1968 L1970 **AI IM** *020 †20,03 ‡
GREEN, Robert Michael. 300 FLEET ST, STE 100 15220 #035-15-1975 L1976 **FM** *020 †18
GREEN, Todd David. 3705 5TH AVE, CHILDREN'S HOSPITAL OF PIT 15213 #041-12-2001 L2006 **AI** *020 †55,03
GREEN, William T, Jr. 3705 5TH AVE 15213 #024-01-1960 L1969 **ORS** *071 †40
GREENAMYRE, John Timothy. 3501 5TH AVE, STE 7039 15213 #025-01-1986 L2004 **N IM** *020 †75
GREENBERG, Jacob Joseph. 1400 LOCUST ST, MERCY PRIMARY CARE 15219 #561-01-1974 L1976 **NPM PD** *040 †55
GREENBERG, James Alan. 3705 5TH AVE 15213 #008-02-1972 L1973 **AN PD** *071 †55,05
GREENBERG, Larisa. 320 E NORTH AVE, CANCER CENTER 5TH FL 15212 #913-57-1975 L1996 **ON HO** *020 †20
GREENBERGER, Joel Steven. 200 LOTHROP ST, RAD ONC/3RD FL 15213 #024-01-1971 L1993 **RO** *020 †80
GREENBLATT, David Lee. 9100 BABCOCK BLVD, 2424 TRACI DRIVE 15237 #041-01-1986 L1988 **AN** *020 †05
GREENE, Michael Howard. ■ 15217 #035-48-1980 L1982 **AN PME** *020
GREENLEAF, Robert Martin. ■ 15212 #041-15-2005 L2005 **ORS** *012
GREENLEE, Charles E. ■ 15206 #047-07-1943 L1946 **GP** *020
GREENSPAN, Robin Lee. 4800 FRIENDSHIP AVE 15224 #041-01-1981 L1982 **DR NM** *071 †80,28
GREENSPAN, Susan Lynn. 3471 5TH AVE STE 1110, OSTEOPOROSIS CENTER 15213 #024-01-1979 L1999 **END IMG** *050 †20
GREENWALD, Marni Nicole. 3708 5TH AVE, MED ARTS BUILDING STE 500 15213 #041-12-2002 L2002 **IM** *020 †20
GREER, Julia Butler. ■ 15216 #035-47-1996 L1996 **IM** *100
GREER, William James. 1307 FEDERAL ST, STE 2 15212 #041-13-2000 L2001 **ORS OSM** *020
GREGG, Grace L Stollar. 4221 PENN AVE 15224 #041-12-1943 L1944 **PD CD** *072 †55
GREGORIO, Martin Guy. ■ 15232 #055-02-2004 L2004 **FM** *100
GREGORIO, Remigio Mallari. 181 DOMBEY DR 15237 #748-08-1966 L1972 **PTH CLP** *040 †50
GREGORIO-TENA, Rosita. ■ 15228 #748-01-1958 L1971 **PD GP** *020 †55
GREGOROWICZ, Adrienne Lis. VAMC, UNIVERSITY DRIVE C 15044 #041-12-2001 L2004 **IM** *020
GREHIAN, Sonia Veronica. 3811 OHARA ST, AND C 15213 #016-06-2006 L2006 **P** *012
GREIM, Chas Christopher. 2585 FREEPORT RD, STE 105 15238 #025-07-1980 L1986 **PM** *020 †60
GREINER, Richard George. 230 MCKEE PL, STE 500 15213 #041-14-2004 L2004 **EM** *020
GRENNAN, Martin J, Jr. 120 5TH AVE STE 748, HIGH MARK INC 15222 #041-12-1987 L1987 **MDM AN** *030 †05 ‡
GRENVIK, Ake Nils Adolf. 3550 TERRACE ST, DPC CCM RM 640A SCAIFE HAL 15261 #858-02-1956 L1970 **AN CCA** *030 †05
GREY, Thaddeus Andrew. 519 BROOKLINE BLVD 15226 #759-03-1968 L1984 **FM** *020 †18
GRIBAR, Steven Charles. 200 LOTHROP ST, UNIV OF PITTSBURGH MED CTR 15213 #041-12-2003 L2003 **GS** *012
GRIFFIN, Marilyn. 3811 OHARA ST, & CLI 15213 #016-11-2006 L2006 **CPP** *012
GRIFFITH, David Lowell. 320 E NORTH AVE 15212 #054-04-2005 L2005 **EM** *012
GRILL, Howard Philip. 500 GRANT ST, STE 2210 15219 #024-01-1983 L1990 **CD IM** *020 †20
GRIMES, Bernard Jos. 1400 LOCUST ST 15219 #041-01-1960 L1961 **END IM** *020 †20
GRIMLEY, Sara Rachelle. ■ 15211 #051-01-2001 L2004 **CD** *100
GROB, Daniel Kenneth. 1017 PERRY HWY 15237 #041-12-1995 L1997 **FM** *020 †18
GROFF, Henry Clay. 100 DELAFIELD RD STE 105, 100 MEDICAL ARTS BUILDING 15215 #041-14-1983 L1984 **P** *020 †75
GROFF, Yram Jan. 4815 LIBERTY AVE, # 250 15224 #041-12-1995 L1997 **ORS OSM** *020 †40
GRONDZIOWSKI, Peter M. 490 E NORTH AVE STE 504 15212 #041-12-1989 L1991 **END** *020 †20
GRONER, John Bernhardt. ■ 15201 #422-01-2002 L2007 **PMM** *012
GROUCUTT, William M. 5230 CENTRE AVE 15232 #038-40-1990 L1992 **EM FM** *020 †18
GROVE, Meghan Elizabeth. ■ 15207 #041-12-2003 L2003 **IM** *100 †20
GRUDZIAK, Jan Stanislaw. 3705 5TH AVE 15213 #759-01-1981 L1998 **ORS** *020 †40
GRUEN, Gary Scott. 3471 5TH AVE STE 1010, LILLIAN KAUFMAN BUILDING 15213 #041-13-1983 L1984 **ORS TRS** *020 †40
GRUFFERMAN, Seymour. 432 MOREWOOD AVE 15213 #035-15-1964 L1989 **PD EP** *050 †55
GRUM, Emily Edith. 3459 5TH AVE, NW628 MUH DEPT PACCM 15213 #041-07-1984 L1985 **PUD PCC** *020 †20
GRUMET, Bernard Alan. 6301 FORBES AVE, STE 301 15217 #041-02-1972 L1973 **IM** *020 †20
GSCHWEND, Andreas. 121 MEYRAN AVE, DEPT MED EDUCATION 15213 #869-02-1983 L1993 **HEM ON** *020
GSCHWEND-EIGENMANN, S C. 121 MEYRAN AVE, DEPT MED EDUCATION 15213 #869-01-1982 **PDE** *100
GUEHL, John J, Jr. 4800 FRIENDSHIP AVE 15224 #041-12-1949 L1950 **P** *071 †75
GUEHL, John James. 4815 LIBERTY AVE STE M-25 15224 #041-77-1975, ▲ L1976 **OPH** *020 †35
GUERRA-WALLACE, Melissa. ■ 15218 #905-02-2003 L2005 **PEM** *012
GUEVARRA, Joan Catherine. 320 E NORTH AVE, ALLEGHENY GEN HOSP 15212 #422-01-2003 L2003 **IM** *100 †20
GUGLANI, Seema Khurana. 2585 FREEPORT RD, STE 201 15238 #495-45-1992 L1995 **IM** *020 †20
GUIDO, Richard Scott. 300 HALKET ST, MAGEE-WOMENS HOSP 15213 #035-45-1987 L1990 **OBG** *020 †30
GULATI, Christine Lee. 15 JAMES ROSS PL 15215 #035-15-1991 L1994 **IM** *020 †20
GULATI, Vijay Kumar. 200 DELAFIELD RD, STE 3010 15215 #024-07-1991 L1998 **CD** *020 †20
GULLAPALLI, Ramachandra R. 3550 TERRACE STREET, A711 SCAIFE HALL 15261 #495-73-1999 L2007 **PTH** *012
GULUZIAN, John Krikor. ■ 15232 #038-41-2007 L2007 **TY** *012
GUMERMAN, Lewis Wm. 200 LOTHROP ST STE 710 15213 #041-01-1960 L1961 **NM** *071 †80,28
GUNAWARDENA, Sriya W. 3705 5TH AVE, DIV OF HEM/ONC 15213 #220-01-1981 L1997 **PHO** *020 †55
GUNGOR, Anil. 3705 5TH AVE, 3RD FL 15213 #902-05-1990 L2000 **PDO A** *020
GUNGOR, Neslihan. 3705 5TH AVE, DIV OF ENDOCRINOLOGY 15213 #902-05-1989 L2000 **PDE** *020 †55
GUNN, Scott Richard. 3550 TERRACE ST, 646B SCAIFE HALL 15261 #026-04-1996 L1999 **EM** *020 †16
GUP, Daniel Irvin. 200 DELAFIELD RD, STE 3060 15215 #041-01-1984 L1989 **U** *020 †95
GUPTA, Bhavana. 121 MEYRAN AVE, UNIV HLTH CTR OF PITTSBURG 15213 #496-17-1999 L2004 **FM** *100 †18
GUPTA, Gaurav. 121 MEYRAN AVE 15213 #495-36-2002 L2006 **IM** *012
GUPTA, Kshitij. ■ 15213 #496-09-1994 **IM** *100 †20
GUPTA, Navyash. 100 DELAFIELD RD 15215 #017-20-1991 L1998 **VS** *020 †85
GUPTA, Nikhil. 3708 5TH AVE, DEPT OF MED EDUCATION 15213 #495-36-2004 L2007 **IM** *012
GUPTA, Vipin Kumar. ■ 15235 #495-99-1997 L2004 **GE** *012 †20
GURECKI, John Jos. ■ 15214 #041-12-1981 L1983 **PTH** *020 †50
GURGUN, Melih. ■ 15243 #902-03-1951 L1965 **R OS** *071
GURKLIS, John Anthony, Jr. 7180 HIGHLAND DR 15206 #041-12-1986 L1988 **P** *020 †75
GURSKY, Andrew E. 300 WEYMAN RD, STE 380 15236 #041-12-1949 L1950 **PD** *020 †55
GURSON, Helen Walko. 2018 E CARSON ST 15203 #041-12-1942 L1943 **FM HEM** *071
GURTUNCA, Nursen. 3708 5TH AVE, DEPT OF MED EDU 15213 #902-04-1980 L2006 **PD** *012
GURUMURTHY, Ramya. 3811 OHARA ST, AND C 15213 #038-06-2007 L2007 **P** *012
GUSENOFF, Jeffrey Adam. 3550 TERRACE ST, SCAIFE HALL SUITE 6B 15261 #023-07-2002 L2006 **PS** *020
GUSHCHIN, Ghennady V. 3811 OHARA ST RM E820, AND CLINIC 15213 #913-01-1978 L2002 **P** *020 †75
GUTERSON, John. 23, # 6110 15212 #035-46-1987 L1995 **P** *020 †75
GUTHRIE, Robert Dale. 320 E NORTH AVE, DEPT PED 15212 #041-12-1969 L1982 **NPM PD** *030 †55
GUTKIN, Dmitriy W. ■ 15206 #913-99-1979 L1997 **PTH** *020 †50
GUY, Mark Ward. 620 E OHIO ST 15212 #041-01-1990 L1993 **FM** *020 †18

GUY, Victoria Eldredge. 5230 CENTRE AVE 15232 #041-12-1976 L1991 **IM EM** *020 †20

GUYETTE, Francis Xavier. 230 MCKEE PL, STE 400 15213 #021-01-2001 L2001 **EM** *020 †16

GYALTSONG, Tashi Dolma. ■ 15217 #054-04-2005 L2005 **PD** *012

GYULAI, Ferenc E. 200 LOTHROP ST STE C-200, UNIV OF PITTSBURGH ANETHES 15213 #473-02-1984 L1993 **AN** *020 †05

HA, Glen Jungho. 200 LOTHROP ST 3950, CHILDRENS HOSPITAL RADIOLO 15213 #050-02-1998 L2003 **DR** *020 †20

HAARER, Kelly Anne. 200 LOTHROP ST, RM 4660 15213 #023-01-1995 L1998 **DR** *020 †20

HABEYCH, Miguel Ernesto. 200 LOTHROP ST STE B-400, UPMC DEPT NEUROLOGICAL SUR 15213 #264-09-1989 L2005 **CN N** *012

HABIB-BEIN, Nadia Fouad. 6 UNIVERSITY DRIVE C, VAPHS PATH DEPT 132L-U 15240 #915-02-1980 L2003 **PCP** *020 †50

HACKAM, David. 3705 5TH AVE 15213 #065-06-1992 L2001 **PDS OS** *020 †85

HACKETT, Alyssa Michelle. ■ 15203 #038-40-2006 *012

HACKMAN, Trevor Glenn. ■ 15208 #041-12-2003 L2003 **OTO** *012

HACKNEY, David Nicholas. 300 HALKET ST, DIVISION OF MATERNAL/FETAL 15213 #041-12-2000 L2005 **OBG** *020

HADAM, Jennifer Lynn. 121 WASHINGTON RD 15221 #038-40-2002 L2002 **IM** *020 †20

HADDAD, Tarik J. 490 E NORTH AVE, STE 300 15212 #654-01-2001 L2007 **PCC PUD** *020

HADEED, Samir. 449 ORCHARD SPRING RD 15220 #875-01-1993 L2001 **IC** *020 †20

HADJIPANAYIS, Constantino. 200 LOTHROP ST, STE B-400 15213 #041-02-1998 L2000 **NS** *100

HADJISTAVRINOS, Lucas. ■ 15213 #418-01-1964 L1970 **PD** *100

HAENGGELI, Chas Antoine. 3705 5TH AVE, DEPT NEUR 15213 #869-02-1968 L1976 **CHN** *020 †75

HAEUSSNER, Charles Fred. 100 DELAFIELD RD, STE 301 ST. MARGARET MED. 15215 #041-13-1967 L1968 **GS** *071 †85

HAFEZ, Mohammed Nassoh. ■ 15220 #875-01-1994 L2001 **CCM** *020 †20

HAGEN, Tanya Jeanine. 3200 S WATER ST 15203 #010-02-1998 L2000 **ISM** *020 †20

HAGENKORD, Jill Marie. 121 MEYRAN AVE, UNIV HLTH CTR 15213 #005-11-1999 L2005 **MGP** *012 †50

HAGERICH, Kelley Lynn. ■ 15206 #010-02-2007 L2007 **IM** *012

HAGERT, Carl-Goran A. 3471 5TH AVE, UNIV SURG ASSOC 15213 #858-05-1963 **GS** *020

HAGG, Sigrid Anne. 201 PENN CENTER BLVD, STE 505 15235 #041-12-1969 L1978 **IMG IM** *020 †20

HAHN, Adam W. ■ 15215 #041-01-1960 L1964 **P** *071

HAIDET, Jaime Leigh. 3705 5TH AVE, OF PITTSBURGH 15213 #038-43-2003 L2007 **PDE** *012 †20

HAIGH, John Desmond. 200 LOTHROP ST, PRESBYTERIAN HOSP 15213 #062-01-1978 L1983 **AN** *020 †05

HAIRSTON, John Carl. ■ 15206 #041-12-1954 L1955 **GP** *071

HAKAS, David Roger. 5140 LIBERTY AVE 15224 #041-12-1995 L1999 **NEP** *020 †20

HAKAS, Elizabeth. ■ 15241 #024-16-1996 L1999 **IM** *020

HAKAS, Joseph F, Sr. 2275 SWALLOW HILL RD, STE 2600 15220 #041-12-1957 L1958 **FM** *072 †18

HAKIM, Christine Mary. 200 LOTHROP ST, RADIO/CHP MAIN TOWER 15213 #038-44-1987 L1991 **IM** *020 †80

HALASZYNSKI, Lori Marie. 1789 S BRADDOCK AVE, STE 510 15218 #041-12-1991 L1993 **IM** *020 †20

HALCZENKO, Paul William. ■ 15206 #041-14-2001 L2005 **CCP** *012 †20,55

HALEY, Marsha Lee. ■ 15237 #051-01-2004 L2005 **RO** *012

HALL, Andrew Michael. ■ 15232 #041-12-2007 L2007 **TY** *012

HALL, Daniel E. F1281.2 PUH, 200 LOTHROP ST 15261 #008-01-1999 L2001 **GS** *020 †85

HALL, David Geo. 7171 CHURCHLAND ST, LINCOLN LEMINGTON FAM HLTH 15206 #035-45-1979 L1980 **FM OM** *020 †20

HALL, Denise Michelle. ■ 15228 #041-12-2006 L2006 **AN** *012

HALL, R Norton. 1600 W CARSON ST STE 300, MEDICAL DIRECTOR CIGNA 15219 #041-13-1962 L1963 **NS** *030

HALLOWS, Kenneth Raymond. S976.1 SCAIFE/3550 TERRACE, UNIV OF PITTSBURGH SCHOOL 15261 #035-45-1995 L1997 **NEP** *020 †20

HAMAD, Giselle Genevieve. 300 HALKET ST STE 5518, MAGEE WOMENS HOSP 15213 #023-07-1993 L2000 **GS** *020 †85

HAMEL, Sara Christine. 3705 5TH AVE, CHILDREN'S HOSP OF PITTSBU 15213 #016-06-1982 L1992 **PD** *020

HAMILTON, Ronald Lee. 200 LOTHROP ST 15213 #030-05-1989 L1993 **NP** *030 †50

HAMM, Charles Robt. ■ 15229 #041-12-1958 L1959 **R NR** *071 †80

HAMMER, Maxim Daniel. 200 LOTHROP ST, C-400 PUH 15213 #035-03-1998 L2002 **N** *020 †75

HAN, Liwen. 320 E NORTH AVE, DEPT OF INTERNAL MED 15212 #243-76-1992 L2004 **IM** *100 †20

HAN, Sum Kyung. ■ 15243 #583-10-1966 L1972 **FM** *071

HAN, Yoong Oh. 5200 CENTRE AVE, STE 610 15232 #583-09-1965 L1975 **OBG PHP** *071 †30

HANCHETT, Jeanne Marie. 6301 NORTHUMBERLAND ST 15217 #035-20-1961 L1971 **PD** *020 †55

HANDLER, Steven Mark. 3459 5TH AVE, STE 4E 15213 #033-05-1997 L2000 **IMG** *020 †18

HANKEY, John Clarke. 4800 FRIENDSHIP AVE, W PENN HOSP 15224 #041-02-1978 L1979 **EM IM** *020 †16

HANLON, Dennis Paul. 320 E NORTH AVE 15212 #051-04-1987 L1989 **EM** *020 †16

HANLON, Kim Anne. 3601 5TH AVE, FALK CLINIC RM 585 15213 #041-14-1981 L1982 **EM** *020 †16

HANNEMAN, Douglas Breuer. ■ 15201 #056-06-2007 L2007 **EM** *012

HANNIBAL, Kristin Mary. 3705 5TH AVE, GAP/PRIMARY CARE CENTER 15213 #038-41-1983 L2000 **PD** *020 †55

HANNON, Tamara S. 3705 5TH AVE AT DESOTO ST, DIV OF ENDO 4A RM 400 15213 #017-20-1996 L2004 **PDE** *020 †55

HAPP, Erik Michael. 420 E NORTH AVE STE 116, ALLEGHENY GENERAL HOSPITAL 15212 #041-09-1997 L2002 **AM** *020 †35

HARADIN, Anthony Ray. 1050 BOWER HILL RD, STE 106 15243 #041-12-1963 L1964 **ON HO** *020 †20 ‡

HARCHELROAD, Fred P, Jr. 320 E NORTH AVE 15212 #041-14-1982 L1983 **EM ETX** *020 †16

HARDESTY, Robert Lynch. 200 LOTHROP ST, C 700 PUH UPMC 15213 #041-12-1966 L1966 **TS** *020 †85,90

HARDGROVE, Jacqueline Ann. ■ 15217 #038-43-2007 L2007 **IM** *012

HARDY, Susan E. 3471 5TH AVE, STE 500 15213 #041-12-1996 L2005 **IMG** *020 †20

HARETOS, John. 160 N CRAIG ST 15213 #418-01-1980 L1982 **IM** *020 †20

HAREWOOD, Peter Fabian. ■ 15206 #041-12-2006 L2007 **IM** *012

HARLEY, Barbara M H. 9104 BABCOCK BLVD STE 2111 15237 #024-01-1968 L1981 **PD PDE** *020 †55

HARNER, Christopher D. 3200 S WATER ST, UPMC CTR SPORTS MEDICINE 15203 #025-01-1981 L1983 **ORS** *020 †40

HARPER, Jay Douglas. 3708 5TH AVE STE 500.59 15213 #055-01-1989 L1991 **OM** *030 †70

HARPER, John Jos. 120 5TH AVE, STE 748 15222 #028-34-1965 L1966 **PD MDM** *030 †55

HARRINGTON, Scott. 200 LOTHROP ST 15213 #035-15-1995 L1997 **EM** *020 †16

HARRIS, Anthony Edward. 200 LOTHROP ST, STE 8400 15213 #041-12-1999 L2001 **NS** *020

HARRIS, Bernadette G. 532 S AIKEN AVE STE 201 15232 #028-03-1985 L1987 **IM IMG** *020 †20

HARRIS, Emily Nicole Thom. 3811 OHARA ST 15213 #041-02-2005 L2005 **CPP** *012

HARRIS, Kristen Raye. ■ 15216 #047-06-2003 L2006 **PD** *012

HARRIS, Leon Xavier. 5230 CENTRE AVE 15232 #047-07-2003 L2004 **FM** *100

HARRIS, Pamela Lin. 5230 CENTRE AVE 15232 #047-07-2004 L2004 **FP** *012

HARRIS, Richard Neal. 120 LYTTON AVE FL 1 15213 #041-12-1974 L1975 **IM** *020 †20

HARRIS, Steven Phillip. 9104 BABCOCK BLVD, STE 2103 15237 #035-06-1991 L1993 **PUD CCM** *020 †20 ‡

HARRISON, Anthony Miller. 200 LOTHROP ST, UPMC PRESBYTERIAN F1267 15213 #041-02-1964 L1965 **GS VS** *020 †85

HARRISON, Janet Rose. 300 HALKET ST, # 5407 15213 #041-01-1995 L2004 **GE** *020 †20

HARRISON, Lee H. DESOTO ST., 521 PARRAN HALL/130 15261 #012-05-1982 L1996 **IM** *050 †20

HARROLD, Carol Ruth. 620 E OHIO ST, NORTHSIDE CHRISTIAN HLTH 15212 #007-02-1991 L2007 **IM IMG** *020 †20

HARTMAN, Jamie Y. 4800 FRIENDSHIP AVE 15224 #041-12-1994 L1998 **DR** *020 †80

HARTMAN, Matthew Scott. ■ 15217 #041-12-2002 L2002 **DR** *020 †80

HARTMANN, Susanne. 1350 LOCUST ST STE G102 15219 #016-11-1998 L2000 **IMG** *020 †20

HARTNER, Walter Bruce. ■ 15215 #041-12-1962 L1963 **P IM** *020

HARTSOCK, Robert Jos. 320 E NORTH AVE, ALLEGHENY GEN HOSP 15212 #041-12-1957 L1958 **PTH HMP** *071 †50

HARVEY, Joan. 200 LOTHROP ST, MED/MISC/SCAIFE HALL 15213 #023-07-1974 L1992 **RHU IM** *020 †20

HARWICK, Jean Crandall. 4815 LIBERTY AVE 15224 #041-13-1980 L1982 **OPH** *020 †35

HASHIMOTO, Masayoshi. ■ 15213 #572-70-1987 L1992 **FM** *020 †18

HASHMI, Asima. ■ 15215 #495-21-1972 L1974 ✦

HASHMI, Majid Ali. 4815 LIBERTY AVE STE 334 15224 #495-21-1962 L1974 **CD IM** *020 †20 ‡

HASLEY, Peggy Braasch. 200 LOTHROP ST, 933 WEST-MUH 15213 #041-12-1985 L1986 **IM** *050 †20

HASLEY, Steve Kinneman. 535 SMITHFIELD ST, STE 1030 15222 #041-12-1984 L1985 **OBG** *020 †30

HASSAN, Danyal. 2030 ARDMORE BLVD, STE 125 15221 #704-20-1996 L2001 **NEP** *020 †20

HASSAN, Shuja. 5200 CENTRE AVE, STE 211 15232 #704-21-1987 L1997 **IMG** *020 †20

HASSELMAN, Carl Thomas. 200 DELAFIELD RD, STE 1040 15215 #036-07-1994 L1996 **ORS** *020 †40

HASSOURI, Hassan. 9104 BABCOCK BLVD STE 2116, PASSAVANT PROFESSIONAL BLV 15237 #517-01-1969 L1984 **N** *020 †75

HATHAWAY, Bridget Cara. 203 LOTHROP ST 15213 #041-12-2001 L2001 **OTO** *020

HATTLER, Brack G, Jr. 200 LOTHROP ST STE C700 15213 #035-20-1961 L1964 **TS** *071 †85,90

HAUGHT, Justin Michael. ■ 15239 #055-01-2005 L2006 **D** *012

HAUN, Paul Long. ■ 15213 #244-04-1973 L1975 **AN** *020

HAWKINS, Andrew Richard. 5230 CENTRE AVE 15232 #051-04-2003 L2003 **FM** *020 †18

HAWKINS, Michelle Yvette. ■ 15218 #038-45-1990 L1993 **IM** *020 †20

HAYBRON, David Mcclure. 4815 LIBERTY AVE, STE 156 15224 #038-40-1988 L2001 **TS GS** *020 †85,90

HAYES, Jennifer Lynn. 300 HALKET ST, DEPT OF OB/GYN/REPRODUCTIVE 15213 #024-07-1999 L2005 **OBG** *020

HAYETIAN, Fernando Daniel. 4800 FRIENDSHIP AVE, DEPT OF SURGERY 15224 #132-01-1996 L2003 **GS** *012

HAYKIN, Martha Ellen. ■ 15232 #012-01-2001 L2006 **N** *100

HAYN, Matthew Henry. 3471 5TH AVE, STE 700 15213 #041-12-2003 L2003 **U** *012

HAZEL, Elizabeth W. 1330 OLD FREEPORT RD, STE 1A 15238 #041-12-1986 L1988 **OBG** *020 †30

HAZLETT, Nancy Sturgis. 401 SHADY AVE STE D107 15206 #041-12-1988 L1992 **CHP** *020 ‡

HE, Mei. 320 E NORTH AVE, ALLEGHENY GEN HOSP 15212 #243-47-1993 L2003 **CN** *012

HEALEY, Jeffrey Mark. ■ 15232 #041-12-2007 L2007 **TY** *012

HEATH, George Tilton. 320 E NORTH AVE 15212 #055-01-1992 L1994 **AN** *020 †05

HEBERT, Randy Scott. 200 LOTHROP ST STE 9, MONTEFIORE HOSPITAL 15213 #023-07-1995 L2002 **IM** *020 †20

HECK, Harry John, III. 1622 LOWRIE ST 15212 #422-01-1982 L1983 **IM AM** *020 †20

HECKLER, Frederick Roger. 320 E NORTH AVE 15212 #024-07-1966 L1982 **PS HS** *020 †85,65 ‡

HECKMAN, Jason T. ■ 15237 #035-45-2001 L2006 **GS** *100

HEDAYATI, Behzad. 320 E NORTH AVE, DEPT OF MED EDU 15212 #517-11-2001 L2006 **RNR** *100

HEGAZI, Refaat Abdel-Fatt. 3550 TERRACE ST, RM 572-B SCAIFE HALL 15261 #915-06-1989 L2006 **IM** *100

HEGDE, Vinayak Anant Padm. 4800 FRIENDSHIP AVE, WESTERN PENNSYLVANIA HOSP 15224 #495-17-2002 L2004 **CD** *012 †20

HEIDELBERGER, Cory Patric. ■ 15217 #049-01-2007 L2007 **EM** *012

HEIDENREICH, Fred P, Jr. 107 GAMMA DR, STE 107 15238 #041-12-1993 L1999 **OP** *020 †40

HEIDER, Amer. 121 MEYRAN AVE 15213 #875-01-2001 L2005 **PTH** *012

HEIL, Kurt Matthew. 5700 CORPORATE DR, STE 700 15237 #041-02-1995 L1998 **FM** *020 †18

HEILBRUNN, Steven Mark. 100 DELAFIELD RD, STE 303 15215 #041-01-1981 L1987 **CD IM** *020 †20 ‡

HEIN, Alethea Ann. ■ 15206 #036-01-2007 L2007 **TY** *012

HELFRICH, David John. 151 HINKEL RD 15229 #041-12-1983 L1984 **RHU IM** *020 †20

HELKOWSKI, Jeffrey Lee. 4800 FRIENDSHIP AVE 15224 #041-09-1991 L1996 **AN** *020

HELKOWSKI, Wendy Marie. 2000 MARY ST 15203 #041-02-1992 L1996 **PM** *020 †60

HELMI, Seyed Mehdi. 5230 CENTRE AVE, SHADYSIDE HOSP 15232 #517-05-1974 L1976 **OBG GS** *100

HEMADRI, Amit. 1500 5TH AVE, DEPT OF INTERNAL MED 15219 #495-99-1999 L2007 **IM** *012

HEMPHILL, Richard W. ■ 15238 #041-12-1953 L1954 **OBG OS** *071 †30

HEMSTREET, Mitzi K. 1160 INGOMAR HEIGHTS RD, WESTERN PA ANESTHESIA ASSO 15237 #043-01-1994 L2002 **AN** *020 †05

HENDERSON, Maryanne J. 1405 SHADY AVE 15217 #041-77-1990, ▲ L1991 **PM** *020 †60

HENDRICKX, Hans Henricus. 3260 5TH AVE 15213 #660-04-1977 L1982 **AN** *050

HENNIGAN, Allison Langfor. ■ 15235 #048-02-2005 L2005 **N** *012

HENNING, George Thomas. 900 OSAGE RD 15243 #038-40-1994 L2001 **RO** *020 †80

HENNON, Don Leroy. 9576 PERRY HWY, STE 103 15237 #041-12-1963 L1964 **GS** *020 †85

HENNON, Kimberly Ann. 100 S JACKSON AVE 15202 #041-13-1993 L1995 **EM** *020 †16

HENNON, Mark William. 320 E NORTH AVE, ALLEGHENY GENERAL HOSPITAL 15212 #035-06-2002 L2002 **GS** *012

HENNON, Robert Peter. 9100 BABCOCK BLVD 15237 #041-07-1991 L1994 **GS** *020 †85

HENRY, Jessica Ann. 4800 FRIENDSHIP AVE, 3RD FL 15224 #041-09-1998 L2001 **NPM** *020 †55

HENRY, Leland T, Jr. 4815 LIBERTY AVE, STE 154 15224 #025-01-1956 L1957 **IM** *020 †20

HENRY, Randall Scott. 9100 BABCOCK BLVD 15237 #041-12-1985 L1986 **DR GS** *020 †80

HENRY, Sarah Elizabeth. ■ 15213 #041-12-2008 *012

HENZEL, Mary Kristina. ■ 15207 #020-02-2006 L2006 **PM** *012

HEPLER SMITH, Elizabeth. 9401 MCKNIGHT RD, ARCADIA CENTER STE 304A 15237 #041-01-1983 L1985 **P** *020 †75

HEPLER-SMITH, Michael. 9800A MCKNIGHT RD, STE 204 15237 #041-01-1979 L1981 **PD DIA** *020 †55

HEPPNER, Richard Lee. 5140 LIBERTY AVE 15224 #008-01-1967 L1972 **CD IM** *071 †20

HERATH, Priyantha Pushpa. 3471 5TH AVE, SUITE 811 KAUFMANN BLDG 15213 #220-02-1995 L2002 **N** *100

HERB, Christine Marie. ■ 15224 #041-13-2007 L2007 **IM** *012

HERB, Robert William. ■ 15235 #041-01-1962 L1966 **GE IM** *071 †20

HERBERMAN, Ronald Bruce. 5150 CENTRE AVE, STE 500 15232 #035-19-1964 L1986 **ON IM** *050 †20

HERBERT, David Leonard. 200 LOTHROP ST, ROOM 4895/MAIN TOWER 15213 #143-03-1968 L1975 **DR** *020 †80

HERES, Edward K. 320 E NORTH AVE 15212 #010-02-1983 L1993 **AN PME** *020 †05

HERLICH, Andrew. 1400 LOCUST ST, DEPT OF ANESTHESIOLOGY UPM 15219 #305-01-1984 L1986 **AN** *040 †05 ‡

HERMAN, Brian Andrew. ■ 15235 #041-09-1984 L1987 **CD IM** *020 †20

HERMAN, Jay Bernard. 532 S AIKEN AVE, STE 210 15232 #041-12-1979 L1980 **U** *020 †95

HERMAN, Julius. ■ 15232 #041-12-1939 L1940 **FM** *071

HERNANDEZ, Cesar Mario. ■ 15203 #561-17-1988 L2000 **OB** *012 †20

HERNDON, Oliver W. 500 LEWIS RUN RD, STE 105 15122 #005-11-1996 L1999 **IM** *020 †20

HERON, Dwight Earl. 5230 CENTRE AVE 15232 #035-45-1995 L1997 **RO** *020 †80

HERRINGA, Ryan John. ■ 15215 #056-05-2006 L2006 **P** *012

HERRLE, Scott Robert. 200 LOTHROP ST, UPMC MONTEFIORE HOSPITAL, 15213 #041-12-2003 L2003 **IM** *020 †20

HERRON, Matthew Ryan. ■ 15238 #038-43-2006 L2006 **EM** *012

HERSHENSON, Lee M. 1000 INTEGRITY DR, ASSOCIATES INC 15235 #041-12-1949 L1950 **GE IM** *072 †20 ‡

HERSHEY, Richard E. 1400 LOCUST ST 15219 #041-12-1950 L1951 **NS** *071 †25

HERTLE, Richard William. 203 LOTHROP ST 15213 #038-44-1984 L1989 **OPH PO** *020 †35

HERTZBERG, Todd Michael. 300 HALKET ST, RADIOLOGY DEPT 15213 #035-09-1991 L1997 **DR OS** *020

HERTZOG, James Edward. 1800 WASHINGTON RD 15241 #041-12-1957 L1958 **OM AM** *030 †70

HESS, Rachel. 200 LOTHROP ST, MUH 9S 15213 #034-01-1997 L1999 **IM** *050 †20

HETRICK, William David. 1400 LOCUST ST, ANESTHESIOLOGY MERCY HOSP 15219 #041-12-1969 L1970 **AN** *071 †05

HEWIE, Sheila Patrice. 1060 SCAIFE HALL DEPT-ANES 15261 #016-02-1979 L1982 **AN PD** *020

HEYL, Louis Wm. 1020 CENTER AVE 15229 #041-09-1980 L1980 **FM** *020

HEYMAN, Rock Alan. 3471 5TH AVE 15213 #038-40-1985 L1986 **N SME** *020 †75

HICKEY, Gavin William. ■ 15221 #035-45-2006 L2006 **IM** *012

HICKEY, Robert Wm, Jr. 3705 5TH AVE 15213 #041-02-1985 L1988 **PD** *020 †55

HIGGINBOTHAM, Monique R. 3705 5TH AVE, DIVISION OF CHILD ADVOCACY 15213 #038-41-1990 L2000 **PD OS** *020 †55

HIGGS, Craig Louisalbert. 320 E NORTH AVE, DEPARTMENT OF PEDIATRICS 15212 #016-45-2003 L2007 **MPD** *020 †20

HIGMAN, Henry Booth. 3471 5TH AVE, KAUFMANN BLDG NEUROLOGY DP 15213 #023-01-1955 L1967 **N R** *071 †75

HILAL, Elias Youssef. 1350 LOCUST ST STE 309 15219 #605-01-1970 L1977 **OTO HNS** *020 †45

HILDEBRANDT, Carl Andrew. 5808 EVA ST 15206 #025-01-1986 L1987 **PD** *020 †55

HILL, John Burkett. 4815 LIBERTY AVE, STE 158 15224 #041-12-1957 L1958 **ON HEM** *071 †20

HILL, Justin James. ■ 15211 #045-01-2002 L2005 **N** *012

HILL, Lyndon Michael. 300 HALKET ST, OBGYN/MAGEE WOMENS HOSP 15213 #035-09-1972 L1985 **OBG MFM** *020 †30

HILLER, Walter W, Jr. 603A MCKNIGHT PARK DR 15237 #049-01-1960 L1962 **P OS** *020 †75

HILMI, Ibtesam Abbass. 200 LOTHROP ST, PRESBYTERIAN HOSPITAL 15213 #528-01-1976 L1996 **AN** *020 †05

HILTON, Christie J. ■ 15243 #041-77-2007, ▲ L2007 **IM** *012

HIMMELBERGER, James Allen. 15218 #041-12-1977 L1980 **IM** *020 †20,16

HIMMELHOCH, Jonathan M. ■ 15238 #024-01-1964 L1974 **P PA** *050 †75

HINCHLIFFE, Joseph G. ■ 15238 #010-02-1960 L1961 **P PYA** *071

HINDES, Susannah Rebecca. 121 MEYRAN AVE, DEPT FM 15213 #035-15-2007 **FP** *012

HINDMARSH, Dale J. 4 ALLEGHENY CTR 15212 #025-07-1976 L1979 **CHP** *020 †75

HINKLE, David Alan. 3471 5TH AVE, KAUFMAN BLDG STE 811 15213 #023-01-1997 L1999 **N** *020 †75

HIRA-BRAR, Shabneet K. 3811 OHARA ST RM E807, UNIV OF PITTSBURGH MED CTR 15213 #495-43-1997 L2006 **PFP** *100 †75

HIRKO, Mark K. 4815 LIBERTY AVE, STE 140 15224 #038-45-1989 L2006 **VS GS** *020 †85

HIRO-OKA, Nobutaka. 5230 CENTRE AVE, UPMC SHADYSIDE 15232 #572-76-1995 L2001 **FM** *100 †18

HIRSCH, Barry Eliot. 203 LOTHROP ST 15213 #041-01-1977 L1978 **OTO NO** *020 †45

HIRSCH, David James. 230 MCKEE PL, STE 500 15213 #024-16-2005 L2005 **EM** *012

HIRSCH, Eugene Zachary. 15206 #038-06-1957 L1996 **IM PLM** *071

HIRSCH, Raphael. 3705 5TH AVE 15213 #016-11-1983 L2002 **PD RHU** *020 †55

HIRSCH, Stanley Alan. 5200 CENTRE AVE, STE 307 15232 #041-12-1957 L1958 **VS GS** *020 †85

HIRSCH, Stuart David. 401 SHADY AVE C203 15206 #041-12-1964 L1965 **P OS** *020 †75

HIRSHBERG, Richard Wm. ■ 15241 #041-09-1961 L1962 **GP** *071

HISAMATSU, Yoshikazu. ■ 15206 #572-45-1992 L2003 **IM** *100

HITCHCOCK, John. ■ 15238 #035-01-1958 L1964 **PYA** *071 †75

HO, Andrew Manlap. 3471 5TH AVE STE 1010 15213 #005-11-2002 L2002 **ORS** *100

HO, Johnan. ■ 15228 #038-44-2000 L2003 **PTH** *100 †50

HO, Ken Sujin. 200 LOTHROP ST RM N713, UPMC-MONTEFIORE 15213 #023-01-2004 L2004 **IM** *020 †20

HO, Kevin. 3550 TERRACE ST, S931 SCAIFE HALL 15261 #035-01-1987 L2002 **NEP** *020 †20

HO, Monto. A427 CRABTREE HALL, GRADUATE SCH OF PUBLIC HLT 15261 #024-01-1954 L1962 **IM ID** *071 †20

HO, Yee Chung. 810 WOOD ST STE 1 15221 #244-02-1974 L1975 **GP** *020

HOBBS, Joseph Kyle. ■ 15229 #038-40-2004 L2005 **NS** *012

HOBERMAN, Alejandro. 3705 5TH AVE, PEDS/ONE CHILDREN PL 15213 #132-01-1984 L1991 **PD** *040 †55

HO CAIN, Kitty Uyen-Uyen. ■ 15235 #041-13-2004 L2004 **DR** *012

HOCKING, Stephen Nicholas. 1400 LOCUST ST 15219 #143-06-1986 L1988 **NS** *012

HODAK, Steven Paul. 6301 5TH AVE, STE 580 15206 #010-02-1999 L2005 **IM** *020

HODGDON, Alan K. 1501 LOCUST ST, STE 403 15219 #048-13-1988 L1990 **EM** *040 †16

HODGES, Allen Roger. 211 N WHITFIELD ST 15206 #010-03-1974 L1979 **OS PD** *050

HOFFMAN, Amber M. 3705 5TH AVE, DRS CHP 15213 #041-12-1999 L2001 **PD** *020 †55

HOFFMAN, Charlotte. 160 SOUTHERN AVE, SERVICES 15211 #005-06-1993 L1995 **P** *020 †75

HOFFMAN, Erika Lee. OAKLAND VA MEDICAL CTR, UNIVERSITY DR C 15240 #041-09-1990 L1992 **IM** *020 †20

HOFFMAN, Marcus Keith. ■ 15213 #041-12-2007 L2007 *012

HOFFMAN, Robert Miles. ■ 15208 #036-07-1978 L1979 **PUD** *020 †20

HOFFMANN, Ludwig G. 4200 5TH AVE 15261 #409-33-1972 **AN** *100

HOFKOSH, Dena. 3705 5TH AVE, PEDS/ONE CHILDRENS PL 15213 #035-19-1979 L1981 **PD** *020 †55

HOFSTETTER, Mark. 101 DRAKE RD STE C, ST CLAIR COMMONS CTR 2ND F 15241 #038-40-1976 L1985 **ID IM** *020 †20

HOGAN, William Richard. 200 LOTHROP ST # 8084 15213 #041-02-1993 L1995 **IM** *062 †20

HOGGE, William Allen. 300 HALKET ST, MAGEE-WOMENS HOSPITAL 15213 #051-01-1973 L1992 **OBG CG** *050 †19,30

HOHING, Charles Conrad. ■ 15220 #041-12-1956 L1957 **OBG** *071 †30

HOHMANN, Heather Lyn. 300 HALKET ST, MAGEE WOMENS HOSPITAL 15213 #035-48-2002 L2006 **OBG** *012

HOHMANN, Thomas Chas. PASSAVANT HOSP, DEPT MED 15237 #041-12-1954 L1955 **PM** *071 †60

HOLDER, Deborah Lee. 3705 5TH AVE 15213 #038-43-1994 L2005 **CHN CN** *020 †75

HOLLENBAUGH, Fonda Jo. ■ 15228 #054-04-1984 L1985 **EM FM** *020 †18

HOLLERAN, Kathleen Erin. 320 E NORTH AVE, MED CLINIC 15212 #025-07-2002 L2002 **IM** *020 †20

HOLLINGER, Chester Boyd. ■ 15238 #305-01-1985 L1988 **IM CCM** *020 †20

HOLLOWAY, Shane Eugene. 5150 CENTRE AVE STE 414, UPMC CANCER PAVILION 15232 #054-04-1999 L2006 **GS** *020 †75

HOLST, Jennifer Pennock. 5200 CENTRE AVE, STE 211 15232 #041-12-1999 L2005 **END** *020

HOLST, Seth Andrew. 2400 ARDMORE BLVD, STE 200 15221 #041-12-1998 L1998 **OPH** *020 †35

HOLTZMAN, Matthew Peter. 5150 CENTRE AVE, STE 420 15232 #035-08-1999 L2004 **SO GS** *020 †85

HOLZER, Brian Keith. ■ 15241 #041-15-2001 *020

HOLZINGER, Elmer John. 519 EDGEWOOD RD 15221 #041-12-1954 L1955 **IM** *020 †20

HOMANN, Joseph Francis. 4800 FRIENDSHIP AVE, WEST PENN HOSPITAL 15224 #005-12-1967 L1992 **GS** *040 †85

HOMAYOUN, Houman. 200 LOTHROP ST, STE 503 15213 #517-01-1999 L2007 **IM** *012

HOMROK, Katherine Alice. 901 WEST ST, STE B 15221 #041-12-1987 L1989 **FM** *020 †18

HONG, Andrea Sunglyun. 200 LOTHROP ST, UPMC-PUH 15213 #036-07-2005 L2006 **DR** *012

HONG, Eric Anson. ■ 15213 #041-12-2006 L2007 *012

HONG, Feiyu Francis. 121 MEYRAN AVE 15213 #067-01-2003 L2005 **IM** *012

HONG, Justin Sup. 121 MEYRAN AVE, UNIV HLTH CTR 15213 #016-42-2007 L2007 **PM** *012

HONG-BARCO, Pablo. 5200 CENTRE AVE, STE 216 15232 #649-01-1965 L1974 **TS VS** *020 †85,90

HONKALA, Timothy Keith. 180 FORT COUCH RD, STE 400 15241 #038-44-1985 L1991 **ORS OSM** *020 †40 ‡

HOON, John Harvey. ■ 15239 #041-12-1947 L1948 **GP OS** *020

HOOTMAN, John Kenneth. 713 WASHINGTON RD 15228 #041-12-1947 L1948 **OPH** *071 †35

HOOVER, Alan Dale. 1400 LOCUST ST, STE 5105 15219 #041-12-1974 L1974 **IM** *020 †20

HOOVER, Darren Loran. 400 PENN CENTER BLVD, BLDG 4 15235 #028-03-1982 L1987 **OPH** *020 †35

HOOVER, Larry Jos. 1400 LOCUST ST 15219 #041-12-1980 L1981 **IM IMG** *020 †20 ‡

HOOVER, Rachel Ann. ■ 15209 #041-13-2006 L2006 **IM** *012

HOPPE, Susan Allison. ■ 15203 #044-14-1998 L2001 **IM** *020 †20

HOQUE, Sabina. ■ 15232 #023-01-2005 L2005 **IM** *012

HORBINSKI, Craig Michael. ■ 15209 #035-06-2003 L2003 **NP** *012 †50

HORCHNER, Nadezhda V. 5230 CENTRE AVE, UPMC SHADYSIDE 15232 #050-02-2007 L2007 **IM** *012

HOROWITZ, Michael Bruce. 200 LOTHROP ST 15213 #035-45-1988 L1990 **NS** *020 †25

HORTON, Charles Newton. 15206 #048-04-2004 L2004 **AN** *012

HORTON, John Allen. 2000 MARY ST 15203 #054-04-1993 L1998 **PM SCI** *020 †60

HORVATH, David Albert. 20 CEDAR BLVD STE 205 15228 #041-13-1975 L1978 **D** *020 †15

HORVITZ-LENNON, Marcela. 3811 OHARA ST, AND CLINIC 15213 #231-03-1987 L2004 **P PHP** *020 †75

HORWITZ, Mara Jean. 3601 5TH AVE RM 586 15213 #035-01-1987 L1989 **END** *020 †20

HOSANAGAR, Avinash. 3811 OHARA ST, AND C 15213 #495-52-1999 L2004 **CHP** *012

HOSSEINZADEH, Keyanoosh. 200 LOTHROP ST, RM 3950 CHP MAIN TOWER 15213 #065-06-1992 L2005 **DR** *020 †80

HOTCHKISS, John Robt, Jr. CARE MEDICINE, DEPT OF CRITICAL 15261 #016-02-1988 L2004 **PUD** *020 †20

HOUDA, Joseph Harry. 1400 LOCUST ST 15219 #041-12-2003 L2003 **GS** *012

HOUGH, Bruce Oliver. ■ 15235 #011-04-1998 L2000 **HO** *012 †20

HOUGHTON, Ashley Mc Garry. 3459 5TH AVE, NW 628 MONTEFIORE 15213 #010-02-1996 L2006 **PCC** *012

HOUSAM, Ryan Ann. ■ 15218 #023-01-2007 L2007 **PD** *012

HOUSTON, Mary Jo. 1000 INTEGRITY DR, STE 100 15235 #041-09-1985 L1986 **FM** *020 †18

HOWELL, Gina Moonsuh. ■ 15213 #041-12-2007 L2007 *012

HOWLAND, Robert Herbert. 200 LOTHROP ST, M115 UNIVERSITY CTR 15213 #026-04-1986 L1987 **P PYG** *050 †75

HOWRYLAK, Judie Ann. 15203 #021-01-2003 L2003 **PCC** *012 †20

HOY, Ronald James. DESOTO & OHARA ST 15213 #143-03-1939 L1977 **DR** *071

HOZAKOWSKA-RUBIN, Ewa M. 300 FLEET ST, STE 100 15220 #759-03-1981 L1995 **IM** *020 †20

HRACH, Catherine R. 1000 BOWER HILL RD, ST CLAIR HOSPITAL 15243 #016-11-1995 L2000 **EM** *020 †16

HREBINKO, Ronald Lee, Jr. 5200 CENTRE AVE, STE 211 15232 #041-12-1986 L1987 **U** *020 †95
HRIBAR, Stephen Richard. 9104 BABCOCK BLVD, STE 2120 15237 #041-13-1995 L1997 **ORS** *020 †40
HRIESIK, Claudia. 835 N MEADOWCROFT AVE 15216 #409-38-1996 L2000 **CRS** *012 †85
HSIEH, Margaret. 200 LOTHROP ST 15213 #033-06-1996 L1999 **EM** *020 †16
HSU, Chia C. ■ 15213 #244-01-1976 L1993 **PTH** *020
HSU, Eileen. 6418 JACKSON ST 15206 #010-02-2002 L2002 **PCC** *012 †20
HUAMAN VARGAS, Gonzalo. 121 MEYRAN AVE 15213 #737-01-1998 **IM** *012
HUANG, Allen. ■ 15206 #038-41-2005 L2005 **PM** *012
HUANG, David Tom. DEPT OF CRITICAL MEDICINE, 646B SCAIFE HALL 15261 #035-09-1998 L2001 **EM CCM** *020 †16
HUANG, Grace Chon-Huey. 3811 OHARA ST, AND CLINIC 15213 #025-01-1994 L1994 **P** *020 †75
HUANG, Gregory Shannon. ■ 15206 #038-41-2005 L2005 **GS** *012
HUANG, Peng-Yun Angela. 3708 5TH AVE, DEPT OF MED EDUCATION 15213 #143-02-2002 L2005 **IM** *012
HUANG, Ted Ling. 200 LOTHROP ST, W933 MONTEFIORE BLDG 15213 #016-45-2004 L2007 **IM** *100 †20
HUANG, Yunzhong. 4800 FRIENDSHIP AVE 15224 #243-47-1991 L2001 **AN** *020 †05
HUBERT, Mark G. ■ 15221 #048-04-2004 L2004 **ORS** *012
HUDAK, Robert. 3811 OHARA ST 15213 #038-44-1992 L1999 **P** *020 †75
HUDSON, Mark Edward. 5230 CENTRE AVE, DEPT OF ANESTHESIOLOGY/CCM 15232 #041-02-1988 L1990 **AN** *020 †05
HUEBNER, Julius John. 1307 FEDERAL ST, STE 2 15212 #025-01-1983 L2002 **ORS OTR** *020 †40
HUEBNER, Laura K. ■ 15217 #025-01-1983 L2002 **IM** *020 †20
HUEN, Arthur Chihcheng. ■ 15217 #016-06-2006 L2006 **D** *012
HUGHES, Christopher M. 1000 BOWER HILL RD, ST CLAIR HOSP 15243 #038-44-1984 L1987 **CCM IM** *020 †20
HUGHES, Geo Van Guilder. 9100 BABCOCK BLVD 15237 #041-12-1945 L1946 **IM** *072 †20
HUGHES, James Michael. 210 MILLVIEW DR 15238 #917-22-1967 L1983 **RO** *071 †80
HUGHES, Lisa M. 490 E NORTH AVE, STE 406 15212 #041-09-1996 L1999 **OBG** *020 †30
HUGHES, Nolan Philip. 15218 #041-02-2006 L2006 **P** *012
HUGHES, Steven John. 200 LOTHROP ST 15213 #026-08-1993 L2000 **CCS** *020 †85
HUGHES, Thomas Barry, Jr. 1307 FEDERAL ST, STE 2 15212 #041-01-1996 L2000 **ORS** *020 †40
HUGHES-DOICHEV, Rachel A. 320 E NORTH AVE 15212 #041-13-1999 L2007 **CD** *020 †20
HUI, Sifong Elise. ■ 15213 #041-12-2008 L2008 **IM** *012
HUMPHREYS, Linda. 3811 OHARA ST 15213 #047-05-1986 L1990 **CHP P** *030 †75
HUNG, Por-Tying. 829 WOOD ST 15221 #385-02-1959 L1977 **OPH** *020 †35
HUNGERFORD, Olena Grygori. 320 E NORTH AVE, ALLEGHENY GENERAL HOSPITAL 15212 #913-10-1999 L2007 **IM** *012
HUNTER, Doris M. 154 N BELLEFIELD AVE 15213 #016-11-1951 L1952 **PYA P** *071 †75
HURITE, Francis Gerard. 1835 FORBES AVE 15219 #010-02-1959 L1965 **OPH** *020 †35
HURWITZ, Dennis Jay. 3109 FORBES AVE, STE 500 15213 #023-01-1970 L1976 **PS CS** *020 †85,65
HUSAIN, Anwar. ■ 15232 #020-02-2007 L2007 **PD** *012
HUSAIN, Sohail Nabeel. ■ 15212 #016-06-2002 L2006 **HSO** *012
HUSSAIN, Sabiha M. 320 E NORTH AVE, 4TH FL 15212 #495-74-1997 L2005 **NEP** *020 †20
HUSSEIN, Basem M. 7070 FORWARD AVE 15217 #065-09-1990 L1998 **RNR** *020 †80
HUTCHINGS, Lorraine S. 1000 CLIFFMINE RD, PARKWEST ONE/SUITE 110 15275 #063-01-1992 L1996 **FM** *020 †18
HUTCHINSON, Jessica Jean. 1400 LOCUST ST, OF PITTSBURGH 15219 #041-02-2004 L2004 *100
HUTCHISON, Sarah Elisabet. ■ 15217 #038-06-2005 L2006 **OBG** *012
HUWE, Trina Marie. 200 LOTHROP ST, DEPT OF ANESTHESIOLOGY 15213 #041-12-2001 L2001 **AN** *100 †05
HUYNH, Priscilla. ■ 15213 #023-12-1996 L2001 **NS** *020
HWANG, Lisa Margaret. 105 BRAUNLICH DR, STE 450 15237 #041-14-1993 L1996 **PD** *020 †55
HWANG, Maisie. 4070 BEECHWOOD BLVD 15217 #051-04-1991 L1993 **FM** *020 †18
HYDE, Bruce. 240 MT LEBANON BLVD, PEDIATRICS SOUTH 15234 #041-13-1982 L1983 **PD** *020 †55
HYLAND, John Arthur, Jr. 320 E NORTH AVE, RADIATION ONCOLOGY 15212 #038-43-1990 L1995 **RO** *020 †80
IANNUZZI, C Charles. 2115 NOBLE ST 15218 #165-04-1961 L1962 **FM OS** *071 †18
IBRAHIM, Nesreen Saad Ahm. 4 ALLEGHENY CTR, CENTER,8TH FL 15212 #915-03-1993 L2006 **CHP** *012
ICHIKAWA, Diane Chiyo L. 850 CLAIRTON BLVD, STE 3100 15236 #041-12-1980 L1981 **OBG** *020 †30
IE, Han-Yo. 5230 CENTRE AVE 15232 #660-03-1990 **IM** *100
IKE, Diana Ugo. UNIV PITTSBURGH SCH OF MED 15261 #041-12-1991 L1993 **IM** *020 †20
ILIESCU, Anca Valeria. ■ 15217 #781-01-1996 L2001 **CD** *100 †20
ILKHANIPOUR, Kamyar. 320 E NORTH AVE, DEPARTMENT OF RADIOLOGY 15212 #041-12-1993 L1997 **DR** *020 †80
ILKHANIPOUR, Kaveh. 1501 LOCUST ST, STE 403 15219 #041-12-1985 L1986 **EM** *020 †16
ILYAS, Mohammad. 15215 #704-04-1967 L1973 **R** *020 †80
IM, Annie Pearl. ■ 15217 #035-48-2006 L2006 **IM** *012
IMLER, Erin Lynne. ■ 15235 #041-12-2007 L2007 **FP** *012
IMRO, Amy Katherine. 4815 LIBERTY AVE, STE 321 MELLON PAVLN 15224 #041-09-1998 L2001 **OBG** *020
INDORATO, Leroy Salvatore. 6343 PENN AVE, # 201 15206 #041-12-1967 L1968 **PD OS** *020 †55
INDYK, Justin A. ■ 15229 #035-48-2003 L2004 **PDE** *012 †55
INGRAM, Michael Douglas. 1000 BOWER HILL RD 15243 #026-04-1979 L1982 **AN** *020 †05
INNASIMUTHU, Antony Lesli. 200 LOTHROP ST, STE 503 15213 #495-59-2002 L2007 **IM** *012
INSERRA, Diane Wishnow. 651 HOLIDAY DR, FOSTER PLZ 5 15220 #033-05-1989 L1992 **D** *020 †15
IONESCU, Diana Nora. 121 MEYRAN AVE 15213 #781-03-1995 L2001 **PTH** *100 †50
IQBAL, Zafar. ■ 15214 #704-01-1962 L1972 **GS** *020 †85
IRACKI, Daniel Andrew. 110 FORT COUCH RD 15241 #041-07-1979 L1980 **PUD IM** *020 †20
IRANI, Jihad Shawki. 3937 BUTLER ST 15201 #605-02-1994 L2006 **FM** *020 †18
IRANI, Kaikobad J. 200 LOTHROP ST 15213 #010-01-1989 L2005 **CD IM** *020 †20
IRANI, Plomarz Rustom. ■ 15217 #047-05-2005 L2005 **EM** *012
IRBY, Susan Kathleen. 7555 SALTSBURG RD, GREATER PGH MED ASSOC-UPMC 15235 #051-04-1979 L1982 **IM** *020 †20

IRVIN, Frances E C. 6023 HARVARD SQ 15206 #065-01-1990 L1994 **FM** *020 †18
ISAAC, Mohsen Abdalla. 4800 FRIENDSHIP AVE, RADIATION ONCOLOGY 15224 #915-02-1994 L2002 **RO** *020 †80
ISAACS, Gilbert Herman. 320 E NORTH AVE, ALLEGHENY RADIOLOGY 15212 #023-01-1959 L1968 **NM END** *071 †28
ISAACSON, Yisrael Arieh. UNIV DR C, VETERANS ADMIN HOSP. 15217 #035-46-1980 L1987 **GE IM** *020 †20
ISHIZAWAR, David Chang. ■ 15207 #041-12-2001 L2001 **CD** *100
ISIBOR, Tolulope Osamudia. ■ 15212 #047-06-2004 L2004 **DR** *012
ISIK DEMIRCI, Sukriye A. ■ 15241 #041-12-2004 L2004 **IM** *020
ISKYAN, Kara Melinda. ■ 15206 #038-41-2005 L2005 **MEM** *012
ISLAM, Mohammed Fakhrul. 4727 FRIENDSHIP AVE, STE 340 15224 #160-02-1983 L1998 **HO** *020 †20
ISMAEL, Mohamed M. 35 STANCEY RD 15220 #915-04-1978 L1990 **P PYG** *020 †75
ISMAIL, Saad Usman. 1518 FORBES AVE, MCAULEY MEDICAL ASSOCIATES 15219 #496-21-1999 L2002 **IM** *012
ISMAIL, Suad Abduljabbar. 490 E NORTH AVE, STE 400 15212 #539-06-1983 L1999 **CD** *020 †20
ISMAIL-BEIGI, Farhad. 1000 INTEGRITY DR, ASSOCIATES INC 15235 #047-05-1964 L1971 **GE IM** *020 †20 ‡
ISOM, Corinne Elizabeth. ■ 15208 #041-12-2004 **DR** *012
ISRAEL, Barbara Anne. 320 E NORTH AVE, ALLEGHENY GENERAL HOSP DEP 15212 #041-12-1987 L1990 **NPM PD** *020 †55
ISSA, Dany Hassib. 200 LOTHROP ST, GEN INTERNAL MEDICINE MUH 15213 #605-01-1999 L2005 **IM** *012
ISTVANIC-ZDRAVKOVIC, Smilj. 815 FREEPORT RD, DEPT OF PATHOLOGY 15215 #957-02-1992 L2006 **PCP** *100 †50 ‡
ITO, Sawa. 3708 5TH AVE, DEPT OF MED EDU 15213 #572-29-2002 L2006 **IM** *012
ITOMAN, Erick Moriatsu. ■ 15217 #014-01-2004 L2007 **CCM** *012
ITSKOWITZ, Alan Lee. 6301 FORBES AVE, STE 301 15217 #041-09-1964 L1966 **IM** *072 †20
ITSKOWITZ, Marc Samuel. 320 E NORTH AVE 15212 #047-07-1998 L2000 **IM** *020 †20
ITZKOFF, Jerome Matt. 5200 CENTRE AVE STE 207, CARDIOVASCULAR ASSOCIATES 15232 #035-19-1975 L1978 **CD** *020 †20
IVANOV, Emil Hristov. 3811 OHARA ST, DEPT OF PSYCHIATRY 15213 #198-03-1995 L2002 **P** *100 †75
IVANOVA, Valentyna. 320 E NORTH AVE, ALLEGHENY GEN HOSP 15212 #913-86-1997 L2006 **IM** *012
IVEY, Timothy. ■ 15206 #010-03-1965 L1966 **ORS** *020
IWATSUKI, Shunzaburo. 3601 5TH AVE, FALK CLINIC RM 585 15213 #572-58-1965 L1981 **GS IM** *020 †85
IYER, Vish Venkatesh. 30 HIGH ST 15223 #495-04-1981 L2000 **FM** *020 †18
JACKMAN, Stephen V. 3471 5TH AVE, STE 700 15213 #008-01-1994 L2004 **U** *020 †95
JACKOVIC, Marcy L. 815 FREEPORT RD, UPMC-ST MARGARET 15215 #041-77-2000, ▲ L2001 *020
JACKSON, Christann Louise. 4800 FRIENDSHIP AVE 15224 #041-12-1980 L1981 **OBG MG** *020 †19,30
JACKSON, John Brian. 200 LOTHROP ST, UNIVERSITY OF PITTSBURGH M 15213 #023-01-2003 L2003 **DR** *012
JACOB, N J. 200 LOTHROP ST, 431 SOUTH,MONTIFIORE HOSPI 15213 #495-44-1985 L1992 **P** *020 †75
JACOB, Rolf Gunter. 3811 OHARA ST, UNIVERSITY OF PITTSBURGH 15213 #858-02-1971 L1979 **P** *050 †75
JACOB, Timothy Douglas. 9104 BABCOCK BLVD, STE 3111 15237 #041-13-1988 L1990 **GS** *020 †85
JACOBS, Bruce Lee. ■ 15238 #047-05-2004 L2004 **U** *012
JACOBS, Richard Patrick. 532 S AIKEN AVE, STE 414 15232 #017-20-1965 L1971 **U** *020 †95
JACOBS, Samuel Angel. 5150 CENTRE AVE 15232 #035-45-1971 L1976 **HO IM** *020 †20
JACOBSON, Michael Joseph. 3811 OHARA ST, WPIC 15213 #038-06-2002 L2002 **P** *100
JACOBSON, Sansea Lynn. 3811 OHARA ST 15213 #041-12-2004 L2004 **P** *012
JADALLAH, Khaled Ali Yous. ■ 15228 #561-01-1987 L2001 **IM** *100 †20 ‡
JAFFE, Ronald. 3705 5TH AVE DEPT PATH 15213 #836-01-1969 L1977 **PP PTH** *020 †50
JAFFE, Thomas Michael. 200 DELAFIELD RD, STE 3060 15215 #038-06-1990 L1997 **U** *020 †60
JAGGA, Priya. ■ 15215 #759-06-2000 L2005 **OBG** *012
JAHANGEER, Ahmed. 10 DUFF RD, STE 301 15235 #704-15-1987 L2000 **CHP** *020
JAIN, Abhishek. 3811 OHARA ST, AND 15213 #038-44-2006 L2006 **P** *012
JAIN, Nandita. 4800 FRIENDSHIP AVE, DEPT MED 15224 #496-07-2001 L2005 **IM** *012
JAIN, Rajiv. UNIV DR C, VA PITTS HLTH CARE SYSTEM 15240 #495-48-1972 L1975 **ON IM** *030 †20
JAIN, Samay. ■ 15218 #051-01-2000 L2006 **N** *100 †75 ‡
JAIN, Sandeep Kumar. 200 LOTHROP ST 15213 #016-06-1996 L2004 **CD** *020 †20
JAIN, Sheena K. 3550 TERRACE ST, A SCAIFE HALL OF HLTH PROF 15261 #041-12-2008 *012
JAKACKI, Regina Irene. 3705 5TH AVE 15213 #041-01-1985 L1987 **PHO OS** *020 †55
JAKYMEC, Andres. DESOTO AT OHARA STS 15213 #935-04-1972 L1977 **AN** *020 †05
JALIJALI, Armand L. 15219 #748-01-1988 L1995 **NEP** *020 †20
JAMESON, Angus Macintosh. ■ 15206 #035-03-2007 L2007 **EM** *012
JAMNBACK, Lisa Ann. 4 ALLEGHENY CTR 8TH FL, DEPT OF PSYCHIATRY 15212 #041-12-1988 L1990 **CHP P** *040 †05,75
JAN, Sophia. ■ 15232 #035-08-2005 L2005 **MPD** *012
JANAKIRAMAN, Abirami. 320 E NORTH AVE 15212 #305-01-2005 L2007 **IM** *012
JANARDHANAN, Ravi. 9401 MCKNIGHT RD, ARCADIA CENTER BLDG SUITE 15237 #495-04-1976 L1981 **GE** *020 †20
JANEWAY, Timothy. 5200 CENTRE AVE, STE 415 15232 #025-01-1963 L1967 **ORS HS** *071 †40
JANG, David H. 230 MCKEE PL STE 500, OF PITTSBURGH 15213 #024-07-2006 L2006 **EM** *012
JANI, Niraj D. 200 LOTHROP ST, OF GASTROENTEROLOGY 15213 #035-45-2000 L2000 **GE** *100 ‡
JANICIJEVIC, Jelica. ■ 15241 #041-13-2006 L2006 **IM** *012
JANICKE, George Henry. 9100 BABCOCK BLVD 15237 #041-12-1968 L1969 **EM** *020 †16
JANKOWITZ, Brian Thomas. 200 LOTHROP ST, STE B400 15213 #041-13-2003 L2003 **NS** *012
JANNELLI, Dorothy Frances. 5 GATEWAY CTR 15222 #041-09-1986 L1988 **IM** *012
JANNETTA, Carol Marie. ■ 15217 #041-12-1988 L1991 **ORS** *020
JANNETTA, Peter Jos. 200 LOTHROP ST 15213 #041-01-1957 L1958 **NS GS** *020 †85,25
JANOSKO, Mark Richard. 200 LOTHROP ST 15213 #041-07-1992 L1994 **IM** *020
JANOSKO, Rudolph E M. 161 N DITHRIDGE ST 15213 #041-12-1956 L1957 **P PYA** *020 †75
JARAMILLO, Beverly Ann. 105 BRAUNLICH DR STE 220 15237 #011-02-1978 L1987 **ON OBG** *020 †30
JARRETT, Fredric. 5200 CENTRE AVE, STE 705 15232 #024-01-1967 L1981 **GS VS** *020 †85

■ = Address Information Privacy Protected

JARVIS, James Robert. 120 LYTTON AVE, 1ST FL SIDE A 15213 #041-12-1996 L1999 IM *020 †20

JASNOSZ, Katherine Mary. 542 4TH AVE 15219 #035-06-1980 L1982 FOP PTH *062 †50

JASTAN, Rasmiyah Majdy. ■ 15232 #605-04-2002 L2005 FP *012

JASTHY, Sri Lakshmi. 4800 FRIENDSHIP AVE, STE 2303 15224 #495-50-1998 L2001 HO *012

JASTI, Harish. 200 LOTHROP ST, MONTEFIORE HOSPITAL, W933 15213 #035-19-1998 L2001 IM *020 †20

JASTI, Kishan Kumar. ■ 15220 #496-24-1998 L2001 IM *020

JAVADI, Parvin Patricia. ■ 15228 #517-05-1964 L1973 AN *072

JAVAHERIAN, Tracy Nicole. 3811 OHARA ST 15213 #041-12-2005 L2005 P *012

JAVED, Nosheen. 4800 FRIENDSHIP AVE 15224 #704-09-2001 L2003 CD *012 †20

JEFFRIES, C Stephen. 1000 BOWER HILL RD 15243 #041-12-1983 L1984 PD *020 †55

JEREMITSKY, Elan. 320 E NORTH AVE, ALLEGHENY GENERAL HOSPITAL 15212 #035-08-1997 L2001 GS *020 †85

JERNIGAN, Paula Marie. 5200 CENTRE AVE, STE 610 15232 #041-12-1997 L1999 PCC *020 †20

JEVAJI, Indira P. 1400 LOCUST ST, MERCY HOSPITAL 15219 #495-65-1982 L1995 PD *020 †55

JEVAJI, Padmarao. ■ 15237 #495-21-1984 L1997 IM *020 †20

JEW, Edward W, Jr. 650 WASHINGTON RD 15270 #041-12-1953 L1954 GS GE *071 †85

JEYABALAN, Arundhathi. 300 HALKET ST, UNIV OF PITTSBURGH MED CTR 15213 #025-01-1994 L2000 OBG *020 †30

JEYABALAN, Geetha. 200 LOTHROP ST, RM F-675 15213 #025-01-2002 L2002 GS *012

JHAMB, Manisha. 4800 FRIENDSHIP AVE, WESTERN PENNSYLVANIA HOSPI 15224 #495-45-2004 L2006 IM *012

JHAMB, Mohit. 4800 FRIENDSHIP AVE, WESTERN PENNSYLVANIA HOSPI 15224 #495-45-2004 L2006 IM *012

JHO, Hae Dong. 320 E NORTH AVE, JHO INSTITUTE FOR MIN 7TH 15212 #583-06-1971 L1983 NS OS *020 †25

JIANG, Shao. 3705 5TH AVE 15213 #041-14-1999 L2004 PS *020 †65

JIDARIAN, Anoush. 121 MEYRAN AVE, UNIV HLTH CTR 15213 #033-05-2001 L2007 TS *012 †85

JIMENEZ, Eduardo Leon. PO BOX 38563 15238 #308-01-1958 L1972 P IM *020

JINDAL, Ankur. 1400 LOCUST ST, MERCY HOSPITAL 15219 #496-59-2005 L2007 IM *012

JINDAL, Rishi. ■ 15213 #041-12-2008 *012

JOCSON, Vicente Locsin. 200 LOTHROP ST, PRESBYTERIAN HOSP 15213 #748-02-1956 L1968 OPH *012

JOHAN, Morton. 230 N CRAIG ST, VISTA BEHAVIORAL 15213 #010-01-1946 L1955 PYA *071 †75

JOHN, Lawrence Richard. 100 DELAFIELD RD 15215 #038-06-1977 L1978 FM *020 †18

JOHNJULIO, William Keith. 1400 LOCUST ST 15219 #018-03-1995 L1998 FM *020 †18

JOHNSEN, Anna-Margareta. 490 E NORTH AVE, STE 107 15212 #409-12-1965 L1981 IM PA *020 †20

JOHNSON, Barbara Ann. 3811 OHARA ST 15213 #025-01-1985 L1987 CHP P *020 †75

JOHNSON, Brian Michael. ■ 15232 #041-13-2006 L2006 IM *012

JOHNSON, Bruce Allen. 3459 5TH AVE RM NW628, MONTEFIORE UNIV HOSPITAL 15213 #038-40-1986 L1988 PUD IM *020 †20

JOHNSON, Bruce Leonard. 203 LOTHROP ST, EAR & THROAT INSTITUTE 15213 #041-02-1960 L1961 PTH *020 †50

JOHNSON, Jennifer Petra. 3811 OHARA ST, AND C 15213 #041-02-2005 L2005 P *012

JOHNSON, John Degraft. ■ 15216 #038-41-1996 L2006 TS *012

JOHNSON, John Prentiss. 3550 TERRACE ST, 937 SCAIFE HALL 15213 #051-04-1971 L1991 NEP *020 †20

JOHNSON, Jonas Talmadge. 200 LOTHROP ST, STE 500 15213 #035-15-1972 L1979 OTO HNS *020 †45

JOHNSON, Marshall M, Jr. 1425 BEAVER AVE, PITTSBURGH BLACK ACTION DR 15233 #047-07-1952 L1959 GP OS *071

JOHNSON, Nathan Allen. 3705 5TH AVE, CMT STE 4895 15213 #005-19-2001 L2004 DR *012

JOHNSON, Richard Barrett. 580 S AIKEN AVE 15232 #041-14-1982 L1984 ID IM *020 †20

JOHNSON, Ronald Robt. 300 HALKET ST 15213 #041-12-1983 L1984 GS *020 †85

JOHNSTON, James Ray. 3550 TERRACE ST 15261 #041-12-1979 L1980 NEP IM *020 †20

JOHNSTON, Jann M. 1400 LOCUST ST, BLDG D 15219 #041-14-1979 L1980 END *020 †20

JOHNSTON, Robert Thos. 1400 LOCUST ST, STE 5106 15219 #041-09-1973 L1974 IM OM *020 †20

JOHNSTONE, Graham Findlay. 107 GAMMA DR, STE 107 15238 #041-12-1970 L1974 ORS *020 †20

JOLLY, Shashank. ■ 15213 #495-34-1987 L2006 TS *012 †85

JONES, Alvin Christopher. ■ 15261 #041-12-2008 *012

JONES, Frank Edward. 3200 PARK LANE DR, INTRACORP-MEDICAL DEPT 15275 #025-01-1969 L1988 GS OS *062 †85

JONES, George James. 320 E NORTH AVE 15212 #041-12-1970 L1974 U *020 †95

JONES, Joseph Orduma. 3601 5TH AVE, STE 3A 15213 #917-28-1996 L2002 ID *012

JONES, Keisha Andrene. 15217 #051-04-2002 L2006 OBG *100

JONES, Kristen Elizabeth. ■ 15206 #021-01-2007 L2007 *012

JONES, Larry Martin. 1400 LOCUST ST 15219 #017-20-1977 L1980 GS TRS *020 †85

JONES, Michael C. ■ 15235 #041-02-2006 L2006 DR *012

JONES, Miroslawa. 300 HALKET ST, MAGEE DEPT PATHOLOGY 15213 #759-09-1978 L1993 ATP *020 †50

JONES, Robert Tudor, Jr. 1400 LOCUST ST 15219 #041-12-1971 L1972 R PD *071 †80

JONES, Russell Edward. 200 LOTHROP ST, N713 15213 #041-13-2004 L2004 IM *012 †20

JONES, Sandra Marie. 320 E NORTH AVE, 5TH FLR SOUTH TOWER 15212 #038-45-1995 L1998 CRS *085,10

JONES, Steven Robt. 4190 BROWNSVILLE RD 15227 #038-41-1981 L1982 OTO *020 †45

JONES, William C. 400 45TH ST 15201 #041-12-1953 L1955 PTH *071 †50

JONES, Yemisi. ■ 15206 #041-12-2008 *012

JONES-IVY, Sonya Uda. ■ 15218 #041-12-2001 L2001 OBG *100

JOOSTE, Edmund Hilton. 3705 5TH AVE, DEPT OF ANESTH 15213 #836-03-1995 L2005 AN *100 †05

JORGENSON, Joel Jonathan. 200 LOTHROP ST, DEPT OF RADIOLOGY 15213 #041-13-1996 L2001 DR *020 †80

JOSEPH, Andrew Harry. 120 LYTTON AVE, STE 300 15213 #041-13-1970 L1971 IM *020 †20

JOSEPH, Benson Pullikkoti. ■ 15232 #035-03-2005 GS *012

JOSHI, Amar Bharat. ■ 15221 #041-12-2006 L2006 TY *012

JOSHI, Manohar Janardan. 5230 CENTRE AVE 15232 #495-23-1959 L1973 CD IM *074

JOSHI, Rama M. 5230 CENTRE AVE, STE M-205 15232 #495-22-1985 L1990 AN OS *020 †05

JOSHI, Renu Ashwin. 320 E NORTH AVE 15212 #496-60-2003 L2006 OBG *012

JOSHI, Sheela Kishor. OF PITTSBURGH, UNIV HLTH CTR 15261 #041-12-2003 L2006 END *012 †20

JOVIN, Franzisua Fruzsina. 200 LOTHROP ST 15213 #409-25-1994 L1999 IM *020 †20

JOVIN, Tudor Gheorghe. 200 LOTHROP ST, C-400 PUH 15213 #409-25-1994 L2000 N *020 †75

JOYCE, Judith Marie. ■ 15238 #048-13-1983 L1989 NM DR *030 †80,28

JOZEFCZYK, Patricia B. 420 E NORTH AVE, STE 206 15212 #041-12-1974 L1975 N *020 †75

JOZWIAK, Mariola R. 900 MT ROYAL BLVD, GPMA UPMC 15223 #759-04-1985 L1994 IM *020 †20

JUANG, David. ■ 15215 #038-45-2003 L2003 CCS *020

JUDD, Barry Lewis. 540 N NEVILLE ST, STE 102 15213 #038-43-1983 L1984 P *020 †75

JUDELMAN, Kevin Marc. 320 E NORTH AVE, ALLEGHENY GEN HOSP 15212 #143-06-2002 L2006 IM *012

JUENG, Carl Friedrich, Jr. 919 SETTLERS RIDGE RD 15238 #034-01-1982 L1994 RO IM *020 †20,80

JUGAN, Carol Agnes. 3705 5TH AVE, OF PITTSBURGH 15213 #041-13-2000 L2000 PAN *012

JUHAS, Elizabeth Anne. ■ 15232 #041-15-2008 *012

JUKIC, Drazen Marijan. 5230 CENTRE AVE RM WG0214, UPMC SHADYSIDE DERM 15232 #957-01-1993 L1998 DMP ATP *020 †50

JULIAN, Thomas Benj. 320 E NORTH AVE, ALLEGHENY GEN HOSP 15212 #041-12-1976 L1977 GS *020 †85

JUMAA, Mouhammad Aghiad. 121 MEYRAN AVE, DEPT OF INTERNAL MED 15213 #875-01-2002 L2004 N *012

JURCZAK, Renata Izabela. 135 CUMBERLAND RD, STE 200 15237 #759-04-1994 L2000 *100 †75

JUSELIUS, Whitney E. 121 MEYRAN AVE, UNIV HLTH CTR 15213 #007-02-2003 L2007 CD *012 †20

KABAZIE, Abraham John, Jr. 320 E NORTH AVE 15212 #041-07-1992 L1996 APM *020 †05

KABB, Aaron Leonard. ■ 15212 #016-42-2005 L2005 IM *012

KACZOROWSKI, David James. 200 LOTHROP ST, ROOM F-675 PRESBYTERIAN HO 15213 #023-07-2003 L2003 GS *012

KACZOROWSKI, Denise Anne. ■ 15243 #055-01-1991 L1993 IM *020 †20

KACZOROWSKI, Susan Lynn. 320 E NORTH AVE, ALLEGHENY GENERAL HOSPITAL 15212 #041-13-1987 L1989 CCP *020 †20

KAD, Rishi. ■ 15205 #496-43-1998 L2001 CD *012 †20

KADIWAR, Kavita Rajnikant. ■ 15213 #035-45-2007 L2007 P *012

KAHLOON, Arslan Akbar. 3708 5TH AVE, UNIVERSITY HEALTH CENTER 15213 #704-25-2004 L2006 IM *012

KAHN, Charles Edward. 3811 OHARA ST, OFC 11 15213 #041-12-1997 L1999 P *020 †75

KAIRIS, Edwin James. 600 GRANT ST, U.S. STEEL TOWER, 41ST FLO 15219 #041-12-1992 L1995 PD *030 †55

KAISER, Erin Michelle. ■ 15218 #041-02-2006 L2006 PD *012

KAITHACKACHALIL, Shirley. 320 E NORTH AVE 15212 #495-99-1989 L1999 P *012

KALAN, Amanda Meloura. ■ 15206 #038-41-2003 L2006 OBG *020

KALDAS, Hoda Kamel Halim. 3550 TERRACE ST, A919 SCAIFE HALL 15261 #915-02-1995 L2001 NEP *100 †20

KALE, Hrishikesh Arwind. 9100 BABCOCK BLVD 15237 #496-36-1996 L2006 RNR *100 †80

KALE, Vasudha Hrishikesh. 3705 5TH AVE, MT 3950 15213 #496-38-1998 L2007 DR *020

KALEIDA, Phillip Henry. 3705 5TH AVE, GENERAL ACADEMIC PEDIATRIC 15213 #020-02-1974 L1982 PD *040 †55

KALIAPPAN, Robert. 230 MCKEE PL STE 500, OF PITTSBURGH 15213 #016-06-2006 L2006 EM *012

KALIDINDI, Ravi Kumar. ■ 15232 #496-69-2004 L2006 FP *012

KALIM, Roshan. 103 GREENVALLEY CT 15220 #495-77-1997 L2005 FM *020 †18

KALIMAN, Edward Geo. 200 BROWNSVILLE RD 15227 #035-09-1983 L1984 CD IM *020 †20

KALLA, Richard Leob. 5140 LIBERTY AVE 15224 #041-12-1960 L1961 IM NM *071 †28

KALRO, Brinda Narain. 300 HALKET ST, MAGEE WOMENS HOSPITAL 15213 #495-75-1987 L1998 OBG *020

KAMAT, Nitin M. A 919 SCAIFE HALL, 3550 TERRACE STREET 15261 #495-17-1989 L2001 NEP IM *020 †20

KAMAT, Sonal Nitin. ■ 15238 #495-17-1995 L2007 PTH *100

KAMEL, Adham Samy. 320 E NORTH AVE 15212 #915-02-1998 L2004 IM *100

KAMERER, Donald B. 200 LOTHROP ST, UPPTLRYNGLGY EYE & EAR 15213 #041-13-1959 L1960 OTO OS *071 †45

KAMINSKI, Robert John. 300 HALKET ST, STE 4750 15213 #041-12-1974 L1975 OBG *020 †30

KAMPNER, Stanley Laurence. ■ 15208 #005-15-1963 L1965 ORS *071 †40

KAMPSCHULTE, Peter S. 3705 5TH AVE DEPT AN 15213 #407-21-1961 L1972 AN OS *020

KANAAN, Hilal Azzam. 200 LOTHROP ST, STE B400 15213 #025-07-2004 L2004 NS *012

KANAKAMEDALA, Satish B. 4506 PENN AVE 15224 #495-11-1981 L1993 GE IM *020 †20

KANAL, Emanuel. 200 LOTHROP ST, DEPARTMENT OF RADIOLOGY - 15213 #041-12-1981 L1983 DR RNR *020 †80

KANBOUR, Amal Ibrahim. 300 HALKET ST, MAGEE WOMENS HOSP DPT PTH 15213 #528-01-1971 L1985 PTH PCP *020 †50

KANBOUR, Anisa Irbahim. 300 HALKET ST, PATH/MAGEE WOMENS HOSPITAL 15213 #528-01-1957 L1972 ATP PCP *020 †50

KANDEL, Arie. A-1305 SCAIFE HALL, DEPT OF ANESTHESIA AND CCM 15261 #045-04-1989 L1992 AN *020 †05

KANDERI, Tanuja. ■ 15206 #495-11-1995 L2007 NM *100 †28

KANDIL, Hossam Mohamed. 200 LOTHROP ST, 9019 FORBES TOWER 15213 #915-03-1981 L1996 GE IM *020 †20

KANE, John Jos. 158 MAIN ENTRANCE DR 15228 #041-13-1971 L1972 OBG *020 †30

KANE, Kevin Martin. 1400 LOCUST ST, STE 103 15219 #038-40-1972 L1975 ON HEM *020 †20

KANE, Timothy Dennis. 3705 5TH AVE 15213 #035-15-1992 L2001 GS PDS *020 †85

KANEL, Keith Thos. 320 E NORTH AVE 15212 #041-12-1983 L1984 IM *020 †20 ‡

KANG, James D. 3471 5TH AVE, SUITA 1010 15213 #039-01-1986 L1987 ORS GS *020 †40

KANG, Jasbir S. 1000 COMMERCE DR, STE 1002 15275 #495-27-1976 L1984 P PYG *020 †75

KANG, Robert H. 1350 LOCUST ST STE G103 15219 #016-06-1993 L2003 PS HS *020 †65

KANIA, Robert Jos. 4815 LIBERTY AVE, MELLON PAVILION 15224 #016-43-1967 L1980 GE IM *020 †20

KANIECKI, Robert Gerard. 120 LYTTON AVE, STE 300 15213 #028-02-1988 L1992 N *020 †75 ‡

KANN, Jeffrey Neal. 300 CHAPEL HARBOR DR, STE 300 15238 #041-12-1991 L1996 ORS OFA *020 †40

KANN, Jules. 128 N CRAIG ST 15213 #869-01-1959 L1961 OS OM *020 †18

KANN, Steven Enright. 300 CHAPEL HARBOR DR, STE 300 15238 #041-12-1990 L1992 HS *020 †40

KANNAN, Muralidhar. 320 E NORTH AVE 15212 #495-16-1999 L2005 P *012

KANSAL, Sheru Kumar. 4800 FRIENDSHIP AVE 15224 #035-06-2004 L2005 IM *020

KANT, Jeffrey Alan. 3550 TERRACE ST, S 701 SCAIFE HALL 15213 #016-02-1975 L1983 PTH CMG *020 †50,19

KANT, Tapan Naval. 317 CLIMAX ST, HILLTOP COMMUNITY HEALTHCA 15210 #041-13-2002 L2002 **FM** *020 †18

KANTARTZIS, Stamatis Nich. ■ 15232 #041-12-2007 L2007 **TY** *012

KANTER, Adam Scott. 200 LOTHROP ST, UPMC PRESBYTERIAN, SUITE A 15213 #050-02-2001 L2007 **NS** *100

KAO, Amy H. 3500 TERRACE ST S721, BIOMEDICAL SCIENCE TWR 15261 #035-08-1997 L2000 **RHU IM** *050 †20

KAPADIA, Shernaaz Behram. 3801 MCKNIGHT EAST DR, FL 1 15237 #041-13-1995 L2001 **AI** *020 †55,03

KAPLAN, Alicia Joy. 1200 REEDSDALE ST 15233 #016-42-1997 L2003 **P** *020

KAPLAN, Peter Donald. 490 E NORTH AVE, STE 300 15212 #016-11-1967 L1974 **PUD IM** *020 †20

KAPLAN, Richard Mark. 4800 FRIENDSHIP AVE, W PENN HOSP 15224 #041-12-1992 L1994 **EM** *020 †16

KAPLAN, Robert. 4800 FRIENDSHIP AVE, STE 2303 15224 #041-09-1990 L1993 **HO IM** *020 †20

KAPLAN, Sandra M Solon. 300 HALKET ST 15213 #024-05-1959 L2001 **CLP HEM** *020 †50 ‡

KAPOOR, Rachna. 1400 LOCUST ST, MERCY HOSPITAL 15219 #035-03-2003 L2003 **PD** *100 †55

KAPOOR, Wishwa Nath. 200 LOTHROP ST, GEN MED/933 W MONTEFIORE H 15213 #028-02-1975 L1979 **IM** *050 †20

KAPOSI-NOVAK, Pal. 3550 TERRACE STREET, A711 SCAIFE HALL 15261 #473-01-2001 L2007 **PTH** *012

KAR, Erica D. 200 LOTHROP ST, ASSISTANT PROFESSOR UPMC D 15213 #041-13-2001 L2007 **PDR** *100 †80

KARAMCHANDANI, Nilima Tej. 4800 FRIENDSHIP AVE, DEPT PED 15224 #496-38-1970 L1974 **NPM PD** *020 †55 ‡

KARAS, Mark. 619 MOUNT ROYAL BLVD 15223 #011-03-1976 L1977 **FM EM** *020 †18

KARASIC, Raymond Bennett. 3705 5TH AVE, CHILDREN'S HOSP OF PITTSBU 15213 #023-07-1977 L1978 **PD PEM** *020 †55,16

KARJOO, Sara. ■ 15217 #035-15-2007 L2007 **PD** *012

KARLIK, Jeffrey Scott. 1015 W VIEW PARK DR, KARLIK OPHTHALMOLOGY 15229 #041-12-1995 L1997 **OPH** *020 †35

KARLOVITS, Stephen M. 320 E NORTH AVE, DEPT RAD/ONC 15212 #038-41-1993 L1999 **RO** *020 †80 ‡

KARP, Jordan Friedman. 232 N CRAIG ST 15213 #041-12-1998 L2002 **P PYG** *050 †75

KARPIE, John Christopher. ■ 15214 #035-06-2005 L2005 **ORS** *012

KARPINSKI, Stephen J, Jr. ■ 15237 #010-02-1963 L1965 **AN** *071 †05

KARPOV, Oksana. 1400 LOCUST ST 15219 #041-78-2007, ▲ L2007 **IM** *012

KARR, Steven Paul. ■ 15237 #041-12-1976 L1977 **DR** *020 †80

KARSLIOGLU, Esra. 121 MEYRAN AVE, UNIV HLTH CTR OF PITTSBURG 15213 #902-05-2002 L2004 **END** *012 †20

KART, Barry H. 200 LOTHROP ST STE 710 15213 #041-13-1969 L1970 **DR** *020 †80

KARTAN, Roopa. 446 LINCOLN AVE, BELLEVUE PEDIATRICS 15202 #041-12-1993 L1996 **PD** *020 †20

KARTHIKEYAN, Tharun. ■ 15217 #041-12-2005 L2005 **ORS** *012

KARWOWSKI, Christine Ann. 121 MEYRAN AVE, UNIV HLTH CTR 15213 #759-18-2003 L2007 **PG** *012

KASDAN, Lanie Alyse. 1400 LOCUST ST STE G103, UPMC CANCER CENTER AT MERC 15219 #041-12-2001 L2004 **HO** *020 †05

KASDAN, Richard Bruce. 1515 LOCUST ST, OF PITTSBURGH 15219 #041-12-1972 L1973 **N** *020 †75

KASEER, Bahaa Aldeen. 200 LOTHROP ST, STE 503 15213 #875-02-2005 L2007 **IM** *012

KASIEWICZ, James Edward. 4800 FRIENDSHIP AVE, DEPT OF SURGERY 15224 #041-13-2004 L2004 **GS** *012

KASSAM, Amin B. 200 LOTHROP ST 15213 #065-01-1991 L1997 **NS** *020

KASSYK, Monika A. 2020 ARDMORE BLVD, STE 300 15221 #759-03-1988 L1994 **FM** *020 †18

KASZA, Jason Richard. 320 E NORTH AVE, ALLEGHENY GENERAL HOSPITAL 15212 #017-20-2003 L2003 **GS** *012

KATHJU, Sandeep. UNIV. OF PITTSBURGH, 6B SCAIFE HALL 3550 TERR 15261 #025-01-1994 L2000 **PS** *020 †45,65

KATTAN, Jacob Daniel. ■ 15217 #035-47-2007 L2007 **PD** *012

KATYAL, Sanjeev. 4800 FRIENDSHIP AVE 15224 #035-19-1995 L1998 **DR** *020 †80

KATZ, Aviva Lynn. 3705 5TH AVE, STE 4A485 15213 #035-47-1982 L1993 **PDS TRS** *020 †85

KATZ, Carissa L. 3436 WILLIAM PENN HWY, BLDG 2 15235 #041-12-1994 L1997 **IM** *020 †20 ‡

KATZ, David Leland. 1 BIGELOW SQ, STE 729 15219 #041-12-1961 L1962 **GYN** *020 †30

KATZ, Harry Robt. 1020 BOWER HILL RD 15243 #041-02-1973 L1974 **RO** *020 †80

KATZ, Kenneth Darren. 200 LOTHROP ST 15213 #035-48-1996 L2003 **EM ETX** *020 †20,16

KATZ, Richard Gutman. 3500 5TH AVE 15213 #023-07-1968 L1976 **HS** *071 †85,65

KATZ, William Edward. 200 LOTHROP ST, SCAIFE HALL S563 15213 #038-40-1986 L1987 **CD IM** *020 †20

KATZIN, Dick. 0 UNIVERSITY DRIVE C 15240 #035-20-1965 **OPH** *071 †35 ‡

KAUFER, Gerald Ira. 1000 BOWER HILL RD 15243 #041-12-1963 L1964 **GS VS** *020 †85 ‡

KAUFFMAN, David Earl. 1501 LOCUST ST, STE 224 15219 #045-01-1992 L1996 **OBG** *020 †30

KAUFMAN, Sidney Stanley. 5200 CENTRE AVE STE 609 15232 #041-12-1941 L1942 **GS** *072 †85

KAUFMANN, David Louis. 1501 LOCUST ST, STE 224 15219 #035-46-1994 L2000 **NS** *020 †25

KAUFMANN, Robert A. 3471 5TH AVE 15213 #041-13-1997 L1999 **HS** *020 †40

KAUL, Bupesh. 200 LOTHROP ST, ANESTH/SCAIFE HALL 15213 #495-45-1980 L1997 **AN** *020 †05

KAUL, Rita. 1900 MURRAY AVE, STE 206 15217 #495-08-1980 L1997 **PD** *020 †55

KAUMA, Scott Wm. 4815 LIBERTY AVE STE 330, ALLEGHENY HEALTH SYSTEM 15224 #056-05-1982 L2003 **REN GYN** *075 †30 ‡

KAUR, Lakhvir. 320 E NORTH AVE, DEPT OF MED EDU 15212 #495-43-2000 L2006 **IM** *012

KAUR, Manpreet. 320 E NORTH AVE, ALLEGHENY GEN HOSP 15212 #495-03-2004 L2006 **IM** *012

KAURA, Amit. ■ 15203 #661-02-2004 L2005 **IM** *012

KAUSHIK, Alka Sharma. 4800 FRIENDSHIP AVE 15224 #496-07-1979 L1989 **AN DR** *020 †05

KAUSHIK, Ved Prakash. 4725 MCKNIGHT RD STE 107 15237 #495-45-1978 L1989 **CRS GS** *020 †85,10

KAVIC, Suzanne Marie. 4815 LIBERTY AVE, MELLON PAVILLION STE 330 15224 #047-07-1994 L2006 **OBG** *020 †30

KAWAI, Akihiko. 3811 OHARA ST 15213 #572-29-1983 **TS** *020

KAYE, Judith Evelyn. 5000 MCKNIGHT RD 15237 #550-02-1985 L1990 **CHP P** *020 †75

KAYE, Walter Hyman. 3811 OHARA ST, IROQUOIS BLDG ROOM 600 15213 #038-40-1970 L1986 **P N** *050 †75

KAZIENKO, Betsy Shook. 4424 PENN AVE, STE 104 15224 #055-01-1999 L2002 **RHU** *020 †20

KEATON, Altorous Raymon. ■ 15241 #024-01-1993 L1997 **OPH** *100

KEDDIE, Roland Thos F. 1000 BOWER HILL RD 15243 #041-12-1957 L1958 **EM LM** *071 †18

KEELEY, Samuel B. 200 LOTHROP ST, C-800 15213 #020-02-1978 L1999 **TS** *020 †90,85

KEENAN, Donald M. 300 HALKET ST 15213 #041-12-1989 L1998 **GS** *020 †85

KEENAN, Robert James. 320 E NORTH AVE, DEPT OF THORACIC SURGERY 15212 #060-01-1984 L1989 **TS** *020 †85

KEENER, Matthew Thomas. ■ 15213 #041-12-2005 L2005 **P** *012

KEHRL, Thompson. 230 MCKEE PL STE 500, OF PITTSBURGH 15213 #023-01-2005 L2005 **EM** *012

KEIDAR, Rimona. 121 MEYRAN AVE, UNIV HLTH CTR OF PITTSBURG 15213 #550-02-1994 L2000 **NPM** *012

KEIM, Peter Jos. ■ 15222 #041-12-1963 L1964 **FM** *030 †18

KEITH, Jonathan David. ■ 15221 #041-12-2006 L2006 **PS** *012

KELJO, David John. 3705 5TH AVE 15213 #041-01-1977 L2001 **PG PD** *020 †55

KELLEHER, Peter Marvel. ■ 15212 #041-02-2002 L2007 **HSO** *012

KELLER, Bradley Barth. 3705 5TH AVE 15213 #041-14-1985 L2002 **PDC PD** *020 †55

KELLEY, David Edmond. UNIV OF PITTSBURGH, E-1140 BST 15261 #023-01-1978 L1987 **END IM** *050 †20

KELLEY, Donald L. 3636 BLVD OF THE ALLIES 15213 #041-12-1979 L1980 **CLP BBK** *020 †50

KELLEY, Joseph Leo, III. 300 HALKET ST 15213 #028-34-1985 L1986 **GO OBG** *020 †30 ‡

KELLUM, John Alston, Jr. 200 LOTHROP ST 15213 #038-43-1988 L1992 **CCM IM** *020 †20

KELLY, Bruce. 2585 FREEPORT RD, STE 105 15238 #041-14-1977 L1978 **FM** *020 †18

KELLY, Edward Geo. 363 VANADIUM RD 15243 #056-06-1967 L1971 **ORS OSS** *071 †40

KELLY, Jonathan David. 5825 5TH AVE, # A305 15232 #036-05-2003 L2003 **EM** *010 †16

KELLY, Karen Ann. 7180 HIGHLAND DR, VA MEDICAL CENTER 15206 #041-13-1980 L1982 **P** *020 †75

KELLY, Kevin M. 420 E NORTH AVE, STE 206 15212 #041-12-1984 L1984 **N IM** *020 †75 ‡

KELLY, Thomas James. 3347 FORBES AVE, STE 303 15213 #024-07-1972 L1977 **GE** *020 †20

KELLY, Thomas John. 1400 LOCUST ST, MERCY HOSP 15219 #038-41-2004 L2006 **PM** *012

KEMPEN, Paul Martin. 200 LOTHROP ST, UPMC 15213 #409-05-1981 L1987 **AN IM** *020 †05

KENKRE, Rajendre B. ■ 15235 #495-01-1971 L1979 **N** *020

KENNA, Marita D. 3811 OHARA ST 15213 #056-06-1951 L1952 **CHP PYA** *071 †55,75

KENNARD, David Wm. ■ 15213 #917-25-1947 L1977 **P** *030

KENNEDY, David F. ■ 15217 #041-02-1953 L1954 **P** *072 †75

KENNEDY, Francis Bryan. 200 DELAFIELD RD, CLINICAL CARDIOLOGY 15215 #041-12-1955 L1956 **CD** *071 †20

KENNEDY, Margaret. 4800 FRIENDSHIP AVE # 2303, WESTERN PENN CANCER INST 15224 #759-11-1988 L2002 **HEM VM** *020 †20

KENNEDY, Shirley Ann. 5900 PENN AVE, NOVUM PHARM RESEARCH SVCS 15206 #041-14-1983 L1984 **EM FM** *020 †18

KENNEDY, Susan Mary. 3705 5TH AVE # 2ND 15213 #539-05-1980 L1989 **NP** *020 †50

KENNERDELL, John Shirk. 420 E NORTH AVE, DEPT OF OPHTHALMOLOGY 15212 #041-13-1961 L1964 **OPH N** *071 †35

KENT, Charles Joseph. 1835 FORBES AVE, 1401 FORBES AVENUE 15219 #038-06-1992 L1997 **OPH FPS** *020 †35

KENT, Georgia Lynn. ■ 15234 #041-01-1975 L1976 **OBG** *020 †30

KENT, Sara Antoinette. 200 LOTHROP ST RM C924, UPMC PRESBYTERIAN 15213 #026-08-1995 L1995 **HMP** *020 †50

KENTOR, Michael Leon. 3550 TERRACE ST, A-1305 SCAIFE HALL 15261 #041-12-1976 L1977 **AN** *020 †05

KEOUGH, William Lawrence. 320 E NORTH AVE, ALLGHANY GENERAL HOSP 15212 #024-16-1999 L2001 **PDI** *020 †55

KERR, John Fergus. 200 LOTHROP ST 15213 #143-10-1987 *100

KESLINGER, Lynn Sherry. 320 E NORTH AVE 15212 #035-08-1983 L1986 **AN** *020 †05

KESSLER, Otto Francis. 5230 CENTRE AVE 15232 #041-12-1959 L1960 **OBG** *071 †30

KETTEL, Jessica Candelora. 3811 OHARA ST, AND C 15213 #041-12-2005 L2005 **P** *012

KHACHI, Gerald Jerry. 3550 TERRACE PLACE, UPMC 15261 #539-04-2000 L2005 **PS** *012 †85 ‡

KHAJAVI, Mohammad. 1400 LOCUST ST DEPT RAD 15219 #517-01-1966 L1977 **R** *020

KHAJURI, Vishwanath M B. 1501 LEBANON CHURCH RD 15236 #496-01-1980 L1992 **IM** *020 †20

KHAKHKHAR, Sima P. ■ 15232 #016-42-2007 L2007 **PD** *012

KHALID, Mian Kamal. 4800 FRIENDSHIP AVE, STE 2303NT 15224 #704-21-2000 L2006 **HO** *012

KHALID, Muhammad R. OF PITTSBURGH, UNIV HLTH CTR 15261 #704-25-1998 L2007 **CCM** *012

KHALIL, Patricia Elias. ■ 15206 #605-02-2002 L2006 **NEP** *012 †20

KHALILI, Behrooz. 180 FORT COUCH RD, STE 450 15241 #517-01-1970 L1978 **OBG** *020 †30

KHAN, Akhtar Sultan. 3459 5TH AVE, N-756.3 UPMC MONTEFIORE 15213 #704-09-1993 L2000 **CCS TTS** *020 †85

KHAN, Bilal Mohammad. 320 E NORTH AVE, ALLEGHENY GENERAL HOSPITAL 15212 #704-25-2003 L2006 **GS** *012

KHAN, Mashukur Rahman. 1400 LOCUST ST, MERCY HOSP PITTSBURGH 15219 #160-01-1991 L2001 **IM FM** *020 †20 ‡

KHAN, Milly P. 5230 CENTRE AVE, STE 339 15232 #160-02-1980 L1994 **FM** *020 †18

KHAN, Noor Afshan. 1515 LOCUST ST 15219 #704-25-1996 L2001 **IM** *020 †20

KHAN, Shabana. ■ 15213 #035-08-2007 L2007 **P** *012

KHAN, Shakeel Ahmed. 3811 OHARA ST, RM NO1175 15213 #704-08-1986 L1999 **P** *020 †75

KHAN, Waseem Khalid. 1400 LOCUST ST, MERCY HOSP OF PITTSBURGH 15219 #035-45-2007 L2007 **TY** *012

KHAN, Ziauddin. 4800 FRIENDSHIP AVE 15224 #704-02-1989 L1993 **IM** *100

KHANDHAR, Sameer J. ■ 15227 #038-44-2003 L2003 **CD** *012

KHANZADA, Mohammed A. 5230 CENTRE AVE, UPMC SHADYSIDE HOSPITAL 15232 #704-08-1991 L1996 **CCA** *020 †05

KHASNABIS, Sukamal. 2000 MARY ST, UPMC SOUTHSIDE HOSPITAL 15203 #495-39-1962 L1973 **PTH FOP** *020 †50

KHAVANDGAR, Simin. 121 MEYRAN AVE, DEPT OF NEUROLOGY 15213 #517-01-2001 L2004 **N** *012

KHEHRA, Raman Deep. 320 E NORTH AVE 15212 #496-03-2002 L2005 **IM** *012

KHETARPAL, Sharad Kumar. 5230 CENTRE AVE, SHADYSIDE HOSPITAL, 2ND FL 15232 #496-09-1979 L1993 **AN** *020 †05

KHOSLA, Nidhi. 4800 FRIENDSHIP AVE, WESTERN PENNSYLVANIA HOSP 15224 #495-45-1995 L2005 **OBG** *100

KHOURY, Firas George. 3550 TERRACE ST, A915 SCAIF HALL 15261 #875-01-1992 L2001 **NEP** *100 †20

KHURANA, Ajay Kumar. 2181 GARRICK DR 15235 #041-12-1999 L2001 **IM** *020 †20

KHURANA, Ramesh Chander. 700 WASHINGTON RD 15228 #495-36-1964 L1971 **NTR END** *072 †20 ‡

■ = Address Information Privacy Protected

KIAZAND, Mehrshid. 1400 LOCUST ST, MERCY HOSP-PITTSBURGH 15219 #517-23-2001 L2004 IM *020 †20

KIDO, Takaaki. 3380 BLVD OF THE ALLIES, STE 390 15213 #654-01-2001 L2002 GS *020

KIELMAN, Michael Jos. 5230 CENTRE AVE 15232 #041-12-1980 L1980 EM *020 †16

KIELY, Sharon Cabrina. 4800 FRIENDSHIP AVE 15224 #010-02-1984 L1988 IM PDS *030 †20

KIESAU, Marin Lynn. 3705 5TH AVE, 3RD FLOOR CHOB 15213 #041-02-1998 L2004 PD *020 †55

KIETZ, Daniel Armin. 3705 5TH AVE 15213 #409-23-1994 L2003 RHU *020 †20,55

KILARU, Deepika. 320 E NORTH AVE 15212 #496-62-2004 L2005 IM *012

KILKENNY, Laurie Ann. 1350 LOCUST ST, STE 308 15219 #035-19-1996 L2001 PCC *020 †20

KILPELA, Brian Andrew. 4721 MCKNIGHT RD STE 209N, PED ALLIANCE NORTHLAND 15237 #041-12-2002 L2002 PD *020 †55

KILPELA, Donald Andrew. 4721 MCKNIGHT RD STE 209N, PEDIATRIC ALLIANCE - NORTH 15237 #041-12-1974 L1975 PD *020 †55

KILPELA, Kyra Marie. ■ 15237 #041-15-2005 L2008 EM *012

KIM, Cathy L. 320 E NORTH AVE, DEPT OF RADIOLOGY 15212 #024-05-1996 L2002 DR *020 †80

KIM, Changhee. ■ 15206 #048-16-1999 L2004 PD *020

KIM, David Young. 121 MEYRAN AVE 15213 #041-01-2007 L2007 TY *012

KIM, Dong Hoon. ■ 15237 #028-34-1997 L2000 PCC *020 †20

KIM, Gene. ■ 15232 #041-12-2007 L2007 TY *012

KIM, Hanna. ■ 15206 #051-07-2003 L2007 CD *012

KIM, Ivone E. ■ 15232 #043-01-2007 L2007 PD *012

KIM, John Albert. ■ 15232 #041-12-2002 L2002 EM *020 †16

KIM, Joseph Uk. 320 E NORTH AVE 15212 #043-01-1989 L1992 AN *020 †05

KIM, Sang Won. 200 LOTHROP ST, STE C-800 15213 #048-12-1996 L1996 TS *100 †85

KIM, Seungwon. ■ 15238 #035-15-1998 L2006 OTO *100 †45

KIM, Stacy June. ■ 15237 #038-44-2003 L2007 PCP *012 †50

KIM, Sung Yong. ■ 15238 #583-03-1962 L1972 DR R *020 †80

KIM, Thomas Y. 5700 BUNKERHILL ST # 40 15206 #026-04-2003 L2007 AN *020

KING, Barbara Lynne. 3433 WILLIAM PENN HWY, MEDEXPRESS 15235 #041-12-1981 L1982 EM *012 †16

KING, Charles Christopher. 200 LOTHROP ST 15213 #008-01-1987 L1988 PD *020 †16

KING, Dale Eugene. ■ 15206 #041-12-2004 L2004 PD *012 †55

KING, Edwin Bennett, II. 1580 MCLAUGHLIN RUN RD, STE 208 15241 #041-02-1998 L2001 PD OS *020 †55

KING, Leo M. ■ 15243 #041-12-1953 L1954 U *071 †95

KING, Linda Ann. 200 LOTHROP ST, MUH - 933WEST 15213 #016-06-1995 L1999 IM *020 †20

KINNANE, Janet Mary. 3705 5TH AVE 15213 #024-01-1989 L1994 PD *020 †20

KINSEL, Alvin Anthony. 815 FREEPORT RD 15215 #041-12-1955 L1956 OM GP *071

KIPROFF, Paul Michael. 320 E NORTH AVE, ALLEGHENY RADIOLOGY 15212 #041-02-1984 L1985 VIR *040 †80

KIRK, Jacquelyn Marie. ■ 15241 #051-04-1949 L1971 D *071 †15

KIRKWOOD, John Munn. 5717 CENTRE AVE, HILLMAN CANCER RESEARCH 15206 #008-01-1973 L1986 HO IM *050 †20

KISHIDA, Akihiro. ■ 15217 #572-29-1978 L1990 OS GS *020 †85

KISILEVSKY, Robert. U-PGH GRAD SCH PH PATH 15213 #067-01-1962 PTH OS *050 †50

KISLOFF, Barry. 200 LOTHROP ST, DIVISION OF GASTROENTEROLO 15213 #035-19-1970 L1976 GE IM *020 †20 ‡

KISNER, Robert Garland. 211 N WHITFIELD ST, STE 410 15206 #047-07-1969 L1970 OBG *020 †30

KISS, Joseph Elmer. 3636 BLVD OF THE ALLIES 15213 #010-02-1978 L1979 HEM ON *020 †20

KISS, Lawrence Philip. ■ 15203 #035-48-2001 L2006 PTH *100 †50

KISS, Zoltan Steven. DESOTO & OHARA ST, DEPT RAD 15213 #143-03-1964 R *030

KISSLINGER, Benjamin L. 7180 HIGHLAND DR, PRIM.CARE, PURPLE TEAM 130 15213 #038-06-1998 L2000 IM *020 †20

KIYOTA, Ayano. 3708 5TH AVE, DEPT OF MED EDU 15213 #572-65-1998 L2006 FP *012

KIZINA, Christopher Allen. 5124 LIBERTY AVE 15224 #041-13-2004 L2005 AN *012

KLAIN, Miroslav. 3459 5TH AVE, DEPT OF AMESTHES 15213 #286-02-1951 L1973 AN CCA *071 †05

KLEIN, Alan Howard. 1307 FEDERAL ST, STE 2 15212 #041-12-1988 L1990 ORS *020 †40

KLEIN, Herbert A. 200 LOTHROP ST 15213 #035-01-1960 L1980 NM *020 †28

KLEIN, Janene Hecker. 320 E NORTH AVE, ALLEGHENY GEN HOSP 15212 #051-07-1986 L1987 EM *020 †16

KLEIN, Richard M. 580 S AIKEN AVE, STE 320 15232 #010-02-1972 L1975 FM EM *020 †16

KLEIN, Sanford Morton. ■ 15213 #041-12-1956 L1958 AN *071

KLEIN-PATEL, Marcia Ellen. ■ 15243 #035-05-2006 L2006 OBG *012

KLEPCHICK, Paul Richard. ■ 15243 #041-15-2001 L2001 DR *012

KLEYMAN, Thomas Ralph. 3550 TERRACE ST., RENA L DIVISION A919 SCAIF 15261 #028-02-1978 L1988 NEP IM *050 †20

KLIBER, Allison Anna. 7171 CHURCHLAND ST 15206 #041-07-1996 L1998 FM *020 †18

KLINE, Alex James. ■ 15213 #051-01-2004 L2004 ORS *012

KLINESTIVER, Donald G, Jr. 9365 MCKNIGHT RD, STE 300 15237 #055-02-1988 L1990 IM *020 †20

KLINGMAN, Daisy. 3811 OHARA ST, AND C 15213 #035-19-2005 L2005 P *012

KLIONSKY, Bernard L. 15217 #041-09-1952 L1961 PTH *071 †50

KLITSCH, Neal John. ■ 15218 #041-12-2005 L2005 DR *012

KLOESZ, Jennifer Lynn. 300 HALKET ST, DEPT OF PEDS MAGE WOMENS 15213 #038-40-1995 L1997 NPM *020 †55

KLUFAS, Christina Irene. 1400 LOCUST ST, CRITICAL CARE MEDICINE 15219 #035-15-1988 L1991 AN *012 †20

KLUG, Gerald David. 3528 BLVD OF THE ALLIES 15213 #422-01-1981 L1985 IM *020 †20

KLUGH, Jimmy R. 3433 WILLIAM PENN HWY, PENN CENTER EAST 15235 #048-15-1999 L2004 EM *020 †16

KLUNE, John Robert. ■ 15213 #041-12-2008 *012

KLUNK, William Edward. 130 DE SOTO ST, ROOM 705 PUBLIC SECTOR BUI 15261 #028-02-1984 L1985 P *050 †75

KNAUSS, Courtney Allison. ■ 15232 #041-12-2008 *012

KNOX, Mark Allan. 5215 CENTRE AVE 15232 #041-14-1979 L1980 FM *040 †18

KNUPP, Donna L. 4381 MURRAY AVE 15217 #010-02-1978 L1979 FM *020 †18

KNUTSEN, Christian Conrad. 230 MCKEE PL, STE 500 15213 #041-14-2000 L2000 EM *100

KO, Judy. 15219 #041-02-2005 L2005 IM *012

KOBALY, David John. 9576 PERRY HWY, STE 100 15237 #041-12-1973 L1974 OPH *020 †35

KOCHANEK, Patrick M. 3705 5TH AVE 15213 #016-02-1980 L1986 PD EM *020 †55

KOCHIK, George Jerome. 9100 BABCOCK BLVD 15237 #041-14-1987 L1989 GPM *020 †18

KOCHUPURA, Peter Varkey. 200 LOTHROP ST, CTR MED 15213 #035-09-2000 L2004 SME *012 †20

KODALI, Sobhan. 4800 FRIENDSHIP AVE 15224 #495-52-2004 L2005 IM *012

KODURI, Sailaja. 211 N WHITFIELD ST, STE 590 15206 #495-11-1983 L1992 IM *020 †20

KOENIG, Maria Elizabeth. 2 HOT METAL ST, 2ND FL 15203 #035-03-2005 L2005 EM *012

KOENIG, Mark Allen. 105 GAMMA DR, STE 300 15238 #025-01-1978 L1979 PD *020 †55

KOFLER, Julia. 3708 5TH AVE, DEPT OF MED EDUCATION 15213 #154-07-1997 L2005 PTH *012

KOHLI, Susan Marie. ■ 15208 #041-12-2005 L2005 IM *012

KOHNEN, Sharon Krug. ■ 15221 #041-02-2005 L2005 P *012

KOIMATTUR, Arwind Gowind. 4815 LIBERTY AVE, STE 156 MELLON PAVILION 15224 #495-35-1969 L1976 TS VS *012

KOJIMA, Hajime. 5215 CENTRE AVE 15232 #572-12-2000 L2003 FM *100 †18

KOKALES, John Geo. 120 LYTTON AVE 15213 #041-12-1973 L1974 IM IMG *020 †20

KOLARIK, Russ Carl. 5230 CENTRE AVE, STE 206 15232 #038-43-1995 L1999 IM PD *020 †20,55

KOLB, Norman Randall. 5230 CENTRE AVE, UPMC SHADYSIDE FAMILY MED 15232 #041-12-1982 L1983 FM *040 †18

KOLIBASH, Christopher P. 320 E NORTH AVE, ALLEGHENY GENERAL HOSPITAL 15212 #055-01-2003 L2004 IM *100 †20

KOLLS, Jay Kennedy. 3705 5TH AVE 15213 #023-01-1985 L2003 CCM PD *020 †20,55

KOLMEN, Barbara Kass. 256 SWEET GUM RD 15238 #048-02-1957 L1984 PD *071 †55

KOLOBOV, Anton. ■ 15217 #913-81-1993 L2002 IMG *100 †20

KOLTER, Joseph Paul, Jr. 1000 BOWER HILL RD 15243 #041-12-1975 L1976 GS VS *030 †85

KOLTHOFF, Marta C. 300 HALKET ST, DEPT OF OB/GYN/RS 2ND FL 15213 #035-06-2000 L2001 MG *100 †19

KOMAN, Christopher Glenn. 8135 PERRY HWY 15237 #041-12-1994 L1996 FM *020 †18

KOMARLU, Rukmini Rajaratn. 3705 5TH AVE, OF PITTSBURGH 15213 #496-39-1997 L2007 PDC *012 †55

KOMEN, Sutinee. ■ 15241 #891-02-1976 PD *075

KOMERALLY, Sangeeta Laksh. 4800 FRIENDSHIP AVE 15224 #495-98-2005 L2006 IM *012

KOMETIANI, Peter Zurab. 121 MEYRAN AVE, DEPT MED 15213 #038-43-2006 L2006 IM *012

KONDAVEETI, Kotayya. 4815 LIBERTY AVE STE 453 15224 #495-50-1969 L1981 GE *020 †20

KONDZIOLKA, Douglas S. 200 LOTHROP ST STE B-400, UPMC -DEPARTMENT OF NEUROL 15213 #065-01-1985 L1990 NS *020 †25

KONO, Yuriko. 200 LOTHROP ST, STE 503 15213 #572-32-2003 L2007 IM *012

KOO, Betty Kuen Kuen. 3705 5TH AVE, CHILDRENS HOSP 15213 #462-01-1975 L2000 CN *020 †75

KOOROS, Kian Said. 9104 BABCOCK BLVD 15237 #517-01-1962 L1970 CD IM *020 †20

KOOZEKANANI, Roshan Sara. 3811 OHARA ST, STE 274 THOMAS DETRE HALL 15213 #038-40-1995 L1999 OS P *020 †20,75

KORMOS, Robert Leslie. 200 LOTHROP ST 15213 #065-06-1976 L1987 TS *020

KORNBLITH, Paul Lee. 2516 JANE ST, PRECISION THERAPEUTICS, IN 15203 #041-02-1962 L1968 NS *071 †25

KORVEK, Scott Jason. 320 E NORTH AVE, STE 249 15212 #024-05-2001 L2001 EM *100 †16

KORYTKOWSKI, Mary Teresa. 3601 5TH AVE, FALK RM 550 15213 #036-01-1982 L1989 END IM *050 †20

KOSEMPA, Damian Carl. ■ 15218 #056-06-2007 L2007 ORS *012

KOSSOVSKY, Nir. 200 S LINDEN AVE 15206 #016-02-1983 L1985 ATP *062 †50

KOSTOV, Dean Borissov. ■ 15218 #041-12-2004 L2004 NS *012

KOSTYAL, John Louis. ■ 15236 #041-12-1940 L1941 OBG *071 †30

KOTAGAL, Vikas. ■ 15217 #026-04-2007 L2007 IM *012

KOTEKAL, Nagaraj. 1400 LOCUST ST, MERCY HOSPITAL 15219 #496-01-1980 L2000 AN *020

KOTTAPALLY, Srinivas M. ■ 15238 #495-62-1978 L1983 RO *020 †80 ‡

KOUMPOURAS, Fotios. ■ 15238 #422-01-2000 L2007 RHU *020 †20

KOURKLINSKI, Andrei Kazim. 320 E NORTH AVE, DEPT INTERNAL MEDICINE 15213 #912-07-1999 L2005 IM *012

KOVATCH, Anthony Louis. 9000 PERRY HWY STE 120, PED ALLIANCE - ARCADIA DIV 15237 #041-09-1977 L1981 PD *020 †55

KOVKAROVA-NAUMOVSKI, Eliza. ■ 15228 #957-04-1988 L2008 *100

KOZEL, Jennifer Marie. ■ 15202 #017-20-2004 L2004 PD *012 †55

KOZOVSKA, Milena Evlogiev. 522 ALPHA DR 15238 #913-05-1984 L2005 PTH DMP *100 †50

KRACKOW, Jeffrey D. ■ 15208 #041-15-2003 L2003 CD *012 †20

KRAEMER, David Warren. ■ 15220 #041-01-1954 L1955 OBG *071 †30

KRAEMER, Kevin Lawrence. 200 LOTHROP ST, MUH W920 15213 #005-02-1989 L1995 IM *020 †20

KRAK, Michael. 300 HALKET ST 15213 #041-12-1949 L1950 PD *071 †55

KRAKER, Jennifer Lynn. ARTS BUILDIN, STE 503 MEDICAL 15213 #550-04-2006 L2007 P *012

KRAKORA, Steven. ■ 15228 #041-15-2001 L2001 *012

KRALIOS, Constantine. 9335 MCKNIGHT RD, STE 220 15237 #418-01-1997 L2002 OBG *020 †20

KRAMER, Thomas Danl. 3000 BROWNSVILLE RD, STE C 15227 #041-12-1992 L1999 ORS *020 †40

KRANS, Elizabeth Ellen. ■ 15232 #027-01-2005 L2005 OBG *012

KRASINSKAS, Alyssa Marie. 200 LOTHROP ST, UPMC PRESPITERIAN A610 15213 #035-45-1994 L1997 ATP *020 †50

KRASOWSKI, Matthew David. 200 LOTHROP ST, DEPT OF PATHOLOGY/5834 MAI 15213 #016-02-2001 L2005 PTH *020 †50

KRAULAND, John Edward. 320 E NORTH AVE 15212 #041-13-1981 L1982 AN *020 †05

KRAUS, David Ross. 200 DELAFIELD RD, STE 1040 15215 #041-12-1965 L1969 ORS *020 †40

KREBS, Matthew Justin. ■ 15217 #041-15-2004 L2004 AN *012

KREINDLER, James Levin. 3705 5TH AVE, 3RD FLOOR/MAIN TOWER 15213 #035-47-1998 L2007 PDP *030 †55

KREISS, Christianna Maria. 200 LOTHROP ST, DIV OF GASTROENTEROLOGY 15213 #409-40-1993 L2000 GE *020 †20

KREMSER, Charles Allan. 3380 BOULEVARD OF THE ALLS, STE 1 15213 #025-01-1977 L1978 OBG *020 †20

KREPS, S Alexandra. 128 N CRAIG ST, STE 217 15213 #041-12-1982 L1983 P CHP *020 †75

KRESH, Norman Nathan. 540 N NEVILLE ST 15213 #041-12-1958 L1959 P CHP *071 †75

KREUTEL, Amy Haas. 200 LOTHROP ST, RADIOLOGY - UNIV OF PITTSB 15213 #041-12-2001 L2001 DR *020 †80

KREUTZER, Jacqueline. 3705 5TH AVE 15213 #132-01-1987 L1999 PDC *020 †55

KRIDGEN, Pamela Lofink. 300 HALKET ST, STE 1338 15213 #041-12-1991 L1993 OBG *020 †30

KRIFCHER, Emanuel. 6301 FORBES AVE, STE 300 15217 #275-01-1960 L1963 IM CD *020

KRIMER, Leonid Semion. 121 MEYRAN AVE, UNIV HLTH CTR OF PITTSBURG 15213 #913-81-1984 L2003 P *100

KRISHNA, Priya Darshini. 2000 MARY ST 15203 #028-46-1997 L2004 **OTO** *020 †45
KRISHNAMURTHY, Prema. 200 LOTHROP ST, C-WING PRESBYTERIAN UNIV H 15213 #495-16-1982 L2000 **PAN** *100 †05
KRISHNAMURTI, Lakshmanan. 3705 5TH AVE 15213 #495-73-1980 L2001 **PD HO** *020 †55
KRISHNAMURTI, Uma. ■ 15238 #496-07-1986 L2001 **PTH** *100 †50
KRISHNAN, Eswar. 3500 TERRACE ST, S709 BST SOUTH 15261 #495-31-1993 L2002 **RHU IM** *050 †20
KRISKY, David Mark. ■ 15237 #041-12-1999 L2001 **PTH** *020
KRISTAN, William Gerard. 9100 BABCOCK BLVD # EM 15237 #041-12-1980 L1980 **EM** *020 †16
KRISTOFIC, John D. 9909 FRANKSTOWN RD 15235 #041-13-1974 L1975 **IM CD** *020
KRIVAK, Thomas Carl. 300 HALKET ST 15213 #038-40-1994 L2005 **OBG** *020 †30
KROBOTH, Frank James. 200 LOTHROP ST, GEN MED/933 W MONTEFIORE 15213 #035-15-1976 L1977 **IM** *020 †20
KROHN, Kelly Dean. 1350 LOCUST ST, STE 300 15219 #030-06-1983 L1990 **RHU** *020 †20
KROPF, Eric Jon. ■ 15217 #010-02-2003 L2003 **ORS** *012
KROSS, Dean Ellis. 155 N CRAIG ST STE 110 15213 #008-01-1977 L1983 **CD IM** *020 †20
KROTEC, Joseph Wm. 5750 CENTRE AVE, STE 395 15206 #041-09-1954 L1955 **FM** *071 †18
KRUGH, James Wm. 200 LOTHROP ST 15213 #041-12-1970 L1976 **AN GS** *020 †05
KRUPSKI, Carol Ann. 850 CLAIRTON BLVD STE 3100 15236 #041-12-1982 L1983 **GYN OBG** *020 †30 ‡
KU, Andrew. 320 E NORTH AVE, ALLEGHENY RADIOLOGY 15212 #035-01-1984 L1984 **DR NS** *020 †80
KUAN, Shih-Fan. 200 LOTHROP ST 15213 #244-02-1977 L2002 **PTH** *020 †50
KUBIK, Carolyn Janet. 665 RODI RD, FL 2 15235 #010-01-1977 L1979 **REN GYN** *020 †30
KUBRIN, Gail M. 4416 PENN AVE 15224 #050-02-1982 L1983 **P** *074 †75
KUCHERA, Susan Alverna. ■ 15206 #041-14-2006 L2006 **FP** *012
KUCHIPUDI, Kavita. ■ 15213 #038-45-2008 *012
KUFFNER, Haruko A. 3601 5TH AVE STE 580 15213 #043-01-1994 L2002 **END IM** *020 †20
KUKLINCA, Arlington Geo. 4 PARKWAY CTR, QUEST DIAGNOSTICS 15220 #041-12-1966 L1967 **PTH** *020 †50
KULICK, Aaron Francis. 5140 LIBERTY AVE 15224 #041-13-1997 L2005 **NEP** *020 †20
KULKARNI, Aparna. 22 FORBES TER, # 22 15217 #048-04-1995 L2005 **GE** *020 †20
KULLER, Lewis Henry. AS26 CRABTREE GSPH/EPID 15261 #010-01-1959 L1973 **CD GPM** *050 †70
KUMAR, Suneel. ■ 15232 #025-01-2006 L2007 **DR** *012
KUMMANT, Peter Karl. 1400 LOCUST ST, MERCY HOSP OF PITTSBURGH 15219 #041-12-1984 L1985 **GS** *020 †85
KUNDRAT, Mary Louise. 120 5TH AVE # P4205, HIGHMARK BLUE CROSS 15222 #041-02-1975 L1976 **IM IMG** *030 †20
KUNKEL, Herbert G, Jr. 4800 FRIENDSHIP AVE 15224 #305-01-1984 L1985 **PM** *020 †60
KUNKLE, Amy Kathleen. ■ 15212 #041-77-2007, ▲ L2007 *012
KUNSCHNER, Alan John. 300 HALKET ST 15213 #561-01-1966 L1968 **GO GYN** *020 †30
KUNSCHNER, Lara Jeanne. 420 E NORTH AVE, EAST WING OFFICE BLDG, STE 15212 #041-12-1994 L2000 **N ON** *020 †75
KUPEC, Evan George. 1400 LOCUST ST, MERCY HOSP OF PITTSBURGH 15219 #055-01-2007 L2007 **TY** *012
KUPFER, David Jerome. 3811 OHARA ST, WPIC-ROOM E-210 15213 #008-01-1965 L1973 **P** *030 †75
KUREMSKY, Dale Alexander. 1000 BOWER HILL RD, STE 201 15243 #041-12-1970 L1971 **U** *071 †95
KUREMSKY, Jeffrey Griffin. ■ 15241 #010-01-2008 *012
KURLAND, Geoffrey. 3705 5TH AVE 15213 #005-11-1973 L1988 **PD PDP** *020 †55,03
KUROWSKI, Brad Gerald. ■ 15206 #038-06-2004 L2004 **PM** *012
KUSH, Frank Henry. 4815 LIBERTY AVE, STE G25 15224 #041-12-1972 L1973 **IM IMG** *020 †20
KWAK, Eunice J. 3601 5TH AVE, 3A FALK MEDICAL BUILDING 15213 #035-06-1991 L2001 **OBG** *020 †30
KWIATKOWSKI, Katherine An. ■ 15232 #041-12-2004 L2004 **P** *012
KWOH, Chian Kent. 3500 TERRACE ST, S702 BST 15261 #016-11-1979 L1986 **RHU IM** *050 †20
KWON, Lanna Sook. 15222 #036-01-2004 L2004 **IM** *100 †20
KWON, Soon-You. ■ 15232 #041-12-2007 L2007 **TY** *012
KWON, Soonhak. ■ 15237 #583-04-1988 L1995 **CHN** *020 †55
KWON, Younghoon. DEPT OF CRITICAL CARE MEDI, 3550 TERRACE STREET 6TH FL 15261 #583-04-1999 L2003 **CCM** *012 †20
KYRIACOPOULOS, John D. 200 LOTHROP ST 15213 #418-01-1952 L1968 **CD IM** *071 †20
LABIB, Dina Atef. 15211 #038-44-1998 **PM** *020
LABRIOLA, Leanne Terese. ■ 15213 #041-77-2006, ▲ L2006 **IM** *012
LABUDA, Joseph M, II. 2101 GREENTREE RD, STE B101 15220 #055-01-1984 L1985 **FM** *020 †18
LACARIA, Teresa Maria. OF PAT, UNIV OF PITTSBURGH DEPT 15261 #041-12-2004 L2004 **PTH** *010
LACE, Thomas Edward. 300 HALKET ST 15213 #041-12-1976 L1977 **AN PD** *020 †55,05
LACKNER, David Francis. 400 PENN CENTER BLVD, STE 555 15235 #041-12-1984 L1986 **R DR** *020 †80
LACOMIS, David. 200 LOTHROP ST, NEURO/F878 PRESBYTERIAN 15213 #041-14-1987 L1992 **N NP** *020 †75
LACOMIS, Joan Marie. 200 LOTHROP ST, SCHOOL OF MEDICINE RADIOL 15213 #041-14-1988 L1993 **DR** *020 †80
LADENBURGER, Regan Nichol. ■ 15218 #020-12-2006 L2006 **EM** *012
LADHAM, Shaun Antony. 542 4TH AVE 15219 #064-01-1992 L1997 **FOP** *020 †50
LAGANA, Stephen M. ■ 15213 #041-12-2008 *012
LAGEMANN, Gerritt Michael. 320 E NORTH AVE, DEPT RAD 15212 #038-40-2006 L2007 **DR** *012
LAGNESE, John Michael. 103 GAMMA DR STE 120 15238 #032-01-1978 L1979 **FM** *040 †18
LAGNESE, Keith Richard. 615 WASHINGTON RD, STE TL4 15228 #041-12-1994 L1998 **IM** *020 †20
LAGNESE, Margaret A. 3705 5TH AVE 15213 #032-01-1978 L1984 **PD** *020 †55
LAHOUD-RAHME, Manuella S. ■ 15206 #605-03-1999 L2005 **PDC** *100 †55
LAI, Stephen Yenzen. 203 LOTHROP ST 15213 #005-02-1998 L2000 **OTO** *020 †45
LAING, Patrick Gowans. ■ 15238 #352-07-1945 L1960 **ORS** *071 †40
LAKDAWALA, Shabbir S. 2912 GLENMORE AVE, SHABBIR LAKDAWALA MD PC 15216 #495-01-1974 L1978 **IM GP** *020 †20
LAKKAPPA, Bharath Kanthra. 2100 WHARTON ST, STE 620 15203 #495-37-1995 L2001 **IMG** *100 †20
LAKKIS, Fadi Geo. 200 LOTHROP ST, W1542 BIOMEDICAL SCIENCE T 15261 #605-01-1985 L2005 **NEP IM** *020 †20
LALL, Raj Kumari. 7180 HIGHLAND DR, HIGHLAND DRIVE CAMPUS 15206 #495-11-1978 L1989 **P** *020

LALLY, Margaret Sue. 1382 OLD FREEPORT RD, 1ST. FL. REAR 15238 #041-12-1985 L1986 **D** *020 †15
LALLY, Michael Edward. 1350 LOCUST ST STE 205 15219 #025-01-1977 L1979 **VS GS** *020 †85
LAMB, Jason Jay. 4815 LIBERTY AVE, STE 158 15224 #051-01-1996 L2000 **TS** *020 †85,90
LAMB, Jennifer Dana. ■ 15217 #041-12-2005 L2005 **PD** *012
LAMBERTON, Wm Frederick. ■ 15212 #041-14-1977 L1978 **IM OS** *071 †20
LAMBERTY, Phillip Edward. 3459 5TH AVE, UPMC MONTEFIORE NW 628 15213 #041-01-1997 L2000 **PCC** *050 †20
LAMBORE, Sanjay. 3705 5TH AVE 15213 #495-92-1983 L2003 **PD** *020 †55
LAMM, Inna V. 2400 ARDMORE BLVD, STE 301 15221 #913-69-1994 L2000 **IM** *020 †20
LAMONT, Patricia Anne. ■ 15217 #010-02-2003 L2003 **HO** *012 †20
LAMPERSKI, Christopher V. ■ 15237 #041-12-1978 L1980 **IM** *020 †20
LANAUZE, Harry E. 328 CURRY HOLLOW RD 15236 #047-07-1961 L1962 **GP FM** *020
LANDA, Jose Gonzalez. 4800 FRIENDSHIP AVE, DEPT PTH 15224 #847-04-1966 L1972 **PTH** *020 †50
LANDAU, Philip Meyers. 217 TIMBER RIDGE RD, CHOICE CARE PHYSICIANS, PC 15238 #041-12-1976 L1977 **IM** *020 †20
LANDEN, Deborah Dena. ■ 15217 #025-07-1976 L1977 **PHP** *050
LANDERMAN, Nathaniel S. 3471 5TH AVE STE 603 15213 #041-13-1955 L1956 **A IM** *020 †20,03 ‡
LANDIS, Jonathan Carl. 100 S JACKSON AVE 15202 #048-02-1991 L1993 **EM** *020 †16
LANDIS LEWIS, Deborah Lyn. ■ 15206 #041-12-2007 L2007 **OBG** *012
LANDRENEAU, Rodney Jerome. 200 DELAFIELD RD 15215 #021-05-1978 L1990 **TS CD** *020 †85,90
LANDRY, Jo-Anne Marie. 15221 #016-43-2004 L2007 **IM** *012 †20
LANDVOIGT, Maple Timothy. 3705 5TH AVE, OF PITTSBURGH 15213 #055-01-2002 L2006 **PDP** *012 †20,55
LANDY, Michelle. ■ 15217 #041-12-2008 *012
LANERI, Giovanni. 4800 FRIENDSHIP AVE, # 3420 15224 #308-03-1982 L1983 **NPM PD** *020 †55
LANFORD, Lizabeth Miller. 3705 5TH AVE 15213 #005-18-1988 L1990 **PDC** *020 †55
LANG, Howard Norman. ■ 15236 #041-12-1961 L1962 **IM A** *071 †03
LANG, John Jos. 1001 BRINTON RD 15221 #023-12-1987 L2001 **FM** *020 †18
LANG, Robert Scott. 121 MEYRAN AVE, UNIV HLTH CTR 15213 #041-13-2007 L2007 **AN** *012
LANGA, Victoria Margaret. 1515 LOCUST ST, 2ND FL 15219 #035-01-1978 L1988 **HS ORS** *020 †40
LANTZY, Alan. 4800 FRIENDSHIP AVE, DEPARTMENT OF PEDIATRICS 15224 #041-12-1976 L1977 **PD NPM** *020 †55
LANZ, James K, Jr. 5200 CENTRE AVE, STE 211 15232 #041-12-1985 L1988 **PUD CCM** *050 †20
LANZ, Richard Kiern. 603 WASHINGTON RD STE 300 15228 #041-12-1967 L1971 **PD** *020 †55
LANZAROTTA, Joseph James. 1004 ARCH ST 15212 #561-01-1979 L1981 **EM** *020 †16
LA PIDUS, Andrew Scott. UNIVERSITY DRIVE C, VA HOSPITAL 15240 #033-05-1987 L1997 **DR** *020 †80
LAPP, Daniel Paul. 117 N NEGLEY AVE 15206 #055-01-1993 L1995 **FM** *020 †18
LAREAU, Susan Michelle. 300 HALKET ST 15213 #051-01-2004 L2004 **OBG** *012
LARKIN, Sarah Bernadette. 111 SHERIDAN ST 15209 #041-12-2002 L2002 **FM** *020 †18
LARRAZABAL, Johanna De Lo. 320 E NORTH AVE 15212 #748-31-2000 L2002 **IM** *020 †20
LARSEN, Matthew Justin. 15237 #049-01-2006 L2006 **AN** *012
LARSON, James Wesley, III. 3471 5TH AVE, STE 1010 15213 #041-12-2003 L2003 **ORS** *012
LARSON, Jeffrey Arnold. ■ 15226 #010-02-2007 L2007 *012
LASOTA, Melissa Ann. 15237 #041-13-2005 L2005 **AN** *012
LASSEK, William Day. 15217 #024-05-1968 L1988 **FM PHP** *030 †18
LASSITER, Anthony T. ■ 15217 #010-03-1977 L1989 **N** *020 †75
LATEEF, Mujahed. 110 ROESSLER RD, STE 100D 15220 #665-01-1999 L2001 **APM** *020 †60
LATONA, Carmen Ross. 320 E NORTH AVE 15212 #016-43-2000 L2001 **DR** *100 †80
LATTANZI, Daniel Raymond. 1000 BOWER HILL RD STE 3 15243 #028-34-1978 L1980 **OBG** *020 †30 ‡
LATUSKA, Richard Francis. 9100 BABCOCK BLVD 15237 #041-09-1980 L1981 **GE** *020 †20
LAUER, Karen Baker. 420 E NORTH AVE 15216 #041-02-1980 L1986 **OPH OS** *020 †35
LAUFE, Marc David. 5200 CENTRE AVE STE 304 15232 #041-01-1981 L1984 **PUD IM** *020 †20
LAUGHNER, Julie Ann. ■ 15261 #041-12-2008 *012
LAUGHON, Sarah Katherine. 300 HALKET ST, DEPARTMENT OF OB/GYN/RS 15213 #051-04-2000 L2006 **OBG** *020
LAVEE, Jacob. 200 LOTHROP ST, PRESBYTERIAN HOSP 15213 #550-02-1977 L1989 **TS** *020
LA VERDE, George Charles. ■ 15221 #041-12-2008 L2008 *012
LAVERY, Laurie Lynn. 3459 5TH AVE 15213 #023-01-1994 L1998 **IMG** *020 †20
LAVIGNE, Gregory Scott. 1307 FEDERAL ST, STE 2 15212 #035-03-2000 L2001 **ORS OAR** *100
LAW, Stuart Chas, Jr. 4727 FRIENDSHIP AVE, STE 240 15224 #050-02-1984 L1986 **AN PD** *020 †05 ‡
LAW, William. 969 GREENTREE RD, STE 107 15220 #038-41-1976 L1978 **CHP** *050 †75
LAWLER, Robert Alan. 200 LOTHROP ST 15213 #041-02-1980 L1982 **AN** *020 †05
LAWLOR, Maureen. 1401 FORBES AVE, FMC THREE RIVERS 15219 #041-13-1981 L1982 **NEP** *020 †20 ‡
LAWSIN, Loredo Manuel. OF PITTSBURGH, UNIV HLTH CTR 15261 #045-04-1996 L2007 **CCM** *012 †20
LAWSKY, Alan Richard. ■ 15217 #010-01-1968 L1975 **DR** *020 †80
LAWSON, Alton Lionel. 4111 PENN AVE 15224 #033-06-1978 L1981 **OBG** *020 †30
LAZAREV, Mark Gregory. 121 MEYRAN AVE 15213 #041-12-2002 L2005 **GE** *012 †20
LAZOL, Judith Panergo. 3705 5TH AVE, OF PITTSBURGH 15213 #748-01-1990 L2007 **PDC** *012
LE, Stephanie. 4735 CLAIRTON BLVD, JEFFERSON PAIN AND REHAB 15236 #035-08-1998 L2009 **PM PME** *020 †60
LE, Thu. 4735 CLAIRTON BLVD, JEFFERSON PAIN & REHABILIT 15236 #035-08-1997 L2003 **PM PME** *020 †60
LEBDA, Paulette Louise. ■ 15222 #016-43-2005 L2006 **DR** *012
LE BEAU, Shane Otto. 3601 5TH AVE, FALK MEDICAL BUILDING, SUI 15213 #038-40-1999 L2003 **END** *020 †20
LEBOVITZ, Emily Suzanne. 1046 LYNDHURST DR 15206 #041-15-2003 L2003 **OBG** *020
LEBOVITZ, Jerome J. 1350 LOCUST ST, STE 105 15219 #041-02-1952 L1953 **IM OS** *020
LEBOVITZ, Paul Jay. 1307 FEDERAL ST STE 301 15212 #035-46-1987 L1988 **GE IM** *020 †20
LECHMANICK, Eugene A. 8135 PERRY HWY 15237 #041-77-1978 L1979 **FM** *020 †18
LECKIE, Steven Koufman. 15232 #024-16-2007 L2007 **ORS** *012
LEDONNE, Karen Arlene. 8601 OLD PERRY HWY 15237 #041-02-1986 L1986 **AN** *020 †05
LEE, Amy Hyounjoung. 121 MEYRAN AVE 15213 #055-01-2003 L2006 **PCC** *012 †20
LEE, Angell. 400 45TH ST, MEDICAL EDUCATION 15201 #065-05-1994 L1998 **PM** *100 †60

LEE, Annie Sang. ■ 15221 #041-12-2004 L2004 **GS** *100
LEE, Ashley Bradley. 200 LOTHROP ST, F392 PUH 15213 #016-43-1993 L1999 **CD** *020 †20
LEE, B Young W C. 200 MEYRAN AVE STE 217, UNIVERSITY OF PITTSBURGH 15213 #583-03-1960 L1972 **FM** *071
LEE, Edward Seunghoon. ■ 15221 #041-12-2001 L2001 **IM** *020
LEE, Euhan John. 200 LOTHROP ST, MONTEFIORE 628NW 15213 #033-05-2002 L2002 **PCC** *012 †20
LEE, Foo Tack. 5200 CENTRE AVE, STE 610 15232 #583-01-1959 L1973 **OBG ON** *020 †30
LEE, Grace Jung. 190 LOTHROP ST, STE 145 15213 #024-05-1992 L1996 **D** *020 †15
LEE, Janet Sojung. 3459 5TH AVE, UNIF OF PITTS MED CTR 15213 #010-02-1995 L2004 **PCC** *050 †20
LEE, Jenifer Elizabeth. 200 LOTHROP ST 15213 #024-05-1987 L1990 **CD** *020 †20
LEE, Jerome. ■ 15206 #041-12-2006 L2006 **AN** *012
LEE, John Keun-Sang. 4735 CLAIRTON BLVD 15236 #583-03-1969 L1977 **PM OS** *020 †60 ‡
LEE, John Youngkeun. 200 LOTHROP ST, DEPT OF NEUROSURGERY/STE B 15213 #033-06-1998 L2001 **NS** *100
LEE, Joon Sup. 200 DELAFIELD RD 15215 #036-07-1988 L1996 **CD** *020 †20
LEE, Joonyung. 5200 CENTRE AVE, STE 211 15232 #008-01-1998 L2000 **ORS** *020 †40
LEE, Kang H. 3550 TERRACE ST 15213 #917-03-1987 L1994 **CCM IM** *020
LEE, Kenneth Kwockwah. 200 LOTHROP ST 15213 #016-02-1981 L1988 **GS** *020 †85
LEE, Lucia Soondong. ■ 15237 #583-03-1948 L1964 **AN** *071
LEE, Margaret Sue. ■ 15232 #005-19-2004 L2006 **FSM** *012 †18
LEE, Robert Edward. ■ 15208 #041-12-1956 L1957 **PTH CLP** *071 †50
LEE, Seung Joon. 515 S AIKEN AVE 15232 #035-48-2002 L2003 **APM** *020 †20,05
LEE, Stephen Erwin. 969 GREENTREE RD, STE 107 15220 #016-02-1980 L1981 **CHP** *020 †75
LEE, Sungmin. ■ 15232 #012-01-2002 L2003 **DR** *100 †80
LEE, Teh Min. 300 HALKET ST STE 2324, MAGEE WOMENS HOSP 15213 #024-07-1992 L1994 **OBG** *020 †30
LEE, Vincent. ■ 15213 #041-12-2008 *012
LEE, Vincent John. ■ 15228 #041-02-2001 L2001 **RO** *020 †80
LEE, W P Andrew. 3550 TERRACE ST, 690 SCAIFE HALL 15261 #023-07-1983 L2002 **HS PS** *020 †85,65
LEE, Yang Wen. ■ 15205 #244-04-1969 L1974 **FM** *020 †18
LEEN, Raymond Lam Shang. 4800 FRIENDSHIP AVE, WESTERN PENNSYLVANIA HOSP 15224 #917-10-1964 L1971 **RO** *071 †80
LEERS, Steven A. 100 DELAFIELD RD 15215 #024-16-1978 L1987 **VS** *020 †85
LEFF, Bernard. ■ 15206 #041-12-1956 L1957 **OTO OS** *071 †45
LEFF, Louis Edward. 532 S AIKEN AVE, STE 201 15232 #041-01-1985 L1986 **IM** *020 †20
LEGA, Mark. 320 E NORTH AVE 15212 #016-06-1983 L1986 **PUD IM** *020 †20
LEGGAT, Merrideth Ann. 300 HALKET ST, DEPT OBGYN/MAGEE-WOMENS HS 15213 #051-01-2001 L2001 **OBG** *040
LEGNARD, Elizabeth Anne. ■ 15205 #041-12-2004 L2004 **GS** *012
LEHANE, Christina Marie. 3705 5TH AVE 15213 #041-02-2003 L2006 **PD** *020 †55
LEIFER, Joyce Susan. 3705 5TH AVE 15213 #038-06-1980 L1985 **PD** *020 †55
LEMARQUAND, Wendy Jane. 6023 HARVARD SQ, CARE CENTER 15206 #067-01-1982 L1998 *020 †18
LEMASTER, Abigail Rebecca. ■ 15237 #038-43-2007 L2007 **OBG** *012
LEMBERSKY, Barry Craig. 300 HALKET ST 15213 #041-07-1981 L1982 **ON HEM** *020 †20
LEMLEY, Diana Kay. ■ 15238 #041-12-1975 L1976 **IM** *020 †20
LEMONCELLI, Gary Louis. 4727 FRIENDSHIP AVE, STE 180 15224 #036-05-1975 L1976 **IM** *020 †20
LENAHAN, Susan Ellen. ■ 15206 #041-14-1997 L2002 **DMP** *020 †50
LENG, Wendy Wunching. 3471 5TH AVE, STE 700 15213 #024-07-1991 L2001 **U** *020 †95
LENKEY, Joseph Lewis. 1000 BOWER HILL RD, DEPART OF MEDICAL IMAGING 15243 #041-09-1978 L1979 **DR** *020 †80
LENTZSCH, Suzanne. 200 LOTHROP ST 15213 #408-30-1990 L2006 *020
LENZE, Eric Juckeland. 3811 OHARA ST, BT 764 15213 #028-02-1994 L1998 **PYG** *020 †75
LEONG, Paul Liwah. 4815 LIBERTY AVE, STE 443 15224 #008-01-1999 L2001 **OTO** *100 †45
LERBERG, David Bedford. 4815 LIBERTY AVE STE 156 15224 #023-07-1969 L1971 **TS** *020 †85,90
LESACA, Timothy Gordon. 1200 REEDSDALE ST 15233 #055-01-1984 L1987 **CHP P** *020 †75 ‡
LESNOCK, Jamie Lee. 300 HALKET ST 15213 #047-05-2005 L2005 **OBG** *012
LEUNG, Keith Wah. ■ 15217 #025-01-2005 L2005 **IM** *012
LEVARI, Itamar. ■ 15217 #041-13-2004 L2005 **IM** *012
LEVARI, Itzchak. 2020 ARDMORE BLVD, STE 300 15221 #308-11-1987 L1992 **FM** *020 †18
LEVENSON, David J. 5140 LIBERTY AVE, RENAL ENDOCRINE ASSOS 15224 #041-02-1976 L1987 **NEP IM** *020 †20
LEVICK, Marvin Howard. 200 LOTHROP ST 15213 #041-12-1960 L1961 **IM GE** *071
LEVIN, Harry. 3811 OHARA ST RM 134 15213 #041-12-1972 L1974 **P** *020 †75
LEVIN, James E. 3705 5TH AVE, CHILDRENS HOSP 15213 #016-02-1988 L2006 **PD ID** *020 †55
LEVIN, William Ira. 200 LOTHROP ST, UPMC MONTEFIORE SUITE 933W 15213 #041-12-1988 L1991 **IM** *020 †20
LEVINE, Arlene Bradley. 320 E NORTH AVE 15212 #024-01-1979 L2002 **CD IM** *020 †20
LEVINE, Arthur Saml. STE 401, 3350 TERRACE STREET 15261 #016-42-1964 L2001 **PHO ID** *030 †55
LEVINE, Barry Lee. 1738 N HIGHLAND RD, STE G101 15241 #041-13-1986 L1987 **P** *020 †75
LEVINE, Macy Irving. 3347 FORBES AVE 15213 #041-12-1943 L1944 **AI PUD** *020 †20,03
LEVINE, Nancy. 4800 FRIENDSHIP AVE STE N2, WESTERN PENNSYLVANIA HOSPI 15224 #035-48-1985 L2000 **FM** *020 †18
LEVINE, Phillip Ross. ■ 15215 #041-12-1957 L1958 **IM OM** *071 †20 ‡
LEVINE, Sheldon R. 6343 PENN AVE, # 201 15206 #041-12-1967 L1968 **PD** *020 †55
LEVINE, Theodore Barry. 320 E NORTH AVE 15212 #165-01-1973 L2002 **CD** *020 †20
LEVITT, Susanna Blau. 1000 BOWER HILL RD 15243 #041-07-1980 L1984 **PTH PCP** *020 †50
LEVY, Matthew Evan. BST 1140E, 200 LOTHROP ST 15261 #041-13-2001 L2001 **END** *020 †20
LEVY, Reinhardt D. 3500 5TH AVE STE 205 15213 #016-42-1953 L1953 **FM** *071 †18
LEVY, Ryan Matthew. 200 LOTHROP ST, PUH DEPT SURGERY/PUH F1263 15213 #041-12-2001 L2001 **GS** *012
LEWEN, Robert Michael. 420 E NORTH AVE, STE 116 15212 #016-42-1980 L1988 **OPH R** *020 †35
LEWINSOHN, Gavriel. ■ 15217 #550-01-1963 **IM** *050
LEWIS, David Alan. 3811 OHARA ST 15213 #038-40-1979 L1987 **P IM** *050 †20,75 ‡
LEWIS, Gus Jonathan. ■ 15213 #041-77-2007, ▲ L2007 **IM** *012
LEWIS, Gwendolyn Marie. 230 MCKEE PL, STE 500 15213 #041-14-2003 L2003 **EM** *100 †16
LEWIS, Howard T, Jr. 1049 JEFFERSON RD 15235 #041-12-1943 L1944 **GPM GP** *071
LEWIS, Jennifer Louise. 490 E NORTH AVE, STE 107 15212 #041-12-1997 L1999 **IM** *020 †20
LEWIS, Jessica Helen. 812 5TH AVE 15219 #023-07-1942 L1955 **HEM** *072
LEWIS, John Derek. ■ 15218 #016-42-2005 L2005 **DR** *012
LEWIS, Richard Peter. 5750 CENTRE AVE STE 370 15206 #041-12-1973 L1974 **GS VS** *020 †85 ‡
LEWIS, Thomas Jacob, Jr. 1307 FEDERAL ST, STE 300 15212 #041-12-1960 L1961 **U** *071 †95
LEWY-WEISS, Vered Dvora. 1405 SHADY AVE, THE CHILDREN'S INSTITUTE 15217 #035-09-1993 L1996 **PDE** *020 †55
LEY, John Theodore. 121 MEYRAN AVE, DEPT OF ANESTHESIOLOGY 15213 #038-43-2006 L2006 **AN** *012
LHEUREAU, Thomas Vero. 100 S JACKSON AVE, SUBURBAN GENERAL HOSP 15202 #041-07-1994 L1998 **GS** *020 †85
LI, Fanghong. ■ 15207 #243-72-1990 **PTH** *012
LI, Shih-Tzung. 3811 OHARA ST 15213 #036-01-2003 L2003 **CHP** *012
LIANG, Alicia Fonseca. ■ 15209 #047-05-2005 **PTH** *012
LIANG, Han-Chun. 3811 OHARA ST 15213 #047-05-2005 L2005 **P** *012
LIANG, Hongmei. ■ 15237 #243-46-1993 L2005 **HO** *012 †20
LIANG, Marc Danl. 580 S AIKEN AVE STE 203 15232 #038-41-1978 L1979 **PS** *020 †85,65
LIANG, Maria. 200 LOTHROP ST 15213 #041-12-1971 L1973 **N** *071 †75
LIANG, Ruomei. 121 MEYRAN AVE 15213 #244-09-1985 L2005 **FP** *012
LIANG, Ye. ■ 15217 #243-39-1987 L2003 **CN** *012
LIBMAN, Ingrid Marianne. 3705 5TH AVE 15213 #132-04-1991 L2001 **PDE** *020 †55
LIBMAN, Stuart Ellwyn. 615 WASHINGTON RD STE 107 15228 #038-06-1978 L1979 **CHP** *020 †75
LICHTENSTEIN, Steven E. 3705 5TH AVE, DEPT OF ANESTHESIOLOGY 15213 #041-07-1984 L1986 **AN** *020 †05
LICKERMAN, Erik David. ■ 15206 #016-11-1993 **PTH** *100
LIEBE, Karl Frederick. ■ 15216 #016-43-2004 L2004 **PM** *012
LIEBE, Magdalena K. 133 SLEEPY HOLLOW RD 15216 #016-43-2004 L2004 **FM** *100 †18
LIEBER, Paul Spencer. 107 GAMMA DR STE 200, GAMMA SURGERY CENTER, LLC 15238 #016-42-1986 L1988 **PM** *020 †60
LIEBERMAN, Frank Scott. 5150 CENTRE AVE, CANCER PAVILION, 5TH FLOOR 15232 #016-02-1979 L1999 **N** *050 †75
LIEBERMAN, Rhett Howard. 3705 5TH AVE 15213 #041-13-1996 L1998 **PEM** *020 †55
LIEBLER, George Andrew. 1000 BOWER HILL RD 15243 #010-01-1962 L1963 **TS** *071 †85,90
LIGGETT, Joseph G. ■ 15235 #041-12-1953 L1954 **GS** *071 †85
LIGHT, Wilma Charlean. 3801 MCKNIGHT EAST DR, FL 1 15237 #041-02-1971 L1976 **AI PD** *020 †55,03
LIM, Suzy Ann. ■ 15232 #041-12-2008 *012
LIMA, Breno Da Rocha. 200 LOTHROP ST, STE 503 15213 #187-32-2004 L2007 **IM** *012
LIMA, Claudio A B. 5200 CENTRE AVE STE 216 15232 #187-14-1972 L1976 **CD** *020 †85,90
LIMAURO, David Louis. 1350 LOCUST ST, STE 406 15219 #036-05-1992 L1994 **GE** *020 †20
LIMCUANDO, Vera Hope. 22 COLONY OAKS DR 15209 #041-02-2002 L2002 **IM** *100
LIN, Carol. 200 LOTHROP ST STE W933, GENERAL INTERNAL MED, MON 15213 #016-06-2001 L2005 **OBG** *100
LIN, Caroline. ■ 15232 #034-01-2004 L2007 **IM** *012 †20
LIN, Charles. ■ 15237 #041-12-2007 L2007 **TY** *012
LIN, Hugo. ■ 15213 #035-15-2004 L2004 **END** *012 †20
LIN, Jenny Hanching. ■ 15217 #056-05-2006 L2006 **PD** *012
LIN, Luke. 4800 FRIENDSHIP AVE 15224 #244-04-1972 L1979 **DR RNR** *020 †80
LIN, Philana Ling. 3705 5TH AVE 4B320, PITTSBURGH 15213 #038-44-1996 L2000 **PDI** *020 †55
LIN, Ridwan. ■ 15206 #041-14-2003 L2007 **N** *100
LIN, Rong Chung. 829 WOOD ST 15221 #244-04-1972 L1977 **U** *020 †95
LINCOLN, Danforth N. UNIV OF PITTSBURGH, DEPT OF FAMILY MED & EPID 15260 #035-48-1990 L1992 **FM** *020 †18
LINDBLAD, Douglas Scott. 3705 5TH AVE 15213 #048-04-1999 L2001 **PD** *020 †55
LINDEN, Peter Ken. 200 LOTHROP ST 15213 #041-09-1984 L1988 **CCA ID** *020 †20
LINDENBAUM, Jorge. 3000 BROWNSVILLE RD, UPMC 15227 #132-01-1972 L1974 **IM OS** *020 †20
LING, Bruce Sanchi. 200 LOTHROP ST, MUH-SUITE 818E 15213 #025-01-1993 L1999 **GPM** *020 †20
LIPAPIS, Christy Nick. 1400 LOCUST ST 15219 #041-12-1959 L1960 **IM OM** *071
LIPPE, Richard David. 5200 CENTRE AVE, STE 616 15232 #041-02-1963 L1964 **END IM** *020 †20
LIPUT, Joseph H, Jr. 5140 LIBERTY AVE, C/O RENAL-ENDOCRINE ASSOC, 15224 #041-12-1979 L1980 **NEP** *050 †20
LISCHNER, Mark I. ■ 15237 #041-77-2007, ▲ L2007 **AN** *012
LISTER, John. 4800 FRIENDSHIP AVE, STE 2303 15224 #065-05-1978 L1992 **HO** *020 †20
LITTLE, Andrew Francis. UNIV PITTSBURGH MED CTR., DEPT OF RADIOLOGY 15213 #143-02-1982 L1994 **DR** *020
LITTLE, Gregory Scott. 1000 INTEGRITY DR, STE 100 15235 #025-12-2000 L2001 **FM** *020 †18
LITTMANN, Robert. 738 OHIO RIVER BLVD 15202 #035-09-1965 **U** *071 †95
LIU, Betty. 2000 MARY ST 15203 #035-09-1990 L1990 **PM** *020 †60
LIU, Collins Yuchen. 121 MEYRAN AVE, DIV OF NEPHROLOGY 15213 #035-09-2004 L2004 **N** *012
LIU, Xin. 4800 FRIENDSHIP AVE, PENNSYLVANIA HOSPI 15224 #243-70-1995 L2005 **AN** *012
LIU, Yulin. ALLEGHENY GEN HOSP, DEPT PATH 15212 #243-76-1984 L1999 **PCP** *020 †50
LIU-CUNNINGHAM, Penny P. 320 E NORTH AVE, DEPARTMENT OF ANESTHESIA 15212 #019-02-1992 L2002 **AN** *020 †05
LLOYD, David Allden. 3705 5TH AVE 15213 #917-20-1965 L1984 **PDS** *020
LLOYD, Jon C. 5750 CENTRE AVE STE 370 15206 #049-01-1968 L1973 **GS OS** *020 †85
LLULL, Ramon. 200 LOTHROP ST 15213 #847-11-1988 L1998 **PS** *100
LO, Alan Manlone. 230 MCKEE PL STE 500, OF PITTSBURGH 15213 #035-03-2006 L2006 **EM** *012
LO, David Yung-An. ■ 15237 #016-06-2004 L2007 **GE** *012 †20
LO, Marvin Yukming. ■ 15232 #005-02-2002 L2007 **OSM** *012
LOBAS, David Michael. 9104 BABCOCK BLVD STE 5110 15237 #041-12-1971 L1976 **N IM** *020 †75 ‡
LOBES, Louis Anthony, Jr. 3501 FORBES AVE STE 500, RETINA-VITREOUS CONSULTANT 15213 #035-20-1970 L1977 **OPH** *020 †35
LOBL, Andrew Barbrow. 1004 ARCH ST, NORTH SHORE FAMILY HEALTH 15212 #010-01-1995 L2000 **FM** *020 †18
LOBL, Lawrence Tolstoi. 401 SHADY AVE STE D107 15206 #010-01-1964 L1970 **P** *020 †75 ‡
LOBUR, Paul T. 1400 LOCUST ST # 5121 15219 #041-12-1978 L1979 **IM** *020 †20
LOGAN, David Anthony. 5500 CORPORATE DR, STE 240 15237 #041-12-1994 L1997 **OBG** *020 †30

LOHIYA, Piyush Suresh. 1400 LOCUST ST, MERCY HOSP-PITTSBURGH 15219 #496-36-1999 L2005 **IM** *012

LOHR, Charles Edward. ■ 15232 #055-01-2004 L2004 **DR** *012

LOHR, Patricia Ann. 300 HALKET ST, DEPT OF OB/GYN/RS 15213 #005-06-2001 L2005 **OBG** *100 †30

LOLAK, Sermsak. 100 N BELLEFIELD AVE, STE 442 15213 #891-01-1997 L2007 **P** *020 †75 ‡

LOMBARD, Lisa Alison. 2000 MARY ST 15203 #025-07-1999 L2001 **PM** *020 †60

LOMBARDI, Benito. 3811 OHARA ST 15213 #561-11-1952 **PTH** *050

LONDON, Barry. 200 LOTHROP ST, SCAIFE HALL S-572 15213 #035-46-1987 L1995 **CD IM** *050 †20

LONE, Usman Mahmood. ■ 15213 #041-15-2008 L2008 *012

LONG, Gregory Scott. 320 E NORTH AVE, 7TH FL 15212 #041-12-1991 L1994 **ON IM** *020 †20

LOPEZ, Aileen Jaro. ARTS BUILDIN, STE 503 MEDICAL 15213 #748-02-2004 L2007 **FP** *012

LOPEZ, Angel. 200 LOTHROP ST, SCAIFE HALL/S-560 15213 #042-01-1986 L2001 **CD** *020 †20

LOPEZ, Oscar Luis. 3501 FORBES AVE, STE 830 15213 #132-03-1980 L1994 **N** *050 ‡

LOPEZ ALBAITERO, Andres. 121 MEYRAN AVE, UNIV HLTH CTR OF PITTSBURG 15213 #649-31-2000 L2005 **OTO** *012

LOPEZ CHAVEZ, Ariel. 121 MEYRAN AVE 15213 #649-60-2002 L2005 **IM** *012

LORENZ, Stephen A, III. 100 DELAFIELD RD 15215 #041-09-1969 L1970 **OTO HNS** *020 †45

LORVIDHAYA, Petchara. ■ 15238 #891-03-1971 L1977 **AN** *100 †05

LOSEE, Joseph Edward. 3705 5TH AVE 15213 #035-45-1994 L1999 **PS** *020 †65

LOTZE, Michael Thos. 200 LOTHROP ST, SURG GEN/NESE BARKAN ANNEX 15213 #016-06-1974 L1990 **GS IG** *012

LOUX, Tara Jean. ■ 15217 #001-02-2005 L2005 **GS** *012

LOVALLO, Amanda Cathleen. 230 MCKEE PL, STE 500 15213 #041-12-2004 L2004 **PEM** *012

LOWDER, Jerry Lane. 300 HALKET ST, DEPT OF OB/GYN 15213 #036-08-1999 L2003 **OBG** *100 †30

LOWE, Mark Evan. 3705 5TH AVE 15213 #011-02-1984 L2003 **PD GE** *050 †55

LOWENGRUB, Jeffrey A. 3811 OHARA ST 15213 #035-45-1985 L1986 **P PD** *020 †75,55

LOWENGRUB, Katherine Moss. 3811 OHARA ST 15213 #035-45-1985 L1986 **PYG** *020 †75

LOWENSTEIN, Robert Aaron. 211 N WHITFIELD ST, STE 475 15206 #016-42-1966 L1983 **CHP P** *020 †75

LOWERY, Willa Dean. ■ 15237 #011-02-1959 L1965 **OBG** *071 †30

LOZANNE, Karl Angelo. 200 LOTHROP ST, STE B-400 15213 #008-01-2002 L2002 **NS** *012

LU, Amy Hweimei. 200 LOTHROP ST, LOTHROP 3950 15213 #035-01-1998 L2001 **DR** *020 †80

LU, Angela Hsingcheng. 15222 #041-12-2003 L2003 **CN** *012

LU, Eduardo Chua. 2000 MARY ST 15203 #748-08-1969 L1973 **FM GS** *020

LUBETSKY, Martin Joel. 3811 OHARA ST, WPIC-UPMC 15213 #025-07-1981 L1984 **P CHP** *020 †75

LUCKIEWICZ, Halina E. 9104 BABCOCK BLVD STE 1113 15237 #759-03-1991 L1997 **IM** *020 †20

LUCKIEWICZ, Paul J. 320 E NORTH AVE, PITTSBURG 15212 #759-03-1991 L1998 **AN** *020 †05

LUDKIEWICZ, Wayne Steven. 2100 WHARTON ST, STE 307 15203 #007-02-1982 L1983 **EM FM** *020 †18

LUDWIG, Karl David. ■ 15237 #041-12-1960 L1961 **P** *071

LUKETICH, James David. 200 LOTHROP ST 15213 #041-07-1986 L1988 **TS** *020 †90,85

LUM, Milton Yew Fai. 4800 FRIENDSHIP AVE 15224 #064-01-2005 **GS** *012

LUMISH, Robert Malcolm. 101 DRAKE RD STE C, ST CLAIR COMMONS CTR 2ND F 15241 #041-02-1970 L1971 **ID OS** *020 †20

LUNDQUIST, Thomas Geo. 425 HOLIDAY DR, FOSTER PLAZA 2 15220 #023-07-1991 L1993 **PD PHP** *030 †55

LUNSFORD, Lawrence Dade. 200 LOTHROP ST 15213 #035-01-1974 L1975 **NS DR** *020 †25

LUO, Jianhua. UPMC, LOTHROP STREET 15261 #243-77-1983 L1998 **PTH** *020 †50

LUPARELLO, Frank J. ■ 15234 #035-08-1953 L1954 **IM OS** *071 †20 ‡

LUPETIN, Anthony Robt. 320 E NORTH AVE, ALLEGHENY RADIOLOGY 15212 #035-08-1976 L1981 **DR** *020 †80

LUST, Wouter J P H. 1385 SCAIFE HALL 15261 #165-04-1988 L1992 **AN** *020

LUSTBERG, Lisa Rose. ■ 15218 #041-12-2002 L2005 **PHO** *012 †55

LUTHER, Joseph Harold. 200 LOTHROP ST 15213 #041-12-1993 L2001 **AN** *020 †05

LUTINS, Jay Allan. 5750 CENTRE AVE, STE 430 15206 #051-04-1985 L1987 **U GS** *020 †95

LYJAK-CHORAZY, Anna Julia. 6301 NORTHUMBERLAND ST, CHILDRENS INST 15217 #041-07-1960 L1961 **PD** *071 †55

LYNCH, Edward F, Jr. 4800 FRIENDSHIP AVE, WEST PENN HOSP DEPT PATH 15224 #038-44-1988 L1993 **PTH HMP** *020 †50

LYNCH, James Michael. 3705 5TH AVE 15213 #043-01-1975 L1980 **PDS** *020 †85

LYNCH, James Patrick. 15232 #041-15-2003 L2003 **CD** *100 †20

LYNCH, Michael James. 230 MCKEE PL STE 500, OF PITTSBURG 15213 #041-12-2004 L2004 **ETX** *012

LYONS, John Michael, Jr. ■ 15209 #005-06-2001 L2005 **GE** *012

LYONS, Troy Danean Bryant. 1000 INTEGRITY DR, PREMIER PEDS 15235 #041-13-1997 L1999 **PD** *020 †55

MA, Edward. ■ 15241 #035-08-1998 L2003 **IM** *020 †80

MAALOUF, Fadi Toufic. 3811 OHARA ST, BFT 3 15213 #605-01-2001 L2007 **CHP** *100 †75

MABRY, Michael Edwin. ■ 15215 #036-07-1980 L1992 **N IM** *071 †20

MACALUA, Irene Carampatan. 121 MEYRAN AVE 15213 #748-07-2003 L2006 **FP** *012

MAC DONALD, George F. 450 HOLLAND AV 15221 #041-12-1952 L1953 **CRS** *072 †10

MAC DOUGALL, James Howard. 1050 BOWER HILL RD STE 3 15243 #036-05-1981 L1982 **CD IM** *020 †20

MAC GINNITIE, Andrew J. 3705 5TH AVE, PHYSICIANS 15213 #016-02-1998 L2004 **AI** *100 †55,03

MACGOWAN, Guy A. 200 LOTHROP ST, 9019 FORBES TOWER 15213 #539-06-1986 L1994 **CD** *020

MACHIRAJU, Usha. ■ 15238 #495-70-1971 L1979 **PM** *020 †60

MACHIRAJU, V R. 5200 CENTRE AVE, STE 216 15232 #495-50-1969 L1978 **TS CD** *020 †85,90

MACK, Diana. 3811 OHARA ST 15213 #016-11-1976 L1981 **CHP** *074

MACKECHNIE, Cheryl Anne. ■ 15218 #041-12-2007 L2007 *012

MACKETT, Charles W, III. 3518 FIFTH AVE, UPMC DEPT OF FAMILY MEDICI 15261 #035-15-1982 L2005 **FPG** *040 †18

MACKEY, Christine Lynn. 320 E NORTH AVE 15212 #032-01-2000 L2003 **IM** *020 †20

MAC LEOD, Bruce Alan. 1004 ARCH ST 15212 #038-41-1987 L1989 **EM** *030 †16

MAC LEOD, Gordon K, Jr. 130 DESOTO STREET, UNIVERSITY OF PITTSBURGH 15261 #038-41-1960 L1975 **IM PHP** *071 †20

MAC MURDO, Stanley Dale. 8150 PERRY HWY, STE 311 PERRYMONT BLDG 15237 #041-12-1976 L1977 **AN** *020 †05

MACPHEE, Edward Robert. ■ 15212 #033-06-2004 L2004 **P** *012

MAC PHERSON, David Scott. 0 UNIVERSITY DRIVE C, 933 W MONTEFIORE HOSP 15240 #016-06-1981 L1990 **IM GP** *050 †20

MAC PHERSON, Trevor A. 300 HALKET ST, DEPT OF PATHOLOGY-MWH/UPMC 15213 #836-02-1970 L1978 **ATP** *030 †50

MADAN, Suneeta. 3520 5TH AVE 2ND FL, CHILDRENS HOSP OF PITTSBUR 15213 #496-07-1978 L1995 **OS PD** *020 †55,19

MADDEN, Michael Anthony. 120 5TH AVE, SUITE FAP 733 15222 #010-02-1978 L1981 **FM** *030 †18

MADHAVAN, Vasantha C. 21 YOST BLVD, STE 216 15221 #495-09-1975 L1982 **CD IM** *020 †20

MADHOK, Ricky. 200 LOTHROP ST, STE 3400 DEPT OF NEUROSRGY 15213 #033-05-2003 L2003 **NS** *012

MADIGAN, Michael Charles. ■ 15202 #047-05-2007 L2007 *012

MADOFF, Henry Robt. 5200 CENTRE AVE 15232 #035-19-1953 L1961 **CD TS** *071 †85,90

MAENZA, Richard Louis. 1400 LOCUST ST 15219 #008-02-1992 L1994 **EM** *020 †16

MAESHIRO, Rika. ■ 15217 #025-01-1987 L1990 **PHP IM** *030 †70,20

MAGAJI, Vasudev Govardhan. 1400 LOCUST ST, MERCY HOSPITAL 15219 #496-22-2004 L2007 **IM** *012

MAGGARD, Kamala Dawn. ■ 15237 #016-42-2004 L2006 **P** *012

MAGNOTTA, John Anthony. 1307 FEDERAL ST, STE 2 15212 #041-14-1984 L1986 **PM IM** *020 †20,60

MAGOVERN, George J, Jr. 320 E NORTH AVE, SURGERY CENTER 15212 #041-12-1978 L1985 **TS** *020 †85,90

MAGOVERN, George Jerome. 490 E NORTH AVE STE 302, ALLEGHENY PROF BLDG 15212 #056-06-1947 L1958 **TS CD** *071 †85,90

MAH, Francis Sung-Il. 203 LOTHROP ST 15213 #038-43-1995 L1999 **OPH** *020 †35

MAHER, John Campbell. 5230 CENTRE AVE 15232 #010-02-1978 L1982 **OPH** *020 †35

MAHER, Thomas David, Jr. 320 E NORTH AVE, SURGERY CENTER 15212 #010-02-1974 L1980 **TS** *020 †85,90

MAHESHWARY, Rishi Kumar. 320 E NORTH AVE, DEPT OF DIAGNOSTIC RADIO 15212 #038-44-2004 L2005 **DR** *012

MAHFOOD, Christina Marie. 3705 5TH AVE, CHILDREN'S HOSP 15213 #654-01-2004 L2007 **CHN** *012

MAHIDHARA, Seshamamba. 9100 BABCOCK BLVD 15237 #495-21-1963 L1972 **PTH** *020 †50 ‡

MAHMOOD, Burhanuddin. 300 HALKET ST, MAGEE WOMENS HOSP 15213 #704-25-1991 L1997 **NPM PD** *020 †55

MAHMOOD, M Khalid. 2275 SWALLOW HILL RD 15220 #704-04-1972 L1978 **IM** *020 †20

MAHMUD, Hussain. 200 LOTHROP ST, STE 503 15213 #704-25-2005 L2007 **IM** *012

MAHONEY, John Francis. 200 LOTHROP ST 15213 #041-12-1990 L1990 **EM ETX** *040 †16

MAHYAR, Babak. ■ 15212 #517-01-1999 L2006 **IM** *100

MAI, Evelyn F. 3811 OHARA ST 15213 #025-01-2003 L2003 **SME** *012

MAIER, John S. ■ 15213 #016-11-1998 L2001 **FM** *020

MAIER, Robin Marie. ■ 15217 #016-11-1998 L2000 **FM** *020 †18

MAIVALD, Pavel. ■ 15241 #286-02-1956 L1972 **AN** *071

MAJESKO, Alyssa Alina. ■ 15201 #041-12-2003 L2003 **IM** *100 †20

MAJEWSKI, Philip Mel. 320 E NORTH AVE, ALLEGHENY GENERAL HOSPITAL 15212 #025-07-1990 L1992 **OM** *020 †16,70

MAJKIC, Dushan. 3028 BROWNSVILLE RD, BRENTWOOD MEDICAL GROUP 15227 #035-09-1993 L1995 **IM** *020 †20

MAJMUDAR, Vasanti Harshit. 9104 BABCOCK BLVD, STE 5113 15237 #495-48-1968 L1982 **OBG** *020 †30

MAKAM, Alok. ■ 15219 #665-01-2006 L2007 **AN** *012

MAKAROUN, Michel S. 5200 CENTRE AVE, STE 211 15232 #605-01-1978 L1981 **VS** *020 †85

MAKAROUN, Silva A. 3705 5TH AVE 15213 #605-01-1978 L1982 **PD PDE** *050 †55

MALAY, Mary Beth. 9100 BABCOCK BLVD 15237 #041-07-1994 L1999 **GS** *020 †85

MALAYIL, Johnpaul. ■ 15241 #041-15-2007 L2007 **IM** *012

MALEC, Lynn Marie. ■ 15206 #056-05-2006 L2006 **MPD** *012

MALEK, Siamak. 121 MEYRAN AVE, UPMC MONTEFIORE N-713 15213 #035-48-2005 L2005 **IM** *012

MALEY, Richard Hardy, Sr. ■ 15236 #041-12-1956 L1957 **GP** *071

MALHOTRA, Saurabh. 3708 5TH AVE, UNIVERSITY HEALTH CENTER 15213 #496-09-2002 L2006 **IM** *012

MALIK, Khalid Javaid. 490 E NORTH AVE, STE 300 15212 #704-01-1977 L1998 **PCC** *020 †20

MALINA, Amanda Nicole. 300 HALKET ST, MAGEE-WOMENS HOSPITAL 15213 #041-12-2004 L2004 **OBG** *012

MALIVER, Deborah Sarah. 401 WOOD ST STE 1600 15222 #035-46-1982 L1985 **IM** *020 †20

MALLEK, Gregory William. ■ 15217 #040-02-2006 L2006 **OBG** *012

MALLIKARJUN, Mahesh Rudra. 910 5TH AVE, STE 910 LSK BLDG UPMC ANES 15219 #495-09-1993 L2001 **AN** *020

MALLINGER, Mark Lee. 300 HALKET ST, STE 5120 15213 #041-12-1984 L1989 **OBG** *020 †30

MALLY, Abhijith Dev. ■ 15241 #041-15-2008 *012

MALLY, Ashith. 2101 GREENTREE RD, STE B101 15220 #495-37-1983 L1993 **IM** *020 †20

MALOY, Elmer J. 1406 AMANDA AVE 15210 #041-12-1951 L1952 **GP OS** *071

MALTMAN, Michael Eric. 320 E NORTH AVE, DEPT OF INTERNAL MED 15212 #422-01-2005 L2005 **IM** *012

MAMALADZE, Vasil. 4800 FRIENDSHIP AVE, PENNSYLVANIA HOSPI 15224 #913-23-1992 L2006 **AN** *012

MAMATAS, Emanuel E. 133 JEFFERSON RD, STE 6 15235 #915-02-1983 L1985 **IM IMG** *020 †20

MAMMEN, Oommen Kandathil. 3811 OHARA ST, PSYCHIATRY 15213 #495-37-1982 L1994 **P CHP** *020 †75

MAN, Li-Xing. ■ 15217 #041-01-2005 L2005 **OTO** *012

MANALAC, Fernando Jacinto, Jr. 320 E NORTH AVE, ALLEGHENY GEN HOSP 15212 #422-01-2005 L2006 **IM** *012

MANCINI, Alfred Michael. ■ 15238 #561-01-1973 L1981 **DR NM** *030 ‡

MANCUSO, Teresa. ■ 15211 #041-12-2002 L2002 **OBG** *012

MANDEL, Ellen May. 3705 5TH AVE, ENT DEPT CHILDS HOSP 15213 #041-12-1975 L1977 **PD** *050 †55

MANDELL, David Louis. 3705 5TH AVE 15213 #023-01-1996 L2001 **PDO** *020 †45

MANDENBERG-SIEBER, Anne R. ■ 15232 #025-01-1948 L1951 **OS AN** *071

MANDERS, Ernest Kelvin. 200 LOTHROP ST 15213 #024-01-1972 L1982 **PS** *020 †65,85

MANDIC, Maja. 200 LOTHROP ST, STE 503 15213 #957-02-1998 L2007 **IM** *012

MANGALMURTI, Sarang S. ■ 15232 #035-19-2001 L2005 **CD** *012 †20

MANGILI, Alessandro Carlo. 230 MCKEE PL STE 500, OF PITTSBURGH 15213 #024-07-2005 L2005 **EM** *012

MANGIONE, Michael Paul. 3550 TERRACE ST, A-1305 SCAIFE HALL 15261 #041-12-1992 L1995 **AN** *020 †05

■ = Address Information Privacy Protected

MANNHEIMER, Jack. 500 N LEWIS RUN RD, STE 129 15122 #041-12-1966 L1967 RHU *020 †75 ‡

MANOLE, Mioara Daciana. 3705 5TH AVE 15213 #781-03-1997 L2001 PD *020 †55

MANRIQUE, Marievic G. UNIV OF PITTSBURGH MED CTR, CRITICAL CARE MED 15261 #748-01-1984 L2001 CCA *012 †05

MANSON, David Eliezar. ■ 15221 #041-01-1981 L1983 DR PD *050 †55,80

MANSOUR, Wissam Bader. 3550 TERRACE ST, SCAIFE HALL, SUITE 651 15213 #605-01-2002 L2003 CCM *012 †20

MANSURIA, Suketu Mohan. 300 HALKET ST, DEPT OBG 15213 #011-02-1999 L2001 OBG *100 †20

MANTHA, Venkata R. 300 HALKET ST 15213 #495-65-1980 L1997 AN *020 †05

MANTIA, August Maurice. 3811 OHARA ST 15213 #036-05-1974 L1975 AN *020 †05 ‡

MANTIA, Gina Marie. 300 HALKET ST 15213 #035-48-2004 L2004 OBG *012

MANUSOW, David Norman. 400 45TH ST 15201 #062-01-1975 L1986 OPH *35

MANYAM, Harish. 320 E NORTH AVE, ALLEGHENY GEN HOSP 15212 #654-01-2004 L2005 IM *012

MANZETTI, Gene Wm. 850 CLAIRTON BLVD STE 2300 15236 #041-12-1972 L1974 TS VS *020 †85,90

MANZI, Susan. 300 HALKET ST STE 1750, LUPUS CTR OF EXCELLENCE 15213 #041-12-1985 L1988 RHU IM *020 †20

MAPARA, Markus Yashavant. 5117 CENTRE AVE, CANCER CENTER 15213 #409-37-1992 L2005 *020

MARANCHIE, Jodi Kathleen. 5200 CENTRE AVE, STE 211 15232 #016-06-1993 L2006 U *020 †95

MARASCO, Joseph A, Jr. 400 PENN CENTER BLVD, STE 555 15235 #041-12-1957 L1958 R *071 †80

MARCH, Lewis Edward. ■ 15218 #038-06-1973 L1983 EM *020 †20,16

MARCH, Vicki. 120 LYTTON AVE 15213 #041-01-1984 L1985 IM *020 †20 ‡

MARCHL, William Henry. ■ 15235 #041-12-1964 L1965 CHP *020

MARCINI, Amy B. 100 BEAR RUN DR 15237 #041-15-2003 L2003 ORS *012

MARCOS, Amadeo. 3459 5TH AVE, UPMC MONTEFIORE, N 725 15213 #935-07-1987 L2002 TTS GS *020

MARCSISIN, Michael James. ■ 15206 #041-12-2007 L2007 P *012

MARCUCCI, James William. 363 VANADIUM RD, US HEART & VASCULAR, PC 15243 #041-12-1975 L1976 CD IC *020 †20

MARCUCCO, Elisa. ■ 15217 #010-01-2006 L2006 PD *012

MARCUS, Dawn Showalter. 5750 CENTRE AVE, STE 400 15206 #035-15-1986 L1989 N *020 †75

MARCUS, Revital Michelle. 15217 #016-01-2007 L2007 IM *012

MARCUS, Richard J. 320 E NORTH AVE 15212 #035-15-1987 L1990 NEP *020 †20

MARDERSTEIN, Eric Lance. 200 LOTHROP ST, RM F1263 15213 #051-01-1998 L2001 CRS *100

MARES, Aaron Vid. ■ 15203 #041-13-2007 L2007 IM *012

MARIN, Robert Steven. 3811 OHARA ST 15213 #035-46-1971 L1979 P *050 †75

MARINA, Anna Leonidovna. ■ 15219 #913-02-1996 L2005 IM *012

MARINO, Natalie Gloria. ■ 15261 #041-12-2007 *012

MARKLE, Cyrus P. ■ 15238 #647-12-1937 L1938 OM GS *071 †85

MARKOWSKI, Maciej Piotr. 121 MEYRAN AVE, UNIV HLTH CTR OF PITTSBURGH 15213 #759-18-1998 L2005 N *012

MARKS, Deborah A. ■ 15237 #041-13-2004 L2004 PTH *012

MARKS, Fred Stuart. 1000 INTEGRITY DR, STE 200 15235 #041-12-1954 PD PDA *071 †55

MARKS, Latoia Monneque. ■ 15212 #041-15-2008 *012

MARKS, Paul Howard. 5200 CENTRE AVE, STE 211 15232 #065-01-1986 L1991 ORS *012

MARKS, Stanley M. 5115 CENTRE AVE, FL 3 15232 #041-12-1973 L1974 HEM ON *020 †20

MARMOL, Aimee Kopnicky. 300 CEDAR BLVD 15228 #041-13-1996 L1998 IM *020 †20

MARONE, Luke Keith. 5200 CENTRE AVE, STE 211 15232 #024-07-1996 L2003 VS *040 †85

MARQUARDT, Merlin Delano. 320 E NORTH AVE 15212 #056-05-1971 L1989 ATP NP *020 †50

MARQUEZ, Jose M. 320 E NORTH AVE, DEPT ANES 15212 #011-03-1977 L1979 AN *020 †05

MARQUEZ, Victor. 15230 #649-01-1949 L1967 GP PTH *071 †50

MARQUIS, Belinda. ■ 15217 #035-48-2007 L2007 PD *012

MARR, Lawrence Bruce. 3550 TERRACE ST, A-1305 SCAIFE HALL 15261 #064-01-1975 L2002 AN *020

MARRERO, Miguel Angel. 4955 STEUBENVILLE PIKE, STE 364 15205 #038-06-1986 L1992 REN OBG *020 †30

MARRONE, Gary Chas. 490 E NORTH AVE, STE 302 15212 #023-07-1980 L1989 TS *020 †85,90

MARROQUIN, Oscar Clemente. ■ 15217 #429-02-1996 L2000 CD *020 †20

MARSH, James Wallis, Jr. 200 LOTHROP ST 15213 #004-01-1979 L1986 DR *020 †85

MARSHALL, Krista Lynn. ■ 15206 #041-12-2007 L2007 FP *012

MARTI, Erin Elizabeth. 815 FREEPORT RD, UPMC ST. MARGARET HOSPITAL 15215 #041-12-2005 L2005 FP *012

MARTICH, George Danl. 3559 TERRACE ST, SCAIFE HALL STE 602B 15261 #055-01-1985 L1990 CCM IM *030 †20

MARTIN, Benjamin Fredric. 4815 LIBERTY AVE STE 331 15224 #026-08-1997 L1999 FM *020 †18

MARTIN, Charles D. 2213 BROWNSVILLE RD 15210 #016-43-1947 L1948 GP *071

MARTIN, Fredric Wm. 4815 LIBERTY AVE, STE 331 15224 #041-02-1967 L1968 IM IMG *020 †20

MARTIN, Jerry Geo. 300 HALKET ST, MAGEE-WOMEN HOSP 15213 #048-12-1961 L1986 MFM *020 †30

MARTIN, Joel Edwin. 4815 LIBERTY AVE 15224 #041-02-1994 L2002 IM *020 †20

MARTIN, Juan Jose. 121 MEYRAN AVE 15213 #649-03-1998 L2006 NS *012

MARTIN, Judith Marie. 3705 5TH AVE AT, DESOTO ST 15213 #035-47-1991 L1993 PD ID *050 †55

MARTIN, Peter Shawn. 320 E NORTH AVE 15212 #055-01-1997 L1999 EM *020 †16

MARTIN-GILL, Christian. 230 MCKEE PL, STE 500 15213 #051-01-2005 L2005 EM *012

MARTINO, Micahel L. 1000 BOWER HILL RD, DEPT. EMERGENCY MEDICINE 15243 #041-12-1997 L2001 EM *020 †16

MARTONE, Christine Senese. 100 DELAFIELD RD STE 202 15215 #016-43-1969 L1971 P PFP *062 †75

MARTONE, Louis Henry. 100 DELAFIELD RD STE 202 15215 #016-06-1970 L1971 D *020 †15 ‡

MARTYN, Slava. 5230 CENTRE AVE 15232 #913-69-1989 L2001 AN PAN *020 †05

MARWAH, Shashi. 2388 OAKVIEW DR, TORRANCE STATE HOSPITAL 15237 #495-36-1972 GP *020 †50

MASERATI, Matthew Benjami. 121 MEYRAN AVE, DPET OF NEURO SURGERY 15213 #035-01-2005 L2005 NS *012

MASON, Holly Robin. ■ 15217 #024-07-2005 L2006 D *012

MASOOD, Anwar. 1400 LOCUST ST 15219 #704-02-1987 L1995 *100

MASSELLA, Elizabeth W. 651 HOLIDAY DR, FIVE FOSTER PLAZA 15220 #038-06-1987 L1990 PD *020 †55

MASSUCCI, James Edward. 1000 BOWER HILL RD 15243 #041-12-1988 L1990 AN *020 †05

MASTANDREA, Carl Albert. 4414 PENN AVE 15224 #561-17-1961 L1964 IM CD *071

MASUD, Ali. 121 MEYRAN AVE, UNIVERSITY HEALTH CENTER 15213 #704-01-2001 L2005 IM *012

MATA, Maria De Las Nieves. 3705 5TH AVE STE 3950, CHILDREN'S HOSPITAL OF PIT 15213 #132-01-1980 L2007 DR *020 †80

MATASY, Victoria Lynn. 651 HOLIDAY DR, 5 FOSTER PLAZA 15220 #038-43-1990 L1993 IM *020 †20

MATEUSZCZYK, Jaroslaw. ■ 15213 #759-03-1989 L2007 CCM *012 †20

MATHAI, Koshy Mathews. 121 MEYRAN AVE, UNIV HLTH CTR 15213 #048-12-2006 L2006 AN *012

MATHAROO, Paul Singh. 1400 LOCUST ST, OF PITTSBURGH 15219 #011-03-2006 L2006 AN *012

MATHEW, Anna. 2585 FREEPORT RD, STE 105 15238 #825-01-1975 L1980 OM IM *020 †20,70

MATHEW, Elizabeth. ■ 15238 #495-27-1970 L1977 *020

MATHIE, Laurie W. 4424 PENN AVE, STE 104 15224 #041-15-2000 L2000 RHU *020 †20

MATHIER, Michael Arthur. 200 LOTHROP ST, MEDICINE/SCAIFE S 559 15213 #035-01-1990 L1997 CD IM *020 †20

MATOKA, Derek John. ■ 15217 #016-43-2002 L2002 U *012

MATSUBARA, Haruka. 5230 CENTRE AVE, UPMC SHADYSIDE 15232 #572-29-2001 L2004 IM *100 †20

MATTHEW, Elizabeth Morrow. ■ 15238 #065-01-1974 L1977 P *020 †75

MAURO, Craig Stephen. ■ 15232 #041-12-2004 L2004 ORS *012

MAVANUR, Arun Anantharam. 5150 CENTRE AVE RM 414, DIVISION OF SURGICAL ONCOL 15232 #496-21-1989 L2007 GS *100 †85

MAVRINAC, Joan Michele. 13 PRIDE ST 15219 #041-14-1982 L1986 PD *020 †55

MAXWELL, Ned G. ■ 15213 #056-06-1945 L1960 IM PTH *071

MAY, Stanley Chas. 5230 CENTRE AVE 15232 #041-02-1979 L1981 IM *020 †20

MAYERNIK, Curtis Vincent. 4416 PENN AVE, CHEN LIN-LI MD 15224 #010-02-1985 L1992 P *020

MAZARIEGOS, George V. 3705 5TH AVE 15213 #016-06-1986 L1989 GS CCS *020 †85

MAZZEI, Joseph M. 125 7TH ST 15222 #041-12-1945 L1946 DR *072

MC ADAMS, David John. 200 LOTHROP ST, UPMC MONTEFIORE, RM E815 15213 #010-02-1998 L2000 IM *020 †20

MCAFFEE, Richard Harmon. 121 MEYRAN AVE, DEPT OF ANESTHESIOLOGY 15213 #010-01-2005 L2005 AN *012

MC ALLISTER, Florencia Ma. 3708 5TH AVE 15213 #132-04-2000 L2005 IM *012

MC ALLISTER, Jeanann R. 1200 REEDSDALE ST 15233 #041-12-1996 L1998 P *020 †75

MC ANINCH, Brett Liana. 3705 5TH AVE 15213 #041-12-2003 L2006 PEM *012 †55

MC ASSEY, Janine Michelle. 200 LOTHROP ST, UPMC MONTEFIORE SUITE 9W93 15213 #035-06-1997 L1999 IM *020 †20

MC AULEY, Clyde Edward. 320 E NORTH AVE, ALLEGHENY GENERAL HOSPITAL 15212 #041-12-1979 L1980 CCS *020 †85

MC BEE, William Carr, Jr. ■ 15228 #055-01-2003 L2007 OBG *100

MCBURNEY, Christine Ann. 15261 #041-12-2007 L2007 IM *012

MC CAFFERTY, Leo Raymond. 580 S AIKEN AVE STE 530 15232 #041-13-1981 L1988 PS *020 †65 ‡

MC CAFFREY, Francis M. 3705 5TH AVE 15213 #041-14-1980 L1993 PDC PD *020 †55

MCCAGUE, Annabinney. ■ 15213 #041-12-2008 *012

MC CAGUE, James Jos. 1350 LOCUST ST STE 311, MERCY PROFESSIONAL OFFICE 15219 #067-01-1969 L1974 U GS *020 †95

MCCALL, Matthew James. 4815 LIBERTY AVE STE GR 15224 #041-13-2004 L2004 IM *100 †20

MC CANDLISH, Mitchel Lee. 4800 FRIENDSHIP AVE 15224 #041-02-1986 L1987 EM *020 †16

MCCARDLE, Hilary Susan. ■ 15221 #011-02-2006 L2006 PD *012

MC CARRAN, William Joseph. ■ 15237 #024-16-2001 L2007 NPM *100

MC CARTHY, Kenneth Robt. ■ 15237 #035-08-1979 L1980 EM *020 †16

MC CARTHY, Maria A. ■ 15213 #035-19-2003 L2003 CHP *012

MC CARTY, Kenneth S, Jr. 200 LOTHROP ST, DEPT MEDICINEDEPT PATHOLOG 15213 #036-07-1972 L1993 PTH END *020 †50,20

MC CAULEY, Jerry. 3550 TERRACE ST, RENA DIV/TRANSPLANT A909 15213 #032-01-1977 L1984 NEP IM *020 †20

MCCAULEY, William John. 431A S ATLANTIC AVE 15224 #918-01-1992 L2001 IM *100

MC CAUSLAND, Julie Beth. 230 MCKEE PL, STE 400 15213 #041-09-1996 L2001 EM *020 †16

MC CHESNEY, Daniel Dwight. 15208 #041-12-2002 L2002 IM *100

MC CLAIN, Edward James. 200 DELAFIELD RD, STE 1040 15215 #041-01-1957 L1958 ORS *071 †40

MC CLINTOCK, W Creighton. ■ 15214 #041-12-1947 L1948 CD IM *071

MC CLOSKEY, Carol Ann. 3380 BOULEVARD OF THE ALLS, ALLIES, SUITE390 15213 #041-12-1997 L2000 GS *020 †85

MC CLUSKEY, Kevin Michael. ■ 15222 #041-12-1998 L2002 VIR *100 †80

MC COLLUM, George Richard. 3528 BOULEVARD OF THE ALLS 15213 #041-12-1957 L1958 FM *072 †18

MCCOMB, Jennifer Gonzalez. 3459 5TH AVE, NW 628 MUH 15213 #035-03-2002 L2005 PCC *012 †20

MC COOK, Barry Moore. 200 LOTHROP ST, DEPT OF RADIOLOGY 15213 #011-03-1984 L1995 DR *020 †80

MC COOL, Charles Michael. 4390 CAMPBELLS RUN RD 15205 #038-40-1972 L1974 IM END *020 †20

MCCORMICK, Andrew Allen. ■ 15206 #041-12-2007 L2007 MPD *012

MC CORMICK, Lee Hamilton. 2708 BROWNSVILLE RD 15227 #041-12-1958 L1959 FM ADM *020 †18

MCCRAY, Justin Neil. ■ 15224 #041-12-2007 L2007 AN *012

MC CURRY, Kenneth R. 200 LOTHROP ST STE C-700 15213 #011-03-1987 L1997 TS CD *020 †85,90

MC DONALD, Robert H, Jr. 3500 5TH AVE STE 200 15213 #016-43-1959 L1966 PA IM *072

MC ELHATTAN, Shirley A. 120 LYTTON AVE, STE 3B 15213 #041-02-1998 L2000 IM *020 †20

MCELLISTREM, Mary C. 3601 5TH AVE STE 3A 15213 #047-05-1993 L1996 ID *020 †20

MCENANEY, Ryan Michael. ■ 15217 #028-34-2007 L2007 *012

MC FADDEN, Kathryn Alicia. ■ 15217 #041-12-2001 L2001 PTH *020 †50

MC GAFFEY, Ann Louise. 5321 PENN AVE 15224 #040-02-1977 L1980 FM *040 †18

MC GAFFIN, Kenneth Robert. 200 LOTHROP ST, UPMC-S559 SCAIFE HALL 15213 #010-02-1999 L2001 CD *020 †20 ‡

MC GARRITY, Amy Lynne. 1580 MCLAUGHLIN RUN RD, STE 208 15241 #035-15-1989 L1991 PD *020 †55

MCGARVEY, Jeremy Ray. ■ 15232 #041-12-2008 *012

MC GAVIN, Cameron Lindsay. 3811 OHARA ST, WESTERN PSYCHIATRIC INSTIT 15213 #003-01-2000 L2001 **PFP** *100 †75

MC GEE, Elizabeth Ann. 204 CRAFT AVE 230, INSTITUTE 15213 #047-06-1989 L2000 **OBG** *020 †30

MC GEE, James Barry, Jr. 200 LOTHROP ST 15213 #021-06-1988 L2001 **GE IM** *040 †20

MC GILL, Rita L. 320 E NORTH AVE, 4TH FLOOR, SOUTH TOWER 15212 #024-16-1985 L1986 **NEP IM** *020 †20

MC GOUGH, Richard Louis. 5200 CENTRE AVE, STE 211 15232 #041-12-1996 L2004 **ORS** *040 †40

MC GRANAHAN, Shannon H. 9335 MCKNIGHT RD 15237 #041-09-1996 L1999 **OBG** *020 †30

MC GRATH, Kevin Michael. 200 LOTHROP ST 15213 #041-02-1992 L2001 **GE** *020 †20

MCGRATH, Michael Thomas. ■ 15211 #035-45-2007 L2007 **EM** *012

MC GRAW, Donald J. 580 S AIKEN AVE STE 100 15232 #035-48-1976 L1982 **OM IM** *020 †70

MC GUIRE, Sean Patrick. 4800 FRIENDSHIP AVE 15213 #041-12-1981 L1982 **EM** *020 †16

MCHAYLEH, Wassim Marwan. ■ 15219 #605-02-2002 L2006 **HO** *012 †20

MCHUGH, Gregory Leo. ■ 15232 #056-06-2008 *012

MC HUGH, Richard Dennis. 3550 TERRACE ST, UNIV OF PITT PHYS ANES 15261 #041-12-1974 L1978 **AN** *020 †05

MC INTIRE, Sara Charlotte. 3705 5TH AVE 15213 #005-19-1984 L1990 **PD** *020 †55

MC INTYRE-SELTMAN, K. 300 HALKET ST, MAGEE-WOMANS HOSPITAL 15213 #041-07-1979 L1980 **OBG** *040 †30

MCIVOR, William Raymond. 200 LOTHROP ST, C-WING 15213 #056-05-1990 L1993 **AN** *020 †05

MC KEATING, John Anthony. 1501 LOCUST ST, STE 304 15219 #041-12-1985 L1986 **GS VS** *020 †85

MC KEE, Claude W. ■ 15219 #041-12-1937 L1938 **GP A** *071

MC KENRICK, Crystal Lynn. 320 E NORTH AVE 15212 #041-15-2000 L2001 **EM** *020 †16

MC KEVITT, Dennis. 140 LOCUST ST, MERCY HOSPITAL 15202 #021-06-1998 L2006 **CCM** *020 †20

MC KINNON, John Ernest. ■ 15237 #715-01-1995 L2002 **ID** *100 †20

MCKINNON, Megan Heather. ■ 15217 #028-02-2004 L2004 **MEM** *012

MCLAUGHLIN, Brian Thomas. 121 MEYRAN AVE, UPMC MONTEFIORE N-713 15213 #035-48-2006 L2006 **IM** *012

MC LEAN, Gordon Kennedy. 4800 FRIENDSHIP AVE, THE WESTERN PENNSYLVANIA H 15224 #032-01-1975 L1976 **VIR R** *020 †80

MC LEAN, Kia Maureen. 683 SCAIFE HALL, 3550 TERRACE STREET 15261 #036-07-2003 L2003 **GS** *020

MCLENNAN, John D. ■ 15213 #060-01-1991 L1996 **GPM P** *100

MC LINDEN, Sean. 612 CALIFORNIA AVE 15202 #041-12-1985 L1986 **N** *020

MC MAHON, Deborah Kay. 3601 5TH AVE, FALK CLNC BLDG RM 611 15213 #041-13-1981 L1987 **ID IM** *050 †20

MC MAHON, Kelly Patrice. 9104 BABCOCK BLVD STE S107 15237 #041-12-1997 L1999 **IM** *020 †20

MC MAHON, Patrick Jos. 2100 JANE ST 15203 #041-13-1987 L1990 **ORS OSM** *020 †40

MC MASTER, James Henry. 1307 FEDERAL ST 15212 #041-13-1964 L1966 **ORS OAR** *071 †40

MCMORROW, Kari Maureen. ■ 15243 #041-15-2007 L2007 **TY** *012

MC MULLEN, Laura Lea. ■ 15217 #041-12-2004 L2004 **PD** *020 †55

MC MURRAY, Jessica Marie. 3459 5TH AVE, MUH NW628 15213 #041-02-2000 L2001 **PCC** *020 †20

MC NALL, Pearl G. ■ 15243 #041-12-1949 L1950 **AN** *071 †05

MC NAMARA, Dennis Michael. 200 LOTHROP ST 15213 #024-01-1987 L1994 **CD** *020 †20

MC NAMARA, Michael James. 200 LOTHROP ST, N713 15213 #038-06-2001 L2001 **HO** *012

MC NANIE, Jamie Melissa. 6343 PENN AVE 15206 #038-40-2000 L2001 **PD** *020 †55

MC NEIL, Melissa Ann. 200 LOTHROP ST, MEDICINE 15213 #041-12-1980 L1981 **IM IMG** *040 †20

MC NULTY, Barbara Mary. 4615 FORBES AVE, CCP OAKLAND 15213 #041-12-1975 L1978 **PD ADL** *020 †55

MC NUTT, Rebecca Anne. 230 MCKEE PL STE 500, OF PITTSBURGH 15213 #008-01-2007 L2007 *012

MC PHERSON, Elizabeth W. 300 HALKET ST, DEPT OF GENETICS 15213 #054-04-1975 L1990 **MG PD** *020 †55,19

MC QUONE, Shelly Jeanne. 4815 LIBERTY AVE, STE 443 15224 #051-01-1990 L1998 **OTO** *020 †45

MC SORLEY, John, III. 580 S AIKEN AVE, STE 201 15232 #055-01-1966 L1967 **D** *020 †15

MC TIGUE, Kathleen Mary. 200 LOTHROP ST, 9W MONTEFIORE UNIVERSITY H 15213 #008-02-1996 L2002 **GPM** *020 †20

MC VAY, William Jos. 4627 5TH AVE 15213 #010-02-1959 L1960 **OPH** *072 †35 ‡

MC VERRY, Bryan James. 3459 5TH AVE, UPMC MONTEFIORE NW 628 15213 #010-02-1997 L2005 **PCC** *050 †20

MEADOWS, Amy Lynn. ■ 15243 #008-01-2008 L2008 *012

MEANS, John Ryan. 1400 LOCUST ST 15219 #539-03-2000 L2001 **GS** *020 †85

MECS, Sandor. 1000 BOWER HILL RD, STE 213 15243 #473-01-1984 L1986 **OBG** *020 †30

MEDHEKAR, Anjali. 320 E NORTH AVE 15212 #495-32-1988 L2001 **CHP** *100 †75

MEDHI, Monisha. ■ 15237 #496-02-1984 L2001 **IMG END** *020 †20

MEDICH, David Stanley. 320 E NORTH AVE, 5TH FL S TOWER 15212 #038-40-1987 L1989 **CRS GS** *020 †85,10

MEDICH, Gretchen Elsasser. 4727 FRIENDSHIP AVE, STE 240 15224 #038-06-1986 L1987 **AN IM** *020 †20,05 ‡

MEDINA-FLORES, Rafael. 200 LOTHROP ST 15213 #649-31-1994 L2001 **NP** *050 †50

MEDSGER, Thos Arnold, Jr. RM S721 BST, UNIV OF PITTSBURGH SCH OF 15261 #041-01-1962 L1966 **RHU IM** *030 †20

MEHOK, Ronald Geo. 5820 CENTRE AVE, GREATER PITTSBURGH ORTHOPA 15206 #041-12-1966 L1967 **ORS** *020 †40

MEHROTRA, Ateev. 230 MCKEE PL, STE 600 15213 #005-02-1999 L2006 **MPD** *020

MEHTA, Amish Manhar. 4727 FRIENDSHIP AVE, STE 200 15224 #041-12-1997 L1999 **CD** *020 †20

MEHTA, Arpita Indravadan. ■ 15206 #024-07-2005 L2005 **OTO** *012

MEHTA, Harshad Ratilal. 1050 BOWER HILL RD STE 308 15243 #495-17-1972 L1977 **CD IM** *020 †20

MEHTA, Kiran. 9100 BABCOCK BLVD 15237 #041-09-1991 L1994 **RO** *020 †80

MEHTA, Kiran Dalichand. 9100 BABCOCK BLVD 15237 #495-48-1982 L1988 **IM** *020 †20

MEHTA, Yogini Rohit. 2000 MARY ST, UPMC SOUTHSIDE 15203 #495-01-1970 L1972 **AN** *020

MEIER, Carmen B. 15221 #038-41-2003 L2003 **GE** *012 †20

MEISLER, Arnold Irwin. 5150 CENTRE AVE 15232 #035-19-1956 L1979 **HO HEM** *071 †20

MEISNER, Dennis James. 5115 CENTRE AVE, FL 3 15232 #041-12-1980 L1989 **ON HEM** *020 †20

MEISTER, Donald Glenn. 9100 BABCOCK BLVD 15237 #041-12-1954 L1955 **GP** *071

MELANI, Kenneth Rudolph. 120 5TH AVE, STE 3116 15222 #036-05-1979 L1980 **IM** *030 †20

MELEAN, Fernando Enrique. 200 LOTHROP ST, UPMC-PUH C-WING 15213 #935-03-1993 L2005 **AN** *020 †05

MELHEM, Mona Fouad. 113 WESPORT DR, VA MEDICAL CENTER 15238 #915-02-1980 L1984 **PTH** *020 †50

MELHEM, Samer Rami. ■ 15238 #041-12-2008 *012

MELLORS, John Watson. 3550 TERRACE ST, STE 818 15213 #032-01-1978 L1991 **IM ID** *050 †20

MELNICK, Brian Marshall. 3550 TERRACE ST, A-1305 SCAIFE HALL 15261 #041-14-1977 L1980 **AN** *020 †05

MELNICK, Melvin Philip. 530 MARSHALL AVE 15214 #041-09-1972 L1973 **CHP P** *020 †75 ‡

MELOTTI, Peter Morris. 1350 LOCUST ST, STE 105 MERCY PROF BLDG 15219 #561-01-1961 L1963 **PM** *071 †60

MENDELSOHN, Sylvia Rachel. 401 SHADY AVE STE A204 15206 #041-09-1977 L1979 **P CHP** *020 †75

MENDELSON, Samuel Robt. 9100 BABCOCK BLVD 15237 #041-12-1975 L1976 **OBG** *071 †30

MENDELSON, Stephen Abram. 3705 5TH AVE 15213 #016-02-1989 L1997 **ORS** *020 †40

MENG, Li. A-1305 SCAIFE HALL, DEPARTMENT OF ANESTHESIOLO 15261 #243-44-1982 L1998 **AN PHP** *020 †05

MENIN, April Marie. ■ 15217 #041-77-2007, ▲ L2007 **OBG** *012

MERENSTEIN, Joel Harvey. 3937 BUTLER ST 15201 #041-12-1960 L1961 **FM** *020 †18

MERICK, Rudolph Edward. 559 TRUMBULL DR 15205 #041-12-1982 L2000 **IM** *020 †20

MERKOW, Leonard Philip. ■ 15217 #056-05-1962 L1964 **IM PTH** *075 †50

MERMAN, Rita Borisovna. 5230 CENTRE AVE, STE 205 15232 #913-32-1988 L2002 **AN** *020 †05

MEROLA, Christina Ann. ■ 15238 #041-12-2008 *012

MEROVICH, Barbara. 121 MEYRAN AVE, UNIV HLTH CTR OF PITTSBURG 15213 #132-10-1998 L2004 **IM** *020 †20

MERTZ, Kristen Jean. ■ 15232 #008-01-1987 L1988 **PHP** *020 †70

MESORAS, Michael Anthony. 5313 CAMPBELLS RUN RD, TWO MARQUIS PLAZA, SUITE 3 15205 #041-14-1980 L1981 **FM** *030 †18

MESSNER, Kevin Lee. 1307 FEDERAL ST, STE 2 15212 #041-07-1997 L1999 **EM ESM** *020 †16

METRO, David George, Jr. 3471 5TH AVE STE 910, LILIANE S. KAUFMANN BUILDI 15213 #041-12-1994 L1997 **AN** *020 †05

METZGER, Charles W. 100 S JACKSON AVE 15202 #041-12-1943 L1944 **GP** *071

MEYER, Mark William. 7171 CHURCHLAND ST, EAST LIBERTTY FAMILY HEALT 15206 #046-01-1993 L1995 **FM** *020 †18

MEYER, Viveca Ann. 3811 OHARA ST 15213 #051-07-1980 L1982 **CHP** *020 †75

MEYERS, Louis L. ■ 15213 #041-12-1951 L1952 **GYN OS** *071 †30

MEZA, Manuel Elliott. 3705 5TH AVE #041-02-1985 L1991 **R PDR** *020 †80

MIASKIEWICZ, Stasia L. 930 SCAIFE HALL 15261 #041-14-1983 L1984 **END IM** *020 †20

MICHAELS, Bernard I. 400 PENN CENTER BLVD, STE 810 15235 #041-12-1942 L1943 **PD** *071 †55

MICHAELS, Marian Gail. 3705 5TH AVE RM 4B320, PEDS INFECTIOUS DISEASES 15213 #041-01-1985 L1987 **PD ID** *020 †55

MICHAELS, Milton Meyer. ■ 15232 #041-12-1954 L1955 **IM HEM** *071 †20

MICHAELS, Richard H. 3705 5TH AVE 15213 #035-01-1953 L1961 **PD ID** *071 †55

MICHALOPOULOS, George. 200 LOTHROP ST 15213 #418-01-1969 L1991 **PTH** *050 †50

MICHEL, Gerard Elliott. 1004 ARCH ST 15212 #041-12-1971 L1973 **EM AM** *070

MICKIEWICZ-MARCINKOWSKA, E. 320 E NORTH AVE 15212 #759-03-2001 L2005 **P** *012

MICKUS, Timothy John. ■ 15233 #047-05-2004 L2005 **DR** *012

MICUCCI, Chad Joseph. ■ 15229 #055-01-2004 L2004 **ORS** *012

MIDDLETON, Donald Bell. 200 DELAFIELD RD, STE 2030 15215 #035-45-1972 L1978 **IM PD** *040 †20,55

MIDDLETON, Jennifer Laura. 5321 PENN AVE, UPMC ST MARAGARET BLOOMFLD 15224 #038-40-2003 L2003 **FM** *100 †18

MIDIAN-SINGH, Robin S. 1307 FEDERAL ST, STE 301 15212 #305-01-2001 L2004 **GE** *020

MIGALY, Peter. 1200 REEDSDALE ST 15233 #473-01-1981 L1996 **P** *020 †75

MIKNEVICH, Maryann. 1350 LOCUST ST, STE 409 15219 #041-12-1980 L1981 **PM** *020 †60 ‡

MIKOLICH, Brandon M. 320 E NORTH AVE, DIVISION OF CARDIOLOGY 15212 #041-15-2002 L2002 **CD** *012 †20

MIKULLA, John Michael. 2400 ARDMORE BLVD STE 200 15221 #041-12-1974 L1975 **OPH** *020 †35

MILBRANDT, Eric Benjamin. ■ 15217 #017-20-1996 L2003 **PCC** *050 †20

MILLAR, Deborah Louise. 5230 CENTRE AVE, SHADYSIDE HOSPITAL DEPT OF 15232 #041-12-1985 L1987 **DR OS** *020 †80

MILLER, Annette F. 240 MOUNT LEBANON BLVD 15234 #065-01-1994 L1998 **PD** *020 †55

MILLER, Benjamin Galen. ■ 15213 #041-12-2004 L2004 **PD** *012 †55

MILLER, Brian Andrew. ■ 15224 #041-12-2007 L2007 **FP** *012

MILLER, Clarke T. 1004 ARCH ST 15212 #041-13-1973 L1975 **EM** *020 †16

MILLER, David Scott. 50 MOFFETT ST 15243 #041-14-1985 L1986 **IM HPI** *020 †20

MILLER, Edward B. 3500 5TH AVE 15213 #041-01-1982 L1983 **RHU IM** *020 †20

MILLER, Eric Scott. 5230 CENTRE AVE, SHADYSIDE HOSPITAL 15232 #035-20-1976 L1988 **OBG FM** *020 †30,18

MILLER, Jeanine Helena. ■ 15237 #051-07-2004 L2004 **EM** *100

MILLER, Kelly Ann. 3705 5TH AVE 15213 #041-13-1990 L2001 **PDS** *012 †85

MILLER, Kimberly V. ■ 15221 #043-01-2004 L2006 **TY** *012

MILLER, Laura Leigh. 815 FREEPORT RD 15215 #041-02-2004 L2004 **FM** *020 †18

MILLER, Margaret Ann. 1400 LOCUST ST 15219 #041-12-1986 L1987 **DR** *020 †80

MILLER, Mark David. 3811 OHARA ST 15213 #041-12-1981 L1983 **P** *050 †75

MILLER, Ralph J, Jr. 1307 FEDERAL ST, STE 300 15212 #041-12-1984 L1986 **U** *020 †95

MILLER, Susan Ann. 3705 5TH AVE 15213 #041-12-1982 L1983 **PDC PD** *020 †55

MILLER, William B. 1425 BEAVER AVE, P.B.A. INCORPORATED 15233 #041-12-1948 L1949 **IM** *071

MILLER, William Harold. 532 S AIKEN AVE 15232 #041-09-1957 L1958 **TS** *071 †85,90

MILLIN, Cynthia Angela. ■ 15206 #011-02-2006 L2006 **P** *012

MILLMAN, Eric. 3705 5TH AVE, CHILDREN'S HOSP OF PITTSBU 15213 #023-01-1989 L2002 **PDR** *020 †80

MILLS, Thomas Cooke. ■ 15232 #016-11-1981 L2005 **P PHP** *071 †75

MINES, Samuel Chas. ■ 15243 #041-12-1963 L1964 **A IM** *020 †03

MINEV, Evgueni Minev. 200 LOTHROP ST, W933-MUH 15213 #198-01-1995 L2006 **NEP** *012

MINNO, Alexander Mackey. 120 LYTTON AVE 15213 #041-12-1947 L1948 **IM RHU** *071

MINSHEW, Nancy Jean. 3811 OHARA ST # 454, IROQUOIS BLDG STE 208 15213 #028-02-1974 L1984 **P PD** *050 †75

■ = Address Information Privacy Protected

MIRANDA, Aurora Marcelo. 4815 LIBERTY AVE, STE 321 15224 #748-02-1975 L1982 **OBG** *020 †30

MIROWITZ, Scott Alan. 200 LOTHROP ST 15213 #028-02-1985 L2000 **DR AR** *020 †80

MIRSKY, Robert Stewart. 600 GRANT ST, U.S. STEEL TOWER, 41ST FLO 15219 #035-08-1985 L2007 **FM** *020 †18 ‡

MIRZA, Lubna. 1400 LOCUST ST, MERCY HOSP-PITTSBURGH 15219 #704-17-1999 L2008 **IM** *012

MISAGE, John Raymond. 3520 5TH AVE 15213 #041-12-1962 L1963 **IM CD** *071 †20

MISHRA, Michael Donald Vi. 121 MEYRAN AVE, DEPT RAD 15213 #055-01-2006 L2007 **DR** *012

MISHRA, Seema Shyam. 3705 5TH AVE 15213 #025-07-2003 L2003 **PD** *020 †55

MISJA, Matthew Edward. ■ 15202 #038-45-2002 L2002 **EM** *100 †16

MISKIMMIN, Renee Lynn. 11 STANWIX ST, HEALTH AMERICA/HEALTH ASSU 15222 #041-13-1994 L1996 **IM** *020 †18

MISRA, Nilanjana. ■ 15206 #495-13-1996 L2006 **PDC** *012

MISSRY, John Jacob. 5701 CENTRE AVE, STE L3 15206 #021-01-1990 L1992 **OPH** *020 †35

MISTRY, Amita Thakor. ■ 15224 #048-02-2002 L2007 **SP** *012

MITCHELL, Fenton Martin. 4221 PENN AVE 15224 #041-12-1957 L1958 **CD IM** *071 †20

MITCHELL, Galen Wesley. 3471 5TH AVE, STE 811 15213 #019-02-1984 L1998 **N IG** *020 †75

MITRA, Sanjay. ■ 15237 #496-09-1992 L2007 **NPM** *012 †55

MITRAKOU-FANARIOTIS, A. 200 LOTHROP ST, PRESBYTERIAN HOSP 15213 #418-01-1980 **END** *100

MITRE, Blima K. 9100 BABCOCK BLVD, PASSAVANT HOSPITAL 15237 #176-03-1967 L1972 **PTH PCP** *062 †50 ‡

MITRE, Marcia Carmen. ■ 15217 #041-12-1998 L2000 **GE** *020 †20

MITRE, Ricardo Javier. 925 BRIGHTON RD 15233 #176-03-1967 L1972 **GE IM** *020 †20

MITRO, William M. 15243 #028-34-1944 L1945 **FM** *071

MIZIKOWSKI, Stanley G, Jr. 9100 BABCOCK BLVD 15237 #041-07-1998 L2000 **EM** *020 †16

MIZRACHI, David. 4800 FRIENDSHIP AVE, STE 3410-NT 15224 #041-13-2002 L2002 **DR** *100 †80

MLECKO, Lawrence Matthew. 9104 BABCOCK BLVD, STE 4106 PASSAVANT PROFESS 15237 #016-11-1959 L1960 **GE IM** *071 †20

MLECKO, Michael Lawrence. 9000 PERRY HWY, STE 210 15237 #041-13-1997 L2000 **GE** *020 †20

MOALLI, Pamela Ann. 300 HALKET ST, MAGEE WOMENS HOSPITAL 15213 #016-06-1994 L1996 **OBG** *020 †30

MODI, Jashwantlal B. 4815 LIBERTY AVE STE GR-4 15224 #495-22-1972 L1980 **CD IM** *020 †20 ‡

MODIC, Christopher Wm Jos. 1000 BOWER HILL RD 15243 #038-06-1972 L1973 **DR VIR** *020 †80

MODY, Neeta Satish. ■ 15213 #041-02-2001 L2001 **DR** *012

MOESLEIN, Fred Martin. 3705 5TH AVE, CHP MT SUITE 3950 15213 #038-06-2001 L2007 **DR** *100 †80

MOGHTADERI, Sam. ■ 15222 #035-46-2002 L2007 **HSO** *012

MOGUILLANSKY, Diego. ■ 15232 #132-01-2000 L2002 **PDC** *012 †20,55

MOHAMED, Imtiaz. ■ 15237 #704-01-1974 L1999 **GE** *100

MOHAN, Deepika. ■ 15232 #012-05-2001 L2003 **CCS** *012 †85

MOHAN, Janani. 1500 5TH AVE, DEPT OF INTERNAL MED 15219 #495-59-2006 L2007 **IM** *012

MOHAN, Niveditha. 3601 5TH AVE, STE 2B 15213 #495-04-1992 L2005 **RHU** *020 †20

MOHAN, Pankaj. 490 E NORTH AVE, STE 307 15212 #038-40-1993 L1999 **CD** *020 †20

MOHANKA, Ravi Rajendrapra. 3708 5TH AVE, DEPT OF MED EDUCATION 15213 #495-83-1998 L2006 **TTS AS** *020

MOHN, Kimball Willis. 1400 LOCUST ST, MERCY HOSPITAL 15219 #041-09-1975 L1976 **IM** *040 †20

MOHR, Michael Harry. 200 LOTHROP ST, STE C-212 15213 #041-12-1998 L2000 **AN** *020 †05

MOHTASEBI, Yasaman. 1400 LOCUST ST 15219 #517-12-2002 L2006 **IM** *012

MOKKAPATTI, Rupa. 9104 BABCOCK BLVD, STE 1106 15237 #495-65-1985 L1999 **IM** *020 †20

MOLENAAR, Donald Michael. 100 BAYER RD, BLDG 6 15205 #026-08-1976 L1999 **OM IM** *030 †70

MOLLEN, Kevin Patrick. 200 LOTHROP ST, F675 PUH 15213 #035-06-2001 L2001 **GS** *012

MOLNAR, Theodore John. 400 PENN CENTER BLVD, STE555 15235 #041-01-1983 L1985 **DR** *020 †80

MONACO, Edward A, III. ■ 15209 #035-01-2006 L2006 **NS** *012

MONAH, Ronald O, Jr. 490 E NORTH AVE STE 204 15212 #017-20-1978 L1980 **IM CD** *020 †20

MONAHAN, Daniel Jos. 200 DELAFIELD RD, STE 2030 15215 #028-34-1990 L1992 **FM** *020 †18

MONDZELEWSKI, James Peter. 1145 BOWER HILL RD, STE 205 15243 #038-40-1973 L1976 **OPH** *020 †35 ‡

MONEDERO, Pablo. ■ 15213 #847-01-1983 L1996 **CCA** *040

MONGA, Dulabh Kaur. 5150 CENTRE AVE 15232 #495-43-1994 L2001 **HO** *020 †20

MONTELLESE, Phyllis B. 5230 CENTRE AVE, RM 519 SCH OF NURSING 15232 #035-45-1979 L1985 **FM** *040 †18

MONTES, Anne Camille Alte. ■ 15232 #748-01-2003 L2006 **FP** *012

MONTGOMERY, Sean Day. 815 FREEPORT RD, EMERGENCY DEPT 15215 #041-15-2001 L2004 **EM** *020 †16

MONTI, Daniel. 1200 REEDSDALE ST, MERCY BEHAVIORAL HEALTH 15233 #924-01-1989 L2000 **P CHP** *020 †75

MONTINI, John. 717 WASHINGTON RD 15228 #041-02-1986 L1987 **IM** *020 †20

MONTOYA, Mario Ignacio. 3705 5TH AVE, KAUFMANN MEDICAL BLDG. SUI 15213 #041-12-2003 L2003 **AN** *100

MOOMIAIE, Remo M. A.. 4800 FRIENDSHIP AVE, DEPT OF GME 15224 #473-02-2002 L2006 *100

MOORE, Henry Rahsaan. ■ 15232 #016-11-2002 L2007 **CCS** *012

MOORE, Jason Elliot. 3550 TERRACE AVE, 651 SCAIFE HALL 15261 #033-06-1998 L2002 **CCM** *020 †20

MOORE, Patricia E. 3471 5TH AVE, STE 811 15213 #041-07-1973 L1981 **N** *020 †75

MOORE, Patrick Stephen. ■ 15217 #049-01-1985 L1990 **GPM** *020 †70

MOORE, Robert Yates. 3471 5TH AVE STE 811, UNIV PITTS 15213 #016-02-1957 L1991 **N CHN** *020 †75

MOORE-FORBES, Yolanda A. 1400 LOCUST ST, DEPT PED 15219 #041-12-1989 L1991 **PD** *020 †55

MOOSSY, John. UNIV PITTSBURGH SCH MED 15261 #021-01-1950 L1965 **NP N** *050 †75,50

MOOSSY, John Jefferson. 200 LOTHROP ST 15213 #021-01-1980 L1986 **NS** *020 †25

MORAITIS, Constantine Z. 230 LOTHROP ST 15213 #041-12-1947 L1948 **OPH** *071 †35

MORATO, Daniela Elvira. ■ 15213 #023-01-2006 L2006 **OBG** *012

MORELAND, Larry Wayne. UNIVERSITY OF PITTSBURGH, 3500 TERRACE ST 15261 #055-01-1983 L1984 **RHU** *020 †20

MORELAND, Morey Sargent. 3705 5TH AVE, CHILDRENS HOSP PITTSBURGH 15213 #035-45-1965 L1989 **ORS** *071 †40

MORELL, Victor Onofre. 3705 5TH AVE 15213 #042-02-1988 L1991 **TS** *020 †85,90

MORETTI, James Michael. 2589 WASHINGTON RD, STE 423 15241 #041-09-1979 L1980 **FM** *020 †18

MORGAN, Allan V. 230 N CRAIG ST # 510 15213 #010-01-1933 L1934 **IM GE** *071 †20

MORGAN, Matthew Breinholt. ■ 15216 #049-01-2003 L2005 **DR** *012

MORI, Mari. ARTS BUILDIN, STE 503 MEDICAL 15213 #572-08-2003 L2007 **FP** *012

MORINE, Susan Ann. ■ 15221 #041-12-2004 L2004 **CHP** *012

MORITA, Shigeki. ■ 15217 #572-12-1980 L1991 **TS GS** *020

MORITZ, Michael Laredo. 3705 5TH AVE 15213 #016-02-1991 L1999 **PN** *020 †55

MORKOUS, Sameh Serry Wasf. 3705 5TH AVE, CHILDREN'S HOSP 15213 #915-03-1994 L2004 **CHN** *012 †55

MORONE, Natalia Emily. 200 MEYRAN AVE STE 200 15213 #025-12-1993 L2003 **MPD PD** *020 †55,20

MORREALE, Steven Charles. 5230 CENTRE AVE 15232 #012-05-2005 L2005 **FP** *012

MORRIS, David Wayne. 1130 PERRY HWY, PINES PLAZA 15237 #041-12-1988 L1990 **FM** *020 †18

MORRIS, Karen Guckert. ■ 15202 #041-12-1988 L1991 **PD** *020 †55

MORRISON, Bruce Wm. 200 DELAFIELD RD, STE 2010 15215 #041-01-1984 L1985 **OBG** *020 †30

MORRISON, Linda Ying. ■ 15206 #026-04-2007 L2007 **EM** *012

MORRISROE, Shelby Nicole. ■ 15232 #010-02-2003 L2003 **U** *012

MORRISSEY, Suzanne K. 1307 FEDERAL ST STE 301, ALLEGHENY GENERAL HOSPITAL 15212 #041-15-2002 L2002 **GE** *012 †20

MORSE, William Scott. 1000 BOWER HILL RD 15243 #041-09-1978 L1979 **DR** *020 †80,16

MORSHEDI, Mojgan. 5230 CENTRE AVE 15232 #517-01-1994 L2002 **IM** *020 †20

MORTON, Margaret Sue. 4070 BEECHWOOD BLVD STE 5 15217 #041-09-1984 L1985 **FM FPG** *020 †18 ‡

MOSCHOS, Stergios. ■ 15215 #418-01-1997 L2002 **HO** *100 †20

MOSER, Arthur James. 200 LOTHROP ST 15213 #028-02-1989 L1996 **GS SO** *020 †85

MOSES-KOLKO, Eydie L. 3811 OHARA ST 15213 #023-01-1995 L1997 **P** *020 †75

MOSESSO, Vincent N, Jr. 200 LOTHROP ST 15213 #041-12-1988 L1990 **EM** *020 †16

MOSIER, Stephen Kimberly. 2000 MARY ST, SOUTH SIDE HOSP-ANESTLGY 15261 #035-08-1998 L2001 **AN CCA** *020

MOSKOWITZ, Howard Samuel. 121 MEYRAN AVE, DEPT OF OTOLARYN 15213 #035-20-2006 L2006 **OTO** *012

MOSLEY, Mark Richard. 645 OVERLOOK DR, CHOICECARE PHYSICIANS, PC 15216 #041-12-1976 L1977 **IM** *020 †20

MOSS, Deborah Rose. 3705 5TH AVE, CHILDREN HOSP PITTSBURGH 15213 #016-06-1987 L1989 **PD** *020 †55

MOSTOUFIZADEH, Mahpareh. 565 COAL VALLEY RD, DEPT LAB FL 4 BIBRO 15236 #517-01-1973 L1987 **PTH** *030 †50

MOTEN, Marriyam. 111 UNIVERSITY PL 111-CU, VA MEDICAL CTR /CARDIOLOGY 15213 #704-02-1981 L1993 **CD IM** *100 †20

MOTOYAMA, Etsuro. 3705 5TH AVE 15213 #572-05-1957 L1979 **AN PD** *020 †05

MOTURI, Hemlata. 420 E NORTH AVE, EAST WING, SUITE 205 15212 #495-72-1993 L2000 **END** *020 †20

MOUDED, Majd. 3459 5TH AVE, UPMC MONTIFIORE NW 628 15213 #024-07-1999 L2006 **PCC** *100 †20

MOUL, Douglas Edward. 3811 OHARA ST E-1119 15213 #005-06-1985 L1996 **P SME** *050 †75

MOUNTZ, James Michael. 200 LOTHROP ST 15213 #038-06-1981 L2003 **NM DR** *050 †80,28

MOURACHOV, Pavel V. 1307 FEDERAL ST, STE 300 15212 #041-01-1998 L2000 **U** *020 †95

MOUSA, Emad Youhanna. 4800 FRIENDSHIP AVE, DEPT OBGYN 15224 #915-02-1998 L2004 **OBG** *020

MOUSSA, Imad. ■ 15206 #875-02-1984 L1998 *071

MOUTINHO, Maria Elizabeth. 600 GRANT ST FL 41, GATEWAY HEALTH PLAN 15219 #047-07-1980 L2003 **PD** *030 †55

MOZELESKI, Dean Stephen. ■ 15232 #422-01-2003 L2003 **PMM** *012

MRVOS, Diana Lois. 9100 BABCOCK BLVD 15237 #024-01-1982 L1983 **OPH** *062 †35

MRVOS, Donald Miles. ■ 15238 #041-12-1955 L1956 **OBG** *071 †30

MUDDANA, Venkata Narasimh. 5230 CENTRE AVE, ROOM 341 SCHOOL OF NURSING 15232 #495-50-1999 L2003 **IM** *100 †20

MUDER, Robert Richard. 311 S CRAIG ST, STE 300 15213 #041-12-1977 L1979 **ID IM** *040 †20

MUELLER, Derk August. ■ 15218 #020-12-2004 L2007 **CCP** *012 †55

MUELLER, Jeffrey Schiller. 320 E NORTH AVE, DEPT OF RADIO 15212 #036-01-2000 L2000 **DR** *100 †80

MUHLY, Wallis Taylor. ■ 15221 #041-12-2006 L2006 **AN** *012

MUKADAM, Syana Sorab. ■ 15218 #026-04-2002 L2005 **PEM** *012

MUKHERJEE, Koushik. 1200 REEDSDALE ST 15233 #495-38-1993 L2000 **P** *020

MULDOON, Matthew F. ■ 15232 #016-11-1984 L1985 **PA IM** *050 †20

MULHERN, Lawrence Michael. MERCY HOSP 15219 #041-12-1960 L1961 **RHU IM** *071 †20

MULLICK, Prabir Kumar. 4608 PENN AVE 15224 #496-04-1975 L1984 **P N** *020

MULLINS, Stephen Darrell. ■ 15232 #047-06-1982 L1992 **CHP PHP** *020 †75

MULSANT, Benoit H. 3811 OHARA ST 15213 #067-03-1984 L1987 **P PYG** *020 †75

MULTARI, Heather N. ■ 15239 #041-77-2003, ▲ L2003 **AN** *100

MULUK, Satish Chandra. 320 E NORTH AVE, CARDIOVASCULAR SURGERY CEN 15212 #024-05-1985 L1994 **VS** *020 †85

MULUK, Visala Sarmishta. 0 UNIVERSITY DRIVE C, GENERAL MED/VA HOSP 15240 #495-50-1990 L1994 **IM** *020 †20

MULUKUTLA, Suresh Raghu. 200 LOTHROP ST, DIVISION OF CARDIOLOGY 15213 #035-20-1996 L1999 **CD** *020 †20

MUMMA, Bryn Elissa. ■ 15221 #041-01-2007 L2007 **EM** *012

MUNIN, Michael Craig. 2000 MARY ST 15203 #041-02-1988 L1991 **PM** *020 †60

MUNIZ, Melissa. ■ 15213 #041-12-2008 *012

MUNK, Marcdavid. 414 S CRAIG ST 15213 #041-02-2003 L2003 **EM** *100 †16

MUNOZ, Ricardo Alfonso. 3705 5TH AVE 15213 #264-12-1982 L2002 **PDC** *020 †55

MUNSON-YOUNG, Adam. ■ 15224 #051-07-2007 L2007 **AN** *012

MURALI, Srinivas. 320 E NORTH AVE, ALLEGHANY GENERAL HOSPITAL 15212 #495-53-1980 L1985 **CD IM** *020 †20

MURCKO, Regina Gabrielle. 9335 MCKNIGHT RD, STE 220 15237 #041-07-1991 L1994 **OBG** *020 †30

MURDOCH, Geoffrey Howard. 200 LOTHROP ST, DEPT OF PATHOLOGY, PRESBYT 15213 #005-18-1984 L2003 **ATP NP** *020 †20

MURPHEY, Stephen Martin. 3801 MCKNIGHT EAST DR, FL 1 15237 #033-05-1968 L1972 **AI PD** *020 †55,03

MURPHREE, Megan Lynn. ■ 15224 #020-12-2008 L2008 *012

MURPHY, Arthur I, Jr. ■ 15213 #041-01-1943 L1946 **GS OS** *071 †85

MURPHY, Timothy Dennis. 3705 5TH AVE, PEDIATRIC PULMONOLOGY/CF 15213 #054-04-1982 L1993 **PD PDP** *020 †55

MURRAY, Andrew Walter. 3550 TERRACE ST, A1305 SCAIFE HALL 15261 #836-04-1994 L2000 **AN** *020 †05

MURRAY, Holt Nicholas. 3550 TERRACE ST., 655 SCAIFE HALL 15261 #038-40-2000 L2003 **CCM EM** *020 †16

MURRAY, John Martin. 5230 CENTRE AVE, EMERGENCY DEPT 15232 #041-01-1988 L1990 **EM** *020 †16

MURRAY, John Morton, Jr. 5230 CENTRE AVE, EMERGENCY DEPT 15232 #051-01-1989 L1990 **FM** *020 †18

MURRAY, Pamela Jane. 3705 5TH AVE, PEDITRICS/ONE CHILDRENS PL 15213 #041-07-1978 L1980 **ADL GYN** *020 †55

MURRAY, Peter Dow. 6023 HARVARD SQ 15206 #026-04-1992 L1995 **P** *020 †75

MURTAGH, Eileen Marie. ■ 15206 #038-06-2004 L2004 **MPD** *012

MURTHY, Hema Latha. ■ 15237 #495-94-1991 L1996 **IM** *074 †20

MUSAHL, Tina. 1000 INTEGRITY DR, ASSOCIATES INC 15235 #045-01-1998 L2001 **GE** *020 †20 ‡

MUSAHL, Volker. 121 MEYRAN AVE, DEPT OF INT MED 15213 #409-05-1998 L2003 **ORS** *012

MUSGRAVE, Ross H. ■ 15213 #041-12-1943 L1944 **OS PS** *071 †65

MUSICK, Tiffany. 5230 CENTRE AVE, SON BUILDING, RM 538 15232 #051-01-2001 L2001 **FM** *020 †18

MUSSER, William Stuart. ■ 15217 #035-03-1992 L1995 **N CN** *020 †75

MUTETWA, Solomon Mapeto. ■ 15232 #775-01-1988 L2006 **FP** *012

MUTO, Carlene Ann. 200 LOTHROP ST, 1215 KAUFMANN BLDG 15213 #041-13-1993 L1996 **ID** *020 †20

MYERBURG, Michael Mallard. ■ 15238 #041-12-2000 L2001 **PCC** *100 †20

MYERS, Delynne Joan. ■ 15238 #021-01-1980 L1988 **ON HEM** *020 †20

MYERS, Eugene Nicholas. 2000 MARY ST 15203 #041-13-1960 L1961 **OTO HNS** *020 †45 ‡

MYERS, Thomas Gerald, III. ■ 15211 #041-13-2005 L2006 **ORS** *012

MYNSBERGE, Ashley Ann Sue. 121 MEYRAN AVE, DEPT OBG 15213 #016-06-2007 **OBG** *012

MYRON, Carol Showalter. 300 CEDAR BLVD 15228 #041-01-1985 L1986 **IM** *020 †20 ‡

NACE, David Andrew. 3459 5TH AVE 15213 #041-13-1990 L1993 **IMG** *020 †20

NADLER, Leigh Howard. 1050 BOWER HILL RD, STE 208 15243 #016-42-1984 L1990 **CRS** *020 †85,10

NADOUR, Wadih. 320 E NORTH AVE 15212 #875-01-2001 L2005 **IM** *012

NAGELKIRK, Joan Ellen. 3 MARINER CT, RUSSELLTON - HARMR HLTH CT 15238 #047-06-1982 L1984 **IM** *020 †20

NAGHSHIN, Jahanbakhsh. ■ 15206 #517-06-1996 L2002 **PCC** *012 †20

NAGHSHINEH, Nima. ■ 15206 #041-12-2008 *012

NAGUIT, Michael Jason Rag. ■ 15222 #748-10-2004 L2007 **P** *012

NAHUM, Elmer. 320 E NORTH AVE, DEPT OF RADIOLOGY 15212 #023-01-1990 L1997 **DR** *020 †80

NAIR, Bronwyn Eileen. 200 LOTHROP ST, UNIV OF PITTSBURGH 15213 #041-15-2003 L2004 **DR** *012

NAIR, Madhusudanan. 9100 BABCOCK BLVD 15237 #495-01-1975 L1978 **VS GS** *020 †85

NAIR, Pradeep K. ■ 15222 #041-15-2003 L2003 **CD** *012 †20

NAKAGAWA, Kohhei. ARTS BUILDIN, STE 503 MEDICAL 15213 #572-74-1997 L2007 **FP** *012

NAKAMURA, Mamoo. 121 MEYRAN AVE, UNIV HLTH CTR OF PITTSBURG 15213 #572-34-1993 L2004 **IM** *100 †20

NALAMADA, Pranitha Reddy. 4800 FRIENDSHIP AVE, WESTERN PA HOSP 15224 #496-01-2000 L2003 **PMM** *012

NALESNIK, Michael Andrew. 200 LOTHROP ST 15213 #033-06-1977 L1979 **PTH** *020 †50

NALIN, Daniel Jos. 615 WASHINGTON RD, STE TL4 15228 #561-17-1983 L1986 **IM** *020 †20

NANDIPALLI, Koteshwara Ra. ■ 15220 #495-11-2000 L2005 **FP** *012

NAPOLEON, Louis Nicola. 1150 BOWER HILL RD 15243 #561-01-1938 L1942 **GP** *071

NARAIN, Harold. ■ 15237 #850-01-1976 L1983 **OBG** *020 †30

NARASIMHAMURTHY, Suman. 320 E NORTH AVE, ALLEGHEN GEN HOSP 15212 #495-09-1989 L2004 **CHP** *012

NARASIMHAN, Seethalakshmi. ■ 15209 #495-31-1968 L1983 **IM** *071

NARAYAN, Raj Athi. 340 PEARL ST, RESIDENTIAL CARE SERVICES 15224 #038-43-2000 L2001 **P** *020

NARAYANAN, Krishna. 8400 PERRY HWY, STE 102 15237 #495-59-1983 L1993 **PS OS** *020

NARCISSE, Yanouchka D. 4800 FRIENDSHIP AVE, DEPT OF OB/GYN 15224 #041-12-2003 L2003 **OBG** *020

NARDUZZI, Jo Ann Virginia. ■ 15241 #041-12-1962 L1963 **END DIA** *071 †20

NARENDRAN, Rajesh. 200 LOTHROP ST, UPMC PRESBYTERIAN, B-938 15213 #495-16-1995 L2006 **P** *020 †75 ‡

NARESH, Amber. ■ 15206 #021-01-2005 L2005 **OBG** *012

NARITA, Masashi. 121 MEYRAN AVE, DEPT OF INTERNAL MED 15213 #572-39-1994 L2004 **IM** *100

NASH, David Reinthal. 3705 5TH AVE, CHILDREN'S HOSPITAL PITTSB 15213 #038-41-1989 L1994 **AI** *020 †03,55 ‡

NASH, Kenneth Clayton. 3811 OHARA ST, # E819 15213 #020-02-1990 L1992 **CHP** *030 †75

NASHAR, Khaled. 200 LOTHROP ST, UPMC MONTEFIORE STE 933W 15213 #875-02-1997 L2002 **IM** *020 †20

NASIR, Khurram. 121 MEYRAN AVE, UNIV HLTH CTR OF PITTSBURG 15213 #704-21-1999 L2005 **IM** *100

NASR, Isam Waddah. 121 MEYRAN AVE 15213 #605-01-2003 L2005 **GS** *020

NASR, John Yacoub. 3708 5TH AVE, DEPT OF MED EDU 15213 #605-01-2004 L2006 **IM** *012

NASTASI, Byron Edward. 121 MEYRAN AVE, DEPT RAD 15213 #016-01-2006 L2007 **DR** *012

NATALIE, August Anthony. 15201 #017-20-2006 L2006 **IM** *012

NATARAJAN, Sathiavathi Se. ■ 15214 #496-33-1997 L2007 **FP** *012

NATH, Parineesha. 4800 FRIENDSHIP AVE, WESTERN PENNSYLVANIA HOSPI 15224 #495-78-2000 L2006 **IM** *012

NATHAN, Swami. 4 ALLEGHENY CTR 8TH FL, DEPT PSYCHIATRY AGH 15212 #495-16-1969 L1981 **P** *020 †75 ‡

NATION, David Andrew. ■ 15232 #041-12-2008 *012

NAU, Gerard Jos. E1256, 200 LOTHROP STREET 15261 #016-02-1990 L2003 **ID** *020 †20

NAUGLE, Ingrid Erika. 26 NEWGATE RD, I 15202 #407-23-1965 L1969 **DR GP** *020 †80

NAUMOVSKI, John. 121 MEYRAN AVE, UNIV HLTH CTR OF PITTSBURG 15213 #957-04-1988 L2004 **FM** *100 †18

NAUS, Gregory Jay. 200 LOTHROP ST 15213 #035-20-1980 L1987 **ATP** *020 †50

NAUTIYAL, Amit. 200 LOTHROP ST, DEPT OF MED 8 NO STE 869-2 15213 #495-14-1995 L2005 **IM** *100 †20

NAVALGUND, Yeshvant Ashok. 1400 LOCUST ST, DEPT OF ANESTH MERCY HOSP 15219 #665-01-1999 L2000 **PME AN** *020 †05

NAVOLOTSKAIA, Olga. ■ 15237 #913-51-1991 L2005 **PTH** *100 †50

NAVRKAL, Harvey Jos. ■ 15219 #030-05-1990 L2005 **PM** *012

NAYAK, Jayakar V. 200 LOTHROP ST, STE 500 15213 #041-12-2003 L2003 **OTO** *012

NAYAK, Narayan Tellar. 1501 LOCUST ST, STE 224 15219 #495-37-1965 L1973 **NS N** *071 †25

NAYAK, Shanteri Umesh. 320 E NORTH AVE, ALLEGHENY GENERAL HOSPITAL 15212 #495-09-1974 L1978 **NM RO** *020 †28 ‡

NAYAK, Smita. 200 MEYRAN AVE, STE 200 15213 #033-05-2000 L2006 **IM** *020

NAZARNIA, Soheyla. 200 LOTHROP ST, STE N463 15213 #902-05-1989 L1995 **AN** *005

NDAGANO, Annette Matovu. 4411 STILLEY RD, STEEL CITY PEDIATRICS 15227 #905-01-1988 L1997 **PD** *020 †50

NDIMBIE, Oliver Kimka. 7643 FRANKSTOWN AVE, DIRECT MEDICAL ASSOCIATES 15208 #010-03-1983 L1988 **PTH** *020 †50

NEAL, Matthew David. ■ 15227 #041-12-2006 L2006 **GS** *012

NEASE, Emily Kathryn. 3705 5TH AVE, CHILDREN'S HOSPITAL OF PIT 15213 #055-01-2005 L2005 **PD** *012

NECHES, William Harold. 3705 5TH AVE, CHILDREN'S HOSPITAL 15213 #035-08-1965 L1972 **PDC** *071 †55

NEE, Martin Patrick. 1501 LOCUST ST, MD BUILDING/SUITE 405 15219 #041-02-1978 L1979 **PS** *071 †85,65

NEEDLEMAN, Herbert Leroy. 3811 OHARA ST 15213 #041-01-1952 L1953 **P** *050 †55,75

NEEPER, Ronald. 4411 STILLEY RD, STE 3 15227 #026-08-1990 L1999 **CHN** *020 †75

NEGROIU, Andreea Mihaela. 121 MEYRAN AVE 15213 #781-01-2001 L2005 **IM** *012

NEGROIU, Costin Catalin. 3471 O LSK BLDG 15213 #781-01-2001 L2005 **AN** *012

NEISH, Carol Lu. 363 VANADIUM RD, STE 101 15243 #041-12-1989 L1991 **D** *020 †15

NELLAS, Constantine Louis. 490 E NORTH AVE 15212 #041-02-1956 L1957 **IM RHU** *020 †20

NELMS, Justin Kristofer. ■ 15203 #050-01-2004 L2004 **GS** *012

NELSON, Bruce Neal. 135 CUMBERLAND RD, STE 202 15237 #055-01-1978 L1983 **IM** *020 †20

NELSON, Jared Wynn. ■ 15207 #018-03-2005 L2005 **DR** *012

NELSON, Joel Byron. 5200 CENTRE AVE, STE 211 15232 #016-06-1988 L1999 **U** *020 †95

NELSON, John Paul. 401 SHADY AVE STE D108 15206 #024-01-1967 L1982 **P PYG** *020 †75

NELSON, Lawrence James. 777 CLAIRTON BLVD 15236 #041-12-1970 L1971 **GP** *020

NELSON, Theodore Chas. 5016 ALDEN DR 15220 #869-01-1965 L1966 **FM D** *071

NEMEC, Jan. 200 LOTHROP ST 15213 #286-13-1987 L2006 **CD** *020 †20

NEMOIANU, Andrei T. 3811 OHARA ST 15213 #025-01-2003 L2003 **PFP** *012

NERA, Marie Sherleen Estr. 320 E NORTH AVE, ALLEGHENY GEN HOSP 15212 #422-01-2006 L2006 **IM** *012

NERAVETLA, Soumya Reddy. ■ 15214 #038-44-2004 L2004 **GS** *012

NESBIT, Chadd Eric. ■ 15206 #035-06-2005 L2005 **EM** *012

NESS, David Eli. 105 BRAUNLICH DR STE 480 15237 #008-01-1979 L1987 **P** *020 †75

NESS, Roberta. 130 DE SOTO STREET, UNIVERSITY PITTSBURG 15261 #035-20-1984 L1988 **OS IM** *020 †20

NETRAVALI, Mahesh A. 3801 MCKNIGHT EAST DR, FL 1 15237 #035-15-2002 L2005 **AI** *020 †55,03

NETTROUR, Lewis Fairbanks. 9104 BABCOCK BLVD, STE 2120 15237 #041-12-1965 L1972 **ORS** *071 †40

NETTROUR, W Scott, III. 9104 BABCOCK BLVD, STE 2120 15237 #041-12-1964 L1971 **ORS** *071 †40

NEVIN, Amy Gates. 317 CLIMAX ST 15210 #016-02-1999 L2001 **PD** *020 †55

NEWCOMER, Janet Strellec. 100 DELAFIELD RD STE 101 15215 #041-12-1989 L1991 **FM** *020 †18

NEWMAN, Anne Barbara. 130 N BELLEFIELD AVE, RM 532 15213 #041-12-1982 L1984 **OS IM** *050 †20

NEWMAN, Benny. ■ 15228 #517-08-1974 L1982 **OBG** *020

NEWTON, Ernest Douglas. 4815 LIBERTY AVE, MELLON PAVILION 15224 #047-06-1970 L1983 **PS** *075 †65

NEWTON, Rex Harlan, Jr. 3 MARINER CT, RUSSELLTON - HARMR HLTH CT 15238 #041-12-1945 L1946 **PM** *071 †60

NEY, Eugene Coleman. ■ 15241 #019-02-1956 L1961 **GS GP** *071

NG, Brian Yin. ■ 15221 #035-15-2002 L2002 **GE** *012 †20

NG, Jason Michael. OF PITTSBURGH, UNIV HLTH CTR 15261 #055-01-2004 L2004 **END** *012 †20

NG, Kim Swee. ■ 15228 #825-01-1987 L1990 **CCA** *020

NG, Yue Harn. 200 LOTHROP ST, UPMC-MUH 15213 #067-01-2002 L2002 **NEP** *100 †20

NGAN, Kakei. ■ 15206 #043-01-1999 L2005 **DR** *020 †80

NGHIEM-DAO, Dai. 320 E NORTH AVE 15212 #941-01-1968 L1987 **GS TTS** *040 †85

NGUYEN, Alexander Phong. ■ 15232 #034-01-2002 L2004 **DR** *012

NGUYEN, Bryant Huy. ■ 15212 #010-02-2004 L2007 **CD** *012 †20

NGUYEN, Jessica Mai. ■ 15213 #041-12-2006 L2006 **AN** *012

NGUYEN, Minhhong Thi. 3550 TERRACE ST, SCAIFE HALL, SUITE 871 15261 #041-13-1988 L1991 **ID** *020 †20

NGUYEN, Thanh Giang. 100 DELAFIELD RD, STE 212 15215 #021-01-1997 L2006 **CCM** *020 †20

NGUYEN, Vu Tu. 5717 KENTUCKY AVE 15232 #030-05-1999 L2001 **PS** *020

NGWU, Ogundu Obioha. 200 LOTHROP ST 15213 #690-01-1990 L2001 **CD** *020 †20

NICASSIO, Anthony. 193 43RD ST 15201 #041-09-1976 L1978 **IM GP** *020 †20

NICHOLS, Lawrence Carl. 200 LOTHROP ST, STE 224 15219 #056-05-1982 L1992 **ATP ID** *020 †50

NICKELL, Patton Vanmeter. 4 ALLEGHENY CTR, DEPT.OF PSYCHIATRY/AMBULAT 15212 #055-01-1983 L1984 **P IM** *020 †20,75

NICOLAU-RADUCU, Ramona Em. ■ 15237 #781-04-1988 L2004 **AN** *012

NICOLESCU, Anton Cristian. SCAIFE HALL, STE 640, 3550 TERRACE STREET 15261 #781-01-1982 L1997 **CCM** *020 †20

NICOTERO, James Anthony. 4221 PENN AVE 15224 #041-12-1962 L1963 **NEP IM** *020

NIELAND, Michael Louis. 875 GREENTREE RD, QUEST DIAGNOSTICS INC 15220 #024-01-1964 L1973 **D DMP** *020 †15

NIELAND-FISHER, Nancy S. 190 LOTHROP ST, STE 145 15213 #055-01-1967 L1973 **D RHU** *020 †15

NIGBOROWICZ, Ronald J. 4815 LIBERTY AVE, STE G25 15224 #041-12-1973 **IM** *020 †20

NIGGEMYER, Keith Alan. 9104 BABCOCK BLVD, STE 2103 15237 #055-01-1998 L2001 **PCC** *020 †20

NIKIFOROVA, Marina Nikola. ■ 15238 #913-32-1985 L2006 **PTH** *020 †50

NILLES, Kathleen Margaret. ■ 15217 #041-12-2008 *012

NIMGAONKAR, Vishwajit L. 3811 OHARA ST, RM 443 15213 #495-27-1991 L1992 **P** *020 †75

NIRANJAN, Ajay. 200 LOTHROP ST 15213 #495-05-1988 L2003 *020

NIREN, Neil Martin. 9102 BABCOCK BLVD, STE 206 15237 #030-06-1978 L1981 **D** *020 †15

NISAR, Humera. 121 MEYRAN AVE 15213 #704-25-2003 L2005 **IM** *012

NISAR, Saira. 121 MEYRAN AVE 15213 #704-25-2003 L2005 **IM** *012

NISENBAUM, Marcia R. 5750 CENTRE AVE, STE 230 15206 #041-07-1976 L1977 **IM HEM** *020 †20

NISTA, Joseph Anthony. 532 S AIKEN AVE 15232 #028-34-1957 L1969 **OPH** *020

NITIYANANT, Wannee. 200 LOTHROP ST, PRESBYTERIAN HOSPITAL 15213 #891-02-1970 **END IM** *020 †20

NITYANAND, Mala. ■ 15217 #495-05-1979 L1986 **PD** *020

NOBEL, Helen Virginia. ■ 15206 #041-07-1939 L1940 **FM** *071

NOECKER, Robert John. 203 LOTHROP ST 15213 #036-01-1990 L2003 **OPH IM** *020 †35

NOFZIGER, Ryan Anthony. ■ 15232 #038-43-2007 L2007 **PD** *012

NOFZINGER, Eric Allen. 3811 OHARA ST 15213 #038-40-1987 L1989 **P SME** *050 †75

NOH, Sungran Sonya. 850 CLAIRTON BLVD, STE 3100 15236 #035-46-1990 L1994 **OBG** *020 †30

NOORBAKHSH, Hossein. 180 FORT COUCH RD, STE 450 15241 #517-01-1970 L1978 **OBG** *020 †30

NORBUTT, Craig Steven. ■ 15261 #041-12-2007 L2007 *012

NORDMAN, Bethany Leigh. ■ 15227 #041-14-2006 L2006 **IM** *012

NORDMAN, Cory Robert. ■ 15227 #041-12-2006 L2006 **GS** *012

NORRIS, David C. 4800 FRIENDSHIP AVE, SUITE 333, MELLON PAVILLIO 15224 #041-13-1952 L1953 **P** *071

NORRIS, John Randolph. 781 PINE VALLEY DR, PLUM PEDIATRICS 15239 #041-12-1994 L1996 **PD** *020 †55

NORTHINGTON, William E, III. 230 MCKEE PL STE 500, OF PITTSBURGH 15213 #036-01-2002 L2002 **EM** *020 †16

NOTICEWALA, Anand Hasmukh. 5500 CORPORATE DR, STE 240 15237 #496-49-2001 L2002 **OBG** *020

NOVAK, Matthew John. ■ 15232 #041-15-2003 L2003 **NEP** *012 †20

NOVELLI, Enrico Maria. ■ 15213 #561-03-1996 L2001 **HO** *012

NOVERO, Carlette Palacios. ■ 15219 #748-28-1993 L2005 **FP** *012

NOVILLA, Manuel Rosapapan. 288 TARA DR, PLEASANT HILLS 15236 #748-07-1962 L1971 **EM GS** *020 †16

NOVITSKAYA, Dina. ■ 15217 #041-12-2003 L2003 **DR** *012

NOWAK, Tina Lynne. 9100 BABCOCK BLVD 15237 #041-12-1986 L1987 **AN** *020 †05

NOWALK, Andrew John. ■ 15218 #041-12-1999 L2001 **PDI** *100 †55

NUFFIELD, Edward Jos A. 3811 OHARA ST 15213 #143-03-1947 L1971 **CHP P** *071 †75

NULL, Harry Matthew. 15237 #041-12-1969 L1970 **GS VS** *071 †85

NUSBACHER, Jacob. ■ 15217 #016-42-1963 L1982 **HEM** 030

NUSSBAUM, Arthur Joseph. 8273 BRITTANY PL 15237 #021-01-1971 L1972 **DR VIR** *020 †80 ‡

OAKLEY, Christine Irene. ■ 15217 #055-01-2006 L2006 **IM** *012

OAKLEY, Gerard Joseph, III. ■ 15217 #055-02-2006 L2006 **PTH** *012

OAKLEY, Nigel Wingate. 3811 OHARA ST 15213 #352-03-1958 **OS** *050

OBBEHAT, Amir. 320 E NORTH AVE, ALLEGHENY GENERAL HOSPITAL 15212 #422-01-2007 L2007 **IM** *012

OBEID, Makram Mohammad. 121 MEYRAN AVE, UNIV HLTH CTR OF PITTSBURG 15213 #605-01-2004 L2005 **PD** *012

O'BRIEN, Alison Theresa. 317 CLIMAX ST, HILLTOP COMMUNITY HEALTHCA 15210 #041-01-2000 L2007 **FM** *100 †18

O'BRIEN, Ann Margaret. 300 HALKET ST, DEPT PATH 15213 #539-04-1969 **PTH** *100

O'BRIEN, Gerard. 651 HOLIDAY DR, # 5 FOSTER PLZ 15220 #539-05-1981 L1993 **FM** *020 †18

O'BRIEN, Robert Gary. 733 WASHINGTON RD 15228 #041-12-1959 L1960 **GYN** *071 †30

OCHALSKI, Pawel Grzegorz. ■ 15217 #033-06-2005 L2005 **NS** *012

OCHOA, Erin R. 200 LOTHROP ST, STE E739 15213 #012-05-1996 L1999 **PTH** *020 †50 ‡

OCHOA, Juan B. 200 LOTHROP ST, F1264 15213 #264-13-1982 L1995 **CCS TRS** *050 †85

OCHS, Mark Wilson. 3471 5TH AVE, STE 1112 15213 #036-01-1987 L1988 **OS** *020

O'CONNELL, Bryan Daniel. ■ 15218 #041-02-2006 L2006 **IM** *012

O'CONNELL, Michael John. 320 E NORTH AVE, ALLEGHENY GENERAL HOSPITAL 15212 #026-04-1969 L2002 **ON** *050 †20

O'CONNOR, John Paul. 400 45TH ST 15201 #041-13-1957 L1958 **RO GYN** *071 †30

O'CONNOR, Mary Kelly. ■ 15237 #041-07-1974 L1975 **IM** *071 †20

O'CONNOR, Siobhan Marie. OF PAT, UNIV OF PITTSBURGH DEPT 15261 #036-01-1998 L2004 **PTH** *012 †30

ODAGIRI, Kunio. 3705 5TH AVE DEPT RAD 15213 #572-32-1967 **R PTH** *020 †80

ODDIS, Chester Vincent. S 703 BIOMEDICAL SCIENCE T 15261 #041-14-1980 L1981 **RHU IM** *020

O'DONNELL, Walter Frank. 1401 FORBES AVE, STE 330 15219 #041-12-1967 L1970 **U** *020 †95

OESTERLING, Everett F, Jr. 2165 POOR RICHARDS LN 15237 #041-02-1961 L1962 **NM PTH** *020 †50,28

OFFERMAN, Joop. 6740 REYNOLDS ST 15206 #660-02-1977 L1985 **FM FPG** *020 †18 ‡

OGILVIE, Jennifer Braemar. 3550 TERRACE ST., 497 SCAIFE HALL 15261 #024-01-1997 L2005 **GS** *020 †85

OGLE, Kim Alison. 6343 PENN AVE, # 201 15206 #038-40-1980 L1988 **PD** *020 †55

OGONOWSKI, Julie Ann. ■ 15217 #041-12-2007 L2007 **PD** *012

OGREN, Eric Andrew. 3601 5TH AVE 15213 #030-05-1980 L1993 **N IM** *020 †75

OGUNRINDE, Olukayode Ayo. 121 MEYRAN AVE, DEPT OF NEUROLOGY 15213 #036-01-2004 L2005 **N** *012

OH, Kook Sang. 200 LOTHROP ST, RADIOLOGY/ROOM PUH 1ST FL 15213 #583-02-1961 L1971 **PDR** *020 †80

OH, Michael Yang-Hoon. 420 E NORTH AVE, STE 302 15212 #005-06-1996 L2001 **NS** *020 †25

O'HARA, Kevin Robt. 9100 BABCOCK BLVD 15237 #035-15-1975 L1981 **R** *020 †80

OHORI, Nobuyuki Paul. 200 LOTHROP ST 15213 #051-04-1987 L1989 **ATP** *020 †50

OIDE, Shiho. 200 LOTHROP ST, STE 503 15213 #572-35-2003 L2007 **IM** *012

O'KEEFE, Stephen J D. 200 LOTHROP ST 15213 #917-23-1971 L2002 **GE NTR** *050

OKEKE, Nnamdi E. ■ 15213 #041-12-2008 *012

OKONKWO, David Okwudi. 200 LOTHROP ST 15213 #051-04-2000 L2006 **NS** *020

OKUBADEJO, Gbolahan O. 3471 5TH AVE, KAUFMANN MEDICAL BUILDING 15213 #023-07-2002 L2007 **ORS** *020

OKWIYA, Victor Kyle. 5200 CENTRE AVE STE 610, MEDICAL THORACIC ASSOCIATE 15232 #010-03-1996 L1998 **CCM** *020 †20

OLBRICH, Christopher D. 7175 SALTSBURG RD 15235 #041-02-1992 L1994 **FM** *020 †18

OLEARCHYK, Andrew S. 320 E NORTH AVE, CVI I 15212 #759-03-1961 L1970 **TS VS** *020 †85,90 ‡

OLECK, Joanne Rose. 3358 5TH AVE 15213 #041-12-1994 L1998 **OBG** *020 †30

OLEKSAK, William Alan. ■ 15219 #041-02-2004 L2004 **IM** *020 †20

OLENIC, Gregory W. 651 WOODCREST DR 15205 #055-01-2000 L2001 **AN** *020 †05

OLIPHANT, Sallie Sherrod. ■ 15217 #036-01-2006 L2006 **OBG** *012

OLIVA, Jose Gerardo. 1307 FEDERAL ST STE 301, ALLEGHENY CENTER FOR DIGES 15212 #042-01-1996 L1998 **GE** *100 †20

OLSEN, Karl Raymond. 3501 FORBES AVE, STE 500 15213 #016-06-1980 L1990 **OPH OS** *020 †35

OLSON, Jamie Beth. ■ 15218 #051-04-2007 L2007 **IM** *012

OLSON, Peter Ralph. 320 E NORTH AVE #026-04-1969 L1976 **PTH PCP** *020 †50

OMALU, Bennet Ifeakandu. 542 4TH AVE 15219 #690-04-1991 L1998 **NP FOP** *062 †50

OMANA, Evelyn Tan. 121 MEYRAN AVE 15213 #748-10-1999 L2005 **FP** *012

O'NEILL, Brian Timothy. ■ 15218 #049-01-2008 *012

O'NEILL, Michael James. ■ 15232 #041-12-2008 L2008 *012

ONG, Adrian Weihuan. 320 E NORTH AVE, ALLEGHENY GEN HOSP 15212 #024-05-1990 L2002 **TRS CCS** *020 †85

ONISHI, Tomifumi. 3708 5TH AVE, DEPT OF MED EDU 15213 #572-32-2003 L2006 **IM** *012

ONUMA, Kazuya. 300 HALKET ST, MAGEE WOMENS HOSP-PATHLGY 15213 #572-76-1990 L2003 **SP** *100

ONWERE, Joyce Linda. 200 LOTHROP ST, DEPT OF ANESTHESIOLOGY 15213 #041-12-2003 L2003 **AN** *020

ONYENEKWU, Nkeiruka Ngozi. ■ 15206 #021-05-2007 L2007 **MEM** *012

OOI, Heo Jeng. ■ 15220 #012-01-2005 L2005 *100

OPPERMANN, Timothy Edward. 1400 LOCUST ST, MERCY HOSPITAL 15219 #055-01-2003 L2003 **GS** *012

ORAKZAI, Sarwar Hassan. 121 MEYRAN AVE, DEPT OF INTERNAL MED 15213 #704-25-2002 L2004 **IM** *100 †20

ORAVITZ, Todd Matthew. 3550 TERRACE ST, A-1305 SCAIFE HALL 15261 #041-12-1994 L1997 **AN** *020 †05

ORCHARD, Trevor John. 3512 5TH AVE 15213 #917-18-1974 L1979 **OS END** *050 ‡

OREBAUGH, Steven Lee. 2000 MARY ST, UPMC SOUTHSIDE HOSPITAL 15203 #041-13-1986 L1989 **AN EM** *020 †05,16

ORENSTEIN, David Mark. 3705 5TH AVE 15213 #038-06-1973 L1984 **PDP PD** *020 †55

ORENSTEIN, Susan Roth. 303 CHURCH LN, 303 CHURCH LANE 15238 #038-06-1977 L1984 **PG PD** *020 †55

ORGANIST, Michele Lynn. 5140 LIBERTY AVE 15224 #035-19-1991 L1993 **IM** *020 †20

ORIE, John Richard. 9104 BABCOCK BLVD 15237 #041-12-1947 L1948 **A IM** *071

ORIE, Judith Ellen. 490 E NORTH AVE, STE 400 15212 #041-12-1978 L1979 **CD** *020 †20

ORLANDO, Quentin. 320 E NORTH AVE, ALLEGHENY GEN HOSP 15212 #041-78-2000, ▲ L2001 **IC** *012

ORLANDO, Salvatore John. 3705 5TH AVE 15213 #038-41-1959 L1962 **PHO HEM** *020 †55

ORR, Donald Paul. 1000 BOWER HILL RD, DEPT OF MED IMAGINE 15243 #041-12-1976 L1977 **DR** *020 †80

ORR, Richard Andrew. 3705 5TH AVE 15213 #055-01-1977 L1980 **CCP PD** *040 †55

ORTIZ, Ernesto M. ■ 15219 #737-01-1971 L1975 **OBG** *100

ORTIZ, Eugene Santos. 4117 LIBERTY AVE, DRAKE COUNSELING CTR 15224 #748-01-1983 L2000 **P** *020 †75

ORTIZ, Luis Alberto. 100 TECHNOLOGY DR, RM 557 15219 #264-13-1983 L2002 **IM** *020 †20

ORTIZ-AGUAYO, Roberto J. 3811 OHARA ST 15213 #042-01-2002 L2002 **OS** *100 †55

OSAWA, Ryosuke. 121 MEYRAN AVE, DEPT ID 15213 #572-03-2001 L2007 **ID** *012 †20

OSBORN, Jennifer Lynn. 9100 BABCOCK BLVD 15237 #038-40-1990 L1993 **ON** *020 †20

OSBORNE, Anwar Dayan. 320 E NORTH AVE 15212 #045-01-2003 L2003 **MEM** *012

OSEIWUSU, Abena Afrah. ■ 15206 #023-01-2003 L2007 **CD** *012 †20

O'SHURA, John Shane. 230 MCKEE PL STE 500, OF PITTSBURGH 15213 #041-15-2006 L2006 **EM** *012

OSOFSKY, Michael Gary. ■ 15232 #010-02-2007 L2007 **TY** *012

OSOFSKY, Murray V. 540 N NEVILLE ST STE 103 15213 #035-15-1957 L1961 **GYN** *020 †30 ‡

OSORIO, Maria Joana. ■ 15232 #770-04-2004 L2007 **PD** *012

OSSOWSKI, Kathryn Lynn. ■ 15221 #016-02-2005 L2005 **OTO** *012

OST, Michael Cecil. 3471 5TH AVE, KAUFMAN MEDICAL BUILDING, 15213 #035-47-1998 L2006 **UP** *100

OSTER, Marc Howard. ■ 15217 #011-02-1993 L2006 **IM** *020 †20

OSTERLOH, Chas Thos, Jr. 320 E NORTH AVE 15212 #041-12-1942 L1943 **GP** *071

O'SULLIVAN, Cornelius P. ■ 15235 #539-03-1962 L1986 **DR GP** *020

O'TOOLE, James Dennis. 5200 CENTRE AVE STE 703 15232 #028-34-1966 L1971 **CD IM** *020 †20 ‡

O'TOOLE, James Patrick. 320 E NORTH AVE, ALLEGHENY GENERAL HOSPITAL 15212 #028-34-1999 L2001 **PS** *012 †85

O'TOOLE, Joseph Frederick. 5200 CENTRE AVE, STE 703 15232 #028-34-1997 L2000 **CD** *020 †20

O'TOOLE, Kevin Scott. 200 LOTHROP ST 15213 #041-12-1983 L1984 **EM** *020 †16

OTTE, Robert Wm. 1000 INTEGRITY DR, STE 102 15235 #051-04-1985 L1986 **AI IM** *020 †20,03

OTTESON, Todd David. 3705 5TH AVE 15213 #010-02-1999 L2004 **PDO** *020 †45 ‡

O'TUAMA, Lorcan Alabhaois. 3705 5TH AVE 15213 #539-03-1963 L2006 **DR PD** *020 †75,28

OU, Kuang Yu. 7405 IRVINE ST 15218 #244-02-1971 L1976 **GP** *020 ‡

OURY, Tim David. 200 LOTHROP ST 15213 #036-07-1994 L1998 **PTH** *020 †50

OUYANG, Tao. 121 MEYRAN AVE, DEPT OF RADIO-CHP MT 3950 15213 #035-01-2003 L2003 **DR** *012

OVERTON, Mark Howard. 5200 CENTRE AVE, STE 211 15232 #040-02-1981 L1992 **IMG IM** *020 †20

OWENS, E Reese. ■ 15238 #041-13-1946 L1947 **ORS** *071 †40

OWENS, Gregory Randolph. 3471 5TH AVE, STE 1117 KAUFMANN BLDG 15213 #041-01-1974 L1975 **PUD CCM** *040 †20

OWENS, Scott Roland. 200 LOTHROP ST, PRESBYTERIAN HOSP. - RM. 15213 #025-07-1999 L2006 **PTH** *020 †50

OWENS, Stephanie Michele. 300 HALKET ST, MAGEE WOMENS HOSPITAL 15213 #054-04-2004 L2004 **OBG** *012

OWONIKOKO, Taofeek Kunle. 5150 CENTRE AVE, UPMC CANCER PAVILION 15232 #690-05-1992 L2007 **HO** *012 †20

OZOLEK, John Anthony. 3705 5TH AVE, DEPT OF PATH 15213 #041-12-1989 L1992 **PP** *100 †55,50

PACEK, Corey Andrew. ■ 15223 #041-02-2005 L2005 **ORS** *012

PACELLA, Charissa. 200 LOTHROP ST, RM CL06 15213 #041-12-1998 L2000 **EM** *020 †16

PACELLA, John Jude. 200 LOTHROP ST 15213 #041-12-1998 L2000 **IC** *020 †20

PACHUCKI, Janusz S. ■ 15217 #759-07-1989 L1995 **END** *020 †20

PACHUSKI, Janna. ■ 15232 #041-14-2006 L2006 **PD** *012

PADIVAL, Simi. ■ 15217 #038-06-2006 L2006 **MPD** *012

PADOVAN, Gordon. 200 LOTHROP ST, STE C-800 15213 #957-01-1988 L2002 *020

PADUA, Alan A. ■ 15206 #748-31-2001 L2007 **FP** *012

PAGANO, Robert John. 1050 BOWER HILL RD, STE 305 15243 #033-06-1983 L1984 **GE IM** *020 †20

PAGE, Signi Amanda. 3811 OHARA ST, AND C 15213 #011-02-2006 L2006 **P** *012

PAGNOTTO, Mary Amanda. 4721 MCKNIGHT RD, STE 209N 15237 #010-02-2004 L2004 **PD** *020 †55

PAGNOTTO, Michael R. ■ 15213 #035-01-2004 L2004 **ORS** *012

PAI, K Gopalkrishna. 850 CLAIRTON BLVD STE 3300 15236 #495-37-1966 L1973 **PD ADL** *020 †55

PAIK, Soon-Myoung. 320 E NORTH AVE, NSABP PATHOLOGY SECTION 15212 #583-01-1981 L1984 **ATP** *050 †50

PAINTER, Michael James. 3705 5TH AVE 15213 #025-01-1965 L1973 **CHN PD** *020 †55,75

PAINTER, Thomas Driscoll. 200 LOTHROP ST, 9W26 MONTEFIORE UNIVERSITY 15213 #048-12-1974 L1975 IM *020 †20

PAK, Samuel Pyong. 200 LOTHROP ST, UPMC PRESBYTERIAN, E-177 15213 #003-01-2002 L2006 **NM** *100

PALANISAMY, Subramaniam. 4520 PENN AVE 15224 #495-16-1966 L1973 **TS CD** *071 †85,90

PALCHICK, Bryce Allen. 275 CURRY HOLLOW RD, FL 1 15236 #025-01-1978 L1993 **FM IM** *020 †20,18

PALEKAR, Alka. 5230 CENTRE AVE DEPT PATH 15232 #495-01-1966 L1974 **PTH PCP** *020 †50

PALEOS, K Casey Alexander. ■ 15261 #041-12-2007 **P** *012

PALEVSKY, Paul Marc. 200 LOTHROP ST 15213 #016-06-1981 L1982 **NEP IM** *050 †20 ‡

PALEY, Kristina. ■ 15232 #035-20-2003 L2003 **D** *012

PALKO, David Bryan. 1000 BOWER HILL RD 15243 #041-12-1987 L1989 **DR** *020 †80

PALKO, Michael James, III. 5230 CENTRE AVE 15232 #010-02-1985 L1986 **DMP PTH** *020 †50

PALMA, Alexander. 320 E NORTH AVE 15212 #305-01-2005 L2006 **MEM** *012

PALMER, Arthur Harvey. 1501 LOCUST AVE 15219 #011-02-1964 L1971 **NS** *071 †25

PALMER, Brittany Ann. ■ 15219 #051-07-2006 L2006 IM *012

PALMER, Michael Paul. ■ 15226 #041-15-2008 L2008 *012

PALUS, Bernard Robt. 10 DUFF RD 15235 #016-43-1964 L1965 **D** *020 †15

PAN, Raymond Juienshih. 1200 REEDSDALE ST 15233 #008-02-1998 L2001 **P CHP** *020 †75

PAN, Stephen. ■ 15213 #041-12-2007 **IM** *012

PAN, Sylvia S F. 3811 OHARA ST 15213 #242-17-1946 L1964 **OS NM** *020

PANA, Zinovia D. ■ 15224 #418-01-1990 L1995 **IM** *100

PANAHANDEH, Abolhassan. 4725 MCKNIGHT RD STE 212 15237 #517-01-1962 L1971 **CRS GS** *010,85 ‡

PANCHAL, Amar Mahendra. 4800 FRIENDSHIP AVE 15224 #495-22-2004 L2007 **IM** *012

PANDIAN, Sujatha. 4 ALLEGHENY CTR, 8TH FL 15212 #308-12-1997 L2000 **P** *020

PANDIT, Devayani I M. 4815 LIBERTY AVE STE 340 15224 #495-22-1966 L1973 **OBG** *020 †30 ‡

PANDIT, Indravadan N. 532 S AIKEN AVE STE 308, UPMC AIKEN MED BLDG SUITE 15232 #495-22-1961 L1972 **CD IM** *020 †20 ‡

PANDIT, Santosh Makarand. 9104 BABCOCK BLVD STE 3114 15237 #495-83-1976 L1982 **IM CD** *020 †20

PANI, Paolo. 3811 OHARA ST 15213 #561-02-1965 **OS** *075

PANICHEEWA, Sucheelar. ■ 15241 #891-02-1977 L1985 **AI RHU** *100

PANKO, Laura Michelle. 3705 5TH AVE, REFERRAL SERVICE 15213 #038-43-2002 L2002 **PD** *020 †55

PANTCHEVA, Mina Blagoeva. 203 LOTHROP ST, UPMC EYE AND EAR INSTITUTE 15213 #198-01-1998 L2004 IM *100

PAPACHRISTOU, Georgios Io. 200 LOTHROP ST 15213 #418-03-1996 L2002 **GE** *020 †20

PAPACHRISTOU, Marios Dimi. 200 LOTHROP ST 15213 #011-04-2004 L2005 **DR** *012

PAPAS, Spiro Nicholas. 200 DELAFIELD RD, STE 1040 15215 #041-12-1980 L1981 **ORS OS** *020 †40

PAPAZIAN, Ara. 1 ALLEGHENY CTR STE 240 15212 #902-01-1960 L1967 **AN** *071 †05

PAPE, Hans-Christoph. 3471 5TH AVE, STE 1010 15243 #409-38-1988 L2005 **ORS** *020

PAPPAS, Michael Thos. 15241 #041-12-1959 L1960 **AN** *071 †05

PAPPAS, Thomas Michael. 1000 BOWER HILL RD, ST CLAIR HOSP 15243 #041-12-1985 L1986 **AN** *020 †20

PAPPO, Orit. UNIV PITTSBURGH SCH MED, DEPT PATH 15261 #550-01-1984 **PTH** *040

PARADIS, Milo Richard V. ■ 15228 #047-06-1957 L1970 **GP** *075

PARADISE, Jack Leon. 125 DESOTO ST, CHILDREN'S HOSP OF PITTSBU 15213 #023-07-1947 L1955 **PD OS** *050 †55

PARAG, Yoav. 121 MEYRAN AVE, UNIV HLTH CTR OF PITTSBURG 15213 #550-01-2000 L2005 **DR** *012

PARANJPE, Deval Mohan. 420 E NORTH AVE, STE 116 15212 #043-01-1999 L2001 **OPH** *020 †35 ‡

PARDA, David Stephen. 320 E NORTH AVE 15212 #011-04-1988 L1998 **RO IM** *020 †20,80 ‡

PARE, Amelia Arianne. 2535 WASHINGTON RD, STE 1121 15241 #041-09-1992 L1999 **PS** *020 †65

PAREPALLY, Haranath. 9000 PERRY HWY, STE 310 15237 #495-57-1979 L1996 **P** *020 †75

PAREPALLY, Shailaja. 9104 BABCOCK BLVD, STE 6118 15237 #495-21-1983 L1997 **END IM** *020 †20 ‡

PARIKH, Bharati Kiran. 2370 W GATE DR 15237 #495-22-1969 L1979 **AN** *020 †05 ‡

PARIKH, Pratik Sharadbhai. 320 E NORTH AVE, ALLEGHENY GENERAL HOSP 15212 #495-23-1997 L2001 **CD** *012 †20

PARIKH, Rahul Atul. 121 MEYRAN AVE 15213 #496-38-2001 L2006 **IM** *012

PARIKH, Tejas Nikunj. ■ 15201 #021-06-2005 L2005 **PM** *012

PARIS, Paul Marc. 200 LOTHROP ST 15213 #041-12-1976 L1981 **EM IM** *020 †20,16

PARK, Andrew Sungjae. ■ 15217 #041-12-1999 L2001 **IM** *100 †20

PARK, Brian J. 203 LOTHROP ST, DEPT OF OTOLARYNGOLOGY, SU 15213 #035-15-2002 L2007 **OTO** *100

PARK, James Sungsik. ■ 15232 #035-06-2001 L2004 **GE** *012

PARK, Sang Chong. 3705 5TH AVE, CHILDREN'S HOSP 15213 #583-10-1963 L1972 **PDC** *020 †15

PARK, Sunwoo. 88 FORT COUCH RD, STE 100 15241 #041-12-2001 L2001 **PD** *100 †55

PARK, Taewoo. ■ 15243 #038-06-2005 L2005 **P** *012

PARKER, Ronnie Coward. 532 S AIKEN AVE, STE 201 15232 #045-01-1983 L1984 **IM** *020 †20

PARKINSON, Michael Donald. ■ 15217 #010-01-1979 L1984 **PHP** *030 †70

PARKS, William Antone, Jr. ■ 15238 #028-02-1988 L2007 **PTH** *020 †50

PARNESS, Jerome. 3705 5TH AVE, DEPT OF ANESTHESIOLOGY 15213 #035-46-1985 L1987 **AN** *050 †05

PARRISH, James Edward. 420 E NORTH AVE, STE 205 15212 #028-34-1957 L1965 **END OS** *020 †20

PARSONS, John Andresen. 200 LOTHROP ST STE 710 15213 #035-15-1946 L1961 **RO** *071 †80

PARVEZ, Rizwan. ■ 15221 #035-06-2007 L2007 **P** *012

PARVIAINEN, Eeva L K. 300 HALKET ST, MAGEE WOMEN'S HOSPITAL 15213 #001-02-1995 L2004 **OBG** *020 †30

PASCUA, Frederick Nick. ■ 15241 #010-01-2005 L2005 **IM** *012

PASH, Christopher Alan. 1910 COCHRAN RD, MANOR OAK TWO-SUITE 490 15220 #041-12-1987 L1988 **IM** *020 †20

PASSARELLI, Ralph William. 200 DELAFIELD RD, STE 1040 15215 #051-01-1997 L2001 **ORS** *020 †40

PASSELTINER, Patricia. 160 SOUTHERN AVE 15211 #422-01-1987 L1995 **P** *020 †20,75

PASSERO, Christopher J. A 915 SCAIFE HALL, 3550 TERRACE STREET 15261 #043-01-2002 L2002 **NEP** *100 †20

PASTOR, Christopher Georg. ■ 15237 #041-13-2005 L2005 **IM** *012

PASTOR-SOLER, Nuria Maria. 3550 TERRACE ST, A915 SCAIFE HALL - DEPT OF 15261 #041-02-1996 L2000 **NEP** *020 †20

PASUNUR, Deepika. 4815 LIBERTY AVE, STE G25 15224 #495-65-1995 L1997 **IM** *020 †20

PATAKI, Robert Scott. PO BOX 81619 15217 #035-09-1989 L1993 **FM** *020

PATEL, Amit. 200 LOTHROP ST, PITTSBURGH MED 15213 #038-06-1998 L2002 **TS** *020

PATEL, Amy. ■ 15213 #050-02-2004 L2004 **MPD** *012

PATEL, Chandrakant R. ■ 15211 #495-23-1974 L1986 **NM** *020 †28

PATEL, Falguni Harilal. 320 E NORTH AVE, ALLEGHENY GEN HOSP 15212 #759-12-2005 L2006 **IM** *012

PATEL, Gautam P. 1361 REDFERN DR 15241 #495-22-1970 L1981 **R OS** *020 †80

PATEL, Hitendra R. 1000 INTEGRITY DR, ASSOCIATES INC 15235 #495-23-1987 L1995 **GE** *020 †20 ‡

PATEL, Jigneshkumar Bhogi. 3705 5TH AVE 15213 #495-23-1998 L2005 **NPM** *012 †55

PATEL, Jitesh Arvind. 320 E NORTH AVE, ALLEGHENY GERERAL HOSPITAL 15212 #033-06-2003 L2003 **GS** *012

PATEL, Kaushikkumar Kanti. 320 E NORTH AVE 15212 #495-23-2001 L2005 **IM** *012

PATEL, Kush Shashikant. ■ 15241 #038-44-2008 *012

PATEL, Kusum Bhikhu. 200 LOTHROP ST, UPMC-PRESBYTERIAN HOSPITAL 15213 #035-08-1995 L2002 **GS** *020 †85

PATEL, Mamta Dahyabhai. 121 MEYRAN AVE 15213 #495-89-2004 **FP** *012

PATEL, Maulikkumar Bipinc. 320 E NORTH AVE 15212 #495-89-2000 L2002 **PCC** *012 †20

PATEL, Minaxi. 330 CURRY HOLLOW RD 15236 #495-76-1971 L1981 **AI** *020 †55

PATEL, Mitva Jashu. 200 LOTHROP ST, UNIV OF PITTSBURGH MED CEN 15213 #025-12-2001 L2006 **DR** *020 †80

PATEL, Ranoo Rajendrakum. ■ 15232 #041-12-2008 *012

PATEL, Rita Maganbhai. 3471 5TH AVE, STE 910 15213 #654-01-1981 L1984 **AN** *040 †05 ‡

PATEL, Sanjay Arun. 1350 LOCUST ST, STE 308 15219 #041-12-1996 L1998 **PCC** *020 †20

PATEL, Satish Ramanbhai. ■ 15237 #495-76-2000 L2003 **NEP** *012 †20

PATEL, Susanj Shantu. 4800 FRIENDSHIP AVE 15224 #035-19-1995 L1995 **DR** *020 †80

PATEL, Vikram Kumar P. 3705 5TH AVE RM 7469, DEPARTMENT OF ANESTHESIA 15213 #495-22-1993 L2000 **PAN** *020 †50

PATERSON, David Leslie. 3601 5TH AVE STE 3A, FALK BLDG 15213 #143-05-1988 L2001 **ID** *020

PATHE, Neeta Prasad. 4800 FRIENDSHIP AVE 15224 #495-83-2001 L2005 **IM** *012

PATIL, Shankar. 4800 FRIENDSHIP AVE 15224 #495-09-1959 **PUD** *050

PATNI, Mayuri. ■ 15235 #495-20-2000 L2004 **IM** *020 †20

PATRINA, Yuliya. 3705 5TH AVE, CHILDREN'S HOSP 15213 #913-07-1981 L2006 **CHN** *012

PATRINOS, Demetrios C. 2585 WASHINGTON RD STE 111, SUMMERFIELD COMMONS 15241 #041-12-1997 L1998 **GS** *020

PATTERSON, Brandy. ■ 15237 #011-02-2004 L2004 **IM** *020 †20

PATTERSON, Katherine L. 901 WEST ST, STE B 15221 #047-05-1991 L1993 **FM** *020 †18

PATTERSON, Kevin Russell. 3520 5TH AVE, LOWER LEVEL KEYSTONE BUILD 15213 #035-09-2003 L2003 **P** *100

PATTERSON, Michael D, Sr. 3866 BAYTREE ST 15214 #041-12-1980 L1982 **IM** *020 †20

PATTERSON, Scott Paul. 1000 BOWER HILL RD 15243 #038-40-1998 L2001 **DR** *020 †80

PATTI, Mitchell James. 200 DELAFIELD RD, STE 2040 15215 #035-08-1986 L1988 **CCM** *020 †20

PATTON, Anna Margaret. 4800 FRIENDSHIP AVE 15224 #041-07-1943 L1944 **OBG** *071 †30

PAUL, Dina Eleni. 425 HOLIDAY DR, FOSTER PLAZA 2 15220 #041-14-1997 L1999 **IM** *020 †20

PAUL, Maria Ann. 363 VANADIUM RD, STE 15 15243 #041-14-1991 L1994 **D** *020 †15

PAUL, Richard. 3705 5TH AVE 15213 #041-12-1961 L1962 **PD** *071 †55

PAUL, Rogi. 5230 CENTRE AVE 15232 #495-01-1983 L1995 **IM** *020 †20

PAULIUKONIS, Laima Terese. 3705 5TH AVE, CHILDRENS HOSPITAL PITTSBU 15213 #041-01-1986 L1989 **AN** *020 †06

PAULOS, Mark R. 3436 WILLIAM PENN HWY, PENN CENTER, BLDG 2, SUITE 15235 #028-02-1998 L2000 **IM** *020 †20

PAUTLER, Stanislav. 400 45TH ST 15201 #286-02-1953 L1969 **AN GP** *071 †05

PAVELKO, Jennifer Renee. ■ 15232 #038-44-2006 L2006 **FP** *012

PAVLIC, George John. 4725 MCKNIGHT RD 15237 #041-12-1956 L1957 **ON HEM** *071 †20

PAVLICK, Geno Joseph. 1000 INTEGRITY DR, STE 100 15235 #041-14-1994 L1996 **FM** *020 †18 ‡

PAWELSKI, Lisa Alexandra. 3424 WILLIAM PENN HWY, BLDG 2 15235 #041-12-1986 L1988 **D IM** *020 †20,15

PAZIN, George James. 969A SCAIFE HALL 15261 #041-12-1964 L1968 **ID IM** *071 †20

PEARCE-SMITH, Beverly. 4800 FRIENDSHIP AVE 15224 #067-01-1983 L1988 **AN** *020 †05

PEDUZZI, Trina Lynn. 317 CLIMAX ST, HILLTOP COMMUNITY HEALTH C 15210 #041-12-1998 L2000 **PD ADL** *020 †55

PEEL, Robert Louis. 200 LOTHROP ST, PRESBYTERIAN HOSP 15213 #041-12-1968 L1969 **PTH** *020 †50

PEITZMAN, Andrew Bertram. 200 LOTHROP ST, F1281 PRESBYTERIAN HOSP 15213 #041-12-1976 L1977 **GS TRS** *020 †85

PELKOFER, Cletus G. ■ 15213 #041-12-1950 L1951 **DR R** *071

PELLEGRINI, Ronald Virgil. 9104 BABCOCK BLVD, STE 5105 15237 #041-02-1963 L1964 **TS** *020 †85,90

PELUSO, Leeann. 100 DELAFIELD RD 15215 #038-44-2000 L2000 **GS** *020

PENCHANSKY, Lila. 125 DE SOTO ST 15213 #132-01-1962 L1977 **GP** *050 †50

PENNANT, Marjorie Angella. ■ 15212 #041-14-2001 L2005 **END** *012 †20

PENNATHUR, Arjun. 3705 5TH AVE 15213 #495-95-1985 L2004 **TS** *020 †90,85

PENROD, Louis Edmund. 3471 5TH AVE, STE 201 15213 #041-12-1984 L1986 **PM SCI** *030 †60

PEREIRA, Telma Carvalho. 320 E NORTH AVE, ALLEGHENY GENERAL HOSP - 15212 #187-33-1998 L2001 **PTH PCP** *020 †50 ‡

PEREPLETCHIKOV, Alexandre. ■ 15217 #913-36-1988 L2006 **SP** *012 †50

PEREZ, Andrew, IV. 1350 LOCUST ST, STE 308 15219 #048-02-1995 L1997 **PCC** *020 †20
PEREZ, Horacio Anibal. ■ 15203 #132-01-1976 L1979 **PTH** *020
PEREZ, Kevin Anthony. 4778 LIBERTY AVE 15224 #035-01-1993 L2001 **ID** *020 †20
PEREZ, Ruth Elizabeth. ■ 15237 #042-01-1999 L2001 **EM** *020 †16
PERLIN, Mark Wm. ■ 15217 #016-02-1984 L1984 **OS DR** *062
PERLMUTTER, David Hirsch. 3705 5TH AVE 15213 #028-34-1978 L1979 **GE PD** *050 †55
PERLMUTTER, David Alan. ■ 15232 #041-12-2004 L2007 **U** *012
PERRI, Francis R. 1050 BOWER HILL RD STE 302 15243 #010-02-1953 L1954 **GS** *071 †85
PERRI, Jeffrey Allen. 1050 BOWER HILL RD STE 302 15243 #010-02-1990 L1993 **GS** *020 †85
PERRI, John Anthony. UNIVERSITY DR C, RM 11W-122 15240 #041-12-1959 L1960 **ORS** *072 †40
PERRICELLI, Brett C. 3471 5TH AVE, STE 1010 15213 #041-12-2002 L2002 **ORS** *012
PERRIERA, Lisa Kim. ■ 15203 #035-48-2003 L2007 **OBG** *100
PERROTTA, Charles, Jr. 3811 OHARA ST, WPIC ROOM 689 15213 #041-12-1988 L1990 **CHP P** *020 †75 ‡
PERRY, Yaron. ■ 15217 #550-01-1994 L2003 **TS** *012 †85
PERRYMAN, Charles Richard. 4815 LIBERTY AVE, STE 437 15224 #035-20-1942 L1945 **R** *075 †80
PERRYMAN, Stephen Edward. 2920 W LIBERTY AVE 15216 #004-01-1990 L1993 **FM** *020 †18
PESKE, Kristen Emily Mest. 4800 FRIENDSHIP AVE, DEPT OBG 15224 #041-77-2006, ▲ L2006 **OBG** *012
PETERS, Jeffrey Lee. 7180 HIGHLAND DR, HIGHLAND DRIVE VAMC 15206 #038-06-1980 L1981 **P PYG** *030 †75 ‡
PETERS, Vaughan. ■ 15226 #041-12-1955 L1956 *020
PETERSON, Alison Reichard. 7180 HIGHLAND DR # 1324-H, VAMC 15206 #035-06-1985 L1986 **PM N** *020 †75,60
PETERSON, Arleen Margaret. 200 LOTHROP ST, PUH-DEPT OF RADIOLOGY 15213 #041-12-1984 L1990 **DR RNR** *020 †80
PETERSON, Beth Anne. 230 MCKEE PL STE 500, OF PITTSBURGH 15213 #035-06-2005 L2005 **EM** *012
PETERSON, Curtis Lee. ■ 15238 #035-06-1987 L1989 **IM** *020 †20
PETERSON, Mary Elizabeth. 300 HALKET ST, STE 1338 15213 #051-01-1990 L1995 **OBG** *020 †30
PETERSON, Suzanne E. 300 HALKET ST, DEPT OB 15213 #054-04-2003 L2003 **OBG** *020
PETILLA, Mariano Enriquez. 532 S AIKEN AVE, STE 501 15232 #748-01-1960 L1971 **TS GS** *020
PETRAS, Laslo. ■ 15237 #649-14-1980 L1986 **P** *020
PETRO, Daniel Paul. 5115 CENTRE AVE 15232 #041-02-2000 L2001 **HO** *020 †20
PETROLLA, Justin J. 3471 5TH AVE STE 201 15213 #038-44-2004 L2004 **PM** *012
PETROPOULOU, Kalliopi A. 200 LOTHROP ST, SUITE 3950 CHP MAIN TOWER 15213 #418-02-1985 L1994 **DR** *020 †80
PETROV, Andrej A. 3459 5TH AVE, UPMC MONTEFIORE NW 628 15213 #957-02-1997 L2001 **AI** *100 †20,03
PETRUSCAK, Jaroslaw. 128 NORTH CRAIG ST, PARK PLAZA STE 603 15213 #847-01-1952 L1962 **AN** *071 †05
PETTEGREW, Jay Wesley. 3811 OHARA ST 15213 #016-11-1969 L1984 **P** *020 †75
PETTIFORD, Brian Lamar. 5200 CENTRE AVE STE 715, SHADYSIDE MEDICAL OFFICE B 15232 #041-12-1996 L2001 **TS** *020 †85,90
PEZZONE, Kimberly Tillery. 1580 MCLAUGHLIN RUN RD, STE 208 15241 #041-12-1991 L1993 **PD** *020 †55
PEZZONE, Michael Angelo. 200 LOTHROP ST, 9019 FORBES TOWER 15213 #041-12-1994 L1996 **GE** *020 †20
PFAEFFLE, Hugo Hermann. PASSAVANT HOSP ANES 15237 #649-01-1963 L1970 **AN** *071 †05
PFINSGRAFF, Joan Lange. ■ 15237 #032-01-1979 L1982 **IM** *074
PHADKE, Aparna Suresh. ■ 15238 #496-38-1995 L2002 **PAN** *100 †05
PHAN, Phu Gia. ■ 15213 #041-12-2004 L2008 **IM** *100
PHELPS, Tracy Lee. ■ 15206 #041-12-2007 L2007 **FP** *012
PHILBIN, Terence J. 1400 LOCUST ST, STE 5109 15219 #016-43-1983 L1985 **IM** *020 †20 ‡
PHILLIPS, Chester A, III. ■ 15241 #041-01-1969 L1972 **AN** *071 †05
PHILLIPS, Dennis Jos. 1307 FEDERAL ST, STE 2 15212 #041-07-1992 L1997 **OSM** *020 †40
PHILLIPS, John Chas. 1726 E CARSON ST 15203 #012-05-1969 L1971 **CD IM** *020 †20
PHILLIPS, Mary L. 121 MEYRAN AVE, LOEFFLER BUILDING, ROOM 30 15213 #917-03-1989 L2006 *100
PHILLIPS, Scott Thomas. 3028 BROWNSVILLE RD, BRENTWOOD MEDICAL GROUP 15227 #041-02-1995 L1997 **IM** *020 †20
PHILLIPS, William Watson. 9000 PERRY HWY, STE 210 15237 #041-09-1976 L1978 **GE** *020 †20
PHITAYAKORN, Preyaratt T. ■ 15241 #891-02-1971 L1974 **AN** *071 †05
PHRAMPUS, Erin Doherty. 3705 5TH AVE 15213 #051-07-1998 L2001 **PEM** *020 †55 ‡
PHRAMPUS, Paul Edward. 230 MCKEE PL, STE 300 15213 #051-07-1997 L1999 **EM** *020 †16
PHU, Phan Tho. ■ 15213 #005-19-2002 L2003 **PD** *020 †55
PICCIOTTI, Isabella M. 3705 5TH AVE, CHILDRENS HOSP OF PGH 15213 #051-01-1981 L1985 **AN** *020 †55,05
PICCOLI, Louis A. 3459 5TH AVE 15213 #016-11-1980 L2005 **IMG IM** *020 †20
PICKLE, Daniel E, Jr. 5618 KENTUCKY AVE 15232 #055-01-1985 L1987 **AN** *020 †05
PIERCE, Alice Marie. 400 HOLIDAY DR, STE 101 15224 #041-13-1988 L1991 **TS CD** *020 †85,90
PIERCE, Kim Marie. 300 HALKET ST, STE 5710 15213 #041-12-1998 L2000 **IM** *020 †20
PIEROTTI, Aldino Louis. 730 HOLIDAY DR, STE 140 15220 #041-01-1992 L1994 **EM CCA** *020
PIERRI, Joseph N. 3811 OHARA ST, WESTERN PSYCHIATRIC INSTIT 15213 #016-02-1992 L1995 **CHP** *020 †75
PIETRAGALLO, Louis Danl. 101 DRAKE RD, STE B 15241 #041-02-1972 L1973 **HEM IM** *020
PIFALO, William Bradley. 2304 COLONY CT, HIGHMARK BLUE CROSS BLUE S 15237 #561-01-1980 L1983 **CD IM** *030 †20 ‡
PIGALARGA, Rodolfo. 121 MEYRAN AVE 15213 #561-23-2002 L2006 **GS** *100
PIL, Tricia Huang. 5676 STEUBENVILLE PIKE, STES C AND D 15205 #041-01-1996 L1998 **PD** *020 †55
PILCH, Yosef Hayim. ■ 15217 #023-07-1959 L2003 **GS** *071 †85
PILEWSKI, Joseph Mark. 3601 5TH AVE, FALK 4 LUNG CTR 15213 #035-45-1987 L1988 **PUD CCM** *020 †20
PINCHASIK, Dawn Elyse. ■ 15213 #041-15-2007 L2007 **PD** *012
PINEVICH, Anthony John. 1649 PINEHURST CT 15237 #038-44-1985 L1986 **IM NEP** *030 †20
PINKOFSKY, Harold Bertram. 3811 OHARA ST, TDH OF WPIC 15213 #035-09-1989 L2002 **P** *020 †75
PINSKY, Michael Raymond. 3550 TERRACE ST, 606 SCAIFE HALL 15213 #067-01-1974 L1981 **CCM PUD** *050 †20
PIPER, Russell Weldon. 3708 5TH AVE, STE 500 MEDICAL ARTS BLDG 15213 #041-14-1978 L1979 **FM OM** *020 †18

PIPPIN, Barbara Ann. 201 LOTHROP ST, UPMC 15213 #041-12-1995 L1996 **PM** *020
PIRAINO, Beth Holley. 3504 5TH AVE STE 200, UNIV OF PITTSBURGH 15213 #041-07-1977 L1978 **NEP** *020 †20
PIRRIS, John. 1307 FEDERAL ST, STE 300 15212 #418-01-1957 L1965 **U** *071 †95
PIRRIS, Stephen M. 200 LOTHROP ST, STE B-400 15213 #041-12-2002 L2002 **NS** *012
PITETTI, Raymond. 3705 5TH AVE 15213 #041-13-1992 L1994 **PE PD** *020 †55
PITTLE, Howard Scott. 5247 BROWNSVILLE RD, WHITEHALL FAMILY MED 15236 #041-02-1991 L1993 **FM FPG** *020 †18 ‡
PIZON, Anthony Francis. 200 LOTHROP ST 15213 #038-43-2001 L2001 **ETX** *020 †16
PLAKSEYCHUK, Anton Yuriev. 3471 5TH AVE, KAUFMAN BLD S1010 15213 #913-03-1987 L2003 **ORS** *012
PLANINSIC, Raymond M. 200 LOTHROP ST 15213 #035-47-1986 L1987 **AN IM** *020 †20,05
PLOWEY, Edward. ■ 15229 #016-11-2005 L2005 **PTH** *012
PLOWMAN, Judith Lynn. 106 BERKELEY MEADOWS CT 15237 #041-12-1992 L1994 **IMG** *020 †20
PLUNKETT, Francis Xavier. 9104 BABCOCK BLVD, STE 2120 15237 #041-12-1975 L1977 **ORS** *020 †40
PODGAINY, Helen Joan. 300 HALKET ST 15213 #036-07-1971 L1973 **PD** *020 †55
POKHARNA, Renu Kishor. 3471 5TH AVE 15213 #495-30-1985 L2000 **FM** *100
POLAM, Chandrasekhara R. 4727 FRIENDSHIP AVE, STE 200 15224 #495-70-1975 L1979 **CD** *020 †20
POLAN, William Steele. 9100 BABCOCK BLVD 15237 #041-02-1965 L1969 **FM GS** *075
POLANCO, Patricio Marcelo. ■ 15213 #737-10-2000 L2007 *100
POLINSKI, Leonard J. 3805 BRIGHTON RD 15212 #308-03-1983 L1985 **IM** *020 †20
POLITO, Antonella. ■ 15232 #035-08-2007 L2007 **PD** *012
POLIZIO, Anna M. ■ 15237 #759-10-1963 L1987 **R NM** *020 †80,28
POLLACK, Dean Nelson. 5200 CENTRE AVE, STE 316 15232 #035-09-1982 L1986 **OBG** *020 †20
POLLACK, Ian Fredric. 3705 5TH AVE 15213 #023-07-1984 L1985 **NS** *020 †25
POLLER, William Richard. 320 E NORTH AVE, ALLEGHENY GENERAL HOSP CAN 15212 #041-12-1968 L1975 **R** *020 †80 ‡
POLLICE, Eugene Adelmo. ■ 15205 #561-01-1973 **FM** *020
POLLICE, Philip Adelmo. 1400 LOCUST ST 15219 #041-01-1991 L1997 **OTO** *020 †45
POLLICE, Philip George. 1699 WASHINGTON RD, STE 400 15228 #561-01-1961 L1964 **AN OS** *071 †05
POLLOCK, Avrum N. 3705 5TH AVE, DEPT OF RADIOLOGY 15213 #062-01-1988 L1993 **R PDR** *020 †80
POLLOCK, Bruce Godfrey. 3811 OHARA ST 15213 #065-01-1979 L1983 **P PA** *020
POLLOCK, Gary Fredrick. 1004 ARCH ST 15212 #051-01-1995 L1997 **EM** *020 †16
PONS, Wanda Katiuska. 320 E NORTH AVE, ALLEGHENY GEN HOSP 15212 #308-05-1998 L2002 **IM** *100
PONTIUS, Robert Gilmore. ■ 15232 #041-01-1947 L1957 **TS** *071 †85,90
POORNIMA, Indu G. 320 E NORTH AVE, DEPT OF NUCLEAR CARDIOLOGY 15212 #495-16-1992 L2000 **NC CD** *020 †20
POPESCU, Alexandra. ■ 15232 #781-01-2001 L2005 **N** *012
POPESCU, Laura Mihaela. 15206 #781-01-2004 L2007 **IM** *012
POPKO, Brian Matthew. 100 S JACKSON AVE, ALLEGHENY GENERAL HOSPITAL 15202 #041-07-1997 L2000 **EM** *020 †16
POPKO, Stacey Hope. 2581 WASHINGTON RD, STE 211 15241 #041-07-1996 L1996 **MPD** *020 †20,55
POPLI, Gagandeep Singh. 320 E NORTH AVE, ALLEGHENY GEN HOSP 15212 #495-03-1998 L2001 **P** *100
PORTER, Elizabeth S. ■ 15216 #041-01-1986 L1987 **PHP FM** *074 †70,18
PORTER, Lynne E. ■ 15215 #041-02-1973 L1978 **GE** *074 †20
PORTMAN, Mary Ann. 300 HALKET ST 15213 #041-13-1975 L1976 **OBG** *020 †30
POST, Andrew Ronald. 306 S HIGHLAND AVE # 504 15206 #041-01-1999 *100
POST, James Christopher. 320 E NORTH AVE, ALLEGHENY GENERAL HOSPITAL 15212 #011-03-1993 L1990 **PDO** *020 †45
POTOKA, Douglas A. 3705 5TH AVE 15213 #023-07-1996 L2001 **PDS** *020 †85
POTOKA, Karin Plummer. ■ 15238 #041-12-2008 L2008 *012
POTTER, Robert Hugo, Jr. 5700 CORPORATE DR, STE 700 15237 #041-12-1982 L1983 **FM** *020 †18
POTTS, Jonathan Matthew. 320 E NORTH AVE, ALLEGHENY RADIOLOGY 15212 #143-01-1986 L1995 **VIR NM** *020 †20
POTTS, Lynn Marie. 113 CURRY HOLLOW RD 15236 #051-04-1997 L1999 **FM** *020 †18 ‡
POUNDS, Lois Ann. ■ 15206 #041-12-1965 L1974 **PD** *030 †55
POVEDA, Herberto. UNIV OF PITTS, DEPT RAD 15213 #264-01-1967 L1980 **R DR** *020 †80
POWELL, Angela Maude. 200 LOTHROP ST, EEI BLDG STE 500 15213 #016-06-2000 L2001 **OTO** *020
POWELL, Nina Nicole. 3520 5TH AVE STE 205, MEDICAL GENETICS 15213 #566-01-1998 L2002 **MG** *012 †55
POWELL, Thomas Ray. JMA BLDG, SUITE 270 15236 #038-40-1990 L1997 **IM NEP** *020 †20
POWER, John A, Jr. 490 E NORTH AVE, STE 405 15212 #041-07-1983 L1984 **CD** *020 †20
POWER, Thomas F. 490 E NORTH AVE, STE 301 15212 #539-03-1985 L1991 **CD IM** *020 †20
POWERS, Karen Ann. 100 DELAFIELD RD 15215 #041-14-1984 L1985 **IMG IM** *040 †20
PRABHU, Anil. 1050 BOWER HILL RD STE 301 15243 #495-37-1980 L1983 **IMG** *020 †20 ‡
PRABHU, Asha. ■ 15243 #495-37-1990 L1996 **P** *020 †75
PRABHU, Nalina. 1050 BOWER HILL RD STE 301 15243 #495-37-1981 L1984 **IM** *020 †20 ‡
PRABHU, Shakuntala. 1050 BOWER HILL RD 15243 #495-21-1953 L1973 **EM OBG** *020
PRAIRIE, Beth Ann. 300 HALKET ST, MCGEE-WOMENS HOSPITAL 15213 #034-01-2002 L2008 **GPM** *012
PRALL, Nicole C. 580 S AIKEN AVE, UPMC SHADYSIDE PLACE 15232 #003-01-2002 L2007 **DMP** *012
PRANIEWICZ, Mary Jane. 815 FREEPORT RD 15215 #041-12-1985 L1986 **EM** *020 †16
PRASAD, Adusumilli S. ■ 15222 #495-50-1989 L2000 **TS** *100
PRASAD, Amitesh. 200 LOTHROP ST, UPMC DEPARTMENT OF RADIOLO 15213 #041-13-1992 L2000 **DR** *020 †80
PRASAD, Konasale Muniraje. 3811 OHARA ST, RM 422 15213 #496-01-1993 L2001 *020 †75
PRASAD, Vutla Venkata S. 2000 CLIFFMINE RD, PARK W TWO/STE 110 15275 #495-58-1973 L1998 **GPM EM** *075
PRASANNA, Vikram. ■ 15213 #041-12-2008 *012
PREISMAN, Richard Chas. ■ 15243 #016-02-1965 L1969 **P** *020 †75
PREISNER, Ruth Marie. 130U UNIVERSITY DRIVE C, DEPARTMENT OF VETERANS AFF 15240 #041-01-1984 L1986 **IM** *020 †20
PREISS, Jennifer Ellen. 651 HOLIDAY DR, FOSTER PLAZA 5 15220 #036-07-1986 L1991 **IM PD** *020 †20,55

■ = Address Information Privacy Protected

PRENDERGAST, John Michael. 1910 COCHRAN RD, STE 525 15220 #539-06-1972 L1987 **IMG IM** *020 †20

PRETTER, Paul Donald. ■ 15238 #165-04-1960 L1962 **IM OM** *071

PREVEDELLO, Daniel Monte. 200 LOTHROP ST 15213 #187-08-2000 L2008 *020

PREZZIA, Charles Paul. 600 GRANT ST, RM 468 15219 #038-40-1981 L1998 **OM EM** *030 †70,18 ‡

PRICE, David Bryan. 1400 LOCUST ST 15219 #020-02-1988 L1990 **GS VS** *020 †85

PRICE, Fredric V. 4815 LIBERTY AVE, STE 127 15224 #020-02-1986 L1987 **GO GYN** *020 †30 ‡

PRIMACK, Brian Adam. 3518 5TH AVENUE 15261 #012-05-1999 L2001 **FM** *020 †18

PRIMAVERA, James Michael. 815 FREEPORT RD, UPMC ST. MARGARET 15215 #035-46-1993 L2004 **PTH NP** *020 †50

PRIMEAU, Michelle Marie. 3811 OHARA ST, AND C 15213 #038-06-2007 L2007 **P** *012

PRIN, William. ■ 15208 #023-07-1957 L1960 **HEM PD** *020 †55

PRINCE, Jose Manuel. 15217 #008-01-2000 L2001 **GS** *012

PRINGLE, Jacqueline M. 12 EASTERN AVE, STE 204 15215 #041-13-1981 L1984 **P ADP** *020 †75

PRINGLE, Robert Wm. 300 FOX CHAPEL RD 15238 #041-12-1944 L1945 **OM** *071 †20

PRISK, Victor Robert. 3471 5TH AVE, STE 1010 15213 #016-11-2001 L2001 **OFA** *012

PROBST-SISKA, Jamie Lynn. 100 DELAFIELD RD, 100 MEDICAL ARTS, SUITE 31 15215 #038-41-2003 L2003 **FM** *020 †18

PROCHOWNIK, Edward Victor. 3705 5TH AVE 15213 #016-02-1978 L1992 **HEM** *050 †55

PROKHOV, Vassil Kosta. 1050 BOWER HILL RD STE 309 15243 #957-04-1958 L1981 **CD** *020 †20

PROSTKO, Edward Richard. 1050 BOWER HILL RD, STE 203 15243 #016-43-1974 L1981 **NS** *020 †25

PROTELL, Peter Holt. ■ 15232 #031-01-2007 L2007 **EM** *012

PROVENZANO, Mark Anthony. 9104 BABCOCK BLVD, STE 2103 15237 #010-01-1990 L1993 **PCC** *020 †20

PRYJDUN, Olena. ■ 15213 #913-89-1995 L2001 **AN** *100 †05

PRYMA, Daniel Alexander. 200 LOTHROP ST, DEPARTMENT OF RADIOLOGY 15213 #016-43-2002 L2005 **IM** *100 †28

PUCEVICH, Brian Edward. ■ 15238 #010-02-2007 L2007 **IM** *012

PULOS, George D. ■ 15213 #418-01-1987 L1995 **CD** *100 †20

PUNTURERI, Anthony Jos. UNIVERSITY DR C 15240 #041-12-1940 L1941 **IMG IM** *020 †20

PUROHIT, Avinash. 1400 LOCUST ST, DEPT OF PEDIATRICS 15219 #496-03-1986 L2000 **NPM** *020 †55

PURPURA, Lawrence James. 2000 MARY ST 15203 #748-10-1981 L1982 **IM** *020 †20

PUSATERI, Dorothy Walker. 320 E NORTH AVE, ALLEGHENY GENERAL HOSPITAL 15212 #020-02-1985 L1986 **IM** *020 †20

PUSATERI, Joseph Paul, Jr. 3347 FORBES AVE, STE 303 15213 #041-13-1980 L1981 **GE EM** *020 †20

PUSWELLA, Amal Les. ■ 15213 #041-12-2004 L2004 **IM** *020 †20

PUTHENPURAYIL, Kurian J. 815 FREEPORT RD 15215 #023-07-1998 L2001 **DR** *020 †80

PUYANA, Juan Carlos. 200 LOTHROP ST, TRAUMA GENERAL SURGERY 15213 #264-04-1983 L2001 **GS TRS** *020 †85

PYMAR, Helen Christina. 300 HALKET ST, MAGEE WOMENS HOSP 15213 #065-05-1994 L1998 **OBG** *100

QAMAR, Mohammad Zeeshan. 121 MEYRAN AVE, DEPT OF INTERNAL MED 15213 #704-25-2002 L2004 **NEP** *012 †20

QAYYUM, Azmat. 1321 5TH AVE, STE 202 15219 #704-21-1988 L2000 **PUD** *020 †20

QU, Lirong. 3636 BLVD OF THE ALLIES 15213 #243-20-1983 L2001 **PTH** *020 †50

QUELER, Evan D. ■ 15203 #104-01-2004 L2005 **PM** *012

QUICK, Sharon M. 3705 5TH AVE, CHLDRNS HOSP OF PITTSBURGH 15213 #028-02-1988 L1997 **AN** *020 †05,55

QUIGLEY, Matthew Richard. 420 E NORTH AVE, EAST WING SUITE 302 15212 #016-06-1981 L1987 **NS** *020 †25 ‡

QUILINO, Anna Marie Aguas. 5215 CENTRE AVE 15232 #748-31-2000 L2003 **FM** *100 †18

QUINLAN, Joseph John. 200 LOTHROP ST, UPMC-PRESBYTERIAN C-223 15213 #041-01-1984 L1986 **AN** *020 †05

QUINLIN, Robert Francis. 200 DELAFIELD RD, STE 1000 15215 #041-12-1974 L1975 **GS** *020 †85

QUINTERO, Andres Javier. ■ 15232 #041-14-2006 L2006 **ORS** *012

QUINTERO, Miguel Javier. 144 S 20TH ST 15203 #264-04-1967 L1973 **OPH** *020 †35

QUIVERS, Eric Stanley. 3705 5TH AVE 15213 #010-03-1983 L2004 **PDC PD** *020 †55

QURESHI, Irfan Riaz. ■ 15205 #004-01-2004 **GS** *100

RABIN, Bruce S. 200 LOTHROP ST 15213 #035-06-1969 L1972 **CLP** *020

RABINOVITZ, Asaf. ■ 15217 #035-46-2007 **IM** *012

RABINOVITZ, Mordechai. 2205 BEECHWOOD BLVD 15217 #550-02-1975 L1989 **GE HEP** *020

RABINOWITZ, Jerry Paul. 5173 LIBERTY AVE 15224 #041-01-1977 L1978 **FM PG** *020 †18

RABKIN, Michael Scott. 522 ALPHA DR 15238 #030-07-1984 L1989 **DMP** *020 †50

RACH-BORETSKY, Karen Lee. 320 E NORTH AVE 15212 #041-12-1984 L1985 **AN CCM** *030 †05

RADFAR, Arash. 5230 CENTRE AVE, RM WG02.18 15232 #024-07-2000 L2006 **DMP** *020 †50

RADFAR, Fereydoon. 2987 W LIBERTY AVE 15216 #517-05-1977 L1981 **P ADM** *020 †75

RADFAR, Nezame. 733 WASHINGTON RD, STE 211 15228 #517-01-1967 L1976 **PDE END** *040 †55

RADFAR, R Hoorazar. 733 WASHINGTON RD, STE 211 15228 #517-01-1968 L1976 **IM END** *020

RADFAR, Soraya Z. 20 CEDAR BLVD STE 204 15228 #517-06-1978 L1985 **P** *020 †75

RADHAKRISHNAN, Anita Umay. 320 E NORTH AVE, ALLEGHENY GEN HOSP 15212 #496-23-2006 L2006 **IM** *012

RAFFENSPERGER, John A. 100 DELAFIELD RD, STE 105 15215 #041-12-1985 L1987 **PUD CCM** *020 †20

RAFIEE, Bahman. ■ 15238 #517-08-1990 L2002 **MSR** *020

RAFKIN, Harry Steven. 5200 CENTRE AVE, STE 610 15232 #396-32-1984 L1987 **CCM IM** *020 †20

RAGER, Ronald. 875 GREENTREE RD, STE 117 15220 #035-19-1973 L1977 **VS** *062 †55

RAGHAVAN, Aarti. 300 HALKET ST, MAGEE WOMENS HOSP 15213 #496-23-2002 L2007 **NPM** *012

RAGHAVAN, Mythili L. ■ 15206 #041-12-2008 *012

RAGINS, Naomi. 4716 ELLSWORTH AVE 15213 #016-02-1951 L1955 **PYA CHP** *075 †75

RAGNI, Margaret Victoria. 3636 BLVD OF THE ALLIES 15213 #041-12-1975 L1976 **HEM** *050

RAGOWANSI, Ashvin T. 4815 LIBERTY AVE, STE 448 15224 #041-12-1987 L1993 **NS** *020 †25

RAHBAR, Rodeen. 320 E NORTH AVE, ALLEGHENY GENERAL HOSPITAL 15212 #055-02-2001 L2001 **VS** *012 †85

RAHMAN, Aref Mohammad. 200 LOTHROP ST, SCAIFE HALL, B 571.3 15213 #041-15-2002 L2005 **CD** *012 †20

RAHMAN, Mohammad Mohsin. 1400 LOCUST ST 15219 #704-02-1982 L2002 **DR VIR** *020 †80

RAINA, Amit. 121 MEYRAN AVE, DEPT OF INTERNAL MED 15213 #495-48-1999 L2004 **IM** *100 †20

RAJA, Ali Iftikhar. ■ 15203 #704-01-1998 L2007 **NS** *012

RAJAGOPALAN, Navin. 200 LOTHROP ST 15213 #038-40-2000 L2003 **CD** *020 †20

RAJAKUMAR, Kumaravel. 3705 5TH AVE, CHILDRENS HOSP PITTSBURGH 15213 #495-04-1982 L1995 **PD** *040 †55

RAJASEKHARA RAO, Gutti. ■ 15238 #495-11-1960 L1974 **NP** *020 †50

RAJAVEERAIAH, Kodali. 9100 BABCOCK BLVD 15237 #495-39-1965 L1976 **R** *020 †80

RAJENDIRAN, Swaminathan. 15237 #495-66-1987 L1999 **PTH** *100 †50

RAJI, Mohammad Reza. ■ 15215 #517-03-1971 L1981 **DR OS** *071 †80

RAJUPET, Gopinath. 2585 FREEPORT RD, STE 201 15238 #495-99-1984 L1993 **IM** *020 †20

RAKHSHAN, Mohammad. 320 E NORTH AVE 15212 #517-03-1966 L1973 **PTH** *020 †50

RAKITT, Tina Susanne. ■ 15208 #041-12-2003 L2003 **PG** *012 †55

RALPHE, John Carter. 3705 5TH AVE 15213 #035-08-1997 L2004 **PDC** *020 †55

RAMACHANDRAN, Radha. ■ 15217 #496-23-2003 L2006 **EM** *020 †16

RAMAEKER, Devon Marie. 15217 #046-01-2007 L2007 **OBG** *012

RAMAIYAH, Senthil Prakash. 200 LOTHROP ST, STE 503 15213 #495-94-2003 L2007 **IM** *012

RAMAKRISHNA, Nagamalli. 100 DELAFIELD RD, STE 301 15215 #495-16-1972 L1976 **GS VS** *020 †85

RAMALAKSHMI, Santhanam. ■ 15237 #495-66-1994 L2001 **NEP** *100 †20

RAMALINGAM, Suresh Sakkar. 5150 CENTRE AVE STE 552 15232 #495-59-1992 L2000 **HO** *050 †20 ‡

RAMAN, Asha. 4314 PENN AVE 15224 #495-09-1972 L1981 **IM CD** *020 †20

RAMANATHAN, Ramesh C. 3380 BOULEVARD OF THE ALLS, STE 390 15213 #495-04-1988 L1994 **GS** *020 †85

RAMANI, Gautam Venkat. 200 LOTHROP ST, STE 5B 15213 #041-02-2000 L2001 **CD** *020 †20

RAMANI, Ravi Neelakantan. 200 LOTHROP ST 15213 #495-73-1994 L2001 **CD** *020 †20

RAM-DEV RAO, Kasuganti. 1501 LOCUST ST STE G6 15219 #495-57-1967 L1973 **CD IM** *020 †20

RAMESH, Makum L. 200 LOTHROP ST 15213 #495-33-1972 L1980 **CD IM** *020 †20

RAMKUMAR, Mohan. 3550 TERRACE ST, A919 SCAIFE HALL 15213 #496-09-1995 L2000 **NEP IM** *020 †20

RAMRATNAM, Mohun. ■ 15232 #016-06-2004 L2007 **IM** *100 †20

RAMS, James John. ■ 15238 #010-02-1955 L1970 **CD TS** *071 †85,90

RAMSAY, Obie Lou. ■ 15217 #041-15-2003 L2003 **RHU** *012

RANA, Jamal Sabir. 200 LOTHROP ST, UPMC PRESBYTERIAL HOSPITAL 15213 #704-25-2000 L2005 **IM** *012

RANA, Sandeep Singh. 420 E NORTH AVE, STE 206 15212 #495-45-1984 L1995 **N** *020 †75 ‡

RANA, Sangeeta. 200 DELAFIELD RD 15215 #495-07-1986 L1995 **FM** *020 †20

RANCURELLO, Michael David. 320 E NORTH AVE 15212 #038-43-1977 L1978 **CHP P** *020 †75

RANDHAWA, Parmjeet Singh. 200 LOTHROP ST 15213 #495-45-1980 L1990 **PTH** *020 †50

RANEY, David Franklin. 200 LOTHROP ST, M115 UNIVERSITY CTR 15213 #047-05-1981 L1993 **CHP P** *030 †75

RANIER, George Joseph. 200 LOTHROP ST, PRESBYTERIAN HOSPITAL 15213 #041-12-1994 L1997 **AN** *020 †05

RANII, Carmello Angelo. 4800 FRIENDSHIP AVE 15224 #041-12-1946 L1947 **IM** *020

RANKIN, Robert Charles. 1050 BOWER HILL RD, STE 206 15243 #016-06-1974 L1980 **OBG** *020 †30

RANPURIA, Reena Kishor. A 915 SCAIFE HALL, 3550 TERRACE ST. 15261 #035-15-2002 L2002 **NEP** *020 †20

RAO, Anshul Mocherla. ■ 15237 #038-43-2006 L2006 **IM** *012

RAO, B Venkat. 5200 CENTRE AVE STE 206 15232 #495-57-1967 L1973 **CD IM** *020 †20

RAO, C V Sunder Ram. 9104 BABCOCK BLVD, STE 4106 15237 #495-16-1978 L1992 **CD IM** *020 †20

RAO, Chitra Kancherla. 6000 PARK PLAZA DR, STE 303 15229 #038-44-2005 L2005 **IM** *012

RAO, Goutham. 815 FREEPORT RD, ST MARGARET MEM HOSP 15215 #067-01-1993 L1996 **FM** *020 †18

RAO, Kasuganti Tumala. ■ 15238 #495-11-1972 L1979 **GPM EM** *020

RAO, Nalini G. 5750 CENTRE AVE, STE 230 15206 #495-45-1970 L1976 **ID IM** *050 †20 ‡

RAO, Rayasam Harsha. 3601 5TH AVE, RM #580 FALK BLDG 15213 #495-73-1974 L1985 **END IM** *020 †20

RAO, Uma Navaratna M. 200 LOTHROP ST 15213 #495-09-1969 L1990 **ATP** *020 †50

RAPHAEL, Brenda L. 300 HALKET ST 15213 #041-02-1988 L1990 **AN** *020 †05

RAPKIN, David Allen. ■ 15213 #041-13-2005 L2005 **OBG** *012

RAPTIS, Anastasios. 5115 CENTRE AVE, 3RD FL 15232 #418-04-1986 L2004 **HEM** *020 †20

RASTEGAR FASSAEI, Hooman. 121 MEYRAN AVE 15213 #517-05-1999 L2005 **AN** *012

RASTOGI, Priya. 300 HALKET ST 15213 #038-45-1997 L2001 **HO** *020 †20

RATHI, Vikas K. 320 E NORTH AVE, DIVISION OF CARDIOLOGY, AL 15212 #496-03-1996 L2001 **CD** *020 †20

RATHORE, Daleep K. ■ 15241 #496-03-1983 L1994 **P** *020 †75

RAULT, Raymond Marcel. 3550 TERRACE ST, A-909 SCAIFE HALL 15213 #917-29-1967 L1979 **NEP IM** *020 †20

RAVANO, Rowena Pingul. 4800 FRIENDSHIP AVE, FAMILY PRATICE PROGRAM 15224 #748-10-1997 L2005 **FP** *012

RAVEENDRAN, Bindu Ponnu. 300 HALKET ST, MAGEE WOMENS HOSP 15213 #038-44-2004 L2007 **NPM** *012

RAVINDRAN, Cholapurath Ni. 1500 5TH AVE, DEPT OF INTERNAL MED 15219 #495-44-1996 L2007 **IM** *012

RAVIPATI, Lakshmi Narasim. 1500 5TH AVE, DEPT OF INTERNAL MED 15219 #495-65-1998 L2007 **IM** *012

RAVISHANKAR, Ramalingam. 1350 LOCUST ST, STE 409 15219 #495-04-1990 L1999 **PM** *020 †60

RAVITSKIY, Larisa. ■ 15217 #035-19-2002 L2007 **PRD** *012 †15

RAY, Atanu. 4800 FRIENDSHIP AVE, GRADUATE MED EDUCATION 15224 #965-01-1983 L1993 **GS** *100

RAY, Richard Louis. 1307 FEDERAL ST, STE 2 15212 #041-12-1969 L1996 **ORS** *020 †40

RAYMOND, Jane Molnar. 320 E NORTH AVE 15212 #043-01-1986 L1989 **IM HEM** *020 †20

RAZ, Yael. 203 LOTHROP ST 15213 #005-14-1995 L2002 **OTO** *020 †45

RAZAK, Eathar Asim. 200 LOTHROP ST, SCAIFE HALL, SUITE B571.3 15213 #528-07-1995 L2002 **OTO** *012

READ, Thomas Edward. 4800 FRIENDSHIP AVE, 4600N DEPT OF SURGERY 15224 #005-02-1988 L2001 **GS CRS** *020 †85,10

READE, Michael Charles. 3550 TERRACE ST, STE 605 SCAIFE HALL 15261 #143-03-1996 L2005 **IM** *012

RECALDE, Scott Eric. 4381 MURRAY AVE 15217 #041-12-1997 L1999 **FM** *020 †18

RECAVARREN ASENCIOS, Rosem. OF PAT, UNIV OF PITTSBURGH DEPT 15261 #737-06-2002 L2004 **PTH** *012
RECIO, Rolando G. 400 PENN CENTER BLVD, STE 100 15235 #748-08-1959 L1969 **OBG** *071 †30
REDA, Frank A, Jr. 1000 BOWER HILL RD, SUITE 311 ST CLAIR HOSPITA 15243 #051-04-1952 L1958 **GYN** *071 †30
REDDY, Cara Elizabeth. 3471 5TH AVE, STE 201 15213 #041-15-2002 L2002 **PM** *100 †60
REDDY, Lakshmi Kakivaya. 117 N NEGLEY AVE 15206 #011-02-2000 L2001 **FM** *020 †18
REDDY, Lakshmi Kundhur. 200 LOTHROP ST, # FBT-SUIT 15213 #495-65-1997 L2000 **IM** *100 †20
REDDY, Pesara Sudhakar. 200 LOTHROP ST, PRESBYTERIAN HOSP 15213 #495-49-1962 L1972 **CD** *020 †20
REDDY, Ravinder Dwaram. 3811 OHARA ST 15213 #495-37-1981 L1993 **P** *050 †75
REDDY, Sudhir Nadvaluru. ■ 15232 #055-01-2005 L2005 **IM** *012
REDDY, Venkataramana Kodu. 1400 LOCUST ST, MERCY HOSP-PITTSBURGH 15219 #495-11-1997 L2005 **IM** *012
REDDY, Venkatlaxman B. 514 BELTZHOOVER AVE 15210 #495-50-1988 L1994 **IM** *020 †20
REDDY, Vivek Kotha. 200 LOTHROP ST, PUHC400 15213 #041-15-2002 L2002 **IM** *100
REDLINGER, Richard Edward, Jr. ■ 15236 #041-15-2006 L2006 **GS** *012
REDNER, Robert Laurie. 200 LOTHROP ST, HEMATOLOGY/SCAIFE HALL 15213 #024-01-1980 L1991 **HEM ON** *020 †20
REECE, Garry John. DESOTO & OHARA ST, DEPT RAD 15213 #143-01-1969 L1978 **DR** *020
REED, Darrell Kent. 1370 OLD FREEPORT RD # 1B, STE 1B 15238 #038-40-1975 L1981 **GE** *020 †20
REEDER, Jennifer Gordon. 200 LOTHROP ST, UPMC 15213 #033-06-2003 L2003 **HO** *012 †20
REEL, Charles M. ■ 15243 #041-12-1951 L1952 **OPH** *071 †35
REESE, Charles Edward. 1515 LOCUST ST 15219 #041-14-1980 L1981 **IM GE** *040 †20
REESE, Timothy Herman. 1425 BEAVER AVE, PBA 2ND STEP 15233 #038-43-1974 L1987 **EM** *075
REEVES, Matthew Fontaine. 300 HALKET ST, DEPT OF OB/GYN 15213 #024-01-1999 L2004 **OBG** *020 †30
REFAAT, Marwan Mouhamed. 121 MEYRAN AVE, DEPT CD 15213 #605-01-2003 L2007 **CD** *012 †20 ‡
REGUEIRO, Carol Ronk. 320 E NORTH AVE 15212 #041-09-1992 L1997 **IM** *020 †20
REGUEIRO, Miguel Duclos. 200 LOTHROP ST 15213 #041-09-1992 L1997 **GE** *020 †20
REHDER, John Gordon. 320 E NORTH AVE, AGH NUCLEAR CARDIOLOGY 15212 #028-34-1980 L1986 **CD** *020 †20,28
REHDER, Karen Viestenz. 580 S AIKEN AVE, STE 500 15232 #028-34-1982 L1986 **GYN** *020 †30
REICH, Jay Howard. 200 LOTHROP ST 15213 #035-09-1995 L2000 **EM** *020 †16
REIDBORD, Howard Elliott. 815 FREEPORT RD 15215 #041-12-1959 L1960 **PTH FOP** *020 †50
REIDER, Jodie Alton. 200 LOTHROP ST, E1140 BIOMEDICAL SCIENCE T 15261 #041-12-2002 L2002 **END** *012 †20
REIDY, Edward Donahue. 9104 BABCOCK BLVD, STE 2120 15237 #035-06-1994 L1998 **PM** *020 †60
REIDY, Margaret Eileen. 9365 MCKNIGHT RD, STE 300 15237 #035-06-1985 L1986 **PM** *071 †60
REILLY, James Brannigan. ■ 15228 #041-12-2005 L2005 **IM** *012
REILLY, James Jos, Jr. ■ 15208 #041-01-1972 L1980 **GS NTR** *020 †85
REILLY, Patrick Gerard. 1350 LOCUST ST, STE 308 15219 #539-06-1987 L1990 **PUD CCM** *020 †20
REINHARDT, Adam Lewis. 3705 5TH AVE, DEPARTMENT OF RHEUMATOLOGY 15213 #030-05-2002 L2005 **PPR** *012 †55
REIS, Alan Jan. 540 N NEVILLE ST STE 104 15213 #016-42-1995 L1998 **P** *020 †75
REIS, Evelyn Cohen. 3414 5TH AVE, DIV OF GENERAL ACADEMIC PE 15213 #024-01-1987 L1994 **PD** *040 †55
REIS, Steven Eric. 200 LOTHROP ST, UNIV OF PITTS MED CTR 15213 #024-01-1987 L1994 **CD IM** *020 †20
REISINGER, Keith Stewart. 1580 MCLAUGHLIN RUN RD, STE 208 15241 #041-12-1969 L1975 **PD PHP** *020 †55
REMPE, Brian David. 320 E NORTH AVE 15212 #016-45-1999 L2001 **EM** *020 †16
RENTON, Alan Cameron. 918 PARK AVE, STE 112 15234 #041-12-1965 L1969 **PS HS** *020
REPKA, Steven Edward. 4800 FRIENDSHIP AVE, N TOWER 15224 #041-13-2003 L2003 **DR** *012
RESHMI, Chandrappa S. 2409 BROWNSVILLE RD, C.S. RESHMI, M.D., INC. 15210 #495-35-1963 L1972 **OPH** *071 †35
RESNICK, Neil Martin. 3520 5TH AVE, KEYSTONE BLDG., STE 300 15213 #005-11-1977 L1999 **IMG U** *050 †20
RESNICK, Paul H. 200 DELAFIELD RD, STE 1040 15215 #010-02-1975 L1977 **ORS** *020 †40
RESTAURI, Nicole Lynne. ■ 15202 #041-12-2003 L2003 **DR** *012
REYES, Jorge Dionisio. 3601 5TH AVE, FALK CLINIC 15213 #187-06-1979 L1988 **GS TTS** *020 †85
REYES-LITTAUA, Maria Chri. ■ 15213 #748-10-1986 L2003 **PM** *020
REYNOLDS, Chas Felder, III. 3811 OHARA ST, WESTERN PSYCHIATRIC INSTIT 15213 #008-01-1973 L1974 **P PYG** *050 †75
REYNOLDS, Stacy Lynn. ■ 15228 #041-15-2000 L2000 **EM** *012 †55
RHEE, Diane Chungmin. ■ 15232 #041-12-2008 *012
RHEE, Robert Young. 5200 CENTRE AVE, STE 211 15232 #035-45-1988 L1995 **VS** *020 †85
RHODES, David H, Jr. 1835 FORBES AVE 15219 #041-12-1953 L1954 **OPH OS** *020 †35
RIANO, Felix Antonio. 4800 FRIENDSHIP AVE, DEPT OF SURGERY 15224 #264-19-1986 **GS** *012
RIAZ, Freaha. 4800 FRIENDSHIP AVE, DEPT OF GME 15224 #704-21-2005 L2006 **FP** *012
RIBAUDO, Janice. 563 E END AVE 15221 #035-15-1988 L1990 **FM** *020 †18
RICCELLI, Antonio Mariso. 250 MT LEBANON BLVD, STE 306 15234 #041-14-1989 L1991 **IM** *020 †20
RICE, Eileen Marie R. 200 DELAFIELD RD STE 2000 15215 #041-12-1974 L1975 **N** *020 †20,75
RICE, Jeffrey Ryan. ■ 15239 #041-13-2006 L2006 **GS** *012
RICE, Marc. 4815 LIBERTY AVE STE M56 15224 #041-12-1972 L1974 **CD IM** *020 †20
RICHARD, Charles Whiting. 3811 OHARA ST 15213 #038-40-1981 L1985 **P** *050
RICHARD, Scott Daniel. 300 HALKET ST, MAGEE WOMENS HOSPITAL/UPMC 15213 #035-03-2001 L2005 **OBG** *100
RICHARDS, Charles H. 3550 TERRACE ST, A-1305 SCAIFE HALL 15261 #024-05-1983 L1985 **AN PME** *020 †20,05
RICHARDS, Stephanie S. 5200 CENTRE AVE, STE 405 15232 #023-07-1992 L1995 **P PYG** *040 †75
RICHARDSON, James Robert. ■ 15237 #035-45-2002 L2006 **CD** *012 †20
RICHARDSON, Vanessa. 490 E NORTH AVE, STE 504 15212 #024-05-1978 L1980 **END IM** *020 †20
RICHARDSON, Ward Michael. ■ 15212 #041-12-2004 L2004 **GS** *012
RICHETTI, Joseph F. 3089 SUSSEX AVE 15226 #041-12-1992 L1994 **IM** *020 †20
RICHMAN, Jory Donald. 1350 LOCUST ST, STE 220 15219 #038-06-1986 L1992 **ORS** *020 †40
RICHTER, Erik. ■ 15223 #036-01-2003 L2004 **DR** *012
RICHTER, Tor. ■ 15213 #024-01-1951 L1981 **OM IM** *071 †20
RICK, Roxanne Kimberly. 1913 W CARSON ST 15219 #308-11-1986 L1987 **IM** *020
RICKIN, Eric David. 3811 OHARA ST, & CLINIC 15213 #038-41-2000 L2001 **P** *100 †75 ‡
RIDDLER, Sharon Anne. 200 LOTHROP ST, INFECTIOUS DIS/SCAIFE HALL 15213 #056-06-1986 L1991 **ID PD** *020 †55,20
RIDGWAY, William M. 5725 BASIC SCIENCE TOWER 15261 #035-45-1989 L1998 **IM** *020 †20
RIGAS, Christina Easther. ■ 15237 #017-20-2003 L2006 **PCC** *012
RIJHWANI, Ashok. 3708 5TH AVE, DEPT OF MED EDU 15213 #495-27-1990 L2005 *100
RIKE, Paul Miller. 4625 5TH AVE 15213 #041-12-1938 L1939 **IM CD** *071 †20
RILEY, Bernard John. 4221 PENN AVE 15224 #041-12-1959 L1960 **OBG** *071 †30
RINGER, Geoffrey W. ■ 15217 #051-07-2001 L2001 **GS** *020
RINGGER, Chad Michael. ■ 15237 #018-03-2006 L2007 **DR** *012
RIOS PEREZ, Jorge Arturo. 121 MEYRAN AVE 15213 #737-01-2003 L2006 **IM** *012
RIPEPI, Antonio John. 500 LEWIS RUN RD, STE 101 15122 #041-02-1993 L1999 **GS** *020 †85
RIPEPI, Philip Pasquale. 500 LEWIS RUN RD, STE 101 15122 #041-12-1960 L1961 **GS** *020 †85
RITCHEY, Arthur Kim. 3705 5TH AVE 15213 #038-41-1972 L1998 **PHO PD** *020 †55
RITTENBERGER, Jon Charles. 230 MCKEE PL, STE 400 15213 #041-12-2002 L2002 **EM** *020 †16
RIVENBURGH, Matthew Brian. ■ 15232 #041-12-2007 L2007 **EM** *012
RIVERA, Marcus Richard. ■ 15213 #033-05-2001 L2004 **PG** *100 †55
RIZK, Nashaat N. 200 DELAFIELD RD 15215 #915-04-1984 L1998 **AN** *020 †05
RIZK, Sherif Labib. 532 S AIKEN AVE, STE 501 15232 #016-01-1981 L1987 **CRS GS** *020 †10,85
RIZK, Wafia Kamel. ■ 15235 #330-02-1952 L1971 **OBG FM** *071
ROBA, Laurie Ann. 1326 FREEPORT RD, STE 200 15238 #035-06-1988 L1991 **OPH** *020 †35
ROBB, Jessica Fiester. ■ 15217 #041-12-2008 *012
ROBBINS, Terrance James. ■ 15232 #041-02-1961 L1962 **IM** *071 †20
ROBERGE, Raymond Jos. 300 HALKET ST, MAGEE WOMEN'S HOSPITAL 15213 #308-03-1981 L1984 **EM** *020 †16,70
ROBERT, Stephen Mark. 3705 5TH AVE 15213 #004-01-2001 L2005 **CCP** *012 †55
ROBERTS, James Michael. 204 CRAFT AVE, STE 610 15213 #025-01-1966 L1991 **OBG EP** *050 †35,30
ROBERTS, Jan Neal. 490 E NORTH AVE, STE 204 15212 #038-41-1978 L1980 **IM** *020 †20
ROBERTS, Linda Palone. 5230 CENTRE AVE 15232 #041-07-1972 L1973 **IM IMG** *020 ‡
ROBERTS, Mark Stenius. 200 LOTHROP ST, STE 600 15213 #024-07-1984 L1993 **END** *050 †20
ROBERTS, Michelle Maura. UNIV OF PITTSBURGH, E1140 BIOMEDICAL SCI TWR 15261 #036-07-1983 L1984 **END IM** *020 †20
ROBERTS, Seth Belote. 230 MCKEE PL, STE 500 15213 #051-04-2001 L2001 **EM** *020 †16
ROBERTSON, Douglas Duncan, Jr. 200 LOTHROP ST, MUH RM NE 520-3 15213 #010-02-1982 L1984 **ORS R** *020 †80
ROBINSKY, Boris. 5230 CENTRE AVE 15232 #913-13-1964 L1985 **PTH** *020
ROBINSON, Eric Paul. 200 DELAFIELD RD, PAIN MEDICIN 15215 #001-06-1995 L2007 **PMM** *012 †05
ROBINSON, John Norton. 9100 BABCOCK BLVD 15237 #010-01-1963 L1972 **TS VS** *020 †85,90
ROBINSON, Keven Mara. ■ 15232 #041-02-2005 L2005 **MPD** *012
ROBINSON, Wm Overholt. ■ 15206 #041-01-1948 L1949 **EM GS** *030 †85
ROBISON, Walter James, Jr. 1039 BROOKLINE BLVD 15226 #051-04-1976 L1977 **IM** *020 †20
ROCHE, Karen Ruth. 9365 MCKNIGHT RD, STE 200 15237 #041-12-1975 L1976 **PS CS** *020 †65
ROCK, Jason Edward. 3811 OHARA ST, RM 134 15213 #038-40-2003 L2003 **CHP** *012
ROCKACY, Douglas David. 3519 COLBY ST, STE 500 15214 #036-01-2000 L2001 **EM** *020 †16
ROCKACY, Matthew Jason. ■ 15210 #041-12-2006 L2006 **IM** *012
RODEBERG, David Anthony. 3705 5TH AVE 15213 #056-05-1989 L2006 **PDS** *020 †85
RODEMANN, Joseph Franklin. ■ 15243 #016-43-2003 L2007 **GE** *012 †20
RODNAN, Joan Bernstien. CHILDREN'S HOSP 15213 #035-19-1950 L1960 **PD OS** *040
RODOSKY, Mark Wm. 2000 MARY ST 15203 #035-47-1987 L1989 **ORS** *020 †40
RODRIGUEZ, Aurelio. 320 E NORTH AVE, STE 594 S TOWER 15212 #737-01-1968 L2000 **TRS** *020 †85
RODRIGUEZ, Eric Gibson. 3459 5TH AVE 15213 #010-01-1979 L1985 **IM IMG** *020 †20
RODRIGUEZ, Graciana. ■ 15232 #132-09-1990 **CHN** *100
RODRIGUEZ, Kenneth David. ■ 15222 #041-12-2007 L2007 *012
ROESEL, Daniel M. ■ 15219 #038-75-2007, ▲ L2007 *012
ROGAL, Michael J. ■ 15206 #041-01-1977 L1978 **ORS** *020 †40
ROGERS, Robert Mark. 3459 5TH AVE, NW628MUH 15213 #041-01-1960 L1961 **PUD IM** *030 †20
ROGERS, Steve. 1323 HEBERTON ST 15206 #038-45-1984 L1985 **OPH** *020 †35 ‡
ROGULA, Tomasz. ■ 15232 #759-01-1993 L2006 **GS** *100
ROH, Ellen Kimberly. ■ 15232 #041-12-2002 L2004 **D** *012
ROH, Mark Stephen. 320 E NORTH AVE 15212 #038-40-1979 L1980 **GS** *020 †85
ROLL, Julius Peter. 1350 LOCUST ST, STE 408 15219 #038-40-1975 L1987 **OPH** *020 †35 ‡
ROLLINS-RAVAL, Marian Ali. ■ 15232 #036-01-2006 L2006 **PTH** *012
ROLLMAN, Bruce Lawrence. 230 MCKEE PL, STE 600 15213 #041-02-1988 L1995 **IM** *050 †20
ROMA, Rebecca S. 1200 REEDSDALE ST 15233 #041-12-2001 L2001 **P** *100 †75
ROMAND, Jacques A. 367 LEHIGH AVE 15232 #869-04-1981 L1992 **CCA** *020
ROMBERGER, James A. 300 HALKET ST 15213 #041-14-1975 L1984 **PD** *020 †55
ROMEO, Ryan Christopher. 300 HALKET ST, MAGEE HOSPITAL 15213 #041-14-1995 L1998 **AN** *020 †05
ROMERO-CACES, Gloria M. 777 PENN CENTER BLVD, STE 600 15235 #748-01-1979 L1992 **PTH** *020 †50
ROODMAN, Garson David. 151U UNIVRSTY DRV C #2E114, VA PITTSBURGH HLTHCARE SYS 15240 #020-12-1973 L2001 **HEM IM** *050 †20
ROONEY, Edward Francis. 514 BELTZHOOVER AVE 15210 #010-02-1958 L1959 **FM GS** *075 †85
ROOSEN, Christina. ■ 15238 #935-07-1993 L2003 **PAN** *020
ROPER, Carol Kalinowski. 3601 5TH AVE, DERM CLINIC 15213 #041-12-2000 L2001 **D** *020 †15
ROQUE, Dana Marie. ■ 15213 #036-01-2007 L2007 **OBG** *012
ROSADO, Zenaida. 1000 CLIFFMINE RD STE 210, ROBINSON OB/GYN ASSOC 15275 #041-12-1998 L2001 **OBG** *020 †30
ROSAS, Ivan Orlando. 3459 5TH AVE, DIVISION OF PULMONARY 15213 #264-01-1991 L2005 **PCC** *020 †20
ROSE, Carol Elaine. 200 LOTHROP ST 15213 #011-02-1978 L1979 **AN** *020 †05
ROSEN, Clark Alan. 203 LOTHROP ST 15213 #016-01-1989 L1995 **OTO OS** *020 †45
ROSEN, Johanna R. ■ 15221 #051-04-2006 L2006 **PD** *012
ROSEN, Jules. 3811 OHARA ST 15213 #038-41-1978 L1985 **P CHP** *040 †75

■ = Address Information Privacy Protected

ROSEN, Paul. 3705 5TH AVE 15213 #035-06-1997 L2003 **PPR** *020 †55

ROSEN, Rochelle. 2000 MARY ST 15203 #041-12-1977 L1978 **EM** *020 †16

ROSENBERG, Cynthia N. 326 PENN CTR BLVD, HEALTH DIALOG PENN CTR W 15235 #041-12-1982 L1983 **FPG** *030 †18 ‡

ROSENBERG, George Larry. 201 S HIGHLAND AVE, STE 102 15206 #020-02-1977 L1981 **GYN OBS** *020 †30

ROSENBERG, Paul R. 532 S AIKEN AVE, STE 520 15232 #035-08-1978 L1983 **OPH** *020 †35 ‡

ROSENBERG, Pinchas Philip. ■ 15217 #016-06-2001 L2007 **OPH** *020

ROSENBLUM, David Harry. ■ 15217 #041-12-1976 L1976 **GS** *071 †85

ROSENFELD, Rochelle Lynn. ■ 15217 #017-20-2002 L2007 **GS** *100

ROSENGART, Matthew R. 200 LOTHROP ST, F1266.1 15213 #001-02-1995 L2004 **TRS GS** *020 †85

ROSENKRANZ, Margalit E. ■ 15217 #041-12-1998 L2006 **PPR** *020 †55

ROSENSTOCK, Jason Bruce. 3811 OHARA ST, INSTITUTE AND CLINIC 15213 #043-01-1992 L1994 **P** *040 †75

ROSENTHAL, Bruce Wayne. 1400 LOCUST ST, MERCY HOSP 15219 #041-13-1979 L1981 **OS** *020 †55,16

ROSINI, Rita Marie. 4800 FRIENDSHIP AVE 15224 #041-07-1945 L1946 **PD** *071

ROSKOPH, Jay Alan. 3550 TERRACE ST, A-1305 SCAIFE HALL 15261 #038-40-1987 L1989 **AN** *020 †05

ROSS, Gerald J. 400 PENN CENTER BLVD, STE 555 15235 #041-13-1986 L1987 **DR** *020 †80

ROSS, James Stevenson. 619 MOUNT ROYAL BLVD 15223 #041-12-1954 L1955 **GP** *020

ROSS, Judy Deivernois. 1050 BOWER HILL RD, STE 205 15243 #041-12-1992 L1995 **GS** *020 †85

ROSSI, Albert Jos, Jr. 3811 OHARA ST 15213 #041-12-1976 L1977 **P** *020 †75

ROSSI, Joseph Anthony. 4800 FRIENDSHIP AVE, THE WESTERN PENNSYLVANIA H 15224 #038-44-1987 L1992 **CCM PUD** *020

ROSSI, Michelle Ida. 3459 5TH AVE 15213 #035-47-1988 L1990 **IMG IM** *020 †20

ROSSMAN, Gerald Geo. 490 E NORTH AVE, STE 200 15212 #041-09-1984 L1985 **IM** *020 †20

ROTENSTEIN, Deborah. 1789 S BRADDOCK AVE, STE 294 15218 #041-12-1978 L1981 **PDE PD** *020 †55 ‡

ROTH, Kimberly Raquel. 3705 5TH AVE 15213 #051-01-1999 L2001 **PEM** *020 †55

ROTH, Loren Henry. 200 LOTHROP ST 15213 #024-01-1966 L1974 **P PHP** *020 †75

ROTH, Ronald Neal. 200 LOTHROP ST 15213 #041-12-1982 L1983 **EM** *020 †16

ROTHENBERG, Mitchell H. 9100 BABCOCK BLVD 15237 #023-01-1986 L1992 **ORS** *020 †40

ROTHERAM, Edward Brook. 320 E NORTH AVE 15212 #041-01-1959 L1960 **IM** *071 †20

ROTHFUS, William Edward. 320 E NORTH AVE, ALLEGHENY RADIOLOGY 15212 #035-45-1976 L1977 **DR** *020 †80

ROTHSCHILD, Adam Scott. ■ 15217 #016-11-2000 L2001 **FP** *012

ROTHSCHILD, Jeffrey Mark. 1400 LOCUST ST, MERCY HOSPITAL 15219 #056-06-1978 L1981 **CCM IM** *020 †20

ROTTGERS, Stephen Alexand. UNIV OF PITTSBURGH, 3550 TERRACE STREET 15261 #048-04-2007 L2007 **PS** *012

ROTTINGHAUS, David M. 320 E NORTH AVE 15212 #038-43-1998 L2000 **EM** *020 †16

ROUX, Louis A D. 3811 OHARA ST DEPT CCA 15213 #836-02-1966 **CCA** *020

ROWLAND, James Joseph. 5500 CORPORATE DR, STE 240 15237 #041-13-1994 L1996 **OBG** *020 †30

ROWLAND, Norris D, Jr. ■ 15211 #041-02-1951 L1952 **GP OS** *075

ROWLAND, Paul Leslie, III. 4221 PENN AVE 15224 #041-12-1990 L1992 **PD** *020 †55 ‡

ROY, Louise. 121 MEYRAN AVE, DEPT MED EDUCATION 15213 #067-02-1987 L1992 **AN** *020

RO-YIM, Sandy H. 420 E NORTH AVE, STE 406 15212 #024-07-1993 L2000 **D** *020 †20,15

ROZEN, Shari Evalynn. 275 CURRY HOLLOW RD, ARBOR PROFESSIONAL CENTER 15236 #041-02-2002 L2002 **FM** *020 †18

ROZIN, Leon. 542 4TH AVE 15219 #913-89-1955 L1983 **LM** *071

RUBERTSSON, Sten I. ■ 15228 #858-03-1984 L1995 **CCA** *020

RUBIN, Fred Howard. 5200 CENTRE AVE, STE 211 15232 #041-14-1975 L1977 **IMG IM** *040 †20

RUBIN, Harvey Martin. 1580 MCLAUGHLIN RUN RD, STE 208 15241 #041-09-1966 L1967 **PD NPM** *071 †55

RUBIN, J Peter. 200 DELAFIELD RD 15215 #024-07-1992 L2002 **PS** *020 †85,65

RUBIN, Joshua Tarbut. 6950 BLENHEIM CT 15208 #010-01-1979 L1990 **SO** *020 †85

RUBIN, Lore Reich. 400 45TH ST 15201 #035-19-1954 L1964 **PYA P** *071 †75

RUBIN, Seth Ryan. 5215 CENTRE AVE, UPMC SHADYSIDE 15232 #041-12-1999 L2001 **FM** *020 †18

RUBINSTEIN, Debra Nan. 300 HALKET ST, STE 0610 15213 #041-12-1982 L1983 **OBG** *020 †30

RUBINSTEIN, Roee Elan. 15213 #028-02-2004 L2004 **PS** *012

RUBIO, Wilfredo V. 9100 BABCOCK BLVD 15237 #748-01-1967 L1973 **GP** *020

RUCEKOVA, Alica. 100 TECHNOLOGY DR, RM 553 15219 #286-03-1996 L2006 **GPM** *012

RUDIN, Jennifer Ellen. 4800 FRIENDSHIP AVE 15224 #035-46-1979 L1980 **ID IM** *020 †20

RUDKIN, Victor Marvin. 705 S LINDEN AVE 15208 #041-13-1974 L1975 **IM GE** *020 †20

RUDOLPH, Joseph Philip. 328 CURRY HOLLOW RD 15236 #041-14-1975 L1978 **A FM** *020 †16

RUEGER, Raimund Geo. ■ 15238 #407-19-1954 L1962 **OTO HNS** *071 †45

RUFFNER, Robert John. 5200 CENTRE AVE STE 710, CARDIOVASCULAR ASSOCIATES, 15232 #023-07-1981 L1983 **CD IM** *020 †20

RUGGIERO, Renato. 414 S CRAIG ST 15213 #561-23-1982 L1998 **TS CD** *020 †85,90

RUHL, Anna Mary. 200 LOTHROP ST, UPMC MONTEFIORE, N713 15213 #025-01-1998 L2000 **IM** *020 †20

RULIN, Marvin Calvin. HALKET ST, MAGEE WOMENS HOSPITAL 15213 #016-42-1954 L1960 **OBG** *072 †20

RUMBLE, Thomas Reid. 4815 LIBERTY AVE, MELLON PAVILION 15224 #012-05-1971 L1971 **P PYG** *071 †75

RUMSCH, Bernard James. ■ 15217 #869-05-1950 L1973 **FOP PTH** *072

RUNCO, Angelo S. 4221 PENN AVE, FL 4 15224 #041-12-1950 L1951 **PD** *071 †55

RUNGRUANG, Bunja Jane. 300 HALKET ST, MAGEE-WOMENS HOSPITAL 15213 #001-02-2005 L2005 **OBG** *012

RUPP, Richard Witt. 121 MEYRAN AVE, DEPT OF RADIO -CHP MT 3950 15213 #010-01-2000 L2005 **DR** *012

RUSCHER, Adam. 320 E NORTH AVE, DEPT OF 15212 #067-01-2004 L2004 **EM** *100

RUSSAVAGE, James Michael. 3550 TERRACE ST, 678 SCAIFE HALL 15213 #041-12-1987 L1990 **PS** *020 †65

RUSSELL, Marsha Yolanda. ■ 15235 #566-01-1997 L2007 **PDI** *012 †20,55

RUSSELL, Mary Louise. 3705 5TH AVE 15213 #041-07-1983 L1989 **PM** *020 †60,55

RUSSELL, Teresa Danielle. ■ 15220 #035-06-2002 L2002 **PPR** *012

RUSSMAN, Richard B. 1050 BOWER HILL RD, STE 308 15243 #041-09-1964 L1965 **CD PUD** *020

RUSSO, Linda Marie. 3705 5TH AVE 15213 #030-06-1998 L2001 **PDC** *030 †55

RUTKOSKI, John Daniel. ■ 15221 #041-13-2006 L2006 **GS** *012

RUTMAN, Deanna Love. 1910 COCHRAN RD 15220 #041-12-1981 L1982 **OBG** *020 †30 ‡

RUTOVIC, Zorica. 5119 CLAIRTON BLVD 15236 #957-02-1984 L1996 **FM** *020 †18

RUZICZKA, Linda Ann. ■ 15209 #041-12-1986 L1986 **OPH** *071 †35

RYAN, Alexander Thomas. 5230 CENTRE AVE, PRESBYTERIAN SHADYSIDE 15232 #041-12-2006 L2007 **TY** *012

RYAN, Manijeh. ■ 15220 #517-01-1994 L2007 **PM** *012

RYAN, Neal David. 3811 OHARA ST, UNIVERSITY OF PITTS SCH OF 15213 #008-01-1978 L1984 **CHP P** *020 †75

RYAN, Steven James. 530 MARSHALL AVE, THE PRESSLEY RIDGE SCHOOLS 15214 #030-05-1983 L1993 **CHP P** *020 †75

RYBKA, Witold Boleslaw J. 311 S CRAIG ST, STE 300 15213 #065-01-1972 L1991 **ON HEM** *020 †20

RYCHECK, Russell Rule. GRAD SCHL OF PUB HLTH UNIV, RM A 510 CRABTREE HALL 15261 #041-12-1975 L1978 **PHP GPM** *040 †70

RYDZE, Richard Anthony. 425 1ST AVE, SECOND FLOOR 15219 #041-12-1975 L1976 **IM** *020 †20

RYDZE, Robert Anthony. ■ 15243 #038-41-1944 L1948 **GP P** *071

RYMER, David Bryan. 320 E NORTH AVE 15212 #055-01-1983 L1986 **AN** *020 †05

RYTEL, Michael Jan. 5820 CENTRE AVE, GREATER PITTSBURGH ORTHOPA 15206 #016-06-1990 L1995 **ORS** *020 †40

SAAD, Reda Shibl. 320 E NORTH AVE, ALLEGHANY GEN HOSP 15212 #915-03-1983 L2001 **SP** *100 †50

SAALBACH, Christine. 5230 CENTRE AVE 15232 #051-04-1984 L1985 **FM** *020 †18

SAALOUKEH, Michel. 1400 LOCUST ST, DEPARTMENT OF PEDIATRICS 15219 #875-03-1997 L2001 **NPM** *020 †55

SABA, Samir F. 200 LOTHROP ST, CVI PUH B535 15213 #605-01-1993 L2000 **ICE** *020 †20

SABEH, Christina Marie. 200 LOTHROP ST 9S, GENERAL INTERNAL MEDICINE 15213 #041-13-2001 L2001 **IM** *020

SABO, Daniel P. 5230 CENTRE AVE 15232 #041-12-1991 L1994 **AN** *020 †05

SABOL, Joseph Geno. 4800 FRIENDSHIP AVE, WEST PENN HOSPITAL 15224 #041-13-1988 L1990 **IM** *020 †20

SACCO, David Russell. 300 CEDAR BLVD 15228 #041-12-2000 L2003 **IM** *020 †20

SACCO, Russell John. 5200 CENTRE AVE, STE 603 15232 #041-12-1971 L1972 **IM IMG** *071 †20 ‡

SACHS, Murray. 5200 CENTRE AVE, STE 211 15232 #041-12-1957 L1958 **PUD IM** *020 †20

SACHSE, Brett Allen. 320 E NORTH AVE, ALLEGHENY GENERAL HOSPITAL 15212 #041-15-2001 L2001 **GS** *020

SADLER, James Lorin. ■ 15236 #041-12-2004 L2004 **AN** *012

SADOVSKY, Yoel. 204 CRAFT AVE, MAGEE WOMENS RESEARCH INST 15213 #550-01-1986 L2007 **OBG MFM** *050 †30

SADOWSKI, Hubert F. 1000 BOWER HILL RD RM 106 15243 #025-07-1969 L1971 **IM** *071 †20

SAFAR, Douha. 1400 LOCUST ST, BLDG D 15219 #875-02-1989 L1996 **END** *020 †20 ‡

SAFATLE-RIBEIRO, Adriana. ■ 15213 #187-04-1987 **GE** *020

SAFAVI, Haleh. ■ 15237 #517-05-2000 L2008 **IM** *020 †20

SAFDARIAN, Nastaran. ■ 15232 #048-15-2005 L2005 **IM** *012

SAFIER, Robert Adam. 3705 5TH AVE 15213 #550-02-1999 L2002 **CHN** *020 †55,75

SAFYAN, Eric Lee. 1400 LOCUST ST 15219 #041-12-1981 L1986 **ON HEM** *020 †20

SAFYAN, Susan L. 660 WASHINGTON RD, STE 201 15228 #005-14-1981 L1986 **D** *020 †10 ‡

SAGAN, Elizabeth Rose. 300 HALKET ST, STE 2541 15213 #041-12-1979 L1982 **U** *020 †95

SAH, Mukesh. 3811 OHARA ST, WESTERN PSYCH INST & CLC 15213 #495-45-1983 L1998 **P** *020 †75

SAH, Neera Bansal. 300 HALKET ST 3RD FL, RM 3510 15213 #495-45-1984 L2000 **AN** *020 †05 ‡

SAHAI, Rohit Kumar. 200 LOTHROP ST, DEPARTMENT OF SURGERY 15213 #025-01-2001 L2001 **GS** *100 †85

SAHAI, Vaibhav. 1400 LOCUST ST, MERCY HOSPITAL 15219 #495-03-2004 L2007 **IM** *012

SAHNI, Ramona. 815 FREEPORT RD # PATH, ST MARGARET MEM HOSP 15215 #495-08-1967 L1979 **PTH** *071 †50

SAHOVEY, James R. 5608 WILKINS AVE 15217 #010-02-1975 L1978 **IM** *020 †20

SAHOVIC, Entezam Asim. 4800 FRIENDSHIP AVE, STE 2303 15224 #957-08-1978 L2006 **HEM ON** *020 †20

SAHUD, Andrew Graham. ■ 15217 #016-42-2000 L2005 **ID** *100 †20

SAHUD, Hannah. 5738 WILKINS AVE # 1A 15217 #016-42-2000 L2005 **PD** *020 †55 ‡

SAIFEE, Kutub Mohamedbhai. 490 E NORTH AVE, STE 302 15212 #495-01-1961 L1969 **TS** *020 †85,90

SAIGAL, Sonia. 320 E NORTH AVE 15212 #496-07-1994 L1999 **IM** *020 †20

SAITO, Reisuke. VET ADMIN HOSP PATH 15240 #572-28-1959 L1970 **PTH** *071 †50

SAITZ, Edward Wilde. ■ 15238 #041-12-1961 L1962 **PD** *030 †55

SAKAI, Tetsuro. 121 MEYRAN AVE 15213 #572-01-1989 L2001 **AN** *100 †05

SAKAMOTO, Sara Beth. ■ 15261 #041-12-2007 L2007 **OBG** *012

SAKOLSKY, Dara Jennifer. 3811 OHARA ST 15213 #041-13-2000 L2001 **P** *050 †75 ‡

SALADIN, Lois J D. 232 N CRAIG ST, 130 N BELLEFIELD ST 15213 #041-13-1958 L1959 **CHP P** *071 †75

SALADINO, Richard Anthony. 3705 5TH AVE 15213 #028-03-1985 L2000 **PD PEM** *020 †55

SALAMA, Marybeth Pope. 235 ALPHA DR, STE 101 15238 #041-12-1988 L1990 **FM** *020 †18

SALANGSANG, Jo-Anne Marie. 121 MEYRAN AVE 15213 #748-02-1996 L2006 **ID** *012 †20

SALATA, Rose Ann J. 320 E NORTH AVE 15212 #041-14-1980 L1981 **END IM** *020 †20

SALERNI, Rosemarie. UNIVERSITY DR, CARDIOLOGY 15235 #035-08-1968 L1969 **CD** *071 †20

SALGADO POGACNIK, Javier. 4800 FRIENDSHIP AVE, SUITE 4600 NORTH TOWER 15224 #132-02-2004 L2007 **GS** *012

SALIBA, Zeina. ■ 15217 #051-04-2008 L2008 *012

SALIBI, Naman. 200 LOTHROP ST, STE 5C 15213 #605-01-1973 L2006 **NS** *020 †25

SALIM, Debra Lynn. 1400 LOCUST ST, MERCY PRIMARY CARE 15219 #055-02-2003 L2003 **IM** *100 †20

SALONIA, Rosanne. ■ 15221 #305-01-2002 L2005 **CCP** *012 †55

SALUJA, Arpit. ■ 15232 #496-09-2003 L2005 **FP** *012

SALVOZA, Manuel Ijares. 320 E NORTH AVE, ALLEGHENY GEN HOSP 15212 #748-01-1963 L1973 **CD** *071

SAM, Mammen Ashish. 1400 LOCUST ST 15219 #048-02-2003 L2003 **IM** *020 †20

SAMADANI, Siroos. 532 S AIKEN AVE 15232 #517-01-1962 L1971 **TS** *071 †85,90

SAMII, Soraya Mehraban. 200 LOTHROP ST STE B535, UPMC-PRESBYTERIAN 15213 #041-14-1997 L1999 **ICE** *100 †20

SAMPHIRE, John. 9100 BABCOCK BLVD 15237 #061-01-1995 L2002 *020

SAMUEL, Amber Rachael. 121 MEYRAN AVE, MAGEE-WOMEN'S HOSP 15213 #048-04-2006 L2006 **OBG** *012

■ = Address Information Privacy Protected

SAMY, Hazem Mahmoud. 203 LOTHROP ST 15213 #915-04-1986 L2005 **OPH** *020 †35 ‡
SANDBERG, Joyce A B. ■ 15241 #041-07-1954 L1955 **GP** *071
SANDBERG, Theodore Ernest. 100 BAYER RD, BLDG 6 15205 #045-01-1948 L1950 **OM IM** *030
SANDERS, Aimee. ■ 15217 #038-40-2003 L2003 **IM** *020 †20
SANDERS, Mark Helms. 0 UNIVERSITY DRIVE C, PULMONARY/VA HOSP 15240 #035-15-1974 L1982 **PUD IM** *020 †20
SANDERS, Michael Kevin. 200 LOTHROP ST 15213 #001-06-1998 L2006 **GE** *020 †20
SANDERS, Robert Wyman. ■ 15217 #016-42-2005 L2005 **EM** *012
SANDHU, Imran Khalid. 1400 LOCUST ST 15219 #704-02-1998 L2001 **IM** *100 †20
SANDHU, Rajdeep Singh. ■ 15205 #032-01-2000 L2005 **VS** *020
SANDHU, Rupinder. 1400 LOCUST ST 15219 #912-01-1998 L2002 **IM** *100 †20
SANDHU, Saima Imran. 1400 LOCUST ST, MERCY HOSPITAL 15219 #704-06-2003 L2007 **IM** *012
SANDO, Isamu. 200 LOTHROP ST, PRESBYTERIAN HOSP 15213 #572-28-1952 **OTO PTH** *050
SANDRONI, Stephen Eugene. 320 E NORTH AVE, ALLEGHENY GENERAL HOSPITAL 15212 #035-09-1978 L2001 **NEP IM** *020 †20
SANDSON, Gerald B. 401 SHADY AVE STE A-1 15206 #041-12-1963 L1964 **CHP P** *020
SANDULACHE, Vlad Constant. ■ 15261 #041-12-2008 *012
SANDY, Edward Allen. 300 HALKET ST, MAGEE-WOMEN'S HOSPITAL 15213 #051-07-1984 L2008 **OBG** *020 †30
SANFILIPPO, Andrea Michel. 300 HALKET ST, MAGEE WOMEN HOSP 15213 #020-02-2006 L2006 **DR** *012
SANFILIPPO, Joseph S. 300 HALKET ST, MAGEE WOMENS HOSP 15213 #016-42-1973 L1998 **REN GYN** *020 †30 ‡
SANFILIPPO, Kristen Marie. ■ 15217 #028-03-2007 L2007 **IM** *012
SANGHA, Amandeep Singh. 320 E NORTH AVE, STE 206 15212 #495-03-1997 L2003 **N** *100 †75
SANGIMINO, Mark Jos. 1307 FEDERAL ST, STE 2 15212 #041-02-1990 L1996 **DR OP** *020 †40
SANGL, John David. ■ 15218 #041-15-2007 L2007 **EM** *012
SANGRUJEE, Kannika L. S JACKSON AVE 15202 #891-03-1966 L1973 **AN** *020 †05
SANIKOMMU, Vijaya Bharath. ■ 15237 #495-50-1998 L2002 **CD** *012 †20
SANTORA, Dawn Marie. 3601 5TH AVE, FALK MEDICAL BLDG, SUITE 3 15213 #041-12-1989 L1992 **RHU** *020 †20
SANTORA, Frank James, Jr. ■ 15237 #561-01-1970 L1973 **GS** *071
SANTOS, Arthur Magno. 532 S AIKEN AVE 15232 #748-10-1972 L1974 **TS** *075 †85,90
SANTUCCI, Francesco. 4747 LIBERTY AVE 15224 #041-07-1983 L1985 **IM** *020 †20
SAPPATI, Shailaja Reddy. 200 LOTHROP ST RM 3950, MAIN TOWER 15213 #495-65-1997 L2004 **DR** *100 †80
SAPPINGTON, Penny Lynn. 200 LOTHROP ST 15213 #041-14-1994 L1999 **CCM ID** *020 †20
SARANGARAJAN, Ranganathan. 3705 5TH AVE, DEPT PATH CHP 15213 #495-17-1988 L1996 **PP** *020 †50
SARI, Colleen E. 5655 BRYANT ST STE 108 15206 #048-14-1985 L1996 **P CHP** *020 †75
SARKAR, Chaitali. 1400 LOCUST ST 15219 #495-38-2004 L2006 **IM** *012
SARMA, Rajkumar R. 12 EASTERN AVE, STE 100 15215 #496-01-1988 L2000 **PYG** *020
SARMA, Shashikala. 2585 FREEPORT RD, STE 201 15238 #495-62-1989 L1995 **IM** *020 †20
SARNAIK, Ajit Ashok. 3705 5TH AVE, 6TH FLOOR PCCM 15213 #025-07-2002 L2005 **CCP** *012 †55
SARNER, Joel Braude. 200 LOTHROP ST 15213 #041-13-1983 L1984 **AN PAN** *020 †05
SARSHAR ILKHANIPOUR, Z. 200 LOTHROP ST 15213 #517-01-1958 L1983 **R OS** *020
SARUMI, Molade. 3601 5TH AVE, STE 3A 15213 #917-34-1999 L2005 **CCM** *012 †20
SASATOMI, Eizaburo. 121 MEYRAN AVE 15213 #572-81-1989 L2003 **SP** *100 †50
SATHE, Geeta Ganesh. ■ 15213 #041-14-2007 L2007 **PM** *012
SAU, Indranil. 3705 5TH AVE, DEPARTMENT OF PEDIATRIC SU 15213 #495-02-1996 L2007 **PDS** *012
SAUER, Cary Gordon. 3705 5TH AVE, CHP - PEDIATRIC GI DEPT 15213 #056-05-2002 L2005 **PG** *012 †55
SAUEREISEN, Sandra Chase. 3937 BUTLER ST 15201 #041-09-1992 L1994 **FM PHP** *040 †18
SAUNDERS, Cathy Lynne. 320 E NORTH AVE, ALLEGHENY GEN HOSP 15212 #041-07-1991 L1993 **OBG** *020 †30
SAUNDERS, Timothy S. 1400 LOCUST ST, MERCY HOSP OF PITTSBURGH 15219 #041-15-2007 L2007 **TY** *012
SAWYER, Kelly Nicole. ■ 15222 #047-05-2006 L2006 **EM** *012
SAWYER, Patricia Heather. 100 S JACKSON AVE, ALLEGHENY GENERAL SUBURBAN 15202 #021-01-1987 L1989 **EM** *020 †16
SAXENA, Shashank. 3550 TERRACE ST, A-1305 SCAIFE HALL 15261 #496-09-1993 L1999 **APM** *020 †05
SCALERCIO, Anthony Ralph. 1400 LOCUST ST 15219 #041-12-1977 L1979 **DR** *020 †80
SCANSETTI, Giuliana T. 300 HALKET ST, MWH DEPT PATHOLOGY 15213 #561-20-1974 L1988 **PTH** *020 †50
SCARAMUCCI, John Carl. 4140 BROWNSVILLE RD 15227 #041-12-1957 L1958 **GYN** *071 †30
SCHACHTER, Allan Bert. 5750 CENTRE AVE, STE 430 15206 #016-42-1967 L1969 **U** *020 †95
SCHACHTER, Joseph. 401 SHADY AVE, NO 202B 15206 #035-19-1952 L1968 **PYA CD** *071 †75
SCHAFFER, Ted Curran. 619 MOUNT ROYAL BLVD 15223 #051-04-1979 L1980 **FM FPG** *040 †18 ‡
SCHAFFNER, Kenneth F. 220 N DITHRIDGE ST, APT 802 15213 #041-12-1986 *050
SCHAITKIN, Barry Michael. 200 DELAFIELD RD 15215 #041-14-1984 L1986 **OTO GS** *020 †45
SCHANER, Paul Jos. 1400 LOCUST ST 15219 #041-12-1963 L1964 **AN** *071 †05
SCHAPIRO, Rolf Lutz. 320 E NORTH AVE, ALLEGHENY RADIOLOGY 15212 #038-06-1964 L1979 **R** *071 †80
SCHAUBLE, Thomas Lee. 9102 BABCOCK BLVD, STE LL1 15237 #041-13-1983 L1984 **PUD IM** *020 †20
SCHEATZLE, Mark David. 320 E NORTH AVE 15212 #038-40-1993 L1995 **EM** *020 †16
SCHEEL, Michael John. 180 FORT COUCH RD 15241 #041-12-1998 L2000 **ORS** *020 †40
SCHEGG, Tracy Regina. ■ 15232 #031-01-2007 L2007 **CPP** *012
SCHELER, Carl Elmer. 815 FREEPORT RD 15215 #041-09-1978 L1979 **IM EM** *020 †20,16
SCHERER, Joseph. 713 WASHINGTON RD 15228 #063-01-1999 L2001 **OPH** *020 †35
SCHEUER, Mark Louis. 3471 5TH AVE STE 811, LILIANE KAUFMANN BLDG 15213 #016-02-1983 L1996 **N OS** *020 †75
SCHIANO, Michael Todd. 320 E NORTH AVE, ALLEGHEN GEN HOSP 15212 #422-01-2003 L2003 **IM** *020 †20
SCHILKEN, Robert Edward. 1307 FEDERAL ST, STE 2 15212 #041-12-1990 L1994 **ORS** *020 †40
SCHILLO, Robert Edward. ■ 15217 #038-40-2004 L2004 **HO** *012 †20
SCHIMPFF, Scott Nelson. ■ 15215 #422-01-2002 L2006 **APM** *020
SCHIRO, Brian Jason. ■ 15227 #021-05-2004 L2005 **DR** *012
SCHKROHOWSKY, Joshua Guen. ■ 15237 #023-07-2006 L2006 **ORS** *012
SCHLAR, Lisa Pearl. ■ 15217 #003-01-1993 L2000 **FM** *020 †18
SCHLESINGER, Abigail B. ■ 15224 #041-12-2000 L2004 **P** *100 †75
SCHMIDHOFER, Mark. 200 LOTHROP ST, A-333 15213 #056-06-1976 L1977 **CD** *020 †20
SCHMIDT, Christopher C. 1307 FEDERAL ST, STE 2 15212 #056-05-1989 L1993 **ORS** *020 †40
SCHMIDT, Karen Russell. 3705 5TH AVE, CHILDREN'S HOSPITAL OF UPM 15213 #030-05-1987 L2006 **MG SP** *020 †19
SCHNECK, Francis Xavier. 128 N CRAIG ST 15213 #010-02-1987 L1989 **U** *020 †95
SCHNECK-JACOB, Stephanie. 1307 FEDERAL ST 15212 #041-13-1987 L1991 **OP OS** *020 †40
SCHNEIDER, Beth A. 300 CEDAR BLVD, (MT.LEBANON INTERNAL MEDIC 15228 #041-12-1993 L1995 **IM** *020 †20
SCHNEIDER, Michael Philip. 5900 CORPORATE DR, STE 150 15237 #047-06-1984 L1984 **OPH** *020 †35
SCHOEDEL, Karen Elizabeth. 200 LOTHROP ST, UPPPTHLGY - BMDCL SCNCE TW 15213 #051-04-1987 L1990 **BBK** *020 †50
SCHOEN, Robert E. 200 LOTHROP ST 15213 #035-01-1984 L1991 **GE** *020 †20
SCHOR, Nina Tabachnik. 3705 5TH AVE, PEDS/ONE CHILDRENS PL 15213 #035-20-1981 L1986 **OS** *050 †55,75
SCHORSTEN, Melissa Marie. ■ 15229 #038-44-2005 L2005 **PD** *012
SCHRAGIN, Jeffrey Gerard. 5115 CENTRE AVE, PEDC/GROUND FL 15232 #028-03-1988 L2002 **IM** *020 †20
SCHRAUT, Wolfgang Hans. 200 LOTHROP ST 15213 #409-16-1970 L1988 **GS** *020 †85
SCHROEDER, Maryellen Ann. 7175 SALTSBURG RD 15235 #041-12-1987 L1989 **FM** *020 †18
SCHUCHERT, Matthew James. 2000 MARY ST 15203 #023-07-1994 L1997 **TS** *020 †85,90
SCHUCHERT, Vaishali Dixit. 200 LOTHROP ST, F1267 15213 #041-12-1994 L1997 **TRS CCS** *020 †85
SCHUIT, Kenneth Edward. 125 DE SOTO ST 15213 #051-01-1974 L1978 **ID PD** *050 †55
SCHULHOFF, John Wm. 1400 LOCUST ST, STE 5110 15219 #035-19-1971 L1974 **U** *020 †95
SCHULMAN, Douglas Seth. 500 GRANT ST, STE 2210 15219 #023-07-1981 L1988 **CD IM** *020 †20
SCHULTHEIS, Clyde John. 1400 LOCUST ST 15219 #041-12-1980 L1987 **DR** *020 †80 ‡
SCHULZ, Nicholas Theodore. 125 HASTINGS ST, 125 HASTINGS ST 15206 #041-12-1982 L1986 **IM ON** *020 †20
SCHUMACHER, Carol Ann. ■ 15204 #028-78-1978, ▲ L1979 **N OBG** *071
SCHUMAN, Joel Steven. 203 LOTHROP ST 15213 #035-47-1984 L2003 **OPH** *020 †35 ‡
SCHUSTER, James Morton. 4725 MCKNIGHT RD, STE 104 15237 #020-02-1985 L1986 **P** *030 †75 ‡
SCHWARTZ, Anna Rebecca. 230 MCKEE PL STE 500 15213 #041-01-2005 L2005 **EM** *012
SCHWARTZ, Daniel Norman. ■ 15238 #803-09-1933 L1935 **OTO OPH** *071
SCHWARTZ, Eric Gerald. ■ 15212 #016-11-2002 L2007 **HSO** *012
SCHWARTZ, Eric David. 200 LOTHROP ST, NEURORADIOLOGY, ROOM D132 15213 #023-07-1995 L1999 **RNR** *020 †80
SCHWARTZ, Jonathan Eric. 4200 5TH AVE 15260 #035-19-1989 L1992 **IM** *100
SCHWARTZ, Leonard. 5525 NORTHUMBERLAND ST 15217 #041-12-1952 L1953 **P PYA** *071 †75
SCHWARTZ, Raymond Barry. 2000 MARY ST, UPMC, SOUTH SIDE 15203 #048-04-1965 L1968 **AN** *020 †05
SCHWARTZ, Robert Jay. 200 LOTHROP ST 15213 #008-02-1982 L1995 **EM GPM** *020 †70,16
SCHWARTZMAN, David S. 200 LOTHROP ST, UNIVERSITY OF PITTSBURGH 15213 #035-19-1985 L1992 **CD IM** *020 †20
SCHWARTZMAN, Gregory Jay. 9100 BABCOCK BLVD 15237 #041-13-1995 L1997 **DR** *020 †80
SCHWARZ, Samuel David. ■ 15211 #023-01-2005 L2006 **DR** *012
SCHWEER, James Glenn. ■ 15217 #012-05-2001 L2007 **RNR** *020 †80
SCHWENTKER, Frederic Noel. 200 LOTHROP ST 15213 #023-07-1960 L1965 **U** *020
SCHWERHA, Joseph John. 200 LOTHROP ST 15213 #055-01-1966 L1967 **OM GP** *030 †70
SCHWINDT, Mary Lina. 8000 MCKNIGHT RD 15237 #016-11-1974 L1975 **FM NM** *020 †18
SCIOSCIA, Eugene A, Jr. 490 E NORTH AVE 15212 #041-12-1985 L1989 **OBG** *020 †30
SCIULLI, Robert Louis. 320 E NORTH AVE, RADIOLOGY DEPT 15212 #041-12-1974 L1975 **DR** *020 †40,80
SCIURBA, Frank Carl. 3471 5TH AVE, STE 1211 15213 #016-02-1982 L1984 **PUD IM** *020 †20
SCKOLNICK, Joshua Scott. ■ 15217 #038-06-2004 L2004 **GS** *100
SCLABASSI, Robert Jos. 200 LOTHROP ST 15213 #041-12-1981 L1998 **CN** *020
SCOGLIETTI, Vincent C. HIGHLAND DR 15206 #056-06-1943 L1944 **IM OM** *071
SCOLIERI, Sun Kim. 200 LOTHROP ST, PUH F392 15213 #038-06-1999 L2002 **IC** *100 †20
SCOPAZ, Kristen Alyse. ■ 15232 #041-12-2008 *012
SCOTT, C Paul. 401 SHADY AVE STE C202 15206 #038-06-1968 L1972 **P PYA** *020 †75 ‡
SCOTT, David Alan. 3520 5TH AVE, STE 300 15213 #010-01-1997 L1999 **IM** *020 †20
SCOTT, John Harvey. 4800 FRIENDSHIP AVE 15224 #041-12-1954 L1955 **PUD IM** *071 †20
SCOTT, Randolph Dante. 4800 FRIENDSHIP AVE, WESTERN PENNSYLVANIA HOSP 15224 #036-08-2006 L2006 **OBG** *012
SCOTT, Thomas F, Jr. 420 E NORTH AVE, STE 206 15212 #055-01-1985 L1989 **N** *020 †75 ‡
SCOTT, Victor Leslie. 3705 5TH AVE 15213 #035-08-1982 L1988 **AN IM** *020 †20,05
SCOURAS, Nicole Elaine. ■ 15201 #035-06-2006 L2007 **AN** *012
SCUTARU, Irina. 1400 LOCUST ST, MERCY HOSPITAL 15219 #781-04-2001 L2006 **IM** *012
SEAGER, Adair Dalzell. 320 E NORTH AVE, ALLEGHENY GENERAL HOSPITAL 15212 #422-01-2007 L2007 **IM** *012
SEALEY, Marylynn. 4800 FRIENDSHIP AVE, DEPT OF INTERNAL MEDICINE 15224 #041-13-1995 L1997 **IM** *020 †20
SEDGH, Jacob. ■ 15213 #005-18-2005 L2006 **OTO** *012
SEDHAIN, Suresh Raj. 320 E NORTH AVE 15212 #704-04-2001 L2005 **P** *012
SEEL, Michael Jude. 4815 LIBERTY AVE 15224 #041-12-1992 L1996 **ORS** *020 †40
SEEMUNGAL, Ian Ainsley. 320 E NORTH AVE, ALLEGHEN GEN HOSP 15212 #305-01-2004 L2005 **IM** *012
SEETHALA, Srikanth. 1400 LOCUST ST, MERCY HOSPITAL 15219 #495-11-2003 L2007 **IM** *012
SEEWALD, Tracy Robin. 3436 WILLIAM PENN HWY, STE 166 BLDG 2 PENN CTR 15235 #041-12-1986 L1987 **IM** *020 †20
SEFTCHICK, Michael Willia. ■ 15232 #041-13-2005 L2005 **EM** *012
SEGAL, Barry Gerald. 6301 FORBES AVE, STE 100 15217 #836-01-1981 L1987 **FM** *020 †18
SEGAL, Ricardo. 200 LOTHROP ST, UNIV OF PITTSBURGH 15213 #132-04-1967 L1978 **NS PMM** *020
SEGEL, David Peter. 200 LOTHROP ST, W919, UPMC 15213 #024-01-1960 L1965 **IM NEP** *020 †20
SEGRETI, Eileen Marie. 4815 LIBERTY AVE STE 321, MULTISPECIALISTS, P C 15224 #036-07-1988 L2003 **GO GYN** *020 †30
SEGURA, Bradley Jay. 3705 5TH AVE, DEPARTMENT OF PEDIATRIC SU 15213 #025-01-2002 L2007 **PDS** *012

■ = Address Information Privacy Protected

SEGURA, Susana. 320 E NORTH AVE, ALLEGHENY GEN HOSP 15212 #935-07-1996 L2004 IM *020 †20

SEHGAL, Rajesh. ■ 15238 #495-03-2000 L2006 HO *012 †20

SEIP, Rebecca Ann. 320 E NORTH AVE, DEPT EMER MED 15212 #039-01-1982 L1987 EM GS *020 †16

SEKHON, Amandeep Kaur. 320 E NORTH AVE, ALLEGHENY GEN HOSP 15212 #495-43-2000 L2002 NEP *012

SEKHON, Sandeep Kaur. 320 E NORTH AVE, ALLEGHENY GENERAL HOSPITAL 15212 #495-29-2001 L2006 IM *012

SEKHON, Sandeep Singh. 2201 LENOX OVAL 15237 #495-43-1999 L2001 GE *020

SEKULA, Raymond Francis, Jr. 420 E NORTH AVE, STE 302 15212 #010-02-2000 L2001 NS *020

SELKER, Robert Geo. ■ 15243 #041-12-1957 L1958 NS *071 †25

SELL, Harry Wm, Jr. 1501 LOCUST ST, STE 304 15219 #041-13-1980 L1982 GS AS *020 †85

SELTMAN, Howard Jeffrey. ■ 15221 #041-07-1979 L1980 PTH *071 †50

SELTMAN, Martin I. 901 WEST ST, STE B 15221 #041-07-1978 L1979 FM FPG *040 †18

SELVAGGI, Kathy Jane. 4815 LIBERTY AVE, STE 435 15224 #041-14-1985 L1986 ON HEM *020 †20

SELVAGGIO, Adriana M. 100 DELAFIELD RD, STE 212 15215 #041-13-1981 L1987 NEP IM *050 †20

SEMENOV, Igor V. ■ 15241 #913-02-1996 L2001 PAN *100 †05

SEMINS, Howard. 4815 LIBERTY AVE, STE 338 15224 #023-01-1968 L1969 GS EM *020 †85 ‡

SENAN, Pushpendra. 4520 PENN AVE STE 100 15224 #495-31-1963 L1971 TS CD *071 †85,90

SENTER, Howard Jay. 4815 LIBERTY AVE 15224 #024-07-1973 L1981 NS *020 †25

SEO, Su-Hun. ■ 15206 #041-12-2007 L2007 IM *012

SEPULVEDA, Antonia Rogado. 15217 #770-02-1984 L2000 PTH *020 †50

SEPULVEDA, Jorge P. ■ 15217 #770-02-1984 L2000 PTH *020 †50

SERBIN, Scott Ronald. 490 E NORTH AVE STE 305 15212 #041-12-1982 L1983 PD *020 †55

SERENE, Harry Elton. 1400 LOCUST ST 15219 #030-06-1969 L1970 GS *020 †85

SERRAO, Rocco Thomas. ■ 15213 #041-12-2008 †012

SERVAN-SCHREIBER, David. 5230 CENTRE AVE, RM 323SON 15232 #067-04-1984 L1987 P OS *020 †75

SESKI, Jan Casimir. 3358 5TH AVE 15213 #025-01-1973 L1981 GO GYN *020 †30

SESSOMS, Frank Eugene. 211 N WHITFIELD ST, STE 590 15206 #047-07-1974 L1976 FM EM *020 †18

SETHI, Jigme. 200 LOTHROP ST 15213 #495-73-1991 L2000 PCC *020 †50

SETHI, Pradeep K. 4800 FRIENDSHIP AVE, WESTERN PA HOSP DEPT PATHO 15224 #495-73-1980 L1995 PTH OS *020 †50

SETHUMADHAVAN, Vijaya P. ■ 15220 #041-59-1991 L1998 NEP *100 †20

SETLIK, Daria Elizabeth. 200 LOTHROP ST, UPMC-PUH 15213 #033-05-2004 L2005 DR *012

SEVERANCE, Alin James. 3811 OHARA ST, AND C 15213 #035-01-2007 L2007 P *012

SHABALOV, Olga. 5200 CENTRE AVE, STE 703 15232 #913-16-1990 L1997 CD IM *020 †20 ‡

SHACKELFORD, Jason Michae. ■ 15202 #041-13-2006 L2006 IM *012

SHACKNEY, Stanley Emanuel. 320 E NORTH AVE, ALLEGHENY GENERAL HOSP 15212 #024-01-1964 L1983 IM HO *050 †20

SHADDUCK, Richard K. 4800 FRIENDSHIP AVE, STE 2303 15224 #035-15-1962 L1969 HEM ON *020 †20

SHADE, Daniel Anthony, Jr. 490 E NORTH AVE, STE 303 15212 #041-13-1992 L1994 PCC *020 †20

SHAFFER, Stacey Lee. 200 LOTHROP ST, MONTEFIORE HOSPITAL 15213 #051-01-2003 L2003 IM *020 †20

SHAFFER, Walter Lee. 580 S AIKEN AVE, MOSS-WEIGEL AND ASSOCIATES 15232 #041-13-1965 L1966 OBG *020 †30

SHAH, Ajit Natverlal. 200 LOTHROP ST STE 710 15238 #495-22-1979 L1986 NM *020 †28

SHAH, Amar Bhupendra. 5921 HOWE ST, UNIT 301 15232 #035-48-2001 L2004 DR *020 †80

SHAH, Anisha Bhupendra. ■ 15206 #035-48-1999 L2002 CD *100 †20

SHAH, Ankur Raju. 320 E NORTH AVE, ALLEGHENY GEN HOSP 15212 #495-76-2001 L2002 CD *020 †20

SHAH, Ashish Rajesh. ■ 15213 #041-12-2008 *012

SHAH, Bhavesh Bhupendra. 320 E NORTH AVE 15212 #422-01-2000 L2006 GE *012 †20

SHAH, Hemal Vasant. ■ 15227 #033-05-2003 L2003 CD *012 †20

SHAH, Manisha Chirag. 320 E NORTH AVE, ALLEGHENY GENERAL HOSPITAL 15212 #495-23-1997 L2006 OBG *012

SHAH, Moneal Bipin. 320 E NORTH AVE 15212 #038-44-2004 L2007 CD *012 †20

SHAH, Mukesh Vasantlal. 1000 BOWER HILL RD STE 209 15243 #495-01-1974 L1980 GE IM *071 †20

SHAH, Nirav Arvind. 3550 TERRACE STREET, A915 SCAIFE HALL 15261 #035-08-1998 L2000 NEP *020

SHAH, Parin Mukesh. ■ 15241 #495-01-1979 L1984 PTH *020

SHAH, Samirkumar J. 1360 OLD FREEPORT RD, STE 1A 15238 #495-23-1987 L1993 CD IM *020 †20

SHAH, Sapana Jayantilal. ■ 15232 #041-02-2006 L2006 PD *012

SHAH, Sohail Rashmi. ■ 15208 #048-16-2003 L2005 GS *012

SHAH, Veeral Shailesh. ■ 15232 #041-12-2008 *012

SHAH, Vipul Manhar. ■ 15217 #041-12-2008 *012

SHAH, Vipul Sharadbhai. 1400 LOCUST ST, MERCY HOSP-PITTSBURGH 15219 #495-23-2001 L2005 IM *012

SHAHAR, Avner. 6683 RIDGEVILLE ST 15217 #550-02-1986 L1994 FPG *100 †20

SHAHEEN, Anne. 3380 BOULEVARD OF THE ALLS, STE 1 15243 #038-40-1995 L1997 OBG *020 †30

SHAIKH, Muhammad Ilyas M.. 3811 OHARA ST, WPIC 15213 #496-38-1993 L2001 P *020 †75

SHAIKH, Nader. 3705 5TH AVE, GENERAL ACAD PEDS 15213 #041-13-1997 L2002 PD *055 †55

SHAKOOR, Asif. 320 E NORTH AVE, ALLEGHENY GEN HOSP 15212 #422-01-2004 L2004 IM *020 †20

SHALABY, Alaa A. 111 UNIVERSITY PL, PITTSBURGH VA HEALTHCARE S 15213 #915-04-1986 L1999 CD *020 †20

SHALABY, Khalid Mohamed. 5230 CENTRE AVE RM 322, DEPT OF SURGERY 15232 #915-04-1989 L2001 GS SO *020

SHAMBLIN, Jerry Douglas. 9400 MCKNIGHT RD 15237 #055-01-1965 L1969 OTO A *020 †45

SHANAHAN, James Francis, IV. ■ 15241 #010-02-2000 L2003 CD *020 †20

SHANNON, Kelly T. 815 FREEPORT RD, DEPT OF ANESTHESIA 15215 #048-04-1988 L1991 AN *020 †05

SHANNON, Marcia Timko. 300 HALKET ST, DEPT OF ANESTHESIOLOGY 15213 #048-04-1988 L1992 AN *020 †05

SHANNON, Richard Patrick. 320 E NORTH AVE 15212 #008-02-1980 L1997 CD IM *020 †20

SHAPIRA, Edith Laura. 401 SHADY AVE STE A205 15206 #041-12-1980 L1982 P *020 †75

SHAPIRO, Ezra David. ■ 15213 #016-42-1977 L1980 PM *020 †60

SHAPIRO, Morry. ■ 15217 #041-12-1942 L1943 IM PUD *071

SHAPIRO, Ronald. 3459 5TH AVE, UPMC MONTEFIORE7 SOUTH 15213 #005-11-1980 L1986 TTS GS *020 †85

SHARE, Sarah Marie. 15237 #038-43-2005 L2005 PTH *012

SHARIF, Saima. 320 E NORTH AVE 15212 #704-02-1994 L2002 HO *100 †20

SHARMA, Arun. ■ 15232 #041-12-2008 *012

SHARMA, Ashish. 15206 #495-03-2002 L2007 IM *012

SHARMA, Brahma N. 9365 MCKNIGHT RD, UPMC CARDIOVASCULARY STE 7 15237 #495-30-1976 L1989 CD *020 †20

SHARMA, Sandeep Bagotra. 128 N CRAIG ST, STE 100 15213 #422-01-1998 L2001 NEP *020 †18,20

SHARMA, Shaifali. ■ 15219 #041-15-2001 L2001 DR *012

SHARMA, Sunil Kumar. 2000 MARY ST 15203 #495-20-1989 L2000 GS *020 †85

SHARMA, Tarun Kumar. 320 E NORTH AVE, ALLEGHENY GEN HOSP 15212 #422-01-1998 L2007 GE *012 †20

SHARMA, Usha. 10986 FRANKSTOWN RD 15235 #495-77-1973 L1978 END IM *020 †20

SHARMA, Vidhu Kumar. 1004 ARCH ST 15212 #051-04-2001 L2001 FM *020 †20

SHARMA, Vivek. 3459 5TH AVE, UPMC MONTEFIORE, 7 SOUTH 15213 #495-90-1993 L1999 ORS *020 †18

SHARRER, Margaret C. ■ 15235 #041-07-1957 L1958 OPH *071 †35

SHARTS, Michael Charles. 200 LOTHROP ST, STE B-400 15213 #017-20-2000 L2001 NS *020

SHAUGHNESSY, Michael John. ■ 15238 #041-12-1965 L1966 U *071 †95

SHAVER, James Alvin. 200 LOTHROP ST 15213 #041-09-1959 L1960 CD IM *020 †20

SHAVER, Verne Clifford. ■ 15235 #041-12-1954 L1955 CD IM *071 †20

SHAW, Jay Thomas. 1000 BOWER HILL RD, STE 213 15243 #495-01-1968 L1977 OBG *020 †30

SHAW, Peter Haywood. 3705 5TH AVE 15213 #035-46-1994 L2000 PHO *020 †55

SHAW-STIFFEL, Thos Alvin. 3471 5TH AVE, STE 916 15213 #067-01-1981 L2002 GE HEP *020 †20

SHAY, Paul Larew. 815 FREEPORT RD, UPMC ST MARGARET 15215 #041-12-1976 L1977 AN *020 †05

SHEAHAN, Daniel Gerald. 5230 CENTRE AVE, INT PATHOLOGY SHADYSD HOSP 15232 #539-03-1959 L1984 PTH OS *020 †50

SHEAR, Mary Katherine. 3811 OHARA ST, UNIVERSITY OF PITTSBURGH S 15213 #024-07-1972 L1992 P IM *020 †20,75

SHEAR, Shoshanna L. 3811 OHARA ST, WESTERN PSYCHIATRIC INSTIT 15213 #041-01-1999 L1999 P CHP *020 †75

SHEDRO, Hector. ■ 15238 #132-01-1961 L1976 CD IM *020 †20

SHEEHAN, Mary Patrice. 580 S AIKEN AVE, SHADYSIDE PLACE 15232 #539-06-1983 L1994 D *020 †15

SHEKAR, Saraswathy. 200 LOTHROP ST, DEPT OF ANESTHESIA 15213 #495-66-1987 L1999 AN *020 †05

SHELESKY, Gretchen. ■ 15209 #041-12-2005 L2005 FP *012

SHELLENBARGER, David Rex. ■ 15217 #041-13-2006 L2006 EM *012

SHEN, Xinglei. ■ 15206 #041-12-2007 L2007 TY *012

SHENDE, Manisha R. 200 LOTHROP ST, C-800 15213 #495-96-1989 L2006 TS *020 †85,90

SHEPPARD, Scott Franklin. 3471 5TH AVE STE 1010, DEPT OF ORTHOPAEDIC SURGER 15213 #025-01-1992 L1995 ORS *072

SHEPTAK, Peter Edward. 200 LOTHROP ST # B400, PRESBYTERIAN UNIV HOSP 15213 #041-12-1963 L1964 NS *020 †25

SHERMAN, Frederick Scott. 3705 5TH AVE 15213 #008-01-1975 L1988 PDC PD *020 †55

SHESTAK, Kenneth C. 300 HALKET ST, RM 2541 15213 #024-07-1976 L1984 PS OS *020 †85,65

SHETTY, Manohar. 5200 CENTRE AVE STE 603 15232 #495-37-1977 L1996 P *020 †75

SHEU, Yun Robert. ■ 15213 #038-06-2007 L2007 TY *012 †4

SHIFERMAN, Gennady Mikhai. 3550 TERRACE ST, A SCAIFE HALL OF HLTH PROF 15261 #041-12-2008 *012

SHIKORA, Evan S. 300 HALKET ST, STE 5770 15213 #018-75-1990, ▲ L1990 OBG *020 †30

SHILL, Talmage Legrand. ■ 15237 #051-04-2002 L2003 DR *020 †80

SHIMBERG, Joanna Ursula. ■ 15218 #016-42-2005 L2005 PD *012

SHIMER, Adam Lynn. 3471 5TH AVE STE 1 15213 #051-01-2002 L2002 ORS *100

SHIN, Hyunchul John. ■ 15241 #583-02-1958 L1971 GP OS *020 †20

SHIN, Joyce Ja Hyun. 320 E NORTH AVE 15212 #305-01-2003 L2004 AN *012

SHINDE, Dilip Digambar. 300 HALKET ST, MAGEE WOMENS HOSPITAL 15213 #496-38-1979 L2000 DR *020 †80

SHINDE, Trupti Shrikantra. 320 E NORTH AVE 15212 #496-51-2005 L2006 IM *012

SHINDEL, Betty Elaine. 300 HALKET ST, FL 3 15213 #041-07-1996 L2001 DR *020 †80

SHINOZUKA, Hisashi. UNIV PITTSBURGH MED SCH 15261 #572-20-1954 L1974 PTH *050 †50

SHIPKOVITZ, Harvey Danl. 1024 MAIN ST 15215 #038-41-1972 L1974 FM OM *020

SHIPLEY, Randal Kris. 320 E NORTH AVE, ALLEGHENY GEN HOSP 15212 #422-01-2005 L2005 IM *012

SHIRTS, Brian Hanson. ■ 15217 #041-12-2008 *012

SHIVELY, John Grant. 320 E NORTH AVE 15212 #041-12-1959 L1960 DR CCM *071 †20

SHNEIDER, Benjamin L. 3705 5TH AVE 15213 #016-02-1986 L2007 PD *020 †55

SHOENTHAL, Donald Ray, Jr. 1020 CENTER AVE 15229 #055-01-1987 L1989 FM *020 †18 ‡

SHOGAN, Jeffrey Edward. 5115 CENTRE AVE, FL 3 15232 #041-12-1982 L1983 ON HMP *020 †20

SHOLDER, Arnold Jay. 1050 BOWER HILL RD 15243 #016-11-1979 L1986 U *020 †95

SHOOK, Willis D, III. 1350 LOCUST ST STE 410 15219 #041-12-1973 L1974 PS HS *020 †65

SHORT, Tracee Chavawn. 15216 #048-13-2006 L2006 GS *012

SHOSTAK, Michael. 200 LOTHROP ST, M115 UNIVERSITY CTR 15213 #035-46-1968 L1980 P *020 †75

SHOYKHET, Michael Ilya. ■ 15217 #041-12-2005 L2005 CCP *012

SHRAGER, Daniel Stephen. 6315 FORBES AVE, STE B16 15217 #041-12-1968 L1969 P *020 †75

SHREINER, David Paul. 320-12-2064 15213 #041-02-1964 L1965 NM HEM *072 †20,28

SHRESTHA, Ruchi. 15212 #496-04-1999 L2007 DR *012

SHTRAHMAN, Benjamin. 9104 BABCOCK BLVD, STE 1107 15237 #041-12-1990 L1993 N *020 †20

SHTRAHMAN, Eta Ospovat. 7180 HIGHLAND DR 15206 #913-50-1967 L1982 IM *020

SHTRAHMAN, Matthew. ■ 15217 #041-12-2007 L2007 TY *012

SHUCKETT, Paul. ■ 15217 #062-01-1975 L1979 PDO *020

SHUE, Eveline H. ■ 15213 #041-12-2008 L2012 *012

SHUFORD, Gregory Alan. 402 BEAR RUN DR 15237 #010-02-1994 L1995 AN *100

SHUGARMAN, Ryan Scott. 3811 OHARA ST, WESTERN PSYCH INST & CLNC 15213 #023-01-2004 L2004 **P PFP** *012
SHUM, Leo Mengtah. 230 MCKEE PL STE 500, OF PITTSBURGH 15213 #041-12-2006 L2006 **EM** *012
SHUPAK, Avigdor. UNIV PITTSBURGH SCH MED, DEPT OTOLAR 15261 #550-03-1979 **OTO** *040
SHUSTER, Inna Leonidovna. ■ 15217 #913-79-1989 L2002 **PM** *100
SHYMANSKY, John Stephen. 1515 LOCUST ST, OF PITTSBURGH 15219 #055-01-1986 L1986 **N** *020 †75
SICKERI, Joanne Christine. ■ 15237 #041-15-2002 L2002 **RHU** *100 †20
SIDANI, Ramzi Scott. ■ 15209 #038-43-2006 L2006 **EM** *012
SIDDIQUI, Nasir Ahmed. 121 MEYRAN AVE, DEPT RAD 15213 #038-06-2006 L2007 **DR** *012
SIDDIQUI, Sharifuzzama. ■ 15214 #495-93-1982 L2007 **P** *012
SIDONIO, Robert Francis. ■ 15218 #001-02-2004 L2007 **PHO** *012 †55
SIEGENTHALER, Michael P. 200 LOTHROP ST 15213 #869-02-1991 L2006 **TS** *020 †85,90
SIGNORELLA, Arthur P. 1000 BOWER HILL RD STE 213 15243 #041-12-1991 L1993 **OBG** *020 †30
SIGURDSSON, Luther. 3705 5TH AVE, CHILDRENS HOSP 15213 #484-01-1988 L1995 **PG** *020 †55
SIKER, Ephraim S. ■ 15228 #035-19-1949 L1953 **AN** *071 †05
SILAO, Anne Balagtas. 121 MEYRAN AVE 15213 #748-10-2002 L2006 **FP** *012
SILK, Ann. 1012 S BRADDOCK AVE 15218 #041-12-2008 *012
SILVAGGIO, Vincent Jos. 200 DELAFIELD RD, STE 1040 15215 #041-12-1987 L1989 **ORS OSS** *020 †40
SILVEIRA, Fernanda De Pin. 3601 5TH AVE, STE 3A 15213 #187-03-1998 L2003 **ID** *100 †20
SILVER, Susan Anne. 200 LOTHROP ST 15213 #038-06-1988 L1998 **PTH** *020 †50
SILVERBLATT, Bernard L. ■ 15217 #041-12-1938 L1939 **OTO** *071 †45
SILVERMAN, Alan Ronald. 5001 CENTRE AVE, FL 3 15213 #035-08-1971 L1978 **D DMP** *020 †15 ‡
SILVERMAN, Gary Arthur. 300 HALKET ST, MAGEE WOMEN'S HOSPITAL 15213 #016-02-1984 L2004 **PD** *020 †55
SILVERMAN, Jan Franklin. 320 E NORTH AVE, DEPT PATH ALLEGHENY GEN HO 15212 #051-04-1970 L1997 **PTH PCP** *020 †50
SILVERMAN, Jerry Danl. 5460 DARLINGTON RD 15217 #041-12-1944 L1945 **PUD IM** *071
SILVERMAN, Mark Steven. 1400 LOCUST ST 15219 #065-09-1983 L1990 **END DIA** *020 †20
SILVERMAN, Mendel. ■ 15232 #041-12-1946 L1947 **PD** *071 †55
SILVERMAN, Stuart Lee. 1515 LOCUST ST, OF PITTSBURGH 15219 #010-02-1985 L1987 **N** *020 †75
SILVERSTEIN, Chas Edward. 88 FORT COUCH RD, STE 100 15241 #023-07-1977 L1978 **PD** *020 †55
SILVESTRI, Sara Beth. ■ 15217 #041-12-2005 L2005 **PD** *012
SIM, Hyun S. 3 OLD TIMBER TRL 15238 #583-06-1968 L1981 **AN** *020 †05
SIM, Kah-Ming. ■ 15217 #825-01-1982 L1990 **CCA** *100
SIMASEK, Madeline. 5230 CENTRE AVE, SHADYSIDE HOSP FAMILY MED 15232 #041-13-1979 L1980 **PD** *040 †55
SIMBRA, Maria Estela. 3471 5TH AVE, STE 810 15213 #041-12-1993 L1995 **N CN** *071 †75
SIMHAN, Hyagriv Nara. 300 HALKET ST, STE 0610 15213 #024-05-1995 L1998 **OBG** *020 †30
SIMHI, Eliahu. 3705 5TH AVE, ANESTHESIOLOGY 15213 #550-02-1989 L1993 **AN** *020 †05
SIMMONDS, Robert Thompson. 300 HALKET ST, STE 1338 15213 #035-45-1977 L1978 **OBG** *020 †30
SIMMONS, Richard Lawrence. 497 SCAIFE HALL, 3550 TERRACE STREET 15261 #024-05-1959 L1987 **GS ON** *030 †85
SIMMONS, William. 5230 CENTRE AVE DEPT ANEST, UPMC PRESBYTRN SHADYSDE HP 15232 #026-08-1981 L1986 **AN PD** *020 †05
SIMON, Laura Haley. 5230 CENTRE AVE, PRESBYTERIAN SHADYSIDE 15232 #032-01-2007 L2007 **MPD** *012
SIMON, Marc Alan. 200 LOTHROP ST 15213 #023-01-1998 L2001 **CD** *050 †20
SIMON, Peter Morgan. 200 LOTHROP ST, PRESBYTERIAN HOSPITAL 15213 #024-16-2004 L2004 **EM** *020
SIMONE, Samuel Thos. 1350 LOCUST ST STE 205 15219 #041-13-1975 L1976 **VS GS** *020 †85
SIMONS, Jeffrey Philip. 6516 LILAC ST 15217 #028-02-2000 L2001 **PDO** *020 †45
SIMS, Cynthia Cline. 300 HALKET ST, STE 0610 15213 #055-01-1983 L1989 **OBG MFM** *020 †30
SIMS, Robin Louise. 7227 HAMILTON AVE, PRIMARY CARE HEALTH SERVIC 15208 #041-13-1981 L1983 **PD** *020 †55
SINDHI, Rakesh Kumar. 3705 5TH AVE 15213 #495-73-1981 L1998 **GS** *020 †85
SINGBARTL, Kai. 3550 TERRACE ST, C/O J KNAPP, CCM, 613 SCA 15261 #409-20-1996 L2005 *100
SINGH, Amarpreet. 3811 OHARA ST RM E807, UNIV OF PITTSBURGH MED CTR 15213 #495-03-2000 L2006 **PFP** *100 †75
SINGH, Deepinder. 320 E NORTH AVE 15212 #495-36-2003 L2005 **IM** *100
SINGH, Gagandeep. 1400 LOCUST ST, MERCY HOSPITAL 15219 #422-01-2005 L2006 **FP** *012
SINGH, Geeta. ■ 15237 #495-39-1969 L1974 **FM RO** *071
SINGH, Gurmit. 3601 MCKNIGHT EAST DR 15237 #495-03-1982 L1987 **FM** *020 †18
SINGH, Harpriya. 320 E NORTH AVE 15212 #495-43-2000 L2003 **GE** *012 †20
SINGH, Jagjit. 815 FREEPORT RD, UPMC ST MARGARET 15215 #495-10-1982 L1988 **PTH PCP** *020 †50
SINGH, Jaspaal. 200 LOTHROP ST, UPMC # 901 KAUFMANN BLDG 15213 #422-01-1996 L1999 **PM** *020 †60
SINGH, Navdeep. 490 E NORTH AVE, STE 300 15212 #495-43-1998 L2004 **PCC** *020 †20
SINGH, Nina. ■ 15209 #495-03-1979 L1983 **ID** *020 †20
SINGH, Saket. 4800 FRIENDSHIP AVE 15224 #495-37-2001 L2004 **AN** *100 †05
SINGH, Tina R.. ■ 15232 #495-37-2002 L2006 **FP** *012
SINGLETON, Karen A. ■ 15218 #051-04-2002 L2006 **GPM** *012
SINGLETON, Richard Harold. ■ 15218 #051-04-2004 L2004 **NS** *012
SINHA, Latika. 200 LOTHROP ST 15213 #495-13-1995 L2001 **IM** *100 †80
SIOUFI, M Firas. 3471 5TH AVE STE 811 15213 #605-01-2000 L2002 **CN** *020 †75
SIPARSKY, Nicole Fanya. ■ 15213 #024-05-2001 L2007 **GS** *100 †85
SIRAJ, Nejib Salih. 320 E NORTH AVE, ALLEGHENEY GENERAL HOSPITA 15212 #366-02-1995 L2004 **IM** *100 †20
SIRINTRAPUN, Sahussap J. 5150 CENTRE AVE, STE 301 15232 #028-03-1999 L2007 **PTH** *020
SIRIO, Carl Alexander. 200 LOTHROP ST 15213 #033-06-1984 L1985 **IM CCM** *050 †20
SISK, Thomas Matthew. 2509B SIDNEY ST 15203 #041-02-2002 L2006 **FSM** *100 †18
SISKA, Peter Allen. 3471 5TH AVE, KAUFMANN BUILDING SUITE 10 15213 #038-41-2003 L2003 **ORS** *012
SIT, Dorothy K Y. 1211 WINTERTON ST 15206 #065-01-1992 L2003 **P** *020 †75
SITWAT, Bilal. ■ 15220 #704-02-2001 L2005 **CHN** *012
SIVAKANTHAN, Jamuna. 4810 LIBERTY AVE, STE 1000 15224 #913-89-1989 L1997 **PM** *020 †60
SIVAM, Sheila. ■ 15206 #064-01-2003 L2007 **PCC** *012 †20
SIVANESAN, Swarna Priya. 190 LOTHROP ST, 145 LOTHROP HALL 15213 #012-21-2004 L2007 **D** *012
SKANDHAN, Amith. 1400 LOCUST ST, MERCY HOSPITAL 15219 #496-69-2004 L2007 **IM** *012
SKELLY, Thomas Danl. 4411 STILLEY RD, STE 3 15227 #010-01-1963 L1968 **PD GS** *071 †55
SKINKER, Benjamin M, III. 5215 CENTRE AVE 15232 #051-04-1991 L1993 **FM OBG** *020 †18
SKINNER, James W. 1125 PERRY HWY, # 41 15237 #025-01-1945 L1947 **PD** *071 †55
SKOLNICK, Kenneth Brian. 119 ROCK HAVEN LN, STE 604B 15228 #041-12-1974 L1975 **OTO** *020 †45
SKONER, David Peter. 320 E NORTH AVE, DEPT OF ALLERGY ,ASTHMA & 15212 #041-13-1980 L1983 **AI A** *020 †55,03
SLATER, Anne Catherine. ■ 15213 #028-46-2003 L2006 **PEM** *012 †55
SLAYMAKER, Elizabeth P. 1000 W VIEW PARK DR, STE 1 15229 #041-12-1998 L2001 **FM** *020 †18
SLIVKA, Adam. 200 LOTHROP ST 15213 #035-47-1988 L1994 **IM GE** *020 †20
SLOMKA, Juliette Marie. 7180 HIGHLAND DR, VA PITTSBURGH HEALTHCARE S 15206 #025-07-2004 L2004 **IM** *020 †20
SMALDONE, Marc Christophe. ■ 15207 #035-48-2004 L2004 **U** *012
SMALL, George Alan. 420 E NORTH AVE, STE 206 15212 #041-02-1988 L1993 **N** *020 †75 ‡
SMALL, Judith Ann. 420 E NORTH AVE STE 406 15212 #035-45-1978 L1982 **D** *020 †15
SMETANKA, Cynthia Ann. 3459 5TH AVE, UPMC MONTEFIORE 7 SOUTH 15213 #041-13-1996 L2001 **TTS IG** *020 †85
SMITH, A J Conrad. 200 LOTHROP ST, CARDIOLOGY/SCAIFE HALL 15213 #005-02-1987 L1994 **CD** *020 †20
SMITH, Albert T, Jr. 4800 FRIENDSHIP AVE 15224 #041-09-1976 L1978 **FM OS** *075 †18
SMITH, Brenda Catherine. 320 E NORTH AVE 15212 #055-02-1981 L1987 **NEP IM** *020 †20
SMITH, Brett Robert. 1307 FEDERAL ST, STE 2 15212 #041-07-1997 L2001 **ORS** *020 †40
SMITH, Bryan Scott. ■ 15212 #017-20-2002 L2004 **DR** *012
SMITH, Christina Ann. 4 ALLEGHENY CTR, EIGHTH FLOOR 15212 #035-06-1993 L1995 **P** *020 †75
SMITH, Craig Martin. ■ 15224 #035-09-2001 L2005 **CCP** *012
SMITH, Cynthia Lee. 6301 NORTHUMBERLAND ST, THE CHILDREN'S INSTITUTE 15217 #035-20-1979 L1988 **PM** *075 †55,60
SMITH, Darren M. UNIV OF PITTSBURGH, 3550 TERRACE STREET 15261 #043-01-2005 L2007 **PS** *012
SMITH, Deane Edgar. 320 E NORTH AVE, GERERAL SURGERY 15212 #041-15-2005 L2005 **GS** *012
SMITH, Elliot Lyle. 320 E NORTH AVE DEPT IM 15212 #041-09-1992 L1994 **IM** *020 †20
SMITH, Francis Anthony. 1200 CENTRE AVE 15219 #010-02-1943 L1944 **IM CD** *071
SMITH, Gregory Norman. 7175 SALTSBURG RD 15235 #041-12-1979 L1980 **FM** *020 †18
SMITH, Gregory Thos. 490 E NORTH AVE, STE 400 15212 #041-02-1982 L1985 **CD** *020 †20
SMITH, Hilary R. ■ 15208 #043-01-2006 L2006 **PD** *012
SMITH, Jan Danl. 200 LOTHROP ST 15213 #836-03-1961 L1972 **AN CCA** *071 †20,05
SMITH, John Roger. 100 FOREST HILLS PLZ 15221 #045-01-1986 L1987 **FM** *020 †18 ‡
SMITH, Kenneth Jos. 200 MEYRAN AVE, STE 200 15213 #041-02-1979 L1980 **IM OS** *050 †20
SMITH, Rahsaan Cain. 320 E NORTH AVE 15212 #041-14-2001 L2001 **CD** *012
SMITH, Rebecca Leigh. ■ 15217 #041-15-2003 L2007 **CCP** *012 †55
SMITH, Robert Wm. ■ 15261 #041-02-1956 L1957 **CD IM** *071 †20
SMITH, Ross H, Jr. ■ 15238 #041-12-1951 L1953 **R** *071 †80
SMITH, Warren S. 5700 CORPORATE DR, PORP BLDG 3 STE 700 15237 #041-12-1981 L1982 **FM** *020 †18
SMITHERMAN, Thomas Cecil. 200 LOTHROP ST 15213 #001-02-1967 L1990 **CD IM** *020 †20
SMOOKLER, Amy Elizabeth. 320 E NORTH AVE, ANEGHERY GENL HOSP 15212 #041-12-1996 L1999 **EM** *020 †16 ‡
SMUCKLER, Aaron G. ■ 15217 #035-15-2003 L2007 **MPD** *020 †55
SMYTHE, Jason Jack. 121 MEYRAN AVE, DEPT OF RADIO CHP MT 3950 15213 #025-01-2004 L2005 **DR** *012
SNEDIKER, Daniel Garrett. 230 MCKEE PL, STE 500 15213 #010-02-2004 L2004 **EM** *020
SNELL, Edward Delbert. 1307 FEDERAL ST, STE 2 15212 #041-14-1991 L1993 **FSM** *020 †18
SNITZER, Arnold Judah. 748 N NEGLEY AVE 15206 #041-12-1960 L1961 **FM** *020 †18
SNODGRASS, Steven Michael. ■ 15221 #041-02-2005 L2005 **PD** *012
SNYDER, James Victor. 200 LOTHROP ST 15213 #041-02-1966 L1971 **AN CCA** *050 †05
SNYDERMAN, Carl Henry. 200 LOTHROP ST STE 500, EYE & EAR INST 15213 #016-02-1982 L1983 **OTO HNS** *020 †45
SOBH, Nessreen Nancy. ■ 15232 #025-07-2007 L2007 **IM** *012
SODAGAM, Archana. 4800 FRIENDSHIP AVE, DEPT MED 15224 #495-98-2005 L2006 **IM** *012
SOFFRONOFF, Pierce. 300 HALKET ST, STE 1338 15213 #048-02-1974 L1975 **GYN** *020 †30
SOHNEN, Adam Edmund. 532 S AIKEN AVE, STE 201 15232 #012-05-1993 L1995 **IM** *020 †20
SOKOS, George Gus. 320 E NORTH AVE, AGH INTERNAL MEDICINE 15212 #055-75-1999, ▲ L2001 **CD** *012 †20
SOLAI, Lalithkumar K. 3811 OHARA ST, WPIC 721 15213 #495-59-1991 L1997 **P PYG** *020 †75
SOLARI, Mario Giulio. 3550 TERRACE ST, SCAIFE 69, UNIVERSITY OF PITTSBURGH 15261 #024-07-2003 L2003 **PS** *012
SOLIMAN, Doreen Emile. 3550 TERRACE ST, A-1305 SCAIFE HALL 15261 #915-02-1984 L2000 **AN** *020 †05
SOLOFF, Paul Harris. ■ 15243 #041-12-1970 L1977 **P** *050 †75
SOLOMON, Edward A. 9100 BABCOCK BLVD, DEPARTMENT OF RADIOLOGY 15237 #025-76-1994, ▲ L2000 **DR** *020
SOLOSHATZ, Leslie Beth. 9000 PERRY HWY, STE 120 15237 #041-01-1994 L1996 **PD** *020 †55
SOLOSKO, David. 320 E NORTH AVE 15212 #041-12-1969 L1971 **AN** *020 †05
SOLTER, Alan Warren. 9104 BABCOCK BLVD, PASSAVANT PROFESSIONAL BUI 15237 #008-01-1972 L1973 **D** *020 †15
SOLTYS, Kyle Ansel. 3705 5TH AVE 15213 #024-05-1995 L2003 **GS** *020 †85
SOMAL, Jatinder Singh. 1824 CAREY WAY NO 2 15203 #306-01-2000 L2000 **CCA** *100 †05
SOMAN, Prem. 200 LOTHROP ST 15213 #495-98-1988 L2001 **CD** *020 †20
SOMERS, Keith Saml. 6343 PENN AVE, # 201 15206 #041-09-1985 L1986 **PD** *020 †55
SOMMER, Deborah Lee. 1 BIGELOW SQ, STE 729 15219 #038-40-1979 L1980 **OBG** *020 †30
SOMOGYI, Dan Mitchell. 5230 CENTRE AVE, UPMC SHADYSIDE 519 SON BLD 15232 #065-10-1994 L1996 **FSM** *020 †18
SOMOGYI, Sarit Leba. 2020 MONONGAHELA AVE 15218 #550-02-1996 L1998 **FM** *020 †18
SONBOLIAN, Nasser Jacob. 200 LOTHROP ST 15213 #517-06-1968 L1978 **AN** *020 †05
SONEL, Ali F. UD-111C, VA PITTSBURGH HLTHCARE SYS 15240 #902-05-1990 L1999 **CD IM** *020 †20

■ = Address Information Privacy Protected

SONERU, Codruta Nicoleta. 3705 5TH AVE, OF PITTSBURGH 15213 #781-03-2000 L2007 PAN *012

SONG, Angela Yunyoung. ■ 15206 #041-12-2003 L2005 PS *012

SONG, Dennis Yong. SCAIFE HALL, STE 6B, 3550 TERRACE STREET 15261 #041-12-2001 L2001 GS *020

SONG, Ruiping. 121 MEYRAN AVE 15213 #243-47-1996 L2006 IM *012

SONG, Tae Ho. 320 E NORTH AVE, ALLEGHENY GENERAL HOSPITAL 15212 #583-02-2000 L2006 GS *012

SONG, Walter Jungho. 1307 FEDERAL ST, SECOND FLOOR 15212 #035-09-2002 L2007 HSO *012

SONI, Ajay. ■ 15261 #041-12-2004 L2004 OPH *012

SONIS, Meyer. 15208 #041-09-1943 L1944 CHP P *071 †75

SORAN, Atilla. 300 HALKET ST STE 2601, MAGEE WOMENS HOSPITAL 15213 #902-03-1989 L2007 *100

SORIANO, Claver Sayson. 1811 BLVD OF THE ALLIES 15219 #748-10-1974 L1981 OBG *020 ‡

SORR, Edward Mark. 1835 FORBES AVE 15219 #041-02-1967 L1971 OPH *020 †20

SORTINO, Antonio. 400 HOLIDAY DR STE 101 15220 #561-12-1979 L1983 TS *020 †85,90

SOSO, Michael John. 120 LYTTON AVE, STE 300 15213 #005-11-1979 L1981 N *020

SOTELO, Jessica Erin. ■ 15218 #048-04-2008 *012

SOTEREANOS, Dean Geo. 1307 FEDERAL ST STE 2 15212 #041-09-1984 L1985 ORS GS *020 †40

SOTEREANOS, Nicholas G. 1307 FEDERAL ST, STE 2 15212 #041-09-1986 L1987 ORS CD *020 †40

SOTOODEHFAR, Rahim. 9104 BABCOCK BLVD STE 5112 15237 #517-03-1968 L1975 GE IM *020 †20

SOUAIBY, Salim. 4595 MCKNIGHT RD 15237 #913-16-1996 L2003 FM *100

SOUKIASIAN, Harmik. 200 LOTHROP ST, STE C700 15213 #005-06-1998 L2007 TS *100 ‡

SOUNDERARAJAH, Kandan. ■ 15213 #220-01-1959 L1964 P PYG *071

SOWA, Gwendolyn Ann. 2000 MARY ST 15203 #056-05-2000 L2005 PM *020 †60 ‡

SOWERS, Wesley Eugene. 400 45TH ST # 2E, ST. FRANCIS MED CTR 15201 #016-06-1982 L1992 P *020 †75

SPAGNOLETTI, Carla Leigh. 200 LOTHROP ST, 9E923 MUH GIM 15213 #041-12-2001 L2001 IM *020

SPAHR, Jonathan Edward. 3705 5TH AVE RM 3765 15213 #041-02-1998 L2001 PDP PUD *020 †20,55

SPANARD, Russell Amos. ■ 15205 #041-13-1955 L1956 GP *071

SPANGLER, Marion Lee. 121 MEYRAN AVE, DEPT RAD 15213 #035-09-2006 L2007 DR *012

SPATARU, Oana Valentina. 3708 5TH AVE, DEPT OF MED EDU 15213 #781-08-2001 L2006 N *012

SPEAKMAN, Julie Ann. ■ 15211 #041-15-2008 *012

SPEAR, Alison Heather. 230 MCKEE PL, STE 500 15213 #035-03-1998 L2000 EM *020 †16

SPEARMAN, Michael Patrick. 4800 FRIENDSHIP AVE 15224 #028-34-1988 L1993 RNR *020 †80

SPEARS, Noel Barbara. 3705 5TH AVE, DESOTO WING 15213 #016-06-1996 L1999 PEM *020 †55

SPECTOR, Zebulon Zachary. ■ 15232 #041-12-2008 *012

SPENCER, Abby Lyn. 230 MCKEE PL STE 600 15213 #041-12-2002 L2005 IM *100 †20

SPENCER, Lori Anne. 190 LOTHROP ST, STE 145 15213 #041-12-2004 L2004 P *012

SPERLING, Mark Alexander. 3705 5TH AVE 15213 #143-02-1962 L1989 PDE PD *071 †55

SPERO, Joel A. 816 MIDDLE ST, TOM BACZO 15212 #010-02-1970 L1974 HEM IM *071 †20

SPERRY, Jason Lee. ■ 15238 #038-06-1997 L2007 CCS *100 †85

SPEZIALI, Giovanni. 200 LOTHROP ST, C700 15213 #561-15-1988 L2006 *020

SPIESS, Alexander Marcus. 1307 FEDERAL ST, SECOND FLOOR 15212 #016-11-2000 L2005 HS *100

SPIKER, Duane Gerald. 3811 OHARA ST, WESTERN PSYCHIATRIC INSTIT 15213 #038-40-1971 L1975 P *020 †75

SPINA, Horacio A. 1050 BOWER HILL RD STE 303 15243 #132-02-1968 L1973 P *020 †75 ‡

SPINKS, Theodore James. 3705 5TH AVE 15213 #035-01-1999 L2005 NS *020

SPINOLA, Anthony. 120 LYTTON AVE, STE 100A 15213 #041-12-1995 L1998 IM *020 †20

SPIRO, Richard Marc. 200 LOTHROP ST 15213 #001-06-1998 L2000 NS *020 †25

SPOEHR, Luther W. 720 PERRY HWY 15229 #041-12-1943 L1944 GP *071

SPRINGER, Sarah H. 4070 BEECHWOOD BLVD 15217 #041-12-1988 L1990 PD *020 †55

SPYRIDAKI, Melina. 320 E NORTH AVE 15212 #286-11-2001 L2005 P *012

SQUIRES, Janet Endress. 3705 5TH AVE 15213 #017-20-1976 L2003 PD *020 †55

SQUIRES, Robt Hilton, Jr. 3705 5TH AVE 15213 #048-02-1977 L2003 GE PD *020 †55

SREERANGARAJAN, Sumana Hi. 121 MEYRAN AVE 15213 #496-22-2005 L2006 FP *012

SRINIVAS, Narain. 400 PENN CENTER BLVD, STE 555 15235 #495-17-1988 L1993 DR *020 †20

SRINIVASA, Nangali S. 11624 KELEKET DR 15235 #495-33-1978 L1993 NEP IM *020 †20

SRINIVASAN, Malini. 3550 TER-S707 SCAIFE, UNIV OF PITTSBURGH 15261 #495-04-1990 L1999 PTH *020

SRINIVASAN, Rajagopal. ■ 15222 #012-05-2002 L2007 EM *020

SRINIVASAN, Sukanya. 200 DELAFIELD RD 15215 #041-09-1997 L1999 FM *020 †18

STACHURA, Irene. 320 E NORTH AVE, ALLEGHENY GEN HOSPITAL 15212 #759-10-1961 L1977 PTH CLP *071 †50

STAFFORD, Marshall W. 100 DELAFIELD RD 15215 #041-02-1990 L1992 OPH *020 †35

STAFFORD, Regis Wm. 3500 5TH AVE 15213 #030-06-1963 L1964 CD IM *071 †20

STAHLFELD, Kurt Richard. 1400 LOCUST ST, MERCY HOS OF PITTSBURGH 15219 #041-12-1986 L1987 GS *020 †85

STALENSKI, Walter Stephen. 3550 TERRACE ST #A1305, UPMC DEPT OF ANESTHESIOLGY 15261 #055-01-1984 L2003 AN *020 †05

STALTER, Michelle Nicole. ■ 15209 #003-75-2007, ▲ L2007 FP *012

STANG, Michael Tracey. 200 LOTHROP ST, RM F1263 15213 #030-05-2000 L2001 GS *012

STANISH, Frank Xavier. 1004 ARCH ST 3RD FL, MERCY PROVIDENCE HOSPITAL 15212 #065-09-1968 L1969 OPH *020 ‡

STANKO, Kenneth Mark. 401 SHADY AVE STE A204 15206 #041-12-1977 L1981 P CHP *020 †75 ‡

STANKO, Ronald Thos. 200 LOTHROP ST, PITTSBURGH UNIV MED CTR 15213 #041-12-1973 L1974 NTR IM *050

STANKOVICH, Mara Julie. 320 E NORTH AVE 15212 #041-09-1995 L1999 EM *016

STARR, Matthew Todd. ■ 15232 #034-01-2007 L2007 IM *012

STARZ, Terence Weaver. 3500 5TH AVE, STE 401 15213 #041-02-1971 L1973 RHU IM *020 †20

STARZL, Thomas Earl. 3601 5TH AVE 4TH FL, FALK CLINIC 15261 #016-06-1952 L1981 GS TS *071 †85,90

STAUB, Brian Albert. ■ 15228 #041-12-2007 L2007 IM *012

STAUBER, Ziva. 168 ROCKWELL LN 15218 #041-13-1995 L2001 N *020 †75

STAVRIDES, Alexander. 146 N BELLEFIELD AVE 15213 #418-02-1953 L1964 PTH *071 †50

STAVRIDES, Marcia Mears. ■ 15213 #041-12-1961 L1962 PD *071 †55

STECKEL, Alan Jeffrey. 5140 LIBERTY AVE 15224 #041-07-1980 L1981 IM IMG *020 †20

STEED, David Luther. 2019 HAMPSTEAD DR 15235 #041-12-1973 L1974 GS *020 †85

STEFANOVIC-RACIC, Maja. 200 LOTHROP ST, E1140 BSTW 15261 #957-02-1989 L2001 END *020 †20

STEFKO, Susan Tonya. 203 LOTHROP ST 15213 #041-12-1997 L1997 OPH *020 †35

STEIN, Bradley Danl. 1 CHATHAM CTR, STE 700 15219 #041-12-1990 L1993 CHP P *020 †75

STEIN, Thomas Michael. 320 E NORTH AVE, ALLEGHENY GEN HOSP 15212 #041-14-1982 L1988 EM *040 †16

STEINMAN, Richard Arthur. 3600 FORBES AVE STE 405 15213 #041-01-1987 L1989 HEM *050 †20

STEINMAN, Sharon Lynn. 15222 #055-02-1999 L2007 SP PCP *100 †50

STENGER, Elizabeth Obrien. ■ 15206 #041-12-2006 L2006 PD *012

STEPHAN, Thorsten. ■ 15213 #407-21-1965 L1973 DIA END *071 †20

STEPT, Leonard Aaron. 200 DELAFIELD RD, STE 3060 15215 #041-12-1963 L1964 U *071 †95

STEPT, William Jos. 5230 CENTRE AVE 15232 #041-12-1960 L1961 AN OS *071 †05

STERN, Jamie Lynn. 4815 LIBERTY AVE, STE GR-30 15224 #041-07-1991 L1996 GPM *020 †20

STERN, Robert M. 300 HALKET ST STE 4750 15213 #041-12-1978 L1979 OBG *020 †30

STERNLICHT, Harold Craig. 1200 REEDSDALE ST 15233 #035-15-1985 L1986 CHP *020 †75 ‡

STERRETT, Stephanie Eliza. 969 GREENTREE RD, STE 100 15220 #041-12-2004 L2004 PD *020 †55

STETTEN, George De Witt. ■ 15238 #035-15-1991 L1992 OS *050

STEWART, Andrew Fyfe. 202 LOTHROP ST, BIOMEDICAL SCIENCE TOWER E 15261 #035-01-1974 L1997 END IM *020 †20

STEWART, Douglas Paul. 4923 CENTRE AVE, 4923 CENTER AVENUE 15213 #025-01-1990 L1992 PD *020 †55

STEWART, Ellen Claire. ■ 15217 #041-12-1982 L1986 OBG *071 †30

STEWART, Holly Ellen. 1200 REEDSDALE ST 15233 #041-12-2002 L2002 P *100

STEWART, James A, Jr. 7227 HAMILTON AVE 15208 #047-07-1951 L1952 GP *071

STEWART, Mervin S. 5859 BEACON ST, APT 3007 15217 #041-12-1953 L1954 P PYA *020 †75

STEWART, Susan Leigh. 3200 S WATER ST, CENTER FOR SPORTS MED 15203 #024-01-2001 L2001 ORS *020

STEWART, William D. 1400 LOCUST ST STE 2375 15219 #041-12-1944 L1945 AN *072 †05

ST GERMAIN, Natasha. ■ 15251-04-2007 L2007 GS *012

STIEFEL, Lori Ann. 5215 CENTRE AVE 15232 #038-40-1990 L1992 FM *040 †18

STIFEL, Elizabeth A N. 901 WEST ST, STE B 15221 #041-12-1967 L1968 FM *040 †18

STILE, Sabato Anthony. 3811 OHARA ST, WPIC RUN 279TDH 15213 #016-43-1969 L1975 ADP P *030 †75

STILES, Wendy Laura. 1465 MOHICAN DR 15228 #024-05-2000 L2001 DR *020 †80

STILLER, Ronald A. 5200 CENTRE AVE, STE 211 15232 #010-01-1982 L1983 PCC CCM *020 †20

STILLWELL, Terri Lynn. ■ 15232 #021-01-2005 L2005 PD *012

STINE, Amy Ruth. 8150 PERRY HWY, STE 332 15237 #023-01-1985 L1986 FM *020 †18

STIPPLER, Martina. ■ 15218 #154-02-2001 L2001 NS *012

STOFMAN, Guy Marc. 1350 LOCUST ST 15219 #041-02-1984 L1985 PS OTO *020 †45,65

STOICI, Roxana Manuela. 121 MEYRAN AVE, UNIV HLTH CTR OF PITTSBURG 15213 #781-04-2001 L2004 FM *020 †18

STOLLER, Ronald Gary. 5115 CENTRE AVE, FL 3 15232 #024-01-1971 L1978 ON IM *020 †20

STOLLER, Scott H. 1145 BOWER HILL RD, STE 205 15243 #035-03-1989 L1994 OPH *020 †35

STOLZER, Bertrand Lubell. 3601 5TH AVE, ARTHRITIS CTR FLK BLDG 15213 #035-19-1947 L1954 RHU IM *071 †20

STONE, Charles Sherry. 11 BRILLIANT AVE 15215 #041-09-1959 L1960 ORS OSS *020 †40

STONE, David Allan. 3200 S WATER ST, UPMC CENTER FOR SPORTS MED 15203 #033-05-1980 L1987 FSM *020 †60,18

STONE, Walker Harrison. ■ 15218 #067-01-1958 L1959 GS *072

STONE, William Arthur. 3459 5TH AVE, DEPT ANES 15213 #041-12-1962 L1963 AN *030 †05

STONEBRAKER, Vincent C. 1000 BOWER HILL RD, KEYSTONE ANESTHESIA CONSUL 15243 #055-01-1989 L1992 AN PME *020 †05

STOREY, Ashley Margaret. 4800 FRIENDSHIP AVE, STE 459 15224 #041-02-1991 L2005 AN *020 †05

STOREY, Mark Allen. 1711 MERRIMAN ST 15203 #038-43-1989 L1992 AN *020 †05

STOWELL, Keith R. 3811 OHARA ST 15213 #023-01-2004 L2004 P PYG *012

STRACCI, Peter F. 490 E NORTH AVE STE 202 15212 #055-75-1983, ▲ L1985 CD *020 †20

STRAH, Heather Marie. ■ 15219 #018-03-2007 L2007 IM *012

STRAKA, John Anthony. 100 S JACKSON AVE, FL 6 15202 #030-06-1966 L1967 OTO PS *020 †45 ‡

STRAKA, Matthew Burrill. 4815 LIBERTY AVE, STE 443 15224 #010-02-1997 L2000 OTO *020

STRAKA, Michelle R. 5500 CORPORATE DR, STE 100 15237 #010-02-1995 L1999 DR *020 †80

STRAMAT, John Michael. 1400 LOCUST ST, MERCY HOSPITAL OF PITTSBUR 15219 #041-13-1980 L1981 IM *040 †20

STRANDBERG, Gayle Lois. 3811 OHARA ST 15213 #041-12-2003 L2003 CHP *012

STRASSNIG, Martin Thomas. 121 MEYRAN AVE, UNIV HLTH CTR OF PITTSBURG 15213 #154-01-1999 L2003 P *100

STRAUSS, Alexander Sangor. 3811 OHARA ST 15213 #016-06-2005 L2005 P *012

STRAWBRIDGE, Heather D. 3705 5TH AVE, OF PITTSBURGH 15213 #038-44-2004 L2005 PDP *012

STRELEC, Stephen Ronald. 200 LOTHROP ST # C200, UPMC DEPT OF ANESTH 15213 #041-14-1976 L1977 AN CD *020 †05 ‡

STREMPLE, John Francis. 3454 FORBES AVE 15213 #056-06-1963 L1971 GS GE *071 †85

STRIMLAN, Charles Vaughn. 2100 JANE ST STE 601, RSCH TYLR BLDG-N 15203 #041-14-1971 L1976 PUD IM *020 †20

STROLLO, Diane C. 200 LOTHROP ST, 9019 FORBES TOWER 15213 #023-12-1981 L1988 DR *020 †80

STROLLO, Patrick J, Jr. 3459 5TH AVE STE NW628, MONTEFIORE UNIVERSITY HOSP 15213 #023-12-1981 L1993 PUD SME *050 †20

STRONG, Theressa B. 713 WASHINGTON RD 15228 #041-12-1983 L1985 OPH *020 †35

STROUD, Hilary Anne. 525 MOUNT PLEASANT RD, NORTHVIEW HEIGHTS 15214 #005-18-1976 L1979 FM *020 †18

STUART, John Albert. 120 LYTTON AVE, STE 275 15213 #041-07-1986 L1987 IM *020 †05

STUART, John Chas. 200 DELAFIELD RD, STE 2020 15215 #060-01-1968 L1969 OPH *020 †35

STUCKERT, Joseph John. ■ 15243 #041-12-2008 *012

STUDENSKI, Stephanie Anne. 3459 5TH AVE 15213 #019-02-1979 L2002 IMG RHU *050 †20

STULL, Dennis Francis. 5215 CENTRE AVE, STE 100 15232 #036-05-1998 L2000 IM *020 †20

STUPI, Angela Mary. 4424 PENN AVE, STE 104 15224 #041-07-1976 L1978 RHU IM *020 †20

STURM, Mary Frances. 5230 CENTRE AVE, EMERGENCY DEPARTMENT 15232 #038-43-1987 L1989 EM *020 †16

STYPULA, Mark Oliver. 4800 FRIENDSHIP AVE, DEPT OF ANESTHESIA 15224 #035-09-1981 L1986 **AN PD** *020 †55,05

STYPULA, Richard W, Jr. 103 WILLOW RD 15238 #041-12-1978 L1979 **AN PD** *020 †55,05

SU, Erik Ryan. ■ 15213 #051-07-2001 L2001 **CCP** *100 †55

SU, Ruthie Rebecca. 3471 5TH AVE, KAUFMANN MED BLDG STE 700 15213 #035-47-2005 L2005 **U** *012

SUARES, Gregory Alan. 320 E NORTH AVE 15212 #021-05-2004 L2005 **EM** *012

SUBBIAH, Yamini. 320 E NORTH AVE 15212 #496-23-2003 L2004 **IM** *100 †20

SUBRAMANIAN, Srilakshmi. 4800 FRIENDSHIP AVE, STE N221 15224 #495-21-2004 L2007 **FP** *012

SUCATO, Gina Suzanne. 3705 5TH AVE, ADOLESCENT MEDICINE 15213 #041-01-1995 L2000 **PD ADL** *020 †55

SUDHEENDRA, Deepak. ■ 15213 #035-09-2001 L2006 **DR** *012

SUFFOLETTO, Brian Paul. ■ 15221 #016-43-2003 L2003 **EM** *100

SUFFOLETTO, Matthew Scott. 200 LOTHROP ST, SCAIFE HALL S564 15213 #041-12-2001 L2001 **CD** *012

SUJATA, Mandayam Chokkama. 3520 5TH AVE, WPIC C&L SERVICE 15213 #495-04-1994 L2001 *020 †75

SUKANICH, Aurapin. 3 MARINER CT, ST MARGARET MEML HOSP 15238 #891-02-1969 L1974 **PD PHP** *020 †55,03

SUKANICH, Kriengsak. 2100 JANE ST, STE 112 15203 #891-02-1969 L1974 **GS** *020 †85

SUKAROCHANA, Kamthorn. 3705 5TH AVE 15213 #891-02-1951 L1963 **PDS** *071 †85

SUKHAVASI, Sujatha. 3705 5TH AVE, OF PITTSBU 15213 #495-50-1999 L2006 **PAN** *020

SUKUMVANICH, Paniti. 300 HALKET ST 15213 #035-06-1997 L1999 **OBG** *020

SULLIVAN, Daniel Richard. 9100 BABCOCK BLVD, UPMC PASSAVANT HOSPITAL 15237 #041-02-1976 L1977 **AN LM** *020 †05

SULLIVAN, Erin Ann. 200 LOTHROP ST, UPP DEPT OF ANESTHESIOLOGY 15213 #021-05-1986 L1998 **AN CD** *020

SULLIVAN, Lawrence X. ■ 15238 #041-12-1941 L1942 **OS** *072 †85

SULLIVAN, Lawrence X, Jr. 4815 LIBERTY AVE, # 156 15224 #041-12-1980 L1988 **TS** *020 †85,90

SULLIVAN, Maureen L. 815 FREEPORT RD, RADIOLOGY 15215 #010-02-1981 L1986 **DR NR** *020 †80

SULTAN, Shahjahan. ■ 15213 #041-12-2008 L2008 *012

SUN, Min. 200 DELAFIELD RD, 200 MED ARTS BLDG, SUITE 3 15215 #243-47-1993 L1999 **HO** *020 †20

SUNDARAM, Palanisamy. 333 ELM CT 15237 #495-04-1969 L1974 **PD** *020 †55 ‡

SUNDARAM, Sudha. 5700 CORPORATE DR, MERCY FAMILY HEALTH ASSO N 15237 #495-94-1985 L1998 **FM** *020 †18

SUNDARAM, Vinay. 15213 #035-19-2004 L2007 **GE** *012 †20

SUNG, Duk II. 125 MILLVIEW DR, 125 MILLVIEW DRIVE 15238 #583-04-1968 L1980 **RO** *020 †80 ‡

SUNG, Hiro. OF PITTSBURGH, UNIV HLTH CTR 15261 #033-05-2004 L2007 **CCM** *012 †20

SUNG, Jimmy Chiyun. ■ 15217 #016-11-1999 L2006 **GS** *020

SUNSERI, Maria Josephine. 4815 LIBERTY AVE, MELLON PAVILION STE M-02 15224 #041-12-1987 L1992 **SME N** *020 †75

SUPRASONGSIN, Chittiwat. ■ 15213 #891-04-1985 L1996 **PDE** *100

SUPRENANT, Valmore Joseph. ■ 15224 #041-13-2005 L2005 **GS** *100

SURAMPUDI, Ramana K. 100 S JACKSON AVE 15202 #495-50-1969 L1974 **PTH** *020 †50

SURESH, Tunga. ■ 15228 #495-04-1988 L2007 **PAN** *012

SURESHKUMAR, Kalathil K. 320 E NORTH AVE 15212 #495-44-1990 L1996 **NEP** *020 †20

SURYAWALA, Bijal Manoj. 1400 LOCUST ST, MERCY HOSPITAL 15219 #104-01-2005 L2005 **IM** *012

SUSEN, Anthony F. 5750 CENTRE AVE, STE 400 15206 #024-01-1945 L1953 **NS** *071 †25

SUSKI, David Allen. 9100 BABCOCK BLVD, EMERGENCY DEPARTMENT 15237 #041-12-1995 L1997 **EM** *020 †16

SUTKIN, Gary. 300 HALKET ST, DEPT OF OB/GYN/RS ROOM 232 15213 #016-06-1996 L1998 **OBG** *020 †30

SUTTON, Ernest Loran. 200 LOTHROP ST, GASTROENTEROLOGY DIVISION 15213 #016-11-1973 L2007 **GE IM** *020 †20

SUTTON, Roger Delbert. ■ 15228 #041-01-1960 L1961 **CD** *071

SUVICK, Michael Alfred. 1000 BOWER HILL RD 15243 #036-08-1994 L1997 **AN** *020 †05

SUVOROV, Yevgeniy. 320 E NORTH AVE 15212 #913-05-1994 L2006 **P** *012

SUWANNARAT, Pim. 3705 5TH AVE, DEPT OF GENETICS 15213 #891-03-1998 L2007 **MG** *100 †55,19

SUYAMA, Joe. 230 MCKEE PL, STE 500 15213 #041-12-1998 L2002 **EM** *020 †16

SWABY, Milton Eduardo. ■ 15207 #010-02-2002 L2003 **PM** *100

SWAN, Barbara Ellen. 1307 FEDERAL ST 15212 #041-02-1981 L1984 **PM OS** *020 †60 ‡

SWAN, Christopher Henry. ■ 15261 #041-12-2007 **IM** *012

SWAN, Danna Carol. 130 7TH ST, STE 1140 15222 #055-01-1967 L1981 **FM OM** *020 †18

SWANSON, Gary Nathan. 4 ALLEGHENY CTR, DEP TO PSYCHIATRY-8TH FLOO 15212 #025-07-1986 L1991 **CHP** *020 †75

SWANSON, Joel Wm. 320 E NORTH AVE, ALLEGHENY GENERAL HOSPITAL 15212 #035-47-1987 L1988 **AN IM** *020 †05

SWARTZ, Holly A. 3811 OHARA ST, DEPRESSION & MANIC DEPRESS 15213 #035-46-1990 L1997 **P** *020 †75

SWARTZ, William Michael. 5750 CENTRE AVE STE 180 15206 #007-02-1972 L1980 **PS HS** *020 †65

SWEET, Robert Alan. 3811 OHARA ST 12TH FL 15213 #023-01-1984 L1990 **P** *020 †75

SWEGAL, Otto F. 1074 GREENTREE RD 15220 #041-12-1952 L1953 **GP** *071

SWENSEN, Harold Edward. 5750 CENTRE AVE, STE 300 15206 #041-12-1958 L1959 **ORS N** *071 †40

SWENSEN, Nancy Jean M. ■ 15238 #041-12-1959 L1960 **AN** *071 †05

SWENSON, David Lewis. DELAFIELD RD, H JOHN HEINZ VA PROG CARE 15240 #051-01-1982 L1983 **IM IMG** *020 †20

SWERDLOW, Steven Howard. 200 LOTHROP ST 15213 #024-01-1975 L1992 **PTH** *050 †50

SWITALA, Regis Tyrone. 3550 TERRACE ST, A-1305 SCAIFE HALL 15261 #041-12-1994 L1996 **AN** *020 †05

SYED, Aladdin Zafar. 768 SCRUBGRASS RD 15243 #495-65-1968 L1976 **CD IM** *020 †20

SYNOWIC, Andrea. ■ 15228 #041-77-2007, ▲ L2007 **IM** *012

SZABO, Katherine Botuyan. 9100 BABCOCK BLVD 15237 #041-09-1998 L2002 **AN** *020 †05

SZAFRANSKI, John Anthony. 815 FREEPORT RD 15215 #041-12-1992 L1994 **FM** *030 †18

SZANTO, Katalin. 3811 OHARA ST, WESTERN PSYCHIATRIC INST 15213 #473-01-1980 L1999 **P** *100 †75

SZIGETHY, Eva M. 3705 5TH AVE, DEPT OF PSYCHIATRY 15213 #035-45-1993 L2005 **CHP** *020 †75

SZULMAN, Aron E. 300 HALKET ST 15213 #352-01-1945 L1964 **ATP OS** *072 †50

TABACHNICK, Theodore M. 401 SHADY AVE STE D103 15206 #041-12-1961 L1962 **P PYA** *071

TABAS, Debra L Horowitz. 339 6TH AVE, FL 5 15222 #041-12-1983 L1986 **IM** *020 †20

TABAS, Gary Howard. 5200 CENTRE AVE, STE 211 15232 #041-01-1975 L1976 **IM IMG** *040 †20

TABASSUM, Vajeeha. 1400 LOCUST ST 15219 #496-34-2002 L2006 **IM** *012

TABBA, Shadi Hani. ■ 15211 #575-02-2001 L2006 **PDE** *012 †55

TABET, Jean-Claude. ■ 15219 #067-02-1982 L1988 **OTO** *100 †45

TABOR, Ellen Kathleen. 4800 FRIENDSHIP AVE 15224 #055-01-1982 L1983 **DR** *020 †80

TADAJWESKI, Edward Joseph. 200 LOTHROP ST, RM S553 SCAIFE HALL 15213 #041-12-2000 L2001 **IC** *012 †20

TADAKI, Carl Joseph. 1400 LOCUST ST 15219 #021-01-2003 L2003 **GS** *012

TADIC, Stasa Dusan. 200 LOTHROP ST, BGC, UPMC MONTEFIORE 4E 15213 #957-06-1987 L2001 **IMG** *100

TADIKAMALLA, Raghu Ram. 200 LOTHROP ST, SCAIFE HALL, SUITE S553 15213 #028-02-2002 L2005 **CD** *012 †20

TADJZIECHY, Mahnaz. 3550 TERRACE ST, A-1305 SCAIFE HALL 15261 #517-01-1974 L1980 **AN** *020 †05

TAFFE, Elisa Claire. 320 E NORTH AVE, ALLEGHENY GEN HOSP 15212 #041-12-1998 L2000 **IM VM** *020 †20

TAFFE, Kevin Michael. 320 E NORTH AVE, ALLEGHENY GENERAL HOSPITAL 15212 #041-12-2001 L2001 **IM** *020

TAGGERT, Charles. 2585 FREEPORT RD, STE 201 15238 #041-13-1980 L1981 **FM** *020 †18 ‡

TAGLIATI, Kelsi Erin. ■ 15212 #041-14-2004 L2004 **AN** *012

TAITELBAUM, Ben. 4117 LIBERTY AVE, DRAKE BUILDING/2ND FLOOR 15224 #056-05-1962 L1965 **P** *020 †75

TALBOTT, John Bartlett. 1515 LOCUST ST, OF PITTSBURGH 15219 #016-11-1973 L1974 **N** *020 †75

TALLERICO, Samuel Jos. 4815 LIBERTY AVE G-25 15224 #041-12-1979 L1980 **IM** *020 †20

TALREJA, Neetu. ■ 15213 #495-37-2004 L2006 **IM** *012

TAMBOURATZIS, Thomas M. ■ 15234 #418-01-1994 L1994 **IM** *020 †20

TAMRAZOVA, Seda Sergueevn. ■ 15217 #913-15-1991 L2005 **IM** *012

TAN, Andrea Y. ■ 15206 #041-12-2003 L2003 **PMM** *012

TANDIN, Alessia. ■ 15212 #561-03-1994 L2001 **GS** *100

TANEJA, Pravin Atamprakas. 3705 5TH AVE, DEPARTMENT OF ANESTHESIOLO 15213 #496-30-1993 L2002 **PAN** *100 †05

TANHEHCO, Yvette Co. ■ 15213 #041-12-2008 L2008 *012

TANNING, Howard Michaels. 15215 #016-42-1964 L1967 **OPH** *071 †35 ‡

TANTISIRA, Boonrak. ■ 15238 #891-02-1965 L1967 **AN PA** *071 †05

TANZER, Peter Price. 3471 5TH AVE, STE 402 15213 #010-01-1978 L1981 **IM IMG** *020 †20

TAORMINA, Darrin Anthony. 3 MARINER CT, MEDICAL DIRECTOR HARMER OU 15238 #020-12-1995 L1998 **AN** *020 †05

TAPOLOW, Harvey Philip. 10 E NORTH AVE 15212 #033-05-1965 L1970 **P** *075

TAR, Leslie. 1926 E CARSON ST 15203 #035-45-1981 L1984 **RHU LM** *020 †20,70,03

TARIM, Omer Faruk. 3705 5TH AVE, PITTSBURGH/DEPT ENDOCRINOL 15213 #902-05-1982 L2002 **PD** *020 †55

TARNOPOLSKY, Rafael. ■ 15217 #187-06-1947 L1969 **OTO A** *071 †45

TARPEY, Margaret Mary. 200 LOTHROP ST, # W1358 BST 15261 #036-07-1981 L2005 **AN** *050 †05

TARR, Carly Hwangivime. ■ 15217 #041-12-2007 L2007 **EM** *012

TAUXE, W Newlon. 200 LOTHROP ST, UNIVERSITY OF PITTSBURGH 15213 #047-06-1950 L1983 **NM PTH** *072 †50,28

TAVARES, Alexandre Garcia. 3811 OHARA ST 15213 #187-11-1998 L2004 **P** *020

TAVAREZ, Melissa Maria. ■ 15206 #035-01-2007 L2007 **PD** *012

TAWBI, Hussein Abdul-Hass. 121 MEYRAN AVE 15213 #605-01-2001 L2002 **HO** *012 †20

TAYAL, Ashis Hari. 420 E NORTH AVE, STE 206 15212 #024-07-1994 L1997 **VN** *100 †75,20 ‡

TAYLOR, David Mcdonald. 200 LOTHROP ST 15213 #143-02-1978 *100

TAYLOR, Jennifer Lynn. ■ 15217 #010-02-1999 L2003 **EM** *020

TAYLOR, Mark Aaron. 9100 BABCOCK BLVD 15237 #016-43-1992 L1994 **AN CCA** *020 †05

TAYLOR, Paul M. 300 HALKET ST 15213 #023-07-1951 L1951 **PD** *071 †55

TAYLOR, Sharon L. 5900 CORPORATE DR, STE 150 15237 #035-03-1989 L1991 **OPH** *020 †35

TAYLOR, Yvette L. 8989 FRANKSTOWN RD 15235 #041-12-1998 L2000 **FM** *020 †18

TAZELAAR, John Pieter. ■ 15237 #025-01-1991 L2001 **PTH** *020 †50

TCHEN, Christina K. ■ 15222 #035-09-2002 L2007 **PD** *100 †55

TCHIRKOW, George. 1050 BOWER HILL RD, STE 208 15243 #010-02-1970 L1982 **CRS** *020 †85,10

TEDROW, John Rahul. 121 MEYRAN AVE, DEPT OF PULM/CRIT CARE 15213 #036-01-2003 L2006 **PCC** *012

TEEPLE, Edward. 5230 CENTRE AVE, UPMC PRESBY. SHADYSIDE HO 15232 #033-05-1977 L1983 **AN PM** *020 †05

TEIMOORI NOBANDEGANI, Seey. ARTS BUILDIN, STE 503 MEDICAL 15213 #517-05-1996 L2007 **FPP** *012

TELESCO, Richard R. 3705 5TH AVE, DIVISION OF PEDIATRICS 15213 #035-06-2000 L2007 **NPM** *020 †55

TEMELES, Roy Sherman. ■ 15235 #051-04-1947 L1954 **ORS** *071 †40

TENENOUSER, Barry. 2020 ARDMORE BLVD, STE 300 15221 #041-12-1961 L1962 **FM FPG** *071 †18

TENICELA, Ruben. 200 LOTHROP ST 15213 #737-01-1960 L1963 **PME AN** *071 †05

TEOT, Lisa Anne. 3705 5TH AVE 15213 #010-01-1986 L2002 **PTH ATP** *020 †50

TEPE, Paul Gerard. 969 GREENTREE RD 15220 #041-12-1991 L1993 **IM** *020 †20

TEPPERMAN, Barry. 0 UNIVERSITY DRIVE C 15240 #065-01-1975 L2004 **RO** *020 †80

TERKEL, Frederick J. ■ 15235 #041-12-1960 L1961 **FM** *071

TERSAK, Jean Marie. 3705 5TH AVE 15213 #041-12-1993 L1995 **PHO** *020 †55

TESAR, David Wm. 717 DUNCAN AVE, P O BOX 101627 15237 #038-06-1992 L1994 **N** *100 †75

TESSARO, Anne Neering. 9104 BABCOCK BLVD 15237 #041-07-1961 L1963 **R** *071 †80

TESSLER, Ellen Eva. 3705 5TH AVE, OF PITTSBURGH 15213 #041-14-2003 L2003 **AI** *012

TETLOW, Frank Nield. ■ 15241 #041-12-1942 L1943 **GS** *071

TEUTEBERG, Jeffrey John. 200 LOTHROP ST, STE S550 15213 #016-02-1996 L2004 **CD** *020 †20

TEUTEBERG, Winifred Grese. ■ 15217 #016-43-1998 L2004 **IM** *020 †20

TEVEROVSKY, Esther Jenny. ■ 15244 #041-12-2008 L2008 *012

TEW, James Dinsmore, Jr. 3811 OHARA ST, WPIC 15213 #041-12-2001 L2001 **PYG** *100 †75

TFAYLI, Hala Mounir. 121 MEYRAN AVE 15213 #605-01-2001 L2005 **PDE** *012

THAETE, Frank Leland. 200 LOTHROP ST 15213 #041-14-1983 L1984 **DR** *020 †80

THAI, Ngoc Luong. 3459 5TH AVE, UPMC, MONTEFIORE, 7 SOUTH 15213 #041-12-1997 L2002 **GS** *020 †85

THAKKAR, Shyam J. 200 LOTHROP ST, UPMC MONTEFIORE, N713 15213 #041-13-2001 L2001 GE *012

THAKUR, Ajay Kumar. 121 MEYRAN AVE 15213 #672-03-2004 IM *012

THAMMAN, Ritu. 490 E NORTH AVE, STE G104 15212 #016-06-1991 L1997 CD IM *020 †20

THEIN, Khin Kyaw Kyaw. 121 MEYRAN AVE 15213 #209-01-2002 L2005 FP *012

THEISEN, Renee Lynn. ■ 15206 #025-01-2005 L2005 EM *012

THIMONS, Joseph Anthony. 4800 FRIENDSHIP AVE 15224 #041-12-1991 L1994 AN *020 †05

THIRUMALA, Parthasarathy. 200 LOTHROP ST, UPMC PRESBYTERIAN PUH B-40 15213 #495-16-1998 L2003 CN *020 †75

THIRUMALA, Raghukumar Dee. 3550 TERRACE ST, 616 SCAIFE 15261 #495-04-2000 L2006 IM *020 †20

THIRUNAVUKARASU, Pragathee. ■ 15221 #495-04-2005 L2006 GS *100

THOMAS, Andrew Wm. 3285 BABCOCK BLVD 15237 #055-01-1990 L1993 GE *020 †20

THOMAS, Arthur Dutton. 5750 CENTRE AVE STE 430, THE CENTER FOR UROLOGIC 15206 #041-01-2000 L2001 U *020 †95

THOMAS, Ernestine Augusta. ■ 15213 #041-12-2008 *012

THOMAS, Herbert Edwin. 6301 FORBES AVE, STE 105 15217 #065-05-1956 L1961 P PYA *020 †75

THOMAS, Jason Preston. 4727 FRIENDSHIP AVE, STE 340 15224 #033-06-1994 L1996 HO *020 †20

THOMAS, John Wesley. ■ 15237 #047-07-1959 L1962 P *071

THOMAS, Lisa Ann. 100 N BELLEFIELD AVE STE 3 15213 #032-01-2000 L2001 P CHP *020 †75 ‡

THOMAS, Nini Chalakkal. 200 LOTHROP ST, SCAIFE HALL S 563 15213 #495-63-2001 L2004 IM *100 †20

THOMAS, Philip George. ■ 15213 #495-73-1976 L1994 *020

THOMAS, Robert Drexel. 3380 BLVD OF THE ALLIES, STE 1 15213 #041-12-1980 L1981 OBG *030

THOMAS, Ronald Lee. 320 E NORTH AVE, ALLEGHENY GENERAL HOSP 15212 #041-12-1981 L1991 MFM *020 †30

THOMAS, Stephen Michael. 105 BRAUNLICH DR STE 410 15237 #005-11-1984 L1984 PME *020 †05

THOMPSON, Ann Ellen. 3705 5TH AVE 15213 #024-07-1974 L1977 CCP AN *020 †05,55

THOMPSON, Arthur H, Jr. ■ 15209 #041-12-1960 L1961 P *071 †75

THOMPSON, John Watson. 200 LOTHROP ST, E-177 PUH 1ST FL UPMC MED 15213 #041-02-1976 L1977 DR *020 †80

THOMPSON, Kenneth Stewart. 6108 KENTUCKY AVE, 3811 OHARA ST 15206 #024-05-1982 L1991 P *020 †75

THOMPSON, Mark Ewing. 200 LOTHROP ST, CARDIOLOGY/VA HOSP 15213 #041-12-1965 L1966 CD IM *020 †20

THORPE, Steven Walter. ■ 15229 #047-05-2007 L2007 ORS *012

THORSON, Heidi Leigh. 300 HALKET ST RM 2232DE, OF OB 15213 #046-01-2003 L2007 MG *012

THUPPAL, Madhavan. 969 GREENTREE RD, STE 107 15220 #495-70-1978 L2000 P *020 †75

THURM, Leah Michelle. 121 MEYRAN AVE, UNIV HLTH CTR 15213 #035-08-2004 L2007 PG *012 †55

TIANGCO, Beatrice J. 121 MEYRAN AVE, DEPT MED EDUCATION 15213 #748-02-1987 L1995 ON *100

TIEGEL, William James. ■ 15238 #041-12-1965 L1966 FM *071 †18

TILSON, Michael Wayne. 9100 BABCOCK BLVD, DEPT OF ANESTHESIOLOGY 15237 #036-01-1978 L1990 AN *020 †05

TILSTRA, Sarah Anne. ■ 15261 #041-12-2007 L2007 IM *012

TIMBUS, Arthur Iulius. ATTN MARLENE MARREE, ALLEGHENY GENERAL HOSPITAL 15212 #781-01-1998 L2007 P *012

TINDLE, Hilary Aurora. 3459 FIFTH AVE, 933 MONTEFIORE 15261 #016-02-1996 L2005 IM *020 †20

TIRMAL, Vivek Vijay. 121 MEYRAN AVE, DEPT CCS 15213 #495-37-2000 L2007 CCS *012

TISHERMAN, Samuel Aaron. 3550 TERRACE ST, 638 SCAIFE HALL 15261 #041-12-1985 L1986 GS CCS *020 †85

TISZA, Veronica E Benedek. ■ 15213 #473-01-1937 L1962 CHP P *020 †55,75

TOBEY, Allison Beatriceja. ■ 15218 #041-12-2006 L2006 OTO *012

TOBIA, Stephen William. 300 HALKET ST, OF UPMC 15213 #011-02-2004 L2004 OBG *012

TOBIAS, Adam Zuckerman. ■ 15232 #041-12-2006 L2006 EM *012

TOBON, Hector. 200 LOTHROP ST, PATH/BIOMEDICAL SCIENCE 15213 #264-06-1961 L1968 PTH *020 †50

TODO, Satoru. 200 LOTHROP ST, FALK CLINIC 15213 #572-12-1972 L1990 GS *020

TOH, Elizabeth. 200 DELAFIELD RD 15215 #825-01-1991 L2001 OTO *020 †45

TOKARS, Roger Phillip. 521 E BRUCETON RD 15236 #016-02-1979 L1991 RO *020 †80

TOLENTINO, Aida M. 404 BIGHAM ST 15211 #748-08-1967 L1973 IM OBG *020

TOLMAN, Kenneth James. ■ 15237 #051-04-2001 L2003 DR *100

TOMA, Catalin. 200 LOTHROP ST 15213 #781-02-1996 L2002 IC *020 †20

TOMACRUZ, Moses Godofredo. ■ 15232 #748-31-2002 L2005 FP *012

TOMASI, Andrew Brandon. 4800 FRIENDSHIP AVE, THE WESTERN PENNSYLVANIA H 15224 #005-19-2000 L2006 EM *100 †16

TOMLEY, John Edward. ■ 15218 #041-12-1955 L1956 PD *020 †55

TONEY, Rachel Celeste. ■ 15212 #051-01-2003 L2007 GE *012 †20

TONG, Der-Long. 7405 IRVINE ST 15218 #244-01-1978 L1983 IM *020 †20

TOOMKOSITA, Vorachati. SOUTH SIDE HOSP 15203 #891-02-1970 L1976 GP *020 †20

TOPOZ, Irina Arkadyevna. ■ 15201 #007-02-2007 L2007 PD *012

TORABI, Maha. 200 LOTHROP ST, UPMC-PUH 15213 #517-08-2000 L2004 DR *012

TORMENTI, Matthew Justin. 15217 #041-12-2006 L2006 NS *012

TOROK, Frank Steven. 1000 BOWER HILL RD 15243 #041-14-1978 L1979 DR *100 †18,28,80

TOROK, Justin Steven. 15216 #041-14-2004 L2004 DR *012

TOROK, Kathryn Seraphin. ■ 15216 #041-14-2004 L2004 PPR *012

TORRES-TREJO, Alejandro. 5230 CENTRE AVE 15232 #649-26-1986 L2002 N *020 †75

TOTTEN, Jennifer Anne. ■ 15228 #035-45-2005 L2005 IM *012

TOWER, Irene M. ■ 15214 #048-15-2004 L2004 GS *012

TOWERS, Adele E. 450 MELWOOD AVE, LOWER LEVEL 15213 #008-02-1986 L1987 IMG IM *020 †20

TOWERS, Jeffrey Dalton. 200 LOTHROP ST, DEPT RAD 15213 #008-02-1986 L1989 DR *062 †80

TOYODA, Yoshiya. 200 LOTHROP ST 15213 #572-30-1990 L2005 *020

TRACHTENBERG, Lee Alan. 1145 BOWER HILL RD STE 201 15243 #041-12-1971 L1972 PS HS *071 †65

TRAN, An Long. ■ 15218 #035-15-2006 L2006 IM *012

TRAN, Huy Dinh. 4800 FRIENDSHIP AVE, DEPT RAD 15224 #041-15-2006 L2007 DR *012

TRAN, Jerry Loc. ■ 15232 #038-40-2005 L2005 IM *012

TRAN, Minhduc. 3937 BUTLER ST 15201 #016-76-2005, ▲ L2005 FP *012

TRAN, Quyen-Anh Dai. 15237 #041-14-2007 L2007 OBG *012

TRANG, Lien Bach. UNIVERSITY DRIVE C, VAMC ASPIMWALL DIVISION 15240 #941-01-1978 L1983 IM *020 †20

TRAPP, Christine Marie. ■ 15216 #008-02-2005 L2005 PD *012

TRAUB, Kevin Bradley. 200 DELAFIELD RD STE 3060 15215 #035-19-1996 L2002 U *020 †95

TRAY, Brian Patrick. 121 N HIGHLAND AVE STE 333, ALLEGHENY WOMEN'S CENTER 15206 #023-01-1984 L1993 OBG *020 †30

TRAYNOR, Owen Thomas. 230 MCKEE PL STE 400, PENNSYLVANIA 15213 #050-02-1993 L1995 EM *020 †16

TREDENNICK, Tara D. ■ 15219 #043-01-2007 L2007 TY *012

TREGER, Albert. 9104 BABCOCK BLVD 15237 #035-19-1955 L1967 CD IM *071 †20

TRELLIS, Dan R. 3347 FORBES AVE, STE 303 15213 #036-07-1985 L1991 GE IM *020 †20

TRELLIS, Emil Sherman. 15217 #041-02-1957 L1958 P *071 †75

TRENIN, Andrey. 320 E NORTH AVE 15212 #913-16-1989 L2003 IM *020 †20

TRETTIN, Shanthi. ■ 15206 #041-12-2004 L2004 P *012

TRIMMER, Michael Norman. 1004 ARCH ST 15212 #041-12-1973 L1974 EM IM *020 †20,16 ‡

TRIPP, Adam C. ■ 15212 #035-15-2006 L2007 P *012

TRIULZI, Darrell J. 200 LOTHROP ST, PATH/BIOMEDICAL 15213 #035-03-1985 L1985 PTH BBK *030 †50

TRIVEDI, Alok Vikramkumar. 4800 FRIENDSHIP AVE, DEPT FM 15224 #495-22-2003 L2006 FP *012

TRIVUS, Robert Howard. 615 WASHINGTON RD, STE 504 15228 #041-09-1961 L1963 P PA *020 †75

TROEN, Philip. 3601 5TH AVE, FALK RM 580 15213 #024-01-1948 L1964 END IM *040 †20

TROIANO, Mark Anthony. 3550 TERRACE ST, A-1305 SCAIFE HALL 15261 #041-13-1987 L1989 AN *020 †20

TROIANOS, Christopher A. 4800 FRIENDSHIP AVE, WESTERN PENNSYLVANIA HOSPI 15224 #041-12-1985 L1986 AN CD *020 †05

TROMBETTA, Mark Gerard. 320 E NORTH AVE, ALLEGHENY GEN HOSP 15212 #041-09-1985 L1986 RO *020 †80 ‡

TROMBLEY, Irene Kay. ■ 15241 #012-05-1976 L1978 PTH *020 †50

TSAI, Christopher Gordon. 200 DELAFIELD RD, STE 2040 15215 #010-02-1998 L2001 PCC *020 †20

TSAI, Theodore Leonard. 3708 5TH AVE, STE 500 15213 #035-03-1996 L1998 IM *020 †20

TSAI, Wilson Shuchun. 200 LOTHROP ST, UNIVERSITY OF PITTSBURGH M 15213 #033-35-1999 L2002 TS *012 †85

TSAY, Jawad. ■ 15206 #054-04-1999 L2005 RNR *100 †80

TSCHAKALOFF, Alexander. 68 SCAIFE HALL 15261 #409-43-1986 L1990 PS *020

TSIRONIS, Irene. 1350 LOCUST ST, STE 408 15219 #038-40-1981 L1987 OPH *050 †35

TSOPELAS, Nicholas. 3811 OHARA ST STE 275, DEPT OF PSYCH 15213 #418-01-1984 L2003 PYG P *020 †75

TSUKUI, Hiroyuki. 3708 5TH AVE, DEPT OF MED EDU 15213 #572-15-1995 L2006 *100

TSUNG, Allan. ■ 15237 #035-08-2000 L2001 GS *012

TUASON, Dominick Anthony. 121 MEYRAN AVE, DEPT OF ORTHOPAEDIC SURG 15213 #041-01-2005 L2005 ORS *012

TUBLIN, Mitchell Evan. 200 LOTHROP ST 15213 #035-06-1988 L1992 DR *020 †80

TUCHINDA, Jalit. 2100 JANE ST, STE 603 15203 #572-01-1970 L1973 CD *020 †20

TUCHINDA, Kanchana V. 2100 JANE ST, STE 603 15203 #572-01-1970 L1973 PD GP *020 †55

TUCHMAN, Jay B. 3705 5TH AVE 15213 #035-46-2003 L2007 PAN *012

TUCKER, James Newman. 35 GAMMA DR, STE 300 15238 #035-01-1978 L1979 PD *020 †55

TUCKER, Jon Barry. 1145 BOWER HILL RD, THIRD FLOOR 15243 #041-01-1984 L1985 ORS OSM *020 †40

TUCKER, Sonny Willie, Jr. 320 E NORTH AVE, ALLEGHENY GENERAL HOSPITAL 15212 #041-07-1997 L2000 VS *012

TUEL, Wesley David. ■ 15217 #055-02-2005 L2005 DR *012

TULLY, Bryan Paul. 320 E NORTH AVE, ALLEGHENY GENERAL HOSPITAL 15212 #319-07-2005 L2007 EM *012

TULSKY, Asher Arthur. 5200 CENTRE AVE, STE 211 15232 #016-42-1985 L1997 IM *040 †20

TUMMALAPALLI, Krishna V. 5200 CENTRE AVE STE 206 15232 #495-62-1977 L1983 CD *020 †20 ‡

TUMULURU, Rameshwari V. 3811 OHARA ST 15213 #495-65-1982 L1986 P *020 †75

TUNE, Adam Decatur. ■ 15228 #048-13-2006 L2007 *012

TUREN, Selahattin. 3708 5TH AVE, DEPT OF MEDEDU 15213 #902-05-1999 L2006 IM *012

TURKAY, Atac. 3500 TERRACE ST RM S718, DIV OF RHEUMATOLOGY 15213 #902-03-1984 L2001 RHU *020 †20

TURNER, Amy Beth. 3708 5TH AVE, DEPT OF MEDICAL EDUCATION 15213 #011-75-2005, ▲ L2005 OBG *012

TURNER, Andrew Robert. 4200 5TH AVE, DEPT HEM 15261 #067-01-1972 L1974 IM HEM *050 †20

TUROCY, John Francis. 300 HALKET ST, RM 1651 15213 #041-12-1989 L1991 MG *012 †30

TURTURRO, Michael Anthony. 1400 LOCUST ST, MERCY HOSPITAL 15219 #035-15-1987 L1989 EM *020 †16

TURZAI, Lidia Comini. 4923 CENTRE AVE 15213 #041-12-1991 L1993 PD *020 †55 ‡

TUTTLE, Alfred. 5750 CENTRE AVE STE 510 15206 #041-09-1936 L1937 GS *071

TWAN, Steven Aung Myint. 4411 STILLEY RD, STE 3 15227 #209-01-1986 L1998 PD *020 †55

TYLER, Sarah Louise. ■ 15221 #036-07-2006 L2006 PD *012

TYLER-KABARA, Elizabeth C. 3705 5TH AVE 15213 #047-05-1997 L1999 NS NSP *020

TYNDALL, Christine Susan. 400 PENN CENTER BLVD, STE 810 15235 #033-05-1979 L1980 OBG *071 †30

TYSON, Scott Leland. 240 MOUNT LEBANON BLVD 15234 #041-12-1979 L1984 PD *020 †55

TZENG, Edith I. 200 LOTHROP ST, A1010 PUH 15213 #016-02-1990 L1992 GS *020 †85

UBINGER, William N. VET ADMIN MED CTR, DEPT FAM PRACTICE 15206 #005-14-1964 L1965 FM *020 †18

UCHAL, Miroslav. 320 E NORTH AVE, 5TH FLOOR, S TOWER 15212 #286-06-1986 L2004 GS *100

UCHINO, Ken. 200 LOTHROP ST, PUH C-400 15213 #035-19-1997 L2003 N *020 †75

UDREA, Dan Mario. 320 E NORTH AVE 15212 #781-01-2001 L2006 P *012

UDREA, Maria Nicoleta. 4800 FRIENDSHIP AVE, WESTERN PENNSYLVANIA HOSP 15224 #781-01-2001 L2004 OBG *012

UKPEDE, Johnson Akpoba. ■ 15206 #422-01-2006 L2007 AN *012

ULHOACINTRA, Alice Barbos. ■ 15220 #041-15-2006 L2006 IM *012

UMAPATHY, Chandraprakash. 1400 LOCUST ST, MERCY HOSPITAL 15219 #495-59-2003 L2006 IM *012

UMERAH, Stella Anayo. 7227 HAMILTON AVE 15208 #690-15-2000 L2002 FM *020 †18

UNG, Kenneth Kiang. 1748 JANCEY ST 15206 #041-12-1979 L1980 **FM** *020 †18

UNGAR, Ira Jay. ■ 15241 #038-06-1984 L1999 **EM** *020 †16

UNLIGIL, Peri. 200 LOTHROP ST, UPMC MONTEFIORE 9 SOUTH 15213 #067-01-1994 L1996 **IM** *020 †20

UNRUH, Mark Lynn. 3550 TERRACE ST, A909 SCAIFE HALL 15261 #016-02-1996 L1999 **NEP** *020 †20

UPADHYAYA, Ameet Rajanika. ■ 15235 #041-12-2004 L2006 **DR** *012

UPADHYAYA, Margi Jaypraka. ■ 15217 #025-07-2006 L2006 **PD** *012

UPDIKE, Glenn Michael. 300 HALKET ST 2232 15213 #041-12-1998 L2002 **OBG** *020 †30

URBACH, Andrew Harley. 3705 5TH AVE, PEDS/ONE CHILDRENS PL 15213 #035-06-1979 L1980 **PD CCM** *020 †55

URBAN, Agnieszka S. 3705 5TH AVE 15213 #759-07-1991 L2006 **PN** *020 †55

URETSKY, Scott. ■ 15217 #035-08-2004 L2004 **N** *012

URIBE, John Peter. 4815 LIBERTY AVE, STE G25 15224 #649-14-1992 L1997 **IM GPM** *020 †70,20

URIBE, Julieta Giron. ■ 15212 #649-14-1993 L1995 **IM** *100

URISH, Kenneth Lynn. ■ 15232 #041-12-2008 *012

URKIN, Jacob. UNIV HLTH CTR DEPT MED 15260 #550-04-1981 L1992 *020

URREA, Christian Phillip. ■ 15203 #041-15-2008 *012

USKOVA, Anna Alexandrovna. 3471 5TH AVE, STE 910 15213 #913-03-1989 L2001 **AN** *020 †05

UTBERG, John Robert. 9335 MCKNIGHT RD, STE 220 15237 #041-13-1962 L1964 **OBG** *071 †30

UY, Nonita T Lim. 300 HALKET ST, DEPT ANES 15213 #748-10-1965 L1973 **AN** *020 †05

UZOMBA, Rosemary Nnenna. ■ 15217 #035-45-1992 L2005 **AN** *020 †05

VACCA, Jennifer Lynn. ■ 15216 #041-12-2005 L2005 **IM** *012

VAEZI, Alec Ebraim. 200 LOTHROP ST 15213 #869-04-1998 L2004 **OTO** *100

VAGLEY, Richard Thos. 5989 PENN CIR S, PITTSBURGH INST OF PLASTIC 15206 #041-02-1968 L1969 **PS** *020 †65

VAGNUCCI, Anthony Hillary. 3601 5TH AVE, FALK MEDICAL BLDG ROOM 587 15213 #561-07-1954 L1966 **END IM** *071 †20

VAISLEIB, Inna I. 3705 5TH AVE 15213 #913-04-1987 L2000 **CHN** *020 †75

VAKA, Srinivas Reddy. 1500 5TH AVE, INTERNAL MED RESDNCY 15219 #495-50-1997 L2008 *100

VALAKH, Vladimir. 320 E NORTH AVE, ALLEGHENY GEN HOSP 15212 #041-15-2006 L2007 **RO** *012

VALCARCEL, Sofronio J. ■ 15237 #748-01-1960 L1969 **AN** *071

VALENTINE, James Cooper. ■ 15216 #023-12-2005 L2007 *100

VALENTINE, Lee Swenson. 128 HAWTHORNE ST 15218 #041-02-1975 L1976 **GE IM** *050 †20,16

VALENZA, Thomas Chas. 9100 BABCOCK BLVD 15237 #041-12-1980 L1980 **EM** *020 †16

VALERIANO, James Philip. 420 E NORTH AVE, STE 206 15212 #041-12-1980 L1984 **N** *020 †75

VALERIO, Anna Francesca L. ■ 15232 #748-02-2002 L2005 **FP** *012

VALERIO, Ian Lee. ■ 15235 #020-12-2004 L2004 **PS** *012

VALLABHANENI, Geetha Devi. ■ 15220 #495-11-2000 L2008 **IM** *012 †20

VALLABHANENI, Raghuveer. ■ 15203 #033-05-2001 L2001 **GS** *012

VALLANO, Gary. 4701 BAPTIST RD, STE 208A 15227 #041-12-1985 L1987 **CHP P** *020 †75

VAMADEVAMURTHY, M. 7110 CHURCH ST 15202 #495-33-1965 L1979 **IM RHU** *020 †20

VANACHARLA, Saroja. ■ 15224 #495-21-2003 L2007 **IM** *012

VANCE, Robert A. 9100 BABCOCK BLVD, UPMC PASSAVANT 15237 #055-01-1986 L2003 **AN** *050 †05

VAN COTT, Ann Cecile. 200 LOTHROP ST 15213 #035-09-1988 L1990 **N** *020 †75

VANDERBILT, Mark David. 4815 LIBERTY AVE, STE GR-30 15224 #026-04-1986 L1992 **IM** *020 †20

VANDEUSEN, Mathew Aaron. 320 E NORTH AVE, ALLEGHENY GENERAL HOSPITAL 15212 #041-13-2000 L2001 **TS** *100 †85

VAN FLEET, Timothy A. 300 HALKET ST, MAGEE-WOMENS HOSPITAL 15213 #038-45-1983 L1984 **EM FM** *030 †18

VAN LONDEN, G.J.. ■ 15221 #660-04-2000 L2001 **HO** *100

VARAT, Murray Aaron. 6950 ROSEWOOD 15208 #035-08-1962 L1971 **CD IM** *071 †20

VARCELOTTI, Jorge Raul. 1400 LOCUST ST 15219 #132-02-1972 L1978 **GS EM** *020 †85

VARGA, Jeffrey M. 320 E NORTH AVE 15212 #041-02-1983 L1984 **AN PME** *020 †05

VARGHESE, Juno Elizabeth. 4800 FRIENDSHIP AVE, FAMILY PRACTICE PROGRAM 15224 #496-34-2001 L2003 **FP** *012

VARGHESE, Rekhi Puthen Ve. 200 LOTHROP ST, 8E 15213 #496-34-1993 L2002 **CD** *012 †20

VARGO, Scott Michael. 320 E NORTH AVE 15212 #041-09-1996 L1998 **IM** *020 †20

VARLEY, William J. ■ 15234 #041-12-1953 L1954 **R** *071 †80

VARON, Daniel. ■ 15213 #264-04-1995 L2006 **P** *020

VASSILIEV, Dmitri V. 320 E NORTH AVE 15212 #913-15-1987 L1999 **APM** *020 †05

VASUDEVAN, Sanjay Shankar. 200 LOTHROP ST, SCAIFE HALL, SUITE B571.3 15213 #495-04-1993 L2002 **CD** *012 †20

VATNER, Daniel Feller. ■ 15211 #016-02-2007 **IM** *012

VATS, Abhay. 3705 5TH AVE 15213 #495-36-1987 L1998 **PN** *020 †55

VATS, Kalyani Rai. 300 HALKET ST, DEPT OF PEDIATRICS 15213 #495-79-1986 L2000 **NPM** *012

VAUGHAN, Christina Lynn. 121 MEYRAN AVE 15213 #035-06-2006 L2006 **N** *012

VAUGHAN, Paul Matthew. ■ 15228 #041-13-1979 L1980 **EM MDM** *020 †16

VAULXSMITH, Petronilla M. 3811 OHARA ST, PSYCHIATRY 15213 #033-06-1989 L1991 **P** *020 †75

VAVASSORI, Carla. ■ 15206 #561-14-1984 L1994 **IM** *100 †20

VAYONIS, Andrew Geo. 320 FORT DUQUESNE BLVD, GATEWAY TOWERS STE 380 15222 #041-14-1988 L1990 **AI IM** *020 †20,03 ‡

VAZQUEZ, Jorge Antonio. 1307 FEDERAL ST STE 301 15212 #042-01-1978 L1981 **NTR IM** *020

VEERAGANDHAM, Gautami. 373 BURROWS ST 15213 #496-24-1988 L2001 **CHP P** *020 †75

VEITIA, Nestor Adolfo. 121 MEYRAN AVE, DEPT OF PLASTIC SURG 15213 #041-02-1998 L2001 **PS** *012

VELA, Deborah Cecilia. 320 E NORTH AVE 15212 #319-03-1996 L2003 **PTH** *100

VELASQUEZ, Natalie Dawn. 3811 OHARA ST, AND C 15213 #010-01-2006 L2006 **P** *012

VELAZQUEZ, Karen L Brady. 117 N NEGLEY AVE, EAST END COMMUNITY HEALTH 15206 #041-12-1996 L1998 **FM** *020 †18

VELDKAMP, Peter Jakob. 3347 FORBES AVE, FIRST FLOOR 15213 #001-02-1992 L2003 **ID** *100 †20

VELEZ-GIRALDO, Juan R. ■ 15213 #847-11-1988 L1992 **END** *100 †20

VELEZ-LONDONO, Rodrigo. ■ 15243 #264-03-1954 L1976 **GP OBG** *071

VELLODY, Kishore. 3705 5TH AVE, CHILDRENS HOSP OF PGH 15213 #016-11-2002 L2005 **PD** *100 †55

VELUCHAMY, Vivekanand. 3705 5TH AVE, CHILDREN'S HOSP 15213 #496-39-2000 L2007 **CHN** *012 †55

VENEZIANO, Giorgio Carl. ■ 15206 #038-06-2007 L2007 **AN** *012

VENGALA, Srinivas. ■ 15237 #495-65-1995 L2000 **CD** *012 †20

VENKAT, Arvind. 320 E NORTH AVE, DEPT OF EMERGENCY MEDICINE 15212 #008-01-2000 L2007 **EM** *020 †16

VENKATARAMAN, Ramesh. 139 NINETEEN NORTH CT 15237 #495-59-1994 L2000 **CCM** *020 †20

VENKATARAMAN, Shekhar T. 3705 5TH AVE 15213 #495-53-1980 L1984 **CCA CCM** *020 †55

VENKATESAN, Malathi. 490 E NORTH AVE, STE 204 15212 #495-59-1986 L1995 **IM** *020 †20

VENKATESH, Seshaiyengar. 100 DELAFIELD RD STE 211 15215 #495-33-1976 L1995 **OPH** *012 †35

VENTURA, Van Arthur Suva. 1400 LOCUST ST 15219 #748-01-1999 L2004 **IM** *020 †20

VENTURA, Xenia Yu. 1400 LOCUST ST, MERCY HOSPITAL 15219 #748-01-1999 L2007 **IM** *012

VERALDI, Kristen Louise. 3459 5TH AVE, DIV OF PULMONARY, ALLERGY& 15213 #041-12-2001 L2007 **PCC** *100

VERDREAM, E Anthony. 4778 LIBERTY AVE 15224 #041-13-2002 L2002 **ID** *020 †20

VERGIS, Emanuel N. 5230 CENTRE AVE 15232 #041-12-1991 L1993 **ID** *020 †20

VERMA, Anupam Yatish. ■ 15238 #495-96-2000 L2003 **IM** *020 †20

VESCAN, Allan Dave. 3708 5TH AVE, DEPT OF MED EDU 15213 #065-06-2001 L2006 *100

VESIO, Kenneth D. 5200 CENTRE AVE STE 206 15232 #041-13-1984 L1989 **CD IM** *062 †20

VEY, Edwin K. ■ 15238 #041-12-1948 L1949 **OPH** *071 †35

VIADANA, Enrico. 4716 ELLSWORTH AVE 15213 #561-03-1964 **PTH** *020

VICTOR-VEGA, Cassandre St. ■ 15221 #041-12-2007 L2007 **TY** *012

VIJAYALAKSHMI, Duraisamy. 1400 LOCUST ST 15219 #495-04-1994 L2005 **PM** *012

VIJAYKUMAR, Puvalai M. 5125 LIBERTY AVE 15224 #495-16-1978 L1988 **ICE IM** *020 †20

VILAIYUK, Soamarat. 3708 5TH AVE, DEPT OF MED EDUCATION 15213 #891-04-1997 L2006 *100

VILANOVA, Jose Maria. ■ 15208 #132-01-1953 L1962 **P N** *030

VILLA, Chet Ridall. ■ 15243 #038-41-2007 L2007 **PD** *012

VILLANUEVA, Flordeliza S. 200 LOTHROP ST 15213 #024-05-1984 L1987 **IM CD** *020 †20

VILLAR, Kenneth Sanchez. 3708 5TH AVE, DEPT OF MED EDUCATION 15213 #748-10-1997 L2005 **FP** *012

VILLASENOR, Mariano M. ■ 15237 #748-01-1956 L1968 **GP IM** *071

VILLELLA, Edward Robt. 102 WOODBRIDGE DR, CARE CTR 15237 #028-34-1969 L1971 **GS** *020 †85

VINSON, Carey Thos. 120 5TH AVE, SUITE FAP 733 15222 #020-02-1978 L1984 **FM FPG** *030 †18

VINTA, Sandhya Rani. ■ 15213 #496-22-1999 L2002 **AN** *012

VIRJI, Mohamed A. 200 LOTHROP ST 15213 #905-01-1969 L1979 **CLP PCH** *020 †50

VIRK, Amneet. ■ 15205 #495-03-2001 L2007 **RHU** *012 †20

VISOIU, Adrian. 200 LOTHROP ST, BENEDUM GERIATRIC CTR., 4E 15213 #781-01-1993 L1998 **IMG** *020 †20

VISWESWARAN, Shyam. ■ 15217 #495-53-1987 **N** *100

VITALE, Melissa Ann. 3705 5TH AVE, PITTSBURGH, PEM, 15213 #023-07-2003 L2003 **PEM** *012 †55

VITEK, Wendy Susan. ■ 15217 #035-45-2005 L2005 **OBG** *012

VITI, Craig Geo. 200 DELAFIELD RD STE 2040, PULMONARY CONSULTANTS - UP 15215 #041-02-1988 L1990 **PUD** *020 †20

VIVAS, Carlos Alberto. 1307 FEDERAL ST, STE 300 15212 #132-09-1972 L1989 **U** *020 †95

VIVAS, Yoel Rafael. ■ 15209 #935-07-2001 L2005 **CD** *012 †20

VLAHOS, Patrick James. ■ 15241 #041-77-1979, ▲ L1980 **AN PHP** *071

VOCKLEY, Gerard. 3460 5TH AVE, RANGOS BLDG 2ND FL 15213 #041-01-1984 L2003 **MG PD** *020 †19,55

VOGEL, Amy Kathleen. 3471 5TH AVE, STE 901 15213 #016-06-1996 L2000 **PM** *020 †60

VOGEL, Tracey Marie. 300 HALKET ST, MAGEE WOMENS HOSPITAL 15213 #041-12-1993 L2001 **AN** *020 †05

VOGEL, Victor Gerald. 300 HALKET ST 15213 #041-13-1978 L1995 **ON OS** *050 †20,70

VOGELEY, Eva Anne. 300 HALKET ST 15213 #041-12-1975 L1976 **PD LM** *020 †55

VOGLER, Andrea. ■ 15208 #011-03-2001 L2005 **EM** *020 †20

VOGLER, Barbara. 120 LYTTON AVE, STE 250 15213 #011-03-2001 L2005 **N** *100 †75

VOIGT, Andrew Howard. 200 LOTHROP ST, SCAIFE HALL, S559 15213 #041-12-1998 L2000 **ICE** *100 †20

VOIGT, Laura Ward. 5608 WILKINS AVE STE 202, THE WILKINS BUILDING 15217 #041-12-1999 L2002 **PD** *020 †55

VOLK, David William. 3811 OHARA ST, WPIC 15213 #041-12-2004 L2004 **P** *012

VOLKIN, Robert Leonard. 101 DRAKE RD, STE B 15241 #041-12-1975 L1976 **HEM ON** *020 †20 ‡

VOLOSHIN, Denise Kreider. 200 LOTHROP ST, W635 MONTEFIORE UNIV HOSP 15213 #041-02-1989 L1991 **ID** *020 †20

VOLOSKY, Robert Louis. 4778 LIBERTY AVE 15224 #010-02-1985 L1989 **ID** *020 †20

VOLPE, Carmine Michael. 4800 FRIENDSHIP AVE, 4N DEPT OF SURGERY 15224 #041-07-1984 L1985 **GS** *020 †85

VON DER PORTEN, Kenneth. 110 FORT COUCH RD 15241 #048-16-1986 L1987 **PYG P** *020 †75

VORA, Nirav Amit. 200 LOTHROP ST, STE C406 15213 #001-02-2001 L2005 **N NRN** *020 †75

VORNICU, Maria Diana. 4815 LIBERTY AVE, WPMA 15224 #781-02-2000 L2004 **IM** *100 †20

VRIES, John Kenric. 125 DESOTO ST, CHILDREN'S HOSPITAL OF PIT 15213 #905-01-1966 L1979 **NS** *020 †25

VU, Cong Huy. 4800 FRIENDSHIP AVE, WESTERN PA HOSP 15224 #005-18-2007 **GS** *012

VUCHINICH, Theodore, III. 9104 BABCOCK BLVD, STE 2103 15237 #041-12-1987 L1990 **PUD** *020 †20

VUCINICH, Dana. 3601 5TH AVE, FALK, ROOM 585 15213 #048-04-1988 L1990 **END** *020 †20

VUJEVICH, Justin John. 100 N WREN DR, DERMATOLOGY AND COSMETIC S 15243 #016-06-2000 L2003 **D** *020 †15

VUJEVICH, Marion Mark. 100 N WREN DR 15243 #539-05-1966 L1967 **D PS** *020 †15

VUKMIR, Rade B. 13 PRIDE ST 15219 #041-12-1986 L1987 **IM EM** *020 †16

WACHOWSKI, Katharine Sue. ■ 15218 #056-05-2005 L2005 **PD** *012

WACHS, Hirsh. ■ 15217 #016-06-1956 L1957 **N** *071 †75

WACHTEL, Stephen. 3811 OHARA ST DEPT PTH 15213 #055-02-1990 L1995 **PTH** *020 †50

WACHTMAN, Galen Samuel. UNIVERSITY OF PITTSBURGH, 3550 TERRACE STREET 15261 #041-12-2004 L2004 **PS** *012

WADAS, Richard John, Jr. 2 HOT METAL ST 2ND FL, QUANTUM ONE 15203 #033-06-1996 L1998 **EM** *020 †16

WADE, Marcia Jane. 201 N CRAIG ST 15213 #008-01-1978 L1994 **PUD IM** *030 †20

WADHAWAN, Anita. ■ 15217 #495-03-1967 **OBG** *100

WADHWA, Rajindar Kumar. 850 CLAIRTON BLVD 15236 #495-45-1966 L1972 **AN PME** *020

WADHWA, Saroj Rajindar. 4815 LIBERTY AVE 15224 #495-01-1968 L1972 **GYN** *020 †30

WAGNER, Daniel R. ■ 15206 #409-06-1985 L1998 **CD** *100

WAGNER, Kerstin. ■ 15206 #409-40-1992 L1998 **PDC** *100

WAGNER, Michael M. 200 LOTHROP ST, FORBES TOWER, SUITE 8084 15213 #035-19-1979 L1990 **IM** *020 †20

WAHBA, Baher Nabil Naguib. 1500 5TH AVE, INTERNAL MED RESDNCY 15219 #915-02-2000 L2008 *100

WAHEED, Amina. 4800 FRIENDSHIP AVE, WESTERN PENNSYLVANIA HOSP 15224 #704-20-2002 L2006 **FM** *100

WAHLGREN, Christina Marie. 190 LOTHROP ST, 145 LOTHROP HALL 15213 #054-04-2006 L2006 **D** *012

WAHRENBERGER, Jack Todd. 620 E OHIO ST 15212 #041-12-1991 L1993 **FM** *020 †18

WAHRENBERGER, Maria E. 1000 W VIEW PARK DR, STE 1 15229 #041-12-1991 L1993 **IM** *020 †20

WAJANAPONSAN, Non. OF PITTSBURGH, UNIV HLTH CTR 15261 #891-02-1999 L2005 **CCM** *012 †20

WAJANAPONSAN, Yaowarat. 3708 5TH AVE, DEPT OF MED EDUCATION 15213 #891-05-2000 L2006 *100

WAKIM, Najib G. 300 HALKET ST, STE 5150 15213 #605-01-1978 L1991 **REN** *040 †30

WALBERG, Harry Willard. 100 S JACKSON AVE 15202 #041-12-1952 L1953 **IM CD** *071

WALD, Michael Edward. 580 S AIKEN AVE, STE 300 15232 #016-42-1963 L1964 **PUD IM** *020 †20 ‡

WALD, Niel. 5422 NORMLEE PLACE 15261 #035-19-1948 L1958 **OM CCG** *071

WALIA, Rohit. ■ 15212 #496-38-1997 L2005 **DR** *012

WALKER, Delphine Lacretia. ■ 15219 #025-12-2002 L2006 **AN** *012

WALKER, Levi. 211 N WHITFIELD ST STE 710 15206 #041-12-1984 L1986 **IM** *040

WALL, John Nolan. 100 S JACKSON AVE 15202 #041-12-1955 L1956 **OBG** *071 †30

WALLACE, Dustin Mark. ■ 15220 #038-43-2007 L2007 **IM** *012

WALLACE, Luisa Paula. 300 HALKET ST, FL 3 15213 #005-12-1995 L1999 **DR** *020 †80

WALLACE, Michael Lloyd. 522 ALPHA DR 15238 #010-01-1991 L2001 **DMP** *062 †50

WALLEN, Jason M. 121 MEYRAN AVE, UNIV HLTH CTR 15213 #067-01-2001 L2007 **TS** *012 †85

WALLER, Louis Clarence. ■ 15208 #041-12-1947 L1949 **GP** *071

WALLIA, Tegendra Singh. 4800 FRIENDSHIP AVE 15224 #495-20-1967 L1974 **CD IM** *020 †20

WALLS, Andrew Louis. ■ 15228 #041-12-2004 L2004 **PTH** *012

WALSH, Arthur Campbell. 161 N DITHRIDGE ST 15213 #060-01-1943 L1964 **P** *072

WALSH, John J. ■ 15215 #035-09-1953 L1954 **U** *071

WALSH, Nicolette C. 5230 CENTRE AVE 15232 #055-01-1987 L1989 **FM** *020 †18

WALSON, Karen Hallermeier. ■ 15217 #041-12-2002 L2005 **CCP** *012 †55

WALTER, C Lee. 4815 LIBERTY AVE, STE GR-30 15248 #041-12-1961 L1962 **CD IM** *020

WALTER, Kevin A. 200 LOTHROP ST 15213 #023-07-1995 L2002 **NS** *020 †25

WALTERS, Mary Grace. ■ 15213 #041-12-2001 L2001 **P** *100 †75

WALTERS, Timothy Charles. ■ 15218 #051-04-2007 L2007 **IM** *012

WALVEKAR, Rohan Ramchandr. 200 LOTHROP ST 15213 #496-36-1998 L2006 *100

WALZ, Richard Collins, III. ■ 15232 #017-20-2007 L2007 **EM** *012

WANAMAKER, Kelly. ■ 15202 #041-15-2008 L2008 *012

WANG, Henry Eng. 230 MCKEE PL STE 400, UNIVERSITY PITTSBURGH MED 15213 #033-06-1997 L2000 **EM** *050 †16

WANG, Norman Chungshing. ■ 15213 #016-06-1998 L2008 **ICE** *100 †20

WANG, Xue. 320 E NORTH AVE 15212 #243-70-1986 L2000 **DR** *100 †80

WANG, Zheng. 2585 FREEPORT RD, STE 105 15238 #243-79-1983 L2000 **PM** *020 †60

WANGU, Zoon. ■ 15202 #045-14-2007 L2007 *012

WARD, Barbara H. 5500 CORPORATE DR, STE 100 15237 #041-12-1993 L1997 **DR** *020 †80

WARD, John Francis. 1400 LOCUST ST 15219 #041-12-1957 L1958 **PTH** *071 †50

WARD, Lynne Bobetta. ■ 15217 #041-12-1984 L1984 **IM** *020 †20

WARD, William Timothy. 3705 5TH AVE, STE 3330 15213 #041-12-1977 L1984 **OP** *020 †40

WARDE, Deirdre Marie. 320 E NORTH AVE, ALLEGHENY GENERAL HOSPITAL 15212 #539-03-2005 L2007 **IM** *012

WARDE, Donal. 320 E NORTH AVE 15212 #539-03-1972 L1976 **CD IM** *020 †20

WARNER, Robert Haines. 1050 BOWER HILL RD, STE 206 15243 #041-12-1976 L1984 **OBG** *020 †30

WARSHAFSKY, Gene Benj. 2740 SMALLMAN ST STE 300 15222 #041-09-1977 L1979 **IM IMG** *062 †20

WASHINGTON, Christopher B. ■ 15206 #041-12-2006 L2006 **GS** *012

WASKO, Mary C Morgan. S 704 BIOMEDICAL SCIENCE T 15261 #036-01-1983 L1984 **RHU IM** *020 †20

WATCHKO, Jon Freeman. 300 HALKET ST, DEPT PEDS MAGEE WOMENS HOS 15213 #041-12-1980 L1987 **NPM PD** *050 †55

WATERS, Janet Robinson. ■ 15232 #010-01-1986 L2005 **N** *030

WATERS, Jonathan Hale. 300 HALKET ST, DEPT OF ANESTHLGY STE 3510 15213 #010-01-1986 L2004 **AN BBK** *030 †05

WATKINS, Colleen Marie. BIOMEDICAL SCIENCE TOWER, 3500 TERRACE STREET, 7TH F 15261 #055-01-1999 L2002 **RHU IM** *020 †20

WATKINS, Gloria Jean. 300 HALKET ST, MAGEE WOMENS HOSIPTAL PATH 15213 #041-07-1979 L1980 **PTH** *062 †50

WATKINS, Walter David. 5920 BRAEBURN PL 15232 #007-02-1975 L1992 **AN** *030

WATSON, Andrew Rose. 200 LOTHROP ST 15213 #035-01-1997 L2000 **GS** *020

WATSON, David Benjamin. 3471 5TH AVE, DEPT OF NEUROSURGERY 15213 #055-01-1999 L2004 **N** *020 †75

WATSON, Gregory Allen. ■ 15202 #041-12-2000 L2001 **GS** *012

WATSON, R Scott. 3705 5TH AVE, PED CRITICAL CARE MED 15213 #041-01-1993 L2000 **CCP** *020 †55

WATSON, Scott Karl. 3705 5TH AVE 15213 #048-15-2006 **PD** *012

WATTERS, Edmond Clair. 100 DELAFIELD RD 15215 #010-01-1968 L1971 **OPH** *020 †35

WATT-MORSE, Margaret L. 300 HALKET ST, DEPT OBGYN 15213 #016-11-1985 L1989 **MFM OBG** *020 †30

WATTS, Tamia Jovonne. 121 MEYRAN AVE, UNIV HLTH CTR 15213 #025-07-2007 L2007 **PM** *012

WATZMAN, Dean. 5200 CENTRE AVE, STE 610 15232 #305-01-1996 L2007 **PCC** *020 †20

WAX, Randy Stuart. ■ 15217 #065-01-1994 L1998 **CCM IM** *100 †20

WAXMAN, Evan Lewis. 203 LOTHROP ST 15213 #035-47-1994 L1999 **OPH** *020 †35

WAYNE, Dennis Owen. 4424 PENN AVE 15224 #025-07-1969 L1970 **P ADP** *020 †75

WAYNE, Sigrid. ■ 15217 #018-03-1997 L2005 **SP** *012

WEARDEN, Peter Drew. 3705 5TH AVE 15213 #055-01-1993 L2001 **TS** *020 †85,90

WEAVER, Miles Lance. 320 E NORTH AVE, ALLEGHENY GENERAL HOSP 15212 #038-43-1981 L1982 **GS** *020 †85 ‡

WEAVER-AGOSTONI, Jacquelin. 5215 CENTRE AVE, UPMC SHADYSIDE FAMILY HEAL 15232 #041-78-2002, ▲ L2002 **FM** *040 †18

WEBBER, Audra Meredith. ■ 15218 #041-12-2007 L2007 **TY** *012

WEBBER, Steven Alan. 3705 5TH AVE, PEDIATRIC CARDIOLOGY 15213 #917-02-1983 L1991 **PD** *020 †55

WEBER, Anne M. 605 DRIFTWOOD DR 15238 #023-01-1987 L2000 **OBG** *020 †30

WEBER, David Robt. 5200 CENTRE AVE, STE 203 15232 #023-01-1981 L1983 **IM ID** *020 †20

WEBER, Lawrence W N. 5750 CENTRE AVE STE 270 15206 #041-12-1973 L1977 **AI PD** *020 †55,03

WEBSTER, Marshall Wm, Jr. 3600 FORBES AVE, UPP/ DIV PSD 15213 #023-07-1964 L1966 **VS CD** *030 †85,90

WECHSLER, Harry Leon. ■ 15213 #036-07-1947 L1949 **D** *071 †15

WECHSLER, Lawrence R. 200 LOTHROP ST, C426 PUH 15213 #041-01-1978 L1979 **N IM** *020 †20,75

WECHSLER, Richard L. ■ 15213 #041-12-1947 L1948 **GE IM** *071 †20

WECHT, Cyril H. 1119 PENN AVE, STE 404 15222 #041-12-1956 L1957 **PTH FOP** *020 †50

WECK-TAYLOR, Karen E. 3550 TERRACE ST, PATHOLOGY/701 SCAIFE HALL 15213 #036-07-1988 L1998 **PTH** *020 †50

WEDEMEYER, Phillips Pope. 1400 LOCUST ST 15219 #023-07-1962 L1970 **PHO PD** *020 †55

WEDEMEYER, W Anne Little. 3705 5TH AVE 15213 #041-12-1962 L1965 **PDC** *071 †55

WEEDN, Victor Walter. 4400 5TH AVE, CARNEGIE MELLON UNIV 15213 #048-12-1979 L2006 **FOP PTH** *030 †50

WEGLOWSKI, Jennifer. 3705 5TH AVE 15213 #033-06-1998 L2000 **PD** *020 †55

WEGNER, Rodney Ervin. ■ 15261 #041-12-2007 L2007 **TY** *012

WEGRECKI, Adrianna Katarz. 620 E OHIO ST 15212 #759-12-1997 L2004 **IM** *020 †20

WEGRZYNOWICZ, Denise D. 210A ROBINSON PLAZA THREE, STE 210A 15205 #041-77-1997, ▲ L1998 **FM** *020 †18

WEHBI, Fadi Said. ■ 15232 #605-04-2002 L2005 **FP** *012

WEI, Lawrence Ming. 200 LOTHROP ST 15213 #041-12-1982 L1984 **TS VS** *020 †85,90

WEIGEL, Alonzo L. 200 LOTHROP ST, GEN/NESE BARKAN ANNEX 15213 #041-12-1951 L1952 **GS EM** *071 †85

WEIGEL, John Earl, Jr. 5230 CENTRE AVE 15232 #041-12-1954 L1955 **OBG** *071 †30

WEIGLE, Justin Thomas. ■ 15237 #041-13-2008 *012

WEIN, Thomas Philip. 5140 LIBERTY AVE 15224 #041-13-1976 L1977 **IM IMG** *020 †20

WEINBAUM, David L. 4778 LIBERTY AVE 15224 #024-05-1975 L1981 **ID IM** *020 †20

WEINBERG, Ariella Toby. ■ 15217 #016-42-2007 **IM** *012

WEINBERG, Joel Howard. 5200 CENTRE AVE, STE 211 15232 #041-12-1976 L1981 **PUD IM** *020 †20

WEINBERG, Lee Martin. 5200 CENTRE AVE STE 409, UPP GASTROENTEROLOGY 15232 #041-12-1976 L1981 **IM GE** *020 †20

WEINBERGER, Irving G. 2101 GREENTREE RD, STE 105 15220 #033-05-1971 L1974 **OPH** *020 †35 ‡

WEINER, Daniel Jerome. 3705 5TH AVE 15213 #025-01-1993 L1998 **PDP** *020 †55

WEINER, Debra Kaye. 5750 CENTRE AVE, STE 400 15206 #028-03-1983 L1998 **IMG RHU** *050 †20

WEINFELD, Mieczyslaw. 6301 FORBES AVE, STE 300 15217 #759-10-1974 L1979 **IM** *020 †20

WEINGARTEN, Jeremy Adam. 200 LOTHROP ST, UPMC MONTEFIORE N713 15213 #035-48-2001 L2001 **PCC** *012

WEINKLE, Jonathan. 200 JHF DR, SQUIRREL HILL HEALTH CENTE 15217 #041-12-2004 L2004 **MPD** *012

WEINSTEIN, Barbara Jane D. 1910 COCHRAN RD, STE 740 15220 #041-07-1968 L1969 **R** *071 †80

WEINSTEIN, Gary S. 3471 5TH AVE, STE 1115 15213 #041-12-1978 L1979 **OPH PS** *020 †35 ‡

WEIS, Ty David. ■ 15215 #026-04-2005 L2006 **AN** *012

WEISBORD, Steven Darrow. A919, 3550 TERRACE STREET 15261 #010-01-1997 L1999 **NEP** *020 †20

WEISMAN, Richard Alan. 1515 LOCUST ST, OF PITTSBURGH 15219 #041-01-1969 L1970 **N** *020 †75

WEISS, Brian Paul. 1400 LOCUST ST, OF PITTSBURGH 15219 #024-07-2006 L2006 **DR** *012

WEISS, Elissa Maria. 224 PENN AVE 15221 #041-13-1978 L1979 **IM** *020 †20

WEISS, Kurt Richard. 121 MEYRAN AVE 15213 #041-02-2003 L2003 **ORS** *012

WEISS, Michael David. 3705 5TH AVE, STE 3950 15213 #005-14-1985 L2006 **VIR DR** *020 †80

WEISS, Victoria Ann. 603 WASHINGTON RD, STE 300 15228 #041-01-1993 L1996 **PD** *020 †55

WEISSFELD, Joel Lawrence. 130 DESOTO ST, DEPT OF EPIDEMIOLOGY GSPH 15261 #023-07-1981 L1990 **IM** *050 †20

WEISSMANN, Amos. ■ 15217 #409-06-1973 L1981 **IM** *100

WEKSLER, Benny. 200 LOTHROP ST STE C700, UNIVERSITY OF PITTSBURGH M 15213 #187-03-1987 L1994 **GS** *020 †90,85

WELKON, Celeste Jean. 240 MOUNT LEBANON BLVD 15234 #041-12-1979 L1981 **PD ID** *020 †55

WELLS, Alan H. ■ 15261 #043-01-1988 L1999 **PTH OS** *050 †50

WELSH, John P. 4727 FRIENDSHIP AVE, STE 300 15224 #041-15-2003 L2003 **D** *100 †15

WENNERBERG, Anne E. ■ 15261 #020-02-1980 L1991 **BBK ATP** *030 †50

WENZEL, Sally Ellen. 3459 5TH AVE, UNIV OF PITTS MED CTR 15213 #011-03-1981 L2006 **PUD IM** *020 †20

WERNER, Robert Stuart. 1020 BOWER HILL RD 15243 #041-01-1987 L1992 **RO** *020 †80

WERRIES, Gerard Joseph. 300 CHAPEL HARBOR DR, STE 300 15238 #041-12-1997 L2000 **OSS ORS** *020 †40

WESCHLER, Barbara Rae. ■ 15217 #041-12-1979 L1980 **P** *074

WESSEL, Henry Bernard. 3705 5TH AVE, PEDS/ONE CHILDRENS PL 15213 #041-12-1969 L1970 **CHN PD** *020 †55,75

WEST, Robin. 2000 MARY ST 15203 #010-01-1997 L2002 **OSM** *020 †40

WESTMAN, Helen A Rash. 3705 5TH AVE, DEPT ANESTHES 15213 #020-12-1973 L1975 **AN** *020 †05

WESTMORELAND, Samuel Will. 3811 OHARA ST, AND C 15213 #041-12-2005 L2005 **P** *012

WESTRICK, Edward Ryan. ■ 15206 #041-12-2006 L2006 **ORS** *012

WETSCHLER, Stanley Singer. 3028 BROWNSVILLE RD, BRENTWOOD MED GROUP 15227 #041-12-1969 L1970 **IM** *071 †20

WETTICK, Elizabeth S. 3708 5TH AVE, STE 500 15213 #041-01-1998 L2000 **FM** *020 †18

WETTSTEIN, Robert Mark. 401 SHADY AVE, STE B103 15206 #005-14-1976 L1984 **P PFP** *020 †75

WEY, Jane Shufun. 5150 CENTRE AVE, STE 414 15232 #005-18-1999 L2006 **GS** *100

WHALEN, Jason George. 660 WASHINGTON RD, STE 201 15228 #041-12-2002 L2002 **D** *020 †15

WHEELER, Matthew Timothy. ■ 15261 #041-12-2007 L2007 **EM** *012

WHETSTONE, Joseph Laurenc. ■ 15203 #041-12-2007 L2007 **TY** *012

WHITCOMB, David Clement. 200 LOTHROP ST 15213 #038-40-1985 L1991 **GE IM** *020 †20
WHITE, Laura Elizabeth. ■ 15211 #422-01-2001 L2007 **HSO ORS** *012
WHITE, Michael John. 320 E NORTH AVE, ALLEGHENY GEN HOSPITAL 15212 #056-05-1980 L1986 **PS GS** *020 †85,65
WHITE, William Abraham. 1400 LOCUST ST 15219 #028-46-2006 L2006 **GS** *012
WHITEFORD, John Ryan. 1501 LOCUST ST STE 403 15219 #041-12-2000 L2001 **EM** *020 †16
WHITEHURST, Steven Lee. 200 LOTHROP ST, PUH C201 15213 #001-02-1984 L1990 **AN** *020 †05
WHITMAN, Robert Sheldon. 5230 CENTRE AVE 15232 #041-12-1954 L1955 **IM** *071
WHOLEY, Mark H. 5230 CENTRE AVE 15232 #041-09-1953 L1954 **R CD** *020 †80
WHYTE, Allyson Jean. 230 MCKEE PL, STE 500 15213 #036-01-2005 L2005 **EM** *012
WHYTE, Ellen Marie. 3811 OHARA ST, RM BT764 15213 #035-06-1995 L1999 **PYG** *020 †75
WIBLE, Leroy Creesy. 1400 LOCUST ST STE 2375 15219 #041-12-1962 L1963 **AN OS** *071 †05
WICKERHAM, Donald L. ■ 15213 #041-12-1976 L1981 **ON** *050
WIESENFELD, Harold C. 200 LOTHROP ST 15213 #067-01-1987 L1992 **OBG ID** *020 †30
WILBERGER, James E, Jr. 420 E NORTH AVE, STE 302 15212 #051-04-1978 L1979 **NS** *020 †25 ‡
WILCOX, Julia Wu. 1000 BOWER HILL RD 15243 #041-12-1990 L1993 **PM** *020 †60
WILCOX, Mark Spencer. 1350 LOCUST ST, STE 409 15219 #038-40-1990 L1992 **PM** *020 †60
WILDER, Bruce Lord. 436 7TH AVE STE 1050 15219 #024-07-1966 L1973 **NS LM** *020 †25
WILEY, Clayton. 200 LOTHROP ST 15213 #005-18-1981 L1993 **NP ATP** *050 †50
WILEY, Kimberly Annice. ■ 15220 #020-12-2000 L2001 **GS** *100
WILHELM, Dorothy Tan. 100 DELAFIELD RD 15215 #055-01-2004 L2004 **FM** *020 †18
WILKINS, Clyde Smith, Jr. 320 E NORTH AVE, ALLEGHENY GENERAL HOSPITAL 15212 #422-01-2007 L2007 **IM** *012
WILKOSZ, Patricia Ann. 200 LOTHROP ST, UPMC MONTEFIORE, 4 WEST 15213 #041-12-2001 L2001 **PYG** *100
WILLIAMS, Brenda Anne. 1350 OLD FREEPORT RD # 1A 15238 #038-40-1984 L1985 **VM FM** *020 †18
WILLIAMS, Brian Alan. 2000 MARY ST, UPMC SOUTH SIDE ANES 15203 #038-44-1991 L1994 **AN** *050 †05
WILLIAMS, Elizabeth Lynne. 1 ALLEGHENY ST STE 340, ALLEGHENY ANESTHESIOLOGY 15217 #143-03-1972 L1996 **AN** *020 †05
WILLIAMS, Frankie E. 3550 TERRACE ST, SCAIFE HALL 15261 #048-12-1956 L1956 **OS P** *030
WILLIAMS, Jeffrey L. 200 LOTHROP ST, STE 559 15213 #041-15-1999 L2003 **ICE** *012 †20
WILLIAMS, John Phillip. 3550 TERRACE ST, A-1305 SCAIFE HALL 15261 #048-04-1979 L1998 **AN UCM** *040 †05
WILLIAMS, Katherine V. 121 MEYRAN AVE, DEPT MED EDUCATION 15213 #038-44-1991 L1993 **END** *020 †20
WILLIAMS, Lynne Louise. 6023 HARVARD SQ, EAST LIBERTY FAMILY HEALTH 15206 #041-12-2002 L2002 **MPD** *020 †20,55
WILLIAMS, Nakia Venise. ■ 15232 #025-12-2007 L2007 **PD** *012
WILLIAMS, Princess Anne. 1350 LOCUST ST, STE 409 15219 #036-01-1983 L1988 **ID IM** *071 †20
WILLIAMS, Robert Lucien. 320 E NORTH AVE, ALLEGHENY GENERAL HOSPITAL 15212 #033-05-1990 L1995 **RNR** *020 †80
WILLIAMS, Rodney Jay. 3811 OHARA ST, UPMC/WPIC 15213 #038-40-2003 L2003 **CHP** *012
WILLIAMS, Shelley W. 3705 5TH AVE, DEPT PEDIATRIC NEUROLOGY 15213 #036-05-1990 L1992 **CHN** *020 †55,75
WILLIAMS, Steven Cranston. 651 HOLIDAY DR 15220 #008-02-1979 L1980 **IM** *020 †20
WILLIS, Paul Michael. 1050 BOWER HILL RD, STE 309 15243 #041-12-1994 L2000 **GS** *020 †85
WILLOCHELL, Teri Ann. 1515 LOCUST ST 15219 #041-09-1994 L1996 **IM** *020 †20
WILMOT, Alissa Lindsey. ■ 15222 #041-01-2007 L2007 **PD** *012
WILMOT, Andrew Spencerhub. ■ 15222 #041-01-2007 L2007 **TY** *012
WILSON, Chas Reginald, Jr. 4815 LIBERTY AVE 15224 #041-12-1955 L1956 **IM** *071 †20
WILSON, David Oscar. 580 S AIKEN AVE STE 400 15232 #041-12-1980 L1981 **PUD OM** *020 †20,70
WILSON, Dorothy Vickrey. 3811 OHARA ST, AND CLINIC 15213 #041-12-1999 L2001 **P** *020 †75
WILSON, George W. ■ 15215 #041-09-1943 L1944 **EM GS** *071 †85
WILSON, Jennifer Ann. 9100 BABCOCK BLVD, UPMC PASSAVANT HOSPITAL, D 15237 #041-14-2000 L2001 **DR** *020 †80
WILSON, John Travis. 121 MEYRAN AVE, UPMC MONTEFIORE N-713 15213 #035-45-2005 L2005 **IM** *012
WILSON, Julie Ann. 1200 REEDSDALE ST 15233 #041-07-1990 L1996 **P** *020 †75
WILSON, Stephen Andrew. 7171 CHURCHLAND ST, LINCOLN LEMINGTON FAM HLTH 15206 #041-12-1995 L1997 **FM** *040 †18
WILSON, William Lawrence. 1000 BOWER HILL RD 15243 #041-13-1955 L1956 **IM CD** *071
WIMBUSH, Tracy E. 230 MCKEE PL, STE 500, DEPARTMENT OF EMERGENCY ME 15213 #035-45-2000 L2007 **EM** *020 †16
WIN, Karen. ■ 15206 #041-12-2007 L2007 **GS** *012
WINKLER, Martin. ■ 15235 #041-12-1964 L1965 **OPH** *071 †35
WINSTON, Brion Mackie. 121 MEYRAN AVE, PRESBY UNIV HOSP 15213 #035-08-2003 L2007 **CD** *012 †20
WINTER, Peter Michael. 3471 5TH AVE, STE 910 15213 #035-45-1962 L1979 **AN OS** *030 †05
WINTERS, Slava Michael. 5232 CENTRE AVE 15232 #035-15-2001 L2005 *020 †16
WINTZ, Phyllis Wocklish. 200 LOTHROP ST 15213 #041-07-1979 L1991 **DR** *020 †80
WISHNEW, Jessica Meredith. ■ 15217 #041-12-2008 L2008 *012
WISNER, Katherine Leah. 3811 OHARA ST, WOMEN'S BEHAVIORAL HLT CAR 15213 #038-06-1980 L1981 **P CHP** *020 †75
WISNESKI, John Thos, Jr. 3471 5TH AVE, STE 1111 15213 #028-02-1981 L1982 **IM IMG** *020 †20 ‡
WISSINGER, H Andrew. 400 45TH ST 15201 #041-12-1956 L1963 **ORS HS** *072 †40
WISSINK, Scott David. ■ 15224 #026-04-2003 L2003 **FSM** *100 †18
WITCHEL, Selma F. 3705 5TH AVE 15213 #041-12-1978 L1981 **PD PDE** *050 †55
WITHERS, James Scott. 1400 LOCUST ST, STE 5120 15219 #041-12-1984 L1986 **IM** *040 †20
WITTMAN, Catherine A. 121 MEYRAN AVE, UPMC MONTEFIORE N-713 15213 #035-48-2005 L2005 **IM** *012
WIZOREK, Joseph John. 200 LOTHROP ST, STE F1277 15213 #010-02-1998 L2007 **TS** *020 †85
WOELFEL, George Frederick. ■ 15241 #056-06-1944 L1951 **GS** *071 †85
WOELFEL, George Frederick. 400 HOLIDAY DR, STE 101 15220 #056-06-1978 L1986 **TS** *020 †85,90
WOELFEL, Susan Kathryn. 3550 TERRACE ST, A-1305 SCAIFE HALL 15261 #055-01-1978 L1982 **AN** *020 †05
WOLF, Albert Anthony, III. 850 CLAIRTON BLVD, STE 3300 15236 #041-12-1997 L1999 **PD** *020 †55 ‡
WOLF, William Michael. 200 LOTHROP ST, SCAIFE HALL, RM B-571.3 15213 #010-02-1999 L2006 **CD** *012 †20
WOLFE, Sarah Elizabeth. ■ 15224 #018-03-2007 L2007 **CPP** *012
WOLFE, Steven Richard. ■ 15234 #041-78-2002, ▲ L2002 **FM** *020 †18
WOLFERT, Allen Ira. 1050 BOWER HILL RD, ST CLAIR PROFESSIONAL BUIL 15243 #035-46-1977 L1988 **NEP IM** *020 †20
WOLFSON, Allan Barry. 1400 LOCUST ST 15219 #041-01-1972 L1973 **EM IM** *020 †20,16
WOLFSON, Bernard. 1400 LOCUST ST, MERCY HOSPITAL 15219 #803-05-1951 L1962 **AN** *040 †05
WOLFSON, David Hugh. 5608 WILKINS AVE, STE 202 15217 #041-12-1987 L1991 **PD ADL** *020 †55
WOLFSON, Jerome Howard. 5608 WILKINS AVE, STE 202 15217 #035-08-1955 L1960 **PD** *071 †55
WOLFSON, Sidney K, Jr. 300 TECHNOLOGY DR 15219 #016-02-1958 L1959 **GS NS** *072
WOLK, Brad Jeffrey. ■ 15217 #036-05-1979 L1980 **EM OM** *020 †16
WOLK, David Arthur. 3471 5TH AVE STE 811, DEPT OF NEUROLOGY, KAUFMAN 15213 #023-07-1998 L2001 **N** *020
WOLLMAN, Michael R. 3705 5TH AVE 15213 #035-08-1968 L1974 **PHO PD** *020 †55
WOLLSTEIN, Ronit. 2000 MARY ST 15203 #550-01-1990 L2006 **HS** *020
WOLMARK, Norman. 320 E NORTH AVE, ALLEGHENY GENERAL HOSP 15212 #067-01-1970 L1973 **GS SO** *050 †85
WOLSKI, Michal Jacek. ■ 15261 #041-12-2007 L2007 **IM** *012
WOLYNN, Todd Howard. 850 CLAIRTON BLVD STE 3300 15236 #041-12-1992 L1994 **PD SME** *020 †55
WONG, Alfonso Cielo, Jr. 2000 MARY ST 15203 #748-01-1964 L1971 **EM IM** *020
WONG, Anthony Chiyin. ■ 15202 #003-01-2006 L2006 **MEM** *012
WONG, Eric Andrew. ■ 15213 #041-12-2008 *012
WONG, Julielynn Y. 3550 TERRACE ST, DEPT OF PLASTIC SURGERY 15261 #065-05-2005 L2006 **PS** *012
WONG, Timothy Chungtin. 200 LOTHROP ST, SCAIFE HALL S553 15213 #035-19-2002 L2006 **CD** *012 †20
WONGCHAOWART, Boonnum. 2000 MARY ST 15203 #572-01-1974 L1975 **P CHP** *020 †75
WOO, Shirley. ■ 15212 #045-01-2001 L2001 **OBG** *020 †30
WOOD, John Michael. 3347 FORBES AVE, STE 303 15213 #038-06-1972 L1977 **GE IM** *020 †20
WOOD, Randolph Benjamin. 200 LOTHROP ST, MUH ANESTH N463 15213 #041-07-1995 L1997 **AN PME** *020 †05
WOOD, William Anthony. 200 LOTHROP ST STE 500 15213 #036-01-2004 L2004 **OTO** *012
WOODBURN, Mark Abraham. 121 MEYRAN AVE, DEPT OF FAMILY MEDICINE 15213 #041-15-2006 L2006 **FP** *012
WOODYEAR, Dawna Hoyle. 373 BURROWS ST, MATHILDA THEISS HEALTH CTR 15213 #023-01-1985 L1986 **FM** *020 †18
WOOLHANDLER, Robert A. 5562 WILKINS AVE 15217 #035-06-1973 L1975 **GP** *020
WOOTEN, Amber Nicole. ■ 15201 #039-01-2006 L2006 **GS** *012
WOOTEN, Anna Ivanovna. 4800 FRIENDSHIP AVE 15224 #036-08-2000 L2001 **GS** *020
WORF, Amanda Erin. ■ 15217 #047-06-2007 L2007 **PD** *012
WORRALL, V Thomas. 200 DELAFIELD RD, STE 1040 15215 #047-05-1969 L1971 **OS** *071 †40
WOTRING NORMAN, Melissa M. 177 PINECREST DR 15237 #039-01-1990 L1996 **IM** *020 †20
WRAGG, Robin Eleanor. 7180 HIGHLAND DR, VA MEDCL CTR BHVRL HLTH 11 15206 #054-04-1975 L1977 **P PD** *020 †55,75
WRENN, Edward Howard. 100 FOREST HILLS PLZ 15221 #036-01-1991 L1994 **FM** *020 †18
WRIGHT, Barbara. ■ 15217 #024-01-1955 L1966 **PHP GP** *071 †70
WRIGHT, Bruce A. 110 FORT COUCH RD, STE 2 15241 #041-12-1988 L1990 **P** *020 †75
WRIGHT, David Griffith. 420 E NORTH AVE, STE 206 15212 #021-01-1972 L1977 **N** *020 †75 ‡
WRIGHT, George C, Jr. ■ 15236 #041-12-1949 L1952 **GP OM** *071
WRIGHT, George Jesse, Jr. 4401 PENN AVE 15224 #041-01-1942 L1943 **N P** *071 †75
WRIGHT, Glenda Vanessa. ■ 15235 #566-01-1998 L2006 **PDI** *012 †55
WRIGHT, L Alan. 110 FORT COUCH RD, STE 2 15241 #041-12-1963 L1967 **P PYG** *020 †75
WRIGHT, Rollin Michelle. 3471 5TH AVE, KAUFMAN BLDG STE 500 15213 #035-03-1999 L2005 **IMG** *020 †20
WRIGHT, Vonda Joy. 2000 MARY ST 15203 #016-02-1999 L2001 **ORS** *020
WU, Christine Mona. 3550 TERRACE ST, A915 SCAIFE HALL 15261 #023-07-1998 L2001 **NEP** *020 †20
WU, Eric C. 1400 LOCUST ST, OF PITTSBURGH 15219 #041-12-2006 L2006 **TY** *012
WU, Roger Donald. ■ 15219 #023-01-2007 L2007 **IM** *012
WU, Tong. 200 LOTHROP ST 15213 #243-54-1982 L1999 **PTH** *020 †50
WU, Xianren. 121 MEYRAN AVE, DEPT OF ANESTHESIA 15213 #243-58-1986 L2005 **AN** *012
WUCHER, Frederick P. 1580 MCLAUGHLIN RUN RD, STE 208 PINEBRIDGE COMMONS 15241 #041-12-1960 L1961 **PD** *071 †55
WUKICH, Dane Kent. 2100 JANE ST, STE 7100 15203 #010-02-1982 L1987 **ORS** *020 †40
WYLIE, Mary E. DESOTO AT OHARA STS 15213 #016-11-1977 L1990 **P** *071 †05
WYNERT, Stephen John. 320 E NORTH AVE, ALLEGHENY GEN HOSP 15212 #305-01-2004 L2004 **IM** *012
XIA, Yaqin. 5608 WILKINS AVE, STE 100 15217 #243-21-1987 L2002 **FM** *020 †18
XIAO, Gary Shengguang. 20 OAKHURST CIR 15215 #243-38-1986 L2001 **GS** *100 †19,85
YAAKOVIAN, Michael David. ■ 15213 #041-02-2004 L2004 **GS** *012
YADAV, Dhiraj. 5200 CENTRE AVE, STE 211 15232 #496-02-1993 L2006 **GE IM** *020 †20
YAEGASHI, Makito. ■ 15213 #572-44-1997 L2005 **CCM** *100 †20
YAMAKAWA, Harushige. 5230 CENTRE AVE 15232 #572-34-1970 L1974 **IM** *020 †20
YAN, Chaohua. 320 E NORTH AVE 15212 #243-39-1986 L2005 **IM** *100
YAN, Jun. 320 E NORTH AVE, DEPARTMENT OF ANESTHESIOLO 15212 #243-76-1992 L2001 **AN** *020 †05 ‡
YANAGA, Katsuhiko. ■ 15217 #572-12-1979 L1981 **OS GS** *020
YANDORA, Kristin Ann. ■ 15216 #041-78-2003, ▲ L2003 **N** *100
YANG, Charles Inshik. ■ 15203 #001-02-1995 L2004 **AN PD** *020 †05
YANG, Linda Chihua. 300 HALKET ST, MAGEE-WOMENS HOSPITAL 15213 #025-01-2002 L2006 **OBG** *100
YANG, Nelson Minhuey. ■ 15212 #041-13-2007 L2007 **EM** *012
YANKURA, David John. ■ 15213 #041-12-2008 L2008 *012
YANKURA, John A. 1000 BOWER HILL RD 15243 #041-12-1978 L1979 **DR NM** *020 †80 ‡
YANOWITZ, Toby Debra. 300 HALKET ST, RM 4302 15213 #035-46-1991 L1997 **NPM** *020 †55
YAROS, John Gregory. 363 VANADIUM RD 15243 #041-12-1976 L1977 **FM** *020 †18
YARYGINA, Anna S. ■ 15232 #041-12-2008 *012
YATES, Adam Michael. 1501 LOCUST ST, STE 403 15219 #038-40-2002 L2002 **EM** *020 †16
YATES, Adolph J, Jr. 5200 CENTRE AVE, STE 211 15232 #023-07-1984 L2004 **ORS** *020 †40
YATES, Anthony Pat. 339 6TH AVE 15222 #010-01-1973 L1974 **IM PUD** *020 †20
YATES, Helen. ■ 15238 #539-06-1983 L1990 **AN** *020 †05
YATSUBA, Ekaterina. 320 E NORTH AVE 15212 #913-09-1999 L2002 **OBG** *100

YAUCH, John Allen. 1515 LOCUST ST 4TH FL 15219 #041-02-1967 L1971 **OBG** *071 †30

YAZER, Mark Harris. 3636 BLVD OF THE ALLIES 15213 #065-09-2000 L2004 *100

YAZIGI, Nasr Issa. 3550 TERRACE STREET/A-SCAI, UPMC/DEPT OF ANESTHESIOLOG 15261 #781-04-1990 L2001 **AN** *100

YEAGER, Jill Marie. ■ 15213 #055-01-2004 L2004 **CPP** *012

YEALY, Donald Matthew. 200 LOTHROP ST 15213 #041-07-1985 L1986 **EM** *020 †16

YEASTED, Claire. 1369 WASHINGTON RD 15228 #038-41-2008 *012

YEASTED, George Alan. 1000 BOWER HILL RD, ST. CLAIR HOSPITAL 15243 #041-12-1974 L1975 **IM** *020 †20

YECK, Jennifer Anne. ■ 15229 #041-02-2006 L2006 **EM** *012

YEH, Andol Stephen. 2135 TEAL TRCE 15237 #038-40-2003 L2003 **EM** *100 †16

YELLON, Robert Forrest. 3705 5TH AVE, CHILDREN'S HOSP OF PITTSBU 15213 #035-48-1986 L1991 **PDO GS** *020 †45

YENDE, Sachin Purushottam. 3550 TERRACE ST, 6TH FLOOR, SCAIFE HALL, 64 15261 #496-38-1995 L2005 **PCC** *100 †20

YENNAM, Sudhakar Reddy. 3550 TERRACE ST, A-1305 SCAIFE HALL 15261 #495-62-1989 L2002 **AN** *020 †05

YEUNG, Alison Yukning. ■ 15232 #041-12-2006 L2006 *012

YIM, John Hosei. UNIVERSITY OF PITTSBURGH, 497 SCAIFE HALL 15261 #005-11-1992 L2000 **GS** *020 †85

YIN, Ming. ■ 15243 #243-44-1982 L2002 **PTH** *020 †50

YIN, Xiao-Ming. 200 LOTHROP ST, UPPPTHLGY - BMDCL SCNCE TW 15213 #243-16-1982 L1998 **PTH** *020 †50

YING, Yulan Mary. ■ 15213 #035-48-2003 L2003 **OTO** *012

YINGVORAPANT, Nori V. ■ 15241 #891-02-1959 L1972 **DIA IM** *071

YIP, Linwah. ■ 15238 #041-02-1999 L2006 **GS** *100 †85

YOKOYAMA, Itsuo. ■ 15220 #572-58-1974 L1987 **OS GS** *020

YOSSA, Casey Lynn. ■ 15238 #041-15-2006 L2006 **GS** *012

YOST, Christine O'Neill. 88 FORT COUCH RD, STE 100 15241 #041-12-2000 L2001 **PD** *020 †55 ‡

YOST, Richard Owen. 9104 BABCOCK BLVD STE 21 15237 #041-09-1975 L1977 **PD** *020 †55

YOUNAS, Nizar Ahmad. UPMC, A915 SCAIFE HALL 15261 #704-25-2002 L2004 **NEP** *012 †20

YOUNES, Hashem Ali. DEPT OF MED EDUCATION SUIT, UNIVERSITY HLTH CTR 15213 #605-01-2001 L2003 **HO** *012 †20

YOUNG, Donna Corinne. 1000 BOWER HILL RD 15243 #035-09-1989 L1991 **IM OM** *062 †20

YOUNG, Felicia Dale. 7227 HAMILTON AVE, PRIMARY CARE HEALTH SVCS., 15208 #041-14-1997 L1998 **FM** *020 †18

YOUNG, Jerome M. 7180 HIGHLAND DR 15206 #020-02-1966 L1989 **P** *020 †75

YOUNG, Jessica Sukwah. ■ 15219 #041-02-2005 L2005 **GS** *012

YOUNG, Joseph Chas. 420 E NORTH AVE, STE 304 15212 #028-34-1971 L1974 **TRS GS** *020 †85

YOUNG, Zachary Timothy. ■ 15238 #654-01-2005 L2008 **IM** *012

YOUNGDAHL, Donald Arthur. ■ 15222 #041-13-1953 L1959 **OBG** *071 †30

YOUNT, John Armstrong. ■ 15239 #041-12-1941 L1942 **IM** *071 †20

YOUSE, Don C, Jr. ■ 15233 #011-03-1984 L1991 **FM** *075 †18

YOUSEF, Mai. 301 CASTLE SHANNON BLVD 15234 #875-01-1992 L2001 **FM** *020 †18

YOUSEM, Samuel Alan. 200 LOTHROP ST 15213 #023-01-1981 L1987 **ATP** *050 †50

YU, Jing. RM 707 SCAIFE HALL, UNIV OF PITTSBURGH DEPT OF 15261 #243-16-1993 L2002 **PTH** *100

YU, Victor Lin-Kai. INFECTIOUS DISEASE SECTION, VA MEDICAL CENTER 15240 #026-04-1970 L1978 **ID IM** *050 †20

YUAN, Lily. 300 HALKET ST 15213 #038-06-1967 L1969 **PD** *020 †55

YUAN, Yu. 320 E NORTH AVE, ANESTHESIA DEPT AGH 15212 #243-92-1986 L2001 **AN** *020 †05

YUE, Esther Lokyan. ■ 15217 #025-01-2007 L2007 **PD** *012

YUNES, Anisa S. 1731 DOMINION DR 15241 #160-02-1987 L1992 **IM** *020 †20

YURCISIN, Basil Michael. ■ 15203 #016-45-2003 L2003 **GS** *012

YUREK, Bryan Andrew. ■ 15212 #041-12-2005 L2005 **EM** *012

ZACCARDI, James Peter. 1400 LOCUST ST, STE G6 15219 #041-01-1963 L1965 **IM** *020 †20

ZAIDI, Syed Fazal Abbas. 200 LOTHROP ST STE C400, UPMC STROKE INSTITUTE 15213 #704-02-2001 L2007 **N** *100

ZAISER, Deborra Kim. 320 E NORTH AVE 15212 #041-02-1979 L1982 **EM IM** *020 †20,16

ZAJKO, Albert Barth. 230 LOTHROP ST, PRESBYTERIAN UNIVERSITY HO 15213 #041-01-1975 L1978 **DR** *040 †80

ZAK, Vitaliy. 4800 FRIENDSHIP AVE 15224 #913-97-1995 L2001 **IM** *020

ZAKHARY, Sammy Alfred. 320 E NORTH AVE, ALLEGHENY GENERAL HOSPITAL 15212 #035-03-1999 L2001 **VS** *020

ZALENSKI, Dianne Marie. 5230 CENTRE AVE STE 307, SCHOOL OF NURSING 15232 #041-12-2000 L2001 **IM** *020

ZALSTEIN, Salomon. 320 E NORTH AVE 15212 #143-02-1979 *100

ZANAROS, George. 1307 FEDERAL ST, SECOND FLOOR 15212 #035-03-2002 L2007 **HSO** *012

ZANCOSKY, Krysia Lynne. 4800 FRIENDSHIP AVE 15224 #041-78-2002, ▲ L2002 **GE** *012 †20

ZANGWILL, Donald Penn. 15243 #024-01-1953 L1961 **IM ID** *071 †20

ZARETSKAYA, Marina. 1350 LOCUST ST, STE 402 15219 #913-06-1987 L1999 **CN N** *020 †75

ZARINEH, Alireza. 4800 FRIENDSHIP AVE 15224 #517-01-1998 L2005 **PTH** *012

ZAVARAS, Katerina A. 3705 5TH AVE 15213 #418-02-1974 L1987 **PD** *020 †55

ZAW, Kyaw Thuya. 121 MEYRAN AVE, DEPT OF FAMILY MED 15213 #209-01-2002 L2006 **FP** *012

ZAWADZKI, Barbara Eva. ■ 15206 #041-12-1975 L1976 **IM** *020 †20

ZEBALLOS, Tatiana Milenka. 88 FORT COUCH RD, STE 100 15241 #270-02-1999 L2004 **PD** *020

ZEH, Herbert John, III. 5150 CENTRE AVE, UPMC CANCER PAVILION 15232 #041-12-1994 L2002 **GS** *020 †85

ZEHEL, Wendell Evans. 110 FORT COUCH RD, STE 3 15241 #041-12-1960 L1961 **GS** *071 †85

ZEHR, Kenton James. 200 LOTHROP ST 15213 #041-14-1989 L2006 **TS** *020 †85,90

ZEIGLER, Zella Rose. 3636 BLVD OF THE ALLIES 15213 #041-12-1968 L1970 **HEM** *020

ZELKOVIC, Audrey Ann. ■ 15237 #041-07-1965 L1966 **PD** *071 †55

ZELLE, Boris Alexander. 121 MEYRAN AVE 15213 #409-07-2000 L2005 **ORS** *012

ZELT, Roger Paul. 713 WASHINGTON RD 15228 #024-01-1980 L1981 **OPH** *020 †35 ‡

ZENATI, Marco. 200 LOTHROP ST 15213 #561-30-1986 L1993 **TS** *020

ZERBY, Stephen Andrew. 414 S CRAIG ST # 176 15213 #041-02-1994 L1996 **PFP** *020 †75

ZERNICH, Milas. 4 AUTUMN PATH LN, CHOICECARE PHYSICIANS, PC 15238 #041-12-1976 L1978 **IM IMG** *020 †20 ‡

ZERVOS, Irene J. 9100 BABCOCK BLVD 15237 #055-01-1990 L1994 **AN** *020 †05

ZHANG, Alexandra Yan. 190 LOTHROP ST, STE 145 15213 #243-16-1998 L2007 **D** *020 †15

ZHANG, Amy Duoxi. ■ 15213 #041-12-2008 *012

ZHANG, June Yun. ■ 15212 #056-06-2003 L2006 **AI** *012 †55

ZHANG, Li-Ming. 200 LOTHROP ST, C WING DEPT ANESTHESIOLOGY 15213 #243-76-1985 L2004 **AN** *020

ZHANG, Yuqing. 121 MEYRAN AVE 15213 #243-92-1983 L2005 **NM** *012

ZHAO, Hongcheng. 121 MEYRAN AVE 15213 #243-47-1991 L2003 **PM** *100

ZHOU, Zhihong. 121 MEYRAN AVE 15213 #243-47-1995 L2005 **IM** *012

ZHU, Wen. ■ 15215 #243-47-1994 L2001 **OPH** *100

ZIAUDDIN, Mohammed Firdos. 5150 CENTRE AVE, RM 414 15232 #016-11-1995 L2005 **GS** *020 †85

ZIDAR, Bernard Luke. 200 DELAFIELD RD, STE 3050 15215 #041-12-1969 L1972 **ON HEM** *020 †20

ZIELINSKI, David Michael. 200 LOTHROP ST, 9 SOUTH MONTEFIORE 15213 #035-48-2003 L2004 *012

ZIELKE, Andrzej K. 200 LOTHROP ST 15213 #759-06-1980 L1995 **CCA** *020 †05

ZILLWEGER, William Scott. 9100 BABCOCK BLVD 15237 #654-01-1982 L1992 **IM OS** *020 †20 ‡

ZIMMERMAN, Darin Michael. ■ 15213 #041-12-2008 L2008 *012

ZIMMERMAN, Erica Lynne. 3708 5TH AVE, STE 500 15213 #010-01-1994 L2000 **IM** *020 †20

ZIMMERMAN, George Richard. 4190 BROWNSVILLE RD 15227 #041-09-1993 L1999 **IM** *020 †20

ZIMMERMAN, Richard Kent. 3518 5TH AVE, DEPT OF FAM MED-U OF PGH 15261 #038-40-1986 L1991 **FM GPM** *050 †70,18

ZIMMERMAN, Ronald Lee. 1350 LOCUST ST, STE 409 15219 #041-12-1962 L1963 **PM** *072 †60

ZIMMERMAN, Todd Michael. 2020 ARDMORE BLVD, STE 300 15221 #041-13-1995 L1997 **FM** *020 †18

ZINELIS, Stylianos A. 4800 FRIENDSHIP AVE, WEST PENN HOSPITAL 15224 #418-01-1980 L1983 **GE** *020 †20

ZISKIND, Zelda. 200 LOTHROP ST 15213 #041-07-1937 L1938 **GP GYN** *071

ZISKO, John William. 5230 CENTRE AVE 3RD FL, SON BLDG 15232 #041-12-2002 L2002 **IM** *100 †20

ZISOWITZ, Carol. 6714 KELLY ST, HOMEWOOD OUTREACH 15208 #041-12-1981 L1982 **P ADP** *020 †75

ZITELLI, Basil John. 3705 5TH AVE, DIAGNOSTIC REFERRAL CENTER 15213 #041-12-1971 L1978 **PD** *020 †55 ‡

ZITELLI, John Albert. 5200 CENTRE AVE, STE 303 15232 #041-12-1976 L1977 **D DS** *020 †15 ‡

ZITNER, George Louis. ■ 15232 #010-02-1964 L1965 **CHP P** *071 †75

ZIVIC, Edward Joseph. 9909 FRANKSTOWN RD 15235 #041-12-1962 L1963 **FM** *020 †18 ‡

ZIVKOVIC, Sasa. 200 LOTHROP ST, PUH F875 15213 #957-01-1992 L2001 **N** *020 †75

ZNOY, Joseph Marion. 110 FORT COUCH RD 15241 #051-04-1959 L1965 **GS** *071 †85

ZORN, Kristin Kelley. 300 HALKET ST 15213 #001-02-1997 L2005 **OBG** *020

ZORUB, David Shakir. 5200 CENTRE AVE, STE 617 15232 #021-01-1970 L1976 **NS** *020 †25

ZUBENKO, George Stephen. 3811 OHARA ST, RM 1516 15213 #041-12-1981 L1983 **P IMG** *050 †75

ZUBERBUHLER, James Robt. 3705 5TH AVE 15213 #041-01-1955 L1956 **PDC** *030 †20

ZUBRITZKY, Stephen A. 408 45TH ST 15201 #041-12-1952 L1953 **CD IM** *071 †20

ZUCKERBRAUN, Brian Scott. 200 LOTHROP ST 15213 #016-06-1997 L2000 **GS** *100 †85

ZUCKERMAN, Katalin Dekany. 2500 BALDWICK RD 15205 #165-03-1982 L1985 **FM** *020 †18

ZUCKERMAN, Myles. 2500 BALDWICK RD 15205 #165-03-1982 L1985 **FM** *020 †18

ZULEY, Margarita Audino. 300 HALKET ST, UNIVERSITY OF ROCHESTER ME 15213 #041-12-1991 L1995 **DR** *020 †20

ZULFIQAR, Sara. ■ 15232 #055-01-2006 L2006 **IM** *012

ZWEIG, Neal. ■ 15217 #041-12-1961 L1963 **IM** *020 †20

ZYCZYNSKI, Halina M. 300 HALKET ST, OBGYN/MAGEE WOMENS HOSP 15213 #035-03-1985 L1986 **GYN** *040 †30

ZYMEK, Pawel Tomasz. ■ 15232 #759-01-1998 L2005 **IM** *012

PITTSTON — LUZERNE

BORMES, Robert E. ■ 18640 #016-43-1951 L1952 **GS** *071

BRUNO, Joseph Nunzio, Jr. 1099 S TOWNSHIP BLVD 18640 #035-09-1962 **R OS** *071

FENSTER, Bradley David. 1099 S TOWNSHIP BLVD, STE E 18640 #010-02-1996 L2001 **IC** *100 †20

JORDAN, William J. 171 N MAIN ST 18640 #065-09-1968 L1969 **OPH** *020 †35

LAUER, Laura Michelle. ■ 18640 #041-77-2007, ▲ L2007 *012

LAZAR, Richard John. 57 N MAIN ST 18640 #041-02-1978 L1979 **FM** *020 †18

LICATA, Guy Joseph. ■ 18640 #041-13-2000 **EM** *100

LOMBARDO, Joseph Michael. 49 BROAD ST STE 4 18640 #016-43-1964 L1965 **GP IM** *020 †18

MC MENAMIN, Deborah J. 426 HIGHWAY 315 18640 #041-07-1977 L1980 **GS CD** *075

SPAGNOLINI, Luigi. 57 N MAIN ST 18640 #561-11-1992 L2004 **FM** *020

STUCCIO, Dominick A. ■ 18640 #041-09-1949 L1950 **U** *071 †95

PLAINS — LUZERNE

ABRANTES, Fernando J. 200 S RIVER ST 18705 #770-01-1953 L1965 **GS VS** *071 †85

ADLER, Michael Laurence. 201 N MAIN ST 18705 #035-46-1993 L1999 **END** *020 †20

BANERJI, Sipra. PO BOX 1810 18705 #495-02-1972 L1982 **FM** *020 †50

BYRON, Thomas Wm. 220 S RIVER ST 18705 #032-01-1975 L1981 **ORS HS** *020 †40

CASTERLINE, Peter F. 200 S RIVER ST 18705 #028-34-1969 L1969 **HNS GS** *020 †85

COREY, Peter John. 200 S RIVER ST 18705 #041-09-1955 L1956 **GS** *071 †85

DALESSANDRO, David Arthur. 667 N RIVER ST 18705 #041-02-1990 L1992 **CD** *020 †20

DAS, Nirode C. 667 N RIVER ST, STE 201 18705 #041-09-1963 L1975 **CD IM** *020 †20

DE ROJAS, Juan Jose, Jr. 200 S RIVER ST 18705 #041-13-1980 L1981 **GS** *020 †85

ELLIS, John Henry, IV. 667 N RIVER ST 18705 #041-09-1979 L1981 **CD IM** *020 †20

GERHART, Clark. 200 S RIVER ST 18705 #041-09-1990 L1992 **GS** *020 †85

GRIVER, Avner R. 11 GALLAGHER DR 18705 #048-04-1992 L1996 **PM IM** *020 †60

KHOUDARY, Raymond. 190 S RIVER ST 18705 #875-02-1983 L1992 **AI PD** *020 †55,03

KIM, Eugene D. 220 S RIVER ST 18705 #035-45-1991 L1997 **ORS** *020 †85

LITCHMAN, Jos Francis, Jr. 220 S RIVER ST, LINDEN MEDICAL GRP 18705 #041-09-1980 L1981 **FM EM** *020 †16,18

LUCCHINO, David Byron. 200 S RIVER ST 18705 #041-09-1960 L1962 **GS TS** *020 †85,90

PERNIKOFF, Barry Jay. 200 S RIVER ST, PLAINS TOWNSHIP 18705 #041-14-1991 L1991 **GS** *020 †85,10

SHEIKH, Feroz Ahemad. 200 S RIVER ST, SURGICAL SPEC WYOMING VLY 18705 #495-35-1970 L1986 **GS CRS** *020 †85,10

TURISSINI, Thomas John. 667 N RIVER ST, STE 201 18705 #041-02-1982 L1983 CD IM *020 †20
VOLPETTI, George Wm. 200 S RIVER ST 18705 #016-43-1969 L1970 GS *020 †85
WITT, Paul Jos. 59 E CAREY ST, PAUL J WITT MD 18705 #305-01-1984 L1984 FM EM *020 †18 ‡
WOOD, Marlene Bird. 670 N RIVER ST STE 102 18705 #048-14-1984 L1985 FM EM *020 †18
YAVORSKI, Chester Chas. 200 S RIVER ST 18705 #010-02-1989 L1993 VS *020 †85

PLEASANT GAP – CENTRE

ALLATT, Richard Douglas. 550 W COLLEGE AVE 16823 #065-10-1978 L1993 PM FM *020 †60
BILLY, Gregory George. 550 W COLLEGE AVE 16823 #041-14-1993 L1997 PM *020 †60
KEENAN, Barbara Frances. 550 W COLLEGE AVE, COMPREHENSIVE REHAB SERVIC 16823 #005-14-1980 L1998 PM *020 †60
MC CAUL, Colin Patrick. 550 W COLLEGE AVE 16823 #033-06-2002 L2005 PM *020 †60
RATNER, Jeffrey Alan. 550 W COLLEGE AVE 16823 #041-09-1978 L1979 PUD IM *020 †20

PLEASANT HILLS – ALLEGHENY

AVOLIO, Guy. 695 CLAIRTON BLVD, MEDEXPRESS URGENT CARE, LL 15236 #422-01-1987 L1990 EM *020 †20
GOSS, Lisa Ann. 695 CLAIRTON BLVD 15236 #041-12-1998 L2000 FM *020 †18

PLEASANTVILLE – VENANGO

ZEHNER, James Maurice. 231 N MAIN ST 16341 #041-12-1977 L1978 FM *020 †18 ‡

PLYMOUTH – LUZERNE

BREAKSTONE, Louise A. 215 E MAIN ST 18651 #041-13-1983 L1984 FM *020
MC SWEYN, Norman F. 546 W MAIN ST 18651 #062-01-1943 OS *100
RONDINA, James Benj J. 253 E MAIN ST 18651 #041-09-1970 L1971 FM GYN *020 †18

PLYMOUTH MEETING – MONTGOMERY

APPELBAUM, Laurie R. 512W TOWNSHIP LINE RD, SCHOOL 19462 #056-05-1978 L1989 CHP PD *020 †75
BALISTOCKY, Marvin H. ■ 19462 #041-09-1951 L1953 OPH *071 †35
BAYLSON, Frances P Batzer. 5217 MILITIA HILL RD, PHILADELPHIA FERTILITY INS 19462 #041-07-1972 L1973 REN GYN *020 †30
BELLO, Justine Ann. ■ 19462 #041-15-2006 L2006 FP *012
BEVILACQUA, Dante J, Jr. PO BOX 743 19462 #041-09-1965 GP *075
BHANDARY, Mallika Manoj. ■ 19462 #495-09-1991 L2002 SP *100
BINNICK, Steven Arthur. 531 W GERMANTOWN PIKE, STE 201 19462 #041-09-1973 L1974 D DMP *020 †15 ‡
BIRCH, Gerald Alexander. ■ 19462 #665-01-1999 L1999 IM *100
BOELLNER-KAHN, Alicia A. 3031 WALTON RD STE C101 19462 #035-20-1991 L1993 PD *020 †55 ‡
BRAINSKY, Ada. 3043 WALTON RD, SUITE 150 HEALTH ADVOCATE 19462 #264-04-1989 L1999 PD *020 †55
BROWN, Arthur Stuart. 523 PLYMOUTH RD 19462 #035-01-1970 L2002 N *074
CARRASCO, Lee R. 1000 GERMANTOWN PIKE 19462 #041-02-1999 L2000 *020
CHEIKIN, Michael Irwin. 832 GERMANTOWN PIKE, STE 3 19462 #035-08-1980 L1987 N ORS *020 †60
CHIN, Songok Susan. 3031 WALTON RD STE C101 19462 #041-13-1998 L2000 PD *020 †55
CHUNG, Kyung Yil. ■ 19462 #583-02-1968 L1994 AN *020
CORSON, Barry. 649 W GERMANTOWN PIKE, STE 200 19462 #041-02-1968 L1969 FM *020 †18
DEHORATIUS, Danielle M. 531 W GERMANTOWN PIKE, STE 200 19462 #041-02-2002 L2005 D *020 †15
DEIN, Robert Allen. 140 W GERMANTOWN PIKE, WOMENS HEALTH CARE GROUP 19462 #041-01-1983 L1984 OBG *020 †30
DENICK, Cheryl Ann. 850 GERMANTOWN PIKE 19462 #041-13-1990 L1992 EM *020 †16
DESAI, Sandhya Krishnan. ■ 19462 #025-01-2000 L2000 AI *020 †55,03
DURKIN, R Torsney. 1000 GERMANTOWN PIKE, STE A3 19462 #010-02-1977 L1978 N *020 †75
EL MALLAH, Mohamed Gaafar. 140 W GERMANTOWN PIKE, WOMENS HEALTH CARE GROUP 19462 #915-03-1978 L1995 OBG *020 †30
EVANS, John Bernard. 3031 WALTON RD, C101 19462 #041-13-1985 L1986 PD *020 †55
FERRARA, Frank Michael. 123 FALCON WAY 19462 #041-14-1979 L1981 AN *020 †05
FISCHER, Mark Brian. 531 W GERMANTOWN PIKE, STE 101 19462 #041-13-1996 L2001 FM *020 †18
GEISSER CHRISTENSEN, Krist. ■ 19462 #041-15-2007 IM *012
GOREN, Elihu Norman. 633 W GERMANTOWN PIKE 19462 #035-46-1973 L1975 DIA END *020 †20
GROSSMAN, Larry Bruce. 777 W GERMANTOWN PIKE 19462 #041-14-1973 L1974 AN *020 †05
HAMAKER, Lisa Lynn. 633 W GERMANTOWN PIKE, STE 105 19462 #041-14-2002 L2002 END *012 †20
HEATH, David D. 531 W GERMANTOWN PIKE, STE 101 19462 #041-13-1951 L1959 GP *071 †18
HENDLER, Barry Hersh. 1000 GERMANTOWN PIKE 19462 #041-07-1973 L1977 OS *020
HOCHFELD, Marla Beth. 102 BLACK WALNUT LN 19462 #041-09-1988 L1998 RHU *020 †20
HUGHES, Eugene P, Sr. ■ 19462 #041-02-1948 L1949 GS TS *071 †85
JACOBS, Jeffrey Alan. 850 GERMANTOWN PIKE, CONCENTRA MEDICAL CENTER 19462 #024-05-1986 L2005 GPM GS *020 †70
KAKARIA, Parul J. 633 W GERMANTOWN PIKE, STE 105 19462 #010-01-1999 L2006 END IM *020 †20
KEILANY, Bashar. 117 WOODBINE WAY 19462 #875-01-1973 L1976 EM IM *020 †20,16
KEILANY, Raghda Tabbara. ■ 19462 #875-01-1973 L1980 OBG *075 †30
KIM, Yong Soon Ahn. ■ 19462 #583-03-1960 L1967 AN *071
KONERU, Ramesh. ■ 19462 #495-62-1989 L1997 PYG *020 †75
LEE, Jin Hee. ■ 19462 #041-15-2008 *012
LEHRER, Michael Stephen. 531 W GERMANTOWN PIKE, STE 200 19462 #041-01-1998 L2001 D DS *020 †15

LEONE-PAK, Lisa Diane. 140 W GERMANTOWN PIKE, WOMENS HEALTH CARE GROUP 19462 #041-13-1994 L1996 OBG *020 †30
LEVIN, Bruce Jay. 111 W GERMANTOWN PIKE 19462 #041-09-1983 L1984 P PYA *020 †75
LI-BURNS, Xiaobin. 850 GERMANTOWN PIKE, CONCENTRA MED CTR 19462 #243-45-1982 L1996 IM *020 †20
LIN, Yi. ■ 19462 #035-01-2001 L2006 GS *100
LOCHETTO, Frank John, III. ■ 19462 #041-12-1993 L1996 PD *020
LONGACRE, Jane Mooney. 3031 WALTON RD, STE C101 19462 #041-02-1980 L1982 PD *020 †55 ‡
LU, Ravy Sreng. 140 W GERMANTOWN PIKE, WOMENS HEALTH CARE GROUP 19462 #041-13-1994 L1996 OBG *020 †30
MACKAY, Donna Jane. 531 W GERMANTOWN PIKE, STE 201 19462 #011-02-1977 L1978 D *020 †15
MASH, Marlene Julia. 1000 GERMANTOWN PIKE, STE C3 19462 #041-13-1982 L1983 D FM *020 †18,15
MC CARTHY, Jennifer M. 531 W GERMANTOWN PIKE, STE 101 19462 #051-04-1991 L1993 FM *020 †18
MENON, Radha Vankawala. ■ 19462 #041-15-2005 L2005 IM *012
NOBEL, Joel J. 5200 BUTLER PIKE, ECRI 19462 #041-02-1963 L1964 OS *071
PARK, Ho Hyun. 37 E GERMANTOWN PIKE, STE 301 19462 #583-02-1958 L1970 CHP P *020
PEVAR, Joel Bertram. 531 PROFESSIONAL BLDG, FORMANCE PHYSICIAN SVC INC 19462 #041-07-1981 L1982 FM *020 †18
PHATAK, Meena Vijaya. ■ 19462 #495-23-1957 L1972 GYN *020 †30
QUINT, Andrew Robt. 633 W GERMANTOWN PIKE, STE 105 19462 #010-01-1979 L1983 END IM *020 †20
RABSON, Joseph A. 1000 GERMANTOWN PIKE, STE E1 19462 #035-46-1977 L1981 PS *020 †65
REALYVASQUEZ, J A. ■ 19462 #005-06-1967 L2000 ORS PDS *020 †40
REID, Daniel Wm. 531 W GERMANTOWN PIKE, STE 101 19462 #041-07-1981 L1982 FM *040 †18
REIS, Maria T Abella. 1041 GERMANTOWN PIKE 19462 #748-01-1982 L1985 P PYG *020 †75
SEMBROT, William B. ■ 19462 #041-13-1958 L1959 IM PUD *071 †20 ‡
STANTON, David C. 1000 GERMANTOWN PIKE 19462 #041-01-1992 L1992 FPS PSH *020
STEPHENSON, Patricia Ann. 523 PLYMOUTH RD, INTRACORP 19462 #041-07-1980 L1982 OBG *020 †30
STRIAR, Jeffery Howard. 531 W GERMANTOWN PIKE, STE 203 19462 #165-04-1972 L1978 N IM *020
TORNETTA, Frank Jos. ■ 19462 #041-09-1946 L1947 AN *071 †05
TREAT, James Rich. ■ 19462 #041-01-2002 L2002 D *100 †15
TSAI, Douglas Byejeh. ■ 19462 #041-13-2002 L2002 VIR *012 †80
TUNG, Ru-Lin Ko. ■ 19462 #385-02-1960 L1968 PTH *071 †50
WHITMAN, Mark Allan. 580 W GERMANTOWN PIKE, PLYMOUTH PLAZA BUILDING 19462 #041-09-1947 L1948 OM PD *071
WILLIAMS, Ayasha Ldaire. ■ 19462 #041-13-2004 L2004 PM *012
WISER, Alan. 531 W GERMANTOWN PIKE 19462 #041-13-1976 L1977 FM *020 †18
WOLFE, Jonathan Todd. 531 W GERMANTOWN PIKE, STE 200 19462 #010-02-1990 L1995 D *020 †20,15
WOLK, Thomas Allen. 3043 WALTON RD, STE 150 19462 #050-02-1975 L1976 PD *030 †55 ‡
WOOD, Andrew Scott. 3031 WALTON RD, STE C101 19462 #041-01-2000 L2001 PD *020 †55
ZEBROWSKI, Sandra Marie. 110 DONNA DR, PLYMOUTH MEETING 19462 #041-13-1985 L1990 P CHP *030 †75 ‡

POCONO LAKE – MONROE

DIENER, Ian Lance D. ■ 18347 #041-01-1971 L1972 FM *020 †18
KITCHEN, James G, II. ■ 18347 #041-01-1942 L1943 FM *071
MIRAGLIA, Richard James. ■ 18347 #036-05-1973 L1974 FM *071 †18
PTAKOWSKI, George Anthony. ■ 18347 #759-10-1985 L1986 FM AM *020 †18

POCONO LAKE PRESERVE – MONROE

LOWRY, Barbara Sawyer. ■ 18348 #041-13-1954 L1955 PTH MM *071 †50

POCONO PINES – MONROE

BOND, James Phillips. ■ 18350 #041-01-1963 L1964 ON HEM *071 †20
CHASE, Zina Z. ■ 18350 #913-23-1963 L1987 IM *071
VEERARAGHAVAN, Gowri. ■ 18350 #496-21-2000 L2006 IM *020 †20

POCOPSON – CHESTER

LABRAGUE, Miguel Apura. ■ 19366 #748-09-1973 GS *100

POINT MARION – FAYETTE

SIMKOVICH, Valerie Ann. ■ 15474 #055-01-1993 L1997 AN *020

POINT PLEASANT – BUCKS

CHAILLE-ARNOLD, Linda Mar. ■ 18950 #041-02-2004 L2004 EM *100
WOODMAN, Thomas Johnson. ■ 18950 #041-13-1954 L1955 P *071

PORT MATILDA – CENTRE

BLUE, Rebecca Suzanne. ■ 16870 #010-02-2008 *012
BUTLER, David K. 116 FOREST GLEN CIR 16870 #048-14-1999 L2002 MPD *020 †20,55
WELZ, Bettina Maxine. ■ 16870 #041-14-1986 L1991 P IM *071 †75,20

PORTAGE – CAMBRIA

KARDUCK, John Steven. 3670 PORTAGE ST, STE 105 15946 #041-12-1975 L1976 **FM** *020 ‡
RATCHFORD, Donald Francis. 3670 PORTAGE ST, STE 105 15946 #041-02-1994 L1996 **FM** *020 †18
SHIKARA, Amina Izzaldin. 3670 PORTAGE ST, STE 105 15946 #528-01-1991 L2002 **FM** *020 †18

POTTSTOWN – CHESTER

CHUNG, Don Young. 730 S HANOVER ST 19465 #041-15-2001 L2003 **IM** *020
COPELOVITCH, Lawrence A. ■ 19465 #035-03-2001 L2004 **PN** *100 †55
DAVIDHEISER, Sharon I. 88 GLOCKER WAY, # 123 19465 #041-07-1991 L1994 **IM** *020 †20
D'ERAMO, Gregory Vincent. ■ 19465 #041-13-2003 L2003 **PM** *100
FLEISCHER, Sharon Jill. 730 S HANOVER ST 19465 #033-05-1997 L2004 **FM** *020 †18 ‡
GOWEN, George F. ■ 19465 #041-02-1952 L1953 **OS GS** *071 †85
GREEN, Nieta Michelle. 730 S HANOVER ST 19465 #041-02-2001 L2003 **IM** *020
HERMANN, Robert Frank, Jr. 730 S HANOVER ST 19465 #041-13-1996 L1998 **FM** *020 †18
LUPAS, John Albert. 730 S HANOVER ST 19465 #041-09-1959 L1962 **PD FM** *020 †55
PADILLA, Gliceria S. ■ 19465 #748-01-1957 L1969 **GP** *071
PLUMMER, Robert Arch. ■ 19465 #041-13-1966 L1967 **FM** *071 †18
SALINDONG, Jaime P. ■ 19465 #748-01-1954 L1968 **AN GS** *071
STROW, Jennifer Ernst. ■ 19465 #041-77-2006, ▲ L2006 **IM** *012
TURCHIN, Louise Helen. ■ 19465 #041-02-1982 L1983 **AN** *020 †05
WINTER, Fred Shipman. ■ 19465 #019-02-1944 L1950 **R OS** *071 †80
YOUNG, Deborah Anne. 730 S HANOVER ST 19465 #033-06-1982 L1983 **FM** *020 †18
YUHAS, Thomas Richard. 1177 CHESTERSHIRE PL, POTTSTOWN SURGICAL ASSOICA 19465 #041-12-1986 L1987 **VS GS** *020 †85
ZABAT, Phil-Edric Cepeda. 730 S HANOVER ST 19465 #748-21-2000 L2006 **FM FSM** *020 †18

POTTSTOWN – MONTGOMERY

ADLER, Jason Paul. 717 E HIGH ST 19464 #041-13-2004 L2004 **DR** *012
AKBAR, Ramzan Shaheedha. 1600 E HIGH ST, STE C 19464 #495-59-1990 L2000 **PM** *020 †60
ALTMAN, Adam Jeffrey. 1503 SUNSET DR, STE 5 19464 #024-16-1985 L1989 **OPH** *020 †35
ANDERSEN, John Martin. 933 N CHARLOTTE ST, STE 3-A 19464 #308-03-1980 L1987 **FM FPG** *020 †18
ANTHONY, John Aubrey. 1133 E HIGH ST 19464 #041-13-1946 L1947 **GP** *072
ARONSKY, Michael Allan. 3277 W RIDGE PIKE 19464 #011-04-1993 L1998 **OPH** *020 †35
BAMAN, Rakesh Ishwarlal. 1591 MEDICAL DR 19464 #016-11-1989 L1992 **CD IM** *020 †20
BANSAL, Harinder K. 1630 E HIGH ST, BLDG 1 19464 #654-01-1981 L1984 **P ADM** *020 †75
BEHR, Edith Delmar. 1590 MEDICAL DR, STE A 19464 #041-07-1985 L1987 **GS** *020 †85
BELLUS, John Jos. 1600 E HIGH ST 19464 #041-02-1957 L1958 **PTH ATP** *071 †50
BHAMBHANI, Girish Mohan. 1600 E HIGH ST 19464 #422-01-2004 L2004 **FM** *020
BIGELOW, Karen Smith. 1555 MEDICAL DR, BROOKSIDE FAMILY PRACTICE, 19464 #041-09-1987 L1989 **PD** *020 †55
BITTENBENDER, Susan E. 933 N CHARLOTTE ST 3B 19464 #041-14-1994 L1998 **D** *020 †15
BLACKSTONE, Peter Eric. 1591 MEDICAL DR 19464 #028-78-2000, ▲ L2001 **IM** *020
BOLMANN, Andrew R. 1600 E HIGH ST 19464 #067-02-1965 L1970 **P** *020 †75
BRICKHOUSE, Neal Angelo. 1600 E HIGH ST, DEPT OF ANESTHESIA 19464 #036-08-1991 L1997 **AN** *020 †05
CAIN, James Patrick. 411 APPLE ST, POTTSTOWN 19464 #041-13-1971 L1972 **FM FPG** *020 †18
CANO, William Guillermo. 1603 E HIGH ST STE C 19464 #847-03-1992 L2002 **PM** *020 †60
CHANG, Clayton Wo. 933 N CHARLOTTE ST 19464 #010-01-1978 L1981 **IM** *020 †20
CHAPIS, Gregory John. 1603 E HIGH ST, STE C 19464 #041-13-1988 L1990 **PM** *020 †60
CHAPIS, Nicholas John. 13 ARMAND HAMMER BLVD 19464 #041-09-1959 L1960 **GYN OBS** *071 †30
CINCO, Victorio Bisquera. 1600 E HIGH ST 19464 #748-01-1965 L1973 **EM GS** *071 †16
COOPER, Alan Edward. 1601 MEDICAL DR, ORTHOPAEDIC ATHLETIC MED 19464 #041-09-1989 L1994 **OSM** *020 †40
D'ANDREA, Linda Ann. 600 CREEKSIDE DR STE 611, BRANDYWINE INST OF ORTHPED 19464 #041-13-1990 L1990 **ORS OSS** *020 †40
DANKMYER, Christopher C. 1603 E HIGH ST, STE C 19464 #041-02-1988 L1990 **PM PME** *020 †60
DE GROOT, Melanie D. 800 HERITAGE DR, STE 900 19464 #016-42-1987 L1995 **PD** *020 †55
DE VANNA, Thomas. 1600 E HIGH ST, POTTSTOWN MEMORIAL MDCL CT 19464 #038-41-1979 L2001 **DR** *020 †80
DEVINEY, John Patrick. 1591 MEDICAL DR 19464 #041-13-1968 L1969 **IM** *020 †20
DHAWAN, Rajiv. 1591 MEDICAL DR 19464 #496-09-1985 L1997 **CD** *020 †20
DI PILLO, Mark Alan. 1503 SUNSET DR, STE 5 19464 #035-08-1983 L1989 **OPH** *020 †35
DONAHUE, John Richard. 1569 MEDICAL DR 19464 #041-02-1976 L1977 **OS ORS** *020 †40
DUSABE-ZIHERAMBERE, Lilian. ■ 19464 #550-04-2005 **MPD** *012
ELURI, Ramesh Babu. 1600 E HIGH ST, POTTSTOWN MEMORIAL MEDICAL 19464 #495-70-1980 L1997 **PYG** *020 †75
ERICKSON, Jacob Neil. ■ 19464 #041-15-2008 *012
ESKRA, Benjamin David. 1590 MEDICAL DR, STE A 19464 #041-02-2000 L2005 **PS** *020
FLEISCHER, Deborah Ellen. 1591 MEDICAL DR, POTTSTOWN MEDICAL SPECIALI 19464 #041-09-1989 L1991 **GE** *020 †20
FRANZ, Pamela Jamene. 1600 E HIGH ST, POTTSTOWN MEMORIAL MEDICAL 19464 #041-02-1991 L1994 **EM** *020 †16
GAFFNEY, Edmund James. 64 N HANOVER ST 19464 #038-41-1960 L1962 **CRS GS** *020 †85
GALIDO JR, Perfecto. 1600 E HIGH ST 19464 #748-11-1981 L2002 **AN** *020
GARCIA-MUNOZ, Richard. 1600 E HIGH ST, POTTSTOWN MEM MED CTR 19464 #033-06-1992 L1997 **AN PME** *020 †05
GOLDBERG, Alan H. 1555 MEDICAL DR, BROOKSIDE FAMILY PRACTICE, 19464 #041-02-1979 L1980 **FM** *020 †18
GOLDBERG, David Sherman. 1503 SUNSET DR, STE 5 19464 #011-04-1991 L1997 **OPH PO** *020 †35
GOONEWARDENE, Ian Michael. 1591 MEDICAL DR 19464 #041-13-1995 L1997 **IM** *020 †20
HABIBA, Umai. 1590 MEDICAL DR, TODAY'S KIDS PEDIATRICS 19464 #495-59-1988 L1996 **PD** *020 †55
HAMEED, Burhan. 1591 MEDICAL DR 19464 #704-01-1994 L2001 **GE** *020 †20
HARPUL, Loraine G. ■ 19464 #041-77-1981, ▲ L1981 **ATP CLP** *071 †50
HERBST, Bernadette Ann. 1630 E HIGH ST BLDG 5 19464 #041-07-1967 L1971 **N** *071
HORSTMAN, Rosemary. 1600 E HIGH ST, POTTSTOWN MEM MED CNT 19464 #041-07-1989 L1991 **EM** *020 †16
HOVE, Christopher R. 2023 E HIGH ST 19464 #041-13-1996 L2007 **FPS OTO** *020 †45 ‡
KABLER, Ronald Lee. 2103 E HIGH ST, TRI COUNTY UROLOGIC ASSOC 19464 #041-02-1972 L1973 **U** *020 †95
KALEMBA, Johanna M Del'Re. 13 ARMAND HAMMER BLVD, STE 100 19464 #041-07-1969 L1970 **R** *020 †80
KAMOUN, Layla. 1560 MEDICAL DR, SANATOGA OPHTHALMOLOGY ASS 19464 #041-01-1993 L1997 **OPH** *020 †35
KAPLAN, Sheldon Jay. 1503 SUNSET DR, STE 5 19464 #010-01-1965 L1976 **OPH OS** *020 †35
KENNEY, Lawrence Edward. 1560 MEDICAL DR, SANATOGA OPHTHALMOLOGY 19464 #041-13-1982 L1982 **OPH** *020 †35
KLOMBERS, Lee Alan. 1503 SUNSET DR, STE 5 19464 #041-12-1986 L1991 **OPH** *020 †35
KRANTZLER, Joseph David. 1591 MEDICAL DR 19464 #016-42-1979 L1981 **CD IM** *020 †20
KROMASH, Marvin Henry. 1590 MEDICAL DR 19464 #041-09-1965 L1966 **PD** *020 †55
LAGUNILLA, Juanito Lopez. ■ 19464 #748-07-1955 L1967 **EM GP** *071
LAMBO, Michael John. 1611 MEDICAL DR, CENTER 19464 #056-05-1988 L1992 **RO** *020 †80 ‡
LEVIN, Kimberly Anne. 1600 E HIGH ST 19464 #041-02-1994 L2001 **HMP** *100 †50
LIBERACE, Ettore Val. 1600 E HIGH ST 19464 #041-01-1965 L1966 **PTH** *020 †50
LIGNELLI, Gregory Joseph. 1630 E HIGH ST, BLDG 5 19464 #041-13-1962 L1963 **NS N** *071 †25
LIPTON, Glenn Emmanuel. 600 CREEKSIDE DR, STE 611 19464 #041-13-2001 L2001 **ORS** *020
LISS, Frederic Eliot. 2081 E HIGH ST, PHOENIXVILLE ORTHOPEDIC 19464 #041-13-1985 L1986 **ORS HS** *020 †40
LOEPER, Donald Jos. 1600 E HIGH ST 19464 #041-09-1954 L1955 **FM** *071 †18
MAHMOOD, Edna Zia. 1503 SUNSET DR, STE 5 19464 #704-06-1969 L1980 **OPH** *020
MALLOY, Barry Chas. 1503 SUNSET DR, STE 5 19464 #024-16-1985 L1996 **OPH** *020 †35
MANZO, Thomas Louis. 1329 E HIGH ST 19464 #010-02-1974 L1975 **OPH** *020 †35 ‡
MASHRU, Rakesh P. 600 CREEKSIDE DR, STE 611 19464 #033-05-2000 L2001 **ORS** *100
MC CLOSKEY, Michael D. 1600 E HIGH ST 19464 #041-02-1981 L1989 **DR** *020
MCDONOUGH, Renee Lynn. 1555 MEDICAL DR, BROOKSIDE FAM PRAC & PED 19464 #011-02-1996 L2000 **MPD** *020 †20,55
MENKOWITZ, Elliot. 1200 E HIGH ST, STE 307 19464 #041-13-1967 L1970 **ORS GP** *020 †40
MOVVA, Rajesh. 1600 E HIGH ST, POTTSTOWN MEMORIAL MEDICAL 19464 #495-21-1996 L2004 **IM** *020 †20
NEILSON, Robert Norman. 13 ARMAND HAMMER BLVD 19464 #041-13-1982 L1987 **OBG OS** *020 †30
NOWACKI, Stanley M. ■ 19464 #041-13-1935 L1936 **GP PUD** *071
OLSTAD, Claire B. 800 HERITAGE DR, STE 900 19464 #048-14-2001 L2004 **PD** *020 †55
PADILLA, Jaime Saulo. 13 ARMAND HAMMER BLVD 19464 #748-01-1958 L1968 **ORS GYN** *071 †30
PARIS, Scot David. 1590 MEDICAL DR, STE A 19464 #033-06-1991 L1993 **CRS GS** *020 †10,85
PELL, John Joseph. 2081 E HIGH ST, PHOENIXVILLE ORTHOPEDIC 19464 #041-13-1973 L1974 **ORS** *020 †40
PERCH, Gerald Alan. 2103 E HIGH ST, TRICOUNTYH UROLOGIC ASSOC 19464 #041-02-1959 L1960 **U** *071 †95
PERILSTEIN, Michael D. 13 ARMAND HAMMER BLVD, CHESTNUT PROF BLDG 19464 #041-02-1975 L1976 **RHU IM** *020 †20 ‡
PERRY, David Mark. 1600 E HIGH ST, POTTSTOWN EMERG DEPT 19464 #041-14-1988 L1990 **EM FM** *020 †18
PHAM, An Huu. 1591 MEDICAL DR 19464 #041-09-1987 L1988 **PCC** *020 †20
PIOTROWSKA, Lucy B. 1600 E HIGH ST 19464 #041-07-1953 L1954 **AN GS** *071 †05
POPOLOW, Michael Leonard. 1591 MEDICAL DR 19464 #041-02-1966 L1967 **IM** *020 †20 ‡
PRIMACK, Jonathan David. 1503 SUNSET DR, STE 5 19464 #028-02-1995 L2005 **OPH** *020 †35
PRONESTI, George Raphael. 3277 W RIDGE PIKE 19464 #041-02-1985 L1995 **OPH** *020 †35
RAMACHANDRAN, Siva Kumar. 1569 MEDICAL DR, STE 100 19464 #495-02-1985 L1998 **PCC** *020 †20
RAMAN, Manjula Kandaa. 13 ARMAND HAMMER BLVD, STE 100 19464 #495-94-1989 L1998 **IM** *020 †20
RODRIGUEZ, Gilberto E. 5 S SUNNYBROOK RD, STE 400 19464 #041-13-1967 L1968 **AI PD** *020 †55,03
RONNERMANN, Drew Paul. 1591 MEDICAL DR 19464 #035-09-1974 L1975 **GE IM** *020 †20
RORICK, Nicholas Richard. 1600 E HIGH ST, PMMC/RADIOLOGY DEPT 19464 #030-06-1966 L1978 **R NM** *020 †80,28
ROSS, Elisa Karen. 13 ARMAND HAMMER BLVD 19464 #041-01-1996 L1998 **OBG** *020 †30
RUBENSTEIN, Glenn Martin. 1600 E HIGH ST, POTTSTOWN MEMORIAL MED CTR 19464 #035-15-1987 L1991 **AN** *020 †05
SANDS, Earl Edwin. 1597 MEDICAL DR 19464 #041-09-1982 L1985 **OBG** *071 †30
SAUNDERS, Richard Michael. 13 ARMAND HAMMER BLVD 19464 #035-09-1982 L1987 **PUD IM** *020 †20 ‡
SAYLOR, Richard F. 1600 E HIGH ST 19464 #041-02-1973 L1974 *030 †85
SCHAAF, H William. 2081 E HIGH ST, PHOENIXVILLE ORTHOPEDIC 19464 #041-13-1977 L1979 **ORS IM** *020 †20,40
SCHANK, Dennis Jos. 1591 MEDICAL DR 19464 #041-13-1986 L1987 **FM** *040 †18
SHULMAN, Leib. 353 KING ST 19464 #065-06-1968 L1981 **GP EM** *020
SONG, Wei. 1600 E HIGH ST, CANCER CTR 19464 #243-16-1987 L1998 **HO IM** *020 †20
SOTOMAYOR, Antonio E. 1569 MEDICAL DR 19464 #308-03-1978 L1983 **N** *020
SPENCER, Stephen E, Jr. 1610 E HIGH ST 19464 #041-02-1996 L1998 **EM** *020 †16
STEVENS, Jeffrey A. 1600 E HIGH ST, POTTSTOWN MEMORIAL CAN CTR 19464 #041-77-1997, ▲ L1998 **HO IM** *020 †20
STOLAR, Neal Myles. ■ 19464 #016-11-1990 L1994 **P** *020 †75
SWAAB, Ronald Louis. 1591 MEDICAL DR 19464 #035-03-1990 L1993 **HO IM** *020 †20
TEEHAN, Geoffrey Stephan. 13 ARMAND HAMMER BLVD #102, CHESMONT PROFESSIONAL BLD 19464 #041-02-1998 L2005 **NEP** *020 †20
THUNE, Michael Edward. 1600 E HIGH ST, POTTSTOWN MEMORIAL-RADIOLO 19464 #035-46-1993 L1998 **DR** *020 †80
TIWARI, Suman. 1611 MEDICAL DR, POTTSTOWN REGIONAL RADIATI 19464 #033-05-1996 L2001 **RO** *020 †80 ‡
TOUEY, Charles Vincent. 1597 MEDICAL DR, WOMAN'S HEALTHCARE 19464 #041-13-1993 L1996 **OBG** *020 †30
TUCKER, Maria Antoinette. 1597 MEDICAL DR, WOMENS HEALTHCARE PC 19464 #041-12-1991 L1994 **OBG** *020 †30
VELASCO CHUA, Chong Heim. 1600 E HIGH ST 19464 #242-46-1959 L1975 **AN** *071
VICKERMAN, Charles Edward. 2135 E HIGH ST 19464 #041-02-1974 L1976 **D** *020 †15
VILLEGAS, Antonio Cruz. 1600 E HIGH ST 19464 #748-01-1955 L1972 **PTH** *020 †50

■ = Address Information Privacy Protected

WEBER, Steven Jay. PO BOX 775 19464 #561-17-1980 L1983 **ID** *020 †20
WERNER, Elliot Bruce. 1503 SUNSET DR, STE 5 19464 #041-01-1971 L1982
   OPH OS *035 ‡
WHITMOYER, Stephen Ronald. 1600 E HIGH ST, PMMC RADIOLOGY 19464
   #041-02-1991 L1993 **DR VIR** *020 †80
WHITTAKER, Richard P. 1200 E HIGH ST, STE 307 19464 #041-01-1966 L1967 **ORS** *020 †40
WILLIAMSON, Joshua Blaine. 800 HERITAGE DR, STE 900 19464 #055-01-2002 L2006
   PSM *020 †55
WORLEY, Gari Lynn. 1569 MEDICAL DR, STE 202 19464 #040-02-2000 L2002 **IMG** *100 †20
YABLON, Jeffrey Steven. 1600 E HIGH ST, NEUROSURGERY - PMMC 19464
   #041-09-1980 L1986 **NS** *020 †25
ZACCHEI, Anthony C. 3277 W RIDGE PIKE 19464 #041-02-1991 L1996 **OPH** *020 †35
ZELLEY, Lee Seitz. 13 ARMAND HAMMER BLVD, 3RD FL 19464 #041-09-1970 L1971
   OBG *020 †30
ZIMMERMAN, Lamar T. ■ 19464 #041-09-1952 L1953 **AM GP** *075
ZOBIAN, Edward Jos. 1503 SUNSET DR, STE 5 19464 #041-01-1966 L1970 **OPH GP** *020 †35

POTTSVILLE – SCHUYLKILL

ABRAHAM, David James. 48 TUNNEL RD, STE 202 17901 #041-02-1992 L1994 **OSS** *020 †40
AHLUWALIA, Harwinder S. 1630 MOUNT HOPE AVE 17901 #495-37-1975 L1983 **PUD IM** *020
AKBAR, Mohammad Masood. 26 S CENTRE ST 17901 #704-01-1973 L1976 **OTO** *020 †45 ‡
ALMIRON, Flaviano Abuan. 420 S JACKSON ST 17901 #748-08-1970 L1975 **GP** *100
ASLAM, Mohammad. 101 MILL CREEK AVE 17901 #704-04-1967 L1974 **N** *020 †75
BAJWA, Zarar Mansoor. 1851 W END AVE 17901 #704-16-1990 L1998 **PD** *020 †55
BANE, Denis Melvin. 106 S CLAUDE A LORD BLVD 17901 #041-13-1969 L1970 **CD IM** *020 †20
BARNETT, Charles Fred. 420 S JACKSON ST 17901 #308-07-1982 L1986 **GP FM** *075
BEAUSANG, Thomas Robt. 529 TERRY REILEY WAY 17901 #007-02-1976 L1978 **PD** *020 †55
BEDWAY, Joseph John, Jr. ■ 17901 #041-02-2008 †012
BEMILLER, Carl Richard. ■ 17901 #041-02-1958 L1959 **CD IM** *020 †20
BINDIE, Richard Peter. 420 S JACKSON ST, POTTSVILLE HOSPITAL 17901 #041-13-1966 L1967
   PTH *050
BIZUP, Thomas Jos. 700 E NORWEGIAN ST #016-43-1955 L1956 **GP EM** *071
BLUM, Haywood. 700 E NORWEGIAN ST, GOOD SAMARITAN REG MED CTR 17901
   #041-09-1981 L1982 **EM** *020
BORAN, Robert Paul, Jr. 700 E NORWEGIAN ST, GOOD SAMARITAN REG M C 17901
   #041-02-1978 L1979 **ORS OAR** *020 †40
BORAN, Thomas V, Sr. 100 SCHUYLKILL MEDICAL PLZ, # 205 17901 #041-01-1982 L1983
   OTO FPS *020 †45
BOYSEN, Homer Wilson. 420 S JACKSON ST 17901 #041-02-1946 L1947 **GP** *071
BRACONARO, Francis John. 420 S JACKSON ST, POTTSVILLE HOSPITAL 17901
   #041-02-1972 L1973 **EM IM** *020 †20
CALIENDO, Mark Vincent. 420 S JACKSON ST 17901 #041-09-1993 L2001 **VIR** *020 †80
CHANDRA, Abhinav Binod. 700 E NORWEGIAN ST 17901 #496-55-2001 L2007 **HOS** *020 †20
CHAUDHRY, Rajnish Pratap. 1 NORWEGIAN PLZ, STE 205 17901 #495-03-1973 L1995
   N *020 †75
CHAWLUK, John Bohdan. 48 TUNNEL RD STE 101, EVERGREEN PROFESSIONAL STS 17901
   #023-07-1979 L1981 **N DR** *020 †75
CHOUDHRY, Babar Murtaza. 700 E NORWEGIAN ST 17901 #704-02-1987 L1998 **PYG** *020
COCHRAN, William John. 700 SCHUYLKILL MANOR RD, STE 3 17901 #041-14-1979 L1987
   PG PD *055
CONRAD, Joe Elvin. 601 E NORWEGIAN ST #041-13-1944 L1945 **DR NM** *072 †80
CROLEY, James Talbot. 529 TERRY REILEY WAY 17901 #047-06-1943 L1944 **FM PD** *020
CUPINO, Elmer. 450 WASHINGTON ST 17901 #649-38-1984 L1992 **CHP P** *020 †75
DANKMYER, Frederick L. 419 W MARKET ST 17901 #041-02-1963 L1964 **OPH** *071 †35
D'ARCO, Daniel John. 111 S CENTRE ST, PENN MUSCLE & BONE 17901 #035-03-1990 L1992
   ORS *020 †40 ‡
DASTAGIR, Muhammad Tariq. 420 S JACKSON ST, WARNE CLINIC 17901 #704-02-2000 L2005
   IM *020 †20
DAWSON, Michael H O. 739 E NORWEGIAN ST 17901 #917-25-1969 L1984 **ORS** *020 †40
DI NICOLA, Arturo N. 420 S JACKSON ST, POTTSVILLE HOSP & WARNE CL 17901
   #041-02-1989 L1993 **AN** *020 †05
DOHERTY, Thomas Wayne. 205 E LAUREL BLVD 17901 #041-14-1997 L2001 **IM** *020 †20
DUBOWITZ, Leslie. ■ 17901 #836-02-1969 L1978 **EM FM** *020 †18
ELBERFELD, Gregory John. 420 S JACKSON ST 17901 #041-09-1987 L1988
   DR NM *020,80,28
FAROOQ, Mohammad T. 1666 MOUNT HOPE AVE 17901 #704-01-1982 L1995 **PM** *020 †60
FONASH, Theresa Marie. 420 S JACKSON ST 17901 #041-07-1987 L1989 **IM EM** *020 †20
FRABLE, Dean Geo. 700 E NORWEGIAN ST 17901 #047-06-1970 L1973 **IM** *071 †20
FREED, Clarence Landis. 1 NORWEGIAN PLZ 17901 #041-13-1972 L1974 **PS DS** *020 ‡
FREELAND, Cynthia Ann. 700 E NORWEGIAN ST 17901 #041-14-1993 L1995 **IM** *020 †20
GARG, Ajay Paul. 420 S JACKSON ST 17901 #308-12-1989 L1993 **IM EM** *020
GIANFAGNA, William Jos. 225 DEERFIELD DR 17901 #051-01-1980 L1982 **PD** *020 †55
GIOMARISO, Joseph Hall. 420 S JACKSON ST, EMERGENCY DEPARTMENT 17901
   #010-02-1984 L1985 **EM IM** *020 †20
GOMBOLA, Jonathan. ■ 17901 #041-15-2007 L2007 **IM** *012
GRAVES, Lynda C. 1851 W END AVE 17901 #024-16-1978 L1979 **FM FPG** *020 †18 ‡
GRECO, Robert Michael. 48 TUNNEL RD, STE 204 17901 #041-02-1985 L1986 **IM CD** *020 †20
GREEN, Charles Edward. 48 TUNNEL RD, STE 104 17901 #023-01-1977 L1980 **GE IM** *020 †20
GRUBE, Timothy G. 171 RED HORSE RD, STE 1 17901 #041-77-1995, ▲ L1997 *020
GRYNYSHIN, Ivan M. 420 S JACKSON ST, THE POTTSVILLE HOSPITAL 17901
   #913-42-1992 L2004 **AN** *020 †05
GUASTAVINO, Thomas David. 420 S JACKSON ST 17901 #033-05-1982 L1988 **ORS** *020 †40 ‡
HALE, Thomas King. 420 S JACKSON ST 17901 #041-09-1943 L1944 **GP** *071
HAWLEY, Richard Chas. 315 W MARKET ST 17901 #035-15-1972 L1984 **GE IM** *020 †20
HEFFNER, George William. 206 SCHUYLKILL AVE, BLDG 100 17901 #041-02-1984 L1987
   IM CD *020 †20
HEISTAND, Landis Claude. 700 SCHUYLKILL MANOR RD, ORTHOPEDIC ASSOCS 17901
   #041-13-1964 L1968 **ORS** *071 †40
HUSSAIN, Aijaz. 420 S JACKSON ST 17901 #495-74-1995 L2005 **IM IMG** *020
JENKINS, Barry Lynn. 420 S JACKSON ST, CLINICATTN MED STAFF OFFIC 17901
   #024-01-1984 L1986 **AN** *020 †05
KASPER, David Andrew. ■ 17901 #041-77-2007, ▲ L2007 *012
KAULBACK, Kyle Rice. 420 S JACKSON ST, POTTSVILLE HOSPITAL 17901 #041-02-1988 L1990
   IM *020 †20

KHAN, Sultan Feroze. 26 S CENTRE ST 17901 #704-01-1969 L1981 **OTO ORS** *020 †45 ‡
KHOLOUSSY, A Mohsen. ■ 17901 #915-02-1969 L1977 **GS** *071 †85 ‡
KIM, Choong Whan. ■ 17901 #583-10-1974 L1979 **OBG** *020 †30
KIMMEL, Robert Monroe. 575 E NORWEGIAN ST 17901 #041-13-1987 L1993
   PS HS *020 †65,85
KO, Chan Sung. 212 MAHANTONGO ST 17901 #583-01-1947 L1970 **GP** *071
KREWSON, David Paul. 171 RED HORSE RD, STE 1 17901 #041-77-1991, ▲ L1992
   OBG *020 †20
KRUSZEWSKI, Stefan P. 450 WASHINGTON ST 17901 #024-01-1977 L1984 **P ADP** *030 †75 ‡
KUMAR, Ashok. 420 S JACKSON ST, 420 S JACKSON STREET 17901 #495-29-1978 L2002
   AN *020
KUMAR, Ashok J. 420 S JACKSON ST 5, POTTSVILLE HOSP 17901 #495-31-1975 **IM** *100 †05
KUMAR, Madhurima. 700 E NORWEGIAN ST 17901 #496-04-1976 L1978 **EM** *020 †16 ‡
LATIF, Naeem. 700 E NORWEGIAN ST 17901 #704-24-1993 L2004 **IM** *020
LAYCHOCK, Anna Marie. 420 S JACKSON ST 17901 #041-07-1984 L1985 **DR** *020 †80
LEE, Jang Woo. 101 W MARKET ST, THOMPSON BLDG STE 311 17901 #583-04-1964 L1972
   OBG *020 †30
LEIB, Pamela Louise. 118 MAHANTONGO ST 17901 #041-02-1981 L1983 **P** *020 †75
LEVIN, Joshua Marc. 700 SCHUYLKILL MANOR RD, STE 5 17901 #041-13-2003 L2003
   D *020 †15
LIN, Ching-Ho. 420 S JACKSON ST 17901 #385-02-1965 L1972 **OBG** *020 †30
LIN, Hsiung-Tso. ■ 17901 #385-01-1967 L1975 **IM** *020
LOK, Mai-Pai. 59 BRYN MAWR AVE 17901 #243-43-1959 L1977 **AN** *071
MALANTIC, Ann Valerie. 106 S CLAUDE A LORD BLVD 17901 #033-05-1994 L2000 **PM** *020 †60
MALIK, Maqsood Ahmad. 106 S LORD BLVD 17901 #704-01-1966 L1978 **CD IM** *020 †20
MALIK, Sajjad Masood. ■ 17901 #041-15-2006 L2006 **IM** *100
MARINO, Glen Anthony. 420 S JACKSON ST, WARNE CLINIC DEPT REHAB 17901
   #055-07-1987 L1992 **PM** *020 †60
MARSHALL, David Saml. 205 E LAUREL BLVD 17901 #041-13-1942 L1943 **IM CD** *071
MC LAUGHLIN, Thomas Wm. 700 E NORWEGIAN ST, GOOD SAMARITAN REG MED CTR 17901
   #041-02-1977 L1978 **IM OS** *030
MEERAN, M Mohamed. 420 S JACKSON ST 17901 #495-42-1972 L1983 **VS GS** *020 †85
MODY, Nitesh Satish. ■ 17901 #041-77-2007, ▲ *012
MODY, Smita S. ■ 17901 #495-17-1970 L1973 **AN** *020
MUNIR, Muhammad. 106 S CLAUDE A LORD BLVD, MEDICAL ARTS BLDG 17901
   #704-04-1964 L1972 **IM** *020 †20
MUNNELLY, Kevin Peter, Jr. 1544 ROUTE 61 HWY S, STE 6192 17901 #035-08-1991 L1995
   AN *020 †05
NARULA, Amrit Pal. 106 S CLAUDE A LORD BLVD 17901 #495-78-1978 L1986 **GE IM** *020 †20
NIDDODI, Prakash Nayak. 420 S JACKSON ST, CLINIC 17901 #495-65-1991 L2001 **AN** *020 †05
NOLL, Kathleen Rose. 700 E NORWEGIAN ST, GOOD SAMARITAN HOSP 17901
   #041-01-1982 L1984 **AN** *020 †20
O'CONNOR, Robert Donald. 700 E NORWEGIAN ST 17901 #035-08-1948 L1977
   OS CD *071 †20
PETERS, Robt Harrison, III. 48 TUNNEL RD 17901 #041-02-1978 L1979
   GE IM *020 †20
PIERDON, Steven Bradley. 1400 MAHANTONGO 17901 #025-07-1979 L1983 **PD** *062 †55
POLLOCK, Whitney E. 700 SCHUYLKILL MANOR RD 17901 #041-77-1999, ▲ L1999 **OBG** *020
PUJARA, Devi Mahendra. 1630 MOUNT HOPE AVE, DEVI. M. PUJARA 17901
   #495-48-1971 L1980 **AN** *020 †05
PUJARA, Mahendrakumar M. 1630 MOUNT HOPE AVE 17901 #495-22-1970 L1978
   PHP *020 †95
PURCELL, Stephen M. 700 SCHUYLKILL MANOR RD, STE 5 17901 #016-76-1980, ▲ L1988
   D *020 †15
PUZZI, Joseph Vincent. 100 SCHUYLKILL MEDICAL PLZ, THROAT ASSOC P.C./STE 205 17901
   #035-47-1994 L1997 **OTO GS** *020 †45
RAHIMI, Mohammad Ismail. ■ 17901 #118-01-1972 **IM** *100
RAO, Yashoda. 106 S CLAUDE A LORD BLVD 17901 #495-33-1979 L1989 **IM NEP** *020 †20
RASHID, Abdul. 693 PORT CARBN SNT CLR HWY 17901 #704-04-1963 L1973 **IM PUD** *020 †20
REIMER, Craig Lee. 407 W MARKET ST 17901 #422-01-1982 L1983 **IM** *020 †20
RUSSO, John Frederick. 700 E NORWEGIAN ST, GOOD SAMAR REG MED CTR 17901
   #033-05-1961 L1971 **PTH HMP** *020 †50
SAIFULLAH, Muhammad Faisa. 420 S JACKSON ST 17901 #704-02-1999 L2003 **IM** *020 †20
SCHAEFFER, Carol Miller. 206 SCHUYLKILL AVE, BLDG 100 17901 #041-09-1988 L1990
   IM *020 †20
SHAH, Syed G M. 106 S CLAUDE A LORD BLVD 17901 #704-01-1972 L1979 **IM NEP** *020 †20 ‡
SHAKIL, Mohammad Sualeh. 100 SCHUYLKILL MEDICAL PLZ, # 106 17901 #704-02-1979 L1996
   ORS OSS *020
SINGH, Rajendra. 1630 MOUNT HOPE AVE 17901 #495-20-1976 L1984 **AI ID** *020 †55,03
SINGLA, Satish Chander. 700 SCHUYLKILL MANOR RD, STE 7 17901 #495-21-1976 L1982
   HO IM *020 †20
SLIMMER, Samuel Chas, Jr. 420 S JACKSON ST, POTTSVILLE HOSPITAL 17901
   #041-13-1965 L1966 **EM OM** *071 †16
SLUSSER, Stephen O. 48 TUNNEL RD, STE 104 17901 #041-14-1989 L1992 **GE** *020 †20
SRINIVASAN, Raji. 700 E NORWEGIAN ST, VA CLINIC, GSRMC 17901
   #496-28-1996 L2002 *020 †15
SWAIN, Stephen Scott. 100 SCHUYLKILL MEDICAL PLZ, STE 202 17901 #041-13-1982 L1984
   IM *020 †20
TANANIS, Leonard John. ■ 17901 #041-02-1954 L1955 **OPH OS** *071 †35
UZOUKWU, Uchenna Cosmas. 450 WASHINGTON ST 17901 #690-02-1989 L1996 **P** *020
VESUWALA, Nimeshkumar Dil. 48 TUNNEL RD, STE 203 17901 #495-89-1999 L2004 **IM** *020
VISOT-FERNANDEZ, Luis R. 300 SCHUYLKILL MEDICAL PLZ, SCHUYLKILL
   REHABILITATION 17901 #649-01-1956 L1986 **PM OS** *020 †60
WAHHAB, Abdul. 420 S JACKSON ST 17901 #704-04-1964 L1973 **GS** *020 †85
WALDMAN, Richard Evan. 700 E NORWEGIAN ST 17901 #041-12-1990 L2004 *020
WALL, Norman M. 200 E ARCH ST, AMERICAN REHAB CENTER 17901 #041-01-1939 L1940
   IM CD *072 †20
WATT, John Martin. ■ 17901 #041-02-2008 *012
WEIZER, Ilene Katz. 541 W BACON ST, A WOMAN'S CHOICE 17901 #041-09-1990 L1992
   OBG *020 †30
WHEELER, Thomas Brooks. 100 SCHUYLKILL MEDICAL PLZ, STE 201 17901
   #041-07-1987 L1988 **ORS HS** *020 †40
WONG, Henry Chen. 700 E NORWEGIAN ST, DEPT OF ANES 17901 #051-04-1987 L1991
XENOPHON, James C. 541 W BACON ST 17901 #041-02-1984 L2005 **OBG** *020 †30
YANKOSKY, Jean Algefia. 420 S JACKSON ST 17901 #041-07-1956 L1957 **GP PD** *075

■ = Address Information Privacy Protected

ZAFAR, Ghaffar Ahmad. 100 SCHUYLKILL MEDICAL PLZ 17901 #704-01-1968 L1974 **PD** *020 †55

ZHAO, Jing Cheng. 201 E LAUREL BLVD 17901 #243-47-1984 L2001 **IM** *020 †35

ZIMMERMAN, Robert M, Jr. 171 RED HORSE RD, STE 1 17901 #041-77-1988, ▲ L1989 **OBG** *020 †30

PRESTO – ALLEGHENY

BANSAL, Surendra Kumar. 9011 SHERWOOD CT 15142 #495-29-1961 L1971 **DR** *020 †80

DATTU, Mohamed Raza. ■ 15142 #422-01-1998 L2000 **P** *020 †75

PELLETIER, Catherine E. ■ 15142 #041-15-2002 L2002 **EM** *020 †16

PHANSE, Kalyani M. 250 CHERRY HILL DR 15142 #495-01-1965 L1973 **OBG** *062 †30

RUBENSTEIN, Leonard S. 101 CAMBRIDGE DR 15142 #041-12-1960 L1961 **FM IM** *020 †18

YARUSSI, Frank Anthony. 1090 SAINT MELLION DR 15142 #041-12-1963 L1964 **R** *020

PROSPECT – BUTLER

FLETCHER, Gordon Thos. ■ 16052 #060-01-1958 L1959 **OPH GS** *020

PROSPECT PARK – DELAWARE

PATEL, Mukesh Ambalal. 1421 LINCOLN AVE 19076 #435-23-1977 L1980 **IM GP** *020 †20

STEWART, Michael John. 1401 LINCOLN AVE 19076 #561-25-1982 L1983 **IM** *020 †20

PUNXSUTAWNEY – JEFFERSON

ARNOUK, Nabil. 1464 N MAIN ST STE 14 15767 #875-02-1983 L1988 **OBG** *020 †30

BIZOUSKY, Franklin S. 1000 WOODLAND AVE 15767 #041-09-1956 L1957 **EM** *071 †16

CHAMBERS, Martin Lee. 200 E MAHONING ST, STE 1 15767 #041-14-1988 L1990 **IM** *020 †20

CHERIAN, R George. 803 W MAHONING ST 15767 #495-37-1970 L1977 **OBG** *020 †30

COSTA, Jose M Lins. 81 HILLCREST DR 15767 #187-11-1968 L1978 **PTH** *020 †50

DAJANI, Zuhdi Mohamed. 720 W MAHONING ST, STE 300 15767 #528-01-1981 L1991 **CD IM** *020

DICKSON, James Robt. 81 HILLCREST DR, PUNXSUTAWNEY HOSP 15767 #041-12-1985 L1986 **EM** *020 †16

DINGCONG, Luisito. 81 HILLCREST DR, PUNXSUTAWNEY HOSPITAL 15767 #748-12-1981 L1994 **P** *020

ELDER, Jay Edward. 83 HILLCREST DR, PUNXSUTAWNEY MED ASSOCS 15767 #041-09-1983 L1986 **IM IMG** *020 †20

FIGALLO, Eduardo Miguel. MEDICAL ARTS BUILDING 15767 #737-01-1955 L1974 **AN** *071 †05

FUGATE, Douglas Scott. 720 W MAHONING ST, STE 200 15767 #041-09-1984 L1985 **ORS** *020 †40

FUGATE, Kenneth Kethledge. 525 N MAIN ST 15767 #654-01-1982 L1984 **IM** *040 ‡

GRIEBEL, Stephen. 81 HILLCREST DR, STE 2500 15767 #041-09-1995 L1999 **OPH** *020 †35

KAUFMAN, Theodor Irving. 83 HILLCREST DR, STE 104 15767 #035-08-1993 L2001 **GS** *020 †85

KERNICH, Joseph John. 83 HILLCREST DR, PUNXSUTAWNEY MED ASSOCS 15767 #041-13-1982 L1986 **EM FM** *020 ‡

KHALAF, Mohammad Kamal A. 81 HILLCREST DR, PUNX SUTAWNEY AREA HOSPITA 15767 #875-01-1975 L1981 **DR** *020 †80

KHAN, Kanwal Shehzadi. 81 HILLCREST DR, STE 2200 15767 #704-21-1995 L2004 **OBG** *020

LAMBIOTTE, Charles O, Jr. 81 HILLCREST DR, PUNXSUTAWNEY AREA HOSPITAL 15767 #045-01-1993 L1995 **FM** *072 †18

LAMBIOTTE, Patricia P. 200 E MAHONING ST 15767 #028-03-1992 L1994 **FM** *020 †18

LEWIS, John Ralph. 1464 N MAIN ST, STE 9 15767 #064-01-1979 L1999 **OTO** *020 †45

LINGENFELTER, Kyle Andrew. 83 HILLCREST DR, STE 2600 15767 #041-12-1989 L1991 **GS** *020 †85

OSUNDEKO, Olusola A. 83 HILLCREST DR STE 106, ENDOCRINE CLINIC 15767 #690-06-1985 L1999 **IM END** *020 †20

PRADHAN, Gunjan S. 81 HILLCREST DR, DRMG PEDIATRICS 15767 #496-38-1998 L2001 **PD** *020 †55

SALDANA, Idel. 81 HILLCREST DR 15767 #748-01-1955 L1965 **GP** *075

SANTOS, Gaspar Alcaraz. 81 HILLCREST DR 15767 #748-01-1955 L1968 **PD GP** *071 †55

SHETTY, Jagadeesha. 720 W MAHONING ST, STE 200 15767 #495-72-1987 L1998 **PM PMM** *020 †60

SILVA, Jose Americo S, Jr. 81 HILLCREST DR 15767 #187-01-1995 L2000 **HO** *020 †20

STATES, Phillip John. 1464 N MAIN ST STE 5 15767 #041-13-2001 L2003 **FM EM** *020 †18

QUAKERTOWN – BUCKS

ADIBI, Fereydoon. 750 S WEST END BLVD 18951 #517-01-1967 L1981 **OBG** *020 †30 ‡

ALBRECHT, James Bernard. 256 TRUMBAUERSVILLE RD 18951 #041-13-1973 **FM FPG** *020 †18

BALSHI, James Donald. 1021 PARK AVE, STE 203 18951 #041-02-1980 L1981 **VS GS** *020 †85 ‡

BAXTER, Ric Alan. 200 APPLE ST STE 2 18951 #041-07-1978 L1982 **FM** *020 †18

BENJAMIN, Robert. 1021 PARK AVE, STE 10 18951 #041-13-1973 L1974 **P ADP** *020 †75 ‡

BERCES, Csaba Gyorgy. 1021 PARK AVE, STE 101 18951 #473-01-1997 L2001 **IM** *020 †20

BERMAN, Steven Howard. 1021 PARK AVE, STE 203 18951 #024-07-1984 L1985 **GS** *020 †85

BONEKEMPER, Thomas Wayne. ■ 18951 #041-09-1969 L1970 **IM** *071 †20

BURKE, Gerrianne. 1021 PARK AVE 18951 #041-13-1994 L1996 **IM** *020 †20

BUTTRAM, Harold Eugene. ■ 18951 #039-01-1958 L1969 **GP** *020

CAMPBELL, Chas Eugene M. 127 S 5TH ST, THE ATRIUM STE 200 18951 #041-01-1972 L1974 **OPH** *020 †35

CEVALLOS, Eduardo. 541 S WEST END BLVD 18951 #737-01-1969 L1975 **PD N** *020 †55

CHAI, Chiu Ling. ■ 18951 #041-09-1957 L1958 **FM** *071 †18

EICHER, Wendell Paul. 750 S WEST END BLVD 18951 #017-20-1969 L1970 **GS** *020

FILIPOWICZ, Thomas Alan. 1021 PARK AVE, ST LUKES QUAKERTOWN HOSP 18951 #010-02-1979 L1983 **EM OM** *020 †16

GRANSON, Marc Allen. 1021 PARK AVE, STE 203 18951 #041-13-1977 L1982 **VS** *020 †85 ‡

HAMILTON, Elizabeth. 750 S WEST END BLVD, GRANDVIEW MEDICAL PRACTICE 18951 #030-06-1996 L1999 **OBG** *020 †30

HANES, David Paul. 91 LAUREL CT 18951 #041-13-1999 L2000 **IM** *020

HELMOLD, Karl Wm. 28 S 14TH ST 18951 #033-05-1988 L1994 **ORS** *020 †40

HO, Vu Uy. ■ 18951 #041-13-2006 L2006 **IM** *012

JENKINS, Russell Hayden. 24 S 14TH ST 18951 #041-13-1971 L1972 **IM** *020 †20

KELLEY, Denise Christine. ■ 18951 #041-09-1997 L2001 **FM** *020

KENEPP, Darwin Lee. 1021 PARK AVE 18951 #041-09-1974 L1975 **EM OM** *020

KIM, Yung Sup. 1021 PARK AVE 18951 #583-02-1952 L1962 **IM CD** *071

LEWIS, Daniel A. 1021 PARK AVE 18951 #041-77-2000, ▲ L2001 **AN** *020 †05

LINN, Sheldon Hal. 200 APPLE ST, STE 5 18951 #041-09-1985 L1986 **OBG** *020 †30

MARION, Paul Milton. 200 APPLE ST STE 2 18951 #041-09-1981 L1982 **FM OM** *020 †18

MOISE, Adriana Gabriela. 541 S WEST END BLVD 18951 #041-09-1992 L1999 **VS** *020 †85 ‡

OSKIN, Timothy Clyde. 1021 PARK AVE, STE 203 18951 #041-09-1992 L1999 **VS** *020 †85 ‡

PERELSON, Allen Mark. 1021 PARK AVE 18951 #035-08-1976 L1984 **FM GS** *020

PEREZ, Ana Maria. 1021 PARK AVE, ST LUKES QUAKERTOWN HOSP 18951 #035-46-1979 L1986 **EM** *020 †16

PEREZ-GUARDIOLA, Lydia. 2100 QUAKER POINTE DR, STE 102 18951 #056-06-1950 L1953 **OPH** *020

POWELL, John Preston. ■ 18951 #041-01-1985 L1986 **P** *020 †75

RAMANATHAN, Deborah. 241 JUNIPER ST 18951 #495-04-1969 L1983 **FM EM** *020 ‡

REINOLD, Kevin Grant. 256 TRUMBAUERSVILLE RD 18951 #033-06-1992 L1997 **FM** *020 †18

ROBERTS, Robert J. 401 W BROAD ST 18951 #065-05-1977 L1980 **FM** *020

ROSENFELD, Joel Chas. 1021 PARK AVE, STE 203 18951 #041-02-1974 L1975 **VS GS** *040 †85 ‡

SCHMIDT, Diane Norlaine. 1021 PARK AVE, STE 200 18951 #041-02-1993 L1998 **END** *020 †20

SCHWARTZ, Jon Howard. 1021 PARK AVE, QUAKERTOWN INTERNAL 18951 #041-09-1975 L1978 **IM** *020 †20

SHOEMAKER, David M. 256 TRUMBAUERSVILLE RD 18951 #041-02-1951 L1952 **GP** *071 †18

SMITH, Stephen Heilman. 28 S 14TH ST 18951 #041-02-1972 L1977 **ORS** *020 †40

SPRINGER, Jay Mark. 1021 PARK AVE, STE 200 18951 #041-13-1975 L1976 **END IM** *020 †20

STAUFFER, Daniel J. 1021 PARK AVE, STE 203 18951 #041-02-1982 L1983 **FM** *020 †18

STRZELECKI, Zigmund F. 1021 PARK AVE 18951 #041-13-1974 L1975 **ORS** *020 †40 ‡

TE, Tomas Tan. 361 S 11TH ST 18951 #748-01-1965 L1967 **OPH** *071 †35

TWARDZIK, David Edward. 1021 PARK AVE STE 30 18951 #041-02-1998 L2000 **D** *020 †15

VASTA, Alfred Gabriele. 750 S.W. END BOULEVARD 18951 #041-02-1974 L1975 **IM** *020

WEIBEL, Paul Wesley, Jr. 1021 PARK AVE, QUAKERTOWN INTERNAL 18951 #041-14-1980 L1981 **IM** *020 †20

WILLIHNGANZ, Walter Diehl. 401 W BROAD ST 18951 #041-13-1968 L1975 **GS EM** *020 †85

WILSON, Thomas Gregory. 200 APPLE ST, UPPER BUCKS FAM MED CTR 18951 #041-02-1983 L1984 **FM** *020 †18

YAZDANYAR, Ali. 1021 PARK AVE, STE 202 18951 #517-01-1965 L1985 **PD PDC** *020 †55

ZITARELLI, Joseph Anthony. 1021 PARK AVE 18951 #041-09-1983 L1984 **GS GP** *020 †85

QUARRYVILLE – LANCASTER

NAFZIGER, John Kenneth. 331 STONY HILL RD 17566 #051-01-1979 L1982 **FM** *020 †18

RIPCHINSKI, Michael R. 317 W CHESTNUT ST, WALTER L AUMENT FAMILY HLT 17566 #041-14-2003 L2003 **FM** *020 †18

STEWART, Ashton Tatnall. 625 ROBERT FULTON HWY 17566 #041-01-1944 L1951 **PM GP** *072

VOLLMAR, William Richard. 203 COMMERCE DR STE G, DIAMANTONI AND ASSOC 17566 #051-04-1989 L1991 **FM** *020 †18

RADNOR – DELAWARE

BANCOFF, Carl. ■ 19087 #035-20-1965 L1969 **CD** *062

BOXER, Arthur David. ■ 19087 #041-02-1961 L1962 **P PFP** *020 †75

BRUZA, John Michael. 250 KING OF PRUSSIA RD, PENN MEDICINE AT RADNOR 19087 #039-01-1991 L1997 **IM** *020 †20

BUI, Stephanie K. 250 KING OF PRUSSIA RD, STE 25 19087 #041-01-1999 L2003 **MPD ADL** *020 †20,55

DECKELBAUM, Lawrence I. 145 KING OF PRUSSIA RD R2, JOHNSON & JOHNSON 19087 #024-01-1979 L1988 **CD IM** *050 †20

DEMOPOULOS, Laura Ann. 250 KING OF PRUSSIA RD 19087 #035-19-1986 L1996 **CD** *020 †20

DHAWAN, Rajnee. 320 KING OF PRUSSIA RD, STE 120 19087 #496-09-1989 L1999 **IM** *020 †20

EPSTEIN, Jonathan Alan. ■ 19087 #024-01-1988 L1996 **CD** *020 †20

EPSTEIN, Paul Elliott. 250 KING OF PRUSSIA RD, PENN MEDICINE AT RADNOR 19087 #024-07-1966 L1969 **PUD IM** *020 †20

FISHMAN, Neil Owen. 250 KING OF PRUSSIA RD, PENN MEDICINE AT RADNOR 19087 #041-13-1983 L1984 **IM** *020 †20

FLEISCHMAN, Carol Rose. 250 KING OF PRUSSIA RD, MODULE G PENN MEDICINE AT 19087 #041-09-1986 L1987 **IM** *020 †20

FOSNOCHT, Kevin Michael. 250 KING OF PRUSSIA RD, PENN MEDICINE AT RADNOR 19087 #041-14-1993 L1996 **IM** *020 †20

GOODMAN, Lowell I. ■ 19087 #008-01-1951 L1986 **P PA** *071 †75

GRIPPI, Michael Anthony. 250 KING OF PRUSSIA RD, PENN MEDICINE AT RADNOR 19087 #041-01-1976 L1977 **PUD CCM** *020 †20

HALPERN, Casey Harrison. ■ 19087 #041-01-2007 L2007 **GS** *012

HENRY, David Holden. 250 KING OF PRUSSIA RD, STE 1B 19087 #041-01-1975 L1976 **ON HEM** *020 †20

HERMAN, Barry Keith. ■ 19087 #024-07-1980 L2003 **CHP MDM** *030 †75 ‡

HERMAN, Ellen N. ■ 19087 #048-14-1978 L2003 **CHP P** *020 †20

HOWARTH, Marilyn Veronica. 250 KING OF PRUSSIA RD, WORKWELL PENN MEDICINE RAD 19087 #033-05-1986 L1989 **OM IM** *020 †20

HUMPHREY, David M. 555 E LANCASTER AVE 3 19087 #020-02-1969 L1991 **AN** *030 †05

HUNTLEY, Arthur Carson. ■ 19087 #041-02-1955 L1960 **P MDM** *071 †75

JEFFERY, Maren Elizabeth. 250 KING OF PRUSSIA RD, PENN MEDICINE AT RADNOR 19087 #041-01-2000 L2001 **CD** *020 †20

KIST, Joseph Michael. 250 KING OF PRUSSIA RD, DEPARTMENT OF DERMATOLOGY 19087 #033-05-1999 L2003 **D** *020 †15

KOSSEIM, Laura Marie. 250 KING OF PRUSSIA RD, PENN MEDICINE AT RADNOR 19087 #035-01-1994 L1996 **IM** *020 †20

KUBO, Janice Kay. 250 KING OF PRUSSIA RD, STE 2C 19087 #035-20-1982 L1985 **IM** *020 †20

LALLY, Kate Marie. 320 KING OF PRUSSIA RD, STE 120 19087 #008-01-2002 L2002 **IM** *020 †20

LAVERAN-STIEBAR, Rudolf F. ■ 19087 #154-07-1952 L1962 **P** *071

LEVIN, Gene David. 250 KING OF PRUSSIA RD, RD STE 2F 19087 #041-02-1967 L1968 **ORS** *020 †40

LINDNER, Marie Alice. ■ 19087 #016-42-1978 L1988 **NTR CD** *050 †20

MASSARO-GIORDANO, Mina. 1230 GULPH CREEK DR 19087 #041-13-1994 L1997 **OPH** *020 †35 ‡

MCALLISTER, Ronald Eric. 170 N RADNOR CHESTER RD, STE 300 19087 #064-01-1976 L1977 **GP PHM** *050

MC CLOSKEY, Richard V. 145 KING OF PRUSSIA RD, R 2 19087 #035-45-1960 L1965 **ID IM** *050 †20

OLER, Allison. 250 KING OF PRUSSIA RD, PENN HEALTH FOR WOMEN 19087 #016-02-1994 L1997 **IM** *020 †20

OLEX, Andrew James. 320 KING OF PRUSSIA RD, STE 120 19087 #041-09-1976 L1977 **IM** *020 †20

OSTERHOLM, Jewell L. ■ 19087 #028-02-1957 L1963 **NS** *071 †25

PACROPIS, Richard Frank. 320 KING OF PRUSSIA RD, STE 120 19087 #041-02-1982 L1983 **IM** *020

PIASECKI, Barbara A. 250 KING OF PRUSSIA RD, STE 1B 19087 #023-01-1997 L2001 **GE** *020 †20

PITTELLI, Joseph Jerome. 145 KING OF PRUSSIA RD 19087 #041-02-1962 L1972 **PD** *030 †55

POPIK, Sharon Roberta. 19087 #041-14-1994 L1997 **IM** *020

REES, Victoria Anne. 1 RADNOR CORPORATE CTR, COVANCE 19087 #041-07-1991 L1997 **IM PHM** *050 †20

ROSEN, Lisa Stein. 250 KING OF PRUSSIA RD 19087 #038-40-1984 L1986 **OBG** *020 †30

ROSEN, Mark Alan. 250 KING OF PRUSSIA RD, PENN MEDICINE AT RADNOR 19087 #035-01-1994 L2000 **DR** *020 †80

ROTH, Rudolf Richard. 250 KING OF PRUSSIA RD 19087 #023-12-1981 L2001 **D FM** *020 †15

SERLETTI, Bonnie Lou. 250 KING OF PRUSSIA RD 19087 #035-45-1990 L2005 **OBG** *020 †30

SILVESTRY, Frank Eric. 250 KING OF PRUSSIA RD, PENN CARDIAC CARE 19087 #041-01-1990 L1993 **CD IM** *020 †20

SLATTERY, Sara Ann. 250 KING OF PRUSSIA RD, PENN MEDICINE AT RADNOR MO 19087 #041-01-1997 L2000 **IM** *020 †20

SMULLENS, Stanton Noel. 259 N RADNOR CHESTER RD, STE 290 19087 #041-02-1961 L1962 **VS TS** *072 †85,90

SOSTEK, Mark Bertram. 250 KING OF PRUSSIA RD, PENN MEDICINE AT RADNOR 19087 #024-07-1986 L1998 **GE IM** *050 †20

SPARKMAN, Thorne, Jr. 250 KING OF PRUSSIA RD, PENN MED AT RADNOR 19087 #041-13-1965 L1969 **IM** *020

STADDON, Arthur Petrie. 250 KING OF PRUSSIA RD, STE 1B 19087 #041-01-1972 L1973 **ON HEM** *020 †20

STEELE, George Horace, Jr. 250 KING OF PRUSSIA RD, PENN MEDICINE 19087 #036-01-1981 L1992 **IM** *020 †20

SWITZKY, Martin Baker. ■ 19087 #041-14-1995 L1997 **P** *020 †75

THOMAS, Preethi Pramod. 250 KING OF PRUSSIA RD, STE E 19087 #495-31-1994 L1999 **RHU** *020 †20

THOMPSON, Sarah Gustafson. 250 KING OF PRUSSIA RD, PENN MEDICINE AT RADNOR 19087 #035-20-1997 L1999 **IM** *020 †20

TOBEY, Raymond Eugene. ■ 19087 #024-07-1958 L1982 **AI** *072 †05

TROTT, Edward Ashley. 250 KING OF PRUSSIA RD 19087 #041-02-1990 L1996 **OBG REN** *020

WHEELER, Bernadette C. 250 KING OF PRUSSIA RD 19087 #005-02-1986 L2001 **OBG** *020 †30

WHITAKER, Timothy Malone. 145 KING OF PRUSSIA RD, WYETH-AYERST RESEARCH 19087 #036-05-1984 L1997 **P** *020 †75

WILLENBUCHER, Robert F. ■ 19087 #035-01-1985 L1986 **GE IM** *020 †20

WILLIAMS, John Pasquale. ■ 19087 #041-01-2000 L2004 **CHP** *012

RANSHAW – NORTHUMBERLAND

WARDEH, Ahmad. 7 ANTHRA PLAZA CTR, SR 61 17866 #875-01-1992 L1998 **PCC** *020 †20

READING – BERKS

ABADIER, Nagi H. 145 N 6TH ST, FL 2 19601 #915-04-1972 L1995 **OBG** *020 †30 ‡

ABTAHI, Parvaneh. 301 S 7TH AVE, STE 355 19611 #041-13-1995 L1998 **NEP** *012

ABUBAKAR, Rezner Hernande. PO BOX 16052, READING HOSPITAL & MEDICAL 19612 #748-08-1994 L2007 **FP** *012

ACHARYA, Bikash. PO BOX 16052, READING HOSPITAL & MEDICAL 19612 #495-13-1971 L2007 *020

ACHARYA, Bikash. PO BOX 16052, 6TH-SPRUCE STS 19612 #672-04-2005 **IM** *012

ADAM, Suzanne E. 3909 PERKIOMEN AVE 19606 #041-77-2003, ▲ L2003 **FM** *020 †18

ADAMEC, Thomas Alan. ■ 19605 #016-02-1976 L2002 **PTH** *020 †50

ADELEYE, Adetoun Oluyemis. ■ 19605 #690-05-1998 L2005 **IM** *012

ADIGUN, Adegboyega Quadri. ■ 19606 #690-05-1990 L2003 **IM** *100

AGOURIDIS, Nicholas T. 200 N 13TH ST, STE 308 19604 #418-01-1954 L1967 **OBG** *071

AHMED, Fatima Sughra. ■ 19610 #704-01-1946 L1982 **IM IMG** *020 †50

AHMED, Saifuddin. ■ 19610 #704-01-1946 L1966 **IM OS** *020 †20

AILAWADI, Maneesh. 301 S 7TH AVE, STE 315 19611 #016-42-1997 L2006 **TS** *100 †85

ALI, Mohammed. 2500 BERNVILLE RD, ST JOSEPH MED GROUP HOSPIT 19605 #495-65-1982 L2001 **IM HOS** *020 †20

ALLEN, David Wayne. 4 PARK PLZ 19087 #041-13-1983 **NS** *020 †25

ALLEN, Jennifer E. 1623 MORGANTOWN RD 19607 #035-15-1998 L2001 **IM PLM** *020 †20

ALLEY, Samie Abbas. 1146 ELM ST 19604 #041-09-1963 L1968 **GS** *071 †85 ‡

ALTOMARE, John Frank. 301 S 7TH AVE, STE 215 19611 #041-13-1999 L2001 **GE** *020 †20,55

AMBARIAN, Anne Patricia. 838 PENN ST 19602 #041-13-1994 L1996 **FM** *040 †18

AMIN, Ali. 301 S 7TH AVE, STE 1070 19611 #033-06-1988 L1992 **VS GS** *020 †85

ARENA, Cristan Marie. PO BOX 16052, READING HOSPITAL & MEDICAL 19612 #023-01-2005 L2005 **OPH** *012

ARIAS LARACUENTE, Felipe. 501 WASHINGTON ST, STE 308 19601 #308-03-1988 L2000 **FM** *020 †18

ARMSTRONG, Allison A. PO BOX 16052, READING HOSPITAL & MEDICAL 19612 #048-13-2007 L2007 **IM** *012

ASCANIO, Guido, Jr. ■ 19606 #041-13-1981 L1982 **AN** *020 †20,05

AWAN, Zahid Farooq. 1733 PENN AVE 19609 #308-10-1987 L1996 **P** *020 †75

AYNARDI, Jay Marc. 301 S 7TH AVE, STE 210 19611 #041-12-1980 L1982 **IM IMG** *020 †20

BABITT, Wendy Lauren. 6 SPRUCE ST, STE 132 19611 #041-02-2001 L2001 **ID** *100

BABU, Vijay Gutti. PO BOX 16052, READING HOSPITAL & MEDICAL 19612 #041-14-2008 L2008 *012

BAMBERGER, P Kurt. 301 S 7TH AVE, STE 315 19611 #041-02-1990 L2000 **GS** *020 †85

BANEY, Philip John, IV. 3212 KUTZTOWN RD 19605 #041-13-1997 L1999 **FM** *020 †18

BATCHELDER, Barron. 6TH AND SPRUCE ST 19611 #005-14-1971 L1972 **AN** *020 †05

BAXTER, Donald Michael. 301 S 7TH ST, STE 2120 19602 #041-13-1980 L1981 **FM FPG** *040 †18

BAZARNIC, Margaret Louise. 601 SPRUCE ST, CENTER 19602 #041-07-1981 L1983 **DR** *020 †80

BEAUPARLANT, Heather M. 145 N 6TH ST 19601 #041-77-2007, ▲ L2007 **FPP** *012

BEETEL, Christopher John. 301 S 7TH AVE, STE 1120 19611 #041-02-1958 L1964 **TS VS** *071 †85,90

BERNE, Douglas Jacques. 301 S 7TH AVE 19611 #041-14-1989 L1991 **P** *020

BITETTO, Nicola. 2605 KAISER BLVD, BERKS CARDIOLOGISTS LTD 19610 #035-09-1964 L1972 **CD IM** *072

BLECKER, Daniel. 2230 RIDGEWOOD RD, STE 100 19610 #035-09-1993 L1995 **GE** *020 †20

BOEHMLER, William John. 1200 BROADCASTING RD # 200 19610 #041-01-1964 L1969 **P** *020 †75

BOLTON, Gregory C, Jr. 4885 DEMOSS RD, STE 101 19606 #041-13-1994 L1996 **OBG** *020 †30

BONACCORSI, Diane Therese. 1903 MORGANTOWN RD 19607 #016-43-1980 L1983 **FM** *020 †18

BONNER, James Jos. 1940 N 13TH ST, STE 207 19604 #041-13-1983 L1984 **OBG** *020 †30

BORGATTA, Louis. 2605 KAISER BLVD, BERKS CARDIOLOGISTS LTD 19610 #035-09-1986 L1987 **CD** *020 †20

BRACKBILL, Elizabeth Jean. ■ 19610 #041-02-1979 L1980 **GP** *020

BRACKBILL, Robert M. 3200 READING CREST AVE 19605 #041-02-1979 L1981 **IM IMG** *020 †20

BRANDT, Susana Zamora. 838 PENN ST, THE READING HEALTH DISP 19602 #737-09-1984 L2004 **FM** *020 †18

BROWN, Anitra Gabrielle. ■ 19605 #001-06-2006 L2006 **OBG** *012

BROWN, Patti Schaebler. 1623 MORGANTOWN RD 19604 #041-02-1986 L1987 **PM** *020 †60

BRZOZOWSKI, Lawrence A. 1940 N 13TH ST, STE 203 19604 #035-08-1973 L1978 **N** *020 †75

BUB, Ivan. 225 N KENHORST BLVD 19607 #836-02-1981 L1987 **FM ADM** *020 †18

BUCH, Sandhya Yadunandan. 145 N 6TH ST, FAMILY HEALTH 19601 #495-74-1969 L1979 **FM** *020 †18

BURNEY, Ghaus Us Samad. ■ 19603 #308-03-1988 **P** *020

BUZAS, Jerome Walter. 2650 WESTVIEW DR 19601 #041-13-1974 L1975 **D** *020 †15

BYBEL, Nicholas. 3701 STOUDTS FERRY BRDG RD, RIVERVIEW PARK 19605 #041-09-1961 L1962 **GP GS** *071

CAIRNS, Lucy Janet. 455 PENN AVE 19611 #023-07-1984 L1986 **OPH** *020 †35

CALATA, Eliseo R. 1623 MORGANTOWN RD 19607 #748-02-1970 L1976 **PM** *020 †60

CARIM, Hyder Mohamed. 2240 RIDGEWOOD RD, STE 100 19610 #495-21-1960 L1970 **PD PHO** *071

CARLSON, Arthur S. ■ 19606 #035-20-1952 L1986 **NM PTH** *072 †50,28

CARLSON, Stephen Edward. 606 COURT ST, STE 308 19601 #035-20-1976 L1981 **GE IM** *020 †20

CARTER, Frank Moulton. 301 S 7TH AVE, STE 100 19611 #041-13-1984 L1988 **CRS GS** *020 †85,10

CASEY, John D, Jr. 4885 DEMOSS RD, STE 102 19606 #041-13-1984 L1985 **ORS** *020 †40

CAVORSI, Joseph Peter. 2201 RIDGEWOOD RD STE 190 19610 #561-17-1977 L1982 **GS VS** *020 †85

CHAKRABARTI, Debanjana. PO BOX 16052, READING HOSPITAL & MEDICAL 19612 #495-12-1996 L2007 **FP** *012

CHASTKA, Edward Anthony. 999 BERKSHIRE BLVD STE 130 19610 #051-01-1988 L1992 **P** *020 †75

CHAUDHARY, Ashok. PO BOX 16052, 6TH-SPRUCE STS 19612 #672-02-2004 L2007 **IM** *012

CHELIUS, Alan B. 523 CARSONIA AVE, CARSONIA FAMILY PRACTICE 19606 #041-09-1981 L1982 **FM** *020 †18

CHMIELEWSKI, Steven R. 415 READING AVE 19611 #041-02-1991 L1996 **DR** *020 †80

CHOWDHURY, Abdur Rab. 8 N 11TH ST 19601 #704-11-1964 L1973 **GE IM** *020 †20

CHRIST, Peter Jos. 215 N 12TH ST, P O BOX 316 19604 #041-02-1979 L1981 **PTH OS** *020 †50

CHRISTIE, David James. SIXTH AVE SPENCER 19603 #041-13-1968 L1972 **EM** *020

CHWIECKO, Paul J. 623 N 5TH ST 19601 #011-02-1996 L1998 **FM** *020 †18

CIFELLI, Enrico Anthony. 2500 BERNVILLE RD 19605 #305-01-1999 L2001 **IM** *020 †20

CLARK, Jennifer Susan. 1731 OLIVE ST 19604 #041-13-2002 L2002 **EM** *100 †16

COBB, Brian Jay. ■ 19605 #019-02-2004 L2004 **OBG** *012

COMESS, Raymond Rueben. ■ 19602 #051-01-1943 L1946 **GS OBG** *071 †85

COMITE, Harriet. 1260 BROADCASTING RD 19610 #008-01-1977 L1982 **D** *020 †15

CONSOLI, Deborah Marie. 301 S 7TH AVE, STE 365 19611 #010-02-1979 L1981 **OS** *020 †30

CONTE, Tracy Lyn. ■ 19606 #041-14-1996 L1999 **IM** *020 †20

CORONA, Claudia. PO BOX 16052, DEPT OF INTERNAL MED 19612 #308-13-2002 L2004 **IM** *020 †20

CRANDALL, Tonie Camardese. 301 S 7TH AVE, STE 245 19611 #024-07-1981 L1983 **GYN** *020 †30

DALAL, Hansa S. ■ 19605 #495-17-1970 **P** *100

DAYAL, Nimeshkumar Amritl. ■ 19606 #836-01-1992 L2005 **IM RHU** *012

DEACH, Robert A. ■ 19606 #020-02-1951 L1952 **GP** *071

DEANGELIS, Christina T. 3611 PERKIOMEN AVE, READING OB/GYN PC 19606 #041-14-1998 L2000 **OBG** *020 †30

DELLINGER, Robert Karl. 4201 POTTSVILLE PIKE 19605 #041-12-1979 L1985 **OM FM** *020 †18

DEMKO, Trudy Martha. 301 S 7TH AVE, STE 355 19611 #041-14-1991 L1994 **NEP** *020 †20

DEPUE, Scot Mason. ■ 19610 #023-12-1991 L2005 **EM** *020 †16

DERSH, Jerome. 606 COURT ST, STE 200 19601 #041-13-1954 L1955 **OPH** *071 †35

DESJARDINS, George P, Jr. 2500 BERNVILLE RD, ST JOSEPH'S HOSP & MEDICAL 19605 #041-09-1974 L1975 **EM** *020 †16

DETHOFF, John Comppen. 11 FAIRLANE RD, COMMONWEALTH ORTHOPAEDIC A 19606 #041-02-1978 L1979 **ORS** *020 †40

DE VEAUX, Richard Knowles. PO BOX 16052, MATERNAL-FETAL MED,TRHMC 19612 #041-09-1978 L1980 **OBG MFM** *020 †20

DIAMOND, James Jos. ■ 19611 #041-13-1948 L1949 **GS OS** *071 †85

DIMINO, Tara Lynn. 2605 KAISER BLVD, BERKS CARDIOLOGISTS LTD 19610 #041-09-1998 L2006 **ICE** *020 †20

DODSON, Lisa A. 12TH & WALNUT STS 19603 #041-09-1992 L1996 **AN** *020 †05

DONAHUE, Denise Marie. ■ 19610 #041-13-1983 L1985 **GP OM** *020

■ = Address Information Privacy Protected

DOOLEY, Thomas Wm. 40 KENHORST BLVD, LAMANNA-DOOLEY PLASTIC SUR 19607 #028-03-1983 L1989 **PS HS** *020 †65
DOSHI, Nipa Rajnikant. 301 S 7TH AVE, SUITE 200, DOCTORS' OFFICE 19611 #041-09-1995 L1998 **FM** *020 †18 ‡
DOUGHERTY, John Joseph. 301 S 7TH AVE, STE 245 19611 #041-09-1996 L2005 **OBG** *020 †30
DUCKETT, Kelly D. ■ 19610 #041-78-2004, ▲ L2004 **OBG** *012
EAGER, Jon Michael. 301 S 7TH AVE, STE 1020 19611 #041-13-1972 L1973 **GYN** *020 †30 ‡
EARLY, Robert F, Jr. SIXTH AVE AND SPRUCE ST 19611 #041-02-1984 L1985 **AN** *020 †05
EBERSOLE, Thomas Michael. 301 S 7TH AVE, STE 365 19611 #011-02-1973 L1975 **OBG** *020 †30
EDMUNDS, Elizabeth H. 514 CARSONIA AVE 19606 #041-07-1975 L1977 **FM** *020 †18
EINSIG, H J. 3227 PERKIOMEN AVE 19606 #041-09-1992 L1995 **PM ISM** *020 †60
ELSACCAR, Ossama Ahmed. 6 SPRUCE ST 19611 #915-02-1999 **OBG** *012
ERCOLE, Mario Anthony. 19 N 6TH ST STE 300, SVC ACCESS & MGMNT 19601 #041-13-1975 L1976 **CHP P** *020 †75
ERTEL, D Gregory. 2230 RIDGEWOOD RD, STE 100 19610 #041-09-1979 L1981 **GE IM** *020 †20
FAIZ, Saba. PO BOX 16052 19612 #704-06-2003 L2005 **IM** *012
FARBER, Harold Irwin. ■ 19610 #038-40-1941 L1942 **IM CD** *071
FAROOKI, Aamer Zahid. 301 S 7TH AVE, DOCTORS OFFICE BUILDING 19611 #036-07-1998 L2004 **DR** *020 †80
FARRELL, Bonnie Jean. 600 MUSEUM RD 19611 #041-13-1985 L1987 **IM** *020 †20
FEASTER, Marshall M, III. 301 S 7TH AVE, ASSOCIATES OF READING 19611 #036-01-1974 L1982 **TS** *020 †85,90
FERENCHICK, Timothy A. 3701 PERKIOMEN AVE 19606 #041-15-2000 L2001 **FM** *020 †18
FERRY, Gerald Williams. 2209 QUARRY DR, STE C30 19609 #041-13-1974 L1975 **OBG** *020 †30
FIEO, Andrew Gerard. 4885 DEMOSS RD, STE 101 19606 #041-14-1992 L1996 **OBG** *020 †30
FISCHER, Edward Clarence. 301 S 7TH AVE 19611 #041-13-1968 L1969 **R** *071 †80
FLORES, Evelyn Ruth M. 1940 N 13TH ST, STE 203 19604 #748-10-1971 L1976 **N OS** *020
FLORES-POSADAS, Margaret. 1555 SCHUYLKILL AVE 19601 #748-16-1990 L2000 **FM** *020 †18
FORMAN, Daniel. PO BOX 16052, BERKES HEMATOLOGY & ONCOL 19612 #033-75-1996, ▲ L1997 **HO** *020 †20
FRANCO, Frank Andrew. ■ 19610 #041-09-1953 L1954 **IM** *071
FRANCOIS, Max Brenor. 124 N 8TH ST 19601 #440-01-1964 L1970 **GP AN** *020
FRANK, Jeffrey Bruce. 1212 LIGGETT AVE 19611 #041-01-1971 L1972 **OBG IM** *020 †30
GANAS, Christie L. 2494 BERNVILLE RD, STE G02 19605 #041-02-1995 L1998 **OBG** *020 †30
GANSNER, Robyn Kay. 1623 MORGANTOWN RD 19607 #041-02-1985 L1986 **PM** *020 †60
GENT, Michael Lawrence. ■ 19610 #041-15-2007 L2007 **TY** *012
GHASSI, Dimple. PO BOX 16052, DEPT OF INTERNAL MED 19612 #496-17-1999 L2005 **IM** *012
GHATTAS, Janette Gobran. 120 N PROSPECT ST, STE F 19606 #915-05-1967 L1992 **OBG** *020 †30 ‡
GIACCIA, Amato. 600 SCHUYLKILL AVE 19601 #561-17-1957 L1963 **GP** *071
GIERINGER, Roberta L. ■ 19606 #041-09-1989 L1991 **IM** *020 †20
GILMORE, Irvin W. SIXTH AVE & SPRUCE ST 19603 #041-02-1951 L1952 **FM GP** *020
GIVENS, Charles Thomas. 2209 QUARRY DR, STE C34 19609 #654-01-1995 L1998 **FM** *020 †18
GOLDENBERG, Marat. 2494 BERNVILLE RD STE 203 19605 #041-13-1998 L2000 **VS** *020 †85
GOODE, John Gerald, Jr. 2500 BERNVILLE RD, ST JOSEPH MEDICAL CENTER 19605 #024-05-1979 L1984 **AN PD** *020 †55,05
GRABIAS, Stanley L, Jr. 2201 RIDGEWOOD RD, STE 200 19610 #041-02-1967 L1971 **ORS** *020 †40
GRAHAM, Barry Edward. 301 S 7TH AVE, STE 1020 19611 #041-09-1971 **OBG** *020 †30
GRANADOS, Nicanor Gomez. 1555 SCHUYLKILL AVE 19601 #748-01-1967 L1973 **FPG IMG** *020 †18
GRANADOS, Suzita Noche. 130 N PROSPECT ST, ST LAWRENCE PEDIATRICS 19606 #748-01-1967 L1974 **PD** *071 †55
GRANITO, Joseph Louis. SIXTH AVE SPRUCE ST 19603 #041-01-1973 L1974 **EM** *020 †16
GREENBERG, Robert Ned. 2211 QUARRY DR, STE E61 19609 #041-09-1979 L1981 **GS** *020 †85
GROSS, Lawrence Seymour. 6 HEARTHSTONE CT, STE 201 19606 #041-13-1966 L1975 **PD** *020 †55
GURSKI, Karen Jane. 2494 BERNVILLE RD, # G02 19605 #041-14-1992 L1997 **OBG** *020 †30
HABIB, Tamam. ■ 19610 #409-21-1998 L2001 **IM** *100
HALASZ, Mirela Iuliana. 2201 RIDGEWOOD RD, SIXTH AVE AND SPRUCE ST 19610 #781-01-1994 L2001 **PYG** *020 †75
HANJURA, Girdhari Lal. 120 PROSPECT ST 19606 #495-21-1960 L1975 **ON IM** *071 †20
HANNA, Ezzat Azmi. 600 HIGH BLVD 19607 #915-04-1974 L1980 **FM** *020 †18
HANNA, Hoda Zaki. 125 S 5TH ST 19602 #915-04-1973 L1983 **P** *020 †75
HASSAN, Joseph Robt. 3200 READING CREST AVE 19605 #041-01-1982 L1983 **IM** *020 †20
HASSEL, Jeffrey Louis. 640 WALNUT ST, STE 204 19601 #041-13-1976 L1978 **IM** *020
HATAMIZADEH, Parta. PO BOX 16052, READING HOSPITAL & MEDICAL 19612 #517-01-1998 L2007 **IM** *012
HAWKE, William. 6TH & SPRUCE 19611 #041-13-1965 L1966 **AN** *020 †05
HEILIG, Sara Jane. PO BOX 16052, READING HOSPITAL & MEDICAL 19612 #041-14-2008 L2008 *012
HEIN, Edward W. 2210 RIDGEWOOD RD, STE 100 19610 #025-01-1974 L1985 **AI PD** *020 †55,03
HEISEY, John Claymon. 30 VILLAGE CENTER DR 19607 #041-13-1972 L1973 **IM** *020
HELLER, Fredericka S M P. 530 KENHORST BLVD 19611 #041-01-1980 L1981 **OBG** *020 †30 ‡
HEMTASILPA, Somkiat. ■ 19601 #891-06-1990 L1999 **SCI** *020 †60
HENRY, Scott Eric. ■ 19608 #028-02-1998 L2007 **TS** *100
HIGH, Bertrand John. 4885 DEMOSS RD STE 200 19606 #041-02-1976 L1978 **IM** *020 †20
HINRICHS, Thos Frederick. R-BLDG 6 & SPRUCE 19611 #030-05-1961 L1979 **PM** *071 †60
HOFFMAN, Neil Allan. PO BOX 16052 19612 #056-05-1967 L1979 **ATP FOP** *062 †50
HOLM, Eric Kristian. 606 MUSEUM RD 19611 #041-13-1969 L1970 **NS** *020 †25
HORNER, Scott Alan. 640 WALNUT ST, STE 305 19601 #041-12-1986 L1991 **U** *020 †95
HOWE, Elizabeth W. 1235 ELM ST 19604 #010-02-1993 L1996 **EM** *030 †16
HU, Huchun. ■ 19608 #041-13-2002 L2004 **AN** *100 †05
HUSSAIN, Ambreen. 6 SPRUCE ST, STE 132 19611 #305-01-1999 L2003 **ID** *020 †20
JAY, Wendell Thos, Jr. ■ 19610 #036-07-1948 L1950 **IM** *071 †20
JENCKES, George, III. 950 N WYOMISSING BLVD, STE 100 19610 #041-13-1983 L1984 **IM** *020 †20 ‡
JIMERSON, Cedric C. ■ 19607 #035-20-1943 L1949 **GS TS** *071 †85
JOHNSTON, Dorothy. ■ 19603 #041-07-1936 L1937 **P CHP** *071 †75
JOLLY, Dara Dorsey. PO BOX 16052 19612 #305-01-2003 L2004 **OBG** *012
JONES, Irving H. 1623 MORGANTOWN RD 19607 #005-12-1953 L1960 **PM PHP** *071
JONES, Robert S, Jr. 6 SPRUCE ST, STE 132 19611 #041-77-1987, ▲ L1988 **ID** *020 †20
KANE, Brian Roger. 600 HIGH BLVD, CENTER 19607 #041-13-1996 L1998 **FM** *020 †18
KANG, Joseph T. 131 N 5TH ST 19601 #308-10-1987 L1995 **FM** *020 †18
KAO, Winifred Wei. 1 GRANITE POINT DR, STE 300 19610 #033-06-1987 L1989 **OTO HNS** *020 †45
KAOURIS, Leonidas P. PO BOX 16052, READING HOSP MED CTR 19612 #041-14-1992 L1994 **FM** *020
KARABELNIK, Don. 225 KENHORST BLVD 19607 #836-02-1969 L1977 **FM ADM** *020 †18
KASE, James Jos. 145 N 6TH ST 1ST FL, ST JOSEPH FAMILY & WOMENS 19601 #016-43-1958 L1959 **IM** *020 †20
KASTENBAUM, Hannah Asne. ■ 19607 #041-02-2007 L2007 **PTH** *012
KEARNEY, John Mauger. ■ 19606 #041-01-1954 L1961 **GS** *071 †85
KELLEHER, Mary Eileen. 838 PENN ST, READING HEALTH DISPENSARY 19602 #035-01-1994 L2002 **FM** *020 †18
KELLER, Lynwood Vincent. ■ 19610 #041-01-1943 L1944 **IMG GP** *071
KERSHNER, George Henry. ■ 19611 #041-02-1970 L1975 **EM** *020 †16
KHALIL, Carl G. ■ 19606 #041-12-1967 L1968 **CHP P** *075 †75
KHAN, Rahman M. 146 S 5TH ST, BERKS PSYCH INC 19602 #495-65-1995 **P** *020
KHOCHE, Swapnil. PO BOX 16052, READING HOSPITAL & MEDICAL 19612 #496-09-1999 L2007 **IM** *012
KILLIAN, Caleb L, III. 145 N 6TH ST 19601 #041-02-1953 L1954 **FM IM** *020 †18 ‡
KIM, Dosik. 2608 KAISER BLVD, RESPIRATORY SPECIALISTS 19610 #583-01-1997 L2006 **PCC** *020 †20
KIMBALL, Daniel B, Jr. 1711 HAMPDEN BLVD, HOSPICE ST JOHN 19604 #051-01-1965 L1989 **IM HEM** *071 †20 ‡
KINTZI, Harry Edward. 1623 MORGANTOWN RD 19607 #051-04-1976 L1977 **EM OM** *020 †16
KISKADDON, Karrie Lynne. ■ 19605 #305-01-2005 L2005 **FP** *012
KLEINER, Anton John. 6TH AND SPRUCE STS, READING HOSP MED CTR 19603 #041-01-1970 L1971 **GYN** *040 †30
KLEPPINGER, Dorothea C B. 1300 LANCASTER AVE 19607 #041-09-1948 L1949 **IMG** *071
KOLB, Naomi Souder. 3909 PERKIOMEN AVE 19606 #041-07-1978 L1979 **FM** *020 †18
KOPERNIK, Lidia M I. ■ 19603 #759-04-1938 L1958 **P PUD** *071
KOREY, Joseph John, Jr. 12TH & WALNUT STS 19603 #041-02-1975 L1976 **OBG** *020 †30
KOWALSKI, Wendy Jo. ■ 19605 #041-14-1998 L2003 **NPM** *020 †55
KRALJEVIC, Juan. 403 N 13TH ST, BERKS MEDICAL SPECIALISTS 19604 #231-03-1969 L1978 **IM HEM** *020 †20
KUTSCHER, Harlan Austin. ■ 19606 #035-01-1975 L1980 **U MDM** *071 †95
LAKSHMIN, Murali. ■ 19607 #495-98-1981 L1983 **AN** *020 †05
LA LUNA, Louis. 2230 RIDGEWOOD RD, STE 100 19610 #033-05-1992 L1995 **GE IM** *020 †20
LA MANNA, John Vincent. 40 N KENHORST BLVD 19607 #041-02-1977 L1978 **PS HS** *020 †85,65
LATTIN, Gary Marc. 2605 KAISER BLVD, BERKS CARDIOLOGISTS LTD 19610 #023-01-1967 L1972 **CD** *020 †20
LAZOR, Jerome Michael. 1623 MORGANTOWN RD 19607 #041-13-1992 L1995 **IM** *020 †20
LEAMAN, Kristine Marchalo. 3701 PERKIOMEN AVE, READING OB/GYN 19606 #033-06-1998 L2000 **OBG** *020 †18,30
LEASURE, Nick Chas. PO BOX 16052, READING HOSP & MED CTR 19612 #041-09-1983 L1984 **ON HEM** *020 †20
LEE, Jung Sook. 320 ABINGTON DR 19610 #583-04-1973 L1978 **FM** *020 †18
LEE, Soong Gong. 215 N 12TH ST 19604 #583-02-1969 L1979 **R** *020 †80
LEVAN, Joseph Raymond. ■ 19610 #041-09-1991 L1996 **GS** *020 †85
LEVINE, Alan Paul. 30 VILLAGE CENTER DR 19607 #041-14-1984 L1985 **IM** *020 †20
LEVY, Paul Fredric. 6 HEARTHSTONE CT STE 303 19606 #041-01-1978 L1983 **GE IM** *020 †20
LI, Yanyan. PO BOX 16052 19612 #243-32-1990 L2006 **FP** *012
LIN, Chao-Ren. 12TH-WALNUT ST B-316, ST JOSEPHS HOSP 19603 #308-03-1987 L1993 **PD** *100
LIN, Melissa Amy. 30 VILLAGE CENTER DR 19607 #035-08-1995 L1998 **IM** *020 †20
LLOYD, Edgar Chas. ■ 19606 #041-09-1954 L1955 **OS AN** *030 †05
LODER, Donald Irvin. 12TH & WALNUT STS 19603 #041-77-1960, ▲ L1961 **FM** *071
LOGUE, James Gibson, III. 145 N 6TH ST 19601 #649-01-1980 L1985 **AN** *020
LONG, Timothy John. PO BOX 16052, READING HOSPITAL & MEDICAL 19612 #041-13-1995 L1998 **IM** *020 †20
LONGARINI, Ricardo. 2913 WINDMILL RD, STE 7 19608 #649-14-1981 L1986 **IM** *020 †20
LONGENECKER, Benj E, Jr. ■ 19610 #041-02-1949 L1950 **FM** *071 †18
LONGENECKER, Stephen C. 4885 DEMOSS RD, STE 102 19606 #041-13-1986 L1987 **ORS OAR** *020 †40
LORD, William H. 1991 STATE HILL RD 19610 #041-13-1960 L1961 **FM GP** *071 †18
LOWRY, W Norwood. ■ 19609 #041-02-1957 L1958 **P** *020
LU, Meide. 301 S 7TH AVE, DOCTORS' OFFICE BLDG, STE 19611 #243-45-1984 L2002 **HO** *020 †20 ‡
MAIDANSKY, Igor. ■ 19607 #041-13-1988 L1991 **AN** *020 †05
MALAK, Timothy Michael. 5 HEARTHSTONE CT STE 105 19606 #041-13-1984 L1986 **GS** *020 †85
MANCANO, Louis David. 301 S 7TH AVE, STE 2120 19611 #041-13-1984 L1985 **FM** *040 †18
MANCANO, Mary Ann. 2500 BERNVILLE RD, ST JOSEPH MED CTR-PEDS 19605 #041-13-1986 L1988 **PD** *020 †55
MANCUSO, Christopher Jude. 4885 DEMOSS RD, STE 102 19606 #041-02-1994 L1996 **ORS** *020 †40
MANNEPULI, Giri. 3535 N 5TH STREET HWY 19605 #495-50-1989 L1997 **FM** *020 †18
MANUBAY, John M. 1555 SCHUYLKILL AVE 19601 #748-08-1989 L1991 **FM** *020 †18
MAQBOOL, Fauzia Ovais. 6 HEARTHSTONE CT, STE 201 19606 #704-06-1987 L1994 **PD** *020 †55
MAQBOOL, Ovais. 1211 ELM ST 19604 #704-16-1986 L2001 **FM** *100 †18
MARTIN, John Albert, Jr. 11 FAIRLANE RD, COMMONWEALTH ORTHOPAEDIC A 19606 #041-02-1985 L1986 **ORS OSM** *020 †40
MARYNIAK, Girard Michael. 1234 PENN AVE 19610 #041-13-1979 L1980 **OBG** *020 †30
MASAND-RAI, Anirudh. 2230 RIDGEWOOD RD, STE 100 19610 #495-36-1986 L1993 **GE** *020 †20
MASSARO, Marcie Beth. ■ 19606 #041-77-2007, ▲ L2007 **IM** *012
MAZUZ, Meir. 2605 KAISER BLVD, BERKS CARDIOLOGISTS LTD 19610 #550-01-1977 L1979 **CD** *020 †20
MAZZA, Patrick A, Jr. 730 N 5TH ST 19601 #041-02-1950 L1951 **FM** *071 †18
MCHALE, Staci Leigh. ■ 19607 #048-15-2004 L2004 **OBG** *012
MEHARG, John Geo, Jr. 11 E LANCASTER AVE 19607 #035-20-1968 L1970 **IM** *020 †20 ‡
MELE, Aparna. 301 S 7TH AVE, STE 215 19611 #010-01-2001 L2001 **GE** *020

MIFUNE, Yoshinobu. 2603 KAISER BLVD, STE 204 19610 #422-01-1998 L2001 **FM UM** *020 †18

MINEHART, Charles Richard. 2605 KAISER BLVD, BERKS CARDIOLOGISTS LTD 19610 #041-41-1973 L1976 **CD EM** *020 †20

MINOUEI, Mohammadreza. ■ 19605 #517-16-1994 L2007 **IM** *020 †20

MITCH, Alison Mary. 1623 MORGANTOWN RD 19607 #033-06-1996 L2003 **PM** *020 †60

MODI, Mayank R. 2605 KAISER BLVD, BERKS CARDIOLOGISTS LTD 19610 #495-22-1988 L1996 **CD** *020 †20

MOKEDE, Catherine Ruth. ■ 19609 #035-03-1978 L1980 **FM** *074 †18

MONDALA-OCBO, Elisa V. ■ 19607 #748-01-1960 L1971 **AN** *071 †05

MOSER, John Christian. 1623 MORGANTOWN RD 19607 #041-09-1979 L1980 **FM FPG** *040 †18

MOTZ, Lisa Marie. 1991 STATE HILL RD 19610 #041-13-1996 L1999 **IM** *040 †20

MUALLEM, Hanna S. 6TH SPRUCE STS 19603 #748-01-1987 L1988 **OS** *020

MUSTAFA, Anila. PO BOX 16052, DEPT OF MED EDU 19612 #704-26-2000 L2006 **IM** *012

MUSTAFA, Helwey. ■ 19606 #011-75-2005, ▲ L2005 **IM** *012

MUVDI, Bichara Charles. 120 PROSPECT ST, ST LAWRENCE MEDICAL ASSOCI 19606 #016-11-1980 L1983 **IM IMG** *020 †20

NATALE, William Kenneth. 6TH AVE & SPRUCE ST, READING HOSP MED CTR 19603 #041-12-1973 L1994 **PTH LM** *030 †50

NAVONE, Katharine A N. 145 N 6TH ST, STE 1 19601 #561-17-1988 L1993 **FM** *020 †18

NAYAK, Leena H. 838 PENN ST, READING HEALTH DISPENSARY 19602 #016-43-1995 L1998 **FM** *020 †20

NEMEROFF, Jeffrey Brian. 215 N 12TH ST 19604 #035-09-1988 L1994 **DR NM** *020 †80,28

NGUYEN, Kimlien. 130 PROSPECT ST, ALLERGY & ASTHMA MED CTR 19606 #038-40-1984 L1993 **AI IM** *020 †20,03

NIEHLS, Beverly Jean. 120 PROSPECT ST 19606 #041-02-1983 L1984 **FM** *020 †18 ‡

NOLLER, Thomas Hans. 526 PENN ST, CARLOS FONSECA MEDICAL CTR 19602 #016-01-1982 L1985 **FM** *020 †20

NUTTING, Ron Dell. 301 S 7TH AVE, ASSOCIATES OF READING 19611 #016-06-1981 L1992 **TS GS** *020 †85,90

ORFF, Mary Clarke. ■ 19608 #041-13-1958 L1959 **GP OS** *072

ORR, Danielle Jacquelyn. PO BOX 16052, READING HOSPITAL & MEDICAL 19612 #051-07-2005 L2005 **FP** *012

OSMAN, Ziad Saleh. PO BOX 16052, READING HOSPITAL & MEDICAL 19612 #913-06-1998 L2007 **FP** *012

PACIULLI, Raffaele. 11 FAIRLANE RD 19606 #561-11-1956 L1963 **ORS** *071 †40

PADIYAR, Ramdas Badrigi. 200 N 13TH ST, STE 203 19604 #495-09-1974 L1978 **AN** *020 †05

PAGOLU, Pavani David. PO BOX 16052 19612 #495-70-2001 L2005 **IM** *012

PANDIT, Niraj P. 2605 KAISER BLVD, BERKS CARDIOLOGISTS LTD 19610 #041-07-1986 L1988 **CD** *020 †20

PARCELLA, Phyllis Anne. SIXTH AVE SPRUCE ST ANES, DEPT 19603 #041-01-1982 L1983 **AN** *020 †05

PARIKH, Shirish Nanalal. 1800 HAMPDEN BLVD 19604 #495-48-1977 L1984 **IM** *030

PARK, Yong Il. 1270 BROADCASTING RD 19610 #033-05-1996 L2003 **SCI** *020 †60

PATADIA, Chandrakant C. 2309 ALSACE RD 19604 #495-23-1965 L1972 **IM GP** *071 †18

PAYER, Jean Marie. 301 S 7TH AVE, STE 245 19611 #033-05-1985 L1987 **OBG** *020 †30

PELLEGRINI, Vincent A. 301 S 7TH AVE, STE 245 19611 #041-02-1974 L1975 **OBG** *020 †30

PERKINS, Philip Graham. 6 HEARTHSTONE CT, STE 106 19606 #917-05-1971 L1990 **ORS** *020

PEW, Joseph Newton. 3200 READING CREST AVE 19605 #041-01-1978 L1979 **IM** *020 †20

PIEGARI, Guy Nicholas, Jr. 2605 KAISER BLVD, BERKS CARDIOLOGISTS LTD 19610 #032-01-1978 L1986 **CD IM** *040 †20

PIERSON, Nicholas Stephen. PO BOX 16052, READING HOSPITAL & MEDICAL 19612 #041-14-2008 L2008 *012

PIFER, John F. 11 TRANQUILITY LN 19607 #028-78-1962, ▲ L1973 **FM OBS** *071

PIMENTEL, Agustin. PO BOX 16052, READING HOSPITAL & MEDICAL 19612 #132-01-2003 L2006 **IM** *012

PINKUS, Michael. ■ 19604 #022-75-2007, ▲ L2007 **IM** *012

POLINSKY, Ronald John, Jr. 2605 KAISER BLVD, BERKS CARDIOLOGISTS LTD 19610 #033-05-2000 L2003 **CD** *020 †20

POLITZER, Frank Eric. 2605 KAISER BLVD, BERKS CARDIOLOGISTS LTD 19610 #035-46-1980 L1988 **CD IM** *020 †20

POMERANTZ, Philip Abraham. 403 N 13TH ST, BERKS MEDICAL SPECIALISTS 19604 #041-02-1971 L1976 **IM** *020 †20

POSADAS, Christopher B. 1555 SCHUYLKILL AVE 19601 #748-12-1989 L1999 **FM FPG** *020 †18

POWELL, Debra Lynn. ■ 19606 #041-14-2003 L2003 **ID** *012 †20

PRADHAN, Rajesh. PO BOX 16052, READING HOSPITAL & MEDICAL 19612 #672-04-2004 L2006 **IM** *012

PRADHAN, Sagun. PO BOX 16052, READING HOSPITAL & MEDICAL 19612 #672-02-2001 L2006 **IM** *012

PRUZINSKY, Stephen R. ■ 19607 #041-09-1955 L1956 **GP** *071

PUGH, Christopher Johnne. ■ 19603 #041-77-2005, ▲ L2005 **OBG** *012

PUGLIESE, Peter Thos. 4408B POTTSVILLE PIKE 19605 #041-01-1957 L1958 **OS PTH** *071

PUTNAM, Mark Ambrose. 640 WALNUT ST, BORNEMAN PSYCHIATRY 19601 #041-13-1988 L1990 **P CHP** *020 †75

QUIRANTES, Mirta. 301 S 7TH AVE, READING DIAGNOSTIC CLINIC 19611 #308-03-1986 L1992 **IM** *020

RAHMANIAN, Nader. 1416 PENN AVE 19610 #041-09-1987 L1988 **IM IMG** *020 †20 ‡

RAI, Simi Masand. 301 S 7TH AVE, STE 220 19611 #496-17-1989 L2001 **ON** *020 †20

RAVETZ, Pamela Caryn. 3909 PERKIOMEN AVE 19606 #041-13-1997 L1999 **FM** *020 †18

REES, David Barker. 301 S 7TH AVE STE 3220 19611 #041-13-1975 L1976 **ORS** *020 †40

REEVES, Ralph Milton. 560 VAN REED RD STE 203, VAN REED PROF BLDG 19610 #012-05-1965 L1972 **P** *020 †75 ‡

REIMELS, Brian Michael. 3701 PERKIOMEN AVE 19606 #654-01-2001 L2001 **FM** *020 †18

RESTREPO, James Price. 985 BERKSHIRE BLVD STE 101 19610 #041-01-1982 L1984 **OTO** *020 †45

RIFAI, Aicha. 640 WALNUT ST, BORNEMAN PSYCHIATRY 19601 #875-02-1979 L1988 **IM P** *020 †20,75

ROACH, Thomas Carson. ■ 19608 #020-02-1953 L1954 **P IM** *071

ROGERS, Mark Wayne. PO BOX 16052, READING HOSPITAL & MEDICAL 19612 #041-13-2007 L2007 **TY** *012

ROSENZWEIG, Seth Edward. 301 S 7TH AVE, STE 215 19611 #035-01-1982 L1987 **GE IM** *020 †20 ‡

ROWAN, Sandra Kelsey. ■ 19604 #035-09-1960 L1962 **PD** *071 †55

ROZANSKI, Stanley J. 145 N 6TH ST 19601 #041-09-1944 L1945 **GP** *071

SABADO, Jeremiah James. ■ 19607 #041-13-2007 L2007 **TY** *012

SAHOO, Kashi Nath. 12TH & WALNUT STS, DEPT OF RAD THERAP 19603 #495-13-1965 L1976 **RO** *020 †80

SALEEM, Tipu-Faiz M. ■ 19607 #704-01-1995 L2001 **END** *020 †20

SALHA, Hani Hasan. 2605 KAISER BLVD 19610 #539-06-1992 L1997 **CD** *020 †20

SAPIRA, Joseph Danl. ■ 19606 #041-12-1961 L1962 **IM P** *040 †20

SCORNAVACCHI, Jos Mario. ■ 19610 #041-09-1945 L1946 **U** *071 †95

SCOVERN, Henry. 2000 STATE HILL RD 19610 #010-01-1975 L1982 **PDA RHU** *020 †20,03

SEDA, Hector John. 1 GRANITE POINT DR, STE 300 19610 #041-02-1964 L1965 **OTO** *071 †45

SEIDEL, Eric Conan. 6TH & SPRUCE AVE 19611 #010-01-1978 L1979 **EM FM** *020 †18 ‡

SERGI, Michael Anthony. 40 BERKSHIRE CT, READING PEDIATRICS 19610 #010-02-1987 L1992 **PD** *020 †55

SERGI, Tiffany Clarke. 40 BERKSHIRE CT, READING PEDIATRICS, INC. 19610 #010-02-1986 L1992 **PD** *020 †55

SEXTON, George L, Jr. ■ 19610 #041-02-1953 L1954 **GYN** *071 †30

SHAFFER, Irvin Geo. 145 N 6TH ST 19601 #041-02-1940 L1947 **AN** *071 †05

SHAH, Harnish V. ■ 19610 #495-23-1964 L1972 **PD GE** *071 †55

SHAPIRO, Robert Eric. 2605 KAISER BLVD, BERKS CARDIOLOGISTS LTD 19610 #041-13-1993 L2002 **CD** *020 †20

SHARMA, Pathanjali P V. 2494 BERNVILLE RD, STE 203 19605 #495-72-1971 L1993 **TS GS** *020 †85

SHIN, Ann Kyungwohn. 6 SPRUCE ST, STE 132 19611 #041-13-1996 L2000 **ID** *020 †20

SHULTZ, Thomas Eugene. THE READING HOSP MED CTR 19603 #041-13-1958 L1959 **PTH FOP** *050 †50

SILVERMAN, Edward James. 606 MUSEUM RD, BERKS GENERAL MED GROUP, P 19611 #041-02-1981 L1982 **IM** *020 †20

SIMMONDS, Veronica Laine. 145 N 6TH ST 19601 #022-75-2005, ▲ L2005 **OBG** *012

SINGH, Robert S. 2494 BERNVILLE RD, STE 203 19605 #654-01-1997 L2002 **VS** *020 †85

SINGH, Vijay. 120 PROSPECT ST, 120 PROSPECT ST 19606 #495-99-1990 L1996 **IM** *020 †20

SINITSA, Michael L. 11 FAIRLANE RD, SUITE GROUND B 19606 #913-50-1985 L1998 **FM** *020 †18

SMAGINA, Elena Evgenievna. PO BOX 16052 19612 #913-01-1991 L2004 **FM** *020 †18

SMOKER-JOHNSTON, Cynthia. 225 N KENHORST BLVD, BERKS FAMILY PRACTICE 19607 #041-01-1988 L1990 **FM** *020 †18

SOFOWORA, Gbemiga Gboyega. PO BOX 16052, READING HOSPITAL & MEDICAL 19612 #690-05-1989 L2004 **CD** *012 †20

SOKOLOFF, Joel David. 3905 LYNN AVE 19606 #422-01-1981 L1982 **AN** *020 †05

SOLANKI, Rajendra H. 2605 KAISER BLVD, BERKS CARDIOLOGISTS LTD 19610 #011-75-1994, ▲ L1997 **IM** *020 †20

SOTOMAYOR, Matilde R. 145 N 6TH ST 19601 #042-03-1980 L1984 **FM** *020

SPANGLER, Martin L, Jr. 145 N 6TH ST 19601 #041-77-1958, ▲ L1959 **FM** *071

SRIDHAR, Gopalan. 555 RAYMOND ST, BERKS PEDIATRICS 19605 #495-94-1992 L2003 **PD** *020 †55

STELLA, Victoria G. 145 N 6TH ST, ST JOSEPH FAMILY CARE 19601 #422-01-1982 L1983 **FM** *020 †18

STELMACH, Peter. ■ 19604 #024-05-1975 L1982 **IM** *030 †20

STOUDT, Donald Earl. ■ 19609 #041-02-1955 L1956 **N OS** *071 †75

STRAUSE, Harold L, Jr. 530 CENTRE AVE 19601 #041-02-1949 L1950 **OPH** *071 †35

STRIEB, Heidi D. ■ 19603 #041-77-2005, ▲ L2005 **OBG** *012

STRUNK, Harold A. ■ 19608 #010-01-1939 L1940 **AN** *071 †05

SULLUM, Daniel Shimon. 640 WALNUT ST, BORNEMAN PSYCHIATRY 19601 #041-09-1980 L1981 **P PYG** *020 †75 ‡

SUWAN, Manee. 1623 MORGANTOWN RD 19607 #891-01-1971 L1974 **PM** *020 †60

TASE, Douglas Sheperd. 11 FAIRLANE RD, COMMONWEALTH ORTHOPAEDIC A 19606 #041-13-1981 L1982 **ORS** *020 †40

TEMPLE, Michael John. ■ 19610 #065-06-1992 L1998 **DR** *100 †80

THAPALIYA, Prakash. ■ 19610 #672-02-2001 L2005 **IM** *012

THOMAS, Robert F, Jr. 301 S 7TH AVE, STE 230 19601 #041-02-1980 L1989 **GS** *020 †85

THOMAS, Sherlonda Shaw. PO BOX 16052, DEPT OF OB/GYN 19612 #051-07-2005 **OBG** *012

TIETBOHL, Ralph Harry. 3909 PERKIOMEN AVE 19606 #041-13-1953 L1954 **FM** *071

TOM, Barry Michael. 415 READING AVE 19611 #041-09-1985 L1986 **DR RNR** *075 †80

TOMKIEWICZ, Thaddeus. 3535 N 5TH ST, DOCTORS CONVENIENT CARE 19605 #041-09-1961 L1962 **GP** *071

TOSO, Gianfranco. 1 GRANITE POINT DR, STE 300 19610 #561-01-1956 L1963 **OTO HNS** *071 †45

TRAVERS, John Joseph, Jr. 1075 BERKSHIRE BLVD 19610 #035-09-1993 L1993 **FM** *020 †18

TSUMOTO, Sandi Masako. PO BOX 16052, READING HOSPITAL & MEDICAL 19612 #014-01-2006 L2006 **FP** *012

TUMELTY, Daniel Sean. 600 HIGH BLVD 19607 #041-07-1990 L1992 **FM** *020 †18

VAN DEN BOSCH, John Thos. 1075 BERKSHIRE BLVD, STE 950 19610 #041-13-1972 L1973 **IM** *020 †20

VASSEUR, Bernard Gerard. 301 S 7TH AVE, ASSOCIATES OF READING 19611 #409-10-1983 L1983 **TS TTS** *020 †85,90

VELAZQUEZ, Milka Elsa. 14 PHILADELPHIA AVE 19607 #924-01-1986 L1997 **PD** *020 †55

VIPUL, Kumar. PO BOX 16052, READING HOSPITAL & MEDICAL 19612 #496-42-2002 L2006 **IM** *012

VU, Son. 1075 BERKSHIRE BLVD, STE 950 19610 #041-14-1997 L1999 **FM** *020 †18

WAXLER, Andrew Reed. 2605 KAISER BLVD, BERKS CARDIOLOGISTS LTD 19610 #041-01-1992 L1995 **CD** *020 †20

WEAVER, Kent Eby. 2509 PERKIOMEN AVE 19606 #041-13-1963 L1964 **FM** *020 †18

WEAVER, Mary F Pendergast. 145 N 6TH ST 19601 #041-13-1963 L1964 **GP** *071

WEINSTEIN, Richard Jos. 1000 TUCKERTON CT 19605 #001-06-1982 L1992 **FM OM** *020 †70,18

WEST, William J, Jr. 4885 DEMOSS RD, STE 101 19606 #041-02-1986 L1987 **OBG** *020 †30

WHEELOCK, Dana Whitham. PO BOX 16052, READING HOSP & MED CTR 19612 #041-02-1990 L1994 **FM** *100

WIRTH, Frederick H, Jr. PO BOX 16052, THE READING HOSPITAL AND M 19612 #021-01-1967 L1995 **NPM PD** *020 †55

WIRTH, Timothy Mark. 3200 READING CREST AVE, READING CREST MEDICAL ASSO 19605 #041-09-1983 L1984 **IM** *020 †20

WISWESSER, George Andrew. 524 FRANKLIN ST 19602 #041-02-1966 L1967 **P** *020 †75

WITTELS, Emanuel. 225 KENHORST BLVD # M 19607 #836-02-1970 L1977 **FM GP** *020 †18

WOCH, Gustaw. 6 HEARTHSTONE CT, STE 201 19606 #759-04-1992 L2003 **PD** *020 †55

WONG, James. 225 N KENHORST BLVD 19607 #041-02-1967 L1973 **IM ID** *020 †20

WOOLLEY, Daniel Scott. 2494 BERNVILLE RD, STE 207 19605 #041-13-1991 L1993 **TS TTS** *020 †90,85

WOYNAROWSKI, David M. 301 S 7TH AVE, STE 225 19611 #041-13-1987 L1989 **IM** *020 †20

■ = Address Information Privacy Protected

YASMEEN, Nikhat. 640 WALNUT ST, BORNEMAN PSYCHIATRY 19601 #495-62-1993 L2001 PYG *020 †75
YEE, Maria Ruiza A. 2201 RIDGEWOOD RD STE 400 19610 #748-02-1981 L1990 P *020 †75
ZERBY, Jeffrey Chas. 301 S 7TH AVE STE 365, DOCTORS OFFICE BLDG. 19611 #041-13-1975 L1976 OBG *020 †30
ZHANG, Ying. PO BOX 16052 19612 #243-21-1988 L2004 FM *100
ZINNER, Eli S. 145 N 6TH ST, ST JOSEPH FAMILY AND WOMEN 19601 #041-01-1988 L1990 OBG *020 †30
ZOBIAN, David Charles. 301 PENN AVE, STE 200 19611 #041-13-2004 L2004 PD *100
ZOLGHADR, Siavash. 606 COURT ST, STE 308 19601 #517-05-1962 L1973 GE IM *020

RECTOR – WESTMORELAND

PALMER, William Ewing. 2199 ROUTE 381 15677 #041-13-1957 L1958 R NM *020 †80,28

RED LION – YORK

ABDULBAAQEE, Nailah Musli. ■ 17356 #047-07-2007 L2007 FP *012
BOYD, Bradley Lowell. ■ 17356 #016-76-2007, ▲ L2007 *012
BUTZ, Todd Michael. 3065 WINDSOR RD, WELLSPAN MEDICAL GROUP 17356 #041-02-1990 L1992 IM *020 †20
CHODROFF, Charles Henry. 3065 WINDSOR RD 17356 #035-20-1981 L1983 IM *075 †20
DEMPSEY, Joseph William. 3065 WINDSOR RD 17356 #041-14-1999 L2002 PD *020 †55
DOUTHITT, Luke Michael. ■ 17356 #047-20-2007 L2007 GS *012
HOLLIDAY, Nicole. ■ 17356 #022-75-2007, ▲ EM *012
HORNYAK, Daniel John. ■ 17356 #023-01-2007 L2007 EM *012
KEPHART, Fred Wm. 3065 WINDSOR RD 17356 #041-09-1977 L1978 IM *020 †20
KIRBY, James Edward. 3065 WINDSOR RD 17356 #023-01-1973 L1978 PD *020 †55
KRIEGER, Steven Mark. 3065 WINDSOR RD 17356 #041-13-1978 L1979 IM *020 †20
LOGAN, David Jos. ■ 17356 #007-02-1966 L1975 EM GS *020
OWEN, Cynthia Mae. 3065 WINDSOR RD 17356 #023-01-1990 L1993 IM *072 †20
PATEL, Dipak. 3065 WINDSOR RD 17356 #041-09-1990 L1994 IM *020 †20
VIRIASSOV, Peter V. ■ 17356 #022-75-2007 L2007 EM *012

REEDSVILLE – MIFFLIN

CANNON, Carman J. ■ 17084 #010-02-1949 L1952 OS OPH *071
DIXON, Robert E. ■ 17084 #041-09-1953 L1954 OBG *071 †30
PEARSON, Thomas O. 8 SHELLY DR 17084 #041-14-1986 L1988 N *030 †75
QUINN, Philip L. 131 HONEY CREEK RD 17084 #028-78-1959, ▲ L1960 GP OS *071

REINHOLDS – LANCASTER

BITNER, Richard L. RD 1 PEARTOWN RD BOX 143 17569 #041-01-1964 L1965 AN *020 †05
ZIMMERMAN, Heidi Lynn. 554 WILLOW ST 17569 #041-14-1984 L1986 FM *020 †18

RENFREW – BUTLER

AGATE, Weien. ■ 16053 #243-45-1982 L2002 IM *020 †20
COTTINGTON, Gordon M. ■ 16053 #054-04-1954 L1955 PDS *071 †40
REGINELLA, Ruthane Franca. ■ 16053 #041-14-1988 L1991 DR *020 †80

RENOVO – CLINTON

ADVINCULA, Rizalito B. 1001 PINE ST, COMMUNITY CLINIC 17764 #748-07-1963 L1971 EM FM *020 †18 ‡
CONLY, Frank L. 924 HURON AVE 17764 #041-02-1980 L1981 GP IMG *020
LENNON, David John. 1001 PINE ST 17764 #010-03-2000 L2003 FM *020 †18

REYNOLDSVILLE – JEFFERSON

BRANDON, Milton Boyd. PA ROUE 830 EAST 4 MILES, NORTH OF I-80 EXIT 15 ON 15851 #041-02-1942 L1946 PM GP *071
DE VITTORIO, Armond A. ■ 15851 #041-13-1939 L1940 GP *071
MURRAY, Carroll Arthur. ■ 15851 #041-13-1948 L1949 FM *071 †18
VARACALLO, Albert Louis. 5 N 3RD ST 15851 #041-14-1983 L1985 FM FPG *020 †18 ‡
WINEBERG, Jennifer. 22 WELLS DR 15851 #041-09-1995 L1997 FM *020 †18 ‡

RICES LANDING – GREENE

GOSAI, Jayesh Babarpuri. 1895 JEFFERSON RD 15357 #495-76-1983 L1987 IM *020 †20

RICHBORO – BUCKS

ABIR, Isaac. 56 NEWTOWN RICHBORO RD 18954 #517-01-1958 L1970 PD PHO *020 †55
ABRAHAM, Nina Faryl. ■ 18954 #041-02-2007 L2007 IM *012
CHAWLA, Kanwaljit Kaur. ■ 18954 #041-15-2008 *012
CHUN, Monica Joohee. ■ 18954 #041-13-2008 OBG *012
CURTIN, Kelly Anne. ■ 18954 #041-77-2007, ▲ L2007 *012
DEVER, Lynn Garvin. 130 ALMSHOUSE RD, STE 400 18954 #041-13-1986 L1988 PD *020 †55 ‡
DOMSKY, Richard Alan. 132 GLENIFFER HILL RD 18954 #035-01-1982 L1983 AN EM *020 †05
DONEGAN, Ryan Patrick. ■ 18954 #020-12-2006 L2006 ORS *012
GOLDBERG, Fredric Howard. ■ 18954 #041-02-1988 L1990 AN PME *020 †05
GOPPOLD, Ronald Wm. 95 ALMSHOUSE RD, STE 103 18954 #041-13-1975 L1976 EM IM *020 †18
GOSWAMI, Vardhana. ■ 18954 #495-96-1988 L1998 IMG *020 †20
GRIFFIN, Robert Stewart. ■ 18954 #024-01-2007 L2007 IM *012

JAFFE, Brian Chad. ■ 18954 #041-02-2008 L2008 *012
KOFF, Richard Allen. 130 ALMSHOUSE RD, STE 600 18954 #654-01-1983 L1985 FM OM *020
KOLBER, Lauren Rachel. 130 ALMSHOUSE RD, STE 202A 18954 #033-05-1981 L1982 D *020 †15
KORN, Scott Harvey. ■ 18954 #041-02-1981 L1986 IM RHU *050 †20
NOCERA, Lisa Marie. ■ 18954 #035-06-1990 L1992 APM *020 †05
OXENBERG, Jacqueline Clar. ■ 18954 #041-77-2007, ▲ L2007 *012
ROSEN, Matthew Marc. ■ 18954 #041-02-2005 L2005 GS *012
SHAH, Jaykumar H. 862 2ND STREET PIKE 18954 #495-17-1969 L1978 FM *020 †18
SHAH, Vijaya J. 862 2ND STREET PIKE 18954 #495-01-1970 L1978 FM IM *020 †18
SOLIS, J Andrew. 130 ALMSHOUSE RD STE 100 18954 #043-01-1980 L1983 IM *020 †20
ZEIGEN, Scott Richard. 130 ALMSHOUSE RD, STE 202B 18954 #033-06-1982 L1983 OPH *020 †35

RICHEYVILLE – WASHINGTON

COLANTONI, William. EMERY ROAD 15358 #041-12-1951 L1952 AN *071 †05

RICHLAND – LEBANON

GARRETT, John Cleland. 1109 STOUCHSBURG RD 17087 #035-15-1973 L1976 AN *020 †05
SCARBOROUGH, Bethann Mari. ■ 17087 #051-01-2008 *012

RIDGWAY – ELK

ABELEDA, Joselita M. 99 HOSPITAL ST 15853 #748-07-1983 L1997 PD *020 †55 ‡
COFFMAN, Peter William. 425 HYDE AVE 15853 #020-02-1993 L2001 P *020 †75
COROSO, Joseph Graham. 94 HOSPITAL ST 15853 #035-03-1977 L1978 FM *020 †18
HOLWICK, Philip Bradshaw. 94 HOSPITAL ST 15853 #019-02-1964 L1968 D *071
ORDIWAY, M Vernon. 94 HOSPITAL ST 15853 #041-13-1958 L1959 P AM *071 †75
REDDY, Medapally Pradeep. 94 HOSPITAL ST, PROFESSIONAL OFFICE BLDG 15853 #495-21-1984 L1995 P *020 †20
THOMPSON, William Weir. 107 CENTER ST 15853 #041-12-1948 L1949 GP PHP *071
UDARBE, Guillermo G. 225 SOUTH ST, STE 1 15853 #748-07-1965 L1981 FM *020 ‡

RIDLEY PARK – DELAWARE

ABDULLAH, Ibrahim. ■ 19078 #024-01-2001 L2001 GS *012
ALDERFER, Gill Robt. 100 E CHESTER PIKE, PROFESSIONAL ARTS BLDG 19078 #041-02-1968 L1975 GYN *020 †30
ALLEN, Samuel Disston. 23 W CHESTER PIKE STE 101 19078 #041-13-1963 L1965 U *020 †95
ALREZ, Aymen. 1 BARTOL AVE, CARDIOVASCULAR GROUP LLC 19078 #781-01-1985 L2006 CD *020 †20 ‡
AL-SAYYAD, Mohammad F. 175 E CHESTER PIKE, TAYLOR HOSPIAL 19078 #875-01-1977 L1985 GS EM *020
ANDRAHENNADY, Sisira K. 175 E CHESTER PIKE, DEPT OF ANESTHESIOLOGY 19078 #220-01-1986 L2000 AN *020 †05
ANIS, Nadeem Asghar. 175 E CHESTER PIKE 19078 #495-83-1990 L2005 IM *020 †20
BADRA, Michel. 23 W CHESTER PIKE 19078 #847-02-1971 L1974 PUD IM *020 †20
BERGMAN, Martin Jan. 8 MORTON AVE STE 304 19078 #056-06-1982 L1983 RHU IM *020 †20
BHOGAL, Daljit Kaur. 8 MORTON AVE, STE 103 19078 #305-01-2000 L2000 IM *020 †20 ‡
BOGART, Lee Howard. 33 W CHESTER PIKE 19078 #035-46-1981 L1987 HEM IM *020 †20
BRODSKY, John. 23 W CHESTER PIKE 19078 #035-09-1963 L1963 GP PHP *020
BRUNNER, Douglas James. 175 E CHESTER PIKE 19078 #654-01-1981 L1982 PM *020 †60
CAMPELLONE, Alfred D, Jr. 175 E CHESTER PIKE, TAYLOR HOSPITAL 19078 #041-07-1989 L1993 GS *020
CHOUDHRY, Vijay Lakshmi. 101 DUTTON ST 19078 #496-07-1984 L1998 IM *020 †20
CLAY, Christina Marie. 33 W CHESTER PIKE 19078 #016-06-1985 L1995 ON IM *020 †20
CUCULINO, Gregory Philip. 175 E CHESTER PIKE, DEPT OF EMERGENCY MEDICINE 19078 #041-07-1996 L1998 EM *020 †16
DARNALL, Jeffrey Thos. 1 BARTOL AVE STE 103 19078 #047-05-1976 L1977 IM ID *020 †20
DAVIS, Wm Edward Kelly. 1 BARTOL AVE, STE 15 19078 #041-09-1966 L1967 U *020 †95
DIAMANDI, Mihai Vasile. 175 E CHESTER PIKE, TAYLOR HOSPITAL 19078 #781-01-1992 L2005 IM *020 †20
DI GIOVANNI, Anthony Jos. 175 E CHESTER PIKE 19078 #041-09-1967 L1968 AN *020 †05
DOOKHAN, Marlene J. 100 E CHESTER PIKE, PROFESSIONAL ARTS BUILDING 19078 #051-04-1991 L1993 OBG *020 †30
ENNIS, Peter Douglas. 8 MORTON AVE, STE 305 19078 #041-09-1993 L1996 HO *020 †20
GASKIN, Annmarie Avonda. 175 E CHESTER PIKE 19078 #035-15-1994 L1998 N *020 †75
GINSBURG, David Saul. 100 E CHESTER PIKE 19078 #041-02-1978 L1981 OBG *020 †30
GITTER, Howard Ted. 1 BARTOL AVE, STE 10 19078 #041-09-1981 L1982 CD IM *020 †20
GOLDSTEIN, Jerome Benj. 100 E CHESTER PIKE 19078 #048-02-1976 L1981 GYN *020 †30
GORDON, Stuart Leon. 1 BARTOL AVE, PREMIER ORTHOPAEDIC & 19078 #041-02-1981 L1982 ORS *020 †40
GROSSINGER, Bruce H. 23 W CHESTER PIKE STE 301, SPECIALISTS, P.C. 19078 #041-77-1985, ▲ L1985 N *020 †75
GROSSINGER, Steven D. 23 W CHESTER PIKE STE 301 19078 #041-77-1987, ▲ L1988 N *020 †20,75
HADLEY, David Kenneth. 204 E CHESTER PIKE, PHYSICIANS FOR WOMEN 19078 #041-01-1997 L2005 OBG *020 †30
HERRERA, Anibal Felix. 8 MORTON AVE, STE 305 19078 #275-01-1960 L1963 GE IM *071 †20
HOLST, Hazel Irene. 15 MORTON AVE 19078 #041-07-1958 L1962 PS GS *071 †85,65
JONES, Yvonne Lenell. 175 E CHESTER PIKE, DEPT ANESTHESIA 19078 #010-03-1984 L1987 AN *020
JOSUE, Stanley Bandolon. 175 E CHESTER PIKE, 1ST FL 19078 #035-19-2004 L2007 IM *100
KING, Tamika Latoya. 175 E CHESTER PIKE, EMERGENCY DEPARTMENT 19078 #041-02-2002 L2005 EM *100 †16
KOCHAR, Gurpreet Singh. 101 DUTTON ST 19078 #495-43-1977 L1985 CD IM *020
KUROKI, Helen Kane. 175 E CHESTER PIKE 19078 #041-01-1988 L1992 OBG *020 †30
LAPES, Melvyn Jay. 33 W CHESTER PIKE 19078 #051-01-1969 L1970 HEM ON *020 †20
LAVERY, Doriann Lee. ■ 19078 #041-02-2008 L2008 *012

LIEB, George. 23 W CHESTER PIKE, STE 201 19078 #308-12-1986 L1988 **PUD IM** *020 †20
LIM, Osmundo Uy. 175 E CHESTER PIKE, TAYLOR HOSPITAL 19078 #748-01-1964 L1973 **EM GP** *020 †16
LOOSE, Jeffrey Howard. 175 E CHESTER PIKE, TAYLOR LAB 19078 #041-09-1984 L1985 **PTH** *020 †50
LUY, Irwin C. 175 E CHESTER PIKE, TAYLOR HOSPITAL 19078 #748-08-1991 L1999 **AN** *040 †05
MALUMED, Jeffrey. 1 BARTOL AVE, PREMIER ORTHOPAEDIC & 19078 #035-09-1983 L1989 **ORS** *020 †40
MEHALICK, Pamela G. 23 W CHESTER PIKE STE 200 19078 #041-77-1981, ▲ L1982 **PD** *020
MENDEZ, Armando A. 1 BARTOL AVE, PREMIER ORTHOPAEDIC & 19078 #041-02-1985 L1986 **ORS** *020 †40
MIKHAIL, Majid H. 8 MORTON AVE, STE 305 19078 #528-01-1976 L1992 **HEM** *020 †20
MORANZ, Joel Gross. 100 E CHESTER PIKE 19078 #041-01-1972 L1973 **OBG** *020 †30
NAKHODA, Khozaim Zein. 175 E CHESTER PIKE 19078 #495-23-1983 L2001 **NM** *020 †80,28
NUNAG, Robert Dizon. 23 W CHESTER PIKE STE 200, CHILDRENS MEDICAL ASSOC 19078 #041-02-1992 L1995 **PD** *020 †55
O'MOORE, Paul Vincent. 175 E CHESTER PIKE 19078 #041-01-1983 L1993 **DR** *020 †80
PATEL, Rajesh J. 23 W CHESTER PIKE, STE 201 19078 #495-23-1984 L1991 **PUD IM** *020 †20
RATNER, Richard Ronald. 100 E CHESTER PIKE 19078 #041-09-1973 L1974 **IM CD** *020
RHODES, Robert Alexander. 1 BARTOL AVE STE 105 19078 #041-01-1980 L1981 **D** *020 †15 ‡
RIZZO, John S. 8 MORTON AVE, STE 101 19078 #010-02-1977 L1978 **OPH** *020 †35
ROTOR-MAKILAN, Marilyn L. 175 E CHESTER PIKE, 4TH FL 19078 #748-01-1977 L1984 **PM** *020
ROUSH, Robert Kenneth, Jr. 8 MORTON AVE, STE 305 19078 #033-05-1985 L1986 **ON HEM** *020 †20
ROVITO, Marc Anthony. 8 MORTON AVE, STE 305 19078 #041-13-1988 L1990 **ON** *020 †20
RUBY, Samuel Robt. 1 BARTOL AVE, CARDIOVASCULAR GROUP LLC 19078 #041-02-1976 L1979 **CD IM** *020 †20
RUFFINI, John Justin. 8 MORTON AVE 19078 #041-02-1983 L1983 **OPH** *020 †35
SALUK, Patricia. 175 E CHESTER PIKE 19078 #041-09-1981 L1983 **DR** *020 †80 ‡
SANJAY, Rashmi. 33 W CHESTER PIKE 19078 #496-22-1997 L2002 **HO** *020 †20
SAXON, Andrea Mary. 8 MORTON AVE, STE 101 19078 #041-09-1984 L1985 **OPH** *020 †35
SEEDOR, John Wade. 8 MORTON AVE, STE 207 19078 #041-09-1979 L1982 **GE ICE** *020 †20
SHORE, Stephen Arthur. 8 MORTON AVE, STE 305 19078 #041-09-1984 L1990 **HEM ON** *020 †20
SHOTWELL, Barbara Ann. 204 E CHESTER PIKE 19078 #041-02-1989 L1993 **GS OS** *020 †85
SINOR, Cleve Raydean. 175 E CHESTER PIKE 19078 #051-04-1998 L2006 **IM** *020 †20
SOLAN, Andrew James. 33 W CHESTER PIKE 19078 #035-03-1974 L1980 **ON HEM** *020 †20
SPRANDIO, John David. 8 MORTON AVE, STE 305 19078 #041-13-1980 L1981 **HEM** *020 †20
STAFFORD, Calvin R, Jr. 175 E CHESTER PIKE 19078 #041-09-1971 L1972 **N SME** *020 ‡
STARER, Larrimore J. 8 MORTON AVE, STE 101 19078 #041-02-1951 L1952 **FM** *071 †35
SVOBODA, Jakub. 8 MORTON AVE, STE 305 19078 #008-01-2000 L2001 **HO** *020 †20
TADDUNI, Gregory. 1 BARTOL AVE, PREMIER ORTHOPAEDIC & 19078 #035-46-1982 L1984 **ORS HS** *020 †40
TIONGSON, Jose G, Jr. 103 E RIDLEY AVE 19078 #748-01-1968 L1973 **IM CD** *020 †20
TORRENCE, Michael Bruce. 23 W CHESTER PIKE, STE 200 19078 #019-02-1974 L1977 **PD** *020 †55
WANG, Dorothy Y. ■ 19078 #041-02-2008 *012
ZEE, Kate Christie. ■ 19078 #041-07-1975 L1976 **EM** *075
ZIBELMAN, Mark. 8 MORTON AVE 19078 #041-09-1973 L1974 **IM** *020 †20
ZUBERI, Lubna M. 8 MORTON AVE, STE 301 19078 #704-25-1988 L1994 **END** *020 †20

RILLTON — WESTMORELAND

BAKSHI, Viharika Kiran. 2976 CLAY PIKE 15678 #495-96-1972 L1977 **FM** *020 †18
WONG, Kevin Michael. 2976 CLAY PIKE 15678 #024-05-1979 L1980 **FM** *020 †18

RIMERSBURG — CLARION

MARGUGLIO, A Eugene. 101 E BROAD 16248 #005-17-1962 **GP GS** *071

RINGTOWN — SCHUYLKILL

KONITZER, Patrick Thomas. 22 RIDGE RD 17967 #035-46-1997 L2001 **AN** *020
REINBOLD, Marion J E. ■ 17967 #024-15-1942 L1943 **AN** *075

RIVERSIDE — NORTHUMBERLAND

ALLEN, John Lewis. PO BOX 68, 9TH AND AVENUE F 17868 #041-01-1946 L1947 **P** *071 †75
BEILER, David Davis. ■ 17868 #024-01-1947 L1953 **RO DR** *071 †80
CLARK, Michael Jonathan. ■ 17868 #020-02-2005 L2005 **GS** *012
CURRID, John Michael. PO BOX 279 17868 #539-04-1969 *100
LUTTON, Jeffrey Scott. ■ 17868 #010-02-2006 L2006 **ORS** *012

ROARING BROOK TOWNSHIP — LACKAWANNA

UTZ, Jeffrey Peter. ■ 18444 #041-09-1994 **PD** *100

ROARING SPRING — BLAIR

BRIDENBAUGH, Robert Paul. ■ 16673 #041-02-1960 L1961 **FM IM** *071 †18
BURKET, Ramon Clyde. 100 NASON DR STE 103 16673 #041-13-1961 L1962 **FM** *020 †18
CASTEL, Joseph A. 105 HILLCREST DR, NASON PEDIATRICS 16673 #654-01-1988 L1993 **PD** *020 †55
CREVECOUER, Roland. 105 NASON DR 16673 #035-19-1991 L2002 **PDC** *020 †55
FULCHIERO, Gregory John. 121 JUNE DR 16673 #041-09-1970 L1971 **ORS** *020 †40
GRUMBINE, Rowena T. 105 HILLCREST DR, NASON PEDIATRICS 16673 #748-01-1989 L1995 **PD** *020 †55
HARVEY, Charles, Jr. 121 JUNE DR 16673 #041-77-1986, ▲ L1987 **ORS OP** *020
HIMES, Ralph Francis, Jr. 99 NASON DR 16673 #041-02-1954 L1955 **OPH** *071 †35

HOUK, Allison Joan. 100 NASON DR STE 101, COVE FAMILY PRACTICE INC 16673 #038-06-1997 L1999 **FM** *020 †18
JONES, Larry Wm. 99 NASON DR 16673 #041-12-1966 L1967 **OPH** *020 †35
JONES, Renee Lynne. 99 NASON DR 16673 #041-14-1995 L1998 **OPH** *020 †35
KIRSCH, William Jos. NASON HOSP 16673 #010-02-1961 L1962 **PTH NM** *020 †50,28 ‡
LAMBE, Helen Anne. 104 HILLCREST DR, NASON OBSTETRICS & GYNECOL 16673 #041-14-1993 L1996 **OBG** *020 †30
LETTIERI, Michael A. 105 NASON DR 16673 #654-01-1984 L1994 **EM TRS** *020 †18
LOCKE, Darron B. 100 NASON DR STE 101 16673 #033-06-1990 L1992 **FM** *020 †18
MOLTER, Michael W. 121 JUNE DR 16673 #041-78-1999, ▲ L2002 **PM** *020 †60
PETTINGER, Maria Therese. 105 NASON DR 16673 #048-02-1997 L2001 **DR** *020 †80
PIKE, Debra Susan. 4 NASON DR STE 4 16673 #041-12-1979 L1980 **OBG** *020 †30
PORT, Joshua. 121 JUNE DR 16673 #041-01-1988 L1990 **OSM** *020 †40
ROWE, Angela Wai-Chung. 121 JUNE DR 16673 #016-76-1994, ▲ L1999 **ORS** *020
SINDER, Andrew Feder. 105 HILLCREST DR, NASON PEDIATRICS 16673 #035-03-1992 L1994 **PD** *020 †55
SINGER, Robert Joseph. 121 JUNE DR 16673 #028-79-1991, ▲ L1995 **ORS** *020
SOLLENBERGER, Laura B. 100 NASON DR STE 101 16673 #041-14-1988 L1990 **IM** *020 †20
UM, Steve Sanghoon. 105 NASON DR, NASON HOSP 16673 #041-09-1988 L1990 **FM** *020 †18

ROBESONIA — BERKS

ASLAM, Mohammed. PO BOX 115 19551 #495-33-1968 L1978 **FM EM** *020 †18
BAHORIK, Claudia J. ■ 19551 #041-77-1990, ▲ L1991 **FM OM** *020 †18 ‡
CITRO, Laurence A. ■ 19551 #035-06-1969 L1970 **DR** *071 †80
HENNING, Justin Robert. ■ 19551 #041-02-2008 *012
SCHWEIZER, Robert Roy. ■ 19551 #041-13-1956 L1957 **FM** *071 †18

ROCHESTER — BEAVER

COLE, Marty. 218 W WASHINGTON ST, P O BOX 1629 15074 #047-20-1996 L1998 **FM** *020 †18
HELMICK, Wayne Wm. 349 YORK AVE 15074 #041-12-1958 L1959 **FM** *071 †18
KONRAD, Mark Geo. PENN BEAVER MED CTR INC 15074 #020-02-1947 L1956 **DR** *071
MALLEY, Erin Elizabeth. 176 VIRGINIA AVE 15074 #041-12-1993 L1997 **CHP** *020 †75
MENON, Kanthi. 176 VIRGINIA AVE 15074 #495-44-1986 L2000 **P** *020
VASSILENKO, Mikhail. 175 VIRGINIA AVE 15074 #913-72-1984 L1997 **P** *020 †75
ZAMBELLI, George R. 380 ADAMS ST 15074 #028-34-1973 L1977 **OPH** *020 †35

ROCKLEDGE — MONTGOMERY

BOLNO, Charles Martin. 404B HUNTINGDON PIKE 19046 #041-77-1974, ▲ L1975 **ORS** *020 ‡
CASAIA, James Frank. ■ 19046 #308-03-1981 L1984 **DR GP** *020
GAUGHAN, William John. 600 HUNTINGDON PIKE, 1ST FL 19046 #041-09-1983 L1984 **NEP IM** *020 †20
GOMEZ DUMARAN, Delfa. 120 HUNTINGDON PIKE, STE 101 19046 #748-01-1966 L1973 **IM PD** *071
KANTOR, James Gordon. 120 HUNTINGDON PIKE, STE 200 19046 #018-75-1975, ▲ L1976 **PD** *020
MOORE, Jay Richard. 120 HUNTINGDON PIKE, STE 100 19046 #041-01-1961 L1963 **NEP IM** *020 †20
REID-FIGHERA, Deirdre Ann. 120 HUNTINGDON PIKE, LOWER LEVEL 19046 #041-15-2000 L2004 **RHU** *020 †20
SELHAT, Jorj Fethullah. 120 HUNTINGDON PIKE 19046 #902-10-1952 L1966 **IM** *020
TRAN, Hong Thi. 120 HUNTINGDON PIKE, STE 101 19046 #024-05-1993 L1996 **IM** *020 †20

ROGERSVILLE — GREENE

DUER, Nathan Browning. 140 CHURCH ST 15359 #041-02-1984 L1987 **FM** *020 †18
MARTIN, John Paul. 140 CHURCH ST 15359 #055-75-2000, ▲ L2003 **FM** *020 †18 ‡
NOFTZGER, Martha Roe. 140 CHURCH ST 15359 #041-12-1987 L1989 **FM** *020 †18

RONKS — LANCASTER

CONWELL, Jason Edward. 29 EASTBROOK RD 17572 #041-14-2003 L2003 **FM** *020 †18
DUPREY, James G. 29 EASTBROOK RD 17572 #024-07-1977 L1982 **FM** *020 †18
HESS, John Clair. 29 EASTBROOK RD 17572 #041-02-1983 L1984 **FM** *020 †18 ‡
JACKSON, Richard David. 29 EASTBROOK RD 17572 #035-06-1983 L1984 **FM** *020 †18
MCKNIGHT, Stephanie Ann. 29 EASTBROOK RD, EASTBROOK FAMILY HEALTH CE 17572 #041-13-2004 L2004 **FM** *020 †18
SIEGRIST, Jay Donald. 29 EASTBROOK RD, EASTBROOK FAMILY HLTH CTR 17572 #041-14-1972 L1973 **IM PD** *020 †18 ‡

ROSE VALLEY — DELAWARE

BLOCKLYN, Maurice J. ■ 19063 #041-01-1937 L1938 **DR OS** *071
COOPER, Edwin N, Jr. 15 ORCHARD LN 19086 #041-01-1950 L1951 **AN** *071 †05
DE MASI, Leon Gregory, III. ■ 19086 #041-13-1979 L1980 **PHP** *020 †70
ERB, William Henry, Jr. ■ 19086 #041-01-1966 L1967 **GS** *071 †85
KNOBLE, Sefi Rebecca. ■ 19086 #035-03-1988 L1992 **IM IMG** *020 †20
KURTZ, Michael Ben. ■ 19063 #041-01-1964 L1969 **PD** *071 †55
RUSSELL, Marie Olivieri. ■ 19086 #041-02-1970 L1972 **PD PHO** *071 †55

ROSLYN — MONTGOMERY

COLLINS, Tarita N. ■ 19001 #041-77-2007, ▲ **P** *012
FRENCH, Andrea Lee. ■ 19001 #035-09-2003 L2005 **GS** *012
MATULLO, Kristofer S. ■ 19001 #041-13-2003 L2005 **ORS** *012
PONCIANO, Ever Ivan. ■ 19001 #041-15-2007 L2007 **IM** *012
SHEEHAN, Shawn Martin. ■ 19001 #041-77-2007, ▲ **EM** *012

SMITH, Patricia M Henney. 2661 WOODLAND RD 19001 #041-12-1952 L1953 **NTR** *072
SMITH, William Paul. 2661 WOODLAND RD 19001 #041-09-1948 L1949 **NTR** *072 †30
SOLOMON, Donald Henry. ■ 19001 #041-15-2004 L2004 **OTO** *012

ROYERSFORD — MONTGOMERY

ALI, Somera Ashraf. 420 W LINFIELD RD, STE 1000 19468 #704-01-1995 L2003
    END IM *020 †20
AYLWARD, John James. 600 CHURCH ST 19468 #033-05-1978 L1981 **IM** *020 †20
BETTS, Laurie Morris. ■ 19468 #035-48-1989 L2001 **IM** *020 †20
BROWN, Mark Spencer. 420 W LINFIELD RD, STE 1000 19468 #041-09-1983 L1985 **IM** *020 †20
DABBACK, De Witt T. 17 N 4TH AVE 19468 #041-02-1952 L1953 **GP** *071
FAHMY, Wasfy Fahim. 420 W LINFIELD RD, STE 102 19468 #330-02-1967 L1975 **SO** *020 †85
FREEHAFER, John Foster. 420 W LINFIELD RD, STE 1000 19468 #041-13-1975 L1976
    IM END *020 †20
GELDER, Mark Stephen. ■ 19468 #051-01-1982 L1984 **GO GYN** *020 †20,30
HOVICK, Edward Thos. 420 W LINFIELD RD, STE 100 19468 #041-07-1988 L1991
    NEP *020 †20 ‡
KANDIEL, Ahmed Elsayed. 420 W LINFIELD RD, STE 1000 19468 #035-19-2001 L2003 **GE** *020
KOVALOVICH, Kellen Karl. 420 W LINFIELD RD, STE 1000 19468 #041-13-1991 L1994
    GE HEP *020 †20
MALONEY, Kathleen Ann. ■ 19468 #041-07-1971 L1981 **N CHN** *020 †75
MARK, Raymond. ■ 19468 #041-01-1959 L1968 **PTH** *040 †50
MARON, John J. 336 SPRING ST BOX 226 19468 #035-19-1950 L1951 **FPG** *071
NAEGLE, Matthew Bowes. 420 W LINFIELD RD, STE 1000 19468 #041-13-1973
    RHU IM *020 †20 ‡
NGUYEN, Hang Thi. 420 W LINFIELD RD, STE 1000 19468 #051-04-2001 L2003 **IM** *020
NOVELL, Laura Ann. 240 MINGO RD 19468 #028-34-1997 L2004 **VIR** *020 †80
REAL, Mark Barry. 420 W LINFIELD RD, STE 1000 19468 #041-13-1979 L1980 **IM IMG** *020 †20
ROSA, Deborah Maria. 420 W LINFIELD RD, STE 102 19468 #041-07-1985 L1991
    GS VS *020 †85
ROTHSTEIN, Norman Zel. 420 W LINFIELD RD, STE 1000 19468 #041-01-1977 L1979
    CD *020 †20
SODICOFF, Eric Jay. 420 W LINFIELD RD, STE 1000 19468 #041-13-1996 L1999 **IM** *020 †20
STEPANSKY, David Wayne. 420 W LINFIELD RD, STE 1000 19468 #041-02-1978 L1979
    IM OS *030 †20
VINCA, Martin Joseph. 420 W LINFIELD RD, STE 102 19468 #041-02-1994 L2004 **GS** *020 †85
WONDERLING, Julia Loeffle. 590 WASHINGTON ST 19468 #041-15-2004 L2007 **EM** *020

RUFFS DALE — WESTMORELAND

SMITH, Kelly Marie. ■ 15679 #005-02-2004 L2004 **IM** *100

RUSSELL — WARREN

BORGER, Lee James. RR 1 BOX 1066 16345 #041-12-1944 L1945 **EM PD** *071
REINHARD, Harold J. ■ 16345 #041-02-1953 L1956 **P N** *071 †75
RILEY, Veryl M Long. OLD WARREN JAMESTOWN RD 16345 #041-12-1949 L1950 **OBG** *072

RUTLEDGE — DELAWARE

HUTH, Bradley Joseph. ■ 19070 #038-41-2005 L2006 **RO** *012
JOHNSON, Philip E P. ■ 19070 #041-13-1980 L1981 **OTO** *020 †45
TEACHEY, David Trent. ■ 19070 #051-07-1999 L2002 **PHO** *100 †55

RYDAL — MONTGOMERY

FORCE, Thomas Burris. ■ 19046 #041-13-1957 L1958 **GYN** *071 †30
FRANK, Martin N. ■ 19046 #041-09-1951 L1952 **CD IM** *020 †20
GREENBAUM, Charles H. ■ 19046 #041-02-1954 L1955 **D** *071 †15
HURST, J Paul, Jr. ■ 19046 #036-01-1957 L1958 **P** *071
KAMDAR, Jay C. ■ 19046 #041-09-1961 L1968 **IM IMG** *020 †18
KRAMER, Jeffrey Allan. ■ 19046 #041-15-2000 L2001 **EM** *020 †16 ‡
KRICK, Earl Shaffer. ■ 19046 #041-09-1942 L1943 **FPG** *071
KURITZKES, Fedor Anselm. ■ 19046 #869-01-1956 L1958 **PD ADL** *071 †55
LAMSBACK, Edward Gary. 1441 LEWIS RD ROADD-4 19046 #041-09-1980 L1981 **IM** *020 †20
MALMUD, Leon S. 971 FRAZIER RD 19046 #041-01-1965 L1966 **NM IM** *072 †28
NEWMAN, Leroy. ■ 19046 #041-02-1949 L1950 **PD** *071 †55
O'NEILL, James F. ■ 19046 #041-02-1936 L1937 **GS TS** *071 †85,90
PAWLYSZYN, Julian. ■ 19046 #407-10-1949 L1957 **PA P** *071
PIROMRUEN, Watcharee. ■ 19046 #891-02-1974 L1977 **PD** *100 †55
PROENCA, Ricardo Benros. ■ 19046 #035-08-1999 L2001 **IM** *020 †20
SCHWARTZ, David Saml. 972 FRAZIER RD 19046 #041-02-1973 L1974 **IM CD** *050 †20
WEISBEIN, Jessica Lee. ■ 19046 #041-01-2006 L2006 **EM** *012
ZAGERMAN, Abraham Jack. ■ 19046 #041-13-1953 L1954 **IM** *071

SAEGERTOWN — CRAWFORD

COLLIS, Ernest Leonard. 700 ERIE ST 16433 #063-01-1994 L1997 **FM** *020 †18
VUKMER, George J. ■ 16433 #041-09-1963 L1964 **DR GP** *071 †80

SAINT CLAIR — SCHUYLKILL

SCHETTINI, Bruno. 502 S 2ND ST 17970 #035-48-1982 L1993 **IM OM** *020 †20

SAINT DAVIDS — DELAWARE

BJORNSSON, Thorir Dan. 539 SAINT DAVIDS AVE 19087 #484-01-1971 L1988 **PA** *050

JOHNSON, Caroline Carlson. ■ 19087 #023-01-1979 L1986 **ID IM** *062 †20
JOSHI, Manuja. ■ 19087 #496-04-1996 L2002 **IM** *020 †20
KIM, Bong-Soo. ■ 19087 #583-10-1991 L2004 **NS** *012
PERKINS, David Philip. 418 E LANCASTER AVE 19087 #038-40-1987 L1989 **IM** *020 †20 ‡
REED, Karin Anne. ■ 19087 #041-15-2008 *012
ROCK, Alice Louise. 500 E LANCASTER AVE, NUMBER 118 C 19087 #016-45-1987 L2002
    PHO *020 †55
TALBOT, George Harrison. PO BOX 7440 19087 #008-01-1975 L1976 **ID IM** *050 †20
VAN DE BEEK, M Louis. ■ 19087 #041-09-1982 L1983 **FM IM** *020 ‡
WEINSTOCK, Andrew I. 435 E LANCASTER AVE, NUMBER 217 19087 #041-01-1978 L1979
    GS OS *020 †85
YUM, Keuk Yong. 236 RAVENSCLIFF RD, SAINT DAVIDS PA 19087 19087 #583-02-1960 L1971
    GS *020 †85 ‡
ZHANG, Yutong. 435 E LANCASTER AVE, STE 1 19087 #243-39-1982 L1998 **PM** *020 †60

SAINT MARYS — ELK

CARUSO, David Michael. 761 JOHNSONBURG RD, STE 240 15857 #041-14-1978 L1979
    FM *020 †18
CHEN, Lei. 149 PENN RD 15857 #243-81-1986 L2000 **OBG U** *020
CIENCIVA, Rosemaria J. 1095 MILLION DOLLAR HWY 15857 #041-14-1978 L1979 **FM** *020 †18
ESHBACH, Ted Brubaker. 761 JOHNSONBURG RD, STE 310 15857 #041-13-1974 L1975
    ORS *071 †40
FLORES, Emilio G, Jr. 763 JOHNSONBURG RD 15857 #748-08-1974 L1981 **DR NM** *020 ‡
FUEG, Adrienne. 761 JOHNSONBURG RD, STE 120 15857 #035-08-1994 L2007 **GS** *020 †85
GERO, Tibor Julius. 763 JOHNSONBURG RD 15857 #305-01-1983 L1988 **EM IM** *020
GORLOWSKI, John Michael. 761 JOHNSONBURG RD, STE 360 15857 #041-13-1992 L1995
    PD *020 †55
HACKETT, James L, Jr. 1114 WINDFALL RD 15857 #010-02-1958 L1962 **IM CD** *071
HALL, Michael Maurice. 177 WASHINGTON ST 15857 #035-15-1985 L1986 **FM** *020 †18
JOHE, David Howard. 761 JOHNSONBURG RD, STE 210 15857 #055-01-1977 L1982
    ORS EM *020
JOLLY, Raj Kumar. 20 N MICHAEL ST 15857 #495-73-1974 L1977 **OTO PS** *020 †45
JOSEPH, Kadankavil C. 761 JOHNSONBURG RD, STE 130 15857 #495-31-1969 L1979
    GS *020 †85
KELLY, John Stephen. 763 JOHNSONBURG RD 15857 #041-14-1973 L1974 **EM** *020
KULLING, David Lee. 763 JOHNSONBURG RD 15857 #409-16-1979 L1980 **EM FSM** *020 †18 ‡
LIN, Wu-Jan. 761 JOHNSONBURG RD STE 150 15857 #244-04-1970 L1977 **OBG** *020
LU, Luis Washington. 765 JOHNSONBURG RD 15857 #737-06-1975 L1982 **OPH** *020 †35 ‡
MANACK, Leo Michael. 763 JOHNSONBURG RD, ERHC/LABORATORY 15857
    #055-01-1988 L1992 **BBK** *020 †50
MOCLOCK, Michael Anthony. 136 STATE ST, KEYSTONE MEDICAL ASSOCIATE 15857
    #041-07-1990 L1992 **FM** *020 †18
PATANKAR, Jayant L. 763 JOHNSONBURG RD, ELK REGIONAL HEALTH CENTER 15857
    #305-01-1984 L1985 **FM EM** *020 †18
PATEL, Rameshbhai S. 763 JOHNSONBURG RD, ST MARYS HEALTH CENTER 15857
    #495-22-1985 L1999 **IM** *020 †20
PERNESKI, Robert Louis. ■ 15857 #041-01-1954 L1955 **ORS** *071
POULLIOTT, Jerome Wm. ■ 15857 #041-13-1955 L1956 **EM GS** *071 †85
RUDICK, Donald Henry. 761 JOHNSONBURG RD, STE 350 15857 #035-09-1970 L1995
    U *020 †95
SALINAS, Joe Ariel. 763 JOHNSONBURG RD 15857 #048-12-1978 L1993 **PTH** *020 †50
SARGINGER, Larry James. 136 STATE ST 15857 #041-13-1981 L1982 **FM FPG** *020 †18
SCHMIDT, Robert Jos. 177 WASHINGTON ST 15857 #048-14-1978 L1979 **FM OS** *020 †16,18
SHARKEY, Dennis Aloysius. ■ 15857 #041-01-1954 L1955 **PTH** *071 †50
SORG, Maurus Leonard. 136 STATE ST 15857 #041-14-1978 L1979 **FM EM** *020 †18,16
SORIANO, Manuel G, Jr. 763 JOHNSONBURG RD 15857 #748-08-1960 L1968 **U EM** *020
STEELE, David Q. 761 JOHNSONBURG RD 15857 #041-12-1951 L1952 **ORS OS** *071 †40
STOKES, Dean H. 767 JOHNSONBURG RD 15857 #065-05-1982 L1994 **FM** *020
SUBRAMANY, Narayanaswamy. 761 JOHNSONBURG RD STE 130 15857 #495-33-1971 L1980
    GS *020 †85
TANDON, Bevan. 604 SUNSET RD 15857 #051-07-2008 *012
THAKER, Upendra N. 763 JOHNSONBURG RD 15857 #035-09-1985 L1993 **AN PMM** *020 †05 ‡
VALDES, Conrado Acosta. 763 JOHNSONBURG RD 15857 #748-07-1972 L1977 **AN** *020
VIJAYVARGIYA, Prabhu D. ■ 15857 #495-30-1982 L1987 **PCC IM** *020 †20
VIJAYVARGIYA, Rashmi. 761 JOHNSONBURG RD STE 110, ELK REGIONAL HEALTH
    CENTRE 15857 #496-02-1986 L1995 **NEP IM** *020 †20
WERNER, A Wm. 763 JOHNSONBURG RD 15857 #041-12-1975 L1976 **DR PDR** *071 †80

SAINT THOMAS — FRANKLIN

TURCHI, Pierre B. 175 SAINT THOMAS EDENVL RD 17252 #396-30-1976 L1983 **FM** *020 †18

SALISBURY — SOMERSET

BELL, Shawn Leroy. PO BOX 66, 231 ORD ST 15558 #041-15-2000 L2002 **FM** *020 †18

SALIX — CAMBRIA

FELIX, Robert John. ■ 15952 #041-15-2004 L2004 **IM** *020

SALLADASBURG — LYCOMING

WEST, Stanley Q, Jr. RR 973 BOX 447 17740 #041-02-1952 L1953 **GP OS** *075

SALTSBURG — INDIANA

BOULWARE, George Robert. ■ 15681 #010-03-1962 L1969 **GS OS** *071
MC GAUGHRAN, Alan Lee. 101 9TH ST 15681 #041-14-1985 L1986 **FM** *020 †18
MC KELVEY, Paul G, Jr. 101 9TH ST 15681 #041-01-1953 L1954 **GP** *071

PUTNAM-HORNBY, Suzanne. 101 9TH ST 15681 #003-01-1998 L2000 **FM** *030 †18

SANATOGA – MONTGOMERY

SHIN, Yong Shik. 600 CREEKSIDE DR STE 609, SUNNY BROOK VLG 19464 #583-08-1969 L1973
P *020

SANDY LAKE – MERCER

CABREROS, Lorie Joan Q. ■ 16145 #748-10-1990 L1997 **PCC** *020 †20

SARVER – BUTLER

BHAT, Kiran Banari. 619 S PIKE RD 16055 #038-40-1995 L1997 **PD** *020 †55
GREENBAUM, James K. 619 S PIKE RD 16055 #024-01-1951 L1952 **PD** *072 †55
HEILMAN, Marlin Stephen. ■ 16055 #041-01-1959 L1960 **OS GP** *030
HUGHES, James Lafayette. 16055 #041-09-1967 L1968 **CD** *071 †20
HUGHES, Jane Schilling. 16055 #041-02-1966 L1967 **DR** *071 †80
KELLY, Robert Wm. 110 LINCOLN DR 16055 #036-05-1973 L1981 **GS** *020 †85
KEPPEL, Kenneth Robt. 619 S PIKE RD, CHILDREN'S COMMUNITY CARE 16055
#036-07-1985 L1986 **PD** *020 †55
LAZARCIK, Gabriel Joseph. ■ 16055 #038-44-2001 L2001 **AN** *020 †05
RUDERT, William Alvin. ■ 16055 #041-12-1974 **OS** *050
VOGEL, Saralyn Sue. 619 S PIKE RD 16055 #041-13-1978 L1996 **PD** *075 †55

SAXONBURG – BUTLER

FIORAVANTI, Fred Karl. PO BOX 625, 132 PITTSBURGH ST 16056 #041-12-1980 L1981
FM *020 †18

SAYLORSBURG – MONROE

GORMAN, Daniel James. ■ 18353 #041-15-2007 L2007 **TY** *012
SEHRA, Kankanady Heera. PO BOX 1059 18353 #495-16-1952 L1974 **FM P** *071 †18

SAYRE – BRADFORD

ABBAS, Ibraheem. 1 GUTHRIE SQ, DEPT OF MED EDUCATION 18840 #704-21-2003 L2005
IM *012
ABOUFARES, Ali Fares. 1 GUTHRIE SQ, GUTHRIE CLINIC 18840 #605-01-1996 L2005
IC *020 †20
ACHARJI, Subasit. 1 GUTHRIE SQ, DEPT OF INTERNAL MED 18840 #495-36-2002 L2004
IM *020 †20
ADANIEL, Tanguile Agana. 1 GUTHRIE SQ 18840 #748-08-1969 L1977 **AN** *020
AHMED, Ibrahim Mohamed. 102 DESMOND ST 18840 #915-02-1981 L1992 **PD** *100 †55
AJGAONKAR, Mandar Shrikri. GUTHRIE SQUARE, ROBERT PACKER HOSP 18840
#495-06-2005 L2008 *100
ALLERTON, Jeffrey Paul. 1 GUTHRIE SQ, GUTHRIE CLNC 18840 #024-07-1986 L2006
ON HEM *020 †20 ‡
AMBE, Ronald Wanki Ngwa. ■ 18840 #010-03-2003 L2003 **GS** *012
ANDRES, Christopher. 1 GUTHRIE SQ 18840 #041-07-1993 L1995 **FM** *020 †18
ANWAR, Saeed. 1 GUTHRIE SQ, DEPT OF ANESTH 18840 #704-04-1989 L2004 **AN** *020 †05
AUGUSTIN, Toms. 1 GUTHRIE SQ 18840 #495-63-2003 L2006 **GS** *012
AWOTWI, Joseph Kwamina. GUTHRIE SQUARE, ROBERT PACKER HOSP 18840
#286-07-2006 L2008 *012
BABAYAN, Zaruhi. 1 GUTHRIE SQ, GUTHRIE CLINIC CARDIOLOGY 18840 #913-38-1995 L2007
CD *100 †20
BALTZER, Jeffrey Wayne. 1 GUTHRIE SQ 18840 #041-13-1980 L1982 **FOP** *020 †50
BANNISTER, Kyra Heather. 200 N WILBUR AVE, GUTHRIE CLINIC 18840 #035-01-1984 L1989
AN *020 †05
BANSAL, Amit Behari. 1 GUTHRIE SQ, ROBERT PACKER HOSPITAL 18840 #496-09-2005 L2006
IM *012
BASSI, Kuldeep Kumar. ■ 18840 #496-43-1997 L2007 **GS** *012
BEHM, Robert John. ■ 18840 #056-05-2007 L2007 **GS** *012
BELARDI, Francis Gabriel. 1 GUTHRIE SQ, GUTHRIE CLINIC LTD 18840 #030-06-1973 L2000
FM *030 †18
BELLO-LIM, Rebecca. 1 GUTHRIE SQ 18840 #748-01-1963 L1973 **AN OS** *074
BHATTI, Mohammad Azeem. 1 GUTHRIE SQ 18840 #060-01-1992 L2000 **U** *020 †95
BHENDE, Siddharth Kishore. ■ 18840 #305-01-2003 L2003 **GS** *012
BISHOP, Poni S Bolinger. 200 N WILBUR AVE, GUTHRIE MEDICAL CENTER 18840
#041-09-1972 L1973 **EM** *020 †16
BISHOP, Richard Lee. 200 N WILBUR AVE, DEPT SURG 18840 #041-09-1972 L1975
EM *020 †16
BLACK, Mark Anthony. ■ 18840 #047-07-2007 L2007 **GS** *012
BOBRA, Deepali Ajitkumar. 1 GUTHRIE SQ, GUTHRIE-ROBERT PACKER HOSP 18840
#495-22-1997 L2004 **FM** *100 †18
BOROK, Thomas L. 1 GUTHRIE SQ 18840 #035-19-1977 L1992 **RO ON** *020 †80 ‡
BOSELLI, Bruce David. 1 GUTHRIE SQ 18840 #035-20-1957 L1964 **ON HEM** *071 †20
BOYEK, Michael Francis. 1537 ELMIRA ST, SAYRE OUTPATIENT CLINIC 18840
#041-13-1978 L1979 **FM** *020 †20
BOYIADJIS, Harris. ■ 18840 #473-04-1996 **CD** *012 †20
BROKETA, Goran. 1 GUTHRIE SQ, GUTHRIE CLINIC, LTD. 18840 #957-01-1987 L1996
HO HEM *012
BROWN, Daniel Jos. GUTHRIE SQUARE, GUTHRIE CLNC 18840 #035-15-1983 L1987
AN *020 †05
BROWN, Deryck Winston S. 1 GUTHRIE SQ 18840 #566-01-1980 L1998 **FM** *020 †18
BUCKTHAL, Paul Edward. 1 GUTHRIE SQ 18840 #035-15-1970 L1973 **N** *020 †75
BUNAO, Romulo Macugay. ■ 18840 #748-01-1955 L1964 **GE IM** *020
CADY, William Walter. GUTHRIE MEDICAL CENTER 18840 #041-13-1971 L1972
NEP IM *020 †20

CAGIR, Burt. 1 GUTHRIE SQ, DEPT OF SURG 18840 #902-03-1984 L1996 **GS CRS** *020 †85
CAREY, Kevin Vincent. GUTHRIE MEDICAL CENTER 18840 #035-19-1973 L1978 **GE** *020 †20
CARTAGINESE, Peter. 1 GUTHRIE SQ 18840 #561-06-1981 L1985 **IM** *020 ‡
CHANDIRAMANI, Vijay Hari. 1 GUTHRIE SQ, DEPT OF MEDICAL EDUCATION 18840
#495-39-2001 L2005 **IM** *012
CHAUDHARY, Sumblina Aslam. 1 GUTHRIE SQ, GUTHRIE CLINIC 18840 #704-22-1987 L2001
DR *020 †80
CHAVDA, Keyur Anilkumar. 1 GUTHRIE SQ, DEPT OF MEDICAL EDUCATION 18840
#495-22-1997 L2005 **GS** *012
CHOI, Sam Kwang. 200 N WILBUR AVE, GUTHRIE MEDICAL CENTER 18840
#583-09-1969 L1974 **R N** *020 †75,80
CHOUDRY, Shazia Hafiz. 1 GUTHRIE SQ, GUTHRIE CLINIC 18840 #045-01-1999 L2004
AN *020 †05
CHOUHDRY, Iftikhar-Ahmad. 1 GUTHRIE SQ 18840 #704-04-1972 L1997 **HO IM** *020 †20
COHEN, Robert Edward. GUTHRIE MEDICAL CENTER 18840 #023-07-1972 L1973
ORS *020 †40
COOROS, James Charles. ■ 18840 #035-15-2004 L2004 **GS** *012
DALAL, Gunjan Miteshbhai. 1 GUTHRIE SQ, DEPT OF MED EDUCATION 18840
#496-41-2003 L2005 **IM** *012
DAMIAN, Richard Anthony. 1 GUTHRIE SQ 18840 #035-15-1989 L1992 **GS CCS** *085
DELUGE, Gerri Lynne. 1 GUTHRIE SQ, GUTHRIE-ROBERT PACKER HOSP 18840
#305-01-2004 L2005 **FM** *100
DENNEN, Timothy James. 330 N KEYSTONE AVE 18840 #041-02-1984 L1986 **FM** *075 †18
DESHMUKH, Narayan. 112 JOY ST 18840 #495-21-1964 L1973 **VS GS** *020 †85
DESHMUKH, Pramod M. GUTHRIE SQUARE, GUTHRIE CLNC 18840 #495-96-1979 L1990
CD *020 †20
DE SIO, Felix Jos. GUTHRIE MEDICAL CENTER 18840 #041-09-1979 L1980 **NEP IM** *020 †20
DEVARAKONDA, Srinivas San. 1 GUTHRIE SQ 18840 #495-21-2003 L2005 **IM** *012
DEVINE, Terence Moody. 1 GUTHRIE SQ, GUTHRIE CLINIC 18840 #035-09-1976 L1983
OPH *020 †35
DIENHART, Karl Josef. 200 N WILBUR AVE, GUTHRIE MEDICAL CENTER 18840
#407-34-1959 L1972 **CD IM** *071 †20
DISTEFANO, Kenneth Louis. 1 GUTHRIE SQ, GUTHRIE-ROBERT PACKER HOSP 18840
#665-01-2005 L2006 **FP** *012
DONDAPATI, Satya Sree. 1 GUTHRIE SQ 18840 #495-49-2003 L2005 **IM** *012
DUGGAL, Saket Kumar. ■ 18840 #035-47-2006 *100
DURAKOVIC, Asaf. 1 GUTHRIE SQ, ROBERT PACKER HOSP 18840 #065-10-1975 L1982
NM IM *072 †28 ‡
EDDIB, Abdulmagid Ali. 1 GUTHRIE SQ, DEPT OF MED EDU 18840 #613-02-2004 L2006
GS *012
ELLER, Richard Lee. 1537 ELMIRA ST 18840 #017-20-1979 L1980 **IM** *020 †20
ELLIS, George Leroy. GUTHRIE MEDICAL CENTER 18840 #041-07-1979 L1980 **EM** *020 †16
EPHLIN, Karen Ann. 1 GUTHRIE SQ 18840 #041-15-2001 L2001 **PD** *020 †55
ESRIG, Barry Chas. 1 GUTHRIE SQ, GUTHRIE CLINIC 18840 #035-46-1971 L2007
TS *020 †85,90
ESWARAN, Manivel Kumaran. 1 GUTHRIE SQ, ROBERT PACKER HOSPITAL 18840
#496-23-2002 L2005 **IM** *012
EVANS, Lewis C, II. ■ 18840 #035-01-1974 L1978 **CD IM** *071 †20
FALKENBERG, Gisela H G. 1 GUTHRIE SQ 18840 #407-05-1956 L1971 **AN** *020 †05
FEDELE, Charles Robert. 1 GUTHRIE SQ, GUTHRIE CLINIC 18840 #561-01-1970 L1977
D *020 †15 ‡
FISHER, Philip Clinton. 1 GUTHRIE SQ 18840 #041-09-1975 L1980 **EM** *020 †16
FLEURY GUZMAN, Andres Raf. ■ 18840 #035-01-2001 **GS** *012
FLYNN, Richard John. GUTHRIE MEDICAL CENTER 18840 #041-02-1967 L1973 **N** *020 †75
FOSTER, Richard Burton. GUTHRIE MEDICAL CENTER 18840 #035-09-1975 L1988 **DR** *020 †80
FREIJE, James Edward. 1 GUTHRIE SQ, GUTHRIE CLINIC 18840 #035-15-1985 L1991
OTO HNS *050 †45
FRIEDENBERG, William Robt. GUTHRIE SQUARE 18840 #041-02-1967 L1998
ON HEM *071 †20
GAJANANA, Deepakraj. ■ 18840 #496-39-2005 L2007 **GS** *012
GARCIA, Carlos Alberto. 1 GUTHRIE SQ, GUTHRIE CLINIC 18840 #264-11-1986 L1997
IM *020 †20
GEORGETSON, Michael James. 1 GUTHRIE SQ, FL 3 18840 #041-02-1985 L1986
GE IM *020 †20
GERGEL, Thomas James. 1 GUTHRIE SQ 18840 #035-06-1998 L2003
RO *020 †80
GHELLAI, Ali Mahmud. 1 GUTHRIE SQ 18840 #613-02-1988 L2002 **GS** *020 †85
GOHEL, Jagruti Pankaj. 1 GUTHRIE SQ, ROBERT PACKER HOSPITAL 18840
#495-48-2002 L2006 **FP** *012
GOLDBERG, Steven Eric. 1 GUTHRIE SQ 18840 #041-09-1979 L1980 **CD IM** *020 †20
GORSKI, Deborah A. 1 GUTHRIE SQ 18840 #041-09-1983 L1985 **IM** *020 †20
GOTTLIEB, Philip Danl. 1 GUTHRIE SQ 18840 #035-15-1977 L1988 **R** *020 †80
GU, Jeng Yul. 1 GUTHRIE SQ 18840 #583-02-1962 L1973 **R** *020 †80
GUPTA, Sushil. 1 GUTHRIE SQ, GUTHRIE CLINIC LTD 18840 #495-36-1972 L1998 **VS** *020 †85
GUR, Ilia. 1 GUTHRIE SQ, ROBERT PACKER HOSPITAL 18840 #550-03-2004 L2006 **GS** *012
HAN, Anping. 1 GUTHRIE SQ 18840 #243-53-1984 L2006 **FP** *012
HARI PRASAD, Sendil Kumar. 1 GUTHRIE SQ 18840 #496-23-2001 **IM** *012
HERBST, Lee Jordan. 1 GUTHRIE SQ, 1 GUTHRIE SQ 18840 #035-15-1994 L1998 **OBG** *020 †30
HINSMAN, John Abner M, Jr. 1 GUTHRIE SQ 18840 #050-02-1965 L1966 **IM** *071 †20
HIRUNSRI, Panit. 1 GUTHRIE SQ 18840 #891-03-1986 L1999 **IM HEM** *020 †20
HO, Peter Ying Chuen. 1 GUTHRIE SQ, GUTHRIE CLINIC 18840 #038-41-1976 L2002
RO *020 †80
HODA, Tahirul. 330 N KEYSTONE AVE 18840 #495-75-1982 L1991 **FM** *020 †18 ‡
HOMAN, Mal Rolland. 1 GUTHRIE SQ, GUTHRIE CLINIC LTD 18840 #041-09-1985 L1986
END IM *020 †20
HUDOCK, Michael Jos. 1 GUTHRIE SQ, GUTHRIE CLNC LTD OPHTHAL 18840
#035-15-1981 L1982 **OPH** *020 †35
HUDOCK, Stephen Albert. 1 GUTHRIE SQ 18840 #035-15-1981 L1982 **OPH** *020 †35
HUSSAIN, Muzzaffar. 1 GUTHRIE SQ, ROBERT PACKER HOSPITAL 18840 #704-01-2004 L2007
IM *012
HUSSAIN, Sarwat. 1 GUTHRIE SQ 18840 #704-01-1970 L2004 **DR** *020 †80
INGERICK, Brent S. ■ 18840 #041-77-2001, ▲ L2001 **FM** *020 †20
JINDAL, Mohit. 1 GUTHRIE SQ 18840 #495-29-2003 L2007 **IM** *012
JOHNSON, Glen. 1 GUTHRIE SQ 18840 #649-33-1982 L1984 **AN** *020
JOSEPH, E. J. Priyadarshi. ■ 18840 #495-08-2001 L2003 **IM** *020 †20
JOY, Christopher Robt. 1 GUTHRIE SQ, GUTHRIE CLINIC 18840 #008-02-1984 L1994
DR VIR *020 †80

KAHN, Ronald Lee. 200 N WILBUR AVE, GUTHRIE MEDICAL CENTER 18840 #023-01-1977 L1980 IM *020 †20

KANAGALA, Vikram Swaroop. GUTHRIE SQUARE, ROBERT PACKER HOSP 18840 #495-50-2005 L2008 *100

KAPOOR, Anil. 1 GUTHRIE SQ 18840 #064-01-1991 L1998 U *020 †95

KASS, Younis. 1 GUTHRIE SQ 18840 #407-21-1958 L1966 CD IM *020

KHALID, Mona. 1 GUTHRIE SQ, DEPT OF MED EDUCATION 18840 #704-01-2004 L2007 IM *012

KHAN, Sabeen. 1 GUTHRIE SQ, DEPT OF MED EDU 18840 #704-04-2001 L2006 FP *012

KIKKAWA, Kazutoshi. ■ 18840 #572-16-1955 L1963 R *071 †80

KILARU, Malathy Latha. 1 GUTHRIE SQ, DEPT OF MED EDUCATION 18840 #496-35-2003 L2006 IM *012

KING, Joseph T. ROBT PACKER HOSP 18840 #035-06-1973 L1977 PTH CLP *020 †50

KISSELL, Kerri Ann. 1 GUTHRIE SQ 18840 #041-15-2004 L2006 IM *100 †20

KOH, Han Suk. 1 GUTHRIE SQ 18840 #231-01-1992 L1997 N *020 †75

KOSTICK, Richard. 1 GUTHRIE SQ, GUTHRIE CLINIC 18840 #033-75-1986, ▲ L1989 DR OS *020

KUCHELAN, Deepa. 1 GUTHRIE SQ, GUTHRIE CLNC 18840 #495-59-2001 L2002 IM *020 †20

KUKREJA, Sandeep Singh. 1 GUTHRIE SQ, ROBERT PACKER HOSPITAL 18840 #496-59-2002 L2006 IM *012

KUMAR, Manjula. 1 GUTHRIE SQ 18840 #495-41-1968 L1996 P *020

KYAW, Yadana. 1 GUTHRIE SQ, ROBERT PACKER HOSPITAL 18840 #209-01-2005 L2007 IM *012

LASH, Bradley Walter. ■ 18840 #035-15-2006 L2006 IM *012

LEE, Ferrol J. GUTHRIE MEDICAL CENTER 18840 #024-01-1974 L1983 END IM *020 †20

LEE, Marvin Soonmook. 1 GUTHRIE SQ 18840 #583-03-1963 L1972 AN PMM *020

LEE, Rachel Duane. 1 GUTHRIE SQ 18840 #024-07-1975 L1991 D IM *020 †20,15

LEE, Sally Soyoung. ■ 18840 #033-05-1998 L2000 NEP *020 †20

LEWIS, Paulette Valencia. 1 GUTHRIE SQ 18840 #024-01-1994 L1997 IM *020 †20

LIKHI, Rishi. 1 GUTHRIE SQ 18840 #495-73-2004 L2005 IM *012

LIU, Yi. 1 GUTHRIE SQ, GUTHRIE CLINIC 18840 #243-45-1990 L2005 FP *012

LIVELY, Henry S. GUTHRIE SQUARE 18840 #041-13-1952 L1956 A IM *071

LOCKARD, John Wm, Jr. 1 GUTHRIE SQ, GUTHRIE CLINIC LTD 18840 #041-01-1988 L1991 AN PME *020 †05

LUBELL, Richard R. 1766 ELMIRA ST # 184 18840 #035-06-1980 L2005 OBG *020 †30

MACKLER, Gerald Lawrence. 1 GUTHRIE SQ, GUTHRIE CLNC 18840 #035-01-1963 L1967 ON HEM *071 †20

MADNI, Syed Ali. 1 GUTHRIE SQ, DEPT OF MED EDU 18840 #704-25-2001 L2005 IM *012

MAGUIRE, John Walter. 1 GUTHRIE SQ, GUTHRIE CLINIC 18840 #035-09-1967 L2002 U *020 †95

MAHMOOD, Khalid. ■ 18840 #704-01-1962 L1994 OTO HNS *071 †45 ‡

MAHON, Frank Bernard, Jr. 1 GUTHRIE SQ 18840 #028-34-1965 L1965 U *071 †95

MANNAN, Abdul. 1 GUTHRIE SQ 18840 #496-17-2000 L2005 IM *100

MARDANI, Fareed Nazir. GUTHRIE SQUARE, ROBERT PACKER HOSP 18840 #495-96-2006 L2008 *012

MASHAS, Wayne Edward. 1 GUTHRIE SQ 18840 #033-05-1984 L2001 CCS CRS *020 †85,10

MATHUR, Jagrati. 1 GUTHRIE SQ, DEPT OF INTERNAL MED 18840 #495-37-2003 L2005 IM *012

MATTHEWS, Joseph Ignatius. GUTHRIE SQUARE 18840 #030-06-1969 L1999 IM PCC *020 †20

MC DONALD, Thomas J, Jr. GUTHRIE MEDICAL CENTER 18840 #041-09-1983 L1984 GE HEP *020 †20

MC GURK, Charles R. 1 GUTHRIE SQ, BEHAVIORAL SCIENCE BLDG 18840 #030-06-1975 L1976 P *020 †75

MCVAY, Bryan Michael. ■ 18840 #040-02-2004 L2004 GS *012

MENDIBLE PORRAS, Mariana. ■ 18840 #935-01-2001 L2004 GS *012

MEYER, Kenneth K. ■ 18840 #016-06-1951 L1967 GS ON *071 †85

MINNS, Eric Christopher. ■ 18840 #048-15-2003 L2003 GS *012

MOODY, Robert Adams. GUTHRIE MEDICAL CENTER 18840 #016-02-1960 L1981 NS *071 †25

MORCOUS, Shaker Joseph Sh. ■ 18840 #915-09-2004 L2007 GS *012

MURPHY, Barbara L. 1537 ELMIRA ST, SAYRE VA OUTPATIENT CLNC 18840 #033-05-1983 L1991 IM *020 †20

NARAYANAN, Edathil Keloth. GUTHRIE SQ, GUTHRIE CLINIC 18840 #495-04-1960 L1972 PD *071 †55

NARAYANAN, Surya. 1 GUTHRIE SQ 18840 #495-16-1971 L1991 ATP *020 †50

NORVILLE, Kim Joanne. 1 GUTHRIE SQ, GUTHRIE CLINIC 18840 #566-01-1985 L2006 PCC IM *020 †20

O'BRIEN, Edward Thomas. 1 GUTHRIE SQ, GUTHRIE CLINIC 18840 #010-02-1979 L1980 ON IM *020 †20

OLAYO, Alvaro Alfonso. GUTHRIE SQ, DEPT FAM PRAC 18840 #264-05-1991 L2003 FM *020 †18

PACANOWSKI, John Paul. GUTHRIE MEDICAL CENTER 18840 #041-02-1966 L1967 PD *020 †55

PALIWAL, Himanshu Harihar. 1 GUTHRIE SQ, ROBERT PACKER HOSPITAL 18840 #495-23-2002 L2007 FP *012

PARCERO, Augusto Francisc, Jr. 1 GUTHRIE SQ, ROBERT PACKER HOSPITAL 18840 #748-01-2001 L2007 FP *012

PELKOWSKI, David John. 109 TARA PKWY 18840 #041-09-1983 L1984 CD IM *020 †20

PETRINIC, Bambi. ONE GUTHRIE SQUARE, DEPT FAM MED 18840 #654-01-2003 L2005 FP *012

PINSKY, Alexander J. 1 GUTHRIE SQ 18840 #913-15-1979 L2001 PD *020 †55

POKORNY, George Roy. 1 GUTHRIE SQ 18840 #035-03-1981 L1986 ORS *020 †40

PORTER, Burdett R. 1 GUTHRIE SQ, GUTHRIE CLINIC LTD 18840 #026-08-1988 L1990 AN PME *020 †05 ‡

PRABHU, Sheela. 1 GUTHRIE SQ, GUTHRIE CLINIC LTD 18840 #495-09-1998 L2001 IM *020 †20

PRAKASH, Rachita. 1 GUTHRIE SQ, ROBERT PACKER HOSPITAL 18840 #495-45-2005 L2006 IM *012

PRASAD, Kavitha Sudnagunt. 1 GUTHRIE SQ, FAM PRAC RES PROG 18840 #496-35-2000 L2002 FM *100

PROULX, Gary Miller. 1 GUTHRIE SQ, GUTHRIE CLINIC LTD 18840 #024-01-1992 L2002 RO *020 †80

RACHLIN, Leslie S. 1 GUTHRIE SQ 18840 #041-12-1978 L1979 FM *020 †18

RADIN, Edward James. 200 N WILBUR AVE, GUTHRIE MEDICAL CENTER 18840 #020-12-1981 L1982 IM ADL *020 †20

RAMAN, Gita. 1 GUTHRIE SQ 18840 #495-74-1968 L1976 AN *020 †05

RAMAN, Sucharita. 1 GUTHRIE SQ, GUTHRIE CLINIC 18840 #495-04-1981 L1998 EM IM *020 †20

RAMANI, Karthik. 1 GUTHRIE SQ, DEPT OF GME 18840 #496-34-2004 L2006 IM *012

RAZA, Ahamed. 1 GUTHRIE SQ, GUTHRIE CLINIC 18840 #495-44-1990 L2005 AN *100 †05

REYNOLDS, Dermot M. 1 GUTHRIE SQ, ORTHOPEDIC CLINIC 18840 #065-01-1995 L2003 *020 †40

RIAZ, Wasif. 1 GUTHRIE SQ, ROBERT PACKER HOSPITAL 18840 #704-04-2001 L2007 IM *012

RILLORAZA, Francisco. ■ 18840 #748-02-1989 L1996 PS *020 †65,85

ROSE, Frederick Burton. GUTHRIE MEDICAL CENTER 18840 #035-03-1970 L1977 ID IM *020 †20

ROUSE, Steven Bryan. GUTHRIE MEDICAL CENTER 18840 #065-06-1977 L1982 OBG *020 †30

RUSSIN, Stanley J, Jr. 1 GUTHRIE SQ, GUTHRIE CLINIC 18840 #041-09-1983 L1984 IM *020 †20

RYAN, Debra A. GUTHRIE MEDICAL CENTER 18840 #041-09-1983 L1984 FP *012

SALEEM, Sadaf Ahmed. 1 GUTHRIE SQ, GUTHRIE-ROBERT PACKER HOSP 18840 #704-02-1996 L2004 FM *100 †18

SAMPSON, Lawrence Nathan. 1 GUTHRIE SQ, GUTHRIE CLINIC 18840 #008-01-1986 L1995 VS *020 †85

SANDHU, Pritpal. 1 GUTHRIE SQ 18840 #166-01-1999 L2005 FP *012

SARGENT, Syreeta Megin. ■ 18840 #041-02-2006 L2006 EM *012

SARPATWARI, Vilas. 1 GUTHRIE SQ 18840 #495-21-1975 L2003 AN CCM *020

SCHECHTER, David. 1 GUTHRIE SQ 18840 #035-45-1984 L1987 CD *020 †20

SCOPELLITI, Joseph Armine. GUTHRIE MEDICAL CENTER 18840 #041-09-1979 L1980 GE IM *020 †20

SHACKOUR, Mazin. ■ 18840 #875-01-2002 L2005 GS *012

SHAH, Ashok R. 1 GUTHRIE SQ 18840 #495-23-1975 L2002 CD IM *020 †20

SHAH, Jay Pravinkumar. 1 GUTHRIE SQ 18840 #495-76-1993 L2001 P CHP *020 †75

SHAH, Kairav Jitendra. GUTHRIE SQUARE, ROBERT PACKER HOSP 18840 #495-17-2006 L2008 *012

SHANK, Gregory Scott. 1 GUTHRIE SQ, ROBERT PACKER HOSPITAL 18840 #005-12-1999 L2001 GS *020 †85

SHARMA, Ram Charitra. 1 GUTHRIE SQ, 2 RED INT MED 18840 #495-15-1977 L1996 IM *020 †20

SHEIKH, Mohd Raashid Ali. GUTHRIE SQUARE, ROBERT PACKER HOSPITAL 18840 #495-51-2004 L2007 *012

SHELLING, Richard Edmund. GUTHRIE MEDICAL CENTER 18840 #041-01-1964 L1965 IM *020 †20

SHENFIELD, Henry Thos. 1 GUTHRIE SQ, GUTHRIE CLINIC 18840 #023-01-1972 L1980 D IM *020 †20,15

SHRESTHA, Rabin. 1 GUTHRIE SQ 18840 #672-05-2002 IM *012

SIDHU, Manavjot Singh. 1 GUTHRIE SQ, ROBERT PACKER HOSPITAL 18840 #495-43-2006 L2007 IM *012

SIEGEL, Bonita Hazel. 220 DESMOND ST 18840 #056-05-1991 L1993 N *020 †75 ‡

SINGH, Khushwinder. 1 GUTHRIE SQ, ROBERT PACKER HOSP 18840 #496-09-2004 L2006 IM *012

SINGH, Rana Khushdeep. 1 GUTHRIE SQ, ROBERT PACKER HOSPITAL 18840 #496-59-2004 L2007 IM *012

SINGHEL, Kenneth John. 1 GUTHRIE SQ 18840 #035-15-1990 L1994 IM *020 †20

SODUMS, Marcis T. 1 GUTHRIE SQ, CARDIOLOGY GUTHRIE MED CTR 18840 #016-02-1976 L1986 CD IM *020 †20

SOMMER, John Thos. 1 GUTHRIE SQ 18840 #051-01-1972 L1980 U *020 †95 ‡

SPORN, Daniel Primes. GUTHRIE CLINIC, DEPT OF CARDIOLOGY 18840 #010-02-1985 L1986 CD IC *020 †20

SRA, Jaspinder Singh. 1 GUTHRIE SQ, DEPT OF MED EDU 18840 #496-09-2004 L2006 IM *012

STRIFF, Russell John, Jr. 1 GUTHRIE SQ 18840 #005-06-1965 L1995 ORS *020 †40

SUAREZ, Paul Adrien. GUTHRIE SQUARE, GUTHRIE CLINIC LTD 18840 #041-02-1981 L1996 ORS *020 †40

SWETERLITSCH, Paul Reed. ■ 18840 #041-02-1961 L1967 ORS *071 †40

TERWILLIGER, Jerry Wayne. GUTHRIE MEDICAL CENTER 18840 #035-45-1979 L1983 PD *020 †55

THEM, Theodore F. 1 GUTHRIE SQ, GUTHRIE CLNC 18840 #654-01-1987 L1991 OM IM *020 †20,70

THEOHAROUS, Lewis N. 193 S KEYSTONE AVE 18840 #041-09-1960 L1962 GS *071

THOMAS, John M. GUTHRIE MEDICAL CENTER 18840 #803-03-1958 L1960 TS *020 †85

THOMAS, Mathew. 1 GUTHRIE SQ, GUTHRIE SQ 18840 #495-80-1999 L2004 GS *012

THOMPSON, Carson Jos. 1 GUTHRIE SQ, GUTHRIE CLINIC DEPT NEURO 18840 #041-13-1976 L1977 NS *020 †25

TRIKHA, Gaurav. 1 GUTHRIE SQ, ROBERT PACKER HOSPITAL 18840 #496-59-2005 L2006 IM *012

TROSTLE, Douglas Ray. 1 GUTHRIE SQ, GUTHRIE CLNC LTD 18840 #041-09-1978 L1979 GS *020 †85

TRUDEAU, Genevieve M. 1 GUTHRIE SQ, GUTHRIE CLINIC LTD 18840 #041-15-1999 L2002 FM *020 †18

VANDERMEER, Thomas J. GUTHRIE SQUARE, GUTHRIE CLINIC 18840 #051-04-1990 L1998 GS *020 †85

VANDYKE, Esther Mae. 1 GUTHRIE SQ, FAMILY PRACTICE CTR 18840 #041-13-1996 L1998 FM *020 †18

VENKATESH, Govindarajan. 1 GUTHRIE SQ, GUTHRIE CLINIC LTD. 18840 #495-04-1981 L2002 CD *020 †20

WALSH, James Jos. GUTHRIE SQUARE, GUTHRIE CLINIC 18840 #028-34-1983 L1992 IM VS *020 †20

WALTERS, Virginia Lee. 1 GUTHRIE SQ, GUTHRIE CLINIC 18840 #041-02-1979 L2001 PTH GYN *062 †30

WEAVER, Donald Robt. ■ 18840 #041-13-1956 L1981 PTH *071 †50

WEAVER, Matthew Donald. ■ 18840 #041-13-2005 L2005 FP *012

WILSON, James Le Roy. 1 GUTHRIE SQ 18840 #041-02-1961 L1962 FM *020 †18

WILT, John Wm. ■ 18840 #041-02-1959 L1960 IM GE *020

WISEMAN, Jeffrey Scott. 1 GUTHRIE SQ 18840 #041-07-1984 L1985 GS *020 †85,10

YAEGER, Thomas Anthony. GUTHRIE SQUARE, DEPT FAMILY PRACTICE 18840 #005-14-1978 L1994 FM *020 †18

ZAMA, Nche. 1 GUTHRIE SQ, GUTHRIE CLINIC 18840 #038-41-1986 L1993 TS *020 †85,90

ZEHR, Ralph Danl. GUTHRIE MEDICAL CENTER 18840 #035-15-1964 L1965 R OS *020 †80

ZEID KEILANI, Zeid Mahmou. 1 GUTHRIE SQ, ROBERT PACKER HOSPITAL 18840 #575-01-2004 L2006 GS *012

ZHOU, Dalai. 1 GUTHRIE SQ, GUTHRIE-ROBERT PACKER HOSP 18840 #243-45-1993 L2005 FP *012

SCENERY HILL – WASHINGTON

KEARNS, Thos Raymond, Jr. ■ 15360 #038-41-1986 L1987 EM *020 †16

SCHNECKSVILLE – LEHIGH

BROWN, Daniel Forman. ■ 18078 #035-15-1994 L1999 **NP** *020 †50 ‡
GONZALEZ, Humberto Javier. ■ 18078 #649-06-1959 L1965 **P** *071 †75
KOSTENBLATT, Susan Elaine. 4520 PARK VIEW DR, PARKLAND FAMILY HEALTH CTR 18078 #035-15-1979 L1983 **FM** *020 †18
KUCIRKA, Susan Jean. 4110 INDEPENDENCE DR, STE 300 18078 #041-02-1983 L1984 **D** *020 †15
LEE, Eric Scott. 4866 HILTON RD 18078 #014-01-1981 L2000 **DR** *020 †80
LENHART, Jack Andrew. 4520 PARK VIEW DR, PARKLAND FAMILY HEALTH CTR 18078 #025-01-1975 L1977 **FM FPG** *020 †18
RYDER, Kenneth G, Jr. 4955 ROUTE 873 18078 #041-14-1984 L1985 **FM** *020 †18
SHALABY, Marc. ■ 18078 #036-01-1998 L2001 **IM** *020 †20

SCHUYLKILL HAVEN – SCHUYLKILL

BILINSKI, Carol Ann. 4 S GREENVIEW RD 17972 #041-02-1991 L1993 **PD** *020 †55
CHRISTENSON, Mary E. ■ 17972 #041-07-1971 L1973 **EM GPM** *020
CUBLER, Edward Wm. ■ 17972 #041-02-1945 L1946 **GP** *071
LADO, Michael. ■ 17972 #041-12-1955 L1956 **OBG** *071 †30
RUBRIGHT, Herbert C, Sr. 401 UNIVERSITY DR 17972 #041-13-1953 L1956 **GP** *020 †18
RUBRIGHT, Herbert C, Jr. 401 UNIVERSITY DR 17972 #041-14-1978 **FPG PYG** *020

SCHWENKSVILLE – MONTGOMERY

BARON, Bernard Wm. ■ 19473 #041-02-1955 L1956 **IM** *020
BORA, Gulderen N. ■ 19473 #902-10-1958 L1967 **P** *071
DEBIAS, Dennis Anthony. 1000 GRAVEL PIKE, STE 400 19473 #041-02-1986 L1987 **FM** *020 †18
HILL, Gregory George. ■ 19473 #010-01-1997 L2007 **FM** *020 †18
REBONG, Maria V. ■ 19473 #748-08-1988 L1997 **IM** *020
SAWHILL, David Lee. ■ 19473 #041-12-1963 L1969 **PTH** *030 †50
SCHWENK, Edward B, Jr. ■ 19473 #025-07-1947 L1963 **P** *071
STUBA, Stella. 1023 SCENIC VIEW DR 19473 #041-13-1955 L1956 **FM** *071
YANG, York Chiang. 596 MAIN ST, SCHWENKSVILLE FAMILY PRACT 19473 #041-02-1996 L1999 **FM** *020 †18

SCOTRUN – MONROE

ANCIER, Stephen Lee. 424 BUTZ LN 18355 #033-05-1979 L1984 **EM FM** *020

SCOTTDALE – WESTMORELAND

PARK, In Bum. 109 CROSSROADS RD, STE 6 15683 #583-02-1981 L1985 **PM OS** *020 †60
POLAKOVSKY, Andrew Gerard. 310 MULBERRY ST 15683 #038-44-1992 L1995 **FM** *020 †18
SALOOM, Albert Geo. 103 MARKET ST 15683 #605-01-1958 L1959 **FM OS** *072
TA VOULARIS, Marjorie O. ■ 15683 #041-12-1966 L1967 **P PFP** *020 †75 ‡

SCRANTON – LACKAWANNA

ABBAS, Huda A. 746 JEFFERSON AVE 18510 #528-01-1998 L2007 **IM** *012
ABDA, John, Jr. 1027 MOOSIC ST 18505 #041-09-1963 L1964 **IMG GS** *020 †16
ABUGHNIA, Haitham Abdulna. 746 JEFFERSON AVE, DEPT OF MED EDUCATION 18510 #613-02-1996 L2005 **IM** *100 †20
ADAMO, Louis C. 1789 N KEYSER AVE 18508 #422-01-1989 L1992 **IM** *020 †20
ADONIZIO, Christian S. 5 MORGAN HWY, STE 8 18508 #041-02-1996 L1998 **HO** *020 †20
AKKALADEVI, Srinivas. 746 JEFFERSON AVE, SCRANTON-TEMPLE 18510 #495-65-2002 L2006 **IM** *012
ALBERT, Mark John. 6 WILLIAM DR, MT. MARGARET ESTATES 18505 #422-01-1981 L1984 *020
ANDREYCHIK, David Andrew. 125 SCRANTON POCONO HWY 18505 #041-02-1987 L1989 **ORS OSS** *020 †40
ANDRIOLE, Joseph Paul. 1800 MULBERRY ST 18510 #065-09-1963 L1969 **GYN REN** *071 †30
ANEJA, Krishan Kumar. 321 SPRUCE ST STE 429, 4TH FL BANK TWR BLDG 18503 #495-45-1966 L1973 **IM DIA** *020 †20
ARONICA, Michael Jos. 475 MORGAN HWY 18508 #041-02-1958 L1959 **PM GP** *030 †60
ARORA, Subhash C. 746 JEFFERSON AVE 18510 #495-03-1971 L1977 **AN** *005
ARTABANE, Thomas Aziz. 748 QUINCY AVE, STE A 18510 #065-09-1968 L1969 **IM** *020 †20
ASANTE, Nelson K. 326 ADAMS AVE, SCRANTON COUNSELING CENTER 18503 #412-01-1987 L2001 **P** *020 †75
ASGHER ALI, Abbas. 746 JEFFERSON AVE, SCRANTON-TEMPLE RESIDENCY 18510 #495-17-1999 L2005 **IM** *012
AURIEMMA, William Stephen. 1800 MULBERRY ST 18510 #041-09-1991 L1993 **CRS GS** *020 †85,10
BACCOLI, Michael John. 802 JEFFERSON AVE 18510 #035-15-1992 L1997 **N SME** *020 †75
BAJAJ, Rajiv Kumar. 746 JEFFERSON AVE 18510 #495-45-1971 L1994 **AN** *020 †05
BALAVINAYAGAM, Indiran. 746 JEFFERSON AVE 18510 #496-35-1999 L2006 **IM** *012
BANNON, Charles James. 743 JEFFERSON AVE, LL WOUND CARE CTR 18510 #041-02-1962 L1963 **GS** *071 †85 ‡
BANNON, Joseph Patrick. 236 PENN AVE 18503 #041-02-1987 L1989 **CRS GS** *020 †85,10 ‡
BANSAL, Pardeep. 746 JEFFERSON AVE 18510 #913-47-2002 L2006 **IM** *012
BARAKAT, Adel Roland. 700 QUINCY AVE 18510 #330-02-1963 L1971 **ORS HS** *071 †40
BARAX, Charles Nathan. 1800 MULBERRY ST, COMMUNITY MED CTR 18510 #550-02-1985 L2001 **DR ATP** *020 †80
BARBAREVECH, Christopher. 517 ASH ST, STE 1 18509 #041-02-1992 L1994 **GE** *020 †20
BARRASSE, Linda D'Andrea. 746 JEFFERSON AVE 18510 #041-02-1981 L1982 **CD IM** *020 †20
BARRERA-MARTINEZ, Juan C. 802 JEFFERSON AVE, MCAULEY BUILDING 5TH FL 18510 #649-02-1979 L1980 **N CN** *020
BASTING, Gregory Gerard. 5 MORGAN HWY, P O BOX 2029 18508 #033-06-1984 L1985 **PM IM** *030 †60
BEDNARZ, Lucian Paul. 5 MORGAN HWY, STE 4 18508 #041-13-1992 L1994 **PM** *020 †20
BEHLKE, Richard Theodore. 401 ADAMS AVE STE 201, PHYSICIAN HEALTH ALLIANCE 18510 #041-09-1987 L1989 **OBG** *020 †30

BEKELE, Tamrat. 746 JEFFERSON AVE 18510 #366-01-1990 L1998 **IM GP** *020 †20
BENJAMIN, Wallace F. ■ 18508 #041-02-1972 L1973 **GP** *071
BESETTY, Ramashesai. 746 JEFFERSON AVE, SCRANTON-TEMPLE 18510 #495-58-2002 L2007 **IM** *012
BHALODIA, Uchit Vallabhda. 746 JEFFERSON AVE, SCRANTON-TEMPLE 18510 #495-22-2003 L2007 **IM** *012
BIANCARELLI, Susan Marie. 746 JEFFERSON AVE 18510 #041-13-1987 L1989 **IM** *020 †20
BIN, Wei. 746 JEFFERSON AVE, RESIDENCY PROG 18510 #243-47-1990 L2003 **PCC** *012 †20
BLASKO, Edward Conrad. 748 QUINCY AVE, STE 3B 18510 #041-02-1982 L1983 **GS** *020 †85
BLUM, Jeffrey Todd. 435 SCRANTON CARBONDAL HWY, VIEWMONT MEDICAL SERVICES 18508 #011-04-1993 L2002 **RNR** *020 †80
BOLAND, Thomas Stanley. 200 MIFFLIN AVE 18503 #010-02-1991 L1993 **OPH** *020 †35
BOLUS, Charles M. 321 SPRUCE ST, BANK TOWERS, STE 529 18503 #561-01-1970 L1972 **PS** *020
BORIOSI, Guido Domnick. 475 MORGAN HWY 18508 #041-02-1965 L1966 **P** *020 †75
BORMES, Gregory Wm. 321 SPRUCE ST, STE 200 18503 #010-02-1992 L2000 **PS** *020
BOROWSKI, Gregory David. 3 W OLIVE ST, # 2ND-FLR 18508 #041-09-1979 L1980 **END IM** *020 †20
BORRA, Bolliaih. 1800 MULBERRY ST 18510 #495-50-1971 L1977 **R OS** *020 †80
BORUAH, Pranjal Kumar. 746 JEFFERSON AVE, SCRANTON TEMPLE 18510 #495-78-1997 L2008 *100
BREWINSKI, Margaret Mary. ■ 18505 #036-05-2003 L2006 **GPM** *012 †55
BROWDIE, David Abraham. 746 JEFFERSON AVE 18510 #038-06-1964 L1993 **TS PDS** *050 †85,90
BROWN, Sylvan. 125 SCRANTON POCONO HWY 18505 #041-02-1971 L1972 **RHU IM** *020 †20
BRUTICO, Anthony Carmen. 940 JEFFERSON AVE 18510 #041-13-1980 L1981 **OTO HNS** *020 †45 ‡
BRUTICO, Carmen A, Jr. 700 QUINCY AVE, EXECUTIVE OFFICES 18510 #041-14-1980 L1981 **IM** *020 †20
BURIK, Alexander J. 746 JEFFERSON AVE 18510 #016-43-1947 L1949 **OBG** *020
BURKE, Michael Anthony. 5 MORGAN HWY 18508 #010-02-1984 L1987 **RO** *020 †80
BURNS, Richard John, Jr. 321 SPRUCE ST STE 60 18503 #041-77-1993, ▲ L1994 **OBG** *020
CACCIAMANI, John. 746 JEFFERSON AVE, MERCY HOSPITAL 18510 #010-02-1968 L1976 **PUD** *020 †20
CASEY, Kevin. 720 MADISON AVE 18510 #041-13-1976 L1984 **TS** *020 †85,90
CAWLEY, Thomas. 101 CONROY ST 18505 #041-07-1973 L1974 **PTH** *020 †50
CECH, Rosanne. 3 W OLIVE ST, 2ND-FLR 18508 #041-09-1979 L1980 **A** *020 †55
CENERA, Caramarie. ■ 18510 #041-15-2006 L2006 **GS** *012
CERON, Gabriel. 435 SCRANTON CARBONDAL HWY, VIEWMONT MEDICAL SERVICES 18508 #264-01-1963 L1977 **R** *020 †80
CESARE, Joseph Giulio. 327 N WASHINGTON AVE, STE 808 18503 #030-06-1965 L1966 **ORS** *020 †85
CHANDRAGIRI, Sanjay S. 401 ADAMS AVE 18510 #495-37-1992 L1998 **P ADM** *020 †75 ‡
CHAUDHRY, Ayesha. 746 JEFFERSON AVE 18510 #704-21-2002 L2005 **IM** *012
CHIAVACCI, Anthony Leo. 1800 MULBERRY ST 18510 #308-03-1980 L1983 **FM EM** *020 †18 ‡
CHILSON, Rebecca Grimaud. 746 JEFFERSON AVE 18510 #005-12-1999 L2002 **PD** *020 †20
CHO, Sung Choo. ■ 18505 #583-01-1962 L1974 **PTH** *071
CHRISTOFORATOS, Demetrius. ■ 18509 #418-01-1967 L1982 **AN PME** *020
CHUN, Joseph. 5 MORGAN HWY, STE 4 18508 #035-75-1999, ▲ L2004 **PM PME** *020 †60
CHUNG, C K. 4 TIFFANY DR 18505 #583-01-1962 L1974 **PS** *020 †65
CIANNI, Ronald J. 517 ASH ST, # 1 18509 #010-02-1969 L1974 **GE IM** *020 †20
CIPRIANO, John Jos. 1416 MONROE ST, STE 204 18509 #654-01-1982 L1987 **IM** *020 †20
COCHRAN, Terence Alan. 1360 WYOMING AVE, STE 104 18509 #038-40-1970 L1970 **VS** *020 †85
COGNETTI, Peter Anthony. 802 JEFFERSON AVE 18510 #041-02-1983 L1984 **FM** *030 †18
COLLERAN, Kevin Raymond. 743 JEFFERSON AVE, STE 102 18510 #041-14-1998 L2003 **ORS** *020 †40
CONABOY, Patrick Danl. 802 JEFFERSON AVE 18510 #010-02-1986 L1989 **FM** *020 †18
CONDEFER, Kelly Ann. ■ 18510 #041-12-2001 L2007 **N** *100 †75
COSTELLO, Pamela Jo. 212 LINDEN ST 18503 #035-06-1992 L2000 **NS** *020
CRUCIANI, Mark. 1418 WYOMING AVE 18509 #010-02-1984 L1989 **RHU** *020 †20
CURTIN, Eugene Augustine. 743 JEFFERSON AVE, GENERAL SERVICES BLDG 18510 #041-02-1955 L1956 **OBG** *071 †30
D'ALESSANDRI, Robert. 150 N WASHINGTON AVE, 7TH FLOOR MEDC 18503 #035-09-1971 L2007 **IM ID** *030 †20
DAVIS, Harold Jos. 746 JEFFERSON AVE 18510 #041-02-1978 L1982 **GYN GP** *020 †30
DAVIS, Robert Van Schoick. 200 MIFFLIN AVE 18503 #041-02-1959 L1960 **OPH** *071 †35
DECK, Charles Steven. 802 JEFFERSON AVE 18510 #067-01-1978 L1980 **IM** *020 †20
DECSEPEL, John. 1800 MULBERRY ST 18510 #010-02-1995 L2002 **GS** *020 †85
DE GENNARO, Louis P. 940 JEFFERSON AVE, AND THROAT 18510 #016-43-1967 L1968 **OTO** *020 †45 ‡
DE LA FUENTE, Luis F. 700 QUINCY AVE, MOSES TAYLOR HOSPITAL 18510 #748-10-1992 L2000 **NPM** *020 †55
DELSERRA, Joseph John. 401 ADAMS AVE, STE 303 18510 #041-13-1984 L1988 **GS** *020 †85
DEMKO, Joseph Nicholas. 1800 MULBERRY ST, COMMUNITY MC 18510 #041-13-1958 L1959 **FPG FM** *071 †18
DEMPSEY, James Gonzaga. 746 JEFFERSON AVE 18510 #041-13-1958 L1963 **GS** *071 †85
DEMPSEY, William James. 1822 MULBERRY ST 18510 #422-01-1981 L1984 **EM FM** *020 †18
DENIS, Leonard Julian. 743 JEFFERSON AVE 18510 #067-01-1978 L1987 **CD** *020 †20
DEOPURIA, Ramesh Hansraj. ■ 18505 #495-17-1960 L1972 **FM OBG** *071
DIAKIW, John. 748 QUINCY AVE STE 1A, PHYS BLDG MOSES TAYLOR HOS 18510 #041-07-1979 L1980 **IM** *020 †20 ‡
DOHERTY, John Henry, Jr. 743 JEFFERSON AVE, STE 102 18510 #041-02-1975 L1980 **ORS** *020 †40
DOLUNAY, Mehmet Ozer. 1800 MULBERRY ST, RADIOLOGY DEPT 18510 #902-10-1963 L1987 **R** *071 †80
DONOVAN, Robert Jos. 326 ADAMS AVE 18503 #041-01-1947 L1953 **P** *071 †75
DORMANS, Adrian Anthony. 700 QUINCY AVE 18510 #422-01-1983 L1984 **FM EM** *020 †18
DRESSEL, Christopher Jos. 746 JEFFERSON AVE STE 3 18510 #041-12-1973 L1978 **IC IM** *020 †20
DROZDICK, John, III. 748 QUINCY AVE, PHA OB/GYN STE 2A 18510 #041-09-1996 L2000 **OBG** *020 †30
DWEIK, Mahmood O. 640 MADISON AVE 18510 #575-01-1993 L2001 **PCC** *020 †20
DZWONCZYK, Thomas David. 746 JEFFERSON AVE 18510 #041-07-1988 L1990 **CD IM** *020 †20
EAGEN, Jeremiah Wm. 802 JEFFERSON AVE, 4TH FL MCAULEY 18510 #041-01-1969 L1978 **NEP IM** *020 †20 ‡

■ = Address Information Privacy Protected

EISNER, Steven Benj. 919 JEFFERSON AVE 18510 #041-02-1978 L1979 **CD END** *020 †20
ELLIOTT, Nina L. 700 QUINCY AVE 18510 #041-77-1996, ▲ L1997 **FM** *020 †18 ‡
EMANUELSON, Richard G. 5 MORGAN HWY 18508 #035-06-1980 L1986 **ON HEM** *020 †20 ‡
EPSTEIN, Scott Kiev. 5 MORGAN HWY, STE 4 18508 #041-13-1990 L1992 **PM** *020 †60
ESCALANTE, Elizabeth N. 1812 MULBERRY ST 18510 #737-01-1980 L1987 **PD** *020 †55
FAGERBURG, Rodger Eugene. 748 QUINCY AVE 18510 #016-02-1976 L1977 **ID IM** *020 †20
FARLEY, Timothy John. 746 JEFFERSON AVE, MERCY HOSPITAL 18510 #035-08-1985 L2001 **R IM** *020 †80
FARRELL, Robert Edward. MEDICAL ART BUILDING, RADIOLOGICAL GROUP INC 18503 #041-02-1962 L1963 **R** *020 †80
FARRELL, Timothy Jude. 401 ADAMS AVE STE 303 18510 #041-02-1990 L1993 **GS** *020 †85
FARRELL, William John. MEDICAL ART BUILDING, RADIOLOGICAL GROUP INC 18503 #041-02-1961 L1962 **R** *071 †80
FELINS, Kelly Jayne. 426 MULBERRY ST STE 412 18503 #041-14-1988 L1990 **P** *071 †75
FITZPATRICK, W David. 746 JEFFERSON AVE 18510 #041-02-1992 L1998 **CD** *020 †20
FOGLEY, Anees Robt. 802 JEFFERSON AVE 18510 #041-02-1977 L1979 **IM** *020 †20
FRATTALI, Mark Anthony. 940 JEFFERSON AVE 18510 #041-09-1989 L1992 **OTO** *020 †45
FROOZAN, Homayoon. 120 N KEYSER AVE 18504 #917-23-1964 L1972 **N** *020
FURMAN, Andrew Colton. 1800 MULBERRY ST, COMMUNITY MEDICAL CENTER 18510 #041-15-2000 L2002 **EM** *020 †16
GALANAKIS, Stylianos. 746 JEFFERSON AVE 18510 #418-01-1989 L2001 **CD IC** *020 †20
GANDHI, Sanjay Manilal. 959 WYOMING AVE, SCRANTON PRIMARY HEALTHCAR 18509 #495-23-1989 L1998 **PD** *020 †55 ‡
GARCIA, Lidia Y. ■ 18505 #308-02-1975 L2003 **PD** *020
GAUNA, Alberto Ma. Angele, Jr. 746 JEFFERSON AVE, SCRANTON-TEMPLE RESIDENCY 18510 #748-01-1997 L2005 **IM** *012
GAVIN, John R. 746 JEFFERSON AVE, STE 104 18510 #010-02-1951 L1952 **FM OS** *020 †18
GENTILEZZA, Kenneth Willi. 5 MORGAN HWY, STE 4 18508 #422-01-1984 L1985 **PM** *020 †60
GEORGETTI, Debra. 440 N MAIN AVE 18504 #041-13-1995 L1997 **PD** *020 †55 ‡
GETTS, Roger T. 802 JEFFERSON AVE, DEPT OF NEPHROLOGY 18510 #041-77-2000, ▲ L2001 **NEP** *020 †20
GHIGIARELLI, Christopher. 327 N WASHINGTON AVE, STE 808 18503 #010-02-1996 L2000 **ORS** *020 †40
GIBBONS, Robert Francis. ■ 18509 #041-09-1943 L1948 **IM** *020
GILHOOLEY, Michael Gerard. 1789 N KEYSER AVE 18508 #041-13-1992 L1994 **IM** *020 †20
GILLICK, Alan Paul. 327 N WASHINGTON AVE, STE 808 18503 #041-14-1982 L1983 **ORS** *020 †40
GOLDSTEIN, Erroll J. 743 JEFFERSON AVE STE 304 18510 #396-02-1978 L1983 **OBG** *020 †30
GOLDSTONE, Sheldon B. 746 JEFFERSON AVE 18510 #041-02-1944 L1945 **D** *071 †15
GONZALEZ, Jose L. 625 TAYLOR AVE, CMC 1800 MULBERRY ST 18510 #041-14-1980 L1982 **DR** *020 †80
GRAD, Charles Thos. 201 SMALLACOMBE DR, LACKAWANNA MEDICAL GROUP P 18508 #041-13-1972 L1973 **GE IM** *020 †20
GRADY, Eugene Paul. 327 N WASHINGTON AVE, STE 808 18503 #010-02-1991 L1993 **RHU** *020 †20
GRADY, Patrick J. 746 JEFFERSON AVE 18510 #010-02-1981 L1984 **AN** *020 †05
GRANDY, John Paul. 700 QUINCY AVE, MOSES TAYLOR HOSPITAL 18510 #033-05-1984 L1995 **NPM PD** *020 †55
GRATZ, Richard Edward. 201 SMALLACOMBE DR 18508 #041-07-1978 L1979 **IM** *020 †20 ‡
GRECO, Joseph Peter. 1173 CLAY AVE 18510 #033-06-1988 L1990 **IM** *020 ‡
GUNDINAPALLYA KAKIMALLAIAH, . 746 JEFFERSON AVE 18510 #496-20-2002 **IM** *012
HAMM, Francis Edward. 748 QUINCY AVE, STE 2A 18510 #010-02-1986 L1988 **OBG** *020 †30
HAN, Sun Tak. 802 JEFFERSON AVE 18510 #583-06-1971 L1976 **CD IM** *020 †20
HARTMAN, Charles Richard. 1800 MULBERRY ST, COMMUNITY MED CTR 18510 #019-02-1966 L1995 **END IM** *030 †20
HEIM, William Jos. 5 MORGAN HWY, STE 8 18508 #041-02-1969 L1970 **ON HEM** *020 †20
HENSLER, Theresa Marie. ■ 18504 #305-01-1999 L2002 **IM** *100
HOLLA, P Shripathi. 321 SPRUCE ST STE 707 18503 #495-09-1970 L1981 **NS** *020 †25
HOLLAND, Sanford J. 700 QUINCY AVE, C/O DEPARTMENT OF ANESTHES 18510 #035-06-1972 L1979 **AN CCA** *020 †05
HUANG, Chau. 201 FRANKLIN AVE 18503 #243-50-1966 L1973 **CD IM** *020 †20
HUBBARD, Charles Jos. 327 N WASHINGTON AVE, STE 808 18503 #024-07-1987 L1998 **ORS** *020 †40
HUFFMAN, Philip Anthony. ■ 18510 #041-02-1998 L2006 **IM** *020 †20
HYZINSKI, Martin Bernard. 743 JEFFERSON AVE 18510 #041-01-1979 L1981 **HEM ON** *050 †20
IRUKULLA, Pavan Kumar. 746 JEFFERSON AVE, SCRATON-TEMPLE RESIDENCY 18510 #495-37-2001 L2005 **IM** *012
JACOBS, Kenneth M. 746 JEFFERSON AVE 18510 #035-08-1976 L1983 **PUD IM** *020 †20
JONES, James Curtiss. 802 JEFFERSON AVE, 4TH FL 18510 #005-02-1969 L1999 **TS GS** *020 †85,90
JONES, Seth Martin. 802 JEFFERSON AVE 18510 #041-02-1986 L1987 **N IM** *020 †75
JORDAN, Jerome W. 204 MIFFLIN AVE, N.E.I. AMBULATORY SURGICAL 18503 #041-02-1971 L1972 **OPH** *020 †35 ‡
JORDAN, W Edward, III. 5 MORGAN HWY 18508 #041-02-1976 L1977 **HEM ON** *020 †20
KACZANOWSKA, Wieslawa K. 1611 E ELM ST 18505 #759-03-1952 L1972 **P** *020
KALRA, Amandeep. 746 JEFFERSON AVE, RESIDENCY PROG 18510 #495-43-2001 L2005 **IM** *012
KANDALA, Krishnachaitanya. 746 JEFFERSON AVE 18510 #495-73-1999 L2005 **IM** *012
KAREHA, Louis Geo. 1822 MULBERRY ST 18510 #041-02-1943 L1944 **GP IM** *075
KARUMBAYA, Ramola. ■ 18505 #495-33-1970 L1978 **NS VS** *071
KAUR, Dipinpreet. 746 JEFFERSON AVE, SCRANTON-TEMPLE 18510 #495-43-2005 L2008 *100
KAVILLE, Robert W. 1020 W LACKAWANNA AVE 18504 #041-13-1985 L1986 **IM EM** *020 †20
KAZMIERSKI, Daniel Jos. 1789 N KEYSER AVE 18508 #041-13-1990 L1992 **FM** *020 †18
KEHRLI, Henry J. ■ 18509 #041-13-1936 L1937 **OS** *071
KEHRLI, William Henry. 1390 WYOMING AVE 18509 #041-13-1965 L1966 **OPH** *020 †35
KELLEY, Kristine. 225 PENN AVE 18503 #048-12-1983 L1984 **GS VS** *020 †85 ‡
KHADEMI, Jamshid. 1800 MULBERRY ST, DEPT ANESTHIOLOGY 18510 #517-01-1984 L1998 **AN** *020 †05
KHALIL, Yasser Khalid. 746 JEFFERSON AVE, SCRANTON-TEMPLE RESIDENCY 18510 #528-04-1995 L2004 **IM** *020 †20
KIM, Eul Kyung. 1822 MULBERRY ST, COMMUNITY MEDICAL CENTER 18510 #583-03-1971 L1987 **PD NPM** *020 †55
KLAMP, Douglas Karl. 743 JEFFERSON AVE STE 1 18510 #023-07-1988 L1997 **IM** *020 †20
KLINE, Michael A. 746 JEFFERSON AVESTS, DEPT OF ANESTHESIOLOGY 18505 #041-02-1990 L1992 **AN** *020 †05
KLINGERMAN, Michael Rober. ■ 18505 #305-01-2001 L2001 **IM** *020
KOCH, Lear Von. 720 MADISON AVE 18510 #048-04-1972 L1979 **TS VS** *020 †85,90
KOLUCKI, Frank Ralph, Jr. 748 QUINCY AVE, 2A 18510 #010-02-1992 L1996 **OBG** *020 †30
KUNDURU, Seshidhar Reddy. 746 JEFFERSON AVE, SCRANTON-TEMPLE 18510 #495-65-1999 L2007 **IM** *012
KURTZER, Yitzchok Barry. 1405 MULBERRY ST, MULBERRY MEDICAL CENTER 18510 #661-01-1985 L1988 **IM EM** *020
KUTZ, John Anthony. 225 PENN AVE 18503 #041-02-1993 L1996 **VS** *020 †85 ‡
LAHODA, Joseph Gregory. 746 JEFFERSON AVE, MERCY HOSPITAL 18510 #010-02-1984 L1990 **DR VIR** *020 †80
LALOS, Alexander T. 517 ASH ST, STE 1 18509 #041-01-1985 L1991 **GE HEP** *020 †20
LA LUNA, Francis J. 743 JEFFERSON AVE STE 205 18510 #035-06-1968 L1973 **ON HEM** *071 †20
LANGIERI, Gary. 201 FRANKLIN AVE 18503 #033-05-1989 L1991 **CD IM** *020 †20
LARAR, Gerald N. 435 SCRANTON CARBONDAL HWY, VIEWMONT MEDICAL SERVICES 18508 #011-02-1990 L1998 **DR NM** *020 †80,28
LAURY, Joel Jerome. 3 W OLIVE ST, # 2ND-FLR 18508 #035-46-1990 L1995 **AI** *020 †20,03
LAWRENCE, Salvatore A, Jr. 475 MORGAN HWY 18508 #041-09-1983 L1985 **IM** *020 †20
LEE, Kyung Chan. 1027 PITTSTON AVE 18505 #583-01-1966 L1977 **GS** *020
LENA, Marie S. 1800 MULBERRY ST 18510 #220-04-1986 L1997 **PD** *020 †55
LENAHAN, Terrence Patrick. 802 JEFFERSON AVE, MCAULEY BLDG MERCY HOSP 18510 #041-02-1987 L1988 **PUD CCM** *020 †20
LESKO, Samuel Matthew. ■ 18510 #041-02-1977 L2000 **EP FM** *050 †18
LEVINSON, Nat Elliot. 435 SCRANTON CARBONDAL HWY 18508 #041-02-1978 L1979 **PUD CCM** *020 †20
LEVINSON, Sander Jay. 746 JEFFERSON AVE, STE 303 18510 #041-02-1969 L1970 **PUD IM** *020 †20
LILIK, Kenneth Wm. 311 MULBERRY ST 18503 #041-07-1976 L1982 **CHN CN** *020 †55,75 ‡
LINDHOLM, Dale David. 746 JEFFERSON AVE 18510 #026-04-1957 L1978 **IM NEP** *071
LIZANO, Violeta Marina. 201 SMALLACOMBE DR 18508 #737-01-1980 L1988 **PD** *020 †55 ‡
LUKOSE, Ludy. 746 JEFFERSON AVE, SCRANTON-TEMPLE 18510 #495-59-2003 L2006 **IM** *012
LUNDIN, John P. 746 JEFFERSON AVE 18510 #038-44-1992 L2001 **ICE CD** *020 †20
MADDEN, Kevin Gerard. 802 JEFFERSON AVE 18510 #035-08-1979 L1984 **N** *020 †75
MAKHOUL, Waseem. 746 JEFFERSON AVE 18510 #875-02-2000 L2004 **IM** *100 †20
MALLOY, Edwin Stephen. 327 N WASHINGTON AVE, STE 808 18503 #016-43-1969 L1970 **ORS** *020 †40
MANAHAN, Ferdinand Javier. 239 PENN AVE, FORUM PLAZA 18503 #748-02-1980 L1989 **NEP IM** *020 †20
MARAVELLI, Ammie J. 746 JEFFERSON AVE, MERCY HOSPITAL SCRANTON 18510 #035-03-1997 L1999 **EM** *020 †16
MARINER, David Raymond. 125 SCRANTON POCONO HWY 18505 #010-02-1980 L1985 **VS GS** *020 †85
MARINO, Joseph N. 746 JEFFERSON AVE 18510 #041-02-1942 L1943 **FM** *072
MARSILI, Mark A. 429 SCRANTON CARBONDAL HWY, DERMATOLOGY 18508 #041-02-1988 L1991 **D** *020 †15 ‡
MARTIN, Richard Alan. 125 SCRANTON POCONO HWY, GEISINGER MED GROUP SCRANT 18505 #041-02-1978 L1979 **FM** *020 †18
MARVANIA, Julie Jayantila. 746 JEFFERSON AVE, SCRANTON-TEMPLE RESIDENCY 18510 #495-48-2001 L2003 **IM** *020 †20
MAXWELL MC NULTY, K. 748 QUINCY AVE, STE 2A 18510 #041-09-1997 L2000 **OBG** *020 †30
MAZZA, Dominic Louis. 500 WHEELER AVE 18510 #041-14-1977 L1990 **P PYA** *020 †75
MC CORMACK, Patricia Anne. 101 MARY LN 18505 #041-02-1986 L1987 **GYN** *020
MCDONALD, Mary Ann. 802 JEFFERSON AVE, STE 301 18510 #035-03-1985 L1989 **IM** *020 †20
MC GEEHAN, John Francis. 743 JEFFERSON AVE 18510 #041-01-1977 L1978 **IM** *020 †20
MC GUIRE, Edward J. 746 JEFFERSON AVE 18510 #028-34-1943 L1944 **R** *071 †80
MENZEL, Paul Herbert. 201 FRANKLIN AVE 18503 #041-13-1965 L1966 **CD IM** *071
MILANI, Frank Angelo. 201 SMALLACOMBE DR 18508 #041-02-1959 L1960 **IM CD** *020 †20
MIRZA, Wasique. 959 WYOMING AVE, SCRANTON PRIMARY HEALTH CE 18509 #704-21-1992 L1999 **IM** *020 †20
MITRI, Ghada Mitri. 746 JEFFERSON AVE 18510 #875-01-1994 L1997 **IM** *020 †20
MITTAL, Basant Kumar. 1401 ELECTRIC ST 18509 #496-04-1976 L1981 **IM PD** *020 †20,55
MONTELLA, Michael Kirk. 743 S MAIN AVE 18504 #041-02-1986 L1987 **IM** *020 †20
MOORE, Michael Francis. 802 JEFFERSON AVE 18510 #035-03-1971 L1979 **GS CD** *020 †85
MORGAN, Vernon Wm, Jr. 743 JEFFERSON AVE 18510 #041-01-1965 L1966 **OBG** *071 †30
MORI, Hugo. 225 PENN AVE 18503 #041-02-1962 L1963 **U** *071 †95
MOSKEL, Peter. 746 JEFFERSON AVE 18510 #306-01-1983 L1988 **IM** *020 ‡
MOTT, Brian D. 1800 MULBERRY ST, CARDIOTHORACIC SURGERY LLC 18510 #067-01-1992 L2001 **TS** *020 †85,90
MRUTHYUNJAYA, Manasi. 746 JEFFERSON AVE 18510 #496-34-2004 L2006 **IM** *100
MURNIN, Patrick Jos. 3 W OLIVE ST, # 2 18508 #041-09-1985 L1986 **IM IMG** *020 †20
MUSINIPALLY, Sunil. 746 JEFFERSON AVE, SCRANTON-TEMPLE RESIDENCY 18510 #495-65-2001 L2004 **IM** *020 †20
NEALON, Gerard. 1209 SWETLAND ST 18504 #041-13-1995 L1997 **IM** *020 †20
NEVILLE, Edwin C. 746 JEFFERSON AVE 18510 #028-34-1951 L1972 **TS VS** *071 †85,90
NEWTON, Charles Thos. 120 N KEYSER AVE 18504 #041-02-1960 L1961 **N PN** *020 †75
NOWAK, Miroslawa A. 125 SCRANTON POCONO HWY 18505 #759-08-1990 L2003 **RHU** *020 †20
O'BOYLE, Tomas Anthony. 802 JEFFERSON AVE 18510 #010-02-1960 L1968 **PD** *071 †55
O'BRIEN, Richard P. 700 QUINCY AVE 18510 #010-02-1982 L1983 **EM GP** *020 †16
OCONER, Joseph Noel Napiz. 746 JEFFERSON AVE 18510 #748-01-1998 L2006 **IM** *012
O'DONNELL, Michael J. 429 SCRANTON CARBONDAL HWY, DERMATOLOGY 18508 #041-02-1986 L1988 **DS D** *020 †15 ‡
ONOFREY, David. 225 PENN AVE, DELTA MEDIX 18503 #035-09-1982 L1988 **GS CCM** *020 †85 ‡
OPSASNICK, Stephen Gary. 700 QUINCY AVE 18510 #041-09-1987 L1988 **IM** *020 †20 ‡
ORAM, Melvin. ■ 18505 #010-01-1953 L1954 **FM** *071 †18
OTAROD, Jila Kaberi. 201 SMALLACOMBE DR 18508 #517-11-1995 L2004 **IM** *020 †20 ‡
OXLEY, Cubyson Marcus. 746 JEFFERSON AVE, DEPT OF ANESTHESIA 18510 #035-46-1999 L2004 **AN** *020 †05 ‡
PACZKOWSKI, Karen. 748 QUINCY AVE 18510 #041-07-1978 L1979 **IM CD** *074 †20 ‡
PALANDJIAN, Khatchadour B. 475 MORGAN HWY 18508 #561-17-1957 L1975 **CHP P** *020 †75 ‡
PALEPU, Rajendra Prasad. 746 JEFFERSON AVE, SCRANTON-TEMPLE 18510 #495-37-2002 L2007 **IM** *012
PALUSHOCK, Sharon. 475 MORGAN HWY 18508 #422-01-1985 L1987 **END IM** *020 †20

■ = Address Information Privacy Protected

PANCOAST, Stephen Jos. 748 QUINCY AVE, STE 301B 18510 #035-01-1972 L1979 ID IM *020 †20

PANDYA, Varsha Jadunath. 1615 E ELM ST, FRIENDSHIP HOUSE 18505 #495-76-1972 L1982 P CHP *020

PATEL, Ashokkumar C. 326 ADAMS AVE 18503 #495-83-1976 L1983 P SME *020 †75

PATEL, Bharatkumar K. 517 ASH ST STE 1 18509 #495-17-1985 L1988 GE IM *020 †20

PATEL, Bhupendra R. 475 MORGAN HWY 18508 #495-23-1969 L1978 IM *020 †20

PEAIRS, Randall Ray. 200 MIFFLIN AVE 18503 #041-09-1985 L1986 OPH *020 †35

PELIAS, Anastasios J. 1401 MULBERRY ST 18510 #418-01-1972 L1976 TS GS *071 †85,90

PELICCI, Leroy Jos. 748 QUINCY AVE 18510 #041-14-1975 L1977 N P *020 †75

PERRY, Anthony Michael. 802 JEFFERSON AVE, STE 301 18510 #041-13-1964 L1975 IM DIA *020 †20

PETERS, John Wm. 700 QUINCY AVE 18510 #041-02-1977 L1978 PUD CCM *020 †20

PHILBIN, Joseph F. 1736 SANDERSON AVE 18509 #041-13-1979 L1980 IM *020 †20

PICZON, Oscar Y. 239 PENN AVE 18503 #748-11-1970 NEP IM *020 †20

PICZON, Severino Y. 475 MORGAN HWY 18508 #748-01-1955 L1969 N *020

PIRO, Frank Anthony. 1800 MULBERRY ST 18510 #041-13-1968 L1971 R *020 †80

PLATT, Howard Allen. 475 MORGAN HWY 18508 #041-02-1961 L1962 NS *071 †25

POHUTSKY, Karen Ruth. 1800 MULBERRY ST 18510 #041-07-1970 L1971 FM R *020 †28,18

PRADHAN, Raju. 746 JEFFERSON AVE, SCRANTON-TEMPLE 18510 #672-02-2000 L2007 IM *012

PREATE, Donald Louis. 225 PENN AVE 18503 #041-01-1967 L1968 U *071 †95 ‡

PREATE, Donald Louis, Jr. 225 PENN AVE, DELTA MEDIX PC 18503 #041-02-1995 L1997 U *020 †95 ‡

PRITCHYK, Keith Michael. 940 JEFFERSON AVE, NORTHEAST EAR, NOSE AND TH 18510 #010-02-1999 L2003 OTO *020 †45

PUHALLA, Cyril M James. 326 ADAMS AVE, SCRANTON COUNSELING CENTER 18503 #041-02-1973 L1974 CHP P *020 †75

QURESHI, Nabeel. 746 JEFFERSON AVE, SCRANTON-TEMPLE RES PROG 18510 #704-21-1991 L1993 IM *100

RABIN, Marc Howard. 401 ADAMS AVE, STE 202 18510 #041-09-1991 L1995 OBG *020 †30

RABINOVICH, Aaron. 225 PENN AVE, DELTA MEDIX, PC 18503 #025-07-2000 L2006 GS *085

RAMAKRISHNA, Srinivasarao. 517 ASH ST, # C 18509 #495-09-1974 L1981 PUD SME *020 †20

RAMOS, Julio Anibal. 743 JEFFERSON AVE, STE 102 18510 #305-01-1996 L2000 RHU PCP *020 †20

RANCIER, Lee Floyd. 327 N WASHINGTON AVE, MEDICAL ARTS BLDG. 18503 #035-15-1969 L1970 DR *071 †80

RAO, Madhava Seshagiri. 201 FRANKLIN AVE 18503 #495-09-1972 L1979 CD IM *020 †20

RATHI, Prabodh Deokaran. 746 JEFFERSON AVE, SCRANTON-TEMPLE 18510 #496-30-1993 L2006 IM *012

RAWLINSON, Keith Francis. 1800 MULBERRY ST, 3RD FL 18510 #917-20-1967 L2000 OBG MFM *020 †30

RESNICK, Raymond S. 746 JEFFERSON AVE, STE 305 18510 #035-08-1987 L1997 CD IC *020 †20

RICH, John Templer, Jr. 327 N WASHINGTON AVE, STE 808 18503 #041-02-1988 L1990 HS *020 †40

ROBERTS, David Edward. ■ 18505 #041-13-1996 L2001 GPM *020

ROE, Thomas Michael. 746 JEFFERSON AVE 18510 #010-02-1989 L1992 CD IM *020 †20

ROGALLA, Charles S. 401 ADAMS AVE, OB-GYN CONSULTANTS LTD 18510 #010-02-1971 L1973 OBG *071

ROGAN, Michael John. 125 SCRANTON POCONO HWY 18505 #033-05-1982 L1990 IM PD *020 †20,55 ‡

ROMANACE, Jean Pierre. 475 MORGAN HWY 18508 #396-27-1970 L1992 PM *071 †60

ROSIECKI, Michael Walter. 1390 WYOMING AVE 18509 #016-43-1968 L1969 OPH *020 †35

ROSS, Vincent Luch. 440 N MAIN AVE 18504 #016-43-1966 L1967 PD *020 †55 ‡

RUBIN, Emma. 475 MORGAN HWY 18508 #913-32-1974 L1987 IM *020 ‡

RUDEL, Harry W. ■ 18505 #041-13-1950 PA *071

RUDOLPH, Kenneth Harold. 802 JEFFERSON AVE 18510 #041-13-1977 L1978 DIA IM *020 †20

RUPPENTHAL, John Bruce. 748 QUINCY AVE 18510 #041-01-1969 L1970 IM *020 ‡

RUTTA, David. 517 ASH ST, STE 1 18509 #041-13-1983 L1988 GE IM *020 †20

RUZBARSKY, Joseph John. 746 JEFFERSON AVE 18510 #041-02-1977 L1980 AN *020 †05

RYCZAK, Mary. 475 MORGAN HWY 18508 #041-09-1980 L1982 ID IM *030 †20

SALAM, Marguerite Meien. 746 JEFFERSON AVE, DEPT OF PATH/LAB 18510 #041-12-1992 L1994 PTH *020 †50

SALAZAR, Jose Delfor. 1822 MULBERRY ST 18510 #737-05-1971 L1980 NPM PD *020 †55

SALEEM, Mohammad Anwar. 475 MORGAN HWY 18508 #495-50-1973 L1980 IM FM *020

SAMPATH-KUMAR, Sridhar. 746 JEFFERSON AVE STE 305, GREAT VALLEY CARDIOLOGY 18510 #495-73-1991 L1998 IC *020 †20

SARNOWSKI, Robert Jos. 802 JEFFERSON AVE 18510 #041-02-1964 L1965 NS *020 †25

SAVATTERI, Miriam. 746 JEFFERSON AVE 18510 #286-03-1996 L2003 IM *020 †20

SCHECHTER, Jay Franklin. 746 JEFFERSON AVE, STE 305 18510 #041-14-1977 L1984 D IM *020 †20,15

SCHMALTZ, Harry Walter. 327 N WASHINGTON AVE, STE 808 18503 #041-13-1983 L1984 ORS *020 †40

SCHUMAN, Robert Allen. 327 N WASHINGTON AVE, MEDICAL ARTS BLDG. 18503 #023-01-1971 L1975 R *071 †80

SCIALLA, Salvatore Jos. 5 MORGAN HWY, STE 8 18508 #033-05-1971 L1980 HEM ON *020 †20 ‡

SEIGLE, Walter E. ■ 18510 #041-02-1960 L1961 AN *071 †05

SETHI, Arjinder Pal Singh. 746 JEFFERSON AVE, STRP MERCY HOSPITAL 18510 #495-45-1987 L2002 IM *040 †20

SETHI, Harneet. 746 JEFFERSON AVE 18510 #495-45-1988 L2002 IM *020 †20

SEVERS, Gregg. 429 SCRANTON CARBONDAL HWY, DERMATOLOGY 18508 #041-77-2003, ▲ L2003 D *020

SEWATSKY, Mary Finan. 700 QUINCY AVE, EMGY DEPT MTH 18510 #041-13-1981 L1982 EM IM *020 †20 ‡

SHADEROWFSKY, Laura. 959 WYOMING AVE 18509 #041-14-1995 L2000 PD *020 †55 ‡

SHADZEKA, Edwin. 1800 MULBERRY ST 18510 #217-01-2000 L2007 IM *020 †20

SHAH, Rahmat. 746 JEFFERSON AVE 18510 #704-01-1966 L1975 AN *020 †05 ‡

SHAIKH, K A. 1822 MULBERRY ST, COMMUNITY MEDICAL CENTER 18510 #495-28-1965 L1988 GS OS *020 †85

SHANDER, Ernest Gerard. ■ 18509 #041-02-1948 L1949 AN GP *071

SHARMA, Meera Vedraj. 5 WATRES DR 18505 #495-01-1966 L1978 RHU IM *020 †20

SHELDON, Douglas Levi. 429 SCRANTON CARBONDAL HWY, DERMATOLOGY 18508 #041-14-1975 L1976 D *020 †15 ‡

SHERWIN, Edward Alan. 517 ASH ST, # 1 18509 #035-03-1976 L1985 GE IM *020 †20

SHETH, Jignesh Yasmin. 746 JEFFERSON AVE, DEPT OF MED EDUCATION 18510 #495-26-2004 L2006 IM *012

SHETTY, Ajay. 802 JEFFERSON AVE 18510 #495-73-1986 L1996 PCC *020 †20

SHETTY, Shubhra Marwaha. 746 JEFFERSON AVE, STRP 18510 #495-73-1990 L1996 ID IM *020 †20

SHOLI, Abdallah Mohammad. 5 MORGAN HWY, STE 8 18508 #575-01-1994 L1999 HO *020 †20

SIBAI, Jehad. 746 JEFFERSON AVE, SCRANTON-TEMPLE 18510 #875-01-2001 L2006 IM *012

SIEMINSKI, Lynne. 700 QUINCY AVE #010-02-1995 L1997 IM CD *020 †20 ‡

SIMPSON, Roy W. 746 JEFFERSON AVE 18510 #041-02-1951 L1952 GP *071

SINGH, Rohit G. 1800 MULBERRY ST, (ANESTHESIA OFFICE #135) 18510 #495-08-1994 L2004 APM *100 †05

SKETTINO, Joseph Alfred. 200 MIFFLIN AVE 18503 #561-11-1962 L1964 OPH *071

SLOVAK, James P. 321 SPRUCE ST STE 1200 18503 #041-09-1972 L1973 P CHP *020 †75 ‡

SMERALDI, Alessandro G. 1360 WYOMING AVE STE 104 18509 #035-46-1998 L2005 GS VS *100 †85

SMITH, Catherine S. 401 ADAMS AVE STE 306 18510 #041-13-1983 L1987 MFM OBG *020 †30

SMOLKO, Milan John. 802 JEFFERSON AVE 18510 #036-07-1977 L1984 U *020

SOLIMAN, Zaher Selim. 2324 BOULEVARD AVE 18509 #654-01-1986 L1992 IM EM *020

SOMA, Joseph J. 120 N KEYSER AVE 18504 #010-02-1951 L1953 A OTO *071

SPEICHER, Julie Marie. 746 JEFFERSON AVE 18510 #041-13-1986 L1987 IM *020 †20

SREEDHAR, Devathi. 746 JEFFERSON AVE, SCRANTON-TEMPLE 18510 #496-22-2004 L2007 IM *012

STAHL, Russell Frank. 1800 MULBERRY ST 18510 #035-19-1983 L1985 TS CD *020 †85,90

STEFANELLI, James L. 225 PENN AVE 18503 #041-02-1985 L1986 U GS *020 †95 ‡

STEHLIKOVA, Martina. 746 JEFFERSON AVE, SCRANTON-TEMPLE RESIDENCY 18510 #286-11-1991 L2005 IM *012

STEINDEL, Carl Ralph. 233 PENN AVE 18503 #041-02-1966 L1967 ORS *020 †40

STELLA, Joseph E. 125 SCRANTON POCONO HWY, GEISINGER MEDICAL GROUP 18505 #041-13-1978 L1979 FM *020 †18

STRAND, Cynthia Elizabeth. 700 QUINCY AVE, MOSES TAYLOR HOSPITAL 18510 #054-04-1985 L2003 NPM PD *020 †55

SWIFT, Frank Louis, Jr. 18509 #010-02-1948 L1953 PD *071 †55

SWISHER, Charles Lee. 746 JEFFERSON AVE 18510 #051-01-1968 L1975 EM *020 †16

THOMAS, Linda Joanne. 746 JEFFERSON AVE 18510 #048-04-1994 L1998 MPD PD *020 †20,55

THOMAS, Lisa C. 5 MORGAN HWY, STE 8 18508 #041-07-1991 L1993 HEM IM *020 †20

TINSLEY, Bria Marie. 746 JEFFERSON AVE, RESIDENCY PROG 18510 #041-13-2003 L2003 IM *020 †20

TOGIAS, Kyriakos N. 746 JEFFERSON AVE, MERCY HOSPITAL 18510 #418-01-1966 L1976 R *020 †20

TOMASSONI, Andrea Marissa. 201 ADAMS AVE STE 202 18503 #041-14-1996 L2006 OBG *020 †30

TOMASZEWSKI, Theodore J. 743 JEFFERSON AVE, STE 102 18510 #010-02-1994 L1997 ORS *020 †40

TRACY, Gerald Paul. 746 JEFFERSON AVE, STE 305 18510 #041-01-1967 L1968 CD IM *071 †20

TUROCK, Michael John. 397 N 9TH AVE 18504 #016-43-1971 L1972 FM *020 †18 ‡

UDOMSAK, Paramin. 201 SMALLACOMBE DR, LACKAWANNA MEDICAL GROUP 18508 #891-02-1970 L1977 GP GS *020 †20

UROSKIE, Theodore W. 401 ADAMS AVE, STE 202 18510 #041-09-1970 L1971 OBG *071

VANSTON, Vincent Jay. 746 JEFFERSON AVE, SCRANTON TEMPLE RESIDENCY 18510 #041-13-1989 L1992 IM *020 †20

VEKARIA, Kishor-Kumar S. 1800 MULBERRY ST 18510 #495-23-1978 L1985 AN PME *020 †05

VENTURA, Cecilia F. 959 WYOMING AVE 18509 #748-08-1967 L1978 PD *020

VERA, Luis Angel. 1800 MULBERRY ST 18510 #308-03-1982 L1990 NPM *020 ‡

VILOGI, Joseph Paul. 746 JEFFERSON AVE 18510 #041-02-1979 L1980 EM *020 †16

VORA, Kapila Suresh. 1800 MULBERRY ST 18510 #495-96-1970 L1976 R *020 †20

VOYCE, Stephen John. 700 QUINCY AVE 18510 #041-09-1984 L1987 CD IM *020 †20

WALLER, Louis Chas. 700 QUINCY AVE 18510 #036-07-1942 L1943 IM EM *072

WANDALOWSKI, John Gerald. 18509 #041-09-1967 L1973 IM CD *075 †20

WERNER, Donald J. 746 JEFFERSON AVE 18510 #018-03-1949 L1950 GP *075

WILCOX, Kenneth Robt. 720 MADISON AVE 18510 #005-15-1978 L1988 TS GS *020 †85,90

WILSON, James S. ■ 18504 #016-42-1986 L1987 FM *020 †20

WITOWSKI, John Jos. 2601 STAFFORD AVE 18505 #041-13-1965 L1973 DR *071 †80

WOLK, Michael David. 5 MORGAN HWY, STE 4 18508 #041-12-1988 L1992 PM *020 †60

WRIGHT, Robert Emmett. 746 JEFFERSON AVE, SCANTON-TEMPLE RES PROG 18510 #041-13-1965 L1966 ON HEM *030 †20

YANNI, Anthony Jos. 1789 N KEYSER AVE 18508 #041-09-1992 L1994 IM *020 †20

YEAGER, Henry Clay. 746 JEFFERSON AVE 18510 #041-01-1969 L1975 NEP CCM *020 †20

ZALE, Anthony Geo. 1538 WYOMING AVE 18509 #041-02-1942 L1943 ORS *072

ZAYDON, Ann Clarice C. 811 MULBERRY ST 18510 #041-07-1976 L1977 END IM *020 †20 ‡

ZEGLEN, Kurt Thos. 120 N KEYSER AVE 18504 #041-09-1981 L1982 DR NM *020

ZENKER, Joanne Margaret. 429 SCRANTON CARBONDAL HWY, DERMATOLOGY 18508 #041-07-1980 L1982 D *020 †15 ‡

SECANE – DELAWARE

AGRAWAL, Shilpa. ■ 19018 #496-22-1994 *100

AHMAD, Imran. 151 S BISHOP AVE 19018 #704-01-2000 L2004 IM *020

ALADE, Ekunolaola Abimbol. ■ 19018 #041-01-2008 *012

ALI, Tayyab. ■ 19018 #704-01-1998 L2002 IM *020 †20

CHANNAMSETTY, Ramu. ■ 19018 #495-11-1996 L2007 IM *100 †20

FRANCIOSI, James Paul. ■ 19018 #056-06-2001 L2003 PG *012

JAWA, Pankaj. ■ 19018 #495-08-2004 L2007 IM *012

KAVETI, Vamshi Krishna. ■ 19018 #495-21-2004 L2007 IM *012

KELLEHER, Stephanie. ■ 19018 #041-77-2007, ▲ *012

KHAIRI, Shafaq. ■ 19018 #704-02-1998 L2004 IM *012

MAHFOUZ, Reda Fouad. ■ 19018 #915-02-1985 L1995 IM *100

MINNELLA, James Matthew. 831 PROVIDENCE RD, MERCY MEDICAL ASSOCIATE PR 19018 #041-09-1975 L1978 IM *012

RAJAGOPALAN, Viswanathan. 151 S BISHOP AVE, APT M117 19018 #495-66-1983 L2002 GS *020 ‡

RAMESH, Pathasarathy. ■ 19018 #495-16-1991 IM *100

SIDHU, Preetinder Singh. ■ 19018 #495-29-1996 L2006 **OBG** *100

SELINSGROVE - SNYDER

BATES, Ollice, Jr. 21 MILL RD 17870 #041-09-1971 L1972 **NEP IM** *020 †20
BATMAN, Brian Allen. 21 SUSQUEHANNA VALLY ML DR, SUN ORTHOPAEDIC GROUP 17870 #041-14-1993 L1998 **ORS** *020 †40
BRITTON, Eric Lance. ■ 17870 #041-01-1996 L1997 *100
CHLEBOWSKI, James Edward. 21 SUSQUEHANNA VALLY ML DR, STE A 17870 #041-12-1990 L1992 **FM** *020 †18
COLE, Charles Louis, Jr. 11 9TH ST 17870 #041-13-1987 L1988 **ORS** *020 †40
COTTRELL, David Chadwell. 113 N MARKET ST 17870 #041-01-1959 L1960 **ORS** *071 †40
DEL CASTILLO, Juan Julio. 1000 ROUTE 522, SELINSGROVE CENTER 17870 #737-01-1958 L1967 **GP** *071
DOMINICK, Thomas Francis. 11 9TH ST 17870 #041-13-1992 L1994 **ORS** *020 †40
DOTTERER, Christine S. 113 N MARKET ST 17870 #041-02-1979 L1980 **FM** *020 †18 ‡
EDINGER, Andrew Martin. 935 ROUTE 522, EMSF SELINSGROVE 17870 #041-02-1987 L1989 **FM** *020 †18
FREDERICK, Kevin Dale. ■ 17870 #041-15-2005 L2005 **DR** *012
FURIA, John Patrick. 21 SUSQUEHANNA VALLY ML DR, SUN ORTHOPAEDIC GROUP 17870 #047-05-1989 L1995 **OSM** *020 †40
GABALA, John Michael. ■ 17870 #028-34-1957 L1958 **FM** *071 †18
JHAVERI, Amit Rohit. 113 N MARKET ST 17870 #496-21-1995 L2000 **PM** *020 †60
KARP, Steve. 1420 N SUSQUEHANNA TRL, SUSQUEHANNA VALLEY CANCER 17870 #035-09-1992 L1998 **RO** *020 †80
KOBYLINSKI, Maria Susan. 201 ROOSEVELT AVE 17870 #422-01-1998 L2000 **IM** *020 †20
KORINCHAK, Jerome L. 1000 US HIGHWAY 522 17870 #041-02-1980 L1981 **FM** *020 †18 ‡
KUMAR, Ashok V S. 1575 N OLD TRL 17870 #495-59-1985 L1999 **HEM** *020 †20
MOWAD, Christen Maria. 113 N MARKET ST 17870 #041-01-1991 L1994 **D** *020 †15
NESPOLI, Anthony Michael. ■ 17870 #041-02-1972 L1973 **FM GS** *020
PAGANA, Charles Carl, II. 21 SUSQUEHANNA VALLY ML DR, STE A 17870 #041-13-1991 L1993 **FM** *020 †18
PETERS, Lidia Elisabeta. 1000 ROUTE 522 17870 #132-02-1965 L1997 **FM** *020 †18
SCHOENFELDER, Steven J. 201 ROOSEVELT AVE 17870 #023-01-1985 L1986 **IM PD** *020 †20,55
SEMIAN, John Alan. ■ 17870 #033-05-1995 L2002 **GS** *020 †85
SERVANO, Pedro O, III. 201 ROOSEVELT AVE, GEISINGER-SELINSGROVE 17870 #748-08-1979 L1995 **FM** *020 †18
SMITH, Glen Edwin. ■ 17870 #041-13-1960 L1961 **IM** *071
SRIVASTAVA, Poonam. 1575 N OLD TRL 17870 #495-54-1979 L1982 **ON HEM** *020
STRICKLAND, Fred Wm, Jr. PO BOX 148 17870 #001-06-1976 L1982 **P** *020 †75 ‡
TOLAN, Myra B. 113 N MARKET ST 17870 #023-01-1997 L2003 **PM** *020 †60
TRAPP, Donald Chas. ■ 17870 #041-13-1955 L1956 **U** *071 †95
VISUDTIBHAN, Anannit. ■ 17870 #891-04-1984 L1994 **CHN** *020
WEADER, William Michael. ■ 17870 #041-13-1961 L1962 **FM EM** *071 †18
YAHYA, Taher Mohamad. 113 N MARKET ST 17870 #605-01-1974 L1995 **NEP** *020 †20
YAVOREK, Henry Geo, Jr. 1 COMMERCE AVE 17870 #041-02-1985 L1986 **GS VS** *020 †85
ZOLA, James Albert. 201 ROOSEVELT AVE 17870 #041-09-1994 L1996 **MPD PD** *020 †20,55

SELLERSVILLE - BUCKS

AIMETTE, Alexander Argeiw. 700 LAWN AVE 18960 #033-06-1976 L1977 **OPH** *020 †35
ALDERFER, Arthur James. 670 LAWN AVE, STE 4A 18960 #041-13-1965 L1966 **GYN** *020 †30
ALDERFER, James Todd. 670 LAWN AVE, STE 3A 18960 #041-01-1991 L1993 **CD** *020 †20
ALTMAN, David Sigmund. 711 LAWN AVE, BUILD 2 18960 #041-02-1985 L1986 **U VS** *020 †95 ‡
ARSUAGA, Jorge Enrique. 700 LAWN AVE 18960 #042-01-1988 L1992 **VIR** *020 †80
ASOM, Angela E. 700 LAWN AVE 18960 #690-06-1988 L1996 **PD** *020 †55 ‡
BAILEY, Wellesley Earl, Jr. 807 LAWN AVE 18960 #041-09-1998 L2001 **P** *020
BARONE, Frances Ann. 700 LAWN AVE 18960 #041-13-1965 L1966 **PD** *020 †55
BARRER, Mitchell Jay. 700 LAWN AVE, GRAND VIEW ANESTHESIA ASSO 18960 #041-01-1972 L1973 **AN** *020 †05
BLOCK, Steven. 920 LAWN AVE 18960 #041-09-1976 L1977 **GYN** *020 †30
BUMGARDNER, James Larson. 711 LAWN AVE 18960 #041-13-1978 L1979 **ORS** *020 †40
CASEY, Steven Edward. 711 LAWN AVE, STE 3 18960 #041-13-1988 L1990 **ORS** *020 †40
CHU, Andrew Sunwen. 700 LAWN AVE, CHOP CONNECTION GRAND VI 18960 #041-02-1991 L1993 **PD** *020 †55
CLIPP, Samuel Wm. 711 LAWN AVE, STE 1 18960 #041-13-1956 L1957 **R RO** *020 †80
CORALNICK, Jeffrey Roy. 700 LAWN AVE 18960 #041-13-1990 L1996 **DR** *020 †80
CORRADO, Sandra Harris. 920 LAWN AVE, STE 4 18960 #047-07-1974 L1981 **IM ON** *020 ‡
COYLE, Thomas J, Jr. 670 LAWN AVE STE 1A 18960 #041-13-1983 L1984 **GS VS** *020 †85
CRASTNOPOL, David Howard. 700 LAWN AVE, GRAND VIEW ANESTHESIA ASSO 18960 #033-05-1983 L1988 **AN PD** *020 †55,05
DAVID, Richard Allan. 700 LAWN AVE 18960 #041-13-1990 L1993 **DR** *020 †80
DAVIS, Campbell Mortimer. 807 LAWN AVE 18960 #041-02-1967 L1988 **P** *020 †75
DAVIS, Robert A. 700 LAWN AVE 18960 #654-01-1981 L1982 **FM** *020 †18
DIX, David Grant. 700 LAWN AVE 18960 #041-01-1988 L1992 **PDR R** *020 †80
DOBROTA, John Stephen. 817 LAWN AVE 18960 #041-09-1965 L1966 **GE IM** *020 †20
DULCEY, John Jos, Jr. 670 LAWN AVE 18960 #041-02-1977 L1978 **IM** *062 †18,20
FERRY, Jane Ann. 700 LAWN AVE 18960 #041-13-1980 L1982 **EM** *030 †16
FINKELSTEIN, Gary Stan. 670 LAWN AVE, STE 1A 18960 #041-13-1974 L1975 **GS** *020 †85
FODERARO, Anthony Edward. 700 LAWN AVE 18960 #041-14-1982 L1982 **DR** *020 †80
FREEMAN, Marc David. 700 LAWN AVE, GRAND VIEW ANESTHESIA ASSO 18960 #041-13-2000 L2002 **AN** *020 †05 ‡
GEETTER, Philip H. 711 LAWN AVE 18960 #041-02-1970 L1972 **OPH** *020 †35 ‡
GERSTEIN, Matthew Ian. 711 LAWN AVE 18960 #035-08-1998 L2001 **U** *020 †95
GILL, Lewis Martin, Jr. 817 LAWN AVE 18960 #041-02-1980 L1982 **GS** *020
GODSHALL, Richard Wambold. 711 LAWN AVE, CENTER-BLDG #3 18960 #041-02-1959 L1960 **ORS** *020 †40
GORDON, Jeffrey Neil. 920 LAWN AVE, STE 3 18960 #012-05-1988 L1996 **U** *020 †95
GREENSPAN, Mitchell Miles. 3 LIFE MARK DR, ASSOCIATES PC 18960 #041-02-1974 L1975 **CD IM** *020 †20
GUARINO, James Carmen. 670 LAWN AVE, STE 3A 18960 #041-13-1991 L1993 **IM CD** *020 †20
GUIDERA, Ann Chien. 711 LAWN AVE 18960 #035-01-1987 L1989 **OPH IM** *020 †35

HANES, David John. 670 LAWN AVE 18960 #041-01-1990 L1992 **OBG** *020 †30
HANSEN, Carl Anthony. 711 LAWN AVE STE 3 18960 #067-01-1961 L1967 **ORS** *071 †40
HARKNESS, Julia B. 700 LAWN AVE 18960 #041-13-1993 L1996 **PD** *020 †55
HASSAN, Farhat N. 700 LAWN AVE 18960 #704-15-1984 L1996 **PD** *020 †55
HERMANY, Paul Roger. 3 LIFE MARK DR, ASSOCIATES PC 18960 #041-13-1982 L1983 **CD IM** *020 †20 ‡
HIGHTOWER, Martin Craig. 700 LAWN AVE, GRAND VIEW HOSPITAL 18960 #021-05-1987 L1988 **RO** *020 †80
HOLLANDER, Irwin Joel. 700 LAWN AVE 18960 #041-02-1972 L1973 **PTH IM** *020 †20,50
HUANG, Abby Irene. 817 LAWN AVE 18960 #023-01-1986 L1987 **ID** *020 †20
HURLEY, James Michael. 711 LAWN AVE, STE 3 18960 #041-13-1988 L1990 **ORS** *020 †40
HUTCHINGS, Diana M. 711 LAWN AVE, STE 1 18960 #041-01-1980 L1984 **DR** *020 †80
JUNG, Jennifer Lee. 700 LAWN AVE 18960 #583-03-1964 L1970 **AN** *071
KAUFMAN, Alan Carl. 920 LAWN AVE, SUMMIT SOUTH 18960 #035-15-1968 L1969 **ON IM** *020 †20
KNERR, Sheila Maureen. 700 LAWN AVE 18960 #036-07-1993 L1997 **PD** *020 †55
KOELSCH, Robert Ralph. 712 LAWN AVE, ROCKHILL MED ARTS CENTRE 18960 #165-01-1960 L1962 **D** *071
KOZIUPA, Diana Maria. 807 LAWN AVE 18960 #041-01-1978 L1979 **P** *020 †75 ‡
KRATZ, Richard Todd. 711 LAWN AVE 18960 #041-13-1995 L1997 **PD** *020 †55 ‡
KRATZ, Vernon Halteman. 700 LAWN AVE 18960 #041-09-1963 L1964 **P** *020 †75
KUCER, Frank Thos. 817 LAWN AVE 18960 #041-02-1974 L1975 **GE** *020 †20 ‡
KUCER, Kathleen B. UPPER BUCKS MED ARTS BLDG 18960 #041-02-1976 L1977 **D** *020 †15
KUDES, Mark Andrew. 670 LAWN AVE, STE 3A 18960 #041-13-2001 L2007 **CD** *020
KYRIAKOS, Raymond Joseph. 700 LAWN AVE 18960 #033-05-1993 L1999 **DR** *020 †80 ‡
LANDAU, Richard Evan. 920 LAWN AVE STE 3 18960 #010-01-1983 L1984 **U GS** *020 †95
LESKA, Linda Lavin. 700 LAWN AVE, DEPT OF PATH GRANDVIEW HOS 18960 #041-09-1976 L1978 **PTH** *020 †50
LEVIN, Morris. 711 LAWN AVE, STE 1 18960 #041-09-1967 L1968 **DR GP** *020 †80
LINDLEY, Michelle Claudia. 700 LAWN AVE 18960 #041-12-1998 L2002 **PD** *020 †55 ‡
LOUX, Norman L. 807 LAWN AVE 18960 #041-09-1946 L1947 **P** *071
LUKASZEWSKI, Kathleen. 817 LAWN AVE 18960 #033-75-1999, ▲ L2001 **GE** *020 †20
MANDATO, Philip A. 700 LAWN AVE 18960 #041-78-2002, ▲ L2002 **AN** *020
MARKOS, Ronald Peter. 817 LAWN AVE 18960 #041-09-1988 L1990 **GE** *020 †20
MARTIN, C Edwin. 711 LAWN AVE STE 1, GRANDVIEW RADIOLOGY ASSOCI 18960 #041-01-1963 L1964 **DR** *020 †20
MARTIN, Charles Edwin, Jr. 700 LAWN AVE 18960 #041-01-1991 L1998 **DR** *020 †80 ‡
MASS, Marion E. 700 LAWN AVE, CHOP CONNECTION 18960 #036-07-1994 L1999 **PD** *020 †55
MAZZA, Ida L. 3 LIFE MARK DR, ASSOCIATES PC 18960 #935-07-1992 L2000 **CD** *020 †20
MELTZER, Ronald Seymour. 711 LAWN AVE 18960 #033-05-1968 L1975 **U** *020 †95 ‡
MIKETTA, Rose Martha. ■ 18960 #041-07-1972 L1973 **N** *075
MOSKOFF, Lane A. 670 LAWN AVE, STONERIDGE OBSTETRICS & 18960 #041-13-1994 L1997 **OBG** *020 †30
MOYER, John Phillip. 3 LIFE MARK DR, ASSOCIATES PC 18960 #038-06-1970 L1971 **CD IM** *020 †20
NASE, Donald Frederick. 700 LAWN AVE 18960 #041-09-1963 L1964 **CD IM** *071 †20
NEWTON, Anne F. 807 LAWN AVE 18960 #041-13-1983 L1984 **P ADP** *020
NYI, Corinne Ann. ■ 18960 #041-01-1988 **PTH** *071
OMANA, Jess Elento. 700 LAWN AVE 18960 #748-01-1967 L1972 **OBG** *020 †30
OSWALD, Christopher Todd. 3 LIFE MARK DR, ASSOCIATES PC 18960 #041-02-1999 L2005 **CD IM** *020 †20
PAGAN, John Joseph. 670 LAWN AVE, STE 1A 18960 #023-01-1991 L1996 **GS** *020 †85
POBRE-SO, Josephine. 807 LAWN AVE 18960 #748-10-1979 L1995 **P PYG** *020
PRICE, Richard Taylor. 700 LAWN AVE 18960 #041-02-1956 L1957 **FM** *071
RILLING, David Carl. 670 LAWN AVE, STE 1A 18960 #041-09-1966 **GS VS** *020 †85
RISING, David Carl. 711 LAWN AVE, STE 3 18960 #041-02-1966 L1973 **ORS OSM** *071 †40
ROSEN, Randy Allen. 700 LAWN AVE, BIO-MEDICAL APPLICATIONS O 18960 #011-02-1981 L1986 **NEP** *020 †20
ROSS, Abraham. 700 LAWN AVE 18960 #038-41-1972 L1974 **AN** *020 †05
ROTHSCHILD, Jill Green. 700 LAWN AVE, CHOP CONNECTION AT GRANDVI 18960 #041-01-1992 L1994 **PD** *020 †55 ‡
SCHILLER, Ruth Phyllis. 711 LAWN AVE 18960 #041-07-1966 L1967 **PD** *071 †55
SCOZZAFAVA, Thomas John. 700 LAWN AVE 18960 #035-15-1991 L1998 **AN** *020 †05
SHEARBURN, Edwin W, III. 920 LAWN AVE STE 4 18960 #051-01-1972 L1975 **GS** *020 †85
SHOWALTER, James Grove. 807 LAWN AVE 18960 #041-09-1982 L1986 **CHP P** *020 †75
SIBLEY, Robert Emmett. 700 LAWN AVE 18960 #035-01-1978 L1984 **DR VIR** *020 †80
SLAGEL, Scott Alan. 700 LAWN AVE, GRAND VIEW HOSPITAL 18960 #016-11-1982 L1983 **EM** *020 †16
SNYDER, Lorraine Claire. 920 LAWN AVE, THE SUMMIT, SOUTH 18960 #041-01-1999 L2001 **HO** *030 †20
SOUDER, Ronald Lee. 711 LAWN AVE 18960 #041-02-1973 L1976 **PD MM** *020 †55
STELLA, Christopher Robt. 700 LAWN AVE 18960 #035-46-1981 L1989 **EM IM** *020 †20,05,16
STRAM, Michelle. 3 LIFE MARK DR, ASSOCIATES PC 18960 #035-06-1984 L1989 **CD** *020 †20
TRAVIS, David A. 670 LAWN AVE, STE 3A 18960 #041-77-1990, ▲ L1991 **CD** *020 †20
ULASEWICZ, Catherine C. 711 LAWN AVE 18960 #033-06-1981 L1983 **OPH** *020 †35 ‡
VIZER, Mark Benj. 920 LAWN AVE 18960 #041-02-1971 L1972 **OBG** *020 †30
WALTON, Joseph Doyle. 670 LAWN AVE, STE 3A 18960 #041-09-1996 L1999 **CD** *020 †20
WEIDNER, Paul Louis. 711 LAWN AVE, STE 3 18960 #041-13-1982 L1983 **ORS** *020 †40
WENGER, Jay Agnew. GRAND VIEW HOSP 18960 #041-13-1954 L1955 **R RO** *071 †80
WILKINS, H Jeffrey. ■ 18960 #041-13-1988 L1990 **FM** *050 †18
YOUNG, John Lamotte. 700 LAWN AVE 18960 #041-13-1963 L1964 **FM GP** *071 †18
ZEMEL, Walter Geo. 920 LAWN AVE, THE SUMMIT - SUITE #10 18960 #041-02-1968 **OTO** *020 †45
ZURMUHL, Martin Allen. 700 LAWN AVE, EMERGENCY DEPARTMENT 18960 #041-02-1989 L1991 **IM** *020 †20

SENECA - VENANGO

ARIAS, Johnny Manuel. 100 FAIRFIELD DR 16346 #001-06-1988 L2005 **DR** *020 †28,80
BATTEN, Dean. 100 FAIRFIELD DR 16346 #036-07-1998 L2001 **DR** *020 †80
BEALS, Norman K, III. 1 PARK WAY 16346 #422-01-1984 L1986 **FM** *020 †18
BITTNER, Donald Frederick. 100 FAIRFIELD DR 16346 #038-41-1988 L1993 **DR** *020 †80
BOARDMAN, John Works. 100 FAIRFIELD DR 16346 #056-05-1994 L2003 **DR** *020 †80
BURDETTE, D Duke. 100 FAIRFIELD DR 16346 #025-01-1990 L2005 **DR** *020 †80

BUSH, Todd Allen. 3742 STATE RT 257, ANDRE BUSH INTERNAL MEDICI 16346 #041-02-1989 L1991 **IM** *020 †20
CAVIN, Lillian Whitley. 100 FAIRFIELD DR 16346 #045-01-1982 L2003 **DR** *020 †80
CHESAR, Thomas, Jr. 100 FAIRFIELD DR 16346 #041-09-1992 L1994 **FM** *020 †18
CIABATTONI, Steven Emmet. 100 FAIRFIELD DR 16346 #010-02-1987 L2005 **DR** *020 †80
CLARK, Gordon Penner. PO BOX 803 16346 #025-07-1965 L1975 **EM** *020 †55,16
COOK, Nicholas A. 100 FAIRFIELD DR 16346 #016-43-1981 L1982 **HO IMG** *020 †20
DAVIS, Bridgett Kathleen. 100 FAIRFIELD DR 16346 #041-12-1972 L1973 **PTH IG** *030 †50
DINGES, Susan. 100 FAIRFIELD DR 16346 #035-15-1988 L2004 **DR** *020 †80
FEE, William Homer, Jr. 3512 STATE ROUTE 257, STE 108 16346 #036-07-1968 L1974 **IM PUD** *020 †20
FEMOVICH, David Alan. 3744 STATE ROUTE 257 16346 #041-12-1986 L1995 **PS** *020 †65
GOODING, Britta Meghan. 100 FAIRFIELD DR 16346 #024-05-1995 L2005 **DR** *020 †80
GOODPASTOR, Wm Edward. 100 FAIRFIELD DR 16346 #654-01-1981 L1982 **P** *020 †50
GRAMATOVICI, Razvan N. 100 FAIRFIELD DR 16346 #781-01-1966 L1982 **RO** *020 †80
GRENNAN, Jason Edward. 100 FAIRFIELD DR 16346 #030-05-1999 L2005 **DR** *020 †80
GRYSEELS-LA ROCHELLE, A. 3334 STATE RT 257 16346 #165-01-1984 L1990 **END PDE** *020 †20,55
GUTSTEIN, Laurie Lynn. 100 FAIRFIELD DR 16346 #016-06-1985 L2003 **DR** *020 †80
HAMM, Glenn Gordon. 3512 STATE ROUTE 257, HOPE PEDS 16346 #019-02-1982 L1983 **PD** *020 †55
HELLER, Howard Todd. 100 FAIRFIELD DR 16346 #035-08-1992 L1997 **DR** *020 †80
HOLT, Peter David. 100 FAIRFIELD DR 16346 #036-07-1990 L2005 **PDR** *020 †80
JAKSHA, Jonathan Andrew. 100 FAIRFIELD DR 16346 #030-06-1996 L2005 **DR** *020 †80
JONEJA, Savita. 3529 STATE ROUTE 257 16346 #495-85-1981 L1993 **IM** *020 †20
JONES, Thomas Beverly. 100 FAIRFIELD DR 16346 #047-06-1971 L2004 **DR** *020 †80
JUPIN, John Albert. 100 FAIRFIELD DR, UPMC NW DEPT EMER MED 16346 #055-01-1971 L1983 **EM FM** *020 †16
KAPLAN, Liat Joy. 100 FAIRFIELD DR 16346 #035-20-1998 L2004 **DR** *020 †80
KEATS, Joel Benner. 100 FAIRFIELD DR 16346 #038-40-1972 L1977 **R GP** *020 †80
KENNEY, Gerard Francis. 3744 STATE ROUTE 257 16346 #041-14-1990 L1993 **GE IM** *020 †20
KLENA, James William. 100 FAIRFIELD DR, UPMC NORTHWEST 16346 #041-13-1995 L1997 **TS** *020 †85,90
KOTTLER, Nina Ellen. 100 FAIRFIELD DR 16346 #024-16-2000 L2005 **DR** *100 †80
LA ROCHELLE, Gerald E, Jr. 3334 STATE RT 257 16346 #165-01-1984 L1990 **RHU PD** *020 †20,55
MASON, Charles Elbert. 100 FAIRFIELD DR 16346 #016-11-1963 L1969 **R** *020 †80
MC CARTER, Samuel Bethier. 100 FAIRFIELD DR 16346 #041-13-1956 L1957 **R** *071 †80
MCKERNAN, Margaret Grant. 100 FAIRFIELD DR 16346 #048-02-1999 L2005 **DR** *100 †80
MILLER, Christopher James. 100 FAIRFIELD DR 16346 #048-13-1990 L2003 **DR NM** *020 †80,28
MILLER, K Sloan. 100 FAIRFIELD DR 16346 #007-02-1999 L2005 **DR** *020 †80
MIN, Joonhong J. 100 FAIRFIELD DR 16346 #005-11-2000 L2005 **DR** *020 †80
NORCONK, James Jos, Jr. 100 FAIRFIELD DR 16346 #011-02-1981 L2004 **DR IM** *020 †80 ‡
O'CONNOR, John Vincent. 100 FAIRFIELD DR 16346 #028-34-1969 L1980 **DR NM** *020 †80
PADALINO, Michael James. 3744 STATE ROUTE 257 16346 #035-08-1977 L1982 **GE IM** *020 †20
PETTINGER, Thomas Wm. 100 FAIRFIELD DR 16346 #048-12-1990 L2005 **DR** *020 †80
RAMIREZ, Jorge A. 100 FAIRFIELD DR 16346 #042-01-1994 L2004 **DR** *020 †80
RUSNACK, Douglas William. 100 FAIRFIELD DR 16346 #035-01-1998 L2004 **DR** *020 †80
SALERNO, Mark David. 100 FAIRFIELD DR, UPMC NORTHWEST 16346 #051-04-1983 L1992 **DR VIR** *020 †80
SHONNARD, John Waldron. 100 FAIRFIELD DR 16346 #041-12-1972 L1973 **PTH CLP** *020 †50
SNYDER, Bradley Jay. 100 FAIRFIELD DR 16346 #028-02-1990 L2004 **DR** *020 †80
SUK, Jin Hong. 100 FAIRFIELD DR 16346 #583-01-1962 L1971 **PTH** *020 †50
SWITZER, Gary Lee. 100 FAIRFIELD DR 16346 #030-06-1984 L1986 **AN** *020 †05
SWOPE, Stephanie H. 100 FAIRFIELD DR 16346 #028-34-2000 L2005 **DR** *020 †80
TONSETH, Rolf Peter. 100 FAIRFIELD DR 16346 #061-01-1988 L2005 **DR NM** *020 †80,28
VREELAND, Thomas Henry. 100 FAIRFIELD DR 16346 #021-06-1990 L2002 **DR EM** *020 †80,28
YOUNGER, Perry Ward. 3744 STATE ROUTE 257 16346 #026-04-1994 L1998 **OPH** *020 †35
ZEHNER, Janet Aileen. 100 FAIRFIELD DR 16346 #041-12-1977 L1979 **DR** *020 †80

SEVEN FIELDS – BUTLER

BADWAY, David Maynard. 300 NORTHPOINTE CIR, STE 103 16046 #041-14-1983 L1984 **OBG** *020 †30
BENNI, Abd Alrahman M. ■ 16046 #875-01-1994 L2007 **PMM** *012 †05
CHAUDHRY, Sidhartha. ■ 16046 #496-09-1998 L2007 **DR** *100 †80
FAILLA, Jack Paul. 200 NORTHPOINTE CIR, STE 101 16046 #056-06-1968 L1969 **ORS** *020 †40
FERA, William Anthony, III. 100 N POINTE CIR, STE 103 16046 #041-07-1997 L1999 **FM** *020 †18
GALLIS, Christine Menzel. 300 NORTHPOINTE CIR, STE 103 16046 #041-12-1990 L1992 **OBG** *020 †30
JEWELL, Brian Foster. 200 NORTHPOINTE CIR, STE 101 16046 #038-43-1987 L1993 **OSM** *020 †40
LABELLA, Christina M. 300 NORTHPOINTE CIR, STE 103 16046 #035-15-1991 L1993 **OBG** *020 †30
LANGHANS, Mark Jos. 200 NORTHPOINTE CIR, STE 101 16046 #016-06-1985 L1986 **OSM** *020 †40
LIEFELD, Paul Albert. 200 NORTHPOINTE CIR, STE 101 16046 #041-12-1979 L1980 **ORS OSS** *020 †40
LOBERANT, Norman Gary. 300 COVINGTON CT 16046 #041-02-1970 L1971 **EM** *020 †16
MC ELWAIN, Mariann. 300 NORTHPOINTE CIR, STE 102 16046 #038-43-1992 L1995 **OTO** *020 †45
MC NULTY, Larry Paul. 300 NORTHPOINTE CIR, STE 103 16046 #051-01-1983 L1984 **OBG** *020 †30
MORGANTI, Christania Jean. 100 NORTHPOINTE CIR, STE 101 16046 #031-01-1997 L1999 **PD** *020 †55
SCOTT, Howard Kessel, Jr. 100 N POINT CIR STE 101 16046 #028-03-1965 L1986 **PD** *020 †55
SMITH, Tanya Elizabeth. 300 NORTHPOINTE CIR, STE 103 16046 #008-01-2000 **OBG** *020
SOOSE, Ryan Jeremy. 300 NORTHPOINTE CIR 16046 #041-12-2002 L2002 **OTO** *020
SWORD, Andrew James. 300 N POINT CIR, STE 103 16046 #025-01-1999 L2001 **OBG** *020 †30
THOMAS, Victor John. 200 NORTHPOINTE CIR, STE 101 16046 #041-02-1979 L1981 **ORS** *020 †40
WALTRIP, Nicole Marie. 300 NORTHPOINTE CIR, STE 103 16046 #023-07-1996 L1998 **OBG** *020 †30

SEVEN VALLEYS – YORK

KURZ, Richard Bruce. 9803 SUSQUEHANNA TRL S, RD 22 BX 175 17360 #041-13-1981 L1982 **IM PD** *020 †20
KURZ, Susan Diane. 9803 SUSQUEHANNA TRL S 17360 #041-13-1981 L1981 **GP** *020

SEWARD – INDIANA

BALDINUCCI, Henry. 6872 ROUTE 711 STE 7 15954 #561-03-1986 L1988 **IM** *020
SAHLANEY, William J. THOMPSON STREET 15954 #041-12-1949 L1950 **FM** *071

SEWICKLEY – ALLEGHENY

ALVIN, Ernest E, Jr. WAY HOLLOW RD 15143 #041-09-1951 L1954 **PS** *071
ARORA, Alpa Dharia. 525 LOCUST PL 15143 #023-01-1998 L2001 **PD** *020 †55
BACKUS, Ronald Murray. 121 GROVE STREET EXT, P O BOX 586 15143 #038-40-1956 L1959 **P** *020 †75
BAGIC, Anto. ■ 15143 #957-01-1987 L2005 *020 †75
BARBER, James Jon. 301 OHIO RIVER BLVD, STE 204 15143 #010-03-1980 L1985 **PS** *020 †65
BARTON, Michael Edward. 720 BLACKBURN RD, SEWICKLEY VALLEY HOSPITAL 15143 #041-13-1997 L1999 **EM GP** *020 †16
BAUMWELL, Ivan Adam. 400 BROAD ST, STE 2020 15143 #035-06-1982 L1986 **OPH** *020 †35
BELL, Michael Charles. 301 OHIO RIVER BLVD, STE 202 15143 #041-12-1964 L1969 **OTO AI** *020 †45
BERNAT, Karl Richard, Jr. 701 BROAD ST, STE 4B 15143 #041-02-1995 L1998 **IM** *020 †20
BERRY, George Jos. ■ 15143 #016-43-1956 L1962 **P PFP** *071
BIKOWSKI, Joseph B, Jr. 500 CHADWICK ST 15143 #010-01-1971 L1978 **D** *020 †15
BOGDEWIC, Thomas Alan. 525 LOCUST PL 15143 #041-14-1975 L1976 **FM** *020 †18
BOWERS, Le Roy W. ■ 15143 #041-12-1951 L1952 **FM OM** *071
BROOKS, Daniel Herbert. ■ 15143 #041-12-1965 L1966 **GS TS** *071 †85,90
BROOKS, Theodore C. ■ 15143 #308-08-1984 L1994 **PTH** *020
BROWN, Richard Victor. 720 BLACKBURN RD 15143 #041-09-1978 L1979 **IM** *020 †20
CAHILL, David John. 525 LOCUST PL 15143 #023-01-1983 L1984 **PD PDA** *020 †55
CAROSELLA, Nicholas W. 111 HAZEL LN, STE 300 15143 #051-04-1983 L1992 **P N** *020 †75
CASE, Bonnie Kirstein. 1606 CARMODY CT, STE 202 15143 #021-01-1992 L1996 **IM** *020 †20
CHEKAN, Edward Gerald. 701 BROAD ST, 4TH FLOOR PODC 15143 #041-07-1992 L1995 **GS** *020 †85
CHUNG, Daniel. ■ 15143 #759-04-1999 L2006 **PCP** *020 †50 ‡
CLARK, Kevin David. 1099 OHIO RIVER BLVD, OPHTHALMOLOGY ASSOCIATES 15143 #028-02-1989 L1993 **OPH** *020 †35
CLARKE, Charles Edward. 1099 OHIO RIVER BLVD 15143 #041-12-1946 L1947 **IM** *020 †20
CLOSE, Kelly B. ■ 15143 #041-12-1998 L2000 **EM** *020 †16
COLLIER, Paul Edward. 701 BROAD ST 15143 #008-01-1979 L1981 **VS GS** *020 †85
COMERCI, John T, Jr. ■ 15143 #041-13-1988 L1999 **OBG** *020 †30
CORRAL, David Anthony. 701 BROAD ST, STE B 15143 #035-15-1989 L1991 **U** *020 †95
D'COSTA, Queenie Mousumi. ■ 15143 #495-39-1990 L2004 **CCP** *100 †55
DHAGAT, Varsha S. ■ 15143 #495-22-1969 L1982 **PTH** *020
DIAS-MANDOLY, Phillip C F. 111 HAZEL LN, STE 300 15143 #496-15-1975 L1988 **P** *020 †75 ‡
DOEBLER, Robert W. 701 BROAD ST 15143 #035-15-1970 L1977 **U** *020 †95
DOYLE, Thomas Arthur. 720 BLACKBURN RD 15143 #035-01-1989 L1989 **EM** *020 †16
DUBNER, Paul Floyd. 525 LOCUST PL 15143 #041-12-1981 L1982 **PD ADL** *020 †55
DUCKMAN, Henry Hana. ■ 15143 #649-01-1972 L1977 **ORS OS** *020
ERICKSON, Eric Ralph. 3048 SCOTTISH RITE LN 15143 #065-06-1954 L1961 **PTH** *020 †50
EVANS, Richard S. ■ 15143 #041-13-1951 L1952 **FM** *071
FELIX, Michael Dominic. 111 HAZEL LN, STE 100 15143 #010-02-1987 L1989 **GS** *020 †85
FENDERSON, Mary Beth. ■ 15143 #038-40-1988 L2006 **IM** *020 †20
FERRERO, Bruce Roger. 720 BLACKBURN RD, DEPT. OF ANESTHESIOLOGY 15143 #041-01-1981 L1983 **AN** *020 †05
FIJEWSKI, Todd Robert. 720 BLACKBURN RD 15143 #055-01-1998 L2001 **EM** *020 †16
FRONDUTI, Robert Lucian. 2599 WEXFORD BAYNE RD, STE D 15143 #041-02-1966 L1967 **OBG** *020 †30 ‡
FRYE, Jeffrey Howard. 720 BLACKBURN RD 15143 #041-14-1986 L1987 **EM** *020 †16
FUOSS, Mark J. 720 BLACKBURN RD 15143 #041-12-1987 L1988 **OBG** *020 †30
GANNON, Jeanne Elizabeth. WAY HOLLOW RD 15143 #041-12-1960 L1961 **AN** *071
GODFREY, Janet Signe. 2591 WEXFORD BAYNE RD, STE 206 15143 #041-12-1993 L1995 **IM** *020 †20
GOODMAN, George Benj. 701 BROAD ST 4TH FL 15143 #041-09-1976 L1981 **PUD CCM** *020 †20,16
GRAFF, Daniel Marshall. 701 BROAD ST, SEWICKLEY VLY PEDIATRICS 15143 #041-12-1979 L1987 **PD** *020 †55
GRAHAM, Deborah. ■ 15143 #016-42-1985 L1987 **PD P** *020 †55
GRAHAM, Thomas Robt. ■ 15143 #041-12-1971 L1972 **IM** *071 †20
GUYTON, Catherine Ann. ■ 15143 #011-02-1982 L2001 **IM** *020 †20
HADDAD, George Richard. 525 LOCUST PL 15143 #033-05-1961 L1966 **PD A** *020
HAJI-DJAFARI, Azizeh. 720 BLACKBURN RD, SEWICKLEY PATHOLOGISTS 15143 #517-01-1968 L1976 **PTH** *020 †50
HARRIS, Barry Conway. ■ 15143 #036-07-1958 L1964 **CD IM** *071 †20
HAVER, Paul Minor. BLACKBURN ROAD 15143 #041-12-1952 L1953 **GP OM** *071
HENNESSEY, David Huber. 701 BROAD ST, SEWICKLEY VALLEY PEDS 15143 #041-02-1971 L1978 **PD** *020 †55
HENRY, Edgar S, Jr. ■ 15143 #041-12-1953 L1954 **OPH** *071
HOGAN, Richard Chandler. 701 BROAD ST 4B 15143 #001-02-1989 L1991 **IM** *020 †20
HOUSE, Nancy S. 419 WALNUT ST 15143 #041-07-1990 L1994 **DMP** *020 †15
JOHE, Samuel Sang-Woo. ■ 15143 #583-02-1950 L1979 **GP** *020
KAPADIA, Silloo Behram C. ■ 15143 #495-04-1964 L1969 **PTH** *071 †50
KASRAIE, Neptune B. 1 WINTERBURY LN 15143 #517-05-1964 L1975 **AN** *020 †05
KE, Katherine C. 1106 OHIO RIVER BLVD, STE 604A 15143 #041-01-1992 L1995 **FM** *020 †18
KENNY, Kevin Jos. ■ 15143 #539-05-1956 L1974 **FM** *030 †18
KETZAN, Tibor. 720 BLACKBURN RD, SEWICKLEY VLY HOSP 15143 #473-02-1972 L1979 **PM** *020 †60

■ = Address Information Privacy Protected

KITCHEN, Sarah Beth. ■ 15143 #016-06-1986 L1986 **ATP** *075 †50
KORDUNSKY, Lana. 722 BLACKBURN RD, SEWICKLEY VLY HOSP PATH 15143 #913-15-1983 L2004 **PCP** *100 †50
LAMBERT, Jerry Vernon, Jr. 607 CHESTNUT RD 15143 #027-01-1987 L2002 **EM** *020 †16
LAVELLE, Lori A. 303 CAMPMEETING RD 15143 #041-77-2000, ▲ L2001 **RHU IM** *020
LECKEY, Ronald David. 720 BLACKBURN RD, SEWICKLEY HOSPITAL 15143 #041-12-1995 L1997 **EM** *020 †16
LEE, Ook Jai. 720 BLACKBURN RD 15143 #583-10-1966 L1973 **OBG** *020 †30
LILJESTRAND, Janet L D. 525 LOCUST PL 15143 #023-07-1973 L1983 **PD** *074 †55
LOPEZ SOLIS, Roberto Carl. ■ 15143 #649-30-1986 L2003 **TTS** *020
LYNCH, Mary Gerard. 115 WITHEROW RD 15143 #023-07-1980 L1980 **OPH** *020 †35
LYNCH, Richard E, Jr. ■ 15143 #041-13-2002 L2006 **AN** *100 †05
MAHA, Alia Marie. 600 EAST DR 15143 #038-45-1995 L1997 **P** *071 †75
MAHA, Robert John, Jr. ■ 15143 #041-12-1988 L1990 **EM OM** *020 †16
MALIT, Fiorello Gomez. 720 BLACKBURN RD 15143 #748-02-1965 L1971 **AN** *071 †05 ‡
MANJOO, Qurashia. ■ 15143 #539-06-1982 L1986 **IM** *020 †20
MANNAM, Sudhakar Babu. ■ 15143 #495-57-1989 L2004 **APM** *020
MARASOVICH, William A. 701 BROAD ST, JOHN F MOYER JR MD 15143 #038-44-1987 L1992 **OTO** *020 †45
MARINSTEIN, Rhea A. 525 LOCUST PL 15143 #033-05-1990 L1992 **FM** *020 †18
MC CARGO, Sara G. ■ 15143 #023-07-1999 L2006 **OS** *075
MC COY, William Howard. RR 4 15143 #041-02-1972 L1973 **OS** *075
MC GEORGE, Francis R. 720 BLACKBURN RD 15143 #041-12-1944 L1945 **GP** *071
MEDIC, Walter T. 720 BLACKBURN RD 15143 #041-12-1952 L1953 **GP** *075
MEDITCH, James S, Jr. 701 BROAD ST, STE 4B 15143 #035-47-1991 L1993 **IM** *020 †20 ‡
MILLER, Clarence M, Jr. ■ 15143 #041-02-1946 L1950 **PTH** *071 †50
MOYER, John F, Jr. 701 BROAD ST 15143 #041-13-1952 L1953 **OTO A** *071 †45
MULHERKER, Amita Harshal. ■ 15143 #496-26-1994 L2002 **IM** *020 †20
MUNOZ, Alfredo N. 720 BLACKBURN RD, DEPT EMER 15143 #319-01-1970 L1972 **EM PD** *020 †55,16
MUSHER, Jeremy Seth. 549 BEAVER ST 15143 #023-01-1978 L1990 **P** *062 †75
NADLER, Daniel James. 111 HAZEL LN, STE 102 15143 #032-01-1975 L1982 **OPH** *020 †35
NAGEL, Susan Entress. ■ 15143 #041-12-1995 L1997 **FM** *020 †18
NAGIN, Joshua G F. 720 BLACKBURN RD, SEWICKLEY VALLEY HOSP-ED 15143 #035-20-1975 L1978 **EM IM** *020 †20,16
NEGRINI, Barbara. 525 LOCUST PL 15143 #041-01-1993 L1995 **PD** *020 †55
NORBUT, Alan Michael. 720 BLACKBURN RD, SEWICKLEY PATHOLOGISTS 15143 #041-13-1976 L1977 **PTH PCH** *020 †50
OBAGI, Suzan. 1603 CARMODY CT, STE 103 15143 #041-12-1996 L1999 **D** *020 †15
O'DONNELL, Chris Thos. 1099 OHIO RIVER BLVD 15143 #038-41-1983 L1985 **IM** *020 †20
OELHAF, Robert Charles, Jr. 720 BLACKBURN RD, SEWICKLEY VALLEY HOSPITAL 15143 #041-14-1995 L1997 **EM** *020 †16
PAVLIS, Robert Jos. 1099 OHIO RIVER BLVD, OPHTHALMOLOGY ASSOCIATES 15143 #041-12-1958 L1959 **OPH** *020 †35
PLAZA PONTE, Mario Tomas. 701 BROAD ST, STE D 15143 #132-01-1976 L1982 **CRS GS** *020 †85,10
PRESS, Allan Jay. 1099 OHIO RIVER BLVD, OPHTHALMOLOGY ASSOCIATES 15143 #035-15-1967 L1969 **OPH** *020 †35
PROVENZANO, Rosario W. ■ 15143 #024-07-1940 L1941 **PD** *050 †55
PYLE, Wilson Koehler. ■ 15143 #038-41-2005 L2005 **DR** *012
RAMESH, Vimala. ■ 15143 #495-04-1988 L2001 **AN** *100 †05
RAO, Poornima. ■ 15143 #913-92-1995 L2001 **END** *100 †20
RIZK, Labib Shehata. ■ 15143 #330-02-1949 L1969 **FM IMG** *071
SABATELLE, Robert Chas. 701 BROAD ST 15143 #035-09-1965 L1972 **OBG** *071 †30
SANTEE, Veronica. 720 BLACKBURN RD 15143 #035-19-1996 L2002 **FM** *020 †18 ‡
SCHAEFER, Kathleen Lisa. 701 BROAD ST, STE 4B 15143 #422-01-2002 L2002 **IM** *020 †20
SCHMIDT, Gregory William. 111 HAZEL LN, STE 102 15143 #005-02-2003 L2007 **OPH** *100
SCIBILIA, James Peter. 525 LOCUST PL 15143 #023-01-1983 L1984 **PD** *020 †55
SELKOVITS, Sidney. 720 BLACKBURN RD 15143 #803-09-1937 L1940 **GP PM** *071
SHAHABI, Ladan. 1603 CARMODY CT, BLAYMORE CT, STE 103 15143 #025-01-2003 L2007 **D CS** *020 †15
SHAJIHAN, Nasim. 111 HAZEL LN, ALLEGHENY GENERAL HOSPITAL 15143 #495-44-1994 L2001 **CHP** *020 †75
SHICK, Hubert. 1606 CARMODY CT B, BLAYMORE I SUITE 202 15143 #041-02-1993 L1995 **M** *020 †20
SHINN, Sarah Beth. 2591 WEXFORD BAYNE RD, STE 206 15143 #041-07-1984 L1990 **IM** *020 †20 ‡
SHOENER, John Allen. 701 BROAD ST 15143 #041-02-1955 L1956 **CD IM** *072 †20
SINU, Apolonia. 111 HAZEL LN, STE 300 15143 #781-01-1988 L1999 **P** *020 †75
SMITH, Benjamin Vergon. 301 OHIO RIVER BLVD 15143 #024-01-1958 L1969 **GS VS** *071 †85
STAUFFER, Susan Kay. 720 BLACKBURN RD, 52 WICKLEY VALLEY HOSPITAL 15143 #025-01-1976 L1980 **EM OM** *020 †16
STRUM, David Paul. 1637 STONE MANSION DR 15143 #064-01-1980 L1988 **AN CCM** *062 †05
SUBRAMANIAM, Kathirvel. ■ 15143 #495-94-1992 L2005 **AN** *100 †05 ‡
SWAN, David Michael. 525 LOCUST PL 15143 #041-02-1981 L1984 **FM** *020 †18
UIHLEIN, Thomas Wm. 400 BROAD ST STE 2020 15143 #038-41-1985 L1999 **OPH** *020 †35
WAGNER, James David. 201A OHIO RIVER BLVD 15143 #041-02-1983 L1984 **IM** *020 †20
WALKER, Gregory Edward. 720 BLACKBURN RD 15143 #041-13-1994 L1996 **IM** *020 †20
WEICHT, Carole-Jay Ciaio. 720 BLACKBURN RD 15143 #041-13-1993 L1996 **IM** *020 †20
WELLNER, Linda Jean. 325 MEADOW LN 15143 #041-14-1976 L1985 **DR** *071 †80
WHEATLEY, Clayton Andrew. ■ 15143 #024-07-1977 L1983 **EM** *020 †16
WILCOX, Geoffrey Howard. 111 HAZEL LN, STE 100 15143 #041-12-1984 L1985 **GS** *020 †85
WISLER, Andrew Charles. 525 LOCUST PL 15143 #023-07-1996 L1999 **PD** *020 †55

SHADE GAP — HUNTINGDON

MARTIN, Sharon Eunice. 22965 CROGHAN PIKE 17255 #023-07-1996 L1998 **GP** *020 †20

SHADYSIDE — ALLEGHENY

KAVANAGH, Eoin Carl. ■ 15232 #539-06-1997 L2005 *100

SHAMOKIN — NORTHUMBERLAND

BUENDIA, Marylou Javier. 2 E SUNBURY ST 17872 #748-01-1974 L1984 **PD** *020
CEFALU, Elizabeth Muddima. 255 W SPRUCE ST 17872 #021-01-1995 L1999 **MPD** *020 †20,55
DONMOYER, Duane Robert. 255 W SPRUCE ST 17872 #041-14-1996 L1998 **FM** *020 †18
GEHRIS, James Carl. ■ 17872 #041-09-1954 L1955 **GP GS** *071
KHANNA, Sudhir Kumar. 239 W COMMERCE ST 17872 #495-43-1971 L1973 **IM HEM** *020 †20
KORT, Joseph Francis. 519 N ROCK ST 17872 #041-13-1979 L1981 **FM** *020
MILLER, Wayne Robt. 255 W SPRUCE ST 17872 #041-01-1988 L1990 **IM** *020
PERALTA, Juan Obar. 141 E SUNBURY ST 17872 #748-01-1963 L1973 **R** *020 †80 ‡
SINGH, Gurdial. 239 W COMMERCE ST 17872 #495-43-1969 L1979 **P PYG** *020 †75
SPOCK, Nicholas. 300 N SHAMOKIN ST 17872 #041-02-1957 L1958 **IM IMG** *071 †18
STEN, Jon David. 550 W WALNUT ST 17872 #041-09-1971 L1974 **IM CD** *020 †20

SHAMOKIN DAM — SNYDER

FERGUSON-AVERY, Sally Jo. 3057 N SUSQUEHANNA TRL 17876 #012-22-2001 L2001 **MPD** *020 †20,55
MUNIR, Mohammad M. 99 BALDWIN BLVD 17876 #704-01-1968 L1973 **IM** *020 †20 ‡
SPANGLER, Robin Michelle. 3166 N OLD TRL, SHAMOKIN DAM HEALTH CENTER 17876 #041-13-1987 L1989 **FM** *020 †18
TAVARES, Joseph Francis. 3166 N OLD TRL 17876 #308-03-1980 L1984 **FM PTH** *030 †50,18

SHARON — MERCER

ALLEN, Robert Wm. 32 JEFFERSON AVE 16146 #025-07-1956 L1962 **R** *071 †80
BEH, Walter Philip. 740 E STATE ST 16146 #495-29-1969 L1972 **U** *020 †95
BLANK, John Edward. 1 S SHARON GEN HOSP 16146 #041-12-1955 L1956 **P** *071
BOLOTIN, Joseph Howard. 197 E SILVER ST, STE 2 16146 #038-06-1938 L1948 **IM IMG** *072 †20
BREVETTA, Richard Jos. ■ 16146 #035-08-1963 L1970 **OPH** *020
BUTCHKO, Andrew Wm. ■ 16146 #041-01-1955 L1956 **IM** *071 †20
CHLPKA, Paul Martin, Jr. 585 E STATE ST 16146 #041-07-1996 L1999 **PD** *020 †55
CUNNINGHAM, John Thomas. 197 E SILVER ST, STE 2 16146 #041-09-1998 L2001 **PD** *020 †55
D'AMORE, David Lee. 740 E STATE ST 16146 #038-40-1977 L1979 **IM IMG** *020 †20
ESPEJO, Rafael Antonio. 740 E STATE ST 16146 #308-01-1985 L2002 **AN** *020 ‡
FELDER, Mitchell Steven. 87 STAMBAUGH AVE, STE 2 16146 #561-17-1983 L1988 **N IM** *020 †75
GALLAGHER, John Patrick. 1 DAYTON WAY BLDG B 16146 #033-06-1983 L1987 **OBS GYN** *020 †30
GEORGE, Gregory Anthony. 62 STRAWBRIDGE AVE 16146 #649-35-1980 L1984 **FM** *020 †18 ‡
GIORDANO, Joseph Anthony. 32 JEFFERSON AVE, STE 204 16146 #041-09-1976 L1977 **IM** *020
GREENBURG, Morren J. 89 ELM AVE, SHARON COMMUNITY HEALTH 16146 #041-02-1958 L1959 **FM OM** *020
GUERDAN, Bruce Robinson. 740 E STATE ST 16146 #305-01-1985 L1986 **EM AM** *020 †18
HAM, Tong Ho. 740 E STATE ST 16146 #583-03-1962 L1973 **FM GS** *020 †18
ISKANDER, Magdy K. 745 E STATE ST 16146 #915-02-1975 L1986 **RHU IM** *020 †20
KCOMT, Christian Alberto. 94 W CONNELLY BLVD, SHARON COMMUNITY HEALTH CE 16146 #737-09-1999 L2002 **P** *020
LAZAR, Jeffrey Carl. 740 E STATE ST 16146 #308-07-1983 L1986 **PUD IM** *020 †20
MAKHOUL, Samer Saleim. 740 E STATE ST 16146 #875-02-1992 L2000 **CCM** *020 †20
MARCHETTO, Barry Edward. 740 E STATE ST 16146 #041-12-1988 L2000 **R** *020 †80
MARTELL, Catherine Lynn. 740 E STATE ST 16146 #041-12-1983 L1986 **IM** *074 †20
MAURER, Emil A, Jr. 740 E STATE ST, SHARON REGIONAL HEALTH SYS 16146 #041-15-2001 L2001 **AN** *020
MOORE, John Hayward. 740 E STATE ST 16146 #001-06-1980 L1981 **EM** *020
MORGENSTERN, Robert Bruce. 32 JEFFERSON AVE STE 214 16146 #041-12-1983 L1984 **IM** *020
OSMAN, Ashraf Ibrahim. 740 E STATE ST, CARDIO-THORACIC SURGICAL 16146 #915-02-1989 L2001 **TS GS** *020 †85
PATEL, Harshad Chhotalal. 89 ELM AVE, STE B 16146 #495-23-1976 L1993 **P CHP** *020
PENA, Alice Mercedes. ■ 16146 #035-47-1978 L1990 **EM** *020 †16
QUAGLIO, Nannette Dorothy. ■ 16146 #035-08-1962 L1970 **OPH** *071 †35
RAU, Ramnath. 94 W CONNELLY BLVD, SHARON COMMUNITY HEALTH CE 16146 #495-09-1964 L1973 **CD IM** *020
RAZZAK, Ashraf. 701 E STATE ST 16146 #704-02-1989 L1998 **AN** *020
SANDERSON, Vincent R A. 1181 E STATE ST 16146 #041-02-1964 L1968 **OPH GP** *071 †35
SEGARRA, Sergio S. 740 E STATE ST, SHARON REGIONAL HEALTH SYS 16146 #308-07-1982 L1983 **EM FM** *020 †18,16 ‡
SHETTY, Nandalike S. 740 E STATE ST 16146 #495-37-1964 L1988 **AN** *071
STOUDT, Karl Donald. 89 ELM AVE, STE C 16146 #041-13-1964 L1966 **FM PD** *020
STYPULA, Richard W. ■ 16146 #035-20-1949 L1950 **PD** *071 †55
VAN ZANTEN, Henry Chas. 740 E STATE ST 16146 #041-13-1981 L1982 **EM FM** *020 †18
WANG, Sheng Chi. 740 E STATE ST 16146 #385-01-1964 L1973 **PTH** *020 †20
WASSIL, John Geo, Jr. 912 E STATE ST STE B 16146 #041-03-1971 L1972 **OTO A** *020
WOODINGS, Samuel Geo. 89 ELM AVE, SHARON COMMUNITY HEALTH CE 16146 #041-12-1960 L1961 **FM** *071 †18
YARBORO, Theodore Leon. 755 DIVISION ST 16146 #047-07-1963 L1964 **FM** *072 †18

SHARON HILL — DELAWARE

ADIGA, Suchetha. 1 HOOK RD 19079 #495-33-1991 L1998 **PCP** *020 †50
JOHNSON, Michael Dennis. 1315 TRIBBETT AVE 19079 #025-01-1979 L1981 **GS** *020 †85
KASTURIRANGAN, Usha. 800 CHESTER PIKE, DELAWARE COUNTY 19079 #495-08-1974 L1983 **P** *020
SOH, Misook Lee. 800 CHESTER PIKE 19079 #583-03-1971 L1975 **P** *020 †75
STULPIN, Michael Dennis. 940 CHESTER PIKE 19079 #041-02-1979 L1980 **FM** *020
VON SCHLICHTEN, Alexander. 800 CHESTER PIKE 19079 #041-13-1961 L1963 **P** *020 †75

SHARPSVILLE — MERCER

BALING, Larry Edward. 935 FOREST LN 16150 #041-12-1977 L1979 **IM IMG** *020 †20 ‡

■ = Address Information Privacy Protected

FALK, Edward Chas. ■ 16150 #041-12-1943 L1944 **GS** *071
LANGE, Paul C, Jr. 6 E SHENANGO ST 16150 #041-12-1978 L1979 **IM** *020 †20
PERFETT, Alfred Anthony. ■ 16150 #041-12-1955 L1956 **OBG** *071 †30
ROTH, Michael A. 6 E SHENANGO ST 16150 #018-75-1963, ▲ L1964 **FM** *071
VANZANTEN, Aaron Nicholas. ■ 16150 #041-13-2007 L2007 **FP** *012

SHAVERTOWN – LUZERNE

ALMEKY, Ibrahim Moustafa. ■ 18708 #915-03-1997 L2004 **IM** *020 †20
ANZALONE, Angelo Anthony. 2391 HUNTSVILLE RD 18708 #561-17-1973 L1975
    FM EM *020 †18 ‡
BUCAN, Michael. ■ 18708 #041-02-1947 L1948 **FM** *071 †18
CISNEROS, Luis Arturo. ■ 18708 #649-14-1994 L1999 **IM** *020 †20
COLLINI, Francis Jos. ■ 18708 #035-08-1982 L1989 **PS GS** *020 †85,65
CUYEGKENG-JOSE, Cynthia R. 915 TIMBER GROVE RD 18708 #748-02-1975 L1981
    AN PME *020 †05
DOUDS, Gregory Logan. ■ 18708 #056-06-2004 L2004 **NS** *012
FAGAN, Terrence James. ■ 18708 #038-06-1966 L1966 **PUD IM** *020 †20
KOSLOSKY, Kourtney Jarrel. ■ 18708 #041-14-2008 *012
LISS, Arthur. 124 WAKEFIELD RD, WINDSOR FARMS 18708 #748-08-1979 L1984 **DR** *020
MILLER, Debra Thompson. ■ 18708 #041-09-1982 L1985 **FM** *074 †18 ‡
PETERS, Robt Harrison, Jr. ■ 18708 #041-02-1941 L1942 **GP GS** *071
SILVERSTEIN, Daniel K. 112 WELLINGTON RD 18708 #033-05-1977 L1983 **CD IM** *020 †20

SHAWANESE – LUZERNE

SGARLAT, Joseph Robt. ■ 18654 #024-05-1943 L1944 **ORS** *071 †40

SHELOCTA – INDIANA

POBER, Kenneth Alex. RT 422 W 15774 #561-01-1976 L1979 **IM** *020

SHENANDOAH – SCHUYLKILL

HASHIN, Kimberly Ann. 229 N MAIN ST 17976 #041-14-1993 L1996 **IM** *020 †20
HOUSHMAND, Cyrus. 25 N MAIN ST 17976 #517-05-1971 L1981 **IM ON** *020 †16
HU, James W T. 239 W CENTER ST 17976 #244-01-1967 L1973 **FM** *071
PLATT, Benjamin Blieden. 25 S MAIN ST 17976 #041-09-1964 L1965 **IM IMG** *071 †20
RANGANATH, Gubbi Nagaraj. 229 N MAIN ST 17976 #495-33-1975 L1988 **IM** *020 †20

SHERMANS DALE – PERRY

TROSTLE, Lori Carole. 4570 VALLEY RD 17090 #041-13-1990 L1993 **FM** *020 †18

SHICKSHINNY – LUZERNE

GILLIES, Richard. ■ 18655 #024-05-1959 L1960 **AN** *071 †30
KOWALSKI, Michael Kenneth. 319 APACHE DR 18655 #041-13-1971 L1999 **OBG** *020 †30 ‡
SMITH, Gary Marshall. 26 N MAIN ST 18655 #041-09-1979 L1980 **FM** *020 †18
UY, Joshua Daniel. 9 S MAIN ST 18655 #025-01-2000 L2004 **FM** *020 †18

SHILLINGTON – BERKS

BONNER, Mary Josephine. 101 W LANCASTER AVE 19607 #041-01-1980 L1981 **IM** *020
DI FLORIO-BRENNAN, T. 517 E LANCASTER AVE 19607 #041-01-1998 L2000 *020
GINSBERG, Gary. 429 E LANCASTER AVE 19607 #035-08-1981 L1986 **U** *020 †95
JONES, Marion L Kittle. ■ 19607 #005-12-1954 L1962 **PM P** *071
KASTENBAUM, Michael. 101 W LANCASTER AVE 19607 #041-13-1973 L1974 **IM** *020 †20
LEISAWITZ, Elliott Gene. 101 W LANCASTER AVE 19607 #041-02-1973 L1974 **IM** *020 †20
LOUGHEAD, John Rea. 223 E LANCASTER AVE 19607 #041-02-1954 L1955 **GYN** *071 †30
MORAN, Anna M.. ■ 19607 #759-03-2000 L2002 **PTH** *100
MULLIGAN, Robert L. ■ 19607 #041-02-1951 L1952 **NM R** *071 †80,28
OLINGER, Nancy Carmita. ■ 19607 #319-02-1989 L2006 **FP** *012
REED, Mark Saml. ■ 19607 #041-01-1947 L1948 **CLP PTH** *071 †50
SHIPPEN, Eugene R, III. 9 E LANCASTER AVE 19607 #041-09-1972 L1973 **END PTX** *020 †18
VALENCIA, Celedonio C. ■ 19607 #748-01-1954 L1969 **EM** *071

SHINGLEHOUSE – POTTER

BARKE, James N. PO BOX 668 16748 #305-01-1986 L1987 **FM EM** *020 †18

SHIPPENSBURG – CUMBERLAND

ADAMS, Lynn Irwin. 46 WALNUT BOTTOM RD 17257 #041-13-1959 L1960 **GP** *020
ANGSTADT, Terry Lee. ■ 17257 #041-13-1974 L1990 **FM OM** *020 †70,18
BEHTA, Babak. 46 WALNUT BOTTOM RD, SHIPPENSBURG FAMILY PRACTI 17257
    #041-02-1997 L2000 **FM** *020 †18
BRENEMAN, John Wm. 67 W KING ST 17257 #041-13-1967 L1968 **FM** *071 †18
BRYSON, Karen Frances. 46 WALNUT BOTTOM RD 17257 #041-14-2001 L2004 **FM** *020 †18
COVINGTON, Saundra Ella. 601 ROXBURY RD 17257 #033-05-1974 L1992 **P** *020
FREEMAN, Albert Wm. 411 S FAYETTE ST 17257 #041-02-1936 L1937 **FM** *072
FREEMAN, James Wm. 91 FOGELSANGER RD 17257 #041-02-1991 L1994 **FM** *020 †18
FREEMAN, William Albert. PO BOX 128, 5 WILLOW RUN 17257 #041-02-1964 L1965
    FM *020 †18
GLASS, Constance I. 46 WALNUT BOTTOM RD 17257 #035-47-1991 L1997 **OBG** *020 †30
HEINE, Laurice Ann. 46 WALNUT BOTTOM RD 17257 #041-14-1990 L1993 **OBG** *020 †30
LEBOW, Howard M. 46 WALNUT BOTTOM RD 17257 #051-04-1977 L1999 **FM IMG** *020 †18

MERCHANT, Ralph Preston. ■ 17257 #023-01-1963 L1966 **GP** *075
OSER, Sean Michael. 411 S FAYETTE ST 17257 #041-12-2000 L2001 **FM** *020 †18
OSER, Tamara Kay. 411 S FAYETTE ST 17257 #041-12-2000 L2003 **FM** *020 †18
RASCHID, Sohael M. 46 WALNUT BOTTOM RD 17257 #010-01-1985 L1986 **OBG** *020 †30
SHEIKH, Fauzia G. 601 ROXBURY RD 17257 #704-06-1979 L2001 **PYG** *020 †75
STEINOUR, Thomas Anthony. 411 S FAYETTE ST, VMG 17257 #010-02-1980 L1987
    FM *020 †18
STETSON, Derwood Lynn. 46 WALNUT BOTTOM RD, SHIPPENSBURG FAMILY PRACTI 17257
    #050-02-1963 L1964 **GP** *020

SHIPPENVILLE – CLARION

CLARK, Richard Allen. ■ 16254 #028-78-2004, ▲ L2004 **AN** *012
DENNING-BOLLE, Sara J. ■ 16254 #022-75-2005, ▲ L2007 **IM** *100
MC GOWAN, Emma Knight. ■ 16254 #041-09-1984 L1985 **OPH** *071

SHOEMAKERSVILLE – BERKS

ZIMMERMAN, Debra Lynn R. 513 REBER ST 19555 #016-11-1974 L1976 **IM** *020 †20

SHREWSBURY – YORK

CAMPBELL, Sean Christian. 15 CONSTITUTION AVE, EPCO PLAZA 17361 #011-03-1989 L1992
    PD *020 †55
DELLA PENNA, Niccolo Deno. ■ 17361 #016-06-2001 L2006 **P** *100 †75
ESPINAL, Fanny E. 6 CONSTITUTION AVE 17361 #035-15-2001 L2006 **PD** *020 †55
KUHNS, Stacey Becker. 50 OLD FARM LN 17361 #041-09-1983 L1984 **FM** *020 †18
MAHMUD, Riffat. 73 E FORREST AVE, STE 14 17361 #704-21-1980 L1994 **IM** *020 †20
MARDINEY, Michael R, Jr. 15 CONSTITUTION AVE 17361 #033-05-1960 L1998 **AI IM** *020 †03
MILLER, Jed Lee. 6 CONSTITUTION AVE 17361 #005-14-2001 L2004 **PD** *020 †55
MOORE, David Hutchinson. 6 CONSTITUTION AVE 17361 #041-01-1985 L1992 **PD** *020 †55
NUSSBAUM, Allen S. 6 CONSTITUTION AVE 17361 #041-13-1979 L1982 **PD** *020 †55
O'BRIEN, John David. 6 CONSTITUTION AVE 17361 #050-02-1995 L1998 **PD** *020 †55
PEDONE, Amy Beth. 16312 MOUNT AIRY RD, SOUTHERN FAMILY MEDICINE, 17361
    #051-01-2001 L2001 **FM** *020 †18
STRAUSBAUGH, Janet T. 6 CONSTITUTION AVE 17361 #005-12-1978 L1982 **PD AN** *020 †55,05

SIMPSON – LACKAWANNA

TOMSYKOSKI, Adam J. ■ 18407 #010-02-1950 L1952 **GS** *020

SINKING SPRING – BERKS

AINSWORTH, George Edward, Jr. 308 KENTUCKY AVE, BERKS DERMATOLOGY PC 19608
    #020-02-1981 L2002 **D** *020 †15
ALTMAN, Robin Aaron. 2909 WINDMILL RD, SPRING PSYCHOLOGICAL ASSOC 19608
    #036-01-1989 L1991 **CHP** *020 †75
AVELLA, Berard Nicholas. 2913 WINDMILL RD, STE 7 19608 #041-13-1968 L1969 **IM** *020 †20
CAMPANELLA, Peter Carl. 3855 PENN AVE 19608 #041-02-1992 L1995 **OPH** *020 †35
DI SALVO-TUCKMAN, Maria. ■ 19608 #422-01-1987 L1993 **PD** *020 †55
EAGER, Jonathan David. 412 ARROWHEAD TRL 19608 #041-14-2000 L2002 **FM** *020 †18 ‡
ERMOLD, Donald Raymond. ■ 19608 #041-13-1957 L1958 **FM** *071 †18
GALLEN, John H. 2950 VAN REED RD, WILSHIRE SINKING SPRING 19608 #041-09-1964 L1965
    GP *020
HASAN, Nazia. ■ 19608 #010-01-2007 **IM** *012
KIM, Namjin. ■ 19608 #035-48-1998 L2006 **PCC** *100 †20 ‡
LE, Brian Huanthai. ■ 19608 #041-14-2000 L2001 **NP** *020 †50
LEE, Kiwhang K. 4 BRENTWOOD DR 19608 #583-02-1963 L1999 **P** *020 †50
MAJMUDAR, Neha. ■ 19608 #010-01-1998 L2004 **IM** *020 †20
METZGAR, Holly E. ■ 19608 #041-77-2000, ▲ L2001 **OBG** *020 ‡
NEUBERT, Alfred Geo. 9 KNOLLWOOD DR, RD # 5 19608 #041-09-1989 L1992 **MFM** *020 †30
OLA, Conrada C. ■ 19608 #748-10-1965 L1978 **P** *020
PADAYHAG, Elisa Valera. ■ 19608 #748-07-1956 L1983 **P PD** *071
PEARAH, J David. 3855 PENN AVE 19608 #041-13-1963 L1964 **OPH** *071 †35
PEREZ-DE ARMAS, Jorge V. ■ 19608 #042-03-2003 L2003 **HO** *012 †20
SHAH, Kartik Jitenora. ■ 19608 #033-06-1999 L1999 **VIR** *020 †80
STROBEL, George E, Jr. 1068 FRITZTOWN RD 19608 #024-01-1962 L2002 **PME PMM** *071 †05
SWIERCZYNSKI, Sharon Lynn. ■ 19608 #023-07-2000 L2003 **HMP** *100 †50
VIJAYVARGIYA, Indira. ■ 19608 #495-74-1978 L1985 **P OS** *020
WOODRUFF, Frieda Wagoner. ■ 19608 #041-01-1955 L1956 **GP** *020

SKIPPACK – MONTGOMERY

KILGOUR, William S. ■ 19474 #041-01-1949 L1950 **P** *071 †75

SLATINGTON – LEHIGH

HAHN, Robert J. ■ 18080 #305-01-1988 L1996 **AN** *020 †05
KHADPE, Jay. ■ 18080 #041-02-2006 **EM** *012

SLIGO – CLARION

VARNER, Lewis Robt. PO BOX 158, 1643 BALD EAGLE ST 16255 #041-02-1964 L1965
    EM OM *020 †16

SLIPPERY ROCK – BUTLER

EISLER, Robert Leroy. 605 KELLY BLVD 16057 #041-12-1955 L1956 **P** *020 †75

■ = Address Information Privacy Protected

FLEMING, Elenor Jane. RR 4 BOX 135A 16057 #041-12-1948 L1949 **PHP** *071
KREIDER, Randy Melvin. 1 MORROW WAY, MC LACHLAN STUDENT HEALTH 16057
   #041-14-1984 L1985 **FM** *020 †18
MC DONALD, Michael Alan. 565 KELLY BLVD 16057 #055-01-1989 L1992 **FM** *020 †18

SMETHPORT — MCKEAN

MAGNO, Ferdinand Lyndon Q. 406 FRANKLIN ST 16749 #748-01-1992 L1998 **FM** *020 †18
SMITH, Kent Kasper. ■ 16749 #041-02-1965 L1966 **R** *071 †80

SMITHFIELD — FAYETTE

ENGLISH, Robert Saml. 2160 SPRINGHILL FURNACE RD 15478 #041-09-1959 L1963
   D *072 †15
ENGLISH, Robert Samuel, Jr. 2160 SPRINGHILL FURNACE RD 15478 #055-01-1995 L1999
   D *020 †15
GONZALEZ, Marcia Annette. ■ 15478 #024-01-1980 L1998 **GS** *020

SOLEBURY — BUCKS

CICCONE, Patrick Edwin. PO BOX 391, 5590 SHETLAND DR 18963 #041-01-1970 L1971
   PA P *050 †75

SOMERSET — SOMERSET

ANDERSON, Thomas M, Jr. 225 S CENTER AVE 15501 #045-01-1979 L2000 **DR** *020 †18,80
BACESKI, Deborah Anne. 105 W CHURCH ST 15501 #041-12-1977 L1978 **IM** *020 †20
BAKER, Daniel Mark. 225 S CENTER AVE 15501 #036-05-1993 L1998 **DR** *020 †80
BARNHART, Jonathan Lynn. 225 S CENTER AVE 15501 #041-12-1991 L1994 **EM** *020 †16
BATTAGLIA, Paul Gerard. RR 5 15501 #035-09-1984 L1987 **AN** *020 †05
BATTISTA, David Richard. 224 TWIN LAKE RD, C/O TWIN LAKES CENTER 15501
   #041-07-1986 L1989 **ADM FM** *020 †18
BHASKAR, Ambat Gopinath. 225 S CENTER AVE, SOMERSET COMMUNITY HOSP 15501
   #495-04-1961 L1983 **PTH HEM** *071 †50
BLASKO, Suzanne Heather. 225 S CENTER AVE 15501 #041-14-1992 L1994 **FM** *020 †18
BRENNAN, John Thos, Jr. 4324 GLADES PIKE 15501 #036-07-1977 L1986 **FM PHP** *030 †18
CAMACHO, Charles Edward. 229 S KIMBERLY AVE STE 200 15501 #014-01-1997 L2001
   OBG *020 †30
CAMACHO, Rita Nicol. 329 S PLEASANT AVE 15501 #041-13-1997 L2001 **FM** *020 †18
CAMPBELL, Barbara Jean. 223 S PLEASANT AVE STE 301 15501 #036-01-1976 L1986
   ORS PDS *020 †40 ‡
CUBE, Aurora P V. 322 W PATRIOT ST, VILLANUE VA 15501 #748-01-1957 L1977 *071
CUBE, Henry M. 332 W PATRIOT ST 15501 #748-01-1950 L1973 **NS N** *020 †25
DAGHESTANI, Aiman N. 314 S KIMBERLY AVE, SOMERSET ONCOLOGY CENTER 15501
   #875-02-1974 L1983 **ON HEM** *020 †20
DESAI, Jayesh Bhashkarrai. 226 E CHURCH ST, STE B 15501 #495-89-1982 L1988
   PUD IM *020 †20
DE VRIES, Jan R J. 228 SIEMON DR, SIEMON'S LAKEVIEW MANOR ES 15501
   #660-03-1952 L1962 **FM** *071 †18
GHATAGE, Prakash P. 225 S CENTER AVE, SOMERSET HOSPITAL 15501 #495-34-1967 L1981
   EM IM *020 †16
GO, Peter T. 867 W MAIN ST, PTG PROFESSIONAL BLDG 15501 #748-01-1973 L1982
   GS *020 †85
GROF-TISZA, George E. 225 S CENTER AVE, SOMERSET HOSPITAL 15501 #308-08-1983 L1987
   IM *020
HASSANI, Fariba. 105 W CHURCH ST 15501 #654-01-1988 L1997 **IM** *020 †20
HONG, Jae Ui. 321 E MAIN ST, # 100 15501 #583-01-1991 L1996 **IM** *020 †20
KARUMUDI, Anjaneyulu. 245 W RACE ST 15501 #495-57-1972 L1997 **P** *020 †75
KASHURBA, Glenn Jos. 113 S CENTER AVE 15501 #041-14-1982 L1983 **CHP P** *020 †75
KATES, Jonathan Louis. 1590 N CENTER AVE, SOMERSET ORTHOPEDICS 15501
   #041-02-1975 L1976 **ORS OSM** *020 †40
KIM, Jinchul. 314 S KIMBERLY AVE, SOMERSET ONCOLOGY CENTER 15501
   #583-03-1970 L2007 **RO** *020 †80
KOBAN, James Michael. 245 W RACE ST, BEDFORD-SOMERSET MH/MRPROG 15501
   #041-14-1990 L1992 **P** *020 †75
KOSSOW, Ronald Jay. 314 S KIMBERLY AVE, 21ST CENTURY ONCOLOGY 15501
   #035-09-1995 L2000 **RO** *020 †80
KRAMER, Robert Edward. 314 S KIMBERLY AVE, SOMERSET ONCOLOGY CENTER 15501
   #041-14-1979 L1980 **BBK IM** *030 †20
LAVANIER, Jeffrey Allan. ■ 15501 #041-02-1986 L1989 **EM** *020 †16
LIMCUANDO, Emiliano L. 401 S CENTER AVE 15501 #748-08-1962 L1973 **GP** *020 ‡
MOITRA, Shomendra Kumar. SOMERSET COMM HOSP EMER 15501 #495-39-1967 L1981
   EM GS *020 †85,16
NAIR, V Krishnan. 126 E CHURCH ST, STE 2400 15501 #495-31-1967 L1980 **CD IM** *020 †20
NATH, Devarshi. 329 S PLEASANT AVE 15501 #008-02-1995 L1998 **FM** *020 †18
NICHOLSON, John Francis. 329 S PLEASANT AVE 15501 #047-05-1958 L1958 **PD PP** *050 †55
NOVAK, Victor F, II. 223 S PLEASANT AVE STE 302 15501 #654-01-1982 L1986 **GS GE** *020 †85
OLIVER-SMITH, David R. 223 S PLEASANT AVE, STE 102 15501 #024-05-1985 L1987
   NS *020 †25
ORLIDGE, Arthur E. 225 S CENTER AVE 15501 #041-02-1949 L1950 **FM P** *071 †18
PAREKH, Anil K. 225 S CENTER AVE, STE 433 15501 #495-37-1989 L1997 **P** *020 †75
PESSOLANO, Francis Xavier. 196 POVERTY NOOK RD, SOMERSET HOSPITAL 15501
   #561-01-1979 L1982 **DR** *020 ‡
PRADHAN, Kumuda Ranjan. 1019 SUNSET DR, UNIT-1 15501 #496-05-1986 L2006 **GS** *020 †85
ROBERTS, Jeremy Allan. ■ 15501 #055-01-2001 L2006 **FM** *100
SAADAT, Mohammad J. 105 W CHURCH ST 15501 #654-01-1988 L1993 **GE** *020 †20
SALAMEH, Jawad Abdulsalam. 792 N CENTER AVE, SOMERSET MEDICAL ART BUILD 15501
   #575-01-1983 L1991 **NEP IM** *020
SCHMIDT, Gary Louis. 1590 N CENTER AVE, SOMERSET ORTHOPAEDICS 15501
   #041-14-2000 L2001 **ORS** *100
SHANK, Paul Wayne. 223 S PLEASANT AVE 15501 #035-20-1971 L1991 **U PD** *020 †95
SHARIAT, Iraj. 107 W PATRIOT ST 15501 #517-01-1962 L1981 **OPH PM** *020

SHUSTER, Joseph. 226 E CHURCH ST # B, OPHTHALMIC ASSOCIATES 15501 #060-01-1962
   OS *050
SINGH, Ajay Pratap. 225 S CENTER AVE 15501 #495-15-1970 L1977 **PD** *020 †55 ‡
SMITH, Ann Gleysteen. 339 W UNION ST 15501 #010-01-1985 L1998 **FM** *020 †18
SREDY, Michelle Renee. 614 S FRANKLIN AVE 15501 #041-14-1992 L1994 **PD** *020 †55
SURESHKUMAR, Thambipillai. 245 W RACE ST 15501 #220-01-1982 L1996 **P** *020 †75
TANG, Lihui. 225 S CENTER AVE, # 433 15501 #243-44-1984 L2003 **P** *020
TENSUAN, Leonardo S, Jr. 433 W MAIN ST 15501 #748-01-1959 L1971 **IM** *020
THOMAS, George Kalaikathi. 225 S CENTER AVE, DPT ER 15501 #495-52-1980 L1984
   EM GS *020 †16
TRAN, Nghia Van. RR 5 15501 #941-01-1974 L1983 **GP PTH** *020
VAN ANTWERP, Kenneth J. 1590 N CENTER AVE, STE 115 15501 #041-13-1980 L1981
   FM *020 †18
VELEZ, Rafael I. 225 S CENTER AVE, SOMERSET HOSPITAL ANESTHES 15501
   #041-09-1980 L1982 **AN** *020 †05
WONG, Albert, Jr. 142 E CHURCH ST 15501 #649-01-1969 L1970 **OBG** *071
WOOLSLAYER, Paul Ronald. RR 5 15501 #041-09-1960 L1963 **GP P** *071
YAROS, Mark Francis. 329 S PLEASANT AVE 15501 #041-02-1982 L1983 **FM** *020 †18
ZEILER, Wm Bartholomew. ■ 15501 #041-12-1945 L1946 **PTH NM** *072 †50,28

SOUDERTON — MONTGOMERY

AHUJA, Saranbir Singh. 3456 BETHLEHEM PIKE, FL 2 18964 #038-06-1999 L2005 **PD** *020 †55
ANTHONY, Kara Beth. ■ 18964 #036-07-2003 L2003 **ID** *012 †20
BARNES, Donald J. ■ 18964 #028-78-1957, ▲ L1958 **GP NTR** *071
BIMSON, Steven Scott. 777 ROUTE 113 18964 #041-13-1988 L1990 **FM** *020 †18
CAOILI-SANTOS, Arrene Bee. 3456 BETHLEHEM PIKE, FL 2CD 18964 #748-02-1990 L1998
   AI *020 †55
DE WINDT, Alejandro V. ■ 18964 #308-12-1986 *071
DUDICK, David Edward, Jr. ■ 18964 #041-02-2007 L2007 **IM** *012
FILOGRANA, Kathleen. 3456 BETHLEHEM PIKE 2ND FL 18964 #041-01-1996 L1998
   PD *020 †55 ‡
HART, Heather Kirk. 777 ROUTE 113 18964 #020-12-1995 L1997 **FM** *020 †18
JUNOD, John Bernard. 3456 BETHLEHEM PIKE, SKYVIEW MEDICAL CENTER 18964
   #041-13-1986 L1987 **FM** *020 †18
LANE, Barbara. 3456 BETHLEHEM PIKE, FL 2CD 18964 #033-06-1982 L1983
   PD PDC *020 †55 ‡
NUSCHKE, John David. ■ 18964 #041-09-1957 L1958 **FM** *071 †18
ROESING, Tracey Lynn. 3456 BETHLEHEM PIKE 18964 #041-15-2000 L2001 **FM** *020 †18 ‡
ROUSCHE, Lori Eileen. 777 ROUTE 113 18964 #041-07-1988 L1990 **FM** *020 †18
SOUDER, Christian L R. ■ 18964 #041-09-1937 L1938 **P** *071

SOUTH ABINGTON TOWNSHIP — LACKAWANNA

BOCCAGNO, Phillip Anthony. 231 NORTHERN BLVD, STE C 18411 #041-09-1980 L1981
   IM *020 †20
DE LEO, Caesar A. ■ 18411 #041-02-1938 L1947 **IM** *071
DESAI, Arundev Dahyabhai. 120 WELSH HILL RD, ARUNDEV D DESAI 18411
   #495-22-1970 L1979 **FM GP** *020 †18
DESAI, Meena. 120 WELSH HILL RD 18411 #495-22-1969 L1982 **IM PUD** *020 †20
HASSANEIN, Wael Hamdy. 1143 NORTHERN BLVD, # 138 18411 #915-04-1993 L2003
   AN *020 †05
HIJAZI, Saadeddine A E. 231 NORTHERN BLVD 18411 #915-04-1968 L1977 **GS EM** *020 †85
HYLAND, Bernard V. ■ 18411 #041-02-1950 L1951 **U OS** *071 †80
KASIM, Kasim Mohamed. ■ 18411 #528-04-1993 L2006 **IM** *012
KIZER, John Dallas. ■ 18411 #005-19-1984 L1996 **GS** *020 †85
LEE, Edward Yang. 537 VENARD RD 18411 #583-04-1968 L1976 **CHP P** *020 ‡
MARIANI, Stephen Saml. ■ 18411 #016-02-1976 L1982 **DR NM** *071 †80 ‡
MAZZONI, Marcel Mark. 2 LAKESIDE CMN 18411 #025-07-1994 L1998 **OBG** *020
MORAN, Kurt Paul. 611 MORGAN HWY 18411 #654-01-1984 L1988 **IM** *020
MORITZ, Mordekhai. ■ 18411 #550-01-1958 L1972 **GE M** *071
NELSON, Anders Per. 110 LAYTON RD 18411 #041-09-1987 L1989 **PD** *020 †55
OSUNTOKUN, Oladapo Richar. ■ 18411 #690-02-1987 L2005 **P** *020 ‡
OSUNTOKUN, Titilayo O. ■ 18411 #690-02-1989 L2005 **IM** *020 †20
RUZBARSKY, Allison Leigh. ■ 18411 #041-02-2007 L2007 **IM** *012
SCALERA, Melissa Maria. 790 NORTHERN BLVD, ABINGTON PROFESSIONAL PLAZ 18411
   #033-05-1997 L2005 **OBG** *020 †30
SILBERT, Richard Ross. 703 GREEN TREE DR 18411 #041-13-1976 L1977 **P PYG** *020 †75 ‡
SOLIMAN, Manal Daniel G. ■ 18411 #330-03-1966 L1975 **GS VS** *020 †85
SOROKANICH, Steve, Jr. 231 NORTHERN BLVD 18411 #041-02-1981 L1986 **OPH** *020 †35
SZYMANSKI, Mark Brian. 233 NORTHERN BLVD, STE 1 18411 #305-01-1990 L1996
   PTH DMP *062 †50
VENTRE, Susan Ann. 239 NORTHERN BLVD 18411 #033-05-1962 L1964 **PD** *020 †55
WILCOX, Brian David. 790 NORTHERN BLVD, WOMENS CARE CENTER 18411
   #035-03-2001 L2002 **OBG** *020 †30

SOUTH MOUNTAIN — FRANKLIN

BHARGRAVE, Usha A. 10058 S MOUNTAIN RD, SOUTH MOUNTAIN RESTORATION 17261
   #495-20-1969 L1975 **PD GP** *020 †55
CHRISTIE, Linda J. 10058 S MOUNTAIN RD, SOUTH MOUNTAIN RESTORATION 17261
   #041-01-1985 L1987 **IM** *100 †20
GOGLIN, Brett W. 10058 S MOUNTAIN RD 17261 #422-01-1982 L1987 **END IM** *020
STRITE, Joseph O. 10058 S MOUNTAIN RD 17261 #041-13-1952 L1953 **PYG P** *071 †75
SUDDARTH, Sterling Baker. 10058 S MOUNTAIN RD, S MOUNTAIN RESTORATION CTR 17261
   #041-01-1947 L1959 **PYG GP** *071 †55

SOUTH WAVERLY — BRADFORD

LAVIN, Michael Ray. 356 LODER ST 18840 #035-08-1990 L2000 **P** *020 †75

SOUTH WILLIAMSPORT – LYCOMING

BALDYS, James Steven. 699 HASTINGS ST 17702 #041-13-1984 L1985 **FM** *020 †18

SOUTHAMPTON – BUCKS

ARONSON, Marvin E. ■ 18966 #041-13-1952 L1953 **FOP GP** *030 †50
BOOKER-CARTER, Cheryl A. 1111 STREET RD STE 312, SOUTHAMPTON PSYCH ASSOCS 18966 #041-13-1985 L1986 **P** *020
BRODY, Leonard Alan. 283 2ND STREET PIKE, STE 120 18966 #041-13-1979 L1980 **ORS OSM** *020 †40 ‡
CHALFIN, Robert Jay. 501 STREET RD, STE 101 18966 #041-13-1994 L1997 **IM** *020 †20
CLARK, Michael Edward. 207 LAKESIDE PARK 18966 #041-13-1995 L1998 **PD** *020 †55
COLLIER, Cheryl Ann. 735 DAVISVILLE RD, 2ND FL 18966 #041-13-1989 L1992 **IM** *020 †20
DYAKOVETSKY, Eugene. 201 LAKESIDE PARK 18966 #913-21-1981 L2000 **IM** *020
ENGLAND, Robert Walter. ■ 18966 #041-77-1956, ▲ L1957 **FM OMM** *071
FITZSIMMONS, Amy Susan. 44 SECOND STREET PIKE, STE 200 18966 #041-07-1989 L1991 **PM** *020 †60
FLANAGAN, James Wm. ■ 18966 #041-09-1978 L1979 **FM EM** *020 †18
GORDON, Jeffrey Alan. 319 2ND STREET PIKE 18966 #041-01-1991 L1995 **OPH** *020 †35
GORDON, Marvin Ralph. 773 2ND STREET PIKE 18966 #041-09-1983 L1984 **IM GP** *020 †20
HAN, Stella Insook. 319 2ND STREET PIKE 18966 #035-19-1991 L2000 **OPH** *020 †35
ILANGOVAN, Kumar. ■ 18966 #016-43-2007 *012
ILANGOVAN, Saroja. ■ 18966 #495-66-1973 L1977 **NP PTH** *071 †50
ILANGOVAN, Somasundaram. ■ 18966 #495-66-1970 L1973 **GE IM** *071 †20
JAFFEE, Lee. 57 STREET RD, STE E 18966 #028-78-1986, ▲ L1988 **PD** *020 †55 ‡
KHADILKAR, Mangala Vivek. ■ 18966 #495-96-1972 L1978 **CHP P** *020
KHADILKAR, Vivek V. 1045 STREET RD 18966 #495-96-1972 L1978 **FM** *020
KLEIN, Marcia Miriam. 207 LAKESIDE PARK, LAKESIDE OFFICE PARK 18966 #035-08-1990 L1994 **PD** *020 †55
KREMER, Svetlana I. ■ 18966 #913-50-1973 L2000 **AN** *020
LEM, Craig Richard. 207 LAKESIDE PARK, SOUTHAMPTON PEDIATRIC ASSO 18966 #308-10-1984 L1989 **PD** *020 †55
LYONS, Robert C. ■ 18966 #041-01-1945 L1946 **PTH** *072 †50
MANNHERZ, Robert E. 283 SECOND STREET PIKE, STE 120 18966 #041-13-1979 L1980 **OSM ORS** *020 †40
MECKLER, David Ira. 57 STREET RD, STE E 18966 #035-46-1986 L1993 **PD** *020 †55 ‡
NEDJAR, Mona Lisa. 319 2ND STREET PIKE, TRI-COUNTY EYE PHYSICIANS 18966 #035-09-1998 L2004 **OPH** *020 †35
NEWBERG, Aaron Nelson. 57 STREET RD, STE E 18966 #041-09-1961 L1962 **PD PDA** *072 †55 ‡
PAO, David S C. 1018 STREET RD, STE 201 18966 #035-01-1969 L1972 **OPH** *020 †35
PERELSHTEYN, Simon. ■ 18966 #913-03-1947 L1985 **GP** *071
PRINCE, Richard Blair. 319 2ND STREET PIKE, AND SURGEONS 18966 #041-01-1983 L1984 **OPH** *020 †35
ROJAVIN, Yuri. ■ 18966 #041-13-2005 **GS** *012
ROTH, Jerry M. 501 STREET RD, STE 101 18966 #041-02-1982 L1983 **IM** *020 †20 ‡
SALEM, Anthony Walter. 283 2ND STREET PIKE, STE 120 18966 #041-13-1962 L1963 **ORS** *020 †40
SCHRAMM, Kathleen Ann. 1111 STREET RD, STE 312 18966 #041-07-1981 L1983 **CHP P** *020 †75
SCHWARTZ, Lauren Faith. ■ 18966 #041-13-1992 L1998 **NS** *020
SHIRAZIMAJD, Mahshid. 501 STREET RD 18966 #041-13-1997 L2000 **IM** *020 †20
TANCOR, Benito. 130 ALMSHOUSE RD 18954 #561-10-1958 L1964 **OBG** *071 †30
TORNEA, Razvan S. 1111 STREET RD, STE 312 18966 #781-01-1986 L1994 **CHP** *020 †75
WANG, He. ■ 18966 #243-72-1988 L2006 **PTH** *012
WARRENDER, William F. 781 2ND STREET PIKE 18966 #041-09-1959 L1960 **IM GP** *071
ZALUT, Scott Eric. ■ 18966 #041-77-2007, ▲ L2007 *012
ZURMUHL, Rezso. ■ 18966 #473-01-1952 L1964 **P** *075

SPANGLER – CAMBRIA

OWENS, Thomas Andrew. CRAWFORD AVE & 1ST ST 15775 #041-02-1980 L1981 **EM** *020
PARONISH, Christopher B. CRAWFORD AVE & 1ST ST 15775 #041-12-1993 L1995 **FM** *020 †18
PARONISH, William John. 1203 BIGLER AV 15775 #041-02-1982 L1983 **FM** *075 †18

SPRING BROOK TOWNSHIP – LACKAWANNA

DE CESARE, Raymond C. ■ 18444 #041-14-1995 L1999 **OBG** *020 †30
NAUSS, Thomas Jos. ■ 18444 #041-01-1944 L1945 **PS HS** *071 †65

SPRING CITY – CHESTER

ELKO, Barbara Anne C. 103 PERCHERON DR 19475 #041-07-1992 L1999 **FM** *020 †18 ‡
JIN, Pamela Ying. 11 INDEPENDENCE DR 19475 #243-45-1991 L1996 **IM** *020 †20
STILES, Jeffrey Douglas. 7 COOKS GLEN RD 19475 #024-05-2000 L2001 **DR** *100 †80

SPRING CREEK – WARREN

HILEMAN, James Daugherty. RR 1 16436 #041-13-1954 L1955 **AN OS** *071

SPRING GROVE – YORK

FARRINGTON, Howard Henry. 22 ROTH CHURCH RD, SPRING GROVE PROFESSIONAL 17362 #041-13-1996 L1998 **FM** *020 †18
FAULKNER, Nancy Ann. 22 ROTH CHURCH RD 17362 #054-04-1993 L2004 **FM** *020 †18
RUSSELL, Roy Dallas. ■ 17362 #035-09-1977 L2004 **AN** *020 †05
RUSSELL, Shawn Elaine. ■ 17362 #035-09-1977 L1978 **P** *020

SPRING HOUSE – MONTGOMERY

CHESNICK, Steven Robt. 909 SUMNEYTOWN PIKE, STE 103 19477 #041-12-1974 L1979 **OTO** *020 †45
ERINOFF, Jeffrey W. 727 NORRISTOWN RD, ROHM & HAAS 19477 #041-77-1987, ▲ L1988 **OM PTX** *030 †70
FIFE, Daniel. RESEARCH INSTITUTE, R.W.JOHNSON PHARMACEUTICAL 19477 #026-04-1975 L1990 **GPM PD** *050 †55,70
GOMBERG, Jack Alan. PO BOX 246, 748 BETHLEHEM PIKE 19477 #041-01-1973 L1974 **P** *020 †75 ‡
MASS, Lawrence David. 909 SUMNEYTOWN PIKE, STE 206 19477 #041-02-1996 L1998 **IM** *020 †20 ‡
MILLER, Alan Michael. 909 SUMNEYTOWN PIKE, STE 103 19477 #038-40-1969 L1972 **OTO FPS** *020 †45
NELSON, Barry Kenneth. 809 BETHLEHEM PIKE 19477 #041-13-1976 L1978 **P ADP** *020 †75 ‡
PAMUKCU, Fevzi Seyfullah. ■ 19477 #902-01-1953 L1965 **IM GE** *071
PAMUKCU, Rifat. ■ 19477 #056-05-1983 L1995 **GE IM** *030 †20
PEGUS, Cheryl Bridget. 1121 BETHLEHEM PIKE, STE 60-284 19477 #035-20-1988 L1990 **CD IM** *020 †20
TATE, Fredericka Cecilia. 909 SUMNEYTOWN PIKE, STE 203B 19477 #041-13-1969 L1970 **P** *020
WEISHAR, Margo Lynne. 909 SUMNEYTOWN PIKE, STE 204 19477 #041-01-1984 L1993 **D IM** *020 †20,15
WOLF, Melvyn Arnold. 909 SUMNEYTOWN PIKE, STE 201 19477 #041-02-1967 L1968 **OPH** *020 †18
WOLFERT, Irwin Howard. 909 SUMNEYTOWN PIKE, STE 205 19477 #041-02-1984 L1989 **FM** *020 †18

SPRING MILLS – CENTRE

BLOOM, James R, Jr. ■ 16875 #041-12-1984 L1985 **PM EM** *020 †60
DOLL, Christina Benamati. 4570 PENNS VALLEY RD, STE 1 16875 #041-01-1985 L1986 **GP** *020 ‡
WOOLLEY, Paul Oswald, Jr. 4570 PENNS VALLEY RD, STE 1 16875 #008-01-1964 L1977 **GP GPM** *020

SPRINGDALE – ALLEGHENY

BAJWA, Jatinder Singh. 831 PITTSBURGH ST 15144 #495-43-1973 L1999 **IM** *020
MC CORMICK, Timothy P. 412 COLFAX ST 15144 #041-09-1985 L1987 *020

SPRINGFIELD – DELAWARE

ADLER-LAVAN, Marthe E. ■ 19064 #041-02-1987 L1987 **PTH IM** *020
AHLUWALIA, Kumkum. 196 W SPROUL RD, STE 205 19064 #035-15-1994 L1997 **PD** *020 †55
ALEXANDER, Chas Meredith. 920 W SPROUL RD 19064 #016-02-1958 L1960 **OPH** *020 †35
AREM, Marcia Susan Clark. 196 W SPROUL RD, STE 205, CROZER-KEYSTONE HEALTHPLEX 19064 #008-01-1977 L1979 **PD PHO** *020 †55
ARSHT, Edwin David. 463 W SPROUL RD 19064 #041-02-1955 L1956 **FM A** *071 †18
BARRIOS, Ronald. 965 BALTIMORE PIKE, STE B3 19064 #308-03-1980 L1982 **IM IMG** *020 †20
BASCH, Bruce Jonathan. 965 BALTIMORE PIKE, STE B3 19064 #041-09-1969 L1970 **IM** *020 ‡
BERKSON, David Arnold. 1260 E WOODLAND AVE, STE 200 19064 #041-14-1995 L1997 **FSM FM** *020 †18
BLANNETT, John Donald. 965 BALTIMORE PIKE 19064 #041-02-1976 L1977 **CD IM** *020 †20
BOUCHER, Kari Williamson. 100 W SPROUL RD, STE 120 19064 #041-09-1997 L1997 **D** *020 †15
BUCKLEY, Maureen Elise. 1260 E WOODLAND AVE STE 20, PRACTICE R 19064 #041-15-2001 L2001 **FM** *020
CALLAGHAN, Anne Teresa. 196 W SPROUL RD STE 205, CROZER-KEYSTONE HELTHPLEX 19064 #035-15-1987 L1989 **PD** *020 †55
CAM, Kristin Mary. ■ 19064 #041-02-2006 L2006 **PD** *012
CARRIGAN, Robert Boyd. 232 SUMMIT RD, 3400 SPRUCE STREET 19064 #041-01-1999 L2001 **HS** *020
CELLUCCI, Michael Francis. ■ 19064 #041-02-2004 L2004 **PD** *100 †55
CHAWLA, Manoranjana. ■ 19064 #496-14-1980 L1995 **NM** *020
CHOPRA, Arun. ■ 19064 #010-01-2000 L2003 **CCP** *100
COLLINA, Steven James. 196 W SPROUL RD, STE 110 19064 #011-04-1997 L1999 **FSM** *020 †18
COX, N Adele. 1260 E WOODLAND AVE, DELAWARE COUNTY PARTIAL HO 19064 #041-07-1985 L1986 **P** *020 †75
CRAWFORD, Nancy Wilson. 100 W SPROUL RD, STE 100 19064 #035-46-1981 L1987 **OPH** *020 †35
CRAWFORD-FAUCHER, Amy D. 1260 E WOODLAND AVE, FAMILY HEALTH 19064 #041-07-1994 L2001 **FM** *020 †18
DE CARO, Mary Magdalene. 100 W SPROUL RD 19064 #041-09-1988 L1990 **FM** *020 †18 ‡
DECENA, Arsenio A, Jr. 62 SAINT DAVIDS RD, RALLING GREEN PARK 19064 #748-01-1964 L1978 *020
DECENA, Zenaida B. ■ 19064 #748-01-1967 L1983 **OS** *020
DE MARIA, Louis Carl, Jr. 1260 E WOODLAND AVE, STE 200 19064 #041-02-1973 L1986 **IMG FM** *050 †18
DUNN, Wayne Hamilton. 100 W SPROUL RD, STE 100 19064 #016-01-1991 L1997 **OPH** *020 †35
ERDMAN, Amy. 196 W SPROUL RD, STE 110 19064 #018-75-1996, ▲ L1997 **FM** *020 †18
EVERLOF, Sherman Wm. 24 E SPRINGFIELD RD 19064 #041-02-1960 L1961 **OBG** *020 †30
FEIGENBAUM, Lloyd Jay. 190 W SPROUL RD 19064 #035-09-1972 L1976 **EM** *020 †16
GHADERI, Mahmoud. 100 W SPROUL RD STE 220, SPRINGFIELD 19064 #028-79-1993, ▲ L1994 **OTO** *020
GIBBS, Sean Lawrence. 1260 E WOODLAND AVE # 200 19064 #038-40-2002 L2005 **FM** *020 †18
GINSBURG, Leonard Harold. 100 W SPROUL RD, PAVILION II STE 100 19064 #041-01-1984 L1990 **OPH DIA** *020 †35
GORRIE, Edward Patrick. 130 S STATE RD 19064 #041-02-1973 L1974 **IM** *020 †20

GUPTA, Renu. ■ 19064 #495-29-1982 L2003 **IM** *020
HAREWOOD, Karen Annette. ■ 19064 #010-03-1996 L2001 **FM** *020 †18
HAYES, Joseph L. ■ 19064 #041-77-1961, ▲ L1962 **FM** *071
HERNZ, William Jos. 1050 BALTIMORE PIKE 19064 #308-11-1985 L1989 **OS P** *020
HERRERA, Anibal Walfredo. ■ 19064 #275-01-1934 L1969 **IM** *072
HOGARTY, Alexa Nana. 100 W SPROUL RD, STE 221 19064 #035-01-1990 L1994 **PDC** *020 †55
HOSTETLER, Lisa Wiebe. 100 W SPROUL RD, HLTHPLX PAV II STE 120 19064
  #048-14-1990 L1992 **D** *020 †15 ‡
HUNN, Richard Hayes. 965 BALTIMORE PIKE 19064 #041-02-1990 L1992 **CD** *020 †20
IOZZI, Louis. ■ 19064 #041-02-1949 L1950 **U** *071 †95
JAVID, Zeeshan. ■ 19064 #041-15-2006 L2006 **P** *012
KAHN, Deborah. 100 W SPROUL RD, STE 224 19064 #016-01-1997 L2000 **IMG** *020 †20
KEARNEY, Martin James. ■ 19064 #041-09-1943 L1946 **GP OS** *020
KEEL, Shannon Kathleen. 1260 E WOODLAND AVE, STE 200 19064 #007-02-2000 L2006
  FM *020 †18
KENT, Maria Candice. 1260 E WOODLAND AVE, CROZER KEYSTONE CENTER FAM 19064
  #033-05-2000 L2001 **FM** *020 †18
KERSUN, Jonathan Michael. 356 MADISON RD 19064 #035-45-1991 L1993 **P** *020 †75
KLINGEN, Donald John, Jr. 1260 E WOODLAND AVE 19064 #041-02-1997 L2001 **FM** *020 †18
KORNIENKO, Walter A. 196 W SPROUL RD, STE 106A 19064 #023-07-1980 L1987
  CD IM *020 †20
KOWNACKI, Vincent Peter. ■ 19064 #041-09-1957 L1958 **GS** *071 †85,16
KRAKOW, Samuel Louis. 1260 E WOODLAND AVE, STE 200 19064 #041-13-2005 L2005
  FP *012
LA PORTA, Edward Wm. 196 W SPROUL RD, STE 106A 19064 #035-48-1983 L1989
  CD IM *020 †20
LEARDI, Robert Kline. ■ 19064 #041-09-1964 L1965 **PTH HEM** *071 †50
LEBEDDA, James David. 196 W SPROUL RD, STE 106 19064 #041-09-1976 L1977
  HO IM *020 †20
LEE, Jonathan Kevin. 196 W SPROUL RD, STE 205 19064 #041-12-2002 L2005 **PD** *020
LEHMAN, Gregory M. 1001 BALTIMORE PIKE # 111, MERCY MED ASSOC 19064 #041-77-1976,
  ▲ L1977 **IM** *020 †20
LICHT, Daniel Jacques. 100 W SPROUL RD, STE 221 19064 #033-05-1997 L1999
  CHN *020 †55,75
LIPSON, Susan Rose. 1260 E WOODLAND AVE 19064 #041-02-2003 L2003 **FM** *020 †18
LOOBY, Catherine Rose. ■ 19064 #041-07-1988 L1990 **PTH** *020 †50
MAHON, Katherine Mary. ■ 19064 #041-02-2006 L2006 **FP** *012
MARTIN, Daniel Scott. 9 N BROOKSIDE RD 19064 #041-02-1999 L2001 **FM** *020 †18
MARVIN, Robert Fleming. 190 W SPROUL RD 19064 #041-13-1965 L1968 **CD IM** *020 †20 ‡
MAXWELL, Lisa Catherine. 1260 E WOODLAND AVE, STE 200 19064 #033-06-2002 L2002
  FM *100 †18
MIRIN, Mischa Pablo. 190 W SPROUL RD 19064 #016-06-2001 L2001 **EM** *020 †16
NAGLE, Walter Wm. 891 BALTIMORE PIKE, SPRINGFIELD DIAGNOSTIC IMG 19064
  #024-01-1948 L1955 **DR** *071 †80
NATHAN, Nirmala Senthil. 196 W SPROUL RD, STE 106 19064 #495-04-1986 L1997
  HO *020 †20 ‡
ORIORDAN, Martin Jos. 965 BALTIMORE PIKE 19064 #041-02-1987 L1988 **CD IM** *020 †20
OTTO, Nicole Janelle. 196 W SPROUL RD, HEALTHPLEX SPORTS MEDICINE 19064
  #041-15-2002 L2002 **FSM** *100 †18
PRETTELT, Adolfo E. 1260 E WOODLAND AVE # 200 19064 #264-05-1990 L1997 **FM** *020 †18
RAFF, Barry. 196 W SPROUL RD, STE 106A 19064 #035-09-1977 L1983 **CD IM** *020 †20
RAGONESI, Susan Beth. 100 W SPROUL RD 19064 #041-09-1982 L1983 **PD** *020 †55 ‡
RIESE, Matthew John. ■ 19064 #056-06-2004 L2007 **HO** *012 †20
RISER, Sharon Judith. 1489 BALTIMORE PIKE # 250, ASSOC SPRINGFIELD PSHYCHOL 19064
  #035-19-1983 L1984 **P** *071 †75
ROSEN, Bruce Jay. 190 W SPROUL RD 19064 #041-02-1976 L1977 **OBG** *020 †30
SAVOY, Margot Latrese. 1260 E WOODLAND AVE, CENTER FOR FAMILY HEALTH 19064
  #023-01-2002 L2002 **FM** *020 †18
SAYEED, Mohammad. 201 FOULKE LN 19064 #704-02-1989 L1996 **IMG** *020 †20
SCHAAF, Richard Dixon. 196 W SPROUL RD, STE 106A 19064 #041-13-1981 L1982
  CD IM *020 †20
SCHEINER, Robin Beth. 100 W SPROUL RD STE 120, HEALTHPLEX PAV II 19064
  #041-13-1986 L1987 **D** *020 †15
SECUNDA, Steven Kalman. 1050 BALTIMORE PIKE 19064 #035-20-1966 L1967 **P** *020 †75 ‡
SHUE, Holly Renee. ■ 19064 #041-12-2002 L2002 **PD** *100 †55
SHUSMAN, Robert Solomon. 190 W SPROUL RD 19064 #041-02-1981 L1982 **FM** *020 †18
SMITH, Bradley Jason. 1260 E WOODLAND AVE, STE 200 19064 #041-02-2003 L2003
  FSM *020 †18
TEY, Peter Hauw-Djien. ■ 19064 #506-01-1962 L1989 **DR** *071 †80
TRIMOR, Fay Ann Inigo. ■ 19064 #033-06-2006 L2006 **PD** *012
TROCHIMOWICZ, Mark S. 1260 E WOODLAND AVE STE 20, PRACTICE R 19064
  #041-02-2001 L2001 **FM** *100 †18
TROTZKY, Margret Sue. 196 W SPROUL RD STE 205, CROZER-KEYSTONE HLTH PLEX 19064
  #041-01-1980 L1981 **PD** *020 †15
WANG, Peter Shih-Hao. ■ 19064 #035-09-2005 L2005 **DR** *012
WARNING, William Jos, II. 1260 E WOODLAND AVE, STE 200 19064 #041-02-1988 L1990
  FM FSM *020 †18
WIDER, Saul. 359 SPRING VALLEY RD 19064 #869-01-1962 L1965 **PD OS** *071
WILLIAMS-PARK, Kimberlee. 196 W SPROUL RD, STE 207 19064 #041-77-1993, ▲ L1995
  FM *020 †18
ZAMOSTIEN, Paul Stanley. 190 W SPROUL RD 19064 #041-02-1973 L1977 **OBG** *020 †30

SPRUCE CREEK – HUNTINGDON

CUSATIS, Deborah C. ■ 16683 #041-14-1999 *071

SQUIRREL HILL – ALLEGHENY

SEETHALA, Raja Ram. ■ 15217 #041-02-2001 L2001 **SP** *100 †50

STARRUCCA – WAYNE

COOK, Homer Elms. ■ 18462 #041-09-1941 L1942 **OBG** *071

STATE COLLEGE – CENTRE

ADAMS, Jonathan David. 1850 E PARK AVE STE 312 16803 #041-02-1981 L1982 **FM** *020 †18
AL-HASHEM, Hashem Youssef. 200 SCENERY DR 16801 #422-01-1999 L2006 **GE** *020 †20
ALMOKADEM, Salah M. 1850 E PARK AVE, STE 201 16803 #915-03-1984 L2006 **IM** *020 †20 ‡
ANDERSEN, Stacy Lynn. ■ 16801 #005-12-2006 L2006 **IM** *012
ANDERSON, Karen Marie. 2520 GREEN TECH DR 16803 #041-14-1995 L1998 **FM** *020 †18
ANSONG, Kwabena. 200 SCENERY DR, GEISINGER HEALTH SYSTEM 16801
  #412-01-1975 L1980 **U** *020 †95
ARBUTINA, David Robt. 200 SCENERY DR 16801 #041-09-1980 L1981 **GS** *020 †85
AUKERMAN, Douglas F. 1850 E PARK AVE STE 112 16803 #055-01-1998 L2003 **FM** *020 †18
AYLWARD, Howard Jos, Jr. 3180 W COLLEGE AVE, # 326 16801 #047-05-1970 L2002
  RHU IM *020 †20
AYOUB, William Thos. 200 SCENERY DR 16801 #041-13-1978 L1979 **RHU** *020 †20
BAKER, Jeffrey Hopkins. 724 S ATHERTON ST, # 200 16801 #041-14-1982 L1983
  FM OBS *020 †18
BANACH, Michael James. 2525 GREEN TECH DR, STE A 16803 #041-01-1993 L1995
  OPH *020 †35
BANERJEE, Amal. ■ 16801 #308-11-1987 L1994 **PD** *020 †55
BARNES, William Stephen. 3901 S ATHERTON ST, STE 2 16801 #041-14-1977 L1978
  GS *020 †85
BARNES, William Tutt. 3901 S ATHERTON ST STE 2 16801 #016-06-1946 L1951
  VS GS *071 †85,90
BASCOM, Karen D. 251 EASTERLY PKWY, STE 102 16801 #041-09-1993 L1995 **IM** *020 †20
BELL, Evan Thos. 1850 E PARK AVE, STE 201 16803 #041-01-1980 L2007 **ID IM** *020 †20
BEM, Thomas Paul. 501 ROLLING RIDGE DR 16801 #041-13-1973 L1979 **EM IM** *020 †20,16
BERESNY, Gerald M. 611 UNIVERSITY DR 16801 #035-06-1971 L1976 **OTO HNS** *020 †45
BHAGAT, Monica. ■ 16803 #041-14-2008 *012
BHAVSAR, Anantkumar D. ■ 16801 #495-17-1973 L1978 **IM** *020
BISHOP, Wayne Edwin. 116 COLONIAL CT 16801 #041-12-1957 L1958 **PD ADL** *020
BITTERLY, Thomas Jos. 200 SCENERY DR 16801 #016-06-1975 L1986 **HS GS** *020 †65
BONNETT, Kathryn Anne. 1850 E PARK AVE, STE 302 16803 #038-45-1991 L1995
  D PD *020 †15
BOSHA, Philip John, III. 1850 E PARK AVE STE 112 16803 #041-15-2000 L2002
  FM FSM *020 †18 ‡
BOSWELL, John Iverson, III. 1315 W COLLEGE AVE STE 303 16801 #051-01-1981 L1986
  CHP P *020 †75
BRINK, Lela W. 2520 GREEN TECH DR, STE D 16803 #033-05-1977 L1980 **PD CCP** *020 †55
CALLAHAN, Mary Frances. 2520 GREEN TECH DR, STE D 16803 #041-13-1985 L1986
  FM *020 †18
CAMAZINE, Scott Merritt. 357 OAKWOOD AVE 16803 #024-01-1978 L1995 **EM** *050
CARDELL, Anthony Francis. 1850 E PARK AVE, STATE COLLEGE P.C. 16803
  #041-13-1988 L1990 **CD IM** *020 †20
CARLETON, John F, Jr. 3048 ENTERPRISE DR, VETERANS OUTPATIENT CLINIC 16801
  #024-16-1980 L2001 **FM EM** *020 †18
CARLSON-RAQUET, Elizabeth. 1850 E PARK AVE, CENTRE MEDICAL SCIENCES BL 16803
  #016-42-1992 L1999 **OBG** *020 †30
CHANDER, Ankit Roy. ■ 16803 #023-07-2005 **NM** *012
CHAPUTA-CHERRY, Melanie M. 1850 E PARK AVE, STE 301 16803 #041-02-1985 L1989
  OBG *020 †30
CHARLES, Kristine Kopp. 2520 GREEN TECH DR, STE D 16803 #041-14-1989 L1991
  OBG *020 †30
CHERRY, Kenneth Lynn, Jr. 476 ROLLING RIDGE DR SU, UNIVERSITY ORTHOPEDICS & S 16801
  #041-02-1985 L1986 **ORS** *020 †40
CHOE, Thomas Sungsoo. ■ 16803 #035-48-1999 L2006 **EM** *020 †16
CLAIR, Gerald F. 232 S BURROWES ST 16801 #041-02-1956 L1957 **OBG** *020 †30
COGGINS, David Allen. 2520 GREEN TECH DR, STE D 16803 #036-01-1987 L1999 **PD** *020 †55
COOK, Gregory Dale. 26 HIGH MEADOW LN 16803 #038-06-1979 L1980 **EM** *020 †16
COOK, Jeffrey Michael. 2520 GREEN TECH DR, STE D 16803 #055-02-2003 L2003 **PD** *020 †55
COPPES, John Chas, Jr. 200 SCENERY DR 16801 #041-13-1985 L1987 **IM** *020 †20
COX, Jay Shelton. 101 REGENT CT, SPORTS MEDICINE CENTER 16801 #041-02-1958 L1989
  ORS *020 †40
COX, John Baldwin. 1850 E PARK AVE, CENTRE MEDICAL SCIENCES BL 16803
  #010-01-1983 L1989 **AI PUD** *020 †20,03
CUDWORTH, George Hitchon. 904 OUTER DR 16801 #539-06-1965 L1993 **AN** *071
DANNEKER, Dale Allan. 1800 E PARK AVE, ATTN: CREDENTIALING 16803 #041-12-1969 L1970
  GS *020 †85
DAULER, Thomas Pearce. 320 ROLLING RIDGE DR, STE 100 16801 #017-20-1965 L1982 **P** *020
DAVIDOWSKI, Thomas A. 1393 N ATHERTON ST 16803 #041-14-1985 L1986 **D** *020 †15
DE CARLE, A John. 320 ROLLING RIDGE DR, STE 100 16801 #068-01-1993 L1996 **P** *020 †75
DEITCH, Helen R. 1850 E PARK AVE STE 301, ASSOC 16803 #041-13-1997 L2003 **GYN** *020 †30
DEITCH, John Richard. 1850 E PARK AVE STE 112, SPORTS MEDICINE 16803
  #041-13-1997 L2003 **OSM** *020 †40
DELOZIER, Jennifer Lynne. 3048 ENTERPRISE DR, BLD. #1 FERGUSON SQUARE 16801
  #041-02-1994 L1996 **FM** *020 †18
DENNISTON, Sky April. ■ 16803 #041-13-2006 L2007 **IM** *012
DEPENBUSCH, Joseph Walter. PO BOX 378 16804 #018-03-1981 L1983 *020 †50
DERDEL, Jerome David. 1800 E PARK AVE, MT NITTANY MEDICAL CENTER 16803
  #561-01-1978 L1980 **RO** *020 †80
DERSTINE, Timothy Hans. 320 ROLLING RIDGE DR, STE 100 16801 #041-13-1992 L1995
  P ADP *020 †75
DIXON, Richard Hoyt. 1850 E PARK AVE, CENTRE MEDICAL SCIENCES BL 16803
  #036-07-1969 L1974 **ON HEM** *071 †20
DONELAN, Stephen Michael. 1850 E PARK AVE, STE 201 16803 #038-43-1993 L2002
  NEP *020 †20
DORSEY, Daniel Collins. 1850 E PARK AVE, STE 201 16803 #055-01-1993 L2001
  END IM *020 †20
DOUCETTE, Fred John. 1850 E PARK AVE, STE 301 16803 #065-01-1995 L1999 *020 †30
DRANOV, Jonathan. 1850 E PARK AVE, CENTRE MEDICAL SCIENCES BL 16803
  #041-01-1969 L1974 **NEP IM** *020 †20
DUNNE, Gay Diane. 137 S PUGH ST 16801 #041-13-1972 L1973 **D** *071 †15 ‡
DUNNE, James Howard. 137 S PUGH ST 16801 #041-13-1968 L1969 **D** *071 †15 ‡
DURKIN, David James. 1850 E PARK AVE 16803 #654-01-1982 L1984 **AN** *020 †05
DURNING, Barbara J F. ■ 16801 #055-01-1973 L1981 **N P** *100
EATON, Jeffrey Gray. 1850 E PARK AVE, CENTRE MEDICAL SCIENCES BL 16803
  #036-05-1988 L1990 **CD** *020 †20

■ = Address Information Privacy Protected

EDWARDS, James Clifford. 100 SCENERY DR 16801 #021-01-1985 L1986 **EM** *020 †20
EIDSVOOG, Carol A. 637 BENJAMIN CT 16803 #037-01-1984 L1999 **P** *020 †20
ENGROFF, Stephen Louis. 200 W BEAVER AVE STE 100 16801 #023-01-1999 L2003 **HNS OMF** *020
FAMIGLIO, Gregory. 19 COLONNADE WAY, STE 117 16803 #041-02-1986 L1990 **IM AN** *020 †05
FARAG, Atif Victor. 1850 E PARK AVE 16803 #915-09-1979 L2000 **AN** *020 †05
FEASTER, Craig Sherman. 110 RADNOR RD 16801 #041-14-1996 L2000 **CHP P** *020 †75
FEESE, Eric James. 1800 E PARK AVE, MOUNT NITTANY MEDICAL CENT 16803 #041-09-1997 L1999 **EM** *020 †16
FEFFER, Michael Jos. 1850 E PARK AVE 16803 #035-08-1987 L1993 **AN** *020 †05
FICK, James Richard. 3901 S ATHERTON ST 16801 #018-03-1986 L2004 **NS GS** *020
FISHER, John Theodore. 507 LOCUST LN 16801 #041-01-1957 L1959 **OPH** *020 †35
FISHER, Mary Ellen. 1800 E PARK AVE, MT NITTANY MEDICAL CENTER 16803 #043-01-1989 L1992 **DR** *020 †80
FLANAGAN, Michael Patrick. 1850 E PARK AVE STE 312, PENN STATE FAMILY MED 16803 #023-01-1987 L1990 **FM** *020 †18
FLEAGLE, Genevra Stone. ■ 16801 #041-07-1946 L1947 **PHP GP** *071
FLIPSE, Wendell Scott. ■ 16803 #041-01-1979 L1980 **EM FM** *020 †18,16
FLIS, Pawel Robert. 1850 E PARK AVE 16803 #759-06-1991 L2003 **AN** *020
FORD, John Pegram. 1850 E PARK AVE, GMSA 16803 #035-01-1974 L1993 **ON** *020 †20
FOUGEROUSSE, Carl Edward. ■ 16801 #035-45-1969 L1992 **IM P** *020 †75
FOX, Olin Mackay. 320 ROLLING RIDGE DR, STE 100 16801 #036-01-1982 L1983 **P** *020 †75
FREEMAN, Marla Ann. 185 HAYMAKER CIR, MARLA A. FREEMAN, MD LLC 16801 #010-03-1991 L2001 **AN** *020 †05
GARCIA, Marian. 233 EASTERLY PKWY 16801 #041-13-1973 L1975 **FM GP** *020 †18
GARRISON, David Dwight. 2520 GREEN TECH DR, GEISINGER 16803 #051-07-1980 L1985 **FM** *020 †18
GASLIGHTWALA, Irphan E. 200 SCENERY DR 16801 #048-04-2000 L2006 **GE** *020
GESELOWITZ, Ari Reuben. 1800 E PARK AVE, CENTRE DIAGNOSTIC IMAGING 16803 #041-14-1986 L1990 **DR** *020 †80
GILL, Shaheen. 1800 E PARK AVE 16803 #704-06-1981 L2002 **PD** *020 †55
GLENN, Jerry David. 3901 S ATHERTON ST 16801 #041-02-1973 L1984 **GS** *020 †85
GORDON, Judit. ■ 16801 #041-13-2005 L2005 **IM** *012
GRINE, Kristen Mariana. 1850 E PARK AVE, STE 312 16803 #041-77-2003, ▲ L2003 **FM OBS** *020 †18
GUILLARD, Frank. 905 UNIVERSITY DR, STE 1 16801 #041-02-1978 L1979 **IM IMG** *020 †20
GUILLARD, Paul. 905 UNIVERSITY DR, STE 1 16801 #041-02-1981 L1982 **IM** *020 †20
HALL, Robert L. 905 UNIVERSITY DR 16801 #041-01-1953 L1954 **IM CD** *071 †20
HALL, Robert Michael. 3901 S ATHERTON ST 16801 #041-13-1986 L1991 **VS** *020 †85
HAMLETT, Frank Jos. 1830 S ALLEN ST 16801 #041-14-1990 L1995 **CHP** *020 †75
HARDYK, Angela. 1850 E PARK AVE, CENTRE MED & SURG ASSOC 16803 #017-20-1998 L2002 **OBG** *020 †30
HARGLEROAD, John A, II. ■ 16801 #041-13-1946 L1947 **GP FM** *071
HARVATINE, Laura Lynn. 320 ROLLING RIDGE DR, STE 100 16801 #041-14-1998 L2001 **P** *020 †18
HAUCK, Anna J. ■ 16801 #024-05-1952 L1956 **PDC PD** *071 †55
HEDRICK, Joseph Henry. ■ 16803 #041-01-2005 **GS** *012
HENRY, Charlotte Amber. ■ 16801 #041-02-2006 L2006 **PTH** *012
HENRY, Michael Bernard. 1800 E PARK AVE 16803 #051-07-1992 L1994 **EM** *020 †16
HENRY, Sheldon Dean. 200 SCENERY DR 16801 #038-40-1987 L1989 **CD IM** *020 †20
HESS, William Fred. 2520 GREEN TECH DR, STE D 16803 #011-04-1981 L1990 **OSS ORS** *020 †40
HEYWOOD, Susan Elizabeth. 1850 E PARK AVE 16803 #035-15-1980 L1983 **CD IM** *020 †20
HILLMAN, Freddie A. 710 EDGEWOOD CIR 16801 #308-03-1980 L1982 **P** *020
HOVICK, Theodore J, Jr. 1850 E PARK AVE, STE 301 16803 #041-14-1985 L1998 **OBG** *020 †30 ‡
HOWSARE, Charles Robt. 1850 E PARK AVE, STE 310 16803 #023-12-1992 L2000 **OM GPM** *030 †70
HSIEH, Timothy Mingder. 1850 E PARK AVE, CENTRE MEDICAL AND SURGICA 16803 #035-09-1998 L2006 **IMG** *020 †20
HUNTER, Robert John. 611 UNIVERSITY DR STE 214 16801 #010-01-1972 L1973 **OTO** *020 †45 ‡
HYLBERT, K William. 1800 E PARK AVE, MT NITTANY MEDICAL CTR 16803 #041-13-1979 L1980 **P ADP** *020 †75
HYMAN, Brian Alan. 1850 E PARK AVE, STE 201 16803 #041-15-2001 L2001 **N** *020 †75
JENSEN, Gordon Lee. 1850 E PARK AVE, STE 201 16803 #035-20-1984 L1988 **NTR IM** *020 †20
JONES, J Alfred. ■ 16803 #011-02-1972 L1976 **IM** *071 †20
JONES, John Howard, Jr. ■ 16803 #041-14-1977 L1983 **VS** *020 †85
JULIAN, Joseph, Jr. 908 STRATFORD CT 16801 #041-02-1971 L1990 **PM N** *020 †60
JUSTICE, William Howard. 1850 E PARK AVE 16803 #041-14-1995 L1999 **AN** *020 †05
KASSAB, Hannah J Lott. 208 W HAMILTON AVE, BOX 117 16801 #041-13-1952 L1953 **IM GPM** *071 †20
KEIL, Stephen Mac Calmont. 200 SCENERY DR 16801 #036-05-1972 L1977 **CD IM** *020 †20
KELLOGG, Lori Flores. 1800 E PARK AVE 16803 #041-15-2002 L2002 **AN** *020 †05
KELMENSON, Edward. 1850 E PARK AVE 16803 #023-01-1981 L2003 **AN** *020 †05
KELSEY, Alice Middleton. 200 SCENERY DR 16801 #025-12-1988 L1991 **IM** *020 †20
KENNEDY, John Peter. 2520 GREEN TECH DR, GEISINGER MEDICAL GROUP 16803 #025-12-1996 L2006 **OBG** *020 †30
KEWITT, Gregory Frank. 474 WINDMERE DR STE 202 16801 #048-13-1998 L2001 **OMF** *020
KILE, Laurie Blair. 248 E CALDER WAY, STE 303 16801 #051-04-1993 L1996 **P** *020
KING, A Reauelle. 200 SCENERY DR, GEISINGER MEDICAL GROUP 16801 #035-15-1999 L2002 **FM** *020 †18
KISH, Robert Stephen. ■ 16801 #041-13-1965 L1966 **U OS** *071 †95
KLINKE, Elizabeth Shaw. 3901 S ATHERTON ST 16801 #051-01-1993 L1996 **PD PHP** *020 †55
KOBERNA, Paul Andrew. 200 SCENERY DR 16801 #038-40-1990 L1997 **IM CCM** *020 †20
KONSTANCE, Richard P, II. 1850 E PARK AVE, CENTRE MEDICAL AND SURGICA 16803 #041-15-1999 L2007 **IC** *020 †20
KOPP, Nelly. 1800 E PARK AVE 16803 #660-01-1956 L1960 **PD** *071
KOZMINSKY, Mark Edward. 2505 GREEN TECH DR STE A1 16803 #025-07-1976 L1985 **D** *020 †20,15
LAL, Rasik Behari. 119 S BURROWES ST, STE 604 16801 #495-21-1974 L1976 **P CHP** *030 †75
LANNING, Richard C. 2525 GREEN TECH DR, STE A 16803 #035-01-1971 L1977 **OPH** *020 †35
LESCANIC, Michael Louis. 1850 E PARK AVE, STE 103 16803 #041-13-1976 L1987 **AN** *020 †05
LEVIN, Scott Michael. ■ 16801 #041-13-2001 L2006 **OSM** *100
LEVINE, Joel Irwin. 2171 SANDY DR 16803 #035-08-1963 L1987 **RO D** *020 †80
LICHTENSTEIN, Jeffrey L. 1800 E PARK AVE 16803 #047-06-1973 L1982 **GE IM** *020 †20
LOPEZ, Rafael. 1002 GREENBRIAR DR 16801 #308-01-1976 L1992 **U** *020
LUMADUE, Jeanne A. 1850 E PARK AVE, STE 205 16803 #023-07-1990 L2004 **PTH** *020 †50
LYNCH, James Michael. 1850 E PARK AVE STE 112 16803 #028-03-1984 L1988 **FSM FM** *020 †18
MAGNANI, Thomas Jos. 3296 SHELLERS BND, UNIT 111 16801 #041-09-1957 L1958 **PTH** *071 †50
MALINICH, Thomas Richard. 1800 E PARK AVE, MOUNT NITTANY MEDICAL CENT 16803 #035-06-1998 L2006 **EM PLM** *020
MANDETTA, Donald Frank. 1850 E PARK AVE, STE 201 16803 #036-07-1968 L1976 **GE IM** *020 †20
MARCOVITCH, Adam Jason. 507 LOCUST LN, WERNER EYE ASSOCIATES 16801 #041-12-2000 L2006 **OPH** *100 †35
MARKS, Asher Michael. ■ 16801 #041-13-2006 **PD** *012
MARTIN, James Stanton. 101 REGENT CT 16801 #041-14-1993 L1999 **OSM** *020 †40
MARTIN, Thomas John. 1850 E PARK AVE, THE PENNSYLVANIA STATE UNI 16803 #041-12-1960 L1961 **PD PSM** *071 †55
MASON, Charles W, Jr. SHORTLIDGE & POLLOCK RDS 16802 #041-12-1953 L1954 **GP OS** *071
MATEER, John Eugene. 200 SCENERY DR 16801 #041-14-1973 L1981 **N** *020 †75
MAXIN, Charles Wm. 200 SCENERY DR 16801 #041-02-1974 L1976 **FM IMG** *030 †18
MAYERS, Stanley P, Jr. ■ 16803 #041-01-1953 L1954 **PHP** *072 †70
MC CLELLAN, Christopher S. 101 REGENT CT 16801 #041-78-2000, ▲ L2001 **ORS** *020
MC CUBBIN, Mary Louisa. ■ 16803 #040-02-1994 L2000 **P** *020
MC LANE, Rogers Dubose. 251 EASTERLY PKWY, STE 102 16801 #041-02-1970 L1971 **IMG FM** *020 †18
MEBANE, Tom Sperring. 251 EASTERLY PKWY 16801 #041-01-1945 L1950 **GP** *071 †55
MENTYKA, Robert Anthony. 200 SCENERY DR 16801 #041-09-1980 L1981 **AI IM** *020 †20,03
MIKESELL, Jerry Forrest. 1393 N ATHERTON ST 16803 #038-40-1981 L1985 **D** *020 †15
MILLARD, Roberta Lee. 1850 E PARK AVE, STE 112 16803 #041-14-1986 L1989 **IM** *020 †20 ‡
MITCHELL, Gary Alan. ■ 16801 #041-12-1965 L1967 **IM** *040 †20
MONTALBO, Antonio Africa. 253 EASTERLY PKWY 16801 #748-02-1964 L1973 **OPH** *071 †35
MULHATTEN, Donald Edward. 200 SCENERY DR, GEISINGER 16801 #041-13-1959 L1960 **GP** *071
NABAVI, Abdollah. 315 S ALLEN ST STE 223 16801 #517-01-1971 L1979 **P N** *020
NEWCOMB, Brian David. 1800 E PARK AVE, CENTRE COMMUNITY HOSPITAL 16803 #023-01-1997 L2000 **EM** *020 †16
NICHOLAS, W Channing. 1800 E PARK AVE 16803 #041-01-1957 L1958 **EM CD** *071 ‡
NNEBE, Nkiruka Sandra. 1850 E PARK AVE, STE 302 16803 #539-06-2001 L2005 **IM** *020 †20
O'CONNOR, Francis J. 738 W AARON DR, RAD ONCOLOGY SERVICES 16803 #024-07-1951 L1990 **RO R** *072 †80
OLIVER, Robin Ella. 1850 E PARK AVE, CENTRE MEDICAL/SURGICAL AS 16803 #041-02-1991 L1995 **OBG** *020 †30
O'SHEA, John Gerard. 1850 E PARK AVE, STE 301 16803 #051-07-1980 L1981 **OBG** *020 †30
PANDOLPH, Stephen Jos. 1528 MARTIN ST 16803 #041-09-1978 L1981 **FM** *020 †18 ‡
PARRY, John Kevin. 200 SCENERY DR 16801 #041-07-1988 L1993 **N** *020 †75
PASQUARIELLO, Rick D. 1850 E PARK AVE, STE 302 16803 #041-09-1995 L1997 **IM** *020 †20
PATTERSON, Yvonne Annette. 2520 GREEN TECH DR 16803 #038-44-1983 L1989 **PD** *020 †55
PEPE, Peter Francis. 1850 E PARK AVE, CENTRE MEDICAL SCIENCES BL 16803 #041-13-1966 L1967 **RHU IM** *020 †20
PERSIC, Louis Anthony, Jr. 1800 E PARK AVE, DEPT RAD 16803 #004-01-1966 L1971 **DR NM** *071 †80,28
PHEASANT, Thomas Ralph. 2525 GREEN TECH DR, STE A 16803 #038-06-1970 L1973 **OPH OS** *020 †35 ‡
PIATT, John E, III. 200 SCENERY DR 16801 #041-02-1977 L1978 **FM** *020 †18 ‡
PILGRAM, Ralph E, Jr. ■ 16803 #041-13-1950 L1951 **GP** *071
POLANSKY, Janet L. 1528 MARTIN ST 16803 #041-09-1978 L1984 **FM** *020 †18
POWERS, Danae Maria. ■ 16801 #035-03-1981 L1983 **AN** *020 †05
PRENSKY, Jay Gary. 2525 GREEN TECH DR, STE A 16803 #023-01-1978 L1983 **OPH** *020 †35
PRINCE, Edward Raymond. 2520 GREEN TECH DR, STE D 16803 #041-13-1979 L1980 **FM** *020 †18
PRO, Jeffrey Willis. 1850 E PARK AVE, STE 302 16803 #051-07-1993 L1996 **IM** *020 †20
PURNELL, John Straw, Jr. ■ 16801 #041-02-1954 L1955 **AN** *071 †05
QIU, Juan. 1850 E PARK AVE, STE 312 16803 #243-33-1986 L2003 **FM** *020 †18
RAMONDELLI, Salvatore M. 200 SCENERY DR 16801 #561-01-1976 L1978 **GS CD** *020 †85
RAQUET, Robert Adam. 1850 E PARK AVE, STE 302 16803 #016-42-1992 L1999 **IM** *020 †20
RIBEIRO, Sady Manoel T. 911 UNIVERSITY DR, PAIN MANAGEMENT CLINIC 16801 #187-29-1973 L2006 **IM** *020 †20
ROBERTS, Philip G, Jr. ■ 16803 #041-13-1965 L1966 **ORS OAR** *071 †40
ROCCO, Jack Frank. 101 REGENT CT 16801 #041-13-1992 L1995 **ORS** *020 †40
ROCKOWER, Roger Alan. 1800 E PARK AVE 16803 #041-13-1972 L1973 **DR** *071 †80
ROESHOT, Douglas E. 101 REGENT CT, UNIVERSITY ORTHOPEDICS CEN 16801 #041-13-1986 L1987 **ORS** *020 †40
ROHRBECK, Charles Wesley. 251 EASTERLY PKWY 16801 #041-01-1958 L1959 **OBG** *071 †30
RORABAUGH, James Douglas. 200 SCENERY DR 16801 #041-02-1990 L1993 **CRS** *020 †85,10
ROSENBERGER, Laura Horst. ■ 16801 #041-02-2008 *012
ROY, Emile Pierre, III. 1850 E PARK AVE, STE 201 16803 #041-14-1983 L1985 **N** *020 †75
SALEEBY, Hussam George. 3048 ENTERPRISE DR, VA OUTPATIENT CLINIC 16801 #875-01-1984 L1998 **IM** *020 †20
SCHELL, Gary Franklin. 501 ROLLING RIDGE DR, CENTRE HEALTH NETWORK 16801 #041-09-1976 L1979 **FM OM** *020 †18
SCHUCK, Eric Joseph. 2024 COUNTRY GLENN LN, EJ SCHUCK PEDIATRICS 16801 #012-05-1994 L2000 **PD** *020 †55
SEBASTIANELLI, Wayne Jos. 1850 E PARK AVE, STE 112 16803 #035-45-1983 L1988 **ORS OSM** *020 †40
SEPICH, Rodney Milan. ■ 16803 #041-02-1990 L1993 **IM** *020 †20
SERENE, James Wm. 1850 E PARK AVE, STE 112 16803 #036-05-1975 L2006 **ORS** *020 †40
SERENE, Mary Bruce M. ■ 16801 #036-05-1975 L1975 **AN** *071 †05
SHEARS, Mark Cyril. 1800 E PARK AVE 16803 #040-02-1983 L1986 **DR** *020 †80
SHERBONDY, Paul Strawn. 1850 E PARK AVE, STE 112 16803 #041-13-1994 L2000 **ORS** *020 †40
SHERMAN, Alan Wm. ■ 16803 #024-05-1971 L2004 **ORS GS** *020 ‡
SOLIC, John Jos. 1850 E PARK AVE 16803 #041-12-1976 L1981 **PUD IM** *020 †20
STEINDORF, Paul H. 1800 E PARK AVE, MOUNT NITTANY MEDICAL CENT 16803 #048-13-1988 L1993 **DR** *020 †80
STEPHENSON, Laura Lee. 1850 E PARK AVE, STE 301 16803 #023-01-1982 L1994 **OBG** *020 †30

■ = Address Information Privacy Protected

STERNER, David Chas. 1850 E PARK AVE 16803 #036-05-1988 L1995 **AN** *020 †05
STEVENSON, Karen B. 845 WALNUT SPRING LN 16801 #021-05-1986 L1992 **CHP PD** *020 †75
STEVENSON, Karen Terese. ■ 16801 #041-13-2006 L2006 **EM** *012
SZABO, Emil Robt. 251 EASTERLY PKWY 16801 #041-01-1975 L1976 **OBG** *020 †30 ‡
TAYLOR, William Fitzhugh. 2520 GREEN TECH DR, STE D 16803 #036-01-1998 L2004 **FM** *020 †18
TIBBELS, Ewing Wiley. 477 E BEAVER AVE, STE 150 16801 #041-13-1958 L1959 **OTO A** *020
TORRETTI, Joel Anthony. 476 ROLLING RIDGE DR SU, DARTMOUTH HITCHCOCK MED CT 16801 #041-14-2001 L2001 **ORS** *020
TRUONG, Steven Ngoc. 2525 GREEN TECH DR, STE A 16803 #024-01-2001 L2007 **OPH** *020 †35
TRUSKY, Jeanette Ina. 1850 E PARK AVE, STE 301 16803 #041-01-1981 L1982 **OBG** *020 †30
TRYBUS, Adam Geo, Jr. 611 UNIVERSITY DR 16801 #041-12-1986 L1987 **DR** *020 †80
TURSKY, Rosemarie J. ■ 16801 #041-07-1940 L1941 **PD** *071 †55
TYNDALL, William Andrew. 101 REGENT CT 16801 #041-02-1997 L2003 **OSM** *020 †40
ULBRECHT, Jan Stanislav. 1850 E PARK AVE, CENTRE MEDICAL SCIENCES BL 16803 #917-09-1979 L1983 **END DIA** *020 †20
VANKIRK, John Robert, Jr. 200 SCENERY DR, GEISINGER MEDICAL GROUP 16801 #041-09-1997 L2003 **PCC** *020
WEAVER, Robert P. ■ 16803 #041-13-1953 L1954 **OPH** *071 †35
WEIMER, Gregory Ross. 1800 E PARK AVE 16803 #041-14-1978 L1979 **DR** *020 †80
WERNER, David Bernes. 507 LOCUST LN 16801 #050-02-1973 L1978 **OPH PD** *020 †35
WEST, Edward. 511 N BURROWES ST 16803 #041-02-1953 L1955 **GP** *072
WHEELER, Leigh D. 2520 GREEN TECH DR, STE D 16803 #041-14-1979 L1980 **FM** *020 †18
WILD, Robert Marshall, Jr. 905 UNIVERSITY DR 16801 #051-01-1970 L1977 **U** *020 †95
WILLIAMS, Robt Xavier, Jr. ■ 16803 #010-02-1961 L1963 **EM FM** *020 †18,16
WOLFE, David Wm. 200 SCENERY DR, COUNTY 16801 #041-14-1979 L1980 **HEM ON** *020 †20
WONG, Ling Gut. ■ 16801 #038-41-1942 L1953 **PD GP** *071
ZEIGLER, David Crandall. 611 UNIVERSITY DR 16801 #041-13-1976 L1978 **OPH** *020 †35
ZIFF, Theodore Lee. 1800 E PARK AVE 16803 #041-09-1979 L1984 **EM IM** *020 †16
ZODA, Albert Ralph. 1800 E PARK AVE 16803 #041-09-1982 L1999 **CD IM** *020 †20

STEELTON – DAUPHIN

SHAIKH, Arif Mahmood. 239 S FRONT ST 17113 #305-01-1987 L1992 **FM** *020 †18

STEVENS – LANCASTER

BALEANU-MALLOZZI, Raluca. 34 SCHOOL LN 17578 #781-01-1985 L1990 **PM** *020 †60
BITTNER, Amanda Joyce. 75 W CHURCH ST, ALLERGY & ASTHMA CENTER 17578 #041-14-1996 L2001 **AI** *020 †20,03
BRELVI, Joanna Ellen. 63 W CHURCH ST, DENVER FAMILY PRACTICE 17578 #038-44-1991 L2003 **FM** *020 †18
CARROLL, Laurence Edward. 73 W CHURCH ST, HYPERTENSION AND KIDNEY 17578 #041-01-1971 L1976 **NEP IM** *020 †20
KAUFMAN, Clark Robt. 75 W CHURCH ST, ALLERGY & ASTHMA CENTER 17578 #038-40-1975 L1986 **AI PD** *020 †55,03
LOCKEY, Stephen D, III. 75 W CHURCH ST, ALLERGY & ASTHMA CENTER 17578 #041-13-1963 L1970 **A IM** *020 †20,03
TITI, Mark Jos. 75 W CHURCH ST, ALLERGY & ASTHMA CENTER 17578 #023-01-1988 L1990 **AI IM** *020 †20,03

STEWARTSTOWN – YORK

GEMMILL, Reginald B. 24 SPRINGWOOD AVE 17363 #041-02-1955 L1956 **GP** *071
GOSSWEILER, Robert Lee. ■ 17363 #035-03-1959 L1991 **EM** *071 †55
PIERSON, Dean Lawrence. ■ 17363 #041-13-1967 L1968 **D DMP** *071 †15

STILLWATER – COLUMBIA

VARKER, Carolyn Branson. 241 HONEYTOWN RD 17878 #041-07-1960 L1964 **PD** *071 †55

STONEBORO – MERCER

FILE, James C. LINDEN ST 16153 #041-12-1951 L1952 **GP** *071
REDDY, Pushpamala P. 4352 GREENVILLE SNDY LK RD 16153 #495-65-1963 L1973 **NM R** *020 †28,80

STOYSTOWN – SOMERSET

BENNER, John Randall. 136 S PINE AVE BOX 340, MED. ASSOCIATES OF BOSWELL 15563 #038-40-1994 L1996 **FM** *020 †18

STRABANE – WASHINGTON

CIMINO, William Lewis. ■ 15363 #017-20-1958 L1958 **AN** *020

STRAFFORD – DELAWARE

RANGANATH, Radhika. 85 OLD EAGLE SCHOOL RD 19087 #016-42-1994 L1999 **OBG** *020 †30
ROCK, Edwin Palmer. ■ 19087 #005-11-1998 L2002 **HO** *100 †20

STRASBURG – LANCASTER

BRENTON, Nancy Mc Tear. 1135 HAMPDEN DR, GRP AT STRASBURG FAMILY 17579 #041-01-1996 L2000 **FM** *020 †18
CHAMBERS, Richard K, Jr. S JACKSON AT FUNK ST 17579 #041-77-1954, ▲ L1957 **PM** *071

HECKMAN, Celeste Silvers. 1135 HAMPDEN DR, GRP AT STRASBURG FAMILY 17579 #041-01-1996 L1998 **FM** *020 †18
MORTON, D Holmes, II. 535 BUNKER HILL RD 17579 #024-01-1983 L1986 **PD** *020 †55
PARSONS, Suzanne Lynne. 1135 HAMPDEN DR, GRP AT STRASBURG FAMILY 17579 #011-03-2002 L2002 **FM** *020 †18
PUTNEY, Christopher James. 1135 HAMPDEN DR, GRP AT STRASBURG FAMILY 17579 #035-15-1994 L1996 **FM** *020 †18
RUTT, John Mark. ■ 17579 #041-09-1963 L1964 **FM OBS** *071
STEINKE, Walter Dennis. 241 N DECATUR ST 17579 #055-75-1985, ▲ L1986 **FM** *020
STRAUSS, Kevin Adams. 535 BUNKER HILL RD, CLINIC FOR SPECIAL CHILDRE 17579 #024-01-1998 L2001 **PD** *020 †55
THOMPSON, Kenneth Wayne. ■ 17579 #041-02-1977 L1978 **ADM GP** *020

STROUDSBURG – MONROE

ARGESON, Andrea Constance. RR 14 BOX 7492 18360 #033-05-1995 L1999 **PD** *020 †55
BHATTACHARJEE, Dulal. RR 7 18360 #160-01-1975 L1995 **IM END** *020 †20
BRAATZ, Timothy Paul. 100 PIONEER LN, STE 5 18360 #035-06-1997 L2003 **DR** *020 †80
CHAKRAVORTY, Subhajit. 1172 W MAIN ST STE B, ISL LIMITED 18360 #496-09-1993 L2002 **PFP** *020
CHAUDHRY, Ahmad N. 1112A N 9TH ST 18360 #035-48-2003 **GS** *100
CHERRY, William E. 300 NORTON RD 18360 #040-02-1985 L1986 **CHP P** *020
CHERRY, William Richard. ■ 18360 #011-02-1988 L1990 **AN** *020 †05
CIBISCHINO, Lindy Lee W. RR 7 BOX 7492, DOGWOOD LANE 18360 #033-05-1990 L1996 **PD** *020 †55
DAVIDSON, Cary A. RR 7 BOX 7491, RR 7 BOX 7491 18360 #035-15-1982 L1985 **FM** *075 †18
DAVIS, Bruce C. 1803 W MAIN ST 18360 #654-01-1981 L1983 **FM** *020 †18
DE, Sulagna. 300 STROUD BUILDING, ROUTE 611 18360 #690-03-1986 L1997 **IM** *020 †20,70
ESOLEN, Lisa Marie. ■ 18360 #032-01-1987 L1995 **IM** *020
FARRELL, John Scott. 100 PIONEER LN, STE 5 18360 #041-02-2000 L2001 **DR** *100 †80
FINCH, Alberta M. ■ 18360 #041-13-1950 L1951 **PD FM** *071 †18
FOGLIA, Ginamarie. ■ 18360 #033-75-1993, ▲ L2005 **ID PHP** *050 †20
FRANGOS, James Nicholas. 100 PIONEER LN, STE 5 18360 #041-09-1980 L1984 **DR** *020 †80
GO, Sian T. 615 MAIN ST, # 308 18360 #005-19-1976 L2002 **IM GP** *030
GONZALEZ SANCHEZ, Edulfo. 1172 W MAIN ST STE B 18360 #726-01-1971 L1977 **P** *020 †75
HOBBIE, Christopher N. 100 PIONEER LN, STE 5 18360 #008-01-1991 L1996 **DR** *020 †80
IANNONE, John Patrick. 100 PIONEER LN, STE 5 18360 #422-01-1989 L1996 **RNR** *020 †80
IKRAM, Mohammad. 1172 W MAIN ST, ISL LTD 18360 #704-09-1991 L2002 **P** *020
KALE, Oludolapo Oluseun. 1172 W MAIN ST 18360 #690-01-1992 L2000 **P** *020 †75
KRISHNAMOORTHY, Divya. 1172 W MAIN ST STE B 18360 #496-44-1999 L2005 **CHP** *020 †75
LEVINSON, Ilan Simha. 1172 W MAIN ST STE B 18360 #550-04-1986 L1995 **P PMM** *020 †75
LYNCH, Christopher B. RR 7 BOX 7492, & DOGWOOD 18360 #018-75-1979, ▲ L1989 **PD** *020 †55
MATHEW, Reena Kalathil. 1172 W MAIN ST STE B 18360 #496-32-1996 L2003 **PYG** *020 †75
MEMON, Parvez. RR 1 PMB 170, BOX 11005 18360 #704-08-1982 L1994 **FM** *020 †18
MUTHIAH, Sethuraman. 6977 ROUTE 611 18360 #495-04-1978 L1997 **IM** *020 †20
RACCIATO, Peter Jos. 1036 N 9TH ST 18360 #041-13-1974 L1975 **OPH** *020 †35 ‡
ROSEMAN, Harry Robt. ■ 18360 #028-44-1942 L1943 **OS** *075
SALVA, Steven Martin. 1251 DREHER AVE 18360 #041-02-2001 L2001 **U** *020 †95
SCHECTER, Benjamin Chas. 411 MAIN ST, STE 100A 18360 #041-02-1966 L1967 **ADM GP** *020
SMITH, Robin Lisa. 100 PIONEER LN, STE 5 18360 #008-01-1992 L1994 **U** *020 †95
STALLMAN, Jamie Scott. 100 PIONEER LN, STE 5 18360 #041-02-1997 L2002 **RNR** *020 †80
SULLUM, Jonathan Chaim. 100 PIONEER LN, STE 5 18360 #041-09-1976 L1977 **DR** *020 †80
WALLINGFORD, James Lane. RR 3 BOX 3360 18360 #041-13-1978 L1983 **PUD CCM** *020 †20

SUGAR NOTCH – LUZERNE

BAER, John Chas. 250 WALNUT ST 18706 #023-01-1982 L2002 **OPH** *020 †35
BISCHOFF, Cynthia M. 200 WALNUT ST 18706 #021-01-1988 L1994 **OBG** *020 †30
BOBECK, Joseph John. MAIN & CONNOR ST 18706 #041-09-1940 L1946 **FM** *020 †18

SUGARLOAF – LUZERNE

AHMAD, Tahira Hameed. ■ 18249 #704-06-1972 L1979 **GS OPH** *050
DESSEN, Edgar Lee. ■ 18249 #041-01-1939 L1940 **DR** *071
DUFFY, Terence Francis. 5 S MAIN ST 18249 #422-01-1984 L1985 **PM IM** *020 †20,60
FRONTERA, John. 115 JEFFREY DR 18249 #051-07-1991 L2000 **N** *020 †75
GORSKI, Eugene Danl. 19 BANKS AVE 18249 #041-09-1981 L1982 **FM** *020 †18
GUNDERSON, Robert Lloyd. ■ 18249 #016-06-1944 L1959 **ORS** *071 †40
KHOSA, Nancy. ■ 18249 #495-51-1969 **FM** *100
RUTKOWSKI, Mark Gregory. ■ 18249 #041-09-1985 L1986 **AN** *071
STISH, Wesley Girard. ■ 18249 #561-17-1935 L1937 **GP** *020
YAMULA, Stanley Jos. ■ 18249 #041-09-1944 L1945 **GS** *071

SUMMIT HILL – CARBON

O'GUREK, David Thomas. ■ 18250 #041-14-2008 L2008 *012
PERILLI, Elizabeth M. 32 W LUDLOW ST 18250 #041-02-1998 L2001 **FM** *020 †18 ‡
PERILLI, Gretchen Anne. ■ 18250 #041-02-2001 L2003 **END** *020

SUNBURY – NORTHUMBERLAND

AKHTAR, M Nayeem. 1214 LINE ST 17801 #495-15-1981 L1992 **GE IM** *020 †20
ALMOND, Charles Richard. ■ 17801 #041-13-1963 L1964 **FM** *040 †18
ARISUMI, Susan Kazuko. 385 STATE ST 17801 #023-01-1985 L1986 **FM** *020 †18
BERLOT, Catherine Hester. ■ 17801 #005-11-1988 *100
BODMER, Meral S. 350 N 11TH ST 17801 #902-03-1954 L1965 **GP P** *071
BORYS, Susan Faith. 385 STATE ST 17801 #041-09-1985 L1986 **IM** *020 †20
BRANCATO, Chris. 330 N 12TH ST 17801 #035-09-1986 L1992 **CD** *072 †20
BUENDIA, Antonio V Bernal. 350 N 11TH ST 17801 #748-01-1975 L1984 **DR** *020 †80

CATALANO, Anthony C. 300 WASHINGTON AVE 17801 #561-17-1982 L1985 **GS VS** *020
DELGADO, Juan Fernando. 330 N 12TH ST, GEISINGER WOMENS HLTH CLC 17801 #737-01-1959 L1963 **GYN** *020 †30
FABIAN, Andrew. 385 STATE ST 17801 #759-10-1982 L1983 **FM** *020 †18
FASANO-BHANGDIA, Maria M. 350 N 11TH ST 17801 #041-09-1993 L1999 **PTH** *020 †50
FOLDES, Steven Istvan. ■ 17801 #473-01-1950 L1960 **AN** *071 †05
FOLDES, Veronika M. ■ 17801 #473-01-1950 L1961 **GP PD** *071 †55
GIBBS, Winfield Scott. ■ 17801 #035-19-1954 L1959 **R** *071
HEPNER, Thomas Arthur, Jr. 385 STATE ST 17801 #041-13-1989 L1991 **IM** *020 †20
KNEIFATI, Ahmed. 350 N 11TH ST 17801 #875-02-1973 L1977 **ORS** *020 †40
KRISHNAN, Geeta K. 1214 LINE ST STE A 17801 #495-17-1971 L1979 **OTO** *020 †45
NASIR, Mahmood. 512 MARKET ST 17801 #704-01-1981 L1987 **N** *020
NINOS, John C. 337 ARCH ST 17801 #035-06-1980 L1981 **FM** *020 †18
PAGANA, John Patrick. 1072 MARKET ST 17801 #041-13-1972 L1973 **FM** *071 †18 ‡
PATEL, Purshottam N. 1214 A LINE ST B 17801 #495-01-1965 L1977 **U OS** *020 ‡
SAMAD, Mohammad Abdul. 350 N 11TH ST 17801 #704-01-1968 L1973 **IM** *020 †20
STONER, Gary. 330 N 12TH ST 17801 #055-02-1989 L1992 **OBG** *020 †30
TILVA, Prafulchandra K. 350 N 11TH ST 17801 #495-48-1972 L1977 **DR** *020
VARMA, Sreelatha C. 385 STATE ST 17801 #495-50-1985 L2005 **IM** *020 †20
WILSON, Dorothy G. ■ 17801 #041-13-1951 L1952 **GYN** *071 †30
YANOVIAK, Pamela Wenger. 2728 MILE HILL RD 17801 #041-14-1985 L1986 **IM** *020 †20

SUSQUEHANNA – SUSQUEHANNA

DE WITT, Warren Stephen. 400 TURNPIKE ST 18847 #041-13-1978 L1981 **FM** *020 †18
HACKER, Richard Keith. 400 TURNPIKE ST 18847 #024-05-1984 L2005 **EM FM** *020 †18 ‡
MIRZA, Adnan. 400 TURNPIKE ST, BARNES-KASSON HOSPITAL 18847 #704-01-1997 L2005 **CCM** *020 †20
MORAN, Ernesto. 400 TURNPIKE ST 18847 #341-01-1960 L1964 **OBG** *071
MUDIPALLI, Vasudeva Ranji. ■ 18847 #495-70-1995 L2005 **FM** *020 †18
PATEL, Bhupendra R. 400 TURNPIKE ST 18847 #495-23-1980 L1985 **IM** *020 †20
PATEL, Pravinchandra K. ■ 18847 #495-22-1979 L1985 **IM GP** *020
PATEL, Ramesh Chandra. 400 TURNPIKE ST 18847 #495-23-1959 L1980 **OBG** *020 †30
PURKAYASTHA, Arindam. 400 TURNPIKE ST 18847 #495-39-1964 L1973 **GS GP** *020 †85 ‡
REMAKUS, Bernard Leo. 400 TURNPIKE ST 18847 #041-13-1978 L1979 **IM EM** *020 †20 ‡
SARAN, Madhukar. 405 PINE ST 18847 #495-15-1964 L1976 **PUD IM** *020 †20
SHAH, Mahendra Kantilal. 400 TURNPIKE ST 18847 #495-22-1969 L1979 **IM HEM** *020
SHELLY, William Dayton. 400 TURNPIKE ST 18847 #041-13-1973 L1974 **GS** *020 †85

SUTERSVILLE – WESTMORELAND

RYCKMAN, William F. 127 AMERICAN LN 15083 #035-06-1971 L1975 **FM** *071 †18 ‡

SWARTHMORE – DELAWARE

AINSLIE, Eleanor Ruth. ■ 19081 #041-02-2008 *012
BAKER, Arthur Gorham, Jr. ■ 19081 #041-01-1961 L1965 **VS GS** *071 †85 ‡
BELASCO, Andrea Laurie. 110 PARK AVE # 3 19081 #007-02-1980 L1981 **P OBG** *075 †75
BROUSSARD, Delma Lynn. ■ 19081 #024-01-1984 L1986 **GE PD** *062 †55
CHUIPEK, Stephanie Ann. 630 FAIRVIEW RD, STE 210 19081 #032-01-1982 L1984 **PD NPM** *020 †55 ‡
FEINGOLD, Joseph L. ■ 19081 #041-13-1949 L1950 **GP EM** *071 †85
FLEHARTY, Heather Maria. 500 COLLEGE AVE 19081 #005-11-2008 *012
FRASER, David Wm. ■ 19081 #024-01-1969 L1970 **OS PHP** *030 †20
GALLATIG, Kathleen Marie. ■ 19081 #041-02-2004 L2005 **PD** *012
GREEN, Lawrence. 315 MAPLE AVE 19081 #041-02-1964 L1965 **N CN** *071 †75
HANNA, Michael Stuart. ■ 19081 #008-02-1983 L1990 **CD PA** *020 †20
HELLMAN, Fredric Neil. ■ 19081 #041-13-1985 L1987 **FOP PTH** *062 †50
JENKINS, Dorothy S. 700 S CHESTER RD 19081 #041-01-1987 L1988 **IM** *020 †20
KARCH, Robert Daniel. ■ 19081 #010-02-2000 L2006 **PD** *100 †55
KATZEN, Nicholas. ■ 19081 #836-01-1982 L1994 **GE** *020 †20
KAUFMAN, Ralph Mark. 100 PARK AVE 19081 #041-09-1986 L1987 **P** *020 †75
KOETHE, John David. 451 RIVERVIEW RD 19081 #041-13-1982 L1985 **NEP IM** *020 †20
MC CARTHY, Geo Edward, Jr. ■ 19081 #041-02-1962 L1963 **RO NM** *071 †80,28
MC CURDY, Dino E P. ■ 19081 #041-01-1939 L1940 **IM CD** *071 †20
PURRINGTON, Amy C. ■ 19081 #016-02-1997 L2000 **PHM IM** *062 †20
ROBEN, George B. 110 PARK AVE APT 3 19081 #041-07-1982 L1985 **CHP P** *020 †75
ROBINSON, Nancy Beth. ■ 19081 #024-05-1981 L1982 **NPM PD** *020 †55
SOEIRO, Damon Randall. ■ 19081 #035-46-2006 L2006 **DR** *100 †80
STREIFF, Katrina. 107 RUTGERS AVE, STE 4 19081 #041-07-1976 L1977 **P PYA** *020 †75
SUM, Eva Elizabeth. ■ 19081 #020-02-2002 L2002 **GE** *020 †20
TENNEY-SOEIRO, Rebecca L. ■ 19081 #035-46-2001 L2006 **PD** *100 †55
TRINKLEY, David Russell. 700 S CHESTER RD, STE A 19081 #041-09-1992 L1994 **IM** *020 †20
TSAI, Peter Ching. ■ 19081 #035-19-2002 L2007 **HSO** *012
VON UNANGST, H S. SWARTHMORE MEDICAL CTR 19081 #041-01-1959 L1960 **P** *020
WELLIVER, Meng Xu. ■ 19081 #041-14-2006 L2006 **RO** *012
WIESNER, Irving Seymour. 300 S CHESTER RD STE 102 19081 #041-01-1966 L1967 **P** *020 †20,75
WILKINSON, Harold Arthur. ■ 19081 #041-13-1953 L1954 **FM** *071 †18
WILKINSON, Roselise D H. ■ 19081 #041-13-1953 L1954 **CHN PD** *071
WITZLEBEN, Camillus Leo. ■ 19081 #028-34-1957 L1973 **PTH** *030 †50

SWEET VALLEY – LUZERNE

GROBLEWSKI, Edward A. ■ 18656 #041-02-1955 L1956 **GP** *071

SWIFTWATER – MONROE

DECKER, Michael Donahue. 0 DISCOVERY DR, AVENTIS PASTEUR 18370 #016-01-1978 L1979 **ID IM** *050 †20

GORDON, Daniel Matthew. 1 DISCOVERY DR 18370 #048-14-1979 L2006 **ID IM** *050 †20
GREENBERG, David Paul. 1 DISCOVERY DR, SANOFI PASTEUR 18370 #048-04-1982 L1996 **PDI PD** *030 †55
JOHNSON, David Rue. 1 DISCOVERY DR, AVENTIS PASTEUR 18370 #056-05-1984 L2004 **PD PHP** *062 †55
RUBEN, Frederick Leon. 1 DISCOVERY DR, SANOFI PASTEUR 18370 #036-07-1964 L1964 **ID IM** *050 †20

SWISSVALE – ALLEGHENY

BOGGS, Mercedes Allysia. ■ 15218 #041-15-2008 L2008 *012
FALLIN, Heath Alexander. ■ 15218 #036-01-2005 L2005 **AN** *012
KHAN, Salman Raza. ■ 15218 #704-02-1997 L2005 **PDP** *012
NICHOLAS, James Elbert. ■ 15218 #041-12-1975 **IM** *020 †20,16

SWOYERSVILLE – LUZERNE

BRADY, John Peter. 1212 MAIN ST 18704 #041-09-1983 L1984 **IM IMG** *020 †20 ‡
CHUNG, Hi-Young. 11 GRANDVILLE DR 18704 #583-02-1957 L1968 **OBG IM** *020

SYKESVILLE – JEFFERSON

DELA TORRE, Henry Gacrama. 37 VAN NESS ST 15865 #748-11-1973 L1982 **GP** *020

TAFTON – PIKE

DAVIS, Charles M, Jr. ■ 18464 #041-01-1956 L1957 **ORS** *071 †40

TAMAQUA – SCHUYLKILL

AYDIN, Kemalettin. ■ 18252 #902-03-1953 L1973 **GS** *071
BARDAWIL, Lawrence Wadi. 301 W BROAD ST 18252 #024-07-1979 L1985 **GE IM** *020 †20 ‡
BOBICK, Frank Jos. 301 E BROAD ST 18252 #041-12-1974 L1975 **OPH** *020 †35 ‡
HOUSER, Angela Grace. 37 MEDICAL CROSSING RD, MAHONING VALLEY EYE CENTER 18252 #041-02-1990 L1994 **OPH** *020 †35
HOUSER, Ben Philip, Jr. RR 3 18252 #041-02-1963 L1964 **OPH** *071 †35
HOUSER, Benjamin Philip. RR 3 18252 #041-02-1934 L1935 **OPH OTO** *071 †45
KIM, Inkyo. 9 LAFAYETTE AVE 18252 #583-01-1972 L1993 **IM** *020 †20
KUMAR, Anil. ■ 18252 #495-01-1998 L2006 **IM** *020 †20
LACEY, Sean Robert. 301 W BROAD ST 18252 #041-14-1994 L2004 **GE** *020 †20
LAGAN, Jane Ruth. ■ 18252 #041-02-1988 L1990 **FM** *062 †18 ‡
LENYO, George Edward. 23 CLARRYAN ST, HOMETOWN 18252 #041-02-1955 L1956 **FM GP** *071
LIAW, Michael Ming Tong. ■ 18252 #385-02-1959 L1972 **GS PS** *071
LUCIER, Alfred Charles. 31 MEDICAL CROSSING RD 18252 #035-03-1961 L1967 **OPH** *071 †35
NEWMAN, Donald Arthur. 37 MEDICAL CROSSING RD 18252 #020-02-1984 L1987 **OPH** *020 †20
SHABLIN, Brian Keith. 253 CLAREMONT AVE 18252 #041-13-1996 L1998 **IM** *020 †20

TARENTUM – ALLEGHENY

BANKS, Matthew Christian. 413 E 4TH, STE 217 15084 #041-14-1998 L2003 **DR** *020 †80
BARNICLE, Daniel James. 413 E 4TH AVE, STE 217 15084 #030-06-1983 L1987 **R** *020 †80
BRAND, Carol Elsie. 301 5TH AVE, RUSSELLTON PEDIATRICS 15084 #054-04-1979 L1982 **PD** *020 †55
BROWN, Robert. 413 E 4TH AVE, STE 217 15084 #035-19-1944 L1945 **IM RHU** *071 †20
BUCK, David Steele. 413 E 4TH AVE, STE 217 15084 #041-12-1985 L1987 **DR NR** *020 †80
CASTILLO, Francisco A. 413 E 4TH AVE, STE 217 15084 #748-01-1971 L1977 **R** *062
CHEN, Lijia. 413 E 4TH AVE STE 217, RADIOLOGIC CONSULTANTS, LT 15084 #243-33-1982 L2006 **DR** *100 †80
DE PIPPO, Paul Alexander. 413 E 4TH AVE, STE 217 15084 #035-03-1984 L1989 **DR** *020 †20,80
DUDA, John Jacob, Jr. 413 E 4TH AVE STE 217 15084 #041-14-1987 L1994 **DR** *020 †80
FERLAN, Lawrence. 317 E 1ST AVE 15084 #041-12-1960 L1961 **GP** *020
GLICK, Kenneth Asher. 301 E 1ST AVE STE C 15084 #041-14-1978 L1984 **GE IM** *020 †20
GRAVES, Chester David. 413 E 4TH AVE, STE 217 15084 #048-13-1983 L1987 **DR** *020 †80
GRAY, Samuel. 320 E 3RD AVE 15084 #041-12-1960 L1961 **IM CD** *071 †20
GREALISH, Robert James. 413 E 4TH AVE, STE 217 15084 #041-12-1974 L1975 **FM** *030 †18
HAAS, Donald Delmont. 413 E 4TH AVE, STE 217 15084 #041-12-1972 L1973 **DR** *020 †80
HEIDENREICH, Fred Paul. 320 E 3RD AVE 15084 #041-12-1962 L1963 **CD IM** *071 †20
HEILMAN, John Danl. 320 E 3RD AVE 15084 #041-01-1965 L1968 **IM PUD** *020 †20
HENCK, Mark Edward. 413 E 4TH AVE, STE 217 15084 #041-14-1991 L1993 **DR** *020 †80
HRBEK, Todd Alan. 413 E 4TH AVE, STE 217 15084 #038-41-1997 L2002 **VIR R** *020 †80
KEARNEY, Joseph Anthony. 413 E 4TH AVE, STE 217 15084 #041-09-1980 L1981 **DR** *020 †80
LIPSITZ, H David. 301 1ST AVE 15084 #041-02-1975 L1976 **GE IM** *020 †20
LOLLEY, David Marcus. 301 E 1ST AVE STE B, CARDIAC SURGEONS INC 15084 #021-01-1968 L1984 **TS VS** *020 †85,90 ‡
LYNCH, James Robert. 413 E 4TH AVE, STE 217 15084 #028-34-1968 L1971 **R IM** *020 †80
MARTIN, Margaret Leffler. 317 1ST AVE 15084 #422-01-2000 L2001 **FM** *020 †18
MEALS, Margaret E. 320 3RD AVE 15084 #041-12-1983 L1984 **IM IMG** *020 †20
MEYER, David Grant. 413 E 4TH AVE, STE 217 15084 #035-20-1979 L1980 **R** *020 †80
MICHEL, Elliot Morton. 215 1ST AVE 15084 #038-40-1976 L1977 **N** *020 †75
PAIVA, John De. 207 ALLEGHENY ST, BILLING OFFICE 15084 #041-09-1986 L1987 **DR IM** *020 †80
PIRL, Keith Gordon. 301 5TH AVE 15084 #038-06-1992 L1997 **PD** *020 †55
SHIN, David Hyunjoon. 317 1ST AVE, FERLAN MEDICAL ASSOCIATES 15084 #038-40-1994 L1997 **IM** *020 †20
SIMONE, Frank John. 413 E 4TH AVE, STE 217 15084 #041-12-1979 L1980 **DR** *020 †80
SIVAKUMAR, Usha. 415 E 4TH AVE, STE 3 15084 #495-59-1987 L1999 **IM FM** *020 †20

SLAUNWHITE, Rebecca M. 301 5TH AVE, CHILDRENS COMMUNITY PEDIAT 15084 #035-48-1999 L2004 **PD** *020 †55
THORNBURG, Alan James. 413 E 4TH AVE, STE 217 15084 #041-14-1984 L1986 **DR** *020 †80
UBER, Gabrielle. 317 E 1ST AVE 15084 #041-14-1996 L1998 **FM** *020 †18
WALSH, Thomas Francis. 413 E 4TH AVE, STE C 15084 #308-03-1982 L1983 **U** *020 †95

TAYLOR – LACKAWANNA

CALDWELL, Douglas Robt. 648 N MAIN ST, REDI-CARE MEDICAL CENTER 18517 #041-14-1984 L1986 **GP OM** *020
MALINA, John Jos. ■ 18517 #030-06-1956 L1957 **AM GP** *030
PERRONE, David Francis. 648 N MAIN ST 18517 #050-02-1978 L1979 **IM** *020
SEBASTIANELLI, Kenneth J. 816 S MAIN ST 18517 #041-07-1986 L1987 **IM** *020 †20

TELFORD – MONTGOMERY

BUI, Minh. 11 N MAIN ST 18969 #041-13-1987 L1989 **IM** *020 †20
COHAN, Hal. 211 TELFORD PIKE, FRANCONIA OFFICE 18969 #041-13-1988 L1991 **FM OM** *020 †18
KRISAK, Lisa Ann. ■ 18969 #041-02-2002 L2005 **EM** *020
KYRIAKOS, Raymond Jamil. ■ 18969 #605-01-1955 L1968 **GP U** *020
MEYER, Robert James. ■ 18969 #008-02-1984 L1986 **PUD IM** *020 †20
O'DRISCOLL, Kelly Anne. 211 TELFORD PIKE 18969 #041-02-2004 L2004 **FM** *020 †18
PFROMMER, James Henry. ■ 18969 #041-09-1954 L1955 **FM** *071
PFROMMER, James Michael. ■ 18969 #041-09-1983 L1984 **P PA** *020 †75
ROSE, Kelly Marie. 211 TELFORD PIKE, INDIAN VALLEY SHOPPING CTR 18969 #041-02-2000 L2001 **FM** *020 †18
SPEIGLE, Joanne Brenneman. ■ 18969 #051-04-1989 L2000 **DR** *020 †80
THATCHER, Jeffrey David. 211 TELFORD PIKE, FRANCONIA OFFICE 18969 #041-02-1983 L1985 **IM** *020 †20
TRAVERS, John. ■ 18969 #033-06-1982 L1987 **P** *020 †75

TEMPLE – BERKS

DENARO, Anthony Thomas. 704 HAY RD, BERKSTREATMENT CENTER 19560 #039-01-1969 L1973 **CHP P** *020 †75
JACOBSON, Martin Aaron. 4201 KUTZTOWN RD, MUHLENBERG MED ASSOC 19560 #035-46-1974 L1978 **IM** *020 †20 ‡
REYNER, Peter Cooper. 4201 KUTZTOWN RD 19560 #041-09-1982 L1984 **IM** *020 †20
ZAPATA, William Anthony. 4201 KUTZTOWN RD, MUHLENBERG MED ASSOC 19560 #035-46-1975 L1978 **IM** *020 †20

THOMASVILLE – YORK

MC FARLAND, Michael John. ■ 17364 #041-13-1992 L1995 **EM** *020 †16

THOMPSON – SUSQUEHANNA

RHODES, Robert Stephen. ■ 18465 #005-02-1971 *100

THORNDALE – CHESTER

ABBAS, Syed Qasim. ■ 19372 #704-02-2000 L2007 **FP** *012
ARAYATA, Felixberto Reyes. ■ 19372 #748-02-1956 L1970 **EM** *071
ARAYATA, Liduvina B C. ■ 19372 #748-01-1957 L1971 **P PD** *020
BERNBAUM, David Jonathan. 3025 C G ZINN RD 19372 #041-01-1974 L1975 **CD IM** *020 †20
HODESS, Arthur Bart. 3025 C G ZINN RD 19372 #035-01-1974 L1975 **CD IM** *020 †20
INSALATA, Robert Anthony. 3629 LINCOLN HWY 19372 #035-09-1962 L1963 **IM** *020 †20
JARDINE, Jill. 32 SKYVIEW LN 19372 #041-13-1993 L1999 **P** *020
JAWAD, Basil Sadik. 3149 LINCOLN HWY 19372 #330-04-1970 L1980 **IM** *020 ‡
LEVIN, Gary Jan. 3000 ZINN RD 19372 #041-02-1973 L1974 **OPH** *020 †35
LUMINAIS, Steven Kean. 3000 C G ZINN RD 19372 #035-20-1979 L1981 **OPH IM** *020 †35
METKUS, Thomas Stephen. 3025 C G ZINN RD 19372 #041-02-1978 L1979 **IM** *020 †20
SABADISH, Michael Paul. 3025 C G ZINN RD 19372 #041-09-1998 L2000 **ICE** *020 †20
SCHMIDT, Robert Edward. 3628 LINCOLN HWY 19372 #041-13-1970 L1971 **IM** *020 †20
TROY, Alan Duncan. 3025 C G ZINN RD 19372 #041-01-1977 L1979 **CD IM** *020 †20
UY, Nenito Pinero. 3628 LINCOLN HWY 19372 #748-11-1974 L1983 **GS SO** *020 †85

THORNTON – DELAWARE

CHAUDHRY, Hina Waheed. ■ 19373 #024-01-1991 L1993 **CD** *020 †20
HUTCHINS, Francis L. ■ 19373 #010-03-1945 L1946 **OM GP** *072
LAROSA, Christopher John. ■ 19373 #041-14-2004 L2004 **PN** *012 †55

THROOP – LACKAWANNA

ALOCCI, Michael. 100 DUNMORE ST 18512 #561-19-1988 L1992 **IM** *020
BARRETT, Michael Joseph. 631 SANDERSON ST 18512 #041-02-1993 L1995 **IM** *020 †20
CASSONE, Gary John. 100 DUNMORE ST 18512 #561-01-1971 L1977 **U** *020 †95
CLAUSS, Thomas F. 515 GEORGE ST 18512 #041-02-1951 L1952 **FM** *071 †18
HODGSON, Eric John. ■ 18512 #023-01-2002 L2007 **OBG** *100
MEYER, Thomas Louis. ■ 18512 #748-09-1978 L1980 **P** *020 †75
SERINE, Enrico Anthony. 100 DUNMORE ST 18512 #038-43-1975 L1981 **IM** *020 †20 ‡
SIROTNAK, John Jos. 434 DUNMORE ST 18512 #041-02-1959 L1960 **OTO** *020 †45
SIROTNAK, John Jos, III. 434 DUNMORE ST 18512 #041-02-1988 L1990 **OTO HNS** *020 †45
WESTON, Wayne Louis. 100 DUNMORE ST 18512 #041-07-1985 L1986 **IM** *020 †20

TIDIOUTE – WARREN

SIVAK, Stanley John. 224 MAIN ST 16351 #041-14-1974 L1975 **GP** *020

TITUSVILLE – CRAWFORD

DONOVAN, Byron Lee. 406 W OAK ST 16354 #041-12-1982 L1983 **AN** *020
DUNN, Joseph Patrick. 406 W OAK ST, TITUSVILLE AREA HOSPITAL 16354 #010-02-1961 L1962 **GP** *020
DUTT, Anil Kumar. 150 W CENTRAL AVE, STE 3 16354 #004-01-1986 L2006 **GS EM** *020 †85
ENGLISH, Gregory Richard. ■ 16354 #041-14-2007 L2007 **GS** *012
ESTRADA, Susan Victoria. 406 W OAK ST 16354 #748-02-1993 L1997 **IM** *020 †20
FAN, Young Chung. 119 E MECHANIC ST 16354 #385-04-1966 L1973 **GS OS** *020
FERREIRA, Leonard Aubrey. 602 W CENTRAL AVE 16354 #033-06-1987 L1991 **OBG** *020 †30
KUMAR, Harinath V. 422 N MONROE ST 16354 #495-21-1963 L1975 **U** *020 †95
LEVENDORF, Keith David. 406 W OAK ST 16354 #041-12-1982 L1983 **AN** *020 †05
LEWIS, Arthur Alan. ■ 16354 #041-14-1984 L1985 **FM** *020 †18
LOS, Brian Anthony. 339 W SPRING ST, STE 102 16354 #041-12-1994 L1996 **IM** *020 †20
MC ALLISTER, Scott J. 339 W SPRING ST STE 102 16354 #041-12-1992 L1994 **IM** *020 †20
MUNOZ, Maria Lourdes N. 339 W SPRING ST STE 103 16354 #041-10-1983 L1993 **PD** *020 †55
NAZZARO, Ralph. 406 W OAK ST 16354 #041-09-1971 L1977 **GS** *071 †85
NECAS, Michael Gerard. 107 E BLOSS ST 16354 #005-18-1980 L1985 **OPH** *020 †35
RUO, Nori Yuehshuan. 339 W SPRING ST 16354 #016-06-1993 L1996 **PD** *020 †55
SHIM, Chungja C. 406 W OAK ST 16354 #583-08-1969 L1979 **PTH** *020 †50
SONNENBERG, William Robt. 119 E MECHANIC ST 16354 #041-12-1980 L1981 **FM** *020 †18
WEEKS, Ruthellen Denise. 12248 N PERRY RD 16354 #041-02-1981 L1983 **OBG** *020 †30
WHALEN, Richard Benedict. 339 W SPRING ST STE 102 16354 #038-40-1992 L1995 **IM** *020 †20
WILKENS, James Burton, Jr. 322 W MAIN ST 16354 #035-01-1983 L1988 **IM** *020 †20

TOBYHANNA – MONROE

ASHRAF, Mohammad. 11 HAP ARNOLD BLVD, TOBYHANNA ARMY HEALTH CLIN 18466 #308-12-1988 L1994 **IM** *020
CHAUDHRY, Sakina Azhar. 445 STERLING RD 18466 #704-08-1967 L1980 **FM EM** *020
CONAHAN, Joseph Bernard. 100 COMMUNITY DR, STE 204A 18466 #030-06-1969 L1970 **OPH** *020 †35
DE FRANK, Frank Nicholas. 100 COMMUNITY DR STE 102, MOUNTAIN FAMILY CARE 18466 #041-14-1980 L1981 **FM** *020 †18
GRIMALDI, Matthew Porter. ■ 18466 #041-13-2007 *012
KEULER, Marc Michael. 100 COMMUNITY DR, STE 203 18466 #041-07-1982 L1983 **IM** *020 †20 ‡
LIPPIN, Richard Arthur. 11 HAP ARNOLD BLVD, TOBYHANNA ARMY DEPOT 18466 #041-13-1971 L1972 **OM PHP** *030 †18,70
NEGVESKY, Gerald Joseph. 100 COMMUNITY DR, STE 204A 18466 #010-02-1996 L2000 **OPH** *020 †35
SHAIKH, Ayesha. 300 COMMUNITY DR STE E 18466 #704-06-1974 L1980 **PD** *020 †55
SIPOWICZ, Carl Peter. 100 COMMUNITY DR, STE 209 18466 #041-09-1965 L1966 **ORS** *020 †40
SORENSEN, Christian Finn. 100 COMMUNITY DR, THE READING HEALTH DISPENS 18466 #033-06-1990 L1992 **FM** *020 †18
WEISS, Carl Broock. 100 COMMUNITY DR, STE 204A 18466 #035-20-1962 L1963 **OPH AM** *072 †35
ZADEH, Ali Mohammad. ■ 18466 #517-01-1964 L1987 **GS TS** *020 †16

TOPTON – BERKS

BECKER, Ward Geoffrey. 1 S HOME AVE 19562 #041-02-1974 L1975 **FPG IMG** *020 †18
FEGLEY, Homer Burkert. ■ 19562 #041-09-1934 L1936 **EM** *071
HAUSER, Raymond Jos. 1 S HOME AVE, THE LUTHERAN HOME AT TOPTO 19562 #041-02-1974 L1975 **FPG FM** *020 †18
MUEHLHAUSER, William Otto. ■ 19562 #041-02-1946 L1947 **GP** *071

TORRANCE – WESTMORELAND

ANANDA-MAHENDIRAN, Muttu. HWY 217 SOUTH 15779 #220-02-1972 L1995 **P** *020
CULBERTSON, Clayton Elden. TORRNCE STATE HOSPITAL 15779 #041-12-1959 L1961 **GYN** *071 †30
ESKENASY, Martinez. TORRANCE ST HOSP CLIN LAB 15779 #429-01-1967 L1978 **PTH** *020 †50
ISSAC, Lisa Ruth. HWY 217 SOUTH 15779 #041-12-1979 L1981 **GP DR** *030
OLAVE, Raul Antonio. HWY 217 SOUTH 15779 #264-02-1950 L1968 **GP GPM** *071
RASHID, Kausar. HWY 217 SOUTH 15779 #495-21-1974 L1985 **FM** *020
SCHULTZ, Theodore A. HWY 217 SOUTH 15779 #010-01-1952 L1954 **P IMG** *071
SCOTT, Kincy J, Jr. TORRANCE STATE HOSP 15779 #048-02-1953 L1965 **P** *071
UDDIN, Faiyaz. PO BOX 111, TORRANCE STATE HOSP 15779 #495-21-1979 L1984 **IM** *020
YUN, Jinha. HWY 217 SOUTH 15779 #583-06-1967 L1976 **P** *020

TOWANDA – BRADFORD

BADAMO, Francis Patrick. RR 1 BOX 3J, PHYSICIAN CARE, P.C. 18848 #041-01-1970 L1971 **GS CD** *020 †85
BECKER, Stephen Ernest. RR 6 18848 #023-01-1981 L1982 **FM** *020 †18
BENDO, John Geo. RR 1 BOX 3J, HOSPITAL DR 18848 #035-19-1971 L2001 **U** *020 †95
BLACK, Ronald Anthony. RR 1, BOX 3J 18848 #005-12-1997 L2001 **FM** *020 †18
BRADSTREET, Richard Perry. 1 HOSPITAL DR 18848 #011-04-1987 L1990 **PTH** *020 †50
CAMA, Joseph. 520 MAIN ST 18848 #561-01-1978 L1980 **FM OBG** *020 †18
CARLOS, Fernando S. RR 1, BOX 3J 18848 #748-16-1988 L1996 **PD** *020 †55
CHALABI, Samim Mohamad. 1 HOSPITAL DR 18848 #605-01-1981 L2000 **GS** *020 †85
FERENZI, James Charles. 12 WALNUT ST 18848 #041-09-1984 L1987 **GS VS** *020

■ = Address Information Privacy Protected

GABALDONI, Louis V. RR 1 BOX 3J, 1 HOSPATAL DR 18848 #023-01-1978 L1985 **OBG** *020 †30
GEORGIU, Edward Virgil. ■ 18848 #041-12-1990 L1994 **AN** *020 †05
GEORGIU, Flory. 1 HOSPITAL DR 18848 #781-01-1959 L1973 **OBG** *020 †30
GEORGIU, Virgil. 1 HOSPITAL DR 18848 #781-01-1959 L1973 **OTO A** *071
GOODRICH, Kenneth Bernard. RR 1 BOX 3J, 1 HOSPITAL DR 18848 #041-01-1979 L1980 **OBG** *020 †30
MAC KAY, Bruce Russell. ■ 18848 #050-02-1957 L1964 **END DIA** *071 †20
MAST, Clarence, Jr. RR 1, BOX 3J 18848 #041-13-1970 L1971 **GPM** *020 †18
MAYLOCK, John Vincent. 7 COLONIAL DR, GUTHRIE CLINIC LTD 18848 #041-02-1992 L1995 **FM** *020 †18
MC INTYRE, John F. RR 1, BOX 3J 18848 #004-01-1972 L1973 **GP** *020
MEIKLE, George Chas, II. RR 5, P.O. BOX 31 18848 #041-02-1985 L1987 **EM OBG** *020 †18
MENDEZ SANCHEZ, Vicente A. RR 1 BOX 3J, HOSPITAL DRIVE 18848 #308-05-1984 L1988 **IM ATP** *020
PAVLOU, William James. RR 1 BOX 4B, COLONIAL DRIVE 18848 #041-09-1982 L1991 **FM RO** *020
PERRY, Raymond Allen. RR 1, BOX 197B 18848 #041-13-1968 L1969 **IM** *071 †20
RAYNE, David Thomas. 1 HOSPITAL DR, MEMORIAL HOSPITAL 18848 #008-02-1993 L1998 **NR** *020 †80,28
SABA, Adnan. COLONIAL DR 18848 #875-01-1986 L1995 **IM** *020 †20
TAMA, Lawrence. 1 HOSPITAL DR 18848 #041-01-1953 L1954 **GS GYN** *030 †85
TAMA, Lawrence Ellis. RR 1 BOX 3J 18848 #041-13-1986 L1987 **FM** *020 †18
TRAMONTANA, Jorge. RR 6, BOX 6089 18848 #737-01-1957 L1965 **GS CD** *020 †85
WINSTON, Ralph B. RR 6, RD #1 BOX 250 18848 #051-04-1949 L1953 **IMG IM** *071 ‡

TRAFFORD — WESTMORELAND

AHMAD, Afaq. 1005 KINGS CT, EMERGENCY DEPARTMENT 15085 #704-15-1979 L1991 **PUD** *020 †20
BUCAR, John R. ■ 15085 #016-42-1948 L1952 **OS GP** *072
DUGAN, Charles Thomas. 101 ORCHARD DR, UNIV OF PITTS CTR LEVELG 15085 #041-09-1987 L1989 **FM** *020 †18
GAROFOLO, Edward Joseph. 101 ORCHARD DR 15085 #041-12-1994 L1996 **FM** *020 †18
JOHNSON, Gary Edward. 503 CAVITT AVE 15085 #041-13-1978 L1980 **FM** *020 †18
LEUKHARDT, Susan Lea. ■ 15085 #041-12-1976 L1977 **IM IMG** *071 †20
POGUE, Jackson S. ■ 15085 #041-12-1938 L1939 **GP** *071
ZDRALE, Nikolai S. ■ 15085 #957-02-2006 *100

TRANSFER — MERCER

ECKARD, Joyce Crisafulli. 1291 RUTLEDGE RD, RUTLEDGE PROFESSIONAL OFFI 16154 #038-45-1990 L1992 **FM** *020 †18
NYSTROM, Joel Erik. 1291 RUTLEDGE RD 16154 #041-12-1975 L1976 **FM** *020 †18

TRAPPE — MONTGOMERY

STEPANSKY, William. 580 W MAIN ST 19426 #041-02-1952 L1953 **FM IM** *071 †18
WILTON, Susan R. 753 W MAIN ST, STE D 19426 #041-07-1989 L1994 **OPH** *020 †35

TREVOSE — BUCKS

ANZOLA PARRA, Edmundo. 3600 HORIZON BLVD STE 300 19053 #935-01-1975 L2004 **IM CD** *062
COLUMBUS, William Francis. 4626 E STREET RD, COLUMBUS LASER & VISION IN 19053 #041-14-1991 L2000 **OPH IM** *020
DRUCKMAN, Myles Christoph. 3600 HORIZON BLVD, STE 300 19053 #065-10-1989 L2002 **FM** *030
KROLL, Barry Scott. 4829 E STREET RD, STE 100 19053 #041-09-1992 L1994 **PD** *020 †55 ‡
LAWRENCE, Najia Claudine. ■ 19053 #010-02-2004 **OBG** *012
PELTAN, Harold Lee. 4626 E STREET RD 19053 #025-01-1993 L2000 **OPH** *020 †35
VASSALLUZZO, Francis Jos. 4979 OLD STREET RD 19053 #041-09-1956 L1957 **GP** *072
WITKIN, Evelyn Davis. 4979 OLD STREET RD, STREET ROAD SURGERY CENTER 19053 #041-13-1975 L1977 **ORS** *020 †40

TREXLERTOWN — LEHIGH

ANASTI, James N, Jr. 6900 HAMILTON BLVD, TREXLER MALL REAR 18087 #041-13-1982 L1995 **OBG** *020 †30
BARANKO, Kristin Menconi. 6900 HAMILTON BLVD, ABC FAMILY PEDIATRICIANS 18087 #041-13-1998 L2007 **MPD** *020 †20,55
GOFF, Elizabeth. 6900 HAMILTON BLVD 18087 #008-02-1989 L1991 **PD** *020 †55
HELWIG, Anne M. 6900 HAMILTON BLVD 18087 #041-02-1993 L1995 **PD** *020 †55
MC NEILL, Kevin Anthony. 6900 HAMILTON BLVD 18087 #033-05-1994 L2007 **FM** *020 †18
PELLINI, Timothy Michael. 6900 HAMILTON BLVD, HEALTH CENTER AT TREXLERTO 18087 #041-15-1999 L2007 **OBG** *100 †30
SANDOVAL, Victorino A, Jr. 6900 HAMILTON BLVD 18087 #748-10-1983 L2002 **FM** *020 †18
WILSON, Brian David. 6900 HAMILTON BLVD BOX 127 18087 #041-02-1984 L1985 **FM** *020 †18

TROUT RUN — LYCOMING

GINTER, George Carroll. ■ 17771 #041-09-1954 L1955 **AN** *071 †05

TROY — BRADFORD

ABRAHAM, George P. 125 CENTER ST 16947 #495-98-1970 L1987 **EM UCM** *020
AKULA, Venkata Ravi S. 280 ELMIRA ST 16947 #495-58-1993 L2006 **CD** *020 †20
CHIVATE, Jayant Gajanan. 125 CENTER ST 16947 #495-22-1977 L2001 **GS** *020 †85
GOOD, Vance Ariel. 125 CENTER ST 16947 #041-02-1975 L1976 **IMG IM** *020 †20
MEHTA, Jay Kumar. 280 ELMIRA ST 16947 #495-20-1978 L2005 **OBG** *020 †30

WOOD, Kari S. 125 CENTER ST 16947 #041-14-2004 L2004 **FM** *020 †18

TRUCKSVILLE — LUZERNE

ANSELMI, Lanning Albert. 206 CARVERTON RD 18708 #041-02-1977 L1978 **FM** *020 †18
LATZKO, Paul Jos. 206 CARVERTON RD 18708 #041-09-1982 L1983 **FM** *020 †18

TUNKHANNOCK — WYOMING

GARDNER, John Carl. 133 W TIOGA ST 18657 #041-02-1982 L1983 **FM** *020 †18
HULL, Donald Frank, III. 110 TRIEBLE DR, STE 1 18657 #023-07-1978 L1987 **GS EM** *020 †85
KELLMAN, Ian Arthur. 880 SR 6 W, TYLER MEMORIAL HOSPITAL 18657 #035-08-1966 L1976 **R NM** *020 †80
LANDIS, Ray Laverne. ■ 18657 #041-13-1967 L1968 **FM OBS** *071 †18
LINDNER, Henry Hudson. 166 W TIOGA ST 18657 #041-02-1984 L1996 **GPM** *020
LINKER, Seth Paul. 110 TRIEBLE DR, STE 1 18657 #024-07-1993 L1999 **OTO** *020 †45 ‡
MATTEI, Dennis Michael. 110 TRIEBLE DR, STE 1 18657 #041-13-1985 L1988 **IM** *020 †20 ‡
RUSSELL, Gary Dwight. 880 SR 6 W 18657 #039-05-1987 L1989 **FM** *020 †18
RUSSELL, Susan Eastberg. ■ 18657 #039-05-1987 L1989 **FM** *020 †18
STONE, Cheryle Ann. 1 KIM AVE, STE 10 18657 #038-44-1985 L1988 **FM** *020 †18
THOMPSON, Sue Wilkinson. ■ 18657 #023-01-1977 L1978 **GP OS** *020
WALKER, William Rost. 886 SR 6 W, FL 4 18657 #012-01-1982 L1984 **OBG NTR** *020 †30
WEINTRAUB, Harvey. 181 W TIOGA ST, CHILDREN'S SERVICE CENTER 18657 #041-02-1961 L1962 **CHP P** *020 †75
WILLIAMS, Daniel Chowen. 71 HOLLOW CREST RD, STE 3 18657 #023-07-1999 L2002 **MPD** *020 †20,55
ZURAD, Edward Gerald. 880 SR 6 W 18657 #041-02-1982 L1983 **FM OM** *020 †18

TURTLE CREEK — ALLEGHENY

DAMESHEK, H Lee. ■ 15145 #024-07-1963 L1966 **HO** *071 †20
VASUDEVAN, Sapna. 112 PENN AVENUE EXT 15145 #495-37-1990 L2000 **IM** *020 †20

TYRONE — BLAIR

BASILE, Joseph Anthony. 3 HOSPITAL DR, CLAY AVENUE MEDICAL CENTER 16686 #561-17-1970 L1973 **ORS** *020
BAUMGARTEN, Thomas. 1 HOSPITAL DR, TYRONE HOSPITAL 16686 #308-03-1980 L1984 **IM** *020 †20
BAUMGARTEN, Thomas Wm. 1 HOSPITAL DR 16686 #025-01-1948 L1949 **GS** *020 †85
BENDER, Barry Lee. 3 HOSPITAL DR, CLAY AVENUE MEDICAL CENTER 16686 #041-13-1975 L1977 **CD IM** *075
BLACK, Howard Matthew. 1 HOSPITAL DR 16686 #024-07-1986 L1987 **CRS GS** *020 †85,10
DE JULIA, Jerome Joseph. 3 HOSPITAL DR, TYRONE MEDICAL ASSOCIATES 16686 #561-25-1986 L1993 **IM** *020
DINGER, John Michael. 1 HOSPITAL DR 16686 #041-12-1985 L1986 **AN** *020 †05
FRYE, Veryl Fell, Jr. 1 HOSPITAL DR 16686 #020-02-1962 L1987 **EM GS** *020 †85
FUGATE, Howard, III. 1 HOSPITAL DR 16686 #041-02-1983 L1984 **IM** *020 ‡
HEIMER, Jeffrey Lewis. 1 HOSPITAL DR 16686 #041-14-1982 L1983 **OPH** *020 †35
JOHNSON, John Harlem. 1 HOSPITAL DR, TYRONE HOSP 16686 #047-05-1987 L1989 **AN** *020 †05
LEVINSON, Lawrence Steven. 1 HOSPITAL DR 16686 #308-03-1980 L1983 **IM FM** *020 ‡
LEWIS, Kathryn Huxtable. ■ 16686 #008-01-1959 L1966 **PD GPM** *071 †55
LINDSAY, David Allen. 1 HOSPITAL DR, TYRONE HOSPITAL 16686 #308-11-1984 L1986 **FM EM** *020 †18
PARENTE, Romulo Quezado. 2 HOSPITAL DR, TYRONE HOSPITALMED CTR 16686 #187-10-1968 L1975 **GP** *020
PARKER, Gerald Belmont. ■ 16686 #041-02-1988 L2002 **MG** *020 †20
PATEL, Kishor D. 3 HOSPITAL DR, TYRONE MED ASSOC 16686 #495-48-1982 L1992 **PD** *020 †55
PAZMINO, Roy Rolando. 2 HOSPITAL DR 16686 #035-46-1984 L1988 **GYN** *020 †30
SANTILLAN, Victor H. 1 HOSPITAL DR 16686 #737-03-1971 L1976 **GS GP** *020 †85
WIEGERING, Carlos. 2 HOSPITAL DR 16686 #847-04-1971 L1977 **GS IM** *020

ULSTER — BRADFORD

BIANCARELLI, Joseph Paul. RR 1 BOX 13, SHESHEQUIN RD 18850 #422-01-1991 L1994 **IM** *020
LEE, Noelle Elizabeth. ■ 18850 #041-14-2007 L2007 **FP** *012

UNION CITY — CRAWFORD

ALLANIGUE, Rogelio M. 65 E HIGH ST 16438 #748-01-1967 L1972 **IM** *020 †20
CRUZ, Rogelio A. 20 W HIGH ST 16438 #748-01-1958 L1968 **GS GP** *071
GURDJIAN, Edwin Stephens. RR 1 BOX 68 16438 #025-07-1961 L1970 **NS** *020 †25
KING, Andrew Wm. 130 N MAIN ST, UNION CITY FAMILY PRACTICE 16438 #023-12-1988 L1992 **FSM** *020 †18
MOORE, Nathan Marc. 130 N MAIN ST, BOX 111 16438 #041-09-1991 L1993 **FM** *020 †18

UNION DALE — SUSQUEHANNA

HUNTER, Robert Matthew. ■ 18470 #041-13-1988 L1991 **IM** *020 †20
KALLISH, Marvin Newton. ■ 18470 #041-02-1958 L1959 **ORS** *020 †40

UNIONTOWN — FAYETTE

AKHTAR, Naeem. 300 SPRING CREEK LN 15401 #704-16-1982 L1999 **AN** *020
ALLEN, Janice G. 1 S MOUNT VERNON AVE 15401 #043-01-1976 L1977 **IM** *020 †20

ASTHANA, Shobha. 500 W BERKELEY ST 15401 #495-21-1978 L1989 **N PD** *020 †55,75

BALASUBRAMANIAM, M. 140 WAYLAND SMITH DR 15401 #495-61-1966 L1990 **PD** *020 †55

BALASUBRAMANIAN, Raj. 300 SPRING CREEK LN 15401 #495-59-1989 L1993 **GE** *020 †20

BALASUBRAMANIAN, M. 140 WAYLAND SMITH DR, UNIONTOWN MEDICAL PAVILLIO 15401 #495-33-1979 L1984 **PTH** *062 †50

BALL, Brandon Michael. 205 EASY ST STE 202 15401 #055-01-1996 L2001 **GS** *020 †85

BARANOWSKI, Ursula. 140 N BEESON AVE 15401 #759-01-2002 L2003 **FM** *020 †18

BHATT, Naresh Indravadan. 60B CONTINENTAL ONE, LEBANON AVENUE 15401 #496-38-1972 L1977 **END** *020 †20 ‡

BLAKE, Paul Maxwell, III. 500 W BERKELEY ST, UNIONTOWN HOSPITAL 15401 #055-01-1999 L2006 **IM** *020 †20

BLASS, David Chesney. 205 EASY ST, STE 202 15401 #055-01-1971 L1971 **EM GS** *020 †85

BLUMENSCHEIN, Gertrude. 30 DELAWARE AVE 15401 #041-12-1950 L1951 **FM** *071 †18

BOBAK, Wladyslaw. 500 W BERKELEY ST 15401 #759-01-1975 L1983 **IM** *020 †20

BONADIO, Peter M. 2 W MAIN ST 15401 #041-12-1968 L1969 **DR** *020 †80

BORLAND, Randall David. 205 EASY ST, STE 105 15401 #038-40-1987 L1996 **PM** *020 †60

BRAUN, Jean B. 105 BIERER LN LOWR LEVEL 15401 #012-01-1968 L1971 **D** *020 †15 ‡

BRINKLEY, Ben Paul. 253 S MOUNT VERNON AVE, FAMILY BEHAVIORAL RESOURCE 15401 #048-04-1978 L2003 **P** *020 †75

CALABRESE, Charles R. 300 SPRING CREEK LN 15401 #028-78-1986, ▲ L1987 **GE IM** *020 †20

CAMELE, Robert Alan. 2 W MAIN ST, STE 110 15401 #055-01-1981 L1983 **DR** *020 †80

CARDENAS, Florencio Pajar. 205 EASY ST, 101 PROFESSIONAL PLAZA 15401 #748-01-1963 L1970 **U** *020

CARVER, Margaret A. ■ 15401 #041-12-1950 L1951 **GYN** *071 †30

CONLEY, Sean Michael. 500 W BERKELEY ST 15401 #041-14-1998 L2000 **FM** *020 †18 ‡

CONTE, Corinne Cecelia. 140 N BEESON AVE 15401 #041-14-1984 L1985 **IM** *020 †20

CUTLIP, Marija. 100 NEW SALEM RD 15401 #957-02-1989 L2003 **P** *020 †75

DALESSIO, Anthony. 500 W BERKELEY ST, UNIONTOWN HOSPITAL 15401 #016-42-1993 L1995 **EM** *020 †16

DIXIT, Niranjan D. 211 EASY ST, 220 PROFESSIONAL PLAZA II 15401 #495-23-1966 L1980 **IM PUD** *020 †20 ‡

EBERTS, Brian Wesley. 100 NEW SALEM RD, CRCSI 15401 #041-12-1986 L1988 **P** *020 †75

FELIX, Sherif Albert. 500 W BERKELEY ST 15401 #915-02-1978 L1989 **AN** *020 †05 ‡

FIALA, Anita Georgine. 86 MCCLELLANDTOWN RD 15401 #055-01-1992 L1995 **FM** *020 †18

FLORES, Concepto Monje. 315 MORGANTOWN 15401 #748-01-1968 L1976 **EM IM** *020 †20

GABRIEL, Pete. ■ 15401 #030-06-1966 L1967 **DR** *071 †80

GALLO, James Peter. 649 CHERRY TREE LN 15401 #041-12-1977 L1978 **OPH** *020 †35

GOEBEL, Roger Allen. 500 W BERKELEY ST 15401 #026-04-1983 L1984 **EM** *020 †16

GOODMAN, David Baer. 500 W BERKELEY ST 15401 #041-12-1954 L1955 **IM** *071 †40

HART, Philip Lawrence. 2 W MAIN ST, STE 110 15401 #010-01-1968 L1969 **DR NM** *071 †80

HARTLEY, Paul Alexander. 202 JACOB MURPHY LN, STE 201 15401 #051-01-1984 L1988 **IM ON** *020 †20

HRITZ, Jeffrey Alan. 300 SPRING CREEK LN 15401 #041-12-1985 L1987 **AN** *020 †05

IANNAMORELLI, Anthony S. 104 MCCLELLANDTOWN RD 15401 #041-14-1981 L1983 **ID** *020 †20

JAMES, Jeffrey Robt. 280 MCCLELLANDTOWN RD, STE A 15401 #041-09-1991 L1994 **ID** *020 †20

JANICIJEVIC, Milena. 500 W BERKELEY ST, DEPT ANESTHESIA 15401 #957-02-1975 L1980 **AN** *020 †05

JIN, Byunghak. 126 BARY LN 15401 #583-02-1963 L1972 **GS OS** *071 †85

JOSHI, Kishor Eknath. 25 HIGHLAND PARK DR, STE 201 15401 #495-23-1965 L1973 **IM CD** *020 †20

JOSHI, Usha K. PO BOX 726 15401 #495-20-1969 **PD GP** *020

JUNEJA, Manie. 202 JACOB MURPHY LN, STE 201 15401 #495-45-1997 L2002 **IM IMG** *020 †20

KAPHENGST, Karla J. 86 MCCLELLANDTOWN RD 15401 #024-05-1997 L2005 **FM** *020 †18

KAPLAN, Richard S. 60 CONNELLSVILLE ST STE D, UNIONTOWN MEDICAL REHAB PC 15401 #011-02-1990 L1995 **PM AM** *020 †60

KHOURY EDDE, Pierre. 205 EASY ST STE 108, PROFESSIONAL PLZ I 15401 #605-01-1997 L2002 **PCC SME** *020 †20

KIM, Myoung Sup. 121 PROFESSIONAL PLAZA 15401 #583-02-1960 L1976 **OBG** *071

KRAUS, John Francis. 300 SPRING CREEK LN 15401 #041-12-1983 L1984 **AN** *020 †05 ‡

KUNKEL, Mary E Harvey. ■ 15401 #041-07-1952 L1953 **IM** *071

LEE, Kuk Seung. 20 HIGHLAND PARK DR, STE 301 15401 #583-12-1973 L1990 **PM** *020 †60

LEE, Ying Pan. 205 EASY ST 15401 #242-28-1953 L1966 **GS GP** *071

LENGYEL, Robert John. 2 W MAIN ST, STE 110 15401 #023-12-1990 L1992 **DR** *020 †80

LOBO, Ronald Patrick. 100 NEW SALEM RD, STE 116 15401 #704-02-1990 L1997 **P** *020 †75

MAENDEL, Christopher M. 500 W BERKELEY ST 15401 #035-03-1994 L1997 **FM** *020 †18

MANDAVA, Karuna Sree. 500 W BERKELEY ST, THE UNIONTOWN HOSPITAL 15401 #495-50-1994 L2000 **N CN** *100 †75

MARQUEZ, Pedro A. 2 W MAIN ST, STE 416 15401 #264-01-1963 L1970 **DR** *071 †80

MBOCK-THERMITUS, S A. 140 WAYLAND SMITH DR 15401 #495-44-1996 L2001 **PD** *020 †55

MC MONAGLE, Carey Lee. 650 CHERRY TREE LN 15401 #041-09-1974 L1975 **IM** *020 †20

MEDINA, Roldan Garrido. 60 CONNELLSVILLE ST 15401 #748-02-1964 L1970 **GS** *020 ‡

MITCHELL, William Jos. 180 N GALLATIN AVE 15401 #010-02-1955 L1966 **ORS** *020 †40

MOORE, Charles A. 2 HIGHLAND PARK DR 15401 #055-01-1984 L1988 **OPH** *020 †35

MORRISON, Serena Ann. 2 HIGHLAND PARK DR 15401 #010-02-2001 L2007 **OPH** *020

MURELLO, David Michael. 650 CHERRY TREE LN 15401 #041-14-1977 L1978 **CD IM** *020 †20 ‡

NADARAJAH, Ravindran. 160 WAYLAND SMITH DR, STE 204 15401 #539-06-1991 L2001 **OTO A** *020 †45

NAHHAS, Daniel Elias. 205 EASY ST STE 204, OB/GYN-PROFESSIONAL PLAZA 15401 #605-01-1990 L1999 **OBG** *020 †30

NELSON, Owen A. 150 WAYLAND SMITH DR, # A 15401 #005-18-1978 L1980 **ORS** *020 †40

NGUYEN, Duy B. 169 S MT VERNON AVE 15401 #942-01-1970 L1995 **PD** *020 †55

NOCHE, Cesar N. 500 W BERKELEY ST 15401 #748-01-1961 L1979 **FM** *071 †18 ‡

OLIVERIO, Anthony John. 10 HIGHLAND PARK DR 15401 #055-01-1967 L1974 **OTO GP** *020 †45

PATEL, Subodh G. 205 EASY ST, STE 106 15401 #495-22-1974 L1979 **U NEP** *020 †95

PATHAK, Praveen Chandra. 25 HIGHLAND PARK DR, STE 200 15401 #025-07-1997 L2002 **CHP P** *020 †75

PATNAM, Sridhar Venkata. 202 JACOB MURPHY LN, STE 201 15401 #495-21-1978 L1985 **IM** *020 †20

PATRICIO, Alejandro M. 25 HIGHLAND PARK DR 15401 #748-07-1961 L1973 **OBG EM** *020

PERACHA, Sajid Mumtaz. 100 WOODLAWN AVE, STE 300 15401 #704-16-1989 L2000 **HO** *020 †20

PERRY, Evelyn Skeen. 500 W BERKELEY ST, DEPT OF PATH 15401 #027-01-1990 L1999 **PTH** *020 †50

PINEDA, Honorio Gueco. 500 W BERKELEY ST 15401 #748-08-1963 L1977 **GS CD** *075

PISH, Richard Jos. 20 HIGHLAND PARK DR, STE 202 15401 #041-14-1985 L1986 **IM** *020 †20

POPAT, Rajnikant N. 104 DELAWARE AVE STE 244 15401 #495-01-1967 L1993 **OBG GPM** *020 †30

POPE, Mary Anne. 125 CHAFFEE ST 15401 #055-01-1981 L1987 **CHP P** *020

PRESSMAN, Ari Edward. 104 DELAWARE AVE, STE 100 15401 #065-09-1995 L2002 *020 †40

PUJANI, Perveen Ali B. ■ 15401 #704-02-1986 L2004 **PD** *075 †55

REILLY, Michael Jos. 205 EASY ST STE 202 15401 #038-43-1981 L1986 **AS GS** *020 †85

REILLY, Phillip Eugene. 7 S MOUNT VERNON AVE 15401 #030-06-1966 L1967 **GP EM** *020 †18

RODRIGUEZ-FLORES, May. 315 MORGANTOWN ST STE 7000 15401 #748-08-1971 L1982 **FM** *020 †18

RUTHARDT, Frederick, Jr. 300 SPRING CREEK LN 15401 #041-02-1983 L1984 **GE IM** *020 †20

SAEED, Atif. 140 N BEESON AVE 15401 #704-02-1989 L1998 **ID** *020 †20

SARADAR, Riad. 25 HIGHLAND PARK DR # 203 15401 #875-01-1971 L1973 **IM** *020 †20

SAVARIRAYAN, Sunil S. 205 EASY ST, STE 101 15401 #495-40-1991 L1998 **U** *020 †95

SHAIKH, Qamar Ul Islam. 100 WOODLAWN AVE, STE 275 15401 #704-02-1986 L2004 **NPM PD** *020 †55

SHAPIRO, Robert Edward. 211 EASY ST 15401 #055-01-2000 L2005 **OBG** *020 †30

SINGH, Vijai Pal. 500 W BERKELEY ST, UNIONTOWN HOSPITAL 15401 #495-03-1963 L1973 **DR RO** *020

SLOAN, Charles Robt. 500 W BERKELEY ST 15401 #041-12-1955 L1956 **GP** *071

SOBOL, Aaron Lee. 139 W FAYETTE ST 15401 #041-14-1996 L1996 **OPH** *020 †20

SPINUZZA, Thomas John. 2 W MAIN ST, STE 110 15401 #041-02-1983 L1985 **DR** *020 †80

SRIDHARAN, Malini. 100 WOODLAWN AVE, STE 275 15401 #495-09-1972 L1986 **PD** *020 †55

STOKES, Robert Fraser. 300 SPRING CREEK LN, STE 201 15401 #041-01-1988 L1993 **GE IM** *020 †20

SYED, Ghousia Parveen. 140 WAYLAND SMITH DR 15401 #495-21-1978 L1996 **PD** *020 †55

TAGHIZADEH, Firooz. 205 EASY ST, STE 107 15401 #517-03-1966 L1979 **GS** *020 †85

TAYLOR, Judith Elizabeth. 20 HIGHLAND PARK DR, ALBERT GALLATIN HOSPICE 15401 #919-02-1978 L1988 **RO PLM** *020 †80

TEICH, Bruce Edward. 500 W BERKELEY ST 15401 #041-13-1981 L1988 **EM FM** *020 †18

THOMAS, Biju Koshy. 211 EASY ST 15401 #495-96-1995 L2002 **GS** *012

TIMOTHY, Sheila H. 2 HIGHLAND PARK DR STE 201 15401 #495-37-1972 L1993 **PD** *020 †55

TRIPATHI, Gauri Satish. 100 WOODLAWN AVE, STE 300 15401 #495-98-1987 L1995 **HO** *020 †20

TROPP, Rory. 500 W BERKELEY ST, ATTN: MEDICAL STAFF OFFICE 15401 #035-08-1983 L1992 **EM** *020 †16

TTOFI, Christopher S. 500 W BERKELEY ST 15401 #019-02-1990 L1998 **APM** *020

TULLIUS, Charles David. 500 W BERKELEY ST, UNIONTOWN HOSP 15401 #041-02-1989 L1991 **AN** *020 †05

VANEK, Josef Jan. 205 EASY ST STE 202 15401 #035-15-1989 L1995 **GS TS** *020 †85

VILLAVICENCIO-NOCHE, L. 500 W BERKELEY ST 15401 #748-01-1961 L1974 **EM FM** *020 †18

WACHTEL, Andrew S. 500 W BERKELEY ST 15401 #048-04-1950 L1954 **P U** *040 †75

YADAGANI, Veerunna C. 205 EASY ST 15401 #305-01-1992 L1995 **CD** *020 †20

ZUBCHEVICH, Emira D. RR 6 15401 #154-07-1943 L1964 **P CHP** *071 †75

UNIVERSITY PARK – CENTRE

FAISON, Hattie Mae. UNIV HEALTH SERVICES, ROOM 140 RITENOUR BLDG 16802 #036-01-1980 L1983 **IM** *020 †20

HANDTE, Gordon Carl. 33 RITENOUR HEALTH CTR 16802 #010-01-1980 L1985 **PTH FOP** *020 †50 ‡

HEINBACH, Robt Allen, Jr. 124 RITENOUR BLDG, PENN STATE UNIV WMEN HLTH 16802 #041-13-1977 L1978 **GYN** *020 †30

JOHNSON, Ellen I. 311 MOORE BLDG, UNIVERSITY 16802 #010-02-1977 L1987 **P** *020 †75

KAMEROW, Harry Nachlas. 33 RITENOUR HEALTH CTR 16802 #010-01-1985 L1991 **PTH IM** *020 †50

KOLAR, Brian Jos. 33 RITENOUR HEALTH CTR 16802 #028-02-1992 L1997 **PTH** *020 †50

LOGAN, Lewis Paul. 143 RITENOUR BUILDING, UNIVERSITY HEALTH SERVICE 16802 #041-14-1978 L1979 **EM FM** *020 †16,18

MURRAY, Paul Dennis. 33 RITENOUR HEALTH CTR 16802 #030-05-1997 L2003 **PCP** *020 †50

SCHIFF, Steven John. 212 EARTH ENGINEERNG SCNCS, PENN STATE UNIV 16802 #036-07-1980 L1988 **NS NSP** *050 †25

SPEAR, Margaret Ellen. 216 RITENOUR BUILDING, PENN STATE U HLTH SRVCS 16802 #035-47-1977 L1988 **IM GYN** *020 †20

TINGLEY, Stephen Thatcher. PENN STATE UNIV, RITENOUR BLDG 16802 #041-02-1986 L1987 **FM** *020 †18

VAUTOUR, Raymond Jos. 33 RITENOUR HEALTH CTR 16802 #024-05-1986 L1991 **PTH** *020 †50

UPLAND – DELAWARE

BANGERA, Natasha. POB I STE 302, CROZER-CHESTER MEDICAL CEN 19013 #496-31-2003 L2007 **PD** *012

GUPTA, Dimpy. POB I STE 302, CROZER-CHESTER MEDICAL CEN 19013 #495-35-2001 L2007 **PD** *012

PANITHI, Ranjani. POB I STE 302, CROZER-CHESTER MEDICAL CEN 19013 #495-21-2004 L2007 **PD** *012

SANAKA, Sirish. BROAD AND VINES ST 19013 #495-65-2000 L2003 **IM** *100 †20

SERU, Saritha. POB I STE 302, CROZER-CHESTER MEDICAL CEN 19013 #495-11-2003 L2007 **PD** *012

SYED, Salma Sumrana Khuda. POB I SUITE 302, CROZER-CHESTER MC 19013 #496-44-2006 L2008 *012

UPPER BLACK EDDY – BUCKS

HEINZ, Kristann. ■ 18972 #041-01-2002 L2002 **GPM** *020

■ = Address Information Privacy Protected

HOLLAND-HULL, Norman E. ■ 18972 #407-16-1959 L1963 **P** *020
JETTE, Christine Ann. ■ 18972 #054-04-2008 *012

UPPER DARBY – DELAWARE

AMONI, Samuel Sunday. 6800 MARKET ST, WINDELL MURPHY MD AND ASS 19082 #024-05-1968 L1972 **OPH GPM** *020 †35
ANTHONY, Eleanor M. ■ 19082 #041-01-1941 L1943 **IM PUD** *071
ASAMOA, Godson Kande K. 7408 W CHESTER PIKE 19082 #412-01-1990 L2001 **PD** *020 †55
BEBOS, Achilles. ■ 19082 #041-15-2007 L2007 **EM** *012
BOBB, Marvin L. ■ 19082 #041-09-1951 L1958 **IM CD** *075
BOYLE, Denis Andrew. 111 LONG LN 19082 #041-02-1948 L1949 **PM R** *071 †60
BOYLE, Denis Andrew, Jr. 111 LONG LN 19082 #010-02-1980 L1981 **PM** *020
CHANG, Suk Chul. 382 AVON RD 19082 #583-02-1948 L1970 **PTH** *020 †50
CHUNG, Insung. ■ 19082 #041-15-2006 L2006 **AN** *012
CIRIGLIANO, Danl Anthony. 67 LONG LN, STE 200 19082 #305-01-1982 L1985 **PM** *020
EDMONDSON, Andrew Charles. ■ 19082 #041-01-2008 *012
EVERTS, Leslie Elizabeth. 1 S STATE RD, STE A 19082 #041-02-1990 L1992 **FM** *020 †18
HART, Gerard Thos. 54 GARRETT RD, CLINIC CARE ASSOCS UNIV PA 19082 #033-06-1983 L1984 **FM** *075 †18
HSIEH, Yehchiu. 51 HAMPDEN RD 19082 #385-02-1958 L1971 **PD** *020 †55
ISAJIW, George. 7012 PENARTH AVE 19082 #041-02-1970 L1971 **IM GP** *020 †20
ISLAM, Kazi Monirul. 392 AVON RD 19082 #160-06-1975 L1994 **PD** *020 †55
JUNEJA, Ish. ■ 19082 #495-36-1964 L1974 **N IM** *075
KALTSIDIS, Charalampos. ■ 19082 #418-02-1995 **IM** *100
KAUR, Paramjit. ■ 19082 #495-77-1999 L2006 **GS** *100 †85
KINDER, Roy Russell, Jr. 35 BRANDON RD 19082 #055-01-1970 L1972 **D** *020 †15 ‡
KUNTZ, Andrew Frederic. ■ 19082 #051-01-2005 L2005 **ORS** *012
MALOLES, Orlando Z, Jr. ■ 19082 #748-08-1977 L1983 **FM** *020 †18 ‡
MARKAKI, Vassiliki E. ■ 19082 #418-01-1990 **P** *100
MARTINEZ, Augusto R. PO BOX 418, 7000 LUDLOW ST 19082 #649-14-1981 L1988 **PD** *020 †55
MATHEW, Sara. ■ 19082 #041-13-2006 **IM** *012
MCMENAMIN, Joseph Patrick. ■ 19082 #041-01-1978 L1981 **LM** *075
MURPHY, Windell Henry. 6800 MARKET ST 19082 #035-46-1981 L1983 **OPH** *020 †35
NGUYEN, Sandy Loan. ■ 19082 #041-13-2005 **FP** *012
PHAN, Nghia. 6800 MARKET ST, # 4H 19082 #041-01-1972 L1979 **IM PD** *020 †20
PIDIKITI, Ravindernath. ■ 19082 #495-21-1979 L2004 **IM** *012
RAAB, David C. 109 N FAIRVIEW AVE 19082 #041-77-2001, ▲ L2001 *020
SASAN, Amritpal Singh. ■ 19082 #495-10-1992 L2007 **P** *012
SIGURDARDOTTIR, Laufey Yr. 34TH ST & CIVIC CTR BLVD, DIV NEURO 19082 #484-01-1993 L2000 **CHN** *100 †55,75
SRIVASTAVA, Brij Behari L. 434 LONG LN 19082 #649-33-1980 L1986 **IM ON** *020
STRAHS, Gerald. 1 N LINDEN AVE 19082 #649-33-1980 L1981 **IM FM** *062 †28
TSIRAKOGLOU, Nikolaos. 792 GARRETT RD 19082 #418-02-1965 L1983 **OBG** *071
WEISS, E Norman. ■ 19082 #041-77-1972, ▲ L1973 **GP** *071
WHELAN, Stephen Thos. LUDLOW&BRANDON RD 19082 #041-01-1940 L1941 **D** *071 †15
ZACHARATOS, Mario Alexand. ■ 19082 #041-14-2007 L2007 **FP** *012

UPPER HOLLAND – BUCKS

AQUINO, Michael A L. ■ 19053 #748-02-1994 L1998 **IM** *020 †20

UPPER SAINT CLAIR – ALLEGHENY

COOK, Chris Cecil. ■ 15241 #055-02-1997 L2006 **TS** *012 †85
MC CARTER, John Christian. 2600 OLD WASHINGTON RD, MEDEXPRESS SOUTH HILLS, LL 15241 #038-43-1997 L2002 **EM** *020 †16

UWCHLAND – CHESTER

TAYLOR, Terrelynn Ann. ■ 19480 #055-02-1997 L1999 **FM** *020 ‡

VALENCIA – BUTLER

KAHN, Yunkoo Raymond. ■ 16059 #583-02-1951 L1964 **GS ORS** *071
LIDDELL, Joseph S. 267 KYLE RD 16059 #041-12-1941 L1942 **EM FM** *071
NUNNA, Sitalakshmi C. ■ 16059 #495-11-1962 L1973 **GP** *071
RAWA, Randy Scott. ■ 16059 #041-14-1994 L1998 **AN** *020 †05
WARGO, Peter John. ■ 16059 #041-12-1946 L1947 **OBG GP** *071

VALLEY FORGE – CHESTER

CHANCHIEN, Laura Jahlin. PO BOX 851, ABC BOARD OF INTL MINISTRI 19482 #034-01-1995 L1998 **FM** *020 †18
COHEN, Allan Mayer. ■ 19481 #041-09-1964 L1968 **DR VIR** *040 †80
PARAJON, David Gustavo. ■ 19482 #038-06-1993 L1993 **GPM** *020 †20

VALLEY VIEW – SCHUYLKILL

HARRING, Maynard Lenwood. ■ 17983 #041-13-1959 L1960 **GP** *071
LUPOLD, Georgetta Diane. 105 W MAIN ST 17983 #041-02-1974 L1975 **FM** *020 †18

VANDERBILT – FAYETTE

RITTENHOUSE, David Willia. ■ 15486 #041-02-2006 L2006 **GS** *012

VANDERGRIFT – WESTMORELAND

LAMPERT, Dana Mirela. 235 LONGFELLOW ST 15690 #781-01-1995 L2001 **IM** *020 †20
LUNDIE, William Mc Kenzie. 134 WASHINGTON AVE 15690 #010-01-1962 L1968 **IM** *071 †20
ONG, Michael Co. 235 LONGFELLOW ST 15690 #748-01-1991 L1998 **IM** *020 †20
PATEL, Mohan Maganlal. 235 LONGFELLOW ST 15690 #917-01-1977 L1980 **IM** *020 †20
STRUM, Dwight M. 179 COLUMBIA AVE 15690 #041-12-1962 L1963 **GP** *020

VENETIA – WASHINGTON

ALLISON, Andrew C. ■ 15367 #016-76-1993, ▲ L1994 *020
ARMFIELD, Samuel L, III. ■ 15367 #025-01-1973 L1974 **DR** *071 †80
CLARK, Allan Wm. 267 QUAIL RUN RD 15367 #038-41-1987 L1997 **CHP** *020 †75
CORTINOVIS, Chas Richard. 165 BITTERSWEET CIR 15367 #041-13-1976 L1977 **AN OM** *020 †05,70
HAUS, Harry Louis. 112 BITTERSWEET CIR 15367 #035-03-1986 L1987 **FM** *030 †18
JENIFER, Kip Dean. ■ 15367 #038-43-1994 L1997 **EM** *020 †16
LEE, Peggy Lin. ■ 15367 #041-02-1999 L2001 **D** *020 †15
ROH, Terry Jos. 101 TIMBER OAK CT 15367 #038-45-1987 L1988 **CHP** *020 ‡
ROSE, Brian Edwin. ■ 15367 #021-01-2001 L2005 **EM** *020 †16
SICONOLFI, Ernest Peter. ■ 15367 #041-01-1966 L1968 **DR MDM** *071
SZKLINSKI, Brian Joel. 251 HILL PLACE RD 15367 #041-14-1992 L1994 **FM** *020 †18
TULLOCK, William C. ■ 15367 #047-06-1982 L1984 **AN FSM** *020 †05
WANG, Songtao. ■ 15367 #243-03-1988 L1999 **PTH** *020 †50

VERONA – ALLEGHENY

BALESTRINO, Vincent M. 5769 SALTSBURG RD, MEDICAL ARTS BUILDING 15147 #041-13-1979 L1980 **FM** *020 †18
BROWN, Dana Kenneth. 5769 SALTSBURG RD, RENAISSANCE FAMILY PRACTIC 15147 #038-44-1993 L1995 **FM** *020 †18
BUCHANAN, Gibson Packer. ■ 15147 #023-07-1944 L1948 **PD** *071 †55
BURNS, Ilene Timko. 5769 SALTSBURG RD, RENAISSANCE FAMILY PRACTIC 15147 #023-07-1989 L1991 **FM** *020 †18
CHEPKO, Margaret I W. ■ 15147 #041-09-1946 L1961 **FM EM** *020
GITTINGS, Jean M Ottaway. ■ 15147 #352-11-1948 L1954 **OS** *020
GITTINGS, Paul Edgar. ■ 15147 #041-12-1943 L1944 **OBG OS** *071 †30
HAGBERG, Margaret Mary. 6039 SALTSBURG RD 15147 #016-06-1981 L1983 **OBG** *071 †30
HANNA, Dwight C, III. 500 ROUTE 909 # C-8, LONGWOOD AT OAKMONT 15147 #041-12-1946 L1947 **PS** *071 †85,65
KEVISH, Barbara Sue. 5769 SALTSBURG RD, RENAISSANCE FAMILY PRAC 15147 #041-12-1993 L1995 **FM** *020 †18
LACE, Richard E. ■ 15147 #041-01-1942 L1945 **PD** *071 †55
NEALON-HARMEIER, Rita. ■ 15147 #041-12-1939 L1940 **PD OS** *071
PRIYA, Prabhaka. 6149 SALTSBURG RD 15147 #305-01-1999 L2001 **IM** *020 †20
RICHARDSON, Geo Stevens. ■ 15147 #051-04-1955 L1964 **OS PS** *071 †65
SCARSELLATO, John N. ■ 15147 #561-01-1960 L1963 **OM OBG** *071 †30
SIEBER, William Karl. ■ 15147 #041-12-1941 L1942 **PDS** *071 †85
WHITEFORD, John Kenney. ■ 15147 #041-12-1968 L1969 **EM GS** *075 †16
WILSON, Brian Keith. 5769 SALTSBURG RD, MEDICAL ARTS BUILDING 15147 #024-16-1997 L1999 **FM** *020 †18

VILLANOVA – DELAWARE

AGARWAL, Pasha. ■ 19085 #495-45-1965 L1973 **PTH PCP** *020 †50
ALLES, Steven J. ■ 19085 #035-15-2001 L2001 **GPM** *020 †70
AMEEN, Vanessa Zalena. 2041 STONERIDGE LN 19085 #566-01-1978 L1991 **PD GE** *020 †55
ANTHONY, Forrest Harold. ■ 19085 #040-02-1976 L1984 **IM** *030
BARTONE, Francis F. ■ 19085 #041-02-1957 L1958 **UP GS** *071 †85,95
BELLO, Jean Pauline. 625 RADNOR VALLEY DR 19085 #041-13-1973 L1975 **PHO** *020 †55
BLEIER, Benjamin Saul. ■ 19085 #041-01-2004 L2004 **OTO** *012
BLEIER, Henry Robt. ■ 19085 #035-20-1973 L1974 **P PYG** *040 †75
BOSTIAN, L Edgar. ■ 19085 #056-06-1949 L1969 **P ADM** *071
BUCH, Cathy A. ■ 19085 #035-03-1980 L1983 **OBG IM** *071 †30
BURNS, Carrie. ■ 19085 #033-06-2001 L2004 **IM** *100
CHE, Chau Bao. ■ 19085 #041-15-2008 *012
CRAWFORD, Mary Newell. ■ 19085 #041-01-1949 L1950 **IG BBK** *062 †55
CUI, Chunhua. ■ 19085 #243-55-1993 L2007 **PTH** *012
DESAI, Meena S. 1501 MOUNT PLEASANT RD 19085 #041-07-1986 L1987 **AN PME** *020 †05 ‡
DEWAN, Abha. ■ 19085 #495-77-1984 L2001 **PD** *020 †55
DOEFF, Jan Willem. ■ 19085 #660-01-1955 L1961 **P IMG** *072 †75
EGAN, Michael Frederick. 365 CEDAR LANE 19085 #023-01-1983 L1984 **P** *020 †75
ETEMAD, Kambeze. 2008 STONERIDGE LN 19085 #043-01-1993 L1997 **P** *020
EVANS, Helen Glover. ■ 19085 #051-04-1936 L1969 **IM** *075
EVANS, Jacquelyn Rose. 1623 COUNTY LINE RD 19085 #064-01-1978 L1994 **NPM** *020 †55
FREIMUTH, Erich Jos. ■ 19085 #041-13-1958 L1959 **N** *071 †75
FREIMUTH, Joan Maria Sapp. ■ 19085 #041-13-1957 L1958 **CHP P** *071
FRIEDMAN, Paul Aaron. ■ 19085 #024-01-1969 L1986 **IM OS** *020 †20
GIESECKE, Susan Bennett. ■ 19085 #041-01-1973 L1974 **DR** *062 †80 ‡
GOLDENER, John Francis. 217 RADNOR CHESTER RD 19085 #010-02-1974 L1975 **PD OS** *020 †55
HELZNER, Eileen Cohler. ■ 19085 #041-13-1972 L1973 **PA FM** *050 ‡
ILDEFONSO, Valentine T. ■ 19085 #748-01-1953 L1967 **ATP** *071 †50
JACOB, Leonard S. ■ 19085 #041-07-1978 L1979 **PA** *071
JAVA, Domingo J, Jr. ■ 19085 #748-10-1966 L1973 **PTH EM** *020 †50
KATZ, Janice Eileen D. ■ 19085 #041-07-1974 L1975 **IM** *020 †20
KATZ, Richard Hildon. ■ 19085 #041-09-1974 L1975 **PUD** *050 †20
KAUFMANN, Berwind Norman. ■ 19085 #041-01-1956 L1964 **GP EM** *020
KIRKLAND, Michele. ■ 19085 #041-02-1984 L1985 **AN OS** *020 †05
KLINE, Irwin Kaven. ■ 19085 #038-06-1957 L1969 **PTH CLP** *071 †50
KOLFF, Jacob. ■ 19085 #038-06-1965 L1978 **TS** *071 †85,90
KRAIN, Raymond. ■ 19085 #041-09-1951 L1952 **D OS** *020 †15

KUSMIREK, Joanna. ■ 19085 #759-03-1992 L2007 **FM** *020 †18
LAFRANCE, Norman David. 304 GRAMONT LN 19085 #003-01-1977 L1997 **IM NM** *050 †20,28
LEE, David Inkoo. ■ 19085 #005-12-1995 L1997 **U** *020 †95
LIU, Jimin. ■ 19085 #243-43-1983 L1996 **IM** *020 †50
MALIOT, Jerry Clayton. 533 N SPRING MILL RD 19085 #025-07-1972 L2001 **NEP IM** *020 †20
MARCOVICI, Mia. ■ 19085 #781-01-1959 L1969 **CHP P** *020 †75
MAURIELLO, Charles A. PO BOX 570 19085 #041-77-1968, ▲ L1969 **ORS OS** *071
MC SHANE, John Michael. 734 E LANCASTER AVE 19085 #041-13-1987 L1995 **FM FSM** *020 †18
MENDELS, Joe. ■ 19085 #836-02-1961 L1973 **P PA** *050
MONZO, Rosemarie C. ■ 19085 #041-09-1997 L2003 **FM** *020 †18
NOWOSLAWSKI, Joseph F. 1211 LAKEMONT RD 19085 #025-12-1974 L1975 **EM** *020
PARK, Jae Hoon. ■ 19085 #035-19-2006 L2006 **AN** *012
PEDIGO, James Monroe. ■ 19085 #047-06-1960 L1964 **P PYA** *020 ‡
PELLETIER, Glenn Jeffrey. ■ 19085 #032-01-1991 L1998 **TS** *020 †85,90
PELTZ, Dieter Erich. ■ 19085 #407-19-1956 L1963 **PDS GS** *071 †85
PLATT, Marc Jay. 1501 MOUNT PLEASANT RD 19085 #649-14-1981 L1983 **AN IM** *020 †05
PRESSMAN, Edmund Norman. ■ 19085 #041-01-1960 L1961 **AN** *071 †05
PRIVETTE, Melinda Hill. 20 ALDWYN LN, DEPARTMENT OF PSYCHIATRY 19085 #036-01-1987 L2001 **P** *020 †75
RATHER, Manzoor Ahmed. 88 WOODSTONE LN 19085 #495-51-1983 L1998 **IM** *020 †20
ROSATO, Francis Ernest, Jr. ■ 19085 #041-02-1999 L2002 **GS** *100 †85
ROSENBERGER, Melissa Dawn. 1501 MOUNT PLEASANT RD, NOVA ANESTHESIA PROFS, PC 19085 #024-07-2001 L2005 **AN** *020 ‡
SCHERTZMAN, Donald S. 1501 MOUNT PLEASANT RD 19085 #035-06-1982 L2000 **AN** *020 †05
SERRUYA, Mijail Demian. ■ 19085 #043-01-2005 L2007 **N** *012
SERRUYA, Roberto Jose. ■ 19085 #132-06-1970 L1973 **P** *020 †75
SIMMONS, David Alan. ■ 19085 #041-01-1977 L1980 **DIA IM** *020 †20
SOKOL, David Marvin. ■ 19085 #041-09-1965 L1970 **TS** *020 †85,90
STOLOFF, Vanessa Valensi. ■ 19085 #041-02-2000 L2001 **FM** *020 †18 ‡
SYEED, Mehmooda. ■ 19085 #496-01-1986 L2000 **END** *100 †20
TAUB, Rebecca Anne. ■ 19085 #008-01-1978 L1986 **IM** *020 †20
TEPPER, Lloyd Barton. ■ 19085 #024-01-1957 L1976 **OM** *030 †70
TOWNSEND, Arlene J. ■ 19085 #041-09-1979 L1981 **FM** *074 †20
VOJTA, Christopher Locke. 1346 PARTRIDGE LN 19085 #041-01-1995 L1997 **IMG** *020 †20
WALSH, Megan Elizabeth. 800 LANCASTER AVE, VU BOX 0052 19085 #035-19-2008 *012
WEIMER, Susan Minnette. ■ 19085 #005-06-1990 L1996 **P** *100 †75
WINTER, Mark Stephen. ■ 19085 #032-01-1978 L1983 **AN** *020 †05

VINTONDALE – INDIANA

NAYAK, Krishen Kesav. ■ 15961 #495-73-1970 L1989 **P** *020

WALLINGFORD – DELAWARE

ALEXANDER, Paul Gregory. 7 MALLARD MILL RUN 19086 #038-06-1991 L1994 **GP EM** *020
BARTLETT, F Lewis. ■ 19086 #050-02-1951 L1956 **P** *071
BILGUTAY, Sabahattin. ■ 19086 #902-03-1957 L1974 **P** *071
BRANES, Laurel Ann. ■ 19086 #026-02-1981 L1987 **FM** *071
BRITT, Klara. ■ 19086 #759-08-1970 L1980 **IM** *075
CARNAHAN, David H. ■ 19086 #048-14-1998 L2006 **IM** *020 †20
COGBILL, Andrew John. ■ 19086 #005-18-1978 L1997 **AN IM** *071 †20,05
CRIDEN, Louis Everett. 602 W BROOKHAVEN RD 19086 #041-02-1965 L1966 **GYN** *062 †30
DANISH, David Michael. ■ 19086 #038-06-2007 L2007 **P** *012
GLAUSER, Terry Ann. ■ 19086 #041-02-1981 L1983 **PHP PM** *075 †16
GOLDMAN, Richard Jay. ■ 19086 #016-06-1961 L1964 **IM** *071 †20
GOLDSHLAG COOKS, Roberta. ■ 19086 #035-19-1984 **P** *075
GURIJALA, Vidyasagar R. ■ 19086 #495-62-1973 L1982 **P** *020
HOFMEISTER, Eric Paul. 120 N PROVIDENCE RD 19086 #023-12-1993 L2001 **ORS** *020 †40
HUANG, Jui-Han J. ■ 19086 #038-06-1996 L2003 *100 †50
HUSHION, William Francis. ■ 19086 #041-02-1960 L1961 **GP OM** *071
HYLAND, Kristen Anne. ■ 19086 #041-01-2008 *012
JEFFERIS, Tamar Virginia. 19 N PROVIDENCE RD 19086 #020-12-1976 L1977 **EM** *020
JENKINS COTHRAN, Shannon. ■ 19086 #041-02-2004 L2004 **OBG** *012
KARIM, Mohammed Fazlul. ■ 19086 #041-02-1976 L*100
LOCKSLEY, Herbert B. ■ 19086 #024-01-1949 L1952 **NS** *071 †25
MC BRIDE, Thomas Jos. PO BOX 519, 121 E POSSUM HOLLOW RD 19086 #041-02-1948 L1950 **IM OS** *071 †20
MC CADDEN, Jos Aloysius. 613 MORRIS LN 19086 #041-02-1956 L1957 **FM OM** *020 †18
MORLEY, Robert R. ■ 19086 #035-45-1960 L1961 **OBG** *071 †30
MORLEY, S Ann R Mahew. ■ 19086 #035-01-1956 L1960 **OBG FM** *020
MORSE, Steven Dale. 447 SAYBROOK LN 19086 #041-01-1977 L1978 **EM** *020 †20,16
MYINT, Maung A. ■ 19086 #209-01-1977 L1993 **SP** *020 †50
ORSEY, Andrea Dahlman. 100 S PROVIDENCE RD 19086 #008-02-2001 L2001 **PHO** *100 †55
PAIK, Hee Hae. ■ 19086 #583-03-1944 L1970 **IMG** *071
PALOS, Lorraine Cecile. ■ 19086 #041-02-1982 L1983 **PD** *072 †55
RUMSEY, William Potter. ■ 19086 #041-13-1943 L1944 **GM GS** *071 †85
SALAM, Haseeda Abdul. ■ 19086 #495-31-1979 L1992 **IM** *020 †20
SKOBELOFF, Emil Marshall. 103 BRENT DR, STE 5 19086 #041-07-1990 L1992 **EM** *020 †16
SZCZEPANIAK, John P. ■ 19086 #041-09-1943 L1946 **GS GP** *071
TURNER, Joseph Ellis. ■ 19086 #041-09-1945 L1948 **GP** *071
WELSH, Judith B. ■ 19086 #041-01-1966 L1971 **PD** *071 †55
WHITAKER, H Craig. ■ 19086 #041-01-1958 L1959 **OBG** *071 †30
ZHENG, Xinglong. ■ 19086 #243-62-1984 L2003 **PTH** *020 †50

WALNUTPORT – NORTHAMPTON

CRESSMAN, Debra Ellen. 215 N BEST AVE 18088 #041-07-1989 L1991 **FM** *020 †18
HENTOSH, John Paul. ■ 18088 #041-02-1963 L1964 **PD GP** *071 †55
LANGAN, Robert C. 330 N BEST AVE, STE A 18088 #035-03-1996 L2003 **FM** *020 †18
YABLONSKI, Thomas Edward. 215 N BEST AVE 18088 #041-02-1987 L1990 **FM** *020 †18

WARFORDSBURG – FULTON

DE MONTIGNY, Lionel H. ■ 17267 #056-05-1961 L1968 **GPM** *030

WARMINSTER – BUCKS

ARONSHTEYN, Adele Rutman. ■ 18974 #913-05-1957 L1985 **IMG IM** *071
BALINT, Steven Eldon. 995 CAROUSEL DR 18974 #033-06-1994 L1997 **IM** *020 †20
BAXI, Nilay Manojkumar. 866 W BRISTOL RD, VALLEY PEDIATRICS 18974 #047-20-2004 L2007 **PD** *020 †55
BEKEN, Ferhan. 205 NEWTOWN RD, STE 107 18974 #902-21-1985 L1996 **N PME** *020 †75
BETOF, Melissa Lauren. ■ 18974 #041-15-2008 *012
BRECHER, Jeffrey Alan. 205 NEWTOWN RD STE 219 18974 #041-09-1974 L1975 **IM** *020
BRONFMAN, Alexander. 225 NEWTOWN RD 18974 #913-18-1958 L1984 **GP GS** *071
CAHAN, Michael Stuart. 225 NEWTOWN RD 18974 #035-19-1966 L1970 **PD** *020 †55 ‡
CAWLEY, Michael Francis. 1190 OLD YORK RD STE A, HARTSVILLE PROF VILLAGE 18974 #024-16-1984 L1987 **PD PM** *020 †60,55
CHARNEY, Richard Howard. 205 NEWTOWN RD STE 101 18974 #041-02-1970 L1971 **U** *020 †95
CHIN, Byoung-Kwon. 225 NEWTOWN RD 18974 #583-10-1965 L1973 **IM OS** *020 †20
COHEN, Harris Brian. 225 NEWTOWN RD 18974 #041-02-2000 L2001 **FM** *020 †18 ‡
COUSENS, Elisabeth M C. 615 SAINT DAVIDS AVE, WARMINSTER FAMILY PRACTICE 18974 #919-05-1964 L1996 **FM** *020 †18 ‡
DANTULURI, Phani K. 215 NEWTOWN RD 18974 #043-01-1997 L2004 **HS** *020 †40
DOBASH, Gregory Charles. 225 NEWTOWN RD, WARMINSTER HOSPITAL 18974 #041-15-2000 L2002 **FM** *020
DOMBKOSKI, Walter Jos. ■ 18974 #041-13-1955 L1957 **GS** *071 †85
FATIMA, Sumayya. ■ 18974 #496-27-1997 L2004 **IM** *020 †20
GERARD-CIMINERA, Judy Lee. 225 NEWTOWN RD 18974 #041-07-1982 L1983 **FM OM** *020 †18
GOODMAN, Michael Scott. 205 NEWTOWN RD STE 213 18974 #041-02-1976 L1981 **U** *072 †95
GRANDFIELD, Kathryn Laura. ■ 18974 #041-02-2008 *012
GROSS, Maurice David. 225 NEWTOWN RD 18974 #041-13-1979 L1980 **FM PLM** *020 †18
HAMILTON, Jennifer Lynn. 225 NEWTOWN RD, DREXEL FAMILY PRACTICE ASS 18974 #033-06-2001 L2006 **FM** *020 †18
HARRIS, Rosemary Monica. 225 NEWTOWN RD 18974 #041-09-1988 L1992 **FM** *020 †18
HEGEDOSH, Natalia Star. 600 LOUIS DR, STE 206A 18974 #913-70-1985 L2006 **FM** *020 †18
HICKS, Michael James. 225 NEWTOWN RD, WARMINSTER HOSPITAL 18974 #008-02-1978 L1980 **EM IM** *020 †20,16
JAIRAM, Colin Xephary. 225 NEWTOWN RD 18974 #010-03-2005 L2005 **FP** *012
JUDD, James David. 225 NEWTOWN RD 18974 #041-13-1980 L1981 **FM** *020 †18
KAPLAN, Gerald Frank. 225 NEWTOWN RD 18974 #041-02-1968 L1970 **GS** *071 †85
KARABELL, Sheldon. 205 NEWTOWN RD, STE 220 18974 #041-02-1967 L1968 **IM** *020 †20
KNAPP, Michael Allan. 205 NEWTOWN RD STE 219 18974 #021-05-1976 L1979 **IM IMG** *020 †20
LA FLEUR, Carolyn. 225 NEWTOWN RD, WARMINSTER HOSP 18974 #024-07-1981 L1996 **AN** *020 †05
LIEBMAN, Irvin Marvin. 205 NEWTOWN RD STE 216, WARMINSTER, PA 18974 #041-02-1961 L1962 **D AI** *071 ‡
LIEM, Han. ■ 18974 #506-01-1956 L1969 **P** *071 †75
MANN, Harold J. ■ 18974 #041-02-1951 L1952 **OBG** *071 †30
MANUEL, Eduardo B. ■ 18974 #748-01-1967 L1973 **GS IM** *100
MARCELIS, John Francis. 10000 ANNS CHOICE WAY 18974 #041-13-1987 L1990 **IM IMG** *020 †20
MARFATIA, Sudhir K. 168 KASI CIR, STE 217 18974 #495-01-1965 L1973 **CD IM** *071 †20
MARFATIA, Usha Sudhir. 205 NEWTOWN RD, STE 204 18974 #495-01-1971 L1973 **ON HEM** *020 †20
MUNDIATH, Violeta R. 225 NEWTOWN RD 18974 #737-06-1967 L1981 **PTH** *020 †50
NAPER, Kristin Nichole. ■ 18974 #041-02-2003 **GE** *012
NGUYEN, Christopher Vinh. ■ 18974 #041-13-2003 L2003 **SP** *012 †50
OXENBERG, Gary Lee. 225 NEWTOWN RD 18974 #422-01-1980 L1982 **IM** *020
PADDOCK, Brad. 1035 W BRISTOL RD STE B, IVYLAND MED CTR 18974 #041-13-1998 L2000 **FM ADM** *020 †18 ‡
PATEL, Prabha Harshad. 225 NEWTOWN RD 18974 #496-38-1971 L1979 **PTH** *020 †50
PERLMAN, Abraham. ■ 18974 #041-02-1949 L1950 **P** *071 †55,75
PRIVOROTSKY, Galina. 205 NEWTOWN RD, STE 210 18974 #661-01-1988 L1989 **PD** *020 †55
RAVETZ, Paul Lawrence. 615 SAINT DAVIDS AVE 18974 #041-01-1959 L1960 **GP** *020 ‡
SAUL, Michael Gary. ■ 18974 #035-09-1975 L1976 **GP** *071
SAXENA, Varun. 205 NEWTOWN RD STE 217 18974 #495-45-1976 L1978 **CD IM** *020 †20
SCHELKUN, Paul Michael. 158 YORK RD 18974 #001-02-1990 L1991 **OMF CFS** *020
SCHIOWITZ, Robert Fuerth. 205 NEWTOWN RD, STE 108 18974 #041-02-1982 L1984 **GS TRS** *020 †85
SCHWARTZ, Peter L. 10000 ANNS CHOICE WAY, SENIOR CAMPUS PHYSICIANS 18974 #024-07-1976 L1978 **IM** *020 †20
SENSENIG, Rachel Lingwah. ■ 18974 #041-15-2004 L2004 **GS** *012
SHAH, Amit Jitendrakum. 225 NEWTOWN RD, OFFICE OF CLINICAL STAFF S 18974 #033-06-2003 L2007 **M** *100
SHEPARD, Cynthia Ann. 10000 ANNS CHOICE WAY 18974 #033-06-1983 L1997 **IM** *020 †20
SHIPKIN, Paul M. 1200 OLD YORK RD, STE 210 18974 #035-46-1971 L1973 **N OS** *020 †75
SILVERBERG, Alan Lee. 205 NEWTOWN RD, STE 207 18974 #024-01-1978 L1980 **ID IM** *020 †20
SORDONI, Susan F. 225 NEWTOWN RD, WARMINSTER HOSPITAL 18974 #041-07-1997 L2000 **FM** *020
SOWINSKI, Sharon M. 205 NEWTOWN RD, STE 210 18974 #041-77-1999, ▲ L1999 **PD** *020
SUGAR, Ronit Zipora. 205 NEWTOWN RD, STE 108 18974 #041-09-1982 L1984 **GS VS** *020 †85
SWEET, Stephanie. 215 NEWTOWN RD 18974 #035-47-1992 L2000 **HS** *020 †40
SYDNEY, Albert David. 225 NEWTOWN RD 18974 #024-05-1972 L1974 **P** *020 †75
TAX, Richard Loren. 225 NEWTOWN RD 18974 #035-20-1970 L1973 **OPH** *020 †35
TOKAREK, Robert Michael. 1190 OLD YORK RD, ABINGTON DERMATOLOGY 18974 #041-01-1992 L1994 **D** *020 †15
TOLAND, Susan Johanna. ■ 18974 #041-07-1992 *100
URIBE, Leon Camilo. 225 NEWTOWN RD 18974 #264-05-1997 L2006 **FSM** *020 †18
WERNER, Joseph Henry, Jr. 866 W BRISTOL RD, VALLEY PEDIATRICS WARRIN 18974 #041-09-1965 L1966 **PD** *020 †55

WOHL, Milton A. WARMINSTER PROF BLDG, ORTHOPEDIC ASSOCIATES PC 18974 #041-13-1949 L1950 **ORS** *072 †40
YANG, Marjorie Frances Uy. 225 NEWTOWN RD 18974 #748-02-1996 L2005 **FM D** *100
YEH, Julie Ann. 225 NEWTOWN RD 18974 #033-05-2000 L2001 **FM** *040 †18

WARREN – WARREN

AHMAD, Javed. 103 W SAINT CLAIR ST 16365 #495-15-1991 L2003 **FM** *020 †18
AHMED, Niaz. 2 W CRESCENT PARK 12, WARREN GENERAL HOSPITAL 16365 #495-21-1973 L1980 **AN** *020 †05
AL-OMAR, Osama. 410 MARKET ST 16365 #875-02-1996 L2007 **UP U** *020
ALTMAN, Arthur Alan. 2 W CRESCENT PARK 16365 #041-01-1957 L1958 **PTH** *071 †50 ‡
BENTZ, Charles Roger. 2 W CRESCENT PARK, WARREN GEN HOSP 16365 #047-05-1970 L1975 **EM FM** *020 †18
BERTA, Julius Wm. 2 W CRESCENT PARK 16365 #041-12-1968 L1975 **R RO** *020 †80
BEUGER, Mark. 514 W 3RD AVE 16365 #660-07-1988 L1995 **P ADP** *020 †75
BIALAS, Paul Anthony. 103 ST CLAIR ST 16365 #041-02-1973 L1974 **IM** *020 †20
BROWN, John Edward. ■ 16365 #041-13-1954 L1955 **GP AN** *020
CESAR, Isabelita T C. 14 CONEWANGO AVE 16365 #748-01-1977 L1990 **P** *020
CHARBONNEAU, Rene. PO BOX 249 16365 #067-02-1958 **P** *020
CLARK, Edward Coe, Jr. 2 W CRESCENT PARK, RENAL CARE OF WARREN, LLC 16365 #028-02-1971 L1976 **OPH** *020 †35
CLIFFORD, Frank David. 143 PLEASANT DR, FAMILY MEDICINE OF WARREN 16365 #041-02-1980 L1981 **FM** *020 †18
COOMBS, Dale Timothy. 145 PLEASANT DR 16365 #055-02-1991 L1994 **PD** *020 †55
DAVISON, James Marshall. 1401 MARKET ST 16365 #028-79-1979, ▲ L2006 **OBG** *020 †30
DENLINGER, Lee Evans. 2 W CRESCENT PARK 16365 #041-02-1974 L1975 **IM** *020 †20
EIDBO, Joel Richard. 2 W CRESCENT PARK 16365 #026-04-1986 L1992 **PTH** *020 †50 ‡
ENDRES, Jay Evan. 514 W 3RD AVE 16365 #422-01-1982 L1983 **FM** *020 †18
FINO, Julius Anthony. 308 MARKET ST 16365 #041-12-1943 L1944 **OBG U** *071 †30
FLICKINGER, Bridget Biala. ■ 16365 #041-02-2005 L2008 **EM** *012
FURMAN, Donald Jack. PO BOX 727, 315 SECOND AVE 16365 #041-12-1954 L1955 **PTH HMP** *071 †50
GABRESKI, Robert Gregory. 410 QUAKER HILL RD 16365 #561-01-1976 L1979 **IM** *020
GALVAO, Luiz Felipe. 2 W CRESCENT PARK 16365 #187-18-1988 L1997 **IM** *020 †20
GOTTWALD, Dan Henry. 103 W SAINT CLAIR ST, RM 1D 16365 #038-43-1984 L1991 **ORS** *020 †40
GRISHAVER, Herman. ■ 16365 #035-46-1964 L1993 **N** *071 †75
GUPTA, Sarv Krishan. 33 MAIN DR, WARREN STATE HOSPITAL 16365 #495-43-1954 L1973 **P** *020 †75
GUPTA, Vinodini. ■ 16365 #495-12-1964 L1973 **P** *071 †75
HARRINGTON, John Leonard. ■ 16365 #041-12-1955 L1956 **P** *071 †75 ‡
HEINTZMAN, John D. 514 W 3RD AVE 16365 #065-05-1993 L1997 **CHP** *020 †75
IGNACIO, Jose Yap. 2 W CRESCENT PARK 16365 #748-02-1964 L1987 **P** *074
IGNATIUS, Paul Franklin. ■ 16365 #041-01-1968 L1969 **ORS** *071 †40
ISMAIL, Mahmoud I. 2 W CRESCENT PARK, WARREN GENERAL HOSP 16365 #915-03-1989 L2006 **IM IMG** *020 †20
JOHN, John Puthenpurac. 514 W 3RD AVE, DEERFIELD BEHAVIORAL HEALT 16365 #035-06-1991 L1993 **P** *020 †75
JOHNSON, Van Warren. 103 ST CLAIR ST 16365 #036-07-1971 L1972 **ORS** *020 †40
JUSZCZYK, Monika Anna. 2 W CRESCENT PARK, DEPT OF INTERNAL MEDICINE 16365 #759-10-1996 L2007 **IC** *020 †20
KORB, Leroy Jay, Jr. 2 W CRESCENT PARK, CANCER CARE CENTER 16365 #055-01-1986 L1991 **RO U** *020 †80
KOURTU, Mohamed Abdillahi. 2 W CRESCENT PARK, WARREN GENERAL HOSPITAL 16365 #915-02-1987 L1993 **AN** *020 †05
KUHNEN, Walter H. 2 W CRESCENT PARK 16365 #010-02-1975 L1983 **GP DR** *020 †80
LAPINSKI, Michael Walter. 2 W CRESCENT PARK 16365 #033-05-1974 L1978 **PTH CLP** *020 †50
LAREAU, Lawrence Germain. 2 W CRESCENT PARK 16365 #041-02-1983 L1985 **DR** *020 †80
LEVINSON, Alan H. 33 MAIN DR 16365 #165-04-1969 L1980 **PM NM** *100
MAC KENZIE, Chas Edward. ■ 16365 #041-09-1965 L1967 **GS** *071 †85
MALJOVEC, Joseph John, Jr. 1401 MARKET ST STE B, CONEWANGO CENTER 16365 #041-13-1979 L1980 **OBG** *020 †30
MC AFOOS, Gary Lynn. 103 W SAINT CLAIR ST, RM 2D 16365 #041-14-1983 L1984 **GS** *020 †85
MC CONNELL, David M, Jr. 145 PLEASANT DR 16365 #036-07-1971 L1972 **PD** *020 †55
MC INTOSH, Brian Fred. 2 W CRESCENT PARK, WARREN GENERAL 16365 #041-13-1974 L1975 **EM** *020 †18,16
MC LEAN KLEIN, Alexandria. PO BOX 249 16365 #041-13-1945 L1947 **P N** *030 †75
MC NETT, Dale La Rue. 1043 E 5TH AVE 16365 #041-12-1976 L1977 **IM GE** *020 †20
MEGILL, Douglas Flint. 2 W CRESCENT PARK, WARREN GENERAL 16365 #010-02-1979 L1989 **EM OM** *030 †16
MORGAN, Walter Raymond. 2 W CRESCENT PARK 16365 #041-02-1957 L1958 **U** *071 †95
NGUYEN, Patrick P. 143 PLEASANT DR 16365 #048-78-1995, ▲ L1998 *020
NORTON, Charles Bryan, Jr. 514 W 3RD AVE, DEERFIELD BEHAVIORAL HEALT 16365 #036-07-1966 L1975 **P** *020 †75
O'BRIEN, Timothy James. 103 W SAINT CLAIR ST 16365 #041-02-1990 L1992 **OPH** *020 †35
OLUWOLE, Olakunle Kayode. 103 W SAINT CLAIR ST RM 2D, WARREN SURGEONS INC 16365 #035-01-1997 L2006 **GS CCS** *020 †85
PIERSON, Gregory Gerard. 2 W CRESCENT PARK 16365 #041-13-1986 L1992 **EM** *020 †18,16
PRICE, Robert Keith. 143 PLEASANT DR 16365 #051-01-1981 L1982 **FM AN** *020 †18
RAO, Nagaraj Shikarpur L. 33 MAIN DR, WARREN STATE HOSPITAL 16365 #495-37-1970 L1984 **FM** *020
RASSIGA, Anne Louise. 2 W CRESCENT PARK, WARREN GENERAL HOSPITAL 16365 #024-01-1966 L1997 **HO IM** *020 †20
ROBERTSON, John Lampe. 44 GLADE AVE 16365 #041-01-1954 L1955 **IM** *071
ROEDERER, Ernesto. 514 W 3RD AVE, DEERFIELD BEHAVIORAL HEAL 16365 #008-01-1986 L1993 **P** *020 †75
SANGHI, Jodh K. 106 PENNSYLVANIA AVE W 16365 #495-12-1949 L1973 **P** *075 †75 ‡
SCHULTZ, William George, Jr. 2 W CRESCENT PARK 16365 #035-15-1996 L2000 **FM** *020 †18
SERENA, Thomas E. 103 W SAINT CLAIR ST, RM 2D 16365 #041-14-1986 L1987 **GS VS** *020 †85
SHARAF, Robert George. 2 W CRESCENT PARK 16365 #041-13-1962 L1965 **FPG** *020 †18
SIMONSEN, Ronald William. 2 W CRESCENT PARK 16365 #041-13-1962 L1965 **FPG** *020 †18
SMITH, Robert G. PO BOX 6 16365 #035-06-1949 L1957 **GS** *071

STANTON, Timothy Scott. 114 MAIN AVE 16365 #010-01-1991 L1994 **IM** *020 †20
SUTTON, John Joseph, Jr. 103 W SAINT CLAIR ST 16365 #035-09-1988 L1994 **FM** *020 †18
THOMAS, Sunny Arikupurath. 145 PLEASANT DR 16365 #495-44-1982 L1993 **PD** *020 †55 ‡
TOOTELL, Mason. ■ 16365 #038-06-2005 L2007 **FM** *020 †18
VAN DAMIA, Donald N. ■ 16365 #028-34-1965 L1966 **FM** *071 †18
VASILE, Alexandru Lucian. 514 W 3RD AVE, TUFTS NEW ENGLAND MEDICAL 16365 #781-01-1996 L2001 **CHP** *100
WALTERS, William Stuart. 514 W 3RD AVE 16365 #041-12-1946 L1947 **FM GS** *071
WILLIAMS, Kenneth Lee. 143 PLEASANT DR 16365 #041-09-1982 L1983 **GPM** *020 †18

WARRENDALE – ALLEGHENY

KRYSINSKI, Terrance R. 16000 PERRY HWY, STE TWO 15086 #041-13-1995 L2000 **GP GS** *020
MAC ISAAC, David B. 125 WARRENDALE BAYNE RD, STE 200 15086 #041-78-2000, ▲ L2001 **FM** *020 †18
WEBB, Robert Mark. 1 WILLIAMSBURG PL STE 250 15086 #038-40-1980 L1982 **P** *020 †75

WARRINGTON – BUCKS

APPLESTEIN, Bruce. 847 EASTON RD, STE 2800 18976 #041-13-1966 L1967 **CD IM** *020 †20
BAUER, Kelly Ann. 1432 EASTON RD, STE 2C 18976 #055-01-1995 L2002 **CHP P** *020
BROAD, Todd Howard. 847 EASTON RD 18976 #041-02-1982 L1983 **AN** *020 †05
BROOKS, Matthew Michael. ■ 18976 #041-13-2005 L2005 **EM** *012
CASTEL, Jose Michael. 630 EASTON RD 18976 #566-01-1972 L1973 **FM** *020 †18
DAVID, Karen W. 1432 EASTON RD, STE 3G 18976 #041-13-1995 L1997 **PD** *020 †55
EBERHARDT, Herman L. ■ 18976 #041-77-1957, ▲ L1958 *071
ENDO, Raymond Noboru. 847 EASTON RD 18976 #041-13-1986 L1987 **PD** *020 †55
ENGLE, Eileen. 847 EASTON RD, STE 2300 18976 #041-09-1979 L1980 **GYN** *020 †30
FONSLICK, Janee Ann. 1380 EASTON RD, ABINGTON OB GYN 18976 #041-12-1993 L1996 **OBG** *020 †30
GALELLA, Nancy Marie. 1380 EASTON RD, ABINGTON OB GYN 18976 #033-05-1989 L1991 **OBG** *020 †30
GIUFFRE, Adrienne Marie. ■ 18976 #041-09-1976 L1978 **GS** *020 †85
GUIDERA, Steven Allan. 847 EASTON RD, STE 2800 18976 #035-01-1987 L1990 **CD** *020 †20
HOCKFIELD, Hal Scott. 1380 EASTON RD 18976 #041-13-1985 L1986 **IM IMG** *020 †20
HOFMANN, Melissa Anne. ■ 18976 #041-01-2006 L2006 **PD** *012
JAURIGUE, Venerando G. ■ 18976 #748-01-1957 L1968 **GS OS** *072 †85
JOSON, Raymond M, Jr. 847 EASTON RD 18976 #041-02-1985 L1989 **AN** *020 †05
KATZ, Theodore Thos. 1127 MAIN ST, VALLEY SQUARE PLASTIC SURG 18976 #041-09-1972 L1980 **PS CS** *020 †85,65 ‡
KRESSLY, Susan J. 1432 EASTON RD, STE 3G 18976 #041-13-1986 L1987 **PD** *020 †55
MAHONEY, James William. 1380 EASTON RD 18976 #041-13-1995 L1998 **IM** *020 †20
MANDEL, Elisa Beth. 847 EASTON RD, STE 2700 18976 #041-09-1990 L1992 **IM** *020 †20
MARTINEZ, Maritza Andrea. 1380 EASTON RD, ABINGTON OB GYN 18976 #041-15-2000 L2001 **OBG** *020
MC ALLISTER, Joseph Cyril. 1380 EASTON RD 18976 #041-09-1987 L1988 **IM** *020 †20
MC DONALD, Steven Mark. 847 EASTON RD 18976 #018-03-1988 L1992 **AN** *020 †05
MOORADD, Michael Geo. 847 EASTON RD, STE 2800 18976 #050-02-1986 L1987 **CD IM** *020 †20
NORRY, Elliot Chas. 1380 EASTON RD 18976 #035-19-1989 L1991 **GE IM** *020 †20
NOVER, David Allen. 1432 EASTON RD STE 2C 18976 #033-06-1985 L1989 **P** *020 †75
O'CONNOR, Jennifer Ann. 304 CEDAR WAXWING DR 18976 #041-15-2001 L2003 **FM** *020 †18
POEHLMANN-BUCKLEY, Nancy. 847 EASTON RD 18976 #041-09-1987 L1988 **PD** *020
REICHLE, Frederick Adolph. 2169 CRESTWALD TER 18976 #041-13-1961 L1962 **GS VS** *020 †85
ROBERTS, Alice Kathleen. 1380 EASTON RD, ABINGTON OB GYN 18976 #041-01-1999 L2002 **OBG** *020
SEGAL, Robert. 2600 KELLY RD STE 100, DISCOVERY LABS INC 18976 #836-03-1980 L1994 **NEP IM** *050 †20
SEJOUR, Farly. ■ 18976 #033-06-2000 L2001 **OBG** *020 †30
SHAPIRO, Marcelle Joy. 847 EASTON RD 18976 #041-13-1980 L1982 **DR** *020 †20,80
SHUKLA, Rohitkumar S. ■ 18976 #496-38-1963 L1973 **OBG** *071 †30
SIH, Philip Gregory. 1380 EASTON RD, ABINGTON OB GYN 18976 #041-13-1984 L1985 **OBG** *020 †30
SLOAN, Stephen Brian. 847 EASTON RD, STE 2800 18976 #038-40-1991 L1998 **ICE** *020 †20
SPRINGER, Cathy Ann. 847 EASTON RD, STE 2500 18976 #041-09-1988 L1990 **PD** *020 †55
TANNENBAUM, David Scott. 1380 EASTON RD, ABINGTON OB GYN 18976 #041-01-1991 L1993 **OBG** *020 †30
TOLTZIS, Melanie Cohen. 847 EASTON RD, STE 2700 18976 #041-07-1989 L1991 **FM** *020 †18
WANNER, Jeffrey Lee. 1380 EASTON RD 18976 #033-06-1995 L1997 **IM** *020 †20
WARSETSKY, Sarah Irene. 1380 EASTON RD, ABINGTON OB GYN 18976 #041-14-2000 L2001 **OBG** *020
WEILER, Jutta. ■ 18976 #407-02-1967 L1970 **EM** *071
WILLS, Roselyn Aguila. 847 EASTON RD, STE 2700 18976 #041-07-1990 L1992 **FM** *020 †18
WULC, Allan Edward. 847 EASTON RD STE 1500 18976 #041-01-1980 L1982 **OPH CS** *020 †35 ‡

WARRIORS MARK – HUNTINGDON

VELKOFF, Cyril L. ■ 16877 #010-01-1944 L1950 **GS CRS** *071

WASHINGTON – WASHINGTON

ACKERMAN, Robert Jos. 95 LEONARD AVE 15301 #033-05-1975 L1976 **FM** *020 †18
ADLER, Jon S. 151 N FRANKLIN ST, WASHINGTON DIAGNOSTICS 15301 #041-02-1965 L1966 **FM** *071 †18
ALBERTS, Melvin Chas. 378 W CHESTNUT ST, STE 106 15301 #041-12-1970 L1973 **N** *020 †75
ALIZRAY, Imad Garwan. 155 WILSON AVE, EMERGENCY DEPARTMENT 15301 #875-01-1986 L2006 **FM** *020 †18
APREA, Richard Anthony. 155 WILSON AVE 15301 #055-02-1997 L1999 **EM** *020 †18
AVOLIO, Armando. 125 N FRANKLIN DR, STE 1 15301 #048-04-1989 L1991 **ORS** *020 †40

BARSOUK, Tatyana. 378 W CHESTNUT ST, STE 106 15301 #913-10-1993 L2001 *020 †75

BAYER, Joseph Francis. ■ 15301 #041-12-1956 L1957 PD *071 †55

BEACHLER, John Sutherland. 95 LEONARD AVE 15301 #041-12-1970 L1972 ORS *020 †40

BEEL, John Addis. 155 WILSON AVE, THE WASHINGTON HOSPITAL 15301 #007-02-1976 L1977 DR *071 †80

BENTON, Owen D. ■ 15301 #020-02-1952 L1958 P *071 †75

BERKEY, Kent Elliot. 1025 JEFFERSON AVE 15301 #051-01-1988 L1990 N P *020 †75

BIGLEY, Joel David. ■ 15301 #055-01-2007 L2007 *012

BISCHOF, Lee R. 155 WILSON AVE, DEPT OF ANESTHESIA 15301 #055-75-1991, ▲ L1994 AN PME *020 †05

BONITATIBUS, Ernest J. 460 WASHINGTON RD, STE 7 15301 #055-01-1975 L2002 EM FM *020 †16

BRENNAN, Catherine Joan. 100 RIDGE AVE, VETERANS ADMIN CLINIC 15301 #422-01-1995 L2002 IM *020

BROWN, Dennis Paul. 95 LEONARD AVE STE 301 15301 #005-06-1981 L1986 GS *020 †85

CANTERNA, Anthony Chas. 460 WASHINGTON RD, GABRIELS PLZ STE 8 15301 #561-01-1970 L1974 ORS OSM *020 ‡

CASTRO, William Guillermo. 155 WILSON AVE 15301 #055-01-1981 L1982 DR NM *020 †28,80

CHETTUR, Vinod Kumar. 155 WILSON AVE, EMERGENCY DEPT 15301 #016-43-1996 L2001 IM *020 †20

CHOI, Kou-Sun. ■ 15301 #583-08-1965 L1981 IMG *030

CLEMENTS, James Keith. 190 N MAIN ST 15301 #030-05-1976 L1977 FM *020 †18

CONROY, William Patrick. 155 WILSON AVE 15301 #041-12-1991 L1996 DR *020 †80

COOK, Richard Allen, II. 95 LEONARD AVE, BUILDING 2 - 2ND FLOOR 15301 #041-02-2005 L2005 FP *012

COOK, Scott Anthony. 155 WILSON AVE, THE WASHINGTON HOSPITAL 15301 #041-07-1998 L2000 FM *020 †18

COPPULA, Robert J. 90 W CHESTNUT ST, STE 500 15301 #561-01-1967 L1969 IM IMG *020 †20

CORKUM, Douglas J. 155 WILSON AVE 15301 #065-01-1978 L1983 EM *020 †16

CORWIN, Douglas Thomas, Jr. 400 LOCUST AVE 15301 #041-02-1993 L1996 IM *020 †20

COTUGNO, Bruce Michael. 90 W CHESTNUT ST, STE 125LL 15301 #035-09-1988 L1993 N *020 †75

CRAMER, Nancy Jean. 50 E WYLIE AVE 15301 #041-12-2000 L2001 FM *020 ‡

CULLEN, Paul Thos. 95 LEONARD AVE 15301 #041-02-1976 L1978 FM *040 †18

DAVIS, Dennis. 50 E WYLIE AVE 15301 #041-13-1977 L1978 FM *020 †18

DAVIS, James E. 750 E BEAU ST 15301 #041-13-2000 L2001 OPH *100 †35

DONOFRIO, Robert J. 95 LEONARD AVE 15301 #035-45-1976 L1978 ORS *020 †40 ‡

DOUGHERTY, Michael James. 155 WILSON AVE, LEVEL G 15301 #016-02-1988 L1990 RO *020 †80

DOWNER, William Robt. 155 WILSON AVE, WASH HOSP 15301 #041-12-1986 L1987 DR PTH *020 †80

DUNCAN, Sarah Carolyn. 90 W CHESTNUT ST, STE 400 15301 #041-15-1999 L2001 FM *020 †18

DUTTA, Tarit Kanti. 155 WILSON AVE, WASHINGTON HOSPITAL 15301 #495-78-1966 L1984 RO ON *020 †80

EDGAR, Kenneth Alan. 155 WILSON AVE, THE WASHINGTON HOSPITAL 15301 #025-01-1993 L1998 DR RNR *020 †80

EISLEY, Matthew John. 155 WILSON AVE 15301 #056-06-1986 L1988 DR *020 †80

ESHBAUGH, Natasha. 155 WILSON AVE 15301 #041-13-2000 L2001 FP *012

FAGIOLETTI, Robert Jos. 457 TYLER AVE 15301 #055-01-1969 L1970 FM *020 †18 ‡

FALCIONE, Michael. 100 RIDGE AVE, CROSSING THE JORDAN CHRIST 15301 #041-12-1996 L1998 FM *020 †18

FAUST, Michael David. 95 LEONARD AVE, STE 501 15301 #055-01-1995 L1997 PD *020 †55 ‡

FECHER, Alison Marie. 155 WILSON AVE, WASHIGTON HOSPITAL 15301 #422-01-1999 L2001 GS *100 †85

FELICE, Civie David. 95 LEONARD AVE, STE 501 15301 #041-12-1975 L1976 PD *020 †55 ‡

FOLEY, Edward Lewis, Jr. 400 JEFFERSON AVE, CORNERSTONE CARE PED ASC 15301 #041-12-1971 L1972 PD GP *020 †55

FOX, Craig Douglas. 2 WILSON AVE 15301 #041-12-1980 L1981 FM *020 †18 ‡

FRAME, David Crawford. 95 LEONARD AVE STE 201 15301 #041-13-1971 L1973 ORS OTR *020 †40

FRIEDMAN, Laurence Erik. 90 W CHESTNUT ST, TEREDESAI MC CANN & 15301 #045-01-1989 L1994 NEP IM *020 †20

FRIEDSAM, Patricia Lee. 400 LOCUST AVE 15301 #041-07-1978 L1980 IM *020 †20

FUCHS, David Vincent. 155 WILSON AVE 15301 #041-13-1976 L1977 EM FM *020 †18,16

FUERST, Nicholas E. 151 N FRANKLIN ST 15301 #035-06-1974 L1975 FM *020 †18

GOLDMAN, Tatiana. 1025 JEFFERSON AVE 15301 #913-06-1984 L2006 N *020

HAHN, Richard M. 880 S MAIN ST 15301 #041-12-1978 L1979 IM IMG *020 †20

HALL, John Henry, Jr. ■ 15301 #041-13-1946 L1947 IM *071 †20

HALLMARK, Christopher Ala. ■ 15301 #048-04-2006 L2006 DR *012

HART, Richard Brant, Jr. 90 W CHESTNUT ST, STE 500 15301 #041-13-1992 L1994 ID *020 †20

HEADLEY, Chauncey Roger. ■ 15301 #041-13-1956 L1957 OBG *071 †30

HESS, Grant Ephraim, Jr. ■ 15301 #041-12-1939 L1940 GP *071

HILGER, Jeffrey Scott. 155 WILSON AVE 15301 #041-12-1988 L1991 DR VIR *020 †80

HILL, Becki Sue. 155 WILSON AVE, WASHINGTON HOSPITAL 15301 #055-02-1994 L1997 RO *072 †80

HISRICH, Glenn Dale. ■ 15301 #038-40-1962 L1969 ORS *071 †40

HOLT, Daniel Lee. 181 W BEAU ST, WESTVIEW FAMILY HEALTH ASS 15301 #041-14-1990 L1992 FM *020 †18

HOSPODAR, Mark Edward. 378 W CHESTNUT ST, STE 106 15301 #041-12-1988 L1990 N *020

JACKSON, Grant Wells. ■ 15301 #049-01-2005 L2005 FP *012

JAMES, David Lee. ■ 15301 #041-07-1995 L2003 FM *062

JAYAKUMAR, Subramoniam. 764 LOCUST AVE 15301 #495-37-1966 L1975 NEP IM *020 †20

JENSEN, Amy Violet. ■ 15301 #041-15-2007 L2007 FP *012

KARAMCHETI, Anand. 208 WELLNESS WAY 15301 #495-58-1968 U UP *020 †95 ‡

KELLY, James Christopher. ■ 15301 #041-02-2008 *012

KELMINSON, Stephen B. 155 WILSON AVE 15301 #048-02-1986 L1996 DR *020 †80

KIRSHEN, Michelle Rae. 155 WILSON AVE 15301 #012-05-1991 L1996 DR NM *020 †80,28

KOLINER, Charles Michael. 400 LOCUST AVE 15301 #035-01-1971 L1982 PUD IM *020 †20

KOVSCEK, Annastasia Marie. ■ 15301 #041-14-2005 L2006 FP *012

KREBS, James Arthur, Jr. 880 S MAIN ST 15301 #041-12-1974 L1976 IM *020 †20

KROSNOFF, Michael. 95 LEONARD AVE 15301 #041-02-1964 L1965 GS CD *071 †85

LAMB, Mary Parks. 95 LEONARD AVE 15301 #051-01-1995 L1997 FM FSM *020 †18

LANDAY, Ronald Allan. 1385 WASHINGTON RD, STE 101 15301 #041-12-1973 L1974 A PD *020 †55,03 ‡

LANE, John Fairbanks. 805 RUPLE LN, PHYSICAL MED & REHABILITAT 15301 #038-06-1954 L1979 PM PTH *071 †60

LARSON, Paul Robert. 95 LEONARD AVE 15301 #024-16-2002 L2002 FM *100 †18

LEE, Lawrence Houchung. 155 WILSON AVE 15301 #041-14-1994 L2001 PTH *020 †50

LESLIE, Scott David. ■ 15301 #055-01-2004 L2004 GPM *012

LEUKHARDT, David Bryan. 155 WILSON AVE 15301 #041-12-1988 L1991 DR *020 †80

LEWIN, Melissa Jean. 90 W CHESTNUT ST, STE 400 15301 #041-12-2003 L2006 FM *020 †18

MALINAK, Christa Marie. 190 N MAIN ST, DERIENZO FAMILY PRACTICE 15301 #025-07-1998 L2001 FM *020 †18

MALLY, Amarjith N. 155 WILSON AVE, THE WASHINGTON HOSPITAL 15301 #495-37-1977 L1992 AN EM *020

MAMROS, Mark Allen. 181 W BEAU ST, WASHINGTON FAMILY DOCTORS 15301 #041-13-1987 L1989 FM FPG *020 †18

MANNING, Christopher M. 95 LEONARD AVE 15301 #041-12-1999 L2001 ORS *020

MANOJBHAI, Patel. 300 CAMERON RD 15301 #495-23-1972 L1983 P *020 †75

MC BEE, Alden Gay. 155 WILSON AVE, WASHINGTON HOSP PATH DPT 15301 #055-01-1975 L1976 PTH *020 †50 ‡

MC MAHON, William Jos. 155 WILSON AVE, RAD DEPT-WASHINGTON HOSP 15301 #041-12-1960 L1961 R *071 †80

MEDWICK, Gerald Richard. 155 WILSON AVE 15301 #041-77-1980, ▲ L1981 RO *020 †80

MEGALUDIS, Alexis M. 997 N MAIN ST, STE 2 15301 #041-07-1983 L1985 HEM ON *020 †20

MEISNER, Robert James. ■ 15301 #041-02-2008 *012

MERZI, Allen John. 575 MCKINLEY AVE 15301 #038-40-1968 L1970 GS VS *020 †85

MIKHAIL, Mona R. 1385 WASHINGTON RD 15301 #915-04-1980 L1994 P *020 †75

MILLER, David Lee. 1385 WASHINGTON RD, STE 101 15301 #038-40-1964 L1967 A PDA *020 †55,03

MINTEER, Jeffrey F. 155 WILSON AVE 15301 #041-02-1977 L1979 FM PLM *040 †18

MIZIKAR, William Edward. 155 WILSON AVE, THE WASHINGTON HOSPITAL 15301 #041-12-1993 L1996 AN *020 †05

MORALES, Rafael Angel. 400 LOCUST AVE 15301 #042-03-1981 L1985 CCM IM *020 †20

MUHLY, Jennifer. 181 W BEAU ST, CENTERVILLE CLINICS INC 15301 #055-01-2000 L2002 FM *020 †18

NABORS, Eric David. 95 LEONARD AVE 15301 #041-12-1989 L1994 ORS *020 †40

NADER, Dena R. 155 WILSON AVE 15301 #041-07-1998 L2000 FM *020 †18

NANGIA, Sunaina. 1008 STONECREEK LN 15301 #496-07-1994 L2001 FM *020 †18

NAWROCKI, Joseph Steven. 90 E MAIDEN ST 15301 #041-12-1990 L1992 HNS *072

NICHOLLS, Samuel G. ■ 15301 #041-12-1950 L1951 GP *071

NIES, Gerald Frederick. 155 WILSON AVE 15301 #041-02-1958 L1960 AI OTO *071 †45

ODASSO, David Peter. 155 WILSON AVE, BOX AK 15301 #041-09-1989 L1991 AN *020 †05

PALUMBO, Michael Joseph. 1385 WASHINGTON RD, STE 101 15301 #041-14-1998 L2003 AI *020 †55,03

PALUSO, Eugene Francis. 380 W CHESTNUT ST 15301 #561-01-1965 L1967 OTO *020 †45

PALUSO, John R. 1480 JEFFERSON AVE 15301 #561-01-1965 L1967 R *071

PANUCCI, Debra Jean. 155 WILSON AVE 15301 #055-01-1986 L1987 IM PM *020 †20,60

PARESO, James Dwight. 95 LEONARD AVE STE 301 15301 #041-12-1970 L1973 GS EM *020 †85

PATAKI, Richard Stephen. 155 WILSON AVE 15301 #035-09-1962 L1975 PTH *020 †50 ‡

PEARSON, William Paul. 155 WILSON AVE 15301 #010-02-1964 L1972 *030 †30,16

PENDERGAST, William James. 90 W CHESTNUT ST 15301 #041-12-1990 L1992 IM *020 †20

PENSOCK, John Frank. 155 WILSON AVE 15301 #041-14-1995 L1998 IC *020 †20

PESACRETA, Matthew George. 90 W CHESTNUT ST, TEREDESAI MC CANN & 15301 #041-12-1998 L2001 NEP *020 †20

PFRIMMER, Wayne Jos. 997 N MAIN ST, STE 2 15301 #041-12-1970 L1974 HEM ON *020 †20

PHARES, Pascal Alain. 155 WILSON AVE, EMERGENCY DEPARTMENT 15301 #048-04-2004 L2004 FM *020 †18

PHILLIPS, Thomas Grant. 95 LEONARD AVE 15301 #041-09-1979 L1980 FM *040 †18

PLATTO, Michael Jon. 240 WELLNESS WAY, WR CAMERON WELLNESS CTR 15301 #023-01-1985 L1989 PM *020 †60

RAJAWAT, Yadavendra Singh. 50 BERRY RD, DONOHUE CARDIOLOGY ASSOCIA 15301 #495-30-1989 L2001 IC *020 †20

REEVES, Michael Jay. ■ 15301 #038-45-2005 L2005 FP *012

REIBACH, Andrew Mark. 95 LEONARD AVE 15301 #041-12-1991 L2000 FM *020 †18

REILLY, William M, Jr. ■ 15301 #041-12-1943 L1944 OPH *071 †35

RICCI, Anthony N, II. 123 WASHINGTON ST # 233 15301 #041-12-1993 L1995 PM *020 †60

RICHARDSON, James Elwood. ■ 15301 #055-01-1969 L1970 GP *071

ROSENBLUM, Bret Abraham. 460 WASHINGTON RD, STE 7 15301 #041-02-1990 L1992 FM *020 †18

RUBEN, Malcolm Edward. ■ 15301 #023-07-1948 L1951 U *071

SAHETA, Sanjaya Narayan. 50 BERRY RD 15301 #422-01-1995 L1998 IC CD *020 †20

SALVITTI, E Ronald. 750 E BEAU ST 15301 #041-13-1963 L1964 OPH *020 †35

SCHEIB, Frederick Jude. 212 WILSON AVE 15301 #041-12-1975 L1976 OPH *020 †35

SCHELLINCK, Edward Martin. 155 WILSON AVE 15301 #061-01-1972 L1976 FM GPM *020

SCHMELTZ, Ralph. 86 WELLNESS WAY 15301 #035-08-1967 L1968 END IM *020 †20

SCHMIELER, George Carl. 95 LEONARD AVE, STE 401 BLDG #1 15301 #023-01-1962 L1965 FM OM *030 †18

SEAMAN, David Edward. 90 W CHESTNUT ST STE 410 15301 #038-43-1988 L1991 RHU IM *020 †20

SHARER, Jill Ann. 181 W BEAU ST 15301 #041-02-2002 L2002 FM *020 †18

SHERWOOD, Mylaina Lyn. ■ 15301 #041-15-2006 L2006 FP *012

SIERRA, Kimberley Ann. ■ 15301 #041-13-2006 L2006 FP *012

SILVIS, Harry Jos. 400 LOCUST AVE 15301 #041-12-1975 L1976 IM *020 †20

SIX, John David. 95 LEONARD AVE, FAMILY PRACTICE RESIDENCY 15301 #041-02-2003 L2003 FM *020 †18

SLOMIANY, Walter Paul. 95 LEONARD AVE 15301 #041-13-1986 L1987 FM *020 †18

SMITH, Perry Clare, Jr. 764 LOCUST AVE 15301 #010-02-1954 L1955 NM IM *071 †28,20

SOMEN, Leyla Inci. 378 W CHESTNUT ST STE 205, CENTER INC 15301 #902-04-1968 L1983 P *020

SOMMERFIELD, Richelle Cer. 95 LEONARD AVE, BLDG 2 15301 #041-12-2001 L2003 PD *020 †55

SPEICHER, Monica Lee. 95 LEONARD AVE 15301 #041-02-2000 L2001 FM *020 †18

SPROWLS, Jay R. 155 WILSON AVE 15301 #041-13-1950 L1951 GP OBG *071

STINELY, Regis William. 155 WILSON AVE 15301 #041-12-1955 L1956 PTH *071 †50

TEREDESAI, Pradip R. 90 W CHESTNUT ST, TEREDESAI MC CANN & 15301 #496-38-1972 L1976 NEP IM *020 †20

TIBBENS, George Filmore. ■ 15301 #041-02-1947 L1948 OPH *071 †35

■ = Address Information Privacy Protected

TIHANSKY, Dennis P. ■ 15301 #011-02-1978 L1982 **DR VIR** *071 †80
TOBIN, Karen. 378 W CHESTNUT ST STE 106 15301 #038-40-1989 L1993 **N** *020 †75 ‡
TRUSNOVIC, William Danl. ■ 15301 #041-12-1989 L1996 **IM** *020
TURNER, Morris Edward. 90 W CHESTNUT ST, STE 400 15301 #041-12-1973 L1974 **OBG** *020 †30
UY, Henry Tan. 155 WILSON AVE, DEPT OF RADIOLOGY 15301 #748-01-1956 L1970 **R** *071 †80
VAN CURAN, Keith W. ■ 15301 #049-01-2005 L2005 **FP** *012
VAN STRIEN, Adrian R, Jr. 400 LOCUST AVE 15301 #041-13-1966 **IM** *071 †20
VERSTRAETEN, Thierry C. 750 E BEAU ST 15301 #165-07-1984 L1987 **OPH OS** *020 †35
VORE, Kimberle Keller. 95 LEONARD AVE 15301 #038-41-1986 L1987 **FM** *040 †18
WALTERS, Phyllis Jean. 155 WILSON AVE 15301 #041-09-1981 L1982 **DR** *020 †80
WALTHER, Brenda Lee. ■ 15301 #041-12-1989 L1991 **FM** *020 †18
WATERS, Michael Nelson. 10 SAMUEL DR 15301 #041-12-1988 L1991 **EM** *020
WEIMER, Joseph Clarence. ■ 15301 #016-43-1953 L1958 **GS AN** *071 †85
WEINSTEIN, Maryann Brandt. 95 LEONARD AVE, FAMILY PRACTICE CENTER 15301 #041-07-1980 L1983 **FM FPG** *020 †18
WEST, Cynthia G. 90 W CHESTNUT ST, TEREDESAI MC CANN & 15301 #041-02-1981 L1982 **IM NEP** *020 †20
WHITING, Donald Mark. 380 W CHESTNUT ST STE 101 15301 #041-02-1985 L1986 **NS** *020 †25
WICK, Matthew Edwin. ■ 15301 #041-12-2007 L2007 **FP** *012
WILDENHAIN, Philip M. 155 WILSON AVE 15301 #041-12-1986 L1987 **DR VIR** *020 †80 ‡
WILLIS, Amber Dionne. ■ 15301 #048-04-2006 L2006 **FP** *012
WILSON, John Steven. 100 WELLNESS WAY 15301 #041-14-1986 L1994 **CD** *020 †20
WODLINGER, Paul Meredith. 400 JEFFERSON AVE 15301 #051-01-1974 L1988 **PD PHP** *020 †55
WOLZ, Dean Eric. 100 WELLNESS WAY 15301 #055-01-1988 L1990 **CD IM** *020 †20
WORSHTIL, Mark Eric. WA HOSP DEPT FAM PRAC 15301 #041-12-1973 L1974 **FM** *040 †18
XIE, Qizhi. 90 W CHESTNUT ST, TEREDESAI MC CANN & 15301 #243-52-1986 L2002 **NEP** *020 †20
ZIMMERMAN, Gregory James. ■ 15301 #026-04-2008 L2008 *012

WASHINGTON CROSSING – BUCKS

BERES, Joseph Casimir. ■ 18977 #041-09-1954 L1955 **DR** *071 †80
BONNET, Philip Laurence. 1086 TAYLORSVILLE RD 18977 #041-09-1969 L1970 **P** *020
COHEN, Ernest. ■ 18977 #041-13-1962 L1963 **GS** *071 †85
FALK, Arthur Edward. 10 DECISION WAY E 18977 #035-01-1947 L1955 **OBG** *020 †30
FRANK, Paul Emerson. ■ 18977 #041-02-1956 L1957 **OPH** *071 †35
GALIETTA, Maryann C. ■ 18977 #041-09-1967 L1969 **FPG GP** *020
GASTON, Noreen Hurley. ■ 18977 #041-07-1983 L1986 **IM** *020 †20
GOLD, Henry Jay. ■ 18977 #041-09-1960 L1963 **FM** *020 †18
GONZALEZ-JIMENEZ, Enrique. ■ 18977 #041-13-1952 L1963 **OPH** *071 †35
HEISEN, Peter Roger. ■ 18977 #041-01-1969 L1970 **IM ID** *020 †20
HOWELL, Amanda Pilar. ■ 18977 #041-15-2005 L2008 **EM** *012
KAHN, James Brodie. ■ 18977 #024-01-1967 L1993 **ID IM** *050 †20
MAURO, David John. ■ 18977 #041-13-1966 L1998 **PTH** *020
MINO, David Edmond. ■ 18977 #041-13-1978 L1983 **ORS** *062 †40 ‡
PERRINE, Jane Ellen. ■ 18977 #041-07-1955 L1957 **P** *030
PORTMAN, Ronald Jay. 1231 RIVER RD 18977 #032-01-1976 L2007 **PN PD** *020 †55
RICCIARDELLI, Charles. 19 MILYKO DR 18977 #561-11-1970 L1972 **ORS PD** *040 †40
VILLA, Gabriele L. ■ 18977 #561-03-1955 L1967 **R** *071 †80
WAGNER, Kenneth Lawrence. 1082 TAYLORSVILLE RD, STE 2 18977 #041-13-1964 L1969 **P** *020
WHITNEY, Chas Candee, III. 1121 GENRL WSHNGTN MM BLVD 18977 #041-02-1990 L1992 **FM** *020 †18

WATERFORD – ERIE

EBY, Carl. 991 ROUTE 19 N STE B, HERITAGE PRIMARY CARE 16441 #041-09-1987 L1988 **FM** *020 †18

WATSONTOWN – NORTHUMBERLAND

DOUGLAS, Ray Thomas. 300 E 8TH ST 17777 #041-07-1994 L1996 **FM OBG** *072 †18
MOWERY, Andrew Donald. ■ 17777 #041-77-2007, ▲ L2007 **IM** *012
REGALADO, Regulus Doctura. ■ 17777 #748-02-1965 L1973 **EM GS** *071 †85
YANNACCONE, Robert. ■ 17777 #041-02-1947 L1948 **GP OS** *071

WATTSBURG – ERIE

SUSI, Joseph Albert. ■ 16442 #041-13-1980 L1981 **FM** *020 †18

WAVERLY – LACKAWANNA

HORCHOS, Donald David. MAIN STREET 18471 #041-09-1961 L1962 **PM** *071 †60
JARVIS, Margaret A E. ■ 18471 #051-04-1989 L1999 **ADM P** *030 †75
WITHERS, David John. PO BOX 36, MARWORTH 18471 #035-15-1980 L2004 **EM GS** *020 †16
WOLK, Melvyn H. CLINTON ST 18471 #050-02-1960 L1963 **PDA PD** *071 †55,03

WAYMART – WAYNE

AHLUWALIA, Swadesh Kaur. ■ 18472 #495-29-1965 L1981 **GP** *020
MIZIANTY, Thomas Jos. 11 MIZIANTY LN 18472 #041-02-1975 L1976 **OM GP** *020
MORTON, Robert John. 27B WOODLANDS DR 18472 #035-08-1981 L1984 **PD** *020 †55
OREHEK, Allen James. ■ 18472 #041-02-1995 L1997 **MPD PD** *020 †20,55

WAYNE – DELAWARE

BAKER, Joshua Fitzgerald. ■ 19087 #041-01-2005 L2005 **IM** *012

BARRY, William John. 999 OLD EAGLE SCHOOL RD, STE 118 19087 #041-09-1961 L1962 **R** *062 †80
BASSIRI, Hamid. ■ 19087 #041-01-2004 L2004 **PD** *100
BECKER, Gary Lee. 229 LANSDOWNE AVE 19087 #041-02-1971 L1972 **D IM** *020 †20,15
BEERS, Michael Francis. 402 MIDLAND AVE 19087 #041-01-1985 L1986 **PUD** *020 †20
BIERLY, Mahlon Z, Jr. ■ 19087 #041-02-1946 L1947 **LM GPM** *071 †55
BOCOBO, George G. 999 OLD EAGLE SCHOOL RD, STE 118 19087 #748-02-1976 L1988 **DR NM** *020 †80
BOYER, Donald Lee. ■ 19087 #041-01-2005 L2005 **PD** *012
BRECHER, Chad William. ■ 19087 #043-01-1998 L2006 **DR** *020 †80
BROWN, Nathan. ■ 19087 #041-13-1931 L1932 **GP** *071
BROWN, Richard Allen. ■ 19087 #654-01-1981 L1981 **GP** *020
BUERKLIN, Ellen Marie. ■ 19087 #041-13-1970 L1971 **END DIA** *050
CANTAFIO, Ralph. ■ 19087 #041-02-1950 L1951 **OM GP** *071
CAPPOLA, James Jos. 1275 DRUMMERS LN, THE COVALENT GROUP, INC 19087 #649-33-1983 L1984 **IM CLP** *050
CARR, Molly Corbett. ■ 19087 #035-01-1994 L1996 **END** *050 †20
CHARAGUNDLA, Sridhar Rao. ■ 19087 #041-01-1999 L2004 **DR** *020 †80
CHRISTIE, Thomas. ■ 19087 #803-05-1952 L1965 **PA** *072
CHUNG, Christine Angela. 860 E SWEDESFORD RD 19087 #041-02-1991 L1993 **OPH** *020 †35
CLEMENTI, Nancy Durst. 555 E LANCASTER AVE 19087 #051-04-1977 L1979 **IM** *050 †20
CLOSE, Sally. ■ 19087 #041-07-1969 L1970 **AN** *020 †05
COFFEY, John Francis. ■ 19087 #917-30-1962 L1974 **NEP IM** *020
CORREA-MEYER, Paulo. 295 OLD EAGLE SCHOOL RD 19087 #187-25-1966 L1982 **OPH** *020
CUCURULLO, Albert Joseph. ■ 19087 #561-01-1971 L1979 **PTH** *050
CURTIS, John Ashton, Jr. 110 W LANCASTER AVE, STE 230 19087 #035-01-2001 L2001 **ETX** *020 †16 ‡
DE PAOLA, Alphonse F. ■ 19087 #561-17-1954 L1955 **FM OBG** *072 †18
DIGIACOMO, Philip John, III. ■ 19087 #041-02-2008 *012
DONNELLY, Marie R. 425 HOMESTEAD RD R9 19087 #041-07-1966 L1967 **P PYA** *020
DORRANCE, William L. ■ 19087 #041-13-1947 L1949 **P** *071 †55
DOYLE, Robert. ■ 19087 #041-02-1953 L1954 **GYN** *071 †30
DUPONT, Frank Albert, III. 999 OLD EAGLE SCHOOL RD, STE 118 19087 #024-05-1985 L1990 **DR IM** *020 †80
ENGLANDER, Stacey Ellen. ■ 19087 #028-02-1996 L1999 **D** *020 †15
FARLEY, Faith Ann. 201 S ABERDEEN AVE 19087 #041-07-1983 L1988 **DR** *020 †80 ‡
FIELD, Hilary V. 110 W LANCASTER AVE STE 3 19087 #917-18-1976 L1985 **PD** *020 †20
FRIEDMAN, Carl Jeffrey. ■ 19087 #020-12-1970 L1984 **IM GE** *071 †20
GILLESPIE, Barbara Ann W. ■ 19087 #051-04-1975 L1980 **IM ID** *020 †20
GORDON, Harold Mark. 418 E LANCASTER AVE 19087 #024-07-1977 L1979 **PD NPM** *020 †55
GOURLEY, Ian Scott. ■ 19087 #918-01-1988 L1999 **PTH** *050
GOYAL, Maheep Kumar. 999 OLD EAGLE SCHOOL RD, STE 118 19087 #041-02-1988 L1991 **DR** *020 †80
GREENBERG, Steven Marc. 999 OLD EAGLE SCHOOL RD, STE 118 19087 #024-05-1989 L1994 **DR AR** *020 †80 ‡
HALAK, Mary Nguyen. ■ 19087 #041-02-2003 L2003 **IM** *100
HANDWERGER, Beth Allison. 271 E SWEDESFORD RD 19087 #035-45-1996 L2000 **OPH** *020 †35
HASHEMI, Nikroo. ■ 19087 #517-12-1999 L2004 **GE** *012
HERMAN, Bjorn. ■ 19087 #035-01-2007 **OTO** *012
HOFFMAN, David Jos. 651 KNOX RD 19087 #035-15-1988 L1990 **NPM** *020 †55
HOOK, Vicki Sue Bair. 489 DEVON PARK DR, STE 312 19087 #041-07-1972 L1974 **P** *020 †75
HUG, Bruce Alan. ■ 19087 #028-02-1997 L2000 **BBK** *020 †50
JESSANI, Naushad R. 121 N WAYNE AVE STE 300 19087 #704-02-1986 L1997 **P CHP** *020 †75
JONES, Mable Lee Smith. 999 OLD EAGLE SCHOOL RD, STE 118 19087 #021-05-1975 L1992 **DR** *020 †80
KANE, Daniel Merrick. 860 E SWEDESFORD RD 19087 #041-13-1972 L1973 **OPH** *020 †35
KATZ, Arie. 295 E SWEDESFORD RD 19087 #550-02-1993 L2002 **END** *020
KERR, John Herbert. 418 E LANCASTER AVE 19087 #041-09-1960 L1961 **IM** *071
KIM, Philip Sunghan. 744 W LANCASTER AVE STE 11, DEVON SQUARE II 19087 #016-43-1992 L1996 **AN PMM** *020 †05
KLEIN, Lisa. 999 OLD EAGLE SCHOOL RD, STE 118 19087 #035-20-1989 L1992 **RNR** *020 †80
KNEELAND, John Bruce. 200 W LANCASTER AVE, WAYNE MRI OF PENN 19087 #041-02-1978 L1990 **DR** *020 †80
KRICH, Karen Luann. ■ 19087 #041-07-1980 L1982 **IM** *074 †20
LAFFEY, Patricia A D. 999 OLD EAGLE SCHOOL RD, STE 118 19087 #016-12-1972 L1974 **DR** *020 †80
LANCHONEY, Diana Mallory. ■ 19087 #041-01-1997 L2000 **IM** *020 †20
LEI, Benjamin Wing. ■ 19087 #010-02-1969 L1975 **PA** *075
LEONG, Ronald Wing. 201 KING OF PRUSSIA RD 19087 #028-02-1981 L1981 **IM** *050 †20
LEVY, David Welsh. 999 OLD EAGLE SCHOOL RD, STE 118 19087 #041-13-1982 L1983 **N R** *020 †80
LIU, Steven Si. ■ 19087 #041-01-2006 L2006 **AN** *012
LOVELAND, Margaret Jean. ■ 19087 #065-01-1970 L1997 **PUD** *020 †20
MAC INTYRE, Amy M. 121 N WAYNE AVE, STE 300 19087 #024-07-1999 L2002 **P** *020 †75
MADONIA, William James. ■ 19087 #035-19-1994 **P N** *100
MAHBOUBI, Mona. ■ 19087 #041-02-2008 L2008 *012
MARCUCCI, Lisa. 303 W LANCASTER AVE, PMB 302 19087 #041-02-1991 L1993 **GS** *020 †85
MARREN, Amy S. ■ 19087 #041-13-1997 **EM** *100
MC ELFRESH, Chas Warner. ■ 19087 #041-13-1958 L1959 **P CHP** *071
MENARDKATCHER, Paul Andre. ■ 19087 #041-01-2005 L2005 **IM** *012
MIN, Htun. ■ 19087 #209-01-1982 L1997 **PTH** *020 †50
MINERVA, Joanne. 121 N WAYNE AVE STE 300 19087 #539-04-1994 L2000 **CHP P** *020 †75
MOOREVILLE, Ruth. 110 W LANCASTER AVE 19087 #550-01-1978 L1981 **PD** *020 †55
MORGENSTERN, Kenneth Eli. 123 BLOOMINGDALE AVE, STE 102 19087 #041-07-1995 L1997 **OPH** *020 †35
MURPHY, Judith Heyer. 466 DEVON PARK DR, NYCOMED AMERSHAM IMAGING 19087 #041-07-1975 L1978 **CD NM** *020 †20,28
MURPHY, Mary Harlan. ■ 19087 #041-07-1973 L1974 **EM** *071 †16
NAGY, Pamela Belmont. 241 CONESTOGA RD B 19087 #010-01-1999 L2005 **IM** *020 †20
NASER, Jeffrey Allen. 121 N WAYNE AVE STE 300 19087 #025-01-1991 L1993 **CHP** *020 †75
NEAL, Hunter S. ■ 19087 #023-01-1950 L1953 **GS TS** *071 †90,85
NEGRON, Ana Margarita. 680 TWIN BRIDGE DR 19087 #041-02-1973 L1975 **FM** *040 †18
NEWMAN, Karen Siegel. ■ 19087 #041-13-1987 L1988 **P** *020 †75
NGUYEN, Toan Thanh. ■ 19087 #041-15-2000 L2003 **GE** *020 †20

OTTENWELLER, Mark R. ■ 19087 #021-05-1977 L1978 **IM** *020 †20

PAE-WEINSTEIN, Susan. 200 W LANCASTER AVE 19087 #041-01-1993 L1998 **DR** *020 †80

PECKHAM, George Jos. GLOBAL HEALTH PARTNERSHIPS 19087 #010-02-1966 L1968 **NPM PD** *071 †55

PINHEIRO, Lisa Winer. 999 OLD EAGLE SCHOOL RD, STE 118 19087 #041-02-1993 L1999 **DR** *020 †80

PRESTON, Samuel David. 400 E LANCASTER AVE 19087 #041-13-1969 L1970 **GP** *071 †18

PUDER, Pamela S. 999 OLD EAGLE SCHOOL RD, STE 118 19087 #035-47-1989 L1997 **DR** *020 †80

QUINN, Thomas Jos, Jr. 999 OLD EAGLE SCHOOL RD, STE 118 19087 #041-02-1991 L1993 **DR** *020 †80

RAMASWAMI, Ravishankar. ■ 19087 #495-17-1985 **IM** *100

ROSE, Robert E. 125 E SWEDESFORD RD, STE 111 19087 #017-20-1952 L1953 **FM PHP** *071 †18

RUBIN, Jonathan Douglas. 999 OLD EAGLE SCHOOL RD, STE 118 19087 #035-48-1988 L1995 **DR** *020 †80

RUBIN, Peter Erwin. ■ 19087 #035-45-1967 L1976 **OS** *020 †20

SABERIN-WILLIAMS, Mojdeh. 85 OLD EAGLE SCHOOL RD, GYNECOLOGY 19087 #041-01-1996 L1998 **OBG** *020 †30

SAINT-ARMAND, Guirlette. ■ 19087 #649-35-1990 L1994 **IM** *020 †20

SARIS, Teresa Alexandra. 418 E LANCASTER AVE 19087 #041-09-1988 L1990 **IM** *020 †20

SCHAFRANK, Scott Neil. 995 OLD EAGLE SCHOOL RD, STE 304F 19087 #035-20-1986 L1993 **D** *020 †15

SCHATZ, Melanie Beth. 85 OLD EAGLE SCHOOL RD, GYNECOLOGY 19087 #041-13-2002 L2002 **OBG** *020 †30 ‡

SCHNALL, Mitchell Dennis. 200 W LANCASTER AVE, WAYNE MRI OF PENN 19087 #041-01-1986 L1989 **DR** *020 †80

SCOLLAN, David Francis. ■ 19087 #023-07-2002 L2005 **CD** *012 †20

SCOTT, J Clifford. ■ 19087 #041-01-1933 L1934 **CHP** *071

SIEPSER, Steven B. 860 E SWEDESFORD RD 19087 #035-08-1974 L1976 **OPH** *020 †35 ‡

SMITH, C Ross. ■ 19087 #270-02-1983 L1984 **PD** *020 †55

SQUIRES, Fredric Barton. 999 OLD EAGLE SCHOOL RD, STE 118 19087 #041-13-1991 L1993 **DR** *020 †80

STALLKAMP, Jonathan Brady. 241 CONESTOGA RD, STE B 19087 #041-02-2000 L2005 **IM** *020 †20

STRICKLAND, S Clyde. ■ 19087 #064-01-1944 L1951 **PA IM** *071

SUH, Sang John. ■ 19087 #583-01-1957 L1973 **GS GP** *071

TAGUE, Kelly Mooney. ■ 19087 #041-02-1991 *075

TARGUM, Steven David. 575 E SWEDESFORD RD, STE 101 19087 #035-47-1973 L1989 **P** *050 †75

TAYLOR, Mary Scanlon. 200 W LANCASTER AVE 19087 #041-07-1980 L1981 **R** *020 †80

TOROSIAN, Michael Harry. 30 HIGHFIELD LN, THE READING HOSPITAL & MED 19087 #041-01-1978 L1980 **SO** *020 †85

TREAT, Joseph Anthony. ■ 19087 #041-13-1979 L1988 **ON** *020 †20

UNDERWOOD, Stephen Geo. 136 W WAYNE AVE 19087 #035-19-1973 L1990 **CHP** *075

VOULALAS, Debra Susan. 528 W BEECHTREE LN, 528 WEST BEECHTREE LANE 19087 #035-46-1980 L1990 **PD** *040 †55

WARDEN, Anne Elizabeth. ■ 19087 #041-02-1997 L2000 **EM** *020 †16

WEBER, Margaret Ellen. 555 E LANCASTER AVE 19087 #041-01-1987 L1988 **OBG** *030

WILDEMORE, John Keen. 744 W LANCASTER AVE, DEVON SQUARE II, SUITE 230 19087 #041-02-2001 L2001 **D** *020 †15

WILLIAMS, Erica Hove. ■ 19087 #041-01-1999 L2001 **FOP** *020 †50

WILLIAMSON, Paul K. 145 KING OF PRUSSIA RD, ROAD R-2-3 19087 #024-16-1979 L1982 **RHU IM** *020 †20

YARDNEY, Marc Jonathan. 241 CONESTOGA RD # B 19087 #041-01-1981 L1982 **IM IMG** *020 †20

YELAMANCHILI, Aarati. ■ 19087 #041-13-1999 L2007 **IM** *020 †20

WAYNESBORO — FRANKLIN

AMALFITANO, Thomas Guy. 5 ROADSIDE AVE, MID-ATLANTIC ORTHOPEDIC SP 17268 #035-48-1987 L1994 **ORS** *020 †40 ‡

ANDREWS, Christopher S. 45 ROADSIDE AVE 17268 #041-15-1999 L2002 **GS TRS** *020

BLANCHET, Garrett H. 6155 ANTHONY HWY 17268 #024-07-1978 L1987 **FM** *020 †18

CARD, Scott Alan. 1051 E MAIN ST 17268 #422-01-2003 L2006 **IM** *020 †20

CHAUDHRY, Muhammad Rafiq. 1051 E MAIN ST 17268 #654-01-1981 L1985 **IM** *020 †20

CHO, Cho. 45 ROADSIDE AVE, 2ND FL 17268 #209-01-1990 L1997 **IM** *020 †20

CHOI, Sang Youl. ■ 17268 #583-08-1974 L1983 **AN** *020 †05

CODA, Louis Evis. 501 E MAIN ST, C/O WAYNESBORO HOSPITAL 17268 #041-09-1985 L1993 **IM PD** *020 †20,55

COLLINS, David Andrew. 501 E MAIN ST, WAYNESBORO HOSPITAL 17268 #035-03-1978 L2006 **AN** *020 †05

CRYER, Theodore Hudson. 1647 E MAIN ST 17268 #023-01-1972 L1977 **OPH IM** *020 †35

DAUT, Ellen E Dugan. 501 E MAIN ST, WAYNESBORO HOSPITAL LAB 17268 #025-01-1963 L1969 **PTH** *020 †50

EDWARDS, Bruce Neil. 200 E MAIN ST, ROBINWOOD ORTHOPAEDIC SPEC 17268 #041-14-1980 L2008 **ORS** *020 †40

FARAH, J Ramsay. 501 E MAIN ST 17268 #605-01-1972 L1984 **PD ADL** *020 †55

FLINT, Robert Daniel, Jr. 501 E MAIN ST, EMERGENCY DEPARTMENT 17268 #023-01-1999 L2005 **EM** *020 †16

GARCIA, Domingo Alcantara. ■ 17268 #748-01-1953 L1971 **IM** *071

GLASS, Louis Leonard. 501 E MAIN ST 17268 #035-47-1991 L1996 **U** *020 †95

GOLDMAN, Robert Franklin. 1051 E MAIN ST STE 2 17268 #038-43-1976 L1984 **IM IMG** *020 †20

HAQ, Mohammad Shamsul. 23 WALNUT ST 17268 #704-01-1979 L1989 **IM** *020 †20 ‡

HAREN, William Edward. 501 E MAIN ST 17268 #041-13-1983 L1984 **U** *020 †95

HESS, Charles Franklin. ■ 17268 #023-01-1953 L1955 **FM** *071

HESS, David Robt, Jr. 501 E MAIN ST 17268 #023-01-1963 L1964 **FM** *020 †18

HESS, Reuben David. 501 E MAIN ST 17268 #041-14-1985 L1989 **IM PD** *020 †20,55

HINTERKOPF, John Peter. 45 ROADSIDE AVE 17268 #016-06-1965 L1977 **GS TRS** *020 †85

HOFGAARD, Henrik A. 500 E MAIN ST 17268 #693-01-1982 L2004 **ORS GS** *020

HOLOBINKO, Joseph Newton. 200 E MAIN ST, ROBINWOOD ORTHOPAEDIC SPEC 17268 #041-14-1996 L2004 **ORS** *020 †40

JANICKA, Iwona Joanna. 501 E MAIN ST, WAYNESBORO HOSPITALIST PRO 17268 #759-12-1989 L1998 **OBG OBS** *020 †18

KIRK, Daniel Lee. ■ 17268 #010-01-1943 L1944 **IMG** *071

KUMAR, James S. 501 E MAIN ST 17268 #495-76-1975 L1998 *020

LAMBIOTTE, Benjamin Jos. 204 W MAIN ST 17268 #039-01-1957 L1963 **GPM GP** *071 †70

LESSARD, Jean Vickers. 12525 N WELTY RD 17268 #041-12-1985 L1988 **OBG** *020 †30

LEWIS, Gary Wm. 501 E MAIN ST, FRANKLIN COUNTY HEART CENT 17268 #305-01-1985 L1986 **CD IM** *020 †20

LORENTSEN, Kevin John. 501 E MAIN ST, HEMATOLOGY SERVICES 17268 #023-07-1989 L1995 **ON HEM** *020 †20

LYON-LOFTUS, Diana Joan. 6155 ANTHONY HWY 17268 #025-12-1975 L1984 **FM** *020 †18

LYON-LOFTUS, Gregory Thom. 501 E MAIN ST 17268 #025-12-1977 L1984 **FM FPG** *020 †18

MATHIAS, Norbert Paul. 501 E MAIN ST 17268 #041-02-1977 L1979 **EM** *020 †16

MC KEE, Terrence Ian. 45 ROADSIDE AVE 17268 #060-01-1993 L1995 **GS** *020 †85

MC KENZIE, James Gray. 501 E MAIN ST 17268 #004-01-1961 L1976 **R** *020 †80

MC KENZIE, Merrill B. 501 E MAIN ST, WAYNESBORO HOSPITAL 17268 #035-06-1980 L1985 **FM EM** *020 †20

MILFORD, Richard Stuart. 5 ROADSIDE AVE 17268 #035-47-1983 L1989 **ORS** *020 †40

MILLER, Joseph Jay. ■ 17268 #041-13-1948 L1949 **GP** *071

NGEOW, Yin Keong. 501 E MAIN ST 17268 #624-01-1974 L1983 **AN PUD** *020 †05

PATTERSON, Donald Allen. 501 E MAIN ST, ROBINWOOD ORTHOPEDIC 17268 #041-09-1969 L1976 **ORS** *071 †40

PRICE, Todd Ashley. 501 E MAIN ST, WAYNESBORO HOSPITAL 17268 #011-02-1988 L1990 **AN** *020 †05

QURESHI, Jehanzeb. 1933 MARKET SQUARE BLVD, WAYNESBORO MEDICAL ASSOCIA 17268 #704-02-1980 L1996 **IM** *020 †20

QURESHI, Mahpara. 501 E MAIN ST 17268 #495-45-1990 L2006 **IM** *020 †20

REIHARD, Kathryn Anita. 501 E MAIN ST, WAYNESBORO HOSPITAL 17268 #041-02-1985 L1989 **EM** *020 †16

RISHI, Fouzia. 27 VISTA DR STE 3 17268 #704-02-1979 L1996 **PD PDC** *020 †55

ROTH, Mark David. 45 ROADSIDE AVE, SURGICAL ASSOCIATES 17268 #041-07-1992 L1996 **GS** *020 †85

SLETTEN, Stein M. 500 E MAIN ST 17268 #693-01-1987 L2004 **ORS** *020

STAPLEFORD, Edmund M. ■ 17268 #065-06-1953 L1961 **OBG OS** *071

TEETER, James Herring. 501 E MAIN ST 17268 #023-01-1954 L1957 **GS** *071 †85 ‡

TERNES, Robert Jos. 1051 E MAIN ST STE 2 17268 #041-13-1975 L1978 **IM OS** *020

WALLICK, Peter Glenn. 5 ROADSIDE AVE 17268 #041-02-1982 L1991 **PS HS** *020 †85,65

WAYNESBURG — GREENE

BAKTH, Shamsher. 350 BONAR AVE 15370 #160-06-1971 L1975 **CD IM** *020 †20

BEN, Kevin Chas. 350 BONAR AVE, GREEN COUNTY MEMORIAL HOSP 15370 #308-07-1982 L1986 **IM** *020 †20

BORIS, Jami Lynn. 430 E OAKVIEW DR 15370 #055-01-1998 L2002 **MPD** *020 †55,20

BUTERBAUGH, John Carl. 350 BONAR AVE 15370 #041-02-1961 L1962 **GS** *020

CHAYAPRUKS, Prayun. 189 E HIGH ST 15370 #891-02-1966 L1974 **IM IMG** *020 †55,20

CHURCH, Daniel Alan. 246 ELM DR 15370 #055-01-1998 L2001 **PD** *020 †55

COSTELLO, John M, Jr. 350 BONAR AVE, 3RD FL 15370 #041-12-1985 L1986 **CD IM** *020 †20

DESAI, Shirish Balvantrai. 1150 7TH ST 15370 #495-23-1969 L1980 **U** *020 †95

DIXON, Byron Duane. ■ 15370 #654-01-2004 L2008 **EM** *012

DONLEY, Darrell Lee. 1135 8TH ST 15370 #055-01-1995 L1997 **IM** *020 †20

FALOR, Stanley E L. 350 BONAR AVE 15370 #010-01-1964 L1965 **GP OM** *020

FRAZIER, John Earl, II. 350 BONAR AVE, 3RD FL 15370 #041-13-1966 L1967 **CD IM** *020 †20

GOULATIA, Amit. 1150 7TH ST 15370 #495-45-1992 L1996 **PCC** *020 †20

GROVER, Sukhdev Singh. 1150 7TH ST 15370 #495-03-1966 L1973 **PUD UM** *020 †20

HARPER, Morris Earl. ■ 15370 #024-01-1975 L1991 **IM** *020

HART, Neil James. 350 BONAR AVE, 3RD FL 15370 #028-34-1968 L1982 **CD** *020 †20

HORANI, Mohammed Nabil. 350 BONAR AVE 15370 #075-01-1971 L1973 **AN** *020

HUFFMAN, Charles R. ■ 15370 #041-02-1951 L1952 **GP OBG** *071

JACKSON, Timothy Kevin. 1115 E HIGH ST 15370 #038-41-1981 L1982 **END IM** *020 †20

JOAQUIN-WU, Jane Tio. 205 CRAGO AVE 15370 #748-07-1969 L1978 **GP** *075 ‡

KAPOOR, Rajeshwar Dayal. 1150 7TH ST 15370 #495-45-1973 L1977 **IM PCC** *020 †20

LESLIE, David Cleland. 343 E ROY FURMAN HWY, STE 104 15370 #041-13-1969 L1970 **OBG** *071 †30

LIU, Chaonan. ■ 15370 #242-50-1966 L1974 **IM** *100 †20

MARTINEZ, Ferdinand Anton. ■ 15370 #748-02-1999 L2007 **GS** *020 †85

MERING, Thomas Wood. 54 N MORRIS ST 15370 #056-06-1943 L1944 **OBG** *071

MULLANEY, Dennis Timothy. 350 BONAR AVE, GREENE CO. MEMORIAL HOSPIT 15370 #045-01-1976 L1990 **EM IM** *020 †20

NEGREY, Amy R. 430 E OAKVIEW DR, STE A 15370 #041-02-1996 L1999 **FM** *020 †18

O'CONNELL, C Leonard, Jr. 66 S CHURCH ST 15370 #041-12-1944 L1945 **IMG** *071

OWENS, Michael Ray. 350 BONAR AVE 15370 #051-04-1987 L1989 **EM IM** *020 †20

PATTERSON, Arthur J. 7TH ST & BONAR AVE 15370 #041-12-1944 L1945 **GS** *071 †85

PATTERSON, Arthur J, Jr. 112 VALLEY AVE STE A 15370 #041-02-1978 **GS EM** *020 †85

PERRY, John Killebrew, Jr. 350 BONAR AVE 15370 #027-01-1990 L1999 **AN** *071 †05

PILLAI, Pushkalai R. 190 BONAR AVE 15370 #495-42-1972 L1990 **P** *020

PIZZI, Wilson Bryan. 7TH ST & BONAR AVE 15370 #041-12-1942 L1943 **N IM** *071

REYES, John Leeds. 350 BONAR AVE 15370 #748-02-1973 L1975 **PTH BBK** *020 †50

SCHROEDER, George. 350 BONAR AVE, GREENE COUNTY MEMORIAL HOS 15370 #065-02-1982 L1986 **UCM** *020 ‡

STACHER, Eric Durell. 142 W HIGH ST 15370 #561-01-1974 L1978 **PD** *020

TSAI, Jer-Yuan. 1150 7TH ST 15370 #243-50-1967 L1974 **IM** *020 †20

VORA, Prafullchandra D. 249 ELM DR 15370 #495-01-1973 L1980 **CD IM** *020 †20

WU, Shin Shen. 205 CRAGO AVE 15370 #244-06-1969 L1976 **IM** *020 †20 ‡

ZIMMERMAN, Sherry M. 343 E ROY FURMAN HWY, STE 105 15370 #041-12-1994 L1996 **FM** *020 †18 ‡

WEATHERLY — CARBON

SECHERESIU, Emilia. 500 1ST ST, A & E MEDICAL ASSOCIATES, 18255 #781-03-1985 L1992 **IM** *020 †20

WELLSBORO — TIOGA

ANDERSON, John D, III. ■ 16901 #041-01-1951 L1953 **AN** *071 †05

BAIR, Robert C. 32-36 CENTRAL AVE 16901 #041-02-1950 L1951 **GS OBG** *071 †85
BECKER, Victor Paul. 103 WEST AVE 16901 #035-45-1996 L1999 **FM** *020 †18
BELLINGER, Edward Lee. 15 MEADE ST 16901 #041-13-1977 L1978 **U** *020 †95
BILDER, Mary Joan Horan. 103 WEST AVE, WELLSBORO LAUREL HEALTH CE 16901 #035-09-1969 L1973 **PD** *020 †55
BRECHBILL, Ivan Theodore. 5 EAST AVE 16901 #041-13-1963 L1964 **GS** *020
CAHILL, David Morton. 15 MEADE ST STE L5 16901 #654-01-1980 L1986 **GS GYN** *020
CALLENBERGER, George J. 9 WATER ST 16901 #041-13-1946 L1947 *071
CALLENBERGER, Ronald W. 9 WATER ST 16901 #041-13-1969 L1970 **ORS** *071
CAVANAUGH, Michelle Lynne. 7 WATER ST, GUTHRIE CLINIC LTD 16901 #041-14-1997 L1999 **FM** *020 †18
CLARK, Barry A. 1B MAIN ST 16901 #035-06-1980 L1983 **PD ADL** *020 †55
COOLIDGE, William Adams. 24 WALNUT ST, DAVID F GILLUM MD 16901 #041-13-1958 L1964 **GP** *071
DALE, Leonard Ervin, II. 101A WEST AVE 16901 #016-02-1970 L1971 **R NM** *020 †28,80 ‡
DOTY, John Patrick. 7 WATER ST, GUTHRIE CLINIC LTD 16901 #035-09-1975 L2000 **FM** *020 †18
ERWAY, Preston Mosch. 24 WALNUT ST 16901 #041-13-1958 L1991 **FM** *071 †18
GAFFORD, Grady D. 15 MEADE ST STE U1 16901 #001-02-1974 L1981 **OPH** *020 †35
GILLUM, David Frank. 24 WALNUT ST, GUTHRIE CLINIC 16901 #041-13-1963 L1964 **FM** *071 †18
GUELIG, Edmund P. 103 WEST AVE, WELLSBORO FAMILY PRACTICE 16901 #055-01-1988 L1990 **FM OBG** *020 †18
HARPST, Lisa Lynnelle. 7 WATER ST, GUTHRIE CLINIC 16901 #038-06-1995 L1998 **FM** *020
HESS, Edward Robt. 48 PEARL ST 16901 #041-09-1973 L1975 **GS GYN** *020 ‡
HOWE, Willard Arthur. 142 MAIN ST 16901 #025-07-1978 L2001 **FM EM** *020 †18,16
KNISLEY, Kent Remine. 32 FISCHLER ST 16901 #054-04-1983 L1984 **EM FM** *020 †18
MASON, Kevin Thos. ■ 16901 #041-07-1978 L2005 **FM AM** *020 †70,18
MEYERS, Lee Carroll. 7 WATER ST 16901 #041-15-2001 L2001 **FM** *020
NESPOLA, Anthony Morgan. 15 MEADE ST 16901 #041-13-1972 L1973 **IM** *020 †20
PFISTERER, David Alan. 7 WATER ST, GUTHRIE CLINIC LTD 16901 #041-07-1993 L1996 **FM** *020 †18
REICH, William Paul. ■ 16901 #054-04-1965 L1972 **PTH** *020 †50 ‡
RICE, Laura J. 22 WALNUT ST 16901 #025-12-1996 L2001 **EM** *020 †16
ROBERTS, Herbert R. 1 MAIN ST 16901 #028-03-1976 L2002 **OBG** *020 †30
SAYRE, Andrew John. 830 N CALLAHAN RD 16901 #041-14-1978 L1979 **EM** *020 †18,16
TERRY, John Martin. 58 WEST AVE 16901 #041-14-1977 L1978 **IM IMG** *020
THOMAS, Frank Ardell. 15 MEADE ST 16901 #041-02-1967 L1968 **IM** *030 †20
TOLINS, Christine L. 32-36 CENTRAL AVE 16901 #035-06-1975 L1981 **EM FM** *071 †18
TOWNSEND, Darryl Edward R. ■ 16901 #067-01-1955 L1969 **OBG** *071
VENTURANZA, Lucille E. 1873 SHUMWAY HILL RD 16901 #748-10-1965 L1979 **P** *020 †75
WONG, Edgar. SSM HSP CENTRAL AVE 16901 #063-01-1980 L1983 **EM** *020

WELLSVILLE – YORK

KUSHNER, Lois Jane Newman. ■ 17365 #041-09-1956 L1957 **R** *071 †80
MOYER, Shawn Steven. 7489 CARLISLE RD 17365 #041-02-1998 L2001 **FM** *020 †18

WERNERSVILLE – BERKS

CLEMENTS, William T. 260 E WASHINGTON ST 19565 #041-02-1980 L1981 **FM OS** *020 †18
DEMMY, Merlyn Ray. WERNERSVILLE STATE HOSP, CHIEF OF CLINICAL SERVICES 19565 #041-02-1956 L1957 **P** *071
DE VINE, Raylene Ann. 6 W PENN AVE 19565 #010-03-1968 L1983 **PD** *020 †55
FISHER, William C. ■ 19565 #035-01-1949 L1953 **D** *071 †15
KRAYBILL, Harold Erb. WERNERSVILLE STATE HOSP 19565 #041-01-1965 L1966 **P FM** *020 †18,75
LIGHT, Frederick W, Jr. ■ 19565 #023-07-1930 L1934 **CLP** *071 †50
LUTZ, Wilbur M. ■ 19565 #041-01-1941 L1942 **P** *071 †75
PADAYHAG, Matias Medalle. RT 422 SPORTSMANS RD 19565 #748-07-1956 L1980 **PTH** *071
RUBRIGHT, George La Mar. ■ 19565 #041-13-1946 L1947 **GP GYN** *071
SILVERMAN, Myron Harvey. WERNERSVILLE STATE HOSP 19565 #041-12-1966 L1967 **P CHP** *020
VITOLO-GALLO, Emilia. WERNERSVILLE STATE HOSP 19565 #041-09-1985 L1986 **P** *020 †75

WESCOSVILLE – LEHIGH

RENTLER, Russell Jos. 6083 HAMILTON BLVD 18106 #033-05-1985 L1986 **IM** *020 †20
VELARDE, Mark Edward. 6083 HAMILTON BLVD, SHEPARD HLS FMLY PRACTICE 18106 #033-05-1993 L1997 **FM** *020 †18

WEST ALEXANDER – WASHINGTON

COREY, Norman Francis, Jr. 278 MCDONALD RD 15376 #041-12-1980 L1982 **IM** *074 †20

WEST CHESTER – CHESTER

ABBOTT, Joseph Leo. 600 E MARSHALL ST 19380 #041-02-1954 L1955 **GYN** *072 †30
AGARWAL, Rajat Kumar. ■ 19380 #305-01-2001 L2002 **FM** *100
AKINS, Jennifer. 600 E MARSHALL ST 19380 #041-02-1994 L1997 **OBG** *020 †30
ALARCON, Jose Edgar. 440 E MARSHALL ST 19380 #341-01-1969 L1976 **IM** *020 †20
ALLAN, Mary Berninger. 606 E MARSHALL ST, STE 111 19380 #041-01-1955 L1956 **CD IM** *020 †20
ALTHOEN, Morgan C. ■ 19380 #025-01-1998 L2007 **DR** *012
ANDERSEN, Donald H. 915 OLD FERN HILL RD, BLDG B 19380 #041-02-1989 L1994 **U** *020 †95
ARAKAWA, Gordon K. ■ 19380 #024-05-2003 L2004 **DR** *012
ASHBURN, Theodore Thomas. ■ 19380 #024-01-1999 L2007
ASKINAS, Alan Michael. 600 E MARSHALL ST STE 305, CHESTER COUNTY OBGYN ASSOC 19380 #016-11-1980 L1984 **OBG** *020 †30
ATHANAS, Efthimios. ■ 19382 #561-01-1963 **PD** *071 †55

ATLAS, Douglas Leonard. 520 MAPLE AVE, STE 4 19380 #041-02-1998 L2000 **IM** *020 †20
BAICHI, Matthew M. 915 OLD FERN HILL RD 19380 #035-15-2000 L2006 **GE** *100 †20
BARRIS, Bruce J. 1103 PAOLI PIKE 19380 #041-13-1979 L1981 **IM N** *020 †20 ‡
BATIPPS, Francis Webb. ■ 19380 #010-03-1955 L1960 **OM U** *071
BAY, Kimberly C. 795 E MARSHALL ST, STE 301-307 19380 #041-01-1995 L2002 **PD** *020 †55
BAY, Nicholas William. 1460 CHESTNUT CT 19380 #041-01-1994 L1997 **FM** *020 †18
BEASLEY, James Edwin. ■ 19382 #041-01-1994 *100
BEAUGARD, Mark E. 520 MAPLE AVE STE 1 19380 #028-34-1975 L1976 **OTO** *020 †45
BEHRENS, Edward Malachi. ■ 19382 #041-01-2002 L2002 **PD** *100 †55
BELLAIRE, Cheryl Renee. 795 E MARSHALL ST, STE 304 19380 #025-01-1992 L1995 **OBG** *020 †30
BENNER, John Henry. 915 FERN HILL RD, STE ONE 19380 #041-02-1973 L1974 **ORS OFA** *020 †40
BENTLEY, Eugene Allan, Jr. 701 E MARSHALL ST, CHESTER COUNTY HOSP DEPT P 19380 #041-09-1958 L1959 **CLP PTH** *071 †50
BERKOWITZ, Richard David. ■ 19380 #024-07-1954 L1960 **IM** *071 †20
BERMAN, Dennis A. 440 E MARSHALL ST, STE 201 19380 #041-13-1977 L1978 **ON HEM** *071 †20
BERNBERG, Lawrence. ■ 19382 #041-01-1971 L1972 **AN** *071 †05
BIERL, Charlene Marie. ■ 19382 #024-05-2005 L2005 **PTH** *012
BISACCIA, Leonard Jos. ■ 19382 #050-02-1943 L1985 **R** *071 †80
BLYDENBURGH, Susan M. ■ 19382 #035-15-1983 L1985 **FM** *020 †18,70
BOBMAN, David Eric. 915 OLD FERN HILL RD 19380 #041-13-1986 L1991 **GE IM** *020 †20
BOCHER, Jack. 701 E MARSHALL ST 19380 #041-02-1960 L1961 **ORS LM** *071 †40
BOIS, Richard Thos. ■ 19382 #028-34-1984 L1994 **EM** *020 †16
BONANNI, Loretta Doreen. 795 E MARSHALL ST, STE 301-307 19380 #041-02-1978 L1979 **PD** *020 †55
BONNER, Hugh, Jr. 701 E MARSHALL ST, DEPT OF PATH 19380 #041-13-1967 L1968 **PTH HEM** *020 †50
BORISLOW, Steven Mark. 701 E MARSHALL ST 19380 #041-01-1993 L1999 **DR** *020 †80
BOWEN, Anne C. 1646 W CHESTER PIKE, STE 21 19382 #041-12-1984 L1985 **IM** *020 †20
BOYADJIS, Terrence A. 790 E MARKET ST, STE 245 19382 #308-07-1982 L1985 **P** *020 †75
BRIONES, Mariele Calderon. 795 E MARSHALL ST, STE 102C 19380 #020-02-1998 L2001 **END** *020 †20
BROWN, Earl Howard. ■ 19382 #041-02-1973 L1974 **EM** *020 †16
BUCHANAN, Aurora S. ■ 19382 #748-07-1956 L1965 **FM AN** *071
BURKE, Bernard Steven. 795 E MARSHALL ST STE 201 19380 #041-02-1979 L1980 **IM** *020 †20
CANTARELLA, Gina Marie. ■ 19380 #041-13-2004 L2004 **OBG** *012
CANTRELL, Cheryl Kaye. 1308 BIRMINGHAM RD 19382 #039-01-1980 L1982 **P** *020 †75
CARTER, Edward Philip. 701 E MARSHALL ST, CHESTER COUNTY HOSPITAL 19380 #041-12-1989 L1996 **DR** *020 †80
CATALANO-CAMPBELL, Jamea. 1450 E BOOT RD, STE 700A 19380 #041-07-1997 L2001 **D** *020 †15
CHAMBERS, Aaron Andrew. ■ 19380 #023-07-2004 L2007 **PD** *100 †55
CICCARELLI, Stephanie Lee. 701 E MARSHALL ST, GLASGOW MEDICAL ASSOCIATES 19380 #036-05-1993 L1997 **IM EM** *020 †20,16
CLAUHS, Ronald P. 701 E MARSHALL ST 19380 #041-13-1977 L1978 **OBG** *020 †30
COLLINS, Kenneth Patrick. 915 OLD FERN HILL RD, BLDG B 19380 #038-43-1982 L1987 **U** *020 †95
CONN, Coulson Alan. 440 E MARSHALL ST 19380 #041-01-1964 L1968 **PD** *020 †55
DAMIANO, Michael David. 1450 E BOOT RD, STE 700A 19380 #035-20-1986 L1990 **D** *020 †15
DAMMERMAN, Ryan Scott. ■ 19380 #035-01-2002 L2003 **FM** *020 †18
DE BACCO, Paul. 909 E BOOT RD 19380 #041-13-1992 L1994 **FM** *020 †18
DEBAPTISTE, Celeste E. 440 E MARSHALL ST, STE 101 19380 #041-13-1988 L1991 **OBG** *020 †30
DELANEY, Melissa Leigh. 606 E MARSHALL ST, STE 205 19380 #041-77-1993, ▲ L1994 **OBG** *020 ‡
DESJARDINS, Jay Arnold. ■ 19380 #041-01-1955 L1956 **IM OS** *071 †20
DESTAFENO, John J. ■ 19380 #035-03-2001 L2007 **OPH** *100 †35
DICKTER, Steven Jos. 701 E MARSHALL ST 19380 #041-02-1987 L1989 **FM** *020 †18
DI SESA, Verdi Jos. 701 E MARSHALL ST, THE CHESTER COUNTY HOSPITA 19380 #041-01-1976 L1977 **TS CD** *020 †20,85,90
DONNELLY, Joseph C, Jr. 794 JEFFERSON WAY, HERSHEY'S MILL 19380 #041-13-1956 L1957 **VS TS** *020 †85,90
DUNBAR, Nancy Robin. 1546 MCDANIEL DR 19380 #041-13-1988 L1990 **P ADP** *020 †75
EARLEY, Willie Roger. 1008 BALA FARMS 19382 #016-11-1989 L2005 **P** *020 †75
EDWARDS, Clifford Newton. 1615 E BOOT RD, # L308 19380 #062-01-1946 L1960 **U** *071
EFSTRATIOU, Alain. 531 MAPLE AVE 19380 #418-01-1981 L2003 **CD IM** *020 †20
ELLISON, Norig. ■ 19380 #041-01-1961 L1964 **AN** *020 †05
EMERY, Donald Lee. 701 E MARSHALL ST, INTENSIVE CARE UNIT 19380 #041-02-1981 L1988 **PUD IM** *020 †20
ERESO, Glenn Louis. 701 E MARSHALL ST, WEST CHESTER ANESTHESIA AS 19380 #051-04-2004 L2004 **AN** *012
FATTU, James Michael. ■ 19382 #017-20-1973 L1993 **IM PHM** *071 †20
FAUNCE, James George, III. ■ 19380 #041-09-1962 L1963 **OBG** *071 †30
FENDRICK, Jeffrey Scott. 440 E MARSHALL ST, 3RD FLR STE 300 19380 #041-02-1988 L1990 **PD** *020 †55
FERNANDEZ, Elizabeth Ann. ■ 19380 #041-02-2008 *012
FISCHETTI, John Leo. ■ 19382 #035-08-1954 L1988 **IM CD** *072 †20
FLANAGAN, John Chas, Jr. ■ 19380 #041-02-1957 L1958 **IM** *020 †20
FLORENCE, Daphne Jo. 708 E MARSHALL ST, WEST CHESTER ANESTHESIA AS 19380 #041-02-1999 L2000 **AN** *020
FONTANELLA, Mary Nichole. ■ 19382 #041-13-2007 L2007 **TY** *012
FOXX, William F. ■ 19382 #038-40-1952 L1957 **DR RO** *071 †80
FUKUCHI, Steven Gitaro. 915 OLD FERN HILL RD 19380 #016-06-1994 L1999 **GS** *020 †65
GALLO, Eduardo Felix. ■ 19380 #132-02-1969 L1974 **DR RNR** *020 †80
GARBER, Scott Jeffery. 708 E MARSHALL ST 19380 #041-13-1989 L1992 **AN** *020 †05
GARDNER, Alan Mathews. 606 E MARSHALL ST, STE 112 19380 #041-02-1970 L1971 **P** *020 †75
GAZEK, Miguel German. 323 E MARSHALL ST 19380 #132-02-1970 L1977 **IM CD** *075
GEDDES, Giselle Jeannette. 600 E MARSHALL ST, STE 303 19380 #041-13-1987 L1989 **IM** *020 †20
GELMAN, Ricardo. 701 E MARSHALL ST 19380 #038-06-1983 L1984 **EM** *020 †16
GEMIL, Corazon G. 795 E MARSHALL ST STE 201 19380 #748-01-1967 L1972 **OBG** *020 †30

GEMIL-CORRAL, Angelita G. 795 E MARSHALL ST, STE 201 19380 #748-01-1964 L1979 GYN *020

GILMAN, Steven Brian. ■ 19382 #035-03-1978 L1984 DR *020 †80

GOLD, Steven K. ■ 19380 #043-01-1994 *100

GONZALEZ, Ralph, Jr. ■ 19382 #041-13-2007 L2007 *012

GRAHAM, Garth Kinsey. ■ 19380 #024-01-1947 L1974 IM *071 †20

GREENBERG, Bernard. 440 E MARSHALL ST STE 201, CHESTER CNTY HEMATOLOGY 19380 #035-46-1966 L1967 HO ON *020 †20

GROSSMAN, David. 440 E MARSHALL ST, STE 201 19380 #033-05-1982 L1986 HEM *020 †20

GUNNING, Marylisa. 21 TURNER LN, EMBASSY COURT 19380 #041-02-1985 L1988 FM *020 †18

HACK, David Walter. ■ 19382 #033-05-1996 L1999 FM *020 †18

HALL, Estill F. ■ 19380 #020-02-1951 L1951 PHP GPM *071

HANCHAK, Nicholas Andrew. ■ 19382 #024-01-1990 L1992 IM *020 †20

HANDLER, Robert Isaac. 390 E BOOT RD 19380 #020-02-1978 L1982 CHP P *020

HANNA, Robert Howard. 701 E MARSHALL ST 19380 #010-03-1958 L1959 GP OBG *072

HANSON, Teresa Sanchez. 701 E MARSHALL ST 19380 #056-06-1948 L1951 OBG *075 †30

HART, Kathryn Y D. ■ 19380 #041-09-1974 L1976 DR *075 †80

HATTI, Runa Shivkumar. ■ 19382 #041-02-2007 IM *012

HEALD, James Irwin. 701 E MARSHALL ST 19380 #041-02-1980 L1982 PTH PCP *020 †50

HELLER, Harry Eddy. 8 S WAYNE ST, COUNTY, INC 19382 #035-09-1977 L1981 OBG *020 †30

HERRING, Steven Jeffrey. 1450 E BOOT RD, STE 600B 19380 #041-02-1985 L1986 FM *020 †18

HERTZ, Barry Chester. 520 MAPLE AVE STE 3, PULMONARY DISEASES LTD 19380 #041-01-1975 L1976 PUD IM *020 †20

HEWITT, Maureen Rose. 440 E MARSHALL ST 19380 #021-05-2001 L2001 HO *020

HEWSON, William Claude. ■ 19380 #041-13-1954 L1956 LM GP *071

HIMMELSTEIN, Fred Raymond. ■ 19382 #041-14-1979 L1980 EM FM *020 †18,16

HIRSCH, Susan Lenore. ■ 19382 #035-03-1981 L1983 GS *020 †85

HOBERMAN, Maury. ■ 19382 #041-02-1960 L1961 OTO PS *071 †45

HOTMER, Dianne. 600 E MARSHALL ST, STE 305 19380 #041-07-1989 L1992 OBG *020 †30

HURLEY, Harry J, Jr. 1101 PAOLI PIKE 19380 #041-02-1949 L1950 D *020 †15

HURLEY, Jeffrey Peter. 1101 PAOLI PIKE 19380 #024-05-1984 L1988 D DMP *020 †15

HUSAIN, Azam. 531 MAPLE AVE 19380 #495-21-1959 L1971 IM CD *071 †20

HUXSTER, Robert Hugh. 915 FERN HILL RD, STE ONE 19380 #041-02-1978 L1979 ORS HS *020 †40 ‡

HYKEL-MALONE, Nancy C. 42 E STREET RD 46 19382 #041-07-1983 L1985 IM *020 †20

JAN, Mian Arshad. 531 MAPLE AVE 19380 #704-09-1974 L1983 CD IM *020 †20

JOHNSON, Lisa Bowen. 1646 W CHESTER PIKE, STE 21 19382 #041-13-1987 L1989 IM *020 †20

JOLLY, Athena T. 850 PENNS WAY 19382 #418-01-1970 L1993 OM IM *030 †20,70

JUNG, Jennifer Warren. ■ 19380 #041-02-2003 L2003 DR *012

KAETEN, Gisela Eva M. ■ 19380 #407-25-1952 L1962 GP *071

KAMINSTEIN, David S. ■ 19382 #561-17-1973 GE IM *075 †20

KANE, Diana L. 701 E MARSHALL ST, CHESTER COUNTY HOSPITAL-ER 19380 #041-13-1997 L1999 EM *020 †16

KANE, Matthew Stephen. 795 E MARSHALL ST, STE 102C 19380 #065-09-1984 L1985 END IM *020 †20

KATARIA, Vinod Kumar. 529 MAPLE AVE 19380 #496-14-1981 L1986 IM EM *020 †20

KELTON, Franklin C. ■ 19382 #041-01-1945 L1946 IMG *072 †18

KELTON, Franklin C, Jr. 401 N FRANKLIN ST 19380 #041-02-1974 L1975 FM *020 †18,16

KENAWY, Azza Ezzel Arab. 1511 MCDANIEL DR 19380 #915-04-1987 L1997 IM *020 †20

KERN, George W. 520 MAPLE AVE STE 6 19380 #041-02-1970 L1971 AI PD *020 †55,03

KESTER, Walter L. ■ 19380 #041-01-1949 L1950 GP *071

KHAN, Shabih Urrehman. 603 PERRY DR 19380 #704-02-1996 L2002 IM CCM *020 †20

KHATTAK, Mohammad Yunas. ■ 19380 #704-09-1965 L1976 GS *100 †85

KIM, Ilhoon. 453 LYNETREE DR 19380 #583-02-1957 L1972 IM *071 †20

KIMLESS-GARBER, Debra B. ■ 19382 #033-05-1987 L1989 AN IM *020 †05

KORBONITS, Charles Wm. 701 E MARSHALL ST 19380 #041-02-1946 L1950 OBG *071 †30

KRASNER, Lauren Jill. 701 E MARSHALL ST, DEPT OF ANESTHESIA/ 19380 #041-13-1989 L1991 CCA *020 †05

KRISHNAN, Shanti. 440 E MARSHALL ST, STE 330 19380 #495-01-1983 L1990 PD *020 †55

KURYAN, Alex Sibu. 915 OLD FERN HILL RD 19380 #041-15-1999 L2001 GE *020 †20

LACAVARO, Jules Anthony. ■ 19380 #561-17-1966 L1968 GE *071

LANDRUM, Lorena Robin. ■ 19382 #025-07-1997 L2006 ICE *012 †20

LAUFER, Elizabeth Ursula. ■ 19380 #041-07-1956 L1957 OBG *020 †30

LAWTON, Gregory. 440 E MARSHALL ST STE 300, KIDS FIRST WEST CHESTER 19380 #041-02-1996 L1998 PD *020 †55

LEBOUTILLIER, Martin, III. 701 E MARSHALL ST, CHESTER CNTY C V SURGERY 19380 #035-01-1990 L1998 TS *020 †85,90

LEIGH, Flora Bongsoon. ■ 19382 #041-07-1961 L1979 OM *071

LEVIN, Russell Lee. 701 E MARSHALL ST, THE CHESTER COUNTY HOSP 19380 #041-13-1984 L1985 AN PME *020 †05

LEWIS, Earl Thurman. ■ 19380 #041-02-1954 L1965 PA IM *071

LEWIS, Jerry Parker. ■ 19382 #016-11-1957 IM HEM *071 †20,19

LEWIS, Joseph Gerard. 915 OLD FERN HILL RD, BLDG A 19380 #041-02-1986 L1987 CD *020 †20 ‡

LIANG, I-Hsun. 467 BALA TER E 19380 #035-09-2008 *012

LIFSCHITZ, Meyer D. ■ 19380 #024-05-1967 L1968 NEP IM *050 †20

LIMPERT, George Henry. 1205 W CHESTER PIKE, RR 3 19382 #036-05-1985 L1988 FM *020 †18

LISS, Robert Phillip. 915 OLD FERN HILL RD, STE B200 19380 #035-08-1985 L1990 OPH *020 †35

LOBO, Christopher Jos. 1601 MCDANIEL DR, STE 50 19380 #495-17-1974 L1978 OBG *020 †30

LOEB, Debra Gail. 701 E MARSHALL ST 19380 #041-07-1983 L1984 AN *020 †05

LUTCAVAGE, Christopher M. ■ 19382 #041-02-1999 GS *020

MAC KENZIE, Norman D. PO BOX 15 19381 #041-13-1943 L1944 GP OS *075

MAHER, John Patrick. 601 WESTTOWN RD, STE 290 19382 #035-08-1960 L1964 PHP IM *030

MALCOLM, Carol Elizabeth. 440 E MARSHALL ST STE 3 19380 #041-13-1996 L1998 PD *020 †15

MANION, David Patrick. 1450 E BOOT RD, STE 700A 19380 #041-02-2002 L2006 D *020 †15

MANSFIELD, Richard John. 600 E MARSHALL ST STE 305, OB/GYN ASSOCIATES OF 19380 #033-05-1989 L1992 OBG *020 †30

MARSHALL, Martye Lois. 701 E MARSHALL ST 19380 #012-01-1983 L2004 IM OS *020 †20

MATTHEWS, Helen Chang. 701 E MARSHALL ST, 4TH FLOOR PEDIATRICS 19380 #025-01-1993 L1998 PD *020 †55

MAUD, Patricia A. 1450 E BOOT RD, STE 600B 19380 #041-01-1978 L1979 FM *020 †18

MC ALEER, David J. ■ 19380 #041-13-1951 L1952 GS *071 †85

MC CABE, James Leo, Jr. ■ 19380 #041-02-1959 L1960 END *071

MC CARTER, Anne A. ■ 19380 #041-09-1992 L1996 OTO *062 †45

MC CAUSLAND, Drew. 606 E MARSHALL ST STE 107 19380 #041-09-1969 L1970 D DMP *020 †15

MC GEEHAN, John Thos. 701 E MARSHALL ST 19380 #041-02-1944 L1945 R NM *072 †85,80

MERSON, Erich Rudolph. 701 E MARSHALL ST 19380 #154-02-1967 L1970 GP *072

METRY, Nawal G. 1536 MCDANIEL DR 19380 #330-04-1966 L1971 AI A *020 †55,03

MICHENER, Todd Andrew. 915 OLD FERN HILL RD, STEADMAN HAWKINS CLINIC 19380 #047-05-2001 L2001 ORS *100

MIKURIYA, Beverly A. 701 E MARSHALL ST, EMERGENCY DEPT 19380 #041-13-1973 L1976 IM *020 †20,16

MILLER, Carrie Nicole. 915 OLD FERN HILL RD 19380 #035-19-2001 L2001 GE *020

MONTGOMERY, Bruce Barrick. ■ 19380 #041-02-1960 L1961 OBG *020 †30

MORTENSEN, Eric Rudolph. ■ 19382 #024-01-1990 L1997 GE *020 †20

MUDGIL, Anaeth V. 440 E MARSHALL ST, STE 100 19380 #035-03-1993 L2001 OPH PO *020 †35

MURDOCH, Winslow Wm. 1450 E BOOT RD STE 300A, GOSHEN EXECUTIVE CENTER 19380 #041-02-1986 L1987 FM *020 †18

MURPHY, Andrew Wm. 520 MAPLE AVE STE 6 19380 #041-14-1992 L1994 AI *020 †20,03

MURRAY, Audrey. ■ 19382 #539-06-1961 L1976 GP *071

MYERS, Boyd Corson. 1205 W CHESTER PIKE 19382 #051-04-1973 L1977 FM *020 †18

NAGLE, Willard F. 1450 E BOOT RD, STE 330A 19380 #035-06-1961 L1986 IMG NEP *072

NAIDU, Ramarao. ■ 19382 #209-01-1958 L1979 AN *074 †05

NALIN, David Robt. ■ 19382 #035-03-1965 L1988 ID GE *071 ‡

NEIBLUM, David R. 915 OLD FERN HILL RD 19380 #041-13-1989 L1991 GE *020 †20

NEILAN, Joyce S. ■ 19382 #055-01-1991 PD *074

NEUBURGER, Kenneth Jay. 725 MARSHALLTON THORNDL RD 19380 #035-03-1980 L1981 EM *020 †20,16

NEWMAN, Clyde F, Jr. 1580 MCDANIEL DR 19380 #041-01-1946 L1947 OBG *071 †30

NGUYEN, Doyen Thi. ■ 19382 #041-13-1981 L1983 PTH NS *020 †50

NOLAN, Gerald Patrick. ■ 19380 #041-09-1954 L1955 OBG *071 †30

NYPAVER, Annette Lynn. 701 E MARSHALL ST 19380 #041-13-1986 L1990 PD *020 †55

OEHLER, Sharon Denise. 440 E MARSHALL ST STE 300 19380 #025-07-1980 L1983 PD *020 †55

OH, Eun Joo. 520 MAPLE AVE 19380 #023-01-2002 L2002 IMG *020 †20

OSMICK, Mary Jane. ■ 19382 #041-13-1981 L1983 IM *020 †20

PAI, Reina D. 915 OLD FERN HILL RD 19380 #035-03-2001 L2006 GE *020

PAREKH, Nehal Vijay. 223 SNOWBERRY WAY 19380 #496-25-1999 L2002 RHU *012 †20

PATEL, Maya Bhagubhai. 23 DOE RUN CT 19382 #495-17-1955 L1975 P *020 †75

PATTON, Gerald Morgan. 795 E MARSHALL ST, STE 102 19380 #011-02-1987 L1988 VS *020 †85

PELLINI, Brian Michael. ■ 19382 #041-02-2006 L2007 GS *012

PELLINI, Michael John. ■ 19380 #041-02-1997 L1999 FM *030

PENNINGTON, Neil Douglas. 795 E MARSHALL ST STE 307 19380 #306-01-1984 L1985 PD *020 †55 ‡

PEREIRA, Gilberto R. 701 E MARSHALL ST, 2ND FLOOR NEONATOLOGY 19380 #187-18-1966 L1975 PD NPM *020 †55

PEREZ, Elena Elizabeth. 701 E MARSHALL ST, 4TH FLOOR PEDIATRICS 19380 #011-03-1998 L2000 PD *020 †55,03

PEREZ, Ricardo Antonio. 701 E MARSHALL ST 19380 #042-03-1998 L2007 IM *020 †20

PERSONS, Carol Ann Marie. ■ 19382 #041-13-1975 L1976 P *040 †75

PETERS, Gary Richard. ■ 19380 #005-14-1980 L1998 PA *050 †20

PINSKY, Karen L. 701 E MARSHALL ST, COUNTY HOSPITAL 19380 #067-01-1991 L1995 AN *020 †55

PINTO, Rupal Christine. ■ 19382 #041-12-2007 L2007 *012

PLATT, Marc Lee. 531 MAPLE AVE, WEST CHESTER CARDIOLOGY 19380 #016-06-1974 L2005 CD IM *020 †20

PLUMMER, William, III. ■ 19382 #041-01-1950 L1951 DIA IM *071

POOLE, Catherine Ann. ■ 19382 #040-02-1958 L1997 PDR *071 †80

RAYMUNDO, L Antone. ■ 19380 #056-06-1988 L1989 AN *020

RHOADS, Donelle Lynn. 795 E MARSHALL ST, STE 102 19380 #041-13-1995 L1998 GS *020 †85

RIVIELLO, Michael Saml. 1152 N NEW ST 19380 #021-01-1964 L1965 OM GS *071

ROBERTS, Alfred S, Jr. ■ 19382 #041-09-1946 L1947 P *071 †75

ROBERTS, John Hahn. 701 E MARSHALL ST, THE CHESTER COUNTY HOSP 19380 #041-13-1980 L1986 HOS PUD *020 †20

ROBINSON, Theodore Alan. 440 E MARSHALL ST, STE 300 19380 #041-01-1963 L1964 PD *071 †55

RODRIGUEZ, Claudio E. ■ 19382 #308-05-1995 *100

ROHRMAYER, Francis P, Jr. ■ 19380 #041-01-1944 L1945 OBG GP *071

ROMISHER, Marc Kenneth. 708 E MARSHALL ST 19380 #041-02-1978 L1979 AN *020 †05

RONKIN, Sheila Lee. 701 E MARSHALL ST, CHESTER COUNTY HOSPITAL 19380 #033-05-1982 L1984 MFM *020 †30

ROSEN, Michael Stuart. 795 E MARSHALL ST STE 101 19380 #041-07-1979 L1980 RHU IM *020 †20 ‡

ROSS, Maria Alotzker. ■ 19380 #041-07-1970 L1971 R *020 †80

ROWGHANI, Mohammad I. 701 E MARSHALL ST 19380 #517-06-1962 L1973 OBG *071 †30

ROZMUS, Gemma Greiner. 300 LAWRENCE DR STE B, CVIM 19380 #041-13-1992 L1996 IM *020 †20

RUBENSTONE, Jeanne Chris. 701 E MARSHALL ST 19380 #041-09-1983 L1986 EM *020 †16

RUSSELL, Bertram Royce, Jr. 701 E MARSHALL ST, CHESTER COUNTY HOSPITAL 19380 #041-02-1976 L1977 R *020 †80

RUSSELL, James Clyde, Jr. ■ 19382 #028-03-1971 L1971 AN *020 †05

RUSSELL, Pamela Brown. 701 E MARSHALL ST 19380 #041-01-1981 L1983 NPM *020 †55

RUSSO, Ronald Francis. 300 LAWRENCE DR STE B, COMM VOLUNT IN MED 19380 #041-13-1958 L1959 FM *071 †18

SARAN, Bruce Robert. 915 OLD FERN HILL RD, BLDG B 19380 #035-06-1988 L1992 OPH *020 †35 ‡

SAUL, Marjorie Ruth. 1246 W CHESTER PIKE STE 30 19382 #041-12-1979 L1980 P *020 †75 ‡

SAUL, Scott Howard. 862 BOLING BROOKE RD 19382 #041-12-1979 L1980 PTH *020 †50

SCHAAF, Homer Dixon. ■ 19382 #035-19-1948 L1975 PTH *071 †50

SCHAAF, Sara A Chubb. ■ 19382 #041-13-1947 L1949 GP *071

SCHWAMM, Harry Alfred. ■ 19380 #869-07-1957 L1978 PTH *071 †50

SCHWARTZ, Andrew Eric. 915 OLD FERN HILL RD 19380 #035-09-1984 L1985 GE IM *020 †20

SCHWARTZ, Lori Ellen. 795 E MARSHALL ST, STE 301-307 19380 #041-15-2002 L2002 **PD** *020 †55

SCHWENK, Eric Stephen. ■ 19380 #041-02-2008 L2008 *012

SCIARA, Christine M. 1595 PAOLI PIKE STE 105 19380 #041-13-1980 L1981 **D** *020 †15

SCOTT, Pamela Phyllis. 795 E MARSHALL ST, STE 102 19380 #041-07-1976 L1978 **GS** *020 †85

SEEDOR, John Wm. ■ 19382 #041-09-1954 L1955 **GP OM** *071

SEIDNER-JOSEPH, Elyse L. 600 E MARSHALL ST STE 205 19380 #035-01-1986 L1993 **GE IM** *071

SHAPIRO, Scott Eric. 25 RIDINGS WAY 19382 #041-13-2000 L2000 **CD** *020 †20

SHENKIN, Henry Arnold. ■ 19380 #041-02-1939 L1941 **NS** *071 †25

SHILLINGFORD, Robert Paul. 440 E MARSHALL ST STE 300 19380 #041-02-1958 L1959 **PD** *020 †55

SHRIKANTHAN, Michele Sora. ■ 19382 #041-12-1995 L2001 **IMG** *020 †20

SIDDIQUI, Msalim Unnabi. ■ 19382 #041-13-2007 **IM** *012

SINGER, Jerome. 1488 QUAKER RDG 19380 #041-02-1966 L1967 **PD** *030 †55

SKALINA, Mary Ellen L. 701 E MARSHALL ST, DIVISION OF NEONATOLOGY 19380 #035-01-1976 L1986 **NPM** *020 †55

SPEIDEL, Francis Xavier. 215 WILLIAM PENN BLVD 19382 #041-13-1977 L1978 **EM** *020 †16

STARK, Bruce Ira. 915 OLD FERN HILL RD, BLDG B 19380 #025-01-1978 L1979 **OPH** *020 †35

STEIN, Herman Joseph. ■ 19382 #041-01-1962 L1963 **DR** *071 †80

STEINBERG, Mark Harold. ■ 19382 #005-11-1977 **PHM ON** *050 †20

STEINER, Craig Michael. 915 OLD FERN HILL RD, BLDG B, GROUND FLOOR 19380 #041-12-1987 L1991 **AN** *020 †05

STEWART, William Wayne. ■ 19380 #041-09-1943 L1946 **ORS** *071

STIPE, Barbara Lynn. 701 E MARSHALL ST, THE CHESTER COUNTY HOSPITA 19380 #011-04-1993 L1996 **PD** *020 †55

STRETTON, Jean Brubaker. 520 MAPLE AVE 19380 #041-09-1979 L1980 **IM IMG** *020 †20

STRODE, Marshall D. 708 E MARSHALL ST 19380 #041-13-1971 L1972 **AN** *020 †05

STRUCKMEYER, Doris Lee A. ■ 19380 #051-04-1956 L1966 **IM GPM** *071

SUNOO, Jane. 520 MAPLE AVE, STE 4 19380 #038-06-1995 L1998 **IM** *020 †20

TAM, Isaac Ti-Yuen. 440 E MARSHALL ST, WEST CHESTER 19380 #041-01-1975 L1977 **IM** *020 †20

TAUBER, Danna. 701 E MARSHALL ST 19380 #021-01-1997 L2000 **PDP** *020 †55

TEDESCHI, Michele Teresa. 440 E MARSHALL ST, STE 501 19380 #041-13-1992 L1995 **HO** *020 †20

THANGADA, Parineetha. 701 E MARSHALL ST 19380 #496-33-1997 L2002 **IM** *020 †20

THAYU, Meena. 701 E MARSHALL ST, 4TH FLOOR PEDIATRICS 19380 #008-01-1999 L2002 **PD** *020 †55

TIRK, Kirby Stuart. 708 E MARSHALL ST 19380 #056-05-1980 L1990 **AN** *030 †05

TISCHLER, James F. ■ 19382 #041-09-1977 L1981 **IM** *020 †20

TOMAYKO, John F, Jr. ■ 19382 #041-12-1985 L1989 **ID IM** *020 †20

TRAJTENBERG, Jorge A. 915 OLD FERN HILL RD, BLDG B 19380 #132-02-1974 L1978 **GS** *020 †85

TROJAK, Joseph Edward. 1646 WEST CHESTER PIKE, STE 12 19382 #041-09-1975 L1976 **IM MG** *020 †20,19

TROSTLE, Henry S. 915 OLD FERN HILL RD STE 3, FERN HILL CMPS BLDGE A 19380 #041-02-1952 L1981 **OM AM** *071

TROUT, Robert Gates. ■ 19380 #041-09-1947 L1948 **TS** *072 †85,90

TULLAI, John. ■ 19382 #041-09-1959 L1961 **AN** *071

TURAN, Ekrem S. 701 E MARSHALL ST 19380 #902-01-1947 L1975 **OBG** *071 †30

TURNER, Erica. 795 E MARSHALL ST, STE 307 19380 #050-02-1987 L1990 **PD** *020 †55

TURNER, Roberta Virginia. ■ 19380 #051-01-1983 L1985 **IM** *020 †20 ‡

TWARDY, Bernadette E K. 1500 QUAKER RDG, HERSHEY'S MILL 19380 #041-07-1957 L1958 **PM** *071 †60

UHLMAN, Richard Chas. 606 E MARSHALL ST, STE 207 19380 #041-13-1955 L1956 **U** *071 †95

VAN AS, Andre W W. ■ 19380 #836-01-1960 L1980 **PUD IM** *020

WANG, John Kai. 701 E MARSHALL ST, CHESTER COUNTY HOSPITAL IC 19380 #041-02-1995 L2006 **PUD** *020 †20

WARD, Michael John A. 915 OLD FERN HILL RD # 1B 19380 #041-02-1976 L1977 **ORS HS** *071 †40

WARDEH, Ghassan Louis. 617 COACH HILL CT 19380 #528-04-1989 L2004 **PUD** *020 †20

WEIMAR FITZPATRICK, J A. ■ 19380 #041-02-2005 L2005 **FP** *012

WEINBERG, Laurence Mark. 915 OLD FERN HILL RD 19380 #024-05-1976 L1984 **GE** *020 †20

WERRIN, Ronald J. 440 E MARSHALL ST, PENN PRIMARY CARE OF WC 19380 #041-13-1977 L1978 **IM** *020 †20 ‡

WHITE, Joseph Geo. 606 E MARSHALL ST, STE 207 19380 #016-02-1963 L1973 **U** *071 †95

WINKLEY, Geoffrey. 701 E MARSHALL ST 19380 #048-13-1991 L1996 **EM** *020 †16

WIRSHUP, Mary Brennan. 300 LAWRENCE DR STE B, COMMUNITY VOLUNTEERS IN ME 19380 #051-07-1984 L1985 **FM** *020 †18

WITTERHOLT, Kenneth A. 795 E MARSHALL ST, STE 102 19380 #010-01-1986 L1991 **GS** *020 †85

WOLF, Charles Robt. 915 OLD FERN HILL RD, # 1-BLDG 19380 #041-12-1959 L1960 **ORS** *071 †40

WOUTERSZ, Theodore Bruce. ■ 19382 #041-02-1956 L1957 **OBG** *071 †30

WU, David Harold. ■ 19380 #035-15-1978 L1995 **ID IM** *050

ZELENSKA, Tetyana Aleksee. 1450 E BOOT RD, STE 200A 19380 #913-05-1994 L2007 **FM** *020 †18

WEST CONSHOHOCKEN – MONTGOMERY

BRODERSON, Hal Stuart. 100 FRONT ST, STE 1350 19428 #020-12-1983 L1984 **OS** *030

COOPERMAN, Harry Alan. 405 SPRING GARDEN LN 19428 #041-07-1981 L1983 **DR** *020 †80

FITZGIBBONS, Richard P. 100 FOUR FALLS CORPORT CTR, STE 312 19428 #041-13-1969 L1970 **P FM** *071

RUSH, Janet Elaine. ■ 19428 #038-40-1979 L1982 **CD IM** *050 †20

SMOGER, David Lee. ■ 19428 #041-13-2003 L2003 **DR** *012

SMOGER, Tracy Levitt. ■ 19428 #041-13-2004 L2004 **PTH** *100

WEST GROVE – CHESTER

BARKASY, Linda C. 316 E BALTIMORE PIKE 19390 #041-02-1999 L2002 **PD** *020 †55

BARKASY, Michael Augustus. 1011 W BALTIMORE PIKE, STE 7 19390 #041-02-1999 L2002 **FM** *020 †18

BELSON, Arthur Bachman. 1011 W BALTIMORE PIKE #203 19390 #041-09-1983 L1985 **OPH** *020 †35

BLOCK, Daniel B. 227 E EVERGREEN ST 19390 #041-13-1989 L1991 **P** *020 †75

BREARLY, Wayne Robt. 1015 W BALTIMORE PIKE 19390 #055-01-1983 L1985 **GS** *020 †85

CALLAHAN, Bonnie C. 1011 W BALTIMORE PIKE, STE 301 19390 #041-02-2003 L2003 **IM** *100 †20

D'AMATO, Samuel Lawrence. 1015 W BALTIMORE PIKE 19390 #035-09-1964 L1970 **DR** *020 †80

DE MICHELE, Andrew Henry. 1011 W BALTIMORE PIKE, MOB- STE 106 19390 #041-09-1993 L1996 **GS** *020 †85

DENITZIO, Robert P. 1015 W BALTIMORE PIKE 19390 #010-02-1981 L2001 **FM** *020 †18

DE SIMONE, Gregory Geo. 1015 W BALTIMORE PIKE, S.C.C.M.C. 19390 #041-09-1977 L1980 **IM** *020 †20,16

DIEFENDORF, Herbert Wm. ■ 19390 #008-01-1941 L1947 **IM A** *071 †20

DOYLE, Russell Gordon. 1011 W BALTIMORE PIKE 19390 #041-13-1954 L1955 **AM GP** *075

DROP, Deborah Bross. 390 VINEYARD WAY, STE 501 19390 #051-07-1999 L2007 **PD** *020 †55

DUA, Jayant Kumar. BALTIMORE PIKE, S CHESTER CO MEDICAL CTR 19390 #495-55-1973 L1986 **AN** *020 †05

DURAN, Daniel Nathan. 1011 W BALTIMORE PIKE, STE 7 19390 #041-02-1999 L2002 **FM** *020 †18

GAGE, Tracy Sue. 1015 W BALTIMORE PIKE, DEPT. OF RADIOLOGY 19390 #017-20-1985 L2000 **DR GS** *020 †80

GAMBHIR, Vibha Pal. 1015 W BALTIMORE PIKE 19390 #041-15-1999 L2001 **EM** *020 †16

GARCIA, Dominador I. 1015 W BALTIMORE PIKE, SOUTHRN CHSTR CNTY MDCL CT 19390 #748-08-1961 L1972 **EM FM** *071

GLUCK, Joseph Lawrence. ■ 19390 #035-20-1947 L1954 **IM** *071 †20

GOOD, Cynthia Jane. 1015 W BALTIMORE PIKE, SOUTHRN CHSTR CNTY MDCL CT 19390 #038-45-1987 L1990 **FM** *020 †18

HAO, Qingzhong. 1011 W BALTIMORE PIKE 19390 #243-21-1984 L2002 **AN** *020 †05

HAPLEA, Seth S. 1011 W BALTIMORE PIKE, STE 202 19390 #036-07-1993 L1995 **N CN** *020 †75

HENRY, George Keith. 1011 W BALTIMORE PIKE, OB/GYN SUITE 208 19390 #041-02-1995 L1997 **OBG** *020 †30

HOFFMAN, David F. 1015 W BALTIMORE PIKE 19390 #041-02-1990 L1993 **FM** *020 †18

KOTLIAR, Sophia Natalie. 1015 W BALTIMORE PIKE 19390 #033-06-1989 L1994 **BBK** *020 †50

KRISHNA, Bhupendra. 1011 W BALTIMORE PIKE, STE 202 19390 #495-36-1962 L1971 **FPS HNS** *071

LANGERAK, C. ■ 19390 #007-02-1950 L1950 **P EM** *071

LOWE, Cheryl Fala. 390 VINEYARD WAY, STE 501 19390 #041-02-1991 L1994 **PD** *020 †55

MONDOA, Emil Isume. 1015 W BALTIMORE PIKE, MED STAFF OFFICE 19390 #690-01-1981 L1992 **PD** *020 †55

MONIHAN, James Michael. 1015 W BALTIMORE PIKE 19390 #041-02-1984 L1998 **PTH BBK** *020 †50

NEILAN, Barbara Ann. 1011 W BALTIMORE PIKE, STE 105 19390 #033-05-1966 L1979 **ON HEM** *020 †20

OST, Mary-Anne. 1011 W BALTIMORE PIKE, STE 7 19390 #654-01-1981 L1983 **FM FPG** *020 †18

PLUMB, Jennifer M. 1015 W BALTIMORE PIKE, MEDICAL CENTER 19390 #028-46-1980 L2000 **PS GS** *020

RESWEBER, Scott Andrew. 1015 W BALTIMORE PIKE, JENNERSVILLE REGIOWAL HOSP 19390 #021-05-1988 L1998 **EM** *020 †16

RISHI, Mazhar. 1015 W BALTIMORE PIKE 19390 #704-02-1984 L1987 **PTH PCP** *020 †50

ROGOWSKI, Raymond A. 1015 W BALTIMORE PIKE 19390 #041-02-1960 L1961 **PTH** *071 †50

ROSSI, Ralph Anthony. 1015 W BALTIMORE PIKE 19390 #041-13-1972 L1973 **DR** *020 †80

ROY, Mary Nulty. 1015 W BALTIMORE PIKE, SOUTHRN CHSTR CNTY MDCL CT 19390 #047-07-1985 L1987 **DR** *020 †80

SANT RAM, Deepak. 1015 W BALTIMORE PIKE 19390 #495-45-1966 L1973 **AN IM** *020 †20

SCHEID, Vicky L. 390 VINEYARD WAY, STE 501 19390 #048-14-1988 L1993 **PD** *020 †55

SNOW, James Byron, Jr. ■ 19390 #024-01-1956 L1972 **OTO** *071 †45

STEWART, Michael Paul. 1011 W BALTIMORE PIKE, STE 106 19390 #041-02-1975 L1976 **GS VS** *020 †85

SUPPIAH, Kathiresan. 1011 W BALTIMORE PIKE, STE 201 19390 #305-01-2000 L2006 **HO** *020 †20

URIBE, Jorge Rafael. 1011 W BALTIMORE PIKE, STE 112 19390 #935-01-1998 L2001 **GE** *100 †20

WILLARD, Jennifer M. 316 E BALTIMORE PIKE 19390 #036-01-1996 L1997 **PD** *020 †55

WOZNIAK, Timothy Francis. 1011 W BALTIMORE PIKE, MEDICAL OFFICE BLDG, SUITE 19390 #041-01-1971 L1972 **ON IMG** *020 †20

YOUNG, Sherice Debra. 1011 W BALTIMORE PIKE, STE 101 19390 #010-03-1996 L2005 **OBG** *020

WEST HAZLETON – LUZERNE

STISH, Eugene Robt. 600 PENN ST 18202 #041-13-1984 L1986 **FM** *020 †18

WEST HOMESTEAD – ALLEGHENY

CHEN, Tai-Wen. 495 WATERFRONT DR E, STE 210 15120 #041-13-1993 L1995 **PCC** *020 †20

COSHAREK, Robert Frank. 207 W 7TH AVE, NOVACARE OCC HEALTH SERVIC 15120 #041-12-1976 L1977 **FM** *020 †18

WEST LAWN – BERKS

DENBY, Robert Anthony. 25 STEVENS AVE 19609 #041-13-1959 L1960 **GP** *071

LATMAN, Stephen Frederick. 2130 PENN AVE 19609 #041-13-1968 L1969 **ORS LM** *020 †40

NG, Joseph Soonyau. ■ 19609 #005-12-1998 L2001 **OBG** *100 †30

PLYMYER, Ray E. 19609 #010-01-1952 L1954 **A IM** *071 †20,03

STARSNIC, Janice. 2208 QUARRY DR STE 206 19609 #041-02-1978 L2002 **D DMP** *020 †15

VENIER, Leon Henry. 2209 QUARRY DR UNIT B-2 19609 #041-02-1968 L1969 **PM** *020 †60 ‡

WEST MIFFLIN – ALLEGHENY

ANNEAR, William C. 2027 LEBANON CHURCH RD 15122 #539-06-1989 L1992 **FM** *020 †18

BAIRD, James Wilson. W MIFFLIN MNR 15122 #023-07-1968 L1971 **IM PM** *071 †20

BAKER, Evan Edward. ■ 15122 #041-12-1992 L1998 **PTH** *020 †50
BECK, Ronald Chas. 2027 LEBANON CHURCH RD 15122 #035-48-1984 L1985 **FM** *040 †18
BHAT, Mohan Rama. 2027 LEBANON CHURCH RD, CENTURY III MEDICAL ASSOC. 15122 #495-09-1995 L2004 **IM** *020 †20
BOSCARINO, Martin Anthony. 9970 MOUNTAIN VIEW DR 15122 #041-15-2001 L2007 **OPH** *020 †35
BUSQUETS, Miguel Antonio. 9970 MOUNTAIN VIEW DR 15122 #036-07-1996 L2001 **OPH** *020 †35 ‡
CHAKRAPANI, Raja Mohanan. 1872 HOMEVILLE RD 15122 #495-31-1977 L1995 **IM** *020 †20
CHICO, Lauro. 1451 LEBANON SCHOOL RD 15122 #748-01-1966 L1972 **OM FM** *020
CIBIK, Lisa Marie. 9970 MOUNTAIN VIEW DR 15122 #041-12-1983 L1983 **OPH** *020 †35
EDINGER, James Thomas. ■ 15122 #041-12-2003 L2003 **PTH** *012
GOLDSTEIN, Keith Stuart. 814 PITTSBRGH MCKSPRT BLVD, BECHTEL BETTIS INC 15122 #305-01-1982 L1986 **FM OM** *020 ‡
JEW, Edward W, III. 1907 LEBANON CHURCH RD 15122 #041-12-1985 L1987 **IM** *020 †20
JEWART, Brian Harry. 9970 MOUNTAIN VIEW DR 15122 #041-12-1989 L1991 **OPH** *020 †35 ‡
KRAFTOWITZ, Robt Elliott. 2027 LEBANON CHURCH RD, CENTURY 111 MEDICAL ASSOCI 15122 #024-07-1978 L1983 **IM IMG** *020 †20
LANGOL, George, Jr. 1907 LEBANON CHURCH RD 15122 #041-12-1962 L1963 **PD** *071 †55
LWIN, Tint. 925 IRWIN RUN RD 15122 #209-01-1968 L1980 **R** *020
MENON, Madhusudan. 1872 HOMEVILLE RD 15122 #495-44-1990 L2000 **IM** *020 †20
MILLIGAN, Robert S. 2027 LEBANON CHURCH RD 15122 #041-12-1953 L1954 **GP** *071
NAIR, Sreelatha C. 2027 LEBANON RD 15122 #495-63-1983 L1997 **IM** *020 †20
NAIRN, John Patrick, Jr. 9970 MOUNTAIN VIEW DR 15122 #010-02-1988 L1990 **OPH** *020 †35
OLEGARIO, Louis Teodorico. 1907 LEBANON CHURCH RD, STE 240 15122 #748-19-1991 L2002 **PM PME** *020 †60
PETERS, Randolph Morgan. 1907 LEBANON CHURCH RD, AMI/EDWARD W JEW III,MD&AS 15122 #041-01-1991 L1994 **IM** *020 †20
PROVAN, Charles Andrew. 1815 PENNSYLVANIA AVE 15122 #041-12-1954 L1955 **GP OS** *071
SARACCO, Thomas Raymond. 500 LEWIS RUN RD 15122 #041-12-1943 L1944 **FM** *072
SCHUMAN, Linda Jean. 1907 LEBANON CHURCH RD 15122 #041-13-1985 L1997 **FM** *020 †18
SONGSANAND, Prachark. 2328 WORTON BLVD 15122 #891-01-1965 L1973 **GS GP** *071
SYEDA, Asma Masrath. 2027 LEBANON CHURCH RD 15122 #495-62-1995 L2001 **FM** *020 †18
XU, Sharon Xiaowen. 1451 LEBANON SCHOOL RD, HEALTH SERV 15122 #243-45-1985 L2000 **OM** *020 †70
ZIMMER, Daniel Vaughn. 9970 MOUNTAIN VIEW DR 15122 #038-43-1987 L1993 **OPH** *020 †35

WEST MILTON – UNION

CALLAWAY, Sara B. ■ 17886 #041-77-2006, ▲ L2006 **OBG** *012
FROMOWITZ, Frank Bernard. 58 SANDRA LEE BLVD 17886 #041-02-1973 L2002 **ATP** *020 †50
SMITH, Ashlee Linn. ■ 17886 #041-77-2006, ▲ L2006 **OBG** *012

WEST NEWTON – WESTMORELAND

CAMPBELL, Eric Fletcher. 115 S 2ND ST 15089 #010-02-2000 L2001 **IM** *020 †20
HUGHES, William Morgan. ■ 15089 #041-13-1948 L1949 **FM CD** *071 †18
MC GROGAN, Frank Patrick. 155 MOUNT PLEASANT RD 15089 #041-12-1985 L1986 **FM** *020 †18
PANAHANDEH, Matthew Reza. 115 S 2ND ST 15089 #041-02-1996 L1999 **IM** *020 †20
RIHN, Christopher Thomas. 115 S 2ND ST 15089 #041-15-2000 L2003 **IM** *020 †20

WEST PITTSTON – LUZERNE

ALEXANDERIAN, Harry. 1010 SUSQUEHANNA AVE 18643 #407-21-1958 L1964 **GP OS** *072
BROWN, Michael V. ■ 18643 #041-15-2008 *012
SAMMON, Mary Ross. ■ 18643 #041-02-2007 L2007 *012

WEST POINT – MONTGOMERY

ALEXANDER, Charles Michae. 770 SUMNEYTOWN PIKE, WP39-162 19486 #005-06-1977 L1994 **END IM** *050 †20
BRILL-EDWARDS, Patrick A. PO BOX 4, BLB22 19486 #065-10-1982 L2001 **IM** *020 †20
CHODAKEWITZ, Jeffrey A. BL3-4 CLNICAL RESEARCH 19486 #008-01-1981 L1992 **ID IM** *050 †20
CHOW, Joseph W. PO BOX 4, MAILSTOP BL 3-4 19486 #041-02-1984 L1988 **ID IM** *050 †20
CLARK, Liana Roxanne. 770 SUMNEYTOWN PIKE, # WP97-A343 19486 #010-03-1988 L1993 **ADL PD** *062 †55
FARTHING, Charles Frank. PO BOX 4, 770 SUMNEYTOWN PIKE 19486 #671-01-1976 L2008 **ID IM** *030 †20
FLICKER, Michele Rhona. PO BOX 4, MERCK RESEARCH LABORATORIE 19486 #028-02-1976 L1977 **IM OS** *062 †20
HYER, Randall Nelms. PO BOX 4, MERCK AND CO INC (WP97A-27 19486 #036-07-1993 L1994 **GPM** *020 †70
ISAACS, Robin David. PO BOX 4 19486 #671-02-1982 L1989 **IM ID** *020 †20
MELTON, Mary Elaine. SUMNEYTOWN & BROAD HM-216, MERCK & CO INC CLNCL DEVEL 19486 #016-11-1985 L1993 **END IM** *050 †20
MODUR, Vijayanand R. PO BOX 4, SUMNEYTOWN PIKE 19486 #495-35-1990 L1997 **PTH** *020 †50
MOZLEY, P David, Jr. 770 SUMNEYTOWN PIKE, WP42-210 19486 #036-08-1984 L1985 **NM NUP** *050 †28
PECK, Harold Mitchell. MERCK SHARP AND DOHME 19486 #038-06-1945 L1945 **OS** *030
POWELL, William John, Jr. MERCK SHARP DOHME RES LABS 19486 #035-01-1961 L1963 **CD IM** *050 †20
REINES, Scott Alan. MERCK SHARP DOMME LABS 19486 #035-46-1976 L1979 **P** *050 †75
SHARRAR, Robert Gene. PO BOX 4 19486 #041-01-1966 L1973 **PHP IM** *030 †20
SHER, Sanford Paul. MERCK INST THERAPEUTI RES 19486 #028-02-1977 **OS** *062

WEST READING – BERKS

AILAWADI, Radhika. 301 S 7TH AVE, STE 245 19611 #038-45-1998 L2006 **OBG** *020 †30

BELCH, Richard Zbigniew. 301 S 7TH AVE STE 100DOB, THE READING HOSP & MED CTR 19611 #016-11-1974 L1977 **GO GYN** *020 †30
BELL, Richard T. 301 S 7TH AVE, STE 305 19611 #041-02-1972 L1973 **PUD IM** *020 †20 ‡
BOHNENBLUST, Walter R, Jr. 301 S 7TH AVE, STE 225 19611 #041-13-1979 L1981 **IM** *020 †20
BOROFSKY, Michael Allen. 401 BUTTONWOOD ST 19611 #041-12-1984 L1986 **RHU IM** *020 †20
BRAVIDIS, Demetrius Elias. 301 S 7TH AVE STE 2020 19611 #418-01-1994 L1999 **CD IM** *020 †20
BRIGHAM, Robert Allan. 301 S 7TH AVE, STE 1070 19611 #025-07-1977 L1989 **VS GS** *020 †85
BROCKMAN, Paul Scott. 301 S 7TH AVE STE 2070 19611 #023-01-1982 L1985 **PM** *020 †60
BROWN, Michael T. 301 S 7TH AVE, STE 350 19611 #041-02-1986 L1990 **GS SO** *020 †85
CARLSON, John Edward. 301 S 7TH AVE STE 135, 6TH AND SPRUCE STS 19611 #056-05-1983 L1985 **DR** *020 †80
CARUANA, Bruce Jos. 301 S 7TH AVE, STE 215 19611 #917-04-1983 L1985 **GE IM** *020 †20
CESCON, Terrence Paul. 301 S 7TH AVE STE 270, ASSOCIATES, LTD 19611 #041-09-1988 L1991 **HEM ON** *020 †20
CHESEN, Neil. 301 PENN AVE, STE 100 19611 #041-02-1983 L1984 **OPH IM** *020 †20,35
CHIRIELEISON, Rocco Frank. 301 S 7TH AVE, STE 225 19611 #041-13-1965 L1966 **IM** *071 †20
CHONG, Young J. 301 S 7TH AVE, STE 135 19611 #035-48-1966 L1968 **RNR** *020 †16,80
CHOPRA, Akhil. 6TH AVE & SPRUCE ST, DEPT MED 19612 #496-09-2001 L2002 **HO** *012 †20
CLOSE, Richard Alan. 601 SPRUCE ST 19611 #041-13-1972 L1973 **NS GS** *020 †25
COFFEY, James Augustus. 301 S 7TH AVE, STE 1070 19611 #035-19-1980 L1992 **VS GS** *020 †85
COLOZZI, Louis Arthur, Jr. 6TH AVE & SPRUCE ST, READING ANESTHESIA ASSOC 19611 #035-15-1982 L1987 **AN** *020 †05
DABROWSKI, G Paul. 6TH AVE & SPRUCE ST, B BLDG 4TH FL 19611 #028-34-1990 L1997 **GS TRS** *020 †85
DASIKA, Uday K. 301 S 7TH AVE 19611 #035-03-1994 L1999 **TS CD** *020 †85,90
DEB, Bhaskar. 6TH AVENUE & SPRUCE ST, READING ANESTHESIA ASSOC 19611 #041-13-1989 L1994 **AN CCA** *020 †05
DE BENEDICTIS, Kenneth J. 6TH AVE & SPRUCE ST 19612 #041-02-1962 L1963 **ID AI** *071 †20,03
DERR, Craig Alan. 6TH & SPRUCE ST, HOSPITALIST SERVICES 19611 #041-13-1979 L1980 **IM** *020 †20
DE SANCTIS, Jos James, Jr. 301 S 7TH AVE STE 210 19611 #041-13-1968 L1969 **IM** *020 †20
DE VOS, Wayne Calvin. 301 S 7TH AVE, STE 100 19611 #016-11-1990 L1998 **GS CRS** *072 †85,10
DUFFY, Scott Smith. 301 S 7TH AVE, STE 225 19611 #041-02-1971 L1972 **IM** *020 †20
EMKEY, Kenneth David. 301 S 7TH AVE STE 21 19611 #041-09-1972 L1973 **IM GE** *020 †20
EMRICH, Russell Earl. 301 S 7TH AVE, 16052 ZIP 19612 19611 #041-15-1999 L2001 **FM** *020 †18
ERLIKH, Tatyana. 301 S 7TH AVE, STE 225 19611 #913-50-1993 L2000 **IM** *020 †20
FALLON, Edward C, III. 301 S 7TH AVE STE 135, W READING RADIOLOGY ASSC 19611 #041-13-1971 L1976 **DR** *020 †80
FAUST, Donald Strickner. 6TH AVE & SPRUCE ST 19612 #041-09-1960 L1961 **RO** *071 †80
FEHNEL, Stephen Henry. 301 S 7TH AVE STE 245, C/O WOMENS CLINIC LTD 19611 #041-02-1977 L1978 **OBG REN** *020 †30
FELDMAN, Adam Howard. 301 S 7TH AVE, DOCTORS OFFICE BLDG/STE 20 19611 #041-13-1992 L1994 **CD** *020 †20
FILSTEIN, Marc Robt. 6TH AVE & SPRUCE ST 19612 #035-47-1975 L1977 **PTH BBK** *020 †50 ‡
FINNERAN, William C, III. 301 S 7TH AVE STE 2 19611 #010-02-1991 L2001 **CD IM** *020 †20
FLYNN, Anne M. 301 S 7TH AVE STE 3070 19611 #023-12-1984 L1996 **GS** *020 †85
FREEMAN, Margaret Louise. 6TH AVE & SPRUCE ST 19612 #041-13-1980 L1981 **PTH DMP** *020 †50
GEORGE, David Lloyd. DEPT OF MEDICINE, READING HOSPITAL 19612 #024-01-1978 L1983 **RHU** *040 †20
GEYER, David Wayne. 6TH AVE & SPRUCE ST 19612 #035-45-1984 L1985 **AN** *020 †05
GHOUBRIAL, Jaylaine. 301 S 7TH AVE STE 245 19611 #041-13-1999 L2001 **OBG** *020 †30
GOKAL, Deepam. 6TH & SPRUCE, T R H M C 19609 #836-01-1984 L2001 **IM** *020 †20 ‡
GOROUHI, Fariborz. 6TH AVE SPRUCE ST, DEPT OF MED 19611 #517-01-2001 L2004 **IM** *100 †20
GREENE, Richard Joel. 6TH AVE & SPRUCE ST 19612 #033-05-1969 L1975 **AI PD** *020 †55,03
GRETH, Warren Edward. 401 BUTTONWOOD ST 19611 #041-01-1973 L1978 **RHU** *020 †20
HAAS, Michael Lester. 6TH AVE & SPRUCE ST 19612 #033-06-1996 L2001 **RO** *020 †80 ‡
HANLEY, Terrance Patrick. 301 S 7TH AVE 19611 #041-09-1992 L1995 **GS** *020 †85
HARDISKY-O'ROURKE, Jo-Ann. 301 S 7TH AVE, STE 120 19611 #041-02-1982 L1983 **FM OBS** *020
HELINEK, Gerard L. 301 S 7TH AVE 19611 #041-13-1972 L1981 **DR RNR** *020 †55,80
HERMANOVICH, John, Jr. 301 S 7TH AVE STE 2020 19611 #041-02-1974 L1975 **CD IM** *020 †20
HEY, E Berry, Jr. 301 S 7TH AVE, STE 2020 19611 #041-01-1958 L1959 **CD** *020 †20 ‡
HIEHLE, John Frederick. 6TH AVE & SPRUCE ST 19612 #041-02-1960 L1961 **DR** *071 †80
HOLDSWORTH, Charles M. 6TH AVE & SPRUCE ST 19612 #041-02-1980 L1981 **AN IM** *071 †20,05
HOPE, Earl Jos. 301 S 7TH AVE, STE 2020 19611 #023-07-1987 L1995 **CD IM** *020 †20
HOPKINS, John Edward. 6TH AVE & SPRUCE ST, THE READING HOSP MED CTR 19611 #041-13-1989 L1992 **AN** *020 †05
HUNTER, John Sidney. 6TH AVE & SPRUCE ST 19612 #041-13-1939 **GP** *071
JAXHEIMER, Eric Chas. 301 S 7TH AVE, STE 1070 19611 #041-02-1977 L1983 **VS** *020 †85
JOHNSON, Craig Herbert. 601 SPRUCE ST 19611 #041-13-1973 L1974 **NS** *020 †25
JOHNSON, William Thos. 6TH AVENUE & SPRUCE ST, READING ANESTHESIA ASSOC 19611 #041-01-1974 L1975 **AN** *020 †05
JONES, Camille Nicole. 6TH AVE & SPRUCE ST 19612 #023-01-1997 L2002 **IM** *020 †20
KAPLAN, Lawrence Michael. 415 READING AVE 19611 #035-08-1976 L1982 **DR NM** *020 †80 ‡
KATZ, Stephen K. 6TH AVE & SPRUCE ST 19612 #041-02-1976 L1999 **PD ADL** *020 †55 ‡
KIMBALL, C E Jensen. 301 PENN AVE, STE 200 19611 #051-01-1965 L1989 **PD DBP** *020 †55
KIMMEL, Craig Alvin. 301 S 7TH AVE, STE 3120 19611 #041-13-1981 L1982 **OTO HNS** *020 †45
KOLVA, Donald Gary. 301 S 7TH AVE STE 240 19611 #041-07-1986 L1988 **N** *020 †20
KOSLOW, Michael. 301 S 7TH AVE, DOCTORS OFFICE BUILDING 19611 #041-13-1983 L1984 **CD IM** *020 †20
LANDIS, Richard. 6TH AVE & SPRUCE ST 19612 #041-13-1965 L1966 **EM** *020
LANE, Charles Darrell. 6TH AVE & SPRUCE ST 19612 #041-13-1964 L1965 **PTH** *071 †50
LIFT, Varsha Shukla. 301 PENN AVE, STE 200 19611 #305-01-1987 L2006 **PD** *020 †55
LLOYD, Benjamin John. 6 AVENUE & SPRUCE ST 19611 #041-09-1988 L1991 **HOS** *040 †20
LU, Li-Hong. 6TH AVE & SPRUCE ST 19612 #243-46-1982 L2001 **PM** *020 †60
LUSCH, Charles Jacque. 301 S 7TH AVE, STE 220 19611 #041-13-1961 L1962 **ON HEM** *020 †20 ‡

LYNCH, James Daniel. 301 S 7TH AVE STE 2020 19611 #041-09-1975 L1976 **CD IM** *020 †20

MALICK, Gerald Paul. 301 S 7TH AVE STE 325 19611 #041-13-1963 L1964 **GYN** *071 †30

MARCHINSKI, Leonard Jos. 301 S 7TH AVE, STE 3020 19611 #041-07-1981 L1982 **HS** *020 †40

MARSHALL, Jeffrey Scott. 6TH AVE & SPRUCE ST 19612 #041-09-1986 L1998 **AN** *020 †05

MASSENGALE, Alexander T. 301 S 7TH AVE STE 115 19611 #041-13-1969 L1970 **OBG** *020 †30 ‡

MATHIS, James Gertler. 6TH AVE & SPRUCE ST 19612 #010-02-1979 L1981 **AN AM** *020 †05 ‡

MELE, Carl Dominic. 301 S 7TH AVE, STE 215 19611 #041-13-1997 L1999 **GE HEP** *020 †20 ‡

MENGES, Job Franklin, Jr. 301 S 7TH AVE, STE 3020 19611 #041-13-1962 L1963 **ORS** *071 †40

MOFFITT, Vincent John. 301 S 7TH AVE STE 3170 19611 #041-13-1973 L1974 **PD** *020 †55

MUNION, Gail Lynn. 6TH AVENUE & SPRUCE ST, READING ANESTHESIA ASSOC 19611 #041-14-1982 L1983 **AN** *020 †05

NAING, Grace. 561 CHESTNUT ST 19611 #041-13-1997 L1999 **FM** *020 †18

NICHOLAS, Peter Daniel. 401 BUTTONWOOD ST 19611 #041-13-1977 L1978 **RHU IM** *020 †20

NOBLE, Samuel Ross. 200 READING AVE STE 102 19611 #041-02-1986 L1987 **PM** *020 †60

NYDEGGER, Charles C. 301 S 7TH AVE 19611 #041-09-1982 L1984 **CD OS** *020 †20

O'NEILL, Bernard Jos. 301 S 7TH AVE, STE 320 19611 #041-14-1975 L1976 **N IM** *020 †20,75

OPLINGER, Arthur F. 6TH AVE & SPRUCE ST 19612 #041-13-1963 L1964 **FM** *071 †18

O'SHEA, Daniel Jerome. 301 S 7TH AVE, WEST READING RADIOLOGY ASS 19611 #028-34-1999 L2004 **DR** *020 †80

PALLAS, Randolph Scott. 301 S 7TH AVE, DOCTORS OFFICE BUILDING 19611 #012-01-1979 L1987 **CD IM** *020 †20

PATTON, Jarret Royce. 206 S 6TH AVE, CHILDREN'S HEALTH CENTER 19611 #038-06-1999 L2002 **PD** *020 †55

PENTA, John Michael. 301 S 7TH AVE STE 305 19611 #041-02-1969 L1970 **OTO** *020 †45

PERLMUTTER, Gordon Saml. 6TH AVE & SPRUCE ST 19612 #050-02-1965 L1966 **R** *071 †80 ‡

PETERSON, Tory Rob. 301 S 7TH AVE STE 365 19611 #049-01-2003 L2003 **OBG** *020

PLUCINSKY, Francis C. 6TH AVE & SPRUCE ST 19612 #041-13-1971 L1972 **AN** *071 †05

PORTER, William Ralph. 6TH AVE & SPRUCE ST, READING ANESTHESIA ASSOC 19611 #041-14-1988 L1992 **AN** *020 †05

PROBST, Susan Jane. 6TH AVE & SPRUCE ST 19612 #041-13-1977 L1980 **OBG** *020 †30

PSARROS, Thomas. 601 SPRUCE ST 19611 #035-47-1999 L2005 **NS** *100

RADOSH, Lee Jay. 301 S 7TH AVE, STE 2120 DOCTORS OFC BLDG 19611 #041-13-1997 L1999 **FM** *020 †18 ‡

RAFF, Thomas Chaney. 301 S 7TH AVE, STE 2120 19611 #051-04-1990 L1992 **N IM** *020 †75 ‡

REED, Clifford Anthony. 301 S 7TH AVE, STE 240 19611 #036-05-1975 L1976 **N IM** *020 †75 ‡

REHR, Roger Bruce. 301 S 7TH AVE, DOCTOR'S OFFICE BUILDING 19611 #035-03-1978 L1979 **CD IM** *020 †20

REICHARD, Richard Curvin. 6TH AVE & SPRUCE ST 19612 #041-13-1962 L1963 **GP FM** *071

REIGH, Ernest Edward. 601 SPRUCE ST 19611 #041-12-1954 L1955 **NS** *071 †25

RIDDLE, Renee E. 206 S 6TH AVE 19611 #041-02-1999 L2006 **PD** *020 †55

RIST, Kevin Ernest. 301 S 7TH AVE, STE 2020 19611 #032-01-1978 L1992 **ICE CD** *020 †20

RODRIGUEZ, Ricardo Alan. 6TH AVE & SPRUCE ST, READING ANESTHESIA ASSOC 19611 #041-13-1989 L1995 **AN** *020 †05

ROHRBACH, Anne M. 301 S 7TH AVE, STE 225 19611 #035-15-1995 L1997 **IM** *020 †20

ROMEO, Michael A. 301 S 7TH AVE, STE 135 19611 #041-77-2000, ▲ L2001 *020 †80

ROTENBERG, Larry Abraham. 6TH AVE & SPRUCE ST 19612 #061-01-1963 **PFP P** *020 †75

SACCO, Matthew Anthony. 415 READING AVE 19611 #041-01-1981 L1983 **DR** *020 †80

SCHADDER, Cynthia Ann. 301 S 7TH AVE, STE 3170 19611 #041-14-1994 L1997 **PD** *020 †55

SCHLAFF, Sheldon. 301 S 7TH AVE STE 245 19611 #028-02-1962 L1971 **END DIA** *020 †20

SCHLESINGER, Diana M. 301 PENN AVE STE 200, ALL ABOUT CHILDREN PEDIATR 19611 #041-07-1980 L1981 **PD PDP** *020 †55 ‡

SCHWARTZ, Peter Alan. 6TH AVE & SPRUCE ST 19612 #024-05-1966 L1986 **OBG** *071 †30

SCORNAVACCHI, Joseph M. 301 S 7TH AVE, STE 3220 19611 #041-13-1973 L1974 **ORS OAR** *020 †40

SERRIAN, John Louis, Jr. 301 S 7TH AVE STE 2020, WEST READING LTD 19611 #041-13-1989 L1991 **CD** *020 †20

SHADDUCK, Sneed Patrick. 6TH AVE & SPRUCE ST, READING ANESTHESIA ASSOC 19611 #041-13-1987 L1990 **AN** *020 †05

SHAFFER, Eugene Michael. 301 S 7TH AVE STE 310 19611 #041-02-1973 L1981 **GS AS** *020 †85

SHAW, Robert Joseph. 6TH AND SPRUCE ST, DEPT OF RADIOLOGY 19611 #033-06-2001 L2007 **DR** *020 †80

SHULTZ, Barry S. 301 S 7TH AVE, STE 340 19611 #035-06-1968 L1969 **U** *071 †95

SHUMAN, John Ferris. 301 S 7TH AVE, STE 130 19611 #041-01-1964 L1965 **PUD** *020 †20

SIMONS, Jeffrey Steven. 6TH AVE & SPRUCE ST, READING ANESTHESIA ASSOC 19611 #033-06-1988 L1991 **AN** *020 †05

SMITH, Barton Lowell. 301 S 7TH AVE, STE 215 19611 #035-20-1964 L1971 **GE IM** *071 †20

STEFFY, David Frederick. 301 S 7TH AVE, STE 210 19611 #051-07-1983 L1986 **IM** *020

STRANGARITY, Joseph W. 6TH AVE & SPRUCE ST 19612 #041-13-1985 L1986 **FM** *020 †18

SUTHERLAND, Robert Dale. 301 S 7TH AVE, STE 3220 19611 #041-13-1981 L1982 **ORS** *020 †40

SWEET, William Arthur. 301 S 7TH AVE 19611 #018-03-1966 L1970 **GS** *020 †85

SZARKO, Carol J Herman. 6TH AVE & SPRUCE ST, READING ANESTHESIA ASSOC 19611 #041-01-1966 L1967 **AN OS** *020 †05

TOMASSI, Anthony Thomas. 301 S 7TH AVE, STE 200 19611 #041-13-2004 L2004 **FM** *020

TRONCALE, Joseph Alder. 6TH AVE & SPRUCE ST 19612 #001-06-1979 L1988 **FM** *020 †18

TRUEX, Raymond Carl. 601 SPRUCE ST, NEUROLOGICAL SURGERY 19611 #041-13-1967 L1968 **NS** *020 †25

ULMER, Lorie Anne. 301 S 7TH AVE STE 3170 19611 #041-07-1996 L1999 **PD** *020 †55

VELAZQUEZ, Maria Antonia. 6TH AVE & SPRUCE, READING HOSP MED CTR 19611 #042-01-2002 L2006 **P** *020

WALKER, Nancy Jane. 401 BUTTONWOOD ST 19611 #065-10-1998 L2004 **RHU** *020 †20

WANG, Baoqing. 601 SPRUCE ST 19611 #243-21-1986 **CN** *020

WANG, Karen Eisenhart. 206 S 6TH AVE, CHILDREN'S HEALTH CENTER 19611 #024-05-1998 L2002 **PD** *020 †55

WEAVER, Timothy Vincent. 301 S 7TH AVE, STE 200 19611 #041-14-2004 L2004 **FM** *020 †18

WEISBERG, Jerome Stephen. 401 BUTTONWOOD ST 19611 #041-09-1968 L1969 **RHU IM** *020 †20

WESTCOTT, Richard Jerrell. 301 S 7TH AVE 19611 #041-13-1959 L1960 **GS** *072 †85

WIENER, Stephen G. 6TH AVE & SPRUCE ST 19612 #041-09-1965 L1967 **D** *071 †15

WINN, Randall Scott. 301 S 7TH AVE 19611 #019-02-1976 L1982 **NR DR** *020 †80,28

WORRELL, Lindsay A. 6TH AND SPRUCE ST, THE READING HOSP & MED CTR 19611 #566-01-1989 L2007 **NPM PD** *020 †55 ‡

YUEN, Albert. 6TH AVE & SPRUCE ST 19612 #035-03-1980 L1987 **RO** *020 †80 ‡

ZONIES, David Cowley. 301 S 7TH AVE STE 205 19611 #016-06-1962 L1963 **CD** *071 †20

WEST SUNBURY – BUTLER

ASHBY, Marshall Woodson. ■ 16061 #010-03-1957 L1980 **EM GS** *071 †85

WEST WYOMING – LUZERNE

ADAJAR, Marie Juliette B. 812 SHOEMAKER AVE, INTERNAL MEDICINE PARTNERS 18644 #748-01-1991 L2001 **IM** *020 †20

WESTFIELD – TIOGA

MILLER, Susan J. 222 CHURCH ST 16950 #041-12-1994 L1996 **FM** *020 †18

WEXFORD – ALLEGHENY

ADHAR, Meena. 11676 PERRY HWY, STE 2204 15090 #496-07-1975 L1988 **END PD** *020 †55

AKINDELE, Olusola A. ■ 15090 #690-02-1979 L1996 **EM OM** *020 †70

ALVAREZ, Rene Jesus, Jr. 425 MCKEAN DR 15090 #041-01-1990 L1992 **CD IM** *020 †20

BAJAJ, Girish. ■ 15090 #495-45-2001 L2006 **IM** *100 †20

BAKER, Matthew Stephen. ■ 15090 #041-12-2008 *012

BAKER, Stephen Duane. 2500 BROOKTREE RD, STE 200 15090 #041-12-1972 L1973 **FM** *020 †18

BALOURIS, Chris Anthony. 7000 STONEWOOD DR, STE 200 15090 #041-12-1984 L1986 **OPH** *020 †35

BEGG, Frank Richard. 1000 STONEWOOD DR, STE 110 15090 #041-12-1956 L1957 **CD OS** *040 †20

BERGMAN, Elisabeth Calvo. 11676 PERRY HWY STE 1308 15090 #132-04-1980 L1983 **END DIA** *020 †20

BISBEY, Ryan James. ■ 15090 #035-45-2006 L2006 **TY** *012

BIYANI, Archana Kailash C. ■ 15090 #495-20-1992 L2005 **END** *100 †20

BOCHKORIS, Matthew John. ■ 15090 #041-13-2005 L2005 **PD** *012

BULUSU, Mamatha V R. ■ 15090 #496-24-1993 L2004 **SP** *100

BUTERBAUGH, Glenn Allen. 6001 STONEWOOD DR 15090 #041-12-1979 L1979 **ORS HS** *020 †40

BUTTER, Desiree Beth. 101 BRADFORD RD, STE 220 15090 #041-12-1994 L1996 **FM** *020 †18

CAMERON, Julie Frances. 6400 BROOKTREE CT, STE 230 15090 #019-02-1988 L1993 **IM** *020 †20

CARMEN, Thomas Fred. 11676 PERRY HWY 15090 #041-13-1985 L1986 **FM** *020 †18

CASTEEL, Mark Allen. 3000 STONEWOOD DR, STE 120 15090 #055-01-1998 L2001 **DR** *100 †80

CERCONE, Ronald Gino. 3000 STONEWOOD DR STE 200 15090 #055-01-1981 L1982 **U** *020 †95

CHALFANT, Richard S. 9000 BROOKTREE RD, STE 400 15090 #041-02-1973 L1974 **OBG** *020 †30

CHALIFOUX, Thomas Michael. ■ 15090 #041-12-2003 L2003 **AN** *100

CHAMOVITZ, Irvin. ■ 15090 #020-02-1946 L1950 **CHN** *071 †55

CHEN, Zong Fu. ■ 15090 #243-78-1983 L2001 **APM** *100 †05

CHENG, Kenneth Paul. 1000 STONEWOOD DR, STE 310 15090 #041-12-1984 L1985 **PO OPH** *020 †35 ‡

CHENG, Kensei. 1000 STONEWOOD DR, STE 310 15090 #572-03-1958 **OPH OS** *040

CINICOLA, John Thos. 105 BRADFORD RD, STE 100 15090 #055-01-1987 L1990 **IM** *020 †20

CLARKE, Kofi. 102 TANGLEWOOD DR, WEST PENN MEDICAL ASSOCIAT 15090 #412-01-1989 L1996 **IM** *020 †20

COLE, Daniel Jos. 3000 STONEWOOD DR, STE 200 15090 #041-02-1984 L1985 **U** *020 †95

COLELLA, Joseph James. 145 REICHOLD RD 15090 #041-12-1986 L1988 **GS** *020 †85

COLLINS, Lawrence A. 3000 STONEWOOD DR STE 200 15090 #010-02-1964 L1968 **U** *020 †95

CRANDALL, Theodore L. 9930 GRUBBS RD, STE 100 15090 #041-01-1973 **ON HEM** *020 †20

DAYAN, Stephen Alan. 2108 SHADOW GLEN CT 15090 #396-11-1973 L2004 **P** *020 †50

DESAI, Anup Mahesh. ■ 15090 #041-02-2003 L2003 **FM** *100 †18

DISCHMAN, Gregory David. 6400 BROOKTREE CT 15090 #041-09-1989 L1991 **IM** *020 †20

DJOKIC, Divna. ■ 15090 #957-02-1992 L2005 **PDI** *020 †55

DVERGSTEN, Jeffrey Arthur. ■ 15090 #026-04-1993 L2007 **CCP** *020 †55

ELLIOTT, George Michael. ■ 15090 #041-13-2002 L2006 **EM** *020

FABRY, Edward Irwin, Jr. 10339 PERRY HWY 15090 #041-12-1947 L1948 **U** *071 †95

FLOYD, S L. 11676 PERRY HWY, STE 3306 15090 #041-12-1985 L1986 **OBG** *020 †30

FOLKE, Richard Patrick. 3000 STONEWOOD DR, STE 120 15090 #016-43-1984 L2002 **DR** *020 †80

FRANCKEN, Gregory Jos. 3000 STONEWOOD DR, STE 120 15090 #041-09-1986 L1987 **R IM** *020 †80

FRANCO, Thomas Jude. 3000 STONEWOOD DR, STE 120 15090 #041-12-1993 L1998 **R VIR** *020 †80

FRYE, Paul Edward. 11676 PERRY HWY STE 2100 15090 #055-01-1977 L1991 **P** *020 †75 ‡

FULLER, Mark Guthrie. 10592 PERRY HWY # 226 15090 #055-01-1981 L1990 **IM P** *030 †20,75

GATIAL, Joseph Edward. ■ 15090 #041-13-2004 L2004 **PD** *020 †55

GEHRIS, Robin Paige. 11279 PERRY HWY, STE 108 15090 #041-12-1997 L1999 **D** *020 †55,15

GERENYI, Andrew Geo. ■ 15090 #041-12-1964 L1965 **FM** *071 †18

GILLESPIE, Mary Patrice. 119 VIP DR, STE 202 15090 #021-01-1980 L1982 **P** *020 †75

GINDE, Kaustubh Motilal. ■ 15090 #495-98-1995 L2006 **VIR** *100 †80

GLUCKMAN, Robert Joel. 9930 GRUBBS RD STE 100, NORTH PARK PROF BLDG 15090 #041-12-1980 L1981 **HEM IM** *020 †20

GOLDSTEIN, David Meyer. 2500 BROOKTREE RD, STE 300 15090 #025-01-1982 L1985 **PM NTR** *020 †60

GRAND, Aaron Gavin. 6001 STONEWOOD DR FL 2 15090 #008-01-1996 L2004 **HS PS** *020 †65

GUILINGER, Ruth Ann. ■ 15090 #041-14-1989 L1993 **PUD** *020 †20

HABIB, Adnan Naeem. ■ 15090 #764-25-1998 L2000 **PCC** *020 †20

HAGBERG, William Chas. 6001 STONEWOOD DR 15090 #016-06-1981 L1983 **ORS HS** *020 †40

HARNIST, Kimberly Sue. 9000 BROOKTREE RD, STE 402 15090 #038-43-1987 L1992 **DR** *020 †80

HILLMAN, Todd Alan. ■ 15090 #038-40-1997 L2002 **OTO** *100

HUGGINS-PUHALLA, Shanon. ■ 15090 #038-44-2001 L2007 **IM** *100 †20

HUST, Frederick. 3000 STONEWOOD DR, STE 120 15090 #035-06-1972 L1976 **R** *020 †80 ‡

IMBRIGLIA, Joseph Ettore. 6001 STONEWOOD DR 15090 #041-09-1970 L1976 **ORS HS** *020 †40

JEAN, Raymond David. 309 RUSTIN WAY 15090 #024-05-2003 L2003 **GS** *020

JOHN, Chad Eric. 11279 PERRY HWY, STE 105 15090 #041-12-1971 L1973 **PD** *020 †55

KANANI, Prapti Mulraj. 3500 BROOKTREE RD, STE 204 15090 #495-01-1984 L1999 **PDC PD** *020 †55

KLINESTIVER, Donald G. 500 BLAZIER DR 15090 #055-01-1964 L1967 **GP** *020

KRAMPERT, Stephen Douglas. 3000 STONEWOOD DR 15090 #035-03-2001 L2007 **DR** *020 †80

KRAUSE, Helen Fox. 3101 WEXFORD RD 15090 #024-07-1958 L1959 **OTO AI** *071 †45

KREIT, John Wm, Jr. ■ 15090 #036-07-1981 L1991 **PUD CCM** *020 †20

KRESS, Douglas Wayne. 11279 PERRY HWY, STE 108 15090 #041-02-1992 L1995 **D** *020 †15

KRIVINKO, Dennis Michael. 9000 BROOKTREE RD, STE 400 15090 #041-04-1977 L1978 **OBG** *020 †20

KROB, Mary Jeanne. ■ 15090 #018-03-1978 L1986 **TRS GS** *020 †85

KULKARNI, Arvind V. ■ 15090 #495-22-1963 L1996 **RO R** *020 †80

KURRA, Geeta. ■ 15090 #496-24-1998 L2007 **HO** *012 †20

LAMB, Michael G. 9500 BROOKTREE RD, STE 100 15090 #041-12-1979 L1982 **IM** *020 †20

LAMPERSKI, Lloyd Geo. 7000 STONEWOOD DR, STE 151 15090 #041-12-1980 L1981 **IM PMM** *020 †20

LATTARI, Vincent Aldo. 3000 STONEWOOD DR, STE 120 15090 #041-12-1993 L1996 **VIR R** *020 †80

LI, Guizhu. ■ 15090 #243-64-1983 L2004 **SP** *020 †50

LOBERANT, Leslie Anne. 11676 PERRY HWY STE 1201, WEXFORD PROFESSIONAL BLDG 15090 #041-02-1998 L2000 **FM** *020 †18

LO DICO, Mark. 1000 STONEWOOD DR, STE 300 15090 #035-15-1988 L1992 **PMM** *020 †05

LOVE, Joseph Robt. 117 VIP DR STE 120 15090 #041-12-1957 L1958 **FM FPG** *071 †18 ‡

LOWDER, Ralph J, Jr. ■ 15090 #041-12-1946 **R** *071

LUCAS, Donna. 213 EDELWEISS DR 15090 #041-07-1986 L1987 **AN** *020 †05

LYNN, Charles Alan. 3000 STONEWOOD DR, STE 120 15090 #025-07-1968 L1974 **DR** *020 †80 ‡

MAKKAR, Louka T. ■ 15090 #915-04-1976 L1992 **FM PCP** *020

MALIT, Paulita Yuvienco. ■ 15090 #748-01-1956 L1968 **AN OS** *071 †05

MARQUIS, Marian Kay. ■ 15090 #041-12-1995 L1997 **EM** *020 †16

MARRYSHOW, Basil Albert. ■ 15090 #010-03-1962 L1967 **ORS OS** *071

MARSH, Christopher R. ■ 15090 #038-41-2002 L2003 **HO** *012 †20

MAVANUR, Manju Arun. ■ 15090 #495-17-1992 L2007 **NEP** *012 †20

MC CANDLESS, Cara Lynne. 11676 PERRY HWY, STE 2100 15090 #005-18-1995 L1997 **CHP** *020 †75

MC GHEE, Elaine. 11279 PERRY HWY, STE 105 15090 #041-12-1975 L1976 **PD** *020 †55

MELLINGER, John C. 821 MULBERRY CT, 821 MULBERRY COURT 15090 #041-12-1988 L1990 **OBG** *020 †30

MISRA, Sutanu. ■ 15090 #038-40-2000 L2006 **AN** *020 †05

MITROS, Mark Michael. 3000 STONEWOOD DR STE 110 15090 #025-01-1983 L1989 **PM** *020 †20

MOHSIN, Jamil Chaudhry. 10513 FOREST HILL DR 15090 #056-06-1996 L2000 **IC** *012 †20

MORIARTY, Richard Wm. 119 VIP DR STE G4 15090 #041-12-1966 L1967 **PD** *020

OCHOA, Efrain Ricardo. ■ 15090 #036-05-2005 L2005 **DR** *012

O'ROURKE, Bridget Anne. 2400 CORPORATE DR, STE 100 15090 #041-02-2001 L2003 **FM** *020 †18

O'ROURKE, Howard John. ■ 15090 #035-45-2006 L2006 **DR** *012

ORZA, Florin Mihai. ■ 15090 #781-05-1991 L2002 **AN PME** *020 †05

PADIYAR, Krishna Rama. ■ 15090 #051-04-1997 L2000 **OM FM** *020 †70

PECMAN, Joanna. ■ 15090 #041-07-1940 L1941 **OM OBG** *071

PELZ, Geoffrey Benjamin. ■ 15090 #243-46-1984 L2004 **GS** *012

PIFER, Gerald Warner. 901 HIGHLANDER CIR, FEDERAL NORTH BUILDING 15090 #041-13-1965 L1966 **ORS** *020 †40 ‡

PONTZER, Mary Verderame. 11676 PERRY HWY, STE 2309 15090 #041-07-1979 L1981 **P** *020 †75

QUINT, Donald Herman. ■ 15090 #041-12-1959 L1960 **PTH CLP** *071 †50

QUIVERS, William W, Sr. ■ 15090 #047-07-1953 L1954 **PD PDC** *071

RABINOWITZ, Philip Frank. 306 RUSTIN WAY 15090 #035-03-1989 L1991 **IM** *020 †20

RAGHAVAN, Murugan. ■ 15090 #495-16-1997 L2002 **CCM** *100

RAJASENAN, Kiran Kumar. 9930 GRUBBS RD, STE 100 15090 #041-09-1996 L1999 **HO** *020 †20

RAVES, John James. 909 HIGHLANDER CIR 15090 #041-12-1976 L1977 **GS TRS** *020 †85 ‡

RAVINDRAMURTHY, T. 6400 BROOKTREE CT STE 230 15090 #495-16-1987 L1998 **IM** *020 †20 ‡

REST, Carl Christian. ■ 15090 #041-12-2000 L2004 **AN** *020 †05

RHEINBOLT, Joshua A. ■ 15090 #035-01-2004 L2006 **ORS** *100

ROBERTS, Thom Richard. 11279 PERRY HWY, STE 105 15090 #041-12-1971 L1973 **PD GP** *020 †55 ‡

ROSNER, Joel Louis. 4500 BROOKTREE RD 15090 #041-13-1997 L2003 **DR** *020 †80

RU, Kun. ■ 15090 #243-46-1992 L2005 **PTH** *100 †50

RUEDA, Juan Luis. 10010 VALLEYVIEW CT 15090 #847-11-1968 L1997 **P IMG** *020

RUTKOWSKI, Robert, Jr. 11279 PERRY HWY, STE 105 15090 #041-12-1993 L1995 **IM** *020 †55

SAGINI, Dennis Onkoba. 6001 STONEWOOD DR, HAND & UPPEREX CENTER 15090 #041-13-2002 L2007 **HSO** *012

SAVOPOULOU, Cornelia. ■ 15090 #418-01-1998 L2002 **CCS** *100 †85

SAYLOR, Randall Martin. 3000 STONEWOOD DR, STE 120 15090 #041-09-1978 L1980 **DR** *020 †80

SCHERI, Tad Daniel. 117 VIP DR STE 120, AND SCHERI FAMILY PRACTICE 15090 #041-12-1999 L2001 **FM** *020 †18

SCHINDLER, John Thomas. ■ 15090 #041-12-1993 L1997 **CD** *071 †20

SCHNEIDER, Robert Edward. ■ 15090 #041-12-1954 L1955 **GP OS** *071

SCHORR, Neal Alan. 2400 CORPORATE DR STE 100 15090 #041-12-1982 L1983 **FM** *020 †18 ‡

SCHWERIN, William F, Jr. PO BOX 207 15090 #041-12-1952 L1953 **GP** *071

SENITA, George Robt. ■ 15090 #041-02-1946 L1947 **OPH** *071 †35

SHAHZAD, Uzma. 147 BLUE HERON DR, ALLEGHENY GENERAL HOSPITAL 15090 #704-02-1997 L2005 **ID** *020 †20 ‡

SHAW, Sheng Cheong. ■ 15090 #495-52-1972 L1980 **DR** *020 †80

SHINN, Elliott T. 6200 BROOKTREE RD, STE 110 15090 #024-07-1953 L1960 **P** *020 †75 ‡

SIMKINS, Jo Marie. 11676 PERRY HWY, STE 3206 15090 #028-34-1979 L1984 **GS** *071 †85

SOLANO, Francis X, Jr. 106 BRECKENRIDGE DR 15090 #041-09-1980 L1981 **IM** *020 †20 ‡

STILES, Helen Daniels. ■ 15090 #019-02-1986 L1989 **PD** *074 †55

STILES, Joel R. ■ 15090 #019-02-1991 *100

STRAYHORN, Joseph M, Jr. 11676 PERRY HWY STE 1200, WEXFORD PROFESSNL BLDG I 15090 #016-06-1974 L1981 **CHP P** *020 †75 ‡

STREETS, David Trigg. ■ 15090 #041-15-2005 **ORS** *012

TIPPET, Paul David. 3000 STONEWOOD DR, STE 300 15090 #041-12-1982 L1988 **REN OBG** *020 †30

TYMA, Cathy Soffer. 9000 BROOKTREE RD STE 402, WOMENS IMAGING NORTH 15090 #041-07-1983 L1993 **DR** *020 †80

TYMA, Thomas Allen. 150 LAKE DR STE 109 15090 #041-07-1983 L1993 **RHU IM** *020 †20

UIHLEIN, Arlette Harper. ■ 15090 #038-43-1988 L1999 **PTH** *012 †18

VALLEJO, Manuel C, Jr. 10059 OAKRIDGE DR 15090 #055-01-1992 L1996 **AN** *020 †05

VASSILIEVA, Polina S. ■ 15090 #913-15-1988 L2001 **PYG** *020 †75

VENKAT, Veena L. ■ 15090 #041-12-2001 L2007 **PG** *020 †55

VOGRIN, Tracy Marie. 10562 FOREST HILL DR 15090 #041-12-2003 L2003 **EM** *100

WAHL, Loretta Janine. 1290 PLEASANT HILLS RD 15090 #025-01-1987 L1989 **FM** *020 †18

ZEMEL, Sharon. 5000 STONEWOOD DR, STE 100 15090 #041-01-1984 L2003 **END PD** *020 †55

ZHANG, Qin. ■ 15090 #243-46-1991 L2006 **AN** *100

WHITAKER – ALLEGHENY

RUSHE, Karen Reisiger. ■ 15120 #028-02-2005 L2007 **U** *100

WHITE DEER – UNION

CORINES, Peter James. PO BOX 1000, GREG UNIT #51244-054 17887 #035-20-1973 L1976 **GS** *075 †85

WHITE HAVEN – LUZERNE

DEL GATTO, Louis John. 827 OLEY VALLEY RD, WHITE HAVEN CENTER 18661 #035-09-1973 L1981 **PD FM** *020 †55

FITZMAURICE, John Wm. PO BOX 19 18661 #010-02-1944 L1945 **RHU GP** *071

SHAH, Asmita C. 827 OLEY VALLEY RD, WHITE HAVEN CENTER 18661 #495-23-1980 L1985 **IM** *020

TOGUT, Myra R. ■ 18661 #035-09-1962 L1983 **PD OS** *071 †55

WALDMAN, John. PO BOX 87 18661 #869-01-1963 L1968 **PTH** *071 †50

WHITEHALL – LEHIGH

BIENIEK, Marzena Lilana. 352 5TH ST 18052 #759-01-1984 L1991 **RHU IM** *020 †20

FREI, Steven Paul. ■ 18052 #041-02-1981 L1982 **EM FM** *020 †16,18

GROVER, Narinder. 1401 FAIRMONT ST 18052 #495-45-1979 L1981 **FM** *020 †18

HABERERN, Edward John. 4205 LEHIGH ST 18052 #041-02-1960 L1961 **FM GP** *020 ‡

HOANG, Hieu Trong. ■ 18052 #041-15-2004 L2004 **AN** *012

HOSKINS, Nicholas Anthony. ■ 18052 #028-34-2008 *012

MALDONADO-COLON, Edgardo. ■ 18052 #042-03-2001 L2003 **IM** *020

MEDINA, Lisa Hammond. 1111 6TH ST 18052 #917-10-1980 L1985 **FM** *020 †18

NOR, Eugene Basil. 3691 CRESCENT CT E, STE 100 18052 #041-13-1997 L2000 **FM** *020 †18

OLOUFA, Ashraf Mohamed. ■ 18052 #915-02-1985 L1998 **P IM** *020 †75

SHARMA, Rohit. ■ 18052 #495-45-2003 L2003 **GS** *012

SPIKOL, Louis Eric. 1111 6TH ST 18052 #041-02-1984 L1985 **FM** *071 †18

SPRAGUE, William L. 1700 PEACHTREE CIR 18052 #041-02-1988 L1993 **FM** *020

VAUGHN, Robert Wm. 3000 FELLOWSHIP DR 18052 #041-13-1983 L1984 **FM FPG** *020 †18

WALTHER, Brian S. ■ 18052 #041-77-2004, ▲ L2008 **D** *012

YACOUB, Wael. 450 PERSHING BLVD, WHITEHALL MED & DENTAL 18052 #875-01-1993 L2002 **FM** *020 †18

WILCOX – ELK

SMITH, Gerald Michael. ■ 15870 #041-77-2007, ▲ L2007 *012

WILKES BARRE – LUZERNE

ADAJAR, Mario Lopez, Jr. 157 BEAR CREEK BLVD, PLAINS TOWNSHIP 18702 #748-01-1990 L1999 **IM** *020 †20

AGARWAL, Akash Deep. ■ 18702 #024-05-2000 L2001 **NS** *020

AKACH, Samir. 575 N RIVER ST, WILKES BARRE GENERAL HOSP 18764 #875-01-1999 L2004 **IM HOS** *020 †20 ‡

ALDAY, Senen N. 25 CHURCH ST, GEISINGER SOUTH W-B 18702 #748-10-1983 L1998 **AN** *020 †05

ALJARI, Jamal M.. 3 WILCOX DR, P O BOX 567 18705 #875-01-1983 L2001 **IM** *020

ALLARDYCE, Thomas James. 150 MUNDY ST 18702 #041-02-1990 L1992 **ORS** *020 †40 ‡

AMOACHI, Guenadi S. 575 N RIVER ST, ATTN: MEDICAL STAFF OFFICE 18764 #913-50-1982 L2005 **DR** *020 †80

ANDERSON, Robert S. 18701 #041-13-1937 L1942 **PHP ID** *071

ANDREWS, Joseph John. 87 E MAIN ST 18705 #041-02-1991 L1993 **GE** *020 †20

ANDREWS, Peter James. 195 E MAIN ST 18705 #041-02-1959 L1960 **FM** *071

ANDREWS, Peter James, Jr. 575 N RIVER ST 18764 #041-02-1985 L1986 **GS OS** *020 †85

ANEJA, Rita. ■ 18702 #495-34-1969 L1976 **PTH** *020

BANERJI, Barun. 25 CHURCH ST 18765 #495-38-1965 L1982 **ON HEM** *020 †18,20

BANSAL, Sanjeev Kumar. N RIVER & AUBURN STS 18764 #495-29-1999 L2005 **FP** *012

BASTA, Mafdy Nazir. ■ 18702 #915-04-1988 L2006 **AN** *020 †05

BATERIWALA, Samir Niranja. ■ 18702 #495-22-1991 L2005 **IM** *100

BATOK, Gary Raymond. 1000 E MOUNTAIN BLVD, VALLEY MEDICAL BUILDING 18711 #041-09-1979 L1980 **EM** *020 †16,20

BAUTISTA-DATOR, Carmen Sa. ■ 18764 #748-21-1998 L2001 **FM** *100

BAXI, Nilesh Husmukhlal. 575 N RIVER ST 18764 #495-89-1983 L1994 **P** *020

BEGUM, Umme Habiba. 1000 E MOUNTAIN DR 18711 #160-02-1992 L2004 **HO** *020 †20

BELIKOVA, Natalia. 1111 E END BLVD 18702 #913-13-1980 L2003 **IM** *020 †20
BELL, Mark H. 11 GALLAGHER DR 18705 #041-09-1984 L1989 **PME PMM** *020 †05
BENKINNEY, James Allen. 1000 E MOUNTAIN DR 18711 #041-09-1985 L1986 **EM** *020 †16
BERGER, Steven. ■ 18701 #396-05-1938 L1958 **P** *020
BERLEY, Benjamin S. 25 CHURCH ST 18765 #016-06-1946 L1948 **IM PUD** *071
BERNATH, Albert M. 1000 E MOUNTAIN DR 18711 #041-12-1972 L1976 **ON MG** *020 †20
BERNSTEIN, Richard Carl. 1000 E MOUNTAIN BLVD, GEISINGER MEDICAL GROUP 37 18711 #038-44-1987 L2004 **PCC CCM** *020 †20
BLAUM, Louis Chas, Jr. 25 CHURCH ST 18765 #041-02-1972 L1973 **TS GS** *020 †85,90
BLIDNER, Martin D. 150 MUNDY ST, MAC 2 BLDG 18702 #748-10-1975 L1981 **RHU IM** *020 †20
BLUM, Richard Harvey. 545 N RIVER ST, STE 230 18702 #041-13-1974 L1975 **IM PUD** *020 †20
BOHINSKI, Stanley T. 25 CHURCH ST 18765 #041-77-1988, ▲ L1989 **FM** *020 †18
BOHN, Mark Wm. 25 CHURCH ST 18765 #041-09-1980 L1981 **FM** *020 †18
BONITA, Louis Biagio. 234 S RIVER ST 18702 #021-01-1974 L1975 **FM** *071 †18
BOONIN, Alan Lee. 25 CHURCH ST 18765 #041-09-1977 L1978 **FM** *020 †18
BOULEGHLEM, Samia. ■ 18702 #125-03-1989 L2004 **IM** *100 †20
BOUND, Linda Mae. 575 N RIVER ST, WILKES BARRE GENERAL HOSPT 18764 #047-05-1981 L1983 **PTH** *020 †50 ‡
BOYLE, Grace Klimek. 1000 E MOUNTAIN BLVD, VALLEY MEDICAL BUILDING 18711 #041-07-1981 L1982 **DR PDR** *050 †80
BRIN, Kenneth Philip. 1000 E MOUNTAIN DR 18711 #035-19-1975 L2001 **CD IM** *020 †20
BROBYN, Charles Wilmer. ■ 18705 #041-09-1944 L1945 **AN** *071 †05
BRUNO, Anthony Dominic. 1000 E MOUNTAIN BLVD 18711 #030-06-1998 L2007 **PS** *020 †85
BUCCI, Frank Anthony, Jr. 158 WILKES BAR TWNSHP BLVD, STE 201 18702 #033-05-1985 L1992 **OPH** *020 †35
BUTCOFSKI, James Stephen. 166 HANOVER ST, STE 302 18702 #041-02-1963 L1967 **FM PD** *020 †18
CALLAGHAN, Daniel A, Jr. 1000 E MOUNTAIN BLVD, VALLEY MEDICAL BUILDING 18711 #041-13-1981 L1984 **AN** *020 †05
CANSECO-BERBANO, Rachel. 166 HANOVER ST, STE 105 18702 #748-10-1988 L2002 **IM** *020 †20
CARBAUGH, Rudy Allen. 1000 E MOUNTAIN BLVD 18711 #045-04-1994 L2004 **PD** *020 †55
CASALE, Alfred Stanley. 1000 E MOUNTAIN DR 18711 #023-07-1980 L2000 **TS** *020 †90,85 ‡
CASSAGNOL, Hans Patrique. 1000 E MOUNTAIN DR, OB/GYN DEPT 18711 #008-02-1998 L2002 **OBG** *020 †30
CHANG, Sin Chen. 1111 E END BLVD 18711 #244-01-1967 L1977 **FM FPG** *020 †18
CHEN, Kai-Chyr. 1111 E END BLVD, VAMC DPT OF RADIOLOGY 18711 #385-03-1959 L1979 **R** *020 †80
CHINIMILLI, Maheswari. N RIVER & AUBURN STS 18764 #495-11-2001 L2006 **FP** *012
CIMOCHOWSKI, Geo Eugene. 670 N RIVER ST, STE 206 18705 #041-02-1967 L1990 **TS** *020 †85,90
COHEN, Tom. 575 N RIVER ST 18764 #041-09-1980 L1981 **FM** *071 †18
COOPER, David R. 744 KIDDER ST, THE KNEE CENTER 18702 #041-02-1971 L1972 **ORS OSM** *020 †40 ‡
COOPER, Helen Claire. ■ 18702 #041-09-1947 L1948 **IM CD** *071
CORREALE, Christine E. 1000 E MOUNTAIN BLVD, MEDICAL CENTER 18711 #041-14-1997 L2002 **D DS** *020 †15
COSLETT-CHARLTON, Lynne M. 545 N RIVER ST, STE 100 18702 #041-02-1995 L1998 **OBG** *020 †30
CROCKETT, Samuel R, III. 1000 E MOUNTAIN DR, GEISINGER WY VALLEY MED CE 18711 #051-04-1991 L2001 **AN** *020 †05
DALSANIA, Atul Odhavji. 1111 E END BLVD, VA HOSPITAL 18711 #495-48-1989 L1996 **IM** *020 †20
DANISHANKO, Albert Geo. 25 CHURCH ST 18765 #041-02-1956 L1957 **GP** *020
DAWSEY, John Marshall. 575 N RIVER ST 18764 #041-09-1985 L1987 **DR** *020 †80
DE ANTONIO, Angela Marie. 1000 E MOUNTAIN BLVD, GEISINGER WYOMING VALLEY 18711 #041-02-1984 L1985 **IM PUD** *020 †20
DECKER, Gary Raymond. 107 LOOMIS ST 18702 #010-02-1987 L1988 **ID IM** *020 †20
DECKER, Marylouise Susan. 107 LOOMIS ST 18702 #010-02-1993 L1998 **ID IM** *020 †20
DE GENNARO, Patrick Jos. WILKES-BARRE GEN HOSP 18764 #016-43-1963 L1964 **R RNR** *071 †80 ‡
DELUNA, Carlo Marte. 545 N RIVER ST, STE 240 18702 #035-06-1990 L2005 **NS** *020 †25
DE ROJAS, Juan Francisco. 1111 E END BLVD 18711 #275-01-1949 L1968 **GS** *071
DESAI, Pramtheshkumar K. 545 N RIVER ST 18702 #495-23-1989 L1998 **PUD** *020 †20
DESAI, Sandhy. 545 N RIVER ST, STE 230 18702 #495-20-1992 L2001 **IM** *020 †20
DEVINE, Sean Thomas. 1000 E MOUNTAIN BLVD 18711 #041-09-1998 L2001 **PCC** *020 †20,55
DOSHI, Sanjaykumar J. ■ 18702 #495-48-1985 L2000 **IM** *020 †20
DRAPIEWSKI, Vincent Albin. 166 HANOVER ST, RM 1022 18702 #041-02-1963 **IM IMG** *020 †20
DYSINGER, Calvin Jon. 1000 E MOUNTAIN DR, MEDICAL CENTER 18711 #051-01-1984 L2003 **AN IM** *020 †05
EASOW, Georgey Thattaruzh. 62 EAGLE CT 18706 #496-21-1997 L2003 **IM** *020 †20
EATEDALI, Lida. 306 INDIAN CREEK DR 18702 #517-12-1994 L2001 **IM** *100 †20
ECONOMOPOULOS, George. 35 W LINDEN ST, STE 340 18702 #418-01-1974 L1998 **TS** *020 †85,90
EMILCAR, Jean. ■ 18702 #041-14-1997 L2001 **AN** *020 †05
EVERLINE, Clayton Austin. 1000 E MOUNTAIN BLVD 18702 #665-01-2003 L2007 **IM** *100 †20 ‡
FARHI, Farideh Tabatabai. 1084 HIGHWAY 315 BLVD 18702 #517-01-1972 L1991 **GP** *020
FATEMI, Jalal Boushehri. 35 W LINDEN ST, STE 220B 18702 #517-01-1962 L1972 **TS GS** *020 †85,90
FEERICK, John P. 1111 E END BLVD, DEPARTMENT OF VETERANS AFF 18702 #010-02-1978 L1982 **N PM** *020
FEINSTEIN, Peter Alan. 150 MUNDY ST, JOHN HEINZ INSTITUTE 18702 #043-01-1975 L1979 **ORS** *020 †40 ‡
FEUDALE, Frances A. 133 N RIVER ST, ASSISTANT DEPARTMENT 18711 #041-77-1995, ▲ L1996 **EM** *020 †16
FILLER, Joseph John. 575 N RIVER ST, WBGH ANESTHESIA DEPT 18702 #041-13-1982 L1984 **AN IM** *020 †20,05
FINCH, Oliver Timothy. 177 S GRANT ST 18702 #495-08-1967 L1981 **IM AN** *020
FIROUZI, Masoud. 1111 E END BLVD, MEDICAL SERVICE VIMC 18711 #517-05-1978 L1996 **GE** *020 †20
FISHER, D Michael. 175 S WILKES BARRE BLVD 18702 #041-14-1991 L1994 **FM** *020
FLETCHER, Linda L. 1000 E MOUNTAIN DR, GEISINGER HEALTH SYSTEM 18711 #024-01-1986 L2006 **NM R** *020 †80,28
FREEDMAN, Louis Jay. 1010 E MOUNTAIN BLVD 18711 #041-01-1974 L1975 **OBG** *020 †30 ‡
FRYE, John Wm. 545 N RIVER ST STE 100 18702 #041-01-1975 L1976 **OBG** *020 †30
GARCIA, Nestor Torres. 575 N RIVER ST, WILKES BARRE GENERAL HOSPT 18764 #748-01-1973 L1988 **PTH** *020 †50
GARRI, Richard Francis. 1000 E MOUNTAIN BLVD, CENTER/EMERGENCY DEPT/ MC 18711 #035-46-1995 L2005 **EM** *020 †16
GELL, Jennifer Sue. 1130 HIGHWAY 315 BLVD 18702 #041-09-1991 L1999 **OBG** *020 †30
GHOSH, Martha Sue. 1000 E MOUNTAIN DR 18711 #041-07-1991 L1993 **GE** *020 †20
GIBBONS, Gerald P. 575 N RIVER ST 18764 #010-02-1976 L1977 **IM** *020 †20
GIORDANO, Nicholas D. 575 N RIVER ST 18764 #038-06-1975 L1978 **IM IMG** *020
GRAHAM, E Joan. 575 N RIVER ST, WB6H 18764 #041-77-1975, ▲ L1977 **NM R** *071 †80,28
GRANA, Vicente P. 166 HANOVER ST, STE 303 18702 #748-08-1966 L1973 **TS** *020 †85 ‡
GRASSO, Michael James. 150 MUNDY ST 18702 #041-15-2000 L2001 **IM** *020 †20
GRINAWAY, George Aaron. COR N RIVER & AUBURN STS, WILKES-BARRE GENERAL HOSP 18764 #047-06-1967 L1967 **PTH FOP** *020 †50
GROSS, Mitchell Jay. 1000 E MOUNTAIN BLVD, VALLEY MEDICAL BUILDING 18711 #033-05-1983 L1985 **N** *020 †75
GRYCZKO, Gerald Anthony. 47 S WASHINGTON ST, BUREAU OF DISABILITY 18701 #041-02-1963 L1972 **OTR** *020 †40
GUSTITUS, Gaye C. 175 S WILKES BARRE BLVD 18702 #041-77-2000, ▲ L2001 **FM** *020 †18
HARABIN, Katarina. 1111 E END BLVD 18711 #286-11-1968 L1985 **IM NEP** *020 †20
HARDAWAY, Alfred Eugene. 25 CHURCH ST 18765 #016-42-1979 L1987 **DR NM** *020
HAROSTOCK, Michael Danl. 35 W LINDEN ST STE 220 18702 #010-02-1981 L1983 **TS GS** *020 †85,90
HARRIS, Ronald Irwin. 1010 E MOUNTAIN DR, DEPT ENDO 18711 #021-01-1975 L1978 **END IM** *020 †20
HARTZ, Leo Mitri. 19 N MAIN ST 18711 #010-01-1974 L1975 **FM MDM** *030 †18 ‡
HOGG, Judith Elaine. 1111 E END BLVD, VA MED CTR 18711 #024-05-1970 L1971 **N CN** *020 †75
HOLMES, Todd Jeffry. 25 CHURCH ST 18765 #010-02-1986 L1989 **IM** *020 †20
HORA, James Francis, II. 1000 E MOUNTAIN BLVD, GALEN MEDICAL GROUP 18711 #016-43-1990 L1993 **N** *020 †75
HUNTINGTON, Richard A. 175 S WILKES BARRE BLVD, GEISINGER KISTLER CLINIC 18702 #041-14-1995 L1998 **FM** *020 †18
HUSAIN, Zahid. 150 MUNDY ST, ALLIED MED ARTS BLDG 18702 #160-02-1972 L1980 **RHU IM** *020 †20
HUSSAIN, Abul F Z. ■ 18702 #160-02-1977 L1998 **IM** *020
IMBROGNO, Michael S. 3 OAK CTR 18702 #561-06-1981 L1986 **PD NPM** *020 †55 ‡
INDECK, Matthew Chas. 1000 E MOUNTAIN BLVD, GEISINGER SPECIALTY CLINIC 18711 #021-01-1979 L1985 **TRS GS** *020 †85
JACOB, Emmanuel Egipto. 1000 E MOUNTAIN DR 18711 #748-01-1977 L1982 **PM** *020 †60
JANERICH, Albert David. 672 N RIVER ST, STE 101 18705 #041-02-1977 L1978 **PM** *020 †60
JOSEPH, Raymond Guido. 1130 HIGHWAY 315, STE B 18702 #041-12-2000 L2001 **NEP** *020 †20
JOSEPH, Raymond John. 165 CAREY AVE 18702 #041-09-1977 L1978 **GP** *020
JUDGE, James W, Jr. ■ 18702 #010-02-1951 L1952 **OPH** *020 †35
JULIUS, Ernest Leo. 150 MUNDY ST 18702 #041-01-1980 L1981 **FM FPG** *020 †18
KACZOROWSKI, Eugene. 8 CHURCH ST, STE 214 18702 #759-12-1969 L1981 **OBG** *020 †30
KALAKUNTLA, Radhakrishna. 1000 E MOUNTAIN DR 18711 #495-65-1994 L2006 **GE** *020 †20
KANERIA, Pareshkumar Hars. ■ 18702 #495-48-1995 L2004 **IM** *100 †20
KAO, Yu Song. 25 CHURCH ST 18765 #244-04-1966 L1976 **N** *020 †75
KASAYAPANAND, Wittawat. 335 S FRANKLIN ST, FRIENDSHIP HOUSE 18702 #891-07-1989 L2000 **P** *020
KASHATUS, William Chas. 166 HANOVER ST 18702 #041-09-1959 L1960 **IM HMP** *071 †50 ‡
KASPAR, Hanna J. 1000 E MOUNTAIN BLVD 18711 #605-01-1984 L2006 **PTH CLP** *020 †50
KATLIC, Mark Richard. 1000 E MOUNTAIN DR, GEISINGER WYOMING VALLEY 18711 #023-07-1977 L1983 **TS GS** *020 †85,90
KEETON, Nancy Cone. 744 KIDDER ST 18702 #010-02-1982 L1989 **DR** *020 †80
KERRIGAN, Patrick Jos. 476 HAZLE ST 18702 #041-77-1984, ▲ L1985 **GP** *020
KIM, Hyung Bae. 545 N RIVER ST STE 210 18702 #583-01-1968 L1977 **OBG** *020 †30
KIM, Steve Hosuk. 1000 E MOUNTAIN BLVD, MC 37-62 18711 #035-01-1987 L2006 **GS** *020 †85
KISTLER, David Walter. 175 S WILKES BARRE BLVD, CENTRAL WILKES BARRE 18702 #041-09-1947 L1948 **FM** *071 †18
KLINE, Gerard Louis. 175 S WILKES BARRE BLVD 18702 #041-02-1989 L1991 **FM** *020 †18 ‡
KLINE, John Anthony, Jr. 150 MUNDY ST 18702 #041-02-1993 L1996 **PM PME** *020 †60
KODALI, Sathish. 1111 E END BLVD, VA MEDICAL CENTER 18711 #495-50-1989 L1995 **ICE** *020 †20
KODIAL, Sukhwinder Singh. N RIVER & AUBURN STS 18764 #495-29-1993 L2005 **FP** *012
KOLESSAR, David Jos. 1000 E MOUNTAIN BLVD, GEISINGER WY VLY MED CTR 18711 #041-13-1987 L1988 **ORS OAR** *020 †40 ‡
KOVAL, Joseph Chas. 19 N MAIN ST 18711 #010-02-1980 L1987 **PUD CCM** *020 †20
KRAFCHIN, Ira Chas. 1130 HIGHWAY 315 BLVD, THE PLASTIC SURGERY CENTER 18702 #035-08-1976 L1983 **PS HS** *020 †65
KRAMER, Arnold. 1084 HIGHWAY 315 BLVD 18702 #036-07-1963 L1972 **PD PDA** *020 †55
KRAUSE-BRUCKER, Wilma. 1111 E END BLVD 18711 #041-07-1972 L1980 **OPH** *020 †35
KREEL, Barbara Janice. 1000 E MOUNTAIN DR 18702 #035-47-1984 L1989 **OTO** *020 †45
KRYWICKI, William Jos. 1000 E MOUNTAIN DR 18711 #041-02-1977 L1978 **ORS OSM** *020 †40
KUCHEMBA, Leonard Adam. 25 CHURCH ST 18765 #654-01-1986 L1989 **IM** *020
KURZWEIL, Steven J. 6 WILDFLOWER DR 18702 #748-08-1981 L1987 **U** *020 †95
LANDRY, Roger Francis. 500 SCOTT ST 18702 #024-07-1972 L1995 **AM OM** *030 †70
LAWRENCE, Gary Wm. 175 S WILKES BARRE BLVD 18702 #041-02-1977 L1985 **PD ADL** *020 †55
LEASE, John Richard. 1111 E END BLVD, VA MEDICAL CTR 18711 #024-01-1971 L1979 **ORS** *020 †40
LEE, Samuel. 1000 E MOUNTAIN DR, DEPT OF ANESTHESIA 18711 #244-06-1973 L1982 **AN** *020 †05
LENTINI, Joseph A. 672 N RIVER ST, STE 105 18705 #041-02-1951 L1952 **OS GP** *072
LEVANDOSKI, Diana C. 1000 E MOUNTAIN DR 18711 #041-09-1984 L1985 **OPH** *020 †35
LEVCHUK, Vera. 1111 E END BLVD, DEPT OF VET AFFAIRS MED CT 18711 #913-05-1990 L2006 **NEP IM** *020 †20
LICO, Serrie C. 1000 E MOUNTAIN DR 18711 #041-09-1989 L1999 **TS** *020 †85,90
LONG, Paul Robt. 1000 E MOUNTAIN BLVD, VALLEY MEDICAL BUILDING 18711 #041-02-1976 L1977 **D IM** *020 †15
LOPEZ DEL CASTILLO, Kharme. N RIVER & AUBURN STS, DEPT OF FAMILY PRACTICE 18764 #748-21-1998 L2006 **FP** *012
LOWE, Diane Alison. 575 N RIVER ST, WILKES BARRE GENERAL HOSPT 18764 #041-14-1980 L1986 **FM** *020 †18
LURASCHI, Maria Cristina. 1111 E END BLVD 18711 #561-17-1955 L1966 **PTH** *071 †50
MADEIRA, Robert Gordon. 1000 E MOUNTAIN DR MZ35-37, GEISINGER MEDICAL GROUP 18711 #041-13-1998 L2000 **IM** *020 †20

MALIK, Aslam M.. 1111 E END BLVD, DEPT OF INTERNAL MED 18711 #704-21-1985 L2004 **IM** *100 †20
MALIK, Uzma. 1000 E MOUNTAIN DR 18711 #704-25-1989 L2005 **DR** *020 †80
MANCIA, Bonita Madelyn. 25 CHURCH ST 18765 #041-09-1978 L1979 **OBG** *020 ‡
MANRIQUE, Jose Vicente. 166 HANOVER ST 18702 #847-09-1967 L1973 **CD IM** *020 †20
MC BURNEY, John Wallace. 620 BALTIMORE DR 18702 #012-05-1981 L2005 **N** *020 †75
MC LAUGHLIN, Kevin P. 575 N RIVER ST, WILKES BARRE GENERAL HOSPT 18764 #308-08-1983 L1986 **IM** *020 †20 ‡
MC RIPLEY, James Ronald. 1000 E MOUNTAIN BLVD, VALLEY MEDICAL BUILDING 18711 #032-01-1980 L1986 **U** *020
METGUD, Hema Annappa. 1111 E END BLVD, VA MEDICAL CENTER 18711 #495-97-1991 L1999 **IM** *020 †20
MEYER, Arthur Nathaniel. 1000 E MOUNTAIN BLVD, VALLEY MEDICAL BUILDING 18711 #041-02-1961 L1962 **ON HEM** *020 †20 ‡
MIAN, Nabeela Z. 1111 E END BLVD, VA MEDICAL CENTER 18711 #704-06-1986 L1996 **RHU** *020 †20
MOHIUDDIN, Mohammed. 1000 E MOUNTAIN DR 18711 #495-21-1968 L1976 **RO ON** *020 †80
MORANO, H Joyce. 1111 E END BLVD, VAMC GERIATRICS & EXT CARE 18711 #035-08-1982 L1983 **IMG IM** *020 †20
MOSES, George Peter. 166 HANOVER ST 18702 #041-02-1962 L1963 **GS TS** *020 †85
MUFTI, Amjad Idris. ■ 18702 #704-09-1983 L2001 **IM** *020 †20
MUFTI, Tehmina. ■ 18702 #704-24-1989 L2005 **IM** *012
MURPHY, Mary L Resinski. 110 S PENNSYLVANIA AVE 18701 #041-07-1958 L1959 **PD** *071
MURTHY, Radhakrishna. ■ 18702 #495-50-1963 L1971 **U** *020 †95
NADKARNI, Prashant V. 1000 E MOUNTAIN DR 18711 #495-17-1991 L1995 **END IM** *020 †20
NADKARNI, Prashant V. 100 E MOUNTAIN BLVD, GEISINGER WYOMING VLY MED 18702 #624-01-1982 L2005 **END DIA** *100
NAKKACHE, Victor B. 166 HANOVER ST, STE 202 18702 #132-01-1974 L1988 **NS** *020 †25
NAZNEEN, Asra. N RIVER & AUBURN STS, DEPT FAM PRAC 18764 #495-21-1998 L2003 **FM** *100
NAZZIOLA, Eric Anthony. 575 N RIVER ST, WILKES-BARRE GENERAL HOSPI 18764 #035-19-1995 L2007 **EM** *020 †16
NEWMARK, Zephron Gabriel. 1000 E MOUNTAIN BLVD, MAIL STOP 37-37 18711 #011-03-1975 L2004 **OTO** *020 †45
NIEZGODA, Paul Edward. 1000 E MOUNTAIN DR, GEISINGER HEALTH SYSTEMS 18711 #041-14-1977 L1978 **GE** *020 †20
NIKAM, Smita Shivprasad. ■ 18702 #496-42-1999 L2006 **IM** *100
NIRMUL, Dharamraj. 1111 E END BLVD, VETERANS AFFAIRS MED CTR 18711 #836-05-1968 L1994 **GS VS** *020 †85
O'DONNELL, George James. 272 S RIVER ST 18702 #041-02-1948 L1949 **PD** *071 †55
OLSHEMSKI, Frank Chas. 575 N RIVER ST 18764 #041-09-1984 L1985 **FM** *020 †18
OW YONG, Henry. 1111 E END BLVD, VETERANS ADMINISTRATION HO 18711 #209-01-1981 L1998 **IM** *020 †20
PADEN, Drue Robt. 150 MUNDY ST 18702 #041-09-1977 L1978 **FM** *020 †18
PANDE, Chhavi. N RIVER & AUBURN STS, DEPT OF FAMILY PRAC 18764 #496-07-2000 L2004 **FM** *100 †18
PANDE, Vinit Kumar. 150 MUNDY ST, WILKES-BARRE 18702 #035-08-1997 L2001 **PM** *020 †60
PARENT, Kevin. 1000 E MOUNTAIN DR 18711 #041-02-1965 L2004 **GE IM** *072 †20
PATEL, Kamlesh R. 1111 E END BLVD 18711 #495-22-1989 L1997 **IM** *020 †20
PATEL, Satish Devnathbhai. DEPARTMENT OF RADIOLOGY, WILKES-BARRE GENERAL HOSPI 18764 #495-23-1974 L1980 **R RNR** *020 †80
PELCZAR, Eugene Walter. 171 STANTON ST 18702 #041-02-1962 L1963 **GP** *071
PENUGONDA, Dwaraki Bai. 166 HANOVER ST 18702 #495-11-1961 L1974 **PD PHO** *020 †55
POLSANI, Srilatha. 560 WILDFLOWER DR 18702 #495-57-1997 L2006 **IM** *100 †20
POMPEY, Daniel Thos. 48 SARATOGA CT 18702 #041-02-1958 L1959 **AN** *071 †05
POTERA, Leo Paul. 80 E NORTHAMPTON ST 18701 #016-43-1971 L1972 **IM** *020 †20
POTORSKI, Robt David Jos. 545 N RIVER ST, STE 220 18702 #308-03-1982 L1983 **CD IM** *020 †20
PRASAD, Shishir Chandra. 166 HANOVER ST STE 3 18702 #495-24-1963 L1972 **GS VS** *020 †85
PRATER, John Mark. ■ 18705 #041-09-1986 L1987 **FM** *020 †18
PREBOLA, William Ronald. 150 MUNDY ST 18702 #041-02-1988 L1990 **PM IM** *020 †60
PRESPER, John Herve. 1000 E MOUNTAIN DR, GEISINGER MEDICAL GROUP 18711 #035-08-1969 L1984 **NS** *020 †25
PUGAZHENDHI, Vasanthi. 8 CHURCH ST, STE 414 18702 #495-42-1988 L2005 **PDP** *020 †55
PUMA, Samuel Jos. 25 CHURCH ST 18765 #041-09-1940 L1941 **GS** *071
PUTPRUSH, Joseph Ronald. 575 N RIVER ST 18764 #041-13-1976 L1977 **PTH** *020 †50
QUIERY, Albert Thos. 1000 E MOUNTAIN DR 18711 #035-46-1984 L1991 **HEM BBK** *020 †20 ‡
QUILO, Lino A. 25 CHURCH ST, GEISSINGER SOUTH WB 18765 #748-01-1966 L1978 **EM GP** *020
RAINEY, Catherine Marie. 500 SCOTT ST 18702 #041-14-1983 L1984 **IM** *020 †70 ‡
RAJAGOPAL, Mini. N RIVER & AUBURN STS, WYOMING VALLEY HLTH CARE S 18764 #495-31-1994 L2004 **FM** *100
RHEE, Chung-Kwang. 1111 E END BLVD 18702 #583-06-1964 L1974 **P** *020 †75
RICHTERMAN, Ronald L. N RIVER AND AUBURN STS, DEPT OF RADIOLOGY 18764 #035-46-1983 L1985 **DR** *020 †80
RITZ, George. 150 MUNDY ST, MUSCULOSKELETAL INSTITUTE 18702 #041-09-1988 L1992 **ORS** *020 †40
RODRIGUEZ, Alfonso. 1130 HIGHWAY 315, STE B 18702 #042-01-1980 L1987 **OS NEP** *020 †20
ROE, Robert Everett. 1000 E MOUNTAIN DR 18711 #025-01-1966 L1986 **OBG** *020 †30
ROHDE, Thomas Lee. 110 S PENNSYLVANIA AVE, COMMUNITY COUNSEL SRVICE 18701 #056-05-1974 L1993 **P** *020
ROOTS, Bridget Diana. 1000 E MOUNTAIN DR 18711 #035-46-1986 L2005 **OBG** *020 †30
ROSENBLATT, Stanley A. 150 MUNDY ST 18702 #041-02-1962 L1964 **N** *072 †75
ROSS, David Stuart. 1000 E MOUNTAIN BLVD, M C 37-51 18711 #041-09-1992 L1994 **IM ISM** *040 †20
ROSSI, Patricia A V. RR 1 18702 #041-07-1967 L1968 **PD** *074 †55
ROSTOCK, Robert Anthony. 50 ROOSEVELT TER 18702 #041-14-1979 L1983 **RO** *020 †80
ROTH, Mary Elizabeth A. 1000 E MOUNTAIN BLVD 18711 #041-01-1971 L1972 **FM FPG** *030 †18
ROTHSCHILD, John Albert. 1130 HIGHWAY 315 BLVD, W-B 18702 #035-20-1969 L1971 **NEP IM** *020 †20
ROTHSTEIN, Stephen Allan. 19 N MAIN ST, 8TH FL 18711 #045-01-1971 L2002 **FM EM** *020 †16
RU DUSKY, Basil Michael. 15 PUBLIC SQ STE 208 18701 #041-12-1959 L1960 **CD IM** *020 †20
RUGGIERO, Nicholas Jos. 575 N RIVER ST 18764 #041-02-1966 L1967 **CD IM** *071
RUPP, Michael Donald. 166 HANOVER ST, STE 305 18702 #041-09-1987 L1988 **CD** *020 †20
RUSIN, William Aloysius. 35 W LINDEN ST STE 320 18702 #041-13-1963 L1964 **OTO** *071 †45
SAHILLIOGLU, Refik. 166 HANOVER ST 18702 #902-10-1962 L1971 **PUD IM** *075
SAIDMAN, Lester Michael. 575 N RIVER ST 18764 #041-13-1942 L1943 **FM EM** *071
SALZANO, Laura Jo. 1000 E MOUNTAIN BLVD, GEISINGER GENERAL SURGERY 18711 #041-07-1995 L2002 **SO GS** *020 †85
SAMONTE, Alexies Osorio. 8 CHURCH ST, 4TH FL 18702 #748-01-1988 L2001 **PD PN** *020 †55
SANTOS, Francisco F. 1111 E END BLVD, MENTAL HYGEINE CLNC-VAMC 18711 #748-25-1984 L1993 **P** *020 †75
SATYAM, Dasa S. 25 CHURCH ST 18765 #496-01-1971 L1976 **AN** *020 †05
SAWYER, Charles Spencer. 1000 E MOUNTAIN DR 18711 #035-45-1984 L1989 **IM** *020 †20 ‡
SCARANO, Domenico. 1000 E MOUNTAIN BLVD, GEISNGER MEDICAL GROUP 18711 #561-17-1952 L1965 **TS GS** *020 †85,90
SCHAEFER, David Carl. 1000 E MOUNTAIN DR 18711 #051-07-1992 L1994 **GE** *020 †20
SCHELL, Frank James, Jr. N RIVER AND AUBURN STS, WILKES-BARRE GEN HOSP EMER 18764 #067-01-1977 L1978 **EM FM** *020 †18,16
SCHIOWITZ, Mark Fuerth. 545 N RIVER ST, STE 20 18702 #041-02-1978 L1980 **GS CCS** *020 †85
SCHUCKER, Jodi Lynn. 1000 E MOUNTAIN DR 18711 #041-13-1991 L1993 **MFM** *020 †30
SCHULMAN, Norman. 25 CHURCH ST 18765 #561-01-1968 L1974 **RO** *020 †80
SCHWITER, E Jos. 1000 E MOUNTAIN DR 18711 #041-14-1976 L1977 **CD IM** *020 †20
SCIANDRA, Lucyann Marie. 107 LOOMIS ST, INFECTION SPECIALISTS 18702 #041-77-1993, ▲ L1994 **ID IM** *020
SCINICO, Mark Wm. 268 HIGHLAND PARK BLVD, NORTHEASTERN MED CENTER 18702 #308-07-1983 L1986 **OM IM** *020 †20
SEDOR, David John. 150 MUNDY ST, MAC IV 18702 #041-09-1985 L1987 **NS GS** *020 †25
SEHGAL, Vishal. 9B CHEROKEE SQ 18702 #495-78-2000 L2006 **IM** *020 †20
SHAH, Anilkumar T. 166 HANOVER ST 18702 #496-38-1961 L1986 **CD IM** *071 †20
SHAH, Jyoti Ramesh. 575 N RIVER ST 18764 #495-48-1972 L1980 **P IM** *020 †75
SHAIKH, Mohammad Ali. 1111 E END BLVD, DEPT. OF VETERANS AFFAIRS 18711 #517-01-1954 L1985 **GS** *020 †85,90
SHANKAR, Uday Rangappa. 1111 E END BLVD, VET AFFAIRS MED CTR 18711 #306-01-2000 L2004 **IM** *020 †20
SHEA, Paul Leo. ■ 18702 #041-14-2006 L2006 **PD** *012
SHEPPARD, Steven Richard. 20 NORTH ST, MOUNTAIN VIEW OB/GYN 18705 #055-75-1983, ▲ L1984 **OBG** *020
SHERWOOD, Arthur Walter. 1000 E MOUNTAIN DR, MEDICAL CENTER 18711 #035-45-1966 L1967 **GP** *071 †18
SHERWOOD, John Wm. 575 N RIVER ST 18764 #033-05-1963 L1964 **FM OBG** *071 †18
SHROFF, Farook Kassamali. 166 HANOVER ST 18702 #495-23-1970 L1974 **CD IM** *020 †20
SIDDIQUI, Shahid Nusrat. ■ 18702 #704-02-1987 L2003 **IM** *020
SINGH, Deepak. 1000 E MOUNTAIN BLVD, GEISINGER HEART HOSPSITAL 18711 #041-13-1993 L1999 **TS** *020 †85,90
SINGH, Magan Pal. 25 CHURCH ST, MERCY HOSPITAL 18765 #495-05-1982 L1994 **AN** *020 †05
SKONIECZKI, Stanley R, III. 670 N RIVER ST STE 102, WATERFRONT PROFESSIONAL PA 18705 #041-07-1991 L1993 **EM** *020 †16
SMEDLEY, William Paul. 575 N RIVER ST 18764 #016-43-1960 L1961 **GS OM** *020 †85
SMITH, Henry F, Jr. 575 N RIVER ST 18764 #041-02-1983 L1987 **PUD IM** *020 †20
SOLGAMA, Pareshkumar C. 110 S PENNSYLVANIA AVE, COMMUNITY CONS SVCS 18701 #495-22-1991 L1999 **P** *020 †75 ‡
SONCAYAON, Mila S. ■ 18702 #748-01-1989 L1996 **PTH** *020 †50
SOTELO, Carlos E. 1000 E MOUNTAIN DR, GEISINGER HEALTH SYSTEM 18711 #737-09-1993 L2007 **PCC** *020 †20
SOTIROPOULOS, George P. 21 CHURCH ST., GEISINGER PEDIATRIC URGENT 18765 #028-34-1982 L2003 **PD** *020 †55
SPEACE, George Francis. 1130 HIGHWAY 315 BLVD, VALLEY SURGERY CENTER INC 18702 #041-02-1972 L1973 **PS** *020 †65
STANKOSKI, John Anthony. 150 MUNDY ST STE 4 18702 #561-01-1984 L1987 **IM** *020 †20 ‡
STERNLIEB, Sanford B. 35 W LINDEN ST STE 210 18702 #869-05-1953 L1955 **ORS** *071 †40
STRANG, David Jesse. 1111 E END BLVD 18711 #056-05-1962 L1990 **D** *020
STUCCIO, Joseph Jerome. ■ 18705 #041-09-1956 L1957 **U** *071 †95
SUSSMAN, Jonathan. VET ADMIN HOSP, DEPT MED 18711 #035-19-1964 L1965 **IM** *020 †20
TALATI, Dineshkumar C. 166 HANOVER ST STE 105, MD ASSOC BLDG 18702 #495-22-1974 L1985 **PUD IM** *020 †20
TALEGHANI, Mohammad Foad. N RIVER & AUBURN STS 18764 #517-08-1983 L2005 **FM** *100
TALUKDER, Mohammad Ali. 1000 E MOUNTAIN BLVD, GEISINGER WYOMING VALLEY M 18711 #033-05-2000 L2001 **DR** *100 †80 ‡
TASKAR, Devesh Ramesh. N RIVER & AUBURN STS 18764 #495-17-1996 L2005 **FM** *100
THEROUX, John Francis. 335 S FRANKLIN ST 18702 #048-02-1984 L2006 **P CHP** *020 †20,75
THOMAS, Justin. ■ 18702 #495-63-1981 L1997 **IM** *020 †20
TOGIAS, Afrodite. 110 S PENNSYLVANIA AVE 18701 #418-01-1966 L1976 **FM PD** *020
TOGUT, Allen John. 166 HANOVER ST, STE 202 18702 #035-20-1960 L1993 **TS PME** *020 †85,90
TORONY, Jeannie A. 575 E MAIN ST, FOX HILL 18702 #305-01-1984 L1989 **FM** *020
UDOSHI, Mallapa B. 166 HANOVER ST 18702 #495-35-1967 L1981 **IM CD** *020 †20
URANGA, Rebecca Sue. ■ 18701 #054-04-2007 L2007 **OBG** *012
VARMA, Krishnan R. 1111 E END BLVD, VA MEDICAL CENTER 112 18711 #495-31-1967 L1975 **U** *020 †95
VELNATI, Aparna. ■ 18702 #495-50-1994 L2007 **DR** *020 †80
VELUSWAMY, Ragupathy. 575 N RIVER ST 18764 #495-94-1971 L2007 **PD** *020 †55 ‡
VIJAYARAMAN, Pugazhendhi. 1000 E MOUNTAIN DR 18711 #495-42-1991 L2005 **CD** *020 †20
VILLAROSA, Anthony Romero. 1000 E MOUNTAIN DR 18711 #748-01-1994 L2005 **CD NC** *020 †20 ‡
VO, Kim-Loan Thi. ■ 18702 #840-01-1967 L1981 **PUD** *020 †20
VRABEC, Keith Gerard. 1000 E MOUNTAIN DR 18702 #041-07-1990 L1994 **EM** *020 †16
WAGSHUL, Adam David. 1000 E MOUNTAIN BLVD, MC 37-51 18711 #023-01-1996 L1999 **ORS** *020 †40
WEISER, Nelson J. 1111 E END BLVD, USVA MED CTR 18711 #035-19-1943 L1990 **IM CCM** *020 †20
WEISS, William. 144 MUNDY ST 18702 #041-09-1977 L1979 **PUD** *020 †20
WHALEN, Edward Michael. ■ 18701 #041-13-1942 L1943 **P** *071 †75
WIRJOSEMITO, Salimi A. 1111 E END BLVD 18711 #506-03-1971 L1998 **GS EM** *020 †85
YAP, Englok. 1130 HIGHWAY 315 BLVD, 0S-315 18702 #041-02-1990 L2006 **AN PME** *020 †05
YATSONSKY, David James. 175 S WILKES BARRE BLVD, GEISINGER MEDICAL GROUP 18702 #035-15-1991 L1993 **IM** *072 †20

ZALATIMO, Akram Abdallah. 545 N RIVER ST, STE 110 18702 #915-04-1974 L1980
OBG *020 †30 ‡
ZAMAN, Rubina. 575 N RIVER ST 18764 #704-18-1980 L1993 PD *020 †55
ZAMANIAN YAZDI, Ali Reza. 1111 E END BLVD, VETERANS ADMINISTRATION HO 18711
#517-04-1975 L2002 IM *100
ZAVACKI, John. 216 N RIVER ST, COURTHOUSE SQ TOWERS #640 18702 #041-13-1962 L1966
D *020 ‡
ZEGER, Steven Allen. 545 N RIVER ST STE 100 18702 #308-03-1982 L1984 OBG *020 †30 ‡
ZEVENEY, Dennis Jos. 25 CHURCH ST 18765 #010-01-1966 L1972 GS *071 †85
ZHANG, Xiaohong. 1000 E MOUNTAIN DR 18711 #243-39-1982 L2005 PTH *100

WILKINSBURG – ALLEGHENY

AYERS, Cynthia G. 221 PENN AVE, STE 1500 15221 #010-03-1968 L1969 IM *020 †20
BAZRON, Herbert, Jr. 224 PENN AVE STE B 15221 #041-12-1984 L1985 IM *020 †20
FLETCHER, Douglas Danl. 221 PENN AVE, STE 1700 15221 #051-01-1981 L1984
IM IMG *020 †20
GILLETTE, Noel John. 225 PENN AVE 15221 #041-12-1960 L1961 GP *071
IANCU, Albert L. 225 PENN AVE 15221 #041-12-1942 L1943 U *071 †95
KHAN, Abdul Qayyum. 200 PENN AVE 15221 #704-02-1990 L1995 IM *020 †20
KONDAVEETI, Radhika. 225 PENN AVE 15221 #422-01-1999 L2001 IM *020 †20
SINCHIOCO, Ceferino S. 225 PENN AVE, LIFECARE HOSP-PITTSBURGH 15221
#748-01-1964 L1973 AN GS *071
SLAYTON, Robert Ira. 221 PENN AVE STE 1100 15221 #035-15-1978 L1979 P PYG *020 †75
STIEBEL, Victor Gordon. 225 PENN AVE 15221 #016-42-1984 L1992 IM P *020 †75
WEINSTEIN, Elizabeth. ■ 15221 #041-12-2002 L2002 IM *100 †20
WILSON, Jeffrey Chas. 221 PENN AVE STE 1100 15221 #048-14-1982 L1983 P *020 †75
WITTIG, Robert Link. 225 PENN AVE 15221 #028-34-1961 L1966 P *020

WILLIAMSBURG – BLAIR

SIEMS, Laura Jane. 306 PLUM ST 16693 #041-13-1995 L1998 FM *020 †18

WILLIAMSPORT – LYCOMING

ABDEL-MESSEIH, Adel A. 1100 GRAMPIAN BLVD, DIVINE PROVIDENCE HOSPITAL 17701
#915-03-1964 L1980 ON HEM *020 †20
ALAMY, Sayed Shaheer. 1100 GRAMPIAN BLVD 17701 #118-01-1981 L2006 P *020
AMBROSE, David Noble. 699 RURAL AVE 17701 #041-13-1977 L1978 FM OBS *040 †18
AMEREE, Baryalay. 777 RURAL AVE, WILLIAMSPORT HOSPITAL 17701 #286-03-1983 L1996
IM *020 †20
AMSLER, Fred Ritts. 1738 E 3RD ST, # 316 17701 #041-13-1959 L1960 ORS *071 †40
ANDERSON, Elizabeth E. 1205 GRAMPIAN BLVD, STE 1A 17701 #033-06-1988 L1990
FM *020 †18
ANTONETTI, Thomas Blane. 777 RURAL AVE 17701 #041-13-1986 L1987 FM *020 †18
ARGUE, Stephen Harold. ■ 17701 #030-06-1980 L1980 FM *020
AUFIERO, Thomas Xavier. 777 RURAL AVE, CARDIOTHORACIC SURGERY 17701
#041-14-1983 L1984 TS *020 †90,85
BAGDADI ALHASHIMI, Maher. 777 RURAL AVE DEPT ER, WILLIAMSPORT HOSL 17701
#875-01-1979 L1982 EM IM *020 †20,16
BAILEY, John Harvey, Jr. 699 RURAL AVE 17701 #041-14-1989 L1991 ORS OSM *020 †40
BANKS, William Walter. 1705 WARREN AVE, STE 205 17701 #035-45-1974 L1975 OTO *020 †45
BELLES, Terry Alan. 145 SHAFFER ST, BELLES HOFSTROM & 17702 #041-13-1975 L1976
FM *020 †18
BELTZ, William Richard. 1100 GRAMPIAN BLVD, WOUND CENTER 17701 #016-11-1970 L1977
GS VS *020 †85
BERING, Joseph Paul, Jr. 777 RURAL AVE, SUSQUEHANNA CARDIOLOGY ASS 17701
#041-02-1988 L1990 CD IM *020 †20
BIANCO, Teresa Irene. 1100 GRAMPIAN BLVD, DIVINE PROVIDENCE HOSPITAL 17701
#048-04-1996 L2001 P *020 †75
BLOISO, Glenn Thos. 1705 WARREN AVE, STE 206 17701 #035-46-1980 L1986 U *020 †95
BLOM, Bohen M Ferrari. 777 RURAL AVE 17701 #004-01-1959 L1979 PTH *020 †50
BLOM, Johannes. 1100 GRAMPIAN BLVD, DIVINE PROVIDENCE HOSPITAL 17701
#660-04-1955 L1979 ON HEM *071 †20
BOYLE, Michael Francis. 777 RURAL AVE, EMERGENCY SERVICES/WILLIAM 17701
#051-07-1988 L2006 EM *020 †16
BOZIC, Albert Francis P. 57 E 4TH ST 17701 #041-09-1941 L1942 OPH *071
BRACE, Matthew James. 699 RURAL AVE 17701 #041-15-2005 L2005 FP *012
BRANTON, Susan Ann. 699 RURAL AVE, STE 104 17701 #041-13-1992 L1995 GS *020 †85
BRAUN, Jeffrey William. 1201 GRAMPIAN BLVD, STE 2E 17701 #012-01-2002 L2002
FM *020 †18
BRAUNEGG, Paul W, Jr. 777 RURAL AVE, STE 400 17701 #041-12-1984 L1985 AN *020 †05
BRESTICKER, David Hyman. 1705 WARREN AVE STE 301 17701 #041-12-1987 L1988
FM *020 †18
BURKE, Thomas V. 777 RURAL AVE 17701 #041-07-1980 L1981 PUD CCM *020 †20
BURKHART, Linda Louise. 1705 WARREN AVE 17701 #051-04-1990 L1992 GS *020 †85
BURKS, John Mallory. 777 RURAL AVE 17701 #035-01-1970 L1977 CD *020 †20
BURNS, John Thos. 777 RURAL AVE, THIRD FLOOR SOUTH 17701 #039-05-1989 L1991
GE PG *020 †20,55
BUSSANICH, Anthony. 777 RURAL AVE 17701 #561-11-1992 L1996 IM *020
BUTKIEWICZ, Bernard L. 777 RURAL AVE 17701 #041-14-1980 L1982 DR *020 †80
BYLER, Philip Ray. 1205 GRAMPIAN BLVD 17701 #011-03-1975 L1978 FM *020 †18
CALCE, John Vincent. 1100 GRAMPIAN BLVD 17701 #035-15-1972 L1977 NM END *020 †20,28
CALVERT, Terri Lynn. 904 CAMPBELL ST STE 301 17701 #041-14-1988 L1991 P *020 †75
CAMPANA, Joseph Francis. 151 E 3RD ST 17701 #041-13-1944 L1945 OTO OPH *071 †45
CAREY, Patrick Jos. 1100 GRAMPIAN BLVD 17701 #041-77-1983, ▲ L1984 ORS OSM *020 †40
CHANG, Mona Pinghua. 777 RURAL AVE 17701 #035-19-1986 L1989 FM *020 †18
CICCARELLI, Lee Michael. 1251 RURAL AVE 17701 #036-05-1978 L1979 IM IMG *020 †20
COLLINS, Leonard Robt. 777 RURAL AVE, FL 6 17701 #041-13-1977 L1979 OBG *020 †30
CONNOLLY, Thomas Carroll. 1705 WARREN AVE 17701 #041-09-1984 L1986 ORS *020 †40
COOPER, Kenneth L. 777 RURAL AVE 17701 #041-13-1950 L1951 OBG *071 †30
CROLL, Scott Douglas. 699 RURAL AVE, STE 104 17701 #041-09-1989 L1991 GS *020 †85

DE LEON, Mary Jeanne S. 1100 GRAMPIAN BLVD 3RD FL 17701 #748-01-1991 L2004
END IM *020 †20
DE MAY, Joseph. 338 RUSSELL AVE 17701 #047-05-1985 L1992 PD *020 †55
DI SIMONE, Ronald Enrico. 1705 WARREN AVE 17701 #041-09-1982 L1983 ORS *020 †40 ‡
DOWD, Sabrina Kay. 699 RURAL AVE, STE 201 17701 #020-12-1994 L1997 D *020 †15
DUNSTON, John Henry. ■ 17701 #010-01-1968 L1969 GS *075
DURRANI, Jameel Farrukh. 777 RURAL AVE, LUNG CTR 17701 #704-04-1992 L2005
PCC SME *020 †20
DURRWACHTER, Kenneth Robt. 1705 WARREN AVE STE 208, KENNETH R DURRWACHTER MD
P 17701 #041-09-1989 L1991 FM *020 †18
EBERSOLE, Russell Edgar. 1705 WARREN AVE, STE 301 17701 #023-12-1984 L1993
PD *020 †55
ECKER, Herbert A, Sr. 420 W 4TH ST 17701 #041-01-1946 L1947 PS *071 †65
ECKER, Herbert A, Jr. 777 RURAL AVE 17701 #041-02-1976 L1978 PS HS *020 †65
EISTER, Donald Howard. ■ 17701 #041-02-1945 L1946 GP PD *020
ENGLISH, Joseph Gartland. 1100 GRAMPIAN BLVD 17701 #041-13-1959 L1960 EM GP *020
ESAA, Durriya S. 1201 GRAMPIAN BLVD STE 2C 17701 #035-19-1985 L1991 OPH *020 †35
ESAA, Shabbir Abbas. 1100 GRAMPIAN BLVD 17701 #008-02-1984 L1990 DR *020 †80
EZERO, Abby Borow. ■ 17701 #035-15-2006 L2006 FP *020
FAJARDO, Arturo Abrantes. ■ 17701 #748-01-1969 L1981 R RO *020 †80
FARRINGTON, Quinne R. 1100 GRAMPIAN BLVD, 5TH FL 17701 #051-07-2001 L2005
P *020 †75 ‡
FAUSNAUGHT, Todd Wayne. 2134 W 4TH ST, WEST END FAMILY PRACTICE 17701
#041-02-2000 L2001 FM *020 †18
FINCH, Clyde Mitchell. 699 RURAL AVE 17701 #048-16-2003 L2003 N *020
FINN, David Richard. 777 RURAL AVE 17701 #041-01-1970 L1971 PUD CCM *020 †20
FISCHER, Joel Stuart. 800 W 4TH ST, STE 104 17701 #041-14-1984 L1990 OPH *020 †35
FRANCE, Robert Orville. 1100 GRAMPIAN BLVD 17701 #023-01-1967 L1973 DR R *020 †80
FREY, David M. 1201 GRAMPIAN BLVD 17701 #023-12-1989 L2000 OPH *020 †35
FRIES, Gene Thos. ■ 17702 #041-09-1955 L1956 PTH *071 †50
FUNK, Frederick C, Jr. 949 WESTMINSTER DR 17701 #041-13-1971 L1972 FM *020 †18
GAYLOR, Michael Stephen. ■ 17701 #041-12-1972 L2003 P *075 †75
GEHRON, William Henry, Jr. ■ 17701 #041-02-1944 L1944 U *071 †95
GEORGY, Farouk Mickail. 699 RURAL AVE, STE 306 17701 #330-04-1965 L1971 OBG *071 †30
GESSNER, Jonathan Dale. 777 RURAL AVE, WILLIAMSPORT HOSP MED CTR 17701
#104-01-2004 L2004 FM *020
GIORDANO, Guy Alphonse. 1201 GRAMPIAN BLVD 17701 #041-02-1981 L1992 FM *020 †18
GLASER, Kenneth Ian. 1100 GRAMPIAN BLVD 17701 #035-47-1986 L1990 RO *020 †80
GLUNK, Daniel James. 904 CAMPBELL ST STE 201 17701 #041-09-1984 L1985 IM OS *020 †20
GOMBOSI, Russell Lewis. 904 CAMPBELL ST STE 103, SUSQ INT MED AND PED ASSOC 17701
#041-14-1986 L1991 IM PD *020 †20,55
GOULDIN, Judith Ann. 777 RURAL AVE, THE WILLIAMSPORT HOSP 17701 #041-09-1972 L1977
NM IM *020 †20,28
HAAS, Angela Nicholas. 1205 GRAMPIAN BLVD, STE 1A 17701 #041-13-1993 L1995
FM *020 †18
HAMM, William G. 777 RURAL AVE, SUSQUEHANA HEALTH SYSTEM 17701 #041-09-1948 L1949
FM *071
HAMPTON, Robin Wheeler. 777 RURAL AVE 4TH FL 17701 #001-06-1994 L2003 ID *020 †20
HANNAGAN, Francis James. 777 RURAL AVE, WILLIAMSPORT HOSPITAL 17701
#024-07-1978 L1988 IM *020 †20,16
HARER, Jendy Yon. 699 RURAL AVE 17701 #041-77-2006, ▲ L2006 FP *012
HEERE, Barbara Ann. 904 CAMPBELL ST STE 201 17701 #041-14-1980 L1981 IM *020 †20
HEILMANN, Timothy Michael. 699 RURAL AVE 17701 #041-02-1983 L1984 FM *020 †18
HENDERSON, K Wayne. 1201 GRAMPIAN BLVD, STE 3E 17701 #041-13-1960 L1961
IM HEM *071
HERBST, Vincent Paul. 904 CAMPBELL ST STE 206 17701 #041-02-1981 L1982 D GP *020 †15
HERRINGTON, Pamela Jean. 1205 GRAMPIAN BLVD, CORNERSTONE FAMILY HEALTH 17701
#035-15-1989 L1991 FM *020 †18
HESS, Donald Walter. 777 RURAL AVE, WILLIAMSPORT PEDIATRIC 17701 #041-14-1976 L1977
FM *020 †18
HILL, Shannon Nicole. 777 RURAL AVE, DEPT FM 17701 #041-78-2007, ▲ L2007 FP *012
HIPPLE, Randall Fraser. 777 RURAL AVE 17701 #041-01-1960 L1961 GYN *071 †30
HOFFMAN, Michael Voss. ■ 17701 #049-01-2001 L2007 ORS *100
HOFSTROM, Glen Theodore. 145 SHAFFER ST, BELLES HOFSTROM & 17702
#033-05-1976 L1977 FM *020 †18
JAVED, Asif. 777 RURAL AVE 17701 #704-01-1982 L1994 IM *020 †20
JONES, Michael Wm. 2034 LYCOMING CREEK RD 17701 #033-05-1983 L1984 FM *020 †18
JONES, Veronica Valerie. ■ 17701 #041-14-1977 L1983 OBG *020
JUDSON, William Whiting. 904 W 4TH ST 17701 #041-02-1970 L1971 IM *020 †20
KAISER, Ralph Henry. 6 E MOUNTAIN AVE 17702 #041-13-1967 L1968 PD *020 †55
KEENAN, William F, Jr. 699 RURAL AVE 17701 #024-16-1978 L1979 FM D *040 †18
KENT, Sarah C. 1201 GRAMPIAN BLVD, STE 2E 17701 #041-14-2003 L2007 FM *100 †18
KINKEAD, Kevin Poultney. 777 RURAL AVE 17701 #041-12-1989 L1991 AN *020 †05
KIRK, William Edward. 454 PINE ST 2ND FL 17701 #028-34-1959 L1960 P CHP *020 †75
KOLB, Aaron Jay. 777 RURAL AVE 17701 #041-14-1978 L1979 OM FM *020 †70,18
LALLI, Joanne Marie. 1201 GRAMPIAN BLVD 17701 #035-19-1983 L1986 IM *020 ‡
LAMADE, Charles Dietrick. 777 RURAL AVE, FL 6 17701 #041-12-1979 L1983 OBG *020 †30 ‡
LARSON, Theodore Stephen. ■ 17701 #041-13-1958 L1959 R DR *071 †80
LAUTH, William Brian. 777 RURAL AVE, WILLIAMSPORT HOSPITAL 17701 #016-43-1977 L2007
EM IM *020 †20,16
LIDDELL, Albert Gallatin. 904 CAMPBELL ST, STE 101 17701 #041-12-1963 L1964
ORS *062 †40
LIGHTMAN, David Abbott. 800 W 4TH ST STE 104 17701 #021-01-1980 L1986 OPH *020 †35
LOPATOFSKY, David James. 145 SHAFFER ST, BELLES HOFSTROM & 17702
#041-07-1988 L1990 FM *020 †18
MANCHESTER, George Alden. 777 RURAL AVE 17701 #050-02-1979 L1980 EM FM *030 †18
MANGANO, Robert Anthony. 204 CURTIN ST 17702 #041-09-1987 L2000 PDC PD *020 †20,55
MARCEAU, Michael James. 1100 GRAMPIAN BLVD, FIFTH FLOOR 17701 #028-34-1985 L1988
P *020
MASON, Nathan Ray. 777 RURAL AVE, WILLIAMSPORT HOSPITAL 17701 #550-04-2006 L2006
FP *012
MATTIACE, William. 1705 WARREN AVE, STE 301 17701 #041-02-1989 L1991 FM *020 †18
MC CAULEY, William C. 777 RURAL AVE 17701 #051-01-1970 L1974 PUD CCM *020 †20
MC CLAIN, James Bernard. 777 RURAL AVE, STE 400 17701 #041-77-1981, ▲ L1982
AN FM *020 †18,05

MC GARY, Suzan Cowart. 777 RURAL AVE 17701 #048-02-1987 L1989 **TS** *020 †85,90
MEHTA, Pankajbala G. 777 RURAL AVE, 6TH FL 17701 #495-22-1969 L1979 **OBG** *020 †30
MELTON, Delia Christina. 1205 GRAMPIAN BLVD C, CORNERSTONE FAMILY HEALTH 17701 #041-13-1988 L1990 **FM** *020 †18
MERRICK, James Gerard. 1705 WARREN AVE, STE 201 17701 #018-03-1975 L2007 **PDP AI** *020 †55,03
MILLER, Jay Kenneth. 1100 GRAMPIAN BLVD 17701 #001-06-1978 L1979 **FM OS** *020 †18
MINTZER, Harry Dean. 777 RURAL AVE, STE 400 17701 #041-77-1981, ▲ L1982 **AN** *020 †05
MORAN, John Kevin. 1749 MCCONNELL DR 17701 #041-09-1987 L1992 **DR** *020 †80
MORENO, Manuel V. 2015 BENTLEY DR 17701 #748-11-1969 L1979 **AN** *020
MULLER, Robert Leopold, Jr. ■ 17701 #041-13-2006 L2006 **FP** *012
MURPHY, Edith Lechner. ■ 17701 #035-20-1951 L1952 **IMG** *071
NAGEL, David Bruce. 1100 GRAMPIAN BLVD, DIVINE PROVIDENCE HOSPITAL 17701 #041-02-1980 L1981 **RO** *020 †80
NANGIA, Geeta. 1100 GRAMPIAN BLVD, FIFTH FL 17701 #024-05-2002 L2007 **CHP** *100 †75
NARDONE, Donald Thos. 777 RURAL AVE, HEART & LUNG CTR 17701 #041-02-1985 L1987 **CD IM** *020 †20
NARWAL, Rawan. 699 RURAL AVE, WILLIAMSPORT HOSPITAL 17701 #654-01-2006 L2007 **FP** *012
NESBITT, Alexander R. 1201 GRAMPIAN BLVD 17701 #010-01-1981 L1984 **FM FPG** *020 †18
NICOTERA, Anthony Louis. 1100 GRAMPIAN BLVD 17701 #041-09-1964 L1967 **P N** *020
NIDITCH, A Scott. 1705 WARREN AVE, STE 206 17701 #035-09-1988 L1994 **U** *020 †95
NIELSEN, Richard Craig. 777 RURAL AVE 17701 #041-01-1969 L1971 **FM** *020 †18
NJOKU, Godwin Nwannewuihe. 777 RURAL AVE 17701 #305-01-2001 L2002 **FM** *100
O'HARA, Mary Beth. 904 CAMPBELL ST STE 102 17701 #041-77-1993, ▲ L1994 **PD** *020 †55
OKE, Luc Magloire. ■ 17701 #170-01-1990 L2007 **CD** *100
OLINSKY, Stuart Martin. 777 RURAL AVE 17701 #033-05-1976 L1981 **N** *020 †75
PAGANA, Timothy James. 1705 WARREN AVE, STE 304 17701 #041-13-1975 L1976 **GS** *020 †85
PAGANA, William Jos. 904 CAMPBELL ST, STE 103 17701 #041-13-1991 L1993 **IM PD** *020 †55,20
PAI, Sujata Mangalore. 1201 GRAMPIAN BLVD, STE 3A 17701 #495-41-1987 L1993 **RO** *020
PARK, Young Won. 777 RURAL AVE 17701 #583-09-1969 L1982 **PM** *020 †60
PASTORE, Timothy Paul. 777 RURAL AVE 17701 #041-07-1991 L1993 **AN** *020 †05
PATEL, Harshad Rambhai. 1100 GRAMPIAN BLVD, DIVINE PROVIDENCE HOSPITAL 17701 #495-23-1971 L1977 **DR R** *020 †80
PATEL, Shailesh Dinbandhu. 777 RURAL AVE 17701 #041-02-1991 L1994 **AN** *020 †05
PECK, William James. 904 CAMPBELL ST STE 202 17701 #041-02-1977 L1978 **FM** *020 †18
PEPPERMAN, Larue Everett. ■ 17701 #041-09-1954 L1955 **OM FM** *071
PETERS, C A P, II. 1100 GRAMPIAN BLVD 17701 #036-01-1979 L1980 **EM FM** *020 †18
PHAM, Hung Tony. 777 RURAL AVE 17701 #654-01-2001 L2003 **FM** *100
PHAM, Luan Vong. ■ 17701 #041-14-2008 L2008 *012
PILUIKO, Vitaly V. 1201 GRAMPIAN BLVD, STE 3E 17701 #913-86-1983 L2004 **TS VS** *020 †85,90
PLUMMER, Robert Earl, Jr. 1100 GRAMPIAN BLVD 17701 #041-09-1968 L1969 **R GP** *020 †80
POLIS, Mark Jan. 1705 WARREN AVE 17701 #035-06-1977 L1983 **U SO** *020 †95 ‡
PORTUESE, Thomas John. ■ 17701 #035-15-2007 L2007 **FP** *012
POWERS, Francis M, Jr. 1100 GRAMPIAN BLVD, CANCER TREATMENT CENTER 17701 #035-45-1971 **RO** *020 †80
PURCELL, Robt Edward, Jr. 777 RURAL AVE, 3RD FLOOR SOUTH 17701 #035-09-1981 L1986 **GE IM** *071 †20
QUERIMIT, Jorge Ancheta. 777 RURAL AVE 17701 #748-01-1954 L1962 **GS** *020
QUINTANA, David. 1100 GRAMPIAN BLVD 17701 #035-15-1995 L1998 **VIR** *020 †80
RACKISH, Mark Adam. 699 RURAL AVE 17701 #005-06-1978 L1991 **ORS** *020 †40
RAJJOUB, Rodwan Khaled. 1100 GRAMPIAN BLVD 17701 #875-01-1972 L1979 **NS** *020 †25
RAJJOUB, Samer Rodwan. ■ 17701 #010-01-2008 *012
RANDOLPH, Victor Lawrence. 777 RURAL AVE 17701 #023-07-1970 L2004 **ON IM** *020 †20
REDKA, James Wilson. 1205 GRAMPIAN BLVD, CORNERSTONE FAMILY HEALTH 17701 #041-02-1972 L1977 **FM** *020 †18
REILLY, Christopher E. 1705 WARREN AVE STE 206, SUSQUEHANNA UROLOGY ASSOC. 17701 #048-04-1995 L2001 **U** *020 †95
REKHALA, Vijay Kumar. 699 RURAL AVE, STE 301 17701 #495-21-1979 L1983 **P** *020 †75
RIGAL-LIZARDI, Rene R. 1201 GRAMPIAN BLVD 17701 #042-01-1971 L1973 **PME AN** *020 †05
ROBINSON, Warren L, Jr. 1100 GRAMPIAN BLVD, SUSQUEHANNA CANCER CENTER 17701 #041-02-1978 L1987 **ON HEM** *020 †20
ROCKOFF, Steven Drew. 1705 WARREN AVE, STE 206 17701 #010-02-1987 L1992 **U** *020 †95 ‡
RODGERS, Charles Jack. 1100 GRAMPIAN BLVD 17701 #041-02-1947 L1948 **GP** *071
ROMAN, Edwin. 777 RURAL AVE 17701 #042-02-1990 L1997 **PM** *020
SCHIFFERLI, Janice. 699 RURAL AVE 17701 #041-78-2005, ▲ L2005 **FP** *012
SCHILDT, Mark Anthony. 699 RURAL AVE, FAMILY PRACT RESIDENCY 17701 #041-13-2000 L2001 **FM** *020 †18
SENULA, Ann Naomi. ■ 17701 #005-11-1987 **OS NTR** *040
SENULA, Gerhard Carl. ■ 17701 #005-11-1986 L1987 **EM FM** *020 †16
SHAFIQUE, Mohammad. 777 RURAL AVE, SUSQUEHANNA CARDIOL 17701 #704-01-1971 L1981 **CD IM** *020 †20
SHAH, Arshad Ali. 777 RURAL AVE 17701 #704-09-1994 L2006 **IM** *020 †20
SHAHIN, Khalil Fouad. 777 RURAL AVE 17701 #473-01-2001 L2002 **FM** *020 †18
SHAW, Gordon Allan, Jr. 1100 GRAMPIAN BLVD 17701 #038-06-1971 L1977 **DR** *020 †80
SHEARER, Donald Ebner. 777 RURAL AVE 17701 #041-02-1963 L1965 **GP** *071
SHENBERGER, Keith Norman. 1100 GRAMPIAN BLVD 17701 #032-01-1977 L1978 **RHU IM** *020 †20
SHOEMAKER, Margrit Mary. 1100 GRAMPIAN BLVD 17701 #041-12-1983 L1984 **END IM** *020 †20
SHU, Jason C. 1100 GRAMPIAN BLVD 17701 #244-04-1968 L1975 **OBG** *020
SILBERG, Robert Dean. 777 RURAL AVE, STE 400 17701 #055-01-1990 L1994 **AN** *020 †05
SIMMS, Aaron Dwight. 777 RURAL AVE, THE WILLIAMPORT HOSPITAL 17701 #005-18-1984 L1985 **FM EM** *020 †20
SOMERS, William Robt. 777 RURAL AVE, 3RD FLOOR SOUTH 17701 #036-07-1970 L1976 **GE IM** *020 †20
SOUNDARARAJAN, Ranganatha. 245 GRAMPIAN BLVD 17701 #495-04-1957 L1971 **U GS** *020 †95
STABLER, Craig Lauren. 1100 GRAMPIAN BLVD 17701 #041-02-1981 L1987 **ORS OSM** *020 †40
STAUBLY, Ronald Tyne. 1705 WARREN AVE STE 304, WOODLAND RD 17701 #023-01-1972 L1995 **FM** *071 †18
STAYER, Glenn Alan. 204 CURTIN ST 17702 #048-15-1981 L1987 **CHN PD** *020 †55
STEFANILE, Luke Adam. 777 RURAL AVE, HOSPITALIST SERVICE 17701 #305-01-2000 L2003 **IM** *020
STEINBACHER, Bernard Carl. 777 RURAL AVE 17701 #041-15-1999 L2000 **IM** *040 †20
STEVENSON, Rodrick A. 699 RURAL AVE, STE 104 17701 #047-07-1985 L1992 **GS** *020 †85
STRALEY, Richard Kirk. 1705 WARREN AVE, THE COSTELLO CENTER 17701 #041-01-1966 L1967 **ORS** *071 †40
STRYKER, Allan Kent. 1201 GRAMPIAN BLVD 17701 #020-02-1972 L1985 **PS** *020 †65 ‡
SUTER, Harry Jos. 699 RURAL AVE 17701 #041-09-1965 L1966 **CD TS** *020 †85,90
TANNER, Rebekah Ellen. 777 RURAL AVE 17701 #550-04-2003 L2003 **FM** *020 †18
THOMAS, Karen Leigh. 1100 GRAMPIAN BLVD 17701 #041-02-1996 L1998 **FM** *020 †18
THOMAS, Ralph Edward. 777 RURAL AVE, WILLIAMSPORT HOSPITAL & ME 17701 #023-01-1991 L1994 **AN** *020 †05
TIGNOR, Richard Franklin. 699 RURAL AVE 17701 #041-01-1962 L1963 **OPH** *071 †35
TIMKO, Carrie Ann William. 777 RURAL AVE 17701 #041-15-2000 L2002 **FM OBS** *020 †18
TOBIASZ, Christopher. 777 RURAL AVE 17701 #035-19-1981 L1986 **CD IM** *020 †20
TODHUNTER, William James. 699 RURAL AVE, STE 104 17701 #041-13-1979 L1984 **GS** *020 †85
TRAUTWEIN, Robert Chas. 777 RURAL AVE 17701 #024-07-1980 L1994 **CD** *020 †20
TUFFAHA, Hani Jawdat. 904 CAMPBELL ST 17701 #915-02-1971 L1982 **NS** *020 †25 ‡
VANDORT, Martin B. 777 RURAL AVE 4TH FL, OFFICE OF INFECTIOUS DISEA 17701 #220-03-1993 L2007 **ID** *020 †20
VERZELLA, Jeffrey N. 699 RURAL AVE, FAMILY PRACTICE GROUP 17701 #035-15-1982 L1989 **FM** *040 †18
WADE, Franklin Geo. ■ 17701 #041-13-1944 L1945 **GS** *071
WAGNER, Christopher Andre. 777 RURAL AVE 17701 #550-04-2005 L2005 **FP** *012
WAGNER, William John. 777 RURAL AVE 17701 #041-13-1970 L1975 **GP** *020
WALGAMPAYA, Dakshina Nama. ■ 17701 #422-01-2000 L2008 **IM** *020 ‡
WALLACE, Thomas E. 1705 WARREN AVE STE 301 17701 #041-13-1989 L1991 **FM** *040 †18
WALMER, Lynnwood Allen. 460 RIVER AVE 17701 #041-14-1976 L1977 **OPH** *020 †35
WASILEWSKI, Charles L, Jr. 1201 GRAMPIAN BLVD 17701 #041-02-1963 L1966 **D** *071 †15
WEAVER, Don Kent. ■ 17701 #017-20-1959 L1971 **PTH** *071 †50
WEBER, Seth Ian. 777 RURAL AVE 17701 #041-12-1983 L1993 **IM** *020 †20
WEBER, Stephen Florian. 777 RURAL AVE, # 4TH-FL 17701 #016-45-1982 L1988 **ID IM** *020 †20
WEISNER, Michael Jos. 777 RURAL AVE 17701 #041-14-1982 L1983 **FM** *020 †18
WIEGAND, Rosemary Abate. 701 NORTHWAY RD, SAMUEL SCHRACK DO PC 17701 #041-14-1994 L1996 **FM** *020 †18
WILLIAMS, A Claude, Jr. 994 VALLAMONT DR 17701 #045-01-1964 L1972 **P** *020 †75
WOLFE, Daniel Elmer. 777 RURAL AVE 17701 #041-01-1971 L1972 **DR** *071 †80
WOLFSON, Steven J. 1201 GRAMPIAN BLVD, STE 2F 17701 #035-01-1982 L1988 **GE** *020 †20
WOROBEC, Russell Nick. 699 RURAL AVE, STE 203 17701 #025-01-1946 L1954 **ORS** *071 †40
WYSHOCK, Edward Gerard. 1100 GRAMPIAN BLVD, DIVINE PROVIDENCE HOSPITAL 17701 #041-09-1979 L1981 **HEM IM** *050 †20
YANOFSKY, Charles Sylvan. 699 RURAL AVE, STE 302 17701 #035-09-1977 L1981 **N** *020 †75 ‡
YEALY, Wendell Holmes. ■ 17701 #035-01-1948 L1949 **DR** *071 †80
YOON, Chan. 1100 GRAMPIAN BLVD 17701 #583-02-1957 L1966 **DR NM** *071 †80
YOUNG, David Edmond. ■ 17701 #024-07-2005 L2005 **FP** *012

WILLOW GROVE – MONTGOMERY

ALBURGER, Philip David. 2400 MARYLAND RD, STE 20 19090 #041-13-1969 L1970 **ORS OSM** *040 †40
ANDREWS, Ronald P. 2400 MARYLAND RD STE 40 19090 #041-01-1965 L1966 **RHU IM** *020
BABIAK, Olesh. 2701 BLAIR MILL RD, STE 30 19090 #041-09-1986 L1987 **AN PME** *020 †05
BARRER, Steven Jon. 2510 MARYLAND RD, STE 185 19090 #041-09-1976 L1977 **NS NSP** *020 †25
BARTLETT, Frederick H, Jr. 2729 BLAIR MILL RD, STE A 19090 #041-01-1948 L1950 **OBG** *071 †30
BERGER, Alan S. 1001 EASTON RD, STE 106 19090 #041-13-1977 L1978 **OTO** *020 †45
BLUMENTHAL, Sherry Luber. 2701 BLAIR MILL RD, STE C 19090 #041-02-1982 L1984 **GYN** *020 †30
BOOTH, Kevin Richard. 2701 BLAIR MILL RD, STE 8 19090 #025-01-1985 L1987 **N OS** *020 †75 ‡
BORTHWICK, Laura Ann. 15 YORK RD 19090 #041-14-1995 L2000 **OBG** *020 †30
BRAHMABHATT, Shyam N. 2400 MARYLAND RD, STE 20 19090 #041-13-1999 L2002 **OSM** *020 †40
BREZIN, Joseph Henry. 1036 EASTON RD 19090 #010-02-1972 L1973 **NEP IM** *020 †20 ‡
BURKE, James Murray, Jr. 2701 BLAIR MILL RD, STE 8 19090 #035-45-1978 L1985 **N OS** *020 †20,75
CHERNER, Rachmel. 1003 EASTON RD, REGENCY TOWERS STE 106 19090 #041-02-1955 L1956 **END IM** *020 †20 ‡
CHESNER, David Jonathan. 2400 MARYLAND RD STE 40 19090 #041-77-1993, ▲ L1995 **IM** *020
COENEN, Verena Hermine. 2729 BLAIR MILL RD, STE A 19090 #007-02-1994 L1996 **OBG** *020
COLLINS, Deirdre Murray. 735 FITZWATERTOWN RD 19090 #041-02-1984 L1992 **IM NEP** *020 †20 ‡
COOK, James Hunter. 2701 BLAIR MILL RD, STE 8 19090 #041-07-1993 L2001 **N OS** *020 †75
COOPER, Jeffrey. 723 FITZWATERTOWN RD 19090 #041-07-1973 L1975 **OTO AI** *020 †45
CRAFT, David Victor. 2400 MARYLAND RD, STE 20 19090 #041-02-1988 L1990 **OSM** *020 †40
CURLEY, Eugene Mascucious. ■ 19090 #041-14-2004 L2004 **IM** *012
DANIAL, Joseph Wadie. 3941 COMMERCE AVE 19090 #915-04-1980 L1997 **P** *020 †75
DAVOLOS, Dominick D. ■ 19090 #035-20-1949 L1952 **CD IM** *071
DEAN, Gregory Edwin. 2701 BLAIR MILL RD, STE 6 19090 #035-01-1988 L1995 **U** *020 †95
DE JESUS QUINONES, Felipe. 2300 COMPUTER RD, # 25 19090 #042-01-1957 L1962 **R DR** *071
DERSHAW, Stuart Zane. 15 YORK RD 19090 #041-09-1974 L1975 **OBG** *020 †30
DIAMOND, B Franklin. 2701 BLAIR MILL RD, STE 8 19090 #041-12-1967 L1968 **N SME** *020 †75
DIGREGORIO, Catherine J. 2701 BLAIR MILL RD, STE 30 19090 #041-09-1994 L1998 **APM** *020 †05
DI GREGORIO, Guerino John. PO BOX 480 19090 #041-09-1978 L1979 **PA IM** *020
DOMBKOSKI, Ruth Ann. 2701 BLAIR MILL RD, STE 30 19090 #041-13-1983 L1984 **AN** *020 †05
EASLEY, Eva D Hayden. 2701 BLAIR MILL RD, STE 30 19090 #033-75-2002, ▲ L2002 **AN** *020 †05
EISNER, Elana Rose. 2400 MARYLAND RD STE 40 19090 #041-01-1995 L1998 **RHU** *020 †20

ETTER, Mark Stewart. 2701 BLAIR MILL RD, ABINGTON SURGICAL CENTER 19090 #041-02-1975 L1979 **AN** *020 †05

FERRARA, Bradley John. 2325 MARYLAND RD STE 200 19090 #041-13-1996 L1999 **IM** *020 †20,60

FLEEKOP, Philip Donald. 2300 COMPUTER RD, STE M66 19090 #012-05-1981 L1984 **AI IM** *020 †20,03

FRANKLIN, Charles M, Jr. 2400 MARYLAND RD, STE 40 19090 #035-15-1981 L1982 **RHU IM** *020 †20

FREITAS, Lawrence. 735 FITZWATERTOWN RD, U-MASS MEDICAL CENTER 19090 #305-01-2002 L2007 **NEP** *020 †20

FRYER, Larry Anton. 200 FITZWATERTOWN RD 19090 #041-01-1964 L1965 **P** *030

GALLANT, Gregory Gerald. 2400 MARYLAND RD, STE 20 19090 #008-02-1989 L1994 **HS OSM** *020 †40

GAUSLING, Sharon Mesmer. ■ 19090 #047-06-1986 L1989 **PD** *020 †55

GECHLIK, Glen Brian. 1120 FAIRCHILD ST, 913 MDS 19090 #035-19-1995 L1996 **IM** *020 †20

GHANTOUS, Victor E. 735 FITZWATERTOWN RD 19090 #605-02-1990 L1999 **NEP IM** *020 †20

GINSBURG, Silas J. 2300 COMPUTER RD, GCSF OB GYN ASSOCS 19090 #041-01-1952 L1953 **GYN** *071 †30

GOPEZ, Jonas Joaquin. 2510 MARYLAND RD, STE 185 19090 #041-02-1996 L2000 **NS** *020

GRATCH, Michael James. 2400 MARYLAND RD, STE 20 19090 #041-13-1976 L1977 **ORS OSS** *020 †40 ‡

HALE, Pamela Muschek. 2701 BLAIR MILL RD, STE 30 19090 #041-13-1993 L1998 **APM** *020

HAMILTON, Keith William. ■ 19090 #041-01-2006 L2006 **IM** *012

HAUSER, Adam Chas. 2701 BLAIR MILL RD, STE 30 19090 #035-15-1988 L1991 **AN** *020 †05 ‡

HILLIARD, Rhadjena Pilar. ■ 19090 #035-47-2001 **GPM** *100

HSU, Victor Weiteh. 2400 MARYLAND RD, STE 20 19090 #041-13-2001 L2001 **ORS** *020 †20

HUPPERT, Leonore Charles. 2300 COMPUTER RD, STE 44 19090 #041-01-1972 L1973 **REN GYN** *020 †30 ‡

JACKS, Fred D, Jr. 1675 EASTON RD 19090 #041-09-1976 L1978 **IM** *071

JOSE, Sherry. 2701 BLAIR MILL RD, STE 30 19090 #495-37-1992 L2004 **APM** *020 †05

JUNKIN, David Maclean. 2701 BLAIR MILL RD STE 35, ABINGTON SURGICAL CENTER 19090 #041-13-1966 L1967 **ORS OSM** *020 †40

KEATING, Paul J, Jr. 2701 BLAIR MILL RD, STE 30 19090 #041-13-1983 L1984 **AN** *020 †05

KELLY, Kevin John. 2701 BLAIR MILL RD, STE 6 19090 #010-02-1980 L1995 **PD** *020 †55

KREMER, Anatoly I. 2701 BLAIR MILL RD, STE 30 19090 #913-50-1983 L1998 **AN PME** *020 †05 ‡

KUTE, Neelima Mukund. 106 YORK RD 19090 #495-97-1991 L2002 **FM** *020 †18

LEVIN, Steven Paul. 701 EASTON RD 19090 #041-02-1986 L1987 **PM** *020 †60

LEVIT, Lawrence Scott. 2701 BLAIR MILL RD, STE 30 19090 #041-09-1984 L1986 **AN** *020 †05

LEWIS, Stephen Fraser. 2300 COMPUTER RD, EXECUTIVE MEWS SUITE H-43 19090 #036-05-1989 L1992 **N** *020 †75

LIM, Maria Roselyn Cua. 2701 BLAIR MILL RD, STE 8 19090 #748-02-1986 L2000 **N** *020 †75

LONG, Tanika Reontae. 2701 BLAIR MILL RD, STE 30 19090 #041-15-2002 L2002 **AN** *020

LOPATIN, Mark Alan. 2400 MARYLAND RD, STE 40 19090 #041-07-1983 L1984 **IM RHU** *020 †20

MARLOWE, Jennifer Leigh. 221 DAVISVILLE RD 19090 #041-07-1988 L1990 **FM** *020 †18

MARPLE, Jill Ann. 701 EASTON RD 19090 #032-01-2001 L2002 **PM** *020 †60

MC GRATH, Glenn Alan. 2300 COMPUTER RD, EXECUTIVE MEWS, SUITE H 39 19090 #041-14-1987 L1988 **END** *020 †20

MEAGHER, Richard John. 2510 MARYLAND RD, WILLOWOOD STE 185 19090 #033-06-1996 L1998 **NS** *030

MILLINER, David H C. 2701 BLAIR MILL RD, STE 30 19090 #917-23-1972 **AN** *020 †05 ‡

MOREHOUSE, Todd C. 1001 EASTON RD, STE 106 19090 #041-77-1999, ▲ L2001 **OTO** *100

NACHMAN, Jeffrey Alan. 2701 BLAIR MILL RD, STE 30 19090 #041-13-1987 L1988 **AN** *020 †05

NACHMAN, Michael Gordon. 2701 BLAIR MILL RD, STE 6 19090 #035-01-1979 L1984 **UP** *020 †95

PAPARSENOS, Achilles Theo. 2500 MARYLAND RD STE 130 19090 #033-06-2001 L2007 **END** *020 †20

PARKANSKY, Inessa. 735 FITZWATERTOWN RD 19090 #041-13-1999 L2001 **NEP** *020 ‡

PECORELLA, Wendy A. 3941 COMMERCE AVE, MEMORIAL HOSPITAL 19090 #041-07-1996 L1999 **P** *020

PEREZ, Finuccia. 2701 BLAIR MILL RD, STE C 19090 #041-15-1999 L2001 **OBG** *020 †30

PICCONE, Carolyn Anne. 2701 BLAIR MILL RD STE C 19090 #041-13-1992 L1994 **OBG** *020 †30

PLATIA, Maria Pia. 2300 COMPUTER RD, STE 44 19090 #041-12-1977 L1988 **OBG END** *020 †30

PLOTKIN, Lenore Roberts. 3525 WELSH RD 19090 #041-09-1987 L1988 **IM** *020 †20

PRIPSTEIN, Stephen. 2601 BLAIR MILL RD STE 1 19090 #041-13-1966 L1970 **R DR** *020 †80

RAMAN, Meena. 2701 BLAIR MILL RD, STE 30 19090 #496-38-1995 L2001 **AN** *020 †05

RAPPE, Sandra Michelle. 2701 BLAIR MILL RD, STE C 19090 #010-02-1997 L2000 **OBG** *020 †30

RICE, Thomas Brendan. 411 QUIGLEY AVE 19090 #041-13-2003 L2003 **PCC** *012

RODRIGUEZ, Anthony R. 2701 BLAIR MILL RD 19090 #005-14-1989 L1991 **FM** *020 †18

ROTH, Jonathan Adrian. 2701 BLAIR MILL RD, STE 6 19090 #041-01-1994 L1997 **UP U** *020 †95

RUBIN, Jeffry Fredric. 2400 MARYLAND RD, STE 20 19090 #041-02-1971 L1972 **ORS** *020 †40

SALINAS, Cynthia Lee. 2701 BLAIR MILL RD 19090 #005-02-2002 L2005 **FM** *020 †18

SANTANGELO, Samuel Chas. 2400 MARYLAND RD 19090 #041-13-1954 L1955 **ORS** *071 †40

SCHAPIRE, Phyllis G. 2701 BLAIR MILL RD, STE 30 19090 #041-14-1989 L1991 **AN** *020 †05

SCHOR, Robin Cheryl. 3941 COMMERCE AVE 19090 #041-07-1981 L1986 **P ADP** *020 †75

SEIDMAN, Michael Jeffrey. 2510 MARYLAND RD, STE 175 19090 #041-13-2002 L2002 **HO IM** *012 †20

SELLERS, Jeffrey Christop. ■ 19090 #041-12-2004 L2004 **OBG** *012

SHAH, Roshani Pranav. ■ 19090 #495-23-2002 L2007 **IM** *012

SIROTA, Robert Alan. 735 FITZWATERTOWN RD 19090 #008-01-1973 L1979 **NEP IM** *020 †20 ‡

SNIPES, Edward Ralph. 735 FITZWATERTOWN RD 19090 #041-02-1984 L1985 **NEP IM** *020 ‡

STACK, John M, Jr. 15 YORK RD 19090 #041-02-1968 L1971 **OBG** *020 †30

STAR, Andrew Michael. 2400 MARYLAND RD 19090 #016-06-1982 L1983 **ORS** *020 †40

STOPPER, Stephen Martin. ■ 19090 #041-02-2003 L2007 **CD** *012 †20

SULLIVAN, Patricia Ann. 2701 BLAIR MILL RD, STE C 19090 #041-13-1978 L1980 **OBG** *020 †30

TAKEI, Takahisa Robt. 2400 MARYLAND RD, STE 20 19090 #024-05-1989 L1995 **HS** *020 †40

THETGYI, Katherine. 701 EASTON RD 19090 #209-01-1962 L1983 **PM** *020 †60

TOBKIN, Mary A. 3525 WELSH RD 19090 #041-13-1998 L2001 **IM** *020 †20

TSAI, Arthur. 735 FITZWATERTOWN RD 19090 #023-07-2001 L2004 **NEP** *020

UDDOH, Cordelia Nkolika. 608 EASTON RD STE C, PREMIERE VISION LASER CENT 19090 #041-01-1995 L1995 **IM** *020 †35

UKROPEC, Dusty I Mahosky. 2701 BLAIR MILL RD 19090 #041-02-1997 L1999 **FM** *020 †18

WATERS, George Edward, III. ■ 19090 #041-13-2006 L2006 **IM** *012

WEISMAN, David Calkins. 2701 BLAIR MILL RD, STE 8 19090 #041-14-2000 L2006 **N** *100 †75

WEISS, Ned M. 2500 MARYLAND RD, STE 130 19090 #041-09-1980 L1981 **END DIA** *020 †20

WOLF, John Henry, Jr. 2400 MARYLAND RD 19090 #041-13-1962 L1964 **ORS** *020 †40

WOODLAND, Mark B. 2300 COMPUTER RD, STE 44 19090 #010-01-1985 L1987 **GYN OBS** *040 †30

YOON, Michael Sungshick. 2510 MARYLAND RD, STE 185 19090 #051-01-1994 L1997 **NS** *020 †25

YUDIS, Melvin. 735 FITZWATERTOWN RD 19090 #041-02-1963 L1964 **NEP IM** *020 †20 ‡

ZAONTZ, Mark Randall. 2701 BLAIR MILL RD, STE 6 19090 #010-02-1979 L1988 **UP** *020 †95 ‡

ZHOU, Jialin. 2701 BLAIR MILL RD, STE 30 19090 #243-46-1986 L2002 **AN** *020 †05

ZIGERMAN, Herbert L. ■ 19090 #041-77-1955, ▲ L1957 **FM RHU** *072 †18

WILLOW STREET – LANCASTER

ANDRIAN, Mihaela. 226 WILLOW VALLEY LAKES DR, STE F 17584 #781-01-1989 L2004 **IM** *100 †20

ARMSTRONG, Charles Daniel. 222 WILLOW VALLEY LAKES DR 17584 #051-04-1973 L1980 **PD PDA** *020 †55

BEELEN, Matthew James. 222 WILLOW VALLEY LAKES DR, STE 1600 17584 #025-01-1999 L2001 **FM** *020 †18

BROWN, H Zane. ■ 17584 #041-01-1957 L1964 **OPH** *071 †35

BRUBAKER, J Kenneth. 222 WILLOW VALLEY LAKES DR, STE 1600 17584 #041-09-1970 L1971 **FM** *020 †18

BYLER, Arthur Byron. ■ 17584 #041-09-1955 L1956 **FM** *071 †18

CRITCHLOW, Robert J. ■ 17584 #041-02-1950 L1951 **R** *071 †80

DIEHL, Daniel Lee. 222 WILLOW VALLEY LAKES DR 17584 #041-02-1981 L1982 **FM** *020 †18

FENIMORE, Pia Boben. 222 WILLOW VALLEY LAKES DR 17584 #041-02-1999 L2002 **PD** *020 †55

GROSH, John L. ■ 17584 #041-13-1950 L1951 **IM HEM** *071 †20

HURSH, Dale Keith. 222 WILLOW VALLEY LAKES DR, STE 1600 17584 #041-02-1989 L1991 **FPG FM** *020 †18 ‡

JOHNS, Milton W. ■ 17584 #041-02-1953 L1954 **EM** *071

JUDSON, G Vernon, Jr. ■ 17584 #041-02-1938 L1939 **FM** *071 †18

KAEBNICK, Ernest Elliott. ■ 17584 #041-01-1962 L1963 **OPH** *071 †35

KING, Ann Marie. 222 WILLOW VALLEY LAKES DR, LANCASTER FAM MED ASSOC 17584 #041-02-1995 L1997 **FM** *020 †18

KRAYBILL, Leon Sherer. 222 WILLOW VALLEY LAKES DR, STE 1600 17584 #041-13-1985 L1986 **FPG FM** *020 †18

LOWELL, Fred Milton. ■ 17584 #041-13-1961 L1971 **P** *072 †75

MC DOUGAL, Robt Curtenius. ■ 17584 #038-06-1969 L1970 **P** *071 †75

MIELNIK, Anne Louise. ■ 17584 #041-02-2006 L2006 **FP** *012

PRATT, Robert Stewart. 25 NOLT AVE, WILLOW STREET FAMILY HEALT 17584 #036-05-1977 L1978 **FM OBS** *020 †18

SCHMITT, John James. 222 WILLOW VALLEY LAKES DR, RM 1900 17584 #024-07-1987 L1988 **FM** *020 †18

SCHUBERT, John Jos. 222 WILLOW VALLEY LAKES DR, NEPH ASSOCS LANCASTER LTD 17584 #041-02-1959 L1961 **NEP IM** *071 †20

SPITLER, William Meller, III. 222 WILLOW VALLEY LAKES DR, STE 1800 17584 #041-14-1972 L1973 **OPH** *020 †35

SPRAGUE, Grover Jos. ■ 17584 #035-08-1943 L1973 **IM** *071

THATCHER, Allyson P. 25 NOLT AVE 17584 #051-04-1989 L1991 **FM** *020 †18

WAGNER, Richard S, Jr. ■ 17584 #041-13-1951 L1952 **AN** *071 †05

WIELAND, Winfried Gordon. 222 WILLOW VALLEY LAKES DR, STE 1900 17584 #033-06-1992 L1994 **FM** *020 †18

WITMER, Donald Boyer. ■ 17584 #041-02-1944 L1944 **GP** *071

WILMERDING – ALLEGHENY

DHAR, Veena. 419 WESTINGHOUSE AVE 15148 #496-07-1975 L1992 **FM** *020 †18 ‡

WIND GAP – NORTHAMPTON

AVERBACH, Marcus Aaron. 6695 SULLIVAN TRL, STE 201 18091 #041-12-1997 L2005 **CD** *020 †20

BORICK, Sheila Mary. 131 S BROADWAY 18091 #045-01-1982 L1986 **FM** *020 †18

COLON-DELGADO, Rafael I. 6693 SULLIVAN TRL 18091 #847-05-1977 L1993 **PD** *071 †55

DE FRANCO, Albert Basil. 497 BUSHKILL PLAZA LN 18091 #308-08-1982 L1986 **FM** *020 †18

GILBERT, Christopher B. 6689 SULLIVAN TRL 18091 #033-05-1995 L1997 **OBG** *020 †30

KAUFMANN, Bruce Mark. 6695 SULLIVAN TRL 18091 #041-01-1971 L1972 **OBG** *020 †30

KIM, James Byung-Jin. 5 S BROADWAY, LLC 18091 #035-75-1987, ▲ L1991 **PM** *020 †60

KITEI, Robert A. 6695 SULLIVAN TRL 18091 #041-02-1989 L1993 **OPH IM** *020 †35

KITEI, William J. 6695 SULLIVAN TRL 18091 #041-02-1975 L1976 **OPH** *020 †35

KOHAN, James Michael. PO BOX 306 18091 #051-01-1979 L1980 **SME PUD** *020 †20

MARTINEZ-RAMOS, Maria A. 6693 SULLIVAN TRL 18091 #042-01-1978 L1981 **PD OS** *020 †55

MENDOZA, Mayra Ivette. 6693 SULLIVAN TRL 18091 #042-03-2001 L2003 **PD** *020 †55

NOLL, Richard John. ■ 18091 #041-13-1990 L1991 **IM** *075

POWELL, Mark Wright. 131 S BROADWAY 18091 #045-01-1983 L1986 **FM** *020 †18

SALLASH, Robert John, Jr. 6689 SULLIVAN TRL 18091 #041-13-1966 L1967 **OBG** *020 †30

SARAVITZ, Eugene Martin. 6695 SULLIVAN TRL 18091 #041-13-1986 L1986 **OPH OS** *020 †35

SCOBLIONKO, David P. 6695 SULLIVAN TRL, STE 201 18091 #041-13-1976 L1985 **CD IM** *020 †20

SKUTCHES, Joseph Matthew. 6689 SULLIVAN TRL 18091 #041-02-1957 L1958 **GYN** *020 †30

SUN, Kenneth Paul. PO BOX 266, 382 EPPS ST 18091 #035-06-1989 L1995 **APM** *020

TAVERNA-MILLER, Karen E. 6689 SULLIVAN TRL 18091 #041-15-2003 L2003 **OBG** *020

VAN GAALEN, Adriaan Johan. 6689 SULLIVAN TRL 18091 #660-07-1980 L1982 **OBG** *020 †30

WIND RIDGE – GREENE

CYGAN, David. 548 DODDS RIDGE RD 15380 #649-14-1980 L1984 **EM IM** *020

■ = Address Information Privacy Protected

WINDBER – SOMERSET

AGUILERA, Amelia Gahol. 600 SOMERSET AVE 15963 #748-01-1960 L1977 **OBG** *020

AGUILERA, Bonifacio Tan. 600 SOMERSET AVE 15963 #748-01-1961 L1976 **GS TS** *020 †85,90

AHLERS, Paul. 600 SOMERSET AVE, WINDBER MEDICAL CENTER 15963 #019-02-1974 L1976 **EM** *020 †16

ANDERSON, Amy Lynn. 600 SOMERSET AVE, ANEX 2 15963 #041-13-1996 L1999 **OBG** *020 †30

AWAN, Rashid. 700 5TH ST STE 101 15963 #649-33-1981 L1984 **ON** *020 †20

BOROUMAND, Masood. 700 5TH ST, MEDICAL ARTS BLDG STE 103 15963 #517-01-1968 L1985 **PD PHO** *020 †55

CIACCHELLA, Arthur Paul. 600 SOMERSET AVE 15963 #041-12-1985 L1987 **DR NM** *020 †80

COMAS, Michael Gus. 700 5TH ST, STE 104 15963 #654-01-1986 L1989 **FM OS** *020 †18

CORRENTE, Lisa A. 600 SOMERSET AVE 15963 #422-01-1997 L2004 **DR** *020 †80

CRAIG, Dianna. 600 SOMERSET AVE 15963 #048-13-1994 L1996 **GS** *020 †85

DICK, Sally Miller. 600 SOMERSET AVE 15963 #041-12-1965 L1966 **EM FM** *020

DONROVICH, Paul John. 401 12TH ST 15963 #041-07-1975 L1976 **FM IMG** *020 †18

DUNN, Michael Andrew. 620 7TH ST, WINDBER RESEARCH INST 15963 #016-06-1971 L1972 **GE** *050 †20

ECKENRODE, James Andrew. 600 SOMERSET AVE, WINDBER MED CENTER 15963 #041-13-1971 L1972 **EM GS** *030 †85 ‡

EPSTEIN, Beverly. 700 5TH ST 15963 #748-08-1988 L1992 **N PM** *020 †75

FORMAN, Howard Irv. 600 SOMERSET AVE 15963 #041-07-1988 L1992 **DR** *020 †80

FURIGAY, Rodolfo Lazo. 609 SOMERSET AVE 15963 #748-01-1961 L1970 **GS GP** *020 †85 ‡

GLASS, Samuel Louis. 421 PARK PL 15963 #051-04-1975 L1979 **OPH** *020 †35

GOLDEN, Lisa Waslo. ■ 15963 #041-07-1997 L1999 **EM** *020 †16

GRAY, Jerry Leroy. 1510 JEFFERSON AVE 15963 #041-12-1972 L1973 **IM** *020 †20 ‡

GRAY, Patrick Michael. 1510 JEFFERSON AVE 15963 #041-13-2001 L2004 **IM** *020 ‡

GWAN-NULLA, Daniel Nvakob. 600 SOMERSET AVE, WINDBER MEDICAL CENTER 15963 #041-01-1995 L1997 **TS** *020 †85,90

GWAN-NULLA, Meesha B. 600 SOMERSET AVE, WINDBER PROFESSIONAL SRVCS 15963 #035-15-1994 L1998 **IM** *020 †20

HAHM, Michael Sungjoon. 600 SOMERSET AVE 15963 #010-03-2000 L2001 **DR** *020

HERBICK, William T. 600 SOMERSET AVE 15963 #041-12-1980 L1987 **DR** *020 †80

HOANG, Kiet Anh. 600 SOMERSET AVE 15963 #941-01-1972 L1986 **R** *020 †80

KEMP, De Witt Edward, III. 600 SOMERSET AVE 15963 #012-05-1968 L1983 **GS PLM** *020 †85

KRAMER, Gary Scott. 600 SOMERSET AVE 15963 #041-13-1993 L1995 **VIR** *020 †80

MALIK, Noman Ahmed. 600 SOMERSET AVE 15963 #704-01-1995 L2006 **DR** *020 †80

MARLEY, Kim Russell. 600 SOMERSET AVE 15963 #025-07-1983 L2004 **GS GP** *020 †85

MC SURDY, Bruce James. 600 SOMERSET AVE, WINDBER MEDICAL CENTER 15963 #038-41-1990 L1998 **AN** *020

MORRELL, Roger Wm. 600 SOMERSET AVE, WINDBVER OB-GYN ASSOC 15963 #018-75-1973, ▲ L1974 **OBG** *020 †30

PARK, Neil III Hyung. 609 SOMERSET AVE 15963 #583-01-1966 L1971 **OBG GP** *020 †30

PHULWANI, Prakash. 600 SOMERSET AVE 15963 #495-30-1973 L1979 **EM FM** *020 †16

ROBERTS, Handel Jay. ■ 15963 #305-01-1994 L1999 **IM** *075

SANTIAGO, Diosdado. 403 12TH ST STE B 15963 #748-08-1987 L1991 **IM** *020

SCHWAB, Gwendolyn Marie. 620 7TH ST, WINDBER RESEARCH INST 15963 #055-01-2004 L2004 **IM** *012

STASCHAK, Michael Carmen. 600 SOMERSET AVE 15963 #041-12-1975 L1977 **LM OS** *030

SULER, Sima. 500 SOMERSET AVE 15963 #957-08-1988 L2001 **FM** *020 †18

VOLOSHIN, Michael D. 700 5TH ST, STE 101 15963 #041-09-1989 L1991 **ON HEM** *020 †20

WOLFE, Patrick Wayne. 600 SOMERSET AVE 15963 #041-12-1979 L1980 **DR** *020 †80

WINFIELD – UNION

ABLAYAO, Shiyi. ■ 17889 #041-02-1992 L1995 **PMM** *012 †05

TENEDIOS, George. 795 FELMEY RD 17889 #024-07-1980 L1982 **AN** *020 †55,05 ‡

WOMELSDORF – BERKS

BIGOS, Edward Thos. 1137 W PENN AVE, CONRAD WEISER MEDICAL 19567 #041-07-1982 L1983 **FM** *020 †18 ‡

DIETRICH, Scott Allan. 1137 W PENN AVE, CONRAD WEISER MEDICAL 19567 #041-13-1989 L1991 **FM** *020 †18

NAGLE, Arlington Adam. ■ 19567 #041-01-1943 L1944 **FM** *071

ROKE, Albert David. 1137 W PENN AVE, CONRAD WEISER MEDICAL 19567 #041-01-1973 L1974 **FM** *020 †18

WUMMER, Brian Anthony. 1137 W PENN AVE 19567 #041-09-1956 L1957 **FM** *071

WOODLYN – DELAWARE

KODUMAL, Luis Ezpeleta. 1245 JEFFERSON AVE 19094 #748-01-1968 L1974 **IM GE** *020

WORMLEYSBURG – CUMBERLAND

ALTAKER, Lawrence Lewis. 1013 MUMMA RD STE 203 17043 #041-02-1962 L1963 **P AM** *020 †75

BARSANTI, Ronald Gregory. 532 N FRONT ST, SUSQUEHANNA SURGEONS, LTD 17043 #051-04-1983 L1985 **GS** *020 †85

CASAL, Rolando Apolinario. 532 N FRONT ST 17043 #748-01-1963 L1971 **GS** *020 ‡

ESPOSITO, Joseph Paul. 532 N FRONT ST, SUSQUEHANNA SURGEONS LTD 17043 #035-20-1978 L1980 **GS VS** *020 †85

FROEHLICH, Arthur David. 532 N FRONT ST 17043 #035-45-1967 L1975 **GS CD** *020 †85

GRAF, Kenneth Walter. 532 N FRONT ST 17043 #041-09-1970 L1971 **GS CRS** *020 †85

LEONE, Timothy Adam. 532 N FRONT ST, SUSQUEHANNA SURGEONS 17043 #041-77-2002, ▲ L2003 **GS** *020

LIM, Heng-Feng. 1000 N FRONT ST 17043 #041-13-1963 L1965 **CD IM** *071 †20

MOFFITT, George Reily, Jr. 1000 N FRONT ST 17043 #041-01-1947 L1948 **CD** *071 †20

PAGE, Michael Jerome. 532 N FRONT ST 17043 #010-01-1975 L1979 **GS VS** *020

PARK, Nae Hong. 1000 N FRONT ST, STE 400 17043 #583-04-1966 L1972 **OTO HNS** *071 †45

PETER, Anastasius Omar. 532 N FRONT ST 17043 #041-14-1987 L1989 **GS** *020 †85

POOL, Marjorie Kishpaugh. ■ 17043 #023-01-1944 L1945 **PD** *072

RADTKE, Nancy Le Compte. 1000 N FRONT ST, MOFFITT HEART & VASCULAR G 17043 #051-04-1983 L2001 **CD IM** *020 †20

SAVORY, William John. 532 N FRONT ST 17043 #041-09-1954 L1955 **GS** *071 †85

TORP, Lisa Kim. 532 N FRONT ST, SUSQUEHANNA SURGEONS, LTD 17043 #011-02-1990 L1992 **GS** *020 †85

WORTHINGTON – ARMSTRONG

PAUL, Jay. 497 BEAR ST 16262 #041-14-1971 L1972 **PUD CCM** *020 †20 ‡

WRIGHTSVILLE – YORK

BRIGHTER, Jennifer Marie. 6415 LINCOLN HWY, GRP AT TWIN ROSE PRIM 17368 #041-15-2002 L2002 **FM** *020 †18

DANIELS, Bret Anthony. 6415 LINCOLN HWY, GRP AT TWIN ROSE PRIM 17368 #041-01-1989 L1995 **FM** *020 †18

EBUOMA, Lilian Olubukola. ■ 17368 #023-01-2007 L2007 **TY** *012

HUSSAR, Eric Fix. 6415 LINCOLN HWY, GRP AT TWIN ROSE PRIM 17368 #041-13-2002 L2002 **FM** *020 †18

MAGILL, D Thais. 6415 LINCOLN HWY, GRP AT TWIN ROSE PRIM 17368 #035-08-1999 L2001 **FM** *020 †18

SCHUCKER, Scott Alan. 6415 LINCOLN HWY, GRP AT TWIN ROSE PRIM 17368 #041-09-1997 L2003 **FM** *020 †18

SHAH, Shefali M. 6415 LINCOLN HWY, GRP AT TWIN ROSE PRIM 17368 #008-02-1991 L1998 **FM** *020 †18

SNYDER, William Barry. ■ 17368 #041-14-1999 **P** *100

YOUNG, Brian J. 6415 LINCOLN HWY, GRP AT TWIN ROSE PRIM 17368 #035-15-2001 L2001 **FM** *020 †18

WYALUSING – BRADFORD

MANLEY, Charles Roscoe. RR 3 BOX 83D 18853 #067-01-1969 L1977 **AN** *020

WEBB, Paul Richard. PO BOX 700 18853 #050-02-1983 L1986 **IM OM** *020

WYCOMBE – BUCKS

BUCHER, Robert Geo. CHERRY LN 18980 #041-02-1954 L1955 **FM** *071 †18

WYNCOTE – MONTGOMERY

BAER, Samuel. ■ 19095 #041-01-1933 L1935 **CD IM** *071 †20

BAKER, Barrie Ruth. 1015 SERPENTINE LN 19095 #041-07-1991 L1994 **EM FM** *020 †18

BRILLMAN, Nathan. ■ 19095 #041-02-1957 L1958 **IM GP** *072 †18

CLAYTON, Charles H, Jr. 2827 W CHELTENHAM AVE 19095 #041-13-1976 L1977 **FM** *020 †18

COGEN, Jacob Franklin. ■ 19095 #041-02-2005 L2007 **FP** *012

DRUM, Elizabeth T. ■ 19095 #041-13-1986 L1987 **AN** *020 †05

FLEEGLER, Earl Jason. 25 WASHINGTON LN, STE 16 THE WYNETE HSE 19095 #041-02-1965 L1966 **HS** *020 †85,65

GIORDANO, Luca. ■ 19095 #561-17-1993 L2000 **GS** *100 †85

GOLDSTEIN, Jeffrey I. ■ 19095 #041-01-1993 *074

GREENBERG, Leonard Fred. 325 GRIBBEL RD 19095 #041-02-1959 L1960 **CD IM** *071

GREENSPON, Samuel Edwin. ■ 19095 #041-13-1937 L1938 **GP** *071

HADEH, Anas. 8480 LIMEKILN PIKE, APT M10 19095 #875-01-2000 L2001 **PCC** *100

HALBERT, Steven Carl. 2442 ASHBOURNE RD 19095 #041-13-1979 L1989 **IM EM** *020 †20,16

HARWICK, Robert Dean. DEAVER RD 19095 #035-20-1947 L1956 **HNS OS** *071 †85

HERBERT, Bettina. 270 BENT RD 19095 #025-12-2001 L2002 ***100** †60

HURWITZ, Elliott L. ■ 19095 #024-05-1974 L1990 **N** *075

JACKSON, Tiffaney Schree. ■ 19095 #010-03-2006 L2006 **IM** *012

JAFFE, Jeremy Robt. ■ 19095 #041-13-1991 L1995 **AN** *020 †05

JEON, Mary Eun. ■ 19095 #035-46-2007 **FP** *012

JOEBSTL, Barbara C. ■ 19095 #051-07-1984 L1986 **RHU PPR** *020 †20,55

JONES, James Gregory. 8480 LIMEKILN PIKE 1211 19095 #041-13-1991 L1994 **P** *020

JONES, Kaya Joy. ■ 19095 #041-02-2007 L2007 **FP** *012

JONES, Robyn Rachelle. 1010 ARBORETUM RD 19095 #041-13-1981 L1982 **OBG** *062 †30

KNEE, Norman Stanley. ■ 19095 #041-77-1957, ▲ L1958 **LM FM** *071

KNOWLTON, Christin A. ■ 19095 #035-48-2006 L2007 **RO** *012

KUPTSOW, Rubin Raymond. ■ 19095 #041-77-1940, ▲ L1957 *071

MARGOLIS, Stephen Harold. 25 WASHINGTON LN STE 22C 19095 #041-02-1971 L1972 **IM** *020

MARTIN, Kisha Monique. 1400 REDWOOD LN 19095 #041-15-1999 L2001 **EM** *012

MATTHEWS, Warren Bruce. 8101 WASHINGTON LN, STE 101 19095 #041-02-1977 L1978 **FM** *020 †18

MEDINA, Carlos Reydell. ■ 19095 #042-03-2003 L2003 **GS** *012

NAIR, Seema. ■ 19095 #495-44-1999 L2006 **IM** *012

PASHUPATHI, Rudrappa. ■ 19095 #495-35-1955 L1981 **IM P** *072

PORTNER, William Jay. 7915 GREEN LN 19095 #016-42-1976 L1977 **R DR** *020 ‡

REICHART, James Paul. ■ 19095 #041-13-2004 L2004 **NEP** *012 †20

RUDNICK, Herman D. ■ 19095 #041-09-1943 L1944 **P** *020 †75

SCOTT, Henry. ■ 19095 #010-03-1964 L1965 **GP** *071

SHORTEN, Suzanne Marie. 8101 WASHINGTON LN, STE 101 19095 #041-15-2000 L2001 **FM** *020 †18 ‡

SINGH, Madhusree. 201 STONEHOUSE LN 19095 #495-38-1995 L2001 **IM** *020

SLIZOFSKI, Walter Jos. ■ 19095 #047-05-1974 L1986 **NM DR** *020 †80,28

STREETS, Gerald Martin. ■ 19095 #047-07-1986 L1987 **P** *020

TABUENA, Amelia Lourdes A. 25 WASHINGTON LN, SUITEC-13 19095 #748-02-1979 L1984 **PM PME** *020

VIVAS-COLON, Iris M. 8460 LIMEKILN PIKE 708 19095 #042-03-2003 L2003 **P** *020

WALTZER, Frederick N. ■ 19095 #041-01-1949 L1951 **OPH** *071

■ = Address Information Privacy Protected

ZIMMERMAN, Edward. 8460 LIMEKILN PIKE PH18-1 19095 #041-77-1954, ▲ L1957
GP FM *071

WYNDMOOR – MONTGOMERY

BARBOT, Donna Jean. 8200 FLOURTOWN AVE, STE 2 19038 #035-08-1978 L1980 GS *020 †85

BARDIN, Simeon Leo. 8200 FLOURTOWN AVE, STE 6 19038 #035-08-1978 L1994 IM IMG *020 †20

BUTCHER, Jeffrey Louis. 8200 FLOURTOWN AVE, STE 2 19038 #041-15-2000 L2001 CRS *020 †85

COHEN, Jonathan. ■ 19038 #033-05-1999 L2004 ID *020 †20

DE PACE, Nicholas Louis. 805 E WILLOW GROVE AVE, NEW LIFE CARDIOVASCULAR CA 19038 #035-47-1978 L1980 CD *020 †20

DOGHRAMJI, James. 551 E EVERGREEN AVE 19038 #041-02-1989 L1991 EM IM *020 †20

GOREN, Norman Jack. 1400 CROMWELL RD 19038 #041-01-1946 L1947 CHP P *072 †55

JABLONSKI, Miroslawa S. ■ 19038 #033-05-1999 L2004 CD *012 †20

KAGEN, Richard D. 8200 FLOURTOWN 19038 #024-05-1980 L1981 IM *020 †20

KISTENMACHER, John C, Jr. ■ 19038 #041-13-1950 L1951 GS *071 †85

KREITZ, Keith Allan. 8200 FLOURTOWN AVE, STE 2 19038 #041-15-1999 L2006 GS *020 †85

KYLE, Maryellen S. 8200 FLOURTOWN AVE STE 7 19038 #045-01-1979 L1983 IM *020 †20

LOPEZ, Rafael H. 805 E WILLOW GROVE AVE 19038 #748-01-1958 L1972 IM CD *071

MAHBOOB, Hina. ■ 19038 #495-51-2001 L2005 IM *012

MATTEUCCI, Walter V. 8103 ARDMORE AVE 19038 #041-02-1946 L1947 IM A *072 †20

MORLEY, Jonathan. 8200 FLOURTOWN AVE, WYNDHILL PROF CENTER STE 4 19038 #035-19-1974 L1975 P PYG *020 †75

NELSON, William Carl, Jr. ■ 19038 #041-09-1980 L1983 IM *020

OBENRADER, Mark Francis. 8200 FLOURTOWN AVE, STE 5 19038 #041-13-1980 L1981 FM *020 †18

RABINOWITZ, Aliza Bella. 8200 FLOURTOWN AVE STE 7 19038 #041-01-2002 L2002 IM *020 †20

ROSENBERG, Morton. ■ 19038 #041-09-1947 L1948 PD PDI *071 †55

SALGADO GONZALEZ, Gonzalo. ■ 19038 #035-01-2001 L2004 IM *100

SPIELBERGER, Karen Ann M. 8200 FLOURTOWN AVE 19038 #041-07-1987 L1988 IM *020 †20

SULLIVAN, Richard Anthony. 8601 STENTON AVE 19038 #035-15-1955 L1987 PM *071 †60

THOMPSON, Coralee Gene. 8801 STENTON AVE 19038 #054-04-1989 L1994 FM *020 †18

TRAMUTA, Gregory J. 8200 FLOURTOWN AVE, STE 4B 19038 #035-06-1974 L1975 P PYA *020 †75

TRILNICK, Ida Muriel. ■ 19038 #132-01-1978 L1984 P *074 †75

WEBER, Amy Elizabeth. 912 E WILLOW GROVE AVE 19038 #041-12-1996 L2000 OPH *020 †35

WHITE, Ammie Marie. ■ 19038 #041-15-2007 L2007 TY *012

WHITENACK, Stephan Harris. 8200 FLOURTOWN AVE, SUITE10 19038 #041-02-1974 L1975 GS TS *020 †90,85

WIVEL, Ashley E. 531 E MERMAID LN 19038 #008-01-1998 L2007 EM *020 †16

ZUBRITZKY, Martha M. 8200 FLOURTOWN AVE, STE 7 19038 #041-01-1985 L1986 IM *020 †20 ‡

WYNNEWOOD – MONTGOMERY

ABELSON, Denis Maurice. 100 E LANCASTER AVE # 451, LANKENAU MED BLDG E 19096 #352-07-1951 L1962 IM *020

ABRAMSON, Sandra Vicki. 100 E LANCASTER AVE, STE 356 19096 #041-07-1984 L1985 CD IM *020 †20

ABU-ZAHRA, Khalil Wasfi. 109 STRAWBRIDGE CT, HUP 19096 #575-01-1993 L2006 RNR *020

AHLSWEDE, Karl Melvin, Jr. 100 E LANCASTER AVE, STE 280 19096 #041-02-1988 L1990 GS *020 †85 ‡

AHN, Max. 100 E LANCASTER AVE 19096 #041-01-1996 L2002 U *020 †95

ALBERTSON, Richard Potter. 1001 CITY LINE AVE, GREEN HILL EC 306 19096 #041-13-1963 L1963 AN *071 †05

ALDRICH, Jennifer Lee. 100 E LANCASTER AVE, STE 164 19096 #035-45-1992 L1994 ID *020 †20

ALI, Aneela Ashraf. 100 E LANCASTER AVE, CANCER CTR MOB 19096 #704-06-1998 L2002 HO *020 †20 ‡

ALI, Zonera Ashraf. 100 E LANCASTER AVE, STE B20 19096 #704-01-1995 L2000 IM *020 †20

ALTER, Milton. 100 E LANCASTER AVE, LANKENAU HOSPITAL, STE 567 19096 #035-06-1955 L1964 N OS *071 †75

ANTONIADES, John. 100 E LANCASTER AVE 19096 #418-01-1960 L1981 RO NM *071 †80,28

ANTOSH, Lucinda Stephanie. 100 E LANCASTER AVE, DEPT OF MED EDUCATION 19096 #041-78-2005, ▲ L2005 OBG *012

ANYAOGU, Obiageli Enuma. 100 E LANCASTER AVE, LANKENAU HOSPITAL 19096 #038-45-2005 L2007 IM *012

AROUH, Albert. ■ 19096 #041-02-1956 L1957 R *071 †80

ASUBIARO, Waheed Abiodun. 100 E LANCASTER AVE, LANKENAU HOSPITAL 19096 #690-05-1988 L2002 IM *100

AUGUST, Charles Saul. ■ 19096 #024-01-1962 L1976 PHO HEM *071 †55

BADOSA, Francisco. 100 E LANCASTER AVE, LANKENAU HOSP MSB STE 275 19096 #847-01-1964 L1985 GS OS *020 †85

BAILEY, Scott Higgins. 100 E LANCASTER AVE, STE 216W 19096 #035-48-1983 L1989 OBG *020 †30

BAILLIE, Daniel Robert. 100 E LANCASTER AVE, DEPT OF GENERAL SURGERY 19096 #539-04-2004 L2004 GS *012

BAUM, Sheldon F. 100 E LANCASTER AVE, LANKENAU HOSPITAL 19096 #041-01-1955 L1976 NM *071 †28

BECK, Aaron Temkin. ■ 19096 #008-01-1946 L1953 P *071 †75

BENOR, Sharon. 100 E LANCASTER AVE, STE 422 19096 #041-01-2002 L2002 TS *012 †85

BENTIVOGLIO, Lamberto G. 100 E LANCASTER AVE # 380 19096 #561-03-1951 L1963 CD *071 †20

BENZ, Robert Lawrence. 100 E LANCASTER AVE, STE 130 19096 #041-02-1978 L1980 NEP IM *020 †20

BERKELEY, Abiona Virginia. 100 E LANCASTER AVE, LANKENAU HOSPITAL 19096 #005-02-2004 L2004 AN *012

BERNSTEIN, Larry Norman. 100 E LANCASTER AVE, DEPT OF REHAB MED 19096 #035-15-1983 L1984 PM OS *020 †60

BERRY, John William, Jr. 100 E LANCASTER AVE, MAIN LINE EMERGENCY 19096 #041-15-2000 L2001 EM *020 †16

BERRY, Tami Lee. 100 E LANCASTER AVE, LANKENAU HOSPITAL 19096 #305-01-2007 L2007 GS *012

BHATIA, Avnish K. ■ 19096 #041-15-2002 L2008 HO *012 †20

BILELLO, Michel. ■ 19096 #005-11-2000 L2002 DR *100 †80

BLACKMAN, Ryan Graham. ■ 19096 #041-77-2007, ▲ L2007 *012

BLATT, Bruce Ian. 100 E LANCASTER AVE 19096 #041-02-1984 L1985 IM *020 †20 ‡

BONN, Joseph. 100 E LANCASTER AVE, LANKENAU HOSP 19096 #051-01-1979 L1986 VIR DR *020 †80

BONO, Bartholomew Raymond. ■ 19096 #041-13-1996 L2000 ID *020 †20

BOYD, Robert T, III. ■ 19096 #041-01-1950 L1951 GS *071 †85

BRENNAN, Edward Jos. LANKENAU HOSP 19096 #041-13-1989 L1994 GS PHM *050 †85

BREST, Norman Alan. 100 E LANCASTER AVE, STE 561 19096 #041-02-1979 L1980 OBG *020 †30

BULATOVA, Julia Igorivna. 100 E LANCASTER AVE, LANKENAU HOSPITAL 19096 #913-05-2004 L2006 GS *012

BURHAN, Umber. 100 E LANCASTER AVE, LANKENAU HOSPITAL 19096 #704-01-2000 L2001 NEP *100 †20

BURKE, M Susan. 100 E LANCASTER AVE, LANKENAU INTERNAL MEDICINE 19096 #041-01-1979 L1980 IM IMG *020 †20

BURTON, Frederick Douglas. 1455 CITY AVE 19096 #047-07-1981 L1984 IM *020 †20

BUSHICK, James Bryan. ■ 19096 #041-01-1989 L1989 IM *030

BUSHRA, Elizabeth Ann. 1719 POWDER MILL LN, PRESBYTERIAN MEDICAL CENTE 19096 #041-09-1994 L1996 EM *020 †16

BUSHRA, Joseph Sarwat. 100 E LANCASTER AVE, MAIN LINE EMERGENCY 19096 #041-02-1996 L1998 EM *020 †16

CANDELORI, Carmen Danl. ■ 19096 #041-09-1961 L1962 GP AN *071

CANTOR, Jillan Beth. ■ 19096 #041-02-2007 L2007 P *012

CAO, Yimei. ■ 19096 #041-13-1998 L1999 IM *020

CAPLAN, Howard Joel. 100 E LANCASTER AVE, 463 LANKENAU MBE 19096 #041-02-1972 L1974 N IM *020 †20,75 ‡

CAPUZZI, David Michael C. 100 E LANCASTER AVE 19096 #041-02-1964 L1965 END CD *050 †20

CARP, Leon Moses. ■ 19096 #041-09-1940 L1941 IM CD *071

CARP, Ned Zachary. 100 E LANCASTER AVE, STE 275 19096 #041-13-1984 L1985 GS *020 †85

CASEY, Rosemary Delourdes. 100 E LANCASTER AVE, OFC 436 19096 #024-01-1975 L1976 PD *020 †55

CASH, Stephen Laurence. 100 E LANCASTER AVE # 253E 19096 #035-15-1978 L1984 HS ORS *020 †40

CHAMOUN, George N. 100 E LANCASTER AVE STE 356 19096 #605-01-1981 L1986 IM CD *020 †20

CHANG, Gordon Yinwei. 100 E LANCASTER AVE 19096 #041-01-1988 L1997 NPM *020 †55

CHARATZOGLOU, Georgios M. ■ 19096 #418-02-1987 L2000 AN *020

CHASTENEY, Mark Edward. 100 E LANCASTER AVE 19096 #041-02-1983 L1984 OBG *020 †30

CHAUHAN, Nisha Kaur. ■ 19096 #023-01-2007 L2007 *012

CHEATLE, Patrick Philip. ■ 19096 #041-13-2007 L2007 EM *012

CLARKE, Catherine Faye. 100 E LANCASTER AVE # 135W 19096 #008-02-1983 L1984 IM IMG *020 †20 ‡

CLAVES, Jennifer Lee. 300 E LANCASTER AVE, STE 304 19096 #041-14-1997 L1999 IM *020 †20

COADY, Paul M. 100 E LANCASTER AVE, 380 LANKENAU MED SCIENCE B 19096 #041-13-1984 L1985 CD IM *020 †20

COHEN, David Andrew. 100 E LANCASTER AVE, 330 LANKENAU MOB WEST 19096 #041-09-1983 L1984 IM *020 †20

COLLINS, Lauren Gustafson. ■ 19096 #041-02-2002 L2002 FPG *100 †18

COMBER, Bernard Edward. 100 E LANCASTER AVE 19096 #041-01-1959 L1961 PYA *020 ‡

COREY, Donald Jerry. 100 E LANCASTER AVE, STE 161 19096 #016-01-1974 L1975 IM *020 †20

COTLER, Marc D. 35 E WYNNEWOOD RD 19096 #041-07-1974 L1976 AI PD *020 †55,03

COUTSOUMARIS-HAUGHTON, I. 100 E LANCASTER AVE 19096 #035-19-1952 L1956 CHP PD *020

CRIMMINS, Terri Kathleen. ■ 19096 #048-04-2003 L2005 P *100

CSANALOSI, Irma Buko. ■ 19096 #473-01-1944 L1966 P *071 †75

CURTIN, Andrew Jos. 100 E LANCASTER AVE, LANKENAU HOSPITAL 19096 #041-02-1983 L1985 DR RNR *020 †80

DARUWALA, Cherag Aspi. 100 E LANCASTER AVE, LANKENAU HOSPITAL 19096 #041-15-2003 L2003 GE *012 †20

DAUM, Gary Stuart. 100 E LANCASTER AVE, MAIN LINE PATHOLOGY 19096 #041-09-1983 L1988 PTH *020 †50

DAVIS, Daniela Hoffmann. ■ 19096 #032-01-1996 L1998 CCP *020 †55

DEBAKKER, Carol Judith. 100 E LANCASTER AVE, LANKENAU HOSPITAL 19096 #041-09-1985 L1987 PM *020 †60

DELANEY, William E. LANKENAU MEDICAL BLDG 19096 #041-02-1953 L1954 IM PTH *071 †50,28,20

DEL CORRAL, Gabriel Alfon. 100 E LANCASTER AVE, LANKENAU HOSPITAL 19096 #649-14-2005 L2005 GS *012

DE MAIO, John Gerard. 100 E LANCASTER AVE 19096 #041-01-1982 L1984 NPM PD *020 †55 ‡

DESOUZA, Bryan Xavier. 100 E LANCASTER AVE, SUITE 312, SOUTH ANNEX 19096 #008-01-1985 L1994 N CN *020 †75

DESSAIN, Scott Kendall. 100 E LANCASTER AVE, STE 227 19096 #008-01-1994 L2002 HO *020 †20

DIEFES, Gerard John. 1001 CITY AVE, BLDG 113 19096 #041-09-1992 L1996 PCC SME *020 †20

DI MONTE, Diane Karen. 100 E LANCASTER AVE 19096 #041-07-1981 L1982 PTH *075 †50

DIXIT, Sanjay. ■ 19096 #495-67-1992 L2000 ICE *020 †20

DOHERTY, Henry Jos. ■ 19096 #028-34-1958 L1959 AN P *071 †05

DORFMAN, Murray L. 1001 CITY LINE AVE # WA105 19096 #035-09-1949 L1950 IM OS *020

D'ORSI, Angela Vincenza. 100 E LANCASTER AVE, DEPT PM & R 19096 #035-15-1989 L1991 PM *020 †60

DORWART, Bonnie Brice. 100 E LANCASTER AVE 19096 #041-13-1968 L1969 RHU IM *071 †20

DOUGHERTY, Malvin John. ■ 19096 #041-02-1954 L1955 OPH *071 †20

DOUGHERTY, Michael Jos. 100 E LANCASTER AVE, 356 LANKENAU MEDICAL BLDG 19096 #041-01-1968 L1969 CD *020 †20

DRAZNIN, Julia. ■ 19096 #007-02-1997 L2000 HO *020 †20

DREYFUSS, Arnon Itzchak. ■ 19096 #550-01-1981 L1999 HEM ON *071 †20

DUNN, Matthew Alan. 100 E LANCASTER AVE, LANKENAU HOSPITAL 19096 #041-02-2007 L2007 **GS** *012

DUNTON, Charles Jos. 100 E LANCASTER AVE, MOB EAST STE 661 19096 #041-02-1980 L1981 **OBG GYN** *020 †30

EL-HAJJ, Rita. 100 E LANCASTER AVE, 222 LANKENAU HOSPITAL MOB 19096 #605-01-1987 L1997 **END IM** *020 †20

ELLIS, Jeffrey Bennett. 300 E LANCASTER AVE, STE 303 WYNNEWOOD HOUSE 19096 #041-02-1998 L2000 **IM** *020 †20

ERHARD, Daniel T. 100 E LANCASTER AVE 19096 #041-02-1951 L1952 **AN** *071 †05

ESBERG, Douglas Bernard. 100 E LANCASTER AVE, STE 556 19096 #035-09-1994 L1997 **ICE** *020 †20

ESKREIS, Naftali. ■ 19096 #561-01-1939 **P** *071

EZEKOWITZ, Michael David. 100 E LANCASTER AVE, STE 556 19096 #836-02-1970 L2000 **CD NM** *050 †20

FARNON, Christa U. ■ 19096 #407-07-1965 L1972 **GP FPG** *071 †70

FAVA, George E. 742 CHERRY CIR 19096 #024-07-1977 L1978 **OPH** *020 †35

FEDDER, Stephen L. 100 E LANCASTER AVE, STE 655 19096 #035-19-1981 L1982 **NS GS** *020 †25

FELDMAN, Ella Sitchin. ■ 19096 #041-09-1976 L1977 **RHU IM** *020 †20

FENTON, Bradley Wayne. ■ 19096 #024-01-1976 L1978 **IM ID** *020 †20

FERNANDEZ, Carmella. 100 E LANCASTER AVE, ANNENBERG CONF CTR - G10 19096 #033-06-2006 L2006 **IM** *012

FINKLE, John Kennedy. 621 MONTGOMERY SCHOOL LN 19096 #035-19-1990 L1992 **CD ICE** *050 †20

FISHMAN, Victor Martin. 100 E LANCASTER AVE, 252 LANKENAU MED BLDG EAST 19096 #035-46-1994 L1996 **GE** *020 †20

FLEISHMAN, Ervin Saphir. 100 E LANCASTER AVE, STE 365 19096 #041-02-1971 L1972 **IM** *020 †20

FRANK, Evan David. 100 E LANCASTER AVE, LANKENAU MED OFFICE BLD ST 19096 #041-01-1982 L1987 **AN PMM** *020 †05

FRIEDMAN, David Frederick. 370 AUBREY RD 19096 #041-01-1984 L1986 **PHO BBK** *062 †55

FRITZ, Karen Ingeborg. 901 POWDER MILL LN 19096 #008-02-1990 L1992 **NPM PD** *020 †55 ‡

GABUZDA, Thomas Geo. 100 E LANCASTER AVE, CANCER CENTER LANKENAU HOS 19096 #024-01-1955 L1965 **HEM ON** *071 †20

GALATI, Sandijo. ■ 19096 #041-15-2008 *012

GALINSKY, David Elliot. 100 E LANCASTER AVE, STE 467 19096 #041-13-1971 **IMG OS** *020 †20

GALLEN, Christopher C. ■ 19096 #012-05-1980 L1982 **N P** *030 †75

GARAY, Carlos Antonio. ■ 19096 #042-01-1991 L1993 **HO IM** *050 †20

GEFEN, Jonathan Yoav. 100 E LANCASTER AVE, MSB 275 19096 #041-02-1997 L2004 **GS** *020 †85

GEFEN, Ron. 100 E LANCASTER AVE, LANKENAU HOSP 19096 #041-02-2004 L2004 **DR** *012

GERHARD, Wilhelm. 100 E LANCASTER AVE, STE 210 LANKENAU MOB SOUTH 19096 #409-15-1970 L1976 **GS** *020 †85

GERSON, Leroy T. 300 E LANCASTER AVE STE 10 19096 #041-13-1961 L1965 **IM CD** *040

GIANGIULIO, Louis Michael. 23 E WYNNEWOOD RD 19096 #041-02-1999 L2005 **PD** *020 †55

GILGORE, Gary Steven. LANKENAU MED BLDG STE 130 19096 #041-02-1967 L1968 **NEP IM** *020 †20

GILMAN, Paul Barth. 100 E LANCASTER AVE, STE B20 19096 #041-02-1976 L1980 **ON HEM** *020 †20

GLAZER, Robert Morris. ■ 19096 #041-02-1962 L1963 **ORS** *071 †40

GOLDEN, Jeffrey Alan. ■ 19096 #041-01-1988 L1996 **NP PTH** *020 †50

GOLDMAN, Scott Michael. 100 E LANCASTER AVE, 280 LANKENAU MEDICAL SCI B 19096 #041-02-1976 L1977 **ORS** *020 †85,90

GOLDMANN, Bonnie J. ■ 19096 #035-46-1977 L1979 **IM** *020 †20,16

GOLDMANN, David Robt. 224 ALMOS LN 19096 #024-01-1972 L1973 **IM END** *020 †20

GOLDSTEIN, Ari Benjamin. ■ 19096 #041-02-2007 **IM** *012

GOLDSTEIN, Larry Edwin. 602 ARGYLE CIR 19096 #041-02-1973 L1974 **U GS** *020 †95 ‡

GOLLOMP, Stephen Michael. 100 E LANCASTER AVE, STE 161 19096 #035-03-1976 L1981 **N CN** *020 †75

GOODSTINE, Lynette B. 100 E LANCASTER AVE, SUIE 415 19096 #041-07-1977 L1979 **IM** *020 †20

GORBY, Charles Kenderdine. 100 E LANCASTER AVE 19096 #041-02-1959 L1960 **IMG PA** *071

GORDON, Eleanora C. ■ 19096 #008-01-1949 L1951 **PD** *071 †55

GORDON, Gary Victor. 137 LANKENAU MED BLDG 19096 #008-01-1973 L1976 **RHU GP** *020 †20 ‡

GOREN, Robert Alan. ■ 19096 #041-09-1977 L1979 **DR** *020 †80

GREEN, Alfred I. ■ 19096 #041-77-1950, ▲ L1957 **PD GP** *071

GREENE, Joshua Matthew. 780 PERIWINKLE LN 19096 #041-13-2001 L2001 **OPH** *020 †35

GREENSPON, Lee Wm. 100 E LANCASTER AVE, STE 230 19096 #041-13-1976 L1978 **PUD** *020 †20

GREGORY, Susan Ann. 100 E LANCASTER AVE, STE 230 19096 #038-43-1986 L1987 **PUD CCM** *020 †20

GROSS, Joan Paull. ■ 19096 #041-07-1961 L1962 **P PYA** *020

GROSSMAN, David Hollander. 100 E LANCASTER AVE 19096 #041-01-1976 L1978 **EM IM** *020 †20,16

GROSSMAN, Eric Joel. ■ 19096 #041-13-1966 L1967 **AN** *020 †05

GUPTA, Prasad D.. 100 E LANCASTER AVE, LANKENAU HOSPITAL 19096 #495-38-1990 L2003 **CD** *012 †20

HAAB, Jean Elizabeth. 300 E LANCASTER AVE, WYNNWOOD HOUSE, SUITE 303 19096 #041-02-1994 L1997 **IM** *020 †20

HABER-COHEN, Andrea Diane. ■ 19096 #024-01-1980 L1984 **HNS** *071

HAGG, Michael Joseph. 100 E LANCASTER AVE 19096 #041-09-1993 L1995 **U** *020 †95

HARPER, Glenn Robt. 100 E LANCASTER AVE, STE 556 19096 #041-07-1985 L1986 **CD IM** *020 †20

HARRIS, Basil Mark. 100 E LANCASTER AVE, LANKENAU HOSP EMGY DEPT 19096 #041-02-2002 L2002 **EM** *020 †16

HARRIS, David Thorme. 100 E LANCASTER AVE, MAIN LINE EMERGENCY 19096 #024-01-1968 L1970 **ON HEM** *020 †20

HATHTHOTUWA, Eranga K. 100 E LANCASTER AVE # 380, MED SCIENCE BLDG 19096 #913-92-1988 L1997 **CD** *020 †20

HAYWARD, R Bradley. 1111 BERWIND RD 19096 #041-02-1977 L1978 **GS CRS** *020 †85

HEACOCK, Kevin Floyd. 100 E LANCASTER AVE, LANKENAU HOSPITAL 19096 #041-14-2005 L2005 **IM** *020

HEIDARY, Godrattollah. 100 E LANCASTER AVE, LANKENUA HOSPITAL 19096 #517-01-1965 L1973 **AN** *020 †05

HEIGHTCHEW, Kimberly Ann. 100 E LANCASTER AVE, MAIN LINE PATHOLOGY 19096 #033-05-2000 L2001 **PTH** *020 †50

HELLER, Alvin Gordon. 100 E LANCASTER AVE, STE 330 19096 #041-02-1971 L1972 **IM CD** *071

HENCI, Teuta. ■ 19096 #041-15-2002 L2002 **PD** *020 †55

HERLYN, Antje Marianne. ■ 19096 #005-02-2007 L2007 **IM** *012

HERNANDEZ, Maribel. 100 E LANCASTER AVE, STE 556 19096 #005-11-1985 L1989 **CD ICE** *020 †20

HILLIS, Matthew Blair. ■ 19096 #035-01-2001 L2001 **ICE** *012 †20

HINER, Linda Beth. ■ 19096 #017-20-1970 L1976 **PD PN** *071 †55

HOLTZ, David Olof. 100 E LANCASTER AVE 19096 #041-02-1998 L2000 **GO GYN** *020

HOLZMAN, Eliezer Josef. ■ 19096 #550-02-1978 L1987 **NEP DR** *020 †20

IMAIZUMI, Shotaro. 100 E LANCASTER AVE, MAIN LINE PATHOLOGY 19096 #187-04-1971 L1981 **PTH IG** *020 †50

INGERMAN, Mark Jeffrey. 100 E LANCASTER AVE, STE 164 19096 #041-02-1981 L1982 **ID IM** *020 †20

ISAACSON, Howard. 100 E LANCASTER AVE 19096 #041-02-1946 L1947 **OBG** *020 †30 ‡

JACQUETTE, Mary Ellen. 100 E LANCASTER AVE 19096 #041-09-1980 L1982 **NPM PD** *020 †55

JALALI, Shailen. 100 E LANCASTER AVE, STE 233 WEST MOB 19096 #041-02-1985 L1986 **AN PMM** *020 †05 ‡

JANARTHANAN, Sakthipriya. 100 E LANCASTER AVE, LANKENAU HOSPITAL 19096 #495-04-1995 L2003 **IM** *100 †20

JATLA, Muralidhar. ■ 19096 #038-40-2002 L2005 **PG** *012 †55

JAYALAKSHMI, Shyamalan. ■ 19096 #495-53-1962 L1973 **OBG** *020 †30

JIAO, Zhen. 100 E LANCASTER AVE, LANKENAU HOSPITAL 19096 #243-44-1989 L2005 **IM** *012

JONAS, Larry. 100 E LANCASTER AVE, STE 456 19096 #041-01-1976 L1977 **PS OTO** *020 †45,65

KAMBIN, Sheila Parvin. 100 E LANCASTER AVE, STE 458 19096 #041-15-2001 L2001 **OBG** *020

KANDARPA, Madhu. 100 E LANCASTER AVE, LANKENAU HOSPITAL 19096 #495-58-1993 L2003 **NEP** *012 †20

KAO, Stephanie Y S S. ■ 19096 #244-05-1991 L1997 **IM OM** *020 †20

KAPLAN, Glenn Stuart. 100 E LANCASTER AVE 19096 #041-13-1978 L1979 **NPM PD** *020 †55

KARTEN, Russell Jeffrey. 100 E LANCASTER AVE, MAIN LINE EMERGENCY 19096 #033-06-1999 L2002 **EM** *020 †16

KATZ, Jessica Beth. 100 E LANCASTER AVE, 452 LANKENAU MOB EAST 19096 #035-46-1992 L1995 **HO** *012 †20

KAUFMANN, Herbert J. ■ 19096 #869-01-1951 L1975 **PDR** *062 †80

KESHGEGIAN, Albert A. 100 E LANCASTER AVE, MAIN LINE PATHOLOGY 19096 #041-01-1975 L1976 **CLP ATP** *030 †50

KESSLER, Ada. ■ 19096 #550-02-1982 **R** *100

KHAN, Amiduzzaman A. 100 E LANCASTER AVE, STE 356 19096 #160-03-1988 L2000 **IC** *100 †20

KIM, Ellen A. ■ 19096 #583-01-1984 L2002 **NPM** *020 †55

KIRKPATRICK, Thanh Giang. ■ 19096 #050-02-2002 L2007 **PD** *012

KITCHEN, James Gordon, III. 100 E LANCASTER AVE, 356 LANKENAU MED BLDG EAST 19096 #041-01-1968 L1969 **CD** *020 †20

KLEIN, Lynn Michele. 100 E LANCASTER AVE, 461 LANKENAU MED BLDG 19096 #041-07-1988 L1993 **D** *020 †15

KNOLL, Sandra Lee. 100 E LANCASTER AVE, 3 WEST PEW BLDG 19096 #028-02-1980 L2006 **IM** *020 †20

KOCOVIC, Dusan Z. 100 E LANCASTER AVE, STE 556 19096 #957-02-1982 L1994 **CD** *020 †20

KOENIG, George J. ■ 19096 #041-77-2003, ▲ L2003 **GS** *012

KOHLER, Fritz Peter. 361 E LANKENAU MED BLDG 19096 #041-01-1956 L1957 **U** *071 †95

KOHOUT, Jaromir. 100 E LANCASTER AVE, DEPT GS 19096 #286-13-2001 L2002 **GS** *012

KOLASINSKI, Sharon Lee. 540 HANSELL RD 19096 #035-19-1985 L1986 **RHU IM** *030 †20

KOMMURI, Anand. 100 E LANCASTER AVE, DEPT MED 19096 #495-58-1997 L2007 **IM** *012

KONDA, Sumitra Sai. 100 E LANCASTER AVE, LANKENAU HOSPITAL 19096 #495-21-2001 L2006 **IM** *012

KOPROWSKA, Irena. ■ 19096 #759-03-1940 L1961 **PTH** *020 †50

KOSINSKI, Lauren Amelia. 100 E LANCASTER AVE, 330 LANKENAU MOB, WEST 19096 #005-02-1992 L2005 **CRS** *012 †85

KOTAK, Rajesh. 100 E LANCASTER AVE, LANKENAU HOSPITAL 19096 #422-01-2007 L2007 **GS** *012

KOTLER, Michael Justin. 100 E LANCASTER AVE, LANKENAU HOSPITAL 19096 #025-01-2007 L2007 **IM** *012

KOTLOFF, Leon. ■ 19096 #041-13-1941 L1942 **IM GP** *071

KOWEY, Peter Russell. 100 E LANCASTER AVE, STE 556 19096 #041-01-1975 L1976 **CD IM** *020 †20

KRAUSE, Marilyn. ■ 19096 #010-02-1966 L1969 **PD CHP** *020

KUDSI, Omar Yusef. 100 E LANCASTER AVE, LANKENAU HOSPITAL 19096 #875-02-2004 L2006 **GS** *012

KUNTZ, Catherine Lynn. 100 E LANCASTER AVE, STE 230 MEDICAL BUILDING 19096 #041-01-1998 L2001 **PCC** *100 †20

LACHMAN, Tim. 100 E LANCASTER AVE, BLDG. 19096 #041-01-1967 L1968 **N RO** *020 †75 ‡

LALLY, James Arthur. 100 E LANCASTER AVE, STE 558 19096 #041-02-2000 L2004 **IC** *012 †20

LANDE, Leah. 100 E LANCASTER AVE, STE 230 19096 #041-01-1997 L2006 **PCC** *020

LANGAN, Edward L, III. 100 E LANCASTER AVE, LANKENAU MED BLDG STE 551 19096 #041-02-1971 L1972 **OBG** *020 †30

LANGDON, Ira Danl. ■ 19096 #020-02-1943 L1954 **OM** *071

LANGER, Burton Harris. 100 E LANCASTER AVE, 400 LANKENAU MED BLDG SOUT 19096 #041-01-1986 L1987 **PD** *020 †20

LAVI, Nimrod. 610 LATHAM DR 19096 #550-01-2001 L2007 **ICE** *012 †20

LAWRENCE, John Todd Rutte. ■ 19096 #041-01-2003 L2003 **ORS** *012

LAWSER, Amy L. 100 E LANCASTER AVE, SOUTH 114 19096 #041-13-1999 L2001 **IM** *020 †20

LEE, Sena Jessica. 259 E LANCASTER AVE 19096 #035-20-2003 L2004 **D** *100 †15

LEHMAN, Amanda Young. 100 E LANCASTER AVE, LANKENAU HOSPITAL 19096 #041-02-2007 L2007 **IM** *012

LENCHNER, Gregory Steven. 1001 CITY AVE 19096 #035-01-1975 L1976 **PUD CCM** *020 †20

LESSER, Bettina Beth. 100 E LANCASTER AVE 19096 #041-01-1991 L1993 **PD PHP** *020 †55

LEVETAN, Claresa Sharon. 100 E LANCASTER AVE, 222 LANKENAU HOSPITAL MOB 19096 #012-05-1983 L2002 **END IM** *020 †20

LEVIN, William Phillip. ■ 19096 #550-02-1998 L2001 **RO** *020 †80

LEVINE, Samuel Abraham. ■ 19096 #035-19-1953 **PM IM** *071 †60

LEWIS, William John. 33 LANKENAU MED BLDG W 19096 #041-02-1970 L1971 **OTO PS** *020 †45

LIEBMAN, Ronald. ■ 19096 #041-01-1966 L1967 **CHP P** *020 †75

LING, Henry Tsewei. 100 E LANCASTER AVE, SUITE 140 LANKENAU MED BLD 19096 #041-02-1986 L1988 **IM** *020 †20

LIPPA, Robert Leo. 100 E LANCASTER AVE, MAIN LINE EMERGENCY 19096 #024-16-1983 L1995 **EM IM** *020 †20

LIU, Huiqiu. 100 E LANCASTER AVE 19096 #243-76-1990 **IM** *062

LIU, Jennifer. 100 E LANCASTER AVE, LANKENAU HOSPITAL 19096 #021-01-2003 L2003 **PTH** *012

LIVORNESE, Lawrence L, Jr. 100 E LANCASTER AVE, STE 164 19096 #033-05-1986 L1988 **ID IM** *020 †20

LONSDORF, Richard G. 100 E LANCASTER AVE 19096 #041-01-1946 L1947 **P PFP** *072 †75

LOTHE, Pradeep A. 300 E LANCASTER AVE, WYNNEWOOD HOUSE SUITE 105A 19096 #495-19-1973 L1991 **IM** *020 †20

LUARDO, Edwin G. ■ 19096 #748-09-1967 L1973 **P** *020

MAGARGEE, Edward Russell. 100 E LANCASTER AVE, STE 414 19096 #041-02-1986 L1987 **IC CD** *020 †20

MAGUIRE, Joseph Ignatius. 100 E LANCASTER AVE, STE 256 19096 #041-02-1983 L1983 **OPH** *020 †35 ‡

MAHMOOD, Ayesha. ■ 19096 #704-16-1992 L2004 **CN** *020

MAHNE, Anton. 100 E LANCASTER AVE, LANKENAU HOSPITAL 19096 #308-13-2003 L2005 **DR** *012

MAMILLAPALLI, Padmaja Dev. 100 E LANCASTER AVE 19096 #495-58-1990 L2005 **IM** *012

MANKO, Michael Alfred. 100 E LANCASTER AVE # 114 19096 #041-13-1957 L1958 **IM ID** *072 †20

MANLEY, Donelson Reeve. 100 E LANCASTER AVE, STE 314 19096 #004-01-1959 L1966 **OPH** *020 †35

MANN, Barry David. 100 E LANCASTER AVE, 275 LANKENAU MEDICAL SCIEN 19096 #041-01-1975 L1993 **GS** *020 †85

MARGOLIES, Lucas Zahir. 100 E LANCASTER AVE, STE 161 19096 #041-13-1999 L2001 **N** *012 †75

MARGOLIS, Mitchell Lee. ■ 19096 #041-02-1977 L1978 **PUD** *020 †20

MARGOLIS, Richard Craig. ■ 19096 #308-03-1986 L1989 **CHP** *020 †75

MARJON, Philip Louis. 100 E LANCASTER AVE, LANKENAU HOSPITAL 19096 #034-01-2007 L2007 **IM** *012

MARKS, Gerald. 100 E LANCASTER AVE, 330 LANKENAU MOB W 19096 #041-02-1949 L1951 **CRS** *071 †85,10

MARKS, John H. 100 E LANCASTER AVE, MOB WEST 330 19096 #041-02-1989 L1991 **CRS** *020 †85,10

MARKSON, Victor I. 1001 CITY AVE 19096 #018-03-1937 L1938 **CD IM** *071

MARLINO, Teresa Adele. 100 E LANCASTER AVE, STE 458 MOB EAST 19096 #041-02-1996 L1999 **OBG** *020 †30

MARTIN, George L. 100 E LANCASTER AVE # 237, LANKENAU MED BLDG 19096 #016-42-1975 L1977 **A PUD** *020 †20,03 ‡

MATHEW, Seema. 100 E LANCASTER AVE 19096 #693-02-2003 L2005 **OBG** *012

MATHEWS, Robert John. 100 E LANCASTER AVE, LANKENAU HOSPITAL 19096 #308-13-2003 L2005 **IM** *012

MATHUR, Tarun. 100 E LANCASTER AVE, MOB EAST, STE 558 19096 #041-02-2002 L2005 **CD** *012 †20

MATOTH, Israel. ■ 19096 #550-01-1983 L1994 **CHN** *020

MAUS, Douglas Charles. ■ 19096 #041-01-2001 L2001 **N** *100

MAUS, Marcela Valderrama. ■ 19096 #041-01-2005 L2006 **IM** *012

MC BREARTY, Francis X, Jr. 100 E LANCASTER AVE 19096 #041-02-1971 L1972 **PTH IM** *100 †20,50

MC CONNELL, Edward L, Jr. ■ 19096 #041-02-1944 L1945 **OBG** *071 †30

MC GEEHIN, Frank C, III. 100 E LANCASTER AVE, 356 LANKENAU MEDICAL BLDG 19096 #041-13-1980 L1981 **CD IM** *020 †20

MCKAY, George Robert. 100 E LANCASTER AVE, DEPT OF MEDICAL EDUCATION 19096 #041-77-2005, ▲ L2005 **IM** *012

MCMAHON, Maureen. 100 E LANCASTER AVE, OFC 436 19096 #041-07-1995 L1997 **PD** *020 †55

MEGERIAN, Raffi G. 100 E LANCASTER AVE, 467 LANKENAU MOB, EAST 19096 #041-15-1999 L2001 **IMG IM** *020 †20

MERIN, Robert Gillespie. ■ 19096 #035-20-1958 L1981 **AN** *071 †05

MEYER, Thomas James. 100 E LANCASTER AVE, LANKENAU MED BLDG W SUITE 19096 #041-02-1986 L1993 **PUD IM** *020 †20

MEZEY, Alan Lowell. 100 E LANCASTER AVE, STE 39 19096 #041-02-1989 L1991 **IM** *020 †20

MICHAELSON, Janet M. 100 E LANCASTER AVE # 400 19096 #041-01-1976 L1978 **PD** *020 †55 ‡

MIDDLEMAN, Dori H. 300 E LANCASTER AVE, WYNNEWOOD HOUSE STE 306B 19096 #041-13-1987 L1988 **P CHP** *020 †75

MINIMO, Corrado. 100 E LANCASTER AVE, MAIN LINE PATHOLOGY 19096 #561-23-1986 L1998 **SP PTH** *020 †50

MIROSHNICHENKO, Gennady. 100 E LANCASTER AVE # 301, DEPT OF OB/GYN 19096 #913-95-1994 L2005 **OBG** *012

MOE, Kyaw. 100 E LANCASTER AVE, LANKENAU HOSPITAL 19096 #209-01-1996 L2003 **IM** *020 †20

MOHAMMED, Ilyas Khan. 100 E LANCASTER AVE, LANKENAU HOSPITAL 19096 #495-21-2002 L2006 **IM** *012

MOHAMMED, Khaja Salahuddi. 100 E LANCASTER AVE, LANKENAU HOSP 19096 #495-21-2001 L2006 **IM** *012

MONFERRE, Adriana Thelma. 100 E LANCASTER AVE, LANKENAU HOSPITAL, 3 WEST 19096 #041-13-1994 L1996 **IM** *020 †20

MONTGOMERY, De Witt H, Jr. 100 E LANCASTER AVE, CITY LINE 19096 #041-01-1953 L1954 **PYA P** *020 ‡

MOON, Hye Won. ■ 19096 #583-19-1990 L2005 **P** *100

MORRIS, James Andrew. 300 E LANCASTER AVE 19096 #041-13-1976 L1977 **IM** *020 †20

MOVSOWITZ, Colin Milton. 100 E LANCASTER AVE, STE 414 19096 #836-02-1985 L1992 **ICE CD** *020 †20

MURRAY, Gambrill Breton. 100 E LANCASTER AVE, LANKENAU MED BLDG STE 140 19096 #041-02-1995 L1997 **IM** *020 †20

MUSCO, Simone. 100 E LANCASTER AVE, THE LANKENAU HOSPITAL 19096 #561-04-1995 L2001 **ICE** *012

MYERS, Sage Renee. ■ 19096 #024-16-2003 L2007 **PEM** *012 †55

NAIDE, David. 100 E LANCASTER AVE, 356 LANKENAU MED BLDG E 19096 #041-09-1960 L1961 **CD IM** *072

NANSTEEL, John Frederich. 300 E LANCASTER AVE 19096 #041-02-1975 L1976 **IM** *020 †20 ‡

NARAYANASWAMY, Girija. ■ 19096 #495-16-1993 L2001 **IM** *020

NARAYANASWAMY, Srinivasa. 100 E LANCASTER AVE 19096 #495-09-1996 L2005 **IM** *012

NASR, Daniel Mark. 100 E LANCASTER AVE, LANKENAU HOSPITAL 19096 #041-02-2004 L2004 **AN** *012

NEDELCOVICIU, Radu Alexan. 100 E LANCASTER AVE, LANKENAU HOSPITAL 19096 #781-04-2001 L2007 **GS** *012

NELSON, Gandhi A Dixon. ■ 19096 #220-01-1956 L1974 **OBG** *071 †30

NELSON, Pathmathevy. ■ 19096 #220-01-1956 L1976 **PTH** *071 †50

NEMEC, Jacqueline Eve. ■ 19096 #041-07-1963 L1964 **PYG** *071 †75

NOGAMI, Suzanne Sakaye. 100 E LANCASTER AVE, LANKENAU HOSPITAL 19096 #041-02-2006 L2006 **OBG** *012

NOONE, Robert Barrett, Jr. 100 E LANCASTER AVE, STE 275 19096 #041-01-1993 L1997 **CRS** *020 †85,10

NORTHRUP, Bruce Edgar. ■ 19096 #038-40-1965 L1974 **NS** *020 †25

NTAMBI, James Alfred. 100 E LANCASTER AVE, ANNENBERG CONF CTR. - G10 19096 #023-07-2006 L2006 **IM** *012

O'CONNOR, Colleen E. 100 E LANCASTER AVE, 3 PEW 19096 #024-07-2002 L2005 **IM** *100

ODABASHIAN, Arthur. ■ 19096 #517-01-1961 L1965 **PD** *071

O'DONNELL, Ward John. 100 E LANCASTER AVE, CLINIC D 19096 #041-02-1988 L1991 **IM** *020 †20

O'HARA, Julie Ann. 100 E LANCASTER AVE, ANNENBERG CONF CTR - G10 19096 #041-15-2006 L2006 **IM** *012

OLSON, Timothy Steven. ■ 19096 #051-01-2006 L2006 **PD** *012

ORFANIDIS, Nicholas Thoma. ■ 19096 #041-13-2005 L2005 **IM** *012

ORLIN, Anton. ■ 19096 #041-01-2006 L2006 **OPH** *012

PAHLAJANI, Niraj Hiro. 100 E LANCASTER AVE, LANKENAU HOSPITAL 19096 #033-06-2004 L2004 **RO** *012

PARISH, Daniel Howard. ■ 19096 #041-02-2007 L2007 *012

PARK, John J. 100 E LANCASTER AVE, MOB W STE 233 19096 #041-02-1994 L1996 **APM** *020 †05

PASCUA, Monina Farrah. ■ 19096 #041-15-2003 L2003 **GE** *012 †20

PATCHEFSKY, David Stuart. 100 E LANCASTER AVE, MAIN LINE EMERGENCY 19096 #041-02-1997 L1999 **EM** *020 †16

PATEL, Rajiv Arvind. 100 E LANCASTER AVE, MEDICAL OFFICE BLDG EAST 19096 #017-20-1996 L2000 **CD IM** *020 †20

PAULETTO, Ferrel Jo. 100 E LANCASTER AVE, STE 558 19096 #055-01-1966 L1970 **CD IM** *071 †20

PEDEN, Margaret Marie. 100 E LANCASTER AVE, #461 MED BLDG EAST 19096 #051-07-1992 L1994 **OBG** *072 †30

PEMBERTON, Clifford H. 100 E LANCASTER AVE, STE B20 19096 #041-02-1978 L1980 **HO** *020 †20

PETERSON, Amy L H. ■ 19096 #056-05-2004 L2007 **PDC** *012 †55

PETERSON, Donald Duane. 100 E LANCASTER AVE, STE 230 19096 #024-01-1975 L1976 **PUD SME** *020 †20

PFEFFER, William Harry. 100 E LANCASTER AVE, EAST SUITE 563 19096 #041-01-1974 L1975 **REN GYN** *020 †30 ‡

PHIAMBOLIS, Thomas Paul. 100 E LANCASTER AVE, STE 375 19096 #041-02-1979 L1980 **CD IM** *020 †20

PHILLIPS, Russell Evan. 100 E LANCASTER AVE, 31 LANKENAU MEDICAL BLDG W 19096 #038-06-1973 L1974 **P** *020 †75

PICKERING, J Edward. 100 E LANCASTER AVE # 316 19096 #019-02-1958 L1963 **IM CD** *020 †20 ‡

PINNAMANENI, Sridhar. 100 E LANCASTER AVE, LANKENAU HOSPITAL 19096 #495-50-1991 L2003 **PM** *100

PISKORSKI, Leonard. 100 E LANCASTER AVE, OFFICE OF MED EDUCATION 19096 #042-03-1991 L1992 **IM** *100

POHLEN, Judith Mary. ■ 19096 #671-02-1986 L2002 **NM** *100 †28

PORCELAN, Jane B. 100 E LANCASTER AVE, LANKENAU HOSPITAL, STE. 43 19096 #041-07-1983 L1985 **OBG** *030 †30

POSNER, Jerahme Seth. ■ 19096 #035-46-2001 L2004 **EM** *020 †16

PREHATNY, John Richard. ■ 19096 #041-02-1957 L1958 **GS OS** *071 †85

PRESS, Arthur Jos. LANKENAU HOSPITAL 19096 #024-07-1964 L1969 **DR** *071 †80

PROMISLOFF, Robert A. 1001 CITY LINE AVE, WB113 19096 #041-77-1973, ▲ L1974 **PCC IM** *020 †20

PULLMAN-MOOAR, Sally W. 100 E LANCASTER AVE, STE 418 19096 #038-41-1980 L1982 **RHU IM** *020 †20

PYM, John. 100 E LANCASTER AVE 19096 #143-01-1972 L1999 **TS CD** *020 †20

QAYYUM, Imran. 100 E LANCASTER AVE 19096 #704-01-1987 L1996 **NPM** *020 †55 ‡

RADHAGOPALAN, Selvaratnam. 100 E LANCASTER AVE, STE 307 19096 #422-01-1993 L1998 **IM CD** *020 †20

RAFEEK, Hashmi. 100 E LANCASTER AVE 19096 #496-23-2003 L2006 **IM** *012

RAI, Jitha. 100 E LANCASTER AVE, 3 ROSENGARTEN BUILDING 19096 #495-37-2002 L2002 **GE** *012

RAMAKRISHNAN, Vidyasagar. 100 E LANCASTER AVE 19096 #495-42-1997 **GS** *012

RATHI, Sandeep. 100 E LANCASTER AVE, LANKENAU HOSPITAL 19096 #041-02-2004 L2004 **PM** *012

RED, Donald Eufford. 100 E LANCASTER AVE, LANKENDOU HOSPITAL 19096 #048-02-1959 L1959 **DR** *020 †80

REDFIELD, Robert Ray, III. ■ 19096 #023-01-2006 L2006 **GS** *012

RENBAUM, Leslie Sharon. 609 ARGYLE CIR, PENNSYLVANIA HOSPITAL 19096 #016-42-1996 L1998 **OBG** *020 †30

RENTSCHLER, Stacey Lynn. ■ 19096 #035-47-2004 L2004 **CD** *012 †20

RENZI, Paula Marie. 100 E LANCASTER AVE, ANNENBERG CONF CTR - G10 19096 #041-77-2007, ▲ L2007 **IM** *012

RIEKE, Matthew Blaine. ■ 19096 #041-01-1998 L2000 **IM** *071

RILEY, Catherine Anne. 100 E LANCASTER AVE, LANKENAU HOSPITAL 19096 #041-15-2003 L2003 **PCC** *012 †20

RINGPFEIL, Franziska. 339 E LANCASTER AVE, RINGPFEIL ADVANCED DERM 19096 #409-25-1994 L1999 **D** *020 †15

RITCHIE, Marianne T. LANKENAU MEDICAL BLDG EAST 19096 #041-02-1980 L1982 **GE IM** *020 †20

RITTERMAN, Richard Bruce. 100 E LANCASTER AVE 19096 #016-42-1981 L1984 **NPM** *020 †55

ROBINSON, Elizabeth Joy. 23 E WYNNEWOOD RD RE 19096 #035-08-1990 L1995 **PD** *020 †55

RODRIGUEZ, Ellana Jeanett. LANCASTER CITY LINE 19096 #308-13-2002 L2003 **DR** *012

RODRIGUEZ, Hugo Federico. 100 E LANCASTER AVE 19096 #308-01-1955 L1969 **R** *020 †80

RODRIGUEZ, Nicole Dionesi. 100 E LANCASTER AVE, LANKENAU HOSP DEPT SURG 19096 #308-13-2001 L2008 **GS** *012

ROLING, Daniel B. 259 E LANCASTER AVE 19096 #041-01-1997 L1999 **D** *020 †15 ‡

ROMANELLI, Jeanine Elena. 100 E LANCASTER AVE, STE 380 19096 #041-13-1997 L2001 **CD** *020 †20

ROMANOFF, David. 100 E LANCASTER AVE 19096 #035-46-1971 L1972 **IM IMG** *020 †20

ROSE, Elizabeth Kirk. ■ 19096 #041-01-1926 L1929 **PD GPM** *071 †55

ROSEMAN, Richard Lee. 1428 MANOA RD 19096 #041-13-1980 L1981 **IM** *020 †20

ROSS, Michael Jordan. ■ 19096 #035-47-1997 L1999 **FSM** *012 †16

ROTHMAN, Irwin. 1001 CITY AVE, # 1117 19096 #005-15-1962 L1975 **P N** *071

ROTHMAN, Steven Alan. 100 E LANCASTER AVE, STE 556 19096 #041-13-1988 L1991 **CD** *020 †20

RUBENSTEIN, David Lloyd. 100 E LANCASTER AVE, STE 650 19096 #041-13-1984 L1985 **OSM ORS** *020 †40

RUSHTON, Scott Allen. 100 E LANCASTER AVE, STE 250E 19096 #041-02-1993 L1995 **ORS** *020 †40

RUSSELL, William Randall. 100 E LANCASTER AVE, STE 275 19096 #041-02-1983 L1984 **GS CRS** *020 †85

RUTTER, William Albert. ■ 19096 #041-02-1957 L1958 **P** *040

RYAN, Linda Ann. ■ 19096 #045-01-1993 L2005 **P** *020 †75

SAIDI, Firas Fadhil Jaaz. 100 E LANCASTER AVE, STE 467 19096 #528-07-1994 L2003 **IM IMG** *020 †20

SAKET, Daniel David. ■ 19096 #008-01-2003 L2004 **DR** *012

SAMUELS, Louis Edward. 100 E LANCASTER AVE, STE 280 19096 #041-09-1987 L1989 **TS** *020 †85,90

SANCHEZ, Blanca Secades. ■ 19096 #275-01-1951 L1977 **PM** *071

SANCHEZ, Laura Elena. 261 TOMKENN RD 19096 #038-40-1987 L1991 **CHP** *020 †75

SANTORE, Louis Xavier. 100 E LANCASTER AVE, SUITE 36 MOB -WEST 19096 #041-13-1980 L1981 **OPH** *020

SANTORO, Jerome. 100 E LANCASTER AVE, 164 LANKENAU MED BLDG EAST 19096 #041-13-1972 L1973 **ID IM** *030 †20

SATINSKY, Jonathan David. 100 E LANCASTER AVE STE 39, LANKENAU MEDICAL BLDG 19096 #041-01-1967 L1968 **IM CD** *071 †20

SAVARD, Marie Ann. ■ 19096 #041-01-1976 L1978 **IM** *020 †20

SAWIN, Henry Scofield, Jr. 100 E LANCASTER AVE, STE 375 19096 #041-01-1971 L1972 **CD IM** *020 †20

SCHERMER, Cathie Melissa. 100 E LANCASTER AVE, LANKENAU HOSPITAL 19096 #041-13-2004 L2004 **GS** *012

SCHETMAN, William Robt. 100 E LANCASTER AVE, STE 330 19096 #041-02-1986 L1988 **IM** *020 †20

SCHILLING, John Francis. 100 E LANCASTER AVE, LANKENAU HOSP DEPT RAD 19096 #041-02-1981 L1983 **DR** *020 †80

SCHLEIFER, Charles Robt. 100 E LANCASTER AVE, STE 130 19096 #041-02-1970 L1971 **NEP IM** *020 †20

SCHNALL, Robert Ira. 100 E LANCASTER AVE 19096 #041-13-1982 L1983 **U** *020 †95

SCHULMAN, Elliott A. 100 E LANCASTER AVE, STE 452 MOB E 19096 #035-06-1974 L1979 **N** *020 †50

SCHWAB, Robert H. ■ 19096 #041-02-1957 L1958 **CD IM** *020 †20

SCOLNICK, Edward Mark. 811 WICKFIELD RD 19096 #024-01-1965 L1982 **OS IM** *020

SHAH, Sheetal Hemendra. 100 E LANCASTER AVE, ANNENBERG CONF CTR - G10 19096 #020-12-2007 L2007 **IM** *012

SHAHIN, Ammar Said. 100 E LANCASTER AVE, LANKENAU HOSPITAL 19096 #575-01-1999 L2005 **IM** *012

SHAIK, Zakir Husain. 100 E LANCASTER AVE, LANKENAU HOSPITAL 19096 #495-21-2000 L2007 **IM** *012

SHAPIRO, Timothy Alan. 100 E LANCASTER AVE # 380, MED SCI BLDG 19096 #008-01-1985 L1986 **CD** *020 †20

SHARE, Isaiah Anatole. 100 E LANCASTER AVE 19096 #016-11-1947 L1953 **P PYA** *020 †75 ‡

SHARMA, Anuradha. 100 E LANCASTER AVE, LANKENAU HOSPITAL, 3 SOUTH 19096 #495-03-1986 L1998 **IM** *020 †20

SHEIKH, Najmi Ishaque. ■ 19096 #209-01-1975 L1979 **PM** *020 †60

SHELANSKI, Sharon Lillian. 100 E LANCASTER AVE 19096 #041-07-1983 L1985 **AI IM** *020 †20

SHERWIN, Nancy Marie. 100 E LANCASTER AVE, THE LANKENAU HOSPITAL 19096 #041-09-1979 L1980 **NM DR** *020 †80,28

SHERWOOD, Jennifer Beth. 100 E LANCASTER AVE 19096 #035-48-1994 L1998 **U** *020 †95

SHYAMALAN, Nelliate C. ■ 19096 #495-53-1963 L1973 **IM CD** *071 †20

SIDDIQUI, Adnan Karim. 100 E LANCASTER AVE, STE 556 19096 #704-02-1993 L2002 **CD** *012 †20

SIEGFRIED, Jay Worth. 100 E LANCASTER AVE 19096 #038-41-1978 L1979 **PM** *020 †60

SIGLER, Miles Harold. 100 E LANCASTER AVE, STE 130 19096 #035-20-1955 L1957 **NEP IM** *071 †20 ‡

SILVER, Bruce Goodman. 300 E LANCASTER AVE 19096 #041-02-1974 L1975 **IM OS** *020 †20

SIMMONS, Barry Brent. ■ 19096 #041-02-2004 L2004 **FPG** *012 †18

SIRCA, Florica Cristina. ■ 19096 #781-04-1992 L2001 **IM** *100

SIRIPURAPU, Veeraiah. 100 E LANCASTER AVE 19096 #917-34-2000 L2004 **GS** *012

SLAVIN, Dorothy Ann. 100 E LANCASTER AVE, STE 164 19096 #041-07-1991 L1993 **ID IM** *020 †20

SLOANE, Manuel Harold. ■ 19096 #041-77-1951, ▲ L1959 **NM** *071 †28

SMALLS, Arlene Janice. 100 E LANCASTER AVE, AREA B15 19096 #035-01-1990 L2007 **OBG** *020 †30

SMINK, Robert Danl, Jr. 100 E LANCASTER AVE, 275 LANKENAU MSB 19096 #038-06-1966 L1971 **GS** *020 †85

SMITH, Amy Michelle. 100 E LANCASTER AVE, LANKENAU MOB W STE 135 19096 #010-01-2008 *012

SMITH, Bradford Davison. 33 LANKENAU MED BLDG W 19096 #041-12-1982 L1983 **OTO HNS** *020 †45

SMITH, Cynthia Dickinson. 100 E LANCASTER AVE, CLINIC D 19096 #035-01-1993 L2000 **IM** *020 †20

SMOLAR, Andrew Ian. 300 E LANCASTER AVE STE 20, WYNNEWOOD HOUSE 19096 #035-48-1987 L1992 **P** *020 †75

SNOOK, Mary Ellen. 100 E LANCASTER AVE, LANKENAU MEDICAL BLDG E S 19096 #033-05-1989 L1991 **PD** *020 †55

STACEY, William C. ■ 19096 #038-06-2002 L2006 **N** *100 †75

STEHLE, Norman Scott. 100 E LANCASTER AVE, STE 441 19096 #041-07-1988 L1990 **P** *020 †75

STEIN, Steven Harry. 307 VIOLET LN 19096 #836-01-1990 L1997 **HO** *020 †20

STEINBERG, Amanda Lee. ■ 19096 #035-46-1997 L2001 **IM** *020 †20

STRICKLAN, Daphne Griggs. 100 E LANCASTER AVE, 212 LANKENAU MOB SOUTH 19096 #041-09-1992 L1995 **IM** *020

SUKUMARAN, Nishanth. 100 E LANCASTER AVE, OFFICE OF MED EDU 19096 #495-63-1999 L2005 **IM** *012

SUPERDOCK, Keith Robt. 100 E LANCASTER AVE, STE 130 LMB WEST 19096 #041-02-1986 L1993 **NEP IM** *020 †20

SUTILLA, Constance B. 100 E LANCASTER AVE, RADIOLOGY DEPT LANKENAU HO 19096 #041-07-1988 L1994 **DR** *020 †80

SWAIN, Timothy Whitzel. 100 E LANCASTER AVE, LANKENAU HOSPITAL, DEPT. O 19096 #016-11-1999 L2000 **TS** *020

TAKIEDDINE, Nadia. 100 E LANCASTER AVE, LANKENAU HOSPITAL 19096 #875-01-1998 L2006 **IM** *012

TAYLOR, Marcia Robin. 1213 WEYMOUTH RD 19096 #008-01-1980 L1982 **D** *020 †15

TEEHAN, Brendan Patrick. 100 E LANCASTER AVE # 130, LANKENAU MED BLDG 19096 #033-05-1963 L1970 **NEP IM** *071 †20

TENG, Jinnwien. 23 E WYNNEWOOD RD 19096 #008-02-2002 L2002 **PD** *020 †55

TENNEKOON, Gihan I. 420 BOLSOVER RD 19096 #917-23-1964 L1995 **N OS** *050 †75

THIRUMARAN, Rajesh Prem A. 100 E LANCASTER AVE, STE 30 19096 #495-94-1994 L2001 **HO** *012 †20

TING, Rosalind Yi-Ming. ■ 19096 #242-16-1945 L1968 **PD OS** *072

TOMASELLO, Donald N. 100 E LANCASTER AVE 19096 #041-02-1969 L1977 **TS** *020 †85,90

TOPJIAN, Alexis Ann. ■ 19096 #035-01-2001 L2001 **CCP** *100 †55

TRAN, Khoa Quang. 100 E LANCASTER AVE, STE 114 19096 #035-09-1999 L2002 **IM** *020 †20

TUBB, Benjamin Edward. ■ 19096 #048-04-2002 L2007 **DR** *100 †80

TULLY, John Owen. 100 E LANCASTER AVE, LANKENAU HOSPITAL 19096 #041-02-2005 L2005 **IM** *012

UMRUDDIN, Zia Mohamed. 100 E LANCASTER AVE, LANKENAU HOSPITAL 19096 #496-39-1996 L2003 **NEP** *012 †20

URIBE, Alexander. 100 E LANCASTER AVE, STE 275MSB 19096 #264-04-1978 L1979 **VS GS** *020 †85

USATCH, Ben Robert. 100 E LANCASTER AVE, MAIN LINE EMERGENCY 19096 #041-02-1998 L2000 **EM** *020 †16

VAGANOS, Steve A. 100 E LANCASTER AVE, STE 414 19096 #041-07-1983 L1984 **CD IC** *020 †20 ‡

VALSDOTTIR, Elsa Bjork. 100 E LANCASTER AVE, LANKENAU HOSPITAL 19096 #484-01-1997 L2007 **GS** *020 †85

VAN UITERT, Bonnie Lynn. 205 OLD FOREST RD 19096 #041-02-1977 L1979 **ID IM** *020 †20

VAUGHN, Beverly Marie. 100 E LANCASTER AVE, STE 353E 19096 #041-13-1978 L1980 **GYN** *020 †30

VEET, Laure Lynn. 1715 POWDER MILL LN 19096 #041-13-1993 L1995 **IM** *020 †20

VEKSLER, Ekaterina Sosil. ■ 19096 #041-02-2001 L2001 **AN** *100 †05

VIGG, Avanti. 100 E LANCASTER AVE, OFFICE OF MED EDUCATION 19096 #496-27-2003 L2006 *100

VILLARS, Jean Frederick. 100 E LANCASTER AVE 19096 #024-01-1980 L1982 **P** *020 †85,90,75

VOLKMAN, Edward A. ■ 19096 #010-03-1968 L1974 **P** *020 †75

VOMMI, Srinivas. 100 E LANCASTER AVE, LANKENAU HOSPITAL 19096 #495-58-1997 L2005 **IM** *012

VROMAN, Craig Richard. 100 E LANCASTER AVE, MOB EAST, STE 256 19096 #041-13-2003 L2004 **OPH** *100

WALLACE, Elizabeth Anne. ■ 19096 #671-02-1986 L1999 **IM END** *020 †20

WANG, Alvin N. ■ 19096 #041-77-2007, ▲ L2007 **EM** *012

WANG, Chunyang. ■ 19096 #243-44-1993 L2003 **CN** *012

WATSON, Barbara May. 215 OLD GULPH RD 19096 #836-02-1974 L1984 **OS PD** *020 †20

WEINBERG, Carroll Arnold. ■ 19096 #051-01-1955 L1962 **P PYA** *072 †75

WEINSTEIN, Donald Stanley. ■ 19096 #041-13-1970 L1971 **DR** *020 †80

WEISER, Madeleine. 23 E WYNNEWOOD RD RR 19096 #041-07-1978 L1980 **PD** *020 †55

WEISS, David. ■ 19096 #024-05-1987 L1995 **P** *020 †75

WEISS, Jordan Barry. ■ 19096 #035-19-1963 L1971 **GE IM** *071 †20

WEISS, Rochelle Rudolph. 259 E LANCASTER AVE 19096 #041-01-1993 L1995 **D** *020 †15

WEISS, Theodore. LANKENAU MED BLDG 19096 #038-06-1966 L1973 **P CD** *020 †75 ‡

WELLER, Gregory Eugene. ■ 19096 #041-12-2005 L2005 **AN** *012

WESLEY, Carl Christopher. 100 E LANCASTER AVE, ANNENBERG CONF CTR - G10 19096 #041-02-2005 L2006 **AN** *012

WILKES, Adam Lewis. 100 E LANCASTER AVE, MAIN LINE EMERGENCY 19096 #041-02-1991 L1994 **IM** *020 †20

WILLIAMS, Edward Shepard. 100 E LANCASTER AVE, STE 451 19096 #041-02-1975 L1976 **IM** *020

WOFSEY, Alan Ross. 100 E LANCASTER AVE RM 5, LANKENAU MED BLDG EAST 19096 #023-07-1972 L1972 **P** *020 †75

WOLF, Laurence Rand. 100 E LANCASTER AVE, STE 650 19096 #024-01-1983 L1989 **ORS** *020 †40

WOLFSTEIN, Judith. ■ 19096 #550-02-1990 L1997 **RNR** *020 †80

WRIGLEY, Michael Sterling. 100 E LANCASTER AVE, 317 LANKENAU MEDICAL OFFIC 19096 #041-02-1973 L1974 **OM IM** *020 †20,70 ‡

XU, Yanping. ■ 19096 #243-47-1986 **IM** *100

YALAMANCHI, Lakshmana Rao. 100 E LANCASTER AVE, LANKENAU HOSPITAL 19096 #495-58-1988 L2003 **IM** *100 †20

YAN, Ganxin. 100 E LANCASTER AVE, STE 556 19096 #243-65-1983 L2000 **ICE** *020 †20

YIH, Donald Franklyn. 100 E LANCASTER AVE, 356 LANKENAU MEDICAL BLDG 19096 #040-02-1979 L1981 **CD IM** *020 †20

YOUCHA, Sharon Hilda. 331 PENN RD 19096 #008-01-1984 L1986 **P** *020 †30 ‡

ZEGER, Erik Leroy. 100 E LANCASTER AVE, MAIN LINE ONCOLOGY HEMATOL 19096 #041-15-1999 L2005 **HO** *020 †20

ZELOUF, David Steven. 100 E LANCASTER AVE, STE 650 19096 #035-46-1987 L1997 **HS** *020 †40

ZEMBA-PALKO, Vlasta. 100 E LANCASTER AVE, MAIN LINE PATHOLOGY 19096 #957-01-1980 L1991 **PTH** *020 †80

ZERVOS, Denis G. ■ 19096 #418-01-1942 L1958 **R NM** *071 †80

ZGONIS, Miltiadis Holger. ■ 19096 #035-03-2004 L2006 **ORS** *012

ZILBERBERG, Tatiana S. LANKENAU HOSP DEPT PTH 19096 #913-35-1983 L2001 **HMP** *020

ZISKIND, Michele J. 100 E LANCASTER AVE, STE 456 19096 #051-04-1979 L1980 **D** *020 †15

WYOMING – LUZERNE

AMBRUSO, Victor Thos. 1523 W 8TH ST 18644 #041-09-1967 L1968 **NS** *071 †25

COAR, George Robt. 155 WYOMING AVE 18644 #041-02-1981 L1982 **OPH** *020 †35

■ = Address Information Privacy Protected

FERRARO, Michael Mark. 19 COLONIAL CT 18644 #041-09-1978 L1982 **GYN** *020 †30
KONECKE, Melita M. ■ 18644 #041-09-1981 L1983 **FM** *020 †18
KONECKE, Ron J. 26 HIGHWOODS RD 18644 #041-09-1979 L1983 **DR VIR** *020 †80
KRUGER, Erik Forrest. 155 WYOMING AVE 18644 #016-42-1995 L2003 **OPH** *020 †35
LANGE, Eva. ■ 18644 #759-03-1968 L1983 **IM END** *020 †20
MACAREO, Louis Robert. ■ 18644 #021-01-1999 L2001 **GS** *020
MCGRAW, Joseph Patrick. 155 WYOMING AVE 18644 #041-13-1991 L1999 **OPH** *020 †35 ‡
MODARES, Fariba. 389 WYOMING AVE 18644 #517-01-1989 L1997 **PUD** *020 †20
MORRISON, Joseph Francis. 155 WYOMING AVE 18644 #041-13-1975 L1976 **OPH** *020 †35
PUGLIESE, Joseph Francis. ■ 18644 #010-02-1954 L1955 **OPH** *071 †35
REISER, Harvey James. 155 WYOMING AVE 18644 #036-07-1985 L1987 **OPH** *020 †35
SAVAGE, Donald Jos. 155 WYOMING AVE 18644 #041-02-1977 L1982 **OPH** *020 †35
SCROBOLA, Charles Cooney. ■ 18644 #041-02-1957 L1958 **GP** *020
SCROBOLA, Charles J. 638 WYOMING AVE 18644 #422-01-1984 L1985 **GE IM** *020 †20 ‡
SHARKEY, Thomas George. 155 WYOMING AVE 18644 #041-02-1977 L1978 **OPH** *020 †35
SZULBORSKI, Robert George. 155 WYOMING AVE 18644 #041-01-1988 L1992 **OPH** *020 †35

WYOMISSING – BERKS

AHMED, Saeeduddin. ■ 19610 #005-14-1988 L1989 **P** *020 †75
AITA, Paul Chas. ■ 19610 #041-09-1966 L1967 **GS VS** *020 †85
ALLEN, David Walton. ■ 19610 #020-02-1948 L1985 **P PYA** *071 †75
ALWEIS, Richard L. 1991 STATE HILL RD #043-01-1999 L2007 **IM** *020 †20
ANDERSON, John Bethune. 1340 PENN AVE 19610 #041-02-1969 L1970 **OBG** *071 †30
ANZALONE, Salvatore. 2240 RIDGEWOOD RD, STE 100 19610 #011-03-1986 L1988 **PD** *020 †55
ATWELL, Margaret S. ■ 19610 #041-01-1986 L1987 **IM OM** *020 †20
AVEDISSIAN, Michael Gober. 1320 BROADCASTING RD 19610 #041-02-1982 L1983 **CD** *020 †20
BANCO, Stephen Patrick. 1270 BROADCASTING RD 19610 #041-02-1996 L1998 **ORS** *020 †40
BANDALA, Leonard Chester. 2752 CENTURY BLVD, SURGICAL INSTITUTE OF READ 19610 #016-11-1984 L1991 **AN PME** *020 †05 ‡
BARBERA, Charles F. 1508 MEADOWLARK RD 19610 #041-13-1993 L1995 **EM** *020 †16
BARRETT, James Philip. 1235 PENN AVE STE 302, CTR FOR PAIN CONTR PC 19610 #035-03-1970 L1971 **AN PME** *020 †05 ‡
BARRY, Jonathan Edward. 1235 PENN AVE, STE 302 19610 #016-06-2000 L2004 **APM** *020 †05
BEEM, John William. 1 GRANITE POINT DR 19610 #041-13-1962 L1963 **OPH** *071 †35
BEETEL, Thomas Charles. 2603 KAISER BLVD STE 104 19610 #041-02-1997 L2002 **GS AS** *020 †85
BERNE, Cheryl Ann. ■ 19610 #041-14-1989 L1994 **BBK** *020 †50
BIALAS, Henry Norman. ■ 19610 #041-13-1957 L1958 **GP** *071 ‡
BRAUN, Maria Antonia. 931 PENN AVE, FAM MED ASSOC OF WYMSNG 19610 #847-01-1986 L1991 **FM** *020 †18
BROWN, Linda Eileen. 2 MERIDIAN BLVD 19610 #041-07-1979 L1984 **NEP IM** *020 †20
BUNDY, Jason Thomas. 1235 PENN AVE, STE 302 19610 #036-01-2002 L2002 **PMM** *012
BURKE, Joseph William. 45 BUCKINGHAM DR 19610 #041-13-1994 L1997 **DR** *020 †80
BURNS, Donald Thos. 1500 PENN AVE 19610 #041-01-1957 L1963 **OPH** *071 †35
CALDER, Peter David. 1802 PAPERMILL RD 19610 #041-14-1986 L1990 **OPH** *020 †35 ‡
CANNER, Gary Chas. 2201 RIDGEWOOD RD 19610 #043-01-1977 L1979 **ORS** *020 †40
CARIM, Moiz Mohamed. 2630 WESTVIEW DR, CARIM EYE AND RETINA CTR 19610 #041-07-2001 L2007 **OPH** *020 †35
CARLSON, Lynn Barbara. 1340 PENN AVE 19610 #041-07-1981 L1984 **OBG OCC** *020 †30
CEFARATTI, Michael D. 2630 WESTVIEW DR, CARIM EYE AND RETINA CTR 19610 #041-02-1962 L1963 **OPH** *020 †35
COHN, C Harold. ■ 19610 #041-02-1948 L1949 **TS CD** *071 †85,90
DATLOF, Steven Barry. 999 BERKSHIRE BLVD, STE 130 19610 #035-45-1983 L1984 **P** *020 †75
DE GUZMAN, Franklin D. 1200 BROADCASTING RD, STE 200 19610 #748-10-1978 L1994 **P** *020
DEIBERT, David Clayton. 560 VAN REED RD STE 304 19610 #041-13-1974 L1981 **END IM** *020 †20
DIETRICH, Patricia Diane. ■ 19610 #041-07-1974 L1983 **FM** *020 †18
DI RENZO, Dennis Peter. 40 BERKSHIRE CT 19610 #041-14-1980 L1983 **PD** *020 †55
DONATO, Anthony A, Jr. 1991 STATE HILL RD 19610 #041-12-1994 L1996 **IM** *020 †20
DRIBEN, Jeffrey Scott. 985 BERKSHIRE BLVD, STE 101 19610 #041-02-1991 L1999 **OTO GS** *020 †45
EHRLICH, Irving. 1330 PENN AVE 19610 #041-09-1974 L1975 **DR OS** *020 †80
EICHER, Geary M, Jr. ■ 19610 #041-12-1954 L1955 **PTH FOP** *071 †50
ELLENBERGER, Pamela Marie. 50 COMMERCE DR, BERKS PLASTIC SURGERY 19610 #041-14-1985 L1993 **PS** *020 †65
EMKEY, Ronald Danl. 1235 PENN AVE, STE 305 19610 #041-09-1965 L1966 **RHU IM** *020 †20
EZARD, Rebecca R. 2240 RIDGEWOOD RD, STE 100 19610 #041-14-1989 L1992 **PD** *020 †55
FEINBERG, Stanford Saml. 2 MERIDIAN BLVD 19610 #041-07-1979 L1984 **N SME** *020 †20,75
FLEISCHER, Alan Neil. 1075 BERKSHIRE BLVD, STE 900 19610 #748-08-1977 L1983 **U** *020 †95
FRANK, Laura Beth. ■ 19610 #041-02-1999 L2001 **EM** *020 †16
GABRIEL, Beverley E. 1991 STATE HILL RD, READING HOSPITAL CENTER FO 19610 #033-05-1994 L2001 **IMG** *020 †20
GALLAGHER, Francis John. 1235 PENN AVE, STE 305 19610 #041-15-2000 L2001 **RHU** *100 †20
GERHART, George Roy. ■ 19610 #041-02-1958 L1959 **FM OM** *071 †18
GHANTA, Ravi Kishan. 2230 RIDGEWOOD RD, STE 100 19610 #038-44-1999 L2006 **GE** *020 †20
GILFILLAN, Andrew Geo, III. 2240 RIDGEWOOD RD STE 100 19610 #041-13-1965 L1966 **PD** *071 †55
GOLDMAN, Alla. ■ 19610 #913-09-1984 L1995 **FM** *020 †18
GORDON, Michael Ephraim. ■ 19610 #041-13-1969 L1970 **R** *071 †80
GREGOR, Richard John. 2603 KAISER BLVD, 1ST FL 19610 #041-13-1991 L1995 **DR** *020 †80
GRUBER, John W. ■ 19610 #041-01-1960 L1961 **CD IM** *071 †20
GUAY, Robert C. 1848 READING BLVD 19610 #011-04-1984 L1991 **OS R** *020 †80
HARRIS, Constantine F. 1320 BROADCASTING RD, STE 200 19610 #041-01-1999 L2001 **U** *020 †95
HASSON, Dawn Marie. 1340 PENN AVE 19610 #041-07-1995 L1999 **OBG** *020 †30
HEFFERNAN, John Michael. 950 N WYOMISSING BLVD, BERKSHIRE HEIGHTS 19610 #010-01-1980 L1983 **IM AS** *020 †20
HELINEK, Thomas Gerard. 2603 KAISER BLVD, 1ST FL 19610 #041-02-1985 L1986 **DR** *020 †80

HENRY, John Martin. 1320 BROADCASTING RD, STE 200 19610 #023-07-1988 L1991 **U** *020 †95
HESKETT, Bret Earl. ■ 19610 #019-02-2007 L2007 **OBG** *012
HILDRETH, Eugene A, Jr. ■ 19610 #051-01-1947 L1954 **IM NEP** *071 †20,03
HO, John Jen-Yeang. 999 BERKSHIRE BLVD, STE 130 19610 #051-01-1984 L1985 **P** *020 †75
HOFFMAN, David Althouse. 1330 PENN AVE 19610 #041-01-1957 L1958 **GYN OS** *071 †30
HORAN, Jennifer Lawrence. 40 BERKSHIRE CT, READING PEDIATRICS INC 19610 #032-01-1990 L1994 **PD** *020 †55
HSU, Tsung Hua. 1235 PENN AVE, STE 302 19610 #012-01-2002 L2007 **APM** *020 †05
HUBBARD, Raymond Jos. 40 BERKSHIRE CT, READING PEDIATRICS INC 19610 #010-02-1985 L1988 **PD** *020 †55
IZZO, Domenic C, Jr. 1802 PAPERMILL RD 19610 #041-09-1982 L1983 **OPH** *020 †35 ‡
KALIYADAN, Antony George. ■ 19610 #041-02-2007 L2007 **IM** *012
KELLY, Johanna. 40 BERKSHIRE CT 19610 #034-01-1992 L1997 **PD** *020 †55
KOHL, Thomas David, Jr. 867 BERKSHIRE BLVD, STE 100 19610 #041-14-1996 L1998 **FSM** *020 †18
KROL, Ronald Casimir. 2608 KAISER BLVD 19610 #041-14-1980 L1984 **PUD CCM** *020 †20
KU, James. 2603 KAISER BLVD, STE 104 19610 #041-02-1992 L1995 **GS CCS** *040 †85
KURUVILLA, Supriya. ■ 19610 #495-28-1996 L2007 **PP** *100 †50
LABENSKI, James Peter. ■ 19610 #041-13-1984 L1985 **IM** *020 †20
LEE, Jung Sin. 1320 BROADCASTING RD, STE 200 19610 #583-02-1976 L1985 **ON IM** *050
LEE, Jung-Pil. 1320 BROADCASTING RD, STE 200 19610 #583-02-1964 L1972 **U** *020 †95
LEONI, Joseph Vincent. 1320 BROADCASTING RD, STE 200 19610 #041-01-1969 L1970 **U** *020 †95
LEWIS, Elaine Renee. 2603 KAISER BLVD, 1ST FL 19610 #041-07-1984 L1985 **R** *020 †80
LICATA, Anthony. 1320 BROADCASTING RD 19610 #035-01-1997 L2000 **CD** *020 †20
LUECKE, Gail Anne. 2603 KAISER BLVD, 1ST FL 19610 #028-02-1983 L1985 **DR** *020 †80
LUTZ, Charles Kevin. 985 BERKSHIRE BLVD, STE 101 19610 #024-05-1984 L1986 **OTO HNS** *020 †45
MAIORANA, Salvatore L. ■ 19610 #041-13-1953 L1954 **OBG** *071 †30
MALSTROM, Michael Alan. 1 GRANITE POINT DR, STE 100 19610 #041-13-2004 L2004 **OPH** *012
MARCUS, Jerome I. PO BOX 6467 19610 #041-13-1975 L1976 **CLP** *071 †50
MARIGLIO, Joseph A. 2608 KAISER BLVD 19610 #030-06-1978 L1983 **PUD CCM** *020 †20
MARR, Paul James. 1235 PENN AVE, STE 102 19610 #033-05-1998 L2000 **FSM** *020 †18
MC BRYAN, Donald John, Jr. 950 N WYOMISSING BLVD 19610 #041-09-1994 L1996 **IM** *020 †20
MENGEL, Roger Grant. ■ 19610 #035-15-1968 L1974 **PUD IM** *071 †20
MENON, Sanand R. 40 BERKSHIRE CT, READING PEDIATRICS 19610 #035-09-1996 L2000 **PD** *020 †55
MERCURIO, Teresa Marie. ■ 19610 #020-02-1973 L1974 **PLM ON** *020 †20
MIGLIARINO, Luciano. 1424 PENN AVE 19610 #041-13-1993 L1995 **FM** *020 †18
MILLAN, Liz P. ■ 19610 #048-16-2006 L2006 **OBG** *012
MILLER, Jay Blaine. 1320 BROADCASTING RD, STE 200 19610 #035-20-1974 L1980 **U** *020 †95
MINTZ, Paul Sander. 200 READING BLVD, 200 READING BLVD 19610 #056-06-1982 L1983 **AN CCM** *020 †05
MITNICK, Paul David. 625 SPRING ST 19610 #035-20-1974 L1975 **NEP CCM** *020 †20
MORRISSEY, E James, Jr. 1121 PENN AVE 19610 #041-09-1957 L1965 **ORS** *071 †40
MOYER, Carey Anne. ■ 19610 #041-14-1998 L2001 **IC** *020 †20
MUALLEM, Nabil Salim. 1330 PENN AVE 19610 #748-01-1980 L1983 **OBG** *020 †30
MUHLENBERG, John Peter G. 1125 BERKSHIRE BLVD, STE 100 19610 #041-01-1954 L1955 **PD** *071 †55
MUIR, Robert Warren. 1629 W THISTLE DR 19610 #041-01-1960 L1962 **GS CD** *020 †85
NAGY, Robert. 560 VAN REED RD STE 302 19610 #041-01-1974 L1978 **D** *020 †15
NELSON, Robert Eugene. 2201 RIDGEWOOD RD, STE 400 19610 #036-07-1997 L2003 **P** *020 †75
NORD, D Scott. 2201 RIDGEWOOD RD 19610 #041-01-1982 L1983 **ORS** *020 †40
OLOWOLAFE, Yinka Adenike. 513 VAN REED RD 19610 #041-12-2001 L2004 **PD** *020
O'NEILL-RICE, Elizabeth A. 2603 KAISER BLVD, 1ST FL 19610 #041-09-1977 L1983 **DR EM** *020 †80
OPLINGER, Michele S. 2603 KAISER BLVD, 1ST FL 19610 #041-13-1991 L1995 **DR** *020 †80
O'ROURKE, David Brian. 560 VAN REED RD STE 306 19610 #041-09-1983 L1984 **FM** *020 †18
ORQUIZA, Clodualdo S, Jr. 1320 BROADCASTING RD, STE 200 19610 #748-02-1957 L1966 **U** *020 †95
PAN, Edward Ledesma. 2025 HALE CT 19610 #748-08-1967 L1971 **ORS** *020
PAOLINI, Mauro John. 2240 RIDGEWOOD RD, STE 100 19610 #041-01-1960 L1961 **PD** *071 †55
PATTILLO, Beverly Alison. 1991 STATE HILL RD, RPS PHYSICAL MEDICINE 19610 #035-09-1989 L1993 **PM** *020 †60
PATTILLO, Robert William. 1320 BROADCASTING RD 19610 #024-05-1988 L1993 **CD IM** *020 †20
PELLECCHIA, Dennis John. 2603 KAISER BLVD, SPRING RIDGE/3RD FLOOR 19610 #041-13-1984 L1986 **AN** *020 †05
REED, Tiffany Linn. ■ 19610 #041-77-2006, ▲ L2006 **IM** *012
REEDY, Brian Keith. 50 COMMERCE DR, BERKS PLASTIC SURG 19610 #041-01-1991 L1994 **PS OS** *020 †65
REIFSNYDER, William H, III. 2000 CAMBRIDGE AVE 19610 #041-02-1951 L1952 **IMG CD** *071 †20
REUBEN, Mark Steven. 40 BERKSHIRE CT, READING PEDIATRICS INC 19610 #041-02-1973 L1974 **PD** *020 †55
REYES-GARZA, Amaro Sergio. ■ 19610 #649-30-1981 L1988 **CHP P** *020 †75
ROBERTSON, John Jos. ■ 19610 #041-12-1961 L1962 **GP** *071 †18
ROTHFLEISCH, Richard. 2608 KAISER BLVD 19610 #035-09-1985 L2002 **PUD CCM** *020 †20
RUDOLPH, Robert Isaac. 1134 PENN AVE 19610 #041-01-1971 L1972 **D** *020 †15 ‡
RUMPF, Christopher Barton. 50 COMMERCE DR, BERKSHIRE HEALTH PLAN 19610 #041-13-1979 L1980 **IM** *020 †20
RUSSO, Michael Bernard. 2605 KAISER BLVD, NAVAL MEDICAL CENTER 19610 #041-13-1994 L2007 **CD** *100 †20
SACHENIK, Michael Leon. 2603 KAISER BLVD, 1ST FL 19610 #035-45-1989 L1992 **DR** *020 †80
SACKS, David. 2603 KAISER BLVD, 1ST FL 19610 #041-01-1980 L1982 **VIR** *020 †80
SCHEIRER, Jorge Jose. 1991 STATE HILL RD, RPS INTERNAL MEDICINE 19610 #041-13-1989 L1991 **IM** *020 †20
SCHLECHTER, Benjamin. 2603 KAISER BLVD STE 207 19610 #016-42-1988 L1995 **PS** *020 †65 ‡
SELEY, Jeffrey Douglas. 2201 RIDGEWOOD RD STE 400 19610 #011-04-1996 L2000 **P** *020 †75
SHAH, Sajjad Haider. 2608 KAISER BLVD 19610 #422-01-1996 L1999 **PCC SME** *020 †20

SHAPIRO, John Alan. 2608 KAISER BLVD 19610 #041-01-1979 L1981 **PUD CCM** *020 †20 ‡
SIHELNIK, Stephen Adam. 1320 BROADCASTING RD, SUTIE 200 19610 #047-06-1977 L1994 **U** *020 †95
SKORPINSKI, Edward W. 40 BERKSHIRE CT 19610 #023-07-1991 L1993 **PD** *020 †55,03
SMITH, Raymond Leigh. ■ 19610 #041-13-1966 L1967 **PS GS** *071 †65
SOFFER, Stephen Randolph. 2201 RIDGEWOOD RD 19610 #041-01-1986 L1992 **ORS HS** *020 †40
SOUDERS, Thomas Bright. 1802 PAPERMILL RD 19610 #041-01-1965 L1966 **OPH** *020 †35 ‡
SPILLERMAN, Ruth Massuda. 2240 RIDGEWOOD RD, STE 100 19610 #016-06-1994 L1999 **PD** *020 †55
STARBUCK, David Lea. 50 COMMERCE DR, BERKSHIRE HEALTH PLAN 19610 #038-06-1967 L1996 **PD MDM** *030 †55
STELMACH, John Paul. 1235 PENN AVE, STE 102 19610 #041-13-1987 L1988 **OTR OSM** *020 †40
STELMACH, Paul. 2608 KAISER BLVD 19610 #041-14-1983 L1985 **PUD CCM** *020 †20
STOLZ, Jonathan Lavery. 18 JUNCO DR 19610 #041-13-1969 L1970 **R** *071 †80
TAM, Timothy Luwen. 2240 RIDGEWOOD RD, STE 100 19610 #041-15-2001 L2004 **PD** *020 †55
TCHANG, Felix Kia-Ming. ■ 19610 #396-03-1963 L1991 **PTH** *071 †55
TELLEZ, Francisco Luis. 1802 PAPERMILL RD 19610 #035-19-1988 L1996 **OPH** *020 †35
TEREFENKO, Kevin Michael. 1235 PENN AVE, STE 102 19610 #010-02-1995 L2001 **ORS** *020 †40
TEXTER, David Edward. ■ 19610 #041-13-1974 L1975 **IM** *020 †20,16
THOTT, Kurian. ■ 19610 #045-37-2000 L2004 **OBG** *012
TIMKO, John Vincent. 560 VAN REED RD, STE 301 19610 #041-13-1991 L1993 **P** *020 †75
URFFER, Peter Harcourt. 36 WYOMISSING BLVD 19610 #041-12-1995 L2002 **IM** *020 †20
VAN DEN BOSCH, Elaine S. ■ 19610 #041-13-1945 L1946 **GP** *071
VILLANUEVA, Beata Mistica. ■ 19610 #748-01-1957 L1969 **PTH** *020
WAGNER, Brent Joseph. 2603 KAISER BLVD, 1ST FL 19610 #041-02-1985 L1987 **R** *040 †80
WARTLUFT, Leah Rose. 2630 WESTVIEW DR 19610 #041-13-1999 L2003 **OPH** *020
WEIDNER, Sandra Lee. 2240 RIDGEWOOD RD, STE 100 19610 #041-13-1985 L1988 **PD** *020 †55
WHIKEHART, Richard Eric. 1235 PENN AVE, STE 206 19610 #035-46-1980 L1987 **P** *020 †75
WILL, Peter M. 1320 BROADCASTING RD 19610 #143-05-1975 L1995 **CD** *020 †20
WINANS, Lewis Edward. 950 N WYOMISSING BLVD 19610 #041-02-1971 L1972 **IM** *020 †20
WINSTON, Norman J. 124 LUCINDA LN 19610 #041-13-1949 L1950 **R** *071 †80
ZELNICK, Eric Brian. ■ 19610 #041-13-1975 L1980 **GE IM** *071 †20

WYSOX — BRADFORD

LIVERIGHT, Timothy Fouch. RR 2 BOX 247F 18854 #041-13-1971 L1997 **FM** *030 †70,18
SWEET, Constance Maybell. PO BOX 341 18854 #041-02-1994 L1997 **FM** *020 †18

YARDLEY — BUCKS

ABAD, Mario Diaz, Jr. 1596 PAGE DR 19067 #748-02-1984 L1993 **IM** *020 †20
ABRAHAM, Susan Anisha. ■ 19067 #041-15-2002 L2004 **IM** *100
AITA, Daren Jos. 103 FLORAL VALE BLVD, MERCER-BUCKS ORTHOPAEDICS 19067 #041-09-1992 L1997 **HS ORS** *020 †40 ‡
AMOIA, Andrea Catalano. 385 OXFORD VALLEY RD, STE 311 19067 #041-13-1999 L2001 **PD** *020 †55
ANTONUCCI, Donna Lynn. 301 FLORAL VALE BLVD, FLORAL VALE PRO BLDG PK 19067 #041-07-1984 L1985 **DBP PD** *020 †55 ‡
ARONIN, Tsodik. ■ 19067 #913-33-1954 L1985 **GP** *020
ATILLASOY, Evren. 1552 SURREY BROOK CT 19067 #041-01-1987 L2000 **HEP GE** *072 †20
BABALAKIN, Abiola Haolat. ■ 19067 #690-01-1991 L2001 **CHP** *020 †75
BALLEK, Ronald Edward. 301 OXFORD VALLEY RD #404A 19067 #041-13-1973 L1974 **IM HEM** *020
BALSAMO, Anthony Jos. 111 FLORAL VALE BLVD, # B 19067 #041-07-1974 L1976 **ORS** *020 †40
BARAG, Perry. 301 OXFORD VALLEY RD, STE 804 19067 #038-41-1969 L1970 **IM GE** *020 †20
BAUGHN, Steven Peyton. 680 HEACOCK RD, STE 250 19067 #048-04-1973 L1981 **IM** *020 †20
BERMAN, Edel. ■ 19067 #836-02-1954 *030
BERNAL, Guillermo Jose. 805 FLORAL VALE BLVD 19067 #042-03-1986 L1990 **PM** *020 †60
BIERNAT, Fay Molly G. ■ 19067 #422-01-1982 L1984 **IM** *030
BLUMENTHAL, Jerome Barry. 301 OXFORD VALLEY RD, STE 301B 19067 #035-08-1962 L2001 **P** *020 †75
BLUMENTHAL, Melvin S. ■ 19067 #041-01-1968 L1969 **CD IM** *050 †20
BRESLIN, Kenneth Spencer. 301 OXFORD VALLEY RD, STE 701 19067 #041-02-1987 L1988 **GE IM** *020 †20
BRODKIN, Bruce Ira. 668 STONY HILL RD 19067 #010-01-1967 L1994 **OBG** *020 †30
BROOK, John Henry. ■ 19067 #056-06-1981 L1985 **GPM PHP** *020
BROOKMAN, Harvey Walter. 301 OXFORD VALLEY RD, STE 104A 19067 #561-01-1973 L1974 **OBG** *075
BUDD, Catherine Belford. ■ 19067 #041-01-1993 L1996 **OBG** *020 †30
BURKE, Alan M. 301 OXFORD VALLEY RD, STE 1902B 19067 #035-06-1976 L1978 **ORS NM** *020
CAMPANELLI, Carmen David. 903 FLORAL VALE BLVD 19067 #041-02-2001 L2002 **D** *020 †15
CARUSO, John, Jr. ■ 19067 #024-05-1949 L1981 **OM IM** *071 †20,70
CAUTILLI, George Peter. 115 FLORAL VALE BLVD, STE 115 19067 #041-02-1986 L1987 **ORS OS** *020 †40
CAUTILLI, Richard Anthony. 115 FLORAL VALE BLVD STE C, CAUTILLI ORTHO SURG SPEC 19067 #041-02-1958 L1959 **ORS** *071 †40
CENCI, Judith Ann. 903 FLORAL VALE BLVD 19067 #041-02-2000 L2002 **D** *020 †15
CHEN, Esther Hsiu-Hsin-Hu. ■ 19067 #244-02-2005 L2007 **FP** *012
CHEN, Roland Sangone. 909 FLORAL VALE BLVD 19067 #041-01-1993 L1997 **IM** *075 †20
CHIRAYATH, Mercy. ■ 19067 #495-63-1974 L1983 **IM** *020 †20
CIMINO, Ernest John. 1666 EDGEWOOD RD, STE 2 19067 #035-19-1982 L1989 **PS** *020 †65
COHEN, Steven Wm. 301 OXFORD VALLEY RD, STE 804 19067 #041-02-1982 L1983 **GE IM** *020 †20
COLARUSSO, Frank J. 103 FLORAL VALE BLVD, MERCER BUCK ORTHOPEDICS 19067 #041-77-1996, ▲ L2006 **PM** *020
CRYER, Dennis Robt. 530 ASPEN WOODS DR 19067 #035-46-1977 L1980 **PHM MG** *030
DAVE, Rishi Bhasker. ■ 19067 #041-13-2007 L2007 **IM** *012

DE FRANCESCO, Josephine C. ■ 19067 #041-13-1948 L1950 **AN** *071 †05
DESAI, Hemlata. ■ 19067 #495-17-1972 L1976 **PTH** *020 †20
DESAI, Narendra Babulal. 1296 QUARRY COMMONS DR, 100 E LEHIGH AVE 19067 #495-01-1981 L2001 **IM** *020
DEVINE, Maryann. 2603 STERLING RD 19067 #010-02-1990 L1993 **CCS CCM** *020 †20
DOUGHERTY, Charles Oscar. 62 S MAIN ST, YARDLEY MEDICAL CENTER 19067 #041-02-2000 L2001 **FM** *020 †18
DOUGHERTY, Thomas J. ■ 19067 #041-02-1950 L1951 **IM PUD** *071
DUNAIEF, David Matthew. ■ 19067 #035-48-2004 L2006 **IM** *100
EBERHART, Joseph Carl. 62 S MAIN ST, YARDLEY MEDICAL CENTER 19067 #041-13-1960 L1961 **FM** *071 †18
ENG, Benjamin. ■ 19067 #035-20-1983 L1984 **PM** *030 †60
ESHAGHI, Ghasem. 201 FLORAL VALE BLVD 19067 #517-01-1988 L2003 **OSS** *030
ESTRIN, Jason Todd. 777 TOWNSHIP LINE RD, STE 200 19067 #041-15-2002 L2002 **IM HO** *100 †20
EVANGELISTA, Cleofe P. 301 OXFORD VALLEY RD #403A 19067 #748-08-1968 L1983 **IM** *020
FAROOQUI, Fozia. ■ 19067 #704-26-1997 L2004 **IM** *020 †20 ‡
FIRTH, Brian Garriock. ■ 19067 #836-02-1971 L1990 **CD** *062 †20
FORD, Edward James. 103 FLORAL VALE BLVD 19067 #033-05-1980 L1988 **ORS** *020 †40 ‡
FRIED, Fern Moldwin. 903 FLORAL VALE BLVD 19067 #035-19-1985 L1993 **D IM** *020 †20,15
GOKCEN, Eric Cemil. 103 FLORAL VALE BLVD 19067 #041-02-1988 L1994 **ORS OSS** *020 †40 ‡
GOLDBERG, Harvey Elliott. 777 TOWNSHIP LINE RD 19067 #035-08-1969 L1972 **IM** *020 †20
GOLDFARB, Richard Marc. 301 OXFORD VALLEY RD #1104 19067 #016-42-1983 L1987 **GS TRS** *020 †85
GOLDSTEIN, Walter Carl. ■ 19067 #016-42-1955 L1963 **IM PUD** *071 †20
GORDON, Michael Stuart. ■ 19067 #041-13-1989 L1992 **AN** *020 †05
GORDON, Muriel M. 1248 BRIDLE ESTATES DR 19067 #041-13-1990 L1992 **DR** *020 †80
GORELLI, Lucy Ann. ■ 19067 #033-05-1983 L1984 **GP** *020
GOULD, Stanley. ■ 19067 #035-09-1955 L1961 *071 †55
GREENBERG, Linda Wolf. ■ 19067 #041-07-1997 L2000 **PD** *020 †55
HARDESTY, Wm Harriman. 488 BIG OAK RD 19067 #041-01-1958 L1959 **VS GS** *020 †85
HO, Hsin-Tsung. ■ 19067 #244-04-1978 L1984 **PTH** *020 †50
HOFFMAN, Meredith Leigh. ■ 19067 #041-13-2000 L2002 **IM** *100
HOSSEINI, Seyedeh Shokouh. ■ 19067 #517-06-1998 **IM** *012
HOWARD, Campbell Palmer. ■ 19067 #039-01-1974 L1975 **PDE PD** *020 †55
HOWELL, John Taylor, III. 62 S MAIN ST 19067 #035-01-1980 L1982 **FM** *020 †18
HUFNAL-MILLER, Carrie Ann. ■ 19067 #041-02-1984 L1985 **NPM** *071 †55
IRWIN, John Thos. 680 HEACOCK RD, STE 201 19067 #033-05-1974 L1975 **ORS** *020 †40
JACOBSON, Arnold Fred. ■ 19067 #041-13-1980 L1981 **NM** *020 †20,28
JONES, Charles Bronston. ■ 19067 #035-20-1961 L1977 **PTH NM** *071 †50,28
KELLY, Sheila Ann. ■ 19067 #041-13-1986 L1987 **IM** *071 †20 ‡
KIM, Deborah Miyoung. ■ 19067 #041-02-2008 *012
KIM, Joseph Kihoon. ■ 19067 #041-13-2007 **IM** *012
KISHORE-KUMAR, Ranganna. ■ 19067 #495-72-1980 L1984 **N PME** *020 †75
KRAVATZ, Alan Marc. 777 TOWNSHIP LINE RD 19067 #035-15-1992 L1996 **IM** *020 †20 ‡
KUTNER, Barry Neil. 301 OXFORD VALLEY RD, STE 801A 19067 #035-15-1982 L1983 **OPH** *020 †35
LARKIN, Michael J J. ■ 19067 #010-02-1945 L1953 **OBG OS** *071 †30
LAROCCA, Sandro. 103 FLORAL VALE BLVD, MERCER BUCK ORTHOPAEDICS 19067 #041-02-1995 L1997 **ORS** *020 †40 ‡
LEBOVITZ, Philip Lewis. 407 FLORAL VALE BLVD 19067 #041-12-1966 L1970 **CD** *020 †20
LEEGARD, Robert Lloyd. ■ 19067 #041-13-1962 L1963 **AN** *071
LEVENBERG, Mark E. 209 FLORAL VALE BLVD 19067 #011-75-2002, ▲ L2003 **D** *020
LEVENTHAL, Linda. 385 OXFORD VALLEY RD, STE 312 19067 #041-09-1988 L1990 **D** *020 †15
LEVIN, Richard Leslie. ■ 19067 #010-01-1967 L1968 **D** *071 †15
LIGHT, Richard Todd. ■ 19067 #035-45-1975 L1997 **HEM CLP** *050 †20,50
LOWE, Stephen Jay. 111 FLORAL VALE BLVD, STE B 19067 #041-13-1970 L1971 **ORS** *020 †40
MAJID, Abdul. ■ 19067 #495-21-1992 L2002 **IM** *020 †20
MANALO, Maria Fatima R. ■ 19067 #748-01-1974 L1982 **FM** *020
MANNINO, Anthony J. 515 RIVER RD 19067 #308-10-1983 L1986 **IM** *020 †20
MARTINETTI, Paul. 800 TOWNSHIP LINE RD, STE 400 19067 #035-45-1997 L1997 **GP FM** *020
MAZIARZ, Dennis Michael. 680 HEACOCK RD, EDGLEWOOD VILLAGE EXECUT P 19067 #033-05-1971 L1973 **PD** *020 †55
MEMON, Nahid. ■ 19067 #704-16-1993 L2004 **IM** *020 †20
MILLER, Randolph John. 680 HEACOCK RD, STE 101 19067 #041-02-1984 L1985 **PD** *020 †55
MILLER, Rebecca Christine. ■ 19067 #041-15-2008 *012
MIRSKY, Robert Stuart. 777 TOWNSHIP LINE RD 19067 #012-01-1980 L1984 **IM** *020 †20
MITCHELL, Florence. ■ 19067 #033-05-1991 L1994 **DR** *100
MOGUL, Robert. ■ 19067 #041-02-1978 L1979 **IM** *020 †20
MONKOWSKI, Alfred Matthew. 81 BIG OAK RD, STE 104 19067 #041-02-1970 L1977 **IM FM** *020 ‡
MONTGOMERY, Michael O. ■ 19067 #035-01-1982 L1999 **CD IM** *020 †20
MORGAN, Joseph Jairus. ■ 19067 #041-09-1984 L1985 **PA GP** *050
MOSKOWITZ, Irwin Arthur. 933 PRINCESS DR 19067 #035-46-1962 L1988 **ORS** *020 †40
MULTAK, Alexander. 18205 CORNERSTONE DR 19067 #041-13-1984 L1985 **AN** *020 †20,05 ‡
NOBLE, Shanta J. ■ 19067 #495-27-1959 L1973 **PD** *071 ‡
NOLAN, John P, Jr. 103 FLORAL VALE BLVD 19067 #041-02-1982 L1983 **ORS** *020 †40 ‡
NOLAN, Sheila Margaret. ■ 19067 #041-13-1998 L2005 **PDI** *012 †55
ONORATO, Anna Theresa. ■ 19067 #041-09-1944 L1945 **GP PD** *071
PATEL, Rakesh Bhupendrabh. ■ 19067 #495-22-1994 L2006 **PUD** *020 †20
PAUL, Sindy Michelle. ■ 19067 #041-13-1983 L1984 **PHP** *062 †70
PEACOCK, Samuel Moore, Jr. 201 FLORAL VALE BLVD 19067 #041-01-1948 L1949 **OS N** *030
PEDROTTY, Francis W, Jr. ■ 19067 #041-02-1952 L1953 **GS** *071 †20
PENA, Rafael Eduardo. 407 FLORAL VALE BLVD 19067 #264-04-1992 L1998 **ICE** *100 †20
PESKIN, Steven Ross. 780 TOWNSHIP LINE RD 19067 #012-05-1982 L1988 **IM** *030 †20
PETERS, Ray Francis. 680 HEACOCK RD STE 101, EDGEWOOD VILLAGE EXECUTIVE 19067 #041-13-1975 L1982 **PD** *020 †55
POPPER, David. 301 OXFORD VALLEY RD, STE 701 A-EAST BLDG 19067 #033-05-1978 L1982 **GE IM** *020 †20
RABIN, Elizabeth Watts. 605 FLORAL VALE BLVD 19067 #033-06-1988 L1992 **IM** *020 †20
RAFELSON, Stephen Arnold. 301 OXFORD VALLEY RD # 70 19067 #041-01-1972 L1982 **GE IM** *020 †20
RAJAN, Jennifer Ray. 903 FLORAL VALE BLVD 19067 #038-40-1995 L1999 **D** *020 †15
RAUH, Donald Albert. 306 FLORAL VALE BLVD 19067 #038-06-1980 L1987 **P CHP** *020 †75
RETIZOS, Nenita B. ■ 19067 #748-01-1974 L1993 **P** *020

ROSADO, Miriam. 680 HEACOCK RD STE 205, EDGEWOOD PROFESSIONAL PLAZ 19067 #033-05-1981 L1983 **IM** *020 †20

ROSENMAN, Howard D. 385 OXFORD VALLEY RD, STE 312 19067 #035-08-1975 L1979 **D** *020 †15

ROZENGARTEN, Michael J. 407 FLORAL VALE BLVD, MERCER BUCKS CARDIOLOGY 19067 #035-08-1997 L2005 **ICE** *100 †20

RUSSELL, Lucille Joyce. ■ 19067 #010-03-1982 L1982 **AN PHM** *050

SAGNIP, Cesar Oro-Ni J. ■ 19067 #748-02-1953 L1959 **OS AN** *020

SAMODIO, Evelyn Interior. ■ 19067 #748-08-1971 L1983 **FM** *074

SAMSON, Jose Mansilungan. ■ 19067 #748-01-1971 L1979 **GP** *020

SCHACHTER, Lee Richard. ■ 19067 #035-08-1999 L2006 **U** *020 †95

SHAH, Daksha Rajnikant. ■ 19067 #495-22-1969 L1973 **PTH FOP** *062 †50 ‡

SILBER, Neil Sheldon. 301 OXFORD VALLEY RD, STE 305B 19067 #035-09-1975 L1978 **IM** *020 ‡

SISACK, Michael John. 903 FLORAL VALE BLVD, YARDLEY DERMATOLOGY ASSOC 19067 #033-06-1991 L1997 **D** *020 †20,15 ‡

SMALL, Daniel Alan. 680 HEACOCK RD 19067 #041-01-1982 L1983 **OBG** *020 †30 ‡

STERNBERG, Lauren Jenine. 903 FLORAL VALE BLVD 19067 #016-42-2001 L2007 **D** *020 †15

STOLLSTEIMER, George T. 111 FLORAL VALE BLVD, STE B 19067 #041-13-1991 L1993 **ORS OSM** *020 †40

SULLIVAN, Andrew Landi. 62 S MAIN ST BOX 364 19067 #041-13-2000 L2001 **FM** *020 †18 ‡

SUSSMAN, Steven Andrew. 909 FLORAL VALE BLVD 19067 #041-07-1980 L1981 **OBG** *020 †30 ‡

TABOADA, Javier Gustavo. ■ 19067 #737-03-1966 L1979 **N P** *071 †75 ‡

TAYLOR, Jillian Smith. 306 FLORAL VALE BLVD 19067 #048-12-1998 L2002 **P PYA** *100

THOMAS, Elizabeth. 385 OXFORD VALLEY RD, STE 311 19067 #495-16-1987 L1996 **PD** *020 †55

TOM, Karen Ann. 3405 STERLING RD 19067 #041-09-1987 L1989 **NEP** *020 †20

UMALI, Melecio Joyag. ■ 19067 #748-07-1966 L1980 **FM** *020 †18

URBANIAK, Thomas Frank. 73 E AFTON AVE 19067 #041-09-1964 L1965 **ORS** *020 †40

VANDERPOOL, Ramon Antonio. ■ 19067 #308-01-1971 L1978 **N** *071

VENEGAS, Julio Cesar. ■ 19067 #737-01-1955 L1963 **GP GE** *075

VEPURI, Varalaxmi. 301 OXFORD VALLEY RD, SUITE # 403 A 19067 #495-50-1980 L1992 **FM EM** *020

VORSANGER, Gary Joel. ■ 19067 #035-47-1984 L1985 **AN IM** *050 †20,05

WANG, Ching-Jen. 103 FLORAL VALE BLVD 19067 #385-02-1965 L1971 **ORS PTH** *020 †40 ‡

WEINBERG, Auren Steve. 385 OXFORD VALLEY RD, STE 311 19067 #495-45-1997 L1999 **PD** *020 †55 ‡

WIDLITZ, A Robt. ■ 19067 #803-09-1940 **GP A** *071

WIDLITZ, Michael David. ■ 19067 #010-01-1977 L1983 **OTO A** *020 †45

WILLIAMS, Eric James. ■ 19067 #033-05-1996 L2000 **IM** *020

WILSON, Dorota Michalek. 385 OXFORD VALLEY RD, STE 312 19067 #041-15-2000 L2001 **D** *020 †15

WILSON, Lance Brian. 777 TOWNSHIP LINE RD, 2ND FL 19067 #041-13-1982 L1983 **FM EM** *020 †18

WITMAN, H John, Jr. ■ 19067 #041-09-1944 L1955 **PD OS** *072

YEKTA MOAZAMI, Delaram. ■ 19067 #517-29-1993 **IM** *012

ZAMBITO, Kimberly Lynn. ■ 19067 #041-15-2002 L2002 **ORS** *100

YEADON – DELAWARE

BAGGOTT, Mary Ratner. ■ 19050 #016-43-1965 L1973 **OS GP** *075

HARRIS, Bernard Amiel. ■ 19050 #041-14-1980 L1981 **FM** *020 †70 ‡

SHATOUHY, Joseph. 433 S LANSDOWNE AVE 19050 #875-01-1962 L1969 **ORS PM** *020 †40,60

SMITH, James Riley. ■ 19050 #041-09-1985 L1986 **IM** *075 †20

WILLIAMS, Michael Anthony. ■ 19050 #041-13-1986 L1987 **CD** *062 ‡

YEAGERTOWN – MIFFLIN

PARMAR, Rasik Bachubhai. 310 S MAIN ST, P O BOX 430 17099 #495-48-1980 L1989 **N** *020

YORK – YORK

ADAM, Marilyn. ■ 17403 #042-03-1982 L1985 **P** *075

AGARWAL, Nikhileshwer N. 15 WYNTRE BROOKE DR 17403 #495-45-1970 L1981 **GS PHL** *020 †85

AHLBRANDT, Duane Edward. 2690 SOUTHFIELD DR 17403 #041-09-1983 L1984 **GE IM** *020 †20

ALPERT, Jeffrey Robt. 1946 SECURITY DR 17402 #050-02-1972 L1973 **VS GS** *020 †85

AL-SHUNNAR, Buthainah M. 25 MONUMENT RD, STE 292 17403 #539-06-1991 L1999 **PS GS** *020

ALTMAN, Michael Elimelech. 25 MONUMENT RD, STE 297 17403 #035-46-1990 L1997 **OPH** *020 †35

ALUR, Pradeep. 1001 S GEORGE ST, WELLSPAN HEALTH 17403 #495-65-1985 L2005 **NPM** *055

AMMON, Wallace Keith. 1101 EDGAR ST 17403 #055-02-2001 L2005 **FM** *020 †18

AMSBAUGH, Glenn Allan. 1001 S GEORGE ST 17403 #041-13-1971 L1972 **OTO HNS** *071 †45 ‡

AMSTERDAM, James Todd. 1001 S GEORGE ST, ED ADMIN YORK HOSPITAL 17403 #041-07-1980 L1981 **EM MDM** *030 †16

ANDREWS-MURRAY, Gayle. 292 SAINT CHARLES WAY 17402 #041-07-1983 L1985 **END IM** *020 †20

APPLEFELD, Randy Michael. 1001 S GEORGE ST 17403 #550-02-2001 L2005 **AN** *020 †05

ARBITTIER, Douglas Andrew. 1001 S GEORGE ST 17403 #041-01-1991 L1994 **AN** *020 †05

ARISTIMUNO, Begona. 360 SAINT CHARLES WAY, CHRISTIANNE SCHOEDEL, MD 17402 #042-02-1985 L1989 **PO IM** *020 †35

ARMAH, Kwasi Ofori. 520 GREENBRIAR RD 17404 #033-05-1993 L1995 **RNR** *020 †80,28

ARORA, Pawan Kumar. 310 PINE GROVE COMMONS 17403 #495-03-1991 L1998 **IM IMG** *100 †20

ARUNKUMAR, Punitha. 1001 S GEORGE ST, YORK HOSP 17403 #496-23-1993 L1999 **IM ID** *020 †20

AWAN, Hasan Abdulrehman. 1001 S GEORGE ST 17403 #305-01-2004 L2004 **IM** *020 †20

AWAN, Khadija. 1001 S GEORGE ST 17403 #704-01-1999 L2007 **OBG** *012

AWAN, Maryam. 1001 S GEORGE ST, DEPT OBG 17403 #704-01-2002 L2003 **OBG** *012

AYYANATHAN, Arulnithi. ■ 17403 #496-23-1998 L2007 **IM** *012

AZAR, Albert. 1575 BANNISTER ST STE 4, YORK GUIDANCE CENTER 17404 #154-02-1962 L1972 **CHP** *020

BACASNOT, Jerome Vincent. 1001 S GEORGE ST, YORK HOSP 17403 #422-01-2004 L2004 **EM** *012

BACCON, Jennifer Wells. ■ 17403 #041-01-2005 L2005 **NP** *012

BAKER, David Gerard. 1001 S GEORGE ST 17403 #041-13-1982 L1986 **AN GPM** *020 †05

BAKER, Richard Henry. 25 MONUMENT RD, STE 140 17403 #035-20-1990 L1992 **IM** *020 †20

BARCLAY, Peter Michael. 1001 S GEORGE ST 17403 #041-14-1996 L1998 **IM** *020 †20

BARRON, Todd Franklin. 370 SAINT CHARLES WAY, WELLSPAN NEUROLOGY PEDIATR 17402 #035-47-1985 L1987 **CHN** *020 †55,75

BASELLI, Edgar Carlos. 2350 FREEDOM WAY, STE 102 17402 #041-14-1995 L1999 **U** *020 †95

BASIOUNY, Khaled Fouad. ■ 17402 #001-02-2004 L2004 **GS** *012

BAUER, Thomas Lee. 25 MONUMENT RD, STE 220 17403 #041-02-1965 L1966 **SO** *020 †85

BECKER, Brent Albert. ■ 17403 #023-01-2007 L2007 **EM** *012

BEEKEY, Cyrus Ezra, Jr. 300 PINE GROVE COMMONS, PINE GROVE ADULT MED 17403 #041-02-1968 L1969 **IM NEP** *020 ‡

BELL, Debra Ann. 2775 N GEORGE ST 17406 #048-16-2004 L2004 **FM** *020 †18

BELUR SHIVANANDA, Madhu N. 1001 S GEORGE ST 17403 #496-22-2000 L2005 **IM** *012

BENE, Catherine Helen. 2915 E PROSPECT RD 17402 #041-13-1978 L1979 **OPH EM** *020 †35

BENE, David Jos. 2300 PLEASANT VALLEY RD, P O BOX 3528 17402 #748-08-1987 L1993 **OPH OS** *020 †35

BENE, Natalie I. 205 SAINT CHARLES WAY 17402 #024-05-2000 L2003 **D** *020 †15

BENENSON, Ronald S. EMERGENCY DEPT, YORK HOSPITAL 17405 #023-01-1977 L1978 **EM** *020 †20,16

BENSI, Debora Elena. 1001 S GEORGE ST 17403 #132-12-2001 L2007 **FP** *012

BERING, Thomas Gerard. 1001 S GEORGE ST, YORK HOSPITAL 17403 #041-01-1980 L1982 **AN** *020 †05 ‡

BERNSTINE, Earl L. ■ 17403 #041-02-1955 L1956 **GS** *071

BHAMIDI, Anuradha. 924 COLONIAL AVE STE B, BROCKIE INTERNAL MEDICINE 17403 #495-58-1984 L1999 **IM** *020 †20

BHARGAVE, Geeta Ashutosh. ■ 17403 #041-13-2008 *012

BHATTACHARYA, Ishan. 25 MONUMENT RD, STE 250 17403 #016-02-1982 L2007 **GE IM** *020 †20

BICE, Douglas Edward. 4222 LINCOLN HWY, STONY BROOK FAMILY MEDICIN 17406 #023-01-1995 L1998 **FM** *020 †18

BILBROUGH, Meagan L. 325 S BELMONT ST, MEMORIAL HOSP 17403 #041-78-2005, ▲ L2005 **IM** *012

BILDER, Matthew Brett. 1945 QUEENSWOOD DR 17403 #041-14-1994 L1998 **OPH** *020 †35

BISCOTAKIS, Evangelos. 1001 S GEORGE ST, YORK HOSP 17403 #654-01-2004 L2005 **FP** *012

BIXLER, Brian Loren. 1855 POWDER MILL RD, ORTHOPAEDIC & SPINE SPCLTS 17402 #041-14-1993 L1996 **ORS** *020 †40

BLEDSOE, Ralph Daniel. 1001 S GEORGE ST 17403 #055-02-2001 L2001 **EM** *020 †16

BLOCK, Lisa Mendel. 3542 CONCORD RD 17402 #012-05-1987 L2003 **P CHP** *020 †75

BLOOM, Glenn Robert. ■ 17402 #016-45-2007 L2007 **EM** *012

BLOTZER, John Wolfe. 1001 S GEORGE ST 17403 #023-01-1972 L1976 **IM RHU** *040 †20

BOHRN, Michael Alan. 1001 S GEORGE ST, YORK HOSPITAL EMERGENCY DE 17403 #041-09-1998 L2000 **EM** *020 †16

BOINAPALLY, Nivedita. 1575 BANNISTER ST STE 1 17404 #495-70-1995 L2000 **FM** *020 †18

BOJJA, Lavanya. 1001 S GEORGE ST, YORK HOSPITAL 17403 #496-24-2003 L2006 **FP** *012

BOLLAMPALLI, Vidyasagar R. 1720 S QUEEN ST STE 140 17403 #495-65-1978 L1986 **PD** *020 †55

BORN, Michael Wm. 2295 S GEORGE ST 17403 #035-20-1980 L1985 **PS HS** *020 †65,85

BORNT, Marsha Dawn. 25 MONUMENT RD, STE 230 17403 #023-01-1972 L1973 **GYN** *020

BOUDER, Thomas G. 1001 S GEORGE ST, YORK HOSPITAL 17403 #055-01-1991 L1993 **PCC** *020 †20

BOWMAN, Eric Paul. 1001 S GEORGE ST, YORK HOSP DEPT EMERG MED 17403 #041-14-1994 L1996 **EM** *020 †16

BOYLE, Liam Eamonn. 25 MONUMENT RD, STE 294 17403 #539-04-1970 L1973 **ON HEM** *020 †20

BRAGINSKIY, Roman N.. 1575 BANNISTER ST, YORKTOWNE FAMILY MEDICINE, 17404 #913-33-1988 L2003 **FM** *100 †18

BREIN, Kenneth Robt. 1945 QUEENSWOOD DR 17403 #041-01-1982 L1983 **OPH** *020 †35

BRENZA, Stephen John. 520 GREENBRIAR RD 17404 #041-12-1979 L1987 **R** *020 †80

BRIDE, Thomas P. 1001 S GEORGE ST 17403 #041-77-1974, ▲ L1975 **AN PD** *020 †55,05

BRILLHART, Aaron Martin. ■ 17403 #054-04-2005 L2005 **EM** *012

BRUSSE, Dawn M. 80 WYNTRE BROOKE DR, WHITE ROSE FAMILY PRACTICE 17403 #023-01-1997 L2000 **FM** *020 †18

BUENAVENTURA, Percival O. 1575 BANNISTER ST, STE 7 17404 #033-06-1990 L1992 **TS** *020 †85,90

BURCHMAN, Corey Andrew. 400 PINE GROVE COMMONS, YORK HOSP PAIN RELIEF 17403 #010-01-1983 L1992 **AN PME** *020 †05

BURD, Joyce Kopicky. 292 SAINT CHARLES WAY 17402 #023-07-1980 L1999 **RHU IM** *020 †20

BURDETTE, Rebecca Gwen. 310 PINE GROVE COMMONS 17403 #055-01-1992 L1995 **OBG** *020 †30

BURGESS, Wayne C, Jr. 1101 EDGAR ST, WELLSPAN READYCARE 17403 #051-04-1988 L1993 **FM OS** *020 †18

BUSHWICK, Bruce Micah. 1001 S GEORGE ST 17403 #023-01-1982 L1983 **FM FPG** *040 †18

BUTERA, Vincent. ■ 17403 #041-13-1971 L1972 **ORS** *071 †40

BUTLER, Ivan Lewis. 2319 S GEORGE ST 17403 #041-09-1962 L1963 **NS** *071 †25

BUZOGANY, Joseph Arpad. 1600 S GEORGE ST 17403 #038-40-1992 L1995 **P** *020 †75

CAMITTA, Francine Deborah. ■ 17402 #041-09-1963 L1964 **END** *071 †20

CAPLAN, Faina. 300 PINE GROVE COMMONS 17403 #023-01-1994 L1999 **IMG** *020 †20

CAPLAN, Steven Eric. 205 SAINT CHARLES WAY 17402 #035-19-1992 L1996 **D** *020 †15 ‡

CARDONA, Michelle Anne. ■ 17402 #041-02-2006 L2006 **FP** *012

CAROE, Alan Edward. 1001 S GEORGE ST 17403 #048-12-1983 L1989 **PTH BBK** *020 †50 ‡

CARPENTER, Cathy Penton. 80 WYNTRE BROOKE DR 17403 #023-01-1982 L1983 **FM** *020 †18

CARTER, Joseph H, Jr. 3015 EASTERN BLVD 17402 #041-09-1962 L1963 **OBG** *071 †30

CARTER, Renee Naomi. 1001 S GEORGE ST, DEPT OF SURGERY 17403 #035-09-2005 L2005 **GS** *012

CASTRONUOVO, John J. 1001 S GEORGE ST 17403 #035-09-1974 L2006 **GS** *020 †85 ‡

CATTERALL, Mark Francis. 2775 N GEORGE ST 17406 #035-09-1996 L1998 **FM** *020 †18

CHACKO, Anju Mathews. 1001 S GEORGE ST, YORK HOSPITAL 17403 #496-35-2002 L2007 **FP** *012

CHELLIAH, Aruna. 292 SAINT CHARLES WAY, WELLSPAN ENDOCRINOLOGY-WMG 17402 #495-42-1993 L2004 **IM** *020 †20
CHEN, Douglas Norman. 1030 PLYMOUTH RD, YORK PSYCH ASSOC 17402 #041-13-1991 L1993 **P** *020 †75
CHEN, Xiaoling Shawn. 1001 S GEORGE ST 17403 #243-21-1986 L2000 **AN** *020 †05 ‡
CHERRY, Scott M. 955 S GEORGE ST 17403 #041-02-1977 L1979 **N** *020 †20,75
CHINWALLA, Imtiaz M.. 1001 S GEORGE ST, DEPT OF SURGERY 17403 #495-28-1989 L2004 **GS** *100
CHRISTMAN, Nichole Lee. 1001 S GEORGE ST, T HART FAMILY PRACTICE CTR 17403 #041-02-2006 L2006 **FP** *012
CHU, Kimwai. 25 MONUMENT RD, STE 260 17403 #035-08-1989 L1992 **AN** *020 †05
CHUN, Deborah Heeran. ■ 17402 #041-13-2006 L2006 **EM** *012
CLANCY, Keith David. 1001 S GEORGE ST, YORK HOSPITAL 17403 #030-06-1992 L1999 **GS TRS** *020 †85
COHEN, David Louis. 1855 POWDER MILL RD, ORHTO & SPINE SPECIALISTS 17402 #041-13-1972 L1973 **ORS OTR** *020 †40
COHEN, Merrill Alan. 1001 S GEORGE ST 17403 #041-13-1965 L1972 **EM** *020 †16
CONWAY, Nancy Kathleen. 1207 S QUEEN ST 17403 #033-06-1996 L1998 **FM** *020 †18
CORDTS, Grace Ann. 290 SAINT CHARLES WAY 17402 #023-01-1986 L1989 **IM** *020 †20
COSTA, Jonathan Leeds. 1850 NORMANDIE DR 17408 #016-02-1972 L1997 **PM APM** *020 †60
CRAIG, Richard Alfred. 1001 S GEORGE ST 17403 #041-02-1977 L1979 **AN** *020 †05
CROVATTO, Arthur Chas. ■ 17403 #008-01-1954 L1961 **U** *071 †95
DABB, Richard Wm. 25 MONUMENT RD STE 292 17403 #041-13-1969 L1975 **PS GS** *020 †85,65
DALY, Richard Harold, Jr. 1930 SECURITY DR 17402 #027-01-1978 L1979 **FM** *020 †18
DAMEWOOD, Marian D. 1001 S GEORGE ST 17403 #023-07-1978 L2000 **REN OBG** *030 †30 ‡
DANG, Hongduc Vu. 1001 S GEORGE ST, DEPT OF SURGERY 17403 #010-02-2004 L2004 **GS** *012
DANYO, John Jos. ■ 17403 #041-02-1959 L1960 **ORS HS** *071 †40
DAVIS, Abby Warner. 1001 S GEORGE ST, YORK LAB ASSOC YORK HOSP 17403 #041-14-1994 L1996 **PTH** *020 †50 ‡
DAVIS, James H. ■ 17402 #041-01-1952 L1953 **FM** *071
DAVIS, Justin Brian. 1001 S GEORGE ST, DEPT EM 17403 #012-01-2007 L2007 **EM** *012
DAVIS, Robert Morris. 50 WYNTRE BROOKE DR 17403 #041-02-1963 L1964 **PS GS** *071 †85,65
DAVULURI, Surendra Babu. 1001 S GEORGE ST 17403 #496-31-1995 L2005 **AN** *020
DAYA, Samantapudi Krishna. 1001 S GEORGE ST 17403 #496-39-1997 L2001 **IM** *020
DE FALCIS, Daniel Carmine. 1850 NORMANDIE DR, CENTRAL PENNSYLVANIA REHAB 17408 #041-14-1994 L1998 **PM** *072 †60
DEISHER, Samuel W. ■ 17403 #041-13-1952 L1953 **OBG** *071 †30
DEITRICH, Claudia Nicki. 1001 S GEORGE ST 17403 #035-45-1976 L1986 **AN** *020 †05
DE LOS ANGELES-SICILIA, M. 1850 NORMANDIE DR 17408 #010-01-1993 L1997 **PM** *020 †60
DELP, Andrew Taylor. 1001 S GEORGE ST, YORK HOSP FAM PRAC CTR 17403 #041-13-1985 L1992 **FM** *020 †18
DELP, William Taylor. ■ 17408 #041-13-1954 L1955 **OBG** *071 †30
D'EMILIO, Mary Theresa. 140 PINE GROVE COMMONS, CENTER FOR AGING 17403 #010-02-1978 L1979 **FM** *020 †18
DENG, Ping Na. 1001 S GEORGE ST, YORK HOSP 17403 #243-21-1993 **OBG** *012
DEREWITZ, Daniel Lee. 1001 S GEORGE ST 17403 #041-09-1975 **AN** *020 †05
DERRICK, David Alan. 1001 S GEORGE ST 17403 #033-05-1987 L1992 **PTH** *020 †50 ‡
DE SANTI, Joseph Vincent. 204 SAINT CHARLES WAY, UNIT E367 17402 #010-02-1992 L2004 **FM** *020
DEVLIN, Joseph Michael. 116 S GEORGE ST, STE 200 17401 #041-02-1980 L1982 **FM** *020 †18
DILLON, Michael Burton. 25 MONUMENT RD, STE 292 17403 #010-02-1972 L1987 **GO GYN** *071 †30
DILTS, Stephen Leist, Jr. 1600 S GEORGE ST, WELLSPAN BEHAVIORAL HEALTH 17403 #007-02-1993 L1997 **P** *020 †75
DOHERTY, John Christopher. 1001 S GEORGE ST 17403 #041-09-1994 L1996 **FM** *020 †18
DOLAND, Cherylann. 110 PINE GROVE COMMONS, ANESTHESIA ASSOCIATES OF Y 17403 #041-14-1984 L1985 **AN** *020 †05
DOLINA, Marina. 25 MONUMENT RD, STE 190 17403 #913-09-1992 L2001 **PCC** *020 †20
DONTU, Vijaya Saradhi. 1001 S GEORGE ST, YORK HOSP 17403 #495-58-1994 L2004 **IM** *012
DORSCH, Carole Ann. 292 SAINT CHARLES WAY, APPLE HILL MEDICAL CENTER 17402 #023-07-1968 L1988 **RHU** *071 †20
DOUGLASS, Paul Howard. 4222 LINCOLN HWY 17406 #041-02-1970 L1971 **OBG U** *020 †30
DRESSLER, Anne Marie. 1001 S GEORGE ST 17403 #422-01-2004 L2004 **FM** *100
DROLET, Julie. 1600 6TH AVE, STE 117 17403 #067-02-1983 L1997 **OBG** *020 †30
DUE, Christopher Franklin. 1001 S GEORGE ST 17403 #023-01-1985 L1986 **IM** *020 †20
DUNCAN, Ralph Emerson. 25 MONUMENT RD STE 100, APPLE HILL MEDICAL CENTER 17403 #051-04-1971 L1979 **U** *020 †95
DURICA, Allision Renee. ■ 17402 #041-14-1999 L2001 **OBG** *100
EAGLE, Perry Alan. 191 LEADERS HEIGHTS RD 17402 #023-01-1967 L1970 **ORS HS** *071 †40
EBONG, Constance Nzelle. 1101 EDGAR ST STE A, WELLSPAN BEHAVIORAL HEALTH 17403 #217-01-1988 L2005 **ADP** *020
ECHTERLING, Christopher K. 605 S GEORGE ST, STE 200 17401 #041-14-1992 L1994 **FM** *030 †18
EDWARDS, Earl Wilbert. ■ 17402 #042-03-1992 L2005 **FM** *020
EFIOM-EKAHA, Daniel Natha. 25 MONUMENT RD, STE 294 17403 #690-01-1995 L2006 **HO** *100 †20 ‡
EID, Mark Philip. ■ 17406 #023-07-2006 L2007 **D** *012
EITEL, David Richard. 1001 S GEORGE ST, YORK HOSPITAL 17403 #065-06-1973 L1982 **EM** *020 †16
ELLIOTT, C D. 2180 WHITE ST # 316 17404 #418-01-1955 L1963 **P** *020
EL-MAGHRABI, Essam A. 1001 S GEORGE ST 17403 #915-03-1980 L1996 **AN** *020 †05
ESCARO, Danilo Umali. 1001 S GEORGE ST 17403 #748-01-1963 L1970 **PTH** *071 †50
ESKRIDGE, Timothy Howard. 940 S QUEEN ST 17403 #023-01-1974 L1978 **OPH** *020 †35
ETIENNE, Gracia. 1855 POWDER MILL RD 17402 #041-14-1995 L2005 **ORS** *020 †40
ETTER, Russel Harry. 55 WYNTRE BROOKE DR 17403 #041-13-1964 L1965 **FM** *020 †18
FASANO, Mary Theresa. 110 PINE GROVE COMMONS 17403 #033-06-1986 L1991 **AN** *020 †05
FASANO, Michael John. 110 PINE GROVE COMMONS, ANET ASSOC OF YORK 17403 #041-14-1986 L1990 **AN** *020 †05
FAWCETT, Robert Sayers. 1001 S GEORGE ST 17403 #018-03-1975 L1979 **FM FSM** *040 †18
FAZIO, Gregory Paul. 25 MONUMENT RD STE 200 17403 #010-02-1982 L1993 **CD ICE** *020 †20
FERRARO, Katarzyna K. 1001 S GEORGE ST, EMERGENCY DEPT 17403 #041-14-1999 L2001 **EM** *020 †16
FERRENTINO, Frank Louis. 1001 S GEORGE ST, MKB 17403 #010-02-1979 L1986 **NPM PD** *020 †55 ‡
FIELDING, Lawrence Peter. 1001 S GEORGE ST, YORK HOSPITAL 17403 #917-26-1964 L1997 **GS CRS** *030
FIGDORE, Meg Kistler. 1693 S QUEEN ST 17403 #041-02-1993 L1996 **OBG** *020 †30
FIGUEREDO, Marius. ■ 17402 #495-52-1986 L2001 **PCC** *100 †20
FILER, Robert B. 130 LEADERS HEIGHTS RD 17403 #041-09-1981 L1985 **REN** *020 †30
FILER, Wanda Diane. 1010 PLYMOUTH RD 17402 #041-09-1983 L1987 **FM** *020 †18
FLACCAVENTO, Frederick G. 1001 S GEORGE ST 17403 #023-01-1981 L1983 **AN PME** *020 †05
FLOWERS, Brian Kenny. 924 COLONIAL AVE, STE G 17403 #023-01-1986 L1995 **OTO HNS** *020 †45
FOLEY, Theodore Thomas. ■ 17402 #016-42-2004 L2004 **GS** *012
FORNEY, John Poole. 1001 S GEORGE ST, YORK HOSPITAL 17403 #305-01-2005 L2005 *100
FORSYTHE, Danny William. 1001 S GEORGE ST 17403 #010-02-1994 L1997 **AN** *020 †05
FOSTER, Edwin Neil. 1938 SECURITY DR 17402 #023-01-1985 L1986 **IM** *020 †20
FOSTER, Lisa Marie. 1575 BANNISTER ST, STE 4 17404 #016-11-1995 L1995 **P** *020 †75
FOTI, Gregory Patrick. 1001 S GEORGE ST 17403 #654-01-2004 L2004 **FM** *020 †18
FOUNTAIN, Steven James. ■ 17406 #017-20-2004 L2005 **EM** *012
FOX, Kevin Loren. 1001 S GEORGE ST 17403 #055-01-2000 L2001 **EM** *020 †16 ‡
FRANCOIS, David Thos. 292 SAINT CHARLES WAY 17402 #028-34-1980 L1993 **RHU IM** *020 †20
FREUNDEL, Roseann Janine. YORK HOSP 17405 #055-75-2005, ▲ L2005 **OBG** *012
FREY, Jeffrey Allen. 1001 S GEORGE ST 17403 #041-09-1982 L1984 **IM** *020 †20
FRIEDMAN, Neal Matthew. 1803 MOUNT ROSE AVE, STE B5 17403 #041-13-1973 L1974 **DIA END** *020 †20
FRIEDRICH, Roland. 2690 SOUTHFIELD DR 17403 #308-03-1981 L1983 **GE** *020 †20
FRIEDRICH, Tomas. 2240 S QUEEN ST 17402 #305-01-1981 L1983 **FM GP** *020 ‡
FULTON, William O. ■ 17403 #041-02-1943 L1944 **FM** *071
FURMAN, Michael Bruce. 1855 POWDER MILL RD, ORTHO & SPINE SPECIALIST 17402 #041-13-1990 L1992 **PM PMM** *020 †60 ‡
GALUSKA, Michael Andrew. ■ 17402 #041-14-2005 L2005 **EM** *012
GARBER, Edward H. 325 S BELMONT ST 17403 #041-02-1976 L1977 **GS** *020 †85 ‡
GARG, Ashwani Kumar. 1001 S GEORGE ST 17403 #495-29-2001 L2006 **IM** *012
GEISELMAN, Douglas Luther. 2449 W PHILADELPHIA ST 17404 #041-13-1977 L1978 **FM** *020 †18
GHEBREKIDAN, Habte. 1001 S GEORGE ST, DEPT OF INTERNAL MEDICINE 17403 #041-13-2001 L2006 **IM** *012
GIBBLE, Leon Wagner. 1001 S GEORGE ST 17403 #023-01-1979 L1981 **IM** *020 †20
GILL, Daljeet Singh. ■ 17402 #917-24-1989 L1999 **IM** *100
GILRAIN, Kenneth James. 1001 S GEORGE ST, DEPT EM 17403 #041-15-2007 L2007 **EM** *012
GLORIOSO, Robert Chas. 1001 S GEORGE ST 17403 #023-01-1981 L1982 **FM** *020 †18
GO, Asceline So. 116 S GEORGE ST, FAMILY FIRST HEALTH 17401 #748-16-1988 L1998 **FM** *020 †18
GOBEL, Reginald Trudo. 1600 S GEORGE ST 17403 #030-06-1944 L1947 **P** *071
GOCHOCO, Jacinto J. 1001 S GEORGE ST 17403 #748-02-1952 L1960 **PTH** *071 †50
GOEDECKER, Mark Anthony. 1001 S GEORGE ST, DEPARTMENT OF 17403 #041-14-1997 L2003 **FM** *020 †18
GOLDSTEIN, Craig Evan. 1001 S GEORGE ST 17403 #041-02-1998 L2000 **IM** *020 †20
GOLLAPALLI, Sunil Kumar. ■ 17403 #495-58-2002 L2007 **IM** *012
GOOD, Garth Monroe. 924 COLONIAL AVE, STE G 17403 #041-13-1995 L1997 **OTO** *020 †45
GOODSTEIN, Michael Howard. 325 S BELMONT ST 17403 #035-46-1987 L1988 **NPM** *020 †55
GORDON, Becky. ■ 17406 #041-15-2005 L2005 **FP** *012
GREEN, Michael Raymond. ■ 17403 #010-02-1972 L1985 **PUD PCC** *020 †20 ‡
GREENBERG, Reuben. ■ 17403 #024-15-1939 L1940 **GP OS** *071
GROFF, Steven Kenneth. 1855 POWDER MILL RD, ORTHO & SPINE SPECIALIST 17402 #051-01-1991 L1993 **ORS** *020 †40
GROLMAN, Dennis Michael. 1855 POWDER MILL RD, ORTHOPAEDIC & SPINE SPECIA 17402 #836-03-1970 L1976 **AN PME** *020 †05
GROSS, Donald Richard. ■ 17403 #041-09-1948 L1949 **AN** *071 †05
GROSSBART, Douglas Scott. 1001 S GEORGE ST, DEPT ROTAT 17403 #033-05-1993 L1993 **OS** *100
GROSSI, Lewis Geo, Jr. 1001 S GEORGE ST, YORK HOSPITAL 17403 #041-01-1968 L1969 **EM IM** *040 †20,16
GROSSMAN, Robert Steven. 1001 S GEORGE ST 17403 #035-09-1980 L1991 **CCM IM** *040 †20
GROVE, Glenn Pershing. ■ 17403 #023-07-1943 L1950 **GS CRS** *072 †85
GROVE, William Kirkwood. 1001 S GEORGE ST 17403 #041-13-1960 L1962 **OPH** *071 †35
GUREGHIAN, Patricia A H. ■ 17403 #041-07-1963 L1964 **R DR** *071 †80
GUZZARDI, Lawrence Jos. 54 N HARRISON ST, WHITE ROSE AMBULANCE 17403 #041-02-1971 L1980 **FM EM** *020 †16
HALDIPUR, Namrata. 1001 S GEORGE ST 17403 #496-22-1991 L2003 **IM** *020 †20
HAMILTON, Kimberly Joy. 292 SAINT CHARLES WAY 17402 #036-01-1996 L2001 **RHU** *020 †20
HARBERGER, James Henry. ■ 17403 #011-02-1978 L1979 **FM FPG** *020 †18
HARGEST, Thomas E, Jr. 1030 PLYMOUTH RD 17402 #041-13-1988 L1991 **FM** *020 †18
HAROOTUNIAN, Richard. 1001 S GEORGE ST 17403 #041-01-1968 L1969 **IM** *020 †20,18
HARRIS, Anne Earle. ■ 17404 #051-01-1984 L1991 **PME AN** *071 †55,05
HARRISON, Rita B. 1001 S GEORGE ST, DEPT OF FAMILY MEDICINE 17403 #008-02-1995 L1999 **FP** *012 †50
HARTMANN, Peter Martin. 1001 S GEORGE ST, YORK HOSPITAL 17403 #023-01-1971 L1977 **P** *030 †75,18
HASSAN, Mohamed H. 302 SAINT CHARLES WAY 17402 #915-03-1983 L1997 **NEP** *020 †20
HASSINGER, Kathryn K. 1693 S QUEEN ST 17403 #041-07-1985 L1986 **OBG** *020 †30 ‡
HAWK, David Lee. 1 W MARKETWAY W STE 3, YORK CITY BUREAU OF HLTH 17401 #041-01-1971 L1972 **PHP FM** *030 †18
HEILMAN, Catherine B. 1001 S GEORGE ST 17403 #023-01-1992 L1994 **FM** *020 †18
HEIRD, Steven B. 191 LEADERS HEIGHTS RD, STE 105 17402 #023-01-1984 L1985 **VS SO** *020 †85
HEMPLING, Ronald Elliott. 35 MONUMENT RD 17403 #039-01-1973 L1997 **GO GYN** *050 †30
HENDERSON, Charles F. 1001 S GEORGE ST, DEPT IM 17403 #033-05-1995 L2007 **IM** *012 †18
HENDERSON, Thomas James. 1001 S GEORGE ST, DEPT OF EMERGENCY MEDICINE 17403 #041-15-2006 L2006 **EM** *012
HENRIKSEN, Daniel Scott. 1601 S QUEEN ST, WHITE ROSE SURGICAL 17403 #041-07-1990 L1992 **GS** *020 †85
HERMAN, Ronald James. 1001 S GEORGE ST 17403 #041-01-1961 L1962 **CD IM** *071 †20
HERMANN, Jeffrey William. 300 E 7TH AVE 17404 #041-07-1997 L1999 **P CHP** *020 †75
HERTZ, Gail Sharon. 2860 CAROL RD, PEDIATRIC HEALTH ASSOCIATE 17402 #041-14-1997 L2000 **PD** *020 †55

■ = Address Information Privacy Protected

HICKEY, Andrew Edward, Jr. 300 PINE GROVE COMMONS 17403 #010-03-1968 L1971 FM FPG *020 †18

HINES, Lisa Sarah. ■ 17404 #048-13-1997 L1999 IMG *020

HIRSH, Marc Alan. 25 MONUMENT RD, STE 194 17403 #035-03-1977 L1987 ON HEM *020 †20

HO, Clement Tat-Shing. 25 MONUMENT RD, STE 294 17403 #919-03-1979 L1986 ON HO *020 †20

HODZIEWICH, Tatiana Alyci. ■ 17403 #023-01-2005 L2005 FP *012

HOFFMAN, David Jos. 1001 S GEORGE ST 17403 #041-14-1972 L1973 IM *020 †20

HOFFMANN, Barbara Landis. 3321 WHITEFORD RD 17402 #041-09-1983 L1984 FM *020 †18

HOFMANN, Douglas Jos. 1855 POWDER MILL RD 17402 #041-12-1982 L1984 ORS *020 †40

HOOVER, Benjamin A, II. ■ 17403 #041-01-1963 L1964 IM IMG *020 †20

HOPKINS, Lisa Anne. ■ 17402 #016-42-2005 L2005 GS *012

HORST, Stephanie Anne Sch. ■ 17403 #041-14-2006 L2006 GS *012

HOSSLER, Eric Winfield. ■ 17404 #047-20-2005 L2005 D *012

HOWARD, Renee. 2860 CAROL RD 17402 #036-01-1976 L2007 PD ADL *020 †55

HOWIE, Matthew Ross. 605 S GEORGE ST, STE 200 17401 #023-01-1997 L1999 FM *020 †18 ‡

HUDAK, Mary Joanne. 1001 S GEORGE ST 17403 #041-07-1978 L1979 IM EM *020 †16,20

HUDSON, Clifford C. 1232 GREENSPRINGS DR 17402 #041-01-1968 L1969 IM *020 †20

HUITT-CORCORAN, Carla J. 1796 3RD AVE 17403 #030-06-1986 L1991 OM *030 †70

HUMBURG, Burt Clifton. 1803 MOUNT ROSE AVE, STE B3 17403 #019-02-2002 L2005 IM *012

HURTT, Stanley Derrick. ■ 17402 #041-12-2002 L2002 PTH *100 †50

IANNINI, Paul Bernard. 1001 S GEORGE ST, YORK HOSPITAL 17403 #008-02-1972 L2007 ID IM *030 †20

INGLIS, Cherie Michelle. 1001 S GEORGE ST 17403 #041-14-2005 L2005 FP *012

IV, Caliste Ny. 1001 S GEORGE ST, DEPT OF SURGERY 17403 #056-06-2004 L2005 GS *012

JACKSON, Jay R. 25 MONUMENT RD, STE 140 17403 #023-01-1974 L1975 OBG *020 †30

JACOBUS, Paula Ann. 1938 SECURITY DR 17402 #041-01-1984 L1985 IM IMG *020 †20

JAIN, Nitesh Kumar. ■ 17403 #496-22-2000 L2007 IM *012

JENSEN, Lynn Sprague. 1001 S GEORGE ST, DEPT OF EMERG MEDICINE 17403 #025-01-1975 L1976 EM *020 †16

JOHNSON, Adrienne Ruth. 1930 SECURITY DR 17402 #041-14-1996 L1998 FM *020 †18

JOHNSON, Dean Eliot. 1001 S GEORGE ST, YORK HOSPITAL EMERGENCY DE 17403 #051-04-1992 L1994 EM *020 †16

JOHNSON, Dennis Edward. 25 MONUMENT RD, STE 220 17403 #041-13-1989 L1995 GS *020 †85

JOHNSON, Dennis Robt. 1693 S QUEEN ST 17403 #036-01-1973 L1982 OBG *020 †30

JOHNSON, George Mark. 1001 S GEORGE ST 17403 #041-09-1963 L1964 OBG *071 †30

JOHNSTON, Robert Bernard. 605 S GEORGE ST, YORK HOSPITAL 17401 #010-02-1964 L1968 PD N *040 †55

JONES, David Bruce. 1001 S GEORGE ST 17403 #005-14-1980 L1995 PTH *020 †50 ‡

JONES, Karen Elizabeth. 1001 S GEORGE ST, YORK HOSPITAL 17403 #011-03-1989 L1992 IM *020 †20

KANNARKATT, Annie J. 25 MONUMENT RD, STE 294 17403 #495-63-1987 L2000 HO *020 †20

KARKHANIS, Kundan Anil. 1001 S GEORGE ST, YORK HOSP 17403 #496-44-1999 L2004 RHU *012

KATARI, Vijay Sekhar. 1001 S GEORGE ST, YORK HOSPITAL 17403 #495-58-1992 L2003 IM *020 †20

KAY, Kathleen Barrett. 924 COLONIAL AVE STE B, BROCKIE INTERNAL MEDICINE 17403 #033-05-1986 L1999 IM *020 †20

KEEPORTS, Richard Lee. 1001 S GEORGE ST, 25 MONUMENT RD 17403 #041-01-1966 L1970 PUD IM *071 †20

KEHM, Vincent A. ■ 17403 #041-02-1944 L1944 AN *071

KELLEY, Brian M. ■ 17402 #011-75-2004, ▲ L2004 EM *012

KENNA, Denise Mary. 1936 POWDER MILL RD 17402 #041-02-1982 L2001 PS GS *020 †65

KENNEDY, Karen Dee. 35 MONUMENT RD 17403 #041-14-1989 L1991 CHP P *020 †75

KEPNER, Andrew M. 1001 S GEORGE ST, YORK HOSP-DEPT EMERG MED 17403 #041-13-1998 L2001 EM *020 †16

KEPNER, Diane M. 80 WYNTRE BROOKE DR 17403 #041-02-1997 L1999 FM *020 †18

KHAN, Sadia R. 292 SAINT CHARLES WAY 17402 #041-02-2002 RHU *020 †20

KHANNA, Apurv. 302 SAINT CHARLES WAY 17402 #495-05-1992 L2006 NEP *050 †20

KHAWAJA, Ali Imran. 1855 POWDER MILL RD, ORTHO AND SPINE SPECIALIST 17402 #704-21-1997 L2007 PM *020

KHERA, Jena Rajinderrut. 370 SAINT CHARLES WAY, WELLSPAN NEUROLOGY 17402 #038-43-2002 L2007 PD *100

KIRAN, Zahra. 1001 S GEORGE ST 17403 #704-21-1995 L2007 FP *012

KITTRELL-MC MILLAN, D. 1575 BANNISTER ST, YORKTOWNE FAMILY MEDICINE 17404 #041-09-1981 L1982 FM IMG *020 †18

KLEIN, Michael Allen. 1855 POWDER MILL RD 17402 #035-08-1979 L1983 AN IM *020 †20,05

KLIMES, Ronald Louis. ■ 17402 #023-01-1962 L1963 FM *071

KLINE, Jack Arthur. 25 MONUMENT RD, STE 140 WELLSPAN MEDICAL G 17403 #041-01-1963 L1964 IM IMG *072 †20 ‡

KLINEK, Michelle M. 2605 JOPPA RD 17403 #035-45-1990 L1992 AI PD *020 †55,03

KLUFAS, Swiatoslau John. ■ 17404 #047-16-1958 *075

KNUDSON, Conrad Harrison. 1207 S QUEEN ST 17403 #051-01-1996 L1998 FM *020 †20

KONCHAR, William Carl. 1803 MOUNT ROSE AVE, B3 17403 #041-02-1977 L1978 FM *020 †18 ‡

KOUSEN, Morton. 1001 S GEORGE ST 17403 #023-01-1973 L1974 OBG *071 †20

KRAMER, David A. 1001 S GEORGE ST, YORK HOSP/DEPT EM 17403 #028-34-1981 L1999 EM *040 †16

KRAUS, Richard Edward. 520 GREENBRIAR RD 17404 #041-09-1969 L1975 DR *020 †80

KUKRIKA, Miodrag Dusan. 25 MONUMENT RD, STE 294 17403 #957-02-1962 L1970 HEM ON *071 †20

KUMAR, Rajesh. 300 PINE GROVE COMMONS 17403 #496-38-1999 L2008 IMG *012 †20

KURTZ, Adelle. 1001 S GEORGE ST 17403 #041-02-1993 L1995 IM *012

KURUP, Priyesh Pankajaksh. 1001 S GEORGE ST 17403 #495-28-2001 L2005 IM *012

LAMANTEER, Michael John. 1001 S GEORGE ST 17403 #041-02-1996 L1998 IM *020 †20

LAMPE, William Thos, II. BROCKIE MEDICAL CTR, ASSOCIATED INTERNISTS INC 17403 #041-02-1957 L1958 IM *071

LANDER, Jeffrey Richard. 309 LEADERS HEIGHTS RD, LEADER HGTS EYE CENTER 17402 #038-43-1980 L1982 OPH *035

LANDIS, Robert Chester. 1001 S GEORGE ST 17403 #041-09-1965 L1966 PD *020

LANDIS, William A. 1001 S GEORGE ST, YORK HOSPITAL 17403 #011-04-1982 L1983 IM *020 †20

LANPHER, Gregory B. 1620 S QUEEN ST 17403 #051-01-1980 L1985 AI IM *020 †20,03

LAPES, George Anthony. ■ 17403 #023-01-1967 L1968 P AM *020 †75

LAUCKS, Samuel Simon, II. 1601 S QUEEN ST, WHITE ROSE SURGICAL ASSOC 17403 #041-02-1981 L1982 CRS GS *020 †10,85

LAUCKS, Stanley Philip. 7 RATHTON RD 17403 #041-01-1978 L1979 DR *020 †80

LAUCKS, Stephen O. 2080 SPRINGWOOD RD, PAIN MED OF YORK LLC 17403 #041-01-1979 L1980 PMM ADM *020 †05 ‡

LAW, Michelle M. ■ 17403 #048-78-2006, ▲ L2006 EM *012

LAWRENCE, John Jeffrey. 1693 S QUEEN ST 17403 #041-14-1989 L1992 OBG U *020 †30

LE, Kimthuy. 1001 S GEORGE ST, DEPT EM 17403 #020-02-2007 L2007 EM *012

LEBOUITZ, Stanton Saml. 1936 POWDER MILL RD 17402 #041-09-1968 L1969 D *020 †15 ‡

LEE, Michael Yiming. ■ 17403 #041-14-2007 GS *012

LEKAWA, Thaddeus. ■ 17403 #041-12-1961 L1962 FM *071 †18

LETOCHA, Charles Edward. 1945 QUEENSWOOD DR 17403 #041-01-1970 L1971 OPH *020 †35

LEVIN, Bradley Howard. 1001 S GEORGE ST 17403 #036-05-1976 L1987 TS *020 †85,90

LEVINE, Charles Bruce. 1001 S GEORGE ST 17403 #023-01-1984 L1989 AN *020 †05

LIJOI, Andre Francis. 1001 S GEORGE ST 17403 #010-02-1980 L1988 FM FPG *020 †18

LIJOI, Laurie M. ■ 17403 #023-01-1980 L1987 FM OS *074 †18

LILIE, Steven. 924 COLONIAL AVE STE B 17403 #035-46-1990 L1992 IM *020 †20

LIS, Edward T. ■ 17403 #038-06-1950 L1951 FM FPG *071

LISS, Jonathan. 1001 S GEORGE ST 17403 #041-13-1980 L1982 NPM PD *020 †55 ‡

LITRENTA, David Edward. 2141 PENNSYLVANIA AVE, CONCENTRA MEDICAL CENTER 17404 #023-01-1961 L1962 OM GPM *020 †20

LITT, Jeffrey S. ■ 17404 #041-78-2006, ▲ L2006 TY *012

LOCKWOOD, Tammy Jean. 302 SAINT CHARLES WAY, PINNACLE HEALTH HARRISBURG 17402 #051-04-2001 L2002 IM *020

LYND, Clifford Warren, Jr. 1946 SECURITY DR, YORK ENDOVASCULAR SOLUTION 17402 #041-02-1971 L1972 VS GS *020 †85

MAC DOUGALL, Howard H. 1207 S QUEEN ST 17403 #050-02-1946 L1949 FM *071 †18

MAC DOUGALL, Robert D. ■ 17403 #041-13-1950 GP OM *071 †18

MACKENZIE, Iain L. 25 MONUMENT RD, STE 250 17403 #917-10-1961 L1970 GE *071

MACLER, Henry Humbert, Jr. 1855 POWDER MILL RD, DEPARTMENT OF ANESTHESIA 17402 #035-03-1974 L2007 AN *020 †05

MADAPOOSI, Sudhakumar. 3542 CONCORD RD, WELLSPAN BEHAVIORAL HEALTH 17402 #495-16-1988 L2001 P *020 †75

MADDOX, Lee Alexander. 25 MONUMENT RD, STE 190 17403 #023-01-1997 L2003 PCC *020 †20

MADUFORO, Aloysius C. ■ 17315 #041-13-1999 GS *100

MAGID, Warren Paul. 110 PINE GROVE COMMONS, ANESTHESIA ASSOC OF YORK I 17403 #023-01-1971 L1974 AN GP *020 †05

MAJKOWSKI, Adam Edward. ■ 17404 #048-02-2005 L2005 EM *012

MALLORY, Roslyn Vernice. 1001 S GEORGE ST, DEPT OB 17403 #010-03-2006 L2006 OBG *012

MANN, Scott Russell. 80 WYNTRE BROOKE DR, WHITE ROSE FAM PRACTICE 17403 #023-01-1992 L1994 FM *020 †18

MANZELLA, John P. 1001 S GEORGE ST, FL 4 17403 #035-06-1974 L1979 ID IM *020 †20

MASCHKE, Stuart Paul. 325 S BELMONT ST 17403 #038-40-1980 L1987 AN *020 †05

MATHAI, John. ■ 17403 #495-31-1960 L1970 TS *071 †85,90

MATHEWSON, John William. 1001 S GEORGE ST 17403 #422-01-2004 L2004 GS *012

MATSUURA, Dean Hideo. 302 SAINT CHARLES WAY 17402 #041-09-1992 L1995 NEP *020 †20

MATZ, Whitney Rothschild. ■ 17403 #041-01-2004 L2004 EM *012

MAY, Anthony Crofton. 290 SAINT CHARLES WAY 17402 #010-02-1995 L2005 N OS *020 †75

MC CABE, Jennifer. 1001 S GEORGE ST 17403 #023-01-1999 L2001 FM *020 †20

MC CARTER, Pamela Young. 2339 S GEORGE ST, SPRINGDALE PEDIATRIC MEDIC 17403 #041-07-1985 L1987 PD *020 †55

MC CONVILLE, John Hayes. 1001 S GEORGE ST, DEPT OF MEDICINE 17403 #035-03-1968 L1976 ID IM *071 †20

MC CULLOUGH, Alice Q. 1001 S GEORGE ST 17403 #041-14-2000 L2001 IM *100 †20

MC CULLUM, Kevin John. 25 MONUMENT RD, STE 200 17403 #010-01-1986 L1988 CD *020 †20

MC CULLUM, Nancy Naylor. 1936 POWDER MILL RD 17402 #010-01-1986 L1988 FM *020 †18

MC CURLEY, Scott Darren. 1001 S GEORGE ST, YORK HOSPITAL 17403 #041-13-1996 L1999 EM *030 †16

MC GRAW, Thomas P J. ■ 17402 #028-79-1964, ▲ L1965 AN *071

MC GREGOR, Deborah. 2141 PENNSYLVANIA AVE 17404 #025-01-1977 L1984 PHP GP *030

MC GUINN, William James. 1001 S GEORGE ST 17403 #028-34-1981 L1983 AN IM *020 †20,05

MCHEDLISHVILI, Gela Givi. 45 MONUMENT RD, STE 200 17403 #913-23-1988 L1997 NEP *020 †20

MC KEAGUE, Mark Alan. 25 MONUMENT RD, STE 140 17403 #041-14-1994 L1998 IM *020 †20

MEDINA, Lidio Wilfrido. ■ 17402 #726-01-1967 L1985 EM IM *020 †16

MEHTA, Bena Piyush. ■ 17402 #041-14-2005 L2005 EM *012

MENCHEY, Milton James. 924 COLONIAL AVE STE B, BROCKIE MED CTR 17403 #010-01-1970 L1971 IM *020

MILLER, James Andrew. 1 W MARKET ST, STE 202 17401 #041-14-1977 L1978 FM *020 †18

MINGLE, John Joseph. 290 SAINT CHARLES WAY, WELLSPAN NEUROLOGY 17402 #422-01-2001 L2005 N *020 †75

MINHAS, Omar Sajjad. 1575 BANNISTER ST, STE 1 17404 #704-20-2000 L2004 FM *020

MOHAN, Chandra. 380 SAINT CHARLES WAY, WELLSPAN NEPHROLOGY 17402 #495-04-1976 L2001 NEP IM *020 †20

MOHAN, Chandra A M. 308 SAINT CHARLES WAY, WELLSPAN DIALYSIS - YORK 17402 #495-09-1970 L1983 CD *020 †20

MOLINARO, Anthony D, Jr. ■ 17402 #041-02-1974 L1975 FM *020 †18

MONGIA, Rajkumar. 110 PINE GROVE COMMONS, ANESTHESIA ASSOCIATES OF Y 17403 #496-09-1994 L2005 AN *100 †05

MONK, John S, Jr. 25 MONUMENT RD, STE 220 17403 #041-02-1982 L1983 GS *020 †85

MOORTHY, Gita. 2200 S GEORGE ST 17403 #495-37-1979 L1988 N NP *020 †75

MOQUIN, Ross Bassett. 1001 S GEORGE ST, MKB 17403 #010-02-1957 L1973 ON HEM *075 †20

MORAN, Roberto Antonio. 1001 S GEORGE ST, DEPT OF EMERGENCY MEDICINE 17403 #010-03-2006 L2006 EM *012

MORITZ, Michael J. 1855 POWDER MILL RD 17402 #041-12-1977 L1979 ORS HS *020 †40

MORREELS, Chas Louis, Jr. ■ 17403 #023-01-1961 L1962 R *071 †80

MORRISON, Kevin Scott. 1001 S GEORGE ST 17403 #041-01-1986 L1989 AN *020 †05

MORROW, Walter James. 2550 KINGSTON RD, STE 205 17402 #016-45-1983 L1984 FM *020 †55,18

MOSSER, Jeffrey Francis. 2200 S GEORGE ST 17403 #023-01-1977 L1981 N *020 †75

MOSSER, Robert S. 2200 S GEORGE ST 17403 #023-01-1951 L1982 **N** *020 †55
MOTACKI, Joseph Frank. 3550 CONCORD RD, EAP BEHAVORIAL HLTH 17402 #041-15-2000 L2001 **PYG** *020
MOTTER, Leo Justin. 1001 S GEORGE ST 17403 #023-01-1999 L2001 **IM** *020 †20
MOYER, Alyssa. 1001 S GEORGE ST 17403 #041-02-1997 L1999 **IM** *020 †20
MPINGA, Ebondo. ■ 17403 #024-07-1993 L2003 **GS CCS** *020 †85
MUDGE, Kimberlee. 25 MONUMENT RD, STE 260 17403 #055-02-1991 L1994 **GS** *020 †85
MUNIR, Muhammad Shahzeb. ■ 17408 #781-02-2001 **IM** *012
MURPHY, Jennifer Lynne. 1001 S GEORGE ST, YORK HOSP MOTHER-CHILD 17403 #023-01-1987 L1994 **PD** *020 †55
MURRAY, Cheryl Gallagher. 1001 S GEORGE ST 17403 #041-14-1983 L1984 **PTH** *071 †50 ‡
MURRAY, Richard John, Jr. 25 MONUMENT RD, STE 109 17403 #051-01-1981 L1983 **PUD CCM** *020 †20
MURUDKAR, Preeti Meghnath. 2159 WHITE ST, STE 11 17404 #496-55-2001 L2005 **FM** *020 †18
MUZZIO, Kevin Robt. 25 MONUMENT RD, STE E140 17403 #041-02-1991 L1993 **IM** *020 †20
NACHTIGALL, Jonathan. ■ 17408 #041-77-2007, ▲ L2007 *012
NAGIB, Nancy Dia. 1001 S GEORGE ST, DEPT OF FAMILY PRACTICE 17403 #041-14-2005 L2005 **FP** *012
NASIR, Munima. 1001 S GEORGE ST, DEPT OF FAMILY PRATICE 17403 #704-25-1996 L2007 **FP** *012
NEWTON, Frederic Kendall. 1855 POWDER MILL RD 17402 #045-01-2003 L2007 **PM** *020
NICHOLAS, Bradley Eugene. 1001 S GEORGE ST 17403 #041-13-1960 L1961 **GP** *071
NICHOLSON, Kathryn Anne. 380 SAINT CHARLES WAY 17402 #041-14-1998 L2006 **NEP** *020 †20
NICHOLSON, Philip G, Jr. 1001 S GEORGE ST, BROCKIE INTERNAL MEDICINE 17403 #023-01-1996 L1998 **IM** *020 †20
NICHOLSON, Thomas Joseph. 25 MONUMENT RD, STE 260 17403 #041-14-1996 L1999 **CRS** *020 †85,10
NOUR, Samah K.M.. 1001 S GEORGE ST 17403 #539-06-2001 L2004 **GS** *100
NULLIAH, Shirdi. 1001 S GEORGE ST, YORK HOSP 17403 #495-37-2003 L2007 **FP** *012
NWOSU, Nnenna Ngozi. ■ 17402 #690-04-1997 L2007 **FP** *012
OLKOWSKI, Steven T. 25 MONUMENT RD STE 297 17403 #010-02-1981 L1990 **OPH** *020 †35 ‡
ONOBRAKPEYA, Olufunmilayo. 292 SAINT CHARLES WAY, WELLSPAN ENDOUINOLOGY 17402 #690-05-1988 L2001 **END** *020 †20
ORNDORFF, Eric Michael. 110 PINE GROVE COMMONS 17403 #041-02-1999 L2003 **AN** *020 †05
OWENS, John David. ■ 17402 #023-01-1973 L1974 **PTH** *020 †50 ‡
PANDELIDIS, Kirk Nicholas. 1855 POWDER MILL RD 17402 #041-14-1985 L1986 **ORS OSS** *020 †40
PANDELIDIS, Pandelis K. 1600 S GEORGE ST 17403 #418-01-1952 L1961 **P** *020 †75
PANDELIDIS, Steven M. 25 MONUMENT RD STE 220, APPLE HILL SURGICAL ASSOCI 17403 #041-14-1987 L1988 **GS** *020 †85
PARCHURI, Vatsala Devi. 1001 S GEORGE ST, YORK HOSP 17403 #495-50-1997 L2001 **IM** *020 †20
PARGAMENT, Robert Ian. 1001 S GEORGE ST 17403 #023-01-2001 L2004 **IM** *020
PARIKH, Tejas Dinesh. ■ 17408 #041-13-2007 L2007 **GS** *012
PARRA, Jose Ricardo. 25 MONUMENT RD, STE 105 17403 #007-02-1994 L2005 **VS** *020 †85
PASARILLA, Paul Michael. ■ 17404 #048-16-2003 L2003 **GS** *012
PASUMARTHY, Lakshmi S. 25 MONUMENT RD, STE 140 17403 #495-21-1994 L2000 **IM** *020 †20
PATEL, Alpa Pravinbhai. 292 SAINT CHARLES WAY 17402 #028-34-1994 L1997 **END** *020 †20
PATEL, Dipti Y.. 1001 S GEORGE ST, 4TH FL 17403 #759-06-2001 L2007 **IM** *100 †20
PATEL, Minesh Nitinkumar. ■ 17408 #496-44-2005 L2007 **IM** *012
PATEL, Rajesh. ■ 17406 #495-37-2000 **FM** *020
PATEL, Rakesh Bhanuprasad. 1001 S GEORGE ST, DEPT OF PEDS 17403 #422-01-1999 L2006 **PDI** *020 †55
PATEL, Snehal B.. ■ 17408 #305-01-1999 L2003 **FM** *020 †18
PATEL, Vipul Ghanshyambha. 1001 S GEORGE ST, BROCKIE HOSPITALIST 17403 #496-54-2003 L2007 **IM** *020
PATIL, Prashant Veerangow. 1001 S GEORGE ST, DEPT IM 17403 #496-01-2002 L2007 **IM** *012
PATIL, Sumukh Balaji. ■ 17402 #051-04-2003 L2003 **DR** *012
PEARCE, Steven Rowan. 1001 S GEORGE ST 17403 #028-34-1979 L1985 **AN** *020 †05
PERCHELLET, Stephen Jerem. ■ 17402 #019-02-2006 L2006 **EM** *012
PINDZOLA, J Ander. 1001 S GEORGE ST 17403 #023-01-2002 L2006 **EM** *012
PINNOW, Jeffery Matthew. ■ 17403 #026-04-2007 L2007 **EM** *012
PIZZIKETTI, Robert John. 1 W MARKET ST STE 202 17401 #041-13-1987 L1988 **FM** *020 †18
PLITT, Calvin Edwin. 25 MONUMENT RD, STE 201 17403 #023-01-1977 L2003 **CD EM** *020 †20
PODIUK-KLUFAS, Halyna I. ■ 17402 #407-16-1958 **GP** *012
POLLACK, Marc Lewis. 1001 S GEORGE ST, DEPT OF EMERG MED YH 17403 #649-33-1980 L1983 **EM ESM** *020 †20,16
POLLAK, Brian Michael. 25 MONUMENT RD, STE 140 17403 #041-12-1996 L1998 **IMG** *020 †20
POPA, Alina Lorena. 116 S GEORGE ST, FAMILY FIRST HEALTH 17401 #781-01-1999 L2005 **ID** *020 †20
PRATS, Ignacio. 25 MONUMENT RD STE 260 17403 #021-01-1984 L1994 **GS SO** *020 †85
PRENDERGAST, Michael Jos. 25 MONUMENT RD STE 100, APPLE HILL MEDICAL CENTER 17403 #041-02-1962 L1963 **U GS** *071 †95
QUARTEY, Seth Mac. 1001 S GEORGE ST, FL 4 17403 #051-04-1989 L1999 **ID** *020 †20
RAHEJA, Divisha. 1001 S GEORGE ST 17403 #495-29-2004 L2007 **IM** *012
RAHIM, Shamila. 1001 S GEORGE ST, YORK HOSPITAL 17403 #041-13-2003 L2006 **IM** *020
RAHN, Mary Elizabeth. 8 WYNTRE BROOKE DR 17403 #051-04-1974 L1975 **P** *020 †18,75
RAMAGE, Ann Louise. 1575 BANNISTER ST, YORK HLTH SYST MED GRP 17404 #041-07-1981 L1984 **FM** *020 †20
RANEN, Neal Gilbert. 1491 S QUEEN ST 17403 #024-16-1988 L1996 **P** *020 †75
RAO, Paul Gurudath. ■ 17403 #051-01-2006 **P** *012
RAO, Usha G. 1001 S GEORGE ST 17403 #496-38-1972 L1982 **AN** *020 †05
REDDY, V Saraswathi. 110 PINE GROVE COMMONS, PA, INC. 17403 #495-65-1966 L1977 **AN** *020 †05
REIF, Robert Edward. ■ 17402 #023-01-2002 L2002 **CN** *020
REILLY, Charles Mullany. 605 S GEORGE ST STE 200, YORK HOSP-DEPT PEDIATRICS 17401 #041-01-1955 L1956 **PD** *071 †55
REINHARD, Ronald James. 1001 S GEORGE ST 17403 #041-01-1964 L1965 **IM** *020 †20
REXRODE, William Oehme. 151 HIGHLAND RD 17403 #041-01-1963 L1965 **PUD IM** *071 †20
RHOADS, Jonathan E, Jr. 1001 S GEORGE ST 17403 #024-01-1964 L1974 **GS TS** *020 †85,90
ROACH, Chad Jeremy. 1001 S GEORGE ST, DEPT EM 17403 #016-02-2007 L2007 **EM** *012

ROBERT, Stacey G. 1001 S GEORGE ST, FAMILY PRACTICE ADMIN 17403 #023-01-1999 L2001 **FM** *020 †18
ROBERTSON, Joanne M. ■ 17402 #024-16-1980 L1980 **EM** *075 †16
ROBINSON, George Raymond. 25 MONUMENT RD STE 190, APPLE HILL MED CTR 17403 #055-01-1987 L1988 **PCC CCM** *020 †20
ROBINSON, Joseph Edgar. 325 S BELMONT ST, MEMORIAL HOSPITAL 17403 #032-01-1992 L1996 **AN** *020 †05
ROBINSON, Leslie Elaine. 605 S GEORGE ST, STE 200 17401 #041-14-1979 L1981 **OBG** *020 †30
ROGERS, Edward Q, Jr. 140 PINE GROVE COMMONS 17403 #023-01-1983 L1984 **IM** *020 †20
ROLLINGS-MAZZA, Pamela P. 1600 S GEORGE ST 17403 #063-01-1996 L2001 *020 †75
RONEY, Thomas James. 2251 EASTERN BLVD 17402 #649-14-1973 L1986 **FM** *020 †18
ROTHROCK, Gilmore Morrow. 25 MONUMENT RD, STE 220 17403 #041-02-1958 L1959 **GS VS** *071 †85
ROZZI, Heather Valentine. 1001 S GEORGE ST, YORK HOSPITAL DEPT OF EMER 17403 #041-14-2001 L2001 **EM** *020 †16
RUBI, Jorge Ulises. 296 SAINT CHARLES WAY 17402 #023-01-1996 L1998 **IM** *020 †20
RUDIS, Steven Peter. 325 S BELMONT ST, EMERGENCY DEPARTMENT 17403 #010-01-1989 L2002 **EM** *020 †16
RUMSEY, Colleen H. 1001 S GEORGE ST, YORK HOSP ED ADM 17403 #041-14-2000 L2001 **EM** *020
RUSSO, Anthony F. 1420 6TH AVE, MEMORIAL BEHAVIORAL HEALTH 17403 #030-06-1974 L1988 **P ADP** *071 †75
RUTLAND, Hedley E. 914 W MARKET ST 17401 #023-01-1933 L1934 **GP** *071
RYSCAVAGE, Thomas Stephen. 2200 S GEORGE ST, MEDFORD PROFESSIONAL CENTE 17403 #010-02-1973 L1975 **ORS** *020 †40 ‡
SALAZAR, Louis Fernando. 1001 S GEORGE ST 17403 #033-06-1986 L1991 **AN** *020 †05
SALTER, Ridgley Paul. 2775 N GEORGE ST 17406 #041-14-1996 L1998 **FM** *020 †18
SAMELSON, Leo. ■ 17403 #024-01-1952 L1955 **IM** *071 †20
SANSTEAD, John Kenneth. 296 SAINT CHARLES WAY 17402 #041-02-1976 L1978 **IM** *020 †20
SANTANIELLO, Robina Renee. 1112 PENNSYLVANIA AVE 17404 #041-14-1987 L1990 **FM** *020 †18
SCARITO, Elizabeth Alice. 1938 SECURITY DR, ASSOCIATES IN ADULT MEDICI 17402 #023-01-1992 L1994 **IM** *020 †20
SCARPELLI, David Jos. 1001 S GEORGE ST 17403 #035-15-1989 L1992 **FM** *020 †18
SCHENDEL, Paul Burnett. 302 SAINT CHARLES WAY 17402 #026-04-1979 L1990 **NEP CCM** *020 †20
SCHIRK, Steven Karl. 1001 S GEORGE ST, YORK HOSP EMERGENCY DEPT 17403 #041-14-1984 L1985 **EM** *020 †16
SCHLAGER, Charles Edward. 1 W MARKET ST, STE 202 17401 #041-01-1957 L1958 **FM** *020 †18
SCHMITZ, Thomas Jos. 1001 S GEORGE ST 17403 #041-14-1986 L1988 **AN** *020 †05
SCHOEDEL, Christianne. 360 SAINT CHARLES WAY 17402 #023-01-1991 L1996 **PO OPH** *020 †35 ‡
SCHONAUER, Thomas David. 1 RATHTON RD 17403 #041-02-1966 L1967 **PD** *020 †55
SCHRADING, Walter Alan. 1001 S GEORGE ST, YORK HOSPITAL 17403 #041-12-1986 L1987 **EM** *020 †16
SCHULZ, J Albert. 1600 S GEORGE ST 17403 #041-01-1964 L1965 **P CHP** *020 †75
SCOTT, Sharon Lee. 25 MONUMENT RD, STE 140 17403 #065-10-1992 L1994 **IM** *020 †20
SCOTT, Thomas Rodger. 1001 S GEORGE ST 17403 #041-14-1986 L1987 **GS** *020 †85
SEIBERT, Richard H. ■ 17403 #041-01-1950 L1951 **IM CD** *071 †20
SEVRIN, Amanda Hope. 2651 FAIRWAY DR 17402 #041-01-2001 L2003 **ID** *012 †20
SEYDEL, Teresa Jane. 1010 PLYMOUTH RD 17402 #023-01-2004 L2004 **FM** *020 †18
SHAH, Shalini Bharat. ■ 17404 #041-15-2005 L2005 **FP** *012
SHAPIRO, Steven Lewis. 1001 S GEORGE ST 17403 #051-07-1982 L1988 **NPM PD** *020 †55
SHARMA, Chetan Lall. 1001 S GEORGE ST, YORK HOSP 17403 #495-37-2003 **FP** *012
SHEARS, Larry. 1575 BANNISTER ST, STE 7 17404 #055-01-1991 L1993 **GS** *020 †85,90
SHI, Cindy Quingxin. 1001 S GEORGE ST, YORK HOSPITAL 17403 #243-16-1983 L1999 **DR** *020 †80,28
SHORB, Andrew Reed. 924 COLONIAL AVE, STE G 17403 #041-14-2001 L2006 **OTO** *100 †45
SHUE, William Martin. 1601 S QUEEN ST 17403 #041-02-1961 L1962 **OS GS** *071 †85
SICILIA, Bruce E. 1850 NORMANDIE DR 17408 #041-07-1988 L1994 **PM PMM** *020 †60
SICURANZA, Michael John. 1855 POWDER MILL RD 17402 #023-01-1985 L1990 **ORS EM** *020 †40
SIDDOWAY, Lyle Amos. 1001 S GEORGE ST 17403 #023-07-1979 L1989 **CD IM** *020 †20
SIMON, Nicolas. 1001 S GEORGE ST DEPT OBT 17403 #165-03-1961 L1976 **OBG** *030 †30
SINGAL, Brenda Bouchard. 1620 S QUEEN ST, YORK PEDIATRIC ASSOC 17403 #023-07-1991 L1993 **PD** *020 †55
SINGAL, Rajesh. 1620 S QUEEN ST, YORK PEDIATRIC ASSOCIATES 17403 #023-07-1991 L1993 **PD** *020 †55
SIPE, Paul Gray. 1601 S QUEEN ST, WHITE ROSE SURGICAL 17403 #041-12-1984 L1987 **CRS GS** *020 †85,10
SIPPLE, Daniel P. ■ 17403 #018-75-2003, ▲ L2007 **PM** *020
SIROLLY, Kendra Walker. 2339 S GEORGE ST, SPRINGDALE PEDIATRIC MEDIC 17403 #021-01-2002 L2002 **PD** *020 †55
SIU, David Suiwai. 302 SAINT CHARLES WAY 17402 #038-06-1999 L2005 **NEP** *100 †20
SLOAN, Richard Walter. 1001 S GEORGE ST, YORK HOSP 17403 #041-14-1977 L1978 **FM PA** *040 †18
SMALL, Richard Elwood. ■ 17408 #023-01-1955 L1956 **FM** *071 †18
SMALLEY, Arthur Jedson. 1001 S GEORGE ST 17403 #035-06-1986 L1990 **AN** *020 †05
SMITH, Mark Alan. 25 MONUMENT RD STE 250 17403 #023-01-1986 L1988 **GE** *020 †20
SMOLKO, James Michael. 1750 5TH AVE, FIRST FLOOR 17403 #041-12-1985 L1986 **AN** *020 †05
SMOLKO, James Regis. 110 PINE GROVE COMMONS, ANESTHESIA ASSOC OF PA INC 17403 #041-12-1961 L1962 **AN** *020 †05
SOENEN, Sherry Lau. 25 MONUMENT RD STE 140, APPLE HILL INTERNAL MEDICI 17403 #023-01-2003 L2003 **IM** *100
SOLOMON, Sam John. 25 MONUMENT RD, STE 200 17403 #041-09-1979 L1981 **CD IM** *020 †20
SONG, Suzette Jimi. 1855 POWDER MILL RD 17402 #041-02-1993 L1996 **ORS** *020 †40
SOPCHAK, Michael Andrew. 1001 S GEORGE ST 17403 #035-15-1976 L1985 **AN** *020 †05 ‡
SOTIRESCU, Dan. 25 MONUMENT RD STE 294, CANCER CARE ASSOCIATES OF 17403 #781-01-1986 L2000 **HO IM** *020 †20
SPANGLER, Donald Bruce. 1001 S GEORGE ST, YORK HOSPITAL 17403 #041-13-1963 L1964 **OBG** *071 †30
SPANGLER, Michael S. 1600 6TH AVE STE 114 17403 #041-78-2003, ▲ L2003 **IM** *020

■ = Address Information Privacy Protected

SPEARS, Laura Smith. 490 SHADY DELL RD 17403 #041-01-1979 L1982 **D** *020 †15 ‡

SPERANZA, David Nicholas. 2690 SOUTHFIELD DR 17403 #016-43-1981 L1989 **GE IM** *020 †20 ‡

SROUR, James Winston. 2690 SOUTHFIELD DR 17403 #023-01-1976 L1978 **GE IM** *020 †20

STAHL, Amanda Michelle. 1001 S GEORGE ST 17403 #654-01-2007 L2007 **OBG** *012

STEIN, Jonathan Ian. 1001 S GEORGE ST 17403 #041-01-1995 L1997 **AN** *020 †05

STEVENS, Bryan James. 3542 CONCORD RD 17402 #041-12-1971 L1976 **P** *020 †75

STOJAN, George. DEPT OF MEDICAL AFFAIRS, YORK HOSP 17405 #957-02-2005 L2008 *100

STRANG, Clyde Arthur. 2350 FREEDOM WAY, STE 102 17402 #023-01-1977 L1979 **U** *020 †95

SUAN, Eric Pinn. 199 S YALE ST 17403 #008-01-1986 L1987 **OPH** *020 †35

SULLIVAN, James Jos. 325 S BELMONT ST 17403 #011-75-1987, ▲ L1991 **PM** *020 †60

SUPPIAH, Ravichandran. 325 S BELMONT ST, DEPARTMENT OF ANESTHESIOLO 17403 #495-95-1992 L2005 **AN** *020 †05

SWAMIDOSS, Stephenson S P. 1850 NORMANDIE DR 17408 #495-04-1971 L1976 **PTH PCP** *071 †50 ‡

TABATABAI, Seyed E. 25 MONUMENT RD, STE 294 17403 #020-02-1994 L1995 **HO** *020 †20

TALLURI, Satish Chandra. 310 PINE GROVE COMMONS, APOLLO INTERNAL MEDICINE 17403 #495-58-1984 L1998 **IM** *020 †20

TAMEO, Michael Nathan. 1001 S GEORGE ST 17403 #665-01-2002 L2002 **VS** *012

TAUTKUS, Barbara. 1001 S GEORGE ST 17403 #422-01-1983 L1984 **PD** *020 †55

TAYLOR, Bradley Scott. 1575 BANNISTER ST, STE 7 17404 #012-05-1993 L1995 **TS** *020 †85,90

TERRY, Shawn Michael. 1001 S GEORGE ST, TRAUMA SVC YORK HOSP 17403 #030-06-1994 L2000 **TRS GS** *020 †85

THIEME, Heather Anne. 1001 S GEORGE ST 17403 #422-01-2002 L2003 **GS** *012

THOMAS, Elise F. 1620 S QUEEN ST 17403 #035-45-1990 L2007 **PD** *020 †55

THOMAS, Latona Martha A. 26 S YALE ST 17403 #041-02-1976 L1977 **OBG** *020 †30

THOMAS, Mazhuvanchery A. 1001 S GEORGE ST DEPT EM 17403 #495-27-1961 L1986 **EM** *020 †16

TIRUCHELVAM, Junia P. 1207 S QUEEN ST 17403 #220-01-1974 L1985 **FM** *020 †18

TIRUCHELVAM, Vasudevan. 25 MONUMENT RD, STE 260 17403 #220-01-1974 L1985 **GS** *020 †85

TOLERICO, Paul Howard. 25 MONUMENT RD STE 200 17403 #041-14-1993 L1995 **CD** *020 †20

TOMHE, Yaseen Ahmad. 25 MONUMENT RD, STE 105 17403 #875-01-1972 L2002 **VS** *020 †85

TRANCHITELLA, Vincent J. 1855 POWDER MILL RD 17402 #041-14-1989 L1992 **PM OS** *020 †60

TRIANTAFYLLOU, Steven J. 1855 POWDER MILL RD 17402 #041-14-1985 L1986 **ORS OSS** *020 †40

TULL, John Woodring. 469 W MARKET ST 17401 #041-02-1966 L1967 **OPH** *071 †35

TUMMALA, Vijaya Laxmi. 1927 QUEENSWOOD DR J 2, YORK HILLS APARTMENTS 17403 #495-58-1994 L2002 **IM** *020 †20

TUNG, William Siao-Ping. 25 MONUMENT RD, STE 105 17403 #023-07-1992 L2006 **VS** *020 †85

TURKEWITZ, David. 605 S GEORGE ST, STE 200 17401 #035-47-1978 L1979 **PD PEM** *040 †55

TYNDALL-SMITH, Althea Pat. 1001 S GEORGE ST, DEPT OF FAMILY MEDICINE 17403 #041-15-2005 L2005 **FP** *012

UHLMAN, Eric James. 2350 FREEDOM WAY STE 102 17402 #041-13-1989 L1991 **U** *020 †95

UNWIN, William Michael. 1693 S QUEEN ST, THE WOMENS HLTHCR GRP 17403 #033-01-1985 L1987 **OBG** *020 †30

UPDIKE, Furman Titus, Jr. 2339 S GEORGE ST, SPRINGDALE PEDIATRIC MEDIC 17403 #041-02-1961 L1962 **PD** *071 †55

VAID, Sachin. 1001 S GEORGE ST 17403 #495-45-2001 *012

VAIDA, Razvan Theodor. 1101 EDGAR ST, STE A 17403 #781-01-1996 L2001 **P** *020 †75

VAIDYA, Sharad Mohan. ■ 17402 #039-01-2005 L2005 **IM** *100

VANDEN BOSCHE, Marie Lynn. 2775 N GEORGE ST 17406 #023-01-1997 L1999 **FM** *020 †18

VAN GIESEN, Peter James. 1855 POWDER MILL RD 17402 #041-13-1971 L1972 **ORS HS** *020 †40

VAN SANT, Alan Eugene. 9 RATHTON RD, SPRINGDALE MED CTR 17403 #041-01-1961 L1963 **PM** *020 †60

VAN WYK, Rita E. 300 PINE GROVE COMMONS 17403 #836-03-1970 L1974 **FM** *020 †18

VEEK, Kristina Michelle. ■ 17404 #056-06-2008 *012

VEGA, David Daniel. 1001 S GEORGE ST, YORK HOSPITAL 17403 #041-14-2002 L2002 **EM** *020 †16

VENTURA, Melencio C, Jr. 2860 CAROL RD, PEDIATRIC HEALTH ASSOCIATE 17402 #051-04-1991 L1994 **PD** *020 †55

VERMA, Navin. 302 SAINT CHARLES WAY 17402 #495-23-1994 L2002 **NEP** *020 †20

VIBHAKAR, Dev Bharat. ■ 17404 #028-79-2006, ▲ L2007 **GS** *012

VIBHUTI, Veeranna Somashe. 1001 S GEORGE ST 17403 #495-35-2001 L2007 **IM** *012

VIRGILIO, Lawrence Adam. 17403 #035-15-1970 L1975 **PTH** *020 †50

VISCO, Denise Lennick. 1880 KENNETH RD, STE 1 17408 #041-02-1991 L1995 **OPH** *020 †35

VOHRA, Surinder Pal Singh. 1600 6TH AVE, STE 101 17403 #495-45-1984 L1993 **ON HEM** *020 †20

VOORSTAD, Theodoor A. 605 S GEORGE ST, STE 200 17401 #165-08-1992 L1996 **IM** *020 †20

VU, Thao Hoang. ■ 17403 #035-19-1998 L2002 **AN** *020

VU, To-Nhu Hoang. 1001 S GEORGE ST 17403 #041-14-1993 L2003 **AN PME** *020 †05

VU, Tuan Hoang. 290 SAINT CHARLES WAY, WELLSPAN NEUROLOGY 17402 #041-14-1989 L2002 **N** *050 †75

WAGNER, Clayton Wm. 1855 POWDER MILL RD 17402 #021-01-1988 L1999 **ORS** *020 †40

WALDROP, Charles Danny. 1001 S GEORGE ST, YORK HOSP-DEPT OF PEDS 17403 #036-07-1977 L1989 **PD ADL** *020 †55

WALKER, Ryan Mcgarry. 1001 S GEORGE ST 17403 #654-01-2007 L2007 **GS** *012

WALLET, Joshua Michael. ■ 17403 #041-02-2004 L2004 **GS** *012

WALLO, Elise A. 1001 S GEORGE ST, DEPT OF EMERGENCY 17403 #041-15-2005 L2005 **EM** *012

WALTZ, Karen Marie. 1934 SECURITY DR, YORK DERMATOLOGY 17402 #041-02-1992 L1997 **D** *020 †15

WAMPLER, M John. 2164 TALL OAKS LN 17403 #041-01-1957 L1958 **IM** *020

WANG, Pin. 2690 SOUTHFIELD DR, GASTROENTEROLOGY ASSOC OF 17403 #243-63-1983 L2004 **GE** *020 †20

WARNER, Carleen Talbot. 1010 PLYMOUTH RD 17402 #037-01-2001 L2001 **FM** *020 †18

WASSEF, Sherif Botros. 1001 S GEORGE ST, RADIOLOGY DEPARTMENT 17403 #915-04-1984 L1999 **VIR** *020 †80

WEAVER, Richmand Garrison. 325 S BELMONT ST 17403 #041-77-1954, ▲ L1959 **GP** *071

WEIGNER, Michael Bradley. 1001 S GEORGE ST 17403 #041-14-1994 L2001 **EM** *020 †16

WEINER, Fredric Roy. 120 SCARBORO DR 17403 #041-02-1972 L1973 **FM** *030 †18

WELLS, Erik Martin. 1001 S GEORGE ST, DEPT OF EMERGENCY MEDICINE 17403 #041-14-2006 *012

WHITNEY, Jonathan Paul. 1001 S GEORGE ST, BROCKIE HOSPITALISTS 17403 #051-07-1981 L1982 **IM** *020 †20

WILLIAMS, Glenn Roger. 1620 S QUEEN ST, YORK PEDIATRIC ASSOCIATES 17403 #041-14-1986 L1989 **PD** *020 †55

WILSON, David Geo. 1001 S GEORGE ST 17403 #041-14-1990 L1992 **FM** *072 †18

WILSON, Michael Andrew. 1001 S GEORGE ST 17403 #023-01-1988 L1990 **FM** *020 †18

WILSON, Ray Austin. ■ 17402 #023-01-1957 L1958 **FM** *071

WILSON, Robert Vincent. 2350 FREEDOM WAY, STE 102 17402 #010-02-1980 L1989 **U** *020 †95

WILT, Kenneth E. 413-13-1951 L1952 **TS GS** *071 †85,90

WINAND, Andrew Todd. 1001 S GEORGE ST, BROCKIE HOSPITALISTS 17403 #041-13-1990 L1993 **IM** *020 †20

WINAND, David Alan. 25 MONUMENT RD, STE 105 17403 #041-13-1996 L1998 **VS** *020 †85 ‡

WIRSZTEL, Hillel. 1001 S GEORGE ST, YORK HOSPITAL 17403 #654-01-1996 L2006 **FP** *012

WOERTHWEIN, Kenneth F. 1575 BANNISTER ST, YORKTOWNE FAMILY MEDICINE 17404 #016-11-1970 L1971 **FM FPG** *020 †18

WOLFE, William Scott. 1 W MARKET ST, STE 202 17401 #231-05-1995 L2000 **FM** *020 †18

WOLFGANG, Jill Ann. 1001 S GEORGE ST, YORK HOSPITAL 17403 #041-14-1998 L2000 **ID** *020 †20

WONG, Ming-Der. 1934 SECURITY DR 17402 #385-02-1964 L1975 **IM** *071 †20

WOO, Samuel. 1001 S GEORGE ST, YORK HOSP EMERG DEPT 17403 #023-01-1994 L1996 **EM** *020 †16

WOODARD, Jameson Dean. 1001 S GEORGE ST 17403 #130-02-2007 L2007 **IM** *012

WOODARD, Stacey Lee. 1001 S GEORGE ST 17403 #130-02-2007 L2007 **OBG** *012

WOODS, Anne Mary. 2159 WHITE ST 17404 #010-01-1976 L1977 **FM** *071 †18

WRIGHT, John Andrew. 1001 S GEORGE ST 17403 #030-06-1997 L2004 **PTH** *020

YACOUB, Sherif Fikry. 25 MONUMENT RD, STE 94 17403 #915-04-1984 L2007 **RO** *020 †80

YEE ARMAH, Shawyin. 1600 6TH AVE, PROFESSIONAL CTR STE 113 17403 #033-05-1993 L1998 **OPH** *020 †35

YINGER, Mark David. ■ 17403 #041-15-2007 L2007 *012

YOHE, William Calvin. 1001 S GEORGE ST 17403 #041-01-1948 L1951 **IM RHU** *071

YOO, Heui Gyeong. 924 COLONIAL AVE STE B, BROCKIE INTERNAL MEDICINE 17403 #023-01-1997 L2007 **IM** *020 †20

YORK, Terry Neal. 325 S BELMONT ST, RADIOLOGY DEPT 17403 #055-75-1988, ▲ L1989 **R** *020

YOST, Samuel Anthony, Jr. 50 WYNTRE BROOKE DR 17403 #041-09-1992 L1997 **PS** *020 †65

YSLA, Roy Gilbert. 1681 KENNETH RD 17408 #409-39-1972 L1987 **PM** *020 †60

YUEN, Nelson. 1101 EDGAR ST, URGENT CARE - WELLSPAN HEA 17403 #041-02-2001 L2004 **FM** *020 †18

ZACHARIAH, Philip T. 924 COLONIAL AVE STE B 17403 #005-12-1992 L2005 **IM** *020 †20

ZAMMAM, Sawsan Yasen. 1600 6TH AVE, STE 114 17403 #875-01-1989 L2002 **IM** *020 †20

ZARFOS, Morgan Lehr. ■ 17403 #041-01-1943 L1944 **IM** *071

ZELIS, David William. 1620 S QUEEN ST, YORK PEDIATRIC MEDICINE 17403 #041-12-2001 L2004 **PD** *020 †55

ZEMO, Peter Lehman. 924 COLONIAL AVE 17403 #041-02-1962 L1965 **OTO** *020 †45

ZENG, Rong Wendy. 1001 S GEORGE ST 17403 #243-76-1991 L2003 **OBG** *020

ZIMBERG, Gary Bryant. 1600 S GEORGE ST 17403 #051-07-1981 L1983 **P** *020 †75

ZUBROD, Gordon Joshua. 1001 S GEORGE ST, THOMAS HOST FAM PRACTICE 17403 #041-14-2000 L2005 **FM** *020 †18

YORK HAVEN – YORK

HERROLD, Warren Constans. ■ 17370 #041-02-1944 L1945 **FM** *071

YORK SPRINGS – ADAMS

NOLT, Jeffrey Scott. 408 MAIN ST, ADAMS CUMBERLAND FAMILY ME 17372 #041-09-1986 L1987 **FM** *020 †18

RILEY, Jessica Lenai. ■ 17372 #041-01-2007 L2007 **EM** *012

SAUERS, Crystal Ann. ■ 17372 #041-13-2006 L2006 **EM** *012

YOUNGSVILLE – WARREN

ELVIR AVILA, Ramon. 400 E MAIN ST, PRIMARY HEALTHCARE ASSOCIA 16371 #649-01-1968 L1973 **FM** *071 †18

ORZANO, Jennifer Anne. 115 7TH ST 16371 #010-02-1998 L2005 **IM** *020 †20

TURBESSI, Albert Jos. 400 E MAIN ST 16371 #055-01-1965 L1967 **FM** *020 †18

YOUNGWOOD – WESTMORELAND

MILLS, Steven English. 505 N 4TH ST 15697 #041-07-1994 L1996 **IM** *020 †20

STROH, Andrew Michael. 505 N 4TH ST 15697 #041-12-1977 L1979 **GS** *020 †85

ZELIENOPLE – BUTLER

PFOFF, Robert Michael. 400 W CULVERT ST, HEALTH AND WELLNESS CENTER 16063 #041-12-1981 L1985 **IMG PLM** *020 †20

SWAN, Reyer O. ■ 16063 #041-02-1949 L1950 **GP** *071

WEIDENHAMER, Monica L. 626 W NEW CASTLE ST 16063 #038-43-1984 L1987 **PD PDC** *020

ZIONSVILLE – LEHIGH

COOK, Richard Paul. 5802 CHESTNUT ST, ZIONSVILLE FAMILY PRACTICE 18092 #041-09-1977 L1978 **FM** *020 †18

TRUSCOTT, Kenneth D, Jr. 5802 CHESTNUT ST, ZIONSVILLE FAM PRAC 18092 #041-02-1985 L1986 **FM** *020 †18 ‡

ADJUNTAS – ADJUNTAS

BALLESTER, Gory. PO BOX 435 00601 #042-01-2005 **DR** *012

CUEVAS-SANABRIA, Edwin. 6 CALLE RIUS RIVERA 00601 #649-14-1984 L1990 *020

DECLET-MANZANET, Antonio. 26 CALLE MUNOZ RIVERA 00601 #649-14-1977 L1979 **GP** *020

GONZALEZ-SEPULVEDA, Jose. ■ 00601 #847-04-1955 L1966 **GP** *020

MARTINEZ PEREZ, Juan C. ■ 00601 #042-04-1993 L1994 **IM** *020

MILAN, Rafael A. CALLE SAN JOAQUIN 00601 #847-04-1962 L1966 **IM OS** *071

MURPHY-RIVERA, Francisco. 19 CALLE SAN JOAQUIN 00601 #042-03-1991 L1994 **FM** *020 ‡

PEREZ FRONTERA, Sigrid D. 32 CALLE MUNOZ RIVERA 00601 #042-04-2005 L2006 *100

PEREZ-VALENTIN, Jose R. 32 CALLE MUNOZ RIVERA 00601 #847-17-1983 L1988 **GP** *020

QUILES LOPEZ, Ricardo Lui. ■ 00601 #649-30-2003 L2003 *100

RAMOS, Rigoberto G. 35 CALLE MUNOZ RIVERA 00601 #042-01-1986 L1989 **CD IM** *020

ROMAN, Alexis E. ■ 00601 #847-06-1987 L1994 *020

ROMAN, Jaime Luis. ■ 00601 #042-02-2004 **IM** *012

SEPULVEDA PAGAN, Nydia Iv. ■ 00601 #649-30-2002 L2004 *100

TORRES PAGAN, Mayra Ivett. 10 CALLE MUNOZ RIVERA 00601 #649-14-1994 L2001 *020

VELEZ-ALICEA, J Daniel. 4 CALLE JOSE V BOSCH 00601 #649-14-1980 L1984 **GP** *020

YELTON-ROSSELLO, Peter J. 57 CALLE SAN JOAQUIN 00601 #308-04-1990 L1992 **IM** *020

AGUADA – AGUADA

ACEVEDO, David. HC 3 BOX 29965, 0 CARR 417 HM 2 00602 #649-35-2001 L2002 *020

ACEVEDO RUIZ, Omar. HC 5 BOX 12748 00602 #649-14-2003 L2006 *100

ALERS LOPEZ, Carlo M.■ 00602 #649-14-2003 L2005 *100

BAEZ MURPHY, Gloria E. 115 CALLE COLON 00602 #847-01-1965 L1974 **FM GP** *020

BATLLE, Elsie. ■ 00602 #649-14-2000 **FP** *100

BERMUDEZ-MORENO, Edgardo. 259 CALLE COLON, CENTRO DE CUIDADO CARDIO 00602 #649-14-1982 L1992 **IC CD** *020 †20

CAJIGAS, Yanniris. ■ 00602 #042-01-2006 **FP** *012

CHAPARRO, Marjorie Susan. ■ 00602 #033-05-1997 L1997 **PD** *100

CLAUDIO, Manuel. ■ 00602 #308-03-1983 L1987 **GP** *020

COLOMBANY, Hector Javier. ■ 00602 #649-14-1996 L1996 **CD** *020

CONCEPCION, Stephanie A. ■ 00602 #649-14-1996 L1997 *020

CORONA-AMARO, Juan M. HC 59 BOX 4930 00602 #649-09-1983 L1990 **IM** *020

CRESPO, Margarita. 201 CALLE LA PAZ 00602 #649-18-1986 L1990 **GP** *020

CRUZ MIRANDA, Sonia E. ■ 00602 #308-03-1983 L1991 **PD** *020

DIAZ SOTO, Manuel Enrique. ■ 00602 #308-03-1985 L1992 **GP** *020

ECHEVARRIA-SANTIAGO, Luis. 278 CALLE MARINA 00602 #042-03-1980 L1984 **PD** *020

GALLOZA LAGUER, Hector N. PO BOX 336 00602 #649-14-2001 L2003 *100

GALLOZA-SERRANO, Edgardo. ■ 00602 #847-02-1980 L1984 **PD** *020

GONZALEZ, Mario Roberto. ■ 00602 #042-03-2006 **P** *012

GONZALEZ ESCLAVON, Edna. 311 CALLE COLON 00602 #308-03-1977 L1980 *020

GONZALEZ-MORET, Hector E. PO BOX 94, 24 BO ASOMANTE CARR 115 00602 #042-01-1970 L1973 **PD OS** *020

GONZALEZ MUNOZ, Carmen E. C/O PO BOX 461, CALLE COLON #86 00602 #308-02-1986 L1988 **END** *020

GONZALEZ-SANCHEZ, Roberto. 125A CALLE COLON 00602 #308-03-1981 L1988 **IM** *020

LAUSELL, Victor S. 152 CALLE PAZ 00602 #847-01-1963 L1968 **GP OS** *020

MENDOZA, Jose Carlos. 76 CALLE ESTACION 00602 #308-04-1988 L1995 *020

MENDOZA, Jose R. 76 CALLE ESTACION 00602 #847-10-1963 L1966 **OBG** *072

MERCADO, Katia Larisa. ■ 00602 #042-01-2000 L2003 **FM** *020 †18 ‡

MUNIZ MOLINERO, Carlos. 76 CALLE COLON 00602 #649-14-1992 L1994 **IM** *020

ORTEGA, Hiram. C/O APARTADO 998, CALLE COLON #93 00602 #308-03-1983 L1986 **PD** *020

ORTEGA, Hiram Daniel. ■ 00602 #042-01-2006 **IM** *012

PAGAN, Elizabeth. 103 URB MONTEMAR, BOX 368 00602 #042-01-1994 L1997 **PD** *020 †55

PAGAN-OCASIO, Vannessa. 7 LAS CASONAS 00602 #042-01-1997 L2001 **P** *020

POUR-AHMADI, Navid. ■ 00602 #308-13-2001 L2005 *100

QUESADA, Angel Manuel. ■ 00602 #649-14-1999 L1999 **FM** *020

QUINONEZ, Evaristo. CR 58, 0.2 CARR 417 00602 #308-06-1983 L1991 **GP** *020

QUINONEZ CARRABALLO, Fredd. PO BOX 7000, SUITE 238 00602 #308-01-1990 L1990 *020

QUINTANA VALENTIN, Jose E. HC 3 BOX 35130, BO MALPASO 00602 #042-04-1996 L1999 *020

RAMIREZ, Leonardo Javier. 34 URB SAN FRANCISCO, CALLE C 00602 #042-02-1996 L1998 **IM** *020

RAMIREZ LORENZO, Humberto. BUZON A-604 BO CARRIZAL 00602 #308-03-1980 L1983 *020

RAMOS MENDEZ, Alberto. 137 CALLE COLON BOX 1076, CENTRO DE MEDICINA ESPECIA 00602 #042-03-1984 L1986 **FM** *020 †18

REYES VALE, Victor M. ■ 00602 #042-04-2000 L2001 **IM** *020

RIOS, Felix Francisco. 311 CALLE COLON 00602 #308-03-1977 L1980 **GP** *020

RIVERA, Erik X. ■ 00602 #042-03-2008 *012

RIVERA, Solimayli. 251 CALLE LA PAZ 00602 #308-04-2001 L2003 *100

RIVERA MATOS, Julio E. 278 CALLE COLON 00602 #308-03-1982 L1986 **GP** *020

RIVERA-SIFONTES, Tomas H. 251 CALLE PAZ 00602 #649-14-1975 L1980 **FM** *020

RODRIGUEZ, Arleen M. 59 CALLE ESTACION 00602 #042-01-1993 L1997 **FM** *020 †18

RODRIGUEZ ROSA, Jose E. HC 56, 00685 SAN SEBASTIAN 00602 #308-03-1983 L1991 *020

ROMAN, Jorge Orlando. PO BOX 56 00602 #649-35-2002 L2003 *100

ROSA, Yolanda Varela. C/O BOX 202, CALLE COLON #111 00602 #308-03-1981 L1983 **GP** *020

RUIZ LORENZO, Yamilcis J.. ■ 00602 #649-14-2003 L2005 **IM** *012

SANCHEZ MERCADO, Aida M. HC 3 BOX 36210, 3.2 ARR 417 00602 #042-04-1995 L1997 *020

SANCHEZ-VAZQUEZ, Carmen I. ■ 00602 #847-10-1973 L1976 **FSM** *020

SANTIAGO, Antonio. ■ 00602 #649-35-2001 L2003 *100

SANTIAGO, Ariel Crespo. ■ 00602 #308-06-1981 L1991 **GP** *020

SANTIAGO, Ivonne Y. ■ 00602 #042-04-1997 L1998 **FM** *020

SANTIAGO, Mayra L. ■ 00602 #042-04-1996 L1997 **PD** *020

SANTIAGO CRESPO, Nelson E. ■ 00602 #308-06-1981 L1993 *020

SANTIAGO-NEGRON, Juan A. 278 CALLE MARINA 00602 #308-02-1976 L1978 **FM** *020

SOTO-VILLARRUBIA, Carlos. 230 CALLE MARINA 00602 #042-03-2003 **IM** *020

TORRES, Miguel. PO BOX 628, 141 CALLE COLON 00602 #308-06-1983 L1991 **GP** *020

VALENTIN, Jannette. ■ 00602 #649-14-2002 L2004 *100

VARELA, Noemi C. 278 CALLE MARINA, STE 3 00602 #042-01-1990 L1999 **RHU** *020 †20

VARGAS, Gladys. ■ 00602 #042-04-1981 L1983 *020

VAZQUEZ-MENDEZ, Cristino. ■ 00602 #847-10-1972 L1975 **PD N** *071

VEGA HERNANDEZ, Aristides. 266 CALLE MARINA 00602 #847-16-1980 L1986 **IM** *020

VILLARRUBIA, Hector J. ■ 00602 #042-03-2002 L2006 **OPH** *100

ZENO CALERO, Gloria Enid. 137 CALLE COLON, P O BOX 1076 00602 #042-03-1984 L1986 **IM** *020

ZUNIGA-HIDALGO, Julio Ces. ■ 00602 #308-10-1990 L2005 **FM** *020

AGUADILLA – AGUADILLA

ACEVEDO, Edgar N. PO BOX 250186 00604 #042-01-2006 **PD** *012

ACEVEDO, Gloria I. PO BOX 4409 00605 #308-01-1984 L1990 **GP** *020

ACEVEDO-ACEVEDO, Jose Ang. ■ 00603 #649-35-1995 L1996 *020

ACEVEDO ACOSTA, Gilbert. CARR AGUADILLA SAN JUAN 00605 #308-01-1984 L1987 **IM** *020

ACEVEDO-LAZZARINI, Luis G. 18 AVE KENNEDY, GOOD SAMARITAN HOSPITAL 00603 #042-01-1973 L1975 **ORS FM** *020

ACEVEDO LEBRON, Angelic. ■ 00603 #649-14-2000 L2001 **GP** *030

ACEVEDO MARTY, Luis Jaime. ■ 00603 #649-14-2000 L2003 **FM** *020

AGUILAR PANTOJA, Agustin. HC 1 BOX 12145 00603 #649-43-1983 L1990 **OM** *020

ALCARAZ, Luis G. 23 CALLE BETANCES, P O BOX 99 00603 #042-01-1987 L1991 **OPH** *020 †35

ALDARONDO-BADILLO, Robert. PO BOX 1297 00605 #308-03-1982 L1984 **GP** *075

ALERS-CABRERA, Ramon. CARRETERA #2 KM 12604, INTERIOR 00604 #308-03-1978 L1980 **IM** *030

ALERS FERNANDEZ, Roberto. 24 AVE SEVERIANO CUEVAS, STE 106 00603 #847-05-1985 L1989 **IM** *020

ALSAEID, Mayra. ■ 00603 #042-02-1986 L1989 **PD** *075 †55

ALVAREZ CASTILLO, Augusto. PO BOX 3948, 39 AVE QUENNEDY 00605 #847-08-1964 L1970 **GP** *020

APONTE, Luis Arcangel. 233 BELT RD 00603 #847-05-1974 L1977 **FM** *020

APONTE GARRIDO, Miguel A. 703 CALLE BELT, RAMEY SHOPPING CTR 00603 #042-04-1996 L1998 **GP PME** *020

ARANA-MARTIR, Alma Ines. PO BOX 250612, RAMEY 00604 #308-03-1984 L1992 **OS** *020

ARROYO-FELICIANO, Miguel. 100 AVE MONTEMAR 00603 #847-09-1968 L1971 **PD** *020

AVILES MUNOZ, Nelson J. PO BOX 605703, 0.2 BO JOBOS ISABE 4466 00605 #042-04-1995 L1997 **FM** *020

AVILES VAZQUEZ, Hector M. PO BOX 725, SAN ANTONIO 00605 #042-04-1996 L2003 *020

BADILLO, Kenneth N. ■ 00604 #042-01-2005 **DR** *012

BAEZ SANTIAGO, Eric A. PO BOX 250515 00604 #847-05-1974 L1977 **IM** *020

BARRETO, Concepcion. PO BOX 250490, DOCTOR CONCEPCION BARRETO 00604 #308-03-1981 L1985 **OM GP** *020

BARRETO PAGAN, Enrique. PO BOX 492, 00604 LAS VILLAS-RAMEY- 00605 #308-02-1978 L1981 *020

BATLLE, Rafael Arturo. PO BOX 3756 00605 #308-01-1938 L1970 **U** *020

BEAUCHAMP-ROCHE, Francis. C/O P.O.BOX 5116, AVE KENNEDY #44 OFIC #1 00605 #308-06-1986 L1989 **GS** *020 †85

BECERRA, Arturo. PO BOX 4022 00605 #649-01-1959 L1968 **GS GP** *020

BERRIOS, Ingrid Alicea. 22A CALLE PROGRESO, PO BOX 86 00603 #308-03-1980 L1991 **P FM** *020

BURGOS-DECLET, Nilda. 89 CALLE 2, URB GARCIA 00603 #847-05-1977 L1979 **P IM** *020

BURGOS-TRINIDAD, Hector I. 164 CARR 107 REPTO LOPEZ 00603 #847-06-1982 L1990 **GS** *020 †85

CABAN, Michael Abel. 148 CALLE D, BASE RAMEY 00603 #649-14-2002 L2003 *100

CABAN, Oscar. ■ 00603 #649-14-1993 L1995 **IM** *020

CALERO, Carmen Mercedes. 11 CALLE BETANCES BOX 133 00603 #042-01-1971 L1973 **PD** *020

CALERO-CEREZO, Fernando M. 16 AVE SAN CARLOS, SEGUNDO PISO 00603 #847-06-1964 L1967 **D** *020

CANCIO, Juan Francisco. PO BOX 4043, AVE MONTEMAR S N VILLA HAY 00605 #847-04-1968 L1971 **IM** *020

CARDONA BADILLO, Carlos R. 6 AVE LOS ROBLES 00603 #308-13-2000 L2005 *100

CASTA MENDEZ, Ida M. CARR AGUADILLA SAN JUAN 00605 #847-10-1964 L1968 **GS GP** *020

COLOMER, Carmen Elsa. PO BOX 250015 00604 #042-01-2005 L2005 **P** *012

COLOMER-MONTES, Alberto L. 24 AVE SEVERIANO CUEVAS, AGUADILLA MED PLZ 00603 #308-03-1977 L1980 **OBG** *020

COLON-RIVERA, Jose E. ■ 00605 #308-03-1981 L1984 **NEP IM** *020

CORDERO PUPO, Julio C. 1 CARR 107 STE 1 00603 #275-01-1971 L2001 **GP ADM** *020

CRUZ-HERNANDEZ, Rosa M. 1 AVE SAN CARLOS, C/O FCIA LA MILAGROSA 00603 #042-02-1982 L1985 **PD** *020 †55

CUBERO-DIAZ, Yolanda. ■ 00603 #649-14-2002 L2002 *020

DAABOUL, George H. ■ 00603 #847-10-1960 L1968 **IM** *020

DE FRIAS, Fidel Clemente. 27 AVE SEVERIANO CUEVAS, REPTO LOPEZ 00603 #308-01-1976 L1983 **PTH** *062

DE LA ROSA, Ignacio. PO BOX 3696 00605 #264-02-1952 L1970 **PD** *071

DEL VALLE CALERO, Mayra L. BOX 4968 00605 #308-03-1982 L1996 **GP** *020

DIAZ, Jose A. BO CEIBA BAJA, CARR 110 KM 0.3 00604 #308-03-1985 L1992 **GP** *020

ELIAS GONZALEZ, Jose L. ■ 00604 #042-04-2001 L2003 *100

FALTO-DETRES, Pedro Cesar. 168 CALLE PROGRESO 00603 #847-06-1982 L1986 **IM** *020

FERNANDEZ PEREZ, Sandra M. ■ 00604 #649-14-1993 L1995 **PD** *020

FIGUEROA, Eduardo. CARR AGUADILLA SAN JUAN 00605 #042-01-1976 L1981 **DR** *020 †80

FIGUEROA-MEJIAS, Miguel E. 166 CALLE MARINA 00603 #308-03-1979 L1979 **OM** *020

GARCIA, Gustavo Francisco. ■ 00603 #649-14-2006 L2006 *100

GARCIA-JIMENEZ, Jose J. 536 AVE VICTORIA 00603 #042-04-1980 L1983 **CD IM** *020

GARRATON, Manuel. 2 CALLE PROGRESO STE 203 00603 #042-01-1972 L1975 **OPH** *020 †35

GONZALEZ, Jessica. ■ 00603 #042-03-2006 **PD** *012

GONZALEZ GARCIA, Roberto. ■ 00605 #847-06-1983 L1989 *100

GONZALEZ VISBAL, Maria I. 179 CALLE SAN RAFAEL, REPARTO LOPEZ 00603 #042-01-1972 L1974 **IM DR** *020

GUZMAN RODRIGUEZ, Tamara. ■ 00603 #649-14-2002 L2004 *100

HERNANDEZ, Carlo A. URB. MARBELLA, STREET A #15 00603 #042-01-1993 L1997 **EM** *020

HERNANDEZ, Yadira. ■ 00603 #042-02-1994 L2002 **PYG** *020 †75

HERNANDEZ-ROSADO, Jose R. 24 AVE SEVERIANO CUEVAS, STE 208 ATUADILLA MED PLZ 00603 #847-08-1981 L1984 **GE IM** *020 †20

HERRERA-LOPEZ, Rafael. ■ 00603 #847-10-1960 L1963 **IM OS** *020

HUMBERTO, Rivera. ■ 00603 #649-14-2001 L2003 *020

IGARTUA-JULIA, Edward G. 167 AVE PEDRO ALBIZU CAMPS, REPTO LOPEZ 00603 #847-08-1979 L1983 **GP EM** *020

INFANZON-SANTOS, S. BO BORINQUEN, CARR. 107 KM 2.2 00603 #308-03-1980 L1986 **GS** *020

JIMENEZ, Jose Rafael. 101 CALLE LOS CIPRESES 00603 #308-03-1982 L1997 *020

JIMENEZ MENDEZ, Alejandro. 15 CALLE BETANCES, ESQ CARDONA 00603 #847-05-1972 L1975 **OPH** *071

KALANTAR LOPEZ, David H. PO BOX 5291, H3 CARR 112 L3 00605 #649-14-1992 L1994 *020

KUILAN COLLAZO, Juan A. 2053 PEDRO ALBICU, SUITE 2 EMB 323 00603 #649-14-2000 L2001 **EM** *020

LEDESMA, Ramon Gabriel. ■ 00603 #308-01-1957 L1973 **GP** *020

LIPSETT-RODRIGUEZ, A. C/O PO BOX 4036, HOSPITAL DR PEDRO J ZAMORA 00605 #042-03-1980 L1983 **GP** *020

LLAVONA, Eric E Ortiz. PO BOX 5255 00605 #308-06-1983 L1986 **AN** *020

LOPERENA, Eleuterio. 42 CALLE COMERCIO 00603 #847-03-1955 L1958 **IM** *020

LOPEZ, Raul E, Jr. ■ 00604 #016-11-1996 L2002 **OPH** *071

LUGO, Jose E. BARRIO BORINQUEN, CARR. 107 KM 2.8 00604 #308-03-1982 L1984 **OBG** *020

LUIGI-SANCHEZ, Giancarlo. 162 CALLE SAN RAFAEL 00603 #308-04-1981 L1988 **OTO GS** *020

MAIR CASTILLO, Alfred. PO BOX 3942, AVENIDA SERVERIANO CUEVAS 00605 #847-08-1974 L1977 **IM** *020

MALAVE GOMEZ, Angel B. 2 CALLE PROGRESO, STE 202 00603 #649-14-1974 L1974 **U** *020 †95

MARQUEZ-TORO, Carlos R. C/O P.O. BOX 5116, AVE KENNEDY #44 OFIC #1 00605 #649-14-1982 L1985 **GS** *020 †85

MARTINEZ, Adriano H. 169 CALLE SAN RAFAEL, REPARTO LOPEZ 00603 #308-02-1977 L1987 **GP** *020

MARTINEZ, Manuel A. 2 CALLE PROGRESO STE 304, C/O P.O. BOX 908 VICTORIA 00603 #042-01-1988 L1992 **PM** *020 †60

MARTINEZ-FIGUEROA, Ana L. 39 AVE KENNEDY, REPTO LOPEZ 00603 #847-05-1980 L1982 **PD** *030

MATOS, Francisco A. 19 AVE SEVERIANO CUEVAS, REPTO LOPEZ 00603 #042-01-1981 L1985 **OBG** *020

MATTAR TUMA, Musa. ■ 00603 #847-04-1963 L1975 **FM** *020

MEDINA, Roberto Edwin. 703 BELT RD, RAMEY 00603 #042-01-2002 L2008 **DR** *012

MEDINA AGOSTINI, Annette. 43 AVE SEVERIANO CUEVAS, STE 1 00603 #042-04-1991 L1993 **GP** *020

MEDINA-GAUD, Ismael. 43 AVE SEVERIANO CUEVAS, S-1 00603 #847-08-1971 L1974 **OBG GP** *020

MEDINA-PEREZ, Luis A. CARR AGUADILLA SAN JUAN 00605 #847-04-1969 L1971 **OBG** *020

MEDINA RIVERA, Stella Ira. ■ 00603 #308-13-2003 L2006 *100

MENDOZA MENDOZA, Pedro. 65 CALLE PROGRESO # 2B 00603 #231-01-1942 L1958 **PD** *071

MICHEL GOMEZ, Rosa Luz. G-284 MARBELLA 00603 #308-01-1980 L1986 **GP** *020

MILAN MUNIZ, Ivan. 32 CALLE PROGRESO 00603 #649-01-1956 L1959 **OBG** *020

MIRANDA, Ada S. CARR AGUADILLA SAN JUAN 00605 #308-03-1976 L1979 **PD** *030

NAVARRO, Cecile. ■ 00603 #042-01-1993 L1998 **ID** *020

NEGRON MERCADO, Juan A. PO BOX 250634 00604 #649-13-1993 L1996 *020

NIEVES, Mayra. PO BOX 60401 PMB 174 00604 #042-02-1999 L2002 **FM** *020 †55

NOBLE MARTINEZ, Mario. ■ 00603 #847-05-1976 L1978 *020

OBEN, Marcelo. 25 AVE SEVERIANO CUEVAS, REPTO LOPEZ 00603 #042-01-1976 L1981 **GS** *020

OLAVARRIA-CORREA, Gloria. CEIUELO D 295 B RAMSEY 00603 #847-02-1981 L1983 *020

ORAMA, Lispoldo J. LOOP 137 LAS VILLAS, RAMEY FIELD 00604 #308-03-1982 L1986 **OM FM** *020

ORTEGA CRUZ, Hiram J. HC 1 00603 #649-14-2001 L2002 *020

ORTIZ GONZALEZ, Maria D. PO BOX 4409 00605 #308-01-1984 L1995 **PD GP** *020

ORTIZ HERNANDEZ, Gerardo. CALLE 5 C-31, URB VISTA ALEGRE 00603 #649-14-2004 L2006 *100

PADIN, Albertino. CARR #2 KM 122.2 00603 #042-01-1986 L1989 **IM CD** *020

PEREZ, Arnaldo Enrique. ■ 00605 #042-01-2005 L1988 **IM** *012

PEREZ-ORTEGA, Jose Luis. BO BORINQUEN, CARR #107 KM 2.7 00604 #308-01-1976 L1978 *020

PEREZ-VAZQUEZ, Almanzar. SAN ANTONIO, AVENIDA RAMEY #20 00605 #308-02-1976 L1984 **GP** *020

POU DE SANTIAGO, N, II. G-9 GROUND FLOOR, BUEN SAMARITAIN HOSPITAL 00603 #042-02-1992 L1995 **OBG** *020

QUINONES, Janice. HC 5 BOX 52608, 8.5 STREET 110 # 608 00603 #042-03-2000 L2001 **ADP** *100

QUINONES, Ramon. ■ 00604 #847-02-1958 L1963 **GP** *020

QUINONES, Samuel. 127 HARRISON DR, RAMEY 00603 #847-05-1977 L1979 **FM** *020

QUINONES-HERNANDEZ, Jaime. CARR AGUADILLA SAN JUAN 00605 #308-01-1986 L1990 **GP** *020

QUINTANA PIPPINS, Brenda. 19 CALLE A, JARDINES DE BORINQUEN 00603 #649-14-2002 L2005 *100

RAMOS-RODRIGUEZ, Nisislay. BOX 306 00603 #308-03-1985 L1989 *020

RECART-SCHROEDER, Johanna. CARR 107 KM 2.8 00604 #308-03-1983 L1984 **FM** *020 †18

RICO, Carmen Maria. HC 1 BOX 16614 00603 #649-14-2001 L2004 *010

RIVERA, Carmen Vivian. 111 CALLE CROWN, RAMEY 00603 #308-03-1982 L1986 **OM** *030

RIVERA, Jose Etan. 2 CALLE PROGRESO STE 302, AGUADILLA X-RAY OFFICE 00603 #042-03-1983 L1987 **DR PD** *020 †55,28,80

RIVERA, Luis H. CARR 459 BO CALERO #7 00603 #847-08-1979 L1981 **IM** *020

RIVERA CARPIO, Gustavo D.. ■ 00605 #042-03-2008 L2012 *012

RIVERO, Enrique. ■ 00603 #308-03-1983 L1986 **GP** *020

RIVERO CALZADILLA, R. ■ 00603 #275-01-1951 L1973 **GP** *071

ROBLES CORTES, Pablo J. PO BOX 142 00603 #649-14-2000 L2000 *020

RODRIGUEZ, Wandaliz. ■ 00605 #649-14-1998 L2001 *020

RODRIGUEZ BURGOS, Samuel. ■ 00603 #308-04-2001 L2005 *100

RODRIGUEZ-ORTIZ, F. 19 AVE SEVERIANO CUEVAS #I, REPTO LOPEZ 00603 #308-01-1979 L1983 **IM END** *020

RODRIGUEZ RIOS, German. PO BOX 3262 00605 #649-14-1992 L1994 *020

ROMAN VARGAS, Zaida. 18A CALLE MUNOZ RIVERA 00603 #308-01-1981 L1994 **GP** *020

ROSA CARDONA, Juan M. 109 CALLE KALBERER, RAMEY 00603 #847-06-1975 L1978 **GP** *020

ROSARIO, Maria M. PO BOX 3893 00605 #308-03-1983 L1991 **GP** *020

ROSA RIVERA, David. ■ 00603 #847-23-1979 L2004 *100

RUIZ CRESPO, Osvaldo. ■ 00603 #649-30-2001 L2003 *100

SALMA AYMAT, Ervin A. ■ 00603 #649-14-1999 L2001 *020

SANABRIA HILERIO, Nelson. 6 CALLE D, VILLA LINDA 00603 #042-04-2004 L2005 *100

SANCHEZ, Janice. 703 BELT RD, RAMEY 00603 #308-01-1985 L1987 **GP** *020

SANCHEZ, Luis. 55 AVE SEVERIANO CUEVAS 00603 #847-08-1969 L1980 **IM** *020

SANTIAGO, Waldo. 23 AVE SEVERIANO CUEVAS, REPTO LOPEZ 00603 #042-03-1986 L1991 **GE IM** *020

SANTIAGO ANDUJAR, Ismael. ■ 00604 #308-03-1982 L1989 *020

SANTOS, Diana I. 14 CALLE PROGRESO, PMB 55 00603 #308-03-1978 L1981 **GPM** *020

SANTOS LLANOS, Rafael. 626 CALLE 16, VISTA VERDE 00603 #308-01-1981 L1987 *020

SEPULVEDA, Jaime Noel. LOPEZ URB HILDA ST #104 00603 #308-03-1981 L1985 *020

SERRA-SEMIDEI, Edgar. 25 AVE SEVERIANO CUEVAS, REPTO LOPEZ 00603 #847-11-1974 L1977 **GS** *020

SOLA, Jessica. ■ 00603 #042-01-2008 *012

SOTO, Melvin. PO BOX 3891 00605 #649-14-1994 L1996 **GP** *020

SOTO GONZALEZ, Edwin D. 2053 AVE PEDRO ALBIZU CMPS, CAMPOS #3 00603 #308-03-1983 L1986 **GP** *020

SOTOMAYOR, Lisa Michelle. ■ 00604 #308-13-1998 L2003 **IM** *020 †20

SUAREZ ZAVALETA, James Wm. NO BOX 929, MUNOZ RINERA 13TH STREET 00605 #847-01-1957 L1964 **GP OS** *020

TOFANI, Mari Silvia. 18 AVE KENNEDY, PO BOX 5295 AVE. 00603 #042-02-1998 L2001 **IM** *020 †20

TORRES, Ernesto A. ■ 00605 #847-04-1960 L1965 **OBG** *020

TORRES, Sandra Enid. 105 KALMER DR 00603 #649-14-1995 L1998 **PD** *020

URBINA AYUSO, Rubiel Elen. ■ 00603 #649-14-2003 L2004 *100

VALLE, Luis Angel. ■ 00603 #308-13-2000 L2005 *100

VAZQUEZ, Roberto. 24 AVE SEVERIANO CUEVAS, STE 205 00603 #042-01-1981 L1986 **U GS** *020 †95

VELEZ, Heriberto. 152 AVE PEDRO ALBIZU CAMPS, REPTO LOPEZ 00603 #308-03-1983 L1990 **GP** *020

VELEZ, Luis Esteban. PO BOX 250648, RAMEY STATION 00604 #649-01-1963 L1970 **GP** *020

VICTOR, Juan M. ■ 00603 #308-01-1986 L1989 *075

VILLANUEVA LAGUER, Hector. ■ 00603 #042-04-1981 L1983 **PD** *020

VILLANUEVA LAGUER, Ismael. ■ 00603 #308-03-1978 L1981 **IM** *020

ZAMBRANA, Neyda R Najul. 24 AVE SEVERIANO CUEVAS, STE 108 00603 #042-04-1983 L1985 **FPG FM** *020

AGUAS BUENAS – AGUAS BUENAS

BUXO-DIAZ, Yadira Ibet. PO BOX 777 00703 #308-03-1979 L1981 **GP** *020

CAMILO, Edwin. PO BOX 1149 00703 #308-03-1983 L1986 **GP** *020

COTTO, Maribel. ■ 00703 #042-03-2006 **IM** *012

CRUZ RIVERA, Saul. 5 CALLE ANTORCHA 00703 #847-06-1973 L1976 **IM** *020

ESTERAS, Doris Margarita. HC 3 BOX 15319 # 174 KM 00703 #042-03-1997 L2000 **PM** *020 †60

FLORES LOPEZ, Regino. ■ 00703 #847-04-1962 L1966 **GS** *020

GONZALEZ-GOMEZ, Alfredo. 5 CALLE ALBIZU CAMPOS, # 3 00703 #308-03-1978 L1982 **GP** *020

NEGRON ROSARIO, Ana I. HC 2 BOX 12918 00703 #308-03-1982 L1995 **GP** *020

PASTRANA MALDONADO, Pablo. PO BOX 1283 00703 #308-03-1985 L1991 *020

RAMIREZ, Eric Jose. HC 3, BOX 15319 00703 #042-03-1997 L2002 **PM** *020 †60

RIVERA, Ariel. ■ 00703 #042-02-1995 L1999 **PM** *020

ROSA-CARTAGENA, Felix J. HC 2 BOX 14178 00703 #042-01-1985 L1987 **EM** *030

ROSARIO ROSARIO, Raul. PO BOX 718 00703 #308-03-1991 L2004 *100

SERRANO, Ana E.. HC 1 BOX 6583 00703 #649-14-2000 L2004 *100

TATUM-GOMEZ, Alma Flora. 9 CALLE PIO RECHANI 00703 #042-02-1992 L1997 **PD** *020

AGUIRRE – GUAYAMA

RIVERA, Jose Enrique. ■ 00704 #042-01-2006 **IM** *012

AIBONITO – AIBONITO

ABRAHAM, Jose Ramon S. C/O P.O. BOX 564, C.D.T. AIBONITO, P.R. 00705 #308-03-1976 L1978 **GP** *020

AFANADOR, Wilfredo. 100 CALLE JOSE C VAZQUEZ 00705 #308-06-1983 L1995 **FM** *020

ALVAREZ-SWIHART, Roberto. DEPT OF INTERN MEDICIN, MENNOMITE GENERAL HOSP 00705 #042-03-1980 L1983 **RHU IM** *020 †20

ARROYO MATOS, Jose Ramon. 156 CALLE BALDORIOTY N 00705 #308-01-1982 L1986 **OM GP** *020

BELTRAN MORALES, Francisco. VILLA ROSALES E-29 00705 #649-14-2000 L2003 **FM** *020

BREWSTER, Kenneth Willard, III. PO BOX 536, BARRIO PASTO 00705 #649-14-2004 L2005 *100

CANAS, Luis Roberto. BO ASOMANTE CARR 162 KM 1 00705 #847-02-1973 L1977 **IM** *020

CASTRESANA, Josue. 102 EDF PROFESIONAL # 102 00705 #042-01-1986 L1990 **NEP IM** *020 †20

CEPERO, Carlos. PO BOX 1326 00705 #308-04-1982 L1987 **IM** *020

COLLAZO, Jose A. EDIF PRO HSOP MENONITA 306 00705 #042-01-1985 L1986 **ORS OP** *020 †40

COLON, Enid Mercedes. BO ASOMANTE 00705 #308-03-1984 L1987 *020

COLON, Jose A. ■ 00705 #042-01-1962 L1966 **OBG** *020 †30

COLON, Manuel Colon. 60 CALLE DEGETAU 00705 #847-06-1966 L1971 **GP** *071

COLON COLLAZO, Janine S. ■ 00705 #042-04-1997 L1999 **FM** *020

CRUZ ESPARRA, Migdalia. HC 2 BOX 7988, 21 CALLE BOHIQUE 00705 #649-14-1990 L1997 **PD** *020

DE LA TORRE FELICIANO, Tan. ■ 00705 #649-14-2002 L2005 *100

DIAZ, Jaime Ivan. ■ 00705 #042-01-1999 L2003 **AN** *020 †05

DIAZ-HERNANDEZ, Jaime M. HC 1 BOX 6527 00705 #042-01-1975 L1979 **FM** *020 †18 ‡

DIAZ SERRANO, Angel E. 203B CALLE JULIO CINTRON 00705 #649-14-1999 L2002 *020

ECHEVARRIA, Maria. 165 CALLE BALDORIOTY N, EDIFICIO CENTRAL OF #7 00705 #649-14-1976 L1987 **GP** *020

ECHEVARRIA ALICEA, Javier. ■ 00705 #308-03-2001 L2004 *100

FUENTES-BORRERO, Carlos R. 53 CALLE BALDORIOTY N 00705 #042-03-1980 L1983 **FM PHP** *020 †18

GONZALEZ-DE PENA, R. 209 CALLE JULIO CINTRON 00705 #308-03-1982 L1984 **CD FM** *020

HERNANDEZ, Nilda Alicia. BOX 21 BO LA PLATA 00705 #847-05-1980 L1984 **IM** *020

HOLGUIN, George Luis. PO BOX 2063 00705 #649-14-1979 L1996 **GP FPG** *020

IBARRA, Eduardo Ortega. 204 CALLE JULIO CINTRON, STE 224 00705 #649-14-1976 L1985 AN PME *030 †05
JORGE, Antonia. ■ 00705 #308-01-1962 L1974 AN *020
LOPEZ RIVERA, Margarita. ■ 00705 #308-07-1984 L1993 PD *020
MALAGA, Nicolas Argelia. CALLE 1 B4 CAMPO REY 00705 #737-01-1963 L1972 OBG OS *020
MARQUEZ-RODRIGUEZ, Luis B. 202 CALLE JULIO CINTRON, STE 219 00705 #308-03-1977 L1980 OBG
MARRERO, Rafael L. REPARTO ROBLES A 83 00705 #042-01-1989 L1992 FM *020 †18
MARRERO-CANINO, Jeanette. 124 CALLE BALDORIOTY S, BOX 152 00705 #042-03-1988 L1991 PD *020 †55
MARTINEZ OLIVIERI, Edgar. 60 CALLE DEGETAU N 00705 #308-04-1990 L1992 *020
MARTINEZ-ZORTIZ, Maria M. ■ 00705 #042-01-1996 L1999 FM *020
MEDINA, Rafael E. 6 CALLE RAMON FLORES 00705 #042-01-1987 L1990 GE IM *020 †20
MEHNE, David Karl. ED PROF HOSP MENOITA 306 00705 #003-01-1976 L1985 ORS OS *020 †40
ORTIZ, Sigfredo. ■ 00705 #308-03-1981 L1981 GP *020
PABON-LOPEZ, Monserrate. 64 CALLE JOSE C VAZQUEZ, AIBONITO 00705 #308-03-1976 L1979 OBG *020
PEREZ SANTIAGO, Pedro A. ■ 00705 #042-04-1998 L1999 FM *020
PIETRI, Jose Antonio. 102 CALLE FLORES 00705 #308-03-1991 L2003 GPM GP *020
RIVERA-ALVARDO, Juan B. 67 CALLE RAMON FLORES 00705 #847-06-1975 L1978 GP *020
RIVERA-COTTO, Angel Raul. 156 CALLE BALDORIOTY N 00705 #847-04-1977 L1982 IM *020
RODRIGUEZ, Edwin F. PO BOX 1450 00705 #042-03-1990 L1993 IM *020
RODRIGUEZ-DAVID, Hector I. ■ 00705 #847-03-1982 L1984 PD *020
RODRIGUEZ-GOTAY, Gladys. 53N CALLE BALDORIOTY S 00705 #042-03-1980 L1983 FM *020
ROSARIO, Vidal. PO BOX 1390 00705 #042-01-1980 L1985 PDS GS *020 †85
SANCHEZ COLON, Nestor P. PO BOX 2042 00705 #042-01-1975 L1981 D PTH *050 †15
SANCHEZ-LLAVONA, Vivian M. ■ 00705 #308-04-1980 L1982 *020
SANCHEZ-RODRIGUEZ, Carlos. ■ 00705 #042-01-1985 L1988 EM *020
SANTIAGO, Carmen Y. REPARTO BELLA VISTA C20 00705 #042-01-1991 L1995 PD *020
SANTIAGO, Luis R. 56 CALLE PEDRO ROSARIO 00705 #042-01-1994 L1998 OPH *020 †35 ‡
SANTIAGO-RODRIGUEZ, Juan. ■ 00705 #042-01-2004 L2006 *012
SANTIAGO-SANCHEZ, Carlos. PO BOX 2053 00705 #308-04-1988 L1991 GS *020 †85
SANTIAGO-TORRES, Wilfredo. C/O P.O. BOX 1508, RAMON FLORES STREET 105 00705 #847-05-1975 L1978 PD *020
SANTOS VEGA, Madelaine O. PO BOX 1082, D-42 00705 #308-03-1984 L1995 PD *020
SILVA-MORENO, Juan Ramon. #109, CALLE DEGETAU SUR 00705 #308-04-1982 L1986 PD *020
SUAREZ ABRAHAM, Carlos R. ■ 00705 #042-01-1972 L1976 PD *050 †55
TOROORTIZ, Ana Cristina. ■ 00705 #042-03-2007 IM *012
TORRES-TORRES, Nancy. ■ 00705 #042-01-2004 FM *100 †18
VELARDE, Francisco J. ■ 00705 #649-14-1983 L1996 PD *020
VELEZ, Angel Gilberto. 120 CALLE JOSE C VAZQUEZ 00705 #308-03-1983 L1991 GP OS *020

ANASCO – ANASCO

AGUILERA-MONTALVO, Jorge. PO BOX 171, BO MARI 2.1 CARR 402 00610 #847-08-1972 L1990 *050
AQUINO, Rafael A.. PO BOX 494 00610 #308-03-1995 L2003 *020
AVILES, Miligsa. ■ 00610 #649-14-1994 L1997 *020
CARRERO SOTO, Edras. PO BOX 1878 00610 #649-14-1994 L1997 *100
COLLAZO AROCHO, Sylvia. RR 2, 5602 BUZAN 00610 #308-03-1977 L1988 FM *020
COLON TIRADO, Amarilys. ■ 00610 #649-14-2003 *020
CRUZ, Felix Jorge. PO BOX 429 00610 #308-03-1999 *100
GONZALEZ, Adolfo. URB.VILLAS DE AVASCO 00610 #649-14-1997 L1998 FM *020
GONZALEZ, Ernesto Jose. ■ 00610 #649-14-1992 L1993 *020
GONZALEZ DEL RIO, Evelyn. RR 2, 9 OFIC EDIF BOSQUES MOCA 00610 #308-01-1989 L1995 PD *020
GONZALEZ RAMOS, German R. ■ 00610 #042-04-1993 L1995 PD *020
HERNANDEZ, Miguel Angel. ■ 00610 #308-03-1985 L1996 FM *020
INFANTE-RODRIGUEZ, Jose M. ■ 00610 #308-01-1956 L1972 GP *071
LAMOUR, Ferol Fils. 9 CALLE IBANEZ, ERQ PADRE BERNAZAR 00610 #649-01-1975 L1989 GP *020
MARTINEZ POLANCO, Jose T.. RR 2 BOX 8168 00610 #308-03-2000 L2004 *100
MENDEZ RODRIGUEZ, Fabian. 79 CALLE SOL BOX 566 00610 #847-02-1976 L1978 GP *020
MENDOZA IRIZARRY, Rafael. CARR 109 KM 4.9 INT RR-03 00610 #042-04-1999 L2001 FM *020
MONTALVO-CORDERO, Jose H. ESQ ANGELES, 65 DE INFANTERIA #51 00610 #024-06-1947 L1954 IM FM *072
MONTALVO LORENZO, Dolca. ■ 00610 #308-03-1980 L1986 FM *020
MORALES RECIO, Francisco. ■ 00610 #308-04-2000 L2002 *020
MUNIZ ROSADO, Carlos M. ■ 00610 #649-14-1976 L1978 IM *020
ODIOTT SANCHEZ, Betzaida. PO BOX 224 00610 #649-14-1993 L2003 *100
ODIOTT SANCHEZ, Felix M. CALLE H1 2 P O BOX 224 00610 #649-14-1993 L1996 *020
OSORIO-CUEVA, Edisson H. 15 CALLE LA ROSA 00610 #308-03-1977 L1982 GP *020
PAGAN MORALES, Eric N. ■ 00610 #649-14-1989 L1992 *020
RAMIREZ MENDEZ, Hector J. ■ 00610 #649-14-2004 L2005 *100
RAMIREZ-NIEVES, Jacqueline. ■ 00610 #308-03-2000 L2004 GP *100
RAMIREZ PRATTS, Sasha Mai. RR 2 BOX 2901, BO CAR 4 CARR 402 HM 0 00610 #649-14-2003 L2005 *100
REYES CRUZ, Luis D. ■ 00610 #308-01-1987 L1995 OBG *020
REYES LARA, Dolores. ■ 00610 #275-02-1985 L2002 *020
RIOS, Ivette. PO BOX 1390, 2 AVENIDA 65 DE INFANTERIA 00610 #847-06-1973 L1976 FM *075
RIVERA, Maria Michelle. ■ 00610 #649-14-2002 L2004 *100
RIVERA-ANTONGIORGI, Nikaur. ■ 00610 #042-01-2008 *012
RIVERA-BARBOSA, M. ■ 00610 #042-01-1995 L1998 GS *020
RIVERA-ROSADO, Francisco. 65 INFANTRY #65 00610 #847-04-1969 L1971 IM *020
ROCHE-ASENSIO, Manuel. ■ 00610 #847-06-1973 L1980 FM *020
RODRIGUEZ, Roselis Y. NUM APDO 1203 00610 #308-03-1985 L1991 GP *020
ROMAN-MATIAS, Manuel. ■ 00610 #308-03-1978 L1983 GP *020
ROSADO, Jaime Antonio. PO BOX 345 00610 #649-35-1992 L1995 *020
ROSADO, Pedro Jaime. 52 CALLE DAGUEY, BOX 163 00610 #308-03-1982 L1984 GP *020
ROVIRA, Sonia I. ■ 00610 #308-02-1991 L1996 IM *020
RUIZ, Brenda M.. PO BOX 486 00610 #649-35-2001 L2004 *100

SANTOS ALLENDE, Jose Raul. RR 2 BOX 8288, URB JARDINES DE DAQUEZ 00610 #308-04-1984 L1993 *020
TORO VELEZ, Edgardo. ■ 00610 #649-14-2002 L2004 *100
TORRES CABAN, Alberto L. 90 CALLE 65 INFANTERIA 00610 #649-14-1997 L2002 FM *020
VALENTIN, Ana Luz. ■ 00610 #042-03-1981 L1990 PD *020
VALENTIN-GONZALEZ, Nelson. ■ 00610 #649-14-1985 L1992 PD *020
VELEZ-GONZALEZ, Mario O. ■ 00610 #308-03-1983 L1990 *020
VELEZ-VALENTIN, Edgardo. 141 URB SAGRADO CORAZON 00610 #042-01-1958 L1960 PD *071
VIGO PAREDES, Elvin. ■ 00610 #308-03-1984 L1989 GS *020

ANGELES – UTUADO

CINTRON-MENDEZ, Hector R. ■ 00611 #308-03-1980 L1983 IM *020

ARECIBO – ARECIBO

ABREU VALENTIN, Roberto Y. HC 1, BOX 10835 00612 #308-03-2000 L2006 *100
ACEVEDO TACORONTE, Jose. CALLE A #18, URBANIZACION MARTELL 00613 #308-01-1985 L1995 FM *020
ACOSTA RUIZ, Melvyn. 53 CALLE DOMINGO RUBIO, URB VILLAMAR 00612 #847-10-1961 L1964 IM *020
ALCANTARA CARDI, George D. PO BOX 140401 00614 #308-04-1990 L1992 *020
ALCANTARA NUNEZ, Veronica. PO BOX 2265 00613 #649-26-1991 L2003 *100
ALICEA CUEVAS, Nicolas. ■ 00613 #308-03-1982 L2002 *020
ALLENDE VAZQUEZ, Jose A. 55 CALLE PALMA 00612 #042-03-1984 L1989 U *020
ALONSO SUAREZ, Maria P. BO. SAN DANIEL, ARECIBO MEDICAL CENTER 00612 #847-06-1971 L1975 OBG *020
ALVAREZ, Melissa Marie. ■ 00612 #042-01-2007 *012
ANTONMATTEI RIVERA, Sadi. PO BOX 141899 00614 #847-11-1975 L1980 DR OS *020 †80 ‡
ANTONSANTI, Daina Iveliss. ■ 00612 #649-14-2003 L2005 *100
AREVALO, Alberto Enrique. 163 CALLE ANTONIO R BARC, STE 104 00612 #042-02-1994 L1999 NEP *020 †20
ARIAS, Fernando J. 1216 AVE MIRAMAR STE 1, CENTRO TRANSPLANTE DE CABE 00612 #308-03-1980 L1983 GS *020
ARROYO, Raul M. 65 AVE BARBOSA, STE 105 00612 #042-01-1988 L1994 U *020 †95
ARROYO-BALLESTEROS, Luis. ■ 00614 #847-06-1962 L1967 GP *020
ARROYO GRAU, Jose G. 55 NICOMEDES RIVERA 00612 #847-01-1965 L1969 PD *020
ARROYO OTERO, Adrian. ■ 00612 #847-05-1985 L1992 FM *020
AZZARO GONZALEZ, David. 323 AVE JOSE DE DIEGO, AFOCINA DR DAVID AZZARO 00612 #308-03-1996 L2003 OBG *020
BAERGA, Frances. 172 CALLE RODZ IRIZARRY 00612 #042-02-1997 L2000 OBG *020
BAGUE, Ismael. PO BOX 141348 00614 #132-01-1993 L1998 FM *020
BALL-ROSA, Francisco E. ■ 00613 #308-04-1983 L1987 PD *020
BARRETO URDAZ, Nabal E. PO BOX 141254 00614 #308-03-1999 L2003 *020
BARRIOS, Sigifredo C. 101 CALLE GONZALO MARIN 00612 #847-05-1975 L1979 OBG *020
BARRIOS BARRETO, Jose F. ■ 00612 #308-03-1984 L1990 *020
BARRIOS ROMACHO, Fransisco. PO BOX 142481 00614 #649-14-2000 L2001 GP *020
BERMUDEZ, Lillian Emilia. PO BOX 140700, 166 DELFIN OLMO ST 00614 #042-01-1977 L1983 GP *020
BERRIOS, Fermin Heribel. 6 ST F 9 UNIVERSITY GDNS 00612 #308-03-1980 L1988 PD *020
BETANCOURT COLLAZO, Sandra. PO BOX 143853 00614 #308-03-2002 L2005 *100
BETANCOURT-MEDINA, Luis F. PO BOX 935 00613 #308-01-1985 L1988 IM *020
BEY VINAS, Blanizza Lorra. ■ 00613 #649-14-2001 L2002 PD *020
BONILLA, Julia. ■ 00614 #042-01-1977 L1980 FM *020 †18
BORRERO, Carlos Manuel. PO BOX 140275 00614 #649-14-2002 L2004 *100
BRAVO, Eileen. ■ 00612 #042-03-2006 *012
BRAVO, Maria Pilar. HC 2, 20 ARECIBO MEDICAL CTR 00612 #042-01-1997 L1999 OBG *020
BRAVO VELAZQUEZ, Diego. BO. SAN DANIEL, ARECIBO MEDICAL CENTER 00612 #847-06-1970 L1975 NPM PD *020
CABAN MARTINEZ, Jorge L. ■ 00613 #308-03-1982 L1992 *020
CANCEL, Edgar A. ■ 00612 #042-04-1989 L1990 GP *020
CANDELARIO, Edwin. PO BOX 140279, AZUL1 URB VIS 00614 #042-01-1977 L1983 *020
CARRANZA DE LEON, Norma L. ■ 00613 #308-01-1975 L1977 FM NTR *074
CARRASQUILLO GARCIA, E. 55 CALLE PALMA 00612 #308-03-1979 L1985 GP *020
CARRO, Jose Antonio. 540 AVE MIRAMAR, STE 5 00612 #042-01-1985 L1987 IM *020 †35
CASTRO, Justiniano. 49 CALLE MORELL CAMPOS, URB GARCIA 00612 #042-01-1987 L1992 HO IM *020 †20
CEPERO, Efrain Antonio He. B13 MARTELL 00612 #308-03-1983 L2005 *100
CEREZO-MAGAN, Eduardo. 55 CALLE PALMA 00612 #847-04-1969 L1976 AN PME *020
CHABRIER, Mario. 263 CALLE RUIZ BELVIS 00612 #308-01-1987 L1989 FM *020
COKER, Jackie H. ■ 00613 #847-04-1957 L1960 GP IM *075
COLON, Angel Francisco. ■ 00614 #042-01-1991 L1996 PM *075 †60
COLON, Felix Luis. PO BOX 143952 00614 #308-04-1987 L1992 GP *020
COLON, Jose A. HC 1 BOX 4829 00612 #308-07-1984 L1995 PD *020
COLON, Rolando. 54 AVE BARBOSA 00612 #308-03-1985 L1995 GP *020
COLON-NEBOT, Rolando. C/O P.O. BOX 668, ANDRES OLIVER 56 00613 #847-05-1967 L1969 ORS *071 ‡
COLON-RODRIGUEZ, Manuel A. 101 CALLE GONZALO MARIN 00612 #649-14-1977 L1979 OBG *020
CORREA RODRIGUEZ, Miguel. BO. ISLOTE II #73 00612 #308-04-1999 L2003 FM *020
COTT ROSARIO, Hector M. 55 CALLE PALMA 00612 #308-03-1978 L1981 FM EM *020
CRUZ-RODRIGUEZ, H L. 55 NICOMEDES RIVERA 00612 #847-05-1972 L1974 PD NPM *075
CUEVAS, Elizabeth. ■ 00612 #649-14-2003 L2004 *100
DAVID, Nasim Salomon. 107B CALLE RODZ IRIZARRY 00612 #308-01-1980 L1986 PD *020
DAVILA, Jose Roberto. 53 CALLE ANDRES GARCIA, URB GARCIA 00612 #042-01-1998 L2001 IM *020 †18
DAVILA COLON, Edgardo. PO BOX 144200 PMB 045 00614 #649-14-1992 L1995 *020
DE JESUS, Elizabeth. Diego. ■ 00614 #847-06-1970 L1978 GP *020
DE LA CRUZ, Francisco. ■ 00614 #042-01-1974 L1976 PD *040 †80
DELGADO, Enrique. ■ 00613 #847-10-1962 L1969 IM HEM *071
DELGADO, Gloria A. PO BOX 143114, CARR 653 K21 HATO ABCJO BA 00614 #308-03-1982 L1986 GP *020

DELGADO, Marta. JOSE C BARBOSA ST, ARECIBO MEDICAL PLZ STE 10 00612 #308-04-1984 L1986 **NEP** *020 †20
DELGADO, Rafael. 320 AVE R RIVERA AULET 00612 #649-14-1992 L1997 **FM** *020
DELGADO RODRIGUEZ, Fernand. PO BOX 1613 00613 #275-06-1978 L2000 *020
DELIZ, Rafael J. PO BOX 141057 00614 #042-01-1988 L1992 **PUD IM** *020 †20
DEL RIO CORDERO, Jose R. PO BOX 143112 00614 #649-14-1988 L1992 *100
DE ROZAS, Rosalia Peralta. BOX 513 AVE BARBOSA 51 00613 #847-10-1968 L1974 **GP** *020
DIAZ-GARCIA, Julio. KM 69 8-BO SANTANA, CARRETERA #2 00612 #847-04-1960 L1963 **GP** *071
DIAZ GONZALEZ, Luis M. ■ 00612 #308-03-1982 L1986 **GP** *020
DIAZ-SANTANA, Eloy. 55 CALLE PALMA 00612 #847-02-1970 L1973 **OBG** *020
DIEZ-SIFONTES, Antonio J. 55 CALLE PALMA 00612 #649-14-1978 L1980 **IM** *020
ENCARNACION CONCEPCION, Ed. PO BOX 144100 PMB 168 00614 #308-03-1989 L2003 *100
ESTREMERA, Maria Del Mar. ■ 00612 #042-01-2004 **CHP** *012
FERNANDEZ, Rosangela Luis. 147 CALLE LOS HEROES, URB ZENO GANDIA 00612 #649-14-2000 L2001 **IM PHP** *040 †20
FERRA GEYLS, Alberto. 520 AVE SAN LUIS 00612 #847-06-1982 L1990 **GP** *020
FIGUEROA, Antonio L, Jr. 19 AVE JOSE DE DIEGO, CENTRO CARDIOLOGICO DEL NO 00612 #042-01-1986 L1992 **CD** *020 †20
FONT, Victor Rodriguez. I13 CALLE 10 UNIV GRDNS 00612 #847-12-1981 L1986 **FM** *020
FRANCESCHI, Eddie V. ■ 00613 #847-02-1972 L1979 **FM** *020
FRANCO RENTA, Rafael. 4 CALLE COBALLES GANDIA, URB VILLA SERENA 00612 #847-02-1974 L1978 **FM** *030
FRIAS, Francisco M. 66 AVE DE DIEGO STE 204 00612 #042-01-1963 L1968 **U** *020 †95
FUENTES-FERRER, Jose J. REGIMIENTO 65 ST 00612 #275-01-1948 L1973 **U** *071
FUENTES-INGUANZO, Jose J. 531 AVE MIRAMAR, BOX 3102 00612 #308-03-1980 L1984 **GYN** *020
GALVA, Roberto Antonio. C/O P. O. BOX 1658, CALLE BARBOSA #50 00613 #649-18-1983 L1990 **IM RHU** *020
GARCIA, Ana Cristina. ■ 00614 #042-01-2007 *012
GARCIA, Francisco M. 47 CALLE MORELL CAMPOS, URB GARCIA 00612 #042-01-1982 L1986 **IM CD** *020 †20
GARCIA, Jose Guillermo. 330 CALLE SANTA INES, URB EL PARAISO 00612 #847-05-1973 L1976 **PD** *020
GARCIA, Margarita Rosa. ■ 00613 #042-01-1979 L1983 **N** *020
GARCIA ACEVEDO, Obed Rene. PO BOX 3130 00613 #649-14-2003 **FM** *020
GARCIA CUEVAS, Millan J. PO BOX 2604 00613 #042-04-2000 L2001 **P ADM** *020
GARCIA LLORENS, Miguel A. 64 CALLE TRINA PADILLA 00612 #042-02-1992 L1996 **OPH** *020
GARCIA LUCIANO, Angel L. PO BOX 1057, ARECIBO 00613 #847-05-1978 L1985 **GP** *020
GARCIA SANABRIA, Samuel. F41 CALLE 8, URB LOS LLANOS 00612 #847-04-1964 L1967 **IM** *020
GARCIA SANTALIZ, Domingo. ■ 00613 #847-04-1962 L1965 **PD** *071
GARCIA-TORRADO, Millan. 55 NICOMEDES RIVERA 00612 #042-01-1955 L1961 **GS OS** *071 †85
GIL DELGADO, Carlos A.. ■ 00612 #649-14-2004 L2005 *100
GINES, Carmen L. CALLE KL 16, JARD ARECIBO 00612 #847-05-1975 L1981 **GP** *020
GOITIA-RIOS, Dario Manuel. 50 AVE BARBOSA 00612 #308-03-1984 L1988 **N** *020
GONZALEZ, Bernardo Amadis. 318 CALLE URPILA 00612 #649-03-1990 L1992 **GS OS** *020
GONZALEZ, Dorabelle. ■ 00614 #308-01-1977 L1980 **GP** *020
GONZALEZ, Mariano Enrique. 540 AVE MIRAMAR, STE 3 00612 #042-01-1985 L1990 **OTO** *020 †45
GONZALEZ, Raphy Alexis. PO BOX 141322 00614 #649-14-2002 L2003 *100
GONZALEZ, Ruben David. 163 CALLE ANTONIO R BARC 00612 #042-04-1985 L1986 **PD** *020
GONZALEZ, William. ■ 00612 #308-03-1979 L1990 **GP** *020
GONZALEZ-COLON, Luis R. 55 CALLE PALMA 00612 #847-05-1973 L1975 **GE IM** *020
GONZALEZ CRUZ, Julio E. ■ 00613 #847-01-1965 L1968 **FM** *020
GONZALEZ DELGADO, Ismael. 50 CALLE ANDRES OLIVER 00612 #308-03-1983 L1994 *020
GONZALEZ-DEL ROSARIO, S. ■ 00613 #649-01-1976 L1980 *020
GONZALEZ VEGA, Lorna. ■ 00612 #649-14-2004 L2006 *100
GONZALEZ VIRUET, Guelmi. ■ 00612 #649-14-2000 L2002 *100
GORROCHATEGUI, Martin. ARECIBO SHOPPING CTR 00612 #042-01-1980 L1985 **NEP IM** *020 †20
GRAU, Jose. HOSP CAYETANO COLL Y TOSTE 00612 #847-01-1966 L1968 **ORS** *071
GUERRIER, Max. BO SANTANA, CARR #2 KM 66 7 00612 #847-02-1973 L1977 **GP** *020
GUILLEN FIGUEROA, Juan A. 56 CALLE ANA L SUSONI 00612 #308-01-1967 L1975 **P** *020
HERNANDEZ, Cesar R. HC 3, 2.3 CARR 635 00612 #847-05-1970 L1973 **OBG** *020 †30
HERNANDEZ-VELAZQUEZ, Jose. ■ 00613 #308-01-1950 L1961 **OTO** *020
HOTESSE-DIAZ, Tania A. C/O P.O. BOX 289, AVDA. JOSE DE DIEGO #229 00613 #308-01-1971 L1977 *020
IGUINA, Fermina M. ■ 00613 #847-04-1952 L1961 **GP** *071
IGUINA, Flora M. ■ 00613 #847-04-1952 L1961 **GP** *071
IGUINA DE HERNANDEZ, Olga. 165 CALLE SAN FELIPE 00612 #042-01-1957 L1959 **IM OBG** *072
IGUINA-MELLA, Luis E. 158 AVE JOSE DE DIEGO, EDIF CABAN, AVE. 00612 #308-03-1977 L1984 **GS VS** *020
IGUINA MORA, Martin A. ■ 00613 #847-04-1952 L1955 **OPH** *071
IGUINA REYES, Luis E. REGIMIENTO 65 ST 00612 #847-04-1960 L1966 **GP** *020
JAMES, Magdalena Bernat. ■ 00613 #042-04-1985 L1986 **P GP** *020
JANER GARCIA, Jorge R. SEGURO DEL ESTADO, CORPORACION DEL FONDO DEL 00614 #847-10-1966 L1969 **GS** *020
JIMENEZ, Elias R. BOX 1863 00613 #847-01-1968 L1974 **P** *020
JIMENEZ, Jose Francisco. 6 VILLA ANGELA 00612 #308-01-1969 L1979 **GP** *020
JIMENEZ COLON, Eliza M. ■ 00612 #308-04-1999 L2002 *100
JIMENEZ COLON, Natalia Za. ■ 00612 #308-04-2001 L2004 *100
JIMENEZ-GONZALEZ, Juan R. ■ 00612 #042-04-1989 L1992 **AN** *020
JIRAU, Juan Luis. ■ 00612 #042-03-2004 **PM** *100
JOVE JIMENEZ, Rafael A. 109 CALLE ANTONIO R BARC, STE 3 00612 #042-01-1972 L1974 **OBG** *020 †30
JOVE-MATOS, Denisse. 109 CALLE ANTONIO R BARC, STE 3 00612 #042-02-1999 L2000 **OBG** *020 ‡
LAGO, Lourdes Roxana. ■ 00614 #042-03-2008 *012
LAGO EXPOSITO, Maria E. ■ 00614 #275-01-1992 L2006 *100
LAGUILLO, Carlos R. 16 CALLE ANA L SUSONI 00612 #042-04-1989 L1990 **GP** *020
LAGUILLO RODRIGUEZ, P. 418 AVE JOSE DE DIEGO, BOX 413 00612 #847-04-1958 L1962 **GP** *020
LAMA, Victor. ■ 00614 #308-01-1955 **GS GP** *020
LAMA GATTAS, Victor M. ■ 00614 #308-03-1983 L1987 **GP** *030
LASSALLE, Cesar Augusto. ■ 00612 #042-01-2007 *012
LOPEZ, Hector Felipe. 459 AVE R RIVERA AULET, URB GARCIA 00612 #649-14-1996 L1996 **IM** *020
LOPEZ, Myrna L. 65 AVE BARBOSA, STE 102 00612 #042-01-1988 L1991 **END IM** *020
LOPEZ-LOPEZ, Ricardo. PO BOX 141408, 2.9 CARR 492 00614 #649-14-2003 *020
LOPEZ ROJAS, Salvador. 62 CALLE PRINCIPAL, JAREALITO ARECIBO 00612 #649-18-1983 L1991 **GP** *020
LOPEZ SANTIAGO, Sandra. URB DUHAMEL #43 00612 #308-01-1986 L1989 **GP** *020
LOPEZ VAZQUEZ, Myrtha. V1 CALLE 16, VILLA LOS SANTOS 00612 #042-04-1986 L1989 *020
MAGRANER FOLCH, Miguel A. ■ 00612 #847-04-1957 L1960 **PM** *020
MALDONADO, Ferdinando. PO BOX 9921, COTTO STATION 00613 #308-03-1981 L1989 **GP** *020
MARCANO RIVERA, Manuel E. 115 CALLE ARIOSTO CRUZ 00612 #308-03-1979 L1990 **GP** *020
MARIN, Juan Rafael. PO BOX 140413 00614 #649-14-2000 L2001 **FM** *020
MARRERO, Miriam. ■ 00612 #308-01-1982 L1996 **GP** *020
MARRERO-NIEVES, Jose. C/O P.O. BOX 1905, URB ARECIBO GARDENS 4 #54 00613 #042-04-1985 L1986 **GP EM** *020
MARRERO-RUSSE, Jaime L. 55 CALLE PALMA 00612 #042-03-1981 L1985 **PM IM** *020 †60
MARTINEZ, Angel Luis. BO ISLOTE 11 7 00612 #042-04-1984 L1987 **GP** *020
MARTINEZ, Evelyn. 155 CALLE HERNANDEZ HUERTS 00612 #308-03-1977 L1980 **PD** *072
MARTINEZ, Jose J.. PO BOX 971 00613 #308-03-1983 L2003 *100
MARTINEZ, Luis Manuel. ■ 00614 #847-06-1974 L2002 **EM** *020
MARTINEZ-FERNANDEZ, Nitza. 94 CALLE PRINCIPAL, P O BOX 799 00612 #649-14-1980 L1982 *020
MARTINEZ-MORALES, Hugo E. ARECIBO MED CTR 205 00612 #042-01-1981 L1984 **FM** *020 †18
MARTINEZ-RIVERA, Pedro A. HC 3 BOX 22191, 2.4 CARRETERA 635 00612 #042-04-1986 L1988 **GP** *020
MARTINEZ RODRIGUEZ, Rafael. P O BOX 35` SABANA HOYOS, SEC CANDELARIO SABANA HO 00688 #308-03-1983 L2003 **GP** *100
MARTINEZ-SANCHEZ, Hector. HOSP DISTRICTO 00612 #847-10-1964 L1970 **GP** *020
MARTINEZ SANDIN, Hugo. ■ 00614 #847-04-1958 L1961 **FM PD** *071
MARTINO-DIAZ, Juan Rafael. G5 CALLE MARGINAL, VISTA AZUL 00612 #042-02-1992 L1997 **FM** *020
MATEO, Yadira G. ■ 00614 #042-01-1990 L1995 **DR** *020
MATEO, Zacarias A. ■ 00612 #308-01-1986 L1996 **OBG FM** *020
MATOS-MEDINA, Manuel A. 162 CALLE RODZ IRIZARRY, BOX 696 00612 #308-03-1979 L1979 **AN** *020
MELERO, Luis D. ■ 00613 #649-34-2005 L2006 *100
MELERO-MUNOZ, Arturo Juan. E39 CARR #653, CALLE FRATERNIDAD 00612 #308-03-1977 L1979 **EM GP** *020
MENDEZ, Herminio. C29 CALLE 3, URB LOS LLANOS 00612 #308-03-1988 L2003 *100
MENDOZA, Mario R. 165 CALLE SAN FELIPE 00612 #308-01-1952 L1958 **IM CD** *020
MERCADO-JIMENEZ, Manuel A. 32 AVE JOSE DE DIEGO 00612 #308-03-1977 L1978 **FM** *020
MIRANDA, Jose Luis. ■ 00613 #847-04-1973 L1976 **PTH** *020
MIRANDA JIMENEZ, Ada L. 165 S FELIPO ST 00612 #308-01-1954 L1958 **PD OS** *020
MOCOROA, Elena. PO BOX 9576, COTTO STATION 00613 #847-06-1973 L1977 **PD** *020
MOLINA ADAME, Clara. 51 CALLE GAUTIER BENITEZ 00612 #042-04-1983 L1985 **GP** *020
MONROIG GARCIA, Samuel A. ■ 00614 #042-04-1997 L1999 **FM** *020
MONTALVO, Carlos N. PO BOX 140729 00614 #847-04-1956 L1959 **OPH** *020
MONTALVO, Luis. 404 AVE DE DIEGO 00612 #042-03-1985 L1987 **OPH** *020
MONTALVO-BONILLA, Carlos. 51 CALLE GAUTIER BENITEZ 00612 #847-20-1980 L1982 **PUD IM** *020 †20
MONTANO, Lourdes. ■ 00612 #042-04-1988 L1990 **GP** *020
MORALES, Alga S. 1 CALLE P MORA ACOSTA, URB SAN LORENZO 00612 #042-01-1985 L1987 **AN** *020
MORAN BETANCOURT, Yadira. HC 5 BOX 93480, 2A ST B-8 00612 #649-14-2003 *020
MUNIZ RIVERA, Gaspar. 52 AVE DE DIEGO 00612 #847-06-1969 L1971 **FM GP** *020
MUSKUS-ROSARIO, Javier E. 531 AVE MIRAMAR 00612 #042-02-1994 L1996 *020
NAGY, Zsolt. ■ 00614 #473-04-1984 L2001 *020
NAJUL, Jose Elias. 55 CALLE PALMA 00612 #042-01-1978 L1983 **GE** *020
NARVAEZ, Julio Carlos. HC 5 BOX 92152 00612 #042-01-2000 L2003 **GS** *100
NARVAEZ, Nelson Yohanny. PO BOX 140928 00614 #649-35-1999 L2000 *020
NARVAEZ REYES, Julio. AVE.DE DIEGO, HOSPITAL DR. SUSONI, INC. 00612 #649-01-1965 L1970 **GS** *020
NIEVES, Jose Luis. PO BOX 970 00613 #308-03-1981 L1989 **GP** *020
NIEVES FELICIANO, Martha. HC 2 BOX 13741, HATO VIEJO 00612 #308-03-1982 L2001 *100
NIEVES MALDONADO, Waleska. APT 2432 00613 #042-04-1990 L1994 *020
NOY, Raul De Jesus. 64 CALLE TRINA PADILLA 00612 #042-01-1974 L1976 **OPH** *020
NUNEZ, Luis Rafael. 8 CALLE COBLS GND URB VILL, COBALLES GANDIA #8 URB VIL 00612 #264-04-1967 L1978 **HO IM** *020
NUNEZ, Teofilo. ■ 00612 #308-01-1982 L1997 *020
OCASIO-CARRION, Magaly N. ■ 00612 #308-03-1982 L1992 **OS** *020
OHARRIZ, Juan Jose. 540 AVE MIRAMAR, STE 2 00612 #042-01-1988 L1991 **GE IM** *020 †20
ONGAY, Jaime. ■ 00614 #308-04-2000 L2003 **GP** *020
ORTEGA ESTRADA, Jose Luis. ISLOTE II NO 56 00612 #308-03-1978 L1985 **FM** *020
ORTIZ MARTINEZ, Juan Carl. 55 CALLE PALMA 00612 #649-14-1993 L1996 **GP** *020
OSORIO GONZALEZ, Brenda I. BZN. 128-E, BO SANTANA 00612 #649-30-2001 L2004 *100
OTOMAN, Raul R. 55 CALLE PALMA 00612 #308-03-1985 L1997 **EM** *020
PADILLA, Efrain. 162 CALLE JOSE RODRIGZ IRZ 00612 #042-04-1980 L1987 **GP** *020
PADRO-ROSADO, Luis H. 42 URB CAMINO DEL VALLE 00612 #308-02-1988 L1993 **GP OM** *020
PARALITICCI, Luis Eduardo. ■ 00613 #308-02-1977 L1980 **GP** *071
PENISTON, Hector Luis. SAN LUIS AVE 00612 #042-01-1991 L1994 **EM** *075 †16
PERAZA, Juan Carlos. ■ 00614 #649-14-1995 L1996 **CD** *020
PERAZA GARCIA, Juan. ■ 00613 #847-10-1965 L1969 **GP OS** *020
PERAZA-TOLEDO, Jorge S. 161 CALLE BETANCES 00612 #847-06-1975 L1982 **GP** *020
PEREZ AMARO, Irma Esther. PO BOX 3252 00613 #308-02-2002 **PD** *012
PEREZ DE MARQUEZ, Witiza. ■ 00612 #042-01-1973 L1975 **PM** *020 †60
PEREZ-GARCIA, Sixto. ARECIBO GARDENS 76 00612 #042-01-1995 L2001 **HO** *020 †20
PEREZ MERCADO, Pedro. ■ 00613 #308-03-1994 L2006 *100
PEREZ OLMO, Rafael. H C BOX 19302 00612 #308-03-1989 L1996 *020
PEREZ-ORENGO, Victor Luis. V1 CALLE 16, LOS SANTOS 00612 #308-03-1977 L1979 *020
PEREZ-PEREZ, Luis A. 55 CALLE PALMA 00612 #308-03-1985 L1991 **IM** *020

■ = Address Information Privacy Protected

PEREZ RODRIGUEZ, Olga M. 56 CALLE ANA L SUSONI 00612 #847-04-1958 L1961 GP OS *020

PEREZ ROSARIO, Anabelle I. ■ 00614 #649-35-2001 L2006 *100

PEREZ-TOLEDO, Rafael. 51 CALLE PALMA 00612 #847-11-1972 L1974 OBG *020 †30

PEREZ-TORRADO, Pablo O. CALLE CELSO BARBOSA #65, ARECIBO MED PLAZA OFIC 103 00614 #847-03-1976 L1980 P *020

PEREZ-TORRES, Gloria M. ■ 00612 #308-03-1977 L1980 *020

PHIPPS DE LLERANDI, C E. 155 HERNANDEZ HUERTAS-543 00612 #308-01-1953 L1961 OBG GP *020

PICON SANTOS, Francis. E1 CALLE 5 URB REGIONAL 00612 #042-04-1987 L1989 IM *020

PINEIRO PEREZ, Cesar F. PO BOX 737, 128-E IN CARE OF PO BUZON 00613 #649-30-2001 L2002 *020

POLANCO MARTINEZ, Manuel. 14 CALLE GONZALO MARIN 00612 #308-01-1982 L1986 GP *020

POU-DE SANTIAGO, Edgar A. 16 CALLE ANA L SUSONI 00612 #042-02-1993 L1995 OBG *020

QUIJANO MARTINEZ, Maricarm. ■ 00612 #042-04-2002 L2003 *020

RAICES, Vanessa Enid. 55 CALLE PALMA 00612 #649-14-2001 L2003 GP EM *020

RAMIREZ, Alberto Javier. 10 PEDRO MORA 00612 #042-01-2000 L2002 GS *020 †95

RAMIREZ COSTA, Alberto L. 62 AVE DE DIEGO 00612 #042-01-1970 L1975 U GS *020

RAMIS-SANCHEZ, Juan R. 50 AVE JOSE DE DIEGO 00612 #042-03-1988 L1995 PM *072

RAMOS-ESCODA, Emilio E. 66 AVE DE DIEGO, OLIVER BLDG STE 304 00612 #308-01-1980 L1983 GS *020

RAMOS NAVARRO, Marcos. ■ 00612 #649-14-1996 L2001 *020

RESTO RIVERA, William. ■ 00612 #042-04-1985 L1989 IM OS *020

REYES, Harry Omar. PO BOX 141434 00614 #308-11-1992 L2004 *100

REYES-MATEO, Felix M. ■ 00612 #041-09-1954 L1955 DR *020

REYES-NIEVES, Pedro. URB TANAMA C-17 00612 #042-01-1984 L1988 DR *020 †80

RIVERA, Cesar Rafael. ■ 00614 #649-14-1993 L1995 *020

RIVERA, Manuel Z. 55 CALLE PALMA 00612 #308-03-1980 L1982 CD *020

RIVERA, Miriam. ■ 00613 #308-03-1982 L1989 GP *020

RIVERA-BIASCOECHEA, Zenon. ■ 00613 #041-13-1948 L1950 CD *071 †20

RIVERA CRUZ, Ciprian. PO BOX 141343 00614 #308-01-1982 L1992 *100

RIVERA-NATAL, Samuel. 55 CALLE PALMA, HOSPITAL DR SUSONI 00612 #308-03-1979 L1981 EM IM *020

RIVERA SCHNEIDER, Ramon L. 57 AVE BARBOSA 00612 #649-14-1990 L1992 AN *020

RIVERA VAZQUEZ, Gisela. ■ 00614 #649-14-2003 L2005 *100

RODRIGUEZ, Dante Amadis. HOSP SUSONI ARECIBO 00613 #308-03-1985 L1990 IM *020

RODRIGUEZ, Jorge Xavier. I8 CALLE H, JARD DE ARECIBO 00612 #649-14-1992 L1995 IM *020

RODRIGUEZ, Jose Antonio. 531 AVE MIRAMAR 00612 #649-35-1991 L1994 OBG *020

RODRIGUEZ, Juan A. ■ 00612 #042-01-1989 L1993 ORS *020

RODRIGUEZ, Justo Pastor. 301 EDIF OLIVER 00612 #847-06-1963 L1966 P *020

RODRIGUEZ, Mayra Ivonne. I8 CALLE H, JARD DE ARECIBO 00612 #042-03-1995 L1997 *020

RODRIGUEZ, Pablo Emilio. 51 CALLE JUAN COLON PADILL 00612 #042-01-1973 L1977 PM *020

RODRIGUEZ, Zoe Marie. ■ 00614 #016-11-1988 L1997 PD *020 †55

RODRIGUEZ-BERMUDEZ, V. PO BOX 140099, 3 CALLE 5 00614 #231-01-1955 L1958 GS AS *020

RODRIGUEZ DUVERGE, Carlos. ■ 00613 #308-02-1993 L1995 *020

RODRIGUEZ-GOMEZ, Jose. 55 CALLE PALMA 00612 #847-05-1970 L1973 OBG *020

RODRIGUEZ-GOMEZ, Julio R. 55 NICOMEDES RIVERA 00612 #308-03-1979 L1979 AN PME *020

RODRIGUEZ MORA, Luis M. ■ 00613 #042-01-1972 L1974 IM *020

RODRIGUEZ QUINONES, Jose. CLIN EL BUEN PASTOR 00612 #035-15-1931 L1931 GS OS *100

RODRIGUEZ-QUINONES, Jose. 21 CALLE MARTE 00612 #308-03-1980 L1982 FM GP *020

RODRIGUEZ RAMIREZ, Jose A. ■ 00612 #649-01-1961 L1967 OM GP *020

RODRIGUEZ RIVERA, Carlos. PO BOX 2476 00613 #649-14-1996 *100

RODRIGUEZ-RODRIGUEZ, Jose. 58 AVE DE DIEGO, OFICINA PROF OB/GYN 00612 #847-10-1968 L1970 OBG *020

RODRIGUEZ ROSADO, Elizabet. PO BOX 2476 00613 #649-14-1996 L2002 *100

RODRIGUEZ UBINAS, Fanny L. PO BOX 140784 00614 #649-14-2004 L2006 *100

ROIG PEREZ, Lazaro. ■ 00614 #275-07-1992 L2002 *100

ROLON MARINA, Jose A.. PO BOX 1934 00613 #649-35-1992 L1996 *020

ROLON-ORENGO, Laura E. PO BOX 9306, COTTO STA 00613 #847-02-1981 L1987 GP *020

ROMAN FELICIANO, Carmen M. REPARTO MARQUEZ, 10-I-10 00612 #308-01-1983 L1985 PD *074

ROMAN-MARTINEZ, Nayda I. ■ 00612 #308-06-1986 L1990 GP *020

ROMAN-VELEZ, Angel Manuel. PO BOX 9576 00613 #847-06-1973 L1977 EM *071

ROSA, Agustin Lopez. PO BOX 832 00613 #308-01-1969 L1971 GP *020

ROSA, Jessica Isabel. BO SANTANA, URB TANAMA BZN 19 00612 #042-01-1999 L2002 END *020 †20

ROSARIO CASILLAS, Johnny. 24 CALLE MORA ACOSTA, URBANIZACION SAN LORENZO 00612 #847-05-1967 L1972 GS *075

RUIZ, Jose L. PO BOX 142378, AVE NUNOZ RIVERA ESQ SAN J 00614 #649-03-1991 L1994 FM *020

RUIZ ARROYO, Hiram A. 129 COLL Y TOSTE, EL SPA PERMETOLOGICO PERM 00612 #847-01-1964 L1969 D *020 †15

RUIZ CORTES, Cinthia E.. ■ 00614 #308-04-2000 L2003 *100

RULLAN, Sara. PO BOX 01649223 00614 #847-01-1969 L1972 PD *020

SALGADO, Carlos A. 575 AVE SAN LUIS 00612 #042-01-1978 L1982 CD IM *020 †20

SALINAS, Viridiana. PO BOX 141633, 3.5 ROAD 651 HATO ARRIB 00614 #649-14-2000 L2001 IM *012

SANCHEZ BRACHE, Ezequias. BOX 1637/OCEAN VIEW 00613 #308-01-1947 L1960 GP OS *020

SANCHEZ LOPEZ, Ricardo E.. PO BOX 664 00613 #042-04-2000 L2002 FM *020

SANTANA-VILLEGAS, Maria L. ■ 00613 #847-02-1971 L1974 PD *020

SANTIAGO, Isamir. ■ 00612 #649-35-2002 L2004 *100

SANTIAGO-SANTIAGO, G. ■ 00614 #042-03-1981 L1986 IM *020

SANTOS, Adelimelid Camila. ■ 00614 #308-04-1992 L2001 *020

SANTOS, Julio A. MIRADOR VISTA AZUL, CALLE NUM 7F-14 00612 #308-03-1985 L1992 *100

SANTOS, Julio A, Jr. 314 CALLE M PEREZ AVILES 00612 #308-01-1972 L1974 FM OS *072

SEOANE, Jesus Gomez. UNIDAD DE SALUD PUBLICA 00612 #275-01-1945 L1966 GP OS *020

SEPULVEDA, Ramonita. ■ 00614 #847-05-1969 L1972 FM DR *020

SERRANO, Waleska Ivette. 235 CALL URGL VILLA TOLEDO 00612 #649-14-1998 L2001 FM *020

SERRANO-GONZALEZ, Roberto. 563 AVE ROTARIO 00612 #847-05-1971 L1974 OBG *020

SERRANO HERNANDEZ, Jose S. ■ 00612 #649-14-2000 L2000 *020

SOMOHANO-ARBIDE, Manuel A. 55 CALLE PALMA 00612 #042-04-1981 L1982 IM *020

SOMOHANO MOSQUERA, Angel. ■ 00613 #275-01-1953 L1955 GS GP *071

SOTO, Anel Grimaris. PO BOX 142806 00614 #649-14-2004 *100

SOTO, Karren Lynn. ■ 00614 #042-01-1991 L1995 P *020

SOTO, Miguel A. ■ 00613 #308-03-1977 L1979 PD *020

SOTOMAYOR, Luis Felipe. ■ 00612 #649-14-2001 IM *020 ‡

SOUFFRONT, Pedro Angel. ■ 00612 #308-03-1981 L1995 *020

TAVAREZ HERNANDEZ, Jesus. HC 2, CORP FONDO SEGURO DEL ESTA 00612 #649-18-1973 L1983 *020

TOLEDO ARMADA, Mildred M. ■ 00612 #042-01-1972 L1974 PD *020 †55

TORRADO, Ramon Francisco. 55 CALLE PALMA 00612 #649-14-1989 L1991 IM *020

TORRECILLAS DE HITA, Rita. 66 AVE JOSE DE DIEGO # 302 00612 #847-10-1967 L1971 GP *100

TORRES, Elizabeth. A12 CALLE MARGINAL, URB JARD 00612 #649-14-1983 L1988 NPM *020

TORRES, Luis Francisco. ■ 00613 #042-03-2007 IM *012

TORRES GONZALEZ, Deliana. ■ 00612 #649-14-2000 L2002 FM *020

TORRES-NADAL, Julio A. ■ 00613 #847-05-1975 L1979 *075

TORRES RIVAS, Miguel Anto. HC 2 BOX 13908 00612 #308-02-2002 L2004 *100

TRINIDAD, Marco Antonio R. PO BOX 141135, 9 CALLE ARCANGEL URB 00614 #308-01-1975 L1981 GP *020

TRUJILLO, Beatriz. 166 CALLE RODZ IRIZARRY 00612 #042-04-1988 L1990 P *020

URDAZ MESTRES, Francisco. ■ 00613 #847-05-1969 L1971 PD *020

URENA CRUZ, Miguel A. 55 CALLE PALMA 00612 #308-01-1978 L1983 *020

VARGAS, Pedro. PO BOX 363 00613 #042-01-1973 L1975 OPH *020

VARGAS ROSADO, Pedro. ■ 00614 #407-26-1940 L1941 OPH *071

VAZQUEZ-CRUZ, Julio A. 52 AVE DE DIEGO 00612 #042-01-1981 L1984 PD *020

VAZQUEZ-LOPEZ, Miguel J. ■ 00612 #308-04-1992 L2001 P *020

VAZQUEZ NIEVES, Mirelys. 73 CALLE N-L, URB JARDINES 00612 #649-14-2004 L2005 *100

VEGA, Senen. ■ 00614 #649-14-1991 L1996 FM *020

VELEZ, Nydia Mercedes. ■ 00612 #042-01-2001 L2004 NPM *100 †55

VELEZ QUINONES, Iriamar. 517 AVE MIRAMAR, STE 2 00612 #649-14-2002 L2003 GP *020

VELEZ-QUINONES, Luis F. PO BOX 141239 00614 #042-04-1988 L1989 PUD IM *020 †20

VELEZ-RIVERA, Lydia E. HC 2 BOX 17238, HATO ARRIBA 00612 #308-03-1983 L1990 GP *020

VERGNE, Ramon A. ■ 00612 #165-01-1941 L1947 GP OS *020

VILLANUEVA, William. 52 AVE DE DIEGO 00612 #042-01-1984 L1986 PCC *020

VILLANUEVA VALDES, Esther. ■ 00612 #308-03-1982 L1995 GP *020

VILLANUEVA VAZQUEZ, Elba. ■ 00612 #847-06-1964 L1969 GP OS *020

VIVONI FARAGE, Victor E. 82 CARR 2 STE 203, ARECIBO MEDICAL CENTER 00612 #042-01-1972 L1974 GS *020

ZENO MORALES, Carmen E. ■ 00612 #847-06-1972 L1975 FM *020

ARROYO – ARROYO

ACAVEDO, Annette. ARROYO COMMUNITY HLTH CTR 00714 #649-14-1993 L1995 *020

APONTE SANTINI, Sandra N. ■ 00714 #042-04-1999 L2002 GP *020

BASTIAN, Harold Samuel. ■ 00714 #649-35-1983 L1989 GP *020

BONELLI-PAGANELLI, Jose A. PO BOX 848 00714 #847-05-1971 L1982 GP *020

COLON MALDONADO, Jose O.. ■ 00714 #649-14-2001 L2002 *020

GUTIERREZ ORTIZ, Maria De. ■ 00714 #649-14-2001 L2004 *100

GUZMAN-VALDEZ, Maximo A. ■ 00714 #308-01-1975 L1978 *100

JORGE FLORES, Jaime. PO BOX 1210 00714 #042-04-1996 L2001 GP *020

LOPEZ, Rodney. CI38 CALLE Y, JARD DE ARROYO 00714 #649-14-2001 L2002 *020

LOPEZ-NIEVES, Roberto. CARR 3 KM 161.8, BO GUASIMAS 00714 #308-07-1982 L1989 FM OM *020 †18

MUNIZ BERDEGUEZ, Maria M. ■ 00714 #649-14-1996 L2002 *020

NAVARRO FIGUEROA, Yamilka. B13 URB LA RIVIERA 00714 #042-04-2002 L2003 *100

PEREZ, Ramon Ramos. 225 CALLE CARIBE, URB ARROYO DEL MAR 00714 #308-03-1982 L1987 P *020

PICART, Zinnia Enid. ■ 00714 #649-14-2000 L2002 *020

QUINONES RAMPOLLA, Carlos. ■ 00714 #649-14-1992 L1995 GP *020

RENDON, Rafael O. CENTRAL LAFAYETTE 00714 #042-01-1984 L1987 PD *020 †55

RIVERA, Jose Enrique. URB JARDINES DE ARROYO, CALLE CCA 1-19 00714 #649-14-1995 L1996 IM *020

RIVERA BADUI, Jose S. 211 CALLE MORSE, PO BOX 818 00714 #847-02-1971 L1973 GS *020

RIVERA-IRIZARRY, Jose V. 211 CALLE MORSE 00714 #649-14-1991 L1992 GP *020

RIVERA IRIZARRY, Miriam L. PO BOX 1210 00714 #649-14-1991 L1995 IM *020

RIVERA VAZQUEZ, Milagros. ■ 00714 #649-14-1990 L1993 *020

RIVERIA IRIZARRY, Jose S. 211 CALLE MORSE, BOX 819 00714 #649-14-1993 L1995 GP *020

ROSS RIVERA, Lorenzo E. PO BOX 450, ARROYOS COMM FMLY HLTH CTR 00714 #042-04-1992 L1994 GP *020

SANTIAGO, Jose Ramon. ■ 00714 #308-03-1985 L1989 GP *020

SOLIS, Edwin. 53 CALLE VIRGILIO SANCHEZ 00714 #308-04-1989 L1991 GP *020

BAJADERO – ARECIBO

GARCIA SANTIAGO, Miguel A. ■ 00616 #649-14-2004 L2006 *100

MEDINA, Luis Alberto. HC 2 BOX 6870, 638 BO DOMING 0.0 CARR 00616 #042-01-1976 L1980 PD *040

REYES, Evelyn. CARR. 638 KM 2.4 00616 #847-04-1977 L1981 IM *020

ROSADO SANTIAGO, Miljan I. HC 1, 2 CEIBA BAJA ST KM 118.9 00616 #649-14-1990 L1994 P *020

SANTIAGO DELGADO, Robin. PO BOX 66 00616 #649-30-2001 L2003 *100

SANTIAGO-GIRONA, Robinson. ■ 00616 #042-04-1985 L1988 GP *020

TORRES-MENDOZA, Ralph. PO BOX 799, 94 AVENIDA PRINCIPAL 00616 #649-14-1980 L1982 *020

BARCELONETA – BARCELONETA

ALVAREZ CORDERO, Lizette. PO BOX 624 00617 #308-06-1986 L1993 *020

BONET PAGAN, Yara A.. PO BOX 445 00617 #308-03-2005 L2006 *100

CALCANO, Nannette. URB LA CATALANA D 41 00617 #308-04-1989 L1992 **PD** *020

CARRION TORRES, Zaida Ive. HC 1 BOX 69492 00617 #649-14-2002 L2004 *100

DAVILA TORRES, Glenda O. PO BOX 822 00617 #649-14-2000 L2003 *100

DIAZ CUEVAS, Bernardo. PO BOX 368 00617 #847-10-1961 L1964 **GP OBG** *020

LOUBRIEL, Francisco J. 14 CALLE CEREZAL, PARC IMBERY 00617 #042-03-1995 L1997 **IM** *020

MARTINEZ VELAZQUEZ, Minely. 803 URB PRADO ALTO 00617 #308-01-1983 L2002 *100

NIEVES-MENDEZ, Adney D. 3 CALLE 8 PARC MAGUEYES 00617 #042-02-2000 L2002 **IM** *020

OTERO CRUZ, Ana I.. PO BOX 658 00617 #308-04-2004 L2005 *100

PEREZ GARCIA, Jose M. 10 CALLE GEORGETTI 00617 #042-04-1990 L1995 **IM** *020

RAMIREZ, Grizelle M. ■ 00617 #042-03-1990 L1994 **FM** *020 †18

RAMOS MENDEZ, Isis D. ■ 00617 #042-04-1998 L2001 **FM** *020

RAMOS-REYES, Pedro Jose. ■ 00617 #847-04-1962 L1964 **GP** *020

REYES, Pedro J. PO BOX 625 00617 #042-01-1984 L1990 **OSS** *040 †40

REYES ROSARIO, Yadira. PO BOX 1885 00617 #649-14-2002 L2004 *100

RIVERA, Joel. ■ 00617 #649-14-2003 L2004 **OBG** *012

RIVERA JIMENEZ, Waldemar. 1 CALLE TOMAS DAVILA, P O BOX 667 00617 #649-14-2003 L2005 *100

RIVERA JIMENEZ, Yonathan. PO BOX 359 00617 #649-14-2003 L2004 *100

RIVERA LABARCA, Rafael. 1 CALLE TOMAS DAVILA, BOX 667 00617 #308-01-1972 L1975 *020

RODRIGUEZ, Arnaldo Ocasio. ■ 00617 #847-10-1966 L1970 **GP** *020

ROSADO MARTINEZ, Edwin. ■ 00617 #042-04-1990 L1995 **PD** *020

RUIZ, Gustavo V. PO BOX 426 00617 #042-04-1993 L1996 **P** *020

RUIZ, Santiago Polly A. PO BOX 1127 00617 #649-14-1994 L2001 *020

RUIZ SANTIAGO, Lesbia I. PO BOX 426 00617 #308-03-1983 L1995 **GP** *020

SANTIAGO COLON, Carmen G. ■ 00617 #847-10-1971 L1978 *020

SOLER-CANDELARIA, Edwin I. PO BOX 552, 38D URB CETALENE 00617 #649-14-1990 L1992 **GS** *020

TIRADO VAZQUEZ, Kareen T.. ■ 00617 #308-04-2000 L2004 *100

TOLEDO, Rafael. PO BOX 205 00617 #042-04-1989 L1989 **GP** *020

TORRES, Angel L. 68 CALLE 2, PARC MAGUEYES 00617 #042-04-1985 L1986 *020

BARRANQUITAS — BARRANQUITAS

ABREU, Nelson. 19 CALLE PADRE BERRIOS 00794 #308-01-1964 L1976 **GP** *030

APONTE, Edgardo R. 103 CALLE BARCELO, HC 1 BOX 4616 00794 #649-14-1989 L1992 **GP** *020

BERRIOS, Madelaine. PO BOX 519 00794 #649-14-1999 L2002 **FM** *020

CASAS-BENABE, Rene. ■ 00794 #041-13-1977 L1982 **IM** *020

COLON, Osvaldo E. PO BOX 759 00794 #042-01-1979 L1982 **PD** *020

COLON, Zidnia Marie. ■ 00794 #308-13-2005 L2006 *100

COLON-ALONSO, Jose. ■ 00794 #847-05-1976 L1978 **GP** *020

COLON MALDONADO, Evaliz. HC 1 BOX 5838 00794 #649-14-2002 L2004 *100

CUADRADO FIGUEROA, F. 00618-9604, BARRANQUITAS PUERTO RICO 00794 #042-02-1981 L1984 **FM** *020 †18

LAUREANO, Angel F. MSC569 00794 #042-01-1985 L1988 **PUD IM** *040 †20

LIMBERT RODRIGUEZ, David. 25 CALLE MUNOZ RIVERA 00794 #042-01-1972 L1974 **PD** *020

LOPEZ, Edgardo R. 76 CALLE BARCELO, APT 429 00794 #042-01-1982 L1985 **FM** *020

LOPEZ, Rafael Angel. PO BOX 699 00794 #042-01-1973 L1975 **CD IM** *020

MARRERO ORTIZ, Carlos E. 8 CALLE BARCELO STE 2 00794 #649-14-1989 L1993 **GS** *100

PAGAN-COLON, Alida. 68 CALLE BARCELO # B 00794 #847-02-1973 L1975 **IM** *020

PEDRAZA-NEGRON, Solimar. 14 CALLE BARCELO 00794 #042-01-2006 **EM** *012

RIVERA, Jose Juan. PO BOX 727, UROLOGO 00794 #042-01-1980 L1987 **U** *020 †95

RIVERA, Mireily. ■ 00794 #042-03-2008 *012

RIVERA, Orlando Enrique. PO BOX 1018 00794 #649-14-2002 L2004 *100

RIVERA-CARTAGENA, Jaime A. ■ 00794 #042-03-1978 L1982 **IM** *020

RODRIGUEZ-ORTIZ, Cristino. 17 CALLE PADRE BERRIOS # A 00794 #042-03-1980 L1982 **OBG** *020

ROSA CARDONA, Angel L. PO BOX 999 00794 #847-05-1979 L1990 *100

ROSARIO, Gabriel Joel. PO BOX 424 00794 #042-02-2007 **TY** *012

SANTINI RODRIGUEZ, Rafael. HC 2 00794 #308-03-1986 L2002 *020

VEGA, Roberto Aponte. 35 CALLE MUNOZ RIVERA, BOX 607 00794 #847-04-1962 L1963 **GP OS** *020

WAH-CHIANG, Roberto. CALLE MUNOZ RIVERA APT15, BX817 00794 #649-02-1959 L1974 **GP GS** *075

BAYAMON — BAYAMON

ACEVEDO, Carlos A. RT 2 K M 11-7 00960 #042-01-1980 L1983 **PD** *020 †55 ‡

ACEVEDO, Jorge Luis. 164 VISTA DE LA BAHIA, URB PANORAMA VILLAGE 00957 #308-01-1986 L1990 **GP** *020

ACEVEDO-SANTOS, Enrique. PO BOX 3010, I-68 SEVILLA BITMORE 00960 #649-01-1955 L1956 **OBG** *020

ACEVEDO SIERRA, Ignacio. AA13 CALLE RIO DUEY, URB RIO HONDO 2 00961 #308-04-1989 L1991 **GP** *020

ACOSTA-ANADON, Carlos A. 207 EDIF MEDICO HERMNS DVL, STE 207 00959 #042-01-1979 L1982 **IM** *020 †20

ACOSTA-CADENA, Surilo I. ZA1 CALLE 36, URB RIVER VIEW 00961 #308-01-1975 L1982 **FM OM** *020 ‡

ACOSTA FERNANDEZ, Jose M.. ■ 00961 #042-04-1997 L2004 **GP** *100

AGRAIT FELICIANO, Mario A. L17 AVE MAGNOLIA, URB MAGNOLIA GDNS 00956 #649-14-1988 L1991 **GP** *020

AGUIRRE, David. ■ 00957 #649-14-2002 L2004 *100

ALAMO-ESTRADA, Pedro. PO BOX 2610 00960 #847-04-1962 L1965 **GS GP** *100

ALBARRAN, Hector J. ■ 00961 #308-03-1983 L1991 **GP** *020

ALBERRO FERNANDEZ, Jose A. ■ 00959 #275-04-1983 L2005 **PD** *020

ALBERTY, Jose Jaime. ■ 00961 #042-01-2007 **GS** *012

ALCANTARA, Adelaida M. ■ 00961 #308-01-1958 L1975 **IM GYN** *020

ALCARAZ, Osvaldo. 804 BAYAMON MEDCL PLZ 00959 #042-01-1977 L1982 **GS** *020

ALDARONDO, Francisco. PO BOX 6999 00960 #042-04-1982 L1986 **IM** *020

ALEJANDRO, Edwin. 106 BAYAMON MEDICAL PLZ, STE 106 00959 #042-01-1986 L1991 **CD IM** *020 †20

ALEJANDRO-GONZALEZ, Adan. X13 CALLE 10, URB FLAMBOYAN GDNS 00959 #042-03-2000 L2002 *020

ALEMANY, William Eugenio. 51 CALLE SANTA CRUZ, ESQ ESTEBAN PADILLA, 00961 #042-01-1981 L1984 **OBG** *020 †30

ALFONSO-SARNELLI, Lizzie. 120 CALLE PRINCIPAL 00957 #308-02-1990 L1996 **OBG** *020

ALICEA BERRIOS, Efrain. TORRE SAN PABLO 00959 #042-01-1963 L1968 **PUD PD** *020

ALICK, Sasha. ■ 00956 #042-03-2008 *012

ALLENDE GINES, Carmen E. 14A COND RIVERSIDE PLZ, 74 SANTA CRUZ ST 00961 #308-03-1979 L1986 **GP** *020

ALTAGRACIA-TARDY, Antonio. 4R34 CALLE ROBLE, LOMAS VERDES 00956 #308-01-1973 L1990 **OPH** *020

ALTAMAR, Gustavo Adolfo. ■ 00961 #042-03-2006 **IM** *012

ALVAREZ, Carlos E. 66 CALLE SANTA CRUZ, STE 310 00961 #308-03-1978 L1980 **GYN** *020 †30

ALVAREZ, Karen Grisselle. PO BOX 60327, U DEL CARIBE ESCUELA MED 00960 #042-03-1998 L2001 *100

ALVAREZ, Lyvia Alaida. ■ 00960 #132-06-1980 L1986 **ATP FOP** *020

ALVELO, Jesus M. 310 BAYAMON MEDCL PLZ #310 00959 #042-03-1980 L1984 **PD** *020 †55

AMADOR, Maria Eugenia. ■ 00959 #275-01-1981 L2005 **PD** *020

ANCALLE, Ingrid Maritza. 113 VISTA DEL MORRO, URB PANORAMA VILLAGE 00957 #649-14-2002 L2004 **NPM** *012 †55

ANDUJAR, Juan David. ■ 00957 #042-03-2002 L2005 **AN** *100

ANGULO VILLANUEVA, Vivan. PO BOX 2382, STE 305 00960 #649-14-1999 L2001 *020

APONTE, Lesbia. 100 PASEO SAN PABLO, STE 203 00961 #042-03-1986 L1992 **N** *020

APONTE, Maysabel. ■ 00959 #042-01-2007 **IM** *012

APONTE, Victor Ivan. 70 CALLE SANTA CRUZ, URB SANTA CRUZ 00961 #042-01-1986 L1996 **DR** *040 †80

APONTE COLON, Jessika. ■ 00957 #308-04-2000 L2002 **PD** *020

APONTE-PEREZ, Lara Milagr. AB15 CALLE RIO FAJARDO, URB RIO HONDO 2 00961 #649-14-1995 L1998 **IM** *020

ARAMBURU, Eloina Leon. ■ 00956 #847-04-1964 L1971 **END IM** *030

ARANGO FRIAS, Celeste M. 501 BAYAMON MEDICAL PLZ, STE 501 00959 #308-03-1979 L1992 *020

ARANGO-FRIAS, Julio Cesar. 606 TORRE SAN PABLO, #68 CALLE SANTA CRUZ 00961 #308-03-1980 L1998 *020

ARANGO-FRIAS, Maria L. 501 BAYAMON MEDCL PLZ #501 00959 #308-03-1979 L1993 **OS** *020

ARIAS, Jose E. 70 CALLE SANTA CRUZ, URB SANTA CRUZ 00961 #042-01-1982 L1984 **PM OS** *020

ARIAS RAMIREZ, Leanis. PO BOX 60327 00960 #275-04-1995 L2004 *020

ARIZMENDI, Angel L. 505 BAYAMON MEDCL PLZ #505 00959 #649-31-1980 L1985 **IM** *020

ARIZMENDI, Norman. 70 CALLE SANTA CRUZ, URB SANTA CRUZ 00961 #042-03-1983 L1986 **FM** *020 †18

ARRAIZA, Francisco Javier. 70 CALLE SANTA CRUZ, URB SANTA CRUZ 00961 #042-01-1997 L2003 **DR** *020 †80

ARRIETA, Francisco. 504 TORRE SAN PABLO 00961 #847-03-1973 L1976 **IM CD** *020

ARZENO, George. 70 CALLE SANTA CRUZ, URB SANTA CRUZ 00961 #035-01-1978 L1984 **OPH** *020 †35

ASENCIO ROSADO, Brendaliz. ■ 00956 #042-04-2001 L2002 *020

AVILES, Jose Luis. 64 CALLE SANTA CRUZ, STE 203 00961 #649-14-1988 L1990 **GP** *020

AYALA, Jose Antonio. 17A CALLE 4, URB BELLA VISTA 00959 #308-03-1982 L1987 **GP** *020

AYALA, Jose Gilberto. ■ 00961 #042-01-2008 *012

AYALA, Velia M. 31-40 AVE MAIN, URB SANTA ROSA 00959 #042-04-1982 L1991 **FM** *020

AYALA-ORTIZ, Madelyn. RR 5 BOX 7662 00956 #042-01-1994 **OS** *100

BADILLO BARRETO, Noel A. RT 2 K M 11-7 00960 #847-05-1973 L1975 **GP OBG** *020

BAEZ ROBLEZ, Mildred E.. ■ 00959 #847-06-2001 L2005 *100

BALESTRA JIMENEZ, Jesus M. HC 67 BOX 100, MANSIONES DE SIERRA TAINA 00956 #847-02-1973 L1977 **PD** *020

BANO, Maria J. TORRE SAN PBLO 802 ST CRUZ 00959 #847-04-1961 L1964 **R** *020

BARRERAS, Miguel F. AVE LAUREL SANTA JUANITA 00958 #042-04-1983 L1986 **EM** *020

BARTOLOMEI, Beatriz. 16-21 AVE AGUAS BUENAS, URB SANTA ROSA 00959 #042-01-1981 L1985 **PM** *020 †60

BATISTA, Sylma. 73 CALLE SANTA CRUZ, STE 212 00961 #042-03-1996 L2005 **PYG** *020

BATLLE-DE LA MAZA, Manuel. 26 CARR 174 URB PALMAR 2 00956 #308-02-1973 L1973 **GP** *020

BAUCAGE-RODRIGUEZ, K. ■ 00961 #042-02-2002 L2005 **PM** *100 †60

BEAUCHAMP, Pedro Jaime. 213 EDIF MEDC SNT CRZ #213 00961 #042-01-1976 L1983 **REN GYN** *020 †30

BECERRA, Merardo Antonio. ■ 00956 #649-17-1999 L2005 **PD** *100

BELTRAN, Jose Luis. 100 AVE R RODRIGUEZ, P O BOX 70 00959 #308-02-1989 L1993 **FM** *020

BELTRAN VIRELLA, Wanda M. 70 CALLE SANTA CRUZ, URB SANTA CRUZ 00961 #308-04-1981 L1986 **IM** *020

BENABE, Julio Edgardo. 125 CALLE ALHELI, URB SAN RAFAEL EST 00959 #042-01-1975 L1981 **NEP IM** *030 †20

BENITEZ, Enrique O. ■ 00956 #275-01-1982 L2001 *100

BERDEGUER, Pedro Federico. PO BOX 395, Z40 AVE LRL 00960 #042-01-1975 L1980 **OTO FPS** *071

BERMUDEZ, Ariel Eduardo. ME30 PLAZA 17, URB MONTE CLARO 00961 #042-03-1989 L1992 **GS** *020

BERMUDEZ, Jose. 100 PASEO SAN PABLO, EDIF DR ARTURO CADILLA ST 00961 #042-01-1995 L1988 **OBG** *020 †30

BERMUDEZ-FRESSE, Maria I. ■ 00959 #042-03-1999 L2000 **PD** *100

BERNAL CABRERO, Delfin. 70 CALLE SANTA CRUZ, URB SANTA CRUZ 00961 #847-01-1955 L1957 **R** *071

BERRIOS, Maria Angelica. 8 F-50 SANTA ELENA 00957 #649-14-2002 L2004 *100

BERRIOS, Rafael. 66 CALLE SANTA CRUZ, INSTITUTO SAN PABLO OFFIC 00961 #042-03-1985 L1989 **OBG** *020 †30

BERRIOS, Rodney. ■ 00958 #042-01-2008 *012

BERRIOS RIVERA, Jorge R. AVE LAUREL SANTA JUANITA 00958 #042-03-1984 L1988 **PM** *020

BETANCOURT, Felix. 70 CALLE SANTA CRUZ, URB SANTA CRUZ 00961 #042-01-1973 L1975 **FM** *040 †18

BETANCOURT-COLLAZO, J. PO BOX 1665 00960 #847-06-1978 L1983 **IM** *020

BICCHI, Liliana Hortensia. 73 CALLE SANTA CRUZ, CARR.#2 KM. 8.5 BO. JUAN S 00961 #308-04-1980 L1989 **P** *020

BISBAL, Jose Eddie. 10-2 AVE AGUAS BUENAS, URB SANTA ROSA 00959 #042-01-1974 L1976 **PM** *020

BLAS, Nancy. H2 CALLE 6, ESTANCIAS DE CERRO GORDO 00957 #649-30-2003 L2005 *100

BOBONIS DE MIRANDA, T. 308 INSTITUTO SAN PABLO, SANTA CRUZ 00961 #042-01-1961 L1963 **CHP P** *020

BONET VELEZ, Ivette C. PO BOX 1617 00960 #649-14-1993 L1996 *020

BOSCH-GOSALVEZ, Enrique F. 410 INSTITUTO SAN PBL #410 00961 #847-08-1979 L1982 PD *020

BOU-GAUTHIER, Elias. J15 AVE BETANCES, URB HNAS DAVILA 00959 #042-03-1983 L1988 PD *020

BRAVO, Wilfredo Eddy. PO BOX 60327 00960 #308-03-2004 IM *012

BRAVO VALVERDE, Ruben L. PO BOX 3050 00960 #308-03-1980 L2002 P *020

BREA, Jose A. 10C EDIF LAS TORRS SR #10C 00959 #308-01-1963 L1976 GS EM *020

BRITO, Rafael Antonio. 70 CALLE SANTA CRUZ, URB SANTA CRUZ 00961 #308-01-1961 L1971 TS *020 †85,90

BULTRON-RODRIGUEZ, Cristin. ■ 00956 #042-01-2004 L2007 EM *020

BUSIGO BORRAS, Miguel E. ■ 00959 #847-05-1982 L1990 GP *020

CABRERA, Carmen Milagros. ■ 00960 #308-03-1991 L2000 FM *100

CABRERA, Pilar A. 70 CALLE SANTA CRUZ, URB SANTA CRUZ 00961 #042-02-1991 L1995 IM *020

CABRERA-DELGADO, Fernando. 307 EDIF MEDICO SANTA CRUZ, STE 307 00961 #042-01-1981 L1983 P *020 †75

CABRERA-OTERO, Sylvia. Z22 AVE LAUREL, LOMAS VERDES 00956 #847-08-1974 L1977 GP UCM *020 ‡

CACHO, Alan Peter. ■ 00959 #308-04-1993 L2002 *100

CAISEDA, Carmen M A-B. 410 INSTITUTO SAN PABLO, CALLE STA CRUZ 00961 #042-01-1961 L1964 PDA PUD *020 †03

CALDERIN, Julio. PO BOX 60327, UNIV CENTRAL DEL CARIBE SC 00960 #042-03-2002 L2005 GS *100 †85

CALDERON, Paulita. CALLE 13 0-4, VERSALLES 00959 #308-03-1981 L1992 GP *020

CALERO, Fernando M. 68 CALLE SANTA CRUZ, TORRE SAN PABLO STE 103 00961 #042-01-1989 L1995 PS *020 †65

CAMPBELL, Joseph Patrick. 2A CALLE LAS FLORES, STE 2A 00959 #007-02-1994 L2000 OPH *020 †35

CAMPOS, Jose A. 70 CALLE SANTA CRUZ, URB SANTA CRUZ 00961 #042-01-1969 L1971 NEP IM *020

CAMPOS, Maribel. 70 CALLE SANTA CRUZ, URB SANTA CRUZ 00961 #042-01-1998 L1999 NPM *055

CAMPOS-SANTIAGO, Zulmari. ■ 00959 #042-03-2005 IM *012

CANALES-QUINTERO, Carlos. ■ 00959 #847-06-1978 L1982 OM GP *020

CANCEL, Mireily. ■ 00961 #042-03-2003 L2006 FM *100 †18

CANDELARIO FERNANDEZ, N. OF MED, UNIVERSITY HOSP UCC SCHOOL 00960 #042-01-1972 L1974 PD OS *075 †55

CANDELAS-RODRIGUEZ, H. 70 CALLE SANTA CRUZ, URB SANTA CRUZ 00961 #847-06-1976 L1982 PD *020

CANER, Raul Orlando. PO BOX 60327, U CENTRAL DEL CARIBE SCH M 00960 #275-03-1992 *100

CANIZARES BAQUERO, O. PO BOX 1005 00960 #847-11-1974 L1977 PS GS *020 †65

CANOVA DIAZ, Carlos. PO BOX 60327, U CENTRAL DEL CARIBE SCH M 00960 #275-01-1993 IM *012

CAPESTANY MATOS, David. PO BOX 8413 00960 #649-14-1992 L1996 *020

CARAZO-CASTILLO, Jorge A. BOX 3016 00960 #869-04-1955 L1958 OBG *020 †30

CARBONELL RAMIREZ, Araceli. PO BOX 56353 00960 #649-14-1991 L2002 *100

CARDE, Pedro Angel, Jr. ■ 00959 #042-03-1991 L1996 NEP *020

CARDENAS, Jose Joaquin. PO BOX 60327, U CENTRAL DEL CARIBE SCH M 00960 #275-01-1990 L2005 FM *020 †18

CARDONA-RAMIREZ, Oscar A. 43 SANTA ROSA MALL STE 15 00959 #847-06-1976 L1979 CHP *020

CARMONA-TORRES, Nestor Lu. ■ 00959 #649-14-2001 L2004 *020

CARO, Osvaldo I. ■ 00959 #042-01-1989 L1993 P *020

CARO ACEVEDO, Eduardo. 32 CALLE PARQUE STE 1A 00961 #847-08-1984 L1989 GP *020

CARRASQUILLO, Hiram A. RT 2 K M 11-7 00960 #847-04-1959 L1962 PD *020

CARRASQUILLO, John Allen. H11 CALLE YORK, VILLA CONTESSA 00956 #042-01-1997 L2000 FM *020 †18 ‡

CARRER RIVERA, Glamadys D. ■ 00956 #042-04-2003 L2004 *100

CARRION, Mercedes. D36 CALLE 15, VILLA DEL RIO BAYAMON 00959 #042-01-1978 L1982 OBG *020

CARRION, Wanda Violeta. 64 CALLE SANTA CRUZ, GALERIA MEDICAL 208 00961 #042-03-1991 L1994 FM *020 †18

CARRION-DIAZ, Yolanda. 3B22 AVE NOGAL, LOMAS VERDES 00956 #649-35-1992 L1996 IM *020

CARRO, Jose Antonio. ■ 00961 #042-02-2004 PM *012

CARTAGENA, Maria Ivelisse. PO BOX 60327, U CENTRAL DEL CARIBE SCH M 00960 #308-02-2002 FP *012

CASANOVA-DIAZ, Angel S. 803 TORRE SAN PABLO 00961 #041-13-1942 L1989 GS *071 †85

CASIANO, Antulio. ROYAL PALM, CALLE ALMACIGO 1-C-4 00956 #649-14-1982 L1986 FM *020 ‡

CASTILLO, Antonio. AL19 CALLE RIO LAJAS, URB RIO HONDO 2 00961 #308-01-1985 L1997 *020

CASTILLO, Evelyn E. ■ 00957 #308-03-1982 L1990 FM *020

CASTILLO, Joel. 1-13 CALLE 1, URB SIERRA BAYAMON 00961 #308-06-1981 L2006 *100

CASTILLO LOPEZ, Miguel A. PO BOX 1334 00960 #308-01-1946 L1958 OS GP *020

CASTILLO-VOLCKERS, E. SUITE 103, PASEO SAN PABLO, FDIF.DR.ARTURO CADILLA 00961 #042-03-1981 L1984 IM *020

CASTRO CRUZ, Julio. PO BOX 60307 00960 #042-04-1991 L2004 *100

CASTRO-MONTANEZ, Leonardo. J13 CALLE 2, EXT VILLA RICA 00959 #042-01-1962 L1967 CD IM *020

CEDENO, Rafael. ■ 00960 #042-03-1988 L1991 FM *020

CESPEDES, Juan J. ■ 00959 #275-03-1983 *100

CESTERO-COLON, Isabel. 409B BAYAMN MDCL PLZ #409B 00959 #847-04-1971 L1975 IM *020

CHACON RIOS, Osana. B7 CALLE SANTA CRUZ, URB SANTA CRUZ 00961 #308-03-1982 L1992 FM *020

CHALOKA, Raymond J. 100 PASEO SAN PABLO, STE 512 00961 #042-01-1991 L1996 U *020 †95

CHEVRES, Myriam Viviana. KK-A STREET 31, ALTURAS DE FLAMBOYA 00959 #649-14-2004 *100

CHEZ, Joaquin Angel. 12 CALLE TIAGOSAN, BOSQUE DE LAS FLORES 00956 #308-01-1983 L1988 GP *020

CHICO, Francisco J. I-J-3 NOGAL AVE RYL PLM 00956 #847-05-1980 L1984 FM IMG *020 †18

CHIESA CEDO, Carlos Juan. 66 CALLE SANTA CRUZ, STE 409 00961 #847-11-1975 L1980 IM HEM *020

CHINCHILLA JIMENEZ, C. UNIV HOSP 00956 #649-26-1981 L1990 P *020

CHINEA, Carmen Maldonado. 41 CALLE DEGETAU 00961 #847-04-1954 L1957 P GP *020

CHRISTENSON, Bernard. 73 CALLE SANTA CRUZ, STE 302 00961 #042-01-1979 L1982 ID IM *020 †20

CINTRON, Hector Luis. NN1 CALLE 32, ALT DE FLAMBOYAN 00959 #042-01-1971 L1973 OBG *020

CIRINO RODRIGUEZ, Juan J.. ■ 00959 #308-06-2001 L2004 *100

COLOM-AVILES, Jesus. PO BOX 2697 00960 #042-01-1955 L1957 U *020 †95

COLON, Marilu. BE25 CALLE AMAZONAS, VALLE VERDE 00961 #042-03-1999 L2002 RHU *020 †20

COLON-PEREZ, Benedicto. STE 602 BAYAMON MED PLAZA 00959 #042-03-1982 L1986 U *020

COLON-RODRIGUEZ, Omaira. ■ 00959 #042-01-1998 L2002 OBG *020

COLON SANCHEZ, Victor A.. PO BOX 3133 00960 #308-01-2000 L2001 *020

COLON SANTINI, Yaditza. ■ 00956 #042-04-1984 L1988 PD *020

CORDOVA-OTERO, Jose A. ■ 00960 #308-03-1985 L1989 FM *020 †18

CORREA, Carlos A. B6 AVE SANTA JUANITA, URB SUNNY HLS 00956 #042-03-1989 L1991 IM *020

CORRIPIO, Ana Isabel. PO BOX 60327, U DEL CARIBE ESCUELA MED 00960 #042-03-1998 L2003 AN *020

CORTES, Ivan. 70 CALLE SANTA CRUZ, URB SANTA CRUZ 00961 #042-03-1984 L1990 OBG *020 ‡

CORTES, Jorge Luis. 68 CALLE SANTA CRUZ # 703, TORRE SAN PABLO 00961 #042-03-1993 L2001 GE IM *020 †20

CORTES, Luz Nilsa. ■ 00957 #042-01-1994 L1998 HO *020

CORTES, Milagro. BD18 CALLE RIO ORINOCO, VALLE VERDE 2 00961 #042-03-1995 L2000 CD *020

CORTES FIGUEROA, Gilberto. 1 AVE AGUAS BUENAS, URBANIZACION SANTA ROSA 00959 #847-02-1971 L1974 OBG *020 ‡

COTTO SANTOS, Cibeles. PO BOX 3376 00958 #649-14-2000 L2003 *100

CRUZ, Abdiel. ■ 00956 #042-01-2003 L2005 GE *012 †20

CRUZ, Rolando J. PO BOX 60327 00960 #649-14-2001 L2003 IM *100 †20

CRUZ-BURGOS, Evelyn. ■ 00958 #042-03-1982 L1995 OS *020

CRUZ FONTANEZ, Lizamar. ■ 00957 #649-14-2003 L2005 *100

CRUZ NIEVES, Jorannie. PO BOX 6942 00960 #649-14-2003 L2005 *100

CRUZ OLIVO, Regino. PO BOX 567, AVE WINSTON CHURCHILL 00960 #308-03-1987 L1990 *020

CRUZ-ORTIZ, Maritza. PO BOX 2387 00960 #308-13-2001 L2004 PD *020

CRUZ RIVERA, Loida. RT 2 K M 11-7 00960 #847-06-1972 L1975 PD PHP *020

CUELI, Adolfo Alfredo. ■ 00956 #308-13-2002 *100

CUEVAS, Harry Richard. 607 BAYAMON MEDICAL PLZ, STE 607 00959 #649-03-1986 L1989 PD *020

CUMBA, Jose Ramon. 51 AVE WEST MAIN # 27, URB SIERRA BAYAMON 00961 #042-01-1976 L1980 OPH *020

CYRILLE, Frantz. PO BOX 60327, PED CENTRAL DEL CARIBE 00960 #649-14-1982 L1999 PD *020

DA COSTA, Yadira S. ■ 00961 #042-03-2001 L2005 N *100 †75

DAVILA, Luis Antonio. ■ 00961 #308-03-1982 L1990 GP *020

DAVIS, Joanna Marie. ■ 00961 #042-03-2007 IM *012

DEBS, Natalio. 100 PASEO SAN PABLO, SUITE 508, EDIF DR A CADIL 00961 #042-01-1981 L1986 PS GS *020 †65

DE LA CRUZ, Antonio A. B1 CALLE SANTA CRUZ, STE 403/404 00961 #042-01-1994 L1998 OSM *020 †40

DE LA CRUZ CAMILO, A A. CALLE 7-218 FLAMINGO HILLS 00957 #308-01-1955 L1972 GP OS *020

DE LA CRUZ ROBLES, Alba E. ■ 00959 #308-01-1989 L2002 GP *030

DE LA TORRE, Eneida Maria. ■ 00961 #042-01-2008 *012

DE LA VEGA, Alberto B. 100 PASEO SAN PABLO, OFIC 408 00961 #042-01-1984 L1987 OBG *050 †30

DEL CAMPO-RIVERA, Lourdes. AVE LOMA VERDE 1C-14B, RM 146 00956 #042-04-1986 L1989 PD *020

DE LEON, Carmen Milagros. 59 CALLE SANTA CRUZ, URB SANTA CRUZ 00961 #042-01-1997 L1999 FM *020

DE LEON-ANTONI, Eduardo. 69 CALLE SANTA CRUZ, URB SANTA CRUZ 00961 #042-01-1957 L1961 PTH CLP *071 †50

DELGADO, Ada Lissette. 902 BAYAMON MEDCL PLZ #902 00959 #042-03-1989 L1993 P *020

DELIZ, Efrain D. B1 CALLE SANTA CRUZ, STE 403-404 00961 #042-01-1985 L1990 ORS *020 †40

DELIZ FIGUEROA, Gladys S.. PO BOX 8156 00960 #308-02-1993 L1996 *020

DEL RIO, Felix G. 100 PASEO SAN PABLO, ARTURO CADILLA BLDG., SUIT 00961 #042-03-1989 L1994 CD *020

DEL RIO, Juan Carlos. 7-8 CALLE 7, URB SANTA ROSA 00959 #308-03-1985 L1991 PD *020

DE MIRANDA, Gilberto L. ■ 00960 #649-14-1991 L1993 *020

DENIS-ROMAN, Luis Alberto. ■ 00956 #308-03-1981 L1985 GP *020

DE PADRO, Teresa Castro. 70 CALLE SANTA CRUZ, URB SANTA CRUZ 00961 #847-10-1956 L1958 PYA P *020

DEPOOL, Magda E. B1 CALLE SANTA CRUZ, CARIMED PLAZA 00961 #042-01-1995 L2000 OPH *020 †35

DE SANZ, Benicia Lebron. LAS TORRES 2B S 00959 #847-10-1957 L1959 P *071

DESCHAMPS-GARCIA, Rafael. 2D CALLE LAS FLORES, BOX2310 00959 #308-01-1959 L1975 GP *072

DE THOMAS, Antonio P, Jr. CARRETERA NUMERO 2 K 8-2 00959 #847-01-1961 L1964 P *071 ‡

DEXTER, Donald Francis. TORRE SAN PABLO, SANTA CRUZ STE 701 00959 #042-01-1971 L1974 PUD IM *020 †20

DIAZ, Arturo. 70 CALLE SANTA CRUZ, URB SANTA CRUZ 00961 #042-01-1980 L1985 U *020

DIAZ, Hector Francisco. C1 CAL 19 URB MAGNOLIA GDN, ROYAL PALM 00956 #042-01-1980 L1983 CCP *020 †55

DIAZ, Marcos Devarie. 70 CALLE SANTA CRUZ, URB SANTA CRUZ 00961 #308-03-1977 L1980 IM *020

DIAZ, Rolando E. 73 CALLE SANTA CRUZ, STE 303 00961 #042-01-1984 L1988 N *020 †75

DIAZ, Santiago. 51-61 CALLE MARGINAL, URB SANTA ROSA 00959 #042-01-1976 L1980 OBG IM *020

DIAZ COLON, Ralph. ■ 00957 #847-14-1981 L1986 PD *020

DIAZ CRUZ, Carmen D.. ■ 00957 #308-03-1982 L2002 GP *020

DIAZ-TORRES, Erving. ■ 00961 #042-03-2000 L2004 PM *020

DIAZ-VARGAS, Manuel A. 68 CALLE SANTA CRUZ # 407, INSTITUTO SAN PABLO 00961 #847-02-1975 L1982 GS *020

DIAZ-VAZQUEZ, Ruben. 66 CALLE SANTA CRUZ, INSTITUTO SAN PABLO, SUITE 00961 #042-01-1980 L1983 **CD IM** *020

DIEPPA, Julio Edgardo. F6 VIA BOGOTA, URB ESTANCIAS 00961 #042-01-1978 L1982 **PM** *020

DIETRICH, Rene. 70 CALLE SANTA CRUZ, URB SANTA CRUZ 00961 #176-01-1966 L1974 **DR NM** *020 †28,80

DIEZ-CARDONA, Elsie M. PO BOX 60327, U DEL CARIBE ESCUELA MED 00960 #042-03-1994 L1999 **PTH** *020

DIPLAN-RODRIGUEZ, Mariel. ■ #042-03-2007 **IM** *012

DOMINGUEZGIRONA, L. 70 CALLE SANTA CRUZ, URB SANTA CRUZ 00961 #042-03-2001 L2003 **FM** *100

DOMINGUEZ PASCUAL, Maria. PO BOX 6727 00960 #308-03-1990 L2002 *100

ECHEVARRIA-CORTES, W. 70 CALLE SANTA CRUZ, URB SANTA CRUZ 00961 #042-01-1995 L2002 **PG** *020 †55

EDNEY WHATTS, Stanley. ■ 00957 #042-04-1983 L1989 **GP** *020

ENCARNACION, Eliseo. BOX 3497, BAYAMON GARDENS 00958 #042-04-1983 L1989 **GP** *020

ENCARNACION, Jeanette P. UNIV CENTRAL DEL CARIBE, DEPT-FAM PRAC 00960 #308-02-1987 L1992 **FM** *020

ENCARNACION KUIL, Cirilo. ■ 00956 #308-06-1986 L1996 *020

ENCARNACION-KUILAN, Edwin. ■ 00956 #308-06-1985 L1991 *020

ENCARNACION MARTE, Roberto. AN2 CALLE 31, REPTO TERESITA 00961 #649-14-2001 L2003 *020

ENTENZA, Fernando. 73 CALLE SANTA CRUZ, STE 201 00961 #042-01-1990 L1995 **P** *020 †75

ESCOBAR PAEZ, Jaime. 36 CALLE MAIN # 51 00957 #264-07-1962 L1963 *100

ESPADA, Javier Rafael. CALLE 5 H-8, RIVERVIEW 00961 #649-14-2002 L2004 **GP** *100

ESTRADA, Carlos J. 70 CALLE SANTA CRUZ, URB SANTA CRUZ 00961 #042-01-1989 L1991 **AN** *020

ESTRELLA, Domingo A. ■ 00961 #308-03-1985 L1989 **GP** *020

EXPOSITO-CARRASQUILLO, A. 75-50 CALLE 64, URB RIVER VIEW 00961 #847-01-1974 L1977 **IM** *020

FABRE, Ricardo Jose. 100 PASEO SAN PABLO 00961 #042-01-1981 L1985 **OBG P** *020

FALCON-TORRES, Felix A. BB2 CALLE 45, JARD DE CAPARRA 00959 #042-03-1980 L1984 **FM** *020 †18

FEIJOO-GONZALEZ, Jose E. 12A CALLE 3, URB FLAMINGO HLS 00957 #308-01-1978 L1980 **GP** *020

FELIBERTI, Norma Arleen D. 44 CALLE DR VEVE 00961 #308-03-1981 L1985 **IM** *020

FELIBERTI IRIZARRY, A. G. 70 CALLE SANTA CRUZ, URB SANTA CRUZ 00961 #847-03-1971 L1975 **EM OS** *020

FELICIANO, Carlos A. ■ 00961 #042-02-2005 **N** *012

FELICIANO, Lourdes J. 100 AVE HOSTOS, VALLE BELLO CHALETS A-13 00956 #042-03-1996 L1998 **ON** *020

FELICIANO MORALES, Wm. 708 BAYAMON MEDICAL PLZ, STE 708 00959 #847-02-1971 L1974 **P** *020

FELIX REYES, Juan J. ■ 00960 #847-04-1955 L1959 **ORS OS** *020

FELIX-TACORONTE, Carmen L. PO BOX 593 00960 #042-01-2005 L2005 **GS** *100

FEQUIERE, Charles Jean. 66 CALLE SANTA CRUZ, STE 506 00961 #042-01-1977 L1981 **NEP IM** *020

FERNANDEZ, Ernesto. PO BOX 60327, U CENTRAL DEL CARIBE SCH M 00960 #275-01-1986 **FP** *012

FERNANDEZ, Ingrid. 70 CALLE SANTA CRUZ, URB SANTA CRUZ 00961 #042-01-1988 L1992 **ID OS** *030

FERNANDEZ, Maria Caridad. PO BOX 60327, U CENTRAL DEL CARIBE SCH M 00960 #275-01-1983 **FM** *100

FERNANDEZ, Pamela. ■ 00956 #042-03-2008 *012

FERNANDEZ-GALLARDO, Judy. 66 CALLE SANTA CRUZ # 508, INSTITUTO SAN PABLO 00961 #308-03-1981 L1987 **P** *020

FERNANDEZ-GARCIA, Ricardo. X12 CALLE 17, URB ROYAL TOWN 00956 #847-04-1968 L1973 **IM END** *020

FERNANDEZ QUESADA, Rafael. 3865 BAY GARDENS 00957 #308-01-1976 L1979 **GP** *020

FERRAN RHEDER, Juan. D14 AVE BETANCES, URB HNAS DAVILA 00959 #847-04-1968 L1970 **GP** *020

FERRER, Carlos, Jr. 405 TORRE SAN PABLO 00961 #308-01-1956 L1963 **GYN** *020

FERRER, Janice. N9 CALLE 1, URB SANS SOUCI 00957 #308-01-1986 L1989 **PD** *020

FERRER, Ricardo M. 70 CALLE SANTA CRUZ, URB SANTA CRUZ 00961 #042-01-1987 L1991 **AN** *020

FERRERIS, Manuel Alberto. 90 AVE RIO HONDO, STE 252 00961 #308-04-2004 L2005 *100

FIGUEROA, Antonio. 70 CALLE SANTA CRUZ, URB SANTA CRUZ 00961 #042-01-1981 L1988 **DR** *050

FIGUEROA, David. MANSIONES DE SIERRA TAINA, CAKKE 3 #4 00956 #649-01-1961 L1966 **HS GS** *020

FIGUEROA, Florentino. ■ 00956 #042-03-1984 L1987 **IM** *020

FIGUEROA, Javier. CALLE 6 APT7 R PLANTATION 00959 #042-01-1992 L1995 **ID** *020 †20

FIGUEROA, Nitza Delcarmen. RR 4, 1.2 CARR 829 00956 #042-01-2000 L2003 **OBG** *020 †30

FIGUEROA, Wanda I. B35 VEREDA REAL, URB VEREDAS 00961 #042-01-1986 L1989 **PD** *040

FIGUEROA CAMARENO, Maria. S30 CALLE 27, ALT DE FLAMBOYAN 00959 #308-01-1983 L1991 **GP** *020

FIGUEROA-FUENTES, F. 70 CALLE SANTA CRUZ, URB SANTA CRUZ 00961 #042-03-1980 L1985 **OBG** *020

FIGUEROA-OCASIO, Marta M. EXTENSION FOREST HILLS, CALLE ATENAS HA-535 00959 #847-02-1982 L1987 **GP EM** *020

FLORES, Jose A. 11 CALLE BETANCES, ESQUINA MARTI 00961 #042-01-1989 L1994 **OPH** *020 †35

FLORES, Vimari Grissel. ■ 00960 #042-01-1998 L2001 *020

FLORES GARCIA, Pedro. RT 2 K M 11-7 00960 #847-06-1973 L1976 **PD** *075

FLORES RIVERA, Arlene. ■ 00960 #042-04-2002 L2004 *100

FLORIAN, Ganimedes. S4 AVE CASTIGLIONI, URB BAYAMON GDNS 00957 #308-01-1980 L1992 **GP** *020

FOSSAS, Jose. 1845 CARR 2 STE 108, BAYAMON MEDICAL PLZ 00959 #042-03-1987 L1988 **GP** *020

FOSSAS LOPEZ, Jose L. 108 BAYAMON MEDCL PLZ #108 00959 #847-04-1957 L1959 **OPH** *020

FRAGA MILLAN, Carlos J. B1 CALLE SANTA CRUZ, CARIMED PLAZA STE 507 00961 #042-01-1988 L1992 **ORS** *020 †40

FRANCESCHINI, Jose A. 73 CALLE SANTA CRUZ # 201, EDIFICIO MEDICO STA CRUZ 00961 #042-01-1980 L1985 **P PYG** *020 †75

FRANCIA PEREZ, Mario Nest. PO BOX 2913 00960 #847-10-2001 L2003 **GP** *100

FUENTES, Anselmo. 107 AVE RIO HONDO 00961 #042-01-1986 L1988 **FM** *020

FUMERO PEREZ, Jose R. 15 E-1 VILLAS DEL RIO 00959 #042-03-1984 L1986 **ORS GS** *020

FUSTER BERLINGERI, R. 306 BAYAMON MEDICAL PLZ #649-14-1972 L1975 **GS AS** *020

FUXENCH, Zaida Z. 66 CALLE SANTA CRUZ, STE 409 00961 #042-01-1977 L1982 *020

FUXENCH, Zelma Z. 66 CALLE SANTA CRUZ # 409, INSTITUTO SAN PABLO 00961 #042-01-1977 L1982 **ID IM** *020

GANDIA-CARO, Rafael. 51-46 AVE MAIN, URB SANTA ROSA 00959 #308-03-1978 L1980 *020

GARAU, Alexis G. CALLE SANTA CRUZ TORRE, HOSPITAL SAN PABLO 00960 #042-03-1985 L1990 **AN IM** *020

GARAU, Priscila. 100 PASEO SAN PABLO, CADILLA BUILDING STE 203 00961 #042-03-1986 L1992 **PG** *020 †55

GARAU, Samuel. TULIPAN ST 224 URB SAN FEO 00956 #056-06-1944 L1945 **IM** *071

GARAU DIAZ, Samuel. 73 CALLE SANTA CRUZ, STE 103, SANTA CRUZ ST. 00961 #649-14-1977 L1979 **R** *020

GARAYALDE, Glenn Jos. ■ 00960 #042-01-1977 L1981 **N** *020

GARCIA, Felipe Antonio. 66 CALLE SANTA CRUZ, STE 405 00961 #042-01-1976 L1981 **CD** *050 †20

GARCIA, Ferdinand. 3-R NO51 EXT LA MILAGROSA 00959 #847-06-1975 L1978 *030

GARCIA, Francisco Javier. ■ 00957 #042-02-2002 L2005 **PM** *100 †60

GARCIA, Harry. 9C CALLE LAS FLORES, VISTA ALEGRE 00959 #042-03-1981 L1985 **P** *020

GARCIA, Juan D. 68 CALLE SANTA CRUZ, TORRE SAN PABLO SUITE 102 00961 #308-01-1967 L1975 **ORS** *020

GARCIA, Luis Amato. ■ 00960 #847-10-1965 L1977 **GP** *020

GARCIA, Madeleine. 102 AVE MINILLAS BAYAMON, STREET #831 KM 8 00956 #649-14-1990 L1996 **ON** *020

GARCIA, Maria Del Carmen. PO BOX 60327 00960 #275-01-1987 **PD** *012

GARCIA, Mario Espinosa. 66 CALLE SANTA CRUZ # 404, INSTITUTO SAN PABLO 00961 #308-02-1975 L1977 **PUD IM** *075

GARCIA, Sylvia Milagros. 904 BAYAMON MEDCL PLZ #904 00959 #308-03-1985 L1989 **HEM** *020

GARCIA, William. F20 CALLE JOSEFINA, URB ROYAL GDNS 00957 #649-14-1992 L2002 **GP** *020

GARCIA MACHADO, Gumersindo. 70 CALLE SANTA CRUZ, URB SANTA CRUZ 00961 #275-03-1974 L1999 **GP** *020

GARDON, Roberto. 308A BAYAMON MEDICAL PLZ, STE 308A 00959 #847-10-1968 L1971 **PD PHP** *020

GARIB-GARCIA, Magaly M. 64 CALLE SANTA CRUZ, GALERIA MEDICA SUITE 209 00961 #308-03-1978 L1981 **PD** *020

GASCOT ZAYAS, Javier. ■ 00956 #042-04-2003 L2004 *100

GENAO ENCARNACION, Maxuel. ZA1 CALLE 36, URB RIVER VIEW 00961 #308-01-1989 L1993 **GP** *020

GERMOSEN CANELA, Altagraci. ■ 00957 #308-01-1958 L1997 **GP** *020

GIL-ESCUDERO, Alcides. 70 CALLE SANTA CRUZ, URB SANTA CRUZ 00961 #847-04-1969 L1972 **NEP IM** *020

GIRON, Jessie. ■ 00960 #308-13-2001 L2003 **IM** *020

GIRONA-LOZADA, Marielys D. ■ 00960 #042-03-2003 L2006 **FM** *100 †18

GODREAU, Roberto. BD2 CALLE RIO AMAZONAS, VALLE VERDE 2 00961 #308-01-1977 L1980 **GP** *020

GOMEZ, Michelle Joanne. ■ 00956 #042-03-2007 **PD** *012

GOMEZ MEDINA, Kenneth J. PO BOX 1641, METROPOLITAN DETENTION 00960 #308-02-1991 L1995 **IM** *020

GONZALEZ, Edgardo. ■ 00957 #649-14-2003 L2005 *100

GONZALEZ, Luis Benjamin. 213 EDIF MEDC SNT CRZ #213 00961 #649-38-1994 L1999 **IM** *020

GONZALEZ, Marybel. ■ 00956 #649-14-1997 L2000 **OBG** *020

GONZALEZ, Reinaldo. 68 CALLE SANTA CRUZ, EDIF. TORRE SAN PABLO SUIT 00961 #308-04-1990 L1992 **IM** *020 †20

GONZALEZ, Sor S. APART 3173 00960 #308-03-1978 L1985 *020

GONZALEZ FUENTES, Sasha M. ■ 00956 #042-04-2000 L2004 *100

GONZALEZ-JOVE, Eduardo A. 70 CALLE SANTA CRUZ, URB SANTA CRUZ 00961 #847-01-1973 L1975 **OBG** *020

GONZALEZ MORALES, Edgardo. DC4 CALLE MONTES, URB VALLE VERDE 3 00961 #308-03-1985 L1994 *020

GONZALEZ PIMENTEL, Victor. BOX 1405 00960 #308-01-1956 L1961 **P GP** *020

GONZALEZ-SALA, Roberto L. 51-39 AVE MAIN, URB SANTA ROSA 00959 #042-03-1981 L1986 **DR** *020 †80

GONZALEZ-SEGARRA, Naggai. ■ 00961 #042-01-2006 **N** *012

GUERRA ASENCIO, Ricardo. BOX 3049 00960 #847-10-1956 L1958 **IM OS** *071

GUZMAN-VIRELLA, Jose R. 66 CALLE SANTA CRUZ, INSTITUTO SAN PABLO STE 40 00961 #042-01-1976 L1981 **U** *020 †95

HAMMERSCHLAG-ICAZA, Bruno. CALLE 22 #301 B 00959 #649-14-1981 L1991 **PUD** *020

HAWATMEH, Ziad Elias Elaw. PO BOX 60327, U CENTRAL DEL CARIBE SCH M 00960 #275-01-1982 L2006 **PD** *100

HERNANDEZ, Angel W. 66 CALLE SANTA CRUZ, STE 501 00961 #042-01-1965 L1969 **CHN PD** *055

HERNANDEZ, Benito. CALLE 3 BLD C8 00961 #649-01-1972 L1978 **OBG** *020

HERNANDEZ, Jeranfel. PO BOX 60327, U CENTRAL DEL CARIBE SCH M 00960 #308-13-2000 L2005 **IM** *020

HERNANDEZ, Jose Miguel. ■ 00959 #042-01-1974 L1976 *020

HERNANDEZ, Nayda I. 70 CALLE SANTA CRUZ, URB SANTA CRUZ 00961 #847-02-1981 L1992 **PD** *020

HERNANDEZ, Nilsa. ■ 00960 #308-03-1984 L1988 *020

HERNANDEZ, Tomas. 73 CALLE SANTA CRUZ, STE 308 00961 #042-01-1968 L1971 **N PHP** *020

HERNANDEZ ABAD, Fermin. ■ 00959 #847-06-1989 L1993 **EM** *020

HERNANDEZ ADAMES, Teodosia. ■ 00959 #308-01-1988 L2004 *100

HERNANDEZ AYALA, Maria I. ■ 00959 #847-06-1976 L1980 **N** *020

HERNANDEZ-COTT, Luis R. 902 TORRE SAN PABLO, 68 CALLE SANTA CRUZ 00961 #042-01-1976 L1981 **OPH** *020 †35

HERNANDEZ-FLORES, Amaury. U19 CALLE LAREDO, VISTA BELLA 00956 #308-01-1978 L1983 **GP** *020

HERNANDEZ-HERNANDEZ, Rene. 809 BAYAMON MEDCL PLZ #809 00959 #847-10-1973 L1976 **RHU IM** *020

HERNANDEZ MARRERO, Armando. 100 PASEO SAN PABLO, SUITE 205 ARTURO CADILLA 00961 #308-03-1984 L1988 **FM** *040

HERNANDEZ-RIOS, Luis J. 73 CALLE SANTA CRUZ, EDIFICIO MEDICO SANTA CRUZ 00961 #024-05-1989 L1991 **GP** *020

HERNANDEZ RODRIGUEZ, David. PO BOX 60327 00960 #649-03-1997 L2002 **IM** *020 †20

HERNANDEZ ROSARIO, Jose R. ■ 00960 #847-04-1974 L1976 *100

HERNANDEZ RUIZ, Manuel. CC20 AVE SANTA JUANITA 00956 #649-01-1962 L1967 OM OS *020

HERNANDEZ TORRES, Antonio. F19 CALLE ISLA NENA, REPTO FLAMINGO 00959 #649-01-1952 L1956 PHP *030 †30

HOY, Leslie. 73 CALLE SANTA CRUZ # 314, SANTA CRUZ PHYSICIAN GRP 00961 #308-04-1991 L1996 FM *020 †18

HUNTER, Robert Franklin. 100 PASEO SAN PABLO, STE 510 00961 #042-01-1978 L1981 ON HEM *020 †20

HUSSEIN, Esam Amin. ■ 00961 #308-03-1984 L2003 PD *020

IGUINA, Jose Gualberto. L53 AVE SANTA JUANITA 00956 #649-14-1985 L1992 GP *020

IRIZARRY, Jose Francisco. 66 CALLE SANTA CRUZ, STE 501 00961 #042-01-1969 L1971 RHU IM *020 †20

IRIZARRY, Pablo Enrique. 304 TORRE SAN PABLO 00961 #042-04-1980 L1984 PD *020

JANER, Walter E. 73 CALLE SANTA CRUZ, EDIF. STA. CRUZ STE 215 00961 #042-01-1993 L2000 GE *020 †20

JASKILLE-ERDMAN, F M. AVE LAUREL SANTA JUANITA 00958 #649-01-1969 L1979 PS *020

JIMENEZ, Aitsa. RR 4, 4.9 CARR 830 HM 0 00956 #649-14-1993 L1995 HEM *020

JIMENEZ, Dorka Maria. ■ 00957 #042-01-2007 *012

JIMENEZ, Edil Obed. ■ 00961 #042-03-2005 ORS *012

JIMENEZ, Manuel Ildefonso. ■ 00957 #308-01-1980 L1988 GP *020

JIMENEZ-GARCIA, Felix A. 1845 CARR 2 STE 410 00959 #649-14-1977 L1979 PG *020

JIMENEZ LOPEZ, Mairamandy. PO BOX 9174 00960 #308-03-1983 L2001 *020

JIMENEZ RIVERA, Brenda M. ■ 00959 #649-14-1999 L2002 *100

JIMENEZ RODRIGUEZ, H O. BB28 AVE SANTA JUANITA, URB SANTA JUANITA 00956 #042-01-1972 L1974 IM END *020

JIMENEZ SALVAT, Ricardo. CARRETAR ESTATAL #2, FONDO SEGURO DEL ESTADO 00961 #847-01-1986 L1993 *020

JONES, Gerty. 608 BAYAMON MEDCL PLZ *608 00959 #440-01-1975 L1984 PM *020 †60

JORDAN, Octavio. 313 EDIF MEDC SNT CRZ #313 00961 #847-05-1969 L1971 GE IM *020 †20

JORDAN-LOPEZ, Tomas. 51-39 AVE MAIN, URB SANTA ROSA 00959 #847-05-1978 L1983 GP *020

JUARBE, Charles. 73 CALLE SANTA CRUZ # 205 00961 #308-03-1978 L1980 OTO HNS *020 ‡

JULIO, William. ■ 00960 #042-03-1999 L2003 PYG *020 †75

LABADIE LABADIE, Gary. 1612 CHALETS DE BAYAMON, AVENIDA RAMON C RODRIGUEZ 00959 #847-05-1969 L1975 GP *020

LA FONTAINE, Ezequiel. ■ 00961 #308-12-1981 L2001 GP *020

LATIMER, Carlos A. 100 PASEO SAN PABLO # 210, ARTURO CADILLA 00961 #042-01-1977 L1980 GE IM *020 †20

LATORRE, Angela Vicent De. PO BOX 20096 00960 #847-01-1958 L1967 OPH OS *074

LAUREANO, Idamar. ■ 00956 #042-01-1992 L1995 FM *020 †18

LEAVITT, Gloria Nahir. ■ 00961 #042-01-2001 L2004 NPM *100 †55

LEAVITT, Karla Michelle. ■ 00961 #042-01-2007 OBG *012

LEBREAULT, Victor F. AN19 CALLE RIO LA PLATA, URB RIO HONDO 2 00961 #308-01-1967 L1975 GS *012

LEBRON LEBRON, Roberto. 341 AVE DOMINICOS, URB MIRAFLORES 00957 #847-01-1974 L1976 GP *020

LECUMBERRY, Maria A. ME60 PLAZA 13, URB MONTE CLARO 00961 #042-01-1983 L1986 PD *020

LEON LEON, Emilio H. CALLE 4 BLQ 9 33 SANTA ROS 00959 #847-08-1972 L1975 GP *020

LERMA-PEREZ, Maria Del C. HOSP REG RUIZ ARNAO 00956 #847-02-1974 L1979 GP *020

LESPIER MENDEZ, Laura E. 68 CALLE SANTA CRUZ, TORRE SAN PABLO SUITE 701 00961 #042-01-1970 L1973 NEP IM *020

LIMARDO DEFENDINI, D. ■ 00959 #042-01-1994 L1999 PTH *020

LINARES, Anthony Raphael. ■ 00960 #308-07-1983 GP *020

LISBOA, Sergio Lebron. SANTA ROSA UNIT 00960 #308-03-1985 L1988 GP *020

LIZARDI-MARTINEZ, Hommy R. 34 CARR 872, URB RIO PLANTATION 00961 #042-04-2002 L2004 GP *020

LLADO, Ivan Jose. 202 INST SAN PABLO, STE 202 00961 #308-02-1979 L1982 CD IM *020 †20

LLAURADOR, Alberto. ■ 00956 #649-14-2002 L2003 *100

LLUBERAS-ORTIZ, Arturo. 7B CALLE LAS FLORES 00959 #847-10-1960 L1963 PM *020

LONGO, Fernando L. 201 TORRE SAN PABLO 00961 #042-01-1965 L1968 OTO GP *020 †45

LOPEZ, Edwin. URB. BELLA VISTA, CALLE 6-F 33 00957 #308-03-1982 L1990 GP *020

LOPEZ, Jaime Pedro. 66 CALLE SANTA CRUZ, STE 306 00961 #042-01-1979 L1983 GYN *020

LOPEZ, Jose Joaquin. 70 CALLE SANTA CRUZ, URB SANTA CRUZ 00961 #042-01-1992 L1994 OPH *020

LOPEZ, Julio Cesar. 1845 CARR 2, BAYAMON MED PLZ STE 309 00959 #042-01-1975 L1980 END IM *020

LOPEZ, Yolanda. 66 CALLE SANTA CRUZ, STE 307 00961 #042-01-1980 L1983 IM *020

LOPEZ-BAEZ, Pablo. 202A SANTA ROSA MALL, SEGUNDO PISO 00961 #847-06-1975 L1977 OTO A *020

LOPEZ-CEPERO, Jose Ramon. 107 CALLE DR VEVE 00961 #308-03-1977 L1979 GP *020

LOPEZ DE ORTIZ, Evelyn. 510 BAYAMON MEDCL PLZ *510 00959 #847-04-1965 L1968 PD *020 †55

LOPEZ DE VICTORIA, Jose R. 68 CALLE SANTA CRUZ # 803 00961 #308-02-1978 L1984 GS EM *020

LOPEZ DE VICTORIA, Orlando. 710 BAYAMON MEDICAL PLZ, STE 710 00959 #042-02-1987 L1991 TS VS *020 †85,90

LOPEZ FIGUEROA, Norma S. 20-20 CALLE 17, URB SANTA ROSA 00959 #847-02-1992 L1995 *020

LOPEZ-HUERTAS, Hector L. ■ 00960 #042-01-2002 L2005 GS *100

LOPEZ MALDONADO, Felix E. CALLE I 361 HRMANAS DVLA 00959 #847-04-1971 L1978 GP GYN *071

LOPEZ-MARTINEZ, Ricardo A. 66 CALLE SANTA CRUZ, STE 406 00961 #042-03-1990 L1991 U *020 †95

LOPEZ-MORALES, Angel. ■ 00961 #308-03-1981 L1986 *020

LUGO, Humberto Luis. 73 CALLE SANTA CRUZ, STE 309 00961 #042-01-1979 L1984 PDS *020 †85

LUGO-D'ACOSTA, Samuel E. ■ 00960 #042-01-1956 L1961 GP OS *020

LUGO-PIAZZA, Edwin I. 504 INSTITUTO SAN PABLO, STA CRUZ 66 00961 #847-06-1970 L1974 NS *020

LUGO-RIGAU, Nelson. PO BOX 1822 00960 #056-06-1948 L1989 R *071 †80

LUINA-PORTILLA, Alejo. 68 CALLE SANTA CRUZ, STE 502 00961 #847-05-1972 L1976 PUD IM *050 †20

LUNA, Victor Arcadio. ■ 00961 #308-01-1960 L1967 IM OS *020

MACHADO GONZALEZ, Richard. RT 2 K M 11-7 00960 #847-02-1963 L1966 OS U *030

MACHADO-MARISCAL, Ricardo. 102 BAYAMON MEDICAL PLZ 00959 #042-02-2003 L2006 IM *100 †20

MADURO, Samuel Irvin. 68 CALLE SANTA CRUZ # 705, TORRES SAN PABLO 00961 #308-03-1984 L1989 FM *020 †18

MAISONAVE BARCELO, Jessica. ■ 00961 #649-14-2003 L2005 *100

MALAVE, Adriel Jose. ■ 00957 #042-01-2005 IM *012

MALAVE, Daisy. PO BOX 236 00960 #649-14-1996 L1997 *020

MALDONADO, Carlos Ismael. ■ 00961 #042-01-2007 P *012

MALDONADO, Juan Antonio. EXT. VILLA RICA, CALLE 5 E-16 00959 #308-04-1983 L1990 GPM OM *020

MALDONADO DE LEON, George. ■ 00959 #308-03-1989 L1998 *020

MALDONADO GONZALEZ, H M. ■ 00957 #308-01-1986 L1988 FM *020

MALDONADO RIVERA, Myriam. ■ 00956 #308-04-1999 L2002 *020

MANCEBO, Luis Alfredo. , LAUREL AVE 00956 #308-01-1983 L2002 PD *100

MANZANO, Marylia. CALLE SANTA CRUZ-70 00960 #649-14-1999 L1999 FM *020 ‡

MARCIAL-ROJAS, Raul A. AVE LAUREL SANTA JUANITA 00958 #056-06-1949 L1954 ATP FOP *030 †50

MARIN-FAVALE, Joanne M. 803B TORRE SAN PABLO, CALLE SANTA CRUZ 00961 #042-01-1990 L1993 DR *020 †80

MARQUEZ, Ruben. 70 CALLE SANTA CRUZ, URB SANTA CRUZ 00961 #308-01-1984 L1986 PD *020

MARRERO, Edith Margarita. AG1 AVE LOMAS VERDES, URB SANTA JUANITA 00956 #308-01-1980 L1983 PD *020

MARRERO, Ernesto R. 66 CALLE SANTA CRUZ, INSTITUTO SAN PABLO SUITE 00961 #847-06-1977 L1981 P OS *020

MARRERO, Ernesto Xavier. ■ 00957 #308-13-2001 L2003 IM *020 †20

MARRERO, Gil M. ■ 00957 #308-03-1982 L1985 GP *020

MARRERO, Juan M. CASA LIN DEL SUR 316 S 17 00959 #042-01-1989 L1992 AN *020

MARRERO, Luis A. 68 CALLE SANTA CRUZ, STE 703 00961 #042-01-1966 L1973 IM GP *020 †20

MARRERO, Luz N. 70 CALLE SANTA CRUZ, URB SANTA CRUZ 00961 #042-01-1983 L1986 IM *020 †20

MARRERO, Ramon. 64 CALLE SANTA CRUZ, GALERIA MEDICAL SUITE 206 00961 #042-01-1984 L1986 GE IM *020 †20

MARRERO, Sandra Enid. AK12 CALLE RIO JAJOME, URB RIO HONDO 2 00961 #042-03-1992 L1997 GS *020 †85

MARRERO MCFALINE, Yanira. ■ 00956 #042-01-2004 IM *100 †20

MARTI, Karen Nereida. ■ 00959 #649-14-2002 *020

MARTINEZ, Andres Antonio. A CARBNL P 16 RES VERSLES 00959 #847-10-1970 L1973 GP *020

MARTINEZ, Cristina Franch. ■ 00956 #042-01-2007 IM *012

MARTINEZ, Edilberto. 73 CALLE SANTA CRUZ 00961 #042-01-1983 L2000 OBG *020 †30

MARTINEZ, Emilio E. RT 2 K M 11-7 00960 #042-04-1980 L1983 EM IM *020

MARTINEZ, Eric. 204 GALERIA MEDICA STE 204, SANTA CRUZ 64 GALERIA MEDI 00961 #042-01-1981 L1988 CHP *020

MARTINEZ, Evelisa. PO BOX 60327, U DEL CARIBE ESCUELA MED 00960 #042-03-1996 L2001 DR *020

MARTINEZ, Frances Aileen. PO BOX 607061, 580 BMS 00960 #042-01-2000 L2003 OBG *020 †30

MARTINEZ, Guillermo E. EDIF MED HERMANAS DAVILA 00959 #042-01-1981 L1986 OTO *020

MARTINEZ, Juan Carlos. 607 BAYAMON MEDICAL PLZ, STE 607 00959 #649-14-1986 L1987 GS *020

MARTINEZ, Manuel Jose. ■ 00960 #042-01-1974 L1982 CD *020 †85,90

MARTINEZ, William Matos. 70 CALLE SANTA CRUZ, URB SANTA CRUZ 00961 #308-03-1982 L1984 GP EM *020

MARTINEZ CANCEL, Zenobio. 41 CALLE DEGETAU 00961 #847-04-1954 L1957 OBG *020

MARTINEZ CRUZ, Joselin. MA-47 CALLE PASEO DEL MONT, URB MONTECLARO 00961 #308-06-1993 L2005 *100

MARTINEZ-DEPENA, Elias. 14 AVE DOMINICOS # 6UR, URB MIRAFLORES 00957 #308-06-1985 L1997 FM *020

MARTINEZ-MALDONADO, Robt. BOX 790 00960 #308-03-1983 L1985 OBG *020 †30

MARTINEZ-MARTIR, Anselmo. ■ 00961 #042-03-1984 L1984 *020

MARTINEZ-MONTANEZ, Victor. BOX 8208 00960 #649-18-1987 L2003 FM *100

MARTINEZ-ORAMAS, Joaquin. PO BOX 2968 00960 #016-06-1950 L1952 IM OM *020

MARTINEZ-RIVERA, Pedro C. 2135 CARR 2, STE 15 PMB 148 00959 #847-06-1977 L1980 FM EM *020

MARTINEZ-SUAREZ, Luis A. ■ 00956 #649-14-1991 L1993 GP *020

MARTINO, Enrique. 70 CALLE SANTA CRUZ 00961 #847-10-1967 L1970 IM *020

MARTINO BERIO, Martin. ■ 00961 #649-14-2004 L2005 *100

MARTINO-MORALES, A. ■ 00961 #042-01-2000 L2002 END *100 †20

MARTIR COLLAZO, Antonio. ■ 00957 #847-06-1976 L1980 *100

MARTORELL, Edgar Manuel. EXT HERMANAS DAUILA 00958 #042-01-1970 L1972 U *075 †95

MATOS, Victor Salas. PO BOX 1801 00960 #737-01-1959 L1968 FM *020

MATOS-MERCADO, Rafael. ■ 00958 #308-03-1985 L1991 IM *020

MATUNDAN, Mitchell M. 73 CALLE SANTA CRUZ, STE 211 00961 #042-03-1997 L2004 IM *020

MAYMI, Jose Amado. 100 PASEO SAN PABLO, AZTURO CADILLA -410 00961 #042-01-1980 L1985 U *020 †95

MAYOL, Pedro M. 70 CALLE SANTA CRUZ, URB SANTA CRUZ 00961 #042-01-1962 L1964 PDP PD *020 †55

MAYORAL-BIGAS, Jose A. VANDA NO 4 TORRIMAR 00956 #847-02-1963 L1966 P CHP *072

MC KENZIE GARAY, Manuel. 909 BAYAMON MEDICAL PLZ, STE 909 00959 #847-06-1972 L1975 OBG *020

MEAUX, Jorge Arturo. 73 CALLE SANTA CRUZ 00961 #042-01-1998 L2001 FM *020

MEDINA, Augusto Cesar. BAYAMON GARDEN STATION 00958 #042-04-1991 L1997 HEM *020

MEDINA, Miguel A. 50-21 CALLE 25, URB SANTA ROSA 00959 #042-03-1993 L1997 FM *020

MEDINA, Sixto Manuel. 405 BAYAMON MEDCL PLZ *405 00959 #042-01-1974 L1976 IM CD *020 †20

MEDINA CLAUDIO, Yanira. AC-1 RIO HONDO, ESPIRITU SANTO 00961 #649-14-2002 L2003 *100

MEDINA-SANTOS, Robustino. URB SANTA ROSA, 24 ST BLQ 44 #2 00959 #847-02-1974 L1976 EM GP *020

MEDINA TOLLINCHE, Jose T. 1850 ROAD #2 00959 #042-01-1954 L1957 R NM *030 †80,28

MEDINA VILAR, Alejandro A. ■ 00961 #847-10-1988 L1994 FM *020

MELECIO, Lemuel. 70 CALLE SANTA CRUZ, URB SANTA CRUZ 00961 #042-01-1979 L1982 PD *020

MELENDEZ, Coralys. ■ 00961 #042-03-2008 *012

MELENDEZ, Enid R. PO BOX 2035 00960 #042-01-1986 L1990 PM *020 †60

MELENDEZ, Maria T. 70 CALLE SANTA CRUZ, URB SANTA CRUZ 00961 #042-01-1971 L1973 PD NEP *020

MELENDEZ, Mario Manuel. 25 CALLE ONGAY, URB SANTA CRUZ 00961 #649-01-1970 L1972 GP *071

MELENDEZ QUINONES, F. 70 CALLE SANTA CRUZ, URB SANTA CRUZ 00961 #024-01-1983 L1991 TS VS *020 †85,90

MELENDEZ-ROSA, Myriam I. 11 CALLE PALMER 00961 #042-03-1986 L1992 PUD IM *040

MENDEZ, Lorely Esther. PO BOX 60327, U CENTRAL DEL CARIBE SCH M 00960 #275-03-1990 PD *012

MENDEZ, Ramon Eduardo. ■ 00959 #308-04-1987 L1990 GP *020

MENDEZ, Zenaida. 201 BAYAMON MEDCL PLZ #201 00959 #042-01-1978 L1983 GS SO *030

MENDEZ DE GUZMAN, R J. E22 CALLE SANTA CRUZ, URB SANTA CRUZ 00961 #847-11-1977 L1980 AN PME *020

MENDOZA, Lourdes Maria. CALLE 2H 32 EXT VILLA RICA 00957 #308-03-1984 L1993 P *020

MENENDEZ, Benny. 73 CALLE SANTA CRUZ, STE 314 00961 #042-01-1986 L1993 EM *020 †16

MENENDEZ-APONTE, Angel J. 316 CALLE 2, HERMANAS DAVILA 00959 #847-04-1979 L1983 TS *020

MENENDEZ RUIZ, Benjamin. ■ 00961 #649-35-1996 L2002 *020

MENESES, Miguel A. EE10 CALLE MARGINAL, VILLA CONTESSA 00956 #042-04-1995 L1996 FM *020

MERCADO, Aurea Yanira. ■ 00957 #649-14-2002 PD *020

MERCADO, Harry. AVE LAUREL SANTA JUANITA 00958 #042-01-1980 L1983 FM *040 †18

MERCADO, Ruben Luis. 70 CALLE SANTA CRUZ, URB SANTA CRUZ 00961 #042-01-1974 L1976 GYN *020 †30 ‡

MERCADO-ARROYO, Alejandro. 70 CALLE SANTA CRUZ, URB SANTA CRUZ 00961 #308-02-1977 L1982 PD *020

MERCED, Gadiel Enrique. ■ 00956 #042-03-2006 TY *012

MICHEO, William F. 66 CALLE SANTA CRUZ, INSTITUTO SAN PABLO STE 30 00961 #042-01-1982 L1986 PM *020 †60

MICHES-VICIOSO, Rafael. ■ 00957 #308-01-1962 L1976 *100

MIDDELHOF, Alberto E. FC1 CALLE ARTURUS, URB IRLANDA HTS 00956 #042-03-2001 L2002 PM *012

MIESES, Eddy. ■ 00959 #042-03-1990 L1995 CD IM *020 †20

MIMOSO, Jose J. 100 PASEO SAN PABLO, CADILLA 00961 #042-01-1961 L1966 OBG *020 †30

MIRANDA, Jose R. 100 PASEO SAN PABLO, EDIT DR A CADILLA 00961 #042-01-1981 L1987 OPH *020

MIRANDA, Maria L. 68 CALLE SANTA CRUZ, TORRE SAN PABLO #605 00961 #649-14-1999 L2002 PD *020

MIRANDA, Mariade L. HH5 CALLE 41, JARD DE CAPARRA 00959 #042-01-1985 L1989 END IM *020 †20

MIRANDA, Mario Cesar. 68 CALLE SANTA CRUZ, STE 606 00961 #042-01-1958 L1961 IM *020

MIRANDA, Roberto Antonio. 00961 #649-14-2003 L2004 GP *100

MIRANDA CASANOVA, Edwin. ■ 00956 #308-01-1972 L1975 PTH *020

MIRANDA CASANOVA, Luis E. 66 CALLE SANTA CRUZ, INSTITUTO SAN PABLO SUITE 00961 #847-01-1958 L1961 OBG *020

MIRANDA-MARTIN, Anselmo. 66 CALLE SANTA CRUZ # 408, INSTITUTO SAN PABLO 00961 #042-03-1981 L1984 IM *020

MIRANDA MIRANDA, Anisha. ■ 00959 #308-04-2004 L2006 *100

MIRANDA-RAMIREZ, Juan M. PO BOX 2669 00960 #649-01-1958 L1963 OTO *020

MIRANDA USUA, Yamil. ■ 00956 #042-03-2008 *012

MOJICA, Jose A. PO BOX 4291, BAYAMON GARDENS STATION 00958 #042-03-1985 L1988 IM *020

MOLINA, Maria D. 20 CALLE SANTA CRUZ, URB SANTA CRUZ 00961 #042-01-1974 L1975 PN PD *020 †55

MOLINARY, Luis. 804 BAYAMON MEDCL PLZ #804 00959 #042-01-1987 L1990 CD *020 †20

MONLLOR, Lilliam. J8 CALLE 9, EXT VILLA RICA 00959 #308-11-1990 L2003 *100

MONTALVO, Carmen I.. 89 CARR 174, URB AGUSTIN STAHL 00956 #649-14-1999 L2002 GP *020

MONTANEZ-FALCON, Rufino. 31-61 AVE MAIN, URB SANTA ROSA 00959 #847-06-1975 L1982 *020

MONTERO, Angel. PO BOX 60327, U CENTRAL DEL CARIBE SCH M 00960 #275-01-1976 PD *100

MORALES, Alvin. 73 CALLE SANTA CRUZ, STE A 00961 #024-01-1985 L1989 AN PME *020

MORALES, Anabelle. 70 PLAZA DEL PARQUE, URB. PASEOS 00961 #042-01-2005 IM *100

MORALES, Esther M. F19 CALLE 7, URB RIVERSIDE PARK 00961 #042-04-1981 L1996 PD *020

MORALES, German Del Rio. 00959 #649-03-1976 L1978 FM *020

MORALES, Ibis. 85 CALLE GORRION, JARD DE BAYAMONTE 00956 #042-03-1984 L1987 PD *020

MORALES, Jose O. 70 CALLE SANTA CRUZ, URB SANTA CRUZ 00961 #042-01-1982 L1984 AN *020

MORALES, Jose Oscar. 70 CALLE SANTA CRUZ, URB SANTA CRUZ 00961 #023-01-1959 L1961 NM IM *020, 28

MORALES, Randolfo. AL17 CALLE 30, URB ROYAL TOWN 00956 #649-35-1986 L1988 GP *020

MORALES ALVARADO, Jose L. 203 EDIF MEDICO SANTA CRUZ, STE 203 00961 #847-10-1966 L1974 OBG *020

MORALES-FERNANDEZ, V. PO BOX 3459 00958 #308-01-1977 L1979 GP *020

MORALES-MORALES, Jose A. 73 CALLE SANTA CRUZ, STE 306 00961 #649-14-1978 L1981 IM *020 †20

MORALES-MORALES, Victor M. COND BAYAMON GDNS 00956 #308-01-1974 L1976 GP *072

MORALES VAZQUEZ, Randolfo. AL017 30TH ST STNT JUAN 00956 #847-09-1965 L1968 OS GP *020

MORA PERAZA, Edwin A. EXT HNAS DAVILA, CALLE K #101 00959 #847-04-1956 L1959 EM OS *030

MORA RUIZ, Edwin A. 503 INSTITUTO SAN PABLO, AVE SANTA CRUZ 00961 #042-03-1980 L1987 GP *020

MOREL, Jaime Jose. SANTA ROSA 00959 #308-01-1980 L2003 *100

MORELL, Andres. ■ 00956 #308-04-1989 L1992 GP *020

MORELL COLBERG, Frances M. PO BOX 60327 00960 #308-02-2002 PTH *100

MOURE-RODRIGUEZ, Sergio. 705 TORRE SAN PABLO 00961 #847-05-1979 L1986 GS *020

MOYSE, Gerard J. ■ 00956 #649-14-1977 L2003 OBG *020

MUNIZ, Eva I. ■ 00960 #042-04-1982 L1984 GP *020

MUNIZ, Luis A. 11-6 CALLE 55, URB ROYAL TOWN 00956 #042-04-1981 L1984 PD *020

MUNIZ, Miguel A. 11-6 CALLE 55, URB ROYAL PALM 00956 #042-04-1982 L1985 GP *020

MUNOZ, Carlos A. RT 2 K M 11-7 00960 #847-04-1962 L1964 AN *020

MUNOZ, Carlos Jose. HOSPITAL HERMANOS MELENDEZ, DEPT OF ANESTHESIA 00959 #042-01-2985 L1992 AN IM *020

MUNOZ-JIMENEZ, Ramon A. GG 36 CALLE 19 ALT 00959 #308-01-1952 L1958 *100

MUNOZ ZAYAS, Roberto. 49 CALLE 1, ALTS DE BAYAMON 00956 #847-05-1955 L1958 GYN FSM *072

MURRAY, Gisela. E2 CALLE 10, REPTO TERESITA 00961 #042-01-2005 L2006 GS *100

NADAL LLUBERES, Jose R. BOX 2313 00960 #308-01-1961 L1976 *020

NATALI, Maria Elena. B24 VEREDA TROPICAL, URB VEREDAS 00961 #308-03-1979 L1983 IM *020

NATER, Manuel. SUITE 706 CARR #2 KM 11.7, BAYAMON MEDICAL PLAZA 00960 #042-01-1968 L1970 OBG GP *020 †30

NAZARIO TOSSAS, Antonio J. JJ9 CALLE VIA PERIFERICA, JARD DE CAPARRA 00959 #847-04-1965 L1970 GS *020

NEGRON, Jose E. 64 CALLE SANTA CRUZ, STE 203 EDIFICID GALERIA 00961 #308-02-1988 L1991 GP *020 †20

NEGRON-RIVERA, Delma. PO BOX 60 00960 #042-03-1980 L1985 OBG *020

NEVAREZ, Gladys. B7 CALLE SANTA CRUZ, URB SANTA CRUZ 00961 #042-01-1975 L1979 PD *020

NIETO ORTIZ, Jose Luis. 2 RES MAGNOLIA GDNS 00956 #847-10-1969 L1972 GP *020

NIEVES, Carlos Manuel. J21 CALLE 2, EXT VILLA RICA 00959 #042-01-1985 L1992 CD *020 †20

NIEVES, Carmen Marisol. P40 CALLE RENO 00956 #042-03-1992 L1995 FM *020 †18

NIEVES, Higinio D. PO BOX 1177, 302B TORRE SAN PABLO 00960 #649-01-1958 L1963 CD IM *072

NIEVES, Sonia Beatriz. ■ 00960 #715-01-1981 *100

NIEVES-REINO, Jesus L. 100 PASEO SAN PABLO, STE 509 00960 #042-02-1985 L1990 U *020

NIEVES-RIVERA, Francisco. 305 BAYAMON MEDICAL PLZ 00959 #042-01-1985 L1992 PDE PD *020 †55

NIEVES-RODRIGUEZ, Mariela. ■ 00959 #042-01-2005 IM *012

NIEVES TABAADA, Adoniran. P10 CALLE PRINCIPAL, PARC VAN SCOY 00957 #847-06-1961 L1965 *020

NINA, Emiliano. EXT HERMANAS DAUILA 00958 #308-01-1949 L1962 PUD A *072

NORIEGA, Elizabeth. ■ 00960 #042-03-2008 *012

NORIEGA, Monserrate. PO BOX 217 00960 #042-01-1985 L1985 OBG *020

NOVOA, Jose Edgardo. 66 CALLE SANTA CRUZ, STE 101 00961 #042-01-1990 L1994 CD *020 †20

OCASIO, Juan Antonio. ■ 00961 #042-01-1977 L1980 OPH *020 †35

OCASIO PANTOJA, Ana Ivett. ■ 00959 #308-07-1984 L2001 *020

OCHOA-SALCEDO, Ramon. B204 COND RIBRS DL R #B204 00959 #042-02-1995 L1996 *020

OLLER NAVARRO, Jose A. EE10 CALLE MARGINAL, VILLA CONTESSA 00956 #847-03-1972 L1975 PD *020

OLMEDO, Luis Fernando. 70 CALLE SANTA CRUZ, URB SANTA CRUZ 00961 #042-01-1977 L1981 PD *030 †55

OPPENHEIMER, Jennifer C. 100 PASEO SAN PABLO # 510, EDIFICIO ARTURO CADILLA 00961 #042-03-1980 L1985 HO IM *020 †20

OQUENDO-CABRERA, Angel. 68 CALLE SANTA CRUZ, STE 402 TORRE SAN PABLO 00961 #847-05-1960 L1963 PD *020 †55 ‡

OQUENDO-VELEZ, Leyda Z. 100 PASEO SAN PABLO, STE 405 00961 #042-02-1994 L1997 FM *020 †18

OROBITG, Francisco. PO BOX 363 00960 #030-06-1950 L1993 R OS *020

ORRACA-FEBRY, Martha E. I7 AVE BETANCES, URB HNAS DAVILA 00959 #649-14-1987 L1990 FM OM *020

ORTEGA, Lucrecia E. 60 CALLE SANTA CRUZ, URB SANTA CRUZ 00961 #308-01-1969 L1976 PD *020

ORTEGA-PRIETO, Roberto. PHA, COND. RIVERSIDE PLAZA 00961 #847-02-1972 L1982 AN *020

ORTEGA-TORRES, Maximino R. 70 CALLE SANTA CRUZ, URB SANTA CRUZ 00961 #308-03-1978 L1980 PD *020

ORTIZ, Eddie. H2 AVE CASTIGLIONI, URB BAYAMON GDNS 00957 #042-01-1996 L1999 FM *020 †18

ORTIZ, Hernan. PO BOX 60327, U DEL CARIBE ESCUELA MED 00960 #042-03-1998 L2000 FM *020

ORTIZ, Janet Pizarro. K5 AVE CASTIGLIONI, URB BAYAMON GDNS 00957 #308-02-1992 L1994 PD *020

ORTIZ, Jorge Luis. ■ 00959 #042-04-1981 L1986 GP *020

ORTIZ, Luis J. 306 TORRE SAN PABLO, STE 306 00961 #042-01-1986 L1986 D *020 †15

ORTIZ, Noel Antonio. PO BOX 2990 00960 #042-01-1973 L1975 CD IM *020

ORTIZ, Noemi. PO BOX 4274 00958 #308-06-1984 L1991 GP *020

ORTIZ, Norma A. RT 2 K M 11-7 00960 #847-04-1961 L1963 OS PD *030

ORTIZ, Omar. ■ 00959 #042-01-2002 L2008 GS *100

ORTIZ BOU, Miguel Angel. CALLE 6 H-1, URB VERSALLES 00959 #308-04-2003 L2006 *100

ORTIZ CINTRON, Edgar. ■ 00957 #649-14-1992 L1995 P *020

ORTIZ GRAULAU, Rafael A. AN19 CALLE JULIA, VILLA RICA 00959 #042-04-1991 L1993 GP *020

ORTIZ RIVERA, Leonardo. ■ 00956 #042-01-1986 L1989 PD *020

ORTIZ-SORRENTINI, Cesar. 66 CALLE SANTA CRUZ, INSTITUTO SAN PABLO SUITE 00961 #847-12-1977 L1979 PD *020

ORTIZ-VALLADARES, Hector. 68 CALLE SANTA CRUZ, STE 103 00961 #308-03-1976 L1978 GP *020

OTERO, Ruben. ■ 00961 #042-04-1981 L1986 IM *075

OTERO BERMUDEZ, Jose. 36 PASEO ROSSY, BO HATO TEJAS 00959 #308-03-1977 L1980 GP *020

OTERO HERNANDEZ, Pedro A. EXT HERMANAS DAUILA 00958 #847-02-1972 L1975 OBG *020

OYOLA MORALES, Jose R. 226 CALLE COMERIO 00959 #042-01-1984 L1987 FM IM *020 ‡

OYOLA-NIEVES, Pedro. 73 CALLE SANTA CRUZ # 416 00961 #847-01-1977 L1981 P *020

OZUNA, Agustina Xiomara. ■ 00956 #308-03-1983 L1991 GP *020

PABLOS DE PARRILLA, G. B7 CALLE SANTA CRUZ, URB SANTA CRUZ 00961 #847-04-1954 L1957 FM EM *020

PABON-NEVAREZ, Ramon. 68 CALLE SANTA CRUZ, TORRE SAN PABLO 00961 #042-01-1960 L1962 GS OS *040 †85

PACHECO, Luis A. ■ 00960 #010-03-1944 L1945 GP OS *020

PACHECO, Olga E. PO BOX 3298, BAYAMON GARDENS STATION 00958 #042-01-1989 L1995 CD *020 †20

PADILLA, Antonio C. PO BOX 60327, U DEL CARIBE ESCUELA MED 00960 #042-03-1998 *100

PADILLA, Jose L. 64 CALLE SANTA CRUZ, STE 103 00961 #042-04-1989 L1991 GP *020

PADILLA, Samuel. ■ 00961 #042-01-2002 L2005 NEP *100 †20

PAGAN, Carlos M Morales. 6 ST D 8 FLAMBOYAN GDNS 00959 #308-04-1983 L1985 GPM PHP *020

PAGAN, Enid. ■ 00957 #649-43-1982 L1990 PD *020

PAGAN MARRERO, Luis R. 2K23 CALLE FLAMBOYAN, LOMAS VERDES 00956 #649-14-1986 L1989 CD *020

PAGAN PAGAN, Jose Domingo. PO BOX 60327 00960 #042-01-1958 L1965 GS *020 †85

PANTOJA, Jose Rosado. BOX 9071 00960 #847-04-1960 L1964 *071

PAOLI BRUNO, Jorge. 70 CALLE SANTA CRUZ, URB SANTA CRUZ 00961 #042-01-1994 L1996 FM *020 †18

PAOLI-BRUNO, Rafael A. 70 CALLE SANTA CRUZ, URB SANTA CRUZ 00961 #042-03-1984 L1990 IM MDM *030

PARRILLA-PABLOS, Maria P. 10 CALLE SANTA CRUZ # B-7 00961 #308-03-1982 L2002 FM *014

PARRILLA-PADILLA, Pedro L. 70 CALLE SANTA CRUZ, URB SANTA CRUZ 00961 #308-03-1976 L1979 OBG *020 †20

PAZ-TREMOLS, Manuel. AVE LAUREL SANTA JUANITA 00958 #275-01-1950 L1976 PUD *020

PEDROSA, Dora. AP & O 2222, CHALETS DE BAYAMON 00959 #042-03-1990 L1994 OBG *020

PEDROZA-SIERRA, Gerardo A. ■ 00956 #649-14-2000 L2004 GP *020

PELAEZ ALLENDE, Adriano V. AVE STA JUANITA STE 154 00957 #275-01-1965 L1975 GP *020

PELAYO, Enrique. PO BOX 60327, U CENTRAL DEL CARIBE SCH M 00960 #275-01-1988 L2005 IM *020 †20

PELET, Jorge I. ■ 00956 #042-01-1987 L1993 GS *020 †85

PENA, Nancy. PO BOX 2609 00960 #308-04-1986 L2003 CHP *100

PERAZA, Antonio. L53 AVE SANTA JUANITA, URB SANTA JUANITA 00956 #042-03-1995 L2000 IM *020

PEREA, Leila Yanin. ■ 00961 #042-01-1979 *075

PEREYO, Jose A. 100 PASEO SAN PABLO, STE 207 00961 #023-01-1959 L1961 CD IM *020 †20

PEREYO, Jose Eduardo. PO BOX 9432, BAYAMON BRANCH 00960 #042-01-1998 L2000 IM *020 †20

PEREZ, Carlos R. Z40 AVE LAUREL, LOMAS VERDES 00956 #042-04-1989 L1991 GP *020

PEREZ, Carmen Maria. 00959 #042-01-1978 L1982 R *020 †80

PEREZ, Emilio A. 70 CALLE SANTA CRUZ, URB SANTA CRUZ 00961 #042-01-1983 L1988 GS *020 †85

PEREZ, Gilberto. PO BOX 60327, U CENTRAL DEL CARIBE SCH M 00960 #275-08-1995 IM *012

PEREZ, Lisette Y. 70 CALLE SANTA CRUZ, URB SANTA CRUZ 00961 #042-01-1988 L1994 OTO *020 †45

PEREZ, Maria Del Carmen. RT 2 K M 11-7 00960 #042-03-1980 L1985 OBG *020

PEREZ, Milton Anthony. RT 2 K M 11-7 00960 #042-03-1981 L1985 PUD IM *020

PEREZ, Pedro A. ■ 00956 #308-03-1987 L1996 *020

PEREZ, Veronica. ■ 00956 #042-03-1994 L1996 FM IM *020 †18

PEREZ ALVAREZ, Brigida L. RR 5 BOX 6705 00956 #847-10-1992 L1994 P *020

PEREZ-ANDREU, Javier J. K1 CALLE 7 BOX 66, VISTA BELLA 00956 #042-01-1991 L1996 DR *020

PEREZ-GUMA, Jose E. 70 CALLE SANTA CRUZ, URB SANTA CRUZ 00961 #042-04-1983 L1985 OBG *040

PEREZ LOPEZ, Naydamar. CALLE STA CRUZ 53 ALTOS 00961 #042-01-1972 L1974 GP *020

PEREZ-LORAN, Edwin Heber. PO BOX 60327, U DEL CARIBE ESCUELA MED 00960 #042-03-2000 L2006 *100

PEREZ MALDONADO, Nicolas. 68 CALLE SANTA CRUZ, OFICINA 401 00961 #042-01-1988 L1992 PM *020 †75

PEREZ MAROS, Nydia Luz. BAVIERA FF47 VILLA CONTESA 00956 #649-14-1994 L1996 GP *020

PEREZ-ORTIZ, Domingo. Z40 AVE LAUREL, URB IRLANDA HTS 00956 #042-01-1955 L1957 GP *072

PEREZ RIVAS, Jose F. 34-1 CALLE 43, URB MIRAFLORES 00957 #847-03-1973 L1975 IM CD *020

PEREZ SOTO, Noel. 70 CALLE SANTA CRUZ, URB SANTA CRUZ 00961 #042-03-1995 L1998 OPH PS *020 †35

PEREZ-TORO, Luis S. 73 CALLE SANTA CRUZ STE 31 00961 #308-04-1991 L1993 FM *020 †18

PEREZ-VEGA, Gladys. 3A CALLE LAS FLORES, STE 3A 00959 #649-01-1974 L1980 GP *020

PEREZ VILLAMIL, Ralph. 70 CALLE SANTA CRUZ 00961 #649-01-1961 L1966 AN *071

PESANTE-PINTO, Jose Luis. 70 CALLE SANTA CRUZ, URB SANTA CRUZ 00961 #847-06-1979 L1982 FM *020 †18

PESQUERA-SEVILLANO, H L. ■ 00959 #847-06-1976 L1979 FM *020

PHILIPPI, William E. 73 CALLE SANTA CRUZ # 407 00961 #042-01-1986 L1992 N *020 †75

PICO-BAUERMEISTER, Jose F. EXT HERMANAS DAUILA 00958 #847-04-1954 L1957 OPH *071

PIETRI, Giovanna C. 73 CALLE SANTA CRUZ STE 20 00961 #042-02-1984 L1986 P *020

PINERO OLMO, Patricia. P62 CALLE 21, URB BELLA VISTA 00957 #649-14-2003 *020

PITA, Ignacio Luis. ■ 00959 #042-01-2001 L2002 N *020 †75

PIZARRO SEVILLA, Ana. ■ 00961 #847-04-1956 L1960 IM *020

PONTON, Juan Igartua. 66 CALLE SANTA CRUZ, INS SQU PABLO STE 401 00961 #847-06-1976 L1981 IM CD *020

POU-DELGADO, Israel. HC 67 BOX 13130 00956 #308-03-1978 L1980 FM *020

PRIETO, Edgardo Jose. ■ 00959 #649-14-1990 L1992 P *020

PRINCIPE-LOPEZ, Jorge L. 70 CALLE SANTA CRUZ, URB SANTA CRUZ 00961 #847-05-1976 L1979 IM *020

QUESADA MARRERO, Angel F. AVE LAUREL SANTA JUANITA 00958 #275-01-1945 L1971 FM OM *020

QUETGLAS, Miguel A. RT 2 K M 11-7 00960 #869-04-1955 L1957 GS HS *072 †85

QUEVEDO, Gerardo. 73 CALLE SANTA CRUZ, STE 204 00961 #042-01-1980 L1985 GS CRS *020 †10,85

QUEVEDO, Juan Manuel, Jr. PO BOX 60327, U CENTRAL DEL CARIBE 00960 #042-02-2007 IM *012

QUINONES, Dorayde. ■ 00957 #042-01-1998 L2000 EM *020

QUINONES-MEJIAS, Rosa. Q6 CALLE 14, UR RIVER VIEW 00961 #308-01-1979 L1982 *020

QUINONES TORRES, Luis A.. COND. TORRES DEL PARQUE, APTO. 810 00956 #649-35-1996 L2003 FM *020

QUINTANA, Humberto O. 66 CALLE SANTA CRUZ, STE 202 00961 #308-03-1981 L1984 CD IM *020 †20

QUINTERO, Greida M. ■ 00957 #649-14-1986 L1995 *020

R, Anibal A Rodriguez. ■ 00959 #308-01-1980 L1997 *020

RAICES, Ohel Soto. ■ 00961 #042-03-1997 L2004 CHP *100

RAMIREZ, Jorge J. 2A CALLE LAS FLORES # 2A, VISTA ALEGRE 00959 #042-01-1961 L1963 OPH IM *020 †35

RAMIREZ, Juan A. BAYAMON MEDICAL PLAZA, OFIC 307 00959 #847-05-1976 L1982 GS *020 †85

RAMIREZ, Moises O.. ■ 00959 #649-14-2003 L2005 *100

RAMIREZ JIMENEZ, Aurea. 10E CALLE LAS FLORES 00959 #649-01-1968 L1971 D *020

RAMIREZ QUINONES, Augusto. PO BOX 2076 00960 #042-01-1964 L1966 PD *020

RAMIREZ-RIPOLL, Miguel A. 11 CALLE BETANCES, INSTITUTO OFTALMICO BAYAMO 00961 #042-02-1995 L1999 OPH *020

RAMIREZ RODRIGUEZ, Milton. ■ 00959 #275-01-1981 L2004 GP *020

RAMIREZ-TANCHEZ, Carlos. 68 CALLE SANTA CRUZ # 803 00961 #042-03-1980 L1985 GS *020 †85

RAMOS, Enrique. 73 CALLE SANTA CRUZ, STE 404 00961 #649-14-1998 L2000 FM *100

RAMOS, Ivan G. 704 BAYAMON MEDICAL PLZ, STE 704 00959 #649-30-1984 L1987 IM *020

RAMOS, Luis E. 73 CALLE SANTA CRUZ, STE 102 00961 #042-01-1984 L1987 OBG *020

RAMOS, Peter. 70 CALLE SANTA CRUZ, URB SANTA CRUZ 00961 #042-01-1992 L2002 PTH IM *020 †50

RAMOS CRUZ, Alberto. 66 CALLE SANTA CRUZ, INSTITUTO SAN PABLO STE 30 00961 #847-02-1978 L1981 ORS *020 †40

RAMOS-DUCOS, Emilio. 51-46 AVE MAIN, URB. SANTA ROSA 00959 #308-10-1983 L1993 FM *020 †18

RAMOS MARTINEZ, Juan C. ■ 00956 #649-14-2001 L2002 *100

RAMOS ORTIZ, Marily. PO BOX 1592 00960 #649-14-2001 L2004 *100

RAMOS PEREZ, Maritza. LILAS B11 00961 #042-04-1999 L2002 FM *020

RAMOS RAMOS, Luz E. CALLE 22 BLD 47 20 STA ROS 00959 #847-08-1980 L1985 *020

RAMOS-RAMOS, Manuel. ■ 00960 #847-04-1956 L1960 PD *020

REYES, Clara Nilda. 808 BAYAMON MEDICAL PLZ, STE 808 00959 #042-01-1980 L1983 PHO PD *020

REYES, Edgar A. 70 CALLE SANTA CRUZ, URB SANTA CRUZ 00961 #042-01-1985 L1993 OTO FPS *020 †45

REYES, Victor Santos. ■ 00959 #649-26-1981 L1987 GP *020

REYES POLANCO, Vanessa. ■ 00961 #649-14-2003 L2005 *100

REYES TINEO, Radhames. 68 CALLE SANTA CRUZ # 803 00961 #847-05-1974 L1976 GS *020

RIESTRA, Jose L. 68 CALLE SANTA CRUZ, TORRE SAN PABLO 904 00961 #042-01-1971 L1980 END IM *020 †20

RIOS, Raul Armando. 100 PASEO SAN PABLO, ARTUZO CADILLA STE 411 00961 #042-01-1981 L1984 PUD IM *020 †20

RIOS, Victor Miguel. ■ 00961 #042-01-1973 L1975 NS *020 †25

RIOS CERVANTES, Jose. SANTA ROSA, AVE. AGUAS BUENAS B-10 #7 00959 #847-02-1976 L1981 P *020

RIOS-LLUVERAS, Arlia M. AA44 CALLE 49, URB REXVILLE 00957 #308-02-1976 L1982 *020

RIOS SANCHEZ, Valerie M. PO BOX 60327 00960 #649-14-2004 PD *012

RIVAS, Cesar Ramon. EXT HERMANAS DAUILA 00958 #847-10-1968 L1970 N *020

RIVAS DIAZ, Lourdes. ■ 00956 #649-19-1992 L1996 *020

RIVERA, Agustin. AVE LAUREL SANTA JUANITA 00958 #042-03-1981 L1986 PD *020

RIVERA, Almi Enid. 70 CALLE SANTA CRUZ, URB SANTA CRUZ 00961 #649-14-2003 FM *020 †18

RIVERA, Anibal. RT 2 K M 11-7 00960 #042-01-1973 L1974 D *020

RIVERA, Barbara Columua. ■ 00957 #308-01-1959 L1978 GP *071

RIVERA, Crispulo M. 602 TORRE SAN PABLO, CALLE SANTA CRUZ 68 00961 #847-06-1965 L1967 PUD IM *020

RIVERA, Edwin. ■ 00959 #308-03-1979 L1985 *100

RIVERA, Enrique Antonio. 70 CALLE SANTA CRUZ, URB SANTA CRUZ 00961 #042-01-1999 L1999 DR *020

RIVERA, Eugenia Ayala. S4 AVE CASTIGLIONI, URB BAYAMON GDNS 00957 #308-01-1984 L1987 PD *020

RIVERA, Fernando. 701 BAYAMON MEDCL PLZ #701 00959 #042-01-1997 L1999 GS *100 †85

RIVERA, Fernando Torres. RT 2 K M 11-7 00960 #042-03-1980 L1987 OBG *020

RIVERA, Hec Manuely. ■ 00961 #649-14-2005 L2005 *100

RIVERA, Herbert A. 31-60 AVE MAIN, URB SANTA ROSA 00959 #042-03-1993 L1997 CD *020

RIVERA, Ildefonso Rivera. 68 CALLE SANTA CRUZ # 506, TORRE DE SAN PABLO 00961 #308-02-1975 L1981 CD IM *020

RIVERA, Ileana. B8 CALLE ABETO, LOMAS VERDES 00956 #042-01-1989 L1992 PD *020 †55

RIVERA, Jose Antonio. PO BOX 60327, UNIV HOSP RAMON RUIZ ARNAU 00960 #649-14-2000 L2002 IM *100

RIVERA, Jose Efrain. 73 CALLE SANTA CRUZ, STE 412 00961 #042-03-1992 L1995 FM *020

RIVERA, Kimberly. 73 CALLE SANTA CRUZ, STE 314 00961 #649-14-2000 L2003 *020

RIVERA, Maria Isabel. 11 CALLE BETANCES 00961 #035-08-1984 L1990 OPH OS *020 †35

RIVERA, Miguel Angel. 41 CALLE SANTA CRUZ, URB SANTA CRUZ 00961 #649-14-1988 L1991 P *020

RIVERA, Norma I. BOX 236, SAN PABLO HOSP 00960 #042-01-1987 L1990 FM *020 †18

RIVERA, Ricardo Enrique. 70 CALLE SANTA CRUZ, URB SANTA CRUZ 00961 #042-03-1998 L2005 DR *020 †80

RIVERA, Roberto. ■ 00960 #042-01-1984 L1988 IM RHU *020 †20

RIVERA, Vivian. ALT.SAN SOUCI, C-7 CALLE 2 00957 #649-14-1999 L2000 FM *100

RIVERA-COLON, Yamil Cesar. ■ 00957 #042-01-2000 L2004 OSS *020

RIVERA COTTES, Nestor A. 405 TORRE SAN PABLO 00961 #847-05-1961 L1964 OBG *071

RIVERA DEL RIO, Jose R. 100 PASEO SAN PABLO, ARTURO CADILLA BLG STE 401 00961 #308-02-1977 L1981 IM CD *020 †20 ‡

RIVERA-LOPEZ, Luis A. RT 2 K M 11-7 00960 #308-01-1974 L1977 FM *020

RIVERA-MALDONADO, Jose H. 274 PASEO C # 0, ALTS DE BAYAMON 00956 #847-09-1954 L1956 IM P *020

RIVERA-NEVAREZ, Jose A. RENO Q # 5 URB VISTA BELLA 00956 #042-01-1998 IM *100

RIVERA ORTIZ, David. BF1 CALLE AMAZONAS 00961 #308-02-1977 L1981 IM *020

RIVERA-PAGAN, Eduardo. AQ8 CALLE RIO SONADOR 00961 #847-04-1974 L1978 GP *020

RIVERA-POLANCO, Jose. 73 CALLE SANTA CRUZ STE 21 00961 #308-03-1977 L1980 P CHP *020

RIVERA-ROMERO, Enrique. PO BOX 2707 00960 #035-08-1952 L1954 CHP OS *040 †75

RIVERA VALDES, Jose Juan. 68 CALLE SANTA CRUZ, TORRE SAN PABLO STE 202 00961 #847-10-1961 L1965 PD *020

RIVERO, Delia Yola. ■ 00959 #737-08-1990 L2003 *100

RIVERO, Jesus. ■ 00960 #308-08-1982 L2005 P *100

RIVERO, Luis Manuel. AVE LAUREL SANTA JUANITA 00958 #649-14-1981 L1984 FM *040

RIVERO MARTINO, Victor Ra. PO BOX 60327 00960 #308-13-2005 IM *012

ROBLES, Luis. ■ 00961 #308-03-1983 L1987 GP *020

ROBLES BARRETO, Maria Y.. ■ 00959 #042-04-2003 L2004 *100

ROBLES RIVERA, Edna I. 110 AVE LOS FILTROS STE 21, COND. PLAZA DE TORRIMAR I 00959 #847-03-1996 L2000 *100

RODRIGUEZ, Blanca I. 73 CALLE SANTA CRUZ, STE 314 00961 #042-04-1981 L1991 GP *020

RODRIGUEZ, Carmen Rocio. PO BOX 60327, U DEL CARIBE ESCUELA MED 00960 #042-03-1999 L2002 *020

RODRIGUEZ, David Danl. PO BOX 60327, U DEL CARIBE #847-10-1974 L1980 U *020 †95

RODRIGUEZ, David Ruben. ■ 00960 #847-02-1978 L1983 IM *020

RODRIGUEZ, Dinamarca. PO BOX 60327 00960 #308-04-1992 L1998 IM *020

RODRIGUEZ, Diomedes R. PO BOX 60327, U DEL CARIBE ESCUELA MED 00960 #042-03-2001 L2004 AN *100

RODRIGUEZ, Elvira. S9 CALLE 5 # 23, URB SANTA ELENA 00957 #847-04-1981 L1989 **PD** *020

RODRIGUEZ, Felicita R. ■ 00959 #847-04-1977 L1980 **PD** *020

RODRIGUEZ, Harry. 2135 CARR 2, STE 15 00959 #649-39-1984 L1990 **GP** *020

RODRIGUEZ, Jaime Enrique. PO BOX 60327, U CENTRAL DEL CARIBE 00960 #042-02-1996 L1998 **IM** *012

RODRIGUEZ, Jose A. 38 CALLE BETANCES 00961 #308-01-1978 L1980 *062

RODRIGUEZ, Juan L. AVE LAUREL SANTA JUANITA 00958 #847-04-1957 L1959 **PHP GP** *020

RODRIGUEZ, Juan M.. ■ 00961 #847-10-1995 L1998 **IM RHU** *020

RODRIGUEZ, Julio Armando. ■ 00959 #042-01-2001 L2003 **IM** *020 †35

RODRIGUEZ, Luz M. ■ 00961 #042-01-1982 L1987 **PTH** *020

RODRIGUEZ, Melanie. ■ 00958 #042-01-2008 *012

RODRIGUEZ, Olga L. 607 BAYAMON MEDCL PLZ #607 00959 #042-01-1967 L1969 **GS** *020 †85

RODRIGUEZ, Wilfredo. CENTRO COMERCIAL ROYAL GAR, CARR 167 00957 #042-04-2002 L2003 *100

RODRIGUEZ, Wilmer. 100 PASEO SAN PABLO, STE 104 00961 #042-01-1979 L1982 **GE** *020 †20

RODRIGUEZ-COLON, Magda I. CARRETERA NUMERO 2 K 8-2 00959 #042-03-1981 L1986 **IM** *020

RODRIGUEZ COLON, Maria. 64 CALLE SANTA CRUZ, GALERIA MEDICA STE 208 00961 #042-01-1989 L1993 **FM** *020 †18

RODRIGUEZ CRUZ, Jose A. ■ 00959 #847-02-1973 L1975 *100

RODRIGUEZ-DIAZ, Oscar A. BX 4191 BAYAMON GARDENS 00958 #847-08-1971 L1974 **GP** *020 †18

RODRIGUEZ-HERNANDEZ, Jose. 68 CALLE SANTA CRUZ, STE 301 00961 #308-03-1978 L1980 **AN EM** *020

RODRIGUEZ MEDINA, Ednaliz. ■ 00961 #649-14-2004 L2005 *100

RODRIGUEZ-NIEVES, Nelson. 68 CALLE SANTA CRUZ # 702, TORRE SAN PABLO 00961 #847-05-1967 L1974 **P** *020

RODRIGUEZ PEREZ, Vilmarie. RR 5 BOX 5334, 11.0 BO DAJ 167 CARR 00956 #042-04-2002 L2003 *100

RODRIGUEZ ROBLE, Juanita. ■ 00960 #308-02-1977 L1979 **PD** *020 †55

RODRIGUEZ RODRIGUEZ, J. AU17 CALLE RIO TURABO, VALLE VERDE 1 00961 #847-05-1964 L1967 **P** *020

RODRIGUEZ-ROSARIO, Arturo. TERMINAL GUEGUAS AMA, BAYAMON OPTICAL 00958 #042-01-1959 L1962 **OPH R** *071

RODRIGUEZ, Carlos Antonio. 64 CALLE SANTA CRUZ, GALERIN MEDICA STE 203 00961 #649-14-1996 L1996 **IM** *020

ROJAS, Maria Libertad. L12 SANS SOUCI 00957 #847-05-1976 L1980 **PD OM** *030

ROMAN, Marina I. PO BOX 9463 00960 #042-03-1981 L1984 **IM** *030

ROMAN, Pedro Eyxarch. B1 CALLE SANTA CRUZ, CARIMED PLAZA , SUITE 309 00961 #649-14-1993 L1995 **IM** *020

ROMAN DIAZ, Felix A. 4X6 AVE CARLOS JAVIR ANDLZ, URB ROYAL PALM 00956 #847-04-1968 L1974 **GP** *020

ROMAN TOLEDO, Jose A. ■ 00959 #847-04-1966 L1970 **P** *071

ROMERO, Arlene. FLAMINGO HILLS, 7TH ST #217 00957 #042-04-1980 L1986 **PD** *020

ROMERO, Domingo. ■ 00959 #308-01-1982 L1996 **GP** *020

ROSA, Martin. ■ 00957 #308-03-1984 L1991 **GP** *020

ROSADO DEL VALLE, Marcos. ■ 00959 #649-01-1958 L1961 **P PHP** *072

ROSADO MAYSONET, Ignerys. ■ 00960 #042-04-2003 L2004 *100

ROSADO ROSA, Saritza I. H26 CALLE 8, URB HNAS DAVILA 00959 #308-03-1984 L1995 **GP** *020

ROSARIO, Marta Isabel. ■ 00956 #042-03-1999 L2002 **FM** *020

ROSARIO ROSARIO, Norbert. EXT ALTURAS DE FLAMBOYAN, CALLE 30 QQ-10 00959 #042-04-1984 L1986 **GP EM** *020

ROSARIO SEISE, Elzebir G. 20 CARR 174 # 28B, URB. STA. ROSA 00959 #042-04-1992 L1993 **FM** *020

ROSARIO TIRADO, Ruben C.. 4 AVE LOS DOMINICOS, URB MIRAFLORES 00957 #649-14-2001 L2001 *020

RUIZ, Carmina. 32 BLQ 54 16 SANTA ROSA 00959 #042-03-1988 L1994 **NM** *020

RUIZ, Hiram Antonio, Jr. 907 BAYAMON MEDICAL PLZ 00959 #042-01-1994 L1998 **D** *020 †15

RUIZ, Jose I. ■ 00961 #042-01-1994 L1996 **EM IM** *020 †16,20

RUIZ, Maria Delc. ■ 00961 #042-03-1988 L1991 **PD** *020

RUIZ, Rafael. 302 INSTITUTO SAN PBL #302 00961 #308-03-1983 L1995 **GP** *020

RUIZ, Rafael Angel. 908 BAYAMON MEDCL PLZ #908 00959 #042-01-1974 L1980 **U** *020 †95

RUIZ ALVAREZ, Felix. 73 CALLE SANTA CRUZ, STE 304 00961 #308-02-1991 L1995 **ID** *020 †20

RUIZ RAMOS, Juan Alberto. CARR #2 KM-11.1, BAYAMON MEDICAL PLAZA 00959 #042-03-1984 L1990 **IM** *020 †20

RULLAN, Ramon Manuel. 68 CALLE SANTA CRUZ, TORRE SAN PABLO 00961 #042-01-1999 L2001 **GE** *020 †20

RUSSE GOMEZ, Limaris. 100 AVE LAUREL, LOMAS VERDES 00956 #649-14-2004 L2006 **IM** *012

SALGADO MITCHELL, Maritza. 2231 CHALETS DE BAYAMON, RL AVE 50 CHALETS BAYAMON 00959 #308-03-1978 L1981 **PD** *020

SALLENT AQUINO, Freddy. PO BOX 60327, U CENTRAL DEL CARIBE SCH M 00960 #308-02-2003 **FP** *012

SANABRIA, John F. ■ 00958 #041-02-1952 L1953 **GS** *020.

SANCHEZ, Angel Radames. MONTE CLARO, PLAZA 5-MA #23 00961 #042-01-1980 L1983 **IM NEP** *020

SANCHEZ, Luis P. B1 CALLE SANTA CRUZ # 307, CARIMED PLAZA 00961 #042-03-1990 L1991 **OSS** *020

SANCHEZ AVILA, Maria Del. ■ 00959 #649-35-1999 L2002 *020

SANCHEZ BETANCOURT, Ivette. 70 CALLE SANTA CRUZ, URB SANTA CRUZ 00961 #649-14-1993 L1995 **PEM** *020

SANCHEZ-BORRERO, Rene. OFICINA 505, INSTITUTO SAN PABLO 00959 #042-01-1979 L1983 **N** *020 †75

SANCHEZ-LONGO, Maria M. 56 CALLE BETANCES, HNAS DAVILA 00961 #308-04-1981 L1986 **PD** *020

SANCHEZ-MILLET, Israel. PO BOX 2105 00960 #847-01-1974 L1976 **PD** *020

SANCHEZ-ORTIZ, Hector. ■ 00957 #847-05-1976 L1979 *020

SANFELIZ RIVERA, Victor M. 70 CALLE SANTA CRUZ, URB SANTA CRUZ 00961 #847-03-1965 L1971 **IM** *020

SAN MIGUEL, Carmen M. 68 CALLE SANTA CRUZ # 406 00961 #042-01-1990 L1994 **D** *020 †15

SAN MIGUEL GONZALEZ, Wilma. J21 CALLE 2, EXT VILLA RICA 00959 #042-04-1997 L2001 **FM** *020

SANTA, Juan Carlos. ■ 00961 #042-01-2004 **PTH** *012

SANTANA, Liza Marie. ■ 00957 #042-01-2001 L2004 **FM** *100

SANTANA-REBOYRAS, Justo. RIO HONDO MED CTR 00961 #042-03-1980 L1984 *100

SANTIAGO, Annette. RIO HONDO 00961 #042-01-1995 L1999 **CCP** *020 †55

SANTIAGO, Ariel. ■ 00958 #042-03-1994 L2000 *020

SANTIAGO, Lynnette. 70 CALLE SANTA CRUZ, URB SANTA CRUZ 00961 #649-14-1998 L2003 **GP** *020

SANTIAGO, Manuel Antonio. PO BOX 596 00960 #649-14-1982 L1993 **GP EM** *020

SANTIAGO, Ruben Jesus. DD4 CALLE 18, ALTURAS DE FLAMBOYAN 00959 #847-08-1985 L1991 **GP** *020

SANTIAGO, Yesenia Delcarm. ■ 00959 #042-01-2004 **IM** *100 †20

SANTIAGO-LUGO, Haydee. 51-46 AVE MAIN, URB. SANTA ROSA 00959 #649-14-1976 L1978 **P PMM** *071

SANTIAGO SOLANO, Carlos M. ■ 00958 #847-05-1981 L1985 **FM** *020

SANTINI, Luis Antonio. PO BOX 1585 00960 #847-04-1967 L1971 **IM** *020

SANTOS, Javier. PO BOX 60327, U DEL CARIBE ESCUELA MED 00960 #042-03-1998 *100

SANTOS, Madeline. ■ 00961 #042-04-1981 L1989 **GP** *020

SANTOS PEREZ, Eduardo. E6 CALLE SANTA CRUZ 00961 #308-01-1942 L1958 **GP PHP** *020

SANTOS-SANTIAGO, Jose L. EA68 CALLE TILO, URB LOS ALMENDROS 00961 #451-01-1977 L1983 *020

SANZ-ORTEGA, Gerardo. 2B CALLE LAS FLORES # 2B 00959 #847-10-1957 L1960 **P** *020

SARRIERA RODRIGUEZ, M A. CONDOMINIO LAS TORRES, OFIC 4A SUR 00960 #847-01-1960 L1962 **IM GE** *071

SASTRE-MARTINEZ, Eduardo. RT 2 K M 11-7 00960 #042-03-1982 L1986 **PD MDM** *020 ‡

SEDA, Jose Oscar. ■ 00959 #042-03-2005 **FM** *100

SEDA-RAMIREZ, Jesus M. 508 BAYAMON MEDCL PLZ #508 00959 #847-05-1974 L1980 **OBG** *020

SEGURA-LUINA, Maria J. ■ 00960 #847-02-1975 L1980 *074

SEGURA-NIEVES, Enrique. 100 PASEO SAN PABLO, STE 408 00961 #308-03-1978 L1980 **OBG** *020

SEIN NAJERA, Ricardo Javi. PO BOX 60327, U CENTRAL DEL CARIBE SCH M 00960 #308-04-2003 **IM** *012

SERRANO, Glory Marie. PO BOX 60327, U DEL CARIBE ESCUELA MED 00960 #042-03-1998 L2001 *020

SERRANO, Juan. PO BOX 1876, 68 SANTA CRUZ ST SUITE 40 00960 #042-03-1988 L1994 **BBK** *020 †50

SERRANO-GONZALEZ, Ina R. AVE LAUREL SANTA JUANITA 00958 #042-01-1961 L1964 **PHO PD** *020 †55

SERRANO OJEDA, Pedro A. PO BOX 958, CARIBBEAN TOMOTHERAPY CTR 00960 #042-02-1994 L2003 **RO** *020 †80

SIERRA, Jesus R. CALLE 14S 33, SANTA MONICA 00957 #042-04-1995 L1997 *020

SILVA, Eliezer Roberto. H-1 ST. 10, SANS SOUCI 00957 #649-35-1999 L2001 **GP** *100 ‡

SMITH, Wanda Ivelisse. C/17 BLG 15 NO 4 STA ROSA 00959 #308-04-1980 L1985 *020

SOBRINO-CATONI, Jose M. 68 CALLE SANTA CRUZ, TORRE SAN PABLO SUITE 503 00961 #042-01-1969 L1974 **IM OS** *020

SOLIS CRESPO, Gloria D L. 20 CALLE SANTA CRUZ, URB SANTA CRUZ 00961 #308-03-1983 L1987 **PD** *020

SOTO, Ruth H. AA1 CALLE 5, REPTO VALENCIA 00959 #308-03-1983 L1986 **ID** *020 †20

SOTO, Zahidee. ■ 00957 #042-03-1995 *100

SOTO-GOITIA, Mayra L. ■ 00961 #042-03-2000 L2004 **FM** *100 †18

SOTO-QUIJANO, David A. 66 CALLE SANTA CRUZ, STE 301 00961 #042-01-1996 L1999 **PM** *020 †60

STUART, Brayan Omar. ■ 00956 #042-01-2004 **BBK** *012

STUART, Elizabeth. G21 CAMINO DE LIRIOS, URB ENRAMADA 00961 #042-01-1983 L1986 **PD** *020 †55

SUAREZ, Carlos Manuel, Jr. ■ 00960 #042-01-2000 **CHP** *012

SUAREZ, Carmen I. 100 PASEO SAN PABLO, STE 202 00961 #042-03-1989 L1994 **PD** *020 †55

SUAREZ, Carmen M. 31-43 AVE MAIN, URB SANTA ROSA 00959 #042-03-1987 L1988 **FM** *020 †18

SUAREZ, Ramon Alberto. 31-43 AVE MAIN, URB SANTA ROSA 00959 #042-01-1977 L1980 **FM** *040 †18

SUAREZ-VILLAMIL, Ramon A. 66 CALLE SANTA CRUZ # 508 00961 #308-03-1982 L1984 **IM CD** *020

TANON, Rafael E. C11 CALLE 1 URB REXVILLE, STATION 00957 #649-01-1966 L1970 **FM** *020

TASCH RAMIREZ, Raymond J. 3A7 AVE LAUREL, LOMAS VERDES 00956 #649-14-1986 L1990 **FM** *020

TEJEDA OYOLA, Maricel. ■ 00959 #308-13-2002 L2004 *020

TIMOTHEE-RIOS, Miguel A. PO BOX 1758 00960 #010-03-1953 L1955 **GP OS** *071

TIRADO OTERO, Maria D. 73 CALLE SANTA CRUZ, EDIFICIO MEDICO SANTA CRUZ 00961 #308-03-1979 L1989 *020

TIRADO-RIVERA, Jorge L. ■ 00959 #649-14-1982 L1982 **PD** *020

TOCUYO, Carmen M. 70 CALLE SANTA CRUZ, URB SANTA CRUZ 00961 #649-14-1987 L1990 **FM** *020 †18

TOLEDO-COLON, Maribel. ■ 00957 #042-03-1993 L1996 **PD** *020

TOLLINCHE, Marcel Phil. 1875 CARR 2, STE 208 00959 #042-01-1974 L1976 **OPH IM** *020

TORANO, Victor A. 802 TORRE SAN PABLO, STE 802 00961 #042-03-1987 L1995 **P ADP** *030 †75

TORO-GRAJALES, Ismael. B7 CALLE SANTA CRUZ, URB SANTA CRUZ 00961 #042-03-1980 L1984 **IMG FM** *020 †18 ‡

TORO MONTALVO, Pedro E. 2U6 AVE LAUREL, LOMAS VERDES 00956 #649-18-1986 L1992 *020

TORRES, Erick. ■ 00958 #042-02-2004 **FM** *100

TORRES, Jaime Gerardo. ■ 00957 #042-03-2006 **P** *012

TORRES, Juan A. EXT HERMANAS DAUILA 00958 #042-01-1967 L1973 **R** *020

TORRES, Juster Manuel. AL21 CALLE 30, URB ROYAL TOWN 00956 #308-02-1988 L1990 **PD** *020

TORRES, Neisa Minerva. 70 CALLE SANTA CRUZ, URB SANTA CRUZ 00961 #042-03-1995 L1997 **PUD** *020

TORRES, Tomas M. 73 CALLE SANTA CRUZ, STE 202 00961 #042-01-1962 L1966 **GS HS** *020

TORRES ALVARADO, Jose. ROYAL TOWN, AVENUE LAS CUMBRES A-35 00958 #847-04-1968 L1975 **FM** *020

TORRES-ALVAREZ, Elba. ■ 00956 #042-03-1997 L2003 **SP** *020

TORRES BERRIOS, Loyda S. HNAS DAVILA, CALLE I, #49 00959 #042-01-1988 L1993 **D** *020 †15

TORRES CABRERA, Benjamin. CALLE 19X2 BAYAMON GARDENS 00957 #847-02-1971 L1975 *020

TORRES MORILLO, Aida Luz. HC 67 BOX 100, MANSIONES DE SIERRA TAINA 00956 #847-02-1973 L1976 **GP PD** *071

TORRES RODRIGUEZ, Leonard. PO BOX 926 00960 #847-04-1966 L1970 **OBG** *020
TORRES SANCHEZ, Jorge L. 74 CALLE ESTEBAN PADILLA 00959 #308-03-1981 L1991 *020
TORRES SEDA, Luis Angel. B7 CALLE SANTA CRUZ, URB SANTA CRUZ 00961 #847-10-1978 L1983 **FM EM** *020
TROCHE, Rodolfo. ■ 00959 #042-03-2000 L2002 **NEP** *020 †20
TRUJILLO, Angel Whatts. CALL 11 I 16 JARD DE CAPA 00959 #649-01-1957 L1957 **GP** *072
ULLOA SARDINAS, Victoria. ■ 00959 #649-14-2001 L2003 **GP** *020
URDAZ-ALVAREZ, Vivian. ■ 00961 #847-08-1975 L1982 **OTO** *020
URQUIA, Maite Ametza. PO BOX 60327, U DEL CARIBE ESCUELA MED 00960 #042-03-1998 L2002 **PM** *020 †60
VALCARCEL-BAEZ, Harry. 73 CALLE SANTA CRUZ, STE 105 00961 #042-04-1981 L1984 **P** *020
VALENTIN, Leonardo I. PO BOX 2698, 202 BAYAMON MEDICAL PLZ 00960 #042-01-1981 L1986 **GS PS** *020 †85
VALENTIN, Oscar Osorio. RT 2 K M 11-7 00960 #847-10-1967 L1976 **PD** *020
VALENTIN-GONZALEZ, Wilmer. PO BOX 2698, 202 BAYAMON MEDICAL PLZ 00960 #308-03-1981 L1983 **GS** *020 †85
VALERO-IRIZARRY, Angel A. 31-43 AVE MAIN, URB SANTA ROSA 00959 #308-03-1980 L1996 **GP** *020
VALLEDOR, Luis Enrique. 105 CARR 2, BAYAMON MEDICAL PLAZA 00961 #042-01-1989 L1995 **OTO HNS** *020 †45
VALLE MEDINA, Abel. ■ 00961 #275-01-1989 L2005 *100
VALLES SANTIAGO, Carmen A. AVE LAUREL SANTA JUANITA 00958 #308-03-1977 L1980 **GP** *030
VARGAS, Luis F. PO BOX 60327 00960 #847-04-1966 L1968 **R GP** *020
VARGAS VALDEZ, Wellington. Z27 CALLE 1, REPTO VALENCIA 00959 #308-04-1989 L1992 *020
VAZQUEZ, Ariane. D10 CALLE 14, VILLA DEL RIO BAYAMON 00959 #042-01-1983 L1989 **IM ID** *020 †20
VAZQUEZ, Carlos A. CLINICA HNOS MELENDEZ 00956 #847-04-1963 L1966 **R** *020
VAZQUEZ, Eduardo R. 901 TORRE SAN PABLO # 901 00961 #042-03-1980 L1987 **GS** *020
VAZQUEZ, Himirce. URB RIBERAS DEL RIO, CALLE 8 B#49 00959 #042-01-1977 L1981 **OBG** *020
VAZQUEZ BAS, Ricardo R. I39 CALLE 8, EXT VILLA RICA 00959 #847-04-1956 L1959 **GP OS** *020
VAZQUEZ DIAZ, Maria Merce. PO BOX 60327, U CENTRAL DEL CARIBE SCH M 00960 #308-13-2001 L2005 **IM** *012
VAZQUEZ-PEREZ, Rafael. RR 5 BOX 5334 00956 #308-03-1990 **GP** *020
VEGA, Gilberto. AU18 CALLE 24, URB SANTA JUANITA 00956 #847-01-1974 L1976 *020
VEGA DE RODRIGUEZ, Gloria. B5 CALLE SANTA CRUZ, URB SANTA CRUZ 00961 #042-01-1958 L1964 **IM OBG** *020
VEGA SUAREZ, Lorna. 73 CALLE SANTA CRUZ # 301, EDIF MEDICO SANTA CRUZ 00961 #649-14-1991 L1993 **PD** *020
VELAZQUEZ, Elena. 66 CALLE SANTA CRUZ, OFICINA 302 00961 #042-03-1991 L1994 **IM RHU** *020
VELAZQUEZ, Magdalena. PO BOX 60327 00960 #649-60-1998 L2005 **PD** *012
VELAZQUEZ, Miguel Ali. ■ 00959 #042-01-2000 L2002 **FPG** *020 †18
VELAZQUEZ CAPO, Wilfredo. RT 2 K M 11-7 00960 #308-01-1971 L1974 **FM** *050
VELEZ, Ivan Francisco. ■ 00956 #042-03-2002 L2005 **IM** *100 †20,28
VELEZ DIAZ, Vilmarie. ■ 00961 #649-35-1999 L2004 *100
VELEZ ROJAS, Angel F. 70 CALLE SANTA CRUZ, URB SANTA CRUZ 00961 #042-03-1981 L1986 **AN GS** *020
VELEZ SANTIAGO, Florencio. ■ 00960 #847-04-1962 L1967 **GP PD** *020
VELEZ SANTIAGO, Vidal. ■ 00961 #649-01-1961 L1964 **PM** *071
VERA-AROCHO, Antonio A. 70 CALLE SANTA CRUZ, URB SANTA CRUZ 00961 #649-14-1980 L1982 **PD** *020
VIANA-REYES, Carlos H. B25 CALLE ISABEL, URB FLAMINGO TER 00957 #308-03-1980 L1984 **GP** *020
VICIOSO DEL ROSARIO, Marga. 100 CALLE 17A APT N-327, COND REXVILLE PARK 00957 #308-04-1990 L2005 *100
VILARO, Charles Edward. J19 CALLE 2 EXT VILLA RICA 00959 #042-01-1981 L1986 **GS** *020 †85
VILARO, James F. J21 CALLE 2, EXT VILLA RICA 00959 #042-01-1984 L1987 **CD IM** *020 †20
VILARO, Juan R. 70 CALLE SANTA CRUZ, URB SANTA CRUZ 00961 #042-01-1980 L1987 **TS VS** *020 †85,90
VILLAFANE, Edwin. 70 CALLE SANTA CRUZ, URB SANTA CRUZ 00961 #308-02-1977 L1979 **IM** *020
VILLAFANE, Ivonne. 100 AVE LAUREL, LOMAS VERDES 00956 #847-12-1976 L1982 **PD** *020 †55
VILLAFANE, Luce Maria. 70 CALLE SANTA CRUZ, URB SANTA CRUZ 00961 #847-04-1968 L1970 **N** *020
VILLALOBOS, Ricardo. ■ 00957 #042-01-2004 L2006 **N** *012
VILLALON-RODRIGUEZ, Edwin. 70 CALLE SANTA CRUZ, URB SANTA CRUZ 00961 #042-03-1980 L1988 **OBG** *020
VILLAMIL, Jose Ramon. PO BOX 69, 2 ROAD STE 408 00960 #847-06-1976 L1981 **GP** *020
VILLANUEVA APONTE, Jose L. B3 CALLE GARDENIA, EXT CAMPO ALEGRE 00956 #308-06-1986 L1991 *020
VILLAREAL-ALEJANDRO, Onier. ■ 00960 #042-01-2004 **EM** *100
VIRELLA, David. 25-11 CALLE 15, URB SANTA ROSA 00959 #042-01-1987 L1991 **AN** *020
ZAMORA, Linda Denisse. ■ 00957 #042-03-2004 **FP** *012
ZAPATA-GUZMAN, Victor A. 9-35 CALLE 4, URB SANTA ROSA 00959 #649-14-1977 L1979 **IM** *020
ZAPATER-RODRIGUEZ, F. BOX 705 00960 #308-02-1974 L1976 **IM** *020
ZAYAS, Carlos Roberto. ■ 00959 #042-01-1999 L2002 **CD** *020 †20
ZAYAS-TORO, Ilia E. B7 CALLE SANTA CRUZ, URB SANTA CRUZ 00961 #042-03-1980 L1984 **FM** *030 †18 ‡

BOQUERON — CABO ROJO

ALBITE VELEZ, Antonio. CARR 101 00622 #847-01-1971 L1974 **OS** *020
BONILLA REYES, Gisel M.. PO BOX 529 00622 #042-04-2003 L2004 *100
CRUZ GARCIA, Luis Saul. PO BOX 426 00622 #649-35-1999 L2001 **GP** *020
DIAZ, Jose Sigfredo. MAYAGUEZ, CALLE MENDEZ VIGO #52 00622 #308-03-1985 L1988 **CHP P** *020
FIGUEROA, Angie G. VILLA TAINA, EDIF. GUARIONEX #304 00622 #308-03-1982 L1992 **GP** *020.
GARCIA BOBE, Carmelo E. PO BOX 432 00622 #847-04-1959 L1961 **P** *071

LOZADA, Antonio. ■ 00622 #654-01-2004 L2007 **IM** *020 †20
LOZADA, Antonio R. ■ 00622 #748-01-1952 L1959 **AN** *071
MARTY LOPEZ, Laura Angeli. PO BOX 328 00622 #649-30-2004 L2006 *100
PLAZA-CASTELO, Bell Karen. CARR. 100 #806, BORQUERON BAY VILLA 00622 #176-01-1999 L2006 *100
ROQUE, Melba N. PO BOX 198, 0.2 CARR 311 00622 #042-01-1989 L1993 **P** *020 †75
RUIZ-IRIZARRY, Santiago. ■ 00622 #847-02-1973 **GP** *075
TOSCA, Maria Lourdes. ■ 00622 #042-03-1994 L1998 **OBG** *020
VARGAS, Carmen Lizzette. PO BOX 309 00622 #649-14-1983 L1988 **GP** *020

CABO ROJO – CABO ROJO

ACARON, Sifredo, III. D-21 M BRACETTI ST, URB BORINQUEN 00623 #042-03-1980 L1984 **HEM GS** *020 †20
ACOSTA, Humberto. 195 CALLE PICAFLOR, QTAS DE CABO ROJO 00623 #308-02-1989 L1992 **FM** *020 †18
ACOSTA, Raul A. 3 REPTO SAN SALVADOR 00623 #308-03-1983 L1987 **GP** *020
ALEMAR ULLOA, Jose Ramon. 38 AVE SANTOS ORTIZ, SAN JOSE PLAZA STE 104 00623 #308-01-1986 L1991 **OBG** *020
ANGLERO, Grizel. COND MIRAMAR C 3 JOYUDA 00623 #042-01-1986 L1989 **PD** *020
APONTE, Jaime Rafael. 74 CALLE BALDORIOTY 00623 #042-03-1990 L1992 **FM** *020 †18
ARROYO SANTIAGO, Waldemar. 45 CALLE CARBONELL 00623 #847-04-1970 L1976 **GP** *072
ASENCIO, Madeline. 56 CALLE CARBONELL # J6, BOX 8 00623 #308-03-1985 L1991 *020
ASENCIO MONTALVO, Dessiren. ■ 00623 #308-03-1979 L2002 **GP** *020
AVILES VAZQUEZ, Osvaldo. ■ 00623 #308-03-1987 L1990 **OBG** *020
BANCH, Walter Anthony. ■ 00623 #042-01-1981 L1986 **OBG** *020
BRACERO PEREZ, Magaly. ■ 00623 #042-04-1996 L2003 *020
CARDONA, Fernando A. 19B CALLE RUIZ BELVIS 00623 #649-41-1983 L1991 **PD** *020
CARO, Wilma. CALLE G-D7 BOX 4, URB MARGARITA 00623 #308-03-1984 L1992 **GP** *020
COBIAN LOGO, Jose L.. PO BOX 623 00623 #649-14-1999 L2000 **GP** *020
COLBERG, Jansen. ■ 00623 #042-01-1996 L1998 **OPH** *020 †35
COLON-QUETGLAS, Edward W. ■ 00623 #042-01-1982 L1986 **P** *071 †75
CRESPO, Pedro. 142 CALLE RUISENOR, QTAS DE CABO ROJO 00623 #308-04-1984 L1992 *020
DE JESUS CARBONELL, A. ■ 00623 #649-01-1959 L1965 **AN** *020
DEL CAMPO, Rafael. HC 1 BOX 6150, 208 MUNOZ RIVERA 00623 #649-14-1998 L2001 *020
DESCARTES, Fernando Sol. ■ 00623 #042-02-2002 L2003 **DR** *020 †80
FAS-FAGUNDO, Nayip. ■ 00623 #041-09-1941 L1941 **GP OS** *020
FERNANDEZ, Noe. PO BOX 684, 47B CALLE MUNOZ RIVERA 00623 #649-14-1975 L1978 **GP FM** *020
FERNANDEZ DEMORIZI, Dayra. ■ 00623 #308-02-1992 L1995 **P** *020
FIGUEROA, Mario J. 63 CALLE CARBONELL 00623 #042-01-1987 L1992 **GS** *020 †85
GARCIA RODRIGUEZ, Angel L. URB BORINGUEN ST 4 I-27 00623 #649-14-1983 L1986 **IM** *020
GUZMAN TENNANT, Juan C.. I21 CALLE RENE MARQUEZ, URB BORINQUEN 00623 #308-02-2003 L2005 *100
HERNANDEZ, Jorge Luis. 87 CALLE SOL, PARC LAS 35 00623 #308-03-1983 L1986 **GP** *020
LOZADA MERCADO, Maria V. 44 CALLE CARBONELL, STE 4 00623 #042-04-1994 L1996 *020
LOZADA SEDA, Luis A. 64 CALLE MUNOZ RIVERA 00623 #847-10-1970 L1975 **FM** *020
LUCIANO, Orlando. PO BOX 1148 00623 #042-01-1987 L1990 **GP** *020 †55
LUGO, Fausto Carlos. ■ 00623 #308-02-1978 L1982 **IM** *020
LUGO OLIVIERI, Hernan, III. PMB 315 PO BOX 5103-315 00623 #649-45-1996 L2003 **GP** *020
MANON, Rogelio Alberto. E28 CAL PDR FLRS URB BORIN 00623 #308-01-1964 L1976 **GP** *020
MARTINEZ, Cindy. PO BOX 5103, PMB 154 00623 #649-35-2000 L2004 **GP** *020
MARTINEZ, Ivonne Arellys. 26 CALLE 4, PARC ELIZABETH 00623 #649-14-1984 L1985 **GP** *020
MATIAS DEL TORO, Jose L. ■ 00623 #042-04-1998 L1999 **P** *012
MONTALVO NAZARIO, Karinell. ■ 00623 #649-14-2001 L2004 *100
MORENO, Edgar Hjalmar. 108 CALLE MUNOZ RIVERA, HOSPITAL METROPOLITANO 00623 #649-14-1993 L1996 **FM** *020
MORENO, Juan L. 20 CALLE MACEO 00623 #042-01-1958 L1960 **GP P** *020
MOSCOSO PINA, Rosa E. 43 CALLE JOSE DE DIEGO, PMB 206 00623 #308-01-1985 L1992 *100
NEGRON, Carmen L. ■ 00623 #042-04-1980 L1989 **GP** *020
NEGRONI-PACHECO, Elba. PO BOX 1330 00623 #308-01-1981 L1983 **PD** *020
NORIEGA ACOSTA, Antonio. ■ 00623 #649-14-1993 L1995 **GP** *020
ORTIZ, Gladys Del Carmen. 44 CALLE RIUS RIVERA, BOX 593 00623 #649-18-1981 L1985 **GP** *020
ORTIZ MEDINA, Rolando. 68 CALLE BALDORIOTY 00623 #649-02-1971 L1973 **FM** *020
PABON, Hector E. ■ 00623 #649-01-1958 L1959 **OBG** *020
PABON REYES, Sibel N. ■ 00623 #042-04-1997 L1998 **FM** *020
PADILLA, Denisse. 3 CALLE B, EXT LA CONCEPCION 00623 #042-01-2001 L2003 **IM** *020
PADILLA-COMAS, Alma L. URB CONCEPCION ALIDA 84 00623 #042-03-1981 L1985 **OBG** *020 †30
PADILLA FERRER, Mildred I. HC 1 BOX 1829 00623 #649-14-1995 L1997 **IM** *020
PAGAN-MORALES, Velma I. URB CIBAO, CALLE BRAU #4 00623 #308-03-1978 L1981 **GP** *020
PARDO MORALES, Plutarco. ■ 00623 #649-01-1957 L1960 **GP OS** *020
PEREZ-TORO, Maria Angeles. ■ 00623 #042-04-1983 L1986 **GP** *020
PINEIRO, Luis Ignacio. 409 CALLE FLAMBOYAN, EXT PARC ELIZABETH 00623 #649-18-1983 L1997 *020
QUINONES, Carlos F. 116 CALLE CORAL # B-6, ALTS DEL MAR 00623 #042-03-1999 L2003 **PM** *020 †60
RAMIREZ, Eric. ■ 00623 #042-01-1984 L1989 **IM** *020 †20
RAMIREZ, Ricardo R. ■ 00623 #847-09-1954 L1956 **OS GP** *071
RAMIREZ LUGO, Delvis. 67 CALLE CARBONELL, BOX 789 00623 #847-04-1964 L1971 **GP** *020
RAMIREZ MENDEZ, Jose M. ■ 00623 #649-18-1979 L1991 **GP** *020
RAMIREZ SOTO, Samuel. ■ 00623 #649-39-1983 L1996 **GP** *020
RAMIREZ-TORRES, Hugo. 75 CALLE BALDORIOTY 00623 #847-10-1963 L1965 **GP** *071
RAMIREZ VELEZ, David A. URB BORINGUEN G 33 6ST 00623 #649-14-1980 L1986 *020
RAMIREZ ZAPATA, Vanessa. ■ 00623 #649-14-2004 L2006 *100
RETEGUIS LUGO, Jaime. ■ 00623 #649-01-1957 L1957 **GS GP** *020
RIVERA NATALI, Luis Anton. ■ 00623 #649-14-2005 L2005 *100
RODIL, Edwin. URB ANA MARIA # I19 00623 #042-01-1987 L1991 **PD** *075
RODRIGUEZ ARCE, Roberto. ■ 00623 #649-14-2003 L2005 **GP** *020
ROMAN RAMIREZ, Arlene M.. PO BOX 891 00623 #649-14-1995 L1997 *100
ROMEU-VELEZ, Jesse. ■ 00623 #042-04-1988 L1991 **CCM PUD** *020 †20
ROSALES, Jose Vicente. ■ 00623 #649-14-1985 L1999 **FM** *020

ROSARIO, Francisco Juan. ■ 00623 #649-30-2001 L2003 *100
RUIZ ZAPATA, Ruben. 48 CALLE HENNA, HC 1 BOX 8527 00623 #308-02-2000 L2002 *020
SEDA, Jaime S. C4 URBN MARGARITA 00623 #847-04-1956 L1971 IMG *071
SILVA IGNACIO, Julio I. SAN JOSE 26 URB RAMIREZ 00623 #649-18-1982 L1990 OM *020
SILVESTRY, Mitchell L. 18.6 CARR 102 00623 #649-14-1982 L1985 OM *020
SILVESTRY-HERNANDEZ, V. 44 CALLE CARBONELL 00623 #308-01-1979 L1983 EM GP *020
SILVESTRY-REYES, Edgar F. 19 CALLE MAXIMO GOMEZ 00623 #847-09-1957 L1978 *071
SOSA, Ivette Marie. ■ 00623 #042-01-2008 *012
SOSA, Ramon Antonio. 21 CALLE RUIZ BELVIS, STE A 00623 #308-02-2001 L2006 GP *020
TORO, Kevin. ■ 00623 #042-04-2000 L2001 *020
TORO PAGAN, Julio. ■ 00623 #649-01-1968 L1969 PUD *020
VARGAS, Sergio A. ■ 00623 #847-10-1964 L1969 GP *020
VARONA CANTELLOR, Alvia I. 44 CALLE CARBONELL STE 1 00623 #649-14-1995 L1997 *100
VAZQUEZ, Alberto Javier. ■ 00623 #649-14-2002 L2003 IM *020
VEGA MACHAL, Hernan E. 5 CALLE SN JRG URB RAMIREZ, QUINONES 35 00623 #042-04-1991 L1993 GP *020
VELEZ MONTIJO, Lionel. ■ 00623 #308-04-1993 L1996 GP *020
VILLABRILLE MORALES, Jose. Q15 CALLE JUAN MORELL CMPS, URB BORINQUEN 00623 #308-03-2000 L2002 FM *020

CAGUAS – CAGUAS

ABREU, Arlene M. B-15 ESTANCIAS DEL LAGO 00725 #042-04-1991 L1992 IM *020
ACEVEDO-MARTY, Iris A. PO BOX 4952 00726 #042-01-1994 L1998 N *020 †75
ACOSTA-AZCONA, Clara. PO BOX 7139 00726 #308-01-1976 L1985 IM *020
ACOSTA ORTIZ, Hilson. 90 LA SERRANIA, URB LA SERRANIA 00725 #649-14-1990 L1992 P *020
ADORNO, Edgardo J.. ■ 00725 #042-01-2005 IM *012
AGUAYO GOMEZ, Irving Jose. 44 CALLE CELIS AGUILERA 00725 #308-03-1983 L1988 GP *020
AGUAYO-MUNOZ, Rafael A. ■ 00726 #847-06-1976 L1979 PM OM *020
AGUIRRE, Georgina. F1 CALLE 4, VILLA DE CASTRO 00725 #042-01-1985 L1988 FM *040 †18
ALAMO, Zacarias. C17 AVE CAGUAX, REPTO CAGUAX 00725 #847-02-1977 L1980 GP ADM *020
ALDRICH, Ismael. PO BOX 845, 2 URB PARADIS STREET A 00726 #042-01-1966 L1970 OTO *030 †45
ALFARO, Ines Maria. 15 AVE MUNOZ MARIN # N-8, VILLA BLANCA 00725 #649-01-1982 L1991 OM *020
ALFONSO MEDINA, Jorge E. 10 AVE LUIS MUNOZ MARIN, URB. VILLA BLANCA 00725 #042-04-1992 L1994 *020
ALMODOVAR, Nelson. 293 PASEO DEL FLAMBOYAN, URB EL VALLE 00727 #042-01-1985 L1988 PD *030 †55
ALONSO, Maria L. I3 CALLE SAN ESTEBAN, URB SAN PEDRO EST 00725 #042-01-1990 L1993 FPG *020 †18
ALVARADO-NORAT, Frankie. PO BOX 8502 00726 #042-01-1956 L1960 CD IM *020
ALVAREZ-DIAZ, Herminio. 34 RES BONNEVILLE HTS #K-6, URB BONNEVILLE HTS 00727 #042-01-1956 L1961 PD *072
ALVAREZ-SOTO, Fernando. ALTOS DE LA FUENTE, K-3 8TH STREET 00726 #042-01-1979 L1982 FM *020
APIZ, Juan Jose. PO BOX 1357, 2 MUNOZ RIVERA 00726 #935-02-1971 L2000 PD *020
APONTE, Luis A. ■ 00725 #042-03-1986 L1995 VS GS *020 †85
APONTE, Rafael. ■ 00726 #042-01-1959 L1961 CD IM *020
APONTE, Zwinda I. ■ 00727 #308-04-1989 L1992 PD *030
APONTE LA LUZ, Felix R. 28 CALLE OPORTO, EST EL VERDE 00725 #042-03-1980 L1986 *020
ARAMBURU GONZALEZ, Amy N. ■ 00727 #308-03-1981 L1995 GP *020
ARCE, Jose Luis. ■ 00725 #042-03-1990 L2004 FM *020
ARCHE-MATTA, Arturo C. BLOQUED EL RETIRO #A6 00726 #847-10-1969 L1972 PM *020 †60
ARCHILLA, Rafael Jaime. Y2 AVE LUIS MUNOZ MARIN, URB MARIOLGA 00725 #308-03-1981 L1985 GP *020
ARROYO, Migna. 46 CALLE TOPACIO, VILLA BLANCA 00725 #308-03-1985 L1992 PD *020
ARROYO MARQUEZ, Beverly A. ■ 00727 #649-14-1999 L2000 PM *020 †60
ARROYO ROSADO, Edwin I. PO BOX 7645 00726 #308-03-1980 L1987 FM PME *020
ARRUZA, Michael John. ■ 00726 #042-01-1992 L1996 OTO *020 †45
ASPARO-PLANA, Rosa. PO BOX 5729 00726 #847-01-1979 L1984 IM *020
AUGUSTIN, Nerva. PO BOX 8071, V38 F D ROOSEVELT ST 00726 #440-01-1978 L2005 P *100
AYALA, Jose M. REG HOSP CAGUAS, DEPT MED 00725 #042-01-1973 L1975 NEP IM *020
BADILLO QUINONES, Jose A. PROFESSIONAL CTR STE 307 00725 #847-04-1958 L1961 IM CD *020
BAERGA LIZARDI, Hector J. C/O P.O. BOX 582, PIO RECHANI #24 00726 #847-09-1969 L1971 FM *074
BAEZ, Antonio Miguel. ■ 00726 #649-14-2002 FM *020 †18 ‡
BAEZ, Emilio A. ■ 00726 #042-01-1996 L2003 GS *020
BAEZ, Emilio J. ■ 00726 #042-01-1991 L1994 PD *020 †55
BAEZ, Julio M. 2 CALLE MUNOZ RIVERA, POBOX 5100 PROF. CENTER 00725 #042-01-1986 L1990 CD *020
BAEZ, Luis G. ■ 00726 #042-01-1995 L1997 GS *020 †95
BAEZ, Virgen Milagros. PO BOX 4956 00726 #042-01-1993 L1998 GE *020 †20
BAEZ-LEON, Rafael. PO BOX 9231 00726 #308-03-1987 L2002 FM *020
BAIZ FALCON, Brenda I. ■ 00727 #042-04-1997 L2001 FM *020
BALBES, Idelisse Raquel. PO BOX 6653 00726 #649-14-1992 L2004 *100
BARCELO, Andres Miguel. PO BOX 4952 00726 #308-02-1979 L1983 IM *020
BARINAS ROBLES, Pablo A. 4 CALLE BALDORIOTY 00725 #308-01-1971 L1993 IM PTH *020 †20
BARRETO-SOLA, Luis Ramon. AVENIDA LUIS MUNOZ MARIN 00725 #035-47-1987 L1992 ORS OSM *020 †40
BATISTA FELIZ, Elpidio. ■ 00727 #308-01-1962 L1975 GP *020
BAYRON, Mayra L Gonzalez. I1 CALLE SAN ESTEBAN, URB SAN PEDRO EST 00725 #042-01-1988 L1991 FPG FM *020 †18
BELMONT RODRIGUEZ, W. I17 AVE MUNOZ MARIN, VILLA CARMEN 00725 #308-03-1983 L1986 IM *020
BENN-BOCANEGRA, Noemi. HC 1 BOX 29030, PMB DEPT 00725 #847-04-1966 L1969 PD OS *020
BERRIOS, Jose Ernesto. ■ 00726 #308-04-1981 L1992 PM *020
BERRIOS BORGES, Victor J. ■ 00725 #308-03-1984 L1988 GP *020
BERROCAL-ZEGARRA, Carlos. ■ 00726 #847-05-1978 L1979 FM PHP *020

BERTRAN, Juan M. AVENIDA LUIS MUNOZ MARIN 00725 #035-20-1943 L1945 ORS *020 †85
BERTRAN, Juan Manuel. D5 AVE DEGETAU, URB SAN ALFONSO 00725 #042-01-1975 L1980 ORS *020
BETANCOURT, Nancy Esther. D5 AVE DEGETAU, URB SAN ALFONSO 00725 #308-03-1982 L1992 GP *020
BETANCOURT ORTIZ, Edwin B. ■ 00727 #649-14-1999 L2002 *100
BEZARES-TORRES, Nicolas. 6 CALLE PROLONGACIN C AGLR 00725 #042-03-1982 L1986 IM *020
BONILLA GONZALEZ, Edwin. PO BOX 4952 00726 #308-03-1982 L1994 *020
BORRAS, Jose Miguel. PO BOX 6629 00726 #847-01-1986 L1991 GP *020
BORRERO SANCHEZ, Lysander. PO BOX 4956 00726 #308-06-1983 L1988 GP *020
BOSSOLO-LOPEZ, Edwin. ■ 00726 #308-03-1978 L1987 GPM *020
BRANA, Angel Rafael. CARRETERA CAGUAS A CIDRA 00725 #847-06-1976 L1979 PHP FM *030 †70
BUONOMO, Emigdio A. ■ 00726 #042-01-1958 L1962 OPH *071
BUONOMO, Luzmarie. BOX 857 00726 #042-01-1991 L1998 DR *020 †80
CABRAL HIDALGO, Angela. 55 CALLE CORL VILLA BLANCA 00725 #308-03-1996 L2002 *100
CACERES DELGADO, Hector L. SUITE 212, COND. PROFESSIONAL CENTER 00725 #847-08-1971 L1975 FM *020
CALDERON, Thea Lynn. ■ 00727 #649-14-1998 L2000 PD *100 ‡
CALVI, Alejandro. ■ 00725 #042-04-1988 L1991 GP *020
CALZADA, Manuel Eduardo. PO BOX 7768 00726 #308-04-1986 L1992 GP *020
CAMACHO, Samuel. 3 AVE DEGETAU, BONNEVILLE HEIGHTS 00727 #847-06-1973 L1975 FM *020
CAMARGO, Edinson. 408 EST DEL REY 00725 #649-14-2000 L2001 *020
CAMINO-LANDRON, Jose R. CARRETERA CAGUAS A CIDRA 00725 #308-02-1973 L1979 PD FM *020
CAMPOS, Guillermo F. A7 CALLE SAN IGNACIO, URB SAN PEDRO EST 00725 #649-14-1994 L1996 EM GS *020
CANETTI-MIRABAL, Luis R. 301 AVE MUNOZ MARIN, URB CONDADO MODERNO 00725 #308-01-1988 L1992 GS *020
CANINO, Alexis. ■ 00727 #042-01-2004 CD *012 †20
CAPELLA, Antonio. AVENIDA LUIS MUNOZ MARIN 00725 #042-01-1978 L1982 FM EM *020
CARABALLO, Gilberto. PO BOX 1118 00726 #042-01-1983 L1984 FPG GP *020
CARAZO-RODRIGUEZ, Brenda. D39 CALLE A, URB BRISAS DEL PARQUE 00727 #042-03-1980 L1984 IM *020
CARAZO-RODRIGUEZ, Jaime. PO BOX 9449 00726 #308-03-1981 L1990 *020
CARBALLEIRA, David A. Q36 AVE MUNOZ MARIN, VILLA CARMEN 00725 #042-01-1984 L1986 IM *020 †20
CARDONA, Dodanid. ■ 00727 #042-03-1999 L2004 CHP *020 †75
CARDONA-DURAN, Rafael F. 146 CALLE B, BDA MORALES 00725 #042-01-1997 L2000 NS *012
CARRION, Juan Luis. CALLE 1 1-8, JARDINAS DE CAGUAS 00725 #308-03-1979 L1989 GP *020
CARRION DE JESUS, Arturo. CALLE 5- B-11, URB VILLA DE CASTRO 00726 #847-06-1976 L1980 GS GP *020 ‡
CARRION DE LEON, Salvador. PO BOX 6330 00726 #308-03-1983 L1986 IM *020
CASTRO HERNANDEZ, Jose Ju. PO BOX 809, F-1 STREET 9 BRISASDEL PAR 00726 #649-14-1989 L2002 *020
CASTRO RIOPEDRE, Luis. BONN GRDNS C 6 L 29 00725 #308-06-1983 L1986 *020
CASTRO TORRES, Gloria Est. PO BOX 1943 00726 #308-03-1986 L2005 *100
CERON, Miguel Enrique. PO BOX 9834, SUITE C-33-C 00726 #042-03-1982 L1987 PD *020 †55
CHAMORRO, Zaida Maria. ■ 00725 #042-01-2004 OBG *012
CINTRON, Amilcar. 4 CALLE BALDORIOTY 00725 #264-05-1970 L1973 END IM *020
CINTRON-LOPEZ, Juan. 2 CALLE MUNOZ RIVERA 00725 #847-06-1971 L1974 IM *020
CLAS, Luis Vicente. PO BOX 4980, LUIS MUNOZ MARIN AVE 00726 #308-03-1980 L1990 EM GYN *020
COLBERG, Graciela. M3 CALLE I, URB BAIROA GOLDEN GATE II 00727 #042-02-1982 L1984 OM GP *020
COLON, Pedro Jose. PO BOX 5307 00726 #042-01-1994 L1998 IC *020 †20
COLON, Victor J. B12 CALLE J, URB VERDE SUR 00725 #042-03-1993 L1999 GE *020 †20
COLON-CASTILLO, Lillian E. ■ 00725 #042-03-1980 L1983 PTH *020
COLON ORTIZ, Pedro J. PO BOX 5307 00726 #847-04-1968 L1971 CD IM *020
CONCEPCION, Carmen B. DE GACUAS REG HSP, DEPT PED 00725 #042-01-1965 L1967 PD *020 †55
CORCINO, Veronica. 4000 AVE LAKEVIEW, STE 1 00725 #649-14-2004 L2004 *100
CORDERO, Hanney M. TRAIL DRIVE G-7, LAKEVIEW ESTATES 00726 #042-01-1992 L1996 DR *020
CORDOVA, Ana Isabel. 200 AVE RAFAEL CORDERO, STE 140 00725 #042-03-1995 L1998 PHO *020 †55
CORREA, Luis Rafael. ■ 00725 #042-01-1987 L1990 OBG *020
CORREA, Raul Grau. ■ 00726 #847-02-1961 L1969 P OS *072
CORREA-CINTRON, Javier R. AVENIDA LUIS MUNOZ MARIN 00725 #308-01-1980 L1981 OBG *020
CORTES, Hector Raul. D5 AVE DEGETAU, URB SAN ALFONSO 00725 #308-03-1982 L1992 GP *020
CORTES RIVERA, Enrique. ■ 00727 #649-14-2000 L2002 FM *020
CORUJO, Yazmin Idalia. 115 TURABO CLUSTERS 00727 #042-01-1996 L1999 HEM *020 †20
COTTO HERNANDEZ, Josefa. B18 CALLE ANGELINO FUENTES, URB IDAMARIS GDNS 00727 #042-04-1996 L2002 FM *020
CRESPO, Myriam. 35 CALLE RUIZ BELVIS 00725 #042-03-1996 L1999 PM *020 †60
CRESPO ZAMORA, Rolando. PO BOX 4956 PMB 495 00726 #275-01-1994 L2002 *020
CRUZ, Floridalia. 2V6 CALLE 24A, URB MIRADOR DE BAIROA 00727 #042-01-1988 L1992 FM *020 †18
CRUZ, Grimanessa. 61 CALLE CELIS AGUILERA 00725 #042-01-1992 L1996 OPH *020 †35
CRUZ, Manuel Omar. ■ 00726 #042-01-2006 GS *012
CRUZADO, Ricardo. PO BOX 7273 00726 #042-01-1998 L2000 VIR *020 †80
CRUZ CRUZ, Flor Patricia. ■ 00727 #649-14-2000 L2002 *020
CRUZ GARCIA, Joanny. H15 CALLE 8, URB CONDADO MODERNO 00725 #649-14-1992 L1995 PD *020
CRUZ-MARTINEZ, Drisde Isa. 1208 CALLE ALMENDRO, PMB 413 00725 #308-04-2000 L2002 *020
CURET RAMOS, Jose A. AVENIDA LUIS MUNOZ MARIN 00725 #847-05-1984 L1988 IM *020
DAVILA, Miguel Angel. ■ 00725 #308-13-1999 L2005 *100
DAVILA, Zaida Iris. CALLE SANTA LUCIA, URB SANTA ELVIRA 00725 #649-14-2003 L2004 *100
DAVILA UVILES, Carlos M. H40 AVE PINO, VILLA TURABO 00725 #847-05-1973 L1976 OBG *020

DE JESUS, Aponte Ramon. ■ 00726 #042-01-1998 L2003 **GE** *020 †20
DE JESUS-ACOSTA, Carolina. ■ 00726 #042-01-2007 **N** *012
DE JESUS-TEJADA, Victor J. PO BOX 7139 00726 #308-01-1976 L1983 **FM** *020
DE JESUS TORRES, Myrna E. X2 AVE LUIS MUNOZ MARIN, URB MARIOLGA 00725 #308-02-1982 L1987 **GP** *020
DE LA VEGA, Gloria M. 152 CALLE GAUTIER BENITEZ 00725 #042-01-1965 L1969 **D OS** *020
DE LEON ALCANTARA, Miguel. ■ 00727 #308-01-1963 L1975 **GP** *020
DELGADO, Luz Eneida. 130 CALLE PLAYERA, URB CONDADO VIEJO 00725 #308-03-1977 L1988 **GP** *020
DELGADO-PEREZ, Diego M. VILLA DEL REY 4 TA, T1 CALLE 1 00725 #847-05-1973 L1977 **GP** *020
DE LOS SANTOS SOLIS, Juan. 121 CALLE OVIEDO, CIUDAD JARDIN DE BAIROA 00727 #308-01-1987 L2003 *020
DEL TORO-MARTINEZ, Ivan E. C9 CALLE 1, ALT DE LA FUENTE 00727 #042-01-1976 L1980 **GYN** *030 †30 ‡
DEL VALLE BELTRAN, Pablo. D11 CALLE D, JARD DE CAGUAS 00727 #042-01-1992 L1995 **FPG** *020 †18
DE MELECIO, Carmen F. PO BOX 5190 00726 #042-01-1961 L1964 **PD** *030
DE RODRIGUEZ, Carolina F. PO BOX 5729 00726 #308-02-1982 L1988 **PD** *020
DE VARONA, Roberto R. P4 CALLE SANTA MARTA, URB SANTA ELVIRA 00725 #042-02-1984 L1987 **IM** *020
DIAZ, Eduardo. ■ 00726 #042-03-1980 L1983 **IM** *020
DIAZ, Eduardo Jose. A40 CALLE MARGARITA, URB SAN ALFONSO 00725 #042-03-1995 L2001 **NEP IM** *020
DIAZ BARRIENTOS, Jose A.. HACIENDA SAN JOSE 531, VIA GUAJANA 00727 #042-04-1996 *100
DIAZ-BORRAS, Lydia A. 202 CALLE GAUTIER BENITEZ, CONSOLIDATED MALL C-1-A 00725 #847-01-1983 L1987 **IM** *020
DIAZ CRUZ, Mildred S.. PO BOX 4952 PMB 99 00726 #308-01-1986 L1990 *100
DIAZ DE QUILES, Ana J. PO BOX 6827 00726 #042-01-1972 L1975 **D** *020
DIAZ-DIAZ, Candido. 14 AVE MUNOZ MARIN, URB NOTRE DAME 00725 #308-03-1980 L1982 **FM** *020
DIAZ FERNANDEZ, Edgard O. 101 ESTANCIAS DEL LAGO, EST DEL LAGO 00725 #649-14-1984 L1988 **PD** *020
DIAZ MARXUACH, Euclides. ■ 00726 #649-01-1955 L1964 **GP** *071
DIAZ MEDINA, Keyla. ■ 00727 #649-14-1999 L2002 *020
DIAZ-RAMOS, Nestor E. AVENIDA LUIS MUNOZ MARIN 00725 #847-10-1970 L1973 **PD** *020
DIEPPA, Diomedes. PO BOX 639 00726 #308-03-1983 L1991 **IM GE** *020 †20
DIEZ-ROSALES, Viriato J. CAGUAS REG HOSP 00726 #308-03-1980 L1985 **AN EM** *020
DOMINGUEZ, Ramon Andres. ■ 00725 #308-01-1978 L1994 **GP** *020
DONES-RODRIGUEZ, Rolando. C PROLONGACIAN TROCHE 1 00725 #308-03-1977 L1982 **GP** *020
DUCOUDRAY, Samadys N. PO BOX 7738, GAUTIER BENITEZ STREET 00726 #042-02-1992 L1996 **GS** *020 †75
DURE, Jean Maurice. AW5 CALLE LUIXA, RES BAIROA 00725 #649-18-1989 L2005 *100
ECHEVERRI, Hernan Alfonso. ■ 00725 #847-04-1982 L2001 **IM** *020
EDWARDS VALQUEZ, Ruben S. 2H35 CONDADO PK BAIROA PK 00725 #308-01-1968 L1976 **GP** *020
ESCOBAR, Edwin. ■ 00725 #847-04-1959 L1963 **OS** *071
ESCOBAR, Enrique. S1 AVE LUIS MUNOZ MARIN, URB MARIOLGA 00725 #042-01-1992 L1995 **OSS** *020 †40
ESPINAL, Kevin Nick. CONDADO 2-H39, BAIROA PARK 00725 #308-03-1982 L1986 **GP** *020
ESTRADA-BIBILONI, F J. BW 9 LAS AMERICAS 00725 #649-01-1958 L1962 **OTO** *072
EUGENIA GOMEZ, Maria. 186 ESTANCIAS DEL LAG #B-1, EST DEL LAGO 00725 #264-03-1974 L1993 *020
FALCON RODRIGUEZ, Tania. CALLE 3 CARRETERA ESTATAL, VILLA DEL REY SECCION 00725 #042-04-2003 L2004 *100
FELICIANO, Briseida E. V28 AVE LUIS MUNOZ MARIN, URB MARIOLGA 00725 #042-01-1987 L1989 **N CN** *020
FELICIANO-HERNANDEZ, Luis. ■ 00727 #847-05-1974 L1978 **P CHP** *020
FERNANDEZ, Hector Manuel. 61 CALLE CELIS AGUILERA 00725 #847-10-1963 L1966 **GPM** *020
FERNANDEZ, Lourdes M. 24 AVE MNZ MRN URB NOTRE D 00725 #308-04-1984 L1986 **PHO** *020
FERNANDEZ MONTALVO, Dora. N11 CALLE CUMBERLAND, VILLA DEL REY 1 00725 #042-04-2000 L2001 **FM** *020
FIGUEROA, Osvaldo A. I17 AVE MUNOZ MARIN, VILLA CARMEN 00725 #042-01-1985 L1988 **CD IM** *020 †20
FIGUEROA, Socorro L. 116 AVE ESTANCIAS DEL LAGO, EST DEL LAGO 00725 #042-01-1987 L1990 **P** *020
FIGUEROA COSME, Carmen R. A5 CALLE BROMELIA, EST DE BAIROA 00727 #308-06-1985 L1987 *020
FIGUEROA-DELGADO, Edwin O. C6 CALLE JOSE VILLARES, APT 1-B 00725 #308-03-1980 L1990 **FPG** *020
FIGUEROA MATOS, Veronica. ■ 00727 #042-01-2006 **OBG** *012
FIGUEROA PEREZ, Felix M. PO BOX 6858 00726 #847-08-1976 L1981 **GS** *020
FIGUEROA RIVERA, Anstrong. ■ 00725 #308-04-2001 L2003 *100
FIGUEROA RIVERA, Ramon L. ■ 00725 #308-01-1983 L1987 **GP** *020
FLORES, David Antonio. CILLA DEL REY, CALLE PRINCIPAL E230 00725 #649-14-1994 L1996 *020
FLORES, Ramses. M23 CALLE 4, URB SAN ANTONIO 00725 #847-06-1991 L1994 **IM** *020
FLORES CRESPO, Jose. F2 CAL C URB BAIROA GOLDEN, GATE 00727 #847-02-1983 L1985 **OM** *020
FLORES-RODRIGUEZ, Eduardo. 33 CALLE BETANCES 00725 #847-10-1970 L1972 **PD** *020
FONSECA, Wanda Socorro. 64 CALLE ACOSTA 00725 #308-03-1982 L1999 **GP** *020
FONSECA-RIVERA, Evelyn M. PO BOX 6330 00726 #308-03-1977 L1989 **IM** *020
FONTANEZ, Julio. AVE MUNOZ MARIN, OFF 121, H.I.M.A. 00726 #847-06-1979 L1990 **GP** *020
FONTANLASANTA, Luis A. 108 LA SERRANIA, URB LA SERRANIA 00725 #042-03-1997 L2000 **ID IM** *020 †20
FORASTIERI, Luis Javier. 1 CALLE NAZARIO, URB NAZARIO 00725 #042-01-1995 L2000 **CN** *020 †75
FORTUNO, Carmen Rosa. ■ 00725 #042-03-2007 *012
FRANCO, Maria. R13-17 CALLE D, URB TURABO GDNS 00727 #042-01-1992 L1995 **PD** *020 †55
FRANQUIZ, Jose M. AB9 CALLE REINA ISABEL, URB. RESIDENCIAL BAIROA 00725 #042-04-1991 L1993 **GP** *020

FUENTES, Andres R. SUITE 106 VILLA BLANCA, PLAZA BAIROA 00725 #308-03-1981 L1986 **GP OM** *020
FUENTES, Jose Angel. 26 CALLE JIMENEZ SICARDO 00725 #308-03-1978 L1994 *020
GARCIA, Robert Jose. 2 CALLE MUNOZ RIVERA # 307, PROFESSIONAL CENTER 00725 #308-03-1983 L2002 **IM** *020
GARCIA, Ruth Marie. ■ 00725 #042-01-2008 *012
GARCIA COLON, Luis O. 9101 URB SERENNA 00727 #308-13-2005 L2006 **GP** *020
GARCIA-DE JESUS, R. 341 PASEO DEL FLAMBOYAN, URB EL VALLE 00727 #042-01-1995 L2001 **PD CCP** *020 †55
GARCIA ELOSEGUI, Sandra E. 107 EST DEL REY, CALLE 2 A-7 00725 #308-03-1984 L1990 **PD** *020
GARCIA-HAROOTIAN, Mayra. CALLE DEL COMERIO B13, URB EL RETIRO, 00725 #308-01-1977 L1982 **IM** *020
GARCIA RIVERA, Julio E. ■ 00725 #649-14-1991 L1993 **IM** *020
GARCIA SANTIAGO, Ernesto. B24 CALLE SAN AGUSTIN, URB SAN PEDRO EST 00725 #649-35-1990 L1993 **GP** *020
GELY DE LA ROSA, Haydee. PO BOX 6973 00726 #042-04-2001 L2002 *100
GELY LATALLADI, Luis M. QUADRANGLE OFF 303, AVE LUUIS M MARIN #50 00725 #847-10-1984 L1991 **CD** *020 †20
GIL BANUELOS, Karen Elisa. PO BOX 4960, PMB 229 00726 #649-14-2000 L2006 *100
GOMEZ, Francisco. PO BOX 370 00726 #042-03-1980 L1986 **DR** *020
GOMEZ, Manuel. ■ 00725 #042-03-1993 L1997 **OBG** *020
GOMEZ, Rene Clemente. 63 CALLE GOYCO 00725 #042-01-1965 L1971 **IM CD** *020 †20
GOMEZ-CARRERA, Ricardo M. 2 CALLE MUNOZ RIVERA, PROFESSIONAL CENTER SUITE 00725 #847-10-1982 L2000 *020
GOMEZ DIAZ, Jackeline. ■ 00725 #042-01-1992 L1993 **IM** *020 †20
GOMEZ MENDOZA, Ramon. CAGUAS REG HOSP, DEPT PED 00725 #308-03-1982 L1989 **PD** *020
GONZALEZ, Antonio F. 63 CALLE PITIRRE, CHALETS DE BAIROA 00727 #042-02-1981 L1990 **CHN PD** *020 †55
GONZALEZ, Falcon-Caro. ■ 00726 #308-06-1986 L1989 **IM** *020
GONZALEZ, Jorge. PO BOX 4952, PMB 373 00726 #042-03-1988 L1995 **CD** *020
GONZALEZ CRUZ, Israel. DQ42 CALLE 42, URB.BAIROA 00725 #042-04-1997 L1999 **FM** *020
GONZALEZ RODRIGUEZ, Angel. 394 CALLE VALENCIA, MANS DE CIUDAD JARDIN BAIR 00727 #847-06-1980 L1994 *100
GONZALEZ RODRIGUEZ, H. ■ 00726 #847-04-1964 L1976 **GP** *020
GONZALEZ TORRES, Emilio R. 201 CALLE GAUTIER BENITEZ, STE 303 00725 #042-01-1982 L1986 **GE IM** *020 †20
GRILLO, Victor Manuel. ■ 00726 #308-07-1983 L1995 **GP** *020
GUADALUPE, Ruben. PO BOX 4956 00726 #308-03-1984 L1995 *020
GUADALUPE-HERNANDEZ, J. S1 AVE LUIS MUNOZ MARIN, PMB 321 00725 #847-06-1979 L1981 **EM** *020
GUARDIOLA RIVERA, Benjamin. ■ 00727 #308-13-2002 **IM** *100 †20
GUERRERO, Francisco. 200 AVE RAFAEL CORDERO, STE 140 00725 #042-01-1994 L1998 **AN** *020
GUTIERREZ, Jorge L. 1074 CALLE GUAJATACA, URB VALLES DEL LAGO 00725 #042-01-1990 L1993 **EM** *020 †16 ‡
GUZMAN, Ivan. 3B6 CALLE BORGONA, VILLA DEL REY 3 00727 #042-03-1993 L1997 **OBG** *020 †20
GUZMAN, Samuel. ■ 00727 #042-01-1999 L2002 **EM** *020 †16
HADDOCK, Ilia Torres. 202 CALLE GAUTIER BENITEZ, CONSOLIDATED MED PLAZA STE 00725 #042-01-1965 L1972 **R** *020
HADDOCK, Jorge M. ■ 00725 #042-01-1965 L1969 **R** *020 †80
HADDOCK, Luis J. ■ 00725 #042-01-2008 *012
HERNANDEZ, Jeffrey. 201 CALLE GAUTIER BENITEZ, STE 303 00725 #042-01-1983 L1986 **GE IM** *020 †20
HERNANDEZ FLORES, Victor. ■ 00727 #649-14-1998 L2000 **GP** *020
HERNANDEZ MENDEZ, Edgardo. 18 CALLE ACOSTA 00725 #308-01-1983 L1991 *100
HURTADO DE MENDOZA, A. 45 CALLE RUIZ BELVIS 00725 #847-04-1963 L1970 **P** *020
IGUINA GOITIA, Arminda. A13 ST 2 00725 #308-03-1978 L1990 *100
IRIZARRY-ARCE, Ivelisse. ■ 00725 #042-03-1991 L1999 **HEM** *020
JIMENEZ, Carlos Enrique. 315 CALLE LANZALOTE, MANS DE CIUDAD JARDIN BAIR 00727 #042-01-2000 L2003 **GE** *020
JIMENEZ, Jose Luis. PO BOX 340 00726 #042-01-1978 L1983 **OPH** *075
JIMENEZ, Julio E. AV. LUIS MONOZ MARIN #50, QUADRANGLE MED CTR 303 00725 #649-40-1984 L1987 **CD** *020 †20
JIMENEZ-FIGUEROA, Eric J. PO BOX 6738 00726 #847-05-1975 L1978 **GP OM** *020
KAREH-CORDERO, Pedro M. 201 CALLE GAUTIER BENITEZ, CONSOLIDATED MEDICAL PLAZA 00725 #042-03-1981 L1984 **CD IM** *020
LABOY PABON, Miguel A. ■ 00727 #649-14-2003 L2004 *100
LARACUENTA, Wallace J. 61 CALLE GOYCO FL 3 00725 #649-14-1989 L1992 **IM** *020
LARACUENTE, Edna Enid. 2 CALLE MUNOZ RIVERA # 312, PROFESSIONAL CENTER BUILDI 00725 #649-35-1999 L2001 **FM** *020
LARAS GARCIA, Linda Rose. PO BOX 9175 00726 #847-08-1980 L1984 **OS OBG** *020 †30
LASANTA-RAMOS, Iris E. H29 AVE PINO, P O BOX 6411 00725 #308-03-1978 L1981 **GP OM** *020
LAZARO, Pedro L. 50 AVE MUNOZ MARIN, STE 305 00725 #042-03-1981 L1987 **P GS** *020
LEBRON, Victor. ■ 00727 #042-01-1972 L1975 **PD** *020
LEROUX-PEGUERO, Cesar R. PO BOX 8727 00726 #308-01-1968 L1981 **GP** *020
LLERENA, Vilma Virgilia. L7 CALLE 2, VILLA NUEVA 00727 #275-01-1975 L2002 **CCM** *020
LOPEZ, Agnes L. 108 LA SERRANIA, URB LA SERRANIA 00725 #042-03-1999 L2002 **IM** *020
LOPEZ, Jorge Alberto. ■ 00725 #649-14-2001 L2003 *100
LOPEZ, Jose Enrique. H7 CALLE D, URB BAIROA GOLDEN GATES 00727 #308-04-1984 L1987 **GP** *020
LOPEZ, Josue. 106 CALLE COLOMBIA, URB BUNKER 00725 #847-05-1976 L1980 **OBG** *020 †30
LOPEZ, Juan Carlos. ■ 00727 #042-02-2005 L2005 **IM** *012
LOPEZ, Maria M. 114 CALLE JAZMIN, URB CONDADO VIEJO 00725 #308-03-1986 L1992 **PD** *020
LOPEZ, Nancy. CAGUAS REG HOSP, DEPT PED 00725 #308-03-1982 L1994 **PD** *020
LOPEZ, Wilfredo. SUITE #119, INTERAMERICAN HOSPITAL 00726 #847-05-1972 L1975 **U** *020
LOPEZ-DEL VICTORIA, A. ■ 00725 #649-01-1956 L1958 **GP** *020
LOPEZ DE VICTORIA, Juan C. ■ 00727 #042-03-2001 L2001 **GS** *020
LOPEZ DE VICTORIA, Raul M. ■ 00726 #649-01-1958 L1963 **GP** *020
LOPEZ LOPEZ, Benigno. 1A CALLE MUNOZ RIVERA #205, CAGUAS SURGICTR 00725 #847-08-1972 L1975 **ORS** *075
LOPEZ RIVERA, Anabel. ■ 00725 #042-01-1985 L1989 **P** *020

LOPEZ VELEZ, Eliud H. AVENIDA LUIS MUNOZ MARIN 00725 #042-01-1963 L1965 PTH PCP *020 †50

LORES-SUAREZ, Manuel E. AVENIDA LUIS MUNOZ MARIN 00725 #847-05-1974 L1986 TS CD *020 †85

LOUBRIEL, Francisco J. ■ 00726 #042-01-1982 L1986 DR *020 †80

LOZADA, Carmen Teresa. 29 CALLE STRN URB EL VERDE 00725 #042-01-1992 L1995 FM FPG *020 †18

LOZADA-RIVERA, Jose L. 43 CALLE CELIS AGUILERA 00725 #042-03-1980 L1983 GP *020

LOZANO, Hector. ■ 00726 #042-01-1999 L2004 GE *020 †20

LOZANO-MENDOZA, Manuel A. H15 PARQ DE LA LUZ, URB BAIROA PARK 00727 #308-03-1978 L1981 GP *020

LUGO-CALZADA, Pedro. 93 CALLE AGUAS BUENAS, URB BONNEVILLE HTS 00727 #847-06-1977 L1979 GP *020

MALDONADO, Angel. PO BOX 8910, AVANZADA, AVE MUNOZ MARIN 00726 #847-05-1974 L1977 AN GS *020

MALDONADO, Ileana. ■ 00726 #042-03-2007 TY *012

MALDONADO ESQUILIN, Lydia. E26 AVE RICKY SEDA, URB IDAMARIS GDNS 00727 #308-01-1985 L1992 GP *020

MALDONADO-MORALES, Gisela. 11 CALLE ONICE, VILLA BLANCA 00725 #042-02-1998 L2001 IM *020 †20

MALDONADO-RODRIGUEZ, M A. 847 VIA PLACIDA, HACIENDA SAN JOSE 00727 #042-01-1979 L1982 FM FPG *040 †18

MANGUAL, Damaris. 2D33 CALLE PINO, VILLA DEL REY 2 00725 #042-01-1995 L1999 P *020

MANITI, Luzminda Singian. PO BOX 5729, CAGUAS REGIONAL HOSP 00726 #748-08-1976 PD *100

MARCANO, Geovannie. ■ 00727 #042-02-1998 L2001 EM *020

MARRERO, Maria Francisca. ■ 00725 #649-14-1990 L1995 GP *020

MARRERO-GUADALUPE, Julio. ■ 00726 #042-03-1992 L1996 FM *020

MARTE, Noemi Davis. F21 CALLE 2, URB BONNEVILLE TERR 00725 #649-14-1971 L1978 FM *020

MARTI, Maria P. 10 CALLE ACOSTA CAGUAS 00725 #042-01-1982 L1986 CD IM *020

MARTINEZ, Ana Hilda. ■ 00726 #042-03-1993 L1996 RHU *020

MARTINEZ, Ana L. U9 CALLE 23, URB TURABO GDNS 00727 #042-04-1993 L1995 *020

MARTINEZ, Elfren Cesar. ■ 00727 #847-05-1983 L1986 IM *020

MARTINEZ, Rafael. 2F1 CALLE JIMENEZ SANJURJO, URB BAIROA PARK 00727 #308-07-1983 L1999 *020

MARTINEZ RIVERA, Johanna. ■ 00727 #042-04-2001 L2002 IM *020

MARTINEZ RODRIGUEZ, Elias. 154 CALLE BUCANO GIGANTE, URB EL VALLE 00727 #308-03-1999 L2004 *020

MARTINEZ-ZAYAS, Gines A. MUNOZ MAYIA AVE, MEDICAL QUAD OFC 205 00726 #042-01-1957 L1959 GE IM *020 †70

MARTI NUNEZ, Rafael. 49 CALLE GOYCO 00725 #847-06-1960 L1964 IM OS *020

MATEO, Fernando Luis. PO BOX 8459 00726 #042-01-1986 L1991 VIR *020 †80

MATOS, Jennifer Eileen. ■ 00727 #042-01-2007 IM *012

MAYMI BURGOS, Wanda E. ■ 00726 #935-04-1989 L1992 *020

MEDINA-ROSARIO, Agustin. ■ 00726 #847-10-1963 L1966 U *020

MELENDEZ, Bebelin. 631 VIA DE LA ERMITA, HACIENDA SAN JOSE 00727 #042-03-1997 L2000 ID *020 †20

MELENDEZ-COLLAZO, Aurora. PO BOX 7829 00726 #847-01-1973 L1976 *020

MELENDEZ TORRES, Lourdes. ■ 00725 #042-04-2000 L2002 FM *020

MENDEZ, Nancy D. CARRETERA CAGUAS A CIDRA 00725 #847-05-1972 L1984 DR PDR *020

MENDEZ MENDEZ, Luis F. PO BOX 4952 PMB 448 00726 #042-04-2004 L2005 *100

MENDEZ NEGRON, Edgar. ■ 00726 #308-13-2002 L2003 IM *100

MENDOZA, Isabel. ■ 00727 #042-01-1979 L1983 FM *020 †18

MENDOZA, Odalys. C/O P.O. BOX 1082, CALLE CELIS AGUILERA #61 00726 #042-01-1989 L1993 OPH *020 †35

MERCADO RODRIGUEZ, Lynneth. A10 CALLE 1, VILLAS LAS MERCEDES 00725 #649-14-2004 *100

MERCADO RODRIGUEZ, Salvado. 54 CALLE AMATISTA, VILLA BLANCA 00725 #042-04-2001 L2002 *020

MIMOSO GONZALEZ, Domingo. 45 CALLE RUIZ BELVIS 00725 #847-04-1959 L1968 GP *020

MIRANDA RIVERA, Benjamin. 45 CALLE TENERIFE, URB PALMAS DEL TURABO 00727 #847-06-1980 L1985 *020

MOLINA, Carmelo. ■ 00726 #649-14-1989 L1991 IM *020

MONTALVO-DIAZ, Isamarie. ■ 00727 #308-13-2003 L2005 *100

MONTANEZ, Nelson. OFICINA A-2, PLAZA DEL CARMEN MALL 00725 #042-03-1980 L1987 ON IM *020 †20

MONTILLA, Julieta. 164 LA SERRANIA, URB LA SERRANIA 00725 #042-03-1997 L2000 FPG *020 ‡

MORALES, Teresita. K13 CALLE BAYAMON, VILLA CARMEN 00725 #042-01-1996 L2000 PM *020

MORALES GONZALEZ, Gloria. PO BOX 4953 00726 #308-03-1982 L1992 *100

MORALES-LOPEZ, Antonio R. 55 CALLE SATURNO, EST EL VERDE 00725 #847-11-1976 L1981 RHU IM *020

MORALES-RODRIGUEZ, Luis R. ■ 00725 #308-01-1956 L1963 *071

MORALES SANCHEZ, Ramon. 2 CALLE PADIAL BOX 451 00725 #847-05-1964 L1989 OBG *020

MORA-QUESADA, Carlos E. ■ 00726 #264-04-1979 L1983 IM *020

MORA QUESADA, Wilfred. 2 CALLE MUNOZ RIVERA, PROFESSIONAL MED CTR 00725 #847-01-1973 L1975 GS *020

MULERO, Maria. LAS AMERICAS BW-6, POLICLINICA BAIROA AVE. 00726 #308-03-1983 L1986 GP *020

MULERO HERNANDEZ, G R. 49 CALLE CELIS AGUILERA 00725 #847-04-1958 L1960 GP *020

MULERO-JIMENEZ, Ricardo. PROFESSIONAL CTR 00725 #030-06-1963 L1967 OTO *071 †45

MUNERO, Hector F. HOSP MUNICIPAL DE GAGUAS 00725 #275-01-1952 L1989 AN OS *020

MUNOZ CAMACHO, Zulma L. H14 CALLE SAN FLORENCIO 00725 #042-04-1993 L1995 GP *020

NAVARRO, Gerardo V. 305 AVE MUNOZ MARIN, URB CONDADO MODERNO 00725 #042-03-1983 L2002 CHP P *020

NAVAS DE LEON, Melba D. C/O BOX 5585, AVE DEGETAU F-13 OFIC 2 00726 #847-04-1968 L1976 GP *020

NAZARIO-MATOS, Cindy M. ■ 00726 #042-01-1996 L2000 *020

NEGRON, Jose A. 62 CALLE ANDALUCIA, CIUDAD JARDIN DE BAIROA 00727 #042-01-1996 L1999 NEP *020

NIEVES, Aida Luz. ■ 00725 #308-03-1982 L1991 GP *020

NOBO, Ulises Lisandro. SAN PABLO CAGUAS, URB MARIOLPA 00725 #132-01-1990 L1996 N *020 †75

NOVOA-CABALLERO, Miguel. ■ 00726 #023-01-1941 L1942 OS GP *072

NUNEZ ARIAS, Angela. ■ 00725 #308-01-1976 L1992 *100

NUNEZ LOPEZ, Jose Antonio. CALLE 15-Z-5 #1, URB TURABO GARDENS II 00725 #042-01-1958 L1962 P *062 †75

ODRIOZOLA-ARUCA, Maria C. B17 CALLE SAN IGNACIO, URB SAN PEDRO EST 00725 #042-03-1981 L1985 PD *020

OLAZAGASTI LEDEE, Ramsis. 8 CALLE AMATISTA, URB. VILLA BLANCA 00725 #649-14-2000 L2002 *100

OLIVER, Armando Luis. CALLE PINO 2D, 28 VILLA DEL REY 00725 #042-01-1998 L2002 OPH *020 †35

OLIVERO-RAMIREZ, Dalvin. CAGUAS REGIONAL HOSP 00725 #308-03-1984 L1991 PD *020

OLLER, Jose Rafael. 558 CALLE BADAJOZ, MANS DE CIUDAD JARDIN BAIR 00727 #042-03-1998 L2001 APM *020

ORTIZ, Ada Nivea. AVE MUNZO MARIN, HOSPITAL HIMA CAQUAS 00725 #042-01-1974 L1976 PD *020 †55

ORTIZ, Carlos Ramon. ■ 00727 #308-04-2000 L2002 *020

ORTIZ, Jose Manuel. G30 CALLE MYRNA VAZQUEZ, VALLE TOLIMA 00727 #042-01-1991 L1994 FM *020 †18

ORTIZ, Jose Miguel. ■ 00726 #042-03-2008 *012

ORTIZ, Maria Delourdes. 86 VIA MIRADERO, HACIENDA SAN JOSE 00727 #042-01-1997 L2001 OPH *020 †35

ORTIZ, Ramon Antonio. A7 CALLE YAHUECA, URB PARQUE DEL RIO 00727 #308-06-1983 L1992 PD *020

ORTIZ-CRUZ, Jose L. ■ 00726 #042-03-1982 L1986 ID IM *020

ORTIZ KIDD, Enrique O. CONSOLIDATED MALL POB 6628 00726 #308-01-1977 L1982 NEP IM *020 †20

ORTIZ MARTINEZ, Jose O.. LEON G-12 VILLA DEL REY 1 00725 #042-04-1997 L2004 *100

OSORIO, Hector. ■ 00727 #308-03-1980 L1995 *020

OSORIO, Yma. ■ 00725 #042-01-2004 OBG *012

OTERO, Juan R, Jr. ■ 00725 #042-01-1983 L1986 IM END *020 †20

OTERO-CASTRO, Diana M. ■ 00726 #042-03-1981 L1982 ID *020

PADILLA, Doris C. PO BOX 6149, K-3 8TH ST 00726 #042-01-1981 L1984 FM *020

PADILLA, Orlando. ■ 00726 #308-06-1991 L1996 IM *020

PAGAN, Ketsy Ivelisse. 2901 PARQ SAN ANTONIO 00727 #649-14-1999 L2002 PD *100

PARDO, Cecilio Francisco. 2 CALLE MUNOZ RIVERA, PROFESSIONAL CENTER, SUITE 00725 #042-01-2000 L2003 P *020 ‡

PATRON, Daniel A. PO BOX 8248 00726 #308-03-1979 L1981 PUD IM *020

PEDROZA, Idalia. 201 CALLE GAUTIER BENITEZ 00725 #042-03-1993 L1996 IM *020

PENA-RUIZ, Jorge L. ■ 00725 #847-21-1982 L1987 PD *020

PENA SANCHEZ, Ricardo E. 60 CALLE TOPACIO, VILLA BLANCA 00725 #308-03-1981 L1989 *020

PERALES, Noel Angel. 145 TURABO CLUSTERS 00727 #308-03-1983 L1991 GP *020

PEREIRA PAPALEO, Rafael A. ■ 00725 #308-04-1987 L1992 IM *020

PEREZ, Amarilis J. M36 CALLE 13, URB CONDADO MODERNO 00725 #042-03-1987 L1991 RHU *020

PEREZ, Angel Daniel. K11 CALLE SANTA LUCIA, URB SANTA ELVIRA 00725 #847-08-1978 L1988 GP *020

PEREZ, Angel G. BONNEVILLE HEIGHTS, AVE PR #1 00725 #042-01-1985 L1986 PM *020

PEREZ, Arturo Enrique. A11 CALLE CAMPECHE, QTAS DE SAN LUIS 2 00725 #649-18-1985 L1990 GP *020

PEREZ BRIONES, Julio A.. ■ 00725 #649-14-1996 L2002 GP *020

PEREZ-NAVARRO, Angel L. PO BOX 5729, DEPT PED 00726 #308-03-1978 L1981 PD *020

PEREZ-ORTIZ, Iris Icela. 179 CALLE BUCANO GIGANTE, URB EL VALLE 00727 #042-01-1994 L1999 OBG *020

PEREZ TORRES, Norma M.. PO BOX 1612 00726 #649-14-2003 L2005 *100

PERFETTO, Melissa. 1074 CALLE GUAJATACA, URB VALLES DEL LAGO 00725 #042-01-1995 L2000 EM *020

PIMENTEL, Ada Elena. PO BOX 8223, FEDERICO A39 EST. DEGETAU 00726 #042-10-1983 L1987 OS PD *020 †55

PINERO SANTIAGO, Mariel. ■ 00725 #042-04-1997 L1999 FM *020

PUJOLS-SILFA, Porfirio A. PO BOX 5729 00726 #308-01-1976 L1986 *020

QUINONES, Cesar Rafael. PO BOX 4985, STE 132 00726 #042-01-1988 L1992 OPH *020 †35

QUINTERO, Edda C. PO BOX 4960, PMB 436 00726 #042-01-1971 L1976 DR *030 †80

QUINTERO, Jose E. CARRETERA CAGUAS A CIDRA 00725 #042-01-1984 L1987 FM *020 †18

RAMIREZ APONTE, Catalino. AVENIDA LUIS MUNOZ MARIN 00725 #847-05-1962 L1966 GS *071

RAMIREZ CASIANO, Miguel A. ■ 00726 #847-10-1969 L1975 *071

RAMIREZ-LIZARDI, Eduardo. ■ 00726 #847-05-1976 L1985 GS *020

RAMOS, Anabelle. ■ 00726 #042-01-1998 L2000 FM *020

RAMOS, Frank. ■ 00727 #308-04-1983 L1990 IM *020

RAMOS, Luis Daniel. PO BOX 8882 00726 #042-04-2003 L2004 *100

RAMOS, Ramon Gerardo. ■ 00725 #847-01-1999 L2003 U *020 †95

RAMOS-MERCADO, Mirian. V40 AVE LUIS MUNOZ MARIN, URB MARIOLGA 00725 #042-04-1991 L1993 PD *020

RAMOS VAZQUEZ, Axel Javie. A 17 AVE DEGETAU 00725 #308-04-2000 L2003 *100

READ, Francisco. ■ 00725 #308-01-1947 L1958 GP *071

RENTAS-MAGAZ, Luis Rafael. CARRETERA CAGUAS A CIDRA 00725 #847-04-1960 L1962 R FM *071

REOYO, Zaida Margarita. 2 CALLE MUNOZ RIVERA, STE 307 00725 #042-03-1993 L2002 P *020

RESTO, Luis A. CARRETERA CAGUAS A CIDRA 00725 #042-01-1985 L1990 FM *020

REYES, Milagros T. PO BOX 5729 00726 #308-02-1982 L1986 PD *020

REYES, Nitzia Betacourt. ■ 00727 #042-03-2000 PD *020

REYES FONTANEZ, Carmen L. ■ 00725 #649-14-1992 L1994 *020

REYES-GARCIA, Mildred M. ■ 00725 #847-10-1969 L1972 PD *075

REYES LOPEZ, Aimee Del C. PO BOX 6479 00726 #308-03-1983 L1986 GP *020

REYES MATOS, Betania. ■ 00727 #649-14-2002 L2005 *100

REYES MORENO, Raul. 3RA SECC VILLA DEL REY, CALLE BORGONA 3B-5 00725 #308-03-1982 L1993 GP *020

REYES-ORTIZ, Arnaldo. 200 AVE RAFAEL CORDERO, STE 140 00725 #308-03-1981 L1983 GP *020

REYES VIZCARRONDO, Antonio. ■ 00726 #042-04-1997 L2001 FM *020

REYNOSO RIVERA, Renato. SJ 115 HACIENDA SAN JOSE 00725 #308-02-1991 L1993 IM *020

RICHARDSON-PEREZ, Edgar L. SUITE 136, HIMA HOSPITAL, E.G.O.S. 00726 #847-05-1977 L1980 OBG *020

RIOS, Myriam Socorro. 155 VIA MATINAL, HACIENDA SAN JOSE 00727 #042-03-1991 L1994 FPG *020 †18

RIOS-CAMACHO, Limary. K13 CALLE BAYAMON, VILLA CARMEN 00725 #042-01-1994 L1997 PM *020 †60 ‡

RIOS-CORUJO, Walter. ■ 00727 #308-04-2000 L2003 *100

RIOS DE LA LUZ, Francisco. 1251 CALLE REINA D LS FLRS, HACIENDA BORINQUEN 00725 #649-14-1990 L1995 IM *020

RIOS DIAZ, Maria Elena. CDT CAGUAS, RAFAEL CORDERO AVE 00725 #649-14-1988 L1995 GP *020

RIVERA, Aminta M. PO BOX 7437 00726 #649-14-1994 L1998 P *100

RIVERA, Ivelisse. CONDADO MODERNO 00725 #042-03-1993 L1998 IM *020

RIVERA, Jorge. CAGUAS REG HOSP, DEPT FLEX 00725 #308-04-1983 L1994 OS *020

RIVERA, Juan Carlos. 90 VIA MIRADERO, HACIENDA SAN JOSE 00727 #042-03-1997 L2001 OBG *020

RIVERA, Marisol. 3 COND SANTA JUANA, CALLE 9 T-3 00725 #042-01-1996 L2000 IM *020

RIVERA, Moises. ■ 00727 #308-03-1983 L1987 PD *020

RIVERA, Pedro Ivan. HC 1, 834 SEC GREEN 2.4 CARR 00725 #042-01-1981 L2003 AN *020

RIVERA, Pedro Luis. PO BOX 4956 00726 #308-03-1982 L1989 GP *020

RIVERA, Pedro Luis. PO BOX 4956, C-9 F32 II 00726 #308-06-1986 L1990 PD *020

RIVERA, Rafael Angel. S1 AVE LUIS MUNOZ MARIN, URB MARIOLGA 00725 #308-04-1990 L1996 PD *020

RIVERA, Rafael Manuel. PO BOX 5489 00726 #042-01-1976 L1980 R *020 †15

RIVERA, Renato. ■ 00726 #042-03-1980 L1983 PD PUD *020 †55

RIVERA, Victor M. 1 CALLE BALDORIOTY 00725 #042-02-1982 L1987 U *020 †95

RIVERA-ARZOLA, Jose Celso. CARRETERA CAGUAS A CIDRA 00725 #649-01-1966 L1974 IM *020

RIVERA BERNARD, Felix C. PO BOX 403 00726 #847-04-1959 L1961 U *071

RIVERA CABALLERO, Pedro A. 1069 CALLE GUAJATACA, URB VALLES DEL LAGO 00725 #042-04-1996 L2006 *100

RIVERA-COLON, Rafael. PO BOX 8939, BU-2 AVE LAS AMERICAS 00726 #308-03-1979 L1983 GP *020

RIVERA-JIMENEZ, Jorge L. 1 CALLE BALDORIOTY, ESG GOYCO 00725 #042-01-1985 L1988 U GS *020 †95

RIVERA-LIZARDI, Francisco. 2 CALLE MUNOZ RIVERA, CENTRO PEDO PROF 00725 #847-01-1960 L1964 PD *020

RIVERA LOPEZ, Ana M. 49 RES TURABO HTS, CARRETERA 172 URBANIZACION 00727 #042-04-1998 L2000 FM *020

RIVERA LUNA, Hiram. PO BOX 6960 00726 #042-01-1986 L1989 NM OS *020 †20,28

RIVERA-MARTINEZ, Oscar. 202 CALLE GAUTIER BENITEZ, CONSOLIDATED MALL 00725 #308-02-1984 L1986 PUD IM *020

RIVERA-MORILLO, Pedro D. A8 AVE MUNOZ MARIN, URB VILLA CRIOLLOS 00725 #308-03-1980 L1982 PD *020

RIVERA NUNEZ, Efrain. PO BOX 4954, STE 110 00726 #308-03-1982 L1989 *020

RIVERA ORELLANO, Olga Dam. CALLE 12 L-4, URB SANTA JUANA 2 00725 #649-35-2004 L2006 *100

RIVERA-REVERON, Cesar A. ■ 00725 #649-03-1990 L1992 NEP *020

RIVERA-RODRIGUEZ, Jose A. F13 AVE DEGETAU, URB BONNEVILLE TERR 00725 #847-06-1970 L1974 *020

ROBLES-MORA, Carlos. 24 CALLE JADE, VILLA BLANCA 00725 #847-05-1977 L1980 GP *020

RODRIGUEZ, Elizabeth. 2B37 CALLE CARLOMAGNO, VILLA DEL REY 2 00725 #308-03-1985 L1990 PD *020

RODRIGUEZ, Jose Rafael. ■ 00726 #042-01-2007 L2007 GS *012

RODRIGUEZ, Luis R. ■ 00725 #042-03-1978 L1981 FM *020

RODRIGUEZ, Marilyn. ■ 00725 #308-02-1986 L1989 GP *020

RODRIGUEZ, Patricia. PO BOX 8038 00726 #308-03-1982 L1990 IM *020

RODRIGUEZ, Virgen M. PO BOX 6168 00726 #042-02-1984 L1987 FM *020 †18

RODRIGUEZ, Vivian Janette. 2 CALLE EXT MUNOZ RIVERA 00725 #308-04-1988 L1991 PD *020

RODRIGUEZ BENITEZ, Jose M. PO BOX 1388 00726 #308-03-1983 L1994 GP *020

RODRIGUEZ-CAY, Jose R. PO BOX 1209 00726 #308-03-1980 L1982 P OS *020

RODRIGUEZ COLON, Juan. ■ 00726 #042-01-1963 L1969 ORS AM *020

RODRIGUEZ-GARRIDO, Miguel. ■ 00726 #042-03-1980 L1984 IM CD *020 †20

RODRIGUEZ-LOPEZ, Hector. ■ 00726 #042-05-1976 L1979 GP *020

RODRIGUEZ MALDONADO, Justo. 2 CALLE MUNOZ RIVERA, STE 312 00725 #649-35-1999 L2001 *020

RODRIGUEZ MARTINEZ, Maximo. 24 CALLE DIAMANTE, VILLA BLANCA 00725 #308-03-1979 L2002 *020

RODRIGUEZ-MONGE, Steven J. PO BOX 9450 00726 #847-10-1987 L1991 IM *020

RODRIGUEZ ROMAN, Edgardo. ST. 2 A 13 00725 #308-03-1978 L1981 *100

RODRIGUEZ ROQUE, Maria De. ■ 00725 #308-01-1982 L2002 *020

ROLDAN, Rossely. ■ 00725 #042-03-2003 P *012

ROLDAN-MILLAN, Pedro. ■ 00725 #042-01-1959 L1968 OBG *071 †30

ROMAN, Jesus Manuel. 24 AVE JOSE GARRIDO, VILLA BLANCA 00725 #649-14-2005 *100 †20

ROQUE AGOSTO, Rafael A. G41 AVE PINO VILLA TURABO 00725 #847-05-1971 L1978 GP *020

ROQUE RODRIGUEZ, Carlos. BONNEVILLE TERRACE, DEGETAU AVE #A-16 00726 #847-06-1976 L1983 GS *020

ROQUE-VELAZQUEZ, Felix R. G41 CALLE PINO, VILLA TURABO 00725 #042-01-1995 L2000 GS *020 †85

ROSADO, Angel. Y26 AVE LUIS MUNOZ MARIN, URB MARIOLGA 00725 #308-02-1989 L1994 END *020

ROSARIO-MULINELLI, Jorge. AVENIDA LUIS MUNOZ MARIN 00725 #042-04-1988 L1992 PG *020

ROSA SOLA, Mabel. I20 CALLE EUCALIPTO, URB ARBOLADA 00727 #649-14-2001 L2003 *100

ROURA, Fernando Eugenio. PO BOX 4960 PMB 229 00726 #649-14-2002 L2003 *100

ROVIRA, Jose F. ST 5-F29 URB CAGUAX 00725 #042-04-1987 L1990 IM *020

RUIZ, Harry Rafael. A7 COND BONNEVILLE, DEGETAU ST 00725 #042-01-1989 L1995 GE IM *020 †20

SAAVEDRA, Maiza Daisy. PO BOX 760 00726 #176-03-1995 L2003 GS *100 †85

SALGUEIRO-BRAVO, Jesus M. 195 CALLE GAUTIER BENITEZ, P O BOX 4961 00725 #042-03-1997 L2000 OBG *020 †30

SANCHEZ FERRERI, Jorge M. APT POSTAL 6599 00725 #028-34-1941 L1942 OPH *071

SANCHEZ-GOMEZ, Jessica. 559 VIA GRANDE, HACIENDA SAN JOSE 00727 #042-01-1998 L2002 AN *020

SANCHEZ VALDES, Jesus H. 630 VIA DE LA ERMITA, HACIENDA SAN JOSE 00725 #847-05-1975 L1978 OM *030

SANTA, Wilfredo G. PO BOX 8907 00726 #042-04-1980 L1986 P CHP *020

SANTANA, Arnulfo Nouel. PO BOX 7738 00726 #308-03-1982 L1986 GP *020 †20

SANTIAGO, Dhalma Cecilia. ■ 00726 #042-02-2004 PD *100

SANTIAGO FIOL, Ivonne M. 61 CALLE GOYCO 00725 #649-14-1988 L1995 IM *020

SANTIAGO-MARTINEZ, Myrta. PO BOX 397 00726 #042-03-1980 L1983 FM *020 †18

SANTOS, Armando J. A11 AVE DEGETAU, BONNEVILLE TERRACE 00725 #042-03-1980 L1984 PD *020

SANTOS ELOSEGUI, Jose Dav. EL VERDE 73 00725 #649-14-2002 L2005 *100

SANTOS GERARDINO, Hector. ■ 00726 #308-01-1969 L1976 *071

SANTOS SANCHEZ, Irma C. CALLE 1-B3 CONDADO MODERNO 00725 #308-03-1987 L1989 *020

SAPUTELLI BARRIOS, Adriana. PO BOX 4985 PMB 204 00726 #308-03-1987 L1999 GP *020

SCOTT-CORA, James Wm. PO BOX 9119 00726 #010-03-1973 L1984 NM PTH *020 †28

SELEM, Lissette. 142 ESTANCIAS DEL LAGO, EST DEL LAGO 00725 #308-03-1986 L2003 P *020

SENERIZ, Rafael. 52 CALLE RUIZ BELVIS, P O BOX 7827 00725 #042-01-1996 L2000 ORS *020 †40

SENQUIZ, Angel Luis. CARRETERA CAGUAS A CIDRA 00725 #042-01-1975 L1979 PD *030 †55

SEPULVEDA PELLICIER, D. PO BOX 6419 00726 #847-05-1971 L1974 GP *020

SERRA, Hector E. ■ 00725 #847-09-1964 L1968 FM *071

SERRANO, Roberto Jose. ■ 00725 #042-01-2008 *012

SERRANO-DOMINGUEZ, J. ■ 00727 #042-01-2002 L2004 PUD *020 †20

SERRANO-SOLIS, Rosa A. 6 CALLE CORCHADO 00725 #056-06-1949 L1952 GYN *071

SERRANO-VAZQUEZ, Alfonso. AVENIDA LUIS MUNOZ MARIN 00725 #847-04-1957 L1960 OBG *071

SILVA, Amarilis. AVENIDA LUIS MUNOZ MARIN 00725 #042-03-1980 L1986 HS GS *020

SILVA, Karen M. 667 VIA DESTELLO, HACIENDA SAN JOSE 00727 #042-01-1996 L1998 EM *020

SOCARRAS, Luis Guillermo. 60 CALLE CAMPIO ALONSO 00725 #275-01-1983 L2003 GP *020

SOLA LOPEZ, Cirilo. ■ 00725 #308-03-1979 L1981 GP *020

SOTO, Ian Ramon. 1 CALLE NAZARIO, URB NAZARIO 00725 #042-01-1995 L2000 GS *020 †85

SOTO-SOLA, Jose J. 2 CALLE MUNOZ RIVERA 00725 #042-01-1962 L1966 PD PUD *020 †55

STEELE LLINAS, Rosa Maria. A36 CALLE MARGARITA, URB SAN ALFONSO 00725 #042-03-1991 L1996 GP *020

SUAREZ CAIMARES, Emilio. ■ 00727 #308-01-1966 L1976 AN *020

SUAREZ IGARTUA, Jaime. PO BOX 9717 00726 #042-03-1996 L1998 FPS EM *020

SUAREZ-TORRES, Humberto. 2 CALLE MUNOZ RIVERA, PROFESSIONAL CTR STE 308 00725 #042-04-1982 L1985 P *020

SUSTACHE, Sonia Ivette. 53 CALLE FEDERICO, EST DEGETAU 00727 #042-01-1977 L1982 OBG *020

TELMONT, Maria De Lourdes. 56 CALLE CELIS AGUILERA 00725 #042-01-1976 L1981 HEM *020

TEXIDOR, Carmen Ivette. PO BOX 4952 00726 #308-03-1988 L1990 GP *020

TIRADO, Guillermo J. ■ 00726 #649-14-1989 L1991 IMG *020

TIRADO, Pedro Antonio. AVENIDA LUIS MUNOZ MARIN 00725 #649-14-1988 L1991 IM *020

TIRADO-GOMEZ, Maribel. ■ 00727 #042-01-1997 L2001 ON *100 †20

TORO, Anibal Jose. ■ 00725 #042-03-1997 L1999 IM *020 †20

TORRES, Francisco J. ■ 00727 #042-01-1991 L1995 AN *020 †05

TORRES, Guillermo. PO BOX 219, 1A CALLE MUNOZ RIVERA 00726 #042-01-1971 L1973 OPH GP *020

TORRES, Nilda Eneida. A7 CALLE YAHUECA, PARQ DEL RIO 00727 #308-01-1986 L1990 GP *020

TORRES, Timoteo. PO BOX 9689, 208 CALLE GAUTIER BENITEZ 00726 #042-01-1979 L1984 U *020 †95

TORRES-GARCIA, Ibel S. ■ 00726 #649-14-1986 L1991 PD *020

TORRES NAVARRO, Nilda. ■ 00726 #042-01-1986 L1990 AN *020

TORRES-PINEDO, Jose A. MIRADOR CALLE 30 2T 51 00725 #308-01-1975 L1979 *020

TORRES-TORRES, Carlos M. ■ 00725 #649-30-1986 L1988 GP PD *062

UBARRI GARCIA, Luisa M. 2 CALLE ANASCO, URB BONNEVILLE HTS 00727 #847-08-1975 L1980 OBG *020

UFRET-PEREZ, Rafael. 107 AVE ESTANCIAS DEL LAGO, CALLE 2-A-7 00725 #308-06-1986 L1988 CD *020

VADI, Nitza N. PO BOX 6449 00726 #847-02-1977 L1980 P *020

VALDES COCHRAN, Jennifer. ■ 00725 #649-14-2002 L2004 *100

VARELA, Edgardo Enrique. CALLE POE E-9, QUINTAS DE SAN LUIS 00725 #042-01-1988 L1993 PM *020

VARGAS, Margarita T. 55 CALLE SATURNO, EST EL VERDE 00725 #308-04-1987 L1989 P *020

VARGAS CORDERO, Jose J. AVENIDA LUIS MUNOZ MARIN 00725 #847-05-1955 L1959 OBG *071 †30

VAZQUEZ, Francisco. ■ 00726 #042-03-1984 L1986 *020

VAZQUEZ, Gonzalo. PO BOX 495225 00726 #042-03-1988 L1991 OBG *020

VAZQUEZ, Martha. PO BOX 5729, DEPT OBG 00726 #042-03-1980 L1985 OBG *020

VAZQUEZ, Sandra I. 140 AVE RAFAEL CORDERO, PMB 455 00725 #042-01-1993 L1997 IM *020 †20

VAZQUEZ-JULIA, Jose M. ■ 00726 #308-02-1974 L1979 *020

VAZQUEZ PEREZ, Ermelinda. ■ 00727 #308-03-1981 L1994 *020

VAZQUEZ-RODRIGUEZ, Angel. 2D29 CALLE PINO, VILLA DEL REY 2 00725 #308-03-1981 L1982 PD *020

VEGA-RODRIGUEZ, Maritza. 63 CALLE TOPC VILLA BLANCA 00725 #847-05-1976 L1979 PD *020

VELAZQUEZ, Angel Manuel. 24 AVE MUNOZ MARIN, VILLA CARMEN 00725 #308-04-1984 L1986 GP *020

VELAZQUEZ, Edwin. CIDRA PR, CARR 734 KM 0.5 00726 #042-01-1987 L1991 PD *020

VELAZQUEZ, Fernando Luis. I19 AVE LUIS MUNOZ MARIN, VILLA CARMEN 00725 #308-03-1984 L1993 IM *020

VELAZQUEZ, Zulma J. CARRETERA CAGUAS A CIDRA 00725 #042-01-1985 L1988 PD *020

VELEZ, Manuel Antonio. ■ 00725 #042-01-2004 L2005 PM *012

VELEZ CORREA, Daniel. ■ 00726 #308-03-1984 L1992 GP *020

VERA GONZALEZ, Agustin. PO BOX 7378 00726 #847-01-1968 L1971 GP *020

VERGARA, Carlos A. PO BOX 4956, S JOSE 00726 #042-01-1982 L1988 GS U *020

VICENTE, Sara Maria. 1 CALLE NAZARIO, URB NAZARIO 00725 #042-01-1995 L2000 PM *020 †60

VIERA, Cynthia. URB CONDADO, CALLE JAZMIN B-127 00725 #042-01-1993 L1997 IM *020 †20

VIERA, Jose R. 201 CALLE G BENITEZ # 201, CONSOLIDATED MEDICAL PLAZA 00725 #042-03-1985 L1988 IM *020

VIERA, Loida E. 2 CALLE PADIAL BOX 451 00725 #042-01-1983 L1986 OBG *020

WHITLOCK, Robert Nolen. 6 CALLE INTENDENTE RAMIREZ 00725 #023-01-1965 L1968 CD IM *020

YAPUR-PALEO, Matilde. 142 ESTANCIAS DEL LAGO, EST DEL LAGO 00725 #847-06-1979 L1987 PD *020

YSERN, Fernando J. PO BOX 8969, 50 AVE MUNOZ MARIN 00726 #042-01-1981 L1984 PD ADL *020 †55

YULIAN, Antonio. I5 CALLE SAN ESTEBAN, URB SAN PEDRO EST 00725 #042-01-1974 L1976 **U** *020 †95
ZAMORA-CORDERO, Lynette. PO BOX 5729, DEPT PED 00726 #847-05-1979 L1981 **PD** *020

CAMUY — CAMUY

ALDIVA HERNANDEZ, Nelson. ■ 00627 #649-14-2003 L2005 *100
BRAVO, Jose Alberto. PO BOX 851 00627 #649-14-2002 L2005 *100
CASANAS ESTRELLA, Jose R. ■ 00627 #042-04-1999 L2001 **FM** *020
CHACON CRESPO, Mary T.. PO BOX 8 00627 #649-14-2002 L2004 *100
CORDERO GUILLAMA, Enery M. PO BOX 850 00627 #308-03-1984 L1998 *100
DELGADO, Irma I. BOX 667 BO PUERTE 00627 #308-03-1982 L1986 **GP** *020
GARCIA, Yussel Carmelo. ■ 00627 #042-01-2007 **IM** *012
GONZALEZ, Pedro Rafael. 1 CALLE IGUINA E 00627 #308-01-1969 L1975 **OBG GP** *020
GONZALEZ CAMUY, Antonio. H67 CALLE 9, URB DEL CARMEN 00627 #308-03-2000 L2003 *100
GONZALEZ MORELL, Juan A. 66 AVE MUNOZ RIVERA E 00627 #308-04-1980 L1994 **GP** *020
HERNANDEZ, Milca Lymarie. HC 5, 488 BO ABRA H 0.6 CARR 00627 #042-01-2000 L2003 **PD** *100
HERNANDEZ LOPEZ, Oscar A. APTO 542 BO ZANJAS 00627 #308-03-1983 L1987 **GP** *020
JIMENEZ-MENDEZ, Rafael A. ■ 00627 #847-05-1974 L1977 **PD** *020
JIMENEZ ORTEGA, Obet. PO BOX 850 00627 #308-03-1984 L2003 *100
LOPEZ, Elsa. 4 CALLE CABAN STE 2 00627 #308-02-1989 L1993 **PD** *020
LOPEZ, Jose Joaquin. C/O P.O. BOX 593, CALLE PERELLO #4 00627 #308-03-1982 L1986 **FM** *020
LOPEZ, Vionette. HC 2, 2 CARR KM 94.7 00627 #649-14-2002 L2004 *100
LOPEZ-LOPEZ, Hilda Luz. ■ 00627 #042-04-1982 L1983 **PD** *020
LUIGI SANCHEZ, Giovanni G. HC 3 BOX 10428 00627 #308-06-1985 L1996 **GP** *020
MARTINEZ MALDONADO, D J. HC 4, MD, HOSPTL SUB REGIONAL PE 00627 #308-03-1978 L1983 *020
MEDINA QUINONEZ, Cesar H. 6 CALLE ESTRELLA S 00627 #042-04-1985 L1993 **GP** *020
MOLINA GONZALEZ, David. ■ 00627 #042-04-2004 L2005 *100
PADILLA, Cesar O. ■ 00627 #042-04-1985 L1992 **P** *020
PEREZ, Brenda Liz. PO BOX 3500, PMB 286 00627 #649-14-2002 L2003 *100
PEREZ, Yamira. HC 2 BOX 6040 00627 #042-03-1988 L1991 **FM** *020
PEREZ VEGA, Mayra E. ■ 00627 #649-14-2000 L2003 *100
RODRIGUEZ, Americo. ■ 00627 #308-03-1981 L1986 **GP** *020
RODRIGUEZ, Francisco R R. PO BOX 508 00627 #308-03-1979 L1981 **FM** *020
ROMAN RONDA, Elizabeth. ■ 00627 #308-01-1990 L1993 *020
SOLER, Yadira Alexandra. ■ 00627 #042-01-2003 **PD** *100 †55
TORO BOBE, Jose M.. PO BOX 455 00627 #308-03-1998 L2002 *020
TORRES DEL VALLE, Mariela. ■ 00627 #649-35-2001 L2002 *020
TOSADO, Adalberto. ■ 00627 #042-01-1990 L1995 *020
VELEZ ARCE, Ramon A. 55 CALLE ESTRELLA N 00627 #847-05-1972 L1975 **GP** *020

CANOVANAS — CANOVANAS

ANSA-VILA, Ramon Martin. 80 CALLE BETANCES 00729 #308-03-1979 L1982 **GP** *020
AYALA, Daniel. ■ 00729 #308-03-1980 L1990 **GP** *020
BADILLO, Julio R. 87 CALLE MUNOZ RIVERA 00729 #042-01-1962 L1970 **PD OS** *020 †55
BUJATER, Antonio Stephen. 71 CALLE AUTONOMIA 00729 #440-01-1946 L1957 **GP** *020
CALDERON, Eva Yvonne. ■ 00729 #649-14-1978 L1989 **GP** *020
CARRASQUILLO, Aleida Yoma. 137 CALLE 6, PARC CENTRAL 00729 #649-14-1999 L2000 **GP** *020
CARRASQUILLO, Maritza. JARDINES DE CANOVANAS, D-16 2ND ST 00729 #042-01-1999 L2002 **IM** *020 †20
CLAUDIO, Pedro Juan. ■ 00729 #042-01-2000 L2003 **FM** *020 †18 ‡
COLON RODRIGUEZ, Diego J. AA8 LOIZA VALLEY MALL 00729 #042-04-1999 L2001 **GP** *020
CORREA-JUSINO, Francisco. B1 CALLE 1, JARD DE CANOVANAS 00729 #308-03-1978 L1981 **GP** *020
COTTO, Migdaliz. ■ 00729 #649-14-2003 L2006 *100
DELGADO, Jorge Rafael. 260 CALLE FLOR DE LIS, URB RIVER GDNS 00729 #737-03-1989 L2006 **GP** *020
DELGADO-RODRIGUEZ, Rebecca. 101 CALLE AUTONOMIA 00729 #042-04-1983 L1985 **GP** *020
FERRIS PLAZA, Roberto A. 61 CALLE PALMER, BOX 525 00729 #308-01-1982 L1992 **GP** *020
GARCIA, Oscar. 58 CALLE CORCHADO, INSTITUTO MEDIC FAMILIAR 00729 #308-03-1980 L1988 **GP** *020
GOMEZ FORTUNA, Mayralisa. ■ 00729 #308-01-1979 L1989 *020
GONZALEZ-SKERRETTE, Juan. 66 CALLE PEPITA ALBANDOZ 00729 #308-04-1987 L1991 **GP** *020
JURADO AGOSTO, Zulma. 18 CALLE PALMER, BOX 10000 URB 445 00729 #042-01-1991 L1994 **OBG** *020 †30
KUTCHER, Roberto B. URB LOIZA VALLEY, C/O BOX 1672 00729 #308-03-1982 L1984 **GP** *020
LASTRA, Pedro Luis. 3 CALLE AUTONOMIA 00729 #308-03-1982 L1984 **GP** *020
LOPEZ, Carmen Antonia. HC 1 BOX 7546, EM6.0 CARR 185 00729 #308-03-1981 L1990 **GP** *020
MARTE, Francisco Rafael. LOCAL AA-3 LOIZA VALLEY 00729 #308-01-1985 L1992 **IM** *020
MENDEZ GARCIA, Joaquin R. BOX 1645, 55 CARR 185 00729 #847-10-1966 L1968 **FM** *020
MERCADO, Jose A. A2 CALLE ACACIA, URB LOIZA VALLEY 00729 #042-01-1992 L1995 **PCC IM** *020 †20
MERCED PASTRANA, Maria V.. PO BOX 10000 PMB 260 00729 #649-14-2002 L2000 *100
MONTEVERDE, Rolando. 55 CALLE JOSE AUBRAY, URB COUNTRY VIEW 00729 #649-14-1988 L1992 **FM EM** *020
MUJICA DEL VALLE, Hilda V. 83 CALLE MUNOZ RIVERA 00729 #308-01-1981 L1993 **FM** *020
PARRILLA, Francisco. ■ 00729 #042-01-2007 **IM** *012
PASCUAL VAZQUEZ, Ricardo. PO BOX 20000, PMB 152 00729 #649-35-1993 L1996 **GP** *020
QUINONES, Justo. 975 CALLE BAUHINIA, URB 00729 #308-04-1993 L1996 **PD** *020
RAMOS, Ruth Evelin. ■ 00729 #308-01-1990 L2003 **FM** *020
REYES, Mayra V. 52 CALLE PALMER, BOX 339 00729 #308-03-1984 L1989 **PD** *020
RIVERA ARTES, Ileana F.. #9621 VILLAS DE CUIDAD JA 00729 #649-30-2002 L2004 *100
RIVERA-MORILLO, Edith E. ■ 00729 #042-03-1988 L1993 **IM** *020
RODRIGUEZ, Hector C. 870 CALLE DIAMANTE, QTAS DE CANOVANAS 00729 #042-02-1990 L1994 **PD** *020

RODRIGUEZ RODRIGUEZ, Alexa. HC 1 BOX 8581, BO LOMAS 00729 #042-04-2004 L2006 *100
ROHENA, Jorge Alberto. ■ 00729 #042-01-2005 **IM** *012
ROMAN, Carlos M. HC 1 BOX 6560KM, BO CAMPO RICO 00729 #847-02-1982 L1990 **GP** *020
ROSARIO, Jessica. ■ 00729 #308-04-2000 L2002 *020
TORRES DE PEREZ, Zulma. PO BOX 20000 00729 #847-10-1964 L1968 **GP** *072
VAZQUEZ, Luz Eneida. URB LOIZA VALLEY, LOIZA VALLEY MALL AA10 00729 #042-01-1981 L1984 **PD** *020
VEGA, Manuel Angel. ■ PO BOX 35000 PMB 20149 00729 #649-14-2005 *100
VEGA-CALZADA, Zaida Iris. 54 CALLE JOSE AUBRAY, URB COUNTRY VIEW 00729 #847-05-1971 L1975 *020
VERGNE, Julio E.. ■ 00729 #308-07-1983 L2004 *100

CAPARRA HEIGHTS — SAN JUAN

MARAVER MARCANO, Juan B. COND LOS PATRICIOS-401 00920 #847-04-1961 L1972 **GP** *100
MILAN, Maria P. ■ 00920 #847-23-1967 L1974 **D** *020
VALENCIA, Miguel. COLLINS 582 SUMMIT HILLS 00920 #042-01-1979 L1982 **PHP PD** *030 †55

CAPARRA HILLS — SAN JUAN

ALVAREZ DE CHOUDENS, Jose. PO BOX 11964 00922 #023-01-1944 L1947 **OS NS** *071 †25
MARCHAND, Juan Ramon. ■ 00922 #021-05-1943 L1945 **OS DR** *072 †80
MARTINEZ DIAZ, Etanislao. PO BOX 11981 00922 #042-01-1970 L1972 **FM** *020 †18
PAGAN, Victor J. PO BOX 11921 00922 #041-13-1951 L1952 **EM FM** *020
PUJADAS, Giovanni Colberg. A2 GREEN VALL GARDEN HILL 00922 #649-01-1951 L1954 **GYN GP** *020
RAMOS-YORDAN, Luis E. PO BOX 10847 00922 #649-01-1947 L1948 *100
RIVERA-OPIO, Milagros. ■ 00922 #847-10-1970 L1975 **PD** *030
ROSSELLO, Pedro Juan. SUCHVILLE NO 8 00922 #008-01-1970 L1977 **PDS GS** *020 †85

CAPARRA TERRACE — SAN JUAN

OMS, Luis J. 1250 JESUS T PINERO AVE 00922 #042-01-1967 L1971 **OPH** *020 †35
RIVERA, Rafael Jose. 1421 CALLE DOVER, URB PUERTO NUEVO 00920 #042-03-2003 L2006 **CD** *012

CAROLINA — CAROLINA

ABREU-FESHOLD, Francisco. 511 AVE SANCHEZ OSORIO, VILLO CONTANA 00983 #847-10-1972 L1975 **GP** *020
ACEVEDO, Luz Maria. D22 CALLE YUNQUESITO, LOMAS DE CAROLINA 00987 #042-03-1983 L1987 **FM IMG** *020 †18
ACEVEDO, Sara G. 5 AVE SANCHEZ OSORIO # G-4, VALLE ARRIBA HTS 00983 #042-01-1990 L1994 **IM** *020
ADAMES, Diogenes Orestes. ■ 00985 #308-01-1987 L1992 **P** *020
AGDAM, Arzhang. ■ 00983 #308-13-2003 L2005 *100
AHMAD-KHADIJAH, Hamdallah. AA5 CALLE MORERA, VALLE ARRIBA HTS 00983 #308-03-1978 L1995 **GP** *020
ALBANDOZ-ORTIZ, Dulce M. S1 CALLE IMPERIAL, PARQ ECUESTRE 00987 #847-05-1974 L1977 **GP** *020
ALICEA-GARCIA, Luz V. VILLA FONTANA, VIA 61 3CN 26 00983 #042-01-1993 L1996 **IM** *020 †20
ALVAREZ-RUIZ, Carlos R. ESTANCIAS DE SAN FERNANDO, STREET #4 B-17, 00985 #308-03-1978 L1983 **PD GP** *020
ANDINO-DONES, Bernardo. CO13 CALLE 125, VALLE ARRIBA HTS 00983 #042-04-1980 L1983 **EM** *020 †16
ARENALDE ARAUS, Margarita. ■ 00987 #649-14-1993 L2003 *100
ARRIETA, Victor R. ■ 00987 #308-04-1983 L1987 **GP** *020
ARROYO-MUNIZ, Maritza. DL13 VIA EMILIA, VILLA FONTANA 00983 #308-03-1976 L1978 **N** *020 †75
AVILES, Osvaldo. F25 CALLE 5, URB ROSA MARIA 00985 #042-04-1988 L1991 **GP** *020
AYALA-SEGUI, Chas Anthony. E7 CALLE MALAGA, URB VISTAMAR MARINA 00983 #308-03-1979 L1982 **EM GP** *020
AYUSO-ROSARIO, Jesus M. J18 CALLE CERRO PENUELAS, URB LOMA ALTA 00987 #847-10-1966 L1978 **GP EM** *020
BACO, Carlos Juan. ■ 00984 #847-12-1994 L1996 **P** *020
BAEZ-SILVA, Carmen. 23-8 AVE ROBERTO CLEMENTE, VILLA CAROLINA 00985 #649-14-1974 L1978 **PD** *020
BALZAC, Maria Delosang. ■ 00987 #042-03-1994 L1997 **P** *020
BARBOSA, Bernadette. 33-8 CALLE 11, VILLA CAROLINA 00985 #042-03-1998 L2001 **PD** *020
BARBOSA, Jesus M. 33-8 CALLE 11, VILLA CAROLINA 00985 #847-10-1968 L1970 **PD** *020
BARBOSA, Rosa L. PO BOX 4467 00984 #847-02-1973 L1977 **OS** *020
BARRETO-SOSA, Sissi Miche. 11-2 CALLE 24, VILLA CAROLINA 00985 #042-02-1998 L2000 **FM** *020
BARRIOS, Rosalie Eunice. 1106 COND PASJS DL ESCRLBL 00987 #042-01-1997 L2001 *020
BARROSO TORRES, Jose Mari. ■ 00985 #305-01-1981 L2001 *020
BERRY POLANCO, Jossepp O. 31-8 CALLE PRAVIA # 8, VILLA ASTURIAS 00983 #308-03-1981 L1986 **GP** *020
BLANCO, Ramon O. VALLE ARRIBA HEIGHTS, MONSERRATE AVE BA-14 00984 #847-04-1965 L1967 **IM** *020
BREA, Mayra E. ■ 00988 #308-01-1982 L1994 *020
CABALLERO, Jose Antonio. ■ 00983 #042-01-1993 L1999 **CHP** *020
CABAN HERNANDEZ, Hector M. CALLE 1 #A2, URB MOUNTAIN VIEW 00987 #308-03-1993 *100
CACERES, Domingo Luis. 3KS8 VIA MYRTA, VILLA FONTANA 00983 #649-14-1984 L1990 **FM** *020 †18
CALDERON-SUAREZ, Aureo. ■ 00985 #847-04-1965 L1969 **GP OS** *020
CAMACHO, Richard. ■ 00984 #042-01-1993 L1995 **OPH** *020
CAMPOS, Victor I. ■ 00987 #847-06-1987 L1991 **GP** *020
CARRERAS-MARTINEZ, Juan. URB VILLA ASTURIAS 31 2 00983 #847-04-1978 L1980 **IM** *020
CASTRO CURET, Gretza Odet. ■ 00983 #649-14-1999 L2002 *020

■ = Address Information Privacy Protected

CESPEDES, Nelsa Rodriguez. ■ 00985 #308-01-1980 L1986 **P** *020

CIURO REYES, Delma Julia. BLOGUC 123 NO 25, AVC ROBERTO CLCMCOTE 00985 #308-06-1982 L1986 **PD** *020

COLLAZO, Victor. ■ 00984 #042-01-1985 L1989 **PTH** *020

COLLAZO PABON, Nancy. BO SANTA CRUZ, CARR 859 KM 2.4 00988 #042-04-1992 L1994 **PD** *020

COLON, Manuel Antonio. ■ 00987 #042-01-2000 L2002 **EM** *100

COLON CARRASQUILLO, Yadirm. ■ 00985 #649-14-2002 L2005 **GP** *020

COLON DIAZ, Rafael Angel. BOX 647 00986 #847-05-1978 L1980 *020

COLON-FONTANEZ, Francisco. 264 CAL TRNTR CIUDAD JARDI 00987 #042-01-1992 L1996 **D** *020 †15

COLON REYES, Ivette. B24 CALLE 4, EST DE SAN FERNANDO 00985 #042-04-2001 L2002 *020

COMAS, Maria R. AA28 CAL 20 JARD DE COUNTR, CLUB 00983 #308-03-1984 L1992 **PD** *020

CORDOVA, Delfin Gines. VILLA CAROLINA, 408 ST BLOG 149 #16 00985 #308-03-1978 L1985 *020

CORRETJER, Gustavo Pedro. ■ 00983 #308-01-1972 L1974 **P** *020

CRUZ, Miguel Angel. 1626 CALLE ALICANTE, URB BAHIA VISTAMAR 00985 #308-03-1980 L1990 **GP** *020

CRUZ, Nilda E. 25 AVE ROBERTO CLEMENTE, BLOQUE 123, VILLA CAROLINA 00985 #847-01-1985 L1989 **PD** *020

CRUZADO, Armando Javier. 1420 CALLE MARBELLA, MANS DE VISTAMAR MARINA 00983 #042-01-2002 L2005 **GS** *100 †85

CRUZ-MALDONADO, Juan. ■ 00986 #847-05-1973 L1984 **GP** *020

CRUZ ROMAN, Olga A.. ■ 00985 #308-01-1992 L2003 *100

CRUZ-SOTO, Luis Orlando. ■ 00988 #042-01-1962 L1966 **GP** *020

DAVILA, Dalya. HC 1 BOX 11136 00987 #649-14-2002 L2005 *100

DE LA CRUZ, Nerina Elvira. ■ 00985 #308-01-1975 L1997 **GP** *020

DEL AMO MOJICA, Fernando. ■ 00987 #308-11-1990 L2005 *100

DE LA ROSA TORREGROSA, N. ■ 00987 #042-01-1957 L1960 **P CHP** *071

DELGADO, Luis Arnaldo. 20 BLVD MEDIA LUNA, PARQUE DE LAS FLORES 1804 00987 #042-03-1991 L1994 **ON** *020

DELGADO-BUTHER, Norma V. 5W7 PARQUE BOLONIA, VILLA FONTANA PARK 00983 #042-01-1999 L2005 **IM** *020 †20

DELGADO-MATOS, Ronald. ■ 00987 #042-04-1987 L1989 **FM** *020 †18

DELIZ, Brenda Lourdes. 9 CALLE 21 BLQ 16, SABANA GARDENS 00983 #042-01-2000 L2003 **N** *100 †75

DE PENA BATISTA, Julio Ma. ■ 00987 #308-13-2000 **EM** *100

DIAZ, Lydia Damaris. E7 CALLE MALAGA, URB VISTAMAR MARINA 00983 #308-03-1981 L1984 **GP** *020

DIAZ CABRERA, Eileen. PO BOX 3185 00984 #649-14-2003 L2004 *100

DIAZ-LOPEZ, Gloria L. C/18 BLO 22 6 VIL CAROLINA 00985 #847-08-1978 L1982 **IM** *020

DIAZ-MONTANO, Rafael. 5H AVE SANCHEZ OSORIO, VALLE ARRIBA HTS 00983 #847-10-1963 L1966 **GP IM** *020

DULUC, Clemencia Isaura. ■ 00988 #308-01-1986 L1992 *020

ESCUDERO, Cesar Augusto. ■ 00984 #737-01-1991 L2003 **FP** *012

FEBO CRUZ, Nancy I.. ■ 00987 #308-04-1999 L2005 *100

FERRER BROOKS, John F. 122 CALLE LL CIUDAD JARDIN 00987 #847-05-1964 L1969 **GP** *020

FIGUEROA, Ilsa Josefina. ■ 00988 #847-08-1981 L1992 **OPH** *020

FIGUEROA RUSSE, Antonio. 529-196-31 VILLA CAROLINA 00985 #847-02-1970 L1974 **GP** *020

FIOL-RODRIGUEZ, Rose E. HE BOX 11043 00987 #847-04-1953 L1956 **NP** *072

FLORES, Victor Luis. ■ 00988 #042-01-1980 L1983 **NEP IM** *020

FONT HERMIDA, Evarista. ■ 00983 #847-10-1966 L1991 **GP** *020

GALDON, Gladys. I17 CALLE RAMON QUINONES, URB E J SALDANA 00983 #042-01-1980 L1983 **FM OS** *030 †18

GARCES-MEJIAS, Kamir. ■ 00987 #308-03-1982 L1990 *020

GARCIA, Enid. ■ 00985 #042-01-1996 L1999 **FM** *020 †18

GARCIA, Juan Edgardo. 36-5 CALLE 14, VILLA CAROLINA 00985 #649-14-1976 L1983 **OBG MFM** *020

GARCIA, Lourdes. MONSERATE AC8 VALLE ARRIBA 00983 #042-01-1988 L1993 **NM** *020 †28

GARCIA, Lourdes Fragoso. ■ 00983 #042-03-1992 L1995 **NPM** *020 †55

GARCIA-CATALAN, Nallix. 51 AVE ROBERTO CLEMENTE, VILLA CAROLINA 00985 #042-01-1999 L2001 **PM** *020 †60

GARIB, George. ■ 00983 #042-03-2007 **IM** *012

GARIB-BAZAIN, Jorge L. ■ 00983 #308-03-1979 L1982 **ID IM** *020 †20

GIUSTI RODRIGUEZ, Alba. A36 CALLE 4, EST DE SAN FERNANDO 00985 #042-01-1984 L1987 **IM** *020

GODREAU, Ayleen I. PO BOX 4492 00984 #042-01-1990 L1993 **PD** *020 †55

GONZALEZ, Carlos Ruben. 104 BB-25 00986 #649-14-1996 L1997 *020

GONZALEZ, Francisco. BJ6 CALLE YAGRUMO, VALLE ARRIBA HTS 00983 #308-03-1982 L1990 **PD** *020

GONZALEZ, Juan A. 44 CALLE PLANTIO, PASEO DEL PRADO 00987 #042-01-1986 L1989 **EM** *030 †16

GONZALEZ, Sheila Ivette. PO BOX 6022 PMB 385 00988 #042-01-1996 L2000 **PCC** *100 †20

GONZALEZ-MARTINEZ, Isaac. 3-1 CALLE 4, URB EDUARDO J SALDANA 00983 #308-01-1984 L1993 *020

GONZALEZ-SOLA, Ariel. 2 RR 471 VIA I VILLA FONTA 00983 #847-04-1964 L1966 **PD** *020

GUERRA, Hector Juan. ■ 00983 #308-13-2004 **IM** *012

GUERRERO, Ricardo Alexis. ■ 00983 #042-01-2003 L2005 **GS** *100

GUERRERO JIMENEZ, Manuel. ■ 00985 #308-03-1987 L1993 *100

GUZMAN, Francisco S. D19 AVE ROBERTO CLEMENTE, VILLA CAROLINA 00985 #042-01-1993 L1998 **P CHP** *020

GUZMAN DE LEON, Rafael A.. ■ 00983 #308-03-1985 L2004 *100

GUZMAN-ORTEGA, Alpha M. VALLE ARRIBA, AVE MONSERRATE BA-24 00984 #847-10-1961 L1964 **R** *071

HERNANDEZ, Miguel H. G10 CALLE POMARROSA, VALLE ARRIBA HTS 00983 #308-01-1982 L1988 **GP** *020 †18

HEUGHES PASCUAL, Clery. #758 AVE CAMPO RICO COUNTR 00983 #308-01-1987 L2003 *100

HORTA VELAZQUEZ, Adline M. ■ 00983 #042-04-2003 L2004 *100

IRIZARRY, Diana. 1508 CALLE MARBELLA, MANS DE VISTAMAR MARINA 00983 #649-14-2001 L2002 **FM** *020

JIMENEZ, Luis Emilio. ■ 00988 #308-01-1982 L1993 **IM** *020

JORGE, Wanda A. ■ 00983 #308-03-1989 L1989 *020

LANDESTOY, Luis E. VIA EMILIE AL 5 00983 #308-03-1981 L1985 **FM** *020

LASTRA, Maria Isabel. 355 PONTEZUELA AVE, URB VISTAMAR 00983 #042-04-1984 L1987 **OM GP** *030

LASTRA MORALES, Rafael. PO BOX 523 00986 #847-10-1960 L1963 **OS** *071

LEON PEDROZA, Hector R. B3 CALLE FERNANDEZ JUNCS N, URB ROSA MARIA 00985 #042-01-1972 L1975 **OPH** *020

LINDERMAN-BARRIENTOS, J. WRI VIA DONNATELLA VIL FON 00983 #847-10-1964 L1970 **GP** *020

LLANOS, Ninci Limari. ■ 00985 #042-01-2003 L2006 **EM** *100

LOPEZ, Dorian Mirella. PO BOX 79662 00984 #042-01-2002 L2003 **APM** *100

LOPEZ-ALVAREZ, Maria J. ■ 00985 #042-03-1993 L1997 **IM** *020

LOPEZ BURREZO, Jose J. 335 CALLE WEST ROSE, CIUDAD JARDIN 00987 #847-21-1984 L1996 **PD** *020

LOPEZ LOPEZ, Michelle. ■ 00985 #042-04-2003 L2004 *100

LOPEZ-NIEVES, Zoilo. CASTELLAUA GARDENS, AVE. GALICIA LL-11#1, 00984 #308-01-1978 L1980 **FM** *075

LOZADA, Jose E. 3K VILLA FONTANA COM # 59, VIA MIRTA 00983 #042-01-1976 L1980 **GYN OBG** *020

MACK, Josefa Rodriguez. A6 CALLE ATUN, URB BAHIA VISTAMAR 00983 #847-04-1973 L1978 *020

MALDONADO, Marcelino E. PO BOX 9177, SUITE 3 ALTOS PLAZOLETA 00988 #308-03-1977 L1979 **GP** *020

MALDONADO, Ramon Q. PO BOX 3689 00984 #035-19-1928 L1934 **OS** *075

MARRERO, Miguel Angel, Jr. 4-5 CALLE 9, SABANA GARDENS 00983 #042-02-1999 L2002 **PD** *100

MARTINEZ, Eduardo Antonio. ■ 00983 #042-01-2004 **PM** *012

MARTINEZ, Felix David. C-502 BLG 218-18 U CAROLIN 00985 #649-14-1999 L2001 *020

MARTINEZ, Miriam. ■ 00987 #042-02-1997 L2000 **PCC** *100 †20

MARTINEZ, Ricardo J. C15 AVE ROBERTO CLEMENTE, VILLA CAROLINA 00985 #042-01-1983 L1983 **EM IM** *020

MARTINEZ, Silma Luz. ■ 00987 #042-03-2001 L2004 **PD** *100

MARTINEZ-ESPADA, Armando. ■ 00984 #649-14-1974 L1978 **GP** *020

MARTINEZ ORTIZ, Manolo. PO BOX 4166 00984 #308-01-1979 L1986 *020

MARTINEZ SANTANA, Ruben D. BQ7 CALLE 109, VALLE ARRIBA HTS 00983 #308-03-1982 L1990 **GP** *020

MATOS, Felix V. ELI LILLY INDUSTRIES INC, KM 12-5 65TH INFANTRY RD 00986 #042-01-1982 L1985 **OM FM** *020 †18

MATOS, Linka. ■ 00987 #042-01-2000 L2002 **APM** *100 †05

MEDINA, Frankie Thomas. ■ 00985 #308-03-1990 L1997 *020

MEJIA-LARA, Servia L. BK12 CALLE 111 JARD D, COUNTRY CLUB 00983 #308-02-1978 L1985 **FM** *020

MEJIAS-SOTO, Ana Hilda. PO BOX 6021 00984 #042-01-1991 L1995 **OPH** *020 †35

MEJIA VALLE, Jorge. ■ 00987 #042-04-2000 L2001 *020

MELLADO LOPEZ, Carlos Raf. ■ 00983 #649-35-2000 L2002 *020

MENDEZ GARCIA, Ileana. ■ 00987 #275-01-1992 L2005 *100

MENDEZ MORALES, Alba N.. ■ 00983 #649-14-2004 L2005 *100

MENDOZA, Veronica. B34 CAL 4 EST DE SAN FERNA, FERNANDO 00985 #308-03-1987 L1994 *020

MERA, Roberto Enrique. ■ 00987 #042-01-2001 L2004 **GE** *012

MIRANDA, Gabriel J. DL13 VIA EMILIA, VILLA FONTANA 00983 #042-01-1989 L1994 **U** *020 †95

MIRANDA, Rafael. ■ 00987 #847-08-1981 L1984 **NEP** *020

MOHAMMAD, Mohammad Rashid. AA4 CALLE MORERA 00983 #308-03-1977 L1980 **PDC PD** *020

MORALES-LEBRON, Nadya M. ■ 00983 #042-01-2000 L2005 *100

MULLINS, Kathryn. E16 CALLE 7, EST DE SAN FERNANDO 00985 #308-03-1980 L1985 **GP** *020

NAVARRO, Francisco V. ■ 00983 #748-01-1943 L1959 **PUD P** *071

NEGRON-PENA, Rafael. ■ 00983 #847-19-1981 L1986 **OBG** *020

NOLASCO GARRIDO, Arturo A. BH16 CALLE 110 APT A, VALLE ARRIBA HEIGHTS 00983 #308-13-2002 L2004 *100

OLIVENCIA, Julie. TEGUCIGALPA 361, ROLLING HILLS 00987 #042-04-1987 L1988 **GP** *020

ORTIZ, Alma Beatriz. ■ 00983 #042-03-1997 L2000 **PCC** *100 †20 ‡

ORTIZ, Erwin Rafael. 24 VILLA FONTANA COM, FIDALGO DIAZ AVE CL-1 ESA 00983 #308-01-1987 L1991 **PD** *020

ORTIZ, Jose Raul. ■ 00984 #308-03-1980 L1988 **GP** *020

ORTIZ, Nerian. 1412 CALLE MARBELLA, MANS DE VISTAMAR MARINA 00983 #042-01-1998 L2000 *020 †55

OSORIO FIGUEROA, Ramon Lu. ■ 00987 #104-01-2006 **IM** *012

PABON PADILLA, Hiram. PO BOX 3185 00984 #649-14-2004 L2006 *100

PADILLA, Olga Maria. URB. ROSA MARIA 00985 #649-14-2004 *100

PAGAN CALO, Guillermo A. 4QN7 VIA JOSEFINA, VILLA FONTANA 00983 #649-14-2000 L2002 **GP** *020

PAGAN-CARDONA, Jannisse. 128 CALLE ALBORADA, PASEO DEL PRADO 00987 #042-01-1992 L1995 **PD** *020 †55,28

PAGAN REYES, Lucila. ■ 00985 #308-01-1970 L2002 *100

PALADINES, Miguel A.. PO BOX 9512, PLAZA CAROLINA STATE 00988 #319-03-1990 L2003 **FM** *100

PASTRANA, Rafael Jaime. PO BOX 79662 00984 #042-01-1999 L2001 **GE** *100 †20

PASTRANA, Ramon Antonio. ■ 00986 #649-14-1980 L1986 **IM** *020

PENA ORTIZ, Irma Iris. ■ 00984 #847-11-1972 L1974 **GP GYN** *020

PERALTA, Altagracia Iris. ■ 00983 #308-01-1983 L1987 **PD** *020

PEREZ ALVARADO, Reynaldo. CALLE MEXICO #385 00987 #042-04-2001 L2002 **U** *020

PEREZ CARRASQUILLO, Eric. ■ 00985 #042-04-1991 L1996 **IM** *020

PEREZ RODRIGUEZ, Julio. ■ 00987 #649-35-1994 L2002 **GP** *020

PEREZ ROLON, Magda D. ■ 00985 #308-03-1982 L1993 **GP** *020

PICHARDO, Jesus R. PO BOX 9699, PLZ CAROLINA STATION 00988 #308-01-1987 L1992 **PD** *020

PINEYRO, Ramon Ricardo. 9 CAROLINA HOUSING 00987 #308-01-1980 L1987 **GP** *020

PORTILLA, Oliva Myriam. 33-2 CALLE 11, VILLA CAROLINA 00985 #308-06-1982 L1993 **FM** *020 †18

PSARRAS, Peter John. ■ 00983 #035-09-1987 L1993 **GS CCS** *020

RABELO, Marielsa. 514 CALLE SEGOVIA, URB VISTAMAR 00983 #042-01-2001 L2003 **END** *100

RAMIREZ, Beatriz. ■ 00983 #308-01-1986 L1989 **CHP** *020

RAMIREZ JIMENEZ, Miguel A. B4 CALLE FERNANDEZ JUNCS N, URB ROSA MARIA 00985 #649-14-1993 L1995 **P GP** *020

RAMIREZ-MERCADO, Angel L. BH8 CALLE 110, VALLE ARRIBA HTS 00983 #042-03-1981 L1983 **IM** *020

RAMIREZ-PAGAN, Lorimar. ■ 00987 #042-01-2005 **PD** *012

REYES, Carlos Efrain. ■ 00987 #042-03-2004 **IM** *012

REYES SOLIS, Maria Elena. 60 CALLE VIOLETA, CIUDAD JARDIN 00987 #042-04-2000 L2002 FM *020

RIBOT RUIZ, Salvador. PO BOX 1800 00984 #308-03-1982 L1990 GP *020

RIOS, Javier Francisco. ■ 00987 #042-03-1999 L2003 GS *020

RIOS, Naomi. ■ 00985 #042-01-2004 PD *100

RIOS-RIVERA, Mildred. ■ 00983 #042-04-1980 L1982 OM FM *071

RIVERA, Mariel. BO7 CALLE 118, VALLE ARRIBA HTS 00983 #649-14-1995 L1997 PD *020

RIVERA FEBRES, Sara. AVEPABLO VELAZQUEZ A13 00985 #042-04-1989 L1992 *020

RIVERA-MELENDEZ, Julio C. ■ 00984 #847-02-1981 L1994 FM *020

RIVERA-PEREZ, Nestor. 4 AVE CAMPO RICO, GARDENS 00983 #308-01-1972 L1974 FM LM *020

ROBAINA-ALVAREZ, Jose M. B14 CALLE PONTEVEDRA, URB VISTAMAR MARINA 00983 #308-03-1979 L1983 EM *020

RODRIGUEZ, Lourdes T.. PO BOX 308, BLV DE LA MEDIA LUNA 00986 #308-03-1992 L2003 FM *020

RODRIGUEZ, Luis. ■ 00984 #847-02-1978 L1980 *020

RODRIGUEZ, Maria Esther. 1 AVE MONSERRATE, URV VILLA FONTANA 00985 #847-08-1974 L1977 GP *020

RODRIGUEZ, Minerva. ■ 00985 #042-04-1988 L1991 GP *074

RODRIGUEZ, Noelia. 5R8 PARQUE ASTURIAS, VILLA FONTANA PARK 00983 #042-01-2005 IM *012

RODRIGUEZ, Sylma Ivette. ■ 00984 #649-14-1999 L2003 FM *020

RODRIGUEZ, Wanda. APT 404, VISTAMAR PRINCESS 00983 #042-01-1992 L1996 DR *020 †80

RODRIGUEZ CHACON, Migdala. PO BOX 312 00986 #042-04-1999 L2001 FM *020

RODRIGUEZ CONTRERAS, M A. ■ 00983 #308-01-1959 L1975 *020

RODRIGUEZ-CRUZ, Gilda D. ■ 00984 #649-14-1982 L1982 IM *020

RODRIGUEZ DELGADO, Ileana. PO BOX 3762 00984 #042-04-1999 L2002 FM *020

RODRIGUEZ DELGADO, Ricardo. PO BOX 3762 00984 #042-04-2004 L2006 *100

RODRIGUEZ-HERNANDEZ, Ralph. ■ 00983 #042-01-2004 L2008 *100 †20

RODRIGUEZ-ROSARIO, Sandra. 72 CALLE GARDENIA, URB LOS CACIQUES 00987 #042-03-1996 L2000 AN *020 †05

RODRIGUEZ TORRES, Efrain. 5A AVE SANCHEZ OSORIO # 3, URB VALLE ARRIBA HTS 00983 #847-05-1973 L1975 *100

RODRIGUEZ VELEZ, Awilda. ■ 00987 #847-02-1985 L1989 *100

ROJAS, Yoel Antonio. ■ 00987 #042-01-2007 GS *012

ROMERO, Ariel Gustavo. L15 CALLE 42 # B48, EXT PARQ ECUESTRE 00987 #042-02-1991 L1995 IM *020

ROMERO URBINO, Sylvia R. B4 CALLE FERNANDEZ JUNCS N, URB ROSA MARIA 00985 #847-05-1978 L1981 *020

ROSARIO, Katyna. ■ 00987 #042-01-2005 P *012

ROSARIO, Norman Rambert. B4 CALLE FERNANDEZ JUNCS N, URB LOS COLOBOS 00985 #847-10-1966 L1968 P *020

ROSARIO, Rosana Teresa. F14 CALLE 8, EST DE SAN FERNANDO 00985 #042-01-1995 L1999 PD *020

ROSARIO BURGOS, Edgardo N. 10 AVE CAMPO RICO, STE 106 00983 #042-04-1984 L1992 PHP MDM *030

ROSARIO PAGAN, Gladynette. ■ 00987 #042-04-2004 L2005 *100

ROSICH, Ivan M. PO BOX 3912 00984 #308-03-1982 L1996 FM *020

ROSICH-BACHS, Walter. APT 1570 VALLE ARRIBA HGTS 00984 #847-05-1977 L1979 *020

SAID ALI, Azzam. 90 BLVD MEDIA LUNA, APARTADO 308 00987 #308-03-1992 L2003 *100

SALGADO, Jodys Lorna. ■ 00984 #042-01-1994 L1999 PM *020 †60

SANCHEZ, Alma Doris. ■ 00983 #035-41-1979 L1999 P FM *020 †18,75

SANCHEZ DUVERSE, Ana R. CALLE MUNOZ RIVERA ESQUINA, FONDO SEGURO DEL ESTADO 00985 #308-01-1983 L1986 OM CHP *075

SANCHEZ MARTINEZ, Rafael. PO BOX 3109 00984 #308-01-1950 L1966 FM *020

SANCHEZ OJEDA, Jose M. ■ 00985 #649-14-2004 L2005 *100

SANCHEZ RODRIGUEZ, Fernand. ■ 00987 #649-14-2001 L2002 IM *100

SANTANA, Maria Altagracia. 10-19 CALLE 14, URB SABANA GDNS 00983 #308-01-1969 L1988 GP *020

SANTIAGO, Miguel A. CARR #3 KM 12.3, 65TH INFANTRY AVE 00985 #042-01-1984 L1988 OPH *020 †35

SANTONI, Yonaida D. ■ 00987 #042-02-2003 EM *100

SIERRA, Vilmary. 129-20 CALLE 70, VILLA CAROLINA 00985 #649-14-2002 L2003 *100

SIERRA-MARTINEZ, Kassandra. ■ 00987 #042-01-2007 FP *012

SOTO, Aurea Nivia. D10 CALLE FLORENTINO ROMAN, VILLA DE SAN ANTON 00987 #649-01-1978 L1991 PD *020

SUAREZ-PARES, Yolanda. ■ 00988 #847-04-1969 L1972 PD *072

TARTAK-SALICRUP, Bernadett. ■ 00983 #305-01-1981 L2004 GP *020

TORREALBA, Ruben. ■ 00983 #042-01-2007 ORS *012

TORRES, Hector Rafael. CALLE 13 BLOQ 34 16 VILLA 00985 #042-03-1991 AN *100

TORRES, Victor Rafael. 6 CALLE DE DIEGO N, JARD DE BUENA VISTA 00985 #042-01-1977 L1980 PD PN *020 †55

TORRES-REYES, Emilio. C6 AVE ROBERTO CLEMENTE, VILLA CAROLINA 00985 #042-01-1960 L1964 R RNR *020 †80

TORRES-VELEZ, Rafael. X1152 AVE PONTEZUELA, URB VISTAMAR 00983 #308-03-1976 L1979 OBG *020

TUDELA, Maria I. ■ 00985 #042-04-1988 L1990 GP *071

UNGER, Nestor Miguel. 768 CALLE CASTELLON, URB VISTAMAR 00983 #132-01-1979 L2002 NEP *020

VARGAS FERNANDEZ, Juan E. EDIF. E APT.1203, COND.VILLAS DE PARQUE ESCO 00987 #308-01-1983 L1997 *020

VARGAS-MORALES, Abelardo. PO BOX 818 00986 #649-14-1977 L1979 GP *020

VARGAS-RIVERA, Abelardo. PO BOX 59 00986 #649-01-1951 L1954 FM OM *020

VASQUEZ SALAZAR, Lisette. 226 CALLE MURCIA, URB VISTAMAR 00983 #308-13-2003 L2005 *100

VAZQUEZ PEREZ, Gilberto. ■ 00985 #308-03-1981 L1994 *020

VAZQUEZ-VALLE, Janessa. ■ 00985 #042-01-2002 L2005 PD *020

VEGA, Rolando Eriel. ■ 00988 #042-12-1992 L1996 OBG *020 †30

VELAZQUEZ CALDERON, Guille. PO BOX 96641 00989 #308-01-1970 L2003 FM *020

VELAZQUEZ-NAVARRO, Sonia. A-312 CATALUNA ST VISTAMAR 00983 #042-04-1989 L1991 IM *020

VELEZ, Eneida Torres. ■ 00983 #308-01-1982 L1985 OM GP *020

VELEZ, Ivonne. ■ 00985 #042-01-2006 *012

VIANA, Maria Engracia. 10 CALLE IGNACIO ARZUAGA W, C/O P.O. BOX 112 CAROLINA 00985 #649-33-1983 L1986 GP *020

VILLALOBOS, Alexis. 1503 CALLE MARBELLA, MANS DE VISTAMAR MARINA 00983 #042-01-1992 L1995 DR *020 †55

VIRELLA, Vivian Eunice. CALLE D BLOQUE #15, APT C 00987 #308-05-1988 L2004 *100

VIZCARRONDO, Ramon. 5 CALLE IGNACIO ARZUAGA E 00985 #649-14-1977 L1979 GP *020

VIZCARRONDO ACOSTA, Noemi. ■ 00983 #847-08-1975 L1978 GP *020

YEJO, Carmen Ana. CALLE 111 BT6-ARRIBA HGTHS 00983 #042-04-1983 L1991 OM GP *020

CAROLINA – SAN JUAN

ACEVEDO-MONTALVO, Angel C. COND CORAL BEACH I, APT 916 00979 #649-01-1955 L1956 GP OBG *075

AGUAYO, Sandra I. 4429 COND PARK PLZ # 1203 00979 #042-04-1988 L1990 PM *020

ALCANTARA, Cesar Danilo. GO35 AVE CAMPO RICO, URB COUNTRY CLUB 00982 #308-06-1991 L1991 GP *020

ALEMAN, Janice Marie. QG11 CALLE 525, URB COUNTRY CLUB 00982 #042-03-1999 L2001 *020

ALGARIN, Elba Hilda. ■ 00982 #847-10-1972 L1974 GP *020

ALVAREZ SANTANA, Hector. ■ 00982 #308-01-1983 L1992 *020

AMADOR, Mirtha D. 21 CALLE MAR DE CHINA, URB VILLAMAR 00979 #035-08-1964 L1967 PD PHP *020

APONTE, Orlando. 221 CALLE GRUS, PARQ DE ISLA VERDE 00979 #042-01-2000 L2004 AN *100 †05 ‡

ARROYO ORTIZ, Eduardo E. 4TA EXT COUNTRY CLUB, 502 OB 8 00982 #042-01-1994 DR *020

AVELLANET, Yaniris Rebecc. ■ 00979 #042-03-2002 OBG *012

AYALA, Rosana. 227B JWB6 QUINTA EXTENSION, COUNTRY CLUB 00982 #308-13-2000 L2005 *100

BARRIENTOS CABEZAS, C. ■ 00979 #847-03-1971 L1975 P *062

BERNAL RAMIREZ, Luis A. APTO 1106 COND LAS GAVIOTA 00979 #042-04-1991 L1994 IM *020

BERTRAN, Nitza. 704 COND TIFFANY, AVE. ISLA VERDE 00979 #042-03-1988 L1993 PD *020

BRITO-BEATO, Neftali R. ■ 00979 #308-01-1979 L1982 CHP *062

BRITO PEGUERO, Yudit Mayt. GARDENIA F #3, LA MARINA 00979 #308-11-1995 L2004 *100

BRUGAL, Yocasta. LAGUNA GARDENS SHOPP CTR, STE 14J 00979 #847-01-1971 L1976 FOP *020 †50

BUONOMO, Blanca E. ■ 00982 #042-04-1990 L1999 IM *020

CABEZAS-MIJUSTE, Maritza. ■ 00979 #308-01-1983 L1985 IM *020

CABRAL JIMENEZ, Denys I.. ■ 00979 #308-01-1990 L2004 *100

CALDERON, Cindy. ■ 00979 #042-01-1984 L1987 NM *020 †28,55

CAMUNAS, Jose F. 1025 CALLE MARGINAL VILLMR, EXT VILLAMAR 00979 #042-01-1987 L1988 FM *020 †18

CANALES, Idaliz. ■ 00979 #042-01-2004 L2008 EM *100

CARDONA, Iris R. AVE CAMPO RICO G0-7, CENTRO PEDIATRICO CTY CLUB 00982 #042-01-1987 L1990 PD PDI *020 †55

CARDONA SOTOMAYOR, A. ■ 00979 #847-04-1969 L1989 AN *020

CASIANO PARRILLA, Luis Ja. ■ 00982 #042-03-2005 *100

CASTILLO VILLAVICENCIO, Fr. PO BOX 810233 00981 #308-01-1985 L2002 *100

CHAFEY, Marisa Castro. 55 CALLE 2 URB VILLAMAR 00979 #035-09-1949 L1954 PD *071

CLAUDIO, Reinaldo. 7 COND ST TROPEZ STE 0, AVE ISLA VERDE 00979 #308-03-1985 L1994 *020

COLON, David W. 2 K OESTE COND LOS PINOS, ISLA VERDE 00979 #042-04-1995 L1997 *020

COLON RIVERA, Malieri. ■ 00982 #649-14-2003 L2005 *100

CORCHADO, Samuel. ■ 00979 #042-01-1957 L1959 PD *071

CORDERO, Efrain. ■ 00979 #042-01-1984 L1997 IM *020 †20

CRUZ, Maria Teresa. 10 AVE LAGUNA STE 207 00979 #042-01-1998 L2000 IM *020 †20

CRUZ, Ramon. PQ28 AVE EL COMANDANTE, URB COUNTRY CLUB 00982 #042-01-1973 L1976 PD *020

CRUZ-LANDRON, Alberto. 207 LAGN GRDNS SHP #207 00979 #042-01-1961 L1965 IM *020

CUADRADO, Marianela. ■ 00982 #042-01-1999 L2002 PM *020 †60

DE ANDINO, Richard M. 6 CALLE MAR CARIBE, EXT VILLAMAR 00979 #041-02-1976 L1980 FM FPG *040 †18

DE DIEGO-PERAL, Gregorio. ■ 00979 #042-04-1981 L1985 IM *020

DEFENDINI, Efrain Antonio. ■ 00979 #023-01-1954 L1957 TS GS *020 †85,90

DE JESUS-VARONA, Marian. 1025 CALLE MARGINAL VILLMR, EXT VILLAMAR 00979 #042-01-1979 L1982 FM *020 †18

DE LEON, Jose Noel. COND CASTILLO DELMAR, STE 1427 00979 #847-04-1960 L1963 OPH *071

DELGADO, Francisco J.. 2 CAROLINA CT, CALLE 19 BLOQ 19 #25 00982 #649-30-2002 L2004 *100

DEL VALLE, Francisco. ■ 00979 #847-04-1968 L1970 GP *020

DEL VALLE ORTIZ, Efrain E. GL14 AVE CAMPO RICO, COUNTRY CLUB 00982 #308-02-1985 L1988 P ADP *020

ESCALERA NAVARRO, Alfredo. 11 CALLE MAR DEL CORAL, URB VILLAMAR 00979 #042-04-1990 L1991 IM *020

FELICIANO, Edgardo. ■ 00979 #649-14-1991 L1996 PD *020

FERNANDEZ FERNANDEZ, Jose. WEST LOS PINOS COND, ROAD 187 APT 6 B 00979 #275-01-1954 L1973 CD IM *071

FLAZ, Marita De Jesus. 81 CALLE PISCIS, URB LOS ANGELES 00979 #042-01-1995 L1999 FM *020

FONT-LOPEZ, Aracelis. ■ 00979 #042-03-1980 L1982 GP *020

FORCHUE, Abraham Lincoln. CAL CARMEN HERNANDEZ 883, URB EL COMANDANTE 00982 #308-01-1955 L1976 GP *020

FORTUNA-EVANGELISTA, A. ■ 00979 #308-01-1968 L1974 R *071

GARCIA, Esther Manas. ■ 00982 #396-06-1961 L1965 NM DR *071 †80,28

GARCIA, Manuel Velez. PQ28 AVE EL COMANDANTE, URB COUNTRY CLUB 00982 #308-01-1981 L1984 PD GP *020

GARCIA, Maria L. ■ 00979 #042-04-1996 L1997 *020

GARCIA OCAMPO, Esther Elo. ■ 00982 #649-14-1979 L1994 *100

GENTINI, Raul Alberto. ■ 00982 #132-02-1995 L2008 FP *012

GOMEZ-ALBA, Jose Rafael. 236 AVE SAN MARCOS, URB EL COMANDANTE 00982 #308-01-1976 L1982 P FM *020

GUINDIN-CUEVAS, Rafael F. 9550 CALLE DIAZ WAY, APT 1019 00979 #308-03-1983 L1990 P OM *020

HERNANDEZ ALONSO, Victor. 5900 AVE ISLA VERDE, PMB 394 00979 #042-04-1991 L1993 GP *020

HERNANDEZ-BARTOLOMEI, R. 203 CALLE FIRMAMENTO 00979 #847-10-1964 L1969 GP *020

HERNANDEZ-PLANAS, Jose. GO35 AVE CAMPO RICO, URB COUNTRY CLUB 00982 #308-03-1973 L1979 *020

HERRERA, Humberto. GP8 AVE CAMPO RICO, URB COUNTRY CLUB 00982 #308-04-1984 L1991 **GP** *020

JIMENEZ, Edgardo Mendez. ■ 00979 #308-01-1981 L1989 **GP** *020

JIMENEZ, Juan F. 53 EAST ST, PALMAR SURG 00979 #051-04-1952 L1954 **PD** *020 †55

JIMENEZ-MESSON, Cesar A. ■ 00979 #308-01-1960 L1968 **AN** *071 †05

JORDAN, Ligia Noemi. 209 CALLE FIRMAMENTO, PARQ DE ISLA VERDE 00979 #847-08-1978 L1990 **GP** *020

LARREGOITY-SANCHEZ, O. 404 AVE SAN MARCOS, URB EL COMANDANTE 00982 #847-05-1977 L1983 **NEP IM** *020

LEDESMA, Gilberto Fragoso. ■ 00979 #847-04-1960 L1963 **IM** *020

LEONARDO, Myriam R. ■ 00981 #016-11-1960 L1963 **EM OBG** *071 †30

MALAGA, Bernardo Francisc. 5859 AVE ISLA VERDE, CORAL BEACH 1101 - II 00979 #649-14-2001 L2003 *020

MALDONADO, Jeannette C. ■ 00979 #042-01-1983 L1985 **AN** *020

MARTINEZ, Ada S. 101 COND MUNDO FELIZ 00979 #308-03-1977 L1980 **GPM FM** *030

MARTINEZ-CAYERE, Rafael. GO5 AVE CAMPO RICO 00982 #042-01-1965 L1969 **N PM** *020

MELENDEZ SANTANA, Vilma. A11 CALLE 1, QTAS DE COUNTRY CLUB 00982 #308-01-1985 L1993 **OM** *020

MERCADO, Josue R. 802 COND PLAZA DEL MAR 00979 #042-03-1982 L1987 **CD** *020 †20

MUNIZ GUTIERREZ, Alba. COND PARK PLZ # 402 00979 #275-01-1952 L1967 **PUD GP** *020

MUNIZ QUIROS, Rosilvia. ■ 00979 #042-04-1997 L1999 **FM** *020

MUNS-GARCIA, Maria Adela. ■ 00979 #042-01-1984 L1989 **DR** *020 †80

NAVEDO ORTIZ, Luis A.. LAGUNA GARDENS I, APT 3-J 00979 #649-14-2004 L2006 *100

NEGRON, Juanita. APT E-22, MONTERREY ESTATES 00979 #042-01-1994 L1997 **PD** *020 †55

NOLASCO-POLANCO, Angel T. VALLE ARRIBA HEIGHTS, AVE MONSERRATE BH-16 00930 #308-01-1966 L1972 **OBG** *020

NUNEZ NIEVES, Juan Rafael. ■ 00979 #042-04-1991 L1993 **CHP** *020

OLIVER, Lynnette Ileana. ■ 00979 #025-12-1978 L1982 **IM** *020 †20

OPPENHEIMER, Jorge J. 2014 CALLE CELESTIAL, URB LOS ANGELES 00979 #308-10-1991 L1997 **OS** *020 ‡

ORTIZ RIVERA, Luis J. AVE COMANDNTE HR 27 CT CLB 00982 #847-01-1962 L1965 **GP** *030

PACHECO, Margarita M. 10 CALLE AMAPOLA, COND. RICOMARAPT #505 00979 #042-04-1996 L1997 **PD** *020

PACHECO ESCOBAR, Sixto A. ■ 00982 #847-06-1992 L1995 **GP** *020

PARES SANTIAGO, Pedro M. 60 CALLE VENUS, URB ATLANTIC VIEW 00979 #308-01-1983 L1992 *020

PAULINO PAYANO, Mario E. 124 CALLE FIRMAMENTO, PARQ DE ISLA VERDE 00979 #308-03-1986 L1995 **PD** *020

PENA, Jose Antonio. ■ 00979 #847-04-1963 L1966 **OBG** *071 †30

PENA ALEMAN, Luz D. ■ 00979 #308-06-1986 L2004 *100

PEREZ MORENO, Gilda. 74 CALLE VENUS FL 2, URB ATLANTIC VIEW 00979 #275-01-1976 L2004 *100

PINEDA ROMERO, Marilyn A. 00982 #308-01-1988 L2006 *100

RAMIREZ, Adriana Milcia. ■ 00979 #308-13-1997 L2002 **FM** *020

RAMOS, Maria Margarita. ■ 00979 #042-01-2005 L2006 **AN** *012

RAMOS GARCIA, Alberto. CONDOMINIO PLAYA DORADA B3 00979 #308-06-1988 L1992 *020

RIVAS, Steven. ■ 00982 #042-01-1992 L2000 **CD** *020

RIVERA, Gustavo. 211 LAGUNA GARDENS SHP CTR, STE 211 00979 #042-03-1992 L2001 **P** *020 †75

RIVERA PEREZ, Maria Nilda. T-2 CORAL BEACH 1207 00979 #308-03-1978 L1986 **GP** *020

RIVIERE, Jean. 5757 AVE ISLA VERDE, COND. OCEAN TOWER 00979 #042-03-1998 L2003 **GS** *100

ROBLES IRIZARRY, Jorge R. 3001 CONDO PLZ #2304, AVE ABE ISLA VERDE 00979 #308-04-1989 L1991 **P** *020

RODRIGUEZ, Elmo. 166 CALLE NIZA, URB EL COMANDANTE 00982 #649-14-1983 L1986 **GP** *020

RODRIGUEZ, Jose Antonio. 237 AVE SAN MARCOS, URB EL COMANDANTE 00982 #308-03-1975 L1978 **GP** *020

RODRIGUEZ, Nicole Mariel. ■ 00979 #042-01-2006 **GS** *012

RODRIGUEZ, Virginia Ana. 25 CALLE C, URB LOS ANGELES 00979 #042-01-1978 L1991 **OPH** *020 †35

RODRIGUEZ-VELEZ, Ruth E. 2007 C BUZELLO COUNTRY CLB 00982 #847-08-1976 L1979 *020

ROIG, Edwin. ■ 00979 #042-01-1970 L1975 **IM** *020 †20

RORIGUEZ RODRIGUEZ, Miguel. ■ 00979 #308-01-1990 L2004 *100

RUIZ, Lydia Irma. ■ 00979 #308-01-1985 L1989 *020

SALEM, Joseph Challita. 200A LAGUNA GARDNS SHP CTR, STE 200A 00979 #847-08-1980 L1991 **PD GP** *020

SANTA, Ulpiano. URB COUNTRY CLUB, PQ 28 AVE COMANDANTE 00982 #042-01-1962 L1964 **OS PD** *030

SANTANA SABINO, Andrea. 321 CALLE GRUS, PARQ DE ISLA VERDE 00979 #308-01-1993 L1997 *020

SANTIAGO, Jorge Luis. STREET B #C24, URB LOS ANGELES 00979 #042-03-1995 L1997 **P** *020

SEGARRA-REYES, Enrique. 134 CAPE SABLE, URB CAPE SEA VILLAGE 00979 #847-06-1977 L1979 **EM** *020

SKEET-WILLIAMS, Claudia. G18 CALLE 5, ALT DE VILLA FONTANA 00982 #308-01-1967 L2005 *100

SOSA DE JESUS, Gloria M. LOS ANGELES, B-36 00979 #042-03-1980 L1991 *020

STELLA CINTRON, Roque C. MARBELLA DEL CARIBE, APARTAMENTO 704 OESTE 00979 #847-10-1969 L1975 **P** *020

SUAREZ-COCA, Coral. ■ 00982 #847-01-1972 L1975 **EM** *020

TARTAK, Carlos. CALLE JOSE TARTAK NO 5 00917 #847-04-1958 L1963 **OPH OS** *020

TORRES TORRES, Jose A. COND PARK PLZ # 74 00979 #649-39-1982 L1986 **IM** *020

TORRES VENTURA, Dinorah. ■ 00979 #308-01-1970 L1974 **ATP** *020

TOUS, Amalia Maria. 649 BO CACAO 00979 #042-01-1986 L1990 **OBG** *020

VARGAS, Lymari. ■ 00979 #042-01-2001 L2004 **AN** *100 †05

VAZQUEZ, Jose Victor Luis. ■ 00979 #042-03-1983 L1987 **GP** *020

VILA, Juan C. 3018 AVE ISLA VERDE 00979 #042-01-1991 L2001 **CD** *020 †20

VILCHEZ, Simeon Hermogene. PMB 328 ISLAVERDE AVE L2 00979 #649-03-1988 L2005 *100

VILLAMIL, Mayra A. OA9 CALLE 500, URB COUNTRY CLUB 00982 #042-01-1990 L1993 **PD** *020 †55

CASTANER — LARES

FLECHA, Miguel. K M 64-2 RT 135 00631 #042-01-1981 L1984 **FM** *020

JUSTINIANO, Lizbette. PO BOX 436 00631 #649-14-2003 L2005 *100

KIDWELL, John Aaron. ■ 00631 #042-01-1957 L1958 **EM FM** *071 †18

MEDINA RIOS, Jennymar. ■ 00631 #649-14-2000 L2003 **GP** *020

PAGAN, Damacio. PO BOX 459 00631 #649-14-2002 L2004 **GP** *020

RIVERA, Hector Luis. K M 64-2 RT 135 00631 #042-03-1985 L1993 **FM** *020

RIVERA TOLEDO, Jose Raul. ■ 00631 #042-02-1994 L1997 **FM** *020

RODRIGUEZ, Jose O. K M 64-2 RT 135 00631 #042-01-1987 L1990 **FM** *020 †18

ROMAN RODRIGUEZ, Ellis A. PO BOX 383 00631 #042-04-1998 L2001 **FM** *020

SANTIAGO, Nydia. KM 64-2, ROUTE 135 00631 #042-03-1984 L1987 **PD** *020 †55

VEGA SOTO, Jose Rafael. ■ 00631 #042-01-1954 L1958 **OM IM** *071

ZAYAS, Eileen. PO BOX 101 00631 #649-14-2002 **FM** *020 †18

CATANO — CATANO

ARROYO-GARCIA, Rosa. 77 CALLE LAS FLORES 00962 #308-03-1977 L1980 **GP** *020

CARRASCAL, Maria Eloisa. 38 CALLE BAHIA S, URB BAHIA 00962 #042-03-1990 L1995 **PD** *020

CARRON-CARBONELL, Claudio. PASEO CYPRES 3073 LEVIT 00962 #308-01-1959 L1969 **GP** *020

CASTRO CASTRO, Carlos M. BARBARA ST NO 36 00962 #649-01-1959 L1966 **OS GP** *074

DAVILA, Yelitza M. 48 CALLE LAS FLORES 00962 #649-14-1991 L1997 **PD** *020

DELGADO-CORTES, Roberto. ■ 00962 #847-05-1980 L1983 **GP** *020

DEL VALLE, Antonio Efrain. 68 CALLE OCEAN DR, URB BAY VIEW 00962 #308-03-1983 L1989 **GP ESM** *020

ESTRADA, Francisco M. PO BOX 362, 131 BARBOSA 00963 #649-14-1983 L1990 **GP** *020

FERNANDEZ, Yanira I. 2 CALLE SANTA ROSA STE A, SECT LA PUNTILLA 00962 #042-01-1992 L1995 **FM** *020 †18

LAUREANO GARCIA, Noemi. RD13 PLAZA DIEZ, URB MARINA BAHIA 00962 #308-03-1983 L1993 **GP** *020

MERLOS-CHICHARRO, Pascual. AVE LA MARINA MF4 MARINA 00962 #308-01-1986 L1987 *020

MIRANDA-APONTE, Edwin. ME7 AVE LA MARINA, URB MARINA BAHIA 00962 #847-08-1981 L1983 **EM** *030

MONTILLA-CRESPO, Jose A. 31 CALLEJON PAZ, BO JUANA MATOS 00962 #847-02-1983 L1986 *020

MORENO-NUNEZ, Luis E. 62 CALLE LAS FLORES 00962 #649-14-1991 L1996 **GPM** *020

MUNOZ-DONES, Eloisa. ■ 00962 #021-01-1948 L1950 **NPM PD** *071 †55

PEREZ, Juan J. ■ 00962 #308-03-1981 L1996 *020

RIVERA, Hector J. MARINA BAHIA, AVE BAHIA R B38 00962 #042-03-1990 L1995 **AN** *020

RIVERA VELAZQUEZ, Itza Ma. ■ 00962 #042-01-2004 **PM** *012

RODRIGUEZ-TRINIDAD, Angel. ■ 00962 #847-04-1976 L1984 *020

TORRES-FERNANDEZ, Placido. 160 AVE BARBOSA 00962 #649-01-1952 L1989 **FM** *075 †18

TORRES MUNOZ, Dinorah. PO BOX 1058 00963 #649-42-1983 L1988 **FM** *020

VELASCO, William. 116 CALLE 14, PROYECTO 141 00962 #042-01-1995 L1998 **EM** *020

VELAZQUEZ, Lorraine Y. ■ 00962 #308-03-1985 L1995 **GP** *020

CAYEY — CAYEY

ACEVEDO, Frank R. 159 AVE MUNOZ RIVERA N, BOX 697 00736 #042-01-1984 L1988 **OPH** *020

ACEVEDO, Jorge Amilcar. 4 CALLE H MENDOZA E 00736 #042-03-1998 L2002 **AN** *020

ADORNO AROOYO, Wilfredo. PO BOX 373453, 1 CARR KM 52.6 00737 #308-03-1985 L1997 *020

AGUIRRE VAZQUEZ, Judith. PO BOX 143 00737 #308-03-1984 L1991 *020

ALVAREZ GUTIERREZ, Jose O. 174 CALLE LUIS BARRERAS S 00736 #308-04-1993 L1995 **GP** *020

ANGEL, Carlos Hernando. 4 CALLE H MENDOZA E 00736 #264-20-1992 L2001 **IM** *020 †20

BURGOS-COTTO, Javier R. CALLE IGUALDAD SOLER #18, LAS MERCEDES 00736 #042-01-1998 L2002 **OBG** *020

BUSSI-GERMOSEN, Pedro R. PO BOX 2311 00737 #308-01-1967 L1980 **GP** *020

CANDELARIO, Rosalie. HC 44 BOX 13719 00736 #649-14-1999 L2001 *020

CARRO-ORTIZ DE CORREA, A. ■ 00737 #041-07-1955 L1957 **GP PHP** *020

CINTRON, Jose Adalberto. 55 CALLE MANUEL CORCHADO 00736 #308-03-1979 L1996 **FM** *020

COCA, Rosa A. 57 CALLE LUCIA VAZQUEZ S 00736 #042-03-1986 L1990 **IM** *020

COLLAZO-NUNEZ, William. ■ 00736 #042-03-1981 L1986 **PD** *020 †55

COLON, Gloria Maria. E52 CALLE A, REPTO MONTELLANO 00736 #042-02-1993 L1996 **CD** *020

COLON, Jose. 12 CALLE HERACIO MENDOZA E 00736 #042-02-1982 L1984 **PM** *020 †60

COLON-FERREIRA, Luis R. 151 AVE LUIS MUNOZ RIVER S 00736 #042-01-1984 L1987 **RHU IM** *040

CORDERO ORSINI, Morgan. E53 CALLE A, REPTO MONTELLANO 00736 #308-03-1981 L1993 *020

CORREA, Andre Erich. ■ 00736 #847-23-1975 L1997 *074

CORREA, Jose Julio. 55 CALLE BARBOSA S 00736 #042-01-1985 L1988 **FM FSM** *020 †18

CORREA-AYALA, Roberto F. 55 CALLE BARBOSA S 00736 #042-01-1955 L1957 **FM** *071 †18

DE JESUS-PEREZ, Luis G. PO BOX 371328 00737 #042-01-1961 L1964 **IM** *071

DELGADO-RODRIGUEZ, Juan A. 53 CALLE HERACIO MENDOZA W, CENTRO PEDIATRICO E CAYAY 00736 #042-01-1979 L1982 **PD ADL** *020

DUCOUDRAY, Federico R. PO BOX 2000 00737 #847-05-1977 L1980 *071

FEBO, Edgardo L. G11 CALLE RUB URB LA PLATA 00736 #308-03-1981 L1987 **GP** *020

FELICIANO, Caleb Enrique. PO BOX 372230 00737 #042-01-2001 L2002 **NS** *012

FELICIANO, Ferdinand. PO BOX A 00737 #308-03-1984 L1989 **GP** *020

FERNANDEZ, Rafael Cesar. 256 AVE JOSE DE DIEGO W 00736 #308-01-1959 L1973 **PD** *020

FERNANDEZ FIGUERAO, M. 67 AVE BALDORIOTY W 00736 #847-05-1975 L1977 **GP** *020

FERNANDEZ-VAZQUEZ, Luis C. 4 CALLE H MENDOZA E 00736 #847-10-1974 L1976 **PD** *020

FLORES TORRENT, Antonio. 4 AVE MUNOZ RIVERA S # 52 00736 #042-03-1981 L1985 *020

GABALDON SOTO, Abner J. PO BOX 6400 PMB 169 00737 #649-34-2005 **GP** *020

GONZALEZ, Marie Desiree. ■ 00736 #042-02-1995 L1998 **FM** *020

GONZALEZ, William R. PO BOX 1570 00737 #847-02-1978 L1980 **PD** *020

GONZALEZ BAUZA, Jose A. 4 CALLE H MENDOZA E 00736 #847-10-1960 L1966 **GP** *020

GONZALEZ-ORTIZ, Elena. CIDRA, CALLE PADILLA EL CARIBE #2 00737 #847-02-1980 L1983 *020

GRANADOS, Pedro Antonio. ■ 00736 #264-11-1986 L2001 **IM** *020

GUTIERREZ-RIVERA, Sylvia. ■ 00736 #042-02-2000 L2001 **PTH** *100 †50

JIMENEZ, Ricardo E. 114 AVE MUNOZ RIVERA S 00736 #308-01-1973 L1990 IM *020

LISBOA, Sandra Noelia. 205 AVE ANTONIO R BARCELO, BO ASOMANTE SEC SABANA 00736 #649-14-1976 L1986 GP *020

LOPEZ, Mayra L. 55 CALLE BARBOSA S, CENTRO MEDICINA DE FAMILIA 00736 #042-03-1989 L1991 FM *020 †18

LUCCA, Aileen D. PO BOX 373070 00737 #042-01-1984 L1987 PD *020

MARINEZ RAMOS, Maria. PO BOX 371696 00737 #042-01-1986 L1988 PD *020

MARTINEZ, Esteban. PO BOX 6400, PMB 380 00737 #042-03-1988 L1991 GS *020

MENDEZ, Freddy Rafael. PO BOX 372876, EDIY PROFESSIONAL DOMINGO 00737 #042-01-1996 L1999 U *020

MENDEZ BENABE, Ruben. PO BOX 6400 00737 #847-02-1982 L1989 *020

MENDEZ SANTIAGO, Jorge L. BOX F 00737 #847-05-1977 L1980 GP *020

MENDOZA-ORTIZ, Juan A. 4 CALLE H MENDOZA E 00736 #042-03-1983 L1986 IM *020

MENDOZA ROSA, Felix. ST. HERACLIO MENDOZA 22 00737 #042-01-1984 L1988 U *020 †95

MORALES, Jose R. PO BOX 43 00737 #042-01-1982 L1985 OBG *020 †30

MUNIZ, Jose Radames. 10 AVE MIGUEL MELENDEZ MNZ 00736 #042-02-1982 L1984 FM FPG *020 †18

MUNIZ, Radames. PO BOX 2315 00737 #065-09-1952 L1953 GP IM *071

NOGUERAS-FUENTES, Carlos. 392 AVE JOSE DE DIEGO W 00736 #847-02-1976 L1978 GP *020

OLIVER PICHARDO, Jaime J. ■ 00736 #847-05-1973 L1976 OM *020

ORTEGA MORETT, Miguel A. PO BOX 1270 00737 #847-10-1966 L1969 PD *020

ORTIZ-PAGAN, Marta R. 4 CALLE H MENDOZA E 00736 #042-03-1981 L1986 IM *020

ORTIZ RAMON, Orlando. ■ 00737 #847-10-1963 L1966 GP *020

OTERO, Arnaldo Jose. 110 CALLE NUNEZ ROMEU E 00736 #649-14-1987 L1989 FM *020

OVALLES, Eurgilia Oneida. PO BOX B 00737 #308-01-1978 L1985 *020

PADILLA VELEZ, Saul. PO BOX 966 00737 #847-04-1958 L1961 GP *020

PEREZ-MARTINEZ, Floren E. 4 CALLE H MENDOZA E 00736 #042-03-1980 L1984 OBG *020

PLAZA, Manuel. PO BOX 373413, URB. CAMPO PRIMAVERA ST. 2 00737 #649-14-1990 L1994 IM *020

POLA-RODRIGUEZ, Harold. 4 CALLE H MENDOZA E 00736 #308-03-1983 L1987 PUD CCM *020

QUILES, Carlos Antonio. PO BOX 6400 PMB 1244 00737 #649-14-2001 L2002 *020

RABELO, Jose A. 4 CALLE H MENDOZA E 00736 #042-01-1984 L1992 D *020 †55,15

RAMIREZ ARIZA, Manuel J. 9 AVE MIGUEL MELENDEZ MUNZ, URB APONTE 00736 #042-01-1975 L1980 GYN *020 †30

RAMIREZ-ARIZA, Victor M. ■ 00737 #847-02-1974 L1980 PD *071

RAMOS, Luis Benigno. 4 CALLE H MENDOZA E 00736 #042-03-1994 L1995 PTH PP *062 †50

RAMOS-PADILLA, Nydia. 55 CALLE CARRION MADURO, PO BOX 1272 00736 #847-08-1976 L1980 AN *020

RIVERA, Don Raymond. PO BOX 372707 00737 #035-09-1972 L1975 CD IM *020

RIVERA-ARGUINZONI, Ramon. PO BOX 193 00737 #035-06-1974 L1975 PTH *020

RIVERA-CERON, Rafael I. 109 AVE MUNOZ RIVERA S, BOX 1088 00736 #308-01-1962 L1968 GP *020

RODRIGUEZ, Edgar I. ■ 00736 #042-01-1990 L1993 OBG *020

RODRIGUEZ, Haydee. 2 CALLE 2, GARDENIA D26 00736 #847-02-1979 L1986 GP *020

RODRIGUEZ, Luis Alberto. ■ 00736 #042-01-2000 L2003 EM *020

RODRIGUEZ, Luis J. 55 CALLE BARBOSA S 00736 #042-01-1993 L1996 FM *020 †18

RODRIGUEZ, Norma Iris. ■ 00737 #308-03-1981 L1991 P *020

RODRIGUEZ-COLON, Celeste. PO BOX 373471 00737 #649-14-1999 L2006 *100

RODRIGUEZ-PAGAN, Jorge L. ■ 00737 #042-01-1959 L1961 GS TS *020 †85

ROSARIO RODRIGUEZ, Elsie. ■ 00736 #649-03-1990 L1992 IM *020

RUIZ, Natalio Figueroa. ■ 00736 #308-02-1973 L1975 IM *020

SAENZ, Carmen Ana. ■ 00737 #847-04-1962 L1964 END PD *020 †55

SANCHEZ-COTTO, Jorge Luis. ■ 00736 #308-03-1982 L1985 IM *020

SANTIAGO, Wilberto. 227 CALLE MARCIAL BOSCH, URB BOSCH 00736 #308-03-1982 L1988 IM *020

SANTIAGO NOA, Victor M. 20620 CALLE MAMEY, BO BEATRIZ 00736 #042-01-1972 L1975 CHP P *020

SANTIAGO-SANTIAGO, Jose E. REPTO MONTELLANO, CALLE B-F-12 00737 #847-06-1979 L1985 *100

SANTOS-RIVERA, Hector A. ■ 00737 #847-02-1976 L1979 IM *020

SEGARRA, Pablo E. PO BOX 696 00737 #847-02-1973 L1977 GP *071

SILVA-FIGUEROA, Victor D. TRATAMIENTO DE CAYEY, CENTRO DE DIAGNOSTICO Y 00737 #308-06-1983 L1987 GP *020

SOTO, Carmen Laura. ■ 00737 #042-01-2007 *012

STACHOLY, Mariela. PO BOX 372618 00737 #042-03-1998 L2000 *020

STACHOLY, Pedro Armando. PO BOX 372618 00737 #275-01-1960 L1971 IM GP *020

SUAREZ ALMEDINA, Luis Ces. PO BOX 373245 00737 #847-21-1981 L1986 PD *020

TORRES HERNANDEZ, Alvin. 4 CALLE H MENDOZA E 00736 #042-04-1988 L1991 IM *020

TRINIDAD MATEO, Marta. JARDINES DEL CARIBE E17 00736 #308-03-1985 L1991 *020

VAZQUEZ, Francisco Jose. 4 CALLE H MENDOZA E 00736 #042-01-1989 L1992 N *020

VAZQUEZ, Gladys Mercedes. ■ 00736 #308-04-2000 L2002 *020

VAZQUEZ, Samuel. 23 CALLE HERACIO MENDOZA E 00736 #042-01-1981 L1985 PD *020

VAZQUEZ-APONTE, Miguel A. C4 CALLE ALMENDROS, URB MIRADOR ECHEVARRI 00736 #847-05-1967 L1978 *020

VEGA, Marta L. PO BOX 1194 00737 #308-03-1982 L1986 FM *020

VEGA-MALDONADO, Miguel A. PO BOX 372950 00737 #042-01-1977 L1982 OTO HNS *020

VELEZ, Frances Marie. ■ 00737 #042-01-2005 N *012

ZAYAS, Fernando Luis. 55 CALLE BARBOSA S, FAMILY MED CENTER OF CAYEY 00736 #042-01-1987 L1991 FM *020 †18

CEIBA — CEIBA

CARLO-COLLAZO, Jose Luis. 294 AVE LAURO PINERO, 12 N11 JARDINES DE CEIBA 00735 #649-14-1978 L1981 GP *020

CARRILLO, Felix. ■ 00735 #042-01-2001 L2004 IM *020 †20

CORDERO POLANCO, Enerolisa. PO BOX 1205 00735 #308-03-1987 L2005 *100

ESTRADA, Isaac Wagner. 297 AVE LAURO PINERO 00735 #649-14-1976 L1979 GP FM *020

FIGUEROA-PACHECO, Jose R. SAN JORGE F4 VILLA PILAR 00735 #847-05-1977 L1982 GP *020

FLOYD, Charles. ROOSEVELT ROAD, US NAVAL HOSPITAL 00735 #019-02-1977 L1990 P *020

FONTANEZ, Agapito. ■ 00735 #847-05-1973 L1976 *020

FONTANEZ, Nydia. ■ 00735 #649-14-2001 L2005 GP *020

GONZALEZ, Richard. ■ 00735 #042-01-1979 L1988 ORS *020 †40

LOPEZ, Fabian Velazquez. 288 AVE LAURO PINERO 00735 #847-05-1975 L1978 GP *020

LOYEZ, Jorge E. ■ 00735 #429-01-1961 L1969 N IM *071 †75

MARCANO ORTIZ, Marie C. ■ 00735 #649-14-2004 L2006 GP *100

MATOS, Ruth Esther. ■ 00735 #308-03-1981 L2005 *100

QUINTERO, Edgar Nelson. ■ 00735 #308-03-1983 L1992 GP *020

RIVERA COLON, Julio. 767 CALLE JOSE ROMERO 00735 #308-03-1984 L1994 GP *020

RIVERA-CRUZ, Carlos. 205 AVE LAURO PINERO, P O BOX 1068 00735 #847-06-1976 L1982 IM *020

RIVERA-MELENDEZ, Ruth E. ■ 00735 #308-03-1983 L1992 IM *020

VILLAMIL RAMOS, Jose Luis. UNIDAD DE SALUD 00735 #847-01-1954 L1956 GP OS *020

ZARRILLO DIPAOLO, Joseph. 205 AVE LAURO PINERO 00735 #649-14-1991 L1995 GP *020

CIALES – CIALES

ALICEA, Eric. 12.3 CARR 149, CIALES PRIMARY HEALTH CARE 00638 #042-03-1988 L1991 IM *020

CAMPOS-LOPEZ, Frank. HC 2 BOX 7151, KM 24.1 BO. CORDILLERA 00638 #847-06-1976 L1979 GP *020

CASTELLANOS, Orestes. ■ 00638 #042-01-1987 L1990 FM *020 †18

COLLAZO GARCIA, Maria A. 25 CALLE JOSE DE DIEGO, INST MEDICO DE CIALES 00638 #308-03-1981 L1993 GP *020

DELGADO SEIJO, Hector F. 55A CALLE PALMER 00638 #308-03-1984 L1990 GP *020

DISDIER-RODRIGUEZ, Carlos. PO BOX 1425 00638 #308-04-1979 L1983 FM *020 †18

GARCIA, Hector Arnaldo. 10 BO CORDILLERA, BOX 341 00638 #042-01-1995 L1996 PDO *020

GARCIA DE COLOM, Luisa M. PO BOX 1385 00638 #042-01-1963 L1966 GP *020

GEYLS-RAMIREZ, Alberto. 5 CALLE PALMER 00638 #047-06-1949 L1951 FM *020

HERNANDEZ REYES, Maria I. 55 CALLE PALMER 00638 #308-03-1985 L1991 GP *020

MARCANTONI, Efrain A. 13 CALLE IGNACIO FERNANDEZ 00638 #042-01-1982 L1985 IM *020

MARRERO, Tomas A. ■ 00638 #847-09-1969 L1989 GP *072

MARTINEZ, Mayra. 51 CALLE PALMER 00638 #042-02-1983 L1986 FM *020 †18

ORTIZ RIVERA, Grisselle E. PO BOX 36 00638 #308-01-2002 L2004 *100

RIVERA MATOS, Rosily. ■ 00638 #308-04-2004 L2005 *100

RODRIGUEZ RIOS, Rafael A. 12 CALLE CORCHADO 00638 #308-03-1981 L1986 GP OS *020

SANABRIA, Arturo E. 49 CALLE PALMER, BOX 1375 00638 #041-02-1952 L1954 GP *072

SASTRE, Alberto. 61 CALLE JOSE DE DIEGO 00638 #308-03-1983 L1984 GP *020

VALENTIN-DE RIVERA, A. 27 CALLE JOSE DE DIEGO 00638 #308-01-1979 L1981 GP *020

CIDRA – CIDRA

BRITT, Andres M. 421 CAM DE LAS MIRAMELINDS, URB SABANERA 00739 #042-01-1989 L1992 EM *020 †16

BURGOS RIVERA, Jorge A. 23 CALLE BARCELO 00739 #308-03-1985 L1989 *020

CALDEVON JIMENEZ, Jorge L. PO BOX 206 00739 #308-02-1990 L1992 *020

CARRASQUILLO, Nelson. 5 RES PRAXEDES SANTIAGO 00739 #308-03-1984 L1990 *020

COLON, Jose Antonio. 429 CAMINO LOS HELECHOS, URB SABANERA 00739 #042-02-1993 L1997 EM *020

COLON-RIVERA, Luis R. 86 CAMINO DEL BOSQUE, URB SABANERA 00739 #042-01-1979 L1981 CHP P *020 †75

COTTO, Roalba. 406 CAM DE LAS MIRAMELINDS, URB SABANERA 00739 #308-03-1984 L1989 PD *020

DEL VALLE, Benjamin. ■ 00739 #308-06-1987 L1989 GP *020

DIAZ FERNANDEZ, Luis A. R. BARCELO #23 00739 #847-02-1976 L1980 *100

DURAN SERRANO, William A.. ■ 00739 #308-04-2002 L2003 *100

FELICIANO, Ruth A. URB SABANERA, CALLE LAS TRINITARIAS #148 00739 #042-03-1987 L1992 ID *020

FIGUEROA ROBLES, Jose M.. ■ 00739 #649-14-2003 L2005 *100

FLORES, Rosa Maria. RR 1 BOX 3942 00739 #649-14-2003 L2006 *100

FOTTE, Manuel Michelen. BLOQUE E-8 00739 #308-01-1961 L1977 EM *020

FRANCO COTTO, Edgardo. PO BOX 1082 00739 #042-04-2001 L2002 *020

FRATTALLONE, Josephine M. ■ 00739 #042-01-1983 L1986 CCP PD *071 †55

FRYE MALDONADO, Aislinn C. PO BOX 1398, 1.5 STATE RD 787 00739 #042-01-1994 L1997 P *020

GRANA DE CHAPPUIS, J. ■ 00739 #041-13-1951 L1952 PD *071

JOHNSON, Sylvia Priscilla. ■ 00739 #847-06-1976 L1981 CHP *020

JUSTINIANO-ACEVEDO, A. ■ 00739 #847-05-1974 L1976 GP *071

LUGO TORRES, Nora M. #167 CAMINO POMAROSA, URB SABANERA 00739 #649-14-1992 L1994 *020

MEJIAS-MATOS, Juanita. SECTOR STA CLARA, BO ARRENAS 00739 #308-01-1987 L1991 *020

NIEVES, Lourdes. 2 CALLE FRANCISCO CRUZ 00739 #042-03-1988 L1991 PM *012 †55

NIEVES RIVERA, Jeovhanni. PO BOX 1512 00739 #042-04-2003 L2005 *100

PEREZ, Ramon. ■ 00739 #042-01-1998 L2000 OBG *020

RESTO, Ivette. ■ 00739 #042-01-1999 L2004 AN *100 †05

REYES ROSARIO, Jorge Y.. BUZON 5309, BO ARENAS 00739 #042-04-2003 L2004 *100

RIVERA, Amilcar. ESQUINA PADILLA EL CARIBE, CALLE ANTONIO R BARCELO 00739 #042-03-1983 L1987 PD *020

RIVERA, Robert. C/O P.O. BOX 459, CALLE BARCELO 46 00739 #649-14-1986 L1989 GP EM *020

RODRIGUEZ, Hector Javier. 2 CALLE FRANCISCO CRUZ, CORPPORACION DE SERVICIOS 00739 #042-03-2001 L2006 OBG *100

RODRIGUEZ-ALBERTORIO, E. JOSE DEDIEGO ST #140 00739 #042-04-1988 L1992 IM *020

RODRIQUEZ, Angel L. RR 2 BOX 5427, KM1.5 INTERIOR 00739 #308-01-1987 L1994 *020

ROMAN, Amaury Arnaldo. 4 CALLE BALDORIOTY 00739 #042-01-1977 L1980 GP OS *020

RONDA LEBRON, Edgardo L. PO BOX 1624 00739 #308-03-1983 L1988 GP *020

ROSADO, Jose Rafael. ■ 00739 #649-14-2002 L2004 *100

SANTIAGO FORTIER, Edgardo. PO BOX 1876 00739 #308-07-1981 L2003 FM *020

SANTOS, Hector Orlando. C/O PO BOX 1832, CARR 734 KM 0.5 00739 #042-01-1980 L1985 PD *020 †55

SOTO, Edgardo. 2 CALLE FRANCISCO CRUZ 00739 #042-01-1985 L1988 FM *020 †18

TORRES, Alberto Fernandez. ■ 00739 #042-02-1976 L1978 GP EM *020

TORRES-MIRANDA, Jose R. PO BOX 1400, 1.5 STATE ROAD 787 00739 #042-02-1989 L1992 P *020 †75

VAZQUEZ, Efrain. ■ 00739 #042-01-1999 L2003 OBG *020

VAZQUEZ AYALA, Edwin. CAMINO POMAROSA, URB SABANERA #167 00739 #649-14-1992 L1994 *020
VEGA-ROLON, Vilma G. C2 CALLE 5, VILLA DEL CARMEN 00739 #042-01-1995 L1998 IM *020 †20
VICENTE, Wilda Rosa. ■ 00739 #042-01-2004 PD *100 †55

COAMO – COAMO

ALVARADO, Hector Manuel. ■ 00769 #649-14-1988 L1992 PD *020
CARATINI SOTO, Felix M. 134 CALLE JOSE I QUINTON 00769 #308-04-1993 L1995 IM *020
CRUZ, Bethzaida Ortiz. HC 1 BOX 14938 00769 #042-02-2000 L2002 FPG *020 †18 ‡
CRUZ, Pedro Juan. 146 CALLE JOSE I QUINTON 00769 #042-01-1971 L1989 CHP P *020
DE JESUS CARTAGENA, Lorna. 4 CAR 702 VILLA DE SAN BLA, APT 1276 00769 #042-04-1998 L1999 FM *020
ECHEVARRIA, Adalina M. ■ 00769 #847-06-1979 L1981 P *020
FRONTERA, Laura. ■ 00769 #042-01-2004 L2007 PD *020 †55
HERNANDEZ, Helder Oscar. ■ 00769 #042-01-2007 IM *012
LARRAURI-RENTA, Jose J. 1 CALLE MARIO BRASCHI 00769 #649-01-1979 L1984 GP *020
LLORENS-QUINONES, Jose. CARR 14 34 A PARCELAS NIAG 00769 #847-14-1983 L1989 *020
MANES, Raul B. 15 CALLE BALDORIOTY 00769 #275-01-1960 L1975 FM *020
MARRERO, Hector Raul. 13 CALLE WILLIE ROSARIO, STE 2 00769 #042-01-1984 L1987 OBG *020
MARTINEZ AJA, Jorge C. 42 CALLE BALDORIOTY 00769 #649-14-1990 L1992 IM *020
MORENO, Anibal. 18 CALLE MARIO BRASCHI 00769 #308-01-1987 L1988 GP *020
MORENO TORRES, Edwin. PO BOX 3003, STE 40 00769 #308-03-1978 L1980 *100
QUESADA, Consuelo Enid. 142 CALLE JOSE I QUINTON 00769 #308-07-1983 L2003 P *020
QUINCOCES-HERNANDEZ, O. 41 CALLE BALDORIOTY 00769 #847-02-1980 L1984 PD *020
QUINONES, Virgen Milagros. ■ 00769 #042-02-2003 P *100
REYES RODRIGUEZ, Roberto. ■ 00769 #042-04-1989 L1991 PD OM *020
RIVERA-GUILBE, Luis Guill. ■ 00769 #308-13-2000 L2004 *100
RODRIGUEZ, Luis Miguel. VILLA MADRID E34 00769 #042-02-1996 L2001 NPM *020 †55
RODRIGUEZ COLON, Jose Raf. ■ 00769 #649-14-2000 L2002 *020
RUBERO, Ruben Alfonso. PO BOX 454 00769 #649-14-2003 L2004 *100
SAEZ VEGA, Milagros Del C. 19 CALLE BALDORIOTY 00769 #042-04-1989 L1991 PD *020
SANCHEZ PADILLA, Francisco. ■ 00769 #308-01-1977 L1986 *020
SANTINI-OLIVIERI, Sonia M. 6 CALLE WILLIE ROSARIO 00769 #042-01-1959 L1963 PD *020
SIMON, Juan Manuel De, Sr. ■ 00769 #308-01-1967 L1976 GP *020
SOLIVAN-MIRANDA, Ramon A. 1 CALLE MARIO BRASCHI 00769 #042-03-1981 L1986 GP OS *020
TORRES, Orlando. 43 CALLE VARSOVIA 00769 #042-03-1988 L1992 IM *020
VAZQUEZ-CRUZ, Mario J. ■ 00769 #042-01-2001 L2004 PAN *100
VEGA, Karim Saleh. 49 CALLE BALDORIOTY 00769 #422-01-1993 L2001 IM *020 †20
VELEZ ALGARIN, Silvia L. ST CARRION MADURO #12 00769 #308-03-1991 L1991 GP *020
ZAYAS MERCADO, Ivan F. ■ 00769 #308-02-2001 L2003 *100

COMERIO – COMERIO

BURGOS-COLON, Edwin P. HC 2, 779 BO PALOMAS 56 RD 00782 #847-10-1963 L1969 P *020
CASTRODAD, Victor R M. PO BOX 1107, 10 SANTIAGO R PALMER 00782 #847-03-1959 L1962 GP IM *072
DIAZ PEREZ, Luis Raul. 1A CALLE JOSE DE DIEGO 00782 #042-03-1980 L1983 FM *020 †18
GONZALEZ, Luis Manuel. ■ 00782 #308-03-1982 L1989 GP *020
LLAVONA, Luis Antonio. 63 CALLE GEORGETTI 00782 #649-14-1989 L1992 GP *020
LUGO, Marie Carmen. BO PINAS ARRIBA APDO 259 00782 #042-03-1992 L1996 PM *020
MEJIAS FRANQUI, Diego. CALLE GEURGETT 14 A 00782 #308-03-1977 L1980 FM *020
NIEVES CRUZ, Ivonne M.. PO BOX 58 00782 #042-04-2003 L2004 *020
PEREZ VEGA, Lissette E. 1A CALLE JOSE DE DIEGO 00782 #649-14-1993 L1996 *020
RIVERA, Francisco Javier. PO BOX 1008, DON ELENA 00782 #649-14-2003 L2004 *100
RIVERA MARTINEZ, Angel S. ■ 00782 #649-14-2002 L2005 *100
RODRIGUEZ RODRIGUEZ, R. 1 CALLE GEORGETTI BOX 137 00782 #308-03-1981.L1985 GP *020
TORRES-BONILLA, Luis E. 85 CALLE GEORGETTI 00782 #847-05-1977 L1980 GP *020

CONDADO – SAN JUAN

ALVAREZ FERRER, Gilberto. ■ 00907 #649-30-2002 L2003 FM *020
BORREGO, Lillian Judith. ■ 00907 #042-01-1997 L2002 NEP *040 †20
CANTO, Roberto Jose. 101 ASHFORD MEDICAL CTR, STE 101 00907 #042-01-1976 L1981 U *020 †95
COLON, Lizzette. 403 ASHFORD MEDCL CTR #403 00907 #042-04-1983 L1986 IMG *020
CURBELO, Pablo Guillermo. 201 ASHFORD MEDICAL CTR, STE 201 00907 #042-01-1957 L1962 U *020 †95
MEDINA, Marta. ■ 00907 #042-02-1993 L1997 P *020

COROZAL – COROZAL

ARROYO-NIEVES, Oscar. 8 CALLE NUEVA, BOX 364 00783 #042-01-1979 L1981 PM *020
BAHRI, Daled. 7 CALLE GANDARA 00783 #042-01-1982 L1985 IM IMG *040
BERIO RAMOS, Francisco. CALLE BOU 49 ALTOS 00783 #308-01-1975 L1977 GP *020
BERIO ROUSSEL, Francisco. 25 CALLE LAS MERCEDES 00783 #649-14-2004 L2006 *100
BETANCES SANTOS, Domingo. PO BOX 1838 00783 #308-04-1984 L1986 PD *020
BOU, Genaro Ramon. 8 CALLE NUEVA 00783 #847-05-1977 L1983 PD *020
CABRERA, Cesar E. ■ 00783 #308-02-1973 L1975 GP *020
CAMACHO, Ezer. ■ 00783 #042-01-2004 *100
CARRO, Francisco E. 19 CALLE NUEVA, BOX 1535 00783 #042-01-1987 L1988 PUD *020 †20
CASAS-LOPEZ, Angeles L. 23 CALLE LAS MERCEDES 00783 #847-06-1977 L1980 GP *020
CASTRO CINTRON, Ricardo J. PO BOX 870 00783 #042-04-2003 L2004 *100
CASTRO-VELAZQUEZ, Ana P. 56 CALLE IDILIO 00783 #042-01-1982 L1989 IM *020 †20
COBIAN TORMOS, Modesto L. CENTRO DE SALUD 00783 #847-05-1956 L1958 PHP GP *030
CORDOVA, Hector R. ■ 00783 #042-01-1981 L1984 NEP IM *020 †20
CRUZ, Hilda Ivonne. ■ 00783 #649-14-1997 L1999 FM *020

DAVILA-FERNANDEZ, Mario R. 16 CALLE GANDARA 00783 #042-04-1984 L1986 OBG *020
DAVILA-GONZALEZ, Luis I. 15.0 CARR 159, BO. PUEBLO 00783 #308-03-1978 L1980 GP *020
FUCILE, Michael Nelson. PO BOX 739, COROZAL HLTH CNTR 00783 #041-13-1982 L1985 FM *020 †18
FUENTES-SANTIAGO, Yasmin. HC 1 BOX 6624 00783 #649-14-1987 L1990 FM *020 †18
GIMENEZ SAFONT, Jose. C/O BOX 677, CALLE BOU #18 00783 #847-01-1954 L1959 OS GP *072
GONZALEZ, Julio Armando. 13 CALLE GANDARA, BOX 1332 00783 #042-03-1982 L1986 OBG *020 †30
GONZALEZ MARCANO, Samuel. 40 CALLE GANDARA 00783 #042-04-2000 L2001 *020
GUZMAN MALDONADO, Yannette. ■ 00783 #308-13-2002 L2004 *100
HASBUN, Diego Rafael R. MARIA DEL CARMEN MALL 00783 #308-01-1967 L1976 *020
JOY, Luis Manuel. HC 1, (RD 159 KM 15.5) 00783 #308-01-1980 L1984 FM FPG *020 †18
MALDONADO RAMIREZ, Mario. 17 CALLE LAS MERCEDES 00783 #308-03-1981 L1983 IM *020
MEDINA FUENTES, Jose F. PO BOX 848 00783 #847-06-1973 L1977 GP *020
NEGRON, Juan Enrique. ■ 00783 #308-13-2000 L2006 *100
ORTIZ, Luis J. PO BOX 209 00783 #308-03-1984 L1988 *020
ORTIZ CALDERO, Miguel. PO BOX 620 00783 #308-01-1978 L1981 *020
ORTIZ-MATOS, Juan L. PO BOX 1117 00783 #308-03-1986 L1989 IM *020
ORTIZ RIVERA, Josefina. HC 3 BOX 14874 00783 #042-04-2003 L2004 *100
RODRIGUEZ, Betty. PO BOX 616 00783 #042-04-1984 L1987 GP *020
SANTOS SANTOS, Ada L. PO BOX 407 00783 #308-03-1993 L2003 *100
SERRANO TORRES, Nelson F. 7 CALLE GANDARA 00783 #042-04-1983 L1986 GP *020
TORRES, Damaris. ■ 00783 #042-03-1994 L1995 N *020 †75
ZUAZAGA RODRIGUEZ, G. ■ 00783 #035-06-1952 L1954 GP *071

COTO LAUREL – PONCE

ABOU ELMAGD, Ahmed. 62 CALLE VIGIA, MANS DEL SUR 00780 #915-03-1982 L1996 IM *020
ALVAREZ DE LA CAMPA, A. ■ 00780 #042-02-2001 L2004 NR *100 †28
ARANDA, Maria Dolores. 6013 PASEO LA CONCORDIA, HACIENDAS DEL MONTE 00780 #847-06-1982 L1986 PD *020 †55
AROCHO, Celso Joel. ■ 00780 #308-04-1991 L1992 AN *020
BAEZ, Richard. 157 CALLE REY FERNANDO, MANS REAL 00780 #042-02-1994 L1997 U *020 †95
BELLVER ESPINOSA, Enrique. ■ 00780 #132-07-1977 L2005 *100
BELMONTE CORDANO, Edgar C. PO BOX 801024 00780 #176-01-1969 L1985 PTH GP *020 †50
BLASINI-SANTIAGO, Rafael. ■ 00780 #021-01-1949 L1953 PD OS *020 †55
CESTERO, Maria Conchita. ■ 00780 #847-06-1975 L1980 AN *020
CORREA, Jose Noel. PO BOX 800967 00780 #025-01-1958 L1963 RO *020 †80
DANET, John Michael. ■ 00780 #649-35-2000 L2003 *020
DIAZ, Henry. 62 CALLE VIGIA # F6, MANS DEL SUR 00780 #308-03-1988 L1998 *020
FAHED-INIGO, George Paul. 304 TORRE SAN CRISTOBAL, GEORGE FAHED 00780 #649-14-1998 L1999 SME *100
FARINACCI, Pedro Noel. 63 CALLE VIGIA, MANS DEL SUR 00780 #042-02-1994 L2000 RNR *020 †80
FERNANDEZ, Rafael Manuel. 201 TORRES SAN CRISTOBAL 00780 #042-01-1987 L1993 ORS *020 †40
FRONTERA TACORONTE, Nestor. ■ 00780 #649-14-1998 L2002 *100
FUMERO, Jose Oscar. 104 CALLE REY FERNANDO, MANS REAL 00780 #042-02-1997 L2002 RNR *020 †80
GALARZA LUGO, Ivonne E. ■ 00780 #042-02-1985 L1997 PD *020 †55
GRILLASCA, Jorge E. 302 TORRES SAN CRISTOBAL 00780 #649-14-1990 L1991 NEP *020
HERNANDEZ, Felix F. ■ 00780 #847-06-1983 L1986 GP *020
HERNANDEZ, Jorge. ■ 00780 #042-01-1985 L1988 OPH *020 †35
IRIZARRY, Luis M. 209 TORRES SAN CRISTOBAL 00780 #042-01-1985 L1988 IM *020
LEON, Juanita Cecilia. 211 TORRE SAN CRISTOBAL 00780 #308-01-1987 L1991 P *020
LUGO, Fabio H. 309 TORRES SAN CRISTOBAL 00780 #042-04-1984 L1986 P OS *020
MAGRANER, Miguel A. ■ 00780 #042-02-1984 L1987 IM *040 †20
MALDONADO TORRES, Ismael. ■ 00780 #649-14-1984 L1986 IM *020
MARTINEZ, Axel Enri. ■ 00780 #042-01-2004 FP *012
MEDINA, Magaly. ■ 00780 #042-02-2005 L2005 AN *020 †05
MEJIA, Dilaury. ■ 00780 #042-02-2007 OBG *012
MELENDEZ, Luis Humberto. ■ 00780 #042-01-1993 L2000 VIR *020 †80
MELENDEZ, Octavio. 311 TORRES SAN CRISTOBAL 00780 #308-03-1989 L1990 OBG *020 †30
MIRO-ROSADO, Aurelio. PO BOX 800676 00780 #308-03-1980 L1982 GP *020 †30
MONTALVO-FIGUEROA, Jose A. 308 TORRE SAN CRISTOBAL 00780 #042-02-1992 L1995 END *020
MUNOZ ALVARADO, Armando L. ■ 00780 #649-14-2003 *020
NAZARIO-ALMODOVAR, F A. 304 TORRES SAN CRISTOBAL 00780 #847-06-1972 L1975 GS FM *020
OLIVER, Soniann. HACIENDAS DEL MONTE I-4 00780 #042-02-2000 PD *100
OLIVIERI, Odette. 308 CALLE SOFIA, MANS REAL 00780 #042-03-1990 L1993 PD *020 †55
OMS, Americo. 506 CALLE EL FLAMBOYAN, URB SOMBRAS DEL REAL 00780 #308-03-1983 L1986 P *020
ORTIZ NEVAREZ, Manuel A. PO BOX 800510 00780 #042-04-1999 L2002 FM *020
ORTIZ ROSARIO, Jaime L. 205A TORRE SAN CRISTOBAL 00780 #042-01-1984 L1989 OTO *020
PADILLA, Maria Del C. SUTIE 206, TORRE SAN CRISTOBAL 00780 #042-03-1983 L1986 IM *020
PEREZ, Zenaida Esther. PO BOX 801054, 58O STATE ROAD PR - 149 00780 #042-02-1998 L2000 OBG *020
PEREZ VARGAS, Wilfredo J. PO BOX 801054 00780 #649-30-2001 L2004 *100
QUILES, Wanda Ivelisse. 305B TORRE SAN CRISTOBAL 00780 #042-02-1993 L1997 P CHP *020
RAMIREZ-MARTINEZ, Jose R. 513 CALLE CASTILLA, MANS REAL 00780 #308-03-1981 L1984 IM *020 †20
REYES RODRIGUEZ, Martha D. ■ 00780 #649-14-1992 L1994 PD *020
RIVERA BERMUDEZ, Lilliam. ■ 00780 #649-30-2001 L2004 *100
RIVERA-DE JESUS, J. 41 CALLE TIBES, MANS DEL SUR 00780 #042-02-1992 L1996 OBG *020
RIVERA-IRIZARRY, Jomarie. 2101 VEREDAS DEL LAUREL 00780 #649-14-2002 L2003 *100
RIVERA PABON, Gerardo. 46 CALLE VIGIA, MANS DEL SUR 00780 #308-03-1983 L1995 GP *020

PUERTO RICO

COTO LAUREL — FAJARDO

RIVERA-RIVERA, Lillian V. PO BOX 801215 00780 #042-01-1990 L1993 **PD** *062 †55
RODRIQUEZ, Jessica. PO BOX 800562 00780 #649-14-2000 L2001 *020
RUIZ, Wanda Ivelisse. 1228 BLVD SAN LUIS, VILLAS DEL LAUREL 1 00780 #847-06-1995 L1997 **FM** *020
SANTA, Jesus J. ■ 00780 #042-01-1995 L1999 **AN** *020
SANTIAGO, Manuel S. 8 CALLE CEIBA, MANS DEL SUR 00780 #042-01-1986 L1990 **AN PME** *020 †05
SANTOS, Claudio Samuel. P O BOX 8002500 00780 #649-14-2001 L2004 *100
SERPA, Miguel Angel. ■ 00780 #042-02-1988 L1995 **NM** *020 †28
SERRANO, Alicia Maria. 145 CALLE REY FERNANDO, MANS REAL 00780 #042-02-1993 L1997 **PD** *020 †55
SOLTERO, Ernesto R. ■ 00780 #042-01-1989 L1997 **TS** *020 †85,90
TORRES, Anibal Robinson. C/O BOX 1144, VISTA POINT B-4 00780 #042-01-1974 L1976 **GS** *020
TORRES, Nadja Ivette. 214 TORRE SAN CRISTOBAL, URB LLANOS DEL SUR 00780 #042-01-1990 L1994 **OPH** *020 †35
TORRES, Orlando Alberto. 202 TORRES SAN CRISTOBAL 00780 #042-03-1988 L1992 **CHN** *020 †55
TORRES, Roberto Luis. ■ 00780 #847-12-1979 L1984 **CD IM** *020 †20
VAZQUEZ RAMIREZ, Lida V. ■ 00780 #042-04-1995 L2001 *020
VERA-MIRO, Jose L. 207 TORRES SAN CRISTOBAL 00780 #042-02-1985 L1988 **CD IM** *020 †20
VILARO-CHARDON, Juan Luis. ■ 00780 #042-02-1989 L1992 **NEP** *020

CULEBRA – CULEBRA

ORTIZ, Juan Ramon. ■ 00775 #308-03-1978 L1985 **GP** *020

CUPEY – SAN JUAN

GONZALEZ, Ramon H. 382 CALLE SAN CLAUD PMB 07, URB SAGRADO CORAZON 00926 #042-01-1993 L1997 **IM** *020 †20
MICHELEN, Eduardo Antonio. ■ 00926 #308-01-1985 L1991 **ON** *020 †20

DORADO – DORADO

ABDALA, Jose Miguel. 410 CALLE MENDEZ VIGO, STE 204 00646 #308-07-1980 L1991 **CD** *020
ACEVEDO, Sandra Ivette. ■ 00646 #042-01-1997 L2000 **PD** *020
ALMIRA SUAREZ, Maria Isab. ■ 00646 #275-01-1994 **PTH** *020
AMEZQUITA, Angel R. JJ4 CALLE PELICANO 00646 #042-04-1981 L1990 **GP** *020
ANDUZE-MENENDEZ, Julio. PO BOX 970 00646 #042-01-1954 L1956 **GP OM** *072
ARROYO, Ricardo J. PO BOX 608 00646 #047-07-1980 L1986 **GE IM** *020
BAEZ, Ignacio J. E13 CALLE MADRE PERLA, URB DORADO DEL MAR 00646 #010-03-1951 L1953 **GP** *020
BAEZ MURPHY, Raymond. ■ 00646 #847-05-1956 L1958 **FM OS** *072
BATALLA, Jorge Lopez. 401 CALLE S 00646 #847-06-1975 L1978 **GP** *020 ‡
BAUZA, Gustavo Jose. ■ 00646 #042-03-2008 *012
BENMAMAN, Moises. ■ 00646 #847-04-1958 L1965 **GS** *020 †85
BEZARES, Erskin. 81 CALLE DIAMANTE, URB LOS PRADOS SUR 00646 #042-01-2002 L2005 **CCP** *012
CANALES TORRES, Josue. AA24 CALLE 3 N, QTAS DE DORADO 00646 #649-14-2002 L2004 **GP** *020
CARRASQUILLO, Efrain. ■ 00646 #042-03-1994 L1999 **RHU** *020
CARRION, Enrique. ■ 00646 #847-10-1970 L1973 **PD PDC** *020
CARRION-VARGAS, Enrique. 216 CALLE METIS, PASEO DEL SOL 00646 #042-01-1993 L1996 **PDC** *020 †55
CINTRON-CASTRO, Reinaldo. STREET 5-H-1, URB JARDINES DE DORADO 00646 #308-03-1977 L1980 **GP** *020
COLLAZO, Michelle Haydee. ■ 00646 #042-03-2002 L2005 **D** *020 †15
COLLAZO, Ramon Luis. ■ 00646 #308-01-1983 L1992 **PD** *020
CONNELLY, Richard P. ■ 00646 #042-04-1992 L1994 *020
CORDERO, Jose. B19 CALLE 3, URB. FLAMBOYAN 00646 #308-01-1980 L1984 **IM** *020
CORRETJER BENVENNUTI, O F. ■ 00646 #649-01-1955 L1957 **OTO** *072
CRESPO, Carmelo A. 338 CALLE MENDEZ VIGO 00646 #308-01-1975 L1977 **EM GP** *020
CRUZ, Eva L. ■ 00646 #042-01-1995 L2001 **DR** *020 †80
CRUZ CORREA, Marcia R. ■ 00646 #042-01-1995 L1996 **GE** *020 †20
DEL VALLE, Carlos Rafael. PO BOX 670 00646 #847-11-1977 L1981 **OPH** *020
DIAZ SOTOMAYOR, William. ■ 00646 #042-03-1981 L1991 **PD** *020
FUMERO, Jaime Francisco. ■ 00646 #042-03-1992 L1995 **ORS** *020
GARCIA ALTIERI, Mauro And. ■ 00646 #042-01-2007 **P** *012
GELPI, Francisco Jose. ■ 00646 #042-01-1994 L1994 *020
GONZALEZ-PEDROSA, Oscar B. 340 CALLE TIBURON, PASEO LAS OLAS 00646 #042-01-1995 L2000 **P** *020
GOSS, Carmen. JJ40 DORADO DEL MAR BLVD, URB DORADO DEL MAR 00646 #042-04-1985 L1988 **PD** *020
GOVEO, Luis Javier. ■ 00646 #042-03-1995 L1998 **PM** *020
GUZMAN, Humberto Manuel. ■ 00646 #042-01-2003 **ORS** *012
HERNANDEZ, Daniel. P16 CALLE SIRENA, URB DORADO DEL MAR 00646 #042-01-1988 L1991 **FM** *020
JOHNSON, Orley Franklin. PO BOX 636 00646 #649-14-1975 L1995 **GP** *071
LAGRANDIER GOMEZ, Olga P. ■ 00646 #649-14-2003 L2005 **FP** *012
LONGO, Marta Klachko. ■ 00646 #033-05-1992 L1997 **EM** *071 †16
LOPEZ, Jose Luis. C3 CALLE MARGINAL STE 9, URB. COSTA DE ORO 00646 #042-01-1995 L1999 **FPG** *020 †18
LOPEZ LOPEZ, Ulises M. Z16 CALLE BRISAS, URB DORADO DEL MAR 00646 #042-01-1978 L1982 **OBG** *020
LUGO-AMADOR, Nannette M. 581 CALLE MAR CARIBE, PASEO LOS CORALES 00646 #042-01-1998 L2004 **EM** *100 †16
LUIGGI CALCERRADA, M. JJ31 CALLE MIRAMAR, URB DORADO DEL MAR 00646 #847-08-1975 L1979 **NPM PD** *020 †55
MARRERO, Ricardo Juan. ■ 00646 #042-03-1998 **GE** *020
MARRERO ORTIZ, Oscar. 716 CAL CCTR URB MONTE BEL 00646 #649-14-2001 L2005 *100

MATOS-CANDELARIA, Wanda A. 375 CALLE MENDEZ VIGO 00646 #649-14-1990 L1992 **PD** *020
MAYMI, Maria Angeli. 585 CALLE MAR CARIBE, PASEO LOS CORALES 00646 #042-01-2001 L2003 **D** *020
MEDINA, Karla Teresa. ■ 00646 #042-03-2004 **PD** *100
MEJIA-CARVAJAL, Carmen R. ■ 00646 #042-02-1998 L2000 **PD** *020
MELECIO, Elliot. ■ 00646 #042-01-1992 L1995 **IMG** *020 †20
MONTALVAN-MIRO, Carlos Ja. ■ 00646 #042-01-2005 **IM** *020
MONTALVAN-RUIZ, Avelino. R18 CALLE MARINA, URB DORADO DEL MAR 00646 #847-02-1978 L1982 **P** *020
MORALES, Ubaldo. 425 CARR 693 PMB 242 00646 #042-01-1975 L1984 **P** *020 †75
NEVAREZ, Edgar Antonio. URB. JARDINES DORADO, CALLE 9 #B-4 00646 #042-03-1992 L1996 **IM** *020
NORIEGA, Rosa Haiffe. ■ 00646 #308-01-1968 L1976 **PTH** *020 †50
NORIEGA-SANCHEZ, Angel. PO BOX 1418 00646 #308-01-1968 L1974 **N P** *020 †75
ONGAY RULLAN, Marietta. ■ 00646 #649-26-1993 L1995 **FM** *020
ORTIZ, Adelaida Teresa. ■ 00646 #042-01-1997 L1999 **IM** *020 †20
ORTIZ, Mirza I. 410 CALLE MENDEZ VIGO, STE 208 00646 #308-02-1993 L1996 **PD** *020
ORTIZ-CARRASQUILLO, Ramon. 106 DORADO BCH E 00646 #847-01-1974 L1976 **IM END** *020 †20
OTERO SURIA, Maria R. 219 CALLE THEBE, PASEO DEL SOL 00646 #042-04-1998 L2000 **FM** *020
PAULINO FADUL, Yesmin L. CALLE VIA MARBELLA 471 00646 #308-03-1995 L2003 *100
PENA-FIGUEROA, Luis A. PO BOX 563, BO MAMEYAL 00646 #308-03-1981 L1990 *020
PEREZ COLON, Dennis. ■ 00646 #042-02-1993 L1995 **DR** *020 †80
PEREZ-IGLESIAS, Salvador. K9 CALLE ESTRELLA DL MR #9, URB DORADO DEL MAR 00646 #042-01-1959 L1962 **OBG** *020 †30
PLAZA, Blanca Iris. 425 CARR 693, PMB 276 00646 #649-14-2002 *020
PORTELA, Juan C. ■ 00646 #042-01-1996 L1997 **OTO** *020 †45
RAMIREZ-HERNANDEZ, Judith. N-3 CALLE MENDEZ DEL MAR 00646 #847-10-1971 L1978 *020
RAMOS RIVERA, Pedro Luis. ■ 00646 #308-03-1984 L1995 *020
RAMPOLLA, Carla Teresita. 386 DORADO BCH E 00646 #042-01-1997 L1999 **OBG** *020
REYES MALDONADO, Oscar. 631 CALLE MAR DE BERING, PASEO LOS CORALES 00646 #308-04-2001 L2003 *100
RIOS, Juan Antonio. 425 CARR 693 PMB 325 00646 #042-01-1995 **ORS** *020
RIOS SANTIAGO, Elfren F. 275 CALLE MENDEZ VIGO 00646 #308-03-1980 L1984 **FM OS** *020
RIVERA-RIVERA, Magali S. P16 CALLE SIRENA, URB DORADO DEL MAR 00646 #042-04-1980 L1985 **PD GP** *020
RIVERA RUIZ, Alex. HH5 CALLE PELICANO, URB DORADO DEL MAR 00646 #649-14-1999 L2002 *100
ROBLES-ORAMAS, Carlos F. 332 CALLE MENDEZ VIGO 00646 #308-03-1980 L1983 **GP** *020
RODRIGUEZ, Marisol. ■ 00646 #042-01-1979 L1984 **RO** *020
ROLON-RIVERA, Jose E. Q14 CALLE PALMAS, URB DORADO DEL MAR 00646 #847-10-1974 L1976 **IM** *020
ROMAN CARLO, Ernesto. ■ 00646 #649-14-2000 L2001 *020
ROMERO SANTANA, Carlos A. BLDG 3 LOT 6 SEC 2 DORAVL 00646 #308-03-1985 L1992 **EM** *020
RUIZ-PEREZ, Fernando. 302 CALLE MENDEZ VIGO 00646 #847-04-1954 L1957 **GP PD** *075
RUIZ-VALE, William Jose, Jr. 362 CALLE SABALO, PASEO LAS OLAS 00646 #042-03-1993 L1996 **OBG** *020
SAADEYORDAN, Ricardo. 386 DORADO BCH E 00646 #042-03-1997 L2001 **U** *020
SANTIAGO APONTE, Rafael A. ■ 00646 #042-04-1997 L1999 **EM** *020
SANZ, Sara Victoria. ■ 00646 #042-03-1991 L1993 **PTH GP** *020 †50
SEGARRA, Omar. ■ 00646 #042-02-2005 **IM** *012
SEPULVEDA-NICHOLS, John P. JJ40 DORADO DEL MAR BLVD, URB DORADO DEL MAR 00646 #042-04-1985 L1986 **IM** *020
SERRANO MEDINA, Nitza Mer. ■ 00646 #042-03-2005 *100
SOLIS MERCADO, Heriberto. ■ 00646 #308-03-1990 L1993 *020
SOTO, Rafael Antonio. ■ 00646 #649-14-1998 L2001 *020
SUAREZ, Maria Soledad. ■ 00646 #042-01-1978 L1989 **PD** *020 †55
TELLO SANTINI, Carminia. E7 CALLE MADRE PERLA, URB DORADO DEL MAR 00646 #308-03-1982 L1994 *020
TIRADO GRACIA, Raul. ■ 00646 #847-10-1956 L1959 **PHP OS** *020
TIRADO-MANZANO, Javier L. 316 CALLE MENDEZ VIGO 00646 #847-10-1985 L1986 **IM** *020 †20
TIRADO MANZANO, Manuel. 316 CALLE MENDEZ VIGO 00646 #847-10-1987 L1990 *020
VELAZQUEZ RODRIGUEZ, N L. PO BOX 864 00646 #847-06-1972 L1978 **CD** *020
WILLIAMS, Robert Thomas. ■ 00646 #042-03-2000 L2001 **PTH** *020

ENSENADA – GUANICA

AVILES, Alberto. ■ 00647 #042-01-1966 L1993 **OBG** *020 †30
HERNANDEZ CASTILLO, Ricard. ■ 00647 #649-30-2004 **IM** *012
JUSINO ROMAN, Ernesto Lui. 48 CALLE FRAGATA, URB. PLAYA DEL SUR, CALLE 00647 #308-02-1998 L2000 **AN** *020
ROMAN, Ludemar Yaliz. ■ 00647 #042-01-2006 **N** *012

FAJARDO – FAJARDO

ABOU EL HOSSEN, Jamil. 410 AVE GENERAL VALERO, OFICINA 409 00738 #308-03-1984 L1995 **IM** *020
AGUILAR FIGUEROA, Nelida. HC 66 00738 #649-14-1999 L2002 *020
ALVARADO LOPEZ, Luis R. 9 CALLE AREYTO, TERR DEMAJAGUA 00738 #649-14-1993 L1996 **GP** *020
ANTRON AVILA, Cristobal A. PO BOX 70005 00738 #308-03-1986 L1992 *020
ARIAS RIOS, Elsa Dolores. ■ 00738 #308-03-1981 L1995 *020
ARRAUT, Juan Carlos. ■ 00738 #649-14-2003 L2005 *100
ARRAUT, Luis Armando. G5 CALLE PRINCIPAL, URB BARALT 00738 #308-03-1981 L1995 **IM** *020
ARRAUT DONADO, Luis. PO BOX 1322 00738 #132-02-1960 L1970 **OBG** *071
AYALA-ROSA, Balbino. G26 CAL 9 URB RAFAEL BERMU 00738 #308-03-1981 L1992 **GP** *020
BAEZ QUINONES, Samara. ■ 00738 #649-14-2002 L2004 *100
BERMUDEZ, Livia M. 303 AVE GENERAL VALERO, OFICINA 202 00738 #042-01-1978 L1982 **GP** *020

BETANCOURT, Nayda. URB EL BATEY, H-2130 CALLE #3 00738 #847-06-1975 L1982 **PD** *020
BIZARRO FANFAN, Cesar Enr. PO BOX 288 00738 #308-03-1982 L2004 *100
CARDONA, Kareen A. ■ 00738 #649-14-1993 L1996 *020
CARRERA, Alberto Manuel. PO BOX 667 00738 #042-01-1979 L1983 **OBG PHP** *030
CARRERA, Maria. 101 CALLE UNION E, URB SANTA ISIDRA 1 00738 #042-02-1983 L1986 **OBG** *020 †30
CINTRON-HERRERA, Jose L. ■ 00738 #042-03-1981 L1983 **OBG GP** *020
COGOLLO PUELLO, Rafael. FAJARDO DIST HOSP 00738 #649-01-1958 L1972 **GP** *020
COLON, Juan Medardo. 303 AVE GENERAL VALERO, OFC 302 00738 #042-01-1973 L1975 **U GS** *100
COLON, Nestor Alberto. 155 CALLE CELIS AGUILERA N 00738 #042-01-1976 L1980 **PD** *020
CONCEPCION MARIN, Julio L. B6 CALLE H, URB MONTE BRISAS 2 00738 #308-03-1984 L2005 **GP** *020
DE JESUS, Miguel A. PO BOX 309, N-2 GETTYSBURG 00738 #042-02-1991 L1996 **GS** *020
DELERME-MARTINEZ, Edsel. 205 CALLE CELIS AGUILERA N, STE 103 EDIFICIO OASIS 00738 #847-02-1967 L1971 **GS OS** *020
DEL ROSARIO ARIAS, Juan E. DEPT OF PUBLIC HEALTH 00738 #308-01-1946 L1958 **PHP OS** *020
DIAZ-BARRIOS, Luis Manuel. 303 AVE GENERAL VALERO, STE 101 00738 #308-01-1979 L1986 **CD IM** *020 †20
DIAZ CARTAGENA, J R. 110 CALLE ANTONIO R BRCL E 00738 #847-02-1972 L1975 **FM** *062
DIAZ-TORRES, Heriberto. 101 CALLE UNION E, URB SANTA ISIDRA 1 00738 #847-04-1960 L1963 **PD OS** *030
ENCARNACION SIACA, Maria. 104 CALLE DIEGO ZALDUONDO 00738 #042-03-1994 L1996 *020
ESQUENAZI, Moises. 10 CALLE UNION E STE 201, FAJARDO MEDICAL PLAZA 00738 #042-04-1981 L1989 *020
FIGUEROA, Myra. CALLE 11 5 7 FAJARDO GRD 00738 #042-03-1990 L1993 **IM** *020
FRANCESCHI, Patricia. ■ 00738 #308-03-1983 L1997 *100
FUENTES-CANALES, Manuel. B21 CALLE 5, URB CRUV 00738 #042-01-1966 L1969 **OBG** *020 †30
GARCIA, Jorge Ivan. ■ 00738 #042-01-2003 L2006 **PM** *100
GARCIA, Luis N. G19 CALLE PRINCIPAL, URB BARALT 00738 #042-01-1990 L1991 **FM** *020 †18
GARIB, Lidia Rosario. 375 AVE GENERAL VALER #101 00738 #042-01-1982 L1986 **PM** *020
GONZALEZ, Nestor. ■ 00738 #649-01-1970 L1974 **FM** *020
GONZALEZ-ALONSO, Luis A. 410 AVE GENERAL VALERO, STE 503 00738 #308-01-1979 L1986 **ORS OFA** *020
HENRY-SANCHEZ, John Tomas. ■ 00738 #042-01-2007 *012
HERNANDEZ ESTRELL, Arturo. ■ 00738 #308-01-1971 L1989 *020
HERNANDEZ-FRAGOSO, I. ■ 00738 #042-01-1957 L1971 **PHP FM** *071 †70
HERNANDEZ LIYIM, Luisa. ■ 00738 #308-03-1981 L1991 **IM** *020
HERNANDEZ-RIVERA, Luis A. 222 AVE B BOX 1311, URB SANTA ISIDRA 1 00738 #308-04-1984 L1987 **PD** *020
IRIZARRY, Carmen Diana. 10B CALLE CELIS AGUILERA S 00738 #308-03-1981 L1993 **GP** *020
IRIZARRY, Carmen G. 267 AVE GENERAL VALERO 00738 #847-04-1962 L1974 **AN PUD** *071
JIMENEZ, Cristobal. 20 CALLE CELIS AGUILERA S, OFFICE GYNECOLOGY BOX 1208 00738 #042-01-1971 L1973 **OBG** *020
JIMENEZ MATTA, Eduardo A. ■ 00738 #649-14-1992 L1994 **EM** *020
JURADO, Juan Antonio. 375 AVE GENERAL VALERO, STE 106 00738 #847-02-1963 L1971 **OPH** *020
JUSTINIANO-DIAZ, Raul T. 11 CALLE ANTONIO R BARCL W 00738 #016-43-1952 L1954 **GS** *020 †85
LAMBOY MEDINA, Ivette M. HC 867 BOX 21787 00738 #649-14-1991 L1995 **GP** *020
LEBRON NAZARIO, Luis D. 267 AVE GENERAL VALERO 00738 #847-04-1957 L1957 **GP OS** *020
LITHGOW RAMIREZ, Yngrid B. APT 908, CONDOMINIO DOS MARINAS II 00738 #649-14-1986 L1993 *020
LOPEZ, Manuel E. 315 AVE GENERAL VALERO 00738 #308-01-1959 L1969 **U** *075
LOPEZ, Sara. PO BOX 70006, 303 AVE GENERAL VALERO 00738 #847-05-1973 L1976 **OS** *020
LOPEZ MADRAZO, Silvio J. 110 CALLE ANTONIO R BRCL E 00738 #275-01-1949 L1972 **OTO PUD** *020
LOPEZ MARRERO, Luis M. PO BOX 1326, CALLE 6E-1 SAN ISI 00738 #847-10-1966 L1975 *020
LUGO, Lydia M. 375 AVE GENERAL VALERO, STE 105 00738 #042-01-1983 L1986 **PM** *020
MARCHENA, Jaime. 410 AVE GENERAL VALERO, SUITE405 00738 #308-03-1982 L1991 **P** *020
MARSHALL, Edwin. 375 AVE GENERAL VALERO, STE 105 00738 #042-01-1983 L1986 **CD IM** *020
MAS DE LEON, Yolanda. OFICINA 201, CALIFICIO MEDICO DEL ESTE 00738 #847-06-1976 L1982 **IM** *020
MATIENZO BOCANEGRA, Iris. PO BOX 966 00738 #847-04-1956 L1960 **PD PHP** *071
MELENDEZ, Jenny G Matta. C-1 URB MELENDEZ 00738 #847-10-1971 L1975 **GP** *020
MELENDEZ, Maritza. PO BOX 1289, CEMA 00738 #042-01-1989 L1992 **IM** *020
MENDEZ, Carmen Ivette. 267 AVE GENERAL VALERO 00738 #308-03-1978 L1980 **PD** *020
MONTALVO, Gloria Iris. PO BOX 667, H1 CARR 194 K1 00738 #042-01-1978 L1979 *020
MONTERO VELAZQUEZ, Jose F. 6 CALLE 3 00738 #847-10-1961 L1968 **GP PTH** *020
MONTES SANTIAGO, Sarita. URB. SANTA ISIDIA 3 EXT, CALLE UNION A-48 AND/OR 00738 #042-04-1991 L1994 *020
MORALES, Edwin Davis. ■ 00738 #847-02-1983 L1986 **GP** *020
MORALES, Miguel Javier. 98 CALLE GARRIDO MORALES E, OFIC 203 FAJARDO 00738 #308-02-1986 L1993 **GP** *020
MUES, Jose Alejandro. PO BOX 70005 00738 #308-03-1981 L1986 **IM** *020
NAZARIO, Ivette Francesch. D5 CALLE LA MILAGROSA 00738 #308-03-1982 L1992 **P** *020
NEGRON AGOSTO, Samuel. 67 CALLE ANTONIO R BARCL W 00738 #042-04-1994 L1995 **GP** *020
NEPTUNE, Reginald. J1 CALLE PRINCIPAL, URB BARALT 00738 #308-01-1974 L1976 **GP** *020
NIEVES-CALCANO, Gilberto. PO BOX 850 00738 #042-01-1954 L1957 **GP** *071
NIEVES SANTOS, Jennifer E. PO BOX 70005, 28.8BO CARR 3 CAROLAR 00738 #042-04-1998 L1999 **FM** *020
ORDONEZ, Luis R. 302 AVE GEN VALERO 00738 #847-06-1959 L1962 **IM CD** *020
ORTIZ, Jose R. PO BOX 70005, F7 CAMINO DEL VALLE 00738 #042-01-1976 L1981 **GS** *020
ORTIZ-FLORES, Sonia Enid. 410 AVE GENERAL VALERO, STE 504 00738 #042-04-1991 L1992 **FPG** *020 †18
ORTIZ RAMOS, Arturo. MUNOZ RIVERA 256 00738 #308-03-1984 L1992 **GP** *020
ORTIZ RIVERA, Eulalio. 267 AVE GENERAL VALERO 00738 #649-01-1962 L1962 **AN** *071
ORTIZ-VELAZQUEZ, Proviana. PO BOX 486 00738 #847-06-1976 L1982 *020
PACHECO MALDONADO, Pedro. HC 66 00738 #649-14-1997 L2000 *100
PALMER, Grace. 55 CALLE DEL CARMEN W 00738 #042-01-1988 L1992 **P** *020

PERELES-MERCED, Angel L. 5 CALLE CELIS AGUILER S #M 00738 #847-08-1971 L1974 **GS** *020
PEREZ, Jaime Roberto B. ■ 00738 #847-17-1981 L1984 **GP** *020
PEREZ, Maria De Lourdes. P O BOX 70011 PMBG7 00738 #308-13-2002 L2005 *100
PEREZ-CRUZ, Luis A. J1 CALLE PRINCIPAL, URB BARALT 00738 #042-03-1981 L1985 **OBG** *074
PEREZ-MALDONADO, Zaida. 810 DOS MARINA 00738 #308-03-1979 L1982 **PD** *020
PEREZ ROMERO, Alberto. CALLE 5 D7 SANTA ISIDRA 1 00738 #308-06-1987 L1994 **GP** *020
PRATTS-RIVERA, Ramon O. G.P.O. BOX 1227, STATE ROAD #3 KM44 00738 #847-12-1977 L1979 **GP** *020
QUESADA, Angel J. 313 AVE GENERAL VALERO, EDIF MED DEL ESTE STE 204 00738 #042-01-1984 L1987 **CD IM** *020
QUINONES, Evaristo. Q46 CALLE SAN MIGUEL, ALTS DE SAN PEDRO 00738 #308-06-1984 L1992 **GP OS** *020
QUINONES-ESQUILIN, Luis A. URB ALTAMIRA, TREET # 8 BLOCK A-21 00738 #847-10-1974 L1978 **GP** *020
REYES CRUZ, David. 375 AVE GENERAL VALERO, STE 108, ESQ MEDICA VALERO 00738 #042-04-1990 L1992 **GP** *020
RIVERA, Meiling. ■ 00738 #042-03-1990 L1993 **PD** *020
RIVERA-SANCHEZ, Yadira M. ■ 00738 #042-02-1998 L2000 **PDP** *020 †55
RODRIGUEZ, Antonio E. CALLE 9, #E6 URB ALTAMIRA 00738 #042-01-1993 L1994 **CD** *020 †20
RODRIGUEZ-GONZALEZ, Wilna. 353 AVE GENERAL VALERO 00738 #042-03-1981 L1987 **GS** *020
RODRIGUEZ-MORAN, Aurora. PO BOX 1247 00738 #308-01-1981 L1988 **PD** *020
ROSA-CEPEDA, Angel. 57 CALLE ISABEL ANDREU E 00738 #308-03-1979 L1982 **GP** *020
ROSA DIAZ, Luis F. D20 CALLE 9 URB ALTAMIRA 00738 #649-14-1997 L1999 **FM** *020
RULLAN, Luis Antonio. G19 CALLE PRINCIPAL, URB BARALT 00738 #042-01-1991 L1994 **IM** *020
SALAMAN, Luis Raul. URB ALTAMIRA ST 8 #A-18 00738 #042-01-1975 L1979 **IM** *020
SANCHEZ, Nestor Colon. 155 CALLE CELIS AGUILERA N 00738 #132-03-1968 **PD** *050
SANCHEZ, Sylvia Margarita. 57 CALLE UNION E 00738 #042-01-1976 L1980 **OPH** *020
SMESTAD, Kenneth Lee. ■ 00738 #042-01-1973 L1975 **IM** *071
SOFFICI, Nelida M. HC 66, BOX 10100 00738 #132-01-1957 L1971 **EM GP** *071
SOLLA-VELEZ, Angel Luis. PO BOX 883, 303 AVE GENERAL VALERO 00738 #847-02-1973 L1976 **PDE PD** *020
SOTO-VELILLA, Rosa. ■ 00738 #847-01-1975 L1980 **PD PHP** *020
TEJEDA, Carlos Manuel. 410 AVE GENERAL VALER #205, TORRE SAN PABLO DEL ESTE 00738 #042-01-1994 L1999 **HO** *020
TORRES-PEREZ, Alfonso. 110 CALLE ANTONIO R BRCL E 00738 #847-08-1973 L1976 **PD** *020 †55
VARGAS RAMOS, Irma N. 10 CALLE UNION E STE 202 00738 #042-04-1989 L1993 *020
VAZQUEZ, Antonio. 210 CALLE ORQUIDEA, LA COSTA GDNS HOMES 00738 #649-14-1999 L2000 **PD** *100 †55
VELAZQUEZ, Miguel. PO BOX 70005, PMB 228 00738 #042-04-1992 L1996 **OBG** *020
VELAZQUEZ LOPEZ, Benjamin. CALLE #132 00738 #649-14-2000 L2002 *020
WETTERER, Howard John. 313 AVE GENERAL VALERO 00738 #308-07-1983 L2002 **GP** *100
YUMET, Raul. ■ 00738 #028-34-1940 L1941 **GP** *071
ZACCHEUS FLORES, Carlos M. ■ 00738 #308-03-1978 L1989 **GP** *020

FLORIDA – FLORIDA

DE LA ROSA SERRANO, Abdias. APT 38 00650 #649-14-2003 L2005 *100
DELGADO TORRADO, Victor M. PO BOX 368, 7 CALLE ANTONIO ALCAZAR 00650 #649-14-1993 L1996 *020
DOMENECH HERNANDEZ, W. 72 CALLE ARIZMENDI, FLORIDA PUERTO RICO 00650 #649-01-1972 L1978 **GP** *020
GUERRERO, Daniel. PO BOX 386, 109 CALLE ARIZMENDI 00650 #847-02-1973 L1978 *020
MESTEY, Nilda. ■ 00650 #308-04-1984 L1987 **GP** *020
RODRIGUEZ PEREZ, Sarahi. PO BOX 352 00650 #308-13-2005 **IM** *012
SANCHEZ, Orlando. HC 1, BOX 3969 00650 #308-04-2004 L2005 *100
VARGAS OLIVERAS, Waleska. ■ 00650 #649-30-2001 L2003 *100
VAZQUEZ SANTOS, Jesus M. 72 CALLE ARIZMENDI 00650 #847-06-1986 L1989 *100

FORT BUCHANAN – BAYAMON

CABALLERO, Gilberto. US ARMY HEALTH CLINIC 00934 #042-01-1980 L1983 **FM** *020 †18

GARROCHALES – ARECIBO

CAMACHO MONTALVO, Darynell. PO BOX 268 00652 #649-14-2000 L2003 *100
FIGUEROA, Eric Noel. HC 52 BOX 4026, HM6 CARR 682 5 00652 #308-01-1990 L1996 **FM** *020
FIGUEROA SERRANO, Leovigil. PO BOX 224, 683 CARR KM 7.9 00652 #308-01-1983 L1996 *020
JELU, Antonio Jose. ■ 00652 #847-04-1967 L1973 **PD** *020
MARTINEZ-CARRASQUILLO, J. DORAL PLAZA #80 00652 #847-06-1984 L1989 **END** *020

GUANICA – GUANICA

ARROYO, Milagros. PO BOX 1452 00653 #042-02-1989 L1993 **PM** *020 †60
BAEZ LOPEZ, Roberto. 3 CALLE VICTOR SALLABERRY 00653 #308-04-1993 L1995 **IM** *020
BRINN-ESPARRA, Orlando. PO BOX 855 00653 #042-04-1983 L1987 **PD** *020
CAMACHO-COLBERG, Jose E. ■ 00653 #847-10-1970 L1972 **GP** *020
DELGADO-PEREZ, Antonio T. ■ 00653 #308-01-1974 L1978 **GP** *020
GALARZA, Ruben. BDE BELPICE #44 00653 #042-01-1974 L1976 **PD** *020
MARTINEZ, Arlene J. CALLE C17 URB SANTA CLARA 00653 #042-01-1993 L1998 **P** *020
MUNIZ, Pascual. 13 CALLE YAGUER 00653 #042-02-1994 L1997 *020
NAZARIO RODRIGUEZ, Ilsa J. 49 CALLE A, URB BAHIA 00653 #649-14-2001 L2003 **PD** *020
PEREZ SANTIAGO, Pedro. PO BOX 972 00653 #308-01-1981 L1987 *020
PRATDESABA, Rodrigo B. 10 CALLE 25 DE JULIO, URB SANTA CLARA 00653 #429-01-1974 L1977 **FM** *020
REYES, Alfonso. ■ 00653 #264-01-1958 **GS** *071

■ = Address Information Privacy Protected

RIOS SANTONI, Lucas J. PO BOX 1303 00653 #847-09-1975 L1978 **GP** *020
RIOS VIVAS, Aitza B. ■ 00653 #042-04-1995 L1996 **PD** *020
ROSADO, Rosana. 42 CALLE 25 DE JULIO 00653 #042-01-1999 L2000 **OPH** *020 †35 ‡
SIBERON NAPOLEONI, Maria. URB STA CLARA-CALLE B-23 00653 #847-02-1972 L1976 **FM** *020
TORRES-ORTIZ, Norman. 15 CALLE BUENAVENTURA QNNS 00653 #847-02-1973 L1976 **PD** *020
VELEZ, Gisela. PO BOX 446 00653 #649-14-2006 *100
VELEZ QUINONES, Luis A. APT 1167 00653 #308-03-1983 L1990 *020

GUAYAMA – GUAYAMA

ACEVEDO, Gilfredy. ■ 00784 #649-14-1990 L1993 **IM** *020
ALBAN, Gladys Myriam. ■ 00784 #649-35-1984 L2002 **FM** *020
ALEJANDRO-BENITEZ, A. 84 CALLE ASHFORD S 00784 #308-03-1979 L1982 **IM** *020
ALVARADO, Ricardo Nelson. ■ 00784 #042-03-2004 **N** *012
ANGELI, Robexi Delrosario. ■ 00785 #042-01-2000 L2005 **GS** *020 †85
ANGLERO-RAMOS, Jose. 69 CALLE DUQUE 00784 #308-03-1979 L1980 **EM** *020
BELLAFLORES CUEBAS, Frank. AVETERANS AVE 00784 #847-04-1956 L1958 **GP OS** *072
BUITRAGO, Hector C. 3 AVE LOS VETERANS, VILLA ROSA 1 00784 #847-04-1956 L1959 **IM** *030
BUITRAGO, Juan C. 128 CALLE ASHFORD S, OFICINA #101 00784 #042-01-1985 L1988 **PUD IM** *020 †20
BURGOS RIVERA, Yanille B. PO BOX 2464 00785 #649-14-2000 L2002 *020
BUSQUETS-PESQUERA, Jamie. 1 URB GIBRALTAR, AVE. ASHFORD 00784 #308-01-1976 L1979 **OBG** *020
CABALLERO, Rafael. C/O P.O. BOX 1558, 2 URB VILLA ROSA #1 00784 #042-04-1981 L1986 **GP** *020
CANDELARIO PIEVE, Alberto. PO BOX 2217 00785 #308-06-1986 L1989 **IM** *020
CARDONA, Alberto. I10 CALLE F, URB ALGARROBOS 00784 #042-01-1988 L1993 **GS** *020 †85
CARDONA ROBLES, Alberto. ■ 00784 #308-03-1982 L1989 *020
CASTANEDA, Angel Luis. PO BOX 10018 PMB 66 00785 #275-01-1970 L2006 **GP GS** *020
CINTRON-JEREMIAS, Hector. C/O PO BOX 2215, CALLE CALIMANO 101 00785 #847-06-1976 L1980 **GP** *020
CONDE, Zidnia M. ■ 00785 #042-01-2007 **IM** *012
CORA-SANTIAGO, Virgilio. BDA STA ANA C137 BUZON 13 00785 #308-03-1980 L1982 *020
CORTES-RIERA, Enrique Ama. AY5 CALLE 54, URB LA HACIENDA 00784 #042-02-2006 **IM** *012
DALMASY, Jose Manuel. POB 711 CALLE 6 C-18 00785 #308-01-1957 L1967 **IM PHP** *071
DAVILA, Roberto Luis. 21 CALLE HOSTOS S 00784 #042-01-1974 L1978 **D DS** *020 †15
DAVILA-LOPES, Juan A. BOX 722 00785 #042-04-1980 L1983 **IM** *020
DUPREY, Alexis. 22 CALLE ASHFORD N 00784 #042-01-1990 L1992 **N** *020
ESTRADA CORIS, Juan. APTO 655 CENTRO DE SALUD 00784 #847-10-1965 L1969 *020
FLORES VAZQUEZ, Nestor J. 71 PARQ INTERAMERICANA 00784 #042-04-1991 L1998 **PUD IM** *020
FOURQUET CRUZ, Jose G. 16 CALLE 3, BDA MARIN 00784 #308-04-1990 L1995 **PD** *020
FRANCESCHI-JUSINO, Edna. ■ 00784 #308-03-1983 L1990 **GP** *020
FRANCO RIVERA, Karina. PO BOX 1957 00785 #649-14-2003 L2005 *100
FRATICHELLII NIEVES, Angel. PO BOX 2187 00785 #649-14-1994 L1996 *100
GODREAU, Eileen Milagros. 214 CALLE REINITA, EL LEGADO GOLF RESORT 00784 #308-03-1984 L1987 **FM** *020 †18
GONZALEZ, Carlos P. ■ 00784 #649-14-1993 L1995 **FM** *020 ‡
HERNANDEZ, Edward. #22 OESTE, CALLE FRANCISCO G BRUNO 00784 #042-04-1988 L1993 **OBG** *020
HUERTAS RAMOS, Angel. ■ 00785 #847-08-1991 L1992 *020
JIMENEZ ALFONZO, Leida M. PO BOX 1680 00785 #308-01-1980 L1992 *020
JIMENEZ-TORRES, Carlos F. PO BOX 1657, ARROYO 00785 #010-01-1943 L1944 **DR** *071 †80
LAJARA, Reyna Isabel. PO BOX 1865 00785 #308-03-1996 L2006 *100
LINARES, Esteban Jose. 11137 LA FUENTE TOWN CTR, STE 11137 00784 #042-03-1991 L1995 **PM** *020 †60
LOPEZ ORTIZ, Edicto. 83 CALLE VICTORIA S 00784 #649-01-1960 L1968 **GP** *071
LOPEZ ORTIZ, Hector L. PO BOX 1957 00785 #649-14-2001 L2003 **GP** *020
LORENZO, Cristina E. ■ 00785 #308-01-1979 L1991 **GP AM** *020
LUGO, Luis A. 7 CALLE BALDORIOTY E 00784 #847-06-1976 L1979 **PD** *020
LUGO-CARMONA, Lilliam Den. ■ 00784 #649-14-2002 *020
LUGO-ZAMBRANA, Ruben. A3 AVE PEDRO ALBIZU CAMPOS, VILLA ROSA 3 00784 #042-01-1983 L1992 **GE IM** *020 †20
MARTINEZ, Hector G. PO BOX 388, 45N PALMER ST 00785 #042-01-1962 L1966 **OBG** *071 †30
MARTINEZ RODRIGUEZ, Rosa. PO BOX 7725 00784 #847-08-1984 L1992 *020
MATOS GUADALUPE, Alberto. ■ 00785 #042-04-1998 L1999 **FM** *020
MATOS VAZQUEZ, Emma. 41 CALLE SAN JOSE W 00784 #308-01-1982 L1992 *020
MELENDEZ, Luis Rafael. PO BOX 2601 00785 #308-04-1980 L1989 **GPM** *062
MIRANDA, Hector J. ST ROSA CLINIC BOX 988 00784 #847-05-1955 L1960 **GP** *020
MIRANDA, Maria Del C. ■ 00784 #042-03-1985 L1990 **IM** *020
MIRANDA-IGLESIAS, Juan J. 92 CALLE DUQUE 00784 #308-04-1985 L1986 **CD** *020
MIRANDA IGLESIAS, Luis R. 128 CALLE ASHFORD S # 104, ASHFORD MEDICAL PLAZA 00784 #042-04-1989 L1994 *020
MORALES, Jose Alberto. PO BOX 1913 00785 #649-14-2001 L2003 *100
MORALES, Sigfredo Santana. 22N CALLE PALMERA, BRISAS DEL MAR 00784 #308-03-1976 L1978 **OBG** *020
MORO, Jose S. PO BOX 1278 00785 #275-01-1960 L1975 **PD** *020
MUBARAK, Marisol Mercedes. CAL 3 B 5 URB REXMANOS 00784 #042-01-1989 L1993 **N** *020
MUBARAK RIZEK, Jose B. 3 B-5, REXMANOR STREET 00784 #308-01-1959 L1971 **FM** *071
MUNET PAGAN, Myrta D.. PO BOX 1601 00785 #308-03-2002 L2004 *100
MUNS-SOSA, Robert John. DR ALEJANDRO BUIHIAGO, GUAYAMA AREA HSP AMBUL DPT 00784 #308-03-1980 L1982 **EM** *020
NAVARRO, Rexie. ■ 00785 #042-04-1997 L1999 **FM** *020 †18
NAVEO MEDINA, Fidias O. AVETERANS AVE 00784 #010-01-1966 L1978 *020
NIDO, Roque C. AVETERANS AVE 00784 #847-06-1978 L1984 **GS** *020
NIDO STELLA, Roque C. PO BOX 1079 00784 #010-03-1951 L1953 **GP GS** *071
ORSINI ORTIZ, Magda. ■ 00784 #308-03-2001 L2004 *100
ORTIZ, Angel Luis. C/O P.O.BOX 1560, CALLE PALMER #44 NORTE 00785 #847-06-1977 L1980 **IM** *020
ORTIZ-BURGOS, Nora Hilda. ■ 00785 #847-06-1976 L1980 **AN** *071
ORTIZ DIAZ, Carlos W. ■ 00784 #308-03-1981 L1986 **PD** *020

ORTIZ RIVERA, Juan D.. ■ 00784 #308-04-1991 L1993 *100
PABON JUSINO, Lizzette C. ■ 00784 #649-43-1986 L2005 *100
PABON-MATEO, Hiram. 3 CALLE ENRIQUE GONZALEZ W, CONSULTORI MEDICO 00784 #847-02-1975 L1978 **FM OM** *020
PALES-AGUILO, Joaquin R. 23 CALLE BALDORIOTY W, ESQUINA LUIS VENEGAS 00784 #847-21-1980 L1984 **GP** *020
PATINO-ARCA, Bolivar. AVETERANS AVE 00784 #737-01-1943 L1958 **PTH FOP** *071 †50
PEDRAZA ORTIZ, Ivemilia. PO BOX 232 00785 #308-03-1984 *100
PERDOMO DE MUBARAK, Olga. PO BOX 478 00785 #308-01-1959 L1971 **GP** *100
PEREZ, Leroy A. PO BOX 1920 00785 #308-03-1983 L1989 **PD** *020
PEREZ-DE JESUS, Armando L. 128 ASHFORD ST 00784 #308-03-1984 L1989 **P** *020
PEREZ RAMIREZ, Ruben A. ■ 00785 #308-06-1984 L1988 **FM** *020
PEREZ-SOTO, Omar. D1 CALLE GLADIOLA, URB GREEN HILLS 00784 #649-14-2003 *020
PLANAS SANTIAGO, Virgen Y. PO BOX 1864 00785 #042-04-2003 L2004 *100
POMALES, Raul Antonio. PO BOX 390 00785 #847-10-1973 L1976 **EM** *020
QUINONES, Angel Miguel. 3 AVE LOS VETERANOS, VILLA ROSA 1 00784 #042-01-1997 L2002 **GS** *020
QUINONES-GONZALEZ, J. 11123 LA FUENTE TOWN CTR, STE 11123 00784 #649-14-1986 L1991 **PD MDM** *020
QUINTANA, Francisco J. CALLE ASHFORD 81 00784 #042-02-1996 L1997 **OBG** *020
RAMOS RODRIGUEZ, Jerry D. PO BOX 183 00785 #042-04-1994 L1995 **PHL GP** *020
RIVAS, Ramon Luis. PO BOX 1739 00785 #042-04-1988 L1991 **AN** *020
RIVERA-FIGUEROA, Marta I. CALLE 2 #1 - VILLA ROSA I 00784 #308-03-1979 L1985 **GP** *020
ROBLES-ROMERO, Jorge L. REXMANOR STREET 6 F-2 00784 #042-04-1988 L1992 **AN** *020
RODRIGUEZ, Carlos R. ■ 00785 #847-04-1958 L1960 **IM** *071
RODRIGUEZ, David Eduardo. ■ 00785 #649-14-2003 L2004 **IM** *100
RODRIGUEZ-FONTANEZ, Jose. ■ 00785 #308-03-1980 L1982 **GP** *020
RODRIGUEZ TORRES, G. PO BOX 1023, CALLE #5C-10 URBANIZACION 00785 #847-04-1963 L1966 **OPH** *020
RUIZ SOTO, Juan A. ■ 00784 #308-01-1990 L1995 **IM** *020
SANCHEZ, Gustavo R. 23 CALLE BALDRIOTY W, LUIS VENEGA CORNER BOX 215 00784 #308-04-1942 L1984 **OBG** *020 †20
SANTIAGO, Dania Luz. ■ 00785 #042-01-2005 **IM** *012
SANTIAGO, Iris Belia. ■ 00785 #649-01-1960 L1971 **PD** *020
SANTIAGO COLON, Juan R.. ■ 00784 #308-03-2003 L2004 **FM** *100
SANTIAGO-FORTIER, Aurelio. 26N CALLE ASHFORD N 00784 #847-02-1974 L1979 **PD** *020
SANTIAGO TEXIDOR, Marisel. CALLE 4 C8 VISTAMAR 00784 #308-03-1982 L1991 *020
SICARD FIGUEROA, David T. ■ 00785 #042-04-1994 L1995 **FM** *020
SOLIVAN, Rosalinda. PO BOX 780 00785 #649-52-1986 L1992 **GP** *020
SOSA-MIRANDA, Hiram. PO BOX 1018 00785 #847-10-1963 L1966 **PD** *020
SOTOMAYOR SANTOS, Melba. ASHFORD ST, #22-N 00784 #042-01-1980 L1984 **N** *020
TORRADO, Luis A. PALES, 2DO PISO, CALLE HOSTOS ESQ VICENTE 00785 #308-03-1982 L1984 **P** *020
TORRES, Mildred. ■ 00785 #649-30-2004 **IM** *012
TORRES RODRIGUEZ, Jose An. ■ 00784 #308-04-2005 **GP** *020
VAZQUEZ, Luis Adiel. ■ 00784 #649-30-2004 *100
VIGO, Myrna L. ■ 00785 #847-03-1972 L1975 **GP** *020
VIZCARRONDO, Manuel. PO BOX 2342 00785 #308-03-1984 L1987 **GP** *020
VIZCARRONDO-ACOSTA, Nilsa. PO BOX 538, CALLE PACIFICO 17 BAJOS 00785 #308-03-1979 L1980 **OBG** *020
YEJO VEGA, Nelia. 74 CALLE E # 19, BDA SANTA ANA 00784 #649-35-2000 L2002 *020
ZAPATA, Arnaldo I. AVETERANS AVE 00784 #042-02-1984 L1989 **CD IM** *020 †20
ZAYAS-BURGOS, Jesus A. PO BOX 24 00785 #042-04-1991 L1991 **PD** *020
ZAYAS-MARTINEZ, Antonio. ■ 00785 #847-02-1975 L1977 **OBG** *020
ZENO, Helios Augusto. PO BOX 2223 00785 #308-06-1984 L1990 **GP** *020

GUAYANILLA – GUAYANILLA

BELTRAN RAMOS, Wilfredo. CALLE 18 R-3, URB SANTA ELENA 00656 #649-14-1998 L2003 *100
CAMACHO, Luis Oscar. ■ 00656 #308-03-1983 L1990 **GP** *020
CASIANO, Ariel. 6 CALLE JOSE DE DIEGO 00656 #649-18-1984 L1990 **GP** *020
CASTILLO, Mario Luis. ■ 00656 #308-03-1985 L1990 **GP** *020
CRUZ, Luis Javier. HC 1, URB STA ELENA M-6 ST 14 00656 #042-02-1993 L1997 **GS** *020
DEMAIO, Jamie Michelle. PO BOX 560086, 20 CALLE CONCEPCION 00656 #042-01-1989 L1992 **GP** *020
FERNANDEZ, Miguel Alberto. 12 CALLE CONCEPCION 00656 #308-01-1986 L1991 *020
FRANCESCHINI, Carmen. 152 CALLE MUNOZ RIVERA INT 00656 #042-02-1983 L1986 **IM** *020
HERNANDEZ RODRIGUEZ, Rafae. ■ 00656 #649-14-2001 L2002 **FM** *020
LOPEZ DE VICTORIA, Carlos. 10 CALLE CONCEPCION, FIRST FLOOR 00656 #308-01-1988 L1993 *020
LUGO, Sylvette Marie. ■ 00656 #649-14-2003 L2005 *100
MELENDEZ BERRIOS, Anthony. C2 CALLE 21, URB STA MARIA 00656 #649-14-1996 *100
MORALES, Zulicka Yexira. ■ 00656 #042-02-2006 L2007 **TY** *012
MORALES-RODRIGUEZ, Luz E. URL STA ELENA 17 00656 #847-04-1959 L1962 **OBG** *071
OLIVERA, Carlos, Jr. P O BOX 56078 00656 #649-14-1994 L1996 *020
ORTIZ, Luz Adina. ■ 00656 #308-02-1991 L1995 **GP** *020
PAGAN, Luis A. ■ 00656 #649-26-1988 L1996 **FM** *020
RAMIREZ MONTALVO, Jorge R. PO BOX 560102 00656 #308-04-2004 L2005 *100
RODRIGUEZ, Hilda Yris. ■ 00656 #308-03-1981 L2003 *100
RODRIGUEZ, Virgilio, Jr. HC 1 BOX 6035, KM4.5 CARR 378 00656 #042-02-1997 L1999 **EM** *020
RODRIGUEZ CALES, Orlando. E10 CALLE 4, SANTA ELENA 2 00656 #649-14-2003 L2005 *100
SANTIAGO, Francisco N. ■ 00656 #847-06-1992 L1995 **FM** *020
SANTIAGO GARCIA, Richard. PO BOX 560810 00656 #649-14-2003 L2005 *100
SEGARRA, Amaury. BOX 242, BO BARRERO 00656 #042-02-1999 L2003 *100 †20
TORRES-VELAZQUEZ, Juan Ca. ■ 00656 #649-14-2000 L2002 *100
VILLA-MEDINA, Juan C. PO BOX 561436 00656 #308-13-2001 L2005 *100
ZAIDI ALLEN, Yamil A.. B6 CALLE 3, VILLA DEL RIO 00656 #308-04-2003 L2005 *100

GUAYNABO – CATANO

ACOSTA, Deborah Antonia. AVE CRISLIDA CRISTALINA, URB LUIS MUNOZ RIVERA 35 00965 #042-01-1997 L1999 **P** *020

APONTE, Orlando. 10E CALLE A BDA VIETNAM 00965 #042-01-1975 L1980 **RHU IM** *072

BERLINGERI, Jose A. ■ 00965 #042-01-1962 L1967 **DR** *020

CIANCHINI QUINONES, F A. ■ 00965 #847-04-1960 L1977 **GP** *020

COLON, Ada Milagros. ■ 00965 #042-03-2003 **FM** *100

DECHOUDENS, Mercedes. ■ 00965 #042-01-1988 L1993 **DR** *020 †80

DE LEON-RIVERA, Teresita. ■ 00965 #042-03-1994 L1999 **DR** *020

ECHEVARRIA, Maria Elena. ■ 00965 #042-02-1998 L2000 **PD** *020 †55

FONTANEZ-NIEVES, Tania Da. ■ 00965 #042-01-2007 **PD** *012

LEBRON MALDONADO, Carmen. 11 CALLE H, BDA VIETNAM 00965 #042-03-1981 L1991 *020

MARTINEZ MENA, Enercida. ■ 00965 #308-01-1994 L2005 *100

MEDIAVILLA DE CONAWAY, C. 15 CALLE H, BDA VIETNAM 00965 #649-18-1971 L1977 **PD** *020

MERCADO-DIAZ, Victor R. 1028 ROOSEVELT AVE 00965 #847-05-1975 L1979 **FM** *020 †18

ORTIZ HERNANDEZ, Carlos F. 4 CALLE B BDA VIETNAM 00965 #847-04-1966 L1968 **OBG** *020

ORTIZ-SANABRIA, Edna G. 45 CALLE DIEGO VEGA, BO AMELIA 00965 #042-02-1986 L1989 **PD** *020

PEREZ, Ricardo. ■ 00965 #042-01-1987 L1988 **FM** *020 †18

PIMENTEL, Milciades A. ■ 00965 #308-01-1950 L1966 **ORS** *040

RIOS, Olga Vanessa. ■ 00965 #042-01-1998 L2006 **N** *100 †75

ROBLES, Maybeth. ■ 00965 #042-01-1984 L1989 **PTH** *020 ‡

ROMAN, Sonia. ■ 00965 #308-03-1981 L1992 **PD** *020

SUAREZ, Samuel Benjamin. ■ 00965 #042-01-1994 L1997 **PUD** *020 †20

VAZQUEZ, Lorraine Marie. ■ 00965 #042-01-1980 L1984 **DR** *020 †80

GUAYNABO – GUAYNABO

ABOUBAKER, Mohamad. ■ 00969 #042-03-1981 L1992 **OBG** *020

ACEBAL, Vivian Lourdes. 407 VIA ESCORIAL, VILLAS REALES 00969 #042-03-1995 L1998 **PD** *020

ACEVEDO, Guillermo. B8 CALLE PONCE, VILLA AVILA 00969 #847-05-1978 L1997 **GP** *020

ACEVEDO, Wida Mercedes. 10 CALLE CARAZO 00969 #308-03-1980 L1984 **PD** *020

ACOSTA, Hector Javier. PO BOX 7891, PMB 677 00970 #042-01-1999 L2001 **EM** *020 †16

AGUAYO, Rosaura. E14 CALLE NUEVA, VILLA CLEMENTINA 00969 #042-01-1984 L1987 **PD** *020 †55

AGUDO, Maria Luisa Arcill. 18 CALLE AZALEA, URB MUNOZ RIVERA 00969 #748-12-1986 L1999 **PD** *020

AIZENMAN, David. ■ 00969 #649-01-1961 **ORS** *020

ALEGRIA-ORTEGA, Ega R. ST 19 NO 31 URB PONCE DE L 00969 #847-03-1976 L1978 **PD** *020

ALEJANDRO, Kathia V. ■ 00966 #042-01-2000 L2004 **GS** *100

ALONSO RODRIGUEZ, Alicia. ■ 00969 #275-03-1994 L2003 **GP** *020

ALONZO, Angelita. 10 CALLE TRUJILLO 00966 #308-01-1986 L1994 *020

ALTIERI, Vanessa. 5 #19 AVE.SANTA ANA, ALTURAS DE TORRIMAR 00969 #649-14-2004 *100

ALVAREZ, Fernando L. ■ 00969 #847-01-1961 L1963 **IM GE** *071

ALVAREZ MOLINA, Carlos J. PO BOX 210, 42 CALLE CARAZO 00970 #308-03-1979 L1987 **GP** *020

ALVAREZ RIVERA, Edwin. A-APOLO ESQ ALEJANDRINO Q5 00969 #042-01-1980 L1983 **OPH** *020

ANDREU, Rene Alfredo. B5 CALLE GENOVA, EXT VILLA CAPARRA 00966 #308-03-1986 L1991 **GP** *020

ANGLERO-RIVERA, Roberto. ■ 00970 #847-10-1958 L1961 **PHP GP** *020

ANTUNEZ, Ivan Dario. 67 CALLE JUAN C BORBON #35, PMB 311 00969 #042-03-1997 L2000 **GE** *020

ARIAS-BENABE, Claudino. URB CERRO REAL # M2 00969 #042-01-1979 L1982 **PM** *020 †60

ARIAS MALDONADO, Luis A. ■ 00969 #308-04-1984 L1987 **GP** *020

ARIZA, Carlos Arturo. 304 EDIF CAPARRA GLRY #304 00966 #042-01-1996 L1998 **IM** *020

ARROYO, Gloria E. ■ 00969 #042-01-1968 L1971 **RO** *020

ARROYO-TORO, Amilcar J. CALLE 10-1F VIC BRAEGGER 00966 #649-01-1958 L1965 **GP** *071

ARZOLA-CASTANER, Daniel. ■ 00966 #042-01-1998 L2002 **ICE** *100 †20

ASTACIO, Esteban Vasquez. 2073 CALLE CLOTO, URB ALTO APOLO 00969 #308-03-1979 L1988 **GP** *020

AXTMAYER, Robert W. ■ 00966 #056-06-1946 L1948 **OBG** *020 †30

AYALA, Maira E. 10 CALLE CARAZO 00969 #042-04-1989 L1991 **ADP CHP** *020

AYALA, Wanda Waleska. ■ 00969 #308-03-1982 L2006 *100

AYALA CUERVOS, Jose Raul. 18-4 CALLE ALCAZAR, URB TORRIMAR 00966 #847-06-1972 L1975 **IM** *020

BADIA CALDERON, Jose M. ■ 00969 #231-01-1955 L1957 **PD** *071 †55

BADILLO, Salvador. ■ 00966 #042-01-1961 L1963 **IM RHU** *071

BAEZ, Jose A. 14B CALLE VANDA, ALT DE TORRIMAR 00966 #042-01-1995 L1997 **PM** *020 †60

BANUCHI, Ivonne M. ■ 00969 #042-01-1984 L1989 **PM** *020

BARRERAS, Jose Rafael. ■ 00969 #042-03-1994 L1995 **DR NM** *020 †80

BARRIOS, Nilka J. 2 CALLE BRILLANTE, CHALETS DE SANTA CLARA 00969 #042-03-1981 L1991 **PHO** *030 †55

BATLLE, Maria Y. 2123 CALLE MILETO, URB ALTO APOLO 00969 #042-01-1995 L1998 **EM** *020 †16

BAYOLO ALONSO, Juan Carlo. ■ 00969 #649-14-2002 L2004 **GP** *020

BEAUCHAMP, Belinda. 369 VIA VERSALLES, VILLAS REALES 00969 #042-01-1986 L1989 **PD** *020 †55

BEAZ, Luis F, Jr. ■ 00969 #042-01-1988 L1992 **AN** *020

BEHAR-YBARRA, Tamara. B27 CALLE 1, VILLAS DE PRADO ALTO 00966 #308-03-1982 L1989 **PD** *030

BELLO GRAFELS, Jesus A. ■ 00969 #042-01-1965 L1967 **IM RHU** *020

BENITEZ, Frank H. C9 CALLE ACUARELA, URB HIGHLAND GDNS 00969 #649-28-1982 L1989 **GP** *020

BERDECIA, Victor Antonio. 1353 CARR 19 00966 #042-03-1989 L1994 **DR** *020

BERDECIA-RODRIGUEZ, Vic. ■ 00966 #847-03-1976 L1981 **FM OM** *020

BERLINGERI-RAMOS, Alma Cr. ■ 00966 #042-01-1988 L2004 **D** *012

BERMUDEZ, Ramon Humberto. ■ 00969 #056-06-1961 L1965 **ID IM** *020 †20

BERRIOS, Ramon Rafael. 301 EDIF CAPARRA GLRY #301, CALLE 107 GONZALEZ GIUSTI 00966 #042-01-1988 L1989 **OPH** *035

BERRIOS DIAZ, Wanda M. ■ 00969 #042-04-1998 L2000 **FM** *020

BERTRAN-PASARELL, Jorge. 35 CALLE JUAN C BORBON, STE 67 PMB 343 00969 #042-01-1994 L1999 **D** *020

BETANCOURT BETANCOURT, L. 21 AVE TERRS DE TINTILLO 00966 #847-10-1972 L1975 **OBG** *020

BLANCO, Jorge A. ■ 00966 #042-01-1967 L1971 **ORS** *020

BLASINI, Ileana Enid. ■ 00969 #042-01-1978 L1984 **PD** *020

BONANO BENITEZ, Juan F. ■ 00969 #042-04-1997 L1999 **OBG** *020

BONES-RODRIGUEZ, Raphael. ■ 00969 #042-03-2001 L2002 **IM** *020

BONETA-GARCIA, Eliseo. JA10 CALLE PASEO DEL PARQU, URB GARDEN HLS 00966 #042-01-1957 L1959 **CLP PD** *020 †18

BONILLA FRANCESCHINI, A. ■ 00966 #042-03-1980 L1986 **PTH** *030

BONNET, Armando Luis. B15 CALLE BENITEZ, VILLA LISSETTE 00969 #042-02-1991 L1998 **DR** *020

BONNET-ALVAREZ, Mayra. 205 EDIF CAPARRA GALLERY, STE 205 00966 #042-03-1981 L1985 **PD OS** *030 †55

BORDEWYK, Roberto P. ■ 00969 #042-01-1981 L1985 **IM** *020

BORRAS, Pedro J. C5 CALLE PALMA SOLA, URB GARDEN HLS 00966 #847-04-1957 L1958 **NS RO** *020 †25

BORRERO, Clarimar. ■ 00969 #042-03-2006 **PD** *012

BOUPRIETO, Elias Antonio. ■ 00969 #042-01-2004 L2006 **IM** *012 †20

BRAVO, Jaime Jose. 165 CALLE REINA ISABEL, URB LA VILLA DE TORRIMAR 00969 #042-01-1977 L1981 **OPH** *035

BUJOSA, Carlos A. 112 CALLE CARAZO 00969 #042-01-1992 L1996 **FM** *020

BURGOS, Rafael A. CALLE 1 J13 LOS FRA NORTE 00969 #042-01-1965 L1968 **IM OS** *020

BURKE RAMIREZ, Petra. 12 CALLE REINA ISABEL, URB LA VILLA DE TORRIMAR 00969 #042-01-1970 L1974 **N** *040

BUSTAMANTE, Horlirio L. CEREIPO 108 ALT STA MARIA 00969 #275-01-1947 L1975 **GP** *020

CABAN, Carmen. 305 CALLE REY FELIPE, URB LA VILLA DE TORRIMAR 00969 #042-01-1967 L1970 **R** *020

CABANAS, Jose Guillermo. ■ 00971 #305-01-2005 **EM** *012

CABEZAS, Ana. 81 CALLE REINA ALEXANDRA, URB LA VILLA DE TORRIMAR 00969 #042-03-2002 L2005 **PD** *020

CABRERA, Carmen M. LOS FRAILES C6-URB LOS FRA 00969 #042-01-1982 L1987 **U** *020 †95

CABRERA DE LA MATA, Luis. E2 CALLE 1, URB PRADO ALTO 00966 #308-02-1991 L1992 **FM** *020

CACERES, Juan. V15 CALLE MONTE DEL ESTADO, COLINAS METROPOLITANA 00969 #042-01-1984 L1987 **FM** *020 †18

CAJIGAS-PICO, Agustin. ■ 00966 #042-01-1958 L1961 **CLP** *071 †50

CALDERA, Jose A.. 58 AVE ESMERALDA, URB MUNOZ RIVERA 00969 #308-02-1993 L1998 **IM** *020

CAMACHO, Nyda Del Rosario. 3013 AVE ALEJANDRINO, FONTAINBLEU PLAZA #102 00969 #042-01-1997 L1999 **D** *020 †15

CAMPOS-RUIZ, Rafael S. 439 CALLE REY LUIS, URB LA VILLA DE TORRIMAR 00969 #042-03-1981 L1984 **IM** *020

CANINO-MOREY, Alfredo A. D6 CALLE HAMILTON 00969 #847-06-1976 L1980 **GP** *072

CANTELLOPS, Jose M. C1 CALLE PARK PL, URB TORRIMAR EST 00969 #308-02-1987 L1992 **PD** *020

CARAZO, Edgardo. J3 CALLE CHURCH HL, URB TORRIMAR 00966 #042-04-1987 L1991 **GP** *020

CARBALLIDO, Jorge. ■ 00966 #275-01-1969 L1998 **FM** *020

CARDONA, Carlos Alfonso. ■ 00969 #042-01-1988 L1991 **IM** *020 †20

CARDONA, Francisco Enriqu. L-9B CALLE TORRIMAR, PATIO HILLS 00966 #649-14-2003 L2005 *100

CARDONA-RAMIREZ, Jose M. ■ 00969 #847-05-1981 L1986 **CD IM** *020

CARDONA-UBINAS, Marciano. ■ 00969 #042-01-1956 L1960 **OS** *072

CARLO, Michelle Marie. ■ 00966 #042-01-1997 L2003 **PD** *055

CARMONA RIVERA, Adaliz. AVE SAN IGNACIO 1500 J206, BALCONES DE SANTA MARIA 00969 #649-14-1999 L2000 *100

CARMONA-VARGAS, Nestor A. 140 CALLE REINA MARIA, URB LA VILLA DE TORRIMAR 00969 #847-01-1974 L1979 **OBG** *020

CARRASQUILLO-ROMAN, Jose. ■ 00970 #308-03-1983 L1988 **PHP** *020

CARRERO, Evelyn. C8 CALLE ZEUS, URB MONTE OLIMPO 00969 #042-01-1982 L1984 **AN CCA** *020 †055

CARRILLO COLON, Hipolito. ■ 00970 #308-03-1983 L1987 **FM** *071

CARTAGENA, Miguel Angel. ■ 00969 #042-01-1974 L1976 **AN** *020

CASAS-LOPEZ, Raul. K12 CALLE REY ARTURO, QTAS REALES 00969 #847-06-1978 L1981 **OM** *020

CASTELLANOS-BRAN, Raul G. PASCUA N7 TERR DE GUAYN 00969 #847-04-1974 L1978 **GP** *020

CASTELLVI, Maria V Armas. 50 CALLE CALISTEMON, EST DE TORRIMAR 00966 #042-02-1986 L1991 **AN IM** *020

CASTRO, Joyce Marie. 19-22 AVE RAMIREZ DE ARELN, STE 7 PMB 65 00966 #042-01-2003 L2005 **PM** *020

CASTRO, Providencia. ■ 00966 #041-07-1943 L1944 **CHP OS** *071

CASTRO AVILA, Rosa Taiwa. C5 CALLE YAGRUMO, COLINAS DE GUAYNABO 00969 #649-14-2000 L2002 *020

CASTRODAD, Eladio V. ■ 00966 #847-06-1969 L1970 **CD IM** *020 †20

CASTRO-SILEN, Jesus A. ■ 00969 #308-03-1978 L1982 **GP** *020

CEDENO GONZALEZ, Cayetano. 274 AVE SANTA ANA # 186 00969 #847-04-1955 L1958 **GP** *020

CEDENO LACLAUSTRA, Nanette. ■ 00966 #649-14-2004 **IM** *012

CERVONI, Walter A. 8 CALLE 10, ALT DE TORRIMAR 00969 #024-05-1949 L1952 **PTH IM** *020 †50

CHIESA, Zelma Charlotte. ■ 00969 #042-01-2008 *012

CID, Dorcas Yadira. ■ 00969 #042-03-1999 **P** *100

CINTRON PINERO, Alex D. ■ 00969 #042-04-2000 L2003 **FM** *020

CLAUDIO, Norma A. ■ 00969 #042-02-1997 L1999 **NPM** *012 †55

CLIMENT-DE VELEZ, C. G5 CALLE SAN JACINTO 00969 #847-06-1974 L1980 **CLP OS** *040 †50

COLIN, Mitsue. ■ 00969 #042-01-1999 *100

COLOM AVILES, Vicente. B.Z.N. 176, COND CHALETS DEL PARQUE 00969 #869-04-1958 L1960 **AN** *071

COLON, Eileen. ■ 00969 #042-03-2003 **IM** *100 †20

COLON, Horacio Rafael. X22 CALLE EL VIGIA, COLINAS METROPOLITANA 00969 #042-01-1998 L1999 **RNR** *020 †80

COLON, Irma N. 53 AVE ESMERALDA, PMB 171 00969 #042-01-1981 L1985 **DR** *020 †80

COLON, Melba Iris. CALLE 1J11, URB. PRADO ALTO 00966 #042-01-1980 L1983 **ID IM** *020 †20

COLON, Minela. ■ 00969 #042-03-2007 **PD** *012

COLON-MENDEZ, Manuel J. ■ 00971 #649-18-1979 L1987 **EM** *020

COLON-STALZER, Ana L. 6-16 CALLE 7 00969 #042-03-1995 **PD** *100

COLON-VELEZ, Helga T. ■ 00969 #847-01-1984 L1988 **P** *020

COMAS, Arsenio Carlos. K3 CALLE BAMBOO DR, URB TORRIMAR 00966 #042-01-1961 L1964 **OBG MFM** *020 †30

■ = Address Information Privacy Protected

CONAWAY, Ralph C. H-15 STREET VILLA CAPARRA 00966 #649-01-1970 L1975 **CD IM** *040

CONDE-ROSA, Ana Marisol. ■ 00966 #042-03-2003 L2005 **ID** *012 †20

CORDOVA, Awilda Arroyo. 71 CALLE ROBLE, EST DE TORRIMAR 00966 #042-01-1971 L1978 **PD** *020

CORTES, Richard. 52 AVE ESMERALDA, URB MUNOZ RIVERA 00969 #042-01-1986 L1990 **PD** *020

CORTES MELENDEZ, Maritza. ■ 00969 #042-04-2004 L2006 *100

CORTES-SANTOS, Hector M. ■ 00966 #042-01-2004 **PM** *020

CORTIJO PADILLA, Ernesto. PO BOX 64 00970 #308-03-1986 L1994 *100

CORZO, Jorge E. I14 CALLE RUISENOR, URB TIERRA ALTA III 00969 #847-06-1973 L1976 **FM PMM** *020 ‡

COTT, Hector. D12 CALLE BUEN SAMARITANO, URB GARDENVILLE 00966 #042-04-2000 L2001 *020

CRESPO-BADILLO, Edgar R. 203 AVE ESMERALDA, URB PONCE DE LEON 00969 #847-03-1974 L1980 **PD** *020

CRUZ, Marinely. ■ 00969 #042-03-2003 **IM** *100 †20

CRUZADO, Gustavo Antonio. O5 CALLE LAS AGUILAS, URB TIERRA ALTA I 00969 #042-03-2000 L2003 **OBG** *020 †30

CRUZ RIVERA, Carlos R. ■ 00971 #308-04-1993 L1995 **GP** *020

CUBANO, Miguel A. D12 CALLE BUEN SAMARITANO, GARDENVILLE 00966 #847-01-1962 L1965 **P GP** *072 †85

CUEBAS, Luz M. 2 CALLE CRISALIDA, URB MUNOZ RIVERA 00969 #042-01-1980 L1985 **OTO HNS** *020

CUESTA, Carlos. A 14 TORREMOLINOS 00969 #649-01-1954 L1980 **OS** *075

CUMBA BERMUDEZ, Nixaliz. B19 BALDWIN WALK, URB BALDWIN PARK 00969 #649-14-2003 L2005 *100

DALMAN LARRINAZA, Marta. ■ 00969 #042-03-1980 L1980 *100

DANGER, Eddyme. ■ 00969 #042-02-2003 L2006 **PM** *020

DAVILA AGOSTO, Emilio J.. A13 CALLE MEADOW LN, URB GARDEN HLS 00966 #649-14-2004 L2006 *100

DE FELIX-DAVILA, Roberto. ■ 00969 #042-01-2001 L2006 **PM** *020 †60

DE JESUS, Orlando. 14 CALLE DIAMNT URB BUCARE 00969 #042-01-1987 L1994 **NS GS** *020 †25

DEJESUS, Ricardo. ■ 00969 #042-01-1999 L2005 **DR** *020 †80

DE JESUS GONZALEZ, Eilyn. ■ 00966 #649-14-1999 L2001 **IM** *020 †20

DE LA CRUZ AVILES, Jaime. 136 CALLE CARAZO 00969 #847-04-1972 L1977 **GP** *020

DE LA PENA, Sylvia L. 274 AVE SANTA ANA, URB TIERRA ALTA III 00969 #847-05-1976 L1979 **PD** *020 †55

DE LA VEGA, Arnaldo. 41 CALLE ALAMEDA, URB MUNOZ RIVERA 00969 #275-04-1976 L2006 **PD** *012

DELGADO-NORIEGA, Sigfredo. ■ 00969 #847-06-1974 L1976 **GP** *020

DEL VALLE-DE TOMAS, Pedro. GARDEN HILLS, VILLAVERDE A-15 00966 #042-04-1993 L1994 **IM** *020

DEL VALLE-VIZCARRONDO, L. D13 CALLE ECUADOR, URB OASIS GDNS 00969 #042-01-1969 L1974 **OPH GP** *020

DE MARQUEZ, Felipa Diaz S. ■ 00969 #041-13-1949 L1951 **GP** *020

DENIZ, Sandra Ivette. ■ 00969 #042-01-2003 L2006 **GS** *012

DE ROLDAN, Frieda Silva. ■ 00970 #042-01-1972 L1974 **NM IM** *040 †28

DIAZ, Francisco J. ■ 00966 #042-01-1996 L1999 **CCP** *020 †55

DIAZ, Jacqueline. ■ 00966 #275-01-1994 **FP** *012

DIAZ, Jose. ■ 00966 #042-03-1988 L1994 **OBG** *020

DIAZ, Manuel. 107 AVE ORTEGON, CAPARRA GALLERY BLDG, SUIT 00966 #308-03-1980 L1987 **P** *020

DIAZ, Mirielle. ■ 00969 #042-02-2006 **PM** *012

DIAZ, Padilla Julio J. 2102 CALLE AGUAMARINA, URB BUCARE GDNS 00969 #308-04-1990 L1992 **RO** *020

DIAZ, Pedro Ernesto. 35 CALLE JUAN C BORBON #67, PMB 383 00969 #042-02-2001 L2006 **RNR** *020 †80

DIAZ, Rodrigo. QUINTAS REALES, N-9 REINA ISABEL 00969 #042-01-1989 L1993 **OBG** *020

DIAZ, Teresa Delpilar. ■ 00969 #042-01-1999 L2001 **OBG** *100

DIAZ-MAISONET, Luis. 2055 CALLE TOPC URB BUCARE 00969 #649-14-1976 L1978 **IM** *020

DIAZ-MONTANEZ, Angel M. D12 CAL GRNT URB PARKVILLE 00969 #021-01-1949 L1951 **PD** *020 †55

DIAZ-REYES, Candido Ariel. ■ 00969 #275-01-1960 L1970 **PD OS** *075

DUBOCQ, Francisco Manuel. ■ 00966 #042-01-1965 L1967 **U** *020

DUBOCQ, Francisco Manuel. ■ 00966 #649-14-1986 L1989 **U** *020

ECHEANDIA FUSTER, Ramon A. ■ 00966 #042-04-1997 L2000 **FM** *020

ECHENIQUE, Luis Ignacio. 534 CALLE TINTILLO, URB TINTILLO HLS 00966 #042-01-1979 L1984 **GS** *020 †85,10

ELIZA-GARCIA, Miguel A. 14 CARR 833, LA CIMA DE TORRIMAR 1404 00969 #847-05-1977 L1979 *020

ESCABI PEREZ, Luis A. A15 CAL GNV EXT VILLA CAPA 00966 #042-01-1970 L1973 **P GS** *020

ESCOBAR-MARTINEZ, Lynn. ■ 00966 #042-02-1992 **OBG** *100

ESPADA, Carmen. EX11 CALLE HERMOSILLA 00969 #042-01-1984 L1989 **OBG** *020

ESPINOSA, Rosa Maria. ■ 00966 #042-04-1981 L1987 **GP** *020

ESQUILIN, Ines O. 36 CAL CRSLD URB MUNOZ RIV 00969 #042-01-1989 L1992 **IM PD** *020 †55

ESTRELLA, Eduardo F. 107 AVE ORTEGON, CAPARRA GALLERY STE 212 00966 #042-01-1998 L2002 **OBG** *020 †30

FABIAN, Carlos Alberto. CARRTERA 177, THE FALLS 00966 #132-06-1972 L1978 **U** *020 †95

FAGET, Guillermo L. 21 AVE WALL, TERRS DE TINTILLO 00966 #847-10-1972 L1975 **OBG** *020

FAGET, Maria Eugenia. 21 AVE TERRS DE TINTILLO 00966 #649-14-2003 L2006 *100

FAGET BETANCOURT, Ana Mar. ■ 00966 #649-14-2003 L2006 **GP** *100

FALCON-CARATINI, Roberto. ■ 00969 #042-03-2000 L2004 **FM** *071

FAURA CLAVELL, Luis. STE 308 00966 #042-03-1980 L1983 **PM** *020

FEBUS LUNA, Adria. ALHAMBRA BLK 17 17 TORR 00966 #847-08-1970 L1977 **FP** *071

FERNANDEZ, Daniel Enrique. N24 CALLE HARDING, URB PARKVILLE 00969 #042-01-1997 L2002 **APM** *020 †05

FERNANDEZ, Enrique. 6-10 RAMIREZ DE ARELLN, URB TORRIMAR 00966 #649-14-1988 L1991 **OS** *020

FERNANDEZ, Jose Alberto. ■ 00969 #275-03-1990 L2005 **HEM** *012 †20

FERNANDEZ, Jose Orlando. ■ 00969 #649-14-2001 L2003 *100

FERNANDEZ-MARINO, Vicente. ■ 00971 #275-01-1953 L1967 **OTO** *072

FERNANDEZ-TORRES, Lionel. MCKINLEY N 38 PARKVILLE 00969 #847-04-1962 L1964 **PM FM** *020

FIGUEROA, Karla Ivonne. 52 AVE ESMERALDA, URB MUNOZ RIVERA 00969 #042-01-1999 L2002 **PD** *020 †55

FIGUEROA, Lissan. ■ 00971 #649-14-2002 L2004 *100

FIGUEROA, Rafael R. ■ 00966 #308-04-1983 L1992 **IM** *020

FLORES, Licette M. 8 AVE VICTOR BRAEGER # E9 00966 #042-01-1986 L1989 **PD** *020 †55

FLORES PADRO, Awilda A. ■ 00966 #847-10-1962 L1967 *071

FONT, Yvonne Marie. ■ 00969 #042-01-2001 L2004 **RHU** *100

FORT, Digna Victoria. 36 CALLE TROPICAL, URB MUNOZ RIVERA 00969 #649-30-1985 L1995 **FM** *020

FORTI, Luis Raul. 3071 AVE ALEJANDRINO, PMB 136 00969 #308-04-1988 L1991 **GP** *020

FORTUNO, Armando. M31 AVE JUAN RAMOS, EXT SANTA PAULA 00969 #042-03-1995 L1998 **P** *020

FOURNIER, Tatiana. ■ 00970 #042-02-2007 **OBG** *012

FRONTERA, Ernesto A. 12 C/PATRICIA SUSAN CT CHL 00966 #042-01-1982 L1986 **P** *020

GALAN VAZQUEZ, Ricardo D. B19 CALLE SEVILLA BILTMORE, URB SEVILLA BILTMORE 00966 #042-04-1989 L1994 *020

GALARZA-ARBONA, Jose Luis. ■ 00969 #847-05-1969 L1971 **P** *020

GARCIA, Beatriz Eugenia. ■ 00969 #042-03-2007 **ORS** *012

GARCIA, Frances Lynn. 115 CALLE REINA MARGARITA, URB LA VILLA DE TORRIMAR 00969 #042-01-1973 L1975 **NPM PD** *030 †55

GARCIA, Jose Antonio. ■ 00969 #275-01-1984 L2006 **IM** *012

GARCIA, Jose Luis. 7 CALLE ONIX, URB BUCARE 00969 #847-06-1980 L1993 *020

GARCIA, Nayda Felicita. 335 VIA LOUVRE, VILLAS REALES 00969 #308-04-1984 L1990 **GP** *020

GARCIA-BLANCO, Mariano A. L11 VILLA CAPARRA CT 00966 #008-01-1984 *100

GARCIA BULLS, Aureo B. 10 CALLE 1, TERRS DE TINTILLO 00966 #847-04-1956 L1959 **GE IM** *071

GARCIA-GARCIA, Jose M. ■ 00969 #847-02-1976 L1983 *020

GARCIA-MEDINA, Jose. ■ 00969 #042-01-1995 L1997 **IM** *020

GARCIA-PALMIERI, Mario R. 27 CALLE DUQUE WINDSOR, EST REALES 00969 #023-01-1951 L1953 **CD IM** *030 †20

GARCIA-RIVERA, Olga Noemi. ■ 00966 #847-08-1977 L1979 **PD OS** *020

GARCIATRIAS, Rebecca P. ■ 00966 #042-03-1999 L2002 **HO** *100

GARCIA-VERGNE, Manuel A. A18 CALLE SERRANIA, URB GARDEN HLS 00966 #847-09-1962 L1965 **OBG** *020

GARRIGA, Lourdes. ■ 00969 #042-02-1994 L1997 **PD** *020 ‡

GAYOL, Priscilla. ■ 00969 #649-14-2002 L2005 *100

GERENA, Fernando. PO BOX 2793, GUAYNABO PUEBLO ST. 00970 #042-01-1992 L1996 **AN PME** *020 †05

GIL-MUNOZ, Betty. ■ 00970 #264-02-1978 L1991 **RO** *020

GIRALDEZ, Laureano August. ■ 00966 #042-01-2007 **OTO** *012

GOMEZ REYNOSO, Marcos A. ■ 00969 #308-03-1985 L1993 **PD** *020

GONZALEZ, Beatriz Celeste. ■ 00966 #042-03-2001 L2004 **PD** *020 †55

GONZALEZ, Carlos Javier. ■ 00969 #042-02-2007 **TY** *020

GONZALEZ, Henry. 331 VIA LOVR VILLAS REALES 00969 #042-01-1993 L1996 **GE** *020 †20

GONZALEZ, Maria Eugenia. 1179 CALLE F, URB MUNOZ RIVERA 00969 #308-03-1981 L1987 **GP** *020

GONZALEZ, Michelle Marie. ■ 00971 #042-01-1999 L2001 **ID** *100 †20

GONZALEZ, Rafael. ■ 00966 #847-10-1964 L1969 **PD** *071

GONZALEZ, Ramon Martinez. ■ 00969 #275-01-1934 L1966 **PUD OS** *020

GONZALEZ, Ricardo Eduardo. ■ 00969 #042-01-1986 L1988 **FM** *020 †18

GONZALEZ BERNAL, Juan M. 1959 CALLE SANDALO, URB SAN RAMON 00969 #847-10-1972 L1974 **GP** *020

GONZALEZ FLORES, B. 17-18 PASEO ALHAMBRA 00966 #041-13-1952 L1955 **U** *020 †95

GONZALEZ GARCIA, Manuel M. ■ 00969 #308-02-1982 L1995 **GP** *020

GONZALEZ MARIN, Ludgardo. ■ 00969 #649-01-1972 L1977 **P OM** *020

GONZALEZ-PONS, Carlos A. 3011 CAMINO ALEJANDRINO, C/O CONDOMINIO VIEW POINT 00969 #308-01-1976 L1981 **IM** *020

GONZALEZ-RAMIREZ, Edgardo. ■ 00969 #042-01-1977 L1983 **ORS OS** *020

GORDO-GONZALEZ, Victor M. ■ 00969 #042-04-1986 L1988 **IM** *020

GOTOS, Juan Antonio. 3071 AVE ALEJANDRINO, STE 140 00969 #042-01-1975 L1979 **PD** *020 †55

GRAU PABON, Iris M. ROBLE BLANCO E-9 SANTA CAL 00969 #308-04-1994 L1997 *020

GROVAS PORRATA, Jorge E. COND.PLAZA ESMERALDA APT.1 00969 #042-04-1997 L1999 *020

GRULLON BAUTISTA, Jeanette. ■ 00966 #308-01-1987 L2002 **FM** *100

GUASP, Glenda Grisselle. ■ 00969 #042-03-1995 L1998 **PD** *020

GUTIERREZ, Maria Del Carm. ■ 00969 #275-04-1992 L2006 **PD** *012

GUZMAN, Aida. ■ 00969 #042-01-1956 L1960 **P** *020

GUZMAN, Giram A. RES GALLARDO GDNS B APT 3 00966 #042-03-1981 L1985 **IM** *100

GUZMAN VILLARONGA, Jorge. ■ 00969 #308-03-1982 L1987 **EM** *020

HADDAD, Mario A. ■ 00969 #308-04-1984 L1988 **IM** *020

HANSBERRY, Edna Rosario. ■ 00969 #847-10-1968 L1970 *074

HERNANDEZ, Gustavo A. 35 CALLE JUAN C BORBON #67, PMB 295 00969 #042-01-1992 L1996 **OPH** *020 †35

HERNANDEZ, Julio R. B0#41 LA COLINA 00969 #042-01-1987 L1992 **ORS OAR** *020 †40

HERNANDEZ, Nilda Ivonne. ■ 00969 #042-01-1977 L1982 **IM** *020 †20

HERNANDEZ-DA PENA, M A. 132 CALLE 21, URB JUAN PONCE DE LEON 00969 #847-04-1959 L1962 **PM GP** *020

HERNANDEZ-GARCIA, E. ■ 00970 #042-01-1994 L1997 **PD** *020

HESS, Jorge. 249 CALLE REY FEDERICO, URB LA VILLA DE TORRIMAR 00966 #847-02-1979 L1985 **GP** *020

HUERTAS-SOLA, Lisette. 53 AVE ESMERALDA, PMB 75 00969 #042-01-1992 L1995 **IM** *020 †20

IGLESIAS, Nayvis. ■ 00969 #275-01-1996 **FP** *012

INESTA, Michael Franklyn. 12 AVE PARQUE DE LOS NINOS, CHALETS DEL PARQUE BOX 118 00969 #042-01-1999 L2001 **CHP** *020

IRIZARRY, Maria De Los A. ■ 00966 #042-04-1988 L1990 **GP** *030

JACA, Ignacio Javier. 40 CALLE VALENCIA, URB TORRIMAR 00966 #035-09-1995 L1999 **GE** *020 †20

JIMENEZ, Eleanor. APT.24A STA.ANA COND., 1026 RD19 VILLA CAPARRA 00966 #042-01-1964 L1968 **PHO PD** *020 †55

JIMENEZ BARREDO, Jesus Li. 42 CALLE ALAMEDA, URB MUNOZ RIVERA 00969 #275-04-1985 L2006 **FP** *012

JIMENEZ DE CAJIGAS, Alma. ■ 00966 #042-01-1957 L1961 **PDC PD** *071

JIMENEZ QUEZADA, Juan V. 8 CAL PRNTSS URB MUNOZ RIV, RIVERA 00969 #308-01-1975 L1983 **GS** *062

JOGLAR, Olga M. 9 CALLE PATRICIA, URB SUSAN CT 00966 #042-01-1973 L1976 **PD PDC** *020 †55

■ = Address Information Privacy Protected

JORDAN-MOREY, Edmundo J. 18 AVE ARBOLOTE, PALMAR DEL RIO I BOX 352 00969 #649-14-1997 L1999 **CD** *100 †20

LAGUNA, Reinaldo Figueroa. ■ 00971 #042-01-1989 L1993 **IM** *020 †28

LAMBOY DE LEON, Aurea M. ■ 00969 #042-01-1991 L1994 **PD** *020

LARA, Rafael. 405 FOUNTAINBLEU VLG 00969 #649-14-2000 L2003 *100

LATOUR, Euyen. ■ 00969 #042-03-2005 **IM** *012

LEBRON, Juan Carlos. ■ 00966 #042-03-2008 *012

LEON FIGUEROA, Hector Rub. ■ 00969 #308-13-2000 L2004 **ON** *012

LEON-VALIENTE, Carla F. ■ 00966 #042-01-1974 L1974 **ID IM** *020

LINARES, Rafael. ■ 00970 #010-03-1963 L1972 **IM HEM** *020 †20

LLITERAS, Olga Milagros. 67 CALLE JUAN C BORBON, PMB220 00969 #042-01-1998 L2001 *020

LLORENS, Amaury Jose. 406 VIA ESCORIAL, VILLAS REALES 00969 #042-03-1994 L1999 **OBG REN** *020 †30

L'OFFICIAL-DESCHAMPS, A. M. ■ 00966 #308-01-1958 L1973 **GYN** *020

LOJO, Liliana. ■ 00969 #042-01-2000 L2006 **PHO** *012

LOPEZ, Lionel Fernandez. 2 CALLE CRISALIDA, URB MUNOZ RIVERA 00969 #042-01-1980 L1985 **OTO HNS** *020

LOPEZ, Luis A. Y2 CALLE ARIZONA, EXT PARKVILLE 00969 #847-06-1960 L1963 **OS PHP** *030

LOPEZ, Nayda T. M8 CALLE REY JORGE V, QTAS REALES 00969 #042-01-1986 L1989 **PD** *020 †55

LOPEZ, Raul Edgardo. SANTA PAULA, CALLE 2J4 00969 #649-14-1988 L1990 *020

LOPEZACEVEDO, Nicolas. ■ 00969 #042-03-2008 *012

LOPEZ-ALMODOVAR, Carlos E. 22 CALLE DIAMANTE, URB BUCARE 00969 #847-10-1966 L1969 **A IM** *020 ‡

LOPEZ-CALDERON, Felix. GUAYNABO MUNICIPALITY, HEALTH DEPT 00970 #042-03-1980 L1984 **PD** *020

LOPEZ DEL VALLE, Felix J. ■ 00970 #042-04-1991 L1995 **GP** *020

LOPEZ-TORRES, Sarah. PO BOX 1078, 307 EDIF CAPARRA GALLERY 00970 #847-03-1980 L1985 **FM** *020 †18

LOPEZ-VELEZ, Alba Nydia. ■ 00969 #308-03-1979 L1981 **GP OM** *020

LORENZO, Claudia. 49 VALLE ESCONDIDO 00971 #042-02-1984 L1986 **PD** *020

LUCIANO, Carlos Alberto. ■ 00969 #042-01-1985 L1998 **N CN** *050 †75

LUGO, Lisette A. L3 CALLE JAGUAS, URB SANTA CLARA 00969 #042-01-1986 L1989 **PD** *020 †55

LUGO LUGO, Tomas. 2115 CAL ANTQ URB ALTO APO, APOLO 00969 #847-04-1964 L1967 **P** *071

MADRID, Alfonso A. 42 CALLE CARAZO 00969 #847-06-1980 L1992 **P** *020

MAESTRE, Carlos C. E5 CALLE A, EST DEL PARQUE 00969 #042-01-1967 L1969 **U** *020 †95

MAISONET, Carmen L. 35 AVE ESMERALDA PMB 135, URB MUNOZ RIVERA 00969 #042-01-1961 L1968 **PD GE** *040

MAISONET-RODRIGUEZ, A. 53 AVE ESMERALDA, PMB 135 00969 #042-04-1984 L1988 **GP** *020

MALAVE FELIX, Leila V. 1 CALLE LUHN, URB VICTOR BRAEGER 00966 #847-12-1976 L1980 **PD CCP** *020

MALAVET, Julia T. GARDEN HILLS ESTATES, 26 2ND STREET 00966 #042-01-1988 L1991 **PD** *020

MALDONADO, Addiss. ■ 00969 #308-01-1986 L1989 **GP** *020

MALDONADO, Alberto Manuel. C16 CALLE MONTEREY, URB EL ALAMO 00969 #042-01-1996 L2001 **TS** *020

MALDONADO, Carlos Nicolas. ■ 00966 #308-01-1966 L1975 **GS** *020

MALDONADO, Mayra. ■ 00969 #042-03-2004 **DR** *020

MALDONADO, Norman I. 16-10 CALLE GRANADA, URB TORRIMAR 00966 #042-01-1959 L1961 **HEM IM** *020 †20

MALDONADO, Pedro Alberto. D18 CALLE DORA SOLER, VILLA LISSETTE 00969 #308-02-1989 L1991 **IM** *020

MALDONADO RIVERA, Felix. 225 CARR 2, VILLA CAPARRA PLAZA 00966 #847-09-1968 L1971 **CHP OS** *020

MANDRY, Rocio Delcarmen. 309 EDIF CAPARRA GALLERY, AVE GONZALEZ GIUSTI #107 00966 #035-01-1988 L1992 **D** *020 †20,15

MARIANI, Aixa M. ■ 00969 #042-01-1964 L1966 **GP OBG** *074

MARIANI, Jose Francisco. 28 CALLE SONATA, URB MUNOZ RIVERA 00969 #649-14-1993 L1995 **PD** *020

MARIN-DE GRACIA, Jesus M. F1 CAL DLD ALT DE SANTA MA, MARIA 00969 #847-02-1983 L1986 **EM GP** *040

MARIN RULLAN, Mimosa. JARDIN N 1 GARDEN HILLS 00966 #025-01-1948 L1949 **PD** *071 †55

MARMORATO, Rossella Maria. ■ 00966 #042-01-2007 **IM** *012

MARQUES, Bernardo Jose. 1353 CARR 19, PMB 502 00966 #010-02-1963 L1967 **DR** *020 †80

MARRERO, Derik Ivan. ■ 00966 #042-01-2004 **GS** *012

MARRERO, Ian Carlos. ■ 00966 #042-01-2000 L2002 **PS** *100 †85

MARRERO-ARROYO, Darwin. E2 CALLE A, EST DEL PARQUE 00969 #308-03-1979 L1984 **PD** *020

MARROIG RIOS, Georgina. ■ 00966 #847-10-1957 L1960 **PDC** *071 †55

MARTIN, Ralph Jesus. ■ 00969 #042-01-2005 **IM** *012

MARTINEZ, Enrique R. ■ 00970 #034-01-1977 L1978 **FM** *020 †18 ‡

MARTINEZ, Francisco Jose. 100 BUEN SAMARITANO # 12A 00966 #042-02-1985 L1990 **FM** *020 †18

MARTINEZ, Glenda. F20 CAL CLVLND URB PARKVIL 00969 #042-03-1989 L1992 **PD** *020 †55

MARTINEZ, Jaime S. 37 CALLE REINA SOFIA, URB LA VILLA DE TORRIMAR 00969 #042-01-1985 L1986 **IM** *020 †20

MARTINEZ, Jose R Melendez. ■ 00971 #042-03-1994 L1996 **IM** *020

MARTINEZ, Palmira. ■ 00970 #042-01-1989 L1994 **OTO** *020 †45

MARTIN-REYES, Elba Rosa. 1 COND LA ARBOLEDA 00966 #275-03-1988 L2005 **IM** *100 †20

MARTORELL, Gerardo S. ■ 00966 #649-01-1961 L1966 **R** *072

MARTORELL, Guillermo M. ■ 00966 #042-01-2003 L2006 **EM** *100

MARXUACH, Acisclo M. 2-14 PASEO ALHAMBRA, URB TORRIMAR 00966 #847-04-1962 L1965 **GE IM** *062 ‡

MAS-RAMIREZ, Manuel. 408 CALLE REINA ISABEL, URB LA VILLA DE TORRIMAR 00969 #042-01-1980 L1985 **GS** *020 †85

MAYOL, Hector Manuel, III. ■ 00969 #042-02-2001 L2002 **IM** *020

MEDINA, Antonio. W1 CALLE 1, URB BELLOMONTE 00969 #042-01-1994 L1999 **OBG** *020

MEDINA-TOLENTINO, G. ■ 00966 #016-43-1950 L1952 **GP** *071

MEJIA BETANCOURT, Luis E. ■ 00969 #319-02-1989 L1991 **GP** *020

MEJIAS LOGRONO, Laura. A14 CALLE I, URB TORREMOLINOS 00969 #308-02-1977 L1982 **PD** *074

MELENDEZ, Jonathan A. ■ 00966 #042-01-1996 L1999 **EM** *020 †16

MELENDEZ, Jorge S. 1142 CALLE K, URB MUNOZ RIVERA 00969 #737-03-1982 L1996 **FM** *020

MELENDEZ, Rafael. B5G CALLE GARFIELD, URB PARKVILLE 00969 #042-01-1976 L1981 **N** *071 †75

MELENDEZ-RIOS, Nyssa Zoe. ■ 00969 #042-01-2007 **IM** *012

MELENDEZ TORRES, Juan B. 536 CALLE TINTILLO 00966 #847-10-1965 L1969 **ORS GS** *020

MENDEZ, Angela M. ■ 00969 #042-01-1982 L1986 **DR IM** *020 †80

MENDEZ, Keimari. ■ 00969 #042-01-2006 **OBG** *012

MENDEZ, Melissa. ■ 00966 #042-01-1995 L1998 **N CN** *020 †75

MENDEZ-BUSO, Carla M. ■ 00966 #042-01-1996 L2004 **P** *020 †75

MENDEZ SEXTO, Ramon. ■ 00966 #042-04-1981 L2003 *020

MENDIOLA DE JESUS, R. 37 CAL TNGR URB ALTO APOLO 00969 #649-01-1960 L1969 **PD OS** *071

MENDOZA MOYA, Samuel. ■ 00966 #308-01-1943 L1958 **OBS GPM** *071

MERCADO, Salvador Mercado. 25 ST 221 URB'PONC DE LEON 00969 #649-14-1974 L1980 **DR PD** *020

MERCADO, Teodoro Hiram. ■ 00966 #649-14-1988 L1992 **CD IM** *020

MERLE, Lydia A. 3071 AVE ALEJANDRINO, STE 231 00969 #042-04-1982 L1988 **PD** *020

MILAN, Livette. 409 CALLE REINA ISABEL, URB LA VILLA DE TORRIMAR 00969 #042-01-1992 L1996 **OBG** *020

MIRANDA, Ana B. URB PARQUE MEDITERRANCO, APT 12 00966 #042-01-1989 L1992 **PD** *075

MIRANDA, Liliana Zo. 35 CALLE JUAN C BORBON #67, PMB 383 00969 #042-02-2001 L2006 **P** *020 †75

MIRANDA, Luis Alexander. 35 CALLE JUAN C BORBON #67, PMB 327 00969 #042-01-1992 L1998 **OSM** *020 †40

MIRANDA BUSTAMANTE, Jorge. PH I PONCE DE LEON GARDENS 00966 #847-04-1959 L1970 **GP** *020

MIRANDA-CORDOVES, Carlos. CALLE 12 24 ALTURAS DE TOR 00969 #649-14-1984 L1986 **GS** *020

MIRANDA-LAMA, Esmeralda. ■ 00966 #042-03-1992 L1996 **PM SCI** *020 †60

MIRANDA REYES, William. 10 AVE WALL, URB TINTILLO GDNS 00966 #847-10-1970 L1972 **PD** *020

MOLINA, Angel M. 9 AVE ESMERALDA, URB MUNOZ RIVERA 00969 #042-01-1986 L1988 **IM** *020 †20

MOLINA DIEZ, Jose R. ■ 00969 #649-14-1976 L1976 **FM** *030

MOLINARI, Maria A. COND GARDEN HILL TOWER, APT 601 00966 #042-01-1999 L2002 **NPM** *020

MOLINARIS, Luis Fernando. 35 CALLE JUAN C BORBON, STE 67 00969 #042-03-1994 L1998 **AN** *020

MOLINARIS, Yolanda M. 254 STATE ROAD 2 STE 1302, COND. CAPARRA REAL 00966 #042-01-1990 L1995 **OBG** *020

MOLINS, Caroline Marie. ■ 00971 #042-03-2007 *012

MONTALVO, Freddie. 2 VIA BERNARDO, URB MONTE ALBERNIA 00969 #042-01-1968 L1976 **PD HEM** *020

MONTALVO, Lisandro, Jr. LA VILLA DE TORRIMAR 00969 #042-01-1999 L2001 **IM** *020 †20

MONTALVO SANCHEZ, L. 12 CALLE REINA ISABEL, URB LA VILLA DE TORRIMAR 00969 #042-01-1970 L1974 **NEP IM** *020

MORALES, Adisbeth. 50 CALLE LOPATEGUI, URB PARKVILLE 105 00969 #042-01-2005 **D** *012

MORALES, David. PHA VILLA CAPARRA 00966 #042-01-1967 L1974 **R** *020

MORALES, Digna Gisela. 110 CALLE CEREIPO, ALT DE SANTA MARIA 00969 #042-03-2003 L2006 **IM** *020

MORALES, Jose Manuel. 35 CALLE JUAN C BORBON #67, PMB 182 00969 #042-01-1988 L1992 **PM** *020 †60

MORALES-MORALES, Manuel J. ■ 00969 #737-01-1959 L1972 **GP** *020

MORALES-PEREIRA, Antonio. ■ 00969 #042-01-1958 L1962 **OBG END** *071 †30

MORA RODRIGUEZ, Brenda I.. PO BOX 332, CONDO VALLES DE TORRIMAR 00970 #308-04-2001 L2003 *100

MORENO, Patricia Rosa. 1142 CALLE K, URB MUNOZ RIVERA 00969 #737-03-1983 L1996 **PD** *020

MORENO-FERRER, Liana A.. ■ 00966 #308-15-1989 L2002 **FM** *020

MULET, Jesus. ■ 00966 #275-05-1985 L2005 *100

MUNIZ, Jesus. C16 CALLE ISABEL LA CATOLC, MANS REALES 00969 #042-01-1984 L1987 **IM** *040 †20

MUNIZ, Juan C. ■ 00969 #042-03-2005 **IM** *100

MUNIZ VARGAS, Luis D. ■ 00969 #308-06-2002 L2004 *100

MURATI, Belkiss Iulianne. ■ 00969 #042-01-2007 **PTH** *012

NADAL, Anaida Josefina. ■ 00969 #649-14-2003 **RHU** *012

NEGRON, Edgardo Aliover. #80 ST 3 APT 302, COND ARC SUCHVILLE 00966 #042-03-1999 L2003 **IM** *100

NERY, Edgar Alejo. ■ 00966 #176-03-1969 L1979 **GS** *020

NERY GOMEZ, Richard Paul. 120 CALLE C, URB ALTO APOLO 00969 #649-14-2003 *020

NG FRANJUL, Joaquin N.. ■ 00969 #308-01-1984 L2002 *020

NIEBLA DIAZ, Osvaldo. 118 CALLE ACUARELA, COND QUINTAVALLE 00969 #275-03-1996 L2004 *100

NIEVES, Daniel Amilcar. ■ 00969 #042-01-1954 L1956 **IM** *020

NIEVES, Myrna. 2501 COND FOUNTAINEBLEU 00969 #042-03-1983 L1988 **PD PHO** *071 †55

NIEVESORTIZ, Omar Noel. ■ 00969 #042-01-2002 L2005 **CD** *012 †20

NOY, Maria Cecilia. K 18 VILLA CAPARRA 00966 #042-01-1988 *100

NUNEZ CORRADA, Jose. ■ 00969 #847-09-1972 L1975 **U GS** *020

OCASIO, Carlos Javier. ■ 00969 #042-01-2007 *012

OCTAVIANI, Clarylee. ■ 00969 #042-01-2001 L2002 **NEP** *100

OJEDA, Willibaldo. ■ 00966 #042-01-2001 L2004 **CD** *012

OLAZABAL, Maria Dolores. ■ 00966 #042-01-1997 L2000 **P** *020

OLAZABAL, Ricardo Manuel. ■ 00966 #010-02-1992 L1997 **RNR** *020 †80

OLIVERAS, Carene Alani. ■ 00969 #042-01-2007 *012

OLIVERO, Herminio Javier. ■ 00966 #042-01-1996 L1999 **OBG** *020 †30

ORDUNA, Elba A. ■ 00969 #042-03-1981 L1984 **PA FOP** *020 †28

ORENGO, Victor. ■ 00970 #649-14-1987 L1991 *100

OROBITG, Francisco J. ■ 00966 #042-03-1986 L1987 **DR** *071

ORTIZ, Arturo A. ■ 00969 #042-01-1992 L1996 **N** *020 †75

ORTIZ, Damarys. D14 CALLE AZALEA, PARQ TORREMOLINOS 00969 #649-14-2003 **IM** *020

ORTIZ, Jose Francisco. ■ 00969 #042-03-1994 L1996 **AN** *020

ORTIZ, Jose Israel. 65 CALLE ADONIS, URB ALTO APOLO 00969 #847-10-1964 L1967 **OS GP** *030

ORTIZ, Juan Carlos. ■ 00966 #042-03-2004 **IM** *100 †20

ORTIZ, Melissa. ■ 00966 #042-01-2005 **OTO** *012

ORTIZ, Milagros. ■ 00969 #308-04-1985 L1990 **P** *020

ORTIZ, Wanda E. F1 CALLE VILLA FLORES 00969 #042-01-1984 L1987 **GE IM** *020 †20

ORTIZ-GOVEO, Elsie M. ■ 00970 #042-01-1996 L1999 **OPH** *020 †35

OSSA QUINTERO, Viviana. ■ 00969 #264-04-1998 L2005 *100

PADILLA, Antolin J. 67 CALLE CARAZO 00969 #042-01-1992 L1995 **FPG** *020 †18

PADILLA, Isabel Teresa. B10 CALLE D, URB ALTO APOLO STATES 00969 #042-01-1984 L1987 **PM** *020

PADILLA-BRUNO, Maria A. B7 CALLE ARTURO RIVERA MJC, URB GARDEN HLS 00966 #042-01-1974 L1976 **D OS** *015

PAGAN, Annette Lydia. 8 CALLE BETANIA, URB MUNOZ RIVERA 00969 #308-02-1976 L1982 **CHP P** *020 †75

PAGAN, John M. ■ 00969 #042-01-1987 L1995 **PS** *020 †65

PAGAN, Juan Antonio. ■ 00969 #649-14-2000 L2002 *020

PAGAN, Vilma I. B4 AVE ALEJANDRINO, VILLA CLEMENTINA 00969 #649-14-1990 L1994 **FM** *020

PAGAN MEDINA, Rafael A.. APT 905, CONDOMINIO EL BOSQUE 00971 #042-04-2003 L2004 *100

PALERMO, Jose Alberto. Q4 CALLE TAYLOR, URB PARKVILLE 00969 #308-01-1980 L1986 **FM** *020

PARALITICCI, Giovanni Ube. ■ 00969 #042-01-2008 *012

PARES MARTINEZ, Luis A. H48 CAL 5 URB TINTILLO GDN 00966 #847-08-1973 L1976 **CD IM** *020

PASTRANA, Jose G. 67 CALLE CARAZO 00969 #308-01-1986 L1988 **GP EM** *030

PENA, Mary Karen. ■ 00966 #042-01-1994 L1998 **N** *020 †75

PENA, Selene. 14-20 CALLE GRANADA, URB TORRIMAR 00966 #042-01-1997 L2002 **P** *020

PENARANDA-SAN JUAN, T. C BARCELONA NO 21 TORRIMAR 00966 #264-05-1969 L1982 *020

PEREZ, Doris Maria. ■ 00970 #042-01-2003 **ID** *012 †4

PEREZ, Francisco A. COND TORRE DE GRAIL APT 10, APT 10K 00966 #132-01-1981 L1986 **GP** *020

PEREZ, Orlando. 8-6 AVE RAMIREZ DE ARELLAN, URB TORRIMAR 00966 #010-02-1995 L1997 *020 †35

PEREZ, Silverio. ■ 00969 #042-01-1981 L1983 **R** *020 †80

PEREZ CHACON, Jose Julio. ■ 00966 #275-02-1975 L2002 **GP** *020

PEREZ-DIAZ, Sergio Amaury. ■ 00969 #308-01-1968 L1976 **FM** *100

PEREZ-ECHEVARRIA, Tricia. HC 1 BOX 5460, 1.3 CARR 834 CAMINO LOS 00969 #042-01-1998 L2000 **IM** *020

PEREZ-LLORENS, Ibrahim. L1 CAL BMB DR URB TORRIMAR 00966 #042-01-1961 L1964 **GE IM** *071

PEREZ MONTE, Juan Enrique. 175 CALLE REINA ISABEL, URB LA VILLA DE TORRIMAR 00969 #042-01-1991 L1998 **DR** *020

PEREZ-ORONOZ, Abdon J. 3013 AVE ALEJANDRINO, COND. FOUNTAINBLUE PLAZA # 00969 #042-01-1970 L1972 **DR** *020

PEREZ-PRADO, Calixto E. PARKVILLE COURT RH 2 #4 00969 #042-01-1956 L1959 **PM** *071

PEREZ-QUIROS, Jose. 74 CALLE REINA ALEXANDRA, URB LA VILLA DE TORRIMAR 00969 #042-03-1984 L1987 **GS** *020 †85

PEREZ RIVERA, Ivan O. ■ 00969 #308-04-2001 L2002 **IM** *020

PEREZ-VIVAS, Hector F. 8-6 AVE RAMIREZ DE ARELLAN, URB TORRIMAR 00966 #042-01-1956 L1959 **OBG** *020

PINE, Michelle Vizcarrond. ■ 00966 #042-01-1997 L1999 **NPM** *020 †55

PIRAZZI-MARQUEZ, Beatriz. 57 AVE LOPATEGUI, VILLAS DE PARKVILLE BOX 46 00969 #042-01-1996 L1998 **EM** *020 †16

PIZARRO, David Orlando. ■ 00969 #042-01-2005 L2005 **OBG** *012

PLA, Alejandro. 1353 AVE LUIS VIGOREAUX, STE 171 00966 #270-02-1998 L2005 **IM** *100 †20

PLACER-ROMAN, Carlos. PO BOX 3825 00970 #649-18-1978 L1982 **ADL PD** *020 ‡

PLAUD, Ricardo. ■ 00969 #308-03-1988 L2002 *020

POLISH, Roger David. ■ 00966 #042-03-1995 L2005 **GE** *020 †20

PORRATO DORIA ACOSTA, A V. 34 CALLE OVIEDO, URB TORRIMAR 00966 #042-01-1969 L1971 **GP PM** *020

POSADA, Jorge Luis. 405 AVE ESMERALDA, STE 102 PMB 403 00969 #270-02-1998 L2004 **NEP** *012 †20

POUEYMIROU, Frank Arthur. A2 CALLE I, PARQ TORREMOLINOS 00969 #056-06-1948 L1952 **IM CD** *071

PRADA, Rafael. 50-18 STREET, PONCE DE LEON 00969 #275-01-1967 L1975 **GP GYN** *071

PRADERE DE WISCOVITCH, A. 58 AVE ESMERALDA, URB MUNOZ RIVERA 00969 #042-03-1984 L1984 **IM** *020

PRATS, Manuel Ramon, Jr. ■ 00969 #042-01-1986 L1991 **DR** *020 †80

PUIG, Jose Luis. ■ 00969 #042-03-1997 L2003 **PM** *020 †60

QUINONES, Myrna Lizette. GUAYNABO, PALOMAS P-II TIERRALTA II 00969 #042-01-1980 L1983 **PD** *020 †55

QUINONEZ, Concepcion. 8 CALLE PATRC URB SUSAN CT 00966 #042-01-1966 L1968 **PD** *030

RAMIREZ, Gilberto. ■ 00966 #042-03-1983 L1986 **FM** *020 †18

RAMIREZ, Irelis. ■ 00969 #042-03-1997 L2000 **N** *020 †75

RAMIREZ, Lionel Alejandro. 146 CALLE CARAZO 00969 #308-03-1981 L1993 **GP** *020

RAMIREZ, Lisannette Marie. ■ 00969 #042-03-2006 **IM** *012

RAMIREZ DE ARELLANO, G A. ■ 00966 #056-06-1949 L1957 **PTH OS** *020

RAMIREZ-ORTIZ, Alvin E. 35 CALLE JUAN C BORBON, STE 67 PMB 163 00969 #308-03-1977 L1982 **AN PME** *020

RAMIREZ-RAMIREZ, Carlos. 20 CALLE ROMA BOX 203, GRANADA PARK APT C 00969 #042-03-1995 L1999 **ID** *020

RAMOS, Rosa Elena. ■ 00969 #042-01-2002 L2006 *100 †80

RAMOS, Viola. ■ 00970 #847-02-1962 L1966 **PM AN** *020

RAMOS CONDE, Andre. ■ 00970 #649-14-1989 L1993 **FM** *020

REYES, Dario Luis. ■ 00969 #847-06-1978 L1989 **GP OM** *020

REYES, Juan Angel. ■ 00971 #308-03-1985 L1992 *100

REYES, Maria Leticia. ■ 00969 #042-01-1996 L1998 **P** *020 †75

REYES, Raul Antonio. MANNSIONES CE TORRIMAR, CALLE 5 BLOG 18 E 4 00966 #035-20-1977 L1980 **PUD IM** *050 †20

REYES-PESANTE, Sara M.. ■ 00969 #308-05-1996 L2004 *100

REYES REYES, Jorge A. 3071 AVE ALEJANDRINO, PMB 247 00969 #847-04-1968 L1970 **OBG** *020

RICHIUSA, Juan Pablo. ■ 00966 #042-02-2003 L2005 **OBG** *012

RIERA MARRERO, Ivan. APT #303, COND. PLAA REAL CAPARRA 00966 #847-04-1959 L1961 **OTO** *072

RIOS, Maricell. 2052 CALLE SATURNO, URB ALTO APOLO 00969 #042-01-1992 L1996 **P** *020 †75

RIOS GARCIA, Rosendo. 20 CALLE UNION, URB SANTA PAULA 00969 #042-01-1963 L1966 **GS** *020

RIVERA, Awilda. ■ 00969 #042-01-1982 L1985 **NPM PD** *020 †55

RIVERA, Edwin. ■ 00969 #649-14-2000 L2001 *020

RIVERA, Javier. N4 CALLE REY JORGE V, QTAS REALES 00969 #042-01-1996 L1999 **PM** *020 †60

RIVERA, Juan Anibal. G1 CALLE 1, URB TERRANOVA 00969 #042-01-1993 L1996 **NPM** *020 †55

RIVERA, Laura. 47 CALLE CARAZO 00969 #042-01-1982 L1985 **PD** *020

RIVERA, Sandra Ivelissa. ■ 00969 #649-14-2004 L2004 *100

RIVERA, Valenie. ■ 00969 #042-01-2002 L2003 **D** *020 †15

RIVERA-DUENO, Jaime. J19 CAL JFRSN URB PARKVILL 00969 #042-01-1960 L1965 **PD** *020

RIVERA JIMENEZ, Jorge. HC 1, 8.3 CARR 3 AVE 65 INF 00971 #042-01-2002 L2005 *020

RIVERA LINARES, Sonia Y. ■ 00970 #042-01-1994 L1997 **GP** *062

RIVERA-PACHECO, Nitza H. ■ 00966 #308-02-1977 L1982 **PD** *030

RIVERA-PANIAGUA, Dennis S. ■ 00969 #041-13-1951 L1952 **PM OS** *071

RIVERA-RIVERA, Jaime O. ■ 00969 #231-01-1956 L1958 **OBG** *020

RIVERA VILCHES, Jose F. 46 CALLE CARAZO 00969 #847-02-1980 L1986 **GP** *020

RIVERA VINAS, Juana I. ■ 00969 #042-01-1984 L1987 **OBG** *020 †30

ROBLES, Nelson A. 19-22 AVE RAMIREZ DE ARELN, STE 7 PMB 304 00966 #847-05-1978 L1982 **HEM ON** *020

ROBLES-IRIZARRY, Lizbeth. ■ 00969 #042-01-2007 L2007 *012

RODRIGUEZ, Antonio Juan. ■ 00966 #051-04-1993 L1997 **OBG** *020 †30

RODRIGUEZ, Astacio Jose A. ■ 00966 #847-10-1960 L1968 *100

RODRIGUEZ, Jaffet Seda. ■ 00969 #649-14-2003 **OBG** *012

RODRIGUEZ, Natividad. APT J-1 SAN JOSE STREET, COND. SAN FCO JAVIER 00969 #042-01-1974 L1976 **P** *020 ‡

RODRIGUEZ, Oscar E. G31 CAL GNV EXT VILLA CAPA 00966 #042-01-1974 L1976 **PD** *020

RODRIGUEZ, Wilfredo. 1971 CAL SNDL URB SAN RAMO 00969 #042-03-1988 L1994 **PM** *020

RODRIGUEZ CEPEDA, Aristide. ■ 00969 #308-01-1976 L1981 *100

RODRIGUEZ-CRUZ, Diana C. GA13 CALLE PALMA SOLA, URB GARDEN HLS 00966 #649-14-1979 L1982 **PD** *020

RODRIGUEZ DONES, Jaime. QQ14 CALLE FEBE, URB APOLO 00969 #847-01-1964 L1966 **PD** *020

RODRIGUEZ-ESCUDERO, Jose. ■ 00966 #042-01-1998 L2001 **IC** *020 †20

RODRIGUEZ MARIAN, Aixa M. ■ 00969 #042-01-1990 L1993 **OBG** *020 †30

RODRIGUEZ ROSSELLO, Luis. ■ 00969 #308-13-2001 L2005 *100

ROMAN VELEZ, Rosario. ■ 00969 #847-06-1974 L1977 **PTH** *020 †50

ROMERO, Carlos Javier. ■ 00969 #042-01-2001 L2004 **GE** *012

ROMERO-GELPI, Carmen A. ■ 00966 #056-06-1948 L1948 **OBG** *071

ROSABAL, Adabell. ■ 00969 #649-14-2002 L2004 *100

ROSADO, Iris Y. V5 CALLE JUAN RAMOS, EXT SANTA PAULA 00969 #042-04-1996 L1997 *020

ROSADO, Luis Angel. 42 CALLE CARAZO 00969 #649-14-1995 L1998 **CD** *020

ROSARIO, Carla Michelle. ■ 00969 #649-14-2002 L2004 *100

ROSELLO, Jose A. A19 CALLE HARDING, URB PARKVILLE 00969 #308-03-1977 L1980 **PD** *020

RUIS, Ana Del Carmen. ■ 00971 #042-01-1979 L1983 **IM** *020

RUIZ, Israel Alejandro. ■ 00966 #308-03-1982 L1990 **GS** *020

RUIZ, William Manuel. 15 CALLE EUGENE, URB VICTOR BRAEGER 00966 #847-01-1977 L1983 **GS OS** *020

RUIZ-ALONSO, Ramon A. E14 CALLE ROMA, EXT VILLA CAPARRA 00966 #042-03-1983 L1987 **IM** *020

RULLAN, John Vincent. ■ 00966 #042-01-1982 L1984 **PHP GPM** *030 †70

RULLAN, Maria Del Carmen. ■ 00966 #042-01-1977 L1982 **PD** *020 †55

SABATER, Amelia. 10 CALLE MIRAMONTE, BOX 738 00966 #308-01-1952 L1958 **PD** *020

SALICRUP, Eumari. ■ 00971 #042-01-1999 L2003 **OBG** *020

SANCHEZ CHEVERE, Luis A. ■ 00969 #847-05-1976 L1990 **EM PD** *020

SANCHEZ-ORTIZ, Ricardo F. A3 CALLE FRANCIA, URB GARDEN CT 00966 #042-01-1996 L2003 **U** *020 †95

SANCHEZ RIVERA, Rafael I. B5 CALLE GARDEN MDW 00966 #847-04-1960 L1962 **OBG** *071 †30

SANCHEZ TARNIELLA, Rafael. ■ 00969 #847-04-1962 L1966 *071

SANCHIDRIAN, Gloria Suau. ■ 00969 #042-03-1998 L2000 **CHP** *020 †75

SAN GABRIEL, Maria S Q. ■ 00969 #748-07-1958 L1968 **PD** *071

SANTIAGO, Hector H. PRADO ALTO, 6TH STREET K-35 00966 #847-01-1961 L1964 **PD** *020

SANTIAGO, Michelle Marie. ■ 00966 #042-01-2005 **PD** *012

SANTIAGO, Nancy. 74 AVE LOPATEGUI, STE 203 00969 #042-03-1981 L1983 **PD** *020

SANTIAGO DE BURGOS, C R. GUAYNABO PUERTO RICO, ST 9 D8 VICTOR BRAGGER 00966 #847-10-1963 L1967 **P CHP** *050

SANTOS, Laura Margarita. ■ 00966 #042-01-2007 *012

SANZ-LEBRON, Carmen Z. DE PARKVILL, CALLE A 21, COLINAS 00969 #042-03-1982 L1985 *020

SANZ-VALDES, Enrique E. A16 AVE RAMIREZ DE ARELLAN 00966 #847-04-1967 L1975 **AN** *020

SARRAGA, Andres Guillermo. ■ 00966 #042-01-2004 **GS** *012

SCHENK, Christian Eberhar. ■ 00966 #042-01-2008 *012

SENIOR, Joham. ■ 00966 #042-03-1981 L1985 **GE IM** *020 †20

SERRANO, Pedro R. 302 VIA ALCAZAR, VILLAS REALES 00969 #042-01-1991 L1994 **NPM** *020 †55

SERRANO MUNIZ, Francisco. 15 AVE ESMERALDA, URB MUNOZ RIVERA 00969 #308-04-1987 L1994 *020

SILVA-COLL, Maria M. ■ 00969 #042-01-1990 L1995 **DR** *020 †80

SOLIS, Edgar A. 35 CALLE JUAN C BORBON, STE 67 00969 #042-01-1987 L1989 **CHN PD** *020

SORRENTINI-MENDEZ, Hector. CALLE 25-274 URB PR DE LEO 00969 #308-03-1979 L1982 *020

SORRENTINO, Jose Lorenzo. G5 CALLE RUISENOR, URB TIERRA ALTA III 00969 #042-01-1986 L1991 **GS AS** *020 †85

SORVILL, Marino. ■ 00969 #308-01-1952 L1968 **ATP** *071 †50

SOTO, Ana Bernice. ■ 00966 #024-05-1977 L1980 **PD** *062 †55

SOTO, Julio Michael. M6 CALLE PATIO HL, URB TORRIMAR 00966 #042-01-1972 L1990 **GS DS** *040

STRUBBE-PLANAS, Leopold. GDNS HILLS PLAZA #333 00969 #308-03-1977 L1984 **GS** *020

TEJADA-VEGA, Inocencia J. CALLE BRZIL DI GRDNVILL 00966 #042-03-1980 L1981 **GP** *020

TELLO, Margarita Ellena. 11 CALLE ACUARELA, URB MUNOZ RIVERA 00969 #308-03-1984 L1992 **GP** *020

TOBAJA LOPEZ, Maria A. ■ 00969 #308-01-1982 L1993 *020

TORMOS, Lee Marie. ■ 00969 #042-01-2003 L2006 **PTH GP** *020

TORRES, Eduardo Ivan. D5 CALLE A, URB GARDEN HLS 00966 #042-03-1996 L1999 **OBG** *020

TORRES, Edwin. ■ 00969 #042-01-1992 L1997 **GS** *020 †85

TORRES, Nydia Esther. G-26 ST VILLA CAPARRA 00966 #847-08-1974 L1978 **GP** *074
TORRES, Wanda Ivellisse. ■ 00970 #042-03-1994 L1996 **ID** *020
TORRES-GARCIA, Alfonso. 0-19 CLLE MCKINLEY, URB PARKVILLE 00969 #308-04-1982 L1985 **GP** *020
TOUS DE JESUS, Horacio Ma. ■ 00969 #042-03-2004 *100
TRINIDAD, Meliana Maria. ■ 00969 #042-01-2005 **IM** *012
TURULL, Marta J. ■ 00966 #042-03-2003 L2006 **IM** *100 †20
URIA DUARTE, Maria I. ■ 00966 #649-14-1985 L1994 *020
VALDERRABANO, Carmen V. CALLE 6A CHALETS DE LA REI 00966 #042-01-1980 L1985 **DR** *020 †80
VALDERRABANO, Jose Luis. ■ 00970 #847-04-1955 L1959 **P** *020
VALLEJO, Ricardo Rafael. ■ 00969 #042-03-1992 L1994 **DR** *020 †80
VAN DAALEN-BADILLO, Larry. 41 CALL CB EST DE TORRIMAR, RIO PIEDRAS 00966 #042-03-1980 L1983 **IM** *020
VAQUER, Rafael Antonio. ■ 00969 #042-03-1980 L1996 **NM** *020 †28
VARGAS-BIRD, Margarita. ■ 00969 #042-01-1994 L1999 **DR** *020 †80
VARGAS DE LEON, Jose J. F2 VIA SAN PAOLO, URB MONTE ALBERNIA 00969 #308-03-1979 L1982 *020
VAZQUEZ, Cesar Augusto. B6 CALLE 5, URB TERRANOVA 00969 #042-01-1978 L1982 **CD** *020 †18,20
VAZQUEZ, Elsie Eileen. 44 CALLE J, VILLA CAPARRA 00966 #042-01-1999 L2001 **P** *020 †55
VAZQUEZ, German. ■ 00969 #042-04-1981 L1984 *020
VAZQUEZ, Jose Manuel. 1982 CALLE SAUCO, URB SAN RAMON 00969 #042-01-1975 L1982 **HEM** *020
VAZQUEZ-ALVAREZ, Angel M. VILLA CAPARRA, STREET J-16 00966 #649-14-1977 L1979 **AN** *020
VAZQUEZ-CASANOVA, Jose O. ■ 00966 #649-01-1954 L1956 **PD** *071
VAZQUEZ-DUENO, Dianette L. 100 CALLE ABERDEEN, URB COLLEGEVILLE 00969 #042-01-2001 L2003 **D** *020
VAZQUEZ-RIQUELME, C. 9D COND DORAL PLAZA, AVE VIGOREAUX, VILLA CAPAR 00966 #847-04-1960 L1962 **PD** *020
VAZQUEZ-RODRIGUEZ, Victor. ■ 00969 #042-03-1989 L1992 **HO** *020
VEGA, Ana Maria. B20 CALLE FLORENCIA, EXT VILLA CAPARRA 00966 #042-01-1981 L1985 **P** *020 †75
VEGA-GONZALEZ, Martin. ■ 00969 #847-05-1981 L1984 *020
VEGA ORTIZ, Carmen Teresa. ■ 00966 #308-03-1983 L1987 **GP** *020
VELA CORDOVA, Rodrigo. J6 VILLA CAPARRA 00966 #649-14-2004 L2005 *100
VELAZQUEZ, Tomas. 80 CALLE CARAZO 00969 #847-10-1959 L1962 **GP** *020
VELAZQUEZ MUNOZ, Braulio. 17B AVE TERRS DE TINTILLO, COND MANSIONES LOS CAOBOS 00966 #308-03-1986 L2004 *100
VELAZQUEZ VERA, Juan. ■ 00969 #649-03-1951 L1959 **PTH GYN** *030 †50
VELEZ, Janet Igdalia. ■ 00969 #042-01-1996 L1999 **FM** *020
VELEZ, Jorge Luis. ■ 00969 #308-03-1984 L1997 *020
VELEZ, Mayra. B23 SOUTHVIEW CT, URB BALDWIN PARK 00969 #042-03-1996 L1998 **ID IM** *020 †20
VELEZ FORTUNO, Jaime. CALLE MADRID VLQ 3 15 00966 #649-01-1957 L1959 **GP PD** *020
VELEZ SEGARRA, Glenise C. 17 CALLE DIAMANTE, URB BUCARE 00966 #042-04-1986 L1987 **GP** *020
VENERO, George. 17 CALLE DIAMANTE, URB BUCARE 00969 #042-04-1986 L1988 **IM** *020
VERGES BONET, Enrique. ■ 00966 #042-04-2003 L2004 **GP** *030 ‡
VIEJO-RULLAN, Francisco A. ■ 00966 #042-01-2004 **NM** *012
VIERAS, Frank. ■ 00966 #042-01-1972 L1980 **NM** *075 †28
VILARO, M M. ■ 00966 #042-01-1981 L1987 **DR** *020 †80
VILLANUEVA, Carmen M. ■ 00969 #042-03-2000 L2002 **RNR** *020 †80
VILLANUEVA, Hector L. ■ 00969 #042-01-1982 L1986 **PD** *020
VILLANUEVA-MEYER, Sylvia. OA10 CALLE PALMA SOLA, URB GARDEN HLS 00966 #649-14-1981 L1984 **IM** *020
ZAMOT, Alberto Luis. ■ 00966 #042-01-2007 **IM** *012
ZARRUK, Alan A. ■ 00970 #042-04-1984 L1988 **GP** *020

GUAYNABO – SAN JUAN

ABREU, Jose R. 401 COND MADRESELVA 00968 #042-01-1964 L1969 **ORS** *020 †40
AGUILU, Dalila Elizabeth. J6 AVE SAN PATRICIO, COND MANSIONES LOS CAOBOS 00968 #847-04-1977 L1986 **CHP P** *020 †75
ALDRICH-NOVOA, Jorge A. ■ 00968 #042-01-1999 L2000 **OTO FPS** *020 †45
ALONSO SANTIAGO, Ramon. G4 AVE SAN PATRICIO, CONDOMINIO EL GENERALIFE A 00968 #847-04-1955 L1957 **P** *020 †75
ALVAREZ-BELTRAN, Franco. D3 CALLE TOPACIO, PARQ SAN PATRICIO 00968 #042-01-1969 L1972 **PD** *020
ALVAREZ-BERDECIA, Antonio. ■ 00968 #042-01-1973 L1975 **NS OS** *071 †25
BAEZ-FRANCESCHI, Daisy. 101 AVE SAN PATRICIO, STE 1010 00968 #042-01-1993 L1998 **IMG** *020 †20
BALLESTE-FRANK, Carmen Ri. ■ 00968 #042-03-1997 L2000 **ID** *020 †20
BATLLE, Francisco A. ■ 00968 #308-02-1989 L1992 **GS** *020 †85
BAYRON VELEZ, Roberto. 2D COND EL CORDOVES, AVE SAN PATRICIO 00968 #042-01-1994 L1998 **AN** *020
BRAGIN, David Ernesto. 101 AVE SAN PATRICIO, STE 870 00968 #042-01-1997 L1999 **CD** *020 †20
CACHO, Agustin A. ■ 00968 #847-04-1971 L1974 **GP PUD** *030
CASELLAS, Nicolas. CALLE 1 STE 10 00968 #042-03-1985 L1986 **OBG** *020 †30
CASTRO PONCE, Teresa. 101 AVE SAN PATRICIO, MIRAMAR PLAZA SSUITE 1140 00968 #042-01-1990 L1995 **N** *020 †75
COLBERG, Pedro Nelson, Jr. 840 COND MARAMAR, 101 SAN PATRICIO AVE. 00968 #308-01-1981 L1986 **P** *020
CONTE-MILLER, Maria S. ■ 00968 #308-04-1982 L1988 **FOP** *020 †50
CUMBA LLAVONA, Gilmarie. AVE DELISA R DE GAUTIER AP, PASEOMONTE 00968 #649-14-2000 L2002 *100
CURET-SALIM, Maria Terisa. 101 AVE SAN PATRICIO, STE 970 00968 #056-05-1995 L1998 **PD** *020 †55
DAVISON, James Wilford. A COND BELEN PH A, CAPARRA HEIGHTS 00968 #033-05-1984 L1993 **FM EM** *020 †18
DE JESUS, Jorge Rafael. 12 CALLE 1, EXT ALTS DE SAN PATRICIO 00968 #042-01-1975 L1981 **END IM** *020

DE LA ROSA, Norman Javier. ■ 00968 #042-03-2001 L2004 **U IM** *012
DEL TORO, Manuel F. CITY VIEW PLAZA STE 115, RD 165 K M 1.2 #48 00968 #042-02-1994 L1998 **OPH** *020 †35 ‡
FERRE, Tiody. ■ 00968 #042-03-1980 L1983 **GP** *071
GARCIA-BARCENA, Rafael. 22 CALLE GONZALEZ GIUSTI, STE 210 00968 #042-04-1981 L1986 **P** *020
GIGANTE BAEZ, Arturo. 101 AVE SAN PATRICIO, MARAMAR PLAZA, SUITE 1130 00968 #847-06-1976 L1982 **OBG** *020
GONZALEZ, Jose Raul. BUCARE H-6 CAPARRA HILLS 00968 #024-01-1972 L1981 **GS** *020 †85
GONZALEZ MONTOYA, Victor. ■ 00968 #649-14-2004 *100
GREGORY, Federico Jose. ■ 00968 #042-03-2000 L2002 **GE** *100 †20
HIDALGO, Alejandro Jorge. ■ 00968 #042-01-2003 L2006 **DR** *012
IRIZARRY RIVERA, Hector L. 90 CARR 165, STE 302 00968 #042-01-1994 L1999 **GS** *020
LASA, Arnaldo Enrique. ■ 00968 #042-03-2005 **IM** *012
LIZARDI, Lourdes. ■ 00968 #042-04-1991 L1992 *020
LOJO, Luis Francisco. ■ 00968 #042-01-2002 L2007 **ORS** *100
MAESO, Patricia Anne. ■ 00968 #042-01-2002 L2004 **OTO** *100
MAESO SCHRODER, Andres. 39 CALLE ESMERALDA, URB GOLDEN GATE 00968 #847-04-1957 L1959 **OTO** *020
MARCHAND COLLAZO, Maria. 5C COND EL JARDIN, J7 AVE SAN PATRICIO 00968 #308-02-1976 L1980 **PD OS** *030
MEDINA, Ana L. 12 EXT ALTURAS DE SAN PAT, ST 1 00968 #042-01-1975 L1980 **PD** *020 †55
MERLE, Santa. ■ 00968 #649-14-1998 L2000 **HO** *100
MOTTA, Ana I.. ■ 00968 #649-14-1996 L2000 **P** *100
MUNIZ, Francisco J. 27 CALLE M RIVERA FERRER, URB SAN PATRICIO 00968 #847-01-1962 L1966 **HEM ON** *030
MUNIZ, Manuel Ramon. 101 AVE SAN PATRICIO, STE 170 00968 #042-01-1978 L1981 **PD** *020 †55
MUNOZ BENEDICTO, Jose L. 100 CARR 165 STE 304, CENTRO INTL. DE MERCADEO I 00968 #308-04-1987 L1992 **IM** *020
MURRAY, Irina Marina. ■ 00968 #042-01-2008 *012
PASTRANA, Vivian Raquel. ■ 00968 #042-03-2000 L2004 **P** *100 †75
PEREZ BAILON, Esteban R. ■ 00968 #042-04-1997 L2000 **FM** *020
QUINONES-JIMENEZ, Frank. ■ 00968 #021-01-1944 L1945 **OTO** *020
RAMIREZ, Rainier. AVE SAN PARTICIO, SAN PATRICIO CHALETS #7 00922 #042-01-1982 L1985 **IM** *020 †20
REYES BAEZ, Gloria. ■ 00968 #042-01-1972 L1974 **PD NPM** *020 †55
RIVERA, Belinda Natalia. ■ 00968 #042-03-2006 L2006 **IM** *012
RIVERA-BOBE, Elizabeth M. ■ 00968 #649-18-1979 L1983 **FM** *020 †18
SANCHEZ-LOPEZ, Carmen D. C54 CALLE DIAMANTE, URB GOLDEN GATE 00968 #308-04-1979 L1983 **GP** *020
SANCHEZ RODRIGUEZ, Carlos. ■ 00968 #649-14-1988 L1992 **IM** *020
SANTIAGO, Fernando Luis. 101 AVE SAN PATRICIO, STE 1180 00968 #042-02-1995 L2000 **N** *020 †75
SOTOMAYOR, Antonio G. J10 AVE SAN PATRICIO, COND SAINT MORITZ APT 1503 00968 #042-01-1976 L1981 **N** *020
SURIA, Jorge L. ■ 00968 #042-01-1971 L1973 **P CHP** *020
TORMES GOTAY, Leila N. 89 CALLE NOGAL, URB ALTURAS STA MARIA 00968 #847-10-1960 L1964 **PD** *030
TORRES-CASTRO, Jadmmal L. 1-7 CALLE EBANO APT-1503 00968 #847-08-1979 L1986 **IM** *020
VALERA, Gilda Isabel. ■ 00968 #042-03-2004 **PM** *012
VEGA RODRIGUEZ, Rosa E. H21 CALLE YAGRUMO, URB CAPARRA HLS 00968 #042-04-1988 L1989 **GPM OM** *030
VELAZQUEZ, Carmen G. 101 AVE SAN PATRICIO, MARAMAR PLZ STE 1150 00968 #042-01-1998 L2001 **PM** *020 †60

GURABO – GURABO

ACEVEDO DENIS, Hector R. ■ 00778 #308-03-1983 L1992 **PD** *020
ALIFONSO, Yamines. ■ 00778 #042-2-2007 **OBG** *012
BENITEZ, Juan A. HC 2, BOX 13814 00778 #308-03-1985 L1995 *100
BERRIOS ECHEVARRIA, H J. ■ 00778 #042-03-1996 L1999 **OBG** *020
BEZARES COLON, Sandra E. ■ 00778 #308-03-1985 L1989 **IM** *020
BEZARES GOMEZ, Lillian E. 343 CAMINO DE LOS LIRIOS, URB SABANERA DEL RIO 00778 #649-14-1990 L1994 **RHU** *020
BORIA-CARCANO, Fausto R. C/O PO BOX 642, C-91 VILLA MARINA 00778 #308-01-1980 L1983 **PM GP** *020
BOU, Carmen Ines. 471 VEREDAS DE LAS AMAPOLS, URB VEREDAS 00778 #042-03-2000 L2004 **EM** *020 †16
BURGOS, Miguel A R. 42 CALLE EL PRADO, URB GRAN VISTA I 00778 #308-03-1979 L1981 **CD IM** *020 †18
CANELLAS CORREA, Karen M. ■ 00778 #042-04-2002 L2005 **GP** *020
CARRASQUILLO, Luz M. ■ 00778 #308-03-1985 L1994 *020
CARRION, Ivelisse E. ■ 00778 #042-02-1994 L1996 **IM** *020
CARRION, Maria Maribelle. #2 SUR, CALLE ZOILO RIVERA MORALES 00778 #308-03-1979 L1987 **GP** *020
CARRION DEL TORO, Carlos. ■ 00778 #042-04-2003 L2004 *100
CORREA, Hector A. 104 CALLE SANTIAGO N 00778 #308-03-1977 L1980 **GP OM** *020
CRUZ BERRIOS, Carina A. A9 CALLE ILUSION, URB HORIZONTE 00778 #042-04-2000 L2002 **FM** *020
CURET CRESPO, Jose A. ■ 00778 #847-05-1955 L1958 **GP P** *020
DE JESUS, Felipe Nicolas. ■ 00778 #649-14-1984 L1988 **GP** *071
DE JESUS CARRION, Julio C. ■ 00778 #308-03-1983 L1995 **GP** *020
DIAZ, Hilda Maria. ■ 00778 #847-04-1967 L1972 **GP** *071
DOPAZO-RODRIGUEZ, Irma. ■ 00778 #649-14-1989 L1992 **PD** *020
FIGUEROA, Luz Delia. VEREDA 23 00778 #042-01-1979 L1983 **D** *020 †15
FRANCESCHI, Gerardo A. 105 CAMINO DE LAS AMAPOLAS, URB SABANERA DEL RIO 00778 #042-01-1988 L1991 **IM** *020
FUENTES MELENDEZ, Luis A. ■ 00778 #308-03-1979 L1982 *100
GANDARA, Roberto Juan. 185 CAMINO DEL MONTE, URB SABANERA DEL RIO 00778 #649-14-1990 L1992 *020
GARCIA, Hermes R. PO BOX 457 00778 #042-04-1980 L1984 **OS GP** *020
GERERA, Milagros Teresa. C/O INT HCO2 BOX 18698, CARR 189 R-933 KM 0.9 00778 #308-03-1981 L1990 **GP** *020

GOMEZ, Maria Isabel. ■ 00778 #649-14-2000 L2001 **FM** *020

GONZALEZ, Nanette Lucien. ■ 00778 #042-01-1997 L2000 **PD** *020

GUERRA, John Alfredo. ■ 00778 #264-09-1992 L2003 **PD** *020 †55

HERNANDEZ, Anissa V. ■ 00778 #042-01-1998 L2002 **P** *020

HERNANDEZ ROSES, Ines. CALLE SAN ANTONIO FINAL, UPR MED SCIENCES CAMPUS 00778 #042-04-1990 L1992 **FM** *020 †18

JIMENEZ, Rafael A. ■ 00778 #021-01-1945 L1948 **IM GP** *071

JORGE, William Alfredo. 343 CAMINO DE LOS LIRIOS, URB SABANERA DEL RIO 00778 #649-14-1992 L1995 **NEP IM** *020

KIDD HAUT, Alvaro A. URB. REINA DE LOS ANGELES, C/7-M19 00778 #308-03-1979 L1995 **GP** *020

LAMEIRO, Alodia. 99 CALLE PASEO, URB GRAN VISTA I 00778 #042-03-1984 L1987 **EM** *020 †16

LEMOINE BELTRE, Marta. D12 CALLE 2, VILLAS DE GURABO 00778 #308-01-1991 L1996 *020

LOPEZ FELIX, Rocio E.. ■ 00778 #649-14-1996 L2005 *100

MANAUTOU, Jose A. 4 CALLE SAN FRANCISCO, EST DE GRAN VISTA 00778 #308-03-1983 L1993 **IM** *020

MARTINEZ COLLAZO, Pedro J. ■ 00778 #308-03-1977 L1980 **EM** *020

MARTINEZ ZAYAS, Ana I. ■ 00778 #308-01-1969 L1981 **FM** *020

MATIAS VALLADARES, Pedro. ANGELES, C 3 B8 URB REINA DE LOS 00778 #847-05-1981 L1990 **GP OM** *030

MENDEZ, Ingrid A. ■ 00778 #042-01-1990 L1994 **PM** *020

MILLAN, Ismenio. A12 CALLE ILUSION, URB HORIZONTE 00778 #308-07-1983 L1994 **FPG** *020 †18

MOJICA, Pablo Luis. ■ 00778 #042-01-1997 L2002 **GS HNS** *100 †85

MONTALVO-ROSA, Milagros. ■ 00778 #308-01-1984 L1994 **OM** *020

MORINGLANE, Michelle. ■ 00778 #042-03-1997 L2000 **PD** *020

MOSQUERA, Rafael A. 40 PLAZA 4, URB GRAN VISTA II 00778 #042-01-1984 L1986 **GE IM** *020

MUNET-QUINTERO, Amilva R. ■ 00778 #042-03-1990 L1995 **IM** *074

NIEVES, Aleida Gricel. 33 CALLE VALLE S, URB GRAN VISTA I 00778 #649-14-2001 L2002 *020

OCTAVIANI-REYES, Melba E. 6 CALLE E E, CAMPAMENTO 00778 #042-02-2000 L2003 *020 †55

ORTIZ, Nestor R. 166 CALLE ANDRES ARS RVR W, CLINICA DE SALUD DEL TURAB 00778 #042-01-1985 L1988 **FM** *020

ORTIZ-FRANCO, Fernando L. PO BOX 863, 101W ANDRES ARUZ RIVERA 00778 #847-02-1973 L1976 *020

ORTIZ TORRES, Angel. 135 CAMINO DE LOS CAOBOS, URB SABANERA DEL RIO 00778 #847-08-1971 L1974 **AN PME** *020

OSUNA, Soraya Torres. ■ 00778 #042-01-1990 L1994 **AN** *020

OTEROFRANQUI, Elisa Angel. ■ 00778 #042-03-2008 *012

OTERO GARCIA, Carmen Soco. ■ 00778 #308-03-1981 L1998 **PD** *020

PARDO, Luis E.. ■ 00778 #649-14-2002 **OBG** *020

PEREZ-LOPEZ, Shirley. ■ 00778 #042-01-2003 **FM** *100 †18

QUINONES, Jose Ramon. CALLE 5N 21, REINA DE LOS ANGELES 00778 #847-02-1982 L1986 **PD** *020 †55

RAMOS, Juan Carlos. 311 CAMINO DE LAS PALMAS, URB SABANERA DEL RIO 00778 #033-05-1999 L2003 **IM** *020 †20

RAMOS-ROMAN, Wilma Rita. REINA DE LOS ANGELES, CALLE NO.7 M-19 00778 #308-03-1977 L1983 **OBG** *020

RAMOS TORRES, Angel L. T7 CALLE 10, URB REINA DE LOS ANGELES 00778 #042-04-1997 L2002 **FM** *020

RIVERA ORTIZ, Jose A. ■ 00778 #042-04-1997 L2000 **FM** *020

ROCAFORT, Angel Luis. ■ 00778 #042-01-1997 L1999 **EM** *020 †16

RODRIGUEZ, Ana. ■ 00778 #042-01-1981 L1983 *020

RODRIGUEZ, Francisco. PO BOX 66 00778 #308-15-1981 L2004 **GP** *020

RODRIGUEZ, Middelia. ■ 00778 #308-01-1984 L1991 **IM** *020

RODRIGUEZ, Rebecca. PO BOX 1277 00778 #042-04-1991 L1994 **FM** *020 †18

ROMAN, Juan Manuel. PO BOX 633 00778 #649-14-1993 L1996 *100

ROSARIO-CASABLANCA, R A. 91 CALLE EL PRADO, URB GRAN VISTA I 00778 #308-02-1984 L1987 **NPM PD** *020

SALGADO, Norma Rosa. ■ 00778 #649-14-2001 **ON** *012

SANABRIA, Pedro. PO BOX 1323, CALLE 2D12 URB VIVERO 00778 #308-03-1978 L1980 **GP** *020

SANCHEZ, Mario L. BARRIO RINCON, APART 468 00778 #308-03-1978 L1981 *100

SANTOS, Jesus Manuel. 197 CALLE SAN JOSE N # 52 00778 #847-02-1973 L1976 **GP** *020

SANTOS, Jesus Manuel, Jr. 52 CALLE SAN JOSE, 1ST FL 00778 #042-02-1994 L1999 **CD** *020

SANTOS, Luis Raul. 3 URB LOS MAESTROS 00778 #308-03-1978 L1981 **GP** *020

SANTOS ELOSEGUI, Shirley. 52 CALLE SAN JOSE, EST DE GRAN VISTA 00778 #042-04-1999 L2001 **GP** *020

SEDA, Miguel Americo. REINA DE LOS ANGELES, 910 S-1 00778 #847-06-1979 L1988 **GP** *020

SERRANO, Alfonso. ■ 00778 #042-02-1985 L1988 **OBG** *020 †30

SIERRA-CABEZUDO, Julio. BO RINCON BN 28 A 00778 #042-03-1981 L1984 *100

TORO, Rafael Velez. PO BOX 619 00778 #649-18-1979 L1985 **GP OM** *020

TORRES, Sara Y. 287 CAMINO DEL MANGO, URB SABANERA DEL RIO 00778 #042-01-1995 L1999 **GP** *020

VAZQUEZ, Ana H. 54 CALLE E SANCHEZ LOPEZ E 00778 #042-01-1982 L1985 *020

VAZQUEZ RAMOS, Adolfo. 9 VCAR, URB LOS FLAMBOYANES 00778 #308-03-2002 L2004 *100

VELAZQUEZ, Freddy Eliud. ■ 00778 #042-03-1996 L1999 **GS** *020

VELEZ DE JESUS, Roberto. HC 2 BOX 19741 00778 #308-03-1979 L1981 **GP ADM** *020

VICENS, Jose L. 44 CALLE HIGUERETA, CIUDAD JARDIN 00778 #042-03-1988 L1992 **PD** *100

VIERA, Marta. URB REINA DE LOS ANGELES, CALLE 2-A10 00778 #847-06-1983 L1986 **GP** *020

VILLAVICENCIO, Juan B. ■ 00778 #308-03-1981 L1986 **IM** *020

ZERPA-SANCHEZ, Henry A. PO BOX 1311 00778 #649-14-1985 L1990 **PD** *020

HATILLO — HATILLO

AGUILAR, Melitsa. ■ 00659 #649-14-2004 L2004 *100

AMADOR-CASTRO, Luz Teresa. ■ 00659 #042-03-1980 L1984 **PD** *074

APONTE PERAZA, Luis A.. ■ 00659 #649-35-2003 L2006 *100

ARANA, Sandra. PO BOX 373 00659 #649-14-2002 L2004 *100

AROCHO, Juan Rene. PO BOX 350 00659 #042-04-1982 L1985 **GP** *020

BENAVIDES MARTINEZ, Rhina. 137 AVE DR SUSONI 00659 #847-06-1977 L2003 *100

CHICO, Carlos Daniel. 112 AVE DR SUSONI 00659 #649-14-1988 L1991 **GP** *020

CRUZ-HERNANDEZ, Hector. 121 AVE DR SUSONI, EQSUINA AVENIDA ROOSEVELT 00659 #035-15-1953 L1954 **PD** *072

CUBANO-MARTINEZ, Cesar. 556 CALLE TRUNCADO 00659 #042-04-1990 L1992 **P** *020

DEL VALLE DIAZ, Angel M. 190 AVE DR SUSONI 00659 #847-08-1968 L1971 **GP** *020

DEL VALLE TORRES, Angel R. PO BOX 1330 00659 #649-14-2000 L2001 *020

FOLCH FERNANDEZ, Alberto. 125 AVE ROOSEVELT 00659 #847-05-1956 L1958 **GP OS** *020

GARCIA, Herminio D. BUZON 212-CARR 130 00659 #021-01-1921 L1923 **GP** *072

GARCIA, Leslie Katherine. ■ 00659 #649-14-2005 *100

GARCIA-LLORENS, Jose A. PO BOX 65, 2 CARR KM 85.7 00659 #649-14-1977 L1979 *020

GONZALEZ, Ismael. ■ 00659 #308-01-1986 L1989 **GP** *020

GONZALEZ, Rafael Pedro. ■ 00659 #308-01-1964 L1975 **OBG IM** *075

JUARBE-MALAVE, Hector M. BO CARRIZALES, CARR 493 KM. 1.0 00659 #847-05-1980 L1982 **FM** *020

LLANES-AGUILAR, Sigfredo. ■ 00659 #847-05-1973 L1978 *020

MOLINA, David. PO BOX 1328 00659 #308-03-1981 L1985 **GP** *020

OLMEDA, Edwin. 119 CALLE VIDAL FELIX 00659 #308-07-1983 L1989 **GP** *020

PADILLA MORALES, Vilma. ■ 00659 #847-06-1989 L1991 **FM** *020

PAGAN, Kayleene Edith. ■ 00659 #042-01-2007 *012

PEREZ PEREA, Miriam L.. PO BOX 2025 00659 #649-14-2002 L2003 *100

PINERO PERAZA, Jose M. ■ 00659 #042-04-1996 L1998 **GP** *020

PORTALATIN, Jose Luis. PO BOX 483 00659 #649-35-1997 L2003 **GP** *020

REYES, Madeline. ■ 00659 #308-01-1995 L2005 *100

RIOS, Laura C. 137 CALLE VIDAL FELIX 00659 #042-01-1985 L1989 **OBG** *020

RODRIGUEZ, German Rene. ■ 00659 #042-02-2002 L2004 **IM** *020

RODRIGUEZ GARCIA, Juan. ■ 00659 #847-10-1967 L1971 **OBG** *020

ROMAN PAGAN, Miguel Angel. HC 1 BOX 10185 00659 #649-14-1989 L1992 **GP** *020

RUIZ MORELL, Emelda. 542 CALLE TRUNCADO 00659 #308-03-1984 L1993 **GP** *020

RUIZ TORRADO, Herminio. 73 CALLE PH HERNANDEZ 00659 #308-06-1981 L1987 **GP** *020

SANCHEZ-MARCHAND, Luis Ma. C/O PO BOX 69001 STE 403, BO. DOMINGUITO ARECIBO, 00659 #308-07-1981 L2003 *100

SANTIAGO, Joseph Luis. ■ 00659 #308-13-2001 *100

SANTOS, Rafaelito B. PO BOX 69001, STE 243 00659 #308-01-1984 L1995 **GP** *062

SANTOS-MONTES, Noel. PO BOX 193 00659 #308-03-1981 L1984 **IM** *020

SILVESTRY, Elvin John. 120 AVE DR SUSONI 00659 #561-01-1965 L1967 **FM** *020

TALAVERA FERRER, Tomas J. HC 4 BOX 48700, BO NARANJITO 00659 #308-03-1985 L1991 *020

TOLEDO-GARCIA, Marilyn. HC6 BOX 10185, KM 2D 00659 #649-14-1990 L1995 **PD** *020

TORO VELEZ, Jose M. 7 CALLE D, PARC SANTA ROSA 00659 #649-01-1955 L1958 **GP** *100

TORRADO, Jose Manuel. ■ 00659 #042-01-1997 L1999 **IM** *020 †20

TORRES MALDONADO, Maria I. ■ 00659 #649-14-2000 L2004 *100

URDAZ GOMEZ, Jose H. 560 CALLE TRUNCADO, CARRETERA #2 HCT815 00659 #847-05-1972 L1975 **GS** *020

HATO REY — SAN JUAN

ALMODOVAR, Ramon I. PARIS ST 126 A 00917 #023-01-1943 L1945 **U** *072 †95

ALONSO, Guillermo. PO BOX 925 00918 #275-01-1948 L1949 **GP** *020

AMEZAGA, Angel Roberto. 426 CALLE PADRE BERRIOS 00917 #308-02-1979 L1982 **OPH** *020

APONTE CORDOVA, Alfredo. 735 AVE PONCE DE LEON, STE 707 00917 #847-06-1971 L1974 **IM** *020

ARANDA, Alvaro U. 735 AVE PONCE DE LEON, STE 716 TORRE AUXILIO MUTU 00917 #042-01-1986 L1991 **PUD CCM** *020

ARROYO, Ana Teresa. ■ 00917 #308-01-1983 L1991 **FM** *030

BADIA GONZALEZ, Evelyn. 735 AVE PONCE DE LEON # P, TORRE MEDICA DEL AUXILIO M 00917 #042-01-1978 L1983 **CHN PD** *020 †75

BARRERAS AVILA, Jose A. 316 COND MAYAGUEZ CT, MAYAGUEZ ST NO 137 00917 #308-10-1985 L2002 *020

BRAU, Ricardo H. 400 F D ROOSEVELT 511 00918 #042-01-1975 L1980 **NS** *020 †25

BRUNO-DOMENECH, Jose Luis. ■ 00917 #649-14-1991 L1993 **FM** *020

CANTALAPIEDRA, Susana. 715 AVE PONCE DE LEON, HOSPITAL AUXILIO MUTUO 00917 #024-07-1991 L1997 **IM** *020 †20

CARDONA AVILES, Nestor. 431 AVE PONCE DE LEON #325 00917 #649-01-1959 L1961 **PM** *020

CARDONA-CANCIO, Nestor. 431 AVE PONCE DE LEON #325 00917 #042-01-1985 L1989 **PM** *020 †60

CARLO, Jose Rafael. CLINICA LAS AMERICAS RM 42 00918 #042-01-1978 L1983 **N** *020 †75

CARLOS, Francisco Jose. 735 AVE PONCE DE LEON #801 00917 #042-01-1981 L1986 **ORS** *020 †40

CASTA-CARDONA, Mayra Merc. ■ 00917 #649-14-1999 L2002 **FM** *020

CASTRO DE JESUS, Rafael E. 152 AVE FD ROOSEVELT 00917 #847-10-1953 L1957 **P** *020

CERRA DIAZ, Jose J. AUENIDA ROOSEVELT 400, STE 307 00918 #042-01-1963 L1968 **GS** *020 †85

CINTRON RIOS, Eloy. 315 DOMENECH AVE 00919 #042-01-1961 L1970 **OBG** *020 †30

COLON-MORALES, Miguel A. CENTER, LAS AMERCIAS PROFESSIONAL 00919 #038-06-1950 L1952 **AN** *020 †05

CORDOVA, Fernando Auibal. 903 COND EL ARANJUEZ 00917 #010-02-1955 L1961 **IM** *071

CRUZ, Gladys M. COND TORRE ALTA APT 7043 00917 #042-03-1981 L1985 **CLP** *020 †50

CUELLAR AVINO, Sonia. PO BOX 2133 00917 #042-04-1991 L1995 **PD** *020

DEL CASTILLO, Alan. 400 ROOSEVELT AVE, STE 410 00918 #917-30-1979 L1990 **P** *020

ECHANDI, Manuel Antonio. ■ 00917 #042-01-1976 L2001 **FM** *030 †18

ECHEGARAY, P P Luis. 735 AVE PONCE DE LEON, STE 716 00917 #042-01-1987 L1990 **PUD IM** *020

ELIAS DE ALONSO, Adelaida. ■ 00917 #041-09-1949 L1952 **PUD IM** *072

ESCOTO VALES, Alejandro A. OFFICE 200, PLAZA LAS AMERICAS 00918 #275-01-1950 L1970 **OS GS** *020

ESPIET MIRAY, Juan A. 431 AVE PONCE DE LEON, STE 701 00917 #847-05-1977 L1981 **IM HO** *020

FERNANDEZ, Carlos. F.D. ROOSEVELT AVE #400, CLINICA LAS AMERICAS 00917 #042-01-1981 L1984 **IM** *020 †20

FERNANDEZ, Carmen A. ROSI 255, BALDRICH 00918 #042-04-1988 L1993 **GP** *020

FERNANDEZ-CERRA, Eugenio. CLINICA FDEZ GARCIA 00919 #023-07-1943 L1989 **OS PUD** *071

FIGUEROA, Wilda. PARIS 243 W 1313 00917 #042-04-1984 L1986 **IM** *020

FIGUEROA-COLON, Jose J. PLAZA MD-4TH FLOOR, TORRE PLAZA LAS AMERICAS 00918 #041-01-1951 L1953 **OS U** *020 †95

FIGUEROA-CRUZ, Wanda Luz. 200 CALLE DUARTE 00917 #042-04-1984 L1986 **IM** *020

FLORES, Jose R. 735 AVE PONCE DE LEON, STE 710 00917 #042-01-1995 L1999 **OBG** *020

FRIAS-ARIAS, Alberto E. 130 AVE FD ROOSEVELT 00917 #308-01-1979 L1982 **PD** *020

GARCIA, David E. OFIC 814 MIDTOWN CONDO 00918 #036-07-1958 L1965 **AI PDP** *071 †55,03

GARCIA-OLIVERAS, Ramon L. 223 STAHL ST 00918 #649-01-1958 L1962 **P CHP** *071

GONZALEZ, Miguel A. 259 CALLE CHILE, INTERIOR D 00917 #847-01-1971 L1974 **P** *030

GONZALEZ DEL ROSARIO, M. 735 AVE PONCE DE LEON, STE 716 00917 #847-06-1977 L1980 **PUD IM** *020

GONZALEZ-RODRIGUEZ, A. 123 EL VEDADO 00919 #847-06-1977 L1982 **ATP CLP** *020 †50

GRAZIADIO, Victor J. HOSP AUXILIO MUTUO 00919 #561-01-1945 L1989 **AN** *075

GUERRIOS, Lourdes. TOWNHOUSE G-501, EL MONTE SUR 00918 #042-01-1990 L1995 **U** *020 †95

HERNANDEZ, Daniel Ivan. 431 AVE PONCE DE LEON, STE 1503 00917 #042-01-1996 L1999 **OBG** *020 †30

IRIZARRY-BULLS, Edgar. PARQUE DE LAS FUENTES, APT 1506 00918 #649-01-1945 L1946 **OPH** *071

JIMENEZ-RIVERA, Jorge L. CLINICA LAS AMERICAS, OFICINA 410 00918 #042-01-1970 L1974 **P** *020

KOLODZIEJ, Frank. 56 CALLE JOSE MARTI, URB EL PRADO 00917 #042-01-1967 L1969 **R RNR** *020

LEON-VALIENTE, Ana I. ■ 00919 #042-01-1968 L1970 **PD** *020 †55

LLAGUNO, Norma. PLAZA 12 H, COND HATO REY 00918 #847-06-1976 L1985 **GP** *020

LOPEZ, Madelyn. 735 AVE PONCE DE LEON, 410 TORRES DE AUXILIO MUTU 00917 #649-19-1993 L1996 **P** *020

LOPEZ-ELIAS, Francisco. ■ 00917 #847-05-1942 L1942 **P** *071

LOPEZ-QUILES, Aida Iris. #17.0, HATO REY PLAZA CONDOMINIUM 00918 #308-03-1976 L1979 **GP** *020

LOWRY, Philip Chas. 362 CALLE PACHIN MARIN, URB UMPIERRE 00917 #042-01-1971 L1973 **GS** *020 †85

LUGO-ALVAREZ, Waldemar. 431 AVE PONCE DE LEON, OFICINA 326 00917 #042-03-1988 L1992 **IM** *020

MALDONADO, Jellytza. 527 CALLEJON C, SECT EL RELINCHO 00917 #649-14-1993 L1996 **IM NTR** *020

MALDONADO-RODRIGUEZ, O. 735 AVE PONCE DE LEON #503, TORRE MEDICA AUXILIO MUTUO 00917 #649-14-1978 L1980 **P** *020

MARCIAL, Luisa Vanessa. 725 AVE PONCE DE LEON, PDA. 371/2 00917 #042-01-1982 L1986 **RO** *020 †80

MARCIAL DE GOMEZ, V E. PRES RAMIREZ 207 BALDRICH 00918 #308-01-1948 L1966 **GP PHP** *020

MARIN-SANTOS, Juan Ramon. PO BOX 2426 00919 #847-10-1969 L1973 **GP** *074

MARRERO-SANTIAGO, Ricardo. 57 CALLE JOSE MARTI, URB FLORAL PARK 00917 #308-03-1977 L1979 **GP** *020

MARTIN, Jose R. 735 AVE PONCE DE LEON, STE 816 00917 #042-01-1993 L1996 **GE IM** *020 †20

MARTINEZ, Hugo Enrique. 400 F D ROOSEVELT 303, CLINICA LAS AMERICAS 00918 #042-01-1978 L1983 **OPH** *020 †35

MARTINEZ, Maria Ivelisse. 40 AVE ROOSEVELT, AMERICAS CLINICA LAS AMERI 00917 #042-01-1978 L1982 **D DS** *020 †15

MARTINEZ, Ronaldo L. 735 AVE PONCE DE LEON, STE 706 00917 #042-03-1987 L1991 **IM** *020

MARTINEZ CRESPO, Cesar. 273 AVE BARBOSA, BDA ISRAEL 00917 #847-04-1960 L1962 **GP** *020

MATOS-SANTIAGO, William. 607 LA TORRE DE PLAZA 00918 #847-10-1968 L1970 **RHU IM** *075

MEJIA, Rosana. EDIF TAMARINDO J-15, COND PARQUE CENTRO 00918 #042-01-2000 L2004 *020

MENDEZ-SANTISTEBAN, J A. ■ 00918 #042-01-1971 L1974 **OS GP** *030

MIRABAL, Ozema Milagros. HATO REY PLAZA 17 L 00919 #308-01-1971 L1976 **P** *050

MIRANDA, Fermin C. 566 CALLE B, UPPR 00917 #042-01-1966 L1970 **PG PD** *020 †55

MIRANDA-FERRER, M, Jr. 735 AVE PONCE DE LEON, STE 202 00917 #847-01-1980 L1984 **OPH** *020

MIRANDA RODRIGUEZ, R. 1 AVE PONCE DE LEON, PROFESIONAL MEDICAL PLAZA 00917 #308-03-1981 L1981 **IM** *020 †20

MONROIG-QUILES, Pedro J. 715 AVE PONCE DE LEON, STE 513 00917 #042-03-1981 L1984 **IM PUD** *020 †20

MONTESERIN MEDINA, Sylvia. 398 DOMENECH AVE 00918 #847-04-1956 L1961 **GP OS** *020

MORALES, Julio Cesar. EL MONTE NORTE APT 728 00918 #042-01-1975 L1979 *020

NEGRON, Carmen Josefina. CONDO HATEO REY PLZ 19A 00918 #042-01-1974 L1976 **DR** *040

NEGRON, Juan Carlos. 265 CALLE HONDURAS, COND DUERO APT 10-D 00917 #042-01-1980 L1983 **IM NM** *020 †28

NERY, Cristina Gomez. G P O BOX 1811 00919 #176-03-1967 L1977 **PTH** *020 †50

NOVAK, Pablo Leonardo. 262 CALLE URUGUAY 00917 #132-04-1985 L2004 *100

OLAZABAL, Angel Jesus. 735 AVE PONCE DE LEON, 735 PONCE DE LEON SUITE 40 00917 #035-20-1971 L1980 **GE IM** *020 †20

ORENGO, Serafin. ATRIUM PLAZA, APT 1104 00918 #042-01-1984 L1988 **CHP P** *020

ORTIZ, Grisel. URBANIZACION HYDE PARK, CLLE RUIS RIVERA APT 270 00918 #042-03-2000 **PM** *100

ORTIZ-QUINONES, Luis A. ■ 00917 #847-06-1975 L1978 **OBG** *020

OTERO-ROQUE, Manuel. 428 CALLE PACHIN MARIN 00917 #275-01-1945 L1953 **GS OS** *020

PABON-LANDRON, Josue A. 735 AVE PONCE DE LEON, OFICINA 415 TORRE AUXILIO 00917 #042-03-1982 L1986 **FM** *020

PAEZ, Rene Antonio. ■ 00919 #847-10-1959 L1968 **OBG** *030

PARRILLA GONZALEZ, Juan R. EL MONTE G 406 00918 #275-01-1944 L1971 **GP PUD** *020

PEROCIER-AGUIRRE, M. 132 CALLE MAYAGUEZ 00918 #308-01-1979 L1981 **P** *020

QUINONES ESTRADA, Maria E. INSTITUTO PSIQUINTUA 00919 #847-04-1963 L1965 **CHP** *020

RAMIREZ, Glenda Emlyn. 275 AVE BARBOSA 00917 #042-03-1993 L1996 **IMG** *020

RAMIREZ, Maria T. EL DUERO 14A HONDURAS 265 00918 #042-01-1992 L1992 **P** *020

RAMIREZ VAZQUEZ, Ana Ines. CALLE J CARBONELL 378 00918 #308-02-1989 L1994 *020

RIOS-MELLADO, Luis R. APT. 21-G, AVENIDA PINERO, CONDOMINIO HATO REY PLAZA 00918 #847-04-1961 L1963 **P GP** *020

RIUTORT, Antonio. PO BOX 191649 00919 #042-01-1977 L1979 **D** *020 †15

RIVAS, Maria Delcarmen. 273 AVE PONCE DE LEON, 15TH FL 00917 #035-01-1988 L1994 **END** *020 †20

RIVERA, Lilia I. AVE ARTERIAL HOSTOS, COND CAPITAL CENTER #306 00918 #042-01-1982 L1986 **OPH OS** *020 †35

RIVERA RIVERA, Angel M. 553 CABO ALVERIO ROOSEVELT 00918 #042-01-1963 L1967 **A** *020 †55,03

RODRIGUEZ, Damara Esther. 121 CALLE COSTA RICA, CONDO EL BILBAO APT 203 00917 #649-14-2002 L2004 *100

RODRIGUEZ, Isabel M. LAMIRANTE PNZN 228 EL VEDD 00918 #042-01-1989 L1992 **CHP** *020 †18,75

RODRIGUEZ, Orlando. 735 AVE PONCE DE LEON, STE 503 00917 #308-02-1991 L1993 **CD IC** *020

RODRIGUEZ, Rafael J. OFIC 205, EDIF CLINICA LAS AMERICAS 00918 #042-01-1971 L1973 **PUD IM** *040

RODRIGUEZ-GINORIO, Henry. 735 AVE PONCE DE LEON, 405 TORRE SUZILO MUTUO 00917 #042-01-1976 L1980 **GYN** *020 †30

RODRIGUEZ-IRIZARRY, Jose. COND EL MONTE SUR 704B 00918 #042-02-1983 L1986 **PD** *020 †55

RODRIGUEZ MOJICA, Wilma. FERNANDEZ ST NO 3 00917 #042-01-1970 L1972 **DR** *020 †80

RODRIGUEZ-OQUENDO, A. BOX 3545 HATO REY STA 00919 #042-01-1986 L1990 **P** *020 †75

ROSA-SANTIAGO, Helen. 601 COND TORRE DE ORO, PLAZA LAS AMERICAS 00917 #042-01-1982 L1985 **FM** *020 †18

RUIZ, Eloy. HOSP AUXLO MUTO, DEPT ANES 00919 #042-01-1962 L1967 **AN GS** *020 †05

RUIZ, Oscar Antonio. CLINICA LAS AMERICAS, F.D.R AVE #400 SUITE 410 00918 #042-01-1978 L1983 **P** *020 †75

SABATER LOPEZ, Homero. ■ 00917 #649-01-1950 L1964 **GS** *071

SANCHEZ, Carmen L. FLORAL PK BETANCES 106 00917 #847-04-1965 L1967 **GP** *020

SEGUNDO GONZALEZ, Urania. 701 COND TORRE ALTA, MEJICO ESQ URUGUAY STS 00917 #847-01-1964 L1967 **IM** *020

SIERRA-GARCIA, Radames. 400 F.D. ROOSEVELT AVENUE, CLINICA LAS AMERICAS 00918 #847-10-1954 L1958 **RHU IM** *071

SILVA-AYALA, Jose Enrique. 735 AVE PONCE DE LEON, STE 603 00917 #649-01-1971 L1974 **VS GS** *020 †85

SILVA MONGE, Luis Danl. ■ 00917 #042-01-1954 L1957 **GP** *072

SOLTERO-VENEGAS, Edmee M. SUITE 402, AMERICAS PROF CENTER 00918 #042-01-1985 L1990 **GS** *020 †85

STIEHL, Walter Leoncio. PO BOX 25 00919 #042-01-1955 **DR OS** *040

TORRES, Carlos F. ■ 00917 #649-01-1969 L1972 **GS U** *071

TORRES SOLIVAN, Ruben. AUENIDA PONCE DE LEON 714 00918 #847-02-1969 L1971 **IM** *020

TOTTI, Noel, III. 735 AVE PONCE DE LEON, STE 716 00917 #042-01-1976 L1981 **PUD IM** *040 †20

TOWNSEND, William Martin. 735 AVE PONCE DE LEON, SUITE 216 TORRE AUXILIO MU 00917 #021-01-1965 L1967 **OPH** *020 †35

VALDES, Leoncio. BOX 738 00919 #308-01-1950 L1958 **GS** *020

VALDESPADA, Argelio H. ■ 00917 #275-01-1952 L1975 *062

VARELA, Benigno Luis. AVE. PONCE DE LEON, HOSPITAL AUXILIO MUTUO 00919 #042-01-1976 L1982 **ON IM** *020 †20

VARELA TIZOL, Manuel. PO BOX 1876 00919 #847-10-1968 L1975 *100

VAZQUEZ, Miguel Angel. 6 CALLE PONCE, UPPR 00917 #042-03-1995 L1999 **OBG** *040 †30

VAZQUEZ-MILAN, Hiram. ■ 00917 #041-09-1943 L1944 **OM IM** *071

VIGO-DIAZ, Jose Joaquin. 435 AVE PONCE DE LEON, HOSPITAL PAVIA HATO REY 00917 #649-14-1976 L1979 **P** *020

WALTERS, Thelma Cristina. 140 AVE ROOSEVELT, CALL BOX 1007 00917 #308-03-1983 L1986 **GP** *020

ZAVALA, Manuel Antonio. 52 CALLE MAYAGUEZ 00917 #042-02-1992 L1995 **IM** *020

HORMIGUEROS – HORMIGUEROS

ALMODOVAR, Luis Anibal. 6 AVE LUIS MUNOZ MARIN 00660 #042-01-1976 L1979 **GS** *020

ARROYO-CORDERO, Tamara C. ■ 00660 #042-01-2007 **P** *012

CARRERO SOTO, Jose A. ■ 00660 #649-19-1997 L1999 **P** *100

CASIANO, Wanda. ■ 00660 #042-01-1992 L1995 **HO** *020

CASTILLO-MORALES, David. ■ 00660 #042-03-1999 L2003 **IM** *020

CHAMAH-MARTINEZ, Eduardo. SAN ANTONIO ST #212, STE 9 00660 #308-01-1986 L1991 **GP** *020

COLBORG, Gustavo Adolfo. N1 CALLE TILO, URB. VALLE HERMOSO ARRIBA 00660 #042-01-1990 L1993 **PS** *020 †85

COLON-PADILLA, Juan. S5 CALLE PINO, VALLE HEMOSO ARRIBA 00660 #042-02-1998 L2000 **IM** *020

DELGADO QUINONES, Carlos. 4 CALLE MONSERRATE, BOX 158 CARR. 2 KM 164 #4 00660 #308-06-1986 L1988 **IM** *020

ESCABI, Fernando Armando. ■ 00660 #042-02-2006 *012

GAUD MORALES, Jorge Luis. ■ 00660 #308-13-2001 L2003 *100

GUTIERREZ MESTRE, Pete A.. PO BOX 446 00660 #308-03-1989 L2004 *100

JIMENEZ, Luz Maria. 2 CALLE LUIS MUNOZ MARIN 00660 #007-02-1997 L1999 **PD** *020 †55

LEBRON SILVA, Harvey W. SK17 CALLE BELLISIMA, VALLE HERMOSO 00660 #649-35-1999 L2002 *020

MACHIN PORRATA, Rafael A.. ■ 00660 #042-04-2003 L2004 *100

NELSON CRUZ, Carl P. 8 CALLE MATEO FAJARDO 00660 #847-02-1978 L1983 **GP** *020

NOEL IRIZARRY, Francisco. 2 CALLE RUIZ BELVIS 00660 #308-04-1990 L1995 **IM** *020

ORTA, Brenda L. 756 CALLE CAFETAL, HACIENDAS CONSTANCIA 00660 #042-04-1996 L1997 **FM** *020

PEREZ-LUGO, Elliot Ernest. ■ 00660 #649-14-2002 *020

POLANCO, Maria De. J12 CALLE 8, HACIENDA LA MONSERRATE 00660 #308-06-1986 L1996 **PD** *020

QUILES, Osvaldo B. 736 CALLE ARBOLEDA, HACIENDAS CONSTANCIA 00660 #042-04-1990 L1992 **OBG** *020

QUILES-RUIZ, Ana Tilde. 14 CALLE SAN ANTONIO # 201 00660 #649-14-1988 L1990 **FM** *020 †18 ‡

QUINONES, Alicia. ■ 00660 #649-14-2002 *020

QUINONES BAYRON, Jacobo E. R10 CALLE CEDRO, VALLE HERMOSO 00660 #042-04-1998 L2000 **FM** *020 ‡

QUINONES ORTIZ, Eileen M. ■ 00660 #308-06-1988 L1992 *020

RAMIREZ DE ARELLANO, A A. ■ 00660 #024-01-1950 L1955 **IM OS** *040 †20

RAMIREZ TORO, Noe. 10 CALLE SAN ANTONIO # 103 00660 #649-14-1983 L1986 **OM GP** *020

RODRIGUEZ, Victor Manuel. SC12 CALLE FLAMBOYAN, VALLE HERMOSO 00660 #649-35-1999 L2002 **FM** *020

ROVIRA MARTINO, Jose. PO BOX 1520 00660 #847-10-1984 L1989 **GP** *020

SAAVEDRA, Arturo, Jr. J1 CALLE AZUCENA, VALLE HERMOSO 00660 #847-10-1974 L1976 **OBG** *020

TORRES, Alba N. ■ 00660 #042-04-1995 L1997 *020

VIDAL CABANAS, Efrain R. N1 CALLE TILO, VALLE HERMOSO 00660 #308-01-1986 L1993 **GS** *020

VILLAMIL, Fernando Luis. 2 AVE LUIS MUNOZ MARIN, MASS GENERAL HOSPITAL 00660 #042-01-2001 L2003 **ORS** *020

HUMACAO – HUMACAO

ABREU, Salvador. 2 CALLE PADRE RIVERA W, POBOX 8486 00791 #847-05-1974 L1977 **IM PUD** *020
ABREUDELGADO, Yamilka. ■ 00791 #042-02-2008 *012
ABREU-GONZALEZ, Fernando. ■ 00791 #042-02-2002 L2003 **IM** *020 †20
AGOSTO, Wanda Ivelisse. 52 CALLE ULISES MARTINEZ 00791 #308-03-1982 L1989 **PD** *020
AGOSTO ALVAREZ, Juan R. 3 CALLE FONT MARTELO E 00791 #847-01-1965 L1969 **FM GP** *020
ALAMO VAZQUEZ, Isabel. PO BOX 8668 00792 #847-05-1974 L1977 **IM CD** *020
ALICEA-RODRIGUEZ, Miriam. 50 CALLE MIGUEL CASILLAS, MUNOZ MARIN ESQ 00791 #042-01-1979 L1982 **PDE** *020
ALLENDE, Myriam Zahydee. 18 CALLE JORGE FRANCESHI, URB PEREYO 00791 #042-01-1974 L1977 **END IM** *020 †20
ALONSO, Angel Antonio. 458 CALLE FONT MARTELO, ROSADO MEDICAL 00791 #847-05-1975 L1980 **IM** *020
ALTIERI, Pablo I. PO BOX 8387 00792 #042-01-1967 L1970 **CD IM** *020 †20
ALVARADO, Elvin. 429 CALLE FLAMBOYAN, URB LOS SAUCES 00791 #308-03-1982 L1989 **GP** *020
ALVARADO-BERCKEMEYER, J. 303 CALLE FONT MARTELO 00791 #847-04-1966 L1974 **OBG OS** *020
ALVAREZ, Luis Reinaldo, Jr. PO BOX 179 00792 #042-01-1998 L2000 **IM** *020
ALVAREZ-RUIZ, Jesus M. 158 CALLE FONT MARTELO 00791 #847-06-1977 L1979 **OBG** *020 †30
APONTE, Ivan Euclides. 263 AVE FONT MARTELO 00791 #042-03-1993 L1996 **ON IM** *020
ARBOLEDA-OSORIO, Bolivar. 3 CALLE FONT MARTELO E 00791 #042-01-1983 L1988 **GS SO** *020 †85
ARNAU RODRIGUEZ, Noel J. 55 CALLE FLOR GERENA S 00791 #042-01-1992 L1996 **PM PMM** *020 †60
ARROYO, Elba I. ■ 00792 #042-03-1998 L2001 **ID** *020 †20
ARROYO, Ernesto. 52 CALLE FONT MARTELO E 00791 #042-01-1970 L1972 **OBG** *020
ARROYO, Esther Noemi. 42 SURFSIDE RD, PALNAS DEL MAR 00791 #025-01-1954 L1956 **GP OBG** *020
ARROYO, Javier Ivan. ■ 00792 #042-03-1995 L2001 **GE** *020 †20
BAGUE, Milagros Nilda. 96 PALMAS DR, PALMAS DEL MAR 00791 #042-01-1998 L2000 *020 †55
BAJANDAS, Ahmed. F9 CALLE JESUS M RIVERA, URB RIVERA DONATO 00791 #042-01-1955 L1959 **AN** *030
BALAGUER, Juan Luis. 52 CALLE FONT MARTELO E 00791 #847-04-1956 L1959 **IM CD** *072
BENITEZ, Gabriel Alberto. ■ 00792 #042-01-2007 *012
BENITEZ, Ramon H. 52 CALLE MUNOZ MARIN, BOX 151 00791 #308-03-1986 L1996 **PD** *020
BERRIOS, Sylvia. ■ 00791 #042-01-2006 **P** *012
BONNIN, Maria Elena. ■ 00791 #042-03-2004 *100
BOURET, Lizzette Marie. 295 PALMAS INN WAY STE 135, PALMAS FAM MED CTR 00791 #042-01-2000 L2003 **FM** *020
BRUGUERAS, Nydia E. 9 CALLE MUNOZ MARIN W 00791 #042-01-1966 L1969 **RHU IM** *020
BURGOS VARGAS, Bolivar. 110 CALLE F MARTELO E, BOX 313 00791 #847-06-1975 L1980 **PD** *020
CAMILO-RODRIGUEZ, Marcia. ■ 00792 #308-01-1965 L1972 **GYN** *062
CAMUNAS, Litza Haydee. ■ 00791 #042-03-2002 L2006 **IM** *100 †20
CARBALLO, Francisco R. 13 CALLE FLOR GERENA N, FLOR GERENA #13, HUMACAO, 00791 #308-03-1984 L1986 **IM** *020
CARDONA-TRAVERSO, Edgar A. 55 CALLE ULISES MARTINEZ N 00791 #042-03-1981 L1988 **GS** *020
CASTRO-SANTANA, Lesliane. ■ 00791 #042-01-2004 **IM** *100 †20
CATARINEU-ANDREU, Nestor. 295 PALMAS INN WAY, STE 130 PMB 195 00791 #847-10-1962 L1964 **N** *020
CHARNECO, Jerry Chas. 63 CALLE FONT MARTELO 00791 #042-01-1972 L1974 **D** *020 †15
CLEMENTE ORTIZ, Monica M.. 100 CARR 908, CUH STATION 00791 #649-14-2004 L2006 *020
COLON-ORTIZ, Edna S. PO BOX 554, 17 CALLE 16C 00792 #308-03-1978 L1981 **GP** *020
CUYAR FERNANDEZ, Jose L. SUITE 409, CORREO CENTRO #58-B 00792 #042-01-1978 L1983 **GS** *020
DAVILA SANDOZ, Mabel. 42 PORT RD PALMAS DEL MA 00791 #847-04-1959 L1963 **CHP** *020
DE LA CRUZ ROSADO, Julio. 300 CALLE FONT MARTELO 00791 #847-06-1971 L1974 **ORS OM** *020
DE LA ROSA, Julio Antonio. PO BOX AE 00792 #308-01-1960 L1969 **OBG** *075
DE LA ROSA-ALMODOVAR, J M. HC 3, 1 PLAZA DEL MAR 00791 #847-10-1975 L1978 **PD** *020
DE LEON, Maria R. PO BOX 284 00791 #847-01-1986 L1994 **PD** *020
DELGADO, Saul. 50 CALLE MIGUEL CASILLAS, P O BOX 8367 00791 #042-01-1962 L1964 **PD OS** *020
DELGADO-VELAZQUEZ, Diana. AVENIDA TEJAS 00791 #308-03-1978 L1982 **GP** *020
DEL TORO, Antonio R. 60 CALLE MUNOZ MARIN 00791 #042-01-1966 L1969 **U** *020
DEL TORO, Antonio R. PO BOX 549, URB EL RETIRO 00792 #042-04-1995 L1997 *020
DEL TORO SANCHEZ, Annette. 60 CALLE MUNOZ MARIN 00791 #042-04-1995 L2002 **GP** *020
DIAZ-NEGRON, Huberto. 3 CALLE FONT MARTELO E 00791 #847-10-1965 L1967 **ORS** *020
DONES, Wistremundo. 332 AVE FONT MARTELO 00791 #042-01-1985 L1990 **CD IM** *020
DUCHESNE LANDRON, Juan. 3 CALLE FONT MARTELO E 00791 #847-04-1956 L1959 **GP** *020
ESPINOSA, Rafael. ■ 00792 #042-01-2984 L2002 *020
ETIENNE, Rufus. PO BOX 305 00792 #042-03-1981 L1984 **AN PME** *020
FERNANDEZ BRITO, Beatriz. 301 AVE FONT MARTELO 00791 #308-03-1987 L1994 *020
FERNANDEZ BRITO, Luis M. 52 CALLE ANTONIO LOPEZ S 00791 #308-06-1989 L1996 **GP** *020
FERNANDEZ-MENA, Manuel D. ■ 00792 #308-01-1950 L1958 **GP GS** *075
FIGUEROA, Miguel. ■ 00791 #847-01-1964 L1973 **PD** *020
FIGUEROA HERNANDEZ, David. ■ 00792 #042-04-1997 L1999 **FM** *020
FIOL-VAZQUEZ, Julio. 3 CALLE FONT MARTELO E 00791 #847-04-1962 L1964 **PM R** *071
FLORES, Luis G. 300 CALLE FONT MARTELO 00791 #042-02-1983 L1987 **OBG** *020
FRANCESCHI JULIA, F J. ■ 00792 #396-06-1937 L1939 **PUD** *071
GARAY, Jose M. ■ 00792 #308-04-1991 L1997 **PD** *020
GARCIA, Miosotis. ■ 00792 #042-03-2004 **PTH** *012
GARCIA, Yazmin L. ■ 00791 #042-04-1993 L1996 *020
GARCIA APONTE, Gloria I. PO BOX 859, RYDER MEM HOSP 00792 #847-05-1973 L1977 *100

GOLDEROS, Francisco Ruben. 3 CALLE FONT MARTELO E 00791 #847-08-1976 L1981 **AN** *074
GOMEZ, Jose A. 9 CALLE FLOR GERENA N 00791 #847-02-1974 L1981 **GS** *020
GONZALEZ, Angel-Rafael. 104 CALLE FONT MARTEL E #2 00791 #308-01-1967 L1975 **PD** *020
GONZALEZ, Ariel Figueroa. 300 CALLE FONT MARTELO 00791 #308-03-1979 L1981 **PD** *020
GONZALEZ-CAMACHO, Luis A. 3 CALLE FONT MARTELO E 00791 #649-14-1979 L1984 **AN PUD** *020
GONZALEZ DIAZ, Juan F. RYDER MEM HOSP POB 489 00792 #847-05-1973 L1975 **EM** *020
GUZMAN, Manuel A. ■ 00791 #042-04-2002 L2003 *100
HERNANDEZ, Eduardo Frank. PO BOX 9131, HUMACAO ST 00792 #042-01-1978 L1981 **IM** *020
HERNANDEZ SEPULVEDA, Ivan. 132 FRINGE DR, URB PALMAS PLANTATION 00791 #308-01-1981 L1986 **GP** *020
HERRERO LUGO, Carmelo E. PO BOX 9120 00792 #649-35-2001 L2002 **FM** *020
HERRERO-TORRES, Carmelo. 300 CALLE FONT MARTELO 00791 #042-01-1969 L1972 **GE IM** *020
JIMENEZ, Mildred. SALIDA HACIA LA PLAYA DE, AVENIDA BLVD RAMAL 3 00792 #308-04-1984 L1987 **GP** *020
LA TORRE, Orlando. 300 CALLE FONT MARTELO, HOSPITAL DR DOMINGUEZ 00791 #042-01-1991 L1995 **AN** *020
LLONA-SANCHEZ, Antonio. 59 CALLE MUNOZ MARIN 00791 #847-04-1959 L1960 **P PHP** *020
LOIRA, Lenis V, Jr. 300 CALLE FONT MARTELO 00791 #275-01-1960 L1972 **GP** *020
LOPEZ, Adaline. 170 CALLE FONT MARTELO 00791 #308-03-1985 L2002 *020
LOPEZ, Agustin J. 334 AVE FONT MARTELO 00791 #308-04-1989 L1992 **IM** *020
LOPEZ, Armando, Jr. ■ 00791 #042-01-1985 L1988 **AN** *020 †05
LOPEZ, Rafael A. 358 CALLE FONT MARTELO, STE 102 00791 #042-01-1987 L1993 **ORS** *020 †40
LOPEZ-MARQUEZ, Jose L. 128 CALLE FONT MARTELO E, CLINICA DEL ESTE 00791 #042-03-1980 L1982 **P** *020
LOPEZ NIEVES, Myrna Iris. ■ 00791 #649-14-1976 L1980 **PD** *020
LOPEZ-RAMIREZ, Elsa V. 67 SUNSET ST, URB SUNRISE 00791 #308-03-1981 L1987 **GS** *020
LOPEZ RODRIGUEZ, Cynthia. HC 11, BOX 12126 00791 #649-14-2003 L2005 *100
LOURIDO FERRER, Heriberto. PO BOX 8887 00792 #308-06-1981 L1987 **P** *020
LOYOLA PEREZ, Angel E. 65 CALLE CARRERAS W, DOLORES CABRERA 65 E ESQ A 00791 #308-03-1985 L1993 **P** *020
LUGO, Wilmer. 170 AVE FONT MARTELO 00791 #308-03-1985 L1992 **GP** *020
LUGO VELAZQUEZ, Agripino. PO BOX 179, ULISES MARTINEZ ST 55 N 00792 #847-05-1973 L1976 **OM** *020
MARCHAN, Luis Augusto. 100 CALLE DUFRESNE W # 90 00791 #042-01-1971 L1974 **R** *020
MARQUEZ, William. 3 CALLE 1, # A1 00791 #042-01-1977 L1980 **FM** *020 †18 ‡
MARRERO-RUSSE, Jose R. PO BOX 859 00792 #042-03-1981 L1985 **AN** *020
MARTINEZ-IRIZARRY, L. 3 CALLE FONT MARTELO E 00791 #396-04-1958 L1958 **GS GP** *071
MARTINEZ-LOPEZ, Loyda. ■ 00792 #042-01-1956 L1959 **GP GPM** *020
MILLAN APONTE, Sharon. ■ 00791 #649-35-2004 L2005 *100
MIRANDA-TRISTANI, G. C/O P.O. BOX 10164, 7 CALLE DUFRESNE (BAJOS) 00792 #308-03-1977 L1980 **HEM** *020
MOJICA, Luz Belinda. 55 CALLE MUNOZ MARIN 00791 #042-02-1998 L2002 **PD** *020
MOLINARY-RUIZ, Marla Y. 116 CALLE LAUREL, URB LOS SAUCES 00791 #042-01-2000 L2002 **PM** *020 †60
MORA BONETA, Pedro A. PO BOX 859, HOSP RYDER MEM,INC 00792 #847-04-1953 L1955 **OBG GP** *071
MUNOZ, Willie. ■ 00791 #308-03-1976 L1983 **AN** *020
MUNOZ NIETO, Jessie. ■ 00792 #308-03-1977 L1987 *020
MURILLO DE REYES, Aida M. 317 CALLE FONT MARTELO, HOSPITAL RYDER MEMORIAL 00791 #649-01-1969 L1975 **FM** *020
NASSAR, Carlos J. PO BOX 9132 00792 #042-01-1994 L1997 **DR** *020 †80
NASSAR, Jose A. 300 CALLE FONT MARTELO 00791 #041-13-1963 L1967 **DR OS** *030 †80
NAVARRETE, Enery. 69 CALLE ULISES MARTINEZ S 00791 #042-01-1975 L1980 **OPH** *020
NAVAS, Manuel Angel. 158 CALLE FONT MARTELO 00791 #042-03-1981 L1986 **OBG** *020 †30
OQUENDO, Carmen V. ■ 00792 #042-04-2002 L2003 *100
OQUENDO, Ruddy H. 4 CALLE PADRE RIVERA W, BOX 8389 00791 #042-10-1971 L1974 **PD** *020
ORTIZ, Julio A. 3 CALLE FONT MARTELO E, HOSP. HIMA FONT MARTELO 00791 #047-07-1948 L1955 **TRS GS** *072 †85
ORTIZ, Julio A, Jr. CALLA CARRERAS 58B, STE 417 00791 #010-02-1982 L1988 **OTO** *020
PANTALEON MENA, Ramon F V. FONT MARTELO 170-BOX 697 00791 #308-01-1958 L1966 **OBG** *020
PAOLI-BRUNO, Ramon N. 5 CALLE DUFRESNE E, MEDICENTRO 00791 #042-01-1980 L1984 **CCM IM** *020
PASTRANA, Griselle. ■ 00792 #042-01-1995 L1997 **FPG** *020 †18
PAULINO, Jose N. PO BOX 8938, B-12 EL RETIRO 00792 #847-01-1967 L1973 **PD** *020
PEGUERO, Roberto E. MUNOZ MARIN NO-104 00791 #308-01-1962 L1979 **GP** *020
PERALES, Marjorie Marie. ■ 00791 #042-03-1995 L1998 **ID** *020
PEREZ, Juan Emilio. 25 CALLE ULISES MARTINEZ 00791 #042-03-1996 L1999 **FM** *020
PEREZ-CASTRO, Ana P. 300 CALLE FONT MARTELO 00791 #847-04-1977 L1982 **GP** *020
PEREZ CORTES, Carlos O. 355 AVE FONT MARTELO, HOSP RYDER MEM 00791 #308-01-1983 L1987 **P** *020
PEREZ-HERNANDEZ, Cesar A. ■ 00792 #847-06-1976 L1980 **GP** *020
PEREZ TORRES, Antonio. VILLA UNIVERSITARIA, VALLE 14 F-36 00791 #308-03-1985 L1993 *020
PEREZ VEGA, Arnaldo. ■ 00792 #847-04-1958 L1961 **OTO** *020
PINO CANO, Ibrahim. ■ 00791 #275-01-1967 L1998 *020
PINTOR MARTINEZ, Augusto. PO BOX 128 00792 #649-14-2000 L2002 **FM** *020
POLISH, Sicila R. PO BOX 284 00792 #847-04-1966 L1974 **PD** *020
PUELL, Jose David. 295 PALMAS INN WAY STE 9 00791 #649-14-1979 L2002 **PD FM** *020 †55 ‡
QUINONES-NIEVES, Benjamin. 111 CALLE FONT MARTELO 00791 #042-01-1978 L1982 **OPH** *020
REYES, Luis M. 3 CALLE FONT MARTELO E # 1, HIMA HUMACAO, INC 00791 #042-01-1985 L1988 **IM END** *040 †20
REYES-LABORDE, Cesar A. PO BOX 300 00792 #041-13-1981 L1985 **P** *020 †75
RIVERA, Gerhardt. 58 CALLE CARRERAS W, CENTRO OB GYN 00791 #042-03-1988 L1992 **OBG** *020 †30
RIVERA, Nestor Orlando. 58 CALLE CARRERAS W 00791 #847-04-1963 L1967 **OBG** *020
RIVERA LOPEZ, Lumarie. 300 CALLE FONT MARTELO 00791 #649-14-2003 L2006 **PTH** *100
RODRIGUEZ, Jose F. 355 AVE FONT MARTELO, STE 401 00791 #308-03-1982 L1985 **IM** *020

■ = Address Information Privacy Protected

RODRIGUEZ TORRES, Pedro J. PO BOX 411 00792 #308-03-1986 L1995 *100
RODRIGUEZ TORRES, Rafael. PO BOX 411 00792 #308-03-1987 L2004 *100
ROLON, Dubal. 300 CALLE FONT MARTELO 00791 #308-04-1985 L1990 **IM** *020
ROMERO, Francisco Javier. 117 AVE FONT MARTELO W 00791 #042-03-2001 L2002 **PM** *100 †60
ROSA, Arnaldo I. 3 CALLE CARRERAS W 00791 #042-01-1992 L1995 **GE** *020 †20
ROSADO CARDONA, Betzaida. 58B CALLE CARRERAS W # 548 00791 #649-14-1988 L1993 *020
ROSA-MARTINEZ, Euelyn. 53 CALLE MUNOZ MARIN 00791 #308-03-1979 L1981 **FM** *030
ROSA-RODRIGUEZ, Jose M. 300 CALLE FONT MARTELO 00791 #847-05-1976 L1979 **GP** *020
ROZON, Manuel, Jr. ■ 00792 #042-01-1972 L1974 **GS** *020
SANCHEZ, Alberto E. CEDRO # 4,PALMAS DEL MAR 00791 #042-01-1954 L1956 **PS** *071 †65
SANCHEZ-RIVERA, Hector L. 158 CALLE FONT MARTELO 00791 #308-03-1978 L1980 **OBG** *020
SANTANA, Lisgelia. ■ 00792 #042-01-2004 L2005 **AN** *012
SANTIAGO, Waldemar E. RYDER MEM HOSP 00791 #025-07-1948 L1951 **PUD** *020
SANTINI VALIENTE, Nancy E. 12 CALLE TURQUESA 00791 #042-01-1992 L1996 **IM PM** *020
SEPULVEDA-ABREU, Ramon. 108 CALLE FONT MARTELO E 00791 #847-05-1974 L1977 **U** *020 †95
SERRANO, Aracelis. PO BOX 247 00792 #649-14-1990 L1992 **PD** *020
SERRANO, Pablo. 54 CALLE MUNOZ MARIN 00791 #042-03-1982 L1989 **CD IM** *020
SERRANO GARCIA, Lillian. 53 CALLE FONT MARTELO E, STE 101 00791 #042-04-1993 L1994 **P** *020
SILVA-BEAUCHAMP, Rene. PO BOX 607 00792 #010-02-1951 L1952 **IM** *075 †20
SMITH, Howard Alan. 355 AVE FONT MARTELO, STE 506 00791 #042-01-1977 L1980 **FM** *020 †18
SOARES, Manuel. 119 CALLE FONT MARTELO E 00791 #042-01-1978 L1983 **ORS** *020
SOSA, Miguel E. 4 CEDRO RD, PALMAS DEL MAR 00791 #042-01-1994 L2000 **GS** *020 †95
SOTO, Manuel Osvaldo. 358 AVE FONT MARTELO, ROSADO MED BLD #102 00791 #042-01-1989 L1992 **ORS** *020 †40
SUERO-PEREZ, Romulo S. 300 CALLE FONT MARTELO 00791 #847-04-1966 L1973 **GS** *020 †85
TEJEDA SANCHEZ, Hector M. PO BOX 8778, 56 MUNOZ MARI 00792 #308-03-1969 L1973 **GP** *020
TORRELLAS, Luis C. PO BOX 9290 00792 #042-01-1993 L1999 **PUD** *100 †20
TORRELLAS, Mari Clara. ■ 00792 #042-03-2004 **PTH** *012
TORRELLAS, Rafael Antonio. ■ 00792 #042-01-1997 L2000 **GS** *020
TORRES, Alexis. ■ 00791 #649-14-1998 L2000 **IM** *100
TORRES-NIEVES, Hector L. 53 CALLE MUNOZ MARIN 00791 #308-03-1978 L1981 **P** *020
VARGAS-RAPOSO, Juan B. C/O BOX 8868, 4 FLOIR GEREUA 00792 #308-01-1965 L1972 **PD** *071
VAZQUEZ TORRES, Otto. ■ 00792 #847-02-1973 L1975 **GP** *020
VAZQUEZ VAZQUEZ, Efrain. 55 CALLE MUNOZ MARIN, P O BOX 9137 00791 #042-01-1970 L1972 **PD** *020 †55
VEGA EMMANUELLI, Jose M. 9 CALLE DUFRESNE 00791 #847-06-1977 L1980 **EM FM** *020
VELAZQUEZ CABRERA, Esther. PO BOX 9128, 5 CARRURAS ST 00792 #042-01-1963 L1966 **PD** *020
VICENS, Rafael Esteban. 300 CALLE FONT MARTELO 00791 #042-01-1973 L1976 **OBG** *020 †30
WEBSTER, Wilfred. 103 PALMAS DR DEL MAR, SUNRISE AT PALMAS MORNING 00791 #042-03-1985 L1990 **OBG** *020
YUMET, Angel M, Jr. PO BOX 726 00792 #035-15-1948 L1951 **CD IM** *020 ‡
ZENON GARCIA, Lesbia M. CALLE A NUM 7 URB 00791 #308-03-1982 L1992 *020

ISABELA – ISABELA

ABREU, Luis Angel. PO BOX 1739 00662 #308-13-2002 L2005 *100
ABREU-ELIAS, Jose. 34 CALLE BARBOSA BOX 748 00662 #649-01-1959 L1961 **FM ADM** *020 †18
ABREU VENTURA, Manuel A. ■ 00662 #308-01-1958 L1969 **FM GYN** *071
ALVAREZ CASTILLO, Alfredo. ST. L. MUNOZ-RIVERA #10 00662 #847-08-1969 L1973 **GP** *020
ALVAREZ-MONTES, Jose R. 94A CALLE SAN ANTONIO 00662 #042-01-1982 L1985 **IM** *020
AQUINO, Fernando Arturo. ■ 00662 #308-01-1955 L1975 **GP** *020
BAHAMUNDI-MORALES, Jose L. ■ 00662 #308-03-1981 L1982 **EM OM** *020
CANABAL-LOPEZ, Manuel. ■ 00662 #847-04-1954 L1956 **PD** *071 †55
CARBONELL, Carlos E. ROAD 459 KM 10.1 00662 #042-01-1983 L1987 **OBG** *020 †30
CASTILLOVEITIA, Pedro D. ■ 00662 #042-04-1989 L1992 **GP** *020
CORCHADO, Amarilis. BO ARENALES ALTOS, BUZON 6-116 D 00662 #042-01-1999 L2001 *020 †75
CORCHADO, Marco A. 7260 AVE AGUSTIN RAMOS CLR 00662 #042-01-1995 L1998 **FM** *020 †18
CORDERO, Saul. PO BOX 123, 2KM CARR 111.5 00662 #042-01-1992 L1998 **RNR** *020 †80
ELIAS, Federico Abreu. PO BOX 747 00662 #308-03-1982 L1984 **FM** *020 ‡
GILROY TORRES, Kelly Sue. 117 BO BAJURAS 00662 #649-35-1998 L2002 *020
GIRALD ROSA, Adrian. ■ 00662 #649-14-1999 L2001 *020
GUEVARA, Carlos Eduardo. ■ 00662 #649-14-2003 *020
HAU, Marta Doris. 61 CALLE OTERO 00662 #308-03-1983 L1986 **GP** *020
HAU-ROSA, Roberto H. 68 CALLE DR GONZALEZ 00662 #308-03-1982 L1985 **GP** *020
HERNANDEZ BLAS, Daniel. ■ 00662 #649-14-2003 L2005 *100
HERNANDEZ CEREZO, Rufilio. INT KM 1.4 CARR 112 00662 #649-14-1982 L1995 *100
HOMS, Patricia. PO BOX 2224 00662 #649-14-2001 L2004 *100
LAMELA, Ethel Christine. 7 CALLE BARBOSA 00662 #042-01-1982 L1985 **PD** *020 †55
LICEAGA SANCHEZ, Juan B. 2 ISABELA BEACH CT, APT 244 00662 #649-14-2001 L2002 *100
LOPEZ, Jose Angel. CALLE MANUEL OTERO #65 00662 #042-01-1979 L1982 **PD** *020
MACHADO PELLOT, Veronica. BUZON 3, BO GALATEO BAJO SECTOR MAC 00662 #649-14-2002 L2003 *100
MALDONADO AVILES, Ildaly. AVE FELIX ALDARONDO, POSTNET PMB #154 00662 #042-04-2003 L2004 *100
MEDINA MONTANO, Teodoro. PO BOX 80000 PMB 487, COND LOS PONCE PLAYERAS 00662 #649-14-2000 L2002 *020
MELON VELEZ, Juan Carlos. ■ 00662 #649-14-2002 L2005 *100
MENDEZ RODRIGUEZ, Andres. ■ 00662 #847-01-1972 L1974 **CD IM** *020
MIRANDA MORENO, Ibelith. ■ 00662 #308-04-2004 L2005 *100
MORALES, Raymond R. ■ 00662 #010-03-1945 L1946 **GP** *074

MORETA, Rafael Angel. 76 CALLE BARBOSA 00662 #308-03-1983 L1986 **PD** *020
NIEVES, Walter. 3285 AVE MILITAR 00662 #042-01-1994 L1998 **OPH** *020 †35
NIEVES GONZALEZ, Luis Raf. 78 RUTA 4 00662 #649-14-2002 L2004 *100
PEREZ, Carmen A. ■ 00662 #042-04-1989 L1992 **GP** *020
PEREZ, Vanessa. PO BOX 743 00662 #649-14-2001 L2003 *100
PEREZ DIAZ, Pedro. 4024 VISTAS DEL HORIZONTE, BO ARENALES 00662 #308-13-2003 L2005 *100
PEREZ-MUNOZ, Ibzan. 7114 AVE AGUSTIN RAMOS CLR 00662 #847-03-1979 L1982 **P FM** *020
PLUMEY RIOS, Jose. ■ 00662 #847-06-1976 L1976 **P** *071
PRATS, Luis Enriqe. PO BOX 743, CARR 459 9.3 AGUADILLA 00662 #649-14-1999 L2002 **FM** *020
RAFOLS-SAAVEDRA, Rafael. PO BOX 503, URBANIZACION LAMELA 00662 #308-03-1980 L1983 **P** *020
RAMIREZ, Carlos R H. ■ 00662 #649-01-1954 L1962 **GP OBG** *020
RAMOS, Marco A. PO BOX 492, URB OTERO ST. MUNOZ RIVERA 00662 #308-03-1978 L1986 **GP** *020
RIVERA, Francisco. PO BOX 521 00662 #847-08-1982 L1984 **GP** *020
RODRIGUEZ, Ellen Dianne. 2993 AVE MILITAR, INTERNAL MEDICINE 00662 #042-03-1993 L1996 **IM** *020
RODRIGUEZ, Gilberto. ■ 00662 #308-03-1981 L1989 **GP** *020
RODRIGUEZ-RAMOS, Jorge. 115 CALLE EMILIO GONZALEZ 00662 #847-06-1978 L1982 **IM** *020
RODRIGUEZ SANTANA, Anibal. PO BOX 80000, PMB 230 00662 #649-14-1999 L2002 *100
ROMERO LOPEZ, Joselito. ■ 00662 #649-14-1993 L1995 **FM** *020
ROMERO LOPEZ, Luis R. 4239 AVE MILITAR 00662 #308-03-1982 L1986 **FM** *020
ROSARIO, Ivan. 401 CALLE PASADENA, SECT CALIFORNIA 00662 #042-04-1986 L1988 **EM** *020
RUIZ, Ricardo. PO BOX 2362 00662 #308-03-1981 L1986 *020
SANTOS, Milagros De Los A. 4 CALLE PINERO 00662 #847-06-1976 L1979 **PD** *020
SEPULVEDA, Angel. BOX 1308 00662 #847-04-1977 L1981 **CD IM** *020
SOLER, Antonio H. ■ 00662 #396-04-1954 L1958 **GP OS** *020
TORRES, Marlene L. 76 CALLE BARBOSA 00662 #308-03-1983 L2004 **GP** *100
TORRES FELICIANO, Jose A. PO BOX 915, 76 CALLE BARBOSA 00662 #847-10-1966 L1969 **IMG FM** *072
VEGA-VEGA, Hector N. EDIFICIO LAB TAVAREZ #7, AVE JUAN HERNANDEZ 00662 #308-04-1983 L1988 **GP** *020
VELAZQUEZ, Ivan Havier. ISABELA, PR, CALLE JESUS DE PINERO #4 00662 #308-04-1987 L1990 **GP** *020
VELEZ CORCHADO, Arbel. ■ 00662 #649-14-2000 L2002 **GP** *020
VELEZ GONZALEZ, Pedro Lui. ■ 00662 #042-02-2007 **P** *012
VELEZ-LUGO, Francisco E. PO BOX 866 00662 #847-04-1965 L1970 **GP** *020
VELEZ ROMAN, Miriam D. 325 CALLE TRINITARIA, URB MANUEL CORCHADO 00662 #042-04-1997 L2001 **FM** *020

ISLA VERDE – SAN JUAN

CUFF-NEGRONI, Charles. APART 1009, COND. COMDESA DEL MAR 00979 #042-03-1980 L1986 **GS** *020
JORDAN-ROJAS, Miguel. CORAL BEACH 1201 T-2 00913 #042-03-1981 L1983 **PM** *020
MARTINEZ, Jose A. COND CORAL BEACH II, APT 212 00913 #042-01-1966 L1971 **GP END** *071 †55
TOMAS, Nery. APT. 119, CONDO ISLA VERDE ESTATES 00979 #308-01-1975 L1978 **GP** *020

JAYUYA – JAYUYA

CARRERAS COELLO, Nilda I. C/O PO BOX 386, 47 CALLE LIBERTAD 00664 #308-03-1982 L1993 **GP** *020
CARRERAS-CUELLO, Fernando. 103 CALLE GUILLERMO ESTEVS 00664 #308-03-1981 L1984 **GP** *020
COLON MALDONADO, Rotceh. 13 CALLE GMO ESTEVES, STE 1 00664 #042-04-1994 L1996 **GP** *020
FIGUEROA ANDUJAR, Jose En. ■ 00664 #308-06-1989 L2003 **GP** *020
FIGUEROA ANDUJAR, Juana. ■ 00664 #308-06-1984 L2003 **FM** *020
FRONTANES, Abymael. ■ 00664 #042-01-2004 **NPM** *012 †55
GUZMAN BURGOS, Maria G. PO BOX 1152 00664 #649-14-2003 L2006 *100
GUZMAN-ORTIZ, Jorge. 2 CALLE CEMENTERIO, CENTRO DE SALUD MARIO CANA 00664 #024-05-1980 L1987 **FM** *020
MARRERO TORRES, Victor R. PO BOX 853, AVE TITO CASTZO, CENTRO 00664 #308-03-1984 L1994 *020
MIRANDA GONZALEZ, Jose M. PO BOX 791 00664 #308-02-1977 L1980 **GP** *020
ORAMA, Carlos Manuel. ■ 00664 #308-03-1983 L1990 **IM** *020
RAMOS RIVERA, Jose. ■ 00664 #308-03-1983 L1984 **GP** *020
RIVERA-RODRIGUEZ, Luis A. 2 CALLE MASSINI 00664 #042-01-1995 L1998 **OPH** *020 †35
RIVERA-ROMAN, Luis. PO BOX 798 00664 #308-01-1976 L1978 **GP** *020
RODRIGUEZ BARRERA, Francis. 1 AVE MATTEI 00664 #649-30-2003 L2005 *020
RODRIGUEZ-ZAYAS, Manuel A. 17 CALLE FIGUERA 00664 #649-14-1979 L1982 **IM** *020
ROMAN VEGA, Juan Manuel. PO BOX 281, SAN FELIPE INTERIOR 00664 #649-14-2001 L2004 *100
SANTIAGO, Giovanny. 96 CALLE GMO ESTEVES 00664 #649-14-1993 L1996 *020
SANTIAGO, Roberto Padua. PO BOX 796 00664 #649-14-1989 L1992 **PUD** *020
VARGAS DE LEON, Francisco. PO BOX 286, 12 CALLE W GONZALEZ 00664 #308-03-1977 L1980 *020
VELAZQUEZ, Vanessa. ■ 00664 #042-01-2007 *012

JUANA DIAZ – JUANA DIAZ

ALVARADO ALVARADO, Gerardo. PO BOX 505, BARRIO LOMAS TOCADILLO 00795 #649-14-2000 L2004 *100
ALVAREZ-RODRIGUEZ, A R. URB VILLA DEL SOL O4 00795 #042-02-1999 L2003 **OBG** *020
ARRAUT, Orlando Marchena. 3 CALLE LA CRUZ STE 2 00795 #308-03-1978 L1981 **IM** *020
BERRIOS ANTUNA, Pedro A. 41 CALLE DEGETAU 00795 #042-04-1998 L2001 **FM** *020
BERRIOS ORTIZ, Pedro A. C/O P.O. BOX 1425, CALLE DEGETAU #41 00795 #847-04-1957 L1960 **GS** *071

COLLADO, Aurelio Miguel. 66 CALLE MUNOZ RIVERA 00795 #308-06-1985 L1988 **IM** *020
COLON GAZTAMBIDE, Jose M. 106 CALLE COMERCIO 00795 #649-18-1980 L1987 **GP** *020
COMAS ROSADO, Francisco. 11 CALLE DR VEVE 00795 #847-09-1964 L1968 **PD GP** *020
DOMINGUEZ MIRANDA, Carlos. 168A CALLE LAS FLORES, JACAGUAX HEALTHCARE GROUP 00795 #308-03-1978 L1981 **GP** *020
ENGEL, Robert A. 46 CALLE 1, URB TOMAS CARRION MADURO 00795 #308-03-1983 L1986 **CD** *020
FALU, Griselle. 175 CALLE ROBLE, EST DE JUANA DIAZ 00795 #847-02-1982 L1990 **GP OM** *020
FIGUEROA RAMOS, Carlos Hi. URB. HNOS SANTIAGO, #71 00795 #649-14-2001 L2004 *100
FRANCO, Luis A. CALLE 6, URB VILLA DEL SOL 00795 #042-01-1986 L1989 **P** *020 †75
GARCIA, Maria T. PO BOX 984 00795 #847-02-1973 L1983 **GP** *020
GOMEZ, Edward Antonio. HC 1 BOX 6335, 8 PARC SALISTRAL CALLE 4 00795 #042-03-1998 L2000 **OBG** *020
HERNANDEZ VIVES, Martin. 4 CALLE LA CRUZ, CDT 00795 #308-03-1981 L1988 **EM** *020
JORGE CARABALLO, Josue. 47 CALLE D, EXT LAS MARIAS 00795 #649-14-2001 L2004 **FM** *020
MARTINEZ, Vinicio Amado. APT. 2B, VILLA DE SAN MARTIN 00795 #308-01-1958 L1974 **IM** *071
MARTINEZ DIAZ, Annette N. 31 CALLE DEGETAU 00795 #042-04-1998 L2001 **FM** *020
MELENDEZ TORRES, Linda M.. ■ 00795 #042-04-2004 L2005 *100
MORCIGLIO, Ariel E. 6 CALLE ANGEL R MORA 00795 #042-04-1995 L1996 **IM** *020
OCASIO MALDONADO, Hilda. 61 CALLE COMERCIO 00795 #847-02-1961 L1964 **IM PUD** *020
ORTIZ, Nancy I. 6 CALLE 1 URB DEL CARMEN 00795 #042-01-1985 L1988 **PD** *020
RIVERA, Hiram. URB JACAGUAX 4 NO 82 00795 #042-01-1991 L1995 **RHU** *020
RIVERA-COLON, Guireida. URB VILLA DEL SOL A-13 00795 #042-02-1996 L1999 **END** *020
RIVERA-CORDOVA, Luis A. 5 CALLE MARIO BRASCHI 00795 #042-03-1980 L1983 **IM** *020
RODRIGUEZ, Brenda. HC 1, 147 CALLE LAS TRINITARIAS 00795 #649-14-1997 L2000 **PD** *100
RODRIGUEZ, Glenda Milagro. ■ 00795 #649-14-2001 L2003 **FM** *020
RODRIGUEZ, Pedro Jaime. #29 ALTOS, CALLE TOMAS CARRION MADURO 00795 #042-01-1979 L1982 **PD** *020 †55
RODRIGUEZ ROCHE, Kermys. PO BOX 488 00795 #649-14-2001 L2004 *100
ROSADO-BRACERO, Angel. ■ 00795 #847-04-1968 L1970 **OBG EM** *020
ROSADO-MONTALVO, Hector L. HC 4 00795 #308-10-1983 L1991 **FM** *020
SANTIAGO TORRES, Rosalia. PO BOX 1733 00795 #308-03-1985 L1991 *100
SANTINI, Francisco A. ■ 00795 #847-10-1969 L1971 **IM** *020
SCHMIDT, Ramon A. 13 CALLE 4, URB LAS FLORES 00795 #308-03-1984 L1987 *020
SILVA GONZALEZ, Theresa M. ■ 00795 #649-14-2001 L2004 **GP** *100
SOSA, Javier. 15 CALLE LUIS F DESSUS, EXT JACAGUAX 00795 #042-02-1999 L2002 **GS** *100
VELEZ GARCIA, Iris Vanesa. ■ 00795 #042-02-1992 L1995 *020

JUNCOS – JUNCOS

ALVAREZ-VALENTIN, Mario. PO BOX 1569 00777 #042-03-1981 L1983 **FM IMG** *020
AMARAL, Hector Luis. ■ 00777 #649-18-1980 L1995 **FM** *020
ANTUNA CINTRON, Jose A. ■ 00777 #847-08-1974 L1978 **GP** *020
ANTUNA MELENDEZ, Ada L.. PO BOX 1540 00777 #649-30-2004 L2006 *100
ARTHUR NOVEL, Rafael Jose. BOX D 00777 #308-01-1962 L1970 **GP PD** *020
ARZUAGA, Iris Janet. HC 1 BOX 5436, KM1 H 2 00777 #042-04-1999 L2001 *020
BERRIOS, Nannette S. PO BOX 1569 00777 #042-03-1981 L1990 **FM** *020
CACERES, Carlos R. PO BOX 747, 1 VALENCIA 00777 #042-01-1988 L1993 **PD** *020
CALDERON, Ismael Colon. PO BOX 1801 00777 #308-03-1983 L1990 *020
CASTRO, Nilda Fidalgo. 8 CALLE TEODOMIRO DELFAU, BOX 2152 00777 #042-03-1983 L1984 **PD** *020
DIAZ-SCHROEDER, Elsie M. CAGUAS , PR (00725), PROF CTR STE 310 00777 #042-01-1993 L1996 **IM PUD** *020 †20
DUVAL, Sigfredo Diaz. 46 CALLE T DELFAU 00777 #308-01-1976 L1984 **FM EM** *020
FERNANDEZ, Amanda D. PO BOX 1801, CALLE MARTINEZ ESQ BEFANCE 00777 #308-03-1983 L1990 *020
FLORES-JIMENEZ, Maria M. 27 CALLE MARTINEZ 00777 #847-02-1976 L1979 *020
HERNANDEZ, Juan. ■ 00777 #847-23-1975 L1978 **FM** *020
HERNANDEZ-DE LEON, Sonia. ■ 00777 #649-09-1973 L1978 *020
HERNANDEZ-MIRANDA, V M. C/O BOX 995, CARR 172 RAMAL 785 KM 4 1 00777 #847-02-1975 L1980 **GP** *020
HERNANDEZ-RODRIGUEZ, Raul. PO BOX 1767 00777 #847-06-1977 L1980 **GP** *020
LORA CRUZ, Livino Antonio. CAGUAS, P.R., HOSPITAL HIMA OFFICINA 122 00777 #308-03-1984 L1995 **IM** *020
MALDONADO GARCIA, Carlos. ■ 00777 #308-13-2002 L2003 **IM** *020
MANTERO HORMAZABAL, Julio. CALLE B 45 BOX 15 URB MADR 00777 #308-03-1982 L1986 **IM** *020
MARIN, Frank, Jr. PO BOX 167 00777 #649-14-2004 L2006 *100
NEGRON GAY, Jorge L. PO BOX 972 00777 #308-03-1980 L1997 *020
NEGRON-VAZQUEZ, Olga. C/O BOX 167, 18 AQUZYBANA ST 00777 #308-03-1980 L1984 *020
NUNEZ, Jackeline. 35 CALLE MUNOZ RIVERA, URB MADRID 00777 #308-04-1992 L1996 **OBG** *020
ORTIZ-MALDONADO, Fernando. PO BOX 1725 00777 #308-02-1977 L1980 **IM** *020
OTERO, Guillermo R. JUNCOS AREA HOSP, BOX P 00777 #042-01-1979 L1979 **PD** *020 †55
PALACIOS MORIONES, F Leon. 40 CALLE LOPEZ HORMAZABAL, URB MADRID 00777 #847-08-1968 L1974 **OBG** *020
PALACIOS VAZQUEZ, Ivan E. 00777 #649-14-1999 L2002 *100
PARRILLA-ORTIZ, Edilio. ■ 00777 #847-05-1975 L1978 *020
PEREZ, Juan Marcelo. ■ 00777 #042-03-2008 *012
PEREZ CURRY, Marisol. PO BOX 1391 00777 #308-13-2002 L2004 *100
RODRIGUEZ, Arnaldoi. ■ 00777 #308-03-1978 L1980 **GP** *020
RODRIGUEZ RAMOS, Edwin. ■ 00777 #308-04-1992 L1995 *020
RODRIGUEZ RIOS, Evelyn. PO BOX 1155, R935 CARR 31 00777 #042-04-2005 L2006 *100
ROSARIO-SANTOS, Rafael. ■ 00777 #847-04-1963 L1966 **AN** *100
SANTORY ORTIZ, Julio. ■ 00777 #042-04-1996 L1997 *020
SANTORY-PENA, Julio. ■ 00777 #847-02-1974 L1977 **GP** *020
SANTOS, Emmanuel. PO BOX 1769 00777 #649-30-2001 L2003 *100
SILVESTRIZ ROHENA, Ricardo. 27 CALLE MARTINEZ 00777 #649-14-1987 L1994 **GP** *020
SOLORZANO, Patty. ■ 00777 #033-05-1997 L2004 **PD** *020
TAPIA TAPIA, Liza Y.. PO BOX 936 00777 #649-30-2002 L2004 *100

TORRES, Luis Alvarez. 4 CALLE ERNESTO CADIZ, URB MADRID 00777 #308-03-1982 L1987 **PD** *020
TORRES, Nicole Edmee. ■ 00777 #042-03-2008 *012
TORRES FLORES, Jose A. ■ 00777 #308-03-1983 L1994 *020
VAZQUEZ, Jorge Edgardo. ■ 00777 #649-14-1997 L1999 **FM** *020
VAZQUEZ, Nelida E. PO BOX 996 00777 #847-04-1971 L1976 **PD** *020

LAJAS – LAJAS

ACOSTA, Jose Arturo. ■ 00667 #847-10-1970 L1973 **GE** *020
ACOSTA MARTINEZ, Alexis. HC 2, BOX 14705 00667 #649-14-2004 L2006 *100
ADYANTHAYA, Aravind E. PO BOX 596, BO CANDELARIA 00667 #649-14-2002 L2005 *100
ALMODOVAR-MARCHANY, Danl. 32 CALLE AMISTAD 00667 #308-03-1980 L1983 **OBG** *020
BERMUDEZ-WEBB, Nini M. ■ 00667 #042-01-1971 L1973 **RO** *071
BRACERO, Julio. ■ 00667 #042-02-2008 *012
COLLADO RODRIGUEZ, Daniel. ■ 00667 #649-14-1999 L2001 *100
CUEVAS AVILES, Lionel, Jr. ■ 00667 #649-03-1987 L1992 *020
ESCABI, Rafael E. 237 CALLE FLAMBOYAN, URB EL VALLE 00667 #042-03-1984 L1987 **FM OBG** *020
GARCIA, Sol Maria. ■ 00667 #042-01-2001 L2004 **PD** *020 †55
GUTIERREZ, Andres Ivan. PO BOX 596, BO CANDELARIA 00667 #649-14-2002 L2005 *100
IRIZARRY, Walter F. URB EL VALLE # 43 00667 #649-01-1963 L1967 **GP** *020
IRIZARRY CAMPERO, Walter. ■ 00667 #649-14-2004 L2005 *100
JIMENEZ, Ricardo Juan. HC 1, 101 AVE SAN PATRICIO GUAY 00667 #042-01-1997 L2002 **PS** *020 †85
LUGO, Maria De Los A. ■ 00667 #042-01-1999 L2001 **FPG** *100 †18
MAURY, Mildred. ■ 00667 #016-11-1994 L2003 **FM** *020 †18
NAZARIO DEL RIO, William. 1 RES LAS AMERICAS 00667 #847-09-1960 L1969 **GS** *071
NAZARIO-PEREZ, Angel R. ■ 00667 #042-01-1956 L1959 **PD PHP** *071
ORTIZ, Sarah Rubi. ■ 00667 #649-14-2002 L2005 *100
PEREZ, Ramon. PO BOX 1549 00667 #649-14-2001 L2003 *100
POTTER, George Leslie. PO BOX 918, MG2 CENTRO MEDICO 00667 #067-01-1955 L1958 **NS P** *071 †25
RAMIREZ, Sadi. PO BOX 903 00667 #649-18-1982 L1987 **GP** *020
RAMIREZ-IRIZARRY, Enrique. 65TH INFANTRY ST #20-B 00667 #847-08-1977 L1980 **GP** *020
RIVERA, Erasmo Asencio. 35 CALLE AMISTAD 00667 #847-02-1972 L1978 **FM** *071
ROSARIO, Ruben Dario. 35B CALLE AMISTAD 00667 #308-04-1994 L2002 **GP** *020
TIRADO-MORALES, Radames. PO BOX 917 00667 #042-03-1983 L1991 **IM** *020
TORRES, Marina Amelia. ■ 00667 #042-01-1998 L2003 **GE** *020
VELEZ FLORES, Edison. ■ 00667 #649-38-1990 L1992 *020
VELEZ-ORTIZ, Ulysses Gary. 41 CALLE AMISTAD 00667 #308-04-1986 L1988 **FM** *020

LARES – LARES

ALICEA GERENA, Idamaris. PO BOX 211 00669 #308-04-2003 L2005 *100
ARIAS-MENDEZ, Carlos E. 54 CALLE COMERCIO, DR PEDRO ALBIZU CAMPUS 00669 #308-01-1976 L1978 **FM FSM** *020
ARIAS MENDEZ, Pedro E.. 54 CALLE PEDRO ALBIZU CMPS 00669 #308-04-2002 L2005 **GP GPM** *020
BALLESTER, Jorge J. ■ 00669 #308-03-1983 L1987 *020
CARDENAS HERNANDEZ, Victor. PO BOX 542 00669 #649-38-2004 L2005 *100
ECHEANDIA, Ramon Felix. PO BOX 19, # 19 00669 #649-18-1983 L1987 **FM** *020
GARCIA-IRIZARRY, Pedro O. PO BOX 1299 00669 #649-31-1979 L1986 **FM** *020
GARRASTEGUI, Francisco A. ALTAMIRA F13 BOX 95 00669 #308-04-1989 L1992 *020
GARRASTEGUI-BIGAS, Maria. C/O PO BOX 95, CALLE VILELLA #8 ALTOS 00669 #308-03-1980 L1983 *020
GONZALEZ-BAUZA, Elba Rosa. ■ 00669 #847-08-1975 L1978 **GP** *075
GONZALEZ CARBIA, A R. 8 CALLE VILELLA 00669 #847-08-1970 L1972 **GP** *020
HERNANDEZ, Luis O. CARR. 111 KM-1.9, CENTRO DE SALUD DE LARES 00669 #042-04-1985 L1988 **GP** *020
JIMENEZ, Juan Bautista. 15 CALLE MUNOZ RIVERA 00669 #042-01-1974 L1976 **PD** *020
JIMENEZ AROCHO, Emilio. 15 CALLE MUNOZ RIVERA 00669 #649-30-2002 L2004 *100
JIMENEZ GONZALEZ, Cristina. ■ 00669 #649-14-2000 L2002 **PD** *100
LOPEZ, Eva I. ■ 00669 #847-06-1977 L1981 **GP** *020
LOPEZ, Jose Javier Lopez. A39 CALLE 2, URB. BUENA VIST 00669 #649-14-1989 L1994 *020
MALAVE, Willie Nelson. PO BOX 819 PMB 513 00669 #308-03-1985 L1989 **PD** *020
MARRERO PEREZ, Edgardo. PO BOX 609, BO LARES 00669 #649-14-2001 L2002 *100
MARTINEZ MENDEZ, Jose M. ■ 00669 #847-06-1972 L1975 **GP** *020
MEDINA, Luis A. BAJADERO 00669 #649-14-1993 L1996 **FM** *020
NIEVES-GONZALEZ, Wanda Iv. HC-4195 00669 #308-04-2004 L2006 *100
PAGAN CORTES, Luis A.. BUZON 372, URB VILLA BORINQUEN 00669 #308-04-2002 L2004 *100
PEREZ LOPEZ, Edgardo. PO BOX 334 00669 #649-14-1997 L2000 *020
PLANELL, Ubaldo. ■ 00669 #649-38-1993 L2001 **FM** *020
PLANELL PABON, Yaralin. ■ 00669 #042-04-2004 L2005 *100
QUILES TORRES, Mairim E.. ■ 00669 #649-14-2002 L2004 *100
RIOS BATTISTINI, Jose A. NUM D-2 BUZON 129, URB ALTAMIRA 00669 #649-18-1979 L1999 *100
RIVERA, David. CARR 129 KM 15.K INT CARR, BO LARES CRUCE MIGAN 00669 #042-01-1987 L1991 **FM** *020 †18
RIVERA GONZALEZ, Ruth. ■ 00669 #847-10-1965 L1976 *100
RODRIGUEZ, Baltazar. PO BOX 3 00669 #042-04-1983 L1985 **GP** *020
RODRIGUEZ, Yadira. ■ 00669 #042-03-2007 *012
RODRIGUEZ CANCEL, Walter. PO BOX 323 00669 #308-03-2003 L2006 *100
ROMAN RIVERA, Maria P. PO BOX 936 00669 #649-30-2002 L2004 *100
SEGARRA, Maria Domitilla. 56 CALLE COMERCIO 00669 #035-45-1974 L1979 **IM** *100
SUAREZ RAMIREZ, Catalino. PO BOX 2111 00669 #308-04-2002 L2005 *100
TORRES-VEGA, Ramon A. ■ 00669 #308-03-1976 L1978 **GP** *020
VALENTIN-MARRERO, Felix A. ■ 00669 #042-03-1980 L1984 **PD** *020
VIVALDI PICO, Jose G. ■ 00669 #042-04-1997 L1999 **FM** *020

LAS MARIAS – LAS MARIAS

JUSTINIANO-FIGUEROA, R. 35 CALLE SAN BENITO 00670 #847-10-1975 L1979 *020

MATOS MONTALVO, Dixon E. PO BOX 345, 25.1 CARR 119 00670 #308-04-1991 L1993 FM *020 †18

ORTIZ, Norberto. PO BOX 23, SERVICIOS MEDICOS LAS MARI 00670 #042-02-1997 L1999 FM *020

PADIN SEGARRA, Maribel. C/O PO BOX 23, CARR 119 KM27.4 PASEO ADRI 00670 #308-03-1982 L2003 *100

PEREZ, Ruben Dario. PO BOX 23 00670 #308-03-1981 L1985 GP GPM *020

LAS PIEDRAS – LAS PIEDRAS

CASIANO, Iris Janet. ■ 00771 #308-03-1982 L1985 GP *030

CASTILLO, Fernando. 4 CALLE 2, REPTO ARENALES 00771 #308-01-1967 L1993 *020

CATONI, Luis Antonio. 219 CALLE BARBOSA 00771 #042-01-1980 L1983 FM FPG *020 †18

CHAPA JUAN, Vicente. PO BOX 9 00771 #847-08-1982 L1986 GP *020

CRUZ DIAZ, Ana Del. ■ 00771 #649-14-2001 L2002 *020

DAUSA, Maria Del Carmen. ■ 00771 #308-03-1982 L1987 GP *020

DAVILA-MARTINEZ, G. BO SABANA 00771 #042-01-1979 L1983 DR *062

DIAZ-ROMERO, Noris Marie. ■ 00771 #042-02-2003 L2006 EM *100 †16

FABIANI-RODRIGUEZ, Miguel. JOSE CELSO BARBOSA 175 00771 #308-03-1980 L1982 GP *020

FERNANDEZ-MONTANEZ, Aida. CALLE JOSE C BARBOSA 100 00771 #308-03-1979 L1988 *020

FIGUEROA, Rocheline. ■ 00771 #649-14-2001 PD *100 ‡

GOMEZ HERNANDEZ, Juan San. PO BOX 233 00771 #649-14-2002 L2004 *100

GOMEZ LOPEZ, Wanda Yadira. C/O PO BOX 1477, VICENTE DE LEON ST. #8 00771 #308-03-1986 L1996 GP *020

GOMEZ TORRES, Jeisa Y.. ■ 00771 #649-14-2000 L2003 IM *012

GONZALEZ-BERRIOS, Nereida. ■ 00771 #042-02-2004 P *012

GUTIERREZ-HERNANDEZ, M. 209 CALLE BARBOSA 00771 #847-09-1970 L1981 OBG *020

HERNANDEZ CRUZ, Juanita. ■ 00771 #847-02-1974 L1979 IM *020

HERRERA, Agueda Isabel. 4 CALLE 2 REPTO ARENALES, HOSPITAL REGIONAL DE CAGUA 00771 #308-01-1969 L1987 GP *020

KIDD, Rafael Oscar. PO BOX 2017 00771 #308-01-1978 L1988 CD *020 †20

LOPEZ-DUGUE, Luz M. BUZON 90 BO COLLORES 00771 #308-03-1979 L1981 GP *020

MACCONE, Marjorie Iris. ■ 00771 #042-03-2004 P *100

MALDONADO-ROSA, Rafael. PO BOX 1848 00771 #847-02-1979 L1983 IM *020

MARTINO, Margarita Sofia. ■ 00771 #042-01-2001 L2005 EM *020

MONSERRATE, Marie Elsie. ■ 00771 #042-03-2008 *012

NADAL, Eduardo. PO BOX 128 00771 #042-01-2005 PM *012

PEREZ-LOPEZ, Cielomar. PO BOX 1722, 1 CALLE POUPART 00771 #042-03-1981 L1982 IM *020

RAMOS RODRIGUEZ, Jose M.. ■ 00771 #042-04-2004 L2005 *100

RENTAS, Hilario Luis. ■ 00771 #308-03-1983 L1986 GP *020

RODRIGUEZ, Carol. 99 CALLE 2, VILLA LAS MERCEDES 00771 #042-01-1993 L1996 PD *020

RODRIGUEZ GOMEZ, Carlos A. P O BOX 2107 PMB 149 00771 #649-19-1992 L1994 *100

RODRIGUEZ GOMEZ, Zulma N. ■ 00771 #308-03-1982 L1990 *020

SANCHEZ-ORTIZ, Adolfo. HUMACAO, HOSPITAL SUB REGIONAL DE 00771 #308-03-1984 L1987 CD *020

SANTIAGO VIGO, Julio M. ■ 00771 #847-01-1965 L1968 IM CD *020

SILVA, Carmen. ■ 00771 #649-14-1989 L1992 FM *020

VALLEJO-ALMEDA, Nelson. ■ 00771 #308-07-1984 L1991 IM *020

VAZQUEZ BALASQUIDE, Maria. 140 CALLE SYROS, URB OLIMPIC PARK 00771 #042-04-2001 L2002 *020

LEVITTOWN – TOA BAJA

ACEVEDO, Vivian I. ■ 00949 #042-03-1994 L2000 P *020

AGOSTO, Mariely. HM23 CALLE RAMON MORLA, URB LEVITTOWN LAKES 00949 #042-01-1993 L1996 PD *020

CALDERON-RODRIGUEZ, R E. BOX 51412 00949 #308-01-1979 L1983 CD GP *020 †20

CAMERO-RAMIREZ, Maria R. SA57 PLAZA 3, MANS DEL SUR 00949 #649-14-1977 L1991 *020

CHICLANA-GONZALEZ, Ivette. MANSION DEL SUR, PLAZA 9-SB-8 00949 #847-05-1977 L1980 GP *020

CRESPO TORRES, Justa M. JT8 CALLE CARMEN SANABRIA, URB LEVITTOWN LAKES 00949 #308-03-1985 L1995 GP *020

FERNANDEZ CABRERA, Fe I. LEILA ESTE U 11 4A SECC 00949 #308-01-1969 L1988 GP *020

GERENA-DELGADO, Ramon. JR1 CALLE LIZZIE GRAHAM 00949 #649-01-1976 L1979 GYN *030

GOMEZ-SALDNA, Wilfred. ■ 00949 #649-14-1998 L2000 FM *100

GRASSETTE, William. DR9 CALLE LAGO CERRILLO, URB LEVITTOWN LAKES 00949 #308-06-1986 L1992 *020

GUILLEN, Fausto Emilio. BN17 CALLE DR H DE CATANO, URB LEVITTOWN LAKES 00949 #847-01-1966 L1977 OM *020

JOAQUIN ALBERTO, Santiago. ■ 00949 #649-14-1977 L1988 *020

MARRERO, Norma I. EE10 CALLE JOSE S ALEGRIA, URB LEVITTOWN LAKES 00949 #649-31-1982 L1989 GP *020

NICOLAU CASTRO, Nayda M. ST 10 B-19, VALPARAISO 00949 #649-10-1971 L1976 *020

ORTIZ, Tulio L. 1173 AVE DOS PALMAS, URB LEVITTOWN 00949 #847-04-1961 L1964 R IM *020

PORRAS BATISTA, James. HF16 CALLE LIZZIE GRAHAM, URB LEVITTOWN LAKES 00949 #847-08-1972 L1975 GP *020

RODRIGUEZ, Carmen E. 1172 AVE DOS PALMAS, URB LEVITTOWN 00949 #847-02-1973 L1978 GPM *020

RODRIGUEZ, Maribel. HG12 CALLE LIZZIE GRAHAM, SEVEN SECTION 00949 #042-03-1998 L2002 IM *020

SANTANA, Hugo. PASEO ALPES C-2210 00949 #042-03-1990 L1992 IM *040

TORRES-CRUZ, Janette. ND11 CALLE RANADA, MANS DEL NORTE 00949 #042-04-1991 L1993 P *020 †75

LOIZA – LOIZA

GUTIERREZ, Jose V. ■ 00772 #649-14-1987 L1994 *020

LICHA, Miguel. 29 CALLE ESPIRITU SANTO, BOX 539 00772 #847-03-1971 L1973 GP *020

LICHA-BAQUERO, Rosa Belen. 29 CALLE ESPIRITU SANTO 00772 #042-01-1979 L1983 GP *074

PAGAN-LOPEZ, Edwin Erieo. 8164 CALLE JAZMIN, VISTAS DEL OCEANO 00772 #042-03-1981 L1986 IM *020

LUQUILLO – LUQUILLO

BALZAC-MERCADER, Jaime. ■ 00773 #396-04-1955 L1958 GP *071

BAQI, Noosha. HC 2, PO BOX 5189 00773 #704-02-1982 L2006 PN *040 †55

BENABE HUERTAS, Ivonne I. 104 CALLE 2, VILLA ANGELINA 00773 #308-03-1982 L1996 *020

CORTES ROSADO, Evelyn. PO BOX 971 00773 #649-14-1979 L1994 *100

CRUZ, Osvaldo L. 2J EDIF BRISAS DE VILOMAR, SUNNY CITY BLDG OFFICE 102 00773 #847-05-1976 L1979 PD *020

ESTEVA-HEAL, Rafael C. 104 CALLE 2, VILLA ANGELINA 00773 #847-08-1979 L1982 GP *020

FEHLER, Werner H. ■ 00773 #407-01-1939 L1970 P ON *071

FERNANDEZ, Eduardo Robert. ■ 00773 #308-03-1997 L2005 *020

GONZALEZ, Maximo A. ■ 00773 #308-01-1980 L1983 *020

GOYECHEA, Miguel Juan. EDIF SUNNY CITY CALLE J6 00773 #847-04-1968 L2001 IM *020

GREGORY PEREZ DE TUDELA, F. 165 CALLE FLORIDA 00773 #649-14-1999 L2003 *100

MONSERRATE, Dennise. PO BOX 1449 00773 #042-03-1990 L1993 PM *020

MUNTANER, Angel Salvador. CEIBA, CALLE RAMOS ANTONINI #22 00773 #308-03-1985 L1989 GP *020

NAZARIO ANTONGIORGI, Iris. C/4 H21 COCO BEACH BX 1558 00773 #308-01-1982 L1994 *020

RIVERA-BOU, Wanda Lucille. PO BOX 596 00773 #649-14-1997 L1998 EM *020 †16

ROBLES, Brenda Lee. N8 CALLE 9, BRISAS DEL MAR 00773 #649-14-2000 L2000 FM *100

ROBLES GONZALEZ, Sol A. CALLE 14 173, PARCELAS FORTUNA 00773 #308-01-1989 L2002 *100

RODRIGUEZ, Miguel Angel. 198 CALLE CARRETA, HACIENDA MARGARITA 00773 #042-01-2000 L2002 IM *020 ‡

RODRIGUEZ JAIME, Iris. PO BOX 375, G5 BRISAS DEL MAR CALLEB 00773 #649-14-1994 L2002 *020

RODRIGUEZ-ROSA, Ricardo E. ■ 00773 #042-01-1996 L1999 OPH *020 †35

ROMERO CLASS, Jessica V. ■ 00773 #042-04-2003 L2004 *100

RUIZ PAGAN, Irma I. BX 515/BRISAS DEL MAR 00773 #847-06-1967 L1970 GP *020

SAMBOLIN, Ivelisse Yvonne. ■ 00773 #042-02-2007 PM *020

SANTANA-BURGOS, Jaime E. SUITE 3, #158, LUQUILLO, URB COLINAS DE LUQUILLO 00773 #308-03-1978 L1981 *020

TORRES, Lizette Marie. 95 CAMINO DEL VALLE, URB PAISAJE DEL LAGO 00773 #042-01-1992 L1995 PD *020

TORRES, Luz E. 256 CALLE MELAO, HACIENDA MARGARITA 00773 #042-01-1966 L1969 PD *020

VAZQUEZ, Leticia. BUZON 5292, BO MATA DE PLATANO 00773 #042-04-1987 L1990 GP *020

VIVAS PARRILLA, Enriqueta. HC 1 BOX 7018 00773 #847-04-1988 L1994 *020

MANATI – MANATI

ABREU GUZMAN, Jose Miguel. 10 CALLE PATRIOTA POZO 00674 #308-03-1983 L1992 *020

AMADOR, Nestor Chacon. PO BOX 1144 00674 #042-03-1997 L1999 FM *020 †18

AMADOR OYOLA, Nestor A. B11 CALLE MARGINAL, URB LOS FLAMBOYANES 00674 #847-06-1971 L1974 U *020 †95

ARROYO-RAMIREZ, Pedro L. ■ 00674 #308-03-1978 L1980 EM *020 †16

BARRETO, Rafael Garcia. PO BOX 392 00674 #308-03-1988 L1990 ON IM *020

BENITEZ, Raul. J16 CALLE ELLIOT VELEZ, URB ATENAS 00674 #042-01-1984 L1988 P *020

BENITEZ-RAMIREZ, Maritza. 115 CALLE PITIRRE, HACIENDA LA MONSERRATE 00674 #042-02-1982 L1985 PD *020

BENJAMIN CASTILLO, Samuel. BOX 8383 00674 #308-01-1983 L1992 *020

BENMAMAN, Coty. CARR 2 K M 47-7 00674 #042-01-1980 L1985 D IM *020 †15

BERTRAN-PENA, Roberto. 1 CALLE JOSE CANDELAS, MANATI MED PLAZA STE 201 00674 #308-06-1986 L1990 GP *020

BLANCO-LUGO, Pedro. CARR 2 K M 47-7 00674 #649-01-1955 L1956 GP *030

CABRERA, Carlos A. ■ 00674 #042-04-1994 L1996 FM *020 †18

CANO-MAHONEY, Angelica M. 1 AVE EL YUNKE, VILLA FORESTAL 00674 #264-05-1991 L1999 PD *020

CAPELLA SERPA, Jose Luis. J7 CALLE HERNANDEZ CARRION, URB ATENAS 00674 #308-04-1983 L1995 PD *040

CAPRE, Joseph. ■ 00674 #042-01-1984 L1987 OBG *020

CARDONA, Regino Rosario. ■ 00674 #847-04-1971 L1977 IM *071

CARDONA MONTES, Agnes. A-8 O'NEILL 00674 #847-06-1993 L1996 *020

CARDONA-SANTOS, Nelson R. PO BOX 1125 00674 #847-04-1959 L1963 OPH *072

CARRION, Carlos Ivan. 5 PUERTA DEL NORTE, LOCAL 14 00674 #042-01-1997 L2002 ORS *020

CASANOVA, Rose J. ■ 00674 #042-01-1975 L1982 PHO PD *020 †55

CASANOVA-PUIG, Maria De P. HERNANDEZ CARION 00674 #308-03-1980 L1982 *020

CASIANO, Felix Manuel. ■ 00674 #649-14-1989 L1991 FM *030

CIDRE, Carlos M. B41 CALLE ELLIOT VELEZ, URB ATENAS 00674 #042-04-1983 L1985 IM *020 †20

COLLAZO-TIRADO, Milton R. PO BOX 491 00674 #847-08-1966 L1969 PD OS *020

COLON, Jose Miguel L. 13 PASEO VICTORIA, URB HACIENDA HERMANAS MENA 00674 #042-01-1979 L1983 OPH *020

CORREA SUAREZ, Jose M. 8 CALLE CELIS AGUILERA 00674 #847-09-1971 L1975 OBG *020

CRUZ, Maria Cristina. PO BOX 2271 00674 #042-02-2003 L2004 N *100

CRUZ MOLINA, Yoel. ■ 00674 #649-14-2005 L2006 GP *100

CRUZ SOTO, Manuel Antonio. PO BOX 1662 00674 #847-03-1974 L1977 IM NEP *050 †20

DE JESUS-TORO, Jose A. PO BOX 138 00674 #847-08-1978 L1980 AN *020

DE LA ROSA ALVAREZ, Ana Y. 100 MAR CHIQUITA CONDOMINI, APT 40 00674 #275-01-1997 L2002 *020

DELGADO-COLON, Victor L. URB FLAMBOYAN, STREET 3 B-24 00674 #308-01-1980 L1985 GP *020

DELGADO REYES, Carlos. ■ 00674 #308-03-1982 L1988 FM *030

DIAZ, Manuel Gaspar. CARR 2 K M 47-7 00674 #042-01-1975 L1980 PD *020

DIAZ-SANABIA, Leonora. RR 2 00674 #308-03-1978 L1981 OM GPM *030

FIGUEROA, Francisco Jorge. J16 CALLE ELLIOT VELEZ, URB ATENAS 00674 #042-01-1971 L1974 A *020

FONT, Frederick J A. C/O PO BOX 1160, URB SAN SALVADOR A-19 00674 #042-01-1977 L1981 RHU IM *020 †20

FONTANET, Francisco Javie. ■ 00674 #649-14-1997 L1999 FM *020

GANDIA-MANTARAS, Luis T. 1 CALLE JOSE D CANDELAS, MANATI MED PLZ STE 106 00674 #042-03-1981 L1984 IM *020

GARCIA CARRASCO, Felix D. GEORGETT ST 32 2ND FLOOR 00674 #308-01-1945 L1954 GP GS *071

GARCIA CARRASCO, Juan J. RR 2, HOSPITAL DOCTOR'S CENTER 00674 #308-01-1967 L1975 OBG *020

GELPI, Angel L. ■ 00674 #042-03-1983 L1986 OBG *020 †30

GIERBOLINI, Giancarlo. 201 MANATI MEDICL PLZ #201 00674 #042-03-1999 L2006 CN *020

GOMEZ, Reinaldo. ■ 00674 #308-01-1982 L1991 GP *020

GOMEZ CAMPORREDONDO, Margi. E2 CALLE HERNANDEZ CARRION, URB ATENAS 00674 #042-04-1996 L1999 FM *020

GONZALEZ, Carlos Enrique. 102 CARR 2, URB ATENAS,C/HERNANDEZ CAR 00674 #042-01-1976 L1980 OBG *020 †30

GONZALEZ, Giovani. B42 CALLE ELLIOT VELEZ, URB ATENAS 00674 #308-03-1981 L1986 GP *020

GONZALEZ-AMPARO, Carlos. PO BOX 1702, 2 CALLE MARGINAL CARR 00674 #308-01-1976 L1983 GS *020

GONZALEZ ANDUJAR, Dorma. PO BOX 1564 00674 #308-02-2002 L2005 *100

GONZALEZ-BARRETO, Jorge. J4 CALLE HERNANDEZ CARRION, URB ATENAS 00674 #042-03-1994 L1999 P *020

GONZALEZ-CASTRODAD, Luis. 3 BO CANTERA, ED BELLA SIEMPRE 00674 #042-03-1980 L1984 OBG *020 ‡

GONZALEZ-MORALES, Orlando. PO BOX 1152, STE 202 TORRE DOCTORS CENT 00674 #308-03-1977 L1980 HS HS *020

GONZALEZ RODRIGUEZ, Jorge. PO BOX 803 00674 #042-04-1999 L2001 FM *020

GRAJALES, Nancy L. PO BOX 1142 00674 #847-06-1996 L1998 FM *020 ‡

GUZMAN LUGO, Luis A. PO BOX 1460 00674 #042-04-1998 L2001 FM *020

GUZMAN-SILVAGNOLI, Sonia. 10 CALLE PATRIOTA POZO, PO BOX 1201 00674 #308-03-1978 L1982 EM GP *020

HERNANDEZ, Nelly G L. PO BOX 44 00674 #847-02-1990 L1995 *020

JAIME CONCEPCION, Shirley. ■ 00674 #308-01-1990 L1994 GP *020

JIMENEZ, Jorge D. C15 CALLE A S, URB FLAMBOYAN 00674 #042-04-1995 L1997 FM *020

LAFONT-PEREZ, Emilio A. ■ 00674 #042-03-1981 L1983 GP *020

LANG, Karl Michael. 8 PUERTA DEL NORTE 00674 #042-01-1982 L1986 PUD CD *020 †20

LASTRA, Jorge J. 201 MANATI MEDICAL PLZ, STE 201 00674 #042-01-1992 L1999 NS *020

LOPEZ, German. B1 CALLE MARGINAL, URB SAN SALVADOR 00674 #042-01-1980 L1993 DR *020

LOPEZ FANTAUZZI, Mayra J. C/O P.O. BOX 1686, CARR #2 KM 50, CDT-MANATI 00674 #308-04-1991 L1994 *020

LOPEZ-GALARZA, Luis A. PO BOX 1069, 2 STREET 00674 #308-03-1979 L1983 GS *020 †85

LOPEZ-LLAVONA, Victor A. HERNANDEZ CARRION 00674 #847-06-1976 L1982 IM *020

LOZADA, Luis R. 1 CALLE JOSE D CANDELAS, STE 206 00674 #042-01-1991 L1996 PTH *020 †50

LUGO, Gaspar Rafael. E18 CALLE MARGINAL, URB. SAN SALVADOR 00674 #847-06-1970 L1973 GYN *020

LUGO MORALES, Jose L. PO BOX 542 00674 #649-14-1998 L2001 *100

MALDONADO, Felix. LOS ROSALES 00674 #308-01-1984 L1986 *020

MALDONADO FORNES, Ramon L. A18 CALLE VENDIG, URB SAN SALVADOR 00674 #847-02-1968 L1995 *020

MARTINEZ, Jose R. PO BOX 1000 00674 #042-01-1978 L1978 GP *020 †20

MARTINEZ, Jose R. EXT SAN SALVADOR, MARGINAL #1 00674 #042-01-1980 L1983 IM CD *020

MARTINEZ DONES, Maria E. J17 CALLE ELLIOT VELEZ, URB ATENAS 00674 #847-05-1977 L1981 IM *020

MASSA, Jose Luis. ■ 00674 #042-03-1995 L2006 P *020

MATEO, Luis Alberto. 105 PASEO DE LA ATENAS 00674 #649-14-1994 L1996 OBG FM *020

MELENDEZ CEBOLLERO, G. ■ 00674 #847-04-1960 L1961 GP *071

MELENDEZ-CEBOLLERO, G. 22 PUERTA DEL NORTE, STE 6 00674 #847-04-1960 L1964 GP *020

MELENDEZ RAMIREZ, Manuel. ■ 00674 #308-04-2000 L2002 *100

MENDEZ-MENDEZ, Domingo. PO BOX 857, 2 JARD DE MONACO 1 B11 CAL 00674 #308-01-1972 L1976 PD *020

MERCADO, Marcos Antonio. 201 MANATI MEDICAL PLZ, STE 201 00674 #042-03-1996 L2002 NS *020

MONSERRATE, Pablo E. CALLE J P REYES LOPEZ J-32, URB ATENAS 00674 #042-03-1992 L1996 FM *020

MONTIJO-DE LA CRUZ, Ibis. 93 PASEO ATENAS, CALLE MCKINLY 00674 #042-03-1981 L1984 GP *020

MORALES RUZ, Queenland. J13 CALLE ELLIOT VELEZ, URB ATENAS 00674 #042-01-1972 L1974 R *020

MUDAFORT, Rafael M. PO BOX 385 00674 #056-06-1944 L1947 PD GP *074

NAVAS NAZARIO, Edward J. PO BOX 989 00674 #308-04-2005 L2006 *100

NAVAS-PEREZ, Edward J. PO BOX 989 00674 #308-03-1977 L1980 EM *020

NEGRON, Dennis E L. 105 MANATI MEDICL PLZ #105, C/O #042-02-1985 L1987 NEP IM *020

NIEVES, Migdalia. 205 PASEO REAL MONTEJO, URB HACIENDA HERMANAS MENA 00674 #042-01-1981 L1984 EM *020 †16

ORRACA, Carlos Guillermo. LOS ROSALES III AVE 3 #7 00674 #042-03-1989 L1991 *020

ORTIZ, Cynthia M. 152 AVE LAS PALMAS, VILLAS DEL MANATI 00674 #847-06-1994 L1996 FM *020

ORTIZ, Jose L. HERNANDEZ CARION 00674 #649-14-1988 L1991 OBG *020

PADILLA, Carmen Gloria. 5 CALLE PATRIOTA POZO 00674 #042-03-1981 L1985 IM *020

PADILLA, Lillian M. PO BOX 1662 00674 #042-01-1991 L1996 NEP *020 †20

PADILLA ROSA, Samuel. J23 CALLE ELLIOT VELEZ, URB ATENAS 00674 #042-04-1983 L1985 IM *020

PADRO-RAMIREZ, Josefina. B14 CALLE MARGINAL, URB LOS FLAMBOYANES 00674 #042-03-1980 L1984 PM *020

PARTIDA-ROBLES, Eduardo. 107 MANATI MEDICL PLZ #108, CALLE JOSE CANDELAS 00674 #649-14-1979 L1983 CD *020

PAULA-PAULINO, Jorge. CARR 2 K M 47-7 00674 #308-01-1969 L1976 OBG *071

PENA VALDIVIA, Raul F. ■ 00674 #042-03-2002 L2006 OBG *100

PEREZ, Javier Antonio. ■ 00674 #042-01-2004 L2004 UM *020

PEREZ, Juan F. J23 CALLE ELLIOT VELEZ, URB ATENAS 00674 #042-03-1994 L1996 IM *020

PEREZ-EMMANUELLI, Juan. J20 CALLE ELLIOT VELEZ, URB ATENAS 00674 #042-01-1981 L1986 OPH *020 †35

PINEIRO, Ricardo Antonio. PO BOX 847 00674 #649-14-2001 L2004 *100

PINEIRO ENRIQUEZ, Maria D. PO BOX 847 00674 #649-14-2004 L2005 *100

QUINTERO, Aida L. HERNANDEZ CARION 00674 #042-01-1985 L1989 D *020 †15

QUINTERO, Francisco J. 200 CARR 2, EDIF. DR PEDRO BLANCO LUGO 00674 #042-01-1985 L1996 IM *020 †20

RAIMUNDI, Jose L. ■ 00674 #308-04-1987 L1991 P *020

RAMIREZ HERNANDEZ, A. CARR 2 K M 47-7 00674 #649-01-1970 L1971 OBG *020

RAMIREZ-SCHON, Gerhart B. ■ 00674 #042-01-1960 L1962 GS TS *020 †85

RAMOS, Edgar J. PO BOX 1142, DR A OTERO LOPEZ HOSP 00674 #042-04-1996 L1997 FM *020

RAMOS, Oscar E. C/O P.O. BOX 1869, MANATI MEDICAL PLAZA 104 00674 #042-01-1984 L1988 PM *020

REYES, Miguel A. 113 CALLE SALMON, EST DE MANATI 00674 #649-14-1993 L1996 PD *020

RIOS, Enrique L. 1 CALLE JOSE CANDELAS, MANATI MEDICAL PLAZA SUITE 00674 #042-01-1996 L1999 IM *020 †20

RIVERA ACOSTA, Walter. A13 CALLE VENDIG, URB SAN SALVADOR 00674 #042-04-2002 L2003 *020

RIVERA ORTEGA, Saul L. PO BOX 1126 00674 #649-14-2003 L2005 *100

RIVERA SANTANA, Patricia. PO BOX 1144 00674 #042-04-1997 L1999 FM *020

RODRIGUEZ, Victor. 200 CARR 2, STE 310 00674 #042-03-1988 L1991 PS *020

RODRIGUEZ-CABRERA, O. MARGINAL #4, EXT SAN SALVADOR 00674 #847-02-1979 L1981 GS *020

RODRIGUEZ NAZARIO, Rafael. PO BOX 1809 00674 #042-04-2004 L2005 *100

ROSA, Luis Ricardo. B43 CALLE ELLIOT VELEZ, URB ATENAS 00674 #649-14-1989 L1994 GP *020 †18

ROSADO, Ofelio. CARR 2 K M 47-7 00674 #308-02-1976 L1980 DR *071

ROSARIO, Nancy. 4 BO CANTERA, C/O BOX 298 00674 #308-04-1988 L1992 GP *020

RUIZ, Apolinar. B1 VILLA MARIA, VILLA MARIA 00674 #847-10-1971 L1975 *020

SAMALOT, Jose M. B11 CALLE MARGINAL, URB FLAMBOYAN 00674 #042-01-1981 L1984 PD *020

SANCHEZ, Victor Israel. 200 CARR 2 STE 206, DR. PEDRO BLANCO LUGO 00674 #649-35-1994 L1998 IM *020

SANTIAGO-DIAZ, Carlos M. HERNANDEZ CARION 00674 #847-06-1976 L1978 GS *020

SASTRE, Raul Rodriguez. CAR MILITAS - KM 49.5 00674 #847-10-1960 L1963 GP *071

SEDA RAMIREZ, Jennifer M.. ■ 00674 #649-14-2003 L2005 *100

SERRANO, Ramon Candido. ROAD NO. 2, HOSPITAL DOCTOR CENTER 00674 #308-01-1987 L1990 OBG *020

TAVERAS, Jose Martin. PO BOX 484 00674 #847-09-1972 L1977 AN *020

TAVERAS CRUZ, Alex R.. ■ 00674 #649-14-2002 L2004 *100

TIRADO SIRAGUSA, Rafael A. 93 PASEO ATENAS, CALLE MCKINLEY 00674 #042-03-1981 L1986 IM *020

TOLEDO, Delia Glisette. B87 CALLE TIRADO GARCIA, URB ATENAS 00674 #042-01-1991 L1995 P *020

VALDES, Edel Walesca. 107 CALLE MCKINLEY STE 1 00674 #042-03-1995 L1998 PD *020

VALDES-ROLDAN, Oscar E. CARR 2 K M 47-7 00674 #042-04-1980 L1984 GP *020

VAN DAALEN-BADILLO, M. CARR 2 K M 47-7 00674 #042-04-1980 L1983 PD *020

VARGAS, Oscar Rafael. 105B CALLE MCKINLEY 00674 #308-03-1978 L1980 GP *020

VASQUEZ, Celeste. ■ 00674 #308-01-1962 L1969 GP *020

VAZQUEZ SOTOMAYOR, Jose. ■ 00674 #308-03-1980 L1986 P *020

VEGA, Ricardo. PO BOX 454 00674 #042-01-1978 L1982 PD *100

VELASCO, Jorge Enrique. ■ 00674 #847-09-1964 L1972 GP *020

VELAZQUEZ, Angela M. MANATI, HOSPITAL DE AREA MANATI 00674 #308-01-1968 L1974 N PD *020

VIERA, Luis Felipe, Jr. CARR 2 K M 47-7 00674 #042-01-1986 L1991 U *020

VILLANUEVA, Salvador E. ■ 00674 #042-01-1996 L1999 EM *020 †16

ZAMBRANO, Ariel Jimenez. PO BOX 44 00674 #847-02-1991 L2002 *020

MARICAO – MARICAO

LLUSA, Jose Maria. CENTRO DE SALUD AP 457 00606 #847-01-1952 L1975 FPS EM *071

READ MEDINA, Pedro. HOSPITAL DE MARICAO 00606 #308-01-1948 L1957 GP *020

MAUNABO – MAUNABO

BUCKWALTER, Lee West. ■ 00707 #041-13-1972 L2003 IM *020

CORTES-ROBLES, Angel Manu. PO BOX 1209 00707 #649-14-1996 L2002 FM *020

DEL POZO-GOMEZ, Huberto. BARCELO #21 00707 #847-02-1977 L1980 GP *020

ECHANDY, Ruben. ■ 00707 #649-01-1967 L1971 FM *071

GARCIA-BURGOS, Jose O. ■ 00707 #042-02-1997 L1999 IM *020 †20

GHAFARI, Dauod. ■ 00707 #035-09-2000 L2003 FM *020

MARIN RAMOS, Carmen J. PO BOX 1209 00707 #649-14-1999 L2003 *100

MARTINEZ MUNOZ, Raul E. CALLE BARCELO' 53 A#3 00707 #308-03-1983 L1986 GP *020

MORALES FIGUEROA, Elianett. 95 CALLE 2, VILLA ALEGRE 00707 #649-14-2004 L2005 *100

RIVERA, Basilisa. HC 1, BO LIZAS 00707 #649-14-1990 L1992 PD *020

SANTIAGO, Leopoldo. PO BOX 1256 00707 #308-03-1979 L2003 *020

TORRES MORALES, Pedro M. ■ 00707 #649-14-1985 L1988 GP *020

MAYAGUEZ – MAYAGUEZ

ABESADA, Jaime Luis. ■ 00680 #042-01-2001 L2002 VIR *100 †80

ACARON-ORTIZ, Sifredo. PO BOX 2132, 55 NSUITE CALLE DR BASORA 00681 #649-01-1955 L1960 OTO A *071

ACEVEDO MONTALVO, Victor. ■ 00682 #649-14-2001 L2002 FM *100

ACEVEDO PEREZ, Frances Mi. ■ 00682 #649-14-1998 L2002 GP *020

ACOSTA, Ramon Delfin. ■ 00682 #042-01-1958 L1963 R GP *071 †80

ACOSTA, Virgen Maria. DE DIEGP 57 E 00680 #042-01-1976 L1980 DR *020

ACOSTA-ALBINO, Domingo. 58 CALLE MEDITACION 00680 #847-06-1976 L1982 IM *020

AGUILO, Guillermo. 114E CALLE MENDEZ VIGO E 00680 #042-01-1993 L2001 DR *020

AGUILO, Oscar. BO LA QUINTA 00680 #051-04-1940 L1942 GS GP *071

AGUILO-DIES, Jose Antonio. PO BOX 661 00681 #028-34-1953 L1957 GP *020

■ = Address Information Privacy Protected

ALAMEDA, Yadiel Alexis. ■ 00680 #042-01-2004 L2006 **OTO** *012

ALBINO-VAZQUEZ, Dennis J. 156 CALLE MENDEZ VIGO E #B 00680 #308-01-1974 L1978 **GP** *020

ALEQUIN, Angel. 15 CALLE DR BASORA N 00680 #042-01-1982 L1985 **OBG** *020

ALICEA, Carlos Alberto S. PO BOX 481 00681 #042-03-1981 L1986 **END** *020

ALICEA, Orlando Campos. DE DIEGO 52 E. 00680 #649-03-1975 L1978 **GP** *020

ALLENDE, Diana L. 64 CALLE MALAGA, URB SULTANA 00680 #308-04-1992 L1996 **PD** *020

ALMODOVAR, Angel R. 410 CALLE LOPE DE VEGA, MANS DE ESPANA 00682 #042-01-1970 L1973 **OBG** *020 †30

ALSINA, Elsa A. ■ 00681 #847-06-1976 L1981 **NPM PD** *075

ALVAREZ, Luis Alfredo. 106 CALLE SANTA CATALINA, BO PARIS 00680 #661-02-2005 **GP** *020

ALVAREZ-SANCHEZ, Rafael A. BARIO SABELOS RD #2 00680 #308-03-1981 L1982 **GP** *020

ALVAREZ-TORO, Urselio. STATE RD 349 00680 #847-01-1955 L1958 **GS PDS** *071 †85

AMEZQUITA-CANDELIER, M. PATOLOGIA CENTRO MED 00680 #847-09-1972 L1981 **GP** *020 †50

APONTE, Antonio. COND CENTRO PLAZA SUITE #2, 64 EAST DE DIEGO STREET 00680 #042-01-1974 L1976 **HO IM** *020

ARCE, Sylvia Yanira. 18 CALLE POST N, HOSPITAL SAN ANTONIO 00680 #042-01-1998 L2001 **NPM PD** *020 †55

ARENAS, Juan Jose. 15 CALLE DR BASORA N 00680 #649-01-1961 L1964 **PD** *072

ARROYO, Milagros. 345 AVE HOSTOS, CARRETERA #2 00680 #042-03-1985 L1988 **OBG** *020

ARROYO-FERRER, Sandra A. 351 AVE HOSTOS, STE 110 00680 #042-01-1988 L1994 **DR** *020 †80

ARROYO LEBRON, Ferdinand. 79 CALLE DR BASORA N 00680 #847-04-1966 L1971 **GP** *020

ARROYO-PENA, Efrain. 392 CALLE POST S 00680 #649-14-1994 L1996 **GP** *020

AYALA-RIVERA, Marco A. 167E CALLE RAMOS ANTONINI 00680 #308-04-1980 L1983 **GP** *020

BABILONIA, Brunilda. 101 COND CESANI W, CALLE DE DIEGO 26 OESTE 00680 #847-01-1977 L1980 **GP** *020

BABILONIA, Michael. 1065 AVE LOS CORAZONES, STE 212 00680 #042-01-1987 L1991 **IM RHU** *020 †20

BACO, German A. ■ 00680 #042-04-1989 L1991 **GP** *020

BAEZ, Jorge Tomas. ■ 00681 #649-14-2000 L2003 **FM** *020

BAEZ, Jose W. 55 CALLE MEDITACION, CEWNTRO SERVICIOS MEDICA 00680 #042-01-1979 L1982 **GE** *020

BAEZ, Lynette M. 276 CALLE NELSON RAMIREZ, URB ENSANCHE RAMIREZ 00682 #042-01-1986 L1989 **OPH PO** *020 †35

BAEZ, Norberto. 770 AVE HOSTOS 00682 #042-01-1993 L2000 **ORS** *020 †40

BAEZ-RIOS, Gilberto. 55 CALLE DE DIEGO E, STE 203 00680 #042-01-1996 L1999 **CD IM** *020 †20

BAFALLUY, Sofia Padilla. 267 CUMBRES LAS MESAS 00680 #231-01-1972 L1976 **AN** *020

BARRETO-AGUERIA, Manuel G. PO BOX 864, 1040 CORAZONES 00681 #847-03-1977 L1980 **GP** *020

BARROCAS, Ana Magaly. 23 BELLA VISTA GDNS 00680 #275-01-1981 L2005 **FM** *020

BAYRON-RAMIREZ, Zelma. BARIO SABELOS RD #2 00680 #042-04-1980 L1983 **PD** *020

BECERRA-ESCOBAR, Jesus. 14 CALLE PERAL N STE 2G 00680 #649-14-1980 L1989 **AN** *020

BENAVENT, Carlyle. PO BOX 3308 00681 #649-01-1956 L1962 **U** *071

BENITEZ, Noemi. 55 CALLE MEDITACION STE 4A 00680 #042-01-1985 L1989 **IM CD** *020 †20

BENITEZ, Wanda Ivelisse. 38 CALLE A, BRISAS DE RIO HONDO 00680 #042-01-1979 L1983 **R RNR** *020 †80

BENITEZ-CORUJO, Manuel A. PO BOX 990 00681 #042-01-1979 L1985 **ORS** *020 †40

BERRIOS, Carmen L. 55 CALLE MEDITACION STE 9A 00680 #847-08-1975 L1979 **GP FM** *020 †80

BIAGGI, Hipolito. ■ 00681 #649-01-1943 L1945 **GP OS** *020

BIDOT DE KINDY, Mayra D. 14 CALLE R MARTINEZ NADL S 00680 #042-04-1985 L1989 **GP** *020

BLONDET, Ricardo Jose. ■ 00680 #649-14-2000 L2002 **IM** *020

BONILLA TORRES, Edgardo. ■ 00682 #847-09-1958 L1959 **N CN** *071

BOOTHBY, Luis T. 103 CALLE DE DIEGO E # 14 00680 #042-01-1975 L1980 **PD** *020 †55

BULLS, Antonio A. MEDITACION 55 C S M 2 B 00680 #649-01-1957 L1959 **GS** *020

BUSQUETS, Jose R. 64 CALLE POST N 00680 #042-03-1980 L1984 **PM** *020

CABAN, Viviana Teresa. PO BOX 6407 00681 #042-02-1999 L2005 **GE** *020 †20

CAMACHO, Aileen. ■ 00682 #042-03-2007 **P** *012

CAMACHO-PASTOR, Ivonne. 162 CALLE RAMOS ANTONINI E 00680 #649-14-1985 L1991 **IM** *020

CAMPOS, Joseph Stephen. ■ 00680 #042-04-1999 L2001 **IM** *020

CAMPOS LOPEZ, Rafael Adol. 52 DE DIEGO 00680 #308-02-2000 L2003 *100

CANCIO, Jose Alberto, Jr. 351 AVE HOSTOS, STE 409 00680 #035-19-1996 L2001 **ORS** *020 †40

CANDELARIO, Karinee. ■ 00681 #649-14-1987 L1990 **GP** *020

CARBONELL, Enrique. 55 CALLE DE DIEGO E, CPR BLDG STE 404 00680 #042-01-1984 L1987 **OBG** *020 †30

CARDONA, Armando O. 55 CALLE DE DIEGO E # 401, CPR PROFESSIONAL BLDG 00680 #308-10-1984 L1994 **PUD** *020 †20

CARDONA, Hiram. 55 CALLE MEDITACION, STE 4A 00680 #042-03-1983 L1986 **IM CD** *020 †20

CARDONA, Victor Jose. 2055 CALLE LUIS XIV, URB LOS VERSALLES 00682 #649-14-1992 L1997 **AN** *020 †05,20

CARLO, Simon E. 64 CALLE MALAGA, URB SULTANA 00680 #649-14-1975 L1978 **GP EM** *020

CARLO, Simon Enrique. 64 CALLE MALAGA, URB SULTANA 00680 #308-04-1992 L1997 **FM** *020

CARLO TORRES, Ananska Mar. ■ 00680 #308-04-2000 L2002 **GP** *020

CARO, Armando I. 55 CALLE DE DIEGO E, STE 403 00680 #042-02-1984 L1986 **PYG** *020

CARO-MARTINEZ, Denise. PO BOX 7999, SUITE 259 00681 #042-01-1997 L2000 **IM** *020 †20

CARREON, Edmundo, Jr. ■ 00680 #649-38-1980 L2006 *100

CARRERA DEL MORAL, Jorge. 15 CALLE DR BASORA N 00680 #042-03-1980 L1985 **R** *020

CARRERO, Astrid Annette. 5 AVE CONDOMINIO, REPARTO FLAMBOYAN 00680 #649-14-2002 L2004 *100

CASASNOVAS-LOPEZ, Desiree. ■ 00680 #042-01-2005 **N** *012

CASIANO, Elisbel. ■ 00680 #042-04-1994 L1996 **GP** *020

CASILLAS JIMENEZ, G S. 15 CALLE DR BASORA N 00680 #847-04-1956 L1960 **FM GP** *075

CEBOLLERO-SANTAMARIA, F C. ■ 00682 #042-01-1992 L1998 **GE** *020 †20

CHOLLET-RODRIGUEZ, Nelly. 421 CAMINO BECHARA, VILLA SULTANITA 00680 #308-03-1982 L1986 **OBG** *020

CHRISTIAN MEJIAS, Jorge. ■ 00681 #649-01-1955 L1962 **PHP GP** *020

CISNEROS, Jose Gomez. 410 AVE HOSTOS 00682 #649-16-1986 **OBG** *100

COLLADO ROSAS, Irvin. 16 CALLE DR NELSON PEREA 00680 #042-01-1983 L1993 **OPH** *020 †35

COLLEY, Ada Teresa Capo. PO BOX 370 00681 #042-01-1956 L1959 **PHP GP** *071

COLLEY-SANCHEZ, Jaime A. PO BOX 370 00681 #042-01-1956 L1961 **GS** *071

COLON FERNANDEZ, Miguel A. ■ 00682 #847-10-1970 L1973 **GP** *020

COLON-LOYOLA, Angel R. 257 CALLE ADUANA STE 333 00682 #042-01-1986 L1991 **DR** *020 †80

COMAS FLORES, Floremil. 3 CALL ARTR DVL URB HOSTOS 00682 #308-02-1990 L1994 *020

CORBALA-CONTRERAS, Alma R. PO BOX 1841 00681 #649-01-1976 L1980 **IM** *020 †20

CRESPO RAFOLS, Jose E. 3A CALLE MEDITACION # 55 00680 #308-01-1971 L1975 **IM** *020

CRUZ, Jesus. 155 CALLE PADRE AGUILERA, BO BUENA VISTA 00680 #308-03-1979 L1991 **GP** *020

CRUZ, Jose Danl. CALLE POST 60N, EDIFICIO POST CTR STE 206 00680 #042-01-1979 L1983 **GP** *020

CRUZ, Luis M. 81 CALLE RONDA, URB SULTANA 00680 #042-01-1981 L1985 **OPH** *020 †35

CRUZ, Miguel A. FRENTE PLAZA DE DIEGO, MENDEZ VIGO 154EESAS #101 00680 #847-06-1975 L1980 **PD** *020

CRUZ ANTEGUERA, William. 58 CALLE MADRID, URB BELMONTE 00680 #847-06-1973 L1977 **GP** *020

CRUZ-ESTRADA, Sonia. 1 CALLE CAPARRA 00680 #308-03-1978 L1980 **GP** *020

CRUZ-LOPEZ, Sudia Luz. ■ 00681 #042-04-1987 L1989 **ID** *020 †20

CRUZ-RIVERA, Juan B. PO BOX 7999 00681 #649-50-1980 L1983 **GP** *020

CRUZ-ROS, Virgilio. CALLE RAFAEL MERDZ G 27 00680 #847-10-1977 L1978 **GP** *020

CRUZ-VARGAS, Diosdina. ■ 00681 #847-02-1974 L1993 **IM** *020

CUMMINGS, Luis E. STATE RD 349 00680 #649-01-1956 L1959 **AN OS** *071

CUMMINGS, Roberto. 4B EDIF LA PALMA 00680 #042-03-1981 L1984 **AN PME** *020

CURBELO, Gustavo Antonio. ■ 00680 #935-07-1986 L2005 *100 †18

DA SILVA, Jaime Jared. 219 CALLE NOGAL, JARD DE GUANAJIBO 00682 #042-01-1995 L1998 **NEP IM** *020 †20

D'BRASIS, Senen Torres. 63 CALLE MENDEZ VIGO E, STE 2A 00680 #649-14-1977 L1982 **PD** *020

D'CRUZ, Oswald Albert. 15 CALLE DR BASORA N, HOSPITAL PEREA 00680 #847-11-1970 L1976 **AN** *071

DE ECHEGARAY-ESPADA, F J. ■ 00681 #847-10-1953 L1955 **GS OS** *071

DE JESUS, Zoraida. BEGONIA NH 5 URB BUENAVENTURA 00680 #042-02-1995 **IM** *100

DE JESUS-CARBONELL, Ramon. ■ 00682 #847-04-1958 L1960 **GS** *020 †85 ‡

DEL RIO, Maria. BARIO SABELOS RD #2 00680 #847-01-1975 L1980 **PD ID** *020 †55

DEL RIO FERRER, Jose M. ■ 00680 #847-06-1993 L1993 **IM** *020

DEL TORO-COLBERG, Rodolfo. ■ 00682 #042-01-1996 L1998 **OPH** *020 †35

DEL TORO RIVERA, Nydia G. 25 CALLE MCKINLEY W 00680 #042-04-1997 L1999 *020

DEL VALLE, Carlos A. ■ 00682 #042-04-1997 L1999 **GP** *020 †18

DEL VALLE, Carlos M. 14 CALLE PERAL N, LA PALMA I H 00680 #042-01-1966 L1970 **HEM ON** *020

DELVALLE HERNAN, Ernesto. ■ 00681 #042-01-2007 **GS** *012

DE STRUBBE, Ivette Ramire. PO BOX 1795 00681 #308-03-1977 L1980 *100

DEYNES, Juan Senyed. 1004 CALLE MAGNOLIA, URB BUENAVENTURA 00682 #042-02-1998 L1999 **IM** *020

DIAZ, Juan Ramon. C/O BOX 1150, 4TH FLOOR, PENAL STREET 00681 #042-01-1973 L1976 **GS** *020 †85,55

DIAZ DE YUNES, Antonia. 15 CALLE DR BASORA N 00680 #308-01-1959 L1969 **FM GP** *020

DIAZ-MARTINEZ, Rafael. 302 CALLE RAMONITA, BELLAS LOMAS MIRADERO 00682 #308-01-1950 L1958 **PUD PHP** *020

DOMINGUEZ-MAQUEDA, Jose. BUZON 1688 00681 #847-02-1983 L1986 **IM** *020

DOVAL CORREA, Armando. ■ 00681 #649-01-1959 L1962 **OBG** *020

DURAN, Normando Greduvel. CALLE NELSON RAMIREZ, ENSANCHE RAMIREZ # 276 00680 #042-03-1991 L1994 **GS** *020

EGOZCUE, Manuel Antonio. ■ 00682 #649-14-2002 L2005 **GP** *100

ENCARNACION JORGE, Cecilia. 2 CALLE CAPESTANY, BO BUENA VISTA 00680 #308-01-1994 L2006 *100

ENRIQUEZ FIGUEROA, Gretche. PO BOX 6613 00681 #649-14-2000 L2002 *100

ESCALONA, Pedro. 268 CALLE MIRAMAR, URB ENSANCHE RAMIREZ 00682 #042-02-1983 L1986 **FM** *020 †18

ESPAILLAT-INCHAUTEGUI, J. 2770 AVE HOSTOS, STE 202 00682 #042-02-1998 L2003 **CHP** *020

ESTEVEZ, Carlos Jesus. 1065 AVE LOS CORAZONES, OFICINA #201 00680 #042-01-1990 L1994 **ID** *020

FELICIANO, Carlos A. 15 CALLE DR BASORA N 00680 #042-04-1980 L1984 **GS** *020

FELICIANO IRIZARRY, Efrain. ■ 00680 #308-03-1983 L2002 **FM** *020

FELIU-ROSADO, Domingo. ■ 00681 #847-05-1983 L1985 **IM** *020

FERIA, Jorge F. BARIO SABELOS RD #2 00680 #042-02-1984 L1987 **PD** *020

FERNANDEZ, Carmen A. ■ 00682 #042-02-1984 L1985 **GP** *020

FERNANDEZ GUTIERREZ, Juan. ■ 00682 #847-03-1955 L1961 **GS** *071

FERRARI, Cristina. ADUANA ST # 1258, STE 185 00680 #008-01-2000 L2002 *020 †35

FERRER ARAEZ, Tomas. BO LA QUINTA 00680 #847-04-1968 L1973 **GP** *020

FIGUEROA, Luis Miguel F. 15 CALLE DR BASORA N 00680 #275-01-1948 L1971 **GP PUD** *071

FIGUEROA, Zoema. ■ 00682 #649-14-2002 L2005 *100

FIGUEROA-AQUINO, Jose M. PO BOX 118 00681 #308-03-1990 L1991 *020

FIGUEROA-DELGADO, Maria A. ■ 00681 #847-02-1974 L1976 **PD GP** *020

FIGUEROA VARGAS, Sandra. ■ 00680 #308-02-2003 L2005 *100

FLORES, Ivonne. ■ 00682 #649-30-2002 L2006 *100

FLORIAN, Moises Medardo. ■ 00680 #649-38-1984 L2000 **PD** *020

FRANCESCHINI, Gilberto A. PO BOX 1019 00681 #042-01-1993 L1998 **DR** *020 †80

FRANQUI, Hilton. ■ 00680 #042-01-2004 **IM** *100 †20

FRONTERA, Francisco Juan. 114B CALLE PILAR DEFILLO 00680 #308-03-1981 L1989 **GP** *020

FRONTERA-COLLEY, Antonio. BOX 496 00681 #056-06-1957 L1961 **DR** *020

FRONTERA-COLLEY, Carlos. MILLONARIOS ST N 27 00680 #042-01-1969 L1973 **R** *020

FUMERO, Ricardo A. C/O P.O. BOX 3129, TORRE PERAL APT 2-C NORTE 00681 #847-01-1968 L1974 **P CHP** *020

GANDARA, Jose R. 19 CALLE POST N 00680 #042-01-1964 L1967 **END DIA** *020

GARCIA, Luis E. ■ 00680 #042-01-2007 *012

GARCIA, Roberto A. BO LA QUINTA 00680 #042-04-1981 L1984 **PM** *020

GARCIA, Roberto Felipe. 5 CALLE PERAL N 00680 #035-19-1986 L1992 **OPH EM** *020 †35

GARCIA, Santos. CALLE DR NELSON PEREU, EDIFICIO DOCTOR'S CTR#27 00680 #308-04-1990 L1991 **PD** *020

GARCIA CEBALLOS, Vivian C. PO BOX 427 00681 #649-14-2003 L2006 **GP** *100

GARCIA RUIZ, Antonio J. 615 CALLE PEDRO A DE ALRCN, MANS DE ESPANA 00682 #847-03-1987 L1996 **OS** *020

GARCIA VELEZ, Juan R. ■ 00682 #308-04-2000 L2004 *100

GAZTAMBIDE MONTES, Japhet. 5A EDIF CENTRO PLZ E, MENDEZ 63 ESTE 00680 #308-04-1992 L1995 GP *020

GOMEZ CURET, Noemi. ■ 00680 #042-04-1998 L2001 FM *020

GONZALEZ, Ivette. 156 CALLE POST S 00680 #649-14-1989 L1991 GP GPM *020

GONZALEZ, Jose. BARIO SABELOS RD #2 00680 #308-02-1976 L1980 NPM PD *020 †55

GONZALEZ, Merbil R. 351 AVE HOSTOS STE 309, EDIF. MEDICAL EMPORIUM 00680 #042-01-1994 L2001 N CN *020

GONZALEZ, Orisel. PO BOX 1629 00681 #042-01-2000 L2003 OBG *100 †30

GONZALEZ, Pedro Antonio. 55 CALLE MEDITACION STE 9A 00680 #649-14-1994 L1997 *020

GONZALEZ-GARCIA, Jose E. 15 CALLE DR BASORA N 00680 #649-01-1961 L1962 AN *071

GONZALEZ-HERNANDEZ, Maria. 52 CALLE DE DIEGO E, CALLE DE DIEGO 00680 #308-02-1977 L1983 GYN *020

GONZALEZ-RIVERA, Jesus. ■ 00681 #042-03-1981 L1987 OBG *020

GONZALEZ RODRIGUEZ, M A. 15 CALLE DR BASORA N 00680 #847-05-1972 L1974 OBG *020

GONZALEZ-TRAPAGA, Justo L. 351 AVE HOSTOS, STE 208 00680 #042-01-1991 L1997 NEP IM *020 †20

GONZALEZ VALENTIN, Betzaid. ■ 00682 #042-01-2004 EM *100

GOYCO, Edwin O. 904 CARR 349, CERRO LAS MESAS 00680 #649-14-1986 L1992 *020

GUARDIOLA, Armando Jose. DE DIEGO 102 ESTE 00680 #042-01-1975 L1980 D *020 †15

GUARDIOLA-PEREZ, Pablo R. 102 CALLE DE DIEGO E 00680 #041-09-1948 L1950 OTO A *020 †45

GUERRA, Angel Rafael. 392 CALLE POST S, MIGRANT HEALTH CENTER, INC 00680 #042-01-1997 L2001 P *020

GUERRERO, Oliver Maurice. 1050 AVE LOS CORAZONES, STE 102 00680 #042-02-1997 L2000 NEP *020

GUZMAN, Angelina. 2A EDIF LA PALMA, DE DIEGO 14 ESQUINA PERAL 00680 #042-01-1967 L1970 GYN OBS *020 †30

HAZIM-FRAPPIER, Rhanda J. ■ 00680 #308-03-1978 L1979 GS *020

HERNANDEZ, Humberto. ■ 00680 #042-01-1957 L1961 IM *071

HERNANDEZ ALVAREZ, Hector. 14 CALLE DE DIEGO E, STE 201 00680 #042-01-1965 L1993 D *020

HERNANDEZ CASIANO, Wilfred. PO BOX 7147 00681 #649-14-1999 L2001 *020

HERNANDEZ FERRE, Astrid T. 50 CALLE TENERIFE, URB SULTANA 00680 #847-04-1966 L1971 PD *020

HERNANDEZ HERNANDEZ, Miria. ■ 00682 #042-04-2003 L2004 *100

HERNANDEZ LOPEZ, Hector N. 201 OFFICE PARK, 14 E DE DIEGO STREET 00680 #042-01-1958 L1962 D IM *020 ‡

HERNANDEZ RAMIREZ, Aaron. PO BOX 9118 00681 #649-38-1985 L2005 *100

HERNANDEZ SOTO, Amarilis. ■ 00680 #649-01-1982 L1990 *020

HERNANDEZ VARGAS, Bismal. CALLE SEQUOIA 94 URB BELM 00680 #649-01-1962 L1967 PM *072

HERNANDEZ VERA, Jose Mate. 601 COND CERRO LINDO, APT 601 00680 #649-14-2003 L2006 *100

HERNANDEZ-VICENS, Julio C. PO BOX 1110 00681 #847-05-1976 L1982 GS CRS *020

IBANEZ, Hector E. DE DIEGO 14 ESTE STE 201 00680 #042-01-1988 L1990 OPH *020 †35

IBANEZ, Jose Enrique. STATE RD 349 00680 #649-01-1958 L1959 GS *020 †85

IBARRA, Margarita P D. PO BOX 1496 00681 #847-10-1964 L1966 OBG *020

IBARRA PEROCIER, Pedro H. PO BOX 1496 00681 #308-03-1984 L2002 *020

ILLANAS CAMACHO, Jose R. STATE RD 349 00680 #308-02-1994 L1996 IM *020

INIGO-AGOSTINI, Emigdio. MARINA STA 2986, RONET 4R MIRADEVO 00681 #041-09-1951 L1953 GP OS *020

INIGO-FAS, Emigdio. BOX 490, CALLEBONET TB MIRA DEVO 00681 #308-02-1976 L1981 IM *020

INIGO-FAS, Jesus A. CLINICA ESPANOLA LA QUINTA 00680 #308-02-1979 L1982 IM *020 †20

INIGO-FAS, Jose F. PO BOX 1265, CLINICA ESPANO LA INC 00680 #308-02-1979 L1983 AN *020

IRIZARRY, Anibal D. GIRALDA 93 ST RESID SULTN 00680 #847-02-1970 L1973 GP *071

IRIZARRY, Tomas H. 55 CALLE MEDITACION STE 4A 00680 #042-01-1968 L1976 DR AM *020 †80

ITURREGUI PAGAN, Juan R. 55 CALLE MEDITACION, CENTRO UROLOGICO DEL OESTE 00680 #042-01-1972 L1975 U *020 †95

ITURRINO, Doris Milagros. ■ 00680 #042-01-2002 L2004 IM *100 †20

ITURRINO ECHEANDIA, Luis. BARIO SABELOS RD #2 00680 #847-01-1963 L1967 P *020

ITURRINO RODRIGUEZ, J L. ■ 00681 #847-04-1955 L1957 GS TS *020 †85,90

JAQUEZ RODRIGUEZ, Anirma. PO BOX 3030, MARINA STATION 00681 #308-02-2002 L2004 *100

JAUME, Francisco H. ■ 00682 #042-02-1997 L2000 CD *020 †20

JAUME-ANSELMI, Francisco. 21 CALLE CORAL, VISTA VERDE 00682 #847-10-1962 L1965 CD IM *020 †20

JAVDAN, Goshtasb. ■ 00680 #308-11-1999 FP *012

JAVIER, Santiago Rosa. PO BOX 1750 00681 #308-03-1980 L1986 *020

JIMENEZ, Juan Ramon. ■ 00682 #042-02-1998 L2000 PD *020

JIMENEZ-CRUZ, Juan Carlos. STATE RD 349 00680 #649-20-1982 OBG *020 †30

JIMENEZ GUERRA, Carlos V. PO BOX 1295 00681 #308-01-1955 L1973 GP *071

JOURDAN, Luis A. POST 60 N STE 207, POST CTR 00680 #042-04-1988 L1990 GP OS *020

JUSTINIANO, Janice. ■ 00682 #042-02-1999 L2004 *020 †35

JUSTINIANO, Maria Emilia. ■ 00682 #042-03-1998 L2006 RHU *100

JUSTINIANO-GARCIA, Jorge. 109 CALLE MENDEZ VIGO E 00680 #308-03-1977 L1984 GS SO *085

JUSTINIANO SANTIAGO, Rose. ■ 00680 #649-14-2001 L2004 *100

KINDY, Paul E. CALLE LUNA 14 SUR 00680 #017-20-1951 L1953 ORS *071

LAGARES, Lysette. ■ 00682 #649-14-1989 L1996 GP *040

LAMEIRO, Juan Ambrosio. ■ 00682 #847-02-1981 L1986 NS *020

LARACUENTE-VAZQUEZ, Pedro. 114E CALLE MCKINNEY E, PLAZA YAQUEZ 00680 #847-10-1974 L1977 OBG *020

LATONI, Jorge David. 27 CALLE NELSON PEREA, STE 105 00680 #025-07-1990 L1995 PS *020 †45,65

LATONI-BENEDETTI, Gerardo. PO BOX 3605 00681 #042-02-1992 L2000 BBK *020 †50

LATONI-CABANILLAS, David. 27 CALLE NELSON PEREA, DOCTORS CENTER 00680 #041-13-1955 L1959 D AN *020 †05,15

LEBRON RIVERA, Roberto. 1050 AVE LOS CORAZONES, STE 102 00680 #847-06-1981 L1984 NEP *020

LE FEVRE, Enrique. 1050 AVE LOS CORAZONES, STE 102 00680 #649-18-1983 L1988 NEP IM *020

LEON, Carina Fabiana. ■ 00682 #132-04-1994 L2004 FM *100

LEON, Jerry Rodriguez. 740 AVE HOSTOS, STE 301 00682 #042-02-1998 L2001 PM *020

LLORENS PEREZ, Santiago. 50 CALLE TENRF URB SULTANA 00680 #847-06-1972 L1975 PD *020

LOPEZ, Arturo M. 22 CALLE DR BASORA N 00680 #042-01-1962 L1970 PDC PD *020 †55

LOPEZ, Edrick Danl. 160 CALLE MENDEZ VIGO E 00680 #042-01-1974 L1976 RHU IM *020

LOPEZ, Jorge Luis. ROAD #2 BLDG #770, MAYAGUEZ OUTPATIENT CLINIC 00680 #042-01-1974 L1982 P N *075

LOPEZ, Luis E. PO BOX 1088 00681 #042-03-1987 L1990 PM *020

LOPEZ, Maritza. ■ 00682 #042-02-1999 L2003 PM *020

LOPEZ CASTANON, Luis. PO BOX 1088 00681 #847-10-1957 L1960 GP OS *020

LOPEZ PADILLA, Pascasio L. LALIZA AA14ALTURAS E 00681 #308-01-1981 L1995 *020

LOPEZ-VAZQUEZ, Daisy Mary. 202 CALLE RAMOS ANTONINI E 00680 #308-03-1981 L1991 OBG *020

LOYOLA, Mario Armando. ■ 00681 #042-01-1975 L1980 CHN PD *050

LOZA, Felipe Adolfo. C2 CALLE PROVIDENCIA, URB SANTA MARIA 00680 #319-03-1982 L1999 *020

LOZADA DE SUAREZ, Ana M D. PO BOX 3245 00681 #649-01-1956 L1960 GP *072

LUGO MELENDEZ, Angel. ■ 00681 #869-04-1957 L1961 OBG *071

LUGO RAMIREZ, Carmen I.. ■ 00682 #649-14-2000 L2004 *100

LUGO RODRIGUEZ, Harry Gui. ■ 00682 #308-03-1978 L2004 *100

LUGO VAZQUEZ, Carlos J. ■ 00680 #649-14-1997 L2002 *100

LUZON-CEBALLOS, Vicente. 77 CALLE TOLOSA, URB SULTANA 00680 #308-01-1959 L1966 OBG OS *020 †30

MACHADO, Ramon Antonio. 50 CALLE TENERIFE, URB SULTANA 00680 #649-03-1994 L1997 PD *020

MALAVE, Manuel Alejandro. PO BOX 6429, MARINA STATION 00681 #649-14-2002 L2004 *100

MALAVE, Ronald. ■ 00680 #042-03-1985 L1989 P PYG *075 †75

MALDONADO, Francisco Jose. 345 AVE HOSTOS, MAYAGUEZ OUT PATIENT CLINI 00680 #042-03-1981 L1985 FM *020 †18 ‡

MANANA, Ana M. ■ 00682 #847-05-1985 L1993 IM *020

MARIANI MOLINI, Pedro A. PO BOX 3304 00681 #649-30-2001 L2003 *100

MARINI-ROMAN, Grace A. 6 CALLE MORELL CAMPOS, BO BARCELONA 00680 #308-04-1981 L1988 CD *020

MARQUEZ-HERNANDEZ, A J. PO BOX 3247 00681 #042-01-1979 L1984 DR *020

MARTINEZ, Ivan Gilberto. AVE. CORAZONES #1065, EDIF MEDICO PROFESIONAL 00680 #042-01-1975 L1980 FM *020

MARTINEZ GARCIA, Luz E.. ■ 00680 #649-14-2000 L2003 *100

MARTINEZ OLMEDA, Oscar Am. 680 MAYGUEZ MALL, CALLE MCKINNEY 111 ESTE 00680 #649-14-1972 L2001 GP *020

MARTINEZ RIVERA, Carlos M. 27 CALLE NELSON PEREA #204 00680 #042-02-1991 L1996 END *020 †20

MARTIR-NEGRON, Arelis Est. 101 CALLE HABACUC 00680 #649-14-2003 IM *012

MATA, Laura. PO BOX 1750, BELLA VISTA HOSP 00681 #649-02-1985 L1988 FM *020 †18

MATTA, Glorimar. ■ 00682 #042-02-1989 L1998 PM *020 †60 ‡

MAYORAL LUBA, Rafael F. PO BOX 2048 00681 #847-01-1970 L1974 GP *020

MEDINA, Gerardo Jose. 1050 AVE LOS CORAZONES, STE 102 00680 #042-01-1998 L2002 IM NEP *020 †20

MEJIAS, Rafael. ■ 00681 #649-14-1988 L1993 *020

MELENDEZ, Samuel, Jr. 770 AVE HOSTOS STE 210 00682 #649-14-1989 L1992 IM *020

MENDEZ, Samuel, Jr. 60 CALLE POST N, EDIF. POST CENTER OFFICE10 00680 #042-01-1986 L1993 CHN *020

MENENDEZ-DE JESUS, Julio. ■ 00680 #847-04-1968 L1970 AN *020

MICAMES, Carlos Gustavo. ■ 00682 #042-01-2000 L2003 GE *100 †20

MONAGAS, Neal Carlos. 55 CALLE MEDITACION STE 6A 00680 #042-01-1976 L1981 GE IM *020

MONZON, Pedro J. 25 CALLE MENDEZ VIGO W 00680 #847-06-1975 L1978 FM OM *020

MORALES-BARRETO, Jose A. 86 CALLE SAN FERNANDO 00680 #847-04-1981 L1985 *020

MORALES LOPEZ, Rosa H.. ■ 00682 #042-01-1996 L2003 *020

MORALES-MEDINA, Elba Iris. 14 PERAL ST, STE 1E LA PALMA 00680 #042-01-1970 L1972 PD *040 †55

MORETA, Renan A. 55 CALLE MEDITACION, STE 8B 00680 #308-01-1961 L1970 OTO *072 †45 ‡

MORETTA-CABRERA, Sonny H. 1065 OFIC 211, AVEMIDA CORA ZONES 00680 #308-01-1964 L1979 EM HS *020

MUNIZ, Bernardo Bibino. 351 AVE HOSTOS, EDIFICIO MED EMP STE 413 00680 #042-04-1989 L1990 P PD *020

MUNIZ, Jose J. 55 CALLE DR BASORA N # 212 00680 #042-01-1986 L1992 PG *020 †55

MUNIZ, Luis Manuel. 136 CALLE PABLO CASALS 00680 #042-03-2004 GS *100

MUNOZ, Arnaldo L. ■ 00680 #035-06-1951 L1959 GYN *071

MUNOZ-GONZALEZ, Eliasin. C/O BOX 850, MENDEZ VIGO 85 OESTE 00680 #649-02-1984 L1988 FM *020 †18

MUZQUIZ III, Moses. 770 AVE HOSTOS, EDIFICIO PROFESSIONAL PLZ 00682 #649-54-1997 L2003 *020

NADAL, Rafael. MEDITACION 55 OFICINA 7A 00680 #042-01-1967 L1969 IM PUD *020 †20

NAVARRO MORALES, Javier A. 6 VILLA CAPITAN 00682 #649-14-2003 L2005 *100

NAVARRO RODRIGUEZ, Jose C. ■ 00680 #308-03-1977 L1980 GS *020

NAZARIO-CINTRON, Efrain. 2308 CALLE REINA DEL SOL, URB LOS VERSALLES 00680 #847-05-1976 L1981 GS *020

NEGRON, Armando. CALLE DEL RIO, 22 N BAJOS 00680 #308-03-1985 L2004 GP *100

NEGRON, Iliana. 81 CALLE RONDA, URB SULTANA 00680 #042-01-1981 L1984 PD *020 †55

NIEVES PEREZ, Vianny Lour. ■ 00680 #649-14-2002 L2003 *100

NIEVES TORRES, Jose A. EDIF MEDICO IV 00680 #847-05-1975 L1982 GS VS *020

OBEN-MARTINEZ, Jorge. 104 CALLE DE DIEGO E # 14, MEDICO DE DIEGO BLDG 00680 #042-03-1981 L1984 OBG *020

OLIVENCIA, Humberto. 15 CALLE DR BASORA N 00680 #308-03-1977 L1980 IM *020 †20

ORTIZ-MARTINEZ, Hector L. 15 CALLE DR BASORA N 00680 #042-01-1983 L1987 PD *020 †55

ORTIZ MENDEZ, Dymary. ■ 00680 #649-14-1997 L2001 *100

ORTIZ-TORRES, Ivette F. MAYAGUEZ MED CTR 00680 #847-08-1974 L1977 GP *020

OTERO RODRIGUEZ, Angel R. ■ 00681 #042-04-1998 L1999 FM *020

PABLOS-DUCLERC, Diego E. PO BOX 1868, OBG 00681 #308-03-1977 L1979 OBG *020

PABON, Salvador E. 80 CALLE TOLOSA, URB SULTANA 00680 #042-04-1990 L1992 P *020

PACHECO, Angel L. 27 CALLE NELSON PEREA, DOCTOR'S CENTER STE 203 00680 #042-04-1984 L1986 PD *020

PACHECO OLIVERAS, Luis A.. 716 CALLE TAURO, VILLAS DEL OESTE 00682 #308-13-2002 L2004 *100

PACHECO-VEGA, Angel A. 27 CALLE NELSON PEREA, DOCTORS CTR STE 203 00680 #042-02-1995 L1999 PD *020

■ = Address Information Privacy Protected

PADILLA, Maria Delcarmen. ■ 00681 #035-46-1988 L1997 **PS** *020
PADILLA-ACOSTA, Roberto. 26 CALLE DE DIEGO W, CONDOMINIO CESANI 00680 #308-03-1978 L1983 **GP** *020
PADILLA-MENDOZA, Jose S. 5 CALLE PABLO CASALS 00680 #649-01-1957 L1963 **PM P** *020
PADUA, Antonio M. 1C EDIF LA PALMA STE 1C 00680 #042-01-1986 L1990 **PUD IM** *020 †20
PAGAN-GORDILS, Emilio. ■ 00681 #847-04-1959 L1963 **P** *020
PALACIOS, Miguel Angel. MARINA STA POB 3714 00681 #028-45-1934 L1954 **OBG** *100
PARDO, Wandaly Ibon. PO BOX 7238 00681 #042-01-2005 **IM** *012
PARDO-MORALES, Antonio. 00681 #847-04-1962 L1973 *030
PAREDES, Gustavo Adolfo. ■ 00680 #429-01-1991 **FP** *012
PERAZZA, Luis Alberto. C/O P.O. BOX 3229, 54-N DR. BASORA STREET 00681 #847-05-1975 L1980 **PD** *020
PEREA, Francisco Jose. 15 CALLE DR BASORA N 00680 #847-01-1969 L1971 **OBG GP** *020
PEREA, Lilianne Emilie. 266 CALLE NELSON RAMIREZ, URB ENSANCHE RAMIREZ 00682 #042-01-1998 L2001 **PD** *020 †55
PEREA, Pedro Roberto. 17 CALLE DE DIEGO W 00680 #847-01-1969 L1971 **IM CD** *020
PEREA-VICENTE, Miguel A. ■ 00680 #042-03-1981 L1985 **FM EM** *075
PEREIRA DIEZ, Alexis. ■ 00682 #649-14-2002 L2005 *100
PEREZ, Alfredo. 60 CALLE MEDITACION 00680 #042-01-1988 L1991 **N** *020
PEREZ, Alfredo. 60 CALLE MEDITACION 00680 #847-06-1977 L1987 **N** *062
PEREZ, Carlos V. STATE RD 349 00680 #042-01-1986 L1985 **ORS** *020 †40
PEREZ, Maria Dolores. 202 CALLE POST N # 50 00680 #308-04-1987 L2000 **PD** *020
PEREZ, Omar Javier. 351 AVE HOSTOS STE 202 00680 #042-03-1992 L1999 **GE IM** *020 †20
PEREZ, Sara Ismari. PO BOX 118 00681 #042-01-1992 L1999 **OTO** *020
PEREZ, Sergio. ■ 00681 #042-02-2005 **IM** *012
PEREZ ACEVEDO, Maria M. BARIO SABELOS RD #2 00680 #649-01-1958 L1968 **P GP** *071
PEREZ ARROYO, Waldemar M. ■ 00682 #649-14-1989 L1996 *100
PEREZ FERNANDEZ, Jose Ant. PO BOX 714 00681 #649-14-1995 L2002 *100
PEREZ LAGUILLO, Luis R. PO BOX 1558 00681 #649-35-1984 L1994 *020
PEREZ-MARRERO, Maria C. ALTURAS DE MAYAGUEZ, CALLELALIZA BC-16 00680 #308-01-1975 L1982 *100
PEREZ-MASPONS, Silverio A. ■ 00682 #275-01-1953 L1972 **GP IM** *020
PEREZ-PEREZ, Pedro E. 55 CALLE DR BASORA N, EDIFICIO MEDICO IV 00680 #847-09-1967 L1970 **GS** *020
PICHARDO ACOSTA, Dominga. ■ 00681 #308-06-1985 L1994 **IM** *020
PLAZA, Marta C. PO BOX 3605 00680 #042-02-1993 L2000 **PP PTH** *020 †50
PLUGUEZ, Franklin. 55 CALLE DE DIEGO E, CPR BUILDING SUITE 101 00680 #308-03-1982 L1987 **IM** *020
PORTALATIN, Ruben. STATE RD 349 00680 #042-01-1978 L1983 **ORS** *020
QUINONES, Maria Teresa. PO BOX 6453 00680 #649-14-2000 L2003 **GP** *020
QUINONES VARGAS, Xiomara. 29 CALLE TOPACIO, VISTA VERDE 00682 #649-35-2002 L2004 *100
QUINTANA MATOS, Carlos A. 59 CALLE ANDALUCIA, URB SULTANA 00680 #042-03-1990 L1999 *020
QUINTANA MUNIZ, V. 27 CALLE PERAL N 00680 #847-10-1974 L1976 **OBG** *020
QUINTERO MORALES, Braulio. 15 CALLE DEL RIO N 00680 #264-02-1973 L1977 **RHU IM** *020 †20
RAMIREZ, Ivan Emilio. ■ 00680 #042-02-2005 **DR** *012
RAMIREZ, Jaime. CALLE POUS 316 SUR 00680 #042-04-1981 L1987 **GP** *020
RAMIREZ, Jose Manuel. 55 CALLE MEDITACION 00680 #010-02-1960 L1965 **PD PDA** *020 †55
RAMIREZ, Luis Osvaldo. 13 CALLE PABLO MAIZ, BO BARCELONA 00680 #042-01-1973 L1975 **GS** *020 †85
RAMIREZ, Miriam Jean. BARIO SABELOS RD #2 00680 #847-04-1968 L1971 **GYN PHP** *030
RAMIREZ, Norman F. 1065 AVE LOS CORAZONES, STE 102 00680 #042-01-1988 L1993 **OP ORS** *020 †40
RAMIREZ, Yolanda. 151 CALLE MCKINLEY E, OFICINA 3 00680 #042-03-1982 L1986 **AN NS** *020
RAMIREZ CORIANO, Lyselle. 2920 COLINAS DE ALTURAS 00680 #042-04-1991 L1995 **PD ADL** *020
RAMIREZ-DE ARELLANO, I. STATE RD 349 00680 #042-01-1983 L1988 **DR** *020 †80
RAMIREZ VINCENTY, Julio A. 18 CALLE OPALO VISTA VERDE 00682 #847-04-1962 L1964 **N** *020
RAMOS, Edwin. ■ 00682 #042-01-2003 L2008 **NS** *012
RAMOS, Pedro Alejandro. ■ 00682 #649-14-1998 L2001 **GP** *020
RAMOS FIGUEROA, Liza Mari. APT 201 CONDOMINIO LAS COL 00680 #649-14-2000 L2002 *020
RAMOS-GONZALEZ, Max. 410 AVE HOSTOS, BO. SABALOS 00682 #308-01-1974 L1977 **AN** *020
RAMOS SANTIAGO, Sonia J. 104 MANS LAS MESAS, CERRO LAS MESAS 00680 #042-04-1990 L1994 *020
RESTO, Keila Susana. 2200 AVE PEDRO ALBIZU CAMP, APT 20 00680 #649-14-2003 L2006 *100
REYES, Francisco J. 1050 AVE LOS CORAZONES, STE 102 00680 #042-01-1995 L1999 **NEP IM** *020 †20
REYES-HERNANDEZ, Tamari. ■ 00682 #308-04-1985 L1989 **GPM** *020
RIOS ORLANDI, Jose Ramon. BONET 323-3B MIRADERO 00680 #649-18-1983 L1986 **GP** *020
RIVERA, Felix Manuel. 20 CALLE POST N OFC 60 00680 #042-03-1995 L2000 **GE** *020 †20
RIVERA, Francisco Javier. 237 LLORENS TORRES, URB ENSANCHE RAMIREZ 00682 #649-14-1995 L1997 **FM** *020
RIVERA, Lourdes M. ■ 00681 #042-01-1980 L1983 **P** *020
RIVERA, Luis Angel. ■ 00682 #649-14-2003 L2005 *100
RIVERA, Miguel Angel. ■ 00680 #847-06-1984 L1988 **GP** *020
RIVERA-ARROYO, Jose M. ■ 00682 #847-01-1971 L1975 **R** *020
RIVERA-BONILLA, Miguel A. 14 CALLE PERAL N STE 1G 00680 #847-04-1957 L1960 **ATP FOP** *062
RIVERA-CORDERO, Moises. 22 CALLE DR BASORA N, OFICINA 2-A 00680 #042-01-1964 L1968 **IM** *020
RIVERA DE LOS RIOS, Angel. BARIO SABELOS RD #2 00680 #042-01-1970 L1972 **D** *020 †15
RIVERA-GONZALEZ, Ramon O. 105 EDIF MEDICO PROFESIONL, AVE CORAZES #1065 00680 #042-03-1981 L1983 **IM** *020 †20
RIVERA MALAVE, Nelson. MAYAGUEZ TERRACE, CALLE 14 P3A 00680 #649-14-1995 L1996 **IM** *020
RIVERA-MISLA, Marisol. 165E CALLE MENDEZ VIGO 00680 #042-04-1988 L1990 **AN** *020
RIVERA-RIVERA, Iveliza. 163 CALLE MENDEZ VIGO E 00680 #308-03-1978 L1983 **GP** *020
RIVERA SANTIAGO, Jose A. 55 CALLE DE DIEGO E, STE 102 00680 #649-14-1989 L1993 **IM** *020

RIVERA-SERRANO, Aracelis. 351 AVE HOSTOS, BOX 6468 00680 #847-04-1979 L1986 **NM IM** *020
RIVERA-SILVA, Irma Nydia. 3034 CALLE RAMON POWER, URB MAYAGUEZ TERRACE 00682 #847-05-1979 L1982 **GP** *020
RIVERA-TORRES, Miguel. ■ 00680 #308-03-1974 L1980 **PD** *020 †55
RIVERA VELAZQUEZ, Jose M. ■ 00682 #649-14-1998 L1999 *020
RODRIGUEZ, Alberto. 351 AVE HOSTOS STE 212, MEDICAL EMPORIUM BUILDING 00680 #042-01-1976 L1981 **CHP P** *020
RODRIGUEZ, Alberto. 434 CALLE JUANITA, URB BELLA LOMAS 00682 #847-03-1981 L1984 **GP** *020
RODRIGUEZ, Carlos Lorenzo. PO BOX 1868 00681 #275-01-1984 **IM** *012
RODRIGUEZ, Edwin. 410 AVE HOSTOS, RAMON E BETANCES HOSPITAL 00682 #042-02-1989 L1998 **RO** *020
RODRIGUEZ, Fritz. PO BOX 1866 00680 #042-03-1993 L1995 **AN** *020
RODRIGUEZ, Gilberto Luis. STATE RD 349 00680 #042-01-1955 L1957 **U** *072 †95
RODRIGUEZ, Karen Maria. ■ 00682 #042-01-2004 **IM** *100 †20
RODRIGUEZ, Karla Michelle. ■ 00682 #042-02-2007 L2007 **P** *012
RODRIGUEZ, Luis Noel. 117 CALLE ESTACION BOX 330, YAQUEZ COMMUNITY CLINIC 00680 #847-04-1956 L1959 **U** *071
RODRIGUEZ, Maria F. 104 OFFICE PARK, STE 104 00680 #042-04-1989 L1993 **P** *020
RODRIGUEZ, Norma Ivette. ■ 00682 #042-01-2000 L2003 **EM** *020 ‡
RODRIGUEZ, Rafael Angel. 21 CALLE DEL RIO N 00680 #042-01-1983 L1987 **OBG** *020 †30
RODRIGUEZ-ACEVEDO, R A. ■ 00680 #847-04-1961 L1964 **OBG** *071
RODRIGUEZ-ACOSTA, Anatila. 82 CALLE TOLOSA, URB SULTANA 00680 #308-03-1979 L1982 **IM** *020
RODRIGUEZ COLON, Yamil. ■ 00681 #649-35-1995 L1999 *020
RODRIGUEZ DIAZ, Grisel. ■ 00682 #308-03-1989 L2004 *100
RODRIGUEZ-LAGUER, Olga. 20 CALLE POST N 00680 #308-03-1981 L1986 **PD** *020
RODRIGUEZ LOPEZ, Elsa A. ■ 00681 #042-01-1968 L1976 **GP** *075
RODRIGUEZ MARTINEZ, Jephte. 711 CALLE COQUI, URB MIRADERO GDNS 00682 #649-14-1997 L2001 **GP EM** *020
RODRIGUEZ MERCADO, Jose A. PO BOX 2374 00681 #308-01-1978 L1989 **GP** *100
RODRIGUEZ-MUNOZ, F I. STATE RD 349 00680 #042-01-1959 L1962 **GS OS** *020
RODRIGUEZ-SANCHEZ, C J. ■ 00680 #847-04-1963 L1972 **PD** *071
ROJAS, Ariel A. ■ 00682 #042-04-1996 L1997 *020
ROJAS DAVIS, Ariel A. BARIO SABELOS RD #2 00680 #847-01-1966 L1968 **P** *020
ROLDAN FLORES, Maria L. 9 CALLE ANTONIO PAOLI 00682 #649-14-1987 L1992 *020
ROMAN, Mario Luis. ■ 00682 #042-02-1995 L1997 **IM** *020
ROMAN, Miguel A. ■ 00682 #042-01-2004 **IM** *012
ROMAN, William. PO BOX 1230 00681 #042-02-2000 L2002 **U** *95
ROMAN, William R. 103 CALLE DE DIEGO E 00680 #847-06-1976 L1981 **U** *020 †95
ROMAN-AVILES, Freddie H. 14 CALLE PERAL N, STE 1E LA PALMA 00680 #847-10-1966 L1968 **OBG** *020 †30
ROMAN-CARLO, Jose C. ■ 00681 #649-14-1980 L1984 **GP OM** *020
ROMAN-CARLO, Rosa Isabel. STATE RD 349 00680 #649-14-1984 L1989 **PUD** *020 †20
ROMAN DE JESUS, Jose C. 21 CALLE DR BASORA N # 939 00680 #847-04-1958 L1960 **AN** *071
ROMAN GRAU, Radames C. BARIO SABELOS RD #2 00680 #042-01-1982 L1986 **OBG** *020 †30
ROMERO, Jesus Antonio. 5 CALLE PABLO MAIZ, BO BARCELONA 00680 #042-01-1990 L1995 **DR** *020
ROSARIO, Carlos V. ■ 00680 #042-03-1980 L1984 **IM CD** *020
ROVIRA, Edwin Osvaldo. 3A EDIF CENTRO PLZ E, MENDEZ VIGO 63 E 00680 #042-01-1974 L1976 **GYN** *020 †30
RUIZ, Carlos Efrain. ■ 00681 #042-01-1996 L2000 **AN** *020 †05
RUIZ RIVERA, Betsy Y. PO BOX 7996, PMB 244 00681 #042-04-1997 L1999 **FM** *020
RUIZ VEGA, Dimas A. PO BOX 850 00681 #308-03-1983 L1989 *020
RUPERTO, Karen. HC 5 BOX 62977 00680 #649-14-2002 L2004 *100
RYSZ, Barbara. 14 CALLE PERAL N, STE 1D 00680 #759-01-1976 L1991 **OBG** *020 †30
SALAS-RIVERA, Javier Conc. PO BOX 5579 00681 #649-14-2000 L2002 **FM** *020
SALAZAR, Elaine Marie. ■ 00681 #042-02-2006 **PTH** *012
SALAZAR, Fernando G. 64 CALLE DE DIEGO E 00680 #042-01-1974 L1976 **OPH** *020 †35
SALIM-MICAMES, Carlos. PO BOX 1092 00680 #132-06-1973 L1980 **GE IM** *020 †20
SANCHEZ, Juan Jose. STATE RD 349 00680 #132-02-1980 L2000 **GS** *020 †18
SANCHEZ MORALES, Carlos. ■ 00680 #847-02-1959 L1961 **PHP** *071
SAN MIGUEL, Lucia. ■ 00682 #308-03-1984 L1989 **P** *020
SANTAELLA, Hamed. PO BOX 1917, MENDEZ VIGO ST. 61 EAST 00681 #042-01-1975 L1979 **OPH** *020
SANTALIZ, William F. 345 AVE HOSTOS, MAYAGUEZ V.A. OUTPATIENT C 00680 #042-01-1984 L1987 **FM** *020 †18
SANTANA, Darline. ■ 00680 #042-01-2008 *012
SANTIAGO, Juan Alberto. PO BOX 2636 00681 #042-01-1994 L1998 **GS** *100
SANTIAGO, Manuel A. PO BOX 3425, MARINA STATION 00681 #308-04-1992 L1994 *020
SANTIAGO, Michelle Joan. 209 PROLONGACION DI 00680 #649-14-2002 L2005 *100
SANTIAGO, Ricardo E. 123 CALLE DE DIEGO E STE 00680 #042-04-1989 L1995 **IM NM** *020
SANTOS-ONODA, Marilyn. PO BOX 7999, STE 200 00681 #308-03-1980 L1985 **IM** *020
SANTOS-PICO, Jose Vicente. 19 CALLE MCKINLEY E 00680 #042-03-1980 L1986 **N** *020
SEDA, Harry. BOX 4185 SALUD STA 00681 #847-06-1992 L1996 *020
SEDA BONILLA, Pedro A. 22 CALLE DR BASORA N 00680 #847-04-1956 L1957 **GS FM** *020
SEPULVEDA, Ismael. 457 CALLE ALMIRANTE, ALT DE MAYAGUEZ 00682 #042-01-1977 L1980 **FM** *020
SEVILLA MOYA, Pascual. ■ 00680 #308-03-1984 L1987 **FM** *020
SINGH, Edward S. 69 CALLE POST N 00680 #308-03-1981 L1987 **GE IM** *020
SOLER-VINCENTY, Luis E. 55 CALLE DR BASORA N OFC 2 00680 #649-01-1962 L1966 **IM NEP** *020
SOTOLONGO, Roberto. 12 CALLE C, MENDOZA 00680 #308-02-2002 **IM** *012
SOTO MUNIZ, Ana Mercedes. 445 AVE GONZALEZ CLEMENTE 00682 #308-03-1980 L1986 **GP PME** *020
SUAREZ, Ana M. 257 CALLE ADUANA, STE 333 00682 #042-01-1986 L1991 **DR** *020
SUAREZ, Ana S. BARIO SABELOS RD #2 00680 #042-01-1981 L1984 **GS PD** *020 †85
SUAREZ, Dennis Frank. PO BOX 1100 00681 #042-01-1976 L1982 **IM RHU** *020 †20
SUAREZ, Francisco R. DE DIEGO 14 ESTE 00680 #042-01-1984 L1987 **OTO PS** *020 †45
SUAREZ, Giselle. ■ 00681 #042-01-1990 L1996 **GS** *020
SUAREZ, Ivan N. PO BOX 6409 00681 #042-01-1988 L1991 **AN PD** *020 †55
SUAU-FERRER, Luis Jose. 55 CALLE MEDITACION, OFICINA 2-A 00680 #042-01-1970 L1972 **HEM ON** *020 †20

SURIEL, Adalgisa Carmen. ■ 00682 #033-05-1985 L1990 **OBG** *020
TIRADO-QUINONES, Gilberto. 52 CALLE DE DIEGO E, BOX 3635 00680 #847-01-1966 L1968 **NS GP** *020
TORO, Betsy Isabel. 19 CALLE CAPARRA, URB PONCE DE LEON 00680 #308-03-1985 L1996 **FM** *020
TORO, Jose Angel. ■ 00682 #649-14-1997 L1999 *020
TORO-FONT, Jose A. 3115 CALLE ATALAYA, ALT DE MAYAGUEZ 00682 #847-05-1975 L1980 **PD** *020
TORRES, Edwin. ■ 00680 #847-06-1982 L1986 **GP** *020
TORRES VAZQUEZ, Carisa. PO BOX 3064, # 601 00681 #042-04-2001 L2002 **GP** *020
TORRES ZAYAS, Luis Angel. 55 CALLE MEDITACION, GPO BOX 1778 00680 #847-10-1970 L1973 **U GS** *020
TREVINO, Arthur Omar. ■ 00681 #042-01-1974 L1977 **IM HEM** *020
TRUJILLO, Oscar. CENTRO MEDICO PATOLOGIA 00680 #264-07-1965 L1981 **PTH** *020 †50
URDAZ, Federico Joue. ■ 00681 #847-05-1974 L1978 *020
URENA, D Amilcar. ■ 00681 #308-01-1976 L1983 **U EM** *020
URRUTIA ALSINA, Marisol. ■ 00682 #042-04-1989 L1990 **PD** *074
VALENTIN, Jaime. ■ 00680 #042-03-1988 L1996 *020
VALENTIN, Jorge Luis. 351 AVE HOSTOS, MEDICAL EMPORIUM 308 00680 #042-04-1981 L1988 **P** *020
VALLE, Daniel Eloy. 50 CALLE TENERIFE, URB SULTANA 00680 #042-01-1995 L2000 **DR** *100 †80
VALLE, Pedro Luis. 50 CALLE TENERIFE, URB SULTANA 00680 #847-08-1970 L1972 **PD** *020
VALLE TIRADO, Oscar. 345 CALLE POST S, BELMONTE CENTRO 00680 #308-03-1985 L1990 *020
VARGAS, Oscar Alberto. 165 CALLE MENDEZ VIGO W 00682 #042-03-1989 L1991 **PS** *020 †85,65
VARGAS, Roberto Luis. ■ 00680 #042-01-1999 L2007 **PTH** *100
VARGAS-RAMOS, Lorna A. 351 AVE HOSTOS, MEDICAL EMPORIUM STE 203 00680 #042-02-2000 L2002 **OPH** *020 †35
VAZQUEZ, Lizmary. ■ 00680 #649-14-2002 L2004 *100
VAZQUEZ, Yadira. 72 CALLE TENERIFE, URB SULTANA 00680 #042-01-1987 L1993 **DR** *020 †80
VAZQUEZ, Yadira. ■ 00680 #649-14-1993 L1996 *020
VEGA, Francisco Cordero. ■ 00680 #847-03-1958 L1962 **PD OS** *071
VEGA LOPEZ, Jesus. ■ 00681 #005-12-1965 L1970 **PTH CLP** *071
VEGA VAZQUEZ, Ricardo. ■ 00680 #042-04-1997 L2000 **FM** *020
VEGA VIVAS, William A. ■ 00681 #308-03-1981 L1994 **GP** *020
VELASCO, Miguel A. 257 CALLE ADUANA, STE 357 00682 #649-14-1986 L1987 **IM** *020
VELAZQUEZ, Marcos. 204 CALLE MCKINLEY E, EDIFICIO PLAZA YAGUEZ 00680 #308-04-1983 L1985 **CD** *020 †20
VELAZQUEZ-ROSADO, Ismael. 917 CALLE TORRECILLAS 00682 #847-05-1984 L1988 **IM** *020
VELEZ COLON, Waika Deniss. ■ 00682 #649-14-2002 L2002 *020
VELEZ-PONCE, Alfredo. BOX 2663 00681 #847-02-1970 L1973 **PM** *072
VELEZ VARGAS, Jose M. 64 CALLE ZARAGOZA, URB BELMONTE 00680 #042-04-1990 L1991 *020
VERAY-ABRAMS, Gilberto. 14 CALLE DE DIEGO E 00680 #847-06-1968 L1971 **IM** *020
VIGO, Miquel Angel. 66 CALLE ALHAMBRA, URB SULTANA 00680 #308-04-1980 L1983 **IM** *020
VILLANUEVA, Pedro Juan. STATE RD 349 00680 #132-01-1961 L1967 **GP** *020
VILLEGAS VAN DER LINDE, Si. ■ 00680 #308-13-2002 L2004 **PD** *100
VINCENTY, Luis R. STATE RD 349 00680 #308-03-1983 L1986 **IM** *020 †20
VIQUEIRA, Jaime Antonio. PO BOX 1780 00681 #042-01-1974 L1977 **PD** *020
WALKER, Marcial A. 97 CALLE FRANCISCO GALANES 00680 #042-01-1992 L1997 **U** *020 †95
WEBER, Jorge Luis. 1050 AVE LOS CORAZONES, STE 102 00680 #042-01-1974 L1976 **NEP IM** *020
WU CHAVEZ, Alexa M.. ■ 00680 #649-14-2004 L2005 *100
ZAMORA, Carlos J. 62 CALLE DE DIEGO E 00680 #847-04-1956 L1958 **FM** *020
ZAMORA, Francisco J. PO BOX 119 00681 #847-04-1955 L1956 **P** *071
ZAMORA, Jose Julian. 57 CALLE ACACIA 00680 #308-04-1982 L1986 **P** *020
ZAMORA ECHEVARRIA, F Jose. PO BOX 119 00681 #308-04-1984 L1986 **OBG** *020

GONZALEZ, Maria Del Mar. HC 2 BOX 11991, 1 CARR 111 # 422 00676 #042-01-2005 **FP** *012
GONZALEZ BADILLO, Orlando. 112 CALLE DON CHEMARY 00676 #308-02-1990 L1995 **PD** *020
GONZALEZ COLON, Anitza O. 51 AVE LA MOCA 00676 #042-04-2000 L2001 **FM** *020
GONZALEZ-FERNANDEZ, M. ROUTE 110 00676 #308-03-1979 L1982 **EM GP** *020
HERNANDEZ, Jesus I. ■ 00676 #042-03-2008 *012
HERNANDEZ CORDERO, Rene E. PO BOX 368 00676 #649-14-1988 L1992 **GP** *020
LARRAZABAL MERCADO, Luis. ■ 00676 #308-03-1984 L1990 *100
LOPEZ LORENZO, Vivian. HC 5 BOX 10763, BARRIO CUCHILLAS 00676 #308-04-2000 L2003 **FM** *020
MARINI-ROMAN, Orlando. 550 CALLE CONCEPCION VERA, HOSPITAL SAN CARLOS 00676 #308-04-1980 L1991 **CD IM** *020
MARTINEZ FORTIER, Felix. ROUTE 110 00676 #847-05-1974 L1980 **OBG** *020
MATIAS, Israel. 506 CALLE ORQUIDEA, URB MOCA GDNS 00676 #649-14-2004 *100 †55
MENDEZ, Jorge Luis. CALLE BARBOSA 255 00676 #308-03-1980 L1987 **GP** *020
MENDEZ CABAN, Domingo. ■ 00676 #847-02-1981 L1987 **FM** *020
MENDEZ CABAN, Yamilette. HC 5 BOX 10785, 444 ST KM 1.2 00676 #042-04-2000 L2002 **GP** *020
MENENDEZ ANDINO, Sandra. C/O P.O. BOX 884, CALLE PEDRO SANTOS #59 00676 #847-02-1981 L1984 **PD** *020
MERCADO TORRES, Lourdes. 205 CALLE JUAN SAN ANTONIO, EDIFICIO BOSQUES OFICINA 1 00676 #649-14-1994 L1996 *020
MONTES ESTEVES, Santiago. ■ 00676 #649-01-1953 L1956 **FM** *020
MONTESINOS ROIG, Teresa R. AGVADILLA PR, AVE. SAN RAFAEL #168 00676 #847-06-1988 L1994 **IM** *020
PEDRAZA, Carlos Ivan. 2 EDIF BOSQUES, CALLE JUAN SAN ANTONIO #1 00676 #308-03-1985 L1986 **IM** *020
PEREZ, Lisandra. 574 CALLE PASCUAS, URB MOCA GDNS 00676 #042-02-1997 L1999 **PCC** *020 †20
PEREZ-CABAN, Wilfredo. EDIFCIO BOSQUES #8, CALLE JUAN SAN ANTONIO 00676 #649-43-1981 L1983 **GP** *075
RAMOS, Luis R. ROUTE 110 00676 #847-04-1956 L1958 **RHU GP** *020
RIVERA VALE, Pablo. 449 CALLE DEL PILAR, URB. LA MONSERRATE 00676 #649-35-1999 L2002 *020
RODRIGUEZ-MENDEZ, Jose E. HC 2 BOX 10837, 444 ROAD KM 3.5 COCHILLA 00676 #847-05-1964 L1967 **EM FM** *030
ROMAN, Abdiel Alexis. ■ 00676 #649-14-2005 L2006 *100
ROMAN, Jorge Luis. ■ 00676 #042-01-2004 L2005 **ORS** *012
RUIZ, Francisco. BARBOSA 153 00676 #847-08-1979 L1989 **PD** *020
RUIZ, Maria Delosa. 65 CALLE PEDRO SANTOS, STE 1 00676 #042-02-1994 L1997 **PD** *020 †55
SALAS, Blanca. 222 CALLE BLANCA E CHICO 00676 #649-14-2001 L2003 *100
SANTIAGO, Norberto. ■ 00676 #847-06-1984 L1988 **ON HEM** *020
SCHMIDT CABAN, Lisa I.. ■ 00676 #649-14-2001 L2003 *100
SOTO, Dialyn De Lourdes. ■ 00676 #042-01-2008 *012
SOTO, Tomas Deynes. ■ 00676 #042-01-1976 L1980 **PD** *020 †55 ‡
SOTO CRUZ, Lemuel O. PO BOX 2692 00676 #042-04-1998 L1999 **GP** *020
STEFAN, Rafael Miguel. ROUTE 110 00676 #308-01-1962 L1972 **PD** *020
TERON, Ivan. 501 CALLE CONCEPCION VERA 00676 #308-02-1990 L1995 **PD** *020
TRAVERSO, Cesar Alberto. ■ 00676 #649-14-2002 L2004 *100
VALE-COLON, Oscar E. ■ 00676 #308-03-1984 L1991 **IM** *020
VARGAS, Manuel. ROUTE 110 00676 #042-01-1979 L1983 **OBG U** *071
VARGAS-CORTES, Jose Del C. ROUTE 110 00676 #847-09-1961 L1970 **AN PHP** *020
VELAZQUEZ RIVERA, Jose T. PO BOX 398, 230 BARBOSA ST 00676 #847-10-1960 L1966 **GP** *071
VELEZ-MORALES, Lilliam. BOX A-1085 00676 #042-03-1988 **FM** *100
VERA QUINONES, Jorge. 65 CALLE PEDRO SANTOS, STE 1 00676 #649-14-1998 L2000 *020 †18
YAPOR-FADUL, Jesus J. PO BOX 1567 00676 #308-02-1979 L1982 *020

MERCEDITA — PONCE

ACEVEDO COLON, Adrian. PO BOX 462 00715 #308-03-1983 L1990 **GP** *020
CASTAING, Pedro Alfredo. ■ 00715 #042-01-1995 L2000 **OS P** *020 †55,75
LATONI-MALDONADO, R. ■ 00715 #042-03-1995 L2003 **VIR** *020
LLUVERAS, Jorge E. PO BOX 2000 PMB 006 00715 #308-03-1981 L1990 **IM** *020
LOPEZ, Hilda Nora. ■ 00715 #042-01-1988 L1992 **AN OS** *062
LUGO-VELEZ, Luis Jorge. PO BOX 712, 1173 FROGANCIA STEET 00715 #308-01-1987 L1992 **ID IM** *020
MONTES CARABALLO, Miguel. PO BOX 603 00715 #649-33-1989 L1993 **GP** *071
NEGRON, Edwin. PO BOX 2000 PMB 56, MERCEDITA 00715 #308-03-1985 L2003 *100
RODRIGUEZ, Jesus Waldemar. PO BOX 664 00715 #649-14-1998 L1999 *020
RODRIGUEZ-SANTIAGO, G A. 105 MICHELLE PLZ STE 105 00715 #308-03-1982 L1985 **GP** *020
ROMERO, Angel E. ■ 00715 #042-01-1983 L1987 **GS PS** *020
WHATTS, Pedro Manuel. ■ 00715 #042-01-1989 L1993 **AN** *020 †05 ‡

MIRAMAR — SAN JUAN

ALVAREZ, Alden Rene. ■ 00907 #275-03-1992 **FP** *012
PAZ, Cintia Alejandra. ■ 00907 #132-01-2001 **FP** *012

MOCA — MOCA

ACEVEDO, Ismael Antonio. ■ 00676 #308-13-2002 L2004 **IM** *012 †20
BUSQUETS, Dionel Vargas. PO BOX 1859, 550 00676 #847-06-1978 L1985 **GS** *020
CABAN, Omar Leonel. ■ 00676 #042-02-2005 **PD** *012
COLON-RAMOS, Simon. 3 CALLE CATALINO VELAZQUEZ 00676 #308-03-1978 L1981 **FM** *020
COLON SOTO, Benito. BARBOSA ST. #250., REG.NUM. 00676 #649-01-1971 L1975 **EM** *020
DIAZ-OTERO, Heberto. ROUTE 110 00676 #308-02-1979 L1982 **OBG** *020
GONZALEZ, Antonio G. 65 CALLE PEDRO SANTOS 00676 #308-01-1976 L1979 **GP** *020
GONZALEZ, Edgardo. ■ 00676 #308-03-1986 L1993 **OBG** *020

MOROVIS — MOROVIS

ALBIZU, Gustavo Rafael. ■ 00687 #306-01-2003 L2005 *100
ALVARADO, Irma. CRUZ ROSARIO 36, BUZON HC-02-5424 00687 #308-04-1985 L1990 **OBG** *020
BERRIOS APONTE, Cruz M. ■ 00687 #042-01-1978 L1982 **PD** *020
BIDOT DE JESUS, Pedro L. 27 CALLE BUENA VIS 00687 #308-06-1987 L1989 **GP** *020
CARRION-SEGARRA, Enrique. 1 CALLE SAN MIGUEL 00687 #847-05-1976 L1982 **PD** *020
DEL RIO, Francisco J. 68 CALLE BALDORIOTY, UPPR 00687 #847-06-1988 L1990 **GP** *020
HEREDIA BURGOS, Carlos. PO BOX 1982 00687 #308-03-1996 L2002 *100
JUSINO, Camila. CARR 159 KM 0 HM 5, BO MONTELLANO 00687 #042-02-1983 L1986 **PD** *020 †55
MARTINEZ, Guillermo. 1 CALLE HERMINIO MIRANDA, CENTRO DE MEDICINA DE FAMI 00687 #308-03-1985 L1991 *020
MARTINEZ, Julia E. 11 CALLE COMERCIO 00687 #042-01-1981 L1985 **DR** *020 †80
MIRANDA, Nicolas J. 3 PASEO FELICIDAD, QTAS DE MOROVIS 00687 #042-03-1995 L2002 *020
MUNOZ, Antolin. 1 CALLE HERMINIO MIRANDA 00687 #308-01-1982 L1991 **GP** *020
PARES, Jose A. 11 CALLE BUENA VIS, BOX 544 00687 #042-03-1988 L1994 **PTH** *100
QUINTERO, Maria R. ■ 00687 #042-01-1984 L1987 **IM** *020
RIVERA GUEVAREZ, Eric E. 5 CALLE PATRON 00687 #308-06-1987 L1994 *020
ROBLES, Enrique Manuel. ■ 00687 #042-01-2007 *012
RODRIGUEZ COLON, Ivan Raf. ■ 00687 #649-30-2002 L2003 *100
RODRIGUEZ-RIOS, Manuel A. 58 CALLE PROGRESO 00687 #308-03-1981 L1984 *020
RUSSE NEGRON, Ramon. 1 CALLE HERMINIO MIRANDA 00687 #847-09-1956 L1958 **FM PHP** *071
TORRES, Ivan. ■ 00687 #649-14-2002 L2003 *100
TORRES MELENDEZ, Jose G. 20 CALLE PRINCIPAL 00687 #308-03-1980 L1985 **GP** *020
TORRES ROBLEDO, Justo L. ■ 00687 #649-14-1999 L2003 *100
UMPIERRE, Eduardo F. 1 CALLE HERMINIO MIRANDA 00687 #042-01-1988 L1992 **FM** *020 †18
VENEGAS, Victor Javier. ■ 00687 #308-04-1989 L1992 **IM** *020
VERA RODRIGUEZ, Roberto. ■ 00687 #275-01-1954 L1976 *071
ZAYAS CINTRON, Jose Ramon. UNIDAD SALUD PUBLICA 00687 #649-01-1955 L1957 **GP OS** *020

NAGUABO – NAGUABO

AGOSTO, Harvey. ■ 00718 #847-05-1970 L1973 **HEM PD** *020
ASTACIO ALMODOVAR, Maria. 36 CALLE 2, URB JUAN MENDOZA 00718 #042-04-1995 L1997 *020
CARRASQUILLO-REYES, Jose. ■ 00718 #308-03-1978 L1981 **OS EM** *020
COLON, Mayra Milagros. ■ 00718 #042-03-1999 L2001 **ID** *100 †20
FELICIANO, Nereida I. ■ 00718 #042-01-1983 L1987 **P** *020
FLORES APONTE, Hector L. 36 CALLE GOYCO 00718 #308-03-1980 L1996 **GP** *020
LOPEZ-RODRIGUEZ, Harry. 1 CALLE VENECIA 00718 #308-03-1978 L1981 **PD** *020
MENDEZ, Carmen D. APT 176 00718 #042-04-1981 L1985 **GP** *020
MOJICA CRUZ, Sixto M. 70 CALLE LAUREL, JARD DEL ESTE 00718 #308-03-1981 L1991 **GP OM** *020
MONROIG, Francisco Javier. ■ 00718 #649-14-2001 L2002 **IM** *100
RIVAS, Amaris R.. ■ 00718 #042-01-2005 **PD** *012
RODRIGUEZ, Marangely. ■ 00718 #649-14-2003 **GP** *020
ROSADO, Heriberto. PO BOX 176 00718 #847-13-1980 L1984 *100
VALLE OLIVERAS, Jose W. PO BOX 548 00718 #042-04-1995 L1996 *020

NARANJITO – NARANJITO

ALICEA-ORTIZ, Ramon. HC 71 BOX -3766, 152 BO CEDRO ARR 10 RD 00719 #308-03-1981 L1982 **GP** *020
ARROYO, Ruy Dan. ■ 00719 #042-01-1975 L1979 **P GP** *071
BURGOS PABON, Aurea D. ■ 00719 #042-04-1994 L1995 **GP** *020
CRESPO, Juan Manuel. ■ 00719 #308-03-1983 L1986 **GP** *020
HERNANDEZ, Maria Del C. PO BOX 372, 73 CALLE IGNACIO MORALES 00719 #042-04-1984 L1986 **FM** *020
MESA, Orestes Santiuste. CENTRO DE SALUD 00719 #275-01-1942 L1972 **IM GP** *020
MOLINA-NIEVES, Eddie W. ■ 00719 #308-03-1980 L1985 *100
MORALES-TORRES, Yanira. ■ 00719 #042-01-1997 L2000 **EM** *020 †16
NARVAEZ NARVAEZ, Carmen B. HC 73 BOX 5793, 0.3 CARR 164 00719 #649-01-1970 L1974 **PD** *020
NAZARIO, Jorge. 42 CALLE GEORGETTI, NARANJITO, PR 00719 #308-04-1984 L1990 **GP** *020
NOVA, Miguel Angel. 30 CALLE GEORGETTI 00719 #308-01-1972 L1979 **FM** *020 ‡
RAMOS-RAMOS, Luis Alberto. CARR 164 KM 5 1 00719 #042-04-1994 L1999 *020
REATEGUI, Melito. 73 CALLE GEORGETTI STE 1 00719 #737-09-1987 L2005 **GP** *020
RIVERA, Clara L. CARR 164 EL DESVIO 00719 #649-14-1983 L1986 **GP** *020
RIVERA, Marimer. ■ 00719 #649-14-2003 L2005 *100
RIVERA BERRIOS, Juan J.. ■ 00719 #649-14-2001 L2003 *020
RODRIGUEZ, Ismael. PO BOX 930, 47 GEORGETTI 00719 #042-01-1992 L1995 **IM** *020
RODRIGUEZ FIGUEROA, Luz Z. PO BOX 386 00719 #042-04-2002 L2003 *100
RODRIGUEZ RODRIGUEZ, Evely. HC 71 BOX 1475 00719 #042-04-2002 L2003 *100

OROCOVIS – OROCOVIS

APONTE, Jose S. 4 CALLE PEDRO ARROYO 00720 #308-03-1984 L1988 **GP** *020
BERRIOS, Antonio Oscar. PO BOX 2120, 288 CARRETERA 155 # 133 00720 #308-03-1981 L1984 *020
CESTERO VARGAS, Aida Luz. ■ 00720 #308-03-1982 L1985 **GP** *020
GONZALEZ, Manuel F. ■ 00720 #042-01-1990 L1995 **DR** *020 †80
GUTIERREZ, Domingo G. 16 CALLE 4 DE JULIO, UPPR 00720 #847-05-1972 L1975 **OBG** *020
MARRERO BURGOS, Francis E. PO BOX 1235 00720 #649-30-2003 L2005 *100
MELENDEZ, Jorge David. PO BOX 986 00720 #042-01-2005 **IM** *012
MONTES BURGOS, Gloria M. 16 AVE LUIS M MARIN 00720 #308-03-1979 L1981 **GP** *020
OTERO, Carlos M. C/O P.O. BOX 2105, AVE LUIS MUNOZ MARIN #2 00720 #042-01-1984 L1987 **FM** *020
POLANCO SOTO, Romualdo. SALIDA A PORAMO 71 00720 #308-01-1969 L1975 *020
RIVERA, Javier. ■ 00720 #308-03-1979 L1981 *020
RIVERA, Nelson E. 16 CALLE 4 DE JULIO, UPPR 00720 #847-05-1978 L1980 **GP** *020
RODRIGUEZ, Carlos E. 5 CALLE LUIS M ALFARO, P O BOX 867-8085 00720 #308-04-1991 L1995 *020
RODRIGUEZ, Eulogio. ■ 00720 #847-04-1956 L1958 *020
RODRIGUEZ, Luis Francisco. 2 CALLE DR UMPIERRE 00720 #308-04-1988 L1992 **FM** *020
SOLIVAN-ROLON, Elinor. ■ 00720 #649-01-1955 L1955 **GP** *062

PALMER – RIO GRANDE

ORTIZ, Carmen Yaismar. PO BOX 374 00721 #649-34-2002 L2006 *100

PATILLAS – PATILLAS

ARROYO-PLAUD, Marta S. BO MARIN BAJO APTO 524 00723 #308-03-1977 L1979 **GP** *071
AYALA-ORTIZ, Francisco. 15 CALLE ALBERTO RICCI 00723 #308-03-1985 L1991 **GP** *020 ‡
BAEZ, Carlos M. ■ 00723 #308-06-1987 L1995 **FM** *020
BERNIER RIVERA, Rosa Ilia. #1 A-26, URB SAN BENITO 00723 #308-04-2001 L2004 *100
BORRERO, Heriberto. ■ 00723 #308-06-1984 L1996 **PD** *020
CINTRON BAERGA, Idamer. A-21, URB SAN BENITO 00723 #649-30-2002 L2004 **GP** *020
DAVILA CINTRON, Joaquin. 2 CALLE CRISTO 00723 #308-03-1983 L1990 **GP** *020
DIAZ, Santiago Santiago. 99 CALLE GUILLERMO RIEFKHL 00723 #847-06-1978 L1980 **GP** *020
GARCIA, Arturo. PO BOX 697, DE SALUD DE PATILLAS, INC 00723 #007-02-1957 L1958 **GP OBS** *071
GARCIA-FELICIANO, Arturo. PO BOX 697, CSF PATILLAS 00723 #649-14-1995 L1997 **GP** *020
GONZALEZ, Manuel. ■ 00723 #847-02-1984 L1991 **GP** *050
LATALLADI, Graciela. ■ 00723 #042-03-2004 **IM** *100 †20
LEBRON, Vivian N. ■ 00723 #308-06-1984 L1996 **PD** *020
LEBRON-RIVERA, Milton. ■ 00723 #042-04-1980 L1982 **PD** *020
LIZARRAGA, Esteban O.. ■ 00723 #042-01-1975 L1984 **FM** *020
MARTINEZ, Heriberto. ■ 00723 #042-03-1993 L1996 **OPH** *020
NIEVES-CRUZ, Nancy. ■ 00723 #308-06-1982 L1985 **IM EM** *020
RAMOS CEDENO, Daphne. H-C BUZON 8544 HC-764 00723 #042-04-1998 L2000 **FM** *020

RIVERA, Andres. PO BOX 103 00723 #042-04-1989 L1991 **P** *020
RIVERA, Marina Eugenia. ■ 00723 #042-01-1981 L1985 **N** *020 †75
RIVERA-POMALES, Luis A. 4 CALLE SANTIAGO IGLESIAS 00723 #308-03-1985 L1986 **IM** *020
ROBLES-BERNIER, Efigenia. ■ 00723 #847-02-1961 L1963 **PM** *075
RODRIGUEZ-POMBAR, Miriam. ■ 00723 #847-09-1980 L1983 *020
SANTIAGO-PEREZ, Maria D. ■ 00723 #042-01-1970 L1972 **PD** *020
VAZQUEZ, Migdoel. BO CACAO BAJO, APT 1319 00723 #308-03-1982 L1986 **GP** *020

PENUELAS – PENUELAS

BONILLA, Onix. HC 1, BOX 12762 00624 #042-02-1999 L2002 **IM** *020 †20
COLBERG-COMAS, Wallace A. DE GRACIA, CALLE-GILBERTO CONCEPCION 00624 #847-10-1962 L1971 **GP** *020
COLON DE JESUS, Lydia E. PO BOX 88 00624 #308-03-1985 L1991 *100
ECHEVARRIA, Ileana Del Ca. PO BOX 999 00624 #649-34-2002 L2004 *100
FELICIANO, Marco A. 44 PENUELAS VALLEY 00624 #042-01-1988 L1991 **IM** *020 †20
FELICIANO-PEREZ, Jose A. HC 2 BOX 861, 159 BO CARACOLES 00624 #649-14-1980 L1984 **IM** *020
FRANQUI, Wilson. 703 CALLE AMALIA MARIN 00624 #042-01-1972 L1974 **PD** *020 †55 ‡
GARCIA COLON, Rafael A. PO BOX 609, 807 LUIS M RIV 00624 #847-06-1976 L1978 **GP** *020
GRANA CASANOVA, Alberto A. ■ 00624 #649-01-1955 L1957 **PD ADL** *020
GREENBERG, Jeffrey M. U3 CALLE 7, ALT DE PENUELAS II 00624 #042-02-1995 L2002 **OBG** *012
LEFEBRE, Amedee. 503 CALLE MUNOZ RIVERA 00624 #649-14-1992 L1994 **IM** *020
LUGO-BONETA, Adalberto. ■ 00624 #308-03-1979 L1989 **PD** *020
LUGO VELAZQUEZ, Josue. ■ 00624 #649-14-2002 L2004 *100
MALDONADO, Pura Maria. Q25 CALLE 16, ALT DE PENUELAS II 00624 #308-01-1986 L1990 **PD** *020
MILANES, Anthony. PO BOX 789, M8 BO MACANA K M 6 H 00624 #042-03-1988 L1990 **IM** *020
MONTALVO, Lizzette. U3 CALLE 7, ALT DE PENUELAS II 00624 #649-14-1991 L1994 **FM** *020
OCTAVIANI, Raul. ■ 00624 #308-03-1978 L1980 **IM** *020
OLIVERAS, Jofgrek. 24 CALLE 2, URB PENUELAS VALLEY 00624 #649-14-2002 *020
OLIVER SEDA, Anibal L. 418 CALLE MUNOZ RIVERA 00624 #847-06-1973 L1977 *020
ORENGO SOLER, Hilda Milag. ■ 00624 #308-03-2002 L2004 *100
ORTIZ-COTTI, Wilson. 703 CALLE AMALIA MARIN 00624 #308-03-1981 L1985 **GE** *020 †20
PANELLI-RAMERY, Jose E. CALLE PENUELAS VALLEY #11 00624 #649-38-1985 L1993 **PD** *020
RUIZ RODRIGUEZ, Eric John. 18I33ALTURAS DE PENUELAS 00624 #308-03-1980 L1994 *020
SANTIAGO, Eric. ■ 00624 #308-06-1987 L1997 *020
SANTIAGO, Maritza. ■ 00624 #042-02-1993 L2002 **P** *020 †75
SANTOS, Kiyomi Maria. 404 CALLE MUNOZ RIVERA 00624 #308-03-1980 L1986 **GP** *020
SIERRA GONZALEZ, Carlos. URB MONTE VERDE #21 00624 #649-14-1991 L1994 **GP** *020
TARAFA, Edgardo. URB MONTE VERDE 19 00624 #649-14-1999 L2001 **FM** *020
VEGA-GILORMINI, Miguel A. PEDRO VELAZQUEZ #628, EDIFICIO AURORA 00624 #042-03-1988 L1992 **OBG** *020 †30
VELAZQUEZ, Elba. BO MACANA 00624 #308-03-1983 L1991 **GP** *020

PONCE – PONCE

ABREU-RIVERA, Alberto. 4844 CALLE LUNA 00717 #847-04-1962 L1964 **NS OS** *020 †25
ACEVEDO, Jacquline Eunice. ■ 00717 #042-02-2005 **IM** *012
ACEVEDO NEGRON, Lorieva. ■ 00716 #308-02-2003 L2005 *100
ACEVEDO-PEREZ, Idali. ■ 00717 #847-05-1974 L1977 **IM IMG** *071
ACEVEDO QUINONES, Maribel. 33 GG-33 00728 #042-04-2000 L2002 **FM** *020
ACOSTA, Luis Alberto. 8129 CALLE CONCORDIA, STE 4A EDIF CONCORDIA 00717 #042-02-1996 L2001 **OBG** *020
ADAMS REYES, Juan B. 4 CALLE VIVES # 108 00730 #308-01-1974 L1997 *020
AGOSTINI RODRIGUEZ, Evelyn. 445 CALLE JUAN H CINTRON, EST DEL GOLF CLUB 00730 #649-14-1993 L1998 *100
AGOSTO MUJICA, Marielba. ■ 00717 #649-14-2002 L2004 **END** *012 †20
ALAYON-ANTA, Gerardo. 2520 CALLE OBISPADO, JARD FAGOT 00716 #042-04-1985 L1988 **CD** *020
ALBARRAN-PORTILLA, Marco. A94 CALLE MARGINAL 00716 #649-01-1974 L1981 **IM OS** *030
ALBORS, Melanie Marie. 909 AVE TITO CASTRO, STE 613 00716 #042-02-1999 L2000 **IM** *020 †20
ALCALA-OCASIO, Diego J. 75 CALLE VIVES 00730 #847-06-1975 L1980 **PD** *020
ALCAZAR, Jose A. 7309 CALLE RAMON POWER 00717 #042-01-1986 L1989 **FM** *020 †18
ALENO MERCADO, Ashie N.. 434 CALLE JACOBO MORALES, EST DEL GOLF CLUB 00730 #649-14-1998 L2003 *100
ALMODOVAR, Evelyn Sakorn. 2907 AVE EMILIO FAGOT 00716 #649-14-2000 L2003 **FM** *020
ALMODOVAR, William. 2162 AVE LAS AMERICAS, VILLA GRILLASCA 00717 #042-02-2001 L2005 **IM** *100
ALSINA-CAPO, Manuel F. 31 CALLE CONCORDIA, EDIFICIO PROFESSIONEL 00717 #041-09-1944 L1949 **U** *071 †95
ALTAMIRANO, Alvaro Jose. 7309 CALLE RAMON POWER 00717 #682-03-1996 **FP** *012
ALVARADO, Luisa Idalia. AVENIDA LAS AMERICAS 00731 #042-01-1975 L1977 **PD** *030 †55
ALVARADO SANTOS, Ana I. ■ 00730 #649-14-1990 L1993 **FM** *020
ALVAREZ, Nelson. 917 AVE TITO CASTRO, P O BOX 336810 00716 #275-01-1995 **OBG** *020
ALVAREZ, Restituto R. BARRIO MACHUELO 00731 #275-01-1955 L1963 **DR OS** *020 †80
ALVAREZ-COLON, Gilberto. ■ 00716 #042-01-1996 L1998 **PD** *020
ALVAREZ RAMIREZ, Flavio E. ■ 00716 #010-02-1946 L1950 **P** *071 †75
ALVAREZ-SANTIAGO, P E. 2916 AVE FAGOT, STE 1 00716 #649-14-1983 L1986 **NEP IM** *020
ALVERIO, Carlos Manuel, Jr. ■ 00716 #042-02-2007 *012
AMADOR, Pedro Juan. 8118 CALLE CONCORDIA # 210, GALERIA PROFESIONAL 00717 #042-02-1997 L2001 **IM** *020 ‡
AMARO, Mirna. BO MACHUELO, DEPT PED 00731 #308-03-1984 L1991 **PD** *020
AMY, Eduardo. PO BOX 7401 00732 #042-01-1975 L1981 **ORS** *020 †40
ANAYA AMALBERT, Blas. 41 INT. CONCORDIA STREET 00731 #847-10-1966 L1968 **IM** *020
ANCA-VAZQUEZ, Yadira Ayle. ■ 00730 #042-02-2007 **OBG** *012
ANDUJAR, Alex Daniel. 7309 CALLE RAMON POWER, SCH OF 00717 #042-03-2003 **FP** *012
ANGLERO ALFARO, Jorge G. 1243 AVE MUNOZ RIVERA, VILLA GRILLASCA 00717 #649-14-1992 L1994 **IM** *020
ANTOMMATTEI, Osvaldo. 1211 AVE MUNOZ RIVERA, VILLA GRILLASCA 00717 #042-01-1978 L1981 **RHU IM** *020 †20

ANTONMATTEI Y MARIANI, R. EX QUIT MOUSER CALLE 5 137 00730 #056-06-1944 L1946 GP OS *020

ANTUNEZ ESTEBAN, Gilberto. 134 CALLE UNION 00730 #847-10-1961 L1965 GP FM *020

APARICIO-COLON, Juan. PONCE REG HOSP 00731 #042-04-1981 L1986 PD *020

APONTE-DE RODRIGUEZ, Elba. 43 CALLE VIRTUD BOX 1067 00730 #847-10-1964 L1973 P CHP *020

APONTE-RIVERA, Hector. ■ 00716 #308-03-1981 L1986 OBG *020

ARCHEVALD, Carlos L. BOX 445 00733 #847-04-1957 L1960 AN *020

AREVALO-ARCEO, Amaury A. 708 CALLE FERROCARRIL # 10 00717 #275-01-1957 L1976 IM *020

ARMSTRONG, Raul A. PONCE BYPASS AVE, PARRA BLDG STE 705 00731 #021-01-1951 L1953 GS CRS *040 †10,85

AROCHO, Maricelis. CALLE 24 W-5PUNTO ORO 00731 #308-04-1988 L1993 *020

AROCHO-MARTINEZ, Victor F. 7Q13 CALLE, EXT SAN ANTONIL 00731 #042-03-1988 L1993 FM *020

ARROYO, Axel. 2213 PONCE BY PASS 00717 #042-03-1988 L1994 PTH *020

ARROYO, Jose Perez. ST 3 NO 440 EXT LA RAMBLA 00731 #649-14-1986 L1989 PD *020

ARROYO NODUI, Herbert A. ■ 00730 #649-14-1982 L1992 *020

ARZOLA, Fernando Jose. ■ 00716 #649-14-2002 *020

ARZOLA, Gladys E. HOSP ONCOLOGICO, BOX 7439, ANEXO #4 00731 #042-03-1981 L1987 ID IM *020

AVILES-GARCIA, Amarilis. CALLE 6 G-5, URB JARDINES FAGOT 00717 #649-14-2004 IM *020 †20

AVILES TORO, Victor M. JOBOS 33 BOX 1406 00717 #847-04-1960 L1964 GS *020

AYALA, Eddie. PO BOX 32278 00732 #042-01-1973 L1975 GS *020

AYALA, Jaime. ■ 00716 #308-03-2001 L2004 *100

BABB, Donald Ferguson. HOSPITAL DE DAMAS 00731 #051-04-1941 L1946 PTH *020 †50

BAEZ, Santiago. ■ 00731 #042-02-1991 L1994 CD *020

BAEZ, Wanda Ivette. 7309 CALLE RAMON POWER 00717 #649-14-1988 L1990 FM *020 †18

BAEZ-COLON, Sonia J. ■ 00730 #042-02-1997 L1999 FM *020 †18

BALDIT, Carlos A. 917 AVE TITO CASTRO 00716 #649-30-1992 PD *012

BALLESTEROS, Maria Del C. 8169 CALLE CONCORDIA # 212, CONDOMINIO SAN VICENTE 00717 #042-01-1987 L1990 RHU IM *020 †20

BANCHS, Maria. 4981 CALLE PELTADA, JARD DEL CARIBE 5 00728 #042-02-1996 L1998 FM *020 †18

BANCHS SEDA, Ruben C.. ■ 00716 #649-14-2003 L2006 *100

BANUCHI RIOS, Cynthia M. 2328 CALLE BARCELONA, URB LA RAMBLA 00730 #649-14-1990 L1994 FM *020

BARNES, Francisco Jose. C-47 EL MONTE 00731 #308-01-1952 L1957 D *071

BARRANCO, Luis A. 2371 AVE LAS AMERICAS 00717 #847-04-1956 L1958 GS TRS *071

BARRANCO-SMEGO, Elizabeth. 280 CALLE MONTERREY, PSM - CAIMED CENTER 00716 #042-03-1982 L1997 ID IM *050

BARTOLOMEI SANTAELLA, R. 8133 CALLE CONCORDIA, STE 102 00717 #649-01-1953 L1954 A PUD *020

BASORA DE GARCIA, G. CONCORDIA 43 STE 310 00731 #847-04-1957 L1960 PTH *020

BATISTA, Jose. 2431 AVE LAS AMERICAS, PORRATA PILA BLD SUITE 211 00717 #042-02-1983 L1985 IM *020

BAUZA-HERNANDEZ, Antonio. ■ 00716 #847-04-1954 L1956 DR *072 †80

BENITEZ, Pedro Luis. A8 CALLE D, URB JACARANDA 00730 #042-01-1974 L1981 IM GP *020 †20 ‡

BENITEZ COLLAZO, Victor. 801 EDIF PARRAS, STE 801 00717 #847-10-1992 L1995 IM *020

BERMUDEZ, Rosa Hilda. ■ 00716 #042-02-2003 OBG *012

BERMUDEZ CABA, Andres D. 303 TORRES SAN CRISTOBAL, COTO LAUREL 00780 #308-04-1986 L1995 IM *020

BERMUDEZ-RUIZ, Gamalier. 9179 CALLE MARINA 00717 #847-08-1974 L1976 IM *020

BERNASCHINA, Claudio P. 2225 PONCE BY PASS, EDIFICIO PARRASUITE 902-90 00717 #042-01-1992 L1997 U *020 †95

BERNIER GONZALEZ, Larry E. CALLE MARINA ESQ FERROCAR 00732 #308-06-1983 L2000 FM *020

BERRIOS, Tamara. 1014 PASEO REAL, VALLE VERDE 00716 #649-14-1999 L2001 GP *020

BISONO BIDO, Juana Dolore. 430 CALLE RUISENOR, URB CAMINO DEL SUR 00716 #042-04-1983 L2002 *020

BLANCO, Jose Angel. 2060 CALLE COLINA, VALLE ALTO 00730 #847-03-1979 L1990 GP *020

BLANCO, Malynie Delmarie. ■ 00730 #042-02-1997 L2001 FM *030 †18

BLASINI, Yvonne Magali. 1484 PASEO FAGOT, JARD FAGOT 00716 #042-01-1979 L1981 PD *020 †55

BOLANOS-AVILA, Guillermo. 909 AVE TITO CASTRO, STE 723 00716 #341-01-1984 L1994 GS TRS *020 †85

BONILLA-COLON, Jorge. 11 CALLE A 00730 #649-01-1954 L1959 ORS OP *072 †40

BORRERO CUELLO, Karla Mic. ■ 00730 #042-04-2005 L2006 *100

BORRERO DE JESUS, Samuel. 1335 CALLE PDR SANTIAGO GR, VILLA RIO CANAS 00728 #308-03-1983 L1995 GP *020

BOSWELL-DE JESUS, Mary A. BARRIO MACHUELO 00731 #308-03-1979 L1980 PD *074

BRACER, William. PONCE BY PASS 00731 #042-01-1962 L1967 GS VS *072 †85

BRAVO, Alfredo A. 301C AVE TITO CASTRO, DW-222 00716 #042-02-1985 L1988 OBG *020

BRAVO-NONES, Alfredo. PO BOX 7468 00732 #847-04-1961 L1964 OM OS *030

BRETON, Hector Rafael. PO BOX 7364 00732 #308-01-1961 L1975 FM *071

BRIGNONI, Manuel Antonio. 8118 CALLE CONCORDIA, GALERIA PROFESIONAL SUITE 00717 #308-06-1983 L1990 P *020

BUONO-ALCARAZ, Juan. ■ 00732 #010-02-1971 L1974 P *020

BUONO-RUIZ, Ivelise. EXTENSION MARIANI A-94 00732 #649-31-1976 L1981 GP *020

BUSH, Henry Tatnall, III. ■ 00731 #308-11-1989 L1998 *020

BUSQUETS, Antonio R. 106 CALLE ATOCHA, BOX 1326 00730 #010-02-1942 L1989 PD OS *071 †55

BUSTILLO, Barbara. PO BOX 7003 00732 #308-03-1983 L1991 GP *020

CABRERA-URRUTIA, Isabel E. 1633 CALLE NAVARRA, URB LA RAMBLA 00730 #132-02-1981 L1987 NPM *020

CADIZ, Julio L. ■ 00716 #649-14-1995 L1997 *020

CALES-PRATICELLI, Xavier. H11 CALLE 12, JARD FAGOT 00716 #308-03-1982 L1987 GP *020

CAMACHO-LANDRON, Carlos A. 2431 AVE LAS AMERICAS # 30, EDIF-A-PORRATA-PILA 00717 #308-02-1989 L1993 PD *020

CAMPOS SANTIAGO, Carmen L. ■ 00716 #649-14-2003 L2005 GP *020

CANCEL, Jeanette. 2225 PONCE BY PASS, OFICINA 1004 00717 #042-02-1987 L1997 IM *020 †20

CANDAMO-ORTIZ, Juan R. 546 CALLE SIERVAS DE MARIA, LA RAMBIA 00730 #847-09-1971 L1973 U *020

CANDELARIO, Suzette. ■ 00716 #649-03-1987 L1989 PD *020

CANGIANO, Jose Alejandro. PO BOX 7105, PMB 595 00732 #042-02-1997 L1999 ON *020

CANNIZZARO, Johnny. 5 CALLE PABELLONES 00730 #847-03-1989 L1995 *020

CANNIZZARO, Joseph. 2060 CALLE COLINA, VALLE ALTO 00730 #847-03-1989 L1993 *020

CAPELLAN-GERMAN, Luis S. ■ 00717 #308-01-1960 L1982 GP *020

CAPESTANY, Roberto A. 9146 CALLE MARINA STE 102 00717 #649-01-1955 L1957 P *020

CAPLLONCH, Zoraida C. 1575 AVE MUNOZ RIVERA, STE 273 00717 #308-06-1988 L1992 IM *020

CAQUIAS, Abner Retamar. ■ 00731 #847-05-1973 L1978 GP *020

CARLO, Victor Manuel. PO BOX 390 00733 #042-01-1961 L1966 TS *020 †85,90

CARRERAS, Emma L. 8169 CALLE CONCORDIA # 211 00717 #042-02-1990 L1994 PM *020 †60

CARRERAS, Reinaldo Jose G. 8169 CALLE CONCORDIA, STE 210 00717 #847-04-1959 L1966 N IM *020

CARRO-PAGAN, Carlos J. 2545 AVE OBISPADO, URB ALHAMBRALUCAS 00716 #308-01-1978 L1983 CD IM *020

CARTAGENA, Edwin Coimbre. PONCE REG HOSP 00731 #308-04-1983 L1986 IM *020

CARTAGENA, Roberto. 108 CALLE MIGUEL RIVR TXDR, EST DEL GOLF CLUB 00730 #042-02-1998 L2001 IM *020 †20

CARTAGENA-MARTINEZ, A. CALLE 7 W #719, LA RAMBLE 00731 #847-01-1972 L1974 PD *071

CASALS SCOTT, Ana. 50 CALLE ISABEL 00730 #041-07-1949 L1955 OBG *071

CASANOVA, Antonio J. AVENIDA LAS AMERICAS 00731 #847-04-1958 L1960 GS *020

CASANOVA FELIX, Gwendolyn. 2213 PONCE BY PASS 00717 #308-04-2004 L2006 IM *012

CASTAING, Pedro Alberto. 63 CALLE VIVES 00730 #847-04-1963 L1965 OBG *020 †30

CASTA-VEGA, Yvonne O. 346 CALLE FALCON, URB CAMINO DEL SUR 00716 #847-06-1978 L1985 GP *020

CASTELLON, Jose Ernesto. ■ 00730 #649-14-1994 L1996 FM *020

CASTILLO, Candida M. BARRIO MACHUELO 00731 #042-04-1981 L1984 NPM PD *020

CASTILLO, Huascar E. 9113 CALLE MARINA # 9, EDIFICIO PONCE DARLINGTON 00717 #308-01-1967 L1971 CRS GS *020

CASTILLO, Javier, Jr. 609 AVE TITO CASTRO, STE 102 PMB 375 00716 #042-03-1980 L1986 U EM *020 †95

CASTROMARTINEZ, Laura Mer. ■ 00717 #042-02-2008 *012

CAYERE, Agustin. ■ 00730 #649-14-1995 L1997 *020

CEBOLLERO, Jose A. ■ 00716 #042-03-1981 L1988 SO GS *020

CEDENO, Ricardo. ■ 00716 #649-14-1998 L2004 *100

CERRA, Javier. 7106 CALLE DIVINA PROVIDNC, URB SANTA MARIA 00717 #042-02-1981 L1984 PM *020 †60

CHARDON, Domingo. 9140 CALLE MARINA, OFICINA 501 00717 #308-01-1985 L1988 PUD IM *020

CHARDON BURGOS, Raul. ■ 00728 #308-01-1977 L2001 *020

CHAVARRI, Maria Begona. 37 CALLE EL VIGIA, P O BOX 2004 00730 #847-05-1982 L1986 GP *020

CHAVES-MUNOZ, German. 3604 CALLE CUMBRE, URB EL MONTE 00716 #042-03-1981 L1982 DR *020 †80

CHAVEZ, Hernando Antonio. ■ 00716 #264-01-1994 L2002 FM *100

CHRISTIAN, Rafael. BO MACHUELO, DEPT PED 00731 #649-35-1986 L1991 PD *020

CID MANSUR, Fares Antonio. 609 AVE TITO CASTR PMB 383, STE 102 00716 #308-03-1983 L1992 CD *020

CINTRON, Kenneth O. 465 CALLE GAVIOTA, URB CAMINO DEL SUR 00716 #042-01-1990 L1995 ORS *020 †40

CINTRON-GARCIA, Miguel A. ■ 00731 #023-01-1944 L1989 OBG *020

CINTRON-LAFONTAINE, Daihan. 917 AVE TITO CASTRO, P O BOX 336810 00716 #042-03-2005 IM *012

CINTRON-ORTIZ, Heriberto. EDIF MORALES NO 2A CONCORD 00731 #649-01-1967 L1971 OTO GS *020

CINTRON-VILLARONGA, J R. 1326 CALLE SALUD, STE 304 00717 #042-01-1961 L1963 GYN *020 †30

CLAVELL, Ivan. PO BOX 1685 00733 #847-04-1954 L1956 OTO OS *071

CLAVELL, Yolanda Carmen. PO BOX 1685 00733 #042-02-1985 L1988 ID IM *020

CLAVELL-MAYORAL, Ulises M. AVENIDA LAS AMERICAS 00731 #847-10-1962 L1964 OBG *030

COFRESI, Heberto. 3505 CALLE LINARES, VALLE DE ANDALUCIA 00728 #649-03-1996 L1998 FM *020 †18

COLLAZO, Carmen I. 2213 PONCE BY PASS, PEDIATRIA-HOSPITAL DAMAS 5 00717 #042-01-1982 L1985 NPM PD *020 †55

COLLAZO, Margarita Rosa. 1681 PASEO VILLA FLORES, LORRAINE MEDICAL STE 202 00716 #042-02-1987 L1989 FM *020 †18

COLLAZO, Pedro Rafael. 46 CALLE MAYOR, P O BOX 5216 00730 #042-02-1996 L2000 FM *020

COLON, Alberto Manuel. 342 CALLE JUAN H CINTRON, EST DEL GOLF CLUB 00730 #042-03-1991 L1995 DR *020 †80

COLON, Carlos. ■ 00716 #042-03-1983 L1991 OSM GS *020 †40

COLON, Derick Enrique. 917 AVE TITO CASTRO, TORRE MEDICA SAN LUCAS STE 00716 #042-02-1994 L1998 PM *020 ‡

COLON, Felix Antonio. 11 CALLE CONCORDIA, CONDOMINIO CONCORDIA 00717 #042-01-1978 L1982 PD *020 †55

COLON, Jeannette Elise. ■ 00716 #042-02-2005 OBG *012

COLON-BONET, Juan. C20 CALLE VIRGO 00716 #035-15-1943 L1946 GS *071 †85

COLON BORRERO, Jose L.. ■ 00731 #308-04-2000 L2001 *100

COLON-GUZMAN, Carlos M. 19 CALLE EL VIGIA 00730 #847-03-1981 L1990 GP *020

COLON-IBANEZ, Ricardo Lui. C2 CALLE 3 JARD FAGOT 00716 #649-14-2001 L2005 *100

COLON PENA, Aristides. PO BOX 331910, AVENIDA LAS AMERICAS 00733 #649-14-2001 L2003 FP *012

COLON-PEREZ, Yvette C. F37 CALLE 3, URB SANTA MARIA 00717 #042-01-1994 L1997 PD *020 †55

COLON-RAMIREZ, Nelly. 1010 PASEO DEL VETERANO, PONCE VA OUTPATIENT CLINIC 00716 #042-02-1995 L1998 IM *020 †20

COLON-SANTIAGO, Doris. 101 CALLE REINA 00730 #847-16-1979 L1984 ON *020

CONCEPCION, Eugenio S, Jr. ■ 00716 #748-02-1964 L1968 TS *020

CONCEPCION, Maryrose G. ■ 00716 #649-14-1996 OBG *020

CORDERO, Rafael Alberto. ■ 00716 #042-02-2006 IM *012

CORDERO-JIMENEZ, Hector M. PO BOX 7386 00732 #847-06-1976 L1983 U *020 †95

CORTES, Carmen. E-7 MONSERRATE QUINTAS MNS 00731 #649-14-1993 L1998 IM *020

CORTES-TORRES, Vanessa. HC 9, HM7 BO TIBES 9 00731 #649-14-2001 L2004 *100

COTTO-MARTINEZ, Carmen R. 3169 AVE JULIO E MONAGAS, URB CONSTANCIA 00717 #308-03-1976 L1979 FOP P *020

COUTO SEPULVEDA, Jose R. 2225 PONCE BY PASS, EDIFICIO PARRA STE 801 00717 #847-06-1975 L1981 CD IM *020

COYA-VILLARAOS, Gloria. ■ 00732 #042-04-1989 L1992 **IM** *020

CREALES, Miguel Huascar. 92 CALLE SOL, ESQUINA TORRE 00730 #308-03-1987 L1994 **P** *020

CRUZ, Edgard Antonio. 2669 AVE LAS AMERICAS, URB CONSTANCIA 00717 #308-04-1991 L1992 **FM** *020

CRUZ, Eduardo Javier. ■ 00732 #042-03-2008 *012

CRUZ, Jose Rafael. ■ 00716 #042-01-1991 L1995 **APM** *020 †05

CRUZ, Lillian. ■ 00716 #042-01-1969 L1971 **DR OS** *020

CRUZ, Myriam Beatriz. 1913 CALLE ZARINA, VALLE REAL 00716 #649-14-1992 L1994 **IM** *020

CRUZ, Ricardo. 609 AVE TITO CASTRO, STE 102 PMB 306 00716 #042-02-1993 L1995 **AN** *020

CRUZ, Sara Enid. ■ 00717 #042-02-2006 L2007 **IM** *012

CRUZ-CORREA, Jesus. PO BOX 8981 00732 #308-03-1978 L1984 **OBG** *075 †30

CRUZ GARCIA, Cesar P. 917 AVE TITO CASTRO, SAN LUCAS 00716 #308-03-1984 L1986 **CD IM** *020

CRUZ LOPEZ, Pablo J.. PO BOX 7161 00732 #308-03-1999 L2003 *100

CRUZ LOPEZ, Victor M. CALLE 159, ESTANCIAS DEL GOLF 00730 #308-03-1999 L2003 *100

CRUZ PEREZ, Ignacio De Je. ■ 00730 #649-14-2001 L2005 *100

CRUZ-RIVERA, Jose. ALTA VISTA CALLE 16 O6 00731 #042-02-1993 L1998 **FM** *020

CUBILES-RICCA, Inara M. AVENIDA LAS AMER 16 ALTOS 00731 #847-02-1980 L1986 **GS** *020

CUMMINGS, Luis E, Jr. 909 AVE TITO CASTRO STE 5, HOSPITAL SAN LUCAS 00716 #042-01-1979 L1982 **AN** *020 †05 ‡

DE CASTRO, Pablo Jose. ■ 00716 #649-14-2002 L2003 *100

DE COLON, Carmen D Colon. PONCE DITRCT HSP, DEPT PED 00731 #847-04-1960 L1962 **PD OS** *020

DEFILLO-SUAZO, Fernando. MAYOR-2B 00731 #308-01-1972 L1975 **IM CD** *020

DE JESUS, Carlos Ivan. PO BOX 7478, DEL VETERANO C/O PO 00732 #042-03-1985 L1991 **P** *020

DE JESUS, Daniel Edgardo. PO BOX 7004, PONCE MED SCH 00732 #042-02-1995 L1999 **FM** *020

DE JESUS, Reynaldo. 8118 CALLE CONCORDIA, STE 210 00717 #042-01-1998 L1999 **NS** *020

DE JESUS, Tomas. JACARANDA F ST NO A 27 00731 #042-01-1973 L1975 **U** *020 †95

DEJESUSGOMEZ, Gustavo A. ■ 00730 #042-01-2002 **GS** *012

DELANOY SUAREZ, Andres M.. ■ 00716 #042-04-2003 L2005 *100

DELGADO-AYALA, Rosa. 917 AVE TITO CASTRO, CLINICA INMUNOLOGIA REGION 00716 #264-05-1974 L1975 **PD PDI** *020 †55

DELGADO-MEJIAS, Edgardo. PONCE DISTRICT HOSP, DEPT SURG 00731 #308-03-1978 L1979 **GS** *020

DELGADO-MOURA, Janitza. 152 RES SANTIAGO IGLESIAS 00730 #042-02-1996 L1999 **IM** *020

DELGADO PONS, Seidy Idali. ■ 00730 #649-14-2003 L2005 *100

DEL PRADO-ESCOVAR, Ramon. 1591 AVE MUNOZ RIVERA, STE 1 00717 #308-02-1976 L1983 **NS** *020

DEL TORO, Emilio. 3348 CALLE DONA JUANA, VISTA POINT 00716 #042-01-1976 L1982 **CD EM** *020 †20

DEL TORO, Sally. ■ 00731 #042-02-1992 L1996 *020

DIAZ, Carlos Gilberto. 2431 AVE LAS AMERICAS, STE 303 00717 #042-01-1989 L1996 **P** *020 †75

DIAZ, Eddie Gerardo. Z16 CALLE 21, URB PUNTO ORO 00730 #042-02-1996 **PTH** *100

DIAZ, Leila Nannette. ■ 00717 #042-02-2000 **PN** *100 †55

DIAZ, Miriam Esther. ■ 00717 #649-14-2001 *100

DIAZ, Nelson Carlos. 138 CALLE 20, JARD DEL CARIBE 00728 #649-14-1999 L2002 *020

DIAZ-BAEZ, Nadja Milagros. 7813 CALLE NAZARET, URB SANTA MARIA 00717 #042-02-1996 L1998 **IM** *020 †20

DIAZ-BAEZ, Soria Lara. ■ 00728 #649-14-1999 L1999 **FM** *020

DIAZ-BORROTO, Oscar R. C/O PO BOX 7822, 2431 AVE LAS AMERICAS 00732 #847-06-1977 L1979 **IM** *020

DIAZ CORTINAS, Rolando. 2621 AVE LAS AMERICAS, URB CONSTANCIA 00717 #275-02-1983 L2002 *020

DIAZ-LOPEZ, Hector Ivan. ■ 00730 #308-03-1980 L1994 **OBG FM** *020

DI MARCO, Anna Maria. ■ 00730 #308-13-2003 **IM** *012

DOBJANSCHI, Sebastian A. 917 AVE TITO CASTRO 00716 #781-04-1991 *100

DOMENECH, Edgar E, Jr. ■ 00716 #042-02-1993 **OTO** *020 †45

DOMINGUEZ ROMERO, Neiza M. PO BOX 8188 00732 #308-13-2001 L2005 *100

DORRINGTON-CUADRA, Elsie. PO BOX 330003 00733 #042-01-1959 L1962 **PD** *071 †55

ECHEVARRIA, Miguel A. 1326 CALLE SALUD STE 105, EL SENORIAL PLZ 00717 #847-06-1976 L1981 **DR** *020

ECHEVARRIA-VARGAS, Alexis. 2933 AVE EMILIO FAGOT 00716 #042-01-1980 L1985 **PM** *020

ECUYER, Jean Paul. ■ 00732 #041-15-2003 L2007 **ACA** *012

ENRIZO, Orlando Caridad. ■ 00717 #042-02-2007 **TY** *012

ESTEBAN MALARET, Rebeca. ■ 00728 #649-14-1999 L2001 *020

FALCON, Jorge L. 503 CALLE LUIS A MORALES 00730 #042-02-2000 L2003 **EM** *020 †16

FEBLES, Vidal A. PO BOX 7443 00732 #042-04-1982 L1988 **GP** *020

FEBO, Marta. 7309 CALLE RAMON POWER 00717 #042-03-1980 L1984 **FM** *040 †18

FELICIANO, Walter. ■ 00732 #649-14-2004 **IM** *040 †20

FELICIANO-NIEVES, Sonia. 1009S EL SENORL PLZ #1009S 00717 #649-01-1971 L1973 **IM** *020

FELIPE, Ivette. 917 AVE TITO CASTRO, P O BOX 336810 00716 #275-01-1990 L2006 **PD** *100 †55

FELIX, Pedro R. ■ 00716 #308-03-1984 L1987 *020

FERNANDEZ, Blanca. 7309 CALLE RAMON POWER, SCH OF 00717 #042-02-2004 **FP** *012

FERNANDEZ, Eliot M. ■ 00716 #308-01-1961 L1974 **PD** *071

FERNANDEZ, Madeline. 2431 AVE LAS AMERICAS, STE 311 00717 #308-03-1984 L1995 **FM** *020 †18

FERNANDEZ AMARAT, Mayra E. A-C CALLE 8, JARDINES DE PONCE 00730 #649-14-2003 L2006 **GP** *100

FERNANDEZ DURAN, Antonio. PONCE BY PASS 00731 #016-43-1945 L1986 **CD IM** *072 †20

FERNANDEZ-GONZALEZ, D. 1203 AVE MUNOZ RIVERA, VILLA GRILLASCA 00717 #042-02-1986 L1989 **PD** *020

FERNANDEZ TAMAYO, Maria E. 2225 PONCE BYP, EDIFICIO PARRA #405 00717 #308-03-1984 L1992 **OBG** *020 †30

FERRERIS CORDERO, R, Jr. PO BOX 5028 00733 #847-09-1957 L1962 **GP** *020

FERRES, Angel Romulo. 3224 CALLE URSULA CARDONA, URB LAS DELICIAS 00728 #308-01-1967 L1977 **IM CD** *020

FERRES, Millie Anne. ■ 00728 #042-02-2006 **OBG** *012

FIGUEROA, Gladysmaria. PO BOX 10419 00732 #649-14-1997 L1999 *020

FIGUEROA-CEDENO, Sonia En. 375 CALLE VICTORIA 00730 #649-14-2004 *100

FIGUEROA GORDIAN, Jeannett. ■ 00716 #649-14-2003 *020

FIGUEROA HOGUES, Fanny G. 935 CALLE ARBOLEDA, VALLE VERDE 00716 #308-03-1976 L1978 **GP** *020

FIGUEROA MUNIZ, Edgardo. 2213 PONCE BY PASS 00717 #308-03-1985 L2005 *100

FINCH, Ana Delia. 4227 CALLE AGUSTIN DAVIU, URB PERLA DEL SUR 00717 #042-04-1983 L1985 **PDC OS** *020

FLORES, Hector L. 2005 CALLE EXTREMADURA, URB LA RAMBLA 00730 #308-03-1982 L1990 **PD** *020

FLORES, Rebeca. PONCE BY PASS 00731 #042-03-1989 L1990 **CD DIA** *020

FLORES, Roberto. BO MACHUELO, DEPT PED 00731 #308-04-1989 L1991 **PD** *020

FLORES CARDONA, Hector D. ■ 00716 #308-03-1982 L1993 **PD** *020

FLORES SANTANA, Hermes. CON ESQ J EDIFICIO MORALES 00731 #042-01-1963 L1967 **EM IM** *020

FONTANELLA, Antonio Rafae. 2213 PONCE BY PASS 00717 #275-01-1988 L2006 **IM** *020 †20

FORNARIS, Abner Jose. ■ 00733 #847-04-1970 L1975 **PD** *071

FRANCO, Heberto Augusto A. JARDNES FAGOT I 11 CALL 12 00731 #847-04-1962 L1965 **AN** *071

FRATICELLI, Victor. 9140 CALLE MARINA, LOCAL 1-4 00717 #308-03-1982 L1985 **IM** *020

FUENTES-FIGUEROA, Hernan. 1675 PASEO LAS COLONIAS, VISTA ALEGRE 00717 #042-03-2000 L2001 **OBG** *020

FUERTES, Jose M. GUADALUPE ST 00731 #847-05-1965 L1969 **IM** *020

GALANO, Luis. GUADALUPE ST 00731 #275-01-1960 L1977 **ORS** *075

GAONA, Carlos Arturo. 1214 AVE MUNOZ RIVERA, REPTO UNIVERSITARIO 00717 #264-01-1982 L2000 **IM** *020

GAONA LEON, Diana Pilar. ■ 00717 #264-11-1999 L2003 **GP** *020

GAONA-REYES, Jaime E. ■ 00730 #264-01-1978 L2003 **GP** *020

GARCIA, Ashley De Jesus. 1326 CALLE SALUD, STE 316 00717 #308-03-1982 L2002 *020

GARCIA, Jose A. 8129 CALLE CONCORDIA, STE 201 00717 #847-08-1974 L1977 **OBG** *020

GARCIA, Jose Milton. MIRAMAR HOUSING II B6, APT 96 00731 #042-02-1997 L1998 **IM** *100 †20

GARCIA-BARRETO, Luis A. 450 CALLE FERROCARRIL, SANTA MARIA MED BLDG #126 00717 #042-02-1990 L1995 **PUD** *020

GARCIA MOLINER, Lucio. EXT LA RAMBLA, G-6-E #552 00731 #847-04-1956 L1960 **IM** *071

GARCIA MONTES DE OCA, C E. BOX 789 00733 #275-01-1952 L1958 **GP** *071

GARCIA PENA, Anette. PO BOX 330191, 21 CASA YAUCO PR 009698 00733 #308-04-1993 L1996 *100

GARCIA-RAMOS, Carlos H. ■ 00716 #847-04-1963 L1968 **AN** *071 †05

GARCIA REYES, Luis F. CALLE C-A51 URB VALLE REAL 00716 #847-01-1959 L1961 **GS** *020 †85

GARCIA-TORRES, Wanda R. PONCE BY PASS 00731 #042-01-1981 L1984 **PD** *020

GERENA, Luis. GUADALUPE ST 00731 #649-14-1977 L1980 **PM** *020 †60

GHIGLIOTTI, Luis Domingo. ■ 00717 #042-02-1993 L1996 **IM** *020

GIANNONI MOLINA, Anibal A. ■ 00730 #308-10-1983 L2004 *100

GILES, Richard Kirk. 4132 CALLE AURORA STE 101 00717 #042-01-1971 L1974 **CD IM** *020

GODOY LOPEZ, Marco A. 1663 CALLE MARQUESA, VALLE REAL 00716 #649-14-1989 L1993 **EM GS** *020

GOMEZ, Jose. 2275 PONCE BY PASS, STE 103 00717 #042-02-1988 L1991 **CD IM** *020 †20

GOMEZ, Pastor. 1110 CALLE VILLA, STE 102 00728 #649-35-1993 L1996 **PD VS** *020

GOMEZ CORDOBA, Gerardo A. 609 AVE TITO CASTRO STE 1, PMB 257 00716 #649-14-1993 L1996 **GP** *020

GOMEZ RODRIGUEZ, Angel M. Y11 CALLE 28, JARD DEL CARIBE 00728 #042-04-2001 L2002 *020

GONZALEZ, Eugenio E. ■ 00716 #847-06-1979 L1990 *020

GONZALEZ, Jenniffer Marie. ■ 00730 #042-03-2006 **EM** *012

GONZALEZ, Marcos A. 316 EL SENORIAL PLZ, SALUD ST NO 10 00717 #847-01-1964 L1967 **OBG** *071

GONZALEZ, Max Ramos. PO BOX 7252 00732 #308-01-1975 **AN IM** *020

GONZALEZ, Miguel Angel. ■ 00728 #649-14-2001 L2003 *100

GONZALEZ, Quintin. 301C AVE TITO CASTRO, STE 368 00716 #264-18-1984 L1991 **AN** *020

GONZALEZ, Renier David. 7309 CALLE RAMON POWER 00717 #308-04-1981 L1985 **FM** *020

GONZALEZ, Roberto. PONCE BY PASS 00731 #042-01-1977 L1982 **OTO** *020 †45

GONZALEZ, Yolanda Esther. 1113 AVE MUNOZ RIVERA, VILLA GRILLASCA 00717 #042-02-1987 L1990 **OBG** *020 †30

GONZALEZ-AGRONT, Nelida. VILLA DE JUAN APT 8 00731 #847-04-1977 L1979 **IM CD** *020 †20

GONZALEZ-ALTIERY, Daniela. 4021 CALLE CARLOS CARTAGEN, COND PLAZA DEL SUR 9-C 00717 #847-08-1977 L1980 **IM GP** *020

GONZALEZ-BERDECIA, Carlos. ■ 00717 #308-03-1979 L1983 **GP FM** *020

GONZALEZ CRUZ, Juan. CALLE M NUM307 00731 #042-04-1992 L1996 **GS** *020

GONZALEZ DEGRO, Carlos J. 609 AVE TITO CASTRO, STE 102 00716 #308-03-1984 L1995 **P** *020

GONZALEZ-FLORES, Jose R. PONCE BY PASS 00731 #041-02-1938 L1939 **CD IM** *072

GONZALEZ-OLIVIERI, R. PARRA BLVD PONCE BY PASS, #501 00731 #847-08-1982 L1986 **GS** *020

GONZALEZ RIVERA, Eduardo. GUADALUPE ST 00731 #308-03-1977 L1980 **AN PME** *020 ‡

GONZALEZ-RODRIGUEZ, S A. Q2 AVE GLENVIEW # W23, URB GLENVIEW GDNS 00730 #042-02-1996 L1997 **ON** *020

GONZALEZ SOTOMAYOR, Antoni. ■ 00728 #042-04-2003 L2004 *100

GONZALEZ TORO, Lazaro F. ■ 00732 #308-01-1958 L1971 **GS** *020

GORDIAN, Servando L. PO BOX 292 00733 #847-10-1964 L1968 **GP** *020

GORROCHATEGUI, Martin Ign. ■ 00716 #042-02-2007 **TY** *012

GOYCO, Pedro G. 8169 CALLE CONCORDIA, STE 301 00717 #042-01-1984 L1987 **PDP** *020 †55

GRAHAM SIERRA, Adrian Bur. ■ 00733 #649-14-1996 L1998 *020

GRANT, Migueline Marie. PO BOX 5096 00733 #308-03-1988 L1993 *020

GUEVARA, Mario E. PAMPANOS 00732 #341-01-1971 L1980 **EM** *020

GUTIERREZ, Astrid Lissett. ■ 00717 #042-02-2007 *012

GUTIERREZ, Lissette. PO BOX 7469, 409 EDIFICIO PARRA 00732 #042-02-1998 L1999 **OBG** *020 ‡

GUTIERREZ-CAMACHO, J H. 613 AVE TITO CASTRO, STE 101 00716 #847-05-1962 L1964 **IM NEP** *020

GUTIERREZ-DORRINGTON, Jorg. 613 AVE TITO CASTRO, STE 101 00716 #024-07-1993 L1994 **OPH** *020 †35

GUZMAN JORGE, Ulises A. PONCE BY PASS 00731 #308-01-1960 L1973 **GP FM** *020

HAIRSTON, Daniel Lancelot. CENTRO MEDICO DE PONCE 00731 #649-14-1972 L1977 **ON HEM** *075

HEREDIA, Nilso A. PO BOX 34129 00734 #275-01-1959 L1977 **GP** *020

HERMIDA, Gil Angel. 8169 CALLE CONCORDIA, STE 309 00717 #275-01-1989 L1998 **IM** *020 †20

HERNANDEZ, Arlene. 2213 PONCE BY PASS 00717 #308-04-2001 L2005 **IM** *012

HERNANDEZ, Ines Maria. 10 CALLE DE DIEGO, URB ALHAMBRA 00716 #042-01-1993 L1996 **IM** *020 †20

HERNANDEZ, Joaquin. BLOCK # 8, APT 215, LAS AMERICAS HOUSING 00731 #042-02-1995 L1998 **FM** *020 †18

HERNANDEZ, Jose Victor. PO BOX 7105, 196 MSC 00732 #308-01-1986 L1989 **GP** *020

HERNANDEZ, Luis E. 307 CARR 10, PO BOX 119 00728 #308-03-1984 L1988 **GP** *020

HERNANDEZ-FELICIANO, T. 615 CALLE FERROCARRIL, URB SANTA MARIA 00717 #847-10-1973 L1976 **OBG** *020

HERNANDEZ-ORTIZ, Alfonso. 2225 PONCE BYP STE 709 00717 #042-02-1985 L1987 **P** *020

HERRERA, Cesar M. CALLE LOLA RODRIGUEZ DE TI, LAS DELICIAS 3618 00728 #649-14-2002 L2004 **FP** *012

HOEPELMAN-NINA, Baron. 212 RIO CANAS, COLISEO SHOPPING CENTER 00731 #308-01-1962 L1969 **GP** *020

IRIARTE, Rafael Ivan. 7309 CALLE RAMON POWER 00717 #042-01-1978 L1982 **FM** *040 †70,18

IRIZARRI, Alfredo. BO MACHUELO, DEPT PED 00731 #308-03-1983 L1987 **PD** *020

IRIZARRY, Edith M. ■ 00780 #042-01-1989 L1996 **DR** *020

IRIZARRY CRUZ, Elmer. CALLE 3-A-1 BOX 7245, URB. RIO CANAS 00732 #308-03-1980 L1993 **OBG** *020

IRIZARRY-GONZALEZ, Lydia. 2431 AVE LAS AMERICAS, STE 304 00717 #308-04-1987 L1991 **PDE PD** *020

IRIZARRY PEREZ, Luis A. 63B CALLE MENDEZ VIGO EXT 00730 #649-01-1958 L1961 **FM** *072

IRIZZARY, Jadira. ■ 00717 #042-02-2005 **PD** *012

ISIDRO, Angel Antonio. ■ 00717 #308-03-1982 L1990 **PTH** *020

ISLA LLAMAS, Javier E. 860 CALLE CORTADA, URB CONSTANCIA 00717 #275-02-1976 L1999 *020

JIMENEZ, Emilio Antonio. ■ 00731 #308-01-1976 L1990 **IM** *100

JIMENEZ, Gilberto. PO BOX 7352, PMB34 00732 #042-02-2002 L2004 **IM** *100 †20

JIMENEZ, Rolando L. 2225 PONCE BY PASS, EDIFICIO PARRA 706 00717 #042-01-1995 L2001 **HO** *020 †20

JIMENEZ, Salvador. PO BOX 330230, CALLE GUADALUPE ATOCHA STA 00733 #025-01-1963 L1987 **TS** *020 †85,90

JOVANE-JARAMILLO, Jorge R. 1114 AVE MUNOZ RIVERA, STE 2 00717 #649-01-1977 L1984 **IM CD** *020

JUSINO-MC DOUGALL, Ismael. PONCE BY PASS 00731 #847-06-1977 L1981 **GP FM** *020

JUSTINIANO, Marcos A. 472 AVE TITO CASTRO, EDIFICIO MARVESA SUITE 205 00716 #308-04-1992 L1996 **FM** *020

LABOY, Osvaldo Ramon. PO BOX 7685 00732 #308-02-1988 L1991 **ID IM** *020

LABOY CONESA, Mirzia. ■ 00716 #649-14-2003 L2005 *100

LABOY ESPADA, Ray Rafael. ■ 00730 #649-14-2004 *100

LABOY-TORRES, Joaquin A. 75 CALLE VIVES 00730 #042-01-1972 L1975 **OBG** *020 †30

LAGO ORSINI, Eva S. ■ 00717 #649-18-1990 L2003 *100

LAM, Vicente. ■ 00732 #042-01-2006 **IM** *012

LAMBERTY-SOLIS, Jaime L. ■ 00717 #847-04-1958 L1962 **PTH** *020 †50

LANAUZE, Hector Jose. PO BOX 1382 00733 #308-01-1984 L1986 **FM** *020

LATORRE, Hector Antonio. 436 CALLE JACOBO MORALES, EST DEL GOLF CLUB 00730 #649-14-1996 L1998 *020

LATORRE GERENA, Adolfo. ■ 00730 #308-01-1974 L1976 **GP** *020

LEBRON, Angel Rafael. 1913 CALLE ZARINA, VALLE REAL 00716 #308-04-2001 L2005 **IM** *020 †20

LEBRON, Jorge Adrian. PO BOX 7101 00732 #308-07-1984 L1993 **PD** *020

LE COMPTE-TORRES, Abelardo. ■ 00716 #042-04-2002 L2004 *100

LEE, Chao. ■ 00716 #042-02-2008 *012

LEON-PEREZ, Roberto. 2225 PONCE BYP, OFICINA 505 00717 #042-03-1981 L1984 **RHU IM** *020 †20

LINARES-RIVERA, Hector D. ■ 00717 #847-05-1973 L1977 **IM OM** *020 ‡

LIZASOAIN, Jose Angel. 2651 CALLE MAYOR, P O BOX 336060 00717 #847-09-1972 L1974 **PD** *020 †55

LLAVONA, Angel F. EXT LA RAMBLA, 7 EAST STREET, #586 00731 #847-04-1954 L1958 **GP OS** *020

LLUVERAS-GONZALEZ, L. 2253 CALLE RITO MOREL CMPS, VILLA GRILLASCA 00717 #042-03-1980 L1986 **GP** *020

LOPEZ, Brenda Ivelisse. URB. PERLA DL SUR 00717 #649-14-2003 *100

LOPEZ, Jorge Juan. 8169 CALLE CONCORDIA, STE 312 00717 #308-03-1983 L1986 **IM** *020 †20

LOPEZ-BUSQUETS, Roberto H. BARRIO MACHUELO 00731 #042-01-1958 L1963 **IM** *020

LOPEZ CASTRO, Luis A. N 772 PERLA DEL SUR 00731 #308-04-1989 L1992 *020

LOPEZ DE ALVAREZ, Ana V. 1668 CAL NVR URB LA RAMBLA 00730 #042-01-1954 L1957 **PD OS** *020 †55

LOPEZ-DEL POZO, Diana O. CALLE C K-96, URB. VISTA ALEGRE 00731 #308-03-1983 L1988 **IM** *020

LOPEZ DEL POZO, Luis Erne. LA RAMBLA, A-11 00731 #649-14-2000 L2001 **FM** *100

LOPEZ DEL POZO, Sergio R. 8169 CALLE CONCORDIA, STE 312 00717 #308-03-1981 L1985 **IM** *020

LOPEZ LOTTI, Sergio E. 8169 CALLE CONCORDIA STE 5, CONDOMINIO SAN VINCENTE 00717 #847-02-1958 L1962 **TS VS** *020

LOPEZ ORTIZ, Yiselle. ■ 00728 #649-14-2002 L2005 *100

LOPEZ RODRIGUEZ, Miguel A. 3153 E FAY 00731 #042-01-1958 L1960 **PD** *020 †55

LOPEZ-SOMOLINOS, Carlos. CONDO SAN VINCENTE 203 00731 #847-05-1962 L1964 **OPH** *075

LOYOLA-MOREL, Ceferino. SAN ANTONIO, STREET 9 F24 URBANIZAIN 00731 #847-02-1972 L1975 **GS** *020

LUGO, Ramon Rafael. ■ 00730 #308-02-1983 L1995 *020

LUGO FRANCISCO, Manuel A. MARGINAL 301 LA RAMBLA 00731 #308-01-1954 L1968 **IM** *100

LUGO-MUNIZ, Carmelo. 1251 AVE MUNOZ RIVERA, VILLA GRILLASCA 00717 #847-10-1970 L1973 **CD OS** *020

LUGO-POCHE, Johnny. 385 CALLE DR PILA # B, PARC EL TUQUE 00728 #649-14-1976 L1978 **FM** *020

LUGO-RODRIGUEZ, Lionel. GUADALUPE ST 00731 #649-01-1975 L1982 **OTO GS** *020

MADERA, Magali. B2 CALLE A, URB JARDINES DE PONCE 00728 #649-14-2002 L2003 *100

MADURO, Luis Gaspar, Jr. 1391 CALLE CASTELLANA, URB LA RAMBLA 00730 #308-03-1988 L1995 **GP** *020

MALAVE DE GARCIA, Judith. ■ 00731 #847-04-1965 L1971 **PD A** *020

MALAVER, Jimmy Arturo. ■ 00716 #308-03-2000 L2004 *100

MALDONADO, Irma C Seda. 4838 CALLE CANDIDO HOYOS, URB PERLA DEL SUR 00717 #308-03-1978 L1984 *020

MALDONADO GONZALEZ, Juan. PO BOX 8884 00732 #649-14-2001 L2004 *100

MALDONADO RODRIGUEZ, Maria. P O BOX 7105 PM 430 00732 #649-14-2000 L2003 *100

MALDONADO SANTOS, Felix E. 9113 CALLE MARINA STE 10, EDIFICIO PONCE DARLINGTON 00717 #308-03-1983 L1994 **P** *020

MARQUES LLITERAS, Magin. STREET 3 B 9 FAGOT 00731 #847-03-1963 L1973 **ORS** *020

MARQUEZ, Javier Ramon. ■ 00717 #042-02-2007 **TY** *012

MARQUEZ-MINONDO, Dianne M. 917 AVE TITO CASTRO 00716 #649-14-2003 **IM** *012

MARTIN, Aurelio. 2431 AVE LAS AMERICAS, EDIF PORRATA-PIZA STE 310 00717 #042-01-1973 L1975 **OPH PO** *020 †35

MARTINEZ, Gabriel A. ■ 00716 #042-02-1990 L1995 **ID** *020 †20

MARTINEZ, Hector Luis. 2279 PONCE BYP, CARIBBEAN MEDICAL CENTER 00717 #649-14-1995 L1996 **IM** *020

MARTINEZ, Jorge Alberto. 1909 CALLE MURCIA, UPB EXT RAMBLA 00730 #847-06-1976 L1981 **END IM** *040 †30

MARTINEZ, Luis Antonio. 450 CALLE FERROCARRIL, SANTA MARIA MEDICAL 00717 #042-02-2004 *100

MARTINEZ, Raymond. DD40 CALLE W27, URB GLENVIEW GDNS 00730 #649-14-1999 L2002 **GP** *020

MARTINEZ, Rosendo Emilio. 401 EDIF PARRAS 00717 #042-03-1980 L1987 **PS HS** *020 †65

MARTINEZ-MALDONADO, M. ■ 00716 #041-13-1961 L1963 **IM NEP** *030 †20

MARTINEZ RODRIGUEZ, Guille. 2213 PONCE BYP 00717 #308-13-2004 L2006 *100

MARTINEZ-SIERRA, Luis. 450 CALLE FERROCARRIL, STE 210 00717 #042-01-1973 L1975 **GE IM** *020

MARTIR, Rafael A. 450 CALLE FERROCARRIL, STE 210 00717 #042-01-1980 L1983 *020

MATOS FIGUEROA, Jorge R. 1405 CALLE GERMN RCKHF SMP, URB LOS ALMENDROS 00716 #649-14-1992 L1994 **IM** *020

MATOS POSTIGO, Eduardo. CALLE Y #767 PAQUITO MONT 00731 #308-03-1983 L1995 **GP** *020

MAUNEY, Weldon Arnold. ■ 00717 #726-01-1996 **CHN** *012

MAYOL, Carlos J. ■ 00728 #308-01-1991 L1995 **FM** *020

MAYORAL-BIGAS, Jorge W. SALUD 10 COND SENORIAL-313 00731 #024-05-1951 L1953 **GE IM** *071 †20

MEDINA, Mariel Joanne. ■ 00716 #042-01-2005 **PD** *012

MEDINA, Nelson Radanes. ■ 00716 #649-14-1992 L1996 **GE** *100

MEDINA, Sonia. 2509 CALLE JOSEPH BENITEZ, URB LAS DELICIAS 00728 #649-14-2000 **PD** *020

MEDINA-AGOSTINI, Ismael. 301 CALLE JUAN H CINTRON, EST DEL GOLF CLUB 00730 #649-14-1996 L1998 *020

MELENDEZ, Gelmaris. ■ 00728 #042-02-2003 L2004 **FM** *100 †18

MELENDEZ, Jose Edgardo. RR11 CALLE 28, EXT ALTA VISTA 00716 #042-02-1996 L2001 **IM** *020 †28

MELENDEZ, Jose R. 3636 CALLE CUMBRE, URB EL MONTE 00716 #042-01-1987 L1990 **CD** *020

MELENDEZ-QUINONES, Jose R. BARRIO MACHUELO 00731 #847-02-1978 L1981 **PD** *020

MELERO-SANTIAGO, Jennie. PONCE DISTRICT HOSP 00717 #847-05-1975 L1981 **PD** *020

MENDEZ, Roberto Juan. 2431 AVE LAS AMERICAS, STE 206 00717 #042-02-1990 L1997 **PS** *020 †65

MENDEZ SANCHEZ, Miguel A. ■ 00730 #847-06-1973 L1978 *020

MENDOZA, Adalberto. ■ 00716 #042-01-1974 L1976 **PTH** *020 †50 ‡

MERCADO, Joanna. PO BOX 7004, PONCE MED SCH 00732 #042-02-2000 L2004 **EM** *100 †16

MERCADO OLAVARRIA, Ramon. ■ 00717 #847-06-1992 L1999 **IM** *012

MERCADO QUINONES, Alfredo. 917 AVE TITO CASTRO, P O BOX 336810 00716 #308-13-2001 **PD** *100

MICHEL, Angel Eugenio. 4 NO 118 JARD DEL CARIBE 00731 #308-01-1977 L1985 *020

MININO-CASTILLO, S. ■ 00730 #308-01-1966 L1972 **PM GP** *020

MIRABAL-RODRIGUEZ, E. 2273 CALLE IGUALDAD, VISTA ALEGRE 00717 #042-01-1983 L1987 **IM** *020 †20

MIRANDA GRAJALES, Graciany. ■ 00730 #042-04-2003 L2004 *100

MIRANDA-GUZMAN, Miguel A. 28 CALLE MARINA 00717 #308-03-1976 L1978 **GP** *020

MIRANDA TIRADO, Glenda Mi. ■ 00717 #308-13-2005 **IM** *012

MIRO-SOTOMAYOR, Pedro A. 450 CALLE FERROCARRIL, STE 302 00717 #847-04-1963 L1965 **IM** *020

MOJICA, Yazmin Milagros. 2153 CAL NGL URB LOS CAOBO 00716 #649-14-2002 **FM** *020

MOLINA, Rafael A. ■ 00717 #042-04-1987 L1988 **CD** *020

MONASTERIO, Manuel H. 3123 CALLE MEMBRILLO, EL MONTE 00716 #847-06-1965 L1975 **ORS** *020 †40

MONASTERIO-HERNANDEZ, J. 2225 PONCE BY PASS, STE 408 00717 #847-17-1979 L1987 **GS** *020 †85

MONTALVO, Raul F. EL MONTE A-9 00731 #042-02-1982 L1986 **IM** *020 †20

MORALES, Juan Alejandro. ■ 00730 #042-02-2005 **EM** *012

MORELL, Manuel A. SUITE 300, EDIF A PORRATA PILA 00715 #042-01-1981 L1985 **PUD IM** *020 †20

MORENO, Militza. ■ 00730 #042-02-2008 *012

MUNOZ, Armando Luiz. 3429 PASEO VERSATIL, VISTA POINT 00716 #308-03-1977 L1978 **OBG** *020

MUNOZ, Carmen Santiago. BARRIO MACHUELO 00731 #042-04-1984 L1986 **IM** *020 †20

MUNOZ, Jorge Fernando. ■ 00716 #042-02-2005 **PD** *012

MUNOZ TORRES, Mario B. GUADALUPE FINAL STREET 00733 #042-01-1960 L1962 **TS** *071 †85,90

MUNTANER RODRIGUEZ, Marie. ■ 00717 #308-04-2004 *100

NADAL-SANTIAGO, William. CALLE C 19 LOS FLAMBOYANCE 00731 #847-08-1963 L1967 **GP OS** *071

NAZARIO DAVILA, Neixa L. ■ 00716 #649-14-1994 L1994 **PD** *020

NAZARIO-LUGO, Jose E. 1777 CALLE MARQUESA, VALLE REAL 00716 #042-02-1996 L1997 *020

NAZARIO TORRES, Nelly. ■ 00728 #308-04-2001 L2003 **GP** *020

NAZARIO-WEBER, Juan A. ■ 00716 #042-02-1981 L1985 **IMG** *020 †18

NEGRON, Carmen Lillian. JARDINES DE PONCE APT #A1 00731 #308-01-1967 L1970 **PTH** *071

NEGRON, Ernesto Jose. ■ 00716 #042-02-2006 **IM** *012

NEGRON COLON, Raul. 412 CALLE SOLIMAR, VILLA DEL CARMEN 00716 #308-03-2001 L2003 *100

NIEVES, Arnaldo Manuel. 7810 CALLE NAZARET, URB SANTA MARIA 00717 #042-03-1990 L1996 **GE IM** *020

NIEVES LOPEZ, Edith Maria. 2213 PONCE BY PASS 00717 #308-03-2005 **PD** *020

NORIEGA-COLLAZO, Maria D. 917 AVE TITO CASTRO, HOSPITAL SAN LUCAS 00716 #042-04-1983 L1985 **PD** *020 †55

■ = Address Information Privacy Protected

OLIVERA-MORENO, Armando. PO BOX 161, MAREGINAL LA RAMBLE 00732 #451-01-1990 IM *100

OLSEN, Lawrence Chas. ■ 00730 #041-02-1972 L1978 ON *075 †20

OMS, Rafael Luis. 2225 PONCE BY PASS STE 301, EDIFICIO PARRA 00717 #042-03-1981 L1986 PM *075 †60

ORTIZ, Alexandra Maritza. 179 CALLE MIGUEL RIVR TXDR, EST DEL GOLF CLUB 00730 #042-02-1997 L2000 OBG *020 †30

ORTIZ, Anabelle. 704 EDIF PARRAS, PONCE BY PASS 00717 #042-01-1994 L1998 OBG *020

ORTIZ, Edgardo J. 2431 AVE LAS AMERICAS, STE 200 00717 #042-01-1977 L1983 OPH OS *020 †35

ORTIZ, Georgina Esperanza. ■ 00730 #847-09-1963 L1964 GP *074

ORTIZ, Julia. 18 CALLE BERTOLY 00730 #308-03-1979 L1990 GP *020

ORTIZ, Sabato Na. ■ 00728 #042-01-2004 GS *012

ORTIZ-COLON, Pedro J. A-28 URB VALLE REAL 00731 #847-03-1976 L1979 PD OS *020

ORTIZ DIAZ, Miguel A. ■ 00717 #649-14-2001 L2004 *100

ORTIZ-GONZALEZ, Jose Luis. GUADALUPE ST 00731 #847-10-1974 L1978 NPM *020

ORTIZ GONZALEZ, Nelida Ma. ■ 00716 #649-14-2003 L2005 IM *012

ORTIZ LOPEZ, Yamillie Sof. PO BOX 8907 00732 #649-14-2001 L2004 *100

ORTIZ-RIVERA, Franklin. JARDINES FAGOT 4 C 11 00731 #649-14-1980 L1985 IM *020

ORTIZ-RIVERA, Juan L. CALLE AG-77, URB VALLE REAL 00731 #847-06-1976 L1979 GP EM *071

ORTIZ-ROSADO, Jose A. 507 CALLE FERROCARRIL, URB SANTA MARIA 00717 #847-13-1977 L1983 GS *020

ORTIZ-ZAVALA, Jose Efrain. ■ 00717 #847-02-1977 L1979 FM EM *020

OTERO, Carlos R. 2225 PONCE BY PASS, PARRA BLDG STE 305 00717 #042-03-1986 L1994 N PMM *020 †75

OTERO, Carolyn. ■ 00717 #308-04-1992 L1993 IM *020

PACHECO-SEGARRA, Elvin J. 3301 CALLE CAOBA, URB LOS CAOBOS 00716 #308-03-1976 L1980 GP *020

PADRO-DIAZ, Ana Amalia. ■ 00717 #847-05-1977 L1982 IM *020 †20

PAGAN COLON, Angel G.. ■ 00730 #649-14-1994 L1996 *100

PAGAN-MEDINA, Urbano. PONCE BY PASS 00731 #847-05-1974 L1977 PD *020

PAGAN-PASCUAL, Victor M. PONCE BY PASS 00731 #042-01-1955 L1957 OPH *020

PAGES-ARROYO, Elaine Mari. ■ 00716 #042-01-2008 *012

PANELLI, Pedro. 909 AVE TITO CASTRO, STE 612 00716 #042-02-1984 L1987 GE *020 †20

PARAVISINI, Ferdinand. A-23 URB MERCEDITA 00731 #649-01-1953 L1955 PD *071

PARRILLA BARRERAS, R H. BARRIO MACHUELO 00731 #042-01-1972 L1976 P *020 †75

PASCUAL CHAGMAN, Victor E. 7309 CALLE RAMON POWER 00717 #737-06-1994 FP *012

PASSALACQUA, Fernando A. 1010 PASEO DEL VETERANO, PONCE VA CLINIC 00716 #042-01-1974 L1980 P *030

PAULINO-PAULINO, Hector F. URB JARDINES DEL CARIBE, NO 4 STREET 121 00732 #308-01-1975 L1983 GP EM *020

PEGUERO, Edwin Nelson. 2225 PONCE BY PASS, OFICINA 1004 00717 #042-02-1986 L1997 N *020 †75

PENA-CARDENAS, Tirso T. 2431 AVE LAS AMERICAS #212 00717 #042-04-1988 L1994 IM *020

PEREIRA SUAREZ, Miguel A. B-127 SANTA MARIA 00731 #847-04-1965 L1968 OBG *020

PEREYO, Neville. 8129 CALLE CONCORDIA STE 6, CONDOMINIO CONCORDIA 00717 #023-01-1964 L1970 D *020 †15

PEREZ, Adrian. PO BOX 7353, HOSP SAN LUCAS GUADALUPE 00732 #042-01-1990 L1993 CD *020

PEREZ, Carlos Amedee. 4TH PISO PONCE BY-PASS, HOSPITAL DAMAS 00731 #042-01-1978 L1984 HEM IM *030 †55

PEREZ, Daniel Jesus. 7309 CALLE RAMON POWER 00717 #275-02-1994 FP *012

PEREZ, Eduardo. 802 EDIF PARRAS, PONCE BY PASS 00717 #042-01-1986 L1988 OPH *020 †35

PEREZ, Hilton Gustavo. 37 CALLE CONCORDIA 00717 #847-04-1956 L1960 IM CD *030

PEREZ, Jesus A. 301C AVE TITO CASTRO, STE 451 00716 #308-06-1983 L1992 *020

PEREZ, Lianette Marie. 620 CALLE AA, PARQUE LOS AIMENDROS #10 00716 #042-02-1996 L2000 OBG *020

PEREZ, Lourdes Rosario. 8118 CALLE CONCORDIA 00717 #308-03-1986 L1990 GP *020

PEREZ, Magali Del Carmen. ■ 00716 #308-03-1982 L1985 GP *020

PEREZ, Marlene Yaritza. 7309 CALLE RAMON POWER, DEPT OF FAMILY PRACTICE 00717 #649-14-2000 L2001 FM *020

PEREZ, Sabdi Jesse. 2213 PONCE BY PASS 00717 #308-04-2004 *100

PEREZ-ARMENDARIZ, Hilton. 3227 CALLE CAFE, URB LOS CAOBOS 00716 #042-03-1988 L1990 HEM *020

PEREZ-ARZOLA, Miguel. 1632 CALLE NAVARRA, URB LA RAMBLA 00730 #023-01-1954 L1957 IM *040 †20

PEREZ-AYBAR, Pedro A. BO MACHUELO, DEPT PED 00731 #308-01-1980 L1985 PD *020

PEREZ-BRISEBOIS, Daniel. 3011 AVE FAGOT, VILLA ESPERANZA 00716 #042-04-1989 L1995 NEP *020

PEREZ-GUADALUPE, Marisol. 917 AVE TITO CASTRO, CLINICA INMUNOLOGIA 00716 #308-03-1981 L1986 IM *020

PEREZ-PEREZ, Edwin. URB ANAYDA 4 ST D 18 00731 #308-03-1980 L1983 PD *020

PEREZ-PEREZ, Milagros E. ■ 00732 #308-03-1980 L1984 PD *020

PEREZ-PRIETO, Manuel. LA RAMBLA CALLE 2 #73 00731 #847-02-1978 L1980 GS *072 †20

PEREZ-ROIG, Manuel. 3110 CALLE ANIBAL, URB. SAN JORGE 00717 #847-04-1954 L1956 OM *020

PIETRI, Richard. ■ 00716 #308-03-1991 L2005 *100

PIETRI, Waleska. ■ 00717 #042-02-1988 L1992 FM *020 †18

PIETRI-MANIANI, Santiago. 35 CALLE MARINA # 2073 00717 #847-04-1956 L1959 PD *020

PIETRI RODRIGUEZ, Rafael. 00717 #649-01-1967 L1969 DR *020

PILLOT, Juan Ramon. AVENIDA LAS AMERICAS, DEPT FAM PRAC 00733 #308-01-1987 L1990 FM *020

PIMENTEL-AWLTREY, Juan C. 1010 PASEO DEL VETERANO 00716 #308-01-1972 L1977 IM *020 ‡

PIMENTEL-LEBRON, Manuel O. 1 CALLE BERTOLY 00730 #308-03-1986 L1990 *020

PINEIRO-MERCADO, Edgardo. ■ 00730 #308-03-1982 L1984 IM *020

PINERO-PARES, Jaime Andre. PO BOX 336810, BO MACHUELO 00733 #305-01-2007 TY *012

PLAZA MALDONADO, Priscilla. PARCELAS AMALIA MARIN, 556 CALLE LOBINA 00716 #649-14-2000 L2002 FM *020

PORTILLA, Jose R. 902 CALLE ZARAGOZA, URB LA RAMBLA 00730 #847-06-1958 L1962 AN *071

POU, Jose Manuel. CALLE A 34 VISTAPOINT 00731 #010-01-1963 L1970 CHP P *072

POU LINES, Angel Eugenio. GUADALUPE ST 00731 #041-13-1953 L1954 PD *071 †55

POU MORALES, Jose Eugenio. ■ 00730 #308-03-1981 L1986 GP *020

PUENTE-CASTRO, Rigoberto. 67 CALLE VIVES 00730 #847-04-1962 L1965 GP GYN *071

PUIG, Hector, Jr. ■ 00716 #042-02-1988 L1994 PUD CCM *071 †20

PUIG, Laura Sofia. 305 CALLE PEDRO FLORES, URB LAS MARGARITAS 00728 #308-11-1985 L2002 PD *020

QUILICHINI ROIG, Carlos A. ■ 00717 #010-01-1937 L1938 GS *071

QUINONES, Eugenio. CALLE 23 U 15 PONCE, PUNTO ORO 00731 #042-01-2000 L2003 OBG *020 ‡

QUINONES CAMPOS, Luis. 35 GG-28, JARDINES DEL CARIBE 00728 #308-03-1988 L2003 *100

QUINONES FERRER, Hiram. 8024 CALLE CONCORDIA, STE 200 00717 #042-01-1985 L1988 OPH *020

QUINONES-ROMEU, Elvin N. 1034 AVE HOSTOS, C/O C.D.T. PLAYA DE PONCE 00716 #847-06-1976 L1981 OBG *020

QUINONES SOTO, Rafael A. DF1 JARDINES DE PONCE 00731 #847-06-1975 L1981 ID IM *050

QUINTERO, Oscar R. ■ 00728 #308-04-1990 L1992 CD *020

RAMIREZ-MARQUEZ, Lucas. 101 CALLE A, EL MONTE 00730 #308-03-1978 L1980 OBG *020 †30

RAMIREZ PEREZ, H. I13 CALLE G, JARD DE PONCE 00730 #308-01-1962 L1973 OBG *020

RAMIREZ-SCHON, T J. BARRIO MACHUELO 00731 #847-10-1964 L1966 ORS HS *072

RAMIREZ-TIO, Fernando. 44 CALLE MAYOR 00730 #010-01-1961 L1963 OPH *071 †35

RAMOS, Angel Luis. DAMAS HOSP, DEPT INT MED 00732 #308-04-1989 L1990 IM *020

RAMOS, Juan Manuel. ■ 00717 #042-02-2007 GS *012

RAMOS, Lilliam Mabel. 501 EDIF PARRAS 00717 #847-08-1982 L1993 GP *020

RAMOS COLON, Janice. 3115 CALLE PORTUGUES, VILLA DOS RIOS 00730 #649-14-2002 L2005 *100

RAMOS MARQUEZ, Edwin. AVENIDA LAS AMERICAS 00731 #847-04-1956 L1959 GE *071

RAMOS-MARTIN, Gerard. 1484 PASEO FAGOT, JARD FAGOT 00716 #042-01-1974 L1976 FM OM *020 †18

REMEDIOS, Carlos, Jr. RAD ONCOLOGY DEPT, PONCE ONCOLOGIC HOSP 00731 #042-02-1986 L1991 RO *020

RENTA-ACEVEDO, Juan C. ■ 00728 #308-04-1990 L1992 GS *020

RENTA-EMMANUELLI, Eduardo. 5 CALLE BERTOLY 00730 #847-05-1979 L1985 GP *020

RENTAS, Evelyn. ■ 00717 #042-02-2001 L2006 IM *100 †20

RENTAS-ORTIZ, Alberto. RAMBLA NO 1 59 00731 #308-03-1976 L1978 IM ID *020

REYES-DE LA PAZ, Myrna. S6 CALLE MARGINAL, JARD FAGOT 00716 #042-01-1980 L1983 PD *020

REYMUNDE, Alvaro. 806 EDIF PARRAS STE 806 00717 #308-03-1984 L1985 GE IM *020 †20

RIMPEL, Robert. 3505 CALLE MESSIER, URB STARLIGHT 00717 #649-18-1980 L1995 P *020

RIOS BENITEZ, Marta I. 2431 AVE LAS AMERICAS, EDIFICIO PORRATA PILA 00717 #042-04-1984 L1989 IM CCM *020

RIOS-RODRIGUEZ, Guillermo. ANESTHESIA DEPT, DAMAS GUILLER E RIOS 00731 #042-01-1962 L1968 AN *071

RIVERA, Alberto. ■ 00716 #042-02-2000 L2005 PM PMM *020 †60

RIVERA, Angel Benito. 609 AVE TITO CASTRO, STE 102 00716 #042-02-1990 L1995 NEP *020 †20

RIVERA, Araceli. D-11, JDNES DE PONCE CALLE C 00731 #042-02-1996 L2001 IM *020

RIVERA, Carlos. PONCE BY PASS 00731 #847-05-1970 L1974 OBG *020

RIVERA, Eugenio. 2431 AVE LAS AMERICAS, STE 300 00717 #042-01-1977 L1981 PUD IM *020

RIVERA, Evelyn. 450 CALLE FERROCARRIL #108, SANTA MARIA MEDICAL BLDG 00717 #042-02-1988 L1991 PM *020

RIVERA, Fernando Garcia. AVENIDA LAS AMERICAS 00731 #847-10-1961 L1968 GS *040

RIVERA, Francisco. 62 CALLE LOS ALMENDROS 00717 #847-06-1979 L1985 GP *020

RIVERA, Francisco J. 62 CALLE LOS ALMENDROS 00717 #042-01-1989 L1993 PDS GS *020

RIVERA, Jorge. PONCE BY PASS 00731 #649-14-1991 L1995 IM *020

RIVERA, Jose. 2436 AVE LAS AMERICAS, PORRATA PILA BLDG STE 306 00717 #042-04-1993 L1996 PD *020

RIVERA, Jose Antonio. PO BOX 10189, 311 CARRETERA 14 NUMBERO 00732 #035-06-1990 L1995 IM *020

RIVERA, Jose Luis. BOX 7456 PAMPANOS STA 00732 #042-01-1973 L1975 OPH *020

RIVERA, Kenneth A.. ■ 00780 #649-14-1994 L1998 *020

RIVERA, Luis H. ■ 00728 #308-03-1986 L1996 IM *020

RIVERA, Muneca Iris. 7309 CALLE RAMON POWER 00717 #042-01-1976 L1980 FM FPG *040 †18

RIVERA, Nelson. PONCE REG HOSP, DEPT MED 00733 #308-06-1986 L1993 IM *020

RIVERA, Nixzaliz Rodrigue. 2213 PONCE BY PASS, HOSP DE DAMAS 00717 #308-04-2004 IM *012

RIVERA, Ruben. 3006 AVE FAGOT, STE 2 00716 #308-03-1978 L1984 PD *020

RIVERA-ABREU, Michelle. ■ 00716 #042-02-2001 L2006 END *012

RIVERA ALICEA, Grisell. 2B6 CAL 54 JARD DEL CARIBE 00728 #308-01-1984 L1994 *100

RIVERA CARRASQUILLO, Frank. ■ 00716 #042-04-2000 L2001 ADP *012

RIVERA ESPARRA, Jose J. 2313 CALLE UNIVERSIDAD, APT 16 00717 #649-14-2000 L2002 *100 †20

RIVERA FELICIANO, Maximo. 602 EDIF PARRAS, PONCE BY PASS 00717 #847-03-1971 L1975 PS *020

RIVERA GUILBE, Jose G. ■ 00732 #649-14-1992 L1994 GS *020

RIVERA-LOPEZ, Luis. PONCE BY PASS 00731 #308-03-1978 L1980 PD *020

RIVERA-MERCADO, Jose Anto. PONCE UNIV HOSP, DEPT OBG 00731 #748-20-1993 L1996 *100

RIVERA-RIOS, Marilia. I18 CALLE MARGINAL N, URB EL MADRIGAL 00730 #847-09-1980 L1984 EM UCM *020 ‡

RIVERA RIVERA, Osvaldo. GUADALUPE ST 00731 #042-04-1980 L1984 IM *020

RIVERA-VAZQUEZ, Angel. PONCE BY PASS 00731 #847-08-1973 L1976 NEP IM *020

RIVERA-VEGA, Alexandra Ma. ■ 00716 #042-02-2007 *012

ROBERTO ORTIZ, Eduardo C. STATION 6 BOX 200, CALLE JOBOS ESQ CONCORDIA 00731 #847-10-1971 L1973 FM EM *020

RODRIGUEZ, Amaury. SAN JOSE, CALLE 1 C-15 00731 #649-35-1990 L1996 *020

RODRIGUEZ, Awilda Garcia. 1034 AVE HOSTOS 00716 #308-02-1977 L1981 IM *020

RODRIGUEZ, Betsy. 1204 CALLE FRANCISCO VASAL, URB LAS DELICIAS 00728 #308-04-1984 L1987 FM *020 †18

RODRIGUEZ, Carlos Omar. ■ 00717 #042-02-2000 L2002 CD *020

RODRIGUEZ, Celso Antonio. 917 AVE TITO CASTRO 00716 #275-01-1989 L2008 OBG *012

RODRIGUEZ, Daisy Rivera. BARRIO MACHUELO 00731 #308-01-1981 L1993 GP CLP *075

RODRIGUEZ, Deborah. 1802A CALLE COVADONGA, URB LA RAMBLA 00730 #649-14-1987 L1993 PD NPM *020

RODRIGUEZ, Dulce J. 100 PASEO DE LA REINA, MIGUEL A P 2703 00716 #308-01-1980 L1987 FM *020

RODRIGUEZ, Edwin. PO BOX 10614 00732 #649-14-2000 L2003 *100

RODRIGUEZ, Ernesto Jose. ■ 00730 #042-02-2006 IM *012
RODRIGUEZ, Ernesto R, Jr. 1203 AVE MUNOZ RIVERA, VILLA GRILLASCA 00717 #847-04-1965 L1969 NEP IM *071
RODRIGUEZ, Helga I. ■ 00732 #308-03-1980 L1986 GP *020
RODRIGUEZ, Ismael. 8129 CALLE CONCORDIA # 601 00717 #042-01-1962 L1966 IM END *020
RODRIGUEZ, Jorge Ivan. ■ 00716 #649-14-2003 ON *012 †20
RODRIGUEZ, Jose. EXT SAN ANTONIO, CALLE 12 I-7 00731 #308-03-1991 L1997 *020
RODRIGUEZ, Jose Antonio. ■ 00717 #042-02-1990 L1994 NPM *020 †55
RODRIGUEZ, Juan F. ■ 00716 #042-01-1983 L1986 CD IC *020 †20
RODRIGUEZ, Luis Alberto. 1984 CALLE FORTUNA, VISTA ALEGRE 00717 #042-02-1994 L2002 OBG *020
RODRIGUEZ, Luis Edil. 1326 CALLE SALUD, STE 103 00717 #308-03-1981 L1984 IM *020
RODRIGUEZ, Marco Antonio. P O BOX 1067 00733 #649-14-1993 L1996 P *020
RODRIGUEZ, Olga D. 917 AVE TITO CASTRO, DE EDUCACION MEDICAGRADUAD 00716 #042-01-1983 L1986 PD *020 †55
RODRIGUEZ, Reinaldo. 609 AVE TITO CASTRO, STE 102 00716 #042-01-1990 L1992 GS *020
RODRIGUEZ, Remy. PONCE BY PASS 00731 #028-34-1944 L1946 NPM *071 †20
RODRIGUEZ, Remy. 2053 PONCE BYP, CENTRAL CARIBE BLDG 00717 #042-01-1979 L1984 DR OS *020 †80
RODRIGUEZ, Ronald Alexis. ■ 00717 #042-02-1995 L1998 OBG *020
RODRIGUEZ, Sandra Isabel. ■ 00717 #264-11-1997 L2003 IM *100 †20
RODRIGUEZ, Teodoro. ■ 00732 #847-05-1978 L1980 *020
RODRIGUEZ, Victor Miguel. 2431 AVE LAS AMERICAS, STE 204 00717 #308-04-1985 L1992 FM *020 †18
RODRIGUEZ-ARIAS, Jaime O. 1484 PASEO FAGOT, JARD FAGOT 00716 #042-01-1978 L1982 FM FPG *020 †18
RODRIGUEZ BARRAL, Lugelina. PO BOX 7361 00732 #308-03-1980 L1984 *100
RODRIGUEZ CARRERAS, Maria. PO BOX 7625 00732 #847-10-1984 L1999 FM *030
RODRIGUEZ GARCIA, Luis H. PONCE BY PASS 00731 #042-10-1964 L1967 P PD *071
RODRIGUEZ-HERNANDEZ, A. PONCE DIST HOSP INT MED 00731 #308-03-1982 L1986 IM *020
RODRIGUEZ RAMIREZ, Julia. 3060 CALLE LA FUENTE, URB PERLA DEL SUR 00717 #319-01-1977 L1994 *020
RODRIGUEZ-RAMOS, Juan. ■ 00717 #308-03-1980 L1983 PD *020
RODRIGUEZ-RAMOS, Ramon. 375 CALLE VICTORIA 00730 #308-03-1980 L1982 *020
RODRIGUEZ RAMOS, Ulises R. AVENIDA LAS AMERICAS 00731 #042-04-1991 L1993 CD *020
RODRIGUEZ RIVAS, Ramon. 16 CALLE MARINA, SUITES 5C & 5D 00717 #042-01-1972 L1974 U *020 †95
RODRIGUEZ VELAZQUEZ, Oscar. 1937 AVE LAS AMERICAS, URB SAN ANTONIO 00728 #649-14-2004 *020
RODRIGUEZ WELLS, Luis G. 1728 CALLE SIERVAS DE MARI, BOX 1669 00730 #649-01-1956 L1960 CD IM *020
ROLON-MIRANDA, Jose A. ■ 00732 #847-02-1979 L1983 IM *020
ROMAN, Ayleen Ivette. ■ 00732 #042-02-2005 PD *012
ROMAN, Lourdes E. HOSPITAL DISTRITO PONCE 00731 #847-10-1965 L1968 PD *040 †55
ROMAN, Ramiro Nelson. 1672 CALLE MRQS VALLE REAL 00716 #042-01-1979 L1982 PD *020 †55
ROMAN HERNANDEZ, A. 1228 AVE MUNOZ RIVERA, REPTO UNIVERSITARIO 00717 #847-10-1965 L1968 ORS *020
ROMERO, Carlos O. AVENIDA LAS AMERICAS 00731 #042-01-1985 L1988 FM *020
ROMERO CALES, Alvin. PO BOX 240, CARR #14 KM 25.9, COAMO 00732 #649-14-1995 L1996 FM *020
ROQUE, Jorge E. PO BOX 332027 00733 #275-01-1988 IM *020
ROSADO, Angie. INT 00731 #042-02-1985 L1989 CD IM *020
ROSADO, Barbara. ■ 00716 #042-01-1997 L1999 GE *100 †20
ROSADO, Elliot Juan. 6 CALLE SULTANA 00717 #308-01-1983 L1989 GP *075
ROSADO, Hector R. DAMAS PISO 7 OFICINA 703, EDIFICIO PARRA ANEXO HOSP 00731 #042-04-1983 L1985 IM *020 †20
ROSADO, Nilma Esperanza. 1326 CALLE SALUD STE 307, CONDOMINIO EL SENORIAL 00717 #042-03-1994 L1997 *020
ROSADO-PACHECO, Pedro A. 10 CALLE SALUD 00717 #010-02-1964 L1968 PD *020 †55
ROSARIO, Lourdes R. 121 CALLE SANTA MARTA 00716 #649-14-1992 L1993 IM *020
ROSARIO-PADUA, Helvetia. 2520 CALLE OBISPADO, JARD FAGOT 00716 #042-04-1987 L1991 CD IM *020
ROSENBLOOM, Carl. ■ 00732 #748-01-1971 L1974 GP *071
ROUBERT RIVERA, Hector L. Q STREET #504, URB PERLA DEL SUR 00731 #042-03-1984 L1986 *020
RUIZ, Amy. 1010 PASEO DEL VETERANO, CLINICA DE VETERANOS PONCE 00716 #042-02-1991 L1995 FM *020 †18
RUIZ, Carla Rosa. 503 CALLE RAMOS ANTONINI, PARC EL TUQUE 00728 #847-02-1983 L1989 IM ADM *020
RUIZ, Hendrick. ■ 00733 #649-14-1999 L2000 FM *020
RUIZ, Oscar Luis. PASEO LA REINA 3303 00717 #308-04-2002 L2005 *100
RUIZ-ABURTO, Javier. ■ 00733 #649-01-1965 L1992 VS CD *020 †85
RUIZ-DEYA, Gilberto. 1715 CALLE JEREZ, EXT ALHAMBRA 00716 #042-02-1994 L2000 U *020 †95
RUIZ ORONOZ, Joaquin E. 2213 PONCE BY PASS 5TH FL, HOSP DAMAS PEDIATRIX 00717 #042-01-1987 L1991 NPM PD *020
RUIZ ORTIZ, Jose Hiram. 7925 CALLE JOSE J HENNA, URB MARIANI 00717 #649-01-1971 L1975 *020
RUIZ-PLA, Helene Marie. HC 9 BOX 17062, KSH7 BO RIO CHIQUITO 00731 #308-03-1985 L2002 IM *020 †20
RUIZ RIVERA, Luis Raul. 49 CALLE AURORA, BOX 1471 PONCE 00717 #847-05-1977 L1981 END IM *020
RUIZ SOLER, Daniel Alfons. ■ 00730 #649-14-2002 IM *100
SAADE, Guillermo. ■ 00731 #649-01-1960 L1962 AN *020
SALAMO PEREZ, Carmen L. CALLE 55YY 8 00731 #042-04-1990 L1995 GP *020
SALICHS, Orlando. 8169 CALLE CONCORDIA, COND. SAN VICENTE 412 00717 #048-12-1950 L1983 GS *020 †85
SALLABERRY, Santiago N. 3120 CAL MMBRL URB EL MONT 00716 #847-01-1962 L1965 RO *020 †80
SALVA-MARIN, Milagros M. AVENIDA LAS AMERICAS 00731 #308-03-1979 L1983 PD *020
SANCHEZ, Carmen Elisa. ■ 00717 #847-03-1972 L1975 PD *020 †55
SANCHEZ-GAETAN, Felipe F. 2225 PONCE BYP, EDIFICIO PARRA STE 705 00717 #847-04-1975 L1982 GS SO *020
SANCHEZ-OCASIO, Jose F. ■ 00780 #847-01-1971 L1975 GS *020

SANTA, Eileen Elisa. 609 AVE TITO CASTRO, STE 102 PMB 559 00716 #042-02-1993 L1994 AN *020
SANTAELLA RIZARRY, Marien. CALLE LUCAS AMADEO 27, URB MAROAMO 5151 00717 #649-14-2003 L2005 *100
SANTANA, Adrian Antonio. 623 AVE CUATRO CALLES, STE 301 00717 #042-02-1995 L2002 U *020 †95
SANTANA, Alba V. ■ 00716 #308-01-1957 L1963 AN *020
SANTANA BAEZ, Brenda S. 1636 CALLE CAPITAN CORREA, BDA MARIANI 00717 #042-04-1991 L1994 *020
SANTIAGO, Carlos Yamil. 917 AVE TITO CASTRO 00716 #308-13-2001 L2004 IM *020
SANTIAGO, Irma D. ■ 00733 #042-02-1986 L2006 FM *020 †18
SANTIAGO, Jose Angel. 507 CALLE SALAMANCA, VILLA DEL CARMEN 00716 #308-03-1984 L1986 IM *020
SANTIAGO, Jose D. 609 AVE TITO CASTRO, STE 102 00716 #042-04-1984 L1992 PG *020
SANTIAGO, Jose Oscar. ■ 00716 #042-02-1997 L2001 PTH *020 †50
SANTIAGO, Nilda. ■ 00728 #042-02-1996 L1999 IM *020
SANTIAGO, Rafael Luis. 1404 CALLE GERMN RCKHF SMP, URB LOS ALMENDROS 00716 #847-02-1978 L1980 GP *020
SANTIAGO, Rosa E. 2225 PONCE BY PASS STE 805, EDIFICIO PARRA 00717 #042-02-1991 L1995 APM *105
SANTIAGO, Sonia. C/O GPO BOX 9016, AVE LAS AMERICAS 1935 00732 #042-02-1984 L1993 IM *020
SANTIAGO ALVAREZ, Jose A. 2225 PONCE BY PASS, STE 809 00717 #042-03-1980 L1985 OBG *020 †30
SANTIAGO BIGAY, Marjorie. ■ 00730 #308-01-1988 L2003 *100
SANTIAGO-BUTLER, William. 2431 AVE LAS AMERICAS, STE 209 00717 #042-04-1980 L1985 OTO HNS *020
SANTIAGO CORREA, Pedro O. 564 CALLE G URB LA RAMBLA 00730 #847-04-1960 L1964 IM OS *020
SANTIAGO CORREA, Rene. EDIF PONCIANA, APT 7A 00731 #847-04-1962 L1966 U *020
SANTIAGO-FLORES, Mario A. ■ 00728 #042-04-2000 L2002 *020
SANTIAGO-GONZALEZ, O. 2606 CALLE MAYOR 00717 #308-06-1981 L1986 VS OS *020 †85
SANTIAGO-MEDINA, Santos M. 4TH STREET A-17, URB VALLE ALTO 00731 #308-03-1977 L1981 OBG *020
SANTIAGO PACHECO, Jose Lu. ■ 00716 #649-14-2000 L2003 *100
SANTIAGO VIVES, Alejandra. CALLE LADY DI, PARQUE LOS ALMENDROS 00716 #649-14-2002 *100 †20
SANTOS-BELLO, Miguel E. 8024 CALLE CONCORDIA, STE 205 00717 #042-01-1989 L1992 AN *020
SANTOS CARABALLO, Norma I. ■ 00728 #308-03-1985 L1991 *020
SANTOS-SURIEL, Rafael A. 83 CALLE UNION, STE 129 00730 #308-01-1981 L1984 GP *020
SANTOS-TORRES, Cosme D. 3011 AVE EMILIO FAGOT, VILLA ESPERANZA 00716 #308-05-1988 L1995 NEP *020
SCARANO, Jenaro Gerardo. 50 CALLE ROOSEVELT, BDA MARIANI 00717 #042-01-1980 L1986 CHN *020 †75,55
SCARANO, Jenaro Gerardo. ■ 00732 #051-04-1944 L1945 PD OS *072 †55
SCARANO GARCIA, Carlos F. PO BOX 7166, BDA MARIANI 00732 #649-14-1984 L1988 PD *020
SEDA-AGRAIT, Pedro Julio. 12 CHALETS DEL BULEVAR 00716 #042-02-1996 L1999 GS *020
SEPULVEDA, Augusto Cesar. 8118 CALLE CONCORDIA, STE 210 00717 #042-02-1997 L1998 IM *020 †20
SEPULVEDA, Julio Armando. GUADALUPE ST 00731 #042-02-1988 L1991 CD *020
SERRANO, Luis A. PRIMER PISO, EDIFICIO ZAMORA 00731 #042-01-1976 L1981 OPH OS *020 †35
SERRANO RODRIGUEZ, Jorge. ■ 00728 #649-14-2000 L2004 GP *040
SHARATZ, Steven Matthew. ■ 00716 #042-02-2008 *012
SILVA, Lilliana Guadalupe. 2621 CALLE CIDRA, URB LOS CAOBOS 00716 #308-06-1983 L1992 GP *020
SILVA MUSALEM, Mariel. 917 AVE TITO CASTRO 00716 #305-01-2005 PD *012
SIMONETTI, Humberto. CALLE GUADALUPE FINAL, HOSP SAN LUCAS 00732 #042-04-1984 L1985 CD IM *020
SOLER, Hiram Martin. 701 EDIF PARRAS, 2225 PONCE BY PASS 00717 #042-02-1992 L2000 GS *020 †85
SOLER, Richard. ■ 00728 #042-02-1990 L1992 AN *020 †05
SOTO, Rafael, Jr. 2431 AVE LAS AMERICAS, STE 102 00717 #042-02-1996 L1997 PD *020
STEWART, Karen Vanessa. 2235 AVE LAS AMERICAS, APT 205 00717 #042-02-1995 L1998 IM *020
SUAREZ, Milagros Del R. BO MACHUELO, DEPT PED 00731 #847-14-1984 L1990 PD *020
TELLADO-RIOS, Ismael. 8182 CALLE CONCORDIA, STE B 00717 #308-13-2003 *100
TERC, Gregorio Enrique. 9140 CALLE MARINA, OFICINA 104 00717 #847-04-1970 L1978 CD IM *020
TIRADO, Felipe. ■ 00732 #042-02-2005 P *012
TORO, Jose Alfredo. PORTALES DEL MONTE D 1801 00732 #649-35-2000 L2003 *100
TORO, Luis Angel. 8129 CALLE CONCORDIA, STE 302 00717 #649-01-1956 L1977 P *020
TORO-BURGUETE, Jorge A. 2225 PONCE BY PASS, STE 701 00717 #042-01-1996 L2000 GS *020 †85
TORO-ORONA, Nannette. 21 CALLE CRISTINA 00730 #649-14-1996 L1998 *100
TORRES, Carlos Velez. ■ 00716 #308-03-1979 L1984 FM *020
TORRES, Edith. PONCE REG HOSP, DEPT MED 00733 #308-03-1990 L1991 IM *020
TORRES, Francisco. ■ 00716 #042-01-2004 L2006 EM *020
TORRES, Iris Eileen. ■ 00716 #042-02-1991 L1995 NPM *020
TORRES, Jorge Luis. ■ 00733 #042-03-1984 L1990 DR *020
TORRES, Monica E. 1550 BLVD MIGUEL POU, PASEO DEL REY #1501 00716 #042-04-1996 L1997 PD *020
TORRES, Nelson. ■ 00730 #649-34-2003 L2005 GP *020
TORRES, Reymundo M.. ■ 00730 #649-02-1989 L2004 FM *100
TORRES, Senen. ■ 00717 #042-02-1998 L2000 IM *020 †20
TORRES ARISTY, George F. ■ 00730 #308-01-1961 L1966 PD *020
TORRES ARROYO, Jo Ann. ■ 00730 #649-14-2003 *020
TORRES-AYBAR, Francisco G. A 26 JACARANDA 00731 #847-01-1963 L1965 PDC PD *055
TORRES BERNIER, Miguel. 2225 PONCE BY PASS, STE 802 00717 #042-01-1985 L1988 OPH *020 †35
TORRES-CABRERA, Hector R. 2431 AVE LAS AMERICAS, PORRATA PILA SUITE 210 00717 #308-03-1977 L1980 FM *020
TORRES COMAS, Emilette. 1910 AVE LAS AMERICAS, URB SAN ANTONIO 00728 #042-01-1991 L1995 AN *020 †05

■ = Address Information Privacy Protected

TORRES-GARCIA, Miriam E. PO BOX 7814 00732 #649-02-1981 L1985 **FM** *020
TORRES LUGO, Gil Kelly. GUADALUPE ST 00731 #308-04-1989 L1992 **GP** *020
TORRES NADAL, Bethzaida. ■ 00716 #649-03-1994 L1997 **FM** *020
TORRES ORTIZ, Julia. PONCE BY PASS 00731 #042-03-1980 L1986 **NEP IM** *020
TORRES-RIVERA, Anabis C. ■ 00716 #042-02-2003 L2003 **OBG** *020
TORRES-RIVERA, Francis J. PONCE REG HOSP, DEPT PED 00731 #308-03-1979 L1982
　PD *020
TORRES-RIVERA, Lourdes. ■ 00732 #847-05-1975 L1980 **PD** *020
TORRES-SERRANT, Maribel.■ 00717 #042-02-1998 L1999 **PD** *020 †55
TORRES TORRES, Myrgia E.. 23 S-7, URB JARDINES DE CARIBE 00731 #649-14-1994 L2002
　FM *020
TORRES-VEGA, Jose E. 450 CALLE FERROCARRIL, STE 210 00717 #042-03-1981 L1984
　IM *020
TORRES VELEZ, Elba I..■ 00716 #649-14-2001 L2002 *020
TORRUELLA, Luis Jaime. 909 AVE TITO CASTRO, STE 822 00716 #042-02-1989 L1991
　GS *020 †85
TOYOS, Onofre Antonio. ■ 00716 #308-01-1966 L1975 *020
TRABANCO, Cesar H. OFICINA 509 5TO PISO, EDIFICIO PARRA CARR #2 00732
　#042-04-1983 L1985 **END IM** *020 †20
TREVINO, Taina Aracelis. ■ 00716 #042-02-2008 *012
VALDEZ, Victor Oscar. 1959 CALLE FORTUNA, VISTA ALEGRE 00717 #308-01-1971 L1979 *020
VALENTIN, Rouseline. 1903 CALLE DR PILA, PARC EL TUQUE 00728 #308-01-1986 L1989
　IM *020
VALENTIN MARI, Maria. 609 AVE TITO CASTRO, STE 102 PMB 295 00716 #649-14-2001
　IM *020
VALENTIN-MARRERO, Luis R. 1117 CALLE CORDILLERA, VALLE ALTO 00730
　#847-06-1975 L1982 **GP** *020
VALENTIN-MENDEZ, Luis G. CALLE 1-64 VILLA ESPERANZA 00731 #649-14-1976 L1979
　OBG *020
VALLE ECHEMENDIA, F A. BARRIO MACHUELO 00731 #275-01-1943 L1943 **GS GP** *040
VALLEJO, Gladys. ■ 00716 #275-01-1974 L2006 *100
VAQUER HERNANDEZ, Ubaldo. JARDINES FAGOT CLE 7 E 22 00731 #847-01-1963 L1968
　IM *020
VARGAS, Jennifer Marie. 3908 CALLE DILENIA, URB BALDORIOTY 00728 #042-02-2003 L2004
　IM *100 †20
VARGAS GONZALEZ, Joyce L. 3019 CALLE DANUBIO, URB RIO CANAS 00728
　#649-14-2000 L2002 **GP** *020
VASQUEZ, Rafael Antonio. 1722 CALLE SIERVAS DE MARI, URB LA RAMBLA 00730
　#270-02-1987 L2002 **IM** *020
VAZQUEZ, Alberto Santos. AVENIDA LAS AMERICAS 00731 #308-03-1977 L1984 **GP FM** *030
VAZQUEZ, Francis. 1203 AVE MUNOZ RIVERA, VILLA GRILLASCA 00717 #042-03-1988 L1992
　NEP *020 †20
VAZQUEZ, Idel All. 7813 CALLE NAZARET, URB SANTA MARIA 00717 #649-14-2002 L2005 *100
VAZQUEZ, Jose Alfredo. 8111 CALLE CONCORDIA # 101, CONCORDIA PROF PLAZA 00717
　#042-02-1993 L1999 **OPH** *020 †35
VAZQUEZ, Maria De Las Mer. ■ 00730 #649-14-2002 L2004 *100
VAZQUEZ, Wilfredo. 2225 PONCE BYP, STE 909 00717 #042-03-1985 L1989 **GE IM** *020 †20
VAZQUEZ MERCADO, Jayson. ■ 00716 #649-14-1998 L2002 **GP** *020
VAZQUEZ RODRIGUEZ, J A. PO BOX 9021, 2225 BYPASS 00732 #847-08-1957 L1959
　GP PD *071
VAZQUEZ SANTIAGO, Carlos. 609 AVE TITO CASTRO, STE 102 PMB 236 00716
　#649-14-2001 L2004 *100
VAZQUEZ-TANUS, Jose. 2225 PONCE BY PASS, STE 707 00717 #042-04-1983 L1989
　CD IM *020
VAZQUEZ-TORRES, Orlando L. 11 CALLE CONCORDIA # 4AB 00717 #847-11-1975 L1980
　PUD IM *020 †20
VEGA LAGARES, Alexandra. 2148 CALLE COLINA, VALLE ALTO 00730 #649-14-2001 L2003
　GP *020
VELAZCO VAZQUEZ, Xiomara. 917 AVE TITO CASTRO 00716 #308-13-2005 **IM** *012
VELAZQUEZ, Hiram Dexter. 944 CALLE ARBOLEDA, VALLE VERDE 00716 #649-14-1986 L1991
　GP *020
VELAZQUEZ, Vanessa S. GIRASOL I-33 VILLA FLORES 00731 #042-02-1990 L1994 **END** *020
VELAZQUEZ-ALMODOVAR, V. PONCE REGIONAL HOSP 00731 #308-07-1984 L1991
　AI *020 †03,55
VELAZQUEZ RIVERA, Griselle. ■ 00717 #649-14-2001 L2002 *020
VELAZQUEZ-TORRES, Roberto. 2431 AVE LAS AMERICAS, STE 105 00717
　#308-03-1981 L1984 **HEM** *020 †20
VELEZ, Hector Antonio. 2213 PONCE BY PASS, HOPITAL DAMAS INC. 00717
　#042-03-2001 L2003 **HEM** *020 †20
VELEZ, Moraima. 1136 AVE MUNOZ RIVERA, REPTO UNIVERSITARIO 00717 #042-01-1970 L1972
　PM R *020 †60
VELEZ-ANDUJAR, Wanda G. 1236 AVE MUNOZ RIVERA, STE 1 00717 #847-05-1977 L1980
　PD *020
VELEZ-GONZALEZ, Herminio. ■ 00732 #847-05-1979 L1982 *071
VELEZ-MALDONADO, Maria Te. PO BOX 8083 00732 #649-14-2002 L2003 *100
VELEZ-MARTINEZ, Nelson. 609 AVE TITO CASTRO # 102, PMB 356 00716 #308-03-1979 L1980
　OBG *020
VENDRELL, Nancy E. 36 CALLE MARINA 00717 #042-01-1966 **OS** *074
VENDRELL, Pedro J. 9174 CALLE MARINA, STE 1A 00717 #847-10-1963 L1966 **OTO HNS** *020
VENDRELL, Pedro Jose, Jr. 2431 AVE LAS AMERICAS, STE 104 00717 #042-02-1995 L1999
　D *020 †15
VENDRELL, Roberto Malcolm. ■ 00730 #042-01-2001 L2005 **GE** *012
VENDRELL - BENITO, Gerardo. ■ 00728 #649-14-2004 *100
VERA RAMIREZ, Mayra. 8169 CALLE CONCORDIA, STE 302 00717 #042-01-1988 L1992 **N** *020
VICENS, Enrique A. PO BOX 8797 00732 #023-01-1950 L1953 **HNS OTO** *071 †45
VICENTY-RIVERA, Sonia T. PO BOX 7004, PONCE MED SCH 00732 #042-02-1998 L2000
　CD *020 †20
VILARINO-MARTINEZ, Jose R. PO BOX 311 00734 #847-04-1975 L1978 *100
VILLA, Jaime R. 2225 PONCE BYP, STE 403 00717 #042-01-1985 L1987 **D** *020 †15
VILLA, Jose. 16 CALLE BERTOLY # B 00730 #308-03-1981 L1987 *020
VINCENTY VILA, Pedro. 1809 CALLE ALCAZAR, URB ALHAMBRA 00716 #847-04-1960 L1962
　OBG *020 †30
WALKER-RIVERA, Rolando. CALLE C-D24, URB LAS MONJITAS 00731
　#308-03-1980 L1982 *020
WEST, Jared Hunter. PO BOX 7004, PONCE SCH OF MED 00732 #042-02-2008 *012
WISCOVITCH, Armando A. 1910 AVE LAS AMERICAS, URB SAN ANTONIO 00728
　#308-03-1978 L1990 **GP IM** *020

WITHERSPOON, Lynell Auror. ■ 00716 #042-02-2007 **OBG** *012
WYS-SOUFFRONT, William A. 15 CALLE CONCORDIA 00717 #030-06-1953 L1955 **A PD** *020
ZABORSKY, Deborah Ann. 37 CALLE TORRES STE 1 00730 #042-02-1999 L2002 **IM** *020
ZAMBRANA-GARCIA, Raul. F-7 QUINTAS DE MONSERRATE 00731 #847-10-1972 L1974
　RHU *050
ZAMBRANA ROSALY, Hjalmar. CALLE C 29 VILLA DEL CARM 00731 #308-03-1980 L1994 *020
ZAMORANO, Gabriel. ■ 00730 #847-01-1949 L1958 **PTH OS** *020 †20
ZAPATA-MOLINA, Nilda J. MEDICAL EDUCATION, HOSPITAL MOLINA NILDA J 00731
　#042-04-1983 L1985 **ID IM** *020
ZARAGOZA, Jose A.. PO BOX 332027 00733 #649-03-1983 *100
ZARAGOZA, Sharon Vanessa. ■ 00716 #649-14-2003 L2005 *100
ZAYAS, Francis Antonio. 2225 PONCE BY PASS, EDIFICIO PARRA SUITE 708 00717
　#042-02-1994 L2002 **GE** *020 †20
ZAYAS CABRERA, Richard I..■ 00730 #042-04-1999 L2002 **FM** *020

PUERTO NUEVO – SAN JUAN

CARRION-DIAZ, Jose L. 18TH NO ST #1364 00920 #308-02-1977 L1980 **OM EM** *020
CRUZ-IGARTUA, Ariel R. 1028 AVE F D ROOSEVELT 00920 #042-01-1982 L1985
　FM FPG *020 †18
LOPEZ BANCELLS, Maribel. ■ 00921 #275-01-1973 L2005 *100
MALDONADO BELANDO, Melvin. 1028 AVE ROOSEVELT, URB PUERTO NUEVO 00920
　#042-04-1992 L1994 **FM** *020
MEDINA-RUIZ, Arturo. 1007 AVE JESUS T PINERO, ASTOR MEDICAL BLDG SUITE 4 00920
　#042-01-1967 L1970 **CD IM** *020
REY-HERNANDEZ, Ayled. 1348 AVE ROOSEVELT, VILLA BORINQUEN 00920
　#308-07-1976 L1981 **NEP** *020 †20
RIVERA, Norma Iris. 1007 AVE JESUS T PINERO 00920 #042-01-1975 L1979 **FM** *020 †18
RIVERA PEREZ, Rafael A. 1007 AVE JESUS T PINERO 00920 #847-10-1966 L1968 **P** *020

PUERTO REAL – FAJARDO

ARRAUT, Harley. ■ 00740 #649-14-1994 L1996 *020
PEREZ, Jefferson. PO BOX 4173 00740 #042-04-1988 L1990 **GP** *020
SAVONA DEL ROSARIO, Julio. PO BOX 251 00740 #308-03-1978 L1979 *100

PUNTA SANTIAGO – HUMACAO

GOMEZ-DE JESUS, Maria A. PO BOX 24, BOULEVARD DEL RIO AVE. 00741
　#649-18-1977 L1989 *020
HALLMAN, Deana. A-18 URB VILLA PALMIRA 00741 #042-01-1983 L1986 **ON HEM** *020
HERNANDEZ-MOUNIER, Maria. C61 CALLE 4, VILLA PALMIRA 00741 #308-03-1977 L1985
　GP *020
MAYMI, Hector Rafael. ■ 00741 #042-01-1999 L2003 **AN** *020
VELEZ, Anibal Toledo. ■ 00741 #847-08-1975 L1978 *020

QUEBRADILLAS – QUEBRADILLAS

ALONSO OLIVERA, Jose F. ■ 00678 #275-01-1927 L1973 **GP** *100
AVILA ABRAMS, Jose R. PO BOX 962 00678 #847-01-1962 L1966 **PD** *020
BARBOSA DE LA CRUZ, Nancy. 155 CALLE SOCORRO 00678 #308-03-1981 L2003 *100
CAMACHO, Migdonio. C/O BOX 1501, CALLE RAMON SAAVEDRA #152 00678
　#847-06-1986 L1991 **GP** *020
CORDERO, Israel A. 63 CALLE SAN CARLOS 00678 #042-03-1987 L1990 **IM** *020
CRESPO, Jose Luis. PO BOX 123 00678 #649-14-2000 L2005 *100
CRUZ-LUNA, Norma Aimee. ■ 00678 #042-01-2007 L2007 **P** *012
DURAN, Gaily. ■ 00678 #649-14-2002 L2004 *100
FONTANILLAS, Jose A. CAR#2 KM 967 BO COCOS 00678 #042-01-1984 L1987 **PD** *020
GERENA, Arnaldo. HC 1 BOX 3785, BO CACAO 113 CARR KM124 00678 #042-04-1987 L1989
　GP *020
HERNANDEZ, Ilia. 63 CALLE SAN CARLOS 00678 #042-03-1988 L1991 **PD** *020 †55
HERNANDEZ, Juan Fco. CARR #2 KM 98.7 BO COCOS 00678 #308-04-1984 L1986 **GP** *020
HERNANDEZ-MORENO, Carlos. ■ 00678 #308-03-1981 L1984 **PD** *020
JIMENEZ, Angel M. HC 2 BOX 9879 00678 #042-03-1986 L1989 **IM** *020
JIMENEZ TOSADO, Zahir Z.. PO BOX 39 00678 #308-04-2004 L2005 *100
LAZZARINI-LUGO, Sigfrido. ■ 00678 #042-01-1958 L1960 **GP** *071
LUGO-LOPEZ, Edgard. ■ 00678 #847-06-1979 L1984 *020
LUGO-SANTIAGO, Diana I. ■ 00678 #308-03-1982 L1985 **PHP EM** *030
MARTIR PELLOT, Jorge. 206 CALLE SAN JUSTO 00678 #042-04-1986 L1988 **OBG** *020
MEJIAS RODRIGUEZ, Gerardo. PO BOX 88 00678 #649-14-1996 L2005 *100
MIRANDA, Ada Yolanda. URB KENNEDY, CALLE TEIQUE LINARES #80 00678
　#308-06-1984 L1997 **FM** *020
MONTILLA RIVERA, Francisco. HC 2 BOX 10005 00678 #308-01-1982 L1991 *020
PAGAN ROMERO, Anibal. PO BOX 903, CALLE MARGINAL DEL PARQUE 00678
　#308-03-1982 L1995 **GP** *020
PAZ FIGUEROA, Anabelle. PO BOX 25000 PMB 48 00678 #308-13-2001 L2004 *100
PEREZ RODRIGUEZ, Andres F. PO BOX 51 00678 #308-03-2001 L2005 *100
RIVERA-OQUENDO, Carmen M. HC 2 BOX 8660 00678 #847-02-1976 L1983 **GP** *020
SAAVEDRA, Armando. ■ 00678 #042-01-1981 **PD** *071
SAAVEDRA-AMADOR, Armando. ■ 00678 #023-01-1951 L1951 **GP** *071
SANCHEZ, Jack Louis. PO BOX 1296, 96 CALLE JOSE LINARES 00678 #308-03-1982 L1990
　GP *020
SERRANO BARRIOS, Jose B. CALLE OCHO BUZON 1888 00678 #429-01-1987 L1995 **GP** *020
TORRES CASTRO, Efrain. CALLE SOCORRO NO 255 00678 #308-03-1981 L1983 **GP** *020
TREJO, Tomas. 82 CALLE SOCORRO 00678 #308-03-1984 L1992 **PD** *020
VERA MUNIZ, Carlos J. ■ 00678 #649-14-1995 L1995 **FM** *020 †18
ZAMOT, Roberto. 117 CALLE RAFOLS 00678 #308-03-1981 L1990 *020
ZENO, Carmelo Eddin. 96 CALLE JOSE LINARES 00678 #308-03-1982 L1985 **GP** *020

RINCON – RINCON

ARCINIEGAS-MEDINA, Norma. 28 CALLE MUNOZ RIVERA OEST, RR 115 00677
　#264-04-1994 L2002 **PD** *020 †55

BNET, Radames Tirado. ■ 00677 #649-14-1976 L1988 *020
CARDONA, Osvaldo Lionel. ■ 00677 #042-01-1989 L1995 END *020
DOMINGUEZ, Angelina. 28 CALLE MUNOZ RIVERA OEST, RR 115 00677 #847-05-1983 L1987 GP *020
GOMEZ, Jesus V. MUNOZ RIVERA 41 OESTE 00677 #847-05-1968 L1976 GP *020
MAXWELL, Raymond J. KM 0.3, CORSEGA, CARR 115/429 00677 #035-09-1951 L1996 D IM *071 †20
RIVERA, Irma. 28 CALLE MUNOZ RIVERA OEST, RR 115 00677 #042-02-1984 L1988 PTH *020 †50
RODRIGUEZ, Edgar A. 28 CALLE MUNOZ RIVERA OEST, RR 115 00677 #308-02-1992 L1996 GP *020 †18
RUIZ, Lynnette. ■ 00677 #649-14-2000 L2003 GP *020
VELAZQUEZ MUNOZ, Melvin J. PO BOX 133 00677 #308-03-1985 L1990 P *020
VELEZ GONZALEZ, Pedro A. 18B CALLE PROGRESO 00677 #847-05-1979 L1989 GP *020

RIO BLANCO — NAGUABO

APONTE, Ana Maria. ■ 00744 #308-01-1981 L1992 GP *020
GUADALUPE CRUZ, Myriam. PO BOX 799 00744 #649-14-2004 L2005 *100
ORTIZ ARES, Neftali. PO BOX 294 00744 #308-01-1982 L1992 GP *020

RIO GRANDE — HUMACAO

AGOSTINI-MARTINEZ, Luis D. B23 CALLE GARCIA DE LA NOC, VILLAS DE RIO GRANDE 00745 #042-01-1969 L1972 OTO *020
ALLENDE SANTOS, Gerardo J. A3 CALLE GARCIA DE LA NOC, VILLAS DE RIO GRANDE 00745 #308-03-1984 L1993 *020
ANDINO, Ada I. ■ 00745 #042-01-1990 L1994 N *020
BERRIOS, Alma Iris. ■ 00745 #042-01-1976 L1983 DR *020
BOURDON, Joany. ■ 00745 #042-01-1999 L2003 FM *020 ‡
CARABALLO, Ramon. L2 CALLE 6, VILLAS DE RIO GRANDE 00745 #649-35-1995 L2002 *020
CARPINTERO-DIAZ, Carlos R. 27 CALLE PIMENTEL, LOWR 00745 #308-01-1981 L1984 *020
CINTRON, Olga Enriqueta. ■ 00745 #042-03-1975 L1978 GP *020
CINTRON MALDONADO, Rosa A. 138 CALLE CUARZO, PEDREGALES 00745 #042-04-1992 L1996 PD *020
DENO ESTEPAN, Americo. DEPT OF PUBLIC HEALTH 00745 #308-01-1948 L1959 PHP OS *020
DIAZ, Angel M. ■ 00745 #308-03-1978 L1981 FM *020
DURAND ROLON, Roberto. PO BOX 2220 00745 #308-03-1979 L1989 *100
ENCARNACION MELENDEZ, Emil. PO BOX 1145 00745 #042-04-2000 L2001 FM *020
FERMIN VALDES, Luis R. PO BOX 43002, STE 151 00745 #308-01-1987 L1990 *020
FIGUEROA, Ana I. AA20 CALLE B, ALT RIO GRANDE 00745 #042-01-1989 L1992 PD *020 †55
FRED, Roberto Rolando. PO BOX 756 00745 #042-01-1980 L1983 *020
GEREN, Roberto. ■ 00745 #308-01-1972 L1976 *071
GONZALEZ BAUZA, Mario E. PO BOX 817 00745 #847-09-1957 L1960 FM OS *072
LEAL, Francisco Portugal. RIO GRANDE, CALLE 4 L-1 URB. VILLAS DE 00745 #308-01-1985 L1989 GP *020
LOPEZ, Manuel E. ■ 00745 #308-03-1981 L1991 GP *020
MALDONADO ROSARIO, Sandra. ■ 00745 #308-03-1978 L1993 *020
MARQUEZ, Raul. ■ 00745 #042-01-1988 L1992 GE *020 †20
MORALES DIAZ, Ismael. ■ 00745 #308-03-1982 L1993 *020
NABAVI TOUMARI, Maryam D. D-20 CALLE MAMEY 421, LOS ARBOLES 00745 #649-14-2002 L2006 *100
NIEVES, Jose R. PO BOX 43002, CALLE 8-I12 COLINAS DEL YU 00745 #847-05-1984 L1991 GP *020
NIEVES-ROMAN, Edward. L2 CALLE 6, VILLAS DE RIO GRANDE 00745 #042-03-1981 L1986 IM *020
ORSINI TORRES, Hernan. CENTRO DE SALUD 00745 #847-04-1962 L1967 P *020
REYES-TINEO, Edmundo R. VILLA DE RIO GRANDE, CALLE 1 M-2 00745 #847-05-1976 L1979 PD *020
RIVERA GARCIA, Abimael. J2 CALLE 2, VILLAS DE RIO GRANDE 00745 #042-04-2001 L2002 *020
RIVERA TORO, Ermelindo. ■ 00745 #847-05-1971 L1976 GP *020
SCORZA, Pedro Cristobal. ■ 00745 #042-03-1987 L1988 IM *020

RIO PIEDRAS — SAN JUAN

ABUOMAR, Jumana Abuomar. ■ 00924 #042-03-2004 IM *100 †20
ABU-USBA, Ibrahim Abdel F. ■ 00921 #308-03-1984 L1995 GP *020
ACEVEDO, Jose Juan. ■ 00921 #042-01-1994 L2001 CD *020
ACEVEDO-CUEVAS, Maritza. E1 CALLE A, URB EL DORADO 00926 #308-07-1982 L2001 GP *020
ACOSTA, Agnes Lyzette. 234 CALLE LAS MARIAS, HYDE PARK 00927 #649-14-1985 L1989 *020
ACOSTA, Luis Guillermo. BE8 CAL 65 URB HILL MANSIO 00926 #308-04-1987 L1990 GP *020
ACOSTA, Mario Pablo. 138 AVE WINSTON CHURCHILL, EL SENORIAL MAIL STATION 00926 #042-01-1988 EM *020
ACOSTA-MIRANDA, Alex M. ■ 00926 #042-01-2001 L2005 GS *100
ACOSTA-OTERO, Andres A. 217 CALLE CORNELL, URB UNIVERSITY GDNS 00927 #023-01-1961 L1969 U *020 †95
ADLAMUY-VIGOREAUX, Geraldi. 1434 CALLE SAN CARLOS, URB ALTAMESA 00921 #042-03-1998 L2000 *020
AGOSTO, Norma E. A2 CALLE LODI URB LUARCA, CENTRO PSICONEUROLOGICO 00924 #847-08-1973 L1976 N OS *020
AGUADO, Antonio Jose. ■ 00926 #042-02-1993 IM *100
ALARCON, Inerio Luis. RR 2, SAN JUAN CAPESTRANO HOSP 00924 #275-04-1988 L2004 *020
ALBINO, Julio A. ■ 00926 #042-04-1990 L1991 GP *020
ALBINO VAZQUEZ, Vivian M. 1129 CALLE HORTENSIA 00926 #042-04-1994 L1996 GP *020
ALBIZU-SANTIAGO, Carmen E. PUERTO RICO MED CTR, U OF PR HLTH SCI CTR 00931 #042-01-1975 L1977 PD *020 †55
ALFONSO, Gishlaine. ■ 00926 #042-01-1986 L1990 N CN *020 †75
ALGARIN, Vladimir. A REYES 412 SN AGUSTIN 00924 #042-03-1994 L2005 *100
ALLENDE-ORTIZ, Nestor. PASEO MAYOR, CALLE #1 D-5 00926 #847-01-1979 L1983 *020
ALONSO, Rafael Enrique. 1922 CALLE JOSE SABOGAL, URB BORINQUEN GDNS 00926 #042-02-1987 L1991 OBG *020 †30

ALONSO-SANTIAGO, Orlando. 1162 CALLE BRUMBAUGH, GARCIA UBARRI 00925 #308-01-1983 L1989 OS *020
ALSINA, Zamarie. W4-11 CALLE CALDRN D L BRC, URB HUCARES 00926 #042-01-1990 L1993 PM *020
ALVAREZ, Jose R. 66 CALLE GEORGETTI 00925 #042-01-1983 L1986 OBG *020 †30
ALVAREZ, Octavio A. COND JARD METP I 10A 00927 #847-06-1973 L1976 EM GS *030
ALVAREZ VELEZ, Felix R. TOWN PARK, 25 TREVI ST 00924 #649-01-1957 L1962 GP *020
ANDINO, Manuel Flores. 885 CALLE CARMEN HERNANDEZ 00924 #847-10-1966 L1970 GP *020
ANDUJAR-LEBRON, Job. ■ 00924 #042-01-1961 L1964 PD *071
ANGULO-JOHNSON, Alberto A. 12 ST 1051 00927 #737-01-1978 L1994 FM *020
ANTIQUE-DELGADO, Julia M. ■ 00926 #847-06-1971 L1977 GP *071
ANTOMATTEY-DIETRICH, A. ■ 00927 #308-02-1990 L1992 IM *020
APONTE CARRASCO, Victor A. 3 CARR 21, URB COOP V BORINQUEN 00921 #308-01-1985 L1988 IM *020
ARABIA, Jose Antonio. 225 HYDE PK AV LAS MARIAS 00927 #042-01-1978 L1981 PM *020 †60
ARANA GARCIA, Reinaldo H. EVERGLADES 1 10 PRK GRDNS 00926 #847-10-1966 L1971 GP *020
ARANGO, Juan Ruben. ■ 00926 #308-04-1986 L1991 GP *020
ARANZAMENDI VEGA, Iris M. 905 CALLE 1 SE, REPTO METROPOLITANO 00921 #308-03-1983 L1996 *100
ARGUELLES-MORAN, Jorge. C10 CAMINO REAL, PASEO DEL PRADO 00926 #308-03-1982 L1991 EM GP *020
ARIAS, Jose Javier. ■ 00926 #042-01-2007 N *012
ARROYO, Georgina. ■ 00928 #308-03-1981 L1995 FM *020
ARROYO, Norma Yamille. PO BOX 21405, SAN JUAN CITY HOSP 00928 #042-01-2001 L2002 HEM *012
ARROYO-DIAZ, Ana. 1 CALLE SANTA ROSA, URB SAN JUAN GDNS 00926 #308-03-1982 L1989 PD *020
ARZOLA, Jorge Luis. F1 CALLE BEACON, URB CAMBRIDGE PARK 00926 #042-01-1974 L1977 PD *040 †55
AVILES RODRIGUEZ, T A D C. 850C CALLE MARGINAL, LA ALAMEDA 00926 #042-01-1972 L1975 PDS *020
AVILES-ROIG, Carlos A. URB DE DIEGO, # 10 APT-A AMARILLO ST 00926 #042-01-1958 L1962 P *030
AYALA, Felix. ■ 00926 #308-03-1985 L1989 *071
AYMAT RODRIGUEZ, A. COLONIAL N 26 PARK GARDENS 00926 #042-01-1982 L1985 *020
AYMERICH, Sixto R. 1729 CALLE LILAS, URB SAN FRANCISCO 00927 #042-01-1969 L1971 OBG *020 †30
BADILLO, Jeannine M. 1216 CALLE ARNAU IGARRAVDS, URB CLUB MANOR 00924 #042-01-1991 L1996 DR *020
BAERGA-VARELA, Luis. 216 CALLE PALMA REAL, URB UNIVERSITY GDNS 00927 #026-08-1999 L2004 PM PMM *020 †60
BAEZ, Pablo J. F1-25 CALLE C, MANS DE VILLANOVA 00926 #042-01-1991 L1995 PM *020
BAEZ-PEREZ, Carlos. REP METROPOLIT 42 SE 1221 00928 #308-01-1967 L1975 GS *100
BALSALOBRE, Carlos. ■ 00926 #042-03-1987 L1994 R *020 †80
BALTHAZAR, Witni. 1015 CALLE 8, VILLA NEVAREZ 00927 #649-35-1988 L2005 *100
BARBOSA, Eugenio Rafael. 1476 AVE SAN IGNACIO, URB ALTAMESA 00921 #042-04-1983 L1985 GP *020
BARQUET-CHEDIAK, Antonio. ■ 00927 #275-01-1949 L1967 HEM CLP *020 †50
BARROSO-AYESTARAN, Anibal. ■ 00926 #042-01-1960 L1960 EM GP *074
BASSA ELMUDESI, Ramon A. ■ 00927 #308-01-1959 L1969 CD *020
BAUZA, Patricia Christina. ■ 00927 #042-03-2006 L2006 P *012
BAYRON JUSTINIANO, Juan J. 1791 CALLE ESTEBAN PADILLA, URB SANTIAGO IGLESIAS 00921 #308-03-1985 L1995 IM *020
BERDASCO PAZ, Aida R. ■ 00924 #847-06-1992 L1995 *020
BERDECIA, Sandra T. 112 CALLE ARZUAGA STE 902, MEDINA PROFESSIONAL CTR 00925 #042-03-1994 L1997 IM *020
BERMUDEZ, Myriam Zahydee. ■ 00927 #042-01-2007 *012
BERMUDEZ-SEGARRA, Ana L. GLACIER G 16 PARK GARDENS 00926 #042-01-1983 L1986 PD *020 †55
BERMUDEZ VELEZ, Jose A. GLACIER NO 16 PK GRDNS 00926 #847-04-1959 L1961 GP OS *071
BERNAL, Maria. 1571 CALLE 2 SO, URB CAPARRA TER 00921 #042-03-1990 L1995 PD *020 †55
BERRIOS, Joalmi. 2 CALLE LAS VILLAS, # 106 00924 #042-03-1999 L2003 P *100
BETANCES, Roberto. 1703 SAN GERARDO 00926 #847-03-1973 L1975 PTH *020 †50
BETANCOURT, Maria Lourdes. 1411 CARR 21, REPTO LANDRAU 00921 #042-01-1978 L1982 D *020 †15
BIBILONI, Juan Jose. 127 MUGAL URB SAN RAMON 00927 #264-05-1969 L1972 ORS *074
BIDO PEREZ, Joaquin C. 913 CALLE RAFAEL MERCADO 00924 #308-01-1953 L1966 AN OS *100
BIGIO, Arleen. ■ 00924 #042-03-1999 L2002 IM *020 †20 ‡
BISHARA, Mariam Nessim Za. PO BOX 21405 00928 #409-10-1994 L2003 IM *100 †20
BLADUELL, Hector A. BOX 21057 00928 #042-01-1962 L1966 OBG *075
BLANES-MAYANS, Francisco. ■ 00924 #847-06-1992 L1998 GS *020 †85
BLAS-SANTAMARIA, Lorenzo. ■ 00926 #847-02-1973 L1976 GP *020
BLEST, Maria Teresa Q. ■ 00926 #737-01-1965 L1973 PD *020
BONET, Nydia. CALL 3-1054 VILL NEVAREZ 00927 #042-01-1978 L1982 PD *020 †55
BONILLA, Vivian R. 1007 AVE MUNOZ RIVERA, OFICINA 1110 AVE 00925 #042-03-1981 L1986 P *020
BONNET DWONE, Antonio. ■ 00926 #847-04-1955 *071
BOQUESANTIAGO, Miguel J. JARDINES DE SAN FRANCISCO, APT 1104 00927 #042-03-2000 L2003 IM *020
BOSCHETTI, Damarys. 1012 CALLE 42 SE, REPTO METROPOLITANO 00921 #042-04-1987 L1991 PD *030
BOTELLO ARACHE, Lepido. JALAPA 1686-VENUS GARDENS 00926 #308-01-1947 L1972 CD *071
BURGOS, Luisa E. ■ 00926 #042-01-1971 L1973 PD *040
CABRERA, Miguel Angel. APTO 204 B, CALLE 14 QUINTAS DE CUPEY 00926 #847-10-1974 L1976 GS *020
CABRET, Roldan. CAMBRIDGE PARK, CHESTNUT HILL D-9 ST 00926 #042-01-1982 L1985 IM *020
CAISEDA, David. 100 GRAND BLVD, STE 112 00926 #042-01-1987 L1996 OBG *020 †30
CALDERON, Roberto Angel. 1162 CALLE BRUMBAUGH, URB. GARCIA UBARRI 00925 #042-03-1995 L1998 IM *020

■ = Address Information Privacy Protected

CALDERON-TORRES, Pilar. ■ 00921 #308-03-1978 L1981 **GP** *020

CALVINO ACOSTA, Lazaro Ma. PO BOX 21405 00928 #275-03-1989 **IM** *012

CAMPIZ, Leonardo Jose. 285 AVE WINSTON CHURCHILL, EL SENORIAL 00926 #308-01-1983 L1990 **GP** *020

CAMPOS-JOVEL, Jose F. 1672 CALLE HIDALGO, VENUS GARDENS URBANIZATION 00926 #341-01-1975 L1984 **IM** *020

CANCELA-MADURO, Carmen T. W7-15 CALLE J BOSCAN, URB LADERAS DE PALMA REAL 00926 #042-01-1990 L1991 **N** *020

CANINO, Alfredo Ivan. ■ 00926 #042-03-1997 L2000 **IM** *020 †20

CARCANO-ALICEA, Gloria E. ■ 00926 #847-03-1976 L1980 **GP** *020

CARDONA, Blanca R. 2043 CALLE BENITO FEIJOO 00926 #847-04-1968 L1970 **PM** *020

CARDONA, Hector Felipe. ■ 00926 #847-02-1959 L1962 **D** *071

CARMINELLI, Luis. 202 CALLE QUENEPA, EXT MILAVILLE 00926 #042-01-1965 L1969 **PD** *020 †55

CARRASCAL CORENA, Jose D. ■ 00924 #308-01-1958 L1967 **GS OS** *020

CARRAZANA, Pedro Domingo. PO BOX 21405, SAN JUAN CITY HOSP 00928 #649-33-1989 L2004 **IM** *100

CARRERAS, Aileen Milagros. 1059 CALLE 14, VILLA NEVAREZ 00927 #308-03-1983 L1989 **PD** *020

CARRO DE PENA, Luz Maria. ■ 00926 #847-04-1968 L1972 **GP** *020

CASADO, Maria P. CALLE G BECQUER #2021 00926 #308-06-1988 L1989 **PD** *020

CASANOVA, Cynthia. 10 CALLE CASIA, VAMC 00921 #042-01-1975 L1983 **P** *020 †75

CASANOVA, Miguel Angel. 1232 CLUB MANOR 00924 #308-01-1971 L1975 **PD** *020

CASTELLS, Martina. ■ 00927 #847-04-1957 L1960 **OS RO** *020

CASTILLO DIAZ, Fidel Erne. PO BOX 21405 00928 #270-02-1998 **IM** *100 †20

CASTRO-MARCHAND, Maria M. ■ 00926 #042-03-1980 L1982 *020

CASTRO MARQUEZ, Elvin F. OSUNA 790 LOS MAESTROS 00923 #308-03-1982 L1988 **OM** *020

CASTRO RODRIGUEZ, Jose M. 22 CALLE MARBELLA, PASEO LAS BRISAS 00926 #042-01-1972 L1974 **RHU IM** *020

CAUSSADE, Eduardo I. 1007 AVE MUNOZ RIVERA, OFICINA 1110 00925 #847-02-1980 L1990 **P GP** *020

CAUSSADE VEGLIO, Gerry J. 1107 CALLE WILLIAM JONES, ALTOS 00925 #308-03-1984 L1986 **FM** *020

CEDENO, Wilma Elena. ■ 00924 #649-14-2001 *020

CEDENO-COTTI, Wilson. CALLE 56 SE URB LA RIVIERA 00927 #847-10-1972 L1975 **GS** *100

CEIDE-ECHEVARRIA, Alberto. ■ 00925 #561-01-1958 L1962 **ATP CLP** *074

CEREZO, Ivan. PO BOX 21405, SAN JUAN CITY HOSP 00928 #308-03-2005 **IM** *012

CERNUDA-MAYMON, Carlos F. ■ 00927 #847-03-1966 L1970 **GP** *020

CHAAR, Brenda Edsali. ■ 00926 #042-03-1999 L2003 **N** *020 †75

CHAVEZ, Omar Ricardo. PO BOX 21405 00928 #935-03-1991 L2007 **IM** *100 †20

CHEVERE, Carlos Manuel. 276 COLUMBIA URB U GRDNS S 00927 #042-02-1989 L1992 **RO** *020

CHEVERE, Sergio. BOX 29519'65 INF STA-FDR C 00929 #042-02-1984 L1986 **FM** *020 †18

CINTRON, Ana Virginia. ■ 00926 #042-01-1980 L1987 **PM** *020 †60

COBOS-AREVALO, Jose M. ■ 00926 #264-01-1960 L1979 **PHP PD** *062

COLBERG-RIOS, Herman. ■ 00926 #004-01-1949 L1990 **PS** *071

COLLAZO, Brunilda. ■ 00924 #042-01-1964 L1966 **PD** *020

COLLAZO, Samuel. 36 CALLE FRANCISCO SOLER, URB EL CEMI 00924 #308-04-1987 L1988 **AN** *020

COLLAZO-BONILLA, Angel L. 52 CAL 2 URB PARK GDNS TOW 00926 #847-06-1976 L1977 **OBG** *020

COLON, Adrian. 66 CALLE GEORGETTI 00925 #042-01-1972 L1977 **OBG** *020 †30

COLON, Alfredo Salomon. 66 CALLE GEORGETTI 00925 #042-01-1977 L1981 **OBG** *020 †30

COLON, Alicia V. URB VENUS GARDEN, ACUARIO 675 ST 00926 #847-03-1973 L1975 **FM PD** *020

COLON, Ana D. ■ 00927 #042-01-1987 L1991 **PD** *020

COLON, Gardine Michelle. ■ 00926 #042-03-2008 *012

COLON, Jose A. ■ 00926 #042-01-1978 L1981 **IM** *020 †20

COLON, Luis Alfredo. ■ 00926 #042-01-1973 L1975 **IM** *020

COLON, Maria D. 1618 CALLE SANTA ANGELA 00926 #042-01-1989 L1993 **PM** *020

COLON, Rene E. 1752 CALLE SANTA BRIGIDA, URB SAGRADO CORAZON 00926 #042-01-1986 L1988 **AN** *020 †05

COLON NEGRON, Gladys E. AZABACHE 832 LA ALAMEDA 00926 #847-06-1974 L1977 **GP** *074

COLON-RIVERA, Egidio S. ■ 00926 #020-02-1942 L1942 **PDC PD** *071 †55

COLON RIVERA, Jose Efrain. 1364 CALLE SAN BERNARDO 00921 #308-03-1981 L1994 *020

CO-MIRO, Gumi. ■ 00924 #308-03-1983 L1993 *020

CORA, Vilma. 1791 CALLE ESTEBAN PADILLA, URB SANTIAGO IGLESIAS 00921 #042-01-1989 L1992 **FPG** *020 †18

CORADIN RUIZ, Ignacio. FERNANDO DE ROJAS #2048, EL SENORIAL 00926 #308-06-1987 L1994 *100

CORDOVA V, Eduardo Danl. ■ 00926 #737-01-1965 L1975 **GP** *020

CORRETJER-BENVENUTTI, J E. SENORIAL MAIL STATION #787, AVE W CHURCHILL 138 00926 #649-01-1959 L1963 **NEP** *072

CORRIA, Filiberto Ramirez. ■ 00928 #396-06-1933 L1972 **OS** *071

CORTES-ALICEA, Marcelino. 810 CALLE KINGSTON, URB LAS AMERICAS 00921 #042-01-1955 L1957 **CD IM** *020

COTTE SANTANA, Walter E. CTR COMERCIAL R PDRS HGHTS 00926 #847-06-1965 L1971 **GP** *020

COTTO RODRIGUEZ, Yolimar. RR 2 BOX 11, SAN JUAN CAPESTRANO HOSP 00926 #308-13-2000 L2004 *100

CRENSHAW-RIVERA, Ryan P. ■ 00926 #042-01-1960 L1964 **CD IM** *071

CRIADO, Rafael. ■ 00927 #847-09-1935 L1959 **OS FOP** *040 †50

CRUZ, Karen. PO BOX 21405, SAN JUAN CITY HOSP 00928 #649-14-2004 **PD** *100

CRUZ CABRERA, Ana Y.. ■ 00924 #649-14-2003 L2005 *100

CRUZ PUMAREJO, William. ■ 00926 #847-02-1959 L1974 **GP** *072

CUBANO, Sylvia. 206 CALLE INTERAMERICANA, URB UNIVERSITY GDNS 00927 #042-01-1991 L1994 **IM** *020

D'ACOSTA LUGO, Ruben A. 125 CALLE NILO, URB EL PARAISO 00926 #649-14-1973 L1990 **EM GP** *030

DAVILA, Francis. ■ 00926 #042-03-1988 L1994 **PTH** *020

DAVILA, Ruth. ■ 00926 #042-01-1973 **IM** *100

DAVILA MONERO, Blanca I. H8 CALLE 13, URB FAIRVIEW 00926 #308-06-1990 L2002 **GP** *020

DE BERRIOS, Luz Toro. ■ 00926 #042-01-1966 L1968 **RO** *020 †80

DE BRITO, Valmir Gomes. ■ 00926 #187-39-1973 L1978 **GP EM** *020

DE JESUS, Nydia Rosa. JARDINES DE VEDRUNA #8 00927 #042-01-1955 L1958 **AN** *071 †05

DE JESUS, Yohana. BE22 CALLE 65A, URB HILL MANSIONS 00926 #042-01-1981 L1984 **PUD** *020 †20

DE JESUS-GONZALEZ, Manuel. ■ 00927 #030-06-1951 L1957 **ATP** *020 †50

DE JESUS-MONGE, Wilfredo. ■ 00926 #042-01-2004 **IM** *012 ‡

DE JESUS RIVERA, Carmen C. 765 AVE SAN PATRICIO, URB LAS LOMAS 00921 #308-02-1979 L1983 **PD NPM** *020 †55

DE LA CRUZ SANTIAGO, S. ■ 00926 #042-01-1960 L1962 **RHU OS** *040

DE LA LUZ QUILES, Osvaldo. 89 AVE DE DIEGO, STE 105 00927 #308-02-1986 L1989 **CHP** *020

DE LA ROSA, Antonio S. ■ 00926 #649-01-1977 L1989 *020

DELGADO-MERCED, Damaris. O6 CALLE ALORA, VILLA ANDALUCIA 00926 #308-03-1977 L1980 **PD** *020

DELGADO OSORIO, Hector L. A49 CALLE SABATINI, URB PARK GDNS 00926 #042-01-1963 L1969 **CD IM** *040

DELGADO-RODRIGUEZ, Jose A. ■ 00926 #308-03-1979 L1982 **FM** *020

DE MARTINO, Maria M. ■ 00926 #042-01-1976 L1981 **CHP P** *075

DE PAZ-REYES, Bernardo A. 35 CALLE GERANIO, URB SAN FRANCISCO 00927 #847-05-1963 L1967 **OPH** *020

DE PERELLANO, Rosa V P. THEIS 1733 RIO PEIDRAS HGT 00926 #308-01-1966 L1975 *020

DE SANCTIS-ALSINA, V. ■ 00924 #308-02-1975 L1983 **PTH** *020

DEVARIE-SANCHEZ, Marcos. ■ 00926 #649-01-1955 L1956 **GP FM** *020

DIAZ, Alberto. 1629 REPTO DE DIEGO RD 838 00926 #042-01-1965 L1970 **CD IM** *020

DIAZ, Diana. ■ 00926 #042-01-1993 L1997 **P** *020 †75

DIAZ, Luis Alberto. ■ 00926 #649-14-1986 L1988 **GP IM** *020

DIAZ-ALBUERNE, Alberto. 158 CALLE LOS MIRTOS, URB HYDE PARK 00927 #275-01-1955 L1975 **GP** *071

DIAZ COLON, Doris. 160 AVE WINSTON CHURCHILL, URB CROWN HLS 00926 #847-05-1975 L1980 **PD** *020 †55

DIAZ-DIAZ, Jose M. 358 CALLE SAN GENARO, URB SAGRADO CORAZON 00926 #042-04-1981 L1987 **NM** *020

DIAZ-ECHEVERRY, Ariel. 970 CALLE 42 SE, REPTO METROPOLITANO 00921 #264-01-1942 **ORS** *020

DIAZ HERRERA, Maria Del. A16 CALLE A, COLINAS DE MONTE CARLO 00924 #308-04-1994 L2005 *100

DIAZ-HERRERA, William. 765 AVE SAN PATRICIO, URB LAS LOMAS 00921 #042-01-1979 L1982 **PD** *020

DIAZ-LOZADA, Francisco J. ■ 00926 #042-04-2003 L2004 **IM** *020

DIAZ MARTINEZ, Hector F. ■ 00927 #847-10-1956 L1962 *020

DIAZ-RODRIGUEZ, Ada Ines. 6 CALLE SANTA ANASTACIA, URB EL VIGIA 00926 #649-01-1971 L1974 **PD OS** *020 †55

DIAZ-RODRIGUEZ, Ruben. ■ 00926 #042-01-1977 L1981 **CD IM** *020

DIAZ-TORRES, Porfirio E. 1021 CALLE GEN DEL VALLE, URB EL COMANDANTE 00924 #308-03-1980 L1983 **CD IM** *020

DIEPPA, Renan Ariel. 982 CALLE 42 SE, REPTO METROPOLITANO 00921 #042-01-1973 L1980 **UP U** *020 †95

DISLA, Temistocles. 1773 CALLE ALCALA, URB COLLEGE PARK 00921 #308-01-1976 L1979 **AN EM** *020

DOMENECH-CRUZ, Sarah E. ■ 00929 #847-05-1968 L1970 **OS GP** *020

DONATE-PEREZ, Dora. RR 9 BOX 808, COLINA REAL 00926 #308-02-1989 L1992 **OBG** *020 †30

DONES, Sonia. 300 CALLE TOLOSA, URB COLLEGE PARK 00921 #042-01-1968 L1970 **R DR** *020 †80 ‡

DORTA, Luis. RR 2 BOX 11 00926 #042-03-1984 L1985 **P** *020

DUENO QUINONES, Jose R. STA EDUVIGIS 1712 SYD COR 00926 #847-05-1976 L1976 *020

ECHENIQUE, Miguel M. 30 CALLE 1A, ALT DE BERWIND 00924 #042-01-1976 L1982 **GS** *040 †85

EDWARDS VALQUEZ, Earl. CALLE 19F19 FAIR VIEW 00926 #308-01-1962 L1976 *020

ELIAS, Gustavo E. AVE 65 INFANTRY, ITURREGUI PLAZA 00924 #847-04-1961 L1963 *020

ELIAS CORREA, Jaime. 1317 CALLE 25, URB MONTE CARLO 00924 #847-05-1969 L1976 **GP** *020

ENCARNACION, Antonio. LL13 CALLE ROSE, ALTS DE BORINQUEN GDNS 00926 #847-10-1971 L1976 **GP** *071

ENRIQUEZ, Olga Lynnette. ■ 00921 #042-01-1978 L1983 **P** *020

ESCABI-MENDOZA, Jose E. ■ 00926 #042-01-1992 L1998 **CD** *020 †20

ESPADA, Anesdi. LIBRAN 356 SAN AGUSTIN 00923 #042-01-1973 L1978 **P** *100

ESPAILLAT JIMENEZ, Josefin. D2 CALLE FRONTERA, VILLA ANDALUCIA 00926 #308-03-1990 L2003 *100

ESTERAS-MARCIAS, Jose V. MIRADOR BORINQUEN GARDENS, C STREET #12 00926 #847-06-1976 L1979 **IM** *020

ESTRADA, Ricardo. CUPEY BAJO, CALLE A E-1 URB EL DORADO 00926 #308-03-1987 L1997 **FM** *020

FABERY, Efrain. COND SKY TOWERS 1 7H, BORINQUEN GARDENS 00926 #847-10-1966 L1969 **GP** *020

FABIAN-ARGUETA, Mirelis. ■ 00927 #042-03-1997 L2000 **ID** *020 †20

FAISCA-ROSADO, Wilfred. D32 CARR 845, URB EXPERIMENTAL 00926 #847-06-1976 L1978 **FM** *020

FAJARDO VARGAS, Blanca St. PO BOX 21405, SAN JUAN CITY HOSP 00928 #264-01-1998 L2003 **IM** *100 †20

FALCON, Ivette. DD29 CALLE JAZMIN, URB BORINQUEN GDNS 00926 #308-03-1982 L1988 **GP** *020

FARIA RODRIGUEZ, Antonio. BOX 30442, 65TH INFANTRY STA 00929 #308-01-1972 L1975 **FM** *071

FELICIANO, Felix M. ■ 00926 #847-04-1961 L1963 **P OS** *020

FELICIANO, Raul. K2 CALLE FARAGAN, VILLA ANDALUCIA 00926 #847-06-1958 L1959 **OS** *020

FELICIANO RODRIGUEZ, D L. 820 AVE ITURREGUI, URB COUNTRY CLUB 00924 #042-03-1996 L2000 **IM** *020

FERNANDEZ, Enrique Rafael. ■ 00926 #042-01-1977 L1980 **FM** *020 †18

FERNANDEZ ABALDE, Lydia. CALLE JONER 113 00925 #847-05-1979 L1983 **P** *020

FERNANDEZ-DURAN, G. ■ 00927 #020-02-1951 L1953 **AN PUD** *072 †05

FERNANDEZ LOPEZ, Carlos. ■ 00926 #847-05-1956 L1958 **GP OS** *020

FERNANDEZ-PEDRO, Cesar. ■ 00926 #847-10-1955 L1958 **GP PD** *071

FERRER, Jose Luis. ■ 00926 #847-04-1955 L1957 **GP** *020

FERRER, Norma D. ■ 00926 #042-01-1989 L1993 **DR** *020

FIGUEROA, Ivan R. 1277 LA RIVIERA, CALLE 54 S.E. 00921 #649-39-1982 L1990 **GP** *020

FIGUEROA, Yolanda. ■ 00921 #042-01-2003 L2006 **CD** *012 †20

FONTANEZ TAPIA, Raquel. 606 CALLE DE DIEGO APT 36, URB GONZALEZ SEIJO 00924 #649-14-2005 **PD** *100

FONT DE SANTIAGO, Osvaldo. 1007 AVE MUNOZ RIVERA, P O BOX 4860 00925 #649-01-1974 L1977 **FM** *020
FONT-QUINONES, Carlos M. ■ 00926 #649-02-1962 L1967 **PM** *075
FRANCO, Jorge Alfonso. ■ 00927 #023-01-1956 L1958 **OPH IM** *020 †35
FREYTES DEL RIO, Rodrigo. SUITE 604, CONDO OLIMPO PLAZA 00927 #847-10-1965 L1968 **P** *071
FRONTERA, Herminio. 1000 AVE MUNOZ RIVERA #203 00927 #010-02-1976 L1980 **IM IMG** *020 †20
FUENTES, Claude E. 112 CALLE ARZUAGA, STE 601 00925 #275-01-1949 L1952 **P** *020 †75
FUERTES, Milton Julio. E25 BERWIND ESTATES 00924 #010-03-1960 L1963 **IM A** *020
GALLARDO-MENDEZ, Antonio. EDIF DARLINGTON APT 5 00925 #308-03-1979 L1982 **GP** *020
GARCIA, Carlos Manuel. RIO PIEDRAS PR00925, JONES WILLIAM 1107 00928 #042-01-1978 L1982 **FM** *020 †18
GARCIA, Carlos Ruben. 980B CALLE SAN SALVADOR, URB LA RIVIERA IND PARK 00921 #042-01-1997 L2000 **PCC** *100 †20
GARCIA, Gabriel. ■ 00926 #042-01-2004 **ORS** *012
GARCIA, Ines E. PARK GARDENS, CALLE ISIPIBU Y 121 00926 #042-01-1988 L1991 **NPM** *020 †55
GARCIA, Luis Fernando. 140 CALLE VIOLETA, URB SAN FRANCISCO 00927 #042-01-1975 L1980 **PM GP** *020
GARCIA, Mario. ■ 00926 #649-14-1986 L1995 *020
GARCIA, Odette Margarita. 1029 CAL TGCGLP URB LAS AM 00921 #042-01-1981 L1984 **PD** *020
GARCIA ARROYO, Madeline. 1382 CALLE 18, URB MONTE CARLO 00924 #308-03-1982 L1991 *020
GARCIA-CASTRO, Jose M. 1180 AVE AMERICO MIRANDA, STE 1B 00921 #042-01-1964 L1971 **OS PD** *071 †19
GARCIA-DOMINGUEZ, G. CLEMSON 318B-UNIV GARDENS 00927 #275-01-1955 L1970 **DR** *020
GARCIA-GARCIA, Guillermo. ■ 00924 #847-10-1959 L1963 **GP OS** *020 †20
GARCIA HUERTAS, Jesus. 4D COND SKY TOWER I, BORINGUEN GARDENS 00926 #308-01-1973 L1975 **EM** *020
GARCIA PALLAS, Maria Vict. PO BOX 21405, SAN JUAN CITY HOSP 00928 #275-03-1990 L2005 **IM** *100
GARCIA-PONT, Pedro H. ■ 00926 #042-01-1955 L1958 **GE IM** *020
GARCIA-RAMOS, Katia. ■ 00926 #042-03-1998 L1999 **DR** *020 †80
GARCIA SAAVEDRA, Jaime. ■ 00927 #847-04-1956 L1959 **P OS** *071
GARCIA-TORRES, Victor. S MARCOS 236 EL COMANDANTE 00924 #042-01-1966 L1968 **GP GS** *020
GARNICA-DE NIEVES, Maria. 1665 CALLE LENA, URB CARIBE 00926 #649-01-1956 L1962 **OM GP** *075
GARRIDO COLLAZO, Jose R. PO BOX 21376 00928 #051-04-1927 L1927 **GP** *071
GERENA DIAZ, Jose Israel. ■ 00926 #847-10-1968 L1971 **U GS** *020
GINARD DE JESUS, Rafael H. 1785 CARR 21, URB LAS LOMAS 00921 #308-02-1998 L2002 **FM** *020
GODREAU, Miguel F. HILLSIDE L2 ST 5 CAIMITO 00926 #024-07-1933 L1934 **IM OS** *071
GOMEZ, Ada R. I-15 CUPEY GARDENS, 11TH STREET 00926 #042-01-1971 L1973 **PD PHP** *030
GOMEZ-ALICEA, Jose Ramon. ■ 00926 #847-04-1966 L1968 **PD OS** *071
GOMEZ HORMAZABAL, Lope M. ■ 00924 #308-03-1984 L1994 **GP** *020
GONZALEZ, Andrea L. A10 CALLE TREVISO, VILLA CAPRI 00924 #042-04-1984 L1987 **P** *020
GONZALEZ, Antonio Romero. L M SOUTHFRONT 500 00926 #649-14-1976 L1978 **GP** *020
GONZALEZ, Carlos Juan. ■ 00925 #649-14-1977 L1979 **GP** *020
GONZALEZ, Carlos Santos. 726 CAL JL ANDN VILLA PRAD 00924 #847-02-1975 L1978 **GP** *020
GONZALEZ, Carmen I. ■ 00927 #042-01-1979 L1983 **PTH** *020 †50
GONZALEZ, Juan. AVE POL 497 LA CUMBRE, STE 330 00926 #042-01-1978 L1983 **CD IM** *062
GONZALEZ, Liz Marie. ■ 00924 #042-02-2006 **P** *012
GONZALEZ, Luis J. ■ 00926 #275-01-1957 L1973 **GP** *020
GONZALEZ, Maria N. ■ 00924 #042-01-1980 L1983 *020
GONZALEZ, Maria-Del-R. LADERAS DE PALMA REAL 00926 #042-01-1980 L1983 **PD** *020 †55
GONZALEZ, Maribelle. ■ 00924 #042-04-1988 L1991 **P** *020
GONZALEZ, Wilma A. ST 21 1323 MONTECARLO 00924 #847-10-1961 L1963 **PM** *040
GONZALEZ ARXER, Rolando J. U3-6 CARR 21, URB LAS AMERICAS 00921 #275-01-1954 L1973 **GS** *020
GONZALEZ-DIAZ, Lourdes I. ■ 00926 #042-03-1980 L1984 *020
GONZALEZ-OLIVERO, Hector. 1000 CALLE LUIS PARDO, URB SAN MARTIN 00924 #847-05-1975 L1979 **GP** *020
GONZALEZ-PIJEM, Lillian. 58 CALLE MALVA, URB SANTA MARIA 00927 #847-01-1970 L1978 **PD PDE** *020 †55
GONZALEZ-QUINONES, Jose O. 818 AVE ITURREGUI, URB CLUB MANOR 00924 #308-01-1988 L1992 **P** *020
GONZALEZ ROBLES, Gisela. 990 CALLE 15 SE, REPTO METROPOLITANO 00921 #042-04-1992 L1995 *020
GONZALEZ-TORRES, Fernando. 167 CAL MMS URB SANTA MARI 00927 #649-14-1978 L1984 **EM** *020
GRANA, Roberto. 1616 CALLE SANTA EDUVIGIS, URB SAGRADO CORAZON 00926 #847-06-1976 L1978 **GP** *020
GRAULAU, Carmen Ana. COND. ALTAMIRA CENTER, CALLW PERSEO 501. APT. 5B 00920 #649-26-1978 L1981 **GP** *020
GREEN-LOPEZ, Lilliam. ■ 00926 #042-03-1980 L1984 **PD** *040 †55
GUERRERO DE PUMAREJO, M. ■ 00926 #847-02-1957 L1973 **PD** *020
GUZMAN ALVARADO, Wilberto. 1716 CALLE PARANA, URB EL CEREZAL 00926 #042-01-1988 L1992 **CD VM** *020 †20
HENN, Carmen E. ■ 00926 #042-01-1984 L1988 **OPH** *020 †35
HERNANDEZ, Boyd. 66 PARK CT 00926 #649-33-1982 L1988 **GP** *020
HERNANDEZ, Genil N. 1305 CALLE 8, URB MONTE CARLO 00924 #042-01-1968 L1970 **PD** *040
HERNANDEZ, Jose Demorizi. D2 CALLE FRONTERA, VILLA ANDALUCIA 00926 #308-01-1972 L1982 **RO R** *020 †80
HERNANDEZ, Pedro Morales. 59 CALLE SANTA ANASTACIA, URB EL VIGIA 00926 #847-01-1972 L1982 **RO R** *020 †80
HERNANDEZ-GUASCH, Rayda. VIA SAN PAOLO F3 MONTE AL 00927 #042-01-1980 L1984 **DR** *020 †80
HERNANDEZ HERNANDEZ, M L. ■ 00926 #275-01-1957 L1973 **OS** *020
HERNANDEZ-LOPEZ, Edgardo. ■ 00926 #847-03-1971 L1974 **CD IM** *020 †20
HERNANDEZ MARTINEZ, Pedro. ■ 00925 #847-05-1979 L1983 **IM END** *071
HERNANDEZ MATOS, Jose A. 1227 EXT SAN AGUSTIN 7 ST 00926 #649-01-1934 L1940 **GP PHP** *071

HERNANDEZ OVIEDO, S A. ANON 178 HIGHLAND PARK 00924 #308-01-1954 L1966 **GP OS** *020
HESTRES-VELEZ, Raymond A. 784 CALLE 5 SO, URB CAPARRA TER 00921 #308-03-1977 L1979 **EM GP** *020
IRIZARRI, Ermelinda M. ■ 00926 #649-01-1960 L1960 **P CHP** *071
IRIZARRY, Arlene. ■ 00921 #042-01-1995 L1998 **PD** *020
IRIZARRY-BENITEZ, Antonio. TIZIN 1618 RIO PIEDRAS HTS 00926 #649-01-1962 L1963 **GP** *020
ITURREGUI PAGAN, Miguel S. ■ 00926 #042-01-1972 L1978 **GS** *020
IZQUIERDO, Natalio E. SUITE 310, TORRESAN FRANASCO 00923 #042-02-1986 L1988 **OS** *020
IZQUIERDO-MORA, Luis A. 1107 CALLE WILLIAM JONES 00925 #042-01-1956 L1958 **FM FPG** *020 †18
JARAMILLO, Eduardo Leon. ■ 00921 #264-06-1981 L2004 **OBG** *020
JAVIER CANDELARIO, Juan. 1790 CALLE BEGONIA, MANS DE RIO PIEDRAS 00926 #042-01-1972 L1974 **IM HEM** *020
JIMENEZ-DIETSCH, Ramon E. 317 PORTAL DE LA REIN #317, AVENIDA MONTE CARLO 00924 #847-01-1963 L1966 **PD OS** *020
JIRAU-TOLEDO, Aquiles. ■ 00927 #308-01-1974 L1979 **AN** *020
JOHNSON POLANCO, Magaly. 2010 CALLE I DE LUZAN, URB EL SENORIAL 00926 #042-04-1993 L1998 *100
LABORDE, Gabriel Enrique. ■ 00926 #308-06-1983 L1997 **FM** *020
LAO, Carlos Roberto. ■ 00926 #042-01-1971 L1973 **CHN PD** *020
LASTRA, Jorge Juan. M8 CALLE ROSA, PARQ DE SANTA MARIA 00927 #847-05-1973 L1975 **CD IM** *020 †25
LASTRA, Rafael. W7-15 CALLE J BOSCAN, URB LADERAS DE PALMA REAL 00926 #042-01-1986 L1989 **CD IM** *020 †20
LAVERGNE CUEVAS, Rafael. ■ 00927 #737-01-1955 L1958 **PD** *071
LAZAGA-COBIAN, Jose N. JESUS T PINERO 300, CENTRACT RADIOLOGY CENTRE 00927 #847-02-1963 L1967 **PD** *020
LAZARO GARCIA, Pedro. ■ 00925 #649-01-1953 L1954 **D** *072
LEBRON-LUGO, Maria I. ■ 00926 #042-01-1979 L1982 **FM** *020
LEON, Annette Vivian. 7 CALLE NEVAREZ # 1102, URB SAN IGNACIO 00927 #042-01-1986 L1989 **NPM PD** *020
LEON, Yaris Arlene. ■ 00927 #042-01-1998 L1999 **OPH GP** *020 †35
LIZASOAIN SANTIAGO, Aida. 1056 CALLE FERROCARRIL 00925 #042-04-1996 L1998 **FM** *020
LLORENS UBARRI, Edgardo. 670 CALLE JULIO ANDINO, VILLA PRADES 00924 #308-03-1980 L1988 *020
LOCKWARD-SERRET, Dulce M. ■ 00924 #308-01-1963 L1977 **GP** *020
LONGO-CORDERO, Rafael. ■ 00927 #023-01-1953 L1955 **NS** *071 †25
LOPEZ, Antonio Garcia-And. 1489 CAL CLV URB ANTONSANT, MEDICAL DOCTOR 00927 #847-04-1966 L1990 **GP** *030
LOPEZ, Jorge Luis. ■ 00926 #042-02-2000 L2003 **EM** *100
LOPEZ, Jose C. ■ 00927 #308-03-1983 L1990 **PD** *020
LOPEZ, Juan. 1017 CALLE GEN DEL VALLE, URB GONZALEZ SEIJO 00924 #847-05-1970 L1972 **D** *020 †15
LOPEZ, Raul H. VILLA NEVAREZ, 1073 8TH STREET 00927 #042-01-1962 L1968 **PD ID** *040 †55
LOPEZ, Ricardo Jose. ■ 00927 #042-01-1978 L1982 **RO** *020 †80
LOPEZ, Victor Mario. ■ 00926 #847-04-1966 L1974 **CLP PTH** *075 †50
LOPEZ, Waldo Edgar. ■ 00927 #028-34-1955 L1958 **DR CD** *072
LOPEZ BONET, Luz Nereida. 927 AVE CAMPO RICO, URB COUNTRY CLUB 00924 #308-03-1985 L1988 **GP** *020
LOPEZ CABAN, Reinaldo. COOP LOS ROBLES APT 815A 00927 #308-03-1981 L1994 *020
LOPEZ ERQUICIA, Maria T.. ■ 00926 #649-14-1989 L1993 *020
LOPEZ RIVERA, Ileana. ■ 00927 #308-01-1985 L1992 *020
LOPEZ-RODRIGUEZ, Carmen A. LAS LOMAS, CARR 21 #U3 2-A 00920 #042-03-1981 L1985 **IM** *020
LOPEZ-SANABRIA, Ulises. ■ 00927 #041-09-1940 L1941 **OS** *020
LOPEZ SUAREZ, Jose August. 170 CALLE ARIZMENDI 00925 #847-09-1980 L2003 **GP** *100
LORENZI, Pedro A. ■ 00924 #042-01-1966 L1970 **GE IM** *020
LOUBRIEL-JIMENEZ, M. 721 HIGHLAND PARK 00924 #847-02-1974 L1976 **GP** *020
LOZADA-VELAZQUEZ, Benj. SAN JUAN CITY HOSP, DEPT MED 00928 #308-02-1977 L1982 **RHU IM** *050
LUGO, Gabriel Eduardo. ■ 00924 #042-03-2008 *012
LUGO, Miguel Angel. 224 CALLE HIMALAYA, URB MONTEREY 00926 #042-01-1973 L1975 **U** *020 †95
LUGO RODRIGUEZ, Jorge E. 1056 AVE MUNOZ RIVERA, OFFICE 606 EDIF FIRST FEDE 00927 #042-01-1955 L1959 **CD IM** *020 †20
LUNA-FLORES, Luis A. LAS LOMAS, CARR #21 T3-7PEY 00921 #847-04-1970 L1975 **FM** *020
MACHADO RAMOS, Gladys I. 114 CAL LS VGS URB LAS CUM, AVDA LAUREL 2M15 LOMAS VER 00926 #847-02-1985 L1994 *020
MAESTRE GARCIA, Ivonne. ■ 00924 #308-01-1985 L1995 **GP** *020
MAISONET, Ruth N. ■ 00921 #042-03-1993 L1997 **OBG** *020 †30
MALDONADO, Alicia. 2026 CALLE FRAY GRANADA, URB EL SENORIAL 00926 #042-03-1989 L1992 **PD** *020
MALDONADO-CORTES, Jose M. 4 CALLE PARANA # S-2, URB EL PARAISO 00926 #847-06-1971 L1974 **GP** *020
MALDONADO FELICIANO, F. ■ 00926 #649-04-1960 L1963 **P** *020
MANGUAL-CASANOVA, T. ■ 00926 #308-03-1977 L1981 **GP** *020
MARCANO-MARCANO, Rafael A. 497 AVE EMILIANO POL # 616 00926 #847-05-1961 L1964 **OBG** *020 †30
MARCEUS, Pierre Antoine. ■ 00927 #649-43-1985 L2005 *100
MARCIAL, Ana Rosa. PASIONARIA 1935 STA MARIA 00927 #042-01-1978 L1982 **OBG** *020 †30
MARCIAL, Raul Armando. CLAVEL M4 PARQUE STA MARIA 00927 #042-01-1977 L1983 **DR** *020 †20
MARCO, Raul. CONSOLIDATED MALL C 10, C 0 STE 922 AVE E POL 497 00926 #042-01-1980 L1984 **N OS** *020
MARGARIDA VINER, Raul. 1652 CALLE PECOS, PARADISE HILLS 00926 #308-06-1987 L1993 *071
MARIN, Nancy. ■ 00926 #042-01-1957 L1961 **IM** *071
MARIN-AVILES, Jesus. ■ 00926 #042-01-1996 L1999 **FPG** *020 †18
MARRERO, Santiago. 1216 CALLE BRUMBAUGH, BO VENEZUELA 00926 #847-10-1979 L1991 **GP** *020
MARRERO-MAS, Milagros. 77 CALLE PARQUE DEL ORIENT, PASEO DEL PARQUE 00926 #042-03-1981 L1986 **IM** *020
MARTIN, Francisco Miguel. 1542 CALLE BORI # B, URB BELISA 00927 #649-14-1979 L1985 **PD** *020

■ = Address Information Privacy Protected

MARTINEZ, Arnaldo. ■ 00926 #042-01-1988 L1992 **IM** *020

MARTINEZ, Candido. 18 REP ALAMEIN 00926 #042-01-1963 L1967 **PM PMM** *020 †60

MARTINEZ, Diana P. 112 CALLE ARZUAGA STE 802 00925 #042-01-1982 L1986 **PO OPH** *020 †35

MARTINEZ, Jose Antonio. 438 CALLE SAN LEANDRO, URB SAGRADO CORAZON 00926 #042-01-1974 L1976 **PD PDE** *030

MARTINEZ, Laura Elaine. 224 CALLE HIMALAYA, URB MONTEREY 00926 #308-02-1974 L1977 **PD** *030 †55

MARTINEZ, Luis Fernando. 1601 CALLE TIBER, URB EL PARAISO 00926 #308-03-1981 L1997 **FM** *020

MARTINEZ, Ruth Natalia. PO BOX 21405, SAN JUAN CITY HOSP 00928 #665-02-2006 **IM** *012

MARTINEZ, Sol M. ■ 00927 #042-03-1983 L1987 **AN** *074

MARTINEZ, Zobeida E. S-3-20 VILLAS DE PARANA 00924 #042-01-1983 L1986 **CHP** *020

MARTINEZ ANDUJAR, Ramon J. ARZUAGA ST, BOX AM 00928 #308-01-1947 L1959 **GP OS** *020

MARTINEZ COLLAZO, Angel P. 927 CALLE CARMEN HERNANDEZ, URB EL COMANDANTE 00924 #308-03-1976 L1980 **GP** *020

MARTINEZ-DEL VALLE, R. 112 CALLE ARZUAGA, 1101 MEDINA CENTER 00925 #847-04-1958 L1962 **PD** *020

MARTINEZ DE POLO, Hilda M. ■ 00927 #041-07-1952 L1953 **PD OS** *071 †55

MARTINEZ-PEREZ, Leonor G. CALLE 12-1074 VIL NEVARE 00927 #308-03-1977 L1980 **PD** *074

MARTINEZ-RIVERA, Luis A. RESIDENCIA DE LA FACULTAD 00923 #042-03-1995 L1997 **FM** *020

MARTINEZ-TABOAS, Maria D. VILLA NEVAREZ 00927 #042-01-1995 L1999 **P** *020

MARTINO TRILLA, Jesus F. ■ 00926 #649-01-1973 L1975 **EM GP** *020

MARTINO-TRILLA, Jose M. 1 #109 PASCO LAS VISTAS II 00926 #649-01-1974 L1976 **IM** *040 †20

MATOS FERNANDEZ, Maria M. ■ 00924 #847-10-1967 L1969 **GP** *071

MATOS-RODRIGUEZ, Luis. ■ 00926 #847-01-1968 L1973 **GP** *020

MATTEI, Antonio. 35 CALLE 4 # S-1, URB SAN IGNACIO 00927 #042-01-1992 L1996 **AN** *020 †05

MEDINA, Antonio Samuel. ■ 00929 #010-01-1943 L1945 **PHP OBG** *062

MEDINA, Maria Menendez. 2007 CALLE JOSE FIDALGO DZ, URB CALDAS 00926 #847-10-1966 L1975 *020

MEJIA SOSA, Jose Manuel. ANTARTICO 436-PUERTO NUEVO 00920 #308-02-1974 L1989 **GP** *020

MELENDEZ, Carlos Manuel. ■ 00926 #847-10-1970 L1973 **N** *020

MELENDEZ, Edwin. 205 CARR 21, VILLA LOS OLMOS 00927 #042-01-1976 L1983 **GE IM** *020

MELENDEZ, Gloria Maria. 00924 #649-26-1977 L1985 **GP** *020

MELENDEZ, Olga I. 11 AVE 65 INFANTERIA, URB ALAMEIN 00926 #042-03-1980 L1984 **NEP IM** *020

MELENDEZ, Raul. SAN JUAN CITY HOSP, DEPT MED 00928 #308-13-1998 L2002 **IM** *020

MELENDEZ, Ulises. 576 CALLE JULIO C ARTEAGA, VILLA PRADES 00924 #042-01-1994 L1997 **NEP** *020

MELINDEZ, Eliut. ■ 00921 #308-03-1982 L1991 **IM** *020

MENA PEREZ, Raysa. PO BOX 21405 00928 #308-01-1991 L2004 **IM** *100 †20

MENDEZ, Jose Maria. ■ 00927 #308-01-1986 L1997 *020

MENDEZ, Olga I. 1672 CALLE VIOLETA, URB BELISA 00927 #042-01-1965 L1969 **PD** *071 †55

MENDOZA, Idalia Carrion-F. ■ 00926 #042-01-1958 L1962 **PD** *030 †55

MENENDEZ-CORRADA, Rodrigo. SUCHVILLE GUAYNABO, 20 SUCHVILLE ST 00922 #041-13-1943 L1943 **HEM IM** *071 †20

MILAN, Juan Arnaldo. 1310 CALLE 25, URB MONTE CARLO 00924 #042-01-1987 L1991 **ID PD** *020

MIRANDA, Maximino. ■ 00926 #042-01-1980 L1983 **FM** *020 †18

MIR-FRANQUI, Cecilia J. ■ 00924 #042-03-1987 L1991 **FM** *020

MIRO CEBALLOS, Jose A. 16TH ST NW 1351 PTO NUEVO 00920 #042-04-1981 L1983 **GP** *020

MOJICA-MORALES, Victor M. ROSE LL 14 EXT BORINQ GDNS 00926 #847-10-1962 L1965 **N** *020 †75

MOLINARIS, Jose Luis. ■ 00926 #847-04-1957 L1960 **BBK** *030 †50

MONJE CORUJO, Jose G. ■ 00926 #561-17-1966 L1975 *100

MONSERRATE-HERNANDEZ, A L. ■ 00921 #847-04-1975 L1980 **OBG** *100

MONTALVO ALAMO, Michele. CALLE 1 A9 COLINAS VERDES 00924 #649-14-1993 L1995 **GP** *020

MONTALVO-FABRELLAS, E. ■ 00926 #649-14-1976 L1978 **P** *020

MONTES-RUIZ, Juan. CARR 21 U-3-4 LAS LOMAS 00921 #042-03-1980 L1983 **FM** *020

MONTOYA, Miguel Angel. PO BOX 21405, SAN JUAN CITY HOSP 00928 #649-14-1993 L2005 **IM** *012

MORA DELGADO, Jose A. 50 CALLE 10 # 1588 00924 #308-03-1984 L1995 **IM** *020

MORALES, Carlos A. ■ 00924 #308-01-1967 L1975 **PTH** *020

MORALES, Frank Esteban. 966 CALLE PUERTO PRINCIPE, URB LAS AMERICAS 00921 #649-03-1993 L1997 **IM** *020

MORALES, Ilia Marie. COLINAS DE MONTE CARLO, CALLE 15 A #41 00924 #042-01-1998 L2003 **PTH** *020

MORALES, Jose A. 1107 CALLE WILLIAM JONES 00925 #042-01-1968 L1970 **PD** *020

MORALES, Jose Bartolo. ■ 00925 #649-14-2002 L2003 *100

MORALES-FERNANDEZ, Rafael. ■ 00926 #847-04-1960 L1967 **ORS** *071

MORENO-MALDONADO, Victor. ■ 00926 #308-03-1979 L1982 *020

MOSCOSO, Ricardo Antonio. ■ 00927 #042-03-1980 L1983 **OBG** *040 †30

MOULIER, Jose Emmanuel. F12 CALLE 10, URB FAIRVIEW 00926 #847-17-1978 L1981 **CHP P** *020

MUNDO, Jorge Angel. ■ 00927 #042-01-1997 L2001 **IC** *100 †20 ‡

MUNOZ VARGAS, Grissel. 1654 CALLE SANTA ANGELA 00926 #649-14-1988 L1994 **PD** *020

NATER-OJEDA, Carlos E. 432 CALLE SAN CLAUDIO, URB SAGRADO CORAZON 00926 #042-01-1958 L1963 **IM HEM** *020

NAVARRO, Maria Teresa. 1711 CALLE SAN JULIAN, URB SAGRADO CORAZON 00926 #847-05-1971 L1978 **CHP P** *020

NAVARRO DE PEDRO, Jose E. 1711 CALLE SAN JULIAN, URB SAGRADO CORAZON 00926 #847-04-1973 L1975 **DR** *020

NAZARIO, Janira. ■ 00927 #042-01-1987 L1992 **CHP P** *100

NAZARIO-FERNANDEZ, Juan A. 138 AVE WINSTON CHURCHILL, STE 533 00926 #042-03-1981 L1985 **EM** *030 †16

NEGRON, Maria E. ■ 00926 #041-13-1959 L1963 **OBG** *071 †30

NEGRON, Nahir. ■ 00926 #042-03-1990 L1994 **P** *020

NEVARES CATALA, Carmen M. DIASY CC1 BAERNQN GRDNS 00926 #847-04-1963 L1967 **PD END** *030 †55

NEVAREZ, Mario R. YELLOWSTONE Y1 2 PK GRDNS 00926 #042-01-1988 L1992 **PD OS** *020 †55

NIEVES, Gil A. AVE E POL 497 STE 202 00926 #042-01-1980 L1983 **FM** *020

NIEVES, Teresa Garnica De. 1665 CALLE LENA 00926 #649-01-1956 L1956 **GP** *072

NOGUERAS RODRIGUEZ, R. E12 CALLE SALAMANCA, URB SANTA ANA 00927 #042-01-1972 L1974 **P** *062 †75

NORIEGA DE QUINTERO, Eliz. ■ 00928 #042-01-1957 L1961 **CHP P** *020

NORMANDIA, Ramses. 798 CALLE HABANA, URB LA RIVIERA IND PARK 00921 #042-01-1998 L1999 **P** *020

NUNEZ TORO, Victor M. ■ 00928 #847-10-1958 L1961 **GP** *072 †50

OBEN MARTINO, Alberto. VILLAS DEL PARANA, CALLE 8S7-23 00926 #308-01-1974 L1978 **FM** *020

OCHOA-GARCIA, James P. ■ 00927 #341-01-1972 **GS** *100

OJEDA, Ivonne L. ■ 00926 #042-01-1982 L1988 **DR IM** *020 †80

OLIVARI, Luis Antonio. SUITE 200, HOSPITAL METROPOLITANO 00922 #042-01-1976 L1981 **RHU IM** *020

OMS, Magali Maldonado. STA MARIA, DIAMELA 1800 00922 #042-01-1967 L1971 **OS PD** *030

OPPENHEIMER ORTIZ, Miguel. 112 ARZUAGA MEDINA CTR 901 00928 #847-01-1962 L1964 **OBS** *020

ORAMA-ALVAREZ, Flora I. ■ 00924 #042-03-1980 L1985 **R** *020

OREA VELA, Juana. PO BOX 21107 00928 #847-04-1960 L1965 **OPH OS** *071

ORRACA-MARTINEZ, Jaime. ST 3-1022 VILLA NEVAREZ 00927 #847-04-1957 L1963 **GP** *020

ORTEGA, Eileen M. COND LOS ROBLES EDIF A, APT 206 00927 #042-01-1990 L1993 **FPG** *020 †18

ORTIZ, Alberto. MEDICAL SCIENCE CAMPUS, UNIVRSITY OF PR 00920 #308-03-1975 L1980 **AN** *020

ORTIZ, Lucy Lymari. PO BOX 21405, SAN JUAN CITY HOSP 00928 #308-13-2005 **IM** *012

ORTIZ, Luis Rafael. ■ 00926 #042-01-2002 *100

ORTIZ, Omar. PO BOX 21405 00928 #649-14-1998 L1999 **PD** *020

ORTIZ DOMENECH, Ramon E. ■ 00929 #308-01-1973 L1978 **PM** *071

ORTIZ-NOLASCO, Reynaldo. 1371 CALLE SAN BERNARDO, URB ALTAMESA 00921 #847-02-1981 L1984 **EM** *020 †16

ORTIZ-RIVERA, Petra J. MIRADOR BERQUN GRDNS C 12 00926 #847-06-1976 L1979 *020

ORTIZ-VEGA, Pablo A. 313 CALLE COLUMBIA # 4 00927 #649-01-1956 L1959 **A** *071

OTERO MALDONADO, Iris N. 1808 CALLE SANTA ISABEL 00926 #042-03-1980 L1984 **IM** *020

OYOLA, Isabel M. ■ 00926 #649-01-1958 L1963 **AN** *071

PABLOS-DUCLERC, Alexis. ■ 00924 #308-03-1978 L1980 **OBG** *020

PABLOS-DUCLERC, Yaidi N. 866 CALLE SARA ISABL SPNCR, URB COUNTRY CLUB 00924 #308-03-1977 L1979 **P** *030

PACHECO, Ricardo. ■ 00926 #042-01-1974 L1977 **PD** *020 †55

PADILLA-LUGO, Amarilis. REPARTO METROPOLITANO, 34 SE # 1197 00921 #042-04-1981 L1985 **NPM PD** *020

PAGAN, Cruz Edgardo. 1315 CALLE 23, URB MONTE CARLO 00924 #308-01-1981 L1992 **GP EM** *020

PAGAN, Evelyn Eugenia. ■ 00927 #649-18-1981 L1992 **GP** *020

PAGAN-GONZALEZ, Dimas. 110 CALLE GEORGETTI 00925 #847-04-1968 L1974 **IM** *020

PAGANI, Wilfredo. 1612 CALLE SANTA PRAXEDES, URB SAGRADO CORAZON 00926 #042-01-1983 L1988 **GE IM** *040 †20

PAGAN-SAEZ, Heriberto. 1619 CALLE SAN JULIAN, URB SAGRADO CORAZON 00926 #042-01-1959 L1962 **PDR** *020

PALACIOS-MARTINEZ, M. 65TH INF STA 30052 00929 #847-08-1978 L1983 **GP** *020

PALERMO GAROFALO, Coromoto. PO BOX 21405, SAN JUAN CITY HOSP 00928 #935-01-1992 **IM** *012

PALMER BENGOA, Judith T. 3 CALLEJON E # II-6, BO VENEZUELA 00926 #042-04-1998 L2001 **FM** *020

PALOU, Maria Ines. ■ 00927 #042-03-1990 L1993 **PM** *020 †60

PARRILLA, Ana M. ■ 00927 #042-01-1986 L1988 *020

PASCUAL, Rohel. ■ 00926 #042-01-1988 L1992 **OBG** *020

PASTRANA OLIVENCIA, Tomas. AMATISTA 15 BUCARE 00926 #308-03-1980 L1986 *020

PELLOT-MORAN, Norberto. ■ 00927 #649-18-1979 L1982 **P** *020

PENA, Ivelisse A. VILLA NEVAREZ, CALLE 31074 00927 #308-01-1982 L1996 *020

PENA FIGUEROA, Jose R. ■ 00926 #308-03-1981 L1993 **GP** *020

PENA-ORMENO, Jose Raul. ■ 00926 #847-01-1967 L1975 **OBS** *020

PERDOMO, Raymond. ■ 00926 #847-06-1975 L1977 **DR R** *020

PEREA LOPEZ, Ramon M. ■ 00926 #042-01-1990 L1993 **CD** *020

PEREZ, Ana Carmen. 1092 CALLE 15, VILLA NEVAREZ 00927 #308-02-1987 L1991 **IM** *020

PEREZ, Edgar Asmir. PO BOX 21405 00928 #308-13-2000 L2004 *100

PEREZ, Yolanda Margenat. 1916 CALLE TRINITARIA, URB SANTA MARIA 00927 #847-08-1974 L1978 **GP** *020

PEREZ-BERDEGUER, Domingo. ■ 00926 #042-04-1988 L1989 **CD** *020

PEREZ-CABALLERO, Hector. PSYCH CTR RESEARCH 00928 #847-10-1962 L1965 **P OS** *020

PEREZ CASELLAS, Rafael Ju. PO BOX 21405, SAN JUAN CITY HOSP 00928 #649-14-2001 **ON** *100

PEREZ-DIEPPA, Ivan Jose. ■ 00926 #847-02-1977 L1982 **PHO PD** *020

PEREZ-GONZALEZ, Dalia E. 799 CALLE 37 SO, URB LAS LOMAS 00921 #308-03-1982 L1987 **P** *020

PEREZ-SANCHEZ, Gilberto. C PRINCPAL 22 LOS CANTZLES 00926 #042-04-1982 L1985 **GP** *020

PEREZ SANCHEZ, Johnny H. 1669 AVE AMERICO MIRANDA, URB LAS LOMAS 00921 #308-03-1988 L1996 **IM** *020

PEREZ-TORRES, Rosa I. URB COLINAS DE MONTECARLO, 40 23 AST 00924 #042-01-1982 L1985 **PD** *071

PICHARDO, Rafael A. 1669 CALLE ORINOCO, URB EL CEREZAL 00926 #308-01-1966 L1975 **GS** *020

PIETRI-RODRIGUEZ, Maria M. 1677 CALLE LILAS, URB SAN FRANCISCO 00927 #847-01-1982 L1986 **PM** *020

PINEIRO-MONET, Ramon. ■ 00926 #042-01-1954 L1957 **D** *020 †15

PINERO, Ramon. ■ 00928 #847-01-1972 L1975 **P** *020

PIZARRO-TORRES, Gladys. F10 CAL TRV PASEO DE LA FU 00926 #847-10-1977 L1982 *020

POLANCO, Victor Manuel. CALLE 8 S O-1416, CAPARRA TERR 00921 #308-01-1985 L1988 **GP** *020

POLONIO DE LUNA, Virgilio. ■ 00921 #308-03-1986 L1991 *020

PONS, Francisco Jimenez. EL SENORIAL MAIL STA 331 00926 #847-02-1981 L1984 **FM** *020

PRINCIPE SNYDER, Lisa A. ■ 00926 #042-04-1988 L1993 **P** *020

PROANO, Cesar H. BX 29517 65TH INFANTRY 00929 #649-01-1971 L1978 **HEM IM** *050

PUJOL, Bianca S. 1208 COND LAS CAMELIAS #11 00924 #308-01-1981 L1993 *020

PUMAREJO, Milagros M. ■ 00921 #042-01-1978 L1982 **PD** *020 †55

■ = Address Information Privacy Protected

8201

QUILES PAREDES, Zaida E. ■ 00925 #847-04-1972 L1975 **GP** *020

QUINONES, Pablo J. ■ 00927 #649-26-1980 L1991 **GP** *020

QUINONES-GUZMAN, Rafael M. ■ 00926 #847-06-1980 L1980 **GP** *020

QUINONES PARDO, Mildred D. 1800 CALLE ALCALA, URB COLLEGE PARK 00921 #308-01-1986 L1993 **PD** *020

QUINTERO, Mariadel C. ■ 00926 #042-01-1988 L1991 **PD** *020 †55

RABELL, Vilma M. 909 CALLE DUKE, DUKE CHALETS TH9 UNIV GARD 00927 #042-01-1971 L1973 **IM** *020

RAMIREZ, Antonio A. ■ 00927 #042-01-1990 L1993 **OBG** *020

RAMIREZ, Carlos Eduardo. 282 AVE JESUS T PINERO, PLAZA EL AMAL 205 00927 #042-01-1981 L1984 **OBG** *020 †30

RAMIREZ, Edwin Lopez. ■ 00926 #847-01-1957 L1961 **PUD** *020

RAMIREZ, Francisco Amador. ■ 00926 #042-02-1999 L2004 **GS** *020 †80

RAMIREZ DE ARELLANO, M D. ■ 00926 #016-06-1941 L1943 **NS** *071 †25

RAMIREZ-SOSA, Magali J. ■ 00924 #308-01-1981 L1982 **FM** *020

RAMON, Eduardo Rafael. 1889 CALLE JUAN SUAREZ, URB FAIRVIEW 00926 #308-03-1983 L1992 **GP** *020

RAMOS, Luis Javier. ■ 00926 #042-02-1999 L2004 **IM** *100

RAMOS, Luis Juan. ■ 00926 #042-03-1997 L1999 *020

RAMOS, Secundino. JOSE DE DIEGO 409 00923 #308-01-1954 L1974 **OS** *071

RAMOS, Victor Manuel. ■ 00921 #042-01-1998 L2000 **PD** *020

RAMOS CUBANO, Jose Ivan. RR 3 BOX 559 00926 #649-14-1976 L1978 *020

RAMOS DE RAMIREZ, Sonia. LAS VEGAS 119 URB LA CMBR 00926 #847-02-1963 L1966 **PHP GP** *071

RAMOS DIAZ, Luis R. 97 CALLE CASIA, PASEO LAS VISTAS II CALLE 00921 #042-04-1996 L1999 **FM** *020

RAMOS HERNANDEZ, Rafael A. ■ 00926 #308-03-1983 L1989 *020

RAMOS MEDINA, Fernando. 913 CALLE SRST URB SEVILLA 00924 #847-05-1956 L1959 **IM** *071

RAMOS-MORALES, Francisco. ■ 00926 #023-07-1950 L1950 **IM** *030

RENTA, Antonio G. 138 AVE WINSTON CHURCHILL, URB CROWN HLS 00926 #042-01-1983 L1987 **CD IM** *020

REYES, Juan Antonio O. ■ 00926 #308-01-1990 **IM** *100

REYES, Lidia Ivette. ■ 00926 #042-01-1979 L1983 **DR** *020 †80

REYMUNDI, Raul. 100 AVE DE DIEGO, URB SAN FRANCISCO 00927 #308-03-1983 L1980 **GP** *020

RIJO, Roosevelt. 2067 CALLE BENITO FEIJOO 00926 #308-01-1985 L1989 *020

RIOS, Maria Del Carmen. 914 BOSQUE REAL COND 00926 #042-01-1981 L1984 **OBG** *020

RIOS, Myrangeliss. ■ 00926 #042-03-2004 **CHP** *012

RIOS, Viola T. ■ 00927 #847-04-1962 L1987 **GP** *020

RIOS MEJIA, Ivette. ■ 00926 #649-14-1989 L1992 *020

RIVERA, Aixa. ■ 00921 #042-03-1988 L1991 **RHU** *020

RIVERA, Carlos Roberto. 99 CALLE MIRADOR, PASEO ALTO 00926 #042-01-1981 L1984 **ID PD** *020 †55

RIVERA, Digna Rafaela. APART 30749 65TH INF ST 00929 #308-01-1979 L1985 *020

RIVERA, Hilda L. 53 CALL HCC URB LOS PASEOS 00926 #042-01-1964 L1967 **NPM** *020 †55

RIVERA, Jose Miguel. MIZAR 454 DOS PINOS 00923 #649-14-2001 L2003 *100

RIVERA, Luis A. 2 CARR 21 # S3, URB COOP V BORINQUEN 00921 #649-14-1978 L1980 **GP** *020

RIVERA, Ramon. 277 CALLE TRUJILLO, LAS CUMBRES-LAURAL 00926 #042-03-1988 L1992 **PM** *020

RIVERA ASENCIO, Victor M. PO BOX 21230 00928 #048-12-1951 L1953 **GP IMG** *071

RIVERA CARTAGENA, Hilda M. ■ 00924 #847-02-1987 L1995 **P** *020

RIVERA COTTES, Victor M. ■ 00927 #847-05-1961 L1961 **GP OS** *020

RIVERA-CRUZ, Ana. ■ 00926 #847-04-1965 L1973 **GS** *100

RIVERA DE ARROYO, Freya. 129 CAL GDLQVR URB EL CERE 00926 #042-01-1954 L1955 **PUD IM** *071

RIVERA-FIGUEROA, Mayra I. 497 AVE EMILIANO POL, STE 451 00926 #649-14-1985 L1987 **HEM ON** *020

RIVERA-HERNANDEZ, G. ■ 00924 #056-06-1947 L1949 **P PA** *075

RIVERA-MASS, Jorge. 3C SECT ALAMAIN 00926 #042-03-1986 L1990 **CHP** *020

RIVERA-VILLANUEVA, Marco. 1024 CALLE 3 SE, URB LA RIVIERA 00921 #308-03-1979 L1982 **GP** *020

ROBERT DE RAMIREZ, M I. ■ 00926 #016-06-1951 L1953 **N** *071

ROBLES, Tanis A. 697 CALLE CIPRES, URB HIGHLAND PARK 00924 #042-01-1966 L1969 **DIA END** *020

RODRIGUEZ, Carmen M. 5 ST S O 976 URB LA RIVIER 00926 #042-04-1983 L1985 **P** *020

RODRIGUEZ, Efrain. ■ 00924 #847-06-1974 L1978 **GP** *020

RODRIGUEZ, Ernesto L. 1029 CALLE TEGUCIGALPA, URB LA RIVIERA IND PARK 00921 #042-01-1982 L1985 **PD** *020

RODRIGUEZ, Federico. RR 2 BOX 11, PSYCHIATRIC HOSP 00926 #308-07-1982 L2005 *100

RODRIGUEZ, Frank A. 2022 CALLE CONCHA ESPINA, URB EL SENORIAL 00926 #042-03-1981 L1986 **PD** *020

RODRIGUEZ, Gilberto. 65TH INF STA 00929 #042-01-1975 L1981 **GS TRS** *020 †85

RODRIGUEZ, Ricardo A. ■ 00926 #042-04-1990 L1991 **PM** *020 †60

RODRIGUEZ, Ruben. 1785 CARR 21, URB LAS AMERICAS 00921 #042-01-1975 L1980 **IM** *020 †55

RODRIGUEZ, Victor Manuel. SANTA ROSA ST ROMANI GRDNS 00926 #308-01-1956 L1970 **PD** *020

RODRIGUEZ, William. ■ 00924 #042-01-1983 L1986 **PUD IM** *020 †20

RODRIGUEZ AJA, Evelyn. ■ 00927 #847-05-1976 L1980 **N** *020

RODRIGUEZ-AMADOR, Arlene. ■ 00926 #042-03-1998 L2004 **GS** *020

RODRIGUEZ ARROYO, Jesus. 158 CALLE LOS MIRTOS, URB HYDE PARK 00927 #042-01-1972 L1974 **GO** *020 †30

RODRIGUEZ-GOMEZ, B. JOSE SABOGAL 1941-BRN GRD 00927 #847-10-1970 L1974 **OBG** *100

RODRIGUEZ GONZALEZ, A. 1056 AVE MUNOZ RIVERA 00927 #042-01-1986 L1995 **VS GS** *020 †85

RODRIGUEZ MARRERO, V. 1385 AVE SAN IGNACIO, URB ALTAMESA 00921 #847-04-1956 L1959 **FM IM** *020

RODRIGUEZ-PEREZ, Agustin. MIMOSA 143 STA MARIA 00927 #847-05-1955 L1959 **OBS GYN** *071 †30

RODRIGUEZ-PEREZ, Carlos O. PO BOX 29683 00929 #847-04-1958 L1960 **R** *020

RODRIGUEZ-PLASENCIA, Luis. 318 CALLE 32, VILLA LOS OLMOS 00927 #275-01-1940 L1940 **D** *071

RODRIGUEZ RAMIREZ, Yolanda. PO BOX 21405 00928 #665-02-2007 **IM** *012

RODRIGUEZ ROBLES, Grisel. APT 1003 B, VILLAS DE MONTECARLO 00924 #649-14-1998 L2004 *100

RODRIGUEZ SANTIAGO, Jose. 1651 CALLE TAMESIS, URB RIO PIEDRAS HTS 00926 #042-01-1960 L1962 **P** *040

ROGES-DIAZ, Adriana. 231 HYDE PARK 00927 #042-03-1981 L1986 **PD** *020 †55

ROJAS, Carlos. 1056 CALLE FERROCARRIL 00925 #649-01-1954 L1962 **OTO** *071

ROJAS DAVIS, Acacia. 1056 CALLE FERROCARRIL 00925 #847-01-1964 L1968 **FM FSM** *020

ROJAS DAVIS, Eli S. 1056 CALLE FERROCARRIL 00925 #649-01-1956 L1957 **P** *020

ROJAS FERNANDEZ, Marco A. 1056 CALLE FERROCARRIL 00925 #649-14-1985 L1992 *020

ROJAS-RUIZ, Josefina. 1056 CALLE FERROCARRIL 00925 #649-14-1990 L1993 **P** *020

ROJAS-RUIZ, Luis C. 1056 FERNOCANNIL 00925 #649-14-1988 L1991 **P PYG** *020

ROLON-MARTINEZ, Felix. 1916 CALLE TRINITARIA, URB SANTA MARIA 00927 #847-08-1976 L1980 **AN** *020

ROMAN-PAGAN, Emma L. URB MONTECARLO, 8TH STREET #1364 00924 #042-03-1980 L1982 **FM** *072

ROMAN-PEREZ, Cesar A. PIRAND 518 ST PURPLE TREE 00926 #308-01-1955 L1968 **GP OS** *071

ROMEUS, Patrick. PO BOX 21405, SAN JUAN CITY HOSP 00928 #440-01-1995 **IM** *012

ROSADO, Julio R. PASADENA B-5, SAN GERARDO 00926 #042-04-1981 L1990 **GP** *020

ROSARIO, Arnaldo Luis. PIRINEOS 163, LA CUMBRE 00926 #308-03-1985 L1990 **GP** *020

ROSARIO, Ricardo. 138 AVE WINSTON CHURCHILL, URB CROWN HLS 00926 #847-04-1974 L1976 **GP** *020

ROSARIO, Rosario I. JASONE NO 1771 CROWN HILLS 00926 #847-05-1975 L1978 **FPS** *020

ROSSO, Diego. ■ 00927 #042-03-1988 L1992 **IM** *020

ROURA, Alejandrina A. ■ 00927 #847-04-1958 L1960 **PM** *020

ROURA, Alexandra Marie. ■ 00927 #042-01-1991 L1994 **PD** *050 †55

RUBIO, Juan M Fernandez. ■ 00926 #275-01-1950 L1974 **P** *020

RUIZ, Edna Maria. 3RD ST C-4 ROMANY PK 00926 #042-01-1981 L1985 **DR** *074

RUIZ, Ismael. ■ 00929 #005-12-1953 L1956 **ORS OS** *071

RUIZ-ROSARIO, William C. ■ 00926 #308-02-1976 L1982 **RO IM** *020

SAAVEDRA-SANQUIRICO, S. 99 CALLE MIRADOR, PASEO ALTO 00926 #042-03-1980 L1983 **ID IM** *020

SAEZ, Florencio, Jr. 216 CALLE PALMA REAL, UNIVERSITY GARDENS 00927 #649-01-1955 L1955 **PM OM** *071 †60

SALOM, Ivy. PO BOX 21405, SAN JUAN CITY HOSP 00928 #275-08-1997 **DR** *012

SANCHEZ, Carlos Guillermo. 24 CALLE 1, VILLA LOS OLMOS 00927 #042-01-1974 L1981 **IM ID** *040 †20

SANCHEZ, Lydia Enid. LAS LOMAS, MARGINAL 1784 00921 #308-04-1993 L1997 *020

SANCHEZ-INFANTE, Juan R. 696 CALLE WASHINGTON, URB LAS CUMBRES 00926 #042-03-1981 L1986 **PTH** *020

SANCHEZ MEANA, Luis F. DEPT OF HEALTH VALLEJO ST 00925 #010-01-1948 L1950 **PHP** *075

SANCHEZ MECEIRA, Ricardo. ■ 00926 #649-35-2000 L2002 *020

SANG-RIVAS, Guillen R. CALLE ANDES 114-MONTE REY 00926 #308-01-1969 L1980 **PTH** *020

SANTA ANA, Alfredo S. 300 CALLE CLEMSON, URB UNIVERSITY GDNS 00927 #649-01-1977 L1988 **GP OM** *020

SANTAELLA, Maria D. C18 CALL TLN URB SANTA ANA 00927 #042-01-1973 L1975 **IM IG** *020

SANTANA, Jorge Luis. 910 CALLE ZUMBADOR, URB COUNTRY CLUB 00924 #042-03-1981 L1987 **ID IM** *020

SANTANA, Jose R. BX 30819 65TH INFANTRY STA 00929 #042-01-1984 L1987 **FM** *020 †18

SANTE-PEREZ, Maria I. SAN JUAN CITY HSP PATH 00928 #847-17-1980 L1983 **PTH** *020 †50

SANTIAGO, Karen Janice. ■ 00926 #042-02-2002 L2005 ON *012 120

SANTIAGO, Monica. PO BOX 21405, SAN JUAN CITY HOSP 00928 #305-01-2005 **IM** *012

SANTIAGO, Norma E. ■ 00927 #042-01-1990 L1995 **GS** *020 †85

SANTIAGO BONILLA, Lilia. ■ 00926 #847-04-1957 L1960 **IM** *020

SANTIAGO BORRERO, Pedro J. B17 CALLE ROBLES, VILLA HUCAR 00926 #042-01-1960 L1963 **PD PHO** *040 †55

SANTIAGO FORTIER, Ramon A. 138 AVE WINSTON CHURCHILL, URB CROWN HLS 00926 #847-03-1975 L1978 **IM** *020

SANTIAGO LAMPON, Maria E. 567 CALLE LODI # 2A, URB TOWN PARK 00924 #847-08-1974 L1976 **CHP FM** *020

SANTIAGO-VELEZ, Francisco. 765 AVE SAN PATRICIO, URB LAS LOMAS 00921 #042-01-1979 L1982 **PD** *020

SANTINI, Ivelisse. LA CAMPINA, ST 1 NO 55 00926 #042-01-1977 L1980 **PD** *020 †55

SANTOS, Ana T. 220 CALLE TERRACE, URB RIO PIEDRAS HTS 00926 #042-01-1996 L2001 **GS** *020 †85

SANTOS, Carmen Isaura. 269 AVE PINERO 00927 #042-01-1980 L1984 **OPH** *020 †35

SANTOS, Ruth Aixa. ■ 00926 #042-03-2000 L2005 *100 †20

SCHAENING, Juan Luis. 910 CALLE GEORGETOWN, URB UNIVERSITY GDNS 00927 #042-01-1995 L1999 **IM** *020

SCHLEIER PAGAN, Robert C. ■ 00929 #042-04-1995 L1996 **FM** *020

SEDA FIGUEROA, Emma Ruth. ■ 00927 #649-14-2001 L2002 *020

SEGAL, Alexander Lee. ■ 00926 #042-03-2001 L2004 **OBG** *020

SEIN, Roberto Jose. ■ 00927 #847-08-1975 L1980 **DR** *020 †80

SEPULVEDA SERRA, Raymond. L4 CALLE CLAVEL, PARQ DE SANTA MARIA 00927 #847-05-1974 L1977 **EM GP** *020

SERRANO-PERNAS, Maria D. 31 CALLE NIZA, PASEO LAS BRISAS 00926 #308-03-1977 L1982 *020

SERRANO-ROBLES, Jose A. TOLIMA K9 PARK GARDENS 00926 #847-05-1972 L1978 **GP FM** *020

SILVA, David. ■ 00921 #042-03-1992 L1996 **OPH** *020

SILVAGNOLI, Jose A. ■ 00921 #042-01-1967 L1969 **PD OS** *020

SIMONS, Jose A. ■ 00927 #042-03-1987 L1994 **PTH** *020

SMITH, Edward Benjamin. ■ 00926 #649-14-1982 L1985 **GP** *020

SOBA NOVEL, Jose Manuel. ■ 00926 #308-01-1956 L1968 **GP** *020

SOLER-RAMIREZ, Ricardo J. ST 5 S O 974 LA RIVERIA 00926 #649-01-1974 L1982 **GP** *020

SOLER-SALAS, Antonio. 430 CALLE SAN LINO 00926 #042-01-1983 L1988 **ORS** *020 †40

SOLTERO-HARRINGTON, Luis. ■ 00927 #016-06-1950 L1951 **GS PDS** *071 †85

SONNI-TIO, Artturi W. ■ 00926 #042-01-1962 L1968 **GP OS** *020

SOSA-PADILLA, Miguel A. C/O P.O. BOX 34093, 1539 PARANA ST EL PARAISO 00926 #308-03-1981 L1985 *020

SOTO-COLON, Sylvette. CALLE B A1 5 MANS DE VILLA 00926 #042-03-1980 L1984 **NPM PD** *030

SOTOMAYOR-VICENTY, Carlos. ■ 00926 #042-03-1981 L1982 **IM** *020

SOTO TAPIA, Edwin. 249 CALLE HIMALAYA, URB MONTEREY 00926 #308-03-1976 L1978 **NPM CCP** *020

SUAREZ SANCHEZ, Helen. ■ 00929 #847-05-1971 L1975 GP *071

TEJEDOR-GONZALEZ, Gerardo. 592 CALLE VERN VILLA CAPRI 00924 #042-04-1983 L1985 P *020

TELUSMA, Jean Junior. PO BOX 21405, SAN JUAN CITY HOSP 00928 #440-01-1991 L2004 IM *100 †20

TOLEDO-ALVERIO, Ernesto L. ■ 00926 #042-03-1980 L1983 GS *020

TORO, Edith P. ■ 00924 #042-04-1987 L1989 IM *062 †20

TORO MONTALVO, Jose E. 1602 CALLE TIGRIS, URB RIO PIEDRAS HTS 00926 #308-01-1987 L1992 GP *020

TORRES, Alwin L. CIPRES 702 HIGHLAND PARK 00924 #042-04-1987 L1990 GP *020

TORRES, Anelys. 1672 CALLE PARANA, URB EL CEREZAL 00926 #042-01-1986 L1990 PM *020 †60

TORRES, Arturo. ■ 00926 #042-01-1986 L1989 OS *020

TORRES, Carlos. ■ 00926 #042-03-1985 L1991 GS *071

TORRES ACOSTA, Astrid L. 1679 CALLE TINTO 00926 #308-06-1983 L1997 *020

TORRES-AGUIAR, Carlos. ■ 00926 #030-06-1956 L1959 GS *071 †85

TORRES-CABRET, Carlos. 419 CALLE SAN JOVINO, URB SAGRADO CORAZON 00926 #847-02-1974 L1988 GP *062

TORRES HERNANDEZ, Delia. ■ 00926 #308-03-1976 L1978 OS *020

TORRESLEON, Rosimar. 2-A6 BERWIND EST 00924 #042-01-1999 L2002 OBG *100 †30

TORRES MIRANDA, Carmen A. ■ 00927 #042-01-1956 L1959 PD GPM *071 †55

TORRES-NIEVES, Armando. PASEO LAS VISTAS, CALLE 1 A-24 00926 #308-03-1982 L1983 ID IM *020

TORRES PACHECO, Ariel. BOX 225 LA CUMBRE STA 00926 #847-07-1971 L1978 *075

TORRES-RODRIGUEZ, Jose D. ALTURAS DE SANTA MARIA, CALLE NOGAL #1970, 00927 #847-10-1971 L1974 OTO *020 †45

TORRES-RODRIGUEZ, Victor. ■ 00927 #035-01-1951 L1953 D *020 †15

TORRES ROSA, Marta Nydia. ■ 00926 #847-06-1969 L1973 AN EM *071

TRELLES, Isaac Ernesto. PO BOX 21405 00928 #737-01-1992 IM *100 †20

TRISAN DE CUEVAS, Marina. ■ 00926 #847-10-1961 L1965 CHP *020

UBINAS, Jose Luis. ■ 00926 #042-03-1981 L1983 APM *020

ULMOS, Guillermo E. AVE E POL 497, STE 574 00926 #682-01-1964 L1974 GS *071

VALDERRABANO, Jose Luis. ■ 00927 #042-01-1977 L1981 DR *020 †80

VALDERRABANO, Olga M S. ■ 00927 #847-04-1955 L1959 P *020

VALDES MELENDEZ, Jorge R. ■ 00927 #308-01-1955 L1960 PDC PD *071

VALDESPINO, Rafael Hector. PO BOX 21405, SAN JUAN CITY HOSP 00928 #275-01-1984 IM *012

VALES HERNANDEZ, Alina E. EL SENORIAL, ANTONIO MACHADO 2019 00926 #847-02-1964 L1967 P *020

VALIENTE MALDONADO, Gloria. 497 AVE E POL STE 86, LA CUMBRE 00926 #308-15-1981 L2002 FM *020

VALLEJO RAMIREZ, Ruben. 105 CALL QNP URB MILAVILLE 00926 #847-01-1965 L1968 D *020

VALLES, Jose Alberto. ■ 00927 #042-01-1988 L1992 IM PUD *020 †20

VANHORNE, Diane Carol. ■ 00927 #649-54-2000 L2005 IM *012

VARGAS, Vivianne Marie. 3 SE URB LA RIVIERA, COND MED CTR PLZ #311 00921 #042-03-2000 L2003 IM *100 †20 ‡

VARGAS, Wildo. 138 AVE WINSTON CHURCHILL, URB CROWN HLS 00926 #042-03-1980 L1982 PM *020

VAZQUEZ, Gilberto V. ■ 00926 #308-03-1984 L1990 END *020

VAZQUEZ-BONILLA, Brunila. U3-4 CARR 21, URB LAS AMERICAS 00921 #042-03-1980 L1982 P *020

VAZQUEZ-DUBEAU, Daisy. ■ 00926 #042-03-1989 L1992 OBG *020 †30

VAZQUEZ-ENCARNACION, B I. ROSELL 13 BRNQN GRNDS 00926 #847-10-1971 L1978 GP *071

VAZQUEZ-MARTIREN, Julia S. 271 AVE WINSTON CHURCHILL 00926 #042-03-1993 L1998 CD *020 †20

VAZQUEZ-VAZQUEZ, Benjamin. CALLE 3 NO 6 VIL LOS OLMOS 00927 #042-03-1980 L1984 PD *020 †55

VAZQUEZ-ZAYAS, Luis E. CALLE IGUZ T 2 7 PRK GRNS 00926 #847-08-1975 L1980 OBG *020

VEGA, Felix R. G1-7 CALLE D1, MANS DE VILLANOVA 00926 #847-02-1973 L1975 P *020

VEGA, Wanda C. 19 CALLE NEVAREZ # 1026 00927 #042-01-1984 L1990 DR *020 †80

VEGA MORAL, Fernando. PO BOX 21405 00928 #649-14-2000 L2000 PD *100

VELASQUEZ, Guillermo. 959 AVE AMERICO MIRANDA, REPTO METROPOLITANO 00921 #264-01-1960 L1970 OPH PTH *020 †50

VELEZ AROCHO, Juan A. 701 CALLE KENNEDY 00926 #308-04-1981 L1992 *020

VELEZ HERRERA, Freddy. ■ 00926 #042-01-1957 L1959 P IM *020

VELEZ PRIETO, Angela. D1 CHESTNUT HILL AVE 00926 #042-04-1995 L1997 *020

VIDAL-OVIEDO, Zaida Maria. ■ 00926 #308-01-1960 L1978 GP *020

VIERA-FIGUEROA, Wilfredo. A5 CAL 1 EXT COLINAS VERDE 00924 #847-02-1976 L1979 GP *020

VILANOVA MARTINEZ, J. ■ 00924 #308-02-1976 L1979 OBG *020

VILELLA SUAU, Felix S. U3-4 CARR 21, URB LAS LOMAS 00921 #028-34-1958 L1961 GS *020 †85

VILLALBA GALAN, Grisselle. 208 CALLE SAN LORENZO, URB RIO PIEDRAS HTS 00926 #649-14-1993 L1996 PD *020

VILLALBA ROMAN, Jorge F. GETTYSBURG N 9 PARK GRDNS 00926 #847-04-1960 L1962 PM EM *072

VILLANUEVA, Jose Eugenio. COND 1ST FEDERAL 911 912 00927 #308-01-1962 L1974 P PFP *020

VIZCARRONDO, Mayra Y. 1749 CALLE SAN ALEJANDRO, URB SAN IGNACIO 00927 #042-01-1990 L1993 PD *020 †55

WAGNER-BEALL, James G. PO BOX 21405 00928 #649-14-1997 L1997 OBG *020

YAPOR, Pedro Jose. LOS CHALETS COURT C-6, CUPEY 00926 #308-01-1985 L2001 PCC *100 †20

ZAGURY, Irmgard G. ■ 00926 #440-01-1948 L1989 PD OS *071

ZEPEDA RIOS, Laura Elena. 119 CALLE SAN PABLO 00926 #649-14-1989 L1993 FM *020 †18

SABANA GRANDE – SABANA GRANDE

ALVERIO-COLON, Carlos M. ■ 00637 #308-03-1979 L1983 GP *020

ANTOMMATTEI, Edwin Bernar. PO BOX 1059 00637 #649-14-2002 L2004 *100

AXTMAYER PRADO, Robert Wm. 17 CALLE RODRIGUEZ SERRA 00637 #042-01-1984 L1987 FM *020 †18

AYALA, Jorge Luis. 6 CALLE 25 DE JULIO, LOWR 00637 #042-01-1984 L1987 IM *020

AYALA, Loyda Raquel. ■ 00637 #042-02-2002 L2004 IM *020

BAEZ AYALA, Edgardo I. ■ 00637 #649-14-2003 L2004 IM *012

BARRIENTOS GAYOSO, Juan M. 22 CALLE BETANCES, LOWR 00637 #649-14-1984 L1990 IM *020

CARCACHE, Elizabeth. 11 RODRIGUEZ SERRA, P O BOX 880 00637 #042-01-1987 L1990 FM *020 †18

CASIANO SANCHEZ, Luis A. 16 CALLE BALDORIOTY 00637 #649-18-1985 L2001 *020

CASIANO SANTIAGO, Edwin. ■ 00637 #649-18-1998 L1999 *020

CORREA-COLON, Wanda Sinia. HC 9 BOX 4674, HM1 CARR 121 6 00637 #847-08-1980 L1982 GP *062

CRUZ, Ernesto L. CALLE 6 NO F 35 URB V ALBA 00637 #308-02-1979 L1981 GP *020

CRUZ-PACHECO, Frances F. ■ 00637 #042-02-2003 L2005 IM *100 †20

DELIZ VARELA, Luis J. 8 CALLE JULIO V NUNEZ 00637 #308-03-1978 L1981 IM *020

DIAZ-MARTINEZ, Jose E. ■ 00637 #308-01-1962 L1976 *071

ESTEVA LORA, Rafael. PO BOX 44 00637 #275-01-1943 L1969 GP OS *072

FELIZ MENDEZ, Nestor J. ■ 00637 #308-01-1981 L1989 *020

GARCIA, Lilliam I. ■ 00637 #042-01-1996 L2000 PD *020 †55

GARCIA RIVERA, Luis. 109 CALLE B, URB EL ARRENDADO 00637 #042-04-1998 L1999 FM *020

GUERRA-TORRES, Norma R. PO BOX 1179, LL5 EXT ALTURAS SAN JOSE 00637 #042-02-1997 L2000 PD *020

GUZMAN-LUGO, Francisco J. ■ 00637 #042-02-1997 L1998 CD *020

HERNANDEZ JAQUEZ, Jose A. PO BOX 428 00637 #308-01-1967 L1975 PD *020

IRIZARRY, Jorge Alberto. 74 CALLE ANGEL G MARTINEZ 00637 #649-40-1986 L1991 GP FPG *020

IRIZARRY, Jorge Luis. 74B CALLE ANGEL G MARTINEZ 00637 #308-03-1981 L2001 GP PME *020

LIMARY, Rosado Vidro. HC 9, 00637 SABANA GRANDE 00637 #649-35-2004 L2006 FM *100

MARTIN, Carmen Leide. HC 10 BOX 8515, 2.8 CARR 121 BO 00637 #935-01-1980 L2002 FM *020

MARTINEZ-MARTINEZ, Luz E. 84 CALLE A G MARTINEZ 00637 #042-03-1981 L1985 IM *020

MIRANDA, Gerardo Enrique. ■ 00637 #042-01-2007 PM *012

MONTALVO, Joseph Alan. ■ 00637 #308-03-1987 FM *100

MONTALVO, Julio R. 65 INFANTERIA #42 00637 #649-01-1954 L1959 GP OS *071

MONTALVO LOZADA, Brian. ■ 00637 #308-03-2002 L2005 *100

NAVARRO, Wilfredo. ■ 00637 #042-03-1997 L2001 DR *020 †80

NAZARIO, Maricarmen. PO BOX 556 00637 #042-01-2006 L2008 DR *012

NEGRON BAEZ, Jorge. HC 9 00637 #649-19-1993 L1996 *100

PACHECO SANTANA, Wanda I. PO BOX 418 00637 #308-03-1978 L1990 *100

PAGAN, Genero. 148B, URB SANTA RITA 00637 #308-03-1986 L1991 GP *020

QUESADA CUPULL, Nuris. 55 CARR 364 00637 #308-04-1980 L1983 GP *020

ROSADO, Anibal. ■ 00637 #649-35-1997 L2000 FM *020

SANTIAGO RAMIREZ, Cristina. PO BOX 424 00637 #649-35-2004 *020

SAPIA-NIEVES, Jose Manuel. ■ 00637 #847-08-1977 L1979 *020

SEDA, Nancy R. 110 AVE 5 DE DICIEMBRE 00637 #042-04-1985 L1987 PD *020

SILVA CHERENA, William. 24 CALLE BALDORIOTY STE 2 00637 #042-04-1992 L1993 GP *020

TORRES, Manuel. ■ 00637 #275-04-1985 L1999 *020

VELEZ, Herminio H. 8 CALLE BETANCES 00637 #042-03-1987 L1991 OBG *020

VIVALDI, Antonio A. CALLE MUNOZ RIVERA #40 00637 #042-04-1995 L1997 GP *020

SABANA HOYOS – ARECIBO

ACEVEDO, Sigfredo. ■ 00688 #649-35-1999 L2003 *020

BORRERO-HERNANDEZ, Idalia. PO BOX 641 00688 #308-03-1982 L1984 GP *020

CRUZ ARRIGOITIA, Elisa. ■ 00688 #308-03-1983 L1992 FM *020

CRUZ-RIVERA, Jaime. ■ 00688 #847-06-1987 L1991 *020

NIEVES MARTINEZ, Carlos R. PO BOX 641 00688 #308-03-1982 L1987 *020

VILLANUEVA GONZALEZ, Wanda. ■ 00688 #649-14-2002 L2002 *020

SABANA SECA – TOA BAJA

RAMOS, Yemina. ■ 00952 #042-01-1995 L1999 APM *020 †05 ‡

VAZQUEZ, Marien. PO BOX 1766 00952 #042-01-2002 L2004 FM *020 †18

SAINT JUST – TRUJILLO ALTO

ALVAREZ-ROBLES, Manuel J. CARR 842 KM 43, CAIMITO BAJO RIO PIEDRAS 00978 #308-01-1969 L1980 IMG FM *020

GEIGEL-OLIVIERI, Annie. ■ 00978 #649-01-1962 L1964 FPG GP *062

SALINAS – SALINAS

CARLO-CHEVERE, Victor L. PO BOX 747 00751 #042-02-1997 L2003 GE *100 †20

DE JESUS CARABALLO, Joel. ■ 00751 #649-14-2002 GE *020 †20

DIAZ DELGADO, Felipe. ■ 00751 #308-03-1976 L1978 GP *020

HERNANDEZ SANZ, Luz E. ■ 00751 #308-01-1954 L1966 OS *020

JUSINO-LOPEZ, Evangelista. ■ 00751 #649-18-1977 L1987 GP *020

LOPEZ PACHECO, Deborah. EXT MONSERRATE E-38 00751 #308-06-1987 L1995 *020

MALDONADO COLON, Bermily. ■ 00751 #649-14-2006 IM *012

MARIN RIVERA, Ferdinand. 25 CALLE MONSERRATE 00751 #308-04-1990 L1996 GP *020

MATEO-MORENO, Yamil. PO BOX 134 00751 #308-03-1978 L1983 GP *020

MENDEZ LOPEZ, Francisco L. PO BOX 851 00751 #308-04-1985 L1989 IM *020

NEGRON, Roberto. EXT LA MARGARITA, CALLE D-E-17 BOX 231 00751 #042-01-1976 L1977 GS *030

ORTEGA ORTIZ, Orlando. SAN MARTIN 4 00751 #308-03-1983 L1988 GP *020

ORTIZ LARA, Pedro Fq. ■ 00751 #308-04-1988 L1993 *020

PAGAN OCASIO, Shirley W. 4 CALLE PADRE VICTOR 00751 #042-04-1992 L1994 *020

POLANCO SOLIVAN, Angel L.. #109 URB. JARDINES DE SALI 00751 #308-03-2002 L2004 *100

RODRIGUEZ ZAYAS, Jose O.. PO BOX 1161 00751 #308-03-1983 L1989 *100

RUIZ, Hector Luis. 25 CALLE MUNOZ RIVERA 00751 #042-02-1987 L1990 IM *020

SANTIAGO TORRES, Johana. 8 RES BELLA VIS 00751 #649-14-2003 L2006 *100

TAULER, Amadeo A. 18 CALLE H, BO PLAYA 00751 #275-01-1962 L1975 **GP** *020
TORRES, Jorge L. 16 CALLE RAFAEL OCASIO 00751 #042-04-1990 L1991 **GP** *020
VALDEZ-SABATER, F A. ■ 00751 #308-01-1955 L1989 **GP** *075

SAN ANTONIO – AGUADILLA

ALBINO CRUZ, Ileana. 1803 CALLE KENNEDY, SAN ANTONIO 00690 #308-03-1983 L1990 *020
FERRERIS VEGA, Manuel. ■ 00690 #847-10-1961 L1969 **GP** *020
NAVEDO FRONTERA, Angel M. PO BOX 785 00690 #308-03-1977 L1980 **FM** *020
RAMOS, Farida Milagros. BO CORRALES, CARR. #2 KM-124.2 00690 #308-03-1983 L1991 **GP** *020

SAN GERMAN – SAN GERMAN

ACEVEDO, Javier. ■ 00683 #305-01-2004 L2008 **IM** *100
ACOSTA, Andres Alejandro. 41 CALLE LUNA 00683 #041-09-1945 L1946 **IM P** *072
ACOSTA-NAZARIO, Waika Yaj. ■ 00683 #308-02-2001 L2003 *100
ACOSTA-ORRACA, Ivan R. 4 CALLE TETUAN 00683 #042-01-1979 L1982 **IM** *020
ACOSTA VIDAL, Victor. 102 CALLE DR VEVE 00683 #042-04-2000 L2002 **FM** *020
ALEMANY-ARANA, Domingo S. ■ 00683 #042-01-1956 L1961 **OS** *075
ALMODOVAR, Roberto. 41 CALLE LUNA 00683 #649-35-1999 L2001 **GP ADM** *020
ALVAREZ, Urselio, Jr. 41 CALLE LUNA 00683 #231-02-1982 L1985 **IMG IM** *020 †20
ALVAREZ COBIAN, Ruben H. 100 CALLE HERNN ALVRZ #103, PLAZA METROPOLITANA 00683 #308-04-1990 L1994 **IM** *020 †20
ALVAREZ JARAMILLO, Jose R. 41 CALLE LUNA 00683 #847-04-1957 L1959 **GS** *020 †85
AMY, Carlos Daniel. PO BOX 5075, PMB 298 00683 #649-14-2002 L2005 *100
ARIZMENDI, Luis Armando. 41 CALLE LUNA, HOSPITAL DE LA CONCEPCION 00683 #308-03-1982 L1984 **GP EM** *050
AVILES, Carlos A. ■ 00683 #042-03-1984 L1990 **P** *020
AYALA, Jose Antonio. 41 CALLE LUNA 00683 #042-01-1984 L1986 **IM** *020
AYALA, Pedro Nolasco. 41 CALLE LUNA 00683 #042-02-2001 L2003 **IM** *020
AYALA-COLON, Angel R. 41 CALLE LUNA 00683 #042-03-1980 L1984 **PD** *020
BACO, Carrie. 41 CALLE LUNA, 00683 #042-02-1996 L1998 **IM** *020
BAEZ-ZARAGOZA, Edwin A. 41 CALLE LUNA 00683 #847-10-1967 L1971 **OBG** *020
BALLESTER ECHEGARAY, Jose. 41 CALLE LUNA 00683 #308-03-1982 L1989 **FM** *020
BITTMAN DE LUGO, Elaine E. LUNA BYPASS CORNER 00683 #847-04-1975 L1981 **PD** *020
CANTELLOPS VEGA, Virgilio. 41 CALLE LUNA 00683 #847-02-1970 L1973 **GP** *020
CARDONA, Luzma Muriel. HC 1, 178.0 CARR 2 00683 #042-02-2001 L2004 **N** *012
CARILLO, Jose Vicente. 41 CALLE LUNA 00683 #847-08-1974 L1979 **EM** *030
CARTAGENA GARCIA, Horacio. 18 CALLE LUNA 00683 #847-04-1957 L1960 **OTO A** *071
CASIANO, Carlos F. ■ 00683 #042-02-1996 L1998 **IM** *020 †20
CHAUDHARY, Shahid M. ■ 00683 #308-03-1990 L2005 *100
COLLAZO VELEZ, Aurelio. CALLE VICTORIA ESQUINA SOL 00683 #847-02-1967 L1977 **GP** *020
COLON BERMUDEZ, Ramon. 13 CALLE CIBELES, URB RETIRO 00683 #308-07-1982 L2001 *020
COLON-SANTIAGO, Maribel. ■ 00683 #649-14-1987 L1992 **GP** *020
CRUZ, Ivette Lourdes. HC 1 BOX 25, SAN GERMAN MEDICAL PLAZA S 00683 #042-03-1993 L1997 **PM** *020 †60
DAVILA, Ramon A. 100 CALLE HERNAN ALVAREZ, STE 107 00683 #042-01-1987 L1993 **ORS TRS** *020
DEL TORO ROMAN, Edgar. 41 CALLE LUNA 00683 #847-05-1964 L1967 **IM** *020
DIAZ COLLAZO, Myrna L. 41 CALLE LUNA 00683 #042-01-1987 L1992 **DR** *020
DIEGUEZ, Nina. PO BOX 285 00683 #308-03-2000 **IM** *012
FERNANDEZ, Clarissa. PO BOX 5075, PMB 338 00683 #649-14-2001 L2004 *100
FERNANDEZ, Pedro J. ■ 00683 #042-04-1988 L1990 **P** *020
FERNANDEZ-CAAMANO, Hostos. PO BOX 99, B-25 EL CONVENTO 00683 #308-02-1981 L1989 **OBG** *020 †30
FERNANDEZ-DURAN, Manuel. ■ 00683 #308-02-1949 L1953 **GYN** *071 †30
FIGUEROA, Alexis. ■ 00683 #649-14-2000 L2002 *020
FLORES, Miriam. ■ 00683 #847-04-1965 L1968 **OBG AN** *020
FORINA, Jose Francisco. 36 CALLE RUIZ BELVIS 00683 #042-04-1991 L1994 **IM FM** *020 †18 ‡
FRAGOSO-VILLANUEVA, G. 15 CALLE JOSE JULIAN ACOST, P O BOX 81 00683 #847-04-1962 L1966 **AN** *071
FRIAS, Luis Alexander. 41 EXT CALLE LUNA, EXT MANS SAN GERMAN 00683 #035-45-1986 L1999 **N** *020 †75
GALIB, Yussef. ■ 00683 #042-02-2005 **IM** *012
GARCES, Monserrate A. ■ 00683 #847-10-1971 L1974 **ORS GP** *030
GONZALEZ MARQUES, Maria E. ■ 00683 #649-14-2002 L2004 *100
GRANA, Robert. PO BOX 285, DEPT OF INTERNAL MED 00683 #308-03-2000 L2008 **IM** *020 †20
GROVAS, Rafael Francisco. 43 CALLE DR VEVE, SAN GERMANIN XRAY-BODY IMG 00683 #042-03-1996 L1998 **DR** *020 †80
GUZMAN REYES, Francisco A. WNA, HOSP DE LA CONCEYUON 00683 #847-10-1965 L1968 **IM** *030
HAMMERSCHMIDT, Cesar R. ■ 00683 #737-01-1948 L1957 **GP GS** *072
HART, Eileen Marie. ■ 00683 #042-02-1988 L1992 **NM** *020 †28
IGARAVIDEZ, Yolanda M. ■ 00683 #847-03-1979 L1985 **GP OM** *020
IGARAVIDEZ, Yolanda Otero. PO BOX 144 00683 #042-02-1996 L1999 **IM** *020
IRIZARRY, Maritza Margari. PO BOX 739 00683 #649-14-1997 L2004 *100
IRIZARRY, Ronaldo. ■ 00683 #042-02-2002 **P** *100
IZQUIERDO RIVERA, Julio E. 100 CALLE HERNAN ALVAREZ, STE 102 00683 #308-02-1980 L1987 **GS** *020 †85
JIMENEZ MORALES, Luz M. PO BOX 159 00683 #649-14-2003 L2005 *100
JOVE, Gloria Rebecca. 41 CALLE LUNA 00683 #042-02-1992 L1997 **IM ID** *020
JUSTINIANO, Rafael Antoni. 11 CALLE LUNA 00683 #042-01-1974 L1977 **GS** *020 †85
LLAVONA GONZALEZ, Orlando. #79 CALLE LUNA ABAJO 00683 #649-30-2002 L2004 *100
LOINAZ-GARRIDO, Diego H. ■ 00683 #308-01-1943 L1961 **GP** *020
LOPEZ GOMEZ, Fanny R. 187 CALLE LUNA, RALI BLDG STE 205 00683 #042-01-1987 L1990 **PD** *020 †55
LOPEZ-LOPEZ, Edson R. 41 CALLE LUNA 00683 #649-01-1959 L1963 **IM** *071
LOPEZ-RODRIGUEZ, Jose H. 41 CALLE LUNA 00683 #847-06-1977 L1981 **IM** *020
LUGO, Maileen. ■ 00683 #649-14-2000 L2002 *020
LUGO, Yannira. ■ 00683 #308-04-2002 L2006 **IM** *100
LUGO-ROSAS, Anibal Javier. ■ 00683 #308-02-1987 L1992 **IM CD** *020 †20

LUGO SEPULVEDA, Anaida E. 41 CALLE LUNA 00683 #847-06-1971 L1974 **PD** *020
MAIZ-ACEVEDO, Roberto E. 100 CALLE HERNAN ALVAREZ, STE 102 00683 #042-02-1996 L1998 **GS** *020
MARTINEZ, Maritza. 41 CALLE LUNA, OFICINA G-5 00683 #649-14-1980 L1985 **IM** *020
MARTY-CARRILLO, Hector. 41 CALLE LUNA 00683 #847-09-1963 L1967 **OTO** *020
MARTY ORTIZ, Ovida. 40 CALLE DR VEVE 00683 #649-18-1978 L1981 *030
MAYMON, Miguel F. 41 CALLE LUNA, HOSPITAL DE LA CONCEPCION 00683 #042-02-1996 L1998 **IM** *020 †20
MEDERO-ROLDAN, Ramon A. ■ 00683 #042-04-1983 L1985 **PD** *020
MEDINA, Enrique. CALLE 2 C-4, URB MANSIONS REALES 00683 #308-03-1981 L1990 **PD** *020
MERCADO, Luis. 41 CALLE LUNA 00683 #042-03-1988 L1993 **IM EM** *020
MONTALVO, Rogelio F. C17 CALLE 4, VILLA INTERAMERICANA 00683 #042-02-1995 L1998 **IM** *020
MONTALVO-ALVAREZ, Ramon A. ■ 00683 #308-03-1976 L1978 **GP FM** *020
MORA NIEVES, Elaine. PO BOX 5075, A-3 URBANIZACION MANSIONES 00683 #042-04-1994 L1996 **GP** *020
NEGRON, Elsie Enid. 153 CALLE LUNA, BOX 1084 SANGERMAN 00683 #308-04-1987 L1990 **GP** *020
NUNEZ-ACEVEDO, Irving. ■ 00683 #308-03-1982 L1984 *020
OJEDA LARACUENTE, Winston. 41 CALLE LUNA 00683 #649-01-1968 L1970 **NEP IM** *030
ORTIZ, Maritza. ■ 00683 #042-04-1996 L1997 *020
ORTIZ RAMOS, Luis C.. 132 ALTOS AVE UNIVERSIDAD 00683 #649-30-2002 L2004 *100
ORTIZ-SAMBOLIN, Hector S. 41 CALLE LUNA, HOSP LA CONCEPCION OFIC 15 00683 #407-16-1965 L1980 **TRS GS** *071
PADILLA, Angel F. 18 CALLE SOL 00683 #028-34-1946 L1949 **R OS** *071
PADILLA, Jorge. 41 CALLE LUNA 00683 #042-03-1992 L1994 **PM** *020
PAGAN IRIZARRY, Wallace. ■ 00683 #649-14-1994 L1997 **GP** *020
PEREZ, Obed. VILLA INTERAMERICANA F3 00683 #042-03-1983 L1989 **END IM** *020 †20
PEREZ BONILLA, Miguel A. ■ 00683 #847-06-1974 L1976 **GP** *020
PEREZ PEREZ, Nilver. ■ 00683 #308-13-2002 L2005 *100
PLANADEBALL-MORENO, Nydia. CALLE ESPERANZA-30 00683 #649-14-1977 L1979 **PD** *020
PONCE-SANTIAGO, Santiago. URB RIVERSIDE 00683 #847-06-1976 L1980 **GP** *074
QUINONES GAMBOA, Armando. 12 CALLE SOL, PO BOX 306 00683 #847-02-1962 L1968 **GS** *020
QUINONES-RIVERA, Radames. 41 CALLE LUNA 00683 #308-06-1982 L1986 **IM EM** *020
QUINTERO-VILELLA, Mario L. ■ 00683 #847-02-1980 L1984 *020
RAMIREZ, Carlos Moises. PO BOX 1868, 76 CALLE VICTORIA 00683 #847-06-1972 L1975 **FM** *020
RAMIREZ ALUSTIZA, Carlos. 12 CALLE LUNA, HOSPITAL L CONCEPCION 00683 #847-10-1966 L1968 **IM CD** *020
RAMIREZ-FARIA, Juan A. BLOCK "E" NO 35, REPARTO UNIVERSIDAD 00683 #847-04-1962 L1975 **FM P** *020
RAMIREZ-IRIZARRY, Angela. 41 CALLE LUNA 00683 #042-01-1960 L1969 **PS HS** *020 †65
RAMIREZ PABON, Esther J. 102 CALLE DR VEVE, SOCIEDAD MEDICA DE SAN GER 00683 #649-01-1965 L1967 **PD** *020
RAMIREZ RAMOS, Jose A. 41 CALLE LUNA 00683 #042-04-1999 L2001 **GP** *020
RAMIREZ-RONDA, Ramon A. 41 CALLE LUNA 00683 #847-06-1977 L1981 **ID IM** *020
RAMIREZ-SOTO, Manuel A. 102 CALLE HERNAN ALVAREZ, PLAZA METROPOLITANA 00683 #649-14-1976 L1979 **GS** *020
RAMOS, Esteban. PO BOX 285 00683 #270-03-2001 **IM** *012
RIOS, Maria Eugenia. ■ 00683 #042-01-1998 L1999 **GE** *020 †20
RIVERA, Alejandro Acosta. 41 CALLE LUNA 00683 #042-01-1982 L1987 **OPH** *020 †35
RIVERA, Fernando J. 41 CALLE LUNA 00683 #847-10-1969 L1972 **IM NM** *020
RODRIGUEZ, Caroline. 43 CALLE DR VEVE, EDIF GROVAS RODRIGUEZ 00683 #042-03-1992 L1999 **DR** *020 †80
RODRIGUEZ, Hector Manuel. 41 CALLE LUNA 00683 #042-01-1986 L1989 **U** *020 †95
RODRIGUEZ, Keyla Pratts. HC 1, 174 BO CAIN A 2 CARR 00683 #042-01-1998 L2000 **PD** *020 †55
RODRIGUEZ, Nelson. 41 CALLE LUNA 00683 #649-14-1985 L1987 **CD IM** *020 †20
RODRIGUEZ-PEREZ, Roberto. 100 CALLE HERNAN ALVAREZ, STE 202 00683 #649-14-1991 L1994 **IM** *020
RODRIGUEZ-SEGARRA, Hector. 41 CALLE LUNA 00683 #847-10-1963 L1968 **U** *020
ROMAN-FELICIANO, Juan C. ■ 00683 #308-03-1977 L1980 **IM** *020
ROSA-AMADOR, Ricardo. ■ 00683 #042-01-1965 L1971 **CLP PTH** *074 †50
RUIZ-DIAZ, Nestor. 2 CALLE COLON 00683 #308-03-1980 L1983 **IM** *020
SANCHEZ, Heriberto A. 11 CALLE LUNA 00683 #649-14-1990 L1996 **GS** *020
SANTAELLA, Mario. 41 CALLE LUNA 00683 #308-01-1985 L1993 **IM** *020
SANTIAGO, Waleska. PO BOX 285, HOSP DE LA CONCEPCION 00683 #665-02-2004 L2005 **IM** *012
SANTIAGO, Wanda Ivette. ■ 00683 #042-04-1995 L1996 **FM** *020
SURIS, Juan Emilio. 11 CALLE LUNA 00683 #042-01-1973 L1979 **GS VS** *020 †85
TORO, Ramon. PO BOX 2945 00683 #042-01-1978 L1981 **RHU IM** *020 †20
TORO, Suzette. PO BOX 677, 18 CALLE LUNA 00683 #042-02-1991 L1996 **END** *020
TORRES, Axel Baez. PO BOX 285, 1 CAR KM 174.1 HOS CONCEP 00683 #042-01-1990 L1995 **PTH** *020 †50
TORRES, Luis A. PO BOX 591 00683 #649-14-2003 L2006 *100
TORRES ACEVEDO, Eddie G. ■ 00683 #308-04-1980 L1984 **GP** *020
TORRES-JUSTINIANO, A. ■ 00683 #308-03-1979 L1983 **IM** *020
TORRES-OLIVER, Luis J. 1 CALLE ESTRELLA, PO BOX 105 00683 #041-09-1944 L1945 **OS PS** *071
TORRES-SOSA, Ivan Efrain. 41 CALLE LUNA 00683 #308-03-1978 L1982 **OBG** *020
TORRES TORRES, Delia. 4A CALLE TETUAN, SECTOR BOSQUE 00683 #649-14-1990 L1995 **PD** *020
TOSSAS, Raymond Ivan. PO BOX 5000-436 00683 #649-14-1993 L1997 **GP** *020
VARGAS, Fredickson Manuel. HC 1, 2 CARR KM 174 SUITE 00683 #649-14-1999 L2000 **IM** *020 ‡
VEGA-CRUZ, Aster Manuel. 41 CALLE LUNA 00683 #042-02-1999 L2001 **IM** *020 †20 ‡
VELEZ, Axel Wilberto. 59 CALLE DR SANTIAGO VEVE 00683 #042-01-1989 L1992 **PUD IM** *020 †20
VELEZ, Rafael. 41 CALLE LUNA 00683 #042-01-1980 L1985 **D PD** *020 †55,15

SAN JUAN – SAN JUAN

ABRAMS, Jose Lemuel. MM1 CALLE ROSE, ALTS DE BORINQUEN GDNS 00926 #042-01-1981 L1984 **IM** *020

ABREU, Antonio Miguel. ■ 00926 #042-01-2002 L2005 **PM** *020 †60
ABREU GARCIA, Miguel E. CALLE MC KINLEY MIRAMAR, 664 SUGUNDO PISO 00907 #308-04-1991 L2000 **ICE** *020 †20
ABRILES, Oscar Rafael. 730 AVE PONCE DE LEON 00918 #737-01-1959 L1966 **GS OS** *020
ABU KHALIL, Nidal. ■ 00907 #649-14-2003 L2004 *100
ACABA, Luis A. 735 AVE PONCE DE LEON #408, TORRE AUXILIO MUTUO 00917 #308-03-1981 L1987 **HEM ON** *020 †20
ACARON-SOUFFRONT, G. ■ 00926 #847-05-1964 L1967 **GS** *020
ACEVEDO, Angel C. 20 CALLE 2, URB. PASEO ALTO 00926 #042-04-1984 L1991 **GP** *020
ACEVEDO, Lourdes Milagros. 1023 CALLE 21 SE, REPTO METROPOLITANO 00921 #042-01-2002 L2004 **IM** *100 †20
ACEVEDO, Luis Francisco. 89 AVE DE DIEGO, STE 105 00927 #649-14-2000 L2003 **P** *100 ‡
ACEVEDO, Maria Esther. ■ 00923 #042-01-1988 L1992 **NM** *020 †28
ACEVEDO, Tomas Agustin. ■ 00907 #041-13-1961 L1969 **U** *020 †95
ACEVEDO, William. PMR 117, VA MEDICAL CTR 00927 #042-03-1987 L1991 **PM** *020 †60
ACEVEDO-FLORES, Midnela. PO BOX 70344, K1H7 CARR 843 00936 #308-03-1983 L1986 **PD** *020
ACEVEDO-REGO, Carlos M. 623 CALLE FCO CASALDUC, VILLA PRADES 00924 #308-03-1984 L1996 **GP** *020
ACEVEDO SOTO, Carlos M.. ■ 00924 #847-06-1997 L2000 *020
ACEVEDO SOTO, Rafael. ■ 00924 #308-04-2002 L2005 *100
ACOSTA, Eduardo. ■ 00926 #042-03-1996 L2002 **DR** *020 †80
ACOSTA, Heriberto. ■ 00928 #042-01-1975 L1980 **N** *072
ACOSTA, Jaime Alberto. ■ 00924 #935-01-1986 L2005 *100
ACOSTA, Melvyn Miguel. 576 CALLE CESAR GONZALEZ, STE 405 00918 #042-02-1991 L1996 **GE** *020
ACOSTA, Onnis. 800 AVE HIPODROMO STE 102 00909 #649-14-2002 L2003 **GP** *020
ACOSTA JIMENEZ, Carlos R. 401 CALLE FERNANDO MONTILL 00918 #308-01-1961 L1968 **U** *020 †95
ACOSTA ROSAS, Pablo A. 511 CALLE ASUNCION, URB PUERTO NUEVO 00920 #847-02-1983 L1986 **GP** *020
ADAMS GONZALEZ, Jaime L. ■ 00909 #847-06-1966 L1969 **GP** *020
ADAMSONS, Karlis. PO BOX 5067, UNIV OF PUERTO RICO 00936 #407-07-1952 L1981 **OBG** *040 †30
ADLER, Eric Tor. 576 CALLE CESAR GONZALEZ, STE 205 00918 #035-09-1990 L1998 **OTO** *020 †45
AGUILAR, Nelson Eduardo. ■ 00921 #275-04-1991 L2006 **CD** *012 †20
AGUILO, Juan Miguel. 510 AVE MUNOZ RIVERA 00918 #042-01-1960 L1964 **IM D** *030 †20
ALAYON LAGUER, Diogenes. PO BOX 70344, 79 CMMS 00936 #649-14-2004 L2006 **IM** *012
ALBANDOZ, Rafael Jose. CALLE 1 26 VILL LOS OLMOS 00926 #042-01-1978 L1982 **OBG** *020
ALCALA-MUNOZ, Carlos R. 239 AVE ARTERIAL HOSTOS, CAPITAL CTR BLD STE 606 00918 #847-21-1981 L1986 **PUD IM** *020
ALCARAZ, Vicente. 572 CALLE CESAR GONZALEZ, BALDRICH 00918 #042-01-1976 L1981 **OPH** *020 †35
ALDAHONDO, Otto Luis. ■ 00926 #042-01-2004 **PD** *100
ALEGRE-HERNANDEZ, Manuel. 1012 CALLE 42 SE, REPTO METROPOLITANO 00921 #649-14-1987 L1991 **END IM** *020
ALFARO-RIVERA, Luis Raul. 421 AVE MUNOZ RIVERA, COND. MIDTOWN, OFFICE 214 00918 #847-01-1969 L1972 **P OS** *020
ALFONSO, Roberto Edgardo. 29 CALLE WASHINGTON, ASHFORD MED CTR 209 00907 #042-01-1976 L1980 **D** *020 †15 ‡
ALFONSO-MARTINEZ, Nancy J. 652 AVE MUNOZ RIVERA, STE 2015 00918 #847-10-1966 L1971 **IM CD** *020
ALFONSO-OLIVERAS, Rafael. 507 CALLE SIR URB ALTAMIRA 00920 #042-01-1958 L1962 **IM GP** *020
ALGARIN, Sheila. 412 CALLE ALCIDES REYES 00923 #042-01-1992 L2001 *020
ALICEA, Nancy E. 400 CALLE ROOSEVELT, STE 407 00926 #042-01-1988 L1992 **PM** *020 †60
ALICEA BERRIOS, Luz M. 1633 CALLE NIEPER, URB EL CEREZAL 00926 #308-03-1980 L1986 **PD** *020
ALICEA-CRUZ, Valeriano. 1519 AVE PONCE DE LEON, FIRST BANK BLDG 00909 #042-01-1969 L1971 **OPH CCS** *020
ALICEA-MELERO, Jose E. 1785 CARR 21, URB LAS AMERICAS 00921 #042-04-1987 L1989 **EM** *020
ALMENAS, Marina. ■ 00926 #308-04-1988 L1992 **FM** *020
ALMODOVAR, Alvin Ariel. 10 CALLE CASIA 00921 #042-01-1999 L2001 **VIR DR** *020 †80
ALMODOVAR, Jose I. PO BOX 70344, 69 CMMS 00936 #042-01-1993 L1994 **OTO** *100 †45
ALMODOVAR, Luis Jose. ■ 00918 #042-01-1999 L2000 **NS** *100
ALONSO, Hector M. 10 CALLE CASIA, EMERGENCY DEPARTMENT 00921 #042-01-1989 L1992 **EM** *020 †16
ALONSO, Jose Alberto. 728 AVE PONCE DE LEON 00918 #308-03-1982 L1984 **P** *020
ALONSO, Norma U. 735 AVE PONCE DE LEON, STE 519 00917 #042-01-1992 L1996 **D** *020 †15
ALONSO-DAFAUCE, Luis. 10 CALLE CASIA, VAMC RAD SVC 114 00921 #042-01-1988 L1993 **DR** *020 †80
ALOU, Juan Jose. SAN JUAN VA HOSP, DEPT OG 00935 #308-02-1974 **IM** *100
ALTIERI-RAMIREZ, Anibelle. 275 CALLE ELEONOR ROOSEVLT, URB ROOSEVELT 00918 #847-17-1978 L1982 **IM OS** *020
ALVARADO, Luis A. ■ 00936 #042-03-1990 L1995 **OBG** *020
ALVARADO, Marieliz. 500 AVE DOMENECH STE 201 00918 #042-02-1991 L1997 **PUD CCM** *020 †20
ALVARADO MELENDEZ, Francis. 10 CALLE CASIA, VA MEDICAL CENTER 00921 #649-14-2002 L2002 **IM** *020 †20
ALVAREZ, Carmen R. 252 CALLE SAN JORGE 00912 #042-01-1981 L1985 **DR GP** *020 †80
ALVAREZ, Elena Del Pilar. ■ 00926 #042-02-1998 L2004 **DR** *100 †80
ALVAREZ, Gilberto Enrique. 1139 CALLE MADRESELVA, MANS DE RIO PIEDRAS 00926 #042-01-2003 L2005 **D** *012 †20
ALVAREZ, Jose Ramon. 735 AVE PONCE DE LEON, OFICINA 818 00917 #847-01-1975 L1981 **PD GE** *040
ALVAREZ, Luis Felipe. PO BOX 190988 00919 #308-04-1985 L1990 **IM** *020
ALVAREZ, Nuria Merced. ■ 00923 #042-01-1981 L1984 **PD** *020
ALVAREZ-GHERSI, Juan F. VETERANS PLAZA STATION, VA MEDICAL CENTER SAN JUAN 00933 #847-04-1965 L1976 **P** *020
ALVAREZ-MATOS, Hiram. 616 COND TORRE ALTA # 616 00917 #847-04-1963 L1967 **OBG** *030
ALVAREZ ROMAGOSA, Jose L. 100 GRAND PASEO BLVD, STE 112 00926 #308-03-1985 L1989 **OBG** *030 †30
AMADOR, Francisco Jose. 300 CALLE CLEMSON, URB UNIVERSITY GDNS 00927 #649-14-1999 *020

AMADOR, Juan Felix. PO BOX 70344 PMB 79, MUNICIPAL HOSPITAL 00936 #042-01-2004 L2006 **DR** *012
AMADOR MELENDEZ, Viviana. 1726 CALLE SANTA BRIGIDA, URB SAGRADO CORAZON 00926 #042-04-1985 L1991 *020
AMADORMIRANDA, Rosana. ■ 00926 #042-01-2002 L2005 **ID** *100 †20
AMARAL, Carmen Elsa. PO BOX 21107 00928 #042-01-1993 L1998 **OPH** *020 †35
AMARO DE JESUS, Myriam. 783 CALLE GUATEMALA, URB LAS AMERICAS 00921 #649-14-1993 L1997 *020
AMILL, Samuel Antonio. 359 AVE DE DIEGO, 06 501 COND DE DIEGO 359 00909 #042-01-1978 L1981 **PUD IM** *020 †20
AMPARO FLORES, Jesus R. ■ 00921 #308-04-1990 L1993 *020
ANDREWS ALMA, Nildaliz. ■ 00920 #042-04-2003 L2004 *100
ANDUJAR, Job E. 10 CALLE CASIA 00921 #042-03-1985 L1989 **IM SCI** *020 †20
ANNEXY, Mamie. 7 COND MADRESELVA 1001 00920 #042-01-1986 L1990 **IM** *020 †20
ANNEXY-MARQUEZ, Roberto A. ■ 00918 #042-01-2004 **IM** *100 †20
ANQUITA, Manuel A. 735 AVE PONCE DE LEON #603, # 735 00917 #042-03-1989 L1994 **GS** *020 †85
ANZIANI RULLAN, Carmen A. 152 CALLE DUARTE 00917 #042-03-1980 L1985 *020
APONTE, Anamar. ■ 00926 #042-01-2007 **OBG** *012
APONTE, Edgardo J. 1451 AVE ASHFORD 00907 #042-01-1990 L1993 **OBG** *020 †30
APONTE, Hector. 166 CALLE GUAJATACA, URB CONTEMPORANEO 00926 #042-02-1982 L1990 *020
APONTE, Jaime Gabriel. ■ 00918 #042-03-2007 **IM** *012
APONTE, Joseph Louis. 252 CALLE SAN JORGE 00912 #023-01-1948 L1950 **A PDA** *071 †55
APONTE, Nestor Sebastian. 105 AVE ARTERIAL HOSTOS, BAYSIDE COVE, BOX 209 00918 #042-01-1996 L2000 **GE** *020 †20
APONTE, Pedro N. 735 AVE PONCE DE LEON, STE 606 00917 #042-04-1989 L1990 **GP** *020
APONTE-CABALLERO, Sergio. ■ 00936 #847-02-1976 L1979 **GP ADM** *020
APONTE-MUNIZ, Maria De L. 37 AVE PONCE DE LEON 00901 #042-04-1985 L1992 **PD** *020
AQUINO, Messalina. 1400 CALLE AMERICO SALAS, APT 302 00909 #308-13-2002 L2006 *100
ARANA, Luis Antonio R. PUERTO RICO MED CTR 00936 #847-06-1978 L1981 **EM GP** *020
ARANDA, Juan M. 411 AVE HOSTOS 00918 #042-01-1967 L1969 **IM** *020
ARBONA, Norberto J. HOSP METROPOLITANO 00921 #042-01-1966 L1970 **N** *020 †75
ARCE, Emilio Alfonso. 420 AVE PONCE DE LEON, MIDTOWN 908 00918 #847-10-1957 L1966 **OPH** *040
ARCE, Julian Pablo. ■ 00923 #042-01-2007 **PTH** *012
ARCE-LOPEZ, Emilio A. 150 AVE DE DIEGO, STE 502 00907 #042-02-1987 L1988 **OPH** *020
ARCE-MATEOS, Felix Pablo. VILLA ITXAS ALDE 2 00935 #847-05-1974 **PTH** *100
ARECES-PEREZ, Manuel. 252 CALLE SAN JORGE 00912 #275-01-1960 L1969 **PD** *071
ARECES PERNAS, Manuel J. ■ 00926 #308-02-1991 L1995 **CD** *020 †20
ARIAS, Jose Ignacio. 585 CALLE LODI, URB TOWN PARK 00924 #042-01-1980 L1983 **IM** *074
ARILL, Oscar. 10 CALLE CASIA, VA MEDICAL CENTER 00921 #042-01-1981 L1984 **IM RHU** *020 †20
ARIZA, Daisy E Alemany. G1 CALLE FRONTERA, CENTRO PEDIACTRY 110 ALTO 00926 #308-01-1960 L1968 **PD OS** *020
AROCHO, Bienvenida. 231 CALLE DUARTE 00917 #308-03-1986 L1990 **GP** *020
ARRILLAGA, Jorge. ■ 00921 #042-03-1993 L1996 **IM** *020 †20
ARROYAVE CORTES, Ignacio. 1730 CALLE YENISEY, URB RIO PIEDRAS HTS 00926 #264-01-1983 L1985 *020
ARROYO, Angel Luis. 87 CALLE MIRADOR, PASEO ALTO 00926 #042-01-1980 L1983 **CD IM** *020
ARROYO, Ivonne Lyzette. PO BOX 70344, 76 CMMS 00936 #042-01-1981 L1984 **PD RHU** *020 †55
ARROYO, Lillian M. ■ 00923 #042-01-1985 L1989 **P** *020 †75
ARROYO, Mara Neysa. 10 CALLE CASIA, VA MED CTR PMR-117 00921 #042-03-1987 L1991 **PM** *020 †60
ARROYO, Miguel Enrique. SUITE#206 DE DIEGO 369, TORRE HOSP SAN FRANCISCO 00923 #042-03-1994 L1995 **PM** *020
ARROYO, Pedro. ■ 00923 #035-01-1952 L1953 **PM** *071 †60
ARROYOAGUIRRECH, Luis A. ■ 00918 #042-01-2002 L2006 **OBG** *020
ARROYO-MARRERO, Blas C. 1451 AVE ASHFORD 00907 #649-26-1978 L1981 **EM** *020
ARROYO-RODRIGUEZ, Rosa N. ■ 00924 #042-01-1969 L1972 **PD** *020 †20
ARRUZA, John Andrew. C31 CALLE 10, PASEO MAYOR 00926 #042-01-1990 L1994 **AN** *020 †05
ARTURI, Luis A. 400 AVE FD ROOSEVELT, STE 206 00918 #042-01-1994 L2003 **GE** *020 †20
ARUS ROSADO, Deborah Enid. 216 CALLE VIENA, URB COLLEGE PARK 00921 #649-14-1987 L1992 **FM** *020
ARZOLA CINTRON, Ivan F. 400 AVE DOMENECH 00918 #042-01-1960 L1969 **IM A** *020 †20
ARZUAGA DELGADO, Rosita. ■ 00936 #308-06-1986 L1989 *020
ASENCIO, Jose E. 10 CALLE CASIA, VA MEDICAL CENTER(11D) 00921 #042-01-1985 L1988 **ID IM** *020
ASENJO, Conrado W. 369 DE DIEGO AVE, TORRE SAN FRANCISCO #602 00909 #042-01-1991 L1995 **GE** *020 †20
ASENSIO-BEAUCHAMP, S H. 37 AVE PONCE DE LEON 00901 #042-01-1956 L1960 **OBG** *020
ASTACIO, Evelyn R. ■ 00927 #042-01-1976 L1980 **PM** *020
ATENCIO, Jeremias. 61 CALLE TAPIA, APT 1A 00911 #264-08-1983 L2004 *100
AULET-MORALES, Frances. ■ 00926 #042-02-1994 L1998 **DR** *020 †80
AVILA, Andres Rafael. ■ 00921 #042-02-2006 **EM** *012
AVILA-CORTES, Lynnette. EL PORTAL DE LOS PINOS, STREET 2-C-49 00926 #042-03-1980 L1984 **IM** *075
AVILES, Angel Manuel, Jr. 607A CALLE DEL PARQUE 00909 #042-01-1997 L2001 **OBG** *020
AVILES, Eric David. 10 CALLE CASIA, VA MEDICAL CENTER 00921 #649-14-2003 **CD** *020
AVILES, Ileana. 1119 CALLE 3, VILLA NEVAREZ 00927 #042-01-2000 L2003 **FPG** *100 †18
AVILES MALDONADO, Wilfredo. 803 AVE HIPODROMO, CLENDO OCCUPACIONAL 00909 #649-14-2003 L2004 **GP** *020
AVILES SERRANO, Angel L. 259 CALLE MANUEL F ROSSY 00918 #308-03-1976 L1989 *020 †30
AXTMAYER, Alfred L. 252 CALLE SAN JORGE 00912 #056-06-1943 L1946 **GS CD** *020 †85
AYALA, Ivan S. ■ 00927 #042-01-1987 L1990 **CD IM** *020 †20
AYALA CARDONA, Heidi M. PO BOX 22895 00931 #649-14-2000 L2001 *020
AYALA-OLIVERAS, Israel. 20 CALLE GLORIMAR, JARD DE CALDAS 00926 #308-03-1978 L1980 **EM** *020
AYALA-RIVERA, Angel Luis. 1451 AVE ASHFORD 00907 #042-01-1955 L1958 **U** *071
AYUSO, Romulo. 10 CALLE CASIA, MEDICAL SERVICES 00921 #042-01-1981 L1987 **IM** *020 †20
AYUSO-RIVERA, Luis A. 36TH ST CAPERRA TERR 00921 #308-07-1982 *100

BACO, Francis Paul. 10 CALLE CASIA # 111, VA CARIBBEAN-MED SVC 00921 #042-01-1981 L1984 **END IM** *030 †20
BACO, Priscila L. 239 AVE ARTERIAL HOSTOS, STE 306 00918 #042-01-1986 L1988 **OPH** *020 †35
BACO-DAPENA, Raul. ■ 00920 #042-01-1956 L1965 **HEM IM** *030
BADIA, David Miguel. ■ 00923 #042-02-2006 *012
BADILLO, Manuel A. ■ 00926 #042-01-1991 L1996 **ORS** *020 †40
BADILLO-BORRAS, Pedro. 1801 AVE PONCE DE LEON, SANTURCE MEDICAL MALL 00909 #847-01-1973 L1976 **PP** *020
BAEZ, Luis. RR 3 # 20 00926 #042-01-1976 L1981 **IM** *020 †20
BAEZ, Miguel Angel. 406 AVE SAGRADO CORAZON, SAN CLAUDIO AVENUE 00915 #042-03-1997 L1999 **GS** *020 †85
BAEZA, Maria Luisa. ■ 00936 #042-01-1986 L1990 **PM** *020
BAEZ DE LEON, Juitza. 148 TURABO CLUSTER 00927 #042-04-2000 L2002 **FM** *020
BAEZ-LORENZO, Javier. ■ 00926 #042-03-2006 L2006 **P** *012
BAEZ-MATOS, Frankie. PO BOX 362706 00936 #042-01-1998 L2000 **NS** *012 †20
BAEZ-RIOS, Miguel Angel. 406 AVE SAGRADO CORAZON, SAN CLAUDIO AVENUE 00915 #847-06-1977 L1981 **EM FM** *020
BAEZ-SANCHEZ, Jose Angel. BORINQUEN TOWERS, BLDG 3 APT 1202 00920 #308-02-1974 L1978 **GP** *020 †30
BALBUENA HEATH, Charles F. PO BOX 364981 00936 #649-14-2002 L2005 *100
BALDIZON-LEON, Cesar A. ONE VETERANS PLAZA 00927 #682-01-1956 L1973 **PTH** *020 †50
BALLESTER, Maria E. PO BOX 8936 00910 #042-01-1986 L1990 **PM** *020 †60
BALLESTER, Veroushka. ■ 00926 #042-01-2007 **IM** *012
BALLESTER SOSA, Blanca M. 261 CALLE SANTA NARCISA, URB COLLEGE PARK 00921 #308-03-1981 L1993 *020
BALSALOBRE, Diana P. ■ 00907 #042-03-1996 L2000 **CN** *020 †75
BALZAC LIZARDI, Rafael. PO BOX 9020144, OLD SAN JUAN STA 00902 #847-05-1955 L1958 **PD OS** *071
BANCHS-PIERETTI, Hector L. URB LA CUMBRE STE 80 AV E 00927 #308-02-1976 L1982 **CCM IC** *020 †20
BANGDIWALA, Dweepkumar I. 138 AVE WINSTON CHURCHILL, URB CROWN HLS 00926 #042-01-1979 L1982 **IM OS** *071 ‡
BANON-SACRISTAN, Carlos. 714 AVE PONCE DE LEON 00918 #847-10-1965 L1972 **IM** *020
BANUCHI, Isabel Maria. 551 CALLE TRIGO 00907 #042-01-1977 L1981 **D** *020
BANUCHI, Ivan Bartolome. 1013 AVE AMERICO MIRANDA 00921 #042-01-1954 L1955 **GP** *020
BANUCHI, Victoria E. ■ 00921 #035-01-2008 *012
BARBANO, Carmela. ■ 00907 #847-04-1967 L1975 *071
BARLETTA-RODRIGUEZ, Ana M. 500 AVE MUNOZ RIVERA, #1 LOCAL 12 COND EL CENTRO 00918 #308-04-1980 L1983 **PD** *030
BARRERAS, Juan Xavier. PO BOX 363146 00936 #308-02-2000 L2005 *100
BARRERAS, Lourdes D. 820 CALLE 13 SO, URB CAPARRA TER 00921 #042-01-1981 L1984 **CHP PD** *020
BARRERAS-ALVAREZ, Manuel. 951 AVE AMERICO MIRANDA, REPTO METROPOLITANO 00921 #649-14-1967 L1979 **GP EM** *020
BARRETO, Edwin David. 200 AVE JESUS T PINERO 00918 #042-02-1993 L1997 **NPM** *020
BARRETO-DOMINQUEZ, A. 1451 AVE ASHFORD 00907 #024-05-1953 L1954 **PS** *020 †65
BARTOLOMEI, Ana. 431 CALLE TNTE CESAR GNZLZ, URB ROOSEVELT 00918 #042-01-1987 L1988 **OPH** *020 †35 ‡
BARTOLOMEI, Jack Tellier. 500 AVE DOMENECH, STE 302 00918 #847-04-1965 L1967 **IM** *020
BARTOLOMEI, Victoria. 431 CALLE TNTE CESAR GNZLZ, URB ROOSEVELT 00918 #042-01-1978 L1982 **OPH** *020 †35
BASSA, Ramon Antonio. 100 CALLE ROSEVILLE, BOX 28 00926 #308-03-1982 L1985 **GP** *020
BATISTA REYES, Juan G. ■ 00923 #308-01-1986 L1991 *020
BATLLE, Cosme Rafael. ■ 00915 #308-01-1958 L1963 **AN** *071 †05
BATTLE, Manuel. MUNICIPAL HOSP SURG DEPT 00935 #308-01-1973 L1983 **GS** *100
BAYO, Alexis Juan, Jr. ■ 00927 #041-02-1986 L1995 **EM TRS** *020 †16
BAYONET-RIVERA, Natalio. 252 CALLE SAN JORGE 00912 #024-07-1963 L1965 **OBG OS** *020 †30
BEATTY, Mark Edward. 1324 CALLE CANADA, URB PUERTO NUEVO 00920 #008-02-1993 L1993 **GPM** *020 †70,55 ‡
BEAUCHAMP, Mayra Cristina. ■ 00927 #042-01-2005 **D** *012
BELTRAN, Lydia Esther. ■ 00921 #042-01-1989 L1991 **FM** *020 †18
BELTRE VICENTE, Luis A. 57 SE #873, REPARTO METROPOLITANO 00921 #308-03-1990 L2004 *100
BENABE, Erika Michelle. ■ 00924 #042-03-2003 *100
BENAVIDES MARTINEZ, Raul. CALLE PARIS-243 00917 #649-01-1958 L1966 **PD** *020
BENERO-NATAL, Eliezer. 564A CALLE JUAN J JIMENEZ, PARQ CENTRAL 00918 #847-01-1977 L1981 **IM** *020
BENITEZ, Ana Marylee. ■ 00919 #042-01-2007 **TY** *012
BENITEZ, Hector. PUERTO RICO MED CTR 00936 #042-01-1974 L1977 **TRS GS** *020
BENITEZ, Maria Cecilia. PO BOX 13028 00908 #042-01-1979 L1982 **IM** *020
BENITEZ-COLON, Carlos R. 400 AVE DOMENECH STE 60, LAS AMERICAS PROFESSIONAL 00918 #308-03-1982 L1994 **GP** *020
BENITEZ COLON, Rafael A.. PO BOX 70171 PMB 076 00936 #308-03-1983 L2004 *100
BENITEZ GONZALEZ, Oscar R. 5 CALLE ARZUAGA NO 24 00925 #847-03-1974 L1978 **GP EM** *020
BENITEZ QUINONES, Arelis. ■ 00927 #649-14-2002 L2004 **GP** *100
BENITEZ RODRIGUEZ, O J. CALLE C FI18 MANS DE VILL 00926 #042-01-1972 L1975 **N** *020
BENMAMAN, Oliva Esther. 525 AVE FD ROOSEVELT, OFIC. #801 00918 #042-01-1981 L1984 **D IM** *020 †15
BENSEN ALMY, Karin S. ■ 00921 #042-01-1982 L1985 *020
BERDECIA, Jose Juan. 37 AVE PONCE DE LEON 00901 #042-01-1993 L1996 **PD** *020 †55
BERIO-MUNIZ, Rafael Lione. ■ 00918 #649-14-2002 L2002 **CD** *100 ‡
BERMUDEZ, Olga Waleska. GPO BOX 5067, UNIVERSITY HOSPITAL 00935 #042-01-1995 L1999 **PM** *020 †60
BERMUDEZ, Rafael R. 29 CALLE WASHINGTON # 308, ASHFORD MEDICAL CENTER 00907 #042-01-1992 L1995 **IM** *020 †20
BERNAL, Delfin V. 102 CALLE A, BDA BITUMUL 00917 #042-03-1985 L1987 **DR VIR** *020
BERNAL, Mario F. 716 AVE PONCE DE LEON 00918 #308-03-1978 L1979 **P** *020
BERNAL-ROSA, Jose F. 336T COND GOLDEN CT II 00918 #016-43-1949 L1952 **HS GS** *072 †85
BERNAL Y DEL RIO, Victor. 446 ENG FERNDO CALDER ORTZ 00918 #770-01-1942 L1942 **PYA P** *071 †75
BERNARDO, Maria Helena. 37 AVE PONCE DE LEON 00901 #649-14-1991 L1994 **PD** *020
BERRIOS, Angel Alonso. 570 CALLE CESAR GONZALEZ 00918 #847-04-1961 L1964 **OBG** *020

BERRIOS, Cesar. MIDTOWN BLDG STE 706, 420 PONCE DE LEON 00918 #847-09-1958 L1962 **OBG** *071
BERRIOS, Juan E. 1580 AVE AMERICO MIRANDA, URB CAPARRA TER 00921 #308-01-1985 L1989 **GP** *020
BERRIOS, Virginia. ■ 00936 #308-03-1981 L1992 **GP** *020
BERRIOS DE BENAVIDES, I. ■ 00926 #847-04-1964 L1968 **IM D** *020
BERRIOS-DELANNOY, Marco A. 500 AVE MUNOZ RIVERA, STE 204 00918 #847-04-1963 L1969 **OTO** *020 †45
BERRIOS ORTIZ, Lisette M. ■ 00924 #042-04-2001 L2002 *020
BERRIOS-PAGAN, Brigido. 403 CALLE DE DIEGO 00923 #042-01-1961 L1963 **GS** *020 †85
BERROCAL, Jose Antonio. 150 AVE DE DIEGO, # 503-509 00907 #042-01-1957 L1960 **OPH** *020 †85
BETANCES-PASTRANA, Pedro. 350D CALLE 32, PMB 68 00927 #649-14-1995 L2002 **GP GPM** *020
BETANCOURT, Benjamin. 1501 AVE FERNANDEZ JUNCOS, BETANCORT BLDG STE 401 00909 #042-01-1968 L1971 **CD IM** *020 †20
BETANCOURT, Jose Joaquin. 150 AVE CARLOS CHARDON, STE 232 00918 #042-01-1974 L1977 **IM** *020
BETANCOURT, Maria C. S6 CALLE PIO BAROJA, URB EL SENORIAL 00926 #042-03-2003 L2005 **IM** *100 †20
BETANCOURT-FERNANDEZ, N. 735 AVE PONCE DE LEON, STE 207 00917 #847-02-1981 L1984 **IM** *020
BETANCOURT GOMEZ, Isabel. ■ 00924 #042-04-1994 L1996 **PD** *020
BETANCOURT-GOMEZ, Nicolas. 735 AVE PONCE DE LEON, STE 207 00917 #847-02-1978 L1981 **GP** *020
BETANCOURT VELEZ, Elba Is. A20 CALLE 1 00921 #649-14-2003 L2005 *100
BIBILONI, Juan J. 802 ASHFORD MEDCL CTR #802 00907 #042-01-1983 L1988 **ORS** *020 †40
BIRD, Jose Miguel. 735 AVE PONCE DE LEON, COND TORRE DE AUXILIO MUTU 00917 #042-03-1983 L1988 **OTO** *020 †45
BIRD SOTO, Hector M. ONE VETERANS PLAZA 00927 #847-06-1961 L1966 **P** *071
BISONO, Pablo R. 626 AVE ESCORIAL, URB CAPARRA HTS 00920 #308-04-1987 L1992 **IM** *020
BLANCO, Rolando Julio. ■ 00926 #649-14-2003 L2005 **IM** *012
BLANCO-URRUTIA, Carla M. ■ 00907 #042-01-1997 L2003 **DR** *100 †80
BLAS, David Elias. ■ 00926 #042-01-2006 **N** *012
BLASINI RIVERA, E Marino. 611 CALLE PAVIA, SUITE 210 PAVIAMED PLAZA 00909 #042-01-1954 L1955 **GS** *020 †85
BLASINI TORRES, Marino. 611 CALLE PAVIA, STE 210 00909 #042-01-1984 L1987 **OPH OS** *020 †35
BLONDET, Maximo Carlos. 206 CALL PJL EXT MILAVILLE 00926 #042-03-1996 L1999 **PUD** *020 †20
BOADA, Robert. ■ 00907 #042-01-1997 L1999 **OPH** *020 †35
BOERAS PUPO, Luis Cesar. 400 AVE DOMENECH, STE 602C 00918 #275-02-1975 L1998 **IM** *020
BOLET, Orlando. ■ 00936 #308-03-1983 L2002 **FM** *020
BONILLA, Melvin A. B4 CALLE POPPY, PARQUE FORESTAL 00926 #042-01-1986 L1989 **PN PD** *040 †55
BONILLA, Migdalia Zoe. ■ 00927 #042-03-2004 **OBG** *012
BONILLA PEREZ, Juan Perez. ■ 00923 #042-03-2005 **FP** *012
BONNEAUX, Phillip Lee. 903 EDIF MEDINA, 112 ARZUARA ST 00925 #042-03-1980 L1984 **RHU IM** *020
BONNET, Luis E. 400 AVE FD ROOSEVELT, STE 101 00918 #042-01-1964 L1968 **DR** *020
BORGES, Hidelisa. 619 AVE PONCE DE LEON, TORRE MEDICA AUXILIO MUTUO 00917 #042-01-1994 L1997 **CD** *020
BORGES, William. ■ 00922 #042-01-2006 **IM** *012
BORIA R DE BLAS, Zaida. 391 AVE DOMENECH 00918 #847-10-1970 L1972 **N** *020
BORRAS, Freddie. 1451 AVE ASHFORD 00907 #847-04-1954 L1957 **PD** *030
BORREGO, Luis G. 13 CAMINO MANGUAL, BO QUEBRADA ARENA 00926 #042-01-1998 L2001 **IM** *100
BORRI, Cesar Oscar. 1652 CALLE SANTA AGUEDA, LES CHALET COURT B4 00926 #042-01-1998 L2000 **IM** *100
BOSCHETTI, Mildred. ■ 00926 #308-06-1987 L1991 **GP** *020
BOSCH-RAMIREZ, Marcial V. 255 CALLE LUNA, VIEJO SAN JUAN 00901 #308-03-1978 L1980 **AN GP** *020
BOSQUE, Lorenzo Edgardo. 145 CALLE GUARAGUAO, URB MONTEHIEDRA 00926 #308-04-1989 L1992 **GP** *020
BOTET, Miguel Vazquez. 386 AVE DOMENECH 00918 #042-01-1975 L1980 **D** *020 †15
BOUET, Rafael. ■ 00926 #042-03-2000 L2004 **GS** *100
BOURDONY, Carlos Juan. 1717 AVE PONCE DE LEON, PLAZA INMACULAD II PH7 00909 #649-01-1971 L1974 **PDE PD** *020 †55
BOVEA, Augusto Cesar. SAN JUAN CTY HOSP SURG 00935 #264-05-1969 **GS** *100
BRACERO, Nabal Jose. 369 AVE DE DIEGO, STE 606 00923 #042-01-1995 L1999 **OBG REN** *020
BRAGANZA, Adam Francis. ■ 00911 #041-15-2005 L2005 **OPH** *012
BRAVO, Evelio F. 400 AVE DOMENECH STE 604, LAS AMERICAS PROF BLDG 00918 #042-01-1980 L1983 **GE HEP** *020 †27
BRAVO, Miguel A. 303 CALLE SOL # 8-B 00901 #847-03-1975 L1978 **P** *020
BRENES CATINCHI, Jason T. ■ 00926 #042-04-2003 L2004 *100
BRIONES, Carlomagno. ■ 00907 #649-14-1994 L1996 *020
BRITO, Carmen Julia. PO BOX 365067 00936 #308-13-2003 **P** *012
BRITO, Hilda Mileidys. ■ 00920 #275-01-1993 L2006 *100 †55
BRUNET, Virgilio. 385 AVE DOMENECH 00918 #042-01-1975 L1980 **GS** *020
BUCARELLI BOBEA, Ana A. 243 CALLE PARIS, PO BOX 1485 00917 #308-01-1988 L2004 *100
BUNKER, Rex James. 37 AVE PONCE DE LEON 00901 #021-01-1944 L1945 **OTO** *072 †45
BURGOS, Carlos Enrique. 1357 AVE ASHFORD # 352 00907 #847-04-1960 L1976 **GP OS** *071
BURGOS GANDIA, Augusto C. 763 CALLE DIANA, URB DOS PINOS 00923 #308-03-1984 L1993 **GP** *020
BUSHBERG, David Allan. 100 GRAND BLVD STE 106A, GALERIA PASEO MALL 00926 #649-14-1989 L1993 **FM** *020
BUSO, Carmen M. ■ 00907 #042-01-1965 **GP** *075
BUSQUETS, Antonio Rafael. 100 CALLE DEL MUELLE, CAPITOLIO PLAZA SUITE 501 00901 #042-01-1998 L2000 **PS** *020 †85
BUSQUETS, Jose Miguel. 150 AVE DE DIEGO STE 605, SAN JUAN HEALTH CENTER 00907 #042-01-1999 L2002 **GP** *020 †45
BUSQUETS VILLEGAS, Jaime. ■ 00936 #308-13-2004 **IM** *012
BUSTAMANTE, Juan Rivera. ■ 00920 #847-05-1977 L1981 **P** *020
BUSTELO MENDEZ, Guillermo. 101 CALLE MATIENZO CINTRON, URB FLORAL PARK 00917 #847-04-1960 L1963 **P** *071

■ = Address Information Privacy Protected

BUXEDA, Roberto. ASHFORD MEDICAL CTR, DEPT OPTH 00907 #041-09-1940 L1941 OPH *071 †35

BUXO, Carlos Adalberto. ■ 00917 #042-01-2000 L2002 **APM** *100 †05

CABALLERO, Baruch. 1801 AVE PONCE DE LEON 00909 #847-20-1981 L1982 **CD** *020

CABALLERO, Carmen. 1114 PUERTO NUEVO NORTE, 16 N.E. ST 00920 #042-01-1972 L1974 **R IM** *020 †28

CABAN, Carlos Augusto. 650 CALLE LLOVERAS 00909 #042-01-1981 L1985 **P** *020

CABRA, Omar Humberto. GPO BOX 5067 00936 #264-01-1987 **FP** *012

CABRAL DE BEAUCHAMP, M. PO BOX 11950, CAPARRA HEIGHTS STATION 00922 #308-01-1982 L1991 **IM** *050 †28

CABRERA, Ariel. ■ 00918 #042-01-1976 L1980 **P** *020

CABRERA, Fernando. ■ 00936 #847-04-1955 L1958 **P LM** *071 †75

CABRERA, Nestor Antonio. 1772 CALLE GLASGOW, URB COLLEGE PARK 00921 #042-01-1983 L1986 **FM IMG** *040 †18

CABRERA-AGUILAR, Rafael. 344 CALLE HECTOR SALAMAN, EXT ROOSEVELT 00918 #308-04-1981 L1989 **P** *020

CABRERA DIAZ, Manuel A. ONE VETERANS PLAZA 00927 #847-05-1978 L1981 **GS** *020

CABRERA-RALDIRIS, Rafael. ■ 00918 #847-01-1965 L1970 **GP** *020

CABRERO, Andres T. ■ 00936 #649-14-1977 L1994 **P** *020 †75

CACERES, William W. 203 CALLE SORBONA, URB UNIVERSITY GDNS 00927 #042-01-1987 L1992 **HEM ON** *020 †20

CACERES BURGOS, Francisco. PO BOX 361774 00936 #042-01-1970 L1977 **PD NPM** *020 †55

CADILLO CHAVEZ, Ronald Ge. PO BOX 365067 00936 #737-01-1998 **GS** *100

CADIZ, Cecilio Jose. 435 AVE PONCE DE LEON 00917 #042-01-1981 L1986 **GS** *020

CAISEDA-GARCIA, David. PO BOX 367128 00936 #042-01-1961 L1965 **P** *030

CAJIGAS, Agustin. ■ 00926 #042-01-1988 L1992 **PTH** *020

CALCAGNO, F Mario. PO BOX 191116 00919 #308-01-1948 L1958 **GP OS** *071

CALDERIN, Mayra M. 650 CALLE LLOVERAS, STE 101 00909 #042-01-1985 L1989 **P** *020 †75

CALDERON, Edith Milagros. 1236B PASEO MONTE REAL 00926 #042-01-1988 L1991 **PD** *020 †55

CALDERON-GUZMAN, Jose L. PO BOX 70344, SAN JUAN MUNICIPAL HOSPITA 00936 #649-14-2001 L2003 **OBG** *100

CALDERON-JULIA, F J. 1801 AVE PONCE DE LEON, STE 301 00909 #042-01-1991 L1995 **P** *020

CALDERON-SITIRICHE, Saml. ■ 00927 #847-04-1978 L1980 **IM CD** *020

CALERO, Mildred. ■ 00918 #847-01-1974 L1976 **PD** *020 †55

CALIMANO, Carlos A. W5-5 CALLE PIO BAROJA, URB HUCARES 00926 #042-01-1971 L1980 **GS VS** *020 †85

CALISTO, Carlos Alberto. ■ 00924 #042-03-2006 **EM** *012

CALVESBERT, David. 252 CALLE SAN JORGE 00912 #042-03-1983 L1993 **PDS GP** *020

CAMAYD-ARAGUNDE, Ricardo. 419 CALLE DUERO, VILLA BORINQUEN 00920 #847-05-1978 L1982 **GP** *020

CAMBARA, Alejandro Enriqu. PO BOX 5067, UNIV OF PR SCH OF MED 00936 #275-01-1995 **PD** *100

CAMERON MORALES, Salia E. ■ 00926 #847-05-1985 L1990 **OM EM** *020

CAMPOS, Miguel Angel, Jr. 650 CALLE LLOVERAS, STE 202 00909 #042-01-1985 L1995 **CD** *020 †20

CAMPOS HERRERA, Loida H. 502 CALLE NORZAGARAY, APT 3 00901 #275-01-1988 L2000 *100

CANALS, Ricardo M. PO BOX 97 00919 #042-01-1991 L1996 **ORS** *020 †40

CANARIO, Quirico Manuel. 576 CALLE CESAR GONZALEZ, STE 403 00918 #308-02-1977 L1987 **GS** *020 †85

CANCEL, Dilany Michelle. ■ 00926 #042-01-2002 L2005 **GE** *012 †20

CANCEL, Jaime L. FERNANDEZ JUNCOS STATION 00910 #042-01-1971 L1976 **GS** *020

CANCEL HENRIQUEZ, T. BOX 10172 CAPRIA HGTS STA 00922 #042-01-1972 L1974 **IM RHU** *040

CANDELARIO, Juan J. ■ 00921 #042-01-1983 L1988 **IM** *020 †20

CANEPA, Luis Enrique. 29 CALLE WASHINGTON, ASHFORD MEDICAL CENTER 00907 #042-01-1973 L1996 **P PYA** *020 †75

CANGIANO-RIVERA, Jose L. 313 AVE DOMENECH STE 101 00918 #042-01-1960 L1970 **NEP IM** *020

CANTO, Eduardo Ignacio. 29 CALLE WASHINGTON, STE 101 00927 #024-01-1999 L2005 **U** *020 †95

CAPELLA, Amaury. 29 CALLE WASHINGTON, STE 405 00907 #041-13-1955 L1960 **GS** *020 †85

CAPELLA-SEGARRA, Carmen. ■ 00924 #847-06-1973 L1977 **ADM** *030

CAPO, Francisco Jose. PAVIA MEDICAL PLAZA, STE 104 00909 #042-01-1973 L1975 **U** *020 †95

CAPRILES, Jose Antonio. ■ 00922 #042-01-1981 L1984 **NPM PD** *030

CARABALLO ALFONSO, Nilka. RR 6 BOX 10992, LOS RIVERAS ST 00926 #649-14-2000 L2000 **PD** *020

CARBALLO, Francisco. 400 AVE FD ROOSEVELT, BOX 304 00918 #042-01-1962 L1966 **OBG** *020 †30

CARDONA, Hector A. 1431 AVE PONCE DE LEON # 6 00907 #042-01-1990 L1995 **U** *020

CARDONA, Jose F. 401 GALERIA LOS PASEOS 00926 #042-03-1985 L1987 **EM** *030

CARDONA, Marga. B6 CALLE PPY PARQ FORESTAL 00926 #042-03-1994 L1998 **DR** *020

CARDONA, Miguel P. 431 AVE PONCE DE LEON, STE 325 00917 #042-03-1989 L1994 **PM** *020

CARDONA, Pablo E. 1451 AVE PONCE DE LEON # 6 00907 #042-01-1982 L1987 **U** *020 †95

CARDONA-CARRASQUILLO, J. 511 CALLE ASUNCION, URB PUERTO NUEVO 00920 #847-17-1985 L1990 **GP** *020

CARLO, Anibal G. 525 AVE FD ROOSEVELT # 8VO, PLAZA LAS AMERICAS 00918 #042-01-1981 L1988 **U** *020 †95

CARLO CHEVERE, Victor J. 570B CALLE JUAN J JIMENEZ, PARQ CENTRAL 00918 #042-01-1994 L1999 **PTH PCP** *020 †50

CARMONA, Carolina. ■ 00926 #649-14-2002 L2004 *100

CARRASCO, Jose I. 10 CALLE CASIA, PATHOLOGY SERVICE 00921 #042-01-1962 L1978 **PTH AM** *020 †50

CARRASQUILLO RODRIGUEZ, Ha. 180 RES MONTE PARK, AVE HOSTOS APT P 00924 #042-01-1998 L1999 **FM** *020

CARRAU, Victor Antonio. ■ 00936 #042-03-1995 **P** *100

CARRERA-GONZALEZ, Tomas R. 220 CALLE DEL PARQUE 00912 #847-05-1972 L1975 **PD NPM** *020

CARRERAS, Jose Antonio. 150 AVE CARLOS CHARDON, STE 232 00918 #042-01-1980 L1984 **OPH ORS** *071

CARRILLO, Rafael J. 37 AVE PONCE DE LEON 00901 #042-01-1982 L1987 **U** *020

CARRILLO, Sol Melisa. ■ 00929 #042-01-2007 **IM** *012

CARRILLO-RIVERA, Rafael O. 735 AVE PONCE DE LEON, STE 409 00917 #042-01-1966 L1971 **U** *020 †95

CARRO, Eric Juan. 00927 #042-01-2000 L2003 **CD** *012

CARTAGENA, Edgardo Fidel. 369 AVE DE DIEGO, STE 308-309 00909 #308-04-1987 L1989 **PUD IM** *020 †20

CARY, Stephen Matthew. 1451 AVE ASHFORD 00907 #056-05-1993 L1996 **FM** *020 †18

CASADO, Griselle. COND LOS ROBLES #106A 00927 #042-01-1999 L2002 **AN** *020 †05

CASAL, Jesus. ■ 00926 #042-03-1989 L1996 **PUD CCM** *020 †20

CASALS BLASINI, Coral Mar. ■ 00907 #042-04-1996 L2002 **FM** *100

CASANOVA, Roberto Luis. 735 AVE PONCE DE LEON, TORRE MEDICA AUXILIO MUTUO 00917 #042-01-1991 L1997 **GE** *020 †20

CASANOVA-DIAZ, Jose R. 179 CALLE HUYKE 00918 #023-01-1937 L1937 **GS ON** *071

CASANOVA-ROIG, Ramon. 513 AVE HOSTOS 00918 #041-13-1960 L1963 **PDA PD** *020 †55,03

CASAS, Ingrid Leticia. 352 AVE SAN CLAUDIO, URB SAGRADO CORAZON 00926 #042-01-2001 L2003 **CHP** *100 †75

CASASNOVAS, Camille Nanet. 00927 #042-01-2007 *012

CASILLAS, Emilio, Jr. 1890 CALLE PETUNIA, URB SANTA MARIA 00927 #847-03-1969 L1972 **OTO** *020

CASILLAS, Stella Marie. ■ 00927 #042-01-2005 *100

CASIMIR, Franchard. PO BOX 20191 00928 #649-47-1984 L2005 *100

CASTANEDA, Luis A. 10 CALLE CASIA, SEE 42-0464 00921 #275-08-1990 **IM** *012

CASTANER, Juan Carlos. 29 CALLE WASHINGTON, STE 207 00907 #035-03-1987 L1993 **OBG MFM** *020

CASTELLANOS PORTELA, Crist. AVE ARTERIAL HOSTOS 00918 #042-04-2001 L2002 *020

CASTILLO, Maria Cristina. ■ 00926 #042-01-2008 *012

CASTILLO, Maruquel. ■ 00926 #042-01-1996 L2001 **N** *020 †75

CASTILLO AVILES, Zenaida. PO BOX 70344 PMB 17 00936 #042-04-2002 L2004 *100

CASTILLO-BARREIRO, Ivette. ■ 00928 #042-03-1981 L1994 **OBG** *020

CASTILLO-BEAUCHAMP, Yamil. ■ 00926 #042-01-2006 **GS** *012

CASTRILLO, Rafael H. 1867 CALLE ACACIA, URB SANTA MARIA 00927 #847-04-1957 L1959 **OTO** *020

CASTRO, Ericka Rivera. 826 CALLE MOLUCAS, URB COUNTRY CLUB 00924 #042-03-1980 L1984 **P** *020

CASTRO, Nancy Ann. ■ 00926 #042-01-2007 **IM** *012

CASTRO, Nydia De Lourdes. 211 CALLE BENITO PERZ GLDS, URB ROOSEVELT 00918 #649-14-2002 L2005 *100

CASTRO, Ricardo. ■ 00926 #042-01-1992 L1996 **AN** *020

CASTRO, Ricardo Oscar. 390 AVE DOMENECH, ASOCIADOS 00918 #042-01-1989 L1994 **DR** *020

CASTRODAD, David A. ■ 00926 #042-01-1989 L1992 **AN** *020 †05

CASTRO-DIAZ, Esteban. 1451 AVE ASHFORD 00907 #042-01-1984 L1986 **GE IM** *020 †20

CATALA, Ricardo L. ■ 00926 #042-03-1989 L1996 **GS** *020

CATASUS, Ubaldo. 239 AVE ARTERIAL HOSTOS, STE 601 00918 #042-01-1967 L1971 **OBS GYN** *020 †30

CAZARES, Rebeca A. PO BOX 70171 PMB 052-PO 00936 #048-14-1989 L1990 **IM** *071

CEDENO, Arturo. 150 AVE CARLOS CHARDON, STE 232 00918 #042-03-1996 L1999 **PUD** *020 †20

CEDENO, Jessica. 735 AVE PONCE DE LEON, STE 502 00917 #042-01-2000 L2001 *020 †35

CEDENO-COTTI, Pablo. ■ 00918 #847-10-1968 L1970 **P** *020

CEDO-GAUDIER, Pedro. 400 AVE DOMENECH, STE 506 00918 #042-01-1969 L1971 **PD** *020

CEPEDA DE COLOTTO, Carmen. 831 CALLE JOSE B ACEVEDO 00923 #042-01-1984 L1986 *020

CERDA, Rigoberto. 385 AVE FELISA RINCON GATR, COND. PUERTO PASEOS 902 00926 #308-01-1963 L1972 **OBG** *020

CESPEDES, Wayca Rebeca. ■ 00924 #042-03-2003 **AN** *100

CESTERO, Herman J. 435 AVE PONCE DE LEON 00917 #042-01-1965 L1970 **PS GS** *071 †85,65

CHABRIEL-GONZALEZ, G. 1500 AVE SAN IGNACIO, BALCONES DE SANTA MARIA H- 00921 #847-06-1977 L1981 **GP** *071

CHABRIER, Lizette. GPO 4867 00936 #042-01-1990 L1993 **D** *020 †15

CHABRIER, Sandra Gisela. ■ 00921 #308-01-1987 L1987 *020

CHAFEY, David H. A 17 PARQUES SAN IGNACIO 00921 #035-09-1950 L1954 **OBG** *072 †30

CHAVIER ROPER, Rolance G. 1107 CALLE WILLIAM JONES 00925 #042-04-1993 L1994 **IM** *020

CHINEA, Hector. B65 CAL 5 COLINAS DE CUPEY 00926 #649-01-1970 L1974 **N** *020

CHIRINO, Maria Elena. 500 CALLE CESAR GONZALEZ 00918 #042-03-1992 L1995 **RHU** *020 †20

CHIROQUE BENITEZ, Luis. MUNOZ RIVERA, PENTAGRAMA #10 00926 #737-03-1989 L1998 *100

CIANCHINI-ANSELMI, Jose L. 501 COND KINGS CT PLAYA CT, 59 CALLE KINGS COURT 00911 #847-04-1959 L1961 **IM CD** *020 †20

CICHOWICZ, Edward Raymond. 497 AVE EMILIANO POL, STE 585 00926 #042-01-1977 L1982 **GE PD** *020

CICHOWICZ, Ivan E. ■ 00926 #042-03-2005 L2005 **P** *012

CINTRON, Cesar. 403 CALLE DE DIEGO 00923 #042-01-1954 L1960 **ORS** *020

CINTRON, Eloy. 400 AVE FD ROOSEVELT, STE 101 00918 #042-01-1995 L2001 **DR** *020 †80

CINTRON, Elsie. 125 CALLE ALELI, URB SAN FRANCISCO 00927 #042-01-1977 L1981 **DR** *030 †80

CINTRON, Marcelino. 37 AVE PONCE DE LEON 00901 #042-02-1985 L1988 **FM** *020

CINTRON, Vilma Luz. A42 CALLE 1, COLINAS VERDE 00924 #308-01-1985 L1987 **PD** *020

CINTRON-DELGADO, Domingo. 400 AVE DOMENECH STE 206 00918 #847-04-1966 L1971 **PD OS** *020

CINTRON-RIVERA, Angel A. 252 CALLE SAN JORGE 00912 #025-01-1945 L1954 **NM HEM** *071 †28

CIPRIAN LIRANZO, Pedro Ni. 275 CALLE PADRE COLON, BO CAPETILLO 00923 #308-01-1985 L2002 **GP** *020

CIRCUNS-QUIROS, Manuel V. SUITE 611, 497 E POL AVENUE 00926 #847-10-1966 L1968 **PD** *020

CISNERO, Maria Del Carmen. GPO BOX 5067 00936 #275-02-1984 **FP** *012

CLAVELL, Luis Antonio. 252 CALLE SAN JORGE, SAN JORGE MEDICAL BUILDING 00912 #042-01-1976 L1980 **PHO ON** *020 †55

COBIAN, Josefina Diaz. ■ 00918 #308-03-1980 L1980 **GP** *020

COIRA, Diego L. ■ 00936 #847-10-1961 L1967 **P** *071

COIRA, Roberto. 1793 CALLE SANTA EULALIA, URB SAGRADO CORAZON 00926 #042-04-1993 L1996 **P** *020

COLACIOPPO, Ricardo Gabri. ■ 00926 #042-01-2004 **CD** *012 †20

COLBERG, Rebekah Cabreras. 00907 #649-01-1955 L1957 **CHP P** *072

COLBERG, Ricardo Edwin. ■ 00921 #042-01-2008 *012

COLEN, Elan Meshilem. ■ 00901 #042-01-2005 **DR** *012

COLLAZO, Leonardo. 403 CALLE DE DIEGO, ESQUINA LOS ANGELES 00923 #042-01-1964 L1967 **GS SO** *020

COLLAZO, Ramon L. 29 CALLE WASHINGTON # 508, ASHFORD MED CTR 00907 #042-01-1987 L1991 **OAR** *020

COLLAZO DE SABATE, Aida. 30 CALLE WASHINGTON STE 1, CONDODO TOWERS CONDOMINIUM 00907 #847-01-1962 L1966 **CHP** *040

COLLAZO LIZARDI, Diego H. 531 CALLE CUEVAS BUSTAMANT 00918 #042-01-1960 L1964 **PD** *020

COLOM, Sebastian A. 400 AVE DOMENECH 00918 #847-01-1956 L1958 **N IM** *020

COLOMBANI, Leslie G. 426 CALLE AGUEYBANA, URB. EL VEDADO 00918 #649-14-1994 L1997 **FM** *020

COLOM-COLL, Ramon M. 554 CALLE JUAN JIMENEZ 00918 #847-01-1964 L1971 **ORS** *020

COLON, Ana L. PO BOX 22678, 6 CALLE JOSE FERNANDEZ 00931 #042-01-1966 L1969 **D IM** *020 †15

COLON, Arturo. ■ 00917 #042-03-2002 L2004 **GS** *100

COLON, Carlos. ■ 00936 #042-01-1962 L1965 **GP OS** *071

COLON, Dorianne. ■ 00917 #042-03-2005 **PD** *012

COLON, Edgardo Miguel. 279 CALLE CONVENTO, SANTURCE 00912 #042-01-1977 L1983 **PS** *020

COLON, Edwin Alberto A. 1353 CALLE OLGA ESPERANZA, URB SAN MARTIN 00924 #042-01-1992 L1995 **PUD** *050 †20

COLON, Elfren Alfredo. ■ 00926 #042-01-2004 L2005 **AN** *012

COLON, Jacqueline M. 586 CALLE GREENWOOD, URB SUMMIT HLS 00920 #308-06-1986 L1989 **GP** *020

COLON, Jorge G. 150 AVE DE DIEGO STE 607, BOX 365026 00907 #847-01-1984 L1993 **GP** *020

COLON, Jose Luis. 576 CALLE CESAR GONZALEZ, STE 203 00918 #042-01-1993 L1998 **GS** *020 †85

COLON, Lissandra. ■ 00926 #042-01-1999 **EM** *100 †16 ‡

COLON, Luis F. RR 2, BOX 116 00926 #649-34-2004 L2005 *100

COLON, Miguel. 89 AVE DE DIEGO STE 105, PMB 446 00927 #042-02-1983 L1984 **ID IM** *020 †20

COLON, Nelson. 1413 AVE FERNANDEZ JUNCOS, STE 2C 00909 #042-01-1986 L1993 **PM** *020 †60

COLON, Raphael Alexis. ■ 00918 #042-03-2006 **EM** *012

COLON, Raul. ■ 00926 #042-01-2005 **GS** *020

COLON, Tamara I. 1451 AVE ASHFORD, PRESBY PRMARY CARE CTR 00907 #042-01-1987 L1989 **GP** *020

COLON, Vilma. 10 CALLE CASIA, VA CARIBBEAN HEALTHCARE SY 00921 #016-11-1980 L1985 **GP** *020

COLON-ARVELO, Cristino R. 554 CALLE CABO ALVERIO, EXT ROOSEVELT 00918 #042-01-1958 L1962 **IM** *020

COLON-DE MARTI, Luz N. E28 CALLE CORRIENTE, URB EL REMANSO 00926 #042-01-1977 L1986 **P CHP** *040 †75

COLON DE RODRIGUEZ, Lydia. 500 AVE MUNOZ RIVERA, PMB 343-LOCAL 00918 #847-04-1962 L1966 **GP** *020

COLON EMERIC, Marelli. 2010 EL MONTE MALL # 2010 00918 #042-01-1994 L2001 **CHP** *020 †75

COLON GORBEA, Diana M. 554 CALLE ALVERIO, EXT ROOSEVELT 00918 #042-01-1985 L1988 **GE IM** *020 †20

COLON-LEON, Jose R. 37 AVE PONCE DE LEON 00901 #308-03-1979 L1982 **PD** *020

COLON MARTINEZ, Jose Luis. PO BOX 361417, 24 RAMON MEDINA ST 00936 #649-01-1954 L1960 **PD OS** *071

COLON MARTINEZ, Mirylsa. ■ 00926 #042-01-2002 L2004 **ORS** *012

COLON NEGRON, Edgar. ■ 00926 #042-01-1984 L1988 **DR** *020 †80

COLON-PAGAN, Juan R. 37 AVE PONCE DE LEON 00901 #042-01-1962 L1965 **GE IM** *020

COLON-PEREZ, Rolando. 1492 AVE PONCE DE LEON # 7, EDIFICIO CENTRO EUROPA 00907 #042-01-1983 L1986 **TS GS** *020 †85,90

COLON-QUETGLAS, Kermit. N43 CALLE ACADIA, URB PARK GDNS 00926 #042-01-1975 L1979 **IM** *030

COLON QUINONES, Juan L. 60 ST BA 19, URB HILL MANSION 00926 #308-13-2003 L2005 *100

COLON-RAMOS, Francisco E. 1822 AVE PONCE DE LEON, HOSPITAL SANCARLOS SANTURC 00909 #803-05-1955 L1957 **ON GYN** *071 †30

COLON-RIVERA, Orlando A. 251 AVE WINSTON CHURCHILL 00926 #649-14-1988 L1991 **GP** *020 †55

COLON-RODRIGUEZ, Ariel G. ■ 00923 #042-01-1959 L1962 **OBG** *071 †30

COLON-RODRIGUEZ, F. 206 CLINICA LAS AMERICAS, HATO 8284 400 ROOSEVELT 00918 #042-01-1964 L1968 **GE IM** *020

COLON-SEMIDAY, Angel J. 728 AVE PONCE DE LEON 00918 #042-03-1993 L1996 **PDP** *020 †55

COLON-TRABAL, Carmen. 121 AVE DOMENECH 00918 #308-03-1980 L1985 **PD** *020

COLON-VELEZ, Jorge G. PO BOX 365026, 150 DE DIEGO AVE 00936 #847-01-1982 L1985 **OM ADM** *020

COLON ZAVALA, Edgardo Mig. ■ 00926 #042-01-2004 **N** *012

CONAWAY, Paul Irvin. PO BOX 362309 00936 #649-01-1970 L1975 **IM** *020

CONCEPCION, Rodolfo A. 809 ASHFORD MEDCL CTR #809 00907 #042-01-1971 L1973 **RHU IM** *072

CONDE, Jose Guillermo. UNIV PR MED SC-GPO 5067 00936 #042-01-1980 L1984 **GPM** *040

CONDE DE BORROGO, Lillian. 1452 AVE ASHFORD, EDIFICIO ADA LIGIA STE 301 00907 #042-01-1962 L1965 **NM IM** *020 †28

CONDERO-LANZAR, Marvalyn. SEGURO DEL ESTADO, CORPORACION DEL FONDO DEL 00936 #308-03-1978 L1980 **FM** *020

CONNELLY, Owen G. ■ 00926 #308-04-1990 L1995 **OBG** *020

CORADIN RUIZ, Rafael. ■ 00926 #308-06-1982 L1992 *100

CORCINO, Jose J. 37 AVE PONCE DE LEON 00901 #042-01-1962 L1966 **HEM IM** *020 †20

CORDERO, Domingo. 310 ASHFORD MEDICAL CTR 00907 #042-01-1965 L1969 **P** *020

CORDERO, Jorge L. ■ 00936 #042-01-1986 L1990 **GS** *020

CORDERO ALONSO, Domingo B. 29 CALLE WASHINGTON, ASHFORD MEDICAL CENTER 00907 #042-01-1972 L1974 **P** *020

CORDERO-RODRIGUEZ, Luis F. ■ 00927 #042-04-1988 L1991 **AN** *020

CORDERO SEPULVEDA, Julio. ■ 00907 #042-04-2004 L2005 *100

CORDERO-TORRES, Wilfredo. B1 CALLE TOMAS AGRAIT, URB CLUB MANOR 00924 #042-03-2003 L2006 **EM** *020

CORDOBA, Fabiola. ■ 00907 #264-10-1985 L2003 **PD** *020

CORDOVA, Gladys Jeannette. PO BOX 21321, 844 ST 1741 PURPLE TREE 00931 #042-03-1980 L1984 **GP** *020

CORONA, Gonzalo Gonzalez. ■ 00917 #649-14-1982 L2005 *100

CORRAL, Claudio Javier. 239 AVE ARTERIAL HOSTOS, STE 105 00918 #024-07-1991 L1999 **PS GS** *020

CORRALES, Yuri Eduardo. 820 AVE ITURREGUI, URB COUNTRY CLUB 00924 #264-06-1991 L2004 **ID IM** *020 †20

CORREA, Cynthia Milagros. SAN JUAN MUNICIPAL HOSP, DEPT PED 00928 #308-03-1985 L1992 **PD** *020

CORREA, Margarita. 1261 AVE AMERICO MIRANDA, REPTO METROPOLITANO 00921 #042-01-1980 L1984 **PM OS** *020 †60

CORREA, Sonia M. 306 CALLE CACERES, LOWR 00923 #042-04-1995 L1996 **FM** *020

CORREA-FLORES, Maria A. 102 CALLE LAS LOMAS, URB LAS CUMBRES 00926 #042-03-1980 L1986 **IM** *020

CORREA-RIVAS, Maria S. ■ 00936 #042-01-1988 L1992 **PTH PP** *020

CORRETJER, Francisco J. 11 CALLE GUARIONEX, HATO REY 00918 #042-01-1990 L1994 **GYN** *020 †35

CORRETJER, Francisco Jose. 1250 AVE JESUS T PINERO, CAPARRA TERRACE 00921 #042-01-1963 L1966 **OBG OS** *020 †30

CORTES, Antonio. 369 DE DIEGO AVE, STE 402 00909 #042-01-1979 L1983 **OBG** *020 †30

CORTES, Cesar Francisco. 183 CALLE DELBREY 00911 #042-01-2005 **DR** *012

CORTES, Francisco. C-2 CAMBRIDGE PK 00927 #042-03-1980 L1985 **GP FOP** *062

CORTES-GELI, Ruben. PO BOX 361223, STE 10-I 00936 #308-03-1980 L1983 **GP** *020

CORTES-MAISONET, Gregorio. 1826 AVE FERNANDEZ JUNCOS, PDA. 26 00909 #649-14-2004 L2005 *100

CORTES MATOS, Nelson. ■ 00919 #847-04-1953 L1956 **GS IM** *020 †85

CORTES ORTIZ, Walter. 1451 AVE ASHFORD 00907 #847-10-1970 L1973 **FM EM** *020 ‡

CORTES-VAZQUEZ, Zaida M. ■ 00922 #056-06-1958 L1971 **GP** *020 †55

COSTA-PEREZ, Martiniano J. 211 COND SEGOVIA 00918 #847-04-1962 L1964 **PD** *071

COSTAS, Haydee. PO BOX 191984 00919 #042-01-1967 L1969 **P** *040 †75

COSTAS, Margarita C. ■ 00918 #051-04-1953 L1955 **PD** *071 †55

COSTAS, Pablo J. 1056 AVE MUNOZ RIVERA, STE 405 00927 #042-01-1992 L1995 **GE** *020 †20

COSTAS, Raul, Jr. ■ 00918 #010-01-1953 L1954 **IM CD** *072 ‡

COSTA-SOTO, Magda. 303 AVE DOMENECH, URB JB HUYKE 00918 #649-14-1976 L1978 **R** *020

COTO RIVERA, Annette E. ■ 00920 #649-14-2000 L2002 *020

COTTO, Hector L. 371 AVE DE DIEGO 00923 #042-01-1967 L1971 **RHU IM** *020

COTTO IBARRA, Luis. 530 CAL ANTLN NN URB LOS I, INGENIEROS HATO REY 00918 #042-01-1977 L1981 **PM** *020

COTTO-MOJICA, Juan Jose. 39 PARQUE MEDICI, PASEO DEL PARQUE 00926 #308-03-1982 L1984 **GP** *020

COX, Rafael A. ■ 00936 #042-01-1966 L1971 **CD IM** *040 †20

CRESPO, Abnel. 700 CALLE EUROPA STE 301, AVE FERNANDEZ JREOS 00909 #649-14-1987 L1990 **IM** *020

CRESPO, Maribel Vionet. 655 CALLE AFRODITA, URB VENUS GDNS 00926 #649-14-1999 L2000 **FM** *020 ‡

CRESPO, Onelia. 1485 AVE ASHFORD, ST MARYS 503 SOUTH 00907 #042-01-1973 L1978 **PD** *030 †55

CRESPO, Oscar. ■ 00910 #042-02-1987 L1994 **DR** *020

CRUZ, Alexis Manuel. 10 CALLE CASIA, DEPT OF INTERNAL MEDICINE 00921 #042-03-2006 **IM** *012

CRUZ, Alma M. PO BOX 190990 00919 #042-01-1984 L1988 **D** *020 †15

CRUZ, Carmen L. 138 AVE WINSTON CHURCHILL, URB CROWN HLS 00926 #042-01-1982 L1987 **D** *020 †15

CRUZ, Hexor G. 1330 CALLE DAMASCO, VILLA BORINQUEN 00920 #042-01-1977 L1983 **PS** *020 †85,65

CRUZ, Jose Abdiel. 606 CALLE ETNA, URB CAPARRA HTS 00920 #308-03-1985 L1986 **FPG** *030

CRUZ, Jose Javier. ■ 00926 #042-03-1997 L1999 **RHU** *020 †20

CRUZ, Mercedes E. DOMENECH AVE 00918 #042-01-1959 L1962 **CD IM** *071

CRUZ, Nancy. 125 CALLE CARITE, URB CROWN HLS 00926 #308-06-1983 L2003 *100

CRUZ, Nivia Esther. ■ 00926 #042-01-1974 L1976 **NEP** *020

CRUZ, Raul F. 2305 CALLE LAUREL, PARK BLVD. 00913 #042-03-1983 L1989 **OS N** *020

CRUZ, Yvette Marie. 435 AVE HOSTOS, URB EL VEDADO 00918 #042-01-2000 L2005 **P** *020 †75 ‡

CRUZADO, Nibaldo Antonio. 500 AVE DOMENECH STE 304 00918 #042-01-1975 L1979 **PD** *020 †55

CRUZADO, Pablo. RR 3 BOX 10, MONTE APOLO 00926 #042-02-1997 L2000 **OBG** *020

CRUZADO-PEREZ, Enrique. 576 CALLE CESAR GONZALEZ, DORAL BANK CTR #408 00918 #847-05-1974 L1977 **OBS GYN** *020

CRUZ-ALICEA, Carmen M. 1114 CALLE DEGETAU, REPTO AMERICA 00923 #847-08-1981 L1983 **GP** *020

CRUZ BARRETO, Roberto. 155 AVE ARTERIAL HOSTOS, GOLDEN CT II BOX 241 00918 #847-05-1963 L1975 **GP** *020

CRUZ-BURGOS, Rosa Ileana. 1519 AVE PONCE DE LEON, FIRST BANK OF 705 00918 #042-01-1980 L1983 **REN GYN** *020

CRUZ CRUZ, Jose Ramon. 400 AVE DOMENECH, STE 602A 00918 #041-13-1960 L1965 **OBG** *030 †30

CRUZ-CUEVAS, Elsie I. 1451 AVE ASHFORD 00907 #042-01-1995 L1998 **IM** *020 †20

CRUZ-JIMENEZ, Mariacarmen. 10 CALLE ACADIA, FISIATRIA (117) 00926 #042-03-1994 L1998 **PM** *020 †60

CRUZ-MARTINEZ, Carlos. ■ 00924 #308-01-1981 L1984 **GP OM** *020

CRUZ-PALOMO, Guillermo. 101 CALLE PINERO, PUEBLO DE RIO PIEDRAS 00925 #042-03-1981 L1983 **IMG GS** *020

CRUZ-VEGERANO, Elisa. 241 AVE WINSTON CHURCHILL, BOX 69 00926 #042-02-1995 L1998 **FM** *020

CRUZ-VILLEGAS, Vanessa. PO BOX 20370, SAN JUAN 00928 #042-01-1996 L1999 **OPH** *020 †35

CUEBAS, Rebeca Awilda. PO BOX 192966 00919 #649-14-2005 **PD** *100

CUEBAS-VAZQUEZ, Jose R. 1882 CALLE SAN JOAQUIN, URB SAN JUAN GDNS 00926 #847-12-1974 L1978 **IM** *062

CUELLAR AVINO, Maria J. 200 COND LA SIERRA DEL SOL, C/O 100 AVE. LA SIERRA #308-03-1982 L1987 **PD PEM** *020

CUELLAR-QUESADA, Pedro E. 1451 AVE ASHFORD 00907 #275-01-1960 L1970 **OBG** *071

CUELLO, Gustavo. ■ 00926 #308-01-1984 L1992 *020

CUEVAS, Edwin A, Jr. 500 AVE DOMENECH, STE 304 00918 #042-03-1980 L1984 **PD** *020

CUEVAS, Javier. 130 AVE WNSTN CHRCHL #PMB1, URB CONTEMPORANEO 00926 #042-03-1997 L2000 **PD** *020

CUEVAS GARCIA, Bernardo. 366 CALLE SARGENTO MEDINA 00918 #682-03-1987 L2001 FM *100

CUEVAS-NATAL, Ramon. 2033 EL SENORIAL, BENITO FEIJOO 00926 #847-10-1961 L1965 P PHP *020

CUNNINGHAM, Ernest L. 1784 CARR 21 00921 #016-06-1965 L1975 PUD IM *040

CURET CUEVAS, Jose O. 400 AVE DOMENECH STE 602B 00918 #042-01-1957 L1963 OBG *020 †30

CUYAR, Liv Jossette. ■ 00926 #042-01-2004 GS *100

DACOSTA, Charlene Edmee. 125 CALLE NILO, URB EL PARAISO 00926 #649-14-2003 L2005 *100

DANOIS, Claude. ■ 00927 #649-18-1991 L2002 IM *020 †20

DAVILA, Jose Aurelio. 469 CALLE FERNANDO CALDER, URB ROOSEVELT 00918 #649-14-1989 L1992 *020

DAVILA, Katherine. ■ 00936 #649-14-1991 L1993 PTH *020

DAVILA, Maria Eugenia. ■ 00911 #042-03-2000 L2004 N *100 †75

DAVILA, Roberto Emilio. PARQUE DESANIGNACIO 3 D23 00921 #042-01-1976 L1980 DR IM *020 †80

DAVILA, William M. 1671 CALLE PLAYERA, URB SANTA MARIA 00927 #308-01-1988 L1992 PD *020

DAVILA FRANCO, Angel M. W5-18 CALLE CERVANTES, URB HUCARES 00926 #308-03-1982 L1991 *020

DAVIS, Mary Paul. 255 AVE PONCE DE LEON, MCS, INC 00917 #041-13-1989 L1990 FM *062 †18 ‡

DAVIS GONZALEZ, Carlos H. ■ 00936 #042-04-1992 L1994 *020

DE AZA HERRERA, Miguel A.. ■ 00911 #308-03-1988 L2005 *100

DE BIEN, Laura. 10 CALLE CASIA, VET AFFAIRS MED CTR 00921 #275-08-1990 P *012

DE CORRAL, Luis Rafael. 1250 AVE PINERO 00921 #042-01-1980 L1984 OPH *035

DEFENDINI, Maria C. 218 CALLE PARQUE, APT 5-A 00925 #042-01-1987 L1991 PD *020 †55

DE JESUS, Angel. CALLE 13 BO SABANA LLANA, PARCELAS FALU 517 00924 #042-01-1995 *100

DE JESUS, Brenda M. C12 CALLE CHESTNUT HL, URB CAMBRIDGE PARK 00926 #042-02-1997 L2000 PD *020 †55

DE JESUS, Luis Alfredo. 37 AVE PONCE DE LEON 00901 #042-01-1978 L1982 PUD IM *020 †20

DE JESUS, Miguel A. 108B ASHFRD MDCL CTR #108B 00907 #042-01-1975 L1980 PD *020 †55

DE JESUS-GONZALEZ, Nilka. ■ 00926 #042-01-2006 PD *012

DE JESUS-PEREZ, Ana R. 875 CALLE ZUMBADOR, URB COUNTRY CLUB 00924 #847-06-1977 L1983 IM EM *020

DE JESUS-VALIENTE, Blanca. B5 CALLE ARROYO, URB EL REMANSO 00926 #649-14-1987 L1995 PD *020

DELA CRUZ, Maritza. 497 AVE EMILIANO POL # 606, URB LA CAMPINA 00926 #308-03-1987 L1992 IM *020

DE LA TORRE, Gabriel. ■ 00922 #042-01-2007 GS *012

DE LA TORRE MADRAZO, F. 400 AVE DOMENECH STE 509 00918 #275-01-1945 L1972 A *071

DEL CASTILLO, Jose. 201 CALLE BLVD DEL VALLE 00901 #847-10-1945 *050

DELCORO, Carlos Rafael. PO BOX 191227, AUXILIO MUTUO HOSPITAL 00919 #042-01-1949 L2003 GS *020

DE LEON, Carmen Julia. 371 AVE DE DIEGO OFC 40, C/O BOX 22612 UBR STA 00909 #847-08-1981 L1985 GS *020

DE LEON, Mari Dolores. ■ 00926 #042-01-1996 L1999 EM *020

DE LEON, Nicolle Franches. ■ 00926 #042-01-2006 GS *012

DE LEON, Noel Stanley. 1250 AVE JESUS T PINERO 00921 #042-02-1994 L1999 OPH *020 †35

DE LEON JIMENEZ, Jose R. 1452 AVE ASHFORD STE 407, COND ADA LIGIA 00907 #042-01-1993 L1998 OTO HNS *020 †45

DE LEON SANTIAGO, S. 1685 CALLE PARANA, URB RIO PIEDRAS HTS 00926 #308-03-1980 L1986 GP *020

DELGADO, Aurea Luz. 19 CALLE ACUARIO, STE 4 00926 #042-01-1997 L1999 D *020

DELGADO, Blas. 252 CALLE SAN JORGE 00912 #042-01-1981 L1984 PD *020

DELGADO, Daphne Vanessa. 37 AVE PONCE DE LEON 00901 #042-02-1992 L1999 PCC *020 †20

DELGADO, Lourdes Maria. W5-35 CALLE CERVANTES, URB HUCARES 00926 #042-01-1994 L1998 PM *020

DELGADO, Madelyn. ■ 00918 #308-03-1974 L1980 PM *020

DELGADO, Maribel. 501 CALLE GUAYANILLA # 23, PARQUE SAN AGUSTIN 00923 #042-01-1997 L1999 PD *020

DELGADO HERNANDEZ, Zaida. 735 AVE PONCE DE LEON, STE 511 00917 #649-14-1990 L1993 IM *020

DEL MURO, Angela B. 1111 CALLE 1, VILLA NEVAREZ 00927 #308-03-1977 L1983 CHP *020

DEL OLMO COLLADO, F. 239 AVE ARTERIAL HOSTOS, STE 601 00918 #308-03-1982 L1986 OBG *020

DE LOS SANTOS, Andreina. PO BOX 192529 00919 #308-02-1978 L1986 P CHP *030

DEL RIO, Juan Antonio. ONE VETERANS PLAZA 00927 #042-01-1975 L1989 IM *020 †20

DEL RIO, Valentin. 10 CALLE CASIA, DEPT OF INTERNAL MEDICINE 00921 #042-03-2006 IM *012

DEL RISCO, Arquimedes Gui. 2026 CALLE GUSTAVO BECQUER, URB EL SENORIAL 00926 #275-04-1976 L2006 *100

DEL ROSARIO, Maria C. 138 CALLE SAN VALENTIN, URB EL PILAR 00926 #042-01-1971 L1973 R *020

DEL ROSARIO-CERVONI, R. 369 AVE DE DIEGO, STE 601 00923 #847-01-1963 L1966 GS *020 †85

DELTORO, Carlos. 1306 AVE MONTE CARLO, APT 216 00924 #649-30-2002 L2004 *100

DEL TORO BEAUCHAMP, Fernan. GPO BOX 5067 00936 #308-03-2005 GS *012

DEL TORO SOTO, Jaime. 652 AVE MUNOZ RIVERA, STE 3195 00918 #847-06-1976 L1979 P *020

DEL VALLE, Antonio I. 273 CALLE SIERRA MORENA, STE 157 00926 #042-01-1992 L1996 PD PG *020 †55

DEL VALLE, Beatriz. CAPARRA TERRACE, CALLE 45.0 #1410 00921 #042-03-1992 L1996 PM *020

DEL VALLE, Juan Rodriguez. 500 AVE JESUS T PINERO, COND. PARQUE DE LOYOLA P.H 00921 #847-04-1961 L1963 N OS *020

DEL VALLE, Justino. 64 CALLE GEORGETTI # 21375 00925 #396-04-1957 L1958 IMG PHP *020

DEL VALLE, Z R Caballero. DOMENECH AVE 00918 #396-04-1957 L1958 GP IMG *020

DE MARI-PRATS, Nitza M. ■ 00936 #042-01-1968 L1974 R OS *020 †80

DEMELLO, Patricia Storino. 1728 CALLE SEGRE, URB RIO PIEDRAS HTS 00926 #042-03-1999 L2004 FM *020

DE MELLO, Walmor Carlos. U PR SCH MED GPO BX 5067 00902 #187-03-1955 CD *040

DE-MERCARDO, Margarita B. ■ 00926 #042-03-1990 L1994 ON *020 †20

DENTON, Jorge Luis H. 106 CALLE MALLORCA, URB UMPIERRE 00917 #008-01-1973 L1975 IM *020 †20

DESEDA TOUS, Jaime E. 121 AVE DOMENECH 00918 #042-01-1970 L1974 PDI PD *020 †55

DE THOMAS, Antonio R. 400 AVE FD ROOSEVELT, STE 101 00918 #042-03-1988 L1992 DR *020

DE TORRES, Francisco R. 1451 AVE ASHFORD 00907 #042-03-1985 L1988 GYN *020 †30

DEVARIE, Clementina. 311 CALLE TERESA JORNET #7, TROPICAL CTS 00926 #308-03-1980 L1989 FM *020

DEVARIE, Livia. ■ 00926 #308-03-1980 L1984 PD *020

DEVARIE, Norma A. 1002 CALLE 44 SE, REPTO METROPOLITANO 00921 #308-03-1984 L1986 IM CD *020

DE VARONA, Miguel Angel. ■ 00926 #042-01-2005 IM *012

DE VARONA, Orlando Ramon. 11 CALLE COSTA AZUL, # BRISAS 00921 #042-01-1974 L1976 GE IM *020

DEVESA, Nancy Carolina. ■ 00926 #042-01-2000 L2003 DR *100 †80

DE VILLAVICENCIO, Nilda C. ■ 00936 #042-01-1969 L1975 D *020 †15

DE ZENGOTITA-SUAREZ, F J. PO BOX 11487, 400 F D ROOSEVELT AVE 00910 #847-11-1976 L1984 OTO *020

DIAZ, Antonio Luis. ■ 00919 #042-02-2005 IM *012

DIAZ, Barbara Andrea. 29 CALLE WASHINGTON # 310, ASHFORD MEDICAL CENTER 00907 #308-03-1978 L1980 P OS *050

DIAZ, Clemente. UPR MED SCIENCES CAMPUS, UNIV PED HOSP 00936 #042-01-1973 L1983 PD *040 †55

DIAZ, Daniel. 735 AVE PONCE DE LEON, STE 714 00917 #042-01-1985 L1989 OBG *020 †30

DIAZ, Flor Maria. 1395 CALLE SAN RAFAEL, DOCTORS COMMUNITY HOSPITAL 00909 #042-04-1989 L1992 GP *020

DIAZ, Janice Mariel. ■ 00926 #042-03-2004 L2005 IM *012

DIAZ, Jose E. ■ 00936 #042-03-1990 L1994 IM *020 †16

DIAZ, Juan Jose. ■ 00921 #042-01-2005 GS *012

DIAZ, Libia Antonia. 1007 COND SEGOVIA APT 1007 00918 #042-01-1984 L1986 NEP IM *040

DIAZ, Maria Del Carmen. A16 CALLE 1 COLINAS VERDE 00924 #275-01-1951 L1969 OS *020

DIAZ, Marta. 369 AVE DE DIEGO, TORRE SAN FRANCISCO, SUITE 00909 #042-03-1997 L1999 IM *020

DIAZ, Porfirio E, Jr. APT 1110, COND. ALTOMONTE 00926 #042-03-1992 L1996 IM CD *020 †20

DIAZ, Rafael Enrique. 100 GRAN BULEVAR PASEOS, SUITE 112 MSC 481 00926 #847-04-1967 L1974 DR *062

DIAZ, Raul. ■ 00919 #042-02-2004 GS *020

DIAZ, Rita Maria. 568B CALLE JUAN J JIMENEZ 00918 #847-10-1969 L1972 PDA PD *020 †55,03

DIAZ, Rolando Elio. PO BOX 5067, UNIV OF PR SCH OF MED 00936 #275-01-1985 L2005 AN *012

DIAZ, Rosa. ■ 00926 #042-01-2007 PD *012

DIAZ, Sara Michelle. 39 COND ALTO MONTE, 100 CARR 842 00926 #042-01-2002 L2005 PD *020 †55

DIAZ, Sonia Esther. 735 AVE PONCE DE LEON, TORRE MEDICA AUX MJTUO 00917 #042-01-1991 L1995 OBG *020

DIAZ ALICEA, Solimar. 1036 CALLE 11, REPARTO METROPOLITANO 00923 #649-14-2004 L2006 *100

DIAZ-BONNET, Luis A. 37 AVE PONCE DE LEON 00901 #010-02-1943 L1989 GS *030

DIAZ-BONNET, Victor M. 37 AVE PONCE DE LEON 00901 #847-04-1956 L1961 OPH *020 †35

DIAZ CORREA, Jose R. 369 CALLE DE DIEGO, STE 210 00923 #042-04-1981 L1984 IM OM *020

DIAZ DE GARAU, Priscilla. ■ 00927 #021-01-1949 L1951 R IM *071

DIAZ FELIX, Roxana. ■ 00926 #649-14-2003 L2008 *100

DIAZ-FERNANDEZ, Maria M. ■ 00918 #649-14-1979 L1983 GP *020

DIAZ GABRIEL, Rafael. ■ 00918 #847-10-1975 L1978 GP *071

DIAZ GARCIA, Franklin. 1 CALLE 3 00901 #308-06-1982 L2003 *100

DIAZ-GIERBOLINI, Adria Te. 305 CALLE ROMANACH, URB BORINQUEN GDNS 00926 #649-14-2002 L2003 *100

DIAZ MENDOZA, Silvino. 708 AVE PONCE DE LEON, HATO REY 00918 #042-01-1983 L1988 OPH TTS *020 †35

DIAZ MORENO, Bruny V. CALLE TORREON AS 17, VENUS GARDENS 00926 #649-14-2000 L2002 IM *100

DIAZ NEGRON, Severiano. 160 AVE WINSTON CHURCHILL, URB CROWN HLS 00926 #847-05-1975 L1978 PD *020

DIAZ-RAMIREZ, Analid T. 3304 COND PLAZA ANTILLANA, APT 3304 00918 #308-03-1987 L2002 *020

DIAZ RIVERA, Antonio L. 807 COND SEGOVIA APT 807 00918 #042-01-1991 L1995 DR *020 †80

DIAZ-RIVERA, Gabriel. ■ 00920 #847-03-1976 L1980 FM *020

DIAZ RIVERA, Rafael Angel. 7 CALLE 10 URB SAN AGUSTIN 00926 #308-06-1982 L2002 FM *020

DIAZ-SANTANA, Pedro. 735 AVE PONCE DE LEON, TORRE AUXILIO MUTUO OFF511 00917 #308-01-1985 L1990 CD *020 †20

DIAZ SOJO, Omar E.. ■ 00926 #649-14-2002 L2005 *100

DIAZ-SOLA, Maritza H. 85 CALLE LIMONCILLO, EXT SANTA MARIA 00927 #308-02-1977 L1982 PD *020

DIAZ-TRANCON, Lorena. 500 AVE JESUS T PINER #100, COND PARQUE DE LOYOLA SOR 00918 #649-14-1987 L1991 IM *040

DIAZ VALCARCEL, Lucy. ■ 00926 #649-14-1987 L1992 *100

DIEZ-DELGADO, Ricardo. ■ 00936 #042-03-1981 L1988 PD P *020

DOGER, Enrique Jacobo. 50 CALLE JUAN P DUARTE 00917 #275-01-1960 L1972 ORS *020

DOLZ DE CASAS, Leticia. 607 CALLE SINAI, URB SUMMIT HLS 00920 #847-06-1976 L1981 OBG *020

DOMINGUEZ ROMERO, A. 611 CALLE PAVIA, PAVIA MED PLZ OF 112 00909 #042-03-1991 L1995 OBG *020

DOMINGUEZ VILLAFANE, Jorge. 1395 CALLE SAN RAFAEL, DOCTORS COMMUNITY HOSPITAL 00909 #042-04-1998 L1999 FM *020

DOSAL-GARCIA, Jose Manuel. ■ 00927 #847-08-1979 L1984 EM *020

DUCOS DE GARCIA, Carmen J. 70 CALLE PINEIRO 00925 #847-10-1963 L1971 GP *020

DUENO, Maria Isabel. ■ 00936 #042-01-1981 L1984 IM GE *020 †20

DUMERVE, Cecile Dorothy. ■ 00921 #308-04-1998 L2007 *100 †55

DUMOIS, Maria Gaubriela. 969 CALLE MARCONI, JARD METROPOLITANO 00927 #042-01-1996 L2000 AN *05

DUQUELA-BARON, Juan L. 728 AVE PONCE DE LEON 00918 #308-01-1966 L1972 CD IM *020

DURAN, Greduvel. 180 AVE HOSTOS, CONDOMINIO EL MONTE SUR 00918 #042-03-1993 L1996 OBG *020

DURE, Marjorie. 502 CALLE ALVERIO, EXT ROOSEVELT 00918 #649-18-1990 *100

ECHAVARRY, Vanessa Olivo. 735 AVE PONCE DE LEON, STE 207 00917 #042-04-1988 L1992 ID *020

ECHAVEZ, Maria Susana. ■ 00936 #042-02-2004 L2006 IM *020 †20

ECHEVARRIA, Esther. ■ 00920 #649-14-2001 L2004 *100

ECHEVARRIA-BEZA, Luis A. ■ 00915 #847-06-1972 L1975 GS *020

ECHEVARRIA-COFINO, Rene R. 422 CALLE AGUEYBANA 00918 #308-03-1978 L1981 PRO GP *020

ECHEVERRIA, Rafael Javier. 201 DE DIEGO AVE, STE 161 00909 #042-01-1996 L2000 P *020

ELIAS, Ivan J. 1604 CALLE ENCARNACION, URB CAPARRA HTS 00920 #042-01-1964 L1966 OBG *062 †30

ENCARNACION, Alice M. 400 AVE DOMENECH STE 305 00918 #042-01-1983 L1986 PD *020

ENCARNACION-CANINO, G. 512 CALLE JUAN J JIMENEZ, PARQ CENTRAL 00918 #042-01-1956 L1958 OS *075

ESCOBAR HERNANDEZ, Samuel. PO BOX 30485 00929 #308-04-1991 L2005 GP *020

ESCRIBANO, Eric S. 29 CALLE WASHINGTON, STE 805 00907 #042-01-1987 L1990 GS *020

ESPINAL URENA, Maximilien. 1395 CALLE SAN RAFAEL 00909 #308-03-1989 L2004 GP *020

ESPINOSA, Manuel Roberto. ■ 00910 #042-01-1997 L1999 DR *020 †80

ESTELA-JOVE, Zoraida E. PO BOX 5067 00936 #042-03-1997 L2002 DR *020 †80

ESTEVE, Lirio. 318 CALLE COLL Y TOSTE 00918 #132-01-1955 L1972 GP *071

ESTRADA-GOMEZ, Marcos. ■ 00936 #649-03-1994 RHU *012 †20

FABELO, Christine Marie. ■ 00927 #042-01-2004 P *012

FAGOT, Gabriel A. ■ 00927 #041-13-1946 L1951 P *071

FALCON, Carlos Francisco. 216 CALLE PALMA REAL, URB UNIVERSITY GDNS 00927 #042-03-1981 L1985 PM *020

FALCON, Laura. 572 CALLE CESAR GONZALEZ, INSTITUTO PANAMERICANO 00918 #042-01-1996 L2001 P *020 †75

FAMILIA DEL VALLE, Christi. 138 AVE WINSTON CHURCHILL, URB CROWN HLS 00926 #042-04-2004 L2005 *100

FANTAUZZI, Rebecca. 265 CALLE SIERRA MORENA, URB LAS CUMBRES 00926 #042-01-1996 L2004 P *020 †75

FEBLES, Francisco. 391 AVE DOMENECH 00918 #010-01-1955 L1957 IM GE *071

FEBLES, Indra. 10 CALLE CASIA 00921 #042-03-1989 L1993 P *020

FEBO, Horidel Guadalupe. 207 AVE DOMENECH, STE 104 00918 #308-01-1986 L1988 END

FEBO, Irma L. PO BOX 365067, UPR SCHOOL OF MEDICINE, PE 00936 #042-01-1986 L1989 PD *020 †55

FEBRES, Yazmin Marie. ■ 00913 #042-01-1996 L1999 EM *040 †16

FELICIANO, Anibal. 369 AVE DE DIEGO, STE 402 00923 #042-03-1986 L1990 IM *020

FELICIANO, Carmen Oliva. SAN PATRIUO AVE, EL JARDIN 5 I 00921 #042-01-1975 L1979 PD *020

FELICIANO, Efrain. 735 AVE PONCE DE LEON, TORRE AUXILIO MUTUO SUITE 00917 #042-03-1989 L1996 CD *020 †20

FELICIANO, Hector Anibal. 37 AVE PONCE DE LEON 00901 #041-09-1953 L1954 FM IM *072 †18

FELICIANO, Melba. ■ 00921 #042-01-1978 L1982 IM *020 †20

FELICIANO, Ricardo. PO BOX 361738, SAN JORGE CHILDREN'S HOSP. 00936 #042-03-1981 L1984 AN *040

FELICIANO, Ruth M. 513 AVE HOSTOS 00918 #847-05-1979 L1991 P *020

FELICIANO, Yanira R. 708 AVE PONCE DE LEON, # 104 00918 #649-14-2002 L2005 *100

FELICIANO RODRIGUEZ, Lino. 1395 CALLE SAN RAFAEL 00909 #847-04-1958 L1960 FM GP *071 †18

FELIX, Luis Armando. 948 CALLE 9 SE, URB LA RIVIERA 00921 #847-08-1982 L1986 IMG FM *020 †18

FERNANDEZ, Aileen Claire. ■ 00902 #042-03-1984 L1992 CD *020

FERNANDEZ, Alberto F. 1760 CALLE LOIZA, STE 201 00911 #035-47-1978 L1987 PTH BBK *020 †50

FERNANDEZ, Alicia Elena. 382 AVE DOMENECH 00918 #042-01-1975 L1979 PD *020 †55

FERNANDEZ, Diana. UNIV DIST HOSP, DEPT RAD 00935 #042-01-1976 L1980 R *020

FERNANDEZ, Fernando R. 708 AVE PONCE DE LEON, STE 104 00918 #847-04-1967 L1969 IM *020 †20

FERNANDEZ, Inti. PO BOX 70344 PMB 160 00936 #275-01-1995 L2005 *100

FERNANDEZ, Jaquelina. 404 CALLE RAFAEL LAMAR 00918 #308-02-1990 L1992 IM *020

FERNANDEZ, Joaquin. 400 AVE DOMENECH, STE 402 00918 #042-01-1985 L1988 FM FPG *020 †18

FERNANDEZ, Jorge Luis. 1250 AVE PINERO 00921 #042-01-1981 L1986 OPH *020 †35

FERNANDEZ, Jose Ramon. ■ 00910 #847-03-1973 L1976 GP *020

FERNANDEZ, Luis A. 735 AVE PONCE DE LEON, STE 601 00917 #042-01-1983 L1986 OBG *020 †30

FERNANDEZ, Nelson Antonio. 135 CAL EBR URB EL PARAISO 00926 #649-01-1955 L1957 NTR *071

FERNANDEZ, Ricardo. ■ 00926 #649-14-2002 IM *100

FERNANDEZ, Samuel A. ■ 00926 #042-01-1985 L1986 OP *020 †40

FERNANDEZ, Sonia Aracelis. 10 CALLE CASIA, VETERANS ADMINISTRATION HO 00921 #308-02-1983 L1988 FM *020 †18

FERNANDEZ-CUEVAS, Jose O. LAGUNA GARDENS EDIF A 9K 00913 #847-04-1966 L1970 P LM *020

FERNANDEZ-FELIBERTI, R. 1451 AVE ASHFORD 00907 #042-01-1957 L1961 ORS OP *072 †40

FERNANDEZ-MARTINEZ, Jose. PO BOX 9020032 00902 #041-01-1955 L1961 CD IM *020 †20

FERNANDEZ MENENDEZ, F. 1451 AVE ASHFORD 00907 #847-10-1959 L1965 OBG *020

FERNANDEZ MOREIRA, M M. 919 CALLE DUKE # 4, UNIVERSITY GARDENS 00927 #308-04-1983 L1989 GP *020

FERNANDEZ-NODA, Esteban I. 2060 EL MONTE MALL, STE 2060 00918 #275-01-1951 L1967 GS OS *020

FERNANDEZ PLA, Restituto. ■ 00911 #847-04-1957 L1960 OBG *020 †30

FERNANDEZ TORRES, Julia I. 900 CALLE FORDHAM, APT 3 00927 #847-01-1980 L1985 *100

FERNANDEZ-VAZQUEZ, Carlos. PO BOX 364364 00936 #847-10-1970 L1973 IM *020

FERREIRA FRONTERA, Luisa. 315 CALLE COLL Y TOSTE, JARD SELLES 00918 #770-01-1943 L1957 GP P *071

FERRER, Jose Luis. PAVIA ST, STE 103 PAVIA MED PLAZA 00909 #041-13-1959 L1964 U *072

FERRER, Lilliane. 400 AVE DOMENECH STE 308 00918 #051-04-1949 L1952 IM *071

FERRER, Luis E. 37 AVE PONCE DE LEON 00901 #042-01-1992 L1997 CLP *020 †50

FERRER, Norman S. 37 AVE PONCE DE LEON 00901 #649-01-1961 L1963 GYN *071

FERRER, Reinaldo A. ■ 00907 #028-34-1945 L1946 OS *030

FERRERO, Jose V. 23 CALLE SAN MELCHOR, URB SAN IGNACIO 00927 #042-02-1990 L1994 IM *020

FERRER-URBINA, Belen M. 200 AVE WINSTON CHURCHILL, STE 202 00926 #308-01-1982 L1984 GP *020

FIDALGO BENETT, Magda Ter. 1630 CALLE SANTA EDUVIGES, URB SAGRADO CORAZON 00926 #649-14-1999 L2003 FM *020

FIGAREDO-LOPEZ, Alfredo. PO BOX 21414 00928 #042-01-1954 L1955 CHP P *020 †75

FIGUEROA, Edna I. 308 CALLE SAN JORGE 00912 #042-01-1984 L1985 PD *020

FIGUEROA, Nayda Rosa. 59 CALLE SANTA ANASTACIA, URB EL VIGIA 00926 #042-01-1976 L1981 RO *020

FIGUEROA, Rafael. ■ 00927 #649-14-1983 L1986 OBG *020 †30

FIGUEROA, Walter. 939 CALLE EIDER, URB COUNTRY CLUB 00924 #308-03-1984 L1992 IM *020

FIGUEROA-BOLIO, Siegfried. 506 AVE HOSTOS, URB EL VEDADO 00918 #649-01-1971 L1974 CRS GS *020 †85

FIGUEROA-LEBRON, Ramon E. STE 229 PL LAS AMERICAS 00918 #847-05-1962 L1964 PUD IM *020

FIGUEROA-LONGO, Juan G. ■ 00908 #042-01-1957 L1959 OBG OS *071 †30

FIGUEROA MENDEZ, Daphne E. ■ 00907 #308-03-1983 L1995 *100

FIGUEROA-OTERO, Carlos A. ■ 00936 #308-03-1976 L1980 AN OS *071

FIGUEROA-OTERO, Ivan. 252 CALLE SAN JORGE, SAN JORGE MED BLDG STE 407 00912 #042-01-1970 L1972 PDS GS *040 †85

FIGUEROA-RAMIREZ, Yolanda. 134 CALLE MORADILLA, URB MILAVILLE 00926 #847-08-1981 L1986 PD *020

FIGUEROA TORRES, Enrique. 2413 CALLE LAUREL 00913 #042-01-1991 L1997 CD IM *020 †20

FITZPATRICK, Carmen Ana. 652 AVE MUNOZ RIVERA #3020 00918 #847-10-1966 L1970 P OS *020

FLORES, Antonio Goicouria. ■ 00912 #275-01-1941 L1970 GP *071

FLORES, Luis Daniel. 369 CALLE DE DIEGO, TORRE SAN FRANCISCO SUITE 00923 #042-01-1997 L2000 HO *020

FLORES, Manuel. ■ 00919 #042-03-1991 IM *100

FLORES, Maria I. 140 COND PAVILLION CT, 161 AVE.CESAR GONZALEZ 00918 #042-01-1991 L1995 EM *020

FLORES, Pedro Pablo. ■ 00936 #737-03-1994 IM *012

FLORES, Ramon Edgardo. 1801 AVE PONCE DE LEON, STE 306 00909 #042-01-1979 L1982 PUD IM *020

FLORES CANCEL, Awilda. ■ 00924 #847-05-1981 L1992 *100

FLORES-DE HOSTOS, Eddy. 405 CALLE DE DIEGO 00923 #308-03-1978 L1980 CD IM *020 †20

FLORES-GALLARDO, Arturo. PO BOX 192381 00919 #020-02-1946 L1950 P *071 †75

FLORES-VILAR, Luis Jorge. 252 CALLE SAN JORGE 00912 #737-01-1957 L1970 PM OM *075

FLYNN, John Manuel. 735 AVE PONCE DE LEON, TORRE AUXILIO MUTUO OFFICE 00918 #042-01-1969 L1976 OP *020 †40

FONTANET, Ricardo. 37 AVE PONCE DE LEON 00901 #042-03-1985 L1985 PD *020 †55

FONTANET-PERFECTO, Hector. I25 VIA LLNRS URB LA VISTA 00924 #042-01-1958 L1960 PD *020 †55

FONTANEZ, Felipe. 371 AVE DE DIEGO 00923 #042-01-1980 L1988 ORS *020

FONTANEZ, Francisco. CMMS 132 BOX 70344 00936 #308-03-1981 L1994 GP *020

FORT, Zhahedia Zhaythsefa. 1716 CALLE SANTA CATALINA, URB ALTAMESA 00921 #649-02-1985 L1995 IM OS *020

FORTUNO, Ramon Oscar. 89 AVE DE DIEGO, PMB-704 STE 105 00927 #042-01-1985 L1988 P PFP *020

FOURNIER, Jose Rafael. ■ 00923 #042-03-1998 L2001 IM *020 †20

FOX, Robert I. ■ 00911 #042-01-1968 L1972 OBG *020 †30

FRAGA, Ivonne. 708 AVE PONCE DE LEON #102, PROFESSIONAL MEDICAL PLAZA 00918 #042-01-1995 L1999 N *020 †20

FRAGUADA-PEREZ, Luis A. 400 AVE DOMENECH STE 502 00918 #042-01-1957 L1960 GS OS *020

FRANCESCHI, Frances M. 2 CALLE MADRID, COND PALMA REAL, APT 2-H 00907 #308-03-1982 L1990 IM *020

FRANCESCHI, Raul G. 29 CALLE WASHINGTON, STE 707 00907 #042-01-1986 L1988 OPH *020 †35 ‡

FRANCO, Alejandro E. ■ 00936 #042-01-1963 L1966 RHU IM *071

FRANCO, Jose Antonio. ■ 00926 #042-01-2006 P *012

FRANCO, Sonia F. ■ 00936 #042-01-1968 L1968 NEP PD *071 †55

FRANCO MOLINI, Carlos M. 513A CALLEJON H, SECT EL RELINCHO 00917 #042-01-1970 L1972 PD *020

FRANJUL, Rafael Enrique. 400 AVE DOMENECH, STE 210 00918 #308-04-1991 L1992 PUD *020

FRANQUI, Francisco. ■ 00927 #308-03-1977 L1980 *020

FRANQUI, Sandra. 17 CALLE MALLORCA, URB UMPIERRE 00917 #042-01-1988 L1992 IMG *020 †20

FRASQUERI, Rosa. 323 CALLE LOIZA, URB LAS CUMBRES 00926 #042-01-1998 L2002 AN *020

FREEMAN, Reginald Warren. UNIV OF P R DEPT OF SURG 00921 #041-09-1955 L1963 GS *020 †85

FREYRE-GONZALEZ, Nilsa I. 268 CALLE SAN JORGE, C/O TULANE ST C-15 SANTA A 00912 #042-03-1981 L1986 PD *020

FRONTERA, Walter R. 2 CALLE MADRID, PALMA REAL 11K 00907 #042-01-1979 L1983 PM PRS *020 †60

FUENTES MEJIA, Gaspar. ■ 00915 #649-14-1994 L1996 *020

FUERTES, Abelardo. ■ 00936 #847-04-1958 L1961 OBG *071

FULLANA, Altagracia. PO BOX 19446 00910 #649-14-1989 L1993 PD *020

FUMERO, Ileana M. 29 CALLE WASHINGTON, STE 310 00907 #042-01-1989 L1992 P *020 †75

FUSTER, Jaime. 1485 AVE ASHFORD, ST MARYS II 1203 00907 #042-01-1967 L1970 P *020

FUXENCH-ORTIZ, Carlos D. AVE DE DIEGO ESQ 40 S 00922 #847-10-1960 L1963 PM *030

GADEA MORA, Carlos Ramon. ■ 00911 #847-10-1967 L1969 GP *030

GALARZA DIAZ, Nestor Jose. 10 CALLE CASIA, POB 33113 VEERANS PLAZA 00921 #042-01-1972 L1976 P OS *020 †75

GALDAMEZ, Gloria Esperanz. GPO BOX 5067 00936 #451-01-1989 FP *012

GALIB FRANGIE, Hamid. 1801 AVE PONCE DE LEON, STE 205 00909 #042-01-1972 L1975 GE IM *020

GALINDEZ ANTELO, William. 89 AVE DE DIEGO STE 105, PMB 714 00927 #847-04-1955 L1960 P OS *071

GALINDO, Eugenia M. ■ 00926 #847-19-1988 L1994 NEP *020 †20

GALVA, Ana Lorena. 735 AVE PONCE DE LEON, STE 603 00917 #042-01-1984 L1988 OPH *020

GALVAN-BIRD, Felix M. 272 CAL PRS URB COLLEGE PA 00921 #042-01-1951 L1956 GP *071

GANDIA, Jorge. 304 CLINICA LAS AMERICAS 00918 #847-10-1964 L1969 OBG *020 †30

GARCIA, Armando Francisco. ■ 00921 #649-14-2002 L2002 ON *020 †20

GARCIA, Carlos D. 400 AVE FD ROOSEVELT, STE 101 00918 #042-01-1991 L1995 NM IM *020 †28

■ = Address Information Privacy Protected

GARCIA, Deniz Esther. ■ 00929 #042-01-1997 L2000 **IM** *020 †20

GARCIA, Enrique Jose. ■ 00917 #042-01-2007 **ORS** *012

GARCIA, Filia S. 513C CALLE ALVARADO, URB ROOSEVELT 00918 #042-04-1994 L1996 **GP** *020

GARCIA, Gabriel J. 1431 AVE PONCE DE LEON, STE 302 00907 #042-01-1987 L1989 **GS CCS** *020 †85

GARCIA, Gaspar Ruben. ■ 00907 #042-01-1993 L1999 **DR** *020 †80

GARCIA, Haydee. 138 AVE WINSTON CHURCHILL, URB CROWN HLS 00926 #042-01-1975 L1980 **PD ID** *040 †55

GARCIA, Humberto. ■ 00920 #275-04-1996 L2005 **IM** *020 †20

GARCIA, Jorge Enrique. ■ 00921 #042-03-2002 L2005 **PM** *100

GARCIA, Luis F. 37 AVE PONCE DE LEON 00901 #042-03-1988 L1992 **IM RHU** *020

GARCIA, Mari T. 200 AVE WINSTON CHURCHILL, STE 201 00926 #042-01-1993 L1998 **N** *020 †75

GARCIA, Maria Elena. PO BOX 365067, DEPT OF DERMATOLOGY 00936 #042-01-2004 **D** *012

GARCIA, Maribel. 252 CALLE SAN JORGE, STE 504 00912 #042-01-1990 L1993 **PHO** *020 †55

GARCIA, Rafael. GPO BOX 5067 00936 #042-01-2002 L2004 **NEP** *100 †20

GARCIA-CASTILLO, Armando. 1451 AVE ASHFORD 00907 #041-02-1943 L1944 **OBG** *071

GARCIA-CASTRO, Juan A. 1462 CALLE ASIA, HOSP PAVIA EMERGY DEPT 00909 #847-06-1973 L1976 **EM** *020

GARCIA DAVILA, Mariela. ■ 00907 #042-04-2002 L2004 *100

GARCIA GONZALEZ, Carlos. ■ 00907 #847-10-1945 L1975 *020

GARCIA-GONZALEZ, Felipe A. ■ 00919 #132-01-1957 L1960 **AN IM** *071

GARCIA-GUBERN, Carlos F. ■ 00919 #042-02-1996 L1998 **EM** *020 †16

GARCIA JAIME, Aracelia. BX 30074 65TH INFANTRY ST 00929 #308-01-1979 L1981 *020

GARCIA LOPEZ, Rafael. 258 AVE PONCE DE LEON 00901 #847-05-1955 L1958 **FM** *071

GARCIA-MANGUAL, Carlos D. 576 CALLE CESAR GONZALEZ, STE 101B 00918 #042-01-1980 L1982 **ORS** *020

GARCIA MORALES, Jose J. 6 CALLE VEREDA, MONTE VERDE REAL 00926 #308-06-1986 L1991 *100

GARCIA-OTERO, Pedro. 258 AVE PONCE DE LEON, PUERTA DE TIERRA 00901 #042-04-1989 L1991 **IM** *020

GARCIA-PENNA, Alexis J. HSPT AXLO MUTUO, HATO REY, PEDIATRIX MED GROUP OF PR 00918 #042-02-1994 L1998 **PD** *020

GARCIA-RAMIREZ, Ivan D. ■ 00927 #308-01-1986 L1990 **FM** *020

GARCIA-RAMIREZ, Ivan H. SAN JUAN BAY MARINA 00902 #010-02-1951 L1952 **AN** *071 †05

GARCIA-RESUSTA, Pilar. ■ 00902 #847-09-1961 L1971 **P** *071

GARCIA-RICARDO, Flor D. PO BOX 5067, DEPT EMER MED 00936 #308-01-1982 L1988 **EM** *020

GARCIA RIOS, Miguel Angel. ■ 00918 #042-01-1957 L1959 **PTH GP** *071

GARCIA-SANTIAGO, Manuel A. 728 AVE PONCE DE LEON 00918 #847-04-1957 L1962 **OBG** *020 †30

GARLAND, Milton G. 369 AVE DE DIEGO, TORRE SAN FRANCISCO SUITE 00909 #308-01-1987 L1991 **IM** *020

GARRATON, Miguel. 369 CALLE DE DIEGO, STE 506 00923 #042-01-1985 L1987 **OTO HNS** *020 †45

GARRIDO, Jose. 37 AVE PONCE DE LEON 00901 #847-06-1957 L1962 **FM GP** *020

GARRIDO, Jose I. PO BOX 190873 00919 #042-01-1991 L1995 **N** *020

GAVILLAN-PABON, Pedro. 709 ASHFORD MEDCL CTR #709, CONDADO 00907 #847-04-1955 L1957 **IM GPM** *020

GAZTAMBIDE VILA, Nieves. 820 EDIF MERCANTIL PLZ, PONCE DE LEON AVE 00918 #847-01-1970 L1973 **PD** *062

GEIL, Kenneth Paul. 10 CALLE CASIA, MINILLAS STA 00921 #020-12-1976 L1983 **P N** *020 †75 ‡

GEORGE, Rebeca. 67 CALLE ORQUIDEA, URB SANTA MARIA 00927 #042-01-1997 L1999 **OBG** *020

GIAMBARTOLOMEI, Elvira. 420 AVE PONCE DE LEON, EDIF. MIDTOWN OFIC. SUITE 00918 #132-02-1970 L1976 **P** *071

GIRALDEZ-CASASNOVAS, Laur. 37 AVE PONCE DE LEON 00901 #847-03-1972 L1976 **HNS GS** *020

GIROD-MORALES, Carlos E. 124 CALLE HUYKE 00918 #023-01-1961 L1963 **CD IM** *020 †20

GODEROS, Carmen G. SAN PATRICIO PLZ STE 147 00901 #847-08-1977 L1980 **PD** *020

GODREAU NEGRON, Miguel F. 369 AVE DE DIEGO, STE 404 00923 #847-01-1970 L1973 **IM PA** *020

GOMEZ, Angel Alberto. ■ 00926 #042-01-2001 L2006 **DR** *020 †80

GOMEZ, Cesar Gerardo. ■ 00926 #042-01-2001 L2004 **PM** *020 †60

GOMEZ, Manuel Francisco. 500 AVE DOMENECH STE 602 00918 #275-01-1978 L1998 *020

GOMEZ, Martha Y.. PO BOX 70344, PMB 232 00936 #649-54-1991 L2002 **END** *020

GOMEZ, Nestor Rafael. 210 CALLE JOSE OLIVER, PMB 1 00918 #935-07-1997 L2003 **GP** *020

GOMEZ, Omar. ■ 00907 #042-01-2004 **PM** *012

GOMEZ, Yolanda. 3 CALLE NOGAL, LAREDAS DE SAN JUAN 00926 #042-01-1985 L1988 **PD** *020 †55

GOMEZ BUENO, Brunilda Noe. ■ 00920 #308-01-1986 L1998 *020

GOMEZ DEL CARPIO, Jimena. PO BOX 5067, UNIV OF PR SCH OF MED 00936 #649-14-2002 L2005 **FM** *100

GOMEZ DUARTE, Cristobal. PAVIA II SUITE 103, 1449 AMERICO SALAS 00909 #264-04-1972 L1980 **GE** *050

GOMEZ-HEREDIA, Xiomara. ■ 00920 #308-02-1980 L1996 **GP** *030

GOMEZ-MARCIAL, Carlos A. ■ 00926 #308-03-1979 L1981 **EM** *020

GOMEZ PEREZ, Ramon. GPO BOX 5067 00936 #275-01-1989 **FP** *012

GOMEZ-VAZQUEZ, Maria A. 185 CALLE COSTA RICA, CON DOMINIO TEIDE 902 00917 #847-10-1976 L1979 **PN** *020

GONZALEZ, Alexis Tomas. ■ 00924 #042-01-2005 **P** *012

GONZALEZ, Alfredo A. PO BOX 70344, 109 CMMS 00936 #847-06-1988 L1992 **PD** *020

GONZALEZ, Ana C. 300 AVE LA SIERRA, BOX 203 00926 #042-01-1971 L1976 **CD IM** *020

GONZALEZ, Angela Ines. RECINTO DE CIENCIAS MED 00936 #308-01-1972 L1977 **OPH** *020

GONZALEZ, Anita Emperatri. 1336 CALLE DECATUR, VILLA BORINQUEN 00920 #682-01-1988 L2005 *100

GONZALEZ, Benigno A. 1001 COND PARQUE DE LOYOLA 00918 #649-14-2000 L2002 *100

GONZALEZ, Benigno Tomas. STATION 00922 #021-05-1942 L1944 **GP GS** *071 †85

GONZALEZ, Carlos Antonio. 667 AVE PONCE DE LEON #351 00907 #042-01-1979 L1982 **IM** *040 †20

GONZALEZ, Edil. 400 AVE DOMENECH STE 312 00918 #042-01-1968 L1970 **D** *020 †15

GONZALEZ, Eduardo. CAL 17 SE 973 REPARTO MET 00922 #649-01-1953 L1955 **P** *071

GONZALEZ, Eduardo Jose. ■ 00926 #042-01-2003 L2005 **GE** *012

GONZALEZ, Eva. PO BOX 21405, SAN JUAN MUNICIPAL HOSP 00928 #042-01-1990 L1994 **END** *020 †20

GONZALEZ, Felix L. PO BOX 192292 00919 #042-04-1995 L1997 **FM** *020

GONZALEZ, Francisco T. CALLE LOS MARIANISTAS 00928 #042-01-1981 L1987 **P CHP** *020

GONZALEZ, German B. 206 PLAZA LAS AMERICAS 00918 #847-10-1962 L1965 **OTO OS** *020

GONZALEZ, Gladys Hazel. ■ 00936 #042-01-1979 L1982 **PD LM** *040 †55

GONZALEZ, Itzia Edmee. 313 AVE DOMENECH, OFICINA 201 00918 #041-14-1992 L1994 *020

GONZALEZ, Ivan F. CMMS NUM. 476 00936 #042-01-1984 L1989 **TS GS** *020 †85,90

GONZALEZ, Ivelisse. EL MIRADOR, CALLE 6 J10 00926 #042-02-1987 L1991 **PM** *020 †60

GONZALEZ, Joel A.. ■ 00926 #649-14-2000 L2003 **FM** *020

GONZALEZ, Jose R. 00927 #042-01-1975 L1980 **D** *040 †15

GONZALEZ, Luis Daniel. 130 AVE WINSTON CHURCHILL, STE 1 PMB 270 00926 #308-03-1982 L1993 **P** *020

GONZALEZ, Maria D. ■ 00921 #042-01-1978 L1984 **CG CBG** *020 †55,19

GONZALEZ, Melba Nydia. 820 AVE ITURREGUI, URB COUNTRY CLUB 00924 #042-03-1995 L2000 **IM** *020

GONZALEZ, Miguel Angel. 10 CALLE CASIA, VA MEDICAL CENTER 00921 #042-01-1993 L1999 **IM** *020 †20

GONZALEZ, Nelson. ■ 00918 #275-01-1987 L2008 **FP** *012

GONZALEZ, Omar Augusto. 177 COND LA SIR DL SL #177 00926 #042-03-1994 L1996 **OTO** *020 †45

GONZALEZ, Omayra L. 100 CALL MRCB PARK GARDENS 00926 #649-14-2001 **ON** *100 †20

GONZALEZ, Rafael A. 368 CALLE DE DIEGO STE CH7, CONDOMINIO CRYSTAL HOUSE 00923 #042-04-1995 L1996 **FM** *020

GONZALEZ, Robert. 369 AVE DE DIEGO, TORRE SAN FRANCISCO #608 00923 #308-01-1982 L1986 **CD IM** *020 †20

GONZALEZ, Rosalinda. VILLA NEVAREZ, #1025 8 ST. 00927 #042-03-1980 L1987 **DR** *020

GONZALEZ, Yvelisse. 514 AVE DE HOSTOS, URB EL VEDADO 00918 #042-01-1979 L1983 **R** *020

GONZALEZ, Zulma Aracelis. 37 AVE PONCE DE LEON 00901 #042-01-1974 L1976 **OS GS** *040 †85

GONZALEZ ALCOVER, Rafael. UNIV OF PR SCH OF MED 00936 #649-01-1955 L1958 **RHU IM** *040

GONZALEZ-ARISTUD, Juan R. 252 CALLE SAN JORGE 00912 #847-05-1964 L1966 **OBG** *072

GONZALEZ AYALA, Nervis A. CALLE AB 21 CALLE 15 00924 #308-01-1986 L1992 *100

GONZALEZ-CARRASQUILLO, A. 900 CALLE CERRA STOP 15, HOMELESS PROJECT 00907 #847-02-1975 L1979 **IM** *020

GONZALEZ-CELADO, Amparo F. 391 AVE DOMENECH 00918 #308-01-1967 L1976 **GP P** *020

GONZALEZ DE MONTALVO, A. 00923 #041-13-1945 L1946 **PHP PD** *072

GONZALEZ-DIAZ, Milagros. SAN JUAN MUNICIPAL HOSP, DEPT PED 00928 #649-18-1983 L1989 **PD** *020

GONZALEZ GARCIA, Rene. PO BOX 360695 00936 #042-04-2003 L2005 *100

GONZALEZ-LIBOY, Gonzalo V. 1441 AVE FD ROOSEVELT 00920 #847-05-1961 L1964 **IM DIA** *040

GONZALEZ LUGO, Carlos M. ■ 00921 #649-14-2000 L2001 **GP** *020

GONZALEZ-MAYDA, Maria Cri. ■ 00920 #042-01-2008 *012

GONZALEZ-MORALES, Eric M. ■ 00918 #042-03-1980 L1985 **GP** *040

GONZALEZ-PARES, Esther. 1056 AVE MUNOZ RIVERA, COND FF DE RD OFFICE 405 00927 #042-01-1956 L1958 **RHU IM** *020 †20

GONZALEZ-RECIO, Ailed. 100 GRAND PASEO BLVD, STE 112 MSC 465 00926 #042-01-1979 L1983 **OBG** *020 †30

GONZALEZ-RIOS, Antonio. 400 AVE DOMENECH, STE 202 00918 #042-01-1955 L1958 **AN OS** *105

GONZALEZ-RUIZ, Ana Ines. 300 AVE LA SIERRA, BOX 203 00926 #042-01-1994 L1998 **PDR DR** *020 †80

GONZALEZ-YANES, German. 10A COND SAN RAFAEL, CALLE ENSENADA 561 00907 #042-01-1987 L1989 **OTO** *020 †45

GORBEA, Enrique Telesforo. G13 AVE LAS PALOMAS, PASEO SAN JUAN 00926 #042-01-1989 L1995 **RNR** *020 †80

GORBEA, Hector Francisco. 1451 AVE ASHFORD 00907 #042-01-1977 L1982 **ID IM** *020 †20 ‡

GORRIN, Jose J. ■ 00926 #042-01-1967 L1972 **OBG** *020 †30

GOSS MERCED, Moraima M. ■ 00926 #042-04-2000 L2001 **FM** *020

GOTAY, Felicita. 497 AVE EMILIANO POL, PMB 913 00926 #042-01-1971 L1973 **PD CCP** *071 †55

GRACIA, Sandra C. 10 CALLE CASIA 00921 #042-02-1981 L1984 **NM IM** *030 †28

GRACIA-RAMIS, Manuel R. 969 CALLE QUITO, URB LAS AMERICAS 00921 #042-01-2001 L2005 **GS** *100

GRACIA-RAMIS, Roberto. ■ 00921 #042-03-2003 **OBG** *020

GRANT, Trevor H. 364 CALLE SAN JORGE, LAS CARMELITAS CONDOMINIUM 00912 #042-01-1965 L1972 **N** *020

GRATACOS, Jose Antonio. 1505 CALLE LOIZA, BOX 137B 00911 #042-01-1974 L1976 **OBG** *020 †30

GREEN, Angel. 650 CALLE SERGIO CUEVAS, CONDOMNIO SEGOVIA DPC 1410 00918 #847-11-1986 L1988 **IM RHU** *020 †20

GRIMANY, Rene Almento. ■ 00926 #649-13-1983 L1986 **GP** *040

GROVAS, Carlos. 435 AVE PONCE DE LEON #B12 00917 #042-01-1967 L1969 **ORS OAR** *020 ‡

GROVAS, Damian Esteban. 2009 CALLE BECQUER, URB EL SENORIAL 00926 #275-01-1992 L2002 **CD** *020

GUARDIOLADOMINGU, Alberto. ■ 00911 #042-03-2004 *100

GUEDE LORENZO, Carmen. ■ 00921 #649-01-2000 L2005 **GP** *030

GUERRA-SANTIAGO, Carlos. 735 AVE PONCE DE LEON, TORRE AUXILIO MUTUO OFFICE 00917 #847-02-1971 L1973 **IM NEP** *020

GUERRERO, Leonel Enrique. PUERTO NUEVO, 268 3 STREET NO 00920 #042-01-1999 L2001 **GS** *020 †95

GUERRERO CALDERON, Juan I. AVE LAS CUMBRES 381 AOT 10, PASEO MONTE 00926 #308-03-1986 L2001 *100

GUERRERO GUERRERO, Rafael. HOSPITAL AUXILIO MUTUO 00936 #275-01-1953 L1957 **FM IMG** *071

GUERRERO MANZANO, Gualbert. PO BOX 20621 00928 #308-01-1982 L1994 *100

GUERRERO MARTE, Felicia. ■ 00920 #308-01-1989 L2004 *100

GUERRERO SANTANA, Soila E. 1699 CALLE SALTILLO, URB VENUS GDNS NORTE 00926 #308-03-1988 L2004 *100

GUERRIDO, Ramon. ■ 00926 #308-01-1986 L1988 **IM** *020 †20

GUEVARA, Luz Minerva. ■ 00936 #264-05-1963 L1965 **CHP P** *071 †75

GUILBE, Nelson. ■ 00926 #042-03-1994 L1998 **AN** *020

GUILLAN NEGRON, Ramon A. ■ 00918 #847-04-1958 L1961 **PTH** *071 †50

GUILLEN, Luis G. 990 CALLE ESPIONCELA, URB COUNTRY CLUB 00924 #042-03-1987 L2004 **OBG** *020 †30

GUINDIN, Adela. PO BOX 11494 00910 #308-03-1983 L2005 *100
GUIOT, Humberto M. PO BOX 363382 00936 #042-01-2001 L2002 **ID** *100
GURREA-DE GARIB, Carmen M. 150 AVE DE DIEGO STE 610, SAN JUAN HLTH CTR 00907 #308-03-1980 L1981 **PTH** *020 †50
GUTIERREZ, Cristella. PO BOX EH, CAPARRA HTS STA 00910 #308-01-1961 L1969 **AN** *020
GUTIERREZ, Roberto. ■ 00924 #042-01-2005 **P** *012
GUTIERREZ, Suzanne Nicoll. ■ 00927 #042-01-2007 **IM** *012
GUTIERREZ-JAIME, Sarah I. ■ 00920 #308-02-1979 L1983 **PD** *020
GUTIERREZ-NUNEZ, Jose J. 10 CALLE CASIA 00921 #042-01-1976 L1981 **ID IM** *030 †20
GUTIERREZ PALMA, Luis V. 1500 AVE LOS ROMEROS, 1215 MONTEHIEDRA 00926 #264-01-1968 L1992 *020
GUZMAN, Aileen. PO BOX 70344, PMB 422 00936 #042-01-1996 L2000 **GE** *020 †20
GUZMAN, Carlos Javier. 385 AVE FELISA R D GTR #80, CONO PUERTO PASEOS 00926 #038-40-1994 L1999 **ID** *020
GUZMAN, Manuel. 369 AVE DE DIEGO, TORRE SAN FRANCISCO #510 00923 #042-01-1991 L1995 **CD** *020 †20
GUZMAN ACOSTA, Manuel. ■ 00936 #024-05-1946 L1947 **LM ORS** *072 †40
GUZMAN-LOPEZ, Luis R. 1395 CALLE SAN RAFAEL 00909 #023-01-1940 L1985 **NS** *071 †25
GUZMAN-LOPEZ, Manuel. 1395 CALLE SAN RAFAEL 00909 #649-01-1952 L1989 **NS N** *071
GUZMAN-NIEVES, David A. 1122 CALLE HORTENSIA, MANS DE RIO PIEDRAS 00926 #847-02-1972 L1980 **EM** *020
GUZMAN-TORRES, Carlos. 523 CALLE SERGIO CUEVAS, PARQ CENTRAL 00918 #042-01-1972 L1976 **CD** *020
HADDOCK-SUAREZ, Lillian. ■ 00923 #041-13-1954 L1956 **END IM** *020 †20
HAWAYEK ALEMANY, Jose R. RIO PIEDRAS STA 00935 #042-01-1972 L1974 **OBG** *030 †30
HEFFELFINGER SANCHEZ, Fran. ■ 00926 #649-14-2004 L2006 *100
HERETER, Jorge A. PO BOX 192349, HATIO REY STATION 00919 #041-09-1943 L1989 **GYN** *020 †30
HERNANDEZ, Angela T. PO BOX 363628 00936 #042-01-1971 L1973 **PD** *030
HERNANDEZ, Benjamin P. 216 CALLE PALMA REAL, URB UNIVERSITY GDNS 00927 #748-01-1971 L1976 **NEP** *100
HERNANDEZ, Carmina. E5 COND SANTA ANA 00927 #042-01-1981 L1985 **DR** *020 †80
HERNANDEZ, Eduardo N. CENTRO COMRCA LAGNA GRDNS 00913 #042-01-1962 L1967 **D** *020
HERNANDEZ, Felipe. 10 CALLE CASIA, VA MEDICAL CENTER 00921 #042-02-1983 L1989 **FM** *020 †18
HERNANDEZ, Frances Marie. ■ 00927 #042-01-2005 **IM** *012
HERNANDEZ, Gabriel E. 1475 CALLE WILSON STE 4A, WILSON MEDICAL BLDG OFIC 4 00907 #042-01-1979 L1982 **IM GE** *020
HERNANDEZ, Hector Ramon. 431 AVE PONCE DE LEON, SUITE 901 FL 9 00917 #042-01-1972 L1974 **IM** *020
HERNANDEZ, Jose Alberto. 150 AVE DE DIEGO, STE 604 00907 #042-01-1977 L1981 **D** *020 †15
HERNANDEZ, Jose Alejandro, Jr. ■ 00924 #308-04-1985 L2004 *100
HERNANDEZ, Juan J. 735 AVE PONCE DE LEON #210, TORRE MEDICA AUXILIO MUTUO 00917 #042-01-1985 L1987 **TS VS** *020 †85,90
HERNANDEZ, Liliam. PO BOX 365067 00936 #275-09-1999 **FP** *012
HERNANDEZ, Michael. 558 CALLE JUAN J JIMENEZ 00918 #042-01-1998 L2002 **PM** *020 †60
HERNANDEZ, Nicolas. ■ 00918 #847-11-1992 L1995 **CHP** *020
HERNANDEZ, Oscar David. 421 AVE MUNOZ RIVERA, OFC 605 00918 #308-01-1963 L1974 **CD IM** *020
HERNANDEZ, Rahadames. 1747 CALLE ALABAMA, URB SAN GERARDO 00926 #308-01-1981 L1991 **GP** *020
HERNANDEZ, Raul Roberto. 29 CALLE WASHINGTON, SUITE 102 ASHFORD MEDICAL 00907 #308-04-1990 L1997 **IM** *020
HERNANDEZ, Vannessa A. ■ 00919 #042-02-2001 **GS** *100
HERNANDEZ, Victor. 1167 CALLE 56 SE, REPTO METROPOLITANO 00921 #308-13-2003 L2006 **GP** *020
HERNANDEZ, Victor Rafael. ■ 00926 #042-01-1997 L1999 **VIR** *020
HERNANDEZ, William. 964 CALLE TRIGUERO, URB COUNTRY CLUB 00924 #042-04-1995 L1997 *020
HERNANDEZ CHUAN, Juan V. 1072 CALLE 19, VILLA NEVAREZ 00927 #308-01-1988 L2002 **PD** *100
HERNANDEZ-CIBES, Juan J. 400 AVE DOMENECH STE 602 00918 #042-01-1957 L1960 **OBG LM** *030 †30
HERNANDEZ-GONZALES, Liza. ■ 00926 #042-01-2002 L2005 **APM** *100 †60
HERNANDEZ-GONZALEZ, J R. TORRE SAN FRANCISCO 609, 369 AVE DE DIEGO 00923 #042-01-1969 L1973 **N** *020
HERNANDEZ-LATORRE, C. ■ 00926 #308-03-1980 L1986 **GS** *020
HERNANDEZ-MONTALVO, M. 9410 AVE LOS ROMEROS, STE 204 00926 #847-08-1981 L1986 **PD** *020
HERNANDEZ-NEVAREZ, Pedro. 1507 SANTURCE 00936 #042-03-1980 L1984 **PD** *020
HERNANDEZ-PEREZ, Ivette. RR 3 BOX 3239 # 1 KM18.5, I.E.S., INC. 00926 #042-03-1984 L1988 **IM** *020 †20
HERNANDEZ-RAMOS, Prisco. 400 AVE DOMENECH STE 305 00918 #847-04-1955 L1960 **OTO** *020
HERNANDEZ-RICOFF, B. ■ 00918 #847-02-1979 L1983 **GP** *030
HERNANDEZ SUCARICHI, J L. PO BOX 70344, 193 CMMS 00936 #847-06-1976 L1980 **GS TRS** *040
HERNANDEZ-VELASCO, B A. 100 GRAND PASEO BLVD, STE 112 00926 #005-02-1997 L2001 **MPD** *100 †20,55
HERNANDEZ VIERA, Edgar C. 369 AVE DE DIEGO STE 607, TORRE SAN FRANCISCO 00923 #042-01-1994 L1999 **N** *020
HERRERA DALMAU, Jose A.. ■ 00927 #275-02-1984 L2005 **GP** *100
HERRERO, Raquel Cristina. 241 AVE WINSTON CHURCHILL 00926 #649-14-2002 **P** *012
HERRERO GRANDA, Manuel. 287 AVE WINSTON CHURCHILL, URB EL SENORIAL 00926 #935-01-1988 L1996 *100
HIDALGO, Jose R. 150 AVE DE DIEGO, SAN JUAN HEALTH CENTRE 00907 #042-01-1965 L1969 **PDP PD** *020
HIDALGO CESTERO, Carlos A. 130 CALLE ELEONOR ROOSEVLT 00918 #649-01-1953 L1954 **PM** *071 †60
HORTA, Juan Manuel. ■ 00926 #042-01-2007 *012
HORTA RUBIO, Jubal H. ■ 00926 #649-01-1958 L1959 **OS GP** *020
HOYO-RUCABADO, Manuel. ■ 00927 #847-04-1954 L1957 **U** *071
HOYOS, Guillermo Jose. 268 AVE PONCE DE LEON, THE HATO REY CTR STE 501 00918 #847-04-1966 L1973 **P CHP** *020

HUERTA, Jose R. 239 AVE ARTERIAL HOSTOS, STE 601 00918 #042-01-1990 L1993 **OBG** *020 †30
HUERTAS, Sarah Enid. ■ 00907 #042-01-1974 L1976 **CHP P** *020 †75
IDALGISA-PIMENTEL, Anicia. 1306 AVE PONCE DE LEON, PUERTO RICO P.O. BOX 70184 00907 #308-01-1963 L1974 **OBG** *020
IFARRAGUERRI, Carlos E. 301 COND MEDICAL PLZ, ASHFORD 00921 #023-01-1961 L1966 **P IM** *020 †75
IGLESIAS, Manuel Javier. ■ 00926 #042-01-2007 *012
IGLESIAS, Martin. 1347 CALLE DECATUR, VILLA BORINQUEN 00920 #847-10-2000 L2001 *100
IGLESIAS-RIVERA, Jose I. ■ 00912 #847-04-1962 L1964 **PS GS** *071
IMBERT, Segundo. PO BOX 70321 00936 #042-03-1995 L2000 **RO** *020 †80
IMBERT-GARRATON, Manuel E. 735 AVE PONCE DE LEON, STE 605 00917 #042-01-1983 L1986 **GE** *020
INFANTE, Ricardo Ariel. 208 CAL DK URB UNIVERSITY 00927 #264-07-1990 L2005 **RHU IMG** *030 †20
INSERNI, Jaime A. 1451 AVE ASHFORD 00907 #042-01-1983 L1987 **NS** *020 †25
IRANZO, Mauro. 138 AVE WINSTON CHURCHILL, PMB 526 00926 #042-01-2000 L2004 **GS** *020 ‡
IRIZARRY, Gladys M. 742 JUNCAL, LOS CAMPOS DE MONTEHIEDRA 00926 #042-01-1995 L2000 **AN** *020 †05
IRIZARRY, Hilda Teresa. 400 AVE DOMENECH, OFICINA 305 00918 #042-01-1996 L2001 **PD** *020
IRIZARRY, Luis Alberto. 391 CALLE SGTO MEDINA, EXT ROOSEVELT 00918 #847-06-1984 L1992 **PD** *020
IRIZARRY, Milton Edgardo. ■ 00927 #042-01-2001 L2006 *100
IRIZARRY, Neila M. 120 COND SIERRA ALTA, 100 AVENUE LA SIERRA 00926 #042-01-1995 L1999 **PD** *020
IRIZARRY, Sergio. ■ 00926 #035-06-1950 L1952 **IM OS** *030
IRIZARRY BAEZ, Rolando. 531A CALLE SERGIO CUEVAS, PARQ CENTRAL 00918 #042-04-1994 L1995 **P** *020
IRIZARRY BONILLA, Marisol. APT 401 CONDO LAS AMERICAS 00921 #308-04-2003 L2004 *100
IRIZARRY GARCIA, Jose R. PO BOX 16752 00908 #042-04-1990 L1991 **OBG** *020
IRIZARRY-GUASCH, Alwin L. 201 AVE DE DIEGO, PLAZA SAN FRANCISCO, STE. 00927 #649-02-1984 L1992 **FM** *020 †18
IRIZARRY MEDINA, Ileana. ■ 00923 #649-14-2002 L2005 *100
IRIZARRY-RAMIREZ, Jose R. 1400 AVE MAGDALENA, EL CONDADO 00907 #308-02-1981 L1983 **EM OM** *020
ISADO ZARDON, Jose A. 735 AVE PONCE DE LEON 00917 #847-04-1971 L1976 **PD** *030
ISALES, Ramon. 128 AVE DOMENECH 00918 #024-05-1910 L1955 **HS GS** *020 †85
ITURREGUI, Miguel Manuel. ■ 00921 #042-01-1999 L2004 **GS** *020 †85
IZAGUIRRE, Bernardo. 29 CALLE WASHINGTON, STE 108B 00907 #847-09-1975 L1981 **PD** *020 †55
IZQUIERDO PRETEL, Guillerm. PO BOX 365067 00936 #737-03-1989 **IM** *012
JACKSON, Jaime Jose. ■ 00921 #042-01-2003 *100
JACKSON-SANABRIA, Modesta. 371 AVE DE DIEGO 00923 #308-03-1978 L1985 *071
JAUNARENA-PEREZ, Pedro R. 400 AVE FD ROOSEVELT, STE 508 00918 #042-01-1961 L1963 **PD** *020 †55
JAVIER, Eric Roberto. 138 CALLE HIJA DEL CARIBE 00918 #042-03-1993 L1995 **GS** *020
JESURUM NATALIO, Daisy J. UNIV PR SCH MED, DEPT PSYCH 00936 #308-01-1964 L1975 **P** *020
JIMENEZ, Baltasar. ■ 00936 #042-01-1966 L1973 **GP** *020
JIMENEZ, Carlos Enrique. PO BOX 6213, O-11 REINA ISABELA GUAYNAB 00914 #042-02-1991 L1993 **NM** *020 †20,28
JIMENEZ, Elena Maria. 572 CALLE CESAR GONZALEZ, BALDRICH 00918 #042-01-1998 L2000 **OPH** *020 †35
JIMENEZ, Emilio. BOX 22678 UNIV STAT 00931 #042-01-1966 L1969 **OBG** *020 †30
JIMENEZ, Lissette. 400 AVE DOMENECH STE 407 00918 #042-01-1986 L1991 **N SME** *020 †75
JIMENEZ, Maurin. ■ 00926 #275-03-1992 L2006 **FP** *012
JIMENEZ, Ruth E. 914 CALLE PAGANINI # LOFT, URB SEVILLA 00924 #042-01-1988 L1997 **EM LM** *020
JIMENEZ, Tomas. 29 CALLE WASHINGTON, DEPT. OF RADIOLOGY, #501 00907 #042-01-1976 L1983 **DR** *020 †80
JIMENEZ-AGOSTO, John. 73 CALLE LIMONCILLO, EXT SANTA MARIA 00927 #847-06-1975 L1980 **GP** *020
JIMENEZ-CARLO, Ricky. 29 CALLE WASHINGTON, STE 202 00907 #042-01-1991 L1996 **GE** *020 †20
JIMENEZ-GARCIA, Jose C. 735 AVE PONCE DE LEON, TORRE AUXILO MUTRO #809 00917 #042-03-1980 L1984 **GE** *020
JIMENEZ-GUEVARA, Jose A. 1395 CALLE SAN RAFAEL 00909 #649-01-1957 L1960 **IM CD** *071
JIMENEZ MEJIA, Jaris J.. 382 AVE SAN CLAUDIO PMB 78, URB SAGRADO CORAZON 00926 #308-03-1990 L2004 *100
JIMENEZ-SIERRA, Edgardo. 813 CALLE TREVI, PASEO DE LA FUENTE 00926 #308-03-1977 L1990 **PD** *020
JIMENEZ-VEGA, Juan. 452 AVE HOSTOS, URB BALDRICH 00918 #042-03-1980 L1983 **PUD IM** *020
JIMENEZ-VELEZ, Jose L. ■ 00918 #028-34-1950 L1953 **AN LM** *071 †05
JOGLAR, Edgardo Rafael. 652 AVE MUNOZ RIVERA, STE 2075 00918 #042-01-1978 L1983 **ORS** *020
JOGLAR, Fernando Luis. ■ 00927 #042-01-1998 L1999 **GS** *020 †85
JOGLAR, Francisco Manuel. 1441 AVE FD ROOSEVELT 00920 #042-01-1973 L1975 **IM** *020 †20
JOHNSON, Charles Douglas. UPR MED SCI GPO 5067 MED 00936 #051-04-1958 L1968 **CD IM** *020 †20
JONES ROSARIO, John A.. ■ 00901 #308-03-1987 L2003 **GP** *020
JORDAN, G H. BOX 10975 CAPARRA HGTS STA 00922 #042-01-1969 L1975 **ORS EM** *020
JORDAN, Marla Esther. ■ 00920 #042-03-2002 **N** *100
JU, Ben Young. 1569 CALLE 34 SW, URB CAPARRA TER 00921 #649-14-2000 L2003 *100
JUAN, Pablo, Jr. ■ 00926 #847-01-1970 L1973 **OBG** *020
JUARBE, Jose A. ONE VETERANS PLAZA 00927 #847-01-1964 L1968 **P GP** *020
JUSTINIANO, Alfredo R. VET AFFAIRS MED CTR, DEPT MED 00927 #649-14-1995 L2000 **NEP** *020 †20
JUSTINIANO, Carlos E. PO BOX 70344, PMB 186 00936 #042-01-1999 L2001 **GS** *012
JUSTINIANO, Hilda. ■ 00927 #042-01-2003 L2004 **D** *012
KAO, Wynn Hugh. GPO BOX 5067, UNIV OF PR SCH MED 00936 #024-01-2004 **D** *012
KAREH, Jose A. 109 CALLE GERANIO, URB SAN FRANCISCO 00927 #042-01-1990 L1995 **CD** *020 †20

■ = Address Information Privacy Protected

KEY, Veronica R. 1452 CALLE, CONDO VALAJADRIA 00907 #042-03-1980 L1984 **APM** *020

KEY-OYOLA, Carlos Andres. 1357 AVE ASHFORD, STE 2 00907 #042-03-1981 L1986 **AN GS** *020

KIANES, Reinaldo E. ■ 00928 #847-03-1975 L1981 **P** *020

KNUDSON, Deborah Lee. ■ 00907 #042-01-2005 **P** *012

KRAFT, Gladys Perez. PO BOX 364563 00936 #042-01-1975 L1980 **DR** *040 †80

LABAT, Ricardo Alberto. C/O P.O. BOX 194478, 716 PONCE DE LEON AVENUE 00919 #132-02-1964 L1972 **GS** *020 †85

LABAULT, Jose Rafael. ■ 00931 #042-01-2008 *012

LABORDE, Janine. 2 CALLE CASIA 00921 #042-02-1996 L2002 **GPM IM** *062

LABOY, Adair Angel. ■ 00910 #042-04-1982 L1988 **NEP** *020

LACHAUSME, Nicole. 954 AVE PONCE DE LEON, PH-H MIRAMAR PLAZA COND. 00907 #847-09-1965 L1973 **AN** *020

LACOMBA-HERNANDEZ, Rafael. 2265 CALLE LOIZA 00913 #308-03-1980 L1986 **GP** *030

LAMOURT-VALENTIN, F. 138 AVE WINSTON CHURCHILL, URB CONTEMPORANEO 00926 #847-03-1976 L1980 **FM GPM** *020

LAO, Florencio. ■ 00926 #042-01-1979 L1983 **PM** *020

LARROY, Karen Liz. S5-12 CALLE CATARATAS, URB EL REMANSO 00926 #042-03-2000 L2003 **IM** *100

LASALA, Javier David. ■ 00912 #042-01-2007 **TY** *012

LA SALLE, Miguel Angel. ■ 00907 #042-01-1991 L1993 **OTO** *020 †45

LASTRA ARACIL, Juan A. 368 AVE DE DIEGO, COND CRYSTAL HOUSE SUITE C 00909 #847-04-1963 L1966 **P** *020

LATABAN, Lidya Margarita. ESTANCIAS DE BLDG 00926 #649-14-1990 L2003 *100

LATONI MALDONADO, David G. 310 DE DIEGO AVE STE 201 00909 #042-01-1985 L1987 **D PTH** *020 †15

LATORRE TORRES, Nestor R. 7A PLAYAMAR CONDOMINIUM 00979 #847-09-1964 L1966 **P** *020

LAUREANO-MARTI, Pablo. 37 AVE PONCE DE LEON 00901 #308-03-1982 L1989 **EM** *020 ‡

LEAL, Ela Francisca. ■ 00936 #275-01-1951 L1974 *071

LEBRON, Francisco A. 435 AVE PONCE DE LEON 00917 #042-01-1955 L1958 **P** *020

LEBRON, Luis Mazon. 40 CALLE CAPRI, PASEO LAS BRISAS 00926 #308-02-1986 L1992 **PD** *020

LEBRON, Migdalia Garcia. 379 AVE DE HOSTOS, URB JB HUYKE 00918 #847-04-1979 L1984 **IM GP** *020

LEBRON-SOTO, Maribel. ■ 00919 #042-01-1995 L1997 **FM** *020 †18

LEON, Felix Ivan. 1395 CALLE SAN RAFAEL 00909 #042-01-1972 L1974 **PUD IM** *020 †20

LEON, Luis Alberto. ■ 00918 #042-01-1978 L1982 **GP** *020

LEON-JIMENEZ, Jose L. ■ 00918 #649-14-1974 L1977 **GP** *075

LESPIER DE JESUS, Izewska. 134 CALLE SAN VALENTIN 00926 #308-03-1982 L1993 **FM** *020

LEVINE, Jeffrey. 5450 AVE DE LA CONSTITUCIO 00901 #649-14-1998 L2004 *100

LE ZOTTE, Lloyd Alvin, Jr. SCH OF MEDICINE UNIV OF PR, UNIV HOSPITAL 00935 #042-01-1960 L1971 **OS IM** *071

LIANO, Angel Luis. 500 AVE DOMENECH STE 402 00918 #042-01-1959 L1964 **GYN** *020 †30

LIANO, Jose L. 500 AVE DOMENECH STE 402, HATO REY 00918 #042-01-1992 L1995 **IM** *020

LIBERATORE, Katia Angelic. PO BOX 191052 00919 #042-01-2005 **CHP** *012

LIBOY, Ivan A. 1250 AVE JESUS T PINERO, CAPARRA TERRACE 00921 #042-01-1967 L1972 **OPH** *020

LIEN, Jane Michelle. ■ 00926 #042-01-1993 L1997 **OBG** *020 †30

LIMA, Jose T. 650 CALLE LLOVERAS, STE 101 00909 #042-03-1986 L1992 **CHP P** *020

LIMA-BEAZ, Bernabe. ■ 00926 #042-01-1947 L1994 **OM GP** *072

LIMARDO, Abner. 120 CALLE DEL SOL, AVE LA SIERRA, COND. SIERR 00901 #042-01-1995 L2000 **ORS** *020 †40

LINARES CASTRO, Maximino. 503 CALLE ROOSEVELT, URB LAS CUMBRES 00926 #042-01-1983 L1986 **PD** *020 †55

LINARES-RIVERA, Esteban. VET ADMIN CTR 00902 #847-10-1963 L1966 **CD IM** *040 †20

LIZARDI, Lorenzo. ■ 00920 #042-01-1968 L1970 **DR** *075

LIZARDO-VIDAL, Francis. 723 CALLE BULGARIA 00920 #308-01-1945 L1958 **TS GS** *020

LLADO, Victor J. 374 CALLE RAFAEL LAMAR 00918 #042-01-1970 L1974 **P** *020

LLADO-DIAZ, Jose R. M4 CALLE CLAVEL, PARQ DE SANTA MARIA 00927 #042-01-1982 L1984 **OPH** *020 †35

LLOMPART, Juan. 1451 AVE ASHFORD 00907 #847-04-1949 L1958 **ORS LM** *062 †40 ‡

LLORENTE JIMENIS, Nestor. 400 AVE FD ROOSEVELT, STE 304 00918 #275-01-1960 L1975 **GP** *071

LLUBERAS-GONZALEZ, Arturo. 1323 CALLE 21, URB MONTE CARLO 00924 #649-14-1987 L1992 **PD** *020

LOINAZ, Maritza Helena. PO BOX 5067 00936 #042-01-2000 L2006 **ORS** *020

LOJO, Juan J. 207 EDIF EL AMAL 00927 #042-01-1972 L1974 **GS** *020 †85

LOPEZ, Adalberto Jose. 116 CAL PMRS LAREDAS DE 00926 #042-02-1993 L1993 **AN** *020

LOPEZ, Adolfo Daniel. 842 CALLE CABRERA, URB CABRERA 00925 #847-04-1999 L2001 *020 †20

LOPEZ, Agustin. 1275 CALLE 11, URB MONTE CARLO 00924 #042-03-1998 L1999 **FM** *020

LOPEZ, Alvin. 969 CALLE MARCONI, JARD METROPOLITANO 00927 #042-01-1996 L2000 **U** *020 †95

LOPEZ, Annette Yolanda. ■ 00925 #042-03-2005 **PD** *012

LOPEZ, Claudia Isabel. ■ 00912 #042-01-2003 **P** *100

LOPEZ, Diana F. 18 CALLE TAFT, HOSPTITAL H.I.M.A. 00911 #042-01-1966 L1969 **PD** *020

LOPEZ, Jose Eugenio. 3 CALLE VERONA, VILLA CAPRI 00924 #042-01-1954 L1956 **CD IM** *040 †20

LOPEZ, Julie. 382 AVE DOMENECH 00918 #042-01-1976 L1981 **PN PD** *040 †55

LOPEZ, Kennice Marie. 1306 AVE MONTE CARLO, COND PORTAL DE LA REINA 21 00924 #649-30-2002 L2004 *100

LOPEZ, Lidy. 138 AVE WINSTON CHURCHILL, URB CROWN HLS 00926 #042-01-1973 L1977 **PD** *020

LOPEZ, Miguel A. 1801 AVE PONCE DE LEON 00909 #042-01-1975 L1980 **IM** *020

LOPEZ, Miguel Angel. 29 CALLE WASHINGTON, STE 403 00907 #649-14-1984 L1986 **PUD** *020 †20

LOPEZ, Orlando. 1427 AVE FERNANDEZ JUNCOS, STE 203 00909 #042-04-1986 L1991 **IM** *020

LOPEZ, Reynold E. 431 AVE PONCE DE LEON, NATIONAL PLAZA STE 328 00917 #042-01-1971 L1973 **SO HNS** *040 †85

LOPEZ, Serafin Candelario. PO BOX 365067 00936 #275-03-1995 **AN** *012

LOPEZ, Vanessa Beauchamp. 138 AVE WINSTON CHURCHILL, PMB 791 00926 #042-02-2005 L2006 *100

LOPEZ-ACEVEDO, Carmen E. 530 CALLE ANTOLIN NIN, URB LOS INGENIEROS 00918 #042-01-1977 L1981 **PM** *020

LOPEZ ACEVEDO, Marjery Na. 10 CALLE CASIA, VA MED CTR 00921 #649-14-2003 L2003 **IM** *100

LOPEZ-ACOSTA, Ramon Luis. PO BOX 11710, S-34 PALMA REAL ST 00922 #308-03-1980 L1989 **FM** *020

LOPEZ-COLON, Esteban. 572 CALLE JUAN J JIMENEZ 00918 #308-03-1982 L1983 **CD IM** *020

LOPEZ-CRUZ, Manuel E. 385 AVE FELISA RINCON GATR, CONDOMINIO PUERTO PASEOS 00926 #847-04-1962 L1964 **P** *020

LOPEZ CUMPIANO, Andres. 500 AVE MUNOZ RIVERA, COND EL CENTRO II, OFICINA 00918 #847-04-1957 L1959 **OS** *020

LOPEZ-DAVILA, Liana E. ■ 00926 #042-01-1990 L1996 **DR** *020 †80

LOPEZ-DE JESUS, Fernando. 1728 CALLE SEGRE, URB RIO PIEDRAS HTS 00926 #042-01-1999 L2002 **CD** *020

LOPEZ-FLORES, B. 201 AVE ARTERIAL HOSTOS, GALERIA I-SUITE 1705 00918 #847-04-1964 L1967 **P** *020

LOPEZ GALARZA, Carmen. 962 CALLE HYPOLAIS, URB CLUB MANOR 00924 #308-03-1984 L1993 *020

LOPEZ-GARCIA, Josefina M. 618 CALLE AUSTRAL, URB ALTAMIRA 00920 #042-03-1981 L1985 **OS PD** *030

LOPEZ-GONZALEZ, F. 00918 #042-01-1995 L1999 **OAR** *020 †40

LOPEZ HIDALGO, Vicente. 500 AVE MUNOZ RIVERA, EL CENTRO 2 STE 607 00918 #042-01-1979 L1984 **NO OTO** *020 †45

LOPEZ-MALPICA, Fernando J. 1728 CALLE SEGRE, URB PURPLE TREE 00926 #042-01-1974 L1976 **AI IM** *020 †20,03,80

LOPEZ-NEGRON, Arturo. 400 AVE DOMENECH, STE 502 00918 #042-03-1981 L1988 **GS** *020 †85

LOPEZ ORTIZ, Rosa Maria. 206 EDIF BARCELONA CT, BARCELONA ST. #113 00907 #649-14-2002 L2005 *100

LOPEZ-PENA, Maricarmen. 202 CALLE GAUTIER BENITEZ, 349 AVENUE FELISA RINCON D 00915 #042-03-1996 L2002 **PPR** *020 †55

LOPEZ-ROCA, Argelio A. 524 CALLE JUAN J JIMENEZ, PARQ CENTRAL 00918 #042-04-1980 L1985 **CHP PFP** *020

LOPEZ RUYOL, Luis R. 371 AVE DE DIEGO 00923 #847-05-1975 L1980 **HEM IM** *020 †20

LOPEZ-TORRES, Rafael A. 304B CALLE 32, VILLA NEVAREZ 00927 #737-10-1993 L2002 **AN** *020

LOPEZ-VALDES, Ivan E. PO BOX 364684 00936 #308-01-1971 L1976 **AN** *020

LORENZO, Hector. 1501 SAN PATRICIO 00920 #847-03-1964 L1967 **R** *020

LOSA, Sonia. ■ 00907 #275-01-1997 **FP** *012

LOUBRIEL, Brenda Liz. 10 CALLE CASIA 00921 #649-14-2003 **IM PCC** *020 †20

LOUBRIEL CARRIO, Advilda. 370 AVE SAN CLAUDIO, URB SAGRADO CORAZON 00926 #308-03-1984 L1992 *020

LOURO, Vera Lucia B D. 1507 AVE PONCE DE LEON, APT 262 00909 #770-03-1979 L2005 **P** *100

LOZADA, David. GPO BOX 5067, UNIV PR SCH MED 00936 #042-03-2005 **NS** *012

LOZADA-COSTAS, Jose A. 576 CALLE CESAR GONZALEZ, STE 503 00918 #042-01-1995 L2001 **ON** *012

LUCCA PELAEZ, Fernando. 200 AVE WINSTON CHURCHILL, STE 202 00926 #042-03-1988 L1991 *020

LUENGO, Antonio Martinez. 1111 CALLE VIEQUES, 400 DOMENECH AVE OFFICE 51 00907 #042-01-1981 L1986 **OBG** *020 †30

LUGARO, Ana Maria. 10 CALLE CASIA 00921 #042-03-2003 L2006 **END** *012 †20

LUGO, Alexander Rafael. 230 CALLE ELEONOR ROOSEVLT, URB EL VEDADO 00918 #042-01-2000 L2001 **D PRO** *020 †15

LUGO, Edwin Ivan. ■ 00926 #042-01-1984 L1989 **ORS** *020

LUGO, Martin Hernan. 208 AVE PONCE DE LEON, PROFESSIONAL MED PLZ #102 00918 #649-14-1997 L1998 **IM** *020

LUGO, Miladi. ■ 00926 #042-01-1974 L1977 **PDE PD** *020 †55

LUGO, Nitza. 241 AVE WINSTON CHURCHILL, CHURCHILL PARK BOX 37 00926 #042-01-1984 L1987 **CCP** *020 †55

LUGO, Tomas F. 1939 CALLE SAN DIEGO, BORINQUEN GARDENS 00926 #042-01-1991 L1994 **ID** *020 †20

LUGO LUGO, Anibal. UNIV OF P R SCH OF MED 00936 #016-06-1943 L1946 **CD** *071 †40

LUZARDO MEJIAS, Rafael R. 405 CALLE SAN FRANCISCO, VIEJO SAN JUAN 00901 #649-14-1988 L1992 *020

MAC DONALD, Gordon R. ROOSEVELT RD 00902 #010-01-1968 L1994 **U** *071 †95 ‡

MACHUCA-PADIN, Fernando. DOMENECH AVE 00918 #042-01-1954 L1956 **A IM** *020 †03

MACOSSAY-NEGRIN, Carlos R. ■ 00907 #649-01-1950 L1956 **IM CD** *071

MAESO GONZALEZ, Edwin. 735 AVE PONCE DE LEON, STE 806 00917 #042-01-1972 L1975 **U GP** *020 †95

MAESTRE, Federico Andres. 357 AVE PONCE DE LEON, PTA DE TPERRA 00901 #042-02-1986 L1988 **OPH** *020

MAESTRE-GRAU, Barbara E. 255 AVE DOMENECH 00918 #042-01-1977 L1982 **PTH** *050

MAGRANER FOLCH, Gabriel A. 511A AVE DOMENECH # 400 00918 #847-05-1953 L1955 **P OS** *020

MAINARDI REYNA, Louis E. ■ 00927 #869-05-1940 L1956 **PHP** *071

MALARET, German Emilio. 1503 CALLE ASIA, 2ND FL 00909 #024-01-1953 L1956 **CD IM** *071 †20 ‡

MALARET-GONZALEZ, Hiram. 37 AVE PONCE DE LEON 00901 #042-01-1979 L1983 **OBG** *020 †30

MALARET-JUARBE, Glenalvan. I6 CALLE 14 URB FAIRVIEW 00926 #649-01-1965 L1968 **GP** *020

MALAVE, Claritsa. 150 AVE CHARDON, STE 659 00918 #042-01-1978 L1982 **OBG** *020 †30

MALAVE, Marisol. 329 CALLE DEL SOL 00901 #042-01-1998 L2000 *020 †55

MALDONADO, Amarilys C. ■ 00918 #042-01-1987 L1992 **DR** *020 †80

MALDONADO, Awilda M. C/O PO BOX 9023994, RIO PIEDRAS 00902 #042-01-1982 L1985 **IM HEM** *020

MALDONADO, Hector I. AVE APOLO ESQ ALEJANDRINO, ALTOS QUICK PHARMACY 00907 #042-01-1981 L1985 **D** *020 †15

MALDONADO, Jimmy Acevedo. ■ 00918 #847-02-1964 L1973 **P GP** *020

MALDONADO, Jose Antonio. 2051 CALLE F DE ROJAS, URB EL SENORIAL 00926 #042-01-2001 L2002 **DR** *012

MALDONADO, Juan Mario. 735 AVE PONCE DE LEON, OFICINA 414 00917 #042-03-1991 L1999 **PS GS** *020

MALDONADO, Mirna. ■ 00921 #042-01-2002 L2004 **END** *020 †20

MALDONADO, Rita Waleska. PO BOX 270119 00928 #847-04-1980 L1995 **IM** *020

MALDONADO-ALEJANDRO, J H. 252 CALLE SAN JORGE 00912 #042-01-1979 L1981 **AN** *020

MALDONADO CATINCHI, Neil. 3A COND WILSON CT, WILSON MEDICAL BUILDING #1 00907 #042-04-1996 L1999 **FM** *020

MALDONADO-FONSECA, Luis J. 373 CALLE RAFAEL LAMAR, EXT ROOSEVELT 00918 #308-03-1979 L1981 *020

MALDONADO MARTY, Angela L. 9415 AVE LOS ROMEROS # 50, PMB 503 00926 #847-10-1969 L1975 **CHP P** *020

MALDONADO MORALES, C. 1664 CALLE PARANA, URB EL CEREZAL 00926 #308-03-1981 L1985 **FM** *020

MALDONADO SIERRA, Eduardo. BOX 4768 00902 #035-01-1936 L1937 **P OS** *050 †75

MALINOW, Iona Krystin. 576 CALLE CESAR GONZALEZ, EDIFICIO DORAL BANK CTR 00918 #035-45-1992 L1998 **PD** *020 †55

MANACH, Jorge, II. COND SANTA ANA 00927 #275-01-1954 L1970 **IM GE** *020

MANGUAL, Amarilys. ■ 00921 #042-04-1987 L1995 **IM HEM** *020

MANGUAL CORDERO, Efren E. 10 CALLE CASIA # 116A, BEHAVIOAL HEALTHCARE 00921 #649-14-1995 L1997 **P** *020

MARCIAL, Jorge Armando. ■ 00911 #042-03-2008 *012

MARCIAL, Victor A. 400 AVE FD ROOSEVELT # 109, CLINICA LAS AMERICAS 00918 #024-01-1949 L1954 **RO ON** *020 †80

MARCIAL-VEGA, Victor A. 400 AVE FD ROOSEVELT, STE 109 00918 #042-01-1984 L1989 **RO ON** *020 †80

MARCOS-MARTINEZ, Maria J. ■ 00927 #847-11-1987 L1992 **PTH** *020 †50

MARCUCCI-RAMOS, Yarima. 505A COND EMILIANO POL, LACUMBRE 00917 #042-04-1997 L1999 *020

MARGARIDA, Carlos Jose. ■ 00936 #035-01-1946 L1946 **OPH** *071 †35

MARIN, Anibal. PO BOX 5067, DEPT MEDICINA DE FAMILIA 00936 #042-01-1966 L1969 **FM** *020 †18 ‡

MARIN, Edgard. PO BOX 9300156, RIO PIEDRAS, PR 00930 #308-02-1986 L1990 **GP** *020

MARIN, Jose Edgardo. 300 AVE LA SIERRA, BOX 28 00926 #042-01-1991 L1996 **GS** *020 †85

MARIN MALDONADO, Daniel. 60 CALLE SOLDADO SERRANO 00911 #308-03-1979 L1982 **P FSM** *020

MARISCAL, Liuska. ■ 00920 #275-01-1997 L2005 **PD** *100

MARMOLEJO MORALES, Alejand. J1 CALLE 5 URB HILLSIDE 00926 #308-01-1983 L1992 *100

MARQUES, Bernardo Jose. 300 AVE LA SIERRA, BOX 21 00926 #042-02-1990 L1995 **DR** *020

MARQUES-BIBILONI, Jose A. 400 CALLE JUAN KALAF 00918 #042-03-1988 L1990 **HO** *020

MARQUES-MARQUES, Jaime. ■ 00926 #042-03-1981 L1985 **EM** *020

MARQUEZ, Enrique. 1829 CALLE ACACIA, URB SANTA MARIA 00927 #042-01-1955 L1958 **TS GS** *020 †85,90

MARQUEZ, Erik. ■ 00926 #042-03-1982 L1988 **GS** *020 †85

MARQUEZ, Ivonne. ■ 00920 #042-01-1985 L1991 **R** *020

MARQUEZ, Luis E. 502 ASHFORD MEDICAL CTR, 29 WASHINGTON ST 00907 #308-01-1980 L1984 **FM** *020

MARQUEZ, Luis G. 1306 AVE FDZ JUNCOS, PDA 19 1/2 00909 #042-04-1994 L1995 **GP** *020

MARQUEZ, Raul H. 29 CALLE WASHINGTON # 403, ASHFORD MEDICAL CTR 00907 #042-03-1983 L1986 **GS AS** *020 ‡

MARQUEZ BABILONIA, Luis G. 1306 AVE FERNANDEZ JUNCOS, PDA 19 1/2 00909 #042-04-1994 L1995 **GP** *020

MARQUEZ FERNANDEZ, S. ■ 00920 #847-10-1965 L1969 *020

MARQUEZ-VALEDON, G. ■ 00926 #042-03-1995 L1997 **FPG** *100 †18

MARRERO, Arnaldo Luis. ■ 00917 #649-14-2003 **IM** *100

MARRERO, Awilda J. ■ 00926 #042-01-1986 L1989 **FM** *020

MARRERO, Camil Ivette. ■ 00926 #042-01-2006 **OBG** *012

MARRERO, Carmen M. 488 CARR 845, URB PURPLE TREE 00926 #042-01-1987 L1990 **FM FPG** *020 †18

MARRERO, Giselle Marie. ■ 00924 #042-02-2006 **PD** *012

MARRERO, Miguel A. 1485 AVE ASHFORD, APT 801-2 00907 #847-04-1955 L1959 **ORS** *071

MARRERO-DAVILA, Astrid M. 435 AVE PONCE DE LEON 00917 #847-08-1978 L1984 **GP** *020

MARRERO-PLAUD, Carlos C. 463 CALLE CESAR GONZALEZ, URB ROOSEVELT 00918 #308-03-1982 L1986 **FM FPG** *020 ‡

MARRERO RIVERA, Miguel A. 300 AVE LA SIERRA, BOX 39 00926 #649-14-1994 L1994 **PAN** *105

MARRERO VAZQUEZ, Carlos M. 138 AVE WINSTON CHURCHILL, URB CROWN HLS 00926 #649-14-2000 L2002 **OBG** *020

MARTI, Myriam. ONE VETERANS PLAZA 00927 #042-01-1976 L1983 **P** *020

MARTIN, Giselle. 735 AVE PONCE DE LEON, TORRE MEDICA AUXILIO OFIC 00917 #042-01-1994 L1998 **OPH** *020 †35

MARTIN, Jose Carlos. 2 RES MONTE PARK, RR 36 BUZON 33 00924 #042-01-1991 L1995 **OBG** *020 †30

MARTIN, Rafael E. 1451 AVE ASHFORD, ESQUINA NAIRM 00907 #649-01-1963 L1965 **D OS** *020

MARTIN, Rafael F. 1451 AVE ASHFORD, LABALERIA STE 611 00907 #042-01-1988 L1992 **D** *020 †15

MARTIN CORDOVA, Alberto M. ■ 00907 #042-03-2008 *012

MARTINEZ, Abelardo. ■ 00921 #847-08-1962 L1974 **P** *020

MARTINEZ, Anisonia Delis. 820 AVE ITURREGUI, URB COUNTRY CLUB 00924 #042-03-1995 L2000 **IM** *020 †20

MARTINEZ, Annette. 735 AVE PONCE DE LEON, STE 507 00917 #042-03-1997 L2000 **RHU** *100 †20

MARTINEZ, Annette E. PO BOX 5067 00936 #042-01-1996 L1999 **N** *020

MARTINEZ, Carlos E. 352 AVE SAN CLAUDIO, STE 164 00926 #308-03-1983 L1987 **GP** *020

MARTINEZ, David Enrique. 215 CALLE ZORZAL, URB MONTEHIEDRA 00926 #042-01-1975 L1981 **IM RHU** *020 †20

MARTINEZ, Enid Eugenia. PO BOX 11266 00922 #035-19-2008 *012

MARTINEZ, Fernando R. 89 AVE DE DIEGO STE 105, PMB 535 00927 #042-04-1993 L1995 **P** *020

MARTINEZ, Gabriel L. ■ 00926 #042-01-2004 L2008 **P** *012

MARTINEZ, Gabriel R. PO BOX 19146 00910 #042-01-1964 L1966 **END IM** *020

MARTINEZ, Hector A. 377 AVE DOMENECH 00918 #308-03-1982 L1986 **IM** *020

MARTINEZ, Hector Javier. ■ 00926 #042-01-2005 **IM** *012

MARTINEZ, Ian A. ■ 00926 #042-03-2017 **IM** *012

MARTINEZ, Jorge L. 2 CALLE MARGARITA, URB MONTEVERDE 00926 #042-01-1981 L1984 **CD IM** *040 †20

MARTINEZ, Jose Antonio. GPO BOX 5067, UNIV PR SCH OF MED 00936 #042-01-2001 L2003 **CD** *012

MARTINEZ, Jose Luis. 400 AVE DOMENECH 00918 #008-01-1978 L1981 **IM** *020 †20

MARTINEZ, Karen Gisela. 645 AVE SAN PATRICIO, URB SAN PATRICIO 00920 #042-01-2001 L2003 **CHP** *020 †75

MARTINEZ, Margarita M. ■ 00917 #042-01-1982 L1994 **PD** *020 †55

MARTINEZ, Mayra L. ■ 00926 #042-01-2003 L2006 **PD** *020 †55

MARTINEZ, Melisa Raquel. ■ 00926 #042-01-2007 **IM** *012

MARTINEZ, Meliza. ■ 00925 #042-01-2004 **END** *012 †20

MARTINEZ, Miguel A. BA42 CALLE 65 URB HILL MNS 00926 #847-13-1974 L1986 **PD** *020

MARTINEZ, Miguel E. 121 CALLE COSTA RICA, URB PINEIRO 00917 #847-10-1961 L1968 **GP OS** *020

MARTINEZ, Nelia Esther. ■ 00926 #847-10-1964 L1969 **GP** *040

MARTINEZ, Roberto. 735 AVE PONCE DE LEON, STE 501 00917 #042-02-1983 L1987 **PUD IM** *020

MARTINEZ, Segundo M. 366 CALLE LUIS MEDINA, APT 7 EDIF MARIBEL 00918 #308-01-1976 L2006 *100

MARTINEZ, Selma. 138 AVE W CHURCHILL, URB CROWN HLS 00926 #042-01-1991 L1995 **PM** *020

MARTINEZ-CANAVATE, F J. W4-20 CALLE CALDRN D L BRC, URB HUCARES 00926 #308-01-1976 L1978 **PTH** *020

MARTINEZ-DIAZ, Luis A. 1219 CALLE CARDENAS, URB PUERTO NUEVO 00920 #308-01-1982 L1991 **GP** *020

MARTINEZ-DURAN, Ricardo. 200 AVE CUPEY GDNS, PLAZA CUPEY GDNS STE 8W 00926 #308-07-1983 L1987 **IM** *020

MARTINEZ MENDEZ, Eugenia. W5-24 CALLE CERVANTES, URB HUCARES 00926 #847-06-1973 L1976 **GP** *020

MARTINEZ OLIVIERI, Roselyn. 1395 CALLE SAN RAFAEL 00909 #649-14-1997 L1999 **IM** *020

MARTINEZ PEREZ, Abraham. ■ 00920 #308-02-1974 L1977 **FM** *020

MARTINEZ-PICO, Amalia. 400 AVE DOMENECH STE 303, LAS AMERICAS PROF CTR 00918 #042-01-1955 L1959 **PDC PD** *020

MARTINEZ-POVENTUD, G. 37 AVE PONCE DE LEON 00901 #847-06-1976 L1981 **HEM ON** *040

MARTINEZ-RIVERA, Deborah. 469 CALLE LUIS MUNIZ SFRNT 00923 #649-14-1986 L1990 *020

MARTINEZ-RIVERA, Diane Ma. CONCORDIA GARDENS III, APART 4D 00924 #308-13-2002 L2004 *100

MARTINEZ RIVERA, Raquel. ■ 00921 #042-01-1972 L1974 **RHU IM** *062

MARTINEZ-RODRIGUEZ, Iris. 404 AVE BARBOSA, CALLE SICILIA 00917 #847-01-1973 L1976 **PD** *020

MARTINEZ-ROIG, Hugo E. 112 CALLE ARZUAGA STE 802 00925 #025-01-1951 L1953 **OPH** *020 †35

MARTINEZ RUIZ, Silvio R. 700 CALLE DR PAVIA FDZ, STE 203 00909 #275-01-1983 L2000 **FM EM** *020

MARTINEZ-SERVINO, Zayda. 7 CALLE SAN CARLOS, MANS DE CALDAS 00926 #847-10-2002 L2004 *100

MARTINEZ-TORRES, Jose L. 500 AVE DOMENECH, STE 401-B 00918 #308-13-1997 L2002 **PD** *100

MARTINEZ TORRES, Loaly E. F10 CALLE CORRIENTE, URB EL REMANSO 00926 #308-03-1984 L1993 **P** *020

MARTINEZ-TORRES, Pedro J. ■ 00907 #847-01-1974 L1978 **P** *071

MARTINEZ VALETTE, Maritza. ■ 00923 #308-01-1983 L2000 **GP** *020

MARTINEZ VILLAFANE, H A. PO BOX 19269 00910 #010-02-1940 L1941 **IM PUD** *071

MARTI NUNEZ, Jose. 210 PLAZA LAS AMERICAS, HATO REY 00918 #847-06-1961 L1965 **OBG** *071

MAS-IRIZARRY, Manuel. 412 AVE DE DIEGO, URB PUERTO NUEVO 00920 #042-01-1959 L1961 **GP** *072

MASSANET, Jose Manuel. ■ 00926 #042-02-2004 **ORS** *012

MASSANET PASTRANA, Carmen. ■ 00924 #308-03-1981 L1996 *020

MASSINI, Juan Carlos. RR 36 BOX 19, CUPEY 00926 #649-14-1989 L1991 **GP** *020

MATANZO-CORTES, Magaly. PO BOX 190907, 190907 SJ 00919 #042-03-1997 L1999 *020

MATEO, Enid Milagros. 9N COND HATO REY PLZ # 9N 00918 #042-01-1975 L1980 **FM** *030 †18

MATOS, Hipolito De Jesus. PO BOX 8062P 00910 #308-01-1982 L2004 *100

MATOS, Jose Gabriel. 1202 HOSTDS 239, CAPITAL CENTER SUR 00918 #042-01-1977 L1981 **OPH** *020 †35

MATOS, Laura I Galindez. 89 AVE DE DIEGO PMB 700, STE 105 00927 #035-09-1992 L1994 **CD** *020

MATOS, Marta Grisel. 200 AVE WINSTON CHURCHILL, STE 301 00926 #649-14-2000 L2002 *020

MATOS, Nelson Felipe, III. ■ 00926 #042-01-2000 L2003 **DR** *100 †80

MATOS-LLOVET, Isabel T. ■ 00926 #042-02-1997 L2003 **PTH** *100

MATTA, Belisario. 1357 AVE ASHFORD, STE 2 00909 #042-01-1971 L1974 **AN OS** *030 †05

MATTA-FONTANET, Evelyn. VET ADMIN MED CTR, DEPT MED 00927 #649-14-1997 L2000 **IM** *020

MATTEI VAZQUEZ, Libertad. ■ 00918 #649-01-1955 L1959 **P CHP** *071

MATTOS, Angel M. 3 CALLE NOGAL, LAREDAS DE SAN JUAN 00926 #041-13-1949 L1951 **FM** *040 †18

MAYOL, Laura Michelle. ■ 00926 #042-01-2008 *012

MAYOL, Magdiel. 369 AVE DE DIEGO 00909 #042-01-1998 L2002 **OSM** *020

MAYO SUAREZ, Teodoro. 652 AVE MUNOZ RIVERA, STE 3140 00918 #275-01-1954 L1970 **OS GS** *020

MC CARTHY, Vilma T. ■ 00926 #042-01-1995 L2000 **P PYG** *020 †75

MCKENZIE GOMEZ, Felix M. 138 AVE WINSTON CHURCHILL, MSC 631 00926 #042-04-2000 L2001 *020

MEDINA, Jose Ramon. 1738 CALLE AMARILLO, BOX 16 00926 #847-05-1961 L1964 **GP** *020 †20

MEDINA, Juan Jesus. 732 AVE PONCE DE LEON 00918 #042-03-1991 L1995 **U** *020

MEDINA, Manuel Antonio. 1801 AVE PONCE DE LEN #304 00909 #042-04-1980 L1983 **HS GS** *020 †85

MEDINA, Margarita. 220 CALLE RUBICON, URB RIO PIEDRAS HTS 00926 #308-03-1995 L2001 **IM** *020 ‡

MEDINA, Rochelly. 400 AVE FD ROOSEVELT, STE 101 00918 #042-03-1999 L2004 **DR** *020 †80

MEDINA CORTES, Julio C. GPO BOX 19715, FDEL JUNCOS STATION 00910 #308-01-1981 L1983 **GP** *020

MEDINA-FIOL, Lourdes. 251 CAL RN MR URB MONTEHIE, MONTEHIEDRAS 00926 #042-03-1982 L1985 **AN** *020

MEDINA PADILLA, Carlos. RR 36, 844 ST KM 3.0CUPEY BAJO R 00926 #847-06-2000 L2002 *020

MEDINA-TORRES, Juan I. 735 AVE PONCE DE LEON, STE 609 00917 #847-10-1968 L1971 **U** *020

MEJIAS, Edwin. 10 CALLE CASIA, SAN JUAN VA MEDICAL CENTER 00921 #042-01-1974 L1976 **RHU IM** *020

MEJIAS, Ismael. 381 AVE FELISA RINCON GATR, COND PSEO MONTE 00926 #649-14-2002 L2004 *100

MELENDEZ, Efrain. 800 AVE HIPODROMO, DOCTORS MEDICAL CTR 301 OF 00909 #042-01-1973 L1974 **IM END** *020

MELENDEZ, Felix. RR 2 BOX 432 00926 #649-14-1988 L1991 **FM** *020

MELENDEZ, Hector. 369 CALLE DE DIEGO, TORRE SAN FRANCISCO SUITE 00923 #847-10-1967 L1970 **AN** *020

MELENDEZ, Maria T. ■ 00927 #042-01-1990 L1995 **DR PDR** *020

MELENDEZ, Melvin. ■ 00907 #042-01-1988 L1994 **GE** *020 †20

MELENDEZ, Miguel Jose. ■ 00926 #649-14-1997 L2002 **GP** *020

MELENDEZ BONILLA, Jorge A. 435 AVE PONCE DE LEON 00917 #042-01-1970 L1972 **GE IM** *020

MELENDEZ-DEDOS, Andres. 369 CALLE DE DIEGO, TORRE SAN FRANCISCO, SUITE 00923 #042-01-1989 L1995 **APM** *020 †05

MELENDEZ POVENTUD, Luis H. 112 CALLE ARZUAGA, STE 605 00925 #042-01-1962 L1966 **IM** *020

MELENDEZ REYES, Edna G. 369 AVE DE DIEGO, TOME SAN FRANCISCO 00923 #042-03-1988 L1991 **END DIA** *020

MELERO, Gustavo Andres. 300 CALLE LS FLRS MONTEHIE, BUZON 643 00912 #042-01-1994 L1999 **OTO** *100 †45

MEMBRENO ZELAYA, Sandra P. ■ 00926 #451-01-1988 L2002 *020

MENA-FRANCO, Hector J. ■ 00910 #308-01-1986 L1992 **RHU IM** *020

MENAR-ALVARADO, Rafael. 3H LAGURIA GARDENS V 00913 #847-01-1975 L1978 *020

MENCHACA, Juan Antonio. 1701 CALLE PARANA, URB RIO PIED HTS 00926 #042-01-1975 L1979 **IM** *020

MENDEZ, Cathia. ■ 00923 #042-03-2005 **IM** *012

MENDEZ, Celia Georgina. 381 AVE DOMENECH, HATO REY 00918 #042-03-1989 L1992 **OBG** *020

MENDEZ, Cristobal. 29 CALLE WASHINGTON, ASHFORD MED CTR #606 00907 #042-01-1973 L1975 **OPH** *020

MENDEZ, Fredeswinda. APT #18-D, CONDOMINIO HATO REY PLAZA 00918 #308-02-1976 L1980 **CHP PD** *020 †55

MENDEZ, Hector M. PO BOX 191258 00919 #042-01-1985 L1987 **CD CCM** *020 †20

MENDEZ, Jose. 735 AVE PONCE DE LEON, STE 807 00917 #042-01-1976 L1980 *020

MENDEZ, Monica. 751 VALLE DEL TOA, LOS CAMPOS DE MONTEHIEDRA 00926 #042-03-1997 L1999 **HEM** *020

MENDEZ, Yolanda. 501 COND CONDADO GDNS #501, COND PLAZA CONDADO 00907 #649-14-1986 L1992 *020

MENDEZ-BRYAN, Carlos R. 400 AVE FD ROOSEVELT, STE 101 00918 #023-01-1965 L1970 **DR** *020

MENDEZ-BUSO, Carlos R. ■ 00926 #042-01-1999 L2005 **DR** *020 †80 ‡

MENDEZ-CASTRO, Hernan F. 150 AVE DE DIEGO, OFICINA 601 00907 #024-05-1965 L1972 **PS GS** *020 †85

MENDEZ-CRUZ, Daniel. PO BOX 365067, MED SCIENCES CAMPUS 00936 #042-03-2003 L2008 **DR** *012

MENDEZ LATALLAD, William. 29 CALLE WASHINGTON, STE 504 00907 #042-01-1992 L1997 **GS** *020 †85

MENDEZ LOPEZ, Jorge Ricar. ■ 00926 #649-30-2001 L2003 **GP** *020

MENDEZ-MOLINA, Carmen. 241 AVE WINSTON CHURCHILL, BOX 48 00926 #042-01-1995 L1998 **AN** *020

MENDOZA, Celsa Rivera. BOX 1898 HATO REY STATION 00919 #847-04-1963 L1969 **P** *071

MENDOZA, Gilberto. PO BOX 70344, PMB 444 00936 #042-01-1991 L1996 **CD** *020 †20

MENENDEZ, Ferdinand C. 116 AVE DOMENECH 00918 #042-03-1990 L1994 **GS** *020

MENENDEZ, Julio C. 479 CALLE LUIS M SOUFFRONT, VILLA GRANADA 00923 #308-03-1978 L1985 **GP** *020

MENENDEZ CORDOVES, F. 435 AVE PONCE DE LEON 00917 #847-01-1968 L1973 **OTO HNS** *020

MERCADO, Abner Joas. PO BOX 365025 00936 #308-07-1986 L2004 *100

MERCADO, Brenda. APRO 903 CALLE MODESTA, CONDOMINIO BELLO HORIZONTE 00923 #042-03-1988 L1995 **PD** *020

MERCADO, Hiram. BOX 11981 CAPARRA HTS STA 00922 #847-04-1964 L1965 **NS** *020

MERCADO, Katherine Ingrid. 10 CALLE CASIA # 116A, BEHAVIORAL HEALTHCARE 00921 #042-03-2004 **P** *012

MERCADO, Trinidad. 1183 CALLE 62 SE, REPTO METROPOLITANO 00921 #649-14-1986 L2002 **IM** *020

MERCADO CORTES, Rosa Mari. 2203 CALLE LOIZA 00913 #308-13-1988 L1999 *020

MERCADO DOMACASSE, Daisy. ■ 00919 #308-01-1983 L2004 *100

MERCADO RAMIREZ, Diahnara. 1375 AVE SAN IGNACIO, URB ALTAMESA 00921 #308-02-2004 L2005 *100

MERCADO-ROSSO, Wilfredo. 735 AVE PONCE DE LEON, STE 81 00917 #847-01-1968 L1971 **IM** *020

MERCEDES ABREU, Ingrid A.. ■ 00924 #308-05-1995 L2006 *100

MERCEDES INOA, Maira. VILLA DEL PARQUE, APT 12H 00909 #308-01-1985 L1993 *020

MEZA-VENENCIA, Veronica. PO BOX 365067 00936 #264-02-2002 **IM** *012

MIESES-LLAVAT, Pricilla E. 29 CALLE WASHINGTON, ASHFORD MED CTR OFC 409 00921 #042-01-1994 L1997 **PM** *020

MILLAN, Ruben. 10 CALLE CASIA, SAN JUAN VAMC 00921 #847-12-1980 L1985 **P** *062

MILLAND, Antonio A. ONE VETERANS PLAZA 00927 #042-01-1983 L1987 **P** *020

MIRANDA, Hector Alejandro. ■ 00926 #042-01-2007 **IM** *012

MIRANDA, Hector S. 365 DE DIEGO AVE STE 409, SAN FRANCISCO TOWER 00909 #042-01-1986 L1990 **N** *020

MIRANDA, Jaime Antonio. ■ 00924 #042-03-2008 *012

MIRANDA RIVERA, Agapito. 400 AVE DOMENECH STE 408 00918 #042-01-1963 L1965 **IM RHU** *020

MIRANDA-RIVERA, Manuel N. 37 AVE PONCE DE LEON 00901 #021-01-1948 L1950 **OPH** *072 †35

MIRO, Arturo. PO BOX 21314 00928 #308-03-1985 L1991 **P** *020

MIRO-DIAZ, Angel J. 369 AVE DE DIEGO, SAN FRANCISCO SUITE 507-50 00909 #308-03-1982 L1989 **IM** *020

MODESTI, Ney. L2 CALLE 12, MANS COLINAS DE CUPEY 00926 #847-01-1958 L1960 **GP PD** *020

MOJICA, Victor Manuel. 653 AVE HIPODROMO, STE 102 00909 #042-01-1989 L1991 **N** *020 †75

MOJICA SANDOZ, Julio. 420 AVE PONCE DE LEON, EDICICIO MIDTWN OFIC 906 00918 #847-04-1958 L1960 **P** *020

MOLINA, Doris N. 369 DE DIEGO AVE, STE 602 00909 #042-01-1991 L1995 **D** *020 †15

MOLINA, Leonardo. 1451 AVE ASHFORD 00907 #042-03-1995 L1999 **OBG** *020 †30

MOLINA, Maribel. 300 AVE LA SIERRA, BOX 105 00926 #042-01-1992 L1995 **PD** *020 †55

MOLINA-OSSERS, Andres Dav. ■ 00928 #308-03-1988 L2005 *100

MONES, Elizabeth. PO BOX 365067 00936 #275-01-1994 **FP** *012

MONROIG ALFONZO, Arnaldo. 400 AVE DOMENECH 00918 #847-04-1956 L1960 **OBG** *020

MONSERRATE, Francisco J. 844 CAL HSTS URB HYDE PARK, RIO PEDRES 00927 #042-01-1993 L1997 **OPH** *020

MONSERRATE-CALDERON, Juan. 29 CALLE WASHINGTON, STE 109 00907 #041-13-1961 L1964 **CD IM** *020

MONSERRATE-COSTA, Salomon. 539A CALLE S CUEVAS BSTMNT, PARQ CENTRAL 00918 #042-01-1961 L1963 **CD IM** *020

MONSERRATE-MATIENZO, Juan. 728 AVE PONCE DE LEON 00918 #847-04-1962 L1966 **PD OS** *020

MONTALVO, Fernando Ivan. ■ 00926 #649-14-1999 L2003 **FM** *020

MONTALVO, Gary Geo. 400 AVE DOMENECH STE 506 00918 #042-01-1976 L1980 **OTO** *020 †45

MONTALVO, Lilybeth. ■ 00910 #042-01-1983 L1986 **PD** *020

MONTALVO, Luis Felipe. 500 AVE DOMENECH, STE 601 00918 #042-01-1977 L1982 **IM HEM** *020 †20

MONTALVO, Magaly Santiago. 1306 AVE FERNANDEZ JUNCOS, 19TH STOP 00909 #308-03-1982 L1989 **FM** *020

MONTALVO-CARBIA, Andres. RR 2 BOX 9 00926 #042-03-1980 L1983 **P ADP** *020

MONTALVO MARRERO, Jose. 253 CALLE CHILE, CONDOMINIO CADIZ PHC 00917 #847-10-1967 L1969 **OBG** *020

MONTALVO-SUAU, Nayda T. ■ 00920 #308-03-1980 L1982 **FM** *020

MONTANER, Luis Felipe. 252 CALLE SAN JORGE 00912 #042-01-1957 L1963 **OS** *071 †55

MONTANO, Luarde Isaac. ■ 00926 #649-14-2003 **CD** *012 †20

MONTES, Angel M. E POL AVE 497 STE 451, LA CUMBRE 00926 #847-05-1985 L1987 **FM** *020 †18

MONTES, Jose Raul. 735 AVE PONCE DE LEON, TORRE MEDICAL STE 813 00917 #042-01-1989 L1993 **OPH** *020 †35

MONTES CARDONA, Hugo. 735 AVE PONCE DE LEON, STE 602 00917 #042-01-1963 L1968 **CD IM** *020 †20

MONTES LUQUIS, Victor M.. 155 CALLE DEL PARQUE # 2C 00911 #649-14-2001 L2005 *100

MONTES RIVERA, Idalina. 911 CALLE ROCHESTER, URB UNIVERSITY GDNS 00927 #042-01-1970 L1975 **PD PHP** *020

MONTIJO CABIYA, Getzaida. 481 CALLE JOSE A CANALS, URB ROOSEVELT 00918 #308-03-1986 L2005 *100

MONTILLA, Jorge J. 500 AVE DOMENECH STE 301 00918 #042-01-1968 L1971 **P PD** *020 †55

MORA-ALDRICH, Olga Maria. ■ 00917 #042-01-2001 L2003 **CHP** *100 †75

MORALES, Francisco J. 37 AVE PONCE DE LEON 00901 #042-01-1982 L1984 **PD** *020

MORALES, Heriberto. 400 AVE DOMENECH STE 408, EDIFICIO LAS AMERICAS 00918 #649-01-1962 L1963 **NEP IM** *020

MORALES, Irma Ivelisse. 37 AVE PONCE DE LEON 00901 #308-03-1980 L1984 **PM PD** *020

MORALES, Javier A. ■ 00926 #042-01-1983 *020

MORALES, Javier Osvaldo. 359 DE DIEGO AVE STE 501, CLNCL RESRCH PUERTO RICO 00909 #042-01-1974 L1976 **ID IM** *020

MORALES, Jeannette. ■ 00926 #042-02-1994 L1997 **PD** *020

MORALES, Johara Denise. ■ 00926 #042-03-1994 L2001 **DR** *020 †80

MORALES, Juan Enrique. ■ 00923 #028-34-1943 L1944 **P** *072 †75

MORALES, Luis A. ■ 00923 #028-34-1944 L1946 **OPH** *071 †35

MORALES, Luis Arsenio. PO BOX 191227 00919 #847-01-1975 L1983 **GS TTS** *020

MORALES, Luis Enrique. 10 CALLE CASIA, VA MEDICAL CENTER 00921 #042-01-1972 L1980 **P** *020

MORALES, Milton E. ■ 00928 #649-14-1976 L1984 **U** *020 †95

MORALES, Myrna I. W7-10 CALLE BOSCAN, URB LADERAS DE PALMA REAL 00926 #042-01-1992 L1997 **CCA** *100 †05

MORALES, Pablo Luis. 37 AVE PONCE DE LEON 00901 #035-01-1946 L1948 **R NR** *071 †80

MORALES BORGES, Raul H. 29 CALLE WASHINGTON, STE 104 00907 #042-04-1990 L1992 **HO IM** *020

MORALES DAVILA, Carlos A.. PO BOX 29646, 65TH INFANTERIA STATION 00929 #649-19-1990 L1997 *100

MORALES-DE FRIAS, Maria I. ■ 00923 #308-01-1979 L1983 **PD** *020

MORALES GARCIA, Alexis V. 954 AVE PONCE DE LEON, MIRAMAR 00907 #649-14-2001 L2003 *100

MORALES-PADRO, Jose M. 420 AVE PONCE DE LEON, MIDTOWN BLDG STE 906 00918 #042-04-1985 L1986 **P** *020

MORALES PUJALS, Omar L. 1729 CALLE YENISEY, URB RIO PIEDRAS HTS 00926 #649-14-2004 L2005 **GP** *020

MORALES-RIVERA, Carmen R. APTO 502 VENUS PLZA C 00917 #847-06-1975 L1978 *020

MORALES-RODRIGUEZ, Nancy. 10 CALLE CASIA, VA MEDICAL CENTER/DEPT. OF 00921 #042-02-2002 L2006 **P** *100 †75

MORALES-SILVA, Virginia. COND IBERIA I, OFH 1 00920 #308-02-1976 L1980 **PD** *020 †55

MORALES SOLIS, R Armando. 28 CALLE LIMONCILLO, EXT SANTA MARIA 00927 #042-01-1992 L2002 **GE** *020 †20

MORA-PINERO, Edna. 435 AVE PONCE DE LEON 00917 #042-01-1986 L1990 **GS** *020 †85

MOREIRA, Juan A. 394 AVE SAN CLAUDIO, URB SAGRADO CORAZON 00926 #042-01-1990 L1995 **N OS** *020

MORELL, Luis Ivan. 100 GRAND BLVD, SUITE 112 MSC 486 00926 #042-03-1997 L1999 **PS** *020 †85,65

MORELL, Samuel. 773 AVE CAMPO RICO, URB CLUB MANOR 00924 #042-04-1987 L1989 **IM** *020 ‡

MORENO, Yahaira. 10 CALLE CASIA, DEPT OF INTERNAL MEDICINE 00921 #042-03-2006 **IM** *012

MORENO RIVERA, Benjamin. PO BOX 9300808 00928 #308-04-2004 L2006 *100

MORET, Andres M. 502 COND ROSARIO, ST 256 00912 #847-01-1964 L1967 **EM GP** *020

MOTTA-VALENCIA, Keryl. ■ 00920 #042-01-1998 L2002 **PM** *020 †60

MOYA, Paquita L. PO BOX 20, EDIFICIOB PHI 00919 #042-01-1983 L1986 **FM** *020 †18

MUJICA, Luisa. 610 COND SEGOVIA, APT 610 00918 #275-04-1987 L2004 *100

MULERO, Jose A. 497 AVE EMILIANO POL, URB LAS CUMBRES 00926 #042-01-1993 L1996 **FM** *020 †18

MUNDO RODRIGUEZ, Luz N. APT 12-G COND 00913 #847-10-1972 L1976 **GP** *020

MUNIZ, Armando J. 708 AVE PONCE DE LEON, OFICINA 204 00918 #308-01-1986 L1990 **IM** *020

MUNIZ, Benjamin. 150 AVE DE DIEGO 00907 #042-01-1992 L1996 **AN** *020 †05

MUNIZ, Eduardo Jose. 67 CALLE ORQUIDEA, URB SANTA MARIA 00927 #042-03-1994 L1998 **OBG** *020 †30

MUNIZ, Gloria Miret. 00921 #847-01-1962 L1974 **CHP P** *040

MUNIZ, Raquel. PO BOX 191235 00919 #308-13-2002 L2004 *100

MUNIZ-LUCIANO, Oscar. 2408 COND PRQ D LS FNTS #2 00918 #042-03-1998 *100

MUNOZ, Aurea Isabel. 703 CALLE MIRAMAR 00907 #025-01-1948 L1949 **PD OS** *071 †55

MUNOZ, Christine Marie. ■ 00926 #042-01-2000 L2001 **D** *020 †15

MUNOZ, Daniel Manuel. ■ 00927 #042-02-2005 **EM** *012

MUNOZ, Humberto Jose. 1431 AVE PONCE DE LEON, STE 402 00907 #042-01-1995 L2000 **GE** *020 †20

MUNOZ, Roberto. 1446 CALLE AMERICO SALAS 00909 #042-01-1975 L1980 **CD IM** *020 †20

MUNOZ, Rogelio Jose. ■ 00927 #042-01-2001 L2006 **DR** *100 †80

MUNOZ-SAN, Maria C. 667 AVE PONCE DE LEON 00907 #649-14-1988 L1990 **PD** *020

MUNOZ VILCHES, Ernesto J. 1451 AVE ASHFORD 00907 #308-03-1984 L1994 **IM** *020

MURCIA, Francisco. 371 AVE DE DIEGO 00923 #847-01-1955 L1958 **OM** *030

MURPHY, Irma L. 10 CALLE CASIA, VA MEDICAL CENTER 00921 #042-01-1987 L1990 **DR** *020 †28

MUSGRAVE, Ernest Eugene. ■ 00907 #042-01-1973 L1975 **IM ON** *020

MUSGRAVE, Irma N. 89 AVE DE DIEGO STE 105, PMB 411 00927 #042-01-1975 L1979 **PD** *020

NADAL, Hector M. ASHFORD MEDICAL CTR, DEPT SURG 00907 #041-01-1943 L1949 **GS** *020 †85

NAJUL ZAMBRANA, Zahira. K7 CALLE 9, URB EL MIRADOR DE CUPEY 00926 #042-04-1984 L1985 **IM** *020

NAREDO VILLAR, Manuel. 158 CALLE JOSE PADIN, URB JB HUYKE 00918 #042-02-1981 L1984 **PM** *020

NARVAEZ, Jesus Manuel. 261 CALLE LUNA 00901 #847-10-1969 L1972 **PD** *020

NARVAEZ, Maria Elena. PO BOX 19237 00910 #308-01-1985 L1987 **GP** *020

NARVAEZ-LUGO, Jessica. 10 CALLE CASIA, DEPT OF INTERNAL MEDICINE 00921 #042-02-2003 L2006 **GE** *012 †20

NAVARRO, Ana Aida. 503 CALLE FRANCISCO SEIN, URB FLORAL PARK 00917 #042-01-1954 L1957 **PD OS** *050 †55

NAVARRO, Anibal A. 65TH INFANTRY AVE STE 205, CONCORD SHOPPING CENTER 00924 #847-10-1966 L1970 **OTO** *020

NAVARRO, Luis Enrique. 369 CALLE DE DIEGO, TORRE SAN FRAN STE 208 00923 #042-03-1989 L1991 **GE IM** *020 †20

NAVAS SENERIZ, Liza M. ■ 00926 #042-04-1999 L2001 **FM** *020

NAZARIO, Angel David. 1708 CALLE AUGUSTA, URB SAN GERARDO 00926 #042-01-1999 L2003 **OBG** *020

NAZARIO, Armando Luis. 400 CALLE ROOSEVELT, URB LA CUMBRE 00926 #042-01-1980 L1985 **ORS** *020 †40

NAZARIO, Glorimar. 1395 CALLE SAN RAFAEL 00909 #042-02-1997 L2000 **IM** *020

NAZARIO, Lelis Laura. 65 AVE LAS BRISAS 00926 #042-03-1993 L1995 **CHP P** *030 †75

NAZARIO, Sylvette. 10 CALLE CASIA 00921 #042-01-1987 L1996 **IM AI** *020 †20,03

NEGRON, Aurea Teresa. 525 AVE FD ROOSEVELT STE 7 00918 #042-03-1996 L2001 **AN** *020

NEGRON, Diana. PO BOX 41045 00940 #042-01-2001 L2003 **PTH** *100 †50

NEGRON, Emma Aurora. ■ 00918 #042-03-1989 L1994 **P** *020

NEGRON, Luis A. 37 AVE PONCE DE LEON 00901 #042-03-1985 L1988 **IM** *020

NEGRON, Luis Humberto. ■ 00918 #308-03-1981 L1986 **GP** *020

NEGRON APONTE, Henry. ■ 00908 #649-01-1958 L1962 **ON OS** *071

NEGRON-MONSERRATE, Mayra. SJ43 CALLE 5TH, URB ENCANTADA 00926 #042-04-1985 L1988 **GPM FM** *020

NEGRON OLMO, Carlos Raul. ■ 00926 #308-07-1982 L2002 **GP** *020

NEVARES, Roberto Luis. 29 CALLE WASHINGTON # 203, ROBERTO L NEVARES 00907 #042-01-1978 L1983 **PS HS** *020

NEVAREZ, Juan Antonio. 1699 CALLE PARANA, URB RIO PIEDRAS HTS 00926 #042-01-1980 L1984 **OPH** *020 †35

NICOLAU, Yania. ■ 00926 #042-03-2008 *012

NIETO-FILIBERTY, Jose R. PMC EL SENORIAL STE 421 00926 #308-04-1983 L1988 **PD** *020

NIEVES, Dalila. ■ 00921 #042-01-2007 **TY** *012

NIEVES, Luis F. 310 CALLE LOS ROBLES, URB LAS CUMBRES 00926 #042-03-1989 L1992 **PUD** *020

NIEVES, Wilfredo Antonio. ■ 00926 #042-02-1986 L1988 **EM** *020 †16

NIEVES COLON, Juan. ■ 00918 #051-04-1927 L1927 **A** *071

NIEVES-GARNICA, Pedro L. 1000 AVE MUNOZ RIVERA, STE 204 00927 #649-14-1983 L1986 **IM** *020

NIEVES LOPEZ, Pedro Luis. ■ 00926 #649-01-1956 L1958 **P** *072

NIEVES VAZQUEZ, Hector D. 252 CALLE SAN JORGE, STE 408 00912 #308-03-1984 L1986 **PD** *020

NIGAGLIONI, Adan. DOMENECH AVE 00918 #042-01-1954 L1957 **GE IM** *072 †20

NIGGEMANN-ZAYAS, Enrique. 1395 CALLE SAN RAFAEL 00909 #275-01-1957 L1972 **PD** *020

NINE-CURT, Jose. ■ 00922 #016-43-1947 L1954 **P** *020

NOVOA, Luis Rafael. 100 GRAND PASEO BLVD, STE 112-178 00926 #042-02-1991 L1996 **AN** *020

NOYA, Diana. 2162 PARK BLVD 00913 #649-14-2003 L2004 *100

NOYA, Jorge Arturo. 29 CALLE WASHINGTON, STE 404 00907 #042-01-1974 L1980 **GS** *020 †85

NUNEZ, Viola Teresa. 400 AVE DOMENECH, STE 511-BRA 00918 #042-03-1990 L1994 **P** *020

NUNEZ-DIAZ, Raul A. 268 CALLE CLEMSON, URB UNIVERSITY GDNS 00927 #847-04-1958 L1961 **P OS** *020

NUNEZ-SANTANA, Graciela I. ■ 00927 #042-01-1954 L1956 **P** *071

OBEN, Karen E. ■ 00926 #042-01-1994 **IM** *100

OCASIO, Kermell Antonio. 508 ASHFORD MEDICAL CTR 00907 #042-01-1981 L1986 **OPH** *020

OCASIO, Maria Elena. 10 CALLE CASIA, SAN JUAN VA MED CTR 00921 #042-03-1999 L2003 **PCC** *100 †20

OCASIO, Rafael A. ■ 00913 #042-01-1988 L1992 **OPH** *020 †35

OCASIO-CABANAS, Kermell A. 508 ASHFORD MEDICAL CTR 00907 #028-34-1949 L1951 **OPH** *020 †35

OCASIO-TASCON, Julio Ange. 1357 AVE ASHFORD, STE 2 00907 #042-03-1993 L1997 **AN** *020 †05

OJEDA, Hector Ivan. ■ 00927 #042-01-2008 *012

OJEDA DE IGLESIAS, A M. MUNICIPAL HOSP, DEPT RADIOL 00935 #042-01-1971 L1975 **R IM** *020 †80

OJEDA FOURNIER, Ernesto R. ■ 00901 #649-14-1996 L1997 *020

OJEDA-RODRIGUEZ, Aileen G. 100 GRAND BLVD, SUITE 112 MSC-440 00926 #042-03-1997 L1999 **PM** *020 †60

OLAZABAL, Francisco. 735 AVE PONCE DE LEON, TORRE DE AUXILIO MUTUO 403 00917 #023-07-1959 L1963 **CD IM** *071 †20

OLIVELLA, Jorge J. PO BOX 360712, 464 CARBONELL ST 00936 #042-01-1967 L1969 **GP DIA** *020

OLIVER, Luis A. 1804 CALLE JAJOME, URB CROWN HLS 00926 #042-01-1968 L1971 **PD** *020

OLIVERAS, Gilberto. ESCUELA DE MEDICINE, DEPTO ANESTESIA UNIV DE PR 00936 #042-01-1985 L1988 **AN** *020

OLIVERAS, Roberto Enrique. 400 AVE FD ROOSEVELT, STE 304 00918 #023-01-1992 L1996 **OBG** *020 †30

OLIVERO, Elvin. ■ 00926 #308-03-1996 L2002 *100

OLIVER PADILLA, German. 1663 AVE AMERICO MIRANDA, URB LAS AMERICAS 00921 #847-09-1957 L1960 **PD OS** *071

OLIVIERI, Vilma Nytza. ■ 00920 #042-01-1986 L1991 **DR** *020 †80

OLIVO, Nestor. 1251 AVE AMERICO MIRANDA, REPTO METROPOLITANO 00921 #042-03-1993 L1996 **IN** *020

OLMEDO, Luis Narciso. ■ 00926 #042-02-1993 L1996 **PM** *020

OLMO-TERRON, Neftali. 30 CALLE WASHINGTON, STE 2 00907 #847-05-1965 L1967 **P PYA** *020

O'NEILL, Carmen Ana. 37 AVE PONCE DE LEON 00901 #847-10-1963 L1967 **PD** *020

O'NEILL, Edward. 281 CALLE TNTE CESAR GNZLZ 00918 #010-01-1947 L1948 **GYN END** *040 †30

O'NEILL, Jose Guillermo. ■ 00920 #042-01-1981 L1986 **TS** *020 †85,90

OQUENDO, Waleska. ■ 00918 #649-18-1984 L1990 **GP** *020

OQUENDO ROSARIO, Francisco. ■ 00926 #042-04-2001 L2005 *100

ORDONEZ, Rosaura J. 300 AVE JESUS T PINERO, URB EL VEDADO 00918 #847-04-1961 L1966 **GP** *071

ORENGO, Ariel Del C. 150 AVE CARLOS CHARDON, STE 232 00918 #308-03-1987 L1994 **IM** *020

ORIA, Guillermo. 4B COND HATO REY PLZ 00918 #042-04-1987 L1989 **GP** *020

ORIA BORROTO, Gonzalo A. ■ 00918 #275-01-1948 L1972 **GP** *020

ORSINI, Rosa. ■ 00926 #042-02-1984 L1987 **NM IM** *020 †28

ORTEGA, Meileen Rubie. ■ 00918 #042-03-1999 L2002 **ON** *100

ORTEGA-GIL, Jorge. 1674 CALLE VERBENA, URB SAN FRANCISCO 00927 #737-06-1965 L1973 **IM CD** *020 †20

ORTEGA-RODRIGUEZ, Jose V. COLINAS VERDES 00936 #847-04-1974 L1976 *020

ORTEGA VIDAURRE, Vilma. 735 AVE PONCE DE LEON, TORRE MEDICA AUXILIO MUTUO 00917 #042-03-1992 L1996 **OBG** *020 †30

ORTIZ, Alfonso A. ■ 00926 #042-03-1983 L1986 **END IM** *020

ORTIZ, Alicia M. ■ 00926 #042-01-1987 L1991 **P** *020

ORTIZ, Enrique Octavio. ■ 00927 #042-01-2005 **IM** *012

ORTIZ, Gerardo L. ■ 00926 #042-02-2000 L2003 **PM** *020

ORTIZ, Hector M. ■ 00936 #042-01-1980 L1985 **U ON** *020 †95

ORTIZ, Idith Rita. 36 RIO PIEDRAS VLY, UNIVERSITY PEDIATRIC HOSPI 00926 #042-01-1979 L1982 **PD** *020 †50

ORTIZ, Jose Antonio. ■ 00918 #042-01-2000 L2004 **P** *020

ORTIZ, Jose David. ■ 00924 #042-03-2008 *012

ORTIZ, Martin. 562 CALLE JUAN J JIMENEZ, HATO REY 00918 #042-01-1977 L1979 **GE IM** *020 †20

ORTIZ, Melany Marie. PO BOX 361085 00936 #649-14-2003 L2005 *100

ORTIZ, Miguel A. 1452 AVE ASHFORD, STE 4 00907 #042-01-1971 L1973 **PUD IM** *040

ORTIZ, Myra Nydia. ■ 00920 #308-03-1985 L1991 **GP** *020

ORTIZ, Nanette Amanda. ■ 00926 #649-14-2002 L2004 *100

ORTIZ, Rafael. 200 AVE WINSTON CHURCHILL, STE 202 00926 #308-03-1985 L1990 **IM** *020 ‡

ORTIZ, Victor N. 89 AVE DE DIEGO STE 105, PMB646 00927 #042-01-1968 L1976 **PDS GS** *020 †85

ORTIZ, Zhamarie. ■ 00927 #042-01-2002 L2005 **GE** *012 †20

ORTIZ-BRACERO, Irma. ■ 00920 #308-02-1979 L1982 *020

ORTIZ-ESPADA, Carlos A. 37 AVE PONCE DE LEON 00901 #847-09-1957 L1960 **PD** *020

ORTIZ-FIGUEROA, Marilyn. 369 AVE DE DIEGO, OFICINA 207 00923 #042-03-1992 L1996 **OBG** *020

ORTIZ-GOMEZ, Cristina. 5 CALLE SAN SEBASTIAN 00901 #042-01-2001 L2004 **FM** *020 †18

ORTIZ-MARTINEZ, Edris J. 594 CALLE YUNQUE, URB SUMMIT HLS 00920 #847-03-1976 L1981 **GP** *020

ORTIZ-ORTIZ, Luis G. ■ 00921 #042-01-1961 L1974 **D OS** *020 †15

ORTIZ PEREZ, Hector E. 1008 CALLE 42 SE, REPTO LANDRAU 00921 #042-01-1972 L1974 **OBG OS** *020

ORTIZ ROLON, Abraham E. 605 EDIF MERCANTIL PLZ 00918 #042-04-1985 L1986 **GP** *050

ORTIZ-ROQUE, Carmen M. 405 CALLE SAN FRANCISC #2B 00901 #042-01-1986 L1993 **OBG** *020 †30

ORTIZ-SIERRA, Hernando G. PR CANCER CENTER, DEPT RAD BOX 5067 00936 #264-03-1965 L1982 **RO** *050 †80

ORTIZ-SUAREZ, Humberto J. ■ 00907 #042-01-1965 L1974 **NS** *071 †25

ORTIZ VIDAL, Rafael. PO BOX 11981 00922 #308-01-1969 L1976 *020

ORTIZ-VILLALOBOS, Moises. ■ 00919 #042-01-1989 L1992 **NEP** *020 †20

OSORIO, Juan Diego. ■ 00936 #649-05-1977 **FM** *020

OSSA DIAZ, Karen I. PO BOX 16726 00908 #649-14-2003 L2005 *100

OSTOLAZA, Ivette. ■ 00918 #649-14-1991 L1994 **FM** *020

OSTOLAZA, Jorge A. 735 AVE PONCE DE LEON, STE 601 00917 #042-01-1985 L1988 **OBG** *020 †30

OSUSA, Virginia. ■ 00908 #042-02-2007 **TY** *012

OTANO, Manuel Etienne. 539A CALLE S CUEVAS BSTMNT, PARQ CENTRAL 00918 #041-13-1961 L1963 **CD IM** *020 †20

OTERO, Jose E. 29 CALLE WASHINGTON, STE 105 00907 #042-01-1994 L1996 **OTO** *100 †45

OTERO GONZALEZ, Carmen D. 00909 #308-01-1988 L1994 *020

OTERO GONZALEZ, Myrta I. 692 CALLE 44, URB FAIRVIEW 00926 #649-14-2000 L2002 **PD** *020

OTERO HERNANDEZ, Rafael. 369 DE DIEGO AVE, STE 202 00909 #308-01-1972 L1975 **ORS** *020

OTERO VIERA, Jose Angel. E31 CALLE 14, QTAS DE CUPEY 00926 #042-01-1972 L1974 **IM** *020

OVALLES, Jose R. 500 AVE MUNOZ RIVERA, PMB 46 00918 #308-01-1975 L1984 **CD IM** *050

OZUAL, Andres. 2004 AVE BORINQUEN 00915 #308-01-1983 L2006 **GP** *020

PACHECO, Eileen Ivonne. 359 AVE DE DIEGO STE 301 00909 #042-01-1977 L1982 **HO IM** *040

PACHECO, Jose Antonio, Jr. PO BOX 365067, OF MED 00936 #042-01-2003 **DR** *012

PACHECO, Monica Marie. ■ 00926 #042-01-2002 L2004 **GS** *100

PACHECO, Paulette Celeste. ■ 00921 #042-01-2007 **GS** *012

PADILLA, Auralyd. ■ 00926 #042-03-2008 *012

PADILLA, Jose Arnaldo. PO BOX 10666 00922 #308-04-1985 L1986 **CD** *020

PADILLA, Maria Eugenia. D19 CALLE 3, HILLSIDE 00926 #042-01-2003 **PD** *100 †55

PADILLA, Miriam. ■ 00918 #042-01-1973 L1973 **PM** *075

PADILLA, Vanessa Lee. ■ 00927 #042-01-2008 *012

PAGAN, Hector D. 100 GRAND BOULEVARD PASEOS, SUITE 112-198 00926 #042-01-1987 L1992 **ORS** *020 †40

PAGAN, Jose Luis. ■ 00926 #042-01-1985 L1990 **GS** *020

PAGAN, Walter. ■ 00926 #042-03-1987 L1992 **P** *020

PAGAN BEAUCHAMP, Desiree. 29 CALLE WASHINGTON # 703, ASHFORD MED CTR 00907 #042-01-1979 L1982 **PD** *020 †55

PAGAN-DURAN, Carmen Y. 166 CALLE ALELI, URB SAN FRANCISCO 00927 #042-03-1993 L1997 **RHU** *020

PAGAN-FERRER, Juan Ramon. 10 CALLE CASIA 00921 #042-01-2007 **IM** *012

PAGAN-GONZALEZ, Benjamin. 138 AVE WINSTON CHURCHILL, URB CROWN HLS 00926 #847-06-1977 L1980 **EM FM** *020

PAGAN ORTIZ, Myrna M. ■ 00926 #042-01-1970 L1972 **GP** *020

PAGAN RIVERA, Yolanda. ■ 00926 #308-06-1986 L1991 *100

PAISAN GALBAN, Ada Georgi. PO BOX 362352 00936 #308-04-2000 L2002 *020

PALACIOS, Miguel A. MEDICINA AVANZ OFICINA 104, HOSPITAL INTERAMERICNAO DE 00922 #042-03-1980 L1983 **IM** *020

PALAU, Miladys Miriam. ■ 00921 #042-01-2007 **PD** *012

PALERM-RINCON, Gabriel. ■ 00907 #847-05-1965 L1969 **GP EM** *020

PALMER, Victor S. 1306 AVE FERNANDEZ JUNCOS, SAN JUAN AIDS PROGRAM 00909 #649-27-1987 L1991 **GP** *020

PALMER-LOPEZ, Arnaldo. ■ 00914 #041-09-1941 L1941 **GS** *071

PALOU, Jose Miguel. ■ 00927 #042-01-1990 L1994 **P** *020

PALOU PUJOLS, Miguel E. FF17 CALLE MAGNOLIA, URB BORINQUEN GDNS 00926 #847-01-1970 L1972 **OBG** *020

PARES, Maria A. ■ 00926 #023-01-1943 L1944 **OBG** *071

PARKER, Richard Lee, Jr. ROOSEVELT RD 00902 #028-34-1985 L1988 **FM** *020 †18

PASARELL, Enrique Antonio. 271 AVE JESUS T PINERO 00927 #042-01-1974 L1976 **PS GS** *020 †65

PASCUAL, Eduardo A. 218 CALLE RUBICON, URB RIO PIEDRAS HTS 00926 #042-01-1992 L1995 **NM IM** *020 †28

PASSALACQUA, Jose R. ■ 00907 #024-15-1932 L1944 **CD IM** *071

PASTOR, Amado Cesar. ■ 00927 #308-01-1942 L1958 **OBG** *020

PAUL, Fritz. RR 7, VILLAS DE CARRAIZO 00926 #440-01-1978 L2005 **PYG** *100

PAULINO, Magda R. ■ 00917 #308-04-1994 L1996 **PD** *020

PAVIA, Antonio M. 431 AVE PONCE DE LEON, NATIONAL PLAZA STE 328 00917 #042-01-1980 L1986 **GS VS** *020 †85

PAVIA, Orestes Antonio. 715 AVE PONCE DE LEON # PA 00917 #042-01-1998 L1999 **ON** *020 †20

PAVIA-VILLAMIL, Antonio. PO BOX 11137 00910 #016-43-1954 L1959 **IM CD** *071

PAYNE, Charles Albert. ■ 00927 #010-02-1957 L1962 **N** *071 †75

PAYNE, Sylvia N. ■ 00927 #010-02-1957 L1962 **PM OS** *071

PEDRAZA, Lourdes Raquel. 252 CALLE SAN JORGE, SAN JORGE MEDICAL BUILDING 00912 #042-03-1982 L1986 **PDP** *020 †55

PEDROGO, Yasmin. 782 CALLE LINCE, URB DOS PINOS 00923 #042-01-2001 L2004 **PD** *100 †55

PEGUERO, Larissa Amelia. ■ 00920 #042-01-2007 *012

PEGUERO VEGA, Jose M. 625 CALLE AUSTRAL, URB ALTAMIRA 00920 #847-02-1972 L1981 **IM** *020

PENA-DE LA VEGA, Lourdes. ■ 00926 #042-01-1997 L1999 **NEP** *020 †20

PENA-GARCIA, Magali. 654 AVE MUNOZ RIVERA, IBM BUILDING STE 1010 00918 #042-01-1969 L1972 **D** *020 †15

PERALTA, Francisco R. PO BOX 21107 00928 #308-01-1954 L1970 **OTO** *020

PERAZZA, Elizabeth. 10 CALLE CASIA, SAN JUAN VETERANS ADMIN 00921 #042-01-1993 L1999 **U** *100 †95

PERDOMO, Jorge W. 735 AVE PONCE DE LEON #701, COND TORRE AUXICIO MUTUO 00917 #308-01-1972 L1981 **ON HEM** *020 †20

PEREDO WENDE, Ruben A. ■ 00902 #176-01-1993 L2004 **RHU** *100 †20

PEREIRA, Miguel A. 1393 AVE SAN IGNACIO, ALTAMESA 00921 #042-04-1996 L1997 **PD** *020

PERELES, Yasmin. 105 AVE DOMENECH STE 207, URB BALDRICH 00918 #308-01-1985 L1989 **GP** *020

PEREZ, Aivlys. 315 AVE DOMENECH 00918 #042-01-1999 L2000 **DMP** *020 †15

PEREZ, Alejandro. 576 CALLE CESAR GONZALZ #5 00918 #042-02-1994 L1998 **PM** *020 †60

PEREZ, Angel Luis. GPO 4867 MED 00936 #042-01-1989 L1992 **PUD** *020

PEREZ, Carmen R. 1221 CALLE NICOLAS AGUAYO, URB EL COMANDANTE 00924 #042-01-1993 L1996 **PD** *020 †55

PEREZ, Charmaine Marie. ■ 00926 #042-03-2000 L2002 **IM** *020 †20

PEREZ, Doris R. CAL 13 SE 1038 REP METRO 00921 #042-01-1988 L1995 **PM** *020

PEREZ, Eladio. 1449 CALLE AMERICO SALAS, SUITE 103 PAVIA II 00909 #042-01-1984 L1987 **GE IM** *020 †20

PEREZ, Elba Antoinette. PO BOX 193868 00919 #308-04-1987 L1999 *020

PEREZ, Elizabeth. 1323 AVE SAN ALFONSO, URB ALTAMESA 00921 #308-02-2004 L2006 *100

PEREZ, Grisselle. 101 CALLE PITIRRE, URB MONTEHIEDRA 00926 #042-01-1994 L1998 **PM** *020

PEREZ, Ivan Ramon. PO BOX 4001 00936 #308-01-1955 L1961 **N CHN** *020

PEREZ, Javier Orlando. ■ 00926 #042-03-2004 L2007 **OBG** *012

PEREZ, Jorge Jose. 390 AVE DOMENECH 00918 #042-01-1980 L1984 **DR** *020 †80

PEREZ, Jose Antonio. 400 AVE DOMENECH, STE 513 00918 #649-14-1995 L1996 **IM** *020

PEREZ, Jose Manuel. ■ 00927 #042-03-2003 L2005 **CD** *012 †20

PEREZ, Juan Ovidio. 37 AVE PONCE DE LEON 00901 #042-01-1978 L1982 **PN** *040 †55

PEREZ, Lines M. 1355 AVE SAN ALFONSO, URB ALTAMESA 00921 #042-01-1995 L1999 **P** *020

PEREZ, Luis E. PDA 19 SANTURCE PR/MED DIR 00908 #308-01-1960 L1977 *020

PEREZ, Marco Antonio. 576 CALLE CESAR GONZALEZ, STE 404 00918 #308-01-1981 L1986 **PD** *020

PEREZ, Maria Isabel. ■ 00915 #042-01-2000 L2003 **PD** *100 †55 ‡

PEREZ, Mario E. ■ 00920 #275-01-1960 L1977 **AN** *020

PEREZ, Mary Rose. ■ 00936 #308-04-1990 L1996 **P** *020

PEREZ, Miriam Teresa. ■ 00936 #308-04-1985 L1992 **GP** *020

PEREZ, Nilda. ■ 00926 #042-01-1999 L2003 **EM** *020 †35

PEREZ, Rafael Andre. 120 AVE LA SIERRA, BOX 147 00926 #042-03-2001 L2003 **GE** *100

PEREZ, Ramon Amaury. ■ 00926 #308-01-1981 L2001 **IM** *020

PEREZ, Raul. 450 AVE PONCE DE LEON #6 00901 #042-01-1973 L1975 **OPH OBG** *020 †35

PEREZ, Rene Eugenio. 203 CALLE SANTA ROSA, URB RIVIERA SENORIAL 00926 #042-01-1981 L1984 **NM** *020

PEREZ, Roberto. 369 DE DIEGO AVE, STE 408 TORRE SAN FRANCISC 00909 #042-01-1983 L1986 **CD IM** *020 †20

PEREZ, Vilma Esther. ■ 00907 #042-01-1991 L1996 **OPH** *020 †35

PEREZ, Yanesa M. 200 AVE WINSTON CHURCHILL, STE 201 00926 #042-01-1990 L1994 **OPH** *020 †35

PEREZ ARROYO, Gregorio. ■ 00929 #649-31-1976 L1981 *020

PEREZ-ARROYO, Hector M. 29 CALLE WASHINGTON, STE 202 00907 #042-01-1991 L1997 **GE** *020 †20

PEREZ-BERENGUER, Juan L. 1760 CALLE LOIZA STE 203, UNIVERSITY PATHOLOGISTS 00911 #275-01-1977 L2004 **NP** *100 †50

PEREZ-BRAYFIELD, Marcos R. ■ 00926 #042-01-1996 L1997 **U** *020 †95

PEREZ-COMAS, Adolfo. 1452 AVE ASHFORD STE 310 00907 #847-01-1967 L1970 **END MG** *020

PEREZ DE LEON, Isabel. ■ 00920 #847-10-1963 L1967 **PD** *071

PEREZ FERNANDEZ, Carlos. PO BOX 10067 00922 #308-01-1983 L1996 **GP** *020

PEREZ FERNANDEZ, Cenia S. 1133 CALLE 9, VILLA NEVAREZ 00927 #308-03-1978 L1988 **GP** *020

PEREZ-GRAU, Maria E. 1427 AVE FERNANDEZ JUNCOS, STE 101 00909 #042-02-1997 L2000 **HEM** *020

PEREZ HERNANDEZ, C. 1306 AVE PONCE DE LEON, RICO/P.O.BOX 70184 00907 #847-02-1964 L1968 **IM R** *020

PEREZ-HERRERO, Hortensia. ■ 00926 #935-07-1984 L1995 *020

PEREZ-LOPEZ, Mildred G. ■ 00926 #308-02-1991 **END** *100 †20

PEREZ-MACHADO, Cesar. ■ 00936 #308-06-1986 L1988 **PD** *020

PEREZMALDONADO, Jose L. ■ 00926 #042-03-2003 **ORS** *012

PEREZ MIRANDA, Rafael. BOX 11656 STA FERNANDZ JUN 00910 #847-04-1977 L1987 **GP** *020

PEREZ-MOLINA, Fabio N. ■ 00921 #308-03-1978 L1980 **OS GP** *020

PEREZ-PABON, Manuel. PO BOX 11850 PMB 277 00922 #042-01-1980 L1983 **IM** *020 †20

PEREZ-RIOS, Deolina. 1233 AVE PINERO, CAPA RRA TER 00920 #847-04-1978 L1980 **GP** *020

PEREZ RODRIGUEZ, Felipe. 150 AVE CARLOS CHARDON, STE 232 00918 #649-01-1961 L1965 **IM** *020

PEREZ-ROMAN, Gerardo E. 576 CALLE CESAR GONZALEZ, DORAL BANK CENTER SUITE 402 00918 #042-01-1993 L1996 **OSM** *020 †40

PEREZ-TORRES, Doel. 200 AVE WINSTON CHURCHILL, STE 406 00926 #042-03-1980 L1984 **GYN** *020 †30

PEREZ VARGAS, Jackeline E. PO BOX 190988 00919 #308-04-1985 L1996 *020

PEREZ-VELEZ, Jorge Anibal. 251 CALLE REINA MORA, URB MONTEHIEDRA 00926 #308-03-1982 L1985 **AN** *020

PERNAS, Martin. ■ 00926 #308-12-1987 L2004 *100

PEROCIER-AGUIRRE, Camille. ■ 00918 #847-09-1964 L1967 **P** *071

PESQUERA, Jose R. 1801 AVE PONCE DE LEN #309, SANTHROC MED MALL 00909 #308-03-1980 L1984 **HEM ON** *020

PETERSEN, Lenka. ■ 00927 #042-03-2008 *012

PETERSON-TAPIA, Yvonne. 1537 CALLE CAVALIERI, URB ANTONSANTI 00927 #847-06-1977 L1980 **P** *020

PEZZOTTI ALVAREZ, Sandra. 1035 AVE ASHFORD, MIRADOR DEL CONDADO 00907 #308-04-1982 L1987 **GP** *020

PICO, Guillermo, Jr. 1473 CALLE WILSON, THE LITTLE TOWER STE 101 00907 #042-01-1970 L1976 **OPH** *071 †35

PICO-SANTIAGO, Guillermo. 1473 AVE WILSON, STE 101 00907 #023-01-1940 L1941 **OPH** *071 †35

PIETRI-RAMIREZ, Annette E. ■ 00924 #042-02-2008 *012

PIJEM-GARCIA, Jesus E. 539A CALLE S CUEVAS BSTMNT, PARQ CENTRAL 00918 #847-10-1966 L1970 **CD IM** *020

PINERO, Luis Roberto. 1789 CALLE CLAVEL, MANS DE RIO PIEDRAS 00926 #649-14-1995 L1997 **PD** *020

PINERO PEREIRA, Alfredo. ■ 00931 #042-01-1983 L1989 **ORS** *020

PINEYRO CRUZ, Juan Ramon. 435 AVE PONCE DE LEON 00917 #308-01-1945 L1958 **GS GP** *020

PIOVANETTI, Ian Kevin. PO BOX 10431 00922 #042-03-1994 L1998 **OPH** *020 †35

PIOVANETTI, Yvette Louise. 400 AVE DOMENECH STE 413 00918 #008-01-1978 L1982 **PD** *020 †55

PIOVANETTI-PEREZ, Jose E. ■ 00926 #042-03-1995 L1997 **OS** *020

PIOVANETTI PIETRI, E. 1250 AVE JESUS T PINERO, CENTRO OFTALMOLOGICO METRO 00921 #042-01-1963 L1967 **OPH** *020 †35

PISKORSKI, Darlene Elaine. 100 AVE LA SIERRA, COND LA SIERRA DEL SOL 00926 #308-03-1984 L1991 **PD** *020

PITTERSON, Felix O. ■ 00936 #847-10-1967 L1977 **P** *020 †75

PIZARRO, Ana Rosa. ■ 00902 #042-03-2007 **TY** *012

PLA, Francisco Jose. ■ 00913 #649-14-1996 L1997 *020

PLANELL, Carlos R. 315 AVE DOMENECH 00918 #847-06-1975 L1983 **PS GS** *020

PLANELL, Israel E. 308 AVE DOMENECH 00918 #042-01-1961 L1964 **D** *071

PLAZA, Jose Luis. 10 CALLE CASIA, VA MEDICAL CENTER 00921 #042-01-1998 L1999 *020

POLANCO, Mirlia L. 660 AVE PONCE DE LEON 00918 #042-01-1984 L1988 **END IM** *020

POLO, Luis Rafael. 29 CALLE WASHINGTON, STE 609 00907 #012-05-1991 L2002 **CHP** *020 †75

POLO-MARTINEZ, Luis M. ■ 00917 #042-01-1959 L1967 **P** *020

POMALES, Sari Y. ■ 00926 #042-01-1991 L1995 **RHU** *020 †20

PORRATA, Jannette. 565 CALLE CABO H ALVERIO, EXT ROOSEVELT 00918 #308-03-1985 L1989 *020

PORRO, Raul Alberto. 1462 CALLE ASIA, FDZ. JUNCOS STATION 00909 #042-01-1981 L1984 **AN PME** *020 †05

PORRO ZAYAS, Raul A. ■ 00920 #275-01-1953 L1968 **AN PUD** *020

PORTELA, Eugenio Antonio. 23 CALLE SAN EDMUNDO, VILLAS DE SAN IGNACIO 00927 #042-01-1974 L1976 **OTO FPS** *020 ‡

PORTELA, Roberto Carlos. ■ 00921 #042-01-2002 L2004 **EM** *100 †16

PORTOCARRERO, Carlos M. 1400 AVE MAGDALENA 00907 #042-01-1980 L1985 **PS GS** *020

POU, Carlos Roberto. 252 CALLE SAN JORGE, SAN JORGE MED BLDG OFC 206 00912 #042-01-1991 L1996 **OPH PO** *020 †35

POUERIE BAEZ, Juan Maria. 890 AVE ASHFORD STE 3 00907 #308-01-1958 L1978 **GP** *020

POVENTUD, Tomas Ulises. 368 AVE DE DIEGO, COND CRYSTAL HOUSE 00923 #042-01-1978 L1982 **PM** *020

PRATTS PONCE DE LEON, I S. 1373 CALLE OLGA ESPERANZA, URB SAN MARTIN 00924 #042-01-1970 L1973 **PM** *020 †60

PRIETO, Carmen. ■ 00926 #042-03-1985 L1988 **NPM PD** *020

PRIETO-RODRIGUEZ, Jorge B. 130 AVE WINSTON CHURCHILL, URB CONTEMPORANEO 00926 #308-03-1976 L1978 **GP** *020

PRIETO ROIG, Ricardo J. ■ 00926 #042-03-2007 **IM** *012

PROSPERO, Carmen Altiery. 10 CALLE CASIA, VETERAN ADMINSTRATION HOSP 00921 #847-06-1965 L1975 **P CHP** *071

PUIG, Gilberto. 252 CALLE SAN JORGE 00912 #042-01-1987 L1991 **CCP** *020 †55

PURCELL-JORDAN, Rene A. 44 CALLE SAUCO, LAREDAS DE SAN JUAN 00926 #042-01-1995 L1999 EM *020

QUEIPO, Rafael. 380 CALLE ANTOLIN NIN, URB ROOSEVELT 00918 #042-03-1993 L1998 FM *020

QUESADA-SUAREZ, Luis. 611 CALLE PAVIA STE 214, PAVIA MEDICAL PLAZA 00909 #308-03-1981 L1981 NEP IM *020

QUIJANO-AYALA, Isabel M. ■ 00920 #649-14-1977 L1979 FM *020

QUILES, Laura Margarita. 521 CALLE BARRANQUITAS, REPTO AMERICA 00923 #649-14-2000 L2004 *100

QUILES RODRIGUEZ, D. ■ 00923 #042-01-2003 L2004 P *100

QUILICHINI, Jose Luis. ■ 00927 #042-02-1985 L1987 GS TS *020

QUINONES, Belkis. GPO BOX 5067 00936 #275-01-1991 PD *012

QUINONES, Eric Adrian. 513 AVE HOSTOS, STE 3 00918 #649-14-1989 L1992 IM *020

QUINONES, Rebecca Bodega. ■ 00918 #042-02-1989 L1993 PM *020 †60

QUINONES, Walter Ivan. FAIR VIEW, 1916 47TH ST 00926 #042-01-1999 L2005 PM *100

QUINONES, William. PO BOX 365067, OF MED 00936 #308-13-2004 L2006 PTH *012

QUINONES CARO, Alfredo. 614 CALLE AUSTRAL, URB ALTAMIRA 00920 #847-10-1965 L1973 *020

QUINONES-DIAZ, Cesar A. 400 AVE DOMENECH STE 605 00918 #042-01-1960 L1963 D DMP *020 †15

QUINONES-RAMIREZ, Xavier. 400 AVE DOMENECH, STE 605 00918 #042-03-1998 L2000 FM *020

QUINONES ROMERO, Edda I. 10 CALLE CASIA, VA MED CTR VA CARBN HLTH 00921 #042-03-1996 L1999 IM *062

QUINONEZ-AYALA, Lester. 900 CALLE CERRA, CALLE JAZMIN, # 8166 00907 #649-14-2001 L2002 *020

QUINQUILLA, Rafael Luis. 117 CALLE PADRE LAS CASAS, URB BALDRICH 00918 #649-01-1951 L1953 OBG *072

QUINTANA, Cid S. 230 CALLE HIMALAYA, URB MONTEREY 00926 #042-01-1985 L1991 TS CD *020 †85,90

QUINTERO, Ana I. 252 CALLE SAN JORGE 00912 #042-04-1989 L1992 PPR EP *050

QUINTERO, Elisa Mercedes. ■ 00927 #042-01-2004 AN *012

QUINTERO, Jose Luis. ■ 00927 #042-01-1977 L1980 PD *020

QUINTERO, Mario E. 00917 #042-01-1998 L2003 PTH *020 †50

QUINTERO-ALFARO, Jose E. 00923 #042-01-1957 L1961 P *020

QUIROZ NARANJO, Victor H. ■ 00931 #308-01-1981 L1993 GP *020

RABINES BURGA, Marco Anto. 10 CALLE CASIA # 116A, BEHAVIORAL HEALTHCARE 00921 #649-14-1997 P *012

RABRI, Graciela Maria. ■ 00926 #042-01-2008 *012

RAFFUCCI-MORALES, F. ■ 00907 #042-03-1982 L1987 GS *020 †85

RAMIREZ, Alcides. ■ 00929 #308-03-1989 L1997 *020

RAMIREZ, Efren E. ■ 00911 #042-01-1954 L1960 P OS *020

RAMIREZ, Eileen. 365 COND DE DIEGO, TORRE SAN FRANCISCO OF 407 00923 #042-03-1988 L1991 IM *020

RAMIREZ, German Guillermo. 263 CALLE FORTALEZA, STE 2A 00901 #042-04-1981 L1989 OS *020

RAMIREZ, Ivelisse. ■ 00936 #042-01-1982 L1985 GE IM *020 †20

RAMIREZ, Juan Jose. ■ 00918 #649-35-1993 L2004 *100

RAMIREZ, Maria Delpilar. 605 COND GOLDEN VIEW PLZ, C- MODESTA 00924 #042-03-1997 L2000 *020

RAMIREZ, Rafael Amilcar. 275 CALLE PADRE COLON, BO CAPETILLO 00923 #308-01-1985 L2002 IM *020 †20

RAMIREZ, Rafael E. 10 CALLE CASIA 00921 #042-01-1964 L1967 NEP IM *030

RAMIREZ, Rene. 369 CALLE DE DIEGO, URB 00923 #042-01-1991 L1995 MG PUD *020 †20

RAMIREZ-BAERGA, Galileo. ■ 00926 #847-04-1959 L1962 R *020

RAMIREZ-CARMOEGA, Mario R. 735 AVE PONCE DE LEON, TORRE AUXILIO MUTUO SUITE 00917 #847-06-1976 L1979 PD *020

RAMIREZ-LUGO, Octavio A. 923 CALLE CARMEN HERNANDEZ, URB EL COMANDANTE 00924 #308-03-1979 L1985 GP *020

RAMIREZ-RIVERA, Jose. 1657 CALLE ADAMS, URB SUMMIT HLS 00920 #008-01-1953 L1957 PUD IM *040 †20

RAMIREZ-RODRIGUEZ, Eli A. 150 AVE CARLOS CHARDON, STE 232 00918 #056-06-1942 L1949 CD IM *072 †20

RAMIREZ-RONDA, Carlos H. PO BOX 363971, 81 CALLE 3 PASEO ALTO 00936 #016-06-1967 L1969 ID IM *020 †20 ‡

RAMIREZ-TORRES, Efrain. WASHINGTON 30 STE#4 00907 #847-05-1973 L1975 OBG *020 †30

RAMIREZ-VAZQUEZ, Jose R. 369 CALLE DE DIEGO, STE 306 00923 #042-01-1980 L1983 GP *020 †20

RAMIREZ VELEZ, Sigrid A. ■ 00926 #649-14-2001 L2003 *100

RAMIREZ VICK, Margarita I. 1838 CALLE BEGONIA, URB SANTA MARIA 00927 #042-01-1989 L1993 END IM *040 †20

RAMIREZ-WEISER, Rafael R. ■ 00936 #041-13-1949 L1952 PTH PCP *020 †50

RAMIREZ ZAPATA, Evelyn. 340 CALLE FOULTON, JARD METROPOLITANO 00927 #308-02-1990 L1992 PUD *020

RAMOS, Alberto Rafael. PO BOX 70344 PMB 355, MUNOZ RIVERA 210 FAJARDO P 00936 #042-03-2003 L2006 N *100

RAMOS, Carmen Teresa. ■ 00907 #042-01-1989 L1996 GS PDS *020 †85

RAMOS, Cristina Juliana. ■ 00923 #042-01-2004 AN *100 †20

RAMOS, Diomedes. ■ 00936 #308-01-1981 L1990 GP *020

RAMOS, Fernando. 400 AVE FD ROOSEVELT, STE 206 00918 #042-01-1990 L1992 GE *020 †20

RAMOS, Irma E. MM1 CALLE ROSE, ALTS DE BORINQUEN GDNS 00926 #042-01-1991 L1994 PD *020 †55

RAMOS, Maria Elvira. 735 AVE PONCE DE LEON, STE 619 00917 #042-03-1995 L1998 CD IM *020 †20

RAMOS, Mario Antonio. 369 CALLE DE DIEGO STE 307, TORRE HOSPITAL SAN FRANCIS 00923 #042-03-1991 L1994 PUD IM *020 †20

RAMOS, Miguel Angel. 00928 #847-04-1963 L1968 ON HEM *020

RAMOS, Nestor Waldo. 311 AVE DOMENECH, URB JB HUYKE 00918 #176-01-1965 L1976 ORS *040

RAMOS, Pedro D. ■ 00936 #847-06-1978 L1981 *020

RAMOS, Rodney. 105 AVE ARTERIAL HOSTOS, BOX 75 00918 #649-14-2003 GP *020

RAMOS, Walter F. ■ 00926 #042-04-1985 L1988 GP *020

RAMOS, Yadira. ■ 00931 #042-03-2005 EM *012

RAMOS-BARROSO, Antonio. 37 AVE PONCE DE LEON 00901 #041-01-1956 L1959 OBG *020 †30

RAMOS DE VELASCO, Julio A. CALLE 10 M-2, URB EL MIRADOR 00926 #649-14-1998 L2001 *100

RAMOS LEON, Lizzette. PO BOX 16117 00908 #308-03-1984 L2004 *100

RAMOS LOZADA, Wilfredo J. ■ 00912 #308-03-1980 L1986 FM *020

RAMOS-PEREIRA, Raul L. 1717 AVE PONCE DE LEN #220 00909 #042-01-1980 L1985 GS *020

RAMOS SOSA, Johanna. ■ 00912 #308-13-2005 *100

RAMOS-UMPIERRE, Enrique. WILSON 1304 75 EL VIGIA 00927 #847-05-1974 L1977 OBG *020

RECIO, Fernando Oscar. 400 AVE DOMENECH, STE 603 00918 #042-01-1959 L1961 U *020

RECURT, Maria Luisa. 29 CALLE WASHINGTON, ASHFORD MEDICAL CTR SRE#41 00907 #042-01-1979 L1982 RHU IM *020

REDONDO, Haydee. ■ 00926 #308-03-1984 L2004 *100

REDONDO, Pedro Rafael. 37 AVE PONCE DE LEON 00901 #042-01-1993 L1998 CD *020 †20

REINA-SANABRIA, Ricardo J. 100 GRAND BLVD, SUITE 112 MSC 313 00926 #042-03-1996 L2001 OAR *020 †40

RENOVALES, Roberto. CALLE 7 S O, CAPARRA TERRACE 00921 #847-02-1963 L1966 GP *071

RESTITUYO-ROSARIO, Angela. 369 CALLE DE DIEGO, TORRE SAN FRANCISCO, SUITE 00923 #042-03-1997 L2000 IM *020

REVERON, Ivan Javier. 100 GRAND PASEO BLVD, STE 112-219 00926 #308-03-1984 L1986 FM *020

REYES, Aitza. 371 AVE DE DIEGO 00923 #649-14-1998 L1999 PD *020

REYES, Angel Luis. ■ 00917 #042-03-2005 EM *012

REYES, Joaquin. 385 AVE DOMENECH, HATO REY, 00918 #308-01-1988 L2003 *020

REYES, Jose Ismael. 220 AVE DOMENECH PMB 176, HATO REY PUERTO RICO 00918 #847-06-1969 L1984 P GP *020

REYES, Jose Samuel. ■ 00926 #042-01-2004 GS *012

REYES, Reinaldo Juan. 100 COND LA SIR DL SL #207 00926 #042-01-1993 L1998 GS *020 †85

REYES, Zayhara. 29 CALLE AZUCENA, URB. RIO PIEDRAS VALLEY 00926 #042-03-2002 L2005 PD *100 †55

REYES MENDEZ, Milciades. ■ 00921 #308-01-1966 L1973 OM GP *020

REYEZ ALICEA, Angel M. 150 AVE CARLOS CHARDON, STE 232 00918 #847-04-1978 L1982 CD IM *050 †20

RIBOUL, Tamara Michelle. ■ 00926 #042-01-2003 PD *020 †55

RICARDO, Ariamsi Armando. ■ 00926 #042-01-2007 IM *012

RICARDO-PENA, Alberto E. 37 AVE PONCE DE LEON 00901 #275-01-1960 L1975 IM *020

RICCI, Fabio. ■ 00926 #042-01-2007 IM *012

RICHIEZ, Kermit J. ■ 00910 #042-01-1988 L1991 GE *020 †20

RIERA, Jose Dimas. 204 ASHFORD MEDCL CTR #204 00907 #010-02-1962 L1966 CD IM *020

RIERA-MARCH, Antonio. PO BOX 70344 00936 #847-06-1975 L1988 OTO GS *020 †45

RIERA MATIENZO, Lorenzo. PO BOX 16557 00908 #275-01-1969 L2000 *100

RIGAU-PEREZ, Jose G. 1324 CALLE CANADA, URB PUERTO NUEVO 00920 #024-01-1975 L1978 PHP PD *020 †55,70

RIOS, Barklay. UNIV DIST HOSP, DEPT PATH 00935 #715-01-1970 PTH *020

RIOS, Grissel. 37 AVE PONCE DE LEON 00901 #042-01-1996 L1999 RHU IM *020 †20

RIOS, Jessica. PO BOX 15, C/O BALCONES DE SANTA MARI 00919 #042-01-2000 L2002 *020 †55

RIOS, Julieva. 48 CALLE CAPRI, PASEO LAS BRISAS 00926 #042-01-1986 L1988 EM *020 †16

RIOS, Sinia Leyinska. ■ 00926 #042-01-1986 L1988 RHU *020

RIOS, Waldemar Charles. 400 AVE DOMENECH, STE 607 00918 #308-13-2000 L2003 IM *020

RIOS-ALONSO, Maria Luisa. 1501 AVE ASHFORD, PARK TERRACE 7A 00911 #847-05-1974 L1980 IM CD *020

RIOS COLLAZO, Juan Jose. 1017 CALLE GEN DEL VALLE 00924 #847-05-1964 L1966 PD *020

RIOS-DONES, Otto. 1576 CALLE CAVALIERI, URB ANTONSANTI 00927 #308-03-1981 L1987 PD *020

RIOS GONZALES, Felix F. UNIV PUERTO RICO SCH MED 00901 #042-01-1991 L1997 CD IM *020 †20

RIOS MOTTA, Miriam E. 458 CALLE PARAGUAY, URB EL PRADO 00917 #042-01-1990 L1996 N CN *020 †75

RIVAS, Carlos M. PO BOX 70344, PMB 155 00936 #042-01-1968 L1970 AN *071

RIVAS, Jose Angel Zayas. 1207 CALLE LUCHETTI, CONDADO 00907 #308-07-1982 L2001 *020

RIVAS, Ricardo Jonathan. ■ 00926 #042-03-2008 *012

RIVE, Ernesto. 422 CALLE SAN LEANDRO, URB SAGRADO CORAZON 00926 #042-01-1965 L1970 GS *020 †85 ‡

RIVERA, Aileen. 400 BO TORTUGO, C/O CONDOMINIO CORDOBA PAR 00926 #042-01-1999 L2002 PD *020

RIVERA, Ana I. ■ 00926 #042-01-1993 L1998 IM *020

RIVERA, Angel L. 1751 CALLE ALCALA, URB COLLEGE PARK 00921 #042-01-1966 L1968 PUD IM *020

RIVERA, Angel Luis. 1785 CARR 21 STE 205, URB LAS LOMAS 00921 #042-01-1965 L1969 NEP IM *020

RIVERA, Aurea Annette. 503 SAN JUAN HLTH CTR #503 00907 #042-03-1998 L2001 IM *020 †20

RIVERA, Bonifacio. 1769 AVE JESUS T PINERO, SUMMIT HILLS 00920 #748-08-1967 L1976 FM *071

RIVERA, Carlos Gilberto. 105 AVE DE DIEGO, URB SAN FRANCISCO 00927 #042-01-1973 L1975 IM *020

RIVERA, Cedric Y. PO BOX 16124, ASHFORD MEDICAL CENTER 00908 #042-03-1982 L1987 OBG GS *020

RIVERA, Denise C. 252 CALLE SAN JORGE 00912 #042-01-1989 L1992 PD PDP *020 †55

RIVERA, Doris. ■ 00918 #042-02-1993 L1996 PD *020 †55

RIVERA, Elvin G. STE A-201, ASHFORD PRESBYTERIAN HOSP 00907 #042-01-1989 L1995 CD *020 †20

RIVERA, Eugenio. ■ 00910 #042-01-1988 L1993 AN *020

RIVERA, Ezequiel. 37 AVE PONCE DE LEON 00901 #042-01-1964 L1967 ON IM *030 †20

RIVERA, Ferdinand. ■ 00918 #649-14-1998 L1999 NEP *100

RIVERA, Gilberto. 735 AVE PONCE DE LEON, TORRE AUXILIO MUTUO SUITE 00917 #042-01-1997 L1999 CD *020 †20

RIVERA, Homero Fernando. ■ 00940 #042-01-1975 L1975 IM *020

RIVERA, Ivan Antonio. ■ 00921 #847-23-1980 L2003 FM *100

RIVERA, John Everett. 175 AVE HOSTOS, COND EL MONTE NORTH A-614 00918 #847-04-1976 L1980 GP *020

RIVERA, Jose Alberto. ■ 00921 #042-01-1973 L1976 IM *020

RIVERA, Jose Andres. 12 AVE LAS MANSIONES, MANS DE SAN MARTIN 00924 #042-03-1998 L2000 IM *020

RIVERA, Jose Francisco. 252 CALLE SAN JORGE 00912 #042-01-1973 L1975 PD PN *020 †55

RIVERA, Jose Rafael. DIAMANTE 29 GOLDEN GATE #649-01-1956 L1959 AN *071

RIVERA, Josue Gerardo. ■ 00921 #042-01-2001 L2006 PM *100 †60

RIVERA, Keila Liz. ■ 00926 #042-02-2006 PTH *012

RIVERA, Maralexis. 73 CALLE COBANA # E-13, LAREDAS DE SAN JUAN 00926 #042-03-1997 L2001 CHP *020

■ = Address Information Privacy Protected

RIVERA, Mariela. ■ 00926 #042-01-2003 **GS** *012

RIVERA, Mariluz. ■ 00926 #042-01-1998 L2000 **CCS** *100 †85

RIVERA, Michelle. GPO BOX 5067, UNIV PR SCH OF MED 00936 #042-01-2001 L2004 **GE** *012 †20

RIVERA, Petion Enrique. 431 AVE PONCE DE LEON, STE 326 00917 #847-06-1984 L1988 **PD** *020

RIVERA, Rafael A. 29 CALLE WASHINGTON # 809, ASHFORD MED CTR 00907 #042-01-1966 L1970 **IM GE** *030

RIVERA, Ruth Malave. PO BOX 9066630 00906 #847-09-1982 L1986 **P OS** *020

RIVERA, Sonia M. 1418 CALLE AMERICO SALAS 00909 #042-01-1966 L1968 **OPH** *020 †35

RIVERA, Victor Jose. 1004 COND PICO CTR # 1004 00907 #042-01-2001 L2004 **EM** *100

RIVERA, Zoraida. PO BOX 29568 00929 #308-03-1981 L1990 **GP OS** *020

RIVERA-BADILLO, Manuel. ONE VETERANS PLAZA 00927 #847-05-1965 L1967 **GP EM** *071

RIVERA CASTRO, Angel. ■ 00913 #042-01-1989 L1995 **OPH** *020 †35

RIVERA-CUBANO, Luis. 30 CALLE WASHINGTON, STE 4 00907 #042-01-1976 L1981 **CHN** *020 †30

RIVERA DE LA VEGA, Raul F. RR 2 BOX 1282 00926 #649-14-1990 L1995 **IM** *020

RIVERA DIAZ, Jorge. 1395 CALLE SAN RAFAEL 00909 #847-04-1955 L1957 **ORS** *020

RIVERA-GARCIA, Rafael L. 1451 AVE ASHFORD 00907 #847-02-1960 L1965 **OTO** *020

RIVERA GOMEZ, Angel A. 554 CALLE ESTOCOLMO, URB CAPARRA HTS 00920 #847-05-1978 L1980 **PHP GP** *030

RIVERA-GONZAGUE, Milagros. PO BOX 21405, DEPT PED 00928 #649-14-1988 L1990 **PD** *020

RIVERA-GONZALEZ, Hector O. 1874 CALLE SAN ALVARO, URB SAN JUAN GDNS 00926 #847-02-1976 L1981 **P OS** *020

RIVERA-HERNANDEZ, Edgardo. 735 AVE PONCE DE LEON, COND. TORRE AUXILIO MUTUO 00917 #042-01-1992 L1996 **APM AN** *020 †05

RIVERA-HERRERA, Jorge L. 252 CALLE SAN JORGE # 203, SAN JORGE MED OFFICE BLDG 00912 #042-01-1988 L1993 **U** *020 †95

RIVERA-MAC MURRAY, S. 1431 AVE PONCE DE LEON, STE 402 00907 #008-01-1985 L1991 **GE IM** *020 †20

RIVERA MARRERO, Amarilis. PO BOX 365067, SCI CA 00936 #649-14-2001 L2002 **NPM** *012 †55

RIVERA-MASS, Arlene M. 344 CALLE HECTOR SALAMAN, EXT ROOSEVELT 00918 #042-03-1991 L1996 **P** *020 †75

RIVERA-MASS, Enrique. 420 AVE PONCE DE LEON, MIDTOWN CONDOMINUM STE 508 00918 #042-03-1980 L1981 **CHP P** *020

RIVERA-MELENDEZ, Jose J. ■ 00936 #042-01-2008 *012

RIVERA-MENDEZ, Raul. 329 CALLE COLUMBIA, URB UNIVERSITY GDNS 00927 #847-06-1978 L1982 **P** *020

RIVERA-MONTALVO, Evelyn. 563 CALLE ARRIGOITIA, EXT ROOSEVELT 00918 #649-33-1985 L1988 **PD PEM** *020

RIVERA MORALES, Iksen. 500 AVE MUNOZ RIVERA, COND. EL CENTRO II, SUITE 00918 #042-03-1987 L1993 **P** *020

RIVERA-MULLER, Adive. 555 CALLE LAVIANA, URB MATIENZO CINTRON 00923 #847-05-1983 L1992 **IM** *020

RIVERA PALACIOS, Francisco. ■ 00926 #649-30-2005 **PD** *012

RIVERA-PAOLI, Marilyn. 8 URB PARQUE DE BUCARE 00926 #042-01-1987 L1989 **IM** *020 †20

RIVERA-PEREZ, Jhomarie. 10 CALLE CASIA # 116A, BEHAVIROAL HEALTHCARE 00921 #042-02-2002 L2006 **P** *100

RIVERA-QUINONES, Hilda E. 29 CALLE WASHINGTON # 605, ASHFORD MEDICAL CENTER 00907 #042-03-1995 L1998 **HEM** *020

RIVERA-REYES, Luis R. ■ 00936 #023-01-1968 L1974 **N PD** *020

RIVERA-RIVERA, Julio V. 150 AVE CARLOS CHARDON, STE 232 00918 #024-05-1943 L1946 **NM IM** *071 †20,28

RIVERA RIVERA, Yolian. N29 CALLE CIRCEO, URB PARK GDNS 00926 #649-30-2000 L2003 **FM** *020

RIVERA RODRIGUEZ, Jose J. 735 AVE PONCE DE LEON # B, TORRE AYZUKUINYTYI STE 511 00917 #042-01-1986 L1988 **CD** *020 †20

RIVERA-ROSA, Edgardo J. 30 CALLE WASHINGTON, STE 4 00907 #042-02-1992 L1996 **OBG** *020 †30

RIVERA TORO, David. PO BOX 194438 00919 #042-01-1989 L1997 **FM** *020 †18

RIVERA-TORRES, Noel Dario. ■ 00927 #308-03-1977 L1979 **EM FM** *071

RIVERA VARGAS, Jorge D. 3T CARR 21 # 4, URB COOP V BORINQUEN 00921 #308-03-1984 L1986 **IM** *020

RIVERA VELAZQUEZ, Gabriel. ■ 00936 #042-01-2007 **IM** *012

RIZEK, Rafael Antonio. C/O PO BOX 363733, HOSPITAL DEL MAESTRO 00936 #308-01-1951 L1958 **IM HEM** *020 †20

ROBLES FONTAN, William. 398A CALLE RODRIGO DE TRIN 00918 #649-01-1955 L1959 **PUD** *020

ROBLES-RIVERA, Carlos R. 431 AVE PONCE DE LEON 00917 #042-01-1994 L1999 **CD IM** *020 †20

ROCA, Fernando Jose. ■ 00923 #042-01-2007 **IM** *012

ROCAFORT, Jose Luis. ■ 00926 #649-30-2004 L2005 *100

ROCAFORT GONZALEZ, R. 650 CALLE LLOVERAS, STE 203 00909 #847-10-1970 L1972 **OBG** *020

ROCA-FRANCESCHI, Diego J. ■ 00907 #021-01-1953 L1955 **IM** *020

RODRIGUEZ, Ada. ■ 00936 #042-01-1987 L1991 **PM** *020

RODRIGUEZ, Adolfo R. C M M S #171 APT 70344 00936 #042-01-1986 L1991 **RHU IM** *020 †20

RODRIGUEZ, Aixa Enid. 1395 CALLE SAN RAFAEL 00909 #649-14-1990 L1992 **HEM** *020

RODRIGUEZ, Arelis. ■ 00926 #649-14-2002 L2006 *100

RODRIGUEZ, Arnaldo Ivan. 365 CALLE BOLIVAR 00912 #042-01-2005 **ORS** *012

RODRIGUEZ, Aymar Mizei. ■ 00919 #042-02-1994 L1998 **IM** *020 †20

RODRIGUEZ, Belinda. ■ 00926 #042-01-1998 L2000 **FM** *020 †18

RODRIGUEZ, Carlos. 160 AVE WINSTON CHURCHILL, # 1104 00926 #042-01-1985 L1987 **U GS** *020

RODRIGUEZ, Carlos Seda. ■ 00926 #042-04-1987 L1989 *020

RODRIGUEZ, David. ■ 00925 #042-01-2007 **TY** *012

RODRIGUEZ, Enrique Juan. 708 COND PARQ DE LAS FUNTS 00918 #847-10-1987 L1992 **N** *020

RODRIGUEZ, Etta Rosa. ■ 00907 #649-01-1957 L1973 **P** *071

RODRIGUEZ, Fernando. ■ 00927 #847-05-1985 L1996 **CCP** *100 †55

RODRIGUEZ, Francisco A. 1230 CALLE 10 SE, URB CAPARRA TER 00921 #308-01-1986 L1992 **IM** *020

RODRIGUEZ, Gilbert. 372 AVE DOMENECH 00918 #308-01-1983 L1987 **IM** *020

RODRIGUEZ, Gloria Maria. GPO 4867 DEPT MED 00927 #042-03-1995 L1998 **CCM** *020 †20

RODRIGUEZ, Hector Luis. 29 CALLE WASHINGTON, ASHFORED MED CTR #603 00907 #023-01-1963 L1969 **PDC** *020 †55

RODRIGUEZ, Heidy Marie. ■ 00926 #042-01-1999 L2005 **DR** *100

RODRIGUEZ, Javier Jesus. 400 CALLE KALAF, PMB 59 00918 #042-01-1997 L2000 **PTH** *020 †50

RODRIGUEZ, Jesus R. 1786 CALLE SAN ALEJANDRO, URB SAN IGNACIO 00927 #042-01-1984 L1986 **AN** *020

RODRIGUEZ, Joaquin. ■ 00927 #275-01-1981 L2004 **IM** *100 †20

RODRIGUEZ, Johnny A. 151 CALLE CESAR GONZALEZ, APT0 4-5503 00918 #308-01-1985 L1995 *020

RODRIGUEZ, Jose Angel. 10 CALLE CASIA, SAN JUAN VA MED CTR 00921 #042-03-2004 L2005 **PM** *012

RODRIGUEZ, Jose Antonio. ■ 00927 #042-01-1985 L1999 **AN** *020

RODRIGUEZ, Jose Rafael. 37 AVE PONCE DE LEON 00901 #308-02-1981 L1985 **PDP CCP** *020 †55

RODRIGUEZ, Jose Victor. 207 AVE DOMENECH STE 103 00918 #042-04-1990 L1991 **FM** *020

RODRIGUEZ, Juan A. PO BOX 364446 00936 #042-01-1964 L1967 **U** *020 ‡

RODRIGUEZ, Luis F. 703 AVE FERNANDEZ JUNCOS 00907 #005-11-1992 L1997 **PS** *020 †65 ‡

RODRIGUEZ, Luis Fernando. 10 CALLE CASIA, HOSPITAL DE VETERANOS 00921 #042-01-1991 L1995 **CD** *020 †20

RODRIGUEZ, Luis Ignacio. PO BOX 5067 00936 #275-04-1984 **PTH** *100

RODRIGUEZ, Luis Manuel. 59 CALLE BETANCES, URB FLORAL PARK 00917 #035-09-1977 L1982 **OBG** *020

RODRIGUEZ, Maria De Los A. 371 AVE DE DIEGO 00923 #042-02-1990 L1993 **FM** *030 †18

RODRIGUEZ, Maribel. PO BOX 366210 00936 #042-01-1989 L1999 **EM** *020 †16

RODRIGUEZ, Mary Ann. 1588 AVE J T PINERO, CAPARRA TERR 00921 #042-01-1973 L1975 **CD IM** *020

RODRIGUEZ, Miguel A. 20 CALLE SANTA ROSA, URB ROMANY GDNS 00926 #042-04-1982 L1986 **GP** *020

RODRIGUEZ, Neftali. 381 AVE FELISA RINCON GATR, PASEOMONTE 1608. 00926 #042-03-1995 L1999 **CD** *020 †20

RODRIGUEZ, Oreli. 271 CALLE JILGUERO, URB MONTEHIEDRA 00926 #042-01-1993 L1998 **IM** *020 †20

RODRIGUEZ, Ovidio. 831 CALLE MARTI, CONDOMINIO MONTECIELO 3-B 00907 #042-01-1959 L1961 **END DIA** *071

RODRIGUEZ, Pablo. PO BOX 70344, PMB 113 00936 #042-01-1983 L1988 **TRS CCS** *030 †85

RODRIGUEZ, Pelayo. 1883 GLASGOW COLLEGE PK 00921 #042-03-1988 **AN** *100

RODRIGUEZ, Porfirio. ■ 00910 #042-01-1988 L1992 **N** *020 †75

RODRIGUEZ, Rafael. ■ 00936 #042-01-1988 L1991 **NS NRN** *040 †25

RODRIGUEZ, Rafael. 501 CALLE GUAYANILLA # 64, COND. PARQUE SAN AGUSTIN 00923 #042-01-1998 L2000 **CHP** *020

RODRIGUEZ, Ramon Luis. 1327 CALLE 23, URB MONTE CARLO 00924 #847-04-1982 L1986 **GS** *020

RODRIGUEZ, Rebecca. ■ 00907 #042-01-1999 L2002 **FM** *020 †18

RODRIGUEZ, Reinaldo J. CALLE LOTUS, BORINQUEN GARDENS 00926 #308-03-1992 L1994 **P** *020

RODRIGUEZ, Ricardo J. ■ 00923 #042-01-1990 L1992 **D** *020 †15

RODRIGUEZ, Roberto. 377 AVE DOMENECH, URB ROOSEVELT 00918 #042-01-1963 L1967 **IM CD** *020

RODRIGUEZ, Rodolfo. 956 AVE A MIRANDA, DPT METRO 00921 #042-01-1969 L1969 **GE IM** *020

RODRIGUEZ, Sandra S. 37 AVE PONCE DE LEON 00901 #042-01-1986 L1989 **PD** *020 †55

RODRIGUEZ, Syliva E. EL MORRO N 15 PARK GARDENS 00926 #042-01-1989 L1992 **FM** *020 †18

RODRIGUEZ, Vanessa Esther. 139 CALLE MIMOSA, URB SANTA MARIA 00927 #042-01-1992 L1995 **RHU IM** *020 †20

RODRIGUEZ, Veronica. 433 CALLE PADRE BERRIOS, URB FLORAL PARK 00917 #042-01-1978 L1981 **PM** *020 †60

RODRIGUEZ-ASTACIO, Jose A. PO BOX 13365 00908 #847-10-1961 L1968 **GP OM** *020

RODRIGUEZ-BOU, Roberto P. ■ 00919 #042-01-2004 **FM** *100

RODRIGUEZ COLLAZO, Victor. ■ 00926 #308-03-1978 L1980 **EM** *020

RODRIGUEZ-COTTO, Benjamin. PO BOX 70344, # 62 00936 #308-03-1973 L1979 **EM GP** *030

RODRIGUEZ CRUZ, Edwin. 252 CALLE SAN JORGE, SAN JORGE MED BLDG STE 408 00912 #042-04-1992 L1996 **PDC MPD** *020

RODRIGUEZ DE LA OBRA, F J. 435 AVE PONCE DE LEON 00917 #847-04-1962 L1965 **IM** *020

RODRIGUEZ DE LEON, Juan R. UNIV DIST HSP, DEPT UROL 00935 #042-01-1970 L1974 **U ORS** *020

RODRIGUEZ-DIAZ, Rafael. 377 CALLE EMORY, REPTO UNIVERSITARIO 00926 #847-06-1971 L1974 **OBG** *020 †30

RODRIGUEZ DIAZ, Sonia G. 112 CALLE ARZUAGA, STE 906 00925 #847-04-1960 L1963 **OBG** *020 †30

RODRIGUEZ-ELIAS, Rosa A. GEORGETTI #66 RIO PIEDRAS 00925 #042-01-1975 L1979 **PD** *020

RODRIGUEZ-EMA, Joaquin F. 601 COND SAN LUIS APT 601 00901 #847-01-1968 L1971 **AN OS** *020

RODRIGUEZ FERER, Jan R. VET ADMIN MED CTR, DEPT MED 00927 #649-14-1997 L1998 **IM** *020

RODRIGUEZ GARCIA, Roberto. 368 AVE DE DIEGO APT 517, COND CRYSTAL HOUSE 00923 #308-01-1988 L2004 *100

RODRIGUEZ GONZALEZ, Edgar. 576 CALLE CESAR GONZALEZ, STE 201 00918 #042-01-1987 L1990 **PUD IM** *020

RODRIGUEZ GUERRERO, Isabel. ■ 00920 #308-03-2000 L2006 *100

RODRIGUEZ GUEVARA, Sila I. 151J COND L SR DL SL #151J 00926 #042-04-1999 L2001 **FM** *020

RODRIGUEZ-HERNANDEZ, Juan. ■ 00936 #308-03-1980 L1981 **N** *020

RODRIGUEZ HERNANDEZ, O. 730 CALLE JULIO ANDINO, VILLA PRADES 00924 #275-01-1964 L1975 *020

RODRIGUEZ-LEON, Ivette. PO BOX 21405, DEPT PED 00928 #308-01-1985 L1991 **PD** *020

RODRIGUEZ LEON, Sebastian. 7 CALLE NEVAREZ # 1102, VILLA LOS OLMOS 00927 #308-01-1981 L1992 **PD** *020

RODRIGUEZ-LOPEZ, Luis A. 299 AVE PINERO, URB HYDE PARK 00927 #042-02-1982 L1986 **DR** *020

RODRIGUEZ-MALDONADO, R. 100 CARMEN HILLS DR, BEVERLY HILLS COURT BOX 10 00926 #042-01-1958 L1964 **OS OBG** *020 †30

RODRIGUEZ MALPICA, Bernie. 138 AVE WINSTON CHURCHILL, URB CROWN HLS 00926 #649-35-2001 L2005 **GP** *020

RODRIGUEZ-MELANI, Jorge. 811 PASEO MONTE 00926 #649-14-1983 L1985 **PD** *020

RODRIGUEZ MERCED, Rafael. 1451 AVE ASHFORD 00907 #847-04-1955 L1958 **OBG** *020

RODRIGUEZ-MILLAN, Pablo. PO BOX 11934 00922 #042-01-1963 L1967 **PDS GS** *071
RODRIGUEZ-MONGE, Edgardo. ■ 00926 #042-04-1991 L1997 **ON IM** *020
RODRIGUEZ-MONTES, Jose R. 728 AVE PONCE DE LEON 00918 #649-01-1960 L1963 **PD OS** *020
RODRIGUEZ-MORALES, Edda L. ■ 00921 #042-04-1989 L1991 **PTH** *020
RODRIGUEZ-ORTIZ, Lydia. 505 AVE DE HOSTOS, URB. BALDRICH, 00918 #308-01-1978 L1983 **END IM** *020
RODRIGUEZ PABON, Nydia. 10 CALLE CASIA, ONES VETERANS PLAZA 00921 #042-01-1990 L1994 **HEM IM** *020 †20
RODRIGUEZ-PACHECO, Edith. ■ 00913 #056-06-1942 L1943 **OBG OS** *072
RODRIGUEZ PENA, Glisette. APT A9, COND LA SIERRA DEL SOL 00926 #042-03-1986 L1988 **PD** *020 †55
RODRIGUEZ-PEREZ, David. ONE VETERANS PLAZA 00927 #407-10-1940 L1942 **TS GS** *071
RODRIGUEZ PEREZ, Hector. 420 AVE PONCE DE LEON, STE 603 00918 #847-01-1971 L1974 **P** *020
RODRIGUEZ-QUINONES, Angel. 33 CALLE MAYAGUEZ, URB PEREZ MORRIS 00917 #847-08-1979 L1983 **IM** *020
RODRIGUEZ-QUINONES, G. 33 CALLE MAYAGUEZ, URB PEREZ MORRIS 00917 #847-08-1974 L1982 **END IM** *020
RODRIGUEZ-QUINONES, I. 1683 CALLE PORTUGUES # 1, URB RIO PIEDRAS HTS 00926 #649-14-1989 L1990 **PD** *020
RODRIGUEZ RAMON, Andres. ■ 00936 #847-04-1956 L1958 **PM LM** *071
RODRIGUEZ RIVERA, Christia. RR 7 BOX 7156, 4.7 CARRETERA 844 00926 #649-14-2003 **IM** *020
RODRIGUEZ-RIVERA, Ingrid. PO BOX 5746 00901 #042-01-1998 L2006 *100
RODRIGUEZ-ROBLES, Jose A. 1395 CALLE SAN RAFAEL 00909 #042-02-1992 L1996 **NM N** *020
RODRIGUEZ RODRIGUEZ, Leona. 210 CALLE HIJA DEL CARIBE, URB LOS MAESTROS 00918 #275-01-1995 L2003 *020
RODRIGUEZ-ROSADO, Samuel. ■ 00926 #020-02-1945 L1946 **U** *020 †95
RODRIGUEZ-RUIZ, Jose A. 435 AVE PONCE DE LEON 00917 #847-01-1963 L1966 **IM RHU** *020
RODRIGUEZ-SANTIAGO, Ana M. PO BOX 21405, DEPT PED 00928 #649-14-1988 L1991 **PD** *020
RODRIGUEZ-SANTIAGO, Jose. ■ 00926 #308-02-1977 L1982 **RHU IM** *020
RODRIGUEZ SERRANO, Hector. MEDICAL SCIENCE CAMPUS, A-802 MAIN BLDG 00936 #042-04-1990 L1992 **FM** *020 †18
RODRIGUEZ-SURO, Agustin. 1056 AVE MUNOZ RIVERA, FIRST FED BLDG SUITE 610 00927 #042-02-1982 L1984 **IM** *020 †20
RODRIGUEZ-TAVERAS, Marino. PUERTO RICO MED CTR 00936 #308-01-1958 L1989 **ORS** *071
RODRIGUEZ-VALLECILLO, E. 29 CALLE WASHINGTON, STE 507 00907 #042-01-1979 L1983 **D** *020 †15
RODRIGUEZ VEGA, Jose R. PRIMER PISO STE 3, CENTRO CARDIOVASCULAR PR 00936 #042-01-1987 L1992 **TS** *020 †85,90
RODRIGUEZ-VELEZ, Jose A. P O BOX 3600-358 00936 #649-01-1979 L1982 **EM** *020
RODRIGUEZ-VELEZ, Roberto. ■ 00926 #042-01-1987 L1991 **DR** *020
RODRIGUEZ-VIGIL, Efrain. 1451 AVE ASHFORD 00907 #847-10-1972 L1974 **IM END** *020 †20
RODRIGUEZ VILLANUEVA, Noel. ■ 00918 #042-04-2002 L2003 *020
RODRIGUEZ WILSON, Jorge E. 1797 CALLE CAMELIA, PMB 91 00927 #042-01-1985 L1989 **ORS** *020 †40
ROGER VELEZ, Alfredo. 164 CALLE WESER, RIO PIEDRAS HGHTS 00926 #308-13-2001 L2005 **GP** *020
ROJAS, Boris. 1451 AVE ASHFORD 00907 #042-01-1971 L1974 **N** *020
ROJAS, Eli Saml. ■ 00918 #010-01-1931 L1931 **D** *071
ROJAS, Fernando. 37 AVE PONCE DE LEON 00901 #042-01-1978 L1983 **ORS** *020 †40
ROJAS-DIAZ, Eli Saml. 420 AVE PONCE DE LEON, STE 801 00918 #847-01-1964 L1966 **OPH** *020
ROJAS-FRANCO, Luis U. 375 AVE DOMENECH 00918 #308-01-1966 L1973 **IM** *020
ROJO, Julio R. PO BOX 9022007 00902 #042-03-1981 L1986 **DR** *062
ROLDAN, Neyla. 153 AVE DE DIEGO STE 201, URB SAN FRANCISCO 00927 #042-04-1987 L1989 **GP** *020 †18
ROLDOS RIVADENEIRA, Fernan. PO BOX 5067 00936 #319-04-1992 **IM** *100
ROMAGUERA, Josefina E. PO BOX 365067, DEPT OBGYN 00936 #042-01-1980 L1983 **OBG** *040 †30
ROMAN, Ana Judith. 1056 AVE MUNOZ RIVERA, S-1003 00927 #396-04-1955 L1960 **N IM** *040
ROMAN, Angel A. PO BOX 365067 00936 #042-01-1967 L1972 **CLP ATP** *030
ROMAN, Juan Carlos. ■ 00926 #649-14-2001 L2002 **IM** *020
ROMAN, Luis A. 574 CALLE CABO H ALVERIO, EXT ROOSEVELT 00918 #042-04-1996 L1997 **IM** *020
ROMAN, Maria Luisa. 420 AVE PONCE DE LEON, STE 701 00918 #308-02-1987 L1992 **P** *020
ROMAN, Maria M. 239 AVE ARTERIAL HOSTOS, STE 205 00918 #042-01-1977 L1982 **OBG** *020
ROMAN-DIAZ, Angel Manuel. H21 CALLE LA PRINCESA, PASEO SAN JUAN 00926 #308-03-1983 L1986 **IM** *020
ROMAN-IRIZARRY, Luis A. 20 CALLE SANTA ANASTACIA 00926 #042-01-1959 L1961 **IM CD** *020 †20
ROMAN MORALES, Reinaldo L. 1173 CALLE MAXIMO ALOMAR, URB SAN AGUSTIN 00923 #042-01-1972 L1974 **OPH** *020
ROMANO AGRAMONTE, Jose O. 1697 CALLE CHIHUAHUA, URB VENUS GDNS NORTE 00926 #308-02-1991 L1994 **EM GP** *020
ROMAN RUIZ, Mygda. ■ 00909 #847-06-1976 *100
ROMANY, Jose L. 59 AVE CONDADO, CONDO ELBAL TOWER APT 7-B 00907 #308-03-1983 L1993 **FM** *020
ROMERO, Douglas J. 131 AVE WINSTON CHURCHILL, STE B 00926 #042-01-1997 L2001 **P** *020 †75
ROMERO, Marialba. ■ 00926 #042-01-2007 **P** *012
ROMERO-BASSO, Juan L. 239 AVE ARTERIAL HOSTOS, STE 806 00918 #020-02-1983 L1988 **ORS** *020 †40
ROMERO DE DIAZ, Iraida. 1021 CALLE GENERAL DEL VAL, URB GONZALEZ SEIJO 00924 #308-03-1980 L1983 **NM IM** *020 †28
ROMERO-GONZALEZ, Antonio. APTO 807, CONDO VALENCIA PLAZA 00926 #308-01-1972 L1978 **FM** *020
ROMERO RAMIREZ, Martin E.. ■ 00922 #042-04-2001 L2005 *100
ROQUES-ORTIZ, Eliseo C. 125 CALLE CARITE, URB CROWN HLS 00926 #847-01-1969 L1976 **PD** *020
ROSA, Elias Rufo. 12 EL MONTE MALL 00918 #042-01-1959 L1965 **OPH** *020 †35

ROSA-ALGARIN, Rafael A. 00925 #042-04-1997 L2001 *020
ROSADO, Amarylis. ■ 00926 #042-01-2003 L2004 **D** *020 †15
ROSADO, Ariel. 369 CALLE DE DIEGO, TORRE SAN FRANCISCO, SUITE 00923 #649-14-2000 L2001 **IM** *020
ROSADO, Carlos S. 10 CALLE CASIA 00921 #042-01-1985 L1988 **NEP IM** *020 †20
ROSADO, Julio E. 600 BLVD LOS ARBOLES # 309, ARBOLES DE MONTEHIEDRA 00926 #042-01-1989 L1996 **NS OS** *020 †25
ROSADO-MATOS, Juan A. 400 RUBLE AVE, STE 408 00918 #308-02-1979 L1983 **IMG IM** *020 †20
ROSADO OROZCO, Kathia E. ■ 00918 #042-01-1994 L2000 **PTH** *020 †50
ROSALES, Claudia P. ■ 00918 #341-01-1993 L2003 **CD** *100 †20
ROSA-PEREZ, Cesar E. PUERTO RICO MED CTR 00936 #024-01-1952 L1959 **R** *020 †80
ROSARIO, Hector M Cott. 239 AVE ARTERIAL HOSTOS, STE 205 00918 #042-01-1979 L1983 **EM FM** *020 †30
ROSARIO, Luis. 138 AVE WINSTON CHURCHILL, URB CONTEMPORANEO 00926 #042-03-1994 L1998 **OBG** *020 †30
ROSARIO, Reinaldo. 652 AVE MUNOZ RIVERA, STE 3170 00918 #042-01-1972 L1974 **D** *020 †15
ROSARIO LEBRON, Sandra E. 400 AVE FD ROOSEVELT, CLINICA LAS AMERICAS, STE 00918 #042-01-1994 L1998 **PUD** *020 †20 ‡
ROSARIO-ROBLES, Ivette. 1449 CALLE AMERICO SALAS, STE 105 00909 #308-03-1982 L1987 **IM** *020
ROSA SILVA, Heber Amaury. 269 CALLE PERU, URB HYDE PARK 00918 #042-01-1954 L1959 **PD OS** *071
ROSICH, Jose A. VET ADMIN CTR 00935 #847-10-1964 L1967 **N OS** *100
ROSSO QUEVEDO, Roberto. D19 CALLE 14, QTAS DE CUPEY 00926 #308-07-1983 L2002 **GP** *020
ROSSY, Madeline. 150 AVE CHARDON, FEDERAL BLDG RM 659 00918 #042-01-1982 L1985 **PD** *030
ROULET PEREZ, Francisco A. ■ 00921 #308-01-1953 L1970 *100
ROURA-ARIAS, Raul. 65 CALLE FALCON, URB MONTEHIEDRA 00926 #042-03-1995 L2000 **ORS** *020
ROURA-ORTIZ, Eugenio E. ■ 00920 #649-14-1979 L1981 **GP** *074
ROURA-SEPULVEDA, Raul. ■ 00926 #847-03-1960 L1963 **ORS** *100
ROURE, Carlos A. ■ 00918 #042-01-1969 L1975 **OBG** *020 †30
ROVIRA, Edwin De Jesus. 410 AVE DE DIEGO, WINDSOR TOWERS 801 00923 #649-14-1994 L1996 **P** *020
ROVIRA, Helen. ■ 00908 #042-02-2005 **EM** *012
ROVIRA, Madelyn. 65 CALLE FALCON, URB MONTEHIEDRA 00926 #042-01-1994 L1998 **PM** *020 †60
RUBIO, Jaime Eli. PASEO MAYOR LOS PASEOS, CALLE 7 F-5 00926 #308-04-1991 L2003 **FM** *020
RUCABADO, Teodosio Jose. ■ 00918 #042-01-1977 L1982 **CD IM** *020
RUIZ, Dorcas Lorraine. PO BOX 5067, UNIV OF PR SCH MED 00936 #042-01-2006 **EM** *012
RUIZ, Elsa Maria. 251 AVE WINSTON CHURCHILL, PARQUE EL SENORIAL BOX 10 00926 #042-01-1997 L2000 **PD** *020
RUIZ, Jaime Francisco. 1801 AVE PONCE DE LEON #26, STE 403 00909 #042-03-1980 L1984 **IM** *020 †20
RUIZ, Jorge Eusebio. PO BOX 194000, PMB 409 00919 #308-03-1982 L1986 **GP** *020
RUIZ, Luis. OFFICE #6, 730 PONCE DE LEON AVENUE 00919 #042-02-1983 L1983 **IM** *020
RUIZ, Rosalina Valcarcel. ■ 00926 #042-01-1990 L1994 **PD** *075
RUIZ, Wanda. ■ 00927 #042-01-1996 L2000 **AN** *020 †05
RUIZ, Yelitza. ■ 00921 #042-03-2001 L2005 **HEM** *012
RUIZ ALVAREZ, Marta O.. 540B CALLE ELMA, URB CAPARRA HTS 00920 #275-01-1980 L2002 **UP** *100
RUIZ FRANCO, Mario A. 396 CALLE SAN CLAUDIO, URB SAGRADO CORAZON 00926 #308-01-1961 L1967 **GP OS** *071
RUIZ-GANDULLA, Ilia. 1299 CARR 844, APT 505 00926 #847-04-1965 L1969 **OPH** *071
RUIZ LOPEZ, Roberto. 1394 CALLE SAN RAFAEL # 10, DOCTORS HOSPITAL MED PAVIL 00909 #042-01-1984 L1987 **IM IMG** *020
RUIZ MERCADO, Glorimar. 212 BAYSIDE CV, C/O 105 HOSTOS AVE. 00918 #042-04-2003 L2004 *100
RUIZ-ROMAN, Jorge. ■ 00907 #649-14-1990 L1992 **ID** *020
RUIZ SERRANO, Denis F. ■ 00926 #042-02-1994 L1999 **CD** *020 †20
RUIZ-TORRES, Ferdinand. ■ 00926 #042-01-1957 L1963 **HEM ON** *020
RUIZ-TORRES, Ramon Luis. 1760 CALLE ALABAMA, URB SAN GERARDO 00926 #847-05-1972 L1978 **GP** *020
RULLAN, Pedro Juan. 735 AVE PONCE DE LEON, STE 512 00917 #042-01-1981 L1987 **HNS OTO** *020 †45
RULLAN-FERRER, Jose A. 1 CALLE CERVANTES # A 00907 #010-02-1949 L1951 **CD IM** *072 †20
RUSSE SANTOS, Jose Ismael. 252 CALLE CONVENTO 00912 #042-03-1981 L1988 *020
SAAVEDRA, Jesus M. 609 CALLE ARAGON, URB PUERTO NUEVO 00920 #847-05-1978 L1982 **CHP P** *020
SAAVEDRA POZO, Fanor Manu. PO BOX 365067, DEPT OF NEUROLOGICAL SURGE 00936 #176-03-2003 **NS** *012
SABATE, Nuria A. 1452 AVE ASHFORD, STE 5 00907 #042-01-1986 L1993 **CHP** *020 †75
SABATER, Roberto Daniel. ■ 00927 #042-01-2007 **TY** *012
SAINT HILAIRE, Temmy G.. ■ 00921 #308-06-1985 L2005 *100
SAINZ DE LA PENA, Diego. 735 AVE PONCE DE LEON, STE 206 00917 #042-03-1981 L1984 **PD** *020 †55
SALAMONE, Lawrence F. 400 AVE DOMENECH STE 412 00918 #042-01-1979 L1984 **IM NEP** *040
SALAS-RUSHFORD, Jaime Ant. 559 CALLE CABO ALVERIO, EXT ROOSEVELT 00918 #042-01-2004 L2006 **IM** *012
SALGADO, Luis R. 138 AVE WINSTON CHURCHILL, URB CROWN HLS 00926 #042-01-1985 L1987 **EM** *020
SALGADO, Victor Manuel. ■ 00926 #042-01-2002 L2004 **CD** *012 †20
SAMPAYO, Hector M. BOX 1809/OLD SAN JUAN STA 00902 #041-12-1948 L1950 **P** *071
SANABRIA, Dario Enrique. PO BOX 365067, OF MED 00936 #726-01-1996 L2003 **PTH** *020 †50
SANABRIA-RIVERA, Ivelisse. CALLE 10, CAPORRA TER 00921 #042-03-1998 **FM** *100
SAN ANTONIO, Ada Marie. 19 CALLE ACUARIO STE 4, VENUS GARDENS PLZ 00926 #042-01-1996 L1999 **IM** *020 †20
SAN ANTONIO, Maria C. 19 CALLE ACUARIO STE 4, SAN ANTONIO MEDICAL VENUS 00926 #042-01-1996 L1999 **FM** *020 †18
SANCHEZ, Alexis. 2 CALLE GAVIOTA, URB LA SIERRA ALTA 00926 #042-01-1999 L2002 **GS** *100 †85

■ = Address Information Privacy Protected

SANCHEZ, Erika Marie. 46 CALLE SAN JUSTO, URB LOS ADOQUINES 00926 #042-03-1999 L2002 *100

SANCHEZ, Ginnette Sanchez. ■ 00917 #308-01-1989 L1996 **FM** *020 †18

SANCHEZ, Jorge. 516B CALLE JUAN J JIMENEZ, PARQ CENTRAL 00918 #042-01-1966 L1968 **D DMP** *020 †15

SANCHEZ, Jose Manuel. 10 CALLE CASIA, VAMC 112 UROLOGY SECTION 00921 #042-01-1980 L1985 **U** *020 †95

SANCHEZ, Juan M, Jr. 262 CALLE CONVENTO APT 1 00912 #042-01-1988 L1991 **PD** *020 †55

SANCHEZ, Julio Ernesto. ■ 00921 #042-02-2000 L2002 **DMP** *100 †15

SANCHEZ, Maria. 150 AVE DE DIEGO STE 705, EDIF SAN JUAN HEALTH CTR 00907 #042-03-1988 L1995 **P PYG** *020

SANCHEZ, Maria Rosario. ■ 00912 #042-01-1996 L1999 **PD** *020

SANCHEZ, Mary Ann. ■ 00926 #042-01-2004 **FM** *100 †18

SANCHEZ, Mirtha A. 714 CALLE DURAZNO, URB PUERTO NUEVO 00920 #308-01-1981 L1997 *020

SANCHEZ, Nilsa Raquel. 1028 AVE ROOSEVELT, URB PUERTO NUEVO 00920 #042-01-1998 L2000 **FM** *020 †18

SANCHEZ, Orlando M. 4 CALLE PARQUE FORESTAL A, POPPY ST 00925 #042-01-1989 L1993 **OBG** *020 †30

SANCHEZ, Samuel. ■ 00926 #042-01-2002 L2003 **D** *020 †15

SANCHEZ-ASTOR, Carlos R. ■ 00922 #649-01-1969 L1970 **GP OS** *020

SANCHEZ COLLAZO, Anamari. ■ 00926 #042-04-1996 L2002 **FM** *020

SANCHEZ-CRUZ, Jorge A. 517 CALLE S CUEVAS BUSTMNT, PARQ CENTRAL 00918 #042-02-1981 L1984 **P** *020

SANCHEZ FERNANDEZ, Jorge. 497 AVE EMILIANO POL, STE 303 00926 #308-02-1979 L1984 **ID IM** *020

SANCHEZ-LONGO, Isis. SAL SALVADOR 960 LAS AMER 00921 #308-04-1982 L1985 **P** *020

SANCHEZ-LONGO, Luis P. DOMENECH AVE 00918 #041-02-1951 L1953 **N** *071 †75

SANCHEZ LUGO, Fermin A. 1028 ROOSEVELT F D AVE 00920 #042-01-1972 L1974 **PDE PD** *020 †55

SANCHEZ-MENDIOLA, Jose R. 100 GRAND BLVD, SUITE #112 MSC 365 00926 #042-01-1991 L1996 **OTO** *020 †45

SANCHEZ-QUILES, Vicente R. SANTA MARIA, C/O SAUCO 1901 URLO 00927 #847-01-1974 L1977 **IM** *020

SANCHEZ-RAFFUCCI, Luis A. 500 AVE MUNOZ RIVERA, CONDOMINIO EL CENTRO I SUI 00918 #010-01-1964 L1968 **P** *020

SANCHEZ-RIVERA, Carlos Ja. ■ 00927 #042-01-2005 **IM** *012

SANCHEZ-RIVERA, Luis A. 252 CALLE SAN JORGE 00912 #847-04-1963 L1966 **IM** *071

SANCHEZ RODRIGUEZ, Ramon. 1 MEDICAL PAVILLION, CALLE SAN RAFAEL 1396 00909 #042-03-1987 L1989 **IM** *020

SANCHEZ ROSSETTI, Jorge F. 382 AVE DOMENECH, HATO REY 00918 #176-03-1961 L1975 **PDC PD** *020 †55

SANCHEZ-VALENTIN, Rafael. 1451 AVE ASHFORD, STE 308 00907 #042-01-1959 L1961 **CD IM** *020

SAN MIGUEL DE JESUS, Luis. 369 AVE DE DIEGO, STE 404 00923 #042-04-1990 L1995 *020

SANTAELLA DE FIGUEROA, G. ■ 00919 #042-01-1956 L1959 **AN** *071

SANTAELLA-JIMENEZ, Alvaro. MAIL STATION 00926 #847-17-1980 L1982 **NPM PD** *020 †55

SANTANA, Jose A. 1451 AVE ASHFORD 00907 #847-05-1974 L1980 **OBG** *071

SANTANA, Jose Raul. C/O CMMS #10, HOSP ONCOLOGICO ISAAC GONZ 00936 #042-01-1979 L1984 **RO** *020 †80

SANTANA FELIZ, Virginia V. ■ 00920 #308-01-1983 L2004 **GP** *020

SANTANA-MEDINA, Josue. 497 AVE EMILIANO POL, PMB 908 00926 #308-02-1974 L1976 **OTO A** *020

SANTANA RODRIGUEZ, Juan J. 1451 AVE ASHFORD, P O BOX 4759 00907 #847-01-1966 L1968 **PDP PUD** *020 †55

SANTANA SANTANA, Heidi. APT PH-20A 00926 #042-04-2001 L2002 *020

SANTIAGO, Angel. 654 AVE MUNOZ RIVERA, 654 PLAZA STE 1016 00918 #847-08-1972 L1975 **ORS** *020

SANTIAGO, Eduardo A. 37 AVE PONCE DE LEON 00901 #042-01-1965 L1967 **GS TTS** *030 †85 ‡

SANTIAGO, Felisa. 1645 CALLE PARANA, URB EL CEREZAL 00926 #042-01-1970 L1972 **PD** *020 †55

SANTIAGO, Hector Manuel. 200 AVE LOS CHALETS, CHALETS DE CUPEY 00926 #042-02-1997 L2000 **CD** *020

SANTIAGO, Jo Ann. 1395 CALLE SAN RAFAEL 00909 #649-14-2001 **IM** *020

SANTIAGO, Joaquin Mojica. 400 AVE DOMENECH STE 502 00918 #847-05-1976 L1979 **GP** *020

SANTIAGO, Jose Angel. 10 CALLE CASIA, VETERANS AFFAIRS MED CENTE 00921 #042-01-2001 L2005 **OBG** *020

SANTIAGO, Jose M. 1451 ASHFORD, STE 609 00907 #042-01-1986 L1989 **ORS HS** *020 †40

SANTIAGO, Marisel M. 37 AVE PONCE DE LEON 00901 #308-04-1987 L1992 **PD** *020

SANTIAGO, Roberto Jose. B17 CALLE ROBLES, VILLA HUCAR 00926 #042-01-1999 L2004 **RO** *020 †80

SANTIAGO APONTE, Luis R. 500 AVE PINERO APT 707 00918 #847-10-1965 L1968 **PD OS** *020

SANTIAGO COLON, Lizette. 700 CALLE EUROPA, STE 305 00909 #649-33-1982 L1993 *020

SANTIAGO HERNANDEZ, Carlos. ■ 00936 #308-03-1982 L2003 **GP** *020

SANTIAGO-HERNANDEZ, M. 29 CALLE WASHINGTON, STE 309 00907 #308-03-1980 L1986 **IM** *020

SANTIAGO-LUNA, Aidarilys. 73 CAL CHLS MANS DE SAN MA, AVE. LOS CHALETS # 200 00924 #042-01-2000 L2004 **P** *020

SANTIAGO-PEREZ, Basilio. 715 AVE PONCE DE LEON # P, HOSPITAL AUXILIO MUTUO 00917 #308-04-1984 L1986 **IM IMG** *020 †20

SANTIAGO-PLAZA, Juan Jose. 1917 CALLE NARCISO, URB SANTA MARIA 00927 #042-01-1959 L1963 **OTO GS** *020

SANTIAGO-RIVERA, Jose N. 239 AVE ARTERIAL HOSTOS, COND CAPITOL CENTER 00918 #042-01-1969 L1972 **OBG** *020 †30

SANTIAGO-RIVERA, Juan E. 00922 #847-01-1962 L1964 **PD** *020

SANTIAGO-SANCHEZ, M. PO BOX 71325, STE 60 00936 #042-01-2001 L2005 **GS** *020

SANTIAGO-SANCHEZ, Michelal. ■ 00924 #042-03-2005 **IM** *012

SANTIAGO SANTIAGO, Jose. ■ 00926 #649-14-2003 **NEP** *020

SANTINI, Manuel A. 371 AVE DE DIEGO 00923 #042-01-1977 L1978 **GE IM** *020

SANTINI-HERNANDEZ, V. 37 AVE PONCE DE LEON 00901 #649-01-1978 L1981 **PD** *020 †55

SANTINI-SANTIAGO, Manuel. 369 CALLE DE DIEGO, TORRE SAN FRANCISCO OF 406 00923 #308-02-1978 L1982 **IM** *020

SANTOS, Ana L. EE3 CALLE POPPY, URB BORINQUEN GDNS 00926 #042-03-1988 L1992 *020

SANTOS, Erick F. 270 C/HARVARD UNIV GRDNS 00927 #042-01-1968 L1970 **P ADP** *020 †75

SANTOS, Hector. PO BOX 365067, MEDICINE, NEURO 00936 #649-14-1997 L2000 **N** *020

SANTOS, Rosa De Jesus. ■ 00920 #042-01-1985 L1988 **PD** *020

SANTOS-APONTE, Eladio. POB 19149 FDEZ JUNCOS STA 00910 #847-02-1980 L1983 **END** *020

SANTOS-BUCH, Miguel A. ■ 00911 #275-01-1945 L1969 **GE IM** *071

SANTOS-DE JESUS, Jose A. 1106 COND PRQ D LS FNTS #1 00918 #042-03-1982 L1985 **AN PME** *020 ‡

SANZ, Marina Jose. 603 EDIF SAN ALBERTO, C/O CALLE CONDADO 605 00907 #042-04-1987 L1989 **P** *020

SARRAGA-AUDINOT, Jose A. 252 CALLE SAN JORGE 00912 #024-01-1945 L1952 **GS** *072 †85

SARRIERA, Otto A. 1534 CALLE 10 SW, URB CAPARRA TER 00921 #308-03-1980 L1993 **GP** *020

SARTORI, Enrico Giorgio. PO BOX 365067, MEDICINE, NEURO 00936 #042-01-2003 L2005 **N** *100

SARTORI, Renato V. CAPITAL CENTER #603, 239 ARTERIAL HOSTOS 00918 #561-14-1963 L1973 **N** *020

SARZALEJO, Luis G. 550 CALLE SERGIO CUEVAS, PARQ CENTRAL 00918 #847-02-1971 L1975 **EM** *030

SASTRE, Gladys Conception. 371 AVE DE DIEGO 00923 #275-01-1973 L1998 **IM** *020

SCHMIDT GONZALEZ, Jorge C. 239 AVE ARTERIAL HOSTOS, CAPITAL CTR SUR STE 202 00918 #649-35-1992 L1996 **GP OS** *020

SCHOOLOV, Yuri Nicolay. 37 AVE PONCE DE LEON 00901 #913-01-1982 L2004 **DR** *020

SCHWARZ, Susana. 576 CALLE CESAR GONZALEZ, DORAL BANK CENTER 403 00918 #042-03-1986 L1989 **OBG** *020 †30

SCHWARZ GOICOURIA, G F. PO BOX 11986 00922 #024-05-1945 L1946 **GP A** *071

SEDA, Felix J. PO BOX 70344, 187 CMMS 00936 #042-01-1990 L1995 **OTO** *020 †45

SEDA, Luis Angel. UNIV PR SCH MED, DEPT PSYCH 00935 #042-01-1973 **P** *040

SEGARRA, Geida L. 1507 AVE PONCE DE LEON, PMB 401 00909 #042-01-1988 L1994 **CD** *020 †20

SEGARRA, Jose A. ■ 00901 #042-01-1964 L1970 **PS** *071 †65

SEGARRA, Lillian Y. ■ 00926 #042-01-1989 L1994 **P** *040 †75

SEGUNDO, Aurelio. 1837 CALLE ACACIA, URB SANTA MARIA 00927 #042-01-1984 L1989 **GS** *020 †85

SEIN, Rafael E. 201 DE DIEGO AVE STE 154 00909 #847-01-1963 L1963 **PM OM** *020

SEIN, Rafael E. 201 DE DIEGO AVE OFC 00909 #847-06-1975 L1980 **PM** *020

SEPULVEDA, Angel Ramon. 574 CALLE CABO H ALVERIO, EXT ROOSEVELT 00918 #308-03-1986 L1990 **IM** *020

SERRA, Jose Enrique. RR 36 BOX 60 00926 #649-14-1984 L1985 **GP** *020

SERRANO, Javier Gustavo. ■ 00921 #042-01-1994 L1999 **PTH** *020

SERRANO DE ORTIZ, Patria. BOX 1804 HATO REY 00919 #056-06-1947 L1949 **GP** *071

SERRANO MUNOZ, Jose A. 735 AVE PONCE DE LEON, TORRE AUXILIO MUTUO STE 70 00917 #847-01-1971 L1973 **CD IM** *020 †20

SERRA RAMIREZ, Rafael E. PO BOX 70250, STE 35 00936 #649-01-1956 L1960 *071

SEVERINO, Norma Soraya. 1631 VIEPER, EL CEREZAL 00926 #308-13-1995 L2005 *100

SHIELDS, Thomas Matthew. ■ 00907 #042-03-2008 *012

SIERRA, Victor. 10 CALLE CASIA, VA HOSPITAL-SAN JUAN 00921 #035-46-1995 L2003 **P CHP** *020 †75

SIERRA LUCIANO, Carmen J. 400 AVE DOMENECH, STE 311 00918 #042-04-1988 L1992 **OBG** *020

SIERRA-ZORITA, Radames. 400 AVE FD ROOSEVELT # 404, CLINICA LAS AMERICAS 00918 #023-01-1979 L1984 **RHU IM** *020 †20

SIFONTE, Myrta Nancy. ■ 00926 #042-02-1994 L2000 **CHP** *020 †75

SILVA, Antonio Ramon, Jr. ■ 00936 #041-01-1957 L1959 **OBG** *071 †30

SILVA, Debora Heidy. 1719 CALLE SANTA EDUVIGIS, URB SAGRADO CORAZON 00926 #042-01-1997 L2000 **PD** *020 †55

SILVA, Jorge Edgardo. 180 COND MONTE BRSS #3-405, URB BORINQUEN GDNS 00926 #042-01-1994 L1997 **OBG** *020

SILVA, Juan J. ■ 00920 #042-03-2007 **TY** *012

SILVA, Nilda Garcia. 342 CALLE HECTOR SALAMAN, EXT ROOSEVELT 00918 #042-04-1983 L1985 **P** *020

SILVA-RAMIREZ, Samuel D. 151 CALLE AMERICA, URB EL PRADO 00917 #042-02-1992 L1996 **OBG** *020

SILVA TORRES, Edgardo R. 500 AVE DOMENECH STE 503 00918 #042-01-1963 L1967 **IM OS** *075

SILVESTRINI, Isis E. ■ 00926 #042-01-1985 L1988 **ATP** *040 †50

SIMONS, Julio S. 400 AVE DOMENECH STE 307 00918 #010-03-1950 L1953 **GP OS** *071

SIMONS, Julio S. 400 AVE DOMENECH, LAS AMERICAS PROF BLGD 307 00918 #042-01-1980 L1985 **GS PS** *020

SNYDER, Lawrence J. ■ 00911 #035-15-1944 L1945 **HS GS** *071 †85

SOBRINO-SUAREZ, Rafael F. DEPT OF MED, UNIV OF PR SCHOOL OF MED 00936 #042-01-1958 L1961 **CD IM** *020

SOBRINO-VICENTE, Rafael. ■ 00917 #847-05-1953 L1971 **U** *071

SOLA GOMEZ, Hector F. 467 CALLE SEIN, URB FLORAL PARK 00917 #847-02-1979 L1992 **GP OS** *020

SOLER, Echeandia Juan B. MUNICIPAL HOSP, DEPT PED 00935 #847-10-1968 L1971 **PD** *020

SOLER, Hiram R. 37 AVE PONCE DE LEON 00901 #042-03-1990 L1992 **HS GS** *020

SOLER BONILLA, Michael F. ■ 00926 #042-04-1996 L1999 **FM** *020

SOLER FAVALE, Hiram R. PO BOX 11981 00922 #847-05-1956 L1956 **GP GS** *071

SOLER ZAPATA, Jose E. 9 CALLE MALVA, URB SANTA MARIA 00927 #847-01-1954 L1957 **CD IM** *071

SOLIS, David Hiram. ■ 00926 #042-01-1998 L2004 **GS** *100

SOLIS, Rafael A. ■ 00926 #042-01-1991 L1995 **GE** *020 †20

SOLTERO, Roxana. ■ 00926 #042-01-2006 **EM** *012

SOLTERO ZAMORA, Luis H. 1801 AVE PONCE DE LEON 00909 #649-01-1982 L1986 **CD** *020

SOMOHANO, Jose Vicente. 652 AVE MUNOZ RIVERA, MONTE MALL SUITE 2065 00918 #042-03-1992 L1995 **OBG** *020

SOMOHANO ARBIDE, Sandra J. 89 AVE DE DIEGO STE 105, PMB 456 00927 #042-01-1984 L1986 **CCP** *020 †55

SOMOZA, Nairys. 10 CALLE CASIA, SEE 42-0464 00921 #275-01-1997 **IM** *012

SORDO-DIAZ, Herminio A. ■ 00936 #275-01-1951 L1951 **FM** *071

SOSA, Candelario Alberto. 1306 AVE FERNANDEZ JUNCOS 00909 #341-01-1974 L1990 **GP PHP** *020

SOSA, Isabel R Fernandez. 359 AVE DE DIEGO, STE 402 00909 #649-14-1979 L1984 **NM IM** *020

SOSA, Jose Antonio. ■ 00918 #041-09-1951 L1955 **GP IM** *071 †18

SOSA, Maria De Los A. 280 AVE DOMENECH # 281, URB BALDRICH 00918 #042-01-1980 L1984 **PM** *020

■ = Address Information Privacy Protected

SOSTRE, Wilma De Oliver. ■ 00926 #847-05-1973 L1980 **IM** *020
SOTO, Maria C. 60 AVE DE DIEGO 00907 #042-04-2002 L2003 **GP** *020
SOTO, Oscar. 2010 EL MONTE MALL # 2010 00918 #042-03-1994 L2001 **RHU IM** *020 †20
SOTO ALARCON, Jose Luis. PO BOX 195232 00919 #649-14-1977 L1979 *020
SOTO GARCIA, Edwin. ■ 00923 #649-14-1986 L2004 *100
SOTO-GAUTIER, Cesar. ■ 00919 #847-10-1962 L1967 **DR** *020
SOTOLONGO, Antonio E. CARR 21 T3 7 LAS LOMAS 00921 #042-01-1976 L1982 **U** *020 †95
SOTO-MALDONADO, Veronica. ■ 00918 #042-01-2000 L2003 **FM OM** *020 †18
SOTOMAYOR, Ramon Kenneth. 300 AVE LA SIERRA 00926 #042-01-1989 L1994 **GS** *020 †85
SOTOMAYOR, Zoilo R. ■ 00926 #035-06-1950 L1954 **IM** *071
SOTOMONTE, Juan Carlos. 576 CALLE CESAR GONZALEZ, STE 502 00918 #264-04-1996 L2005 **ICE** *100 †20
SOTO VEGA, Elisabeth M. 37 AVE PONCE DE LEON 00901 #042-04-1991 L1992 **IM END** *020
STEFANI, Mercedes. 409 ASHFORD MEDICAL CTR, ASHFORD & WASHINGTON 00907 #042-01-1957 L1961 **PM** *020
STELLA ARRILLAGA, Hector. 420 AVE PONCE DE LEON, MID TOWN BUILDING STE 103 00918 #649-01-1969 L1971 **N** *020 ‡
STELLA-ESTEVEZ, Hector J. 421 AVE MUNOZ RIVERA, STE 103 00918 #042-04-1991 L1992 **PCC** *020
STERLING VASQUEZ, Teresa. ■ 00926 #308-01-1960 L1975 **ATP GP** *020
STIEHL, Franz Edward. 435 AVE PONCE DE LEON 00917 #308-06-1986 L1996 **PD** *020
STODDARD LATORRE, Harold. 700 CALLE EUROPA 00909 #308-04-1993 L1995 *020
STOLBERG, Robert Allan. 200 CALLE TETUAN 00901 #023-01-1969 L1980 **P IM** *040 †75
STORER, David F. 735 AVE PONCE DE LEON # 61, HATO REY 00917 #042-01-1970 L1972 **CD IM** *020 †20
SUAREZ, Jose Manuel. 253 CALLE SAN JORGE, BOX 40476 00912 #042-01-1979 L1982 **IM CD** *020 †20
SUAREZ, Juan Carlos. 735 AVE PONCE DE LEON, TORRE AUXILIO MUTUO SUITE 00917 #042-01-2001 L2006 **ORS** *020
SUAREZ, Juan Ramon. 735 AVE PONCE DE LEON, TORRE AUXILIO MUTUO ROOM 5 00917 #042-01-1988 L1994 **ORS** *020 †40
SUAREZ DOMINGUEZ, A J. 735 AVE PONCE DE LEON, STE 819 TORRE MEDIC AUXILI 00917 #042-01-1972 L1974 **GS TRS** *020 †85
SUAREZ-RUIZ, Angela Elena. 37 AVE PONCE DE LEON 00901 #042-02-1985 L1992 **PD NPM** *020 †55
SUASNAVAR-SANDOVAL, Enio. D27 CALLE 8, PASEO MAYOR 00926 #429-01-1983 L1986 *020
SURIS, Dharma Dennise. 00924 #042-01-2005 **P** *012
TABOADA, Ricardo Jose. ■ 00918 #042-03-2006 **AN** *012
TABOAS, Rafael A. 262 CALLE REINA MORA, URB MONTEHIEDRA 00926 #042-01-1982 L1986 **OPH OS** *020 †75,35 ‡
TABOAS, William Rafael. 369 AVE DE DIEGO STE 501, TORRE SAN FRANCISCO 00923 #042-01-1985 L1988 **NEP IM** *020 †20
TABOAS PEREZ, Eduardo P. 525 F.D. ROOSEVELT AVE., CLINICA TABOAS 00918 #042-01-1982 L1986 **OPH** *020
TALAVERA, Alvaro. PO BOX 363305 00936 #682-01-1992 L1999 **HO** *020 †20
TAMAYO, Vivian Margarita. PO BOX 195193 00919 #042-01-2002 L2004 **OBG** *100
TAMPE, Cristian Roberto. 778 VALLE DE LAJAS, LOS CAMPOS DE MONTEHIEDRA 00926 #023-07-1995 L2001 **IM** *020 †20
TARDY, Rodolfo Antonio. 1020 CALLE GEN VALERO, URB DELICIAS 00924 #308-01-1959 L1970 **GYN** *020
TAVAREZ-VALLE, Jose A. PO BOX 360013 00936 #649-14-1977 L1979 **GP** *020
TEJADA GARCIA, Carmen Y. PO BOX 71325 00936 #308-01-1980 L1986 *100
TEJEDOR, Begona. ■ 00926 #042-01-1988 L1992 **PTH** *020
THOMAS VISSEPO, Alejandra. ■ 00921 #649-14-2003 L2005 *100
TIRADO, Yamilet. ■ 00923 #042-01-2004 **OTO** *012
TIRADO GONZALEZ, Gilda. ■ 00921 #847-04-1957 L1961 **OS** *071
TIRADO MARRERO, Lourdes M. 10 CALLE CASIA, DEPT OF INTERNAL MED 00921 #308-13-2002 **IM** *100 †20
TIZOL-GARCIA, Jose. ■ 00908 #056-06-1955 L1958 **IM OS** *020
TOLEDO, Gloria Cibelle. 243 CALLE PARIS 00921 #649-30-2001 L2004 *100
TOLEDO, Hazel A. ■ 00919 #042-01-1997 L1999 **P** *020
TOMASHEK, Kay Marie. ■ 00920 #030-06-1992 L1994 **GPM PD** *050 †70,55
TOMASINI, Juan T. POB 11440 CAPARRA HTS STA 00922 #847-04-1962 L1966 **GE IM** *071 †20
TOMASINI PEREZ, Mario J. DOMENECH AVE 00918 #010-02-1939 L1940 **GS** *072
TOME-DIAZ, Jose M. RADIOTHERAPY INST, 1785 ROAD 21 LAS LOMAS 00922 #847-06-1952 L1960 **R OS** *020 †80
TORNES, Anibal. 111 CALLE BETANCES, URB FLORAL PARK 00917 #275-01-1984 L2004 *100
TORO, Doris H. 10 CALLE CASIA, VA CARRIBEAN HLTH CARE SYS 00921 #042-01-1983 L1986 **GE IM** *020 †20
TORO, Gerardo L. MED, UNIV OF PUERTO RICO SCH OF 00901 #042-01-1991 L1994 **GS** *020
TORO, Joel. 1400 AVE MAGDALENA, THIRD FLOOR 00907 #042-01-1994 L2000 **PS** *020
TORO, Jorge Rafael. 24 CALLE ACEROLA, URB MILAVILLE 00926 #042-01-1990 L1992 **NM** *020 †55,28
TORO, Rafael Orlando. ■ 00927 #042-02-2005 **GS** *012
TORRADO, Mayra G. PO BOX 363724, 23 U5 VISTA AZUL ARECIBO P 00936 #308-03-1983 L1997 **PD** *020
TORRE, Francisco Javier. 735 AVE PONCE DE LEON, OFICINA #712 00917 #042-01-1992 L1998 **NEP** *020 †20
TORRENS, Rafael A. 21D COND HATO REY PLZ #21D 00918 #008-01-1936 L1990 **CD IM** *071 †20
TORRES, Alfonso. ■ 00929 #035-20-1990 L1999 **PUD** *020 †20
TORRES, Allan. ■ 00926 #042-01-1990 L1994 **U** *020 †95
TORRES, Ana Teresa. RR 36 BOX 542, ALTURAS DE SAN JUAN 00926 #308-03-1986 L1993 **GP** *020
TORRES, Angel. 24 CALLE ACEROLA, URB MILAVILLE 00926 #042-01-1963 L1968 **NM IM** *020 †28
TORRES, Ann Marie. ■ 00926 #042-01-2007 *012
TORRES, Brenda Margarita. 302 CALLE SOL 00901 #649-14-2001 L2005 *100
TORRES, Carlos Alberto. 1304 AVE AMERICO MIRANDA, URB CAPARRA TER 00921 #847-08-1983 L1989 **GP** *020
TORRES, Carlos Pelegrin. ■ 00926 #649-14-2004 L2005 *100
TORRES, Carluis. 1070 CALLE 10 NE, URB JULIA IND PARK 00920 #042-01-2000 L2003 **EM** *020 †16
TORRES, Edgar. 1395 CALLE SAN RAFAEL 00909 #308-06-1987 L1991 **GP AM** *020
TORRES, Fernando Javier. ■ 00926 #306-01-2001 **UM** *100
TORRES, Hector M. ■ 00926 #042-01-1988 L1994 **AN** *020 †05

TORRES, Jeancarlo. ■ 00926 #042-03-2006 **PD** *012
TORRES, Jose Antonio. ■ 00919 #649-14-1998 L1999 **IM** *020
TORRES, Jose Vicente. PO BOX 11548, FERNANDEZ JUNCOS STAT 00910 #042-01-1986 L1991 **PTH** *062 †50
TORRES, Juan O. ■ 00921 #847-05-1976 L1978 **GS** *020 †85
TORRES, Luis A. 508 AVE HOSTOS, URB EL VEDADO 00918 #042-01-1969 L1971 **AI** *020
TORRES, Marian. 10 CALLE CASIA, CENTRO LATINOAMERICANO CLE 00921 #042-01-2001 L2006 **FM** *020 †18
TORRES-AGUIAR, Luis R. ■ 00920 #028-34-1944 L1946 **P PHP** *072
TORRES-CASTRO, Ramul E. 652 AVE MUNOZ RIVERA, STE 2070 & 2035 00918 #308-03-1982 L1990 *100
TORRES-COTTO, Carol Loren. ■ 00926 #042-03-2007 **IM** *012
TORRES GOMEZ, Jose M. ■ 00907 #023-01-1943 L1946 **IM CD** *071 †20
TORRES JUSINO, Magda E. PO BOX 195354 00919 #042-03-1981 L1986 *020
TORRES LOPEZ, Pedro Manue. ■ 00924 #649-14-2004 L2005 *100
TORRES-MARTIN, Ana I. ■ 00927 #042-01-1987 L1991 **P** *020 †75
TORRES MARTINEZ, Leslie C. ■ 00926 #649-14-1996 L1999 *020
TORRES NIEVES, Javier. ■ 00926 #649-14-2005 **IM** *100
TORRES-ORTIZ, Angel R. 00907 #308-01-1975 L1977 **GP** *020
TORRES ORTIZ, Luis A. 445 CALLE TNTE CESAR GNZLZ, URB ROOSEVELT 00918 #847-04-1962 L1966 **OBG OS** *071 †30
TORRES PAOLI, Damaris. 00907 #042-01-1992 L1995 **D** *020 †18,15
TORRES-QUINONES, Marta I. 570 CALLE JUAN J JIMENEZ, HATO REY PHATOLOGY ASSOCIA 00918 #042-01-1998 L2006 **DMP** *020 †50
TORRES RAFAEL, Oberto. ■ 00911 #275-01-1987 **IM** *012
TORRES RAMOS, Jose M. 60 CALLE WASHINGTON # 1301, P.O. BOX 13395 SAN JUAN PR 00907 #847-04-1955 L1958 **IM IMG** *020
TORRES-RODRIGUEZ, Amilcar. 500 AVE DOMENECH STE 2 00918 #308-03-1982 L1985 **IM** *020
TORRES RODRIGUEZ, Esther. 37 AVE PONCE DE LEON 00901 #042-01-1972 L1974 **GE IM** *040 †20
TORRES-ROSARIO, Ismael. 735 AVE PONCE DE LEON #705 00917 #042-03-1981 L1986 **HEM HO** *020 †20
TORRES SANTOS, Francisco. 301 AVE DOMENECH, URB JB HUYKE 00918 #042-01-1969 L1972 **DIA END** *020
TORRES SUAREZ, Luis Angel. 527 CALLE JOSE R ACOSTA, URB LOS INGENIEROS 00918 #847-06-1975 L1978 **PD** *020
TORRES-VAZQUEZ, Armando. PO BOX 364904 00936 #042-03-1980 L1988 **OPH** *020
TORROS, Salvador. 1357 AVE ASHFORD, STE 320 00907 #847-01-1971 L1974 **PS HS** *020
TORT SAADE, Pedro Javier. 1733 CALLE THEIS, URB RIO PIEDRAS HTS 00926 #042-03-1998 L2000 **OSM** *020
TORT-SOLA, Cesar. MARIA, Q2 CALLE PETUNIA PQUE STA 00927 #308-03-1977 L1980 **OPH** *020
TOSCA, Gerardo Javier. 202 PASEO LAS CUMBRES, 349 AVE. FELISA R. DE GAUT 00926 #042-03-1994 L1996 **PD** *020 †55
TOSSAS-MOJICA, Maylynn. 369 AVE DE DIEGO, TORRE SAN FRANCISCO, STE 6 00909 #042-01-1990 L1993 **FM** *020 †20
TOWNSEND-PICO, William A. 735 AVE PONCE DE LEON, TORRE AUXILIO MUTRO, SUITE 00917 #016-06-1990 L1996 **OPH** *020 †35
TRAUTMANN, Mark Emil. 373 AVE DOMENECH 00918 #042-01-1991 L1996 **ORS** *020 †40
TRILLA, Emilio F. 400 AVE DOMENECH, CDT TEACHERS HOSPITAL 00918 #041-02-1944 L1947 **D OS** *020 †15
TRIMARCO, Anna Antonia. AIRPORT STA PO BOX 38079 00937 #561-17-1981 *020
TRINIDAD, Juan. 500 AVS LUIS MUNOZ RIVERA, COND EL CENTRO 2 STE 239-B 00918 #847-04-1970 L1974 **OTO** *020 †45
TRINIDAD, Maritza. 138 AVE WINSTON CHURCHILL, BOX 641 00926 #847-08-1978 L1981 **FM** *020 †18
TRIO-MARTINEZ, Isabel. 400 AVE DOMENECH STE 605, DOCTORS' HOME 00918 #042-01-1998 L2000 **FPG** *020 †18
TROCHE, Armando. PO BOX 70171, PMB 108 00936 #649-14-1992 L1994 *020
TROCHE-PANETTO, Michelle. 10 CALLE CASIA, DEPT. OF PSYCHIATRY 00921 #042-03-1998 L2003 **P** *020
TRULLENQUE, Elizabeth. ■ 00927 #042-01-2004 **DR** *012
TRUYOL-VAZQUEZ, Engracia. 383 AVE FD ROOSEVELT, HUMANA PR 00918 #042-01-1961 L1964 **FM EM** *030 †18
TULLA, Michelle Enid. ■ 00917 #042-02-2005 **OBG** *012
UBINAS, Leticia. 89 AVE DE DIEGO # 105 PMB, URB. JARDINES DE SAN FRANC 00927 #308-03-1978 L1981 **P** *020
UBINAS BURGOS, Jeanne. 10 CANDINA VICTORI PLZ 15B 00913 #649-01-1956 L1960 **R OS** *071 †80
ULLOA, Santiago A. ■ 00920 #042-03-1989 L1992 **CRS** *020
UMPIERRE, Sharee Ann. 37 AVE PONCE DE LEON 00901 #024-01-1985 L1991 **GO GYN** *020 †30
UNDA, Roberto Fernando. 1705 CALLE LOIZA, GANDIA OFC BLDG STE 202 00911 #649-14-1981 L2002 **GP** *020
URBISTONDO, Manuel Rene. 200 AVE WINSTON CHURCHILL, URB EL SENORIAL STE 201 00926 #042-01-1989 L1995 **GE IM** *020 †20
UREA, Johanna Glendalie. ■ 00911 #042-01-2005 **IM** *012
URENA, Guido Javier. 1672 CALLE TERRACE, URB RIO PIEDRAS HTS 00926 #308-01-1986 L2003 **PD** *100
VALCARCEL, Carmen G. 131 AVE WINSTON CHURCHILL, STE B 00926 #042-01-1996 L1999 **GP EM** *020
VALCARCEL, Marta Iris. ■ 00918 #042-01-1955 L1959 **PD NPM** *040 †55
VALDERRABANO, Rodrigo Jua. ■ 00927 #042-03-2007 **IM** *012
VALDES, Jose De Jesus. 369 DE DIEGO AVE STE 504, TORRE SAN FRAN 00909 #042-01-1978 L1982 **OBG** *020
VALDES VAQUERO, Aymara. ■ 00907 #308-03-1982 L1987 **GP** *020
VALDEZ, Maritza Ana. RR 6 BOX 9, MONTE HIEDRA 00926 #042-03-1981 L1984 **AN** *040
VALENCIA, Judith. ■ 00936 #275-01-1995 L2007 *100
VALENTIN, Sheila Marie. ■ 00926 #042-01-2005 **D** *012
VALENTIN-COLON, Lisbeth. 1028 AVE ROOSEVELT, URB PUERTO NUEVO 00920 #847-20-1981 L1983 **PD** *020
VALENTIN-MARRERO, Juan N. SABATINI ST C 10 PK GRDNS 00926 #308-03-1980 L1982 **PM** *020
VALENZUELA, Richard Germa. PO BOX 5067 00936 #649-14-1997 **ORS** *012
VALERIO, Nelson Ramon. PO BOX 2124 00922 #308-01-1968 L1973 **PD** *020

VALLE, Ivette. 1479 AVE ASHFORD, CONDADO DEL MAR 00907 #275-01-1991 L2004 **PD** *100
VALLEJO, Carlos Eduardo. ■ 00927 #308-04-2004 L2005 *100
VALLEJO, Orlando. 803 AVE HIPODROMO 00909 #042-02-1993 L1997 **FM** *18
VALLEJO, Ruben Rafael. ■ 00926 #042-03-1986 L1990 **IM** *020 †15
VALLS, Marcos Osvaldo. 610 COND TORRE DE ORO, HATO REY 00917 #847-03-1973 L1975 **GP** *020
VARELA, Alberto M. 431 AVE HOSTOS, INST PSICOTERAPEUTICO 00918 #042-01-1967 L1987 **P CHP** *030 †75
VARELA, Gilberto E. BOX 19630 FRNDNZ JNCS STA 00910 #847-04-1959 L1961 **OS FM** *030
VARGAS, Caridad Susana. 613 CALLE OLIMPIC, URB SUMMIT HLS 00920 #042-01-1999 L2001 **FPG** *100
VARGAS, Dharma Luz. 37 AVE PONCE DE LEON 00901 #023-01-1943 L1945 **PD** *072 †55
VARGAS, Efrain. 29 CARR 873, BO TORTUGO 00926 #042-04-1995 L1997 **GP** *020
VARGAS, Francisco Cid. 390 AVE DOMENECH 00918 #042-01-1980 L1984 **DR** *020 †80
VARGAS, Joaquin, Jr. 1501 AVE FERNANDEZ JUNCOS, STE 401 EDIF BETANCOURT 00909 #649-01-1970 L1971 **EM GP** *020
VARGAS, Luis. 275 CALLE JILGUERO, URB MONTEHIEDRA 00926 #042-03-1992 L1996 **AN** *020
VARGAS, Rosa I. ■ 00931 #042-01-1987 L1991 **P ADP** *020 †75
VARGAS CESAR, Isaac. ■ 00923 #649-38-1996 L2005 **IM** *100 †20
VARGAS-PEREZ, Rene. 611 CALLE DR PAVIA FERNNDZ, STE 109 00909 #042-01-1966 L1968 **IM** *020
VARGAS VIDAL, Hector B.. AVE MUNIOZ RIVERA NO 402, BASIC MEDICAL GROUP 00917 #308-01-1980 L1995 *100
VASQUEZ, Raul Alberto. ■ 00902 #042-01-2007 **GS** *012
VAZQUEZ, Ana Gloria. ■ 00924 #042-03-1992 *100
VAZQUEZ, Basilia I. 114 CALLE ELEONOR ROOSEVLT, 2ND FL 00918 #847-10-1970 L1978 **GP IMG** *020
VAZQUEZ, Guillermo J. ■ 00926 #041-02-1974 L1976 **ID IM** *020 †20
VAZQUEZ, Gustavo. 4 COND SANTA RITA, RUDO DOMINGO MARRERO NAVAR 00925 #308-02-1981 L1990 **OBG** *020
VAZQUEZ, Humberto R. 1507 CALLE PROF AUGST RDRG 00909 #847-10-1970 L1972 **PD** *020
VAZQUEZ, Jose Raul. C6 VIA PANORAMICA, URB LA VISTA 00924 #042-01-1978 L1983 **NM IM** *020 †28
VAZQUEZ, Maria Isabel. ■ 00907 #042-01-2003 L2008 **IM** *012
VAZQUEZ, Marisel De L. 252 CALLE SAN JORGE, STE 307 00912 #042-01-1981 L1984 **N PD** *020 †55,75
VAZQUEZ, Nestor Luis. ■ 00926 #042-01-2000 L2001 *020
VAZQUEZ, Rene. 386 AVE DOMENECH 00918 #042-01-1976 L1980 **OPH PD** *050 †35
VAZQUEZ, Vidal. 21E COND HATO REY PLZ #21E 00918 #042-01-1983 L1986 **CD** *020
VAZQUEZ, Zaira Namir. 2024 CALLE BECQUER, URB EL SENORIAL 00926 #042-02-1996 L1999 **IM** *020
VAZQUEZ-BORRERO, Ileana. 29 CALLE WASHINGTON # 302, ASHFORD MEDICAL CENTER 00907 #042-03-1981 L1985 **P** *020 †75
VAZQUEZ-COBIAN, Liza B. 252 CALLE CONVENTO, HOSPITAL ESPANOL AUXILIO M 00912 #042-01-1999 L2004 **PPR** *020 †55
VAZQUEZ-LUGO, Albert. 525 AVE FD ROOSEVELT # 8VO, PLAZA LAS AMERICAS 00918 #847-06-1973 L1980 **U** *040 †95
VAZQUEZ-OLIVO, Enrique. 435 AVE PONCE DE LEON 00917 #847-06-1977 L1981 **EM PD** *030
VAZQUEZ OTERO, Lourdes M. B36 CALLE 2 COLINAS VERDE 00924 #308-03-1985 L1994 *020
VAZQUEZ PLARD, Julian A. 730 AVE PONCE DE LEON 00918 #042-01-1963 L1967 **DIA END** *020 †20
VAZQUEZ-QUINTANA, Enrique. 655 CALLE PAVIA, STE 301 00909 #042-01-1962 L1964 **GS** *075 †85
VAZQUEZ-ROMAN, Cesar O. 1880 CALLE FRIBURGO, URB COLLEGE PARK 00921 #847-10-1972 L1975 **OS** *020
VAZQUEZ-TORRES, Rafael J. 1809 CALLE SANTA ISABEL, URB EL PILAR 00926 #649-14-1979 L1982 **GP EM** *030
VEGA, Isabel. 1357 AVE ASHFORD, STE 411 00907 #847-10-1981 L1984 **RHU** *020 †20
VEGA, Luis A. 400 AVE DOMENECH, OFICINA 304 00918 #042-01-1962 L1964 **END** *020
VEGA, Marisol. RR 36 BOX 19, PORTAL DE LOS PINOS 00926 #649-14-1989 L1991 **GP** *020
VEGA, Marisol. 501 CALLE ASUNCION, URB PUERTO NUEVO 00920 #843-04-1989 L1993 **PD** *020
VEGA, Maritza. 411 AVE DE DIEGO, URB PUERTO NUEVO 00920 #308-03-1982 L1989 **GP** *020
VEGA, Miguel Angel. ■ 00921 #847-02-1971 L1973 **AN** *020
VEGA, Nayda E. ■ 00907 #042-01-1991 L1995 **OPH** *020 †35
VEGA, Wilma Hernandez. ■ 00926 #042-01-1985 L1989 **PD** *020
VEGA COFRESI, Regina. 8 COND CONCORDIA CT 00907 #308-01-1979 L1981 *100
VEGA FELICIANO, Edwin. 1395 CALLE SAN RAFAEL 00909 #042-01-1970 L1980 **OBG** *020 †30
VEGA-OCASIO, William. MENONITA CAYEY, CENTRO RENAL HOSP 00928 #649-14-2002 L2002 **IM NEP** *020 ‡
VEGA TORRES, Rafael. ■ 00927 #042-01-1989 L1991 **FPG** *020 †18
VEGA VIDAL, Mercedes. ■ 00936 #042-01-1963 L1967 **PDC PD** *020
VEJAS, Eduardo Jose. ■ 00926 #715-01-1983 L2001 **FM** *020
VELA PINERO, Rosendo E. LAGUNA TERR CONDOMIN, APT 10A 00907 #847-04-1957 L1960 **AN PME** *020 †05
VELASCO, Jaime L. 51 CALLE ORQUIDEA, URB SANTA MARIA 00927 #042-01-1966 L1970 **OPH** *020
VELAZQUEZ, Maria I. ■ 00926 #042-01-1970 L1973 **IM ON** *020 ‡
VELAZQUEZ, Marissel. 369 AVE DE DIEGO, STE 308-309 00909 #847-21-1980 L1984 **PUD IM** *020
VELAZQUEZ RODRIGUEZ, John. ■ 00926 #308-03-2002 L2003 *100
VELEZ, Angel D. 607A CALLE DEL PARQUE 00909 #042-01-1990 L1993 **OBG** *020 †30
VELEZ, Daniel Abner. ■ 00926 #042-03-1995 L2005 **TS** *100 †90
VELEZ, Marcos Eli. ■ 00923 #042-01-2004 **IM** *020
VELEZ, Samuel J. ■ 00926 #042-01-1975 L1980 **PDC** *020 †55
VELEZ, Silvio E. 1620 AVE JESUS T PINERO 00921 #042-01-1965 L1969 **PD** *020
VELEZ, Wandsy M. 1095 CALLE WILSON, COND PUERTA DEL CONDADO 15 00907 #042-01-1987 L1997 **IM OPH** *020 †35
VELEZ-BORRAS, Jesus R. ■ 00926 #005-11-1968 L1974 **CHN N** *040 †75
VELEZ-COLON, Elizabeth. ■ 00926 #042-04-1992 L1996 **PD** *020
VELEZ-GARCIA, Enrique O. 369 CALLE DE DIEGO, TORRE SAN FRANCISCO #603 00923 #847-01-1960 L1968 **ON HEM** *020
VELEZ-MERCADO, Edgardo. 400 AVE DOMENECH, STE 513 00918 #649-14-1996 L1997 **IM** *020
VELILLA-IGLESIAS, Manuel. 405 CALLE SAN JORGE, SAN JORGE MEDICAL BUILDING 00912 #649-14-1976 L1976 **OBG** *020
VENTURA, Hugo Francisco. ■ 00910 #308-01-1984 L1988 **IM** *020

VENTURA TAVARES, Neida R. ■ 00910 #308-01-1983 L2005 **PD** *100
VERA COLON, Lumen. ■ 00920 #308-04-1982 L1987 **GP** *020
VERAY TORREGROSA, F X. 400 AVE DOMENECH, STE G020 00918 #847-01-1959 L1961 **CD CCM** *071
VICENTE-PRADO, Maria C. 130 AVE WINSTON CHURCHILL, STE 1 PMB 186 00926 #042-01-2000 L2005 **P** *100 †75
VICENTE Y GONZALEZ, Felix. ■ 00907 #847-04-1965 L1972 **GP** *020
VICENTY-SANCHEZ, Wassilly. 376 CALLE CESAR GONZALEZ 00918 #042-01-1954 L1958 **PD** *071
VICIOSO, Jose. ■ 00918 #308-01-1957 L1969 **OPH** *020
VIDAL, Ana H. ■ 00912 #042-01-1995 L1998 **N** *100
VIDAL, Jorge. 1451 AVE ASHFORD 00907 #042-03-1997 L2002 **OBG** *020
VIDAL, Yamile Enid. ■ 00926 #042-03-2007 *012
VIDAL-FANDINO, Ramon E. 1395 CALLE SAN RAFAEL 00909 #308-03-1980 L1987 **IM OM** *020
VIDAL PALAU, Jesus M. 1410 CAL 46 SW URB LA RIVI 00921 #042-03-1981 L1988 **NM IM** *020
VIERA, Angel. ■ 00911 #042-01-1978 L1986 **PM** *020 †60
VIGO-PRIETO, Juan A. PO BOX 5067, NEUROSURGERY SECTION 00936 #308-04-1982 L1991 **NS** *020 †25
VILA, Karina. ■ 00926 #042-03-2005 **IM** *012
VILA, Luis M. 735 AVE PONCE DE LEON, STE 507 00917 #042-01-1985 L1988 **RHU IM** *020 †20
VILA, Raul. 735 AVE PONCE DE LEON, STE 407 00917 #275-01-1951 L1966 **PTH GP** *071 †50
VILA, Salvador. PO BOX 192349, 735 PONCE DE LEON SUITE 5 00919 #042-01-1976 L1983 **RHU IM** *020 †20
VILARAMIREZ, Raul G. PO BOX 5067 00936 #042-01-1996 L1999 **OTO** *020
VILA-ROSADO, Alicia T. ONE VETERANS PLAZA 00927 #308-03-1982 L1985 **IM OM** *020
VILCHES, Briseida Munoz. EUCALIPTO E5 CAPARRA HILLS 00920 #308-03-1983 L1986 **PD** *020
VILELLA, Olga J. ■ 00919 #847-05-1953 L1959 **OS** *075
VILLAFANA, Myriam. 37 AVE PONCE DE LEON 00901 #042-01-1976 L1981 **GE IM** *020
VILLAFANA-JUSTICIA, C. 1505 CALLE LOIZA BOX 215, PUBLIC HEALTH 00911 #042-01-1956 L1962 **OM** *071 †70
VILLALOBOS, Javier Raul. 478 CALLE TNTE CESAR GNZLZ, URB ROOSEVELT 00918 #308-03-1984 L1991 **GP** *020
VILLALOBOS, Raul David. 1395 CALLE SAN RAFAEL 00909 #308-07-1983 L1999 **FM** *020
VILLAMIL, Irene Sofia. ■ 00926 #042-01-2007 **IM** *012
VILLAMIL ORTIZ, Maria. 256 CALLE CONVENTO 00912 #308-03-1983 L1990 **PD** *020
VILLANUEVA GARCIA, Alberto. 421 AVE MUNOZ RIVERA, COND. MIDTOWN STE 605 00918 #649-14-2000 L2002 **IM IMG** *020
VILLAR, Felix Xavier. ■ 00926 #649-14-2003 L2005 **GP** *020
VILLAR, Maria Belen. ■ 00926 #042-01-2004 **CCP** *012 †55
VILLAR HERNANDEZ, Marla V. ■ 00926 #042-04-1999 L2000 **FM** *020
VILLARINI, Frances Raquel. 663 CALLE ACUARIO, URB VENUS GDNS 00926 #649-14-1997 L2000 **IM** *020 †20
VILLARMARZO, Guillermo. 1451 AVE ASHFORD 00907 #847-05-1974 L1976 **PTH GP** *062 †50
VILLAR-ROBLES, Felix. 29 CALLE WASHINGTON, ASHFORD MED CTR STE 807 00907 #010-03-1973 L1976 **OBG** *020
VILLARUBIA VELEZ, Vivian. ■ 00920 #042-04-1997 L1999 **FM** *020
VILLATE, Claudia. PO BOX 361314 00936 #264-11-1989 L1997 **IM** *020 †20
VILLAVICENCIO, Rafael. 400 AVE FD ROOSEVELT, CLINICA LAS AMERICAS SUITE 00918 #042-03-1996 L2000 **PDC** *020 †55
VINAS-BANCHS, Amelia. 1972 CALLE JOSE FIDALGO DZ, URB CALDAS 00926 #308-02-1977 L1982 *020
VINAS MATIENZO, Jose E. GPO BOX 1755 00936 #847-04-1958 L1961 **P** *020
VINAS SORBA, Luis A. ■ 00907 #847-04-1955 L1958 **OBG** *071 †30
VIRELLA-SANTANA, Wilma. ■ 00917 #041-13-1992 L1997 **PTH** *020 †50
VIRUET, Eduardo J. 713 COND CRYSTAL HOUS #713 00923 #042-01-1994 L1999 **CD IM** *020 †20
VISBAL, Gladys N. 270 C/HARVARD UNIV GONS 00927 #042-01-1967 L1969 **PD** *071 †55
VIVONI GIROD, Francine. 1250 AVE JESUS T PINERO, CAPARRA TERRACE 00921 #042-01-1998 L2000 **OPH** *020 †35
VIZCARRONDO, Francisco J. 562 CALLE JUAN J JIMENEZ, PARQ CENTRAL 00918 #042-01-1976 L1980 **GE** *020
VIZCARRORDO BERRIOS, F. A7 CALLE HUCAR, VILLA HUCAR 00926 #847-06-1976 L1982 **GS** *020
WALKER, Amina Pilar. ■ 00909 #847-08-1983 L1988 **GP** *020
WEBSTER, Evelyn Lightbour. 37 AVE PONCE DE LEON 00901 #064-01-1959 L1961 **FM** *071
WHEELER, Melissa M. ■ 00936 #042-01-2003 L2006 **FM** *100 †18
WILTZ, Othon H. 500 AVE MUNOZ RIVERA, EDIF EL CENTRO 2 SUITE 150 00918 #275-01-1960 L1969 **CRS GS** *020
WISCOVITCH, Adanette. 53 CALLE FALCON, URB MONTEHIEDRA 00926 #042-01-1986 L1989 **PDE** *020 †55
WISCOVITCH, Maria M. ■ 00936 #042-02-1999 L2005 **N** *100 ‡
WOJNA, Valerie Eileen. ■ 00918 #042-01-1984 L1988 **N CN** *050 †75
WOODBURY, Michael A, Sr. 557A CALLE TRIGO 00907 #024-01-1951 L1953 **P PYA** *071 †75
WOODBURY, Michael Aime. 307 CALLE ELEONOR ROOSEVLT 00918 #042-01-1976 L1982 **P CHP** *020 †75
WOOLLIS, Anabel. ■ 00936 #042-01-2001 L2002 **PM** *020
YDRACH, Arturo Andres. 265 CALLE FORDHAM, URB UNIVERSITY GDNS 00927 #042-01-1969 L1976 **IM ON** *071 †20
YORDAN, Raul A. 652 AVE MUNOZ RIVERA STE 2 00918 #847-01-1962 L1967 **OPH** *020
YSLAND-EUSEBIO, Luisa. 371 AVE DE DIEGO 00923 #308-03-1986 L1992 **GP EM** *020
YUNEZ, Canaan. 608 AVE DE DIEGO # 150, URB PUERTO NUEVO 00920 #264-01-1957 L1989 **GP** *020 †18
ZAITER, Juan Jose. 735 AVE PONCE DE LEON, STE 816 00917 #308-01-1972 L1977 **IM** *020
ZALACAIN, Joaquin Fernand. ■ 00926 #042-01-2008 *012
ZALDUONDO, Fernando M. 1508 ROOSEVELT AV, STE 103 00920 #035-01-1989 L1996 **R RNR** *020 †80
ZAMORA, Maria Soledad. 421 AVE MUNOZ RIVERA, STE 913 00918 #847-06-1990 L1991 **PM** *020
ZAPATA-MARTINEZ, Rafael H. 37 AVE PONCE DE LEON 00901 #042-01-1961 L1964 **PD NPM** *071 †55
ZAPATER, Cesar. 811 CALLE VESTA, URB DOS PINOS 00923 #847-06-1966 L1973 **NS** *020
ZARAGOZA, Rafael H. 513 AVE HOSTOS 00918 #042-01-1987 L1994 **AI PD** *020
ZARAGOZA CASANOVA, J R. 525 AVE FD ROOSEVELT, OFC 808 00918 #847-05-1963 L1967 **PD AI** *020
ZARAGOZA-DIAZ, Elizabeth. ■ 00926 #308-03-1985 L1990 **PD** *020

■ = Address Information Privacy Protected

ZAVALA, Hector Gerardo. 239 AVE ARTERIAL HOSTOS, STE 205 00918 #042-03-1993 L1997 OBG *020

ZAVALA, Oscar F. 1210 AVE MAGDALENA, CONDOMINIUM PAJARELLA COND 00907 #319-04-1980 L1991 DR NR *020

ZAYAS, Angie Linda. 737 VALLE DEL TOA, LOS CAMPOS DE MONTEHIEDRA 00926 #042-01-1989 L1996 P *020

ZAYAS, Edna L. 735 AVE PONCE DE LEON, STE 812 00917 #042-01-1975 L1979 PD *020 †55

ZAYAS, Jose A. 369 AVE DE DIEGO STE 404, TORRE SAN FRANCISCO 00923 #308-03-1986 L1992 PUD *020

ZAYAS MERCADO, Adiana E. ■ 00926 #847-06-1973 L1975 IM *020

ZEDA, Evelyn Aimee. B17 CALLE ROBLES, VILLA HUCAR 00926 #042-03-1999 L2004 OBG *020

ZEGARRA, Jan Pierre. 201 AVE DE DIEGO STE 213, SAN FRANCISCO PLZ 00927 #042-01-1974 L1976 HS *020 †85

ZEGARRA-PAZ, Myrna. 29 CALLE WASHINGTON # 609 00907 #042-01-1959 L1967 P CHP *020 †75

ZERBI-ORTIZ, Alfonso. ■ 00922 #042-01-1955 L1957 CD IM *071

ZIERENBERG, Charles E. 138 AVE WINSTON CHURCHILL, MSC 251 00926 #042-01-1982 L1986 ORS GS *020

ZORRILLA, Carmen Dolores. ■ 00918 #042-01-1978 L1982 OBG *050 †30

ZWEIG, Marie. 37 AVE PONCE DE LEON 00901 #042-03-1983 L1988 OBG *020 †30

SAN LORENZO – SAN LORENZO

APONTE, Madeline Marie. ■ 00754 #042-01-2004 L2008 EM *100

BORGES NUNEZ, Maria D. ■ 00754 #042-04-1992 L1994 PD *020

BURGOS SANTA, Jose E. NARCISO VARONA SUAREZ, ST 53 00754 #308-03-1984 L1988 GP *040

BUXO-LICHE, Ovidio. 6E CALLE DE DIEGO E 00754 #847-05-1967 L1976 GP *071

CANDELARIO-FERNANDEZ, Jose. HC 20 BOX 24403, 181 ST KM 3 HM-1 00754 #649-14-1997 L1999 PD *020

CORDERO, Gustavo Adolfo. 7 CALLE MUNOZ RIVERA N 00754 #308-06-1981 L1985 GP *020

CORREA-CORONAS, Rafael. ■ 00754 #028-34-1959 L1964 ID IM *050 †20

CUEVAS, Wilfredo. C18 URB SAN MIGUEL 00754 #308-03-1983 L1986 GP *020

DE JESUS-DIAZ, Victor. PO BOX 1017, 3 URB APONTE 00754 #308-04-1989 L1990 PD *020

DEL VALLE GALLARZA, Luis. MUNOZ RIVERA N05 00754 #847-05-1972 L1975 IM *020

DEL VALLE REYES, Miriam. ■ 00754 #042-03-1981 L1986 GP *020

DIXON, Paul Henry. PO BOX 1298, 100 JOSE DE DIEJO ST 00754 #308-03-1983 L1988 *020

FERNANDEZ HERNANDEZ, Herac. HC 20 BOX 24388, 183 BO QU 10.4 C/O CARR 00754 #847-13-1988 L1995 *020

FRIAS LOPEZ, Jose Maria. T.M.S. 446 00754 #308-01-1960 L1978 *020

GERENA RAMIREZ, Griselle. CALLE LUIS MUNOZ RIVERA, 202 00754 #308-13-2001 L2003 *100

GONZALEZ-CLAUDIO, Glenda. ■ 00754 #042-03-1993 L1996 ID *020 †20

GONZALEZ-PANTOJA, S. PO BOX 1008 00754 #649-20-1978 L1982 FM *020

HERNANDEZ-APONTE, Gloria. 54 CALLE COLON E, BOX 738 00754 #308-03-1979 L1981 GP *020

LOPEZ COMAS, Mirta Iris. 7 CALLE MUNOZ RIVERA N 00754 #308-03-1981 L1991 GP *020

MEDINA DE JESUS, Ernesto. ■ 00754 #308-04-2001 L2003 GP *020

PARRILLA, Marcos Antonio. JOSE TOUS SOTO #108 SOUTH 00754 #042-03-1993 L1996 IM *020

RODRIGUEZ-FRONTERA, Jose. PO BOX 981 00754 #308-03-1981 L1986 GP OM *020

SANTANA-MACHIN, Victor. 54 CALLE VALERIANO MUNOZ W 00754 #042-01-1980 L1983 PD *020

SELLES, Ramon. 50 MUNOZ RIVERA ST BOX U 00754 #847-04-1958 L1962 GP *071

SIACA COLON, Luis Miguel. 1070 L MUNOZ RIVERA FINAL 00754 #649-14-1995 L1997 *100

TORRES-COLON, Cynthia M. PO BOX 1017 00754 #042-04-1983 L1985 PD *020

VELEZ, Luis Torres. 60 CALLE MUNOZ RIVERA N 00754 #847-10-1965 L1969 *071

VERGARA-GOMEZ, Mark Antho. ■ 00754 #042-01-2004 IM *100 †20

VIRELLA TORRES, Jose A. PO BOX 470 00754 #649-01-1958 L1959 GP OS *020

SAN SEBASTIAN – SAN SEBASTIAN

ACEVEDO, Maria Del Carmen. ■ 00685 #042-01-1987 L1990 PD *020 †55

ACEVEDO RODRIGUEZ, Betzy. 27 CALLE HIPOLITO CASTRO 00685 #649-14-2003 L2004 GP *020

AGUILAR AMIEVA, Hector J. 296 CALLE RUIZ BELVIS 00685 #308-03-1983 L1985 GP *020

ALMEYDA VARGAS, Julio E. 21 CALLE EMILIO RUIZ, MD 00685 #308-06-1985 L1988 *020

ANDUJAR-DE CASTRO, A E. 27 CALLE HIPOLITO CASTRO, P O BOX 588 00685 #308-01-1962 L1969 GP *020

AQUINO CEBOLLERO, Ivan G. PO BOX 3159, HATO ARRIBA STATION 00685 #649-14-2000 L2002 *100

AVILES-PEREZ, Juan. 16 CALLE BETANCES APT 783 00685 #649-01-1943 L1989 OS *075

BRIGNONI, Israel Ruiz. PO BOX 1564 00685 #847-06-1974 L1976 GP *020

CANINO CUMMINGS, Angel. ■ 00685 #847-01-1971 L1975 OBG *020

CARDONA, Nesjuan Faelio. PO BOX 1622, RD 111 KM 22 5 BO PIEDRAS 00685 #649-14-2001 L2003 *100

CARDONA BELTRAN, Ricardo. 901 AVE EMERITO ESTRADA 00685 #308-03-1983 L1988 GP *020

CARRILLO TORRES, Ramon E.. PO BOX 37 00685 #649-14-2000 L2002 *100

CASTELLANOS HERNANDEZ, Son. ■ 00685 #308-06-1988 L2003 *100

CASTRO MONTALVO, Osvaldo. HC 2, 0 CARR 423 HCT 1 HATO 00685 #649-14-2003 L2005 *100

CEBOLLERO-PEREZ, Jesus. ■ 00685 #264-04-1977 L1982 PD PEM *020

CHABRIER MENDEZ, Ivan. ■ 00685 #649-43-1978 L1987 *020

COLON-MORALES, Jose H. ■ 00685 #847-08-1958 L1962 GP PHP *071

DE JESUS-QUINONES, Rafael. PO BOX 592 00685 #308-03-1976 L1979 *020

DELGADO, Iris Yanira. PO BOX 661 00685 #649-14-2000 L2001 *020

GARCIA, David Aroldo. ■ 00685 #308-04-1982 L1984 *100

GONZALEZ, Joanne. ■ 00685 #042-01-2001 L2003 PM *020 †60

GONZALEZ MENDEZ, Joel D.. PO BOX 1270, BO HATO REY 00685 #649-14-2001 L2004 *100

GONZALEZ PONCE, Carmen A. PO BOX 5434 00685 #308-03-1982 L1994 *071

GUZMAN, Luis Felipe. 4100 AVE ARCADIO ESTRADA 00685 #308-03-1983 L1990 GP *020

GUZMAN, Olga E. PO BOX 1601, SAM SG BASTIAM 00685 #308-03-1989 L1991 IM *020

IBARRA, Pedro H. PO BOX 204 00685 #847-04-1961 L1966 D *020

JIMENEZ-ESPINOSA, Manuel. ■ 00685 #042-02-1995 L1998 IM *020

LA SALLE-RUIZ, Confesor. 66 CALLE MJ CABRERO, CENTRO CARDIOVASCULAR 00685 #042-03-1980 L1984 IM CD *020

MENDEZ, Erlando. 17 CALLE BETANCES 00685 #308-06-1984 L1992 GP *020

MONTALVO FABRELLAS, Luis. AA5 CALLE 25, EXT VILLA RITA 00685 #649-14-1976 L1978 GP *020

NIEVES, Robert. PO BOX 2053 00685 #042-03-1981 L1987 PD OS *020

NIEVES RAMOS, Arelis Z. ■ 00685 #308-04-1984 L1987 PD *020

NIEVES-RIVERA, Erick. PO BOX 1756, 201 BELUIS 00685 #308-02-1984 L1986 IM *020

NUNEZ, Fernando Cosme. PO BOX 1636, 32 CALLE EMILIO RUIZ 00685 #847-06-1984 L1986 PD *020

PADUA-HERNANDEZ, Adrian. PO BOX 204, 19 MENDEZ LICIAGA 00685 #308-03-1981 L1983 FM *074

PEREZ, Edith Noemi. ■ 00685 #649-14-2002 L2004 *100

PEREZ, Luis Antonio R. HC 2 BOX 18881, 125 BO CAPA MO 44 CARR 00685 #847-01-1968 L1971 PD *020

PEREZ, William. ■ 00685 #042-03-1984 L1987 PDP *020 †55

PEREZ CRUZ, Luis R.. HC 2 00685 #649-14-1998 L2001 *020

PEREZ LOPEZ, Jesus A. ■ 00685 #847-06-1991 L1995 GP *020

PEREZ SOTO, Omar V. PO BOX 369 00685 #649-30-2002 L2004 *100

PUJOLS, Carmen G. 1153 AVE EMERITO ESTRADA, BOX 1607 00685 #847-04-1984 L1988 GP *020

PUJOLS, Maria De Los A. 1153 AVE EMERITO ESTRADA, ESTRADO RIVERA 00685 #847-04-1984 L1987 P *020

QUINTANA, Myrta Yanira. PO BOX 5028, PONCE, PR 00685 #649-14-1998 L1999 FM *020 †18 ‡

RAMOS, Carlos. ■ 00685 #649-14-1988 L1991 GP *020

RAMOS-GOMEZ, Jacobo. PO BOX 1653 00685 #649-14-1955 L1958 DR *020 †80

RIVERA RIVERA, Erika D. ■ 00685 #649-14-2004 L2006 *100

RIVERA RIVERA, Luis D.. ■ 00685 #649-14-2002 L2004 *100

ROBLES, Angela L. 1151 AVE EMERITO ESTRADA 00685 #042-01-1989 L1992 PD *020 †55

ROBLES-CARDONA, Juan S. PO BOX 609 00685 #308-01-1975 L1978 FM IM *020

RODON HERNANDEZ, Diana E. PO BOX 3686 00685 #649-35-1999 L2002 *020

RODON VERA, Nestor A. ■ 00685 #847-08-1975 L1978 P *020

RODRIGUEZ-DELGADO, Iris E. PO BOX 204 00685 #042-01-1999 L2001 CHP *020

RODRIGUEZ VAZQUEZ, E. BOX 486 00685 #308-02-1976 L1978 GP *075

ROSELLO TORRES, Anibal. PO BOX 1803P 00685 #308-03-1982 L2003 *100

RUIZ RAMIREZ, Carmen A.. PO BOX 1636 00685 #847-06-1988 L1994 *075

SOTO, Leslie Ann. ■ 00685 #042-01-2007 *012

SOTO GUERRERO, Yazmin Joh. PO BOX 813 00685 #308-04-2003 L2005 *100

TORRES, Gabriel G. BO PIEDRAS BLANCA 00685 #308-03-1984 L1990 IM *020

TORRES-ACEVEDO, Eric M. BO PIEDRAS BLANCAS, REPARTO UGINAS #10 00685 #308-03-1982 L1984 *020

VARGAS-NAZARIO, Analicia. ■ 00685 #042-01-2006 P *012

VARGAS QUINONES, Cesar I. 4100 AVE ARCADIO ESTRADA, STE 222 00685 #308-03-1985 L1995 GP *020

SANTA ISABEL – SANTA ISABEL

COLL-PEREZ, Maria J. ■ 00757 #847-01-1977 L1980 PD *071

CRUZ RENDON, Louis A. URB VILLA REITRO NORTE C-1 00757 #649-14-1999 L2004 *100

DAVID, Salomon J. 3 CALLE RUIZ BELVIS 00757 #042-01-1991 L1997 *020

DOMENECH, Luis F. 36 CALLE MUNOZ RIVERA, MEDICO CIRUJANO 00757 #308-04-1983 L1989 GP *020

GODINEAUX MANFREDY, Yamilk. HC 1 BOX 3562 00757 #649-14-2003 L2005 *100

GOGLAS, Carlos Alberto. 17200 CALLE MARGARITA, HACIENDA CONCORDIA 00757 #308-06-1987 L2004 *100

GUEVAREZ, Dargee Emid. 2025 CALLE GUARAGUAO, BRISAS DEL PRADO 00757 #649-14-2001 *020

HEAL, David D. 14 CALLE BETANCES 00757 #308-04-1989 L1993 *020

IGUINA-DE LA ROSA, Maria. 7 CALLE CELIS AGUILERA 00757 #308-02-1980 L1986 GP *020 ‡

MARTINEZ-CAMPOS, Jose E. 69 CALLE CELIS AGUILERA, PLAZA DEL PARQUE OFIC. #5 00757 #042-04-1989 L1990 OBG *020

MORENO RODRIGUEZ, Luis A. ■ 00757 #847-10-1970 L1973 GP EM *020

PAOLI BREBAN, Waldemar. ■ 00757 #649-30-2001 L2004 *100

PEREZ OJEDA, Raul. 16 CALLE CELIS AGUILERA, # 788 00757 #847-04-1963 L1966 GP *020

QUESTELL, David Rafael. 30C CALLE BETANCES 00757 #308-03-1984 L1993 IM *020

QUILES ROSAS, Jose Daniel. 54 CALLE MUNOZ RIVERA, BOX 645 00757 #308-03-1983 L1985 GP *020

RODRIGUEZ FERNANDEZ, Ramon. PO BOX 503 00757 #649-14-2000 L2006 *100

RODRIGUEZ-MARTINEZ, H L. ■ 00757 #308-03-1977 L1979 P *020

RODRIGUEZ MEDINA, Hector. ■ 00757 #042-01-2007 *012

SOTO-NOGUERAS, Vicente. 11284 CALLE AMAPOLA, HACIENDA CONCORDIA 00757 #308-03-1979 L1982 PD *020

TOSADO, Juan Antonio. 15408 CALLE FLAMBOYAN, PASEO JACARANDA 00757 #308-02-1999 L2001 OBG *020

VARGAS RODRIGUEZ, Dianabel. ■ 00757 #649-30-2001 L2004 *100

SANTURCE – SAN JUAN

ABRAHAM, Eduardo. PO BOX 6672 00914 #308-01-1973 L1975 OBG *020

ACEVEDO REYES, Angel L. ■ 00907 #042-03-1996 *100

ADORNO RIVERA, Milagros. 182 CALLE PEREZ, COND HEMI APTO C-6 00911 #649-14-1991 L1994 *020

AGUIAR, Olga. ■ 00907 #275-01-1948 L1972 P GP *020

ALBERTY FIGUEROA, Edgardo. 1452 CALLE AMERICO SALAS 00909 #847-03-1972 L1975 PD *020

ALICEA, Dhilma L. 1519 AVE PONCE DE LEON, STE 1119 00909 #042-01-1994 L1997 P *020

ALMODOVAR, Pablo I. 611 CALLE DR PAVI FDZ #201 00909 #042-01-1968 L1970 D PD *020 †15

ALVARADO, Carlos J. ■ 00907 #042-01-1966 L1973 R *040 †80

ALVAREZ, Antolin Jose. 1801 AVE PONCE DE LEON, STE 213 00909 #042-01-1977 L1981 OPH *020

ALVAREZ, Carmen M. 601 COND PARQUE CNTRL #601 00912 #308-03-1987 L1991 **P** *020

AMARANTE, Alfredo Osiris. 65 CALLE SANTIAGO IGLESIAS, CONDADO 00907 #308-01-1963 L1975 **OS** *020

APONTE-MARQUEZ, Rene. ■ 00907 #308-03-1982 L1989 **GP** *020

ARANGUITI, Jose. ■ 00907 #847-04-1965 L1978 **AN** *020

ARROYO, Juan Gerardo. 253 CALLE SAN JORGE, STE 2-A 00912 #042-01-1981 L1985 **PD** *020

ARSUAGA, Jose Lorenzo. CALLE ASIA 1503 5 PISO 22 00909 #042-01-1982 L1987 **OTO** *020 †45

AYALA, Elvia Arelis. 1822 AVE PONCE DE LEON #26 00909 #649-14-2001 L2002 **GP** *020

BAUZA, Julio C. 403 CALLE SAN JORGE 00912 #924-01-1970 L1978 **PDC PD** *020 †55

BERBERIAN, Anahid. 13 CALLE CERVANTES 00907 #913-38-1967 L1980 **GP OS** *020 ‡

BERIO, Maria T. 1451 AVE ASHFORD, STE B 00907 #021-01-1949 L1952 **GYN** *071 †30

BERIO-SUAREZ, Jose M. 1451 AVE ASHFORD STE B 00907 #041-09-1944 L1989 **GE IM** *072

BERROA BAEZ, Cesar August. 101 CALLE DEL RIO 00911 #308-03-2002 L2004 *100

BERROCAL, Maria Hortensia. 150 AVE DE DIEGO, STE 404 00907 #016-11-1986 L1988 **OPH** *020 †35

BLASINI, Aida L. 1503 CALLE ASIA, 1ST FL 00909 #042-01-1982 L1984 **IM** *020 ‡

BORDET VILLA, Fernando. ■ 00909 #308-01-1986 L1993 **GP** *020

BOTI POMBO, Fernando. 662 CALLE HOARE # 14 00907 #132-01-1952 L1975 **GP PD** *020

BUXEDA, Adriano Roberto. 110 ASHFORD MEDICAL CTR 00907 #042-04-1981 L1983 **GP** *020

CABRERA, Jorge Antonio. ■ 00912 #649-14-1995 L1997 *020

CACERES, Mayra Enid. 1462 CALLE PROF AUGST RDRG, FACULTAD MEDICA 00909 #042-03-1996 L2002 **PEM** *020

CAMINO, Richard F. 258 CALLE SAN JORGE, STE 203 00912 #042-03-1983 L1989 **CHP ADP** *020 †75

CAMUNAS DE VAZQUEZ, Maria. ■ 00907 #042-01-1954 L1961 **GP OS** *040

CARABALLO-SANTIAGO, Albert. 00914 #042-01-1980 L1982 **GP** *074

CARDONA, Victor Joaquin. 1462 CALLE ASIA 00909 #042-01-1988 L1995 **PM** *020

CARDONA CAMPOS, Ivan R. 1409 CALLE FERIA # 20 00909 #042-01-1963 L1967 **NS** *075 †25

CARLOS, Ramon. ■ 00907 #847-04-1955 L1957 **AN PTH** *050

CARMONA, Rosalinda. ■ 00907 #042-03-2008 *012

CARRANZA, Arturo. CUVILLAS 554 CURTO A MIRMA 00907 #847-02-1968 L1972 **PM** *020

CARRERAS, Jose Antonio. 1462 CALLE ASIA 00909 #042-03-1981 L1986 **AN PME** *020

CARRO, Eric Francisco. ■ 00909 #042-01-1974 L1976 **NS** *020 †25

CASTANER, Alberto Amador. ■ 00907 #024-01-1944 L1950 **OBG** *071 †30

CASTILLO, Marta Anisia. 304 CALLE SANTA CECILIA, VILLA PALMERA 00912 #275-01-1983 L2005 *100

CASTRO-BETANCES, Geraldo. 107 CALLE SANTA CECILIA 00911 #308-03-1989 L2005 **GP** *020

CAUSSADE, Wilfredo. 1462 CALLE ASIA 00909 #847-10-1966 L1969 **U** *020

CESAR, Aura. 1396 CALLE SAN RAFAEL, SUITE NO. 7 00909 #187-80-1971 L1979 **P** *020

CHINEA, Luis E. 1801 AVE PONCE DE LEON, SUITE #210 00909 #042-01-1987 L1993 **U GS** *095

CHINEA-MARTINEZ, Angel R. 655 CALLE PAVIA STE 101 00909 #847-08-1979 L1983 **N** *020

CHIQUES, Carlos Miguel. 1519 AVE PONCE DE LEON, OFFICE #701 STOP 23 00909 #023-01-1941 L1942 **OPH** *071 †35

CLAUDIO, Jaime Jose. 1462 CALLE ASIA 00909 #042-01-1978 L1982 **FM GPM** *020 †18

COLLAZO, Ernesto Luis. 1503 CALLE ASIA, SECOND FLOOR 00909 #035-19-1986 L1994 **OPH** *072 †35

COLON-DUENO, Luis Armando. ■ 00915 #308-03-1980 L1989 **FM** *020

COLON ROSA, Emma Rafaela. ■ 00907 #847-04-1971 L1975 **GP** *020

COPPOLA, Angelo. 1462 CALLE ASIA 00909 #042-03-1984 L1987 **FM** *020 †18

CORDOVA LOPEZ, Arturo R. 1462 CALLE ASIA 00909 #042-01-1972 L1979 **PUD CCM** *020 †20

CORTES, Rosa A. 1760 CALLE LOIZA, STE 201 COND MADRID 00911 #042-01-1990 L1992 **PTH** *020

CORTES-SOTO, Gregorio A. 1462 CALLE ASIA 00909 #042-04-1984 L1986 **IM** *020

CRESPO-CARRILLO, Jorge. 1462 CALLE ASIA 00909 #308-04-1982 L1988 **U** *020

CRUZ, Arnaldo B. 1396 CALLE SAN RAFAEL, STE 13 MEDICAL PAVILION 00909 #042-01-1981 L1985 **P ADP** *020 †75

CRUZ, Jose Ramon. 1519 AVE PONCE DE LEON, STE 705 00909 #042-01-1993 L1999 **REN** *020 †30

DALMAU, Miguel S. 653 AVE HIPODROMO 00909 #023-01-1943 L1944 **GYN P** *072 †30

DAVILA, Rafael A. STOP 23, 1ST FEDERAL BLGD OFF 305 00909 #649-01-1956 L1959 **GP AM** *072

DAVILA-CINTRON, Luis R. 851 CALLE LAFAYETTE 00909 #649-01-1949 L1959 **PD** *071

DAVILA VELEZ, Jorge L. 1818 AVE FERNANDEZ JUNCOS, PDA. 251/2 00909 #847-05-1966 L1968 **NS** *020

DEDUAL-NIEDERBERGER, E. 611 CALLE PAVIA STE 203, PARADA 22 00909 #042-01-1976 L1981 **PD** *020

DE LA HUERGA-MARTINEZ, D. 1458 CALLE AIBONITO, URB HIPODROMO 00909 #308-01-1951 L1964 **GP** *020

DE LA ROSA, Luis Javier. 1449 CALLE AMERICO SALAS, STE 201 00909 #042-01-1973 L1975 **OBG** *030

DELGADO GONZALEZ, Americo. PO BOX 7306 00916 #275-01-1957 L1963 **GP OS** *071

DELGADO-MEJIAS, Milton O. 519 CALLE FELIPE R GOYCO 00915 #308-03-1978 L1990 **GP** *020

DEL VALLE, Enid Marie. 407 CALLE SAN JORGE, SAN JORGE MED OFFICE BLDG 00912 #042-01-1991 L1995 **PD PPR** *020 †55

DENIZ MARQUEZ, Juan. 1801 AVE PONCE DE LEON, SANTURCE MEDICAL MALL 00909 #847-06-1976 L1981 **OS N** *020

DE PATTERNE, Dolores D. CALLE AIBON 1458 URB HIPOD 00909 #308-01-1951 L1964 **GP PD** *020

DIAZ, Angeles. 1394 CALLE FERIA 00909 #041-13-1943 L1945 **PS GS** *020

DIAZ, Carlos R. 1449 CALLE AMERICO SALAS, STE 102 00909 #042-01-1987 L1990 **CD** *020

DIAZ COLON, Antonio M. ■ 00911 #847-03-1982 L1982 **IM** *020

DIAZ-GARCIA, Dilia. 307 ASHFORD MEDCL CTR #307, CONDADO 00907 #847-10-1978 L1983 **END IM** *020 †20

DIAZ-PRADO, Hector Manuel. CALLE CALMA #57 OCEAN PARK 00911 #275-01-1963 L1975 **GP** *020

DURIEUX-MILLAND, Amarilis. EDIF 651 OF 104, CALLE MANUEL PAVIA 00909 #042-01-1979 L1984 **ORS** *020 †40

ESPINOSA, Angel F. 68 CALLE WASHINGTON 00907 #042-01-1973 L1978 **PDC PD** *020

ESPINOSA BAEZ, Esther M. ■ 00907 #275-01-1951 L1964 **OM PHP** *020

FERNANDEZ, Adry Cecilia. 359 AVE DE DIEGO, OFICINA 301 00909 #042-01-1977 L1982 *020

FERNANDEZ, David Eduardo. 252 CALLE SAN JORGE, OFF 308 SAN JORGE MED BLDG 00912 #042-01-1983 L1986 **PG PD** *020 †55

FERNANDEZ, Orlando Sixto. 150 AVE DE DIEGO, STE 603 00907 #008-01-1979 L1988 **ORS GS** *020 †40

FERNANDEZ, Rene. 1701 AVE PONCE DE LEON, STE 101 00909 #042-01-1983 L1990 **REN** *020 †30

FERNANDEZ ROSA, Carlos A. AV BORENQUIN 2203-BO OBRER 00915 #308-03-1977 L1979 **FM** *020

FERREIRA, Adalgisa J.. 106 CALLE DEL RIO 00911 #308-01-1981 L2006 *100

FIGUEROA, Myrna S. 252 CALLE SAN JORGE, STE 504 00912 #042-01-1985 L1985 **PD** *020 †55

FIGUEROA-CASAS, Jose Luis. 655 CALLE PAVIA 00909 #847-01-1975 L1981 **IM** *040

FLEISHER, T Lawrence. ■ 00911 #042-01-1956 L1960 **D** *071 †15

FLORES-DE JESUS, Glyced. 359 DE DIEGO AVE 5TH FL, STE 501 00909 #847-23-1983 L1988 **FM** *020 ‡

FONFRIAS, Walter L. AVE JOSE DE DIEGO 357 00909 #847-03-1972 L1976 **GS** *020

FONSECA RIVERA, Manuela A. ■ 00912 #308-06-1987 L1991 *020

FORTUNO, Roberto F. 1462 CALLE ASIA 00909 #016-02-1950 L1989 **U** *071 †95

FREYRE-GOMEZ, Jose Luis. 1502 CALLE ASIA STOP 22 00909 #042-01-1958 L1964 **N** *020

FRIAS, Rafael Dolores. 1257 AVE PONCE DE LEON, APT 3A 00907 #308-03-1984 L1988 **GP** *020

FUMERO, Juan. 29 CALLE WASHINGTON, STE 310 00907 #042-03-1988 L1989 **P** *020

GARCIA, Jose Eduardo. ■ 00911 #847-04-1963 L1971 **AN PUD** *020 †05

GARCIA-BIRD, Jorge. 206 ASHFORD MEDICAL CTR 00907 #051-01-1941 L1941 **OBG** *071 †30

GARCIA MEDINA, Benjamin. ■ 00909 #308-01-1963 L1975 *100

GARCIA-RINALDI, Raul. 1462 CALLE ASIA 00909 #042-01-1966 L1979 **TS VS** *020 †85,90

GAUDIER, Frank Antonio. C/O PO BOX 11792, #611 PAVIA ST, STE 113 00910 #308-02-1977 L1979 **DR EM** *020 †80

GIL-DEL ROSARIO, Valentin. 371 SAN JORGE 36 PDA 25 00912 #308-01-1957 L1972 **GP** *020

GOMEZ, Alberto Sanabria. ■ 00911 #042-04-1984 L1986 **GP** *030

GOMEZ DISDIER, Manuel F. SAN JORGE HOSPITAL 00912 #847-04-1958 L1961 **PD** *020 †55

GOMEZ-FORTUNA, Lidia. 1460 CALLE AIBONITO 00909 #308-01-1976 L1984 *020

GONZALEZ, Carlos. 252 CALLE SAN JORGE STE 5, SAN JORGE MEDICAL OFFICE B 00912 #042-01-1979 L1990 **PDO HNS** *020 †45

GONZALEZ, Migdalia. ■ 00911 #042-01-1974 L1976 **CD CCM** *071

GONZALEZ, Sandy Manuel. 1492 AVE PONCE DE LEON, STE 709 00907 #042-01-1979 L1990 **PS HS** *020 †85,65

GONZALEZ-ARROYO, Efrain. 1801 AVE PONCE DE LEON, STE 308 00909 #308-03-1978 L1981 **END IM** *020

GONZALEZ-GIERBOLINI, C. ■ 00914 #847-04-1975 L1985 **OBG** *020

GONZALEZ PEREZ, Rogelio. 1820 AVE FERNANDEZ JUNCOS 00909 #847-02-1967 L1975 **IM** *020

GONZALEZ VICENTE, Sandy. 1492 AVE PONCE DE LEON, STE 709 00907 #847-04-1968 L1973 **FM** *020

GUILIANI-MALDONADO, Julio. ■ 00907 #847-05-1961 L1964 **IM OS** *020

GUTIERREZ, Victor S. 651 CALLE PAVIA # 651 00909 #042-01-1961 L1963 **GS ON** *020 †85

GUZMAN-ACOSTA, Carlos. 655 CALLE EUROPA 00909 #024-05-1946 L1947 **R** *020 †80

HEYLIGER SANCHEZ, Eduardo. 650 CALLE LLOVERAS, EDIF CENTRO PLAZA 00909 #847-04-1966 L1970 **OBG** *020

ISALES, Ramon Fernandez. 1479 ASHFORD 319 CON DEL 00907 #649-01-1956 L1989 **OBG OS** *075

JAVARIZ, Jose Rafael. SUITE 201 STOP 20, 653 HIPODROMO AVE 00909 #649-01-1967 L1972 **GP OS** *020

JIMENEZ, Maria Teresa. 1462 CALLE ASIA 00909 #042-01-1972 L1974 **PUD IM** *020

LANDRON, Jose Ramon. 501 ASHFORD MEDICAL CTR 00907 #042-01-1957 L1962 **DR** *062

LANDRON-GUARDIOLA, Jose R. 501 ASHFORD MEDICAL CTR 00907 #042-01-1978 L1982 **DR** *020 †80

LAZARO, Nancy Marlene. ■ 00912 #042-01-2000 L2002 **PD** *100

LEE-PIMENTEL, Charles Jay. BOX 9207 00908 #869-04-1955 L1957 **OPH** *071 †35

LLINAS-CHULIAN, Juana. PO BOX 14457, BO. OBREROS-STATION 00916 #847-02-1969 L1983 **GP** *020

LOPEZ, Hilton Luis. ■ 00916 #023-01-1938 L1989 **P** *020

LOPEZ DE VICTORIA, Manuel. 1396 CALLE SAN RAFAEL, MEDICAL PAV OFICINA 21-22 00909 #042-01-1960 L1964 **OPH** *020 †35

LOPEZ-ENRIQUEZ, Alberto T. 1462 CALLE ASIA 00909 #042-01-1979 L1983 **HO ON** *020 †20

LOPEZ-GALARZA, Lourdes M. 1394 CALLE SAN RAFAEL, SUITE 10 MEDICAL PAVILLIO 00909 #308-03-1983 L1989 **PD** *020

LOPEZ PONS, Manuel. PROFESSIONAL BLDG 00909 #847-01-1956 L1963 **PD** *020

LUGO DEL TORO, Alberto E. 303 DE DIEGO AVE 00909 #010-02-1952 L1953 **AN PUD** *071 †20

LYNCH, Lauren. 607A CALLE DEL PARQUE, MATERNAL FETAL MEDICINE & 00909 #042-01-1981 L1992 **MFM OBG** *020 †19,30

MALDONADO, Victor Kevin. 275 CALLE CONVENTO, CLINICA DE OJOS MALDONADO- 00912 #042-03-1998 L2004 **OPH** *020 †35

MARCHAN, Roberto F. 1822 AVE PONCE DE LEON 00909 #042-01-1974 L1980 **DR PDR** *020 †80

MARCHAND, Ernesto J. 1462 CALLE ASIA 00909 #028-34-1943 L1946 **IM CD** *072 †20

MARCHAN JASPARD, Ivette. 1511 CALLE LOIZA, PARK MEDICAL BUILDING 00911 #847-04-1956 L1959 **GP** *020

MARCIAL-SEOANE, Manuel A. 1760 CALLE LOIZA, STE 203 00911 #042-01-1979 L1985 **PTH** *020 †50

MARRERO, Pablo Vladimir. 1507 AVE PONCE DE LEON, PDA. 22 00909 #042-01-1985 L1990 **ORS** *020 †40

MATOS VILELLA, Carlos. 1431 AVE PONCE DE LEON, STE 501 00907 #649-14-1988 L1991 **IM** *020

MATTEI, Eduardo. 1396 CALLE SAN RAFAEL, STE 3 00909 #042-01-1971 L1973 **OTO** *020 †45

MATTEI LOUIS, Jorge E. 655 CALLE PAVIA, OFICINA 202 00909 #649-14-1993 L1995 **IM** *020

MEDINA, Eduardo Jose. BOX 9238 FDZ JUNCOS STAT 00910 #847-04-1955 L1958 **R** *020 †80

MENDEZ, Rosario Nereida. 258 CALLE SAN JORGE, SAN JORGE CHILDREN'S HOSPI 00912 #042-03-1991 L1995 **PM** *020 †60

MENDEZ-BEAUCHAMP, Victor. 1462 CALLE ASIA 00909 #847-04-1962 L1965 **CD IM** *020

MENDEZ-CASHION, Dolores. 600 COND SAN JORGE, COND LAS CARMELITAS 12D 00912 #051-04-1937 L1937 **PD** *075 †55

MIRABAL, Miriam R. 252 CALLE SAN JORGE, SN JORGE MED OFC BLDG #401 00912 #042-01-1988 L1997 **PDP** *020 †55

MODESTO, Gilberto. ■ 00915 #308-03-1986 L2005 *100

MONSEGUR BASSATT, Jose R. ■ 00907 #308-04-1981 L1987 *075

MONTALVO, Lillian Marie. 00913 #042-01-1998 L1999 **D** *020 †15

MONTANEZ-DELERME, L. 1462 CALLE ASIA 00909 #847-10-1975 L1978 **IM** *020

MONTILLA-LOPEZ, Fernando. 611 PAVIA FERNANDEZ ST, PAVIA MED PLZ OFFICE 205 00909 #042-01-1961 L1964 **GYN** *020 †30

MORALES, Alcira. PO BOX 6785 00914 #847-01-1971 L1977 **OM** *020

MORALES FERRER, Carmen L. ■ 00907 #042-01-1963 L1966 **PD OS** *020
MORENO, Esteban. ■ 00911 #041-13-1951 L1954 **PTH** *071 †50
MUJICA, Jose Mestre. COND COBONS PLAZA 1910 00912 #847-10-1974 L1989 *020
NARVAEZ, Angel Manuel. 30 CALLE WASHINGTON, STE 3 00907 #649-14-1999 L2001 *020
NEGRON, Jorge Alberto. 1462 CALLE ASIA 00909 #042-01-1977 L1981 **OBG** *020 †30
NIEVES-VALLE, Luis M. 1452 CALLE AMERICO SALAS, STOP 22 00909 #847-10-1963 L1966 **U** *020
NIN-TORREGROSA, Jose Luis. 1801 AVE PONCE DE LEON, SANTURCE MEDICAL MALL 00909 #042-01-1969 L1972 **NEP IM** *020
NUNEZ DE ASMAR, Neida. BOX 12161 LOIZA STA 00914 #041-13-1952 L1953 **PD OS** *071 †55
OCASIO PAOLI, Jose E. ■ 00911 #308-03-1977 L1980 **FM OM** *020
OQUENDO, Luciano, III. 1462 CALLE ASIA 00909 #042-01-1999 L2000 **FM** *020
ORTEGA, Ramon Luis. 1462 CALLE ASIA 00909 #042-01-1974 L1976 **RHU IM** *020 †20 ‡
ORTIZ, Luis Ariel. 352 CALLE DEL PARQUE, NOFFA MEDICAL CENTER 00912 #308-03-1995 L2001 **GP** *020
ORTIZ ARIAS, Claudio. 1822 AVE PONCE DE LEON #26 00909 #308-01-1960 L1975 *020
ORTIZ-CLAS, Wilfredo. 1396 CALLE SAN RAFAEL, STE 15 00909 #847-04-1971 L1974 **FM** *020 ‡
ORTIZ-FREEMAN, Ydalia. 1477 ASHLAND NO 706 00907 #023-01-1941 L1942 **PD CHP** *071 †55
PACHECO MEDINA, Raysa R. 1466 CALLE SAN RAFAEL, URB. HIPODROMO 00909 #308-03-1987 L2004 *100
PAEZ GONZALEZ, Pedro P. 410 COND CONDADO, ASHFORD MEDICAL CENTER 00907 #308-03-1982 L1987 **CD** *020
PANTOJAS CONCEPCION, C. 1801 AVE PONCE DE LEON, STE 306 00909 #042-03-1984 L1988 **RHU IM** *020 ‡
PEREYO, Luis A. SANTIAGO IGLESIAS 65 703 00907 #847-04-1960 L1963 **GP** *071
PEREZ, Carlos E. ■ 00911 #042-02-2001 **OTO** *012
PEREZ, Manuel Roberto. 1462 CALLE ASIA 00909 #042-01-1973 L1976 **DR VIR** *020 †80
PEREZ-FERRARI, Rafael E. ■ 00911 #042-03-1981 L1985 **FM EM** *075
PEREZ LINARES, Jose A. ■ 00907 #847-09-1957 L1961 **AN** *071
PEREZ MARTINEZ, Manuel. 267 COND SAN JORGE, 8B SAN JORGE GARDENS 00912 #847-04-1957 L1961 **GS** *071
PLA MORALES, Francisco J. CALLE AMERICO SALAS 00909 #847-01-1974 L1976 **OBG OS** *020
PLAZA-CARRILLO, Laura C. ■ 00913 #042-01-1989 L1993 **PM** *020
POLANCO-RIVERA, Jose E. 709 CALLE UNION PH MIRAMA 00907 #035-19-1950 L1951 **GP** *071
PORRATA-DORIA, Rafael, Jr. ■ 00911 #021-05-1942 L1943 **GP OS** *071
PORTELA, Ramon M. 1396 CALLE SAN RAFAEL, MEDICAL PAV OFICINA 21-22 00909 #042-01-1965 L1969 **OPH PO** *020 †35
PORTILLA-PINON, Antonio M. ■ 00911 #308-03-1979 L1983 **GP** *020
POU, Antonio. 207 ASHFORD MEDICAL CTR, CONDADO 00907 #042-01-1978 L1982 **OBG** *020 †30
PURAS, Antonio. 1431 AVE PONCE DE LEON, STE 601 00907 #042-01-1971 L1973 **U** *020 †95
QUILES-LUGO, Manuel A. 650 CALLE LLOVERAS, EDIF CENTRO PLAZA STE 103 00909 #042-01-1985 L1987 **CD IM** *020 †20 ‡
QUINONES-RECIO, Rolando. ■ 00911 #847-05-1975 L1978 *020
RAMIREZ, Sergio Ricardo. 1462 CALLE ASIA 00909 #847-09-1957 L1960 **PD** *020
RAMIREZ-PEREZ, Felix. 1822 AVE PONCE DE LEON #26 00909 #847-08-1978 L1982 **EM FM** *020
RAMIREZ SANTONI, David F. 1412 CALLE AMERICO SALAS 00909 #847-04-1957 L1960 **IM CD** *075
RAMIREZ-SMITH, Kenneth. 660 CALLE MIRAMAR 00907 #041-09-1940 L1941 *071
RAMOS, Edwin. 1760 CALLE LOIZA STE 201 00911 #042-01-1980 L1985 **PTH** *030 †50
RAMOS CORTES, Eduardo. 264 CALLE CONVENTO 00912 #042-01-1989 L1995 **PM** *020 †60
RAMOS-PADRO, Rosalina. 104 DONCLLA PTA LAS MARIA 00913 #847-01-1968 L1971 **AN** *020
RAMOS VELEZ, Wanda. 359 AVE DE DIEGO, COND. DE DIEGO SUITE 501 00909 #042-04-1989 L1990 **IM** *020
RAPOPORT, Alan Haskel. 29 CALLE WASHINGTON STE 6, ASHFORD MED CTR 00907 #024-01-1961 L1963 **IM ON** *020 †20
RENGEL, Ricardo E. 707 ASHFORD MEDICAL CTR 00907 #035-20-1952 L1953 **OPH** *071 †35
RENJIFO-ROMERO, Claudio. 1462 CALLE ASIA 00909 #264-05-1972 L1982 **END IM** *020 †20
RICO, Angel Ernesto. ■ 00911 #275-01-1991 L2007 *100
RIFKINSON, Nathan. 309 ASHFORD MEDICAL CTR 00907 #012-05-1936 L1943 **NS** *071 †25
RIGAU MARQUES, Jose M. 1822 AVE PONCE DE LEON #26 00909 #847-04-1955 L1957 **GS PUD** *072
RIOS, Luis Alberto. 1507 AVE PONCE DE LEON, PDA. 22 00909 #042-03-1996 L2000 **ORS** *020 †40
RIVERA, Carmen. 603 AVE HIPODROMO, CONDOMINIO PLAZA 20 APT. 1 00909 #847-04-1982 L1986 **GP** *020
RIVERA, Jaime Jose. ■ 00911 #042-01-1974 L1976 **NM IM** *020 †28
RIVERA, Robert. 1462 CALLE ASIA 00909 #042-01-1993 L1999 **DR** *020 †80
RIVERO, Manuel A. 1760 CALLE LOIZA, STE 201 00911 #042-03-1989 L1994 **PTH** *020 †50
RODRIGUEZ, Arismendy. EDIF 5 APT PH1, ISLA VERDE LAGUNA GAR 00907 #308-01-1976 L1991 **GP** *020
RODRIGUEZ, Benigno F. 1801 AVE PONCE DE LEN #210 00909 #042-01-1976 L1981 **U** *020 †95
RODRIGUEZ, Hector G. 312 DE DIEGO AVE, CENTER BUILDING SUITE 503 00909 #847-13-1956 L1959 **IM** *071
RODRIGUEZ, Juan J. 1396 CALLE SAN RAFAEL, MEDICAL PAVILLION SUITE 4 00909 #042-04-1983 L1986 **P PFP** *020
RODRIGUEZ, Maribel. 359 DE DIEGO AVE, STE 302 00909 #042-01-1975 L1980 **GE IM** *050
RODRIGUEZ, Segundo A, Jr. 611 CALLE PAVIA STE 110, PAVIA MEDICAL PLAZA 00909 #042-03-1989 L1995 **CRS GS** *020 †85,10
RODRIGUEZ-CHRISTENSEN, J. 702 ASHFORD MEDICAL CTR 00907 #847-01-1956 L1961 **ORS** *072
RODRIGUEZ-NEGRON, Luis A. 1394 CALLE SAN RAFAEL, MEDICAL PAVILION #19 00909 #042-01-1954 L1956 **U** *020 †95
RODRIGUEZ-PEREZ, Federico. 1431 AVE PONCE DE LEON, STE 402 00907 #042-01-1985 L1988 **GE NEP** *020 †20
RODRIGUEZ-SAENZ, Jorge L. 260 CALLE CONVENTO 00912 #042-02-1994 L1998 **PM** *020 †60
RODRIGUEZ VECCHINI, Luis. ■ 00907 #847-01-1971 L1975 **P** *020
ROJAS, Luis Raul. 653 AVE HIPODROMO 00909 #042-01-1963 L1971 **OBG OS** *020
ROMERO, Calixto A. 83 CALLE CARIBE 00907 #041-01-1945 L1947 **IM** *071 †20

ROSADO-FIGUEROA, Raul. ■ 00907 #308-03-1985 L1986 **GP** *020
ROSA LAGUER, Ernie. ■ 00908 #308-03-1982 L1996 **GP** *020
ROSARIO ROBLES, Anibal. 1462 CALLE ASIA 00909 #308-03-1983 L1996 **IM** *020
ROSSELLO, Juan A. ■ 00911 #023-01-1938 L1938 **P** *071
SAIS, Carlos J. ASHFORD MEDICAL CTR, ASHFORD MEDICAL CTR 00907 #012-05-1952 L1954 **R** *020 †80
SALGADO MORALES, Juan L. 607A CALLE DEL PARQUE, MATERNAL FETAL & GINECOLOG 00909 #042-03-1984 L1987 **OBG** *020 †30
SANCHEZ, Antonio. 1801 AVE PONCE DE LEON, STE 412 00909 #042-01-1994 L1997 **P** *020 †75
SANCHEZ, Jorge P. 653 AVE HIPODROMO, STE 102 00909 #042-01-1988 L1991 **OBG** *020
SANCHEZ DEL VALLE, M A. 1394 CALLE SAN RAFAEL, MEDICAL PAVILION SUITE 9 00909 #042-01-1969 L1975 **OBG OS** *020
SANDOVAL, Roberto R. 1822 AVE PONCE DE LEON #26 00909 #308-04-1987 L1992 **IM** *020
SANTIAGO, Allan. 705 ASHFORD MEDICAL CTR, STE 705 00907 #042-01-1981 L1984 **IM** *020
SANTIAGO, Dwight Manuel. 306 ASHFORD MEDICAL CTR 00907 #042-01-1973 L1975 **IM ISM** *020
SANTIAGO, Felix. OFICINA 111, CALLE MANUEL PAVIA #611 00910 #042-01-1976 L1981 **ORS** *020
SANTIAGO, Ubaldo Gerardo. 1304 CALLE WILSON APT 85 00907 #042-03-1996 L2000 **IM** *020
SANTIAGO-CORNIER, Alberto. 408 CALLE SAN JORGE, SAN JORGE MED BLDG 00912 #308-03-1985 L1993 **MG PD** *020
SANTIAGO MARQUEZ, Maria. 1004 CALLE CERRA ANDINO 00907 #308-03-1983 L1995 **GP** *020
SEMIDEY, Jose A. ■ 00907 #051-01-1951 L1968 **AN OBG** *020
SHUB, Leonel. 803 AVE HIPODROMO 00909 #042-01-1989 L1992 **EM OM** *020
SIFRE, Ramon Alberto. 1462 CALLE ASIA 00909 #308-04-1982 L1986 **OBG GS** *020 †30
SILVA-FORT, Raul G. 1462 CALLE ASIA 00909 #041-13-1957 L1959 **OBG** *020 †30
SOLTERO-RAMIREZ, Jose M. 1801 AVE PONCE DE LEON, STOP 26 00909 #649-01-1955 L1958 **FM** *030
SUAREZ, Ramon M, Jr. C/O APARTADO 41245, AVE DE DIEGO 303 PDA 22 00940 #051-04-1945 L1946 **IM** *072 †20
TIRADO, Nestor C. ■ 00911 #042-01-1976 L1980 **IM** *020
TORO FREIRE, Cesar Angel. 604 CALLE ELLIOT PL # 6 00907 #042-01-1957 L1962 **GS** *071 †20
TORRES, Antoliano. 1452 CALLE AMRC SLS 2ND FL 00909 #042-01-1974 L1976 **PD** *020
TORRES, Luz E. BOX 7597 00916 #042-03-1980 L1986 **PM** *075
TORRES-COLON, Candido R. 1462 CALLE ASIA 00909 #847-01-1969 L1973 **D** *020 †15
TORRES DE JESUS, Hector R. 609 AVE CONDADO, STE 205 00907 #016-43-1951 L1953 **D LM** *071
TORRES TOMASSINI, Grisel. 1452 CALLE AMERICO SALAS, (ALTOS) 00909 #042-04-2005 L2006 *100
VALENTIN, Richard. 1507 AVE PONCE DE LEON, STE 1C 00909 #042-01-1997 L2001 **ORS** *020 †40
VALES ORTIZ, Pedro Xavier. 1706 PLAZA INMACULAD #1706 00909 #308-02-1989 L1995 **IM** *020
VALLECILLO, Luis A. 1475 AVE WILSON, WILSON MEDICAL BLDG 00907 #016-01-1939 L1940 **SO GS** *071 †85
VAZQUEZ, Reinaldo. 1822 AVE PONCE DE LEON #26 00909 #847-11-1975 L1980 **PD** *020
VELAZQUEZ, Mercedes. ■ 00912 #308-01-1986 L1988 **GP** *020
VERA, Enrique A. DR'S MED BLD HOPDROMO 756 00909 #042-01-1964 L1968 **OBG** *020 †30
VERGES-FLAQUE, Albert. AMER SALAS 1452 PDA22 8657 00909 #035-09-1938 L1972 **U** *100 †95
VILLAVICENCIO-JIMENEZ, R. 1462 CALLE ASIA 00909 #847-01-1965 L1968 **PDC PD** *020
VINAS RODRIGUEZ, Octavio. ■ 00912 #308-01-1940 L1940 **GP** *020
WALTERS O'NEILL, G A. ■ 00907 #847-08-1960 L1963 **PD PDC** *030
WILLIAMS, Norma E. ■ 00915 #308-01-1981 L1986 **FM** *020
ZALDIVAR-BORJAS, Jose L. BOX 12056 LOIZA STATION 00914 #308-03-1979 L1982 *020
ZAYAS-SANTOS, Pedro Jaime. ■ 00915 #847-12-1976 L1981 **FM OS** *020
ZENI, Celso Vittorio. ■ 00911 #561-01-1945 L1954 **AN** *020

TOA ALTA – TOA ALTA

ACOSTA-ROLON, William. 118 CALLE ANTHURIUM, CIUDAD JARDIN I 00953 #847-08-1976 L1980 **PD** *040
AGUILA-GONZALEZ, Lymarie. 1225 CALLE FINLANDIA, URB PLAZA DE LA FUENTE 00953 #042-03-1998 L2000 **D** *020 †15
ALCANTARA, Altagracia A. URB CIUDAD JARDIN 1, CALLE AZALEA #97 00953 #308-02-1988 L1995 **END** *020 †20
ALMONTE, Cesar Augusto. ■ 00953 #308-01-1984 L2004 *100
BAEZ MENDEZ, Luz J. RR 2 BOX 8190 00953 #308-04-2002 L2003 *100
BURGOS BERRIOS, Ivelisse. ■ 00953 #649-14-2001 L2002 *020
BURGOS-RIVERA, Victor M. LEOPOLDO DIAZ STREET #6 00953 #308-03-1977 L1980 **GP** *020
CEPEDA-LARA, Rafael. ■ 00953 #308-01-1978 L1983 **GP** *020
CEREZO DE LA ROSA, Ivan A. 52 CALLE PALMER 00953 #308-03-1983 L1990 **GP** *020
CHEVRES DIAZ, Itza Doris. G21 CALLE 10, VILLA MATILDE 00953 #308-03-1982 L1989 *020
CHINEA, Betty. ■ 00953 #042-03-1994 L1998 **GE** *020 †20
CORREA, Norbert. ■ 00953 #042-01-2001 L2004 **IM** *020
CORREA LUNA, Luis Daniel. ■ 00953 #649-14-2000 L2002 **IM** *100 †20
DE LA TORRE-MORALES, F. RR 3, 0.1 CARRETERA 828 00953 #042-01-1979 L1982 **PD** *020
DEVARIE DIAZ, Marcos E. 1014 CALLE ITALIA, URB PLAZA DE LA FUENTE 00953 #308-03-1981 L1993 *020
DIAZ, Anita. 938 CALLE PORTO SANTO, URB PORTOBELLO 00953 #649-14-1997 L2000 **PD** *020
DIAZ ANDRES, Odelsa Migue. RR 2 BOX 6051 00953 #308-13-1998 L2002 **GP** *020
DIAZ MARTINEZ, Pedro J.. ■ 00953 #649-14-2004 L2006 *100
DIAZ-ROMERO, Wilfredo. ■ 00953 #308-03-1977 L1980 **GP** *020
ECHEANDIA VELEZ, Juan C. 18 AVE PRINCIPAL, COLINAS DE PLATA 00953 #308-03-1977 L1986 **GP** *020
ELIAS RODRIGUEZ, Norma J.. PO BOX 784, 80 BO GALATEO CENTRO CARR 00954 #649-14-2002 L2006 *100
FELICIANO, Guillermo Jose. ■ 00953 #649-35-2002 L2004 *100
FONSECA, Orlando. 204 CALLE 5, JARD DE TOA ALTA 00953 #308-03-1980 L1985 **GP** *020
GONZALEZ, Evelyn. STREET RIO HONDO #15, MONTE CASINO HEIGHTS 00953 #308-03-1984 L1990 **GP** *020

GONZALEZ-AYALA, Tulio J. 27 CALLE CERRO, ALTS DE MONTECASINO 00953 #042-01-1992 L1995 **AN** *020
GUTIERREZ SANTIAGO, Jessic. ■ 00953 #042-03-2007 *012
HAMBURGO LAGARES, Angel R. 263 CALLE ALMACIGO, URB MONTECASINO 00953 #308-01-1967 L1977 **FM EM** *020
JEREZ, Jorge Horacio. 23 ST. RIO HONDO, URB. MONTECASINO HTS 00953 #429-01-1978 L1977 *020
JIMENEZ, Jose Angel. 55 CALLE 1, JARD DE TOA ALTA 00953 #649-20-1978 L1981 **FM** *020
LOPEZ, Maribel. ■ 00953 #649-14-2000 L2002 **FM** *100
LOPEZ, Maribel Rosario. ■ 00953 #308-03-1983 L1988 **OM** *020
LOPEZ RAMOS, Auday. 151 LINCOLN, JARD DE LA FUENTE 00953 #308-03-1987 L1989 *020
LUGO DE JESUS, Javier Ism. ■ 00953 #308-13-2000 L2005 **GP MDM** *030
MAISONET CORREA, Carlos. ■ 00953 #308-03-1982 L1992 *020
MALTES, Ana Felicita. 52 CALLE PALMER 00953 #308-03-1983 L1991 **GP** *020
MARTIN, Juan A. 28 CAMINO DEL MONTE, COLINAS DE PLATA 00953 #649-14-1988 L2002 *020
MATEO, Manuel Esteban. 362 CALLE CASIA, CIUDAD JARDIN III 00953 #308-03-1988 L1995 *020
NIEVES, Paul James, Jr. ■ 00953 #042-03-2002 L2005 **GE** *012 †20
NIEVES VELEZ, Jose L. L2 CALLE 7, URB SAN FERNANDO 00953 #308-03-1981 L1986 **GP** *020
ONGAY RULLAN, Johnny. 23 CALLE REINA 00953 #308-03-1983 L1995 *020
ORTIZ PIETRI, Rafael A. 40 CALLE AZALEA, CIUDAD JARDIN I 00953 #308-03-1977 L1980 **GS** *020
ORTIZ-SANTIAGO, Pedro M. PO BOX 101 00954 #561-01-1951 L1954 **FM** *072
PABON, Marisol. ■ 00953 #042-03-1997 L2000 **PD** *020
PADILLA HERNANDEZ, Hector. PO BOX 178, 4 OFICINA LILLY MINI MALL 00954 #308-03-1982 L1990 *020
PAMIAS PORTALATIN, Eva F.. ■ 00953 #649-30-2000 L2002 **FM** *020
PEREZ, Carlos Ruben. ■ 00953 #308-01-1987 L1991 **GP** *020
PEZZOTTI-ALVAREZ, R. 117 CALLE ANTHURIUM, CIUDAD JARDIN I 00953 #308-04-1981 L1984 **GP** *020
PIZARRO, Carmen Marie. ■ 00953 #649-14-2000 L2001 **FM** *020
PONCE, Guillermo. ■ 00953 #737-09-1987 L2003 **PD** *020 †55
RAMOS MONGE, Ramon Luis. 38 CALLE AZALEA, CIUDAD JARDIN I 00953 #847-10-1966 L1968 **OBG** *020
REYNOSO-MINAYA, Renato S. RR 2 BOX 6225 00953 #308-01-1958 L1963 **GP** *071
RIOS, Eduardo Alfonso. PO BOX 902 00954 #308-03-2001 L2004 **GP** *020
RIOS, William Felix. PO BOX 902 00954 #308-03-2001 L2005 *100
RIVERA, Judy Yvette. PO BOX 697 00954 #649-14-1991 L1993 **P** *020
RIVERA, Yvonne. ■ 00953 #042-01-1995 L1998 **FM** *020 †18
RIVERA ORTEGA, Santiago. ■ 00953 #649-14-2003 *020
ROBLEDO, Miguel Antonio. ■ 00953 #308-03-1985 L1987 **GP** *020
RODRIGUEZ, Edelmiro. ■ 00953 #308-03-1978 L1982 **P** *020
RODRIGUEZ, Raymond. ■ 00953 #308-03-1989 **GP** *100
RODRIGUEZ AGOSTO, Cristoba. ■ 00953 #649-14-1987 L2003 *100
RODRIGUEZ GONZALEZ, Juan. 48 CALLE 1, JARD DE TOA ALTA 00953 #042-01-1973 L1975 **IM CD** *020
RODRIGUEZ RODRIGUEZ, Migue. ■ 00953 #649-14-2001 L2003 **GP** *020
RUIZ, Emerito Ventura. G21 CALLE 10, VILLA MATILDE 00953 #847-06-1975 L1978 **GP** *020
SERRANO, Edna. 65 CALLE SAUCO, CIUDAD JARDIN III 00953 #308-01-1989 L1991 **PD** *020
SIFRE, Jorge L. 83 CALLE ROBLE, CIUDAD JARDIN III 00953 #042-01-1985 L1988 **PM** *020
TALAVERA RUIZ, Denysse E. 16 CALLE BARCELO 00953 #308-03-1980 L1993 *020
TORRES, Belkliz Yanira. 3214 CALLE RIO GUAYABO, PRADERAS DEL RIO 00953 #649-14-2002 L2003 **IM** *020 †20
TORRES-ARROYO, Ernesto. RR 3 BOX 18637 00953 #847-05-1976 L1979 **GP** *020
VAZQUEZ, Hyrza. ■ 00954 #042-01-1998 L2002 **IM** *020 †20
VEGA, Wilda Enid. FUENTE IMPERIAL, MONACO CC-27 00953 #649-14-1980 L1997 *020
VELEZ LOPEZ, Edwin. 495 CALLE ALCANFOR, CIUDAD JARDIN III 00953 #042-03-1984 L1986 **GS** *020 †16
VELEZ RAMOS, Pedro Juan. ■ 00953 #649-35-2001 L2002 *020
VELEZ-RIVERA, Carlos A. 1184 CALLE ANDRES SEGOVIA, URB PALACIOS DE MARBELLA 00953 #042-01-1991 L1996 **PTH** *020 †50

TOA BAJA – TOA BAJA

ALVAREZ, Nilka Yamila. AA4 AVE DON PELAYO, HACIENDA DEL NORTE 00949 #042-03-1989 L1992 **PD** *020
ANDINO, Jose Felix. ■ 00949 #308-03-1981 L1982 **GP** *020
ARIAS, Jessica. ■ 00949 #042-01-2007 **PM** *012
AYALA, Alfredo. ■ 00950 #308-03-1981 L1984 **GP** *020
BAEZ-NAVARRO, Zoraida. SECTOR LA VEGA, CALLE LUZ 16B 00952 #042-04-1983 L1985 **IM** *020
BARRETO, Carlos Alberto. ■ 00949 #042-01-1994 L1999 **N** *020
BELLO-GONZALEZ, Hilton R. ■ 00949 #308-03-1982 L1984 **GP** *020
CABRER, Miguel Angel. ■ 00949 #042-02-2003 L2005 **CD** *012 †20
CANTRES, Onix Joel. ■ 00949 #042-01-2006 **IM** *012
CARDONA, Maria Isabel. 9004 VIA PELICANOS, URB CAMINO DEL MAR 00949 #042-01-1986 L1989 **IM** *020 †20
CARDONA DE JESUS, Damaris. ■ 00949 #649-14-1999 L2004 *100
CARDONA JIMENEZ, Diana. ■ 00949 #042-02-1983 L1986 **IM** *020
CEBALLOS VENTURA, Pedro A. PO BOX 50142, URB LEVIT TOWN 00950 #308-01-1966 L1975 **GP DIA** *020
CEDRES, Myriam. Y26 AVE BLVD MONROIG, URB LEVITTOWN LAKES 00949 #042-01-1977 L1988 **PD** *020
COLLADO-MARCIAL, Jose L. 9506 VIA PELICANOS, URB CAMINO DEL MAR 00949 #649-14-1977 L1984 **IM EM** *020
COLON, Gloria E. ■ 00949 #042-01-1985 L1988 **PD PHO** *020 †55
COMULADA RIVERA, Angel L. Y30 AVE BLVD MONROIG, URB LEVITTOWN LAKES 00949 #042-02-1992 L1997 **IM END** *020
COTTO VEGA, Carlos Gilber. ■ 00949 #847-02-1978 L1981 *100
CRUZ-MENA, Rafael A. ■ 00949 #308-01-1970 L1981 **P** *020
DACOSTA-FIGUEROA, Nelson. 1173 AVE DOS PALMAS, LEVITTOWN, PUERTO RICO 00949 #847-05-1976 L1979 **IM** *020
DECLET CONCEPCIO, Ely. PO BOX 1878 00951 #649-33-1985 L1996 **FM** *020
DE JESUS, Elena Matilde. 8058 PLAZA GAVIOTAS, URB CAMINO DEL MAR 00949 #042-01-1989 L1993 **OBG** *020 †30

DE JESUS RAMOS, Nelson. HN100 CALLE DOMINGO DELGAD, URB LEVITTOWN LAKES 00949 #042-02-1981 L1984 **FM** *020 †18
DIAZ, Damaris Esther. PO BOX 50502, LEVITTOWN 00950 #649-14-2002 L2004 *100
FERMIN LOPEZ, Yolanda M.. PO BOX 50554, LEVITTOWN 00950 #308-01-1993 L2003 *100
FERRER, Ilia N.. URB.LEVITTOWN 00949 #308-07-1982 L1999 **FM** *020
FRAGUADA, Angel Luis. SE25 CAMINO DE LA ZARZUELA, MANS DEL SUR 00949 #042-03-1985 L1987 **OBG** *020 †30
GONZALEZ RODILES, Enrique. 40 CALLE MUNOZ RIVERA 00949 #275-01-1962 L1976 **GP** *020
GUILBE-PEREZ, Lilliam M. LEILA ESTE U 11 4TA 00949 #308-01-1969 L1978 **GP** *020
GUZMAN, Rafael C. 2012 VIA PLAYERA, URB CAMINO DEL MAR 00949 #042-01-1987 L1990 **EM** *030
HERNANDEZ NATER, Owen F. MAGDA EST'F-6 LEVTOWN LKS 00949 #847-10-1965 L1968 **PD** *020
LA SANTA, Doris Gisela. ■ 00949 #042-01-2003 L2006 **FM** *100
LOPEZ-PECUNIA, Pedro. ■ 00949 #042-01-1967 L1969 **OBG** *100
LOPEZ-ROSARIO, Roberto F. AH18 CALLE MAGALY, LEVITTOWN 00949 #042-01-1997 L2000 **OBG** *020
MACIAS DE MOYKA, Servanda. HF16 CALLE LIZZIE GRAHAM, URB LEVITTOWN LAKES 00949 #847-09-1971 L1975 **GP** *020
MARTIR, Sylvia Annette. ■ 00949 #042-02-2002 L2005 **EM** *100
MERCADO, Ismael. PO BOX 52217 00950 #649-14-1998 L2002 **FM** *020
MORALES-FRAGOSO, Nestor E. 2765 AVE DOS PALMAS, STE 103 00949 #847-05-1977 L1982 *020
MORALES HERNANDEZ, Zaidee. ■ 00949 #308-03-1978 L1981 *020
MORALES SEPULVEDA, Sally. ■ 00949 #649-30-2003 L2006 **GP** *020
MOYKA, Charles Rebman R. HF16 CALLE LIZZIE GRAHAM, URB LEVITTOWN LAKES 00949 #847-09-1970 L1976 **GP** *020
NATER BAEZ, Kyra Z. ■ 00949 #042-04-1998 L2000 **FM** *020
NEGRON, Roberto Luis. ■ 00949 #042-01-2007 **IM** *012
NEGRON PEREZ, Jose M. ■ 00950 #042-04-2001 L2002 *020
NIEVES, Yvette Oyola. ■ 00949 #847-01-1975 L1980 *020
NUNEZ SANTIAGO, Waleska. PO BOX 51680, LEVITTOWN STATION 00950 #042-04-2004 **GP** *020
OROZCO, Rodolfo. PO BOX 51911 00950 #308-01-1986 L1992 **FM** *020 †18
ORTIZ, Jorge L. ■ 00949 #308-03-1982 L1990 **GP** *071
ORTIZ, Leslie. LEVITTOWN, MANSION DEL SUR PLZ 9SB4 00949 #308-03-1988 L1994 *020
ORTIZ DIAZ, Efrain. 2020 VIA CARACOLES, URB CAMINO DEL MAR 00949 #649-14-2002 L2002 *020
ORTIZ-GONZALEZ, Gloria E. ■ 00949 #042-01-2008 *012
PADILLA LOPEZ, Evelyn. ■ 00950 #649-35-1992 L1994 **GP** *020
PARDO-HERNANDEZ, C. ■ 00949 #847-01-1965 L1968 **OS** *050
PEREZ, Carlos E. PO BOX 2400 00951 #308-03-1990 L1993 *020
POLANCO, Miguel Angel. PASEO DIAMELA K1276, LEVITTOWN 00949 #308-03-1984 L1997 **GP EM** *020
RAMOS, Jaime. BOX 751, SABANA SECA STA 00951 #042-04-1986 L1991 **P** *020
REYES, Leovigildo A. AA87 CALLE CERVANTES, LEVITTOWN LAKES 00949 #308-01-1958 L1973 **GP** *020
REY LABORDE, Rosario. PASEO CALMA J-3334, 3RA SECCION LEVITTOWN 00949 #042-04-2004 L2005 *100
RIOS, Amaris Enid. ■ 00949 #042-03-2006 **IM** *012
RIVERA, Alma Violeta. AU6 CALLE 18, URB PRADERA 00949 #042-01-1974 L1976 **HO IM** *030
RIVERA CRUZ, Ellen Christ. ■ 00949 #649-14-2005 L2005 *100
RIVERA-LINARES, Rafael A. MANSIONES DEL NORTE, CAMINO BUSTAMANTE NG-9 00950 #308-03-1981 L1995 **OS** *020
RIVERA-MARRERO, Osvaldo. C24 CALLE 5, URB DOS RIOS 00949 #847-02-1963 L1967 **GP** *020
RIVERA-SERRANO, Sheila. ■ 00949 #847-05-1980 L1983 **GP** *020
RODRIGUEZ, Ana Ivette. JR10 CALLE LIZZIE GRAHAM, URB LEVITTOWN LAKES 00949 #308-07-1983 L1991 **GP** *020
RODRIGUEZ, Pedro J. T1568 BOULEVRD AVE STE 252 00949 #042-01-1985 L1987 **CD** *020 †20
RODRIGUEZ, Yerania. ■ 00951 #042-01-2007 **IM** *012
RODRIGUEZ MELON, Saul. PO BOX 51883 00950 #042-01-1960 L1962 **U** *071
RODRIGUEZ-PADILLA, Maria. ■ 00950 #847-05-1978 L1984 *020
ROSARIO PAREDES, Maria. ■ 00949 #308-03-1985 L2005 *100
ROSAS GONZALEZ, Edgardo I. ■ 00951 #649-01-1969 L1976 *100
RULLAN VALENTIN, Grace. JR5 CALLE LIZZIE GRAHAM, URB LEVITTOWN LAKES 00949 #042-03-1984 L1987 **PD** *020
SANTAELLA, Carmen Iris. PO BOX 51562, SOLER EDIFICIO C 00950 #847-05-1978 L1980 **GP** *020
SANTIAGO, William. ■ 00949 #042-01-2001 L2003 **IM** *020
SEPULVEDA, Lourdes Veroni. ■ 00949 #649-14-1998 L1999 **FM** *020 †18
SIERRA-QUINONES, Yolanda. Y35 BLVD MNRG URB LEVITTOW, C/O BOX 51443 LEVITTOWN 00949 #847-06-1977 L1980 **IM** *020
SOLIS MERCADO, Janet. EL PLANTIO, CALLE ROBLE A-5 00949 #308-03-1986 L2003 **FM** *020
TAVAREZ, Maria M. ■ 00949 #042-01-1991 L1994 **FM** *020 †18
TORO SOTO, Robert. PO BOX 50910 00950 #847-10-1975 L1978 **P CHP** *020
TORRES, Walfred. Y25 AVE BLVD MONROIG, URB LEVITTOWN LAKES 00949 #042-01-1997 L2000 **OPH** *020
TORRES-GONZALEZ, Pedro. AVDA BOULEVARD 1324, 4A SECCION LEVITTOWN 00949 #847-11-1974 L1987 **FM** *020
VALDES, Pedro Vazquez. PO BOX 51643, COMMERIO AVE. 00950 #042-03-1981 L1986 **FM** *020
VASQUEZ, Mirta. CALLE 8AK-12 PRADERAS 00949 #649-14-1992 L1997 **PD** *020
VAZQUEZ, Hector A. MAISION JUN VERSALL SC 24 00949 #042-01-1982 L1985 **EM** *020 †16
VEGA, Ricardo. 3011 PLAZA PLAYERA, URB CAMINO DEL MAR 00949 #308-03-1984 L1987 **GP** *020
VEGA RODRIGUEZ, Manfredo. LEVITTOWN 00949 #649-14-2003 *020
VEGA SORRENTINI, Dessie L. PO BOX 51911 00950 #649-02-1986 L1992 **P** *020
VELEZ, Jesus. ■ 00949 #042-01-1981 L1984 **OBG** *020
VIANA, Cesar. B1 CALLE SAN MATEO, URB SAN PEDRO 00949 #042-04-1981 L1983 **PD GP** *020
VILLEGAS, Rebeca D. ■ 00949 #308-01-1976 L1980 *020

TRUJILLO ALTO – TRUJILLO ALTO

AGOSTO, Edil Josue. ■ 00976 #305-01-2005 **EM** *012

ALVERIO, Harry. ■ 00976 #042-01-2004 **PM** *012

APONTE APONTE, Victor A. A42 CALLE 7, TERR DE CUPEY 00976 #308-03-1985 L2001 *020

ARREDONDO MATOS, Angela. A4 CALLE ANICETO DIAZ, URB GOLDEN HLS 00976 #042-04-2000 L2002 **GP** *020

BAEZ FRANCESCHI, Carmen L. 43 PLAZA SUR, URB ALTAVILLA 00976 #042-01-1994 L2000 **PD** *020 †55

BETANCOURT MONZON, Emilio. ENCANTADA, AA 25 ALTAVILLA 00976 #308-02-1980 L1984 **PD** *020

BOND DIAZ, Elaine Joyce. JARDINES TRUJILLO ALTO, CALLE 1 A13 00976 #308-03-1984 L2004 *100

BONILLA, Rosa M. 4 VIA ENCANTADA, URB RIO CRISTAL 00976 #308-04-1981 L1985 **PD** *020

BOU, Carlos R. LE89 VIA PARS URB LANTIGUA, ENCANTADA 00976 #042-01-1995 L1999 **AN** *020

CABRERA, Brendaliz Ortiz. ■ 00976 #042-03-2000 L2002 **OBG** *100

CARBALLO RIVERA, Lourdes. 220 PLAZA WESTERN AUTO, STE 101 00976 #847-04-1969 L1972 **P CHP** *020

CASTILLO, Erick Narciso. 220 PLAZA WESTERN AUTO, STE 101 PMB 199 00976 #682-01-1985 L2004 *100

CASTRO, Luis Amaury. ■ 00976 #042-01-2008 *012

CHABERT, Astrid Myrza. ■ 00976 #042-01-2005 L2005 **PD** *012

CHACON, Ariel. ■ 00976 #042-01-2002 L2007 **ORS** *100

CINTRON BETANCOURT, Angel. PO BOX 1031, 0.5 CARR 8860 00977 #308-13-2001 L2006 **EM** *100

COLON, Minette Marie. 1003 COND MONTECILLOS, ENCANTADA 00976 #042-01-1999 L2002 **PM** *020 †16

CORREA-PONCE, Luis E. E3 CALLE 4 TERR DE CUPEY 00976 #308-03-1980 L1983 **PD OS** *020

CORTES, Nelson. ■ 00976 #042-01-1983 L1987 **GP** *020

CRUZ, Linda. N14 CALLE AA, CIUDAD UNIVERSITARIA 00976 #308-01-1980 L1996 **FM** *020

CRUZ RIOS, Carlos G. CARTAGENA D 54 ST LAGO ALT 00976 #649-01-1956 L1960 **GP** *075

CUEBAS, Ines Delc. A3 CALLE ANICETO DIAZ, URB GOLDEN HLS 00976 #042-01-1995 L1996 **PD** *020 †55

CUEVAS-ZAMORA, Rafael. ■ 00977 #051-04-1946 L1948 **FM PD** *071

DE LA CRUZ CASTELLANOS, Ma. URB.PACIFICA ENCANTADA 00976 #308-04-1988 L1995 *100

DELGADO, Jennifer Marie. ■ 00976 #042-01-2006 **OBG** *012

DIAZ RIVERA, Daniel. ■ 00976 #847-02-1971 L1975 **GP** *020

DIEGUEZ, Niyasdeen. ■ 00977 #042-03-2008 *012

DIEZ, William. ■ 00976 #847-05-1970 L1974 **GP** *020

DIVERSE-DIAZ, Marie D. C20 CALLE LOS AQUINOS, ALT DE FAIRVIEW 00976 #042-01-1982 L1986 **PD** *020

ESPAILLAT, Ramon Ventura. ■ 00976 #308-01-1954 L1969 **PHP GP** *020

FLORES CARMONA, Celestino. 124 VIA PARIS, URB LANTIGUA 00976 #042-04-1991 L1993 *020

FLORES MARTINEZ, Jose. H8 CALLE C E, CIUDAD UNIVERSITARIA 00976 #847-03-1960 L1967 **GP** *020

FONTANEZ, Juan. ■ 00976 #649-14-1995 L1998 **NM** *100

GARCIA, Vilma Milagros. 160 PLAZA SERENA, URB ENTRE RIOS 00976 #308-02-1988 L1992 **P** *020

GARCIA CORTES, Idalia. PO BOX 218 00977 #308-03-1982 L1993 *100

GARCIA FRAGA, Marina. ■ 00976 #308-13-2003 L2005 *100

GINORIO HERNANDEZ, Aileen. ■ 00976 #308-03-1984 L2001 *020

GONZALEZ, Orlando. 220 PLAZA WESTERN AUTO, PMB 377 00976 #042-01-1993 L1997 **OPH** *020 †35

GONZALEZ MENDEZ, Jose Lui. MA8 VIA DEL MONTE, PARQ DEL MONTE 00976 #308-13-2002 L2005 *100

GUERRERO, Andres. 76 CAMINO ALTO, URB LAGO ALTO 00976 #042-01-1985 L1990 **GS CCS** *020 †85

GUIVEN, Annie. ■ 00976 #042-01-1997 L2000 **PD** *020

GUZMAN, Brenda. ■ 00976 #042-01-1996 L1999 **PD** *020 †60

GUZMAN CORTEZ, Wendy. C/O BOX 70, CALLE LA CRUZ #319 00977 #042-04-1993 L1996 **PD** *020

HERNANDEZ-PEREZ, Miguel A. ■ 00977 #649-14-1979 L1984 *020

LDESUSO HERNANDEZ, Jorge. ■ 00976 #308-03-1984 L1994 *020

LEDESMA-MENDES, Alta. ■ 00976 #308-01-1971 L1980 **GP** *020

LOPEZ, Doralice. AA10 CAMINO PANORAMICO, URB ALTAVILLA 00976 #042-04-1988 L1997 *100

LOPEZ, Jorge Luis, Jr. PG43 PLAZA TROPICAL, URB PACIFICA 00976 #042-03-1990 L1994 **AN** *020

LOPEZ, Wilfredo. CALLE PASEO DEL VIENTO, PARQUE DE MONTE MB-62 00976 #042-01-1989 L1992 **OBG** *020 †30

LUCIANO-CABANELLAS, H. ■ 00976 #042-04-1981 L1984 **DIA** *062

MALDONADO, Yasdet. ■ 00976 #042-01-2007 L2007 **GS** *012

MARIN, Maria De Lourdes. ■ 00977 #042-01-1984 L1987 **PTH** *020 †50

MARRERO DIAZ, Lourdes Eni. MA 8 PARQUE DEL MONTE, ENCANTADA 00976 #308-13-2002 L2005 *100

MARTINEZ COTTO, Carmen L. ■ 00976 #308-03-1980 L1980 **P** *020

MATOS, Brenda Enid. 110 VIA ENRAMADA, URB ENTRE RIOS 00976 #042-01-1994 L1996 **CHP** *020

MAYSONET SANCHEZ, Jose I. PG121 VIA ARCOIRIS, URB PACIFICA 00976 #308-06-1986 L1991 *020

MEDINA CRUZ, Victor L. ■ 00976 #042-04-1985 L1987 **GP** *020

MENDEZ, Alicia. J17 CALLE 16, URB ANTILLANA 00976 #042-01-1984 L1989 **HEM ON** *020

MENDOZA RODRIGUEZ, Olga L. ■ 00976 #275-02-1991 L2003 *020

MESORANA, Zoraida. ■ 00977 #308-01-1981 L1998 **PD** *030

MONTANEZ-RAMOS, Victor M. ■ 00976 #649-14-1987 L1990 **PD** *020

MONTILLA-FULLANA, Victor. 13 CALLE CORRIENTES 00976 #308-04-1985 L1987 **PD** *020

MORALES LORA, Jose M.. ■ 00976 #308-01-1986 L2002 *020

MORALES-RALAT, Astrid. 42 TERRALINDA ESTS, URB MONTE TRUJILLO 00976 #042-01-1995 L1998 **FM** *020 †18

MUNIZ, Avid J. AA23 CAMINO PANORAMICO 00976 #042-01-1984 L1988 **IM NEP** *020

MUNIZ, Jorge L. 442 CALLE ANDRES VALCARCEL 00976 #042-01-1984 L1987 **GPM** *020

MUNOZ VASQUEZ, Rafael. ■ 00976 #396-06-1934 L1935 **PHP** *071

OLIVER, Javier Enrique. ■ 00976 #042-01-2002 L2002 **DR** *020 †80

ORELLANA, Jose E. 77 VIA ROMA, URB LANTIGUA 00976 #649-26-1977 L1984 *020

OTERO, Lerac. N47 CALLE U, CIUDAD UNIVERSITARIA 00976 #308-01-1974 L1988 **GP** *020

PAGAN, Luis Manuel. RB25 PLAZA 2, URB RIO CRISTAL 00976 #308-07-1984 L1991 **GP** *020

PARDO-LOPEZ, Maria F. ■ 00976 #847-06-1986 L1992 **PD** *020

PAREDES, Julisa. 3 SAN RAFAEL ESTS, REPTO SAN RAFAEL 00976 #649-14-1997 L2000 **PD** *100 ‡

PEREZ, Luis T. BF25 PLAZA 15, BOSQUE DEL LAGO 00976 #042-01-1987 L1991 **IM** *020

PEREZ-CHIESA, Janet. 220 PLAZA WESTERN AUTO, PMB 381 00976 #308-03-1979 L1980 **N IM** *020 †20

PORTILLA, Peter. ■ 00976 #308-06-1982 L1986 **AN** *020 †05

POVENTUD, Tamara. AN59 PLAZA SAN THOMAS, URB ANTILLANA 00976 #649-14-1993 L1996 **PD** *020

PRIETO MELENDEZ, Jose M. 220 PLAZA WESTERN AUTO, STE 101 00976 #847-10-1966 L1968 **OBG** *020

PUCCIO, Luciano. ■ 00977 #042-01-1979 L1984 **GS** *020 †85

QUILES-CRUZ, Francisco J. ■ 00976 #042-02-2005 **IM** *012

QUINTERO MALDONADO, Eric. RA12 VIA DEL RIO 00976 #308-03-1982 L1995 **GP** *020

RAMIREZ, Miguel Angel. J17 CALLE 16, URB ANTILLANA 00976 #042-01-1983 L1988 **RHU IM** *020

RAMIREZ RUIZ, Luis A. 1 CALLE 2, PARC SAINT JUST 00976 #308-04-1989 L1995 *100

RAMOS GARCIA, Jesus Migue. ■ 00976 #042-01-2008 *012

RENDON, Wilfredo L. ■ 00976 #042-01-1986 L1988 **EM** *020 †16

REYES GONZALEZ, Irma N. ■ 00976 #847-06-1972 L1975 **OS PD** *071

RIVALTA VILA, Ajneb. PO BOX 309, SAINT JUST 00977 #649-14-2002 L2004 *100

RIVERA, Dagmar. PO BOX 416 00977 #649-14-2002 L2006 **GP** *020

RIVERA, Rosario Sixto. ■ 00976 #847-08-1976 L1980 **GPM** *020

RIVERA GOMEZ, Zulmary. 37 CALLE ZAFIRO # 3, MANS SAN RAFAEL 00976 #042-04-2001 L2002 **PD** *100

RIVERA-MARTINEZ, Elba M. ■ 00976 #847-05-1976 L1979 **OS** *020

RODRIGUEZ-DEL RIO, Felix. ER105 PLAZA SILVESTRE, URB ENTRE RIOS 00976 #042-01-1992 L1994 **ORS OFA** *020 †40

ROMAN DE JESUS, Francisco. P O BOX 2179 00976 #308-03-1985 L2002 *020

ROMAN-DIAZ, Miguel Angel. ■ 00976 #308-01-1986 L1988 **FSM FM** *020 †18

ROMERO, Glorianna Maria. 780 CARR 8860, BOX 2928 00976 #042-03-1993 L1999 **OBG** *020

ROSARIO, Javier A. M3 CALLE YUQUIBO, VILLA DE CANEY 00976 #042-04-1995 L1997 **EM** *020

RUIZ, Samuel. ■ 00976 #042-01-1984 L1989 **CHP P** *020 †75

RUIZ-GONZALEZ, Rafael A. ■ 00976 #308-03-1979 L1986 **IM** *020

RUIZ RIVERA, Ramon. PO BOX 1370 00977 #042-04-1999 L2001 **FM** *020

SALGADO DIAZ, Manuel. CALLE 1 A-3 00976 #308-03-1981 L2003 *020

SANABRIA SANTIAGO, Jose. CONDOMINIO PLAZA DEL PARQU, APT 345 00976 #308-04-2003 L2004 *100

SANCHEZ, Tonya Larissa. ■ 00976 #042-01-1999 L2000 **GS** *020 †45

SANCHEZ-RODRIGUEZ, Efrain. ESPRESO TRUJILLO ALTO, EDIF CENTRO 4 OFIC 205 00977 #847-09-1969 L1976 *075 ‡

SANTIAGO, Bartolo. ■ 00976 #042-01-1998 L2000 **NM** *100 †20,28

SANTIAGO, Benjamin. PG90 VIA ARCOIRIS, URB PACIFICA 00976 #042-01-1989 L1991 *020

SANTIAGO, Javier. E-194 CALLE ARACIBO, VILLAS DE CANEY 00976 #042-03-1996 L1998 **FM** *020

SANTIAGO, Julio. CO51 RIO LA PLATA, URB CORRIENTES 00976 #308-03-1986 L1991 **IM** *020

SERRA-MORALES, Frances T. ■ 00976 #847-05-1975 L1980 **OBG** *020

SOTO, Luis Anibal. ■ 00976 #649-14-1983 L1991 **PM** *020

SOTO DEL CUETO, Jorge Enr. ■ 00976 #042-01-2004 **ORS** *012

TALAVERA, Miguel Angel. ■ 00976 #308-03-1982 L1990 **GP** *020

TORRES BONILLA, Yaslin Ev. BOX 2395 APT 201, COND. PATIOS SEVILLANOS 00976 #308-13-2000 L2004 *100

TORRES-PAGAN, Leonardo An. ■ 00976 #042-01-2005 **OTO** *012

TREJO DERIVET, Eduardo. ■ 00977 #308-03-1984 L1995 **GP** *020

TRINIDAD-ESPADA, Eve E. 52 PLAZA TROPICAL, URB PACIFICA 00976 #042-03-1988 L1992 **ID** *020 †20

VALE FLORES, Raul Antonio. AN43 VIA ANTILLANA, URB ANTILLANA 00976 #308-03-1983 L1994 **GP** *020

VALENTIN, Edwin. ■ 00976 #042-04-1989 L1991 **FM** *020

VALENTIN, Miriam. ■ 00976 #042-04-1995 L1997 *020

VARGAS, Adel R. LE94 VIA PARIS, URB LANTIGUA 00976 #308-03-1986 L1991 **PD NPM** *040

VAZQUEZ, Carmen Ana. RA13 VIA DEL RIO, URB RIO CRISTAL 00976 #308-02-1986 L1990 **GP** *020

VEGA, Mara Teresa. ■ 00976 #042-01-2004 **IM** *100

VEGA HERNANDEZ, Vanessa. 6307 AVENTURA, URB ENCANTADA 00976 #042-04-2003 L2004 *100

VEGA-LOPEZ, Orlando. RA9 VIA DEL RIO, URB RIO CRISTAL 00976 #308-03-1983 L1988 **PD** *020

VELAZQUEZ, Rebecca Eunice. ■ 00976 #042-03-2004 *100

VELEZ, Mildred Ivette. ■ 00976 #042-01-1999 L2004 **OBG** *100

VILA, Carlos Acevedo. 209 CASA 4K 20, COLINAS DE FAIR VIEW 00976 #308-03-1983 L2003 *100

VIVAS SANCHEZ, Rodrigo. ■ 00976 #264-05-1987 L2004 **GP** *020

ZALDUONDO, Maria Pilar. 119 PLAZA SERENA, URB ENTRE RIOS 00976 #042-03-1999 L2002 *020

UTUADO – UTUADO

ABREU, Alberto. PO BOX 187 00641 #042-01-1997 L2000 **FM** *020

BENITEZ, Carlos Francisco. A2 URB CABRERA 00641 #308-06-1984 L1988 **GP** *020

BROCO-HERNANDEZ, Dimas. 58 CALLE COLOMER SANCHEZ, P O BOX 597 00641 #308-03-1976 L1978 **GP** *020

CAPARROS, Juan L. 2 CALLE BETANCES 00641 #308-04-1990 L1992 **GP** *020

CAPELLA ACEVEDO, Antonio. 14 CALLE BETANCES, BOX 768 UTUADO 00641 #847-04-1949 L1958 **GP** *020

CARABALLO, Flores Ivan. 7B CALLE DR CUETO, UTUADO, PR 00641 #308-04-1984 L1988 **IM** *020

CORTES SANTIAGO, Jose A. 80 CALLE NUEVO LONDRES 00641 #308-03-1979 L1988 **GP** *020

CRUZ, Rafael A. HERRERA #14 00641 #042-01-1979 L1982 **PD** *020 †55

CUAUTLI, Maria A. PO BOX 1500 00641 #308-01-1984 L1991 *020

CURIEL, David Antonio. 66 CALLE LA PALMA, URB PEREZ MATOS 00641 #308-01-1990 L1994 *020

DE LA PAZ, Diana. PO BOX 1390 00641 #042-03-1981 L1986 **FM** *020 †18

DEL VALLE-TORRES, Rafael. 17 CALLE DR CUETO 00641 #649-14-1989 L1992 **GP** *020

DIAZ, Luis Guillermo. PO BOX 506 00641 #132-01-1958 L1965 **GS** *020

DIAZ, Pedro Jose. ■ 00641 #649-39-1983 L1991 **GP** *020

GIRONA-RIVERA, Wilfrido. ■ 00641 #649-33-1996 L2002 **FM** *020

MALDONADO RIVERA, Juan J. ■ 00641 #308-01-1981 L1985 **PD PDE** *020

MARTINEZ PEREZ, Pedro M. ■ 00641 #308-01-1974 L1976 **GP** *075

MENDEZ DEYNES, Aracelio. ■ 00641 #649-01-1950 L1960 **GP** *020

ONGAY RULLAN, Rafael. 17 CALLE BARCELO 00641 #649-14-1999 L2003 *100

OQUENDO, Juan Eloy. PO BOX 1519 00641 #308-03-1981 L1985 **GP** *020

PAREDES-MICHEL, Julio P. 66 CALLE LA PALMA, URB PEREZ MATOS 00641 #308-01-1968 L1974 **IM** *020

RIVERA-GONZALEZ, Dennis. ■ 00641 #649-39-1982 L1996 **GP GS** *020

RIVERA-VELEZ, Brendaliz. ■ 00641 #042-01-1998 L2003 **PDR** *020

RODRIGUEZ, Tomas Narvaez. PO BOX 1363 00641 #847-10-1974 L1977 **GP** *020

SANTANA GRANDONE, Carlos. 2 CALLE BETANCES 00641 #847-01-1986 L2002 *020

SANTIAGO-RAMOS, Isaac. O3 JESUS M LAGO 00641 #308-03-1979 L1982 *075

TORRES, Mario. ■ 00641 #649-18-1984 L1989 *020

VAZQUEZ, Jose Javier. ■ 00641 #042-03-2006 **P** *012

VELEZ, Roberto. PO BOX 1843 00641 #649-14-1998 L2002 *020 ‡

VILAR, Ismael. 56 CALLE COLOMER SANCHEZ, BOX 128 00641 #028-34-1947 L1950 **OS GP** *030

VEGA ALTA – VEGA ALTA

ALVAREZ, Franco. ■ 00692 #042-01-2005 *100

BALASQUIDES, Juan. ■ 00692 #308-01-1972 L1977 **GP** *020

CEDENO, Gustavo Quintero. ■ 00692 #042-03-1993 L1996 **FM** *020

CHIPROUT, Elly. PITIRRE NO G 1 00692 #042-03-1989 L1992 **IM** *020

COTTERILL, Robert Wm. PO BOX 1689 00692 #005-06-1972 L1973 **OBG MFM** *020 †30

DE JESUS SANTOS, Jorge. CALLE MIRAMAR #282 00692 #042-04-1999 L2001 **FM** *020

GARCIA, Oscar. V26 CALLE 18 URB LA ESPER 00692 #308-03-1986 L2003 *100

GONZALEZ, Rafael. ■ 00692 #042-01-1983 L1990 **PN PD** *020 †55

HONKAN, Vibha Anant. PO BOX 1689 00692 #495-01-1975 L1982 **PD NPM** *020 †55

LAUREANO RODRIGUEZ, Zaida. ■ 00692 #308-03-1984 L2002 **FM** *020

LOPEZ, Harry. ■ 00692 #847-06-1992 L1996 *020

LOPEZ VIZCARRONDO, Frank. RIVERA, CALLE SEIJO ESQ LUIS MUNOZ 00692 #847-04-1956 L1959 **GP** *020

MORALES VAZQUEZ, Jose Lui. ■ 00692 #649-35-1999 L2003 *020

OQUENDO-NEGRON, Iris A. ■ 00692 #042-01-1999 L2002 **FM** *020 †18

OQUENDO VEGA, Claribel. ■ 00692 #649-14-2003 L2004 *100

ORTIZ, Saturnino. 44 CALLE ZORZAL, PARC CARMEN 00692 #308-03-1976 L1978 **GS** *020

OWEN, Frances J. PO BOX 1476, 5 MUNOZ RIVERA ST 00692 #308-03-1978 L1980 **PD** *020

PEREZ, Rafael Aristides. ■ 00692 #308-03-1984 L1990 *020

PEREZ CLAUDIO, Nestor A. ■ 00692 #308-03-1974 L1985 *020

RIOS RODRIGUEZ, Sandra I. 4 CALLE MUNOZ RIVERA 00692 #308-03-1984 L1994 *020

RODRIGUEZ-SOSTRE, Luis. 2 CALLE 1, URB LAS COLINAS 00692 #847-03-1976 L1979 *020

SANTIAGO ARCE, Marisol. PO BOX 1774 00692 #649-14-2003 L2005 *100

SHEHADEH, Mohammad Mahmou. ■ 00692 #042-03-2004 **IM** *100 †20

SOTO-SILVA, Juan G. 53 CALLE GEORGETTI 00692 #041-13-1962 L1964 **P CHP** *020

TORRENS-PETERSON, Wilson. H39 CALLE MARGINAL, URB SANTA RITA 00692 #308-06-1982 L1988 **GP** *020

TORRES, Artemio. ■ 00692 #042-01-2000 L2005 **ORS** *100

VAZQUEZ-RODRIGUEZ, Jose M. 10A CALLE MUNOZ RIVERA 00692 #847-10-1969 L1971 **PD** *030

VERA, Juan A. ■ 00692 #847-10-1971 L1977 *071

ZOUAIRABANI, Mohamed Z. 5A CALLE MUNOZ RIVERA, CENTRO CLC DE VEGA ALTA 00692 #847-08-1978 L1986 **FM** *020

VEGA BAJA – VEGA BAJA

ABREU-RODRIGUEZ, Angel M. ■ 00693 #847-04-1962 L1989 **GP** *020

AGUAYO VICENTE, Brenda M. C5 CALLE 4 URB BRASILIA 00693 #042-04-2001 L2002 *020

ALMONTE, Vinicio Antonio. SAN AGUSTIN A-19 ST, LOS DOMINICOS 00694 #308-01-1985 L1990 **EM** *020

ARMAIZ, Guillermo Rafael. 50B CALLE JOSE JULIAN ACST 00693 #042-03-1980 L1983 **IM** *020

ARROBA, Arturo Leonardo. ■ 00693 #042-03-2005 **P** *012

AVILES-HERNANDEZ, Israel. ■ 00693 #042-01-2001 L2003 **SCI** *100

AVILES MAISONET, Jose A.. ■ 00693 #649-14-2003 L2004 *100

AVILES MAYSONET, Leyza En. ■ 00693 #649-14-2002 L2004 *100

BAEZSORIA, Oscar. ■ 00693 #042-03-1999 L2003 *020

BURGOS, Norberto. 14T19 SAN DEMETRIO 00693 #308-01-1966 L1976 **GP** *071

CASANOVA ORTIZ, William. 34 CALLE JOSE JULIAN ACOST 00693 #847-05-1965 L1968 **FM OS** *020

CASANOVA RIVERA, Erick Al. ■ 00693 #649-14-2002 **FM** *020

CASTRO RIVERA, Samuel G.. ■ 00693 #308-04-2004 L2005 *100

CINTRON, Evelyn. ■ 00693 #649-35-1996 L2002 *020

CINTRON PAGAN, Evelyn. ■ 00693 #042-04-2000 L2001 **FM** *020

CINTRON-RUIZ, Evelyn. ■ 00693 #042-01-1961 L1964 **IM NM** *020 †28

COLMENARES MARTINEZ, Franc. ■ 00693 #308-06-1986 L1992 *100

DE LA ROSA DIAZ, Juan Ang. 420 CAMINO REAL, URB CAMINO DEL SOL 00693 #649-35-2003 *020

DE LEON COLLAZO, Jose F. ■ 00693 #308-06-1986 L1995 **GP** *020

DEL POZO GOMEZ, Edgardo. PO BOX 1296 00694 #308-01-1983 L1992 *020

DOMINGUEZ, Dimaris. ■ 00694 #042-01-1998 L2002 **AN** *020

DOMINGUEZ, Migdalia. ■ 00693 #308-03-1985 L1990 **GP** *020

DULUC-PEREZ, Lourdes A. 501 CAMINO ESTRELLA, URB CAMINO DEL SOL 00693 #308-03-1981 L1993 **FM** *020

ECHEANDIA, Ramon F. C29 CALLE 2, URB. BRASILIA 00693 #308-03-1979 L1986 **GP** *020

ENCARNACION, Hector M. 54 CALLE BETANCES, ALTOS FARMACIA SAN MIGUEL 00693 #847-05-1979 L1987 **GP** *075

FEBLES VALENTIN, Celestina. ■ 00693 #308-03-1988 L1996 *020

FELIPE-HERNANDEZ, D. BO ALGARROBO 00694 #308-01-1969 L1976 **AN** *020

FELIX ZAPATA, Jose. ■ 00693 #308-03-1979 L1984 *100

FELIZ, Marcos A. 48 CALLE JOSE JULIAN ACOST 00693 #308-01-1982 L1995 **GP** *020

FELIZ-LEBREAULT, Rafael. 48 CALLE JOSE JULIAN ACOST, FRENTE IGLESIA VEGA BAJA 00693 #308-01-1968 L1976 **NPM IM** *020

GARCIA, Jose Alberto. PO BOX 828 00694 #308-03-1989 L2004 *100

GARCIA CRUZ, Fernando A. PO BOX 4317 00694 #308-03-1981 L1990 *100

GONZALEZ, Denia E. 333 CALLE ISLA VERDE, VILLAS DE LA PLAYA 00693 #308-03-1985 L1996 **FM** *020

GONZALEZ-ADORNO, Zorelisa. HC 1, 1.2 CARR 645 VEGA BAJA 00693 #649-14-2002 L2004 *100

GUERRERO, Daniel A. CARR #2 KM 39.5, HOSPITAL WILMA VAZQUEZ 00694 #308-01-1969 L1976 **ORS** *020

HERNANDEZ, Hector David A. BO ALGARROBO 00694 #308-03-1980 L1985 **FM** *020

HERNANDEZ, Zulma. ■ 00693 #042-01-1999 L2004 **DR** *100 †80

JIMENEZ, Francisco Javier. ■ 00693 #308-07-1984 L1990 **GP** *020

JIMENEZ, Thomas. ■ 00694 #042-04-1994 L1996 **FM** *020 †18

LAFONTAINE, Francisco. 415 CAL TLN EST DE TORTUGU 00693 #042-02-1983 L1984 **IM** *020

LAUREANO HERNANDEZ, Milvia. ■ 00693 #308-04-2004 L2005 *100

LOPEZ-TAVERAS, Mercedes. B11 CALLE 2, URB VILLA REAL 00693 #847-09-1972 L1978 **OBG** *020

LUNA-GONZALEZ, Carmen I. PO BOX 4646 00694 #308-03-1982 L1988 **PD** *020

MAHMUD HASSAN, Issa M.. ■ 00693 #308-01-1998 L2004 *100

MALDONADO, Juan Carlos. ■ 00693 #042-01-2004 **IM** *100

MALDONADO, Marisol. 28 CALLE RIO INDIO, BRISAS DE TORTUGUERO 00693 #042-03-1995 L1999 **OBG** *020

MARIANO MERCEDES, Victor. 48 CALLE JOSE JULIAN ACOST 00693 #308-01-1969 L1976 **P** *020

MARQUEZ CABAN, Randy O. ■ 00693 #649-14-2003 L2005 *100

MARTINEZ ORRACA, Juan J. 415 AVE FELISA RINCON, URB. SAN DEMETRIO 00693 #649-39-1982 L1993 **FM** *020 †18

MEDEROS, Orelbe. ■ 00693 #042-01-2002 L2004 **AN** *100

MIRANDA, Francisco J. 517 CALLE CAMINO ESTRELLA, URB CAMINO DEL SOL 00693 #042-04-1995 L1997 **FM** *020

MIRANDA-GONZALEZ, Loida. 13 CALLE JOSE JULIAN ACOST 00693 #308-06-1986 L1990 **GP** *020

MORA, Mayra C.. 413 CALLE ALVA, CIUDAD REAL 00693 #308-03-1986 L2003 **FM** *020

MORALES, Maricelis. HC 1 BOX 24153, SUITE #11,CARR 670 INT. 66 00693 #649-14-2000 L2002 *020

MORALES-VAZQUEZ, Noel R. 15 CALLE TULIO OTERO, BOX 4035 00693 #847-09-1965 L1970 **GP** *020

NAZARIO AVILES, Clarissa. PO BOX 949113, SABANA BRANCH 00694 #649-19-2002 L2004 *100

NIEVES, Edwin Girau. 4 CALLE LUIS MUNOZ RIVERA, VEGA ALTA 00693 #308-03-1985 L1992 *020

OJEDA PADILLA, Irivette. 25 CALLE BOQUERON, VILLAS DE LA PLAYA 00693 #042-01-1994 L1998 **FM** *020 †18

ORTIZ MEDRANO, Jose D. ■ 00693 #308-01-1975 L1994 **GP** *020

OTERO-QUINTANA, Jorge. 629 CALLE TURIN, EST DE TORTUGUERO 00693 #649-14-1989 L1992 **OBG** *020

PABON DE VAZQUEZ, Eduarda. ■ 00694 #847-10-1962 L1965 **DIA** *072

PADILLA AQUINO, Ivonne. ■ 00694 #847-02-1990 L1993 **FM** *020

PAGAN AYALA, Benjamin. BALDORIOTY 12 B 00693 #847-10-1960 L1962 **GP GYN** *020

PEREZ, Maria Ivette. CALLE R-1-10, JARDINES VEGA BAJA 00693 #308-02-1985 L1989 **GP** *020

PEREZ-VAZQUEZ, Juan A. 46 CALLE JJ ACOSTA 00693 #847-04-1977 L1983 **GP** *020

RAMIREZ PEREZ, Livia O. 32B CALLE JOSE JULIAN ACST 00693 #308-01-1969 L1975 **PD** *020 ‡

RENTAS SERRA, Eduardo. ■ 00693 #649-45-1995 L1996 **P** *020

RIOS RODRIGUEZ, Reinaldo. ■ 00693 #649-19-1994 L1998 **GP** *062

RIVERA, Marie Liz. ■ 00693 #308-04-1983 L1991 **FM** *020

RODRIGUEZ, Alfredo. PO BOX 4144 00694 #308-03-1982 L1990 **GP** *020

RODRIGUEZ, Carlos J. PO BOX 1733, BO ALGARROB 39 CARR 2 1 00694 #308-04-1989 L1991 **GP** *020

RODRIGUEZ, Jose Miguel. ■ 00693 #042-01-2001 L2002 **CD** *020

RODRIGUEZ, Julio Hiram. PO BOX 72 00694 #847-06-1976 L1979 **IM** *020

RODRIGUEZ, Luz Elenia. ■ 00693 #649-14-1998 L2006 *100

RODRIGUEZ, Mildred I. ■ 00694 #308-01-1986 L1992 **IM** *020

RODRIGUEZ, Raul A. ■ 00694 #042-04-1994 L1996 *020 †18

RODRIGUEZ BORGES, Wm F. 121 CALLE MARGINAL, STE 3 00693 #308-03-1983 L1988 **IM** *020

RODRIGUEZ-PEREZ, Eduardo. ■ 00694 #407-10-1941 L1989 **GS** *072

RODRIGUEZ-PORTELA, Jaime. ■ 00693 #042-04-2000 L2001 *100

RODRIGUEZ SOLIS, Jaime. 780 CALLE ARRAYADO, URB SAN DEMETRIO 00693 #042-01-1970 L1974 **IM** *020

RODRIGUEZ VAZQUEZ, Rafael. PO BOX 2710 00694 #308-03-1993 L2002 **GP** *020

RODRIGUEZ VELLON, Yazmin. ■ 00694 #042-04-1991 L1992 **FM** *020

ROJAS ROMAN, Rafael G. 80 ST JOSE J ACOSTA 00693 #847-10-1964 L1974 **DIA PD** *020

ROMAN BRUNO, Maria E.. ■ 00693 #649-14-1998 L2005 *100

ROSADO, Roberto Rosado. ■ 00694 #308-03-1978 L1994 *020

ROSADO-ROSADO, Rosaura. 7.0 CARR 670, BO. PUGNADO AFUERA 00693 #308-03-1978 L1983 **GP** *020

SANABRIA-TORRES, Olga T. 125 CALLE MARGINAL 00693 #308-02-1979 L1983 **GP** *020

SANTIAGO, Rosangel. APT 555 COND. TORRE VISTA 00693 #649-14-2001 L2005 *100

SANTIAGO RIVERA, Juan. 22 CALLE SAN ALFONSO, URB SAN AGUSTIN 00693 #847-08-1980 L1988 *020

SARMIENTO, Jesus B. 618 CALLE TURIN, EST DE TORTUGUERO 00693 #308-01-1983 L1991 **FM** *020

SOLER, Antonio. ■ 00694 #042-02-2007 **TY** *012

TAVAREZ ALARCON, Luis E.. ■ 00693 #308-03-1979 L1995 *100

TORRES SANCHEZ, Angel T. ■ 00693 #042-04-1998 L2000 **FM** *020

VAZQUEZ PARES, Enrique. BO ALGARROBO 00694 #847-10-1963 L1966 **OBG** *030

VEGA, Ivonne M. ■ 00693 #042-04-1992 L1997 **FM** *020

VELEZ, Hector R. ■ 00693 #042-04-1992 L1997 *020

VELEZ VILLAPLANA, Jose L. ■ 00694 #308-03-1977 L1984 *020

VIDAL RIOS, Agustin Jose. PO BOX 7, CENTRO MEDICO WILMA N VAZQ 00694 #649-14-1990 L1992 **GP** *020

VIEQUES – VIEQUES

CAMPOS-IPEZ, Federico G. 107 CALLE MUNOZ RIVERA, BX GEN 00765 #847-06-1972 L1979 **GPM** *020

DE CARDENAS-VALDES, F. PO BOX 267 00765 #847-05-1980 L1985 **GP** *030

FIGUEROA, Jose Francisco. 334 CALLE ANTONIO G MELLAD, URB ISABEL II 00765 #649-14-1998 L2000 *020

MAC KENZIE, Betzaida M. PO BOX 326, CENTRO DE SALUD 00765 #308-03-1976 L1979 **GP** *020

MERCEDES DE PENA, Eusebio. HC 1, 7 CALLE CORAL FLORIDA 00765 #308-01-1987 L2005 *100

MOYERS, Donna Sue. ■ 00765 #011-02-1977 L1978 **OBG** *020

RICHARDS, Lawrence A S. UNIDAD DE SALUD PUBLICA 00765 #005-12-1934 L1960 **OS** *075

RIVERA, Luis Enrique. ■ 00765 #308-03-1985 L1995 *020

RIVERA-CASTANO, Rafael A. ■ 00765 #042-01-1958 L1961 **PHP GPM** *072 †70

SANCHEZ, Jaime Raul. ■ 00765 #035-46-1985 L1992 **GS** *020

VILLALBA – VILLALBA

ALVARADO, Lizbeth. ■ 00766 #042-02-2002 L2004 **IM** *020 †20

BOURDON-MALDONADO, H. ST BARCEL 43 00766 #308-01-1980 L1982 **IM** *020

CABALLERO MONTEAGUDO, R E. CENTRO DE SALUD 00766 #275-01-1937 L1966 **GP** *020

GARCIA-TRONCOSO, Jose F. ROAD 150 KM 12.2 00766 #308-01-1983 L1986 **GS** *020

GODREAU, Luis Gilberto. PO BOX 6004, 149 ST KM 580 00766 #042-02-1997 L2000 **OBG** *020

NEGRON, Ramon E. 53 CALLE MUNOZ RIVERA, CALLE MUNOZ RIVERS #17 00766 #308-06-1986 L1990 *020

RIEGA-TROYA, Armando. ST MUNOZ RIVERA 16 00766 #847-06-1977 L1982 **FM** *020

RODRIGUEZ, Irma Nydia. HC 1 BOX 4231 00766 #308-06-1982 L1986 **PD** *062

RODRIGUEZ, Jaime Luis. ■ 00766 #042-02-2006 **P** *012

SANCHEZ, Jarvis Jeffrey. ■ 00766 #042-02-2007 **IM** *012

SEDA CORDERO, Ana. 17C CALLE MUNOZ RIVERA 00766 #042-04-1988 L1994 **IM** *020

YABUCOA – YABUCOA

ALVAREZ ZAMORA, Luz M. 4RB ANGELOS NO E 8 00767 #275-01-1948 L1973 *071

BERRIOS-GARCIA, Miguel A. HC 1 BOX 4720 00767 #847-06-1977 L1980 **PM** *020

CARRION-RIOS, Carlos A. 40 CALLE LUIS MUNOZ RIVERA 00767 #847-05-1977 L1979 **GP** *020

CRUZ-RAMOS, Carlos Mario. ■ 00767 #847-06-1975 L1978 **GP** *071

DE JESUS LAZU, Luis Socor. HC 5 BOX 5115, 32 CALLE 8 00767 #275-02-1989 L2005 *100

DELGADO BURGOS, Rafael A. PO BOX 194 00767 #308-03-1981 L1991 *020

DIAZ ROJAS, Hortensia. PO BOX 519, 2 MARDENAR 00767 #308-03-1983 L1990 **PD** *020

FELICIANO, Jose Ivan. PO BOX 490 00767 #042-01-1981 L1984 *020

GARCIA PENA, Zinnia A. PO BOX 2050 00767 #308-04-1993 L1997 *020

GOMEZ-LOPEZ, Juan R. CALLE 1 A-5, URB VILLA HILDA 00767 #847-08-1979 L1982 **IM** *020

GONZALEZ, Cesar A. PO BOX 146 00767 #649-01-1968 L1969 **PD** *020

MELENDEZ TIRADO, Marielly. ■ 00767 #649-14-2003 L2005 *100

PELLERANO ZAYAS, Arturo. 36 CALLE LUIS MUNZ RVR #68 00767 #308-01-1948 L1966 **GP** *020

RAMOS RAMOS, Kimberly. ■ 00767 #649-35-2004 L2005 *100

RIVAS, Hiram Luis. ■ 00767 #042-01-2007 **IM** *012

SANCHEZ, Norma. ■ 00767 #308-06-1985 L2003 *020

SANCHEZ-MARTINEZ, Elsa M. ■ 00767 #847-05-1979 L1984 **IM** *020

SEPULVEDA RIVAS, Ruben. PO BOX 2050 00767 #308-04-1995 L1996 *020

SEPULVEDA-RIVERA, Vanessa. 8 CALLE 3, URB SANTA ELENA 00767 #042-03-1993 L1996 **IM IMG** *020 †20

SOLIS-DIAZ, Awilda. ■ 00767 #308-03-1979 L1983 *020

TORRES-BORGES, Arturo J. 33 CALLE LUIS MUNOZ RIVERA 00767 #042-01-1980 L1983 **FM** *020 ‡

TORRES-MACHIN, Arturo. 33 CALLE LUIS MUNOZ RIVERA, ARTURO TORRES MAGHIN 00767 #051-01-1952 L1954 **FM OM** *071

VERGARA, Victor Luis. 104 CALLE LUIS MUNOZ RIVER 00767 #649-14-1992 L1995 **END IM** *020

YAUCO – YAUCO

ACOSTA VELEZ, Pablo A. 17 CALLE 25 DE JULIO 00698 #649-14-1990 L1992 **IM** *020

ANTOMMARCHI, Loriann. ■ 00698 #649-14-1997 L2002 **FM** *020

ARIAS-MARTINEZ, Tomas. CALLE 9F URB LUCHETTI 00698 #649-08-1938 L1959 **P** *100

AROCHO HERNANDEZ, Luis E. 58 CALLE COMERCIO BOX 3051, # 58 00698 #847-10-1971 L1974 **GP** *020

ARROYO VELAZQUEZ, Nelly. 21 CALLE BALDORIOTY 00698 #649-33-1985 L1994 *020

BAEZ, Jorge Luis. ■ 00698 #042-03-1992 L1997 **IM PM** *020

BERMUDEZ, David Ricardo. ■ 00698 #042-01-1996 L1999 **CD** *020 †20

BIAGGI-LUGO, Alba. ■ 00698 #042-01-1964 L1967 **OBG** *071 †30

BURGOS FERRER, German A. PO BOX 1983 00698 #649-14-2002 L2003 *100

CAMACHO, Maria Del Carmen. ■ 00698 #847-06-2000 L2003 *100

CANABAL ENRIQUEZ, Jose M. ■ 00698 #649-14-1993 L1996 *020

CARRASQUILLO, Ricardo. ■ 00698 #308-02-1991 L1993 *020

CASIANO MALAVE, Jose A. 74 CALLE COMERCIO 00698 #308-01-1985 L1988 **GP** *020

CATALA, Cecilia M. ■ 00698 #649-18-1982 L1986 **GP** *020

DE JESUS CABRERO, Hector. 17 CALLE 25 DE JULIO 00698 #847-05-1973 L1975 **GP** *020

DIAZ, Carlos A. H14 CALLE GARNET, EST DE YAUCO 00698 #042-01-1984 L1988 **OBG** *020

ECHEVARRIA ROMAN, Cynthia. ■ 00698 #649-14-2002 L2005 *100

ESPARZA, Bogart Ricardo. ■ 00698 #649-14-1984 L1995 **P** *020

ESTABIL, Maritza L. 74 CALLE COMERCIO STE 4 00698 #275-01-1980 L2001 **FM** *100

FIGUEROA-MELENDEZ, Victor. 12 CALLE PROL 25 DE JULIO 00698 #308-04-1980 L1983 **NEP IM** *020 †20

FLORES, Axel Doel. 29 CALLE MUNOZ RIVERA, P O BOX 552 00698 #042-02-1994 L1997 **IM** *020

FRANCESCHI, Porfirio. PO BOX 5006 00698 #847-05-1965 L1968 **DR** *020

FRED SANTIAGO, William. PO BOX 708, 200 AVE RAFAEL CORDERO STE 00698 #649-14-2000 L2002 *100

FRONTERA MARIANI, Rene. CALLE 4 #13, URB EL ROSARIO 00698 #308-01-1965 L1969 *020

GARCIA, Edwin Gerardo. 401A COND TORRES NAVEL 00698 #042-02-1993 L1998 **AN** *020

GERALDINO, Julio E. 25 DE JULIO 5 00698 #042-03-1981 L1991 **IM** *030

GONZALEZ, Marinette. ■ 00698 #649-35-2001 L2003 **FM** *020

GONZALEZ CASIANO, Norman. PO BOX 885 00698 #649-14-2000 L2002 *100

GRANA-SANTIAGO, Alberto G. 22 CALLE MATTEI LLUBERAS 00698 #042-03-1983 L1985 **PD** *020

IRIZARRY, Ivan. ■ 00698 #649-14-2002 L2005 *100

IRIZARRY, Ivan Fernando. B24 CALLE 3, VILLA OLIMPIA 00698 #042-01-2001 L2002 **IM** *020

IRIZARRY, Melina. ■ 00698 #042-01-2005 L2005 **IM** *012

IRIZARRY, Saul. ■ 00698 #308-13-2000 L2004 *100

JUSINO-MC DOUGALL, E. ■ 00698 #308-03-1980 L1983 **GP** *020

KOHLER, Hans Jorg. ■ 00698 #409-25-1985 L1987 **PD PSM** *020

LLAURADOR AGOSTINI, Wady. 46 CALLE 25 DE JULIO, CLINICA DE MEDICINA Y CIRU 00698 #308-02-1986 L1988 *020

LOPEZ, Carlos Luis. F2 CALLE DIAMANTE, EST DE YAUCO 00698 #649-14-1995 L1997 **FM** *020

LOPEZ, Jose Amilcar. ■ 00698 #308-06-1981 L1990 **GP** *020

LOPEZ, Wally. ANESTHESIA DEPARTMENT, HOSPITAL DR TITO MATTEI 00698 #042-01-1991 L1995 **AN** *020 †05

LOPEZ MARTINO, Eric. 13A CALLE BALDORIOTY 00698 #308-03-1980 L1985 **IM** *020 ‡

LOPEZ VELEZ, Ricardo Rafa. PO BOX 724 00698 #649-14-2004 L2005 *100

LOYOLA NEGRONI, Santiago. CALLE VIVALDI PACHECO #14 00698 #649-01-1955 L1956 **GP** *072

MALDONADO, Enrique A. ■ 00698 #308-03-1984 L1990 **GP** *020

MARIN, Radames A. BOX 807 URB LUCHETTI 00698 #649-14-1989 L1992 **FM** *020

MARIN ROMAN, Radames C. 65 CALLE COMERCIO 00698 #847-10-1964 L1969 **GP OS** *071

MARTINEZ, Eddanys. F13 CALLE 3, URB BARINAS 00698 #042-01-1996 L1999 **IM** *020 †20

MARTINEZ SUAREZ, Victor M. PO BOX 5160 00698 #649-14-1999 L2004 *100

MATOS MOQUETE, Patricia E. CALLE E BLOQUE E #22, URB COSTA SUR 00698 #308-01-1997 L2005 *100

MEDINA, Arturo. 13 CALLE MATTEI LLUBERAS 00698 #042-01-1976 L1980 **FM PHP** *020 †18

MEDINA, Dennis Luis. ■ 00698 #649-14-1999 L2002 *020

MENAY-JUSINO, Abelardo. ■ 00698 #042-01-1954 L1956 **OS** *020

MENDEZ-RODRIGUEZ, Rafael. 24 CALLE MATTEI LLUBRS #ME, CORNER 00698 #308-03-1982 L1990 **OBG** *020

MERCADO, Carmen Teresa. I68 CALLE 7, VILLAS DEL CAFETAL 00698 #308-03-1982 L1986 **GP** *020

MILLAN CAMACHO, Sandra E.. PO BOX 788 00698 #649-14-2002 L2003 *100

MORALES, Gary Enrique. ■ 00698 #042-01-2008 *012

MORALES NIEVES, Salvador. ■ 00698 #847-01-1962 L1965 *020

MORALES PRADO, Amilcar. ■ 00698 #308-13-2003 L2004 *100

MUNIZ, Agripina. 155 CALLE CLAVEL, HACIENDAS FLORIDA 00698 #649-14-1989 L1992 *100

MUNIZ, Kellie Marlyn. ■ 00698 #649-14-2001 L2005 *100

OLIVARI, Jose A. VILLA OLIMPIA 2 #A-12 00698 #042-04-1980 L1988 **GP** *020

ORTIZ, Daniel. EXT LA QUINTA CALLE 12 M 8 00698 #042-01-1989 L1992 **FM** *020 †18

ORTIZ, Veronica. ■ 00698 #649-14-1991 L1993 *020

PADILLA, Abner Rodriguez. 41 CALLE DR PASARELL 00698 #847-03-1975 L1978 *020

PELLICIER, Manuel A. 521 CALLE MADRID 00698 #042-04-1996 L1997 **GPM** *020

PEREZ BURGOS, Katherine. ■ 00698 #649-14-2001 L2003 *020

PINTADO, Isidoro. URB LUCHETTI 3 C 17 00698 #308-04-1983 L1990 **FM** *020

QUINONES, Rosabel. ■ 00698 #649-14-1997 L1999 **FM** *020

QUIROS-FRANCESC, Daisy. D1 CALLE JASPE, EST DE YAUCO 00698 #308-03-1992 L1999 **PG** *020

RAMIREZ-CARRERO, Rodolfo. CARRETERA 128 K M 10 00698 #042-02-1992 L1995 **OBG** *020

RIVERA LABARCA, Edgardo R. 35 CALLE SANTIAGO VIVALDI 00698 #308-01-1975 L1978 **GP** *020

ROBLES, Brenliz Mercedes. C/O PO BOX 374, F-1 CALLE 2 00698 #649-14-1999 L1999 *100

RODRIGUEZ, Damaris. 2 CALLE 2A, LAS PELAS 00698 #042-01-2000 L2003 **OBG** *020 †30

RODRIGUEZ, Ivan Saml. 13 CALLE MATTEI LLUBERAS 00698 #042-01-1976 L1980 **FM** *020 †18

RODRIGUEZ, Jorge Alejandr. HC 1 BOX 8003, 128 HERNANDEZ ST 00698 #649-14-2003 **IM** *020

RODRIGUEZ, Maria Angeles. 26 CALLE SANTO DOMINGO 00698 #042-01-1995 L1998 **PD** *020

RODRIGUEZ, Melisa Deline. D1 CALLE 2 URB LA QUINTA 00698 #649-14-2002 L2004 *100

RODRIGUEZ RODRIGUEZ, Karen. 243 CALLE SAN RAFAEL, URB SAN FRANCISCO 00698 #042-04-1999 L2000 **FM** *020

RODRIGUEZ-VELEZ, Carlos. 74 CALLE COMERCIO 00698 #847-02-1977 L1979 **GP EM** *020

ROMAN, Gil M. CO PO BOX 196, CALLE COMERCIO #65 00698 #847-10-1965 L1967 *020

ROMERO, Angel. ■ 00698 #649-35-1993 L1996 **IM** *020

ROSARIO MARTINEZ, Carlos. ■ 00698 #042-04-2003 L2005 *100

ROSARIO-PEGUERO, Cesar A. 14 CALLE PASARELL 00698 #308-01-1961 L1978 **PD** *020

ROSAS, Angela Maria. ■ 00698 #649-14-1995 L1998 *020

RUIZ VELEZ, Luz T.. M21 CALLE 12, URB LA QUINTA 00698 #649-14-1998 L2001 *020

SANTIAGO AVILES, Edson L. ■ 00698 #649-14-1991 L1993 **IM** *020

SANTIAGO-CRUZ, Dayna Mila. ■ 00698 #042-01-2005 **IM** *012

SEPULVEDA, Ileana. 35 CALLE MATTEI LLUBERAS 00698 #649-14-1985 L1989 **PD** *020

SILVESTRINI, Marco A. ■ 00698 #847-14-1984 L1990 **FM** *020 †18

TROCHE, Jose Francisco. 35 CALLE MATTEI LLUBERAS 00698 #308-03-1979 L1981 *020

VAZQUEZ-MALDONADO, L. 187 CALLE BOUGANVILIA, HACIENDAS FLORIDA 00698 #042-02-1998 L2001 **PD** *020

VAZQUEZ-QUINTANA, Carlos. 55 CALLE COMERCIO 00698 #308-03-1981 L1984 *020

VEGA PEREZ, Milka. PO BOX 1976 00698 #649-14-2002 L2004 *100

VELASCO-CANEVARO, Luis M. ■ 00698 #847-10-1958 L1961 **GP GYN** *071

VELEZ, Sixto A. C11 CALLE ESMERALDA, EST DE YAUCO 00698 #649-14-1991 L1994 **FM** *020

ADAMSVILLE – NEWPORT

TEST, Charles Edward. ■ 02801 #016-02-1941 L1960 **IM DIA** *072 †20

ALBION – PROVIDENCE

DIAMOND, Amanda Marie. ■ 02802 #037-01-2003 L2003 **CN** *012

BARRINGTON – BRISTOL

ADAMS, Leah Frances. 310 MAPLE AVE STE 105 02806 #043-01-1996 L1996 **IM** *020
ARENA, Andrea Elizabeth. 60 BAY SPRING AVE, UNIT B6 02806 #035-08-1998 L2005 **FM** *020 †18
ARNOLD, Mary L Bertucio. 21 LEE RD 02806 #050-02-1950 L1965 **PD PDE** *071 †55
ASHBA, Jean Krikor. ■ 02806 #330-03-1954 L1968 **PUD IM** *071 †20
ASWAD, Bassam I. ■ 02806 #605-01-1984 L1993 **PTH** *020 †50
BAAKLINI, Diane King. 233 WASECA AVE 02806 #305-01-1984 L1989 **P** *020
BANDYOPADHYAY, Utpala M. 128 UPLAND WAY, DISEASE PREVENTION & CONTR 02806 #495-27-1973 L1992 **PD PHP** *020 †55
BARRETT, Michael Scanlan. 24 LISTER DR 02806 #024-07-1963 L1966 **VS GS** *020 †85
BARROETA, Julieta Elena. ■ 02806 #935-07-2000 L2006 **PCP** *100 †50 ‡
BAYUK, Julian Meyer. ■ 02806 #035-45-1957 L1965 **OS U** *071 †95
BECKER, Daniel Ira. ■ 02806 #008-01-1968 L1990 **DR EM** *020 †80
BERNSTEIN, Marian J S. ■ 02806 #035-19-1958 L1966 **GP** *020
BERNSTEIN, Paul Wm. ■ 02806 #035-19-1960 L1966 **NS** *020
BLUNDIN, Michael Francis. ■ 02806 #041-14-2004 L2004 **PCC** *012 †20
CAPIZZO, Frank. 147 COUNTY RD 02806 #016-01-1974 L1975 **IM IMG** *020 †20
CARDON, Philippe V, Jr. ■ 02806 #035-01-1946 L1980 **IM** *071
CASTANEDA, Roberto Vamba. 5 PINE TOP RD 02806 #748-01-1961 L1970 **PD EM** *071
CHIU, Ritche Cabanas. ■ 02806 #748-19-2001 L2007 **NEP** *012 †20
CLARK, David Dudley. ■ 02806 #035-48-1974 L1979 **NEP IM** *020 †20
CLEGG, Kevin E. 334 COUNTY RD STE D, BARRINGTON PEDIATRIC ASSOC 02806 #043-01-1992 L1999 **PD** *020 †55
COLLINS, Edward Wm. ■ 02806 #043-01-1975 L1977 **PD** *020 †55
DARAKJIAN, Ghazar Henry. ■ 02806 #035-01-1958 L1968 **PD** *071 †55
DE LUCA, Anthony Joseph. 310 MAPLE AVE, STE L05A 02806 #561-11-1988 L1991 **PD** *020 †55
DE LUCA, Frank Gaetano. ■ 02806 #561-01-1955 L1957 **PDS** *071 †85
DE LUCA-VERLEY, Betheanne. ■ 02806 #043-01-1990 L1990 **PD** *020
DENNISON, Jane Mackenzie. 234 MAPLE AVE 02806 #035-01-1980 L1984 **PD** *020 †55
DENNY, Lisa Rachelle. 60 BAY SPRING AVE, UNIT B6 02806 #041-14-2001 L2007 **FM** *100 †18
DEWAN, Anil Krishan. ■ 02806 #917-08-2001 L2002 **PTH** *100 †50
FERRETTI, Marcolino. 234 MAPLE AVE 02806 #025-12-1995 L1995 **PD** *020 †55
FRARY, Richard Dexter. ■ 02806 #024-05-1956 L1961 **IM** *071
FRIEDMAN, Rebecca Mates. ■ 02806 #035-46-2008 *012
GIBBS, Kendall Arthur. 24 BOSWORTH 02806 #043-01-1982 L1986 **OPH** *020 †35
GOLD, Michael Merton. ■ 02806 #035-45-1953 L1958 **OBG OS** *072
GORDON, Paul Clark. 4 BEECH TREE CT 02806 #035-01-1986 L1993 **CD IM** *020 †20
GREENBURG, Joan Paula. ■ 02806 #043-01-1995 L1995 **PAN** *020
GRENANDER-RAUFI, Angela. 234 MAPLE AVE 02806 #043-01-1981 L1984 **PD** *040 †55
HALTZMAN, Scott D. 147 COUNTY RD 02806 #043-01-1985 L1989 **P** *020 †75
HEALEY, Eugene Harding. ■ 02806 #024-05-1965 L1970 **GS VS** *071 †85
HILLEGASS, Ronald Carl. ■ 02806 #041-01-1964 L1973 **ORS** *071 †40
HORTON, Patricia Mary. 334 COUNTY RD 02806 #008-02-1978 L1983 **PD** *020 †55
JOHNSON, Sandra Diane. 310 MAPLE AVE, BARRINGTON URGENT CARE 02806 #025-12-1998 L2004 **FM** *100 †18 ‡
KESWICK, Lisa Ann. 334 COUNTY RD, STE D 02806 #035-03-1998 L1998 **PD** *020 †55
KUHN, Richard E A. ■ 02806 #041-09-1946 L1967 **GS GYN** *071 †85
LAMBERT, Richard K. 2 OLD COUNTY RD 02806 #049-01-1975 L1978 **P** *020 †75
LAPIDUS, Candace Susan. 5 SPINNAKER DR, P O BOX 247 02806 #024-07-1984 L1999 **D PD** *040 †55,15
LEE, Ho Yong. ■ 02806 #583-02-1950 L1972 **PTH** *071 †50
LEITE, Joaquim Da Costa. ■ 02806 #770-03-1959 L1982 **AN** *071 †05
LERISH, Victor David. 334 COUNTY RD STE D 02806 #023-01-1976 L1979 **PD** *020 †55
LOERKE, Catherine Jane. ■ 02806 #008-01-2005 **GS** *100
LUKS-DE PAEPE, Monique E. ■ 02806 #165-08-1983 L1991 **PTH** *020 †50
MANIS, James Geo. ■ 02806 #008-02-1958 L1958 **IM GE** *071
MATES, Susan M. ■ 02806 #035-46-1976 L1982 **OS ID** *050 †20
MC CARTNEY, James Robt. 4 APPLE TREE LN 02806 #035-01-1955 L1980 **P PYG** *071 †75
MCDONNELL, Matthew. ■ 02806 #033-05-2007 L2007 *012
MILLER, Robert Eric. ■ 02806 #654-01-1981 L1986 **N OS** *020
NAJAFI, Emadedin. ■ 02806 #517-01-1959 **U** *020
OH, Mary Ang. ■ 02806 #748-01-1958 L1977 **CLP** *071 †50
PARK, Joel. ■ 02806 #043-01-2000 L2000 **MPD** *020 †20
PARKER, Leonard Jon. 334 COUNTY RD STE D 02806 #035-15-1973 L1976 **PD** *020 †55
PELTZ, Ronni M. 334 COUNTY RD STE D, BARRINGTON PEDIATRIC ASSOC 02806 #035-03-1986 L1989 **PD ADL** *020 †55
QUAS, Michael Vincent. 45 ANNAWAMSCUTT RD, QUAS, MICHAEL 02806 #007-02-1997 L2001 **FM EM** *020 †20,55
RICHARDSON, Tracy Lynn. ■ 02806 #024-01-1974 L1986 **CHP PD** *020 †55
ROGIN, Ellen Barbara. ■ 02806 #035-20-1982 L1987 **P** *020
ROSENBLOOM, Mindy Sharon. 26 BOSWORTH ST, STE 5 02806 #033-06-1985 L1988 **P PYG** *020 †75
SAPOSHKOV, Andrey. ■ 02806 #913-08-1936 **IM OS** *071
SMITH, Peter Stephen. ■ 02806 #869-01-1968 L1977 **PD PHO** *040 †54
STEINER, Sheila S. 70 WATER WAY 02806 #803-05-1952 L1971 **AN** *020
STEPHENS, Karl Frederick. 147 COUNTY RD 02806 #024-07-1962 L1967 **OPH** *020 †35
TAUBER, Walter F. ■ 02806 #035-08-1952 L1957 **OBG M** *072 †30
TAYLOR, Elisabeth Baldwin. 2 OLD COUNTY RD 02806 #016-42-1985 L1989 **P CHP** *020 †75
TAYLOR, Marshall Adams. ■ 02806 #035-09-1955 L1960 **GYN** *030 †30
THANUMALAYA PERUMAL, A. ■ 02806 #495-04-1982 L1995 **NEP** *020 †20
TOSELLI, Carole V. ■ 02806 #032-01-1989 *075
TOSELLI, Richard Mark. ■ 02806 #043-01-1983 L1992 **NS** *020 †25

VAIDYA, Shilpa K. ■ 02806 #495-37-1995 L2000 **IM** *020 †20
VAN ALLEN, Deborah Anne. ■ 02806 #041-01-2004 L2004 **ORS** *012
WANG, Li Juan. ■ 02806 #243-47-1983 L1997 **PTH** *020 †50
WELTMAN, Joel Kenneth. ■ 02806 #035-08-1958 L1968 **AI ID** *071 †03
WESTMORELAND, Kristen Joy. ■ 02806 #050-02-1997 L1998 **PD** *100
WOHLRAB, Kyle Joseph. ■ 02806 #016-42-2003 L2003 **OBG** *100

BLOCK ISLAND – WASHINGTON

GASNER, Walter Gilbert. ■ 02807 #045-01-1936 L1937 **D** *071 †15
STOECKEL, Catherine Roth. ■ 02807 #051-04-1942 L1942 **OBG GPM** *071

BRADFORD – WASHINGTON

HARWOOD, Michael J. ■ 02808 #043-01-2005 L2005 **D** *012
LAIN, Lynn J Crawford. RD 1 TERRACE FARM 02808 #041-12-1968 L1970 **PTH** *100

BRISTOL – BRISTOL

AGUIAR, Liza. ■ 02809 #043-01-2008 *012
BAAKLINI, Michael Youssef. 810 METACOM AVE 02809 #305-01-1984 L1989 **PUD IM** *020 †20
BERNARDO, Anthony A. 345 THAMES ST 02809 #023-01-1954 L1959 **GS** *071 †85
BINDER, Gottfried H. 1180 HOPE ST, MEDICAL ASSOCIATES OF R.I. 02809 #041-13-1957 L2003 **D DMP** *071 †15
BLAZAR, Steven Leonard. 1180 HOPE ST, ORTHOPEDIC GROUP 02809 #024-05-1982 L1987 **ORS** *020 †40
BOWMAN, Kevin Scott. 1180 HOPE ST, ORTHOPEDIC GROUP 02809 #005-19-1993 L2002 **ORS** *020 †40
CALIFANO, Nicholas Alan. 1180 HOPE ST 02809 #561-17-1971 L1974 **GE IM** *020 †20
CALIKYAN, Raffi. 812 METACOM AVE, CEDARZ MEDICAL 02809 #409-19-1987 L1998 **CCM PUD** *020
CHACE, Patricia Ann. 1180 HOPE ST 02809 #041-01-1977 L1978 **IM** *071 †20
CICERCHIA, David John. 1180 HOPE ST, ORTHOPEDIC GROUP 02809 #024-05-1990 L1996 **ORS OSS** *020 †40
CONSTANTINO, Cassandra X. 1180 HOPE ST, MEDICAL ASSOCIATES OF RI 02809 #187-07-1983 L1996 **END IM** *020 †20
DE FOREST, Robert E. 02809 #024-01-1951 L1964 **IM CD** *072 †20
DE MEDEIROS, Victor P. 1180 HOPE ST 02809 #770-01-1950 L1959 **GP** *071
DENNISON, Allen M. 1180 HOPE ST 02809 #035-01-1980 L1982 **IM** *020 †20
EATON, Ashley David. 1182 HOPE ST 02809 #021-06-1994 L2001 **R** *062 †80
FALLON, Michele Paula. ■ 02809 #035-46-1993 L1995 **P** *020 †75
FELDMAN, Michael David. 1180 HOPE ST, ORTHOPEDIC GROUP 02809 #041-01-1987 L1993 **ORS OSM** *020 †40
FILARDO, Debra Sistrunk. 1180 HOPE ST 02809 #048-12-1986 L1996 **PD** *020 †55
FISCHER, Bruce Evan. 1180 HOPE ST 02809 #035-46-1989 L1989 **IM** *020 †20
GASTEL, Jonathan Arieh. 1180 HOPE ST, ORTHOPEDIC GROUP 02809 #035-45-1992 L1992 **OSM** *020 †40
GIBSON, Theodore Knipe. 1180 HOPE ST 02809 #041-02-1956 L1959 **ORS** *071 †40
GRAFF, Steven Neal. 1180 HOPE ST, ORTHOPEDIC GROUP 02809 #035-01-1987 L1994 **ORS HS** *020 †40
HAMILTON, Geoffrey Robert. 1180 HOPE ST 02809 #035-03-1997 L1997 **IM** *020 †20
HARROP, Pamela Ann. 1180 HOPE ST 02809 #050-02-1983 L1985 **IM** *020 †20
HIRSCH, Howard Scott. 1180 HOPE ST, ORTHOPEDIC GROUP 02809 #043-01-1986 L1993 **ORS GS** *020 †40
HOLSTEN, George Henry, III. ■ 02809 #008-01-1963 L1970 **CLP PTH** *030 †50
IANNUCCILLI, Edward A. ■ 02809 #035-03-1965 L1966 **GE IM** *071 †20
IANNUCCILLI, Nicholas D. 1182 HOPE ST 02809 #561-01-1969 L1972 **R DR** *020 †80
JOHNSON, Roy Allen. ■ 02809 #024-05-1959 L1961 **OTO** *071 †45
JONES, Elaine Celeste. 1180 HOPE ST 02809 #045-01-1994 L1995 **N** *020 †75
KNEELAND, John F. 1180 HOPE ST 02809 #024-07-1975 L1993 **PD** *020 †55
LEE, Alison Gladding. ■ 02809 #024-16-2007 IM *012
LEE, Joshua Justice. ■ 02809 #010-02-2006 L2006 **IM** *100
LITCHMAN, Henry Maurice. 1180 HOPE ST, ORTHOPEDIC GROUP 02809 #024-07-1955 L1956 **ORS** *072 †40
MAIA, Anthony Jos. 1180 HOPE ST 02809 #396-06-1978 L1982 **IM ID** *020
MOHLMAN, Leslie C. 1180 HOPE ST, BRISTOL COUNTY MEDICAL CEN 02809 #035-06-2000 L2004 **MPD** *100 †20,55
MOTAMED, Mehrdad. 1180 HOPE ST, ORTHOPEDIC GROUP 02809 #517-01-1960 L1972 **ORS** *071 †40
O'DOWD, Philip Arthur. 652 WOOD ST 02809 #041-01-1977 L1980 **HEM IM** *020 †20
PATRICK-MACKINNON, Susanne. 448 HOPE ST 02809 #024-16-1990 L1995 **N** *020 †75
PERRONE, Howard Francis. 1180 HOPE ST 02809 #035-01-1977 L1979 **IM** *020 †20
POGGI, John Jeffrey. 1180 HOPE ST, ORTHOPEDIC GROUP 02809 #035-45-1986 L2003 **ORS** *020 †40
POLLAN, Susan Barbara. 1180 HOPE ST, ORTHOPEDIC GROUP 02809 #067-01-1982 L1994 **AN PME** *020 †20,05
PRIOLO, Dennis Louis. 1182 HOPE ST 02809 #033-06-1983 L1990 **DR** *020 †80
ROSENTHAL, Charles Mark. 1182 HOPE ST 02809 #035-20-1981 L1987 **DR OS** *020 †80
ROSS, Antonia Labate. 1180 HOPE ST 02809 #041-01-1985 L1988 **IM** *071 †20
ROSS, James Albert. 1180 HOPE ST, MEDICAL ASSOCIATES OF RI 02809 #041-01-1985 L1988 **IM** *020 †20
SCHWARTZ, Stuart Terry. 1180 HOPE ST 02809 #033-06-1984 L1986 **RHU IM** *020 †20
SYDLOWSKI, Paul E. 576 METACOM AVE, BELL TOWER PLZ #11A 02809 #010-02-1967 L1974 **OPH AM** *071 †35
TORF, Alane Beth. 1180 HOPE ST 02809 #023-01-1988 L1988 **IM ID** *020 †20
URBANIAK, Henry S, Jr. 1180 HOPE ST, ORTHOPEDIC GROUP 02809 #041-01-1961 L1969 **ORS** *020 †40
WALSH, Eric Ferguson. 1180 HOPE ST, ORTHOPEDIC GROUP 02809 #043-01-2000 L2000 **HS** *020
WHELAN, Cathleen. 1180 HOPE ST 02809 #035-20-1997 L1997 **IM** *020 †20
ZANGARI, Dominick, Jr. 375 METACOM AVE 02809 #043-01-1986 L1992 **OPH** *020 †35

■ = Address Information Privacy Protected

CENTRAL FALLS – PROVIDENCE

ALTONGY, Gilbert Jos. 1002 BROAD ST 02863 #396-03-1974 L1977 **IM CD** *020 †20

DRAK, Gandhi. 1000 BROAD ST 02863 #875-01-1986 L1997 **IM** *020

EL-GABRI, Tarek Hassanein. 1002 BROAD ST 02863 #915-02-1977 L1984 **OTO HNS** *020 †45

FOSTER, America Joy. 9 CHESTNUT ST 02863 #050-02-1999 L2002 **FM** *020

FREDERICKS, Rose E. 1000 BROAD ST 02863 #035-03-1980 L1982 **IM** *020 †20

GUNASTI, David Kenan. 1000 BROAD ST 02863 #035-08-1992 L1997 **DR** *020 †80

HOGAN, Dawn M. 1000 BROAD ST, NOTRE DAME AMBULATORY CENT 02863 #024-05-1997 L1997 **FM** *020 †18

LONGOBARDI, Vito Anthony. 571 BROAD ST 02863 #473-01-1997 L1998 **IM** *020

LONGOBARDI, Yen. 571 BROAD ST 02863 #035-09-1991 L1994 **PD** *020 †55

MARTIN, Carla Margarita. 1000 BROAD ST, NOTRE DAME AMBULATORY CENT 02863 #033-05-1997 L1997 **MPD** *020 †20,55

MAZLOUM, Naji Waghi. 1002 BROAD ST 02863 #605-01-1985 L1991 **GS** *020 †85

MIRABAL, Ernesto Antonio. 9 CHESTNUT ST 02863 #308-01-1988 L2003 **IM** *020

SAM, David Arthur. 1000 BROAD ST 02863 #032-01-1997 L1997 **FM** *020 †18

TAKHAR, Amrita. 1002 BROAD ST 02863 #495-72-1979 L1986 **IM** *020 †20

VIBHAKAR, Bharat B. 1000 BROAD ST 02863 #495-01-1967 L1977 **CD IM** *020

WAGDI, Safa Fouad. 1002 BROAD ST 02863 #915-03-1967 L1978 **OPH** *020 †35

YAMINE, Chahine Joseph. 1000 BROAD ST 02863 #010-03-1986 L1989 **AN PME** *020 †05

ZELLER, Kimberly Ann. 1000 BROAD ST 02863 #048-12-1995 L1997 **FM** *020 †18

CHARLESTOWN – WASHINGTON

APSHAGA, Bronie J P. PO BOX 677 02813 #024-07-1942 L1951 **AN GP** *071

DE GREGORIO, Jason. ■ 02813 #043-01-2002 L2003 **PTH** *100

DEMIRS, Stuart. PO BOX 910, 4099 OLD POST RD 02813 #035-03-1988 L1992 **IM PD** *020 †20,55

DE PONTE, Ralph Jos. 101 STARRETT DR 02813 #008-01-1961 L1962 **ORS** *071 †40

GAZDER, Aftab A. ■ 02813 #704-02-1968 L1978 **AN** *071

GROVES, Ralph James. 4533 S COUNTY TRL, NARRAGANSETT INDIAN HEALTH 02813 #047-05-1999 L1999 **FM** *020 †18

KRUPP, Brandon Harris. 4160 OLD POST RD, STE 104 02813 #020-02-1989 L1989 **P PYG** *020 †75

MANN, Paul Atkinson, Jr. 4099 OLD POST RD 02813 #035-03-1983 L1990 **FM** *020 †18

SOULE, Robert Monroe. ■ 02813 #024-01-1943 **CD IM** *071 †20

STAHL, Nicholas Mc Leod. ■ 02813 #008-01-1943 L1947 **PDS** *071 †85

STEVENS, Merrilyn Jane. 2A CROSSLAND ST 02813 #035-45-1979 L1982 **IM** *020 †20

VIGNA, Vincenzo. ■ 02813 #561-21-1953 L1983 **AN** *020 †05

CHEPACHET – PROVIDENCE

LASZEWSKI, Zofia K W. PO BOX 733, 11 MONEY HILL RD 02814 #803-01-1950 L1997 **PM IM** *071 †60

MC KITTRICK, Robert E. ■ 02814 #043-01-1996 L1996 **FP** *012

RESNEVIC, George. 895 PUTNAM PIKE 02814 #407-10-1949 L1955 **DR RO** *071

RESNEVIC, Stanislawa. 895 PUTNAM PIKE 02814 #407-10-1949 L1955 **GP** *075

YANNI, Penelope Anne. 264 PRAY HILL RD 02814 #035-03-2000 L2000 **P** *020 †75

COVENTRY – KENT

AGGARWAL, Vinay. ■ 02816 #041-15-2006 L2007 **IM** *012

ALASHARI, Mouied M. ■ 02816 #528-01-1981 L1987 **PTH** *020 †50

ARCAND, Nicole. ■ 02816 #043-01-2002 L2002 **ORS** *100

COLLINS, Daniel Francis. 982 TIOGUE AVE 02816 #539-02-1969 L1973 **EM** *020

DRUCKMAN, Daniel L. 71 SANDY BOTTOM RD 02816 #305-01-1981 L1990 **DR NM** *020 †28,80

FEINER, Neil Frank. ■ 02816 #011-02-1981 L1985 **P** *075

GOCCIA, Richard J. 982 TIOGUE AVE 02816 #023-07-1982 L1985 **EM** *020

GOLOMB, Duane Thos. 766 WASHINGTON ST 02816 #043-01-1983 L1984 **FM** *020 †18

GRILLO, Joseph Frank. 982 TIOGUE AVE 02816 #033-06-1999 L2002 **IM** *020 †20

HEBB, Donald Bruce, III. 1620 NOOSENECK HILL RD 02816 #016-02-1997 L2000 **IM** *020 †20

KAWATU, Rita. 956 TIOGUE AVE, TIOGUE PEDIATRICS 02816 #198-03-1987 L1996 **PD** *020 †55

MANANSALA, Artemio. ■ 02816 #422-01-2001 L2004 **DR** *020 †80

MANOWN, Timothy J. 1620 NOOSENECK HILL RD 02816 #043-01-1992 L1998 **IM** *020 †20

MAYNARD, Jean Maurice. ■ 02816 #067-03-1940 **PHP GPM** *071

O'HAIR, James P. 982 TIOGUE AVE 02816 #035-15-1991 L1992 **FM EM** *020

PLUVIOSE, Fritz. ■ 02816 #440-01-1973 L1981 **IM IMG** *020 †20

TURNER, Joseph P. 982 TIOGUE AVE 02816 #028-78-2000, ▲ L2000 **IM** *020 †20

VAN HAAREN, Wilhelmus A. 71 SANDY BOTTOM RD 02816 #660-05-1959 L1965 **FM IM** *071

ZALDIVIA, Rodolfo E. 71 SANDY BOTTOM RD 02816 #748-08-1967 L1980 **DR OS** *020

CRANSTON – PROVIDENCE

AARONSON, Leroy D. ■ 02905 #035-03-1952 L1953 **D** *071 †15

ABIRI, Mohammed. 725 RESERVOIR AVE STE 306 02910 #517-01-1958 L1968 **GS ON** *020 †85

ABRAHAM, Sany. PO BOX 8269 02920 #495-31-1959 L1972 **IMG GP** *071

ACCAOUI, Ghazi. 17 CLIFFSIDE DR 02920 #330-04-1960 L1967 **GYN** *020 †30

ACHINDIBA, Robert A, Jr. 39 HOWARD AVE, DEPT OF CORRECTIONS 02920 #412-02-1993 L2002 **IM** *020 †20

ALLEN, Gregory G. 1681 CRANSTON ST, STE D 02920 #022-75-2002, ▲ L2002 **IM** *020 †20

ALMAHAMEED, Soufian. ■ 02921 #875-01-1998 L2007 **CD** *100

ANDREOZZI, Mark Peter. 251 PARK AVE 02905 #022-75-1987, ▲ L1988 **OTO A** *020

ANGOV, Nadia. ■ 02920 #023-01-1997 L2001 **PCC** *020

ARIAS, Jose Ramiro. 39 HOWARD AVE, ADULT CORRECTIONAL INSTITU 02920 #132-05-1995 L2003 **IM** *020 †20

BACCARI, Michael Jos. 677 ATWOOD AVE 02920 #010-02-1959 L1964 **IM PUD** *020

BARITEAU, Jason Tyler. ■ 02920 #035-15-2007 L2007 *012

BARONE, Anthony James. 725 RESERVOIR AVE, SRE 303 02910 #561-01-1978 L1981 **OTO** *020 †45

BARONE, Rocco Robt. ■ 02920 #561-01-1957 L1960 **OBG** *071 †30

BEAUPRE, Stephen Raymond. 1312 OAKLAWN AVE 02920 #024-05-1988 L1988 **IM** *020 †20

BELKNAP, Thomas Warren. ■ 02905 #035-45-2003 L2003 **NS** *012

BHARIER, Michael Adrian. 750 RESERVOIR AVE 02920 #018-03-1977 L1994 **D** *020 †15

BIDADI, Khalil. ■ 02920 #517-08-1980 L1995 **P** *100

BLOOM, Frances Feld. ■ 02905 #008-01-1952 L1956 **AN** *071

BLOOM, Max. ■ 02905 #008-01-1952 L1956 **CD IM** *071 †20

BONNER, James Roy. 1150 RESERVOIR AVE, STE 205 02920 #035-45-1988 L1988 **PD PG** *020 †55

BOSCO, Carin Renee. 11 IMPERIAL AVE 02920 #041-12-1991 L2002 **P** *020 †75

BOTELHO, Dennis D. 1500 PONTIAC AVE 02920 #305-01-1988 L1992 **IM** *020 †20

BRANNON, Patrick Jos. 725 RESERVOIR AVE 02910 #050-02-1971 L1978 **CD IM** *020 †20

BROWN, Joanna Doris. 1090 CRANSTON ST, FAMILY HEALTH SERVICES 02920 #035-46-2002 L2002 **ADL** *100 †18

BUONANNO, William Stephen. 35 SOCKANOSSET CROSS RD 02920 #043-01-1985 L1987 **ORS** *020 †40

BURKER, Mark Alexander. ■ 02905 #035-06-2005 L2005 **EM** *012

CAMPBELL, Jos James, Jr. 761 PARK AVE 02910 #050-02-1980 L1981 **IM** *020 †20

CARDI, Alphonse R. ■ 02920 #010-02-1942 L1943 **FM** *071

CARDI, Erminio R. 633 BUDLONG RD 02920 #010-02-1952 L1953 **GS** *071 †85

CARDI, James K. 677 ATWOOD AVE 02920 #654-01-1987 L1988 **IM** *020 †20

CARPENTIER, David. 495 ATWOOD AVE 02920 #043-01-1983 L1990 **EM** *030 †16

CARROTT, Philip Worthingt. ■ 02920 #019-02-2005 L2005 **GS** *012

CAVANAUGH, Timothy. 1090 CRANSTON ST, FAMILY HLTH SRVS 02920 #032-01-1987 L1994 **OPH** *020 †18

CECE, John A. 1150 RESERVOIR AVE, GARDEN CITY TREATMENT CENT 02920 #561-17-1989 L1989 **IM CCM** *020

CERVONE, Richard L. 900 RESERVOIR AVE, GARDEN CITY NEUROLOGY LTD 02910 #308-14-1996 L2002 **N** *071

CHADHA, Ajit Kaur. 1312 OAKLAWN AVE 02920 #495-03-1962 L1972 **OBG** *020 †30 ‡

CHOI, Melissa Lok-Wah. ■ 02905 #043-01-2008 *012

CLARKE, Jennifer Grace. 95 WILMA SCHESLER LN, ACI/WOMEN'S DIVISION 02920 #035-20-1993 L1993 **IM** *020 †20

COHEN, Eve Melissa. ■ 02920 #008-02-2006 L2006 **IM** *012

COHN, Jamieson Vergeront. ■ 02910 #024-05-2007 L2007 **EM** *012

COK, Leo. HOWARD AVE 02911 #957-01-1954 L1962 **P CHP** *071

COLAGIOVANNI, Marco. ■ 02920 #024-07-1942 L1943 **GP** *071

CONKLIN, Frances Phillips. ■ 02920 #010-02-1951 L1956 **RO** *071 †60

CORDERO, Hector. 801 PARK AVE, PARK PEDIATRICS INC 02910 #308-01-1987 L1999 **PD** *020 †55

CORTEZ, Selina Cortez. ■ 02920 #748-02-1983 L1988 **PTH** *020 †50

COYLE, Deirdre Rose. ■ 02905 #035-19-2004 L2004 **OBG** *012

CRAMTON, Rachel Morris. ■ 02910 #041-13-2004 L2005 **PD** *012

CREIGHTON, William Thos. 1150 RESERVOIR AVE, STE 100 02920 #030-06-1981 L1983 **IM PD** *020 †20

CRITCHFIELD, Agatha Spink. ■ 02910 #020-12-2006 L2006 **OBG** *012

DAUM, Stanley W. ■ 02905 #024-01-1949 L1954 **IM** *071 †20

DE JESUS, Elizabeth G. 1596 BROAD ST 02905 #748-20-1993 L1999 **IM** *020 †20

DENARDO, Bradley Domenic. ■ 02921 #043-01-2008 *012

DENUCCI, Sarah M. ■ 02920 #043-01-2007 L2007 **IM** *012

DE RUOSI, Joseph Nicholas. 1150 RESERVOIR AVE, STE 305B 02920 #649-14-1981 L1986 **GP IM** *020

DESAI, Kirit Manubhai. 1681 CRANSTON ST, STE E 02920 #495-28-1975 L1984 **IM** *020 †20

DI LORENZO, Joseph A. 1370 CRANSTON ST 02920 #043-01-1975 L1976 **IM PD** *020 ‡

DI ORIO, John, Jr. 1725 BROAD ST 02905 #035-03-1975 L1977 **OBG** *020 †30

D'UVA, Anthony Domenic. 766 OAKLAWN AVE 02920 #561-01-1956 L1959 **OTO AI** *071

EJNES, Yul D. 75 SOCKANOSSET CROSS RD, STE 301 02920 #043-01-1985 L1989 **IM** *020 †20

ELEVADO, Morris Paul. 1150 RESERVOIR AVE 02920 #035-06-1997 L2003 **GE** *020 †20

FALGUERA, Dominador Q. 1150 RESERVOIR AVE, STE 100 02920 #748-01-1965 L2000 **GP EM** *020

FEDER, Seth. 950 RESERVOIR AVE 02910 #035-09-1976 L1981 **D** *020 †15

FELDMAN, Steven Allen. 1090 NEW LONDON AVE 02920 #050-02-1968 L1973 **P** *020 †55,75

FIGUEROA, Francis Xavier. 975 PONTIAC AVE 02911 #992 1992 **OPH** *020 †35

FINGLETON, James Gerard. 725 RESERVOIR AVE 02910 #041-13-1985 L1993 **TS** *020 †85,90

FOGLEMAN, Kelly Ammann. ■ 02910 #036-01-2004 L2004 **OBG** *012

FRANKEL, Ellen Henrie. 750 RESERVOIR AVE 02920 #035-09-1979 L1987 **D PDD** *020

FRATANTUONO, Peter. 445 BUDLONG RD 02920 #024-07-1950 L1951 **IM CD** *071

FREITAS, Gil Silva. ■ 02905 #024-07-2008 *012

GAJIC, Slobodan I. ■ 02920 #957-02-1956 L1973 **CLP PTH** *071 †50

GALL, Louis Stephen. 1606 PONTIAC AVE 02920 #473-04-1944 **IM P** *020

GARBER, Perry. 934 PARK AVE 02910 #038-41-1961 L1963 **IM** *020

GATES, Erin Alene. ■ 02905 #035-03-2006 L2006 **P** *012

GILMORE, Judith M. 725 RESERVOIR AVE STE 2 02910 #041-07-1972 L1986 **END IM** *020 †20

GILSON, Irving Thomas. 1150 RESERVOIR AVE, STE 203 02920 #010-02-1956 L1960 **CD IM** *020 †20

GOLINI, William John. 725 RESERVOIR AVE, STE 308 02910 #048-02-1974 L1975 **N** *020 †75

GONZALEZ, Maria T. 663 ATWOOD AVE 02920 #308-05-1989 L1996 **P** *020 †75

GORKINA, Ludmila. ELEANOR SLATER HOSPITAL 02920 #913-32-1964 L1985 *020

GRADY, John Patrick. ■ 02910 #024-02-1943 **PD** *071

GRAHAM, Dorothy Faye. ■ 02905 #143-06-1984 L1998 *100

GUNDOGAN, Fusun. ■ 02905 #902-09-1990 L2003 **PTH** *020 †50

GUPTA, Neena Rakesh. 1370 CRANSTON ST, INTERNAL MEDICINE & PEDIAT 02920 #495-13-1987 L2003 **PN PD** *020 †55

HALO, Hugo Hona. 892 OAKLAWN AVE 02920 #748-07-1956 L1967 **P** *071

HARAN, John Patrick, Jr. ■ 02920 #024-16-2007 L2007 **EM** *012

HART, Susan Harper. 39 HOWARD AVE, ADULT CORRECTIONAL 02920 #035-19-1997 L1997 **IM** *020 †20

HEALEY, Terrance Timothy. ■ 02910 #043-01-2003 L2003 **DR** *012

HOLLMANN, Peter Amberg. 351 BUDLONG RD 02920 #043-01-1979 L1980 **IMG IM** *030 †20

HUANG, Hao-Yuan. 333 BUDLONG RD 02920 #244-02-1977 L1982 **IM OS** *020 †20

HUBBARD, Leonard F, Jr. 1150 RESERVOIR AVE STE 301 02920 #050-02-1971 L1980 **HS ORS** *020 †40

HUSAIN, Syed Ghazanfar. ■ 02910 #704-02-1997 L2007 **CRS** *012 †85

INDEGLIA, Robert Anthony. 725 RESERVOIR AVE, STE 1 02910 #010-02-1962 L1970 **GS TS** *020 †85,90

ISSA, Michel Yacoub. STATE GENERAL HOSP 02920 #330-02-1953 L1977 **GPM** *020

■ = Address Information Privacy Protected

ISSARESCU, Patricia Joan. 1150 RESERVOIR AVE 02920 #024-05-1961 L1972 EM IM *020 †20,16

JACOB, Rafik. ■ 02921 #915-04-1993 *100

JAFFEE, Daniel Clement. 725 RESERVOIR AVE, STE 104 02910 #035-03-1998 L2004 U *020 †95

JASSIM, Ismail Mohammad. ■ 02920 #528-01-1948 L1971 U *020

JOSEPH, Plakyil Jos. 1220 PONTIAC AVE, STE 101 02920 #495-63-1980 L1991 HEM *020 †20

KARDOUS, Antioan. 1145 RESERVOIR AVE, STE 301 02920 #875-01-1994 L1996 IM *020 †20

KARKALAS, John. PO BOX 8281 02920 #902-01-1953 L1967 P *071 †75

KARSHBAUM, Stephen H. 725 RESERVOIR AVE 02910 #024-07-1991 L1998 DR IM *020 †20,80

KAUFMANN, Craig Paul. 960 RESERVOIR AVE 02920 #035-09-2002 L2002 P *100

KAYIAROS, Stephen. ■ 02905 #033-06-2005 L2005 ORS *012

KAZIANIS, John Athanasios. ■ 02920 #047-05-2006 IM *012

KESSIMIAN, Marianna Isabe. ■ 02910 #024-05-2007 L2007 P *012

KHURSHID, Shahzad. 333 BUDLONG RD, OFFICE OF HAO HUANG MD 02920 #704-04-1990 L2002 HO *020 †20

KISCH, Ethan H. 1090 NEW LONDON AVE, QUALITY BEHAVRL HLTH 02920 #024-05-1976 L1999 CHP P *020 †75

KODURU, Lalitha. 333 BUDLONG RD 02920 #496-24-1997 L2006 ID *020

KOTHARI, Renu Omprakash. 311 DORIC AVE 02910 #495-30-1972 L1979 CHP *020 †75

KRUSZ, Stephanie J. 750 RESERVOIR AVE 02910 #043-01-1994 L1994 IM *020 †20

KUTTY, Sinan Muhammad. ■ 02910 #033-06-2005 L2005 IM *012

LAMPURI, Cristina. ■ 02905 #035-06-2004 L2005 D *012

LANE, Courtney Ann. ■ 02905 #035-03-2007 L2007 PD *012

LATINA, Joseph Anthony. 1145 RESERVOIR AVE, STE 302 02920 #056-06-1968 L1969 GS *020 †85

LECONTE, Carine Marie. 1150 RESERVOIR AVE STE 205 02920 #035-45-1990 L1990 PD *020 †55

LEE, Chun Kak. 794 PARK AVE 02910 #583-01-1965 L1977 GP *020

LEE, Donald S. 1312 OAKLAWN AVE 02920 #583-04-1969 L1979 PD GP *020 †55

LEE, Marius Peter. 40 RAVEN CIR 02921 #781-01-1971 L1992 PTH *020 †50

LEE, Melissa. 45 KNEELAND ST 02905 #035-06-1999 L1999 PCC *100 †20

LIFFMANN, Kenneth Emil. ■ 02920 #024-01-1958 L1959 GS VS *071 †85

LIZARRAGA, William Anthon. ■ 02905 #047-06-2005 L2005 IM *012

LOMBARDI, Anthony J, Jr. 75 SOCKANOSSET CROSS RD 02920 #043-01-1993 L1993 IM *020 †20

LOMBARDO, Michele L. ■ 02920 #024-05-2004 L2004 GS *012

LOPORCHIO, Salvatore J. 35 SOCKANOSSET CROSS RD 02920 #043-01-1985 L1986 OPH *020 †35 ‡

LOURES, Constantine D. 16 HARVARD ST BOX 8773 02920 #418-01-1942 L1965 P GP *071

MAC LEAN, K Louise. 780 RESERVOIR AVE, STE 117 02910 #064-01-1976 L1989 FM *020 †18

MAIELLO, Louis Robt. 725 RESERVOIR AVE 02910 #561-01-1964 L1969 DR *020

MANANSALA, Violeta M. 600 NEW LONDON AVE, SLATER HOSPITAL RADIOLOGY 02920 #748-01-1964 L1976 DR *062

MARIASH, Evan Michael. ■ 02905 #016-42-2006 L2006 IM *100

MARIORENZI, Michael Peter. 725 RESERVOIR AVE, STE 101 02910 #010-02-1983 L1989 ORS *020 †40

MARKELEWICZ, Robert. ■ 02920 #043-01-2007 L2007 IM *012

MARSELLA, Augustus Fabius. 712 OAKLAWN AVE 02920 #028-78-1947, ▲ L1957 GP AM *071

MARSOCCI, Gerald. 725 RESERVOIR AVE STE 202 02910 #024-07-1967 L1968 GS CRS *020 †85

MAXIM, Raymond Bremner. 1500 PONTIAC AVE 02920 #305-01-1992 L1992 IM IMG *020 †20

MCINTYRE, Amy Kristen. ■ 02910 #043-01-2008 *012

MECHREFE, Adib Mtanios. 1150 RESERVOIR AVE, GARDEN CITY TREATMENT CENT 02920 #875-01-1964 L1976 EM *020 †16

MEHTA, Rupesh R. ■ 02920 #035-15-2005 L2005 IM *012

MELCHIONNA, John Anthony. ■ 02920 #561-16-1957 L1967 P *071

MIGLIORI, Julius C. ■ 02920 #561-01-1957 L1959 AN *020 †05

MIKOLICH, Dennis John. 1150 RESERVOIR AVE, STE 103 02920 #308-06-1980 L1986 ID IM *020 †20

MORRISSEY, Kenneth Jos. 1150 RESERVOIR AVE STE 200 02920 #043-01-1980 L1984 ORS *020 †40

MOURAD, Jack P. 226 AUBURN ST 02910 #396-24-1986 L1989 RHU *020 †20

MUSCO, Paul Sebastian. 725 RESERVOIR AVE STE 201 02910 #010-02-1982 L1987 OPH OS *020 †35

NAIK, Bachu. ■ 02921 #917-18-1965 L1974 IM *071

O'BRIEN, Mark Maddox. 6 HARRINGTON RD - SIMPSON, HALL R 02920 #028-34-1972 L1981 PD *050 †55

O'CONNELL, Jeremiah. 1150 RESERVOIR AVE, X-RAY ASSOCIATES INC 02920 #539-02-1959 L1966 R OS *020 †20

OHNMACHT, Richard Keith. 1145 RESERVOIR AVE, STE 210 02920 #035-45-1986 L1989 PD *020 †55

OPALENSKI, Philip Jos. 725 RESERVOIR AVE 02910 #561-17-1974 L1980 GE IM *020

ORTIZ, Roberto. 925 RESERVOIR AVE 02910 #649-16-1985 L1995 IM END *020 †20

PANCHAL, Rupa J Hasmukhal. 111 HOWARD AVE, ELEANOR SLATER HOSPITAL 02920 #495-76-1993 L2000 IM *020 †20

PANNEERSELVAM, Usha. 351 BUDLONG RD 02920 #495-59-1985 L1996 IM *020 †20

PATEL, Amrut Ramanlal. 1370 CRANSTON ST 02920 #495-89-1980 L1985 IM *020 †20

PATEL, Justin R. ■ 02910 #043-01-2004 L2004 U *012

PELLA, John Anthony. 1150 RESERVOIR AVE STE 305 02920 #561-01-1971 L1974 PUD IM *020 †20

PERL, Alan. 1215 RESERVOIR AVE 02920 #035-06-1977 L1980 DR *075

PETROCELLI, Giovanni. ■ 02920 #561-10-1944 L1957 GP *071

PETROPOULOS, Peter. ■ 02920 #024-05-1985 L1987 CD IM *020 †20

PHILLIPS, Benjamin Zachar. ■ 02905 #043-01-2004 L2004 PS *012

PICKETT, Brian Joseph. 750 RESERVOIR AVE, PARTNERS IN PRMRY CARE INC 02910 #305-01-1999 L1999 IM *020 †20

PLOVER, Jean Ryan. 1660 BROAD ST, JEAN PLOVER, MDFAMILY PRAC 02905 #422-01-1982 L1992 FM *020 †18

POLANCO, Jose Roman. 251 PARK AVE 02905 #035-08-1998 L1998 IM *020 †20

POND, Soneath Lang Hang. 31 ORCHARD ST 02910 #422-01-1995 L1996 IM *020 †20

POSHKUS, Michael Timothy. 39 HOWARD AVE 02920 #035-01-1998 L1998 ID IM *030 †20

POWERS, George Lyman. 1150 RESERVOIR AVE 02920 #024-07-1978 L1983 GE IM *020 †20

PRICE, Ashley Ann. 1090 CRANSTON ST, CCAP-FHS 02920 #016-01-1998 L1998 FM *020 †18

PRIOR, Michael W. 725 RESERVOIR AVE 02910 #010-02-1967 L1975 TS *020 †85,90

QUILES, Rick. ■ 02921 #043-01-2000 L2004 PD *100

QUINN, Donn R. ■ 02920 #035-20-1951 L1956 IM PD *020

RAZA, Syed K. PO BOX 8281, AM BUILDING, HOWARD AVENUE 02920 #704-02-1985 L2001 P PYG *020

RECCHIA, Richard Orland. ■ 02921 #561-01-1963 L1968 GYN *075 †30

REGE, Vishram Bhalchandra. 1220 PONTIAC AVE, STE 101 02920 #495-01-1960 L1969 ON IM *020

RINTELS, Peter Behrle. 1220 PONTIAC AVE, STE 101 02920 #024-01-1983 L1991 HEM *020 †20

RODERICK, Paul Wm. 1150 RESERVOIR AVE 02920 #041-09-1974 L1979 GE *030 †20

ROMANO, Dennis Jos. 1150 RESERVOIR AVE 02920 #308-07-1982 L1997 FM *020

ROSENBERG, Mark. 725 RESERVOIR AVE, STE 102 02910 #033-05-1996 L1996 FM *020 †18

ROUND, Charles Brayton. ■ 02905 #024-01-1942 L1949 GS PHP *071

RUELOS, Jorge Salvador. 1596 BROAD ST 02905 #748-10-1970 L1985 OBG *020

SALISBURY, Matthew T. 1500 PONTIAC AVE 02920 #023-01-2000 L2000 FM *020 †18

SAMBANDAM, S Thirugnana. 1220 PONTIAC AVE STE 201 02920 #495-66-1970 L1978 ON HO *020 †20

SANTA TERESA, Adelino, Jr. ■ 02920 #748-01-1966 L1973 OBG RO *020

SANTA TERESA, Alicia G M. ■ 02920 #748-01-1964 L1978 PTH *071

SARNI, Robert Peter. 725 RESERVOIR AVE 02910 #023-01-1960 L1961 FM OM *020 †18

SAVITZKY, David C. 311 DORIC AVE, MENTAL HEALTH SERVICES 02910 #048-14-1982 L1989 CHP P *020 †75

SCARLATOS, Theodore F. ■ 02920 #561-01-1966 L1982 ORS *071

SCHNETZLER, Jason Thomas. ■ 02920 #038-41-2005 L2005 EM *012

SEARS, Edmund Hamilton. ■ 02905 #043-01-2004 L2004 MPD *012

SELL, Peter J. ■ 02921 #022-75-2003, ▲ L2007 PD *020

SHANNON, Catherine Marie. 65 SOCKANOSSET CROSS RD 02920 #020-02-1984 L1990 DR *020 †80

SHIPLEY, Joshua Leonard. ■ 02905 #041-15-2004 L2004 HO *012

SIEGEL, Matthew S. ■ 02905 #005-11-2003 L2003 CPP *012 †55

SIKET, Matthew Stephen. ■ 02905 #033-05-2007 L2007 EM *012

SOINSKI, Rebecca Elizabet. ■ 02910 #041-02-2008 *012

SORDELLINI, Paul. 619 BUDLONG RD 02920 #561-10-1952 L1957 GP GPM *071

SPALLUTO, Lucy Marie. ■ 02910 #051-01-2006 L2007 DR *012

SPAULDING, Anne Catherine. 39 HOWARD AVE, RI DEPARTMENT OF CORRECTIO 02920 #051-04-1989 L1989 ID OS *020 †20

STEPANIAN, Sevak. ■ 02905 #024-05-2007 L2007 IM *012

STEVENSON, Karen H. 761 PARK AVE 02910 #033-05-1984 L1986 IM *020 †20

STUEBING, Elizabeth Ann. ■ 02905 #038-06-2005 L2005 GS *012

SULLIVAN, Frank Warren. ■ 02920 #054-04-1961 L1967 P *071 †75

SWEENEY, Lynn Ann. ■ 02910 #043-01-2004 L2004 EM *012

SWEN, Jeanne Wrean. 1660 BROAD ST 02905 #005-18-1989 L1989 FM *020 †18

TACTACAN, Pedro Franco. 111 HOWARD AVE, APS BLDG ROOM 2-21 02920 #748-01-1991 L1999 P *020 †75

TARANTINO, Joseph Angelo. 950 RESERVOIR AVE, STE 5 02910 #561-10-1953 L1958 OBG *071

TOMASELLI, Rosario Vito. ■ 02921 #024-07-1955 L1962 ORS RHU *071 †40

TORRADO, Luis Francisco. ■ 02920 #264-01-1954 L1972 GYN GS *020

TOUBIA, Nabil Anis. 1500 PONTIAC AVE 02920 #913-16-1996 L1998 GE *020 †20

TVERSKAYA, Olga V. 712 OAKLAWN AVE, STE 4 02920 #913-05-1985 L1992 IM *020 †20

VARGHESE, Paul George. ■ 02920 #043-01-1994 L1997 CD *020 †20

VITALE, Colleen Concannon. 1145 RESERVOIR AVE, STE 124 02920 #035-09-2003 L2003 PD *020 †55

WASSER, Marvin Stanley. 496 PONTIAC AVE 02910 #561-01-1977 L1978 PD EM *020 †55

WAY, Christopher C. 1150 RESERVOIR AVE STE 204 02920 #035-03-1975 L1985 OPH EM *020 †35

WEAVER, Michael James. 1500 PONTIAC AVE 02920 #038-40-1971 L1976 GS *020 †85

WILSON, Jeffrey Michael. 725 RESERVOIR AVE, STE 102 02910 #041-09-1998 L1998 FM *020 †18

WINTERS, Jeffry Colin. 761 PARK AVE 02910 #028-34-1981 L1984 IM *020 †20

WOOLFALL, Karen Lee. ■ 02920 #043-01-1989 L1989 IM *020 †20

ZAMAN, Mohammad K. ■ 02920 #160-02-1990 L1999 P *020

ZHANG, Cunxian. ■ 02921 #243-39-1983 L2000 PTH *020 †50

ZUENA, Ernest Nicholas. 1370 CRANSTON ST, WEST BAY MEDICAL BUILDING 02920 #561-01-1976 L1978 GS *020 †85

CUMBERLAND – PROVIDENCE

ACKERMAN, Emily Jane. 2140 MENDON RD, URGENT MEDICAL CARE 02864 #041-15-2002 L2002 FM *100 †18

AHMAD, Bashir. 1464 DIAMOND HILL RD 02864 #704-01-1959 L1969 P *020 †75

ALVAREZ, Helena M. ■ 02864 #132-06-1958 L1973 IM CD *071

ALVAREZ, Mario Hector. ■ 02864 #132-01-1955 L1971 CD IM *071

AUSTIN, Gregory James. 2138 MENDON RD, STE 302 02864 #041-12-1980 L1987 ORS HS *020 †40

BAE, David C. ■ 02864 #043-01-2002 L2002 U *012

BALON, Stanley Richard. 175 NATE WHIPPLE HWY 02864 #024-05-1979 L1981 IM *020 †20

BANSAL, Arvind. 175 NATE WHIPPLE HWY, STE 108 02864 #495-36-1997 L2003 PCC *020 †20

BERMON, Maurice. 1464 DIAMOND HILL RD 02864 #024-07-1970 L1976 P *020 †75

BRODY, Sidney I. WHITE HILL LANE 02864 #041-09-1941 L1970 IM A *071 †70

CARROLL, Kristin Ann. 72 HARRISON ST 02864 #010-01-2004 L2004 PD *020 †55

CATALLOZZI, Kenneth Rocco. 2138 MENDON RD, STE 302 02864 #030-06-1980 L1984 ORS *020 †40

CATUCCI, Federico L. 2482 DIAMOND HILL RD 02864 #561-14-1955 L1963 NS OS *071

CHIHLAS, Christopher N. 2138 MENDON RD, STE 302 02864 #051-04-1992 L1997 ORS *020 †40

CONWAY, Stephen Arthur. 2178 MENDON RD, STE 100 02864 #024-07-2002 L2005 PD *020 †55

CROTTY, Maureen Alice. 2 MEEHAN LN 02864 #024-05-1995 L1995 PD *020 †55

ELAHI, Shahid. ■ 02864 #704-02-1993 L2003 P *020

FARNUM, Elisabeth Knight. 30 MARTIN ST, UNIT 30A 02864 #010-01-1990 L1993 FM *020 †18

GUALTIERI, Albert Mario. ■ 02864 #016-43-1970 L1977 DR *020

GUPTA, Krishanu Bappa. 525 BROAD ST, ADVANCED RADIOLOGY 02864 #041-01-1997 L2003 DR *020 †80

HARAPPANAHALLY, Gita Vija. ■ 02864 #495-58-1993 L2006 PD *100 †55

HARKOW, Joel S. 3353 MENDON RD 02864 #024-16-1985 L1986 IM *075 †20

HARRIS, Craig Alan. ■ 02864 #024-07-1963 L1965 **IM** *020
HORNIK, Norbert. ■ 02864 #759-01-1963 L1973 **PD** *020 †55
IOVANEL, Mihaela. 175 NATE WHIPPLE HWY 02864 #781-01-1985 L1993 **IM** *020 †20
JAGANNATH, Yamini Sundar. ■ 02864 #024-07-2006 L2006 **PD** *012
KHABBAZ, Bassam. 2295 DIAMOND HILL RD, FAMILY INTERNAL MEDICINE 02864 #875-01-1983 L1998 **IM** *020 †20
KIM, Charles Jae Haub. ■ 02864 #583-02-1962 L1972 **AN** *020
KLUFAS, Emil Jos. 525 BROAD ST 02864 #407-19-1948 L1954 **GP** *020
KLUFAS, Lydia L. 525 BROAD ST 02864 #041-01-1990 L1991 **D** *020 †15
KORENNAYA, Alla. 175 NATE WHIPPLE HWY, STE 203 02864 #913-58-1983 L1993 **N** *020
LATHAM, Jeffrey Foster. 175 NATE WHIPPLE HWY, STE 202 02864 #038-41-1975 L1976 **CD IM** *020 †20
LEWIS, Kevan Gerard. ■ 02864 #005-14-2004 L2004 **D** *012
LIFRAK, Joseph Timothy. 2138 MENDON RD, STE 302 02864 #043-01-1994 L1994 **ORS** *020 †40
LUNDY, William Howard. 175 NATE WHIPPLE HWY, STE 210 02864 #024-05-1969 L1975 **P** *020
MAKARIOUS, Samir H. 175 NATE WHIPPLE HWY, STE 101 02864 #915-02-1964 L1994 **IM** *020
MALAFRONTE, Pasquale. 2140 MENDON RD, STE 201 02864 #024-07-1971 L1976 **PD** *020 †55
MARIORENZI, Amedeo Louis. 2138 MENDON RD, STE 302 02864 #010-02-1956 L1957 **ORS** *020 †40
MARIORENZI, Louis John. 2138 MENDON RD, STE 302 02864 #043-01-1980 L1982 **ORS OAR** *020 †40
MIGLIORI, Sidney Premer. 2138 MENDON RD, STE 302 02864 #026-04-1988 L1996 **ORS GS** *020 †40
MISSAGHIAN, Amir H. 106 NATE WHIPPLE HWY 02864 #407-16-1958 L1968 **PDA AI** *071 †55,03
MONTI, Emilio James, Jr. 2178 MENDON RD 02864 #010-02-1961 L1962 **PD** *072 †55
NIZETIC, Nina Betty. 525 BROAD ST 02864 #132-01-1962 L1977 **P** *020
O'SHEA, Carol A. 2178 MENDON RD, STE 100 02864 #043-01-1998 L1998 **PD** *020 †55
PEDUTO, Stephanie Maria. 2 MEEHAN LN, BLACKSTONE VALLEY PED 02864 #035-09-1992 L1997 **PD** *020 †55
PHILIPS, Alexander. 106 NATE WHIPPLE HWY, PHYSICIANS OF RHODE 02864 #495-27-1965 L1976 **GS GYN** *020 †85
PHILIPS, Philip A. 106 NATE WHIPPLE HWY, PHYSICIANS OF RHODE 02864 #043-01-1994 L1999 **GS** *020 †85
ROBBIO, Robert Jos. 2140 MENDON RD 02864 #561-17-1978 L1994 **FM** *020 †18
SCHOORENS, Cathy Joan. 106 NATE WHIPPLE HWY, PHYSICIANS OF RHODE 02864 #023-12-1987 L2004 **FM** *020 †18
SIDDIQI, Naeem M. ■ 02864 #704-01-1958 L1971 **U** *071 †95
SINGER, Ira Joel. 2138 MENDON RD, STE 302 02864 #010-01-1978 L1984 **ORS** *020 †40
SKOMOROCH, Zygmunt Witold. 33 OLD WEST WRENTHAM RD 02864 #759-03-1936 **GS** *100 †85
SMITH, Lynn Marie. 2140 MENDON RD, STE 201 02864 #016-02-1990 L1991 **PD** *020 †55
SOUTHER, Jennifer R. 30 MARTIN ST, UNIT 30A 02864 #043-01-1999 L1999 **FM** *020 †18
STARAKIEWICZ, Maria Zofia. 2178 MENDON RD, PRIMA, INC 02864 #759-01-1988 L2005 **PD** *020 †55
TANDON, Ravi. 175 NATE WHIPPLE HWY, STE 108 02864 #495-45-1983 L2000 **IM PCC** *020 †20
TOMEI, John Anthony. ■ 02864 #561-01-1961 L1968 **R** *071
TRULL, Janice. ■ 02864 #041-77-2005, ▲ L2005 **FP** *012
TUCCI, Joseph Ralph. 175 NATE WHIPPLE HWY 02864 #024-05-1959 L1969 **END IM** *020 †20
VERMA, Tilak Kiran. 175 NATE WHIPPLE HWY, STE 108 02864 #495-45-1975 L1981 **IM** *020 †20
WILSON, Scott A. 106 NATE WHIPPLE HWY, PHYSICIANS OF RHODE 02864 #043-01-1997 L1997 **IM** *020 †20
YASIGIAN, Peter Tuma. 2 MEEHAN LN 02864 #915-04-1982 L1984 **PD** *020 †55
YOUNES, Maria Hoyos. 2138 MENDON RD, STE 104 02864 #264-13-1982 L1990 **N PD** *020
ZITER, Jeanne Evelyn. 2 MEEHAN LN, BLACKSTONE VALLEY PEDIATRI 02864 #038-06-1993 L1996 **PD** *020 †55

EAST GREENWICH - KENT

ABBOTT, Brian Gregory. 1377 S COUNTY TRL, RHODE ISLAND CARDIOLOGY CE 02818 #011-03-1995 L2004 **CD** *020 †20
AGATIELLO, Paul J. ■ 02818 #043-01-1981 L1982 **IM** *071 †20
ASHLEY, David W. 1351 S COUNTY TRL, STE 301 02818 #043-01-1992 L1992 **FM** *020 †18
ATALAY, Michael Kemal. ■ 02818 #023-07-1996 L2003 **DR** *020 †80
AZAM, Munawar M. 1351 S COUNTY TRL, STE 215 02818 #704-16-1985 L1995 **IM** *020 †20
AZZOLI, Salvatore Guido. ■ 02818 #016-43-1967 L1973 **GS** *020 †85
BADIAVAS, Evangelos Van. 1351 S COUNTY TRL 02818 #041-02-1990 L1998 **D** *020 †15
BAUM, Carol Lisa. ■ 02818 #041-01-1994 L2008 **PD** *020 †55
BELLINO, Joseph Peter. 1351 S COUNTY TRL, STE 303 02818 #010-02-1964 L1965 **OTO** *020 †45
BERT, John Jos. 1050 MAIN ST 02818 #010-02-1974 L1978 **OBG** *020 †30
BERTHIAUME, Eric Paul. 1407 S COUNTY TRL, BLDG 4 02818 #038-41-1999 L2002 **GE** *020 †20
BERTHOLD, Francis F. ■ 02818 #154-07-1937 L1955 **GP** *071
BLACKMER, Karen. 1351 S COUNTY TRL, STE 301 02818 #024-07-1993 L1993 **FM** *020 †18
BOEKELHEIDE, Kim. ■ 02818 #036-07-1980 L1984 **PTH** *050 †50
BRECHER, Keith R. ■ 02818 #035-03-1991 L1995 **N** *020 †75
BRENDEL, Debra L. 1050 MAIN ST 02818 #043-01-1989 L1989 **OBG** *020 †30
BRODSKY TOMASI, Cheryl K. 1050 MAIN ST 02818 #016-45-1989 L1994 **OBG** *020 †30
BROGAN, Robert Arthur. 27 DIVISION ST 02818 #010-02-1955 L1956 **PD** *020 †55
BRUTUS, Adrien. 4494 POST RD 02818 #649-14-1969 L1977 **PTH** *020
BURNS, Stephen P, Sr. ■ 02818 #024-07-1966 L1973 **R** *071 †80,28
CANDOW, David Lawrence. 1050 MAIN ST UNIT 18 02818 #041-09-1997 L2004 **FM** *020 †18
CARNEY-GODLEY, Kathleen. 2850 S COUNTY TRL UNIT 2 02818 #008-01-1988 L1989 **D** *020 †15
CASERTA, Robert J. ■ 02818 #561-01-1966 L2002 **DR** *020
CHENG, David. ■ 02818 #035-19-1992 L2000 **DR** *020 †20,80
CHOFAY, Dana R. 1377 S COUNTY TRL, UNIT 2A 02818 #050-02-1995 L1995 **IM** *020 †20
CIVIDINO, Victoria. 4480 POST RD, UNIT 7 02818 #132-01-1968 L1992 **RO** *020 †80
CORRAO, William Michael. 1285 S COUNTY TRL, U PULM ASSOCS & ASTHMA CTR 02818 #035-45-1972 L1973 **PUD** *020 †20
COSTELO, Celso Sacay. ■ 02818 #748-11-1972 *020
COSTELO, Lourdes V. ■ 02818 #748-01-1966 L1984 **PD** *020
DA SILVA, Manuel Ferreira. 1405 S COUNTY TRL, STE 510 02818 #043-01-1991 L1991 **HS** *020 †40
DELSESTO, Richard Michael. 2358 S COUNTY TRL 02818 #050-02-1996 L1999 **IM** *020 †20
DEYOUNG, Paula Ann. 1050 MAIN ST 02818 #024-05-1989 L1989 **OBG** *020 †30
DOMAGALSKI, Lisa R. 1050 MAIN ST 02818 #024-07-1991 L1991 **OBG** *020 †30
DONAT, Walter Edward. 1285 S COUNTY TRL, U PULM ASSOCS $ ASTHMA CTR 02818 #043-01-1977 L1979 **PUD CD** *020 †20
DOYLE, Andrea Mary. 1351 S COUNTY TRL 02818 #035-03-1996 L2004 **PS** *020 †85,65
DREW, Thomas Martin. 1377 S COUNTY TRL, RT 2 02818 #035-01-1971 L1977 **CD IM** *020 †20
DU PREE, Marsha Louise. 1050 MAIN ST, UNIT 15 02818 #010-02-1983 L2004 **D DMP** *020 †15
EBERSON, Craig Politt. 1405 S COUNTY TRL, STE 510 02818 #033-06-1995 L1995 **OP** *020 †40
EGER, Renee Ross. 1050 MAIN ST 02818 #024-07-1991 L1991 **OBG** *020 †30
FADALE, Paul D. 1405 S COUNTY TRL, STE 510 02818 #035-06-1981 L1985 **ORS OSM** *020 †40
FERRANTE, Gaetano Jos. ■ 02818 #010-02-1955 L1956 **GP OS** *020
FERRANTE, Karen Jean. ■ 02818 #010-02-1988 L1993 **ON** *020 †20
FLANAGAN, Claire Marie. 1377 S COUNTY TRL, UNIT 2B 02818 #035-47-1979 L1999 **PD** *030 †55
FRANEK, Bruno. 4601 POST RD 02818 #407-01-1944 L1952 **P** *071
FRANKEL, Amylynne Jaccari. ■ 02818 #050-02-2008 *012
FRIED, David Lawrence. 1351 S COUNTY TRL, STE 100 02818 #012-05-1989 L1989 **IM** *020 †20
GANGE, Michele. 1050 MAIN ST 02818 #043-01-1991 L1991 **OBG** *020 †30
GHOREISHI, Siavash. 5835 POST RD STE 110 02818 #517-01-1976 L1986 **PD** *020 †55
GLICKMAN, Denise Fabiola. 1377 S COUNTY TRL 02818 #035-46-1986 L1995 **IM** *020 †20
GRAY, Cheryl Ann. 9 MCGRAW CT 02818 #028-02-2008 *012
GREEN, Andrew. 1405 S COUNTY TRL, STE 510 02818 #035-01-1987 L1987 **ORS OS** *020 †40
GUILFOYLE, Bryan Joseph. 5600 POST RD, UNIT 114-385 02818 #422-01-1989 L1995 **IM** *075
HAAS, Klaus Friedrich. 105 GRANITE DR 02818 #025-01-1965 L1972 **GS VS** *071 †85
HANNA, Cynthia M. 1050 MAIN ST 02818 #041-02-1985 L1988 **OBG** *020 †30
HARRINGTON, Lisa B K. ■ 02818 #024-05-1990 L1997 **IM** *020 †20
HAYDEN, Deborah Marie. 1050 MAIN ST 02818 #036-07-1987 L2001 **OBG** *020 †30
HERU, Michael R. 24 EXCHANGE ST # 2 02818 #566-01-1981 L1992 **IM** *075
HIGHT, Ellen Beth. 1351 S COUNTY TRL, STE 301 02818 #024-05-1992 L1992 **FM** *020 †18
HULSTYN, Michael Jan. 1405 S COUNTY TRL, STE 510 02818 #043-01-1986 L1988 **ORS GS** *020 †40
IANNUCCILLI, Jason D. ■ 02818 #043-01-2005 L2005 **DR** *012
IQBAL, S M Arshad. 4519 POST RD 02818 #704-02-1988 L1996 **N** *020 †75
JOSEPH-DEL VECCHIO, Jane. 168 MAIN ST, EAST GREENWICH OPHTHALMOLO 02818 #038-44-1992 L1992 **OPH** *075 †35
KAGAN, Samuel. 925 MAIN ST 02818 #005-06-1977 L1993 **FM** *020 †18
KATARINCIC, Julia Ann. 1405 S COUNTY TRL, STE 510 02818 #041-12-1989 L1989 **HS** *020 †40
KEATING, Edward Chas. 1377 S COUNTY TRL, RT 2 02818 #917-19-1976 L2000 **CD** *020 †20
KHAN, Shahid Ali. 1351 S COUNTY TRL, STE 215 02818 #704-25-1996 L2002 **IM** *020 †20
KHOURY, Nabil Yaqub. 1050 MAIN ST 02818 #875-01-1959 L1968 **OBG** *020 †30
KOKTURK, Tolga Nizam. 1050 MAIN ST 02818 #035-08-1996 L2000 **OBG** *020 †30
KROESSLER, David Ernest. 1351 S COUNTY TRL, STE 210 02818 #422-01-1982 L1986 **P** *020 †75
LAMBIASE, Joseph John. ■ 02818 #010-02-1943 L1950 **DR OS** *071
LAMENDOLA, Chad E. 925 MAIN ST 02818 #043-01-1997 L2005 **FM** *020 †18
LAWLOR, John B. ■ 02818 #035-08-1950 L1952 **U** *071 †95
LIMBIRD, Richard S, Jr. 1405 S COUNTY TRL, STE 510 02818 #012-01-1976 L1984 **ORS** *040 †40
LIU, Paul Y. 1351 S COUNTY TRL 02818 #024-01-1987 L2002 **PS** *020 †85,65
LONDON, Gerald L. ■ 02818 #396-18-1989 L1990 **EM IM** *020
LUND, Sally Anne. ■ 02818 #024-05-1989 L1989 **PD** *074 †75
MADRAS-STOPA, Karen. ■ 02818 #067-01-1980 L1995 **PD** *020 †55
MANZO, Pierre Robert. 1351 S COUNTY TRL, STE 301 02818 #021-01-1993 L1993 **FM** *020 †18
MCDONNOLD, Mollie Ann. ■ 02818 #048-04-2007 L2007 **OBG** *012
MC GIBNEY, Kevin Jos. 1377 S COUNTY TRL, STE 28 02818 #041-07-1991 L1991 **NPM** *020 †55
MC KENNA, Michael Brian. ■ 02818 #033-05-2000 L2000 **HO** *012 †20
MC MILLAN, Clare O'Leary. 1377 S COUNTY TRL, EAST GREENWICH PEDIATRICS 02818 #041-01-2000 L2003 **PD** *020 †55
MC RAE, Robert G. 1351 S COUNTY TRL, STE 303 02818 #024-07-1976 L1979 **OTO** *020 †45
MEYER, Scott Andrew. ■ 02818 #043-01-2004 L2006 **NS** *012
MIGLIORI, Joseph Louis. ■ 02818 #561-01-1971 L1977 **OPH** *071 †35
MILLERICK, Thomas Jos, Jr. 1351 S COUNTY TRL, # 1 02818 #422-01-1985 L1988 **IM** *020
MORSCH-ROSSEWEIJ, P. ■ 02818 #660-01-1960 L1979 **IMG PD** *020
NIEDELMAN, Adam Fredric. 1377 S COUNTY TRL 02818 #041-02-2000 L2000 **CD** *020 †20
NIGRI, Peter Thos. 1351 S COUNTY TRL, STE 303 02818 #056-06-1969 L1975 **OTO** *020 †45
NOEL, Anne Elizabeth. 1351 S COUNTY TRL 02818 #010-01-1992 L1992 **PD** *072 †55
NOWAK, Mariola Margaret. 1377 S COUNTY TRL, UNIT 2A 02818 #010-01-1994 L1994 **IM** *020 †20
PALUMBO, Mark Angelo. 1405 S COUNTY TRL, STE 510 02818 #024-05-1988 L1992 **ORS** *020 †40
PAOLINO, Thomas Jos, Jr. 4474 POST RD 02818 #010-01-1967 L1969 **P** *020 †75
PARK, Michael Chankwon. ■ 02818 #019-02-2002 L2002 **NS** *012
PEDVIS-LEFTICK, Anita. 1351 S COUNTY TRL, STE 302 02818 #067-01-1974 L1999 **D** *020 †15
PERRY, Adrienne Jessica. 1050 MAIN ST 02818 #024-05-1990 L1990 **OBG** *020 †30
PERRY, Curtis John. 1567 S COUNTY TRL 02818 #043-01-1983 L1990 **OTO** *020 †45
POGACAR, Peter Rok. 1377 S COUNTY TRL UNIT 2B, EAST GREENWICH PEDS 02818 #024-05-1997 L2004 **PD** *020 †55
POGACAR, Srecko. 4474 POST RD 02818 #957-03-1953 L1971 **P NP** *071 †75
POSHKUS, Kristin Mary. 1377 S COUNTY TRL, UNIT 2A 02818 #041-15-2000 L2000 **IM** *020
RANDALL, Rebecca Winslow. 1050 MAIN ST 02818 #038-41-1990 L1990 **OBG** *020 †30
RATHORE, Bharti Chauhan. ■ 02818 #495-98-1995 L1999 **IM** *100 †20
RAVIN, Mary A S. ■ 02818 #024-07-1950 L1952 **IM** *071
REEDER, Laurie Beth. 1351 S COUNTY TRL, BLDG 2 02818 #024-07-1990 L2001 **TS** *020 †90,85
REIBMAN, Bonnie. 1377 S COUNTY TRL, UNIT 2B 02818 #026-04-1978 L1999 **PD** *020 †55
RICCI, Anthony Raymond. 63 CEDAR AVE 02818 #043-01-1984 L1989 **AI IM** *020 †20,03
RICCI, Patricia Cocozza. 1285A S COUNTY TRL 02818 #043-01-1983 L1989 **P** *020 †75
ROCCHIO, Elizabeth Marie. 1050 MAIN ST UNIT 18 02818 #041-09-1997 L2000 **FM** *020 †18
RODGERS, Joseph Lewis, Jr. 463 FRENCHTOWN RD 02818 #051-01-1986 L2000 **ADP** *020 †18

■ = Address Information Privacy Protected

SCHATZ, Sanford Lewis. 33 GREAT RD 02818 #035-09-1967 L1976 **NM DR** *020 †80,28
SCHWAGER, Mark Ian. 1351 S COUNTY TRL 02818 #035-06-1983 L1986 **IM IMG** *020 †20
SHAMIM, Tabassum. 505 STONERIDGE DR 02818 #308-11-1988 L2005 **ADL PD** *020 †55
SILVERSMITH, Howard Gregg. 1351 S COUNTY TRL STE 205 02818 #035-48-1997 L1997 **PD** *020 †55
SLATTERY, John Gormley. 925 MAIN ST 02818 #043-01-1989 L1993 **FM FSM** *020 †18
SMITH, Matthew Joseph. 1351 S COUNTY TRL, STE 220 02818 #065-05-1995 L2003 **PRS PME** *020 †60
SOLGA, Patricia Michelle. 1405 S COUNTY TRL, STE 510 02818 #010-02-1984 L1990 **ORS GS** *020 †40
SPLITEK, Katherine Bonell. ■ 02818 #056-05-2008 *012
SPRARAGEN, Sanford C. ■ 02818 #035-45-1956 L1972 **NM IM** *071 †20,28
STANCHINA, Michael L. 1285 S COUNTY TRL, UNIVERSITY PULMONARY ASSOC 02818 #055-01-1994 L2002 **PCC** *020 †20
STOPA, Edward G. ■ 02818 #067-01-1980 L1993 **NP** *040 †50
TANEJA, Charu. 1351 S COUNTY TRL 02818 #495-45-1990 L1999 **GS** *020 †85
TEREK, Richard Mark. 1405 S COUNTY TRL, STE 510 02818 #016-02-1985 L1993 **ORS SO** *020 †40
TREGER, Flora. 1377 S COUNTY TRL, UNIT 2A 02818 #038-06-1989 L1989 **IM** *020 †20
UPDEGROVE, Randall L. ■ 02818 #043-01-1983 L1994 **OM IM** *020 †70
URBAN, James Robert, Jr. 1000 DIVISION ST, HARBOUR MEDICAL CLINIC 02818 #561-17-1985 L1992 **N** *020
URBANIAK, Leah Marie. ■ 02818 #010-02-2004 L2004 **IM** *012
VECCHIOTTI, Mark Arthur. 1351 S COUNTY TRL, STE 303 02818 #035-20-2001 L2001 **OTO** *020 †45
VEST, Thomas Alfred. ■ 02818 #035-03-1966 L1972 **GYN** *071 †30
VICCIONE, Todd Daniel. 1351 S COUNTY TRL, STE 100 02818 #035-09-1996 L1996 **IM** *020 †20
VOGEL, Benjamin S. 1050 MAIN ST 02818 #035-08-1968 L1973 **OBG GS** *020 †30
WALKER, William Scott. 1050 MAIN ST 02818 #048-12-1984 L1988 **OBG** *020 †30
WILKEL, Caroline Susan. 2850 S COUNTY TRL, UNIT 2 02818 #008-02-1985 L1988 **D DMP** *020 †15
ZINCK, Deborah Anne. 1351 S COUNTY TRL # 20 02818 #035-15-1992 L1992 **PD** *020 †55

EAST PROVIDENCE – PROVIDENCE

ABANILLA, Juanito A. 1970 PAWTUCKET AVE 02914 #748-10-1964 L1972 **IM EM** *020
AKHTAR, Muhammad. 400 WARREN AVE, STE 1 02914 #704-01-1986 L1994 **ON** *020 †20
ALESSI, Joseph Francis. 525 TAUNTON AVE, EAST PROVIDENCE MEDICAL CE 02914 #024-07-1982 L1990 **FM** *020 †18 ‡
AMBY, Alexander Scott. ■ 02914 #043-01-2006 L2006 **FP** *012
ARMENIO, Vincent A. 1 OFFICE PKWY 02914 #305-01-1986 L1989 **IM HO** *020 †20
AYVAZYAN, Herman. 450 VETERANS MEMORIAL PKWY, METACOMET OFFICE PARK BLD 02914 #043-01-1985 L1987 **IM** *020 †20
BELAND, Michael David. 20 CATAMORE BLVD, RHODE ISLAND MEDICAL IMAGI 02914 #024-16-2001 L2002 **DR** *020 †80
BILODEAU, Courtney Clark. ■ 02914 #016-42-2004 L2004 **IM** *100 †20
BOXERMAN, Jerrold L. 20 CATAMORE BLVD, RHODE ISLAND MEDICAL IMAGI 02914 #024-01-1996 L2002 **RNR** *020 †80
BRASSARD, Peter. 1053 S BROADWAY, BRDWY MED TRTMNT CTR LLC 02914 #023-01-1983 L1986 **FM** *020 †18
BREX, Charles John, III. 450 VETERANS MEMORIAL PKWY, BLDG 4 02914 #035-09-1975 L1976 **IM** *020 †20
BURNS, Suzanne Patricia. 900 WARREN AVE 02914 #043-01-1985 L1988 **IM** *020 †20
CALLAGHAN, Joseph F, Jr. 450 VETERANS MEMORIAL PKWY, BLDG 14 02914 #023-01-1968 L1969 **U** *071 †95
CARRUTHERS, Thomas Nichol. ■ 02914 #036-01-2006 L2006 **GS** *012
CHANG, Kevin Jeffrey. 20 CATAMORE BLVD, RHODE ISLAND MEDICAL IMAGI 02914 #041-01-2000 L2006 **DR** *020 †80
CHRISTIAN, Fredric V. 450 VETERANS MEMORIAL PKWY, BLDG 15 02914 #010-02-1972 L1974 **CD** *020 †20
COLDIRON, John Stephen. 2377 PAWTUCKET AVE 02914 #016-02-1962 L1995 **PD MDM** *030 †55
DAVIS, Lawrence Matthew. 20 CATAMORE BLVD 02914 #024-16-1990 L1991 **DR** *020 †80
DI SANTO, David John. 2464 PAWTUCKET AVE 02914 #048-13-1977 L1978 **NS** *020 †25
DRAGOMIRE, Daniel Lee. 314 TAUNTON AVE 02914 #055-02-1997 L1997 **NEP** *020 †20
DROGIN, Jeffrey Howard. 450 VETERANS MEMORIAL PKWY 02914 #038-41-1975 L1976 **IM** *020 †20
ENDRENY, Raymond Guy. 318 WATERMAN AVE 02914 #041-09-1973 L1974 **NEP IM** *020 †20
ETHIER, Matthew David. ■ 02914 #024-16-2007 L2007 **IM** *012
FARRELL, David Sears. 450 VETERANS MEMORIAL PKWY, BLDG 11 02914 #038-41-1976 L1981 **D** *020 †15
FINIGAN, John Ward. 900 WARREN AVE 02914 #056-06-1996 L1996 **PD** *020 †55
FOX, Gregory Alan. 450 VETERANS MEMORIAL PKWY 02914 #038-41-1997 L1997 **PD PDE** *020 †55
GALKIN, Harris Michael. 450 VETERANS MEMORIAL PKWY, STE 401 02914 #043-01-1978 L1981 **OBG** *020 †30
GIL, Holly Cresho. 20 CATAMORE BLVD 02914 #010-03-1998 L2004 **DR** *100 †80
GILMAN, Ronald M. 450 VETERANS MEMORIAL PKWY, BLDG 6 02914 #035-09-1973 L1974 **PUD IM** *020 †20
GOLDING, Daniel M. 20 CATAMORE BLVD, RHODE ISLAND MEDICAL IMAGI 02914 #041-09-1988 L1999 **DR** *020 †80
GOLDSTEIN, Jack Danl. 400 MASSASOIT AVE, STE 200 02914 #005-19-1982 L1991 **ORS** *020 †40
GORDON, Norman Mervyn. 450 VETERANS MEMORIAL PKWY, BLDG 11 02914 #836-01-1979 L1988 **N** *020 †20,75
GRIFFITH, Fred Flynt. 450 VETERANS MEMORIAL PKWY 02914 #035-45-1978 L1980 **N IM** *020 †20,75
GRIFFITH, Robert Thos. 450 VETERANS MEMORIAL PKWY, BLDG 10-1 02914 #035-45-1983 L1986 **PD** *020 †55
HALEBLIAN, George Edward. 450 VETERANS MEMORIAL PKWY, BLDG 14 02914 #005-06-1999 L2007 **U** *100
HANSEN, Cindy Leah. 50 OFFICE PKWY 02914 #043-01-1984 L1987 **FM** *071 †18
HEINL, Andree Fontaine. 450 VETERANS MEMORIAL PKWY 02914 #043-01-1986 L1989 **PD** *020 †55

JAFFEE, Jordana Ruth. 900 WARREN AVE 02914 #035-20-1996 L2004 **IM** *020 †20
JAYARAMAN, Mahesh V. 20 CATAMORE BLVD, RI MEDICAL IMAGING 02914 #043-01-1998 L1999 **RNR** *100 †80
KARCZMAR, Peter. 450 VETERANS MEMORIAL PKWY, BLDG 6 02914 #035-03-1986 L1989 **PUD CCM** *020 †20
KEMPNER, Steven Marc. 900 WARREN AVE 02914 #035-08-1978 L1979 **EM IM** *020 †20,16
KRIZ, Peter Karl. 900 WARREN AVE 02914 #024-07-1996 L1996 **PD** *020 †55
KUPCHAN, Audrey Renee. 900 WARREN AVE STE 400, COASTAL MEDICAL 02914 #035-20-1981 L1984 **IM** *020 †20
KUROSE, George Alan. 450 VETERANS MEMORIAL PKWY, BLDG 4 02914 #028-02-1988 L1988 **IM** *020 †20
LABOVITZ, Alexandra E. 450 VETERANS MEMORIAL PKWY, # 10 02914 #024-05-2000 L2008 **PD** *020 †55 ‡
LANGE, Elizabeth Baird. 900 WARREN AVE STE 200 02914 #041-14-1992 L1992 **PD** *020 †55
LASSER, Joan L. 20 CATAMORE BLVD 02914 #024-05-1966 L1978 **DR** *020 †80
LEVINE, Daniel Jonathan. 450 VETERANS MEMORIAL PKWY, BLDG 15 02914 #035-01-1987 L1990 **CD** *020 †20
LEY, Christopher Walker. 900 WARREN AVE, STE 400 02914 #035-20-1982 L1985 **IM** *020 †20
LIVINGSTON, Linda Susan. 20 CATAMORE BLVD, RHODE ISLAND MEDICAL IMAGI 02914 #016-42-1995 L2002 **DR** *020 †80
LOURENCO, Ana Paula. 20 CATAMORE BLVD 02914 #024-16-2002 L2002 **DR** *020 †80
MAGALLANEZ, Michelle. ■ 02914 #048-13-2005 L2006 **OBG** *012
MALANGA, Michael Robt. 525 TAUNTON AVE, E PROVIDENCE MED CTR 02914 #035-08-1970 L1975 **EM FM** *020
MANDEL, Alex. 328 TAUNTON AVE 02914 #165-06-1975 L1978 **IM** *020
MANLOLO, Joseph John Balb. ■ 02914 #056-06-2007 L2007 **IM** *012
MARCACCIO, John Robt. 450 VETERANS MEMORIAL PKWY, BLDG 14 02914 #024-05-1964 L1966 **U** *071 †95
MARZILLI, Rocco. 1275 S BROADWAY, WATERVIEW VILLA SKILLED NU 02914 #561-01-1962 L1967 **IM GE** *020
MC COY, Charles Edwin. 318 WATERMAN AVE 02914 #041-09-1980 L1988 **NEP IM** *020 †20
MC GOLDRICK, Karen Lee. 450 VETERANS MEMORIAL PKWY, STE 401 02914 #043-01-1980 L1981 **OBG** *020 †30
MC GOOKIN, Edward Dobson. 900 WARREN AVE STE 2 02914 #035-15-1993 L1994 **PD** *020 †55
MC GOWAN, Elisabeth C. ■ 02914 #050-02-2001 L2004 **NPM** *100 †55
MC GOWAN, Kathryn Denise. 450 VETERANS MEMORIAL PKWY 02914 #035-48-1985 L1994 **OBG** *020 †19,30
MEDVE, Ildiko. 314 TAUNTON AVE 02914 #473-04-1987 L1998 **NEP** *020 †20
MEER, Omar. 400 WARREN AVE, STE 1 02914 #704-25-1994 L1996 **IM** *020 †20
MEREN, Tesfaye. 900 WARREN AVE, STE 400 02914 #759-09-1984 L2000 **IM** *020 †20
MILLER, E Bradley. 450 VETERANS MEMORIAL PKWY, BLDG 14 02914 #024-16-1987 L1992 **U** *020 †95
MILLER, Kennon Sewall. 450 VETERANS MEMORIAL PKWY, BLDG 14 02914 #032-01-1987 L2004 **U** *040 †95
MILLER, Valerie Anne. ■ 02914 #041-15-2007 L2007 **P** *012
MORTON, Kathleen Oneil. 450 VETERANS MEMORIAL PKWY, BLDG 6 02914 #026-04-1987 L1993 **IM** *071 †20
MOVSON, Jonathan S. 20 CATAMORE BLVD, RHODE ISLAND MEDICAL IMAGI 02914 #836-02-1982 L1997 **DR NM** *020 †80
MURPHY, S Deborah. 450 VETERANS MEMORIAL PKWY, STE 504 02914 #051-04-1974 L1979 **OPH** *035
MYERS, James Robt. 450 VETERANS MEMORIAL PKWY, BLDG 6 02914 #056-05-1972 L1978 **PCC IM** *020 †20
ORSON, Jay M. 450 VETERANS MEMORIAL PKWY, # 10 02914 #035-09-1953 L1959 **PD PDE** *071 †55
PAGE, Lyman Alexander. 450 VETERANS MEMORIAL PKWY, # 10 02914 #035-01-1957 L1994 **PD END** *030 †55
PARZIALE, John Robt. 450 VETERANS MEMORIAL PKWY, UNIV REHAB INC 02914 #008-02-1983 L1986 **PM PRS** *020 †60
PEPITONE, Jessica L. 450 VETERANS MEMORIAL PKWY, # 10 02914 #041-07-1981 L1984 **PD ADL** *020 †55
POMERANTZ, Michael Aaron. 450 VETERANS MEMORIAL PKWY, BLDG 6 02914 #033-06-1986 L1989 **PUD IM** *020 †20
PRESSMAN, Mitchell Allen. 450 VETERANS MEMORIAL PKWY, BLDG 6 02914 #035-08-1974 L1975 **IM** *020 †20
RADKA, Dale F. 1011 VETERANS MEM PATHWAY 02915 #035-06-1986 L1988 **CHP** *020 †75
ROBERTSON, James F, III. 450 VETERANS MEMORIAL PKWY, # 15 02914 #008-01-1975 L2003 **CD** *020 †20
ROCHA, Anthony V. 387 WATERMAN AVE 02914 #024-05-1976 L1977 **IM EM** *020
SAYEED, Syed Mohammad. 400 WARREN AVE 02914 #704-02-1962 L1974 **N IM** *020 †75
SCHOENFELD, Larry Jay. 900 WARREN AVE, STE 400 02914 #041-02-1977 L1980 **IM** *020 †20
SHAW, Judith Gibbs. 900 WARREN AVE STE 200 02914 #043-01-1978 L1982 **PD** *020 †55
SHERMAN, Charles Bruce. 450 VETERANS MEMORIAL PKWY 02914 #041-09-1981 L1989 **PUD IM** *020 †20
SHREVE, Daniel Trundle. 47 HAZARD AVE 02914 #010-01-1960 L1962 **FM OM** *020 †18
SIENA, Santina Lee. 450 VETERANS MEMORIAL PKWY, STE 401 02914 #035-20-1977 L1982 **OBG** *020 †30
SISKIND, Mark S. 318 WATERMAN AVE 328 02914 #050-02-1983 L1993 **NEP IM** *020 †20
SOMVANSHI, Rahul Arvind. 20 CATAMORE BLVD, RHODE ISLAND MEDICAL IMAGI 02914 #041-01-1999 L2005 **DR** *020 †80
STOCKWELL, Philip Hansen. 450 VETERANS MEMORIAL PKWY, BLDG 15 02914 #035-45-1993 L2001 **CD** *020 †20
TARPEY, Joseph Thos. 450 VETERANS MEMORIAL PKWY 02914 #035-08-1973 L1975 **IM PUD** *020 †20
TAYLOR, Montoya. ■ 02914 #043-01-2008 *012
TOWNSEND, Kimberly J. 450 VETERANS MMRL PKWY #10 02914 #043-01-1993 L1996 **PD** *020 †55
TURACOVA, Daniela. 525 TAUNTON AVE, STE 100 02914 #286-12-1995 L1996 **IM** *020 †20
TURTLE, William James. 450 VETERANS MEMORIAL PKWY, BLDG 10 02914 #035-45-1985 L1989 **PD** *020 †55
UTTER, Wilson Fiske. 900 WARREN AVE, STE 200 02914 #024-07-1954 L1956 **PD** *071 †55
VALDEPENAS, Jesus Bernal. 2447 PAWTUCKET AVE 02914 #748-01-1961 L1978 **GS** *030
VIGLIANI, Marguerite B. 450 VETERANS MEMORIAL PKWY, STE 101 02914 #041-07-1976 L1979 **OBG** *020 †30
VOHR, Fred Harold, Jr. 450 VETERANS MEMORIAL PKWY 02914 #035-03-1964 L1967 **ON IM** *020

■ = Address Information Privacy Protected

WEIGNER, Marilyn Jean. 450 VETERANS MEMORIAL PKWY, BLDG 15 02914 #024-07-1992 L1998 **CD** *020 †20

WONG, Arthur Wang-Yan. 450 VETERANS MEMORIAL PKWY, BLDG 14 02914 #917-18-1982 L1989 **U** *020 †95

WOODFIELD, Courtney Anne. 20 CATAMORE BLVD, HOSP OF UNIV OF PENNSYLVAN 02914 #041-01-2000 L2005 **DR** *020 †80

YESS, James Patrick, Jr. 450 VETERANS MEMORIAL PKWY, BLDG 4 02914 #016-43-2003 L2003 **IM** *020 †20

YOO, Don Chan. 20 CATAMORE BLVD, RHODE ISLAND MEDICAL IMAGI 02914 #035-08-1998 L1999 **DR** *020 †80,28

ZAYAS, Vladislav. 450 VETERANS MEMORIAL PKWY 02914 #043-01-1989 L1989 **N** *020 †75

ZIPIN, Steven Bertram. 318 WATERMAN AVE 02914 #035-08-1970 L1974 **NEP IM** *020 †20

FOSTER – PROVIDENCE

DADEKIAN, Gregory Arsen. ■ 02825 #043-01-2006 **IM** *012

JOO, Christopher Joon. 112 S KILLINGLY RD B 02825 #583-02-1956 L1980 **P** *071

MC CULLOUGH, Ricky Wayne. 48 MOOSEUP VALLEY RD, MCCULLOUGH MEDICAL SERVICE 02825 #054-04-1982 L1983 **IM EM** *050

WACHTEL, Tom Jeffrey. 142A DANIELSON PIKE 02825 #396-08-1973 L1976 **IM IMG** *020 †20

GREENVILLE – PROVIDENCE

CAPALBO, Carmine J. ■ 02828 #010-02-1952 L1953 **GS** *071 †85

LAPROVA, Gina G. 600 PUTNAM PIKE 02828 #043-01-1998 L2002 **FM** *020 †18

QI, Jiafan. ■ 02828 #243-44-1982 L2006 **PCP** *020 †50

RITZAU, Jennifer Mc Innes. 715 PUTNAM PIKE, VILLAGE AT WATERMAN LAKE 02828 #051-04-1997 L2003 **IMG IM** *020 †20

SOTO, Ricardo F. ■ 02828 #748-08-1964 **GP** *020

TONELLI, Alberto F. ■ 02828 #561-21-1959 L1981 **IM HEM** *071

WILEY, Brian D. 47B AUSTIN AVE 02828 #028-78-1995, ▲ L1996 **EM IM** *020

HARRISVILLE – PROVIDENCE

APSHAGA, Albert A. ■ 02830 #024-05-1949 L1957 **AN** *071 †05

MC GREGOR, Alyson Joy. ■ 02830 #024-05-2003 L2003 **EM** *100

HOPE – PROVIDENCE

RENZA, Gregory James. ■ 02831 #043-01-2006 *012

HOPE VALLEY – WASHINGTON

BERTMAN, Jonathan Morris. 1111 MAIN ST 02832 #024-16-1993 L1993 **FM** *020 †18

CAMPAGNARI, Chris A. 923 MAIN ST, WOOD RIVER HLTH SVCS 02832 #024-16-1991 L1994 **FM** *020 †18

CUMMINGS, Stephen Francis. ■ 02832 #011-03-1979 L1980 **EM FM** *020 †16,18

LICHTENBERG, Kristin N. 823 MAIN ST, WOOD RIVER HEALTH SERVICES 02832 #041-12-2001 L2005 **FM** *020 †18

MANLOVE, Lisa M Menard. 823 MAIN ST, WOOD RIVER HEALTH SERV 02832 #043-01-2000 L2003 **FM** *020 †18

REDMER, Amy Louise. 823 MAIN ST, WOOD RIVER HEALTH SERVICES 02832 #016-42-1995 L2004 **FM** *020 †18

SOMVANSHI, Nicole. 1111 MAIN ST, SOUTH COUNTY FAMILY MEDICI 02832 #024-16-1997 L2005 **FM** *020 †18

WHITED, Henry L. ■ 02832 #035-06-1970 L1971 **CD EM** *071 †20

JAMESTOWN – NEWPORT

BARRY, David M. ■ 02835 #041-02-1952 L1953 **NS** *071 †25

BROWN, Josiah Whitney. ■ 02835 #035-08-1946 L1977 **FM** *071 †18

ENGLAND, Joseph John. 20 SOUTHWEST AVE 02835 #050-02-1981 L1984 **FM FPG** *020 †18

GALLAGHER, Richard C. ■ 02835 #024-07-1954 L1964 **GYN** *071 †30

GROSKIN, Stephen D. 20 SOUTHWEST AVE 02835 #035-06-1975 L2007 **FM** *020 †18

KINDER, Robt Saml Lufbery. ■ 02835 #010-01-1959 L1963 **OPH** *071 †35 ‡

POMFRET, Anna. ■ 02835 #539-03-1965 L1967 **PM** *071 †60

POMFRET, David Buckley. ■ 02835 #539-03-1964 L1965 **CD IM** *071 †20

ROCCHIO, Michael Anthony. ■ 02835 #033-05-1968 L1969 **GS** *071 †85

TAMASE, Terri Lee. 1 STERN ST, MIDDLETOWN VA CLINIC 02835 #016-11-1987 L1987 **IM** *020 †20

VENKATESAN, Jay Raman. ■ 02835 #041-01-2002 *100

YASHAR, John. ■ 02835 #517-01-1950 L1958 **CD TS** *071 †85,90

JOHNSTON – PROVIDENCE

ALI, Sumaira. 1524 ATWOOD AVE, STE 336 02919 #704-25-1996 L2002 **IM** *020 †20

ANDREONI, William Jos. 1524 ATWOOD AVE 02919 #561-01-1976 L1982 **OPH** *020

ARCAND, Michel A. 1524 ATWOOD AVE STE 140, CENTER FOR ORTHOPEDICS 02919 #067-03-1990 L1990 **OSM ORS** *020 †40

BACCARI, Janis Lee. 1524 ATWOOD AVE, STE 110 02919 #024-05-1995 L1995 **PD** *020 †55

BELANGER, Michael James. 1524 ATWOOD AVE STE 140, ORTHOPAEDIC SURGERY 02919 #050-02-1993 L1993 **ORS OSM** *020 †40

BELIVEAU, William Joseph. 1524 ATWOOD AVE, ATWOOD MEDICAL ASSOCIATES 02919 #654-01-1994 1989 **PUD CCM** *020 †20

BERSTEIN, Bernard J. 1524 ATWOOD AVE STE 225 02919 #024-05-1972 L1973 **OBG** *071

BURKE, Cyril O, III. 1524 ATWOOD AVE, STE 120 02919 #035-20-1986 L1987 **N IM** *020 †20,75

CATANZARO, Francis Philip. 1524 ATWOOD AVE 02919 #010-02-1948 L1949 **GS OS** *020 †85

CHAZAN, Joseph A. 1526 ATWOOD AVE, DIALYSIS CENTER OF JOHNSTO 02919 #035-06-1960 L1967 **IM NEP** *020 †20

COLAGIOVANNI, Steven Marc. 1524 ATWOOD AVE, STE 322 02919 #024-07-1989 L1989 **U** *020 †95

D'ALESSANDRO, Vincent A. 1857 ATWOOD AVE 02919 #024-05-1960 L1961 **PD** *020

D'AMICO, Richard Peter. 1524 ATWOOD AVE, ATWOOD MEDICAL CENTER 02919 #024-07-1965 L1969 **HEM ON** *072 †20

DE CONTI, Vincent A. 1524 ATWOOD AVE STE 220, ATWOOD MEDICAL CTR 02919 #561-01-1960 L1962 **IM** *071 †20

DIAMANTE, Giulio Gerardo. ■ 02919 #024-05-1993 L1993 **OPH** *020 †35

DIAMOND, Marc W. 1524 ATWOOD AVE, ATWOOD PEDIATRICS 02919 #043-01-1984 L1987 **PD** *020 †55

DI CENSO, Angelo. 1524 ATWOOD AVE STE 445 02919 #561-17-1985 L1989 **IM IMG** *020 †20

DISCHEL, Judith Mund. 985 PLAINFIELD ST, CENTER FOR BEHAVIORAL HEAL 02919 #023-01-1972 L1999 **FM ADM** *071 †18

DI SIMONE, Allan Amalio. ■ 02919 #010-02-1955 L1956 **GS** *020 †85

EMERY, Douglas Francis. 1526 ATWOOD AVE, STE 220 02919 #035-15-1991 L1998 **OTO** *020 †45

FERRI, Federico F. 1539 ATWOOD AVE, STE 101 02919 #561-01-1983 L1985 **IM IMG** *020 †20

FIRST, Leonora. 1524 ATWOOD AVE, STE 110 02919 #038-41-1999 L1999 **PD** *020 †55

FORTUNATO, David John. 1524 ATWOOD AVE, STE 345 02919 #561-01-1975 L1977 **CD** *020 †20

GIOVANNI, Jeannine. 1539 ATWOOD AVE, STE 201 02919 #008-02-1999 L2001 **GS** *100 †85

GOSPER, James Allen. 1524 ATWOOD AVE, ATWOOD MEDICAL ASSOCIATES 02919 #041-09-1971 L1973 **IM** *020 †20

GUTTMACHER, Thomas E. 1126 HARTFORD AVE, TRI TOWN HEALTH CENTER 02919 #035-48-1990 L1990 **FM** *020 †18

HARRISON, Michael J. 1524 ATWOOD AVE, STE 344 02919 #035-47-1986 L2004 **NS** *020 †25

HERNANDEZ, Sophy Yisset. ■ 02919 #043-01-2007 L2007 **IM** *012

JACOBS, Mark Dennis. 1524 ATWOOD AVE, STE 340 02919 #035-46-1975 L1979 **IM** *020 †20

JOHNSON, Frederick M. PO BOX 19427 02919 #010-02-1969 L1972 **ORS** *020 †40

LANNA, Thomas V. 1539 ATWOOD AVE, STE 304 02919 #043-01-1992 L1992 **CD** *020 †20

LATUSZYNSKI, Dorota. ■ 02919 #759-03-1985 L2000 **FOP** *020

LENTRICHIA, Paul Francis. ■ 02919 #035-46-1975 L1976 **GS** *020 †85

LEVY, Jennifer Shari. 1126 HARTFORD AVE, STE 102 02919 #005-02-1993 L1993 **FM** *020 †18

LINSAO, Lydia S. ■ 02919 #748-01-1957 L1980 **GP** *071

MAISEL, Miriam. 1524 ATWOOD AVE, STE 122 02919 #024-05-1992 L1992 **FM** *020 †18

MANOCCHIO, Anthony Robt. 1524 ATWOOD AVE, # D-442 02919 #561-01-1965 L1972 **OBG** *020 †30

MARANO, Albert Joseph. 1526 ATWOOD AVE, STE 200 02919 #654-01-1988 L1993 **N** *020 †75

MARTINEZ, Hernando. ■ 02919 #264-04-1969 L1978 **GP GS** *071

MOSS, David Alan. 1524 ATWOOD AVE, STE 140 02919 #041-09-1992 L1998 **OSM** *020 †40

OLSSON, Leif Eric. 1524 ATWOOD AVE, STE 322 02919 #024-05-1994 L2004 **U** *020 †95

ONG, Warren Andrew. 1443 HARTFORD AVE 02919 #028-46-1992 L1992 **P** *020 †75

O'TOOLE, Maria Michelle. 1524 ATWOOD AVE 02919 #028-34-1979 L1982 **OBG** *020 †30

OTTIANO, Christopher S. 1526 ATWOOD AVE, STE 200 02919 #024-07-1995 L1998 **GS** *020 †85

PASQUARIELLO, Gennaro F. 1524 ATWOOD AVE, C/O ATWOOD PEDIATRICS 02919 #561-01-1965 L1969 **PD** *020

PETRONIO, Domenico C. 1239 HARTFORD AVE, THE TOWN HALL PROFESSIONAL 02919 #561-01-1965 L1969 **PD** *071

POHL, Dieter. 1539 ATWOOD AVE 02919 #409-22-1988 L1999 **GS** *030 †85

POLACEK, Lori. 1524 ATWOOD AVE STE 343 02919 #024-05-1984 L1991 **PS GS** *020 †85,65

RAYNER, Christine Elise. 1443 HARTFORD AVE, GATEWAY HEALTHCARE 02919 #917-20-1995 L1999 **P** *020

REGAN, Daniel Leonard. 1526 ATWOOD AVE, ATMED TREATMENT CENTER INC 02919 #308-07-1982 L1984 **FM** *020 †18

ROTELLI, Anthony Jos. 1524 ATWOOD AVE 02919 #030-06-1974 L1975 **U** *020 †95

SADOVNIKOFF, Gregory. 1526 ATWOOD AVE, STE 220 02919 #041-02-1996 L1999 **FM** *020 †18

SALIBA, Gisele. 1524 ATWOOD AVE, ATWOOD MEDICAL ASSOCIATES 02919 #605-02-1989 L1994 **CD IM** *020 †20

SANACORE, John Anthony. 1524 ATWOOD AVE, STE 110 02919 #038-41-1986 L1989 **PD** *020 †55

SAVORETTI, Alberto R. 1539 ATWOOD AVE, STE 101 02919 #043-01-2004 L2004 **IM** *020 †20

SAVORETTI, Debby P. ■ 02919 #561-01-1987 L1990 **GP PM** *020 †60

SAVORETTI, Frank. 1539 ATWOOD AVE, STE 101 02919 #561-01-1983 L1986 **IM IMG** *020 †20

SCOTT, Stephen M. 1526 ATWOOD AVE # 1 02919 #017-20-1995 L1995 **IM** *020 †20

SHEPLEY, Michael Peter. ■ 02919 #024-01-1992 *100

SIMONE, Valentino Rudolph. ■ 02919 #561-01-1956 **PD PDA** *020 †55

SOMASUNDAR, Sukanya. 1126 HARTFORD AVE, STE 102 02919 #495-04-1990 L2005 **FM** *020 †18

STOUKIDES, John Aristotle. 1126 HARTFORD AVE, STE 102 02919 #024-07-1989 L1989 **IMG IM** *020 †20

TESTA, Anthony Frank. 1524 ATWOOD AVE, SUITE340 02919 #038-41-1973 L1975 **ON IM** *020 †20

TODER, Jay Scott. 1524 ATWOOD AVE, STE 333 02919 #035-03-1979 L1983 **RHU** *020 †20

TSCHIRLEY, Terry Wayne. 1524 ATWOOD AVE, STE 434 02919 #054-04-1973 L1975 **IM** *020

TURNIER, Edgard. 1526 ATWOOD AVE, STE 200 02919 #440-01-1959 L1970 **GS TS** *020 †85,90

UY, Kerstin King. 22 ANGLEWOOD AVE 02919 #748-10-1990 L1994 **P** *020 †75

VACCA, Vincent Fiore. 1524 ATWOOD AVE, STE 225 02919 #561-01-1961 L1964 **GE** *020

VELOSO, Cristina G. 1526 ATWOOD AVE, STE 300 02919 #043-01-1989 L1993 **AN** *020 †05

VELTRI, Frank Albert. 1524 ATWOOD AVE 02919 #561-01-1965 L1972 **D** *020

KINGSTON – WASHINGTON

ASHLEY, Roger Winslow. 6 QUARRY RD 02881 #024-07-1965 L1967 **PD ADL** *020 †55

HOWARD, Carolyn Denise. 6 BUTTERFIELD RD, POTTER BUILDING 02881 #041-01-1990 L2003 **OBG** *020 †30

MC MANUS, James Edward. ■ 02881 #035-19-1947 L1978 **GS** *071 †85

MOHRNHEIM, Johanna E. ■ 02881 #407-21-1949 L1954 **P** *071

PEREIRA, Celina Antonieta. 6 QUARRY RD 02881 #495-01-1964 L1972 **PD ADL** *020 †55

PROCOPIO, Fortunato. 6 QUARRY RD 02881 #050-02-1983 L1988 **PD ADL** *020 †55

WOOD, Pauline F Bucknell. UNIV RI HEALTH SVCS 02881 #008-01-1958 L1963 **OS GYN** *071

LINCOLN – PROVIDENCE

ABU EL-SAMEED, Yaser Mahm. ■ 02865 #575-01-1999 L2004 **PCC** *100

ALIKPALA, Eleuterio G. ■ 02865 #748-01-1954 L1962 **FM** *071
ALPER, Joseph Cyril. 1 COMMERCE ST, NEW ENGLAND 02865 #035-46-1968 L1975 **D OS** *040 †15
AMICARELLI, Anthony Ralph. 6 BLACKSTONE VALLEY PL, STE 3068 02865 #561-01-1973 L1977 **PD OS** *071
APPENFELLER, Rex Wm. 1 COMMERCE ST, STE 2 02865 #019-02-1979 L1980 **IM** *020 †20
ASSER, Seth Michael. 622 GEORGE WASHINGTON HWY, STE 603 02865 #041-01-1980 L2001 **PD CCP** *020 †55
BERAHA, Nathan Barry. 1 COMMERCE ST, STE 2 02865 #016-06-1979 L1985 **PD PDC** *020 †55
BERNAL MENDOZA, Oscar G. 6 BLACKSTONE VALLEY PL, BLDG 5 02865 #264-04-1991 L2003 **N** *020 †75
BLANCHARD, Sharon Grace. 2 WAKE ROBIN RD, UNIT 207 02865 #035-08-1992 L1997 **PD** *020 †55
CHAN, Philip Andrew. ■ 02865 #050-02-2006 L2006 **IM** *012
CHIRKOV, Alexander M. ■ 02865 #913-06-1983 L1993 **FOP** *020
CHLIWON, Irene S. 1 COMMERCE ST, HARVARD COMMUNITY HLTH PLA 02865 #035-48-1984 L1986 **IM** *020 †20
COHEN, Robert H. 1 COMMERCE ST, STE 2 02865 #035-09-1980 L1986 **IM** *020 †20
COLANTONIO, Louis Anthony. 132 OLD RIVER RD 02865 #561-01-1970 L1973 **PD** *020 †55
CRUZ, Antonio Paulino. ■ 02865 #043-01-2006 L2006 **D** *012
CUMMINGS, Michael Lynch. 1 COMMERCE ST, STE 2 02865 #041-14-1987 L1992 **PD** *020 †55
CYRONAK, Andra Katherine. 6 BLACKSTONE VALLEY PL, STE 701 02865 #041-09-1994 L1994 **IM** *020 †20
D'ALESSANDRO, Frank M. 2 WAKE ROBIN RD, UNIT 103 02865 #305-01-1988 L1991 **IM** *020 †20
DE LUCA, Gerald John. ■ 02865 #847-11-1971 L1972 **ORS R** *020
DE LUCA, Linda Anne. 132 OLD RIVER RD, STE 108 02865 #308-07-1981 L1985 **IM** *020 †20
DIPALMA, Stacey A. ■ 02865 #043-01-2008 *012
ELKAREH, Robert E. ■ 02865 #041-13-2003 L2003 **IM** *100 †20
ETIENNE, Alex. ■ 02865 #043-01-1996 L1997 **IM** *020 †20
FITZHUGH, Walter J, III. 8 BLACKSTONE VALLEY PL, 2ND FL 02865 #024-05-1992 L1996 **P ADM** *020 †75
FLYNN, Cheryl Ann. 2 WAKE ROBIN RD 02865 #041-07-1986 L1992 **PD** *020 †55
GAZZERRO, Richard Carmine. 1 COMMERCE ST 02865 #050-02-1972 L1975 **IM CD** *020 †20
GILLEN, Malini Chablani. 1 COMMERCE ST, ANCHOR MEDICAL ASSOCIATES 02865 #038-41-1998 L2001 **PD** *020 †55
GRANDE, Karen Diane. 2 WAKE ROBIN RD 02865 #024-16-1990 L1997 **IM** *020 †20
GREENIER, Vanessa Rebecca. 6 BLACKSTONE VALLEY PL, STE 701 02865 #043-01-1993 L1998 **IM** *020 †20
GUNASTI, Sabri. ■ 02865 #902-01-1956 L1963 **AN** *071
GUPTA, Ravi. ■ 02865 #035-08-2005 L2005 **IM** *012
HAINES, Lisa Miller. 6 BLACKSTONE VALLEY PL, PLACE #702 02865 #035-06-1994 L1994 **PD** *020 †55
HENDERSON, Kathleen Mary. 1 COMMERCE ST, STE 2 02865 #033-06-1985 L1988 **IM** *020 †20
HINES, Thomas Patrick. 6 BLACKSTONE VALLEY PL, STE 306B 02865 #030-05-1985 L1988 **PD** *020 †55
JARBEAU, Jennifer Flynn. 2 WAKE ROBIN RD UNIT 204 02865 #041-09-1998 L2004 **CD** *020 †20
KADMON, David. 132 OLD RIVER RD, STE B2 02865 #035-46-1992 L1997 **RHU** *020 †20
KADMON, Penny Meryl. 132 OLD RIVER RD STE B2 02865 #035-46-1994 L1997 **PDE** *040 †55
KELLY, Oliver. ■ 02865 #539-06-1967 L1977 **AN** *020
KHALIL, Hanan Ibrahim. ■ 02865 #605-01-1997 L2004 **IM** *020 †80
KIZIRIAN, Janice Marion. 2 WAKE ROBIN RD UNIT 104 02865 #038-06-1981 L1984 **IM** *020 †20
KRISHNAMURTHI, V S. ■ 02865 #495-42-1963 L1977 **PD ADL** *020 †55
KUSMA, Bohdan R. ■ 02865 #154-02-1951 L1957 **PD** *072
LEVESQUE, Patrick R. 186 OLD RIVER RD, UNIT 2 02865 #067-02-1959 L1966 **IM** *020
LU, Hua. 6 BLACKSTONE VALLEY PL, BLDG 5 02865 #187-31-1982 L1998 **IM** *020 †20
LUNDSTROM, Gary Karl. 2 WAKE ROBIN RD, NATE WHIPPLE RADIOLOGY 02865 #010-01-1982 L1987 **DR** *020 †80
MALIK, Amer Bashir. 6 BLACKSTONE VALLEY PL, BLDG 5 02865 #917-07-1978 L1990 **GE IM** *020 †20
MANZO, Ginger Lee. 2 WAKE ROBIN RD, UNIT 206 02865 #021-01-1993 L1993 **PD P** *020 †55,75
MC KEOWN, Lynne M. 6 BLACKSTONE VALLEY PL, STE 702 02865 #030-06-2001 L2001 **PD** *020 †55
NADJMI, Bruce Johan. ■ 02865 #517-01-1962 L1974 **U** *071 †95
PAIVA, Christy Marie. ■ 02865 #043-01-2006 L2006 **IM** *100
PAKULA, Susan Lee Berry. 1 COMMERCE ST, STE 2 02865 #043-01-1976 L1979 **PD** *020 †55
RANEY, Jennifer Joy. 1 COMMERCE ST, ANCHOR MEDICAL ASSOCIATES 02865 #041-02-1999 L1999 **FM** *020 †18
REDDY, Ramanamma Chejerla. ■ 02865 #495-50-1974 L1985 *020
SAMMON, Carolyn Marie. 472 GREAT RD 02865 #028-34-2002 L2002 **P** *100
SANTORO, Ralph Frank. 3 PARTRIDGE DR 02865 #561-17-1994 L2000 **IM** *100 ‡
SCARPACI, Francis Leo. ■ 02865 #010-02-1958 L1959 **GS GYN** *071 †85
SHEKARCHI, Khalil. 132 OLD RIVER RD, STE 103 02865 #517-01-1954 L1960 **GS** *020
SIMMONS, Roxanne Allen. 6 BLACKSTONE VALLEY PL, STE 702 02865 #011-04-1991 L1991 **PD ADL** *020 †55
SOWA, Marta Sanchez. 6 BLACKSTONE VALLEY PL, STE 306B 02865 #024-05-1980 L1986 **PD** *020 †55
STEWART, Ronald Mark. ■ 02865 #033-05-1967 L1968 **P CHP** *020
SUPPIRAMANIAM, Sreeharikes. 25 BRIARWOOD RD 02865 #495-04-1989 L1993 **CD** *012 †20
TANEJA, Rashmi. ■ 02865 #495-45-1989 L1997 **PS** *020 †55,65
TEIXEIRA, Richard Lionel. 6 BLACKSTONE VALLEY PL, STE 306B 02865 #050-02-1972 L1975 **PD** *020 †55
VAN NIEUWENHUIZE, Michelle. 132 OLD RIVER RD, STE 108 02865 #473-01-2001 L2005 **IM** *020 †20
VEZZA, Ovid. 4 CHRISTOPHER DR 02865 #561-01-1951 L1954 **GP** *071
VREES, Roxanne Williams. ■ 02865 #043-01-2003 L2003 **OBG** *020
WACKER, Ernest Andrew. 1 COMMERCE ST, ONE COMMERCE ST 02865 #035-01-1958 L1988 **P** *071 †75
WANG, Chin Tsei. ■ 02865 #638-01-1936 **IM** *020
WESTRICK, Judith Blazar. 1 COMMERCE ST, STE 2 02865 #067-01-1989 L1989 **PD** *020 †55
WHALEN, J J. 6 BLACKSTONE VALLEY PL, STE 401 02865 #043-01-1989 L1989 **P PFP** *020 †75
WOLF, Farrah Joyce. ■ 02865 #043-01-2008 *012
YAMADA, Hugo. 6 BLACKSTONE VALLEY PL, STE 502 02865 #187-11-1989 L1996 **CCM IM** *020 †20

LITTLE COMPTON – NEWPORT

BARNARD, Lucinda Burr. 88 WARRENS POINT RD 02837 #035-20-1979 L1982 **END IM** *020 †20
FISHER, Richard Christian. ■ 02837 #041-13-1968 L1969 **ORS** *020 †40
MAC DONALD, Malcolm W. 8 JOHN DYER RD, BOX 188 02837 #050-02-1969 L1975 **IM** *020 †20
QUINN, James V. ■ 02837 #033-06-2000 L2000 **IM** *100 †20

MIDDLETOWN – NEWPORT

CARRELLAS, Robert Anthony. 700 AQUIDNECK AVE, 700 AQUIDNECK AV.BLDG A UN 02842 #035-09-1989 L1992 **FM** *020 †18
CICCHELLI, Robert Ovidio. 850 AQUIDNECK AVE 02842 #035-47-1990 L1996 **IM** *020 †20
CUNNINGHAM, David Francis. 850 AQUIDNECK AVE 02842 #024-07-1987 L1990 **IM** *020 †20
D'AGOSTINO, Ernest. 67 VALLEY RD, SERVICES 02842 #132-01-1949 L1963 **GP** *020 †05
DEL GUERCIO, Paul Vincent. 294 VALLEY RD 02842 #041-12-1986 L1988 **FM** *020 †18
DOBBIN, James Michael. 850 AQUIDNECK AVE, MIDDLETOWN COMMONS B-9 02842 #008-02-1979 L1987 **OTO HNS** *020 †45
ERSTLING, Christopher M. 747 AQUIDNECK AVE 02842 #033-05-1973 L1994 **P PYA** *020 †75
FREEDMAN, Steven Franklin. 850 AQUIDNECK AVE, MIDDLETOWN COMMONS B-9 02842 #021-01-1985 L1992 **OTO GS** *020 †45
GAINES, Alan David. 850 AQUIDNECK AVE, RUSSELL SETTIPANE MD 02842 #035-01-1983 L1988 **A PDA** *020 †55,03
GILL, Christine A. 42 VALLEY RD 02842 #010-02-1982 L1989 **OPH** *020 †35
GORDON, Robert Learmouth. 67 VALLEY RD, SERVICES 02842 #396-04-1965 L1968 **EM GP** *020
GOSCH-BARKER, D John. 16 BLISS MINE RD, NA 02842 #049-01-1957 L1991 **R** *020
GUTIERREZ, Francisco Jose. 850 AQUIDNECK AVE 02842 #341-03-1994 L2000 **IM IMG** *020 †20
JONES, Dennis Edward. 345 VALLEY RD 02842 #008-02-1990 L1999 **ORS** *020 †40
KAZANJIAN, Rosilyn L. PO BOX 4398 02842 #035-47-1975 L1985 **AN** *020 †05
KENYON, Kenneth Ralph. 73 VALLEY RD 02842 #023-07-1969 L2002 **OPH** *020 †35
KLEIN, Farrel Ivan. 127 JOHNNY CAKE HILL RD 02842 #028-34-1981 L1985 **P** *020 †75
KURTIS, James Thos. 1151 AQUIDNECK AVE STE 493 02842 #041-13-1958 L1965 **PTH** *071 †50
KURTIS, Jonathan D. 1151 AQUIDNECK AVE APT 493 02842 #043-01-1996 L2000 **PTH** *020 †50
LEE, Kyung Chul. 67 VALLEY RD, SERVICES 02842 #583-04-1969 L1977 **GP** *020
LEWIS, George Phillip. ■ 02842 #035-09-1959 L1966 **GS GP** *071
MEIER, Gerhard C. ■ 02842 #407-16-1963 L1967 **IM CD** *020 †20
RADLER, Eric Brett. ■ 02842 #033-05-1999 L1999 **IM** *020 †20
REGAN, Wendy P. 700 AQUIDNECK AVE, FAMILY MEDI CENTER 02842 #024-16-1997 L1997 **FM** *020 †18
RIVERA, Jorge. 73 VALLEY RD 02842 #042-01-1998 L2006 **OPH** *020 †35
RUDOLPH, Norman Eric. 333 VALLEY RD 02842 #033-05-1961 L1970 **IM** *071
RYAN, Carol Marie. 1 CORPORATE PL 02842 #028-34-1987 L1990 **IM** *020 †20
SETTIPANE, Russell A. 850 AQUIDNECK AVE, RUSSELL SETTIPANE MD 02842 #035-09-1984 L1986 **A IM** *020 †20,03
STUDDERS, James Philip. 345 VALLEY RD 02842 #025-07-1972 L1979 **ORS** *020 †40
SULLIVAN, Stephen Francis. 73 VALLEY RD 02842 #024-01-1971 L1976 **OPH** *020 †35
TURANSKI, James Julius. 127 JOHNNY CAKE HILL RD, MENTAL HEALTH CENTER 02842 #068-01-1966 L1996 **P** *072
WHITE, Austin Edward, Jr. ■ 02842 #024-05-1968 L1976 **ORS** *020 †40

NARRAGANSETT – WASHINGTON

BASEL, Mitchell Bart. 360 KINGSTOWN RD, STE 102 02882 #035-03-1983 L1984 **GE IM** *020 †20
CESARIO, Carla A. 360 KINGSTOWN RD, STE 200 02882 #043-01-2003 L2003 **FM** *020 †18
COLAVECCHIO, Louis V. 360 KINGSTOWN RD 02882 #043-01-1976 L1978 **D** *020 †15
HEBERT, Anne Marie. 360 KINGSTOWN RD # 207 02882 #032-01-1982 L1984 **PUD IM** *020 †20
HORROCKS, Lisa M. ■ 02882 #035-09-1983 L1989 **IM** *020
KOSTRZEWA, Dariusz. 360 KINGSTOWN RD, STE 200 02882 #035-08-2001 L2001 **FM** *020
LA BOVE, Neil David. ■ 02882 #041-09-1977 L2002 **PUD IM** *020 †20 ‡
LEE, Chang Kwon. 360 KINGSTOWN RD 02882 #583-01-1959 L1972 **GS** *020 †85
MEOLA, Phyllis Angela. ■ 02882 #561-17-1935 **OS** *071
MURDOCCO, James Jos. 360 KINGSTOWN RD 02882 #035-09-1965 L1968 **OTO A** *020 †45
MURPHY, John Alfred. ■ 02882 #010-02-1961 L1962 **GYN** *071 †30
MURPHY, Richard E, Jr. ■ 02882 #035-09-1961 L1963 **ORS** *020 †40
PARMENTIER, A Hilton. 360 KINGSTOWN RD # 208 02882 #305-01-1984 L1996 **P ADM** *020 †75
PUPPI, Leon Denis. 360 KINGSTOWN RD, # 207 02882 #781-01-1984 L1991 **PUD IM** *020 †20
STEIN, Barry Stephen. 89 STRATHMORE ST 02882 #041-02-1974 L1985 **U** *020 †95
YOGARATNAM, Gunaratnam. 21 GARDENIA LN 02882 #220-02-1970 L1975 **AN** *020 †05

NEWPORT – NEWPORT

ADDO, Abena Amoabea. 62 BROADWAY 02840 #412-01-1992 L2002 **IM** *020 †20
ALTREUTER, Richard Wm. 11 FRIENDSHIP ST 02840 #041-02-1971 L1986 **EM** *071 †16
ANDERSON, Richard Coveney. 275 BROADWAY UNIT 2, NEWPORT HOSPITAL 02840 #043-01-1993 L2007 **ORS OTR** *020 †40
ARNOW, Lewis. 33 BULL ST 02840 #035-01-1957 L1962 **PD OS** *020
BATTAGLIA, Tony Gerard. 43 SMITH RD, NAVAL HEALTH CLINIC NEW EN 02841 #021-01-1993 L1994 **FM** *020 †18
BAUMGARTNER, Philip O. 11 FRIENDSHIP ST 02840 #035-01-1955 L1959 **GP** *075
BILLINGTON, Mark Adam. 50 MEMORIAL BLVD 02840 #035-46-1988 L1993 **GS** *020 †85
BLUMEN, Joseph. 23 POWEL AVE 02840 #024-07-1959 L1960 **GP FPG** *072
BOLAR, Sudhir Narayana. 11 FRIENDSHIP ST, NEWPORT HOSPITAL 02840 #496-01-1994 L2004 **AN** *020
BRADLEY, Michael Patrick. 43 SMITH RD, NAVAL HEALTH CLINIC NEW EN 02841 #043-01-2001 L2001 **ORS** *100

BREWER, Edward Slocum. 1 RIGGS RD, NAVAL HEALTH CARE 02841 #024-05-2001 L2001 DR *012

BURG, Casey Joe. 43 SMITH RD, NAVAL AMBULATORY CARE CENT 02841 #046-01-1999 L2001 PD *100 †55

CAPUTI, Anthony P. 15 HAMMERSMITH RD 02840 #024-01-1944 L1949 CD IM *071 †20

CARRELLAS, Anthony T. ■ 02840 #035-09-1949 L1955 PD *071

CASEY, Kathleen Maura. 19 FRIENDSHIP ST 02840 #032-01-1990 L2003 GS *030 †85

CHERNOW, Marvin A. 11 FRIENDSHIP ST 02840 #035-09-1949 L1964 NM PTH *071 †50,28

CLARISSE, Peter Dirk Tom. 11 FRIENDSHIP ST # RAD, NEWPORT HOSPITAL 02840 #010-01-1965 L1970 R *071 †80

COHEN, Elie Jos. 136 RHODE ISLAND AVE 02840 #330-01-1955 L1960 ORS *020 †40

CONNELL, William Michael. 230 BELLEVUE AVE 02840 #010-02-1989 L1991 IM *020 †20

COPPE, David John. 19 FRIENDSHIP ST UNIT 360 02840 #050-02-1971 L1984 GS VS *020 †85

CRONIN, Robert Jos. 1 RIGGS RD, CODE 424 02841 #024-07-1968 L1969 ORS *071 †40

CRUTCHER, Kendall Alan. 43 SMITH RD, NAVALHEALTH CLINIC NEW ENG 02841 #047-20-2001 L2003 AN *020

DELLAVOLPE, Jeffrey David. ■ 02840 #021-01-2008 *012

DEMIERI, Paul Joseph. 43 SMITH RD, NAVAL HEATLH CLINIC NEW EN 02841 #021-01-1994 L1995 FM GP *020 †18

DEROLF, Donald Anthony. 19 FRIENDSHIP ST, UNIT 130 02840 #043-01-1975 L1977 FM *040 †18

DERREZA, Hector. 7 POWEL AVE 02840 #649-04-1992 L1994 IM *020 †20

DHANANI, Hussain Mansur. 11 FRIENDSHIP ST, NEWPORT HOSPITAL 02840 #704-25-1994 L1999 CCM *020 †20

DRENNAN, Dale Clay. 11 FRIENDSHIP ST 02840 #036-07-1972 L1989 PM PD *020 †55,60

DUPLESSIS, Christopher A. 1 RIGGS RD, NAVAL HEALTH CARE 02841 #023-12-2001 L2002 *020

EARP, Ralph Thos. 50 MEMORIAL BLVD, AQUIDNECK MEDICAL ASSOCIAT 02840 #028-03-1974 L1979 IM CD *020 †20

ETTEFAGH, Keivan. 50 MEMORIAL BLVD 02840 #048-12-1984 L1987 PD *020 †55

EVANS, Larry Arthur. 43 SMITH RD 02841 #023-12-1989 L1990 D *020 †15

FANTES, Jackie Sue. 43 SMITH RD, NHCNE NEWPORT 02841 #023-12-1992 L2002 EM FM *020 †18

FAZIO, Roger Frank. 1 RIGGS RD, NAVAL AMBULATORY CARE CENT 02841 #035-09-1993 L2005 PD *020 †55

FINLEY, Joseph C, Jr. 11 FRIENDSHIP ST 02840 #012-05-1995 L1997 OTO *100 †45

FLETCHER, Donald B, Jr. 11 FRIENDSHIP ST 02840 #016-01-1974 L1978 DR *020 †80

FOWLER, Heidi Ann. 43 SMITH RD, NAVAL HEALTH CLINIC NEW EN 02841 #023-12-1983 L1990 P *020

GAILITIS, Janis. ■ 02840 #594-01-1939 L1952 IM *071 †20

GEDNEY, James Christopher. 50 MEMORIAL BLVD, AQUIDNECK MED CTR 02840 #040-02-1977 L1981 OBG *020 †30

GLEASON, James Brian. 11 FRIENDSHIP ST 02840 #041-07-1992 L1992 EM *020 †16

GONZALEZ, Eileen Marie L. 19 BROADWAY, EAST BAY COMM HEALTH CTR 02840 #748-10-1991 L1998 FM *020 †18

GORELICK, David S. 50 MEMORIAL BLVD 02840 #010-02-1988 L1993 IM *020 †20

GREEN, Susan Mary. 19 FRIENDSHIP ST, NEWPORT HOSP/OCCUP HLTH 02840 #026-04-1981 L1983 OM IM *020 †20,70

GRIMES, Martin Osmond. 11 FRIENDSHIP ST 02840 #035-19-1939 L1943 OPH *071 †35

GROSS, Theodore Donald. NAV REG MED CTR NO F 02841 #005-15-1965 PD *020

HALL, Charles Andrew. MEMORIAL BLVD 02840 #008-01-1958 L1966 IM *071

HEBEL, Glenn Arnold. 11 FRIENDSHIP ST, NEWPORT HOSPITAL 02840 #005-18-1991 L1995 EM *020 †16

HERSTOFF, James Kenneth. 75 GIBBS AVE 02840 #024-07-1970 L1974 D *020 †15 ‡

HOLMES, Elaine C. 1 RIGGS RD, ATTN: CREDENTIAL OFFICE 02841 #048-04-1977 L1977 OM *030 †70

HOUSTON, Jeffrey Paul. 11 FRIENDSHIP ST 02840 #024-07-1990 L1998 DR *020 †80

HOUSTON, Paul C. 11 FRIENDSHIP ST 02840 #041-01-1944 L1952 GS *071 †85

HUSAK, Deborah Jeanne. ■ 02840 #025-07-1988 L1989 FM *071 †18

JUDD, Elizabeth. 11 FRIENDSHIP ST 02840 #035-46-1985 L1988 FM *020 †18

KASS, David Jos. 11 FRIENDSHIP ST 02840 #869-01-1964 L1975 P *020 †75

KNOWLAN, Michael Norman. 19 FRIENDSHIP ST UNIT 140 02840 #010-01-1980 L2003 P *020 †75

KNOWLTON, E Abbie Ingalls. ■ 02840 #035-01-1942 IM END *071 †20

KUTCHER, Theodore John. 11 FRIENDSHIP ST 02840 #050-02-1988 L1995 DR *020 †80

LABIAK-MAHER, Catherine. 19 FRIENDSHIP ST, UNIT 340 02840 #035-09-1982 L1987 PD OS *020 †55

LEVIN, William D. 19 FRIENDSHIP ST, UNIT 130 02840 #035-06-1972 L1978 FM *020 †18

MAC DOUGALL, Donald B. 11 FRIENDSHIP ST/PATH 02840 #024-16-1979 L1991 PTH PCP *020 †50

MADDOX, Michael Ray. 43 SMITH RD, NAVAL HEALTH CLINIC NEW EN 02841 #023-12-1985 L1986 OTO *020 †45

MARCOLINO, Marichel Llego. 11 FRIENDSHIP ST, NEWPORT HOSPITAL 02840 #748-15-1994 L2006 IM *100 †20

MARK, Vernon H. ■ 02840 #026-04-1947 L1996 NS N *020 †25

MARTLAND, William Henry. 11 FRIENDSHIP ST 02840 #010-02-1982 L1993 DR NR *020 †80

MC BURNEY, Alexander A. 38 POWEL AVE 02840 #019-02-1958 L1964 U *071 †95

MC DONALD, Brian Robt. 686 CUSHING RD, NAVY WARFARE DEV COMMAND 02841 #026-04-1981 L1985 IM NEP *030 †20

MC WILLIAMS, Terrence R. 11 FRIENDSHIP ST, NEWPORT HOSPITAL 02840 #041-12-1983 L1990 FM FSM *020 †18

MEDEIROS, Grace. 19 FRIENDSHIP ST, BORDEN CAREY STE 160 02840 #035-47-1991 L1996 N *020 †75

MORGERA, Richard V. 11 FRIENDSHIP ST 02840 #043-01-1983 L1984 IM *020 †20

MORSE, Heather Elizabeth. 19 FRIENDSHIP ST, BELLEVUE HOSPITAL 02840 #035-08-2000 L2007 P *020 †75

MUETTERTIES, Mark Conrad. 11 FRIENDSHIP ST, NEWPORT HOSPITAL 02840 #035-20-1998 L1998 EM *020 †16

NORCROSS, Murray Charles. 43 SMITH RD, NAVAL HEALTH CARE NE 02841 #024-16-1987 L1988 FM EM *020 †18

O'CONNELL, Philip Matthew. 43 SMITH RD 02841 #010-02-1993 L1994 FM *020 †18

O'CONNOR, Francis X, Jr. 43 SMITH RD, NAVAL HEALTH CLINIC 02841 #024-07-1987 L1989 GS *020 †85

PARAMESWARAN, Jayanthi. 50 MEMORIAL BLVD, AQUIDNECK MEDICAL ASSOCIAT 02840 #495-53-1992 L1996 IM *020 †20

PEIRCE, Frederick A, Jr. MEMORIAL BLVD 02840 #024-01-1949 L1955 PD ADL *072 †55

PENSA, Gita Savitri. 11 FRIENDSHIP ST, NEWPORT EMERGENCY PHYSICI 02840 #041-01-1997 L2001 EM *020 †16

PETRILLO, Maria Rita. 11 FRIENDSHIP ST, NEWPORT HOSPITAL 02840 #024-05-1994 L1998 EM *020 †16

PIANKA, Joseph Daniel. 29 POWEL AVE, UNIV OF GASTROENTEROLOGY 02840 #035-15-2001 L2001 GE IM *020 †20 ‡

REISER, Barbara. 11 FRIENDSHIP ST, NEWPORT HOSPITAL 02840 #018-03-1979 L1990 PM IM *020 †60

ROCCO, Thomas Robert, Jr. 224 BELLEVUE AVE, UNIVERSITY SURGICAL ASSOCI 02840 #016-42-1993 L1993 CCS *020 †85

ROETTINGER, Walter F. 222 BELLEVUE AVE 02840 #051-01-1972 L1974 PS HS *020 †65

ROSENTHAL, Judi Beth. 19 FRIENDSHIP ST, UNIT 220 02840 #035-06-1985 L1989 OBG *020 †30

ROSENTHAL, Randall Ian. 19 FRIENDSHIP ST, UNIT 220 02840 #035-06-1985 L1989 OBG *020 †30

ROSS, Lesley Suzanne. 43 SMITH RD, NAVAL HEALTH CLINIC NEW EN 02841 #028-34-2001 L2005 *020

ROUS, Stephen Norman. ■ 02840 #035-09-1956 L1957 U *071 †95 ‡

RYAN, John Jos Donald. ■ 02840 #035-01-1941 L1941 GS *071 †85

SALM, Jennifer M. 50 MEMORIAL BLVD 02840 #035-15-1998 L1998 PD *020 †55

SANDERS, Harold Allen. 50 MEMORIAL BLVD 02840 #035-15-1973 L1975 IM *020 †20

SAPERS, Sufala Patil. 11 FRIENDSHIP ST 02840 #043-01-1995 L2000 DR *020 †80

SHOEMAKER, Charles P, Jr. 11 FRIENDSHIP ST 02840 #035-03-1964 L1970 GS OS *071 †85

SMIGEL, Karen Rosalie. 43 SMITH RD, NHCNE NEWPORT 02841 #024-16-1988 L1988 FM *071 †18

SMITH, George Herbert. 43 SMITH RD, NAVAL HEALTH CLINIC NEW EN 02841 #023-12-1997 L2007 AN *020 †05

SPITALNIC, Stuart Jay. 11 FRIENDSHIP ST, NEWPORT HOSPITAL 02840 #035-15-1992 L1992 EM *020 †16

STALLONE, Martin, Jr. ■ 02841 #041-01-2004 L2007 IM *020 †20

STENGEL, Charles Leigh. 11 FRIENDSHIP ST 02840 #041-01-1991 L1997 EM *020 †16

STERN, Kenneth Bernard. 19 FRIENDSHIP ST UNIT 140, THE BORDEN-CAREY BLDG 02840 #023-01-1967 L1986 P CHP *071 †75

SUCSY, Robert James. 43 SMITH RD, NAVAL CLINIC 02841 #024-07-1978 L2007 IM *020 †20

SUTHERLAND, Imende A. POWEL AVE NEWPORT HOSP 02840 #566-01-1971 L1982 OM *020 †60

TETTEY, Peppino Enrico. 11 FRIENDSHIP ST, NEWPORT HOSPITAL 02840 #412-02-1991 L1996 CCM *020 †20

TILMAN, Keri Ann. 11 FRIENDSHIP ST, NEWPORT HOSPITAL, NEPI 02840 #023-01-2003 L2006 EM *020 †16

TOMLINSON, David Robert. 1 RIGGS RD, NAVAL AMBULATORY CARE CENT 02841 #007-02-1997 L2004 FM *020 †18

TORRES, Olga H. ■ 02840 #275-01-1947 L1977 AN *071

ULLMAN, Martha Ann. 50 MEMORIAL BLVD, ASSOCIATES INC 02840 #038-41-1980 L1983 PD *020 †55

VALENTE, James Danl. 1 RIGGS RD, NAVAL AMBULATORY CARE CENT 02841 #024-07-1985 L1986 GS *020 †85

WALKER, Benj Harrison, Jr. 11 FRIENDSHIP ST 02840 #035-01-1985 L1994 EM *020 †16

WALLACE, Alan Robin G. 11 FRIENDSHIP ST 02840 #917-25-1962 L1967 PD ADL *071

WHITE, Joseph Robt. ■ 02840 #018-03-1966 L1967 AN *071 †05

WILNER, Andrew Nathan. 317 AMERICA, STE 317 02840 #043-01-1981 L1987 N IM *062 †20,75

WITKOWSKI, James Bernard. 11 FRIENDSHIP ST 02840 #021-01-2000 L2007 IM *020 †20

ZAKLYNSKY, Orest Vsevolod. 220 BELLEVUE AVE 02840 #035-08-1969 L1981 GS *020 †85

NORTH KINGSTOWN – WASHINGTON

ALONSO, Pilar Guzman. 1950 TOWER HILL RD 02852 #748-10-1993 L1998 ID *020 †20

ASHER, Ira Henry. 65 BOSTON NECK RD 02852 #035-46-1971 L1977 OPH *020 †35

CAPALBO, Robert Anthony. 320 PHILLIPS ST, STE 201 02852 #041-09-1978 L1981 IM *020 †20

CAPALBO, Sylvester A. ■ 02852 #041-09-1939 L1940 GP *071

COGHLIN, Daniel Thomas. 320 PHILLIPS ST, NARRAGANSETT BAY 02852 #008-01-1998 L2001 PD *020 †55

COGHLIN, Thomas James. 65 BOSTON NECK RD 02852 #024-07-1967 L1972 OPH *020 †35

CROTEAU, Richard Jos. PO BOX 347 02852 #024-05-1971 L1976 GS *100 †85

DECK, Michael David Field. 6725 POST RD, XRA MEDICAL IMAGING 02852 #143-03-1961 L2005 DR RNR *020 †80

DE LUCA, Richard Thos. ■ 02852 #308-07-1982 L1986 IM *020

FEMINO, John Peter. 580 TEN ROD RD, MEADOWS EDGE 02852 #043-01-1976 L1978 ADM IM *030 †20

GLOOR, James Drew. 1051 TEN ROD RD, UNIT B-2/10 02852 #055-01-1979 L1980 GP EM *020

GONZALEZ, Michael Joseph. 7260 POST RD 02852 #748-20-1991 L2004 FM *020 †18

HANCE, Robert Vincent. 320 PHILLIPS ST, STE 201 02852 #422-01-1995 L1999 IM *020 †20

HO, Lynn T. 320 PHILLIPS ST, STE 204 02852 #035-19-1986 L1989 FM *020 †18

HURLEY, Robert Peter. 165 DILLABUR AVE, GENERAL DYNAMICS/ELECTRI B 02852 #306-01-1985 L1988 OM FM *020 †18,70

KELLEY, Mark Damien. 1130 TEN ROD RD, STE D103 02852 #024-07-1970 L1996 IM CD *020 †20

KIDDER, Robert Edward. 6725 POST RD, XRA MEDICAL IMAGING 02852 #035-08-1973 L2007 DR VIR *020 †80

LARKIN, Durga Strohl. 65 BOSTON NECK RD 02852 #036-07-1987 L1990 OPH *020 †35

LEVENTHAL, John Michael. 21 HAMILTON ALLENTON RD, 1 WEST 02852 #024-05-1961 L2004 GYN *071 †30

MACHATA, Francis Karl. ■ 02852 #023-01-1947 L1947 OM IM *071

MAILHOT, Terrie Annette. 1130 TEN ROD RD STE D102 02852 #048-14-1985 L1989 CHP P *020 †75

MALTZ, Robert Danl. 320 PHILLIPS ST, NARRAGANSETT BAY 02852 #035-46-1983 L1987 PD *020 †55

MC CARTHY, D John Finbarr. ■ 02852 #035-09-1955 L1956 P *030

MC KEE, Eugene B. 7260 POST RD 02852 #539-04-1961 L1963 FM *020 †18

MURPHY, John Edward. ■ 02852 #016-43-1948 L1956 GP OM *071

MURRAYM, Mary E. 320 PHILLIPS ST, NARRAGANSETT BAY 02852 #035-48-1987 L1992 PD *020 †55

MUSIAL, Sandra Joan. 320 PHILLIPS ST, NARRAGANSETT BAY 02852 #024-16-1993 L1993 PD *020 †55

OLUDOBUN, Joel O. ■ 02852 #690-01-1977 L2000 **IM** *020 †20
PERRY, Richard Warren. ■ 02852 #025-01-1955 L1965 **TS** *020 †85,90
POWERS, Colleen Ann. 420 SCRABBLETOWN RD STE A, KINGSTOWN PEDIATRICS INC 02852 #032-01-1993 L1993 **PD** *020 †55
RAO, Anita A. ■ 02852 #495-21-1978 L1981 **AN** *020 †05
SATHYA, Anuradha. 320 PHILLIPS ST 02852 #495-80-1995 L2001 **FM** *020 †18
SILVERBLATT, Fred Joel. 37 POJAC PT 02852 #035-19-1962 L2001 **ID IM** *030 †20
SIWICKI, David Martin. 211 CIRCUIT DR 02852 #305-01-1984 L1987 **EM FM** *020 †18
SOLOMON, Debra J. 1130 TEN ROD RD STE D204 02852 #024-07-1984 L1987 **P** *020 †75
SVIOKLA, Sylvester C. 580 TEN ROD RD STE B 02852 #024-01-1972 L2005 **ADM EM** *020
TOMS, Mary Eleanor. 6946 POST RD, BEACON HOSPICE 02852 #041-13-1971 L1987 **OS** *020 †60
TRIVETT, Robert Bowen. 35 WEAVER RD 02852 #051-04-1970 L1975 **ADL** *020 †55
VORASINGHA, Erlinda B. 124 LAUREL RIDGE LN 02852 #748-10-1965 L1980 **OBG GP** *020
WEIGLE, Paul Edward. 650 TEN ROD RD, FAMILY SERVICE OF RHODE IS 02852 #033-05-1999 L2004 **CHP** *020 †75

NORTH PROVIDENCE – PROVIDENCE

AIKEN, James Francis. 200 HIGH SERVICE AVE 02904 #016-06-1963 L1974 **R NM** *020 †80,28
ALIZADEH KHOSROSHAHI, A. 1637 MINERAL SPRING AVE 2 02904 #305-01-1995 L1995 **NM IM** *020,28
ALLEGRA, Salvatore R. 200 HIGH SERVICE AVE, ST JOSEPH'S HOSPITAL 02904 #561-01-1947 L1958 **PTH NM** *071 †50,28
AL-YACOUB, Motasem A. 40B STONE TRL 02904 #575-01-1991 L1994 **N** *020 †20,75
AUSTERLITZ, Jeffrey. 830 CHALKSTONE AVE 02908 #043-01-1978 L1979 **IM** *020 †20
AZER, Wadid Samir. 1630 MINERAL SPRING AVE 02904 #915-04-1995 L1999 **IM FM** *020 †20
BALAGUER, Emma Marie. 399 FRUIT HILL AVE 02911 #028-34-1962 L1980 **PHP FM** *071
BELAVAL, Emilio. 200 HIGH SERVICE AVE, DEPT OF EMERGENCY MEDICINE 02904 #042-01-1995 L2002 **EM** *020 †16
BESSAR, Majedah Abdaihame. 630 SMITHFIELD RD, APT 204 02904 #797-01-1991 L1998 *100
BOVIE, Warren Webster. 200 HIGH SERVICE AVE 02904 #035-03-1965 L1973 **DR NM** *020 †80 ‡
CAMBIO, Angelo Joseph. ■ 02911 #024-05-2005 **U** *012
CAMPELLONE, Peter. 1045 CHARLES ST 02904 #561-19-1932 L1948 **GP GS** *020
CARCIERI, David A. 1637 MINERAL SPRING AVE, STE 117 02904 #043-01-1990 L1994 **OBG** *020 †30
CASTILLO, Jorge Julio. ■ 02904 #649-40-1996 L2005 **HO** *012 †20
CIABATTONI, Joseph. 1352 SMITH ST, ATWOOD MEDICAL ASSOCIATES 02911 #008-01-1976 L1977 **IM** *020 †20
CIANCAGLINI, Doreen M. 1169 MINERAL SPRING AVE 02904 #654-01-1990 L1992 **PD** *020 †55
D'ALESSANDRO, Frank Mario. 1515 SMITH ST 02911 #561-01-1960 L1963 **IM END** *020
D'AMATO, Stephen John. 1637 MINERAL SPRING AVE, NORTH PROVIDENCE MEDICAL S 02904 #561-11-1976 L1979 **EM OM** *020 †16
DE LA PENA, Leonor. 200 HIGH SERVICE AVE 02904 #748-01-1968 L1977 **AN** *020
DILIBERO, Lori Catherine. ■ 02904 #043-01-2007 *012
DIONISOPOULOS, Paul. 1637 MINERAL SPRING AVE 02904 #649-14-1985 L1999 **IM** *020
ELLIN, Stephen Richard. 200 HIGH SERVICE AVE 02904 #041-02-1968 L1976 **R NM** *020 †80,28
FARGNOLI, Donald V. 1358 SMITH ST 02911 #561-17-1976 L1980 **OPH** *020
FARINA, Anthony Geo, Jr. 1339 SMITH ST, N PROVIDENCE PRIMARY CARE 02908 #043-01-1991 L1993 **IM** *020 †20
FARINA, Joseph A. 185 HIGH SERVICE AVE 02904 #050-02-1983 L1986 **CD IM** *020 †20
FAZEL, Shawn. 1637 MINERAL SPRING AVE 02904 #665-02-2000 L2002 **IM** *020
FORT, Glenn G. 200 HIGH SERVICE AVE, ST JOSEPH'S HEALTH SERVICE 02904 #847-08-1983 L1988 **ID IM** *020 †20
GAUTHIER, Edward Jencks. 1332 SMITH ST 02911 #024-07-1958 L1959 **IM CD** *020 †20
GEIST, Mark A. 200 HIGH SERVICE AVE 02904 #035-45-1996 L1997 **DR** *020 †80
GIORGIO, Albert. ■ 02904 #561-17-1950 L1953 **GP OBG** *071
GMUER, Cecilia Ann. 200 HIGH SERVICE AVE, DEPT OF PATH FATIMA HOSP 02904 #035-03-1977 L1981 **PTH** *020
HAMMO, Abdel-Hai H. 200 HIGH SERVICE AVE, DEPT OF PEDIATRICS 02904 #575-01-1986 L1996 **PD PG** *020 †55
HANNA, Linda Jane. 214 HIGH SERVICE AVE, CARDIOLOGY & INTERNAL MED 02904 #036-05-1985 L1993 **IM** *020 †28,20
HANUSHEVSKY, Taras. ■ 02911 #407-04-1950 L1955 **IM** *071
HASSAN, Ghinwa Ali. 1630 MINERAL SPRING AVE 02904 #605-01-1995 L2003 **FM** *020 †18
HERRERA, Jose I, Jr. 200 HIGH SERVICE AVE 02904 #748-01-1964 L1989 **AN** *020
HUSAIN, Reema. 200 HIGH SERVICE AVE, ATTENTION: MEDICAL 02904 #704-02-1993 L2001 **PYG** *020
IACOBUCCI, Richard P. 1635 MINERAL SPRING AVE 02904 #561-01-1969 L1972 **CD** *020
IZZI, Joseph A. 1351 SMITH ST 02911 #561-01-1962 L1964 **ORS** *020 †40
IZZI, Joseph Anthony, Jr. 1351 SMITH ST, JOSEPH A IZZI JR MD 02911 #024-05-1996 L1996 **HS** *020 †40
JAMAL, Sameer Mustafa. ■ 02904 #051-04-2005 L2005 **IM** *012
JERALDO, Teresa L. 967 MINERAL SPRING AVE 02904 #231-01-1986 L1992 **PD PG** *020 †55
KAPLAN, Liana. ■ 02904 #913-16-1967 *075
KHERADI, Jerry M. 1637 MINERAL SPRING, AVE 02904 #495-01-1966 L1973 **GE IM** *071
KISE, Kristina Lyn. ■ 02904 #011-03-2007 L2007 **P** *012
KRISHNADASAN, Ravitharan. ■ 02904 #422-01-2000 **HEM** *100 †20
KURL, Rita Sharma. 200 HIGH SERVICE AVE, ST JOSEPH'S HOSP FATIMA UN 02904 #495-10-1980 L1992 **IM** *020 †20
LINSAO, Milagros M. 200 HIGH SERVICE AVE, ASSOCIATES IN ANESTHESIA I 02904 #748-10-1967 L1977 **AN** *020
LOPEZ, Francisco V F. ■ 02904 #748-01-1989 L1994 **HO** *020 †20
MANNA, Gail Angela. 1850 MINERAL SPRING AVE 02904 #561-17-1984 L1989 **IM** *020
MARCACCIO, Vincent F P. 1637 MINERAL SPRING AVE 02904 #561-17-1986 L1990 **IM ADM** *020
MARINI, Diane Reali. 200 HIGH SERVICE AVE 02904 #043-01-1993 L1993 **EM** *020 †16
MARTIN, Brenda Ann. ■ 02911 #021-01-2004 L2004 **OBG** *012
MASSE, Maureen. ■ 02904 #035-01-2002 L2005 **D** *012
MIAN, Sabina Rafiq. ■ 02904 #704-20-2001 L2001 **RHU** *100
MIGLIORI, Stephen Julius. 200 HIGH SERVICE AVE 02904 #041-09-1987 L1995 **GS** *020 †85
MILES-MATTHIAS, Paul. 200 HIGH SERVICE AVE, FATIMA UNIT 02904 #035-06-1978 L1984 **GS** *020
MOONAN, Denis E, Jr. 1515 SMITH ST STE N 02911 #038-06-1974 L1980 **IMG IM** *020 †50

NUNES, Belarmino Augusto. 1637 MINERAL SPRING AVE, STE 103 02904 #770-03-1972 L1978 **IM** *020
OH, Sei Myong. 200 HIGH SERVICE AVE 02904 #583-01-1970 L1984 **AN** *020
PAPARO, Gary Pat. ■ 02904 #024-05-1943 L1946 **FOP** *071 †50
PENG, Jane Feng. ■ 02904 #243-73-1985 L2006 **N** *012
PEREZ, Joseph Lewis. 200 HIGH SERVICE AVE, ATTN: MEDICAL STAFF OFFICE 02904 #035-20-1998 L2002 **FM** *020 †18
PERRY, Keith Arthur. 200 HIGH SERVICE AVE, DEPT OF ANESTHESIOLOGY 02904 #050-02-1985 L1990 **AN** *020 †10
PHARMAKIDIS, Angelo B. 1637 MINERAL SPRING AVE 02904 #418-01-1965 L1980 **IM ON** *020
POLIANSKI, Nickolay Nicko. ■ 02911 #913-22-1996 L2007 **FM** *100
PRINSCOTT, J D. 200 HIGH SERVICE AVE, ST JOSEPH HOSPITAL 02904 #305-01-1982 L1990 **AN** *020 †20
RAHMAN, Riaz. 1352 SMITH ST, ATWOOD MEDICAL ASSOCIATES 02911 #305-01-2002 L2005 **IM** *100 †20
RAJABIUN, Mohamad Taghi. 259 HIGH SERVICE AVE 02904 #517-01-1959 L1968 **TS** *020 †85,90
REYES, Celia Felicitas G. 200 HIGH SERVICE AVE, ST JOSEPH HEALTH SERVICES 02904 #748-02-1992 L2005 **PD** *020 †55
RUSSELL, Warren King. 200 HIGH SERVICE AVE, OUR LADY OF FATIMA HOSPITA 02904 #048-15-1989 L1992 **EM** *030 †16
SABO, Naftali. 214 HIGH SERVICE AVE 02904 #550-02-1976 L1985 **IM CD** *020 †20
SAMAAN, Fadi Elias. ■ 02911 #875-02-1995 L2006 **IM** *100 †20
SCHOENFELD, Alexander L. 200 HIGH SERVICE AVE, ATTN: MEDICAL STAFF OFFICE 02904 #024-05-1994 L1995 **EM** *020 †16
SHANNON, Mark Allen. 200 HIGH SERVICE AVE, OUR LADY OF FATIMA HOSP 02904 #041-07-1985 L1988 **IMG D** *020 †20
SOUTHARD, James B, III. 200 HIGH SERVICE AVE 02904 #024-05-1974 L1980 **AN** *020
SPROCH, Richard Moran. ■ 02904 #041-02-1947 L1998 **R AM** *071 †80
STANKIEWICZ, Andrzej J. 200 HIGH SERVICE AVE, MARIAN HALL 02904 #759-07-1976 L1987 **IM HO** *020 †20 ‡
SUD, Puneet. 1635 MINERAL SPRING AVE, STE 200 02904 #495-19-1993 L1996 **IM** *020 †20
SULLIVAN, John Robt. 200 HIGH SERVICE AVE, FATIMA HOSPITAL 02904 #308-11-1986 L1988 **ON** *020 †20
TREABA, Diana Olguta C. ■ 02904 #781-05-1993 L2005 **SP** *100 †50
VILLARI, Anne Elizabeth. ■ 02904 #035-15-2008 *012
VLACHA, Vasiliki. ■ 02904 #418-04-1987 L1989 **PHO PD** *020 †55
WATERS, K M. 200 HIGH SERVICE AVE 02904 #067-01-1983 L1987 **PTH** *020 †50
WEHBE, Paul Wahib. 1630 MINERAL SPRING AVE 02904 #605-01-1994 L1998 **PD** *020 †55
WEHBE, Tarek. 1630 MINERAL SPRING AVE 02904 #605-01-1990 L1993 **HEM** *020 †20
WEISBLATT, Steven. 200 HIGH SERVICE AVE 02904 #056-06-1983 L1988 **DR OS** *020 †80
WHEELER, Edward Admas, Jr. 13 BROWN ST 02904 #038-41-1976 L1983 **IM AS** *020 †20
YEUNG, Wilbert Derek. ■ 02904 #033-06-2004 L2004 **CPP** *012
YOUNES, Claude Elias. 1300 MINERAL SPRING AVE 02904 #913-92-1981 L1986 **IM** *020

NORTH SCITUATE – PROVIDENCE

CRAWFORD, Kim Jay. 33 DANIELSON PIKE, P O BOX 428 02857 #030-06-1984 L1987 **FM** *020 †18
CURTIS, Sharon R. ■ 02857 #043-01-1987 L1989 **FM** *020 †18
NEWHOUSE, Robert Emmett. ■ 02857 #010-02-1945 L1949 **GS** *071

NORTH SMITHFIELD – PROVIDENCE

COLELLA, Augustine. 1 EDDIE DOWLING HWY, LANDMARK MED CTR FOGERTY 02896 #561-01-1957 L1959 **PTH FOP** *020 †50
CURRY, Laurie Ann. 63 EDDIE DOWLING HWY, STE 1 02896 #035-20-1988 L1996 **OBG** *020 †30
GOTLIB, Tadeusz A. 400 MENDON RD 02896 #561-01-1951 L1961 **IM CD** *071
GUAY, Jean Alphonse. ■ 02896 #035-03-1956 L1959 **ORS** *020 †40
LUKE, Michael Arthur. 501 GREAT RD, STE 205 02896 #035-06-1979 L1985 **GS GYN** *020
MC GUNIGAL, Thomas E, Jr. 116 EDDIE DOWLING HWY 02896 #038-41-1987 L1993 **PM PMM** *020 †60
NASSERI, Afshin. 63 EDDIE DOWLING HWY, STE 7 02896 #308-12-1993 L1996 **IM** *020
RAFAL, Keith W L. 116 EDDIE DOWLING HWY, HEALING CHOICES PC 02896 #010-03-1982 L1985 **PM IMG** *020 †60
SHAH, Zaheer Ahmed. 65 EDDIE DOWLING HWY 02896 #422-01-1995 L1995 **IM** *020
SMITH, Marsha Kay. 501 GREAT RD, STE 104 02896 #010-01-1994 L1998 **OBG** *020

OAKLAND – PROVIDENCE

GUPTA, Rajeev K. 1376 BRONCOS HWY 02858 #496-13-1983 L1994 **IM** *020
HEALEY, Benjamin Rainer. ■ 02858 #539-02-1965 L1971 **OBG** *020 †30

PASCOAG – PROVIDENCE

CHOKSHI, Purvi. 2090 WALLUM LAKE RD, ELEANOR SLATER HOSP, ZABAR 02859 #495-01-1992 L1998 **IM** *020 †20 ‡
DECELLES, Normand Louis. 2090 WALLUM LAKE RD, ZAMBARINO UNIT 02859 #043-01-1984 L1986 **IM** *020 †20
GIOVETTI, Mary Louise. THE BRIDGEWAY, NORTHWEST HEALTH CENTER 02859 #023-01-1985 L1989 **OBG** *020 †18
HOKENESS, Steven Alan. 36 BRIDGE WAY 02859 #026-04-1974 L1976 **IM ADL** *020 †20
PAQUET, Michele Marie. 2090 WALLUM LAKE RD, ZAMBARANO HOSP 02859 #028-34-1978 L1981 **IM** *020 †20

PAWTUCKET – PROVIDENCE

ABDULBAKI, Abdulrahman Mo. 111 BREWSTER ST 02860 #875-01-2004 L2007 **IM** *012
ABOSHADY, Hesham Mohammed. 111 BREWSTER ST 02860 #915-02-1998 L2005 **IM** *012
ADDO, Matilda Adjeley. 111 BREWSTER ST 02860 #412-01-2002 L2005 **FP** *012

AGARWAL, Purva. 111 BREWSTER ST, MEMORIAL HOSP OF RHODE ISL 02860 #496-02-2001 L2004 **IM** *100

AKHTAR, Ali Amin. 111 BREWSTER ST, DEPARTMENT OF MEDICINE 02860 #704-02-1995 L1998 **IM** *020 †20

AKINS, Amy Baumgartner. ■ 02860 #008-02-2007 L2007 **PD** *012

AL-ALWAN, Ali Aziz Hussei. 111 BREWSTER ST 02860 #575-01-2005 L2007 **IM** *012

AL-RAQQAD, Ahmad Kassab. 333 SCHOOL ST, STE 210 02860 #575-01-1994 L2000 **IM** *020 †20

AMBEWADIKAR, Samrat. 42 PARK PL, BLACKSTONE VALLEY CHC 02860 #024-05-2002 L2002 **PD** *020 †55

AMIN, Kim Samir. 333 SCHOOL ST STE 215 02860 #025-01-1980 L1982 **IM** *020 †20

ANANDARAJAH, Gowrie. 111 BREWSTER ST, MEMORIAL HOSPITAL OF R.I. 02860 #036-01-1988 L1992 **FM** *020 †18

ANDERLIND, Christina. 111 BREWSTER ST 02860 #408-30-1992 L2003 **PCC** *012 †20

ANDREONI, Stephen Paul. 111 BREWSTER ST 02860 #305-01-2005 L2005 **FP** *012

ANTHONY, David Campbell. 111 BREWSTER ST, MEMORIAL HOSPITAL 02860 #036-05-1997 L1997 **FM** *020 †18

ARTENSTEIN, Andrew W. 111 BREWSTER ST, DEPT OF MEDICINE 02860 #024-07-1986 L2001 **ID IM** *030 †20

ASAD, Saba. 111 BREWSTER ST 02860 #704-06-2003 L2006 **IM** *012

ASPRY, Karen Elizabeth. 111 BREWSTER ST, MEMORIAL HOSP OF RI 02860 #005-19-1990 L2005 **CD** *020 †20

ATLASOWITZ, Ilan. ■ 02860 #550-02-1986 L1996 *100

BANERJEE, Rekha. PO BOX 865 02862 #495-41-1962 L1975 **AN** *071

BANGALORE KRISHNAIAH, Poor. 111 BREWSTER ST 02860 #496-20-1988 L2007 **FP** *012

BARUCH, Jay Michael. 111 BREWSTER ST, MEM HOSP RHODE ISLAND EMER 02860 #035-48-1990 L2000 **EM** *020 †16

BASH, Bashar. 111 BREWSTER ST, MEMORIAL HOSPITAL OF RHODE 02860 #875-01-1994 L2005 **PCC** *020 †20

BAUTISTA, Joseph Nathan L. 111 BREWSTER ST 02860 #748-10-2005 L2007 **IM** *012

BAZIOTIS, Peter E. 111 BREWSTER ST 02860 #043-01-1990 L1994 **AN** *020 †05

BECKER, Tanya J. 480 ARMISTICE BLVD 02861 #043-01-1998 L1998 **PD** *020

BERMAN, Arnold M. 111 BREWSTER ST 02860 #024-05-1974 L2002 **FM EM** *020 †18

BERMAN, Linda Jill. 541 NEWPORT AVE, SPECTRUM FAMILY HEALTH CAR 02861 #018-03-2000 L2000 **FM** *100 †18

BERTINI, Richard Geo. 60 NORTON ST 02860 #035-03-1958 L1960 **ORS OS** *071 †40

BEYER, Wendy Mcnear. 111 BREWSTER ST 02860 #005-11-2004 L2004 **FM** *100 †18

BHIMANI, Lisa Ann. 407 EAST AVE 02860 #041-09-1997 L1997 **OBG** *100 †30

BONIVART, Arthur Geza. 85 BEECHWOOD AVE 02860 #473-01-1949 L1968 **GS** *071 †85

BORKAN, Jeffrey Michael. 111 BREWSTER ST, BROWN MEDICAL SCH 02860 #038-06-1984 L2001 **FM** *020 †18

BURKE, Robert Thos. 111 BREWSTER ST, DEPARTMENT OF PEDIATRICS 02860 #033-06-1975 L1996 **PD GP** *020 †55

CAMPANILE, Christopher P. 727 EAST AVE, HILLSIDE FAMILY / COMMUNIT 02860 #051-04-1988 L1988 **FM** *020 †18

CAMPANO, Lee Crepeau. ■ 02860 #016-42-2005 L2005 **IM** *012

CANCHIS, P Wilfredo. ■ 02860 #649-40-1987 L1993 **GE** *100

CANNISTRA, Anthony Jos. 333 SCHOOL ST, STE 112 02860 #024-05-1987 L1994 **CD IM** *020 †20

CANNISTRA, Lauralyn. 333 SCHOOL ST, STE 112 02860 #008-02-1987 L1994 **CD IM** *020 †20

CARTER, David Paull. 174 ARMISTICE BLVD, FAMILY MEDICINE SPECIALIST 02860 #165-04-1977 L1980 **FM** *020 †20

CASSERLY, Brian Philip. 111 BREWSTER ST, MEMORIAL HOSPITAL OF RI 02860 #539-04-1999 L2005 **PCC** *012 †20

CASTRO, Maria Ines. 111 BREWSTER ST 02860 #132-03-2003 L2005 **FP** *012

CAVA, John. 333 SCHOOL ST, BLACKSTONE CARDLGY STE 112 02860 #033-05-1987 L2003 **CD** *020 †20

CAVANAUGH, Colleen Paula. 407 EAST AVE, CTR FOR OB/GYN 02860 #043-01-1989 L1989 **OBG** *020 †30

CETERA, Kinga Joanna. 111 BREWSTER ST, DEPT. OF EMERGENCY MEDICIN 02860 #056-06-1996 L2000 **EM** *020

CHANDRAN, Rabin Frank. 111 BREWSTER ST, FAMILY CARE CTR 02860 #054-04-1996 L1996 **FM** *020 †18 ‡

CHANG, Manchin. ■ 02860 #008-02-2007 L2007 **IM** *012

CHERNESKY, Edward Geo. 111 BREWSTER ST 02860 #010-01-1986 L1992 **DR GS** *020 †80

CHOPRA, Pradeep. 102 SMITHFIELD AVE 02860 #495-38-1988 L2000 **AN** *020 †05

CHOU, Lin. 465 EAST AVE 02860 #065-01-1988 L2000 **OPH** *020 †35

CHRISTIAN, Benjamin Powel. ■ 02861 #024-16-2006 L2006 **PS** *012

CIRCIUMARU-GRILLO, Iulia. 111 BREWSTER ST, INTERNAL MEDICINE CLINIC 02860 #781-01-1993 L2002 **RHU** *020 †20

CLEARY, Colleen Anne. 174 ARMISTICE BLVD 02860 #035-48-1986 L1989 **FM** *020 †18

COFFIN, Linda Carol. 169 GEORGE ST, HOSPICE CARE OF RHODE ISL 02860 #032-01-1976 L1984 **IM PLM** *020 †20

CONWAY, Stephen Tristram. 465 EAST AVE 02860 #024-07-1973 L1978 **OPH** *020 †35

CROWLEY, James P. 111 BREWSTER ST, MEMORIAL HOSP OF RHODE 02860 #010-02-1969 L1975 **HO ILI** *040 †20

CULLEN, Leah Oseas. 85 BEECHWOOD AVE 02860 #036-05-1977 L1983 **P OS** *020 †75

CURRAN, Robert Emmet. 333 SCHOOL ST 02860 #035-20-1966 L1974 **OPH PO** *020 †35

CZEKANSKI, Andrew G. ■ 02860 #024-07-1945 L1948 **IM P** *071

DANILOV, Alexey Valeryevi. 111 BREWSTER ST, MEMORIAL HOSP OF RHODE ISL 02860 #913-64-1997 L2004 **HO** *012 †20

DAVID, Sean Patrick. 111 BREWSTER ST, MEMORIAL HOSP OF RI 02860 #054-04-1995 L1999 **FM** *020 †18

DAVIS, Kathryn M. 407 EAST AVE, STE 150 02860 #011-02-2002 L2006 **OBG** *100

DAVIS, Stephen Whitaker. 111 BREWSTER ST, MEMORIAL HOSPITAL OF R.I. 02860 #043-01-1980 L1985 **FM** *020 †18

DELLA TORRE, Thomas D. 333 SCHOOL ST, STE 302 02860 #561-01-1968 L1972 **OTO FPS** *020 †45

DE LOS REYES, Ma. Theresa. 111 BREWSTER ST 02860 #748-01-2002 L2005 **IM** *012

DEMASI, Monica Holly. 111 BREWSTER ST, MEMORIAL HOSPITAL 02860 #038-06-2003 L2003 **FM** *020 †18

DE PALO, Vera Ann. 111 BREWSTER ST, MEM HOSP RI PULMONARY DIV 02860 #561-15-1987 L1994 **IM PCC** *030 †20

DHILLON, Jaspreet Kaur. 111 BREWSTER ST 02860 #495-29-2002 L2006 **IM** *012

DIAZ, Joseph. 111 BREWSTER ST 02860 #043-01-1996 L1996 **IM** *020 †20

DIRKS, Marco Paolo. 588 PAWTUCKET AVE, ORTHOPEDIC GROUP INC 02860 #050-02-1990 L1996 **HS** *020 †40

DORROS, Carol Marjorie. ■ 02860 #024-05-1987 L1989 **IM** *062 †20

DOSA, David Michael. 407 EAST AVE, STE 110 02860 #010-01-1998 L2003 **IMG** *020 †20

DUARTE, Kristina Marie. 111 BREWSTER ST, DEPARTMENT OF FM 02860 #032-01-1995 L1995 **FM OS**

DUBIN, Howard G. 111 BREWSTER ST 02860 #024-16-1980 L1982 **CCM** *020 †20

DU BOIS, Geret Alan. 111 BREWSTER ST 02860 #024-07-1967 L1974 **ORS** *020 †20

EATON, Charles Buckley. 111 BREWSTER ST, CTR FOR PRIMARY CARE & PRE 02860 #035-15-1977 L1990 **FM** *020 †18

ECONOMOS, Michael M S. 247 ROOSEVELT AVE 02860 #035-20-1992 L1996 **OBG** *020

ELKADI, Ghassan Hosni. 111 BREWSTER ST, MEMORIAL HOSPITAL OF RHODE 02860 #915-02-1988 L1998 **IM** *020 †20

ELTIBI, Rami Sabbah. 111 BREWSTER ST, MEMORIAL HOSP OF RHODE ISL 02860 #575-01-2003 L2005 **IM** *012

ELTOMI, Hoda Nabil Fouad. 111 BREWSTER ST 02860 #584-01-2004 L2007 **FP** *012

EMMICK, Christine Marie. 333 SCHOOL ST 02860 #035-03-1993 L1994 **GS** *020 †85

EMPKIE, Timothy Mayne. 89 POND ST, MEMORIAL HOSP DEPT FP 02860 #008-02-1976 L1984 **FM PHP** *040 †18

ENTIN, Esther J. 555 PROSPECT ST, MEMORIAL HOSPITAL OF R.I. 02860 #041-07-1977 L1979 **PD** *020 †55

ETTENSOHN, David Bruce. 73 BEECHWOOD AVE 02860 #038-41-1977 L1983 **PUD IM** *020 †20

FAIN, Elaine Berlinsky. 100 SMITHFIELD AVE 02860 #035-01-1978 L1979 **IM** *020 †20

FELDMAN, Martin Preville. 209 ARMISTICE BLVD 02860 #024-01-1955 L1964 **GS** *020 †85

FINE, Michael David. 727 EAST AVE, HILLSIDE FAMILY / COMMUNIT 02860 #038-06-1983 L1984 **FM** *020 †18

FINGERUT, Jerald Chas. 42 PARK PL 02860 #041-09-1968 L1997 **MDM** *030 †20

FORTIN, Robert Gerard. 720 CENTRAL AVE 02861 #067-03-1955 L1955 **FM GP** *020

FORTUNA, Robert Jos. 211 ARMISTICE BLVD 02860 #033-05-1981 L1985 **ORS** *020 †40

FRAM, Robert Jay. 111 BREWSTER ST, MEMORIAL HOSPITAL OF RI 02860 #024-01-1976 L1997 **IM ON** *050 †20

FREDIAN, April Leigh. 111 BREWSTER ST, MEMORIAL HOSP OF RHODE ISL 02860 #422-01-2006 L2006 **FP** *012

GABRIELIAN, Ara. ■ 02860 #016-42-2002 L2002 **EM** *020 †16

GALLER, Ezra Louis. 333 SCHOOL ST, STE 301 02860 #024-05-1990 L1995 **OPH** *020 †35

GAVALYA, Richard Nelson. 77 BEECHWOOD AVE 02860 #649-01-1964 L1971 **P CHP** *072

GEORGE, Paul Francis. ■ 02860 #043-01-2005 L2005 **FP** *012

GIBSON, Peter Bevier. 333 SCHOOL ST, STE 112 02860 #038-41-1994 L1998 **CD PD** *020 †20

GIL, Alfredo. 407 EAST AVE STE 150, DBA: WOMEN'S CARE, INC 02860 #010-03-1996 L2003 **OBG** *020 †30

GILL, Peter Severin. 333 SCHOOL ST, STE 213 02860 #024-07-1981 L1990 **GS** *020 †85

GLICKSMAN, Arvin S. 249 ROOSEVELT AVE, UNIT 201 02860 #016-42-1949 L1974 **RO ON** *020 †80

GOEL, Ritu. 333 SCHOOL ST, STE 302 02860 #041-02-1993 L1999 **OTO** *020 †45

GOLDBERG, Arnold Ralph. 111 BREWSTER ST 02860 #016-01-1981 L1994 **FM** *020 †18

GOODMAN, Diana Jeanne. ■ 02860 #011-02-2006 L2006 **N** *012

GOWDA, Yalakki. 111 BREWSTER ST, AN 02860 #495-09-1961 L1971 **IM CD** *020

GRAMLING, Robert Eugene. 111 BREWSTER ST, DEPT OF FAMILY MEDICINE 02860 #032-01-1997 L2002 **FM** *040 †18

GREENBLATT, Samuel Harold. 111 BREWSTER ST, MEMORIAL HOSPITAL OF RI 02860 #035-20-1966 L1989 **NS** *020 †25

GUL, Amber. 111 BREWSTER ST 02860 #704-21-2003 L2005 **IM** *012

GUTMAN, Joshua David. 111 BREWSTER ST 02860 #024-05-1973 L1977 **FM IM** *020 †20,18

GUTMAN, Ned Henry. 407 EAST AVE STE 130, GLL CARDIOLOGY 02860 #023-01-1989 L1989 **CD IM** *020 †20

HAHN, Suh Dong. 333 SCHOOL ST STE 107 02860 #583-02-1967 L1974 **CD IM** *020 †20

HAJJIRI, Mohammad Mohamma. 111 BREWSTER ST, MEMORIAL HOSPITAL 02860 #915-04-2003 L2005 **IM** *012

HALLETT, Joseph Jacob, Jr. 111 BREWSTER ST, MEMORIAL HOSP DEPT PEDS 02860 #035-45-1975 L1992 **PHO PD** *020 †20

HANDEL, Todd Evan. 1145 MAIN ST 02860 #025-01-1997 L2001 **PM** *020 †60

HANNA, Louis Elias. 111 BREWSTER ST 02860 #041-09-1943 **FM PD** *071

HARA, Yoshikuni. 111 BREWSTER ST, DEPT HEM 02860 #572-20-1972 L1975 **HEM IM** *050 †20

HARRINGTON, David John. 174 ARMISTICE BLVD 02860 #043-01-1989 L1997 **OBG** *020 †30

HARRISON, Emily Cope. 407 EAST AVE, STE 150 02860 #050-02-2001 L2001 **FM** *020 †18

HASSAN, Linda Rosarina. 73 BEECHWOOD AVE 02860 #035-45-1979 L1983 **ON HEM** *020 †20

HAWWA, Tawfik Farid. 333 SCHOOL ST 02860 #605-01-1980 L1985 **OBG** *020 †20

HEALEY, Paul Jos Michael. 333 SCHOOL ST 02860 #024-05-1958 L1962 **GS VS** *071 †85

HERBERT, Christine V. 407 EAST AVE, STE 120 02860 #043-01-1987 L1987 **IM** *020 †20

HOPPIN, Frederic G, Jr. 111 BREWSTER ST, DEPT MED 02860 #035-01-1960 L1980 **PUD OS** *071 †20

HORDES, Andrew Richard. 333 SCHOOL ST, STE 112 02860 #035-06-1982 L1984 **CD IM** *020 †20

HOSU, Adriana Mirelle. 111 BREWSTER ST 02860 #781-01-1998 L2005 **IM** *012

HOWLAND, Peter A. 50 PARK PL, BLACKSTONE VALLEY CHC 02860 #035-09-1975 L2004 **PD** *020 †55

HUYNH, Linh Xuan. 111 BREWSTER ST, MEMORIAL HOSPITAL 02860 #035-09-2007 L2007 **FP** *012

IFTIKHAR, Sadia. 126 PROSPECT ST, STE 103 02860 #704-22-1994 L1998 **IM** *020 †20

IJAZ, Ambreen. 111 BREWSTER ST 02860 #704-06-2000 L2005 **IM** *012

INTRIERE, Lisa Ann. 111 BREWSTER ST, MEMORIAL XRAY SERVICES 02860 #010-01-1987 L2004 **DR** *020 †80

ISMAIL, Ahmad Mazen Ahmad. 111 BREWSTER ST 02860 #575-02-2001 L2006 **IM** *012

ISSA, Husam I. 111 BREWSTER ST BLDG C-2, MPC, DEPARTMENT OF MEDICIN 02860 #575-01-1995 L2003 **IM** *100 †20

JABLOW, Barbara W. 727 EAST AVE, HILLSIDE FAMILY/COMMUNITY 02860 #021-01-1985 L1986 **FM** *030 †18 ‡

JACOBS, Edward Jeffrey. 111 BREWSTER ST, DEPT EMERGENCY MEDICINE MH 02860 #020-02-1977 L1997 **EM** *020 †16

JAGGER, Samantha Jane. 111 BREWSTER ST, MEMORIAL HOSPITAL 02860 #550-03-2003 L2004 **FM** *100 †20

JAGMINAS, Liudvikas J. 111 BREWSTER ST, MEMORIAL HOSPITAL OF RI, E 02860 #043-01-1987 L1987 **EM OM** *050 †16

JAWORSKI, Rudolf A. 111 BREWSTER ST 02860 #024-01-1943 L1947 **PD** *071 †55

JHUNG, Jhung-Woock. 111 BREWSTER ST, MEM HOSP OF R I PATHOLOGY 02860 #583-02-1966 L1973 **PTH DMP** *020 †50

JOHNSON, Chas Frank, III. 333 SCHOOL ST 02860 #023-07-1964 L1973 **PS** *020 †85,65

JWIED, Majd Kuftan. 111 BREWSTER ST 02860 #575-01-1993 L2003 **IM** *100 †20

KALMOWITZ, Brett David. 333 SCHOOL ST, STE 303 02860 #035-19-1999 L2006 **GE** *020 †20
KAREM, Rakshana Prasanna. 111 BREWSTER ST 02860 #495-11-2002 L2007 **FP** *012
KESSIMIAN, Noubar. 111 BREWSTER ST 02860 #132-01-1973 L1981 **PTH** *020 †50
KHAN, Mohammad A. 126 PROSPECT ST 02860 #704-01-1958 L1975 *020
KHOURY, Amy Fawzi. ■ 02860 #575-01-1993 L1995 **IM** *100 †20
KIESSLING, Louise S. 111 BREWSTER ST 02860 #043-01-1976 L1977 **PD OS** *071 †55
KIRIAKI, Shadi George. ■ 02861 #010-02-2004 L2006 **EM** *020
KLEIN, Michael D. 727 EAST AVE, HILLSIDE FAMILY / COMMUNIT 02860 #043-01-2000 L2003 **FM** *020 †18
KLIPFEL, Adam Augustus. 334 EAST AVE 02860 #035-47-1996 L2003 **CRS GS** *020 †85
KNOWLES, Kenneth Gardner. 111 BREWSTER ST 02860 #024-07-1957 L1958 **ORS OSM** *071 †40
KOLLI, Uma. 111 BREWSTER ST, MEMORIAL HOSP OF RHODE ISL 02860 #495-21-2000 L2003 **FM** *020 †18
KOPEC, Krzysztof Lukasz. ■ 02860 #033-06-2006 L2006 **IM** *012
KORBLY, Nicole Brooke. ■ 02861 #024-16-2006 L2006 **OBG** *012
KOTHAPALLY, Jagan Mohan R. 111 BREWSTER ST 02860 #495-65-2003 L2006 **IM** *012
KUMAR, Tumkur B N. 333 SCHOOL ST, STE 204 02860 #495-33-1966 L1977 **CD IM** *020 †20
KUMAR, Usha. 333 SCHOOL ST STE 102 02860 #495-33-1973 L1977 **IM** *020 †20
LADETTO, John Victor. 73 BEECHWOOD AVE 02860 #035-20-1995 L1998 **PUD CCM** *020 †20
LAGARES-GARCIA, Jorge A. 334 EAST AVE, CLINIC, LLC 02860 #847-01-1992 L2002 **CRS** *020 †85,10
LAMBRECHT, Jon Keith. 407 EAST AVE, SUITE130 02860 #051-07-1983 L1985 **CD IM** *020 †20
LANKHORST, Christina Eliz. 174 ARMISTICE BLVD 02860 #038-06-2004 L2006 **IM** *020 †20
LATIF, Asma. ■ 02860 #019-02-2006 L2006 **IM** *012
LATIF, Syed Rizwan. ■ 02860 #043-01-2008 *012
LAUDENBERG, Bernd. 111 BREWSTER ST 02860 #409-38-2001 L2006 **FP** *012
LAZARUS, Bruce A. 111 BREWSTER ST 02860 #043-01-1981 L1988 **PM** *030 †60
LEE, Kilza. 111 BREWSTER ST 02860 #583-08-1966 L1978 **OBG FM** *020
LEE, Seok Suh. 126 PROSPECT ST 02860 #583-03-1961 L1984 **FM PD** *020 †18
LEVINSON, Paul D. 111 BREWSTER ST, MEMORIAL HOSPITAL OF RI 02860 #010-02-1975 L1984 **END IM** *020 †20
LEWIS, Michelle Janoff. 333 SCHOOL ST, STE 216 02860 #005-14-2001 L2002 **D** *020 †15
LIEVENSE, Stacey Peckham. 333 SCHOOL ST, PARTNERS IN OB/GYN 02860 #041-01-2003 L2003 **OBG** *020
LONG, Nancy Elizabeth. 169 GEORGE ST 02860 #024-16-1998 L1998 **FM** *020 †18
LONG, Richard H, Jr. 111 BREWSTER ST, MEM HOSP OF RI DEPT FP 02860 #041-02-1986 L1988 **FM** *040 †18
LONGOBARDI, Arturo. 111 BREWSTER ST 02860 #561-10-1955 L1964 **CD IM** *071
LOWENHAUPT, Elizabeth A. ■ 02860 #028-03-2002 L2002 **OS CHP** *100 †55
LOWRY, Matthew Harold. 111 BREWSTER ST, DIV OF PULMONARY/CRITICAL 02860 #051-01-1997 L2005 **IM** *020 †20
LUTTMANN, Christopher J. 407 EAST AVE, STE 130 02860 #035-03-1982 L1987 **CD IM** *020 †20
LYSTER, Mary Elizabeth. 42 PARK PL 02860 #043-01-1984 L1987 **FM** *020 †18 ‡
MAGEE, Susanna Marie. 111 BREWSTER ST, MEMORIAL HOSPITAL OF R.I. 02860 #041-02-1998 L1998 **FM** *020 †18
MAMDANI, Shafiq Tajdin. 333 SCHOOL ST, STE 112 02860 #012-01-1994 L1994 **CD** *020 †20
MANSOURATI, Fadi Fouad. 886 MINERAL SPRING AVE 02860 #875-02-1991 L1995 **IM** *020 †20
MARCOUX, David Alfred. 407 EAST AVE, STE 120 02860 #056-06-1988 L1988 **IM** *020 †20
MARTIN, Horace F. ■ 02860 #043-01-1975 L1976 **CLP OM** *071
MARTIN, Thomas James. ■ 02861 #035-09-1956 L1957 **GP** *071
MATHIAS, David Andrew. 111 BREWSTER ST, MEMORIAL HOSP OF RHODE ISL 02860 #671-02-1990 L2006 **FP** *012
MAYNARD, Steven R. 407 EAST AVE, STE 150 02860 #067-01-1986 L1989 **OBG** *020 †30
MC CLOY, Steven Geo. 100 SMITHFIELD AVE 02860 #048-04-1970 L1977 **IM OM** *020
MC COOL, Franklin Dennis. 111 BREWSTER ST, DIV PUD 02860 #028-34-1976 L1981 **IM PUD** *020 †20
MC MACKIN, Naomi. 111 BREWSTER ST, MEMORIAL HOSPITAL OF R.I. 02860 #033-06-2001 L2005 **IMG** *100 †20
MC NAMARA, Megan Jane. 111 BREWSTER ST, EMERGENCY MEDICINE, MEMORI 02860 #024-07-2003 L2003 **EM** *020
MC NICOLL, Lynn. 407 EAST AVE, STE 110 02860 #067-01-1996 L2001 **IMG** *020 †20
MEDEIROS, Carroll E. 407 EAST AVE STE 150, DBA: WOMEN'S CARE, INC 02860 #043-01-1993 L1998 **OBG** *020 †30
MEILA-PREDOVICIU, Felicia. 407 EAST AVE, STE 120 02860 #781-01-1989 L1994 **IM** *020 †20
MEINKE, William Bondesen. 100 SMITHFIELD AVE, URGENT CARE OF PAWTUCKET 02860 #025-01-1978 L2007 **OM OS** *020
MISKOVSKY, John P. 131 BEECHWOOD AVE 02860 #043-01-1996 L1999 **IM** *020 †20
MISRI, Ashish. 111 BREWSTER ST 02860 #495-52-2005 L2006 **IM** *012
MITAL, Priya. 111 BREWSTER ST, MEMORIAL HOSP OF RHODE ISL 02860 #495-45-2002 L2006 **IM** *012
MITCHELL, Cristina L. 727 EAST AVE, HILLSIDE FAMILY / COMMUNIT 02860 #043-01-1997 L1997 **FM** *020 †18 ‡
MOCK, Curtis Alec. 111 BREWSTER ST 02860 #030-06-1983 L1999 **FM FPG** *020 †18
MODESTO, Maria Hope Mayor. 111 BREWSTER ST, MEMORIAL HOSP OF RHODE ISL 02860 #748-01-2000 L2004 **IM** *100 †20
MOHANTY, Nibaran. ■ 02860 #495-13-1973 *075
MONROE, Alicia Denise H. 111 BREWSTER ST 02860 #017-20-1977 L1989 **FM** *040 †18
MORA, Jorge Ignacio. 111 BREWSTER ST, DEPT OF RISK MANAGEMENT 02860 #935-07-1993 L2006 **PCC** *020 †20 ‡
MORENO, Blas. 111 BREWSTER ST 02860 #275-01-1954 L1957 **IM FM** *020 †18
MORTON, John Rollin. 174 ARMISTICE BLVD, WOMEN'S HEALTH CARE SPECIA 02860 #038-41-1999 L2003 **OBG** *020 †30
MOULE, Bernard A. 111 BREWSTER ST 02860 #024-07-1972 L1978 **U** *020 †95
MUJAHID, Nadia. 111 BREWSTER ST 02860 #704-16-2004 L2007 **FP** *012
MUNUSAMY, Venkataraman. 111 BREWSTER ST 02860 #496-69-2004 L2007 **FP** *012
MURPHY, John Brian. 407 EAST AVE, STE 110 02860 #035-08-1980 L1982 **FM FPG** *040 †18
MYERS, Thomas Joel. 333 SCHOOL ST, STE 210 02860 #050-02-1974 L1980 **HEM IM** *050 †20
NACE, Timothy Michael. 209 ARMISTICE BLVD 02860 #010-02-1983 L1995 **FM FSM** *020 †18
NAQVI, Syed Ahsan Mahboob. 111 BREWSTER ST 02860 #704-01-1983 L2007 **IM** *012
NEILL, Marguerite Ann. 111 BREWSTER ST, MEM HOSP OF RI 02860 #010-01-1977 L1988 **ID** *020 †20
NEMR, Saed Sulaiman Moh'D. 111 BREWSTER ST 02860 #560-01-2005 L2006 **IM** *012
NICASTRI, Guy Richard. 111 BREWSTER ST 02860 #010-02-1986 L2007 **GS** *020 †85
NOBLE, George Davis. 333 SCHOOL ST, STE 301 02860 #050-02-1965 L1967 **OPH** *071 †35
NOONAN, Thomas Edward. 333 SCHOOL ST STE 112 02860 #024-07-1991 L1997 **CD** *020 †20
NOTHNAGLE, Melissa Brooks. 111 BREWSTER ST, MEMORIAL HOSPITAL OF RI 02860 #005-02-1999 L1999 **FM** *020 †18
NOWAK, Andrew Anthony. 407 EAST AVE STE 130 02860 #024-16-1998 L2001 **CD** *020 †20
NUNEZ, Maria Lydia Veiga. ■ 02860 #132-01-1953 **GYN** *071
NUNEZ, Nicolas. ■ 02860 #132-01-1955 L1967 **P** *071 †75
OCASIONES, Anna Marie Lla. 111 BREWSTER ST 02860 #748-01-2002 L2006 **IM** *012
OPAL, Steven Michael. 111 BREWSTER ST, DEPT MED 02860 #035-03-1976 L1985 **IM ID** *050 †20
OSHIRO, Hector Raul. 109 BEECHWOOD AVE, C/O CARLOS LIRA, MD 02860 #737-06-1995 L2001 **ID** *020 †20
PACHECO, Cristina A. 174 ARMISTICE BLVD 02860 #043-01-2004 L2004 **FM** *020
PADILLA, Rafael Eugenio. 200 MAIN ST STE 350, ANESTHESIA CARE INC 02860 #043-01-1988 L2000 **AN** *020 †05
PAPAZIAN, Martin Robt. 333 SCHOOL ST, STE 302 02860 #024-07-1987 L1993 **OTO** *020 †45
PAPAZIAN, Vartan. 333 SCHOOL ST 02860 #024-07-1954 L1955 **OTO** *071 †45
PARKER, Annie Lin. 111 BREWSTER ST # PUD, MEMORIAL HOSP RI 02860 #033-05-1988 L1991 **PUD CCM** *020 †20
PATHAK, Atul. ■ 02860 #496-09-1993 **PD** *100
PATROZOU, Eleni. 111 BREWSTER ST 02860 #418-01-2000 L2003 **ID** *012 †20
PAUL, Alfred Anthony, Jr. 465 EAST AVE 02860 #025-01-1988 L2000 **OPH** *020 †35
PAUL, Biswa Nath. 126 PROSPECT ST 02860 #495-02-1958 L1974 **IM CD** *071
PELLISH, Randall Scott. ■ 02860 #024-16-2001 L2001 **GE** *012 †20
PERRY, Fred T. 111 BREWSTER ST 02860 #050-02-1966 L1967 **AN GP** *020 †05
PHILLIPS, Arthur M, Jr. 89 POND ST, INTERNAL MEDICINE CENTER 02860 #035-01-1944 L1947 **OM IM** *071 †20
PHILLIPS, Martin Ralph. 333 SCHOOL ST, UNIVERSITY SURGICAL ASSOCI 02860 #050-02-1973 L1979 **VS GS** *020 †85
POMERANTZ, David Seth. 333 SCHOOL ST, STE 216 02860 #023-01-1991 L1991 **D** *020 †20,15
POWERS, Donya A. 174 ARMISTICE BLVD, STE A 02860 #043-01-1983 L1984 **FM** *020 †18
PRASAD, Shakuntala L. 111 BREWSTER ST 02860 #495-35-1975 L1984 **PM** *020 †60
PRESCOD, Glenn Stephen. 333 SCHOOL ST 02860 #043-01-1989 L1994 **OPH** *020
RAAD, Chafic. 111 BREWSTER ST 02860 #187-03-1958 L1972 **AN** *020
RABATIN, Joseph Stephen. 111 BREWSTER ST, MEMORIAL HOSPITAL 02860 #026-04-1989 L2006 **IM** *020 †20
RAMOS, Dante A. 126 PROSPECT ST 02860 #748-08-1965 L1973 **PD** *020 †55
RHEE, Karen Eunkyoung. 111 BREWSTER ST, MEMORIAL HOSPITAL 02860 #583-15-1993 L2005 **IM** *012
RHODES, Ramona Lagiers. 407 EAST AVE, STE 110 02860 #004-01-2000 L2003 **IMG** *020 †20
RICHARDSON, Dawn Margit. 111 BREWSTER ST, MEMORIAL HOSPITAL OF RHODE 02860 #043-01-1988 L1990 **EM** *020 †16
RIVINUS, Timothy Markoe. 160 BEECHWOOD AVE 02860 #041-13-1970 L1986 **P CHP** *030 †55,75
ROBITAILLE, Marcia Berry. 111 BREWSTER ST, MEMORIAL HOSPTITAL OF RI 02860 #048-04-1998 L2000 **EM** *020 †16
ROBSON, William Lane M. 111 BREWSTER ST, MEMORIAL HOSPITAL 02860 #060-02-1973 L2000 **PD PN** *020 †55
RODRIGUEZ, Edgardo. 111 BREWSTER ST 02860 #308-07-1981 L1985 **AN** *020
RODRIGUEZ, Pablo. 407 EAST AVE, STE 150 02860 #035-06-1981 L1986 **GYN** *020 †30
ROLAND, Fredy P. 333 SCHOOL ST, STE 215 02860 #165-03-1983 L1985 **IM** *020 †20
RUFFIN, Richard Taylor. 111 BREWSTER ST, WOOD 5 02860 #566-01-1999 L2003 **IM** *020
RUSSO, Patricia Maria. 111 BREWSTER ST, MEMORIAL HOSPITAL OF R.I. 02860 #024-07-1990 L1990 **PCC PUD** *020 †20
RUSSO, Pietro. 111 BREWSTER ST 02860 #561-08-1958 L1964 **PD** *071
RUSU, Veronica. 111 BREWSTER ST 02860 #781-01-1978 L2005 **FM** *020 †18
SABBAGH, Ibrahim. 111 BREWSTER ST 02860 #875-01-1972 L1979 **GS CRS** *020 †85
SADANIANTZ, Ara. 333 SCHOOL ST, STE 112 02860 #035-08-1981 L1986 **CD** *020 †20
SALMON, Adrian Alberto. 111 BREWSTER ST 02860 #319-04-2000 L2002 **CCM** *020 †20
SAMOS, Oscar Arana. 85 BEECHWOOD AVE 02860 #176-02-1961 L1967 **IM PUD** *071
SANI, Omeed. 111 BREWSTER ST 02860 #473-02-2003 L2005 **IM** *012
SANJEEVAIAH, Aravind Raj. 111 BREWSTER ST 02860 #496-39-2003 L2007 **IM** *012
SAYEED, Syeda Maria. 111 BREWSTER ST 02860 #704-02-2004 L2007 **IM** *012
SCHNEIDERMAN, Stuart. 102 SMITHFIELD AVE 02860 #024-07-1976 L1993 **AN PME** *020 †05
SCHWARTZ, Stanley. 111 BREWSTER ST 02860 #008-02-1974 L1979 **PTH HMP** *020 †50
SCOTT, H Denman. 111 BREWSTER ST 02860 #035-01-1966 L1968 **IM PHP** *020 †20,70
SETNA, Kurush Faridon. 111 BREWSTER ST, MEMORIAL HOSP OF RHODE ISL 02860 #704-02-1997 L2002 **IM** *100 †20
SHAH, Madhavi. 111 BREWSTER ST, MEMORIAL HOSPITAL OF RI 02860 #024-07-2004 L2004 **FM** *100 †18
SHALTAF, Mohammad M. ■ 02860 #575-01-1990 L1993 **FM** *020
SHAPIRO, Bradley A. 111 BREWSTER ST, MEMORIAL XRAY SERVICES 02860 #024-16-1980 L1984 **DR** *020 †80
SHEIKH, Ayesha Rizwan. 111 BREWSTER ST, MEMORIAL HOSP OF RHODE ISL 02860 #704-21-2003 L2006 **IM** *012
SHUMAN, Pamela. 160 BEECHWOOD AVE, COMMUNITY COUNSELING CENT 02860 #043-01-1991 L1991 **CHP** *020 †75
SIMMONS, Emma M. 111 BREWSTER ST, FAMILY CARE CENTER 02860 #043-01-1991 L1991 **FM** *020 †18
SMETKOV, Olga Marcus. 160 BEECHWOOD AVE 02860 #913-99-1983 L2002 **CHP** *020 †75
SMITH, Stephen Robt. 111 BREWSTER ST 02860 #024-05-1972 L1979 **FM PHP** *030 †18
SOARES, Barbara Lois. 407 EAST AVE, STE 250 02860 #024-05-1992 L2002 **OBG** *020 †30
SOMLO, Agnes Marta. 111 BREWSTER ST 02860 #065-06-1959 L1975 **IM PUD** *071
SOOCH, Divjot Kaur. 111 BREWSTER ST 02860 #495-03-1997 L2007 **FP** *012
SPERBER, Kenneth Farrell. 727 EAST AVE 02860 #041-07-1997 L2000 **FM** *020 †18
STARAKIEWICZ, Janusz E. 111 BREWSTER ST, MEM HOSP OF RI 02860 #759-01-1988 L1998 **PTH** *020 †50
STEFANEC, Tihomir. 188 OAK HILL AVE, MEMORIAL HOSPITAL OF R.I. 02860 #957-01-1992 L2001 **PUD** *020 †20
STUART, Charles Macaulay. ■ 02861 #035-03-2002 L2007 **NEP** *012 †55
SULLIVAN, Rachel Aileen. ■ 02861 #028-02-2003 L2003 **PS** *012
SUMMERHILL, Eleanor Marie. 111 BREWSTER ST, MEMORIAL HOSP 02860 #024-07-1989 L1998 **PCC** *020 †20
TARRO, John Matthew. 333 SCHOOL ST STE 302 02860 #021-01-1992 L1997 **OTO** *020 †45
TARRO, Robert Dennis. 333 SCHOOL ST STE 302 02860 #010-02-1961 L1962 **OTO** *020 †45

■ = Address Information Privacy Protected

TAYLOR, Julie Scott. 111 BREWSTER ST, MEMORIAL HOSPITAL OF R.I. 02860 #024-16-1995 L1995 **FM** *020 †18

TETREAULT-PERRY, J. 407 EAST AVE STE 150, DBA: WOMEN'S CARE, INC 02860 #050-02-1985 L1990 **OBG** *020 †30

THAYER, John B. 111 BREWSTER ST 02860 #024-07-1953 L1959 **ORS** *071 †40

THEALL, Kathy P. 111 BREWSTER ST 02860 #264-18-1989 L1999 **HO** *020 †20

TODOROV, Ludmil. 200 MAIN ST STE 350, ANESTHESIA CARE INC 02860 #409-33-1999 L2005 **APM** *020 †05 ‡

TRONCALES, Frederick Raym. 111 BREWSTER ST, MEMORIAL HOSP OF RHODE ISL 02860 #748-01-2002 L2005 **IM** *012

TRYFOROS, Margaret Ann. 111 BREWSTER ST, MEMORIAL HOSPITAL OF RI 02860 #035-08-1983 L1989 **FM** *040 †18

TYAGI, Shachi. 111 BREWSTER ST 02860 #496-65-2002 L2007 **IM** *012

VIEHMANN, Laura Ruth. 126 PROSPECT ST, MILL RIVER PEDIATRICS 02860 #038-41-1987 L1990 **PD OS** *020 †55

VREES, Matthew Daniel. 334 EAST AVE, RI COLORECTAL CLINIC 02860 #043-01-1997 L1997 **GS** *100 †85,10

WALLACE, Eric Devin. 111 BREWSTER ST, MEMORIAL HOSPITAL OF RHODE 02860 #024-16-2004 L2004 **FM** *020

WEN, Jiaying. 126 PROSPECT ST 02860 #243-47-1988 L1996 **IM** *020 †20

WEYER, Patrick. 111 BREWSTER ST 02860 #869-04-1983 L2005 **PCC** *100

WHITE, Jordan Catherine. 111 BREWSTER ST, DEPT OF FAMILY MEDICINE 02860 #023-01-2006 L2006 **FP** *012

WILLIAMS, Robert Raymond. 407 EAST AVE STE 150, DBA: WOMEN'S CARE, INC 02860 #067-01-1968 L1970 **OBG** *020 †30

WILSON, Mary K. 169 GEORGE ST, HOSPICE CARE OF RHODE ISLA 02860 #019-02-1975 L1985 **HEM PD** *050 †55

WINTERS, Nicole Renee. 111 BREWSTER ST, MEMORIAL HOSPITAL 02860 #024-16-2007 L2007 **FP** *012

WITHERBY, Sabrina Maria. 111 BREWSTER ST, MEMORIAL HOSPITAL OF RHODE 02860 #024-16-2001 L2001 **HO** *100

WONG, Richard. 333 SCHOOL ST 02860 #041-09-1967 L1974 **GS** *071 †85

WUTHRICH, Susan M. 200 MAIN ST STE 350, ANESTHESIA CARE INC 02860 #048-02-1990 L1994 **AN** *070 †05

YAMMINE, Joe Fouad. 111 BREWSTER ST, MEMORIAL HOSPITAL OF RHODE 02860 #605-03-1999 L2006 **ICE** *100 †20

YERNENI, Madhavi N. 407 EAST AVE, STE 120 02860 #495-21-1991 L1996 **IM** *020 †20

ZAYDON, Paul Thos. 115 NEWPORT AVE 02861 #041-07-1980 L1981 **D** *020 †15

ZIELINSKI, Robert James. 103 BACON ST, GATEWAY HEALTHCARE 02860 #035-48-1987 L1991 **P** *020 †75

ZMEILI, Omar Suheil. 111 BREWSTER ST 02860 #575-01-2004 L2007 **IM** *012

ZULQUERNAIN, Syed Akbar. 111 BREWSTER ST 02860 #704-24-2000 **IM** *012

PEACE DALE – WASHINGTON

ABRAHAM, Jacob. 1058 KINGSTOWN RD, S CNTY CHLD&FAM CONSULTNTS 02879 #047-07-1990 L1994 **CHP P** *020

DODDS, Angus Jefferson. ■ 02879 #023-01-1980 L1984 **FM** *075

PORTSMOUTH – NEWPORT

AMBRAD, Jamiel Joseph. 2444 E MAIN RD, LINDENTREE FAMILY HEALTH C 02871 #041-15-1999 L2002 **FM** *020 †18

ASIEDU, Daniel Kwaku. 77 TURNPIKE AVE 02871 #693-02-1990 L1995 **IM** *020 †20

AUDINO, Lawrence Frank. ■ 02871 #064-01-1968 U *071 †95

BOND, Andrea Joanne. 2444 E MAIN RD 02871 #043-01-1993 L1993 **FM** *020 †18

CIBEU, Lew Edgar. ■ 02871 #035-09-1958 L1959 **PD** *020 †55

COULOMBE, Triste M. 77 TURNPIKE AVE 02871 #043-01-1995 L2002 **OBG** *020 †30

DABULIS, Stephanie Ann. ■ 02871 #041-14-1998 L1999 **EM** *020 †16

DIEROLF, Christina C. 77 TURNPIKE AVE 02871 #043-01-1992 L1992 **PD** *020 †55

DRESSLER, Donald P. ■ 02871 #024-07-1953 L1995 **GS** *020 †85

EARDLEY, Daniel P. 2444 E MAIN RD 02871 #025-76-1982, ▲ L1987 **GS** *020

ETTER, Gregg Michael. 109 KING CHARLES DR 02871 #035-15-1990 L1991 **P** *020 †75

FANTES, Thomas Peter. 77 TURNPIKE AVE 02871 #033-05-1988 L2003 **FM** *020 †18

FITZSIMONS, Julie A. 2444 E MAIN RD 02871 #043-01-1992 L1992 **IM** *020 †20

FRASER, Richard Cameron. ■ 02871 #064-01-1948 L1955 **AN PUD** *020

FRAZZANO, Arthur Andrew. 18 HARRIS AVE, ARTHUR A FRAZZANO, M.D. 02871 #033-06-1975 L1977 **FM** *020 †18

HAND, John Joseph. ■ 02871 #010-02-1962 L1971 **IM CD** *020 †20

HOPPER, Charles Lyon. ■ 02871 #008-01-1956 L1964 **GS TS** *071 †85

KOHANNA, Fred Herman. 1847 W MAIN RD, MEDCOR, INC. 02871 #010-01-1978 L1999 **EM** *020 †70,16

KOZEL, Randy Bruce. 112 CLOCK TOWER SQ, DBA AQUIDNECK NEUROLOGY 02871 #010-02-1980 L1999 **N** *020 †75

KRENSAVAGE, Thaddeus J. 2444 E MAIN RD STE 3R, KRENSAVAGE CORPORATION 02871 #028-78-1984, ▲ L1989 **AN** *020

LAMBERT, Barbara A Salago. ■ 02871 #041-07-1972 L1974 **RO R** *071 †80

MC MAHON, Thomas Patrick. 109 CLOCK TOWER SQ, MEDICAL DIRECTOR 02871 #010-02-1980 L1986 **GE** *020 †20

MERRICK, Robert Michael. ■ 02871 #035-09-1969 L1977 **GS OTO** *075

NALLY, John Brendan A. ■ 02871 #539-06-1948 L1958 **GP OM** *071

SANDFORT, Michael Robert. 2444 E MAIN RD 02871 #033-05-1981 L1995 **CRS GS** *020 †10,85

TOMMEY, Frederic. 47 ISLAND AVE 02871 #917-06-1962 L1978 **GP AM** *071

PROVIDENCE – PROVIDENCE

AARON, Daniel Louis. ■ 02906 #035-08-2005 L2005 **ORS** *012

AARON, Roy Kenneth. 2 DUDLEY ST 02905 #035-08-1969 L1981 **ORS** *020 †40

ABBOTT, Gerald Francis. 1 RANDALL SQ 02904 #035-20-1971 L1989 **R** *020 †80

ABBOTT, Jinnette Dawn. 593 EDDY ST 814, RHODE ISLAND HOSPITAL 02903 #016-02-1995 L2004 **IM** *020 †20

ABDEL-KADER, Khaled. ■ 02903 #033-06-2002 L2002 **NEP** *012 †20

ABEDI, Mehrdad. 825 CHALKSTONE AVE, ROGER WILLIAMS MEDICAL CEN 02908 #517-01-1992 L2001 **HO** *020 †20

ABELLAR, Rosanna Garcia. 101 DUDLEY ST 02905 #748-29-1991 L2006 **PP** *012

ABODEELY, Adam Joseph. 593 EDDY ST, RHODE ISLAND HOSP 02903 #016-43-2004 L2004 **GS** *012

ABRAHAM, Amadeo Lucas. 593 EDDY ST, RHODE ISLAND HOSP 02903 #132-09-2001 L2003 **PCC** *012

ABUELO, Dianne N. 593 EDDY ST, DEPT OF PEDIATRIC ENDOCRIN 02903 #035-19-1965 L1976 **CG PD** *020 †55,19

ABUELO, Julian Gary. 593 EDDY ST 02902 #035-19-1965 L1975 **NEP** *040 †20

ABU-HIJLEH, Muhanned Amin. 593 EDDY ST 02902 #575-01-1995 L1996 **PCC** *020 †20

ACKERS, Marta Louise. ■ 02906 #038-06-1992 L1992 **GPM** *020 †70,20

ACUN, Ceyda. 593 EDDY ST, RHODE ISLAND HOSPITAL 02903 #902-03-1996 L2006 **PD** *020 †20

ACUN, Zeki. ■ 02903 #902-03-1993 L2007 **GS** *012

ADAMS, Charles Andrew, Jr. 593 EDDY ST, 4TH FL STE 453 02903 #033-05-1996 L2004 **GS CCS** *020 †85

ADAMS, John Robert. ■ 02903 #036-01-2005 L2005 **IM** *012

ADAMS, Robert John T. ■ 02903 #143-01-1986 **IM** *100

ADDO, Kamel Norteye. 164 SUMMIT AVE, THE MIRIAM HOSPITAL 02906 #043-01-2001 L2002 **CD** *012

ADELSON-MITTY, Jennifer. 164 SUMMIT AVE, FL 2 02906 #035-19-1991 L1997 **ID** *020 †20

ADRAIN, Alyn L. 164 SUMMIT AVE 02906 #043-01-1988 L1990 **GE** *020 †20

AGGARWAL, Suchit. 164 SUMMIT AVE, MIRIAM HOSPITAL ANESTHESIA 02906 #308-13-1999 L2004 **AN** *020 †05

AGRAWAL, Deepak. ■ 02906 #496-38-1997 L2005 **GE** *012 †20

AHMED, Shair Uddin. 593 EDDY ST, RHODE ISLAND HOSP 02903 #003-01-2007 L2007 **GS** *012

AHN, Kwang Won. 825 CHALKSTONE AVE 02908 #583-02-1959 L1972 **IM** *020

AHN, Sunho. 1 RANDALL SQ 02904 #043-01-1997 L1997 **DR** *020 †80

AJUDUA, Stephanie Nkechi. 593 EDDY ST, DEPT MED 02903 #043-01-2007 L2007 **IM** *012

AKBARI, Homayoon Mohammed. 2 DUDLEY ST, STE 470 02905 #033-05-1997 L2004 **CRS GS** *020 †85,10

AKELMAN, Edward. 2 DUDLEY ST 02905 #032-01-1978 L1984 **ORS HS** *020 †40

AKERMAN, Paul Alfred. 33 SANFORD ST 02909 #010-01-1985 L1994 **GE NTR** *020 †20

ALARIO, Anthony J, Jr. 593 EDDY ST, POTTER STE 200 02903 #024-16-1979 L1982 **PD PPR** *020 †55

ALBINA, Jorge Eusebio. 593 EDDY ST, DEPARTMENT OF SURGERY 02903 #132-03-1972 L1983 **NTR** *050

ALEXANDER, Chandran Paul. 593 EDDY ST, RI HOSP 02903 #495-27-1988 L2007 **PG** *012 †55

ALEXANDER, Nicole E. ■ 02903 #035-15-2001 L2005 **ID** *012 †20,55

ALEXANDER, Paul Evan. 345 BLACKSTONE BLVD, CONSULTANTS OF RHODE 02906 #035-47-1971 L1978 **P** *020 †75

AL-GEBORY, Faris Abdul-K. 3 CAPITOL HL, RHODE ISLAND BOARD LICENSE 02908 #528-01-1986 L2003 **GS** *020 †85

AL-HOMSI, Ahmad S. 825 CHALKSTONE AVE 02908 #875-01-1984 L2008 **HO** *020 †20

ALI, Basmaa. 825 CHALKSTONE AVE, ROGER WILLIAMS HOSP 02908 #704-01-1995 L2000 **IM** *020 †20

ALI, Sadaf. ■ 02906 #704-06-1997 L2005 **PYG** *100

ALI, Tanya. 825 CHALKSTONE AVE, ROGER WILLIAMS HOSPITAL 02908 #160-02-1993 L1998 **ID** *020 †20

ALI, Yousaf. 49 SEEKONK ST, RHEUMATOLOGY ASSOCIATES 02906 #917-28-1992 L1999 **RHU** *020 †20

ALIOTTA, Jason Matthew. 593 EDDY ST, 7TH FLOOR APC, RHODE ISLAN 02903 #024-07-1999 L2002 **PCC** *020 †20

ALLEGRA, Marisa Calzolari. 1 RANDALL SQ STE 407 02904 #561-01-1949 L1976 **P** *020 †75

ALLEN, Deborah M.. 593 EDDY ST, RHODE ISLAND HOSP 02903 #143-03-2003 L2003 **ORS** *012

ALLEN, Rebecca Hathaway. 101 DUDLEY ST, DIV OF AMBULATORY CARE 02905 #035-01-2001 L2001 **OBG** *040 †20

ALTENHEIN, Elizabeth L. 100 HIGHLAND AVE STE 308 02906 #024-07-1979 L1985 **GS** *020 †85

ALTER, Mark David. 593 EDDY ST 02903 #041-12-1999 L1999 **OS** *020 †55,75

ALVAREZ, Alice Edith. 593 EDDY ST 02902 #032-01-1985 L1985 **PUD IM** *020 †20

ALVAREZ, Antonio Granados. ■ 02906 #005-11-2006 L2007 **DR** *012

ALVAREZ, Gustavo A. ST JOSEPHS HOSP FATIMA UT 02904 #649-14-1968 L1979 **END IM** *050

ALVAREZ, Victor Enrique. 593 EDDY ST, RHODE ISLAND HOSP 02903 #422-01-1993 L2007 **NP** *012

ALVERSON, Brian Kenneth. 593 EDDY ST, POTTER 115 02903 #041-01-1999 L2005 **PD** *020 †55

AMANULLAH, Siraj. 593 EDDY ST, POTTER 159 02903 #704-25-1996 L2001 **PD** *020 †55

AMARAL, Joseph F. 2 DUDLEY ST STE 470 02905 #043-01-1981 L1983 **GS** *030 †85

AMATO, Charles Paul. ■ 02906 #561-03-1936 L1942 **GP** *071

AMBROISE, Carl H. ■ 02906 #043-01-1994 L1994 **GS** *075

AMODIA, Alesia. 173 WATERMAN ST 02906 #275-01-1948 L1957 **AN** *071 †05

ANCOWITZ, Bret Adam. 148 W RIVER ST, STE 3 02904 #035-47-2000 L2004 **GE** *020 †20

ANDERSON, Angela Clyneta. 593 EDDY ST, DEPT OF EMERGENCY MEDICINE 02903 #038-06-1985 L1990 **EM PD** *020 †55

ANDERSON, Brenna. 101 DUDLEY ST, WOMEN & INFANTS HOSP 3 FL 02905 #043-01-1999 L2006 **MFM OBG** *050 †30

ANDERSON, Kent Lowell. 1 HOPPIN ST STE 202, CORO CENTER 02903 #048-04-1998 L2003 **OPH OS** *020 †35 ‡

ANDERSON, Kristin Lehr. 2 DUDLEY ST, STE G95 02905 #035-03-2002 L2002 **MPD** *020 †20,55

ANDERSON, Maria T. ■ 02906 #024-07-1994 L2001 **ICE** *100 †20

ANDLER, Robert Harold. 593 EDDY ST, RHODE ISLAND HOSPITAL 02903 #051-01-2002 L2002 **PD** *020

ANGERMEIER, Marla C. 148 W RIVER ST, STE 1 02904 #010-02-1979 L1983 **D** *020 †15

ANSA, Francis Beckett. 164 SUMMIT AVE, THE MIRIAM HOSPITAL 02906 #412-02-1990 L2005 **CCM** *100 †20

ANTONIUK, Pamela Marie. 120 DUDLEY ST, STE 201 02905 #033-05-1988 L1993 **PS** *020 †85,65

AOKI, Etsuko. 593 EDDY ST, RHODE ISLAND HOSPITAL 02903 #572-41-1992 L2003 *100

ARONSON, Stanley Maynard. BROWN UNIV MED SCHOOL 02912 #035-19-1947 L1970 **NP EP** *040 †50

ARRIGHI, James A. 593 EDDY ST, RI HOSP MAIN RM 209 02903 #043-01-1987 L2004 **CD NM** *020 †20,28

ARVIZU OLVERA, Jose Manue. 345 BLACKSTONE BLVD 02906 #649-01-2003 L2004 **P** *012

ASKLAND, Kathleen Dawn. 345 BLACKSTONE BLVD, STE 1 02906 #041-07-1996 L2007 **P** *020 †75

ASSOUMOU, Sabrina Annick. ■ 02903 #035-45-2004 L2004 **MPD** *012

ATKINSON, James Mc Donald. 164 SUMMIT AVE, MIRIAM HOSPITAL 02906 #041-09-1997 L1997 IM *020 †20

ATTIULAH, Naureen. 235 PLAIN ST 02905 #704-25-1994 L1996 P *020 †75

AU, Derrick K. PO BOX 8145 02912 #043-01-1981 *020

AZMA, Azin. ■ 02903 #019-02-2008 *012

AZNIF, Calikyan. 825 CHALKSTONE AVE, ROGER WILLIAMS MEDICAL CEN 02908 #902-07-1988 L2002 AN *020 †05 ‡

AZZOUZ, Mohamed. ■ 02908 #125-01-1995 L1996 IM *020 †20

BADOE, Papa Kaku Ebule. 164 SUMMIT AVE, THE MIRIAM HOSPITAL 02906 #041-01-1994 L1994 IM *020 †20

BAFFY, Gyorgy. 55 CLAVERICK ST, RM 413 02903 #473-04-1980 L2001 GE *020 †20

BAHR, Robert Lawrence. 150 E MANNING ST, THE RHODE ISLAND EYE INST 02906 #024-01-1971 L1976 OPH *020 †35

BAIK, Christina Seung. ■ 02903 #035-45-2002 L2002 HO *012 †20

BAILL, Kevin Elliot. 530 N MAIN ST, THE PROVIDENCE CENTER 02904 #041-02-1997 L2006 P *020 †75

BAKER, Jessica Henri. ■ 02906 #040-02-2007 L2007 PD *012

BAKER, Julie Anne. ■ 02909 #035-06-2007 L2007 OBG *012

BALAKRISHNAN, Maya. ■ 02906 #496-23-2004 L2007 NPM *012

BALIOG, Crisostomo Rodrig, Jr. 825 CHALKSTONE AVE 02908 #748-02-2004 L2006 IM *012

BANSAL, Rajnish. 10 DAVOL SQ STE 400, COASTAL MEDICAL 02903 #495-20-1982 L1997 IM *020 †20

BARAM, Michael. 593 EDDY ST 02903 #041-02-1997 L2002 PCC *020 †20,16

BARCOHANA, Yusef. 101 DUDLEY ST 02905 #517-01-1952 L1965 AN *071 †05

BARENDSWAARD, Elsje C. 828 CHALKSTONE AVE, ROGER WILLIAMS MED CTR 02908 #660-03-1985 L2006 SP *020 †50

BARILE, Maria Florence. 593 EDDY ST, RI HOSP 02903 #008-02-2006 L2007 DR *012

BARRALL, David Timothy. 151 WATERMAN ST 02906 #043-01-1981 L1982 PS HS *020 †65

BARRETT, John T. ■ 02906 #024-05-1943 L1944 P *071 †55

BARRON, Christine E. 1 HOPPIN ST STE 2300 02903 #035-08-1995 L1995 PD *020 †55

BARUCH, Joseph. ■ 02906 #154-02-1951 L1957 P *020

BARZILAI, David. ■ 02903 #038-06-2005 L2006 D *012

BAS, John Philip. 1056 HOPE ST 02906 #166-02-2001 L2003 FM *100

BASHKIROV, Maxim Valery. 164 SUMMIT AVE, DEPT OF ANESTH-MIRIAM HOSP 02906 #913-06-1997 L2004 AN *020 †05

BASILE, Francis X, Jr. 285 GOVERNOR ST, THIRD FLOOR 02906 #035-20-1992 L1992 IM *020 †20

BASU, Kim Apala. 593 EDDY ST, PENTHOUSE, MAIN BUILDING 02903 #024-16-1997 L2000 IM *020 †20

BATRA, Kerri Lynn. 2 DUDLEY ST, STE 370 02905 #024-16-2001 L2007 RHU *100

BAUER, Mark Stephen. 830 CHALKSTONE AVE, VAMC-116R 02908 #041-01-1982 L1991 P PA *050 †75

BAUMGART, Megan Ann. 593 EDDY ST, DEPT MED 02903 #035-03-2007 L2007 IM *012

BAYLISS, George P. 593 EDDY ST, APC 9, RHODE ISLAND HOSPIT 02903 #043-01-2003 L2003 NEP *012 †20

BEARER, Elaine Louise. ■ 02906 #005-02-1983 L1986 PTH OS *050 †50

BECKWITH, Curt Guthrie. 164 SUMMIT AVE, THE MIRIAM HOSPITAL 02906 #043-01-1999 L1999 IM *100 †20

BEGOSSI, Giovanni. 593 EDDY ST 02903 #561-09-1994 L2000 GS *012

BEHAR, Jose. 110 LOCKWOOD ST 02906 #737-01-1961 L1976 GE IM *020 †20

BEHESHTI SHIRAZI, Seyed A. 593 EDDY ST, RHODE ISLAND HOSP-LIFESPAN 02903 #517-08-1992 L2005 PTH *020

BEHRENS, Steve Brian. ■ 02906 #305-01-2006 L2007 ORS *012

BEITLE, M David. 695 EDDY ST, STE 11 02903 #041-02-1994 L1994 OBG *020 †30

BELAY, Nebyou. 593 EDDY ST 02903 #035-01-2001 L2001 OS *020

BELL, Ilse. BROWN U BOX G-8264 02912 #043-01-1996 *100

BELL, Mark Richard. 877 CHALKSTONE AVE 02908 #024-07-1993 L1993 IM *020 †20

BELLIN, Leonard B. ■ 02906 #024-07-1945 L1948 P *071 †55

BEN-DAVID, Deborah Helena. 266 WAYLAND AVE 02906 #550-02-1992 L2003 *100

BENDER, George Jesse, III. 101 DUDLEY ST, WOMEN & INFANTS HOSPITAL 02905 #028-34-1999 L1999 NPM *040 †55

BENEDETTO, Bernard John. 2 DUDLEY ST, STE 470 02905 #008-02-1997 L2005 CCS *100 †85

BENEDETTO, Jessica Outwat. 830 CHALKSTONE AVE, VA MEDICAL CENTER 02908 #024-07-2000 L2005 MPD *020

BENNETT, Irwin Kenneth. 35 S ANGELL ST 02906 #016-42-1975 L1989 P CHP *020 †75

BENNETT, Thomas A, III. 300 IVES ST 02906 #025-01-1969 L1974 IM *020 †20

BENUN, Jacques. 593 EDDY ST, AMBULATORY PEDIATRICS 02903 #935-01-1990 L1997 PD *020 †55

BENZULY, Scott Eric. 10 ORMS ST STE 110, PROVIDENCE ANESTHESIOLOGIS 02904 #048-14-1984 L2002 AN *020 †05

BERARD, Roger Gaston. 830 CHALKSTONE AVE 02908 #024-07-1956 L1958 ADM U *020

BERCOVITCH, Lionel Gordon. 593 EDDY ST, APC 10 02903 #062-01-1969 L1977 D OPH *020 †20,15

BERG, Geoffrey H. 160 WAYLAND AVE 02906 #043-01-1975 L1976 IM *020 †20

BERGER, Eric Eliot. 593 EDDY ST, RHODE ISLAND HOSPITAL 02903 #035-06-1980 L1986 CD ICE *020 †20

BERGER, Jacob Russell. ■ 02906 #012-01-2000 L2000 CN *020 †75

BERNARDO, John R, Jr. 110 LOCKWOOD ST 02903 #024-07-1953 L1954 GS EM *020 †85

BERNHARD, Peter Howard. 1165 N MAIN ST 2ND FL, PROVIDENCE UROLOGY, LLC 02904 #025-12-1986 L2007 U GS *020 †95

BERT, Arthur Anthony. 593 EDDY ST, DEPT OF ANESTHESIA 02903 #035-47-1981 L1986 AN PDC *020 †05

BERZ, David. 164 SUMMIT AVE, THE MIRIAM HOSPITAL 02906 #408-30-1999 L2005 HO *012 †20

BESDINE, Richard W. 2 STIMSON ST, BROWN UNIV 02912 #041-01-1965 L2000 IMG IM *030 †20

BESERRA, Frederico Calvet. 825 CHALKSTONE AVE, DEPT OF INTERNAL MED 02908 #187-10-2000 L2006 IM *012

BEVIVINO, Jack R. 120 DUDLEY ST 02905 #010-02-1976 L1977 PS *074 †65

BHALAKIA, Avni Mahendra. ■ 02909 #010-01-2005 L2005 PD *012

BHAT, Dinesh Vithal. 118 DUDLEY ST, UNIVERSITY OTOLARYNGOLOGY 02905 #495-17-1969 L1978 OTO GS *020 †65

BHATT, Reena Anjalie. 2 DUDLEY ST STE 450, RHODE ISLAND HOSP 02905 #041-15-2005 L2005 PS *012

BHATT, Riha Girish. ■ 02906 #051-04-2006 L2006 PD *012

BHATTACHARYA, Baishali. 593 EDDY ST, DEPT RAD APC-12 02903 #672-01-1997 L2004 PTH *020 †50

BIANCHI, Diana Willa. 101 DUDLEY ST 02905 #005-11-1980 L2000 MG NPM *050 †55,19

BIRD, Elizabeth Madeline. 81 IRVING AVE 02906 #008-01-2002 L2006 PD *100 †55

BIRNBAUM, Ariel Edward. 593 EDDY ST, HEMATOLOGY/ONCOLOGY 02903 #038-43-1994 L2003 HO *100

BITAR, Imad. 825 CHALKSTONE AVE, ROGER WILLIAMS HOSP 02908 #875-01-1997 L2002 RHU *012 †20

BLAINE, Theodore Alton. 2 DUDLEY ST, STE 200 02905 #008-02-1993 L2007 OAR *020 †40

BLAKE, Douglas Robt. 593 EDDY ST, DEPT OF ANESTHESIA 02903 #041-01-1973 L1995 AN *020 †05

BLANKENHORN, Brad Douglas. 593 EDDY ST, RHODE ISLAND HOSP 02903 #041-12-2005 L2005 ORS *012

BLAZAR, Andrew Stephen. 101 DUDLEY ST 02905 #024-07-1959 L1962 REN GYN *072 †30

BLECKER, Douglas Leo. 285 GOVERNOR ST, STE 200 02906 #024-07-1999 L2003 IM *020 †20

BLEDSOE, Thomas Arthur. 285 GOVERNOR ST, GOVERNOR ST. PRIMARY CARE 02906 #043-01-1988 L1988 IM *020 †20

BLISS, Cynthia Dawn. 593 EDDY ST, PEDIATRIC EMERGENCY 02903 #035-45-1998 L2003 PD *020 †55

BLISS, James Mott. 593 EDDY ST, RHODE ISLAND HOSP 02903 #021-01-2002 L2002 ORS *100

BLISS, Joseph Mark. 101 DUDLEY ST, DEPT OF PEDIATRICS 02905 #035-45-1998 L2003 NPM *050 †55

BLISS, Thomas Francis. 124 WATERMAN ST 02906 #010-02-1969 L1970 ORS *020 †40

BLOCH, Amy Lynn. 21 PEACE ST 02907 #008-01-1988 L1990 CHP *020 †75

BLOCK, David Robert. 593 EDDY ST, RHODE ISLAND HOSP APC 608 02903 #035-06-2004 L2004 P *012

BLOCK, Stanley Hoyt. 40 CANDACE ST 02908 #008-01-1966 L1977 A PD *030 †03,55

BLOOM, Bradley Jonathan. 593 EDDY ST, RHODE ISLAND HOSPITAL 02903 #016-06-1989 L1995 PD *020 †55

BLUM, Andrew Steven. 2 DUDLEY ST, STE 200 02905 #035-20-1989 L2000 N CN *020 †75

BOARDMAN, Lori Ann. 101 DUDLEY ST, WOMEN AND INFANTS HOSPITA 02905 #035-01-1992 L1992 OBG *020 †30

BODKIN, Sheenagh Mary. 100 DUDLEY ST FL 2, DEPARTMENT OF MEDICINE 02905 #539-06-1991 L1998 IM *020 †20

BOERESCU, Daniela Anca. 593 EDDY ST, RHODE ISLAND HOSPITAL 02903 #781-01-1995 L2003 P *020

BOFETIADO, Cindyjoy M. 593 EDDY ST, RHODE ISLAND HOSP 02903 #010-01-2003 L2003 EM *012

BOGAARS, Hendrik Anthony. 825 CHALKSTONE AVE, DEPT LAB 02908 #660-03-1955 L1965 DMP PTH *071 †50

BOLAND, Robert Jos. 345 BLACKSTONE BLVD 02906 #010-02-1987 L1992 P PYG *040 †75

BOLTON, Jonathan Wilson. 345 BLACKSTONE BLVD 02906 #025-12-1994 L1999 P *020 †75

BONAUTO, Steven Jeffrey. 2 REGENCY PLZ STE 4 02903 #035-15-1986 L1992 CHP *020 †75

BONDALAPATI, Praveen Kuma. 593 EDDY ST, RHODE ISLAND HOSPITAL 02903 #495-62-2001 L2007 IM *020 †20

BONEY, Charlotte Marie. 593 EDDY ST # MPS2, RHODE ISLAND HOSP 02903 #047-06-1988 L1994 PDE *020 †55

BONILLA, Lorena Del Pilar. ■ 02906 #007-02-2007 L2007 IM *012

BORA, Nirali Sudhir. ■ 02906 #025-01-2006 L2006 FP *012

BORLASE, Bradley C. 830 CHALKSTONE AVE, VAMC PROVIDENCE RI 02908 #048-14-1983 L1988 IM GS *020

BORN, Christopher Thos. 2 DUDLEY ST STE 200 02905 #010-02-1979 L2005 ORS *040 †40 ‡

BORNSCHEIN-CHURCH, S. 202 PRAIRIE AVE 02905 #011-02-1991 L1996 IM *020 †20

BORNSTEIN, Michelle Susan. 593 EDDY ST, RHODE ISLAND HOSPITAL 02903 #024-16-2004 L2004 PD *020 †55

BOSTAJI, Muhammad Bassam. ■ 02904 #875-02-1995 L2006 CCM *012 †20

BOSTOM, Leslie Robinson. 593 EDDY ST 02903 #035-08-1990 L1990 D DMP *020 †15

BOSTON, Andrew Gould. 593 EDDY ST 02902 #035-08-1990 L1990 IM CD *050 †20

BOURJEILY, Ghada Ramez. 790 N MAIN ST 02904 #605-03-1992 L2000 PCC *020 †20

BOUSLOUGH, David Bruce. 55 CLAVERICK ST FL 2, U.E.M.F. 02903 #422-01-2001 L2004 EM *100 †16

BOWEN, John Robert. 593 EDDY ST 02903 #067-01-1945 L1953 GS *071 †85

BOWEN, Lawrence Philip. 235 PLAIN ST, STE 304 02905 #024-07-1971 L1978 PS *020 †65

BOWKLEY, Charles William. 593 EDDY ST, DEPT. DIAGNOSTIC IMAGING 02903 #033-06-2003 L2004 DR *012

BOWMAN, Maureen Lynne. 593 EDDY ST 02903 #048-14-2007 L2007 PD *012

BOYAN, Scott M. 97 WATERMAN ST, BOX G 02912 #043-01-1998 *100

BOYD, George Kline. 95 PITMAN ST 02906 #024-05-1955 L1962 PDA *074 †55,03

BOYLE, Jennifer Mary. 202 PRAIRIE AVE 02905 #016-01-1998 L2005 OBG *020 †30

BOYLE, Lisa Diane. 297 PROMENADE ST, CENTER FOR OBSTETRICS & GY 02908 #043-01-1995 L1995 OBG *020 †30

BOYLE, Sarah M. 120 WAYLAND AVE 02906 #043-01-1996 L1996 P *020

BRADEN, William, III. 345 BLACKSTONE BLVD, CONSULTANTS OF RHODE 02906 #024-01-1969 L1974 P *020 †75

BRADSHAW, Katherine Mary. 345 BLACKSTONE BLVD 02906 #041-15-2001 L2001 CHP *100

BRAGDON, Gwynne Allison. 2 DUDLEY ST, STE 200 02905 #041-15-2002 HSO *012

BRAGG, Mason Alexander. ■ 02906 #035-01-2006 L2006 EM *012

BRAMAN, Sidney Stuart. 593 EDDY ST, APC 432 02903 #041-13-1967 L1973 PUD IM *030 †20

BRANCATO, Scott Clayton. ■ 02903 #010-02-2005 L2005 IM *012

BRANTLEY, Eric James. ■ 02903 #047-05-2006 L2006 EM *012

BRAR, Navneet Neetu. ■ 02907 #820-02-2005 L2007 IM *012

BRARD, Laurent. 101 DUDLEY ST, WOMEN'S & INFANTS HOSPITAL 02905 #041-12-1998 L1998 OBG *020

BRAUN, Mark E. 50 MAUDE ST 02908 #041-09-1979 L1980 IM IMG *020 †20

BRAVE, Laura Ann. 345 BLACKSTONE BLVD, BUTLER HOSP 02906 #041-13-2005 L2005 P *012

BREADY, Barrett W. ■ 02906 #043-01-2003 *100

BREEN, Catherine Malooly. 50 MAUDE ST 02908 #036-07-1999 L2002 PTH *020

BREIDING, Paul. 909 N MAIN ST, STE 300 02904 #043-01-1996 L1996 IM *020 †20

BREM, Andrew Saml. 593 EDDY ST, RHODE ISLAND HOSP 02903 #024-07-1974 L1979 PN *040 †55

BRENNAN, Christopher Mich. 825 CHALKSTONE AVE, DEPT IM 02908 #305-01-2007 L2007 IM *012

BRESLIN, Thomas Grimmett. 110 LOCKWOOD ST 02903 #023-01-1961 L1962 U *020 †95

BRIN, Steven Chas. 400 RESERVOIR AVE, STE 1D 02907 #041-07-1980 L1982 IM *020 †20

BRINKMANN, Dirk A. 593 EDDY ST 02903 #836-02-1991 L1995 PTH *100

BRODY, Jeffrey M. 1 RANDALL SQ 02904 #010-02-1982 L1992 DR *020

BROMBERG, Todd Aaron. ■ 02903 #041-13-2005 L2006 N *012

BROTMAN, Roger L. 825 N MAIN ST 02904 #041-09-1973 L1978 RO *071 †80

BROWN, Amy E. 101 DUDLEY ST 02905 #024-07-1999 L2002 **OBG GO** *020 †30

BROWN, Edward Michael. 480 HOPE ST 02906 #016-43-1969 L1974 **P** *020 †75

BROWN, George Francis. ■ 02903 #024-05-2002 L2002 **EM** *020

BROWN, Katherine Mattox. ■ 02903 #012-05-2003 L2004 **D** *100 †15

BROWN, Larry Kenneth. 1 HOPPIN ST, CORO WEST STE 204 02903 #035-01-1976 L1986 **CHP P** *020 †75

BROWN, Linda Lee. 593 EDDY ST, CLAVERICK 2 02903 #041-14-1997 L1997 **PEM** *020 †55

BROWN, Lucy J. 144 WATERMAN ST, STE 1 02906 #043-01-1992 L1992 **P** *020 †55

BROWN, Paul Jeffrey. 825 CHALKSTONE AVE 02908 #008-02-1983 L2005 **P CHP** *020 †75

BROWN, Rebecca Mary. 700 SMITH ST 02908 #041-01-1999 L2005 **IM IMG** *020 †20

BROWNBACK, Kyle Robert. ■ 02904 #019-02-2006 L2006 **IM** *012

BROWNING, Richard Amblard. 593 EDDY ST, RHODE ISLAND HOSPITAL 02903 #043-01-1978 L1981 **AN PD** *020 †55,05

BRUCE, Benjamin Guerard. 593 EDDY ST, RI HOSP 02903 #005-11-2006 L2006 **ORS** *012

BRUNO, John F. 593 EDDY ST 02903 #561-11-1980 **DR** *020 †80

BRUNO, Louis C. 741 SMITH ST 02908 #035-08-1946 L1949 **GYN** *071 †30

BRUNO, Nicholas Paul. 741 SMITH ST 02908 #028-34-1980 L1981 **D DMP** *020 †15

BRYAN, Richard Girard. 150 E MANNING ST 02906 #048-04-1995 L2005 **OPH** *020 †35

BUBLY, Gary. 164 SUMMIT AVE, DEPT MED 02906 #024-16-1987 L1990 **IM** *020 †20,16

BUCHALTER, Matthew Louis. 164 SUMMIT AVE 02903 #043-01-2003 L2003 **IM** *020 †20

BUCHANAN, April Odom. 593 EDDY ST, POTTER 108 02903 #045-01-1999 L2006 **PD** *020 †55

BUCKLEY, Lucy Parisi. 235 PLAIN ST 02905 #035-15-1965 L1983 **PDC** *020 †55

BUCZKO, George Bohdan. 593 EDDY ST, RHODE ISLAND HOSPITAL 02903 #065-01-1976 L1993 **IM AN** *020 †20,05

BURBANK-SCHMITT, Helen E. ■ 02906 #043-01-2007 L2007 **FP** *012

BURGESS, Frederick W. 593 EDDY ST 02902 #043-01-1986 L1993 **AN PMM** *05

BURKE, Matthew Thomas. ■ 02906 #035-03-2006 L2006 **FP** *012

BURKE, Shayna Beth. 593 EDDY ST 02903 #010-01-2007 L2007 **PD** *012

BURNARD, Ralph John, II. 1 RANDALL SQ 02904 #026-04-1965 L1977 **TS VS** *020 †85,90

BURNS, Kristin Marie. ■ 02906 #024-16-2004 L2004 **PD** *012 †55

BURNSIDE, Nancy Jean. 830 CHALKSTONE AVE, PROVIDENCE VAMC 02908 #005-02-1993 L1996 **D** *020 †15

BUROCK, Jeffrey Michael. 164 SUMMIT AVE 2B, THE MIRIAM HOSP 02906 #030-06-1999 L1999 **PYG** *020 †20

BURSTEIN, Jay M. 21 PEACE ST, CORPORATE CARE 02907 #041-09-1986 L2002 **OM** *020 †70

BURTT, Douglas Michael. 164 SUMMIT AVE, THE MIRIAM HOSPITAL 02906 #035-19-1980 L1982 **CD IM** *020 †20

BUSSELEN, Steven Carroll. ■ 02906 #041-13-2005 L2005 **FP** *012

BUSTER, John Edmond. 101 DUDLEY ST, STE FL1 02905 #005-14-1966 L2007 **REN OBG** *020 †30

BUTERA, James Nicholas. 593 EDDY ST 02902 #024-16-1994 L1994 **HO IM** *020 †20

BUXTON, Alfred Eric. 593 EDDY ST 02902 #041-01-1973 L1999 **ICE CD** *020 †20

BUZZI, Kate Renee. 593 EDDY ST, RHODE ISLAND HOSPITAL 02903 #041-15-2006 L2006 **PD** *012

CAHILL, Deborah. 593 EDDY ST, RHODE ISLAND HOSPITAL 02903 #024-16-1985 L1991 **AN** *020 †20,05

CAHILL, Jonathan Francis. ■ 02903 #035-03-2006 L2006 **N** *012

CAIATI, Joseph Michael, Jr. 593 EDDY ST, PROVIDENCE ANESTHESIOLOGIS 02903 #035-01-1995 L2004 **GS** *020 †85,05

CAIATI, Rachel Lynn. ■ 02906 #035-01-2000 L2004 **DR** *100 †80

CALCATTI, Javid A. 21 PEACE ST 02907 #495-51-1993 L2000 **IM** *020 †80

CALDAMONE, Anthony Angelo. 2 DUDLEY ST STE 185 02905 #043-01-1975 L1986 **U PD** *020 †95

CALDARUSA, Marilena. ■ 02906 #032-01-2005 L2005 **IM** *012

CALFEE, Ryan Patrick. 2 DUDLEY ST, STE 200 02905 #028-02-2001 L2001 **HSO** *012

CALLAHAN, Megan Bradley. 593 EDDY ST, DEPT. OF MEDICINE 02903 #024-07-2002 L2003 **IM** *020 †20

CALVERT, Sandra Adamson. 101 DUDLEY ST 02905 #917-25-1976 **NPM** *020

CALVO, Marco Antonio. 41 ROSLYN AVE 02908 #264-02-1965 L1973 **FM IM** *075 †18

CAMENISCH, David Rine. 593 EDDY ST, RHODE ISLAND HOSPITAL 02903 #021-01-2001 L2001 **OS** *100

CAMPBELL, Katherine Thirz. ■ 02906 #024-16-2008 **PD** *012

CAPONE, Antonio. ■ 02940 #561-10-1953 L1957 **P** *071 †75

CARDENAS, Ricardo Alberto. 164 SUMMIT AVE, MIRIAM HOSPITAL DEPT. OF A 02906 #264-04-1990 L2007 **AN CD** *020 †05

CARELLA, Patricia Irza. 164 SUMMIT AVE 02906 #561-01-1972 L1976 **AN** *071

CAREY, Molly Suzanne. ■ 02906 #041-01-2007 L2007 **OBG** *012

CARINO, Gerardo. 164 SUMMIT AVE, MIRIAM HOSPITAL CRITICAL C 02906 #043-01-1999 L1999 **PCC** *100 †20

CARNEVALE, Robert Angelo. 1075 SMITH ST 02908 #035-09-1975 L1977 **CD IM** *020 †20

CARNEY, Wilfred I, Jr. 2 DUDLEY ST STE 470, UNIVERSITY SURGICAL ASSOCI 02905 #041-02-1968 L1977 **VS GS** *020 †20

CARPENTER, Chas Colcock J. 164 SUMMIT AVE, THE MIRIAM HOSP 02906 #023-07-1956 L1986 **IM ID** *040 †20

CARPENTER, Linda Leigh. 345 BLACKSTONE BLVD, BUTLER HOSP 02906 #041-01-1993 L1999 **P** *020 †75

CARPENTER, Randall Lewis. 1 RICHMOND SQ 02906 #025-01-1978 L1979 **AN** *050 †05

CARR, Stephen Richard. 101 DUDLEY ST, WOMEN & INFANTS HOSPITAL 02905 #014-01-1982 L1986 **OBG MFM** *020 †30

CARSON, Sandra Ann. 101 DUDLEY ST, WOMEN AND INFANTS HOSPITAL 02905 #016-06-1977 L2007 **OBG REN** *020 †30

CARTER, Ethel J. 164 SUMMIT AVE 02906 #010-01-1982 L1984 **IM PUD** *020 †20

CARUOLO, Joseph E R. 830 CHALKSTONE AVE 02908 #024-07-1946 L1947 **GS** *071 †85

CARVALHO, Angelina C A S. 830 CHALKSTONE AVE 02908 #770-02-1965 L1977 **HEM IM** *020

CARVALHO, Jaime De Sousa. 830 CHALKSTONE AVE 02908 #770-02-1964 L1977 **NEP IM** *071

CASE, Brady Geronimospe. 593 EDDY ST, RHODE ISLAND HOSPITAL - CO 02903 #024-01-2002 L2006 **CHP** *012

CASHEL, Leslie Elizabeth. 33 STANIFORD ST 02905 #041-13-1972 L1974 **GE IM** *012

CASHORE, William Jos. 101 DUDLEY ST, WOMEN & INFANTS HOSPITAL 02905 #041-01-1966 L1974 **NPM PD** *050 †55

CASILLAS, Mark Anthony. 593 EDDY ST, RHODE ISLAND HOSP 02903 #001-02-2006 L2006 **GS** *012

CASKEY, John David. ■ 02908 #048-02-2007 L2007 **CPP** *012

CASKEY, Melinda Augustine. 101 DUDLEY ST, DEPARTMENT OF PEDIATRICS 02905 #048-02-2003 L2007 **PD** *100 †55

CASSESE, John Albert. 1 RANDALL SQ 02904 #035-19-1994 L2000 **PDR R** *020 †80

CATALDO, Thomas Edward. 2 DUDLEY ST, STE 470 02905 #024-16-1990 L2004 **CRS** *020 †85,10

CEREZO, Carolina S. 593 EDDY ST, RM 126 02903 #748-08-1991 L2000 **PG** *020 †55 ‡

CERMIK, Dilek. 40 CANDACE ST 02908 #902-03-1989 L2004 **OBG** *020

CHA, Jisun. 50 MAUDE ST, ROGER WILLIAMS HOSPITAL 02908 #583-08-2001 L2003 **D** *012

CHA, Sungman. BROWN UNIV BIO MED SCI 02912 #583-01-1954 **PA OS** *050

CHAABAN, Hala Raafat. 101 DUDLEY ST 02905 #605-04-2001 L2006 **NPM** *012

CHADWICK, Doreen Ann. 297 PROMENADE ST 02908 #043-01-1988 L1988 **OBG** *020 †30

CHAFFA, Freydoun Fred. 1 HOPPIN ST, RIGHA 02903 #396-06-1958 L1968 **DR** *075

CHAMMAS AOUN, Nadia M. 825 CHALKSTONE AVE 02908 #605-03-1992 L2007 **IM** *012

CHAMORRO, Jaime. 21 PEACE ST 02907 #264-04-1961 L1970 **ORS** *071

CHAMPION, Vincent Gerardo. ■ 02903 #021-01-2006 L2007 **DR** *012

CHAN, Karen Chilynn. ■ 02903 #035-06-2003 L2005 **DR** *012

CHANDOLIAS, Nikolaos. 593 EDDY ST 02903 #418-01-2002 L2007 **GS** *012

CHANG, Johnny T. 2 DUDLEY ST STE 450, RHODE ISLAND HOSP 02905 #024-07-2006 L2006 **PS** *012

CHANG, Justine Chiu. 593 EDDY ST, WOMEN AND INFANTS HOSPITAL 02903 #043-01-2003 L2005 **OBG** *012

CHANG, Su-Pen B. 164 SUMMIT AVE 02906 #043-01-1988 L2006 **AN CCM** *020 †05

CHAPMAN, Heather Anne. 21 PEACE ST, ST. JOSEPHS PEDIATRIC CLIN 02907 #024-16-1993 L1998 **PD** *020 †55

CHAPMAN, Laura Lynn. 593 EDDY ST, POTTER BLDG, RM 159 02903 #032-01-2002 L2006 **PEM** *012

CHARPENTIER, Kevin Paul. 593 EDDY ST, UNIVERSITY SURGICAL ASSOCI 02903 #024-07-1996 L2006 **GS** *020 †85

CHARTIER, Molly Beth. ■ 02908 #008-02-2003 L2004 **D** *012

CHAUDHRY, Fakhra Saeed. ■ 02906 #033-05-2003 L2004 **DR** *012

CHAUDHRY, Jamil Sadiq. 520 HOPE ST, THE PROVIDENCE CENTER 02906 #704-02-1990 L1994 **CHP** *020

CHAUDHRY, Sadaf. 825 CHALKSTONE AVE, DEPT IM 02908 #024-05-2007 L2007 **IM** *012

CHAUHAN, Nila. ■ 02908 #033-05-2004 L2004 **EM** *012

CHAWLA, Anjulika. 593 EDDY ST, RHODE ISLAND HOSPITAL 02903 #050-02-1995 L2001 **PHO** *020 †55

CHAWLA, Nancy. 593 EDDY ST, FOUNDATION 02903 #041-02-2002 L2006 **EM** *100 †16

CHEAH, Yee-Lee. 593 EDDY ST 02903 #539-06-2000 L2003 **GS** *012

CHEH, Emily. 101 DUDLEY ST, DEPT OBG 02905 #035-01-1996 L1996 **OBG** *020 †30

CHEN, Kenneth Kin-Leung. 101 DUDLEY ST 02905 #143-03-1999 L2008 *100

CHEN, Mimi Y. BROWN UNIVERSITY, BOX G-8197 02912 #043-01-1999 *100

CHEN, Wendy Shihwen. ■ 02908 #043-01-2008 *012

CHEN, William Tzewei. ■ 02903 #041-02-1997 L1997 **GE** *020 †20

CHENOWETH, Marsha Alexis. ■ 02908 #048-14-2005 L2005 **CPP** *012

CHERN, Hueylan. 593 EDDY ST, DEPT OF SURG 02903 #033-05-2002 L2002 **CRS** *012 †85

CHIBWESHA, Carla R. ■ 02905 #043-01-2005 L2005 **OBG** *012

CHIEN, Edward Ks. 101 DUDLEY ST 02905 #016-11-1988 L2004 **OBG MFM** *020 †30

CHILUKURI, Prathima. 825 CHALKSTONE AVE, ROGER WILLIAMS HOSP 02908 #495-50-1994 L2001 **IM** *020

CHIRICO-POST, Jeannette A. 830 CHALKSTONE AVE 02908 #041-07-1968 L1974 **N IM** *040 †75

CHIU, Joanne Sansan. ■ 02903 #043-01-2008 *012

CHIU, Vernon Sy. 825 CHALKSTONE AVE 02908 #748-01-2004 L2005 **IM** *012

CHOI, Kue Chung. 101 DUDLEY ST 02905 #016-43-1994 L1999 **AN** *020 †05

CHOUDHARY, Gaurav. 830 CHALKSTONE AVE, CARDIOLOGY/MEDICAL SERVIC 02908 #495-36-1997 L1997 **CD IM** *020 †20

CHOUFANI, Bassel Michel. 825 CHALKSTONE AVE 02908 #605-03-2002 L2005 **IM** *012

CHRISTAKI, Eirini. ■ 02908 #418-02-2001 L2007 **ID** *012 †20

CHRISTIAN, Robert Bourke. 593 EDDY ST, RHODE ISLAND HOSPITAL 02903 #036-01-2002 L2002 **OS** *100 †55

CHRISTOPHER, Paul Pasqual. 345 BLACKSTONE BLVD, BUTLER HOSP 02906 #024-16-2005 L2005 **P** *012

CHRISTU, Paul Chris. 845 N MAIN ST, STE 1 02904 #027-01-1977 L1989 **OTO HNS** *020 †45

CHUN, Patrick Youngwhan. ■ 02903 #025-12-2004 L2005 **IM** *012

CHUN, Thomas Harry. 593 EDDY ST, PED EMERGENCY MED, RIH 02903 #014-01-1991 L1991 **PD P** *020 †75,55

CHUNG, Maureen A. 2 DUDLEY ST, STE 470 02905 #067-01-1988 L1993 **GS** *020 †85

CHUNG, Samuel Waikee, Jr. 825 CHALKSTONE AVE, MEDICAL EDUCATION 02908 #005-12-2003 L2003 **HO** *012 †20

CIARALLO, Lydia Rita. 593 EDDY ST, POTTER BLDG #206 02903 #041-12-1989 L1994 **PEM** *020 †55

CIELO, Deus Joseph. ■ 02906 #043-01-1996 L1997 **NS** *100

CINEAS, Sybil. 593 EDDY ST, PHYSICIANS OFFICE BLDG STE 02903 #024-01-1995 L1999 **MPD** *020 †20,55

CINQUEGRANA, Oswald Dante. 825 CHALKSTONE AVE 02908 #024-07-1947 L1948 **PM IM** *071 †60

CIOFFI, William Geo, Jr. 593 EDDY ST, APC 431 02903 #050-02-1981 L1994 **GS CCS** *020 †85

CIRILLO, Louis Anthony. 825 CHALKSTONE AVE, DEPT OF EMERGENCY MEDICINE 02908 #050-02-1990 L1997 **EM** *020 †16

CITRON, Jennifer Lynn. 101 DUDLEY ST, DEPT OF PEDIATRICS 02905 #035-45-2002 L2005 **NPM** *012 †55

CLARK, Kristin Anne. 395 WICKENDEN ST, # 2 02903 #050-02-2005 L2005 **PD** *012

CLEMENT, Jeffrey David. 1076 N MAIN ST 02904 #028-34-1987 L1998 **NEP** *020 †20

CLEMENTS, Aine Emma. ■ 02903 #043-01-2005 L2006 **OBG** *012

CLIFFORD, Craig C. 593 EDDY ST, RHODE ISLAND HOSP 02903 #016-01-2005 L2007 **PTH** *012

CLOUTIER, David Robert. 195 COLLYER ST, STE 302 02904 #032-01-1998 L1998 **GS** *020 †85

CLYNE, Brian. 593 EDDY ST, DAVOL-141 02903 #043-01-1997 L2000 **EM** *020 †16

COBB, Sidney. ■ 02912 #024-01-1942 L1974 **PHP** *072 †70

COBURN, Natalie Groce. 593 EDDY ST 02903 #036-01-1998 L1998 **GS** *020 †85

COHEN, Andrew Jonathan. 593 EDDY ST, RHODE ISLAND HOSPITAL 02903 #035-46-1973 L2007 **NEP IM** *020 †20

COHEN, Evan Bruce. 44 W RIVER ST 02904 #023-07-1981 L1986 **GE IM** *020 †20

COHEN, Scott Bryan. 593 EDDY ST, CARDIOLOGY FELLOW/RI HOSPI 02903 #028-34-2003 L2003 **CD** *012 †55

COHEN, Steven Ira. 528 N MAIN ST 02904 #035-08-1968 L1976 **GS VS** *020 †85

COHEN, Steven Irvin. 125 CORLISS ST 2NDFL 02904 #028-34-1971 L1976 **U** *020 †95

COIA, Anthony Garbiel. ■ 02908 #023-07-1998 *100

■ = Address Information Privacy Protected

COLAIACE, William Michael. 825 CHALKSTONE AVE 02908 #024-01-1962 L1969 **R DR** *020 †80
COLASANTO, Lawrence G. 10 ORMS ST, STE 110 02904 #561-01-1971 L1974 **AN** *020 †05
COLEMAN, Geo Vincent, Jr. ■ 02908 #035-20-1946 L1956 **GS** *020 †85
COLEMAN, Reid Wm. 167 POINT ST, CORO 3RD FLOOR 02903 #043-01-1975 L1978 **IM** *030 †20
COLLINS, Bradley James. 164 SUMMIT AVE, THE MIRIAM HOSPITAL 02906 #041-14-2003 L2003 **IM** *020 †20
COLVIN, Gerald A. 593 EDDY ST, DEPARTMENT OF MEDICINE, DI 02903 #041-77-1994, ▲ L2001 **HO IM** *050 †20
COMBS, Christine Mary. ■ 02906 #043-01-2006 L2006 **IM** *012
CONCEPCION, Norberto G. 593 EDDY ST, DEPT OF ANESTHESIA 02903 #748-01-1960 L1972 **AN** *071
CONLEY, Paul Jos. 593 EDDY ST 02903 #041-02-1955 L1960 **IM OS** *030
CONNELL, Nathan Theodore. 593 EDDY ST, RHODE ISLAND HOSPITAL 02903 #011-02-2007 L2007 **IM** *012
CONNOLLY, Jeannine Sluck. 297 PROMENADE ST, CTR FOR OBSTETRICS & GYNEC 02908 #041-15-2001 L2001 **OBG** *020 †30
CONROY, Michelle Leigh. 345 BLACKSTONE BLVD, BUTLER HOSPITAL 02906 #043-01-2003 L2003 **PYG** *012
CONSTANTINE, Herbert P. 3 CAPITOL HL, RHODE ISLAND DEPARTMENT O 02908 #035-06-1953 L1966 **IM PHP** *030
CONSTANTINOU, Maria. 593 EDDY ST, HEMATOLOGY - ONCOLOGY 02903 #305-01-1997 L2000 **HO** *020 †20 ‡
CONTE, John Michael. 49 SEEKONK ST, UNIT 1 02906 #008-02-1978 L1990 **RHU IM** *020 †20
COPPOLINO, Dominic Louis. ■ 02908 #024-07-1947 L1948 **P** *071
CORRE, Giselle Aviva. 33 INTERVALE RD 02906 #056-06-1985 L1989 **P** *020 †75
CORREA, Francisco Jose. 375 ALLENS AVE 02905 #319-04-1999 L2006 **END** *020 †20
CORRIGAN, Dominic Francis. 1 HOPPIN ST, SUITE 200, CORO BUILDING 02903 #024-07-1967 L2003 **END DIA** *020 †20
CORRIGAN, Elizabeth Anne. ■ 02906 #043-01-1975 L1977 **CD IM** *075
CORVESE, Louis A. 110 LOCKWOOD ST 02903 #008-01-1956 L1965 **ORS** *020 †40
CORVESE, William P. 593 EDDY ST 02903 #024-01-1949 L1950 **GS VS** *072 †85
CORWIN, R William. 1 HOPPIN ST, HPHC / NC 02903 #038-40-1973 L1974 **PUD ID** *020 †20
CORWIN, Robert Danl. 1 HOPPIN ST, STE 304 02903 #035-03-1957 L1963 **PDC** *020 †55
COSSOR, Furha Iram. ■ 02907 #028-03-2005 L2005 **IM** *012
COSTELLO, Doris Theresa. 101 DUDLEY ST 02905 #016-43-1987 L1991 **AN IM** *020 †05
COSTELLO, Gina Marie. 593 EDDY ST, PEDIATRICS DEPARTMENT 02903 #422-01-1998 L2005 **PD** *020 †55
COTE, Kim Marie. ■ 02906 #035-45-1985 L1989 **PD** *020 †55
COTE, Phillippe Sylvestre. 285 PROMENADE ST 02908 #050-02-1979 L1988 **ORS** *020 †40
COTTER, Kristen Ann. ■ 02905 #041-12-2004 L2004 **OBG** *012
COTTIERO, Richard Anthony. 1076 N MAIN ST, HYPERTENSION/NEPHROLOGY AS 02904 #024-07-1985 L1990 **NEP IM** *020 †20
COUGHLIN, Gregory Wm, Jr. 10 ORMS ST STE 110 02904 #033-05-1961 L1965 **AN** *071 †05
COUSTAN, Donald Ross. 101 DUDLEY ST 02905 #008-01-1968 L1982 **OBG MFM** *030 †30
COWDIN, Hugh P, Jr. 593 EDDY ST 02903 #030-06-1982 L1984 **AN GS** *020 †05
COYLE, Mara Genevieve. 101 DUDLEY ST, WOMEN AND INFANTS HOSPITAL 02905 #043-01-1986 L1989 **NPM PD** *020 †55
CRAIG, Suzanne Bell. 444 WESTMINSTER ST 02903 #043-01-1980 L1983 **PD NTR** *062 †55
CRAIN, Thomas Fairweather. 164 SUMMIT AVE, DIVISION OF CARDIOLOGY 02906 #035-46-1998 L2004 **CD** *020 †20
CRAYBAS, Norbert Jos. 2 DUDLEY ST, STE 470 02905 #016-43-1970 L1972 **GS** *020 †85
CRIBB, John. 33 STANIFORD ST, UNIVERSITY GASTROENTEROLOG 02905 #043-01-1996 L1996 **GE** *020 †20
CRICHTON, Rebecca J. 695 EDDY ST, STE 22 02903 #008-01-1996 L2001 **OBG** *020 †30
CRISAFULLI, Frederick S. 9 PLEASANT ST 02906 #035-19-1969 L1972 **IM CD** *020 †20
CRISTOFARO, Patricia Ann. 825 CHALKSTONE AVE 02908 #024-05-1980 L1983 **ID** *020 †20
CRONAN, John Jos. 1 RANDALL SQ 02904 #035-03-1976 L1981 **DR** *030 †80
CRONIN, Maureen Susan. 593 EDDY ST, PHY OFF BLDG STE 324 02903 #010-02-2004 L2005 **N** *012
CROWLEY, Carol Ann Cuozzi. 1 HOPPIN ST 02903 #010-02-1969 L1975 **PD HEM** *075 †55
CROWTHERS, Laina Ewan. 695 EDDY ST, STE 21 02903 #008-02-1999 L1999 **OBG** *020 †30
CUCU, Dragos Florin. 164 SUMMIT AVE, MIRIAM HOSPITAL 02906 #781-01-1995 L2005 **CCM** *100 †20
CUMMINGS, Catherine Ann. 593 EDDY ST, POTTER 2 02903 #036-05-1998 L2005 **EM** *020 †16
CUMMINGS, Francis Jos. 825 CHALKSTONE AVE 02908 #051-01-1966 L1969 **ON HO** *020 †20
CURRAN, Alton Jules. 825 CHALKSTONE AVE 02908 #035-09-1954 L1958 **DIA IM** *071 †20
CUSHING, Keith William. ■ 02903 #020-02-2004 L2004 **N** *012
CUSHING-BRESCIA, Anne E. 164 SUMMIT AVE 02906 #024-16-1986 L1991 **IM** *020 †20
CUTITAR, Marlene. 1 RANDALL SQ, STE 402 02904 #043-01-1986 L1988 **GS** *020 †85
CYR, Michele Gail. 111 PLAIN ST, FL 3 02903 #032-01-1979 L1982 **IM** *020 †20
DAAMEN, Maximilian J. 355 ANGELL ST, STE 1 02906 #024-07-1974 L1984 **P** *020 †75
D'AFFLITTI, Joanna Lynn. ■ 02906 #035-08-2007 L2007 **IM** *012
DAHLBERG, Albert Edward. BROWN UNIV, BOX G 02912 #016-02-1965 L1972 **OS** *062
DAHLQUIST, Enold H, Jr. 593 EDDY ST 02903 #024-07-1946 L1955 **PTH BBK** *071 †50
DAILEY, Tanya Lynn. 101 DUDLEY ST, WOMEN AND INFANTS' HOSPITA 02905 #024-07-2002 L2006 **OBG** *100 †30
DALEY, Jean Marie. 593 EDDY ST, RI HOSPITAL NAB 214 02903 #024-07-1984 L1989 **GS** *050 †85
DALIA, Samir M. 593 EDDY ST, DEPT MED 02903 #038-44-2007 L2007 **IM** *012
DALY, Brian Patrick. 345 BLACKSTONE BLVD, BUTLER HOSP 02906 #035-45-2007 L2007 **P** *012
DAMERGIS, Jennifer Anne. ■ 02906 #010-02-2004 L2004 **EM** *012
DANIEL, Michelle Morse. 55 CLAVERICK ST, DEPT OF EMERGENCY MEDICINE 02903 #023-07-2002 L2005 **EM** *020 †16
DAOUD, Ehab Gamil. 164 SUMMIT AVE, THE MIRIAM HOSPITAL 02906 #915-04-1996 L2003 **CCM** *100 †20
DAPAAH-AFRIYIE, Kwame O. 164 SUMMIT AVE, INTERNAL MED INPATIENT SER 02906 #412-02-1986 L1993 **IM** *020 †20
DARENKOV, Ivan Anatolievi. ■ 02903 #913-15-1991 L2003 **PG** *100 †55 ‡
DA SILVA, Manuel Luciano. 2 DUDLEY ST 02905 #770-01-1957 L1963 **IM** *071
DAVIGNON, Kristopher R. 593 EDDY ST, RHODE ISLAND HOSPITAL, DAV 02903 #050-02-1999 L2005 **AN** *100 †05
DAVIS, Gloria T. 593 EDDY ST 02903 #319-04-1994 L1997 **CHP** *020
DAVIS, Nancy L. 10 ORMS ST STE 110 02904 #035-45-1958 L1981 **AN** *075 †05
DAVIS, Robert P. 164 SUMMIT AVE 02906 #024-01-1951 L1967 **NEP IM** *071 †20
DE BENEDECTIS, Carolynn M. 593 EDDY ST, RI HOSP 02903 #010-02-2006 L2007 **DR** *012
DE BLASIO, Peter F, Jr. 1532 SMITH ST 02911 #561-01-1976 L1978 **OPH** *020 †35
DE CHOWDHURY, Roopa. 825 CHALKSTONE AVE 02908 #495-87-2000 L2003 **IM** *100 †20
DEGLI-ESPOSTI, Silvia. 101 DUDLEY ST, WOMEN & INFANTS HOSPITAL 02905 #561-01-1982 L1985 **GE IM** *020 †20
DE GROOT, Anne Searls. ■ 02903 #016-02-1983 L1992 **ID** *050 †20
DEJAGER, Peter Salomon Ch. 593 EDDY ST 02903 #539-04-2001 L2003 **EM** *020
DE LA MONTE, Suzanne M. 593 EDDY ST, RIH APC 12TH FLOOR 02903 #035-20-1977 L2001 **NP PTH** *050 †50
DE LELLIS, Ronald Albert. 593 EDDY ST, RHODE ISLAND HOSPITAL/PATH 02903 #024-07-1966 L2001 **ATP CLP** *030 †50
DELGADO, Gabriel Angel. ■ 02906 #264-12-1998 L2000 **IM HOS** *020 †20
DELLEMONACHE, Paul Michae. 345 BLACKSTONE BLVD, HOUSE REAR 02906 #025-01-2005 L2005 **P** *012
DE MARTINO, Joseph. 235 PLAIN ST 02905 #561-10-1968 L1974 **OBG** *020 †30
DEMERS, Christopher Paul. ■ 02903 #016-06-2004 L2004 **NS** *012
DENNEHY, Penelope Hill. 593 EDDY ST, RHODE ISLAND HOSP 02903 #024-07-1976 L1981 **PD PDI** *030 †55
DENNIS, Ann Margaret. ■ 02906 #034-01-2004 L2005 **IM** *012
DENOFRIO, David. 593 EDDY ST 02902 #024-07-1988 L1999 **CD** *020 †20
DE NUCCI, Thomas Dominic. 825 CHALKSTONE AVE 02908 #043-01-1980 L1982 **GE** *020 †20
DEORCHIS, Douglas Frank. 164 SUMMIT AVE, DEPT OF RADIOLOGY 02906 #010-02-1982 L1990 **DR VIR** *020 †80
DE PRISCO, Claudio. 202 PRAIRIE AVE 02905 #935-01-1993 L2002 **IM END** *020 †20
DESAI, Manish Bhagubhai. 21 PEACE ST 02907 #495-89-1980 L1984 **IM** *020 †20
DE SANTIS, Sandra Joan L. 593 EDDY ST, RI HOSP 02903 #035-03-1983 L2007 **CHP** *012
DESOUZA, Richard Francis. ■ 02904 #024-16-2007 L2007 **IM** *012
DESSIE, Sybil Gloria. ■ 02906 #043-01-2008 *012
DEUTMEYER, Cindy Marie. 593 EDDY ST, RHODE ISLAND HOSP 02903 #422-01-2005 L2005 **GS** *012
DEUTSCH, Allan Mark. ■ 02906 #016-42-1964 L1967 **IM** *071 †80
DEVER, John Bartholomew. 825 CHALKSTONE AVE 02908 #665-01-2006 L2006 **IM** *012
DEVINE, John Gerard, Jr. 31 LUZON AVE 02906 #041-02-1998 L2001 **IM** *020 †20
DEWAN, Sheri. ■ 02908 #016-42-2005 L2005 **NS** *012
DEY, Ranjan. 164 SUMMIT AVE 02906 #496-05-1984 L2002 **AN PME** *020 †05 ‡
DIAMOND, Richard Neil. ■ 02906 #016-42-1969 L1970 **ORS OM** *071
DIBBLE, Christy Leigh. 101 DUDLEY ST STE 1200, DEPARTMENT OF MEDICINE 02905 #022-75-1992, ▲ L1992 **GE** *020 †20
DI BENEDETTO, Joseph, Jr. 193 WATERMAN ST 02906 #024-07-1972 L1976 **ON HEM** *020 †20
DI CLEMENTE, Bruno. ■ 02908 #010-02-1943 **GS** *071 †85
DIGIOVANNA, John Jos. 593 EDDY ST, DEPT OF DERMATOLOGY 02903 #035-15-1976 L1997 **D** *020 †15
DI GIOVANNI, Christopher. 2 DUDLEY ST 02905 #043-01-1991 L1991 **ORS** *020 †40
DILL, Sara Worthing. 593 EDDY ST, UNIV DERMATOLOGY 02903 #005-18-2000 L2001 **D** *020 †15
DI MAIO, Michael. ■ 02903 #023-07-1939 L1942 **IM CD** *071 †20
DI MASE, Joseph Domenic. 33 STANIFORD ST 1ST FL, 33 STANIFORD STREET 02905 #024-07-1958 L1960 **GE** *020 †20
DIMASE, Susan Lacroix. 203 GOVERNOR ST 02906 #035-47-1974 L1975 **P IM** *020 †20,75
DINGMANN, Philip A. 593 EDDY ST 02903 #037-01-1994 L1997 **CHP** *020
DIPETRILLO, Thomas A. 593 EDDY ST, RHODE ISLAND HOSPITAL 02903 #050-02-1986 L1998 **RO** *020 †20,80
DI ZIO, Stephen D. 172 CUSHING ST 02906 #033-05-1976 L1978 **P** *020 †75
DIZOGLIO, Beata E. 695 EDDY ST, BROADWAY OB/GYN 02903 #043-01-2003 L2007 **OBG** *020
DI ZOGLIO, Joseph David. 695 EDDY ST, BROADWAY OB/GYN 02903 #024-07-1963 L1964 **OBG** *071 †30
DIZON, Don Steven. 101 DUDLEY ST 02905 #035-45-1995 L2003 **IM ON** *050 †20
DOBERSTEIN, Curtis E. 1 DAVOL SQ, STE 302 02903 #067-01-1988 L1995 **NS** *020 †25
DOBRILOVIC, Nikola. 208 COLLYER ST 02904 #422-01-1997 L2006 **TS** *100 †85,90
DOBSON, Theron Leroy. 593 EDDY ST, DEPT MED 02903 #025-12-2007 L2007 **IM** *012
DODSWORTH-FELDMAN, B. 55 DORRANCE ST 02903 #043-01-1977 L1980 **OPH** *020 †35
DONAHUE, John Edward. 593 EDDY ST, RHODE ISLAND HOSPITAL 02903 #024-07-1992 L1996 **N NP** *020 †75
DONISE, Kathleen Rae. 593 EDDY ST, RI HOSP-ACUTE PSYCH SVCS 02903 #033-06-2002 L2005 **P CHP** *020 †75
DONNENFELD, Brian Lee. ■ 02903 #010-02-2005 L2005 **AN** *012
DOOBININ, Kathleen A. 593 EDDY ST, UNIV EMGY MED FOUND 02903 #035-15-1993 L2003 **PEM PD** *020 †55
DORFMAN, Gary Stanway. 593 EDDY ST 02903 #008-01-1976 L1981 **VIR DR** *050 †80
DORRIS-GORZEWSKI, Heidi. 1 HOPPIN ST 3RD FL, ANCHOR MEDICAL ASSOCIATES 02903 #043-01-1996 L1996 **IM** *020 †20
DOWBEN, Robert M. 97 WATERMAN ST, BROWN UNIV BOX G B3 02912 #016-02-1949 L1968 **N IM** *030
DOWLING, Joseph L, Jr. 150 E MANNING ST 02906 #024-07-1950 L1952 **OPH** *072 †35
DOYLE, Kathleen Patricia. ■ 02903 #008-02-2005 L2005 **IM** *012
DOYLE, Thomas V. ■ 02906 #869-01-1960 L1962 **IM** *071
DRAZNIN, Charles David. ■ 02906 #025-01-2006 L2006 **EM** *012
DRIMBAREAN, Calin D. 101 DUDLEY ST 02905 #781-01-1990 L1998 **AN** *020 †05
DUBEL, Gregory Joseph. 1 RANDALL SQ 02904 #035-15-1993 L1994 **VIR DR** *020 †80
DUCHARME, Joseph F. 593 EDDY ST, DEPT OF OPHTHALMOLOGY 02903 #043-01-1992 L1992 **OPH** *020 †35
DUFFY, Christine Mary. 111 PLAIN ST, FL 3 02903 #035-20-1998 L1998 **IM** *020 †20
DUFFY, Susan Jane. 593 EDDY ST, DEPT OF EMERGENCY MEDICINE 02903 #043-01-1988 L1993 **PD** *020 †55
DUFORT, Elizabeth Mariann. ■ 02906 #035-06-2002 L2006 **PDI** *012 †55
DUFRESNE, Raymond Geo, Jr. 593 EDDY ST, DERMATOLOGY FOUNDATION OF 02903 #047-05-1980 L1989 **DS IM** *020 †20,15
DUMENCO, Luba Louise. BROWN UNIVERSITY, BOX G-B5 02912 #056-05-1983 L1991 **ON HMP** *050 †20
DUNCAN, John Allison, III. 55 CLAVERICK ST STE 100 02903 #033-06-1986 L1995 **NS** *072 †25
DUNLAP, Whitney Anne E. ■ 02906 #051-07-2005 L2005 **PD** *012
DUPUIS, Carolyn Suzanne. ■ 02906 #035-08-2005 L2005 **DR** *012
DUPUY, Damian Edward. 1 RANDALL SQ 02904 #024-16-1988 L1996 **DR** *020 †80
DURAN, Luisa A. ■ 02912 #043-01-2008 *012

■ = Address Information Privacy Protected

DURON, Vincent Pierre. 593 EDDY ST, RHODE ISLAND HOSP 02903 #035-45-2007 L2007 GS *012

DUSHAY, Kevin Maier. 593 EDDY ST 02902 #035-01-1983 L2003 PUD IM *020 †20

DUVAL, Bernard S. ■ 02906 #035-03-1949 L1953 P *020

DUWAJI, Mazen Sawaf. 593 EDDY ST 02903 #875-01-1978 L1987 PCP *020 †50

DVORAK, Tomas. ■ 02903 #035-01-1998 L2006 RO *012

DVORIN, Richard Lawrence. 293 GOVERNOR ST 02906 #047-07-1974 L1977 PD *020 †55

DWAN, Jennifer Ballard. 111 DUDLEY ST, WIHRI 3RD FL 02905 #025-01-2000 L2004 OBG MFM *100 †30 ‡

DWORKIN, Lance Douglas. 593 EDDY ST 02902 #041-01-1975 L1993 NEP IM *040 †20

DYCKMAN, Jacob. 164 SUMMIT AVE 02906 #035-19-1944 L1953 PTH DMP *020 †50

DYER, Robert Kevin. 593 EDDY ST, DEPT MED 02903 #043-01-2007 L2007 IM *012

DZIOB, John S. ■ 02906 #024-01-1934 L1936 GP OM *071

EARL, Thomas Joseph. ■ 02908 #035-15-2006 L2006 IM *012

EASTON, J Donald. 2 DUDLEY ST, STE 530 02905 #054-04-1964 L1986 N *040 †75

EDEN, Robert E. 2 DUDLEY ST STE 190 02905 #024-05-1989 L1989 PD *020 †55

EDSTROM, Lee Everett. 2 DUDLEY ST STE 460 02905 #038-06-1969 L1982 PS HS *020 †65

EDWARDS, Omega Lavon. 593 EDDY ST 02903 #035-08-2002 L2003 ID *012 †20

EGGLIN, Thomas Kurt. 593 EDDY ST, RIH RADIOLOGY 02903 #054-04-1985 L1998 DR VIR *020 †80

EHRLICH, Michael G. 2 DUDLEY ST 02903 #035-01-1963 L1990 ORS *020 †40

EISEN, Jane L. 345 BLACKSTONE BLVD 02906 #035-19-1977 L1986 P *030 †75

EL AMIL, Zeina Geryes. 825 CHALKSTONE AVE, ROGER WILLIAMS HOSP 02908 #605-03-2005 L2006 IM *012

ELDRIDGE, Justin Paul. ■ 02909 #041-02-2007 L2007 MPD *012

ELDRIDGE, Kathleen Fanjoy. ■ 02903 #041-02-2007 L2007 IM *012

ELFENBEIN, Gerald Jay. 825 CHALKSTONE AVE, ROGER WILLIAM MED CTR 02908 #023-07-1970 L1998 ON HEM *050 †20

ELIAS, Georg. 825 CHALKSTONE AVE 02908 #875-01-1994 L1998 ON HEM *050 †20

ELION, Jonathan. 164 SUMMIT AVE 02906 #043-01-1975 L1989 CD *050 †20

ELLER, Peter Morrison. 164 SUMMIT AVE 02906 #041-09-1981 L1983 IM *020 †20

ELLIOT, Mark Bruckel. 345 BLACKSTONE BLVD 02906 #010-02-2000 L2000 P *020 †75 ‡

ELLSWORTH, Pamela Ida. 2 DUDLEY ST, STE 174 02905 #024-16-1987 L2005 U *020 †95

EL-METWALLY, Dina E. 101 DUDLEY ST, WOMEN & INFANTS HOSP 02905 #915-11-1989 L1996 NPM *100 †55

ELOFSON, Diane Anderson. 124 WATERMAN ST 02906 #035-47-1985 L1989 PD *071 †55

EL-RAYESS, Fadya. 285 CHAD BROWN ST STE A, CHAD BROWN HEALTH CENTER 02908 #010-01-1996 L1999 FM *020 †18

ELSAMRA, Sammy Elsayed. ■ 02903 #033-05-2007 L2007 GS *012

EMGUSHOV, Rinchen-Tzo. 400 RESERVOIR AVE, COASTAL MEDICAL 02907 #041-13-1985 L1987 IM ID *020 †20

ENZER, Yoash. 120 DUDLEY ST STE 104 02905 #038-41-1986 L1988 OPH PS *020 †35

EPSTEIN, Alan. 50 MAUDE ST 02908 #024-05-1985 L1990 GE IM *020 †20

EPSTEIN, David Louis. ■ 02903 #011-02-2005 L2005 IM *012

EPSTEIN, Lynn M Chaikin. 97 WATERMAN ST STE G-A-, BROWN UNIVERSITY 02912 #023-07-1968 L1985 CHP P *050 †75

EPSTEIN, Melvin Harold. 2 DUDLEY ST, STE 505 02905 #023-07-1966 L1985 NS *020 †25

EPSTEIN, Nathan B. 355 BLACKSTONE BLVD, APT 310 02906 #064-01-1948 L1978 P *020 †75

EREKSON, Elisabeth Ann. 695 EDDY ST, CENTER FOR WOMENS SURG 02903 #016-11-2002 L2006 OBG *100

ERICKSON, Allan Douglas. 830 CHALKSTONE AVE, VA HOSPITAL 02908 #035-01-1968 L1977 PUD IG *020 †20

ESPARZA, Alfredo R. 593 EDDY ST 02903 #649-18-1957 L1968 PTH *020 †50 ‡

ESPAT, N Joseph, Jr. 825 CHALKSTONE AVE, DEPT SURGERY PRIOR 4 02908 #013-09-1990 L1992 GS SO *020 †85

ESTRADA, Elkin Orlando. 1076 N MAIN ST, STE 2 02904 #010-03-1997 L1997 NEP *020 †20

ESTRERA, Chloeanne Bompat. ■ 02906 #051-01-2004 L2005 IM *012

EVANGELISTA, Peter Thomas. 1 RANDALL SQ 02904 #008-02-1998 L1999 DR *020 †80

FAGAN, Mark Justus. 593 EDDY ST, JANE BROWN GROND0114 02903 #035-09-1979 L1982 IM *020 †20

FAGGEN, Meredith Gail. 593 EDDY ST, ALDRICH 126 02903 #021-01-2002 L2006 HO *012 †20

FAHEEM, Wajahat. 21 PEACE ST, ST. JOSEPH HOSPITAL FOR SP 02907 #704-01-1994 L2001 PYG *020 †75

FAIZAN, Mohammed Khurram. 593 EDDY ST APC-942 02903 #704-25-1993 L2002 PN *020 †55

FALANGA, Vincent. 50 MAUDE ST, DEPARTMENT OF DERMATOLOGY 02908 #024-01-1977 L1998 D IM *030 †20,15

FALK, Willy. ■ 02906 #396-06-1957 L1969 PTH IM *062 †50

FALKENBERRY, Stephen S. 235 PLAIN ST, STE 204 02905 #048-02-1984 L1994 OBG *020 †30

FALTUS, Frank John. 315 BLACKSTONE BLVD 02906 #024-07-1972 L1974 P IM *020 †75

FAMIGLIETTI, Edward V, Jr. ■ 02906 #024-05-1972 L1995 NP *050

FARICY, Katherine Elizabe. ■ 02904 #041-02-2005 L2005 IM *012

FAUSTO, Nelson. BROWN U DIV BIO MED SCI 02912 #187-04-1961 OS ATP *050

FAWZI, Gamal E A. PROVIDENCE LYING IN HOSP 02908 #915-02-1965 IM *100

FAYNGERSH, Vadim. 10 DAVOL SQ, STE 400 02903 #550-04-2002 L2004 PCC *012 †20

FEARON, Deirdre Mary. 593 EDDY ST, RHODE ISLAND HOSPITAL 02903 #043-01-1996 L1999 PD *020 †55

FEINSTEIN, Pratarnporn C. ■ 02906 #891-02-1960 L1968 CHP P *020 †75

FEIT, Lloyd Robt. 1 HOPPIN ST 02903 #035-08-1984 L1991 PDC PD *020 †55

FELDER, Martin Edward. ■ 02904 #024-07-1956 L1963 GS *071 †85

FELDMANN, Edward. 110 LOCKWOOD ST, STE 324 02903 #024-01-1983 L1988 N *020 †75

FELLER, Edward Roy. 44 W RIVER ST 02904 #033-05-1973 L1980 GE IM *071 †20

FELLER, Joseph Howard. 151 WATERMAN ST 02906 #396-23-1971 L1984 GS CRS *020 †55

FENDERSON, Jacquia Lamees. ■ 02906 #035-45-2008 *012

FENG, Andrew Ku-Hua. 593 EDDY ST 02902 #041-02-1991 L2004 CCP *020 †55

FENG, William Chinglih. 2 DUDLEY ST STE 47D 02905 #043-01-1982 L1989 OS CCS *020 †85,90

FENTON, Maryanne. 593 EDDY ST 02902 #008-02-1989 L2000 HO *020 †20

FERGUSON, Gary M. 2 DUDLEY ST 02905 #024-07-1981 L1998 ORS OAR *020 †40

FERLAND, Roger Jos. 695 EDDY ST, STE 22 02903 #021-01-1980 L1982 OBG OS *020 †30

FERNANDES, Erika. 593 EDDY ST, RIH PEDIATRIC EMERGENCY M 02903 #067-01-1999 L2003 PEM *020

FERNANDEZ, Adela Manuela. 593 EDDY ST 02903 #104-01-2006 L2007 GS *012

FIELD, Carey Jessica. 593 EDDY ST, DEPT MED 02903 #032-01-2007 L2007 IM *012

FILIP, Corina Sanda. ■ 02906 #781-04-1999 L2006 CCM *012 †20

FIORI, Michael Angelo. 482 LLOYD AVE 02906 #035-09-1981 L1986 P *020 †75

FIRTH, Jacqueline Adriana. ■ 02903 #021-01-2006 L2006 MPD *012

FISCHER, Staci. 2 DUDLEY ST, STE 370 02905 #021-05-1990 L2000 ID *020 †20 ‡

FISH, Keith R. 222 RICHMOND ST, STE 110 02903 #043-01-1994 L1994 IM *020 †20

FISHER, Beth Ann. ■ 02903 #041-02-2002 L2002 PCC *012 †20

FISHER-CORN, Meredith Lee. 101 DUDLEY ST 02905 #035-47-1994 L1999 AN *020 †05

FITCH, Rebecca Lynn. ■ 02906 #035-08-2005 L2005 IM *012

FITZGERALD, Kathleen. 120 DUDLEY ST, STE 301 02905 #010-02-1974 L1977 GYN *020 †30

FITZGIBBONS, Peter Gile. 111 REGENT AVE, # 1 02908 #043-01-2004 L2004 ORS *012

FITZPATRICK, Donald P. 593 EDDY ST 02903 #047-07-1953 L1954 IM CD *071 †20

FIXMAN, Laura Beth. 394 ANGELL ST 02906 #024-07-1988 L1993 P PYG *020 †75

FLANAGAN, Patricia J. 593 EDDY ST, RI HOSPITAL 02903 #035-06-1983 L1988 PD *040 †55

FLANDERS, John Douglas. 10 ORMS ST STE 110, PROVIDENCE ANESTHESIOLOGIS 02904 #043-01-1997 L1997 AN *020 †05

FLANIGAN, Timothy Palen. 164 SUMMIT AVE, FL 2 02906 #035-20-1983 L1991 ID IM *020 †20

FLASH, Charlene Antoinett. ■ 02906 #033-06-2006 L2006 MPD *012

FLAXMAN, Bertram Allen. 189 GOVERNOR ST 02906 #008-01-1963 L1968 D *020 †15

FLEISIG, Norbert. 1 RANDALL SQ, STE 304 02904 #008-01-1961 L1967 GS GPM *020 †85

FLEMING-IVES, Kathryn Sca. 345 BLACKSTONE BLVD, BUTLER HOSP 02906 #024-16-2005 L2005 P *012

FLORIN, Robert Allan. 154 WATERMAN ST, STE 3 02906 #008-01-1973 L1977 P *020 †75

FLYNN, Ellen. 101 DUDLEY ST STE 560, WOMENS BEHAVIOURAL HEALTH 02905 #024-16-1999 L2004 P *020 †20

FLYNN, Laura Margaret. ■ 02906 #051-04-2007 L2007 IM *012

FLYNN, Stephen Gerard. ■ 02912 #041-01-2006 L2006 PD *012

FOGGLE, John Lindsey. 593 EDDY ST, UNIVERSITY EMERGENCY MEDIC 02903 #035-45-1989 L2006 EM *100 †20,16

FONDRAN, John Charles. ■ 02903 #038-06-2002 L2007 CRS *100 †85

FORCADA-LOWRIE, Raymundo. ■ 02907 #056-05-2005 L2005 EM *012

FORMAN, Edwin Noel. 593 EDDY ST, DEPT OF PEDIATRICS 02903 #041-01-1960 L1963 PHO PD *020 †55

FORMISANO, Victor R. 194 WATERMAN ST 02906 #024-05-1958 L1962 D OS *020

FORSYTHE, Thomas. 110 LOCKWOOD ST 02903 #024-07-1945 L1952 R OS *020

FOURNIER, Lenore Saulsber. ■ 02907 #024-01-2000 L2001 FM *100

FOWLER, Rachel Lyn. 593 EDDY ST, CLAVERICK 274 02903 #028-02-2004 L2004 EM *012

FOX, Katherine Marie. ■ 02903 #033-06-2008 IM *012

FOX, Sarah Diana. 101 DUDLEY ST, WOMEN AND INFANTS' HOSPITA 02905 #033-06-1993 L1998 OBG *020 †30

FRANCIS, Warren Wm. 110 LOCKWOOD ST 02903 #035-01-1948 L1955 GS VS *071 †85

FRANK, Joseph William. 02909 #017-20-2007 L2007 IM *012

FRATER, Stephan Istvan. ■ 02906 #473-01-1950 L1959 NM DR *071 †80,28

FRATES, Richard Edward. 101 DUDLEY ST, DEPT RA-INFNT 02905 #024-07-1955 L1965 R *071 †80

FREEMAN, Nancy Jane. PROVIDENCE VA HOSP, DEPT OF MEDICINE 02908 #035-09-1981 L1982 ON HEM *020 †20

FRIEDMAN, Aaron Louis. 593 EDDY ST, DEPT OF PEDIATRICS 02903 #035-15-1974 L2004 PD PN *020 †55

FRIEDMAN, Alexander Micha. 101 DUDLEY ST, WOMEN & INFANTS HOSPITAL 02905 #035-47-2005 L2005 OBG *012

FRIEDMAN, Jennifer. 55 CLAVERICK ST, STE 101 02903 #043-01-1996 L2002 PD *020 †55

FRIEDMAN, Jules Martin. 130 WATERMAN ST 02906 #041-02-1969 L1998 N IM *020

FRIEDMAN, Lester M. 593 EDDY ST 02903 #035-45-1950 L1952 IM *071

FRIEDMAN, Michael Alan. 235 PLAIN ST, STE 501 02905 #035-48-1987 L2000 N *020 †75

FRIEDMANN, Peter David. 593 EDDY ST 02903 #024-05-1988 L1999 IM ADM *050 †20

FRIEHS, Gerhard Martin. 2 DUDLEY ST STE 530 02905 #154-01-1988 L1995 NS TRS *040

FRISHMAN, Gary Nathan. 1 BLACKSTONE PL 02905 #035-01-1985 L1991 REN OBG *040 †30

FRITZ, Gregory Kenneth. 593 EDDY ST, RHODE ISLAND HOSPITAL 02902 #024-07-1971 L1985 CHP *050 †75

FROEHLICH, John Alan. 2 DUDLEY ST 02905 #035-45-1983 L1989 ORS *020 †40

FROEHLICH, Wendy Michelle. 593 EDDY ST, RHODE ISLAND HOSPITAL 02903 #005-11-2004 L2004 CPP *012

FUENTES, Karla Patricia. 593 EDDY ST, RHODE ISLAND HOSPITAL 02903 #682-01-1989 L1999 PHO *020 †55

FUENTES, Miguel A. ■ 02906 #231-01-1986 L1992 PD *020 †55

FULTON, Ana Tuya. 593 EDDY ST, DIV OF GERIATRICS 02903 #010-01-2001 L2001 IMG *020 †20

FURMAN, Martin Julian. 345 BLACKSTONE BLVD 02906 #836-01-1978 L1983 P N *020 †75

FYNN THOMPSON, Eric Kojo. 2 DUDLEY ST, RHODE ISLAND HOSPITAL 02905 #024-01-2002 L2002 PS *012

FYOCK, Christopher James. ■ 02906 #045-01-2005 L2005 IM *012

GADGIL, Meghana Dipti. ■ 02906 #033-05-2007 L2007 IM *012

GAETA, Joseph Roland. 235 PLAIN ST 02905 #024-05-1958 L1961 CD IM *020

GAFFNEY, Mary Anne. 101 DUDLEY ST 02905 #032-01-1995 L1995 OBG *100

GAINES, Barbara Miller. 124 WATERMAN AVE 02911 #035-48-1985 L1988 PD *020 †55

GAINES, John Avery. 593 EDDY ST 02903 #035-48-1985 L1987 IM *020 †20

GAITANIS, John Nicholas. 110 LOCKWOOD ST, STE 342 02903 #043-01-1996 L2003 CHN *020 †20

GAITANIS, Melissa. 2 DUDLEY ST, STE 370 02905 #043-01-1996 L2001 ID IM *020 †20

GALE, Stanley Wm. 345 BLACKSTONE BLVD 02906 #008-01-1975 L1978 P OS *020 †75

GAMBARDELLA, Lee S. 593 EDDY ST, 7TH FLOOR PENTHOUSE 02903 #024-05-1996 L1996 IM *020 †20

GAMBLE, Elizabeth Anne. 101 DUDLEY ST 02905 #035-15-1989 L1993 AN *020 †05

GAO, Zhenqiang. 593 EDDY ST, DEPT OF PATHOLOGY 02903 #243-36-1986 L2005 PTH *100 †50

GARDNER, Rebekah Leslie. 593 EDDY ST, APC 5 02903 #035-19-2002 L2007 IM *020 †20

GARNER, Carol Virginia. 164 SUMMIT AVE 02906 #024-07-1980 L1989 CCM ID *020 †20

GARTMAN, Eric John. 593 EDDY ST, RHODE ISLAND HOSPITAL 02903 #035-45-2004 L2004 IM *012

GARVEY, Keelin Ann. 345 BLACKSTONE BLVD, BUTLER HOSPITAL 02906 #024-16-2005 L2005 P *012

GASCON, Generoso G. 593 EDDY ST 02903 #024-05-1962 L1994 N OS *071 †75

GASPAR, Francisco T. ■ 02907 #748-07-1951 GS *100

GASS, Jennifer Suzanne. 101 DUDLEY ST, WOMEN & INFANTS HOSP 02905 #023-01-1987 L1993 GS CCS *020 †85

GAUTAM, Amitabh. 2 DUDLEY ST STE 470, RI HOSP-UNIV SURG ASSOC 02905 #495-45-1981 L2001 TTS GS *020

■ = Address Information Privacy Protected

GAVIN, Cara Mc Laughlin. 593 EDDY ST, RHODE ISLAND HOSP 02903 #023-07-2002 L2002 IM *100 †20

GAZZILLO, Gregory Patrick. ■ 02904 #033-05-2007 L2007 IM *012

GEFFROY, Guy Adrien E. 110 LOCKWOOD ST 02903 #065-09-1956 L1957 N *020

GELLER, Mirfrida Zinovevn. 593 EDDY ST, RHODE ISLAND HOSP 02903 #913-43-1972 L2007 NP *012

GEMIGNANI, Anthony Seth. 593 EDDY ST, RHODE ISLAND HOSP 02903 #010-02-2004 L2007 CD *012 †20

GENG, Amy. 593 EDDY ST, A PC 10TH 02903 #038-40-2002 L2003 D *074 †15

GENTILESCO, Bethany Jane. 593 EDDY ST, RHODE ISLAND HOSPITAL 02903 #035-20-2001 L2006 IM *020

GEORAS, Constantine Steve. 235 PLAIN ST 02905 #418-01-1950 L1958 CD IM *071 †20

GEORAS, Venetia. 593 EDDY ST 02903 #418-01-1951 PD *071

GEORGE, Ronald Lee, Jr. ■ 02903 #012-01-2006 L2006 IM *012

GEORGY, Youssef Habib. 30 BLACKSTONE BLVD 02906 #330-02-1956 L1969 IM CD *071 †20

GERBER, Rebecca Erin. ■ 02908 #043-01-2008 *012

GIBBS, Frantz J, Jr. 593 EDDY ST, DAVOL 141 02903 #024-01-1997 L1997 EM *020 †16

GIBSON, Sharon Elizabeth. 130 WATERMAN ST 02906 #025-01-1987 L1996 PDO *020 †45

GIDEON, Vasant Arjun K C. 375 ALLENS AVE, CARE FOUNDATION INC 02905 #495-21-1956 L1967 PD *020 †20

GIFFORD, David Ralston. 3 CAPITOL HL RM 401, RI DEPARTMENT OF HTH 02908 #038-06-1989 L1995 IM IMG *012

GIFFORD, Deidre Spelliscy. 235 PROMENADE ST, RM 500 02908 #035-20-1987 L1995 OBG PHP *030 †30

GILCHRIST, James M. 2 DUDLEY ST, STE 530 02905 #016-43-1979 L1987 N CN *040 †75

GILLERMAN, Richard Gordon. 593 EDDY ST 02903 #028-03-1984 L1994 AN *020 †05,55

GILLESPIE, Steven Anthony. 164 SUMMIT AVE, DEPT MED 02906 #021-01-1988 L1988 P *020 †75

GILLMAN, Kelvin David. 845 N MAIN ST, STE 7 02904 #067-01-1982 L1995 PD *020 †55

GILSON, Michael Frederick. 1 DAVOL SQ 02903 #035-01-1986 L1990 CD IM *020 †20

GILSON, Thomas Peter. ■ 02904 #041-07-1988 L2006 FOP *050

GINSBERG, Zachary. ■ 02906 #043-01-2008 *012

GINSBERG-PELTZ, Julien Da. ■ 02905 #035-09-2004 L2004 PD *020 †55

GLANTZ, Lisa Kaljot. 593 EDDY ST, DEPT PATH 02903 #043-01-1984 L1992 ATP *020 †50

GLASGOW, Michelle Anne. ■ 02912 #043-01-2008 *012

GLASSER, Lewis. 593 EDDY ST, DEPT PTH APC 1142A 02903 #035-20-1960 L1994 CLP PTH *020 †50

GLEIT, Cindy Ann. ■ 02906 #038-40-2005 L2005 FP *012

GLINICK, Stephen Ernest. 100 HIGHLAND AVE 02906 #035-01-1976 L1977 D IM *020 †20,15

GNEPP, Douglas Robbin. 593 EDDY ST, DEPT PATH APC 12 RI HOSP 02903 #036-07-1974 L1992 ATP *020 †50

GO, Subil Choi. 593 EDDY ST, RHODE ISLAND HOSPITAL 02903 #748-02-1999 L2006 NEP *012 †20

GOAD, Julianne Marie. ■ 02905 #017-20-2005 L2005 CPP *012

GODDARD, Jesse. 593 EDDY ST, RHODE ISLAND HOSPITAL 02903 #422-01-2007 L2007 IM *012

GODDARD, Joan Holly. 1 HOPPIN ST 3RD FL, ANCHOR MEDICAL ASSOCIATES 02903 #043-01-1979 L1985 IM EM *020 †20

GODDARD, Moses Brown. BROWN UNIV BOX G 02912 #043-01-1979 L1988 GS *020 †85

GODLEY, Frederick A, III. 845 N MAIN ST STE 1, ALLIANCE ENT, INC. 02904 #024-05-1983 L1989 OTO FPS *020 †45

GOHH, Reginald Yuchengco. 593 EDDY ST 02902 #047-07-1990 L1990 NEP IM *020 †20

GOKHALE, Sumita. 825 CHALKSTONE AVE, DEPT OF PATHOLOGY 02908 #495-67-1994 L2007 PTH *050 †50

GOLD, Richard Lawrence. 164 SUMMIT AVE, RADIOLOGY DEPARTMENT 02906 #024-16-1982 L1994 DR RNR *020 †20,80

GOLDBERG, Amy Phyllis. 1 HOPPIN ST, CORO WEST 2ND FLOOR 02903 #024-05-1997 L2001 PD *020 †55

GOLDBERG, Richard J. 101 DUDLEY ST 02905 #035-06-1974 L1978 P PYG *030 †75

GOLDFARB, Amy. 400 RESERVOIR AVE, COASTAL MEDICAL INC 02907 #041-07-1998 L1998 IM *020 †20

GOLDMAN, Debra Lynn. 101 DUDLEY ST, WOMEN AND INFANTS HOSPITAL 02905 #024-07-1998 L1998 OBG *020 †30

GOLDMAN, Marc Alan. ■ 02906 #539-03-2001 L2001 NS *012

GOLDSTEIN, Lisa Joyce. 164 SUMMIT AVE, DEPT OF PATHOLOGY 02906 #043-01-1982 L1985 ATP CLP *020 †50

GOLINGER, Ronald Clark. ■ 02940 #035-19-1966 L1992 P ADP *020 †85,75

GOLITKO, Carrie Lynn. ■ 02906 #030-06-2003 L2003 PD *100 †55

GOLOVA, Natalia. 110 LOCKWOOD ST, STE 230 02903 #132-01-1990 L1995 PD *020 †55

GONZALEZ, Jorge Eduardo. 40 CANDACE ST 02908 #264-10-1997 L2004 IM *020 †20

GOODMAN, Mark Norman. ■ 02903 #039-01-2003 L2003 AN *020

GOODWIN, Sarrah Lynne. ■ 02904 #048-13-2005 L2005 EM *012

GOPALAKRISHN, Paari. 593 EDDY ST 02903 #048-13-1999 L1999 IM *020

GOPALAKRISHNAN, Geetha. 593 EDDY ST, MIDDLE HOWE, ROOM 301F 02903 #048-16-1994 L1994 END *020 †20

GORDON, Alan Lester. 345 BLACKSTONE BLVD 02906 #836-01-1979 L1986 P *020 †75

GORDON, Debra Jenny. 35 S ANGELL ST 02905 #035-48-1980 L1988 P CHP *020 †75

GOT, Christopher John. 593 EDDY ST, RI HOSP 02903 #033-05-2006 L2006 ORS *012

GOTTLIEB, Amy Susan. 101 DUDLEY ST, WOMEN & INFANTS HOSPITAL 02905 #016-02-1999 L1999 IM *020 †20

GOULA, Walter Joseph. 164 SUMMIT AVE 02906 #028-34-1995 L1995 IM *020 †20

GRAF, Amanda Elizabeth. ■ 02906 #038-40-2006 L2006 PD *012

GRANAI, Cornelius O, III. 101 DUDLEY ST # GYNONCOL, WOMAN & INFANTS HOSPITAL 02905 #050-02-1977 L1989 GO OBG *020 †30

GRAND, David J. 593 EDDY ST, DEPARTMENT OF RADIOLOGY 02903 #035-47-2000 L2005 DR *100 †80

GRANDA, Chia Sonia. ■ 02903 #014-01-2005 L2005 CPP *012

GRAVALLESE, Peter Michael. 101 DUDLEY ST 02905 #024-07-1992 L1995 AN ORS *020 †05

GRAVENSTEIN, Stefan. 235 PROMENADE ST, RM 500 02908 #038-40-1982 L2007 IMG CCM *050 †12

GRAVES, Theresa Ann. 235 PLAIN ST 02905 #050-02-1985 L1994 GS OS *050 †85

GRAY, Yulia. 825 CHALKSTONE AVE, DEPT OF PATHOLOGY 02908 #033-06-1995 L1996 DMP *020 †50

GREAVES, Wesley Olando Co. 120 ALDRICH ST, RHODE ISLAND HOSPITAL 02905 #187-45-2002 L2005 PTH *012

GREENBERG, Benjamin David. 345 BLACKSTONE BLVD 02906 #011-02-1987 L1999 P *050 †75

GREENBERG, Paul Benj. 1 RANDALL SQ, STE 206 02904 #035-47-1992 L2003 OPH *020 †35

GREENE, Stephanie. 55 CLAVERICK ST STE 100, DEPT OF NEURO SURGERY 02903 #035-03-1998 L2005 NS *020 ‡

GREENSPAN, Neil Robt. 44 W RIVER ST 02904 #035-47-1984 L1990 GE IM *020 †20

GREENWOOD, Virginia Kaye. 164 SUMMIT AVE 02906 #043-01-1987 L1991 AN *020 †05

GREER, David S. BROWN UNIVERSITY BOX G, DEANS OFFICE 02912 #016-02-1953 L1975 IM PM *071 †20

GREER, Teresa Whelan. 530 N MAIN ST, THE PROVIDENCE CENTER 02904 #033-05-1984 L2002 P *020 †75

GREGG, Zachary Andrew. 593 EDDY ST, RHODE ISLAND HOSP 02903 #033-05-2007 L2007 GS *012

GREGORY, Michael David. ■ 02903 #016-01-2005 L2005 N *012

GREVE, Mark Waldron. 593 EDDY ST 02903 #035-46-2002 L2006 EM *100 †16

GRIFFITH, Rogers C. 593 EDDY ST # APC 12, RHODE ISLAND HOSPITAL 02903 #004-01-1972 L1987 ATP HMP *020 †50

GRUPPUSO, Philip Alan. 593 EDDY ST, RI HOSPITAL 02903 #035-45-1977 L1982 DIA PDE *050 †55

GUDDETI, Pallavi. 825 CHALKSTONE AVE, ROGER WILLIAMS HOSP 02908 #495-65-2002 L2004 IM *100

GUGGENHEIM, Frederick G. 345 BLACKSTONE BLVD, BUTLER HOSP 02906 #035-01-1961 L2002 P *020 †75

GUILBERT, Julie Anne. ■ 02903 #024-16-2004 L2004 IM *012

GULINO, Dante. 345 BLACKSTONE BLVD, BROWN UNIV AFFIL HOSPS 02906 #010-02-1997 *100

GUPTA, Aarti. 593 EDDY ST, DEPT MED 02903 #035-06-2007 L2007 IM *012

GUPTA, Nisha. 593 EDDY ST, DEPT OF ANESTHESIA 02903 #043-01-1998 L2007 APM *100 †05

GUPTA, Rakesh. 877 CHALKSTONE AVE 02908 #495-23-1988 L1999 SME PCC *020 †20

GUPTA, Sheela G. ■ 02903 #024-05-2005 L2005 D *012

GURNEY, Ellen L. 202 PRAIRIE AVE 02905 #035-19-1979 L1982 PD *020 †55

GUSTIN, Adam F. 825 CHALKSTONE AVE 02908 #067-01-2003 L2003 DR *012

GUTHRIE, Tracey Michelle. 345 BLACKSTONE BLVD, BUTLER HOSPITAL 02906 #035-45-1995 L1995 P *020 †75

GUTMAN, Deborah C. 593 EDDY ST, DEPT OF EMERGENCY MEDICINE 02903 #043-01-1999 L1999 EM *020 †16

HAAS, Richard Alan. 1 RANDALL SQ 02904 #016-11-1980 L1985 DR *020 †80

HABR, Fadlallah Gabriel. 110 LOCKWOOD ST STE 116 02903 #605-03-1993 L1997 GE *020 †20

HAHN, David K. ■ 02912 #043-01-2008 *012

HAINES, Francis Xavier. 25 S ANGELL ST 02906 #010-02-1975 L1978 P *020 †20

HAJI-MOMENIAN, Shahriar. ■ 02909 #051-01-2004 L2005 DR *012

HALL, Dana Paquette. 50 MAUDE ST 02908 #016-43-1998 L1999 D *020 †15

HALL, Harald Alexander. 50 MAUDE ST 02908 #016-42-2000 L2000 RHU *012

HALLSTEIN, William Chas. 21 PEACE ST, PSYCHIATRIC SERVICES 02907 #035-03-1967 L1997 P *020

HAMADE, Sam. ■ 02903 #308-13-2002 L2006 PCC *012 †20

HAMOLSKY, Milton W. 3 CAPITOL HL, DEPT OF HEALTH ROOM 205 02908 #024-01-1946 L1963 END IM *071 †20

HAMPTON, Brittany Star. 695 EDDY ST 02903 #035-47-1999 L2006 OBG *100 †30

HAN, Jung-Ah. ■ 02906 #035-46-2005 L2005 IM *012

HANDA, Sajeev. 593 EDDY ST, RHODE ISLAND HOSPITAL 02903 #539-06-1991 L1994 ID *020 †20

HANNA, George Michael, Jr. 21 PEACE ST 02907 #308-07-1981 L1985 CD IM *020 †20

HANSEN, Heather Anne. ■ 02903 #016-43-2003 L2003 GS *012

HANSEN, Jared Lee. 593 EDDY ST 02903 #040-02-2004 L2004 PD *020 †55

HANSEN, Katrine Helen. 593 EDDY ST, RI HOSPITAL 02903 #035-15-1985 L1988 PTH *020 †50

HAREL, Zeev. 593 EDDY ST, RI HOSP ADOLESCENT MEDICNE 02903 #550-02-1980 L1994 ADL PD *020 †12

HARINI, Chellamani. 593 EDDY ST, GEORGE BUILDING 02903 #495-04-1989 L2006 CHN *020 †55,75

HARKNESS, Stephen Hayes. 825 CHALKSTONE AVE 02908 #048-04-1973 L1985 AN *071 †05

HARONIAN, Thomas Justin. 164 SUMMIT AVE 02906 #043-01-1989 L1993 EM *020 †16

HARRINGTON, Colin James. 593 EDDY ST, APC 608 02903 #024-07-1988 L1989 P *020 †75

HARRINGTON, David Tobin. 2 DUDLEY ST, STE 470 02905 #024-07-1988 L1997 GS *020 †85

HARRINGTON, J F, Jr. 235 PLAIN ST 02905 #024-07-1983 L1995 NS *020 †25

HARRIS, Jeffrey Earl. 375 ALLENS AVE, PROVIDENCE COMMUNITY HEALT 02905 #041-01-1974 L2005 PHP IM *012

HARRIS, Jennifer Irene. ■ 02906 #041-12-2005 L2005 P *012

HARRISON, Douglas James. 593 EDDY ST, DEPT OF PEDIATRIC HEMATOLO 02903 #033-05-2000 L2007 PHO *100 †55

HARROP, Daniel Smith. PO BOX 603364 02906 #043-01-1979 L1980 P PYG *030 †75 ‡

HART, John Robert. 593 EDDY ST, RHODE ISLAND HOSP 02903 #035-03-2004 L2007 CHP *012

HARTMAN, Douglas Frederic. ■ 02906 #051-01-2006 L2006 EM *012

HARTMAN, Lauren Alyssa. 593 EDDY ST, RHODE ISLAND HOSPITAL 02903 #051-01-2006 L2006 PD *012

HARTMANN, Silvia. ■ 02912 #043-01-2008 *012

HARWELL, Joseph I. 164 SUMMIT AVE, FL 2 02906 #036-01-1993 L1999 ID *020 †20,55

HASAN, Razi. 790 N MAIN ST, RENASSIANCE MEDICAL GROUP 02904 #704-02-1991 L1997 PD *020 †55

HASSAN RAGHEB, Moataz M M. 235 PLAIN ST, STE 501 02905 #915-04-1994 L2004 P *020 †75

HAWASH, Karameh Y. 16 CHATHAM ST 02904 #575-01-1993 L2002 CHN *020 †75

HAYES, Meghan Elizabeth. 101 DUDLEY ST, DEPARTMENT OF MEDICINE 02905 #035-15-1999 L2006 IM *020 †20

HAYES, Micaela Chadwick. ■ 02903 #008-02-2006 L2006 IM *012

HAYES, Robert Clement. 21 PEACE ST 02907 #024-07-1947 L1948 GP OM *020

HAZELWOOD, Senator. 825 CHALKSTONE AVE, ROGER WILLIAMS MEDICL CENT 02908 #041-13-2000 L2005 IM *100

HEIMMEL, Mark Robert. ■ 02903 #033-06-2005 L2006 OPH *012

HEIN, Michael David. 148 W RIVER ST 02904 #305-01-1982 L1989 DIA END *020 †20

HENNESSEY, James Vincent. 1 HOPPIN ST STE 200 02903 #154-01-1977 L1993 IM END *040 †20

HERMAN, Arnold Harvey. 528 N MAIN ST 02904 #019-02-1966 L1974 GS *020 †85

HERRERA-RUBIO, Engelberto. 593 EDDY ST 02903 #341-01-1969 PD *020

HERSHKOWITZ, Melvin. 3 REGENCY PLZ APT 1001E 02903 #035-19-1945 L1972 IM *072 †20

HIGGINSON, Michelle Kraus. 593 EDDY ST, UNIVERSITY DERMATOLOGY INC 02903 #054-04-1996 L1997 D *020 †15

HIGH, Pamela Craig. 593 EDDY ST, APC -6 RIH 02903 #011-03-1976 L1993 PD *020 †55

HILL, Catherine Louise. ■ 02906 #143-01-1989 **RHU** *100

HILLER, Constance R. 13 BROWN ST, BOX 1928 02912 #038-41-1979 L1993 **PD ADL** *075 †55

HILLSTROM, Mary Martha. 164 SUMMIT AVE, DEPT OF RAD THE MIRIAM HOS 02906 #043-01-1988 L1994 **DR** *020 †80

HINCAPIE, Maria Luisa. 345 BLACKSTONE BLVD 02906 #065-06-2004 L2004 **P** *012

HINES, Scott Justin. ■ 02906 #035-03-2005 L2005 **PD** *012

HIRSH, Rebecca L. 593 EDDY ST, DEPT OF INTERNAL MED 02903 #043-01-2003 L2003 **HO** *012 †55,20

HITCHEN, Tracey Leigh. 593 EDDY ST, RHODE ISLAND HOSP 02903 #043-01-2002 L2002 **PD** *020 †55

HITTNER, Kathleen A C. 164 SUMMIT AVE 02906 #024-07-1973 L1979 **AN** *030 †05

HOGAN, Erin Elizabeth. ■ 02908 #025-01-2000 L2002 **IM** *020 †20

HOGAN, John F. 101 DUDLEY ST 02905 #024-01-1948 L1949 **PD PDA** *020 †55

HOHENHAUS, Mary Helen. 164 SUMMIT AVE, STE E 02906 #041-12-2001 L2001 **IM** *040 †20

HOJMAN, Horacio B. 593 EDDY ST, DEPT OF PSYCH/CHILD PSYCH 02903 #132-01-1984 L1997 **CHP** *020 †75

HOLLINGER, Walter A. 21 PEACE ST, ADULT PRIMARY CARE CLINIC 02907 #041-14-2001 L2004 **IM** *020

HOLLINSHEAD, Wm Henry. 3 CAPITOL HL, RI DEPT OF HEALTH RM 302 02908 #026-04-1968 L1975 **PHP PD** *030 †55

HOLMES, William Nathanael. 593 EDDY ST, RHODE ISLAND HOSP 02903 #050-02-2001 L2001 **PDR** *100 †80

HOLUBAR, Marisa Kathleen. ■ 02903 #056-05-2005 L2005 **MPD** *012

HOLZER, Cynthia. 1085 CHALKSTONE AVE 02908 #038-45-1996 L2001 **IM IMG** *020 †20 ‡

HOODA, Barkat S. ■ 02904 #704-25-1991 L1996 **PD** *100 †55

HOPKINS, Richard Alan. 164 SUMMIT AVE, MIRIAM HOSP 02906 #036-07-1974 L1996 **TS** *020 †85,90

HOPKINS, Robert West. 164 SUMMIT AVE 02906 #024-01-1947 L1970 **VS GS** *072 †85

HORVITZ, Abraham. ■ 02906 #031-01-1936 L1941 **GS** *071 †85

HORWITZ, Alexander Earle. ■ 02906 #028-34-1941 L1950 **P** *072 †75

HORWITZ, Harold Milton. 49 SEEKONK ST 02906 #024-07-1968 L1969 **RHU IM** *020 †20

HOSMER, Jennifer Jean. 40 CANDACE ST 02908 #024-05-1984 L1992 **OBG** *020 †30

HOWARD, Katherine A. 593 EDDY ST 02903 #024-05-2004 L2004 **PD** *012

HOY, Erik Alexander. ■ 02906 #033-05-2005 L2005 **PS** *012

HSU, Ellen Hsiao. ■ 02906 #008-02-2007 L2007 **EM** *012

HSU, Natalie H. 32 ALFRED STONE RD 02906 #043-01-1998 L1998 **NEP** *020 †20

HSUEH, Aileen. 593 EDDY ST 430, RHODE ISLAND HOSPITAL 02903 #035-01-2002 L2005 **CCS** *012

HU, Guang. 830 CHALKSTONE AVE, MEDICAL CENTER 02908 #243-44-1982 L1995 **IM** *020 †20

HU, Jingjing. 825 CHALKSTONE AVE, ROGER WILLIAMS HOSP 02908 #243-03-1999 L2005 **IM** *100

HU, Susie Lee-Insung. 593 EDDY ST 02902 #041-09-1997 L2003 **IM** *020 †20

HUANG, Angela Anchiung. ■ 02903 #033-05-2002 L2005 **DBP** *012 †55

HUANG, Qin. 830 CHALKSTONE AVE, DEPT PATHOLOGY-PROV VAMC 02908 #243-71-1980 L1999 **PTH** *020 †50

HUMAYUN, Nousheen Laila. 593 EDDY ST 02903 #024-05-2007 L2007 **PD** *012

HUMAYUN, Shazia S. ■ 02903 #704-25-1989 L1990 **GS** *100 †85

HUNTINGTON, Christopher F. 955 CHALKSTONE AVE, THE ORTHOPAEDIC INSTITUTE 02908 #041-02-1990 L1996 **ORS OSS** *020 †40

HUR, John. 593 EDDY ST 02903 #035-15-1999 L1999 **OAR** *020

HUSSAIN, Saira. 593 EDDY ST BLDG 1S, DEPT OF MEDICINE, C/O S. H 02903 #704-02-1992 L1999 **IM** *020 †20

HWANG, Eugene Ickjin. 593 EDDY ST, RHODE ISLAND HOSPITAL 02903 #036-07-2002 L2002 **PHO** *012

HYDER, Michael Kalil. 1076 N MAIN ST, CARDIOVASCULAR ASSOCIATES 02904 #024-16-1999 L2006 **ICE** *020 †20

IANNOTTI, Harry Michael. 1165 N MAIN ST, STE 20 02904 #024-05-1966 L1970 **U** *020 †95

IBRAHIM, Cecile. 593 EDDY ST 02903 #528-01-1948 L1971 **PD PDA** *020 †55

INGRAFFEA, Adam Anthony. ■ 02908 #042-02-2006 L2007 **D** *012

INGRAHAM, Bette Ann. ■ 02903 #017-20-1976 L1976 **GS** *075

IP, Julianne. BROWN UNIVERSITY, BOX G-A1 02912 #043-01-1978 L1979 **FM EM** *030 †18

IQBAL, Omer Javaid. 825 CHALKSTONE AVE, ROGER WILLIAMS HOSP 02908 #704-21-2000 L2004 **IM** *012

IWAMOTO, Satori. 825 CHALKSTONE AVE, MOHS SURG CLNC WEST 2 02908 #024-01-1989 L2003 **D** *020 †15

IZEMAN, Henry Frank. 593 EDDY ST 02903 #024-07-1958 L1959 **IM IMG** *071 †20

JABBOUR, Melhem Salim. 825 CHALKSTONE AVE 02908 #605-03-2002 L2005 **IM** *012

JACKSON, Benjamin Taylor. DAVIS PK 02908 #036-07-1954 L1989 **GS CD** *071 †85

JACKSON, Kimberly L. 97 WATERMAN ST, BROWN UNIV PROGRAM IN MED 02912 #043-01-2000 *100

JACKSON, Neil David. 101 DUDLEY ST 02905 #024-05-1962 L1990 **GYN OS** *040 †30

JACKSON, Thomas. ■ 02909 #043-01-2008 *012

JACOBS, Elizabeth Sara. 593 EDDY ST, CLAVERICK 2 02903 #041-13-1997 L1997 **PEM** *020 †55

JACOBS, Niama E. ■ 02912 #043-01-2007 L2007 **P** *012

JACOBSON, Sandra Ann. 164 SUMMIT AVE, # 2B 02906 #014-01-1987 L2003 **P IM** *020 †75

JAEGER, Jenifer Leaf. 593 EDDY ST, POB RM 02903 #028-02-1993 L1997 **PD PDI** *050 †55

JAIN, Neeta. 2 DUDLEY ST STE 560, WOMEN AND INFANTS HOSPITAL 02905 #035-06-1992 L1992 **P** *020 †75

JAIN, Samir Fateh. ■ 02903 #661-02-2002 L2006 **IM** *012

JALAL, Nazeer Mohammed. 825 CHALKSTONE AVE, ROGERS WILLIAMS MED CTR 02908 #820-02-2005 L2006 **IM** *012

JAMESON, Philip Jamoulis. ■ 02906 #024-07-1956 L1976 **DR** *071 †80

JAMIESON, Thomas Wm. 830 CHALKSTONE AVE, DEPT OF MD PROV VAMC 02908 #028-34-1976 L1976 **RHU IM** *020 †20

JANIGIAN, Robert H. 120 DUDLEY ST, STE 303 02905 #043-01-1988 L1988 **OPH** *020 †35

JANKOWICH, Matthew Dmitri. ■ 02908 #038-40-1999 L2004 **PCC** *100 †20

JARDINE, John Francis. 593 EDDY ST DEPT EM 02903 #035-08-1996 L1996 **EM** *012 †16

JAVADI, Omid. 97 WATERTOWN ST, BROWN UNIV PROGRAM IN MED 02912 #043-01-1999 L2006 **GS** *020 †85

JAY, Bryan Scott. 690 EDDY ST, RHODE ISLAND VASCULAR INST 02903 #010-02-2001 L2006 **VIR** *100 †80

JAY, Gregory David. 593 EDDY ST, EMERGENCY MEDICINE 02903 #035-48-1990 L1993 **EM** *020 †16

JAYAKRISHNAN, Asha. 101 DUDLEY ST, WOMEN & INFANTS HOSPITAL 02905 #021-01-2005 L2005 **OBG** *012

JEAN, Thomas Wm. 830 CHALKSTONE AVE, VA MEDICAL CENTER 02908 #043-01-1982 L1985 **IM** *020 †20

JEAN-GILLES, Jerome Louis. 593 EDDY ST, RI HOSP 02903 #035-08-2005 L2007 **PTH** *012

JEDNACZ, Jeffrey Aaron. 593 EDDY ST 02903 #025-07-2002 L2003 **DR** *100 †80

JEFFERS, Justin Michael. ■ 02904 #038-43-2006 L2006 **PD** *012

JEGAPRAGASAN, Vaani. ■ 02906 #010-03-2006 L2006 **IM** *012

JELLINEK, Nathaniel Josef. 593 EDDY ST 02903 #024-16-2000 L2004 **D** *020 †15

JENNY, Carole Ann. 593 EDDY ST 02903 #054-04-1972 L1996 **PD** *020 †55

JENOURI, Ilse Maria. 164 SUMMIT AVE, EMERGENCY DEPARTMENT 02906 #035-15-1994 L1994 **EM** *020 †20

JEREMIAH, Jennifer. 111 PLAIN ST, STE 203 02903 #043-01-1989 L1989 **IM** *020 †20

JERNIGAN, Kristel Leigh. ■ 02906 #036-08-2005 L2005 **IM** *012

JIMENEZ MENDEZ, Patricia. 825 CHALKSTONE AVE, ROGER WILLIAMS HOSP 02908 #341-05-2002 L2006 **IM** *012

JOHN, Jasmine. 825 CHALKSTONE AVE, ROGER WILLIAMS HOSP 02908 #495-63-1998 L2002 **IM** *100 †20

JOHNSON, Gary Darrell. 2 DUDLEY ST, STE 555 02905 #041-01-1985 L1990 **N** *020 †75

JOHNSON, Lynne Lalor. 543 EDDY ST, RHODE ISLAND HOSPITAL 02903 #035-01-1969 L1994 **CD IM** *020 †20

JOHNSON, Michael Pitcairn. 285 GOVERNOR ST, STE 370 02906 #035-20-1993 L1996 **IM** *020 †20

JOHNSTON, Robert Ginson M. 830 CHALKSTONE AVE, VA MEDICAL CENTER 02908 #917-29-1969 L1979 **P** *020 †75

JOHNSTONE, Jill Kathleen. ■ 02903 #023-01-2005 L2005 **GS** *012

JONES, Christopher Allen. ■ 02903 #041-02-2006 L2006 **IM** *012

JONES, Kohar. ■ 02906 #008-01-2005 L2006 **FP** *012

JORDAN, Jesse Jos, Jr. 164 SUMMIT AVE 02906 #047-07-1988 L1989 **PTH** *020

JOSEPH, Michael. ■ 02906 #043-01-2008 *012

JOSHI, Premalkumar Parima. 593 EDDY ST, RHODE ISLAND HOSP 02903 #495-23-2000 L2006 **NEP** *012

JOYCE, Donald Robt. 825 N MAIN ST, RADIATION ONCOLOGY ASSOC 02904 #010-02-1986 L1997 **RO IM** *020 †20,80

JUE, Christopher. ■ 02912 #043-01-2006 L2006 **IM** *012

JURCZAK, Annmarie. 297 PROMENADE ST 02908 #035-46-2000 L2004 **OBG** *020

KABA, Chadi Fahed. 50 MAUDE ST, UNIVERSITY MEDICAL GROUP, 02908 #875-01-1997 L2005 **IM** *020 †20

KAHN, Charles Bernard. 49 SEEKONK ST 02906 #007-02-1963 L1974 **END IM** *020 †20

KAHN, David Allen. 188 BENEFIT ST 02903 #048-14-1987 L2000 **P** *020 †75

KAKAR, Kshitij. 593 EDDY ST, RHODE ISLAND HOSP 02903 #495-37-2005 L2006 **GS** *012

KAMAT, Achyut Mihir B. 164 SUMMIT AVE, DEPT OF EMERGENCY MEDICINE 02906 #033-05-1996 L2000 **EM** *020 †16

KAMENETSKY, Elena M. 830 CHALKSTONE AVE 02908 #913-07-1963 L1983 **N** *020 †75

KAMIONEK, Stephen James. 593 EDDY ST 02903 #024-07-1964 L1969 **HS ORS** *040 †40

KANE, Agnes M Brezak. BROWN UNIV, BOX G 02912 #043-13-1974 L1982 **PTH** *050 †50

KANE, Joshua S. 345 BLACKSTONE AVE 02906 #035-08-2004 L2004 **P** *012

KANG, Lana. 2 DUDLEY ST 02905 #005-02-1998 L1998 **HS** *100 †40

KANTOR, Rami. 164 SUMMIT AVE, MIRIAM HOSP 02906 #550-02-1995 L2005 **ID** *100

KAO, Patricia Poyuan. 21 PEACE ST, PEDIATRIC LCINIC 02907 #005-11-2001 L2006 **PD** *100 †55

KAPLAN, David. 164 SUMMIT AVE, EMERG DEPT 02906 #028-02-1973 L1978 **EM OTO** *020 †45,16

KAPLAN, Jerry. ■ 02903 #047-06-1956 L1957 **GS** *071 †85

KAPLAN, Randy. 825 CHALKSTONE AVE, ER ROGER WILLIAM HOSPITAL 02908 #016-42-1996 L1999 **EM** *020 †16

KAPLAN, Sheldon David. 827 N MAIN ST 02904 #035-09-1967 L1968 **IM** *020 †20

KAPLON, Daniel Marc. ■ 02906 #041-14-2003 L2003 **U** *012

KARANASIAS, Petro. 100 HIGHLAND AVE STE 303 02906 #902-10-1971 L1977 **N** *020

KARIM, Kashana. 202 PRAIRIE AVE 02905 #539-06-2002 L2006 **IM** *020 †20

KARIM, Nazreen. 593 EDDY ST 02903 #035-19-2005 L2006 **PD** *012

KARKI, Arjun. 593 EDDY ST 02903 #672-01-1985 L1996 **CCM** *100 †20

KARNIK, Rahool Sudheer. 593 EDDY ST, MAIN BUILDING, RM 209 02903 #024-07-2002 L2006 **CD** *012 †20

KARSAN, Farrok Akber. 164 SUMMIT AVE, DEPT IM 02906 #043-01-1982 **IM** *100 †80

KASIBHATLA, Mohit Sourabh. 50 MAUDE ST, DUKE UNIVERSITY MEDICAL CE 02908 #036-07-2000 L2008 **RO** *100 †80

KASTOFF, Marisa Beth. ■ 02912 #043-01-2007 L2007 **IM** *012

KASZNICA, John Mark. 101 DUDLEY ST, WOMEN AND INFANTS HOSPITAL 02905 #759-03-1979 L2002 **PTH PP** *020 †50

KATSOULAKIS, Nickolas. ■ 02906 #035-15-2004 L2005 **OPH** *012

KATZ, Emily Ruth. 593 EDDY ST, OF CHILD/FAMI 02903 #024-01-2001 L2006 **CHP** *012 †55

KATZMAN, Gary Mitchell. 208 COLLYER ST, MIRIAM HOSPITAL 02904 #025-07-1995 L1995 **CD** *020 †20

KAUFMAN, Joel Matthew. 167 POINT ST, STE 3A 02903 #024-05-1977 L1996 **N MDM** *020 †75

KAWAOKA, John C. 593 EDDY ST 02903 #043-01-2004 L2004 **D** *012

KAWATU, David. 593 EDDY ST, RHODE ISLAND HOSPITAL 02903 #965-01-1986 L1996 **PG** *020 †15

KAZIM, Ali. 593 EDDY ST, MAIN BLDG ROOM 038 02903 #704-21-1984 L1994 **PFP** *020 †75

KAZLAUSKAS, Anthony Jos. 593 EDDY ST 02903 #050-02-1978 L1979 **IM IMG** *030 †20

KAZURA, Alessandra N. 1 HOPPIN ST, STE 500 02903 #043-01-1982 L1990 **CHP P** *050 †55,75

KEESE, Antonia Josefa. ■ 02906 #869-07-1947 L1957 **OS GP** *071

KEITNER, Gabor Istvan. 593 EDDY ST, RHODE ISLAND HOSPITAL 02903 #065-05-1973 L1980 **P** *020 †75

KELLER, Derek Heinrich. ■ 02910 #024-05-2008 *012

KELLER, Martin Barry. 347 BLACKSTONE BLVD, BROWN UNIV-BUTLER HOSP CPS 02906 #035-20-1972 L1990 **P** *020

KELLY, Colleen Renee. 100 DUDLEY ST 3RD FL, GASTROENTEROLOGY PRACTICE 02905 #038-40-1999 L2003 **GE** *020 †20

KELLY, Michael James. 593 EDDY ST, RHODE ISLAND HOSPITAL 02903 #041-15-2002 L2002 **PHO** *012

KELLY, Susan Malkin. 345 BLACKSTONE BLVD, MCLEAN HOSPITAL SOUTHEAST 02906 #024-16-1998 L1999 **P** *020

KELTY, Patrick Jos. 125 CORLISS ST 02904 #010-02-1990 L1998 **U** *020 †95

KEMPANANJAPPA, Thejaswini. 825 CHALKSTONE AVE, ROGER WILLIAMS HOSP 02908 #495-09-2001 L2004 **IM** *100

KENNEDY, Christine Anne. 101 DUDLEY ST 02905 #041-13-1993 L1993 **FM** *020 †18

KENNEY, Bevin Elizabeth. ■ 02906 #024-16-2006 L2006 **IM** *012

■ = Address Information Privacy Protected

KENNEY, Robert Michael. 593 EDDY ST, TRANS CL 02903 #035-46-1979 L1988 **PTH** *030 †50
KERMAN, Karen Lynn. 593 EDDY ST 02903 #038-41-1983 L1989 **N** *020 †75
KERN, Jeremy Robert. ■ 02906 #035-08-2004 L2004 **PD** *012 †55
KERNER, Paul Jason. 100 BUTLER DR 02906 #035-06-1997 L2007 **ORS** *020 †40
KERSTETTER, David L. ■ 02903 #024-05-2004 L2007 **GE** *012 †20
KERZNER, Marvin S. 164 SUMMIT AVE 02906 #561-01-1960 L1962 **IM CD** *020 †20
KESTIN, Anita Susan. 593 EDDY ST, RHODE ISLAND HOSPITAL 02903 #043-01-1980 L1982 **IM** *020 †20
KETCHEDJIAN, Ara. 593 EDDY ST, DEPT OF SURGERY, SURGICAL 02903 #035-15-1997 L1997 **TS** *100 †85
KHAN, Adeel Shahid. 593 EDDY ST, RHODE ISLAND HOSP 02903 #704-25-2002 L2004 **GS** *012
KHAN, Amir Ali. 830 CHALKSTONE AVE, MHBSS, 3RD FL 02908 #704-04-1991 L2007 **P** *020 †75
KHAN, Hafeez Ur Rahman. 825 CHALKSTONE AVE, ROGER WILLIAM HOSP 02908 #704-21-1985 L2000 **AN** *020 †05
KHATIB, Pervez A. 100 CURTIS ST 02909 #704-16-1988 L1997 **FM** *020 †18
KHAUND, Razib. 100 BUTLER DR, UNIVERSITY ORTHOPEDS 02906 #033-05-1992 L1992 **ISM IM** *020 †20
KHETPAL, Vijay. ■ 02903 #047-05-2006 L2007 **OPH** *012
KHODARAHMI, Khodarahm. 1 RANDALL SQ 02904 #517-01-1955 L1968 **R** *071 †80
KHORSAND, Jila. 50 MAUDE ST 02908 #517-08-1976 L1986 **PTH** *020 †50
KHURSHID, Humera. ■ 02906 #704-25-1993 L2000 **HO** *020 †20
KIEKHOFER, William. 353 BLACKSTONE BLVD 02906 #008-01-1951 L1953 **OBG** *071 †30
KIFF, Jane Elizabeth. 593 EDDY ST, POTTER 115 02903 #028-03-1992 L2005 **PD CCP** *020 †55
KILLORAN, Christina E. ■ 02908 #024-05-2004 L2005 **D** *012
KIM, Alice M. 593 EDDY ST, DEPT OF RADIOLOGY 02903 #035-19-2004 L2005 **DR** *012
KIM, Jennifer Ahjin. 97 WATERMAN ST, BROWN MEDICAL SCHOOL 02912 #043-01-2008 *012
KIM, Kyung Min. 593 EDDY ST 02903 #583-08-2002 L2007 **GS** *012
KIM, Sang Mo. 101 DUDLEY ST, OF RHODE ISLAND 02905 #583-06-1950 L1977 **AN** *072
KIM, Soyun. ■ 02906 #043-01-2008 *012
KIM, Stacey Ahrahm. ■ 02908 #048-12-2007 L2007 **PTH** *012
KIM, Young Han. 2 DUDLEY ST, STE 174 02905 #033-06-1990 L1997 **U** *020 †95
KIMBLE, Brian Andrew. 830 CHALKSTONE AVE, PULMONARY DIVISION 02908 #019-02-1995 L1995 **PUD** *020 †20
KIMBRELL, Katherine Cherr. 593 EDDY ST, DEPT EM 02903 #024-01-2007 L2007 **EM** *012
KING, Boyd Peterson. 593 EDDY ST, RI HOSPITAL 02903 #024-07-1968 L1973 **NEP** *071 †20
KIRCHNER, Robert Michael. 593 EDDY ST, DEPARTMENT OF CARDIOLOGY 02903 #041-15-1999 L2006 **CD** *012 †20
KIRK, Malcolm Moore. 2 DUDLEY ST STE 360, CARDIOVASCULAR DIVISION 02905 #041-14-1989 L2000 **ICE** *020 †20
KIRSCHNER, Steven Benj. 825 CHALKSTONE AVE 02908 #308-06-1980 L1986 **GE IM** *020 †20
KITZES, David Louis. 1 RANDALL SQ, STE 307 02904 #035-08-1963 L1970 **CD IM** *020 †20
KLEIN, Donald Edward. 95 PITMAN ST 02906 #024-01-1963 L1970 **A PD** *020 †55,03
KLEIN, Erika Lynn. 18 IMPERIAL PL, UNIT 2D 02903 #038-06-1992 L1996 **OBG** *020 †30
KLEIN, Michael Andrew. 830 CHALKSTONE AVE, DEPT OF PATH&LAB MED VAMC 02908 #025-07-1972 L1982 **PTH** *020 †50
KLEIN, Robert B. ■ 02906 #869-05-1971 L2000 **PDA PD** *020 †55,03
KLIE, Jack Hug. 100 HIGHLAND AVE 02906 #024-07-1966 L1973 **CD IM** *020 †20
KLINGER, James Raymond. 593 EDDY ST 02902 #056-06-1983 L1988 **PUD IM** *050 †20
KLIPFEL, Cindy Ellen. 101 DUDLEY ST, INFANT'S HOSPITAL 02905 #035-47-1996 L2004 **PD** *020 †55
KOBAYASHI, Leo. 55 CLAVERICK ST 02903 #043-01-1998 L2002 **EM** *020 †16
KOCANDRLE, Karel Petr. 825 CHALKSTONE AVE, DEPT RAD 02908 #286-02-1966 L1977 **R** *020 †80
KOCHILAS, Lazaros K. 1 HOPPIN ST, CDRO W (#304) 02903 #418-01-1986 L2002 **PDC** *020 †55
KOELLIKER, Susan Lyn. 1 RANDALL SQ 02904 #038-41-1991 L1995 **DR** *020 †80
KOHLI, Kapil. 825 CHALKSTONE AVE 02908 #495-30-2001 L2005 **IM** *012
KOHN, Robert. 164 SUMMIT AVE, MIRIAM HOSPITAL, FAIN BUIL 02906 #016-11-1985 L1988 **P PYG** *020 †75 ‡
KOJIC, Erna Milunka. 164 SUMMIT AVE, FL 2 02906 #484-01-1992 L1996 **ID IM** *020 †20
KOLACHALAMA, Sireesha. 825 CHALKSTONE AVE, ROGER WILLIAMS HOSP 02908 #495-21-2000 L2003 **IM** *020 †20
KONANUR, Indira D. ■ 02906 #048-78-2007, ▲ L2007 **IM** *012
KONESS, R James. 825 CHALKSTONE AVE 02908 #035-06-1983 L1988 **GS SO** *020 †85
KONSTADOULAKIS, Manoussos. ■ 02906 #418-01-1989 L1993 **GS** *100
KOPP, Matthew Alexander. 164 SUMMIT AVE, THE MIRIAM HOSPITAL 02906 #016-42-1997 L1997 **EM** *020 †16
KOPPELMAN, Michele Claude. 164 SUMMIT AVE 02906 #041-07-1975 L1983 **END IM** *071 †20
KORNEEVA, Marina Nikolaye. ■ 02906 #913-48-1982 L2008 **PDI** *012 †55
KORR, Kenneth Spencer. 208 COLLYER ST 02904 #847-04-1975 L1981 **CD IM** *020 †20
KORTYNA, George, III. 593 EDDY ST, DAVOL 129 02903 #038-40-1979 L1982 **AN** *020 †05
KOSTADINOV, Stefan G. 101 DUDLEY ST, WOMEN AND INFANTS HOSPITAL 02905 #198-05-1991 L2004 **PP** *020
KOSTER, Michael Philip. 593 EDDY ST, DEPARTMENT OF PEDIATRICS 02903 #035-09-2003 L2007 **PDI** *012 †55
KOUNAVIS, Ari None. ■ 02906 #030-06-2004 L2004 **PD** *100
KOYMEN, Altug. 40 CANDACE ST 02908 #028-02-2002 L2006 **OBG** *020
KOZLOFF, Matthew Seth. 2 DUDLEY ST, STE 470 02905 #016-42-2001 L2007 **CCS** *100 †85
KRAMER, Naomi Ruth. 220 W EXCHANGE ST, STE 100A 02903 #041-02-1987 L1987 **PUD SME** *020 †20
KRAMER, Peter David. 196 WATERMAN ST 02906 #024-01-1976 L1982 **P CHP** *062 †75
KRAUSS, Dennis Sherwin. 49 SEEKONK ST 02906 #050-02-1974 L1979 **END IM** *020 †20
KREISS, Jocelyn Hayes. 345 BLACKSTONE BLVD 02906 #043-01-2004 L2004 **P** *012
KREISS, Joshua P. ■ 02906 #043-01-2004 L2006 **N** *012
KRETZSCHMAR, Andrea. 345 BLACKSTONE BLVD, BUTLER HOSPITAL 02906 #048-12-2002 L2002 **P** *100
KROTZ, Stephan Paul. 101 DUDLEY ST, REPRODUCTIVE MEDICINE 02905 #016-06-2002 L2005 **OBG** *100
KROUNER, Andrew D. 150 E MANNING ST 02906 #010-01-1982 L1993 **OPH** *020 †35
KRZYSTOLIK, Magdalena G. 1 RANDALL SQ, STE 206 02904 #016-02-1993 L2000 **OPH** *020 †35
KUCHARSKI, Donna Aileen. 164 SUMMIT AVE, MIRIAM HOSPITAL 02906 #003-01-1992 L1998 **AN** *020 †05
KUMAR, Varun. 593 EDDY ST, RHODE ISLAND HOSPITAL 02903 #028-02-2002 L2002 **PD** *100
KUMMER, Tobias. 593 EDDY ST, DEPT OF EMERGENCY MED 02903 #409-21-2005 L2006 **EM** *012
KUNDAIKAR, Ajita. 593 EDDY ST, DEPT MED 02903 #035-08-2007 L2007 **IM** *012
KUPERMAN-BEADE, Marina. 1 RANDALL SQ, STE 306 02904 #043-01-1994 L2001 **D** *020 †15
KUPPERBERG, Jerald I. 101 DUDLEY ST 02905 #019-02-1975 L1978 **PD GPM** *020 †55
KURKCHUBASCHE, Arlet G. 2 DUDLEY ST STE 180 02905 #005-15-1987 L1995 **PDS** *020 †85
KURTH, Pamela Ann. 593 EDDY ST, RHODE ISLAND HOSPITAL 02903 #550-03-1999 L1999 **OS** *020 †75
KWAIT, Dylan Cool. ■ 02907 #024-16-2008 *012
KWARA, Awewura. 164 SUMMIT AVE, FL 2 02906 #412-01-1992 L2002 **ID** *020 †20
LACOMBE, Angela Jo Goss. 345 BLACKSTONE BLVD 02906 #016-76-2003, ▲ L2003 **P** *100
LACOURSE, Sylvia Marie. ■ 02906 #020-02-2007 L2007 **MPD** *012
LA FLEUR, John Edmond. 164 SUMMIT AVE, DEPARTMENT OF EMERGENCY ME 02906 #035-06-1991 L2004 **EM** *020 †16
LA FONTAINE, Donna Marie. 101 DUDLEY ST, WOMEN AND INFANTS' HOSPITA 02905 #024-16-1986 L1989 **OBG** *020 †30
LAFRANCE, W Curt, Jr. 593 EDDY ST 02903 #012-01-1995 L1995 **N P** *020 †75
LAGA CANALES, Alvaro Chri. ■ 02903 #649-52-2003 L2005 **PTH** *012
LAHIJANI, Javad. 101 DUDLEY ST 02905 #517-06-1967 L1983 **AN** *020
LAI, Chi-Kuang. 830 CHALKSTONE AVE, VA HOSPITAL 02908 #244-04-1969 L1998 **IMG IM** *020 †20,18
LAIRD, Vanessa De Jesus. 825 CHALKSTONE AVE 02908 #715-01-2003 L2007 **IM** *012
LAKHIANI, Chandan N. 593 EDDY ST, C/O HASBRO CHILDREN'S HOSP 02903 #496-38-1990 L1997 **PD** *020 †55
LALLY, Edward Vincent. 50 MAUDE ST 02908 #024-05-1975 L1980 **RHU IM** *040 †20
LALLY, Michelle Ann. 164 SUMMIT AVE, FL 2 02906 #051-01-1993 L1998 **ID** *020 †20
LA MANTIA, Kenneth R. 593 EDDY ST - 129, RHODE ISLAND HOSPITAL 02903 #035-19-1978 L1991 **AN PME** *020 †05
LAMBERT, Lisa Ann. 164 SUMMIT AVE, FAIN 2B 02906 #016-43-2000 L2000 **P** *100 †75 ‡
LAMBIASE, Robert Edward. 1 RANDALL SQ 02904 #035-46-1982 L1987 **DR** *020 †80
LAMPAL, Howard Stewart. 207 WATERMAN ST 02906 #016-42-1958 L1961 **PD** *020
LAMPEN, Katharine Matson. BROWN UNIVERSITY BOX 3670 02912 #035-20-2007 **IM** *012
LAND, Richard Ellis. 21 PEACE ST, # 251-E 02907 #016-06-1956 L1973 **DR NM** *030 †80,28
LANG, H Bickford. 593 EDDY ST 02903 #024-01-1940 L1952 **PD** *071 †55
LANGER, Phillip Raymond. 2 DUDLEY ST, UNIVERSITY ORTH 02905 #010-02-2001 L2004 **OSM** *012
LANNING, Jessica Denise. 593 EDDY ST 02903 #012-01-2007 L2007 **PD** *012
LAPOSATA, Elizabeth Ann. 48 ORMS ST, MEDICAL EXAMINES OFFICE 02904 #023-01-1979 L1993 **FOP ATP** *030 †50
LAPTOOK, Abbot Roy. 101 DUDLEY ST STE 1100, DEPARTMENT OF PEDIATRICS 02905 #035-08-1976 L2003 **PD NPM** *020 †55
LARAJA, Kristin Mary. ■ 02906 #024-07-2007 L2007 **PD** *012
LARKIN, Jerome Martin. 593 EDDY ST, INFECTOUS DISEASE #113 02903 #033-06-1993 L2005 **ID PD** *020 †20,55
LA ROSA, Steven Philip. 593 EDDY ST STE 330, RHODE ISLAND HOSPITAL 02903 #024-05-1992 L2003 **ID** *020 †20
LARSEN, Reynold Thorvald. 1 HOPPIN ST, RIGA 02903 #016-11-1961 L1987 **IM** *071 †20
LARSON, Lucia. 101 DUDLEY ST, WOMEN&INFANTS HOSPITAL 02905 #035-09-1987 L1993 **IM** *020 †20
LASSER, Michael Sidney. ■ 02903 #033-06-2006 L2006 **U** *012
LATHROP, John Champlin. 101 DUDLEY ST 02905 #035-03-1955 L1960 **GO GYN** *020 †30
LAUCHLAN, Stuart Campbell. 101 DUDLEY ST 02905 #919-03-1954 L1977 **ATP** *075
LAUFGRABEN, Marc Jeffrey. 1 HOPPIN ST, STE 200 HALLET CTR DIAB EN 02903 #024-01-1992 L1998 **END IM** *020 †20
LAWRENCE, William Dwayne. 101 DUDLEY ST, WOMEN & INFANT HOSP 02905 #001-02-1979 L2000 **ATP** *020 †50
LAZARUS, Elizabeth. 1 RANDALL SQ 02904 #035-20-1993 L1994 **DR** *020 †80
LEBEL, Jacqueline. 203 S MAIN ST 02903 #035-45-1997 L1997 **CHP P** *020 †75
LEBLANC, Karen Marie. ■ 02906 #041-12-2007 L2007 **FP** *012
LECHNER, Beatrice E. 101 DUDLEY ST, WOMEN & INFANTS HOSPITAL 02905 #409-23-1997 L2002 **NPM** *100 †55
LECHPAMMER, Mirna. 593 EDDY ST, RHODE ISLAND HOSP-LIFESPAN 02903 #957-01-1994 L2005 **PTH** *012
LEDERER, Daniel H. 345 BLACKSTONE BLVD 02906 #038-06-1968 L1975 **IM PUD** *020 †20
LEE, Betty S.. 877 CHALKSTONE AVE 02908 #305-01-2001 L2002 **IM** *100 †20
LEE, Byung Joo. ■ 02906 #005-11-2007 L2007 *012
LEE, Chun Wha. ■ 02906 #583-02-1984 *100
LEE, George. 164 SUMMIT AVE 02906 #024-05-1992 L1992 **NEP** *020 †20
LEE, Hyeon Soo. 593 EDDY ST, DEPT OF PEDIATRICS 02903 #583-01-1985 L2005 *100
LEE, Lawrence Wallace. 285 PROMENADE ST, FOUNDRY ORTHOPEDICS 02908 #035-06-1984 L1990 **ORS** *020 †40
LEE, Moon Oh. 593 EDDY ST, EMERGENCY MED, CLAVERICK B 02903 #005-14-2004 L2005 **EM PEM** *020
LEE, Soon Yung. 227 ANGELL ST 02906 #583-01-1960 L1972 **DR** *020 †80
LEE, Sung-Hee R. 101 DUDLEY ST 02905 #028-02-1992 L2000 **AN** *020 †05
LEE, Wee Kiat. 593 EDDY ST, RHODE ISLAND HOSPITAL 02903 #060-02-2003 L2007 **PCC** *012 †20
LEE, Young Hee. 593 EDDY ST DEPT RAD 02903 #583-08-1973 L1978 **DR IM** *050 †80
LEE, Yun Joo. 101 DUDLEY ST, DEPT OF PEDIATRICS 02905 #047-07-1971 L1993 **PD NPM** *020 †55
LEFEBVRE, Michelle. 593 EDDY ST 02903 #043-01-1996 L1996 **PD** *020 †55
LEFTICK, Marven. 49 SEEKONK ST, UNIT 1 02906 #067-01-1974 L1979 **RHU IM** *020 †20
LEITNER, Joshua Patrick. 593 EDDY ST, RHODE ISLAND HOSP 02903 #041-13-2003 L2007 **CD** *012 †20
LEITNER, Peter. BUTLER HOSP, DEPT PSYCH 02906 #408-30-1982 L1993 **P** *020
LEKAS, Mary Despina. 110 LOCKWOOD ST 02903 #418-01-1957 L1961 **OTO HNS** *071 †45
LE LEIKO, Neal Simon. 593 EDDY ST, RI HOSP MPH 126 02903 #035-09-1971 L2002 **PG NTR** *020 †55
LENCINAS, Claudio Luis. 21 PEACE ST 02907 #132-06-1995 L2005 **IM** *020 †20
LEONARD, Henrietta L. 593 EDDY ST, RI HOSPITAL 02903 #010-01-1982 L1995 **P CHP** *030 †75
LEONE, Louis August. 593 EDDY ST 02903 #024-05-1947 L1960 **ON** *020
LESPINASSE, Maggy. 40 CANDACE ST 02908 #035-09-1989 L1992 **PD** *020 †55
LESSARD, Anne-Marie. 593 EDDY ST 02903 #067-02-1994 L2006 *100
LESTER, Natalie Anne. 345 BLACKSTONE BLVD, BUTLER HOSP 02906 #047-05-2006 L2006 **P** *012
L'EUROPA, Ronald Albert. 193 WATERMAN ST 02906 #030-06-1977 L1978 **HEM ON** *020 †20
LEV, Robert. 50 MAUDE ST 02908 #869-05-1957 L1978 **PTH** *020 †50

■ = Address Information Privacy Protected

LEVECKIS, Renald Vincent. 164 SUMMIT AVE, DEPT MED 02906 #010-02-1990 L1990 IM *020 †20

LEVINE, Laura Beth. 345 BLACKSTONE BLVD, BUTLER HOSPITAL 02906 #024-07-2000 L2000 P *020 †75

LEVINE, Scott Marc. 1 RANDALL SQ 02904 #035-45-1988 L1996 DR *020 †80

LEVINE, Todd Peter. 101 DUDLEY ST, WOMEN AND INFANTS' HOSPITA 02905 #035-09-2002 L2002 CPP *020 †55

LEVY, Mitchell Mark. 593 EDDY ST 02902 #035-06-1977 L1995 IM OS *020 †20

LEWANDER, William Jeffrey. 593 EDDY ST # 141, EMERGENCY MEDICAL SERVICES 02903 #035-46-1979 L1985 PD OS *020 †55

LEWIS, Anna Van Nort. 1 HOPPIN ST, RIGHA 02903 #051-01-1983 L1989 PG PD *020 †55

LEWIS, Carol Teresa. 77 DABOLL ST 02907 #007-02-1980 L1984 PD *020 †55

LEWIS, David Carleton. BROWN UNIVERSITY, BOX G-BH 02912 #024-01-1961 L1975 ADM IM *072 †20

LEWIS, Robert Vickery. 17 WOODBURY ST 02906 #041-01-1943 L1944 IM *020 †20 ‡

LI, Jianqing. 593 EDDY ST, DEPT MED 02903 #041-15-2007 L2007 IM *012

LIBBEY, Norman Peter. 825 CHALKSTONE AVE, ROGER WILLIAMS GENERAL HOS 02908 #025-01-1974 L1979 ATP *020 †50

LICHT, Warren Eliot. 909 N MAIN ST, STE 300 02904 #035-46-1989 L1989 IM *020 †20

LICHTMAN, Herbert Chas. 164 SUMMIT AVE, MIRIAM HOSP DEPT OF MED 02906 #035-08-1945 L1970 IM HEM *071 †20,50

LIDOFSKY, Sheldon. 33 STANIFORD ST 02905 #035-08-1975 L1981 GE *020 †20

LIEBERMAN, Lori Gayle. ■ 02908 #041-15-2001 L2001 RHU *100

LIEBERMAN, Paul Benj. 345 BLACKSTONE BLVD, BUTLER HOSPITAL 02906 #024-01-1975 L1996 P *020 †75

LIEBMANN, Benjamin Otto. ■ 02906 #035-19-2002 L2007 EM *100

LIGUORI, Nancy Leslie. ■ 02906 #035-09-2004 L2004 IM *100

LIM, Sheen. ■ 02903 #041-02-2004 L2004 IM *020 †20

LINAKIS, James Gerard. 593 EDDY ST, RHODE ISLAND HOSPITAL 02903 #008-01-1984 L1989 EM PD *020 †55

LINDQUIST, David Gilbreth. 593 EDDY ST, RHODE ISLAND HOSPITAL 02903 #050-02-1999 L1999 EM *020 †16

LINSCOTT, Mana Kathleen. ■ 02903 #035-06-2003 L2003 IM *020 †20

LINSKY, Russell Allen. 164 SUMMIT AVE, THE MIRIAM HOSPITAL 02906 #004-01-2000 L2004 CD *020 †20 ‡

LITTELL, Nancy Turner. 593 EDDY ST 02903 #035-20-1984 L1986 IM EM *020 †20,16

LIU, Eugene H. ■ 02906 #043-01-2007 L2007 IM *012

LIU, Hsiang Mei. 164 SUMMIT AVE, MIRIAM HOSPITAL 02906 #385-02-1953 L1981 PTH *040 †50

LIUTKUS, Joanne F. 101 DUDLEY ST 02905 #065-10-1990 L1994 *020

LOCKHART, Gregory R. 593 EDDY ST, RHODE ISLAND HOSPITAL 02903 #032-01-1988 L1991 PEM PD *020 †55

LOFERSKI, Barbara Lynn. 593 EDDY ST, RHODE ISLAND HOSP DEPT ANE 02903 #043-01-1987 L1996 AN *020 †05

LOMME, Michele Marie. 593 EDDY ST, RHODE ISLAND HOSPITAL 02903 #007-02-2001 L2001 PTH *100 †50

LONG, Thomas Patrick. 593 EDDY ST 02903 #024-01-1978 L1985 D IM *020 †20,15 ‡

LONKS, John Richard. 164 SUMMIT AVE, STE E 02906 #033-05-1986 L1989 ID IM *020 †20,16

LORVIDHAYA, Peem. 593 EDDY ST 02903 #891-03-1998 L2005 ICE *020 †20

LOSIKOFF, Phyllis Terri. ■ 02903 #550-02-1998 L2001 PD *020 †55

LOUIS, Mariam. 593 EDDY ST, CRITICAL CAR 02903 #067-01-2000 L2007 *020 †20

LOWE, Lynn Clark. 101 DUDLEY ST 02905 #035-03-1975 L1977 OBG *020 †30

LOZANO, Sara Isabel. 593 EDDY ST, SAMUELS 211-EM RES PROG 02903 #024-16-2004 L2004 EM *012

LUBINSKY, Anthony Steven. ■ 02906 #035-08-2006 L2006 IM *012

LUBOW, Gary Philip. 345 BLACKSTONE BLVD, BUTLER HOSPITAL 02906 #038-40-1997 L1998 PYG *100

LUCAS, Phillip Richard. 2 DUDLEY ST STE 370, UNIV ORTHOPEDICS, INC 02905 #056-06-1973 L1974 ORS *020 †40

LUDWIG, Melissa Adams. 345 BLACKSTONE BLVD 02906 #035-45-2004 L2004 P *012

LUKACOVA-ZIB, Ivana. 1 HOPPIN ST, STE 200 02903 #286-11-1994 L2007 END *020

LUNETTI, Thomas Louis. 825 CHALKSTONE AVE 02908 #041-09-1968 L1986 GS *020 †85

LUTTERLOH, Emily Clare. 593 EDDY ST, PEDIATRIC INFECTIOUS DISEA 02903 #017-20-1998 L2003 PDI *100 †20,55

LUU, Martin Thaihoang. 593 EDDY ST, RHODE ISLAND HOSPITAL 02903 #041-15-2006 L2006 PTH *012

LY, John. ■ 02912 #043-01-2008 *012

LYNCH, Michelle Moore. 235 PLAIN ST 02905 #008-02-1993 L1996 CHP *020 †75

MAANI, Zeina Wajdi. 593 EDDY ST 02903 #575-02-2003 L2007 IM *012

MAC ANDREW, Vincent I. 275 RESERVOIR AVE 02907 #041-02-1945 L1946 U *071 †95

MACATANGAY, Bernard Jonas. 825 CHALKSTONE AVE, ROGER WILLIAMS HOSP 02908 #748-02-2001 L2003 ID *012 †20

MACELHANNON, Katherine Ga. 593 EDDY ST, DEPT EM 02903 #012-05-2007 L2007 EM *012

MACINTYRE, Ross Blairlaws. 593 EDDY ST 02903 #035-09-2006 L2007 OPH *012

MACKIE, Stewart Andrews. 593 EDDY ST 02903 #032-01-2007 L2007 PD *012

MAC KINNON, Scott Francis. 593 EDDY ST 02903 #024-16-1988 L1995 AN *020 †05

MACKO, Michael Bendall. 50 MAUDE ST 02908 #035-01-1975 L1976 IM EM *040 †20

MAC LEAN, David Burton. 1 HOPPIN ST STE 200, HALLETT CTR FOR DIAB ENDOC 02903 #060-02-1973 L1987 END IM *050 †20

MADAN, Seema. ■ 02906 #056-06-2005 L2005 P *012

MADDOX, Michael Mccann. ■ 02906 #047-06-2008 *012

MADOM, Ian A. ■ 02906 #035-15-2003 L2003 ORS *012

MAGENDANTZ, Henry G. 528 N MAIN ST UNIT 3, RHODE ISLAND GYN & FERT. S 02904 #036-07-1962 L1979 OBG REN *020 †30

MAHER, James O, III. 2 DUDLEY ST 02905 #035-09-1982 L1988 OSM OAR *020 †40

MAHER, Michael Jos. 5 ARNOLD ST 02906 #050-02-1989 L1989 NEP *020 †20

MAHONEY, Emmy A. 10 DAVOL SQ, STE 400 02903 #041-01-2002 L2002 CD *100

MAINIERO, Martha Beretta. 1 RANDALL SQ 02904 #024-07-1989 L1995 DR *020 †80

MAIZEL, Abby Lee. 50 MAUDE ST 02908 #041-01-1973 L1986 PTH *020 †50

MAJCZAK, Marta Barbara. ■ 02907 #008-02-2007 L2007 CPP *012

MAJERCIK, Sarah Dawn. ■ 02908 #050-02-1997 L1997 GS *020 †85

MALIK, Ruth C. 101 DUDLEY ST, WOMENS AND INFANT HOSP 02905 #748-01-1963 L1971 AN *020

MALINI, Luiz Eduardo. 825 CHALKSTONE AVE 02908 #187-54-2002 L2006 IM *012

MANALO, Rosario Beatriz. 10 DAVOL SQ STE 400 02903 #748-10-1997 L2000 ID *020 †20

MANCINI, James Richard. 2 DUDLEY ST, STE 306 02905 #028-34-1971 L1972 CD *020 †20

MANDANIS, Perry Nicholas. 830 CHALKSTONE AVE, VA MEDICAL CENTER 02908 #045-01-1986 L1989 P *075 †20

MANDELBAUM, David E. 110 LOCKWOOD ST, STE 342 02903 #035-01-1980 L2002 CHN CN *020 †55,75

MANERA, Lisa Marie. 164 SUMMIT AVE, DEPT HEMATOLOG 02906 #024-07-2002 L2006 HO *012 †20

MANLEY, Peter Elliot. 593 EDDY ST, RHODE ISLAND HOSPITAL 02903 #051-04-1998 L2001 PHO *100 †15

MANNING, Carol A. 18 IMPERIAL PL, UNIT 2D 02903 #041-13-1986 L1989 OBG *020 †30

MANNING, Jeffrey Dabrowsk. ■ 02906 #041-14-2006 L2006 FP *012

MANOCCHIA, Augustine, Jr. 1 EMPIRE PLZ 02903 #043-01-1986 L1988 IM *020 †20

MANSELL, Anthony Lynn. POB STE 440 02902 #038-40-1965 L1986 PDP PD *050

MARCACCIO, Edward J, Jr. 2 DUDLEY ST STE 470, PROVIDENCE RI 02905 #035-45-1986 L1993 VS *020 †85

MARCHANT, Douglas J. 101 DUDLEY ST, WOMEN AND INFANTS' HOSPITA 02905 #024-07-1951 L1992 OS *071 †30

MARECEK, Gary Robt. 825 CHALKSTONE AVE 02908 #033-06-1987 L1993 DR *020 †80

MARGOLIS, Peter Scott. 33 STANIFORD ST 02905 #041-07-1989 L1989 GE GP *020 †20

MARINO, Louis John, Jr. 345 BLACKSTONE BLVD, BUTLER HOSPITAL 02906 #035-08-1991 L1996 PYG P *020 †75

MARINO, Paul Lawrence. 164 SUMMIT AVE, STE 221 02906 #051-01-1974 L2007 CCM IM *020 †20

MARKLEY, Daniel James. 593 EDDY ST, DEPT MED 02903 #033-06-2007 L2007 IM *012

MARKLUND, Stephanie Kathle. ■ 02906 #010-02-2005 L2005 GS *012

MARSH, Donald Jay. PO BOX G A113, BROWN UNIV 02912 #005-02-1958 OS *030

MARTIN, Abigail Ellen. 2 DUDLEY ST, STE 180 02905 #048-02-1998 L2007 PDS *012 †85

MARTIN, Edward Wm. 825 CHALKSTONE AVE 02908 #043-01-1979 L1984 IM IMG *020 †20

MARTIN, Saul Avrum. 345 BLACKSTONE BLVD 02906 #068-01-1958 L1978 P *020

MARTINEZ, Mario Italo. 1 WARREN WAY 02905 #341-04-2000 L2006 PD *020

MARWIL, Daniel T. 293 GOVERNOR ST 02906 #025-12-1978 L1982 IM *020 †20

MASING, Raul Alfar. 593 EDDY ST, 593 EDDY ST 02903 #748-19-1990 L2001 APM *020 †05

MASKO, Gabriela B. 825 N MAIN ST, RADIATION ONCOLOGY ASSOC 02904 #024-07-1984 L1987 RO *020 †80

MASKO, John Jos, III. 94 WATERMAN ST 02906 #035-03-1980 L1986 P *020 †75

MASLOW, Andrew David. 593 EDDY ST, DEPT OF ANESTHESIA 02903 #024-16-1988 L1999 AN *020 †05

MASLOW, Gary Ross. 593 EDDY ST, POB 122 02903 #032-01-2004 L2004 CPP *012

MASON, Gary Edward. ■ 02907 #035-46-2007 L2007 PD *012

MASON, William Trafford. 1 HOPPIN ST, STE 3 02903 #038-41-1974 L1979 RHU IM *020 †20

MASOUDI, Obeidah Mahmoud. ■ 02903 #704-01-1987 L1998 PCC *020 †20

MASSI, Mark. 1 HOPPIN ST, CORO WEST 02903 #041-02-2000 L2000 PD *020

MASTROSTEFANO, Pasquale A. 347 BROADWAY 02909 #028-34-1967 L1968 IM GP *020

MATHEWS, Cara Amanda. ■ 02909 #032-01-2005 L2005 OBG *012

MATHEWS, Donnah Lynn. 593 EDDY ST 02903 #010-01-2002 L2002 IM *020 †20

MATHIEU, Peter Louis, Jr. 255 WATERMAN ST 02906 #028-34-1948 L1950 PD PDA *071 †55

MATHIEU, Robert Stephen. 1 HOPPIN ST, ANCHOR MEDICAL ASSOCIATES 02903 #024-07-1984 L1993 IM *020 †20

MATKOVIC, Christopher Mar. 593 EDDY ST, OF CHILD/FAMI 02903 #422-01-2002 L2005 PFP *012

MATTESON, Kristen Anne. 101 DUDLEY ST, WOMEN AND INFANT'S HOSPITA 02905 #024-07-2000 L2004 OBG *100 †10

MATTINGLY, Mark Edward. 10 DAVOL SQ, STE 400 02903 #020-02-1985 L1987 IM CCM *030 †20

MATTINGLY, Patrick Hayne. ■ 02904 #024-01-1969 L1991 GPM IM *020 †20

MATYAS, Bela Tamas. 3 CAPITOL HL, RI DEPT OF HEALTH 02908 #005-18-1985 L1988 OM *020 †70

MAUDE, Jennifer Louise. 909 N MAIN ST, STE 300 02904 #035-45-1990 L1999 IM *020 †20

MAVRICH, Kate Elizabeth. ■ 02906 #041-12-2006 L2006 IM *012

MAXWELL, Edward J. 345 BLACKSTONE BLVD 02906 #043-01-2000 L2001 P *100

MAYER, Kenneth Hugh. 164 SUMMIT AVE 02906 #016-06-1977 L1983 ID IM *050 †20

MAYER, Stephanie Brigitte. ■ 02906 #051-04-2006 L2006 IM *012

MAYNARD, John Francis. 593 EDDY ST 02903 #024-07-1963 L1964 U *071 †95

MAYO-SMITH, William W. 1 RANDALL SQ 02904 #035-20-1984 L1995 DR ORS *020 †80

MAYRIN, Jane V. ■ 02906 #041-15-2003 L2006 IM *100 †20

MAZER, Jeffrey Michael. ■ 02908 #024-07-2002 L2002 PCC *012 †20

MAZZAGLIA, Peter Joseph. 154 WATERMAN ST STE 2, UNIVERSITY SURGICAL ASSOCI 02906 #024-16-1993 L2006 GS *020 †20,85

MCANDREW, Philip Anthony. 148 W RIVER ST, STE 3 02904 #539-06-1995 L2002 IM *020 †20

MC CARTEN, Kathleen Mary. 593 EDDY ST 02903 #041-07-1970 L1996 PDR DR *020 †80

MCCLORY, Jill Anne. 593 EDDY ST, RI HOSP 02903 #654-01-2003 L2003 RHU *012

MC COMBS, H Louis. 593 EDDY ST, DEPT OF PATHOLOGY-APC 12 02903 #041-09-1958 L1964 PTH CLP *020 †50

MCCORMACK, Elise Michelle. 825 CHALKSTONE AVE 02908 #654-01-2005 L2005 IM *012

MCCORNATY, Bryna Judith. 593 EDDY ST, DEPT MED 02903 #024-16-2007 L2007 IM *012

MC COURT, Carolyn K. 101 DUDLEY ST 02905 #030-06-2001 L2005 OBG *100

MCCOY, Jeanne Marie. 593 EDDY ST, RHODE ISLAND HOSPITAL 02903 #038-43-2006 L2006 PD *012

MC CULLY, Kilmer Serjus. 830 CHALKSTONE AVE, VA HOSPITAL 02908 #024-01-1959 L1965 PTH CLP *020 †50

MC DONALD, Charles J. 593 EDDY ST 02903 #010-03-1960 L1968 D IM *030 †15

MCEACHERN, Rebecca Rose. 593 EDDY ST, RHODE IS HOSP-DEPT PED END 02903 #065-05-1996 L2003 PDE PD *012

MC GARRY, Kelly Ann. 593 EDDY ST, RI HOSPITAL, GENERAL INT. 02903 #008-01-1992 L1992 IM *020 †20

MCGOWAN, Christopher Eric. ■ 02906 #041-02-2006 L2006 IM *012

MC GUIRE, Mark Matthew. 593 EDDY ST, EMERGENCY MEDICINE 02903 #035-01-2000 L2000 EM *020 †16

MC ILWAIN, James Terrell. BROWN UNIV DIV BIOMED SCI, BOX G-M4 02912 #021-01-1961 N *040

MC KEE, Jason Q. 2 DUDLEY ST, STE 470 02905 #035-15-2001 L2001 PDS *012

MC KENDALL, Geo Raymond. 593 EDDY ST, RHODE ISLAND HODPITAL 02903 #035-09-1984 L1990 CD IM *020 †20

MC KNIGHT, Pamela Ann. 164 SUMMIT AVE, THE MIRIAM HOSPITAL 02906 #024-16-1987 L1987 N IM *020 †75

MCLAM, Elisha Christine. 593 EDDY ST, RHODE ISLAND HOSP 02903 #050-02-2006 L2006 GS *012

MC LENNAN, James Edward. 1 RANDALL SQ STE 410 02904 #024-01-1967 L1980 **NS** *020 †25

MC MASTER, Philip Robt B. ■ 02906 #023-07-1956 L1982 **P CLP** *072 †50,75

MC NELIS, Francis Leo. 100 DUDLEY ST, ENT ASSOCIATES INC 02905 #041-02-1945 L1947 **OTO** *072 †45

MC NULTY, Brendan David. 164 SUMMIT AVE, FAIN BUILDING, SUITE 390 02906 #024-16-2003 L2006 **HO** *012 †20

MC OSKER, Thomas C. 593 EDDY ST 02903 #035-01-1943 L1944 **NS** *071

MC ROBERTS, Roger Lowell, III. 593 EDDY ST, DEPARTMENT OF PSYCHIATRY 02903 #048-02-2000 L2000 **P** *020 †75

MC TAGGART, Ryan Andrew. ■ 02903 #035-01-1999 L2006 **DR** *012

MEAD, Richard Key. 235 PLAIN ST 02905 #035-20-1956 L1962 **IM CD** *071

MEDEIROS, Antone Arruda. 164 SUMMIT AVE, STE E 02906 #010-02-1961 L1977 **ID IM** *050 †20

MEECH, Sandra Jean. 593 EDDY ST 02903 #007-02-1991 L2001 **PHO** *020 †55

MEGA, Anthony Emmanuel. 164 SUMMIT AVE, FL 3 02906 #032-01-1988 L1992 **ON** *020 †20

MEHARG, Joseph V. 50 MAUDE ST 02908 #035-03-1985 L1988 **PUD IM** *020 †20

MEHTA, Akanksha. BROWN UNIVERSITY, BOX G8264 02912 #043-01-2006 L2006 **U** *012

MEHTA, Dhhananjay A. 101 DUDLEY ST 02905 #495-01-1993 L2001 **AN** *020 †05

MEHTA, Meghal Praful. ■ 02903 #048-04-2001 L2001 **EM** *100 †16

MEHTA, Niharika D. 100 DUDLEY ST, OBSTETRIC & CONSULTATIVE M 02905 #495-01-1994 L2002 **IM** *020 †20

MEISEL, Karl Martin. ■ 02906 #025-12-2007 L2007 **IM** *012

MEISEL, Lauren Elizabeth. ■ 02902 #025-12-2007 L2007 **PD** *012

MEKHJIAN, Ani Tamar. 164 SUMMIT AVE 02906 #038-40-1996 L2000 **EM** *020 †16

MELLO, Michael John. 164 SUMMIT AVE, THE MIRIAM HOSP 02906 #038-41-1986 L1988 **EM IM** *050 †20,16

MELZER, Katherine Elizabe. ■ 02906 #035-06-2006 L2006 **OBG** *012

MEMON, Abdulsattar N. 61 WESTFORD RD, HEMATOLOGY / ONCOLOGY 02906 #495-23-1971 L1977 **IM IG** *020 †20

MENDEZ ALLWOOD, Daniel Ed. 825 CHALKSTONE AVE, ROGER WILLIAMS HOSP 02908 #341-05-2002 L2006 **IM** *012

MENDONCA, Clyde Cassidy. 593 EDDY ST 952, RHODE ISLAND HOSPITAL 02903 #496-46-1998 L2005 **NEP** *020 †20

MERCER FALKOFF, Aleagia M. ■ 02903 #008-02-2006 L2006 **IM** *012

MERCHANT, Roland Clayton. 593 EDDY ST BLDG 14, RHODE ISLAND HOSPITAL 02903 #012-05-1993 L2001 **EM** *020 †16

MERINGOLO, Robert Douglas. 1076 N MAIN ST, CARDIOVASCULAR ASSOC. OF R 02904 #041-02-1969 L1976 **CD IM** *020 †20

MERLINO, Anthony Frank. 655 BROAD ST 02907 #041-02-1956 L1957 **ORS** *071 †40

MERNOFF, Stephen Todd. 877 CHALKSTONE AVE 02906 #035-19-1988 L1993 **N** *020 †75

MERRIAM, Priscilla. ■ 02906 #041-02-2006 L2006 **IM** *012

MERRITT, Elizabeth C. ■ 02906 #043-01-2008 *012

MERTZ, Michelle Jennifer. ■ 02905 #050-02-2006 L2006 **OBG** *012

MESERVY, Zenoa. 345 BLACKSTONE BLVD, BUTLER HOSPITAL 02906 #031-01-1992 L1996 **CHP** *020 †75

MESSARIS, Evangelos. 593 EDDY ST 02903 #418-01-1999 L2005 **GS** *012

MIDKIFF, Brian David. 593 EDDY ST, RIH, DEPT. DIAGNOSTIC IMAG 02903 #016-42-2003 L2003 **DR** *012

MIGLIORI, Michael E. 120 DUDLEY ST, STE 301 02905 #043-01-1982 L1987 **OPH** *020 †35 ‡

MILENO, Maria Denise. 164 SUMMIT AVE, FL 2 02906 #035-47-1988 L1994 **ID** *020 †20

MILLER, Howard Ipanza. 125 CORLISS ST 02904 #035-09-2001 **U** *020 †95

MILLER, Margaret Ann. 100 DUDLEY ST, 3RD FL 02905 #012-05-1992 L1992 **IM** *020 †20

MILLER, Marsha Maxine. ■ 02906 #056-06-1984 L1988 **FM** *020 †18

MILLIGAN, Benjamin Thomas. 157 SUMMIT AVE, THE MIRIAM HOSPITAL 02906 #035-20-2002 L2003 **EM** *100 †16

MILLS, John Peter. 593 EDDY ST, DEPT MED 02903 #033-06-2007 L2007 **IM** *012

MINER, Martin Morris. 164 SUMMIT AVE, THE MIRIAM HOSPITAL 02906 #038-41-1981 L1984 **FM** *020 †18

MINER, Thomas James. 2 DUDLEY ST, STE 470 02905 #043-01-1991 L2003 **GS** *020 †85

MITCHELL, Lindsay B. ■ 02906 #035-15-2003 L2003 **OBG** *020

MITCHNER, Landis. ■ 02940 #043-01-1999 L1999 **P** *020

MITRI, Joanna Habib. 825 CHALKSTONE AVE, ROGER WILLIAMS HOSP 02908 #605-03-2005 L2006 **IM** *012

MODHA, Poonam Kirit. 345 BLACKSTONE BLVD, BUTLER HOSP 02906 #024-16-2005 L2005 **P** *012

MODI, Rushabh. ■ 02906 #043-01-2008 *012

MODY, Vino Chunilal, Jr. 593 EDDY ST 02903 #012-05-1997 L1998 **IM** *100

MOGHBELI, Anoosheh. 593 EDDY ST 02903 #023-01-2005 L2005 **PD** *012

MONAGHAN, Sean Farrell. 593 EDDY ST, RHODE ISLAND HOSP 02903 #033-05-2007 L2007 **GS** *012

MONCHIK, Jack Morton. 154 WATERMAN ST 02906 #041-12-1964 L1973 **END GS** *020 †85

MONCHIK, Keith Oster. 593 EDDY ST, RHODE ISLAND HOSP-LIFESPAN 02903 #305-01-2003 L2003 **ORS** *012

MONTGOMERY, John Beaton. 101 DUDLEY ST 02905 #539-03-1959 L1963 **PD A** *020

MONTROSS, Christine E. 345 BLACKSTONE BLVD, BUTLER HOSP 02906 #043-01-2006 L2006 **P** *012

MONZON SANTANA, Carmen V. 2 DUDLEY ST STE 560 02905 #308-02-1991 L1999 **P** *020 †75

MOODIE, Jennifer Dunbar. 593 EDDY ST 02903 #033-06-2001 L2001 **N** *100

MOORE, Daniel, Jr. 154 WATERMAN ST 02906 #024-07-1953 L1956 **CD IM** *071

MOORE, Richard George. 101 DUDLEY ST, WOMEN & INFANTS HOSPITAL 02905 #060-01-1993 L1999 **OBG** *020 †30

MORALES COLOME, Eduardo J. 825 CHALKSTONE AVE 02908 #341-03-2004 L2007 **IM** *012

MORAN, John Harold. 202 PRAIRIE AVE 02905 #041-13-1968 L1973 **PD** *020 †55

MORCHEN, Sarah Ann. ■ 02906 #033-06-2006 L2006 **FP** *012

MOREIRA, Carla C. ■ 02907 #043-01-2008 *012

MORIN, Melinda Jean. 593 EDDY ST, RI HOSP PED CRITCAL CARE 02903 #024-16-1990 L1990 **CCP** *020 †55

MOROCCO, William Joseph. 2 DUDLEY ST, STE 190 02905 #032-01-1995 L1995 **PD** *020 †55

MORRIS, Tasha Elisa. 345 BLACKSTONE BLVD 02906 #035-01-2002 L2004 **ADP** *020 †75

MORRISON, Clinton Strauss. ■ 02907 #024-16-2007 L2007 **PS** *012

MORRISSEY, Paul Edward. 2 DUDLEY ST, STE 470 02905 #024-16-1988 L1996 **TTS** *020 †85

MOSHER, Pamela Jane. 593 EDDY ST, RHODE ISLAND HOSP 02906 #005-11-2006 L2006 **CPP** *012

MOSKOWITZ, Paula F. 593 EDDY ST 02903 #016-42-1996 L2000 **D** *020 †15

MOSS, Steven F. 110 LOCKWOOD ST, STE 116 02903 #917-30-1985 L2000 **GE** *020 †20

MOST, Albert Stephen. 593 EDDY ST, RHODE ISLAND HOSPITAL 02903 #023-07-1962 L1969 **CD IM** *030 †20

MOUBAYED, Samir Geo. 1 RANDALL SQ STE 205 02904 #330-03-1949 L1968 **OBG** *071 †30

MOULTON, Anne Winthrop. 111 PLAIN ST, FL 3 02903 #035-08-1980 L1982 **IM** *020 †20

MOULTON, Anthony Le Roy. 1 RANDALL SQ STE 414 02904 #035-01-1971 L1991 **TS VS** *020 †85,90

MOURA, Rossana Martins. 100 DUDLEY ST 02905 #187-13-1992 L2001 **GE** *020 †20

MOUSSA, Pierre Bachir. 593 EDDY ST 02903 #024-07-1986 L1989 **IM CD** *020

MUELLER, Lisa Ann. 33 STANIFORD ST 02905 #539-04-1990 L1998 **GE** *020 †20

MUGLIA, Jennie Josephine. 593 EDDY ST 02903 #033-05-1982 L1990 **D IM** *020 †20,15

MUHLEBACH, Stephan George. 593 EDDY ST, DIVISION OF CARDIOLOGY 02903 #008-02-2002 L2002 **CD** *012 †20

MUKAND, John Arun. 21 PEACE ST, ST. JOSEPH HOSPITAL 02907 #056-06-1985 L1989 **PM** *020 †60

MUKKADA, Vincent Antony. 593 EDDY ST, RHODE ISLAND HOSPITAL 02903 #038-41-2002 L2002 **PG** *012

MULCAHEY, Mary Kathryn. 593 EDDY ST, RI HOSP 02903 #035-45-2006 L2006 **ORS** *012

MULLARE, Tracy Kristen. 593 EDDY ST, RHODE ISLAND HOSPITAL 02903 #035-03-2003 L2003 **CPP** *012

MURALI, Jothi. ■ 02908 #012-05-2007 L2007 *012

MURATORE, Christopher S. 2 DUDLEY ST, STE 180 02905 #010-02-1995 L2005 **PDS** *100 †85

MURPHY, Brian Lawrence. 593 EDDY ST, RHODE ISLAND HOSPITAL 02903 #918-01-1987 L1998 **DR** *020 †80

MURPHY, Frederick G. 593 EDDY ST, DEPT OF ANESTHESIA 02903 #024-16-1979 L1985 **AN** *020 †05

MURPHY, Marie Audrey. 593 EDDY ST DEPT DR 02903 #063-01-1986 L1991 **DR** *020 †80

MURPHY, Marjorie A. 1 HOPPIN ST STE 202, CORO CENTER 02903 #043-01-1988 L1997 **OPH OS** *020 †35

MURPHY, Michael Christie. 593 EDDY ST 02903 #024-07-2003 L2003 **EM** *100

MURPHY, Timothy Patrick. 1 RANDALL SQ 02904 #024-05-1987 L1988 **VIR** *020 †80

MURRAY, Anne Lawrence. 239 CRANSTON ST 02907 #005-02-2003 L2003 **OBG** *020

MURUGANANDAN, Krithika Me. 593 EDDY ST, RHODE ISLAND HOSP 02903 #665-01-2006 L2006 **EM** *012

MUSLINER, Thomas Allen. 164 SUMMIT AVE DEPT ENDRO 02906 #024-01-1972 L1977 **END IM** *040 †20

MYERS, Deborah Lee. 695 EDDY ST 02903 #035-48-1981 L1983 **GYN OS** *020 †30

MYERS, Janette Elaine. 11 S ANGELL ST, # 159 02906 #004-01-2000 L2004 **PD** *020 †55

MYINTU, Aye Myint. 345 BLACKSTONE BLVD, BUTLER HOSP 02906 #021-01-2007 L2007 **P** *012

NADGIR, Rohini Narahari. ■ 02908 #041-01-2000 L2000 **DR** *020 †80

NAGDEV, Arun Daulat. 593 EDDY ST, FOUNDATION 02903 #305-01-2000 L2005 **EM** *020 †16

NAGRAJ, Kasthuri D. ■ 02906 #495-03-1957 L1973 **IM** *075

NAH, Yu Jin. 825 CHALKSTONE AVE, DEPT OF MEDICINE 02908 #583-32-2004 L2007 **IM** *012

NAJERA, Gabriel A. 345 BLACKSTONE BLVD 02906 #649-17-1951 L1956 **P** *072 †75

NANDA, Aman. 593 EDDY ST, APC-424 02903 #495-74-1987 L2000 **IM IMG** *020 †20

NANIAN, Kenneth B. 235 PLAIN ST, STE 305 02905 #024-07-1953 L1957 **CD IM** *020 †20

NAPOLI, Anthony Michael. 593 EDDY ST 02903 #010-02-2002 L2002 **EM** *100 †16

NARDONE, Adelaide Grace. 1 WARREN WAY, CHAPEE HEALTH CTR 02905 #035-09-1983 L2001 **OBG** *020 †30

NARSULE, Chaitan Kamalaka. 593 EDDY ST, APC 4TH FL 02903 #033-06-2004 L2004 **GS** *012

NATHAN, Joshua Benjamin. 593 EDDY ST 02903 #016-11-2002 L2002 **P** *012

NATHANSON, Andrew T. 164 SUMMIT AVE, DEPT EM 02906 #024-07-1990 L1994 **EM** *020 †16

NAYAK, Kamakshi Ullal. 50 MAUDE ST 02908 #495-37-1971 L1977 **PTH** *020 †50

NAYLOR, Elizabeth Thompso. ■ 02912 #043-01-2008 *012

NAYYAR, Panjak. 164 SUMMIT AVE, MIRIAM HOSPITAL 02906 #495-73-1985 L2002 **CCA** *020 †05

NAZARETH, Samantha. ■ 02912 #043-01-2008 *012

NAZERALI, Rahim Shiraz. ■ 02903 #032-01-2008 *012

NEAD, Jennifer Anne. 593 EDDY ST, RHODE ISLAND HOSP 02903 #035-15-2006 L2006 **PD** *012

NEIMARK, Ezequiel. 593 EDDY ST, GI MPS-126 02903 #132-01-1995 L2005 **PG** *100 †55

NEMCHENOK, Lina R. 593 EDDY ST, 593 EDDY STREET 02903 #913-69-1983 L2000 **IM** *020 †20

NERENBERG, Rebecca Heidi. ■ 02906 #041-01-2006 **EM** *012

NESTOR, Elizabeth M. 593 EDDY ST, UNIVERSITY EMERGENCY MEDIC 02903 #016-06-1991 L1994 **EM** *020 †16

NEUMANN, David Paul. 1 RANDALL SQ 02904 #035-08-1985 L1995 **DR** *020 †80

NEVEL, Laura Sue. 528 N MAIN ST, UNIT 3 02904 #550-02-1981 L1984 **OBG** *020 †30

NEVOLA, Chad Peter. 120 DUDLEY ST STE 105 02905 #043-01-1997 L2000 **PD** *020 †55

NG, Diana. ■ 02906 #043-01-2003 **GS** *100

NG, Karen Y. 239 CRANSTON ST 02907 #035-15-1998 L2001 **FM** *020 †18

NG, Thomas. 2 DUDLEY ST, STE 470 02905 #065-05-1993 L1993 **GS** *020 †85

NGO, Huan Thanh. 593 EDDY ST 02903 #010-02-2006 L2000 **EM** *020 †16

NICI, Linda Theresa. 830 CHALKSTONE AVE, PROVIDENCE VAMC 02908 #035-08-1984 L1991 **PUD IM** *020 †20

NIJHAWAN, Ank E. 164 SUMMIT AVE, RISE BUILDING 02906 #048-12-2001 L2007 **ID** *020

NILSON, Douglas George. ■ 02908 #016-06-2005 L2005 **EM** *012

NIR, Dan. 825 CHALKSTONE AVE 02908 #041-09-1994 L2004 **DR** *020 †80

NISSENSOHN, Michael I. 1 SLATER AVE 02906 #035-08-1979 L1984 **GE IM** *020 †20

NOEL, Arthur Wayne. 164 SUMMIT AVE DEPT RAD 02906 #010-02-1979 L1985 **DR NM** *020 †80,28

NOGUEIRA, Jennifer Ann. 593 EDDY ST, RHODE ISLAND HOSPITAL 02903 #024-05-1995 L2000 **DR** *020 †80

NOLAN, Patricia Ann. 3 CAPITOL HL 02908 #067-01-1969 L1995 **PHP** *030 †70

NORA, Nedo F. 593 EDDY ST 02903 #737-01-1957 L1963 **PD GP** *020 †55

NOREN, C Georg. 593 EDDY ST, BLDG 123 02903 #858-02-1971 L1994 **NS** *020

NOTO, Richard Bartholomew. 1 RANDALL SQ 02904 #035-45-1982 L1988 **NM DR** *020 †80,28

NOTTAGE, Kerri. ■ 02906 #043-01-2004 L2004 **MPD** *012

NUGENT, Sara Flint. 285 GOVERNOR ST, STE 200 02906 #003-01-1986 L1989 **IM** *020 †20

O'BELL, John Wallace. 593 EDDY ST, DIVISION OF RENAL DISEASES 02903 #038-06-1998 L2004 **NEP** *020 †20

O'BRIEN, Aidan D. 830 CHALKSTONE AVE, PROV VA MED CTR DIV PULM M 02908 #539-05-1989 L1998 **PUD CCM** *020 †20

O'BRIEN, Barbara M. 101 DUDLEY ST 02905 #035-09-1998 L2007 **MFM MG** *020 †30

O'BRIEN, Mary Ellen. ■ 02908 #033-06-2007 L2007 **P** *012

O'DONNELL, Kathryn Elizab. 593 EDDY ST, DEPT MED 02903 #041-13-2007 L2007 **IM** *012

OELTJEN, Sarah Darlene. 593 EDDY ST, CLAVERICK 2 02903 #024-01-2002 L2005 **PEM** *012 †55

OFISI, Joseph Wesa. 593 EDDY ST 02903 #577-01-1998 L2004 **GS** *100

OFSTEAD, Laura Marie. 111 PLAIN ST, 2ND FL 02903 #023-07-1994 L1994 **IM** *020 †20

OGDEN, Neida Quackenbush. 1 WARREN WAY 02905 #067-01-1948 L1954 **PD** *020 †55

OGUNLEYE, Foluso Sunday. 825 CHALKSTONE AVE 02908 #690-06-2001 L2005 **IM** *012

OH, William. 101 DUDLEY ST, WOMEN & INFANTS HOSP 02905 #748-01-1958 L1974 **NPM PD** *020 †55

OKPARA, Nnenna Chinyere. 593 EDDY ST, RHODE ISLAND HOSPITAL GAST 02903 #035-01-2002 L2006 **GE** *012 †20

OLCHOWSKI, Edward C. 827 N MAIN ST 02904 #043-01-1976 L1978 **IM** *020 †20

OLDENBURG, Nicklas B. 825 N MAIN ST 02904 #036-01-1995 L2002 **RO** *020 †80

OLIVA, Jeanne Marie. 285 GOVERNOR ST 02906 #043-01-1994 L1994 **IM** *020 †20

OLIVARES, Alvaro J. 345 BLACKSTONE BLVD 02906 #264-12-1989 L1993 **P** *020 †75

OLIVIERI, Laura Jean. 593 EDDY ST, RHODE ISLAND HOSP-LIFESPAN 02903 #016-02-2003 L2003 **PDC** *012 †55

ORBAN, Zsolt. 593 EDDY ST 02903 #473-01-1992 L1999 **END IM** *020 †20

ORLANDO, Frances Ann. 593 EDDY ST 02903 #041-01-2007 L2007 **PD** *012

OSBORNE, Roanne Michele. 202 PRAIRIE AVE 02905 #894-01-1998 L2004 **FM** *020 †18

OSIECKI, Stephanie T. 164 SUMMIT AVE, DEPT MED 02906 #050-02-1989 L1998 **IM** *020 †20

OTOOLE, Thomas Paschal. ■ 02908 #005-19-1991 L1994 **IM** *020 †20

OTT, Brian Richard. 2 DUDLEY ST, STE 530 02905 #041-02-1979 L1981 **N IM** *020 †20,75

OVERLY, Frank Lamond. 593 EDDY ST, HASBRO CHILDREN'S HOSPITAL 02903 #035-45-1997 L2000 **PD** *020 †55

OWENS, Gregory Randolph. ■ 02906 #005-14-2005 L2005 **PD** *012

OWENS-STIVELY, Judith A. 593 EDDY ST, POTTER SUITE 200 02903 #043-01-1980 L1986 **PD CHP** *020 †55

OYELESE, Adetokunbo A. 55 CLAVERICK ST, STE 100 02903 #008-01-1997 L2004 **NS** *020

OYER, Calvin E. 101 DUDLEY ST 02905 #017-20-1952 L1990 **PP IM** *071 †20,50

PABALAN, Melissa Lynn. ■ 02906 #041-12-2008 *012

PADBURY, James Frederick. 101 DUDLEY ST, DEPT OF PEDIATRICS 02905 #005-14-1973 L1995 **PD NPM** *020 †55

PADMORE, Soenda Euphemia. 239 CRANSTON ST 02907 #041-13-2001 L2004 **FM** *100 †18

PAGIDAS, Kelly. 101 DUDLEY ST, WOMEN & INFANTS HOSPITAL 02905 #067-01-1987 L1998 **OBG** *020 †30

PAGLIA, Michael Joseph. 101 DUDLEY ST, 3RD FLOOR, MFM DIVISION 02905 #041-01-1998 L2005 **OBG MFM** *020 †30

PAGONIS, Constantine. 21 PEACE ST 02907 #018-03-1971 L1974 **IM CD** *071 †20

PAHIGIAN, Vahey Myron. 101 DUDLEY ST 02905 #024-07-1943 L1944 **GS** *020 †85

PAL, Sangeeta. 825 CHALKSTONE AVE 02908 #495-47-2001 L2005 **IM** *012

PALLANT, Adam David. 593 EDDY ST, RM 135 02903 #035-45-1991 L1996 **PD** *040 †55

PALMER, Mary E. 164 SUMMIT AVE, DEPT OF EMERGENCY MEDICINE 02906 #035-08-1990 L1990 **EM** *072 †16

PALMISCIANO, Lynne M. 593 EDDY ST, DAVOL 141 02903 #043-01-1994 L1998 **PD** *020 †55

PALUMBO, Kevin Scott. 33 STANIFORD ST 02905 #038-06-1995 L1995 **GE** *020 †20

PALUMBO, Theodore Carter. 33 STANIFORD ST 02905 #038-06-1990 L1990 **GE** *020 †20

PALUMBO, William Anthony. 80 DEAN ST, PROVIDENCE MEDICAL HLTHCAR 02903 #561-17-1984 L1987 **IM** *020

PANAGOS, Peter David. 593 EDDY ST 02903 #012-05-1994 L2003 **EM** *020 †16

PANUNCIALMAN, Ian Noel Ta. ■ 02908 #748-10-1996 L2006 *100

PANUNCIALMAN, Jaymie Fe P. 825 CHALKSTONE AVE 02908 #748-02-2001 L2005 **IM** *100

PARAB, Anika. ■ 02904 #024-16-2004 L2004 **EM** *012

PAREEK, Gyan. 2 DUDLEY ST, STE 174 02905 #422-01-1998 L2005 **U** *020

PARISI, Alfred Francis. 164 SUMMIT AVE, FL 3 02906 #035-20-1963 L1988 **CD IM** *040 †20

PARKS, Robert Emmett, Jr. BROWN U DIV BIO & MED 02912 #024-01-1945 L1948 **OS** *050

PARRILLO, Joseph M A. ■ 02904 #561-01-1938 **OS GP** *071

PARTRIDGE, Robert Alan. 593 EDDY ST, DEPT OF EMERGENCY MEDICINE 02903 #041-01-1962 L1963 **P PHP** *020 †75

PASCUAL, Sheila Karina Ve. 825 CHALKSTONE AVE, ROGER WILLIAMS HOSP 02908 #748-01-2001 L2004 **HO** *012 †20

PASSERO, Mary Ann. 120 DUDLEY ST, STE 203 02905 #024-01-1969 L1976 **AI PDP** *020 †55,03

PASSERO, Michael Anthony. 50 MAUDE ST 02908 #024-01-1969 L1976 **PUD IM** *040 †20

PATEL, Amar. 593 EDDY ST, COOP 1 02903 #056-06-2002 L2002 **ORS** *100

PATEL, Brian Bhupendra. 593 EDDY ST, 2ND FL 02903 #024-16-2001 L2001 **EM** *100 †16

PATEL, Dipan C. ■ 02904 #041-13-2006 L2006 **GS** *012

PATEL, Mrudula Harish. 909 N MAIN ST, HINES DERMATOLOGY ASSOC IN 02904 #496-38-1968 L1993 **FPS** *020 †18

PATEL, Paras Mohanbhai. 825 CHALKSTONE AVE 02908 #305-01-2004 L2005 **IM** *012

PATTERSON, Danielle Marle. ■ 02906 #035-19-2007 **GS** *012

PATTERSON, Robert Bruce. 486 SILVER SPRING ST 02904 #041-09-1979 L1991 **VS GS** *020 †85

PAUL, Susan Rachel. ■ 02906 #024-16-2005 L2005 **MPD** *012

PAYNE, John Robt. 830 CHALKSTONE AVE 02908 #035-03-1954 L1955 **GP IM** *020

PAZZAGLINI, Nicole Lynne. 101 DUDLEY ST, WOMEN AND INFANTS HOSPITAL 02905 #035-06-1998 L2007 **OBG** *020 †30

PEARIS, Gillian Elliott. 593 EDDY ST, RHODE ISLAND HOSPITAL 02903 #026-04-1998 L1998 **OS** *020

PEARLSTEIN, Teri Beth. 101 DUDLEY ST, WOMEN AND INFANTS HOSPITAL 02905 #035-19-1982 L1988 **P** *020 †75

PENN, Joseph Vincent. 593 EDDY ST, RHODE ISLAND HOSPITAL 02903 #048-02-1992 L1992 **PFP CHP** *020 †75

PENSA, Edward Antonio. 33 STANIFORD ST 02905 #041-01-1997 L2001 **GE** *020 †20

PEPI, Michael Augustine. 235 PLAIN ST, STE 401 02905 #422-01-1982 L1990 **OBG** *020 †30

PERA, Vincent, Jr. 1 HOPPIN ST, CORO WEST 3 02903 #422-01-1983 L1986 **NTR IM** *020

PEREZ, Rafael. 557 BROAD ST 02907 #264-02-1964 L1982 **IM** *071

PERRON-BURDICK, Misa D. ■ 02906 #043-01-2008 *012

PETER, Georges. 593 EDDY ST, PED INF DIS 02903 #024-01-1964 L1973 **ID PD** *062 †55

PETERS, Norman David. 100 HIGHLAND AVE STE 305 02906 #048-02-1971 L1977 **NS** *020 †25

PETTERS, Gail Audrey. 593 EDDY ST 02903 #035-15-1990 L1998 **AN** *020 †05

PEZZULLO, John A, III. 1 RANDALL SQ 02904 #043-01-1995 L1995 **DR** *020 †80

PFISTER, Blair Curtis. ■ 02906 #054-04-2002 L2003 **CPP** *012

PHILIP, Leny. 9 PLEASANT ST, MEDICINE ASSOCIATES 02906 #495-31-1987 L2003 **IM** *020 †20 ‡

PHILIP, Noah Stephen. 345 BLACKSTONE BLVD 02906 #035-03-2005 L2005 **P** *012

PHILLIPS, Katharine Anne. 345 BLACKSTONE BLVD, BUTLER HOSPITAL 02906 #032-01-1987 L1994 **P** *050 †75

PHILLIPS, Raina Maria. ■ 02908 #016-11-2007 L2007 **MPD** *012

PHIPPS, Maureen Glennon. 101 DUDLEY ST, WOMEN & INFANT HOSP 02905 #050-02-1994 L1994 **OBG** *020 †30

PHORNPHURKUL, Chanika. 593 EDDY ST, RIH PEDIATRIC ENDOCRIN 02903 #891-03-1992 L1995 **PDE** *020 †19,55

PIANTINO, Juan Andres. ■ 02903 #132-01-2002 L2007 **PD** *012

PICCOLELLO, Marcelle L. 1 RANDALL SQ 02904 #041-01-1985 L1994 **DR** *020 †80

PICOTTE, Dawn Marie. 345 BLACKSTONE BLVD, BUTLER HOSPITAL 02906 #011-04-1991 L1996 **CHP** *020 †75

PIEBENGA, Elise Claire. 593 EDDY ST, POTTER 115 02903 #041-02-2000 L2005 **PD** *020 †55

PINAR, Mehmet Halit. 101 DUDLEY ST 02905 #902-03-1974 L1990 **PD PP** *030 †55,50

PINCH, Pamela D Rustim. ■ 02906 #352-11-1948 L1956 **IM** *071

PINTO, Jamie Marie. 593 EDDY ST, RHODE ISLAND HOSPITAL 02903 #035-01-2006 L2006 **PD** *012

PINYAVAT, Alan. ■ 02908 #035-19-2006 L2006 **IM** *012

PIRRAGLIA, Paul Anthony. 830 CHALKSTONE AVE # T-32, PROVIDENCE VA MEDICAL CTR 02908 #035-20-1998 L1998 **IM** *050 †20

PISHARODI, Latha Rammohan. 593 EDDY ST, RHODE ISLAND 02903 #495-31-1982 L1999 **PTH** *020 †50

PISZCZEK-GURSES, Ewa Danu. 593 EDDY ST 02903 #654-01-2002 **IM** *020

PIZZARELLO, Martha. 101 DUDLEY ST, TRIAGE DEPT 02905 #010-02-2000 L2000 **OBG** *020

PIZZARELLO, Peter Anthony. 868 ADMIRAL ST, ORTHOPEDIC SERVICES & SPOR 02904 #024-07-2000 L2003 **OSM** *020

PIZZARELLO, Peter Anthony. 868 ADMIRAL ST 02904 #028-34-1967 L1968 **ORS** *020 †40

PLAMONDON, Caroline J. 1 RANDALL SQ, STE 408 02904 #067-02-1991 L1998 **PS** *072 †65

PLANTE, Matthew Joseph. ■ 02908 #043-01-2003 L2003 **ORS** *012

PLETTE, Angela Marie. 164 SUMMIT AVE, FAIN CLINIC 3RD FLOOR 02906 #024-16-2003 L2003 **HO** *012 †20

PNIEWSKI, Helene. ■ 02906 #024-05-1976 L2001 **CHP OS** *020 †55

POCH, Michael A. 2 DUDLEY ST STE 174, RHODE ISLAND HOSPITAL / DE 02905 #043-01-2005 L2005 **U** *012

PODIS, Alan David. 2 DUDLEY ST STE 185 02905 #038-06-1956 L1987 **U** *020 †95

PONNANDAI, Somasundar S. 825 CHALKSTONE AVE, DEPARTMENT OF SURGERY 02908 #495-04-1990 L2005 **GS** *020 †85

POPESCU, Adrian. ■ 02903 #781-01-2001 L2004 **IM** *100 †20

POPPAS, Athena. 2 DUDLEY ST STE 360, RIH CARDIOLOGY 02905 #056-05-1989 L1996 **CD** *020 †20

PORRAS, Gisela Isabel. 593 EDDY ST, RHODE ISLAND HOSPITAL 02903 #935-07-2002 L2006 **DBP** *012 †55

PORTELLI, David C. 164 SUMMIT AVE, THE MIRIAM HOSP 02906 #035-48-1992 L2003 **EM IM** *020 †20,16

POTTER, Clinton Burns. 101 DUDLEY ST 02905 #035-20-1952 L1956 **OBG** *071 †30

POWERS, Kelly Johnson. 593 EDDY ST, DEPT OF RADIOLOGY 02903 #040-02-2001 L2005 **DR** *012

POWRIE, Raymond Oliver. 101 DUDLEY ST 02905 #060-01-1987 L1992 **IM** *020 †20

PRADEEP, Ramarao A. 593 EDDY ST, RHODE ISLAND HOSPITAL 02903 #495-53-1991 L1996 **END** *100 †20

PRADHAN, Deepak Ravindra. ■ 02908 #041-02-2006 L2006 **IM** *012

PRAKASH, Seema. 825 CHALKSTONE AVE, DEPT IM 02908 #032-01-2007 L2007 **IM** *012

PREIS, Ido S. ■ 02912 #043-01-2007 L2007 *012

PRICE, Katharine Anne. 593 EDDY ST, DEPT MED 02903 #035-45-2007 L2007 **IM** *012 †20

PRICE, Lawrence Howard. 345 BLACKSTONE BLVD 02906 #025-01-1978 L1996 **P** *020 †75

PRICOLO, Victor. 2 DUDLEY ST STE 470, UNIVERSITY SURGICAL ASSOC 02905 #561-03-1981 L1988 **GS AS** *020 †85

PRIEBE, Cedric Jos, III. 101 DUDLEY ST 02905 #024-01-1988 L2004 **PD** *062 †55

PRIETO TORRES, Miguel A. 100 CURTIS ST 02909 #935-01-1995 L2002 **IM** *020 †20

PRINCE, Anthony Alexander. PO BOX 4330, BROWN UNIVERSITY 02912 #041-01-2008 *012

PROANO, Lawrence. 593 EDDY ST, DAVAL RM 141 02903 #016-01-1976 L1983 **EM** *020 †16

PROMRAT, Kittichai. 110 LOCKWOOD ST, STE 116 02903 #891-03-1992 L1995 **GE** *020 †20

PUENTE CUELLAR, Napoleon. 825 CHALKSTONE AVE 02908 #341-05-2002 L2005 **IM** *012

PUESCHEL, Siegfried Max. 593 EDDY ST 02903 #407-25-1960 L1975 **PD** *071 †55,19

PUGATCH, David L. 593 EDDY ST 02903 #067-01-1990 L1990 **PDI** *020 †55

PUIUS, Yoram Andrew. 825 CHALKSTONE AVE, DIVISION OF INFECTIOUS DIS 02908 #035-46-2001 L2007 **ID** *100

PURISIMA, Reve Gamba. 593 EDDY ST 02903 #035-15-2005 L2005 **IM** *012

PURVIS, Warren Leslie. 29 ELBOW ST 02903 #027-01-1977 L1985 **P** *075 †75

PUTHAWALA, Mohamedyakub A. 593 EDDY ST 02903 #495-76-1980 L1990 **RO** *020 †80

QUADRI, Syed Misbahullah. ■ 02906 #704-26-1996 L2000 **CCM** *100

QUALLS, Charles Brandon. 345 BLACKSTONE BLVD, CONSULTANTS OF RHODE 02906 #038-06-1970 L1975 **P** *020 †75

QUDDUS, Mohammad Ruhul. 101 DUDLEY ST, DEPT OF PATH W & I HOSP 02905 #160-02-1983 L1994 **PTH** *020 †50

QUESENBERRY, Matthew I. ■ 02906 #024-16-2004 L2004 **IM** *012

QUESENBERRY, Peter Jay. 593 EDDY ST, RHODE ISLAND HOSP 02903 #051-01-1964 L2001 **ON HEM** *050 †20

QUIGLEY, David Grinnell. 110 LOCKWOOD ST 02903 #024-07-1961 L1968 **ORS AM** *071 †40

QUINN, Erica Lashon. 97 WATERMAN ST, BROWN UNIV BOX G-8218 02912 #043-01-2000 **FM** *100

QUINTOS, Jose Bernardo Q. 593 EDDY ST, PEDIATRIC ENDOCRINOLOGY 02903 #748-10-1992 L2000 **PDE** *020 †55

QUIRK, Daniel Mark. 33 STANIFORD ST 02905 #043-01-1991 L1997 **GE** *020 †20

RADANO, Marcella Calhoun. 593 EDDY ST, RHODE ISLAND HOSPITAL 02903 #023-01-2006 L2006 **PD** *012

RADIE-KEANE, Kathy. 825 N MAIN ST, NORTHMAIN RADIATION ONCOLO 02904 #024-07-1986 L1995 **RO** *020 †80

RAGSDALE, Luna I. ■ 02906 #010-01-2003 L2006 **EM** *020 †16

RAKATANSKY, Herbert. 44 W RIVER ST 02904 #024-07-1960 L1966 **GE** *020 †20

RAMACHANDRAN, V. ■ 02906 #041-14-2003 L2007 **CD** *012 †20

RAMASESHU, Madhugiri B. 101 DUDLEY ST 02905 #495-33-1970 L1986 **AN** *075

RAMOS, Alia E. ■ 02912 #043-01-2008 *012

RAMRATNAM, Bharat. 55 CLAVERICK ST, RM 414 02903 #043-01-1993 L1993 **IM** *020 †20

RANA, Aadia Iftikhar. 164 SUMMIT AVE, RISE BLDG RM 141 02906 #001-02-2003 L2006 **ID** *012 †20

RANA, Naveed A. 10 DAVOL SQ, STE 400 02903 #704-01-1996 L1999 **IM** *020 †20

■ = Address Information Privacy Protected

RANA, Sarosh. 101 DUDLEY ST, WOMAN AND INFANTS HOSP 02905 #495-77-1995 L2005 OBG *020

RAO, Sunil Kumar. ■ 02903 #024-07-2004 L2005 OPH *012

RARDIN, Charles Roswell. 695 EDDY ST, STE 12 02903 #035-45-1996 L2003 OBG *020 †30

RASHID, Wasim. 593 EDDY ST, DEPT OF PSYCHIATRY 02903 #704-01-1983 L1999 PYG ADP *020 †75

RASMUSSEN, Steven A. 345 BLACKSTONE BLVD 02906 #043-01-1977 L1983 P *020 †75

RATHORE, Ritesh. 50 MAUDE ST 02908 #496-09-1992 L1997 HO ON *020 †20

RAU, Brian J. 593 EDDY ST, RHODE ISLAND HOSP 02903 #028-46-2005 L2005 PD *012

RAUFI-MOTLAGH, Nooredin. 593 EDDY ST, RI HOSPITAL 02903 #517-01-1966 L1971 AN GS *020 †05

RAUGHLEY, Moune Jabre. 101 DUDLEY ST, WOMEN & INFANTS HOSPITAL 02905 #024-05-2005 L2005 OBG *012

RAUKAR, Neha Parikh. 593 EDDY ST, FOUNDATION 02903 #010-03-2002 L2006 EM *100 †16

RAYMOND, Roger David. 593 EDDY ST, RHODE ISLAND HOSPITAL APC- 02903 #041-02-1966 L1969 CD *020 †20

RAYNER, James Robert J. 593 EDDY ST, RIH DEPT OF EMERGENCY MED 02903 #917-31-1997 L1998 EM *020 †16

REAGAN, John Leonard. ■ 02906 #035-15-2006 L2006 IM *012

RECUPERO, Patricia R. 345 BLACKSTONE BLVD, BUTLER HOSPITAL 02906 #043-01-1985 L1989 P LM *020 †75

REDDY, Shivani Motkar. 593 EDDY ST, DEPT MED 02903 #035-19-2007 L2007 IM *012

REDMOND, Kendal Francis. ■ 02903 #143-05-1993 L2003 VIR *100

REGAS, Frances Cecelia. 593 EDDY ST, DEPT OF ANESTHESIA 02903 #024-01-1992 L1992 PAN AN *020 †05

REGNANTE, Richard Andrew. 164 SUMMIT AVE, MIRIAM HOSPITAL-CARDIOLOGY 02906 #041-15-2002 L2002 CD *012 †20

REIS, Carlos S. 825 CHALKSTONE AVE 02908 #770-02-1979 L1990 IM *100

RENZI, Richard Michael. 164 SUMMIT AVE, MIRIAM HOSPITAL/EMRY MED 02906 #561-01-1984 L1986 EM IM *020 †20,16

RENZULLI, Joseph Frank, II. 195 COLLYER ST, STE 201 02904 #024-05-2001 L2005 U *020 †95

RESNICK, Murray. 593 EDDY ST, RHODE ISLAND HOSP PATH DEP 02903 #550-01-1989 L2002 PTH *020 †50

RESTIVO, Carin Anne. 593 EDDY ST, DEPT MED 02903 #033-05-2007 L2007 IM *012

REXFORD, Linda Louise. 293 GOVERNOR ST 02906 #035-15-1977 L1979 PD *020 †55

REY, Jesus, II. 593 EDDY ST 02903 #132-09-2000 L2002 ORS *012

REYES, Joyce Christine Bo. 593 EDDY ST 02903 #035-45-2005 L2005 IM *012

RHEE, Kyung E. 593 EDDY ST, POTTER BUILDING 02903 #041-13-1999 L2006 PD *050 †55

RICH, Harlan Geo. 110 LOCKWOOD ST, STE 116 02903 #035-01-1986 L1990 GE IM *020 †20

RICH, Josiah Danl. 164 SUMMIT AVE, FL 2 02906 #024-16-1987 L1994 IM ID *050 †20

RICHMAN, Katherine. 243 PLEASANT ST 02906 #043-01-2003 L2004 NEP *012 †20

RICKLER, Kenneth Carl. 345 BLACKSTONE BLVD 02906 #035-06-1972 L1995 N P *020 †75

RIDLEN, Mark Steven. 593 EDDY ST, DEPT OF DIAGNOSTIC IMAGING 02903 #016-42-1982 L1987 DR *020 †80

RIGGS, Suzanne Gracie. 593 EDDY ST, ADOLESCENT MEDICINE 02903 #024-01-1972 L1981 PD *062 †55

RISSER, Jessica Brubaker. ■ 02906 #012-05-2006 L2007 D *012

RIZVI, Syed. 2 DUDLEY ST, STE 530 02905 #704-02-1991 L2001 OS N *020 †20,75

RIZZUTO, Philip Raymond. 120 DUDLEY ST, STE 301 02905 #035-06-1990 L1995 OPH FPS *020 †35

ROBERTS, Barbara D Hudson. 164 SUMMIT AVE, 2ND FL 02906 #038-06-1968 L1977 CD IM *020 †20

ROBERTS, Jeffrey E. 101 DUDLEY ST, WOMEN AND INFANTS' HOSPITA 02905 #061-01-1996 L2004 *020

ROBERTSON, Alexander P. 100 BUTLER DR 02906 #051-01-1997 L1997 ORS *020 †40

ROBIDOUX, Henry Jos, Jr. 2 DUDLEY ST 02905 #035-15-1962 L1965 GS *071 †85

ROBINS, Jared Cory. 101 DUDLEY ST 401, DIV OF REPRODUCTIVE MED & 02905 #035-48-1994 L2007 OBG *020 †30

ROBINSON, Mendell. 164 SUMMIT AVE 02906 #024-07-1953 L1954 NO *071 †45

ROBINSON, William Thomas. 593 EDDY ST, DEPT MED 02903 #035-03-2007 L2007 IM *012

ROBISON, Katina Marie. 101 DUDLEY ST, WOMEN & INFANTS HOSPITAL 02905 #041-12-2002 L2002 OBG *100

ROCCHIO, Anthony. 151 WATERMAN ST 02906 #561-01-1971 L1975 OPH *020 †35

ROCKNEY, Randal Mark. 593 EDDY ST, DEPT OF PEDS 02903 #005-15-1980 L1986 PD *040 †55

RODRIGUEZ, Luisa Isabel. 825 CHALKSTONE AVE, EMERGENCY DEPT. 02908 #035-48-1986 L1990 IM EM *020 †20

RODRIGUEZ, Marina F. 160 WAYLAND AVE, WAYLAND MEDICAL ASSOC 02906 #024-16-1979 L1981 IM *020 †20

RODRIGUEZ, Miguel Angel. 593 EDDY ST 02903 #024-16-2001 L2001 IM *020

RODRIGUEZ-PERIS, Emilio. 21 PEACE ST 02907 #847-16-1995 L1997 IM *020 †20

ROESLER, Thomas Allen. 593 EDDY ST 02903 #054-04-1972 L1996 CHP P *020 †75

ROEVER, Cynthia Patricia. ■ 02908 #305-01-2007 L2007 IM *012

ROGERS, Jamison Eugene. 593 EDDY ST, RHODE ISLAND HOSP 02903 #011-04-2003 L2007 CHP *012

ROGERS, Lindsay Suzanne. ■ 02906 #035-06-2005 L2005 PD *012

ROGG, Jeffrey Michael. 1 RANDALL SQ 02904 #035-19-1982 L1988 RNR DR *020 †80

ROMEROBOSCH, Lilia Maria. 765 ALLENS AVE, PSYCHOLOGICAL CENTERS 02905 #033-05-2001 L2001 OS *100

ROMPF, Patricia Anne. 235 PLAIN ST STE 301 02905 #020-12-1966 L1971 PDC PD *020 †55

ROSAS, Donovan Thomas. 593 EDDY ST, RHODE ISLAND HOSP 02903 #035-45-2004 L2004 PS *012

ROSEN, Karen Joanne. 662 ANGELL ST 02906 #035-01-1991 L1991 P *020 †55

ROSEN, Wilma S Friedman. 345 BLACKSTONE BLVD, BUTLER HOSPITAL 02906 #041-13-1958 L1965 P *020 †75

ROSENBAUM, Arnold Steven. 1 RANDALL SQ STE 20 02904 #041-02-1966 L1972 GS OS *020 †85

ROSENBERG, Jerrold Nathan. 827 N MAIN ST 02904 #010-01-1980 L1987 PM *020 †60

ROSENBLUM DONATH, David E. 825 CHALKSTONE AVE 02908 #319-08-2003 L2007 IM *012

ROSENE, Karen A. 101 DUDLEY ST, OBSTETRICS & CONSULTATIVE 02905 #016-06-1977 L1989 OBG *012

ROSENZWEIG, Andrew Seth. 345 BLACKSTONE BLVD, FIRST FLOOR WELD BUILDING 02906 #025-01-1991 L1998 PYG *020 †75

ROSMARIN, Alan Glen. 164 SUMMIT AVE, FL 3 02906 #033-06-1981 L1989 HEM ON *040 †20

ROSS, Albert Marshall, IV. 593 EDDY ST, PEDIATRIC GASTROENTEROLOGY 02903 #019-02-1985 L1999 GE PG *020 †55

ROTENBERG, Fred Abraham. 10 ORMS ST, PROVIDENCE ANESTHESIOLOGY 02904 #043-01-1981 L1986 AN *020 †05

ROTJANAPAN, Porpon. ■ 02906 #891-04-1999 L2007 IMG *012 †20

ROTONDO, Kathleen Mary. 593 EDDY ST, DEPT OF PED CARDLGY 02903 #050-02-1984 L2003 PDC *055

ROUNDS, Sharon Irene. 830 CHALKSTONE AVE, PROVIDENCE VA MED CTR 02908 #024-07-1972 L1988 PUD IM *050 †20

ROUT, Preeti. ■ 02906 #038-06-2004 L2004 IM *012

ROYE, Gary Dean. 2 DUDLEY ST, STE 470 02905 #011-02-1992 L1998 GS *020 †85

RUBIN, Lewis Phillip. 101 DUDLEY ST DEPT PD 02905 #008-01-1982 L1990 NPM PD *050 †55

RUBIN, Lowell Jay. ■ 02906 #917-22-1964 L1978 P PYA *020 †75

RUGGIANO, John Robt. 347 BROADWAY 02909 #561-01-1968 L1971 P *020 †75

RUGGIERI, Richard J. 160 WAYLAND AVE 02906 #043-01-1987 L1990 IM IMG *020 †20

RUHL, Charles Meredith. 130 WATERMAN ST 02906 #051-01-1993 L1998 OTO *020 †45

RUPANI, Reena Neela. ■ 02903 #008-01-2004 L2005 D *012

RUSSELL, Lorna Weinheimer. ■ 02906 #041-15-2001 L2001 IM *020 †20

RUSSELL, Philip Christian. 345 BLACKSTONE BLVD 02906 #041-15-2001 L2001 P *100 †20

RUSSO, Christen Marie. ■ 02906 #035-08-2008 †012

RUSSO, Eugene A. 21 PEACE ST 02907 #165-04-1963 L1966 NS OS *020

RUTER, Shane J. ■ 02912 #043-01-2007 L2007 IM *012

RYABOY, Lyudmila. 593 EDDY ST, DEPT OF INTERNAL MEDICINE 02903 #035-48-2006 L2006 IM *012

RYAN, John Mark. 285 GOVERNOR ST, SECOND FLOOR 02906 #043-01-1984 L1987 IM *020 †20

RYAN, Maura Elizabeth. ■ 02903 #035-20-2001 L2001 RNR *100 †80

RYBAK, Natasha Renee. ■ 02906 #032-01-2007 L2007 MPD *012

RYDER, Beth Ann. 2 DUDLEY ST STE 470, UNIVERSITY SURGICAL ASSOCI 02905 #024-07-1999 L1999 GS *020 †85

RYDER, Sverre E. ■ 02904 #539-06-1989 L1992 GS *100

RYFF, Arnika Sylvia. 830 CHALKSTONE AVE # MED, VA HOSPITAL 02908 #869-01-1975 IM *100

RYTER, Richard Jos. 164 SUMMIT AVE 02906 #035-20-1973 L1977 IM *020 †20

RYVICKER, Michael Julian. 164 SUMMIT AVE DEPT R 02906 #035-08-1967 L1975 R *020 †80

SABORIO, Manuel E. 10 ORMS ST STE 110 02904 #649-01-1954 L1961 AN *071 †05

SACHS, George Morrison. 2 DUDLEY ST, STE 530 02905 #008-01-1986 L1992 P *050 †75

SACKTON, Dana Hilary. ■ 02903 #041-02-2006 L2006 PD *012

SAFRAN, Howard Philip. 164 SUMMIT AVE, FL 3 02906 #024-05-1987 L1993 HEM ON *020 †20

SAHA, Dalia. ■ 02908 #043-01-2007 L2007 IM *012

SAID, Fuad Riyad. 164 SUMMIT AVE 02906 #575-01-2003 L2005 IM *012

SAID, Nuha Riyad. 50 MAUDE ST 02908 #575-01-1995 L1996 RHU *020 †20

SAKLAD, Sarah G Mazick. ■ 02906 #023-07-1932 P *071 †75

SALAHUDDIN, Kazi M. 520 HOPE ST, PROVIDENCE CTR 02906 #704-02-1985 L1999 CHP P *020 †75

SALAK, Jessica Rose. ■ 02906 #038-06-2004 L2004 OBG *012

SALLOWAY, Stephan P. 345 BLACKSTONE BLVD, BUTLER HOSPITAL NEUROLOGY 02906 #005-11-1985 L1991 P *020 †75

SALMON, Magdi Louis. 21 PEACE ST 02907 #915-02-1987 L1998 END *020 †20

SALTZMAN, Abraham. ■ 02906 #035-08-1943 L1949 IM *071 †20

SALZMAN, Richard S. 164 SUMMIT AVE, "2ND FLOOR, STE 2" 02906 #005-14-1979 L1985 D *020 †15

SAMPATH, Prakash. 118 DUDLEY ST, RHODE ISLAND SUGICAL 02905 #035-01-1992 L1999 NS *020 †25

SAMUELS, William Oscar. 480 HOPE ST 02906 #023-01-1971 L1975 P *020 †75

SANCHEZ-ESTEBAN, Juan Ram. 101 DUDLEY ST, DEPT PEDS WMN INFTS HOSP 02905 #847-03-1980 L1996 NPM PD *050 †55

SANCHEZ METZ, Cristobal E. 825 CHALKSTONE AVE 02908 #319-04-2001 L2005 IM *012

SANDBERG, Anna. 353 BLACKSTONE BLVD, # 3410 02906 #407-15-1951 L1956 PD *071 †55

SANDERS, Henry Albert. 80 OCEAN ST 02905 #048-04-1969 L1973 IM *020 †20

SAPERS, Benjamin Lovell. 539 EDDY ST, UNIVERSITY MEDICINE FOUNDA 02903 #024-01-1996 L2002 IM *020 †20

SAPIR, Paul Edward. 112 PROSPECT ST 02906 #024-01-1959 L1974 P PYA *020 ‡

SAQR, Bachir Joseph. 101 DUDLEY ST, PROGRAM IN WOMANS ONCOLOGY 02905 #605-03-1995 L2002 HO *020 †20

SARIS, Stephen Clayton. 3 DAVOL SQ STE B200, NEUROSURGERY ASSOCIATES 02903 #024-05-1979 L1993 NS *020 †25

SARLAK, Farzaneh. 15 PRATT ST 02906 #043-01-1998 L1998 FM *020 †18

SARLES, Marilyn Dawson. 825 CHALKSTONE AVE 02908 #043-01-1976 L1980 EM IM *020 †20

SARRIS, Michael Elias. 593 EDDY ST 02903 #418-01-1978 L1985 DIA PD *020

SATTAR, Abida Khalil. 101 DUDLEY ST, WOMEN AND INFANTS' HOSPITA 02905 #704-25-1995 L1997 GS *020 †85

SAVIN, Hillel. 825 CHALKSTONE AVE 02908 #550-02-1980 RHU *020

SAVITT, Daniel Lawrence. 164 SUMMIT AVE, DEPT OF EMERGENCY MEDICINE 02906 #024-16-1983 L1987 EM *030 †16

SAWYER, Gregory Alan. ■ 02906 #032-01-2007 L2007 *012

SAX, Harry C. 164 SUMMIT AVE, ADMINISTRATION, RM 255 02906 #023-07-1982 L2005 GS NTR *030 †85

SAXENA, Abha. 593 EDDY ST, RHODE ISLAND HOSP 02903 #001-02-2003 L2006 NEP *012 †20

SCANLAN, James Jean. 1 ELMHURST AVE 02908 #024-01-1947 L1949 ADL FM *071

SCARAMELLA, Thomas Jerry. 480 HOPE ST 02906 #041-01-1969 L1975 P *020 †75

SCHABERG, Frank John, Jr. 58 IRVING AVE 02906 #051-07-1968 L1975 GS VS *020 †85

SCHABERG, Monica J Piana. ■ 02906 #024-05-1968 L1975 PD PHP *030 †55

SCHAEFER, Marc Evan. ■ 02909 #550-02-2003 L2006 PG *012 †55

SCHECHTER, Michael S. 593 EDDY ST, DEPT OF PEDS 02903 #035-06-1975 L2006 PDP PD *040 †55

SCHECHTER, Steven. 1 RANDALL SQ, STE 406 02904 #035-45-1985 L1988 CRS GS *020 †85,10

SCHEPPS, Barbara. 1 RANDALL SQ 02904 #041-09-1968 L1974 R OS *020 †80

SCHIFF, Stephen Frank. 125 CORLISS ST # 207 02905 #051-07-1981 L1992 U *020 †95

SCHIFFMAN, Fred Jay. 164 SUMMIT AVE, FL 3 02906 #035-19-1973 L1983 HEM IM *020 †20

SCHILLING, Albert. 593 EDDY ST, MEDICAL ONCOLOGY 02902 #065-06-1947 L1977 ON *071

SCHINAZI, Helen Athineos. ■ 02906 #330-03-1960 L1969 OPH OS *071 †35

SCHINAZI, Y Jacob. 265 WATERMAN ST 02906 #330-01-1958 L1967 OPH *071 †35

SCHIRMANG, Todd C. 593 EDDY ST 02903 #016-43-2003 L2005 DR *012

SCHLEINITZ, Mark Duncan. 593 EDDY ST MPB-1, OF GIM 02903 #005-11-1995 L2002 IM *020 †20

SCHMID, Hermann Arnold. 11 S ANGELL ST # 246 02906 #869-07-1966 L1987 P PYA *071

SCHRECK, Barbara Carina. BROWN UNIVERSITY BOX 5294 02912 #035-20-2008 *012
SCHREIBER, David. 44 W RIVER ST 02904 #035-15-1980 L1985 **GE** *020 †20
SCHULMAN, Risa Gabrielle. 345 BLACKSTONE BLVD, BUTLER HOSP 02906 #041-13-2006 L2006 **P** *100
SCHULTZ, Corinna Lee. ■ 02906 #041-02-2007 L2007 **PD** *012
SCHWARTZ, Carl. 593 EDDY ST, DAVOL 129 02903 #422-01-1982 L1987 **AN** *020 †20,05
SCHWARTZ, Cindy Lee. 593 EDDY ST, MULTIPHASIC BLDG, ROOM 117 02903 #043-01-1979 L2005 **PHO** *050 †55
SCHWARTZ, Daniel J. PO BOX G8316 02912 #043-01-1998 *100
SCHWARTZ, Harry. 208 COLLYER ST 02904 #056-06-1978 L1980 **CD IM** *020 †20
SCHWARTZ, Robert. 593 EDDY ST, DEPT PD 02903 #008-01-1947 L1974 **PD** *050 †55
SCHWARTZWALD, Jack L. 593 EDDY ST APC5, RHODE ISLAND HOSPITAL 02903 #033-05-1989 L1989 **IM** *020 †20
SCHWARZ, Liese O'Halloran. 11 S ANGELL ST 02906 #051-01-1992 L1994 **EM** *020 †16
SCHWENGEL, Robert H. 1076 N MAIN ST 02904 #010-01-1987 L1993 **CD** *020 †20
SCIANDRA, Katherine Teres. ■ 02903 #035-06-2005 L2005 **PTH** *012
SCOLA, Patricia R Sexton. 593 EDDY ST, # 6 02903 #024-05-1961 L1965 **PD** *071 †55
SENKOTTAIYAN, Neelavathi. 825 CHALKSTONE AVE, ROGER WILLIAMS HOSP 02908 #495-16-1996 L2006 **END** *012 †20
SEPE, Steven Michael. 222 RICHMOND ST, STE 204 02903 #024-05-1982 L1985 **IM** *020 †20
SEPE, Thomas Edward. 33 STANIFORD ST, UNIVERSITY GASTRONLGY 02905 #035-47-1988 L1993 **IM** *020 †20
SHAFFER, Scott Howard. ■ 02906 #033-06-2006 L2006 **P** *012
SHAFI, Humaira. 825 CHALKSTONE AVE, ROGER WILLIAMS MED CTR 02908 #704-21-1999 L2007 **ID** *012 †20
SHAFIE, Shideh. 593 EDDY ST, RHODE ISLAND HOSP 02903 #032-01-2007 L2007 **GS** *012
SHAH, Kinjal Urvil. 593 EDDY ST, DEPT MED 02903 #030-06-2007 L2007 **IM** *012
SHAH, Nehal Atul. ■ 02903 #033-06-2003 L2005 **DR** *012
SHAH, Parul Devidas. 877 CHALKSTONE AVE 02908 #495-85-1985 L1995 **IM** *020 †20
SHAH, Samir Ashok. 44 W RIVER ST 02904 #024-01-1992 L1997 **GE** *020 †20
SHAH-HOSSEINI, Bahram. 101 DUDLEY ST 02905 #517-01-1967 L1974 **OBG** *020 †30
SHAH-HOSSEINI, Reza. 593 EDDY ST 02903 #517-01-1967 L1980 **OBG OS** *020 †30
SHAHID, Sonia. 825 CHALKSTONE AVE, ROGER WILLIAMS HOSP 02908 #704-05-1998 L2002 **IM** *020 †20
SHAHIN, Mohamed Amr A. 593 EDDY ST, POTTER 115 02903 #915-02-1985 L2006 **CCP** *020 †55
SHAHINIAN, Thomas Karekin. 235 PLAIN ST 02905 #561-01-1968 L1972 **GS** *020 †85
SHALON, Linda Beth. 593 EDDY ST, RIH-MPB 126 02903 #016-43-1986 L1992 **PD** *020 †55
SHALVOY, Robert Michael. 2 DUDLEY ST 02905 #033-05-1984 L1990 **ORS OSM** *020 †40
SHAMMAS, Elia. 1 RANDALL SQ STE 302 02904 #330-02-1954 L1968 **P N** *020 †75
SHAMMASS, Demme. 825 CHALKSTONE AVE, ROGER WILLIAMS HOSP 02908 #875-02-1997 L2002 *100
SHAPIRO, Marc Jay. 593 EDDY ST, RI HOSPITAL EMERGENCY 02903 #024-07-1989 L1993 **EM** *020 †16
SHARAF, Barry Louis. 593 EDDY ST, RHODE ISLAND HOSPITAL 02903 #024-05-1983 L1989 **CD IM** *020 †20
SHARKEY, Katherine M. 593 EDDY ST, UNIVERSITY MEDICINE FOUNDA 02903 #016-01-2002 L2007 **OS** *100 †20
SHARMA, Satish Chandra. 830 CHALKSTONE AVE, VA MEDICAL CENTER 02908 #495-55-1969 L1981 **CD IM** *020 †20
SHARP, Jane Randolph. 297 PROMENADE ST 02908 #041-01-1995 L2003 **OBG** *020 †30
SHATTUCK, Thaddeus Theodo. 345 BLACKSTONE BLVD, BUTLER HOSPITAL 02906 #032-01-2005 L2005 **P** *012
SHEA, Lisa Braff. 345 BLACKSTONE BLVD, BUTLER HOSP 02906 #051-01-1990 L1991 **P** *020 †75
SHEEHAN, Edward Paul. 345 BLACKSTONE BLVD 02906 #008-02-2002 **ADP** *100
SHEMIN, Douglas Gabe. 593 EDDY ST 02902 #038-06-1982 L1984 **NEP** *020 †20
SHERMA, Arun Kumar. 593 EDDY ST, RHODE ISLAND HOSP 02903 #038-41-2006 L2006 **GS** *100
SHERMAN, Melissa Jane. ■ 02907 #041-12-2004 L2004 **OBG** *012
SHETTY, Rashmi. ■ 02906 #043-01-2002 L2002 **U** *020
SHETTY, Taranath K. 120 DUDLEY ST 02905 #495-16-1962 L1972 **CHN N** *075
SHETTY-ALVA, Neetha. ■ 02906 #043-01-1999 L1999 **N** *012
SHIBLEY, Heather Lynn. ■ 02906 #041-14-2005 L2005 **P** *012
SHIELD, Paul Harold. 345 BLACKSTONE BLVD 02906 #041-01-1967 L1974 **P PYA** *020 †75
SHIH, Grace Hong. ■ 02906 #011-03-2003 L2005 **FP** *012
SHIN, Victor Hyunkwang. ■ 02903 #035-19-2000 L2003 **CD** *100 †20
SHIRAISHI, Mari Akemi. ■ 02903 #010-02-2006 L2006 **IM** *012
SHOUKEIR, Hatem Toufic. 830 CHALKSTONE AVE 02908 #605-01-1999 L2005 **GE** *020 †20
SHUEY, Iris B. ■ 02906 #035-48-1975 L1976 **P** *020 †75
SHULMAN, Richard Stanley. 1076 N MAIN ST 02904 #024-01-1967 L1975 **CD IM** *020 †20
SICLARI, Michael Stephen. 825 CHALKSTONE AVE, ROGER WILLIAMS MED CTR 02908 #032-01-1985 L1986 **EM IM** *020 †20
SIEDLECKI, Diane R. 1 HOPPIN ST 3RD FL, ANCHOR MEDICAL ASSOCIATES 02903 #010-02-1983 L1991 **IM** *020 †20
SIEGEL, Nathan Ashley. 593 EDDY ST, FOUNDATION 02903 #008-01-2002 L2006 **EM** *100 †16
SIGMAN, Mark. 2 DUDLEY ST, STE 174 02905 #008-02-1981 L1989 **U** *020 †95
SIKOV, William Marshall. 164 SUMMIT AVE, FL 3 02906 #008-01-1982 L1989 **ON HEM** *020 †20
SILVER, Michael Alan. 530 N MAIN ST 02904 #041-01-1971 L1977 **P** *020 †75
SILVERSTEIN, Jared Andrew. 593 EDDY ST, RHODE ISLAND HOSP 02903 #024-07-2004 L2007 **PG** *012 †55
SIMON, Caroline Josephine. 593 EDDY ST 02903 #539-02-2002 L2006 **GS** *012
SIMON, Peter Roy. 3 CAPITOL HL, RHODE ISLAND DEPT OF HEALT 02908 #035-15-1974 L1977 **PD PHP** *020 †70,55
SIMON, Stanley. 1 RANDALL SQ, STE 406 02904 #051-04-1949 L1954 **GS** *071 †85
SIMPSON, Mary Christina. 101 DUDLEY ST, WOMEN AND INFANTS HOSPITAL 02905 #041-13-2004 L2004 **OBG** *012
SINGER, Nancy Moten. 593 EDDY ST, PEDIATRICS DEPARTMENT 02903 #033-05-1993 L1996 **PD** *020 †55
SINGH, Arun Kumar. 2 DUDLEY ST, STE 470 02905 #495-24-1967 L1975 **TS** *020 †85,90
SINGH, Deepika. ■ 02904 #035-08-2005 L2007 **EM** *100
SISSON, Craig Andrew. 593 EDDY ST, EMERGENCY MEDICINE DEPARTM 02903 #025-07-2003 L2003 **EM** *100
SKONIECZKI, Brendan David. ■ 02909 #035-06-2005 L2005 **DR** *012
SKOWRON, Gail. 50 MAUDE ST 02908 #035-01-1982 L1989 **ID IM** *050 †20
SKURKOVICH, Boris. 202 PRAIRIE AVE 02905 #913-15-1978 L1988 **PD PDI** *020 †55
SLAFSKY, S Frederick. ■ 02906 #035-20-1958 L1965 **GS PDS** *071 †85
SLAIBY, Jeffrey Michael. 2 DUDLEY ST STE 470 02905 #050-02-1988 L1988 **VS** *020 †85
SMITH, Caldwell Withers. 690 EDDY ST 02903 #011-03-1973 L1978 **OPH** *020 †35
SMITH, Jean Feibleman. 100 HIGHLAND AVE, STE 203 02906 #043-01-1992 L1994 **IM** *020 †20
SMITH, Jessica L. 593 EDDY ST, POTTER 225 02903 #011-02-2002 L2006 **EM** *020 †16
SMITH, Richard Mark. 235 PLAIN ST 02905 #041-01-1983 L1994 **P CHP** *020 †75
SMITH, William T. 100 HIGHLAND AVE STE 20 02906 #043-01-1996 L2000 **IM** *020 †20
SMULEVER, Romina Paula. 345 BLACKSTONE BLVD, BUTLER HOSPITAL-GERIATRIC 02906 #132-01-1997 L2005 **PYG** *020 †75
SNELLING, Linda K. 593 EDDY ST DEPT PD 02903 #040-02-1982 L1992 **AN CCM** *020 †55,05
SNYDER, Andrew Mark. 593 EDDY ST, RM 131 02903 #008-02-1994 L1996 **PD** *020 †55 ‡
SOARES, Gregory Michael. 593 EDDY ST, DEPT DIAG IMAGING R1H 02903 #024-05-1992 L1992 **DR** *020 †80
SODERBERG, Clarence H. 593 EDDY ST 02903 #024-05-1953 L1958 **GS CD** *071 †85
SOKOLOWSKI, Devin Robinso. ■ 02906 #041-12-2007 L2007 **EM** *012
SOLOMON, David Arthur. 593 EDDY ST, JANE BROWN 5 SOUTH 02903 #024-05-1986 L1989 **P** *020 †75
SOLOMON, Joel Bryan. 339 ANGELL ST, DEPT OF BEHAVIORIAL HEALTH 02906 #035-03-1995 L1997 **OS** *020 †75
SOLTANI-HOSSAINI, Mohsen. 21 PEACE ST 02907 #517-04-1958 L1969 **PTH CLP** *020 †50
SOMBERG, Chutrudee J. 345 BLACKSTONE BLVD, BUTLER HOSP 02906 #043-01-2004 L2007 **P** *012
SOMLO, Laszlo Ivan. 21 PEACE ST # PATH, SAINT JOSEPHS HOSPITAL 02907 #065-06-1959 L1969 **PTH** *020 †50
SOMMERS, Ross. ■ 02906 #550-02-2004 L2007 **NPM** *012 †55
SOMMERVILLE, Lynn. 164 SUMMIT AVE 02906 #043-01-1981 L1986 **IM** *020 †20
SONG, Julie Haiyoung. 593 EDDY ST 02903 #024-07-1993 L1994 **DR** *020 †80
SOONG, Maximillian C. 2 DUDLEY ST STE 200, C/O ROBIN MORIN, ORTHOPEDI 02905 #035-01-2002 L2002 **HSO** *012
SORGMAN, Jay Alan. 148 W RIVER ST 02904 #024-16-1987 L1992 **IM GE** *020 †20
SORRENTINO, Louis V. 345 BLACKSTONE BLVD 02906 #024-05-1947 L1955 **P** *072 †75
SOSA, Andres Fernando. 593 EDDY ST 02903 #935-01-2002 L2003 **PCC** *012 †20
SPADER, Heather Stevens. ■ 02906 #046-01-2007 L2007 **GS** *012
SPAEDER, Michael Campbell. 593 EDDY ST, HASBRO CHILDREN'S HOSPITAL 02903 #010-01-2003 L2003 **CCP** *012 †55
SPALDING, Kirsten Leigh. ■ 02908 #043-01-2008 *012
SPECTOR, Jeremy. 44 W RIVER ST 02904 #047-05-1998 L2004 **GE** *020 †20
SPEICHER, William Joseph. ■ 02906 #041-13-2005 L2005 **IM** *012
SPELLUN, Joel Steven. 148 W RIVER ST, STE 3 02904 #035-20-1982 L1987 **GE** *020 †20
SPENCER, Patricia Kiel. 593 EDDY ST, DEPT OF RADIOLOGY 02903 #024-16-1977 L1981 **DR NM** *020 †80
SPINDELL, Edward. ■ 02906 #024-05-1953 L1960 **ORS** *062 †40
SPOFFORD, Inbar Shani. ■ 02906 #041-14-2005 L2005 **PD** *012
SPRUNG, Sonia. 101 DUDLEY ST 02905 #913-03-1943 L1957 **PD** *071
STACHURSKI, Dariusz Rober. 593 EDDY ST, DEPT OF PATHOLOGY 02903 #759-04-1999 L2004 **PTH** *100
STA INES, Casimira C. 830 CHALKSTONE AVE, VA HOSPITAL 02908 #748-07-1964 L1982 **DR** *020
STAINKEN, Brian Frederick. 825 CHALKSTONE AVE, DEPT OF DIAGNOSTIC IMAGING 02908 #010-02-1983 L2003 **VIR DR** *020 †80
STAITIEH, Bashar Samih. 593 EDDY ST, DEPT MED 02903 #019-02-2007 L2007 **IM** *012
STANCU, Mirela. 825 CHALKSTONE AVE DP, ROGER WILLIAMS MED CTR 02908 #781-01-1991 L1997 **SP HMP** *062 †50
STANLEY, Robert Dirk. 593 EDDY ST, MAIN BLDG., 11TH FLOOR, P. 02903 #422-01-2003 L2007 *100 †20
STANTON, Laura Anne. ■ 02906 #041-15-2007 L2007 **P** *012
STARK, Ryan Jordan. ■ 02903 #010-01-2006 L2006 **PD** *012
STARR, Rebecca Susan. ■ 02906 #035-08-2004 L2004 **IMG** *012 †20
STAUNTON, Charles Edward. 345 BLACKSTONE BLVD 02906 #035-03-1973 L1979 **CHP** *020 †75
STEELE, Dale Wm. 593 EDDY ST, CLAVERICK 244 02903 #050-02-1986 L1992 **PEM PD** *020 †55
STEIGMAN, David Manuel. 235 PLAIN ST, STE 306 02905 #035-19-1985 L1988 **IM** *020 †20
STEIN, Lauren Fischer. ■ 02906 #010-01-2004 L2005 **DR** *012
STEIN, Michael David. 593 EDDY ST 02903 #035-01-1985 L1988 **IM** *020 †20
STEIN, Nancy Loeber. 593 EDDY ST, DEPT OF ANESTHESIA 02903 #005-02-1974 L1990 **AN PD** *020 †05
STEINBERG, Bonnie J. ■ 02906 #035-46-1989 L1996 **P** *020 †75
STEINHOFF, Margaret Mary. 101 DUDLEY ST 02905 #028-02-1983 L1990 **ATP** *020 †50
STEINKELER, Jill Alana. ■ 02908 #024-07-2005 L2005 **DR** *012
STEMP, Ruth G. 530 N MAIN ST 02904 #035-46-1980 L1989 **IM** *020 †20,75
STEPHENS, Bonnie E. 101 DUDLEY ST, DEPT OF PEDIATRICS 02905 #016-06-1997 L2003 **NPM** *020 †55
STEPHENSON, Jodi Lynn. 345 BLACKSTONE BLVD 02906 #035-03-2002 L2002 **P** *100
STERNBERG, Josef. PROVIDENCE VA MED CTR 02908 #913-08-1965 L1987 *020
STEVENSON, Elizabeth Kepp. ■ 02906 #041-15-2007 L2007 **IM** *012
STICKLES, Eric Thomas. ■ 02906 #041-13-2008 L2008 *012
STIENER, Gregory Paul. 339 ANGELL ST 02906 #017-20-1992 L1992 **OS P** *020 †55,75
STONE, Andrew Cowley. 830 CHALKSTONE AVE, VA MEDICAL CENTER 02908 #050-02-1999 L1999 **PCC** *100
STONE, Andrew Douglas. 148 W RIVER ST, STE 3 02904 #035-06-2000 L2006 **GE** *100 †20
STONE, William Mason. 100 HIGHLAND AVE STE 306 02906 #043-01-1976 L1985 **N** *020 †20,75
STONESTREET, Barbara S. 101 DUDLEY ST 02905 #024-07-1972 L1978 **PD** *050 †55
STORY, Errett Taylor. 100 CURTIS ST 02909 #040-02-1995 L1995 **OBG** *020 †30
STOZEK, Michelle Alaise. 111 PLAIN ST, 3RD FL 02903 #041-07-1998 L1998 **IM** *020 †20
STRAUS, John Samuel. 534 ANGELL ST 02906 #308-14-1997 L1997 **IM** *020 †20
STRENGER, Rochelle. 164 SUMMIT AVE, FL 3 02906 #035-46-1982 L1990 **HEM IM** *020 †20
STROM, John O. 124 WATERMAN ST 02906 #035-45-1951 L1957 **N** *071 †75
STRUMINSKY, Jaroslav. 825 CHALKSTONE AVE 02908 #407-20-1952 L1958 **FM** *072
STURAM, Jorge Hugo. 154 WATERMAN ST 02906 #132-02-1961 L1969 **A PDA** *020 †55,03
STUTZ, Stanley John. 21 PEACE ST, ST JOSEPH'S HOSPITAL 02907 #025-07-1970 L1972 **ORS GP** *020 †40
STUTZ, Stanley John, III. ■ 02906 #041-12-2000 L2004 **EM** *020 †16
SUCOV, Andrew Noah. 593 EDDY ST 02903 #041-01-1988 L1991 **EM** *020 †16

■ = Address Information Privacy Protected

SUDHEENDRA, Vijayendra. 164 SUMMIT AVE 02906 #495-35-1992 L2002 **AN** *020

SULLIVAN, James C. 909 N MAIN ST STE 300 02904 #033-06-1993 L1993 **IM** *020 †20

SULLIVAN, James Kevin. 530 N MAIN ST 02904 #008-02-1989 L1990 **P** *020 †75

SULLIVAN, Patrick Kevin. 235 PLAIN ST STE 502 02905 #026-08-1979 L1986 **FPS OTO** *020 †45,65

SUNDARAM, Magesh. 825 CHALKSTONE AVE, ROGER WILLIAMS MEDICAL CEN 02908 #023-01-1990 L2003 **GS SO** *020 †85

SUNDHAR, Joshua Bharat. 825 CHALKSTONE AVE, DEPT IM 02908 #473-04-2006 L2007 **IM** *012

SUNER, Selim. 1 HOPPIN ST, CORO 106 MEDICAL SIM CTR 02903 #043-01-1992 L1992 **EM UM** *020 †16

SUNG, Chien-Ren James. 101 DUDLEY ST, WOMEN & INFANTS HOSPITAL 02905 #244-06-1984 L1990 **PTH PCP** *020 †50

SUNG, Vivian Waiwai. 101 DUDLEY ST, UROGYNECOLOGY 02905 #024-07-1999 L2003 **OBG** *100

SURESH, Deepa. ■ 02903 #496-39-2003 L2007 **PDE** *012

SURTI, Ghulam Mustafa. 345 BLACKSTONE BLVD, BUTLER HOSPITAL 02906 #704-02-1990 L1998 **P PYG** *020 †75

SUSSET, Jacques Georges. 151 WATERMAN ST 02906 #396-06-1953 L1979 **U** *020

SUTTON, Elizabeth Munro. 164 SUMMIT AVE, EMERGENCY MEDICINE DEPARTM 02906 #010-02-1995 L1998 **EM** *020 †16

SUTTON, Trevor Scott. 593 EDDY ST, DEPARTMENT OF ANESTHESIA 02903 #005-02-1991 L1998 **AN** *020 *05

SWEENEY, Joseph Damien. 164 SUMMIT AVE, MIRIAM HOSPITAL 02906 #539-05-1976 L1993 **ON HEM** *020 †20

SWEENEY, Patrick John. 101 DUDLEY ST 02905 #028-34-1971 L1987 **OBG PHP** *030 †30

SWIFT, Robert Michael. 830 CHALKSTONE AVE 02908 #016-02-1979 L1983 **P ADP** *050 †75

SYED, Amber Hameed. 593 EDDY ST, DIV OF CHILD PSYCHIATRY 02903 #704-25-1994 L1996 **OS** *012

SYED, Nilofar Ikram. 593 EDDY ST, DEPT MED 02903 #038-06-2007 L2007 **IM** *012

SZABADOS, Erica Michele. ■ 02903 #010-01-2003 L2003 **CN** *012

TAITANO, Andrew A. ■ 02906 #043-01-2007 L2007 **GS** *012

TAJIRIAN, Ani L. ■ 02906 #043-01-2007 L2007 **IM** *012

TAMAN, Maged Ali F. 21 PEACE ST 02903 #915-03-1981 L1994 **NEP** *020 †20

TAMI, Mario. 49 TRINITY PKWY 02908 #561-01-1953 L1957 **CD IM** *020 †20

TAMMARO, Dominick. 111 PLAIN ST, FL 3 02903 #043-01-1984 L1988 **IM** *020 †20

TAN, John Frederick. 593 EDDY ST, RHODE ISLAND HOSP 02903 #033-06-2005 L2005 **PD** *012

TAN, Pamela. ■ 02912 #035-48-2008 *012

TAN, Tze Woei. 593 EDDY ST 02903 #143-02-2002 L2005 **GS** *012

TAPSCOTT, David P. 202 PRAIRIE AVE 02905 #024-07-1976 L1995 **PD** *020 †55

TAPYRIK, Sarah Ann. ■ 02906 #035-45-2005 L2005 **IM** *012

TARNOFF, Gerald Mark. 345 BLACKSTONE BLVD, BUTLER HOSPITAL 02906 #016-42-1973 L1990 **CHP P** *020 †75 ‡

TASHIMA, Karen Tokie. 164 SUMMIT AVE, THE MIRIAM HOSP 02906 #035-01-1988 L1995 **IM ID** *020 †20

TATE, Charlene Anne. 2 DUDLEY ST, STE 530 02905 #032-01-1990 L1990 **N** *020 †75

TAUSSIG, Hugo. ■ 02906 #781-01-1948 L1955 **CHP PYG** *072

TAVARES, Joao Moreno. 10 DAVOL SQ, STE 400 02903 #770-01-1990 L1998 **ID** *020 †20

TAYLOR, Lynn Erica. 164 SUMMIT AVE, FL 2 02906 #041-12-1997 L1997 **IM OS** *020 †20

TEFFT, Melvin. ■ 02902 #024-05-1958 L1975 **RO** *071 †20

TEJADA-BERGES, Tevor. 101 DUDLEY ST 02905 #067-01-1996 L2001 *020

TELANG, Gladys Hines. 593 EDDY ST # 10, DEPT OF DERM-BROWN UNIV 02903 #035-15-1987 L2002 **DMP PD** *020 †20,15

TENO, Joan Marie. 2 STIMPSON DR 02919 #041-09-1982 L1984 **IM** *020 †20

TERLATO, Joseph Sebastian. 1075 SMITH ST 02908 #035-09-1988 L1992 **CD IM** *020 †20

TETREAULT, Albert F. 593 EDDY ST, R I H MEDICAL FOUNDATION 02903 #024-07-1952 L1955 **IM DIA** *071

THAKER, Sejal Ashok. 10 DAVOL SQ STE 400, COASTAL MEDICAL, INC. 02903 #024-07-2002 L2002 **PCC** *012

THAKKAR, Rajan Krishnakan. 593 EDDY ST, RHODE ISLAND HOSP 02903 #038-40-2006 L2006 **GS** *012

THAKUR, Nikhil Anand. ■ 02906 #032-01-2005 L2005 **ORS** *012

THAO, Xoua. ■ 02907 #043-01-1989 L1989 **FM** *020 †18

THAVASEELAN, Simone. 2 DUDLEY ST STE 174, RHODE ISLAND HOSPITAL / DE 02905 #010-02-2005 L2005 **U** *012

THAYER, Walter Raymond. 2 DUDLEY ST 02905 #024-07-1954 L1958 **GE IM** *020 †20

THIAGARAJAN, Deepak Venka. 164 SUMMIT AVE, THE MIRIAM HOSPITAL 02906 #422-01-2002 L2006 **IMG** *100

THOMAS, Alex. 97 WATERMAN ST, BROWN UNIV PROGRM IN MED 02912 #043-01-2001 L2001 **EM** *020 †16

THOMAS, Lonice Margaret. 239 CRANSTON ST 02907 #035-03-1982 L1985 **PD** *020 †55

THOMAS, Pascale Adelaide. ■ 02908 #440-01-1992 **PD** *100

THOMAS, Tanya Sanita. 345 BLACKSTONE BLVD, BUTLER HOSP 02906 #012-01-2007 L2007 **P** *012

THOMAS, Valerie Ann. 49 SEEKONK ST, DIABETES & ENDOCRINOLOGY A 02906 #024-07-1986 L1991 **END IM** *020 †20

THOMAY, Alan Adolph. ■ 02906 #038-41-2004 L2004 **GS** *012

THOME, Tamara Lynn. ■ 02903 #051-04-2006 L2006 **EM** *012

THOMPSON, Amanda Jane. ■ 02903 #050-02-2006 L2006 **N** *012

THOMPSON, William Richard. 593 EDDY ST 02903 #035-20-1955 L1963 **GS** *071 †85

TIBBETTS, Lance Malcolm. 50 MAUDE ST 02908 #035-47-1974 L1982 **ATP** *050 †50

TIEN, D Robbins. 2 DUDLEY ST, STE 505 02905 #025-01-1983 L1990 **OPH** *020 †35

TILKEMEIER, Peter L. 164 SUMMIT AVE, MIRIAM HOSPITAL 02906 #016-06-1983 L1989 **CD IM** *020 †20

TILTON, Tania Yvonne. ■ 02905 #035-01-2003 L2003 **OBG** *020

TITA, Charles Tita. ■ 02906 #306-01-1991 L2005 **PYG** *100

TJIA, Marcus Wiliang. 345 BLACKSTONE BLVD 02906 #035-47-2002 L2002 **PYM** *012

TO, King W. 1 HOPPIN ST 02903 #043-01-1986 L1991 **OPH** *020 †35

TOBACK, Neil Edward. 593 EDDY ST 02903 #165-04-1969 L1971 **D** *020 †15

TOCCI, Stephen Leonard. 2 DUDLEY ST STE 200, UNIVERSITY ORTHOPEDICS 02905 #041-12-2002 L2002 **ORS** *100

TOLL, Elizabeth T. 593 EDDY ST, STE 224 02903 #035-45-1988 L1996 **IM PD** *020 †20,55

TONG, Iris Ling. 100 DUDLEY ST, CENTER FOR WOMEN'S HEALTH 02905 #035-20-1997 L1997 **IM** *020 †20

TOOLAN, Beth Ann. 40 CANDACE ST 02908 #043-01-1995 L1995 **IM PD** *020 †20,55

TORGAN, Philip Alan. ■ 02906 #024-07-1958 L1965 **GE IM** *071 †20

TORRES, Rafael Arbues. 345 BLACKSTONE BLVD, BUTLER HOSPITAL 02906 #748-02-1992 L2005 **P** *020 †75

TORRES LOPEZ, Paulo Andre. 825 CHALKSTONE AVE 02908 #264-21-2000 L2007 *100

TOSELLI, Alfred. 120 DUDLEY ST STE 105 02905 #561-01-1957 L1959 **PD OS** *071 †55

TOSO, Gerardo Michael. 593 EDDY ST, RI HOSPITAL 02903 #010-01-2000 L2000 **EM** *100

TOUMA, Carol Lynn. ■ 02906 #020-12-2005 L2005 **IM** *012

TOWNE, Gregory James. 593 EDDY ST, DEPT OF ANESTHESIA 02903 #032-01-1979 L1982 **AN IM** *020 †20,05

TRACY, Matthew Ryan. 593 EDDY ST 02903 #067-01-2004 L2004 **IM** *020 †20

TRACY, Thomas Francis. 2 DUDLEY ST, STE 180 02905 #550-02-1981 L1997 **PDS** *020 †85

TRAFTON, Peter Grier. 2 DUDLEY ST 02905 #024-01-1970 L1984 **ORS OTR** *071 †40

TRAN, Hao Anh. 593 EDDY ST, DEPT MED 02903 #041-15-2007 L2007 **IM** *012

TRIEBWASSER, Andrew S. 593 EDDY ST, DEPT OF ANESTHESIA 02903 #035-09-1982 L1989 **PD AN** *020 †55,05

TRIEDMAN, Leonard Jason. 1 BLACKSTONE PL 02903 #024-01-1953 L1954 **GS HNS** *071 †85

TRIEDMAN, Scott A. 825 N MAIN ST 02904 #043-01-1985 L1990 **RO IM** *020 †80

TROISE, Caroline Ann. 1 HOPPIN ST 3RD FL, ANCHOR MEDICAL ASSOCIATES 02903 #011-02-1980 L1982 **IM** *020 †20

TROZZI, Melissa Claire. 593 EDDY ST, RHODE ISLAND HOSP 02903 #021-01-2005 L2005 **PD** *012

TRUNE, Ryan Dean. 825 CHALKSTONE AVE, ROGER WILLIAMS HOSP 02908 #820-02-2005 L2006 **IM** *012

TSAISHIMIZU, Ikue. ■ 02912 #043-01-2007 L2007 **IM** *012

TSIAPALI, Ekaterini Vasil. 101 DUDLEY ST, DEPT OF WOMENS ONCOLOGY 02905 #418-01-1995 L2006 **GS** *100

TSIARAS, William Geo. 1 HOPPIN ST, STE 202 02903 #038-41-1974 L1975 **OPH** *020 †20,35

TSIONGAS, Konstantine N. 24 CORLISS ST RM 370D, U.S. POSTAL SERVICE 02904 #043-01-1978 L1980 **FM** *020 †70

TSZE, Daniel S. ■ 02903 #061-01-2002 L2006 **PEM** *012

TUBBS, Robert James, III. 593 EDDY ST, POTTER BUILDING 2ND FLOOR 02903 #024-16-2002 L2002 **EM** *100 †16

TUNG, Glenn Albert. 1 RANDALL SQ 02904 #028-02-1982 L1991 **R IM** *020 †20,80

TURMERO, Alejandra Ysabel. 100 CURTIS ST 02909 #335-07-1998 L2004 **OBG** *020

TURNER, Jean Douross. ■ 02906 #043-01-2008 *012

TURNER, Jennifer Leigh. 593 EDDY ST, RHODE ISLAND HOSPITAL 02903 #010-02-2004 L2004 **MPD** *012

TURNER, Richard Borden. 120 DUDLEY ST 02905 #024-07-1964 L1970 **IM** *020

TYLER, Erica Jane. ■ 02908 #038-06-2005 L2005 **DR** *012

TYRKA, Audrey Robin. 345 BLACKSTONE BLVD, BUTLER HOSPITAL 02906 #041-01-1999 L1999 **P** *050 †75

TYTELL, Holly Griner. 120 WAYLAND AVE STE 3 02906 #043-01-1978 L2001 **P** *020 †20,16,75

UNDERWOOD, Jody Ann. 593 EDDY ST, RI HOSP DEPT OF PSYCH 02903 #033-05-1995 L1996 **P IM** *020 †20,75

URBAN, John. 593 EDDY ST 02903 #024-05-1971 L1973 **CD IM** *020 †20

URDANG, Elliott Burt. ■ 02906 #035-08-1960 L1967 **CHP** *062

URI, Jonathan David. 593 EDDY ST, DAVOL 129 02903 #021-01-1988 L1991 **AN** *020 *05

UVIN, Susan Cu. 164 SUMMIT AVE, FL 2 02906 #748-02-1982 L1993 **OS GYN** *050

VACCARO, Jonathan Peter. 593 EDDY ST 02903 #043-01-1988 L1990 **DR** *020 †20

VAIDYA, Kedarnath A. 593 EDDY ST, RHODE ISLAND HOSPITAL 02903 #495-73-1992 L2007 **IC** *012 †20

VAKHARIA, Jamsheed B. 1 RANDALL SQ, STE 406 02904 #704-25-1994 L1992 **GS** *020 †85

VALDES, Mauricio Andres. 593 EDDY ST, RHODE ISLAND HOSP-LIFESPAN 02903 #264-04-1993 L2003 **ORS** *012

VALENTE, Jonathan Harris. 593 EDDY ST, DEPT OF EMERG MEDICINE 02903 #038-41-1996 L2001 **EM PEM** *020 †16

VALENTINI, Robert F. BROWN UNIV, BOX G 02912 #043-01-1993 *100

VANPOZNAK, Marisa Elena. 593 EDDY ST, DEPT MED 02903 #032-01-2006 L2006 **IM** *012

VAN VLEET, Marcia Wenner. 101 DUDLEY ST, WOMEN AND INFANT'S HOSPITA 02905 #050-02-1998 L1998 **PD** *040 †55

VARGHESE, Rimini Ann. ■ 02906 #033-06-2005 L2005 **IM** *012

VARMA, Meera. 1 RANDALL SQ, OB/GYN ASSOCIATES 02904 #038-44-2000 L2004 **OBG** *020

VASQUEZ, Jaime. ■ 02906 #043-01-2006 L2007 *012

VASUDEVAN, Sreekala. 825 CHALKSTONE AVE 02908 #495-31-1990 L1995 **RHU** *020 †20

VAZ, Rosalind Marie. 593 EDDY ST BOX 224, RI HOSP DIV ADOLESCENT MED 02903 #067-01-1976 L1987 **PD ADL** *020 †20

VENTETUOLO, Corey E. ■ 02908 #024-07-2003 L2003 **PCC** *012 †20

VERSACI, Armand D. 110 LOCKWOOD ST 02903 #024-01-1947 L1956 **PS** *020 †85,65

VESTNER, Alicelee. 830 CHALKSTONE AVE, PROVIDENCE VAMC-3B BLDG 1 02908 #035-45-2000 L2000 **PYG P** *020 †75

VEZERIDIS, Michael P. 2 DUDLEY ST, STE 470 02905 #418-01-1967 L1983 **GS SO** *020 †85

VIENS, Michael Leo. 825 CHALKSTONE AVE, ROGER WILLIAMS MEDICAL CEN 02908 #023-01-1990 L1995 **DR** *020 †80

VIGNOGNA, Michael Peter. 530 N MAIN ST 02904 #035-03-1991 L1994 **P** *075 †75

VILLA, Jennifer Angelique. ■ 02909 #041-13-2005 L2005 **IM** *012

VILLALBA, Rendueles, II. 235 PLAIN ST 02905 #026-04-1990 L1995 **P** *020 †75

VILLARREAL, Robert J. ■ 02903 #043-01-2005 L2005 **ORS** *012

VILLAZON, Santiago Julio. 10 ORMS ST, STE 220 02904 #008-01-1992 L2002 **OPH** *020 †35

VINOVRSKI, Todd Joseph. ■ 02907 #041-15-2003 L2007 **DMP** *012

VINSON, Amy Elizabeth. 593 EDDY ST, RHODE ISLAND HOSP 02903 #012-01-2006 L2006 **PD** *012

VITELLI, John Silvio. 80 DEAN ST 02903 #561-17-1987 L1993 **IM** *020 †20

VITHIANANTHAN, S. ■ 02906 #035-01-1993 L2007 **CCS** *020 †85

VITO, Louis. 830 CHALKSTONE AVE, DEPARTMENT OF SURGERY 02908 #050-02-1970 L1975 **GS TRS** *020 †85

VITTIMBERGA, Gwenn M. 593 EDDY ST 02903 #043-01-1985 L1987 **D** *020 †15

VIVIER, Patrick Michael. BOX GA4, DEPT OF COMMINITY HLTH 02912 #043-01-1989 L1989 **PD** *050 †15

VOGEL, Renee Golda Stern. 65 ORCHARD AVE 02906 #035-08-1968 L1977 **PTH** *071 †50

VOGNAR, Lidia Antonia. 825 CHALKSTONE AVE 02908 #957-06-2005 L2007 **IM** *012

VOHR, Betty L J M Rohloff. 101 DUDLEY ST, WOMENS INFANTS HOSP 02905 #035-03-1966 L1968 **PD** *020 †55

VOJKOVSKA, Kveta. 790 N MAIN ST, PEDIATRICS - UPPER FLOOR 02904 #286-13-1992 L2002 **PD** *020 †55

VORLOP, Erich David. ■ 02903 #035-06-2005 L2005 **IM** *012

VROCHIDES, Dionisios V. ■ 02903 #418-02-1994 L2000 **GS TTS** *100

VUKCEVIC, Zoran. ■ 02905 #957-01-1992 L2005 **CCS** *100

VYTLA, Naga Sirisha. 825 CHALKSTONE AVE, ROGER WILLIAMS HOSP 02908 #495-11-2001 L2004 **IM** *100

WAGNER, Carrie Leah. 21 PEACE ST, ST JOSEPH PEDIATRIC CLINIC 02907 #025-12-2001 L2001 **PD** *020 †55

WAGNER, Cheryl Ann. ■ 02906 #065-10-1982 **FM** *020

WAGNER, Richard Laverne. 345 BLACKSTONE BLVD, BUTLER HOSP 02906 #008-01-1975 L1983 **P PFP** *020 †75

WAHLBERG, Lars U. 110 LOCKWOOD ST 02903 #048-13-1985 L1987 **NS** *020

WALL, Barry Wayne. 184 WATERMAN ST 02906 #045-01-1990 L1990 **P PFP** *020 †75

WALLACH, Michael Tide. 1 RANDALL SQ 02904 #038-06-1981 L1988 **DR PD** *020 †80

WALLE, Nicholas Leo. ■ 02906 #010-02-2006 L2006 **DR** *012

WALSH, Kathleen Elizabeth. 593 EDDY ST 02903 #010-02-1998 L1998 **PD** *020 †55

WALTERS, Beverly C. 128 N MAIN ST 02903 #065-10-1981 L1993 **NS** *020

WANDS, Jack Raymond. 593 EDDY ST RM 421, G.I. DIVISION 02903 #054-04-1969 L1998 **IM** *020 †20

WANG, Chia-Ching. ■ 02909 #035-48-2005 L2005 **OBG** *100

WANG, Erik Ekai. ■ 02906 #047-05-2007 L2007 **EM** *012

WANG, Feng. 825 CHALKSTONE AVE 02908 #243-16-1993 L2005 **IM** *012

WANG, Scott E. 164 SUMMIT AVE 02906 #024-05-1980 L1991 **PTH PCP** *020 †50

WANG, Xiao-Qing. ■ 02906 #035-09-2008 *012

WARD, Nicholas Shaeffer. 593 EDDY ST 02903 #035-01-1993 L1999 **PCC** *020 †20

WARD, Renee Melva. 695 EDDY ST, CENTER FOR WOMEN'S SURGERY 02903 #005-02-2001 L2005 **OBG** *020

WARDHAN, Pradeep Kumar. 825 CHALKSTONE AVE 02908 #496-09-2002 L2006 **IM** *012

WARRIER, Sarita Shanker. 593 EDDY ST, INTERNAL MEDICINE 02903 #025-01-2005 L2005 **IM** *012

WASSER, Elliot Joseph. ■ 02906 #008-02-2005 L2006 **DR** *012

WATSON, Erik N. 164 SUMMIT AVE, MIRIAM HOSPITAL 02906 #043-01-1987 L1990 **IM** *020 †20

WATTS, Delma-Jean. 593 EDDY ST, HASBRO CHILDREN'S HOSPITAL 02903 #035-03-2003 L2003 **PD** *100 †55

WAXMAN, Michael Jay. 164 SUMMIT AVE, DIVISION OF INFECTIOUS DIS 02906 #024-16-2001 L2003 **EM** *100 †16

WAZER, David Edward. 593 EDDY ST, RHODE ISLAND HOSPITAL 02903 #035-19-1982 L1998 **RO N** *020 †80

WEAVER, Gayle J. 164 SUMMIT AVE, DIVISION OF HOSPITAL MEDIC 02906 #041-02-1990 L2000 **ID** *020 †20

WEBBER, Banice Mordecai. 825 N MAIN ST 02904 #024-07-1947 L1951 **RO** *071 †85,80

WEBSTER, Myles David. 593 EDDY ST, RHODE ISLAND HOSP 02903 #050-02-2006 L2006 **GS** *012

WEIL, Barbara Jane. ■ 02906 #035-46-1991 L1991 **IM** *020 †20

WEINBERG, Marc S. 235 PROMENADE ST, RM 118 02908 #024-05-1977 L1978 **NEP IM** *050 †20

WEINER, Lewis Richard. 1 DAVOL SQ, STE 304 02903 #012-05-1986 L1988 **IM** *020 †20

WEINMAN, Susan Diane. 345 BLACKSTONE BLVD 02906 #035-08-1990 L1998 **N** *020 †75

WEINSIER, Steven Benjamin. ■ 02906 #001-02-2001 L2004 **CD IC** *100

WEINSTOCK, Martin Arthur. 593 EDDY ST 02903 #035-01-1983 L1988 **D PHP** *050 †75

WEINTRUB, James H. 34 BARNES ST 02906 #038-41-1974 L1975 **GS PS** *020 †65

WEISBORD, Aaron King. 593 EDDY ST, DIV OF CARDIOLOGY 02903 #005-14-2002 L2005 **CD** *012 †20

WEISMAN, Barrie Leo. 1056 HOPE ST 02906 #041-02-1964 L1975 **FM A** *020 †03,18

WEISS, Arnold Peter C. 2 DUDLEY ST 02905 #037-01-1985 L1991 **HS ORS** *020 †40

WEISSBURG, Alan Jeffrey. 300 PEARL ST, UNIT 208 02907 #041-12-1976 L1983 **AN PD** *020 †55,05

WEITBERG, Alan Barry. 50 MAUDE ST 02908 #033-05-1976 L1978 **ON HEM** *030 †20 ‡

WELCH, Elizabeth Ann. 100 HIGHLAND AVE STE 306 02906 #035-01-1976 L1978 **D DS** *020 †15

WELCH, Jennifer Greene. 593 EDDY ST, RHODE ISLAND HOSPITAL 02903 #016-02-2002 L2002 **PHO** *012

WELCH, Raymond Henry. 845 N MAIN ST STE 3 02904 #035-03-1981 L1986 **D** *020 †15

WENDELL, Linda Laselle. ■ 02906 #047-06-2004 L2004 **N** *012

WESNER, Lee Vincent. 593 EDDY ST, DEPARTMENT OF ANESTHESIOLO 02903 #051-01-1999 L2005 **AN** *020 †05

WESSELHOEFT, Conrad Wm. 2 DUDLEY ST STE 180 02905 #024-07-1959 L1968 **PDS TS** *020 †85,90

WESTLAKE, Robert Jos. 345 BLACKSTONE BLVD, BUTLER HOSPITAL 02906 #041-01-1961 L1973 **P PYG** *071 †75

WEXLER, William Marshall. 830 CHALKSTONE AVE, PROVIDENCE VA MED CTR 02908 #008-01-1965 L1969 **OTO A** *020 †45

WEYMAN, Albert Krug. 486 SILVER SPRING ST 02904 #035-01-1969 L1976 **TS VS** *020 †85,90

WHEELER, Carol Anne. 101 DUDLEY ST 02905 #041-02-1980 L1990 **REN GYN** *020 †30

WHITAKER, Anne Willis. 339 ANGELL ST 02906 #035-46-1988 L1992 **P** *020 †75

WHITE, Emily Jane. ■ 02905 #051-01-2007 **GS** *012

WHITE, Russell Eli. 2 DUDLEY ST, STE 470 02905 #025-01-1989 L1989 **GS** *020 †85

WIGGINS, Michael Edward. 285 PROMENADE ST 02908 #010-01-1988 L1988 **OSM ORS** *020 †40

WILKERSON, James Arthur. ■ 02906 #043-01-2008 *012

WILKINSON, Joanne E. 164 SUMMIT AVE 02906 #043-01-1995 L1995 **FM** *020 †18

WILKINSON, Tracey Allyson. 593 EDDY ST, RHODE ISLAND HOSPITAL 02903 #047-05-2006 L2006 **PD** *012

WILLIAMS, David Owen. 593 EDDY ST 814, RHODE ISL HOSP 02903 #041-09-1969 L1976 **CD IM** *020 †20

WILLIAMS, Denise E. 830 CHALKSTONE AVE, VETERANS ADMINISTRATION ME 02908 #043-01-1989 L1989 **HO HEM** *062 †20

WILLIAMS, Jennifer Alyssa. ■ 02903 #028-78-2007, ▲ L2007 *012

WILLIAMS, Jennifer Joan. 593 EDDY ST, RHODE ISLAND HOSP 02903 #050-02-2007 **GS** *012

WILLIAMS, Kenneth Alan. 593 EDDY ST, RHODE ISLAND HOSPITAL 02903 #024-16-1984 L1997 **EM** *020 †16

WILLIS, Christine Ann. ■ 02906 #008-02-2006 L2006 **PD** *012

WILLIS, Matthew Dean. ■ 02906 #008-02-2006 L2006 **CPP** *012

WILTERDINK, Janet Lee. 2 DUDLEY ST, STE 530 02905 #043-01-1988 L1988 **N** *020 †75

WINER, Eric Stephen. 593 EDDY ST, RHODE ISLAND HOSPITAL 02903 #036-01-1999 L2005 **IM** *020

WING, Edward Jos. 164 SUMMIT AVE, FL 2 02906 #024-01-1971 L1998 **ID** *030 †20

WING, Elihu Smith, Jr. ■ 02906 #008-01-1946 L1952 **IM** *072 †20

WINN, Brody James. 593 EDDY ST 02903 #654-01-2004 L2005 **PTH** *012

WINTER, Bruce Allan. 101 DUDLEY ST 02905 #010-01-1981 L1985 **AN** *020 †05

WINTROB, Ronald Marvin. 345 BLACKSTONE BLVD, BUTLER HOSPITAL 02906 #065-01-1959 L1982 **P** *030 †75

WISHIK, Jeffrey. 1 RANDALL SQ STE 409 02904 #016-01-1981 L1987 **N LM** *020 †75

WITMAN, Gary B. 235 PROMENADE ST RM 105 02908 #035-08-1975 L1976 **IM ON** *020 †20 ‡

WITOSZKA, Mark Marian. 164 SUMMIT AVE 02906 #759-03-1956 L1978 **AS TRS** *020

WITTELS, Edward Gerard. 164 SUMMIT AVE, FL 3 02906 #035-08-1972 L1977 **HO** *020 †20

WODA, Craig Bryan. ■ 02906 #035-46-2007 L2007 **PD** *012

WOLD, Anne S Devi. 235 PLAIN ST, STE 102 02905 #187-32-1987 L1997 **OBG CG** *020 †19,30

WOLFE, Michael David. 345 BLACKSTONE BLVD 02906 #055-01-2004 L2004 **P** *012

WOLFMAN, Vanessa Audrey. 593 EDDY ST 02903 #023-01-2007 L2007 **PD** *012

WOLFSON, Ivan Stuart. 160 BROAD ST, C/O CROSS ROADS 02903 #041-02-1992 L1992 **FM** *020 †18

WOLSTON, Edward Jonathan. 394 ANGELL ST 02906 #016-06-1976 L1980 **P** *020 †75

WOO, Hyung Chul. 101 DUDLEY ST, DEPARTMENT OF PEDIATRICS 02905 #035-08-2003 L2006 **PD** *012

WOOD, Todd Andrew. 593 EDDY ST, RHODE ISLAND HOSP 02903 #038-06-2004 L2004 **CD** *012 †20

WOODCOME, Harold A, Jr. 690 EDDY ST 02903 #024-05-1972 L1975 **OPH OS** *020 †35

WOODS, Amie Hall. ■ 02906 #035-45-2004 L2004 **EM** *012

WOOLARD, Robert H. 593 EDDY ST, RHODE ISL HOSP ER 02903 #024-16-1979 L1981 **EM IM** *020 †20,16

WOOLF, Mervyn H. 593 EDDY ST, RHODE ISLAND HOSP DEPT OF 02903 #836-01-1984 L1998 **AN** *020 †05

WROBLESKI, Daniel Edward. 827 N MAIN ST, STE 3 02904 #035-01-1973 L1976 **CRS** *020 †10,85

WU, Hank. 830 CHALKSTONE AVE 02908 #270-01-1995 L1999 **CD IM** *020 †20

WU, Qian. 593 EDDY ST, RHODE ISLAND HOSP PATH DPT 02903 #243-40-1984 L1999 **PTH NP** *020 †50

WU, Tony Chaui. 285 GOVERNOR ST 02906 #033-06-1993 L1993 **IM** *020 †20

WU, Wen Chi. 830 CHALKSTONE AVE, PROVIDENCE VA MEDICAL CENT 02908 #244-06-1968 L1974 **AN** *020

YAAR, Israel. 830 CHALKSTONE AVE 02908 #550-01-1965 L1984 **N** *020 †75

YAKIREVICH, Evgeny. 593 EDDY ST, RHODE ISLAND HOSP-LIFESPAN 02903 #913-33-1987 L2004 **PTH** *012

YALCINDAG, Ali. 593 EDDY ST, HASBRO CHILDREN'S HOSPITAL 02903 #902-07-1994 L2003 **PD PPR** *020 †55

YANGO, Angelito F, Jr. 593 EDDY ST 02902 #748-02-1994 L1998 **NEP** *020 †20

YANKEE, Ronald August. 405 PROMENADE ST 02908 #008-01-1960 L1979 **BBK IM** *071

YATCHMINK, Yvette Ellen. 593 EDDY ST, RHODE ISLAND HOSP APC 6 02903 #035-20-1986 L2003 **PD** *020 †55

YATES, Jennifer Kathleen. 2 DUDLEY ST, RHODE ISLAND HOSP 02905 #028-34-2004 L2004 **U** *012

YEH, Chinchin. 593 EDDY ST, RHODE ISLAND HOSP 02903 #035-47-2006 L2006 **GS** *012

YELLE, William Arthur. 825 CHALKSTONE AVE, ROGER WILLIAMS MEDICAL CEN 02908 #024-16-2003 L2007 **AN** *020

YEO, Linda Irene. ■ 02906 #062-01-1988 L1993 **DR** *020 †80

YIP, Agustin Go. 345 BLACKSTONE BLVD, BUTLER HOSP 02906 #748-02-1997 L2004 **P** *012

YOBURN, David Crocker. 1076 N MAIN ST 02904 #035-00-1975 L1987 **NEP IM** *020 †20

YOUNG, Carolyn Te. 405 PROMENADE ST, THE RHODE ISLAND BLOOD CTR 02908 #011-03-1989 L1992 **BBK CLP** *030 †50

YOUNG, Warren K. ■ 02912 #043-01-2007 **PD** *012

YU, Anthony Tak-Po. 825 N MAIN ST 02904 #462-01-1968 L1979 **RO** *020 †80

ZABBO, August. 195 COLLYER ST, STE 201 02904 #043-01-1980 L1986 **U EM** *020 †95

ZACK, Jeffrey Robert. ■ 02906 #024-16-1998 L1998 **EM** *020 †16

ZACKS, Sumner Irwin. 164 SUMMIT AVE 02906 #024-01-1955 L1977 **PTH** *030 †50

ZAFAR, Nadah. 593 EDDY ST, FOUNDATION 02903 #035-08-1989 L2003 **IM EM** *020 †16

ZAFAR, Saadia. 825 CHALKSTONE AVE, ROGER WILLIAMS HOSPITAL 02908 #704-01-1996 L2001 **AN** *020 †05

ZAIDMAN, Jeffrey Scott. 593 EDDY ST 02903 #051-01-2003 L2006 **GE** *012 †20

ZAKAI, Aminadav. 825 CHALKSTONE AVE 02908 #550-03-1986 L1989 **P** *020 †75

ZAMORA, Haidee Roxanne Da. 825 CHALKSTONE AVE 02908 #748-01-2002 L2006 **IM** *012

ZARLENGO, Raymond Paul. 101 DUDLEY ST 02905 #041-14-1991 L1991 **PD** *020 †55

ZARRAGA, Marc Joseph Coz. 825 CHALKSTONE AVE 02908 #748-01-2002 L2006 **IM** *012

ZEITOUN, Omeima Mohamed. 593 EDDY ST 02903 #915-03-1992 L1999 **CHN** *100

ZELDIN, Edmond T. 345 BLACKSTONE BLVD, CONSULTANTS OF RHODE 02906 #065-01-1973 L1988 **P** *020 †75

ZHANG, Ying. 593 EDDY ST 02903 #243-46-1994 L2006 **PTH** *012

ZHENG, Su. 593 EDDY ST, APC 12 RHODE ISLD HOSP 02903 #243-03-1988 L2004 **PTH** *100 †50

ZHOU, Hua. 50 MAUDE ST 02908 #243-65-1982 L2000 **D** *020 †15

ZIEGLER, James Wm. 593 EDDY ST 02903 #011-03-1994 L1995 **PD** *020 †55

ZIENOWICZ, Richard Jos. 2 DUDLEY ST, STE 380 02905 #043-01-1983 L1991 **PS HS** *020 †65,85

ZIMMERMAN, Mark. 235 PLAIN ST 02905 #016-42-1990 L1994 **P** *020 †75

ZIMMERMANN, Bernard, III. 825 CHALKSTONE AVE, ROGER WILLIAMS MED CTR 02908 #055-01-1979 L1980 **RHU IM** *020 †20

ZIMMERMANN, Matthew Scott. ■ 02903 #005-14-2006 L2006 **ORS** *012

ZINK, Brian Jeffrey. 593 EDDY ST, DEPT OF EMERGENCY MEDICINE 02903 #035-45-1984 L2006 **EM** *020 †16

ZIV, Ohad. ■ 02906 #041-12-2001 L2004 **CD** *100

ZOMPA, Justine B. 1 HOPPIN ST, ONE HOPPIN ST 02903 #033-06-1984 L1986 **OBG** *020 †30

ZONNO, Alan Joseph. 593 EDDY ST, RHODE ISLAND HOSP 02903 #041-13-2004 L2004 **ORS** *012

ZUCKERMAN, Joshua David. 2 DUDLEY ST STE 450, RHODE ISLAND HOSP 02905 #016-42-2004 L2004 **PS** *012

ZUCKERMAN, Matthew David. ■ 02904 #025-01-2007 L2007 **EM** *012

ZWETCHKENBAUM, John F. 1056 HOPE ST 02906 #024-05-1985 L1990 **AI IM** *020 †20,03

RIVERSIDE – PROVIDENCE

ADAMS, Cathleen Marie. ■ 02915 #041-14-2007 L2007 **CPP** *012

ANDERSON, Elliott James. ■ 02915 #035-03-2002 L2002 **HO** *012 †20

BASSEN, Daisy Georgette. 1011 VETERANS MEMORIL PKWY 02915 #035-45-2002 L2002 **CHP** *012

BOCHIECHIO, Pamela Joan. ■ 02915 #035-06-2006 L2006 **P** *012

BROWN, William D. 1525 WAMPANOAG TRL STE 206, NEUROPEDIATRIX PC INC. 02915 #043-01-1987 L1988 **CHN N** *020 †55,75

BRUCE, Barbara Ann. 1525 WAMPANOAG TRL, STE 206 02915 #016-42-2001 L2002 **CHN** *020 †75

CAZZANIGA, Stefano Luca. 1525 WAMPANOAG TRL, STE 202 02915 #036-07-1991 L1991 **IM** *020 †20

COL, Marta. ■ 02915 #649-03-1977 L1994 **PD ADL** *040

COWASJI, Shiavax Bomanji. ■ 02915 #704-26-1996 L2008 **IMG IM** *020 †20

DE LA CRUZ, Ponciano. ■ 02915 #748-10-1962 L1974 **IM CD** *075

FARLEY, John Eugene, Jr. ■ 02915 #024-07-1948 L1950 **PD** *072 †55

FARRELL, Timothy William. ■ 02915 #024-16-2004 L2004 **IMG** *012 †18

FESSLER, Sarah Jane. 100 BULLOCKS POINT AVE, EAST BAY FAMILY HEALTH 02915 #038-40-1991 L1991 **FM** *020 †18

FRAGOLA, Louis A, Jr. 1525 WAMPANOAG TRL 02915 #054-04-1963 L1970 **D** *020 †15

GAGNE, Gerard George, Jr. 250 WAMPANOAG TRL, STE 303 02915 #043-01-1999 L1999 **P** *100

GRECO, Richard Germano. 50 AMARAL ST 02915 #024-07-1967 L1973 **PD** *020 †55

HAMILTON, Teresita Smith. 100 BULLOCKS POINT AVE 02915 #035-03-1997 L1997 **FM** *020 †18

HANNA, Edward R. ■ 02915 #330-02-1952 L1970 **IM CD** *020 †20

HOROWITZ, Karyn Jean. 1011 VETERANS MEMORIAL PKWY, BRADLEY HOSPITAL 02915 #008-01-1996 L2002 **CHP** *020 †75

HUNT, Jeffrey Ivan. 1011 VETERANS MEMORIL PKWY, BRADLEY HOSPITAL 02915 #056-06-1984 L1992 **CHP P** *020 †75

INGRAHAM, James William. ■ 02915 #035-06-2006 L2006 **P** *012

JAFFE, Marc Alexander. 38 AMARAL ST 02915 #023-01-1981 L1982 **OBG** *020 †30

JOHNSON, Melvyn. 250 WAMPANOAG TRL, STE 306 02915 #024-05-1943 L1947 **P** *071 †75

KONCSOL, Kathryn Ann. ■ 02915 #041-13-2004 L2004 **IM** *020 †20

KOSTER, Divya. 50 AMARAL ST, RIVERSIDE PEDIATRICS INC 02915 #035-09-2003 L2007 **PD** *100 †55

LEBLANC, Thomas William. ■ 02915 #036-07-2006 **IM** *012

LEE, Amanda Rebecca. ■ 02915 #047-07-1988 L1988 **PTH** *100

LO, Elizabeth Peishih. ■ 02915 #023-01-2006 L2006 **IM** *012

LUSSIER, Mary Leona. 250 WAMPANOAG TRL, STE 204 02915 #016-06-1981 L1991 **N** *020 †75

MEHTA, Sunita. 56 VILLAGE DR 02915 #422-01-1997 L2005 **PD** *020 †55

MINASIAN, Diane Elaine. 100 BULLOCKS POINT AVE, EAST BAY COMMUNITY ACTION 02915 #024-05-1990 L1990 **FM** *020 †18

MUNRO, Dugald. 1525 WAMPANOAG TRL 02915 #025-01-1960 L1964 **OPH** *020 †35

NURCOMBE, Barry. 1011 VETERANS MEMORIL PKWY, OF PSYCHIATRY 02915 #143-05-1956 L1976 **CHP** *030 †75

PAIK, David S. 42 HEMINGWAY DR, NORTHERN RI ANESTHESIA ASS 02915 #583-06-1960 L1971 **AN** *020

PEREZ, Kimberly Joyce. ■ 02915 #010-01-2004 L2004 **HO** *012 †20

PETERS, Todd Erik. ■ 02915 #041-14-2006 L2006 **P** *012

PHILLIPS, Brian Daniel. ■ 02915 #026-03-2003 L1993 **IM** *100 †20

RAMZAN, Usman. ■ 02915 #024-05-2001 L2001 **PCC** *100

SACHS, Henry Thos, III. 1011 VETERANS MEMORIL PKWY 02915 #043-01-1988 L1989 **CHP** *020 †75

SCHWARTZ, James Morris. 1445 WAMPANOAG TRL, UNIT 205 02915 #038-06-1992 L1996 **FM** *020 †18

SCOLA, Francis Hugh. 1525 WAMPANOAG TRL 02915 #024-05-1961 L1965 **R** *020 †80

SINGER, Joseph Bernard. 50 AMARAL ST 02915 #033-06-1993 L1996 **PD** *020 †55

STULIK, Edward James. 1525 WAMPANOAG TRL, STE 202 02915 #035-06-1986 L1988 **IM** *020 †20

SUN, Margaret Ann. 1445 WAMPANOAG TRL # 205 02915 #035-48-1991 L1991 **FM** *020 †18

THAMBAR, Sukumaran Thevat. ■ 02915 #143-03-1989 L1998 *100

TRIVEDI, Harsh. 1011 VETERANS MEMORIL PKWY 02915 #035-47-2000 L2006 **CHP** *100 †75 ‡

WHEELER, Elizabeth Eustis. 1011 VETERANS MEMORIL PKWY 02915 #043-01-1987 L1987 **CHP P** *020 †75

WILBERGER, Michael S. 1445 WAMPANOAG TRL, UNIT 205 02915 #048-02-1976 L1995 **CHP P** *020 †75

WOLD, Marshall Benj. 610 WAMPANOAG TRL 02915 #035-03-1987 L2000 **CHP P** *020 †75

RUMFORD – PROVIDENCE

CORDOVA, Katharine Malory. ■ 02916 #003-01-2005 L2006 **D** *012

HARRISON, Timothy Stone. ■ 02916 #023-07-1953 L1953 **GS TS** *071 †85,90

HOCHBERGER, Daniel A. 400 PAWTUCKET AVE 02916 #024-05-1983 L1985 **IM** *020 †20

HOWRIE, William C F, Jr. ■ 02916 #041-09-1943 L1947 **AN** *071 †05

KARAS, Joseph Stanley. ■ 02916 #035-01-1953 L1958 **IM CD** *071

MAC DONALD, Lisa Ann. ■ 02916 #035-20-1984 L1988 **OBG** *020

MC NAMEE, Augustine Miles. ■ 02916 #024-05-1954 L1959 **AN** *071 †05

O'NEILL, John Crane. ■ 02916 #024-07-1947 L1949 **OM GP** *071

RICCO, Ronald R. 25 CIRCLE ST 02916 #561-01-1963 L1965 **GYN OBS** *020 †30

SAMUEL, Susan Joseph. ■ 02916 #051-04-2003 L2007 **NPM** *012 †55

SANTANA DE RUIZ, Carmen G. ■ 02916 #847-06-1971 L1978 **GP** *020

SCHILLER, Jonathan. ■ 02916 #041-15-2002 L2003 **ORS** *012

TEFFT, Robert J, Jr. ■ 02916 #010-02-1952 L1954 **IM** *071

WIRTH, Pamela P Walker. ■ 02916 #024-01-1967 L1968 **HEM PD** *074

SAUNDERSTOWN – WASHINGTON

GUTHRIE, James Russell. ■ 02874 #035-19-1948 L1971 **FM PD** *071 †55

HARDIMAN, James Francis. ■ 02874 #007-01-1945 **IM** *020

JASO, Hector C. ■ 02874 #649-01-1949 L1958 **P CHP** *071 †75

MC CAY, Thomas Earl. ■ 02874 #055-01-1971 L1996 **EM** *020

ROQUE, John A Jos. ■ 02874 #024-07-1942 L1948 **IM CD** *071 †20,28

TRIOLO, Peter A. ■ 02874 #649-33-1979 L1990 **DR** *072

SLOCUM – WASHINGTON

CARGES-NASIN, Marjorie. ■ 02877 #043-01-1998 L2007 **PD** *020 †55

NASIN, Christopher S. ■ 02877 #043-01-1998 L2001 **FSM** *100 †18

SMITHFIELD – PROVIDENCE

BLEYER, John Michael. 8 CAMBRIDGE CIR 02917 #473-01-1941 L1953 **IM DIA** *071

BRASCH, Peter Chas. 1 THURBER BLVD 02917 #033-05-1986 L1990 **OPH** *020 †35

BRENNAN, Constance Marie. 28 CEDAR SWAMP RD 02917 #024-07-1992 L1992 **OBG** *020 †30

BROSCO, Fred Augustus. 28 CEDAR SWAMP RD 02917 #043-01-1984 L1985 **OBG** *020 †30

CLEMENS, Susan V. 400 PUTNAM PIKE, URGENT MEDICAL CARE 02917 #043-01-1988 L1989 **FM** *020 †20

DIETRICH, Dinusha W. 41 SANDERSON RD, STE 202 02917 #024-07-1996 L1996 **PDI** *020 †55

FRANCAZIO, Lisa Anne. ■ 02917 #041-14-2007 L2007 **IM** *012

GILLETTE, Gregory Mark. ■ 02917 #036-01-1979 L1979 **P IM** *020 †20,75

GUGLIELMI, Anthony. ■ 02917 #561-01-1956 L1958 **AN** *071

HALPREN-RUDER, Daniel H. 400 PUTNAM PIKE STE E 02917 #021-01-1978 L1981 **OS EM** *030 †16

HEERMANN, Bradley Dean. 400 PUTNAM PIKE STE E 02917 #030-05-1990 L1990 **IM** *020

JONES, Wendell Clyde. 400 PUTNAM PIKE STE E 02917 #033-06-1986 L1989 **OS** *020

LEVIN, William Allan. 41 SANDERSON RD, STE 205 02917 #050-02-1975 L1980 **DR IM** *020 †20

MC GRATH, Carolyn Kelly. 400 PUTNAM PIKE STE E 02917 #043-01-1990 L1990 **IM** *020 †20

MOUHAMED-FARID, Ashraf. ■ 02917 #915-04-1992 L2003 **AN PME** *020 †05

PENCHUK, Stephanie Jo. 9 CEDAR SWAMP RD STE 9 02917 #048-14-1985 L1991 **PD** *020 †55

PENSA, Frank Archille. 28 CEDAR SWAMP RD 02917 #561-01-1974 L1976 **OBG** *020 †30

RAMOS, Donald Andrew. 28 CEDAR SWAMP RD 02917 #008-02-1987 L1989 **OBG** *020 †30

VEZZA, Phyllis Rosemarie. ■ 02917 #010-01-1992 L2000 **PTH** *020 †50

SOUTH KINGSTOWN – WASHINGTON

CANCRO, Carol S. 36 S COUNTY COMMONS WAY, UNIT EIGHT 02879 #043-01-1993 L1998 **FM** *020 †18

HENSELER, Laura Jean. 69 SOUTH COUNTY COMMNS WAY, KENT PRIMARY CARE ASSOCIAT 02879 #024-05-1992 L2000 **FM** *020 †18

PEMBROOK, Richard Chas. ■ 02879 #026-04-1963 L1973 **IM CD** *020 †20 ‡

TIVERTON – NEWPORT

BOWEN, Edward H, Jr. ■ 02878 #024-01-1949 L1992 **IM OM** *072

BROWN, Walter Armin. ■ 02878 #036-07-1967 L1975 **P** *020 †75

BRUCH, Hilton Chas. ■ 02878 #012-01-1940 L1975 **AN** *020 †05 ‡

CHERNAYA, Irina. 1105 MAIN RD 02878 #913-97-1985 L2002 **IM** *020 †20

CHERNYY, Vitaliy. ■ 02878 #913-97-1984 L2002 **IM** *020 †20

EVANS, Frederic Marsee. ■ 02878 #035-20-1951 L1994 **P PYA** *020

GRENIER, Nicole Lynn. ■ 02878 #043-01-2006 L2006 **D** *012

HARRISON, Joan T. 550 MAIN RD 02878 #422-01-1986 L2002 **IM** *020 †20

HARTNETT, William Cliffor. 1368 MAIN RD 02878 #035-08-1957 L1959 **GP** *071

KADIN, Marshall Edward. ■ 02878 #016-06-1965 L2002 **HMP DMP** *050

LAMBERT, Paul Henri. ■ 02878 #067-01-1956 L1958 **OBG** *020 †30

MABIE, Kevin N. 1816 MAIN RD, COASTAL ORTHOPAEDIC INSTIT 02878 #024-16-1979 L1996 **ORS** *020 †40

MARTIN, Edward. ■ 02878 #008-01-1940 L1971 **IM** *071 †20

MIGLIACCIO, Anthony Jos. ■ 02878 #035-09-1959 L1960 **GP** *072 †85

PEDREIRA, Alceu Luiz S. ■ 02878 #187-03-1956 L1967 **TS** *071 †85,90

RADOVSKY, Anna Cort. ■ 02878 #024-05-1949 **GP** *020

RAUKAR, George Jeffrey. 1816 MAIN RD 02878 #026-08-1991 L2007 **ORS OAR** *020 †40

SOLAS, George James. ■ 02878 #024-07-1944 L1948 **ORS OS** *071 †40

WORTHINGTON, James Mason. 1816 MAIN RD 02878 #050-02-1981 L2004 **ORS** *020 †40

WAKEFIELD – WASHINGTON

ARRON, Brett Lawrence. 100 KENYON AVE 02879 #021-01-1981 L1993 **AN IM** *020 †05

BADER, David Scott. 70 KENYON AVE, UNIT 103 02879 #035-03-1994 L1999 **CD** *020 †20

BANDOLA, John Jefferys. 70 KENYON AVE UNIT 326 02879 #010-01-1978 L1980 **IM** *020 †20

BARRATT, Paul Frederick. 481 KINGSTOWN RD 02879 #010-01-1974 L1977 **IM** *020 †20

BELLAFIORE, Peter Jos. 70 KENYON AVE UNIT 321 02879 #050-02-1991 L1995 **N** *020 †75

BOWLING, Kathleen Cote. 49 S COUNTY COMMONS WAY 02879 #032-01-1982 L1983 **OBS GYN** *030

BRADY, John Francis. 100 KENYON AVE 02879 #010-01-1964 L1970 **IM** *020

BRANDON, Neil. 70 KENYON AVE, UNIT 103 02879 #550-02-1985 L1990 **CD** *020 †20

BROUSSEAU, Erin Christine. 49 S COUNTY COMMONS WAY 02879 #028-34-2002 **OBG** *020

BROWN, Christopher Coles. 70 KENYON AVE, UNIT B1 02879 #048-04-1980 L2005 **IM ID** *020 †20

BROZA, David John. 70 KENYON AVE, UNIT 103 02879 #035-09-1989 L1995 **CD IM** *020 †20

CAHILL, Terrence F. 49 S COUNTY COMMONS WAY 02879 #010-02-1975 L1976 **GYN** *020 †30

CAIN, J Lincoln. ■ 02879 #041-01-1951 L1990 **R** *071 †80

CAPUANO, Umberto. 70 KENYON AVE, UNIT 25 02879 #043-01-1982 L1987 **GS VS** *020 †85

CARSWELL, Claire Griffin. 55 CHERRY LN 02879 #045-01-1990 L1994 **P** *020 †75

CASCI, Robert J, Jr. 100 KENYON AVE 02879 #016-76-1990, ▲ L1995 **EM FM** *020 †18 ‡

CASSIN, Kathleen A. 70 KENYON AVE, UNIT 323 02879 #043-01-1982 L1988 **OBG** *020 †30

CHEE, Young Shin. 100 KENYON AVE 02879 #583-03-1964 L1988 **AN** *071 †05

CHINN, Robert Kenneth. 100 KENYON AVE, SOUTH COUNTY HOSP 02879 #014-01-1987 L2004 **AN** *071 †05

CHRONLEY, David James. 4979 TOWER HILL RD 02879 #024-05-1974 L1975 **PD ADL** *020 †55

COGHLIN, Barbara M. 70 KENYON AVE UNIT 101 02879 #008-01-1998 L2001 **PD** *020 †55

CONKLIN, Elizabeth. 70 KENYON AVE, STE 25 02879 #050-02-1990 L1990 **GS** *020 †85

CONRAD, Robert Lee. 11 KENYON AVE 02879 #024-05-1960 L1965 **GS TRS** *071 †20

COPPES, Mark Allister. 10 HIGH ST 02879 #035-03-1985 L1995 **OSS ORS** *020 †40

CORCORAN, Celeste C. 70 KENYON AVE UNIT G1 02879 #010-02-1982 L1985 **PD** *020 †55

CORCORAN, J Russell. 70 KENYON AVE STE 21 02879 #010-02-1982 L1985 **IM IMG** *020 †20

CROUSE, Robert James. 100 KENYON AVE 02879 #023-07-1974 L1977 **EM IM** *020 †20,16

CUNNINGHAM, Colette L. 100 KENYON AVE 02879 #539-04-1955 L1967 **PYM ADM** *072

CURHAN, Robert Pevin. 70 KENYON AVE 02879 #025-01-1957 L1974 **GYN** *020 †30

RHODE ISLAND
WAKEFIELD — WARWICK

DAMLE, Nitin Shridhar. 481 KINGSTOWN RD 02879 #025-07-1985 L1987 **IM** *020 †20
DE MORANVILLE, Beatriz M. 70 KENYON AVE, UNITB1 02879 #737-06-1985 L1991 END **IM** *020 †20
DI BIASIO, Heather A. 46 HOLLEY ST, STE 2 02879 #043-01-2002 L2002 **PD** *020 †55
DOWD, Andrew Jos. 70 KENYON AVE 02879 #016-43-1992 L1992 **GS** *020 †85
DRESLIN, J Andrew. 70 KENYON AVE, UNIT 322 02879 #016-43-2000 L2005 **GS** *020 †95
DUGAS, E Brien. 70 KENYON AVE UNIT 324 02879 #041-09-1983 L1988 **GE IM** *020 †20
DUNCAN, Marie Castaldi. ■ 02879 #016-06-1951 L1953 **P PD** *071 †75
FAMIGLIETTI, Bruce Edward. 100 KENYON AVE, S COUNTY HOSP 02879 #024-07-1984 L1988 **IM** *020 †20
FARMER, Ulana V. ■ 02879 #061-01-1971 L2001 *020
FERA, Steven Raymond. 70 KENYON AVE, UNIT 103 02879 #010-02-1981 L1987 **CD IM** *020 †20
FITZGERALD, Jos Benedict. 10 HIGH ST 02879 #010-01-1968 L1970 **ORS OSM** *020 †40
FRANKLIN, Leslie Anne. 70 KENYON AVE, UNIT 321 02879 #038-41-1986 L1989 **IM** *020 †20
GALLAGHER, Michael Dennis. 10 HIGH ST 02879 #036-01-2001 L2001 **ORS** *020
GAZDER, Humayun Mohammed. 100 KENYON AVE, SOUTH COUNTY HOSPITAL 02879 #539-05-1993 L1999 **AN** *020 †05
GIAMPAOLO, Casimiro M. 100 KENYON AVE, DEPT OF PATHOLOGY 02879 #016-02-1970 L1998 **PTH** *020 †50
GILARDETTI, Robert Steven. 691 KINGSTOWN RD 02879 #024-01-1995 L1998 *020
GOLBERG, Mauricio. 100 KENYON AVE 02879 #132-02-1945 L1958 **GP** *072
GRAHAM, John Deiter. 133 MATUNUCK SCHOOL HOS RD 02879 #043-01-1987 L1991 **AN** *020 †05
HASSAN, Raza. 100 KENYON AVE 02879 #704-04-1964 L1973 **AN OS** *071
HEFFERNAN, John Philip. 70 KENYON AVE, UNIT 322 02879 #010-02-1986 L1997 **U** *020 †95
HEINEMAN, Joseph David. 70 KENYON AVE, UNIT 322 02879 #024-05-1994 L2000 **U** *020 †95
HIMMEL, Peter B. ■ 02879 #035-08-1972 L1974 **RHU** *020
HOLZMAN, Martin Ivan. 142 KENYON AVE, SOUTH COUNTY RADIATION THE 02879 #422-01-1982 L1984 **RO** *020 †20,80
HONEYMAN, Joshua N. ■ 02879 #043-01-2008 *012
JOHNSON, Shelly Lynn. 70 KENYON AVE, UNIT 321 02879 #005-11-1989 L1995 **IM** *020 †20
JOSEPH, Jeffrey Francis. 85 KENYON AVE, STE 215 02879 #035-09-1989 L1992 **OBG** *020 †30
KANJEEKAL, Sindu Mary. 24 SALT POND RD STE G2 02879 #065-06-1997 L2003 *100
KENT, Edward A. 100 KENYON AVE, SOUTH COUNTY HOSPITAL 02879 #654-01-1985 L1993 **AN PME** *020 †05
KLONOWSKI, Eva Maria. 1 RIVER ST, THUNDERMIST HEALTH CENTER 02879 #035-06-1980 L1981 **FM** *020 †18
KOZEL, Margaret Keavey. 70 KENYON AVE, STE G-1 02879 #010-02-1980 L1990 **PD** *075 †55
LIANG, Jee-Quang. 100 KENYON AVE, SOUTH COUNTY HOSPITAL 02879 #244-02-1971 L1976 **AN** *020
MANCINI, Mark Jos. 70 KENYON AVE, UNIT 104 02879 #008-02-1992 L1999 **IM** *020 †20
MARCHAND, Robert Cary. 10 HIGH ST 02879 #035-20-1983 L1988 **ORS** *020 †40
MARTIN, Douglas Woodbury. 100 KENYON AVE, SOUTH COUNTY HOSPITAL 02879 #035-45-2003 L2003 **PCC** *012 †20
MATHIEU, Michele Anne. 4979 TOWER HILL RD, SOUTH COUNTY PEDIATRICS 02879 #043-01-2000 L2000 **PD** *020 †55
MC ATEER, Allison Louise. 70 KENYON AVE, UNIT325 02879 #024-07-1995 L1995 **GS** *020 †85
MC DERMOTT, William Hugh. 46 HOLLEY ST 02879 #024-07-1961 L1964 **PD** *020 †55
MC NIECE, Donald M. 24 SALT POND RD STE H1 02879 #035-08-1976 L1979 **IM** *020 †20
MOFFITT, Raymond Edward. ■ 02879 #035-06-1948 L1949 **GE IM** *020 †20
MORA, George. 100 SHADOW FARM WAY 02879 #541-07-1947 L1955 **CHP P** *071 †75
MURPHY, John F. 70 KENYON AVE, UNIT 103 02879 #043-01-1990 L1997 **CD** *020 †20
NOEL, Lauren C. 46 HOLLEY ST STE 2 02879 #043-01-1994 L1994 **PD** *020 †55
O'BRIEN, James Anthony. 49 S COUNTY COMMONS WAY 02879 #539-06-1979 L1983 **OBG** *020 †30
O'MARA, Timothy J. 481 KINGSTOWN RD 02879 #561-03-1986 L1992 **IM** *020 †20
O'NEILL, Joseph James. 70 KENYON AVE, UNIT215 02879 #030-06-1959 L1964 **GYN** *020 †30
O'NEILL, Robert Thos. 70 KENYON AVE, UNIT215 02879 #030-06-1965 L1969 **OBG OS** *020 †30
PAQUETTE, Richard Robt. 55 CHERRY LN 02879 #033-05-1966 L1996 **P CHP** *020 †75
PARSNANI, Murli Mirchumal. 100 KENYON AVE 02879 #495-01-1972 L1982 **AN GP** *020
PARSNANI, Pratibha Murli. ■ 02879 #495-96-1972 L1982 **FM** *020
PESZKE, Michael Alfred M. ■ 02879 #539-03-1956 L1958 **P** *030 †75
PIERIK, Michael G. ■ 02879 #024-07-1950 L1952 **IM OS** *020 †20
POULIOT, Monique L. 481 KINGSTOWN RD 02879 #022-75-1991, ▲ L1991 **IM** *020 †20
RAMEAKA, Lisa Marie. 85 KENYON AVE 02879 #550-02-1998 L2002 **OBG** *020 †30
REED, Lorijean. 100 KENYON AVE 02879 #048-15-2002 L2005 **AN** *020 †05
REYES, Ysabel Viviana. 100 KENYON AVE 02879 #308-04-1995 L2005 **IM** *020 †20
RISICA, Robert Michael. 116 MAIN ST 02879 #047-14-1988 L1997 **OTO** *020 †45
RISINGER, Randall Jay. 10 HIGH ST 02879 #036-05-1999 L2005 **ORS OSM** *020 †40
ROBINSON, Martin E. ■ 02879 #008-01-1951 L1989 **FM** *071
ROMANELLO, Joseph Michael. 70 KENYON AVE, UNIT 104 02879 #008-02-2000 L2006 **NEP** *020 †20 ‡
ROTH, Steven Robt. 1 RIVER ST, OF SOUTH COUNTY 02879 #035-08-1980 L2003 **FM** *020 †18
RUBENSTEIN, Louis J. 100 KENYON AVE, SOUTH COUNTY HOSPITAL 02879 #035-01-1988 L1988 **IM** *020 †20
SABINA, William Henry. 100 KENYON AVE 02879 #024-05-1995 L1995 **EM** *020 †16
SAMALE, Jill Marie. 85 KENYON AVE 02879 #050-02-2000 L2007 **OBG** *020
SAMUEL, Winston. ■ 02879 #496-38-1970 L1977 **P** *020 †75
SARAZEN, Arnold A, Jr. 70 KENYON AVE, UNIT 322 02879 #043-01-1987 L1993 **U** *020 †95
SCHNEIDER, Steven Howard. 85 KENYON AVE 02879 #038-41-2002 L2006 **OBG** *020
SERRA, Robert Michael. 70 KENYON AVE, UNIT 104 02879 #051-01-1974 L1982 **NEP IM** *020 †20
SKUDLAREK-PRETE, Caroline. 49 S COUNTY COMMONS WAY 02879 #035-75-1995, ▲ L2000 **OBG** *020 †30
SMYTHE, James Leighton. 24 SALT POND RD, STE G2 02879 #048-04-1977 L1983 **ON HEM** *020 †20
SPAIGHT, Deborah Ann. 4979 TOWER HILL RD, SOUTH COUNTY PEDIATRICS 02879 #050-02-1991 L2002 **PD** *020 †55
SPICER, Albert Doty. ■ 02879 #008-01-1937 **OS** *071
SUN, Gloria Yu. 481 KINGSTOWN RD, SOUTH COUNTY INTERNAL MEDI 02879 #025-07-1992 L2001 **IM** *020 †20

SZLATENYI, C Stephen. 163 WOODRUFF AVE 02879 #035-03-1977 L1981 **OS** *020 †16
SZTULMAN, Luciano. 49 S COUNTY COMMONS WAY 02879 #187-67-1983 L1999 **OBG** *020 †30
TAFONE, Paul Jos. 100 KENYON AVE 02879 #422-01-1984 L1990 **EM IM** *020 †55,20
THORNTON, Anthony Jay. 55 CHERRY LN 02879 #051-01-1983 L1997 **P** *020 †75
TIPIRNENI, Prabhakar Rao. 24 SALT POND RD STE H2, SOUTH KINGSTONE OFFICE PAR 02879 #495-58-1974 L1985 **OTO HNS** *030
VAN HEMELRIJCK, C L. 100 KENYON AVE 02879 #035-09-1980 L1989 **IM** *020 †20,16
WALSH, John Jos, Jr. 100 KENYON AVE 02879 #024-07-1947 L1954 **EM GP** *020 †85
WEPMAN, Barry Michael. 70 KENYON AVE UNIT 211 02879 #025-07-1972 L1977 **OPH** *020 †35
WHARTON, Gary Gibson. 49 S COUNTY COMMONS WAY 02879 #010-02-1989 L1995 **OBG** *020 †30
WILLIS, Peter Lyndon. 100 KENYON AVE 02879 #039-01-1996 L2002 **FM** *020 †18
WILSON, Douglas Gardiner. 49 S COUNTY COMMONS WAY, SOUTH COUNTY MED OFFICE 02879 #025-01-1976 L1981 **OBG** *020 †30
ZHANG, Shunli. 100 KENYON AVE, SOUTH COUNTY HOSPITAL 02879 #243-46-1982 L1999 **PTH** *020 †50
ZIEGLER, Joy. 70 KENYON AVE, UNIT 101 02879 #043-01-1988 L1995 **PD** *020 †55
ZUERNER, Richard Taylor. 70 KENYON AVE UNIT 322 02879 #024-01-1964 L1972 **U** *020 †95

WARREN – BRISTOL

AMALFITANO, Frank J, Jr. 639 METACOM AVE 02885 #043-01-1989 L1989 **IM** *020 †20
BASSEL, Howard Scott. 639 METACOM AVE 02885 #038-41-1984 L1989 **FM** *020 †18
CALENDA, Charles Carl. 639 METACOM AVE 02885 #770-02-1979 L1982 **OPH** *020
HALLMANN, David Robt. 02885 #024-07-1955 L1962 **R NM** *071 †20,28
KAPLAN, Stephen Robt. ■ 02885 #035-19-1963 L1969 **RHU IM** *040 †20
MARCACCIO, Paul. 639 METACOM AVE 02885 #035-45-1989 L1989 **RHU** *020 †20
PANTALONI, Marcello. ■ 02885 #561-23-1988 L1993 **PS** *100
SALUJA, Sushila. 511 CHILD ST 02885 #495-30-1970 L1983 **AN** *020 †05
ZIBRIDA, Joseph Thomas. 639 METACOM AVE 02885 #041-09-1998 L1998 **IM** *020 †20

WARWICK – KENT

ACKERMAN, Karen Claire. ■ 02886 #033-05-1991 L1992 **DR** *020 †80
AHMED, Hanna N. ■ 02887 #024-07-2004 L2005 **IM** *100 †20
AHMED, Khaja N. ■ 02887 #495-21-1966 L1975 **IM ON** *020 †20
AHMED, Wesam B. 79 POLK RD 02889 #915-12-1991 L2007 **IM** *012
ALFORD, John W. 120 CENTERVILLE RD 02886 #043-01-1997 L1997 **OSM** *020 †40
ALLENDORF, Charles F. ■ 02886 #010-02-1968 L1972 **IM** *020 †20
AMMAR, Maha M. 215 TOLL GATE RD STE 104, TOLLGATE PEDIATRICS 02886 #915-02-1975 L1993 **PD** *020 †55
ANDREANI, Marc Stephen. 455 TOLL GATE RD 02886 #561-01-1981 L1984 **AN IM** *020 †05
APPLEBY, Reid Simpson, Jr. 390 TOLL GATE RD, KENT OPHTHALMOLOGY, INC 02886 #024-07-1963 L1969 **OPH** *071 †35
ARCHABALD, Karen Lorraine. ■ 02886 #008-01-2007 L2007 **OBG** *012
ARMADA, Mary Julie. 45 GILBANE ST 02886 #043-01-1980 L1987 **DR** *020 †80
ASPRINIO, Edward F. ■ 02886 #561-01-1955 L1957 **FOP FM** *071
ATHAS, John Michael. 227 CENTERVILLE RD 02886 #024-05-1996 L2006 **RNR** *020 †80
AUDETT, John Robt, III. 455 TOLL GATE RD, KENT HOSPITAL 02886 #028-34-1981 L1984 **IM** *030 †20
BAFFONI, Frank Anthony. 300 TOLL GATE RD, STE 304 02886 #305-01-1986 L1990 **IM** *020 †20
BAKER, Kenneth. 215 TOLL GATE RD, STE 109 02886 #550-02-1998 L2005 **R** *020 †20
BAL, Jose Abesamis. 455 TOLL GATE RD, KENT COUNTY HOSP 02886 #748-08-1960 L1972 **FOP PTH** *071 †50
BANSAL, Sudhir. 215 TOLL GATE RD STE 309 02886 #495-45-1970 L1989 **END IM** *020 †20
BANSAL, Tej Varna. 215 TOLL GATE RD 02886 #496-07-1973 L1983 **OBG** *020
BARLOW, Jared C. 455 TOLL GATE RD, KENT HOSPITAL 02886 #035-06-1966 L1967 **AN** *020 †05
BARLOW, Jennifer Cushman. 455 TOLL GATE RD 02886 #035-06-1997 L2002 **AN** *020 †05
BARRETT, Joseph T. ■ 02886 #035-03-1951 L1952 **PD GP** *071
BATTAGLIA, Jennifer June. 455 TOLL GATE RD, KENT COUNTY MEMORIAL HOSPI 02886 #046-01-1999 L2006 **IM** *020 †20
BAUTE, Peter Brueckner. 390 TOLL GATE RD, STE 200 02886 #041-09-1960 L1961 **GS OS** *071 †85
BAUTE, Robert Edward. 455 TOLL GATE RD 02886 #041-09-1966 L1970 **MDM IM** *030 †20
BAXTER, John Chas. 469 CENTERVILLE RD, STE 103 02886 #024-07-1958 L1967 **R** *071 †80
BERRY, Lori Lynn. ■ 02889 #043-01-2001 *100
BINEK, Robert Edward. 455 TOLL GATE RD 02886 #025-01-1984 L1993 **VIR DR** *020 †80
BLACK, Richard Alan. 227 CENTERVILLE RD 02886 #035-08-1980 L1985 **DR** *020 †80
BLACKMAN, Carolyn Ruth. 455 TOLL GATE RD 02886 #043-01-1997 L1997 **IM** *020 †20
BLECHMAN, James William. 227 CENTERVILLE RD 02886 #033-05-1993 L1998 **DR** *020 †80
BONNAFFON, Niccole Anne. ■ 02886 #051-07-2004 L2007 **PHO** *012 †55
BONNAR, James Millar, III. 50 HEALTH LN, KENT CENTER 02886 #024-01-1967 L1997 **P** *020 †75
BOREK, Leora Lisa. 227 CENTERVILLE RD 02886 #654-01-1999 L2003 **PYG N** *020 †75
BOYER, Amy Marcia. 455 TOLL GATE RD, KENT HOSPITALISTS 02886 #010-01-2000 L2000 **IM** *020 †20
BRADY, Joseph James. 470 TOLL GATE RD STE 203, KENT SURGICAL ASSO.INC. 02886 #041-09-1987 L1993 **GS VS** *020 †85
BRENNAN, William Francis. 120 CENTERVILLE RD, WEST BAY ORTHOPEDICS 02886 #024-07-1988 L1994 **OSS** *012 †40
BROWN, Gail Rose. 400 BALD HILL RD, STE 501 02886 #016-11-1984 L2007 **PD PHP** *020 †70,55
BROWN, Lorand Reid. 455 TOLL GATE RD 02886 #067-01-1956 L1960 **OBG** *071 †30
BRUTUS, Roland. 455 TOLL GATE RD, KENT COUNTY MEMORIAL HOSPI 02886 #649-14-1972 L1981 **AN** *020
BRUZZESE, Anthony Geo. 45 GILBANE ST 02886 #043-01-1980 L1982 **DR IM** *020 †20,80
CALDARELLI, John Raymond. 227 CENTERVILLE RD 02886 #422-01-1982 L1984 **DR** *020 †80
CALENDA, Alexander. 300 TOLL GATE RD 02886 #770-02-1979 L1982 **U** *020
CALENDA, Alexander Manuel. 300 TOLL GATE RD 02886 #561-01-1956 L1958 **OPH** *020 †35
CALLAHAN, Keith Lee. 470 TOLL GATE RD STE 103, KEITH LEE CALLAHAN MD, P.C 02886 #016-01-1995 L2007 **FM** *020 †18

■ = Address Information Privacy Protected

CAMBRE, April Davidson. 2756 POST RD 02886 #004-01-2002 L2002 **CHP** *100

CANTON, Juan Carlos. 390 TOLL GATE RD, STE 106 02886 #649-06-1982 L1993 **OS** *020 †75

CARDENAS, Alfonso C. 110 MAJOR POTTER RD, 110 MAJOR POTTER ROAD 02886 #035-09-1977 L1980 **EM FM** *020 †18,16

CARON, Evelyne. ■ 02888 #067-01-2001 L2007 *100

CARPENTER, Marshall Webb. 50 NARRAGANSETT BAY AVE 02889 #041-01-1972 L1983 **MFM OS** *020 †30

CASSIET, Alfredo Cesar. 300 TOLL GATE RD STE 301A 02886 #132-01-1952 L1961 **GE** *071

CASTREE, Katherine C. 400 BALD HILL RD, HARVARD PILGRIM HEALTH CAR 02886 #016-02-1978 L1983 **PD** *020 †55

CATE, Stanley E. ■ 02888 #024-07-1950 L1951 **IM** *071

CHANG, William Chin. 1131 WARWICK AVE 02888 #305-01-1981 L1985 **GP FM** *020

CHAVARRIA, Johnny. 929 MAIN AVE 02886 #270-02-1990 L1992 **PD** *020 †55

CHOU, Kelvin Linyu. 227 CENTERVILLE RD, NEURO-HEALTH PAKINSON DIS 02886 #025-01-1998 L2004 **N** *020 †75

CHOU, Norman G. 455 TOLL GATE RD 02886 #043-01-1996 L2000 **EM** *020 †16

CHU, Nelson Jim. 250 CENTERVILLE RD 02886 #024-07-1986 L1993 **IM NEP** *020 †20

CLYNE, Ailis. 400 BALD HILL RD, STE 501 02886 #043-01-1995 L1995 **PD** *020 †55

COBURN, Michael Christian. 470 TOLL GATE RD 02886 #043-01-1988 L1988 **GS** *020 †85

COLAVITA, Mauro Arnold. 166 TOLL GATE RD 02886 #041-02-1983 L1992 **OBG** *020 †30

CONNOLLY, Michael David. ■ 02889 #041-15-2001 L2001 **GS** *012

COOPER, George Norman, Jr. 840 GREENWICH AVE 02886 #033-05-1961 L1971 **TS** *020 †85,90

CORREIA, Manuel. 455 TOLL GATE RD 02886 #033-05-1998 L2001 **EM** *020 †16

COSCINA, William Francis. 227 CENTERVILLE RD 02886 #023-07-1980 L1985 **DR IM** *020 †80

COSGROVE, Christopher J. 1775 BALD HILL RD 02886 #012-01-1995 L2002 **NEP** *020 †20

COTTER, Richard Geo. 455 TOLL GATE RD 02886 #056-06-1964 L1982 **PTH** *020 †50

COUTO, Corey Alexander. ■ 02888 #032-01-2005 L2005 **DR** *012

COX, Jeffrey Matthew. 455 TOLL GATE RD 02886 #038-40-1984 L1989 **EM** *020 †18,16

CRAIGHILL, Marian C. 475 KILVERT ST, STE 310 02886 #005-02-1980 L2005 **OBG PHP** *030 †30

CRAUSMAN, Robert S. 875 CENTERVILLE RD, UNIT 15 02886 #043-01-1988 L1995 **IM PUD** *020 †20

CUDDY, Arthur Barnabus. ■ 02889 #024-07-1941 L1942 **GP IMG** *071

CURIOSO, Wilfredo A. 455 TOLL GATE RD, KENT COUNTY MEMORIAL HOSPI 02886 #748-01-1985 L1992 **EM** *020 †20

DAUKAS, Charles. 566 TOLL GATE RD 02886 #008-01-1955 L1987 **OPH OS** *071 †35

DAVENPORT, Lyman Alan. 227 CENTERVILLE RD 02886 #024-05-1968 L1970 **DR** *071 †80

DAVIS, Leena. 300 TOLL GATE RD 02886 #495-65-1985 L1999 **PD** *020 †55

DAVIS, Mechery Joseph. 300 TOLL GATE RD STE LL6 02886 #495-52-1981 L1999 **IM** *020 †20

DE BARROS, Anthony H. 215 TOLL GATE RD, STE 109 02886 #050-02-1972 L2003 **DR NM** *020 †80

DE CESARE, Danute Regina. 455 TOLL GATE RD 02886 #154-02-1950 L1956 **AN** *071

DE CESARIS, Vincent A. 469 CENTERVILLE RD, STE 103 02886 #050-02-1970 L1972 **DR** *020 †80

DEINDORFER, Barbara Ann. 455 TOLL GATE RD 02886 #035-47-1990 L2001 **EM OM** *020 †16

DENBY, Charles, II. 300 CENTERVILLE RD, STE 101 02886 #043-01-1978 L1982 **P** *020 †75

DENIER, James M. 1131 WARWICK AVE, WARWICK MEDICAL WALK-IN RO 02888 #041-09-1982 L1998 **EM FM** *020 †16

DEROSA, Mary Catherine. 300 TOLL GATE RD, STE 203 02886 #035-15-1978 L1989 **GYN** *020 †30

DI GIACOMO, Ralph A. 215 TOLL GATE RD STE 303 02886 #422-01-1982 L1985 **RHU IM** *020

DILLON, Hope Caldwell. 300 TOLL GATE RD 02886 #035-09-1975 L1978 **RHU IM** *050 †20

DI PRETE, Daniel Anthony. 250 TOLL GATE RD 02886 #043-01-1989 L1989 **DR** *020 †80

DOBRZYNSKI, Robert John. 390 TOLL GATE RD STE 204 02886 #165-04-1970 L1974 **U** *020 †95

DOI, Kei. 45 GILBANE ST 02886 #035-46-1990 L1997 **R** *020 †80

DONNELLY, Edward Michael. 227 CENTERVILLE RD, THE NEUROLOGY FOUNDATION 02886 #032-01-1997 L1997 **CN N** *020 †75

DRURY, Timothy Robt. 455 TOLL GATE RD 02886 #041-14-1974 L1975 **EM OS** *020 †16

DUFF, Brian Edward. 55 LAMBERT LIND HWY, THE ENT CENTER OF RHODE IS 02886 #038-41-1990 L1996 **OTO NO** *020 †45

DYER, Candace Lesley. 390 TOLL GATE RD, STE 200 02886 #043-01-1980 L1982 **GS** *020 †85

DYER, Richard Raymond. ■ 02889 #008-01-1945 L1951 **GS** *071 †85

EASLEY, Samantha Elaine. ■ 02889 #035-06-2003 L2007 **PTH** *100 †50

EHRLICH, Lawrence H. 566 TOLL GATE RD 02886 #035-20-1972 L1999 **OPH** *020 †35

ELLISON, Robert Gary. 400 BALD HILL RD, STE 520 02886 #035-03-1972 L1976 **IM HEM** *020 †20

ENTEZARY, Fakhreddin. 455 TOLL GATE RD 02886 #517-01-1962 L1971 **R** *020 †80

ERINAKES, Christos Harry. 176 TOLL GATE RD UNIT B 02886 #561-11-1977 L1982 **OBG** *020 †30

EXIL, Gerald. 216 TOLL GATE RD 02886 #847-02-1982 L1995 **CHN OS** *020 †55

FAELLA, Michael J. 455 TOLL GATE RD 02886 #561-01-1965 L1968 **N** *071 †75

FIREMAN, Jack M. 857 POST RD 02888 #041-77-1970, ▲ L1971 **FM** *071

FLETCHER, David P. 390 TOLL GATE RD 02886 #043-01-1977 L1979 **PD** *020 †55

FLYNN, Joseph Christopher. 300 TOLL GATE RD 02886 #016-43-1965 L1967 **OBG** *071 †30

FORBES, Elizabeth Ann. 30 HEWETT ST 02889 #007-02-1996 L2001 **PD** *020 †55

FRAZZINI, Vincent I, Jr. 45 GILBANE ST 02886 #038-06-1992 L2006 **R RNR** *020 †80

FRIEDMAN, Joseph Harold. 227 CENTERVILLE RD 02886 #035-01-1978 L1982 **N P** *020 †75

GABRIELE-PERILLI, Ann. 215 TOLL GATE RD, STE 109 02886 #050-02-1982 L1989 **DR** *020 †80

GALINKO, Neal Jeffrey. 400 BALD HILL RD, ANCHOR MED ASSOC-STE 520 02886 #036-05-1982 L1984 **IM** *020 †20

GARRAHAN, William Francis. 215 TOLL GATE RD, STE 206 02886 #010-02-1955 L1956 **ORS** *071 †40

GATES, Jonathan. 455 TOLL GATE RD, KENT HOSPITAL 02886 #067-01-1999 L1999 **IM** *020 †20

GELTZER, Arthur I. 618 TOLL GATE RD 02886 #035-45-1962 L1969 **OPH** *020 †35 ‡

GELZHISER, John Andrew. ■ 02886 #041-15-2004 L2004 **IM** *020 †20

GEORGE, Thomas Henry. ■ 02889 #024-07-1954 L1957 **PD OS** *071

GERMANO, Thomas Gary. 455 TOLL GATE RD 02886 #010-02-1989 L2001 **EM** *020 †16

GILMAN, Owen Bernard. 250 CENTERVILLE RD, BLDG E 02886 #024-07-1963 L1969 **NEP IM** *020 †20

GOLDFARB, Andrea Grace. 455 TOLL GATE RD, KENT WOUND RECOVERY CENTER 02886 #035-45-1996 L2001 **EM** *020 †16

GOLDHABER, Meryl Gail. 227 CENTERVILLE RD 02886 #035-15-1988 L2000 **N** *020 †75

GOODING, Vaughn G, Jr. 120 CENTERVILLE RD 02886 #024-07-1975 L1978 **ORS IM** *020 †20,16,40

GRAVES, Peter Frederick. 455 TOLL GATE RD, ATTN: PHARMACY DEPARTMENT 02886 #024-16-1999 L1999 **EM** *020 †16

GRUMBACH, Nicholas Munroe. 400 BALD HILL RD, ANCHOR MEDICAL ASSOCIATES 02886 #035-47-1996 L1996 **MPD** *020 †20,55

GUGLIELMO, Maria Ann. 300 TOLL GATE RD, STE 101D 02886 #043-01-1992 L1992 **NS** *020 †25

GUILLETTE, Barbara Jean. 3520 POST RD 02886 #008-01-1985 L1990 **OTO** *020 †45

HACKMAN, Edmund Timothy. ■ 02888 #041-02-1942 L1943 **GP OM** *071

HADAMARD, Antoine F O. 300 TOLL GATE RD 02886 #869-04-1970 L1973 **GE IM** *020

HAMBLETT, Katie Marie. 455 TOLL GATE RD, DEPT OF EMERGENCY MEDICINE 02886 #024-16-2003 L2006 **EM** *020

HARRISON, John Robt. 300 TOLL GATE RD 02886 #024-07-1968 L1972 **END IM** *075 †20

HASHMI, Adnan Hasan. 455 TOLL GATE RD 02886 #704-25-1995 L2006 **NEP** *012 †20

HASSID, Samuel H. 1624 WARWICK AVE 02889 #165-01-1946 L1968 **IMG** *072

HAUGHT, Kristen Rae. 215 TOLL GATE RD, STE 109 02886 #055-01-1998 L2006 **DR** *020 †80

HAYES, John Walter. 120 CENTERVILLE RD 02886 #067-01-1968 L1973 **ORS GP** *020 †40

HEINL, Robert, Jr. 455 TOLL GATE RD 02886 #759-01-1984 L1987 **IM** *020 †20

HERARD, Christian Rene. 300 TOLL GATE RD STE 302 02886 #440-01-1967 L1975 **CD FM** *020

HERRING, Daniel B. ■ 02886 #055-01-2006 L2007 **D** *012

HICKS, Allyson Davis. 215 TOLL GATE RD, TOLL GATE PEDIATRICS 02886 #024-07-1990 L1993 **PD** *020 †55

HOLBY, Elizabeth Doble. 455 TOLL GATE RD 02886 #050-02-1988 L1992 **AN** *020 †05

HORWITZ, Robin Lisa. 455 TOLL GATE RD 02886 #047-20-1983 L2005 **P** *020 †75

HSU, Gloria Puye. ■ 02888 #005-11-2005 L2005 **GS** *100

HUMBYRD, Danny Edward. 120 CENTERVILLE RD, WEST BAY ORTHOPAEDICS 02886 #025-01-1978 L1983 **ORS** *020 †40

IACONO, Vincent. 566 TOLL GATE RD 02886 #561-01-1968 L1971 **PS HS** *020

IBRAHIM, Farhat. 470 TOLL GATE RD STE 1 02886 #704-25-1993 L1995 **PCC** *020 †20

ILER, Lynn Elizabeth. 400 BALD HILL RD STE 526, WARWICK MEDICAL BLDG 02886 #043-01-1995 L1996 **D** *020 †15

INFANTOLINO, Michael. 215 TOLL GATE RD, STE 206 02886 #561-17-1977 L1978 **ORS** *020 †40

ISAAC, John, Jr. 390 TOLL GATE RD STE 200 02886 #047-06-1984 L1989 **GS VS** *020 †85

JACEWICZ, George Jerry. 95 TOLL GATE RD 02886 #759-07-1961 L1969 **OTO NO** *020 †45

JACKSON, Amanda Lynn. ■ 02888 #045-01-2007 L2007 **OBG** *012

JAMES, Andriotis. ■ 02889 #008-02-2004 L2004 **CHP** *012

JASA, Lydia Abreu. 400 BALD HILL RD 02886 #748-01-1963 L1974 **IM** *071 †20

JOHNSTON, Leon Mc Tyeire. 400 BALD HILL RD, STE 520 02886 #043-01-1978 L1980 **IM** *020 †20

JONES, Chas Frederick G. 390 TOLL GATE RD, KENT UROLOGY INC 02886 #539-03-1957 L1959 **OS IM** *071

JONES, Curtis Thompson. 390 TOLL GATE RD 02886 #035-09-1975 L1980 **U** *020 †95

JOSEPH, Robbie J. ■ 02886 #043-01-2007 L2007 **P** *012

JOYAL, Steven Vincent. ■ 02888 #043-01-1993 L1993 **IM** *075 †20

KADER, Medhat A. 300 TOLL GATE RD STE 304 02886 #330-04-1949 L1971 **ORS OS** *071 †40

KAHN, Sewell Irby. 2736 POST RD 02886 #045-01-1966 L1972 **NEP IM** *020 †20

KAPOOR, Nidhi. 455 TOLL GATE RD 02886 #041-02-1997 L2003 **EM** *020 †16

KATAMURA, Kathleen Marie. 455 TOLL GATE RD 02886 #032-01-1981 L2000 **EM IM** *020 †20

KATZEN, David Robt. 400 BALD HILL RD, STE 527 02886 #035-46-1979 L1982 **AI** *020 †55,03

KAW, Yao T. ■ 02889 #748-10-1983 L1988 **PCP PTH** *062 †50

KELLY, Charles Stephen. 455 TOLL GATE RD 02886 #033-05-1965 L1973 **OBG** *071 †30

KIM, Chang-Ryul. ■ 02886 #583-13-1984 L1994 **NPM** *100

KOCH, Paul S. 444 QUAKER LN 02886 #024-07-1977 L1978 **OPH** *020 †35

KOCH, Peter, Jr. 566 TOLL GATE RD, KOCH EYE SURGICENTER INC 02886 #024-07-1946 L1947 **AN** *071

KORNWITZ, Norman Alan. 120 CENTERVILLE RD, WEST BAY ORTHOPAEDICS 02886 #024-05-1980 L1985 **ORS** *020 †40

KOTHARI, Omprakash H. 455 TOLL GATE RD DEPT PATH 02886 #496-38-1969 L1976 **PTH** *062 †50

KOYFMAN, Liliya. 2756 POST RD, STE 200 02886 #913-86-1980 L1995 **P** *020 †75

KYROS, William P. 181 CENTERVILLE RD 02886 #422-01-1980 L1986 **P CHP** *020

LANE, Steven Carroll. 450 TOLL GATE RD, MADDOCK CENTER FOR RADIATI 02886 #036-07-1996 L2002 **RO** *020 †80

LANNA, Lucille. 390 TOLL GATE RD, STE 103 02886 #008-02-1984 L1985 **IM** *020 †20

LAURELLI, Henry Edmond. 300 TOLL GATE RD STE 101D 02886 #041-02-1965 L1972 **NS** *020 †25

LEACH, James Bernard. 300 TOLL GATE RD, TOLLGATE RADIOLOGY 02886 #035-09-1956 L1957 **R** *071 †80

LEDDY, Thomas Raymond. 390 TOLL GATE RD 02886 #030-06-1968 L1972 **OPH** *020 †35

LE LEIKO, Sarah Francine. 455 TOLL GATE RD, KENT HOSPITAL 02886 #035-01-2001 L2001 **IM** *100

LENGYEL, Carole Alice. 400 BALD HILL RD, STE 501 02886 #024-01-1987 L2003 **PD** *020 †55

L'EUROPA, Gary Anthony. 227 CENTERVILLE RD 02886 #043-01-1983 L1986 **N** *020 †75

LEYTIN, Victoria. ■ 02889 #008-02-2007 L2007 **EM** *012

LOMBARDI, Anthony L. 470 TOLL GATE RD, STE 102 02886 #030-06-1994 L1994 **IM** *020 †20

LOUGHLIN, Christopher J. 3520 POST RD 02886 #008-02-1992 L2007 **OTO HNS** *020 †45

LOWE, David A. 615 JEFFERSON BLVD 02886 #024-01-1971 L1977 **ID IM** *020 †20

LUKOWICZ, Daniel Francis. 470 TOLL GATE RD 02886 #035-03-1976 L1978 **IM** *020 †20

LUPPI, Lawrence Howard. 400 BALD HILL RD 02886 #050-02-1967 L1974 **ORS** *071 †40

LUZ, David Jos. 390 TOLL GATE RD, STE 200 02886 #561-01-1974 L1981 **GS** *020 †85

MAC ANDREW, Raymond Noel. ■ 02888 #041-02-1947 L1948 **GS PTH** *020 †85

MAC ANDREW, Vincent I, Jr. 455 TOLL GATE RD 02886 #041-02-1984 L1988 **ORS** *020 †40

MACCONAGHY, Lindsay Anne. ■ 02889 #035-45-2007 L2007 **EM** *012

MACHATA, Karl Francis. 455 TOLL GATE RD 02886 #008-01-1979 L1981 **EM FM** *020 †18,16

MAC MILLAN, Jo-Ann P. 300 TOLL GATE RD 02886 #561-01-1975 L1978 **OTO AI** *020

MADDEN, Edwin Jos. 166 TOLL GATE RD, EDWIN J MADDEN MD INC 02886 #035-09-1956 L1965 **ORS** *071 †40

MADDOCK, Philip G. 450 TOLL GATE RD 02886 #539-04-1967 L1983 **RO** *020

MAIER, Patricia Ane. 400 BALD HILL RD, HCHP 02886 #035-09-1981 L1984 **FM** *020 †18

MALIK, Mohsin K. ■ 02886 #043-01-2006 L2006 **D** *012

MANGRAY, Shamlal. ■ 02886 #566-01-1990 L1997 **PTH** *020 †50

MARCACCIO, Beth Gerfin. 400 BALD HILL RD, STE 508 02886 #035-45-1986 L2001 **GYN** *020 †30

MARTINEZ, Howard. 215 TOLL GATE RD STE 202 02886 #011-04-1988 L1991 **ID** *020 †20
MATE, Rena B. ■ 02886 #748-01-1966 L1983 **IM** *020
MATEO-RAMOS, Celia. 455 TOLL GATE RD, KENT CNTY HOSP PATH DEPT 02886 #748-01-1964 L1974 **PTH** *020 †50
MATSIEVSKAYA, Alla. 430 TOLL GATE RD 02886 #913-07-1980 L1998 **PD** *020 †55
MAYER, David Michael. 300 TOLL GATE RD STE 202 02886 #023-07-1975 L1977 **IM** *075 †20
MCATEER, Kristina Eileen. ■ 02886 #050-02-2005 L2005 **EM** *012
MC CAULEY, Thomas. 300 TOLL GATE RD, STE 101B 02886 #043-01-1982 L1986 **OPH** *020 †35
MC CUE, John A. 455 TOLL GATE RD, KENT COUNTY MEM HOSP 02886 #043-01-1976 L1984 **EM** *020 †20,16
MC INTEER, Debbi Michelle. 455 TOLL GATE RD 02886 #048-12-1995 L1995 **P** *020 †75
MCKENNEY, Michelle M. ■ 02886 #022-75-2007, ▲ L2007 **OBG** *012
MC KENNEY, Paul Francis. 455 TOLL GATE RD 02886 #010-02-1980 L1986 **IM MDM** *030 †20
MEATTEY, Heath Ryan. ■ 02889 #021-01-2004 L2007 **IM** *100 †20
MECHREFE, Anthony Pierre. 120 CENTERVILLE RD 02886 #010-01-2000 L2000 **ORS** *100
MEHARG, John R. ■ 02888 #035-03-1952 L1953 **PD** *071
MENNILLO, Ernest P. 215 TOLL GATE RD, STE 104 02886 #035-45-1952 L1954 **PD** *020 †55
MENNILLO, Roger Niles. 215 TOLL GATE RD, STE 104 02886 #036-07-1988 L1993 **PD** *020 †55
MERLINO, Frank. ■ 02886 #024-07-1947 L1950 **CD IM** *071 †20
MERNAN, Andrea Jean. 24 ROSEGARDEN ST 02888 #010-01-1997 L1997 **P** *020 †75
MEROLLI, Alisa Joy. 455 TOLL GATE RD 02886 #041-15-2003 L2003 **IM** *020 †20
MIANO, Salvatore. 659 SANDY LN 02889 #561-01-1958 L1961 **IM AN** *020
MICHAUD, Pierre Ross. 875 CENTERVILLE RD, UNIT 2 02886 #001-02-1989 L1999 **PS** *020 †65
MILLS, Geraldine. 65 JEFFERSON BLVD 02888 #035-01-1984 L1988 **PD IM** *020
MINTZ, Howard Murray. 400 BALD HILL RD, STE 501 02886 #041-12-1981 L1984 **PD** *020 †55
MIRRER, Franklin Everett. 120 CENTERVILLE RD 02886 #008-02-1995 L2001 **ORS** *020 †40
MIRZA, Ehsun Raza. 455 TOLL GATE RD, KENT HOSPTIAL CRITICAL CAR 02886 #704-02-1993 L1999 **CCM** *020 †20
MONTI, James Eric. 455 TOLL GATE RD 02886 #010-02-1997 L1998 **EM** *020 †16
MORGAN, Thomas Frank. 54 JEFFERSON BLVD 02888 #047-07-1970 L1971 **N** *020 †75
MORO-DECASILLAS, Maria L. 227 CENTERVILLE RD 02886 #649-13-1997 L2004 **N** *020 †75
MORRIS, Andrew Bevan. 50 HEALTH LN, KENT COUNTY MENTAL HEALTH 02886 #021-01-1988 L1992 **P** *020 †75
MOTOLA, Baruh B. ■ 02888 #902-01-1951 L1961 **IM CD** *020
MOTOLKO, Michael Alan. 566 TOLL GATE RD 02886 #065-09-1976 L1998 **OPH** *020 †35
MUELLER, Margaret Poole. 455 TOLL GATE RD 02886 #035-47-1993 L1993 **EM** *020 †16
MYERS, Beverly Ann. 1087 WARWICK AVE 02888 #067-01-1961 L1979 **CHP P** *062 †55,75
NAYAK, Ramakrishna N. 455 TOLL GATE RD 02886 #496-38-1966 L1975 **PTH** *020 †50
NAYLOR, Kelli Ann. 455 TOLL GATE RD 02886 #422-01-1996 L2001 **MPD** *020 †20,55
NEELY-WOLD, Patricia Jean. 59 W SHORE RD, UNIT 2 02889 #030-05-1952 L1963 **P** *071 †75
NEWSTEAD, Graham John. 300 TOLL GATE RD STE 204 02886 #035-45-1965 L1970 **PD A** *020 †55
NIETO, Carlos Humberto. 300 TOLL GATE RD STE 301A 02886 #264-04-1963 L1974 **N** *020
NISBET, John Douglas. 390 TOLL GATE RD 02886 #035-09-1956 L1958 **OBG** *071 †30 ‡
NISBET, John Douglas. 390 TOLL GATE RD 02886 #035-09-1963 L1985 **OBG** *020 †30 ‡
NUDELMAN, Judith Ann. 400 BALD HILL RD, ANCHOR MED ASSOCIATES STE 02886 #041-12-1984 L1987 **FM** *020 †18
O' BRIEN, Michael Jos. 455 TOLL GATE RD 02886 #035-08-1990 L1997 **OPH** *020 †35
O'HARE, Brendan Buckley. ■ 02886 #041-15-2007 L2007 **IM** *012
OLSZEWSKI, Adam Jan. 300 TOLL GATE RD, STE 203 02886 #759-03-1999 L2005 **HO** *020 †20
O'ROURKE, William J. 390 TOLL GATE RD 02886 #010-02-1957 L1964 **U** *071 †95
OSORIO, Luis Alejandro. 400 BALD HILL RD, STE 520 02886 #935-01-1994 L2001 **IM** *020 †20
PADAYHAG, Joseph Paul. 215 TOLL GATE RD, STE 301 02886 #056-06-1967 L1972 **PUD IM** *020 †20
PAGLIA, Karlyn Ann. 455 TOLL GATE RD, KENT HOSPITALIST PRACTICE 02886 #041-02-1995 L2005 **IM** *020 †20
PANCHOLI, Amita V. 455 TOLL GATE RD 02886 #021-06-1996 L2003 **EM** *020 †16
PANNEERSELVAM, Soma S. 470 TOLL GATE RD, STE 105 02886 #495-66-1981 L1994 **IM** *020 †20
PAOLUCCI, Iwona. 215 TOLL GATE RD STE 209 02886 #759-07-1998 L2001 **IM** *020
PARKER, Louise Antoinette. A12 - BOX 13, 600 COLE FARM ROAD 02889 #649-02-1960 L1965 **GP OS** *071
PARKER, Virginia Schmidt. 300 TOLL GATE RD 02886 #043-01-1976 L1980 **RHU IM** *020 †20
PATRICK, Mark. 455 TOLL GATE RD 02886 #654-01-1983 L1989 **AN** *020 †05
PAUL, Thankam Mariam. ■ 02888 #917-36-1988 L2003 **PG** *100
PEARSON, David Waldron. 1087 WARWICK AVE 02888 #041-12-1969 L1976 **P N** *020 †75
PEDORELLA, A Jos, Jr. 455 TOLL GATE RD 02886 #024-07-1961 L1962 **OBG** *071 †30
PELTIER, Joseph Robt. 929 MAIN AVE 02886 #010-02-1956 L1957 **PD PDA** *071 †55
PEZZULLO, Steven Raymond. 1131 WARWICK AVE 02888 #561-01-1977 L1981 **EM IM** *020
PHILLIPS, Kenneth Roswell. 455 TOLL GATE RD, KENT HOSPITAL 02886 #048-02-1983 L2006 **PUD IM** *020 †20
PIECH, Melissa Roether. ■ 02888 #008-02-2007 L2007 **IM** *012
PIZARRO, Greg B. 647 JEFFERSON BLVD, SKIN MED & SURG CTR 02886 #748-01-1984 L2002 **ATP** *020 †50
POMEROY, Lisa Echt. 166 TOLL GATE RD, CARING FOR WOMEN 02886 #012-05-1998 L1998 **OBG** *020 †30
POTENZA, Anthony Ralph. 469 CENTERVILLE RD, STE 103 02886 #010-01-1971 L1972 **R** *071 †80
POTTER, Jeffrey Davol. ■ 02888 #024-16-2002 L2003 **DR** *100 †80
PRINCE, Terry Polon. 250 TOLL GATE RD, THE IMAGING INSTITUTE 02886 #033-06-1997 L1997 **DR** *020 †80
PRZYGODA, John Jos. 215 TOLL GATE RD 02886 #024-05-1977 L1978 **HEM HO** *020 †20
QUINN, Donn Richard. 400 BALD HILL RD, STAT CARE 02886 #010-02-1986 L1989 **PUD IM** *020 †20
QUIRK, Catherine M. 300 TOLL GATE RD, STE 201 02886 #023-07-1995 L2000 **D** *020 †15
RACHT, Justin Robert. ■ 02888 #030-06-2000 L2005 **EM** *012
RAISSI, Babak. 227 CENTERVILLE RD 02886 #065-06-1995 L2003 **DR** *020 †80
RAJAN, Jacob. 455 TOLL GATE RD 02886 #690-07-1988 L2004 **AN** *020
READ, Richard. ■ 02888 #067-01-2004 L2007 **PCC** *012
REARDON, Daniel B, II. 390 TOLL GATE RD, STE 200 02886 #021-01-1968 L1975 **GS VS** *020 †85
REBANE, Mari. ■ 02889 #008-01-2003 L2003 **GS** *012
REGAN, Timothy John. 455 TOLL GATE RD 02886 #016-43-2000 L2003 **EM** *020 †16
REILLY, Philip J, III. 120 CENTERVILLE RD, WEST BAY ORTHOPEDICS 02886 #035-01-1984 L1990 **ORS OSM** *020 †40
RICHMAN, Stephen Joel. 566 TOLL GATE RD 02886 #024-05-1966 L1969 **OPH DIA** *020 †35
ROBERTS, Debra L. 226 BUTTONWOODS AVE 02886 #024-05-1995 L2004 **FM** *020 †18
ROBINS, Jerrold. 227 CENTERVILLE RD 02886 #024-05-1983 L1998 **DR IM** *020 †80
RODRIGUEZ, Oscar T. ■ 02886 #748-02-1967 L1974 **AN** *020
ROSSIGNOLI, Paul Louis. 430 TOLL GATE RD 02886 #561-01-1962 L1967 **OTO OS** *071
ROTONDO, Anthony Thos. 455 TOLL GATE RD 02886 #561-25-1984 L1989 **FM** *020
ROWE, David Wesley. 227 CENTERVILLE RD 02886 #035-46-1996 L2004 **RNR** *071 †80
RUDNICKI, Anna Grant. 455 TOLL GATE RD 02886 #024-16-2002 L2002 **PCC** *012 †20
RUHIG, Alexander Sandor. ■ 02886 #154-01-1952 L1961 **P CHP** *071
SADOVNIKOFF, Vsevolod. ■ 02888 #407-07-1947 L1956 **P** *071 †75
SALONGA, Cynthia Meneses. ■ 02886 #748-10-1983 *100
SALZSIEDER, Kenneth H. 470 TOLL GATE RD 02886 #056-05-1973 L1977 **CD IM** *020 †20
SAMSON, Charles Felix. 455 TOLL GATE RD 02886 #035-15-1976 L1979 **IM** *071
SAN ANTONIO, Pamela J. 929 MAIN AVE, JOSEPH R PELTIER MD INC 02886 #028-02-1976 L1984 **PD** *075 †55
SAN ANTONIO, Richard P. 215 TOLL GATE RD STE 305 02886 #028-02-1976 L1984 **CD IM** *020 †20
SARHAN, Osama E. 455 TOLL GATE RD 02886 #915-04-1966 L1977 **IM CD** *075
SAX, Eric. 250 TOLL GATE RD 02886 #024-05-1989 L2005 **DR NR** *020 †80
SCAGNELLI, Alexander. 889 CENTERVILLE RD 02886 #308-07-1982 L1990 **P** *020
SCHOENFELD, Eugene. 455 TOLL GATE RD 02886 #649-01-1963 L1971 **D IM** *020
SCHULMAN, Howard Ethan. 176 TOLL GATE RD UNIT B 02886 #035-45-1990 L1990 **IM** *020 †20
SCOTT, Mark Francis. 390 TOLL GATE RD 02886 #043-01-1986 L1989 **OBG** *020 †30
SCOTT-TILLERY, Kristin D. ■ 02889 #048-13-2005 L2005 **IM** *012
SETTIPANE, Robert Jos. 470 TOLL GATE RD, TOLLGATE ALLERGY AND 02886 #035-09-1985 L1989 **AI PD** *020 †55,03
SHERMAN, Aaron. 300 TOLL GATE RD 02886 #024-05-1983 L1988 **OBG REN** *020 †30
SILVERSTEIN, Jeffrey E. 227 CENTERVILLE RD 02886 #035-09-1991 L1999 **DR** *020 †80
SMEATON, Stephen Michael. 400 BALD HILL RD, STE 511 02886 #026-04-1993 L1993 **EM** *100
SMITH, J Gerald. 469 CENTERVILLE RD STE 102 02886 #035-45-1965 L1970 **GYN** *020 †30
SPARHAWK, Dana Barnett. 2191 POST RD STE 3, CONCENTRA MED CTRS 02886 #035-09-1981 L1991 **OM** *020 †70
SPURRELL, Timothy Patrick. 166 TOLL GATE RD 02886 #008-02-1996 L1996 **OBG** *020 †30
STAUDINGER, Kathleen M. 215 TOLL GATE RD, STE 109 02886 #024-07-1981 L1984 **DR** *020 †80
STEINMETZ, Gregory John. 857 POST RD, ASSOCIATES IN PRIMARY CARE 02888 #033-05-1998 L1998 **FM** *020 †18
STEVENS, Bruce Lawrence. 215 TOLL GATE RD, STE 109 02886 #041-02-1968 L1975 **DR NM** *071 †80,28
STEVENS, Scott Jordan. ■ 02886 #035-15-2005 L2005 **N** *012
STEWART, Michael Nelson. 455 TOLL GATE RD 02886 #561-01-1972 L1976 **GS** *020 †16
STIPICH, Jadranka. 300 TOLL GATE RD 02886 #957-01-1973 L1985 **IM** *020
ST JEAN, Bernard Paul. 470 TOLL GATE RD, STE 203 02886 #561-01-1976 L1980 **GS GE** *020 †85
STOKOE, Usha. 200 TOLL GATE RD STE 204 02886 #495-27-1973 L1995 **FM OBS** *020 †18
TAFT, George Henry. ■ 02886 #041-02-1941 L1942 **CHN PD** *071 †55
THOMAS, Edward Seth. 390 TOLL GATE RD, STE 108 02886 #010-02-1982 L1988 **CD IM** *020 †20
TOMPKINS, Marc Andrew. ■ 02888 #030-05-2004 L2005 **ORS** *012
TORRES, Geronimo S. 50 HEALTH LN, KENT CO MENTAL HEALTH CENT 02886 #748-01-1956 L1968 **P** *071
TROMBATORE, Sebastian. 300 TOLL GATE RD 02886 #561-04-1978 L1986 **GS VS** *020 †85
VARR, William F, III. 220 TOLL GATE RD, STE B 02886 #035-09-1984 L1985 **OPH** *020 †35
VARR, William Francis. 390 TOLL GATE RD, STE 103 02886 #035-09-1956 L1957 **AN** *071 †05
VEGA, Lucille Claudette. 962 WARWICK AVE 02888 #032-01-1997 L1997 **FM** *020 †18
VELIS, Oswaldo R. 21 FISHS LN 02886 #275-01-1953 L1963 **IM CD** *071
VERMA, Sunil Paul. 300 TOLL GATE RD, STE 301C 02886 #422-01-1995 L1995 **IM NEP** *020
VESEY, John Michael. ■ 02886 #041-02-1945 L1948 **R** *071 †80
VIDINS, Eva Ilze. ■ 02886 #065-01-1966 L1975 **GE** *020
VINCE CRUZ, Teodulo T. 455 TOLL GATE RD, KENT HOSPITALISTS 02886 #748-16-1987 L2001 **IM** *020
VINLUAN, Jesus Colendrino. 120 CENTERVILLE RD 02886 #748-01-1963 L1974 **ORS** *020
WAINERMAN, Bertha Wiera. 191 AIRPORT RD 02889 #275-01-1948 L1954 **CHP** *071
WALEK, Thomas Raymond. 200 TOLL GATE RD, STE 102 02886 #043-01-1979 L1980 **PS HS** *020 †65
WANG, Xiaotian. 227 CENTERVILLE RD 02886 #035-47-2000 L2006 **MSR** *100 †80
WEISS, Yvonne Stuy. 455 TOLL GATE RD 02886 #051-04-1985 L1992 **PD CHP** *020 †55
WELCH, Paul Thornton. 455 TOLL GATE RD 02886 #023-07-1954 L1962 **NS** *072 †25
WHALEN, Richard P. 50 HEALTH LN, THE KENT CENTER 02886 #043-01-1986 L1997 **P** *020 †75
WILHELM, Robert Otto. 400 BALD HILL RD, STAT CARE 02886 #010-02-1973 L1979 **IM EM** *020 †20,16
WILLIAMS, Charles Roger. 227 CENTERVILLE RD 02886 #035-45-1983 L2003 **DR** *020 †80
WILLIAMS, Katherine S. 400 BALD HILL RD STE 511, STATCARE 02886 #041-01-1997 L1997 **FM** *020 †18
WLASSICH, Sophie M. ■ 02888 #407-10-1949 L1954 **PD** *071
WOEL, Roxanne Thais. 566 TOLL GATE RD, KOCH EYE CENTER 02886 #036-07-2001 L2005 **OPH** *020 †35
WONG, Daniel Tit-Ho. ■ 02889 #462-01-1953 L1970 **EM GP** *071
WOODRUFF, Kathleen Ruth. 166 TOLL GATE RD 02886 #035-46-1992 L1996 **OBG** *020 †30
YAKAVONIS, Vincent John. 120 CENTERVILLE RD 02886 #035-09-1977 L1982 **ORS** *020 †40
YOUNG, Gregory Robt. 455 TOLL GATE RD 02886 #005-06-1991 L2000 **EM** *020 †16
ZAHREDDINE, Nabil. 215 TOLL GATE RD, STE 206 02886 #913-05-1980 L1994 **OBG** *020 †30
ZAIDI, Najam. 455 TOLL GATE RD 02886 #704-20-1996 L2003 **IM ID** *020 †20 ‡
ZEBEDE-BLANK, Marcela. 455 TOLL GATE RD 02886 #715-01-1988 L1999 **IM** *020 †20

WEST GREENWICH – KENT

DOBRZYNSKI, Robert John. ■ 02817 #422-01-1996 L2001 **END** *020 †20
DURHAM, Todd Duane. ■ 02817 #025-07-2002 L2007 **VIR** *012 †80

WEST WARWICK – KENT

AMFILO, Basil. ■ 02893 #902-01-1955 L1961 **AN** *071 †05

■ = Address Information Privacy Protected

ARCAND, Alfred Albert. 1079 MAIN ST 02893 #067-03-1961 L1961 **FM FPG** *020 †18 ‡
ARCAND, Denise M. 1079 MAIN ST, STE A 02893 #067-04-1998 L2001 **FM** *020 †18 ‡
BARBER, Paul Edward. ■ 02893 #024-07-1946 L1949 **FM OBS** *071
BARROS, Pedro Mariano. 37 WASHINGTON ST 02893 #737-06-1989 L2003 **GE** *020 †20 ‡
CAMPBELL, Nathalie A. 37 WASHINGTON ST 02893 #065-01-1994 L1997 **END** *020 †20
CLARK, Todd Vernon. ■ 02893 #020-12-2005 L2006 **D** *012
DIMEN, Elisa Mapoy. ■ 02893 #748-01-1964 **AN** *020
DIMEN, Raynaldo R. ■ 02893 #748-01-1964 L1984 **PM** *020
HOLMAN, Laura Lee. ■ 02893 #016-11-2007 L2007 **OBG** *012
KEFALAS, Nikolaos D. ■ 02893 #418-01-1995 L2001 **PDE** *100
KHANBHAI, Karim Zool. 37 WASHINGTON ST 02893 #704-25-1993 L1999 **PD** *020 †55
KOWAL, Elizabeth Derose. ■ 02893 #025-07-2006 L2006 **CPP** *012
LEVISS, Jonathan Adam. 1219 MAIN ST, THUNDERMIST HEALTH CENTER 02893 #035-19-1995 L2004 **IM** *020 †20
MACHATA, John Jos. 1219 MAIN ST, THUNDERMIST HLTH CTR 02893 #035-15-1980 L1994 **FM PHP** *020 †18
MACNEVIN, Ryan James. ■ 02893 #023-01-2005 L2005 **IM** *012
MC LEOD, Brian S. 207 QUAKER LN, FL 1 02893 #033-06-1988 L1988 **U** *020 †95
MILLMAN, Richard Paul. 1 JAMES P MURPHY IND HWY 02893 #041-01-1976 L1985 **PUD OS** *020 †20
MORALLO, Lilia Mary. ■ 02893 #748-01-1966 L1985 **PD** *020
O'DONNELL, Benjamin Micha. ■ 02893 #038-43-2007 L2007 **IM** *012
PEIMER, Megan Larin. ■ 02893 #035-01-2004 L2004 **EM** *012
REUSCH, Ursula. ■ 02893 #028-03-2000 L2000 **IM** *100 †20
RUBIO, Alberto S. ■ 02893 #737-01-1957 L1978 **PTH GP** *020
SAWANT, Dilip Dinanath. ■ 02893 #495-01-1975 L1994 **GS TS** *020
SHAPIRO, Jason Michael. ■ 02893 #050-02-2005 L2005 **PD** *012
VIDAL, Jeannette E. ■ 02893 #067-02-1943 L1943 **IM CD** *071

WESTERLY – WASHINGTON

AUTH, John T. 80 BEACH ST 02891 #010-02-1975 L1986 **OBG** *020 †30
BARBER, Paul Edward. 41 EAST AVE 02891 #024-07-1979 L1985 **U** *020 †95
BELGRAVE, Clyde H. 25 WELLS ST 02891 #041-01-1990 L2002 **PTH** *020 †50
BERGERON, John N. 25 WELLS ST 02891 #043-01-1980 L1983 **IM GYN** *020 †20
BINGHAM, Russell Nevins. 25 WELLS ST 02891 #067-01-1971 L1978 **EM FM** *071 †18,16
BOLTON, Peter E. 11 WELLS ST 02891 #561-17-1982 L1985 **IM IMG** *020 †20
BRAN, Carmen Daniela. 80 BEACH ST 02891 #781-01-1995 L2004 **CN** *020 †75
BROGNA, Carlo Gennaro. 101 AIRPORT RD 02891 #024-16-1981 L1986 **N IM** *020 †20,75
BURBELO, Gregory M. ■ 02891 #407-04-1951 L1955 **IM IMG** *071
CAMERON, Alison Gillmor. 25 WELLS ST, ANES ASSOC OF WESTERLY 02891 #021-01-1998 L2003 **AN** *020 †05
CAMERON, David Scott. 17 WELLS ST STE 201 02891 #021-01-1999 L2003 **OTO** *020 †45
CARDI, Paul David. 55 BEACH ST, # 8B2C 02891 #043-01-1984 L1989 **DR IM** *020 †80
CAREY-KUZMIC, Sheila L. ■ 02891 #010-02-1988 L1994 **PD** *020 †55
CELESTINO, Pasquale J. 65 CANAL ST 02891 #024-07-1938 L1940 **GP** *072
CHRISTIAN, Jeffrey Lane. 46 WELLS ST 02891 #005-14-1984 L1989 **GS** *020 †85
CIACCIO, Rachel K. 45 WELLS ST, STE 104 02891 #011-02-1999 L2003 **OBG** *020 †30
COLBY, Jay Michael. 116 GRANITE ST 02891 #041-09-1983 L2003 **DR** *030 †80
CONLIN, William Michael. 25 WELLS ST, THE WESTERLY HOSP EMERGY 02891 #033-05-1978 L1980 **IM EM** *020 †20,16
CRETELLA, Michelle Anne. 45 WELLS ST, STE 20 02891 #008-02-1994 L1999 **PD** *020 †55
CRISAFI, Bartel Robert, Jr. 116 GRANITE ST 02891 #008-02-1993 L2001 **FM** *020 †18
D'ARCY, Christopher A. 45 WELLS ST STE 203B 02891 #043-01-1996 L2001 **RHU** *020 †20
DAUPHINAIS, Richard M. 25 WELLS ST, PATHOLOGY DEPT 02891 #028-34-1961 L1991 **PTH** *062 †50
DESANTIS, Christopher Jos. 25 WELLS ST 02891 #422-01-2003 L2007 **AN** *020
DIFFIN, Daniel Chas. 116 GRANITE ST, WESTERLY RADIOLOGY ASSOCIA 02891 #035-19-1989 L2000 **VIR R** *020 †80
DOERWALDT, Hartmut A. 62 WELLS ST, WESTERLY FAMILY PRACTICE L 02891 #051-01-1983 L2004 **FM** *020 †18
DRAKE, Leslie James. 46 WELLS ST, WESTERLY MEDICAL CENTER IN 02891 #067-01-1953 L1969 **GS GP** *071 †85
DUHIG, Niall Joseph. 45 WELLS ST, WESTERLY HOSPITAL 02891 #010-02-1996 L2003 **PCC** *020 †20
DUKE, Daniella. 25 WELLS ST 02891 #024-01-1992 L1999 **D DS** *020 †15
ELLIOT, A John. 45R EAST AVE 02891 #035-01-1959 L1964 **ORS** *020 †40
ELZAHR, Dina. 45 WELLS ST, STE 201 02891 #033-05-1995 L1995 **PD** *020
ENQUIST, Erik Gunnar. 35 WELLS ST 02891 #007-02-1991 L1991 **U** *020 †95
FELDMAN, Jeffrey Ira. 17 WELLS ST STE 201 02891 #035-15-1986 L1991 **OTO HNS** *020 †45
FOSTER, John Watkins. 116 GRANITE ST 02891 #008-01-1972 L1978 **DR NM** *071 †80 ‡
FOX, Robert Emmett. 45 WELLS ST, STE 203A 02891 #305-01-1992 L1995 **IM** *020
FUSCO, Anthony John. ■ 02891 #561-01-1958 L1962 **PD** *071
GACCIONE, Daniel R. 45 WELLS ST STE 204 02891 #043-01-1985 L1987 **ORS** *020 †40
GARVEY, Anne M. 45 WELLS ST 02891 #016-43-1988 L2000 **PD** *020 †55
GARVEY, John B. 25 WELLS ST, WESTERLY HOSPITAL 02891 #396-04-1969 L1972 **IM** *020 †20
GIANCASPRO, Joseph. 81 BEACH ST 02891 #561-01-1977 L1981 **FM NTR** *020 †18
GILLIE, R Bruce. 11 WELLS ST 02891 #033-05-1974 L1976 **IM END** *020 †20
GOODMAN, Tobias Mark. 25 WELLS ST 02891 #024-05-1966 L1973 **U** *020 †95
GRAHAM, Robert Grantham. 25 WELLS ST 02891 #005-02-1969 L1976 **EM** *071 †16
GRAMLICH, Curt Wilson. 25 WELLS ST 02891 #665-01-2001 L2005 **AN** *020 †05
GRIFFIN, John Peter. 46 WELLS ST 02891 #041-02-2001 L2006 **GS** *020
GRISCOM, Andrew Husted. 9 AVONDALE RD 02891 #041-02-1989 L1997 **EM** *020 †16
HAMBURGER, Adrian Karl. 25 WELLS ST 02891 #011-04-2001 L2006 **APM** *020 †05
HARONIAN, Howard Louis. 25 WELLS ST 02891 #035-20-1987 L1994 **CD IC** *020 †20
HARRISON, Robert W, Jr. WELLS ST WESTERLY HOSP 02891 #041-13-1974 L1984 **EM FM** *020 †18,16
HINTEREGGER, Frances I. 25 WELLS ST, WESTERLY HOSPITAL 02891 #024-16-1976 L1980 **IM PD** *020 †20
HUANG, Ching Bor. ■ 02891 #244-04-1971 L1978 **AN** *020
JACCARINO, Frederick John. 25 WELLS ST 02891 #011-02-1983 L1984 **EM IM** *020 †20
JOST, Erica Elisabeth. 25 WELLS ST 02891 #005-02-1977 L1987 **ID PD** *071 †55
KITTREDGE, Ben Webster. ■ 02891 #051-01-1971 L1976 **PD** *020
KNISLEY, Robert Eugene. 11 WELLS ST 02891 #041-01-1961 L1967 **ON HEM** *020 †20
KONG, Insu. 80 BEACH ST 02891 #035-08-1989 L1999 **OBG** *020 †30
KUTZ, Stephen Michael. 25 WELLS ST 02891 #035-20-1992 L2000 **CD** *020 †20
LAIN, Richard Francis. 25 WELLS ST 02891 #041-12-1968 L1973 **IM** *020 †20
LANZILLO, Chas Francis, Jr. 17 WELLS ST 02891 #035-46-1975 L1984 **OPH** *020 †35
LA PERE, Louis Anthony. ■ 02891 #561-01-1955 L1957 **OBG** *020 †30
LAU, Tse Chiang. ■ 02891 #050-02-2004 L2004 **EM** *012
LAURENZO, Albert John. 153 HIGH ST 02891 #561-01-1965 L1970 **PUD IM** *020 †20
LAVIGNE, Bradford C. 45 WELLS ST STE 103, INC. 02891 #043-01-1979 L1985 **GE** *020 †20
LEADBETTER, Allen Wm. 46 WELLS ST 02891 #023-01-1969 L1976 **GS** *020 †85
LEDDY, Franklin Fraser. 35 WELLS ST 02891 #032-01-1984 L1989 **U** *020 †95
LEHRACH, Christopher Mark. 30 CHESTNUT ST, WESTERLY AMBULANCE CORPS I 02891 #008-02-1995 L1997 **EM FM** *020 †18
LENTZ, Walter Johnson. 46 WELLS ST 02891 #023-07-1973 L1976 **IM IMG** *020 †20
LEONG, Frederic T M. 10 SEABURY DR 02891 #024-07-1968 L1970 **PD** *020 †55
LIN, Foongyi. 25 WELLS ST 02891 #043-01-1994 L1994 **PD** *020 †55 ‡
LOMBARDO, Robert Lawrence. 25 WELLS ST 02891 #561-01-1955 L1961 **IM** *072
MAGUIRE, Kevin. 39 EAST AVE 02891 #024-16-1990 L1997 **PS** *020 †65
MINN, Mary Christine. 25 WELLS ST 02891 #035-19-1991 L1999 **AN PM** *020 †05 ‡
MONTEMARANO, Vincent A. 27 EAST AVE 02891 #035-09-1965 L1976 **GS** *020 †85
NEJMAN, Wendy Rena. 45 WELLS ST STE 203B 02891 #035-48-1997 L1997 **RHU** *020 †20
NEUHAUSER, Andrew P. 45 EAST AVE 02891 #010-01-1983 L1990 **OBG** *020 †30
NILES, Michael Charles. 116 GRANITE ST 02891 #024-05-1996 L2002 **DR** *020 †80
NOYES-DUGUAY, Lisa M. 85 BEACH ST BLDG B 02891 #008-02-1993 L1996 **IM ADM** *020 †20
PACOWSKI, Ingrid. ■ 02891 #041-13-2004 L2006 **IM** *020 †20
PAPA, Alessandro. 25 WELLS ST 02891 #043-01-1984 L1988 **HEM ON** *020 †20
PARKER, Prior Lewis. 17 WELLS ST, STE 201 02891 #035-20-1983 L1991 **OPH** *020 †35
PATEL, Sunit Hemant. 45 WELLS ST, STE 201 02891 #035-09-1997 L2002 **PD** *020 †55
PETER-FAHERTY, A Rita. 35 WELLS ST 02891 #035-03-1994 L1994 **CD** *020 †20
PITKIN, Olive Emma. ■ 02891 #008-01-1947 **PHP PD** *071 †55
POWERS, John Clancy. ■ 02891 #041-02-1957 L1970 **R** *020 †80
RADIN, Laurence Isador. 80 BEACH ST, NEUROLOGICAL GROUP PC 02891 #008-02-1988 L1996 **N CN** *020 †75
RAYNER, Douglas Archer. 80 BEACH ST 02891 #035-09-1961 L1970 **OBG** *071 †30
RIVERA, David Rafael. 45 WELLS ST STE 2020 02891 #010-02-1987 L1996 **OPH** *020 †35
ROBINSON, Mildred Irene. 25 WELLS ST 02891 #039-01-1937 L1940 **PD FM** *072
SANDOVAL, Job Lee. 25 WELLS ST 02891 #748-10-1984 L1987 **IM** *020
SCHEIBER, Jon Frederick. 25 WELLS ST 02891 #035-09-1989 L2004 **CD** *020 †20
SHRIVASTAVA, Kusum. ■ 02891 #495-49-1962 L1978 **NEP PD** *050 †55
SKOBLE, Luisa. 77 FRANKLIN ST, STE D 02891 #035-09-1983 L1995 **PYG** *020 †75
SMALL, Robert Wm, Jr. 45 WELLS ST STE 104, WOMEN'S HEALTH CONSULTANTS 02891 #016-43-1988 L1996 **OBG** *020 †30
SOLIS, Jon Stephen. 17 WELLS ST STE 203 02891 #023-12-1985 L1993 **D DS** *020 †15
SPENS, Nora Helen. WELLS ST PATH DEPT 02891 #352-07-1955 **ATP CLP** *072 †50
STOKES, Russell D. 3 CRESTVIEW DR 02891 #051-01-1978 L1995 **PD EM** *020 †55
STRICKLAND, H Allen. ■ 02891 #045-01-1968 L1976 **R NM** *071 †80,28
SU, Fang Pan. WELLS ST, DEPT ANES 02891 #244-04-1969 L1977 **AN** *020 †05
TAFT, Susan Elizabeth. 25 WELLS ST, ATTN: ER 02891 #422-01-1984 L1988 **FM** *020 †18 ‡
THRAN, Alexandra Nicole. 25 WELLS ST, THE WESTERLY HOSPITAL 02891 #047-05-1988 L2002 **EM** *020 †16
WEST, Edmund Anthony P. 25 WELLS ST 02891 #010-01-1969 L1973 **IM** *020 †20
WILLETTS, Philo F, Jr. 25 WELLS ST 02891 #028-03-1970 L1978 **ORS GS** *020 †40
WOOD, Anne Ernst. 80 BEACH ST 02891 #020-12-1977 L1988 **OBG** *020 †30
WOOD, John Patrick. 80 BEACH ST 02891 #008-01-1958 L1963 **OBG OS** *071 †30
WOODWORTH, Thasia Goodwin. 17 WELLS ST STE 201 02891 #035-03-1971 L1976 **NEP IM** *020 †20
WOODWORTH, Warren F. 17 WELLS ST STE 201 02891 #035-03-1965 L1975 **OTO HNS** *071 †45
YOLEN, Steven Richard. 45 WELLS ST, STE 103 02891 #561-01-1982 L2000 **GE IM** *020 †20
ZEPPIERI, Joseph Peter. 25 WELLS ST 02891 #024-07-1970 L1998 **HS ORS** *071 †40

WOONSOCKET – PROVIDENCE

ABRAHAMS, Heather Pauline. ■ 02895 #035-45-1997 L1997 **P** *020 †75
AHMAD, Irfan. 25 JOHN A CUMMINGS WAY, STE 4 02895 #704-21-1992 L2001 **IM** *100
ALLEN, Scott A. 191 SOCIAL ST, STE 840 02895 #043-01-1991 L1991 **IM** *020 †20
ALVES, Cynthia Marie. 68 CUMBERLAND ST STE 103, RHODE ISLAND CARDIOVASCULA 02895 #043-01-1988 L1988 **CD** *020 †20
ANDERSEN, Edward Paul. 283 POND ST 02895 #024-05-1964 L1972 **OPH** *020 †35
ARIF, Mohammad. 25 JOHN A CUMMINGS WAY # 4 02895 #704-61-1961 L1971 **CD** *020 †20
ATTIA ALLA, Ayman Zeidan. 25 JOHN A CUMMINGS WAY, STE 3 02895 #915-04-1992 L2004 **IM** *020 †20
AUMENTADO, Dennis Jos. 1065 MENDON RD 02895 #748-10-1984 L1991 **N** *020
BASILE, Orazio J. 20 CUMBERLAND HILL RD, WOODSOCKET MED CTR 02895 #561-01-1960 L1962 **D** *020 †15 ‡
BENAVIDES, Jorge. 20 CUMBERLAND ST 02895 #649-02-1953 L1960 **TS** *071 †85,90
BLISS, David B. ■ 02895 #654-01-1985 *100
BONNET-EYMARD, Jacques L. 219 CASS AVE, STE F 02895 #396-18-1971 L1976 **ORS** *020
BOTELHO, Paul Jorge. 283 POND ST, CENTER FOR SIGHT 02895 #024-05-1992 L2004 **OPH** *020 †35
BOURASSA, David Moses. 383 ARNOLD ST, THUNDERMIST HEALTH ASSOC 02895 #038-06-1993 L1996 **PD** *020 †55
BOURGANOS, George. 68 CUMBERLAND ST, STE 103 02895 #418-01-1989 L2000 **CD** *020 †20
BREEN, Christopher J. 219 CASS AVE 02895 #043-01-1995 L2004 **ORS** *020 †40
BURRILL, James David. 560 CUMBERLAND HILL RD, OAKLAND GROVE HEALTH CENTE 02895 #305-01-1984 L1988 **IMG** *062 †20
CERMIK, Omer. 115 CASS AVE 02895 #902-05-1988 L1999 **P** *020 †75
CHOWDHRY, Sapna. 450 CLINTON ST 02895 #495-73-1998 L1999 **ID** *020 †20
COADY, Michael Anthony. 206 CASS AVE, CHAIRMAN OF SURGERY 02895 #010-01-1993 L2005 **TS** *020 †85,90
COHEN, Ronald Harvey. 115 CASS AVE, LANDMARK MEDICAL CENTER 02895 #041-12-1966 L1995 **DR PD** *020 †55,80
COLEY, Andrew Douglas. 115 CASS AVE, DEPT OF EMERGENCY MEDICINE 02895 #043-01-1997 L1997 **EM** *020 †16
CONCILIO, Gerardo. 115 CASS AVE 02895 #561-10-1980 L1992 **PD** *020

■ = Address Information Privacy Protected

CURETON, Edward Ervine. ■ 02895 #352-06-1955 L1979 **P OS** *071 †75

DESMARAIS, Roland John B. 20 CUMBERLAND HILL RD #203 02895 #396-08-1983 L1988 **IM** *020

DE STEFANI, Carlo James. 2385 DIAMOND HILL RD 02895 #028-34-1943 L1946 **FM** *071

DETORIE, Frank Mariano. 115 CASS AVE 02895 #023-01-1964 L1971 **GS GYN** *020 †85

DI ROBBIO, Carl C, Jr. 2345 MENDON RD 02895 #010-02-1971 L1982 **ORS** *020 †40

DODHIA, Ratilal Lalji. 115 CASS AVE, LANDMARK MED CTR WOON 02895 #495-01-1961 L1980 **PTH NM** *071 †50

DUPRE, Ernest Lucien. 115 CASS AVE 02895 #067-02-1953 L1953 **OBG** *071

ELZEFTAWY, Hossam Ahmed M. 25 JOHN A CUMMINGS WAY 02895 #915-04-1987 L2005 **NM** *100 †28

ERFE, Alberto V. 20 CUMBERLAND HILL RD 02895 #748-01-1964 L1974 **IM CD** *020

FANDETTI, Glen Anthony. 68 CUMBERLAND ST STE 103 02895 #010-02-2000 L2007 **IC CD** *020 †20 ‡

FARRELLY, Robert Leo. 115 CASS AVE 02895 #024-07-1956 L1959 **GP** *071

FONTAINE, Roger Jos. 473 S MAIN ST 02895 #067-03-1954 L1957 **IM** *020

FORREST, Julie -. 515 SOCIAL ST, NORTHERN RI COMMUNITH 02895 #917-08-1985 L1994 **P** *020 †75

GALARDY, Jose Angel. 115 CASS AVE 02895 #275-01-1949 L1960 **PTH** *071 †50

GIRACH, Altaf Ahmed. 20 CUMBERLAND HILL RD, UNIT 105 02895 #473-02-1995 L2001 **IMG** *020 †20

GIRARD, Daren Dennis. 115 CASS AVE, LANDMARK MEDICAL CENTER 02895 #024-05-1998 L1998 **EM** *020 †16

HAJ-DARWISH, Yusef. 115 CASS AVE, ATTN: EMERGENCY DEPARTMENT 02895 #875-02-1987 L1998 **IM** *020 †20

HAMBURGH, Monica Elka. 450 CLINTON ST 02895 #035-45-2004 L2004 **PD** *020 †55

HANNA, Wagih F Amin. 2213 MENDON RD 02895 #330-02-1957 L1972 **GYN GP** *020 †30

HOBAN, John J. 115 CASS AVE, LANDMARK MED CTR WOON 02895 #539-04-1956 L1961 **AN** *071

HORNIK, Irena Helena. 115 CASS AVE 02895 #759-01-1953 L1977 **P CHP** *071 †75

HUSSAIN, Syed I. 450 CLINTON ST 02895 #704-15-1987 L1993 **IM** *020 †20

JASA, Cleto Abreu. 115 CASS AVE 02895 #748-07-1957 L1966 **PD** *071

KAHR, Frank Millner. 115 CASS AVE, LANDMARK MEDICAL CENTER 02895 #008-01-1972 L1985 **P** *020 †75

KARANTH, Nikhil Sripathi. 20 CUMBERLAND HILL RD, UNIT 204 02895 #654-01-1998 L2000 **IM GE** *020 †20 ‡

KELLEY, Neal Christopher. 68 CUMBERLAND HILL RD, STE 103 02895 #024-05-1999 L2006 **IC** *020 †20

KELLY, Robert Michael. 283 POND ST, CENTER FOR SIGHT 02895 #035-19-1995 L2002 **OPH** *020 †35 ‡

KHAMIEES, Mohammad. 25 JOHN A CUMMINGS WAY, STE 3 02895 #875-02-1995 L2006 **IM** *100 †20 ‡

KHAN, Faridoon. 219 CASS AVE 02895 #704-01-1960 L1967 **OTO** *020 †45

KHAN, Jibran. 20 CUMBERLAND HILL RD, UNIT 208 02895 #704-01-1984 L1997 **IM GP** *020 †20

KHAN ADIL, Pir Mohammad. 115 CASS AVE 02895 #704-04-1964 L1981 **AN** *020 †05

KIISS, Arno. 38 HAMLET AVE 02895 #407-05-1944 L1956 **IMG GP** *071

LAMOUREUX, Joseph G. ■ 02895 #024-07-1951 L1952 **R** *071

LANDRY, Roland Donald. 25 CUMMINGS WAY 02895 #396-04-1972 L1975 **CD IM** *020 †20

LLAMAS, Cecilia Q. 115 CASS AVE 02895 #748-01-1964 L1973 **PTH** *020

LLAMAS, Ramon Doria. 20 CUMBERLAND HILL RD 02895 #748-01-1962 L1971 **GS GYN** *020 †85

MACHADO, Antonio Fernando. 115 CASS AVE 02895 #275-01-1951 L1957 **GP** *020

MADARANG, Antonio M. ■ 02895 #748-01-1953 L1968 **AN GP** *071

MAKALINAW, Benj Angeles. ■ 02895 #748-01-1952 L1964 **ORS** *020

MATHEW, Mathew Bijoy. 181 CUMBERLAND ST, NRI COMMUNITY SERVICES 02895 #023-07-1998 L2005 **CHP** *020

MEHDI, Syed Raza. 450 CLINTON ST 02895 #704-02-1989 L1997 **IM** *020 †20

MEHTA, Avanish. 20 CUMBERLAND HILL RD, UNIT 105 02895 #495-45-1975 L1998 **IMG** *020 †20

MIECH, Ralph Patrick. 115 CASS AVE 02895 #056-06-1959 L1970 **PA EM** *071

MISIALEK, Michael John. 115 CASS AVE, DEPT OF PATHOLOGY 115 CASE 02895 #024-16-1994 L2004 **PTH** *020 †50

MITRA, Sanchayeeta. 115 CASS AVE, LANDMARK MEDICAL CENTER 02895 #035-09-1995 L2006 **OTO** *020 †45

MUSCHE, Frank Wilbur, Jr. 115 CASS AVE 02895 #024-07-1970 L1972 **DR** *020 †80

NADEEM, Ahmed. 115 CASS AVE, # 2 02895 #704-01-1981 L1999 **HO** *020 †20

NEGREY, Michael Andrew. 255 CASS AVE 02895 #041-02-2000 L2005 **OPH** *020 †35

NELKEN, Beata Felicia. 450 CLINTON ST, THUNDERMIST HEALTH CENTER 02895 #008-02-2001 L2001 **PD** *020 †55

O'CONNELL, Kevin Patrick. 115 CASS AVE, LANDMARK MEDICAL CENTER 02895 #016-42-1990 L1995 **EM** *020 †16

PARK, Chan Hoon. 115 CASS AVE 02895 #583-04-1968 L1976 **FM** *020 †18

PINKES, Victor Alexis. 115 CASS AVE, LMC 02895 #016-42-1993 L2001 **EM** *020 †16

RAMIREZ, Basilia C. 20 CUMBERLAND HILL RD 02895 #748-01-1964 L1974 **IM END** *020 †20

RASMUSSEN, Irma Eugenia. 450 CLINTON ST 02895 #264-15-1989 L2003 **IM** *020 †20

SABBOUR, Hani Mohammed. 25 JOHN A CUMMINGS WAY, STE 4 02895 #584-01-1994 L2002 **CD** *020 †20

SCARANO, Catello Tullio. 385 MENDON RD 02895 #561-20-1958 L1965 **IM GP** *020

SHAFMAN, Timothy David. 115 CASS AVE STE 1, SOUTHERN N.E. REGIONAL CAN 02895 #024-01-1989 L2004 **RO** *020 †80

SHAHZAD, Khurram. 25 JOHN A CUMMINGS WAY, CARDIOLOGY ASSOCIATES INC 02895 #704-09-1993 L2005 **IM CD** *020 †20

SIDDIQ, Sajid. 68 CUMBERLAND ST STE 103 02895 #704-01-1983 L1997 **CD** *020 †20

SMITH, Richard D. 450 CLINTON ST 02895 #010-02-1971 L1989 **PD** *020 †55

SPIZZIRRI, Michael Edward. 385 MENDON RD, STE 2 02895 #561-01-1970 L1976 **GYN** *020

SRIPATHI KARANTH, Airodi. 20 CUMBERLAND HILL RD, UNIT 204 02895 #495-09-1967 L1973 **IM GE** *020 †20

STOLL, David Bachman. 55 HAMLET AVE 02895 #038-43-1978 L1984 **HEM ON** *020 †20

SUMNER-MACK, Robert W. 383 ARNOLD ST 02895 #041-01-1960 L1996 **PHP PD** *071 †55

SUPERCZYNSKI, Christopher. 25 JOHN A CUMMINGS WAY, COMPREHENSIVE HEALTHCARE 02895 #043-01-1997 L1997 **IM** *020 †20

SY, Emilie Ong. 450 CLINTON ST, THUNDERMIST HEALTH CENTER 02895 #748-02-1994 L1998 **PD** *020 †55 ‡

TAYLOR, David K. 450 CLINTON ST 02895 #043-01-1989 L1992 **IM** *020

TOUKAN, Kamel Kamal. 25 JOHN A CUMMINGS WAY 02895 #575-01-1995 L1998 **IC** *020 †20

WANEBO, Harold Jos. 206 CASS AVE 02895 #007-02-1961 L1987 **GS SO** *020 †85

WEHBE, Salim Assaad. 450 CLINTON ST, THUNDERMIST HEALTH CENTER 02895 #605-03-1999 L2005 **OBG** *020 †30

WILLIAMS, Curtis Michael. 38 HAMLET AVE 02895 #033-05-1970 L1993 **R DR** *020 †80

YEARWOOD, Greigstone M. 191 SOCIAL ST, STE 840 02895 #043-01-1988 L1988 **IM** *020 †20

WYOMING – WASHINGTON

PYSARIW, Jacob. ■ 02898 #286-01-1945 **GP** *071

ABBEVILLE - ABBEVILLE

BALLENTINE, Kinchen W, III. 901 W GREENWOOD ST 29620 #047-06-1967 L1992 **DR NM** *020 †80,28
BISHOP, Walter Grady, Jr. 901 W GREENWOOD ST, # 3 29620 #041-01-1963 L1967 **OBG** *020 †30
BONETTI, Juan Miguel. 901 W GREENWOOD ST, STE 9 29620 #012-01-1990 L1993 **PD** *020 †55
CANERO, Martin P, Jr. ■ 29620 #748-01-1964 L1978 **OBG** *071
CARAWAN, Steven T. 2526 HIGHWAY 72 E, CAROLINA BONE AND JOINT CL 29620 #048-02-1989 L1994 **ORS** *020 †40
D'AMORE, Ralph D. 901 W GREENWOOD ST 29620 #035-06-1965 L1994 **EM** *020 †18,16
DURHAM, James Cottrell. 102 ELLIS AVE 29620 #049-01-1968 L1969 **PTH FOP** *020 †50
FORD, James Edward. 100 COMMERCIAL DR, ABBEVILLE NTAL HEALTH CENT 29620 #012-01-1969 L1992 **P PD** *020 †55
FRY, Michael Blair. 420 THOMSON CIR, ABBEVLE AREA MED CTR 29620 #048-04-1971 L1979 **N IM** *020 †75
GONZALEZ, Evangeline G. 901 W GREENWOOD ST 29620 #748-01-1987 L1997 **IM** *020 †20
GONZALEZ, J E Todd M. 901 W GREENWOOD ST STE 6 29620 #748-09-1990 L1997 **IM** *020 †20
GRAY, Charles David. 103 COMMERCIAL DR, LAKELANDS ORTHOPAEDIC 29620 #020-02-1981 L1982 **ORS FM** *020 †18,40
GUY, John Lewis. 102 ELLIS AVE 29620 #045-01-1962 L1962 **EM** *020
HELMUTH, Loren Jay. 901 W GREENWOOD ST 8B 29620 #011-03-1987 L1994 **GS** *020 †85
HENRY, Brian Nelson. 901 W GREENWOOD ST 29620 #011-03-1987 L1988 **FM** *020 †18
JOHNSTON, Bruce Saml. 901 W GREENWOOD ST, BLDG 2 29620 #012-01-1976 L1977 **FM** *020 †18
KOLB, Charles Allen. 901 W GREENWOOD ST, STE 9 29620 #045-01-1983 L1984 **FM** *020 †18 ‡
MARTIN, David Enos. 901 W GREENWOOD ST, ABBEVILLE COUNTY MEMORIAL 29620 #008-01-1957 L1984 **GS** *020 †85
PATTERSON, Lee Andrew. 2526 HIGHWAY 72 E, CAROLINA BONE & JOINT CLIN 29620 #045-04-2002 L2007 **ORS** *020
RODILLO, Heidi E. 901 W GREENWOOD ST 29620 #748-01-1971 L1983 **IM CD** *020
ROSENBERG, Geo Visanska. 208 CHEROKEE ST 29620 #045-01-1941 L1941 **GS OBG** *071
TURNER, Michael Dawes. 200 CARWELLYN RD, ABBEVILLE UROLOGY 29620 #045-01-1976 L1977 **U GPM** *020 †95
WALLNER, Stephen F. ■ 29620 #035-15-1965 L1972 **HEM IM** *030 †20
YOUNG, Edwin Reynolds. 901 W GREENWOOD ST 29620 #047-05-1954 L1956 **U** *071 †95

AIKEN - AIKEN

ALIFF, Colin Lytton. 850 AIKEN MALL DR, DOCTORS CARE AIKEN 29803 #012-01-1997 L2003 **FM PD** *020 †18
ALLEYNE, Cargill Herley. 302 UNIVERSITY PKWY 29801 #008-01-1991 L2005 **NS GS** *020 †25
ALLIE, Adam Albert. ■ 29803 #055-01-2008 *012
AL-SOUDI, Sylva. 131 CHRISTOPHER DOWNS CT, ANMED HEALTH FAMILY PRACTI 29803 #286-02-2001 L2004 **FM** *020
ANDERSON, Jonathan Hal. 770 MEDICAL PARK DR 29801 #045-01-1991 L1998 **U** *020 †95
BAXLEY, John Baynard, Jr. 60 PHYSICIAN DR, STE 200 29801 #020-12-1971 L1978 **FM** *020 †18
BEARD, John Clyde, Jr. ■ 29803 #041-02-1944 L1966 **TS GS** *020
BELL, Beverly Ann. 302 UNIVERSITY PKWY 29801 #060-01-1979 L1984 **PHO** *020 †55
BERTRAND, Styles Leslie. 302 UNIVERSITY PKWY 29801 #048-15-1980 L1983 **OP ORS** *020 †40
BESSON, Cindy G. 121 AURORA PL, WOMEN'S HEALTH ASSOCIATES 29801 #012-01-1985 L1991 **OBG** *020 †30
BESSON, William Tennent. 410 UNIVERSITY PKWY # 2500 29801 #045-04-1989 L1991 **IM** *020 †20
BHATIA, Jatinder Jit S. 302 UNIVERSITY PKWY 29801 #495-73-1975 L1977 **NPM NTR** *020 †55
BLAND, James Laval. 120 DARLINGTON DR 29803 #012-01-1960 L1961 **FM LM** *020 †18
BOEDY, Robert Fredrick. 302 UNIVERSITY PKWY 29801 #011-03-1978 L1978 **NPM PD** *020 †55
BOEHNER, James Francis. 410 UNIVERSITY PKWY, STE 1550 29801 #035-15-1982 L1983 **OBG GP** *020 †30
BOONE, Robert Danl. 410 UNIVERSITY PKWY, STE 1550 29801 #045-04-1983 L1984 **OBG** *020 †30
BOTNICK, Robert Stanley. MEDICAL DEPT/WSRC 29808 #048-04-1958 L1989 **IM OM** *062
BOUTON, S Miles. ■ 29803 #407-01-1934 L1973 **FOP CLP** *071 †50
BOYD, Michael Max. ■ 29803 #005-19-1985 L1991 **PTH** *020 †50
BRANDT, Babette Lenna. ■ 29803 #041-07-1965 L1975 **R** *071 †80
BRANSOME, Edwin Dagobert. 202 UNIVERSITY PKWY 29801 #035-01-1958 L1977 **END IM** *020
BRUKER, William Cason, Jr. 325 COLLETON AVE SE 29801 #012-01-1974 L1980 **DR** *020
BRYAN, Gasnel Emanuel. 202 UNIVERSITY PKWY 29801 #010-03-1974 L1984 **OBG** *020 †30
BUNYAPEN, Chantrapa. 302 UNIVERSITY PKWY 29801 #891-04-1972 L1978 **PD** *040 †55
CAIAFA, Guy Joseph. ■ 29803 #016-42-2001 L2007 **AN** *100 †20
CANNON, Jack Russell. 202 UNIVERSITY PKWY 29801 #019-02-1975 L1979 **DR** *020
CARTER, Karen Lea. 302 UNIVERSITY PKWY 29801 #012-01-1996 L1997 **PD** *020 †55
CHASE, Frank Yates. 410 UNIVERSITY PKWY, STE 2310 29801 #045-01-1997 L2004 **GS** *020 †85
CHESSER, Richard Stewart. 118 PARK AVE SW, STE 100 29801 #045-01-1981 L1992 **D** *020 †70,15
CHOUDHRI, Haroon Fiaz. 302 UNIVERSITY PKWY 29801 #035-01-1993 L2005 **NS** *020 †25
COFER, Tom Will. ■ 29801 #012-01-1968 L1975 **GS** *020
COLBERT, Ronnika Sheneal. 302 UNIVERSITY PKWY 29801 #047-06-2005 L2006 **PD** *012
COLLINS, Jonathan Claude. 206 CENTRE SOUTH BLVD 29803 #045-01-1981 L1982 **PD** *020 †55
CONGER, Blanche M. ■ 29803 #012-01-1981 **PTH** *071
CONGER, Preston De Witt. 410 UNIVERSITY PKWY, STE 1540 29801 #012-05-1979 L1984 **IM CD** *020 †20
CONNER-MOORE, Tammy T. ■ 29803 #036-08-1994 **FM** *100
CONTI, Paul Anthony. 302 UNIVERSITY PKWY, AIKEN REGIONAL MEDICAL CEN 29801 #038-40-1994 L2000 **IM** *020 †20
COOK, John Robt. 2110 WOODSIDE EXECUTIVE CT 29803 #012-01-1973 L1983 **D IM** *020 †20,15
COX, Frederick Eugene. 302 UNIVERSITY PKWY 29801 #024-05-1964 L2002 **ID PD** *020 †55
CRAFT, James Hord. 202 UNIVERSITY PKWY 29801 #045-01-1974 L1976 **DR** *020 †80
CROITORU, Claudia Mirela. 302 UNIVERSITY PKWY 29801 #781-01-1993 L2004 **PTH** *020 †50
CUNNINGHAM, Joseph Romig. 410 UNIVERSITY PKWY # 2100 29801 #038-40-1967 L1976 **GS** *020 †85
DANIELS, Lloyd Barrington. 80 PHYSICIAN DR 29801 #010-03-1972 L1976 **OBG** *020 †30
DEES, Marvin. RM 522, BLDG 719-5N 29808 #025-01-1967 L1985 **FM OM** *020 †18
DEGNAN, Alyssa M. 102 SUMMERWOOD WAY 29803 #041-78-1998, ▲ L2002 **IM** *020 †20
DI BONA, Francis James. 755 MEDICAL PARK DR 29801 #056-06-1969 L1983 **NEP PN** *020 †55
DOLEN, William Kennedy. 302 UNIVERSITY PKWY 29801 #047-06-1977 L1978 **AI PD** *040 †55,03
DURRETT, William E, Jr. 410 UNIVERSITY PKWY, STE 2360 29801 #012-01-1985 L1989 **AN PME** *020 †05
DWYRE, William R. ■ 29803 #065-09-1953 L1961 **PTH** *071 †50
EAVES, Simeon Gilmore. 202 UNIVERSITY PKWY 29801 #045-01-1956 L1956 **GP** *071
EISENBERG, Richard Allen. 410 UNIVERSITY PKWY # 2360, AIKEN NEUROSCIENCES PC 29801 #008-02-1982 L1994 **N** *020 †75
ENNS, Stephen John. 224 GREENVILLE ST NW, AIKEN, S CAROLINA 29801 29801 #019-02-1988 L1990 **CHP P** *020 †75
ENTREKIN, Wayne Gaines. SRS MEDICAL 719A 29808 #045-01-1967 L1967 **OM IM** *020 ‡
ERGUL, Sitki Mehmet. 100 AURORA PL, CAROLINA CANCER CTR 29801 #902-07-1985 L1998 **HO** *020 †20
ESSELMAN, Gregory Hubert. 121 AURORA PL, STE B 29801 #028-02-1993 L2006 **OTO** *020 †45
FALLAW, David Jerold. ■ 29801 #045-01-2006 **IM** *012
FANCEY, Jason Terrence. 302 UNIVERSITY PKWY 29801 #045-04-1996 L2001 **PTH** *020 †50
FISCHBACH, Gary Thos. 721 RICHLAND AVE W STE 200 29801 #010-02-1979 **IM OPH** *020
FISHER, Donald Gene. ■ 29801 #017-20-1956 L1985 **GS** *071 †85
FITCH, Margaret Ann. 1520 TWO NOTCH RD SE 29803 #012-01-1977 L1981 **D** *020 †15
FREDERICK, Robyn Lee. ■ 29801 #045-01-2006 **FP** *012
FREI, Wayne Thos. 410 UNIVERSITY PKWY, STE 2310 29801 #051-07-1990 L1993 **GS** *020 †85
GARRISON, Lesley Glenn. 2259 BEAVER CREEK LN, WESTINGHOUSE SAVANNAH RIVE 29803 #045-04-1983 L1989 **PTH** *020
GAY, Alfonso, Jr. 302 UNIVERSITY PKWY, CAROLINA RADIOLOGICAL ASSO 29801 #038-43-1989 L2004 **R** *020 †80
GIBBS, David Hamilton. 410 UNIVERSITY PKWY, STE 2100 29801 #036-08-1987 L1994 **CRS GS** *020 †85,10
GILL, Ahmad Nadeem. 111 MIRACLE DR 29801 #704-02-1984 L1992 **ON** *020
GILLESPIE, Edward C. ■ 29803 #067-01-1945 L1950 **OBG** *071 †30
GLEICHAUF, John George. 1051 SILVER BLUFF RD, STE A 29803 #035-06-1962 L1979 **OPH** *020 †35
GORDON, Gerald. 102 SUMMERWOOD WAY 29803 #035-01-1975 L1994 **IM ID** *020 †20 ‡
GRANT, Stephen David. 681 SILVER BLUFF RD 29803 #010-02-1984 L1991 **EM** *020 †16
GRANTHAM, Richard Lee. 139 WATERLOO ST SW 29801 #021-05-1976 L1993 **OPH** *020 †35
GRIFFIN, Dixie Dawn. 302 UNIVERSITY PKWY 29801 #012-01-2005 L2007 **PD** *012
GUILL, Margaret Frank. 302 UNIVERSITY PKWY 29801 #012-01-1973 L1974 **PDP AI** *020 †55,03
HAAS, Melvyn Lawrence. 410 UNIVERSITY PKWY, STE 2360 29801 #035-19-1965 L1972 **N SME** *020 †75 ‡
HAGAN, James Lowell. 100 AURORA PL, STE 200 29801 #027-01-1975 L1985 **GS TS** *020 †85
HAMLET, Katherine Renee. 531 SILVER BLUFF RD 29803 #012-01-1992 L1997 **D** *020 †15
HARRIS, Anthony Edwin. 410 UNIVERSITY PKWY 29801 #036-05-1969 L1985 **OTO HNS** *020 †45
HATFIELD, William Henry. ■ 29803 #023-01-1954 L1957 **PHP PD** *071
HESSE, Raymond Danl. 410 UNIVERSITY PKWY, STE 2500 29801 #045-01-1972 L1975 **IM PUD** *020 †20
HEWITT, Charles H, Jr. 2678 WHISKEY RD 29803 #041-09-1976 L1979 **GP** *071
HEYL, Guy Carlisle, Jr. 202 UNIVERSITY PKWY 29801 #051-01-1954 L1964 **ORS** *071 †40
HIGHTOWER, James Osgood. WESTINGHOUSE SAVANNAH RVR 29801 #012-01-1958 L1981 **AM OM** *071 †70
HILL, James Joseph, Jr. 410 UNIVERSITY PKWY, STE 1000 29801 #010-02-1974 L1985 **HS ORS** *071 †40
HOFFMAN, William Hubert. 302 UNIVERSITY PKWY 29801 #056-06-1965 L1966 **END PD** *020
HOLFORD, Douglas Edward. 410 UNIVERSITY PKWY, STE 1000 29801 #005-12-1976 L1982 **ORS** *020 †40
HOOVER, Judith Bottcher. 1518 TWO NOTCH RD SE, PARKSIDE WOMENS' CENTRE 29803 #045-01-1990 L1994 **OBG** *020 †30
HOWINGTON, Jed Weems. 302 UNIVERSITY PKWY 29801 #012-01-1999 L2004 **RO** *020 †80
HUZELLA, Christine E E H. ■ 29805 #352-07-1952 L1960 **P** *071
HUZELLA, Louis Geo. RR 6 BOX 1292 29805 #473-03-1943 L1960 **P** *071 †75
INDER, Harry A. ■ 29801 #067-01-1951 L1955 **OBG** *071 †30
JACKSON, Thomas Ross. 262 EASTGATE DR 29803 #045-04-1987 L1991 **IM PD** *020 †55,20
JACKSON, Walter Osborne. 1840 HUNTSMAN DR 29803 #008-01-1995 L2003 **EM** *020 †16
JAKUBS, Edward J, Jr. 410 UNIVERSITY PKWY, STE 2100 29801 #038-40-1999 L2005 **CRS** *020 †85,10
JAMES, Frederick Martin. 681 SILVER BLUFF RD 29803 #045-01-1987 L1988 **EM** *020 †18,16
JERATH, Rita S. 302 UNIVERSITY PKWY 29801 #917-08-1977 L1981 **RHU PD** *020 †55
KAMEL, Khaled Fouad. 410 UNIVERSITY PKWY, STE 2360 29801 #045-01-1995 L2000 **CN** *020
KANTO, William P, Jr. 202 UNIVERSITY PKWY 29801 #051-01-1966 L2006 **PD NPM** *030 †55
KASSEBAUM, Kenneth Graham. 1135 GREGG HWY, AIKEN BARNWELL MENTAL HLTH 29801 #016-06-1960 L2000 **CHP P** *020
KEISLER, David S, Jr. 410 UNIVERSITY PKWY, STE 2500 29801 #045-01-1974 L1976 **GE IM** *020 †20
KETCHAM, Jeffrey Keith. ■ 29804 #039-05-1984 L1991 **FM** *020 †18
KINSEY, Timothy Richard. 60 PHYSICIAN DR 29801 #055-02-1999 L2006 **PD** *020 †55
KIRCHNER, Allen W, Jr. ■ 29803 #023-01-1973 L1976 **EM OBG** *040 †30
KOGEL, Robert Wynn. 1840 HUNTSMAN DR 29803 #012-01-1999 L2003 **EM** *020 †16
KULE, Bernard John. ■ 29805 #264-04-1988 L1994 **FM** *020
KULIK, Ann Marie. 60 PHYSICIAN DR, AIKEN FAMILY PHYSICIANS 29801 #025-07-1996 L2006 **FM** *020 †18
LEAVENS, Hugh Miller. 103 WATERLOO ST SW 29801 #035-48-1982 L1995 **GE IM** *020
LEE, Alexander. ■ 29803 #012-05-2008 L2008 *012
LEE, Mark Robt. 302 UNIVERSITY PKWY 29801 #016-02-1986 L2004 **NS NSP** *020 †25
LUTHER, Paula Anne. 206 CENTRE SOUTH BLVD 29803 #045-04-2003 L2004 **PD** *020 †55
LUTIN, William Andrew. 302 UNIVERSITY PKWY 29801 #047-05-1981 L1985 **PDC PD** *020 †55

■ = Address Information Privacy Protected

MACOMSON, Samuel Dion. 302 UNIVERSITY PKWY 29801 #012-01-1997 L2004 **NS** *020
MAILE, Cameron James. 1840 HUNTSMAN DR 29803 #017-20-1995 L1996 **EM** *020 †16
MANI, Chitra Subra. 302 UNIVERSITY PKWY 29801 #495-02-1976 L1989 **PD** *020 †55
MANIAM, Prakash Naga. 770 MEDICAL PARK DR, AIKEN CTR FOR UROLOGY 29801 #038-40-1996 L2005 **U** *020 †95
MARTINEZ DE ANDINO, Edwin. 410 UNIVERSITY PKWY, STE 1000 29801 #042-03-1988 L1995 **RHU IM** *020 †20
MASSIE, Richard Vaughan. 410 UNIVERSITY PKWY, STE 1000 29801 #047-06-2000 L2006 **ORS OSM** *020 ‡
MATHEWS, George Wm. ■ 29804 #012-01-1958 L1958 **DR AM** *071 †70
MATTHEWS, John C. ■ 29801 #012-01-1957 L1960 **GP** *071
MC CORMICK, Glenn Edwards. ■ 29803 #012-05-1956 L1956 **D** *071 †15
MC DONOUGH, Colleen Hope. 302 UNIVERSITY PKWY 29801 #012-01-1995 L1998 **PHO** *020 †55
MC KIE, Kathleen Mood. 302 UNIVERSITY PKWY 29801 #045-01-1973 L1974 **PD** *020
MC KIE, Virgil Cranston. 302 UNIVERSITY PKWY 29801 #045-01-1969 L1969 **PHO HEM** *020 †55
MC NALLY, William Geo. ■ 29803 #041-01-1963 L1984 **IM OM** *071
MEEHAN, William Lloyd. ■ 29801 #051-01-1957 L1977 **U** *071 †95
MEHTA, Renuka. 302 UNIVERSITY PKWY 29801 #495-54-1987 L1997 **CCP** *020 †55
MEYER, Theodore Mark. 410 UNIVERSITY PKWY # 2500 29801 #045-01-1974 L1976 **IM ON** *020 †20
MINTER, William Thos, III. ■ 29803 #012-01-1966 L1976 **AN** *071 †05
MINTO, Oletha Rosina. 410 UNIVERSITY PKWY # 1550 29801 #023-07-1998 L2002 **OBG** *020 †30
MISCH, Diane Marie. 1135 GREGG HWY, AIKEN-BARNWELL MENTAL HLTH 29801 #016-06-1988 L1999 **CHP** *012
MONDSCHEIN, Frank J. 102 SUMMERWOOD WAY, INTERNAL MEDICINE ASSOOF A 29803 #041-09-1976 L2006 **IM PUD** *020 †20
MOORE, Clark Daniel. 410 UNIVERSITY PKWY STE 10 29801 #028-34-1972 L1980 **ORS** *020 †40
MOORE, James Norman, III. 216 EDGEFIELD AVE NW, FAMILY MEDCENTERS 29801 #036-08-1999 L2002 **FM** *020 †18
MUMMANENI, Reddiah Babu. 410 UNIVERSITY PKWY, STE 2360 29801 #496-24-1997 L2007 **CN** *020
MUNIZ, Leopoldo M. 101 SUMMERWOOD WAY 29803 #649-04-1981 L1999 **FM OBS** *020 †18 ‡
MUNIZ, Margo Johanna. 410 UNIVERSITY PKWY, STE 2300 29801 #016-45-1997 L2000 **OBG FM** *020 †20
MUNN, David Hill. 302 UNIVERSITY PKWY 29801 #012-01-1984 L1989 **PHO PD** *020 †55
MURPHY, William R. ■ 29803 #004-01-1951 L1980 **PTH** *062 †50
MURRAY, Dennis Lynn. 302 UNIVERSITY PKWY 29801 #025-01-1974 L1975 **PDI PD** *040 †55
NAGNUR, Shreedhar Madhav. 850 AIKEN MALL DR 29803 #496-38-1994 L2000 **IM IMG** *020 †20
NUTT, Alfred W, Jr. MEDICAL DEPARTMENT, SAVANNAH RIVER SITE/WSRC 29808 #016-11-1984 L1985 **GP GS** *020
OLIVER, Gerald D. 1055 SILVER BLUFF RD STE A 29803 #016-42-1979 L1996 **PD IM** *020
ONSTEAD, Charles O, Jr. ■ 29801 #048-12-1951 L1970 **R** *071 †80
ORTIZ, Luis Alfonso. 302 UNIVERSITY PKWY 29801 #737-01-1981 L2001 **PD PN** *020
OWENS, Kenneth Norwood. 202 UNIVERSITY PKWY 29801 #007-02-1948 L1959 **OBG** *071 †30
OWNBY, Dennis Randall. 302 UNIVERSITY PKWY 29801 #038-43-1972 L1977 **PDA** *050 †55,03
PAGE, Dean A. 3000 WOODSIDE EXECUTIVE CT, AIKEN PLASTIC SURGERY PA 29803 #041-12-1988 L2000 **PS** *020 †65,85
PARNELL, Denyse Nicolle. 302 UNIVERSITY PKWY 29801 #143-07-1972 L1983 **PTH** *020 †50
PATEL, Devesh Ramanlal. 755 MEDICAL PARK DR, CSRA RENAL SERVICES LLC 29801 #305-01-2000 L2005 **NEP** *020 †20 ‡
PATHEJA, Harpreet Singh. 110 PEPPER HILL WAY 29801 #017-20-1990 L2000 **OPH** *020 †35
PHILIPP, Mary Katherine. ■ 29801 #045-01-1991 L1993 **CHP** *020
PLATTE, Stephen John. 681 SILVER BLUFF RD 29803 #012-01-1995 L1998 **EM** *020 †16
PLYER, Dianna Louise. ■ 29803 #045-01-2008 *012
PRIOR, William F, Jr. ■ 29801 #012-05-1950 L1954 **GP AN** *071
RATLIFF, Brenda Myers. 410 UNIVERSITY PKWY, STE 2310 29801 #045-04-1983 L1988 **P OS** *020 †75
RATLIFF, Jack Lawrence. 410 UNIVERSITY PKWY, STE 2310 29801 #027-01-1963 L1977 **TS GS** *020 †85,90
ROBERTS, Mark Alexander. 415 BARNWELL AVE NW, AIKEN CTR FOR FAMILY HLTH 29801 #045-01-1979 L1999 **FM IMG** *020 †18
ROBINSON, Ronald Phillip. 302 UNIVERSITY PKWY, RADIOLOGY DEPT. 29801 #051-07-1993 L1994 **DR** *020 †80
RODGERS, William Leitch. ■ 29801 #041-02-1954 L1987 **OM PD** *071 †55
ROUNTREE, James Edwin. 3215 WISE CREEK LN, # 102 29801 #012-01-1942 L1950 **GS** *071
ROYAL, Howard Guilford, Jr. 410 HITCHCOCK BLVD 29801 #045-01-1975 L1976 **FM** *020 ‡
SANTIAGO, Jose Alejandro. 302 UNIVERSITY PKWY 29801 #021-01-1980 L1996 **NS** *020 †25
SCHAAB, Gabriel Sean. ■ 29803 #016-01-2008 *012
SHANNON, Timothy John. 410 UNIVERSITY PKWY, STE 1000 29801 #028-34-1986 L1995 **ORS** *020 †40
SHEKHAWAT, Prem Singh. 302 UNIVERSITY PKWY 29801 #496-03-1983 L1995 **PDE** *020 †55
SHEKHAWAT, Rashmi. 302 UNIVERSITY PKWY 29801 #495-55-1982 L1998 **PPR PD** *040 †55
SKINNER, Selwyn Martin. ■ 29804 #566-01-1966 L1991 **OBG** *071
SKLIZOVIC, Davor. 48 PHYSICIAN DR 29801 #957-01-1978 L1998 **OTO HNS** *020 †45
SMITH, Daniel Jos. 110 PEPPER HILL WAY 29801 #051-04-1986 L1991 **OPH** *020 †35
SMITH, Gregory Eschol. 1135 GREGG HWY, AIKEN-BARNWELL MENTAL HEAL 29801 #012-01-1983 L1986 **P** *020 †75 ‡
SMITH, Joseph Ritchie. 302 UNIVERSITY PKWY 29801 #054-04-1967 L1968 **NS** *020 †25
STAGGS, Clifford D. 681 SILVER BLUFF RD 29803 #048-15-1988 L1989 **EM** *020 †16
STAHURA, Douglas. 755 MEDICAL PARK DR 29801 #038-75-1998, ▲ L2003 **NEP IM** *020
STEINER, David Andrew. 5110 WOODSIDE EXECUTIVE CT 29803 #020-02-1984 L1992 **P** *020 †75
STINSON, Shannon Marie. ■ 29803 #001-02-2005 L2008 **EM** *012
STOEPPLER, Victoria M. 74 PHYSICIAN DR, AIKEN PEDIATRICS 29801 #341-01-1965 L1980 **PD** *020 †55
STRONG, William Bryan. 302 UNIVERSITY PKWY 29801 #041-09-1962 L1966 **PDC PD** *020 †55
SUH, Young S. 2678 WHISKEY RD 29803 #060-01-1986 L1995 **FM** *020 †18
SUHRER, James H, Jr. 302 UNIVERSITY PKWY, IN HOUSE MEDICINE SERVICE 29801 #047-05-1982 L1988 **IM PD** *020 †20,55
SUSSMAN, Hy Chas. 755 MEDICAL PARK DR 29801 #012-01-1960 L1973 **NEP CD** *020 †20
SZYMIK, Bonnie Swasy. 302 UNIVERSITY PKWY 29801 #012-01-1986 L1991 **PTH** *020 †50

TAM, Henry Wingsek. 2678 WHISKEY RD 29803 #045-01-1985 L1986 **FM** *020 †18
TERRY, Robert Cooper. 410 UNIVERSITY PKWY, STE 2310 29801 #045-01-1975 L1976 **GS** *020 †85
THURM-STOPPENHAGEN, Heide. ■ 29803 #409-10-1995 L1998 **CN** *020 †75
TIFFANY, John Burton. 206 CENTRE SOUTH BLVD 29803 #045-04-1995 L1996 **PD** *020 †55
TOMARCHIO, John B. WESTINGHOUSE SAVANAH RIVER 29808 #021-06-1980 L1984 **EM P** *020 †16,70
TOMARCHIO, John Branham. ■ 29803 #045-01-2007 **IM** *012
TOOMER, Anthony Lanell. 102 RIVIERA RD, AIKEN REGIONAL MEDICAL CEN 29803 #025-12-1996 L2000 **DR** *020 †80
TOOMER, Catherine Harmon. ■ 29803 #025-12-1996 L2000 **FM** *020 †18
TORGESON, Carol Morton. 107 BALD CYPRESS CT 29803 #011-02-1983 L1993 **DR** *020
TSAI, Enoch Nai-Chung. 111 GREGG AVE 29801 #011-02-1970 L1976 **OPH** *020 †35
UDANI, Belaben. 60 PHYSICIAN DR STE 200, AIKEN FAMILY PHYS 29801 #496-41-1999 L2004 **FM** *020 †18
ULMER, Benjamin Sanford. 202 UNIVERSITY PKWY 29801 #012-01-1987 L1991 **AN** *020 †05
VAN DER VLIET, Stephen K. 410 UNIVERSITY PKWY, STE 1500 29801 #016-06-1968 L1979 **OPH** *071 †35
VAUGHTERS, Ray Bauer, Jr. 39 VARDEN DR STE D 29803 #021-01-1969 L1972 **FM** *020 †18
VAUGHTERS, Ray Bauer, III. ■ 29801 #045-04-1998 L2001 **END** *020 †20
VENDER, John Richard. 302 UNIVERSITY PKWY 29801 #035-46-1990 L2005 **HNS** *020 †25
VOEGELE, Lothaire D. 137 MIRACLE DR 29801 #016-06-1968 L1972 **TS** *020 †85,90
VOLOSCHIN, Alfredo Daniel. 302 UNIVERSITY PKWY 29801 #132-01-1985 L1992 **N** *020 †75
VON BUEDINGEN, Richard P. 410 UNIVERSITY PKWY, STE 1560 29801 #056-05-1965 L1968 **U AM** *071 †95
WATSON, Randy Dale. 944 DOUGHERTY RD 29803 #045-01-1978 L1982 **IM** *020 †20 ‡
WEDDLE, Douglas Matthew. 1840 HUNTSMAN DR, AIKEN EMERGENCY MED PHYSIC 29803 #011-02-1994 L1999 **EM** *020 †16
WILES, Henry Barnett. 302 UNIVERSITY PKWY 29801 #045-01-1980 L1986 **PDC PD** *050 †55
WILLIAMS, Robert Layton. ■ 29801 #011-03-1991 L2007 **PCP** *050
WINBURN, Virginia Brevard. 410 UNIVERSITY PKWY, STE 2100 29801 #021-01-1986 L2002 **CRS** *020 †85,10
YEH, Edward Weiyan. 681 SILVER BLUFF RD 29803 #001-02-1995 L1998 **EM** *020 †16
YOUMANS, Stephen Causey. 5110 WOODSIDE EXECUTIVE CT 29803 #045-01-1992 L1993 **FM** *020 †18
ZOTOVIC, Danijela Slavko. 410 UNIVERSITY PKWY, STE 2500 29801 #957-02-1988 L1999 **IM** *020 †20
ZOTOVIC, Miroslav B. 68 PHYSICIAN DR 29801 #957-02-1988 L1997 **CCM** *020 †20

ALLENDALE — ALLENDALE

LAFFITTE, Henry L, Sr. 623 MEMORIAL AVE N 29810 #045-01-1947 L1947 **GP GS** *071 †18
LAFFITTE, Henry L, Jr. 623 MEMORIAL AVE N 29810 #045-04-1990 L1991 **FM** *020 †18
WARREN, Thomas Baker, Jr. 623 MEMORIAL AVE N 29810 #045-01-1961 L1961 **FM** *020 †18

ANDERSON — ANDERSON

ABERCROMBIE, Stoney Alton. 2000 E GREENVILLE ST, STE 3600 29621 #045-01-1975 L1977 **FM EM** *040 †18
ABERNETHY, Don L, Jr. 2126 N HIGHWAY 81 29621 #012-22-1992 L1993 **FM** *020 †18
AGHA, Amir M. 2000 E GREENVILLE ST, STE 2700 29621 #704-16-1989 L1995 **RHU** *020 †20
ALBURO, Robert Marcelino. 2000 E GREENVILLE ST, STE 3700 29621 #748-11-2002 L2005 **FP** *012
ALI-HASSAN, Rola Issam. 2000 E GREENVILLE ST, STE 3700 29621 #605-01-2001 L2004 **FM** *100 †18
ALIKHAIL, Mohammad B. 819 N FANT ST 29621 #118-01-1985 L1999 **IM** *020 †20
AMER, Isra Mohammad. 2000 E GREENVILLE ST, STE 3600 29621 #575-01-2001 L2005 **FP** *012
ANDERSON, Arlene Joan. ■ 29621 #041-02-1970 L1989 **END IM** *071 †20
ANDERSON, William Major. 160 PERPETUAL SQ 29621 #045-01-1997 L1999 **IM** *020 †20
ARCHER, Katharine Jane. 1702 E GREENVILLE ST, VA - ANDERSON CO. CLINIC 29621 #010-02-1987 L1994 **P** *020 †75
ARTHUR, Godfried Antwi. 800 N FANT ST 29621 #412-01-1986 L2006 **FP** *012
ATHERLEY, Cheryl Gwyneth. 2000 E GREENVILLE ST, STE 3700 29621 #566-01-1976 L2006 **FP** *012
AUSTIN, James Andrew. 300 E GREENVILLE ST, STE C 29621 #041-12-1987 L2001 **AN IM** *020 †05
AYERS, Mark Andrew. 800 N FANT ST, DEPT OF FAMILY MEDICINE 29621 #045-04-2000 L2002 **IM** *100
BAILEY, Carl Thomas. 800 N FANT ST 29621 #045-01-1994 L1997 **PD** *020 †55
BAILEY, George Osgood. ■ 29625 #045-01-1959 L1959 **FM** *071 †18
BAILEY-DORTON, Chasse M. 813 N FANT ST 29621 #036-08-1993 L1996 **FM** *020 †18
BAILLIE, E Eugene. 800 N FANT ST, ANDERSON AREA MED CTR 29621 #030-05-1967 L1974 **PTH CD** *020 †50
BAKER, Carol Christensen. 300 E GREENVILLE ST, STE C 29621 #051-01-1990 L1996 **AN** *020 †05
BAKER, Dole Parker, Jr. 1206 CORNELIA RD 29621 #041-02-1990 L1995 **OTO A** *020 †45
BAKER, John Mark. 800 N FANT ST 29621 #045-01-1985 L1986 **FM** *020 †18 ‡
BALARAMAN, Balasukanya. 800 N FANT ST 29621 #496-23-2004 L2006 **FP** *012
BAMASHMUS, Abdalla M. 400 N FANT ST STE D 29621 #915-04-1982 L1991 **P** *020
BANKES, Christie Karen. 109 MONTGOMERY DR 29621 #045-01-1995 L2001 **NS** *020 †25
BARNES, Stuart Marshall. 800 N FANT ST 29621 #012-01-1973 L1977 **IM DIA** *020 †20
BATIZY, Szabolcs Gusztav. 2503 N MAIN 29621 #473-01-1981 L1987 **ON IM** *020 †20
BAUCUM, Jimmy Ray. 100 HEALTHY WAY STE 1250, CONSULTANTS PA 29621 #045-01-1987 L1988 **CD** *020 †20
BEBEN, Katherine Elizabet. ■ 29621 #008-02-2007 L2007 **FP** *012
BELK, Robert Blanton. 2000 E GREENVILLE ST 29621 #051-04-1964 L1970 **GYN** *072 †30
BENSEN, Pamela Parke. ■ 29621 #045-04-1971 L2003 **UCM** *020 †16
BISCOPINK, Ronald James. 800 N FANT ST 29621 #020-02-1978 L1988 **PTH GP** *020 †50
BLANTON, Edwin Brunson. 200 MCGEE RD, ANDERSON CO MENTAL HEALTH 29625 #045-01-1971 L1972 **P** *020
BLECKLEY, James Edward. 109 ESSEX DR 29621 #012-05-1955 L1963 **IM** *071 †20
BLEDSOE, Shannon Howard. 160 PERPETUAL SQ, CAROLINA OB/GYN ASSOC PA 29621 #012-01-1999 L2001 **OBG** *020 †30

BOGGS, Chris. 1100 W FRANKLIN ST 29624 #055-02-1993 L1994 **FM** *020 †18
BOLT, William Frank. 801 E GREENVILLE ST 29621 #045-01-1959 L1959 **P OS** *071
BOWIE, Carroll Wendell. 800 N FANT ST 29621 #012-05-1946 L1947 **U** *020 †95
BOYER, Elizabeth Perkins. 4190 HIGHWAY 24 29626 #036-08-1997 L1998 **FM** *020 †18
BRADFORD, Nathan Felding. 2000 E GREENVILLE ST, STE 3700 29621 #027-01-1989 L2002 **IM PD** *020 †20,55
BRAVO, Julian Andres. 200 MCGEE RD, AOP MENTAL HEALTH CTR 29625 #264-08-1998 L2006 **P** *020
BRENNAN, Bridget Aileen. 800 N FANT ST 29621 #012-01-1995 L1998 **EM** *020 †16
BRILL, Paul Allen. 2000 E GREENVILLE ST, STE 2800 29621 #035-06-1991 L1998 **N** *020 †75
BRITENBURG, James Earl. 800 N FANT ST 29621 #020-12-1977 L1978 **EM** *020 †18,16
BROWN, Juan Anthony. 800 N FANT ST 29621 #045-01-1964 L1964 **OTO** *071 †45
BRYANS, Kyle Coreen. 211 S MAIN ST 29624 #030-05-1988 L1996 **DR** *020 †80 ‡
BRYANT, Calvin Don. 4144 CLEMSON BLVD 29621 #045-01-1977 L1978 **FM OS** *020 †18
BUCCI, Michael Naldo. 109 MONTGOMERY DR 29621 #025-07-1983 L1989 **NS** *020 †25
BUICE, William Sims. 2000 E GREENVILLE ST, STE 2500 29621 #045-01-1984 L1989 **GS GE** *020 †85
BURDINE, Steven Elliott. 600 N FANT ST, RESIDENCY 29621 #045-01-2006 L2006 **FP** *012
BURNETT, Carol Patricia. 100 HEALTHY WAY, STE 1260 29621 #045-01-1993 L1998 **PM** *020 †60
BURNS, Bruce Mallory. 211 S MAIN ST 29624 #012-05-1981 L1988 **R DR** *020 †80
CAMP, Edmond Weyman, III. ■ 29625 #045-01-1964 L1964 **P** *075 †75
CAMPBELL, Kenneth S. 801 E GREENVILLE ST 29621 #045-01-1991 L1992 **FM** *020 †18
CARSON, James Harman, Jr. 500 N FANT ST 29621 #045-01-1971 L1987 **PD** *020 †55
CARTER, Sallie A. 500 N FANT ST 29621 #012-01-1986 L1989 **PD** *020 †55
CAYELLI, Maria Aurora O. 813 N FANT ST 29621 #051-07-1995 L1998 **FM** *020 †18
CHANDLER, Veena Mathur. 211 S MAIN ST 29624 #045-01-1995 L1997 **NM** *020 †80,28
CHAPMAN, Tami Jean. 600 N FANT ST 29621 #039-01-2005 L2005 **FP** *012
CHAROWSKI, Artur Adam. 500 N FANT ST, ANMED CHILD HEALTH CTR 29621 #759-08-1986 L2001 **PD** *020 †55 ‡
CHIPMAN, Dennis Clarence. 2315 N MAIN ST STE 119, REGENCY BLDG 29621 #054-04-1959 L1994 **P PFP** *020 †75
CHISOLM, Daniel J. 160 PERPETUAL SQ 29621 #023-01-1980 L1989 **OBG** *071 †30
CIANCIOLO, Amy Rawlings. 600 N FANT ST 29621 #055-01-1997 L1998 **FM** *020 †18
CLEMOW, Christopher Bice. 2000 E GREENVILLE ST, STE 3700 29621 #047-06-2003 L2004 **FM** *100 †18
CLINE, Matthew Kelley. 2000 E GREENVILLE ST, STE 3600 29621 #012-01-1989 L1990 **FM** *040 †18
COOK, Anne. 2000 E GREENVILLE ST, STE 3700 29621 #045-01-1982 L1984 **IM** *040 †20
COOK, Peter August, Jr. 2000 E GREENVILLE ST, STE 3100 29621 #045-01-1983 L1988 **GS** *020 †85
COOKSEY, Erin Lynn. 2000 E GREENVILLE ST, PRIMARY CARE ASSOCIATES 29621 #020-12-2000 L2001 **FM** *020 †18
COUNTS, Scott Stephen. 2000 E GREENVILLE ST, STE 3800 29621 #047-06-1982 L1988 **FM FSM** *040 †18
COUSAR, Carrie Davis. 211 S MAIN ST 29624 #045-01-1992 L1998 **DR** *020 †80
CROCKER, Thomas Pressley. 800 N FANT ST 29621 #045-01-1979 L1980 **PTH** *020 †50
DAMERON, Robert Allen, Jr. 3424 CLEMSON BLVD 29621 #051-04-1962 L1971 **ORS** *020 †40
DAVIES, John Wallace. 800 N FANT ST 29621 #041-02-1991 L1997 **EM** *020 †16,18
DAVIS, Travis Wayne. 2000 E GREENVILLE ST, STE 3700 29621 #045-01-2005 L2005 **FP** *012
DBOUK, Wajdi Ali. 605 E GREENVILLE ST, ANDERSON FAMILY CARE, PA 29621 #605-01-1984 L1996 **FM** *020 †18
DEAN, Arthur Joe, Jr. 1501 N MAIN ST 29621 #036-07-1967 L1972 **D** *020 †15
DEANGELIS, Richard John. 1409 N FANT ST 29621 #055-01-1987 L1991 **DS** *020 †15
DE HOLL, John David. 800 N FANT ST, AN MED HEALTH ADMIN 29621 #051-01-1971 L1975 **ORS** *020 †40
DELLINGER, Eric Henry. 2000 E GREENVILLE ST, STE 4600 29621 #036-08-1986 L1994 **OBG** *020 †30
DERMER, Mark Stephen. 160 PERPETUAL SQ 29621 #030-06-1980 L1987 **OBG** *020 †30
DESPRADEL, Vidal Manuel. 2000 E GREENVILLE ST 29621 #308-05-1989 L2007 **U** *020 †95
DIAF, Rhania. ■ 29621 #125-01-1983 **PTH** *100
DIETER, Benjamin Scott. ■ 29621 #036-08-2007 L2007 **FP** *012
DIN, Zia Ud. 779 SENATE PKWY 29621 #704-09-1983 L1998 **NEP** *020 †20
DODD, Louis Josselin. HWY 252 29621 #187-12-1953 L1969 **P AM** *071
DODDS, Russell E. 404 E CALHOUN ST 29621 #048-16-1982 L1988 **DMP** *020 †50
DONALDSON, Wm Clarence. 800 N FANT ST 29621 #045-01-1979 L1980 **FM** *020 †18
DOSTER, John Eric. 2503 N MAIN ST 29621 #012-01-1991 L1996 **HO** *020 †20
DUCWORTH, Lyman Ashurst, Jr. 800 N FANT ST 29621 #045-01-1975 L1976 **EM GP** *020
DUNCAN, Diana Margaret. 2000 E GREENVILLE ST, STE 3600 29621 #045-04-2004 L2004 **FM** *100 †18
DUNIHO, Timothy Lee. 2000 E GREENVILLE ST, STE 4500 29621 #028-03-1988 L1992 **OBG** *020 †30
EDSALL, Charles Kenneth. 800 N FANT ST 29621 #422-01-2006 L2007 **FP** *012
ELLIS, Elgar Percy, Jr. 800 N FANT ST 29621 #036-05-1955 L1962 **AN** *071 †05
EMANUEL, Benjamin Francis. 800 N FANT ST 29621 #045-01-1986 L1987 **PTH** *020 †50
ETA, Ekong Ito Ekong. 400 N FANT ST, STE A 29621 #690-04-1979 L2000 **IM** *020 †20
EWING, William Robbins. 800 N FANT ST 29621 #045-01-1955 L1955 **GP** *020
FARMER, Joseph Andrew, III. 2000 E GREENVILLE ST, STE 3850 29621 #045-01-1988 L1989 **IM** *020 †20
FENNELL, Chris Dewayne. 800 N FANT ST 29621 #036-01-2000 L2004 **AN** *020 †05 ‡
FINDER-DRAISEN, Andrea S. 2000 E GREENVILLE ST, STE 3000 29621 #041-12-1980 **PD** *020 †55
FLOYD, Winston Cordell. 400 N FANT ST, STE G 29621 #047-07-1973 L1975 **IM** *020 †20
FORD, R Bruce. ■ 29626 #045-01-1957 L1957 **P** *071
FORSTEIN, David Andrew. 2000 E GREENVILLE ST, STE 4600 29621 #041-77-1990, ▲ L2003 **OBG REN** *020 ‡
FOSTER, James Granbery. 2000 E GREENVILLE ST, STE 2500 29621 #011-04-1988 L1993 **GS** *020 †85
FRANKS, Melody Selena. 4190 HIGHWAY 24 29626 #036-08-1996 L1997 **FM** *020 †18 ‡
FRASSINELLI, Paul Mark. 2000 E GREENVILLE ST, STE 2500 29621 #041-02-1993 L1998 **GS** *020 †85
FREEBORN, John Stephen. 1206 CORNELIA RD 29621 #017-20-1972 L1976 **OBG** *075 †30
FREEMAN, Lawson Barry. 800 N FANT ST 29621 #045-04-1989 L1990 **EM FM** *020 †18
FRIALDE, Jose Rene Bauzon. 1702 E GREENVILLE ST, VETS ADM 29621 #748-08-1986 L2004 **IM** *020 †20
GAILLARD, Charles L. 131 BUFORD AVE 29621 #654-01-1997 L2001 **FM** *020 †18 ‡
GAINEY, James Spencer. 2000 E GREENVILLE ST, STE 3600 29621 #045-01-2005 L2005 **FP** *012
GARRIOTT, Randall Owen. 800 N FANT ST 29621 #048-15-1980 L1995 **EM FM** *020 †18,16
GARRIS, Jeffrey Bruce. 2000 E GREENVILLE ST, STE 4600 29621 #036-05-1993 L2006 **OBG** *020 †30
GARRISON, Robert Carlton. 3031 N HIGHWAY 81 29621 #001-02-1958 L1969 **AN** *072 †05
GAUCHER, Jay Paul. 100 HEALTHY WAY, CONSULTANTS PA 29621 #051-04-1986 L1995 **CD** *020 †20
GEISBERG, Harry Irvin. 1657 E GREENVILLE ST 29621 #020-02-1972 L1974 **FM** *020 †18
GILLESPIE, Marion Ray. 1655 E GREENVILLE ST 29621 #045-01-1957 L1957 **OTO** *071 †45
GRAHAM, Mary Higgins. ■ 29625 #047-06-1985 L1990 **PD** *062 †55
GRAHAM, Tony Randall. 800 N FANT ST 29621 #047-06-1987 L1991 **AN** *020 †05
GRIER, John Miller, Jr. 800 N FANT ST 29621 #045-01-1979 L1980 **EM FM** *020 †16,18
GRIER, Michael Tannehill. 100 HEALTHY WAY, STE 1260 29621 #030-05-1994 L1999 **AN PMM** *020 †05 ‡
GRIER, Monica H. 211 S MAIN ST 29624 #030-05-1994 L1999 **DR** *020 †80
GRIFFIN, Basil Manly, Jr. 2000 E GREENVILLE ST, STE 3700 29621 #047-06-1966 L1967 **ORS** *020 †40
GRIFFIN, David. 2000 E GREENVILLE ST, STE 2550 29621 #047-05-1996 L2005 **OBG** *020 †30
GRIMSLEY, William Ross. 2000 E GREENVILLE ST, ANMED FAM MED RESIDENCY PR 29621 #012-21-2007 L2007 **FP** *012
GRISHAM, Daniel W. 1525 N FANT ST 29621 #047-07-1976 L1979 **IM** *020
GUY-CRAFT, Wanda Ellece. ■ 29625 #010-03-2007 L2007 **FP** *012
HADDOCK, Samuel Thompson. ■ 29621 #012-05-1958 L1959 **PD PDI** *071 †55
HAN, Sung Joon. 100 HEALTHY WAY, STE 1260 29621 #422-01-2001 L2006 **APM** *020 †60
HAND, Stephen Harris. 2000 E GREENVILLE ST, STE 1100 29621 #045-01-1983 L1985 **PUD IM** *020 †20
HARDY, Dianne Kaye. 2000 E GREENVILLE ST, STE 3600 29621 #665-01-2006 L2006 **FP** *012
HART, Keith Mc Graw. 2000 E GREENVILLE ST, STE 3000 29621 #012-01-1981 L1984 **PD** *020 †55
HARTER, Newman W, Jr. 2000 E GREENVILLE ST, PRIMARY CARE ASSOCIATES 29621 #045-01-1971 L1972 **FM** *020 †18
HAYFORD, Elizabeth Ann. 2000 E GREENVILLE ST, STE 3700 29621 #038-44-2006 L2006 **FP** *012
HEARN, Henry Branham, IV. 2000 E GREENVILLE ST, STE 4500 29621 #045-01-1977 L1978 **OBG** *020 †30
HELLSTROM, Michael D. 1655 E GREENVILLE ST 29621 #011-04-1987 L1992 **OTO** *020 †45
HENK, Duane Jay. 2000 E GREENVILLE ST, PRIMARY CARE ASSOCIATES 29621 #016-45-1992 L1993 **FM** *020 †18
HENRY, Ralph S. 779 SENATE PKWY, NEPHROLOGY & INT MED OF AN 29621 #017-20-1980 L1981 **NEP IM** *020 †20
HENSARLING, Jeffrey Kirk. 100 HEALTHY WAY 29621 #012-01-1996 L1999 **ORS** *020 †40
HIGGINS, Matthew Stephen. 2000 E GREENVILLE ST, DEPT OF FAMILY MED 29621 #036-08-2007 L2007 **FP** *012
HILL, James Bryan. 500 N FANT ST, ANMED CHILD HEALTH CENTER 29621 #045-01-1995 L1998 **PD** *020 †55
HINNANT, Charles Wm, Sr. 112 ESSEX DR 29621 #045-01-1960 L1960 **FM** *071 †18
HINNANT, Charles Wm, Jr. 112 ESSEX DR 29621 #045-01-1986 L1992 **U UP** *020 †95
HOBBS, Mary Bryan. 705 N FANT ST 29621 #045-04-1998 L2003 **PD** *020 †55
HOHN, Jeffrey Anselm. 800 N FANT ST 29621 #012-01-2001 L2004 **EM** *020 †16
HOLDREDGE, Terry Keene. 3031 N HIGHWAY 81 29621 #012-01-1974 L1976 **PS GS** *020 †65,85
HOLLINGSWORTH, A S, Jr. 404 E CALHOUN ST 29621 #012-01-1968 L1976 **PTH** *020 †50
HOLT, David H, Jr. 211 S MAIN ST 29624 #047-05-1982 L1988 **NM DR** *020
HOLT, David N. 160 PERPETUAL SQ 29621 #035-06-1964 L1972 **GYN** *020 †30
HOPKINS, Rebecca M. 1207 N FANT ST 29621 #036-01-1983 L1984 **FM** *020 †18
HOSSAIN, Kashfia Duza. 400 N FANT ST, STE D 29621 #160-02-1989 L1996 **P** *020 †75
HOSSAIN, Zafar. 819 N FANT ST, CONSULTATIVE INTERNAL MED 29621 #160-02-1988 L1996 **IM** *020 †20
HUBER, Paige Skinner. 211 S MAIN ST 29624 #045-01-1991 L1995 **DR** *020 †80
HUDAK, Craig Matthew. 100 HEALTHY WAY, CONSULTANTS PA 29621 #035-01-1987 L2001 **IC CD** *020 †20
HUFF, Georgia Lou. 600 N FANT ST, ANMED FAMILY PRACTICE CENT 29621 #665-01-2001 L2001 **P** *100
HULLETT, Joel Michael. 800 N FANT ST 29621 #654-01-2006 L2007 **FP** *012
HULLETT, Maggi Leigh. 800 N FANT ST 29621 #654-01-2006 L2007 **FP** *012
HUNT, John Robinson. 703 N FANT ST 29621 #012-05-1969 L1976 **GS AM** *020 †85
HUNTER, Chas Pinckney, III. 1655 E GREENVILLE ST 29621 #018-03-1966 L1973 **OPH AM** *071 †35
HURRAY, Cathy Reeves. 813 N FANT ST 29621 #045-01-2004 L2004 **FM** *100 †18
HURRAY, David Henry. 800 N FANT ST 29621 #045-01-2000 L2001 **DMP** *020 †50
ILG, Boris Alexanderp. 1116 CORNELIA RD, 1116 CORNELIA ROAD 29621 #045-01-1996 L2000 **OPH** *020 †35
IRBY, James Herman, Jr. 1305 MCLEES RD 29621 #045-01-1983 L1984 **FM** *071 †18
ISAKOV, Ingrid Laetitia. 2000 E GREENVILLE ST STE 1, PRIMARY CARE ASSOCIATES 29621 #836-01-1983 L2000 **IMG** *020 †20
JACQUES, Sunil Bonifacio. ■ 29621 #496-15-1994 L2004 **P** *020 †75
JAIN, Ruchika. 500 N FANT ST 29621 #495-45-1992 L1999 **PD** *020 †55
JARRARD, John Carter, Jr. 800 N FANT ST 29621 #045-01-1969 L1969 **AN** *072 †05
JENNINGS, Christopher Ray. 160 PERPETUAL SQ, CAROLINA OB/GYN ASSOCIATES 29621 #045-04-1997 L1998 **OBG** *020 †30
JOGLEKAR, Rajiv. 819 N FANT ST 29621 #495-45-1992 L2001 **IM IMG** *020 †20
JONES, Audrey S. 2000 E GREENVILLE ST, STE 3700 29621 #045-01-2000 L2003 **FM** *020 †18
JONES, Carl Henry, III. 107 KILSPRINGS RD, ANDERSON FAMILY PRACTICE 29621 #045-01-1973 L1974 **FM** *040 †18
JONES, Lewis Mayrant. 800 N FANT ST 29621 #045-01-1964 L1964 **GP** *020
JONES, Paul R. 100 HEALTHY WAY, CONSULTANTS PA 29621 #048-13-1989 L2004 **CD** *020 †20
JORDAN, Edmond Rhodes. 1 SPRING BACK WAY 29621 #045-01-1983 L1984 **GP** *020
KARPIK, William Richard. 800 N FANT ST 29621 #045-01-1974 L1976 **AN** *020 †05
KEENAN, Daniel Allen, Jr. 803 N FANT ST, STE 3B 29621 #038-45-1994 L1995 **IM** *020 †20
KEIZER, Ricky Jay. 801 E GREENVILLE ST, CORNERSTON FAMILY MEDICINE 29621 #001-06-1995 L1996 **FM EM** *020 †18
KELLER, Patrick Lee. 2000 E GREENVILLE ST, STE 3700 29621 #550-04-2003 L2004 **GPM** *012 †18
KELLEY, David L. 800 N FANT ST 29621 #051-04-1960 L1967 **AN** *071 †05

■ = Address Information Privacy Protected

KENNEDY, William Edwards. 1011 ELLA ST 29621 #045-01-1955 L1955 **DR** *071 †80

KENT, Louis Max. 800 N FANT ST 29621 #012-01-1962 L1967 **ORS** *071 †40

KHAN, Khizar Ali. 400 N FANT ST STE D, ANDERSON PSYCHIATRY/PSYCHO 29621 #704-01-1988 L1999 **CHP** *020 †75

KHULORDAVA, Irakli. 819 N FANT ST 29621 #913-07-1993 L2006 **IM ID** *020 †20

KIMBALL, Raymond Michael. 130 HIGHWAY 252, PATRICK HARRIS HOSPITAL 29621 #036-05-1983 L1985 **P** *020 †75

KINSEY, Jeanette C. 800 N FANT ST 29621 #836-01-1975 L1987 **EM** *020 †16

KNOEPP, Louis F, Jr. 2000 E GREENVILLE ST, STE 3100 29621 #021-01-1962 L1971 **CRS** *071 †10,85

KNOEPP, Louis Frederick. 2000 E GREENVILLE ST #3100 29621 #045-01-1993 L2000 **VS GS** *020 †85

KNOEPP, Theresa Greene. 1501 N MAIN ST, CAMP CENTER 29621 #045-01-1993 L1998 **D IM** *020 †20,15

KOPP, James Henry. 301 E GREENVILLE ST 29621 #020-12-1970 L1976 **IM** *020 †20

KRISTENSEN, Erik Alfred. 600 N FANT ST 29621 #305-01-2003 L2006 **FM** *100

KUMAR, Sanjeev. 819 N FANT ST 29621 #495-15-1997 L2005 **IM** *020 †20

KUNKEL, Michael Ray. 2000 E GREENVILLE ST, STE 3850 29621 #051-04-1990 L1998 **IM** *020 †20

KWAK, Jackie J. 414 N FANT ST 29621 #422-01-2000 L2007 **FM** *020 †18

KYLE, David Louis, Jr. 2000 E GREENVILLE ST 29621 #045-04-1986 L1987 **FM OM** *020 †18

LACY, Mark Parnell. 2000 E GREENVILLE ST, STE 4500 29621 #045-01-1980 L1982 **OBG** *020 †30

LANGBEHN, Susan Eileen. 2000 E GREENVILLE ST, STE 3600 29621 #018-03-1990 L2006 **FM** *020 †18

LAZARIASHVILI, Nikolas. 819 N FANT ST, NIKOLOZ LAZARIASHVILI, M. 29621 #913-23-1994 L2001 **ID** *020 †20

LESSEY, Bruce Arthur. 2000 E GREENVILLE ST, STE 4600 29621 #007-02-1984 L2003 **REN OBG** *050 †30

LIDDLE, Katherine Jean. 400 N FANT ST STE E 29621 #020-12-1991 L1992 **AI** *020 †03,55

LOESCHER, Carol M. 605 E GREENVILLE ST 29621 #045-01-1984 L1992 **OBG** *020 †20

LOMINACK, Edward K, Jr. 100 HEALTHY WAY, CONSULTANTS PA 29621 #045-01-1969 L1969 **CD** *020 †20

LONG, Needham Lapsley. 800 N FANT ST 29621 #001-02-1956 L1963 **ATP DMP** *071 †50

LOUDERMILK, Eric Paul. 100 HEALTHY WAY, STE 1260 29621 #025-01-1992 L1997 **AN PME** *020 †05

LUCAS, Thomas Lawman, III. ■ 29621 #045-01-2007 L2007 **FP** *012

LUM, Brian David. 2000 E GREENVILLE ST, STE 3700 29621 #027-01-2005 L2005 **FP** *012

LUMMUS, William Faulkner. ■ 29621 #045-01-1948 L1948 **IM** *071 †20

LUND, Carl Mc Henry. 118 MONTGOMERY DR 29621 #045-01-1972 L1975 **GE** *020 †20

MABIE, Billy Clinton. 2000 E GREENVILLE ST, STE 4600 29621 #019-02-1972 L2002 **MFM** *040 †20,30

MAC DONALD, Aaron Curtis. 109 MONTGOMERY DR 29621 #012-01-1991 L1997 **NS** *020 †25

MAC DONALD, Keremy J. 800 N FANT ST, AAMC-RAD ONC 29621 #012-01-1991 L1995 **RO** *020 †80

MACK, Brandon Vashon. 800 N FANT ST 29621 #016-42-2002 L2002 **AN** *100

MADDOX, Barry Hershel. E GREENVILLE ST, STE 3000 29621 #045-01-1982 L1983 **PD** *020 †55

MALIK, Rajeev. 703 N FANT ST, ANDERSON ONCOLOGY HEMATOLO 29621 #495-45-1977 L1982 **ON HEM** *020 ‡

MALIK, Ravinder. 701 N FANT ST 29621 #495-45-1977 L1983 **RO U** *020 †80

MALINOWSKI, Timothy R. 100 HEALTHY WAY, CONSULTANTS PA 29621 #038-06-1988 L1999 **CD** *020 †20

MALMQUIST, Peter Geo. 2404 MIDWAY RD 29621 #016-11-1978 L1986 **FM** *020 †18

MANLEY, Michael Alan. 200 MCGEE RD, ANDERSON MENTAL HEALTH CTR 29625 #012-01-1981 L1997 **P ADP** *020 †75

MARTIN, Ernest Cleage. 305 W BELTLINE BLVD 29625 #025-12-1986 L1991 **P** *020

MARTIN, Henry Calhoun. 3424 CLEMSON BLVD 29621 #045-01-1963 L1963 **IM HEM** *020 †20

MARTIN, John Baylis, Jr. 2000 E GREENVILLE ST #1100 29621 #045-01-1956 L1956 **IM CD** *071 †20

MARTIN, John W, Jr. 1208 ELLA ST 29621 #045-01-1966 L1966 **GP P** *020

MARTOCCIA, David Stuart. 2000 E GREENVILLE ST 29621 #011-04-1992 L1998 **U** *072

MATTISON, Edward Clifton. 1116 CORNELIA RD 29621 #045-01-1964 L1964 **OPH** *020 †35

MAY, Keith Andrew. 300C E GREENVILLE ST, MUSC - GRADUATE MED EDU 29621 #045-04-2003 L2004 **AN** *020

MAY, Stephen Cuthbert. ■ 29621 #012-01-1956 L1956 **FM AM** *071 †18

MC CANN, David Allen. 800 N FANT ST 29621 #039-05-1982 L1994 **FM GS** *020 †18

MC CARRAGHER, Kevin Scott. 300 E GREENVILLE ST, STE C 29621 #056-05-1984 L1987 **AN** *020 †05

MC COMBS, William Perry. ■ 29625 #045-01-1982 L1983 **FM** *020

MC CORD, Hugh Calvin, Jr. ■ 29621 #045-01-1964 L1970 **CHP P** *071

MC ELVEEN, Timothy S. 2000 E GREENVILLE ST #3100, SURG CLINIC OF ANDERSON PA 29621 #045-04-1990 L1996 **GS** *020 †85

MC ELWEE, Jos Monroe, Jr. 2000 E GREENVILLE ST, STE 3700 29621 #045-01-1986 L1987 **P** *020 †75,18

MEADORS, Marshall L, III. 2000 E GREENVILLE ST, PRIMARY CARE ASSOCIATES 29621 #045-01-1986 L1987 **FM** *020 †18

MELTON, Donny Mark. 109 MONTGOMERY DR, PIEDMONT NEUROSURGICAL GRO 29621 #045-01-1998 L1998 **NS** *020

MERCHANT, Vernon Evans. 1221 N FANT ST 29621 #045-01-1955 L1955 **GS** *071 †85

MEREDITH, Albert O, Jr. ■ 29625 #012-01-1952 L1956 **DR R** *071 †80

MILLER, Paul Bruce. 2000 E GREENVILLE ST, STE 4600 29621 #035-01-1990 L1998 **OBG REN** *020 †30

MILLER, Stephanie Danette. ■ 29621 #028-46-2007 L2007 **FP** *012

MILLON, S John. 100 HEALTHY WAY, HAND SURGERY CENTER PA 29621 #045-01-1989 L1995 **HS** *020 †40

MILLS, James Casper, III. 100 HEALTHY WAY 29621 #021-01-1986 L1993 **ORS** *020 †40

MILLWOOD, Henry Joseph. 800 N FANT ST, ANDERSON EMERGENCY ASSOCIA 29621 #012-01-2001 L2005 **EM** *100 †16

MOCK, Robert Bradley. 300 E GREENVILLE ST, # C 29621 #012-01-1988 L1989 **AN** *020 †05

MOHAN, Gowdhami. 2000 E GREENVILLE ST, STE 1100 29621 #495-42-1983 L1995 **PUD SME** *020 †20

MONAGHAN, Renee Aurich. 800 N FANT ST 29621 #012-01-1994 L1997 **EM** *020 †16

MOODY, Felice Pearl. 2000 E GREENVILLE ST, STE 2300 29621 #051-01-1991 L1997 **PS** *020 †65

MORAN, John Lawrence. 3424 CLEMSON BLVD 29621 #051-04-1964 L1970 **ORS** *071 †40

MORETZ, Christian Bradfor. 2000 E GREENVILLE ST, STE 3700 29621 #036-08-2006 L2006 **FP** *012

MORGAN, Nancy Strom. 2000 E GREENVILLE ST #3000 29621 #036-07-1998 L2001 **PD** *020 †55

MORIARTY, Mark H. 2000 E GREENVILLE ST #3700 29621 #010-02-1981 L1999 **ORS** *020 †40

MORROW, Jeanne Chadwick. 400 N FANT ST, STE D 29621 #748-11-1983 L1989 **P** *020

MORSE, Harold Gleason. 800 N FANT ST 29621 #012-05-1976 **IM CCM** *020 †20 ‡

MOSELEY, Patti K. 2000 E GREENVILLE ST, SUTE 3000 29621 #045-04-1995 L1997 **PD** *020 †55

MUNRO, Joshua David. 800 N FANT ST 29621 #654-01-2006 L2006 **FP** *012

MURRAY, John Hartwell. 100 HEALTHY WAY 29621 #051-01-1990 L1997 **ORS** *020 †40

NALL, Keith Steven. 800 N FANT ST, ANDERSON AREA MEDICAL CENT 29621 #001-02-1994 L1995 **EM** *020 †16

NALL, Laurie Colleen. 2000 E GREENVILLE ST, URGENT CARE 29621 #005-14-1993 L1994 **FM** *020 †18

NEILSEN, Edward Allen. 800 N FANT ST, ANDERSON EMER ASSOC 29621 #045-01-2002 L2004 **FM** *020 †18

NERELLA, Damodhar. 819 N FANT ST 29621 #496-01-1995 L2004 **IM** *020 †20

NILES, De Witt Carroll. ■ 29621 #035-15-1967 L1972 **AN** *020 †05

NOBLE, Lucretia Hurst. 801 E GREENVILLE ST 29621 #012-01-2000 L2002 **FM** *020 †18

NORDEEN, John Howard, Jr. 2000 E GREENVILLE ST, STE 4500 29621 #005-12-1985 L1997 **OBG** *020 †30

NORRIS, Rebecca Woodbury. 2000 E GREENVILLE ST, PRIMARY CARE ASSOCIATES 29621 #045-04-2000 L2007 **FM** *020 †18 ‡

OLIVER, Frank Elery. 2000 E GREENVILLE ST, STE 2800 29621 #036-05-1971 L1979 **N EM** *020 †75

ORR, Clarence Wilson. ■ 29625 #045-01-1940 L1940 **GS** *071 †85

OSBURN, George Hugh. 600 N FANT ST 29621 #021-05-1971 L1982 **IM** *040 †20

PARCHURI, Nandakishore. 2000 E GREENVILLE ST, STE 5000 29621 #422-01-1997 L2005 **HO IM** *020 †20

PARCHURI, Subha. 109 ESSEX DR 29621 #422-01-1997 L2005 **ID** *020 †20

PARKER, Harold Graham. 100 HEALTHY WAY, CONSULTANTS PA 29621 #028-03-1981 L1989 **CD IM** *020 †20

PATEL, Sidharth C. 110 PERPETUAL SQ 29621 #917-10-1981 L1986 **FM** *020 †18

PATTERSON, Eltanya Angeli. 2000 E GREENVILLE ST, STE 3700 29621 #654-01-2004 L2005 **FM** *100

PATTERSON, Patti Jeanette. 2000 E GREENVILLE ST, STE 2800 29621 #027-01-1984 L1988 **N** *020

PENNELL, James Edgar. ■ 29621 #045-01-1959 L1959 **FM OM** *071

PICKLESIMER, Amy Hairston. 2000 E GREENVILLE ST, STE 4600 29621 #038-40-2000 L2006 **OBG** *100 †30

PINNER, Benjamin Carroll. 600 N FANT ST, MEDICINE RESIDENCY PROGRAM 29621 #045-01-2004 L2004 **FM** *020 †18

PLAYFORD, George Alan. 800 N FANT ST 29621 #012-01-1961 L1969 **AN** *020 †05

POTTS, David W. 800 N FANT ST 29621 #035-06-1971 L1981 **ID IM** *020 †20

POWELL, Jerry Ray. ■ 29621 #045-01-1965 L1965 **GS** *071 †85

PURCELL, Jerry Shane. 2000 E GREENVILLE ST, ANMED URGENT CARE 29621 #012-22-1999 L2000 **FM** *020 †18

PURCELL, John Howell. PO BOX 2907, PATRICK B HARRIS PSYCH HOS 29622 #039-01-1968 L2002 **P** *030 †75

PURDY, Nathan Lynn. 600 N FANT ST, AN MED HEALTH FAMILY MEDIC 29621 #104-01-2004 L2005 **FM** *020 †18

QUARTERMAN, Mark Johnson. 2503 N MAIN ST 29621 #012-01-1991 L1993 **D DMP** *020 †15

QUIROS, Melissa. ■ 29621 #012-21-2007 L2007 **FP** *012

RATLIFF, Larry Dennis. 2000 E GREENVILLE ST, STE 3700 29621 #012-01-1973 L1975 **ORS** *071 †85

RAY, Roger Alan. 2000 E GREENVILLE ST, STE 2800 29621 #055-01-1984 L1988 **N** *020 †75

REESE, James Edward. 800 N FANT ST 29621 #045-01-1992 L1998 **EM** *020 †16

REKITO, Anthony William. 800 N FANT ST 29621 #012-01-2000 L2004 **EM** *020 †16 ‡

REYNOLDS, Carolyn Becker. 800 N FANT ST 29621 #045-01-1987 L1988 **IM GS** *020 †20

RHYNES, Antoinette Denise. 2000 E GREENVILLE ST, STE 3600 29621 #045-01-2006 L2006 **FP** *012

RIDER, Ryan Kevin. 800 N FANT ST 29621 #038-43-1993 L1997 **EM** *020 †16

RIESTER, Jane Wyant. 1655 E GREENVILLE ST 29621 #055-01-1980 L1988 **OTO** *020 †45

RIVERA, Michael Armando. 1519 N FANT ST 29621 #048-04-1974 L1978 **OBG** *020 †30

ROEHRS, Matthew Paul. 2000 E GREENVILLE ST, STE 3700 29621 #045-04-2000 L2001 **FM** *020 †18

ROQUE NAZARIO, Elaine. 2000 E GREENVILLE ST, STE 3600 29621 #042-04-2002 L2005 **FP** *012

ROSS, Sam Harry, III. 130 HIGHWAY 252, BOX 2907 29621 #045-01-1970 L1971 **GP OS** *020

ROWITZ, Blair Martin. 2000 E GREENVILLE ST, STE 2600 29621 #016-01-1993 L1998 **GS** *020 †85

RUFF, James M. ■ 29625 #045-01-1946 L1946 **FM** *071

SAHARA, Hikaru. ■ 29621 #012-01-1992 L1995 **PD** *020 †55

SALLEY, Lawton Harris. 1655 E GREENVILLE ST 29621 #045-01-1995 L2000 **OTO** *020 †45

SANDERS, Caroline Healy. 500 N FANT ST, ANDERSON AREA MED CTR FAM 29621 #036-08-2002 L2006 **FM** *020 †18

SANDERS, John Leonard. 100 HEALTHY WAY, HAND SURGERY CENTER PA 29621 #045-01-1992 L1993 **HS** *020 †40

SANDERS, Timothy Joseph. 2000 E GREENVILLE ST, STE 3700 29621 #036-08-2006 L2006 **FP** *012

SANKARA, Ishwara Raghu Pr. 819 N FANT ST 29621 #495-21-2001 L2007 **IM** *020 †20

SCOWCROFT, Charles Wm. 800 N FANT ST 29621 #041-13-1975 L1984 **GE IM** *020

SEEMULLER, Michael Dean. 600 N FANT ST, ANMED FAMILY PRACTICE CENT 29621 #051-04-2000 L2001 **FM** *020 †18

SEILER, Raymond Kirk. 2000 E GREENVILLE ST 29621 #041-09-1985 L1995 **U GS** *020 †95

SEYMOUR, Zachary Gregg. 803 N FANT ST, STE 2B 29621 #045-01-1989 L1990 **IM IMG** *020 †20

SHAKEEL, Muhammad. 779 SENATE PKWY 29621 #704-02-1988 L1998 **NEP IM** *020 †20

SHEIKH, Shahzad H. 118 MONTGOMERY DR, CONSULTATIVE GASTRO 29621 #422-01-1990 L1996 **GE** *020 †20

SHIVERS, Carroll Paul. 300 N FANT ST, STE C 29621 #045-04-1994 L2006 **AN** *020 †05

SHRAMEK, Jeffrey Keith. 2110 N HIGHWAY 81, ANDERSON RADIOLOGY 29621 #045-01-1987 L1988 **RNR R** *020 †80

SIAZON, Laura Dizon. 200 MCGEE RD, ANDERSON OCONEE PICKENS MH 29625 #748-07-1966 L2004 **P** *020

SINGH, Meenakshi. 600 N FANT ST 29621 #496-07-1995 L2003 **FM** *100 †18

SIZEMORE, Kent Brian. 500 N FANT ST 29621 #045-04-1994 L1995 **MG** *020 †55

SMETKA, Vlastimil. 2000 E GREENVILLE ST, STE 3700 29621 #665-02-2006 L2006 *100

■ = Address Information Privacy Protected

SMITH, Julian M, Jr. ■ 29622 #045-01-1971 L1972 **GYN** *071
SMITH, Melinda J. 100 HEALTHY WAY, CONSULTANTS PA 29621 #048-02-1985 L1991 **CD** *020 †20
SOFLEY, Carl Wilson, Jr. 2000 E GREENVILLE ST, STE 3850 29621 #036-01-1986 L1987 **IM** *020 †20 ‡
SOHN, Jae Il. 500 N FANT ST 29621 #583-02-1985 L1996 **PD** *020 †55
SORIANO, Jason A. 2000 E GREENVILLE ST, STE 2800 29621 #748-02-1990 L2001 **N** *020 †75
SOUVIRON, June Marie. 2405 N MAIN ST 29621 #012-01-1990 L1991 **FM** *020 †18
STEVENS, Jeffrey Hollis. 800 N FANT ST 29621 #030-06-1971 L1976 **AN** *020 †05
STOLL, Brett Cadwell. 100 HEALTHY WAY, CONSULTANTS PA 29621 #051-04-1987 L2000 **CD IM** *020 †20
STONE, Joseph Michael. 705 N FANT ST, ANDERSON PEDIATRIC GROUP, 29621 #045-01-2004 L2007 **PD** *020 †55
STRATHERN, David William. 2000 E GREENVILLE ST, STE 2500 29621 #038-43-1993 L2006 **GS** *020 †85
STRAUGHN, Clifton Wade. 605 E GREENVILLE ST, ANDERSON FAMILY CARE 29621 #036-05-1982 L1983 **FM** *020 †18
STUMPFF, James Owen. 800 N FANT ST 29621 #012-01-1999 L2002 **EM** *020 †16
STURTZ, Richard Paul. 1114 CORNELIA RD 29621 #041-13-1979 L1983 **D IM** *020 †20,15
SUGARMAN, Abraham Perry. ■ 29621 #035-09-1973 L1986 **P** *075
SULLIVAN, Thos James, Jr. 803 N FANT ST STE 2C 29621 #045-01-1981 L1990 **CD IM** *020 †20
SWATHWOOD, Todd Cameron. 100 HEALTHY WAY 29621 #036-05-1991 L2004 **ORS** *020 †40
SWAVELY, Melody Eisenman. 800 N FANT ST 29621 #055-02-1988 L1989 **EM** *020 †18
SWENSON, Bradley Paul. 800 N FANT ST 29621 #045-04-1995 L1998 **EM** *020 †16
SYED, Asad A. 2000 E GREENVILLE ST, STE 4700 29621 #704-01-1989 L1996 **PD** *020 †55
SYED, Elzbieta W. 2000 E GREENVILLE ST, STE 4700 29621 #759-06-1983 L1996 **PD** *020 †55
TALBERT, Edgar Leland. PO BOX 2086, 1028 S MAIN ST 29622 #045-01-1975 L1977 **GP FM** *020 ‡
TAMAKLO, Wilberforce K. 800 N FANT ST, ANMED HEALTH 29621 #412-01-1975 L2005 **P DR** *020 †75
TAMMINENI, Anil Kumar. 819 N FANT ST 29621 #495-36-2001 L2005 **IM** *100 †20
TAYLOR, John C, Jr. 800 N FANT ST 29621 #023-07-1945 L1948 **GP** *020
THOMPSON, Charles A. 2000 E GREENVILLE ST, STE 1100 29621 #048-04-1985 L1994 **IM** *020 †20
THOMPSON, Clifford M. 112 ESSEX DR 29621 #045-01-1969 L1969 **U** *071 †95
THOMPSON, Robert G. ■ 29621 #036-07-1946 L1956 **FM P** *071
TILLIRSON, Michael Lee. 800 N FANT ST, ANMED HEALTH SYSTEM 29621 #018-75-1981, ▲ L1987 **EM FM** *020 †18
TOMLINSON, William Victor. 2000 E GREENVILLE ST, ANMED HEALTH CANCER CENTER 29621 #012-01-1981 L1982 **RO** *020 †80
TREASH, Dale Edward. 705 N FANT ST 29621 #017-20-1998 L2000 **PD** *020 †55
TROFATTER, Kenneth F, Jr. 2000 E GREENVILLE ST, STE 4600 29621 #036-07-1979 L2002 **OBG MFM** *020 †30
TUGGLE, Anne Sherrise. 2000 E GREENVILLE ST, STE 3700 29621 #045-04-2002 L2003 **FM** *020 †18
TURNER, David Scott. 800 N FANT ST 29621 #047-05-1990 L1997 **EM** *020 †16
TURNER, William Muirhead. ■ 29626 #045-01-1964 L1964 **IM** *071 †20
TUTEN, Thomas Upshaw. 211 S MAIN ST 29624 #045-01-1981 L1987 **DR** *020 †80
VALVERDE, Rodolfo Jose. ■ 29621 #429-02-1997 L2005 **PYG** *100 †75
VEERABAGU, Manjakkollai P. 130 PERPETUAL SQ 29621 #495-59-1986 L1996 **GE HEP** *020 †20
VESTAL, Tom A. ■ 29621 #036-07-1953 L1962 **GYN** *071 †30
VOGENITZ, William F. 1 SPRING BACK WAY, ANMED HEALTHSOUTH REHABILI 29621 #021-06-1995 L2002 **PM** *020 †60
WACHS, Theodore James. ■ 29621 #030-06-1958 L1980 **P GPM** *071 †70,75
WADEE, Charles F. 1403 E GREENVILLE ST 29621 #412-01-1985 L1996 **IM** *020 †20
WALKER, Harvey Capers. 801 E GREENVILLE ST 29621 #012-01-1961 L1967 **U** *071 †95
WALKER, William W. 800 N FANT ST 29621 #012-05-1971 L1976 **IM PUD** *020 †20
WARE, John Dwight, III. 800 N FANT ST 29621 #012-05-1975 L1979 **CD IM** *020 †20
WENDT, John R. 100 HEALTHY WAY, CONSULTANTS PA 29621 #045-01-1989 L1999 **CD** *020 †20
WHATLEY, Dennis Steven. 2000 E GREENVILLE ST 29621 #045-01-1985 L1990 **U** *020 †95
WILLIAMS, James Christian. 800 N FANT ST 29621 #422-01-2007 L2007 **FP** *012
WILLIAMS, Kenneth Trotter. 801 E GREENVILLE ST 29621 #036-07-1954 L1954 **GS TS** *071 †85
WILLIAMS, Patrick C. ■ 29626 #051-04-1958 L1959 **OBG P** *071 †30
WILSON, Jessie Ruth. 112 MONTGOMERY DR, C/O ANDERSON BONE AND JOIN 29621 #036-05-1987 L1994 **ORS** *020 †40
WINKLER, Danielle Daneen. 2000 E GREENVILLE ST, STE 4500 29621 #001-02-2002 L2003 **OBG** *020
WOODALL, Hunter Earl. 2000 E GREENVILLE ST, STE 3600 29621 #047-05-1983 L1986 **FM PLM** *020 †18
WOODARD, Brett Houghton. 800 N FANT ST 29621 #021-01-1974 L1981 **PTH BBK** *020 †50
WORSHAM, Stephen Ford. 109 BUFORD AVE 29621 #012-22-1991 L1992 **FM EM** *020 †18
WORTHAM, David Todd. 1922 MCCONNELL SPG RD, SPRINGS ROAD 29621 #012-01-1990 L1995 **GE IM** *020 †20
YEBOAH, Samuel Yaw A. 1221 N FANT ST, ENDOCRINOLOGY, P.A. 29621 #412-01-1988 L1995 **END** *020 †20
YON, Joseph Watson, Jr. 211 S MAIN ST 29624 #045-01-1979 L1980 **DR** *020 †80
YOUNG, Natawadee. 2000 E GREENVILLE ST, STE 3700 29621 #028-02-1995 L2004 **FM** *040 †18

ANDREWS — GEORGETOWN

COHN, Charles J, Jr. 102 S COUNTY LINE RD 29510 #012-01-1985 L1986 **NEP IM** *020 †20
DOWNING, Steven Craig. 701 S MORGAN AVE, ANDREWS MEDICAL CENTER 29510 #003-01-2000 L2003 **FM** *020 †18
HASSAN, Hossan Adnan. 701 S MORGAN AVE 29510 #875-03-1996 L2002 **FM** *020 †18 ‡
JONES, Bernard L, Jr. 701 S MORGAN AVE, ANDREWS MEDICAL CENTER 29510 #045-01-1984 L1985 **FM** *020 †18

AWENDAW — CHARLESTON

HEWSON, Michael Wayne. ■ 29429 #021-01-1976 L1978 **EM** *020 †16

NELSON, George Humphry. ■ 29429 #055-01-1962 L1978 **OBG** *071

AYNOR — HORRY

LAWSON, Louie C, Jr. ■ 29511 #045-01-1984 L1985 **GP EM** *020

BAMBERG — BAMBERG

DWIGHT, F Marion. 450 NORTH ST 29003 #045-01-1958 L1958 **FM AM** *020 †18
GLENN, William Darby, IV. PO BOX 528, 498 NORTH ST 29003 #041-01-1992 L1997 **FM** *020 †18
HAYDEN, John Haskell, Jr. 450 NORTH ST 29003 #045-04-2001 L2004 **FM** *020 †18
MC ALHANEY, Danette E. 450 NORTH ST 29003 #045-01-1994 L1995 **FM** *020 †18 ‡
MOSKOW, Herbert Abraham. 450 NORTH ST 29003 #045-01-1967 L1967 **FM** *020 †18
PADGETT, Ronald Dale. 526 NORTH ST 29003 #045-01-1980 L1981 **FM** *020 †18
ROSS, John Richard. 185 MCGEE ST 29003 #045-01-1974 L1976 **VS GS** *020 †85
SHATILLA, Maggie A E M. 509 NORTH ST 29003 #915-02-1983 L1997 **IM** *020 †20
THOMAS, Joseph Deer. 509 NORTH ST 29003 #045-01-1948 L1948 **GP OS** *020 †18
WATSON, Michael C. 498 NORTH ST 29003 #045-01-1953 **FM PHP** *071 †18

BARNWELL — BARNWELL

ARTHUR, Ansermo Lester. 154 WREN ST 29812 #003-01-1987 L1995 **CD PD** *020 †55,20
BATLEY, Nicholas John. 86 WREN ST 29812 #045-01-1998 L2001 **FM** *020 †18
BOYLES, Richard E, Jr. 86 WREN ST, P O BOX 448 29812 #045-04-1985 L1986 **FM** *020 †18
BURNETT, Bryan Allan. PO BOX 1302, 10706 MARLBORO AVE 29812 #422-01-1996 L1999 **PD** *020 †55
CLAYTOR, Philip Pendell. 1184 JACKSON ST 29812 #045-01-1955 L1956 **GP IM** *071
CUNDEY, David William. 154 WREN ST 29812 #041-13-1967 L1990 **CD IM** *020 †20
EAVES, Gregory Lawton. 154 WREN ST 29812 #045-04-1994 L1995 **CD IC** *020 †20
GIBSON, Henry W. 86 WREN ST 29812 #045-01-1950 L1950 **GP OM** *020
HAMDANI, Syeduzair Tanvee. PO BOX 538 29812 #704-02-1998 L2006 **IM** *100 †20
KHAN, Mir Obaidulla. 55 IRVING ST 29812 #495-65-1965 L1977 **GS TS** *020 †85
KHAN, Yasir Arfat. 85 WREN ST, PALMETTO IM & SUBSPECIALIT 29812 #704-20-2001 L2006 **IM** *020 †20
LA ROCHE, Jane Lawton. 811 REYNOLDS RD, BARNWELL CO HOSP 29812 #045-01-1974 L1978 **IM EM** *020 †20 ‡
MOSKOW, A Herbert, Jr. 811 REYNOLDS RD 29812 #045-01-1979 L1980 **OP** *020 †55
PAXTON, Thomas Patrick. 154 WREN ST 29812 #047-06-1988 L2001 **TS** *020 †85,90
PENNINGTON, Don Lavar. 154 WREN ST 29812 #012-01-1965 L1970 **CD IM** *071
SERVICE, Verston Kirk. 85 WREN ST 29812 #305-01-2001 L2004 **FM** *100
SHARAF, Idris Sayed. 154 WREN ST 29812 #704-02-1978 L1998 **CD IM** *020 †20
WARAICH, Afsar M. 85 WREN ST 29812 #704-02-1988 L1996 **GE** *020 †20

BATESBURG — LEXINGTON

ATKINSON, Katherine Joy. 120 W CHURCH ST 29006 #045-01-2004 L2007 **PD** *020 †55
COLEMAN, Octavius Torrez. ■ 29006 #045-01-2008 *012
ROTAN, Stephanie Susan. ■ 29006 #036-05-2007 **EM** *012
SKINNER, Raymond Ralph. 110 E COLUMBIA AVE 29006 #033-06-1988 L1997 **FM** *020 †18

BATESBURG-LEESVILLE — LEXINGTON

AUGUSTINE, Scott Douglas. 338 E COLUMBIA AVE, D/B/A LEXINGTON MEDICAL CT 29070 #045-04-1993 L1994 **OBG** *020 †30
COUNTS, Gurdon Wright. PO BOX 2629, 110 E COLUMBIA AVE 29070 #045-01-1959 L1959 **GP** *020

BEAUFORT — BEAUFORT

ADAMS, John B, II. 989 RIBAUT RD, STE 220 29902 #012-05-1988 L1999 **U** *020 †95
ADAMS, Michael Louis. 1 PINCKNEY BLVD, NAVAL HOSPITAL 29902 #033-05-1998 L2003 **ORS** *020 †40
AINSWORTH, Makini Shani G. 1 PINCKNEY BLVD, NAVAL HOSPITAL BEAUFORT 29902 #041-15-2003 L2005 **IM** *100 †20
AKERS, Richard Edwin, II. 1094 RIBAUT RD 29902 #045-01-1990 L1995 **OPH** *020 †35
ALEA, Paul Joseph. ■ 29907 #047-07-2004 L2005 **GS** *100
ALLEN, Mark Mclean. ■ 29906 #021-01-2002 L2003 **OBG** *020
ALTLAND, Tracy Thompson. 1 PINCKNEY BLVD, OB/GYN DEPT 29902 #023-12-1997 L2005 **OBG** *020 †30
ARVIN, Jon Anthony. 990 RIBAUT RD 29902 #020-12-1985 L1988 **FM** *020 †18
AXELSEN, Frank Orla. ■ 29902 #023-12-2001 L2003 **FM** *020 †18
BAILEY, Andrew Keith. ■ 29907 #039-01-2004 L2004 **PD** *100
BANKOV, Robert Wm. 1 PINCKNEY BLVD BOX 6216A, NAVAL HOSPITAL BEAUFORT 29902 #001-06-1978 L1997 **EM IM** *020 †16
BARKER, Matthew David. ■ 29907 #036-05-2002 L2004 *100
BAYES, Matthew Christian. 1 PINCKNEY BLVD, ATTN: MEDICAL STAFF OFFICE 29902 #028-34-2001 L2003 **PD** *020 †55
BELL, Robert Edward. 955 RIBAUT RD, BEAUFORT MEMORIAL HOSPITAL 29902 #045-01-1986 L1987 **AN GS** *020 †05
BETTLE, Norman. 989 RIBAUT RD STE 310 29902 #408-30-1997 L2004 **N CN** *020 †75 ‡
BILLIG, Eric. 955 RIBAUT RD, BEAUFORT MEMORIAL HOSPITAL 29902 #051-07-2000 L2005 **R** *100 †80
BLACK, William Murray. ■ 29902 #422-01-1982 L1984 **FM** *020 †18
BLALOCK, Clyde Phillip. 955 RIBAUT RD, DEPT OF RADIOLOGY 29902 #012-01-1979 L1999 **R** *020 †80
BLOCKER, Edward Riley. 300 MIDTOWN DR 29906 #045-01-1993 L1994 **ORS** *020 †40
BORISSOVA, Irina. 9 RUE DU BOIS, # A 29907 #913-15-1986 L1998 **IM** *020 †20
BREWER, Paul Chambers. 1096 RIBAUT RD 29902 #051-01-1984 L1994 **D PD** *020 †55,15

BROERMAN, Nicole S. 2403 ALLISON RD, SEA ISLAND PEDIATRICS PA 29902 #012-01-1996 L2002 **PD** *020 †55

BROWN, Kenneth Allen. 1231 RIBAUT RD 29902 #045-01-1982 L1987 **OTO A** *020 †45

BURRUS, Edward Perry, III. 1055 RIBAUT RD, STE 30 29902 #012-01-1987 L1993 **GS PS** *020 †85

BUSH, Charles Anthony. 955 RIBAUT RD 29902 #021-01-1967 L1969 **GS EM** *020 †85

CELSO, Renee Michelle. 1050 RIBAUT RD 29902 #065-06-1979 L2004 **P** *020 †75

CHAHIN, Majd. 1264 RIBAUT RD, STE 200 29902 #875-03-1986 L1995 **HO** *020 †20

CHIAVIELLO, Christine T. 1096 RIBAUT RD 29902 #033-05-1984 L1994 **PD PEM** *020 †55

CHRISTIAN, Don Ray, Jr. 1231 RIBAUT RD 29902 #012-01-1997 L2002 **OTO** *020 †45

CLINE, Richard W. ■ 29906 #005-76-1995, ▲ L1996 **FM** *020 †18

COGGINS, Allahna Allybia. 955 RIBAUT RD 29902 #024-07-2001 L2005 **OBG** *020

COLEMAN, Lawrence R, Jr. 964 RIBAUT RD 29902 #012-01-1984 L1985 **PD** *020 †55

COLLINS, Bradford Scott. 955 RIBAUT RD 29902 #045-01-1983 L1984 **CLP** *020 †50

COLY, Erasme. 990 RIBAUT RD, STE 102 29902 #820-01-1985 L1996 **CD** *020 †20

COURT, Angela Minnick. 1 PINCKNEY BLVD 29902 #038-40-1999 L2001 **P** *020 †75

CREDLE, Joseph Bernard. 22 BURCKMYER DR 29907 #036-01-1966 L1975 **OBG** *020 †30

DAHL, Georg Jonathan. ■ 29907 #051-07-2003 L2003 **PD** *100 †55

DANIEL, John Wm. 955 RIBAUT RD 29902 #017-20-1992 L1993 **AN** *020 †05

DAVIS, Bradley Hall. ■ 29902 #035-01-2004 L2004 *100

DAVIS-TOLBERT, Andra R. 13 MARSHELLEN DR 29902 #024-05-1997 L2001 **OBG** *020 †30

DEAN, Mark Thos. 1076 RIBAUT RD, STE 101 29902 #048-12-1989 L1995 **OSM ORS** *020 †40

DEAN, Warwick R. 46 HONEYSUCKLE LN, LADYS ISLAND 29907 #917-19-1958 L1974 **P OS** *071

DICKERSON, James Wiley. 1005 RIBAUT RD, STE 41 29902 #045-01-1989 L2001 **P** *020 †75

DICKINSON, M Elizabeth. 990 RIBAUT RD 29902 #045-01-1985 L1986 **FM** *075 †18

DICKINSON, Thomas Wheeler. 990 RIBAUT RD 29902 #045-01-1985 L1986 **FM** *020 †18

DICKMAN, Jean Francetta. ■ 29902 #041-07-1954 L1979 **GS OBG** *062 †85

DIPPEL, Roderick T. 300 MIDTOWN DR 29906 #048-02-1994 L1995 **FM** *020 †18

DOWNS, Thomas James. ■ 29907 #065-06-1975 L1976 **FM** *020

DUFF, Thomas Bailey. 955 RIBAUT RD, ATTN: EMERGENCY DEPT. 29902 #055-75-2002, ▲ L2007 **EM** *020 †18

ELLENBERGER, Kurt Richard. 964 RIBAUT RD, STE 1 29902 #038-41-1996 L1997 **PD** *020 †55

ELLENBERGER, Shayla B. 964 RIBAUT RD, STE 1 29902 #012-01-1995 L1996 **PHO** *020 †55 ‡

ELLER, Karen Michelle. 41A MARSHELLEN DR 29902 #036-01-1994 L2000 **AN PMM** *020 †05

ELMORE, James Liddell, Jr. 955 RIBAUT RD 29902 #047-06-1961 L1994 **P** *071 †75 ‡

ESCALANTE, Jose Antonio. ■ 29902 #649-01-1967 L1973 **AN** *071 †05

FLOYD, John Craig. 300 MIDTOWN DR 29906 #045-01-1995 L1996 **FM** *020 †18

FLOYD, Joseph Harry, Jr. 964 RIBAUT RD 29902 #045-01-1979 L1985 **PD** *020 †55

FRIEDMAN, Daniel. ■ 29907 #039-01-1947 L1998 **FM** *071 †18

GAY, Mary St John. 2719 BOUNDARY ST 29906 #021-05-1978 L1979 **P EM** *020

GEORGE, James Joseph, II. ■ 29907 #023-12-1996 L1998 **FM** *100 †18

GLASS, Jason Lee. 1 PINCKNEY BLVD, ATTN: CREDENTIAL OFFICE, N 29902 #041-14-2001 L2002 **FM** *020

GODEJOHN, Angela Lynn. PO BOX 6216A, NAVAL HOSP, 1 PINCKNEY BLV 29902 #023-12-2000 L2001 **FM** *020 †18

GORDIN, Stephen Jacob. 69 BELLEVIEW BLF 29902 #045-01-1987 L1993 **RNR DR** *020 †80

GRAY, John Wm, III. PO BOX 4070 29903 #045-01-1972 L1973 **FM** *071 †18

GRIBB, Joseph Chester. ■ 29907 #041-13-1938 L1939 **GP** *071

GRIM, Pamela Sue. 7 GOVERNORS TRCE 29907 #054-04-1984 L2004 **EM** *030 †16

GROVER, Warren Deacon. 989 RIBAUT RD, STE 310 29902 #041-13-1955 L2001 **PD N** *040 †75,55

HAMMOCK, David A, Jr. 73 SAMS POINT RD, BOX 2104 29907 #010-03-1961 L1976 **OBG** *020 †30

HEASTER, James Matthew. ■ 29902 #055-01-1964 **PD** *020

HILFER, Richard J. ■ 29907 #028-34-1946 L1946 **IM** *071

HODGES, James C, Jr. ■ 29902 #004-01-1944 L1945 **OBG OS** *071 †30

HOHENWARTER, Susan M. 10 RUSH ST 29907 #021-01-1981 L1982 **AN** *020 †05

HORTON, Samuel H, Jr. ■ 29907 #047-06-1941 L1968 **D PHP** *071 †15

HUCKS, Andrea Dell. 989 RIBAUT RD STE 260 29902 #045-01-1995 L1996 **IM** *020 †20

INGEGNO, Joel Michael. 989 RIBAUT RD, STE 300 29902 #035-08-1962 L1991 **GE IM** *020 †20

JANSEN, Christian W. 1 PINCKNEY BLVD, ATTN: CREDENTIAL OFFICE 29902 #065-09-1979 L1985 **EM** *020

JENKINS, Arthur Simons. 300 MIDTOWN DR 29906 #045-01-1957 L1957 **GP EM** *020 †18

JONES, Howell Kevin. 1251 RIBAUT RD 29902 #045-01-1984 L1989 **ORS** *020 †40

KAUFMAN, Lester. ■ 29907 #005-16-1962 L1975 **FM** *071 †18

KELLY, Ken Farrel. ■ 29902 #004-01-1991 L1995 **IM** *020

KESSEL, Steven Royal. 989 RIBAUT RD, STE 260 29902 #055-01-1976 L2000 **IM** *020 †20

KRUEGER, Gordon Earl. 1055 RIBAUT RD, STE 30 29902 #017-20-1973 L1974 **GS** *020 †85

LAW, Tameeka Latrease. ■ 29902 #012-22-2002 L2008 **OBG** *020

LYNN, William Louis, III. 219 SCOTT ST, PMB 284 29902 #023-01-1970 L1980 **GYN** *020 †30

MANAKER, Lawrence Wade. 1 PINCKNEY BLVD, BEAUFORT NAVAL HOSP-E.R. 29902 #032-01-1990 L1996 **EM** *020 †16

MANOS, Peter Nicholas. 1 PINCKNEY BLVD, NAVAL HOSPITAL BEAUFORT 29902 #045-01-1986 L1992 **PUD CCM** *020 †20

MARTIN, William Dennis. 964 RIBAUT RD 29902 #045-01-1997 L1998 **PD** *020 †55

MASON, Julian Lorin, III. 10 MARSHELLEN DR, # A 29902 #045-01-1995 L1998 **FM PTH** *020 †18

MAVRIDIS, Aristides N. RIBAUT RD 29902 #330-03-1959 L1970 **IM PUD** *020 †20

MAZZEO, Paul. 989 RIBAUT RD STE 310 29902 #010-02-1991 L1995 **N** *020 †75

MC CRAY, David Steele. 1050 RIBAUT RD, COASTAL EMPIRE MENTAL HEAL 29902 #004-01-1966 L1994 **CHP P** *020 †75

MC DEVITT, Neil Shaw. 1055 RIBAUT RD STE 30, 1055 RIBAUT RD SUITE 30 29902 #033-06-1997 L2002 **GS** *020 †85

MC NEIL, Edward James. 1055 RIBAUT RD, STE 10 29902 #045-01-1980 L1995 **IM** *071 †20

MIKELL, Oswald Lightsey. 242 LADYS ISLAND DR 29907 #012-01-1976 L1982 **D CS** *020 †15

MOORE, Carol Elizabeth. 990 RIBAUT RD, STE 102 29902 #045-01-1989 L1997 **OBG** *020 †30

MOORE, Ralph Erskine, III. 990 RIBAUT RD, STE 102 29902 #045-01-1989 L1996 **ORS** *020 †40

MULLINS, W Rodney. ■ 29902 #045-01-1958 L1958 **GP** *071

NEWBERRY, William Marcus. 300 MIDTOWN DR 29906 #045-01-1992 L1993 **HO** *020 †20

NGUYEN, William Buske. 1 PINCKNEY BLVD, ATTN: CREDENTIAL OFFICE, N 29902 #048-02-2002 L2004 **GS** *100

NIEMEYER, Mary Helen. ■ 29902 #010-02-1979 L1980 **FM** *020 †18

NOBLE, Gary Winston. 1 PINCKNEY BLVD, ATTN:CREDENTIAL OFFICE 29902 #023-12-1990 L2004 **P** *020 †75

OGUNTOYINBO, Afolabi. 17 SPRING KNOB CIR 29907 #690-02-1970 L1976 **PD OS** *020 †55,16

PEARCE, Holton T, Jr. 1055 RIBAUT RD, STE 30 29902 #045-01-1974 L1976 **GS** *020 †85

PEARSON, Hugh Oliver, Jr. 300 MIDTOWN DR 29906 #036-07-1956 L1959 **FM AN** *071 †18

PELLER, Kelly Antoinette. ■ 29902 #055-02-2005 L2006 *020

PENMAN, Robert Wm. ■ 29902 #919-03-1954 L1974 **PUD** *071

POPE, Gina Yolette. 27 KEMMERLIN LN, PRIMECARE HEALTH CENTER PA 29907 #023-12-1992 L2003 **EM** *020 †16

POWELL, Alton Linwood. ■ 29907 #051-04-1954 L1981 **GP GYN** *071 †30

QUATTLEBAUM, James Tindal. ■ 29901 #045-01-1956 L1956 **P** *071 †75

RADFORD, Ann Elizabeth. 2709 JONES AVE 29902 #041-78-2001, ▲ L2005 **P** *020 †75

RAIMOND, Danielle Marie. ■ 29907 #041-15-2003 L2004 *100 †20

REAMY, Charles Judson. 1050 RIBAUT RD, COASTAL EMPIRE MHC 29902 #055-01-1993 L1994 **P** *020 †75

REHMAN, Saeed Ur. 955 RIBAUT RD, DEPT EMERGENCY MEDICINE 29902 #308-11-1986 L1996 **FM EM** *020 †18

RHODES, David Vincent. 300 MIDTOWN DR 29906 #045-01-1993 L1994 **FM** *020 †18

RILEY, Elizabeth S. 650 DISTANT ISLAND DR 29907 #045-01-1967 L1967 **AN GP** *020

RIPLEY, Daniel C. 10A MARSHELLEN DR 29902 #045-01-1995 L1996 **FM** *020 †18

ROBINSON, Gary Lewis. ■ 29902 #028-03-1961 L2001 **OBG LM** *071 †30

ROBINSON, William Thos. 1 PINCKNEY BLVD, ATTN: CREDENTIAL OFFICE 29902 #027-01-1963 L1978 **GS** *020

ROCERETO, Paul Vincent. 1 PINCKNEY BLVD, ATTN MEDICAL STAFF SERVICE 29902 #019-02-1973 L1974 **AM** *020

ROYAL, Randall Mac. 1264 RIBAUT RD, STE 200 29902 #654-01-2002 L2006 **OBG** *020

RUSHTON, Francis E, Jr. 964 RIBAUT RD 29902 #011-02-1976 L1982 **PD GP** *020 †55

RYAN, Robert Jerome. ■ 29902 #035-08-1938 L1938 **EM CD** *071 †85

SALYER, Thomas Darrell. ■ 29902 #051-04-1978 L1979 **GYN OBS** *075 †30

SALZER, Ralph Francis, Jr. 1076 RIBAUT RD STE 101 29902 #021-01-1981 L1986 **ORS** *020 †40

SEWARDS, Joseph Milo. 1 PINCKNEY BLVD, ORTHO DEPT-NAVAL HOSP 29902 #041-02-2000 L2005 **ORS** *020 †40 ‡

SHENOY, Katapadi Surendra. 990 RIBAUT RD, STE 110 29902 #495-09-1972 L1983 **NEP IM** *020 †20

SHERBERT, Thurman Ray. ■ 29902 #045-01-1967 L1967 **DR** *072 †80

SHIPPEY, Stuart Hunter. 1 PINCKNEY BLVD, ATTN: CREDENTIAL OFFICE 29902 #023-12-1999 L2000 **OBG** *020

SIEGEL, Mark Shafer. 989 RIBAUT RD STE 200, SEA ISLAND OPHTHALMOLOGY, 29902 #001-02-1985 L1986 **EM** *020 †16

SIMMONS, George Heath. 955 RIBAUT RD, LOWCOUNTRY ANESTHESIA 29902 #045-01-2003 L2003 **AN** *020

SISCO, Stephen Ray. 1 PINCKNEY BLVD, NAVAL HOSPITAL BEAUFORT 29902 #012-01-1988 L1998 **GS** *020 †85

SPEARMAN, Wm Lawrence. 955 RIBAUT RD, ANESTHESIA / BEAUFORT MEMO 29902 #045-01-1981 L1987 **AN OS** *020 †05

STEINERT, Harriett R. 1 PINCKNEY BLVD BOX 6216A, NAVAL HOSPITAL BEAUFORT 29902 #045-01-1975 L1977 **GS** *020 †85

STROHMEYER, Scott Everett. 1076 RIBAUT RD, STE 101 29902 #001-06-1992 L2000 **ORS OSS** *020 †40

SUPAN, Samai. ■ 29902 #891-01-1967 L1983 **FM GP** *020 †18

THOMPSON, Gary Allen. 955 RIBAUT RD, DEPT OF ANESTHESIA 29902 #055-01-1989 L1997 **AN PME** *020 †05

TOBER, James Chadwick. 1 PINCKNEY BLVD, NAVAL HOSPITAL BEAUFORT 29902 #016-11-1985 L2004 **VS GS** *040 †85

TOLBERT, Claude Henry, Jr. 13B MARSHELLEN DR 29902 #047-07-1996 L2000 **OBG** *020 †30

TRASK, Samuel Clark. 974 RIBAUT RD 29902 #045-01-1999 L2004 **FM** *020 †18

TREADWAY, Judith. 1050 RIBAUT RD, COASTAL EMPIRE MENTAL HLTH 29902 #917-14-1983 L1993 **P** *020 †75

TWYMAN, Kimberly Ann. ■ 29902 #028-34-2002 L2005 **DBP** *012 †55

TWYMAN, Michael Allen. 1 PINCKNEY BLVD 29902 #028-34-2002 L2005 **IM** *020 †20

VINOSKI, Bernard B, Sr. ■ 29907 #041-12-1953 L1988 **FM AM** *071 †18

VINOSKI, Bernard Benedict. 989 RIBAUT RD STE 300 29902 #654-01-1985 L1991 **GE IM** *020 †20

WASHINGTON, Elijah. ■ 29901 #047-07-1968 L1970 **OBG** *071 †30

WATKINS, David Brenig. ■ 29902 #539-06-1961 L1977 **AN** *020

WERNER, Glenn Leroy. 1264 RIBAUT RD, STE 200 29902 #036-05-1982 L1992 **OBG** *020 †30

ZERDEN, Solomon Glenn. 300 MIDTOWN DR, ATTN: MISSY DAWSON 29906 #036-01-1976 L1992 **DR** *020 †80

BELTON — ANDERSON

HALL, Lee Ellis. 726 ANDERSON ST, PRIMARY CARE ASSOCIATES 29627 #045-01-1998 L1999 **FM** *020 †18

HELLER, Kenneth Bryan. 726 ANDERSON ST 29627 #045-01-1978 L1979 **MDM FPG** *020 ‡

MARTIN, Joe Alan. 726 ANDERSON ST, PRIMARY CARE ASSOCIATES 29627 #045-01-1988 L1989 **FM** *020

MOORE, Justin Mark. ■ 29627 #045-04-2008 *012

NEILSEN, Marie Elizabeth. ■ 29627 #045-04-2008 *012

BENNETTSVILLE — MARLBORO

ACAYLAR, Francis V. 1076 MARLBORO WAY, STE 3 29512 #748-01-1993 L1999 **PD** *020 †55

ANDERS, Scott Gerald. 999 CHERAW ST 29512 #056-06-1997 L2002 **FM** *020 †18

CAIN, Rufus Haynes, III. 999 CHERAW ST, CARESOUTH CAROLINA BENNETT 29512 #045-01-1982 L1983 **FM** *020 †18

CANDELA, Zenaida. 210 W MAIN ST, BENNETTSVILLE PEDIATRIC CL 29512 #748-01-1989 L2002 **NPM** *020 †55

CHEN, Chi Dai. 1040 MARLBORO WAY STE 7 29512 #048-04-1996 L2001 **GS** *020 †85

COOPER, Sandy Tyrone. 1138 CHERAW ST, MARLBORO PARK HOSPITAL 29512 #012-01-1990 L1991 **EM** *020 †18

CRITTENDON, Cindy. 1076 MARLBORO WAY, STE 1 29512 #028-78-1989, ▲ L1994 **OBG** *020

DEMBOSKY, Dell Andrew. 812 FAYETTEVILLE AVE 29512 #308-11-1983 L1990 **PTH** *020 †50

GLASSMAN, Steven Barry. 1138 CHERAW ST 29512 #045-01-1990 L1996 **DR** *020 †80,28

JENNINGS, Douglas, Jr. 999 CHERAW ST 29512 #045-01-1945 L1945 **GP** *071

■ = Address Information Privacy Protected

MANN, Lawrence Casey, III. 1040 MARLBORO WAY, STE 1 29512 #047-07-1997 L2006 **FM** *020 †18

MAY, John. 1138 CHERAW ST 29512 #045-01-1947 L1947 **FM** *071 †18

MC INNIS, David Murray. 304 MARKET ST 29512 #045-01-1969 L1969 **FM** *020 †18

NESTOR, Jonathan. 301 E MAIN ST 29512 #025-07-1983 L1988 **NEP IM** *020 †20

NOBLES, John Ray, Jr. PO BOX 973, 1007 CHERAW ST 29512 #045-01-1981 L1982 **OBG** *020 †30

RUSH, Cyril B. 1138 CHERAW ST 29512 #045-01-1953 L1953 **ORS** *071 †40

SACHDEV, Simi. 1138 CHERAW ST 29512 #496-07-1996 L2003 **CHP** *020 †75

SAJJAMANOCHAI, Sura. 1104 FRANK W EVANS WAY, BENNETTSVILLE DIALYSIS CTR 29512 #891-01-1971 L1980 **NEP IM** *020 †20

SAMARAKOON, Priyan Chanda. 1040 MARLBORO WAY, STE 1 29512 #913-07-1991 L2005 **IM PCC** *020 †20

SNYDER, Herbert Danl. 1040 MARLBORO WAY STE 7 29512 #041-02-1979 L2005 **GS TRS** *085

TAPLITS, Michael Steven. EMERGENCY DEPARTMENT, MARLBORO PARK HOSPITAL 29512 #038-41-1979 L1993 **EM PD** *055

UPSHAW, Thomas Arthur. PO BOX 738, 1138 CHERAW ST 29512 #012-05-1994 L1995 **P** *020 †75

WHITNER, Wm Church, Jr. 102 LINDSAY AVE 29512 #045-01-1969 **FM OS** *020 †18

WILSON, Ben William, Jr. 1040 MARLBORO WAY, STE 1 29512 #045-01-2001 L2002 **FM** *020 †18

BISHOPVILLE — LEE

DANIEL, Roosevelt Gregory. 545 SUMTER HWY 29010 #001-02-2001 L2005 **MPD** *020

HUNT, Leon Ervin. 106 HOSPITAL SQ 29010 #045-01-1960 L1960 **GP** *020

MOZINGO, James Pierce, IV. 545 SUMTER HWY 29010 #045-01-1965 L1965 **IM** *020

PATE, John Bush, Jr. PO BOX 305 29010 #045-01-1980 L1981 **FM** *020 †18 ‡

BLACKSBURG — CHEROKEE

CARLING, Daren Edward. 301 W PINE ST, CAROLINA PEDIATRICS ASSOCI 29702 #010-01-1997 L2002 **PD** *020 †55

DU BOSE, Ladson Lawrence. ■ 29702 #045-01-1955 L1956 **GP** *071

GAMMON, David Brian. 303 W PINE ST 29702 #050-02-1979 L1996 **IM GP** *020 †20

SPILLER, Paul Craig. 303 W PINE ST, STE B 29702 #012-22-1992 L2000 **FM** *020 †18

BLACKSTOCK — CHESTER

MORGAN, Donald Wm. 631 CROFTON RD 29014 #035-06-1960 L1980 **P PFP** *020 †75

BLACKVILLE — BARNWELL

CLARK, William Benj. 22 GARDNER RD 29817 #045-01-1972 L1977 **EM FM** *020

MC KISSICK, Janet Marie. 19430 SOLOMON BLATT AVE N 29817 #051-01-1987 L1988 **FM** *020 †18

BLUFFTON — BEAUFORT

ALEXANDER, Julian Henry. ■ 29910 #917-23-1983 L1997 **PTH** *020 †50

AMLICKE, James Allen. 19 WALDEN LN, RESIDENCE 29909 #035-20-1959 L1961 **ORS** *020 †40

ANFINSON, Scott Michael. 14 WESTBURY PARK WAY # 102 29910 #047-06-1995 L2000 **OPH** *020 †35

ASHWORTH, Halbert Eugene. ■ 29910 #055-01-1962 L1975 **TS** *071 †85,90

BABCOCK, Ralph Alexander. ■ 29910 #025-07-1973 L1974 **PUD IM** *071 †20

BALSHEM, Lyubov. ■ 29909 #913-89-1970 L1982 **PD** *020 †55

BONDO, Shana Catoe. ■ 29910 #045-01-2004 L2007 **PD** *020 †55

BORELLI, Albert Jos, Jr. 18 CLARK SUMMIT DR, MRI AT BELFAIR 29910 #041-09-1987 L1999 **DR** *020 †80

BURHANS, Gregory Louis. ■ 29909 #025-01-1958 L1959 **PTH NM** *071 †50

BURLING, John Nichols. 7 MALLETT WAY, MHUP - BLUFFTON 29910 #033-06-1977 L2007 **OM IM** *020 †20,70,16

CAFFREY, P Raphael. ■ 29909 #028-34-1957 L1957 **PTH** *020 †50

CAVANO, Francis Jos. ■ 29909 #030-06-1967 L1971 **P** *071

CONDIE, Scott Douglas. PO BOX 3066, 16 MINUTEMAN DR 29910 #016-11-1975 L1990 **FM** *020 †18

CONTE, Harry Chas. ■ 29909 #035-09-1954 L1959 **PD** *020 †55

CRAMER, Susan. 38 SHERIDAN PARK CIR STE F 29910 #025-01-1992 L1996 **PM PMM** *020 †60

CROLL, Stephanie Danielle. 80 BAYLOR DR, OPHTHALMOLOGY ASSOCIATES 29910 #036-05-1979 L1987 **OPH** *020 †35

CROSE, Hunter Croxton. 7 MALLETT WAY, MEMORIAL HEALTH BLUFFTON 29910 #045-01-2001 L2004 **FM** *020 †18

CSAKANY, Jo Ann Lynn. 11 ARLEY WAY, STE 102 29910 #001-06-1992 L2001 **OBG** *020 †30

DAVIES, Barbara Lea. 14 OAK FOREST RD, SAVANNAH PLASTIC SURG 29910 #041-02-1983 L1998 **PS GS** *020 †65

DEWBERRY, James Wm. 10 OAK FOREST RD, STE C 29910 #012-01-1972 L1973 **ORS** *020 †40

DONOVAN, Robert James. ■ 29909 #041-12-1960 L1973 **IM AM** *071

ELLIOTT, Terry Lynn. ■ 29910 #055-01-1977 L1978 **FM FPG** *040 †18

FONTANA, John J, Jr. 11 ARLEY WAY, STE 102 29910 #010-02-1967 L1975 **OBG** *020 †30

FORD, Richard Chadwick. 25 CLARK SUMMIT DR, STE F201 29910 #045-01-2002 L2005 **PFP** *020 †75

FROST, James Keane. 29 PLANTATION PARK DR, STE 602 29910 #036-01-1996 L2004 **FM** *020 †18

GINSBURG, Eugene G. ■ 29909 #020-02-1969 L1970 **OBG OS** *071 †30

GIRGIS, Ebeid Shoukry. ■ 29909 #330-04-1956 L1972 **AN** *071

GOODRICH, Jack Knight. ■ 29909 #047-06-1953 L1953 **NM R** *071 †80,28

GOULAS, Mark Thomas. 29 PLANTATION PARK DR, STE 202 29910 #025-07-2000 L2004 **OPH** *020 †35

GRECO, Richard Jude. 29 PLANTATION PARK DR, STE 301 29910 #041-02-1983 L1994 **PS HS** *020 †85,65

HAMMER, Carl. ■ 29909 #869-05-1963 L1965 **P CHP** *020

HEIGES, Bradley Alan. 10 OAK FOREST RD, STE C 29910 #041-13-1995 L2002 **OSS** *020 †40

HOLBROOK, Constance A. ■ 29909 #023-01-1969 L1970 **PTH GP** *071 †50

HOPE, Chas Anderson, II. 10 OAK FOREST RD, STE C 29910 #051-01-1991 L2004 **ORS** *020 †40

JAAKKOLA, Juha Ilmari. 10 OAK FOREST RD, STE C 29910 #012-01-1995 L2002 **ORS** *020 †40

JOHNSON, William Abner, III. ■ 29909 #021-05-1961 L1965 **GYN** *071 †30

KAGAN, Harold Nathan. ■ 29909 #010-01-1943 L1946 **U** *071 †95

KAHN, Bernard. ■ 29909 #005-02-1942 L1942 **ORS** *072 †40

KAMALESON, Sunderraj Mark. 10 OAK FOREST RD, STE C 29910 #047-07-1989 L2004 **HS ORS** *020 †40

KNIGHT, Thomas Edward, Jr. 18 CLARK SUMMIT DR, MRI AT BELFAIR 29910 #038-43-1997 L2004 **DR** *020 †80

KROPP, William Edward. 10 OAK FOREST RD, STE C 29910 #041-02-1987 L1990 **HS** *020 †40

LAGOC-DINGUS, Randy. ■ 29910 #748-14-1988 L2004 **IM** *020 †20

LEONARD, Robert Parton. ■ 29910 #012-05-1964 L1964 **PS HS** *071 †85,65

LOWRY, Lisa Kondrad. 10 OAK FOREST RD, STE C 29910 #036-07-1995 L2004 **FM** *020 †18

LUSIK, Robert Charles. 64 BLUFFTON RD 29910 #035-06-1986 L2002 **FM** *020 †18

MAYO, Richard A. ■ 29909 #024-05-1970 L1971 **GS** *030 †85

MC CARTNEY, Donald K. 10 OAK FOREST RD, STE C 29910 #048-13-1986 L1993 **ORS** *020 †40

MEYER, Hobart. ■ 29909 #021-01-1956 L1956 **OBG** *071 †30

MIKKELSON, Michael Kent. 167 BLUFFTON RD STE C, PO 709 29910 #056-05-1969 L1991 **FM OS** *020 †18

NICHOLSON, Christopher W. 10 OAK FOREST RD, STE C 29910 #038-40-1999 L2007 **ORS** *100

NIVENS, Charles Joseph. 3 PLANTATION PARK DR 29910 #012-01-1994 L1996 **PM OS** *020 †60

NORTON, Lynn E. 11 ARLEY WAY, STE 102 29910 #043-01-1990 L2002 **OBG** *020 †30

ORR, Earl Lawton. ■ 29910 #047-07-1960 L1988 **OBG** *071 †30

PALMER, David Nunez. 10 OAK FOREST RD, STE C 29910 #011-03-1992 L1998 **ORS OSM** *020 †40

PATEL, Kamal Jayantilal. 1 BURNT CHURCH RD 29910 #654-01-2002 L2006 **FM** *020 †18

PECK, Charles A. ■ 29909 #035-19-1978 L1980 **IM RHU** *062 †20

PETERSON, Emil Warn. ■ 29909 #005-12-1958 L1960 **CLP** *071 †50

PETERSON, Heather Anne. 35 SHERBROOK AVE 29910 #026-04-2000 L2008 **PD** *074 †55

PIROS, Judith M. 80 BAYLOR DR, OPHTHALMOLOGY ASSOCIATES 29910 #051-04-1987 L1996 **OPH** *020 †35

RECK, Robert Henry. ■ 29910 #033-05-1970 L1971 **PS TRS** *071 †65

REEVES, Joseph Lane, III. 80 BAYLOR DR, OPHTHALMOLOGY ASSOCIATES 29910 #012-01-1990 L2000 **OPH** *020 †35

REMIGIO, David Jose. 29 PLANTATION PARK DR, STE 202 29910 #010-02-1991 L2001 **OPH FPS** *020 †35

RHANGOS, William Chas. 10 OAK FOREST RD, STE C 29910 #035-01-1957 L1964 **ORS** *072 †40

RHODES, Louis Danl. 12 WATERS AVE 29909 #045-01-1974 L1975 **AN** *020 †05

ROBBINS, Robert S. ■ 29909 #041-12-1952 L1953 **AN** *071 †05

RODRIGUEZ, Eduardo I. ■ 29909 #726-01-1963 L1971 **PM** *020 †60

ROJAS, Rodrigo Falla. 1314 FORDING ISLAND RD 29910 #264-01-1971 L2004 **AN PD** *020 †55

ROSS, Priscilla Jo. 10 OAK FOREST RD, STE C 29910 #016-45-2002 L2006 **APM** *030

RUF, Lawrence Edward. 14 OAK FOREST RD, SAVANNAH PLASTIC SURG 29910 #020-12-1969 L1977 **PS HS** *020 †65 ‡

SHACHAT, David Allen. ■ 29909 #001-02-1963 L1969 **D** *071 †15

SHEILS, Andrew Thos, Jr. 10 OAK FOREST RD, STE C 29910 #012-01-1969 L1970 **ORS** *020 †40

SHEPARD, James Renwick. ■ 29909 #035-19-1960 L1962 **OTO** *071

STOLLER, Leon Justus. ■ 29910 #017-20-1964 L2003 **OBG** *020 †30

SUM, Paul Wm. ■ 29909 #242-09-1949 L1958 **R GP** *071 †80

SUTKER, Benjamin David. 10 OAK FOREST RD, STE C 29910 #036-01-1991 L2008 **HS** *020 †40

TAYLOR, Keith Alexander. ■ 29910 #654-01-1999 L2007 **MPD** *100 †20

THOMPSON, Patricia Anne. 11 ARLEY WAY, STE 102 29910 #055-01-1992 L1996 **OBG** *020 †30

THOMPSON, Richard M. ■ 29910 #055-01-1963 L1964 **DR AM** *071 †80

THORPE, William Parr. 354 BAMBERG DR 29910 #024-01-1973 L1993 **ORS** *071 †40

TORPEY, David Jos, Jr. ■ 29909 #024-01-1960 L1961 **AN** *071 †05

VENDEL, Zoltan R. 23 MUIRFIELD DR 29909 #473-01-1967 L1976 **IM P** *020

VORMOHR, David Wm. 10 OAK FOREST RD, STE C 29910 #017-20-1991 L1996 **FM FSM** *020 †18

WARNER, Geo Watkins, Jr. 29 PLANTATION PARK DR, STE 204 29910 #004-01-1988 L1989 **N** *020 †75

WENIGER, Frederick George. 29 PLANTATION PARK DR, STE 201 29910 #041-12-1999 L2005 **PS** *020 †65

WHELAN, Edward James, III. 10 OAK FOREST RD, STE C 29910 #012-01-1980 L1985 **ORS** *020 †40

WILKES, Leslie La Mar, Jr. 10 OAK FOREST RD, STE C 29910 #012-01-1965 L1965 **ORS** *071 †40

WILSON, James Wm, Jr. 10 OAK FOREST RD, STE C 29910 #036-01-1992 L1998 **OSM** *020 †40

WINKLER, Norman Walter. ■ 29909 #016-02-1965 L1969 **D IM** *071 †15

WOO, Kent Eugene. 10 OAK FOREST RD, STE C 29910 #012-01-1993 L2001 **ORS** *020 †40

ZHU, Weijian. ■ 29910 #243-43-1985 L2006 **PCP** *020 †50

BLYTHEWOOD — RICHLAND

CLARKE, Khalilah Qadi. ■ 29016 #045-01-2008 *012

DAVIS, Jerome Marquis. 13 VERANDA LN 29016 #045-04-1982 L1983 **AN IM** *020 †20,05

FRANCO, Mark. ■ 29016 #041-09-1988 L2007 **IM** *020 †20

HEINZMAN, Diana Michelle. ■ 29016 #055-01-1996 L1999 **PD** *020 †55

HERO, Numa Chas, III. ■ 29016 #021-05-1967 L1980 **P** *020 †75

KIM, Kyung Ja. ■ 29016 #583-03-1958 L1978 **PD** *071

LOPEZ, Carl Herman. 738 UNIVERSITY VILLAGE DR, BLYTHEWOOD URGENT CARE 29016 #033-06-1981 L1984 **FM GPM** *020 †70

LOWMAN, Isom. 101 OAK SPRINGS RD 29016 #047-07-1972 L1980 **NM IM** *020 †20,28

MANCINI, Joseph Louis. ■ 29016 #024-05-1959 L1970 **IM PUD** *075 †20

MATZNER, Jennifer Babette. 11 ROSE HAVEN CT 29016 #035-75-1997, ▲ L2002 **EM** *020

PASZKIEWICZ, Ewa Margaret. ■ 29016 #048-02-1992 L2000 **OTO** *020 †45

SHIN, In Ai Lee. ■ 29016 #583-01-1966 L1977 **CHP PD** *020 †16

TAILLON, Michael Paul. ■ 29016 #045-04-1986 L1987 **FM** *020 †18

BOILING SPRINGS – SPARTANBURG

BAUGH, Jennifer Grondin. 3941 HIGHWAY 9 29316 #045-01-1997 L1998 **FM** *020 †18
BINGHAM, Marc David. 3941 HIGHWAY 9 29316 #021-05-2001 L2003 **FM** *020 †18 ‡
DURHAM, Melinda Sue. 2212 OLD FURNACE RD 29316 #048-04-1991 L1992 **FM** *020 †18
GIBSON, Gregory Leo. 3941 HIGHWAY 9, FAMILY PHYSICIANS OF BOILI 29316 #836-01-1992 L2000 **FM** *020 †18
NORRIS, Kevin Loren. ■ 29316 #012-01-2008 *012

BONNEAU – BERKELEY

RHODES, Charles Edward. 115 W CHURCH ST, LAKESHORE FAMILY MEDICINE 29431 #045-01-1976 L1977 **FM** *020 †18
RODGERS, David Paul. 115 W CHURCH ST 29431 #045-01-1983 L1984 **FM** *020 †18

BOWMAN – ORANGEBURG

MYERS, Denny Richard. ■ 29018 #045-01-2008 *012
PRICE, Anna Brunson. PO BOX 306, 106 CAUSEWAY DR 29018 #045-01-1979 L1989 **GP** *020

BRANCHVILLE – ORANGEBURG

OQUINN, William Esdorn, Jr. ■ 29432 #045-01-1999 L1999 **FM** *020 †18

CALHOUN FALLS – ABBEVILLE

JORDAN, Henry Speir. 535 JACKSON ST 29628 #012-05-1971 L1973 **GS** *020 †85

CAMDEN – KERSHAW

AMEEN, Saied. ■ 29020 #045-01-1957 L1957 **R** *071 †80
BARTSCHAT, Dieter Karl. RR 2 BOX 124 29020 #045-01-1982 *100
BLOCH, Silvia Margit Anna. 2611 LIBERTY HILL RD, KERSHAW COUNTY MENTAL HEAL 29020 #409-32-1981 L1986 **P PYG** *020 †75
BULTMAN, Charles Keene. 2411 BROAD ST 29020 #047-07-1960 L1979 **ORS** *075
CARLTON, Marguerite E. 1346 HAILE ST, PEDIATRIC ASSOCIATES P.A. 29020 #045-01-1986 L1987 **PD** *020 †55
CASEBOLT, Mark Allen. 1102 ROBERTS ST 29020 #005-15-1989 L2005 **GS** *020 †85
CHRISTENBERRY, David Paul. 1001 FAIRLAWN DR, SURGERY LLC 29020 #001-06-1985 L1992 **VS** *020 †18
COPLEY, Donald Joe. 1315 ROBERTS ST, CAMDEN RADIOLOGY ASSOCIATE 29020 #045-01-1980 L1985 **DR** *020 †80
CUNNINGHAM, Kievers L. 1017 FAIR ST, CAMDEN FAMILY CARE 29020 #045-01-2003 L2004 **FM** *020 †18
DAVIS, Robert Edward. ■ 29020 #045-01-1958 L1958 **GS** *071 †85
DIERINGER, Cindy Sue. 1315 ROBERTS ST, KERSHAW COUNTY EMER DEPT 29020 #036-01-1982 L1983 **EM IM** *020 ‡
DUNAWAY, Michael Trayser. 1102 ROBERTS ST 29020 #041-01-1981 L1986 **GS MDM** *020 †85
FAKOURY, Jack Thos. 1315 ROBERTS ST 29020 #045-01-1957 L1957 **R** *020 †80
GILL, Edward Alton. 1102 ROBERTS ST 29020 #012-01-1985 L1990 **GS** *020 †85
GODFREY, Terry Anthony. ■ 29020 #045-04-2001 L2002 **FM** *020 †18
HOLLAND, Alton Truesdale. 1111 MILL ST 29020 #045-01-1964 L1964 **GP** *020
JAMES, Elizabeth Harrah. 312 BLOOMSBURY CIR 29020 #045-04-2001 L2002 **PD** *020
JENKINS, Karin Miller. ■ 29020 #045-04-2004 L2004 **IM** *020 †20
JOSEPH, Thomas Nimmer. 1112 MILL ST, CAMDEN BONE AND JOINT 29020 #045-01-1997 L2003 **ORS OFA** *020 †40
KALUTZ, Theodore Eugene. 1346 HAILE ST 29020 #045-01-1976 L1977 **PD** *020 †55
KING, Leland Hoyt. 1800 ROBERTS ST, OB/GYN DIVISION 29020 #028-34-1989 L1999 **OBG** *020 †30
KUZBARY, Yasseen M. 1315 ROBERTS ST 29020 #165-03-1978 L1987 **DR NM** *020 †80,28
LAWS, Richard A. 1205 LYTTLETON ST 29020 #010-02-1992 L2006 **D** *020 †15
LEWIS, Lawson Wilford, Jr. 615 LAURENS ST 29020 #012-01-1970 L1974 **OPH** *020 †35
MACARUSO, Steven Bruce. 1315 ROBERTS ST, KCMC 29020 #041-14-1978 L1979 **FM EM** *020 †16,18
MARSHALL, Ted Hall, II. 1344 HAILE ST 29020 #045-01-1985 L1986 **IM** *020 †20
MASKELL, John Joseph, Jr. 1315 ROBERTS ST 29020 #045-04-1994 L1997 **FM** *020 †18
MC CORKLE, Francis N, Jr. 1113 MILL ST 29020 #045-01-1953 L1953 **IM CD** *020
MC LEOD, Linda Carol. 1106 FAIR ST 29020 #045-04-1987 L1989 **OBG** *020
MOORE, John Luther. 1800 ROBERTS ST 29020 #045-01-1973 L1974 **OBG** *020 †30
MORTHALA, Sudhakar Reddy. 2039 W DEKALB ST, STE 1 29020 #495-58-1996 L2005 **P PFP** *020 †75
MUNN, Susan Broome. 383 BLOOMSBURY CIR 29020 #045-04-2001 L2002 *020 †18
NORRIS, George Thomas, III. 1315 ROBERTS ST 29020 #045-01-1993 L1994 **EM** *020 †18
PARROTT, Lawrence Huitt. ■ 29020 #036-07-1960 L1973 **ATP CLP** *071 †50 ‡
PIASECKI, Andrew Wiktor. 1112 MILL ST, CAMDEN BONE AND JOINT LLC 29020 #041-13-1995 L2003 **ORS** *020 †40
POLEN, Samuel W, III. 1315 ROBERTS ST 29020 #010-02-1984 L1986 **EM** *020 †18
RILEY, Rebecca C. 1346 HAILE ST, PEDIATRIC ASSOCIATES OF KE 29020 #045-04-2002 L2003 **PD** *020
SCHOOLMEESTER, William L. 2043 W DEKALB ST # 3, STE C 29020 #010-02-1976 L1980 **CD IM** *020 †20
SHAW, F Grayson. ■ 29021 #045-01-1938 L1938 **GS GP** *071
SHAW, James Stuart. 1344 HAILE ST, CAMDEN PRIMARY 29020 #045-01-1970 L1971 **FM** *020 †18
STAHL, Edward Leonard, Jr. 1009A FAIRLAWN DR 29020 #016-43-1968 L1976 **U** *020 †95
THOMAS, Renee B. 1315 ROBERTS ST, DEPT OF PATHOLOGY 29020 #045-01-1990 L1993 **PTH** *020
WILLENS, Barney Avron. 135 COURT INN LN 29020 #011-02-1973 L1974 **DR** *020 †80
WILLIAMSON, Thomas Bright. 1303 MONUMENT SQ 29020 #045-01-1968 **GE IM** *020 †20
ZIMMERMAN, Greta C. 1205 LYTTLETON ST 29020 #028-79-1984, ▲ L1996 **D IM** *020 †20,15

CAMPOBELLO – SPARTANBURG

HUGILL, John Varty. ■ 29322 #187-03-1968 L1972 **PS HS** *020 †65
WALKER, Betsy Jones. ■ 29322 #045-01-1994 L1995 **FM OS** *020 †18
WEBB, Charles Mansfield. ■ 29322 #045-01-1958 **PTH CLP** *071 †50

CARLISLE – UNION

JETER, Allen P. ■ 29031 #045-01-1959 L1959 **FM OM** *072 †18

CAYCE – LEXINGTON

ARORA, Sri Nath. 1115 STATE ST 29033 #495-41-1962 L1976 **IM HEM** *020 †20
PERRY, Christopher David. ■ 29033 #045-04-2002 L2008 **PCC** *012 †20
WARD, Wm Franklin, Jr. 109 EVERGREEN LN 29033 #045-01-1961 L1961 **FM OM** *020 †18

CENTRAL – PICKENS

BROWN, Laura Tanke. ■ 29630 #036-05-2008 *012
DUSENBERRY, James F, Jr. ■ 29630 #045-01-1964 L1964 **DR R** *020
POWELL, Stephen Thos. ■ 29630 #045-01-1969 L1969 **AM FM** *071 †18
SWEATT, Lois Dell. ■ 29630 #045-04-1993 L1994 **FM** *020

CHAPIN – LEXINGTON

ABDULRAHMAN, Amjad. 317 SIENNA DR 29036 #875-02-1988 L2000 **IM** *020 †20 ‡
BENFIELD, Donald Gary. ■ 29036 #023-01-1965 L1965 **NPM PD** *020 †55
BONNETT, Arthur Luther, IV. 119 AMICKS FERRY RD 29036 #045-01-2002 L2003 **PD** *020 †55
BOWERS, Joseph Ford. 1612 CHAPIN RD 29036 #045-01-1980 L1983 **FM** *020 †18
BYRD, Anna Michelle. 557 COLUMBIA AVE, LEXINGTON MED CTR CHAPIN 29036 #036-08-1995 L1999 **IM** *100
CANNON, Edward Francis. 601 WILLOWOOD PKWY 29036 #010-02-1947 L1949 **IM PUD** *020 †20
CARNEY, Scott David. ■ 29036 #038-43-2007 L2007 **PD** *012
DEPRA, Rogelio D. ■ 29036 #748-01-1960 L1973 **GP EM** *071
DIXON, William Merritt. 2001 DUTCH FORK RD 29036 #051-01-1997 L2001 **FM OBS** *020 †18
EVANS, Joseph Ansel, Jr. 1612 CHAPIN RD 29036 #045-01-1979 L1980 **FM** *020 †18
GODINES, Ramiro. ■ 29036 #016-11-1990 L1992 **AN** *020 †05
HEICHBERGER, Lisa Elaine. 2001 DUTCH FORK RD 29036 #035-06-1998 L2002 **FM** *020 †18
ILSLEY, Jeffrey Eaton. 2168 AMICKS FERRY RD, MIDLANDS ED STAFFING 29036 #654-01-2000 L2003 **FM** *100 †18
JOLLEY, Robert B, Jr. 1009 MUDDY FORD RD, RB JOLLEY JR MD 29036 #045-01-1983 L1986 **FM** *020 †18
LAWHEAD, Michael Dorian. 557 COLUMBIA AVE, STE C 29036 #045-01-1983 L1984 **EM** *020 †16
LOVELACE, Oscar Fred, Jr. 2001 DUTCH FORK RD 29036 #045-01-1985 L1988 **FM** *020 †18
MOTYCKA, Thomas Jos. ■ 29036 #048-15-1991 L1992 **EM** *020 †16
PHILLIPS, James Paul. 1612 CHAPIN RD, CHAPIN FAMILY PRACTICE 29036 #045-04-1989 L1990 **FM** *020 †18
REED, Barry Alan. 372 SAINT THOMAS CHURCH RD 29036 #017-20-1974 L1975 **GP** *020
ROBERTS, Douglas Edward. 557 COLUMBIA AVE 29036 #012-01-1985 L1988 **GP** *020
THOMAS, Susan. 1612 CHAPIN RD 29036 #051-04-1980 L1984 **END** *020 †18
TUCKER, Evelyn Rebekah. 557 COLUMBIA AVE, STE B 29036 #045-04-1997 L1998 **OBG** *020 †30
VENEGAS, J Manuel. 1612 CHAPIN RD 29036 #001-06-1994 L1995 **FM** *020 †18
WEST, Glenn A. ■ 29036 #028-34-1947 L1947 **PTH** *071 †50

CHARLESTON – BERKELEY

COX, Steven Carol. ■ 29492 #036-05-1981 L1986 **EM GS** *020 †85
LAUGHLIN, Jennifer Lee. ■ 29492 #422-01-2007 L2007 **EM** *012
LUECKEN, Robert Charles. ■ 29492 #045-01-2000 L2000 **IM** *020 †20
MURPHY, Sean Brendan. ■ 29492 #016-43-2003 L2004 **NEP** *012

CHARLESTON – CHARLESTON

AARONSON, Ian Anthony. 96 JONATHAN LUCAS ST 29425 #917-03-1965 L1991 **UP** *040
ABBEYQUAYE, Kojo Pobee. 9298 MEDICAL PLAZA DR, RESIDENCY PROGRAM 29406 #020-12-2006 L2006 **FP** *012
ABBOUD, Miguel Raul. 171 ASHLEY AVE, MEDICAL UNIV OF SOUTH CARO 29425 #605-01-1981 L1989 **PD PHO** *020 †55
ABDEL-HAFEZ, Ghada Sami. 167 ASHLEY AVE 29425 #575-02-2001 L2008 *100
ABDELRAHMAN, Ibrahim A. 171 ASHLEY AVE, MED UNIV OF SOUTH CAROLINA 29425 #875-01-1992 L1999 **PHO** *020 †20,55
ABEL, Alan Nathan. 7741 DORCHESTER RD, STE C 29418 #045-01-1972 L1973 **GP** *020
ABEL, Anne Sutherland. ■ 29425 #017-20-1973 L1975 **PD** *020 †55
ABERNATHY, James Harry, III. 29403 #045-02-2001 L2006 **AN** *020 †10
ABESS, John Frederick. 46 STATE ST # C 29401 #045-01-1974 L1976 **P PA** *020 †75
ACHANTI, Anand. ■ 29407 #038-41-2007 L2007 **IM** *012
ACKERMAN, Steven Ira. ■ 29412 #016-42-1976 L1994 **DR EM** *020 †80,16
ACKERMAN, Susan R. 169 ASHLEY AVE 29425 #001-06-1991 L1993 **DR** *020 †80
ADAMS, David Benson. 96 JONATHAN LUCAS ST 29425 #051-04-1977 L1986 **GS ORS** *020 †85
ADAMS, Jason Andrew. 29414 #027-01-2004 L2008 **MP** *012
ADKINS, Warren Young, Jr. DEPT OF OTOLARYNGOLOGY, MED UNIV OF S CAROLINA 29425 #045-01-1965 L1965 **OTO** *071 †45
AFRIN, Jill N. 701 E BAY ST, PORT CITY CENTER 29403 #047-05-1988 L1989 **P** *020
AFRIN, Lawrence Brian. 171 ASHLEY AVE, MUSC DIV OF HEM/ONC CSB903 29425 #045-01-1988 L1989 **HO IM** *020 †20
AGARWAL, Amit Kumar. 169 ASHLEY AVE 29425 #495-05-2001 L2008 *100

■ = Address Information Privacy Protected

AGRAWAL, Amit. ■ 29412 #045-01-2000 L2003 **GE** *012 †20
AGRAWAL, Vishal. 169 ASHLEY AVE, MEDICAL UNIV OF SOUTH CARO 29403 #045-01-2002 L2004 **PCC** *012
AGREST, Eliza. ■ 29403 #045-01-2007 L2007 **PD** *012
AHLERT-SMITH, Erica Grace. ■ 29412 #045-01-2003 L2006 **CHP** *012
AHLUWALIA, Raj. 9313 MEDICAL PLAZA DR, STE 302 29406 #048-12-1991 L1999 **DR** *020 †80
AHMED, Qanta Amtul Aala. 96 JONATHAN LUCAS ST, RM 910H 29425 #917-12-1991 L2005 **PCC** *020 †20
AHN, Chadwick Neal. ■ 29414 #020-12-2004 L2004 **OTO** *012
AHN, Gina. 67 PRESIDENT ST 29425 #039-01-2004 L2004 **P** *012
AHO, Michael Robert. ■ 29407 #045-01-2008 *012
AITHAL, Guruprasad Padur. 96 JONATHAN LUCAS ST, STE 210CSB, PO BOX 250327 29425 #341-37-1988 L2000 *020
AJAYI, Adesuyi Adeyinka. MUSC MED CTR 29425 #690-05-1980 L1993 *020
AKHTAR, Jeffrey M. 30 BEE ST, STE 2100 29403 #028-78-2001, ▲ L2005 **IM** *020
ALBANESE, Robert Pasquale. 171 ASHLEY AVE 29425 #036-08-1988 L2000 **P IM** *020 †20,75
ALBENBERG, David Lawrence. 235 CALHOUN ST 29401 #041-13-1994 L1995 **FM** *020 †18
ALDER, Timothy Leslie. ■ 29412 #004-01-2002 L2007 **DR** *020 †80
ALELE, Jimmy M. 171 ASHLEY AVE 29425 #905-01-1988 L2004 **END** *020 †20
ALEXANDER, Constance J. 1954 ASHLEY RIVER RD STE H 29407 #422-01-1995 L2000 **P** *020 †75
ALEXANDER, Erin Tanner. ■ 29412 #012-22-2008 *012
ALFARO, Daniel Virgil. 2093 HENRY TECKLENBURG DR, STE 315 29414 #035-20-1988 L1997 **OPH** *020 †35
ALLEN, James M. ■ 29414 #048-12-2005 L2007 **P** *012
ALLEN, Robert Johnson. 125 DOUGHTY ST, STE 480 29403 #045-01-1976 L1985 **PS** *020 †85,65
ALLISON, John G. 109 BEE ST, VA MEDICAL CENTER 29401 #836-02-1964 L2003 **GS AS** *030 ‡
ALLISON, Lee Lovett. 9298 MEDICAL PLAZA DR, RESIDENCY PROGRAM 29406 #045-01-2006 L2006 **FP** *012
ALLISON, M Allston. 2097 HENRY TECKLENBURG DR, STE 301 29414 #045-01-1989 **IM** *020 †20
ALPERT, Calvert Clay. 171 ASHLEY AVE, DEPT OF ANESTHESIOLOGY 416 29425 #045-01-1975 L1977 **AN** *020 †20
ALVAREZ, Mary Elizabeth. ■ 29412 #021-01-2004 L2004 **MP** *012
ALVAREZ, Sergio Cristian. 169 ASHLEY AVE # 202, DEPT OF GENERAL SURGERY 29403 #231-03-1994 L2002 *020
AMODEI, Laura Ann. 1930 CHARLIE HALL BLVD, CHARLESTON BREAST CENTER 29414 #026-08-1997 L2007 **DR** *100 †80
AN, Yuehuei. 171 ASHLEY AVE 29425 #243-44-1983 L2006 **ORS** *012
ANDELFINGER, Gregor U. MUSC MED CTR 29425 #409-41-1993 L2000 **PDC** *020
ANDERS, Robert Mayer. 316 CALHOUN ST 29401 #021-01-1993 L2000 **EM** *020 †16
ANDERSON, Annette Bilton. 418 FOLLY RD, STE A 29412 #045-01-1996 L1998 **FM** *020 †18
ANDERSON, Erica. ■ 29414 #028-78-2001, ▲ L2005 **RHU IM** *012 †20
ANDERSON, Jeffrey S. 2049 SAVANNAH HWY, EMERGICARE 29407 #045-01-1992 L1993 **EM** *020
ANDERSON, William Dewey. 490 MARTELLO DR 29412 #045-01-1994 L1995 **FM** *020 †18 ‡
ANDRADE GUTIERREZ, Gustavo. 171 ASHLEY AVE 29425 #341-03-2003 L2006 **AN** *012
ANDREOLI, Steven Michael. ■ 29407 #024-05-2007 L2007 **OTO** *012
ANTIA-OBONG, Betty Jean. 2270 ASHLEY CROSSING DR, ASHLEY RIVER FAMILY PHYSIC 29414 #036-01-1981 L1985 **FM** *020 †18
ANTINE, Bartley Evert. 2270 ASHLEY CROSSING DR, STE 100 29414 #038-40-1957 L1965 **OPH** *071 †35
ANTON, Raymond F, Jr. 67 PRESIDENT ST, P O BOX 250861 29425 #033-06-1976 L1980 **P** *020 †75
ANTONOVICH, Diana Dawn. 135 RUTLEDGE ST, FL 11 29425 #035-45-1998 L2005 **D** *020 †15
APPELGREN, Kristie Elizab. ■ 29401 #045-01-2008 *012
APPIAGYEI-DANKAH, Yaw. 96 JONATHAN LUCAS ST, CSB 316 29425 #412-01-1987 L2002 **PD PDE** *020 †55
APPLE, David Craig. 615 WESLEY DR, STE 200 29407 #036-05-1986 L1987 **IM** *020 †20
APPLE, David Jos. 171 ASHLEY AVE 29425 #016-11-1966 L1989 **OPH PTH** *020 †50,35
APPLEBAUM, Mary Lou. 2095 HENRY TECKLENBURG DR, COGENT HOSPITALISTS 29414 #048-02-1979 L1986 **HOS PUD** *020 †20
APPLEBY, Thomas Corbett. 1327 ASHLEY RIVER RD, STE B 29407 #045-01-1985 L1991 **VS GS** *020 †20
ARANA, George Winston. 109 BEE ST, CHARLESTON VA. MEDICAL CEN 29401 #024-07-1974 L1987 **P IM** *020 †75
ARAVAPALLI, Amit. ■ 29414 #036-08-2008 *012
ARBUCKLE, Justin Hubbard. ■ 29412 #016-43-2005 L2005 **OPH** *012
ARDEN, Kathryn B. 4050 BRIDGE VIEW DR # 600 29405 #045-01-1981 L1985 **FM PHP** *030 †18
ARGULA, Rahul Gupta. ■ 29403 #045-53-2005 L2007 **IM** *012
ARMOCIDA, Frank Michael. 169 ASHLEY AVE # 202, DEPT OF GENERAL SURGERY 29403 #045-01-2003 L2004 **ORS** *012
ARMSTRONG, Don Michael. 2070 NORTHBROOK BLVD, STE B9 29406 #036-01-1998 L2002 **OBG** *020 †30
ARNAU, Thomas Brantley. 9313 MEDICAL PLAZA DR, STE 202 29406 #045-01-1981 L1982 **FM** *020 †18
ARTHUR, John Michael. 171 ASHLEY AVE 29425 #018-03-1990 L2001 **NEP** *020 †20
ARVANITIDU, Sofia. 67 PRESIDENT ST 29425 #409-07-2000 L2004 **P** *100
ASKINS, David G, Jr. 171 ASHLEY AVE 29425 #045-01-1960 L1960 **FM** *040 †18
ASPER, Mari Elisabeth. ■ 29407 #045-01-2007 L2007 **P** *012
ASSIA, Ehid Itzhak. 171 ASHLEY AVE DEPT OPH 29425 #550-02-1980 L1991 *020
ATKINSON, Randy M. 18 FARMFIELD AVE 29407 #045-01-1988 L1992 **AN** *020 †05
AUGELLI, Dianne Marie. ■ 29403 #039-01-2005 L2005 **MP** *012
AUSTIN, Linda Smith. 2016 WAPPOO DR 29412 #036-07-1976 L1986 **P** *020 †75
AVERILL, Nathan John. 9298 MEDICAL PLAZA DR, RESIDENCY PROGRAM 29406 #020-12-2006 L2006 **FP** *012
AXON, Robert Neal. PO BOX 250623, 96 JONATHAN LUCAS ST STE 29425 #001-02-2000 L2005 **MPD** *040
BABANOURY, Agha Baba. 171 ASHLEY AVE 29425 #517-01-1960 L1985 **U** *011 †95
BABB, Robert Edgar, III. 9330 MEDICAL PLAZA DR 29406 #045-01-1970 L1971 **GE IM** *071 †20
BACHMAN, David L. 171 ASHLEY AVE 29425 #012-05-1977 L1989 **N SME** *020 †75
BAER, Daniel Shaun. 67 PRESIDENT ST 29425 #035-06-2004 L2004 **CHP** *012
BAGG, Michael. 316 CALHOUN ST 29401 #836-01-1978 L1989 **DR** *020 †80 ‡
BAGG, Stephen Alan. 9330 MEDICAL PLAZA DR, TRIDENT HEALTH SYSTEM 29406 #045-01-2007 L2007 **TY** *012

BAHADORI, Hamid Reza. 125 DOUGHTY ST, STE 460 29403 #473-03-1994 L2004 **N** *020
BAILEY, Byron Nathaniel. 96 JONATHAN LUCAS ST 29425 #001-06-1984 L1985 **NS CD** *020 †25
BAILEY, Laurel Jean. ■ 29412 #016-45-2005 L2005 **IM** *012
BAILEY, Melinda Kay. 171 ASHLEY AVE, DEPT OF ANESTHESIOLOGY 29425 #001-06-1984 L1985 **AN** *020 †05
BAK, Adrian William. 96 JONATHAN LUCAS ST, DIGESTIVE DIS CENTER 29425 #065-09-1992 L1999 **GE** *020 †20
BAKER, Angus Sellers, Jr. 125 DOUGHTY ST, STE 500 29403 #045-01-1967 L1967 **ON HEM** *071 †20
BAKER, Brett Matthew. 125 DOUGHTY ST, STE 100 29403 #023-01-1991 L1999 **ICE IM** *020 †20
BAKER, George Hamilton. ■ 29412 #035-03-2001 L2004 **PDC** *012 †55
BAKER, Jesse David. 171 ASHLEY AVE, ANESTHESIOLOGY MED UNIV OF 29425 #045-01-1973 L1974 **AN** *020 †05
BAKER, Megan Keeffe. 96 JONATHAN LUCAS ST, POB 250613 29425 #038-45-1999 L2003 **GS** *100 †85
BAKER, Robert Denio. 171 ASHLEY AVE, DEPT OF PEDIATRICS 29425 #041-13-1972 L1993 **PD** *020 †20
BAKER, Stephen Kenneth. 67 PRESIDENT ST, DEPT OF PSYCHIATRY 29425 #016-42-1970 L1996 **P** *020 †20
BALDWIN, James G. ■ 29401 #051-01-1972 L1973 **IM HEM** *020 †20
BALIGA, Prabhakar K. 171 ASHLEY AVE, DEPT OF SURGERY 29425 #495-04-1982 L1992 **GS** *020 †85
BALL, Bruce Devon. 2270 ASHLEY CROSSING DR, CONSULTANTS 29414 #045-01-1981 L1982 **AI PD** *020 †55,03
BALL, James Austin. 12 FARMFIELD AVE STE A, HARBOR TOWN PULMONARY 29407 #045-01-1983 L1988 **PUD** *020 †20
BALLENGER, James Caudell. 171 ASHLEY AVE 29425 #036-07-1970 L1983 **P** *030 †75
BALY, William Leroy, Jr. 51 NASSAU ST, HEALTH CENTER 29403 #010-03-1994 L1997 **IM** *020 †20
BANDISODE, Varsha M. 171 ASHLEY AVE, POB 250915 29425 #012-22-1995 L2002 **PDC** *020 †55
BANERT, Melanie. ■ 29412 #035-15-2004 L2004 **AN** *012
BANOV, Charles Harris. ■ 29407 #045-01-1955 L1955 **A IM** *071 †20,03
BANSAL, Vikas. ■ 29403 #012-01-2001 L2004 **N** *100 †05
BARABELL, Greg Matthew. ■ 29403 #035-15-2007 L2007 **PD** *012
BARBER, Michale Jill. 18 E ELLIOTT ST 29401 #045-01-1986 L1987 **AN** *020 †05
BARBOSA, Ernest. 171 ASHLEY AVE, DEPT OF NEUROLOGY MUSC 29425 #005-18-1975 L1990 **OS CHN** *050
BARBOUR, John Richard. ■ 29403 #010-02-2002 L2004 **GS** *012
BARFIELD, Carlysle. 14 FARMFIELD AVE, RHEUMATOLOGY ASSOCIATES 29407 #045-01-1972 L1973 **RHU IM** *020 †20
BARGATZE, Fred Orval. 171 ASHLEY AVE, MUSC ORTHOPAEDIC SURGERY 29425 #020-02-1956 L1985 **ORS** *071 †40
BARILLO, David Jos. 171 ASHLEY AVE 29425 #033-05-1981 L1998 **PS CCS** *020 †85,65
BARKER, John Middleton. 171 ASHLEY AVE, MEDICINE 29425 #011-04-1997 L1998 **PCC** *100 †20
BARKER, Ralph John. ■ 29407 #045-01-2005 L2006 **GS** *012
BARNES, Derrick Jay. ■ 29414 #045-01-2004 L2004 **OBG** *012
BARNWELL, William H, II. 171 ASHLEY AVE 29425 #045-01-1951 L1951 **CD IM** *071 †20
BARON, Lisa Ann. 1930 CHARLIE HALL BLVD 29414 #051-04-1988 L1990 **R** *020 †80
BARTLETT, Anne. ■ 29412 #017-20-2007 L2007 **PTH** *012
BARTLETT, Robert James. ■ 29412 #017-20-2007 L2007 **AN** *012
BASCO, William Thos, Jr. 135 RUTLEDGE ST 29425 #021-05-1992 L1993 **PD** *050 †55
BASHAMBU, Monuj Triven. ■ 29414 #021-01-2006 L2006 **PD** *012
BASILE, Jan Neil. 109 BEE ST, R H JOHNSON VA MED CTR 29401 #051-04-1978 L1979 **IM IMG** *020 †20
BASKETT, Cecelia Marie. ■ 29403 #045-01-2008 *012
BATCHELOR, Emma Charlotte. ■ 29401 #045-01-2008 *012
BATES, Daniel Chesney. 1851 SAM RITTENBERG BLVD 29407 #045-01-1971 L1972 **FM** *020 †20
BATES, George Walker. 2095 HENRY TECKLENBURG DR 29414 #045-01-1944 L2004 **OTO OS** *071 †45
BAYER, Richard Robert. 96 JONATHAN LUCAS ST 29425 #038-40-2007 L2007 **IM** *012
BAZAZ, Sapna. ■ 29425 #496-07-2002 L2004 **GS** *012
BEACH, Paul Kevin. 1327 ASHLEY RIVER RD STE B 29407 #045-01-1997 L2003 **VS** *020 †85
BEALL, Anthony Carter. 9297 MEDICAL PLAZA DR, STE C 29406 #045-01-1992 L1993 **AN** *020 †05
BECKERT, David Robert. ■ 29412 #051-01-2006 L2006 **P** *012
BECKNER, Glen Eric. 9330 MEDICAL PLAZA DR, TRIDENT EMERGENCY PHYSICIA 29406 #045-04-1995 L1998 **EM** *020 †16
BECTON, Lauren Jennifer. ■ 29412 #036-05-2008 *012
BEISCHEL, Charles John. 161 ASHLEY AVE 29425 #045-01-1994 L1996 **OPH FM** *020 †35
BELDECOS, Athena. 326 CALHOUN ST, 3RD FL 29401 #041-12-1998 L2004 **IM** *020 †20
BELDNER, Matthew Allan. 171 ASHLEY AVE 29425 #045-04-2001 L2002 **IM HO** *050
BELL, Norman Howard. 171 ASHLEY AVE 29425 #036-07-1955 L1979 **END IM** *050
BELL, Thaddeus J. 3951 W MONTAGUE AVE 29418 #045-01-1976 L1979 **FM** *075 †18
BELSER, Ritchie Hugh. ■ 29412 #036-07-1946 L1953 **OS ORS** *071 †40
BENICH, Joseph John. 9298 MEDICAL PLAZA DR 29406 #045-01-2005 L2005 **FP** *012
BENICK, Anthony Perry. 520 FOLLY RD, PMB 123 29412 #005-12-1997 L2001 **AN** *020 †05
BENNER, James Michael. 9231 MEDICAL PLAZA DR, STE D 29406 #041-13-1991 L1995 **TS** *020 †85,90
BENNETT, Antionette Akia. ■ 29407 #045-01-2008 *012
BEN SIMON, Ron David. 135 RUTLEDGE ST, STE 1201 29425 #917-36-1991 L2005 *020
BERGMANN, Kenneth J. 326 CALHOUN ST, ST ST308/POB250108 29401 #035-48-1976 L2000 **N** *020 †75
BERMAN, Megan Anne. 9330 MEDICAL PLAZA DR, MUSC - GRAD MED EDU 29425 #016-43-2004 L2004 **IM** *020 †20
BERTRAND, Helen Read. 333 FOLLY RD, STE F 29412 #045-01-1984 L1986 **PD** *020 †55
BESS, Jennifer Grace. 165 ASHLEY AVE, PATHOLOGY & LAB MEDICINE 29425 #045-01-1998 L2001 **PTH** *020 †20
BETHEA, Amy Mc Alpine. 316 CALHOUN ST 29401 #045-01-1982 L1983 **DR** *020 †80
BHAT, Akhlaque Nabi. 96 JONATHAN LUCAS ST 29425 #495-51-1984 L2001 *020
BHATTI, Harvinder Singh. 169 ASHLEY AVE, MUSC- ORTHOPAEDIC SRGY 29403 #045-01-2005 L2005 **ORS** *012
BHAVSAR, Robin Rashmi. ■ 29407 #051-04-2007 L2007 **GS** *012

BIBER, Joseph Moore. 96 JONATHAN LUCAS ST 29425 #045-01-2005 L2005 OPH *012
BICKERSTAFF, Chas Allen, Jr. 452 FOLLY RD, STE A 29412 #012-01-1976 L1978 GE NTR *020 †20
BILIC, Masha. PO BOX 250625, 96 JONATHAN LUCAS ST 29425 #008-01-2000 L2001 PTH *020 †50
BILLINGSLEY, Caroline Cra. ■ 29401 #045-01-2008 *012
BITTO, Donald John, Jr. PO BOX 250333, 169 ASHLEY AVE 29425 #041-02-2002 L2003 DR *012
BJORKSTEN, Oliver James W. 192 E BAY ST STE 302 29401 #056-05-1968 L1974 P *020 †75
BLACK, Amy Gibson. 9298 MEDICAL PLAZA DR 29406 #045-01-2003 L2004 FM *020 †18
BLACKARD, Robert Francis. 9326 MEDICAL PLAZA DR, STE B 29406 #036-05-1969 L1976 AN *020 †05
BLAKE, Gerard Francis. 16 WINDERMERE BLVD 29407 #045-01-1998 L1999 FM *100 †18
BLANTON, John W, Jr. ■ 29412 #045-01-1952 L1952 P *030
BLANTON, Lucas Scott. 169 ASHLEY AVE, MEDICAL UNIVERSITY OF SC-M 29403 #048-02-2005 L2005 IM *012
BLESSING, Walter Dale, Jr. 510 ALBEMARLE RD, SURGICAL ASSOC OF CHARLEST 29407 #045-01-1999 L2005 GS *020 †85
BLEVENS, Kara L. 169 ASHLEY AVE # 202 29403 #047-06-2002 L2004 PD *020
BLUE, Matthew Benjamin. 316 CALHOUN ST, ROPER HOSPITAL EMERGENCY P 29401 #047-20-1996 L1999 EM *020 †16
BLUESTEIN, Ettaleah C. 2145 HENRY TECKLENBURG DR, STE 100 29414 #045-01-1990 L1991 OPH *020 †35
BLUM, Craig Ashley. ■ 29414 #045-01-2005 L2005 GS *012
BLUMENTHAL, Larry Steven. 30 BEE ST STE A 29403 #048-15-1985 L1986 IM GP *020 †20
BOATWRIGHT, Harry Wade. 316 CALHOUN ST 29401 #045-01-1984 L1985 OBG *020 †30
BOATWRIGHT, Kevin Dale. PO BOX 250333, 169 ASLEY AVE RM 202MU 29425 #045-04-1999 L2002 ID *020 †20
BOHLER, John David. 1606 ASHLEY RIVER RD, COASTAL GASTROENTEROLOGY A 29407 #045-01-1998 L1999 GE *020 †20
BOLIN, Eric Daniel. PO BOX 31434 29417 #036-01-2003 L2004 AN *020
BOLSTER, Marcy Behar. 96 JONATHAN LUCAS ST 916H, UNIV OF SOUTH CAROLINA 29425 #036-07-1988 L1991 RHU *020 †20
BOLT, Thomas Richard. 9313 MEDICAL PLAZA DR #202 29406 #045-01-1981 L1982 FM *020 †18
BONG, Christine Janelhayw. ■ 29412 #051-04-2004 L2005 PD *012
BONG, Gary William. ■ 29412 #051-04-2004 L2004 U *012
BONILHA, Leonardo Fator G. ■ 29412 #187-30-1999 L2007 N *012
BONNEMA, David Dirk. ■ 29414 #025-07-2001 L2002 CD *012
BONSALL, Richard Paul. 169 ASHLEY AVE, MUSC - RADIOLOGY 29403 #033-06-2003 L2004 DR *012
BOOK, Sarah Weiss. 171 ASHLEY AVE, DEPT OF PSYCHIATRY 29425 #036-07-1991 L1995 P *050 †75
BOOKER, Harold Edward. 125 DOUGHTY ST STE 460 29403 #017-20-1957 L1988 N *030 †75
BOOZER, Margaret Maybin. 171 ASHLEY AVE 29425 #036-07-1999 L2002 OBG *100 †30
BORG, Keith Thomas. ■ 29412 #045-01-2000 L2006 EM *020 †16
BORTON, Marc Edwin. PO BOX 250333, 169 ASHLEY AVE 29425 #045-01-2005 L2005 GS *020
BOUALI, Henda. PO BOX 250333, 169 ASHLEY AVE 29425 #895-01-1998 L2003 RHU *020 †20
BOURGEOIS, Tracie Danyel. ■ 29414 #021-06-2003 L2004 PTH *100 †50
BOWIE, Esther Michelle. 167 ASHLEY AVE, MED UNIV OF SO CAROLINA 29403 #894-01-1996 L2001 OPH *020 †35
BOWLBY, Deborah A. 96 JONATHAN LUCAS ST, RM 316 29425 #065-01-1999 L2005 PDE *100 †55
BOWLES, Robert Hasselle. 1249 SAVANNAH HWY 29407 #045-01-1971 L1972 ORS *062 †40
BOWMAN, C Michael. 171 ASHLEY AVE 29425 #056-05-1975 L2000 PDP PD *020 †55
BOWMAN, Zachary Scott. ■ 29414 #045-01-2008 *012
BOYER, Alexis Frances. 125 DOUGHTY ST, STE 420 29403 #010-01-1999 L2000 AN *020 †20
BOYLAN, Alice Maxine. 96 JONATHAN LUCAS ST, RM 812CSB 29425 #041-13-1985 L1995 NS *020 †20
BRACALE, Carlos Leopoldo. 171 ASHLEY AVE 29425 #737-06-1996 L2004 PAN *100 †05
BRACEY, Jennifer Earle. ■ 29412 #045-01-2006 IM *012
BRACKEN, Roberta Theresa. 4 JOHNSON RD 29407 #017-20-1973 L1976 FM *020 †05
BRACKETT, Newton C, Jr. 171 ASHLEY AVE 29425 #045-01-1959 L1959 NEP IM *020 †20
BRACKETT, Newton Craig. 96 JONATHAN LUCAS ST, 829 CLINICAL SCI BLDG 29425 #045-01-1987 L1992 GS *020 †85
BRADEN, Jennifer Michele. 171 ASHLEY AVE 29425 #038-41-2000 L2002 PD PEM *020 †55
BRADHAM, Gilbert Bowman. 171 ASHLEY AVE 29425 #045-01-1956 L1956 GS *020 †85
BRADHAM, Robert R. 125 DOUGHTY ST STE 260 29403 #045-01-1951 L1951 TS *020 †85,90
BRADLEY, Scott Mac Millan. 96 JONATHAN LUCAS ST 29425 #024-01-1985 L1995 TS *020 †85,90
BRADSHAW, Marques Levar. ■ 29414 #036-07-2004 L2007 DR *012 †28
BRADY, Courtney. 96 JONATHAN LUCAS ST, DEPT OF MED CSB 803 29425 #041-13-2000 L2001 IM *020 †20 ‡
BRADY, Kathleen Theresa. 171 ASHLEY AVE, DEPT PSYCHIATRY-MUSC 29425 #045-01-1985 L1986 P *020 †75
BRAHEN, Norman Halin. 9297 MEDICAL PLAZA DR #202 29406 #020-02-1981 L1982 AN *020 †05
BRAKE, Daniel Walter. 9313 MEDICAL PLAZA DR #202 29406 #045-01-1966 L1966 FM *020 †18
BRANCH, Kevin Drake. 169 ASHLEY AVE 29403 #047-06-2005 L2005 PTH *012
BRASHEARS, James Henry. ■ 29403 #036-07-2004 L2005 RO *012
BRAVERMAN, Wayne Harris. 669 SAINT ANDREWS BLVD 29407 #041-02-1968 L1974 P *020 †75
BREHMER, William Peter. ■ 29412 #045-01-2008 *012
BRENER, William. 1962 CHARLIE HALL BLVD 29414 #023-07-1974 L1981 GE IM *020 †20
BRENKERT, Timothy Edward. ■ 29414 #038-45-2005 L2005 PD *012
BREWER, Kristen M. 169 ASHLEY AVE, MEDICAL UNIV OF SOUTH CARO 29403 #048-16-2002 L2004 DR *012 †28
BREWER, Thomas Edward. ■ 29401 #048-02-1964 L1967 IM NEP *071
BREWER, Thomas Owen. 171 ASHLEY AVE 29425 #038-41-1991 L1997 EM *020 †16
BRIDGEWATER, Joel Lee. ■ 29414 #007-02-2005 L2005 AN *012
BRIDWELL, Richard Brent. ■ 29403 #045-01-2008 *012
BRILLIANT, Howard London. 1249 SAVANNAH HWY 29407 #016-42-1968 L1975 ORS HS *040 †40
BRINSON, Robert Earl. 8 SAWGRASS RD 29412 #012-01-1977 L1981 FM *020 †18
BRIONES, Kerry Patterson. ■ 29412 #051-04-2004 L2004 IM *100 †20
BRIONES, Marcus Startsman. ■ 29412 #051-04-2004 L2004 ORS *012

BRITTAIN, Eric Stewart. 9330 MEDICAL PLAZA DR, TRIDENT EMERGENCY PHYSICIA 29406 #016-01-2002 L2003 EM *100 †16
BRITTON, John James, Jr. 641 SAINT ANDREWS BLVD, SPECIALISTS 29407 #045-01-1994 L1998 U *020 †95
BROCK, Clive David. 295 CALHOUN ST 29425 #836-02-1964 L1982 FM *020
BRODY, Jason Scot. 9304 MEDICAL PLAZA DR, STE 2 29406 #016-42-2001 L2006 OPH *020 †35
BROERING, Anthony James. ■ 29414 #045-01-2008 *012
BROOKS, Willie. ■ 29407 #047-07-1972 L1973 *075
BROTHERS, Thomas Edward. 171 ASHLEY AVE 29425 #025-01-1983 L1991 VS CCS *020 †85
BROWN, Alan Neil. 96 JONATHAN LUCAS ST # 912 29425 #045-01-1993 L1994 RHU IM *020 †20
BROWN, Dennis Mc Lean. 171 ASHLEY AVE, DEPT. PHYSICAL MED/REHAB 29425 #305-01-1994 L2001 IM *020
BROWN, Francis Mc Guire. VET ADMIN HOSP, DEPT PATH 29403 #012-05-1962 L1969 PTH CLP *020 †50
BROWN, Fred Chas. 171 ASHLEY AVE 29425 #019-02-1971 L2004 GE *020 †20
BROWN, Grace Lorraine. 171 ASHLEY AVE 29425 #041-13-1985 L1992 AN *020 †05
BROWN, Helen Elizabeth. ■ 29414 #045-01-2005 L2005 OBG *012
BROWN, Jerell Ramar. ■ 29414 #036-07-2007 L2007 AN *012
BROWN, Tod Allen. 171 ASHLEY AVE 29425 #041-13-1988 L1992 AN *020 †05
BROWN, W Raymond, III. 9297 MEDICAL PLAZA DR, STE C 29406 #047-06-1993 L1994 AN PME *020 †05
BROWNFIELD, Elisha. 326 CALHOUN ST, CARE CENTER 29401 #051-04-1990 L1997 IM *020 †20
BRYAN, Martha Carolyn. 316 CALHOUN ST, ROPER HOSPITAL 29401 #045-01-1976 L1980 PTH *062 †50
BRYANT, Tanya Jones. 169 ASHLEY AVE, MEDICAL UNIV OF SOUTH CARO 29403 #028-03-2003 L2004 NS *012
BRZEZINSKI, Walter Adam. 171 ASHLEY AVE 29425 #030-06-1978 L1987 IM *040 †20
BUCHMANN, Luke Oliver. ■ 29412 #041-15-2002 L2007 OTO *100
BUCKALOO, Jerrold M. 125 DOUGHTY ST, STE 300 29403 #047-06-1991 L1999 HS *020 †40
BUCKNER, Carl Louis. 165 ASHLEY AVE # 309 29425 #038-41-2004 L2004 PTH *012
BUDEV, Millin Chandu. 2093 HENRY TECKLENBURG DR, STE 313E 29414 #038-43-1999 L2000 OPH *020 †35
BUDISAVLJEVIC, Milos N. 171 ASHLEY AVE 29425 #957-08-1976 L1994 IM NEP *020 †20
BUMGARTNER, James L. 125 DOUGHTY ST, STE 300 29403 #012-05-1977 L1978 N *020 †75
BUNCHER, Jeffrey Wayne. 1124 SAM RITTENBERG BLVD, STE 1 29407 #045-01-1990 L1991 FM PME *020 †18
BUNKE, Charles Martin. 171 ASHLEY AVE, DIVISION OF NEPHROLOGY 29425 #008-01-1977 L1996 NEP *020 †20
BUNTING, Troy Augustus. 615 WESLEY DR, STE 320 29407 #036-01-2000 L2001 IC *020 †20
BURCH, Hunter Rebecca. 9298 MEDICAL PLAZA DR, RESIDENCY PROGRAM 29406 #045-01-2006 L2006 D *012
BURDON, John Carter. ■ 29401 #016-11-1946 L1947 AN *071 †05
BURGES, Gene Elizabeth. 109 BEE ST 29401 #045-01-1984 L1985 D *020 †15
BURNETTE, Jeffrey Dean. ■ 29414 #045-01-2001 L2004 AN *100 †15
BURNS, Frank Avery, Jr. 125 DOUGHTY ST, STE 300 29403 #012-01-1967 L1972 GE *020 †20
BUSBY, Stephen Clark. 9298 MEDICAL PLAZA DR 29406 #045-01-2004 L2004 FM *020 †18
BUSE, Maria Felice Gordon. 171 ASHLEY AVE 29425 #132-01-1954 L1960 DIA END *050 †28
BUSH, Jeffrey Sullivan. 171 ASHLEY AVE 29425 #036-08-1993 L2004 EM *020 †16
BUSH, Kimberly Monique. 67 PRESIDENT ST 29425 #045-04-2003 L2004 CHP *012
BUTLER, Edward George, II. 3600 RIVERS AVE, DERMATOLOGY DEPT 29405 #023-12-1998 L2005 D *020 †15
BUXTON, Geo Edward Preot. 316 CALHOUN ST 29401 #045-01-1957 L1957 AN *020 †05
BYRD, James Kenneth. ■ 29412 #045-01-2007 L2007 OTO *012
BYRD, Larry Newton. 3800 FABER PLACE DR 29405 #045-01-1987 L1990 PD *020 †55
BYRNE, Thomas Karl. 171 ASHLEY AVE 29425 #539-06-1978 L1992 GS *020 †85
CAHILL, John B. 171 ASHLEY AVE, DEPT OF PEDIATRICS 29425 #033-06-1997 L2000 NPM *020 †55
CAIN, Rebecca Louise. 167 ASHLEY AVE, STE 301 29403 #654-01-2000 L2000 AN *020 †05
CAIN, Robert Wm. 615 WESLEY DR, STE 300 29407 #047-05-1986 L1987 IM *020 †20
CAIN, William H. ■ 29412 #045-01-1952 L1952 GS *020 †85
CAIRE, Elsa Cecelia. 2097 HENRY TECKLENBURG DR, STE 312 29414 #021-05-1980 L1987 OBG *020 †30
CALL, Varnie Crigler. 171 ASHLEY AVE, RM 506 29425 #045-01-2003 L2004 MP *012
CALLAHAN, Debra Louise. ■ 29408 #038-40-1996 L2003 BBK CLP *020 †50
CAMERON, Joseph Price, Jr. 125 DOUGHTY ST STE 550 29403 #045-01-1972 L1973 PS *071 †65
CAMPBELL, Jeffrey W. 96 JONATHAN LUCAS ST, CSB, STE 428 29425 #041-02-1991 L2001 NS *020 †25
CAMPBELL, Johnny Phillips. 2095 HENRY TECKLENBURG DR 29414 #045-01-2000 L2005 DR *020 †80
CAMPBELL, Stephen D. 18 FARMFIELD AVE 29407 #038-44-1990 L1993 AN *020 †05
CAMPBELL, William Bradley. 171 ASHLEY AVE, MED UNIV OF SC COLL OF MED 29425 #045-01-2006 GS *012
CANEPA, Elizabeth Anne. ■ 29403 #016-01-2005 L2006 P *100
CANNON, Albert. 171 ASHLEY AVE 29425 #045-01-1949 L1949 CLP PTH *071 †50
CANTEY, Joseph Robt. 135 RUTLEDGE ST, 12TH FLOOR RUTLEDGE AVE 29425 #045-01-1966 L1966 ID IM *040 †20
CAPLAN, Michael Jeffrey. 171 ASHLEY AVE 29425 #008-02-1987 L2004 FOP PTH *020 †50
CAREK, Peter John. 295 CALHOUN ST 29425 #045-01-1987 L1988 FM *020 †18
CARISTI, Kimberly K. 2051 CHARLIE HALL BLVD, COASTAL PEDIATRIC ASSOCIAT 29414 #055-01-1992 L1993 PD *020 †55
CARLO, Jamie Lynn. ■ 29407 #011-02-2004 L2004 PTH *012
CARNEIRO-PLA, Denise M. ■ 29414 #187-73-1995 L2007 GS *020 †85
CARR, Christine Marie. 169 ASHLEY AVE, RM 115 29403 #045-01-1992 L1995 EM *020 †16
CARTER, James Folger. 171 ASHLEY AVE, DEPT OF OB/GYN 29425 #045-01-1975 L1976 OBG *020 †30
CARTER, Jon C. ■ 29408 #028-46-1994 L1998 EM *072 †16
CARTER, Wm Clinton, III. 125 DOUGHTY ST STE 380 29403 #045-01-1974 L1976 U *020 †95
CASAT, Charles Dean. 2900 EVATT LN, STE 106 29405 #024-05-1963 L1984 CHP P *050 †75
CASESA, Annemarie. ■ 29407 #011-03-2005 L2005 P *012
CASON, Lewis Parker. 9326 MEDICAL PLAZA DR # B, TRIDENT ANESTHESIA GROUP 29406 #045-01-1979 L2006 AN *020 †05
CASTELL, Donald O. 96 JONATHAN LUCAS ST, CLINICAL SCIENCE BLDG STE 29425 #010-01-1960 L2004 GE IM *050 †20

■ = Address Information Privacy Protected

CASTELLANO, Joseph John. ■ 29412 #011-04-2005 L2007 **GS** *012

CATE, John Columbus. ■ 29401 #047-06-1967 L1989 **PCH CLP** *071 †50

CAUDILL, Stacy Renee. 9298 MEDICAL PLAZA DR, RESIDENCY PROGRAM 29406 #020-02-2006 L2006 **FP** *012

CAVALIER, Mary Ellen. 135 RUTLEDGE ST, RUTLEDGE TOWER, SUITE 482 29425 #017-20-1999 L2005 **PHO** *020 †55

CAWLEY, Patrick James. 171 ASHLEY AVE 29425 #010-02-1992 L1997 **IM** *020 †20

CECIL, Lindsey Caston. 9298 MEDICAL PLAZA DR, RESIDENCY PROGRAM 29406 #045-01-2006 L2006 **FP** *012

CHAG, Manoj Vrailal. 2095 HENRY TECKLENBURG DR, ST. FRANCIS HOSPITAL ER 29414 #045-01-1984 L1985 **EM FM** *020 †18

CHAIKHOUNI, Amer. 171 ASHLEY AVE 29425 #875-02-1974 L1983 **TS** *020 †85,90

CHAKERIS, Themistocles J. 715 SAINT ANDREWS BLVD 29407 #045-01-1963 L1963 **FM** *071 †18

CHALELA, Julio Alejandro. 96 JONATHAN LUCAS ST, CSB STE 428 29425 #264-01-1988 L2005 **N** *020 †75

CHAMBERS, Elton Ray. ■ 29407 #020-12-2007 L2007 **MPD** *012

CHAMBERS, Jerre Kelly. 316 CALHOUN ST 29401 #045-01-1965 L1965 **OPH** *071 †35

CHAMBERS, Joe Carroll. ■ 29402 #047-06-1956 L1970 **PHP** *030 †70

CHAN, Kwok C. ■ 29403 #462-01-1985 L1992 **PDC** *020

CHANG, Eugene Yin-Min. 628 SAINT ANDREWS BLVD 29407 #051-04-1994 L1995 **OBG** *020 †30

CHANSON, Rhonda Sue. 12 FARMFIELD AVE STE E 29407 #045-01-1993 L2000 **IM** *020 †20

CHAPLIN, Maurice Levar. ■ 29414 #041-12-2005 L2005 **AN** *012

CHARLES, Jane Murrell. 135 RUTLEDGE ST, MEDICAL UNIV. OF SOUTH CAR 29425 #045-01-1988 L1989 **PD** *020 †55

CHAUDRY, Mohammad Imran. 169 ASHLEY AVE, MSC 322 29425 #704-21-2000 L2008 **RNR** *100 †80

CHAVIN, Kenneth David. 171 ASHLEY AVE 29425 #041-13-1987 L1990 **TTS GS** *020 †85

CHAVIS, Pamela Suzanne. 171 ASHLEY AVE 29425 #033-05-1970 L2004 **N OPH** *030 †75,35 ‡

CHEEK, De Anna Bernadette. 96 JONATHAN LUCAS ST, MUSC 29425 #025-07-1979 L1988 **NEP IM** *020

CHEMODUROW, Katherine. ■ 29412 #003-01-2007 L2007 **P** *012

CHENG, Andrew Yenkai. ■ 29401 #045-01-2008 *012

CHERRY, Daniel A. 9330 MEDICAL PLAZA DR, LOWCOUNTRY PATHOLOGY ASSOC 29406 #306-01-1988 L1996 **PTH** *020 †50

CHESNUTT, David Alston. 167 ASHLEY AVE, MUSC - STORM EYE INSTITUTE 29403 #036-01-1995 L2005 **OPH** *020 †35

CHESSMAN, Alexander W. 295 CALHOUN ST 29401 #038-06-1985 L1987 **FM** *040 †18

CHIARAMIDA, Salvatore A. 171 ASHLEY AVE 29425 #035-09-1974 L2001 **CD IM** *030 †20

CHILELLI, Brian James. ■ 29401 #045-01-2008 *012

CHOI, Buying Sue. 18 FARMFIELD AVE 29407 #583-06-1970 L1979 **AN** *020 †05

CHONG, Andre Kheng Ho. 96 JONATHAN LUCAS ST, APT 210 29425 #143-02-1995 L2004 *020

CHRISTIAN, Elizabeth S. 125 DOUGHTY ST, STE 500 29403 #045-01-1982 L1987 **HEM IM** *020

CHRISTIAN, Stephen R. 169 ASHLEY AVE, MUH RM 297 29403 #001-06-2000 L2005 **DR** *020 †80

CHRISTIANSEN, Lydia Ruth. 165 ASHLEY AVE, STE 309 29425 #030-05-2002 L2003 **HMP** *100 †50

CHRISTIE, Scott Douglas. 2100 CHARLIE HALL BLVD, CHARLESTON MHC 29414 #020-02-1984 L1986 **P** *020 †75

CHRISTOPHER, Robert Manni, Jr. ■ 29412 #045-01-2006 L2006 **IM** *012

CHURCH, Lw Preston. 171 ASHLEY AVE 29425 #012-05-1983 L2000 **ID IM** *020 †20

CIFUENTES, Eduardo. 2777 SPEISSEGGER DR, HEALTH SVC 29405 #270-02-1999 L2004 **P** *020 ‡

CIOBOTEA, Mihaela Simona. ■ 29425 #781-02-1991 L2001 **IM** *074 †20

CLANCY, Dawn Henry. 376 CALHOUN ST 29401 #045-01-1985 L1986 **IM** *020 †20

CLANTON, Lauren Leah. ■ 29412 #045-01-2008 *012

CLARE, William Pettigrew. 2095 HENRY TECKLENBURG DR 29414 #045-01-1965 L1965 **IM CD** *020

CLARE, William Pettigrew. 2270 ASHLEY CROSSING DR, STE 170 29414 #045-01-1993 L1994 **IM** *020 †20

CLARK, Andrew Ryan. 67 PRESIDENT ST 29425 #041-15-2005 L2005 **P** *012

CLARK, Charles Nelson, Jr. 125 DOUGHTY ST, STE 420 29403 #047-20-2002 L2004 **AN** *020 †05

CLARK, Christian Dietrich. 169 ASHLEY AVE # 202, DEPT OF INTERNAL MEDICINE 29403 #019-02-2003 L2004 **GE** *012 †40,20

CLARK, Jennifer K. 169 ASHLEY AVE, MEDICAL UNIV OF SOUTH CARO 29403 #019-02-2003 L2004 **MPD** *100 †20,55

CLARK, Stephen David. 96 JONATHAN LUCAS ST 29425 #021-05-2007 L2007 **IM** *012

CLARKE, Harry S, Jr. 96 JONATHAN LUCAS ST # 644, PO BO 29425 #038-43-1987 L2003 **U** *020 †95

CLAY, Louise Bowen. 316 CALHOUN ST, ROPER-ST. FRANCIS 29401 #045-01-1994 L2000 **RO** *020 †80

CLAY, Rayna Ann. ■ 29412 #049-01-2005 L2006 **AN** *012

CLELAND, Jack Wilson. ■ 29412 #045-01-2008 *012

CLEMENTS, Wilson Monroe. ■ 29412 #047-06-1998 L2005 **TS** *012 †85

CLIFFORD, Robert Andrew. 2125 CHARLIE HALL BLVD #2A 29414 #045-01-1996 L1997 **PD** *020 †55

CLUVER, Abbie R. 169 ASHLEY AVE, MEDICAL UNIV OF SOUTH CARO 29403 #045-01-2002 L2004 **DR** *020

CLUVER, Jeffrey Scott. 109 BEE ST 29401 #047-05-2000 L2003 **P** *020 †75

CLYBURN, Ernest Benj. 376 CALHOUN ST 29401 #045-01-1989 L1997 **IM** *040 †20

COCKRELL, Joseph Robt, Jr. ■ 29401 #045-01-1979 L1990 **P N** *020 †25

COFFEY, Charles Stuart. 135 RUTLEDGE ST STE 1130, MUSC 29425 #036-01-2004 L2005 **OTO** *012

COHEN, Jonathan David. ■ 29403 #045-01-2008 *012

COHENS, Portia Nate. ■ 29407 #045-01-2008 *012

COLA, Carol Arthur. 171 ASHLEY AVE 29425 #024-16-1984 L1997 **ON HEM** *020 †20

COLBATH, Gregory Paul. ■ 29407 #045-01-2007 **ORS** *012

COLE, David Jefferson. 171 ASHLEY AVE, DEPT OF SURGERY 29425 #035-20-1986 L1994 **GS ON** *020 †85

COLE, Kali Bliss. ■ 29407 #039-01-2003 L2007 **OPH** *020

COLE, Scott Wesley. PO BOX 250333, 169 ASHLEY AVE RM 202 29407 #039-01-2003 L2007 **RO** *020 †80

COLE, Tracey Jeanne. 18 FARMFIELD AVE 29407 #045-04-2000 L2004 **AN** *020 †05

COLEMAN, Lee R, Jr. 171 ASHLEY AVE 29425 #036-07-1992 L1993 **GS** *020

COLLINS, Kim A. 171 ASHLEY AVE 29425 #012-01-1989 L1994 **FOP** *020 †50

COLLINS, William A. 9330 MEDICAL PLAZA DR 29406 #045-01-1990 L1992 **RO** *020 †80

COLONA, John Andrew. 125 DOUGHTY ST, STE 420 29403 #051-07-2001 L2004 **AN** *020 †05

COLWELL, John Amory. ■ 29401 #016-06-1951 L1981 **END IM** *071 †20

COMBS, James Mobley, Jr. 4115 DORCHESTER RD 29405 #012-01-1979 L2000 **OM** *020 †70

COMERFORD, Lawrence W. 96 JONATHAN LUCAS ST, STE 210CSB 29425 #045-01-1997 L2006 **GE** *100 †20

COMETA, Michael Anthony. ■ 29412 #005-12-2007 L2007 **IM** *012

CONATSER, John Robert. ■ 29407 #045-01-2006 L2006 **OBG** *012

CONDREN, Stacey Renee. 2097 HENRY TECKLENBURG DR, STE 206 29414 #005-06-1998 L2001 **END** *020 †20

CONNOR, Patrick. 96 JONATHAN LUCAS ST 29425 #919-02-1989 L2001 *020

CONRADI, Sandra Epstein. 171 ASHLEY AVE 29425 #038-41-1963 L1973 **FOP ATP** *071 †50

CONWAY, William Feil. 171 ASHLEY AVE 29425 #016-02-1981 L1993 **DR ORS** *020 †80

COOK, C Thomas. 9330 MEDICAL PLAZA DR 29406 #045-01-1963 L1963 **EM OM** *020 †16

COOK, Lori Michelle. ■ 29412 #021-05-2007 L2007 **PD** *012

COOK, William Joel. 135 RUTLEDGE ST, FL 11 29425 #045-01-1992 L1994 **D** *020 †15

COOKE, James Edward. 171 ASHLEY AVE 29425 #050-02-1967 L1974 **AN** *020 †05

COOPER, George, IV. 109 BEE ST, VA MEDICAL CENTER CARDIOLO 29401 #035-20-1968 L1986 **CD** *020 †20

COOPER, Marion Leslie, II. 9298 MEDICAL PLAZA DR 29406 #665-01-2007 L2007 **FP** *012

COOPER, Samuel Lewis. ■ 29407 #045-01-2008 *012

COPPLER, Amy Nichole. 171 ASHLEY AVE 29425 #045-01-2000 L2004 **EM** *020 †16

CORBETT, Keidre Jenkins. PO BOX 250333, 169 ASHLEY AVE RM 202MUH 29425 #045-01-2002 L2005 **NEP** *012 †20

CORDERO, Brunilda. 96 JONATHAN LUCAS ST, CSB 316 29425 #654-01-2002 L2005 **PDE** *012 †55

CORICA, Federico Alberto. 171 ASHLEY AVE 29425 #132-06-1995 L2003 **U** *020

CORLESS, John K. 1962 CHARLIE HALL BLVD 29414 #010-02-1977 L1978 **GE IM** *020 †20

CORN, William Chase. ■ 29401 #045-01-2007 *012

CORNISH-MC TIGHE, Denise. 2100 CHARLIE HALL BLVD 29414 #020-02-1980 L1981 **CHP** *020

CORTES, Cristina N. 96 JONATHAN LUCAS ST, STE 922 29425 #308-03-2000 L2005 **IM** *020 †20

CORTES, Gil Yosue. 135 RUTLEDGE ST, 11TH FL 29425 #042-02-2004 L2005 **D** *012

COSTA, Louis Edward, II. 247 CALHOUN ST 29401 #001-02-1982 L1983 **FPS** *020 †45

COSTA, Milton Sherman. 347 FOLLY RD, JAMES ISLAND MEDICAL CARE 29412 #045-01-1983 L1984 **GP** *020

COSTELLO, Philip. 171 ASHLEY AVE 29425 #917-22-1969 L2004 **DR NM** *020 †80,28

COTTER, John Patrick. 51 NASSAU ST 29403 #047-07-1989 L1994 **FM** *020 †18

COTTINGHAM, Sarah Stevens. 9298 MEDICAL PLAZA DR, RESIDENCY PROGRAM 29406 #045-01-2006 L2006 **FP** *012

COTTON, Peter. 96 JONATHAN LUCS ST CSB210, MEDICAL UNIV OF SOUTH CARO 29425 #917-07-1963 L1994 **GE** *020

COURTOY, Isabelle Marie T. 171 ASHLEY AVE 29425 #165-07-1983 L1987 **PD OS** *020

COVINGTON, M Samuel C. 1209 HIGHWAY 7 STE G, LOW COUNTRY PHYSICIANS 29407 #045-01-1984 L1986 **EM GP** *020

COX, Emily Susannah. 171 ASHLEY AVE, DEPT OF DERM 29425 #045-01-2005 L2005 **D** *012

COYLE, Pamela C. 316 CALHOUN ST 29401 #011-03-1969 L1999 **DR** *075 †80

CRAFT, Brandon Micael. ■ 29414 #055-01-2006 L2006 **IM** *012

CRAIG, Brian Alan. 125 DOUGHTY ST, STE 420 29403 #045-01-2001 L2004 **AN** *100 †05

CRAIG, Michael Lawrence. 171 ASHLEY AVE 29425 #045-01-2001 L2004 **CD** *012

CRAIGIE, James Ernest. 171 ASHLEY AVE 29425 #045-01-1993 L1995 **PS** *020 †65

CRATER, Dana De Bord. 2051 CHARLIE HALL BLVD, COASTAL PEDIATRIC ASSOCIAT 29414 #051-01-1999 L2002 **PD** *020 †55

CRATER, Scott Edmondson. 8 FARMFIELD AVE STE D 29407 #051-01-1999 L2000 **D** *020 †15

CRAWFORD, Fred Allen, Jr. 171 ASHLEY AVE 29425 #036-07-1967 L1979 **TS GS** *030 †85,90

CREASMAN, William Thos. 171 ASHLEY AVE, MEDICAL UNIVERSITY OF S.C. 29425 #048-04-1960 L1986 **GO GYN** *040 †30

CROFFEAD, George S. 2095 HENRY TECKLENBURG DR 29414 #045-01-1950 L1950 **OPH** *071 †35

CROOK, Erik Steven. ■ 29403 #045-01-2005 L2005 **IM** *012

CROTCH-HARVEY, Michael A. 171 ASHLEY AVE, MEDICAL UNIV OF SC 29425 #917-06-1985 L1995 *020

CRUMBLEY, Arthur J, III. 96 JONATHAN LUCAS ST 29425 #028-02-1974 L1986 **CD TTS** *040 †85,90

CRYMES, William Burke. 316 CALHOUN ST 29401 #045-01-1967 **CLP** *020 †50

CRYMES, William Burke, Jr. ■ 29412 #045-01-2003 **DR** *012

CUDDY, Brian Gerard. 2145 HENRY TCKLNBRG #200 29414 #035-03-1987 L1990 **NS OS** *020 †25

CUNNINGHAM, Mary Roseanne. 2231 S HOBSON AVE, RED NCCC 29405 #051-01-2002 L2002 **OSS** *012

CUNNINGHAM, Melissa Anne. ■ 29414 #041-14-2006 L2006 **IM** *012

CUOCO, Frank Anthony, Jr. 25 COURTENAY DR, UNIV OF SOUTH CAROLINA 29401 #010-02-2001 L2006 **ICE** *012

CURRIE, Alton Blue, Jr. 615 WESLEY DR STE 200 29407 #045-01-1964 L1964 **IM** *071

CURRY, Nancy L Stiles. 171 ASHLEY AVE 29425 #041-07-1972 L1981 **DR IM** *020 †80

CUSTER, John Vernon. 1 POSTON RD STE 145 29407 #020-12-1989 L1990 **P PYG** *020 †75

CUTSHALL, Christopher Mic. ■ 29412 #045-01-2008 *012

DALLMAN, Michael Dennis. ■ 29403 #012-01-2006 L2006 **PD** *012

DALTON, James David. 171 ASHLEY AVE 29425 #036-07-1972 L1977 **ORS OS** *020 †40

DALTON, James David, Jr. 171 ASHLEY AVE 29425 #036-07-1990 L1997 **ORS FSM** *020 †40

DALY, Kristin April. 18 FARMFIELD AVE 29407 #035-46-2000 L2004 **AN** *020 †05

DANIEL, Russell Kevin. 542 WAMPLER DR 29412 #012-01-1984 L1988 **AN** *020 †05

DANIEL, Stephen Lewis. 316 CALHOUN ST 29401 #012-05-1978 L1979 **EM P** *020 †16

DANTAS, Bruno Felipe. ■ 29412 #023-01-2004 L2004 **PTH** *012

DANTZLER, Brian Saml. 46 MARKFIELD DR STE A 29407 #045-01-1973 L1974 **PD AI** *020 †55,03

DANTZLER, Todd Ellis. 96 JONATHAN LUCAS ST, STE 210 29425 #045-01-1997 L2007 **GE IM** *020 †20

DARBY, Charles Pinckney. 310 BROAD ST STE 10, CTR FOR CHILD ADVOCACY 29401 #045-01-1959 L1959 **PD ID** *030 †55

DARDEN, Paul Martin, II. 135 RUTLEDGE ST RM 280Q, MED UNIV OF SO CARO 29425 #048-12-1981 L1988 **PD OS** *040 †55

DAVIDSON, Andrew Evin. 2270 ASHLEY CROSSING DR, CONSULTANTS 29414 #041-14-1987 L1998 **AI** *020 †20,03

DAVIDSON, John Leroy, Jr. 18 FARMFIELD AVE 29407 #017-20-1994 L1995 **AN** *020 †05

DAVIDSON, Scott Conrad. 316 CALHOUN ST, ROPER ST. FRANCIS HEALTHCA 29401 #051-07-1994 L1995 **IM** *020 †20

DAVIS, Brian Wayne. ■ 29407 #020-12-2006 L2006 **IM** *012

DAVIS, Craig Carlton. 169 ASHLEY AVE, MEDICAL UNIV. OF SOUTH CAR 29403 #012-05-2002 L2004 **PHO** *012

DAVIS, Grayce Pauline. 171 ASHLEY AVE, SURGERY 29425 #045-04-1998 L2003 **AN** *020 †05

DAVIS, Jacqueline D. 650 ELLIS OAK DR 29412 #045-01-1992 L1993 **PD** *020 †55

DAVIS, John P, Jr. 2270 ASHLEY CROSSING DR, STE 170 29414 #045-01-1988 L1991 **IM** *020 †20

DAVIS, Kimberly Smith. 376 CALHOUN ST 29401 #045-01-1993 L1995 **IM** *020 †20

DAVIS, Lance Lee. 316 CALHOUN ST, ROPER HOSPITAL 29401 #036-01-1997 L1998 **FM** *020 †18

DAVIS, Matthew Pate. 169 ASHLEY AVE, BOX 250333 29425 #047-06-1996 L1997 **PD** *020 †55

DAVIS, Theophilus Hamish. PO BOX 250625, 96 JONATHAN LUCAS ST 29425 #045-01-2000 L2000 **AN** *020

DAVOODI, Puya. 169 ASHLEY AVE, MEDICAL UNIVERSITY OF SOUT 29403 #012-05-2003 L2004 **GS** *012

DAWSON, Claudius Stuart. 16 WINDERMERE BLVD, SUMMERVILLE FAMILY PRACTIC 29407 #045-01-2000 L2000 **FM** *020 †18

DAWSON, Heather Rose. 6518 DORCHESTER RD 29418 #065-01-1980 L1994 **FM FPG** *020 †18

DAWSON, William Thomas, Jr. 125 DOUGHTY ST, STE 200 29403 #045-01-1976 L1981 **IM PUD** *050 †20

DAY, Terrence Anthony. 171 ASHLEY AVE 29425 #039-01-1989 L1999 **OTO HNS** *020 †45

DAYEMO, Kassamo. 1606 ASHLEY RIVER RD 29407 #275-01-1984 L1997 **GE IM** *020 †20

DEAL, Jeffery Lee. 1849 SAVAGE RD 29407 #045-01-1981 L1985 **OTO** *071 †45

DE ANTONIO, Miriam F. 171 ASHLEY AVE 29425 #045-01-1970 L1971 **P** *020 †75

DEATON, Paul Mc Neely, Jr. 3531 MARY ADER AVE # BLD 29414 #036-01-1974 L1975 **IM** *020 †20

DECKER-MULBRY, Mary M. 316 CALHOUN ST, ROPER HOSPITAL 29401 #003-01-1982 L1990 **IM RO** *020 †20,80

DE HAVEN, Ruth Schirmer. 1249A SAVANNAH HWY, ST ANDREWS MEDICAL 29407 #045-01-1982 L1993 **EM** *020

DEL BENE, Victor Enrico. 171 ASHLEY AVE, DEPARTMENT OF MEDICINE 29425 #010-02-1965 L1972 **IM ID** *071 †20

DELLINGER, Bonnie Beyer. ■ 29406 #422-01-2007 L2007 **EM** *012

DEL PORTO, George Bernard. 1470 TOBIAS GADSON BLVD, STE 201 29407 #047-05-1971 L1972 **PD U** *020 †95

DEL ROSARIO, Leonard D. ■ 29412 #028-34-1993 L1994 **IM** *020 †20

DE MASI, Alexander Wm. 615 WESLEY DR, STE 300 29407 #036-05-1959 L1966 **IM** *071 †20

DEMOS, Harry Andrew. 96 JONATHAN LUCAS ST, DEPT OF ORTHO SURG 29425 #045-01-1991 L1997 **ORS** *020 †40

DENNIS, Patrick H, Jr. 116 ASHLEY AVE STE B 29401 #045-01-1984 L1989 **OPH** *020 †35

DENNIS, Patrick Harley. 116 ASHLEY AVE STE B 29401 #045-01-1958 L1958 **OPH** *071 †35

DENNIS, Richard Blake. 615 WESLEY DR STE 100, CHARLESTON, P.A. 29407 #045-01-1979 L1985 **ORS OS** *020 †40

DENNIS, William Albert. 2093 HENRY TECKLENBURG DR, STE 306 29414 #045-01-1981 L1983 **OBG** *020 †30

DEROSIMO, John F, Jr. 25 COURTENAY DR STE 701, MSC 295 29401 #041-12-1994 L2004 **TS** *020 †85,90

DERRICK, Fletcher Carl. 641 SAINT ANDREWS BLVD, SPECIALISTS 29407 #045-01-1958 L1958 **U** *020 †95

DE SAUSSURE, Charlton. 316 CALHOUN ST 29401 #023-07-1945 L1950 **IM** *020 †20

DESOUKI, Mohamed Mokhtar. ■ 29425 #915-02-1990 L2006 **PTH** *012

DEVICENTE, Noah Manuel. ■ 29412 #011-03-2004 L2004 **GE** *012 †20

DE VITO, Peter Carl. 1050 SAINT ANDREWS BLVD 29407 #036-07-1969 L1971 **PS** *020 †65 ‡

DEWAAY, Deborah Julia. ■ 29407 #018-03-2005 L2005 **IM** *012

DEWHIRST, Brian David. 9313 MEDICAL PLAZA DR #202 29406 #019-02-1998 L1999 **FM** *020 †18

DE WITT, Rosalyn Abrevaya. ■ 29413 #025-12-1994 **IM** *100

DIAZ, Vanessa Astrud. 295 CALHOUN ST, MUSC FAMILY MED CTR 29425 #011-02-1999 L2002 **FM** *050 †18

DIBONA, Dee. 4115 DORCHESTER RD, STE 100 29405 #045-01-1994 L1995 **OBG** *020 †30

DILAWAR, Muhammad. 171 ASHLEY AVE, MUSC MEDICAL CENTER 29425 #704-15-1987 L1998 **PDC** *020 †55

DIXON, Damon Brian. 169 ASHLEY AVE, MEDICAL UNIVERSITY OF SOUT 29403 #037-01-2003 L2004 **PD** *100 †55

DIXON, Jennifer Ann. 96 JONATHAN LUCAS ST, MED UNIV OF S CAROLINA 29425 #017-20-2006 L2006 **GS** *012

DIXON, Sewell Hinton, Jr. 1851 SAM RITTENBERG BLVD 29407 #012-05-1964 L2001 **TS CD** *020 †85,90

DO, Jamie Hoitien. ■ 29412 #021-05-2007 L2007 **EM** *012

DOBSON, Joseph Vanlear. 171 ASHLEY AVE 29425 #012-05-1990 L2003 **PD** *020 †55

DOBSON, Richard Lawrence. 135 RUTLEDGE ST, P O BOX 250578 29425 #016-02-1953 L1979 **D** *040 †15

DODDS, Helen M. 109 BEE ST 29401 #045-01-1974 L1976 **PTH** *020 †50

DOELKEN, Peter. 171 ASHLEY AVE 29425 #409-42-1990 L2000 **PCC** *020 †20

DOIG, K Katrina Batson. 171 ASHLEY AVE 29425 #045-01-1983 L1984 **PD** *020 †55

DOLVEN, Sarah Ingrid. 1327 ASHLEY RIVER RD STE B 29407 #045-01-1996 L1998 **END IM** *020 †20

DOMM, Aaron Benjamin. 96 JONATHAN LUCAS ST, STE 210 29425 #038-43-2000 L2007 **GE** *020 †20

DOMM, Kathleen Kang. 2713 DANTZLER DR, SWEETGRASS PEDIATRICS 29406 #038-43-2001 L2007 **PD** *020 †55

DONATELLI, Paul Edmund. 316 CALHOUN ST, HOSPITALIST SERVICE 29401 #045-01-2004 L2008 **IM** *100 †20

DONOVAN-SHERPA, Katherine. 154 WENTWORTH ST 29401 #036-01-1982 L1983 **P N** *020

DORION, Margaret Elaine. ■ 29412 #045-01-2008 *012

DOROCIAK, Jeffery Jos. 2073 CHARLIE HALL BLVD 29414 #045-01-1988 L1989 **GE** *020 †20

DOUGLASS, George Woodward. 2097 HENRY TECKLENBURG DR, STE 201W 29414 #045-01-1965 L1965 **CD** *020

DOYLE, Kelly Elaine. PO BOX 250620, 171 ASHLEY AVE RM 202MUH 29425 #051-04-2003 L2003 **U** *012

DOZIER, Thomas Slade. 169 ASHLEY AVE, MEDICAL UNIV OF SOUTH CARO 29403 #045-01-2003 L2004 **OTO** *012

DRABKIN, Harry Adolph. ■ 29403 #019-02-1977 L2007 **ON HEM** *050 †20

DRAKE, Luke Matthew. ■ 29414 #017-20-2005 L2005 **IM** *012

DRAKE, Michael Thomas. 171 ASHLEY AVE, MED UNIV OF SC COLL OF MED 29425 #045-01-2008 *012

DRUMMOND, Fitzgerald E. 2097 HENRY TECKLENBURG DR, STE 305 29414 #051-04-2000 L2003 **PCC** *020 †20

DRUMMOND, Meredith Joyner. 181 CALHOUN ST, STUDENT HEALTH SERVICES 29424 #051-04-1997 L2003 **IM** *020 †20

DUBICK, Marc Nathan. 2097 HENRY TECKLENBURG DR, STE 203 29414 #020-12-1975 L1999 **AN PME** *020 †05

DUC, Thomas A, Jr. 18 FARMFIELD AVE 29407 #045-01-1983 L1987 **AN GS** *020 †05 ‡

DUCKETT, Ashley Ann. ■ 29412 #045-01-2003 L2007 **MPD** *100,55

DUGAN, Mary Margaret. 171 ASHLEY AVE, ATTN: MEDICAL STAFF OFFICE 29425 #010-02-1980 L2006 **PD** *020

DUKES, Thomas Harmon, III. 125 DOUGHTY ST, STE 460 29403 #036-01-1973 L1978 **N** *020 †75

DUNCAN, Jackson Thomas. 9231 MEDICAL PLAZA DR # A 29406 #045-01-1969 L1971 **CD IM** *020 †20

DUONG, Angie. ■ 29414 #051-04-2007 L2007 **PTH** *012

DURDEN, Angela F. 165 ASHLEY AVE # 309 29425 #021-06-2004 L2004 **PTH** *012

DURHAM, Ralsa Fuller. ■ 29414 #045-01-1971 L1977 **AM GP** *020

DURRENCE, Hugh Dowdy. 418 FOLLY RD 29412 #045-01-1995 L1996 **FM** *020 †18

DUSTAN, Lorraine Rung. 16 FULTON ST 29401 #045-01-1989 L1990 **P** *020 †75

EADS, Robert Stewart, Jr. 12 FARMFIELD AVE, STE E 29407 #051-01-1993 L1994 **IM** *020 †20

EADY, Maya Larah. ■ 29407 #012-01-2007 L2007 **PD** *012

EBERTS, Paul Thomas. ■ 29407 #047-20-2006 L2006 **PTH** *012

EDWARDS, Anne Louise. 2097 HENRY TECKLENBURG DR, STE 322W 29414 #045-01-1986 L1993 **PS** *020 †65

EDWARDS, James Eugene. 67 PRESIDENT ST RM PH243, DEPT OF PSYCHIATRIC 29425 #036-01-1987 L1992 **CHP P** *020 †75

EDWARDS, Jonathan Charles. 96 JONATHAN LUCAS ST, CLINICAL SCIENCES BUILDING 29425 #036-05-1992 L2007 **N** *020 †75

EDWARDS, Malcolm E, Jr. ■ 29412 #001-02-1967 L1980 **CD GP** *074

EDWARDS, Michael Lamar. 9300 MEDICAL PLAZA DR 29406 #047-06-1979 L1986 **CD VS** *020 †85,90

EGAN, Brent. 171 ASHLEY AVE, DIV OF CLINICAL PHARMACOLO 29425 #025-01-1978 L1992 **IM** *020 †20

EGAN, Thomas Christopher. 211 KING ST, CENEGENICS MEDICAL INSTITU 29401 #035-15-1976 L2005 **CD IM** *020 †20

EGEDE, Leonard Ehianu. 135 RUTLEDGE ST RM 1241, MEDICAL UNIV OF SOUTH CARO 29425 #690-06-1990 L1999 **IM EP** *020 †20

EGLESTON, David Dubose. 418 FOLLY RD, STE A 29412 #045-01-1973 L1974 **FM** *020 †18

EGLESTON, Du Bose, Jr. ■ 29414 #012-01-1938 L1947 **GP GS** *071 †85

EHMANN, Carl Wm. ■ 29401 #035-06-1967 L1970 **D** *030 †15

EHRENCLOU, Jesse Orvar. ■ 29407 #045-01-2004 L2004 **AN** *012

EHRENS, Karl Leonard. ■ 29414 #045-01-2008 *012

EICHER, Dorothea Jenkins. 171 ASHLEY AVE 29425 #045-01-1985 L1993 **NPM PD** *020 †55

EL-BAHTIMI, Reem Mohamed. 171 ASHLEY AVE, MEDICAL UNIV OF SC 29425 #915-03-1988 L1997 **PTH** *020 †50

EL-BAYOUMI, Ezzat. ■ 29414 #759-03-1996 L2005 **PCC** *012 †20

ELLERKMANN, Edzard. 169 ASHLEY AVE # 202, DEPT OF ANESTHESIOLOGY 29403 #409-16-1988 L2002 **APM** *012

ELLIOTT, Bruce Michael. 96 JONATHAN LUCAS ST STE 4, MEDICAL UNIVERSITY OF SOUT 29425 #030-05-1977 L1986 **VS GS** *040 †85

ELLIOTT, Laurie Alexis. 3531 MARY ADER AVE, STE C 29414 #045-01-1999 L2004 **OPH** *020 †35

ELLISON, David Michael. 125 DOUGHTY ST, STE 500 29403 #036-07-1984 L1990 **ON HEM** *020 †20

ELLISON, Haskell S. ■ 29412 #045-01-1951 L1951 **IM CD** *020 †20

ELLISON, Wm Blount, Jr. 125 DOUGHTY ST, STE 370 29403 #045-01-1975 L1977 **CD IM** *020 †20

ELLYN, Catherine Kane. 18 FARMFIELD AVE 29407 #045-01-1988 L1989 **AN** *020 †05

EL-ZAWAHRY, Ahmed Mokhtar. 171 ASHLEY AVE 29425 #915-05-1994 L2005 **U** *012

ENTERKIN, Jacob Elidge. 9298 MEDICAL PLAZA DR, RESIDENCY PROGRAM 29406 #036-08-2007 L2007 **TY** *012

EPPS, Amy Rawl. 135 RUTLEDGE ST, STE 1201 29425 #045-01-1998 L1999 **CD** *020 †20

EPTING, Anne Cox. ■ 29401 #045-01-1979 L1980 **AN PME** *020

ERICH, Mark A. 316 CALHOUN ST 29401 #045-01-1987 L2001 **EM** *020 †16

ERIKSON, Christopher Jose. ■ 29414 #036-01-2007 L2007 **GS** *012

ESCOTO, Heather Dawn. 171 ASHLEY AVE 29425 #055-01-2002 L2006 **PHO** *012

ESKRIDGE, Matthew Ramsey. ■ 29412 #036-05-2003 L2004 **U** *012

ESNAOLA, Nestor Felix. 96 JONATHAN LUCAS ST # 420 29425 #023-07-1993 L2004 **GS AS** *020 †85

EVANS, Joshua Timothy. 96 JONATHAN LUCAS ST 29425 #028-34-2004 L2004 **IM** *100 †20

EVATT, Clay Welborn, Jr. 206 BAKER MEDICAL CENTER 29405 #045-01-1957 L1957 **OPH** *071 †35

EVERMAN, Paul Dawson, Jr. 171 ASHLEY AVE 29425 #020-12-1994 L1995 **CHP P** *020 †75

EVERT, Howard Allen. 30 BEE ST, CAROLINA FAMILY CARE 29403 #026-04-1977 L1994 **IM** *020 †20

EZMAN, Lorianne Therese. 2097 HENRY TCKLNBRG #312W 29414 #038-40-1991 L1998 **OBG** *020 †30

FAIAS, Sandra. ■ 29403 #770-02-1999 L2004 *100

FAIRFAX, Amelia. 1483 TOBIAS GADSON BLVD, STE 107 29407 #045-01-1994 L2001 **FM** *020 †18

FAISON, Thomas Gideon. ■ 29407 #045-01-1932 L1964 **OS P** *071 †70

FARMER, Laurance David. ■ 29414 #036-05-2004 L2007 **CD** *012 †20

FARRAR, Emily K. ■ 29403 #045-01-2002 L2004 **RHU** *012 †20

FARRAR, Joshua Daniel. 171 ASHLEY AVE 29425 #045-01-2004 L2004 **OTO** *012

FAYSSOUX, James Erwin. 316 CALHOUN ST, GREENVILLE HOSPITAL SYSTEM 29401 #045-01-1998 L2000 **IM** *020 †20

FECHTER, Cary Erwin. 2270 ASHLEY CROSSING DR, STE 160 29414 #045-01-1979 L1982 **PUD IM** *020 †20

FEINGOLD, Steven Alan. 2095 HENRY TECKLENBURG DR 29414 #036-07-1995 L1999 **EM** *020 †16

FELBER, William John. ■ 29407 #045-01-1971 L1972 **P** *075

FELDMANN, Mark Ernst, Jr. 169 ASHLEY AVE, PO BOX 25033 29403 #051-04-2003 L2004 **GS** *012

FELLER, Douglas Mark. 9297 MEDICAL PLAZA DR, STE C 29406 #038-45-1991 L1992 **AN** *020 †05

FENG, Wuwei. 96 JONATHAN LUCAS ST, STE 309 29425 #243-76-1996 L2006 **N** *012

FENNING, Robert Lawrence. 171 ASHLEY AVE 29425 #050-02-1964 L2001 **ON HEM** *071 †20

FERGUSON, John Matthew. ■ 29412 #045-01-2008 *012

FERMO, Ricardo Jose. 29 LEINBACH DR B, MUSC BEHAVIOR HEALTH 29407 #748-08-1988 L1995 **P** *020 †75

FERNANDES, Jyotika Kanwar. 171 ASHLEY AVE 29425 #495-08-1987 L2002 **IM** *020 †20

FERNANDES, Valerian Lancy. 135 RUTLEDGE ST STE 1201 29425 #495-52-1993 L2002 **IC CD** *020 †20

FERNANDEZ, Jennifer Marie. ■ 29417 #045-01-2008 *012

FERNANDEZ, Luis, Jr. 29407 #051-04-1939 L1946 **IM EM** *020 †20

FERNANDEZ, Luis Alejandro. ■ 29407 #045-01-2007 L2007 **P** *012

FERNANDEZ, Miguel Jacobo. PO BOX 250333, 169 ASHLEY AVE RM 202 29425 #012-22-2004 L2004 **DR** *012

FEUSSNER, John Roy. 96 JONATHAN LUCAS ST, MEDICAL UNIVERSITY OF SC 8 29425 #050-02-1973 L2004 **IM HEM** *050 †20

FICKLING, William Edward. 96 JONATHAN LUCAS ST, STE 210 29425 #917-19-1990 L2001 **GE** *050

FIELD, Gregory Robert. 9329 MEDICAL PLAZA DR 29406 #032-01-1993 L1994 **GS** *020 †85

FIELD, Larry Clark, Jr. PO BOX 250912, 167 ASHLEY AVE STE 301 29425 #016-11-2001 L2006 **CCA** *100 †05

FIGUEROA, Silkia Mercedes. 29414 #042-01-2003 L2008 **PD** *100 †55

FINCH, Bertram Carlos, III. 2145 HENRY TECKLENBURG DR, STE 270 29414 #036-01-1971 L1972 **OBG** *020 †30

FINN, Albert F, Jr. 1879 SAVAGE RD 29407 #035-15-1984 L1992 **AI IM** *020 †50,03,20

FISHER, Carla Suzanne. 96 JONATHAN LUCAS ST 29425 #041-01-2005 L2005 **GS** *012

FISHER, Courtney Meredith. 2095 HENRY TECKLENBURG DR 29414 #035-08-1978 L1983 **U** *020

FISHER, Dennis Jeffrey. 21 GAMECOCK AVE STE E 29407 #045-01-1975 L1977 **GP** *020

FISHMAN, Richard Lee. 9297 MEDICAL PLAZA DR, STE C 29406 #012-01-1989 L1990 **AN** *020 †05

FITTS, C Thos. 2270 ASHLEY CROSSING DR, STE 155 29414 #041-01-1957 L1965 **GS** *071 †85

FITTS, Robert Wade. 2270 ASHLEY CROSSING DR, STE 155 29414 #045-01-1985 L1990 **GS** *020 †85

FITZPATRICK, David Dierks. 2352 ASHLEY RIVER RD 29414 #045-01-1992 L1993 **PM FM** *020 †18

FLAKE, Charles Lee. 2100 CHARLIE HALL BLVD 29414 #045-01-1999 L2001 **CHP** *020 †75

FLOYD, Rebecca Hope. ■ 29412 #045-01-2008 *012

FLUME, Patrick Allen. 171 ASHLEY AVE 29425 #048-13-1987 L1993 **PUD CCM** *020 †20

FOGLE, William Julian, III. 48 COURTENAY DR 29403 #045-01-1968 L1968 **OPH** *071 †35

FOLK, Jeffrey Wayne. 18 FARMFIELD AVE 29407 #045-01-1991 L1992 **APM** *020 †05

FONTENOT, Bennett Boustan. ■ 29412 #021-05-2007 L2007 **GS** *012

FORBUS, Geoffrey Allen. 165 ASHLEY AVE, RM 603 29425 #027-01-1997 L2001 **MPD** *020 †55

FORD, Dee Walker. 96 JONATHAN LUCAS ST, MEDICAL UNIVERSITY OF SC 29425 #023-07-1999 L2002 **PCC** *100 †20

FORNEY, John Joseph. ■ 29403 #048-14-2000 L2003 **FM** *020 †18

FORREST, Leonard Edward. 1941 SAVAGE RD, STE 100E 29407 #041-09-1979 L1993 **PM ORS** *020 †60

FORTNEY, John Arthur. 169 ASHLEY AVE 29403 #012-22-2005 L2006 **RO** *012

FOSTER, Emily Spear. 109 BEE ST, DEPART OF VETERANS AFFAIRS 29401 #045-01-1975 L1976 **IM GE** *020

FOSTER, Richard Plato, Jr. 9330 MEDICAL PLAZA DR, TRIDENT MEDICAL CENTER 29406 #045-01-1980 L1981 **FM EM** *020 †18

FOUST, Milton Jack. 67 PRESIDENT ST, MEDICAL UNIV OF SC-PSYCHIA 29425 #047-05-1984 L1997 **P** *020 †75

FOWLER, Andrew Harold. 135 RUTLEDGE ST, STE 1212 29425 #045-01-2001 L2004 **IC** *012

FOWLER, Sandra Lynn. 96 JONATHAN LUCAS ST, DEPARTMENT OF PEDIATRICS 29425 #047-06-1983 L1990 **PD ID** *020 †12

FOX, Donald Lee. 171 ASHLEY AVE, MED UNIV OF S.C 29425 #051-04-1973 L1975 **IM** *040 †20

FOX, James B. ■ 29414 #045-01-2007 L2007 **P** *012

FOXWORTH, John Michael. 3 GAMECOCK AVE, STE 3048 29407 #045-01-1968 L1968 **P** *071 †75

FRAMPTON, Joel Wyman. 2097 HENRY TECKLENBURG DR, STE 312 29414 #045-01-1977 L1979 **OBG** *020 †30

FRANKEL, Bruce Michael. PO BOX 250616, 96 JONATHAN LUCAS ST STE 29425 #035-15-1994 L2005 **NS** *020 †25

FRANKEL, Loren B. 1364 ASHLEY RIVER RD, ASHLEY RIVER OB/GYN, P.C. 29407 #035-15-1994 L2005 **OBG** *020 †30

FRANKLIN, Cheri Lateisha. 30 BEE ST 29403 #045-01-1999 L2000 **IM** *020

FRANKLIN, John Edward. 316 CALHOUN ST 29401 #024-05-1978 L1993 **FPG IM** *020 †20

FRANZBLAU, Arnold H. 125 DOUGHTY ST, STE 680 29403 #045-01-1951 L1951 **U** *071

FREEDLAND, Philip Norman. 109 BEE ST 29401 #025-07-1965 L1984 **R** *020 †20

FREEDY, John Richard. 9298 MEDICAL PLAZA DR 29406 #045-01-2002 L2004 **FM** *100 †18

FREEMAN, Joel Robt. 109 BEE ST 29401 #012-01-1972 L1975 **IM** *020 †20

FREEMAN, Stephanie Anne. PO BOX 250333, 169 ASHLEY AVE 29425 #020-12-2006 L2006 **OBG** *012

FREI-LAHR, Debra Ann. 171 ASHLEY AVE, MUSC 903 CSB 29425 #016-02-1979 L1989 **IM HO** *050 †20

FREITAS, Eduardo Augusto. ■ 29407 #187-45-2000 L2006 **ID** *012 †20

FRERKING, Ilka Dietlinde. 171 ASHLEY AVE 29425 #409-38-2000 L2007 **AN** *012

FRIEDMAN, Brad Alan. ■ 29412 #012-01-2003 L2007 **PDC** *012 †55

FRIEDMAN, Richard Joel. 1012 PHYSICIANS DR, CHARLESTON ORTHO ASSOC 29414 #065-01-1980 L1986 **ORS** *020 †40

FRITHSEN, Ivar Leslie. 295 CALHOUN ST, DEPT OF FAMILY MEDICINE MU 29425 #041-15-2002 L2004 **FM** *100 †18

FRITZ, Julie Ann. 9298 MEDICAL PLAZA DR, TRIDENT FAMILY MED-RESD PR 29406 #038-41-2007 L2007 **FP** *012

FRY, Parrish Danen. ■ 29412 #045-01-2008 *012

FRYE, Michael Duane. 171 ASHLEY AVE 29425 #020-12-1983 L1986 **PUD CCM** *020 †20

FUDENBERG, Betty S Roof. 171 ASHLEY AVE 29425 #036-07-1949 L1974 **END IM** *071 †20

FUDENBERG, H Hugh. 171 ASHLEY AVE 29425 #016-02-1953 L1975 **IG** *071

FULFER, Jamie Lynn. ■ 29412 #016-45-2004 L2004 **OBG** *012

FULLER, Kathleen Marie. ■ 29407 #045-01-2007 L2007 **AN** *012

FUNKE, Frederick Walter, Jr. ■ 29414 #045-01-2007 L2007 **IM** *012

FUNSCH, David John. 1 POSTON RD, STE 145 29407 #041-14-1981 L1992 **P** *020 †75

FYLSTRA, Donald Lee. 96 JONATHAN LUCAS ST, DEPT.OF OBSTETRICS/GYNECOL 29425 #047-05-1976 L1982 **OBG** *020 †30

GADDY, Bryant Louise. 171 ASHLEY AVE, MED UNIV OF SC COLL OF MED 29425 #045-01-2007 L2007 **P** *012

GADDY, Joe Ellis, Jr. 135 RUTLEDGE ST, 12TH FL 29425 #036-01-1971 L1972 **CD IM** *020 †20

GAGLIARDI, Elizabeth Alex. ■ 29407 #051-01-2005 L2005 **OBG** *012

GAINERS, Madeliene Elaine. ■ 29407 #041-12-2005 L2007 **P** *012

GAJEWSKI, Kelly Kathleen. ■ 29414 #023-07-2002 L2005 **PDC** *012 †55

GALBRIATH, Gillian Mary P. MUSC MED CTR 29425 #917-19-1971 L1981 **IG** *040

GAMBLE, William B, III. 1243 SAVANNAH HWY 29407 #045-01-1978 L1979 **PD** *020 †55

GAME, Daniel K. 2093 HENRY TECKLENBURG DR, 205 EAST 29414 #957-08-1980 L2000 **CCM PUD** *020 †20

GAMM, Stanford Ralph. ■ 29407 #016-11-1943 L1944 **P PYA** *072 †75

GARDNER, Jonathan Parks. ■ 29412 #045-01-2005 L2005 **AN** *012

GARIN, Margaret Marie. ■ 29403 #028-02-2008 L2008 *012

GARIN, Matthew Thomas. ■ 29403 #045-01-2008 *012

GARR, David Ross. 295 CALHOUN ST 29425 #036-07-1972 L1985 **FM** *020 †18

GARROW, Donald Albert. 171 ASHLEY AVE 29425 #305-01-2001 L2004 **GE** *012

GASKINS, Linda Diane. 171 ASHLEY AVE 29425 #045-01-1984 **IM** *020 †20

GASPER, Fulton Jacob. 48 COURTENAY DR 29403 #045-01-1984 L1985 **OPH** *020 †35

GATES, Shola Tenesia. ■ 29414 #010-03-2008 *012

GATGOUNIS, John. 125 DOUGHTY ST, STE 420 29403 #045-01-1964 L1964 **AN** *071

GAULT, Irina Ellen. ■ 29403 #045-01-2008 *012

GAZES, Peter Christopher. 96 JONATHAN LUCAS ST, STE 816 29425 #045-01-1944 L1944 **CD IM** *071 †20

GEER, Andrew Eugene, III. 18 FARMFIELD AVE 29407 #045-01-1990 L1991 **AN** *020 †05

GEER, Charles Carroll. 293 E BAY ST 29401 #045-01-1969 L1969 **IM** *020 †20

GEILFUSS, Charles Jos, III. 9330 MEDICAL PLAZA DR, PATHOLOGY DEPARTMENT 29406 #045-01-1987 L1994 **PTH** *020 †50

GEILS, George F, Jr. 125 DOUGHTY ST, STE 500 29403 #045-01-1990 L1996 **HO IM** *020 †20

GEILS, George Frederick. 125 DOUGHTY ST, STE 500 29403 #045-01-1966 L1966 **HO IM** *020 †20

GEILS, Meghan Ondo. 776 DANIEL ELLIS DR, SEACOAST PEDIATRICS 29412 #001-02-1995 L1997 **PD** *020 †20

GEILS, Wills Christian. 615 WESLEY DR STE 320 29407 #045-01-1992 L1995 **CD** *020 †20

GELFAND, Yevgeny. ■ 29412 #035-08-2006 L2006 **MP** *012

GEORGE, Mark Stork. 171 ASHLEY AVE, MUSIC PSY 29425 #045-01-1985 L1986 **P N** *020 †75

GHAREEB, Cynthia Louise. ■ 29414 #055-01-2007 L2007 **PD** *012

GHEGAN, Mark Drury. 169 ASHLEY AVE, MEDICAL UNIV OF SOUTH CARO 29403 #012-01-2003 L2004 **OTO** *012

GIBERT, Stephen Pierre, Jr. 171 ASHLEY AVE 29425 #012-01-1997 L2001 **AN** *020 †20

GIBLIN, Erica Marie. 96 JONATHAN LUCAS ST, SUITE 409 CSB BOX 250612 29425 #035-15-2002 L2007 **TS** *012 †85

GIBSON, Maria Valdimir. 295 CALHOUN ST, BOX 250192 29425 #913-08-1983 L2002 **FM** *020 †18

GILBRETH, Edward M. 650 ELLIS OAK DR 29412 #045-01-1988 L1989 **CCM PUD** *020 †20

GILKESON, Gary Steven. 171 ASHLEY AVE 29425 #048-12-1979 L1996 **RHU** *050 †20

GILLESPIE, Marion Boyd. 135 RUTLEDGE ST, POST OFFICE BOX 250550 29425 #023-07-1994 L2000 **OTO** *020 †45

GILLEY, Sandra Kaye. 171 ASHLEY AVE, DEPT OF PULMON & CRITIC 29425 #001-06-2004 L2007 **PCC** *012 †20

GILMAN, Charles Samuel. 171 ASHLEY AVE 29425 #008-02-1979 L1980 **EM IM** *020 †20,16

GITTER, Morris Frederic. 2095 HENRY TECKLENBURG DR, EMERGENCY DEPARTMENT 29414 #035-08-1995 L1999 **EM** *020 †16

GLASER, John Arthur. 96 JONATHAN LUCAS ST # 708 29425 #035-45-1982 L1993 **ORS** *020 †40

GLASSMAN, Armand B. 173 ASHLEY AVE, BOX 250504 29425 #010-02-1964 L1976 **CLP NM** *071 †50,28 ‡

GLENN, James Allen Lester. 171 ASHLEY AVE 29425 #045-01-1967 L1967 **CD IM** *020 †20

GLENN, Joshua Brian. 169 ASHLEY AVE 29425 #012-22-2002 L2004 **GS** *012

GODDARD, Emily Reiter. ■ 29407 #051-04-2004 L2004 **P** *012

GODDARD, John Christopher. ■ 29407 #051-04-2004 L2004 **OTO** *012

GOEBEL, Jason Andrew. 135 RUTLEDGE ST STE 1201, HEART & VASC CTR 29425 #036-08-2003 L2006 **CD** *012 †20

GOEDECKE, Aimee Agresta. 1243 SAVANNAH HWY 29407 #045-01-1997 L2001 **PD** *020 †55

GOETZL, Laura Marie. 171 ASHLEY AVE 29425 #005-02-1993 L2005 **OBG** *020 †30

GOLD, Michael Robt. 135 RUTLEDGE ST STE 1201 29425 #007-02-1985 L2002 **CD IM** *020 †20

GOLDSBERRY, Grant Theodor. ■ 29407 #018-03-2005 L2005 **DR** *012

GOLDSBERRY, Jodi Annette. ■ 29407 #018-03-2005 L2005 **IM** *012

GOLDSTEIN, Marshall. 2095 HENRY TECKLENBURG DR, NEONATOLOGY SERVICE 29414 #035-06-1981 L1997 **NPM PD** *020 †55

GOLDSTEIN, Monica M. ■ 29412 #035-06-1981 L1984 **IM** *020

GOLLER, Jeffrey Mark. 109 BEE ST, EMERGENCY DEPARTMENT 29401 #038-41-1986 L1987 **EM** *020 †16

GOMEZ, Juanmanuel. 9330 MEDICAL PLAZA DR 29406 #264-18-1985 L2002 **IM ID** *020 †20

GONSALVES, Wanda Clark. 171 ASHLEY AVE 29425 #020-12-1984 L2003 **FM** *040 †18

GONZALEZ, Javier Hernando. ■ 29414 #264-01-1998 L2005 **PDC** *012

GONZALEZ, Joseph Ivan. 209 FAIRFIELD OFFICE PARK 29407 #649-01-1956 L1987 **OS OM** *072

GOOD, Annemarie E. 1871 SAVAGE RD 29407 #036-05-1999 L2001 **PD** *020 †55

GOODIER, Christopher Gill. ■ 29407 #045-01-2007 L2007 **P** *012

GOODNIGHT, William H, III. 171 ASHLEY AVE 29425 #036-01-1994 L2005 **MFM** *020 †20

GOODROE, Randall Nix. 135 RUTLEDGE ST STE 1201, BOX 250592 29425 #045-01-2001 L2002 **IC** *012

GOPAL, Anjali Rajdeva. ■ 29407 #016-11-2005 L2006 **IM** *012

GOPASETTY, Mahesh Srisail. 96 JONATHAN LUCAS ST 29425 #495-37-1998 L2007 **P** *100

GORDON, Bertha Lynn. 171 ASHLEY AVE, DEPT OF PSYCHIATRY 29425 #836-01-1988 L1995 **P** *020 †75

GORDON, Leonie. 169 ASHLEY AVE, P O BOX 250322 29403 #836-02-1973 L1978 **NM END** *020 †28

GORDY, Stephanie Dawn. 96 JONATHAN LUCAS ST, RM *202 MAIN HOSPITAL 29425 #012-22-2003 L2005 **GS** *012

GOROD, Herbert L. NEAR I-26 & MONTAGUE AV 29418 #011-03-1971 L1972 **P GP** *030 †75

GOTTESMAN, Jay David. 167 ASHLEY AVE STE 301, DEPARTMENT OF ANESTHESIA 29403 #045-01-1988 L1990 **AN** *020 †05

GOURDIN, Theodore G. 1962 CHARLIE HALL BLVD 29414 #045-01-1985 L1986 **GE IM** *020 †20
GOUST, Jean-Michael C. UNIV OF SC 29425 #396-06-1965 L1980 **IG N** *050
GRADY, Jennifer Ann. 96 JONATHAN LUCAS ST 29425 #020-02-2003 L2004 **OTO** *012
GRAF, Christian David. 9330 MEDICAL PLAZA DR, TRIDENT EMERGENCY PHYSICIA 29406 #045-01-1999 L2001 **EM** *020 †16
GRAHAM, Patricia Crim. PO BOX 250333, 169 ASHLEY AVE 29425 #001-06-2006 L2006 **N** *012
GRATZICK, George Elmore. 18 FARMFIELD AVE 29407 #045-01-1984 L1987 **AN** *020 †05
GRAY, Kevin Michael. 67 PRESIDENT ST, RM 230 29425 #045-01-2000 L2001 **P** *100 †75
GRAYSON, John Michael. 125 DOUGHTY ST, STE 370 29403 #045-01-1975 L1978 **CD** *020 †20
GREEN, Mark Ronald. 171 ASHLEY AVE 29425 #024-01-1970 L1997 **ON** *050 †20
GREENBERG, Raymond Seth. 171 ASHLEY AVE, MED UNIV.OF S CAROLINA 29425 #036-07-1979 L2003 **PD** *074
GREER, Elizabeth White. 169 ASHLEY AVE, PO BOX 25033 29403 #045-01-1999 L2003 **NM** *100 †80
GREGG, David, IV. PO BOX 250592, 135 RUTLEDGE AVE STE 1201 29425 #035-01-1999 L2006 **CD** *100 †20
GREGG, Jeffery Rusten. 316 CALHOUN ST, ROPER RADIOLOGISTS, PA 29401 #055-01-2001 L2007 **DR** *100
GREGORIE, Henry B, Jr. 316 CALHOUN ST 29401 #045-01-1953 L1953 **GS TS** *071 †85,90
GRIESEMER, David Arnold. 96 JONATHAN LUCAS ST, MED UNIV SC DEPT NEURLGY 29425 #023-07-1976 L1993 **CHN CN** *030 †75
GRIFFIN, Charles Narey. 171 ASHLEY AVE, MUSC, DEPT OF RADIOLOGY 29425 #010-01-1959 L1966 **DR** *071 †80
GRIFFITHS, John Calvin. 171 ASHLEY AVE 29425 #917-18-1954 L1999 **OS** *071
GRIMM, Bennett Douglas. 71 1/2 LINE ST 29403 #012-01-2006 L2006 **ORS** *012
GRISSETT, Kathleen Brewer. 169 ASHLEY AVE, MEDICAL UNIVERSITY OF SC 29425 #011-04-2003 L2004 **CHP** *012
GROAT, Brian James. PO BOX 250333, 169 ASHLEY AVE 29425 #021-01-2003 L2006 **OPH** *012
GROCE, Jeffery Royce. ■ 29412 #020-02-2001 L2007 **GE** *100
GROSS, John Allen. 171 ASHLEY AVE, MED UNIV OF SOUTH CAROLINA 29425 #038-40-1969 L1979 **N P** *040 †75
GROSS, Richard Henry. 171 ASHLEY AVE, LSB 708 29425 #036-07-1965 L1971 **OP** *040 †40
GROSSMAN, William Jos. 152 RUTLEDGE AVE 29403 #045-01-1972 L1974 **CD** *020 †20
GRUBER, Frank H, Jr. 316 CALHOUN ST 29401 #012-05-1952 L1957 **R CLP** *020 †80,28
GRUBER, Karl Kulle. 9330 MEDICAL PLAZA DR 29406 #045-01-1992 L1994 **PCP** *020 †50
GRUSH, Owen Chas. 171 ASHLEY AVE 29425 #035-45-1964 L1974 **P PHO** *020 †55,75
GUE, Thomas Benjamin. 1483 TOBIAS GADSON BLVD, STE 105 29407 #045-01-1967 L1967 **PD** *020 †55
GUIDRY, Orin Frederick. 25 COURTENAY DR, STE 4200 29401 #021-05-1970 L2007 **AN CCA** *020 †05
GUIMARAES, Marcelo Silvei. PO BOX 250333, 169 ASHLEY AVE 29425 #187-02-1998 L2004 **VIR** *100
GULDAN, George Joseph, III. 169 ASHLEY AVE, BOX 250333 29403 #045-04-2003 L2004 **AN** *020
GULINO, Joseph Leonard. PO BOX 250333, 169 ASHLEY AVE 29425 #051-04-2006 L2006 **P** *012
GUPTA, Monika. 171 ASHLEY AVE 29425 #495-45-1997 L2003 **NEP** *020 †20
GUSTAFSON, Kristina Kay. 135 RUTLEDGE ST 29425 #016-45-2000 L2003 **PD** *020 †55
GWYNETTE, Mcleod F. 29 LEINBACH DR B, MUSC - BEHAVIORAL HEALTH 29407 #045-01-2000 L2006 **P** *020 †75
HABIB, Amos Quintino. ■ 29407 #045-01-2003 **DR** *012
HABIB, David Michael. 171 ASHLEY AVE 29425 #036-05-1983 L1989 **PD** *020 †55
HADZIJAHIC, Neven. 1962 CHARLIE HALL BLVD, CHARLESTON GASTROENTEROLOG 29414 #957-08-1986 L1997 **GE** *020 †20
HAHM, Joon Soo. 171 ASHLEY AVE 29425 #583-13-1975 L1996 *020
HAILE, Julia Springs. 316 CALHOUN ST, ROPER ST FRANCIS HEALTHCAR 29401 #045-01-1981 L2004 **ID** *020 †20
HAINER, Barry L. 295 CALHOUN ST 29425 #010-02-1976 L1977 **FM FPG** *020 †18
HALFORD, Jonathan Jacob. 326 CALHOUN ST 29401 #045-01-1996 L2003 **CN SME** *100 †75
HALL, Laine Marie. ■ 29412 #055-01-2004 L2004 **MP** *012
HALLETT, John Wm. 316 CALHOUN ST, VASCULAR LAB 3RD FLOOR 29401 #036-07-1973 L2004 **VS GS** *020 †85
HALSTEAD, Lucinda Ann. 135 RUTLEDGE ST 29425 #010-01-1981 L1986 **OTO** *040 †45
HALUSHKA, Perry Victor. 173 ASHLEY AVE RM 102BSB, MEDICAL U OF S CAROLINA 29425 #016-02-1970 L1974 **IM PA** *050 †20
HALY, Emily Adams. ■ 29401 #045-01-2004 L2004 **IM** *012
HAM, Forrest Cleave. 2095 HENRY TECKLENBURG DR, DEPT OF RADIOLOGY, ST FRAN 29414 #047-05-1982 L1983 **DR** *020 †80
HAMILTON, Emily Lauren. ■ 29407 #003-01-2007 L2007 **PD** *012
HAMILTON, Jonathan Nathan. 96 JONATHAN LUCAS ST 29425 #051-04-2005 L2005 **U** *012
HAMILTON, Norwood Brent. 1938 CHARLIE HALL BLVD # A 29414 #045-01-1999 L2000 **NEP** *100 †20
HAMMOND, Natalie Annette. 169 ASHLEY AVE, MEDICAL UNIVERSITY OF SC 29403 #045-01-2003 L2004 **OBG** *020
HAMNER, Mark Benj. 109 BEE ST, 116 MENTAL HEALTH VAMC 29401 #036-01-1982 L1991 **P** *020 †75
HAMPTON, Archibald A. 2095 HENRY TECKLENBURG DR 29414 #011-03-1981 L1987 **ID** *020 †20
HAMPTON, Marta Toruno. 635 SAINT ANDREWS BLVD 29407 #011-03-1985 L1987 **D DMP** *020 †15
HAMRICK, Miller Carlton. 96 JONATHAN LUCAS ST 29425 #012-22-2005 L2007 **GS** *012
HANCOCK, Laura Gayle. 171 ASHLEY AVE 29425 #022-75-2003, ▲ L2004 **PFP** *012
HANLEY, Michael. 9298 MEDICAL PLAZA DR, RESIDENCY PROGRAM 29406 #051-01-2006 L2006 **DR** *012
HANNEGAN, Christopher P. 171 ASHLEY AVE, MUSC DEPARTMENT OF RADIOLO 29425 #045-01-1995 L2000 **VIR** *020 †80
HANNEGAN, Sandra Dianne. 8 FARMFIELD AVE STE D 29407 #045-01-1995 L2000 **D** *020 †15
HANNUN, Yusuf Awni. 171 ASHLEY AVE, BASIC SCIENCE BLDG 29425 #605-01-1981 L1985 **HEM** *050
HANSEN, Samantha Ford. PO BOX 250333, 169 ASHLEY AVE 29425 #023-07-2005 L2005 **AN** *012
HARDESTY, Susan Jones. 171 ASHLEY AVE 29425 #036-01-1990 L1991 **P PFP** *020 †75
HAREN, Lydia Ward. 2777 SPEISSEGGER DR 29405 #036-01-1997 L1998 **P** *020 †55
HAREN, William Blake. 109 BEE ST, DEPT OF MENTAL HEALTH 29401 #047-20-1997 L1999 **OS** *020 †20,75
HARGROVE, Kathryn Manning. 2093 HENRY TECKLENBURG DR 29414 #045-01-1987 L1988 **OBG** *020 †30

HARLEY, Russell A, Jr. 169 ASHLEY AVE, STE HD281 29403 #045-01-1965 L1965 **PTH OS** *040 †50
HARMON, Joseph Michael. 316 CALHOUN ST DEPT PATH 29401 #036-01-1970 L1977 **PTH** *020 †50
HARPER, Brock Evan. ■ 29412 #048-02-2005 L2005 **IM** *012
HARPER, Reginald Howard. 334 E BAY ST, STE 161 29401 #045-01-1980 L1987 **OBG** *020 †30
HARPER, Thomas Bailey. 2270 ASHLEY CROSSING DR, CONSULTANTS 29414 #021-01-1973 L1981 **PDA** *020 †55,03
HARRELL, Allen Lamar. 333 FOLLY RD 29412 #045-01-1956 L1956 **PD** *071
HARRELL, Laurie Ray. 9330 MEDICAL PLAZA DR 29406 #045-01-1990 L1991 **RO** *020 †80
HARTSOCK, Langdon All. 171 ASHLEY AVE, MUSC #036-07-1987 L1996 **OTR** *040 †40
HARVEY, Susan C. 167 ASHLEY AVE STE 301, DEPT OF ANESTHESIOLGY, PO 29403 #045-01-1988 L1990 **AN** *020 †05
HARVIN, Glenn Knoell. ■ 29412 #036-08-2002 L2003 **GE** *012 †20
HASAN, Rabiya Khalid. ■ 29425 #055-01-2004 L2004 **CHP** *012
HASKINS, Curtis Dhamel. 316 CALHOUN 29401 #051-04-1988 L1991 **FM EM** *020 †18
HASSELL, Thoroughgood F. ■ 29412 #045-01-1956 L1956 **FM** *071 †18
HATFIELD, Corey Michael. 171 ASHLEY AVE 29425 #020-75-2005, ▲ L2005 **IM** *012
HATZIS, Melanie Taylor. 263 KING ST STE B 29401 #045-01-2001 L2003 **CHP P** *020 †75
HAVARD, Benjamin James. ■ 29401 #021-01-2006 L2006 **PTH** *012
HAVIDICH, Jeana. 171 ASHLEY AVE 29425 #038-44-1993 L1994 **AN PD** *040 †05
HAVIG-LIPKE, Kelly C. 776 DANIEL ELLIS DR, BLDG 2 29412 #011-04-1989 L1991 **PD** *020 †55
HAWES, Robert Holbrook. 96 JONATHAN LUCAS ST, STE 210 CSB DIGSTVE DIS CT 29425 #017-20-1980 L1994 **GE** *020 †20
HAWK, John Chrisman, III. 125 DOUGHTY ST STE 660, CHARLESTON SURG ASSOC PA 29403 #047-05-1971 L1978 **GS SO** *070 †20
HAWKINS, Michael Mills. 316 CALHOUN ST 29401 #045-01-1988 L1991 **IM** *020 †20 ‡
HAY, Edward La Roche. 2093 HENRY TECKLENBURG DR, STE 200 29414 #045-01-1960 L1960 **HS ORS** *071 †40
HAY, J Michael. 167 ASHLEY AVE # 301, MUSC-ANES DEPT 29425 #005-12-1975 L2007 **AN** *020 †05 ‡
HAY, Robert Marshall. 615 WESLEY DR, STE 100 29407 #045-01-1984 L1991 **ORS GPM** *020 †40
HAYES, David Johnchristi. PO BOX 250333, 169 ASHLEY AVE 29425 #005-02-2002 L2004 **GS** *100
HAYES, James Martin, Jr. 615 WESLEY DR, STE 200 29407 #045-01-1964 L1964 **IM** *020 †20
HAYNES, Gary Reid. 165 ASHLEY AVE STE 525-CH 29425 #038-06-1986 L1987 **AN** *020 †05
HAYS, Angela Nicole. 96 JONATHAN LUCAS ST, STE 307CSB 29425 #021-01-2001 L2007 **N CCM** *020
HAZELL, Samuel E. 1859 SAVAGE RD 29407 #035-01-1975 L1980 **GS** *020 †85
HEADDEN, Gary Fletcher. 169 ASHLEY AVE, MEDICAL UNIV OF SC 29403 #045-01-1990 L1991 **IM EM** *020 †20
HEARD, Richard Kirksey. ■ 29412 #027-01-2008 *012
HEBBAR, Airody Keshava. 295 CALHOUN ST, MEDICAL UNIVERSITY OF SC-F 29425 #495-04-1984 L1997 **FM** *020 †18
HEBBAR, Latha. 171 ASHLEY AVE 29425 #495-04-1982 L1997 **AN** *050 †05
HEBRA, Andre. 96 JONATHAN LUCAS ST, # 418-CSB 29425 #045-01-1987 L1988 **PDS GS** *020 †85
HEIKES, Dana Lyle. 247 CALHOUN ST 29401 #035-09-1972 L1998 **PS** *020 †65
HEINECK, Robert Jason. ■ 29414 #045-04-2007 L2007 **AN** *012
HEINS, Henry Carl, Jr. 171 ASHLEY AVE DEPT OB 29425 #045-01-1946 L1946 **OBG** *071 †30
HELDRICH, Cynthia M. 293 E BAY ST 29401 #045-01-1983 L1984 **PD** *020 †55
HENDERSON, Frampton Wyman. 9298 MEDICAL PLAZA DR, UNIVERSITY FAMILY MEDICINE 29406 #045-01-2005 L2005 **FP** *012
HENDERSON, James Alan. ■ 29403 #045-01-2008 *012
HENDERSON, Mary Frances. ■ 29412 #045-01-2007 L2007 **GS** *012
HENDRIX, Grady Hinson. 171 ASHLEY AVE, MUSC 29425 #045-01-1958 L1958 **CD IM** *071 †20
HENKEL, Brody Lars. 96 JONATHAN LUCAS ST, STE 309 29425 #422-01-2006 L2006 **N** *012
HENNEGHAN, Tedric C. 96 JONATHAN LUCAS ST, DEPT OF GENERAL SURGERY 29425 #045-01-2001 L2001 **AN** *100
HENRY, Wesley Dubois. 316 CALHOUN ST 29401 #045-01-1984 L1985 **DR EM** *020 †80
HENSHAW, Melissa Howard. 171 ASHLEY AVE 29425 #045-01-1991 L1992 **PD** *020 †55
HERBERT, Thomas G, Jr. 59 BEE ST 29403 #045-01-1942 L1942 **GYN** *071 †30
HERBSMAN, Tal. PO BOX 250861, 67 PRESIDENT ST 29425 #011-03-2005 L2005 **P** *012
HERMAYER, Kathie Lynn. 96 JONATHAN LUCAS ST, STE 323CSB 29425 #035-03-1981 L1982 **END IM** *020 †20
HERNANDEZ, Antonio M. 2125 CHARLIE HALL BLVD, STE 2B 29414 #748-20-1989 L2007 **IM** *020 †20
HERNANDEZ, Kathleen White. ■ 29403 #021-05-1951 L1969 **PD FM** *071 †55
HERRIN, Mark Thos. 18 FARMFIELD AVE 29407 #001-06-1991 L1992 **AN** *020 †05
HERRING, Katrina R. 9298 MEDICAL PLAZA DR, TRIDENT FAMILY MED RESIDEN 29406 #045-01-2007 L2007 **FP** *012
HERRING, M Noreen Sagedy. 171 ASHLEY AVE 29425 #045-01-1990 L1997 **PM** *020 †60
HERRON, Michael Keith. 171 ASHLEY AVE 29425 #041-12-1988 L2007 **PD** *020 †60
HERWAY, Catherine M. 96 JONATHAN LUCAS ST 29425 #048-13-2003 L2007 **OBG** *012
HERWIG, Kathryn Elizabeth. 171 ASHLEY AVE 29425 #041-15-2005 L2005 **PD** *012
HICKMAN, Cary Stanley. 293 E BAY ST 29401 #045-01-1990 L1991 **IM** *020 †20
HIGGINS, Edmund Safford. 171 ASHLEY AVE 29425 #038-06-1984 L1985 **P FM** *020 †75,18
HIGHLAND, Kristin Bamber. 96 JONATHAN LUCAS ST, MEDICAL UNIV OF SOUTH CARO 29425 #017-20-1993 L1994 **RHU** *100 †20
HIGHSMITH, Jason Michael. 9313 MEDICAL PLAZA DR, STE 305 29406 #051-04-2000 L2006 **NS** *020
HILDRETH, Barbara Putney. 2097 HENRY TECKLENBURG DR, STE 301 29414 #045-01-1986 L1988 **IM** *020 †20
HILL, Charles Sease. 542 WAMPLER DR 29412 #045-01-1986 L1987 **AN** *020 †20,05
HILL, Jeanne Griffin. 171 ASHLEY AVE, MUSC 29425 #045-01-1988 L1989 **DR** *020 †80
HILLEGASS, Michael Gabrie, III. ■ 29412 #036-05-2007 L2007 **AN** *012
HILLIARD, Thomas F. 171 ASHLEY AVE 29425 #038-06-1987 L1988 **FM** *020 †18
HILTON, Ebony Jade. ■ 29401 #045-01-2008 *012
HINSON, Hans Leighton. 109 BEE ST, RALPH H JOHNSON VETERANS A 29401 #036-05-1997 L2003 **IMG** *020 †20
HINSON, Vanessa K. 171 ASHLEY AVE 29425 #409-21-1995 L2003 **N** *020 †75
HIOTT, David Walter. 2655 EVATT LN STE 106, SOLUTIONS 29405 #045-01-1990 L1991 **CHP P** *020 †75
HIOTT, Joann. 293 E BAY ST 29401 #045-01-1986 L1987 **FM** *020 †18

HLAVACEK, Anthony Marcus. 165 ASHLEY AVE, MEDICAL UNIVERSITY OF SC 29425 #048-04-2000 L2004 PD *020 †55

HOANG, Khanh Gien. 171 ASHLEY AVE, MEDICAL UNIVERSITY OF SC 29425 #020-02-1978 L1988 OTO *020 †45

HOCEVAR, Susan Nicole. 135 RUTLEDGE ST 29425 #012-01-2003 L2005 PD *100 †55

HOCH, Isaac. ■ 29407 #008-01-1975 L1977 FM *020 †18

HOCHMAN, Marcelo Luis. 2097 HENRY TECKLENBURG DR, STE 212 29414 #048-13-1985 L1991 GS FPS *020 †45

HODA, Jonathan Andrew. ■ 29414 #027-01-2007 L2007 IM *012

HOFFMAN, Brenda Joyce. 96 JONATHAN LUCAS ST, DIV OF GASTROENTEROLOGY MU 29425 #020-12-1983 L1984 GE IM *020 †20

HOGAN, Edward Leo. 9313 MEDICAL PLAZA DR, STE 310 29406 #024-07-1957 L1973 N *020 †75

HOGUE, Caisson Timber. 9298 MEDICAL PLAZA DR 29406 #665-02-2005 L2005 FP *012

HOLBROOK, David Lindsay. ■ 29414 #012-01-1978 L1992 PTH *020 †50

HOLEMAN, John Vernon. ■ 29403 #020-02-2006 L2006 MPD *012

HOLL, William Howard, III. 9275 MEDICAL PLAZA DR # F 29406 #045-01-1976 L1977 U *020 †95

HOLLAND, Mary Baran. 171 ASHLEY AVE, MUSC 29425 #045-01-1994 L1998 P *100

HOLLOMAN, David Andrew. ■ 29401 #047-20-2006 L2006 PTH *012

HOLLON, Mitchell Fields. 171 ASHLEY AVE #047-06-1983 L1984 AN *020 †05

HOLMES, Andre Reshaun. PO BOX 250333, 169 ASHLEY AVE 29425 #045-01-2006 L2006 IM *012

HOLMES-MAYBANK, Keri Ther. ■ 29407 #045-01-2007 L2007 IM *012

HONNEY, Shanon Lee. 171 ASHLEY AVE, MED UNIV OF SC SCH OF MED 29425 #045-01-2000 L2001 IM *020 †20

HOOD, Judith E Beatty. 18 FARMFIELD AVE 29407 #020-02-1971 L1974 AN *020 †05

HOOKER, Jennifer Ann. 96 JONATHAN LUCAS ST, STE 708CSB 29425 #036-01-2000 L2007 ORS *100

HOOVER, Michael Shane. 9330 MEDICAL PLAZA DR 29406 #036-01-2001 L2004 NPM *020

HOPE, Jason Michael. ■ 29407 #036-01-2007 L2007 PTH *012

HORNIG, Joshua David. 171 ASHLEY AVE 29425 #060-01-1999 L2004 OTO *020 †45

HORRES, Ernest G, Jr. 669 SAINT ANDREWS BLVD 29407 #045-01-1992 L1993 CHP *020

HORST, Taylor Alan. ■ 29407 #024-07-2008 *012

HOURANI, Lara Mae. ■ 29407 #055-02-2007 L2007 MPD *012

HOWARD, Gene Reid. 171 ASHLEY AVE 29425 #023-07-1984 L1991 OPH *020 †35

HOWARD, Leon King, Jr. 9231 MEDICAL PLAZA DR 29406 #045-01-1970 L1971 CD IM *020 †20

HOWELL, James Singleton. 2188 PIERPONT AVE 29414 #045-01-1954 L1954 GP *071

HOWELL, Roy Allen, Jr. 30 BEE ST 29403 #045-01-1948 L1948 IM IMG *020 †20

HSIA, Tainyen. 96 JONATHAN LUCAS ST 29425 #005-11-1996 L2006 TS *100 †85,90

HUBBARD, Joshua Malcolm. 171 ASHLEY AVE, MED UNIV OF SC SCH OF MED 29425 #045-01-2005 L2005 DR *012

HUBER, Michael Gregory. 109 BEE ST, FLOOR 3A VA HOSPITAL 29401 #025-07-1989 L1990 P *020 †75

HUCHINGSON, James Andrew. ■ 29425 #021-01-2006 L2006 P *012

HUDSPETH, Michelle P. PO BOX 250558, 135 RUTLEDGE AVE RM 480 29425 #045-01-1999 L2007 PHO *100 †55

HUESTON, William John. 295 CALHOUN ST, MUSC 29425 #038-06-1983 L1997 FM *020 †18

HUGGINS, Charles Edward. 2145 HENRY TECKLENBURG DR, STE 270 29414 #045-01-1969 L1970 OBG *020 †30

HUGHES, Frances Beth. 349 FOLLY RD, STE B 29412 #045-01-1994 L1995 IM *020 †20

HUGHES, Lisa E. 171 ASHLEY AVE 29425 #045-01-1992 L1997 PD *020 †55

HUGHES, Nikki Tennille. PO BOX 250333, 169 ASHLEY AVE RM 202 29425 #045-01-2006 L2006 FP *012

HULL, Dennis Michael. 9295 MEDICAL PLAZA DR 29406 #024-01-1974 L1976 D *020 †15

HULLETT, Jonathan Bradley. ■ 29414 #051-04-2003 L2007 AN *100

HULVEY, John Thomas, Jr. 9298 MEDICAL PLAZA DR, UNIVERSITY FAMILY MEDICINE 29406 #051-01-2002 L2005 FP *012

HUNTER, Jairy C. 9330 MEDICAL PLAZA DR 29406 #045-01-1993 L1997 FM *020 †18

HUNTER, Steven John. 171 ASHLEY AVE, DEPT OF DIABETES & END 29425 #918-01-1993 L1998 END *020

HURLEY, Donald P. 1483 TOBIAS GADSON BLVD, STE 101 29407 #028-79-1985, ▲ L1992 FM FSM *020 †18

HUSSAIN, Nadeem Ayaz. 96 JONATHAN LUCAS ST 210 29425 #067-01-1992 L2003 *020 †20

HUTCHISON, Florence N. 171 ASHLEY AVE 29425 #027-01-1980 L1989 NEP *050 †20

HUTSON, Arthur C, Jr. 171 ASHLEY AVE, MED UNIV OF S.C. 29425 #045-01-1960 L1960 FM IM *020

HUTTON, Charles Frederick. ■ 29412 #352-11-1944 L1968 DR *071

HUTTON, Martine Anne. 776 DANIEL ELLIS DR, STE 3C 29412 #051-04-1978 L1979 PD *020 †55

IKONOMIDIS, John Sotirios. 96 JONATHAN LUCAS ST, SURGERY, SUITE 409 CSB 29425 #065-01-1989 L2000 TS *020 †85,90

IRSHAD, Abid. 169 ASHLEY AVE 29425 #704-21-1983 L2003 *020 †80

IRVIN, Robert Gilford. 615 WESLEY DR STE 320 29407 #045-01-1971 L1974 CD IM *020 †20

ISENBERG, Amy Virginia. 29425 #036-08-2001 L2001 AN *020 †70

IVESTER, Julius R, Jr. 18 FARMFIELD AVE 29407 #045-01-1982 L1985 AN *020 †05

IWEGBUE, Kwame Nduka. 316 CALHOUN ST, HOSPITALIST SERVICE 29401 #690-06-1993 L2003 GPM *020 †20

JABLON, Eric Paul. 171 ASHLEY AVE, SURGERY 29425 #045-01-1998 L2000 OPH *020 †35

JACKSON, Sherron Mc Queen. 135 RUTLEDGE ST 29425 #012-01-1981 L1982 PD *020 †55

JACOBS, Theodolph H, Jr. 2317 ASHLEY RIVER RD 29414 #010-01-1980 L1981 FM *020 †18

JACOBSON, Leah Bernstein. 9298 MEDICAL PLAZA DR, UNIVERSITY FAMILY MEDICINE 29406 #041-02-2004 L2005 IM *100 †18

JANULYTE, Beatrice. 96 JONATHAN LUCAS ST 29425 #913-96-1999 L2005 END *100

JANZEN, Grant Phillip. ■ 29412 #039-01-2004 L2004 OPH *012

JANZEN, Jennifer Eve. ■ 29412 #039-01-2004 L2004 PD *020 †55

JAVERY, Shahid Mohammed. ■ 29407 #045-01-2006 L2006 IM *012

JEFFCOAT, Alicia Shanta. 171 ASHLEY AVE, MED UNIV OF SC COLL OF MED 29425 #045-01-2006 L2006 AN *012

JENKINS, Carlotta Fitzsim. ■ 29412 #045-01-2008 *012

JENKINS, Margaret Quante. 669 N SHORE DR 29412 #012-01-1949 L1953 PUD PD *071 †55

JENKINS, Mary Ellen Click. 9329 MEDICAL PLAZA DR 29406 #004-01-1959 L1959 AN *071

JENNINGS, Thomas Scott. 1470 TOBIAS GADSON BLVD, STE 110 29407 #011-04-1987 L1988 GO *020 †30

JENRETTE, Jos Malphus, III. 169 ASHLEY AVE, DEPT OF RAD ONC 29403 #045-01-1979 L1980 RO *020 †80

JERNIGAN, Floyd E. 109 BEE ST 29401 #045-01-1976 L1977 IM *020 †20

JERVEY, Charles Stewart. 125 DOUGHTY ST STE 460 29403 #045-01-1989 L1990 N *020 †75

JOHN, Joseph F, Jr. 109 BEE ST, RALPH H. JOHNSON MEDICAL C 29401 #038-06-1970 L1974 IM *020 †20

JOHNSON, Allen Huggins. 171 ASHLEY AVE 29425 #045-01-1962 L1962 IM ID *071 †20

JOHNSON, Amy Karenlouise. ■ 29407 #021-01-2004 L2004 P *012

JOHNSON, Donald R, II. 1941 SAVAGE RD, STE 100E 29407 #045-01-1984 L1985 ORS *020 †40

JOHNSON, Donna Denise. 628 SAINT ANDREWS BLVD 29407 #045-01-1987 L1996 OBG *020 †30

JOHNSON, Eugene G, III. 2095 HENRY TECKLENBURG DR, BON SECOURS ST FRANCIS HOS 29414 #045-01-1971 L1973 R *020 †80

JOHNSON, George M. 171 ASHLEY AVE 29425 #036-01-1977 L1991 ID PD *050 †55

JOHNSON, John Fred. 1941 SAVAGE RD, STE 100E 29407 #654-01-1990 L1995 PM *020 †60

JOHNSON, Robert Martin. 1 CARRIAGE LN STE 201, UNIT B 29407 #045-01-1954 L1954 OS NTR *020

JOHNSON-GOUGH, Catherine. 316 CALHOUN ST 29401 #010-02-1990 L1997 DR *020 †80

JOHNSTONE, Kenneth W. 18 FARMFIELD AVE 29407 #045-01-1987 L1991 AN *020 †05

JOKL, Rudolf. 171 ASHLEY AVE 29425 #286-04-1980 L1994 IM EM *020 †20

JONES, Amy Lorraine. ■ 29412 #012-01-2003 L2004 PDC *012

JONES, Edward Tudur. ■ 29414 #045-01-2005 PTH *012

JONES, Evan Davis. 3325 ASHLEY PHOSPHATE RD 29418 #010-01-1967 L1973 OPH *020 †35

JONES, Gregory Marvin. 2093 HENRY TECKLENBURG DR, STE 310 29414 #045-01-1988 L1992 PM OS *020 †60

JONES, Timothy John. 2270 ASHLEY CROSSING DR, STE 170 29414 #045-01-1991 L1992 IM *020 †20

JOSEPH, Anthony Benjamin. 9330 MEDICAL PLAZA DR 29406 #045-01-2002 L2003 NEP *012 †20

JOUBERT, James Ira. ■ 29403 #021-05-2004 L2004 N *012

JOYE, Todd. 18 FARMFIELD AVE 29407 #045-01-1994 L1996 APM AN *020 †05

JUDSON, Marc Andrew. 171 ASHLEY AVE 29425 #047-05-1980 L1985 IM *020 †20

JURGENS, Valerie Rene. ■ 29407 #016-45-2007 L2007 PD *012

JUST, Markus Ernst. 67 PRESIDENT ST 29425 #409-07-2000 L2004 P *100

KADRY, Bassam. ■ 29412 #016-06-2005 L2006 AN *012

KALIL, Rhonda Suzanne. 3 GAMECOCK AVE STE 306, MAILING: P O BOX 31547 29407 #021-05-1993 L1994 P *020 †75

KALINSKY, Bradley Scott. ■ 29407 #045-01-2008 *012

KALINSKY, Ryan Adam. ■ 29407 #045-01-2005 PTH *012

KALLURI, Meena. ■ 29412 #495-16-2000 L2005 PCC *012 †20

KAMEN, Diane Leigh. 96 JONATHAN LUCAS ST, STE 912 MSC 637 29425 #019-02-1999 L2000 RHU *050 †20

KANAWATY, David Sam. 171 ASHLEY AVE 29425 #065-01-1985 L1988 IM *020 †20

KANE, Arden Merrill. ■ 29401 #035-06-1968 L1969 OTO *020 †05

KANG, Ian Konrad. 135 RUTLEDGE ST, MUSC DEPARTMENT OF PEDIATR 29425 #056-05-2000 L2007 PG *020 †55

KANICH, William Steele. 2095 HENRY TECKLENBURG DR, ST FRANCIS HOSPITAL-EMERGE 29414 #051-04-1999 L2002 EM *020 †16

KANIS, Jessica Marie. ■ 29412 #038-41-2006 L2006 PD *012

KAPLAN, Raymond. 125 DOUGHTY ST, STE 440 29403 #011-03-1972 L1986 PS OTO *020 †45,65

KARNOFSKY, Roberta S. 18 FARMFIELD AVE 29407 #422-01-1988 L1993 AN *020 †05

KASPER, Terrance Jerome. PO BOX 250333, 169 ASHLEY AVE 29425 #026-04-2002 L2003 GS *100

KASTENSCHMIDT, Erin Kimbe. ■ 29403 #045-01-2008 *012

KATIKANENI, Lakshmi Devi. 171 ASHLEY AVE 29425 #495-01-1968 L1981 NPM PD *020 †55

KATIKANENI, Pruthvi Pathi. ■ 29412 #495-36-1966 L1987 CLP PTH *020 †50

KATSANIS, Ward Andrew. 1470 TOBIAS GADSON BLVD, STE 110 29407 #038-41-1990 L1999 OBG *020 †30

KATZ, Stanley Allen. ■ 29414 #045-01-1989 L1990 N *075

KAY, Clive Lawrence. MUSC MEDICAL CTR, DEPT-RAD 29425 #352-08-1987 L1998 DR *020

KEANE, Thomas E. 171 ASHLEY AVE 29425 #539-04-1981 L2002 U *020 †95

KEARSE, Laurie Ann. 171 ASHLEY AVE 29425 #045-01-1989 L1992 FM *020 †18

KEEFE, Jerry Michael. 3424 SHELBY RAY CT 29414 #005-02-1970 L1997 FM OS *020 †18

KEITH, Brad Albert. 96 JONATHAN LUCAS ST, MUSC INT MED RES PROG 29425 #045-01-2002 L2003 IM *100 †20

KELLER, George Theodore. 1483 TOBIAS GADSON BLVD 29407 #045-01-1988 L1989 IM *020 †18

KELLER, Sondra. 67 PRESIDENT ST, MEDICAL UNIV OF SC 29425 #045-01-1992 L1993 CHP *020 †75

KELLY, Patrick Jos. 316 CALHOUN ST, ROBER HOSP DEPT OF EM 29401 #045-01-1984 L1985 EM *020 †16

KELTY, Patrick James. 169 ASHLEY AVE # 202, DEPT OF GENERAL SURGERY 29403 #038-41-2003 L2004 GS *020

KENNEDY, Adele. 171 ASHLEY AVE RM 323 29425 #918-01-1992 L1997 END *020

KENT, Alexander R. 171 ASHLEY AVE 29425 #005-11-1989 L1994 OPH *020 †35 ‡

KENT, David Gregory. MUSC MED CTR 29425 #671-02-1986 L1995 *020

KEOGH, George Paul, III. 125 DOUGHTY ST STE 500 29403 #035-01-1998 L2003 ON HEM *020 †20

KERNS, Randall Eugene. 9326 MEDICAL PLAZA DR # A, TRIDENT ANES GROUP 29406 #041-12-1983 L1984 AN *030 †05

KERRISON, Horry Heriot. 31 SMITH ST 29401 #045-01-1959 L1959 OPH OS *020 †35

KERRISON, John Barnwell. 3531 MARY ADER AVE, STE D 29414 #012-05-1992 L2005 OPH *020 †35

KESLAR, Paula Jean. 2125 CHARLIE HALL BLVD 29414 #041-12-1984 L1998 PDR DR *020 †80

KETCHAM, Amy Shannon. ■ 29412 #045-01-2008 *012

KEY, Janice Dixon. 135 RUTLEDGE ST 29425 #036-01-1980 L1991 ADL PD *040 †55,19

KEY, Lester L, Jr. 135 RUTLEDGE ST RM 381 29425 #036-01-1977 L1991 PD PDE *050 †55

KHALIL, Sherief Nabil. ■ 29403 #045-01-2008 *012

KHAN, Ahsan Mohammed. 109 BEE ST, RALPH H. JOHNSON MEDICAL C 29401 #038-44-1996 L1998 NM *020 †28

KHOR, Christopher Jen L. 171 ASHLEY AVE, STE 421NT 29425 #825-01-1987 L1998 *020

KILPATRICK, Donald Stokes. PO BOX 13509 29422 #045-01-1983 L1986 AN CCM *020 †05

KILPATRICK, Lauren Ann. ■ 29407 #045-05-2007 L2007 OTO *012

KIM, Edward Han. ■ 29412 #011-02-2003 L2004 GS *012

KIM, Eun Young. 96 JONATHAN LUCAS ST, DIGESTIBE DISEASE CENTER 29425 #583-04-1987 IM *020

KING, Dana E. 295 CALHOUN ST 29425 #020-12-1981 L1999 **FM** *050 †18
KING, Lowrey Pearson. 2145 HENRY TECKLENBURG DR, STE 200 29414 #027-01-1983 L1984 **OPH** *020 †35
KING, Peter Jennings. ■ 29407 #045-01-2008 *012
KINI, Sarvotham. 169 ASHLEY AVE 29403 #495-35-1967 L1987 **EM GS** *020 †85,16
KINLAW, William Knox, Jr. 96 JONATHAN LUCAS ST, STE 428CSB 29425 #036-01-1964 L2005 **NS** *071 †25 ‡
KINNEY, Laura Lee. 2097 HENRY TECKLENBURG DR, STE 220 29414 #045-01-1996 L1997 **IM** *020 †20
KIRKER, Eric Blaine. ■ 29412 #035-06-2000 L2005 **TS** *012 †85
KIRKLAND, Thos Alexander. 171 ASHLEY AVE 29425 #036-07-1958 L1966 **U** *071 †95
KIRKPATRICK, Mcneill Palm. ■ 29425 #045-01-2008 *012
KIRSHTEIN, Jonathan W. 18 FARMFIELD AVE 29407 #045-01-1991 L1996 **AN** *020 †05
KISABETH, Charles Wm. 1243 SAVANNAH HWY 29407 #045-01-1988 L1989 **PD** *020 †55
KITCH, Russell David. 10 FARMFIELD AVE, STE A 29407 #051-01-1985 L1991 **OTO HNS** *020 †45
KITCHEN, Michael Steven. ■ 29412 #047-06-1990 L1992 **GS** *020
KITHIANIS, Carrie S. 2100 CHARLIE HALL BLVD, CHARLESTON COMMUNITY MH 29414 #045-01-1998 L2002 **P** *020 †75
KIZILTAN, Hidayet Tarik. ■ 29401 #902-10-1990 L1995 *020
KIZZIAH, Michael Kirk. ■ 29414 #012-22-2005 L2005 **DR** *012
KLAUBER, Carol Kessler. 3800 FABER PLACE DR 29405 #045-01-1978 L1979 **PD** *020 †55
KLECKLEY, John Edgar. 125 DOUGHTY ST, STE 400 29403 #045-04-2002 L2007 **IMG** *012
KLINE, Jeffrey John. 1164C NORTH BLVD 29405 #023-01-1972 L1989 **GE PD** *020 †55
KNIGHT, Anne Bradley. 51 NASSAU ST, FRANKLIN C FETTER HLTH CTR 29403 #045-01-1983 L1984 **FM** *020 †18
KNOEPP, Ursula S. ■ 29401 #047-20-2001 L2003 **AR** *100
KOESTER, Dirk Andrew. ■ 29401 #017-20-2002 L2004 **VIR** *012 †80
KOGOS, Amanda Barre. 9330 MEDICAL PLAZA DR 29406 #021-05-2001 L2006 **MPD** *100 †20
KOGOS, Philip George. 169 ASHLEY AVE, RM 297MUH 29425 #021-05-2001 L2006 **DR** *020 †80
KOHLER, Matthew Fessler. 326 CALHOUN ST 29401 #036-07-1987 L1998 **OBG** *020 †30
KOHLI, Rohit Robin. 171 ASHLEY AVE, MED UNIV SC COLL OF MED 29425 #665-01-2006 L2006 **P** *012
KOKKO, Kyle Pentti. ■ 29407 #045-01-2006 L2006 **ORS** *012
KOLKAS-MC CARRON, Eugenia. 2070 NORTHBROOK BLVD, STE B9 29406 #048-14-1990 L1996 **OBG** *020 †30
KOONCE, James Duval. 9298 MEDICAL PLAZA DR 29406 #047-06-2006 L2006 **DR** *012
KOOPMAN, Richelle D. 171 ASHLEY AVE 29425 #041-12-1993 L2001 **FM** *050 †18
KOPCHINSKI, Bernard J. PO BOX 250333, 169 ASHLEY AVE 29425 #023-12-1996 L2004 **PS** *020 †85
KOREN, James David. 1180 SAM RITTENBERG BLVD, STE 325 29407 #036-01-1982 L2001 **FM** *020 †18
KOTZ, Edward Athony, III. 811 SAINT ANDREWS BLVD, CAROLINA DERMATOLOGY CLINI 29407 #045-01-2001 L2003 **D** *020 †15
KOVAL, Matthew S. 171 ASHLEY AVE 29425 #055-01-1990 L1991 **CHP** *020 †85
KOYA, Laxmi Deepika. 135 CANNON ST STE 403 29425 #495-65-1999 L2004 **IM** *020
KOZEL, Susan Thomas. 169 ASHLEY AVE # 202, DEPT OF PSYCHIATRY 29403 #012-01-2002 L2004 **CHP** *100 †75
KRATZ, John Martin. 171 ASHLEY AVE, MUSC DEPT OF SURGERY 29425 #017-20-1972 L1973 **TS GS** *020 †90,85
KRAUTHAMMER, Yoaav Samuel. ■ 29412 #038-40-2007 L2007 **IM** *012
KREUTNER, Annemarie K K. 71 BULL ST 29401 #035-45-1964 L1970 **OBG ID** *020 †30
KRISHNA, Vibhor. ■ 29407 #495-36-2004 L2006 **NS** *012
KRISHTEIN, Amy J. ■ 29407 #045-01-1991 L1996 **PTH** *020 †50
KRIZA, Karen Louise. 9330 MEDICAL PLAZA DR, TRIDENT EMERGENCY PHYSICIA 29406 #041-07-1997 L2001 **EM** *020 †16
KRUESI, Markus J P. 67 PRESIDENT ST 29425 #033-05-1979 L1999 **CHP P** *050 †75
KRYWKO, Diann Marie. 169 ASHLEY AVE 29425 #025-07-1996 L2008 **EM** *020 †16
KUBACZ, Dean Bernard. ■ 29412 #045-01-2008 *012
KUELLING, Daniel Peter. 171 ASHLEY AVE, DEPT IM 29425 #869-07-1989 L1997 **IM** *020
KUHNS, Gary Francis. 12 FARMFIELD AVE, STE E 29407 #023-01-1983 L1984 **IM** *020 †20
KULBERSH, Jonathan Sol. ■ 29412 #045-01-2005 L2005 **OTO** *012
KULZE, John Chas, III. 171 ASHLEY AVE 29425 #045-01-1985 L1986 **OPH** *020 †35
KUO, Benjamin Sueming. 135 RUTLEDGE ST 11TH FL, MED UNIV OF S CAROLINA 29425 #021-05-2006 L2007 **D** *012
KURENT, Jerome Edward. 135 RUTLEDGE ST RM 1241S 29425 #038-41-1971 L1984 **IMG N** *020 †75
KURTZMAN, Howard Marc. 27 GAMECOCK AVE STE 203 29407 #045-01-1978 L1992 **CHP P** *020 †75
KUSMIREK, Slawomir. 135 RUTLEDGE ST STE 120, MUSC 29425 #759-03-1991 L2005 **CD** *020 †20
KWON, Soon Ho. 171 ASHLEY AVE 29425 #583-13-1988 L2000 **END** *020 †20
LA BRUCE, Arthur M. 9231 MEDICAL PLAZA DR, STE E 29406 #045-01-1964 L1964 **OTO** *020
LACERDA, Ricardo De Oliva. 148 CANNON ST 29403 #187-01-1998 L2006 **VIR** *100
LACKEY, Keith Woodward. 615 WESLEY DR, STE 300 29407 #045-01-1990 L1991 **IM** *020 †20
LAGE, Janice Marie. 171 ASHLEY AVE 29425 #028-02-1980 L1999 **ATP** *020 †50
LAHR, Christopher John. 2097 HENRY TECKLENBURG DR, STE 311 29414 #016-02-1979 L1989 **CRS GS** *020 †10,85
LAI, Hin. 96 JONATHAN LUCAS ST, BLDG 210 29425 #462-02-2001 L2008 *100
LAKE, Brian M. 169 ASHLEY AVE RM 202MUH, MSC 333 29425 #028-79-2004, ▲ L2007 *100
LALLY, Joseph Michael, Jr. 125 DOUGHTY ST STE 330 29403 #033-05-1987 L1992 **OPH** *020 †55
LALLY, Michelle D. 135 RUTLEDGE ST, MEDICAL UNIVERSITY OF SC 29425 #033-05-1987 L1992 **PD** *020 †55
LAMALE-SMITH, Leah Michel. ■ 29414 #018-03-2007 *012
LAMAR, Carlos, Jr. 109 BEE ST 29401 #021-01-1955 L1974 **IM GE** *071 †20
LAMBERT, Lara Christine. ■ 29412 #045-01-2007 L2007 **IM** *012
LAMBERT, Paul Ray. 171 ASHLEY AVE 29425 #036-07-1975 L1999 **OTO HNS** *020 †45
LANE, Darii Ann. 204 W HILL BLVD, 437TH MEDICAL GROUP/SGHQ 29404 #023-12-1996 L2006 **FM** *020 †18
LANFORD, Ronald Vance. ■ 29407 #045-01-1962 L1962 **OPH** *071
LANG, Mary Taggart. 1483 TOBIAS GADSON BLVD, STE 103 29407 #045-01-1993 L1993 **FM** *020 †18
LANG, Pearon Gordon, Jr. 135 RUTLEDGE ST, FL 11 29425 #051-01-1970 L1970 **OS D** *020 †15
LA ROSA, Angela C. 171 ASHLEY AVE 29425 #055-01-1997 L2000 **PD** *020 †55

LARSON, Eric Jon. 171 ASHLEY AVE 29425 #017-20-1995 L1998 **EM** *020 †16
LAUDITO, Antonio. 34 WENTWORTH ST 29401 #561-20-1989 L2003 **TS PCS** *020 †85,90
LA VIA, Mariano Francis. ■ 29412 #561-08-1949 L1999 **CLP PTH** *071
LAW, Kari Beth. ■ 29414 #055-01-2005 L2005 **P** *012
LAWRENCE, Christopher. 171 ASHLEY AVE 29425 #027-01-1997 L2004 **GE** *100 †20
LAWRENCE, Sandra Kay. 171 ASHLEY AVE 29425 #047-20-1991 L1996 **DR** *020 †80
LAY, Deborah. 9330 MEDICAL PLAZA DR 29406 #028-78-2002, ▲ L2005 IM *100
LAZARCHICK, John. 171 ASHLEY AVE 29425 #041-02-1968 L1979 **HEM IM** *050 †20
LEATHERMAN, Sarah Ada. ■ 29407 #045-01-2008 *012
LECKOVA, Katarina. 9330 MEDICAL PLAZA DR, COASTAL INPATIENT PHYSICIA 29406 #422-01-2000 L2006 **IM** *020 †20
LEE, Franklin Carver. 2051 CHARLIE HALL BLVD 29414 #045-01-1983 L1985 **PD EM** *020 †55
LEE, Kimberly Gronsman. ■ 29425 #025-07-1991 L2006 **NPM PD** *040 †55
LEE, William H, III. 349 FOLLY RD, STE 1A 29412 #045-01-1984 L1990 **OPH** *020 †35
LELAND, Thomas Mikell. 1483 TOBIAS GADSON BLVD, STE 103 29407 #045-01-1975 L1976 **OPH** *020 †35
LEMEL, A Lawrence. 1515 ASHLEY RIVER RD # 23D 29407 #038-06-1957 L1965 **OTO** *020 †45
LENTSCH, Eric Jos. 135 RUTLEDGE ST, MSC 550 29425 #020-02-1992 L2006 **OTO** *020 †45
LEON, Stuart Marc. 96 JONATHAN LUCAS ST, MEDICAL UNIVERSITY OF SC 29425 #041-07-1995 L2002 **CCS TRS** *020 †85
LEONG, Swan Swan. 171 ASHLEY AVE, DEPT OF THORACIC ONCOLOGY 29425 #825-01-1987 L1998 *020
LESHER, Aaron Payne. ■ 29401 #036-07-2006 L2006 **GS** *012
LESTER, Mary Elizabeth. 96 JONATHAN LUCAS ST, CSB 426 29425 #012-05-2000 L2005 **PS** *020 †85
LETTAU, Ludwig Alexander. 1938 CHARLIE HALL BLVD 29414 #056-05-1973 L1985 **ID IM** *020 †20
LE VEEN, Eric G. 1744 SAM RITTENBERG BLVD 29407 #035-08-1978 L1979 **GS VS** *020 †85
LEVKOFF, Abner H. 171 ASHLEY AVE 29425 #045-01-1947 L1947 **NPM** *072 †55
LEVY, Elliott Evens. 109 BEE ST, DEPT OF MENTAL HLTH 29401 #045-01-1994 L1999 **P** *020 †75
LEWIN, David Nigelbruno. 171 ASHLEY AVE 29425 #005-14-1991 L1996 **PTH** *020 †50
LEWIS, Alvin Lee. PO BOX 250333, 169 ASHLEY AVE 29425 #045-01-2006 L2006 **P** *012
LEWIS, Andrew Roper. ■ 29412 #045-01-2008 *012
LEWIS, Geoffrey Faber. ■ 29407 #036-05-2007 L2007 **IM** *012
LEWIS, Madelene Carroll. 9298 MEDICAL PLAZA DR, RESIDENCY PROGRAM 29406 #036-08-2006 L2006 **DR** *012
LICHTENSTEIN, Leonard S. 171 ASHLEY AVE 29425 #041-13-1972 L1975 **IM END** *020 †20
LIEL, Yair Auraham. MEDICAL UNIVERSITY 29425 #550-01-1974 L1987 *020
LIEL-COHEN, Noah. MEDICAL UNIVERSITY 29425 #550-04-1983 L1987 *020
LILES, Laura Lee. ■ 29407 #012-22-2007 L2007 **ORS** *012
LIMEHOUSE, Walter E, Jr. 169 ASHLEY AVE, MEDICAL UNIVERSITY OF SC 29425 #045-01-1974 L1975 **EM FOP** *020 †16
LIN, Angello. 171 ASHLEY AVE 29425 #012-05-1992 L2000 **GS** *040 †85
LINDENMAYER, George Earl. 171 ASHLEY AVE DEPT MED 29425 #048-04-1967 **IM** *020
LINDROOTH, Miriam Watson. 295 CALHOUN ST, MEDICAL UNIV OF SOUTH CARO 29425 #036-01-1998 L2002 **FM** *020 †18
LINDSEY, Peggy Susan. 82 ANSON ST, LINDSEY OPHTHALMIC CONSULT 29401 #036-07-1978 L2004 **OPH** *020 †35
LINE, Christopher Costen. 9330 MEDICAL PLAZA DR, TRIDENT HEALTH - EMERG. DE 29406 #012-22-2001 L2005 **EM** *020 †16
LINKER, Robert Polk. 125 DOUGHTY ST, STE 420 29403 #036-01-1959 L1962 **AN** *071
LINTON, Irwin Grier, Jr. 2075 EAGLE LANDING BLVD 29406 #045-01-1978 L1982 **IM** *020 †20
LIPKE, James A. 2270 ASHLEY CROSSING DR, STE 165 29414 #011-04-1989 L1990 **FM** *020 †18 ‡
LIPTON, Morey. STE#C 3605MEETING ST. ROAD, COASTAL OCCUPATIONAL MED 29405 #045-01-1954 L1954 **GS** *020 †85
LISZKA, Heather Anne. 295 CALHOUN ST, DEPT OF FAM MED 29425 #041-12-1999 L2003 **FM** *020 †18
LITTLE, General T. 280 RUTLEDGE AVE 29403 #047-07-1971 L1976 **IMG** *020 †20
LITTON, Thomas C. 9329 MEDICAL PLAZA DR, TRI-COUNTY SURGICAL ASSOC 29406 #020-12-1983 L1984 **GS SO** *020 †85
LIU, Feng. 169 ASHLEY AVE, MSC 333 29425 #243-16-1987 L2005 **N** *012
LIVINGSTON, Ruth Levern. 2270 ASHLEY CROSSING DR, STE 170 29414 #027-01-1982 L1983 **IM IMG** *020 †20
LLOYD, Christine Patricia. 198 RUTLEDGE AVE, STE 8 29403 #023-07-1975 L1981 **P N** *020 †75
LOCKLAIR, Powell Reid, Jr. 125 DOUGHTY ST STE 260 29403 #045-01-1967 L1967 **CD GS** *020 †85,90
LOMINCHAR, Monica D. 2079 CHARLIE HALL BLVD 29414 #270-02-1987 L1995 **IM** *020 †20
LOOPER, James Michael. 169 ASHLEY AVE, MSC 333 29425 #045-01-2005 L2007 **AN** *012
LOPEZ, Steven Gerald. 2777 SPEISSEGGER DR 29405 #047-20-1996 L1998 **P** *020 †75
LOSEK, Joseph Dominic. 171 ASHLEY AVE 29425 #056-06-1977 L2004 **PEM** *020 †55,16
LOUGHRAN, Christopher F. MEDICAL UNIVERSITY 29425 #917-06-1976 L1985 *020
LOUIS, Russell H, Jr. ■ 29407 #020-02-2003 L2004 **EM** *100 †16
LOVELL, Jami Lyn. ■ 29414 #017-20-2006 L2006 **PD** *012
LOWELL, Isabel L Virella. 135 RUTLEDGE ST, STE 279 P.O. BOX 250561 29425 #045-01-1995 L2003 **PDP** *150 †75
LOWNDES-ROSEN, Dyana. 655 SAINT ANDREWS BLVD 29407 #045-01-1967 L1967 **P** *020
LUCAS, Charles Allen. 9330 MEDICAL PLAZA DR 29406 #045-01-1978 L1979 **OBG** *020 †30
LUCAS, David Grice, Jr. 2270 ASHLEY CROSSING DR, STE 155 29414 #012-22-1998 L1999 **GS** *020 †85
LUCAS, John Hume, IV. 9313 MEDICAL PLAZA DR, STE 310 29406 #045-01-1993 L1998 **N** *020 †75
LUCAS, John Thomas, Jr. ■ 29407 #045-01-2008 *012
LUCAS, Thomas Lawman, Jr. 101 RUTLEDGE AVE 29401 #045-01-1976 L1977 **FM EM** *020 †16
LUFF, Matthew Scott. ■ 29401 #047-20-2005 L2006 **IM** *012
LUK, Keith Dip-Kei. MUSC MEDICAL CTR 29425 #462-01-1977 L1991 *020
LUNDY, Allison Nicole. ■ 29403 #010-02-2008 *012
LUTTRELL, Louis Michael. 171 ASHLEY AVE 29425 #051-01-1988 L2003 **END** *020 †20
LUTZ, Myron Howard. 1205 WISTERIA RD, M H LUTZ, MD GYN CARE LLC 29407 #035-19-1964 L1973 **GYN GO** *020 †30
LYNCH, Meghan Elizabeth. ■ 29407 #045-01-2006 L2006 **OBG** *012
MACALUSO, Katie. ■ 29425 #035-06-2007 L2007 **GS** *012
MAC DONALD, Thomas Glenn. 18 FARMFIELD AVE 29407 #045-01-1986 L1987 **AN** *020 †05
MAC DOWELL, Margaret T. 9330 MEDICAL PLAZA DR, TRIDENT REGN'L MEDICAL CEN 29406 #045-01-1989 L1990 **RO** *020 †80

MACE, James Emory, Jr. 171 ASHLEY AVE, MED UNIV OF SC COLL OF MED 29425 #045-01-2006 L2008 **GS** *012

MACFALL, Timothy Allan. ■ 29414 #045-01-2008 *012

MACIAS, Michelle M. 135 RUTLEDGE ST 29425 #048-13-1987 L1993 **PD** *040 †55

MAC ILWAINE, John C. 1836 ASHLEY RIVER RD, STE E 29407 #051-01-1978 L2006 **ORS HS** *020 †40

MACK, Aimar Patrice. 9330 MEDICAL PLAZA DR 29406 #045-01-2001 L2006 **IM** *020

MAC LEAN, Brett Lewis. 1871 SAVAGE RD, PLANTATION PEDIATRICS 29407 #036-05-2001 L2002 **PD** *020 †55

MACPHERSON, Roderick Ian. 171 ASHLEY AVE, MEDICAL UNIV OF SO CAROLIN 29425 #062-01-1958 L1978 **PDR** *020

MADDEN, Matthew Brooks. ■ 29407 #045-01-2007 L2007 **IM** *012

MAGERA, Barbara Ellen. 452 FOLLY RD STE A 29412 #045-04-1988 L1989 **AI ALI** *020 †03,20

MAGINNIS, Michael Allen. ■ 29407 #045-11-1964 L1981 **ORS** *071 †40

MAGRO, Todd Keith. ■ 29401 #047-06-2008 *012

MAGUIRE, William Francis. ■ 29407 #045-01-1947 L1947 **IM** *071

MAGUIRE, William Francis. 615 WESLEY DR, STE 300 29407 #045-01-1985 L1988 **IM** *020 †20

MAHAFFEY, John Earl. 171 ASHLEY AVE 29425 #045-01-1954 L1954 **AN** *020 †05

MAHONEY, Joseph Peter. 29403 #011-05-2007 L2007 **EM** *012

MAIDMENT, Linda Jane. ■ 29407 #048-13-2007 L2007 **IM** *012

MAINIE, Inder Mohan Lal. PO BOX 250327, 96 JONATHAN LUCAS ST S 29425 #918-01-1995 L2005 **GE** *100

MALANOS, George Emmanuel. 316 CALHOUN ST 29401 #045-01-1973 L1974 **NEP** *020

MALCOLM, Robert James, Jr. 67 PRESIDENT ST, CTR DRUG/ALCOHOL PROG 29425 #045-01-1970 L1971 **FM** *020 †75,18

MALONE, Meghan Lynne. 96 JONATHAN LUCAS ST 29425 #035-06-2004 L2004 **GE** *012 †20

MANDANNA, Kanjithanda K. MED UNIV SC TEACH HOSPS 29401 #495-33-1965 **N** *100

MANNING, Rebecca Anna. 96 JONATHAN LUCAS ST, MED UNIV OF S CAROLINA MED 29425 #001-02-2006 L2006 **GS** *012

MANOS, John Peter. 171 ASHLEY AVE 29425 #045-01-1956 L1956 **ID CLP** *071

MANSKER, Deanna Rochelle. ■ 29414 #045-01-2006 L2006 **GS** *012

MARAN, Anbukarasi. 171 ASHLEY AVE 29425 #495-04-2000 L2007 **IM** *012

MARCHELL, Richard Michael. 135 RUTLEDGE ST, FL 11 29425 #035-48-2000 L2005 **D DS** *020 †15

MARCINO, Sara Lang. 1 CARRIAGE LN, STE J 29407 #045-01-2000 L2003 **P** *020 †75

MARCULESCU, Camelia. 171 ASHLEY AVE 29425 #781-01-1993 L2004 **ID** *020 †20

MARDIKIAN, Pascale Nicole. ■ 29403 #396-30-2000 L2007 **P** *012

MARGOLIUS, Harry Stephen. 171 ASHLEY AVE DEPT PHARM 29425 #038-41-1968 L1974 **PA CD** *071

MARIA, Bernard Lee. 173 ASHLEY AVE, STE 409 29425 #067-06-1981 L2003 **PD N** *030 †55,75

MARICA, Livia Sofia. 171 ASHLEY AVE 29425 #781-01-1993 L2004 **AN** *020

MARICQ, Andres Villu. ■ 29412 #005-02-1990 *100

MARICQ, Hildegard Rand. 171 ASHLEY AVE 29425 #165-01-1953 L1975 **RHU P** *071

MARINO, Robert Michael. ■ 29412 #021-05-2004 L2004 **OBG** *012

MARION, Robert Francis. 1247 SAVANNAH HWY, PARKWOOD PROF BLDG 29407 #012-01-1964 L1967 **PD PDA** *075

MARKLAND, Alan Colin. 171 ASHLEY AVE 29425 #352-03-1953 L1985 **U** *071 †95

MARKO, Dale Eugene. ■ 29407 #035-03-2006 L2006 **PYN** *012

MARKS, Richard Dunn. 9330 MEDICAL PLAZA DR 29406 #051-01-1958 L1974 **RO** *071 †80

MARLOW, Troy Jonathan. 1975 MAGWOOD DR UNIT H, TRICOUNTY RADIOLOGY ASSOCI 29414 #045-01-1997 L2002 **RNR** *020 †80

MAROSOK, Randy David. ■ 29414 #030-06-1986 L2006 **ID PD** *020 †20

MARSH, Jonathan Walton. ■ 29407 #045-01-2008 *012

MARSHALL, Alexander Wm. 2270 ASHLEY CROSSING DR, STE 170 29414 #045-01-1977 L1981 **IM** *020 †20

MARSHALL, David T. 171 ASHLEY AVE 29425 #048-12-1995 L2004 **RO** *020 †80

MARSHALL, Ian. 641 SAINT ANDREWS BLVD, SPECIALISTS 29407 #045-01-1989 L1990 **U** *020 †95

MARSHALL, Joseph Neil. 171 ASHLEY AVE 29425 #020-02-1955 L1960 **N** *020 †75

MARTIN, Frank Foster. 44 MARKFIELD DR 29407 #045-01-1963 L1963 **GE IM** *020 †20

MARTIN, Steve Marshall. ■ 29407 #045-01-2005 L2005 **ORS** *012

MARTIN, Temeia Denise. ■ 29425 #010-03-2007 L2007 **MP** *012

MARU, Neal Kevin. ■ 29412 #045-01-2007 L2007 **N** *012

MARZLUFF, Joseph Michael. 9313 MEDICAL PLAZA DR, STE 305 29406 #045-01-1973 L1980 **NS** *020 †25

MASINDET, Sarbabi. 1812 WALLACE SCHOOL RD 29407 #577-01-1981 L1995 **CD** *020 †20

MASIOWSKI, Michael L. 9330 MEDICAL PLAZA DR, PHYSN, TRIDENT REG MED CTR 29406 #048-04-1990 L2000 **EM** *020 †16

MASSEY, Brian Curtis. 169 ASHLEY AVE 29403 #048-16-2004 L2004 **CHP** *012

MASSEY, Marga Faith. 125 DOUGHTY ST, STE 590 29403 #036-07-1993 L2006 **PS GS** *020 †85,65

MASTRIANI, Katherine Sara. ■ 29401 #045-01-2008 *012

MATAWARAN, Ramon Deguzman. 109 BEE ST 29401 #051-07-1985 L1986 **IM** *020 †20

MATHESON, Eric Morgen. 295 CALHOUN ST, MUSC-DEPT OF FAMILY MEDICI 29425 #051-07-2001 L2007 **FM** *020 †18

MATHEUS, Maria Gisele. PO BOX 250322, 169 ASHLEY AVENUE 297 MUH 29425 #187-11-1996 L2007 **RNR** *100

MATSUDA, Koji. 96 JONATHAN LUCAS ST, DIGESTIVE DISEASE CENTER 29425 #572-76-1998 L2000 *020

MAULDIN, Jill Gossett. 171 ASHLEY AVE 29425 #012-05-1992 L1996 **OBG** *020 †30

MAUNG, Peter K. 9231 MEDICAL PLAZA DR # E 29406 #305-01-1996 L2001 **IM IMG** *030 †20

MAURER, Scott Thos. PO BOX 250333, 169 ASHLEY AVE 29425 #023-12-1992 L2003 **PDC** *020 †55

MAXWELL, Andrea Leigh. ■ 29412 #056-06-2006 L2006 **P** *012

MAY, Joshua Stafford. 9298 MEDICAL PLAZA DR, TRIDENT FAMILY MEDICINE 29406 #021-06-2007 L2007 **TY** *012

MCALISTER, Bradwell R, II. 775 WOODWARD RD 29407 #045-01-1989 L1990 **EM** *020 †16

MC BURNEY, Patricia G. 135 RUTLEDGE ST, MEDICAL UNIVERSITY OF SC 29425 #045-01-1997 L1999 **PD** *040 †55

MC CABE, Melissa Ann. 2633 MARSH CREEK DR 29414 #038-41-1994 L1998 **PD** *020 †55

MCCAIN, Joshua William. 9298 MEDICAL PLAZA DR, TRIDENT MEDICAL CENTER 29406 #012-22-2006 L2006 **DR** *012

MCCALL, Jenna Kathleen Ne. ■ 29407 #045-01-2008 *012

MC CANN, Heather Lynn. ■ 29407 #036-01-2002 L2004 **ORS** *012

MC CARTY, Christopher P. 169 ASHLEY AVE, MEDICAL UNIVERSITY OF S C 29403 #004-01-2003 L2004 **CD** *012

MC COTTRY, Cath Mc Kee. ■ 29407 #010-03-1945 L1950 **OBG OS** *071

MC CRAE, Christopher A. 9330 MEDICAL PLAZA DR, TRIDENT EMERGENCY PHYSICIA 29406 #041-01-2002 L2005 **EM** *020 †16

MC CURDY, Layton. ■ 29401 #045-01-1960 L1960 **P** *071 †75

MC CUSKER, Michelle C. 2095 HENRY TECKLENBURG DR 29414 #043-01-1981 L1993 **OBG** *020 †30

MCDONALD, Kristine G. 71 1/2 LINE ST 29403 #012-01-2006 L2007 **IM** *012

MC DONALD, Robert T, Jr. 109 BEE ST 29401 #012-01-1985 L1986 **IM EM** *020 †20

MC DONOUGH, Richard F. 9295 MEDICAL PLAZA DR # C, CAROLINA CANCER & BLOOD CA 29406 #011-02-2001 L2007 **HO** *012

MC ELLIGOTT, James Thomas. ■ 29401 #036-05-2004 L2004 **PD** *020 †55

MC EVOY, John Richard, Jr. 316 CALHOUN ST, DEPT OF PATHOLOGY 29401 #045-01-2001 L2003 **PTH** *020 †50

MC EVOY, Matthew David. ■ 29414 #045-01-2002 L2004 **AN** *100 †05

MC FADDEN, John Angus, II. 1483 TOBIAS GADSON BLVD, STE 202 29407 #051-07-1983 L1992 **ORS HS** *020 †65,85

MC FALL, Tracy Lynn. 109 BEE ST, DEPT PM& R -117 VAMC 29401 #001-02-1986 L1990 **PM** *020 †60 ‡

MC GAHA, Philip James. 293 E BAY ST 29401 #012-01-1993 L1996 **PD** *020 †55

MC GARY, William Brett. 171 ASHLEY AVE 29425 #020-12-1993 L1997 **EM** *020 †16

MCGILL, Douglas Edward. 316 CALHOUN ST, ROPER REHABILITATION HOSPI 29401 #045-01-1990 L1993 **PM** *020 †60

MCGOWAN, Joseph Wilson. 135 RUTLEDGE ST 29425 #045-04-2005 L2005 **D** *012

MC GRAW, Jennifer Carol. 171 ASHLEY AVE, MED UNIV OF S CAROLINA 29425 #001-06-1990 **AN** *020

MC INNES, Benj Kater, III. 9275 MEDICAL PLAZA DR # F 29406 #045-01-1972 L1976 **U** *020 †95

MC INTYRE, Ruth Thomas. 171 ASHLEY AVE 29425 #012-01-1955 L1970 **PD** *071

MC KEE, Kelly Tilson. 171 ASHLEY AVE 29425 #051-01-1941 L1948 **IM A** *071 †20,03

MC KENZIE, Leigh Jayne. 1030 JENKINS RD, STE A 29407 #047-20-1991 L1992 **CHP** *020

MCKILLOP, Caroline Perrin. ■ 29425 #045-01-2006 L2006 **AN** *012

MC LAIN, Christopher P. 615 WESLEY DR, STE 200 29407 #045-04-2002 L2003 **IM** *020 †20

MC LEAN, William Elliot. 28 BRISBANE DR 29407 #045-01-1962 1962 **OBG** *071 †30

MC LEOD-BRYANT, Stephen A. 171 ASHLEY AVE, DEPARTMENT OF PSYCHIATRY 29425 #035-45-1984 L1988 **P MDM** *020 †75

MCMANUS, John Ryan. ■ 29403 #025-01-2008 *012

MC NEAL, Christiane E. 9330 MEDICAL PLAZA DR 29406 #654-01-1992 L1996 **EM** *020 †16

MCNEAL, Karleen Marie. 109 BEE ST 29401 #422-01-1998 L2005 **IMG PLM** *020 †20

MC NELLIS, Edward Leonard. 1849 SAVAGE RD, CHARLESTON ENT ASSOC. 29407 #008-01-1991 L1992 **OTO** *020 †45

MC QUINN, Timothy Chas. 171 ASHLEY AVE, MEDICAL UNIV OF SOUTH CARO 29425 #054-04-1979 L1995 **PDC** *020 †55

MC QUOWN, Sherry Ann. 43 BROAD ST 29401 #045-01-1980 L1994 **FPS** *020 †45

MCRACKAN, Theodore Richar. ■ 29401 #045-01-2008 *012

MC WHORTER, Sarah E. 125 DOUGHTY ST STE 420, ANESTHESIA ASSOCIATES PA 29403 #045-01-1986 L1991 **AN** *020 †05

MEEHAN, Patrick Paul. 9298 MEDICAL PLAZA DR, TRIDENT REGIONAL MEDICAL C 29406 #035-08-2003 L2004 **FM** *100

MEEKINS, Kirk Allen. ■ 29425 #021-01-2004 L2007 **CHP** *012

MEEKINS, Pauline Elise. 169 ASHLEY AVE, MUSC - EMERGENCY MEDICINE 29425 #021-01-2004 L2007 **EM** *100

MEHURG, Shannon Michael. ■ 29414 #036-08-2005 L2005 **IM** *012

MEILER, Mark Jos. 9302 MEDICAL PLAZA DR, STE C 29406 #030-06-1970 L1993 **FM FPG** *020 †18

MELTON, James Willard, Jr. 316 CALHOUN ST 29401 #036-01-1987 L1989 **DR NM** *020 †80,28

MENARD, Mary Kathryn. 96 JONATHAN LUCAS ST, DEPT. OF OB/GYN, SUITE 634 29425 #033-05-1985 L1992 **MFM** *040 †30

MENDEL, Ehud. 96 JONATHAN LUCAS ST, CSB, STE 428 29425 #021-05-1991 L2000 **NS** *020 †25

MENDONCA, Celio Teixeira. 96 JONATHAN LUCAS ST, DEPT OF RADIOLOGY 29425 #187-08-1988 L2001 *020

MENGEDOHT, Daniel Edward. 2095 HENRY TECKLENBURG DR 29414 #045-01-1957 L1957 **PD** *071

MENGEDOHT, Marjorie A M. ■ 29401 #045-01-1957 L1957 **PD** *071 †55

MENNITO, Sarah Harper. ■ 29412 #023-01-2003 L2004 **MPD** *100 †20,55

MERRELL, Christopher Adam. ■ 29414 #038-40-2003 L2007 **PM** *100

MERRILL, William Woodroof. 109 BEE ST, MEDICAL SERVICE-111 29401 #056-06-1971 L2006 **PCC IM** *030 †20

MESA, Laura Cristina. ■ 29403 #045-01-2008 *012

MESSER, Benson Garrick. ■ 29414 #045-04-2008 *012

METCALF, John Stevenson. 171 ASHLEY AVE 29425 #045-01-1974 L1975 **ATP DMP** *020 †50

METCALF, Margaret Ann. 44 FOLLY RD STE C 29407 #048-13-1973 L1975 **PS** *020 †65

METTS, Christopher Lloyd. ■ 29401 #045-01-1997 L1997 *020

MEYER, Ted Albert. 171 ASHLEY AVE, RUTLEDGE TOWER,11TH FLOOR 29425 #016-11-1995 L2004 **OTO** *020

MEYER FRUTOS, Mario Luis. PO BOX 250333, 169 ASHLEY AVE 29425 #726-01-1996 L2002 **HO** *100 †20

MEYERS, Kevin Patrick. ■ 29407 #048-13-2007 L2007 **IM** *012

MICHALEC, Jennifer Ann. ■ 29414 #539-04-2003 L2006 **NPM** *012

MIELCK, Frank Karsten. 165 ASHLEY AVE STE 525 29425 #409-21-1987 L2005 *100

MILLER, Barbara Ann. ■ 29407 #045-01-2007 L2007 **PD** *012

MILLER, Gregg Bruce. 615 WESLEY DR, STE 320 29407 #020-02-1981 L1982 **CD IM** *040 †20

MILLER, Julie Sinclair. ■ 29414 #045-01-2008 *012

MILLER, Melissa Anne. PO BOX 250333, 169 ASHLEY AVE RM 202MUH 29425 #045-01-2001 L2003 **PCC** *012 †20

MILLER, Stephen Clark. 905 PARROT CREEK WAY 29412 #045-01-1983 L1984 **CD** *020 †20

MILLING, David Lee. 46 JONATHAN LUCAS ST, 916 CSB 29425 #045-01-2002 L2004 **HO** *012 †20

MILLS, David Michael. ■ 29412 #038-06-2005 L2005 **PD** *012

MILLS, Jared Clay. ■ 29412 #045-01-2005 L2005 **DR** *012

MILUTINOVIC, Jovan. 171 ASHLEY AVE 29425 #957-01-1953 L1982 **NEP IM** *071 †20

MINNICK, Katherine A. 1565 SAM RITTENBERG BLVD, STE 200 29407 #017-20-1989 L1997 **ID** *020 †20

MINSHALL, Christian. 96 JONATHAN LUCAS ST, CSB RM 418-E 29425 #016-11-1999 L2007 **CCS** *020 †85

MIRONOVA, Marina A. 338 TWELVE OAK DR 29414 #913-61-1978 L1999 **IM** *020 †20

MITCHELL, Holly C Good. 2125 CHARLIE HALL BLVD 29414 #047-05-1989 L1995 **RHU IM** *020 †20

MOAK, Darlene H. 669 SAINT ANDREWS BLVD 29407 #033-05-1980 L1989 **ADP** *020 †75

MOE, Christopher Bradley. 316 CALHOUN ST, DEPT OF EMERGENCY MEDICINE 29401 #045-01-1992 L1993 **EM** *020 †16

MOHR, Lawrence Chas, Jr. 171 ASHLEY AVE 29425 #036-01-1979 L1994 **IM** *020

MOLLOY, Eric Charles. ■ 29401 #539-06-2007 L2007 **IM** *012

MONDRAGON, Cristina. 1938 CHARLIE HALL BLVD 29414 #748-02-1996 L2003 **ID** *020 †20

MONK, Richard Warren. ■ 29412 #045-01-2008 *012

MONROE, Timothy R. 96 JONATHAN LUCAS ST 29425 #010-02-2004 L2004 **NS** *012

MONSERRATE, Ivan Enrique. 109 BEE ST, VA MED CTR RALPH H JOHNSON 29401 #042-03-1991 L1993 **IM** *020 †20

MONTALBANO, Michelle M. 96 JONATHAN LUCAS ST, STE 812 29425 #039-01-1998 L2004 **AI PD** *020 †55,03

MOONEY, James Francis, III. 96 JONATHAN LUCAS ST, CSB 708 29425 #025-07-1987 L2005 **OP** *020 †40

MOORE, Deborah Hazel. ■ 29407 #036-01-1990 L1993 **PD** *020 †55

MOORE, Susan Elizabeth. ■ 29407 #036-08-1989 L1990 **AN** *020 †05

MORAN, William Patrick. 135 RUTLEDGE ST, UNIVERSITY OF SC RUTLEDGE 29425 #010-02-1982 L2005 **IM** *020 †20

MORGAN, Katherine Ann. 171 ASHLEY AVE 29425 #012-05-1998 L2003 **GS** *020 †85

MORGAN, Steve Lewis. ■ 29412 #048-12-2005 L2005 **NS** *012

MORRIS, Allan John. 171 ASHLEY AVE, MEDICAL UNIV OF SC 29425 #803-01-1984 L1995 **GE** *020

MORRIS, John Lee. 2258 LAZY RIVER DR 29414 #045-01-2008 *012

MORRISON, Edward Chisolm. 1327 ASHLEY RIVER RD, STE B 29407 #045-01-1984 L1985 **GS** *020 †85

MOSES, Christopher K. 169 ASHLEY AVE 29403 #038-43-2002 L2004 **RNR** *012 †80

MOSKOS, Vasiliki. ■ 29412 #045-01-1965 L1965 **CHP PYA** *071

MOTLEY, Jarod Ross. ■ 29401 #001-02-2006 L2006 **AN** *012

MUELLER, Melissa Maria. ■ 29401 #045-01-2008 *012

MUGHELLI, Kess Evelyn. ■ 29407 #045-01-2008 *012

MUGHELLI, Olumide. 1843 ASHLEY RIVER RD 29407 #024-07-1980 L1989 **OBG** *020 †30

MUIRHEAD, William R, II. 1483 TOBIAS GADSON BLVD, CHARLESTON HAND GROUP 29407 #035-45-1995 L2005 **HS** *020

MULBRY, Leonard Wm, Jr. 2095 HENRY TECKLENBURG DR 29414 #020-12-1980 L1989 **P ORS** *020 †40

MULCAHY, Hugh Edward. MUSC MED CTR 29425 #539-06-1987 L1999 *020

MULLIS, Diana Lynn. 29 LEINBACH DR B 29407 #045-01-1985 L1990 **P EM** *020 †75

MULVIHILL, Denise Mary. 169 ASHLEY AVE, MEDICAL UNIVERSITY OF SC 29403 #041-07-1971 L1992 **PDR DR** *020 †80

MURPHY, Cynthia Lee. 2070 NORTHBROOK BLVD 29406 #012-01-1989 L1991 **PD** *020 †55

MURPHY, Jennifer Kirsten. 96 JONATHAN LUCAS ST, STE 912 29425 #016-43-1997 L2006 **IM RHU** *012

MURPHY, Rebecca Reid. ■ 29401 #045-01-2005 L2005 **OPH** *012

MURPHY, Wm Martin, Jr. 10 FARMFIELD AVE STE A 29407 #045-01-1965 L1965 **OBG** *071 †30

MURRAY, David Frank. 3600 RIVERS AVE, NAVAL HOSPITAL 29405 #023-12-1993 L2001 **IM** *020 †20

MURRAY, Matthew F. ■ 29412 #048-13-2005 L2006 **DR** *012

MUSGRAVE, Valerie Ann. 9298 MEDICAL PLAZA DR 29406 #045-01-2007 L2007 **FP** *012

MYRICK, Donald Lahugh. 171 ASHLEY AVE 29425 #045-01-1992 L1993 **P** *020 †75

NABORS, Michael Wills. ■ 29412 #038-06-1979 L1982 **OS NS** *020

NAHAS, Ziad H. 67 PRESIDENT ST # 502-N, INSTITUTE OF PSYCHIATRY-MU 29425 #605-02-1992 L1997 **P** *020 †75

NASON, Barron Scott. 128 BULL ST 29401 #047-20-1994 L1997 **EM** *020 †16

NAZON, Herold. SUITE 1A & 1B, 1455 REMOUNT ROAD 29406 #035-47-1982 L1985 **FM** *020 †18

NEAL, Jeffrey Gardner. 135 RUTLEDGE ST 29425 #051-01-2002 L2004 **OTO** *020

NELSON, Kirstin Jo. 171 ASHLEY AVE 29425 #038-40-1994 L2004 **VIR** *020 †80

NESMITH, Deborah Deas. 67 PRESIDENT ST, MUSC -PSHCHIATRY 29425 #045-01-1989 L1990 **CHP** *020 †75

NESMITH, Louie E. 316 CALHOUN ST 29401 #045-01-1943 L1944 **GYN OBG** *071 †30

NEWMAN, Charlotte Anne. 9330 MEDICAL PLAZA DR, TRIDENT EMERGENCY PHYSICIA 29406 #045-01-2000 L2003 **EM** *020 †16

NEWMAN, Roger Beemer. 628 SAINT ANDREWS BLVD 29407 #045-01-1980 L1981 **OBG** *020 †30

NEWTON, Edward Marshall. 1477 TOBIAS GADSON BLVD 29407 #051-01-1994 L1997 **FM** *020 †18

NEWTON, William Bruce. ■ 29401 #045-01-1956 L1956 **P OS** *020

NICKLES, Roy Everette, Jr. 5 FORT ROYAL CT 29407 #045-01-1963 L1963 **D A** *071 †15

NIELSEN, Christopher D. 135 RUTLEDGE ST, STE 1201 29425 #036-05-1990 L1991 **CD** *020 †20

NIEMER, Gregory William. 10 FARMFIELD AVE, STE A 29407 #045-01-1995 L1996 **RHU** *020 †20

NISSMAN, Daniel Bavo. ■ 29412 #036-01-2003 L2005 **DR** *012

NIXON, Daniel Walker. 125 DOUGHTY ST STE 280 29403 #012-01-1969 L1994 **ON** *030 †20

NNADI, Ngozi Patricia. 2090 EXECUTIVE HALL RD, STE 170 29407 #690-06-1991 L2000 **P** *020 †75

NOBLE, Marc Davis. 1962 CHARLIE HALL BLVD 29414 #048-12-1999 L2006 **GE** *100 †20

NOBLES, Ryan Harrison. ■ 29407 #045-01-2008 *012

NOBLET, Nicholas Hershey. ■ 29407 #045-01-2006 L2006 **IM** *012

NOH, Chung Il. ■ 29407 #583-02-1977 L1989 **PDC** *020

NOLTE, Justin Michael. ■ 29414 #055-02-2007 L2007 **N** *012

NOONE, Michael Curran. 1849 SAVAGE RD, PENINSULA ENT & PLASTIC SU 29407 #036-01-1999 L2001 **GS** *020 †45

NORCROSS, Edward Douglas. 171 ASHLEY AVE 29425 #033-06-1983 L1989 **OS GS** *020 †85

NORIEGA, Joyce Argelia. 1364 ASHLEY RIVER RD 29407 #025-01-1995 L2005 **OBG** *020 †30

NORTHAM, Meredith Cates. ■ 29407 #045-01-2008 *012

NOTZ, William Eugene. 1901 ASHLEY RIVER RD, STE 7A 29407 #035-45-1956 L1983 **AN** *020

NOVY, Craig M. 2095 HENRY TECKLENBURG DR, BON SECOURS SAINT FRANCIS 29414 #011-04-1977 L1978 **PTH** *020 †50

NUMAN, Mohammed Tawfiq. PO BOX 250625, 96 JONATHAN LUCAS ST 29425 #797-03-1990 L2000 **PDC** *020 †55

NUROZLER, Feza. 171 ASHLEY AVE, CARDIOTHORACIC SURGERY 29425 #902-05-1986 L1996 **TS** *020

NUSSBAUM, Alan Israel. 14 FARMFIELD AVE, RHEUMATOLOGY ASSOCIATES 29407 #024-01-1977 L1980 **RHU IM** *020 †20

NUTAITIS, Matthew John. 167 ASHLEY AVE, MUSC - STORM EYE INSTITUTE 29403 #023-12-1985 L1991 **OPH** *020 †35

NUYTTENS, Joost Jan. 171 ASHLEY AVE, RADIATION ONCOLOGY 29425 #165-02-1996 L1999 **RO** *020

NWOSU, Victoria Kosonike. 96 JONATHAN LUCAS ST, MED UNIV OF S CAROLINA 29425 #021-01-2005 L2005 **N** *012

O, Seung-Jun. 2097 HENRY TECKLENBURG DR 29414 #001-06-1993 L1994 **PS** *020 †85,65

OATES, James C. 9330 MEDICAL PLAZA DR 29406 #823-07-1991 L1996 **RHU** *050 †20

OBASI, Patrick Chidi. ■ 29412 #010-03-2004 L2007 **GS** *012

OBEID, Lina Marie. 114 DOUGHTY ST, MED UNV SC RM 604STB 29403 #605-01-1983 L1985 **IMG IM** *050 †20

O'BRIEN, Ann Hope Miller. 1467 BURNINGTREE RD 29412 #803-03-1948 L1976 **AN** *075

O'BRIEN, Paul E. ■ 29407 #016-06-1996 L2006 **ON** *020 †20

O'BRIEN, Terrence Xavier. 135 RUTLEDGE ST STE 1201, MEDICAL UNIV OF SC 29425 #005-18-1984 L1993 **CD IM** *020 †20

O'BRYAN, Edward Conyers, III. 96 JONATHAN LUCAS ST 8 29425 #045-01-2004 L2005 **IM** *012

OCKERMAN, Troy James. 125 DOUGHTY ST, STE 420 29403 #019-02-1997 L2006 **AN** *020 †05

O'DELL, William Fred. 171 ASHLEY AVE 29425 #045-01-1970 L1971 **PD** *020 †55

OGAWA, Makio. 171 ASHLEY AVE 29425 #572-16-1964 L1979 **IM HEM** *050 †20

OKAFOR, Chika Nwando. ■ 29414 #038-40-2005 L2005 **IM** *012

OKAZAKI, Norimasa. 171 ASHLEY AVE 29425 #572-54-1976 L1987 **FM** *020

OLADIMEJI, Ojo Moses. 51 NASSAU ST 29403 #690-02-1992 L2004 **IM** *020

OLDFIELD, Baird Dewes. 9330 MEDICAL PLAZA DR 29406 #039-01-1977 L1980 **FM** *020 †18,16

OLDHAM, John Michael. 67 PRESIDENT ST 29425 #048-04-1967 L2002 **P PYA** *030 †75

OLIVER, Eric Richard. 96 JONATHAN LUCAS ST 29425 #038-40-2004 L2004 **OTO** *012

OLIVERIO, Robert R, Jr. 615 WESLEY DR, STE 300 29407 #023-01-1990 L2006 **IM** *020 †20

OLSON, Ricky Lane. 9330 MEDICAL PLAZA DR 29406 #019-02-1997 L2000 **MG** *020 †19,18

OLTMANN, Michael Adolph. ■ 29414 #004-01-2005 L2005 **MPD** *012

O'NEILL, Patrick Jos. 65 JONATHAN LUCAS ST, STE 426CSB 29425 #045-01-1991 L1992 **PS HS** *020 †85

ORAK, John Kenneth. 171 ASHLEY AVE 29425 #010-01-1977 L1983 **PD** *040 †55

ORCUTT, James Michael. 125 DOUGHTY ST, STE 500 29403 #036-05-1990 L1996 **HO** *020 †20

ORLOWSKY, Eric William. ■ 29412 #023-01-2008 *012

ORNSTEIN, Steven M. 171 ASHLEY AVE, DEPT OF FAMILY MEDICINE 29425 #036-07-1981 L1983 **FM** *050 †18

ORSBORN, Jonathan Wade. ■ 29407 #004-01-2007 L2007 **PD** *012

ORTIGOZA, Eric Brum. ■ 29412 #045-01-2008 *012

OSAGUONA, Stephen Efeosa. ■ 29414 #690-06-1994 L2007 **NEP** *012 †20

OSBORNE, Granger C. 10 FARMFIELD AVE, STE A 29407 #045-01-1974 L1975 **OBG** *020 †30

OSGUTHORPE, John David. 135 RUTLEDGE ST, DEPT OF OTOLARYNGOLOGY PO 29425 #049-01-1973 L1979 **OTO A** *040 †45 ‡

OSLIZLOK, Paul Conrad. 171 ASHLEY AVE 29425 #539-04-1979 L1991 **PDC** *020

OSORIO-MCKENNA, Jonathan. ■ 29407 #045-01-2008 *012

OSTA, Walid Aref. 171 ASHLEY AVE, MED UNIV SC COLL OF MED 29425 #605-01-2002 L2004 **AN** *012

OSTEEN, Matthew Beal. 125 DOUGHTY ST, STE 370 29403 #012-22-2000 L2007 **IC** *020 †20

OTHERSEN, Henry B, Jr. 96 JONATHAN LUCAS ST # 418, PED SURG-MUSC POB 250613 29425 #045-01-1953 L1953 **PDS TS** *030 †85,90

OTHERSEN, Henry Biemann. ■ 29401 #045-01-2000 L2004 **P** *020 †75

OTHERSEN, Jennifer B. 164 MARKET ST, # 260 29401 #045-01-2002 L2004 **NEP** *020 †75

OUZTS, John Andrew, III. 1 POSTON RD, STE 120 29407 #012-01-1973 L1975 **P** *020 †75

OVERDYK, Frank Jacob. 171 ASHLEY AVE 29425 #041-01-1990 L1994 **AN** *020 †05

OWENS, Charles Jerry. 316 CALHOUN ST 29401 #045-01-1962 L1962 **NEP IM** *071 †20

PACULT, Artur. 125 DOUGHTY ST, STE 570 29403 #759-01-1979 L1983 **NS** *020 †25

PADGETT, Tamara Mcgowan. 169 ASHLEY AVE RM 202MUH, MSC 333 29425 #045-01-2005 L2005 **P** *012

PAGE-TURNER, Yvette D. 171 ASHLEY AVE, MED UNIV OF SC SCH OF MED 29425 #045-01-1999 L2003 **AN** *020 †05

PAI, Gurpur Shashidhar. 135 RUTLEDGE ST RM 395, MSC 561 29425 #495-09-1971 L1981 **MG CG** *020 †55,19

PAMUKLAR, Ertan. 169B ASHLEY AVE, RM 297 29403 #902-03-1990 L2005 **N** *100

PAOLONE, Timothy John. 171 ASHLEY AVE 29425 #038-45-1989 L1991 **P** *020

PAPAMITSAKIS, Nikolaos. 96 JONATHAN LUCAS ST, #307 CSB 29425 #418-05-1991 L2006 **N** *020 †75

PAPHITIS, Nicholas Walker. ■ 29407 #051-01-2006 L2006 **IM** *012

PAPPAS, Anthony. ■ 29407 #035-08-1946 L1953 **IM CD** *071

PAQUIN, Sarto C. 96 JONATHAN LUCAS ST, MUSC GASTROENTEROLOGY AND 29425 #067-02-1998 L2004 *020

PARASCHOS, Theodore K. 2095 HENRY TECKLENBURG DR 29414 #035-15-2000 L2003 **EM** *020

PARDIECK, David Anthony. 9330 MEDICAL PLAZA DR 29406 #017-20-1970 L1972 **GS** *020 †85

PARIKH, Naval Girish. ■ 29403 #045-01-2008 *012

PARRIS, Jeremy James. 171 ASHLEY AVE 29425 #012-05-2004 L2004 **GP GS** *020

PASALA, Sanjiv. 169 ASHLEY AVE, MSC 333 29425 #028-46-2005 L2005 **PD** *012

PASTIS, Nicholas James, Jr. 2097 HENRY TECKLENBURG DR, STE 305 29414 #038-41-1999 L2003 **PCC** *020 †20

PATEL, Alpesh. 520 FOLLY RD, STE 375 29412 #047-20-2001 L2004 **GE** *012 †20

PATEL, Ashok Valjibhai. 96 JONATHAN LUCAS ST, STE 309 29425 #495-89-1994 L2004 **N** *012

PATEL, Rakesh Maneklal. ■ 29403 #045-01-2008 *012

PATEL, Sagar Hasmukh. ■ 29412 #027-01-2003 L2004 **MP** *012

PATEL, Sunil Jayavant. 96 JONATHAN LUCAS ST, MSC 616 29425 #045-01-1985 L1987 **NS** *050 †25

PATRICK, Celeste Hunt. 171 ASHLEY AVE 29425 #045-01-1982 L1983 **NPM PD** *020 †55

PAUL, Thomas. 96 JONATHAN LUCAS ST 29425 #409-38-1982 L2001 *020

PAULS, Darryl Randolph. ■ 29401 #045-01-2004 L2004 **DR** *012

PAWATE, Sidhu S. 169 ASHLEY AVE, APT 202 29403 #495-35-1989 L2004 **N** *100

PAYNE, John Furman. 9298 MEDICAL PLAZA DR, RESIDENCY PROGRAM 29406 #045-01-2006 L2006 **OPH** *012

PAYNE, Kenneth Mark. 25 COURTENAY DR, MSC 290 29401 #019-02-1982 L1997 **GE IM** *020 †20

PAYNE, Kim Jeanine. 171 ASHLEY AVE 29425 #019-02-1994 L1999 **AN** *020 †05

PAYNE, Rebecca Ann. 169 ASHLEY AVE, MSC 333 29425 #045-04-2005 L2005 **P** *012

PAYNE, Robert Houston, Jr. 4 CARRIAGE LN STE 100, CHARLESTON FAMILY CENTER 29407 #045-01-1972 L1973 **P** *020

PAZO, Adner. ■ 29414 #422-01-2007 L2007 **EM** *012

PEARCE, Melissa Williams. 96 JONATHAN LUCAS ST, STE 634, MSC 619 29425 #011-03-2004 L2004 **OBG** *012

PEASE, David Murrell. ■ 29412 #045-01-1981 L1987 **OBG** *075 †30

PEATROSS, Jessica Laine. PO BOX 250333, 169 ASHLEY AVE 29425 #020-02-2006 L2006 **IM** *012

PEERY, Charles Vance, II. 9231 MED PLAZA DR 29406 #036-07-1968 L1975 **OBG PD** *020 †30

PELIC, Christopher G. 171 ASHLEY AVE, INSTITUTE OF PSYC, 3 NORT 29425 #038-43-2000 L2001 **P** *020 †75

PENN, Daniel Eli. ■ 29407 #045-01-2006 L2006 **IM** *012

PENN, Frances Elizabeth. 171 ASHLEY AVE, MED UNIV OF SC COLL OF MED 29425 #045-01-2006 L2006 **PD** *012

PENNEY, Fletcher Thompson. ■ 29407 #045-01-2001 L2004 **IM** *100 †20

PERIYASAMY, Basker. 169 ASHLEY AVE, P O BOX 25033 29403 #038-43-2001 L2004 **NEP** *012

PERNA, Mark John. ■ 29425 #007-02-2007 L2007 **GS** *012

PEROT, Phanor L, Jr. 96 JONATHAN LUCAS ST, STE 428 29425 #021-01-1952 L1968 **NS** *040 †25

PETERS, Walter Hamilton, IV. ■ 29403 #045-01-2008 *012

PETERSEIM, David Scott. 125 DOUGHTY ST, STE 690 29403 #028-02-1988 L1999 **TS** *020 †90,85

PETERSEIM, Mae Millicent. 171 ASHLEY AVE 29425 #028-02-1988 L1999 **PO** *020 †35

PEURA, Jennifer Lynn. 169 ASHLEY AVE 29403 #016-45-2000 L2003 **CD** *012

PEYSER, Robert Elliott. 1637 SAVANNAH HWY 29407 #012-05-1978 L1983 **OPH** *020 †35

PHELPS, Sarah Hallman. 2095 HENRY TECKLENBURG DR, CHARLESTON ANESTHESIA GROU 29414 #012-05-2001 L2004 **AN** *005

PHILLIPS, James Harrison. 316 CALHOUN ST 29401 #045-01-1977 L1978 **PTH** *020 †50

PHILLIPS, Kevin Daniel. 169 ASHLEY AVE, P O BOX 25033 29425 #051-04-2001 L2003 **RNR** *020 †80

PHILLIPS, Summar Christia. 169 ASHLEY AVE, MEDICAL UNIVERSITY OIF SC 29425 #045-01-2003 L2004 **AN** *020

PICARD, Melissa Mccutcheo. 171 ASHLEY AVE, DEPT RAD 29425 #038-43-2006 L2007 **DR** *012

PIERCE, Paul Geoffrey. 67 PRESIDENT ST 29425 #039-01-2004 L2004 **P** *012

PILCHER, Thomas Alexander. 169 ASHLEY AVE RM 202M, MSC 333 29425 #048-04-1999 L2004 **PDC** *012 †55

PILLAI, R Bhana. 2093 HENRY TECKLENBURG DR, STE 307 29414 #495-80-1982 L1996 **PG** *020 †55

PITTALL, William Bullock. 165 ASHLEY AVE, DPT PED 29425 #051-01-1972 L1985 **NPM PD** *050 †55

PITTMAN, Fred Estes. 109 BEE ST 5TH FL 29401 #035-01-1959 L1969 **GE IM** *050

PITZER, Geoffrey Barrett. ■ 29412 #051-01-2006 L2006 **OTO** *012

PLAYER, Marty Shannon. ■ 29414 #045-04-2001 L2005 **FM** *100 †18

PLOTH, David Wm. 171 ASHLEY AVE 29425 #018-03-1967 L1987 **NEP IM** *050 †20

PLYLER, John Williams. 9313 MEDICAL PLAZA DR, STE 310 29406 #045-01-1984 L1985 **N** *020 †75

POGHOSYAN, Tereza. 169 ASHLEY AVE # 202, DEPT OF RADIOLOGY 29403 #913-38-1996 L2004 **DR** *012

POLETTI, Steven Chas. 1941 SAVAGE RD, STE 100E 29407 #005-15-1985 L1992 **ORS** *020 †40

POLLACK, Matthew Ryan. 9298 MEDICAL PLAZA DR, RESIDENCY PROGRAM 29406 #051-04-2006 L2006 **FP** *012

POLLACK, Ross Brian. 135 RUTLEDGE ST 11TH FL, MSC 578 29425 #010-02-1978 L1982 **D** *020 †15

POLLEHN, Thomas Andrew. 169 ASHLEY AVE, MSC 300 29425 #010-02-1995 L2006 **EM** *020 †16

POPE, John Hilton, Jr. 171 ASHLEY AVE 29425 #045-01-1974 **AN** *075

POPP, Randi Katherine. 1483 TOBIAS GADSON BLVD, STE 103 29407 #011-02-1994 L1997 **FM** *020 †18

POST, Ginell Antoinette. ■ 29425 #016-02-1992 L2007 **PTH** *100 †50

POST, Nicole Renee. ■ 29412 #033-06-2005 L2005 **P** *012

POST, Robert Edward. 9298 MEDICAL PLAZA DR, UNIVERSITY FAMILY MEDICINE 29406 #033-06-2005 L2005 **FP** *012

POSTMA, William Fulton. 171 ASHLEY AVE, MED UNIV OF SC COLL OF MED 29425 #045-01-2006 L2006 **ORS** *012

POTFAY, Jonathan David. ■ 29425 #011-04-2003 L2004 **CD** *012 †20

POURMAND, Eric Pejman. ■ 29412 #017-20-2003 L2007 **AN** *012

POWERS, Eric Randall. PO BOX 250592, 135 RUTLEDGE AVE STE 1201 29425 #024-01-1974 L2005 **CD IM** *020 †20

PRATT-THOMAS, H Rawling. ■ 29401 #045-01-1938 L1938 **PTH** *071 †50

PRESLEY, Bradley Clayton. ■ 29412 #020-12-2008 *012

PRESNELL, Susan Erin. 165 ASHLEY AVE STE 309, MUSC DEPT OF PATHOLOGY 29425 #045-01-1993 L1994 **FOP** *020 †50

PRESTON, Andrea Schroeder. ■ 29425 #038-40-2005 L2005 **PD** *012

PREYER, Lucy Woltz. 1 CARRIAGE LN, STE J 29407 #036-05-1989 L1998 **P** *020 †75

PRIDE, Pamela Jean. 171 ASHLEY AVE 29425 #041-12-1996 L2001 **IM** *020 †12

PRIESTER, Rory A. PO BOX 250333, 169 ASHLEY AVE RM 202 29425 #043-01-2002 L2006 **CD** *012 †20

PRINCIPE, Ralph Francis. 2095 HENRY TECKLENBURG DR 29414 #028-34-1964 L1972 **OBG** *071 †30

PRIOLEAU, Wm Hutson, Jr. 218 ASHLEY AVE 29403 #023-07-1962 L1962 **CD TS** *071 †85,90

PRITCHARD, Paul Baker, III. 171 ASHLEY AVE, DEPT OF NEUROLOGY 29425 #045-01-1969 L1969 **N** *020 †75

PRIVETT, Thomas Allen. 9330 MEDICAL PLAZA DR, CHARLESTON NEUROLOGY ASSOC 29406 #021-01-1993 L2002 **N** *020 †75

PRUITT, Armstead Bert. ■ 29401 #036-05-1959 L1967 **OBG** *072 †30

PRYSTOWSKY, Michael Wayne. 9291 MEDICAL PLAZA DR 29406 #035-09-1977 L1984 **OBG** *030 †30

PSENKA, Tamatha Marie. 171 ASHLEY AVE 29425 #045-01-1996 L1997 **FM** *020 †18

PUCKETTE, Stephen Elliott. 9313 MEDICAL PLAZA DR, BOX 13 29406 #045-01-1957 L1957 **R** *071 †80

PUCKHABER, Ashley Amanda. ■ 29401 #036-05-2002 **PD** *100

PUGH, Kim B. 125 DOUGHTY ST, STE 530 29403 #055-01-1982 L1993 **END** *020 †20

PULICICCHIO, Louis Umile. 9330 MEDICAL PLAZA DR 29406 #010-01-1958 L1959 **OS IM** *071

PULJIC', Igor. 169 ASHLEY AVE # 202, DEPT OF GENERAL SURGERY 29403 #957-01-1997 L2002 **GS** *020

PULLATT, Rana Chitnaranja. 169 ASHLEY AVE RM 202, MSC 333 29425 #495-04-1997 L2003 **GS** *012

PUROHIT, Dilip Manohar. 171 ASHLEY AVE 29425 #495-01-1965 L1976 **NPM PD** *030 †55

PUTNEY, Floyd Johnson. ■ 29412 #041-02-1934 L1967 **OTO HNS** *072 †45

PYLE, Ashley Louise. ■ 29412 #019-02-2007 L2007 **IM** *012

QUATTLEBAUM, Robert Glen. 9298 MEDICAL PLAZA DR, UNIVERSITY FAMILY MEDICINE 29406 #036-01-2005 L2005 **FP** *012

QUATTLEBAUM, Thomas G. 198 RUTLEDGE AVE 29403 #045-01-1971 L1976 **PD** *040 †55

QUIGLEY, Rex Gayle. 1901 ASHLEY RIVER RD, STE 7A 29407 #048-04-1963 L1987 **AN** *071 †05

QUINN, Gerald Joseph. 125 DOUGHTY ST, STE 570 29403 #041-02-1962 L1968 **N CN** *020 †75

QUINN, John Vaden. 1243 SAVANNAH HWY 29407 #021-05-1999 L2005 **PD** *020 †55

RACKOFF, Andrew Ian. 169 ASHLEY AVE, BOX 250623 29403 #038-41-2002 L2002 **GE** *012 †20

RAISPIS, Christopher J. 1670 DRYDOCK DR, BLDG 10A 29405 #045-01-1996 L1999 **FM** *020 †18

RAJAGOPALAN, P R. 96 JONATHAN LUCAS ST CSB40, MEDICAL UNIVERSITY OF SC 29425 #495-09-1964 L1981 **TTS GS** *020 †85

RAJENDRA, Anil Balaji. ■ 29407 #047-06-2007 L2007 **IM** *012

RAMBO, Victor Birch. 109 BEE ST, VA MEDICAL CENTER 29401 #041-01-1952 L1972 **GP GS** *072 †85

RAMES, Laura Jean. 16 FULTON ST 29401 #047-05-1987 L1988 **P** *020 †75

RAMES, Ross Alan. 96 JONATHAN LUCAS ST, MEDICAL UNIVERSITY OF SC U 29425 #047-05-1987 L1988 **U** *020 †95

RAMEY, John Tompkins. 1879 SAVAGE RD 29407 #045-01-2000 L2005 **AI IM** *020 †20,03

RAMSAY, Michael Patrick. 316 CALHOUN ST, PHYSICIANS EMERGENCY DEPT. 29401 #045-01-2000 L2003 **EM** *020 †16 ‡

RAMSETTY, Anita Nellie. ■ 29412 #011-03-2000 L2006 **END** *100 †20

RAMSETTY, Sabena Karina. 171 ASHLEY AVE, DEPT ID 29425 #035-19-2004 L2007 **ID** *012 †20

RAND, John Chrisman. 316 CALHOUN ST, ROPER HOSP, ROPER RADIOLOG 29401 #020-12-1987 L1993 **R** *020 †80

RANDAZZO, William S. 135 RUTLEDGE ST, MSC 561 29425 #396-01-1982 L2007 **PD** *020 †55 ‡

RAO, Anil Gopalakrishna. 169 ASHLEY AVE, MSC 322 29425 #495-09-1994 L2005 **PDR** *100

RAO, Sandhya Radhakrishna. 96 JONATHAN LUCAS ST, CSB404 29425 #495-01-1989 L2001 *020

RAPER, Stacia Dawn. 169 ASHLEY AVE, MEDICAL UNIVERSITY OF SC 29403 #012-01-2003 L2004 **PYG** *012

RASHFORD, Allan Alexander. PO BOX 22645 29413 #018-03-1973 L1977 **PUD** *020 †20

RAUNIKAR, Robert Austin. 171 ASHLEY AVE 29425 #021-01-1987 L1994 **PDC PD** *020 †20

RAUSCH, Ellisa Anne. 9298 MEDICAL PLAZA DR, RESIDENCY PROGRAM 29406 #047-20-2006 L2006 **FP** *012

RAVANEL, Daniel. 2095 HENRY TECKLENBURG DR 29414 #045-01-1968 L1968 **R NM** *020 †80

RAVENEL, James Gaillard. 169 ASHLEY AVE, BOX 250322 29403 #036-05-1992 L2001 **DR** *020 †80

RAVENEL, James Morris. 1962 CHARLIE HALL BLVD 29414 #045-01-1969 L1970 **GE** *020 †20

RAWE, Stephen Elmer. 9275 MEDICAL PLAZA DR # B 29406 #041-01-1969 L1976 **NS** *020 †25

RAY, Brittany Nicole. ■ 29412 #045-01-2008 *012

RAY, Joseph Michael. 109 BEE ST 29401 #020-12-1974 L1976 **IM** *020 †20

RAYMOND, John Richard. 135 CANNON ST, RM 100 29425 #038-40-1982 L1996 **NEP IM** *050 †20

REDDING, Amanda Louise. 96 JONATHAN LUCAS STE 4 29425 #045-01-2006 L2006 **AN** *012

REDER, Michael William. 2270 ASHLEY CROSSING DR, CONSULTANTS 29414 #038-41-2000 L2001 **AI** *020 †20,03

REED, Carolyn Elaine. 96 JONATHAN LUCAS ST 29425 #035-45-1977 L1985 **TS GS** *020 †85,90

REED, John Henry. PO BOX 250333, 169 ASHLEY AVE RM 202MUH 29425 #010-03-1999 L2005 **PDC** *100 †55

REED, Melissa Lynn. ■ 29412 #017-20-2007 L2007 **AN** *012

REESE, Matthew Edward. ■ 29407 #041-12-2006 L2006 **GS** *012

REEVES, Bozman Rell, Jr. 125 DOUGHTY ST, STE 370 29403 #045-01-1970 L1971 **CD IM** *020 †20

REEVES, Eric Rodney. 169 ASHLEY AVE, MSC 333 29425 #021-06-2005 L2005 **IM** *012

REEVES, Scott Townsend. 165 ASHLEY AVE STE 525, P O BOX 250912 29425 #045-01-1987 L1993 **AN** *020 †20,05

REHMAN, Shakaib U. 109 BEE ST, CTR. (11C) 29401 #704-20-1990 L2000 **IM** *020 †20

REIGART, John Routt, II. 135 RUTLEDGE ST RM 280PO, MEDICAL UNIVERSITY OF SC P 29425 #024-01-1967 L1970 **PD GPM** *050 †55

RENE, Ronald Marshel. 109 BEE ST, VA MED CTR DEPT OF SURG 29401 #035-48-1984 L2005 **GS TS** *020 †85 ‡

RENK, Geoffrey Edmund. 2095 HENRY TECKLENBURG DR, ST FRANCIS HOSPITAL 29414 #045-01-1986 L1997 **EM** *020 †16

REUBEN, Adrian. PO BOX 250327, 90 JONATHAN LUCAS ST 29425 #917-30-1969 L2004 *020

REUSCHE, Christian Fernan. ■ 29425 #033-05-2007 L2007 **P** *012

REVES, Joseph Gerald. PO BOX 250617, 96 JONATHAN LUCAS ST STE 29425 #045-01-1969 L1969 **AN PA** *020 †05

REYNA, Ronald Emilio. PO BOX 250333, 169 ASHLEY AVE 29425 #010-01-2001 L2004 **PS** *012

REYNOLDS, Carl Ray. ■ 29407 #036-05-2003 L2007 **CD** *012 †20

REYNOLDS, Jessica Lynn. 169 ASHLEY AVE 29403 #038-43-2001 L2003 **PYG** *100

RHODES, Dolores Yvette. PO BOX 250327, 96 JONTHAN LUCAS ST 29425 #010-03-1998 L2006 **IM** *020 †20

RHODES, Jack Wylan. 1243 SAVANNAH HWY 29407 #045-01-1948 L1948 **PD** *071 †55

RHODES, Malcolm Mcleod. 1243 SAVANNAH HWY 29407 #045-01-1985 L1988 **PD** *020 †55

RICHARDS, James T. 125 DOUGHTY ST STE 400 29403 #045-01-1962 L1962 **GS** *071 †15

RICHARDS, Jeffrey Kendal. 1548 ASHLEY RIVER RD 29407 #051-01-1974 L1977 **OPH** *020 †35

RICHARDSON, George Robert. 1941 SAVAGE RD, STE 100E 29407 #045-01-1993 L1994 **PM** *020 †60

RICHARDSON, Jonathan W. 171 ASHLEY AVE 29425 #028-03-1991 L1994 **P** *020 †75

RICHARDSON, Mary Sharon. 171 ASHLEY AVE 29425 #012-01-1989 L1993 **PTH** *020 †50

RICHARDSON, N Selby, III. 171 ASHLEY AVE 29425 #045-01-1987 L1988 **EM** *020 †16

RICHMOND, Gerald Edmund. 29401 #045-01-2006 **GS** *012

RICHMOND, Vashondra Denet. ■ 29414 #045-01-2008 *012

RICKER, Harry Eugene. ■ 29401 #045-01-1973 L1975 **EM** *020

RIDINGS, Catherine Louise. ■ 29403 #045-01-2008 *012

RIEDER, Jeffrey Stewart. 125 DOUGHTY ST, STE 370 29403 #035-46-1991 L1994 **CD** *020 †20

RINGEWALD, Jeremy Matthew. 165 ASHLEY AVE 29425 #016-11-1994 L2004 **PDC** *020 †55

RISMANI, Mehdi M. 9297 MEDICAL PLAZA DR, STE C 29406 #045-01-1993 L2001 **AN** *020 †05

RITTENBERG, Charles S. 96 JONATHAN LUCAS ST POB25, MEDICAL UNIVERSITY OF SC 29425 #045-01-2000 L2001 **OBG** *100

RITTENBERG, Gerald Mark. 2095 HENRY TECKLENBURG DR 29414 #045-01-1964 L1964 **R** *020 †80

RITTENBERG, Henry Woodrow. ■ 29412 #045-01-1955 L1956 **GP** *071

RITTERSHAUS, Ahren Charle. 165 ASHLEY AVE STE 309, MED UNIV OF S CAROLINA 29425 #051-04-2005 L2005 **PTH** *012

RIVERS, Charles F. 316 CALHOUN ST 29401 #045-01-1953 L1953 **CD** *071

RIVERS, Thomas Pinckney R. 446 FOLLY RD 29412 #045-01-1961 L1961 **OBG** *071 †30

ROANE, Georgia Carlisle. 14E FARMFIELD AVE STE E 29407 #021-01-1990 L1991 **RHU** *020 †20

ROBARDS, Jay Brian. 316 CALHOUN ST 29401 #045-01-1985 L1989 **DR** *020 †80

ROBBINS, David Herbert. 96 JONATHAN LUCAS ST, MEDICAL UNIVERRITY OF S C 29425 #035-47-1999 L2003 **GE** *100 †20

ROBERTS, Donna Rae. 169 ASHLEY AVE, MSC 333 29425 #045-01-1999 L2000 **RNR** *100 †80

ROBERTS, Jason Ray. ■ 29414 #020-12-2004 L2004 **IM** *100 †20

ROBERTS, John M. 171 ASHLEY AVE, SC PSYCH 29425 #028-03-1977 L1981 **P** *020 †75

ROBERTS, John Martin. 169 ASHLEY AVE 29403 #021-06-1987 L1988 **P** *020 †75

ROBERTSON, Henry Clay, III. 171 MOULTRIE STREET, THE CITADEL INFIRMARY 29409 #045-01-1965 L1965 **IM CD** *071 †20

ROBINS, Amy Lynne. 169 ASHLEY AVE, EMERG MED 29425 #038-40-1994 L1997 **EM** *020 †16

ROBINSON, Christopher Joe. 96 JONATHAN LUCAS ST, MEDICAL UNIV OF SOUTH CARO 29425 #045-01-2000 L2002 **OBG MFM** *020 †30 ‡

ROBINSON, John Hollis. 96 JONATHAN LUCAS ST, MSC 613 29425 #041-02-1968 L2004 **PS** *020 †65

ROBINSON, John Michael. 169 ASHLEY AVE RM 202MUH, MSC 333 29425 #041-02-2002 L2007 **PS** *012

ROBINSON, Kenneth Eugene. 614 BLITCHRIDGE RD 29407 #028-03-1977 L1981 **OBG** *020

ROBINSON, Robert Jos. 51 NASSAU ST 29403 #035-08-1974 L1979 **OBG** *020

ROBISON, Jacob Gordon. 171 ASHLEY AVE 424CSB, MUSC 29425 #048-13-1976 L1987 **VS GS** *020 †85

RODELSPERGER, Geo E, Jr. 316 CALHOUN ST 29401 #045-01-1982 L1988 **EM** *020 †16

RODRIGUEZ, Cesar Amaury. ■ 29414 #042-01-2002 L2008 **AN** *100 †05

ROEHRS, Philip Andrew. 169 ASHLEY AVE 29403 #045-04-2002 L2004 **PHO** *012

ROGERS, Hudson Clyde. 9295 MEDICAL PLAZA DR # B 29406 #045-01-1979 L1982 **DS D** *020 †15

ROGERS, Raford Porter, III. ■ 29412 #012-01-2007 L2007 **PTH** *012

ROGERS, Sarah Ann Charike. ■ 29406 #045-01-2007 L2007 **FP** *012

ROJUGBOKAN, Adebola Ade. 51 NASSAU ST, FRANKLIN C FETTE CLINIC 29403 #048-12-1996 L1999 **FM** *020 †18

ROLAND, Patricia Jackson. 125 DOUGHTY ST, STE 420 29403 #021-06-1990 L1991 **AN** *020 †05

ROMAGNUOLO, Joseph. 96 JONATHAN LUCAS ST, DIV OF GAS/HEPTLGY STE 210 29425 #065-01-1994 L2004 **GE** *020

ROMANO, Peter Benjamin. 169 ASHLEY AVE 29403 #051-07-2003 L2004 **DR** *012

ROMERO, Neil Cameron. 169 ASHLEY AVE, BOX 250333 29425 #021-05-2003 L2004 **ORS** *012

RONISH, Elizabeth M. ■ 29412 #001-06-2003 L2004 **HO** *012 †20

ROSEBROCK, Craig Neale. 160 ASHLEY AVE, BOX 250623 29403 #045-01-2002 L2004 **PCC** *012 †20

ROSEBROCK, Geo Luther, Jr. 3531 MARY ADER AVE STE A 29414 #045-01-1970 L1971 **DIA IM** *020 †20

ROSEN, Marianne Way. 776 DANIEL ELLIS DR, STE 1A 29412 #045-01-1985 L1986 **D FM** *020 †15

ROSEN, Samuel Howard. 198 RUTLEDGE AVE STE 8 29403 #001-02-1974 L1981 **P PYG** *020 †75

ROSENBLUM, Michael Alex. 171 ASHLEY AVE, MED UNIV SC 29425 #045-01-2004 L2007 **CD** *012 †20

ROSENBLUM, Raymond. 1565 SAM RITTENBERG BLVD, STE 200 29407 #045-01-1954 L1954 **U** *071 †95

ROSENSHEIN, Ira Lawrence. 1030 JENKINS RD STE A, COASTAL PSYCHIATRY LLC 29407 #045-01-1990 L1996 **P** *020 †75

ROSENTHAL, Peter Alan. 109 BEE ST, RALPH H JOHNSON VA MED CTR 29401 #836-01-1978 L1992 **DR** *020 †80

ROSIER, Presley F. 2316 COSGROVE AVE 29405 #045-01-1997 L1998 **IM** *020 †20

ROSS, Adam T. 135 RUTLEDGE ST, STE 690 29425 #045-01-1995 L2007 **TS** *020 †85,90

ROSS, Andrew Patrick. ■ 29425 #051-07-2007 L2007 **EM** *012

ROSS, Scott Douglas. 125 DOUGHTY ST, STE 200 29403 #051-01-1995 L2007 **TS** *020 †85,90

ROSSILLO, Ludwig Anthony. 4322 BREAM RD 29418 #010-02-1961 L1981 **R** *071 †80

ROUNTREE, Emily Maria. 67 PRESIDENT ST 29425 #045-04-2006 L2006 **P** *012

ROVNER, Eric Scott. 96 JONATHAN LUCAS ST, MSC 620 29425 #035-46-1991 L2004 **U** *020 †95

ROWLAND, Haley Cody. ■ 29403 #045-01-2008 *012

ROWLAND, Melisa Dawn. 171 ASHLEY AVE 29425 #011-04-1990 L1991 **CHP** *050 †75

ROYALL, Lee Morrell. 1962 CHARLIE HALL BLVD, CHAS GASTROENTEROLOGY SPEC 29414 #045-01-1998 L2004 **GE** *020 †20

RUDDY, Jeanmarie Brigid. ■ 29407 #041-02-2005 L2005 **GS** *012

RUMBOLDT, Tihana. 169 ASHLEY AVE # 202, DEPT OF PATHOLOGY 29403 #957-05-1996 L2004 **PTH** *100 †50

RUMBOLDT, Zoran. 171 ASHLEY AVE 29425 #957-01-1989 L2004 **RNR** *020

RUNQUIST, Lars Hokan, Jr. 125 DOUGHTY ST, STE 370 29403 #047-06-1995 L1996 **CD** *020 †20

RUPP, Ned T. 1879 SAVAGE RD 29407 #012-01-1986 L1997 **AI PD** *020 †03,55

RUSHING, Jona Marie. ■ 29407 #018-03-2006 L2006 **OBG** *012

RUSSELL, Roger Alexander. 701 E BAY ST STE 1-435, RUSSELL BIOMED COMPAY 29403 #045-01-1987 L1991 **PTH** *020 †50

RUSTIN, Dowse Danl. 55 BEE ST 29403 #045-01-1966 L1966 **ORS** *020 †40

RUSTIN, Rudolph Byrd, III. 125 DOUGHTY ST STE 770 29403 #045-01-1983 L1989 **CRS GS** *020 †85,10

RUTH, Natasha Mckerran. 135 RUTLEDGE ST, PED RHEU/MSC 561 29425 #045-04-2000 L2002 **PPR** *020 †55 ‡

RYAN, Ashley Beatty. 169 ASHLEY AVE, MSC 333 29425 #001-02-2005 L2005 **OBG** *012

RYAN, David Steven. ■ 29403 #045-01-2006 L2006 **ORS** *012

SAAVEDRA, Heather Rose. 169 ASHLEY AVE 202M, MSC 333 29425 #016-45-2005 L2005 **PD** *012

SABBACK, Michael Steven. ■ 29407 #038-40-1972 L1973 **GS** *071 †85

SADE, Robert Miles. 96 JONATHAN LUCAS ST, STE 409 29425 #035-01-1963 L1975 **TS GS** *040 †85,90

SADLER, Robert Karl. 4480 LEEDS PL W 29405 #045-01-1974 L1977 **OBG** *020

SAEF, Steven Howard. 171 ASHLEY AVE 29425 #011-02-1983 L1995 **EM** *020 †16,20

SAGATELIAN, Michael A. 2073 CHARLIE HALL BLVD 29414 #005-19-1986 L1995 **GE** *020 †20

SAGEL, Julius. 109 BEE ST, VETERAN AFFAIRS MED CTR 29401 #836-02-1964 L1976 **IM END** *030 †20

SAHN, Steven A. 171 ASHLEY AVE, CARE MEDICINE 29425 #020-02-1968 L1983 **PUD IM** *030 †20

SAIFAN, Chadi Gergis. 171 ASHLEY AVE, DEPT ID 29425 #605-03-2003 L2007 **ID** *012 †20

SALDANA, Larissa Marie. ■ 29412 #045-01-2008 *012

SALERNO, Joseph John. 9231 MEDICAL PLAZA DR # A 29406 #550-02-1981 L1994 **CD IM** *020 †20

SALGADO, Cassandra D. 171 ASHLEY AVE 29425 #055-01-1995 L2004 **ID** *020 †55,20

SALISBURY, Marsha W. 2100 CHARLIE HALL BLVD, CHARLESTON MENTAL HEALTH C 29414 #045-01-1992 L1993 **CHP P** *020

SANDBERG, Sarah Anne. ■ 29403 #045-01-2008 *012

SANDERS, John Dixon. 9275 MEDICAL PLAZA DR, STE C 29406 #045-01-1973 L1974 **IM** *020 †20

SANDERS, Paul Walter, III. 1483 TOBIAS GADSON BLVD, STE 107 29407 #045-01-1957 L1957 **U** *071 †95

SANDHU, Monique Kaur. ■ 29407 #045-01-2007 L2007 **IM** *012

SANTOS, Alberto Benito. 171 ASHLEY AVE 29425 #045-01-1976 L1977 **P** *020 †75

SAPP, Heidi Michelle. 96 JONATHAN LUCAS ST 29425 #045-03-2004 L2004 **OBG** *012

SAPP, Robert Bradley. ■ 29407 #047-20-2006 L2006 **IM** *012

SARAF, Naveen. 171 ASHLEY AVE, SURGERY/CARDIOTHORACIC SUR 29425 #495-51-1986 L1998 *020

SARTI, Juan Fernando. ■ 29425 #132-03-1996 L2007 **AN** *012

SASAKI, Aria Naomi. 169 ASHLEY AVE RM 202MU, MSC 333 29425 #028-34-2000 L2004 **DR** *012

SAUNDERS, Allan Jos. 171 ASHLEY AVE, MED UNIV SC 29425 #042-01-2002 L2007 **VIR** *012 †80

SAUNDERS, Richard Ames. 167 ASHLEY AVE, MEDICAL UNIVERSITY OF S.C 29403 #035-01-1973 L1978 **OPH PD** *050 †35

SAVAGE, Andrew John. 169 ASHLEY AVE RM 202MUH, MSC 333 29425 #045-01-2002 L2006 **PDC** *012 †55

SAVAGE, Ashlyn Holstein. ■ 29403 #045-01-2002 L2006 **OBG** *100 †30

SAVAGE, Stephen James. 171 ASHLEY AVE 29425 #035-01-1993 L2004 **U** *020 †95

SAVATIEL, Angela Maria. 10 FARMFIELD AVE, STE A 29407 #002-01-1995 L2004 **OBG** *020 †30

SCARLETT, Leslie Chardkof. 2270 ASHLEY CROSSING DR, STE 100 29414 #045-01-2003 L2004 **OPH** *020

SCHABEL, Frank Milton, III. 18 FARMFIELD AVE 29407 #021-01-1970 L1975 **AN** *020 †05

SCHABEL, Stephen Irwin. 171 ASHLEY AVE, DEPT OF RADIOLOGY 29425 #016-02-1972 L1976 **DR** *040 †80

SCHENKLER, Mark Andrew. 3 GAMECOCK AVE STE 305 29407 #048-14-1992 L1997 **P** *020 †75

SCHERRER, Sara Jane. ■ 29412 #019-02-2007 L2007 **IM** *012

SCHIFFMAN, Noah Ivan. 171 ASHLEY AVE, PHYSICAL & REHABILITATION 29425 #045-01-1998 L1999 **PM** *020

SCHILLER-FLYNN, Anne B. 316 CALHOUN ST, CHARLESTON PATHOLOGY, PA 29401 #036-05-1994 L2005 **PCP** *020 †50

SCHILLING, Andreas. 171 ASHLEY AVE 29425 #045-01-1999 L2001 **RNR** *100 †80

SCHIMPF, Dennis Kenneth. 96 JONATHAN LUCAS ST STE 4, MED UNIV OF S CAROLINA 29425 #305-01-2001 L2006 **PS** *012 †20

SCHLESINGER, Kenneth I. 542 WAMPLER DR 29412 #035-45-1984 L1989 **AN** *020 †05

SCHLESINGER, Todd Eric. 2093 HENRY TCKLNBRG #300, DERMATOLOGY AND LASER CENT 29414 #035-06-1994 L1998 **D** *020 †15 ‡

SCHLOSSER, Rodney Jon. 135 RUTLEDGE ST STE 1130 29425 #026-08-1996 L2002 **OTO AI** *020 †45

SCHNEIDER, Juli Lynn. ■ 29401 #020-12-2004 L2004 **MPD** *012

SCHNELL, James Wm. 2073 CHARLIE HALL BLVD 29414 #045-04-1992 L1997 **GE IM** *020 †20

SCHONHOLZ, Claudio Javier. 169 ASHLEY AVE, MSC 322 29425 #132-01-1980 L2004 **VIR** *020

SCHRAMM, Marjorie E. 28 ELLIOTT ST 29401 #041-13-1973 L1988 **IM** *020 †20,16

SCHREUDERS, Greta S. ■ 29407 #660-04-1955 **OS** *075

SCHUH, Fredric De Graw. 65 GADSDEN ST 29401 #035-01-1960 L1970 **PS** *020 †85,65

SCHUH, Sara E Daley. 135 RUTLEDGE ST, BOX 250561 29425 #035-01-1961 L1970 **PD PHP** *071 †55

SCHULTZE, Jeffrey George. 2125 CHARLIE HALL BLVD, STE 2B 29414 #008-02-1995 L1996 **IM** *020 †20

SCHUMAN, Stanley Harold. MED UNIV OF SC FAM PRAC 29401 #028-02-1948 L1973 **PHP FM** *040 †55

SCHUSTER, Gerald David. 2093 HENRY TECKLENBURG DR, STE 303 EAST MED 29414 #023-01-1956 L1998 **ORS** *020 †40

SCHUTTE, H Del, Jr. 2125 CHARLIE HALL BLVD 29414 #005-12-1984 L1991 **ORS** *020 †40

SCHUYLER, Dean. 669 SAINT ANDREWS BLVD 29407 #035-19-1967 L2002 **P** *020 †75

SCHWARTZBERG, Brian J. 9330 MEDICAL PLAZA DR, TRIDENT MEDICAL CENTER 29406 #012-01-2001 L2004 **EM** *020 †16

SCHWEIGER, Don Albert. 12 FARMFIELD AVE, STE E 29407 #047-05-1972 L1975 **IM** *020 †20

SCHWEPPE, Mark Lindeman. ■ 29407 #045-01-2008 *012

SCOTT, David John. 169 ASHLEY AVE, DIGESTIVE CENTER 29403 #917-04-1989 L2000 **R** *050

SCOTT, Graham Chas. 125 DOUGHTY ST, STE 200 29403 #539-06-1979 L1991 **PUD IM** *020 †20

SCOTT, Lancer Alan. ■ 29412 #036-01-2004 L2007 **EM** *020

SCURRY, Joy Blanton. 1483 TOBIAS GADSON BLVD, STE 107 29407 #045-04-2002 L2005 **FM** *100 †18

S DAVIS, Phillip Brian. 169 ASHLEY AVE RM 20, MSC 333 29425 #045-01-2004 L2004 **NM IM** *012

SEAWRIGHT, Katherine Mich. ■ 29403 #045-01-2008 *012

SEGAL, Mark Jos. 18 FARMFIELD AVE 29407 #003-01-1986 L1996 **AN** *020 †05

SEIDERS, Christopher D. 9330 MEDICAL PLAZA DR, COASTAL INPATIENT PHYSICIA 29406 #036-01-1999 L2004 **IM** *020

SELANDER, Craig Lee. ■ 29407 #045-01-2007 L2007 **GS** *012

SELBY, John Bayne. 171 ASHLEY AVE 29425 #047-06-1946 L1975 **NM END** *071 †28,20

SELBY, John Bayne, Jr. 169 ASHLEY AVE 29403 #045-01-1983 L1997 **VIR R** *020 †80

SELF, Sally Elizabeth. 165 ASHLEY AVE STE 309, MUSC PATH & LAB MED 29425 #047-05-1978 L1979 **PTH CLP** *040 †50

SELTZER, Sidney Marvin. 9304 MEDICAL PLAZA DR 29406 #025-07-1961 L1968 **OPH OS** *020 †35

SENSENEY, Anna Dudley. 171 ASHLEY AVE, DEPT OF INTERNAL MEDICINE 29425 #045-01-1992 L1993 **RHU** *020 †20

SESSIONS, Roy Brumby. 135 RUTLEDGE ST RM 1117, MSC 550 29425 #021-05-1962 L2008 **OTO HNS** *020 †45

SEXAUER, James D. 67 PRESIDENT ST, MUSC PO 250861 29425 #038-06-1962 L1968 **P** *020 †75

SEYMOUR, William W. 34 BROAD ST 29401 #045-01-1951 L1951 **IM OM** *071

SHAFIQ-HODA, Rana. 171 ASHLEY AVE 29425 #704-02-1983 L2000 **PCP** *020 †50

SHAH, Shilpa Narendra. ■ 29414 #045-01-2006 L2006 **PD** *012

SHAIKH, Zahirabanu Shauka. ■ 29407 #496-41-1998 L2006 **ID** *012 †20

SHANMUGABHASKAR, S. 171 ASHLEY AVE RM 404CSD 29425 #495-04-1984 L1996 **GS** *020

SHAPIRO, Robert Lauren. ■ 29412 #045-01-2008 *012

SHAPIRO, Steven Dennis. 1483 TOBIAS GADSON BLVD, STE 102 29407 #045-01-1987 L1988 **MG PD** *020 †19,55

SHARMA, Anand K. 169 ASHLEY AVE, DEPT OF RADIATION ONCOLOGY 29425 #495-77-1983 L2001 **RO** *020 †80

SHARMA, Neeraj K. 316 CALHOUN ST 29401 #012-01-2003 L2004 **IM** *100 †20

SHARPE, Kenneth Allan. 1470 TOBIAS GADSON BLVD, STE 100 29407 #036-01-1979 L1980 **OPH** *020 †35

SHATAT, Ibrahim Fahmi. 96 JONATHAN LUCAS ST, AKRON CHILDRENS HOSP 29425 #575-01-1999 L2007 **PN** *100 †55

SHAWINSKY, Arlene Anne. 776 DANIEL ELLIS DR, STE 2A 29412 #836-01-1979 L1995 **PD** *020 †55

SHEALY, Gerald James. 1483 TOBIAS GADSON BLVD, STE 202 29407 #036-05-1972 L1973 **HS ORS** *020 †40

SHEALY, Ralph Mc Keetha. 171 ASHLEY AVE 29425 #045-01-1978 L1981 **EM** *040 †16

SHEERANI, Mughis Ahmad K. ■ 29407 #704-02-1990 L1996 **N** *020 †75

SHEIL, Amy Terese. ■ 29422 #030-06-2003 L2004 **ATP** *012 †50

SHELDON, William Burtis. 9279 MEDICAL PLAZA DR, STE C 29406 #051-01-1974 L1975 **RHU IM** *020 †20

SHELLEY, William Harrison. 109 BEE ST, ATT: MAIL ROUTE 11C 29401 #045-01-2000 L2001 **IM** *100 †20

SHEPARD, Arthur James, III. 9330 MEDICAL PLAZA DR, TRIDENT HEALTH SYSTEMS 29406 #036-01-1989 L2001 **NPM PD** *020 †55

SHEPARD, Michelle M. 171 ASHLEY AVE 29425 #422-01-1996 L2003 **NEP** *020 †20

SHEPARD, Nicole Petersen. 1871 SAVAGE RD 29407 #036-05-1991 L2002 **PD** *020 †55

SHEREFF, Michael Jos. 2093 HENRY TECKLENBURG DR, STE 201 29414 #016-42-1976 L1998 **ORS** *020 †40

SHERMAN, Elden Paul, Jr. 18 FARMFIELD AVE 29407 #021-01-1980 L1991 **AN** *020 †05

SHETH, Sachin B. ■ 29401 #045-01-2008 *012

SHIRAI, Keisuke. ■ 29412 #572-01-1997 L2005 **HO** *012 †20

SHIRALI, Girish S. 171 ASHLEY AVE 29425 #496-38-1984 L1998 **PD PDC** *020 †55

SHOEMAKER, Wm Herbert, Jr. 21 GAMECOCK AVE, STE D 29407 #036-05-1973 L1978 **FM** *020 †18

SHOFFEITT, John Paul. ■ 29407 #051-07-2007 L2007 **IM** *012

SHORT, Edward Baron. 67 PRESIDENT ST, MSC 861 29425 #045-01-2001 L2003 **OS** *100 †20,75

SIDNEY, Darren Stuart. 171 ASHLEY AVE, MED UNIV SC 29425 #035-08-2003 L2007 **CD** *012 †20

SIEGAN, Mitchell Joseph. 2095 HENRY TECKLENBURG DR, DEPT OF ANESTHESIA 29414 #016-11-1995 L2000 **CCA** *020 †05

SIEGEL, Mark Samuel. 167 ASHLEY AVE 29403 #051-01-2000 L2002 **OPH** *020

SIGMON, Lee Merrell. 316 CALHOUN ST, CHARLESTON PATHOLOGY PA 29401 #045-01-1972 L1973 **PTH DMP** *071 †50

SILGALS, Robert Marshall. 9295 MEDICAL PLAZA DR # C, CAROLINA CANCER & BLOOD CA 29406 #020-12-1978 L1984 **ON IG** *020 †20

SILVER, Richard Michael. 2125 CHARLIE HALL BLVD 29414 #047-05-1975 L1981 **IM RHU** *050 †20

SILVESTRI, Gerard. 171 ASHLEY AVE 29425 #422-01-1987 L1993 **PUD** *020 †20

SIMMONS, Jack Warren, Jr. 2097 HENRY TECKLENBURG DR, STE 312W 29414 #045-01-1980 L1981 **OBG** *020 †30

SIMPSON, Brian Rush. 169 ASHLEY AVE, MEDICAL UNIVERSITY OF SC 29403 #004-01-2000 L2002 **OS** *020 †75

SIMPSON, James Gaston. 48 FOLLY ROAD BLVD 29407 #045-01-1968 L1968 **D** *020 †15

SIMPSON, Wm Maynard, Jr. 295 CALHOUN ST, DEPT FAM MED-PO 29425-0192 29425 #045-01-1972 L1973 **FM FPG** *040 †20

SINGH, Amit Paul. ■ 29412 #012-01-2004 L2004 **AN** *012

SINGH, Avtar Kaur. 109 BEE ST 29401 #495-73-1981 L1987 **ATP HMP** *050 †50

SINHA, Manasi. ■ 29403 #045-01-2008 *012

SINNOTT, Robert Henry. 30 SOCIETY ST 29401 #045-01-1976 L1978 **P** *020

SITES, Ronald Bradley. 701 E BAY ST, CHARLESTON MHC 29403 #045-01-2000 L2002 **P** *020 †75

SKINNER, David John. 316 CALHOUN ST 29401 #024-01-1978 L1983 **DR** *020 †80 ‡

SKINNER, Margaret Leigh. 135 RUTLEDGE ST # 250550 29425 #035-20-2002 L2004 **OTO** *100

SKONER, Judith Marie. 135 RUTLEDGE AVE, BOX 250550 29425 #045-04-1996 L2000 **OTO FPS** *020 †45

SLAVIN, Laurence A. ■ 29401 #165-01-1967 L1969 **N OM** *071

SLOAN, Helen Elizabeth. 38 RADCLIFFE ST 29403 #045-01-1978 L1979 **GP** *020

SMITH, Arthur Richard. 171 ASHLEY AVE 29403 #010-01-1977 L1998 **AN** *020 †05

SMITH, Bert Jackson. ■ 29414 #047-20-2004 L2004 **MPD** *012

SMITH, Brian Newbatt. 109 BEE ST 29401 #016-02-1960 L1965 **NEP IM** *020

SMITH, Charles Donovan. 96 JONATHAN LUCAS ST, STE 418CSB 29425 #036-07-1969 L1978 **PDS PD** *020 †85

SMITH, Charles Leon, Jr. 2095 HENRY TECKLENBURG DR 29414 #004-01-1994 L1997 **IM** *020 †20

SMITH, Edwin Allan. 96 JONATHAN LUCAS ST, 912CSB 29425 #041-12-1979 L1982 **RHU IM** *020 †20

SMITH, Gregory Warren. ■ 29412 #012-01-1981 L1984 **P** *020 †75

SMITH, Jacqueline Marie. ■ 29407 #045-01-2008 *012

SMITH, James Scott. 125 DOUGHTY ST, STE 500 29403 #036-01-1996 L2004 **HO** *020 †20

SMITH, Kirby Judson. ■ 29407 #045-01-2006 L2006 **PD** *012

SMITH, Michael Keith. 169 ASHLEY AVE, MUH RM 202 29425 #045-01-2002 L2004 **CHP** *020

SMITH, Rikki Lynn. ■ 29412 #001-02-2001 L2004 **P** *020 †75

SMITH, Robert Heyward. 316 CALHOUN ST, ROPER HOSPITAL 29401 #045-01-1992 L1999 **VIR** *020 †80

SMITH, Sally Wilson. 263 KING ST STE B 29401 #045-01-1991 L1993 **P** *020 †75

SMITH, Susan Marie. 2750 SPEISSEGGER DR 29405 #041-14-1981 L1982 **FM EM** *020 †18,16

SMITH, William Arthur. 2318 COSGROVE AVE 29405 #045-01-1971 L1973 **NEP** *020 †20

SMOAK, Dahlmon Lewis. 2145 HENRY TECKLENBURG DR, STE 270 29414 #045-01-1969 L1969 **OBG** *020 †30

SMOLKA, Jean Veronica. 171 ASHLEY AVE 29425 #045-01-1997 L1999 **PD** *020 †55

SNIPES, Jonathan Michael. ■ 29403 #045-01-2008 *012

SNYDER, William Huston. 615 WESLEY DR, STE 200 29407 #045-01-1995 L1997 **IM** *020 †20

SOHN, Mimi. 169 ASHLEY AVE RM 20, MSC 333 29425 #583-08-1988 L2005 **N** *012

SOKEVITZ, David T, Jr. 18 FARMFIELD AVE 29407 #045-04-1990 L1992 **AN** *020 †05

SOLOMON, Kerry Dean. 167 ASHLEY AVE 29403 #050-02-1987 L1993 **OPH IM** *020 †35

SOMMER, Holly Michelle. 171 ASHLEY AVE, MED UNIV OF SC COLL OF MED 29425 #045-01-2006 **P** *012

SOMMERVILLE, Jeanine Ann. 204 W HILL BLVD 29404 #005-14-2001 L2005 **FM** *020 †18

SONNTAG, Hans F. 165 ASHLEY AVE 29425 #407-07-1963 L2004 *020

SOOD, Ajay. 169 ASHLEY AVE, ROOM 202 MAIN HOSPITAL 29403 #045-01-2004 L2007 **CHP** *012

SOPER, David Edward. 96 JONATHAN LUCAS ST, STE 634 29425 #011-02-1976 L1996 **OBG ID** *020 †30

SOSNOUSKI, David Stanley. 169 ASHLEY AVE, MEDICAL UNIVERSITY OF SC 29403 #018-03-2003 L2004 **DR** *012

SOSNOWSKI, J Richard. 171 ASHLEY AVE 29425 #045-01-1945 L1945 **OBG** *072 †30

SOULE, Jeremy Ben. 96 JONATHAN LUCAS ST, CSB 816 29425 #055-01-1994 L1999 **END** *020 †20

SOUTHGATE, Wm Michael. ■ 29425 #020-12-1981 L1992 **PD NPM** *040 †55

SOWARDS, Rachel Jean. 169 ASHLEY AVE RM 202M, MSC 333 29425 #055-02-2005 L2005 **MP** *012

SPAMPINATO, Maria Vittori. 169 ASHLEY AVE, MSC 322 29425 #561-23-2001 L2005 **RNR** *020

SPANDORFER, Michael Alan. 2097 HENRY TECKLENBURG DR, STE 305 29414 #012-01-1992 L1998 **PCC SME** *020 †20

SPANN, James Fletcher, Jr. 171 ASHLEY AVE 29425 #012-05-1961 L1985 **CD** *030

SPEARMAN, Erin Vanessa. 169 ASHLEY AVE RM 202M, MSC 333 29425 #012-01-2005 L2005 **MP** *012

SPENCER, B Broxann. 2100 CHARLIE HALL BLVD 29414 #018-03-1989 L1994 **CHP** *020 †75

SPERRY, John Berhart. 198 RUTLEDGE AVE, STE 1 29403 #051-04-1978 L1979 **PD** *020 †55

SPICER, Galin Jackson. 2097 HENRY TECKLENBURG DR, STE 204 29414 #045-01-1998 L2004 **OPH** *020 †35

SPICER, Kenneth Mc Rae. 169 ASHLEY AVE 29403 #045-01-1975 L1979 **NM R** *020 †28,80

SPICER, Kevin Holmes. 152 CANNON ST, STE B 29403 #045-01-1998 L2004 **P CHP** *020

SPICER, Samuel S. 19 BEE ST, MEDICAL UNIV OF SC 29403 #007-02-1939 L1968 **EM** *020 †50

SPINALE, Francis Guy. 171 ASHLEY AVE, CT SURGERY-ROOM 409 CSB 29425 #045-01-1994 L2001 **GS** *020

SPRATT, Eve Garlington. 135 RUTLEDGE ST, MSC 561 29425 #036-01-1987 L1993 **CHP PD** *020 †20

SPRATT, John A. 125 DOUGHTY ST, STE 690 29403 #028-02-1980 L1997 **TS GS** *020 †85,90

SPRINGER, Jeffrey Robert. PO BOX 250620, 96 JONATHAN LUCAS STREET H 29425 #041-15-2004 L2005 **U** *100

SPRINGS, Mathew Scott. 169 ASHLEY AVE RM 202MUH, MSC 333 29425 #045-01-2004 L2004 **AN** *012

SQUIRES, Jerry Ewing. PO BOX 250908, THE MEDI UNIV OF SC; PATH 29425 #055-01-1978 L2007 **PTH** *030 †50

STACHIW, Natalka Daria. ■ 29403 #045-01-2006 L2006 **OTO** *012

STADALSKY, John Scott. 1871 SAVAGE RD 29407 #045-01-1999 L2003 **MPD** *020 †55,20

STALEY, Paul Russell. 12 FARMFIELD AVE 29407 #019-02-1955 L1964 **IM PUD** *071 †20

STANCUT, Eugen. ■ 29403 #045-01-2008 *012

STANITSKI, Carl Leon. 171 ASHLEY AVE 29425 #041-02-1967 L1999 **ORS** *020 †40

STANITSKI, Deborah Faith. 2125 CHARLIE HALL BLVD 29414 #038-41-1980 L1998 **ORS** *020 †40

STAPLES, Charles Tune, Jr. 9330 MEDICAL PLAZA DR, TRIDENT EMERGENCY PHYSICIA 29406 #012-05-2000 L2003 **EM** *020 †16

STAPLETON, Robert Davis. 198 RUTLEDGE AVE 29403 #023-07-1990 L1993 **PD** *020 †55

STAPLETON, Sarah E. 30 BEE ST, CAROLINA FAMILY CARE 29403 #023-07-1990 L1993 **IM** *020 †20

STEELE, Bradley Wells. 641 SAINT ANDREWS BLVD, SPECIALISTS 29407 #017-20-1995 L2000 **U** *020 †95

STEELE, Thomas Elrod. 67 PRESIDENT ST, 5 S IOP 29425 #041-01-1962 L1978 **P** *030 †75

STEENBURG, Scott David. 169 ASHLEY AVE, MEDICAL UNIVERSITY OF SC 29403 #017-20-2003 L2004 **DR** *012

STELTER, Taryn Elizabeth. 1871 SAVAGE RD 29407 #012-01-2004 L2006 **PD** *020 †55

STEPHENSON, Matthew Lee. 9298 MEDICAL PLAZA DR, TRIDENT FAMILY MED-RESD. P 29406 #011-04-2007 L2007 **TY** *012

STEUER, Gebhard Josef. 293 E BAY ST 29401 #045-01-1989 L1990 **FM** *040 †18

STEVENS, Charles Keith. 125 DOUGHTY ST 29403 #041-02-1984 L1996 **AN** *020 †05

STEWART, Lisa Kay. ■ 29412 #038-41-2003 L2004 **OBG** *100

STEWART, Lisa Renee. 1364 ASHLEY RIVER RD 29407 #033-06-1997 L1998 **IM NEP** *020 †20

STEWART, Vernon Brooks. 2095 HENRY TECKLENBURG DR, DEPT OF EMERGENCY MEDICINE 29414 #023-07-1999 L2005 **EM** *020 †16

STEWART, William Chas. 3 S PARK CIR, STE 105 29407 #048-12-1981 L1987 **OPH** *050 †35

STEYER, Terrence Earl. 9330 MEDICAL PLAZA DR 29406 #038-06-1994 L2000 **FM** *040 †18

STICE, Richard Beil. 3 GAMECOCK AVE, STE 304B 29407 #039-01-1967 L1984 **P EM** *020 †75

STICKLER, David Edward. 96 JONATHAN LUCAS ST, STE 428CSB 29425 #055-01-1999 L2005 **CN** *100 †75

STICKLER, Laura Layman. 96 JONATHAN LUCAS ST POB250619 29425 #055-01-1999 L2005 **OBG** *020 †30

STILL, Brian Richard. ■ 29401 #045-04-2006 L2007 **P** *012

STITES, Harold Wm. 125 DOUGHTY ST, STE 695 29403 #028-03-1977 L1998 **CD IM** *020 †20

STOCK, Kent J. 1938 CHARLIE HALL BLVD 29414 #035-75-1991, ▲ L1999 **ID MPD** *020 †20,55

STOKES, James Porter. 169 ASHLEY AVE RM 202M, MSC 333 29425 #045-01-2005 L2005 **GS** *012

STOLL, William David. 169 ASHLEY AVE RM 202M, MSC 333 29425 #045-04-2005 L2005 **AN** *012

STONER, John Chas. 330 CONCORD ST # 7 29401 #021-01-1964 L2007 **OTO AM** *020 †45

STOPKA, Daniel Theodore. PO BOX 250333, 169 ASHLEY AVE 29425 #016-42-2003 L2003 **PD** *020

STOUT, Nancy Michelle. 169 ASHLEY AVE, MEDICAL UNIVERSITY OF SOUT 29403 #021-06-2003 L2004 **PTH** *012

STOUT, Thomas Franklin. 125 DOUGHTY ST, STE 460 29403 #036-08-1991 L1993 **N** *020 †75

STOWE, Claudia Blair. ■ 29412 #045-01-2004 L2004 **IM** *100 †20

STRANGE, Charlton B, III. 171 ASHLEY AVE 29425 #051-04-1982 L1983 **PUD IM** *020 †20

STRAUSS, Edward. 109 WAPPOO CREEK DR STE 2B 29412 #033-05-2002 L2004 **OMF** *020

STROM, Joni L. ■ 29407 #045-01-2008 *012

STRONG, J Wade. 2095 HENRY TECKLENBURG DR, PATHOLOGY 29414 #045-01-1991 L1992 **D** *020 †50

STROUD, Zachary Blaine. ■ 29412 #045-01-2008 *012

STUART, Laura Lee. ■ 29403 #045-01-2008 *012
STUART, Robert Kenneth. 171 ASHLEY AVE 29425 #023-07-1974 L1985 **HO IM** *040 †20
STUART, Scott William. 135 RUTLEDGE ST, MUSC DEVLPMNTL PEDS 29425 #024-07-1997 L2005 **DBP** *012 †55
STURDIVANT, Rachel Lee. 96 JONATHAN LUCAS ST, CSB 826 29425 #001-02-1998 L2000 **NEP IM** *020 †20
STURGES, Amber Anne. ■ 29407 #039-01-2007 2007 **GS** *012
STUTLEY, Jennifer E. 171 ASHLEY AVE, MED UNIV SC DEPT RAD 29425 #917-02-1979 L1996 **DR** *020 †80
SUKIN, Peter Jay. 9326 MEDICAL PLAZA DR 29406 #041-14-1979 L2001 **P** *020 †75
SULLIVAN, Scott Allan. 171 ASHLEY AVE 29425 #020-02-1996 L2003 **OBG MFM** *020 †30
SULTAN, Iyad Yasin. 169 ASHLEY AVE, P O BOX 25033 29403 #575-01-1996 L2002 **PHO** *100 †55
SUMMER, Andrea Pickens. 171 ASHLEY AVE 29425 #045-01-1992 L1996 **PD** *040 †55
SUMMERALL, Charles Pelot. 171 ASHLEY AVE DEPT CARD 29425 #024-01-1955 L1963 **CD IM** *040 †20
SUMRALL, Bradley Thomas. 9330 MEDICAL PLAZA DR, COASTAL INPATIENT PHYSICIA 29406 #012-01-2003 L2004 **IM** *020 †20
SUTCLIFFE, Sara Emily. 33 LEGARE ST 29401 #045-01-1984 L2008 **OBG** *020 †30
SUTTON, Moira. 9330 MEDICAL PLAZA DR, RADIATION ONCOLOGY ASSOCIA 29406 #035-01-2001 L2006 **RO** *020 †80
SWAN, Loretta S. 9330 MEDICAL PLAZA DR 29406 #021-01-1977 L1978 **DR** *020 †80
SWANN, Shawana Monique. ■ 29412 #035-45-2007 L2007 *012
SWENSON, Orvar. ■ 29412 #024-01-1937 L1944 **GS** *071 †85
SWIFT, Steven Edward. 135 CANNON ST 29425 #038-40-1987 L1988 **OBG** *020 †30
SWIGER, Frederick K, Jr. 1660 SAM RITTENBERG BLVD, STE 7 29407 #045-01-1992 L1993 **PTH** *020 †50
SZABO, Tamas Akos. 109 BEE ST, # 112A 29401 #473-01-1995 L2006 **AN** *100 †05
TABER, Andrew Dean. ■ 29407 #045-04-2006 L2006 **IM** *012
TABOR, Dale Raymond. 109 BEE ST 112A, VA MEDICAL CENTER 29401 #004-01-1994 L2000 **APM** *012
TAGGE, Derya Ucar. 109 BEE ST, RALPH H JOHNSON VAMC 29401 #025-01-1987 L1993 **GS** *020 †85
TAGGE, Edward Peter. 96 JONATHAN LUCAS ST, RM 418CSB 29425 #016-43-1982 L1991 **PDS GS** *020 †85
TALBOTT, Ladawn M. ■ 29412 #048-14-2001 L2006 **PS** *012
TANG, Xingchun. ■ 29412 #243-49-1994 L2007 **P** *012
TARNAWA, Edward D. ■ 29425 #048-13-2007 L2007 *012
TATE, William Eugene. 198 RUTLEDGE AVE STE 5 29403 #045-01-1970 L1971 **D** *071 †15
TAVEL, Edward M, Jr. 9326 MEDICAL PLAZA DR, STE C 29406 #045-01-1989 L1993 **AN** *020 †05
TAYLOR, Ann L. 3601C MEETING STREET RD, CDCMHC 29405 #046-01-1983 L1984 **CHP P** *020 †75
TAYLOR, Anna Greta Birch. ■ 29414 #045-01-2005 L2006 **AN** *012
TAYLOR, Ashby Brooke, III. 171 ASHLEY AVE 29425 #051-01-1965 L1973 **PDC PD** *020 †55
TAYLOR, George Jesse. 109 BEE ST, VAMC-CARDIOLOGY 29401 #016-11-1971 L1997 **CD IM** *020 †20
TAYLOR, Jason Michael. ■ 29414 #051-01-2003 L2007 **AN** *100
TAYLOR, Lee Brown. ■ 29403 #045-01-2005 **IM** *012
TAYLOR, Marian Hazelton. 135 RUTLEDGE ST STE 1201 29425 #045-01-1994 L1996 **CD RHU** *020 †20
TAYLOR, Michael Lee. 9330 MEDICAL PLAZA DR, TRIDENT EMERGENCY PHYSICIA 29406 #045-01-1999 L2002 **EM** *020 †16
TAYLOR, Sarah Newell. 165 ASHLEY AVE, MEDICAL UNIVERSITY OF SC 29425 #011-02-1999 L2004 **NPM** *100 †55
TECKLENBURG, Frederick Wm. 171 ASHLEY AVE 29425 #045-01-1979 L1985 **PD** *020 †55
TEED, Ronald Guy William. ■ 29407 #025-01-2003 L2007 **OPH** *100
TEHRANI, Roya Nadji. ■ 29401 #019-02-2006 L2006 **MPD** *012
TEIXEIRA DA SILVA, Gilda. 1054 CLEARSPRING DR 29412 #935-07-1993 L2004 **FM** *020 †18
TEMPLE, Allison C S. 18 FARMFIELD AVE 29407 #051-01-1990 L1998 **AN** *020 †05
TEUFEL, Ronald John, II. 171 ASHLEY AVE 29425 #055-01-2000 L2003 **MPD** *020 †20,55
THARPE, Marion Elizabeth. ■ 29412 #012-22-2004 L2007 **PDE** *012 †55
THIEDKE, Celia Carolyn. 295 CALHOUN ST 29425 #045-01-1984 L1985 **FM** *030 †18
THIERS, Bruce Harris. 135 RUTLEDGE ST, FL 11 29425 #035-06-1974 L1980 **D IM** *020 †15
THOMAS, Bryan Kendall. ■ 29412 #045-01-2008 *012
THOMAS, James Clifford. 135 RUTLEDGE ST RM 12, DEPT OF INTERNAL MEDICINE 29425 #012-01-1970 L1982 **IM DIA** *050
THOMAS, James Gregory. 1565 SAM RITTENBERG BLVD, STE 200 29407 #132-01-1990 L1999 **ID** *020 †20
THOMAS, John David. 171 ASHLEY AVE 29425 #023-07-1956 L1960 **AN** *071 †05
THOMAS, Joseph Deer, Jr. 316 CALHOUN ST 29401 #045-01-1979 L1980 **FM EM** *020 †16,18
THOMAS, Robert Goodwin. 9231 MEDICAL PLAZA DR # E 29406 #036-01-1968 L1975 **GS** *020 †85
THOMAS, Samuel Dwane. ■ 29401 #041-13-1967 L1972 **U** *071 †95
THOMAS, Stephen M. 9298 MEDICAL PLAZA DR, UNIVERSITY FAMILY MEDICINE 29406 #048-04-2005 L2005 **FP** *012
THOMASON, William Bonner. 10 FARMFIELD AVE STE E, CHARLESTON W. PROFESSIONAL 29407 #045-01-1964 L1964 **U** *071 †95
THOMPSON, Hugh Edward. ■ 29412 #012-22-2005 L2005 **IM** *012
THOMPSON, John Edward, III. 2145 HENRY TECKLENBURG DR, STE 100 29414 #045-01-2002 L2006 **OPH** *020 †35
THOMPSON, P H Gordon. 9313 MEDICAL PLAZA DR, STE 202 29406 #019-02-1992 L1998 **FM** *020
THROWER, James Chas. ■ 29412 #045-01-1958 L1958 **AN** *071
TILLMAN, Mary Hardy. 9330 MEDICAL PLAZA DR 29406 #051-04-1992 L1993 **PD** *020 †55
TIMOTHY, Alvin Michael. ■ 29412 #045-01-2001 L2005 **CD** *012 †20
TITUS, Mary Olivia. ■ 29403 #045-01-1999 L2005 **PE** *100 †55
TOBIN, Catherine Dawson. 295 KING ST, CONDO B2 29401 #045-01-2005 L2005 **AN** *012
TOLLEY, James H, Jr. 169 ASHLEY AVE, P O BOX 150300 29403 #045-01-1985 L1988 **EM FM** *040 †18
TOLLIVER, Bryan Keith. 169 ASHLEY AVE, MEDICAL UNIVERSITY OF SC 29403 #020-12-2003 L2004 **ADP** *012
TOMLIN, Michael Keith. 125 DOUGHTY ST STE 420, ANESTESIA ASSOC OF CHARLES 29403 #001-02-1993 L1994 **AN** *020 †05
TOMOV, Svetozar Velikov. 171 ASHLEY AVE, RM 829 29425 #473-01-1997 L2007 **NEP** *012 †20
TOOLE, John Matthew. ■ 29401 #012-05-1998 L2004 **TS** *100 †85,90

TOWNSEND, James M. ■ 29407 #045-01-1973 L1974 **OBG** *020 †30 ‡
TRANG, Vinh Quoc. ■ 29412 #028-34-2007 L2007 **GS** *012
TRANGMAR, Philip Roger. 9298 MEDICAL PLAZA DR 29406 #665-01-2004 L2004 **FM** *100
TRAUB, Shaun Lowell. 96 JONATHAN LUCAS ST 29425 #012-01-2004 L2004 **ORS** *012
TRAYNHAM, John Alton. 1871 SAVAGE RD, PLANTATION PEDIATRICS 29407 #045-01-1997 L2004 **PD** *020 †20
TRAYWICK, Joseph Paul. 2095 HENRY TECKLENBURG DR 29414 #023-07-1973 L1974 **IM** *020
TRIPICIAN, Nichole Rosa. ■ 29414 #011-02-2005 L2005 **IM** *012
TROEDSSON, Carl Per. 9326 MEDICAL PLAZA DR, STE B 29406 #045-01-1999 L2004 **AN** *020 †05
TSAI, Nancey Trevanian. 96 JONATHAN LUCAS ST, VA MEDICAL CENTER 29425 #051-07-1998 L2003 **PM** *020 †60
TSALAPATAS, Anna Kathryn. 18 FARMFIELD AVE 29407 #045-01-1984 L1987 **AN** *020 †05
TUCKER, Warren Glynn. 316 CALHOUN ST, DEPARTMENT OF PATHOLOGY 29401 #020-02-1977 L1982 **ATP CLP** *020 †50
TUMMINELLO, Paola. 96 JONATHAN LUCAS ST, STE 309, P O BOX 250606 29425 #561-10-1988 L2000 **N** *020 †75
TURAN, Tanya N. ■ 29401 #035-15-2000 L2008 **N** *100 †75
TURNER, Jeffrey Shoji. ■ 29414 #063-01-2003 L2007 **HO** *012 †20
TURNER, Justin Harris. 171 ASHLEY AVE, MED UNIV OF SC COLL OF MED 29425 #045-01-2006 **OTO** *012
TURNER, Robert P. 96 JONATHAN LUCAS ST 29425 #030-05-1984 L1997 **N PD** *020 †75,55
TURNER, Ronald Coleman, Jr. ■ 29407 #045-01-2008 *012
TURNER, William Redd, Jr. 171 ASHLEY AVE 29425 #045-01-1962 L1962 **U** *030 †95
TUTEN, Thaddeus Joseph. ■ 29407 #045-01-2002 L2007 **IM** *012
TYLER, Mike Owens. 9313 MEDICAL PLAZA DR, STE 305 29406 #045-01-1976 L1977 **NS** *020 †25
TYOR, William Randolph. 96 JONATHAN LUCAS ST, CSB STE 319 29425 #036-07-1981 L1993 **N** *050 †75
UFLACKER, Renan Petrucci. 171 ASHLEY AVE, DEPT RAD 29425 #187-02-1974 L1996 **VIR R** *020
ULLIAN, Karen J. 1548 ASHLEY RIVER RD 29407 #035-19-1981 L1989 **OPH** *020 †35
ULLIAN, Michael E. 171 ASHLEY AVE, MEDICAL UNIV/SOUTH CAROLIN 29425 #035-19-1981 L1989 **IM NEP** *020 †20
ULMER, Richard Edwards. 2095 HENRY TECKLENBURG DR 29414 #045-01-1961 L1961 **IM** *072 †20
ULOZAS, Erlandas. 96 JONATHAN LUCAS ST, PO BOX 250623 29425 #913-96-1993 L2004 **NEP** *020 †20
UPADHYAYA, Himanshu P. 67 PRESIDENT ST, DEPT OF PSYCHIATRY 29425 #496-38-1991 L1996 **CHP ADP** *020 †75
UPSHAW, Jana K. 135 RUTLEDGE ST, CRITICAL CARE MED UNIV OF 29425 #012-05-1995 L1996 **PD** *020 †55
UPSHUR, Jane C Kesler. 171 ASHLEY AVE 29425 #045-01-1967 L1967 **PTH** *020 †50
USHER, Bruce Warren. 171 ASHLEY AVE 29425 #045-01-1966 L1966 **CD** *040 †20
VALENTINE, Brandon James. ■ 29401 #038-43-2003 L2004 **ORS** *012
VALICENTI, Joseph F. 9330 MEDICAL PLAZA DR 29406 #045-01-1972 L1973 **PTH** *020 †50
VALLEJO, Stacey Louise. 96 JONATHAN LUCAS ST, STE 812CSB 29425 #021-01-2002 L2006 **PCC** *012 †20
VAN BAKEL, Adrian Bennet. 135 RUTLEDGE ST, STE 1201 29425 #020-02-1981 L1984 **CD IM** *020 †20
VANDERGRIFT, William A. 96 JONATHAN LUCAS ST, STE 428 29425 #012-01-2001 L2004 **NS** *012
VAN DORSTEN, James Peter. 171 ASHLEY AVE, MUSC/DEPT OF OB-GYN 29425 #036-01-1971 L1973 **MFM OBG** *040 †30
VANELLS, Becky Lynn. 109 BEE ST 29401 #012-01-2001 L2002 **PCP** *100
VAN HORN, Stephen Earl, Jr. 169 ASHLEY AVE RM 202M, MSC 333 29425 #045-01-2002 L2004 **CD** *012 †20
VANZURA, Yalani Light. 171 ASHLEY AVE 29425 #045-01-1994 L1998 **EM** *020
VARMA, Abhay Kumar. 171 ASHLEY AVE 29425 #495-36-1986 L2004 *020
VASKO, Todd Raymond. 293 E BAY ST 29401 #012-01-1993 L1995 **PD** *020 †55 ‡
VAUGHAN, Rhys Barrington. 96 JONATHAN LUCAS ST, MUSC DIGESTIVE DISEASE CTR 29425 #143-02-1994 L2005 *100
VELA AQUINO, Marcelo F. 25 COURTENAY DR, MSC 290 29401 #429-02-1996 L2004 **GE** *020 †20
VELEZ, Juan Carlos Q. PO BOX 250623, 96 JONATHAN LUCAS CSB RM 29425 #737-06-1998 L2005 **NEP** *100 †20
VELLODY, Ranjith. PO BOX 250333, 169 ASHLEY AVE 29425 #045-04-2001 L2004 **VIR** *100 †80
VENTRE, Marie Olivia. ■ 29412 #021-05-2006 L2007 **N** *012
VERA, Cristian L. 96 JONATHAN LUCAS ST, STE 428CSB 29425 #231-01-1953 L1978 **NS** *020 †25
VESEL, Travis Prentiss. ■ 29403 #045-01-2007 L2007 **GS** *012
VESER, Fredrick Herman. 171 ASHLEY AVE, MEDICAL UNIVERSITY OF SC E 29425 #041-02-1992 L1995 **EM** *020 †16
VETRO, Sam Wayne. ■ 29412 #654-01-1985 L1992 **IM PD** *050
VIAL, Wayne Charles. 1867 SAVAGE RD 29407 #021-05-1977 L1987 **SMI SMP** *020 †20
VICKERS, Jean Ann. ■ 29414 #055-01-2005 L2006 **IM** *012
VICKERS, William Rob. 96 JONATHAN LUCAS ST, MED UNIV OF S CAROLINA MED 29425 #055-01-2006 L2006 **GS** *012
VIDUYA, Sherryjane F. 9330 MEDICAL PLAZA DR 29406 #045-01-1996 L1997 **FM** *020 †18
VILLERS, Margaret Shiras. ■ 29407 #010-02-2003 L2007 **OBG** *100
VIRELLA, Gabriel T. 171 ASHLEY AVE 29425 #770-02-1967 L1979 **ILI** *040
VIRELLA, Marie Lopes. 114 DOUGHTY ST, BOX 250776 29403 #770-02-1967 L1979 **DIA END** *050 †50
VOGT, Mary Jean. 96 JONATHAN LUCAS ST, MUSC CSB 812 29425 #020-12-1987 L1988 **PUD IM** *020 †20
VON MOLL, Lisa Kaye. 109 BEE ST BOX 11C, VA HOSPITAL CHARLESTON 29401 #025-01-1983 L1991 **ID IM** *020 †20
VON MULLEN, Shaughnessy. 9297 MEDICAL PLAZA DR, STE C 29406 #045-01-1988 L1992 **AN** *020 †05
VROMAN, David Tyler. 171 ASHLEY AVE 29425 #023-01-1995 L1996 **OPH** *020 †35
VUJIC, Ivan. 171 ASHLEY AVE 29425 #957-01-1960 L1979 **DR** *071 †80
VUKSANOVIC, Jovanka. 171 ASHLEY AVE 29425 #957-02-2003 L2006 **IM** *012
WADE, Donald F. ■ 29407 #045-01-1960 L1960 **GP** *020 †18
WAGNER, Carol Lynn. 173 ASHLEY AVE, MEDICAL UNIVERSTIY OF SC 29425 #024-05-1986 L1988 **NPM PD** *040 †55
WAGNER, Mark Wm. 171 ASHLEY AVE, DEPT OF PSYCHIATRY 29425 #038-41-1989 L1990 **CHP** *020 †75

WAGNER, Virginia Ellen. 316 CALHOUN ST 29401 #036-01-1986 L1990 **PD PHP** *020 †55

WAKAT, Marshall August. ■ 29401 #045-01-1975 L1998 **NM R** *071 †80,28

WALDEN-COHN, Susan. 171 ASHLEY AVE 29425 #012-01-1985 L1987 **PD** *020 †55

WALKER, Aljoeson. 96 JONATHAN LUCAS ST 29425 #036-08-1989 L1994 **N** *020

WALKER, Kevin Burton. ■ 29407 #045-01-2004 L2004 **AN** *012

WALL, Robert Thorp. 2093 HENRY TECKLENBURG DR, CANCER CENTER PA-STE 318 E 29414 #045-01-1972 L1982 **HO** *020 †20

WALLACE, Chas Thornwell. 171 ASHLEY AVE, MEDICAL UNIV OF SOUTH CARO 29425 #045-01-1969 L1969 **AN** *020 †05

WALLACE, Earl K, Jr. ■ 29412 #041-12-1947 L1955 **ORS** *071 †40

WALLEN, Matthew Charles. 9330 MEDICAL PLAZA DR, TRIDENT EMERGENCY PHYSICIA 29406 #045-01-2000 L2003 **EM** *020

WALLER, John Louis. 171 ASHLEY AVE 29425 #005-12-1971 L2002 **AN** *030 †05

WALSH, Michael Joseph. 171 ASHLEY AVE, MED UNIV SC COLL MED 29425 #012-01-2004 L2007 **PDC** *012 †55

WALTERS, John F. 316 CALHOUN ST 29401 #045-01-1989 L1992 **EM** *020 †16

WALTERS, Joseph Windham. PO BOX 250333, 169 ASHLEY AVE 29425 #045-01-2002 L2004 **P** *020

WALTON, John Scott. 171 ASHLEY AVE 29425 #045-01-1985 L1989 **AN** *020 †05

WALTON, William Nash. 10 FARMFIELD AVE 29407 #045-01-1964 L1964 **IM** *074

WALTON, Zeke Jonathan. ■ 29412 #045-01-2008 *012

WANG, Jessica. ■ 29412 #011-02-2002 L2007 **PCC** *012 †20

WANG, Zhewu Johnson. 109 BEE ST 29401 #243-44-1982 L1996 **P** *020

WARD, Daniel Bascom, Jr. 135 RUTLEDGE ST, FL 11 29425 #045-04-2000 L2001 **D** *020 †15

WARMOTH, James Ernest. 316 CALHOUN ST, REHAB 29401 #045-01-1973 L1974 **PM** *020 †60

WARNER, Frederick. 2095 HENRY TECKLENBURG DR 29414 #041-15-2000 L2003 **EM** *020 ‡

WARR, Phillip David. ■ 29407 #045-01-2004 L2004 **MPD** *012

WARTERS, Robert D. 109 BEE ST 112A, DEPT OF VET AFFAIRS 29401 #048-14-1989 L2006 **AN** *020 †05

WASSERMAN, Daniel. MUSC DEPT/OPH 29425 #264-04-1979 L1990 *020

WATANABE, Jun. 109 BEE ST 29401 #572-45-1979 **END** *100

WATKINS, John Morgan. 169 ASHLEY AVE RM 202M, MSC 333 29425 #017-20-2004 L2005 **RO** *012

WAY, Thomas Justin. ■ 29412 #045-01-2008 *012

WEATHERS, Suzann. 9298 MEDICAL PLAZA DR 29406 #045-01-2006 L2006 **FP** *012

WEBB, Carson Saint Clair. 25 COURTENAY DR, MSC 592 29401 #001-06-2000 L2001 **IC** *012 †20

WEBB, Jack Vickers. ■ 29412 #047-06-1968 L1996 **R** *071 †80

WEBB, Sally Ann. 135 RUTLEDGE ST, MEDICAL UNIVERSITY OF SC 29425 #021-01-1983 L1991 **CCP PD** *020 †55

WEEKS, Johnny C, III. 12 FORMOSA DR 29407 #036-01-1992 L1993 **FM** *100 †18,30

WEINSTEIN, Benjamin L. 67 PRESIDENT ST, 1 NORTH 29425 #045-01-1998 L2000 **P** *020 †75

WEINSTEIN, Mitchell Lee. 125 DOUGHTY ST, STE 420 29403 #045-01-1997 L2003 **AN** *020 †05

WEINSTEIN, Victor John. 1364 ASHLEY RIVER RD 29407 #038-41-1977 L1981 **OBG** *020 †30

WEISS, Avi C. ■ 29425 #024-05-2004 L2007 **U** *100

WEISS, Edgar Jay. 171 ASHLEY AVE 29425 #041-12-1965 L1996 **PYG P** *020 †75

WEISS, Mark Steven. 18 FARMFIELD AVE 29407 #038-41-1985 L1997 **AN** *020 †05

WELBER, Claudia. 217 CALHOUN ST 29401 #025-07-1987 L2000 **GS** *020 †85

WELLS, James D, III. 316 CALHOUN ST, DEPT RADIOLOGY 29401 #045-01-1982 L1987 **DR VIR** *020 †80

WELLS, James Leroy. 169 ASHLEY AVE RM 202M, MSC 333 29425 #045-01-2005 L2005 **IM** *012

WELLS, Sarah Ann. 96 JONATHAN LUCAS ST 29425 #045-01-2006 L2006 **IM** *012

WELSH, Cynthia A. 171 ASHLEY AVE 29425 #037-01-1988 L1998 **NP ATP** *020 †50

WEST, Mark Warren. 9326 MEDICAL PLAZA DR, STE B 29406 #036-08-2002 L2006 **AN** *020 †05

WEST, Timothy Eugene. 1565 SAM RITTENBERG BLVD, STE 200 29407 #017-20-1974 L1975 **ID IM** *020 †20

WHARTON, John Marcus. 135 RUTLEDGE ST STE 1201 29425 #047-05-1980 L2004 **ICE CD** *020 †20

WHEATON, Michael John. 354 FOLLY RD STE 5 29412 #054-04-1999 L2002 **PD** *020 †55

WHELAN, Sean Patrick. ■ 29403 #045-01-2008 *012

WHITE, David Randall. 135 RUTLEDGE ST, STE 1109 29425 #045-01-1998 L2005 **PDO** *020 †45

WHITE, Katherine Schuh. 10 FARMFIELD AVE, STE A 29407 #045-01-1998 L2002 **OBG** *020 †30

WHITE, Lee Thomas. ■ 29412 #027-01-2006 L2006 **PD** *012

WHITMAN, Stanley Howard. ■ 29423 #005-17-1962 L1975 **FM** *071

WHITTLE, John Parrott, Jr. 169 ASHLEY AVE RM 202M, MSC 333 29425 #051-04-2002 L2005 **PHO** *012 †55

WICKLIFFE, Karen Leanne. ■ 29414 #045-01-2007 L2007 **GS** *012

WIGGINS, Travis Frank. ■ 29407 #045-01-2004 L2004 **IM** *100 †20

WILCOX, June Lorraine. 169 ASHLEY AVE # 202 29403 #045-01-2003 L2004 **AN** *020

WILCOX, Michael David. 171 ASHLEY AVE 29425 #045-01-1999 L2004 **CHP** *020

WILDSTEIN, Michael Scott. 418 FOLLY RD STE C, WILDSTEIN SPINE CENTER 29412 #012-21-2000 L2004 **ORS** *020

WILEY, Maria Kathleen. 171 ASHLEY AVE 29425 #020-12-1977 **IM IMG** *040 †20

WILHOIT, Gordon Beale. 9330 MEDICAL PLAZA DR 29406 #051-07-1977 L1981 **FM** *020 †18

WILKHU, Harshdeep Singh. 165 ASHLEY AVE STE 525CH 29425 #654-01-1998 L2001 **AN** *020 †05

WILLIAMS, Byron. 3605 MEETING STREET RD, STE C 29405 #045-01-1969 L1969 **OM** *020 †18 ‡

WILLIAMS, Daniel Clay. ■ 29414 #047-20-2007 L2007 **PD** *012

WILLIAMS, Eleanor Louise. ■ 29407 #001-02-2007 L2007 **C** *012

WILLIAMS, Evan Grant. 169 ASHLEY AVE RM 202M, MSC 333 29425 #028-03-2005 L2005 **MPD** *012

WILLIAMS, Kathleen Farmer. PO BOX 250912, MED UNIV OF S CAROLINA 29425 #045-01-2005 L2007 **AN** *012

WILLIAMS, Kelleace Cheron. ■ 29403 #045-01-2008 *012

WILLIAMS, Naydene Angela. 171 ASHLEY AVE, SUITE 421 NORTH TOWER 29425 #566-01-1989 L1998 *020

WILLIAMS, Nolan Ryan. ■ 29414 #045-01-2008 *012

WILLIAMSON, Edwin O, II. 1836 ASHLEY RIVER RD, STE 393 29407 #047-05-1969 L1970 **PTH PCP** *020 †50

WILLIAMSON, John David. 9298 MEDICAL PLAZA DR, RESIDENCY PROGRAM 29406 #045-01-2006 L2006 **FP** *012

WILLNER, Ira Richard. 25 COURTENAY DR, MSC 290 29401 #035-15-1990 L1997 **GE HEP** *020 †20

WILSON, Eric Mcadams. 96 JONATHAN LUCAS ST 29425 #045-01-2004 L2004 **GS** *012

WILSON, Frederick Allen. 25 COURTENAY DR STE 7100, MSC 290 29401 #035-03-1963 L1991 **GE IM** *020

WILSON, G Fraser. 316 CALHOUN ST 29401 #045-01-1943 **OBG** *071 †30

WILSON, Hugh Mc Coll. 316 CALHOUN ST, ROPER ST. FRANCIS HEALTHCA 29401 #045-01-1969 L1974 **IM END** *020 †20

WILSON, Hugh Mccoll, Jr. ■ 29412 #045-01-1999 L2003 **IM** *020

WILSON, James Parish. 18 FARMFIELD AVE 29407 #012-01-1989 L1990 **AN** *020 †05

WILSON, Jason Aaron. 169 ASHLEY AVE, MEDICAL UNIVERSITY OF SC 29403 #038-41-2003 L2004 **GE** *012

WILSON, Marion Edward, Jr. 171 ASHLEY AVE, 167 ASHLEY AVE P O BOX 250 29425 #045-01-1980 L1981 **OPH PD** *020 †35

WILSON, Stanley Mc Lean. 125 DOUGHTY ST, STE 660 29403 #045-01-1976 L1977 **GS SO** *020 †85

WILSON, William Chisolm. 316 CALHOUN ST 29401 #045-01-1968 L1970 **OBG ON** *020 †30

WIMBERLY, Jason Andrew. 9326 MEDICAL PLAZA DR, STE B 29406 #045-01-2002 L2002 **AN** *020 †05

WIND, Tyler Conway. 169 ASHLEY AVE RM 202M, MSC 333 29425 #051-01-2005 L2005 **ORS** *012

WINELAND, Rebecca Janes. ■ 29425 #008-02-2004 L2004 **OBG** *100

WINGO, Marshall Scott. 641 SAINT ANDREWS BLVD, LOWCOUNTRY UROLOGY CLINICS 29407 #012-05-2001 L2004 **U** *100

WINSTON, Nicole. 169 ASHLEY AVE # 202, DEPT OF NEUROLOGY 29403 #048-16-2003 L2004 **N** *012

WISDOM, Matthew Young. 169 ASHLEY AVE, MEDICAL UNIVERSITY OF SC 29403 #012-01-2003 L2004 **IM** *020 †20

WISE, Sarah Kristen. PO BOX 250550, 135 RUTLEDGE AVE STE 1130 29425 #048-13-2001 L2006 **OTO** *100 †45

WISSMAN, Stephen Marshall. 169 ASHLEY AVE, MEDICAL UNIVERSITY OF SC 29403 #047-06-2003 L2004 **PD** *100 †55

WOERTH, Stanley Dean. 9297 MEDICAL PLAZA DR, STE C 29406 #030-05-1975 **AN** *020 †05

WOFFORD, Charlie Jean. ■ 29403 #045-01-2008 *012

WOLF, Beth Ann. 316 CALHOUN ST, ROPER HOSPITAL 29401 #046-01-1996 L2004 **IM** *020 †20 ‡

WOLFE, Russell Bryan. 831 FOLLY RD, PSYCHIATRY 29412 #021-05-1981 L1987 **CHP P** *020 †75

WOLFMAN, Tamara Eugenia. 96 JONATHAN LUCAS ST, MSC 623 29425 #011-03-1996 L1998 **IM** *020 †20

WOLINSKY, Arthur Philip. 1483 TOBIAS GADSON BLVD, STE 202B 29407 #041-12-1971 L1999 **IM** *020 †20

WOMAC, Daniel John. ■ 29407 #021-01-2007 L2007 **GS** *012

WONG, Jeffrey Gilbert. 96 JONATHAN LUCAS ST, MEDICAL UNIVERSITY OF SC 29425 #049-01-1985 L2004 **IM** *020 †20

WONG, Kai C. ■ 29403 #495-27-1979 L1992 **NEP** *020

WOODS, Roy. 1 CARRIAGE LN 29407 #011-02-1976 L1978 **IM** *020

WOODWARD, William Mc Gill. 10 FARMFIELD AVE 29407 #045-01-1964 **FM** *071 †18

WOOLF, Shane Kelby. 96 JONATHAN LUCAS ST, STE 708 29425 #041-14-1998 L1999 **ORS** *100

WOOTEN, Caroline Felder. ■ 29407 #045-01-2008 *012

WOOTEN, Thos Durrette, Jr. 18 FARMFIELD AVE 29407 #045-01-1977 L1977 **AN** *020 †05

WORIAX, Fredric Carroll. 96 JONATHAN LUCAS ST 29425 #047-07-2004 L2004 **IM** *012

WORSHAM, George F, Jr. 316 CALHOUN ST 29401 #045-01-1974 L1978 **PTH PCP** *020 †50

WORSHAM, Stephen Thos. 1064 GARDNER RD STE 105 29407 #012-01-1977 L1990 **PD** *062 †55

WORTHINGTON, Ward C, Jr. 171 ASHLEY AVE, MUSC 29425 #045-01-1952 *071

WORTHINGTON, Ward C, III. 125 DOUGHTY ST, STE 570 29403 #045-01-1978 L1980 **NS** *020 †25

WRAY, Dannah Wilde. 100 DOUGHTY ST, MEDICAL UNIVERSITY OF SC 29403 #036-07-1993 L2001 **PDI ID** *040 †20

WREN, Mary Kathleen. ■ 29412 #021-01-2006 L2006 **PTH** *012

WRENN, Dene Courtney. 169 ASHLEY AVE RM 202M, MSC 333 29425 #021-01-2005 L2005 **OBG** *012

WRIGHT, Antwana Sharee. ■ 29407 #045-01-2007 L2007 **GS** *012

WRIGHT, Corey Julian. 171 ASHLEY AVE, GEN SURG 29425 #045-01-2007 L2007 **GS** *012

WRIGHT, Griggsby. 165 ASHLEY AVE, MUSC DEPT ANES 29425 #305-01-1999 L2006 **AN** *100

WRIGHT, Justin John. ■ 29403 #045-01-2008 *012

WRIGHT, Tara M. 96 JONATHAN LUCAS ST, DEPT OF PSYCHIATRY 29425 #035-03-2001 L2004 **ADP** *100 †75

WU, Chang Long. ■ 29412 #012-05-2007 L2007 **PD** *012

WURTZ, Kenneth. 6 RIVER REACH WAY 29407 #012-01-1981 L1998 **HEM ON** *020 †20

YACOUB WASEF, Sherif Z. 96 JONATHAN LUCAS ST, CSB 816 29425 #915-04-1994 L2003 **IM END** *020 †20 ‡

YAJNIK, Amit Ramesh. ■ 29401 #045-01-2008 *012

YAJNIK, Amol Ramesh. 169 ASHLEY AVE RM 202M, MSC 333 29425 #045-01-2005 L2005 **PD** *012

YARBROUGH, William Dwight. 9231 MEDICAL PLAZA DR, STE A 29406 #045-01-1998 L2005 **IC** *020 †20

YARBROUGH, William Martin. PO BOX 250333, 169 ASHLEY AVE 29425 #045-04-1999 L2003 **TS** *012 †85

YEOH, Khay-Guan. 171 ASHLEY AVE, MEDICAL UNIV OF SC 29425 #825-01-1987 L1996 **GE** *020

YING, Michelle Seeyuen. ■ 29412 #012-01-2004 L2004 **OPH** *012

YOON, Hawke Hongduk. 169 ASHLEY AVE, BOX 250333 29425 #049-01-2002 L2004 **GS** *100

YOOST, Jennie Lee. ■ 29412 #020-02-2005 L2005 **OBG** *012

YOOST, Timothy Richard. 169 ASHLEY AVE RM 202M, MSC 333 29425 #020-02-2005 L2005 **U** *012

YOUMANS, Donald Harrison. 9298 MEDICAL PLAZA DR, RESIDENCY PROGRAM 29406 #045-01-2007 L2007 **FP** *012

YOUNG, Rodney Bert, III. 171 ASHLEY AVE 29425 #011-04-1981 L1982 **PS** *020 †65

YOUNG, Sara Elizabeth. 171 ASHLEY AVE 29425 #024-05-2001 L2003 **FM** *020

YOUNUS, Jawaid. ■ 29407 #704-01-1985 L1994 **HO** *100 †20

YOUSSEF, Rimon Fawzy. 96 JONATHAN LUCAS ST, CSB 316 29425 #915-02-1998 L2005 **PDE** *012

ZAPTON, Daniel T. 169 ASHLEY AVE 29403 #024-05-2004 L2004 **DR** *012

ZAULS, Andris Jason. 169 ASHLEY AVE, MED UNIV OF SC 29425 #016-02-2006 L2007 **RO** *012

ZAVADZKAS, Juozas Antanas. ■ 29407 #649-14-2003 L2007 **GS** *012

ZEALBERG, Joseph James. 2016 WAPPOO DR 29412 #041-07-1981 L1987 **P** *020 †75

ZERWAS, Emily Jane. ■ 29414 #021-06-2008 *012
ZILE, Michael Robt. 135 RUTLEDGE ST 29425 #016-01-1977 L1988 **CD IM** *020 †20
ZILKOSKI, Monica Ann. 169 ASHLEY AVE RM 202M, MSC 333 29425 #040-02-2005 L2005 **ORS** *012
ZWERNER, Peter L. 171 ASHLEY AVE 29425 #010-01-1982 L2004 **CD IM** *020 †20
ZYBLEWSKI, Sean. 125 DOUGHTY ST, STE 420 29403 #045-01-2002 L2004 **AN** *020 †05
ZYBLEWSKI, Sinai C. 169 ASHLEY AVE RM 202M, MSC 333 29425 #045-01-2002 L2004 **PDC** *012 †55

CHARLESTON – DORCHESTER

AULTMAN, Amanda Turbevill. ■ 29420 #045-01-2008 *012
CATON, Cathryn. ■ 29420 #045-01-2004 L2004 **IM** *100
DUTTON-TRIPLETT, Casey A. 8761 DORCHESTER RD STE 2 29420 #020-02-1998 L2004 **FM** *020 †18

CHARLESTON AIR FORCE BASE – CHARLESTON

ANDERSON, Michael Bret. 204 W HILL BLVD, 437TH MEDICAL GROUP/SGHQ 29404 #021-05-1997 L2005 **DR** *012
BOYD, James Edwin. 204 W HILL BLVD, 437 MDG 29404 #023-12-1995 L1998 *020 †70
GORDON, Pamela Kurz. 204 W HILL BLVD, 437TH MEDICAL GROUP/SGHQ 29404 #041-15-2001 L2003 *020 †18
HAGEMAN, Patrick Albert. 204 W HILL BLVD, 437TH MEDICAL OPERATIONS 29404 #018-03-2002 L2007 **AM GP** *020
KENNARD, Timothy Patrick. 204 W HILL BLVD, 437TH MEDICAL GROUP 29404 #038-06-2004 L2006 **FM** *020 †18
LANE, Donald Jerry. 204 W HILL BLVD, 437TH MEDICAL GROUP/SGHQ 29404 #023-12-1996 L1998 **PD** *020 †55
OBERG, Erik Donald. 204 W HILL BLVD, 437TH MEDICAL GROUP/SGHQ 29404 #045-01-2002 **EM** *012
SWEITZER, Gregory Bret. 204 W HILL BLVD, 437TH MEDICAL GROUP/SGHQ 29404 #023-12-1999 L2001 **FM** *020
VILLARD, Douglas R. 204 W HILL BLVD, 437TH MEDICAL GROUP/SGHQ 29404 #010-02-2005 L2006 **GS** *020
WALKER, Christopher Scott. 204 W HILL BLVD, 437TH MEDICAL GROUP/SGHQ 29404 #019-02-1997 L1997 **FM AM** *020 †18
WESTPHAL, Marie Jane. 204 W HILL BLVD, 437TH MEDICAL GROUP/SGHQ 29404 #018-03-1998 L1999 **PD** *020 †55
WILLIAMS, Marion O Neil. USAF CLINIC 29404 #041-12-1974 **AM PD** *020

CHERAW – CHESTERFIELD

BERSINGER, David Emil. 721 CHESTERFIELD HWY 29520 #051-07-1985 L2002 **OBG** *020 †30
CIOBANU, Mariana Ion. 309 CLYDE AVE 29520 #913-50-1994 L2006 **PD** *020 †55
COGGESHALL, Berryman E. HWY 9 W 29520 #036-07-1952 L1961 **GS GYN** *071 †85
CRISP-LINDGREN, Naoma. 415 STATE RD 29520 #409-38-1981 L1999 **P CHP** *020
DAVIS, Christopher Paul. 721 S DOCTORS DR 29520 #045-04-1993 L1994 **FM** *020 †18
DAVIS, Dorothy Ann. HWY 9 W 29520 #012-01-1976 L1978 **DR EM** *020
GHORRA, Salim Gerard. 715 S DOCTORS DR STE C 29520 #605-03-1991 L2002 **GS VS** *020 †85
GODWIN, Winston Yuvawn. 119 CHESTERFIELD HWY 29520 #045-01-1959 L1959 **FM** *071 †18
HOLDREDGE, Timothy S. ■ 29520 #012-01-1988 L2007 **EM IM** *020
HOLLIS, Angela Lee. 715 S DOCTORS DR, STE B 29520 #041-12-2003 L2006 **FM** *020 †18
HYATT, Frank Fitzwilliam. ■ 29520 #021-05-1962 L1984 **GP** *020
LI, Carl Siao-Te. 110 DOCTORS DR, STE A3 29520 #024-07-1975 L1990 **GP FM** *020
MC LEOD, John F, III. 110 DOCTORS DR STE B2 29520 #045-01-1982 L1991 **FM** *020 †18
MOORE, Donald Geo. HWY 9 W 29520 #045-01-1982 L1983 **FM** *020 †18
MOOREHEAD, Robert B, Jr. 711 CHESTERFIELD HWY, CHESTERFIELD GEN HOSP 29520 #045-01-1970 L1971 **UCM IM** *020
NEWSOM, Joseph K, Jr. PO BOX 809 29520 #021-01-1982 L1983 **FM** *020 †18
NEWSOM, Joseph Kershaw. PO BOX 809 29520 #021-01-1960 L1961 **FM** *020 †18
NOVINGER, Travis Andrew. 723 S DOCTORS DR, PALMETTO FAMILY MEDICINE O 29520 #045-04-1999 L2000 **FM** *020 †18
PETERS, Terrence Edward. PO BOX 151, CHESTERFIELD GENERAL HOSP 29520 #028-34-1964 L1996 **GS CD** *085
QURESHI, Farooq Husain. 715 S DOCTORS DR STE F 29520 #495-21-1965 L1976 **ORS** *020
REYNOLDS, Karen Ghislaine. PO BOX 1357 29520 #033-05-1993 L2000 **FM** *020 †18
SARTIPZADEH, Abdol Azim. HWY 9 W 29520 #517-03-1961 L1976 **R** *071 †80
SCHULTZ, Agnes. 715 S DOCTORS DR STE E 29520 #473-01-1984 L1994 **PD** *020 †55
SMITH, Gregory Craig. ■ 29520 #045-04-1988 L1991 **DR** *020 †80
SOLIMAN, Mohamed S M. 721 S DOCTORS DR 29520 #915-03-1994 L2006 **PUD** *100 †20
THRAILKILL, James C. HWY 9 W 29520 #045-01-1952 L1952 **GP** *020

CHESNEE – SPARTANBURG

DICKERSON, John Graham. 702 S ALABAMA AVE 29323 #045-04-1997 L1999 **FM** *020 †18

CHESTER – CHESTER

ASHE, Malik Eastern. 517 DOCTORS CT, LOWRYS FAMILY MEDICINE 29706 #035-08-2001 L2005 **ESM** *020 †18
BORHANIAN, Kamran. 701 WILSON ST 29706 #033-06-1980 L1985 **GS VS** *020 †85
BRADLEY, Robert Lee. 1 MEDICAL PARK DR, STE A 29706 #036-08-1983 L1996 **IM** *020 †20
BRICE, Charles W, Jr. 29706 #021-01-1950 L1951 *071
CRISLER, Eugene Croxton. J A COCHRAN BY-PASS 29706 #021-05-1956 L1963 **R NM** *071 †80
DODGE, Terry Lee. 1 MEDICAL PARK DR, CHESTER REGIONAL MEDICAL C 29706 #030-05-1972 L1974 **AN** *020
ESTES, Taft Horace. CHESTER CO HOSP, DEPT OBG 29706 #047-06-1965 L1983 **OBG** *075
FREEMAN, Julius Gilbert. 1 MEDICAL PARK DR, CHESTER REGIONAL MEDICAL C 29706 #045-04-1984 L1985 **FM OS** *020 †18

GAMAGE, Anoma Shiromani. 2744 W PINEWOOD, PROVIDENCE NORTH EAST 29706 #917-23-1993 L2007 **FM** *020 †18
GAY, Walter Carlton, III. 524 DOCTORS CT, CATAWBA COMMUNITY MENTAL H 29706 #045-01-1993 L1994 **CHP** *020 †75
GIBBONS, Marion Logan. 517 DOCTORS CT, LOWRYS FAMILY MEDICINE 29706 #045-01-1989 L1996 **PD** *020 †55
GILLELAND, Geoffrey T. 1 MEDICAL PARK DR, ROCKHILL RADIOLOGY ASSOC 29706 #021-06-1995 L2000 **DR** *020 †80
HENTZ, Edwin Caldwell. 1 MEDICAL PARK DR 29706 #045-01-1965 L1965 **PTH GP** *071 †50
HUGHES, Richard Perry. 139 CHURCH ST 29706 #045-01-1975 L1976 **OM** *030
KHAN, Shaheen A. 1 MEDICAL PARK DR, PHYSICIANS OFFICE BUILDING 29706 #704-02-1986 L1996 **IM** *020 †20
KIM, Ronald H. 1 MEDICAL PARK DR, CHESTER REGIONAL MEDICAL C 29706 #583-06-1964 L1976 **AN** *020
LEONARD, Bruce Alan. 1 MEDICAL PARK DR, ROCKHILL RADIOLOGY ASSOC 29706 #035-03-1987 L1992 **DR** *020 †80
LLOYD, Lancelot Augustus. 1 MEDICAL PARK DR 29706 #566-01-1998 L2005 **IM** *100 †20
MARION, Alexander Douglas. 1 MEDICAL PARK DR, PHYSICIANS OFFICE BLDG 29706 #045-01-1982 L1983 **OPH** *020 †35
MATTHEWS, Mark Robt. 1 MEDICAL PARK DR, ROCKHILL RADIOLOGY ASSOC 29706 #030-06-1987 L2004 **VIR DR** *020 †80
MATTHEWS, William Camp. ■ 29706 #051-01-1937 L1937 **OM IM** *071
MC KINNEY, Edward D, Jr. 1 MEDICAL PARK DR, ROCKHILL RADIOLOGY ASSOC 29706 #045-01-1980 L1990 **DR** *030 †80
MELLO-SHROPSHIRE, Lorrie. 1 MEDICAL PARK DR, BLDG 3 29706 #023-01-1991 L1994 **PD** *020
NAUMANN, Eric Paul. 1 MEDICAL PARK DR, BLDG 3 29706 #023-01-1994 L2001 **FM** *020 †18
NEWLANDS, Frank John. 517 DOCTORS CT 29706 #654-01-1997 L2000 **IM** *020 †20
POSTMA, Jan Hendrik, Jr. 1 MEDICAL PARK DR, CHESTER ORTHO SPECIALISTS 29706 #036-01-1974 L1979 **ORS** *020 †40
RAUT, Pratibha P. 830 DAVIS DR 29706 #495-01-1962 L1981 **OBG** *020 †30
RAUT, Premanand Sadanand. 830 DAVIS DR 29706 #495-01-1958 L1981 **GS** *020
REINHARDT, James E, Jr. 1 MEDICAL PARK DR, ROCKHILL RADIOLOGY ASSOC 29706 #045-01-1968 L1968 **DR** *020 †80
REUTER, Robert. 1 MEDICAL PARK DR, ROCKHILL RADIOLOGY ASSOC 29706 #016-11-1996 L2003 **DR** *020 †80
RONDINA, Joseph. 1 MEDICAL PARK DR, BLDG 4 29706 #024-05-1994 L2004 **GS** *020 †85
SALMAN, Robert Michael. 1 MEDICAL PARK DR, ROCKHILL RADIOLOGY ASSOC 29706 #035-03-1987 L1996 **DR IM** *020 †80
SNYDER, Howard Frank. 1 MEDICAL PARK DR, ROCKHILL RADIOLOGY ASSOC 29706 #045-01-1978 L1982 **DR** *020 †80
SODERSTROM, Lawrence Paul. 1 MEDICAL PARK DR, ROCKHILL RADIOLOGY ASSOC 29706 #036-05-1980 L2001 **DR NM** *020 †80,28
STANGAS, Peter A. 1 MEDICAL PARK DR, ROCKHILL RADIOLOGY ASSOC 29706 #034-01-1996 L2001 **R RNR** *020 †80
STONE, Samuel Rogers. 517 DOCTORS CT 29706 #045-01-1980 L1981 **FM** *020 †18 ‡

CHESTERFIELD – CHESTERFIELD

KHAN, Farah Naeem. ■ 29709 #704-25-1997 L2004 **P** *020 †75
PERRY, Jeremiah Buchanan. ■ 29709 #045-01-1948 L1948 **GP** *075
PERRY, William L. ■ 29709 #045-01-1938 L1938 **GP** *071
VAN GELDEREN, Christina B. 500 WEST BLVD 29709 #187-12-1987 L2004 **FM** *020 †18

CLEMSON – PICKENS

BAXLEY, George Timothy. 220 KEOWEE TRL, CLEMSON NEUROLOGY, PC 29631 #045-01-1996 L1997 **N** *020 †75
BROWNING, Virginia Barret. ■ 29631 #045-01-2005 **OBG** *100
CHEEZEM, Wm Leroy Jr. ■ 29633 #045-01-1945 L1945 **EM** *071 †18
COTHRAN, George Edward. 107 WALL ST 29631 #045-01-1978 L1986 **OBG** *020 †30
DE CASTRO, Marlon Cheng. 885 TIGER BLVD 29631 #748-02-1997 L2002 **IM** *020 †20
DUKES, William Eugene. 386 COLLEGE AVE 29631 #045-01-1961 L1961 **FM** *020 †18
FENLON, Timothy Edward. BOX 344054, CLEMSON UNIVERSITY 29634 #035-15-1973 L1998 **FM** *020 †16,18
FLEMING, Daniel James. 885 TIGER BLVD 29631 #040-02-1976 L1977 **OPH** *020 †35
GENTRY, Warren Douglas, Jr. 522 COLLEGE AVE, STE 1 29631 #045-01-1976 L1980 **FM** *020 †18
GRIFFITH, William Victor. 344054 MCMILLAN RD 29634 #045-01-1978 L1979 **GP** *020
HARDER, Byron B, Jr. 100 PERIMETER ROAD, CLEMSON UNIV TRAINING 29633 #045-01-1968 L1968 **FM** *020 †18
HERBERT, James Orlando. 107 WALL ST 29631 #045-01-1972 L1974 **GYN** *020 †30
HERRING, Mandy Engelman. 107 WALL ST 29631 #045-01-1989 L1996 **FM** *020 †18
HOOD, Jason Alexander. 208 KEOWEE TRL 29631 #012-22-1999 L2000 **OBG** *020 †30
HUNTER, William H. 139 ANDERSON HWY 29631 #045-01-1952 L1952 **FM** *072 †18
JAMESON, Lake Hugh, Jr. CLEMSON UNIVERSITY, REDFERN HEALTH CENTER 29634 #045-01-1978 L1984 **FM** *020 †18
JOHNSON, Brian Richard. 931 TIGER BLVD, CLEMSON OPHTHALMOLOGY, PA 29631 #045-01-2003 L2007 **OPH** *020 †18
KING, William Aaron. 885 TIGER BLVD 29631 #045-01-1980 L1981 **FM** *020 †18
LIEBMAN, David. 885 TIGER BLVD 29631 #012-05-1990 L1996 **IM** *020 †20
LIEBMAN, Maria Oliveira. 885 TIGER BLVD 29631 #012-05-1989 L1996 **FM** *020 †18
MAHIN, Harry Paul. 608 CLEMSON DOWNS 29633 #020-02-1942 L1942 **OS GS** *071 †85
MC DONALD, Rose Marie. 344054 MC MILLAN RD, REDFERN HEALTH CENTER 29634 #045-01-1978 L1984 **FM** *020 †18
MILLAR, Donna Johanna. 101 EDWARDS HALL, JOSEPH F SULLIVAN CTR 29634 #001-02-1980 L1982 **IM** *020 †20
MOUZON, Jacqueline R. 398 COLLEGE AVE 29631 #045-01-1999 L2003 **P** *020 †75
PARISI, Joseph L. 931 TIGER BLVD 29631 #065-05-1984 L1994 **OPH** *020 †35
POLLOCK, Ashley Brooke. ■ 29631 #045-04-2005 **IM** *012
SALZARULO, Henry Halbing. 1011 TIGER BLVD, STE 300 29631 #017-20-1967 L1988 **AN ADL** *020 †05
SCOTT, Michael Dean. ■ 29631 #047-05-2002 L2005 **EM** *020 †16
SWANN, Theodore Joseph. 386 COLLEGE AVE 29631 #045-01-2001 L2002 **FM** *020 †18

TOLBERT, Alicia Limbaugh. 522 COLLEGE AVE, STE 1 29631 #045-01-2002 L2003 **FM** *020 †18
VARN, Lucius Pinckney. ■ 29631 #045-01-1955 L1956 **GP** *020
WALSH, Mark David. 386 COLLEGE AVE 29631 #045-04-1996 L1999 **FM** *020 †18 ‡
WILMETH, John Philip. 885 TIGER BLVD 29631 #045-01-1981 L1986 **OPH** *020 †35
WININGER, Andrea Nicole. 107 WALL ST 29631 #047-06-2001 L2004 **OBG** *020 †30
WOLKEN, Mark Stephen. 885 TIGER BLVD 29631 #018-03-1997 L2001 **OPH** *020 †35

CLEVELAND – GREENVILLE

RECIO RESTREPO, Maria Vic. ■ 29635 #264-05-1988 L2005 **N** *020 †75

CLINTON – LAURENS

BACHINSKI, Matthew S. 300 PLAZA CIR, DIGESTIVE DISEASE GROUP 29325 #024-07-1988 L2001 **GE** *020 †20
BARNARD, Edgar Benton. 201 JACOBS HWY 29325 #047-06-1994 L1995 **FM** *020 †18
BEAUDROT, Joseph L, III. 300 PLAZA CIR 29325 #045-01-1982 L1986 **OBG** *020 †30
BOGNAR, Istvan Gabor. 300 PLAZA CIR, STE A 29325 #473-03-1995 L2001 **NEP** *020 †20
BRADOF, James Edward. 100 PLAZA CIR, STE B 29325 #028-02-1974 L1985 **ON HEM** *071 †20
BROWN, Byron Adams. 700 PLAZA CIR, STE N 29325 #045-01-1998 L2002 **OBG** *020 †30
BUDELMANN, Kurt Ronald. 600 PLAZA CIR, MEDICAL ASSOC 29325 #035-15-1991 L1996 **IM** *020 †20
BURGESS, Sally Elaine. 996 MEDICAL RIDGE RD, PIEDMONT PEDIATRICS 29325 #045-01-1999 L2002 **PD** *020
CARTER, Steven Palmer. 300 PLAZA CIR, STE E 29325 #045-04-1990 L1994 **OBG** *020 †30
CORSO, Steven Wm. 100 PLAZA CIR 29325 #045-04-1988 L1997 **ON HEM** *020 †20
DELLAPORTAS, George John. PO BOX 239, WHITTEN CEXTER 29325 #418-01-1958 L1985 **GPM GP** *071 †70
DIXON, Suzanne Davis. 300 PLAZA CIR, STE E 29325 #036-01-1998 L2003 **OBG** *020 †30
EICHELBERGER, John Gary. 300 PLAZA CIR, STE E 29325 #045-01-1967 L1967 **OBG** *020 †30
FORREST, Amy Yvonne. 300 PLAZA CIR, STE E 29325 #045-01-1997 L2001 **OBG** *020 †30
GATCHELL, Keith Calvin. PO BOX 239 29325 #045-01-1975 L1978 **FM** *020
GILCHRIST, William John. 300 PLAZA CIR, DIGESTIVE DISEASE GROUP 29325 #045-01-1981 L1990 **GE IM** *020 †20
GREEN, Bryan Thames. 300 PLAZA CIR, DIGESTIVE DISEASE GROUP 29325 #001-06-1999 L2004 **GE IM** *020 †20
GRUBE, Robert Jos. 801 MUSGROVE ST 29325 #045-01-1955 L1956 **GP** *071
HAGENBUCH, Michelle L. 500 PLAZA CIR, STE J 29325 #048-14-1989 L1990 **FM** *020 †18
HAMRICK, Christine D. ■ 29325 #045-01-1991 L1992 **EM** *020 †20,16
HEDGEPATH, Andrew Witt. 442 PROFESSIONAL PARK RD, LAURENS MENTAL HEALTH CLIN 29325 #045-01-1999 L2001 **P** *020
HIBBITTS, John M. 22971 HIGHWAY 76 E 29325 #048-02-1994 L1995 **OSM** *020 †40
HOBSON, John Richard, Jr. 300 PLAZA CIR, STE E 29325 #036-05-1983 L1989 **VS GS** *020 †85
HUSSAIN, Akhtar. 106 MEDICAL PARK CT 29325 #704-04-1969 L1978 **IM** *020 †20
KATZBERG, Arthur Jos. 801 MUSGROVE ST 29325 #010-02-1938 L1946 **GS ORS** *071 †85
KELLNER, Scott Anthony. 23013 HIGHWAY 76 E 29325 #045-01-1989 L1990 **FM** *020 †18
LANFORD, Jeffrey Edward. 300 PLAZA CIR, STE E 29325 #045-01-1988 L1992 **VS GS** *020 †85
LATOURETTE, Philip Carl. 105 PHYSICIANS PARK DR 29325 #012-01-1986 L1998 **AN** *020 †20,05
LEARY, Julius L, Jr. 300 PLAZA CIR, STE E 29325 #045-01-1980 L1981 **GYN** *020 †30
LONG, Ronald James. 22725 HIGHWAY 76 E 29325 #017-20-1978 L1986 **OBG** *020 †30
MARSHALL, Bruce Alan. 104 MEDICAL PARK CT 29325 #033-05-1974 L1979 **GS** *020 †85
MEEKS, Michael Raymond. 22725 HIGHWAY 76 E 29325 #045-01-1973 L1974 **FM** *020 †18
MILLAR, Mary Elizabeth. PO BOX 239 29325 #045-01-1974 L1975 **GP** *020
MONTGOMERY, Samuel Jacob. 22995 HIGHWAY 76 E 29325 #045-01-1995 L1999 **OPH** *020 †35
MURRAY, Barbara Sharon. 500 PLAZA CIR, STE J 29325 #036-05-1983 L2004 **GS** *020 †85
NAZARIO, Nilsa I. 22725 HIGHWAY 76 E 29325 #042-01-1983 L1987 **PD** *020 †55
OWENS, William Seldon, Jr. 22971 HIGHWAY 76 E 29325 #019-02-1990 L1991 **HS** *020 †40
OWUSU, Anne. 28373 HIGHWAY 76 E 29325 #412-01-1991 L2000 **IM** *020 †20
PARTEE, Peter Mcdonald. 23013 HIGHWAY 76 E 29325 #045-04-1996 L1997 **FM UM** *020 †18
POLLOCK, Karen Prioleau. 996 MEDICAL RIDGE RD 29325 #045-01-1999 L2002 **PD** *020 †55
RAMAGE, Albert A, III. 300 PLAZA CIR, DIGESTIVE DISEASE GROUP 29325 #047-05-1979 L1982 **GE IM** *020 †20
RIDDLE, Harvard Keith, Jr. 22995 HIGHWAY 76 E 29325 #045-01-1993 L1994 **OPH** *020 †35
ROBINSON, Fred Campbell. PO BOX 239 29325 #047-06-1961 L1985 **PD** *030 †55
RUSSELL, John Andrewhaws. 300 PLAZA CIR, STE E 29325 #051-07-1993 L1997 **OBG** *020 †30
SADLER, Patricia Earle. 106 MEDICAL PARK CT 29325 #045-01-1984 L1985 **IM** *020 †20
SADURSKI, Rafal. 300 PLAZA CIR, DIGESTIVE DISEASE GROUP 29325 #759-04-1990 L1999 **GE** *020 †20
SATTERTHWAITE, John R. 105 PHYSICIANS PARK DR 29325 #012-01-1975 L1980 **AN PMM** *020 †05 ‡
STEPHENS, Louis M, Jr. 23013 HIGHWAY 76 E 29325 #045-04-1985 L1986 **FM** *020 †18
STEPHENS, Louis Moore. 23013 HIGHWAY 76 E 29325 #045-01-1960 L1964 **GP** *020 †18
STROUD, Rebecca Ruth. 302 JACOBS HWY, SUITE H NEELY MEDICAL BLD 29325 #045-01-1994 L1995 **FM** *020 †18
TOUSSAINT, Vincent S. 103 MISSISSIPPI DR, MAILING: P O BOX 1006 29325 #660-03-1967 L1977 **GP** *020 †85
ULMER, Enoch G, Jr. 23013 HIGHWAY 76 E 29325 #045-01-1988 L1999 **FM** *020 †18
VAN DAM, Jacquelyn Fletch. 22971 HIGHWAY 76 E, LAURENS COUNTY ORTHOPAEDIC 29325 #010-02-1995 L2001 **PM** *020 †60
WALSH, Stanley Gray, Jr. 23013 HIGHWAY 76 E 29325 #045-01-2000 L2003 **FM** *020 †18
WARD, William Brian. 300 PLAZA CIR, STE A 29325 #045-01-1997 L1998 **IM** *020 †20
WATKINS, Rufus Walter. 1012 MEDICAL RIDGE RD 29325 #045-01-1973 L1974 **GS** *020 †85
WEAVER, Brian W. 22725 HIGHWAY 76 E 29325 #048-02-1993 L1994 **EM** *020 †16
WIGGINS, Raymond Michael. 1012 MEDICAL RIDGE RD 29325 #051-04-1975 L1987 **OBG** *020 †30
WOMACK, John Wesley, Jr. 22725 HIGHWAY 76 E 29325 #021-05-1972 L1982 **OPH** *071 †35

CLOVER – YORK

BROWN, Brian Daniel. 1200 VILLAGE HARBOR DR, CAROMONT FAMILY MEDICINE 29710 #036-01-1998 L2001 **FM** *020 †18

CROTWELL, Henry Frasier. 207 CHURCH ST, FAMILY MEDICINE 29710 #045-01-1972 L1973 **FM** *020 †18
ELLIOTT, Bruce C, Jr. ■ 29710 #045-01-1987 *075
ELLIOTT, Bruce Carleton. 204 CHURCH ST 29710 #045-01-1956 L1956 **FM** *020 †18
HOLMAN, David O'Neal, Jr. 207 CHURCH ST, FAMILY MEDICINE 29710 #045-01-1973 L1974 **FM** *020 †18 ‡
JACIC, Aida. 207 CHURCH ST, FAMILY MEDICINE 29710 #957-10-1998 L2006 **FM** *100 †18
MC BEAN, Mary Ruth. 207 CHURCH ST, FAMILY MEDICINE 29710 #065-01-1978 L1995 **FM** *020 †18
MC CARTHY, Michael J. ■ 29710 #869-01-1960 L1962 **FM PD** *020 †18
MISZKIEWICZ, Steven Craig. 1200 VILLAGE HARBOR DR, CAROMONT FAMILY MEDICINE 29710 #056-06-1986 L1989 **FM** *020 †18
PERRY, Ernest A. ■ 29710 #012-01-1943 L1946 **GP** *071
PRESTON, Lynn Marie. ■ 29710 #016-76-1994, ▲ L2004 **CD** *020 †20
QUEEN, Michael Lance. ■ 29710 #045-01-1980 L1982 **FM** *020 †18
SHULER, Donald Wayne. 207 CHURCH ST, FAMILY MEDICINE 29710 #045-01-1974 L1976 **FM** *020 †18

COLUMBIA – LEXINGTON

ANDERSON, Dennis Roy. 320 HARBISON BLVD, STE 200 29212 #048-04-1975 L1979 **PHL IM** *071 †20
ARCHER, Michelle G. 320 HARBISON BLVD, STE 230 29212 #045-04-1995 L1996 **FM** *020 †18
BEAVER, George Michael. 7037 SAINT ANDREWS RD, LEXINGTON FAMILY PRACTICE 29212 #045-04-1983 L1984 **FM** *020 †18
BEEBE, Charles Curtis, III. 406 SMITHS MARKET RD 29212 #050-02-1963 L1979 **P** *071 †75
BIRDSONG, Claire Lawton. 320 HARBISON BLVD STE 100, HARBISON MEDICAL ASSOC PA 29212 #045-01-1991 L1992 **FM** *020 †18
BLANCHARD, Gerald E. 6168 SAINT ANDREWS RD, DOCTOR'S CARE 29212 #028-34-1946 L1976 **GP GS** *072
BROWN, Daniel C. 117 CRANEWATER DR 29212 #048-04-1998 L1999 **EM** *020 †16
BUZHARDT, J Richard. 320 HARBISON BLVD 29212 #045-04-1982 L1985 **EM** *020
CALLIS, Robert Mackey. 7037 SAINT ANDREWS RD, LEXINGTON FAMILY PRACTICE 29212 #047-06-1974 L1975 **FM** *020 †18
CASHMAN, Allison Leigh. 320 HARBISON BLVD, STE 250 29212 #045-04-2002 L2006 **D** *020 †15
CHAUDHRY, Sofia Shamim. ■ 29212 #045-04-2004 L2004 **IM** *100 †20
CHAVEZ, Jose De Jesus. 17 SURREY CT 29212 #649-01-1967 L1977 **FM P** *020 ‡
CHOW, Rosemary Y-C. ■ 29212 #243-47-1952 L1976 **PUD** *071
CHOW, Thomas. ■ 29212 #045-01-2007 **GS** *012
CLEMENZ, Rebecca. 7039 SAINT ANDREWS RD 29212 #045-01-1984 L1985 **D** *020 †15
CONDOM, Jaime Ernesto. 1102 JAVELIN CT 29212 #847-04-1962 L1963 **GP** *030
DICKSON, Donald Geo. ■ 29212 #030-05-1945 L1945 **PHP** *030 †70
FABIAN, George Thos. ■ 29212 #045-01-1977 L1978 **AM R** *020 †70
FISHMAN, Gerald Allan. 7033 SAINT ANDREWS RD, STE 101 29212 #012-01-1977 L1978 **EM** *020 †16
FULCHER, Gregory Keith. 7033 SAINT ANDREWS RD, STE 205 29212 #045-04-1991 L1992 **FM** *020 †18
FULLER, Sean Douglas. 190 PARKRIDGE DR, STE 220 29212 #045-04-1995 L1998 **FM** *020 †18
GEURKINK, Deanne Nicola. 16 WOODCROSS DR, PALMETTO PED & ADOL CLINIC 29212 #045-04-1996 L1997 **PD** *020 †55
GREENFIELD, Karen. 100 JIMMY LOVE LN 29212 #016-11-1979 L1980 **FM** *020 †18
HAINES, Peter Carlton. 7033 SAINT ANDREWS RD, STE 204 29212 #050-02-1979 L1986 **PS FPS** *020 †65
HARMAN, William Hampton. 7035 SAINT ANDREWS RD, IRMO URGENT CARE 29212 #045-04-1998 L1999 **FM** *020 †18
HUDSON-STANTON, Deidre J. 190 PARKRIDGE DR, STE 250 29212 #038-41-1995 L1997 **FM** *020 †18
HUTTO, Eric Neil. 190 PARKRIDGE DR, STE 250 29212 #045-01-1995 L1998 **FM** *020 †18
JACKSON, Laura B. 7037 SAINT ANDREWS RD 29212 #045-04-2002 L2003 **FM** *020 †18
KALL, Sheldon Bruce. ■ 29212 #041-13-1973 L1976 **PD** *071 †55
KAPP, Lloyd Mccrary, Jr. 16 WOODCROSS DR, PALMETTO PEDIATRIC AND ADO 29212 #045-04-1999 L2000 **PD** *020 †55
KROLL, Stephen James. 338 HARBISON BLVD 29212 #045-01-1974 L1975 **PS HNS** *020 †45,65 ‡
LEVINSON, Benjamin Jon. 7021 SAINT ANDREWS RD, ST ANDREWS MEDICAL PARK 29212 #045-04-1983 L1984 **IM** *020 †18
LONG, Robert Glendon. ■ 29212 #035-03-1964 L1965 **PD IM** *020 †55
MC WILLIAMS, Wm Reece. 320 HARBISON BLVD, STE 250 29212 #045-01-1973 L1974 **D EM** *020 †15
MILLER, Catherine C. 16 WOODCROSS DR 29212 #045-04-1995 L1996 **PD** *020 †55
MILLER, Stewart Clay. 7045 SAINT ANDREWS RD, STE B 29212 #017-20-1986 L1990 **OPH** *020 †35 ‡
MILLS, Melissa Liles. 16 WOODCROSS DR 29212 #045-04-2001 L2002 **PD** *020 †55
MIRRA, Martin Christopher. 320 HARBISON BLVD, STE 230 29212 #036-01-1996 L1997 **GS** *020 †85
MOORE, D Kay Lillard. 16 WOODCROSS DR 29212 #045-04-1986 L1987 **PD** *020 †55
MULLANEY, Darla Maureen R. ■ 29212 #045-01-1976 L1978 **N** *040
MULLANEY, Morgan Eileen. ■ 29212 #045-01-2007 L2007 **IM** *012
MYSLINSKI, Joseph S. ■ 29212 #048-04-1985 L1986 **EM** *020 †16
ODOM, William Thos, II. 7001 SAINT ANDREWS RD, STE B-8 29212 #045-01-1992 L1993 **AN** *020 †05
OLIVER, Caldwell H, Jr. ■ 29212 #035-20-1965 L1971 **ORS HS** *071 †40
OUBRE, Bert Bryant. ■ 29212 #021-05-1968 L2007 **GS GP** *020 †85
PEREZ, Angel. 324 BROKEN HILL RD 29212 #847-09-1994 L2000 **P** *020 ‡
PERRICK, David. 320 HARBISON BLVD 29212 #035-08-1984 L1989 **AI PD** *020 †55,03
POWELL, Olin H, Jr. 7033 SAINT ANDREWS RD, STE 305 29212 #045-01-1973 L1975 **OBG** *020 †30
PRICKETT, Dalton Shuler. 190 PARKRIDGE DR, STE 200 29212 #045-04-1987 L1993 **GS** *020 †85
RAFI, Sadia. 100 JIMMY LOVE LN 29212 #704-02-1976 L2001 **IM PEM** *020 †20
ROTHSTEIN, Jerry Donald. ■ 29212 #051-01-1961 L1970 **DR** *071 †80
RUBIN, Chad Anthony. 190 PARKRIDGE DR, STE 200 29212 #016-45-1989 L1994 **GS VS** *020 †85

SAILER, Tania Aynat. ■ 29212 #847-10-1967 L1976 **CHP PD** *020

SAILER, Vojtech. 6148 SAINT ANDREWS RD 29212 #286-02-1957 L1976 **PD** *020 †55

SCHUMACHER, Sarah Marie. 190 PARKRIDGE DR, STE G100 29212 #022-75-1997, ▲ L2000 **IMG** *020 †18

SEXTON, Robert Earl. 7037 SAINT ANDREWS RD 29212 #020-02-1973 L1974 **FM EM** *020 †18 ‡

SHEALY, Jerri Lynn. 16 WOODCROSS DR 29212 #045-04-1995 L1996 **PD** *020 †55

SILVERIO, Robert Wayne, II. 7033 SAINT ANDREWS RD, STE 305 29212 #012-01-1996 L2000 **OBG** *020 †30

SMITH, Johnny Yates, Jr. 7037 SAINT ANDREWS RD 29212 #045-01-1982 L1983 **FM** *020 †18

STEEN, Ronald Gene. 190 PARKRIDGE DR, STE 220 29212 #045-01-1981 L1982 **EM FM** *020 †16

SUITS, George Steven. 7035 SAINT ANDREWS RD, D/B/A LEXINGTON MED CTR. I 29212 #045-01-1977 L1978 **EM CCS** *020 †85

SWAMINATHAN, Jawahar. 100 JIMMY LOVE LN 29212 #495-53-1988 L2001 **GP GPM** *020

TINIO, Caridad Gutierrez. ■ 29212 #748-01-1967 L1977 **P** *020 †75

VANDE STOUWE, Robt Allen. 320 HARBISON BLVD, STE 280 29212 #035-01-1977 L1983 **AI** *020 †20,03

VEGA, Jose Luis. ■ 29212 #033-05-2003 L2007 **N** *012

VORA, Anant. 23 SURREY CT, ASHWINI 29212 #495-36-1962 L1983 **PD** *071 †55

WALKER, David Benson. ■ 29212 #045-04-2006 **IM** *012

WESTERKAM, William Jos. 320 HARBISON BLVD STE 290 29212 #041-01-1966 L1971 **PD PHP** *020

WHETSELL, Ashley Robt. 7035 SAINT ANDREWS RD, LCHSD, INC. DBA LMC IRMO 29212 #045-01-1981 L1983 **FM** *020 †18

WILLIS, Samuel Marsh, Jr. 190 PARKRIDGE DR, STE 102 29212 #012-05-1980 L1984 **GE IM** *020

YEARLING, Constance. ■ 29212 #007-02-1977 L1981 **PHP PD** *030

COLUMBIA – RICHLAND

AAMIR, Sayed Mohd. 5 RICHLAND MEDICAL PARK DR, 2MP STE 506 29203 #495-77-2003 L2006 **IM** *012

ABDULHAYOGLU, Emil Sefik. 121 PARK CENTRAL DR, # 200 29203 #024-07-1996 L2001 **NEP** *020 †20

ABRAHAM, Koshy O. 121 PARK CENTRAL DR 29203 #048-14-1992 L1999 **NEP** *020 †20

ABRAMCZYK, Jerzy. 1816 CUNNINGHAM RD, CRAFTS-FARROW STATE 29210 #759-04-1957 L1980 **GP** *071

ACKERMAN, Mary Audrey. 166 STONERIDGE DR 29210 #045-01-1988 L1992 **ON** *020 †20

ADAIR, Jennifer Anne. 5 RICHLAND MEDICAL PARK, EM/3RMP STE 350 29203 #035-15-2005 L2005 **EM** *012

ADAMS, Abigail Lynn. ■ 29203 #025-12-2007 L2007 **EM** *012

ADAMS, Julian Calhoun. 1333 TAYLOR ST, STE 1C 29201 #045-01-1963 L1963 **N ADM** *020 †75

ADCOCK, David Filmore. USC SCH MED, DEPT RAD 29208 #045-01-1962 L1962 **R OM** *071 †80,28,70

ADDIS, Kristen Marie. ■ 29209 #045-04-2008 **IM** *012

ADDISON, Katherine Okey. 5 RICHLAND MEDICAL PARK DR, 14RMP STE 400 29203 #045-04-2003 L2004 **PD** *100 †55

ADEBAJO, Adelero Olayinka. 1520 LAUREL ST, KERSHAW COUNTY MEDICAL CEN 29201 #690-01-1997 L2005 **IM** *020

ADKINS, Elijah Stanton. 1 MEDICAL PARK RD, STE 230 29203 #035-01-1984 L1998 **PDS GS** *020 †85

AHUJA, Divya. 2 MEDICAL PARK RD, STE 502 29203 #495-45-1992 L2005 **ID** *100 †20

AKERS, Paul Clayton. CTR, USC THOMASON STUDENT HEALT 29208 #045-01-1973 L1975 **FM** *020 †18

AL-ASSAAD, Zaid Assaad. 6439 GARNERS FERRY RD, WJBDORN VA MEDICAL CENTER 29209 #875-01-1966 L1979 **PTH FM** *020 †50 ‡

ALBERT, Jose, Jr. 1415 BLANDING ST STE 2 29201 #016-01-1981 L1987 **CRS** *020 †10,85

ALBERT, Ruby Maniago. 4605 MONTICELLO RD 29203 #748-10-1991 L1997 **PD** *020 †55

ALBRECHT, Helmut. 2 MEDICAL PARK RD, STE 502 29203 #409-21-1988 L2006 **ID IM** *062 †20

ALDERETE, Joseph Frank. 2 MEDICAL PARK RD STE 404 29203 #041-14-2001 L2003 **ORS** *020

ALEWINE, Joseph Glenn. 4344 BROAD RIVER RD 29210 #045-01-1981 L1982 **FM** *020

ALEXANDER, Milton D, Jr. 1 RICHLAND MEDICAL PARK #4, COLUMBIA CARDIOVAS CLINIC 29203 #045-01-1973 L1975 **CD** *020 †20

ALFORD, J E Watson. ■ 29205 #012-22-1988 L1989 **P** *020 †75

ALIA, Richard Thos. 1730 SAINT JULIAN PL 29204 #035-09-1970 L1972 **CRS GS** *020 †10,85

ALLEN, Albert S. 1100 KORTRIGHT ST 29203 #045-01-1945 L1945 **IM OS** *072

ALLEN, William Baker. 2750 LAUREL ST, STE 305 29204 #047-06-1971 L1980 **TS** *020 †85,90

ALLISON, James R, III. 1301 TAYLOR ST, STE 8A 29201 #036-07-1975 L1978 **EM IM** *020

ALMOND, Carl H. 2 RICHLAND MEDICAL PARK, STE 300 29203 #028-02-1953 L1978 **TS** *071 †85,90

ALSTON, Clarence Butler. 1410 BLANDING ST, STE 115 29201 #041-01-1983 L1988 **IM** *075

ALSTON, Sidney Greaves. 2838 DEVINE ST 29205 #047-06-1958 L1960 **GP P** *020

ALTIERI, James Howard. 229 LONGTOWN RD 29203 #035-03-1993 L2001 **FM** *020 †18

ALVI, Mohammed Imran. 610 FAISON DR, ALCHOL & DRUG ADDICT TREAT 29203 #704-02-1963 L1977 **GP** *020

ALVI, Shahnaz Parveen. 220 FAISON DR 29203 #704-02-1971 L1979 **PD PYG** *020 †55

AMARNATH, Rathnasa B P. 2113 ADAMS GRV STE 200 29203 #495-70-1979 L1989 **PD GE** *020 †55

AMARNATH, Uma Maheswari. 3 RICHLND MDCL PRK DR #400 29203 #495-04-1981 L1989 **NPM OS** *020 †55

AMBROZIAK, Jaroslaw Mark. 2750 LAUREL ST, STE 103 29204 #026-04-1997 L2000 **FM** *020 †18

AMERSON, Theresa Cambre. 5 MEDICAL PARK RD, ATTN: MEDICAL EDUCATION 29203 #045-04-2005 L2005 **IM** *012

AMIN, Bhavesh R. 813 LEESBURG RD 29209 #495-23-1981 L1996 **FM** *020 †18

AMROL, David Joseph. 2 MEDICAL PARK RD, STE 502 29203 #045-04-1998 L2003 **AI** *020 †20,03

AMROL, Jennifer. 4 MEDICAL PARK RD, STE 301 29203 #045-04-1998 L2003 **PD** *020 †55

ANDERSON, Daniel Richard. 3209 COLONIAL DR, PRH - DEPT OF FAMILY MEDIC 29203 #045-04-2006 L2006 **FP** *012

ANDERSON, Julie Nina. 5 RICHLAND MEDICAL PARK, FRAGILE CHILDRENS PROGRAM 29203 #045-04-1999 L2002 **PD** *020 †55

ANDERSON, Thomas Shannon. 3 RICHLAND MEDICAL PARK 29203 #045-01-1997 L2003 **NS** *020 †25

ANDREWS, Neal David. ■ 29203 #045-01-2007 L2007 **EM** *012

ANYAKWO, Gertrude Nkiru. 5 RICHLAND MEDICAL PARK DR, 2MP STE 208 29203 #012-05-2006 L2006 **OBG** *012

APPAH-SAMPONG, Kenneth. 2753 LAUREL ST 29204 #198-01-1985 L1998 **CD** *020 †20

ARASTU, Safdar Husain. 2800 BUSH RIVER RD, GARDENDALE OFFICE PARK #5A 29210 #495-21-1964 L1980 **GS VS** *020 †85

AREFORD, Matthew Lyon. 5 RICHLAND MEDICAL PARK DR, 2RMP STE 402 29203 #036-07-1993 L2004 **GS** *012

ARMSEY, Thos Darnell, Jr. 1930 BLANDING ST 29201 #038-45-1992 L2004 **FM** *020 †18

ARMSTRONG, Kenneth Scott. 1501 MAIN ST, STE 500 29201 #047-06-1974 L1994 **BBK PTH** *020

ASBILL, David S, Jr. 1417 BARNWELL ST 29201 #036-07-1955 L1958 **OPH** *071 †35

ASHLEY, Jonathan Patrick. 3209 COLONIAL DR, FAMILY MEDICINE 29203 #045-01-2005 L2005 **FP** *012

ASKINS, Benjamin Jerome. 3209 COLONIAL DR 29203 #045-01-2005 L2005 **FP** *012

ATKINS, Daphne Lanette. 2015 MARION ST, ADULT CLINICAL SERVICES 29201 #045-01-1990 L1991 **P PFP** *020 †75

AUSTIN, Thomas Cole. 114 GATEWAY CORPORATE BLVD, STE 350 29203 #045-04-2001 L2004 **OBG** *020

AUSTIN, Tom Laxson. 3 MEDICAL PARK RD STE 400 29203 #048-04-1965 L1971 **NPM PD** *071 †56

AVERY, Melissa Vosche. 101 BRANDON HALL RD 29229 #047-06-1996 L1997 **FM** *030 †18

AZIZ, Shahid A. 2 MEDICAL PARK RD, STE 501 29203 #305-01-2007 L2007 **IM** *012

BABCOCK, William Harry. 166 STONERIDGE DR 29210 #012-01-1970 L1978 **ON HEM** *020 †20

BACON, Janice Lynne. 2 MEDICAL PARK RD, STE 107 29203 #011-04-1979 L1980 **OBG** *040 †30 ‡

BAGGETT, Teresa N. 74 POLO RD, PALMETTO PEDIATRICS 29223 #045-01-1978 L1983 **PD** *020 †55

BAGLEY, Tyler Allison. ■ 29223 #045-04-2007 L2007 **PD** *012

BAIR, Curtis Ray. 2 RICHLAND MEDICAL PARK DR, STE 506 29203 #045-04-2006 L2006 **IM** *012

BAJAMUNDE, Lupicino Ico. 6439 GARNERS FERRY RD, DORN VAMC MHCSL 29209 #748-10-1976 L1983 **P** *020 †75

BAKER, Elizabeth Renwick. 2 MEDICAL PARK RD, STE 302 29203 #036-07-1975 L1976 **REN OBG** *074 †30

BAKER, John Kenneth. ■ 29203 #045-04-2007 **IM** *012

BAKER, Ralph Parr, Jr. 1410 BLANDING ST STE 1 29201 #036-07-1980 L1985 **AN** *020 †05

BALAKUMAR, Shangeetha. 3209 COLONIAL DR, PRH - DEPT OF FAMILY MEDIC 29203 #665-02-2006 L2006 **FP** *012

BALDWIN, Phillip Eugene. 166 STONERIDGE DR 29210 #036-05-1975 L1985 **ON HEM** *020 †20

BALLANCE, Julia B. 4 MEDICAL PARK RD, STE 301 29203 #045-01-1982 L1991 **PD** *040 †55

BALLEW, Richard Osborne. 1751 CALHOUN ST RM 0425 29201 #047-06-1956 L1968 **ID PHP** *071

BALLOU, Christopher Bucki. 14 MEDICAL PARK RD STE 400 29203 #045-04-2005 L2005 **MPD** *012

BANK, Robert Louis. 125 ALPINE CIR 29223 #016-43-1974 L1976 **P** *040 †75

BARBER, Jason K. 3209 COLONIAL DR, PRH - DEPT OF FAMILY MEDIC 29203 #010-03-2005 L2006 **GS** *100

BARCHIESI, Alessandro. VET ADMIN CTR 29201 #561-17-1950 L1972 **P** *020 †75

BARKER, Derek Lloyd. 1920 PICKENS ST 29201 #045-01-1999 L1999 **OPH** *020 †35

BARKER, James Alan. 2 MEDICAL PARK RD, STE 205 29203 #019-02-1980 L2004 **PCC SME** *040 †20

BARKER, Michael Glenn, Jr. 3250 HARDEN ST EXT, ADOLESCENT CLINIC 29203 #045-04-1997 L2000 **PD** *020 †55

BARNARD, Karen. 2 MEDICAL PARK RD, STE 502 29203 #836-01-1989 L2004 **END** *012 †20

BARNICK, Vaughn Rex. 2750 LAUREL ST, STE 303 29204 #045-01-1981 L1984 **IM** *020 †20

BARR, William Mc Kendree. TAYLOR & MARION STS 29220 #045-01-1954 L1954 **FM** *071 †18

BARREDA, Joyce Ileana. 5 MEDICAL PARK RD, MEDICAL EDUCATION 29203 #051-01-2000 L2005 **PD** *012 ‡

BARRETT, O'Neill, Jr. 5 RICHLAND MEDICAL PARK, STE 506 29203 #021-05-1953 L1976 **IM HEM** *071 †20

BARRINEAU-WELSH, Robin. 14 MEDICAL PARK RD, STE 400 29203 #045-01-1988 L1989 **P** *020 †75

BARTLETT, Emilie Ziegler. 3250 HARDEN ST EXT, STE 100 29203 #045-04-1998 L1999 **PD** *020 †75

BARTLETT, Robert Laing. 5 RICHLAND MEDICAL PARK 29203 #001-06-1980 L1981 **EM IM** *020 †16

BATES, Le Roy Everett. ■ 29219 #045-01-1945 L1945 **PHP** *071

BAUKNIGHT, Gerald Conrad. 1655 BERNARDIN AVE, STE 300 29204 #045-04-1986 L1994 **CD** *020 †20

BAUMGARTNER, Diane. 2715 COLONIAL DR, CENTER 29203 #045-04-1985 L1986 **CHP** *020 †75

BAXLEY, Elizabeth Ann. 3209 COLONIAL DR, FAMILY MEDICINE CENTER 29203 #045-04-1984 L1985 **FM** *040 †18

BAYARD, Walter John. 5 RICHLAND MEDICAL PARK 29203 #045-01-1975 L1976 **DR** *020 †80

BEASLEY, John Gerald. 1301 TAYLOR ST, STE 1A 29201 #045-01-1989 L1994 **U** *020 †95

BECKSTROM, Kathry J. 5 RICHLAND MEDICAL PARK, COLUMBIA 29203 #056-06-1989 L1993 **AN** *020 †05

BEESBURG, Robert Yardley. 5 RICHLAND MEDICAL PARK DR 29203 #041-01-1989 L1993 **AN** *020 †05

BEINOR, Michael Jos. ■ 29209 #016-06-1970 L1976 **OBG GP** *020 †30

BELADI, Sareh. 5 RICHLAND MEDICAL PARK DR 29203 #654-01-2003 L2004 **FM** *020

BELL, Floyd Ernest, III. ■ 29210 #045-04-2000 L2000 **DR** *100 †80

BELL, Gary Bernard. 11 ATRIUM RIDGE CT 29223 #045-01-1983 L1984 **IM** *020 †20

BELL, Linda J. PO BOX 101106, DIV OF EPIDEMIOLOGY 29211 #048-12-1989 L1994 **IM PHP** *062 †20

BELL, Richard Mcmurtry. 2 MEDICAL PARK RD, STE 300 29203 #020-12-1972 L1985 **GS TRS** *020 †85

BELL, Sara. 4311 HARD SCRABBLE RD 29229 #048-04-1996 L1998 **FM** *020 †18

BELL, Woodrow Anthony. 6941 N TRENHOLM RD, STE I 29206 #045-04-1992 L1995 **FM** *020 ‡

BELLIL, Lisa. 2 MEDICAL PARK RD, STE 506 29203 #045-04-2006 L2006 **AN** *012

BENDECK, John Lawrence. 1333 TAYLOR ST, STE 6A 29201 #042-01-1980 L1991 **NPM PD** *020 †55

BENITEZ, Jose Luis. 3209 COLONIAL DR, FAMILY MEDICINE 29203 #308-03-2004 L2006 **FP** *012

BENNETT, Allan Thompson. 5 RICHLAND MEDICAL PARK DR 29203 #045-01-1995 L1996 **PTH** *020 †50

BENNETT, Neville Geiger. ■ 29205 #045-01-1991 L1992 **IM** *020 †20

BENNETT, William Paul. 1333 TAYLOR ST, BENNETT & MOORE MD'S 29201
#051-04-1956 L1960 **GYN OS** *071 †30

BENNETT-BURNETT, Annette. 2 MEDICAL PARK RD, STE 506 29203 #045-04-2007 L2007
IM *012

BERG, Edward Walter. 3301 HARDEN STREET EXT 29203 #007-02-1962 L1984 **ORS** *050 †40

BERG, Elin Barth. 4608 ARCADIA RD 29206 #693-01-1974 L1995 **P PFP** *020 †75

BERNARDI-EDELSON, Mary. 1333 TAYLOR ST, STE 6A 29201 #035-09-1989 L1998
NPM PD *020 †55

BERVINE, Sharon Lynette. 1228 HARDEN ST, WAVERLY WOMENS HEALTH CLIN 29204
#035-08-1993 L2004 **OBG** *020

BETHEA, James Frank. 1301 TAYLOR ST, STE 3O 29201 #045-01-1977 L1978
ORS OFA *020 †40

BHARGAVA, Ranjana Satyamu. 2 MEDICAL PARK RD, STE 506 29203 #496-21-2004 L2006
IM *012

BHATT, Harikrashna B. PO BOX 2266, DEPT OF MED 29202 #045-04-2006 L2006 **IM** *012

BICKHAM, Dudley Wayne. 45 FAISON DR, SYSTEM/SC DEPT OF MENTAL H 29203
#001-02-1960 L1973 **P** *020

BISER, Christopher H. DORN VETERANS HOSPITALS 29209 #045-01-1957 L1957 **DR GP** *071

BLACK, Henry Cooper, III. 1519 MARION ST, PROVIDENCE HOPSITAL 29201
#045-01-1993 L1994 **VIR** *020 †80

BLACKBURN, Melanie Dawn. 5 MEDICAL PARK RD, MEDICAL EDUCATION 29203
#045-04-2005 L2005 **PD** *012

BLACKMON, Benjamin B. PO BOX 119, SC STATE HOSP 29202 #045-01-1953 L1953
OM GP *075

BLACKMON, Benjamin B, Jr. 1410 BLANDING ST STE 1 29201 #045-01-1980 L1981
AN *020 †05

BLACKMON, Lyndell W. ■ 29223 #045-01-1950 **OPH** *071 †35

BLAKE, Alric Christopher. 1415 BLANDING ST, STE 5 29201 #033-06-1989 L1994
OPH IM *020 †35

BLASKIS, Mark Gerard. 1706 SAINT JULIAN PL 29204 #028-34-1983 L1995 **D** *020 †15

BLINCOW, John Keith. 6439 GARNERS FERRY RD 29209 #030-05-1955 L1965 **ORS** *071 †40

BLOCKER, Rex Alvin. DEPT OF FAM PRAC, PALMETTO RICHLAND MEM HOSP 29203
#047-07-1998 L2000 **FM** *020

BODENHAMER, Tamera Dawn. ■ 29229 #028-46-2002 L2008 **FM** *020 †18

BODISON, Dan Robert, Jr. 4605 MONTICELLO RD 29203 #010-03-1993 L1997 **PD** *020

BOGAN, Richard Keith. 1333 TAYLOR ST STE 5A 29201 #045-01-1970 L1978
SME PUD *020 †20

BOGGS, William Clarence. 6012 HAMPTON RIDGE RD 29209 #045-01-1963 L1963 **GYN** *020

BOLANDER, Franklyn F, Jr. UNIV OF SC, DEPT OF BIOLOGICAL SCI 29208 #036-07-1977
END *050

BOONE, Tasha Matthews. 2117 GERVAIS ST 29204 #045-04-2002 L2003 **FM** *020 †18

BORUCKI, Robert Bruce. 1818 HENDERSON ST 29201 #016-42-1986 L1987 **FM EM** *020 †18

BOSTON, Tisha. 3010 FARROW RD STE 300 29203 #045-04-1998 L1999 **FM** *020 †18

BOUKNIGHT, Daniel P. 1655 BERNADIN AVE, STE 220 29204 #045-04-1993 L1994 **IC** *020 †20

BOUKNIGHT, James G. 3555 HARDEN STREET EXT, UNIVERSITY OF SC SCHOOL OF 29203
#045-01-1989 L1990 **P PYG** *020 †75

BOULWARE, Raleigh James. 7 RICHLAND MEDICAL PARK DR, STE 104 29203
#038-06-1973 L1977 **RO** *020 †80

BOWDEN, Elisabeth Ann. ■ 29201 #045-01-2008 *012

BOWE, Edwin Earl. 5 RICHLAND MEDICAL PARK 29203 #035-09-1955 L1982 **AN** *020 †05

BOYD, Mary Heather. 3201 CORNWALL RD 29204 #045-04-2001 L2002 **P** *020 †75

BOYD, Robert Edward. 3 RICHLND MDCL PRK DR #240 29203 #055-01-1978 L1984
RHU IM *020 †20

BOYD, William Lewis. 2719 MIDDLEBURG DR 29204 #038-40-1977 L1979 **OPH** *020

BOYER, Richard Alan. 2435 FOREST DR, E/R DEPT 29204 #028-02-1976 L1979 **IM** *020 †20

BOYKIN, Alfred B, Jr. 2 MEDICAL PARK RD, STE 501 29203 #045-01-1970 L1972 **IM** *020 †20

BOYKIN, Darrell Jennings. 1410 BLANDING ST STE 1 29201 #045-04-1985 L1986 **AN** *020 †05

BOYTER, Chas Walton, Jr. 6439 GARNERS FERRY RD, DORN VETERANS HOSPITAL 29209
#045-01-1979 L1984 **EM FM** *020 †18

BRABHAM, Angus Mc Kay. 3 RICHLAND MEDICAL PARK DR, STE 240 29203
#045-01-1972 L1973 **RHU IM** *020

BRADHAM, William Simons. ■ 29205 #045-01-1959 L1959 **IM** *071

BRADLEY, Joel Fontaine, III. 2 MEDICAL PARK RD, STE 402 29203 #036-05-2006 L2006
GS *012

BRADLEY, Robert Foster, V. 5 RICHLAND MEDICAL PARK DR 29203 #045-04-2001 L2005
PTH PCP *020 †50

BRADLEY, Shanna Barbara. 2 MEDICAL PARK RD, STE 208 29203 #012-22-2006 L2006
OBG *012

BRADY, Anna M. ■ 29209 #041-07-1951 L1952 **ORS** *071 †40

BRADY, Anna Sue. 411 PRINCE WALES DR 29209 #045-04-1991 L1992 **PD** *020 †55

BRADY, Thomas Francis. 6108 GARNERS FERRY RD, CHILDREN'S CHOICE PEDIATRI 29209
#045-04-1992 L1994 **PD** *020

BRAGA, Djalma Aranha. ■ 29209 #187-08-1963 L1976 **P** *075 †75

BRAGG, John Earl, Jr. 3555 HARDEN ST EXT, STE 104A 29203 #045-01-1998 L1999
CHP *020 †75

BRANDENBURG, Jeffery Hall. 125 ALPINE CIR 29223 #012-01-1992 L1993 **P** *020 †75

BRANNIGAN, Joseph A, Jr. 121 PARK CENTRAL DR 29203 #045-01-1981 L1982
NEP IM *020 †20

BRANNON, Wm Lester, Jr. 3555 HARDEN ST EXT, STE 104A 29203 #045-01-1961 L1961
N *071 †75

BREEN, Robert Jos. 220 FAISON DR, G WERBER BRYAN PSYCHIATRIC 29203
#045-01-1989 L1991 **P** *020 †75

BRENNAN, James Robt. 1740 SAINT JULIAN PL 29204 #012-01-1980 L1985 **END** *020 †20

BRENNAN, Stacey. 17 TECHNOLOGY CIR, PALMETTO GBA 29203 #041-12-1978 L1979
FM MDM *030 †18 ‡

BRENNER, Eric Richard. 1751 CALHOUN ST BX 1011106, DHEC DISEASE CONTROL 29201
#032-01-1973 L1977 **PHP ID** *062 †20

BRETOUS, Lena Marilyn. ■ 29203 #041-02-1999 L2003 **GPM** *020 †70

BRETT, Allan Saml. 1801 SUNSET DR 29203 #041-01-1976 L1997 **IM** *040 †20

BRILL, Alan Howard. 3 RICHLAND MEDICAL PARK, STE 130 29203 #016-42-1970 L1976
OTO PS *020 †45

BRISTOW, Walter J, III. 2739 LAUREL ST, STE 1A 29204 #045-01-1983 L1992 **GE IM** *020 †20

BRIZENDINE, John Brian. 2 MEDICAL PARK RD STE 402 29203 #305-01-2002 L2004 **GS** *012

BRIZENDINE, Sonal Patel. 3209 COLONIAL DR 29203 #305-01-2002 L2004 **FM** *020 †18

BROADUS-LEWIS, Joyce A. 4214 HARD SCRABBLE RD 29223 #010-01-1981 L1984
FM *020 †18

BROCK, Timothy Zachary. 2 MEDICAL PARK RD, STE 402 29203 #012-01-2007 L2007 **GS** *012

BROOK, Argiri Xanthakos. ■ 29223 #045-04-2002 L2003 **PD** *020 †55

BROOKER, Jeff Z. 1625 BERNARDIN AVE 29204 #045-01-1966 L1966 **CD IC** *020 †20

BROWN, Brandon Eric. 2601 LAUREL ST, STE 260 29204 #045-04-2000 L2007 **IC** *100 †20

BROWN, Curtis Cornwell. 5 RICHLAND MEDICAL PARK DR 29203 #045-01-2002 L2004
AN *020 †05

BROWN, Daniel Craig. 3 MEDICAL PARK RD STE 270 29203 #045-01-1987 L1997 **PDP** *020 †55

BROWN, David Eugene, III. 15 RICHLAND MEDICL PARK #2, HOSPITAL DEPT OF MED
EDUCA 29203 #045-04-2000 L2001 **PDP** *100 †55

BROWN, Eric Alden. 3 MEDICAL PARK RD STE 350, DEPT OF EMGY MED 29203
#024-05-2000 L2001 **EM** *020 †16 ‡

BROWN, Franklin B, Jr. 2015 MARION ST, COLUMBIA AREA MENTAL HLTH 29201
#045-01-1985 L1999 **P** *020 †75

BROWN, John Jeffrey. 2 MEDICAL PARK RD STE 402 29203 #041-01-1974 L1980 **GS** *020 †85

BROWN, Melissa Logan. 2 MEDICAL PARK RD STE 402 29203 #045-04-2005 L2006 **GS** *012

BROWN, Pamela Kay. 5 RICHLAND MEDICAL PARK 29203 #038-41-1997 L1998 **FM** *020 †18

BROWN, Rachel Setzler. 3209 COLONIAL DR, PRMH - FAMILY PRACTICE 29203
#024-05-2000 L2001 **FM** *040 †18 ‡

BROWN, Shawnequa L. 5 RICHLAND MEDICAL PARK, DEPT OF MEDICAL EDUCATION 29203
#028-34-2003 L2004 **OBG** *020

BRUCE, Janie Catherine. 2 MEDICAL PARK RD, STE 506 29203 #045-04-2007 L2007 **IM** *012

BRUCE, Travis Osborne. 15 MEDICAL PARK RD, STE 202 29203 #045-04-2000 L2003
P *100 †75

BRUGH, Rex, III. 9 RICHLAND MEDICAL PARK DR, STE 410 29203 #051-04-1971 L1972
U *020 †95

BRUNE, Warren H. ■ 29223 #012-05-1949 L1972 **GS** *071 †85

BRUNSON, George W, Jr. ■ 29206 #045-01-1942 L1942 **DR** *071 †80

BRYAN, Charles Stone. 2 MEDICAL PARK RD, STE 502 29203 #023-07-1967 L1974
IM ID *020 †20

BRYAN, Williams M, Jr. 1333 TAYLOR ST 29201 #045-01-1944 L1944 **GYN** *072 †30

BRYANT, Lisa Henderson. 15 MEDICAL PARK RD STE 300, SUITE 508 29203
#045-04-1986 L1987 **P CHP** *030 †75 ‡

BUCKLAND, John Jason. 3555 HARDEN STREET EXT, STE 104A 29203 #055-75-2004, ▲ L2004
P *012

BUDMAN, Kevin Adam. ■ 29209 #045-04-2008 *012

BUERKERT, John Edward. 121 PARK CENTRAL DR 29203 #056-06-1968 L1991
NEP IM *050 †20

BUFFALOE, Leon, Jr. ■ 29229 #045-04-2008 *012

BULL, Douglas Middleton. 1519 MARION ST 29201 #045-01-1982 L1983 **DR** *020 †80

BUNCH, Robert Holt. 1850 LAUREL ST 29201 #045-01-1975 L1976 **GS** *020 †85

BUNT, Theodore James. 2 MEDICAL PARK RD STE 300, DEPT OF SURGERY 29203
#025-01-1973 L1980 **VS GS** *020 †85

BURCH, Earl Allen, Jr. ■ 29223 #012-01-1975 L1976 **P PYG** *020 †75

BURGIS, Judith Thompson. 2 MEDICAL PARK RD, STE 107 29203 #045-04-1989 L1990
OBG *020 †30

BURKE, James Ryan. 8 RICHLAND MEDICAL PARK DR, STE 400 29203 #012-05-1999 L2007
TS *020 †85

BURNETTE, Harvey L, Jr. ■ 29204 #045-01-1945 L1945 **FM IM** *071

BURNS, Robert Henry, III. 5 RICHLAND MEDICAL PARK DR 29203 #041-01-1968 L1984 **GP** *071

BURNS, Ronald Gibson. 5 RICHLAND MEDICAL PARK DR 29203 #045-01-1975 L1977
PTH *050 †50

BURNSIDE, Alfred F, Jr. 1011 1/2 ARCADIA LAKES DR 29206 #045-01-1952 L1952 **GP OS** *020

BURNWORTH, Craig Marshall. 14 MEDICAL PARK RD, STE 200 29203 #036-01-1999 L2000
FSM *020 †18

BURTON, Olin Marion. 15 MEDICAL PARK RD STE 300 29203 #045-01-1971 L1972 **PD** *040 †55

BUSNARDO, Marc S. 8231 PARKLANE RD, DIV OF PATHOLOGY/CYTOLOGY 29223
#010-02-1981 L1983 **ATP CLP** *020 †50

BUTLER, Charles Mackie. 2 MEDICAL PARK RD, STE 506 29203 #045-04-2006 L2006 **IM** *012

BUTLER, William Manion. 166 STONERIDGE DR, SC ONCOLOGY ASSOCIATES PA 29210
#021-01-1972 L1975 **ON HEM** *020 †20 ‡

BYKOWSKY, Michael John. 1 RICHLAND MEDICAL PARK, STE 200 29203 #033-05-1990 L1995
AI PDA *020 †55,03

BYNOE, Raymond Paul. 2 MEDICAL PARK RD, STE 300 29203 #045-01-1979 L1980
GS TRS *040 †85

CABINESS, Barry Wayne. 74 POLO RD 29223 #045-04-1995 L1996 **PD** *020 †55

CABRAL-MANDANAS, C B. 7901 FARROW RD 29203 #748-01-1961 L1976 **GPM IMG** *020 †70

CAIN, Gregory David. 3209 COLONIAL DR, PHR - DEPT OF FAMILY MEDIC 29203
#045-01-2007 L2007 **FP** *012

CAIN, William. 1330 TAYLOR ST 29220 #045-01-1973 L1975 **OPH** *020 †35

CALDWELL, Jacquette L. 5 RICHLAND MEDICAL PARK, RICHLAND MEMORIAL HOSPITAL 29203
#047-07-1995 L2002 **DR** *020 †80

CALDWELL, Ryan Blaine. 2 MEDICAL PARK RD, STE 506 29203 #654-01-2006 L2006 **IM** *012

CALLIS, Rachel Lynn. 3209 COLONIAL DR, PRH - DEPT OF FAMILY PRACT 29203
#045-04-2006 L2006 **FP** *012

CAMPBELL, Charles Timothy. 1410 BLANDING ST 29201 #045-01-1983 L1985 **AN** *020 †05

CAMPBELL, Jamae Cherie. 1424 FRANKLIN ST 29201 #045-04-2005 L2005 **P** *012

CAMPBELL, Joseph Andrew. 3 RICHLAND MEDICAL PARK, STE 350 29203 #036-08-2004 L2004
EM *100

CAMPBELL, Nioaka Nicole. 3555 HARDEN ST EXT, STE 104A 29203 #045-04-2000 L2001
P *020 †75

CAMPBELL, Robert James. 4500 STUART ST, MONCRIEF ARMY HOSP - ORTHO 29207
#024-07-1999 L2006 **ORS** *100

CAMPS BARASOAIN, Juan I. 1 MEDICAL PARK RD, STE 230 29203 #847-01-1990 L2002
GS *020 †85

CAPELL, Barbara Batchelor. 1410 BLANDING ST, STE 1 29201 #045-04-1991 L1995
AN *020 †05

CARNECKI, Kelli Elizabeth. 14 MEDICAL PARK RD STE 400 29203 #025-76-2005, ▲ L2005
PD *012

CARNES, James Edward. 1333 TAYLOR ST, STE 1C 29201 #045-01-1973 L1976 **N** *020 †75

CARNEVALE, Kevin. ■ 29223 #035-46-1990 **PTH** *100

CARNEY, Patricia I. 2 MEDICAL PARK RD STE 208, SPECIALTY CLINICS, DEPT OB 29203
#010-01-1989 L2000 **OBG** *020 †30

CARPENTER, April Bettina. 15 MEDICAL PARK RD, STE 104 29203 #025-12-2006 L2006 **P** *012

CARROLL, John Michael. 6108 GARNERS FERRY RD, CHILDREN'S CHOICE PEDIATRI 29209
#045-04-1995 L1996 **PD** *020 †55

CARSON, Lee Smith. 140 WILDEWOOD PARK DR, STE F 29223 #045-04-1998 L2002 **D** *020 †15

CARTER, Charles Joseph, Jr. 3209 COLONIAL DR 29203 #045-04-1999 L2000 **FM** *040 †18

CARZOLI, Thomas James. 1301 TAYLOR ST STE 4 29201 #025-07-1974 L1978 **OBG** *020 †30

CASKEY, John Thos. 1410 BLANDING ST, STE 1 29201 #012-01-1980 L1984 **AN** *020 †05

CASTLES, Charles Guy, Jr. TAYLOR & MARION STS 29220 #045-01-1946 L1946 **PD** *071

CASTLES, Charles Guy, III. 14 RICHLAND MED PK D, PEDIATRIC ASSOCIATES 29203 #045-01-1988 L1989 **PD ADL** *020 †55

CASTLES, Joe Blair, III. 14 RICHLAND MED PK D, PEDIATRIC ASSOCIATES 29203 #045-01-2000 L2001 **PD** *020 †55 ‡

CATALANO, Edward Wm. 5 RICHLAND MEDICAL PARK DR 29203 #045-01-1969 L1969 **PTH** *020 †50

CATO, Candace Denise. 3209 COLONIAL DR 29203 #025-01-2005 L2005 **FP** *012

CAUGHMAN, Belton Drafts. 3555 HARDEN STREET EXT 29203 #045-01-1955 L1956 **P CHP** *071 †55

CAUSEY, Harvey Lavoyd, III. 610 FAISON DR, ALCOHOL & DRUG TREATMENT C 29203 #012-22-2000 L2001 **P** *020 †75

CAVANAGH, Joseph Michael. 21 GATEWAY CORNERS PARK, STE 101 29203 #045-04-1992 L1993 **IM** *020 †20

CHAMBERS, Gerald Mc Call. 1519 MARION ST 29201 #045-01-1968 L1968 **R** *020 †80

CHANDLER, Giselle Terry-A. 2 MEDICAL PARK RD, STE 208 29203 #305-01-2006 L2006 **OBG** *012

CHANDLER, Kevin Lenelle. ■ 29209 #016-06-2008 *012

CHARLTON, Nathan Phillip. 3 RICHLAND MEDICAL PARK, STE 350 29203 #011-04-2004 L2004 **ETX** *012

CHEESEMAN, Edward Wm. 4 MEDICAL PARK RD, STE 100 29203 #023-12-1987 L2005 **OPH** *020 †35

CHENG, Richard Z. 5000 THURMOND MALL, STE 207 29201 #243-16-1982 L2001 **IM PTH** *020

CHERUKURI, Sulochana Devi. 2 MEDICAL PARK RD STE 506 29203 #496-24-2000 L2005 **IM** *020 †20

CHESONI, Solomon Nakhisa. 200 SPRINGTREE DR, STE 100 29223 #010-03-1982 L1988 **CD IM** *020 †20

CHETTY, Prishal. ■ 29209 #048-13-2007 L2007 **MPD** *012

CHEUK, Chad Edward. 6439 GARNERS FERRY RD, DEPT. OF SURGERY 29209 #023-01-1990 L1995 **U** *020 †95

CHILLAG, Shawn Alexander. 1801 SUNSET DR 29203 #055-01-1973 L1982 **IM FM** *040 †20

CHOCKALINGAM, Siva K. 1072 WILDWOOD CENTRE DR, STE 150 29229 #495-04-1988 L1994 **GE IM** *020 †20

CHONTOS-KOMOROWSKI, J. 5 RICHLAND MEDICAL PARK, RICHLAND MEM HOSPITAL 29203 #038-43-1984 L1987 **EM** *020 †16

CHORDIA, Mohan Lal. ■ 29209 #495-20-1960 L1976 **FM U** *071 †95

CHOW, Jim C. 3 RICHLAND MEDICAL PARK DR, STE 500 29203 #045-04-1985 L1986 **D DS** *020 †15

CHOWDHURY, Shahryar Majee. ■ 29229 #011-03-2007 L2007 **PD** *012

CHRISTIANSEN, Neal Paul. 166 STONERIDGE DR, SC ONCOLOGY ASSOCIATES PA 29210 #028-02-1981 L1996 **ON IM** *020 †20

CLARE, F Stewart, Jr. 29206 #045-01-1961 L1961 **PTH** *071 †50

CLARK, Robert Masters. 3 MEDICAL PARK RD, STE 310 29203 #045-01-1963 L1963 **NS N** *071 †75,25

CLARK, William Lloyd. 2750 LAUREL ST, PALMETO EYE CLINIC 29204 #036-01-1995 L2000 **OPH** *020 †35

CLARK-BROWN, Annette. 4214 HARD SCRABBLE RD, DOCTOR'S CARE 29223 #016-11-1997 L2004 **FM** *020 †18 ‡

CLARKSON-DILLIHAY, Rai. 1801 SUNSET DR STE 108 29203 #047-07-1983 L1984 **P** *020 †75

CLAYTON, Bradley Allen. 2435 FOREST DR 29204 #016-45-1996 L1997 **P PFP** *020 †75

CLAYTON, James Emery. 2715 COLONIAL DR, COLUMBIA AREA MENTAL HEALT 29203 #045-04-1982 L1994 **P CHP** *020 †75

CLAYTOR, Susan Montgomery. 120 HIGHLAND CENTER DR, STE 100 29203 #045-01-1984 L1985 **PD ADL** *020 †55

CLEMENTSON, Blair Wetmore. 2 MEDICAL PARK RD, STE 506 29203 #045-04-2007 L2007 **IM** *012

CLINE, Brian Power. 76 POLO RD 29223 #045-04-1993 L1994 **FM** *020 †18

CLINE, David Brennan. 3740 FURMAN SMITH RD APT A 29206 #023-12-1991 L2006 **DR EM** *100 †16,80

CLOSE, Timothy Patrick. 710 RABON RD, STE 100 29203 #016-11-1983 L1989 **DR VIR** *020 †80

CODY, David Mark. 5 MEDICAL PARK RD, ATTN: MEDICAL EDUCATION 29203 #036-08-2005 L2005 **FP** *012

COHEN, Kimmerle Christina. 2 MEDICAL PARK RD, STE 402 29203 #654-01-2005 L2006 **GS** *012

COLBY, Randall Stuart. 9 MEDICAL PARK RD, STE 200A 29203 #045-04-1996 L1997 **MG** *020 †19,55

COLE, Shane Parker. 3 MEDICAL PARK RD, STE 350 29203 #012-22-2006 L2006 **EM** *012

COLECRAFT, Catherine M. 2 MEDICAL PARK RD, STE 502 29203 #010-03-1993 L2002 **ID** *020 †20

COLEMAN, Alvin Atwell, III. TAYLOR & MARION 29220 #045-01-1986 L1987 **PTH** *020 †50

COLEMAN, Janice C Lark. 9 RICHLAND MEDICAL PARK DR, STE 620 29203 #035-48-1974 L1976 **OBG** *020 †30

COLLINS, Hampton W, III. 1655 BERNADIN AVE, STE 220 29204 #045-04-1981 L1982 **CD ICE** *020 †20

COLLINS, Ronald Leroy. 1711 SAINT JULIAN PL 29204 #023-07-1970 L1977 **RHU IM** *020 †20

CONE, David Lindsie. 2 MEDICAL PARK RD, STE 203 29203 #045-01-1985 L1986 **FM UM** *020 †20

CONWELL, Wesley Shawn. 1519 MARION ST, PITTS RADIOLOGY 29201 #012-01-2000 L2006 **DR** *100 †80 ‡

COOK, Michael Dale. 121 PARK CENTRAL DR 29203 #004-01-1987 L1992 **NEP** *020 †20

COOPER, Laura Benecki. 1330 TAYLOR ST 29220 #036-01-1991 L1994 **PD** *020 †55

COOPER, Marc Allen. 4500 STUART ST, MONCRIEF ARMY COMM HOSPITA 29207 #016-01-1998 L1999 **OBG** *020 †20

COOPER, Thomas Glenn. ■ 29223 #045-01-1956 L1956 **IMG P** *071

COOPER, Tyler Clark. 3209 COLONIAL DR 29203 #048-13-2003 L2005 **PHP** *020 †70

CORALES, Ed Paquito F. 7901 FARROW RD, COLUMBIA CARE CENTER 29203 #748-07-1968 L2004 **P** *020

CORLEY, Chas Edward, III. 1410 BLANDING ST, STE 1 29201 #045-01-1965 L1965 **AN** *020

COSHAL, Balbir Singh. 2015 MARION ST, COLUMBIA AREA MHC 29201 #495-36-1961 L1990 **CHP P** *020 †75

COX, Ramoth R. 1801 SUNSET DR 29203 #045-01-1989 L1996 **IM** *020 †20

COXE, Charles Robt. UNIVERSITY OF SC, THOMSON STUDENT HEALTH CEN 29208 #045-01-1981 L1982 **FM** *020 †18

CRAFT, Roland Rhystmas. 1850 LAUREL ST 29201 #045-01-2001 L2003 **CCS** *020 †85

CRAIG, Karen Faye. 4821 ARCADIA RD 29206 #045-04-1985 L1986 **FM GS** *020 †18

CRAMER, Stuart Louis. 5 MEDICAL PARK RD, ATTN: MEDICAL EDUCATION 29203 #011-75-2005, ▲ L2005 **PD** *012

CRAWFORD, Pamela Merle. 220 FAISON DR, BRYAN PSYCHIATRIC HOSPITAL 29203 #012-05-1988 L1998 **P** *012

CREWS, Charles F. ■ 29205 #045-01-1947 L1947 **GS** *071

CRIBBS, Floyd Ashton, IV. 3209 COLONIAL DR, PALMETTO RICHLAND HLTH-DEP 29203 #045-01-2006 L2006 **FP** *012

CRIGLER, William Henry. 1910 GREGG ST 29201 #035-45-1973 L1975 **FM** *020 †18 ‡

CRISP, Jeremy Ray. 3209 COLONIAL DR, PHR - DEPT OF FAMILY MEDIC 29203 #045-01-2007 L2007 **FP** *012

CRISWELL, Christopher B. 5 RICHLAND MEDICAL PARK DR 29203 #047-06-1986 L1990 **AN** *020 †05

CROCKETT, Barbara A. 6439 GARNERS FERRY RD, DORN VETERANS HOSPITAL 29209 #041-09-1968 L1969 **P** *020 †75

CROSHAW, Randal Lee. 5 RICHLAND MEDICAL PARK, DEPT OF MEDICAL EDUCATION 29203 #045-04-2003 L2004 **GS** *100

CROSS, Deena Jo. 6439 GARNERS FERRY RD, WJB DORN VAMC 29209 #045-01-1999 L2003 **P** *020

CROSS, Michael Linn. 7901 FARROW RD, SCDMH BLDG 6 29203 #047-06-1996 L2000 **PFP P** *020 †75

CROSSWELL, Hal H, Jr. 100 SUMMIT CENTRE DR 29229 #045-01-1960 L1960 **OPH** *020 †35

CROSSWELL, William Fort. 100 SUMMIT CENTRE DR 29229 #045-01-1971 L1972 **OPH** *020 †35

CRUEA, Steven Lawrence. 3 RICHLAND MEDICAL PARK, STE 350 29203 #045-04-2004 L2004 **EM** *100

CRUTCHER, Julie Anne. ■ 29229 #047-06-2006 L2006 **PD** *100

CRUTCHER, Samuel John. 3209 COLONIAL DR, P H R - DEPT OF FAMILY ME 29203 #047-06-2006 L2006 **FP** *012

CUDA, Theresa Hance. 1410 BLANDING ST STE 1 29201 #045-01-1987 L1991 **AN IM** *020 †05

CUFFE, Steven Paul. 3555 HARDEN ST EXT, STE 104A 29203 #036-05-1982 L1987 **CHP P** *040 †75

CULLUM, Uriel X, Jr. 1520 LAUREL ST, RICHLAND PRIMARY CARE 29201 #045-01-1968 L1968 **NEP IM** *071 †20

CUPPLES, Tommy Earl. 710 RABON RD, WOME'S CARE AT IMAGECARE 29203 #047-06-1978 L1995 **DR** *020 †80

CUTTING, Robert Thos. 2749 LAUREL ST, COLUMBIA PHYSICAL MED.& RE 29204 #024-05-1955 L1984 **OM GPM** *071 †15

CUTURIC, Miroslav. 3555 HARDEN ST EXT, STE 104A 29203 #957-01-1986 L1997 **N** *020 †75

DABRA, Sundeep Kumar. ■ 29209 #045-04-2007 L2007 **MPD** *012

DALAL, Mayank H. 7901 FARROW RD, CBHS FORENSIC CENTER 29203 #495-22-1980 L1999 **P** *020 †75

DALTON, Mary E. 5 RICHLAND MEDICAL PARK DR 29203 #045-01-1986 L1987 **AN** *040 †05

DANIELS, Damon. 114 GATEWAY CORP BLVD, MEDICAL PLAZA 29203 #012-01-1999 L2000 **FM** *020 †18

DANTZLER, Malcolm U. ■ 29205 #045-01-1950 L1950 **PHP PM** *071 †70

DARGAN, Everett Lloyd. 1701 SAINT JULIAN PL, STE 100 29204 #010-03-1953 L1961 **GS TS** *020 †85,90

DARRAGH, Elizabeth Hinton. 1875 HARDEN ST, COLUMBIA FREE MEDICAL CLIN 29204 #045-04-2000 L2001 **FM** *020 †18

DASH, Sangita. 2 MEDICAL PARK RD, STE 502 29203 #496-31-1998 L2004 **ID IM** *020

DA SILVA, Ercio Mario. PO BOX 119, S C STATE HOSP 29202 #187-06-1950 L1962 **CRS GP** *020 †10

DASILVA, Robert Mario. 1930 BLANDING ST 29201 #045-01-1984 L1990 **ORS** *020 †40

DAUM-KOWALSKI, Robin E. 1331 LADY ST 29201 #041-07-1987 L1994 **R** *020 †80

DAVANI, Ali Mohamad. 2200 HARDEN ST, CMJC 29203 #517-07-1965 L1976 **GP FPG** *020

DAVENPORT, Barbara M. 3 MEDICAL PARK RD, STE 400 29203 #025-07-1980 L1995 **P FM** *020 †18,75

DAVES, Kimberly Dinease. 14 MEDICAL PARK RD STE 400 29203 #045-01-2005 L2005 **PD** *012

DAVID, Iosif I. 2100 BULL ST 29201 #781-03-1945 L1976 **P** *075

DAVIS, Barney Mc Coy, Jr. 7520 MONTICELLO RD 29203 #048-02-1970 L2003 **P N** *020 †75

DAVIS, Charles Hammett. 6439 GARNERS FERRY RD, WJBD VA HOSP DERMATOLOGY 29209 #012-01-1976 L1979 **D IM** *020 †20

DAVIS, Deborah Jones. 1228 HARDEN STREET 29201 #045-01-1982 L1998 **OBG** *020 †30

DAVIS, Donen. 1850 LAUREL ST, STE B 29201 #045-01-1995 L2000 **PS** *020 †65

DAVIS, Joshua Collier. ■ 29209 #012-22-2007 L2007 **EM** *012

DAVIS, Myles Donen. 1301 TAYLOR ST, COLUMBIA WOMENS 29201 #045-04-1986 L1987 **OBG** *020 †30

DAVIS, Richard M. 4 MEDICAL PARK RD, STE 100 29203 #016-06-1981 L1987 **OPH** *020 †35

DAVIS, Rufus Jackson. ■ 29204 #045-01-1946 L1946 **GP** *071

DEAL, Roger Wiley. 125 ALPINE CIR 29223 #021-05-1970 L1984 **P** *020 †75

DEAN, Lara C. 3 RICHLAND MEDICAL PARK, STE 350 29203 #048-12-2006 L2006 **EM** *012

DEB ROY, Narayan P. ■ 29223 #704-03-1960 L1976 **ORS** *020 †40

DEDMOND, Barnaby Todd. 2 MEDICAL PARK RD, STE 404 DEPT OF ORTHOP 29203 #036-01-2000 L2001 **ORS** *020 ‡

DEGENHARDT, Charleston Fr, III. 2 MEDICAL PARK RD, STE 506 29203 #045-01-2007 L2007 **IM** *012

DEGENHART, Vincent John. 1410 BLANDING ST, STE 1 29201 #045-01-1977 L1977 **AN PME** *020 †05 ‡

DEHOLL, Paul Douglas. 1910 BLANDING ST, MIDLANDS ORTHOPAEDICS P.A. 29201 #045-04-1997 L2003 **ORS** *020 †40

DE JESUS, Dennis. 3 MEDICAL PARK RD 29203 #024-07-1988 L2002 **DR VIR** *020 †80

DE JONG, Rudolph H. 5 RICHLAND MEDICAL PARK 29203 #005-11-1955 L1994 **PME AN** *071 †05

DELANEY, Joseph Allen. 14 RICHLAND MEDICAL PARK, STE 400 29203 #045-04-2004 L2004 **PD** *020 †55

DE LEON-MAKAPUGAY, Z. 7901 FARROW RD 29203 #748-07-1954 L1976 **IM** *071

DELGADO, Juan L. ■ 29223 #275-01-1934 L1972 **GP** *071

DEMARCO, Paul Vincent. 2 MEDICAL PARK RD STE 502, MARION MEDICAL GROUP, PA 29203 #045-04-1989 L1993 **IM** *020 †20

DEMIAN, Saba. ■ 29223 #915-02-1966 L1974 **PTH** *020 †50

DENKER, Martin Wm. 1330 TAYLOR ST 29220 #023-07-1968 L1973 **P PYM** *020 †75 ‡

DERRICK, Chas Warren, Jr. 4 MEDICAL PARK RD, STE 301 29203 #045-01-1962 L1962 **PD ID** *040 †55

DERRICK, George Lynn. 1920 PICKENS ST, COLUMBIA EYE CLINIC PA 29201 #045-01-1958 L1958 **OPH** *071 †35

■ = Address Information Privacy Protected

DESAI, Gira V. 1301 TAYLOR ST, STE 4K 29201 #495-17-1964 L1983 **AN** *020

DESAI, Nehal. 21 GATEWAY CORNERS PARK, STE 101 29203 #495-89-1990 L1996 **IM** *020 †20

DESAI, Reena Ashok. ■ 29209 #045-04-2008 *012

DESCHAMPS, Edgar Green. 4540 TRENHOLM RD 29206 #045-04-1982 L1983 **IM** *020 †20

DEW, Ronald. 1333 TAYLOR ST STE 3D 29201 #012-05-1953 L1959 **GYN** *020 †30

DIAL, Burke Hood. 2 MEDICAL PARK RD, STE 300 29203 #045-01-1976 L1977 **NS** *020 †25

DICKSON, James Brice. 1333 TAYLOR ST, STE 4G 29201 #045-01-1978 L1987 **OPH FPS** *020 †35

DILLINGHAM, Rex Howland. 1330 TAYLOR ST 29220 #045-01-1962 L1962 **FM** *071 †18

DI PETTE, Donald John. OFFICE OF THE DEAN, UNIV OF SO CAROLINA SCH MD 29208 #041-14-1977 L2007 **IM** *030 †20

DITZLER, Russell Eugene. 1655 BERNARDIN AVE, STE 350 29204 #045-01-1985 L1986 **FM** *020 †18

DIZON, Rosita C. ■ 29210 #748-01-1953 L1994 **IMG IM** *020

DOELLE, Eric August. 5 RICHLAND MEDICAL PARK, RICHLAND MEMORIAL HOSPITAL 29203 #025-01-1993 L1998 **VIR** *020 †80

DOLLISON, Clarence Jos, Jr. 2712 MIDDLEBURG DR STE 101 29204 #045-01-1975 1976 **PD OS** *020

DOMMERS, Martin Paul. 5 MEDICAL PARK RD 29203 #016-11-1978 L1984 **DR** *020 †80

DONALD, Alexander G. 15 MEDICAL PARK RD, STE 103 29203 #045-01-1952 L1952 **P** *071 †75

DOUGLAS, Leonard W, Jr. 2 MEDICAL PARK RD STE 203, UNIVERSITY OF SO CAROLINA 29203 #045-01-1982 L1983 **FM** *020 †18

DOWNIE, David, IV. 1327 RICHLAND ST 29201 #654-01-1981 L1983 **CHP** *020 †75

DRENNAN, Robert Howard. ■ 29209 #045-04-2008 *012

DU BOSE, Hugh H. 2435 FOREST DR 29204 #045-01-1950 L1950 **OS** *100 †20

DUBOSE, Theodore Marion, V. 9 RICHLAND MEDICAL PARK, STE 110 29203 #045-01-1998 L1999 **PD** *020 †55

DUFFEE, Andrew Richard. 2 MEDICAL PARK RD, STE 404 29203 #020-02-2006 L2006 **ORS** *012

DUFFUS, Wayne Andrew. 2 MEDICAL PARK RD STE 502, USC DEPARTMENT OF MEDICINE 29203 #035-46-1995 L1999 **ID** *020 †20

DUNCAN, Joel W. 1655 BERNARDIN AVE, STE 300 29204 #048-15-1988 L1991 **CD** *020 †20

DUNDAS, Brian Scott. 3555 HARDEN ST EXT 29203 #020-12-2005 L2005 **P** *012

DURAND, Tamsin Melodie. 2 MEDICAL PARK RD STE 402, DEPARTMENT OF SURGERY 29203 #422-01-2007 L2007 **GS** *012

DWYER, Richard Gregg. 3555 HARDEN ST EXT, STE 104A 29203 #004-01-2001 L2002 **PFP** *050 †75 ‡

EADY, John La Fon. 2 MEDICAL PARK RD, STE 404 29203 #045-01-1966 L1966 **ORS AM** *020 †40 ‡

EASTERLING, Bruce M. 6439 GARNERS FERRY RD, DORN VA HOSPITAL 29209 #045-01-2001 L2003 **IMG** *020 †18

EBERSOLE, James B. 3301 HARDEN STREET EXT, RICHLAND MEMORIAL HOSPITAL 29203 #016-06-1950 L1974 **FM** *071 †18

ECKENBRECHT, Paul David. 5 RICHLAND MEDICAL PARK 29203 #041-02-1981 L1988 **AN** *020 †05

EDEN, Sharon Inabinet. 9 RICHLAND MEDICAL PARK DR, STE 620 29203 #045-01-1985 L1986 **OBG FM** *020 †30

EDMUNDS, Thomas B, Jr. 2724 MIDDLEBURG DR 29204 #045-01-1995 L2000 **U** *020 †95

EDWARDS, Doran Devon. 17 TECHNOLOGY CIR, BOX 100413 29203 #047-06-1974 L1974 **GS CRS** *030 †85

EDWARDS, Ernest Lee, Jr. ■ 29229 #041-09-1982 L1989 **FM** *020 †18

EDWARDS, Thomas Stanley. TAYLOR & MARION ST, BAPTIST INPATIENT MED ASSO 29220 #038-40-1972 L1975 **IM** *020 †20

EDWARDS, Walter G, Jr. 14 RICHLAND MEDICAL PARK, STE 310 29203 #045-01-1963 L1963 **NEP IM** *071 †20

EGBERT, John Raymond. 5 RICHLAND MED PK DR 29203 #038-06-1979 L1982 **IM** *020 †20

EHRETH, Jeffrey Thos. 9 RICHLAND MED PK, STE 420 29203 #051-01-1989 L1996 **UP** *020 †95

EKMAN, Evan Franklin. 2 RICHLAND MEDICAL PARK, STE 404 29203 #020-12-1991 L1997 **ORS** *020 †40

ELDIN, Mona Mohamed Zahei. 5 MEDICAL PARK RD, ATTN: MEDICAL EDUCATION 29203 #915-02-1996 L2005 **OBG** *100

ELEAZER, G Paul. 1 MEDICAL PARK RD STE 211, USC SCHOOL OF MEDICINE/IM 29203 #045-01-1979 L1986 **IMG FPG** *040 †20

ELGUINDI, Ismail H. 8 DIAMOND LN 29210 #915-03-1946 L1976 **GYN** *072 †30

ELKINS, Anthony Bertram. 1072 WILDWOOD CENTRE DR 29229 #004-01-1996 L1999 **GE IM** *020

ELLIOTT, Eric Thomas. 3 MEDICAL PARK RD, STE 350 29203 #023-07-2006 L2006 **EM** *012

ELLIOTT, Ronald James. 4444 BROAD RIVER RD, C/O KIRKLAND CORRECTION IN 29210 #045-01-1958 L1958 **FM** *071 †18

ELLIOTT, Samuel Curtis. 3209 COLONIAL DR, FAMILY & PREVENTIVE MEDICI 29203 #036-01-1984 L1985 **FM OBG** *020 †18

ELLIS, Julian Baynard, Jr. 1519 MARION ST 29201 #045-01-1961 L1961 **PTH** *071 †50

ELLIS, Sharon Sapir. 1333 TAYLOR ST STE 6B 29201 #041-07-1968 L1972 **NPM PD** *020 †50

ELRAIE, Khaled Fouad. 1072 WILDWOOD CENTRE DR 29229 #915-02-1988 L1998 **GE IM** *020 †20

EMERY, Jacqueline Ann. 5 RICHLAND MEDICAL PARK DR 29203 #020-12-1990 L1997 **PCP** *020 †50

EMMANUEL, Naresh P. 712 RICHLAND ST, STE H 29201 #495-98-1981 L1990 **P** *050 †75

EMMER, Michael H, II. 5 MEDICAL PARK RD STE 6E, MICHAEL EMMER MD IMAC 29203 #045-04-1995 L1996 **IM** *020 †20

ENGELHARDT, Lydia Anne. 3423 WILMOT AVE, C/O WILLIAM RAMBO, JR, MD 29205 #010-02-1980 L1981 **OBG** *020 †30

ENGLES, Todd Henry. 1620 LADY ST STE B 29201 #045-04-1996 L1997 **P** *020 †75

ENRIQUEZ, Eden Barredo. ■ 29223 #748-01-1956 L1977 **P** *071

ERVIN, Michael Lynn. 1 MEDICAL PARK RD STE 300 29203 #036-08-1991 L1993 **OBG FM** *020 †18,30

ESKRIDGE, Charles D, III. ■ 29223 #045-01-1975 L1976 **EM** *020 †16

ESLAVA, Michael Antonio. 4500 STUART ST, MONCRIEF ARMY HOSP 29207 #001-02-1992 L2007 **ORS** *020 †40

ESTABA, Victor. ■ 29209 #935-01-1940 L1976 **IM GE** *071

ETTER, Kevin Mc Kelvey. 6439 GARNERS FERRY RD, VETERANS HOSPITAL 29209 #028-03-1981 L1993 **P** *020 †75

EVANS, Forest Luke, Jr. 5 RICHLAND MEDICAL PARK DR 29203 #045-04-1993 L1997 **AN** *020 †05

EVERETT, Warren Douglas. 4500 STUART ST, USAMEDDAC 29207 #054-04-1972 L1983 **FM AM** *020 †20

EWART, Thomas Wade. 114 GATEWAY CORPORATE BLVD, STE 120 29203 #030-06-1976 L1980 **ORS OSM** *020 †40

EWING, Gary Bogart. 2 MEDICAL PARK RD, STE 203 29203 #005-12-1990 L1995 **GPM** *030 †70

EZEIHUAKU, Christopher Ch. 15 MEDICAL PARK RD 2ND FL, P H R - DEPT OF GERIATRICS 29203 #690-10-1988 L2006 **IMG** *020 †20

FAGTANAC, Juan A. 2100 BULL ST, S.C. DPT OF MENT HLTH 29201 #748-08-1963 L1976 **GP P** *071

FAIRCLOTH, Michael A. 3209 COLONIAL DR 29203 #020-75-2005, ▲ L2005 **FP** *012

FAIREY, John Ormond. 1333 TAYLOR ST STE 2C, COLUMBIA UROLOGICAL 29201 #045-01-1978 L1983 **U** *020 †95

FAIREY, Philip W, Jr. 1333 TAYLOR ST STE 2C 29201 #045-01-1943 L1944 **U** *071 †95

FANN, Stephen Austin. 2 MEDICAL PARK RD, STE 300 29203 #036-08-1998 L1999 **GS** *020 †85

FANT, James Wilks, Jr. 2 MEDICAL PARK RD, DEPT OF MEDICINE 29203 #045-01-1986 L1994 **RHU IM** *020 †20

FARACH, Martin. ■ 29201 #023-07-1988 *100

FARBER, Emmanuel. ■ 29223 #065-01-1942 L1948 **PTH** *071 †50

FARNELL, Allison Smith. 4500 STUART ST, RM 1013 29207 #045-01-2003 L2006 **FM** *020 †18

FARNELL, Edwin Alonzo, IV. ■ 29229 #045-01-2003 L2005 **FM** *020 †18

FARRELL, James Joseph. ■ 29206 #869-07-1975 L1982 **DR** *020

FEDERICI, Thomas John. 4 MEDICAL PARK RD, STE 300 29203 #035-03-2000 L2006 **OPH** *100 †35

FENGLER, Timothy Raymond. 1410 BLANDING ST, STE 1 29201 #016-45-1985 L1989 **AN** *020 †05

FENNELL, Edwin Kinard. 5 RICHLAND MEDICAL PARK 29203 #045-01-1954 L1954 **ORS** *020 †40

FENNELL, William. 6439 GARNERS FERRY RD, DORN VA HOSP DEPT MED 29209 #539-02-1967 L1986 **CD IM** *020 †20

FERLAUTO, Michael James. 7901 FARROW RD, COLUMBIA CARE CENTER 29203 #045-04-2002 L2006 **P** *100 †75

FERNANDEZ, Javier. ■ 29205 #275-01-1960 L1974 **P** *062

FERREOL, Edmundo C. ■ 29223 #748-01-1974 **PTH** *020

FESSLER, Richard Gready. 6439 GARNERS FERRY RD 29209 #045-01-1978 L1979 **FM** *020 †18

FIELDS, James Thelbert. 3 RICHLAND MEDICAL PARK, STE 510 29203 #045-04-2002 L2004 **IM** *020 †20

FILLER, Lilly Stern. 9 RICHLAND MEDICAL PARK DR, STE 620 29203 #045-04-1988 L1989 **OBG** *020 †30

FILLNOW, Patrick Ryan. ■ 29205 #045-04-2008 *012

FINCH, Michael Trezevant. 110 SUMMIT CENTRE DR, SANDHILLS PEDIATRICS 29229 #045-01-1990 L1993 **PD** *020 †55

FINLEY, Charles David. 100 SUMMIT CENTRE DR 29229 #036-08-1992 L1999 **OPH** *020 †35

FINLEY, Sara Katherine. 14 MEDICAL PARK RD, STE 400 29203 #045-04-2003 L2004 **PD** *020 †55

FINN, Mary Foley. 2 MEDICAL PARK RD, STE 404 29203 #048-13-2006 L2007 **ORS** *012

FIRETAG, Brandie Lauren. ■ 29209 #045-04-2008 *012

FISHBURNE, Barron C. 7620 TRENHOLM ROAD EXT 29223 #039-01-1991 L1997 **OPH** *020 †35

FISHBURNE, Skottowe B. DORN VA HOSPITAL 29204 #045-01-1961 L1961 **IM P** *071 †20

FISHER, David Charles. 300 RICE MEADOW WAY 29229 #055-02-1993 L1995 **FM** *020 †18

FITCHETT, Rose. ■ 29290 #045-04-1976 L1989 **OM IM** *020

FITZGIBBON, Rodney. 3000 NE MEDICAL PARK, STE 209 29223 #045-04-1985 L1986 **FM** *020 †18

FITZGIBBON, Timothy A. 3000 NE MEDICAL PARK, STE 209 29223 #045-04-1987 L1988 **FM** *020 †18

FLANAGAN, Clyde H, Jr. 3555 HARDEN ST EXT 29203 #047-06-1966 L1989 **P CHP** *020 †75

FLINT, Kathleen Patricia. ■ 29205 #012-01-1982 L1988 **RHU IM** *020 †20

FLOYD, Dean Allen. 3010 FARROW RD, STE 230 29203 #045-01-1976 L1978 **FM** *020 †18

FLOYD, Willie Cecil. 1333 TAYLOR STREET STE 3-H 29220 #045-04-1999 L2000 **OM IM** *020 †20,70

FONGER, James Douglas. ■ 29206 #062-01-1978 L2004 **TS** *020 †85,90

FORD, David Thos. 5 RICHLAND MEDICAL PARK 29203 #035-03-1989 L1993 **EM** *020 †16

FORD, Gregory Seth. 4 MEDICAL PARK RD, STE 300 29203 #051-07-2005 L2006 **OPH** *012

FORD, Jeffery Carl. 21 GATEWAY CORNERS PARK, STE 101 29203 #045-04-1990 L1992 **PUD** *020 †20

FORD, Sylvia Hampshire. ■ 29209 #035-46-1990 L1995 **NM R** *020 †28

FORNO, Cindy Mai. 3209 COLONIAL DR, PRMH - FAMILY PRACTICE 29203 #024-07-2003 L2004 **FM** *020 †18

FORNO, Philip Christopher. 2 MEDICAL PARK RD STE 404 29203 #024-07-2003 L2004 **ORS** *012

FORSTHOEFEL, Frank Eugene. 1333 TAYLOR ST STE 37 29201 #056-06-1965 L1969 **P** *020 †75

FORTNER, Bryant Reeves, Jr. 2638 TWO NOTCH RD 29204 #045-01-1974 L1977 **PD GP** *020 †55 ‡

FOUCHE, Heyward H, Jr. 1410 BLANDING ST, STE 1 29201 #045-01-1988 L1989 **AN** *020 †05

FOWBLE, Coleman Deane. 1930 BLANDING ST 29201 #045-01-1992 L2001 **ORS** *020 †40

FOX, Kenneth Harrison. 2 MEDICAL PARK RD 29203 #045-04-2004 L2004 **DR** *012

FRANKS, Sherri Elizabeth. 1333 TAYLOR ST, STE 5F 29201 #012-21-1993 L1998 **OBG** *020 †20

FRAVEL, William James. 9 RICHLAND MEDICAL PARK, STE 510 29203 #038-41-1963 L1971 **OTO** *020 †45

FRAZIER, Larry Julian. 5 RICHLAND MEDICAL PARK DR 29203 #045-01-1980 L1983 **AN** *020 †55,05

FREIBERT, Martha C. 125 ALPINE CIR 29223 #045-04-1988 L1989 **CHP P** *020 †75

FRIEDMAN, Harold Ira. 2 MEDICAL PARK RD, STE 300 29203 #051-01-1974 L1984 **PS GS** *020 †85,65

FRIEDMAN, Samuel E. 1519 MARION ST 29201 #048-04-1985 L1990 **DR NM** *020 †80,28

FRIERSON, Richard Lesesne. 3555 HARDEN ST EXT, STE 301 29203 #045-04-1988 L1989 **PFP P** *040 †75

FRINKS, Leslie Elizabeth. 15 MEDICAL PARK RD, STE 200 29203 #045-04-2002 L2003 **P** *020 †75

FUERST, Ronnie Scott. 5 MEDICAL PARK RD, RICHLAND MEMORIAL HOSPITAL 29203 #021-01-1987 L1996 **EM** *020 †16

FULTON, Jeanette Kuhn. 1519 MARION ST, PITTS RADIOLOGY 29201 #038-41-1993 L1999 **DR** *020 †80

FYFFE, Deborah Lynn. 2601 LAUREL ST, STE 110 29204 #036-05-1980 L1983 **OPH** *020 †35

GABR, Usama Abdul Monem. 120 GATEWAY CORP BLVD, STE 440 29203 #915-02-1996 L2005 **PM FM** *020 †60

GAFFNEY, Thomas Edward. 1801 SUNSET DR 29203 #038-41-1957 L1973 **PA** *071

GAINES, Kenneth James. 4840 FOREST DR, PMB 358 29206 #047-06-1972 L2007 **N** *020 †75

GAJADHAR, Rachelle Nicole. 3010 FARROW RD, STE 300 29203 #023-01-1997 L2006 **IMG** *020 †20

GALANG, Juliana Infante. ■ 29223 #748-01-1968 L1977 **PD** *020
GALLMAN, Burnett Wm. 4100 MAIN ST STE 201 29203 #041-09-1975 L1980 **GE IM** *020
GALPHIN, Robert Lee. 1333 TAYLOR ST, PULMONARY ASSOCIATES 29201 #012-01-1958 L1966 **PUD SME** *030
GALVEZ, Rupert. 3209 COLONIAL DR, PALMETTO HEALTH 29203 #011-75-2004, ▲ L2007 **FSM** *012 †18
GAMBLE, Yvette Denise. 1333 TAYLOR ST, STE 6A 29201 #045-04-1998 L2000 **NPM** *020 †55
GANT, Darrel Dean. 6439 GARNERS FERRY RD 29209 #038-40-1958 L1977 **IM** *071 †20
GANTT, Edna Katherine. ■ 29209 #045-04-2008 *012
GARNER, Frederick Tatum. 3000 NE MEDICAL PARK, STE 205 29223 #004-01-1982 L1992 **OTO** *020 †45
GARRICK, John Edsel, Jr. 1519 MARION ST 29201 #045-01-1985 L1989 **DR** *020 †80
GARRISON, Warren Baker. 10 RICHLAND MDCL PRK DR #B 29203 #012-01-1972 L1974 **EM** *020
GATTI, David Joseph. 1333 TAYLOR ST, STE 3A 29201 #035-09-1966 L1969 **GS VS** *020 †85
GEARHART, Shannon Leigh. 3209 COLONIAL DR, FAMILY MEDICINE DEPT. 29203 #017-20-2006 L2007 **FP** *012
GENERAL, Tiffany Chenise. ■ 29209 #045-04-2008 *012
GEORGE, Charmaine Maria. 3010 FARROW RD, STE 220 29203 #010-03-1985 L1992 **IM** *020 †20
GERARD, William Chas. 5 RICHLAND MEDICAL PARK, PALMETO HLTH RCHLD EMERG 29203 #038-43-1990 L1991 **EM** *020 †16
GETTYS, James Riley, Jr. 1519 MARION ST 29201 #045-01-1972 L1973 **DR** *020 †80
GHENT, William Shawn. 6439 GARNERS FERRY RD, WJBD VA HOSPITAL 29209 #045-04-1988 L1989 **IM** *020 †20
GIBBES, Caroline L. 2601 LAUREL ST 29204 #047-05-1975 L1979 **OPH** *020 †35
GIBBON, John. 6439 GARNERS FERRY RD 29209 #352-11-1946 L1979 **P** *071 †75 ‡
GIBBONS, Thomas Eli, Jr. 4416 FOREST DR STE A, DOCTORS CARE FOREST ACRES 29206 #045-01-1981 L1982 **EM** *020 †16
GIBSON, James Jerome, Jr. 5 RICHLAND MEDICAL PARK 29203 #041-12-1970 L1978 **PHP ID** *030 †20,70
GIFFORD, Robert R M. 2 MEDICAL PARK RD, STE 300 29203 #012-05-1969 L1971 **GS IG** *020 †85
GIUDICE, Thomas Patrick. 1333 TAYLOR ST STE 2D, SOTH CAROLINA OB-GYN ASSC. 29201 #045-04-1993 L1997 **OBG** *020 †30
GIURGIUTIU, Dan V. ■ 29205 #045-01-2008 *012
GIZE, Edward A. 1519 MARION ST, PITTS RADIOLOGY 29201 #017-20-2001 L2007 **DR** *020 †80
GLASSER, James Goodwin. 1 MEDICAL PARK RD, STE 230 29203 #033-05-1974 L1988 **PDS** *020 †85
GLAZEBROOK, Thomas S. 2711 MIDDLEBURG DR, STE 101 29204 #045-04-1981 L1986 **OTO** *020
GLEASON, Courtney Nicole. ■ 29205 #045-04-2008 *012
GOINS, Amanda. 5 MEDICAL PARK RD, ATTN: MEDICAL EDUCATION 29203 #055-75-2005, ▲ L2005 **IM** *012
GOISER, John Louis. ■ 29223 #051-01-1960 L1976 **A PD** *071 †55,03
GOLDING, Eugene, Jr. ■ 29201 #036-05-1989 L1990 **GPM** *012 †55
GOLDMAN, Charles R. 15 MEDICAL PARK RD, STE 300 29203 #028-03-1970 L1984 **P** *071 †75
GOLDSTEIN, Francis Peter. 1301 TAYLOR ST, STE 8A 29201 #041-07-1979 L1980 **IM** *020 †20
GONDI, Gandhi. 1410 BLANDING ST STE 1 29201 #495-50-1965 L1977 **AN** *020 †05
GONDI, Gokul. 1410 BLANDING ST, STE 1 29201 #045-04-1999 L2003 **AN** *020 ‡
GONZALEZ, Alfonso. 3 RICHLAND MEDICAL PARK, STE 500 29203 #264-01-1954 L1964 **PTH** *071 †50
GONZALEZ, Alfonso. 3 MEDICAL PARK RD STE 500, COLUMBIA SKIN CLINIC LLC 29203 #649-04-1979 L1994 **DMP ATP** *020 †50
GONZALEZ, M Francisco. 3 RICHLAND MEDICAL PARK, STE 270 29203 #737-06-1970 L1980 **HEM ON** *020 †20
GONZALEZ-MACEIRA, Jorge E. ■ 29210 #275-01-1952 L1963 **P OS** *020
GOODE, Kimberlee Torlanda. 9 RICHLAND MEDICAL PARK DR, STE 620 29203 #041-13-2001 L2005 **OBG** *020 †50
GOTTLIEB, Jack Henry. 2601 LAUREL ST, STE 120 29204 #045-01-1966 L1966 **IM** *020 †20
GOTTSCHALK, Ginny Lee. 3209 COLONIAL DR, PHR - FAMILY MEDICINE 29203 #020-12-2007 L2007 **FP** *012
GOULD, Lindsay Elizabeth. ■ 29209 #045-04-2007 L2007 **EM** *012
GOURDIN, Theodore Stewart. ■ 29203 #045-04-2008 *012
GRACZYK, Sarena G. 1410 BLANDING ST STE 1 29201 #045-04-1987 L1991 **AN** *020 †05
GRANT, Kenneth Fred. 5 RICHLAND MEDICAL PARK DR 29203 #047-06-1973 L2000 **PTH BBK** *020 †50
GRANT, Larry Dale. 1 SCIENCE CT, STE 200 29203 #056-05-1989 L2000 **PTH** *020 †50
GRAU, Rebecca Elizabeth. 5 MEDICAL PARK RD, ATTN: MEDICAL EDUCATION 29203 #012-22-2005 L2005 **PD** *012
GREEN, Carl A. ■ 29201 #047-07-1947 L1952 **OPH** *071 †35
GREEN, Michael Scott. 1930 BLANDING ST 29201 #017-20-1981 L1987 **ORS HS** *020 †40
GREEN, Neely Elizabeth. 5 MEDICAL PARK RD, ATTN: MEDICAL EDUCATION 29203 #020-02-2005 L2005 **EM** *012
GREEN, William E, III. 1330 TAYLOR ST 29220 #012-01-1985 L1994 **P CHP** *020 †75
GREENBERG, Stanley Harris. 9 RICHLAND MEDICAL PARK DR, STE 410 29203 #041-01-1973 L1980 **U** *020 †95
GREENBERG, Stephen Harvey. 2 MEDICAL PARK RD, STE 502 29203 #024-07-1973 L2006 **IM IMG** *040 †20
GREENHOUSE, David L. 3209 COLONIAL DR 29203 #012-05-1989 L1990 **FM** *020 †18
GREENHOUSE, Deborah Marie. 74 POLO RD 29223 #012-05-1989 L1990 **PD** *020 †55
GREENSPAN, Roman. 4500 STUART ST, MONCRIEF ARMY COMMUNITY HO 29207 #305-01-2001 L2004 **FM UCM** *020 †18
GREGG, Anthony Romaine. 2 MEDICAL PARK RD, STE 107 29203 #016-43-1986 L2004 **OBG MFM** *020 †19,30
GRICE, Dina V. 1709 BARNWELL ST 29201 #048-04-1986 L1987 **D** *020 †15
GRIER, Jason Brooks. 14 MEDICAL PARK RD, STE 400 29203 #045-04-2006 L2006 **PD** *012
GRIFFIN, John Bradley. ■ 29206 #048-12-1980 L1982 **GS VS** *020 †85
GRIFFITH, Margaret Irene. ■ 29210 #048-14-2003 L2007 **GPM** *012 †50
GRISWOLD, Marilee Chantal. 7901 FARROW RD, COLUMBIA CARE CENTER 29203 #045-04-1998 L2000 **P** *020
GROOMS, Sarah Gailey. 74 POLO RD 29223 #045-01-1991 L1992 **PD** *020 †55
GROSS, Jeffrey Glenn. 2435 FOREST DR 29204 #051-04-1983 L1989 **OPH** *020 †35
GROSS, Thomas Paul. 1930 BLANDING ST 29201 #023-07-1985 L1994 **ORS** *020 †40
GROSSLIGHT, Kenneth R. 2001 LAUREL ST STE 5A 29204 #011-03-1982 L1986 **AN** *020 †05 ‡
GRUBER, Louis Nover. 15 MEDICAL PARK RD, STE 103 29203 #045-01-1964 L1964 **P** *071 †75

GRUMBACH, Robert Paul. 1333 TAYLOR ST STE 2D, S.C. OB-GYN ASSOCIATES, P. 29201 #045-04-1996 L1997 **OBG** *020 †30
GUERRY, Betty J Richter. ■ 29209 #051-04-1954 L1956 **P IMG** *071
GUERRY, Paul L, III. 1 SCIENCE CT, STE 200 29203 #045-01-1983 L1984 **PTH** *020 †50
GUEST, Keith Alexander. 401 N WOODLAKE DR, SENIOR HEALTH ASSOCIATES 29229 #045-04-1996 L1999 **IMG PLM** *020 †20
GUPTA, Piyush Ratnakar. 5 RICHLAND MEDICAL PARK, DEPT OF FAMILY MEDICINE 29203 #051-04-2001 L2003 **IM** *020
GURAM, Jennifer Nicole. ■ 29209 #045-04-2008 *012
GURAM, Sukhbir Singh. 2 MEDICAL PARK RD STE 404 29203 #045-01-2005 L2005 **ORS** *012
GUSTAFSON, Dennis Herbert. ■ 29223 #035-01-1971 L1972 **ORS** *020 †40
GUY, Jeffrey Alan. 2 MEDICAL PARK RD STE 404, PRMH - UNIVERSITY ORTHOPAE 29203 #024-01-1994 L2001 **ORS** *020 †40
GUYTON, Steven David. 5 MEDICAL PARK RD, ATTN: MEDICAL EDUCATION 29203 #041-12-2005 L2005 **EM** *012
HACKETT, Lynn Hunter. 6439 GARNERS FERRY RD, DORN VA HOSP PSY SCV 116 29209 #045-01-1981 L1988 **P** *020 †75
HADDON, Werner Scott. 424 SHALLOW BROOK DR 29223 #036-01-1985 L2000 **VS** *020 †85
HADSTATE, James Norman, Jr. ■ 29209 #045-04-2008 *012
HAILE, Edward Cantey, Jr. 2750 LAUREL ST STE 203 29204 #045-01-1963 L1963 **OTO** *020 †45
HAILE, Elizabeth Stokely. 110 SUMMIT CENTRE DR 29229 #045-04-2004 L2004 **PD** *020 †55
HALADAY, George Jeffrey. 5 RICHLAND MEDICAL PARK DR 29203 #028-02-1980 L1985 **AN** *020 †05
HALL, Jeffrey W. 3209 COLONIAL DR, LOVELACE FAMILY MEDICINE 29203 #048-15-1988 L1989 **PS HS** *020 †85,65
HALL, Jeffrey Wayne. 3209 COLONIAL DR 29203 #011-03-2000 L2003 **FM** *020 †18
HALL, Rachel Elizabeth. 3209 COLONIAL DR, DEPT OF FAMILY & PREVENTIV 29203 #045-04-1999 L2000 **FM** *020 †18
HALS, Gary D. 5 MEDICAL PARK RD, RICHLAND MEM HOSP 29203 #048-12-1993 L1997 **EM** *020 †16
HAMADA, Allison Kazue. 2117 GERVAIS ST 29204 #010-01-2004 L2008 **FM** *020 †18
HAMILTON, Chas Pequette. 1403 CALHOUN ST 29201 #045-01-1980 L1981 **FM** *020 †18
HAMILTON, Laura Elizabeth. 2435 FOREST DR 29204 #045-04-1994 L1995 **IM** *071 †20
HAMILTON, Stuart Arnim. 4605 MONTICELLO RD 29203 #035-01-1974 L1976 **PD** *020 †55
HAMMETT, David Hall. 3555 HARDEN STREET EXT 29203 #045-08-2001 L2001 **N** *020
HAMMOND, James William. 14 RICHLAND MED PK D, PEDIATRIC ASSOCIATES 29203 #048-12-1967 L1973 **PD** *071 †55
HAMRICK, Dale Rutledge. 124 SPRING VALLEY CT 29223 #045-04-1995 L1996 **IMG** *020
HAMZY, Nada Jumblat. 74 POLO RD 29223 #605-01-1992 L1997 **PD** *020 †55
HANCOCK, Heather Alicia. 5 MEDICAL PARK RD, ATTN: MEDICAL EDUCATION DE 29203 #001-02-2004 L2005 **OPH** *012
HANDLER, Jason Paul. 5 MEDICAL PARK RD, ATTN: MEDICAL EDUCATION DE 29203 #036-05-2005 L2005 **OPH** *012
HANNA, John Harvey. 114 GATEWAY CORPORATE BLVD 29203 #018-03-1979 L1983 **OBG** *020 †30
HARDING, Richard Kent. 3555 HARDEN ST EXT, STE 104A 29203 #005-12-1971 L1979 **CHP P** *030 †75
HARDING, Sally Ashbaugh. 5 RICHLAND MEDICAL PARK DR 29203 #005-12-1971 L1979 **PTH** *020 †50
HARPER, Angela Dauby. 1620 LADY ST, STE B 29201 #045-04-2000 L2001 **P ADM** *020 †75
HARPER, Greta S. 3 MEDICAL PARK RD, STE 110 29203 #036-01-1984 L1985 **PD CCM** *020 †55
HARPER, Kenneth Wayne. 5 RICHLAND MEDICAL PARK DR 29203 #047-06-2006 L2006 **EM** *012
HARRELL, Ira Lee, Jr. 1707 BERNARDIN AVE, STE B 29204 #045-01-1990 L2001 **GS** *020
HARRELL, Rhona M. 1707 BERNARDIN AVE 29204 #045-01-1991 L1992 **IM** *020 †20
HARRIS, Melissa Lynn. ■ 29204 #045-04-2007 L2007 **P** *012
HARRISON, A Franklin. TAYLOR & MARION STS 29220 #045-01-1958 L1958 **GP FM** *020
HARSHANY, Mark Lawrence. ■ 29229 #023-12-2003 L2005 **DR** *020
HARTVIGSEN, Robert Erik. 3000 NE MEDICAL PARK 29223 #045-04-1985 L1986 **FM** *020 †18 ‡
HARTWIG, Hansdavid Robert. ■ 29201 #047-20-2006 L2006 **PD** *012
HARVEY, Allison Leigh. 5 RICHLAND MEDICAL PARK, DEPT EMERGENCY MED 29203 #011-03-1995 L1996 **EM** *020 †16
HASELDEN, Edward W, Jr. 4540 TRENHOLM RD 29206 #036-01-1969 L1975 **IM N** *020 †20,75
HASSAPOYANNES, Constantin. 6439 GARNERS FERRY RD 29209 #418-01-1970 L1985 **CD IM** *050
HASTINGS, Donald M, III. ■ 29229 #012-01-1997 L1998 **FM** *020 †18
HAWES, Anne Colclough. 6439 GARNERS FERRY RD, WJB DORN VA DEPT OF VETERA 29209 #036-01-1976 L1976 **IM N** *020 †75
HAWKSLEY, Vaughan Coleman. ■ 29209 #041-02-1967 L1976 **PTH GP** *071 †50
HAWN, Jason Lee. 14 MEDICAL PARK, STE 400 29203 #045-04-2003 L2004 **PD** *020 †55
HAYES, Michael Thos. 1913 BULL ST 29201 #045-01-1990 L1994 **IM** *020 †20
HAYNES, James Leland. 2 MEDICAL PARK RD, STE 300 29203 #020-12-1966 L1973 **PS OS** *020 †85
HEARON, Thomas Edward, III. 1314 ADGER RD, COLUMBIA CARDIOLOGY CONSUL 29205 #045-01-1969 L1969 **CD IM** *020 †20
HEATH, Jennifer Elizabeth. 3555 HARDEN ST EXT, STE 104A 29203 #045-04-2002 L2003 **CHP** *020 †75
HEATON, Charles Michael. 1519 MARION ST, PITTS RADIOLOGY 29201 #047-20-1997 L1999 **DR** *020 †80
HEDGEPATH, Larry Lee. 4416 FOREST DR, STE A 29206 #045-01-1970 L1971 *020
HEEBNER, Carol A. 5 RICHLAND MEDICAL PARK 29203 #045-01-1990 L1993 **PD** *020 †55
HEGQUIST, Mitchell Henry. 1715 BLANDING ST 29201 #045-01-1980 **GS** *020
HELMAN, Richard Martin. ■ 29206 #047-05-1965 L1972 **GE IM** *071 †20
HENDERSON, David Livingst. 15 MEDICAL PARK RD, STE 141 29203 #038-45-2004 L2004 **P** *012
HENDERSON, Frampton W, Jr. 2750 LAUREL ST, PROVIDENCE FAMILY 29204 #045-01-1976 L1977 **FM FPG** *020 †18
HENDERSON, Hoke F, Jr. 1519 MARION ST 29201 #036-01-1968 L1972 **PTH DMP** *020 †50
HENDERSON, Patrick Ryan. ■ 29209 #045-04-2008 *012
HENDRICKS, Chas Woodrow. 1 RICHLAND MEDICAL PARK, STE 420 29203 #055-01-1974 L1976 **CD IM** *020 †20
HENDRIX, John Walter. 2 MEDICAL PARK RD, STE 506 29203 #045-04-2006 L2006 **IM** *012
HERBERT, John Mitchell. 2 MEDICAL PARK RD, STE 107 29203 #045-01-1976 L1980 **OBG** *020 †30
HERITAGE, Erin C. ■ 29229 #033-06-2007 L2007 **EM** *012
HERLONG, James Henry. 1301 TAYLOR ST STE 1A 29201 #041-01-1963 L1963 **U** *020 †95

HERMAN, James Richard. 1701 DEVONSHIRE DR, STE 101 29204 #012-01-1984 L1985 IM *020 †20

HERNANDEZ, Johan. 3209 COLONIAL DR, P R H - DEPT OF FAMILY MED 29203 #308-03-2004 L2006 FP *012

HERNANDO, Ernesto C. ■ 29223 #748-01-1959 L1978 GP *071

HESS, Daniel Robert. 2 MEDICAL PARK RD, STE 506 29203 #305-01-2007 L2007 IM *012

HESS, Lori Ann. 110 ATRIUM WAY 29223 #004-01-1994 L2003 FM *020 †18

HESTER, Brabham M, Jr. 5900 GARNERS FERRY RD, SOUTH HAMPTON FAMILY PRACT 29209 #045-04-1994 L1995 FM *020 †18

HESTER, Martha Parker. 5900 GARNERS FERRY RD, SOUTH HAMPTON FAMILY PRACT 29209 #045-04-1994 L1995 FM *020 †18

HICK, Joe Bolton. ■ 29223 #007-02-1962 L1990 FM *071 †18

HICKS, John Reddick, II. 1655 BERNARDIN AVE, STE 300 29204 #045-01-1987 L1988 CD IM *020 †20

HICKS, Kimberly Price. 3209 COLONIAL DR 29203 #045-04-2004 L2004 FM *020 †18

HIGH, Patrice Lynnette. 300 RICE MEADOW WAY 29229 #025-76-1999, ▲ L2002 *020

HIGHTOWER, Kimberly. 4605 MONTICELLO RD 29203 #010-01-1998 L2002 PD *020 †55

HILL, Vernetta Jeane. ■ 29229 #045-01-1998 L2000 P *020 †75

HINDERSMAN, John Chas. 2750 LAUREL ST STE 102 29204 #038-41-1969 L1975 OPH IM *020 †35

HIRTH, Victor Albert. 3010 FARROW RD, STE 300 29203 #054-04-1989 L1994 IMG *020 †20

HOFFMAN, Judith A. 6007 RUTLEDGE HILL RD 29209 #041-09-1980 L1984 AN *020 †05

HOLCOMBE, Rice Ross. ■ 29206 #012-01-1959 L1962 AN *071

HOLLADAY, David Carroll. 1333 TAYLOR ST, STE 2D 29201 #045-04-1984 L1985 OBG *020 †30 ‡

HOLLAND, Warren F, Jr. 1655 BRABHAM AVE, STE 220 29204 #036-07-1963 L1970 CD IM *071 †20

HOLLEMAN, Robert C. 9 RICHLAND MED PK DR, STE 270 29203 #045-04-1990 L1991 PN *020 †55

HOLLINS, William Jos, II. 8 RICHLAND MED PK DR, STE 300 29203 #045-01-1981 L1984 CD *020 †20

HOLLOWAY, Jeffrey Paul. ■ 29201 #012-01-2007 L2007 PD *012

HOLSTRUM, Shelly Deanne. 8301 FARROW RD, DEVELOPMNTL PED CLC 29203 #021-01-1994 L2002 PD GP *020 †55

HOLT, Stephen. 2 RICHLAND MEDCL PARK #506 29203 #917-06-1972 L1988 GE *020 †20

HOMER, Dana Lester, III. ■ 29209 #045-04-2008 *012

HONG, Soon Chang. ■ 29223 #243-44-1941 L1974 FM GYN *071

HOOD, Anita Shah. 15 MEDICAL PARK RD, STE 103 29203 #045-04-1987 L2000 P *020 †75

HOOK, Jeffrey Davis. 3000 NE MEDICAL PARK, STE 108 29223 #045-01-1995 L1998 IM *020 †20

HOOK, Marion B. ■ 29206 #045-01-1941 L1941 GS *071

HOOKER, John Freeman, Jr. 29204 #045-01-1967 L1967 OBG *071 †30

HOOKS, Gregory Stuart. 21 GATEWAY CORNERS PARK, STE 101 29203 #045-04-1990 L1997 IM *020 †20

HOOVER, Justin Randall. 2 MEDICAL PARK RD, STE 404 29203 #045-01-2007 L2007 ORS *012

HOPKINS, Christie Benet. 1655 BERNARDIN AVE, STE 300 29204 #036-07-1966 L1977 CD IM *040 †20

HOPKINS, Edward D, Jr. 1920 PICKENS ST 29201 #045-01-1956 L1956 OPH *071 †35

HOPPMANN, Richard Anthony. 1801 SUNSET DR 29203 #045-01-1982 L1990 RHU IM *040 †20

HORGER, Edgar Olin, III. 2 MEDICAL PARK RD, STE 208 29203 #045-01-1962 L1962 MFM OBG *071 †30

HORST, Eric Allen. 1740 SAINT JULIAN PL 29204 #045-04-1988 L1989 END *020 †20

HORVATH, Joseph Alexander. 2 MEDICAL PARK RD #041-13-1988 L1996 ID IM *020 †20

HOUCHINS, Rachel Annette. 3555 HARDEN ST EXT, STE 104A 29203 #047-20-2004 L2004 P *012

HOWARD, Megan Mullaney. 3555 HARDEN ST EXT, STE 104A 29203 #045-04-2003 L2004 CHP *012

HUBBARD, Charles Rast, Jr. 1519 MARION ST 29201 #045-01-1980 L1984 DR *020 †80

HUBBIRD, Robert Douglas. 3 RICHLAND MEDICAL PARK, STE 110 29203 #011-02-1978 L1991 CCP PD *020 †55

HUCKS, Jennifer Ryan. 14 RICHLAND MEDICAL PARK, STE 400 29203 #045-04-2004 L2004 MPD *012

HUDEPOHL, Jamie Ellen. 3209 COLONIAL DR, UNIV. SPECIALTY CLINIC 29203 #020-12-1991 L1992 FM *020 †18

HUFF, Robert Brian. 1655 BERNARDIN AVE STE 100 29204 #021-06-1992 L1996 OPH *020 †35

HUFFMAN, Leroy James. 1301 TAYLOR ST, STE 8A 29201 #023-01-1974 L1978 IM IMG *020 †20

HUGGINS, P Kenneth. TAYLOR AT MARION ST, BAPTIST MEDICAL CENTER 29220 #045-01-1957 L1957 P ADM *071

HUI, Wing Hong. 220 FAISON DR 29203 #244-03-1963 L1976 P *020

HUMMEL, Melissa Hess. 6439 GARNERS FERRY RD, DORN VA HOSPITAL 29209 #045-04-2000 L2001 IM *020 †20

HUMPHREY, Albert. 4100 MAIN ST STE 101 29203 #041-01-1975 L1976 IM *020 †20

HUMPHREY, Alyssa Nicole. 1301 TAYLOR ST 29203 #045-01-2004 L2005 EM *012

HUMPHREY, Stephen Harmes. 8 RICHLAND MEDICAL PARK DR, STE 300 29203 #048-04-1973 L1973 OB IM *040 †20

HUMPHREYS, Roderick J. ■ 29209 #050-02-1948 L1979 GP IM *071 †18

HUMPHRIES, Ellen Cregan. 15 MEDICAL PARK RD, STE 300 29203 #038-06-1985 L2006 IM *020 †20

HUMPHRIES, Geo Badger, Jr. 1519 MARION ST 29220 #045-01-1972 L1974 R *020 †80

HUMPHRIES, John O'Neal. 2 MEDICAL PARK RD CAC502, USC DEPT OF MEDICINE 29203 #023-07-1956 L1979 IM CD *071 †20

HUNT, Leon Ervin, Jr. PO BOX 2266 29202 #654-01-2006 FP *012

HUNT, Patrick Stephen. ■ 29204 #036-01-1996 L1997 EM *020 †16

HURLEY, Brian Wyche. 5 RICHLAND MEDICAL PARK 29203 #010-03-1989 L2004 IM *020 †20

HURT, Henley H. ■ 29205 #045-01-1998 L2000 EM *071

HUSSAIN, Jabran Akhtar. PO BOX 2266 29202 #704-09-2002 IM *012

HUSSAIN, Omar Nomaan. ■ 29209 #045-04-2008 *012

HUTCHINSON, Christopher T. 1301 TAYLOR ST, THREE RIVERS OB/GYN STE 7B 29201 #045-04-1996 L1997 OBG *020 †30

HUTCHINSON, Kyllan J. 5 RICHLAND MEDICAL PARK 29203 #045-04-1995 L1996 PD *020 †55

HUTCHINSON, Manly E, Jr. 1301 TAYLOR ST STE 7B, SUTIE 7-B 29201 #045-01-1962 L1962 OBG *020 †30

HUTCHINSON, Milford B. 114 GATEWAY CORPORATE BLVD 29203 #012-01-1975 L1979 OBG *020 †30

HUTTO, Lisa Slatton. 9 RICHLAND MEDICAL PARK, STE 430 29203 #045-04-1985 L1986 AI IM *020 †20,03

HWANG, Te-Long. 3555 HARDEN ST EXT, STE 104A 29203 #244-03-1970 L1988 N ON *020 †75

HYDE, Claire Jordan. 1800 COLONIAL DR, PALMETTO HEALTH ALLIANCE G 29203 #039-01-1999 L2000 CHP *020

HYDORN, Christopher Rober. 2 MEDICAL PARK RD, STE 404 29203 #023-01-2004 L2004 ORS *012

HYMAN, William Douglas. 5 RICHLAND MEDICAL PARK DR 29203 #045-01-1980 L1987 AN IM *005

HYNES, C Kelly Scott. 1924 BLOSSOM ST 29205 #045-04-1996 L2000 OPH *020 †35

HYNES, John Dewey. 818 BRYSON RD, UCI MEDICAL 29205 #045-01-1995 L1996 FM *020

IGAMA, Juliet Leonido R. 7901 FARROW RD, COLUMBIA CARE CENTER 29203 #748-01-1974 L2003 P *020

ILLANGAKOON, Sabi. ■ 29229 #220-01-1969 L2000 P *020

IMPERIAL, Anthony. ■ 29223 #748-01-1965 L1976 P *020

INGRAHAM, David Michael. 2750 LAUREL ST STE 201, PALMETTO GASTROENTEROLOGY 29204 #045-01-1984 L1985 GE IM *071 †20

IRIZARRY, Eduardo F. 6439 GARNERS FERRY RD 29209 #308-04-1981 L1989 IM *040

ISBELL, David Connor. 8 RICHLAND MEDICAL PARK, RICHARD MEMORIAL HOSPITAL 29203 #051-01-1999 L2006 CD *020 †20

ISEMAN, Daniel Tupper. 2739 LAUREL ST, STE 1A 29204 #045-04-2000 L2006 GE *020 †20

ISKERSKY, Victor Norbert. 3 MEDICAL PARK RD STE 400, PALMETTO HLTH RICHLAND 29203 #409-16-1982 L1987 NPM GS *020 †55

ISLAM, Muhammad M. 9 RICHLAND MEDCL PARK #320, MIDLANDS NEPHROLOGY ASSOC 29203 #160-05-1987 L1994 NEP IM *020 †20

IZARD, Stephen Rogers. 2406 DECKER BLVD, FIRST CARE 29206 #027-01-1974 L1978 IM EM *020 †20

JACKSON, Don Jobe. 1920 PICKENS ST, COLUMBIA EYE CLNC 29201 #036-07-1969 L1982 OPH *020 †35

JACKSON, Jos Porter, Jr. 2435 FOREST DR 29204 #045-01-1974 L1975 ORS HS *020 †40 ‡

JACKSON, Malaka Baharah. 9 MEDICAL PARK RD STE 230, DIVISION OF PEDIATRIC ENDO 29203 #041-01-2000 L2006 PD END *020 †20

JACKSON, Robert Street. 2600 BULL ST 29201 #035-01-1968 L1980 PHP PD *075

JACOB, Jackie Ezra. ■ 29206 #495-02-1949 L1967 GS CD *020 †85

JACOBS, Dean Robt. 8910 TWO NOTCH RD, STE 301 29223 #005-14-1979 L1985 OPH *020 †35

JACOBS, Jeffrey Robert. 5 MEDICAL PARK RD, ATTN: MEDICAL EDUCATION DE 29203 #047-20-2005 L2005 OBG *012

JAFFE, Pierre. 1330 TAYLOR ST 29220 #012-01-1968 L1973 D *020 †15

JAKES, Derek P. 1519 MARION ST, PITTS RADIOLOGY 29201 #048-15-2000 L2005 VIR *020 †80

JAMES, Asha P. 3 RICHLAND MED PK DR # 500, COLUMBIA SKIN CLC 29203 #055-01-1997 L2001 D *020 †15

JAMES, Charles Alston. 9 MEDICAL PARK RD 29203 #036-07-1954 L1954 PD ADL *071 †55

JAMES, William Cleveland. 1910 BLANDING ST 29201 #045-01-1997 L2003 ORS *020 †40

JANI, Rutkumar P. 229 LONGTOWN RD 29229 #495-48-1977 L1991 FM *020 †20

JANKELEVICH, Shirley. 1751 CALHOUN ST, SC DEPT OF HEALTH & ENVIRO 29201 #035-46-1985 L2005 PD ID *062 †55

JEFFORDS, Elizabeth H. 3612 LANDMARK DR, STE B 29204 #045-01-2001 L2003 CHP *020 †75

JENKINS, George Alexander. 2750 LAUREL ST, STE 201 29204 #045-01-1992 L1997 GE *020 †20

JENKINS, Peter Lionel G. PO BOX 202 29202 #917-19-1980 L1986 FOP *020

JENKINS, Spencer James. 2750 LAUREL ST STE 201, PALMETTO GASTROLGY 29204 #045-01-1993 L1997 GE *020 †20

JENNINGS, William Russell. 3 MEDICAL PARK RD, STE 350 29203 #045-04-2003 L2004 EM *100 †16

JETER, Elaine K. 2435 FOREST DR 29204 #045-01-1979 L1981 PTH *030 †50

JIMENEZ, Rosa Maria. 4540 TRENHOLM RD, THE COLUMBIA MEDICAL GROUP 29206 #042-01-1980 L1985 IM *020 †20

JOHNSON, Carlton David. 1100 SHIRLEY ST, PALMETTO SENIOR CARE/ SHAN 29205 #036-01-1988 L1993 IMG *020 †20

JOHNSON, Crystal Yolanda. 1301 TAYLOR ST, STE 7B 29201 #045-04-2001 L2005 OBG *020 †30

JOHNSON, Elizabeth Bradle. 5 MEDICAL PARK RD, ATTN: MEDICAL EDUCATION DE 29203 #051-01-2005 L2005 IM *100

JOHNSON, Graeme H. 8301 FARROW RD, USC DEVELOPMENTAL PEDIATRI 29203 #671-01-1969 L1987 NDP PD *020 †55

JOHNSON, James Henry. 1301 TAYLOR ST STE 7B 29201 #001-02-1971 L1977 OBG *020 †30

JOHNSON, Jo Harold. 2200 HARDEN ST, JR/DOWDY GARDNER NURSING C 29203 #023-07-1963 L1970 CLP PTH *020

JOHNSON, Julie Markworth. 9 MEDICAL PARK RD STE 208, PALMETTO HEALTH RICHLAND 29203 #036-05-2003 L2004 OBG *100

JOHNSON, Kevin Fountain. 2 MEDICAL PARK RD, STE 506 29203 #045-04-2007 L2007 IM *012

JOHNSON, Kevin Michael. 4416 FOREST DR 29206 #01-04-1994 L1995 FM *075 †18

JOHNSON, Lewis Dean. USC SCH OF MED PATH 29208 #007-02-1966 L1979 PTH *040

JOHNSON, Melvin, Jr. 1410 BLANDING ST, STE 1 29201 #047-07-1977 L1981 AN *020

JOHNSON, Reed P. ■ 29210 #010-03-1944 L1945 P OS *072

JOHNSON, Ronald Lee. 4100 MAIN ST STE 201 29203 #038-41-1975 L1981 IM END *020

JOHNSON, William Arnold. 100 SUMMIT CENTRE DR 29229 #045-01-1972 L1973 OPH *020 †35

JOHNSON, William Arnold. 100 SUMMIT CENTRE DR 29229 #045-01-1999 L2003 OPH *020 †35

JONES, Ashley Blackmon. 15 MEDICAL PARK RD, STE 104 29203 #045-01-2006 L2006 P *012

JONES, Benjamin Richard. 1 MEDICAL PARK RD STE 420, COLUMBIA CARDIOVASCULAR CL 29203 #036-05-1980 L1986 CD *020 †20

JONES, Conigliaro. 2117 GERVAIS ST, CENTERS, INC 29204 #047-01-1994 L2001 FM *030 †18

JONES, Frank Collins, Jr. 2823 RIVER DR, GOOD SAMARITAN HEALTH CENT 29201 #012-05-1960 L1991 GS *020 †85

JONES, Gary Mosher. ■ 29223 #019-02-1966 L1976 EM GS *071 †16

JONES, George Tripp. 166 STONERIDGE DR 29220 #045-01-1974 L1980 ON HEM *020 †20

JONES, John Eric. 3555 HARDEN ST EXT, STE 104A 29203 #012-01-1975 L1976 P *040 †75

JONES, Kadijah. 4416 FOREST DR, STE A 29206 #045-01-1995 L1999 FM *020 †18

JONES, Mark Allen. ■ 29229 #047-20-2004 L2004 CCS *012

JONES, Preston Allen. 1333 TAYLOR ST 29201 #045-01-1973 L1977 PUD CCM *020 †20

JONES, Robert Calvin. 2 MEDICAL PARK RD, STE 400 29203 #045-04-2004 L2004 GS *012

JONES, Scot Heath. 1333 TAYLOR ST, DEPT OF EMERGENCY MEDICINE 29220 #045-04-2002 L2003 EM *020 †16

JONES, Sheila Bertha. 1519 MARION ST, PITTS RAD 29201 #028-02-1985 L2006 PDR R *020 †80

JORDAN, Ashby Miner. ■ 29223 #012-05-1965 L1987 OS PD *030 †55

JORDAN, Lee Tyrone. 1709 BARNWELL ST 29201 #012-01-1971 L1975 **DMP** *020 †55,15
JORDAN, Megan Elaine. ■ 29206 #045-04-2008 *012
JOY, Annarosan P. 2701 MIDDLEBURG DR, ASSOCIATES IN INTERNAL MED 29204 #048-12-1996 L2002 **FM** *020 †18
JOYCE, Betty Winfield. 6439 GARNERS FERRY RD, DORN VA MEDICAL CENTER 29209 #036-05-1987 L1988 **IM** *020 †20
JOYE, Jimmy Finley, Jr. 6439 GARNERS FERRY RD 29209 #045-04-1993 L1994 **IM** *020 †20
JUK, Steven Stanley, Jr. 2601 LAUREL ST, STE 260 29204 #036-07-1971 L1974 **CD** *020 †20
JUVEKAR, Madhuri Vishwas. 4214 HARD SCRABBLE RD 29223 #496-38-1998 L2003 **FM** *020
KALUS, Rami. 1301 TAYLOR ST, STE 10A 29201 #024-05-1982 L1990 **PS GS** *020 †65
KAMINER, Sharon Jean. 1 MEDICAL PARK RD STE 410, SCHOOL OF MED/DEPT OF PEDI 29203 #011-02-1980 L2003 **PDC PD** *020 †55
KANITKAR, Dattatraya V. 1301 TAYLOR ST, STE 4K 29201 #495-01-1967 L1981 **OBG** *020 †30
KANTSIPER, Alan Barry. 710 RABON RD STE 100, 5 RICHLAND MEDICAL PARK DR 29203 #016-42-1969 L1973 **DR OS** *020 †80
KAPLAN, Eugene H. 20 SUMMIT PL 29204 #035-19-1951 L1984 **PYA P** *071 †75
KATWAL, Arabindra Bahadur. 2 MEDICAL PARK RD, STE 506 29203 #672-03-2004 L2006 **IM** *012
KEANE, William Richard. 121 PARK CENTRAL DR 29203 #048-12-1972 L1979 **NEP IM** *020 †20
KEESHAN, Susan Jayne. 1301 TAYLOR ST, STE 3L 29201 #045-04-1996 L2000 **OBG** *020 †30
KEIGER, Christina Marie. 4500 STUART ST, MONCRIEF COMMUNITY ARMY HO 29207 #011-03-1986 L1993 **GP** *020 †18
KEISLER, Brian David. 3209 COLONIAL DR 29203 #045-04-2001 L2004 **FM** *100
KEISLER, David Lemuel. 3209 COLONIAL DR 29203 #045-01-1972 L1973 **FM FPG** *040 †18
KEITH, Philip David. ■ 29204 #045-04-2008 *012
KELLEY, Catherine Powers. ■ 29209 #045-04-2008 *012
KEMICK, Mary Lynn Suzanne. 1740 SAINT JULIAN PL 29204 #045-04-1991 L1992 **END IM** *020 †20
KENDALL, Edward M. 2015 MARION ST, HEALTH 29201 #047-07-1982 L1984 **P** *020 †75
KENE-EWULU, Ijeoma Avunan. 2 MEDICAL PARK RD STE 506 29203 #690-04-1987 L2007 **IM** *012
KENNEDY, Richard Mckinne. 6439 GARNERS FERRY RD, DORN VA MEDICAL CENTER 29209 #045-04-1991 L1992 **AN** *020 †05
KERR, Lawrence S. ■ 29209 #012-01-1981 L1982 **IM LM** *071 †20
KESSLER, Stanton Coleman. 1330 TAYLOR ST 29220 #023-01-1969 L2005 **FOP PTH** *020 †50
KHAN, Maliha W. 2113 ADAMS GRV, STE 101 29203 #704-02-1991 L2007 **MPD PD** *020 †55,20
KHETPAL, Anita. 901 SUMTER ST, BYRNES BLDG, 7TH FLOOR 29208 #704-25-1990 L1996 **CHP** *020 †75
KHOKHAR, Jawaad Siddique. ■ 29229 #665-02-2004 L2004 **END IM** *012 †20
KHOURY, John Anthony. 2719 MIDDLEBURG DR, STE 105 29204 #045-04-1991 L1993 **PD** *020 †55
KILLINGSWORTH, R Alston. ■ 29209 #045-01-1978 L1979 **DR** *020 †80
KILPATRICK, Zachary M, Jr. 1519 MARION ST 29201 #012-22-1998 L2004 **DR** *020 †80
KIM, Chun Soo. 110 ATRIUM WAY 29223 #583-01-1969 L1978 **PD FM** *020 †55
KIM, Gunil G. 220 FAISON DR 29203 #583-10-1967 L1979 **P GP** *020 †75
KIM, Monica Boun. ■ 29204 #045-01-2008 *012
KIMBROUGH, Edward E. ■ 29204 #047-05-1953 L1963 **ORS** *071 †40
KIMBROUGH, Edward Ernest. 2739 LAUREL ST, STE 1A 29204 #045-04-1996 L1997 **GE** *020 †20
KINARD, Kimberly Gale. ■ 29209 #045-04-2008 *012
KINDER, Philip Whitaker. 1301 TAYLOR ST, STE 1A 29201 #045-01-1973 L1976 **U** *020 †95
KING, Terry Allan. 6439 GARNERS FERRY RD 29209 #045-01-1982 L1983 **FM EM** *020 †18
KIRBY, Michael James. 220 FAISON DR 29203 #036-01-1972 L2003 **P PYG** *020
KIRKER, William Oswald. ■ 29221 #025-01-1960 L1987 **EM GP** *074
KIRKLAND, James Robert. 914 RICHLAND ST, STE B201 29201 #305-01-1992 L1997 **P** *020
KIRSCHENFELD, Paul M. 1333 TAYLOR ST 29201 #001-02-1979 L2000 **PUD CCM** *020 †20
KLEIMAN, Richard John. 3 RICHLAND MEDICAL PARK, STE 350 29203 #036-05-2004 L2004 **EM** *100
KLEIN, Lawrence. 1 SCIENCE CT, STE 200 29203 #016-06-1963 L1964 **CD** *020 †20
KLEIN, Lawrence Edward. 5 RICHLAND MEDICAL PARK DR 29203 #032-01-1978 L1986 **DMP D** *020 †15 ‡
KLIMOVICH, Brianne. ■ 29204 #041-15-2007 L2007 **EM** *012
KNEECE, Robert Hugh. 6439 GARNERS FERRY RD, DEPT PRIMARY CARE 29209 #045-01-1995 L2005 **MPD** *020 †20,55
KNIGHT, Ellis Mc Henry. 1301 TAYLOR ST, STE 8A 29201 #040-02-1980 L1986 **IM** *020 †20
KNIGHT, James F. 1410 BLANDING ST, STE 1 29201 #039-01-1981 L1985 **AN** *020 †05
KOCHANSKI, Walter. 1 MEDICAL PARK RD STE 110 29203 #068-01-1958 L1967 **ORS** *071 †40
KOCHER, Gary Allen. 1516 GREGG ST 29201 #055-01-1978 L1979 **OPH EM** *020 †35
KOHN, Laurie Fitzharris. 6439 GARNERS FERRY RD, PRIMARY CARE & SUBSPECIALT 29209 #045-04-1999 L2001 **IM** *020
KOLB, Todd A. ■ 29201 #016-42-1972 L1977 **BBK PTH** *020 †50
KOLIBAC, Alexander. 112 DOCTORS CIR STE 104 29203 #065-06-1959 L1965 **ORS** *072
KOMMAREDDI, Santi. ■ 29223 #495-50-1970 L1978 **PTH CLP** *020 †50
KOON, David Edwin. 2 MEDICAL PARK RD, STE 404 29203 #036-05-1965 L1966 **OM FPG** *020
KOON, David Edwin, Jr. 2 MEDICAL PARK RD, STE LL10 29203 #045-04-1992 L1993 **ORS** *020 †40
KOSCIUSKO, Robert Dale. ■ 29204 #023-07-2007 L2007 **EM** *012
KOTCHMAR, Geo Stephan, Jr. 4 MEDICAL PARK RD, STE 301 29203 #045-01-1976 L1977 **PD ID** *020 †55
KOUVOLO, Cathleen Anne. ■ 29205 #045-04-2008 *012
KRANTZ, Brent Elroy. 2 MEDICAL PARK RD, STE 300 29203 #030-05-1969 L1998 **GS** *020 †85
KREBS, Kevin Ward. 1415 BLANDING ST STE 4 29201 #045-01-1992 L1993 **P** *020
KREISER, Catherine Joan. 3003 COLUMBIA AVE 29201 #038-06-1997 L1999 **P** *020 †75
KRESSLER, Carolyn Freda. 1301 TAYLOR ST STE 3L, THREE RIVERS OB/GYN ASSOCS 29201 #041-07-1974 L1981 **OBG** *020 †30
KRUEGER, Heather. 2113 ADAMS GRV, STE 101 29203 #049-01-1985 L1993 **PD** *020 †55
KUDRIK, Fred John. 166 STONERIDGE DR 29210 #038-06-1997 L2002 **HO** *020 †20
KUGLER, Carlos David. 2 MEDICAL PARK RD, STE 404 29203 #935-03-1998 L2004 **ORS** *012
LACSON, Emiliana Saulog. 3605 CARRIAGE HOUSE RD 29206 #748-08-1967 L1977 **GP** *020
LADD, Ricky Alan. 1330 TAYLOR ST 29220 #027-01-1997 L1998 **EM** *020 †16
LAFFITTE, M Tucker, III. 1333 TAYLOR ST, STE 2D 29201 #045-01-1983 L1984 **OBG** *020 †30
LAFFITTE, Moses T, Jr. 1333 TAYLOR ST, STE 5F 29201 #045-01-1955 L1955 **OBG** *071 †30
LAGRASSO, Jeffrey Raymond. 2 RICHLAND MEDICAL PARK, STE 302 29203 #033-05-1999 L2006 **PS** *020 †65
LALL, Ritu. 3 RICHLAND MEDICAL PARK DR, PEDIATRIX MEDICAL GROUP 29203 #495-45-1994 L2003 **NPM** *020 †55
LALLY, Davinder Kaur. 1801 SUNSET DR 29203 #919-07-1983 L1987 **IM** *040 †20
LAMAR, C Scott. 3209 COLONIAL DR, FAMILY MEDICINE 29203 #045-04-1991 L1992 **IMG** *020 †18
LAMBERT-FALLS, Rosemary. 166 STONERIDGE DR, SC ONCOLOGY ASSOCIATES PA 29210 #045-01-1982 L1983 **ON HEM** *020 †20
LAMMIE, John James. 6 MEDICAL PARK RD, FAMILY PRACTICE CENTER 29203 #041-02-1976 L1988 **FM AM** *020 †18
LAMOREAUX, David Chad. 2 MEDICAL PARK RD, STE 404 29203 #035-03-2004 L2004 **ORS** *012
LANCE, Billy J. 3010 FARROW RD, STE 220 29203 #010-03-1977 L1980 **FM** *020 †18
LANDRY, Jason Michael. ■ 29223 #011-04-2007 L2007 **EM** *012
LANE, Henderson Michael. ■ 29209 #023-12-1986 L1988 **EM** *020
LANGSTON, Gordon M. 5 RICHLAND MEDICAL PARK DR 29203 #041-02-1981 L1985 **AN** *020 †05
LAPIDUS, Bernard. ■ 29223 #024-07-1937 L1968 **IM PM** *071 †20
LA PORTE, Patrick J. 5 RICHLAND MEDICAL PARK DR 29203 #041-02-1989 L1993 **AN** *020 †05
LASHLEY, John Richard. 900 ASSEMBLY STREET, COUNSELING CENTER 29208 #045-01-1965 L1965 **P** *071
LAUVER, John Wm. 1519 MARION ST 29201 #017-20-1977 L1978 **DR** *020 †80
LAW, Theodore Wannamaker. 2750 LAUREL ST, PROVIDENCE FAMILY 29204 #045-01-1986 L1987 **FM** *020 †18
LAWTON, Joseph James, III. 2601 LAUREL ST, STE 260 29204 #045-01-1989 L1997 **CD** *020 †20
LAZARO, Andrea Marie. 2712 MIDDLEBURG DR, STE 101 29204 #055-02-1992 L1993 **PD** *020 †55
LEDFORD, Orr Michael. ■ 29205 #045-01-1965 L1984 **GP OS** *075
LEDLIE, Laura Marie. 1749 MARSHALL ST, SANDHILLS PEDIATRIC & ADOL 29203 #045-04-1995 L1996 **PD** *020 †55
LEOTTA, Gus Joseph, III. ■ 29203 #005-02-1999 L2001 **ORS** *012
LEPPARD, Edward M, Jr. 2750 LAUREL ST, STE 305 29204 #045-01-1977 L1978 **TS VS** *020 †85,90
LEUSCHNER, Zachary Robert. ■ 29205 #045-04-2008 *012
LEVERETTE, Deborah. 3612 LANDMARK DR, STE B 29204 #045-01-1976 L1977 **P PYA** *020 †75
LEWIS, William Vernon. 1 SCIENCE CT, STE 200 29203 #005-12-1972 L1977 **PTH** *020 †50
LIN, Tu. 2 MEDICAL PARK RD STE 502, USC DEPARTMENT OF MEDICINE 29203 #385-02-1966 L1977 **END IM** *040 †20
LINDLER, Charlotte E. 14 RICHLAND MED PK D, PEDIATRIC ASSOCIATES 29203 #045-01-1976 L1979 **PD** *020
LINDLER, William W. 1 MEDICAL PARK RD STE 22 29203 #045-01-1973 L1975 **OBG** *071 †30
LINDSEY, William Bradford. 1801 SUNSET DR 29203 #045-04-2003 L2004 **IM** *020 †20
LINFERT, Jennifer. 9 RICHLAND MEDICAL PARK DR, STE 620 29203 #045-01-1999 L2003 **OBG** *020 †30
LITTLE, John Monroe. I-20 29219 #045-01-1976 L1977 **FM IMG** *030 †18
LIVINGSTON, Rita Rena. 3209 COLONIAL DR, FAMILY MEDICAL DEPT 29203 #012-21-2007 L2007 **FP** *012
LIVINGSTON, Timothy Scott. 9 MEDICAL PARK RD, STE 200 29203 #012-01-1994 L2003 **CHN** *020 †75
LLOYD, Stephen Carroll. 1735 TAYLOR ST, SCMEC 29201 #036-07-1975 L1977 **IM GPM** *020 †20
LLOYD, Vincent James. RICHLAND MEMORIAL HOSPITAL 29203 #045-01-1991 L1992 **EM** *020 †16,55
LOBEL, Melanie. 3555 HARDEN ST EXT, STE 104A 29203 #045-01-2002 L2003 **CHP** *020
LOBITZ, Bruce Harlan. 732 SOUTHLAKE RD 29223 #021-05-1990 L1995 **EM** *020 †16 ‡
LOCKLAIR, Matthew Ryan. 5 MEDICAL PARK RD, ATTN: MEDICAL EDUCATION DE 29203 #045-04-2005 L2005 **PD** *012
LOFTON, Kiersten Leigh. 14 MEDICAL PARK RD, STE 400 29203 #045-01-2006 L2006 **PD** *012
LONG, David Lynn. 1410 BLANDING ST STE 1 29201 #055-01-1988 L1989 **AN** *020 †05
LONG, Laura Bird. 2501 FARAWAY DR AX-325 29223 #051-04-1987 L1988 **PHP IMG** *030 †70
LONG, Leslie S. 1410 BLANDING ST, STE 1 29201 #012-22-1987 L1988 **AN** *020 †05
LONGAKER, Dail Wilson. 1850 LAUREL ST, SURGICAL ASSOCIATES 29201 #051-01-1955 L1963 **GS TS** *020 †85,90
LOUGH, Lawrence Ren. 1519 MARION ST, PITTS RADIOLOGY 29201 #045-01-1985 L1991 **DR** *020 †80
LOUNSBURY, Dave Edmond. ■ 29201 #050-02-1979 L1981 **IM N** *020 †20
LOVE, Joseph Danl, Jr. 1333 TAYLOR ST, STE 6F 29201 #051-01-1971 L1975 **PUD IM** *020 †20
LOVERN, Mark Adams. 1519 MARION ST, PITTS RADIOLOGY 29201 #020-02-1985 L1986 **DR** *020 †80
LOWMAN, Anthony Dean. 2739 LAUREL ST STE 1A, COLUMBIA GASTLGY ASSOC 29204 #045-01-1981 L1982 **GE IM** *020 †20
LOWMAN, Philip Eugene. 5 MEDICAL PARK RD, ATTN: MEDICAL EDUCATION DE 29203 #045-04-2005 L2005 **IM** *012
LUCAS, Amy Ashburne. 6439 GARNERS FERRY RD, DORN VA MEDICAL CENTER 29209 #045-04-2002 L2004 **IM** *020 †20
LUCE, William Franklin. 2719 MIDDLEBURG DR STE 103 29204 #045-01-1959 L1959 **IM** *071 †20
LUCKEY, Thomas John. 3 MEDICAL PARK RD STE 350, DEPT OF EMERGENCY MED 29203 #051-07-2006 L2006 **EM** *012
LUIS, Alejandro Jose. 2 MEDICAL PARK RD, STE 402 29203 #270-02-2005 L2006 **GS** *012
LUNSFORD, Alison Joan. ■ 29229 #039-01-2007 L2007 **PD** *012
LUNSFORD, Jerod Lindsey. 3 MEDICAL PARK RD, STE 350 29203 #039-01-2006 L2006 **EM** *012
LYMAN, Gregory Eugene. 1 MEDICAL PARK RD, STE 300 29203 #021-01-1982 L1983 **OBG** *020 †30
LYNCH, Ross David. 1930 BLANDING ST 29201 #036-01-1976 L1982 **ORS OSS** *020 †40
LYNN, Annette Williams. 1801 SUNSET DR 29203 #045-04-1987 L1992 **D** *020 †15
LYNN, Jason Charles. 1519 MARION ST 29201 #047-20-1997 L1999 **DR** *020 †80
LYON, Pamela Ann. 3000 NE MEDICAL PARK, STE 212 29223 #011-03-1992 L1993 **EM** *020 †16
MACATANGAY, Cesar Torres. 220 FAISON DR, G WERBER BRYAN PSYCH HOSPI 29203 #748-07-1963 L1977 **P** *071
MACDONALD, Roderick, Jr. ■ 29204 #045-01-1950 L1950 **OS OPH** *071 †35
MACON, Jonathan Turner. ■ 29209 #045-04-2008 *012
MADDEN, Hervey Mac, Jr. 15 MEDICAL PARK RD STE 141, PRMH - DEPT OF NEUROPSYCHI 29203 #004-01-2004 L2004 **CHP** *012
MAGEE, Michael Allen. 7620 TRENHOLM ROAD EXT, CAROLINA RETINA CENTER, P. 29223 #047-20-1999 L2005 **OPH** *020 †35
MAHON, Melvyn Vanroy. 4100 MAIN ST, STE 102 29203 #010-03-1979 L1985 **CD IM** *020 †20
MAHTAB, Tanvir. 5 MEDICAL PARK RD, ATTN: MEDICAL EDUCATION DE 29203 #045-01-2005 L2005 **FM** *020

■ = Address Information Privacy Protected

MAISCH, Scott Allen. ■ 29205 #027-01-1991 L2006 **DMP** *020 †50
MAKAPUGAY, Fidel T, Jr. 7901 FARROW RD 29203 #748-01-1952 L1976 **P IMG** *071
MALANUK, Robert. ■ 29223 #045-01-1968 L1968 **EM FM** *071 †18
MALANUK, Robert Middleton. 2601 LAUREL ST STE 260 29204 #045-01-1996 L1997 **CD IC** *020 †20
MALCOLM, Gregory Read. 1410 BLANDING ST 29201 #045-04-1984 L1985 **AN** *020 †05
MALONE, Timothy Darnell. 1333 TAYLOR ST, STE 4H 29201 #045-04-1993 L1994 **P** *020 †75
MANGHI, Abdul Qayoom. 724 SOUTHLAKE RD, MIDLANDS CENTER 29223 #704-02-1961 L1976 **IM PUD** *020
MANKTELOW, Anne. 1 MEDICAL PARK RD STE 230 29203 #917-23-1977 L1994 **PDS** *020 †85
MANN, Joshua Russell. 3209 COLONIAL DR 29203 #027-01-1996 L2002 **GPM** *040 †70
MARAGH, Hallene. 1818 HENDERSON ST, STE 201 29204 #566-01-1972 L2000 **PS OTO** *020 †65
MARCILLE, Roxanne. 3 MEDICAL PARK RD, STE 270 29203 #045-01-1980 L1986 **PDP PD** *020 †55
MARCUS, Bradley Jess. 5 RICHLAND MEDICAL PARK DR 29203 #654-01-2001 L2004 **PTH** *020 †50
MARCUS, Matthew Alexander. 1519 MARION ST, PITTS RADIOLOGY 29201 #035-08-1969 L2007 **DR** *100 †80
MARESKA, Michael Charles. ■ 29204 #038-41-1999 L1999 **CN** *020 †75
MARINKOVIC, Milos. 6439 GARNERS FERRY RD # 5W 29209 #957-02-1962 L1995 **ON HEM** *020 †20
MARINO, Robert Frank. ■ 29223 #035-08-1980 L1985 **PHP** *030 †70
MARION, Henry James. 76 POLO RD, LEXINGTON FAMILY PRACTICE 29223 #045-01-1983 L1984 **FM** *020 †18
MARKOWITZ, Bethany Cecili. 5 MEDICAL PARK RD 29203 #045-04-2005 L2005 **OPH** *012
MARLER, Eric D. 9570 TWO NOTCH RD, STE 7 29223 #035-09-1996 L1999 **IM** *020 †20
MARSH, Thomas David. 3 MEDICAL PARK RD # STE400 29203 #045-01-1982 L1983 **NPM** *020 †55
MARSHALL, Michael C. 1333 TAYLOR ST, STE 6F 29201 #045-01-1987 L1988 **PUD IM** *020 †20
MARTIN, Andrew. 3209 COLONIAL DR DEPT FAM 29203 #041-78-2007, ▲ L2007 *100
MARTIN, James Frank, Jr. 1655 BERNARDIN AVE, STE 350 29204 #045-01-1986 L1987 **FM** *020 †18
MARTIN, Jeffery Scott. 8 RICHLAND MEDICAL PARK, STE 400 29203 #012-01-1995 L2005 **TS** *020 †85,90
MARTIN, Thomas Victor. 1330 RICHLAND ST 29201 #023-12-1988 L1999 **P PFP** *020 †75
MARTINEZ, Enrique Lugo. ■ 29210 #308-03-1977 L1980 **OM** *100
MARTURANO, Jo. 1903 GADSDEN ST, STE 204 29201 #036-01-1984 L1985 **P** *020 †18,75
MASON, Elizabeth Jo. ■ 29209 #045-04-2008 *012
MASSEY, Benjamin Diehl. 2750 LAUREL ST, STE 201 29204 #051-04-1975 L1981 **GE IM** *020 †20
MASSEY, Gene Matthew. 2 MEDICAL PARK RD STE 404, ORTHOPEDICS DEPT 29203 #020-02-2006 L2006 **ORS** *012
MATAWARAN, Alfonso J. 220 FAISON DR, BRYAN PSYCHIATRIC HOSPITAL 29203 #748-01-1955 L1979 **P NTR** *071
MATHEWS, Carnetha Nashun. 3555 HARDEN ST EXT, STE 104A 29203 #047-06-2004 L2004 **CHP** *012
MATTHEWS, Margaret Mary. 3010 FARROW RD, STE 300 29203 #036-01-1994 L1997 **IMG** *020
MATTHEWS-BETTS, Cynthia. 1333 TAYLOR ST, STE 3B 29201 #010-03-1985 L1988 **IM** *020
MATTINGLY, Thomas W. ■ 29204 #010-02-1930 L1972 **IM CD** *075 †20
MATTOCKS, Karen Fisher. 4801 MONTICELLO RD 29203 #036-01-1994 L1998 **FPG FM** *020 †18
MATTOX, Thomas Fleming. 2 MEDICAL PARK RD, STE 107 29204 #036-01-1987 L1996 **OBG** *020 †30
MAULDIN, Lawrence Brooks. 1333 TAYLOR ST, STE 1C 29201 #045-01-1972 L1977 **N CHN** *020 †75,55
MAYER, Ruben Luther. 4540 TRENHOLM RD, THE COLUMBIA MEDICAL GROUP 29206 #045-04-1985 L1988 **IM** *020
MAYLATH, Craig Foster. 1801 SUNSET DR 29203 #041-13-1993 L2000 **IMG** *100 †20
MAYSON, Mark James. 1333 TAYLOR ST, STE 6F 29201 #012-01-1989 L1992 **PUD PCC** *020 †20
MAZOUE, Christopher G. 2 MEDICAL PARK RD, STE LL10 29203 #021-05-1997 L2003 **ORS OSM** *020 †40
MAZUMDER, Mridul Kumar. 3555 HARDEN ST EXT, STE 104A 29203 #004-01-2004 L2004 **P** *012
MC CAIN, Richard Sterling. 1812 HAMPTON ST 29201 #045-01-1978 L1979 **ORS OSM** *020 †40
MC CALLUM, Brown James. 6439 GARNERS FERRY RD, WJB DORN VA MEDICAL CENTER 29209 #045-04-2001 L2002 **IM** *020
MC CARDLE, Robert John. 5 RICHLAND MEDICAL PARK 29203 #041-13-1961 L1970 **GS CD** *071 †85,90
MC CLAIN, Virginia Louise. 4416 FOREST DR 29206 #030-06-1990 L1996 **IM** *020
MC CLERKLIN, Patricia A. 112 DOCTORS CIR 29203 #010-03-1983 L1988 **D** *020 †15
MC CLOY, Stanley W, Jr. 3209 COLONIAL DR 29203 #038-40-1994 L2007 **FM OBS** *020 †18
MC CONNELL, Douglas M. 1519 MARION ST, PITTS RADIOLOGY 29201 #021-05-2001 L2007 **RNR** *100 †80
MC CUTCHEON, Ernest P. ■ 29223 #036-07-1959 L1978 **GPM PHP** *071 †70
MCDANIEL, Jeffrey Michael. 3209 COLONIAL DR, PALMETTO HEALTH RICHLAND 29203 #048-14-2005 L2005 **ORS** *100
MC DONALD, Mark James. 3 RICHLAND MEDICAL PARK, STE 110 29203 #028-34-1995 L2001 **PD CCP** *020 †55
MC ELVEEN, Leland Joseph. 166 STONERIDGE DR 29210 #045-01-1979 L1984 **ON HEM** *020 †20
MC FADDEN, Wm Frederick. 610 FAISON DR, MORRIS VILLAGE 29203 #023-12-1981 L1988 *020
MC FARLAND, Dee Edward. ■ 29204 #036-05-1966 L1971 **PTH CLP** *020 †50
MC FARLAND, Kay Flowers. 2 MEDICAL PARK RD, STE 502 29203 #036-05-1966 L1971 **END IM** *030 †20
MC FARLAND, Marion F, III. 5 RICHLAND MEDICAL PARK 29203 #004-01-1974 L1975 **EM OM** *030 †16
MC GREGOR, William Glenn. ■ 29206 #025-01-1976 L1977 **GYN END** *075
MCGRUDER, Kristine Dinh. 3209 COLONIAL DR, FAMILY MEDICINE CENTER 29203 #012-01-2005 L2007 **FM** *020
MC GUIRE, Franklin Riley. 2 MEDICAL PARK RD, STE 502 29203 #020-12-1999 L2006 **PCC** *020 †20

MC HONE, James Samson. 105 OFFICE PARK RD 29223 #012-01-1978 L1979 **ORS** *020 †40
MC HUGH, Terrance Patrick. 5 RICHLAND MEDICAL PARK 29203 #023-01-1974 L1978 **EM** *020 †16
MC KEE, David Franklin. 3 RICHLAND MEDICAL PARK, STE 120 29203 #045-04-1982 L1987 **OTO HNS** *020 †45
MC KENZIE, Charles M, Jr. 14 RICHLAND MEDICAL PRK DR, STE 410 29203 #045-01-1979 L1982 **PD** *020 †55
MC KINNEY, Harry Don, Jr. ■ 29223 #045-01-1974 L1985 **EM** *020
MC KINNEY, Thornton S, Jr. 1333 TAYLOR ST STE 4H 29201 #305-01-1993 L1999 **P CHP** *020 †75
MC LAIN, Wm Campbell, III. 1333 TAYLOR ST, STE 5A 29201 #045-01-1977 L1978 **IM PCC** *020 †20
MC LAUGHLIN, Niall Gerard. 121 PARK CENTRAL DR 29203 #422-01-1999 L2002 **NEP** *020 †20
MC LEAN, George Edwards. 1410 BLANDING ST STE 203 29201 #012-05-1953 L1962 **PS** *071 †85,65
MC MAHON, Carol L. 6439 GARNERS FERRY RD, LIBRARY BUILDING 3 RM 104 29208 #010-03-1980 L1994 **OS FOP** *040
MCMILLAN, Casey Michael. 14 MEDICAL PARK RD #400PH2 29203 #012-01-2004 L2004 **MPD** *012
MCNEELY, Jonathan Warren. 14 MEDICAL PARK RD, STE 400 29203 #030-04-2006 L2006 **MPD** *012
MC NEIL, Deanna Simmons. 2015 MARION ST 29201 #045-01-1985 L1993 **P** *020 †75 ‡
MC NULTY, Samuel Hunt. ■ 29209 #045-04-2008 *012
MC REDMOND, Kevin Paul. 7 MEDICAL PARK RD STE 203, PEDIATRIC HEMATOLOGY/ONCOL 29203 #043-01-1985 L1991 **PHO PD** *020 †55
MC WILLIAMS, Wilson G. 1920 PICKENS ST 29201 #045-01-1979 L1988 **OPH** *020 †35
MEADOWS, Lora Kim. 4540 TRENHOLM RD 29206 #045-04-1982 L1988 **PD** *020 †55
MEADOWS, Robin Stoddard. 3 MEDICAL PARK RD STE 350, DEPT OF EMERGENCY MEDICINE 29203 #045-04-1989 L1990 **PD** *020 †55
MEARES, Guy Maurice, Jr. 1301 TAYLOR ST, STE 7B 29201 #045-01-1966 L1966 **OBG** *020 †30
MEGHADRI, Niveditha. 15 MEDICAL PARK RD STE 104, ALLIANCE/USC S 29203 #495-65-1991 L2002 **CHP** *020
MEIER, Walter Louis, IV. ■ 29203 #012-01-2003 L2004 **EM** *020 †16
MEISNER, Grant Rolland. 5 RICHLAND MEDICAL PARK DR 29203 #025-01-1981 L1984 **AN** *020 †05
MEJIA, Maria Consuelo. PO BOX 119, SC STATE HOSP 29202 #264-05-1959 L1989 **P** *020
MELLETTE, Connie Owen. 5 RICHLAND MEDICAL PARK 29203 #045-01-1970 L1971 **P** *020 †75
MENACHERY, Jose Devassy. 220 FAISON DR 29203 #495-44-1967 L1983 **P N** *020
MENACHERY, Lissy K. ■ 29223 #561-06-1971 L1990 **FM** *020 †18
MENON, Seema. 2 MEDICAL PARK RD, STE 107 29203 #025-07-2001 L2006 **OBG** *100 †30
MEREDITH, William David. 1519 MARION ST 29201 #045-01-1968 L1968 **R** *020 †80
MERIWETHER, Rebecca Ann. 3209 COLONIAL DR, FAMILY & PREVENTIVE MEDICI 29203 #012-01-1979 L2000 **FM** *050 †18
MERLIN, Stephen Irwin. 1620 LADY ST STE B 29201 #012-05-1982 L1988 **ADM IM** *030 †20
MESSERVY, Thomas Walker. 5 RICHLAND MEDICAL PARK 29203 #045-01-1967 L1967 **P AM** *071 †75
METROPOL, Harry Jack. 1333 TAYLOR ST STE 3E 29201 #036-07-1956 L1963 **GS TS** *020 †85,90
METROPOL, Stephen Harry. 1333 TAYLOR ST, STE 3A 29201 #045-01-1985 L1991 **GS** *020 †85
MEYER, Halford Eye, Jr. 2200 HARDEN ST, C. M. TUCKER, JR. NURSING 29203 #422-01-1984 L1991 **IM** *020
MILAS, Monica N. 3209 COLONIAL DR 29203 #020-75-2005, ▲ L2005 **FP** *012
MILES, William L. 2719 MIDDLEBURG DR STE 202 29204 #010-03-1977 L1978 **FM** *020
MILLER, Joseph Henry. 1333 TAYLOR ST # 2-C, STE 3450 29201 #012-05-1956 L1964 **U** *071 †95
MILLER, Mackenzie Lee. 5 MEDICAL PARK RD, ATTN: MEDICAL EDUCATION DE 29203 #055-02-2005 L2005 **PD** *012
MILLER, Mary Kirsten. 610 FAISON DR, MORRIS VILLAGE 29203 #051-01-1981 L2000 **P ADP** *020 †75
MILLER, Michael Shane. ■ 29201 #045-04-2008 *012
MILLER, Scott Duncan. 1706 SAINT JULIAN PL 29204 #025-12-1995 L2002 **D** *020 †15
MILLING, Robert Nicholson. 7901 FARROW RD, WSHPI INPT FORENSICS 29203 #045-01-1958 L1958 **P OS** *071 †75 ‡
MILLUS, Donald Martin. 4311 HARD SCRABBLE RD 29229 #045-04-1999 L2002 **FM** *020 †18 ‡
MILNE, Henry Ludwig, III. 1655 BERNARDIN AVE, STE 100 29204 #045-01-1980 L1984 **OPH** *020 †35
MINARICH, Laurie Annette. 14 MEDICAL PARK RD, STE 400 29203 #038-43-2006 L2006 **PD** *012
MINTZ, Edward G. 100 SUMMIT CENTRE DR 29229 #045-04-1989 L1993 **OPH** *020 †35
MIRTH, Mariachris Antonia. 1730 SAINT JULIAN PL, COLON AND RECTAL SURGEONS 29204 #035-47-1986 L1992 **CRS GS** *020 †85,10
MIRZA, Rukhsana Wajahat. 404 HOGANS RUN 29229 #704-06-1987 L2005 **P** *012
MIRZA, Wajahat A. 404 HOGANS RUN 29229 #704-01-1987 L2000 **P** *020 †75
MISHRA, Manorama. 8301 FARROW RD, MIDLAND CENTER 29203 #495-13-1968 L1983 **GP PD** *020 †55 ‡
MITCHELL, Carl Isaac. 7201 BROOKFIELD RD 29223 #045-01-1974 L1976 **IM GP** *020
MITCHELL, Debra Louise. 6439 GARNERS FERRY RD, DORN VA URGENT CARE CENTER 29209 #045-04-1997 L1998 **IM** *020 †20
MITCHELL, Kenneth B. 4 MEDICAL PARK RD, STE 100 29203 #035-09-1973 L2005 **OPH** *020 †35
MITCHELL, Sonya Diane. 4 MEDICAL PARK RD, STE 301 29203 #047-06-2006 L2007 **OPH** *012
MITTAL, Shalini. 220 FAISON DR, ATTN: MEDICAL STAFF OFFICE 29203 #495-45-1988 L2000 **IMG** *020 †20
MOHIUDDIN, Aziz. 125 ALPINE CIR 29223 #495-21-1978 L1983 **P** *020 †75
MONA, Meredith Lauretta. 4500 STUART ST, FT JACKSON OMH SERVICES 29207 #024-05-1998 L2006 **P** *020 †75
MONROE, Todd Wayne. 2 MEDICAL PARK RD STE 208, DEPT OF OB/GYN 29203 #007-02-2003 L2006 **OBG** *012 †18
MOORE, Edward Eugene. 2 MEDICAL PARK RD, STE 107 29203 #045-01-1974 L1980 **REN GYN** *020 †30
MOORE, Harold Arthur. 1301 TAYLOR ST, COLUMBIA WOMENS 29201 #021-05-1963 L1970 **GYN** *020 †20
MOORE, John Harold. 1301 TAYLOR ST, COLUMBIA WOMENS 29201 #021-01-1989 L1993 **OBG** *020 †30 ‡
MOORE, Kathryn Lohr. 1301 TAYLOR ST, COLUMBIA WOMENS 29201 #020-12-1986 L1991 **OBG** *020 †30

MOORE, Nicholas Kirkby. PO BOX 687 29202 #045-01-1963 L1963 **A IM** *071
MOORE, Thomas Allen, Jr. 4344 BROAD RIVER RD, KIRKLAND 29210 #045-01-1995 L1997 **FM** *020 †18
MOORE-BOWENS, Stacie K. 4540 TRENHOLM RD 29206 #045-04-1995 L1996 **IM** *020 †20
MOORES, Carol Ann. 4500 STUART ST, MONCRIEF ACH 29207 #023-12-1991 L1993 **PHP** *020 †70,18
MORALES, John. TAYLOR & MARION STS 29220 #847-10-1957 L1965 **AN** *071
MORCIGLIO, April Harrell. 3555 HARDEN ST EXT, STE 104A 29203 #045-01-2002 L2004 **P** *012
MORGAN, Harold Clifford. ■ 29204 #012-01-1962 L1967 **P PFP** *020 †75
MORGAN, Jeffrey Demond. 4611 HARD SCRABBLE RD, STE 109 29229 #045-04-1998 L2003 **ORS** *020
MORGAN, Jon Raymond. 1706 SAINT JULIAN PL 29204 #055-01-1967 L1972 **D** *020 †15
MORING, Francine Marie. 1410 BLANDING ST, STE 1 29201 #041-12-1981 L1984 **AN** *020 †05
MORRIS, Douglas Ryan. ■ 29209 #017-20-2003 L2007 **PFP** *012
MORRISON, James Edward. 2 MEDICAL PARK RD, STE 300 29203 #005-19-1990 L2002 **CCS** *020 †85
MORRISON, Sidney Emmett. 1410 BLANDING ST STE 102 29201 #011-03-1981 L1987 **CRS GS** *020 †10,85
MORTHALA, Suneetha R.. 2 MEDICAL PARK RD, STE 502 29203 #308-13-1998 L2006 **IM** *020 †20
MORTON, Glenville Gregory. 5 MEDICAL PARK RD, ATTN: MEDICAL EDUCATION DE 29203 #024-05-2000 L2005 **IM** *012
MOSES, Cheryl Marie. 5 MEDICAL PARK RD, MEDICAL EDUCATION DEPT 29203 #011-03-2005 L2005 **EM** *012
MOSES, Dusty Allen. ■ 29229 #020-12-2005 L2005 **EM** *012
MOSTAFA, Mahmoud Ibrahim. 1301 TAYLOR ST, STE 3L 29201 #915-04-1964 L1977 **OBG** *020 †30
MOURATEV, Gueorgui Lankov. ■ 29209 #198-02-1991 L2003 *020 †20
MOXON, Robert Kerwin. TAYLOR & MARION STS 29220 #041-01-1943 L1963 **IM** *071 †20
MOZINGO, Ellie Bryan. 125 ALPINE CIR 29223 #045-04-1989 L1990 **P** *020
MSIMANGA, Nokuthula Nondu. 3209 COLONIAL DR 29203 #012-01-2004 L2004 **FM** *020 †18
MUBARAK, Philip Fuad. 2113 ADAMS GRV, STE 101 29203 #045-01-1983 L1986 **PD** *020 †55
MURDAUGH, Herschel V, Jr. ■ 29223 #036-07-1950 L1976 **IM** *071 †20
MUSHTAQ, Chaudhry M. 166 STONERIDGE DR 29210 #704-01-1985 L1996 **HO IM** *020 †20
MUTINGA, Nzisa Lynnette. 121 PARK CENTRAL DR 29203 #001-02-1999 L2005 **NEP** *020 †20
NACHTIGAL, Maurice. UN SC SCH MED DEP PATH 29208 #781-01-1957 **ATP MM** *050
NANKIN, Howard Ronald. 2 MEDICAL PARK RD STE 502, DEPT OF INTERNAL MED 29203 #035-15-1961 L1977 **END IM** *020 †20
NARASIMHAN, Kanakasabai L. 2 MEDICAL PARK RD STE 506, PHR - ENDOCRINOLOGY 29203 #495-59-1994 L2007 **END** *012 †20 ‡
NARASIMHAN, Meera. 3555 HARDEN ST EXT, STE 301 29203 #495-49-1991 L1998 **P** *020 †75
NASH, John Raymond. 1301 TAYLOR ST, STE 7B 29201 #045-01-1976 L1980 **OBG** *071 †30
NDIAYE, Fatimah Omar. 1910 GREGG ST 29201 #051-07-1998 L2006 **FM** *020 †18 ‡
NEAL, Christian Demoine. 15 MEDICAL PARK RD, STE 141 29203 #047-07-2006 L2006 **P** *012
NEAL, Green Belton. 3010 FARROW RD, STE 230 29203 #047-07-1971 L1979 **CD IMG** *020
NEGASH, Yohannes. 2435 FOREST DR, MEDICAL STAFF OFFICE 29204 #045-04-1995 L1998 **IM** *020
NEGLIA, William John. 166 STONERIDGE DR 29210 #012-01-1973 L1981 **RO** *020 †80
NELSON, Kenneth Michael. PO BOX 100282, TRICENTURION LLC 29202 #035-01-1960 L1971 **PHP LM** *030
NETTO, Dymphna. 6439 GARNERS FERRY RD, PATHOLOGY & LAB MED (113) 29209 #495-53-1964 L1977 **PTH** *020 †50
NEUBERG, Ronnie W. 7 RICHLAND MEDICAL PARK DR, STE 203 29203 #035-06-1977 L1984 **PHO** *020 †55
NEUFFER, Francis Henry. 120 GATEWAY CORPORATE BLVD 29203 #045-01-1980 L1984 **DR** *020 †80
NEUFFER, Mary Kelly. 1301 TAYLOR ST, COLUMBIA WOMENS 29201 #045-01-1980 L1984 **OBG** *020 †30
NEVILLE, Rufus Lester, Jr. 4344 BROAD RIVER RD, SC DEPARTMENT OF CORRECTIO 29210 #012-01-1965 L1975 **EM** *020
NEWKIRK, John. 1410 BLANDING ST, STE 200 29201 #016-06-1976 L2002 **PS** *020 †65
NEWMAN, Rudolph Mitchell. 100 SUMMIT CENTRE DR 29229 #045-01-1988 L1996 **OPH** *020 †75,35
NEWSOME, Brandi Reynolds. 3 MEDICAL PARK RD, STE 510 29203 #045-04-2003 L2004 **IM** *020 †20
NGO, Thuy Tuong. 1333 TAYLOR ST, STE 1B 29201 #026-04-1988 L1997 **N SME** *020 †75
NICHOLS, Clay Allen. 5 RICHLAND MEDICAL PARK DR 29203 #039-01-1985 L1986 **FOP PTH** *020 †50
NIENHUIS, Michael John. 114 GATEWAY CORPORATE BLVD, STE 330 29203 #045-04-2002 L2004 **FM** *020 †18
NIGGEL, George Michael. ■ 29205 #045-04-1989 L1994 **DR** *020
NILES, Jack Kenneth. ■ 29229 #047-06-1973 L1981 **EM PHP** *020 †16
NORRIS, Thomas Wayne. 2935 COLONIAL DR 29203 #051-01-1986 L1987 **FM** *020 †18
NOTTINGHAM, James Maurice. 2 MEDICAL PARK RD, STE 300 29203 #051-04-1987 L1989 **GS** *020 †85
NOWELL, Maxcy Hook. 5 MEDICAL PARK RD 29203 #045-04-2001 L2002 **EM** *020 †16
NUNNERY, Michael Lee. 76 POLO RD 29223 #045-04-2001 L2003 **FM** *020 †18
NWANAGU, Jonathan Obinna. 1333 TAYLOR ST, STE 3J 29201 #690-04-1988 L1999 **OBG** *020 †18,30
OAKLEY, Susan Holden. 2 MEDICAL PARK RD STE 208 29203 #550-04-2007 L2007 **OBG** *012
OAKMAN, James Howard, Jr. 4 MEDICAL PARK RD, STE 300 29203 #045-04-1991 L1994 **OPH** *020 †35
ODOM, Albert E, Jr. 1301 TAYLOR ST, COLUMBIA WOMENS 29201 #045-01-1983 L1984 **OBG** *020 †30
ODOM, Sara F. 5 RICHLAND MEDICAL PARK DR 29203 #004-01-1993 L1994 **AN** *020 †05
OGBURU-OGBONNAYA, Eleanya. 4801 MAIN ST 29203 #308-07-1983 L1996 **N PMM** *020 ‡
OGUNTOYE, Morohunrant Oku. ■ 29229 #045-04-2008 *012
OHASHI, Yoko. 2 MEDICAL PARK RD STE 208, DEPT OF OB/GYN 29203 #572-36-1994 L2005 **OBG** *100
OKASHA, Issam Asaad. ■ 29223 #915-02-1969 L1981 **IM GE** *020 †20
O'KEEFE, Raymond Eugene. 2241 BUSH RIVER RD 29210 #010-02-1963 L1979 **D** *071 †15
OKEREKE, Nene Nwaobiara N. PO BOX 2266, PALMETTO HLTH ALLIANCE 29202 #690-04-2001 L2004 **IM** *020 †20
OLADIPO, Tiamiyu Jimoh. 5 RICHLAND MEDICAL PARK DR, PALMETTO RICHLAND MEDICAL 29203 #690-05-1994 L2006 **IM** *100 †20
OLEARY, James Allen. 1930 BLANDING ST 29201 #047-05-1993 L2000 **OSM** *020 †40
OLIVER, Barry Durand. 1416 CALHOUN ST, BARRY D OLIVER MD PA 29201 #010-01-1981 L1990 **ORS GS** *020 †40
OLIVER, David Lee. 5 RICHLAND MEDICAL PARK DR 29203 #016-11-1981 L1985 **AN PDS** *020 †05
OLIVER, Eric Tyrell. ■ 29209 #045-04-2008 *012
OLIVER, Hance Hofler. 3209 COLONIAL DR, FAMILY MED CTR 29203 #036-05-2000 L2002 **FM** *020 †18
OLSEN, Gerald Norman. 701 E SPRINGS RD 29208 #027-01-1966 L1981 **PUD** *040 †20
OMOIGUI, Nowamagbe Austin. 114 GATEWAY CORPORATE BLVD 29203 #690-01-1981 L1995 **CD IM** *020 †20
ONUOHA, Jude Okechukwu. 3209 COLONIAL DR 29203 #690-04-1987 L2006 **GPM** *100
ORNELAS, Robert John. 1530 RICHLAND ST 29201 #045-04-2001 L2002 **P** *020 †75
ORTEGA, Rafael De Venecia. 220 FAISON DR, HOSPITAL 29203 #748-01-1957 L1978 **P GP** *071
OSTERMAN, Juraj. 2 MEDICAL PARK RD, STE 502 29203 #957-01-1961 L1979 **END IM** *020 †20
OSTERMAN, Maja. 1135 AUTUMN CIR 29206 #045-04-1993 L1994 **CHP** *020 †75
OSTMEYER, Jeremiah. ■ 29229 #019-02-2006 L2006 **EM** *012
OTTMANN, Shane Erik. 3209 CANNON ST 29205 #028-03-1999 L2005 *020 †85
OWENS, James Cleatus. ■ 29206 #045-01-1964 L1964 **IM** *071
OWENS, William Benjamin. 2 MEDICAL PARK RD, STE 502 29203 #045-04-2000 L2004 **CCA** *020 †16
OZIMEK, Thaddeus Paul. 4500 STUART ST, MONCRIEF ARMY COMMUNITY HO 29207 #041-13-1979 L1982 **P** *020 †75
PABON ROMERO, Diego Ferna. 2 MEDICAL PARK RD STE 402 29203 #264-09-2002 L2005 **GS** *012
PACHECO, Jimmy. 220 FAISON DR 29203 #042-02-1984 L1991 **P** *020 †75
PAI, M Sharada. 3301 HARDEN STREET EXT, RICHLAND MEM HOSPITAL 29203 #495-21-1970 L1981 **NPM** *020 †55
PAINTER, Lauren Jones. 9 RICHLAND MEDICAL PARK, STE 620 29203 #045-04-1998 L1999 **OBG** *020 †30
PAINTER, William Bradley. 3250 HARDEN ST EXT, STE 100 29203 #045-04-1998 L1999 **PD** *020 †55
PAKALNIS, Vytautas A. 4 MEDICAL PARK RD, STE 100 29203 #038-40-1976 L1987 **OPH DIA** *020 †35
PALISIN, Tenley Erin. 5 MEDICAL PARK RD, MEDICAL EDUCATION DEPT 29203 #045-04-2005 L2005 **FP** *012
PARKER, Harris Hartwell. 1850 LAUREL ST, SURGICAL ASSOCIATES OF SOU 29201 #045-04-1998 L1999 **GS** *020 †85
PARKER, Reginald Lionel. 3000 NE MEDICAL PARK, STE 101 29223 #047-07-1982 L1990 **FM EM** *020 †18
PARKS, William B, III. 1410 BLANDING ST, STE 1 29201 #036-08-1990 L1991 **AN** *020 †05
PARRISH, John C, III. ■ 29223 #047-06-1976 L1979 **IM** *020 †20
PARRISH, Mary Mielke. 2725 KNIGHTBRIDGE RD 29223 #047-06-1975 L1979 **PD** *020 †55
PARROTT, John Talley. 1930 BLANDING ST 29201 #045-01-1979 L1979 **ORS** *020 †40
PARSONS, Cara Marie. 2113 ADAMS GRV, STE 101 29203 #055-01-2001 L2003 **PD** *020 †55
PARSONS, Scott Gary. 2113 ADAMS GRV, STE 101 29203 #035-08-1997 L2002 **PD** *020 †55
PASICATAN, Alfonso A. 220 FAISON DR, GW BRYAN PSYCHIATRIC HOSPI 29203 #748-07-1965 L2003 **P** *020
PASICATAN, Susana Tayan. 220 FAISON DR 29203 #748-10-1968 L1981 **P** *020 †75
PASSER, Darin Lee. ■ 29229 #045-04-2004 L2004 **GS** *012
PASZKIEWICZ, Elisabeth J. 6439 GARNERS FERRY RD, VETERANS ADMIN MEDICAL CEN 29209 #048-02-1993 L2000 **GS** *020 †95
PATEL, Dilipkumar C. 1409 DEVINE ST, THOMSON STUDENT HLTH CTR 29208 #539-06-1979 L1982 **FM** *020 †18
PATEL, Jaiprakash N. 21 GATEWAY CORNERS PARK, STE 101 29203 #045-04-1991 L1993 **CD** *020
PATEL, Nitin Amrat. 2 MEDICAL PARK RD, STE 502 29203 #045-01-2002 L2004 **IM** *020
PATEL, Radhika Dilip. 1819 MARSHALL ST 29203 #495-76-1981 L1987 **P** *020 †75
PATEL, Rima Pravin. ■ 29209 #045-04-2008 *012
PATEL, Vallabh Oghadbhai. 2200 HARDEN ST 29203 #495-39-1966 L1982 **GP** *020
PATHAK, Nirav Rameshchand. 3 RICHLAND MEDCL PARK #510, HIM HOSPITAL INT MED 29203 #495-23-1995 L2004 **IMG** *020 †18
PAYSINGER, Benjamin D, Jr. 2750 LAUREL ST STE 203 29204 #045-04-1982 L1987 **OTO** *020 †45
PAYSINGER, Benjamin Danl. ■ 29206 #045-01-1956 L1956 **NS** *071 †25
PAYTON, Terry A. 610 FAISON DR 29203 #012-01-1984 L1985 **FM ADM** *020 †18
PEACOCK, Edgardo Alberto. 2750 LAUREL ST STE 220 29204 #132-09-1972 L1977 **GS** *075
PEEBLES, Charles H, Jr. 2601 LAUREL ST STE 110 29204 #045-01-1951 L1951 **OPH** *071 †35
PEELE, Robert Mc Nair, Jr. 1930 BLANDING ST 29201 #036-05-1976 L1977 **ORS OSM** *020 †40
PELTZ, Eric Stephen. 14 RICHLAND MEDICAL PARK, STE 400 29203 #011-04-2004 L2004 **PD** *020 †55
PENDER, Jennifer Denise. 315 LONG POINTE LN 29229 #036-01-2003 L2004 **CHP** *012
PEREZ, Romeo P. 4500 STUART ST, MONCRIEF ARMY COMMUNITY HO 29207 #748-08-1969 L1978 **OBG** *020 †30
PERKINS, Linda Ann. 2 MEDICAL PARK RD, STE 502 29203 #048-02-2000 L2007 **PCC** *020
PETER, Donny Mathew. 5 MEDICAL PARK RD, MEDICAL EDUCATION DEPT 29203 #039-01-2005 L2005 **IM** *012
PETERSON, Alan Chas, Jr. 1750 LAUREL ST STE 1 29201 #308-11-1986 L1993 **IM** *020 †20
PETIT, Charles David. 3010 FARROW RD STE 300, CAROLINA MEDICAL PLAZA 29203 #055-01-1978 L1987 **FM FPG** *020 †18
PETIT, Scott James. 8 RICHLAND MEDICAL PARK, STE 400 29203 #021-05-1993 L2001 **TS VS** *020 †85,90
PHILBECK, Mary Catharine. 2435 FOREST DR 29204 #045-01-1992 L1996 **EM** *020 †16,55
PHILLIPS, Charles Daniel. 5 RICHLAND MEDICAL PARK DR 29203 #045-04-2001 L2005 **AN** *020
PHILLIPS, James William. 1 RICHLAND MEDICAL PARK DR, STE 420 29203 #045-04-1995 L2003 **IC CD** *020 †20
PHILLIPS, John Henry, Jr. 2 MEDICAL PARK RD STE 404 29203 #048-04-2002 L2004 **ORS** *020
PIEHL, Frederick Chas. 1930 BLANDING ST 29201 #045-04-1986 L1987 **ORS OP** *020 †40
PILLINGER, Carole Lowman. 6439 GARNERS FERRY RD, DORN VA MED CTR #141 29209 #045-01-1981 L1982 **PTH** *040 †50
PILLINGER, David Arthur, Jr. ■ 29223 #045-04-2007 **IM** *012
PINEDA, Jacqueline Y. 6439 GARNERS FERRY RD, PRIMARY CARE & SUSPECIALTY 29209 #935-03-1990 L2004 **IM** *020 †20
PIRICH, Laura Elizabeth. 4 MEDICAL PARK RD, STE 301 29203 #004-01-1992 L2004 **PHO** *020 †55
PITALIA, Amit Ramniklal. ■ 29223 #495-23-1994 L2002 **FM** *020 †18
PITTS, James Wm. 206 LAURIE ST STE 230 29204 #045-01-1973 L1980 **A IM** *020 †20,03

8296

■ = Address Information Privacy Protected

PLANTE, Paul Albert. 21 GATEWAY CORNERS PARK, STE 101 29203 #045-04-1990 L1991 IM *020 †20

PLATT, Tan Jackson. 3209 COLONIAL DR 29203 #035-01-1973 L1985 FM *020 †18

PLYLER, Joseph Aaron. ■ 29204 #045-01-1954 L1954 FM *071 †18

POILETMAN, Robert Michael. 7901 FARROW RD, HALL PSYCHIATRIC INSTITUTE 29203 #041-13-1975 L1982 IMG P *030 †75

POLLOCK, Ralph Chadwick. 3555 HARDEN ST EXT, STE 104A 29203 #045-04-2005 L2005 P *012

POPP, John Wm, Jr. 2739 LAUREL ST, STE 1A 29204 #008-01-1973 L1979 GE IM *020 †20

PORTER, Ronald Cole. 15 RICHLAND MEDICAL PARK, RICHLAND MEMORIAL HOSPITAL 29203 #001-02-1974 L1978 PD *040 †55

POSTIC, Bosko. 2 MEDICAL PARK RD STE 502 29203 #957-01-1955 L1979 ID IM *071 †20

POSTIC, Georges Thomas. 2739 LAUREL ST, STE 1A 29204 #045-04-1996 L1999 IM *020 †20

POSTLES, David Harry. 1333 TAYLOR ST, STE 2D 29201 #035-15-1968 L1974 OBG *020 †30

POSTON, Mary Elizabeth. 1801 SUNSET DR 29203 #045-04-1999 L2000 IM *020 †20

POTTER, Henry Gilbert. 2000 HAMPTON ST, SCDHEC REG 3 29204 #025-12-1980 L2003 PHP MDM *030 †70

POWELL, Caroline Keller. 2 MEDICAL PARK RD, STE 502 29203 #045-04-2001 L2004 IM *050

POWELL, Donald Langston. 2435 FOREST DR, PROVIDENCE HOSPITAL 29204 #045-04-1987 L1988 EM *020

POWELL, Thomas Brian. 121 PARK CENTRAL DR, STE 200 29203 #045-04-2001 L2004 NEP *020

POWERS, Heather M. 5 MEDICAL PARK RD, PALMETTO HEALTH RICHLAND 29203 #036-05-2000 L2004 IM *020 †20

PRABHU, Prakash N. 121 PARK CENTRAL DR, # 200 29203 #495-96-1988 L1999 NEP *020 †20

PRABHU, Satish Manjeshwar. 1410 BLANDING ST STE 1 29201 #495-72-1974 L1979 AN *020 †05 ‡

PRABHU, Vijayas. ■ 29223 #495-35-1974 L1979 PD *020 †55

PRADO, Maria Del Pilar. 3209 COLONIAL DR, PRMH - FAMILY PRACTICE 29203 #264-06-1998 L2004 FM *020 †18

PRASHAD, Jairaj. 1444 BARNWELL ST # B 29201 #010-03-1972 L1979 IM PUD *020 †20

PREWETTE, Ervin Delmar, II. 610 FAISON DR, MORRIS VILLAGE ALC & DRUG 29203 #045-04-2001 L2003 P CHP *020 †75

PRICKETT, Fuller M, III. 1410 BLANDING ST STE 1 29201 #045-01-1994 L1997 AN *020 †05

PRIDGEN, Cynthia Marie. 1228 HARDEN ST, WAVERLY WOMEN'S HEALTHCARE 29204 #038-41-1996 L2001 OBG *020

PRIDGEN, Kaoru Joan. 11 GATEWAY CORNERS PARK P 29203 #305-01-2001 L2004 FM *020 †20

PRIER, Ronald Eugene. 3555 HARDEN STREET EXT, STE 301 29203 #005-06-1976 L1990 P GPM *040 †70,75

PRIVETTE, Troy Williamson. 5 RICHLAND MEDICAL PARK, DEPT OF EMERGENCY MEDICINE 29203 #045-04-1994 L1995 EM *020 †16

PROPST, Charles Robt. 4 MEDICAL PARK RD, STE 301 29203 #045-01-1948 L1948 PD *040 †55

PROSSER, Leverne Marvin. 1 RICHLAND MEDICAL PARK DR, STE 420 29203 #045-04-1996 L1997 IC *020

PRYOR, Wm Watkins, Jr. 6439 GARNERS FERRY RD, DEPARTMENT OF ANESTHESIOLO 29209 #036-07-1981 L1982 AN IM *071 †20,05

PUGH, Kristopher Ra. 4 MEDICAL PARK RD STE 300 29203 #017-20-2003 L2004 OPH *020

PUJARA, Priya Subhash. ■ 29223 #045-01-2007 L2007 MPD *012

PUROHIT, Anil. ■ 29210 #045-01-2007 *012

PUSEY, Frank Olin, Jr. 9 RICHLAND MEDICAL PARK, STE 450 29203 #045-01-1985 L1987 N *020 †75

PYE, Wesley Tanner. 2 MEDICAL PARK RD, STE 506 29203 #045-01-2007 L2007 IM *012

QUALIO, Angie Lea. 3 MEDICAL PARK RD, STE 350 29203 #018-75-2006, ▲ L2006 EM *012

QUAN, Long Thang. 1706 SAINT JULIAN PL, CAROLINAS DERMATOLOGY 29204 #036-07-1996 L2001 D *020 †15

QUINN, John Francis. 90 COWDRAY RD 29223 #035-15-1980 L1983 AN *020 †05

RABIN, Samuel Shane. 2 MEDICAL PARK RD, STE 208 29203 #012-01-2006 L2006 OBG *012

RACHARLA, Sushma. 2435 FOREST DR, PROVIDENCE HOSPITAL MED OF 29204 #495-62-2000 L2006 IM *020

RAHMAN, Ifad Ur. 5 RICHLAND MEDICAL PARK 29203 #308-06-2002 L2007 IM *012

RAHMAN, Saeed Ur. 2001 LAUREL ST STE 5A 29204 #704-21-1988 L1996 PHP *020 †70

RAJU, Pusapati S J. ■ 29223 #495-58-1966 L1975 AN *071

RALEY, Jesse Andrew. 3555 HARDEN ST EXT, STE 104A 29203 #020-12-2005 L2005 P *012

RAMASAMY, Poornema. 2 MEDICAL PARK RD STE 506 29203 #495-59-1999 L2005 IM *012

RAMSEY, Bonnie Jeanne. 3555 HARDEN ST EXT, STE 104A 29203 #045-04-1981 L1982 CHP *020 †75

RAMSEY, Laura Christine. ■ 29205 #007-02-1992 L1994 PD *020 †55

RANDLE, Nikki Anne. ■ 29209 #045-04-2008 *012

RANDOLPH, Lilly. 2719 MIDDLEBURG DR, STE 103 29204 #028-02-1982 L1992 EM IM *020 †20

RAO, Promila Bhatty. 3 RICHLAND MEDICAL PARK, STE 510 29203 #495-08-1996 L2003 IM *020

RAO, Raviprasad Govinda. 3 RICHLAND MEDICAL PARK, STE 400 29203 #495-23-1990 L2004 NPM *100 †55

RAO, Subba M. 2800 BUSH RIVER RD, STE 5 29210 #495-65-1984 L2003 P *020

RATHLE, Jacques Michel. 26 OFFICE PARK CT, MENTAL HEALTH CENTER 29223 #330-04-1959 L1980 P *071

RAVENELL, Dianna Deniece. 4605 MONTICELLO RD, EAU CLAIRE COOP. HLTH CTRS 29203 #047-07-2001 L2005 OBG *020

RAVENELL, Orson Alphonso. ■ 29229 #045-01-2000 L2004 OBG *020 †30 ‡

RAWL, Dana Anthony. 114 GATEWAY CORPORATE BLVD, STE 430 29203 #045-01-1982 L1983 OM AM *070

RAWL, John Callison. 1301 TAYLOR ST, STE 1A 29201 #036-07-1971 L1977 U *020 †95

RAWLINSON, Monica Nicole. 3209 COLONIAL DR, FAMILY PRACTICE 29203 #028-34-2004 L2004 FM *020

RAY, Donna D. 3010 FARROW RD, STE 300 29203 #045-04-1994 L1995 IMG *040 †20

RAYBOURNE, Susan Roberta. 6439 GARNERS FERRY RD, DORN VAMC 111 29209 #012-01-1980 L1985 N CHN *020 †20

RAYMOND, James Irving. 3301 HARDEN STREET EXT 29203 #041-12-1974 L1976 EM IM *020 †20,16

RAYNAL, Holbrook Wyman. 5 RICHLAND MEDICAL PARK 29203 #045-01-1977 L1978 FM FPG *020 †18

RAYNOR, Jeffrey Donald. 220 FAISON DR, G-H STAFF CENTER 29208 #045-04-2002 L2007 P PFP *100

RAZA, Muhammad A. 2 MEDICAL PARK RD 29203 #704-21-1996 L2005 PCC *020 †20

REDDY, Bhagyalakshmi M. ■ 29223 #495-72-1974 L1980 PM *020 †60

REDDY, Pingle Prithvi. 1 MEDICAL PARK RD, STE 230 29203 #495-09-1966 L1981 PDS *020 †85

REDDY, Srinivasa Reddy. 7901 FARROW RD 29203 #495-50-1989 L2008 P *020 †75

REDMOND, Michael David. 1930 BLANDING ST 29201 #012-01-1980 L1989 PM N *020 †60

REED, Julie Anne. 1333 TAYLOR ST, STE 5F 29201 #045-01-1999 L2003 OBG *020 †30

REED, Michael Elmo. 2 MEDICAL PARK RD, STE 203 29203 #045-01-1975 L1976 FM OM *020 †18

REED, Stanmore Edward. 1333 TAYLOR ST STE 5F 29201 #045-01-1964 L1964 OBG *071 †30

REEVES, Jeremy Mark. 2 MEDICAL PARK RD STE 402 29203 #305-01-2005 L2005 GS *012

REID, Albert Lee. 301 WILKES RD 29203 #047-07-1963 L1963 GS *020

REID, Rodney Rene. 6439 GARNERS FERRY RD, DORN VA MED CENTER 29209 #047-05-1987 L1990 IM *020 †20

REID, Tanya Elaine. 114 GATEWAY CORPORATE BLVD, STE 320 29203 #047-07-1988 L1992 AI PD *020

REIGHT, Ian Gregory. ■ 29223 #308-13-2002 L2004 CCS *100

REMKE CLARY, Kristin L. 15 MEDICAL PARK RD, STE 141 29203 #016-76-2007, ▲ L2007 *012

RENTON, David Benjamin. 2 MEDICAL PARK RD, STE 300 29203 #021-05-2001 L2007 GS *020 †85

RESTREPO, Christopher Gar. ■ 29203 #045-04-2007 L2007 PD *012

REYNOLDS, James Calvert. 1318 WESTMINSTER DR 29204 #045-01-1968 L1968 PTH *071 †50

REYNOLDS, Rembert Neal. 1725 DEVONSHIRE DR 29204 #036-05-1972 L1979 GS *020 †85

RHAME, Ellen Elizabeth. 2 MEDICAL PARK RD, STE 506 29203 #045-04-2006 L2006 AN *012

RHINEHART, Rodney Glenn. 8 RICHLAND MEDICAL PARK, STE 300 29203 #045-04-1991 L1992 CD *020 †20

RHODES, Audrey B. 2200 HARDEN ST 29203 #038-43-1980 FM *020 †18

RHUE, Melanie Kaye. ■ 29203 #045-01-2003 L2006 PG *012 †55

RIBER, Ezra B. 2601 LAUREL ST, STE 130 29204 #055-02-1984 L1988 PME IM *020 †05 ‡

RICE, Carryn Nacia. 14 MEDICAL PARK RD 29203 #041-12-2006 L2006 PD *012

RICE, Joseph Sherrard, Jr. 2739 LAUREL ST, STE 1A 29204 #045-01-1971 L1984 GE IM *020 †20

RICH, J Smythe. 1711 RICHLAND ST 29201 #045-01-1984 L1990 FPS OTO *020 †45 ‡

RICHARDS, Frederick Lee. 1410 BLANDING ST, STE 1 29201 #045-04-1988 L1990 AN *020 †05

RICHARDS, Judith Ashley. 2 MEDICAL PARK RD, SUITE 29203 #012-01-2007 L2007 *012

RICHARDSON, Irene Ina. 3010 FARROW RD 29203 #010-03-1985 L1989 IM *020 †20

RICHARDSON, William H, III. 3 MEDICAL PARK RD STE 350 29203 #045-01-1999 L2000 EM ETX *020 †16

RICHESON, Nancy Anne. 1801 SUNSET DR 29203 #051-04-1980 L1981 IM *040 †20

RICHMOND, Gerald Edmund. ■ 29206 #045-01-1965 L1965 R GP *020 †80

RICKENMANN, Laura Herlong. 1749 MARSHALL ST, SANDHILLS PEDIATRICS 29203 #045-04-1999 L2000 PD *020 †55

RIDDLE, James Frank. 2015 MARION ST 29201 #045-04-1986 L1987 P *020 †75

RIDLEY, Stephen F. 4026 CLAREMONT DR, 5 RICHLAND MEDICAL PARK 29205 #045-04-2001 L2002 EM *020 †16

RIKARD, Erin Tiffany. ■ 29204 #045-04-2008 *012

RILEY, Courtney Marie. ■ 29209 #045-04-2008 †012

RISINGER, Jennifer M. 9 RICHLAND MEDICAL PARK, STE 620 29203 #016-11-1993 L2000 OBG *020 †30

RISINGER, Sharon Ann. 5900 GARNERS FERRY RD, SOUTH HAMPTON FAMILY PRACT 29209 #045-01-1985 L1986 FM *020 †18

RIVERS, Cedric Marcel. 223 TURTLE CREEK DR, PRMH 29229 #045-04-2003 L2004 IM *020 †20

RIZVI, Ali Abbas. 2 MEDICAL PARK RD, STE 502 29203 #704-01-1986 L2003 END IM *020 †20

ROBERTS, Carla West. 5 RICHLAND MEDICAL PARK 29203 #045-01-1995 L2001 PHO PD *020 †55

ROBERTS, Michael Clark. 2601 LAUREL ST, STE 260 29204 #045-01-1986 L1987 CD *020 †20

ROBERTSON, Alan Grant. 6439 GARNERS FERRY RD, MCH BLDG #106 29209 #036-05-1971 L1971 P *020 †75

ROBERTSON, Tracy Ellen. 1801 SUNSET DR 29203 #056-05-1986 L1993 IM *020 †20

ROBINSON, Howard James. 1333 TAYLOR ST STE 5 29201 #016-42-1974 L1978 D *020 †15

ROBINSON, Jerry Wayne. 2750 LAUREL ST, STE 303 29204 #045-01-1983 L1985 IM EM *020 †20

ROBINSON, John Galt. 3 MEDICAL PARK RD, STE 350 29203 #047-20-2003 L2004 EM *100 †16

ROBINSON, William Koonce. 3000 NE MEDICAL PARK, STE 108 29223 #021-05-1975 L1978 IM *020 †20

RODRIGUEZ CARABALLO, J E. ■ 29229 #847-02-1973 L1977 EM *020

RODWELL, David Watson, III. ■ 29209 #045-04-2008 *012

ROJAS, Michelle D. 1333 TAYLOR ST 29201 #010-03-1981 L1985 FM *020 †18

ROLLINS, Kristen Haley. ■ 29209 #045-04-2007 L2007 PD *012

ROOT, Jennifer Roxane. 5 RICHLAND MEDICAL PARK DR 29203 #001-02-1993 L1997 AN *020 †05

ROSA, Olga C. 4 MEDICAL PARK RD, STE 203 29203 #042-01-1986 L2004 PD OS *030 †55

ROSANSKY, Rachel Beth. ■ 29206 #045-01-2008 †012

ROSANSKY, Steven Jay. VET ADMIN HOSP, DEPT NEP 29209 #035-06-1972 L1979 NEP IM *020 †20

ROSEFF, Susan D. 2751 BULL ST, AMERICAN RED CROSS 29201 #035-03-1986 L1998 BBK *062 †50

ROSS, Hasell G. ■ 29206 #045-01-1944 L1944 IM *071 †20

ROSS, William Aaron. 5 MEDICAL PARK RD, MEDICAL EDUCATION DEPT 29203 #010-03-2003 L2005 GS *012

ROSSMAN, Rachael. 6439 GARNERS FERRY RD, WJB DORN VAMC 29209 #018-03-1991 L1998 CHP P *020 †75

ROUHANI, Gloria. 5 MEDICAL PARK RD, ATTN: MEDICAL EDUCATION 29203 #305-01-2004 L2005 OBG *012

ROWLAND, Thomas Clifford. 1301 TAYLOR ST, STE 2L 29201 #045-01-1959 L1959 OBG *071 †30

RUDD, Kimberly Butterfly. 3555 HARDEN ST EXT, STE 104A 29203 #045-04-2003 L2004 PYG *012

RUDERMAN, Ann Elizabeth. 6439 GARNERS FERRY RD, DORN VAMC III 29209 #023-01-1974 L1979 IM ID *020 †20

RUPP, Robert H. ■ 29206 #025-07-1943 L1978 OPH *071 †35

RUTH, Erika Jaclyn. 2 MEDICAL PARK RD, STE 402 29203 #045-04-2007 L2007 GS *012

RYAN, Susan B. 2100 BULL ST, WILSON BUILDING 29201 #045-04-1983 L1985 PD *020 †55

SAENZ, Alberto. 6439 GARNERS FERRY RD, B.DORN VETERANS ADMIN. HOS 29209 #737-06-1970 L1974 CD IM *020 †20

SAKARCAN, Abdullah. 9 MEDICAL PARK RD, STE 270 29203 #902-07-1985 L2000 PN *020 †55

SALLEY, Julian A. 1333 TAYLOR ST, STE 2D 29201 #045-01-1953 L1953 OBG *020 †30

SALLEY, Mark Hedrick. 1301 TAYLOR ST, STE 2D 29201 #045-01-1985 L1989 OBG *020 †30 ‡

SALVADOR, Anastacio T. ■ 29209 #748-10-1967 L1980 **AN** *020

SAMMONS, Hubert Douglas. 1330 TAYLOR ST 29220 #001-02-1982 L1983 **EM** *020 †16

SAMPSON, Donald Ray. 101 FIREBRIDGE RD, SOUTH CAROLINA DEPT OF COR 29223 #047-07-1980 L1983 **IM** *020

SANDRAPATY, Kiran Kumar. 3106 DEVINE ST, MIDLANDS HEALTH CENTER 29205 #422-01-2002 L2006 **PM** *020

SARMIENTO, Remedios M. 7901 FARROW RD 29203 #748-07-1958 L1975 *075 **CD IM** *071 †20

SAUNDERS, Donald E, Jr. 3555 HARDEN STREET EXT 29203 #036-07-1955 L1955 **CD IM** *071 †20

SAUNDERS, Kirby Lamont. 5 RICHLAND MEDICAL PARK, RICHLAND MEMORIAL HOSPITAL 29203 #036-01-1995 L1998 **IMG** *020

SAVAGE-JETER, Erica Lache. 3209 COLONIAL DR, P H R - DEPT OF FAMILY PRA 29203 #045-04-2006 L2006 **FP** *012

SAVOCA, William John. 1310 TAYLOR ST, BAPTIST MED CTR RADIO DEPT 29220 #045-01-1988 L1989 **DR** *020 †80

SCARDO, James Allen. 2 MEDICAL PARK RD, STE 107 29203 #036-08-1989 L1990 **OBG** *020 †30

SCHAEFER, Catherine Ann. 1606 HORSESHOE DR, LONGCREEK FAMILY PRACTICE 29223 #045-04-1994 L1994 **FM** *020 †18

SCHENCK, John Bennett. 2 MEDICAL PARK RD STE 502, USC DEPT OF MEDICINE 29203 #045-04-1999 L2001 **END** *020 †20

SCHLAEFER, Edward M, Jr. 5 RICHLAND MEDICAL PARK 29203 #045-01-1950 L1950 **GP** *071

SCHMIDT, Caitlin Georgia. 1301 TAYLOR ST, STE 3L 29201 #036-05-1996 L2000 **OBG** *020 †30

SCHNACKENBERG, Robert C. 1333 TAYLOR ST, STE 4H 29201 #025-01-1961 L1969 **P CHP** †75

SCHULZE, Robert A, Jr. 1 RICHLAND MEDICAL PARK DR, STE 420 29203 #035-01-1971 L1976 **CD** *020 †20

SCHWARTZ, I David. 9 MEDICAL PARK RD, SUITE 230, UNIVER. PEDS. 29203 #028-46-1984 L2000 **PDE PD** *020 †55

SCHWARTZ-WATTS, Donna M. 5 RICHLAND MEDICAL PARK 29203 #045-04-1989 L1993 **PFP P** †062 †75

SCHWARZ, Ferdinand. 1655 BERNARDIN AVE, STE 100 29204 #033-05-1970 L1975 **OPH OS** *071

SCHWARZ, Fred S. 1655 BERNARDIN AVE, STE 100 29204 #035-06-1946 L1947 **GS** *071 †85

SCOTECE, Maria Michelle. ■ 29210 #045-01-2002 L2002 **IM** *100 †20

SCOTT, Thos Bradford, Jr. 7901 FARROW RD 29203 #045-01-1976 L1977 **P FM** *020 †18

SEBASTIAN, Praxedes S. 21 OLD STILL RD, GARNERS FERRY RD 29223 #748-01-1963 L1976 **P** *020 †75

SEGAL, Stephen Dean. 1800 COLONIAL DR, W. S. HALL PSYCHIATRIC INS 29203 #305-01-1995 L1997 **P** *020

SELLERS, Nosizwe Abidemi. 6439 GARNERS FERRY RD, DORN VA HOSPITAL 29209 #045-01-1998 L1999 **IM** *020

SELLORS, William Henry. ■ 29206 #041-12-1948 L1949 **DR** *071

SELPH, James Felder, III. 3555 HARDEN ST EXT 29203 #011-04-2002 L2007 **N CN** *020

SERBIN, Stephen Fredric. 813 LEESBURG RD 29209 #041-14-1976 L1977 **FM OM** *020 †18 ‡

SETZER, Edward Hugh. ■ 29223 #012-01-1963 L1963 **IM** *020 †20

SEXTON, Gregory Alan. 1708 LAUREL ST 29201 #020-12-1982 L1983 **PS** *020 †65

SHAH, Gopi Yogesh. 8 RICHLAND MEDICAL PARK DR, STE 300 29203 #045-04-1996 L1998 **IC** *020 †20

SHAH, Pareshchandra P. 5 MEDICAL PARK RD, DPT RADIOLOGY 29203 #495-23-1970 L1976 **R** *020 †80

SHAH, Payal Naimesh. ■ 29209 #045-04-2008 *012

SHAH, Purnima Shashikant. 6439 GARNERS FERRY RD, PRIMARY CARE SERVICE 29209 #495-76-1976 L1998 **IM** *020 †20

SHANNON, Samuel Rudolph. 2750 LAUREL ST STE 103 29204 #045-01-1959 L1959 **FM** *071 †18

SHARMA, Poornima. ■ 29209 #496-07-1995 L2000 **HO** *020 †20

SHAVER, Timothy Scott. 4605 MONTICELLO RD, EAU CLAIRE COOPERATIVE 29203 #045-04-1999 L2002 **FM** *020 †18

SHEALY, Carl Brent. 121 PARK CENTRAL DR 29203 #045-01-1997 L2003 **NEP** *020 †20

SHEIKH, Asif M Ahmed. 1910 BLANDING ST 29201 #704-02-1966 L1976 **ORS HS** *020 †40

SHELBURG, Jack Le Roy. 1233 WASHINGTON ST, STE 500 29201 #051-04-1962 L1963 **FM GP** *071 †18

SHELDON, Martin Randolph. 3 RICHLAND MEDICAL PARK, STE 510 29203 #045-04-2000 L2001 **IM** *020

SHELTON, Leslie Woodson. 4 MEDICAL PARK RD, STE 301 29203 #027-01-1961 L1975 **PDC PD** *020 †55

SHELTON, Stephen Lee. 5 RICHLAND MEDICAL PARK DR 29203 #036-08-1991 L1992 **EM** *020 †16

SHENOY, Narayan Renjal. 1410 BLANDING ST STE 1 29201 #495-17-1968 L1976 **AN** *020 †05

SHENOY, Naren Surendra. 5 MEDICAL PARK RD, MEDICAL EDUCATION DEPT 29203 #045-01-2005 L2005 **PD** *012

SHEPPE, Joseph Andrew. 1333 TAYLOR ST STE 4A 29201 #055-01-1979 L1985 **CRS GS** *020 †10,85

SHERIDAN, David Paul. ALPINE RD AT I-20, BCBS SOUTH CAROLINA 29219 #018-03-1976 L1988 **GPM PHP** *020 †70

SHISSIAS, Charles George. 1333 TAYLOR ST, STE 1C 29201 #045-01-1994 L2000 **P PS** *020

SHLAPACK, Matthew Andrew. 5 RICHLAND MEDICAL PARK DR 29203 #305-01-2006 L2006 **IM** *012

SHMUNES, Edward. ■ 29206 #011-03-1965 L1974 **D OM** *071 †15

SHOEMAKER, Daniel Adam. ■ 29209 #041-02-1999 L2001 **PD** *020

SHROUDS, Richard Dickson. 74 POLO RD 29223 #045-01-1998 L2002 **PD** *020 †55

SHULER, Claudius Osborne. 1 RICHLAND MEDICAL PARK, STE 410 29203 #045-01-1988 L1989 **PD PDC** *020 †55

SHULER, Megan Dupree. 14 RICHLAND MEDICAL PARK, STE 400 29203 #045-04-2006 L2006 **PD** *012

SIAZON, Pedro Lizano. 309 SHALLOW BROOK DR, SERVICES 29223 #748-01-1956 L2004 **P EM** *020

SIDDIQUI, Saima K. ■ 29223 #704-02-1994 L2003 **GE** *020 †20 ‡

SIEGEL, Lawrence Kenneth. 4 MEDICAL PARK RD, STE 301 29203 #035-03-1968 L1997 **PD OS** *020 †55

SIEVERDES, Kara Amanda. ■ 29229 #045-04-2007 L2007 **P** *012

SILBIGER, Adam Michael. PO BOX 29202 #654-01-2006 L2006 **IM** *012

SILVESTER, Thomas Danl. 1519 MARION ST 29201 #045-01-1990 L1995 **DR** *020 †80

SIMMONS, John R. ■ 29206 #024-05-1950 L1982 **OS OPH** *071 †35

SIMMONS, Tillmon Lee. 2712 MIDDLEBURG DR, CHILD/ADOLESCENT SERVICES 29204 #038-40-1967 L1978 **CHP** *020

SIMONS, Beverly Yvonne. 110 ATRIUM WAY 29223 #012-05-1983 L1987 **FM** *020 †18

SIMPSON, Daniel Gabe. 15 RICHLAND MEDICAL PARK, HOSPITAL DEPT OF MED EDUCA 29203 #045-04-2000 L2001 **EM** *020 †16

SINGH, Archana. ■ 29209 #045-04-2008 *012

SINGH, Harpreet Kaur. 6439 GARNERS FERRY RD 29209 #021-06-1996 L2000 **IM** *020 †20

SKINNER, Hasel Andrews. ■ 29210 #045-01-1950 L1950 **GP** *071

SKINNER, Margaret C S. ■ 29209 #012-05-1962 L1962 **PTH** *071 †50

SKUFCA, Dan W. 5 RICHLAND MEDICAL PARK, ATTN: MEDICAL EDUCATION 29203 #020-12-2004 L2004 **OPH** *012

SLOAN, Charles R. 1750 LAUREL ST, STE 1 29201 #045-01-1948 L1948 **GS GRS** *071

SLOCUM, Richard C. TAYLOR & MARION STS 29220 #035-20-1944 L1953 **U** *071 †95

SMITH, Brian Andrew. 6439 GARNERS FERRY RD, WJB DORN VAMC 29209 #012-05-1976 L1978 **IM PUD** *020 †20

SMITH, Claude Wilson, Jr. 2750 LAUREL ST, STE 305 29204 #045-01-1967 L1975 **TS GS** *020 †85,90

SMITH, David Lee. 76 POLO RD, LEXINGTON FAMILY PRACTICE 29223 #045-04-1997 L1998 **FM** *020 †18

SMITH, Frederic Al. 2750 LAUREL ST, STE 303 29204 #045-04-1992 L1993 **IM** *020 †20

SMITH, Irving Russell, Jr. 1701 SAINT JULIAN PL, STE 201 29204 #010-03-1976 L1980 **OBG** *020 †30

SMITH, Jack Monroe. 114 GATEWAY CORPORATE BLVD, STE 420 29203 #045-01-1961 L1961 **NS** *071 †25

SMITH, Katherine Leigh. ■ 29210 #012-01-2008 *012

SMITH, Kristin Lynn. ■ 29203 #055-02-2007 L2007 **P** *012

SMITH, Larry Click, II. 2113 ADAMS GRV 29203 #055-02-1993 L1996 **PD** *020

SMITH, Lenwood P, Jr. 2 MEDICAL PARK RD, STE 300 29203 #036-05-1982 L1991 **NS NSP** *020 †25

SMITH, Marlo Monique. 47 CATESBY CIR, PEDIATRICS ASSOCIATES 29206 #045-01-1994 L1998 **PD** *020 †55

SMITH, Robert Ernest. 166 STONERIDGE DR 29210 #051-01-1973 L1978 **ON IM** *020 †20

SMITH, Sarah E. 2 MEDICAL PARK RD, STE 107 29203 #036-05-1998 L2002 **OBG** *040 †30

SMITH, Sidney Terrell. 2 MEDICAL PARK RD, STE 107 29203 #045-01-1975 L1976 **OBG** *020 †30

SMITH, Stuart Millar. 6439 GARNERS FERRY RD, WJB DORN VETERAN'S HOSPITA 29209 #305-01-1998 L2001 **IM** *020 †20

SMOAK, Monica Maline. ■ 29210 #045-04-2008 *012

SMOAK, Nakia Lynne. 14 RICHLAND MEDICAL PARK, STE 400 29203 #045-01-2006 L2006 **PD** *012

SMYTHE, Alexander R, II. 1301 TAYLOR ST, COLUMBIA WOMENS 29201 #045-01-1972 L1973 **OBG MFM** *020 †30

SNELL, Cynthia M. 2601 LAUREL ST, STE 110 29204 #045-04-1991 L1992 **OPH** *020 †35

SNIPES, Richard Dean. ■ 29223 #036-07-1942 L1945 **GYN** *071

SNODDY, Elinor L. 100 SUMMIT CENTRE DR 29229 #045-04-1983 L1984 **OPH** *020 †35

SNODDY, Warren M, III. DORN VA HOSP 29201 #045-01-1979 L1981 **U GS** *020 †95

SOBEL, Jack. 2100 BULL ST 29201 #649-01-1953 L1980 **P OS** *020

SOBEL, Joseph B. PO BOX 6170, BLUE CHOICE HEALTH PLAN 29260 #041-13-1994 L1999 **EM** *020 †16

SOBTI, Deepa. 5 RICHLAND MEDICAL PARK 29203 #495-30-1982 L1995 **P** *020

SOLAJA, Mojibola Olayinka. 120 WILDEWOOD PARK DR, STE B 29223 #690-14-1990 L2000 **PD** *020 †55

SONEK, Mojmir Jiri. 1333 TAYLOR ST, STE 3J 29201 #065-09-1979 L1992 **OBG** *020 †30

SOROOS, Jennifer Marie. 74 POLO RD 29223 #056-06-2000 L2004 **PD** *020 †55

SOTO, Danielle Elizabeth. 3 MEDICAL PARK RD STE 350 29203 #045-04-2005 L2005 **EM** *012

SOUDER, Christopher Allen. 5 MEDICAL PARK RD, DEPT OF EMERG MED STE 350 29203 #041-14-2005 L2005 **EM** *012

SPENCER, Herbert R, Jr. 1800 COLONIAL DR 29203 #012-05-1969 L1972 **CHP P** *020

SPERO, Michele Lynn. 1330 TAYLOR ST 29220 #035-08-1983 L1986 **IM** *020 †20

SPINELLI, James Lawrence. 125 ALPINE CIR 29223 #023-12-1982 L2004 **P IM** *020 †20,75

SPINNER-PRYBIS, Michelle. 5 RICHLAND MEDICAL PARK, DEPARTMENT OF PEDIATRICS 29203 #012-01-1998 L1999 **PD** *020 †55

SPIRYDA, Lisa Beth. 2 MEDICAL PARK RD, STE 107 29203 #035-47-2000 L2007 **OBG** *020 †30

SPIVEY, Jerry Allen, Jr. 2 MEDICAL PARK RD, STE 506 29203 #012-22-2007 L2007 **IM** *012

SPOTTS, Eric Steven. 1409 DEVINE ST, THOMSON HEALTH CENTER 29208 #025-12-1987 L1991 **GYN** *020 †30

SRIBNICK, Martha A M. 2701 MIDDLEBURG DR 29204 #035-01-1970 L1976 **PD** *020 †55

SRIBNICK, Michael Gordon. 2701 MIDDLEBURG DR 29204 #047-05-1973 L1974 **IM** *020 †20

SRIBNICK, Richard Lewis. 2701 MIDDLEBURG DR 29204 #047-05-1975 L1979 **IM** *020 †20

SRIBNICK, Wayne Brian. 2701 MIDDLEBURG DR 29204 #045-01-1979 L1982 **IM** *020 †20

SRIKANTIAH, Saraswati C. 3 RICHLAND MEDICAL PARK, STE 510 29203 #495-27-1991 L2000 **IM** *020 †20

SRINIVASAN, Shilpa. 15 MEDICAL PARK RD, GERIATRIC PSYCHIATRY 29203 #473-02-1996 L2005 **PYG** *100 †75

STACY, Jason John. 3209 COLONIAL DR 29203 #056-06-2000 L2003 **FM FSM** *100 †18

STAFFORD, Robert Holden. 1325 HARDEN ST, LRADAC 29204 #045-01-1969 L1969 **OBG** *020 †30

STAHL, Carl E. 6439 GARNERS FERRY RD 29209 #051-04-1949 L1978 **N IM** *071 †20

STAHL, Peter J. 300 RICE MEADOW WAY, RICE CREEK FAMILY MEDICINE 29229 #035-15-1980 L1983 **FM OM** *020 †18

STALLWORTH, James Rast. 5 RICHLAND MEDICAL PARK 29203 #001-02-1976 L1979 **PD** *040 †55

STANDS, James Walter. 1333 TAYLOR ST, STE 2D 29201 #045-01-1975 L1977 **OBG** *020 †30

STANFIELD, Robin Fulmer. 4 MEDICAL PARK RD, STE 301 29203 #045-04-1996 L1997 **PD** *020 †55

STANFIELD, Stephen C. 3 RICHLAND MEDICAL PARK, 3 RICHLAND MEDICAL PARK 29203 #045-04-1996 L1998 **EM** *020 †16

STARR, Gene Farrell. ■ 29206 #045-01-1965 L1965 **P** *071

STEEDMAN, John Geo. 6439 GARNERS FERRY RD, WJB DORN VA HOSP 29209 #045-01-1992 L1993 **CN N** *020 †20

STEELE, James Chas. 2100 BULL ST 29201 #045-01-1955 L1955 **OS IMG** *071

STEELE, John Charles, II. 3555 HARDEN ST EXT, STE 104A 29203 #045-04-2003 L2004 **P** *020

STEEN, Christian Colbert. 3209 COLONIAL DR 29203 #045-01-2002 L2004 **FM** *020 †18

STEPHENSON, Kathryn Anne. 4 MEDICAL PARK RD, STE 301 29203 #025-12-1993 L1994 **PD** *040 †55

STEWART, Ada Denise. ■ 29229 #038-43-2000 L2001 **FM** *020 †18 ‡

STEWART, Nathaniel J. 5 RICHLAND MEDICAL PARK 29203 #012-01-1981 L1982 **EM** *020 †16

STILL, Charles Neal. 6439 GARNERS FERRY RD, DORN VAMC 29209 #045-01-1959 L1959 **N OS** *020 †75

STINSON, Elva Catherine. ■ 29203 #045-01-1979 L1981 **EM** *020

STINSON, Michael Shawn. 2 MEDICAL PARK RD, STE 502 29203 #036-07-1988 L1995 **IM** *020 †20

STONE, Croft William. ■ 29203 #045-04-2006 L2006 **DR** *012

STONE, Monica Ann. 1409 DEVINE ST, THOMSON STUDENT HEALTH CEN 29208 #020-02-1997 L2008 **OBG** *020 †30

STRAUSS, Bernarda E. 1911 THURMOND MALL, GREENWOOD GENETIC CENTER 29201 #011-02-2000 L2007 **MG PD** *020 †19

STROHECKER, James Scott. 2739 LAUREL ST, STE 1A 29204 #036-05-1974 L1979 **GE** *020 †20

STUART, Eugene Washington. 11 GATEWAY CORNERS PARK 29203 #045-01-1994 L2001 **GE IM** *020 †20

STUBBS, Michelle A. 3555 HARDEN ST EXT, STE 104A 29203 #047-20-2003 L2004 **CHP** *012

STUCK, Craig Andrew. 3555 HARDEN ST EXT, STE 104A 29203 #041-02-1982 L1989 **CHP** *020 †75,18

STUCK, Leslie Mills. 1330 TAYLOR ST 29220 #045-04-1989 L1990 **IM** *020 †20

STUCK, William Warren. 8 RICHLAND MEDICAL PARK DR, STE 300 29203 #036-01-1981 L1986 **CD IM** *020 †20

STUCKEY, Melton Roof. 1333 TAYLOR ST, STE 5E 29201 #045-01-1967 L1967 **GP** *020

STUDNICKA, Benedict R. 2701 MIDDLEBURG DR 29204 #045-04-1993 L1995 **IM** *020 †20

SUBER, Dealva Taundolyn. 4100 MAIN ST 29203 #010-03-1986 L1991 **GE IM** *020 †20

SUH, Philip Sang. 4500 STUART ST, MONCRIEF AMC, MCXL-PQ 29207 #035-08-1996 L1998 **D** *020 †15

SULLIVAN, Michael Jeffrey. 1410 BLANDING ST, STE 1 29201 #055-01-1987 L1988 **AN** *020 †05

SUN, Edward R. 3301 HARDEN STREET EXT 29203 #024-01-1968 L1973 **NM OS** *020 †80,28

SURI, Gurvinder Singh. 5 MEDICAL PARK RD, MEDICAL EDUCATION DEPT. 29203 #305-01-2005 L2005 **IM** *012

SUSSMAN, Joel Philip. 115 ATRIUM WAY, STE 127 29223 #050-02-1970 L1975 **PD** *020 †55

SUTTON, John P, III. 2750 LAUREL ST 29204 #045-01-1988 L1994 **TS** *020 †85,90

SUTTON, John Perry. 2750 LAUREL ST, STE 305 29204 #045-01-1963 L1963 **TS** *020 †85,90

SWANSON, Peter Hyde. 7TH FLOOR, BYRNES BUILDING 29208 #025-01-1969 L1984 **P** *040 †75

SWEATMAN, Carl Alden, Jr. 1850 LAUREL ST, BOX 7728 29201 #045-01-1967 L1967 **GS** *020 †85

SWEENEY, William Brian. 1735 TAYLOR ST 29201 #041-09-1983 L2006 **CRS GS** *020 †85,10

SWINTON, Ayanna Yvonne. 15 RICHLAND MEDICAL PARK, HOSPITAL DEPT OF MED EDUCA 29203 #028-34-2000 L2002 **CHP** *020

SWITZER, Paul Kent, III. 29205 #422-01-1983 L1988 **IMG P** *020 †75

SY, Alexander Ong. 5 RICHLAND MEDICAL PARK 29203 #042-02-1986 L2004 **PUD CCM** *020 †20

SYNN, Nung Man. CRAFTS FARROW STATE HOSP 29203 #583-01-1959 L1975 **P** *075

TABER, Joseph Wm. 9 MEDICAL PARK RD STE 420 29203 #045-01-1959 L1959 **N** *071 †75

TABER, Scott Wayne. 1850 LAUREL ST, SURGICAL ASSOCS OF SO CARO 29201 #030-06-1988 L2002 **GS** *020 †85

TAFFONI, Matthew Joseph. 1519 MARION ST, PIEDMONT RADIOLOGICAL ASSO 29201 #055-01-2000 L2003 **DR** *020 †80

TAREKEGNE, Mulugeta. 2435 FOREST DR, 2719 MIDDLEBURG DRIVE 29204 #366-02-1985 L2000 **IM** *020 †20

TAWFIK, Samy Lewis. 1333 TAYLOR ST, STE 4H 29201 #915-03-1981 L2001 **CHP** *020

TAYLOR, Edmund Rhett. 2435 FOREST DR 29204 #023-07-1941 L1955 **GS TS** *072 †85,90

TAYLOR, Jeter Pritchard. 5 RICHLAND MEDICAL PARK, DEPT EMERGY MED STE 350 29203 #036-08-1987 L1988 **EM** *020 †16

TAYLOR, Jonathan David. 3 RICHLAND MED PK DR, STE 350 29203 #045-04-2006 L2006 **EM** *012

TAYLOR, Robt Richard, Jr. 3 MEDICAL PARK RD, STE 320 29203 #045-01-1960 L1960 **N** *071

TAYLOR, Roger Caughman. 4 MEDICAL PARK RD, STE 301 29203 #045-04-1983 L1984 **PD** *020 †55

TAYLOR, Ryan Wilkes. 5 MEDICAL PARK RD, MEDICAL EDUCATION 29203 #045-04-2005 L2005 **IM** *012

TAYLOR, William Getman. 1330 TAYLOR ST 29220 #035-45-1971 L1976 **PD** *020 †55

TECSON, Sheila Liberty. PO BOX 2266, PALMETTO HLTH ALLIANCE 29202 #748-10-2003 L2006 **GS** *012

THAKUR, Devendra Singh. ■ 29209 #045-04-2008 *012

THIAGARAJAH, Candiah. 220 FAISON DR, HOSPITAL 29203 #220-02-1971 L1981 **P** *020 †75

THIENES, Michelle Margari. 3209 COLONIAL DR 29203 #017-20-2004 L2004 **FSM** *012

THIEU, Nguyen Duc. 9 RICHLAND MEDICAL PARK, STE 320 29203 #010-03-1975 L1981 **GE IM** *020

THOMPSON, Charlotte R. 2016 SUMTER ST, THE EYE & FACIAL CENTER, L 29201 #041-09-1992 L2001 **OPH** *020 †35

THOMPSON, Herman Ora, Jr. 1730 HENDERSON ST 29201 #036-01-1968 L1978 **IM D** *020 †20,15

THOMPSON, Joseph Riddle. VA HOSPITAL 29201 #047-06-1981 L1982 **IM** *020 †20

THOMPSON, Scott William. 3 MEDICAL PARK RD STE 120, MIDLAND EAR NOSE THOART 29203 #041-09-1992 L2000 **OTO NO** *020 †45

THOMPSON, Tab Eugene. 2750 LAUREL ST, STE 203 29204 #045-01-1989 L1994 **OTO FPS** *020 †45

THOMPSON, Wm Horace, Jr. 1410 BLANDING ST, STE 1 29201 #021-01-1971 L1978 **AN** *071 †05

THORNE, Diana Louise. 6439 GARNERS FERRY RD, MENTAL HEALTH, 116 29209 #045-01-1995 L2000 **P** *020 †75

THORNHILL, Joshua Taylor. 3555 HARDEN ST EXT 29203 #051-07-1989 L1991 **P** *040 †75

THORNTON, Elbert G. 5 RICHLAND MEDICAL PARK DR 29203 #045-04-1991 L1992 **AN PME** *020 †05

TIMMERMAN, Robert Clifton, Jr. ■ 29210 #045-04-2008 *012

TOBIN, Mary M Tribble. 1121 BRENTWOOD DR 29206 #045-01-1949 L1949 **IM** *071

TODD, Marc Stephen. 9 RICHLAND MEDICAL PARK, STE 110 29203 #045-04-2003 L2004 **PD** *020 †55

TOLHURST, Judith Elaine. 1821 PICKENS ST 29201 #012-05-1988 L1989 **P** *020 †75

TOLIVER-DINGLE, Peggy V. 1301 TAYLOR ST, STE 8A 29201 #021-01-1981 L1990 **IM IMG** *020 †20

TOLLISON, Charles Earl. ■ 29223 #045-01-1957 L1957 **GS OS** *075 †85

TOOMER-CLOWNEY, Deidre L. 2435 FOREST DR 29204 #020-12-1987 L1988 **IM IMG** *020 †20

TORRES, Carlos Miguel. 3209 COLONIAL DR, PHR - FAMILY MEDICINE DEPT 29203 #045-04-2007 L2007 **FP** *012

TOWLE, Justin Anthony. 5 MEDICAL PARK RD, MEDICAL EDUCATION DEPT. 29203 #104-01-2004 L2005 **OBG** *012

TRIBBLE, David Edgar. 1850 LAUREL ST, BOX 7728 29201 #047-05-1954 L1962 **GS CD** *020 †85,90

TRIBBLE, James Benjamin. 1850 LAUREL ST, SURGICAL ASSOCIATES OF SC, 29201 #047-05-1983 L1988 **GS VS** *020 †85

TRIBBLE, Reid Warren. 8 RICHLAND MEDICAL PARK DR, STE 400 29203 #045-01-1987 L1995 **TS CD** *020 †85,90 ‡

TRIPATHI, Ramesh Chandra. 4 RICHLAND MEDICAL PARK, SC EYE INSTITUTE 29203 #495-12-1959 L2003 **OPH** *071

TROGDON, Johnny Warren. 5000 THURMOND MALL, STE 116 29201 #038-44-1990 L1993 **IM** *020 †50

TROSCLAIR, Erik Anthony. PO BOX 2266, PALMETTO HEALTH 29202 #021-05-2006 L2006 **EM** *012

TROYER, Devin J. 2935 COLONIAL DR 29203 #055-01-1987 L1991 **PM** *020 †60

TRUE, Amber Jean. 2435 FOREST DR 29204 #045-04-1996 L1997 **IM** *020 †20

TRUESDALE, Diane Wells. 166 STONERIDGE DR 29210 #045-01-1976 L1977 **RO** *020 †80

TRUJILLANO, Antonio Calvo. ■ 29209 #847-04-1958 L1981 **N** *020 †75

TRULUCK, Richard K, Jr. 2749 LAUREL ST 29204 #045-01-1966 L1966 **ORS** *071 †40

TSAI, Julie Hsinchia. 4 MEDICAL PARK RD, STE 100 29203 #035-03-2000 L2006 **OPH** *020 †35

TSENG, Helen C. 5 MEDICAL PARK RD, MEDICAL EDUCATION DEPT. 29203 #041-14-2004 L2005 **OPH** *012

TUCCI, Monica Cathleen. ■ 29201 #011-75-2005, ▲ L2005 **PD** *012

TULLOS, Julie Marie. 2 MEDICAL PARK RD, STE 208 29203 #654-01-2007 L2007 **OBG** *012

TURNER, James F, II. 5 RICHLAND MEDICAL PARK DR 29203 #038-40-1977 L1985 **AN IM** *020 †05

TUTEN, Thomas Alexander. ■ 29209 #045-04-2008 *012

TWINING, Christine Louise. USC SCH OF MED, BLDG 101 STE 316 29208 #036-07-2001 L2006 **END** *020 †55

UDOH, Moses Elijah. 2435 FOREST DR, PROVIDENCE HOSPITALIST GRO 29204 #306-01-1998 L2002 **IM** *020 †20

UGINO, Michael Ralph. 1930 BLANDING ST 29201 #035-45-1977 L1983 **HS ORS** *020 †40

ULLMAN, Barbara B. 15 MONCKTON BLVD 29206 #045-01-1965 L1965 **D** *020 †15

UMBACH, Richard Earl. 2601 LAUREL ST, STE 260 29204 #001-02-1972 L1978 **CD IM** *020 †20

VADAPARAMPIL, John Annjos. 1519 MARION ST 29201 #045-01-4-2002 L2007 **DR** *020 †80

VAFAI, Radiance E. 5 RICHLAND MEDICAL PARK, DEPT PEDIATRICS 29203 #036-01-2001 L2004 **PD** *020 †55

VAHJEN, Brian Patrick. ■ 29208 #045-04-2006 L2006 **OPH** *012

VALDIVIESO, Jose G. 6439 GARNERS FERRY RD 29209 #737-01-1954 L1971 **ON IM** *020 †20

VALENTIN, Milagros. 1333 TAYLOR ST, STE 4H 29201 #035-06-1991 L2002 **P** *074 †75

VALESKY, Walter Wallace, Jr. ■ 29209 #045-04-2008 *012

VALLINI, Angel Daniel. 6439 GARNERS FERRY RD, WJB DORN VA MED CTR 29209 #132-02-1967 L1974 **N** *020 †75

VALOSEN, John Matthew. 3209 COLONIAL DR 29203 #041-15-2003 L2005 **ORS** *012

VALPEY, Jack Maxwell. ■ 29223 #005-11-1958 L1986 **OBG GP** *020 †30 ‡

VAN ATTA, Julie Christine. 1301 TAYLOR ST, STE 4L 29201 #041-03-1991 L1993 **FM** *020 †18

VANDALE, Erin Taylor. 14 RICHLAND MEDICAL PARK, STE 400 29203 #045-04-2006 L2006 **PD** *012

VANDAM, W Alaric. 5 RICHLAND MEDICAL PARK 29203 #038-45-1997 L2001 **PM** *020 †60

VANDERSTEENHOVEN, Anne M. 5 RICHLAND MEDICAL PARK DR 29203 #045-01-1987 L2001 **PTH** *020 †50

VANDERSTEENHOVEN, Jacob J. 5 RICHLAND MEDICAL PARK DR 29203 #045-01-1987 L2001 **ATP PCP** *020 †50

VARNADOE, James Brent. 15 RICHLAND MEDICAL PARK, STE 202 29203 #045-04-2004 L2004 **IM** *020

VARUGHESE, Beena Kovoor. 2117 GERVAIS ST, WAVERLY FAMILY PRACTICE 29204 #422-01-1999 L2002 **FM** *020 †18

VELLODY, Devi. ■ 29223 #495-44-1969 L1978 **IM** *020 †20

VENN, Tad Alan. 5 MEDICAL PARK RD, ATTN: MEDICAL EDUCATION 29203 #036-08-2005 L2005 **FP** *012

VERNON, Charles Redfearn. 220 FAISON DR 29203 #036-07-1964 L1970 **CD IM** *020

VIDAL, Rachel Wilks. 101 S WACCAMAW AVE, STE 303 29205 #025-01-1995 L1999 **IM** *020 †20

VILLAFRANCA, Eloida A. 2200 HARDEN ST, NURSING CARE CTR, OFFC OF 29203 #748-07-1958 L1998 **P OS** *071

VILLANUEVA, Rodney A. 4500 STUART ST, MONCRIEF ARMY COMM HOSPITA 29207 #023-12-1997 L1998 **P** *020

VO, Kim Van. 9 RICHLAND MEDICAL PARK DR, STE 320 29203 #941-01-1972 L1982 **NEP IM** *020 †20 ‡

VOSS, Frank Richard. 2 MEDICAL PARK RD, STE 404 29203 #024-01-1986 L1993 **ORS OTR** *020 †40

VOSSOUGHI, Faranak. 5 RICHLAND MEDICAL PARK, PALMETTO RICHLAND MEMORIA 29203 #858-02-1992 L2004 **GS** *012

VUNNAMADALA, Kalyan C. PO BOX 2266, PALMETTO HLTH ALLIANCE 29202 #422-01-2006 L2006 **GS** *012

WADDELL, Lisa Friend. 1751 CALHOUN ST, BOX 1011106 29201 #051-04-1988 L1993 **PHP GPM** *030 †70

WADE, Michael Donald. 5 RICHLAND MEDICAL PARK, STE 350 29203 #045-01-1986 L1987 **EM** *020 †16

WADMAN, Peggy Cherie. ADULT OUTPATIENT SERVICES, WILLIAMS S HALL INSTITUTE 29202 #045-04-1997 L1998 **PFP** *020 †75

WAHEED, Nasir. 9 RICHLAND MEDICAL PARK, STE 450 29203 #704-01-1989 L1997 **N** *020 †75

WALCHALK, Lisa Rae. 15 RICHLAND MEDICAL PARK 29203 #038-44-2005 L2005 **EM** *012

WALDRON, Robert Leroy, II. 1330 TAYLOR ST 29220 #024-01-1962 L1980 **R RNR** *020 †80

WALKER, Leo Lauhon. 1330 TAYLOR ST 29220 #036-07-1971 L1974 **END IM** *071 †20

WALKER, Robert Davis. 74 POLO RD 29223 #012-01-1978 L1981 **PD** *071 †55

WALKER, Thurmond Otto. ■ 29204 #045-01-1958 L1958 **GP** *071

WALKUP, Wm Baskin, Jr. 125 ALPINE CIR 29223 #045-04-1991 L1992 **P** *020 †75

WALLACE, James Nicholas. ■ 29209 #045-04-2008 *012

WALLAM, Mohammed N. 6439 GARNERS FERRY RD, WJBD VA MEDICAL CTR 29209 #704-02-1994 L2003 **HO IM** *020 ‡

WALLS, Allan Christopher. 2 RICHLAND MEDICAL PARK, STE 300 29203 #001-02-1986 L1989 **GS** *020 †85

WALSH, Eileen Marie. 2 MEDICAL PARK RD STE 203, UNIVERSITY PRIMARY CARE 29203 #045-01-1990 L1993 **PD** *020 †55

WALSH, John Jos, IV. 2 MEDICAL PARK RD STE 404, UNIVERSITY SPECIALTY CLINI 29203 #041-02-1989 L1996 **HS ORS** *020 †40

WALTER, Arthur Knight. 2435 FOREST DR, X-RAY DEPT 29204 #045-01-1965 L1965 **R** *071 †80

WALTERS, Suzanne Aileen. ■ 29210 #045-01-1992 L1994 **IM** *020

WALTON, Lyle Scott. ■ 29205 #045-04-2008 *012
WALVOORD, Charles Lewis. 4 MEDICAL PARK RD, STE 100 29203 #016-06-1971 L1975 OPH *020 †35
WARD, John Logan. ■ 29204 #045-01-1961 L1961 **PTH** *020 †50 ‡
WARDER, Frank Reid. 2750 LAUREL ST STE 203 29204 #045-01-1968 L1968 OTO HNS *020 †45
WARE, Patrick Lyle. ■ 29209 #045-04-2008 *012
WARRICK, Kenneth Ray. 6439 GARNERS FERRY RD, DEPT OF DERMATOLOGY 29209 #045-01-1971 L1975 **D** *020 †15 ‡
WASHINGTON, Gail D. ■ 29290 #041-14-1983 L1987 **GP EM** *020
WASHINGTON, Joseph W, Jr. 4611 HARD SCRABBLE RD, STE 346 29229 #010-03-1991 L1997 **IM** *020
WASSERMANN, Richard John. 1220 BLANDING ST, PLASTIC SURGERY CONSULTANT 29201 #021-01-1990 L1997 **PS** *020 †65
WATSON, Christopher M. 2 RICHLAND MEDICAL PARK, STE 300 29203 #012-22-2001 L2003 **GS** *020 †85
WATSON, Lakeisha. ■ 29229 #038-45-2004 L2007 **CHP** *012
WATSON, Stephen. 3 MEDICAL PARK RD, STE 400 29203 #045-01-1985 L1986 **PD** *020 †55
WATT, George Winfield. 9 MEDICAL PARK RD, STE 400 29203 #048-02-1972 L2004 **OBG** *020 †30
WEATHERWAX, John Berean. ■ 29205 #023-12-2004 L2005 **FM** *020
WEBBER, Caroline. ■ 29209 #045-04-2004 L2004 **PD** *020 †55
WEBB-WOOD, Sarah. ■ 29204 #045-04-2007 L2007 **PD** *012
WEBER, Max N. VET ADMIN HOSP 29209 #407-23-1950 L1959 **AN** *071 †05
WEE, Daniel. PO BOX 2266, PALMETTO HLTH 29202 #028-02-2006 L2007 **OPH** *012
WEINER, Lawrence S. 1 RICHLAND MEDICAL PARK 29203 #035-15-1970 L1971 **AI PDA** *020 †55,03
WEIR-COX, Kaylene D. 3019 FARROW RD, PREMIER SURGICAL GROUP, LL 29203 #038-40-1999 L2004 **GS** *020 †85
WEISINGER, Andrew Scott. 2712 MIDDLEBURG DR STE 211, CARDIO ANESTH SVCS LLC 29204 #011-02-1992 L1998 **AN TS** *020
WEISS, Howard A. 110 ATRIUM WAY 29223 #018-75-1977, ▲ L1999 **FM** *071
WELDON, Allan Mustard. 4416 FOREST DR, STE A 29206 #045-01-1975 L2008 **FM** *020 †18
WELLS, James Rife. 6439 GARNERS FERRY RD, ENT DEPT DORN VA MED CTR 29209 #011-03-1976 L1991 **OTO HNS** *020 †45
WELLS, John A, III. 2750 LAUREL ST STE 101 29204 #012-05-1986 L1991 **OPH** *020 †35
WELLS, John Anderson, Jr. 2750 LAUREL ST STE 101 29204 #045-01-1962 L1962 **OPH** *035
WELLS, Marion Timothy. 8 RICHLAND MEDICAL PARK DR, STE 300 29203 #051-04-1994 L2001 **IC** *020 †20
WELSH, Jeffrey Alan. 5 RICHLAND MEDICAL PARK DR 29203 #045-01-1989 L1991 **PTH HMP** *020 †50
WENDELL, Richard Preston. PO BOX 2266, PALMETTO HEALTH 29202 #045-01-2005 L2005 **EM** *012
WENDT, Michael Otto. 5 RICHLAND MEDICAL PARK DR 29203 #056-06-1989 L1990 **AN PME** *020 †05
WENNING, Derick Michael. ■ 29205 #021-06-2008 *012
WERNER, Susan Ashton. 3209 COLONIAL DR, PALMETTO HEALTH RICHLAND 29203 #041-12-2004 L2004 **FM** *020
WESSINGER, Kevin Owen. 1330 TAYLOR ST 29220 #045-01-1986 L1989 **PD** *020 †55
WESTCOTT, Allison Marie. 2 MEDICAL PARK RD, STE 208 29203 #038-43-2007 L2007 **OBG** *012
WESTERKAM, William D. 2935 COLONIAL DR, HEALTHSOUTH 29203 #012-05-1990 L1994 **PM** *020 †60
WESTERKAM, William Randal. 2935 COLONIAL DR, HOSPITAL 29203 #036-01-1993 L1997 **PM** *020 †60
WESTON, James Hough. TAYLOR & MARION STS 29220 #001-02-1956 L1960 **OBG** *020
WESTON, Shannon Nelson. 9 RICHLAND MEDCL PARK #110 29203 #045-01-1962 L1964 **PD** *071 †55
WEYANT, Scott Alan. 5000 THURMOND MALL, STE 207 29201 #422-01-2001 L2004 **IM** *020
WEYMOUTH, Richard Jordan. ■ 29223 #056-06-1963 L1964 **GP** *050
WHITAKER, Andrew Jackson. 2100 BULL ST 29201 #012-01-1954 **GP OM** *020 †85
WHITE, James File. 9 RICHLAND MEDICAL PARK, STE 510 29203 #036-07-1959 **HNS PS** *071 †45
WHITE, Robert Warren, Jr. ■ 29203 #012-01-1994 L2006 **GPM** *012
WHITE, Terrell Hilda. 1415 RICHLAND ST 29201 #012-01-1984 L1986 **P** *020 †75
WHITE, Welbourne Andrews. 2601 LAUREL ST STE 110 29204 #045-01-1956 L1956 **OPH** *071
WHITMAN-ELIA, Gail F. 2 MEDICAL PARK RD, STE 107 29203 #016-02-1976 L1995 **REN GYN** *020 †30
WICKER, Christopher Micha. 2 MEDICAL PARK RD STE 502, DEPT OF INT MED 29203 #045-04-2005 L2005 **IM** *012
WIDEMAN, Vanessa K. 114 GATEWAY CORPORATE BLVD, STE 330 29203 #001-02-1999 L2006 **FM AM** *020 †18
WIENECKE, Matthew Mills. 1 MEDICAL PARK RD, STE 410 29203 #039-01-1985 L1989 **PDC PD** *050 †55
WILD, Garner A J. 100 SUMMIT CENTRE DR 29229 #045-01-1997 L1998 **OPH** *020
WILD, Mark David. 1301 TAYLOR ST, STE 7B 29201 #045-01-1997 L1998 **OBG** *020 †30
WILEY, Kelvin James. 10120 TWO NOTCH RD STE 2, ELITE HEALTH CARE INC 29223 #038-45-1998 L2002 **IM** *020
WILLARD, William Grant, IV. 1749 MARSHALL ST 29203 #045-04-1997 L1998 **PD** *020 †55
WILLCOX, Hugh Labarbe, III. 5 RICHLAND MEDICAL PARK, ATTN: MEDICAL EDUCATION 29203 #045-04-2003 L2004 **GS** *012
WILLIAMS, Alana M. 1818 HENDERSON ST, STE 201 29201 #305-01-1992 L1995 **FM** *020
WILLIAMS, Antoinette L. 2 MEDICAL PARK RD, STE 502 29203 #045-04-2001 L2003 **PCC** *012
WILLIAMS, Daniel Mark. 2 MEDICAL PARK RD STE 404 29203 #023-12-2003 L2007 **ORS** *012
WILLIAMS, Eddie Meek, III. 2712 MIDDLEBURG DR, STE 222 29204 #036-07-1974 L1983 **IM PUD** *020
WILLIAMS, Franklin R. 1410 BLANDING ST, STE 1 29201 #045-04-1990 L1994 **AN** *020 †05
WILLIAMS, James A, Jr. 2 MEDICAL PARK RD, STE 107 29203 #045-04-1988 L1989 **GO OBG** *020 †30
WILLIAMS, John Francis. 2435 FOREST DR, DEPT ANES 29204 #012-01-1972 L1978 **AN** *020 †05
WILLIAMS, Luther C, III. 4 MEDICAL PARK RD, STE 301 29203 #045-01-1968 L1974 **CD PD** *020 †55
WILLIAMS, Richard Taylor. 2601 LAUREL ST, STE 260 29204 #045-01-1996 L2003 **CD** *020 †20
WILLIAMS, Sarah G. 1 SCIENCE CT, STE 200 29203 #045-04-1996 L1998 **DMP** *020 †50

WILLIAMS, Vashaun Omar. 5 RICHLAND MEDICAL PARK, PALMETTO RICHLAND MEMORIA 29203 #012-21-2002 L2004 **CHP** *020 †75
WILLIAMS-CARR, Lady. 610 FAISON DR, SC DEPT OF MENTAL HEALTH 29203 #011-03-1989 L2000 **ID** *020
WILLIAMSON, Oliver Wayne. PO BOX 119, S C STATE HOSP 29202 #023-01-1943 L1947 **GP P** *072
WILMOT, Dale A. 4605 MONTICELLO RD 29203 #035-46-1993 L1997 **OBG** *020 †30
WILSON, Dennis Alonzo. 1701 SAINT JULIAN PL, STE 100 29204 #023-12-1981 L1990 **GS** *020
WILSON, Gerald Anthony. 1701 SAINT JULIAN PL, STE 100 29204 #045-01-1974 **GS VS** *020
WILSON, Lynn Lovelace. 4605 MONTICELLO RD 29203 #027-01-1988 L1989 **PD** *020 †55
WILSON, Malissa Gail. 9 MEDICAL PARK RD, STE 630 29203 #045-04-1988 L1989 **IM IMG** *020 †20
WILSON, Wm Drayton, Jr. 2757 LAUREL ST STE 3 29204 #045-01-1977 L1986 **IM PD** *020 †55,20
WINGO, Timothy Dawayne. 3209 COLONIAL DR, DEPT OF FAMILY PRACTICE 29203 #047-06-1998 L2003 **FM** *020 †18
WINN, David Curtis. 2435 FOREST DR 29204 #051-07-1983 L1987 **IM** *020
WINTER, Eric Karl. ■ 29201 #038-06-1998 L1999 **CHP** *020 †75
WISE, Rudolph La Verne. 166 STONERIDGE DR 29210 #045-01-1977 L1978 **HEM ON** *020 †20
WITHERSPOON, B J, Jr. 166 STONERIDGE DR 29210 #045-01-1973 L1974 **RO ON** *020 †80
WITHERSPOON, Patricia W. 3209 COLONIAL DR 29203 #041-14-1992 L1994 **FM** *020 †18 ‡
WOFFORD, Elizabeth D. 2435 FOREST DR, PROVIDENCE HOSPITAL 29204 #045-01-1983 L1989 **ATP** *062 †50
WOFFORD, John Elihu. 1301 TAYLOR ST, STE 1A 29201 #045-01-1983 L1989 **U** *020 †95
WOLDORF, Andrew Houck. 3800 FOREST DR, STE B101 29204 #041-02-1996 L2002 **OPH** *020 †35 ‡
WOLFE, Grant Collins. 2 MEDICAL PARK RD, STE 402 29203 #041-02-2007 L2007 **GS** *012
WOLFE-THOMA, Whitney. 2 MEDICAL PARK RD, STE 107 29203 #045-04-1997 L2001 **OBG** *020 †30
WOOD, Beverly Ann. 4344 BROAD RIVER RD, GILLIAM PSYCHIATRIC HOSPIT 29210 #051-04-1984 L1991 **P CHP** *020 †75
WOOD, Herbert Austin. ■ 29223 #045-01-1965 L1971 **IM CD** *071 †20
WOOD, John Lee. 3 RICHLAND MEDICAL PARK, STE 350 29203 #012-01-2004 L2004 **EM** *020
WOOD, Patricia Ann. 6439 GARNERS FERRY RD, DORN VA MEDICAL CENTER 29209 #026-04-1980 L2000 **HEM ON** *020 †20
WOODS, Shaw Wendi. 15 MEDICAL PARK RD STE 104 29203 #047-07-2006 L2006 **P** *012
WOODWARD, John Maybin. 2435 FOREST DR 29204 #045-01-1980 L1981 **FM** *020 †18
WORD, Bradley Wyatt. 4540 TRENHOLM RD 29206 #047-05-1992 L1995 **IM** *020 †20
WRIGHT, Ben Wallace, Jr. 166 STONERIDGE DR 29210 #045-01-1981 L1982 **RO** *020 †80
WRIGHT, Harry H. 3555 HARDEN ST EXT, NEUROPSYCHIATRY USC/SM 29203 #041-01-1976 L1978 **CHP P** *040 †75 ‡
WRIGHT, James Alan. 1715 BLANDING ST 29201 #041-14-1975 L1978 **FM EM** *020 †85
WRIGHT, Marie Celeste. 707 PAVILLION AVE 29205 #045-01-1976 L1978 **IM EM** *020 †20
WRIGHT, Walter D. ■ 29223 #045-01-1950 L1972 **ORS AM** *072 †40
WUORI, Donald Francis. 8301 FARROW RD, POPLAR BLDG 29203 #035-08-1968 L1984 **PD OS** *020 †15
WYMAN, Frank James. 1333 TAYLOR ST STE 5F 29201 #045-01-1958 **OBG** *071 †30
YAJNIK, Bhavana Ramesh. 1333 TAYLOR ST STE 6A 29201 #495-76-1972 L1978 **NPM PD** *020 †15
YANG, Chang Hsu. 6439 GARNERS FERRY RD 29209 #385-03-1964 L1972 **PTH** *020 †50
YARBROUGH, John Ward. 2750 LAUREL ST, STE 305 29204 #036-05-1967 L1982 **TS** *020 †85,90
YATES, Carl Douglas. 5 RICHLAND MEDICAL PARK DR 29203 #021-01-1981 L1992 **AN** *020 †05
YATES, William Madison. 3713 COVENANT RD 29204 #045-01-1974 L1976 **LM** *075
YEAKEL, Christopher Allen. 5 RICHLAND MEDICAL PARK DR 29203 #041-14-1980 L1986 **AN** *020 †05
YELLAND, Graham. ■ 29206 #050-02-1963 L1979 **PS GS** *071 †85,65
YEON, Philip Alexandre. 2 MEDICAL PARK RD, STE 502 29203 #187-12-1990 L2006 **ID** *020 †20
YIM, Michael Tingfai. 300 RICE MEADOW WAY 29229 #019-02-2003 L2006 **FM** *030 †18
YOGANAND, Shashi Yuvraj. 3209 COLONIAL DR, P R H - FAMILY MEDICINE DE 29203 #305-01-2005 L2006 **FP** *012
YOUNG, Stewart Gregory. 2406 DECKER BLVD 29206 #045-04-1985 L1986 **GP FM** *020
YOUSUFUDDIN, Mohammed. 1333 TAYLOR ST 29201 #495-21-1964 L1979 **GS TS** *020 †85,90
YU, Maria Theresa S. 220 FAISON DR 29203 #748-08-1993 L2000 **P** *020
YUCHONGTIAN, Lyanna Joy S. 4605 MONTICELLO RD, STERLING SHARPE CLINIC 29203 #748-02-1999 L2006 **PD** *100 †55
YUNIS, Muhammad. 1735 TAYLOR ST 29201 #704-04-1971 L1977 **GE IM** *020 †20
ZAFIRUDDIN, Mohammad. 7901 FARROW RD, CRAFT FARROW STATE HOSP 29203 #495-24-1957 L1978 **FM IM** *071 †18
ZELISKO, John Alexander. 5 RICHLAND MEDICAL PARK, COLUMBIA/ PO OFFICE BOX 19 29203 #016-06-1981 L1999 **AN PME** *020 †05
ZHANG, Jing Wei. 1706 SAINT JULIAN PL, CAROLINAS DERMATOLOGY 29204 #243-76-1983 L2002 **DMP** *020 †50
ZHANG, Zaixiao. ■ 29205 #869-05-1997 L2006 **IM** *012
ZITZKE, Ryan Corbin. ■ 29209 #045-04-2008 *012
ZURCHER, Robert Paul. 2750 LAUREL ST 29204 #016-02-1982 L1995 **TS OS** *020 †85,90
ZVEJNIEKS, Peter Andrew. 5 RICHLAND MEDICAL PARK, FL 2CD 29203 #012-01-1993 L1999 **PTH DMP** *020 †50 ‡

CONWAY — HORRY

ADAMSON, James Wellington. 1301 CREEL ST 29527 #045-01-1979 L1981 **IM** *020
ALFORD, Siena Shields. 1210 MAIN ST, RIVERTOWN FAMILY MEDICINE 29526 #028-78-1987, ▲ L1990 **GP FM** *020
ALSTON, Cornelius Lenard. 243 SINGLETON RIDGE RD, UNIT G 29526 #045-04-1988 L1991 **IM** *020 †20
ATZ, Andrew Martin. 300 SINGLETON RIDGE RD 29526 #011-03-1989 L1998 **PDC** *020 †55
BALACHANDRAN, Sivanthan. 834 FARRAR DR, COASTAL KIDNEY CONWAY 29526 #422-01-1996 L2001 **NEP** *020 †20
BALDER, Donald Allen, Jr. 2376 CYPRESS CIR STE 103 29526 #016-11-1991 L1997 **GS VS** *020 †85
BANGCO, Mario Suilan. 170 WACCAMAW MEDICL PRK CT 29526 #748-08-1975 L1994 **N** *020 †75
BHATT, Margaret Sudhir. 152 WACCAMAW MEDICAL PARK, LIGHTHOUSE CARE CENTERS OF 29526 #495-01-1971 L2004 **CHP** *020 †75

BOGDAN, Carol A. 817 FARRAR DR, ASSOCIATED MEDICAL ASSOCIA 29526 #308-11-1987 L2004 **HEM** *020 †20
BOZEMAN, Barbara Jean. 1933 HIGHWAY 544, STE 243 29526 #047-07-1979 L1983 **OBG** *075 †30
CACACE, John. 300 SINGLETON RIDGE RD 29526 #035-47-1987 L2006 **EM** *020 †16
CORONTZES, Stephen A. 600 SINGLETON RIDGE RD, MAGNOLIA PEDIATRICS 29526 #045-04-1987 L1988 **PD** *020 †55
COURBAN, Christo Choukri. 300 SINGLETON RIDGE RD 29526 #035-08-1996 L2005 **EM** *020 †16
COURTNEY, Lollice B. 907 BELL ST 29526 #045-01-1961 L1961 **PD** *020
CZEPOWICZ, Violetta D. 152 WACCAMAW MEDICAL PARK, PARK DR. 29526 #759-01-1983 L1992 **P ADM** *020 †75
DAVES, Reginald Forrest. 8004 MYRTLE TRACE DR, WOMAN'S MEDICAL CENTER PA 29526 #045-01-1969 L1969 **OBG** *071 †30
DEVENYI, Agnes. 164 WACCAMAW MEDICAL PARK 29526 #473-01-1978 L1991 **P** *020 †75
DIETER, Jonathan L. 8014 MYRTLE TRACE DR 29526 #045-01-1973 L1974 **FM** *020 †18 ‡
DOUGHTEN, Richard Merrill. ■ 29526 #036-01-1965 L1983 **AN PD** *071 †55,05
DRAKE, Dennis Allen. 300 SINGLETON RIDGE RD 29526 #047-06-1970 L1985 **AN PME** *020 †55,05
DUCLOS, Martin. 300 SINGLETON RIDGE RD 29526 #035-09-1995 L2004 **IM** *020 †20
DUERK, Donald Laux. ■ 29527 #035-09-1948 L1975 **P GP** *071
EISENMAN, Richard Henry. 2376 CYPRESS CIR STE 100 29526 #035-09-1978 L1990 **GE IM** *020 †20
ELLIOTT, Christopher C. 2376 CYPRESS CIR, STE 300 29526 #045-01-1995 L1997 **OSM** *020 †40
ELLISON, Richard Arthur. 164 WACCAMAW MEDICAL PARK 29526 #041-01-1978 L1980 **P GP** *020 †75
ELMS, John Jay. 834 FARRAR DR 29526 #035-03-1970 L1994 **NEP IM** *020 †20
ENGLEMAN, Robert Allan. 5575 PRIVETTS RD 29526 #041-15-2004 L2007 **IM P** *100
FOGARTY, James D. 394 SINGLETON RIDGE RD, COASTAL UROLOGY CENTER 29526 #035-75-2002, ▲ L2006 **U** *100
GAGNE-SABBAGH, Camille. 8024 MYRTLE TRACE DR 29526 #067-02-1980 L1996 **OBG** *020 †30
GAWITH, Keith Edward. 394 SINGLETON RIDGE RD 29526 #039-01-1986 L1993 **U** *020 †95
GAY, Robert J. 300 SINGLETON RIDGE RD 29526 #035-03-1974 L1979 **PTH CLP** *020 †50
GLENN, Mark Dwight. 164 WACCAMAW MEDICAL PARK 29526 #036-01-1979 L1988 **P** *020 †75
GONZALEZ-ACEVEDO, Alberto. 8028 MYRTLE TRACE DR 29526 #275-01-1963 L1977 **P** *071 †75
GRAHAM-NWANEGWO, Sheree D. 102 LYNN CT, P O BOX 477 29526 #038-43-1988 L1992 **FM** *020 †18
GRESKO, Andrew John. 2376 CYPRESS CIR, STE 102 29526 #045-04-1989 L1992 **CD** *020 †20
GUPTA, Rajan. 241 SINGLETON RIDGE RD 29526 #495-29-1986 L1996 **GE IM** *020 †20
HALYARD, Jeanne A. 1708 OAK ST, HEALTH CARE PARTNERS OF SC 29526 #010-01-1983 L1986 **FM** *020 †18
HARPER, Jennifer Lynn. ■ 29527 #045-01-2001 L2004 **RO** *100 †80
HASKIN, Jack Stewart, Jr. 2376 CYPRESS CIR, STE 300 29526 #045-01-1978 L1979 **HS ORS** *020 †40
HASKIN, Susan Johnson. ■ 29526 #045-01-1980 L1982 **AN** *020 †05
HAYES, Richard Yates. 300 SINGLETON RIDGE RD 29526 #036-05-1995 L1999 **IM** *020 †20
HIERS, William D. 2367 CYPRESS CIR 29526 #036-05-1952 L1953 **N** *071 †75
HOLMES, Harold Buck, Jr. ■ 29528 #045-01-1971 L1972 **GS** *071 †85
HONAKER, Patrick Allen. 300 SINGLETON RIDGE RD 29526 #045-04-1987 L1995 **AN** *020 †05
HUGGINS, John Terrill. 2376 CYPRESS CIR 29526 #045-01-1997 L1998 **PCC** *020 †20
HUMBLES, Frank Forrest. 300 SINGLETON RIDGE RD 29526 #036-08-1986 L1987 **AN PME** *020 †05
INSLEY, Marion C, Jr. 29527 #023-01-1948 L1954 **OTO** *071 †45
JACKSON, Kimberly Shelley. 1210 MAIN ST 29526 #045-01-1994 L1995 **FM FPG** *020 †18
JEANJAQUET, Mark Saml. 300 SINGLETON RIDGE RD 29526 #005-14-1991 L1995 **EM** *020 †16
JOHNSON, Charles W, Jr. 8002 MYRTLE TRACE DR 29526 #045-01-1960 L1960 **IM CD** *020 †20
JOHNSON, Frankie Fairey. ■ 29526 #045-01-1960 L1960 **PM** *072
LEVENSON, Terry Baruch. 8004 MYRTLE TRACE DR 29526 #045-01-1978 L1979 **OBG** *020 †30
LINDSEY, James Melvin, Jr. 8030 MYRTLE TRACE DR 29526 #045-01-1974 L1975 **PD** *020
LINEBACK, Bradley W. 8016 MYRTLE TRACE DR 29526 #045-04-1983 L1984 **OBG** *020 †30
MALLIKARJUN, Ashwin A. 1608 MAIN ST, CAROLINA 29526 #495-09-1994 L1998 **PD** *020 †55
MCCABE, Gregory Thomas. 300 SINGLETON RIDGE RD, CONWAY MEDICAL CENTER 29526 #422-01-2002 L2006 **AN** *100
MC MILLAN, Michael Reid. ■ 29526 #036-07-1967 L1971 **ORS** *071 †40
MERCHANT, Eugenia C. 1608 MAIN ST, HEALTHCARE PARTNERS OF SC 29526 #610-01-1988 L1998 **PD** *020
MILES, Claudia T. 164 WACCAMAW MEDICAL PARK 29526 #022-75-1994, ▲ L2000 **CHP P** *020 †75
MILLS, Camille B. 8002 MYRTLE TRACE DR 29526 #045-01-1985 L1986 **IM EM** *020 †20
MILLS, William Luther. 2376 CYPRESS CIR, STE 300 29526 #045-04-1985 L1986 **ORS** *020 †40
MOSSEY, Mark William. 300 SINGLETON RIDGE RD 29526 #051-01-2002 L2005 **EM** *020 †16
NELSON, Carl Arthur. ■ 29526 #028-02-1939 L1978 **PD PDA** *071 †55
NILES, Vanessa A. 2376 CYPRESS CIR, STE 203 29526 #047-07-1984 L1988 **OBG** *020 †30
NOVIN-BAHERAN, Elham. 300 SINGLETON RIDGE RD, CAROLINA HOSPITALISTS 29526 #654-01-2004 L2007 **IM** *100 †20
PRESLAR, Arthur Josephus. 2376 CYPRESS CIR, STE 300 29526 #048-13-1983 L1988 **ORS** *020 †40
PRICE, Jimmy Douglas. 8016 MYRTLE TRACE DR 29526 #036-05-1973 L1978 **OBG** *020 †30
QUILLEN, Timothy Jos. 394 SINGLETON RIDGE RD 29526 #047-06-1985 L1990 **U** *020 †95
RABON, Brian Melvin. 171 WACCAMAW MEDICL PRK CT 29526 #045-04-1999 L2001 **PD** *020 †55
RANDO, Joseph J. ■ 29526 #010-02-1952 L1961 **U OS** *020 †95
RECORDS, Carl James. ■ 29526 #041-09-1943 L1947 **GP** *071
RICHARDSON, Paul M. 2367B CYPRESS CIR 29526 #045-01-1997 L2002 **IM** *020 †20
ROGOWSKI, John Allen, Jr. 300 SINGLETON RIDGE RD 29526 #005-14-2000 L2005 **EM OS** *020 †16
RUSH, Richard Hudson. 300 SINGLETON RIDGE RD 29526 #045-01-1957 L1957 **GP** *071 †04
SANGTIAN, Alfonso L, Jr. 8030 MYRTLE TRACE DR 29526 #748-11-1979 L1993 **PD** *020 †55
SASSER, Charles Gregory. 8002 MYRTLE TRACE DR, 247582684 29526 #045-01-1967 L1967 **IM PLM** *020 †20
SASSER, Marshall Craig. 394 SINGLETON RIDGE RD 29526 #045-01-1963 L1963 **U OS** *071
SAUNDERS, Henry V. 903 BELL ST 29526 #051-04-1978 L1984 **IM OM** *020 †20
SNYDER, Richard Gale. 235 SINGLETON RIDGE RD, RICHARD G. SNYDER, M.D. PC 29526 #055-01-1982 L1983 *020

STANLEY, Covia Levance. ■ 29528 #035-06-1978 L2003 **PHP OBG** *020
STOKES, Doty Parker. 8028 MYRTLE TRACE DR 29526 #045-01-1972 L1973 **OPH** *071 †35
SUTTON, Darin Vincent. 808 FARRAR DR 29526 #045-04-1994 L2000 **OTO** *020 †45
TAYLOR, Ross. 2376 CYPRESS CIR, STE 300 29526 #051-04-1994 L2000 **ORS** *020 †40
TUCCI, Peter Anthony. ■ 29526 #056-06-1947 L1976 **AN** *071 †05
WALLACE, Edward Alton. 300 SINGLETON RIDGE RD 29526 #045-01-1984 L1987 **AN IM** *020 †05
WASHINGTON, Dode Nobia. 660 SINGLETON RIDGE RD, COASTAL CAROLINA OB/GYN 29526 #024-05-1992 L2002 **OBG** *020 †30
WATSON, Erin Elizabeth. 2376 CYPRESS CIR STE 300, ATTN AMY THOMAS 29526 #036-08-2003 L2007 **PM** *100
WILKINS, Jeffrey Chas. 2376 CYPRESS CIR, STE 300 29526 #021-05-1992 L1996 **PM PMM** *020 †60
WILSON, David Mark. 300 SINGLETON RIDGE RD 29526 #045-01-1987 L1991 **PTH** *020 †50
WILSON, John W, Jr. 8002 MYRTLE TRACE DR 29526 #036-07-1949 L1953 **IM** *020 †20
WILSON, John W, III. 121 WACC MED PK DR, STE B 29526 #045-01-1986 L1987 **IM** *020 †20
WOOD, Joseph Cary. 394 SINGLETON RIDGE RD 29526 #021-01-1993 L1999 **U** *020 †95
WYCHE, Keith Edward. 2376 CYPRESS CIR, STE 102 29526 #026-04-1994 L2002 **CD** *020 †20
YATES, James Wm, Jr. 2376 CYPRESS CIR, STE 300 29526 #045-01-1977 L1978 **ORS** *020 †40

CORDOVA — ORANGEBURG

GAFFNEY, Christopher Earl. ■ 29039 #045-04-2008 *012

COWPENS — SPARTANBURG

HEVENER, Marvin Geo. 5470 N MAIN ST 29330 #051-04-1975 L1976 **FM** *020 †18

CROSS — BERKELEY

RAVENELL, Roneka Leantric. ■ 29436 #045-01-2004 L2004 **RHU** *012 †20

CROSS ANCHOR — SPARTANBURG

BRANT, Elizabeth Jane. ■ 29331 #035-46-2008 *012

DANIEL ISLAND — BERKELEY

ADAMS, Sara Elizabeth. ■ 29492 #045-01-2004 L2004 **IM** *100 †20
CHAFIN, William Aiken. 113 BOUNTY ST, PRMH - INTERNAL MEDICINE 29492 #012-01-2004 L2004 **RHU** *012 †20
DAVIS, Lucy Green. 900 ISLAND PARK DR, STE 101 29492 #045-01-2001 L2003 **FM** *020 †18
GREGORY, J Lewis. 146 FAIRCHILD ST 29492 #036-01-1987 L1996 **MDM PD** *020 †55
HARTZOG, Timothy Hillery. ■ 29492 #036-05-1997 L2006 **PD** *020 †55
HIOTT, Mary Camille. ■ 29492 #045-01-2007 L2007 **GS** *012
HUNTER, Melissa H. 900 ISLAND PARK DR, STE 202B 29492 #045-01-1987 L1988 **FM** *040 †18
JOHNSON, Ian Todd. ■ 29492 #020-02-1999 L2007 **GS FM** *020
LAKE, Piave Pitisci. 271 BERESFORD CREEK ST 29492 #021-01-1997 L2001 **P** *020 †75
LEVIN, Julian Chas. 213 KING GEORGE ST, LEVIN AEROMEDICAL CONSULTI 29492 #045-01-1981 L1991 **FM OM** *020 †70,18
LIVESAY, William J, Jr. 295 SEVEN FARMS DR, STE C197 29492 #055-75-1999, ▲ L2008 **PM** *020 †60
MC CONNELL, Bright, III. 900 ISLAND PARK DR, STE 105 29492 #012-01-1979 L1985 **ORS OSM** *020 †40
MIDDLETON, Francis G. 146 FAIRCHILD ST 29492 #045-01-1966 L1966 **IM ID** *020 †20
MORRIS, Pamela Lee Bowe. 234 SEVEN FARMS DR, CLINIC 29492 #036-07-1981 L1997 **CD IM** *020 †20
NOONE, Tara Aileen. 234 SEVEN FARMS DR, THE CHARLESTON CLINIC LLC 29492 #036-05-1993 L1998 **DR AR** *020 †80
OLIVENCIA, Luis C. ■ 29492 #042-01-1965 L1997 **AM PD** *020 †55
PATE, Andrew Jos. 800 BECKON ST 29492 #045-04-1986 L1991 **AN** *020 †05
PETERS, Leonard Leckel. ■ 29492 #035-45-1967 L1975 **GS** *071 †85
ROBERTS, James R. 1086 BLAKEWAY ST 29492 #048-15-1992 L1997 **PD** *040 †20
SAHN, Eleanor E. 900 ISLAND PARK DR, STE 104 29492 #007-02-1972 L1983 **D IM** *020 †20,15
SHEAHAN, Patrick O'Brien. ■ 29492 #539-02-1997 L2008 *100
SIMPKINS, Carolyn Wong. 295 SEVEN FARMS DR, STE C-169 29492 #036-07-1999 L2003 **IM** *020 †20
SPICER, Leigh Mcrae. 900 ISLAND PARK DR, STE 101 29492 #045-01-2004 L2004 **FM** *020 †18
TRANAKOS, Elizabeth N. ■ 29492 #016-42-1999 L2000 **FM** *020 †18

DARLINGTON — DARLINGTON

BROWN, Harvey Neil. 964 LOCHEND DR 29532 #041-02-1970 L1978 **OBG** *020 †30
COHEN, Alexander Hyman. 201 CASHUA ST 29532 #045-01-1987 L1988 **FM** *020 †18
CONNOR, Gregory Stephen. 701 CASHUA FERRY RD 29532 #016-11-1973 L1975 **DR IM** *020 †18,80
CRICKMAN, Bonnie Lynn. 201 CASHUA ST 29532 #016-45-1983 L1984 **FM** *020 †18
FARINA-MORIN, Cecilia. ■ 29540 #045-01-1978 L1980 **P** *030 †75
HANNA, Brian Ansel. 213 PEARL ST, THE MEDICAL GROUP 29532 #045-04-2001 L2002 **FM** *020 †18
HEASTER, Brian Matthew. 201 CASHUA ST, PEE DEE HEALTHCARE 29532 #045-04-1995 L1996 **IM** *020
HOKANSON, Thomas Brent. 701 CASHUA FERRY RD, MCLEOD FAMILY MEDICINE 29532 #055-01-1977 L1997 **FM** *020 †18
KEITH, John Alvin, III. 105 INDUSTRIAL WAY 29532 #010-03-1996 L1999 **PD** *020 †55
LILLY, D Parker. 701 CASHUA FERRY RD, MCLEOD FAMILY MEDICINE 29532 #012-12-1999 L2000 **FM** *020 †20
MC INNIS, James Daniel. 201 CASHUA ST 29532 #045-01-1962 L1962 **GP** *071
RAINWATER, Chelsea Lurie. ■ 29532 #045-01-2007 L2007 **IM** *012
ROBERTSON, Richard H, Jr. 201 CASHUA ST 29532 #036-05-1974 L1979 **GE** *020 †20

SCHARSTEIN, Jeffery. 701 CASHUA FERRY RD, MCLEOD FAMILY MEDICINE 29532 #045-01-1981 L1982 **FM** *020

THOMAS, Raymond Lenoid. 701 CASHUA FERRY RD 29532 #036-07-1963 L1969 **R** *020 †80

WEINBAUM, Marc. 24 PUBLIC SQ, WEINBAUM PSYCHIATRIC SERVI 29532 #017-20-1979 L1997 **P OS** *020 †75 ‡

WILSON, Thomas Gray. 701 CASHUA FERRY RD, MCLEOD FAMILY MEDICINE 29532 #045-01-1978 L1979 **GS** *020 †85

DAUFUSKIE ISLAND – BEAUFORT

FERRARA, Emily Mc Duffie. 125 MARTINANGEL LN # 50 29915 #045-01-1949 L1949 **AN** *071

ROBERTS, Richard Henry. ■ 29915 #025-01-1961 L1962 **PD** *071

DILLON – DILLON

ALEXANDER, Paul Michael. 301 E JACKSON ST 29536 #064-01-1974 L1980 **FM** *020

ASHLEY, Ricanthony Rene. 301 E JACKSON ST 29536 #017-20-1990 L1996 **DR** *020 †80

BETHEA, Lesa Keen. 207 E MONROE ST 29536 #045-01-1988 L1989 **FM FSM** *020 †18

BLUM, Walter Biercuk. 409 E MADISON ST 29536 #035-19-1968 L1988 **GS TS** *020 †85

BROWN, Michael Nathaniel. 603 N 6TH AVE 29536 #045-01-1977 L1978 **FM** *020 †18

CERNY, Matthew John. 301 E JACKSON ST, SAINT EUGENE MEDICAL CENTE 29536 #010-01-1958 L1981 **R** *020 †80

FREEL, Paul Duane. 603 N 6TH AVE 29536 #036-08-1989 L1995 **FM** *020 †18

GRAHAM, Eric Matthew. 705 N 8TH AVE, STE 3A 29536 #016-11-1999 L2000 **PD** *020 †55

JENSEN, Dennis Michael. PO BOX 1069, 603 N SIXTH AVE 29536 #019-02-2002 L2003 **FM** *040 †18

KELLY, James Jos. 705 N 8TH AVE STE 1A, PROFESSIONAL BUILDING 29536 #010-02-1986 L1990 **IM** *020 †20

MEDINA, Clifford Estewart. 705 N 8TH AVE, STE 1A 29536 #024-01-1998 L2001 **IM** *020 †20

MOHAMED, Fazil Ayube, II. 705 N 8TH AVE, STE 3B 29536 #023-01-1998 L2004 **OBG** *020 †30

PATEL, Pravin R. ■ 29536 #495-58-1978 L1983 **IM FM** *020

RAMIREZ-WELDEN, Yvonne. 705 N 8TH AVE, STE 3A 29536 #042-01-1987 L1991 **PD** *020 †55

SCHEITERLE, Rebecca J. 301 E JACKSON ST, MCLEOD MEDICAL CENTER DILL 29536 #035-06-1979 L2008 **EM** *020 †18

SHEALY, Robin C. 603 N 6TH AVE 29536 #045-04-1987 L1988 **FM** *020 †18

SULLIVAN, Patricia Steadm. 1639 HIGHWAY 301 N, PHYSICIANS HEALTHCARE OF D 29536 #649-35-1986 L1992 **IM** *020

TWOMBLEY, James Michael. 301 E JACKSON ST 29536 #045-01-1974 L1976 **EM** *020

VANCE, Stephen Granville. 603 N 6TH AVE, DILLON FAMILY MEDICINE PA 29536 #036-08-1987 L1988 **FM** *020 †18

WALLACE, James Phillip. 705 N 8TH AVE STE 1A, MMC-DILLON PROFESSIONAL BU 29536 #011-02-1981 L1982 **IM** *020 †20

DUE WEST – ABBEVILLE

ANGEL, Alanna Elizabethbr. 6 COLLEGE ST 29639 #021-06-2002 L2003 **FM** *020 †18

CLARKE, Robert S, Jr. ■ 29639 #045-01-1950 L1950 **GP IM** *071

LESLIE, Karen Elizabeth. 6 COLLEGE ST 29639 #036-08-1994 L1997 **FM** *020 †18

DUNCAN – SPARTANBURG

ADAMS-HUDSON, Brenda L. 1575 E MAIN ST, FAMILY PHYSICIANS 290 29334 #036-01-1976 L1996 **FM FPG** *020 †18

BLACK, Mary Joan. 115 DEACON TILLER CT, ORTHOPEDIC ASSOCIATES PA 29334 #045-01-1990 L1995 **ORS** *020 †40

CORBETT, Bernard Augustus. 500 SQUIRES PT 29334 #005-12-1977 L1979 **FM** *020 †18

CROW, Daniel Ray. 210 FREEMAN FARM RD 29334 #045-01-1993 L1994 **FM** *020 †18

DIMERY, Lee Charley. ■ 29334 #045-01-1954 L1954 **GP** *071

FUNDERBURK, Michael Wayne. 115 DEACON TILLER CT, ORTHOPEDIC ASSOCIATES PA 29334 #045-01-1979 L1981 **ORS** *020 †40

HARLEY, Robert Stephen. 115 DEACON TILLER CT, ORTHOPEDIC ASSOCIATES PA 29334 #045-01-1977 L1982 **ORS** *020 †40

HENDERSON, Michael Ray. 115 DEACON TILLER CT, ORTHOPEDIC ASSOCIATES PA 29334 #036-05-1984 L1992 **ORS OFA** *020 †40

LABOTKA, Adrienne Louise. 500 SQUIRES PT 29334 #047-20-1989 L2003 **FM** *020 †18

MITCHELL, Michael David. 115 DEACON TILLER CT, ORTHOPEDIC ASSOCIATES PA 29334 #045-01-1986 L1987 **ORS OSS** *020 †40

MORROW, Shawn Michael. 237 PENICK DR 29334 #422-01-1998 L2001 **IM** *020 †20

NESMITH, Jason Mark. ■ 29334 #012-21-2008 *012

ROLLINS, Gerald Lee. 115 DEACON TILLER CT, ORTHOPEDIC ASSOCIATES PA 29334 #051-01-1976 L1982 **ORS** *020 †40

SKELTON, John Stuart. 1575 E MAIN ST 29334 #045-01-1984 L1987 **IM** *020 †20

TADDIA, Rachel Elizabeth. ■ 29334 #047-20-2008 *012

TANBONLIONG, Michael O. 1575 E MAIN ST 29334 #748-15-1984 L1996 **FM** *020 †18

EASLEY – PICKENS

ALI, Zahid. 129 FLEETWOOD DR 29640 #704-16-1980 L1997 **CD** *020 †20

ARDIS, Karen Ann. 200 FLEETWOOD DR, PALMETTO HEALTH 29640 #010-03-1990 L1994 **FM EM** *020 †20

ATKINSON, Michael Shane. 115 BRUSHY CREEK RD 29642 #045-04-1999 L2001 **FM** *020 †18

AWAN, Aftab Ahmad. 129 FLEETWOOD DR, FOOTHILLS CARDIOLOGY ASSOC 29640 #704-21-1994 L2000 **CD** *020 †20

BALLINGER, William Henry, Jr. 220 S PENDLETON ST 29640 #045-01-1979 L1988 **OPH** *020 †35

BANKS, Richard A, Jr. 106 JOHN ST, FAMILY PRACTICE & 29640 #045-01-1984 L1985 **FM EM** *020 †18

BAUKNIGHT, Remsen Stewart. ■ 29640 #047-05-1968 L1978 **OTO** *071 †45

BEANE, Scott Douglas. 800 N A ST 29640 #036-08-1989 L1990 **PD** *020 †55

BOATWRIGHT, Roger Dale. 101 RICHARD ST 29640 #045-01-1998 L2001 **IM** *020 †20

BOLINGER, Jony Margrit. 104 FLEETWOOD DR, CENTER EASLEY 29640 #045-01-1995 L1996 **FM** *020 †18

BOWDEN, David Malcolm. 220 S PENDLETON ST 29640 #001-02-1988 L1992 **OPH** *020 †35

BOWICK, Ralph H. ■ 29640 #045-01-1951 L1951 **GS** *071 †85

BRADLEY, Edwin. ■ 29640 #045-01-1952 L1952 **OBG** *071

BRICE, James Clowney, Jr. 104 FLEETWOOD DR 29640 #012-05-1960 L1960 **FM** *071 †18

BULKELEY, William Worthin, III. 207 HUNTINGTON RD 29642 #045-01-2008 *012

CARVER, David Franklin. 200 FLEETWOOD DR 29640 #045-04-1986 L1987 **FM** *020

CHANG, David Pohsun. 101 RICHARD ST 29640 #045-01-1997 L1998 **IM** *020 †20

COTTER, Deanna J. ■ 29642 #047-07-1990 L1995 **FM** *020 †20

COWAN, Claude Chester, Jr. ■ 29642 #047-06-1956 L1958 **PD** *071 †55

COX, Johnny Herman. 403 HILLCREST DR, STE C 29640 #047-20-1982 L1983 **GS** *020

DANGLER, Julie Mac Donald. 700 BRUSHY CREEK RD, FAMILY PRACTICE ASSOCIATES 29642 #012-05-1996 L1999 **FM** *020 †18

DILLON, Harold Dexter, III. 112 JOHN ST, STE 104 29640 #047-20-1993 L2005 **OPH** *020 †35

DOUGLAS, Frederick Gerald. 106 JOHN ST, FAMILY PRACTICE & 29640 #045-01-1969 L1969 **FM** *020 †18

EDENS, Gregory Wayne. 700 BRUSHY CREEK RD, FAMILY PRACTICE ASSOCIATES 29642 #045-01-1995 L1996 **FM** *020 †18

FINLEY, Robert Felix. 704 N A ST 29640 #045-01-1976 L1977 **ORS** *020 †40

FOWLER, Charles Richard. 112 JOHN ST, STE 203 29640 #030-06-1968 L1982 **NEP IM** *020 †20

FOX, Michael Patrick. 1351 CRESTVIEW RD, MOUNTAINVIEW OB GYN 29642 #047-06-1993 L2001 **OBG** *020 †30

FREEMAN, Steven Earl. 764 SACO LOWELL RD 29640 #045-04-1995 L1996 **IM** *020 †20

GARMON, Stacy Blye. 800 N A ST 29640 #045-01-1991 L1991 **GP** *071

GIGUERE, Jeffrey Kent. 109 FLEETWOOD DR STE A, CANCER CTRS OF THE CAROLIN 29640 #036-07-1980 L1990 **ON HEM** *020 †20

GODWIN, Ashley T. 290 ENTERPRISE DR, FOOTHILLS PEDS 29642 #045-01-1998 L1999 **PD** *020 †55

GOUDELOCK, Gary Morgan. 800 N A ST 29640 #012-05-1980 L1982 **PD** *020 †55

GREENBURG, Rolland Edwin. ■ 29640 #016-43-1946 L1978 **OBG** *071

HARDING, Lisa Gay. 1648 GENTRY MEMORIAL HWY 29640 #020-12-1998 L2004 **IM** *020 †20

HOLTON, Geanice. 1648 GENTRY MEMORIAL HWY, FOOTHILLS INTERNAL MEDICIN 29640 #024-05-1995 L1998 **IM** *020 †20

HUMPHRIES, Hiliary Seay. 106 GREEN CREST WAY 29642 #045-04-2001 L2002 **PD** *020 †55

ISKANDAR, Samy Robert. 200 FLEETWOOD DR 29640 #045-04-1998 L2005 **OBG** *020 †30

JAMESON, John Hal. 104 FLEETWOOD DR 29640 #045-01-1941 **GP** *071

JONES, William Kent. 800 N A ST 29640 #045-01-1980 L1982 **PD** *020 †55

JUNKER, David Arthur. 10701 ANDERSON RD 29642 #045-01-1977 L1978 **FM** *020 †18

KANEB, Gretchen Claire. 10701 ANDERSON RD 29642 #422-01-2000 L2007 **FM** *020 †18

KISSAM-WILLIAMS, Barbara. 800 N A ST 29640 #028-34-1994 L2005 **PD** *020 †55

KOCH, William Schumpert. 10701 ANDERSON RD 29642 #045-01-1977 L1978 **FM EM** *020 †18

LAMBERSON, Sandra J W. 112 JOHN ST, STE 105 29640 #017-20-1969 L1976 **D** *020 †15

LANDRY, Patricia. 104 FLEETWOOD DR, CENTER EASLEY 29640 #045-01-1989 L1992 **FM** *020 †18

LEAVITT, Anna Lee Thomas. 800 N A ST 29640 #045-01-1990 L1991 **PD** *020 †55

LEVENTIS, Annemarie C. 200 FLEETWOOD DR 29640 #045-04-1987 L1998 **FM** *020 †18 ‡

LOLLIS, Patrick Grady. 700 BRUSHY CREEK RD 29642 #045-04-1995 L1997 **FM** *020 †18

LOWRANCE, William Lee. 112 JOHN ST, FOOTHILLS UROLOGY 29640 #045-01-1973 L1975 **U** *075 †95

MANSURE, Frank T. ■ 29640 #041-01-1953 L1954 **OS IM** *071

MARTIN, Sloan Pruitt, Jr. ■ 29642 #045-01-1961 L1961 **TS** *071 †85,90

MATHIS, Louis Behrens, Jr. 10701 ANDERSON RD 29642 #045-01-1974 L1977 **FM** *020 †18

MC KINNON, Lynda M. 832 POWDERSVILLE RD 29642 #067-01-1986 L1995 **FM** *020 ‡

OLIVER, Marcia Ann. 115 BRUSHY CREEK RD, OAKTREE MEDICAL CENTRE 29642 #011-03-1991 L1998 **FM** *020 †18

O'QUINN, Joseph Wales. 1027 S PENDLETON ST, STE B-7 29642 #045-01-1990 L1991 **EM** *020 †18

PASUI, Kristine Dee. 112 JOHN ST STE 201 29640 #045-04-1996 L2000 **OBG** *020 †30

PATEL, Jay Sanjay. 115 BRUSHY CREEK RD, OAKTREE MEDICAL CENTRE, PC 29642 #496-36-2001 L2006 **PM** *100 †60

PHIPPS, Myra Aurelia. 303 DACUSVILLE HWY, OCLEMS FREE MEDICAL CLINIC 29640 #012-05-1995 L1998 **FM** *020 †20

PROSTKO, Thomas Richard. 403 HILLCREST DR, STE A 29640 #024-07-1983 L1988 **GE IM** *020 †20

REPIK, Barbara Sue. 106 JOHN ST, FAMILY PRACTICE & 29640 #025-12-1986 L1987 **IM EM** *020 †20

RICHARDS, Carla King. 800 N A ST 29640 #036-08-1988 L1993 **PD** *020 †55

ROBERSON, William Matthew. 112 JOHN ST, STE 103 29640 #012-01-2000 L2002 **ORS** *020

ROGERS, David S. 115 BRUSHY CREEK RD 29642 #649-19-1983 L1998 **N** *075

ROGERS, Dexter Brown. 700 BRUSHY CREEK RD 29642 #045-01-1960 L1960 **GP OS** *071

ROGERS, Malcolm Macdonald. 200 FLEETWOOD DR 29640 #045-01-1987 L1992 **AN** *020 †05

ROGERS, Melissa Reynolds. ■ 29640 #047-20-1987 L1992 **IM** *020 †20

SACCOGNA, Phillip Wm. 115 WHITMIRE RD 29640 #038-44-1990 L1995 **OTO FPS** *020 †45

SCHRIVER, Peter Clark. 764 SACO LOWELL RD 29640 #045-01-1988 L1994 **GS** *020 †85

SCOTT, William Marion, III. 109 FLEETWOOD DR 29640 #045-01-1977 L1978 **FM ADM** *020 †18

SEABROOK, Paul D, Jr. 200 FLEETWOOD DR 29640 #045-01-1970 L1971 **AN** *020

SHEALY, Ernest Gibson. 200 FLEETWOOD DR 29640 #045-01-1956 L1956 **GP** *071

SIM, Rowena Rosalie. 403 HILLCREST DR STE C 29640 #038-43-1988 L1989 **GS** *020 †85

SMITH, George Warren. 106 JOHN ST 29640 #045-01-1956 L1956 **GP** *071

SMITH, Valda Lee. 200 FLEETWOOD DR 29640 #019-02-1991 L1993 **FM EM** *020 †18

SNIPES, Calvin M, Jr. 1648 GENTRY MEMORIAL HWY 29640 #045-01-1982 L1983 **IM** *020 †20

SQUIRES, Cynthia Hart. 700 BRUSHY CREEK RD 29642 #045-01-1982 L1985 **GP** *020

SQUIRES, Herbert Randall. 1351 CRESTVIEW RD, MOUNTAINVIEW OB GYN 29642 #045-01-1980 L1985 **OBG** *020 †30

STROUD, Donna Rook. ■ 29640 #036-05-1970 L1973 **PD** *020 †55

STROUD, Lawrence Edgar. 109 FLEETWOOD DR, STE B 29640 #045-01-1975 L1978 **IM** *020 †20

SWIGER, Barry Reid. 1648 GENTRY MEMORIAL HWY 29640 #045-01-1981 L1982 **IM** *020 †20

THOMPSON, Allan James, Jr. 112 JOHN ST, STE 104 29640 #045-01-1978 L1979 **OPH** *020 †35

TOLLISON, Boyce Griffith. 104 FLEETWOOD DR, CENTER EASLEY 29640 #045-01-1967 L1967 **FM** *020 †18

WALLER, Jerome Howard, Jr. 104 FLEETWOOD DR, CENTER EASLEY 29640 #020-12-1992 L1993 **FM** *020 †18

WALSH, William Carl, Jr. 400 BELLA VISTA DR, STE F 29640 #045-01-1965 L1965 **FM** *020
WARREN, John Movius, Jr. 112 JOHN ST STE 201 29640 #001-06-1976 L1977 **GYN** *020 †30
WASYLENKO, Mark J. 115 BRUSHY CREEK RD, OAKTREE MEDICAL CENTRE PC 29642
#068-01-1975 L2005 **ORS OTR** *020 †40 ‡
WEBB, Leroy. ■ 29640 #051-04-1950 L1951 **GP AN** *071
WELBORN, Michael Keasler. 106 JOHN ST 29640 #045-01-1967 L1967 **FM** *020
WHEELER, William Earl. 403 HILLCREST DR STE C 29640 #027-01-1977 L1991
GS CCS *020 †85 ‡
WILLIAMS, Matthew Paul. 403 HILLCREST DR STE C, EASLEY GENERAL SURGEONS 29640
#028-34-1994 L2005 **GS** *020 †85
WILSON, William Randolph. 290 ENTERPRISE DR, FOOTHILLS PEDIATRICS P.A. 29642
#045-04-1983 L1984 **PD** *020 †55
WINN, Larry Ross. 104 FLEETWOOD DR, CENTER EASLEY 29640 #045-01-1974
FM FPG *020 †18
WYNNE, Morgan Dozier. ■ 29642 #012-05-1955 L1955 **PD** *071

EASTOVER – RICHLAND

ELLISON, Jody. 120 CLARKSON ST, RICHLAND COMM HEALTH CARE 29044
#038-44-1997 L1998 **FM** *020 †18
LYMAN, Frank Lavern. 1325 S CAROLINA RD, BLDG 984 29044 #045-04-1996 L1997 **IM** *020

EDGEFIELD – EDGEFIELD

BARFIELD, William Elliott, Jr. 300 RIDGE MEDICAL PLAZA RD, P O BOX 590 29824
#012-01-1970 L1971 **OBG** *020 †30
GORDINEER, Dale Richard. 200 RIDGE MEDICAL PLAZA RD, EDGEFIELD MEDICAL
CLINIC,P 29824 #045-01-1996 L1998 **FM** *020 †18
GORDINEER, Elizabeth S. 200 RIDGE MEDICAL PLAZA RD, EDGEFIELD MEDICAL CLINIC 29824
#045-01-1993 L1994 **FM** *020 †18
KYLSTRA, Harke Ruurd. PO BOX 590 29824 #660-03-1948 L1973 **GS** *071
LEAPHART, Eleanor Reece. 200 RIDGE MEDICAL PLAZA RD, EDGEFIELD MEDICAL
CLINIC 29824 #045-01-2000 L2001 **FM** *020 †18
MASSEY, Tami Yvonne. 200 RIDGE MEDICAL PLAZA RD, EDGEFIELD MEDICAL CLINIC 29824
#012-01-2002 L2003 **FM** *020 †18
NICHOLSON, Benjamin E, Jr. 200 RIDGE MEDICAL PLAZA RD, EDGEFIELD MEDICAL
CLINIC 29824 #045-01-1961 L1961 **FM** *020 †18
RAINSFORD, George Lynnwoo. 200 RIDGE MEDICAL PLAZA RD, EDGEFIELD MEDICAL
CLINIC 29824 #045-01-1976 L1977 **FM** *020 †18
SINGLETON, Gregory. 29824 #045-04-1989 L1992 **FM** *020 †18
TURNER, Wiley Herbert, Jr. 200 RIDGE MEDICAL PLAZA RD 29824 #045-01-1961 L1961
FM *071 †18
WOOD, Betty Jean. 407 COLUMBIA RD 29824 #045-01-1956 L1958 **OPH** *020 †35

EDISTO ISLAND – COLLETON

CANTEY, Larry Danl. 738 FAIRWAY DR 29438 #045-01-1979 L1980 **FM EM** *020 †18
FARVER, Harry Edwin. ■ 29438 #051-01-1942 L1951 **GS** *071
MC COLLUM, Edward Evelio. 29438 #045-01-1957 L1957 **GP IMG** *071

ELGIN – KERSHAW

BELMAR, Paula Lorena. 1004 EMANUEL ST 29045 #035-09-1990 L1996 **MPD** *020 †20,55
BOLOS-SY, Annabel Mendoza. ■ 29045 #748-02-1986 L2001 **AI** *020 †20
BROADWAY, Anne Lenette. 2510 GREEN HILL RD 29045 #045-04-1995 L1998 **FM** *020 †18
COCHRAN, Robert Anderson. PO BOX 68 29045 #041-13-1946 L1949 **GP** *071
DADHEECH, Girdhar Gopal. ■ 29045 #495-55-1972 L1989 **IM** *020
DAWKINS, Alicia Mcleod. ■ 29045 #045-04-2007 L2007 **OBG** *012
DEFAIL, Anthony J. ■ 29045 #041-77-2004, ▲ L2007 **IM** *020
DU BOSE, John Bratton, III. 1004 EMANUEL ST 29045 #045-01-1971 L1975 **IM** *020 †20
FELICIANO, Harry. ■ 29045 #035-46-1986 L1987 **PHP IMG** *062 †20
HEGLER, Jonathan Howard. 1004 EMANUEL ST 29045 #045-04-1999 L2000 **FM** *020 †18
HOLSTROM, Tallulah F. 1004 EMANUEL ST 29045 #045-01-1992 L1993 **IM** *020 †20
KANG, Min Wook. 1004 EMANUEL ST 29045 #045-04-2000 L2001 **FM** *020 †18
KEARSE, James Carlisle. 1004 EMANUEL ST 29045 #045-01-1982 L1984 **FM** *020 †20
MC ALPINE, James C, Jr. 1004 EMANUEL ST 29045 #045-01-1983 L1984 **FM** *020 †20
MC COTTER, Craig Jennings. ■ 29045 #036-08-1999 L2000 **ICE** *020 †20
PENNEBAKER, Gordon E. 1004 EMANUEL ST 29045 #045-01-1993 L1995 **FM** *020 †18
RASSIWALA, Farida Zakirhu. ■ 29045 #495-17-1998 L2007 **P** *020
SCHEUER, Jack F, Jr. 1004 EMANUEL ST 29045 #045-01-1978 L1979 **IM** *020 †20
SEIDEL, Amy Lynn. ■ 29045 #041-15-2000 L2007 **IC** *020 †20
TAYLOR, Julie Ann. 1004 EMANUEL ST 29045 #051-01-1988 L1995 **IM** *020 †20
TIMMONS, James M, Jr. 1004 EMANUEL ST 29045 #036-07-1971 L1976 **FM** *020 †18
TOLAN, Eliere John. ■ 29045 #781-03-1943 L1974 **P** *072
VANDENBERG, Jena S. ■ 29045 #021-01-1996 L1998 **PTH** *020
WILBERDING, Cynthia Ann. 1004 EMANUEL ST 29045 #025-07-1983 L1997 **IM** *020 †20

ELLOREE – ORANGEBURG

BOLAND, Brian Newton. ■ 29047 #045-01-2008 *012
CARPENTER, Richard L, Jr. 2734 CLEVELAND ST 29047 #045-04-1986 L1987 **FM** *020 †18
HOLMAN, Robert Evans. 375 HUNGERPILLER ST 29047 #045-01-1957 L1957 **GP** *020
JEFFERSON, Gydia Nina. ■ 29047 #020-02-1980 L1982 **IMG** *020

ENOREE – SPARTANBURG

QURESHI, Azhar Mahmood. ■ 29335 #704-01-1965 L1977 **IM** *020 †20

ESTILL – HAMPTON

BHIMBRA, Sudarshan Singh. 60 3RD ST, FAMILY MEDICAL CENTER 29918 #495-73-1985 L1995
NEP *075 †20

FAIR PLAY – OCONEE

MAYS, Harry B. 111 W PINE GROVE RD 29643 #045-01-1949 L1949 **GP** *071

FAIRFAX – ALLENDALE

BYRNE, Thomas Edward. PO BOX 1151 29827 #036-05-1996 L1997 **GP** *020
JONES, Robert Major. PO BOX 990, 333 REVOLUTIONARY TRL 29827 #041-13-1981 L1996
FM *020 †18
KAPOOR, Sushma Surrinder. 1787 ALLENDALE FAIRFAX HWY 29827 #496-26-1999 L2005
FM *020 †18
OSMAN, Hibah. PO BOX 990, PRISON ROAD - OFF HWY 278 29827 #605-01-1995 L2001
FM *020 †18
ROSS, Peter Cromwell. ■ 29827 #012-22-1992 L1995 **FM** *020

FLORENCE – FLORENCE

ADAMS, Robert Stephen. 901 E CHEVES ST, STE 200 29506 #001-02-1977 L1982
GYN *071 †30 ‡
AGNEW, Samuel Gerard. 901 E CHEVES ST, STE 500 29506 #021-01-1984 L2001 **OTR** *020 †40
ALAN, Rodney Kenneth. 901 E CHEVES ST, STE 500 29506 #036-07-2000 L2001 **ORS** *020 ‡
ALEXANDER, Anthony Wayne. 901 E CHEVES ST, STE 100 29506 #047-07-1987 L2000
PM *020 †60
ALEXANDER, Clarence R, Jr. 800 E CHEVES ST, STE 310 29506 #045-01-1991 L1992
FM *020 †18
ALLEN, Harry S, III. 805 PAMPLICO HWY, STE A310 29505 #045-01-1974 L1976 **IM** *020 †20
ALLEN, Scott H. 555 E CHEVES ST, MCLEOD REG MED CTR-RADIO 29506 #045-01-1990 L1996
RNR DR *020 †80
ANDERSON, Gary Blair. ■ 29504 #041-01-1985 L1995 **PCC IM** *020 †20
ANGUS, Joslyn Lloyd, Jr. 555 E CHEVES ST 29506 #045-04-2000 L2003 **FM** *020
ASH, Ezra Mozelle. 555 E CHEVES ST, MCLEOD FAMILY MEDICINE PRO 29506
#045-01-2007 L2007 **FP** *012
ATWOOD, Gerald Francis. 305 E CHEVES ST, STE 100 29506 #016-11-1964 L1992
CCP PDC *020 †55
BAJAJ, Rajesh. 506 E CHEVES ST, STE 202 29506 #495-36-1988 L1996 **HO ON** *020 †20
BAKER, Bennie Lee. 555 E CHEVES ST, ATTN: MEDICAL STAFF OFC 29506 #025-01-1985 L2007
GE IM *020 †20
BAKER, Justin Ashley. 555 E CHEVES ST, MCLEOD FAMILY MEDICINE PRO 29506
#012-01-2004 L2004 **FP** *012
BARDI, Christopher Thos. 1530 MCLURE CT 29505 #045-01-1978 L1979 **PD** *020 †55
BARNARD, Mark Luther. 506 E CHEVES ST 29506 #001-02-1976 L1986 **PUD** *020 †20
BARNETT, Lowell Thos. 800 E CHEVES ST STE 350 29506 #045-01-1967 L1967 **U** *020 †95
BAROODY, Naseeb B, Jr. 555 E CHEVES ST, MCLEOD HOSP DEPT FAM MED 29506
#041-09-1948 L1948 **IM CD** *071 ‡
BAROODY, Waddy G, Jr. 523 S DARGAN ST 29506 #045-01-1949 L1949 **IM GE** *020 †20
BARRETT, Michael Wayne. 305 E CHEVES ST, JETER SKINNER FAMILY 29506
#055-01-1990 L1992 **FM** *020 †18
BEHLING, Donald Archer. 800 E CHEVES ST, STE 310 29506 #045-01-1991 L1992 **FM** *020 †18
BEHLING, Edward Mellard. 800 E CHEVES ST, STE 310 29506 #045-01-1991 L1992
FM *020 †18
BELT, Mark Ellery. ■ 29501 #051-04-1997 L2001 **EM** *020 †16
BERDIN, Heidi Arsua. 805 PAMPLICO HWY, MEDICAL MALL B, STE 230 29505
#748-11-1990 L2006 **CCM** *020 †20
BERRIOS, Julia E. ■ 29501 #308-03-1979 L1981 **GP** *020
BHAT, Krishna Prasad. 1925 HOFFMEYER RD 29501 #654-01-2001 L2005 **PM GP** *020 †60
BISHARA, Lisa Ann. 555 E CHEVES ST 29506 #045-04-1993 L2002 **AN** *020 †05
BISHARA, Tarek Makram. 805 PAMPLICO HWY, STE B210 29505 #045-04-1992 L2002
PTH *020 †50
BLACKWELL, Billy Ray. 555 E CHEVES ST 29506 #045-01-1964 L1964 **IM** *071
BOBBETT, Gordon Howard. ■ 29502 #035-15-1940 L1948 **OTO A** *071 †45
BOLICK, Reginald Sinclair. 800 E CHEVES ST, STE 260 29506 #036-05-1968 L1975 **GS** *020 †85
BOOTH, John Price. 805 PAMPLICO HWY, STE A315 29505 #001-02-1976 L1982
FM ADM *020 †18
BOTTOMY, David Paul. 1706 2ND LOOP RD, ADVANCED CARDIOLOGY CONSUL 29501
#038-06-1971 L2000 **CD IM** *020 †20
BOULWARE, William Norris. 800 E CHEVES ST STE 370 29506 #045-01-1980 L1981
IM *020 †20
BOWMAN, Philip Clinton. 125 E CHEVES ST, FLORENCE 29506 #045-01-1984 L1988 **P** *020 †75
BOYSIA, Frank Thos. 309 W PINE ST 29501 #012-01-1974 L1978 **D** *020 †15
BOZARD, Asbury Cecil, Jr. 901 E CHEVES ST, STE 100 29506 #045-01-1964 L1964
ORS *071 †40
BRATTON, James Rufus, Jr. 800 E CHEVES ST, STE 480 29506 #045-01-1974 L1975
OTO *020 †45
BREAZEALE, Grant Hamilton. 805 PAMPLICO HWY, STE B310 29505 #045-01-1996 L1999
PCC *012 †20
BRENNAN, James Joseph. 901 E CHEVES ST, STE 420 29506 #035-03-1993 L2000 **NS** *020 †25
BRIDGES, Walter Steven. 121 E CEDAR ST 29506 #012-01-1984 L1993 **NPM PD** *020 †55
BROWN, Frank Reginald, III. 305 E CHEVES ST STE 330, DEVELOPMENTAL PEDS,
MEDICA 29506 #028-02-1975 L1984 **PD** *020 †55
BROWNING, Gregory Vincent. 2188 WINDSOR FOREST DR 29501 #045-01-1981 L1982
FM PM *020 †18
BROWNING, John Barrett. 901 E CHEVES ST STE 300 29506 #012-05-1986 L1994
OBG *020 †30
BRUCE, John Larrabee. ■ 29501 #045-01-1931 **GP GS** *071
BUCHER, Matthew Harold. 555 E CHEVES ST, MCLEOD FAMILY PRACTICE 29506
#051-01-2005 L2005 **FP** *012
BURNER, Bruce Ellis. 121 E CEDAR ST, CAROLINAS HOSPITAL SYSTEM 29506
#045-01-1984 L1985 **EM FM** *020 †18

BURNETT, Jimena Cordeiro-. 2437 WILLWOOD DR 29501 #132-02-1993 L2004 **FM** *020 †18
BURNETT, Waldo Emerson. ■ 29501 #035-20-1943 L1980 **P OS** *030
BURNS, Kenneth Scott, Jr. 805 PAMPLICO HWY 29505 #045-01-1996 L1997 **EM FM** *020 †18
CAMPBELL, Sherri Lynn D. 2100 W LUCAS ST 29501 #036-08-1992 L1996 **P** *020
CARDONA, Fe Asuncion. 125 E CHEVES ST, FLORENCE MENTAL HEALTH 29506 #748-01-1961 L1988 **GP FM** *030 †55 ‡
CAUTHEN, Wm Louis, Jr. 805 PAMPLICO HWY, EMERGENCY PHYSICIAN SERVIC 29505 #045-04-1985 L1986 **FM** *020 †18
CHAIPIS, Philip Nicholas. 805 PAMPLICO HWY, FLOYD MEDICAL ASSOCIATES 29505 #033-06-1991 L1996 **GS** *072 †85
CHANDLER, Michael Kenneth. 1925 HOFFMEYER RD, WEST FLORENCE 29501 #045-01-1995 L1996 **FM** *020 †18
CHANDLER, Paul Evert. 901 E CHEVES ST, STE 200 29506 #047-06-1983 L1997 **OBG** *020 †30
CHAPMAN, David Riner. 1523 HERITAGE LN 29505 #011-02-1971 L1975 **GYN** *020 †30 ‡
CHAPMAN, John Marshall. 1590 FREEDOM BLVD, STE D 29505 #045-01-1978 **OBG** *020 †30
CHARNES, Curt Bryant. 1594 FREEDOM BLVD, STE 202 29505 #422-01-2001 L2004 **FM** *020 †18
CHAUDHRY, Anu. 901 E CHEVES ST, STE 360 29506 #495-36-1984 L1996 **OBG** *020 †30
CHELEN, Carl John. 305 E CHEVES ST, STE 220 29506 #041-14-1988 L1998 **CCP PD** *020 †55
CHOKSHI, Brinda Rakesh. 1594 FREEDOM BLVD, STE 305 29505 #045-01-1993 L2000 **IM** *020 †20
CHOKSHI, Rakesh Pravin. 901 E CHEVES ST, STE 100 29506 #045-01-1993 L2000 **ORS** *020 †40
CHOWDHARY, Deepak. 619 S DARGAN ST 29506 #495-36-1983 L2001 **GE IM** *020 †20
CHUNG, Dong Ha. ■ 29501 #583-04-1966 L1986 **P** *020 †75
CLARK, Barry Lee. 901 E CHEVES ST, STE 100 29506 #018-75-1998, ▲ L2004 **FM** *020
CLARK, Pamela Ann. 305 E CHEVES ST, STE 220 29506 #035-06-1990 L1991 **PDE** *020 †55
CLARY, Angela Lynn. 1590 FREEDOM BLVD STE D 29505 #045-01-1991 L1993 **OBG** *020 †30
CLEVELAND, Gregor Geo. 555 E CHEVES ST 29506 #036-01-1987 L1992 **VIR R** *020 †80
COHEN, Scott Douglas. 800 E CHEVES ST, STE 350 29506 #038-40-1996 L2002 **U** *020 †95
COKER, Steven Nathaniel. 1590 FREEDOM BLVD 29505 #045-01-1973 L1975 **OBG** *020 †30
COLBY, Craig Byron. 555 E CHEVES ST, MCLEOD FAMILY MEDICINE PRO 29506 #012-01-2007 L2007 **FP** *012
COLEMAN, Ashley Dan. 555 E CHEVES ST, MCLEOD FAMILY MEDICINE PRO 29506 #001-02-2007 L2007 **FP** *012
COLEMAN, William Liston. 121 E CEDAR ST, P O BOX 100550 29506 #045-01-1960 L1960 **GP** *020
COLLINS, Charles Michael. 204 E CHEVES ST 29506 #045-01-1982 L1983 **PD** *020 †55
CONNER, Gerald Foster. 800 E CHEVES ST, STE 280 29506 #045-01-1995 L2005 **PS** *020
CONNOR, Walter Ernest. 555 E CHEVES ST, MCLEOD FAMILY MEDICINE PRO 29506 #045-04-1984 L1986 **FM** *020 †18
COOPER, Vidette Violette. 1594 FREEDOM BLVD STE 202 29505 #045-01-1997 L2001 **IM** *020 †20
COX, Jesse Thos, Jr. 901 E CHEVES ST, STE 370 29506 #045-01-1979 L1980 **NPM PD** *020 †55
CRANE, Thomas Jefferson. 555 E CHEVES ST, MEDICAL STAFF OFFICE 29506 #045-04-1986 L1990 **IM HOS** *020 †20
CRAYCRAFT, Amy Marie. ■ 29501 #028-46-2002 L2007 **FM** *020 †18
CREEDMAN, Steven Scott. 805 PAMPLICO HWY, DEPT OF RADIOLOGY 29505 #011-03-1978 L1983 **DR** *020 †80
CROWE, Ralph Edwin, III. 555 E CHEVES ST, MCLEOD FAMILY MEDICINE PRO 29506 #012-01-2007 L2007 **FP** *012
CULLETON, John Lloyd. 506 E CHEVES ST, CAROLINA HEALTH CARE 29506 #024-01-1984 L1992 **END IM** *020 †20
CULPEPPER, David Milton. 305 E CHEVES ST, STE 120 29506 #045-04-1984 L1985 **IM** *020 †20
CUNNINGHAM, Christopher G. 305 E CHEVES ST, STE 230 29506 #024-05-1982 L2006 **VS** *020 †85
CURRAN, Michael Manning. 555 E CHEVES ST, RESIDENCY PROGRAM 29506 #045-04-2006 L2006 **FP** *012
CUSTY, Jane Catherine. 555 E CHEVES ST 29506 #027-01-1970 L1971 **AN** *020
CUTLER, Verne Eugene. 309 W PINE ST 29501 #012-01-1970 L1977 **D** *020 †15
CUTRY, Anthony Francis. 805 PAMPLICO HWY, FLOYD MEDICAL ASSOCIATES 29505 #028-34-1995 L2000 **GS** *020 †85
DALES, Linda Mary. 555 E CHEVES ST 29506 #305-01-1995 L2008 **IM END** *020 †20
DANCY, Timothy Ward. 2437 WILLWOOD DR, MC LEOD FAM MED-SPORTS 29501 #036-01-2000 L2004 **FSM** *020 †18
DAVE, Chirag Harkant. 506 E CHEVES ST 29506 #495-76-1991 L2005 **PUD** *020 †20
DAVIDSON, James Michael. 901 E CHEVES ST STE 200 29506 #012-01-1981 L1989 **OBG** *020 †30 ‡
DAVIS, Clarence S, Jr. 611 S DARGAN ST 29506 #045-01-1961 L1961 **R** *071 †80
DAVIS, Richard Franklin. 1530 MCLURE CT 29505 #045-01-1980 L1983 **PD** *020 †55
DAVIS, Roger Allen. 901 E CHEVES ST STE 460 29506 #045-01-1968 L1968 **P** *020
DAWSON, Alfred Gilchrist. 251 W PALMETTO ST 29501 #045-01-1975 L1976 **ORS GP** *020 †40
DAWSON, George Robert, III. 251 W PALMETTO ST 29501 #045-01-1969 L1969 **ORS HS** *075 †40
DEDONIS, James Louis. 1706 2ND LOOP RD 29501 #007-02-1976 L1999 **CD IM** *020 †20
DEHLINGER, Erik. 805 PAMPLICO HWY 29505 #041-13-1994 L1997 **EM** *020 †16
DEHLINGER, Marian. 125 E CHEVES ST, PEE DEE MENTAL HEALTH CTR 29506 #041-13-1989 L1998 **P** *020 †75
DEKLE, Joel Stewart. 1594 FREEDOM BLVD STE 103 29505 #012-01-1965 L1966 **FM** *071 †18
DE LA CRUZ, Maria Lee. 555 E CHEVES ST, RESIDENCY PROGRAM 29506 #020-02-2006 L2006 **FP** *012
DE MICHELE, Domenic John. 125 S CASHUA DR 29501 #010-02-1984 L1990 **N RNR** *020
DENT, John Marshall, III. 410 S COIT ST 29501 #012-01-1986 L1987 **OBG FM** *020 †18,30
DENTON, Patrick Kerry. 901 E CHEVES ST STE 100, PEE DEE ORTHOPAEDIC ASSCS, 29506 #047-05-1995 L2001 **OSM** *020 †40
DERSCH, Stephen Andrew. 1925 HOFFMEYER RD, WEST FLORENCE FAMILY PRACT 29501 #017-20-2000 L2001 **FM** *020 †18 ‡
DICKINSON, Catherine Nico. 555 E CHEVES ST, MCLEOD FAMILY MEDICINE PRO 29506 #020-02-2007 L2007 **FP** *012
DISHAROON, Aimee Lee. 555 E CHEVES ST, RESIDENCY PROGRAM 29506 #045-04-2006 L2006 **FP** *012
DIXON, Woodward Rion, Jr. 1920 2ND LOOP RD 29501 #422-01-1988 L2003 **IM** *020
DOCHERTY, Jon Harrell. 514 S DARGAN ST, STE G 29506 #045-01-1971 L1976 **IM CD** *020 †20
DOCHERTY, Jon Harrell, Jr. ■ 29501 #045-01-1994 L1999 **RHU** *020 †20
DOMAI, Phuonglinh. 1594 FREEDOM BLVD STE 102 29505 #024-07-2001 L2004 **IM** *020 †20
DOZIER, Samuel Griffin. 800 E CHEVES ST, STE 200 29506 #045-01-1998 L1999 **IM** *020 †20
DUCKER, Dwight Fripp. 800 E CHEVES ST, STE 200 29506 #045-01-1991 L1992 **IM** *020
DUDLEY, William Russel. ■ 29506 #041-01-1968 L1986 **AN** *020 †05
DUNBAR, Daniel Hamilton. 555 E CHEVES ST, MCLEOD FAMILY MEDICINE PRO 29506 #045-01-2007 L2007 **FP** *012
DUNLAP, Joseph W, Jr. 901 E CHEVES ST, STE 100 29506 #047-06-1971 L1979 **ORS** *071 †40
EDWARDS, Willie S, Jr. 901 E CHEVES ST, STE 100 29506 #036-01-1981 L1982 **ORS** *020 †40
EFROS, James Howard. 555 E CHEVES ST 29506 #047-07-1993 L1997 **AN** *020 †05
ELDER, Benjamin Brewer. 1530 MCLURE CT, EASTERN CAROLINA PEDIATRIC 29505 #045-01-2004 L2007 **PD** *020 †55
ELLIS, Norman D, Jr. 555 E CHEVES ST 29506 #045-01-1941 L1941 **GS** *071 †85
ELVINGTON, Robert Edward. 901 E CHEVES ST, STE 100 29506 #045-01-1993 L1994 **ORS** *020 †40
EMERSON, Gary Hamilton. 901 E CHEVES ST, STE 300 29506 #045-04-1995 L2002 **OBG** *020 †30
ERVIN, Daniel M. 1523 HERITAGE LN 29505 #045-01-1977 L1979 **OTO FPS** *020 †45
ERVIN, Dewey Nelson. ■ 29506 #021-01-1967 L1974 **ORS** *020 †40
ERVIN, Frank Richard. 555 E CHEVES ST, MCLEOD REGIONAL MED CTR 29506 #041-09-1971 L1977 **ID MDM** *030 †20
EVALDI, Martin Frederick. 805 PAMPLICO HWY 29505 #045-01-1978 L1979 **AN** *020 †05 ‡
EVANS, Walter James. 436 W PALMETTO ST 29501 #021-05-1983 L1995 **N LM** *020 †75
FARISH, C Morrison. 1530 MCLURE CT 29505 #045-01-1974 L1976 **PD** *020 †55
FARNSWORTH, William V. 805 PAMPLICO HWY, STE B210 29505 #045-04-1985 L1986 **PTH** *020 †50
FARRELL, Howard Anthony. 1594 FREEDOM BLVD, STE 206 29505 #035-45-1989 L1998 **OTO** *020 †45
FEASTER, George Ray. 555 E CHEVES ST 29506 #045-04-2002 L2004 **IM** *020
FIORILLO, James Richard. 1012 LINDBERG DR, ANESTHESIOLOGY CONSULTANTS 29501 #024-07-1982 L2005 **AN** *020 †05
FLANDRY, Amy Elizabeth. ■ 29505 #045-01-2006 L2006 **IM** *012
FLOYD, C Edward. 805 PAMPLICO HWY, FLOYD MEDICAL ASSOCIATES 29505 #045-01-1959 L1959 **GS TS** *020 †85
FLOYD, Coleman Lee. 805 PAMPLICO HWY, P O BOX 12757 29505 #045-01-1986 L1992 **AN** *020 †05,55
FOX, Daniel J. 555 E CHEVES ST 29506 #048-13-1992 L1996 **AN** *020 †05
FOX, Mark Andrew. 1203 E CHEVES ST 29506 #045-01-1986 L1989 **IM PLM** *020 †20
FRANCIS, Charlotte L. 901 E CHEVES ST STE 350, PEE DEE REGIONAL FAMILY ME 29506 #012-21-1992 L1993 **FM** *020 †18
FREELS, Douglas Boyd. 901 E CHEVES ST, STE 100 29506 #047-20-1990 L2007 **ORS** *020 †40
FROST, Bryon Kenneth. 555 E CHEVES ST, BOX 100551 29506 #045-01-2000 L2003 **EM** *100 †16
GAMBLE, Homer Franklin. 121 E CEDAR ST 29506 #045-01-1973 L1974 **FM PHP** *020
GAMBLE, Troy Belser, Jr. 805 PAMPLICO HWY, MAUB SUITE 320 29505 #045-01-1980 L1981 **FM** *020 †18
GANDY, Edwin Laverne. 630 N BEAVERDAM DR, 630 BEAVERDAM DRIVE 29501 #045-04-1992 L1995 **EM** *020 †16
GAUSE, John Wesley. 800 E CHEVES ST, STE 260 29506 #045-01-1987 L1992 **GS** *020 †85
GHAMRA, Ziad Walid. 506 E CHEVES ST, CAROLINA HEALTH CARE 29506 #605-01-1998 L2005 **PCC** *020 †20
GILPIN, Albert Thos, Jr. 901 E CHEVES ST, STE 500 29506 #045-04-1984 L1986 **ORS** *020 †40
GOLDSTEIN, Lewis Wm. 653 S COIT ST 29501 #045-01-1978 L1982 **OBG EM** *020 †30
GOWDY, Harold Watson, Jr. 427 ROSEWOOD DR 29501 #045-01-1964 L1964 **PHP** *071 †55
GRAHAM, Carla Camille. 492 W CHEVES ST 29501 #036-08-1991 L1992 **FPS OTO** *020 †45
GREENBERG, Phillip Henry. 805 PAMPLICO HWY, MALL A SUITE #230 29505 #045-01-1973 L1979 **GS** *020 †85
GREENBERG, Stuart Alan. 214 W PINE ST 29501 #045-01-1974 L1980 **U GS** *020 †95
GREENE, Howard Noble. 400 N CASHUA DR, CAROLINAS CENTERS FOR SIGH 29501 #011-02-1985 L2006 **OPH GP** *020 †35
GRIFFIN, Joe Asa. 513 S DARGAN ST, GRIFFIN PLASTIC SURGERY 29506 #045-01-1982 L1989 **PS** *020 †65
GRUBB, Larry Douglas. 555 E CHEVES ST DEPT RAD 29506 #045-04-1983 L1992 **RO** *020 †80
GUPTA, Brijendra. 255 WARLEY ST 29501 #495-12-1986 L2001 **CCM** *020 †20
GUYTON, Eugene Danl, Jr. 214 W PINE ST 29501 #045-01-1970 L1977 **U** *020 †95
HABERMEIER, Hans Karl. PO BOX 6166 29502 #010-02-1963 L1971 **PTH** *071 †50
HALUS, Steven Mc Donell. 805 PAMPLICO HWY 29505 #005-06-1992 L1996 **EM** *020 †16
HAMADEH, Ghassan Nimah. ■ 29501 #605-01-1984 L1987 **FM** *030 †18
HAMRICK, Gerald Cofer, Jr. 555 E CHEVES ST 29506 #055-01-1991 L1995 **AN** *020 †05
HARDAWAY, William Danl. 901 E CHEVES ST, STE 600 29506 #045-01-1973 L1976 **IM CD** *020 †20
HARLAN, Jos Ellsworth, Jr. 901 E CHEVES ST, STE 370 29506 #036-05-1977 L1980 **NPM PD** *020 †55
HARLEY, Al Boyce. 151 E PINE ST 29506 #045-01-1959 L1959 **P CHP** *020
HARRIS, James Mark. 805 PAMPLICO HWY STE A230, FLOYD MEDICAL ASSOCIATES 29505 #045-01-1993 L2006 **GS** *020 †85
HATCHELL, Jeffrey Fulton. 555 E CHEVES ST, RESIDENCY PROGRAM 29506 #045-01-2006 L2006 **FP** *012
HAZELWOOD, Wm Madison. 555 E CHEVES ST, MED STAFF ADMINISTRATION O 29506 #045-01-1972 L1973 **PUD IM** *020 †20
HEALY, R Joseph, Jr. 805 PAMPLICO HWY STE A130 29505 #045-01-1981 L1982 **N** *020
HENDERSON, William N. ■ 29505 #036-07-1946 L1965 **IMG FM** *071 †18
HERRIN, Michael Keith. 2113 SILVERTHORN ST 29505 #011-04-1987 L1988 **AN** *020 †05
HESTER, William Homer. 555 E CHEVES ST 29506 #045-01-1965 L1965 **FM** *040 †18
HICKS, Myers Hampton. ■ 29501 #051-01-1945 L1950 **IM A** *071 †20
HILL, Karen Ritter. 204 E CHEVES ST 29506 #036-08-1992 L1993 **PD** *020 †55
HILL, Samuel Crawford, IV. 555 E CHEVES ST, DEPT OF RADIOLOGY 29506 #036-08-1992 L1993 **DR VIR** *020 †80
HINDMAN, Carey M. 651 S COIT ST 29501 #045-01-1980 L1981 **DR NM** *020 †80
HODGE, Michael Levaun. 1594 FREEDOM BLVD, STE 205 29505 #045-01-1963 L1963 **N** *075 †75
HOFFMEYER, Margaret H. 1594 FREEDOM BLVD, STE 103 29505 #045-01-1982 L1983 **FM** *020 †18
HOLLAND, Evans. 901 E CHEVES ST, STE 600 29506 #045-01-1990 L1997 **CD IM** *020 †20
HOLLAND, Fred Wilson, II. 305 E CHEVES ST, STE 270 29506 #017-20-1986 L2007 **TS** *020 †85,90
HOOKER, Glen Calvin. 251 LAWSON ST 29501 #033-05-1982 L1992 **P PD** *020 ‡
HOPLA, Dan Michael. 800 E CHEVES ST 29506 #039-01-1978 L1986 **OTO** *020 †45
HOTCHKISS, Robert Kenneth. 417 S DARGAN ST 29506 #041-07-1982 L1987 **CHP P** *020 †75

■ = Address Information Privacy Protected

HOWELL, Richard Reber. 555 E CHEVES ST 29506 #041-07-1978 L1984 **FM** *040 †18

HSIA, Michael Hsuehching. ■ 29505 #048-04-2000 L2007 **U** *100

HUCKS, Mark Alan. 901 E CHEVES ST, STE 200 29506 #045-04-2002 L2004 **OBG** *020

HUDGENS, Roy Edward, Jr. 181 E EVANS ST 29506 #045-01-1962 L1962 **AN** *071

HYLER, Daniel Wesley. 1594 FREEDOM BLVD, STE 202 29505 #045-01-1985 L1986 **FM** *020 †18 ‡

HYLER, Randell Allen, Jr. 2510 W SUMTER ST 29501 #045-04-1997 L2000 **IM** *020 †20

HYMAN, Peter Dewitt, Jr. 555 E CHEVES ST 29506 #045-01-1988 L1990 **EM** *020 †16

HYMAN, Vera Church. 805 PAMPLICO HWY, STE B210 29505 #045-01-1969 L1969 **PTH HMP** *020 †50

INMAN, Carolyn Louise. 509 S COIT ST, PALMETTO FAMILY PHYSICIANS 29501 #051-07-1999 L2001 **FM** *020 †18

INTEMANN, Stephen Rease. 805 PAMPLICO HWY, STE B210 29505 #051-01-1976 L1981 **PTH PCP** *020 †50

JACKSON, Andrea Marie. 535 S CHURCH ST, CAROLINAS OBGY ASSOC. 29506 #036-07-1984 L2006 **OBG** *020 †30

JAVED, Arshad. 555 E CHEVES ST, UNIV OF CINCINNATI MEDICAL 29506 #704-01-1989 L2001 **IMG** *020

JEBAILY, Gerard Chas. 555 E CHEVES ST, MCCLEOD FAM MED 29506 #045-01-1973 L1974 **FM** *040 †18

JEBAILY, Patrick John. ■ 29505 #045-01-2008 *012

JETER, Harold H, Jr. 305 E CHEVES ST, STE 160 29506 #051-01-1952 L1954 **FM** *071 †18

JOBE, John Stephen. 805 PAMPLICO HWY, STE B210 29505 #047-06-1991 L1997 **PTH PCP** *020 †50 ‡

JOHNSON, Isaiah Micah. 901 E CHEVES ST, STE 300 29506 #011-03-2003 L2007 **OBG** *020

JOHNSON, Peter Graham. 555 E CHEVES ST 29506 #064-01-1976 L2004 **OM** *020 †70

JONA, Vinod Kumar. 506 E CHEVES ST 29506 #495-57-1994 L2001 **PUD** *020 †20

JONES, Francis Gregg. 555 E CHEVES ST 29506 #045-01-1978 L1979 **AN PME** *020

JONES, Gregory Hugh. 305 E CHEVES ST, STE 270 29506 #012-01-1981 L1988 **TS** *020 †85,90

JORDAN, Charles Milford. 204 E CHEVES ST 29506 #045-01-1969 L1969 **PD** *020 †55

KAMMER, Kenneth Stuart. 305 E CHEVES ST STE 300 29506 #025-01-1973 L1980 **NS** *020 †25

KEISLER, Christel Nicole. 555 E CHEVES ST, MCLEOD FAMILY MEDICINE 29506 #045-04-2005 L2005 **FP** *012

KENT, Ashley Deane. 1929 MOUNTAIN LAUREL CT, STE B 29505 #016-42-1984 L1988 **N IM** *020 †75

KHAN, M Sana Ulla. 555 E CHEVES ST 29506 #496-01-1994 L2004 **P PYG** *020

KHAN, Sanaullah. 901 E CHEVES ST, STE 460 29506 #704-16-1997 *100

KHIANGTE, Zothanmawii. 506 E CHEVES ST, CAROLINA HEALTH CARE 29506 #422-01-2000 L2006 **CCM PUD** *020 †20

KIELAR, Casimir Michal. ■ 29506 #759-11-1963 L1972 **AN** *020

KING, Caleb K. 555 E CHEVES ST, MCLEOD FAMILY MEDECINE CEN 29506 #024-01-1993 L1998 **PG** *020 †55

KING, Reamer Benjamin. 555 E CHEVES ST 29506 #045-01-1994 L1995 **AN** *020 †05

KIRKLAND, John Judson. 110 W PINE ST 29501 #045-01-1971 L1972 **GP PD** *020

KIRKPATRICK, Palmer M, Jr. 619 S DARGAN ST 29506 #045-01-1970 L1972 **GE IM** *020 †20

KLINE, Richard Blake. 2812 CARRIAGE LN 29505 #045-01-1994 L1998 **AN** *020 †05

KOLB, Cynthia Elizabeth. 901 E CHEVES ST, STE 300 29506 #045-01-1993 L1995 **OBG** *020 †30

KOZACKI, Krista Marie. 800 E CHEVES ST, STE 380 29506 #035-06-1991 L1993 **FM** *020 †18

KRAIKIT, Sompong. 255 WARLEY ST 29501 #891-03-1967 L1976 **NEP IM** *020 †20

KRAIKIT, Suwanee. ■ 29501 #891-03-1971 **AN** *074

KRAININ, Fred Mitchell. 901 E CHEVES ST, STE 600 29506 #024-05-1981 L1992 **CD IC** *020 †20

KRISHNAMURTHY, Shedthike. 436 W PALMETTO ST 29501 #496-39-1977 L2002 **CHN** *020 †75

LAMM, James Dominic. 2637 ASCOT DR 29501 #026-04-1983 L2000 **IM** *020 †16

LANCASTER, Michael J. 555 E CHEVES ST, MCLEOD REGIONAL MEDICAL CE 29506 #352-07-1967 L1988 **AN** *020

LEE, Edward Mc Cravy. 800 E CHEVES ST, STE 260 29506 #045-01-1977 L1980 **GS** *020 †85

LEE, Evan Heyward. 805 PAMPLICO HWY, DEPT OF ANESTHESIA 29505 #045-04-1998 L2007 *020 †05

LEE, Frank B, Sr. 1594 FREEDOM BLVD STE 103 29505 #045-01-1942 L1942 **GS GP** *071

LEE, Frank Barnwell, Jr. 805 PAMPLICO HWY, FLOYD MEDICAL ASSOCIATES 29505 #045-01-1975 L1979 **GS VS** *020 †85

LEE, James Devin. 555 E CHEVES ST 29506 #001-06-1991 L1994 **EM** *020 †16

LEE, Margaret Eugenia. 518 OLEANDER DR 29501 #045-01-1983 L1989 **DR** *020 †80

LEE, Paul Gregory. 555 E CHEVES ST 29506 #055-01-1989 L1993 **AN** *020 †05

LENG, Vitt P. 1706 2ND LOOP RD 29501 #891-02-1971 L2004 **CD IM** *020 †20

LEWIS, Thomas Gerald, Jr. 555 E CHEVES ST, MCLEOD PHYSICIAN ASSOCIATE 29506 #045-01-2001 L2004 **EM** *020

LEWIS-CAREY, Mary Beth. PO BOX 100523 29501 #010-01-1995 L2004 **DR** *020 †80

LIANG, Cassie Lai Ku. 825 W EVANS ST 29501 #305-01-2001 L2007 **FM** *020 †18

LITTLE, Dwight Downs. 514 S DARGAN ST, STE G 29506 #045-01-1976 L1993 **IM FM** *020 †20

LIVINGSTON, Mark A. 3201 S CASHUA DR 29501 #045-01-1975 L1976 **P CHP** *020 †75

LORENZ, William Dean. 1925 HOFFMEYER RD 29501 #005-12-1988 L1994 **PM** *020 †60

LOWE, Paul Phillip. 656 S COIT ST, 2715 COLONIAL DRIVE 29501 #019-02-1985 L1997 **P CHP** *020 †75

LUCAS, Jay Luke. 1540 AMERICAN DR 29505 #045-01-1979 L1980 **OTO** *020 †45 ‡

LUSK, Clifford Dale. 901 E CHEVES ST, STE 200 29506 #045-01-1985 L1992 **OBG** *020 †30

LYLES, Kelly Waters. 1594 FREEDOM BLVD, STE 305 29505 #045-04-1990 L1991 **IM** *020 †20

MACDONALD, Allan R. 555 E CHEVES ST, FAMILY MEDICINE RESIDENCY 29506 #035-45-1983 L1990 **FM** *040 †18

MAC PHERSON, Douglas A. 555 E CHEVES ST 29506 #035-03-1988 L1992 **AN** *020 †05

MAHAJAN, Lalit Kumar. 501 S COIT ST 29501 #495-03-1989 L2000 **IM** *020 †20

MAI, Nguyen Thi. 555 W CHEVES ST 29501 #941-01-1961 L1979 **GP N** *071

MALDONADO, Ricardo Antoni. 506 E CHEVES ST 29506 #737-01-1996 L2006 **ID** *020 †20

MALIK, Rajesh. 901 E CHEVES ST, STE 600 29506 #495-73-1983 L2005 **CD** *020 †20

MANN, James Moss, II. 619 S DARGAN ST 29506 #047-05-1999 L2004 **GE** *020 †20

MARKWELL, Harry Stuart. 506 E CHEVES ST, CAROLINA HEALTH CARE 29506 #040-02-1973 L1993 **HEM ON** *020 †20

MASON, Julian Lorin. 901 E CHEVES ST, STE 100 29506 #045-01-1961 L1961 **ORS** *075 †40

MATTHEIS, John Ray. 555 E CHEVES ST, MCLEOD FAMILY MEDICINE CTR 29506 #018-03-1996 L1997 **FM** *020 †18

MATTHEWS, Adora L H. 900 E CHEVES ST, HEALTHSOUTH REHAB HOSPITAL 29506 #010-03-1991 L1995 **PM SCI** *020 †60

MAY, Gregory Arthur. 1706 2ND LOOP RD 29501 #011-02-1985 L2007 **CD IM** *020 †20

MCCLARY, Guy Elton, Jr. ■ 29505 #045-01-2008 *012

MC COWN, Heather Funke. 506 E CHEVES ST 29506 #045-01-1996 L1997 **D** *020 †15

MC COWN, John Samuel. 217 DOZIER BLVD, STE 100 29501 #045-01-1994 L1995 **DR NM** *020 †80,28

MC CUTCHEON, Karen Denise. 555 E CHEVES ST, MCLEOD REG MED CTR 29506 #045-01-1995 L1997 **FM** *020

MC DANIEL, Emily Carolyn. 1590 FREEDOM BLVD, STE B 29505 #045-01-2003 L2007 **OBG** *020

MC DONALD, Thomas Albert. 901 E CHEVES ST STE 440, MCLEOD MEDICAL PARK EAST 29506 #008-02-1996 L1999 **OMF** *020

MC GEE, Edwin Clyde. 555 E CHEVES ST 29506 #045-01-1959 L1959 **GS** *071 †85

MC KAY, Shawn Patrick. 1594 FREEDOM BLVD, STE 206 29505 #041-15-2001 L2006 **OTO** *020 †45

MC LEAN, David Costen. 305 E CHEVES ST STE 100 29506 #047-06-1954 L1960 **PD** *071 †55

MEIERE, Cheney Mell, Jr. 217 DOZIER BLVD, STE 100 29501 #012-01-1973 L1977 **DR** *020 †80

MIELE, Gerald Brian. 506 E CHEVES ST, STE 202 29506 #016-01-1983 L1996 **IM END** *020 †20

MILLER, Lloyd Chas, Jr. 805 PAMPLICO HWY, STE B310 29505 #045-01-1980 L1982 **IM** *020

MILLER, Wendy Leigh. 1920 2ND LOOP RD 29501 #045-01-2002 L2004 **FM** *020 †18

MITCHELL, Sharon S. 805 PAMPLICO HWY, STE B210 29505 #035-06-1994 L2001 **PTH** *020 †50

MOHR, Richard Eugene, III. 555 E CHEVES ST, MCLEOD FAMILY MEDICINE PRO 29506 #045-04-2007 L2007 **FP** *012

MONROE, Berry Bryant. 1001 W SUMTER ST, CARVER COMMUNITY HEALTH CT 29501 #036-07-1948 L1956 **PD PDC** *071

MOORE, Philip C. 2482 ABBEY WAY 29501 #045-01-1990 L2005 **AN** *020 †05

MOORE, Robert Willard. 1498 FREEDOM BLVD, HAND SURGERY ASSOCS 29505 #045-01-1984 L1990 **ORS** *020 †40

MORRIS, Napoleon Lee. 525 S DARGAN ST 29506 #045-01-1965 L1965 **IM** *071

MOSS, John Edward, Jr. ■ 29501 #045-01-1979 L1980 **NPM** *071 †55

MOYER, Joseph Geo. 800 E CHEVES ST, STE 420 29506 #010-02-1983 L1992 **AI PD** *020 †55,03

MURRELL, Amy P. 800 E CHEVES ST, STE 260 29506 #045-01-2000 L2001 **GS** *020 †85

NASO, Nicolette Balister. 901 E CHEVES ST, STE 600 29506 #036-01-1990 L1991 **CD** *020 †20

NASO, William Bernhard. 901 E CHEVES ST, STE 420 29506 #036-01-1990 L1992 **NS** *020 †25

O'BRYAN, Edward C, Jr. 800 E CHEVES ST, STE 200 29506 #045-01-1960 L1960 **CD IM** *020

O'DELL, Barnett E, Jr. 901 E CHEVES ST, STE 200 29506 #045-01-1981 L1982 **OBG** *020 †30

O'KELLY, Frank M. 1108 MEREDITH DR, STE 106 29505 #539-05-1954 L1978 **U** *020 †95

O'KELLY, James Kevin. 1580 FREEDOM BLVD STE 106 29505 #422-01-1986 L1992 **U** *020

O'KELLY, Peter Pius. 805 PAMPLICO HWY 29505 #016-43-1988 L2001 **U** *020 †95

OUYANG, Wen-Ting. 255 WARLEY ST 29501 #613-02-1983 L1999 **NEP** *020 †20

OWEN, James C. ■ 29505 #045-01-1951 L1951 **OBG** *071

PALLES, Louis M, Jr. 1590 FREEDOM BLVD STE C 29505 #041-01-1952 L1952 **OBG** *020 †30

PALLES, Louis M, III. 1590 FREEDOM BLVD STE C 29505 #045-01-1981 L1985 **OBG** *020 †30

PANDE, Amit Vyankatesh. 619 S DARGAN ST 29506 #495-83-1985 L2003 **CD IM** *020 †20

PANDE, Meenakshi Amit. 506 E CHEVES ST, CAROLINA HEALTH CARE 29506 #496-38-1990 L2004 **IM END** *020 †20

PARAMORE, Christopher G. 901 E CHEVES ST, STE 420 29506 #036-07-1987 L2005 **NS** *020 †25

PARKER, Wm Freeman, Jr. 500 S COIT ST 29501 #045-01-1960 L1960 **IM END** *020

PASCHAL, Hudnall Weaver. 1594 FREEDOM BLVD STE 202, PEE DEE FAM PHYS 29505 #045-04-1985 L1986 **FM** *020 †18

PATEL, Supenkuma. 506 E CHEVES ST STE 202 29506 #048-13-1992 L1997 **RHU** *020 †20

PAVY, Michael Dupre. 506 E CHEVES ST, STE 202 29506 #035-15-1975 L1976 **ON HEM** *020 †20

PEARSON, Joseph Millard. 800 E CHEVES ST, STE 260 29506 #045-01-1973 L1978 **GS** *020 †85

PEREZ-GARCIA, Maria Del C. 805 PAMPLICO HWY, STE A315 29505 #275-01-1987 L2005 **FM** *020 †18

PERRY, Lee R, Jr. 555 E CHEVES ST 29506 #045-01-1984 L1988 **AN PME** *050 †05

PETROPOULOS, George. 901 E CHEVES ST, STE 600 29506 #060-01-1993 L2008 **CD** *020 †20

PHILLIPS, Thomas Walter. 1590 FREEDOM BLVD, STE B 29505 #012-01-1973 L1975 **OBG** *020 †30

PHIPPS, Michele Gibbs. 805 PAMPLICO HWY, CAROLINAS HOSPITAL-EMERG M 29505 #012-01-1998 L2004 **EM** *020 †16

PHIPPS, Noel Lange. ■ 29501 #012-01-1998 L2004 **DR** *100 †80

PITIRANGGON, Pongstorn. 514 S DARGAN ST STE D 29506 #891-02-1989 L1998 **NEP IM** *020 †20

PITTARD, John Cameron. 255 WARLEY ST 29501 #045-04-1983 L1984 **NEP IM** *020 †20

PLAYER, Keith Charles. 800 E CHEVES ST, STE 260 29506 #045-01-1994 L1997 **GS** *020 †85

POON, Jonathan Yung-Chi. 555 E CHEVES ST, MCLEOD FAMILY MEDICINE 29506 #012-01-2004 L2004 **FM** *020 †18

POWELL, Joseph Williamson, Jr. 555 E CHEVES ST 29506 #045-01-2006 L2006 **FP** *012

RABON, Larry Deon. 306 S MCQUEEN ST 29501 #045-01-1967 L1967 **U** *020 †95

RAINWATER, Kelly Price. 1590 FREEDOM BLVD STE D, FLORENCE OB-GYN ASSOC INC 29505 #045-01-1990 L1991 **OBG** *020 †30

RAO, Sreenivas V. 506 E CHEVES ST 29506 #495-65-1982 L2000 **ON IM** *020 †50,20

RAZICK, Manver. 619 S DARGAN ST 29506 #012-01-1985 L1991 **GE IM** *020 †20

REINHART, Lars Hans. 555 E CHEVES ST, MCLEOD REGIONAL MED CTR 29506 #048-12-1996 L1999 **EM** *020 †16

REYNOLDS, Brandie Andrews. 555 E CHEVES ST, MCLEOD FAMILY MEDICINE 29506 #045-04-2005 L2005 **FP** *012

REYNOLDS, Mark Andrew. 800 E CHEVES ST, STE 260 29506 #041-13-1986 L1997 **GS** *020 †85

RHEA, Andrew H. 901 E CHEVES ST STE 420 29506 #048-02-1982 L1989 **NS** *020 †25

RICHARDSON, Wendell L. 555 E CHEVES ST, MCLEOD FAMILY MEDICINE PRO 29506 #045-01-1999 L2002 **FM** *020

RICHEY, Robert Mc Intire. 901 E CHEVES ST, STE 430 29506 #021-01-1983 L1991 **IM GE** *020 †20

RIDGES, Lee E. 145 E CHEVES ST, REGION 4 FLORENCE PUB HLTH 29506 #047-07-1980 L1993 **GP** *030

RIES, Kenneth Lange. 805 PAMPLICO HWY, STE B210 29505 #041-12-1995 L2000 **PTH** *020 †50

ROBEY, Dennison Butler. 805 PAMPLICO HWY 29505 #020-02-1971 L1978 **PTH DMP** *020 †50

RODRIGUEZ, David Carlos. 1594 FREEDOM BLVD, STE 202 29505 #012-01-2000 L2002 **FM** *100 †18

ROGERS, Richard Lionel. 1001 W SUMTER ST, CARVER COMM HEALTH CTR 29501 #036-07-1957 L1982 **PD EM** *020 †55

ROSE, Michael Richard. 555 E CHEVES ST 29506 #024-05-1983 L1990 **AN IM** *020 †20,05

■ = Address Information Privacy Protected

ROSS, Steven Robt. 501 S COIT ST 29501 #045-01-1980 L1983 **IM** *020 †20

ROWE, Llewellyn Alexander. 1706 2ND LOOP RD 29501 #051-01-1988 L1994 **CD** *020 †20

ROWSON, Abraham Eric. 555 E CHEVES ST, MCLEOD FAMILY MEDICINE 29506 #045-04-2005 L2005 **FP** *012

RUSSELL, Bradley Stokes. 1444 DEBERRY BLVD, CAROLINAS HOSPITAL SYSTEMS 29501 #045-01-1998 L1999 **EM** *020 †18 ‡

SATTARI, Maryam. PO BOX 100551 29501 #012-05-1999 L2002 **IM** *020 †20

SATTELE, Kevin Macey. 1611 HAZEL DR 29501 #045-04-1995 L1996 **IM** *020 †20

SCHAEFER, Albert James. 901 E CHEVES ST, STE 377 29506 #035-08-1995 L2004 **OBG** *020 †30

SCHOFIELD, John W. 555 E CHEVES ST 29506 #045-01-1950 L1950 **IM** *071

SCHROER, Richard Jos. 305 E CHEVES ST STE 370, GREENWOOD GENETICS CENTER 29506 #036-05-1975 L1978 **OS PD** *020 †55,19

SCOTT, Michele A. 1920 2ND LOOP RD 29501 #045-04-1989 L1992 **EM** *020 †18

SECHTIN, Alan Gray. 805 PAMPLICO HWY 29505 #045-01-1982 L1983 **DR** *020 †18,80

SELTZER, Samuel Eric. 400 N CASHUA DR 29501 #041-14-1983 L1989 **OPH** *020 †35

SHAH, Mahir Ishaq. 2822 CONSTITUTION DR, SANTEE WATEREE MENTAL HEAL 29501 #704-20-1991 L1999 **P** *020 †75

SHANKARNARAYAN, Saikiran. 805 PAMPLICO HWY, STE A315 29505 #496-39-2000 L2004 **FM** *020 †18

SHAW, Christopher Noel. 901 E CHEVES ST, STE 300 29506 #065-06-1982 L1994 **GYN** *020 †30

SHEA, Kevin Wm. 506 E CHEVES ST 29506 #035-08-1991 L1996 **ID** *020 †20

SHELTON, Heather Michelle. 555 E CHEVES ST, MCLEOD FAMILY MEDICINE 29506 #012-22-2004 L2004 **FP** *012

SHERMAN, John Alan. 2011 2ND LOOP RD STE C 29501 #038-45-1994 L1995 **AN PME** *020

SIMMONS, Andrea Suzette. 555 E CHEVES ST, MCLEOD FAMILY PRACTICE 29506 #036-08-2005 L2005 **FP** *012

SINGH, Inderpal. 255 WARLEY ST 29501 #495-29-1986 L1995 **AN** *020 †20

SITTISUNTORN, Orachun. 514 S DARGAN ST STE D 29506 #891-01-1972 L1984 **ON HO** *020 †20

SITTISUNTORN, Sarawadee. 514 S DARGAN ST STE D 29506 #891-01-1969 L1983 **NEP IM** *050 †20

SKINNER, Motte Gilliam. 305 E CHEVES ST, JETER SKINNER FAMILY 29506 #045-01-1982 L1983 **FM** *020 †18

SKINNER, Roland L, III. 1929 MOUNTAIN LAUREL CT, STE B 29505 #045-01-1980 L1981 **N SME** *020 †75

SKINNER, Roland Le Roy. 305 E CHEVES ST STE 160 29506 #045-01-1955 L1955 **FM** *020 †18

SLONE, Allen R. ■ 29501 #045-01-1955 L1955 **OM GP** *071

SMITH, Charlie D, III. 805 PAMPLICO HWY, B300 29505 #045-04-1985 L1986 **TS VS** *020 †85,90

SMITH, Cory Matthew. 800 E CHEVES ST, STE 310 29506 #045-04-2004 L2004 **FM** *020 †18

SMITH, David M. 555 E CHEVES ST 29506 #055-01-1988 L1999 **AN PME** *005

SMITH, Ian Douglas. 1706 2ND LOOP RD 29501 #045-01-1978 L1998 **CD IM** *020 †20

SMITH, James Culpeperhil. 506 E CHEVES ST 29506 #045-01-1999 L2000 **HO** *020 †20

SMITH, Peter Brian. ■ 29501 #051-04-1995 L1999 **IM AN** *005

SOMMERFELDT, Amanda Chari. 555 E CHEVES ST, RESIDENCY PROGRAM 29506 #056-05-2006 L2006 **FP** *012

SONFIELD, John William. 800 E CHEVES ST, STE 260 29506 #045-01-2000 L2004 **GS** *020 †85

SPENCE, Stacey J. ■ 29501 #048-14-1993 L1995 **FM** *020 †18

SPENCE, Thomas F. 204 E CHEVES ST 29506 #048-14-1992 L1995 **PD** *020

SPENCE, Timothy Alexander. 204 E CHEVES ST 29506 #048-14-1991 L1994 **PD ADL** *020

SPENCER, Thomas R, Jr. 555 E CHEVES ST 29506 #045-01-1984 L1985 **RO** *020 †80

SPOHN, Peter John. 251 W PALMETTO ST 29501 #040-02-1977 L1999 **ORS OTR** *020 †40

SPURLING, Timothy John. 619 S DARGAN ST 29506 #035-06-1976 L1985 **GE IM** *020 †20

STEADMAN, Mark Stephen. 1594 FREEDOM BLVD STE 202, PEE DEE FAM PHYS 29505 #045-01-1982 L1985 **FM** *020 †18

STEPHENS, Jeffrey Allen. 203 W ELM ST, STE C 29501 #045-04-1999 L2000 **IM** *020 †20

STOKES, Julius Howard, Jr. 555 E CHEVES ST 29506 #045-01-1967 L1967 **OPH** *071 †35

STOKES, Mark Robertson. 805 PAMPLICO HWY 29505 #045-04-1989 L1994 **OPH** *020 †35

STONEROCK, Charles Edward. 805 PAMPLICO HWY, MEDICAL MALL B 29505 #017-20-1998 L1999 **VS** *020 †85

STOUGH, Amy Jo. ■ 29501 #045-04-1997 L2000 **IM** *074 †20

TATUM, Charles Ruben. 901 E CHEVES ST, STE 300 29506 #045-01-1980 L1982 **OBG** *020 †30

TAYLOR, Edward W. 555 E CHEVES ST 29506 #036-05-1953 L1959 **U** *020 †95

TERRELL, Hilton Pack. 555 E CHEVES ST 29506 #045-01-1975 L1976 **FM** *040 †18

THOMAS, Toby Thundiyil. 555 E CHEVES ST, DEPT OF EMERGENCY MEDICINE 29506 #048-02-2003 L2006 **EM** *020 †16

THOMASON, John Melvin. ■ 29501 #045-01-1965 L1965 **GP GS** *020

THOMPSON, Hugh Smith. 1920 2ND LOOP RD 29501 #045-01-1973 L1974 **AN** *020 †05

THORN, Leanna Fogleman. 555 E CHEVES ST 29506 #036-08-1996 L1999 **EM** *020 †16

TILLAN-HSIA, Katherine Y. ■ 29501 #308-04-1999 L2007 **IM** *020 †20

TOLBERT, Antoinette R. 555 E CHEVES ST, MCLEOD REGIONAL MEDICAL CE 29506 #045-04-1996 L1999 **EM** *020 †16

TOWNS, Danielle Denise. 555 E CHEVES ST, MCLEOD FAMILY MEDICINE PRO 29506 #045-01-2007 L2007 **FP** *012

TRANT, Charles A, Jr. 305 E CHEVES ST, STE 220 29506 #036-08-1989 L1995 **PDC** *020 †55

TRAYNHAM, Edward Eugene. 1594 FREEDOM BLVD, STE 302 29505 #045-01-1979 L1980 **PD** *020 †55

TRULUCK, Chas Harry, Jr. 506 E CHEVES ST, PEE DEE EAR NOSE THROAT 29506 #045-01-1962 L1962 **OTO** *075 †45

TUEL, Stephen M. 2013 2ND LOOP RD 29501 #048-14-1983 L1995 **PM OS** *062 †60

TURBEVILLE, Ellen Patrice. 204 E CHEVES ST, CHILDREN'S MEDICAL CENTER 29506 #045-01-1990 L1990 **PD** *020 †55

TURNER, Robert Edward, III. 506 E CHEVES ST 29506 #045-01-1971 L1972 **RHU IG** *020 †20

TYSON, Duncan Wright. 1594 FREEDOM BLVD STE 202, PEE DEE FAM PHYS 29505 #045-01-1976 L1979 **FM** *020 †18

VANDER LEEST, Robert E. 555 E CHEVES ST, MCLEOD REGIONAL MEDICAL CE 29506 #007-02-1993 L1997 **EM** *020 †16

VAUGHN-HINTON, Wallisa Te. 555 E CHEVES ST, RESIDENCY PROGRAM 29506 #045-04-2006 L2006 **FP** *012

VAUGHT, Winston Wallace. 800 E CHEVES ST, STE 350 29506 #045-01-1981 L1987 **U** *020 †95

VELAZCO, Jorge Francisco. 805 PAMPLICO HWY, HOSPITALIST PROGRAM 29505 #737-01-1996 L2006 **IM** *020 †20

WALL, Brian Patrick. ■ 29501 #045-04-2007 **IM** *012

WARD, Benjamin Kirby, Jr. 214 W PINE ST 29501 #036-01-1967 L1974 **U** *020 †95

WATFORD, Kyle Ernest. 901 E CHEVES ST, STE 500 29506 #045-01-1996 L1998 **ORS** *020 †40

WATT, Nigel Alan Roderick. 901 E CHEVES ST, STE 100 29506 #917-03-1978 L1993 **ORS** *020

WHERREN EMERSON, Mary A. 800 E CHEVES ST STE 240, FAMILY MEDICINE ASSOCS OF 29506 #036-08-2001 L2004 **FM** *020 †18

WHITE, Bruce Welborn, Jr. 400 CHEROKEE RD 29501 #045-01-1969 L1971 **DR** *020 †80

WHITE, Kelvin Darnel. 514 S DARGAN ST STE F 29506 #012-21-1988 L1989 **FM** *020 †18

WHITEHEAD, Alva Weaver. 800 E CHEVES ST, STE 200 29506 #012-05-1971 **IM** *020 †20

WHITEHEAD, Alva Weaver, Jr. 204 E CHEVES ST 29506 #045-01-1998 L1999 **PD** *020 †55

WHITESIDES, Robert Fred, Jr. 651 S COIT ST 29501 #045-01-1975 L1976 **DR** *020 †80

WILLIAMS, Jonathan Scott. 217 DOZIER BLVD, STE 100 29501 #045-01-1992 L1998 **DR VIR** *020 †80

WILNER, Lane Arne. 2501 S VANCE DR 29505 #033-06-1986 L1997 **ON** *020 †20

WINDHAM, Nancy Q. 509 S COIT ST 29501 #021-01-1986 L1990 **GYN** *020 †30 ‡

WOOD, Laurence Willis. 555 E CHEVES ST 29506 #045-01-1959 **CD IM** *071

WOOLERY, Janet Diane. 901 E CHEVES ST STE 460 29506 #010-02-1991 L1997 **P** *020 †75

YOUNGBLOOD, Robt Watkins. ■ 29501 #037-07-1955 L1960 **GS TS** *071 †85,90

FOLLY BEACH — CHARLESTON

ASSERSON, Bowen, Jr. PO BOX 135 29439 #012-01-1970 L1977 **PTH** *062 †50

ECTOR, Walton L. ■ 29439 #045-01-1952 L1952 **PD** *071 †55

KERN, Donna Howard. ■ 29439 #045-01-1996 L1997 **IM** *020

LEATHERS, Stephen Dale. ■ 29439 #012-01-2001 L2006 **EM** *020 †20

MANOS, Toni. PO BOX 49, 1742 E ASHLEY AVE 29439 #045-01-1984 L1985 **EM** *020 †16

RAWLS, Darlene Oxendine. ■ 29439 #036-05-1986 L1987 **IM** *020 †20

SINGH, Erick Raj. ■ 29439 #045-01-2007 L2007 **IM** *012

FORT JACKSON — RICHLAND

BAENS, Hector Santillan. FORT JACKSON ARMY BASE 29207 #748-02-1954 L1989 **GS TS** *020

BLUE, Peter Wm. MONCRIEF ARMY HOSP DEP RA 29207 #016-02-1969 L1985 **NM** *050 †20,28

FROELICH, Edward Geo. FORT JACKSON ARMY BASE 29207 #023-12-1990 L1997 **AN** *020 †05

MYLANDER, Kenneth Wilton. FORT JACKSON ARMY BASE 29207 #038-40-1967 L1977 **GS** *020 †85

NAIK, Asmika Dolatrai. MONCRIEF ARMY HOSP, FAMILY HLTH CTR TMC 29207 #495-89-1977 L1978 **GP** *020

PHELPS, Karen Sue. FORT JACKSON ARMY BASE 29207 #023-12-1990 L1992 **FM** *020 †18

FORT MILL — LANCASTER

BENSON, Matthew Richard. ■ 29707 #550-04-2004 L2007 **PD** *100 †55

CAMPO, Arnold Bernard. 8351 CHARLOTTE HWY 29707 #422-01-1988 L1992 **FM** *020 †18

CULP, Steven Morrow. 8351 CHARLOTTE HWY 29707 #045-01-1989 L1990 **FM** *020 †18

KINGHORN, Mildred Anne. ■ 29707 #045-01-1975 L2003 **PD IM** *050 †55

KURUSU, Shozo. ■ 29707 #572-20-1966 L1973 **U** *020 †95

SEBASTYAN, Andrew John. 9789 CHARLOTTE HWY, STE 1400 29707 #065-09-1985 L1995 **FM** *020 †18

SHARP, Frank. 8351 CHARLOTTE HWY 29707 #422-01-1997 L2000 **FM** *020 †18

SHEALY, Keith Douglas. 8351 CHARLOTTE HWY 29707 #045-01-1981 L1982 **FM** *020 †18

SINGLETON, Shaunese Derae. ■ 29707 #035-09-1998 L2002 **PD** *020 †55

WILLIS, John Brunson. 8351 CHARLOTTE HWY 29707 #045-01-1966 **FM OS** *020 †18

FORT MILL — YORK

BENSON, Christopher Bruce. 1666 HIGHWAY 160 W 29708 #010-02-1989 L1997 **OBG** *020 †30

BERGMAN, James Loring. 1690 HIGHWAY 160 W 29708 #021-01-1973 L1986 **FM** *020 †18

BOTT, Stephen Jos. 1700 FIRST BAXTER XING 29708 #041-14-1981 L1986 **GE IM** *020 †20

CAVALLARO, Richard James. ■ 29708 #047-06-1958 L1958 **MDM AN** *030 †05

COOK, Dexter Lee, Jr. 1698 HIGHWAY 160 W, STE 220 29708 #045-04-1983 L1984 **PD** *020 †55

CULP, Max A. 1690 HIGHWAY 160 W, FORT MILL FAMILY PRACTICE 29708 #045-01-1953 L1953 **FM** *071 †18

EDWARDS, Martha Hill. 1698 HIGHWAY 160 W, STE 220 29708 #051-01-1990 L1997 **PD** *020 †55

FLEISCHER, Thomas Glenn. 1690 HIGHWAY 160 W 29708 #011-04-1978 L1983 **ORS** *020 †40

FLORACK, Arthur John. ■ 29708 #035-15-1957 L1959 **OBG** *071 †30

GARRETSON, Bret Malcolm. 1700 FIRST BAXTER XING 29708 #021-06-1996 L2004 **GE** *020 †20

HEINIG, Michael Forrest. 1690 HIGHWAY 160 W 29708 #036-08-1984 L1985 **ORS** *020 †40

HENRY, William J. 122 CLEBOURNE ST 29715 #045-01-1950 L1950 **FM** *071

HILTON, Ansley Lowder. 1666 HIGHWAY 160 W 29708 #045-04-2002 L2006 **OBG** *020

IANNINI, Julie Patricia. 1700 FIRST BAXTER XING, STE 101 29708 #045-01-2000 L2006 **D** *020 †15

JAMES, Walter S, III. 1690 HIGHWAY 160 W 29708 #036-07-1984 L1989 **ORS** *020 †40

JEMSEK, Joseph Gregory. 1171 MARKET ST, STE 211 29708 #016-11-1974 L1975 **IM ID** *020 †20

KALINSKI, Andrzej Edward. 377 CAROWINDS BLVD, STE 121 29708 #759-01-1984 L1994 **PTH** *020

LEHMAN, William Louis. 1690 HIGHWAY 160 W 29708 #038-06-1977 L1985 **ORS FM** *020 †18,40

MARTIN, Robert Alexander. 1690 HIGHWAY 160 W, FORT MILL FAMILY PRACTICE 29708 #045-01-1955 L1956 **FM** *071 †18

MC CARTHY, William Golden. 1690 HIGHWAY 160 W 29708 #021-05-1985 L1990 **ORS** *020 †40

MC CLELLAND, Robert Craig. 1666 HIGHWAY 160 W 29708 #051-01-1992 L2000 **OBG** *020 †30 ‡

MC GRAW, Eric Wayne. 271 CAROWINDS BLVD 29708 #021-06-1998 L2004 **DR** *100 †80

MC QUEEN, Donald H, III. 1690 HIGHWAY 160 W 29708 #036-01-1967 L1982 **ORS** *020 †40

MILLER, Gregory Atwood. 1666 HIGHWAY 160 W 29708 #051-04-1989 L1996 **OBG** *020 †30

MITCHELL, Hugh B, Jr. ■ 29708 #021-05-1947 L1975 **AM RP** *071

MOBLEY, David Mc Elrath. 502 SIXTH BAXTER XING 29708 #045-01-1979 L1980 **FM** *020 †18

NELSON, David Rolland. 271 CAROWINDS BLVD 29708 #016-01-1985 L2007 **DR NS** *020 †80 ‡

NOURY, John Philip. 377 CAROWINDS BLVD, STE 110 29708 #010-02-1959 L1965 **OS** *020 †05

NUNNERY, Kenneth Edward. 1690 HIGHWAY 160 W 29708 #045-01-1974 L1975 **FM** *020 †18

PATEL, Ami Nirav. ■ 29708 #305-01-2000 L2003 **P** *020 †75 ‡
PATEL, Nirav Narendra. 1700 FIRST BAXTER XING 29708 #422-01-2000 L2006 **GE** *020 †20
PENNINGTON, Larry H. 1700 FIRST BAXTER XING 29708 #045-01-1991 L1998 **GE** *020 †20
PILLAI, Mohan V. 1700 FIRST BAXTER XING, STE 202 29708 #038-44-1992 L2004 **PS** *020 †85,65
POWELL, E Neal, Jr. 1690 HIGHWAY 160 W 29708 #045-01-1982 L1983 **ORS** *020 †40
RABINER, Edwin L. 29708 #041-01-1952 **P** *020 †75
RANDALL, Robt Donald, Jr. 1700 FIRST BAXTER XING, STE 102 29708 #036-05-1975 L1982 **GS** *020 †85
REID, James Robt. ■ 29716 #045-01-1930 L1930 **OM** *071
RENTZ, Jamie Norman. 1690 HIGHWAY 160 W 29708 #045-01-1991 L1992 **ORS** *020 †40
RICHARDSON, Scott Carter. 1700 FIRST BAXTER XING 29708 #025-01-1996 L2002 **GE** *020 †20
ROBINSON, Joe Clarence. 1666 HIGHWAY 160 W 29708 #001-06-1977 L1978 **OBG** *020 †30
RODRIGUE, Randolph Louis. 1700 FIRST BAXTER XING 29708 #021-05-1983 L1991 **GE** *020 †20
ROWLAND, Barbara L. 1666 HIGHWAY 160 W 29708 #036-08-1997 L1998 **OBG** *020 †30
SCHROEDER, Christopher W. 1700 FIRST BAXTER XING, STE 102 29708 #012-01-1982 L1987 **GS VS** *020 †85
SCHWARTZ, Matthew Allen. 1690 HIGHWAY 160 W 29708 #011-04-2001 L2007 **ORS** *020
SHARMA, Deovyaas Shankar. 1354 DOBYS BRIDGE RD 29715 #422-01-1998 L2003 **IM** *020 †20
SISON, Miguel Yap, Jr. ■ 29708 #748-01-1962 L1972 **PD** *071 †55
SOHNER, Mark Wm. 502 SIXTH BAXTER XING, STE A 29708 #038-40-1983 L1996 **IM** *020
START, Susan Jo. 1698 HIGHWAY 160 W, STE 220 29708 #025-01-1990 L2000 **PD** *020 †55
STEADMAN, Paul Ralph. ■ 29715 #011-03-1986 L1987 **OS** *020
TAYLOR, Roy Norman. 1666 HIGHWAY 160 W 29708 #045-01-1981 L1988 **OBG** *020 †30
THIES, Steven David. 1700 FIRST BAXTER XING, STE 102 29708 #028-03-1992 L1997 **GS** *020 †85
TONKOWICZ, Patricia Ann. 1698 HIGHWAY 160 W, STE 220 29708 #019-02-1988 L1991 **PD** *020 †55
WEBER, Karl. 1698 HIGHWAY 160 W STE 140, MEDICAL ASSOCIATES OF FORT 29708 #031-01-1992 L2005 **IM** *020 †20
YANCHIK, Lori Michelle. ■ 29715 #033-06-2002 L2007 **PD** *020 †55
YEARTA, George Marshall. 1690 HIGHWAY 160 W 29708 #011-03-1979 L1980 **FM** *020 †18

FOUNTAIN INN – LAURENS

BLAND, Maynard Wm. 407 N MAIN ST 29644 #045-01-1957 L1957 **GP FM** *020
MAHON, James Roger. 300 S MAIN ST 29644 #045-01-1974 L1976 **EM FM** *020

GAFFNEY – CHEROKEE

ABREU, Alexandre Rocha. 1529 N LIMESTONE ST, UPSTATE LUNG & CRITICAL 29340 #187-88-1996 L2005 **PCC** *020 †20
AHMAD, Manzoor. 707 6TH ST, GAFFNEY MEDICAL CENTER 29340 #704-04-1961 L1976 **GS TS** *020 †85
BARNHILL, Herbert F, II. 722 HYATT ST, PEACHVIEW MEDICAL PARK 29341 #045-01-1979 L1980 **FM** *020 †18
BLAND, Susan Kay. 722 HYATT ST, STE C 29341 #025-07-1983 L1986 **FM** *020 †18
BURDETT, Maureen Gail. 1552 N LIMESTONE ST, STE B 29340 #023-01-1996 L2006 **GS** *020 †85
COX, Robert Dudley, III. 114 N JOHNSON ST, AFFILIATED COUNSELING 29340 #045-01-1967 L1967 **P** *020
CUTCHIN, Richard Carlton. 1530 N LIMESTONE ST 29340 #021-01-1986 L1988 **FM GPM** *020 †18 ‡
DALE, Michael Stephen. ■ 29340 #021-01-1984 L1988 **IM** *020 †20
DE LA CRUZ, Luis Ignacio. 1529 N LIMESTONE ST, UPSTATE LUNG & CRITICAL 29340 #737-06-1998 L2006 **PCC SME** *100 †20
EDWARDS, George Preston. 1530 N LIMESTONE ST 29340 #045-01-1947 L1947 **GP** *071
ENRIGHT, Michael Jos. 724 HYATT ST 29341 #051-07-1981 L1986 **DR** *020 †80
ERB, David Richard. 1529 N LIMESTONE ST, UPSTATE LUNG & CRITICAL 29340 #025-01-1987 L2002 **PUD CCM** *020 †20
FELDMAN, Grigory Jacob. 1529 N LIMESTONE ST, UPSTATE LUNG & CRITICAL 29340 #913-15-1979 L1992 **PUD** *020 †20
FURR, Roy Woodley. 1307 N LOGAN ST 29341 #654-01-1987 L1996 **PD** *020 †55
GHEORGHIU, Bogdan Petru. 406 TIFFANY PARK, STE C 29341 #035-01-1992 L1997 **N** *020 †75 ‡
GUTTA, Shyamala. 140 4TH AVE, MBHS 23 29340 #495-65-1971 L1979 **AN** *020
GUTTA, Venkataiah. 1530 N LIMESTONE ST 29340 #495-62-1967 L1979 **U** *020 †95
HAGUEWOOD, Billy Joe, Jr. 1530 N LIMESTONE ST 29340 #045-01-1998 L2002 **OPH** *020 †35
HAMMETT, Jay. 1530 N LIMESTONE ST 29340 #045-01-1947 L1947 **GP OM** *072
HAQ, Junaid Ul. 1530 N LIMESTONE ST, UPSTATE CAROLINA MED CTR 29340 #704-02-1985 L1999 **AN** *020 †05
HARAKAS, Andrew Peter. 1529 N LIMESTONE ST, STE B 29340 #036-08-1983 L2003 **ORS** *020 †40
HASELL, Rhett Hagood. 1530 N LIMESTONE ST, UPSTATE CAROLINA MED CTR 29340 #045-01-1981 L1993 **AN PD** *020 †55,05
KAEMMERLEN, Robert Wayne. 1341 N LIMESTONE ST 29340 #045-01-1978 L1981 **FM** *020 †18
KALLMAN, David A. 1530 N LIMESTONE ST 29340 #016-11-1981 L1992 **DR** *020 †80
KARNS, Paul Danl. 1531 N LIMESTONE ST 29340 #045-04-1984 L1985 **EM FM** *020 †18
KHAN, Imtiaz A. 1419 N LIMESTONE ST, REGENESIS COMMUNITY HEALTH 29340 #028-78-1995, ▲ L1998 **FM** *020 †18 ‡
KHAN, Shahina Riaz. 226 W ROBINSON ST 29341 #495-65-1975 L1982 **PD ADL** *020 †55
LEWIS, Steven John. 1421 N LIMESTONE ST 29340 #036-01-1993 L1994 **OBG** *020 †30
LINDER, Blucher Lee. ■ 29341 #036-05-1974 L1975 **FM OM** *071
MC INTOSH, Donald Munro. PO BOX 1567 29342 #036-07-1978 L1980 **IM** *020 †20
MIJANOVICH, James Robt. 1307 N LOGAN ST 29341 #016-43-1980 L1985 **PTH OS** *075 †50
MORGAN, Donald Todd. 722 HYATT STE 29341 #045-04-1990 L1991 **FM** *020 †18
MOSS, Alfred Randall. 101 PROFESSIONAL PARK 29341 #045-01-1978 L1980 **OM FM** *020
MUHAMMAD, Rais. 104 PROFESSIONAL PARK 29340 #704-02-1990 L2002 **PDP AI** *020 †03,55
NAZARENO, Marilu L. 1341 N LIMESTONE ST, CHEROKEE FAMILY MED 29340 #748-11-1982 L1998 **FM** *020 †18

NEIGHBORS, Johnny Leo. 1506 N LIMESTONE ST, STE C 29340 #001-06-1985 L1994 **OBG** *020 †30
NELSON, Timothy Charles. 1552 N LIMESTONE ST, GMA GENERAL SURGERY & ENDO 29340 #025-12-1991 L2006 **GS** *020 †85
PATI, Asim Ranjan. 406 TIFFANY PARK, STE A 29341 #495-02-1980 L1996 **IM** *030 †20
PEDERSEN, Arthur Morris. ■ 29341 #030-05-1947 L1972 **P EM** *071
PHILLIPS, Frank F. 104 PROFESSIONAL PARK # A 29340 #047-06-1983 L1988 **ORS** *020 †40
POTES, Ernesto. 406 TIFFANY PARK, STE C 29341 #264-01-1977 L2001 **N PM** *020 †75
RUFFING, Richard Jos. 722 HYATT ST 29341 #025-07-1983 L1986 **FM** *020 †18
SHAH, Ishfaq Hussain. 707 6TH ST, GAFFNEY MEDICAL CENTER 29340 #704-04-1963 L1982 **IM CD** *020
SOHERWARDY, Khalid Naeem. 317 N LOGAN ST 29341 #308-11-1983 L1997 **FM** *020 †18
STEUER, Rudolph Robt, Jr. ■ 29341 #045-01-1956 L1956 **PTH** *071 †50
STOWELL, John Colby. 117 E MONTGOMERY ST 29340 #027-01-1975 L1976 **GS** *020 †85
STROUP, Chas Patrick, Jr. 722 HYATT ST, STE C 29341 #045-01-1974 L1975 **FM** *020 †18
SWAD, Samuel Jay. 1506 N LIMESTONE ST 29340 #045-04-1994 L1997 **FM** *020 †18
WARREN, Lawrence Newton. 1530 N LIMESTONE ST 29340 #045-04-1988 L1991 **DR** *020 †80
WASSON, Marian Jane. 1341 N LIMESTONE ST 29340 #045-01-1977 L1978 **FM** *020 †18
WHEELER, Michael S. 1530 N LIMESTONE ST 29340 #036-01-1977 L1987 **PTH** *071 †50
WING, Donald Webster. 1530 N LIMESTONE ST 29340 #020-12-1985 L1986 **FM** *020 †18
ZAMAN, Fasih Qamar Uz. 371 6TH ST 29340 #704-01-1962 L1976 **IM** *075
ZORTEA, Paulo Leonildo. 406 TIFFANY PARK, STE C 29341 #187-14-1996 L2003 **N** *020 †75 ‡

GALIVANTS FERRY – HORRY

JORDAN, Carla Sanatha. ■ 29544 #045-01-2008 *012

GASTON – LEXINGTON

SIMMONS, Oliver Pope. ■ 29053 #045-04-1998 L2003 **CFS** *100 †45

GEORGETOWN – GEORGETOWN

ADKINS, Henry Grady. 1530 HIGHMARKET ST, MEDICAL BUILDING PA 29440 #045-01-2004 L2004 **FM** *020
AGUERO, Eric George. 2405 N FRASER ST 29440 #038-06-1998 L1999 **RO** *020 †80
AHEARN, Arthur Mason. 1001 N FRASER ST 29440 #035-20-1962 L1973 **ORS** *020 †40
ARCHAMBEAU, Edgar Victor. 606 BLACK RIVER RD 29440 #045-04-1987 L1988 **FM** *020 †18
AUTIO, Dudley Arne. 525 LAFAYETTE CIR, HEALTH 29440 #154-07-1969 L1976 **P** *020
BALLOU, Laurence H, Jr. 1011 N FRASER ST 29440 #038-40-1978 L1981 **GE IM** *020 †20
BLALOCK, George Robt, Jr. 606 BLACK RIVER RD 29440 #045-01-1965 L1965 **GS** *071 †85
BOHAN, Michael Nolan. 2185 N FRASER ST, CAROLINA ORTHOPAEDIC SPECI 29440 #036-05-1995 L2000 **ORS** *020 †40
BURNS, Scott Barron. ■ 29440 #036-05-1999 L2002 **EM** *020
CAMLIN, Richard M, Jr. 1016 HUGER DR 29440 #045-01-1965 L1965 **IM PUD** *020
CERASARO, Thomas Stephen. 580 BLACK RIVER RD 29440 #012-02-1979 L1985 **U** *020 †95
COMEAU, William Raymond. 606 BLACK RIVER RD, DEPT OF ANESTHESIA 29440 #047-06-1988 L2007 **AN** *020 †05
COMPAGNONE, Salvatore Jos. PO BOX 421718 29442 #067-01-1960 L1986 **EM GS** *071 †85
CRANE, Douglas Fountain. 525 LAFAYETTE CIR 29440 #045-01-1974 L1976 **P ADP** *020 †75
CROSBY, Thomas Eugene. 1530 HIGHMARKET 29440 #045-01-1990 L1991 **FM** *020 †18
DECHAMPLAIN, Richard E. 1200 HIGHMARKET ST, STE 200 29440 #045-01-1992 L1993 **OPH** *020 †35
DES CHAMPS, George Thomas. 606 BLACK RIVER RD, GEORGETOWN MEM HOSP 29440 #045-01-1985 L1990 **DR** *020 †80
DONAHUE, Sarah Hletko. 57 JESSAMINE AVE, POST OFFICE BOX 618 29440 #016-43-2000 L2002 **PD** *020 †55
DOYLE, Frances Ingell. ■ 29440 #045-01-1949 L1949 **PD** *071 †55
DROSIEKO, Amanda Guyton. 606 BLACK RIVER RD 29440 #045-01-1998 L2001 **PD** *020 †55
DUVALL, Lance Alden. 1075 N FRASER ST 29440 #045-01-1976 L1977 **FM** *020 †18
EASTERLIN, Whaley W, Jr. 1075 N FRASER ST, WACCAMAW MEDICAL CENTER 29440 #045-01-1969 L1969 **FM GP** *020 †18
EDWARDS, James Bryant, III. 1306 N FRASER ST 29440 #021-01-1964 L1970 **OBG** *020 †30
EWART, Jackson Mc Crea. 903A N FRASER ST 29440 #045-01-1977 L1978 **GS** *020 †85
FORRESTER, James Waldrip. 1101 MEMORIAL LN, BLALOCK & LEE MD'S 29440 #024-01-1953 L1958 **GS** *071 †85
FRANK, Walter Leslie, III. 580 BLACK RIVER RD 29440 #016-11-1988 L1994 **U** *020 †95
FRY, Terry Rae Lentz. 401 MARINA DR 29440 #036-01-1973 L1989 **OTO HNS** *020 †50
GAGLIANO, Theodore E. 1662 SEITTER ST 29440 #035-01-1951 L1977 **P LM** *030 †75
GARNER, Charles David. 2199 N FRASER ST, GEORGETOWN SURGICAL ASSOCS 29440 #045-01-1991 L1996 **GS** *020 †85
GONZALES, Henry Augustine. 153 BRANDON WAY 29440 #005-19-1977 L2004 **OBG** *020 †30
GOODIN, Donald Edward. 2405 N FRASER ST, WACCAMAW ONCOLOGY 29440 #020-12-1996 L1997 **IM** *020 †20
GORDON, Daniel Jos. 606 BLACK RIVER RD 29440 #041-13-1991 L1997 **IM** *020 †20
HARRELL, W Lamar. ■ 29440 #012-05-1958 L1958 **R** *020 †80
HLETKO, Paul John. 57 JESSAMINE AVE 29440 #016-43-1971 L1989 **PD PHO** *020 †55
HOLSCHER, Edward Chas, Jr. 525 LAFAYETTE CIR 29440 #028-03-1965 L1999 **P** *020 †75
JONES, Webster Newton, III. 606 BLACK RIVER RD, GEORGETOWN RADIOLGY ASSOCI 29440 #045-01-1976 L1978 **DR** *020 †80
JOSEPH, Carium. 903 N FRASER ST, STE B 29440 #010-02-1954 L1954 **GYN** *071 †30
JUSTICE, Heather Melelani. 606 BLACK RIVER RD, GEORGETOWN HOSPITAL SYSTEM 29440 #054-04-2004 L2007 **FM** *020
LASRY, Valerie. 1007 N FRASER ST 29440 #067-02-1990 L2005 **OBG** *020 †30
LINDSAY, Mary Ann Haden. 606 BLACK RIVER RD, GEORGETOWN MEM HOSP 29440 #028-46-1980 L1987 **DR** *075 †80
LUMPKIN, Robert L. 606 BLACK RIVER RD 29440 #045-01-1951 L1951 **GYN** *071 †30
MANNING, John Jos. 223 SANDERLING AVE 29440 #422-01-1985 L1991 **EM FM** *020 †16
MC GINLEY, Kent Michael. 606 BLACK RIVER RD 29440 #047-20-1991 L1997 **PTH** *020 †50
MC GRATH, Robert Wm. ■ 29440 #035-09-1954 L1980 **GS** *071 †85
METZ, Matthew J. PO BOX 1000, 469 MARINA DR 29442 #055-01-1998 L2003 **GS** *100 †85
MULLINS, Darren Eugene. 2405 N FRASER ST, WACCAMAW ONCOLOGY 29440 #001-02-1991 L1999 **HO** *020 †20

NATALE, Deborah Rose. 1068 N FRASER ST, DOCTOR'S CARE GEORGETOWN 29440 #041-01-1992 L2002 **EM** *020 †16,20

NICOL, Philip Russell. ■ 29440 #917-23-1974 L1989 **DIA IM** *020 †20

OGBURN, Lanier. ■ 29440 #036-07-1946 L1946 **GS OS** *071

O'LEARY, Kathleen Ann. 525 LAFAYETTE CIR 29440 #035-15-2000 L2004 **P** *020 ‡

ORCHARD, John Lester. 1011 N FRASER ST, WACCAMAW GASTRO 29440 #041-12-1972 L1977 **GE IM** *020 †20

PAINE, Donald Thos Hardy. ■ 29440 #917-23-1945 L1979 **U GS** *071

PARAGAS, Lamberto S. 606 BLACK RIVER RD 29440 #748-08-1987 L1998 **EM** *020 †16,20

RICHMOND, William D, II. 606 BLACK RIVER RD 29440 #051-04-1983 L1984 **EM** *020 †16

RICKS, Robert Edward, Jr. ■ 29440 #045-01-1975 L1981 **OBG** *040 †30

ROSNACK, David Anthony. 1052 HUGER DR # A 29440 #056-06-1999 L2004 **IM** *020 †20

RYAN, James Michael. ■ 29440 #041-02-1972 L1975 **TS GS** *071 †85,90

SALTER, Henry D, III. 1306 N FRASER ST 29440 #045-01-1986 L1987 **OBG** *020 †30

SCHENKER, Florence Susan. 1068 N FRASER ST 29440 #561-01-1976 L1997 **UCM** *020 †16

SEIGLER, Richard Andrew. 606 BLACK RIVER RD, CATSKILL REGIONAL MEDICAL 29440 #422-01-2002 L2007 **MPD** *100 †20,55

SKINNER, Wright S, III. 1001 N FRASER ST 29440 #045-01-1980 L1981 **ORS OP** *020 †40

SMITH, Robert Sidney. 1011 N FRASER ST, WACCAMAW GASTROENTEROLOGY 29440 #045-01-2000 L2006 **GE** *020 †20 ‡

SOWELL, George Alexander. 606 BLACK RIVER RD 29440 #023-01-1956 L1963 **OBG OS** *071 †30

TILLER, Gerald Roberts. 186 COLONY POINTE DR 29440 #021-01-1968 L1971 **OPH** *071 †35

VALLERY, Steven Bruce. 606 BLACK RIVER RD, GEORGETOWN MEMORIAL HOSPIT 29440 #010-02-1993 L2000 **PCP** *020 †50

VARN, George Holland, Jr. ■ 29440 #045-01-1963 L1963 **IM** *071

WHITMAN, Melanie Diane. 57 JESSAMINE AVE, GEORGETOWN PEDIATRIC CENTE 29440 #035-75-2002, ▲ L2005 **PD** *020

WILKINSON, George Albert. 606 BLACK RIVER RD, GMH DEPT OF EMNERGENCY MED 29440 #027-01-1997 L2000 **EM** *020 †16

WILLIAMS, Clifton Lide. ■ 29440 #036-05-1955 L1955 **IM CD** *071

WILLIAMS, Lloyd Benton. PO BOX 916 29442 #045-01-1956 **GP** *020

YOUNG, Carole Marie. 1200 HIGHMARKET ST, STE 200 29440 #048-13-1982 L1987 **OPH** *020 †35

GILBERT – LEXINGTON

MULL, Shane Robert. 4080 AUGUSTA HWY 29054 #045-04-2002 L2003 **FM** *020 †18

SUMMERS, Diane E. ■ 29054 #047-07-1983 L1988 **PTH** *020

GOOSE CREEK – BERKELEY

BARNES, Sylvia Signorelli. 105 SPRINGHALL DR A 29445 #038-44-1990 L1993 **FM** *020 †18 ‡

BEHRENS, Edward Grady. 119 SPRINGHALL DR, CHARLESTON ENT ASSOCIATES 29445 #039-01-1997 L1998 **OTO** *020 †45

CAMPBELL, John White. 100 SPRING HALL DR, CAROLINA FAMILY MEDICINE 29445 #045-01-2004 L2004 **FM** *020 †18

CAMPBELL, Patricia Ann. 110A SPRINGHALL DR 29445 #045-01-1991 L1992 **FM** *020 †18

COKER, Woodrow Jenkins, III. ■ 29445 #045-01-2008 *012

DORN, Marion Douglas, Jr. 118 SPRING HALL DR STE A 29445 #045-01-1975 L1977 **FM EM** *020

HANNA, Donald Timothy. 100 SPRINGHALL DR 29445 #045-01-1982 L1983 **FM** *020 †18

HO, Beng Heng. ■ 29445 #244-02-1970 L1976 **FM** *071 †18

HODGES, Elbert Ray, Jr. 114 SPRING HALL DR, BERKELEY PSYCHIATRIC ASSOC 29445 #045-01-1986 L1987 **P** *020 †75

KLECKNER-POGUE, Zoe Lynn. 101 SPRING HALL DR 29445 #051-04-1995 **PD** *020 †55

LOSADA, Jose E. ■ 29445 #396-06-1959 L1978 **FM** *071

LYMAN, William M. 206 S GOOSE CREEK BLVD 29445 #010-02-1967 L1983 **FM OM** *020 †18

LYNN, Kristi Leann. 501 RED BANK RD 29445 #047-20-1997 L2000 **FM** *020

OBENG, Kwaku. ■ 29445 #041-13-2004 L2008 **DR** *012

PRICE, Beth S. ■ 29445 #045-01-2001 L2003 **FM** *020 †18

RITTENBURY, Margaret E. 107 THOMASON BLVD, BERKELEY COMM MENTAL HLTH 29445 #045-01-1989 L1993 **CHP** *020 †75

ROBINSON, David W, Jr. 149 SAINT JAMES AVE, WORKSITE PARTNERS 29445 #024-16-1993 L1996 **FM** *020 †18

SCARLETT, Matthew David. 119 SPRINGHALL DR, CHARLESTON ENT ASSOCIATES 29445 #048-04-2000 L2001 **OTO** *100 †45

SCHWENZFEIER, Carl W. 119 SPRINGHALL DR, CHARLESTON ENT ASSOCIATES 29445 #011-03-1972 L1977 **OTO FPS** *020

SCOTT, Shaun Noel. 119 SPRINGHALL DR, CHARLESTON ENT ASSOCIATES 29445 #018-03-1996 L2001 **OTO** *020 †45

SUTTERLIN, John Douglas. 7 S ALLIANCE DR, STE 201 29445 #020-12-1994 L1995 **FM** *020 †18

TRANTHAM, Leah Saguil. 120B SPRINGHALL DR, GOOSE CREEK FAMILY MEDICIN 29445 #748-02-1982 L1993 **FM** *020 †18

TUCKER, William Martin. 105A SPRINGHALL DR, PALMETTO PRIMARY CARE PHYS 29445 #012-22-2003 L2004 **FM** *020 †18

WHITFORD, James Edward. 100 SPRINGHALL DR, COMPANION HEALTH CENTER 29445 #035-06-1947 L1984 **GP** *020

GRANITEVILLE – AIKEN

ENGLEE, Mae Jean. 1 HICKMAN ST, GRANITEVILLE FAMILY MEDICA 29829 #308-07-1982 L2004 **FM** *020 ‡

MULLINS, Jessica Lee. ■ 29829 #012-01-2008 *012

PRATT, Donald Clark. 102 RIDGECREST RD 29829 #012-01-1973 L1975 **FM OM** *020 †18

GRAY COURT – LAURENS

BAUMANN, David Paul. ■ 29645 #038-41-1945 L1988 **CD** *071 †20

BOMAR, William Edward. 839 FRIENDSHIP CHURCH RD 29645 #045-01-1956 L1956 **PDS** *071 †85

CHILDERS, William F. 9100 HIGHWAY 14 29645 #045-01-1985 L1986 **FM FPG** *020 †18

MOORE, Alfred Denton, Jr. RR 2 BOX 468 29645 #045-01-1979 L1981 **IM** *020 †20

MOORE, Paul Douglas. 9100 HIGHWAY 14 29645 #045-01-1991 L2002 **FM** *020 †18

NELSON, Christopher Todd. 9100 HIGHWAY 14 29645 #045-04-1998 L1999 **FM** *020 †18 ‡

PARKER, Howard Byron. 9100 HIGHWAY 14 29645 #045-01-1975 L1976 **FM** *020 †18

PATTERSON, Melmoth Suhr. 9100 HIGHWAY 14 29645 #045-01-1973 L1974 **FM FPG** *020 †18

GREAT FALLS – CHESTER

SNEAD, Hollis P, Jr. 308 CHESTER AVE 29055 #045-01-1950 L1950 **FM** *020 †18 ‡

GREENVILLE – GREENVILLE

ABRAMS, Randel Sease. 890 W FARIS RD STE 440, BOX 20 29605 #045-01-1972 L1974 **PDS** *020 †85

ABSHER, John Robt. 274 COMMONWEALTH DR STE A 29615 #051-04-1986 L1999 **N P** *020 †75

ACOSTA, Jerry Lee. 890 W FARIS RD, STE 550 29605 #035-20-1964 L1975 **TS** *020 †85,90

ADAIR, Stefanie Putnam. 701 GROVE RD, MEDICAL EDUCATION 29605 #036-08-2006 L2006 **MPD** *012

ADAMS, Molly C. 1028 N CHURCH ST 29601 #847-06-1987 L1995 **FM** *020 †18

ADCOCK, Kenneth Dan. 11 MEMORIAL MEDICAL DR 29605 #011-03-1963 L1966 **OBG** *071 †30

AFTAB, Huma. 15 ROE RD, POWERSVILLE MEDICAL PARK 29611 #704-06-1988 L2004 **FM** *020 †18

AHMAD, Ambreen Altaf. 27 MEMORIAL MEDICAL DR 29605 #704-02-1975 L2002 **P CHP** *020 †75

ALEXANDER, James Milton. 2310 WADE HAMPTON BLVD 29615 #047-06-1968 L1975 **EM** *020 †16

ALGARY, William Page. ■ 29607 #036-01-1963 L1970 **CD** *071 †20

ALIOUA, Chokri. 1 SAINT FRANCIS DR 29601 #895-01-1987 L1998 **NEP IM** *020 †20

ALLEN, Benjamin Louis, Jr. ■ 29611 #036-07-1964 L1989 **ORS OP** *071 †40

ALLEN, Leighton Chase, Jr. 1210 W FARIS RD #020-02-1989 L1999 **DR** *020 †80

ALMEIDA, Debby Moisao. 130 MALLARD ST 29601 #035-03-2002 L2005 **FM** *100 †18

AMAYA, Sharai Gail. 701 GROVE RD, DEPT OB 29605 #035-03-2002 L2005 **OBG** *012

AMRHEIN, James Allen. 200 PATEWOOD DR, STE A200 29615 #041-12-1969 L2000 **PDE PD** *020 †55

ANDERSON, Carl Eric. 16 WOODLAND WAY 29601 #045-01-1977 L1978 **TS VS** *020 †85,90

ANDERSON, David Gordon. 3 SAINT FRANCIS DR, STE 490 29601 #035-09-1991 L1997 **GS** *020 †85

ANDERSON, Douglas James. 701 CONGAREE RD 29607 #045-01-1977 L1978 **OM IM** *074 †20,70

ANDERSON, Egbert V, Jr. 9 MILLS AVE 29605 #047-05-1969 L1972 **PD** *020 †55

ANDERSON, Erika Maria. 701 GROVE RD, GHS - PEDIATRICS 29605 #045-04-2004 L2004 **PD** *020 †55

ANDERSON, James L, Jr. 1 SAINT FRANCIS DR 29601 #012-05-1943 L1948 **IM** *071

ANDERSON, James L, III. 17 MEMORIAL MEDICAL DR 29605 #045-01-1973 L1975 **IM** *020 †20

ANDERSON, Stephanie Jeani. 701 GROVE RD, GREENVILLE HOSPITAL SYSTEM 29605 #045-01-2001 L2004 **DBP** *012

ANDES, Victoria Giles. 1 CLEVELAND ST STE 200 29601 #045-04-1990 L1991 **FM** *020 †18

ANDROES, Mark Preston. 701 GROVE RD 29605 #019-02-1998 L2004 **VS** *020 †85 ‡

ANNETT, Scott Anthony. 701 GROVE RD, BALCONY STE 4 29605 #051-04-2007 L2007 **MPD** *012

ANSARI, Mohammad Tariq. 200 PATEWOOD DR, BLDG B 29615 #704-02-1984 L1991 **IM PUD** *020 †20

ANTWORTH, Michael Vinton. 1126 GROVE RD 29605 #028-34-1981 L1990 **OPH** *020 †35

APPLEBY, Douglas Claude. 890 W FARIS RD STE 550 29605 #045-01-1983 L1990 **TS CD** *020 †85,90

ARAGON, Leah. 305 TANNER RD, CENTER FOR ADULT & FAMILY 29607 #748-10-1989 L2002 **FM** *020 †18

ARAGON, Rico Amancio G. 877 W FARIS RD 29605 #748-10-1989 L2002 **FM** *020 †18

ARASHINAGUNDI, Siddesha M. 1208 AUGUSTA ST 29605 #495-99-1991 L1998 **IM** *020 †20

ARNOLD, Susan Pearce. 527 MILLS AVE STE 201 29605 #045-02-1991 L1992 **CHP** *020 †75

ASHRAF, Nomaan. 950 W FARIS RD, ATTN: MEDICAL STAFF OFFIC 29605 #024-07-2002 L2006 **ORS** *012

ASHTON, Ronald Lisle. 2 CLEVELAND CT, STE A 29607 #036-05-1973 L1975 **FM** *020 †18

ASSADI, Hamid Seyed. 701 GROVE RD 29605 #305-01-2004 L2005 **FP** *012

ATKISSON, James Donald. 701 GROVE RD 29605 #038-41-1976 L2003 **IM** *020 †20

AVANT, Michael Grant. 701 GROVE RD, 6TH FLOOR SUPPORT TOWER 29605 #045-04-1991 L1997 **CCP** *020 †55

AWAN, Nasir Jalil. 3 SAINT FRANCIS DR, STE 300 29601 #422-01-1999 L2006 **PUD** *020 †20 ‡

BADY, Angela Rolanda. 701 GROVE RD, GHS - INTERNAL MEDICINE 29605 #030-06-2007 L2007 **IM** *012

BAILEY, Carl Columbus, Jr. ■ 29615 #045-01-1960 L1960 **DR** *072 †80

BAILEY, Christopher Willi. 701 GROVE RD, GREENVILLE HOSP. SYS - MED 29605 #048-14-2006 L2006 **GS** *012

BAILEY, Elizabeth Mohler. 8 MEMORIAL MEDICAL CT 29605 #035-48-1990 L1996 **PTH DMP** *020 †50

BAILEY, Erin Mcswain. ■ 29609 #045-01-2008 *012

BAKER, Eric James. 26 ROPER CORNERS CIR, THE SKIN TRUST 29615 #038-43-1982 L1990 **D AM** *020 †15

BAKER, William A, III. 317 SAINT FRANCIS DR, STE 210 29601 #010-02-1984 L1995 **VS GS** *020 †85

BALDEA, Lidia Catrinel. 701 GROVE RD, GHS - INTERNAL MEDICINE 29605 #550-02-2004 L2004 **IM** *020 †20

BALLENGER, James Franklin. 55 CROSS PARK CT, THORACIC/CARDIO ASSOCIATES 29605 #045-01-1970 L1976 **TS** *071 †85,90

BALLENGER, Ottis Moss. ■ 29615 #045-01-1966 L1966 **NS** *071 †25

BALSYS, Roman A. 701 GROVE RD, GHS - INTERNAL MEDICINE 29605 #011-75-2006, ▲ L2007 **IM** *012

BARKSDALE, Collis Lemoird. 15 ROE RD, POWERSVILLE MEDICAL PARK 29611 #025-12-1996 L1998 **FM** *020 †18

BARKSDALE, Rebecca Faith. 106 S CALHOUN ST, FAMILY PRACTICE 29601 #025-12-1996 L1998 **FM** *020

BARNARD, John Michael. 701 CONGAREE RD 29607 #045-01-1964 L1964 IM *071

BARNES, Shanna Leanne. 701 GROVE RD, GHS - INTERNAL MEDICINE 29605 #045-01-2004 L2007 IM *012

BARNETT, James Earl. 701 GROVE RD 29605 #045-01-1954 L1954 FM *072 †18

BARR, Bonnie Lisa. 701 GROVE RD, GHS- DEPT OF GERIATRIC CAR 29605 #045-01-2001 L2004 IMG *100

BARR, James Sinclair. ■ 29615 #803-03-1956 L1961 AN *071 †05

BARTON, Samuel Letcher. 1020 GROVE RD 29605 #051-01-1982 L1989 FM OM *012 †18

BASS, Gary Allen. 131 COMMONWEALTH DR # 310 29615 #045-04-1988 L1989 PD *020 †55

BASS, Virginia Howell. 701 GROVE RD, DEPT OB 29605 #045-01-2005 L2005 OBG *012

BATSON, Walter Arnold, Jr. 35 INTERNATIONAL DR 29615 #012-01-1977 L1978 ORS HS *020 †40

BAUMGARTEN, Tom. 35 INTERNATIONAL DR 29615 #020-02-1989 L1990 ORS OSM *020 †40

BAVEJA, Punit. ■ 29607 #496-22-1999 L2007 ID *020 †20

BAYLISS, Robert D, Jr. 111 DOCTORS DR 29605 #036-05-1984 L1985 IM *020 †20

BEARD, James Harold. 200 PATEWOOD DR, STE A200 29615 #045-01-1978 L1979 PD ADL *020 †55

BECK, Mary Milner. 701 GROVE RD, GHS - OB/GYN 29605 #045-04-2004 L2004 OBG *012

BECKISH, Michael Lawrence. 890 W FARIS RD, STE 510 29605 #026-04-1992 L1996 OP *020 †40

BEHM, Melissa Allen. 701 GROVE RD, DEPT OF PEDIATRICS 29605 #012-01-2005 L2005 PD *012

BELL, Brent Jason. 701 GROVE RD, DEPT OF SURGERY 29605 #035-01-1995 L2006 GS *012

BELL, Jennifer Megan. 701 GROVE RD 29605 #045-04-2005 L2005 GS *100

BENNETT, Grant Whitby. 701 GROVE RD, GREENVILLE HOSPITAL SYSTEM 29605 #004-01-2006 L2006 ORS *012

BENNING, Gurpal Singh. 701 GROVE RD, DEPT OF FAMILY MEDICINE 29605 #305-01-2002 L2004 FM *020

BENSHETLER, Eleanor Gail. 701 GROVE RD, GREENVILLE HOSPITAL SYSTEM 29605 #422-01-1997 L2002 FM *020

BERNING, Eric Lee. 701 GROVE RD, PEDIATRICS 29605 #016-11-1995 L2005 CCP *020 †55

BESSINGER, C D, Jr. 317 SAINT FRANCIS DR # 210 29601 #036-01-1961 L1968 OS *071 †85

BETHI, Naveen Reddy. 545 W BUTLER RD 29607 #495-21-1994 L1999 FM *020 †18

BEVINS, Rachel E. 890 W FARIS RD 29605 #020-75-2007, ▲ OBG *012

BHATIA, Sunil Kumar. 124 MALLARD ST, GREENVILLE MENTAL HEALTH C 29601 #495-45-1985 L1999 CHP *020 †75

BILLINGS, Michael Robt. 701 GROVE RD 29605 #036-05-1978 L1989 EM *020 †16

BISHOP, Aundie Louise. 701 GROVE RD, MEDICAL EDUCATION 29605 #045-04-2006 L2006 GS *012

BISHOP, John Barry. 24 MEMORIAL MEDICAL DR 29605 #012-05-1972 L1979 PS HS *020 †85,65

BIZZELL, Stacy Lynn. 21 ABERDEEN DR 29605 #036-01-1993 L1994 IM *020 †20

BLACKSTON, Barry Clifton. 16 MILLS AVE STE 6, GREENVILLE INTERNAL MEDICI 29605 #045-04-1992 L1993 IM *020

BLACKWELL, Thomas Keith. ■ 29607 #035-01-1987 OS *050

BLEDSOE, Francis H. ■ 29607 #045-01-1953 L1953 NM DR *071 †80,28

BLOODWORTH, Elizabeth F. 130 MALLARD ST 29601 #012-01-1996 L1997 PD *020 †55

BLOODWORTH, James Romey. 111 DOCTORS DR 29605 #012-01-1996 L1997 IM *020 †20

BLOUIN, Gayle Smith. 35 MEDICAL RIDGE DR 29605 #045-01-1976 L1977 GS *020 †85

BLOUIN, Randall Richard. 200 PATEWOOD DR, STE A200 29615 #008-02-1976 L1977 CHN N *020 †18,55

BOARDMAN, Lynn Amy. 890 W FARIS RD, STE 470 29605 #001-02-1991 L2001 OBG *020 †30

BOINEAU, Franklin G, III. 200 PATEWOOD DR STE A200 29615 #045-01-1969 L1969 PN PD *020 †55 ‡

BOINEAU, Maxcy Carroll. ■ 29601 #045-01-1961 L1961 IM *071 †20

BOLDEN, Kelle Danielle. 701 GROVE RD 29605 #051-01-2006 L2006 IM *012

BOLEMON, Britt Haley. 701 GROVE RD, MEDICAL EDUCATION 29605 #012-22-2006 L2006 IM *012

BOND, Brooke Erika. 701 GROVE RD 29605 #012-21-2005 L2005 IM *012

BONNER, Jack Wilbur, III. 701 GROVE RD, MIPH/GHS 29605 #048-12-1965 L1994 P *020 †75

BONNER, Mack S, Jr. 701 GROVE RD 29605 #045-04-1982 L1986 EM *074 †16

BONNER, William Pinckney. 701 GROVE RD 29605 #045-01-1973 L1975 FM FPG *071 †18

BOONE, Norris Ivan. 701 GROVE RD 29605 #051-04-1970 L1973 IM *020 †20

BOOR, Darwin Russell. 4 OLD GROVE RD 29605 #034-01-1983 L1995 N SME *020 †75

BOOTA, Ahmad Mohammad. 3 SAINT FRANCIS DR, STE 300 29601 #875-01-1983 L1996 PUD *020 †20

BORKERT, Daniel Thos. 1809 WADE HAMPTON BLVD, STE 120 29609 #007-02-1984 L2006 FM *020 †18

BOTTS, James Glenn. 1 SAINT FRANCIS DR, HOSPITALIST PROGRAM 29601 #305-01-2003 L2004 IM HOS *020

BOUKEDES, Chris Geo. 1007 GROVE RD, STE B 29605 #045-01-1981 L1982 AN *020 †05

BOUR, Eric Steven. 111 DOCTORS DR 29605 #041-14-1987 L1995 GS TRS *020 †85

BOURDON, Bruce Alan. 125 COMMONWEALTH DR 29615 #045-07-1990 L1997 EM AM *020 †16

BOWE, Andrew Clark. 701 GROVE RD, BALCONY STE 4 29605 #041-77-2007, ▲ L2007 MPD *012

BOWERS, Teresa Anna. 890 W FARIS RD STE 52 29605 #759-01-1985 L1999 ID *020 †20

BRACKBILL, Erin Lee. 130 MALLARD ST, NEW HORIZONS FAMILY HEALTH 29601 #036-01-1999 L2006 PD *020 †55

BRACKBILL, Stephen Paul. 200 PATEWOOD DR, STE B200 29615 #036-01-1999 L2006 GE *020

BRADLEY, Jeffrey A. 135 COMMONWEALTH DR, STE 300 29615 #045-01-1989 L1990 OBG *020 †30

BRADY, Wayne C. 901 W FARIS RD, 2 CROSS CREEK 29605 #045-01-1947 L1947 ORS *071 †40

BRAKE, Daniel Walter, Jr. 215 HALTON RD 29607 #045-01-2000 L2003 FM *020

BRANNAN, India Rachel. 701 GROVE RD, MEDICAL EDUCATION 29605 #012-01-2006 L2006 PD *012

BRANNON, Michael Hamilton. 1210 W FARIS RD 29605 #045-01-1982 L1983 DR *020 †80

BRAY, Cassandra Easley. 2 ROPER CORNERS CIR, CAROLINA MEDICAL CENTER 29615 #045-01-1978 L1979 IM *020 †20

BRAY, Edward Warren, III. 890 W FARIS RD, STE 510 29605 #045-01-1971 L1972 ORS *040 †40

BRENNER, Peter Alan. 1350 CLEVELAND ST 29607 #035-46-1969 L1974 PD *020 †55

BREWER, Charles H, Jr. 121 INTERSTATE BLVD, UNIT 2A 29615 #012-01-1986 L1989 CHP *020 †75

BRIDGEMAN, James L, Jr. 12 ARBORLAND WAY 29615 #036-01-1986 L1987 FM *020 †18

BRIDGES, Tommy Lee. 317 SAINT FRANCIS DR 29601 #045-01-1973 L1975 GS *020 †85

BRODERICK, Denise A. 48 CROSS PARK CT, GREENVILLE GYNECOLOGY GROU 29605 #045-04-1994 L1996 OBG *020 †30

BRODERICK, John Scott. 890 W FARIS RD, STE 510 29605 #047-05-1992 L1993 OTR *020 †40

BROOKER, Reginald John. 3 BUTTERNUT DR, CAROLINAS-GROVE COMMONS 29605 #012-05-1967 L1976 ON HEM *020 †20

BROWN, Anastasia Nicole. ■ 29615 #012-21-2006 P *012

BROWN, Evangeline Joy. 701 GROVE RD, DEPT PEDIATRICS 29605 #045-04-2005 L2005 PD *012

BROWN, James Haskell. 6 CHATEAU DR, PALMETTO INFUSION COMPANY 29615 #012-01-1962 L1970 IM *020 †20

BROWN, Robert O, III. 200 PATEWOOD DR, STE B400 29615 #045-01-1995 L1996 OTO HNS *020 †45

BROWN, Robert Osborne, Jr. PO BOX 26569, 200 PATEWOOD DR BLDG B 29616 #045-01-1969 L1969 OPH *071

BROWN, Robert Rush. 701 GROVE RD, GHS - INTERNAL MEDICINE 29605 #045-04-2004 L2004 IM *020 †20

BROWNE, Beth B. 304 ASHBY PARK LN 29607 #045-04-1996 L1998 FM *020 †18

BROWNE, Louis Patrick. 215 HALTON RD 29607 #020-12-1993 L1994 FM *020 †16

BROWNLEE, Caroline Leigh. 111 DOCTORS DR 29605 #045-04-2002 L2007 IM *100 †20

BRUCE, Curtis Allen. 1202 E BUTLER RD, ALLERGIC DISEASE & ASTHMA 29607 #036-05-1969 L1976 A IM *020 †20,03

BRUCH, John Steven. 877 W FARIS RD, STE D 29605 #051-01-1985 L1998 END *020 †20

BRUNDAGE, Stephanie C. 130 MALLARD ST, NEW HORIZON FAM HLTH SVCS 29601 #011-02-1982 L1989 FM *030 †18

BRYAN, Matthew Everett. 28 MEDICAL RIDGE DR 29605 #045-01-2000 L2003 D *020 †15

BUFFKIN, Terry Lynn. 1142 GROVE RD 29605 #045-01-1974 L1975 OBG *020 †30

BULLOCK, Andrew Ritchie. 52 BEAR DR 29605 #012-01-2002 L2007 U *020

BURDGE, David Clark. 200 UNIVERSITY RDG, DHEC GREENVILLE CO. HLTH D 29601 #010-01-1964 L1970 OBG *020 †20

BURFORD, Jim Douglas. 12 ARBORLAND WAY 29615 #039-01-1973 L1976 FM P *020 †18

BURGER, Carol Talley. 701 GROVE RD 29605 #041-14-1982 L1983 EM *020 †16

BURK, William Jos, III. 1007 GROVE RD, STE B 29605 #045-01-1968 L1968 AN *020 †05

BURKS, Dawn Williams. 1210 W FARIS RD 29605 #045-01-1986 L2000 DR NM *020 †80

BURNETTE, Jos Duncan, Jr. 503 W BUTLER RD 29607 #045-01-1974 L1976 FM *020 †18

BUTCHER, Tracey Ellen. 200 PATEWOOD DR, GREENVILLE 29615 #001-02-2000 L2001 PD *020 †55

BUTLER, Earl Randolph, Jr. 131 COMMONWEALTH DR, STE 310 29615 #045-01-1987 L1989 PD *020 †55

BYRD, Jeremy Michael. 701 GROVE RD, DPET INTERNAL MEDICINE / P 29605 #036-08-2005 L2005 MPD *012

CAGLE, Mary Jo. 213 HALTON RD 29607 #001-02-1986 L1987 OBG *020 †30

CAIN, Michael Steven. 701 GROVE RD, GREENVILLE HOSPITAL SYSTEM 29605 #012-01-2003 L2004 IM *020 †20

CALDWELL, William Elliott. 1 DOCTORS DR 29605 #045-01-1988 L1994 OPH *020 †35

CALL, Mark Douglas. 890 W FARIS RD, STE 520 29605 #045-01-2000 L2002 ID *020

CALLAWAY, Timothy Michael. 701 GROVE RD, DEPT INTERNAL MED 29605 #051-07-2005 L2005 IM *012

CAMERON, Gail Suzzette. 701 GROVE RD, BALCONY STE 4 29605 #566-01-2003 L2007 PD *012

CAMPBELL, Susan Lee. ■ 29607 #045-01-1979 L1987 P *074 †75

CAMPBELL, Ted Ryan. 701 GROVE RD, GREENVILLE HOSPITAL SYSTEM 29605 #048-16-2003 L2004 GS *012

CAMPBELL, Thomas Wm, Jr. 1142 GROVE RD 29605 #045-01-1973 L1974 OBG *020 †30

CAMUNAS, Joseph Anthony. 890 W FARIS RD, STE 320 29605 #011-02-1977 L1986 GS *020 †85

CANCELLARO, Tara. 130 MALLARD ST, NEW HORIZONS FMLY HLTH CTR 29601 #047-20-1999 L2002 PD *020 †55

CANCELLARO, Vito Anthony. 1007 GROVE RD, GREENVILLE ANES 29605 #047-20-2001 L2004 AN *100 †05

CAREY, John Edward. 8 MEMORIAL MEDICAL CT 29605 #045-04-1988 L1989 GS *020 †85

CARITHERS, Mark Everett. 1007 GROVE RD 29605 #012-01-1989 L1993 AN *020 †05

CARITHERS, Richard Alan. 1007 GROVE RD, STE B 29605 #012-01-1983 L1986 AN *020 †05

CARLETON, Amanda Lee. 701 GROVE RD 29605 #041-15-2006 L2006 PD *012

CARSON, Matthew Drayton. 1210 W FARIS RD 29605 #012-01-1973 L1974 DR NM *020 †80

CARSTEN, Christopher G. 890 W FARIS RD, STE 320 29605 #045-01-1992 L1993 VS *020 †85

CARTER, Joseph Wm. 10 ENTERPRISE BLVD 29615 #012-01-1987 L1990 AN *020 †05

CARTER, Shawn Stafford. 701 GROVE RD, GHS - DEPT OF SURGERY 29605 #045-04-2007 L2007 GS *012

CARTLEDGE, Robert B, Jr. 701 GROVE RD, GREENVILLE MEM HOSP 29605 #012-01-2001 L2002 IM *020 †20

CASTELLANI, Lisa M. 701 GROVE RD 29605 #010-02-1998 L2000 PD *071 †55

CATALANA, Paul Vincent. 701 GROVE RD 29605 #035-48-1979 L1980 PD ADL *040 †55

CATANZARO, Joseph M. 317 TANNER RD 29607 #045-01-1988 L1991 D *020 †15

CECKA, Lance Jon. 800 PELHAM RD, NORTH HILLS MEDICAL CENTER 29615 #011-02-1978 L1979 FM *075 †18

CHAMBLISS, Iris Aleta. 701 GROVE RD, GREENVILLE HOSPITAL SYSTEM 29605 #012-22-1999 L2002 IM *020 †20

CHAMBLISS, Thomas V. 111 DOCTORS DR, INTERNAL MEDICINE ASSOC 29605 #048-13-2004 L2004 IM *020 †20

CHANDLER, George Louie. 877 W FARIS RD 29605 #045-01-1977 L1978 IM *020 †20

CHANDLER, Jack Willard. 701 GROVE RD 29605 #045-01-1955 L1956 OS PD *071 †55

CHANDLER, John Cletus. 890 W FARIS RD STE 440 29605 #051-01-1992 L1993 PDS *020 †85

CHANG, Catherine Marie. 200 PATEWOOD DR, BLDG B 29615 #016-43-1999 L2005 PCC *100 †20

CHAPMAN, Shelley Janeece. 890 W FARIS RD, STE 470 29605 #036-01-1990 L1997 OBG MFM *020 †30

CHAROWSKA, Grazyna J. 701 GROVE RD, GREENVILLE HOSPITAL SYSTEM 29605 #759-08-1986 L1999 IM *020 †20

CHILDS, James Wesley. 35 MEDICAL RIDGE DR 29605 #045-01-1964 L1964 GS CD *020 †85,90

CHIVERS, Pamela Canant. 3911 S HIGHWAY 14 29615 #045-01-1982 L1983 PD *020 †55

CHOU, Famin. 1 DOCTORS DR 29605 #025-07-1992 L1998 OPH *020 †35

CHOWDHURY, Saeeda Z. 701 GROVE RD 29605 #160-02-1990 L2005 HEM *012 †20

CHRISTENSEN, Erik Dean. 8 MEMORIAL MEDICAL CT, STE 1 29605 #051-01-1990 L2002 FOP PTH *020 †50

CHRISTMAN, Kathy Lyn. 3 BUTTERNUT DR, CAROLINAS-GROVE COMMONS 29605 #041-14-1987 L1996 ON *020 †20

CICCHILLO, Michael Samuel. 701 GROVE RD, ATTN: MEDICAL STAFF OFC 29605 #038-44-2002 L2006 **GS** *012

CLARDY, Alan Rucker. 701 GROVE RD #011-04-1998 L2001 **FM** *020

CLARK, Andrew Douglas. 701 GROVE RD 29605 #012-01-2006 L2006 **OBG** *012

CLARK, Clifford Dana. 701 GROVE RD, ORTHOPAEDIC SURGERY EDUCAT 29605 #034-01-2003 L2004 **ORS** *012

CLARK, J Ashley Lucas. 1350 CLEVELAND ST 29607 #045-04-1998 L1999 **PD** *020 †55

CLARK, Reese Hunter. 801 GROVE RD 29605 #036-01-1982 L2004 **NPM PD** *020 †55

CLARK, Thomas Bradley. 701 GROVE RD, ATTN: MEDICAL STAFF OFC 29605 #039-01-2005 L2006 **GS** *012

CLARKE, Hugh Adams. 708 GROVE RD 29605 #047-06-1956 L1980 **NS** *071 †25

CLARKSON, Garden Stuart, Jr. 1 SAINT FRANCIS DR, ST FRANCIS HOSPITAL 29601 #045-01-1975 L1979 *020

CLARKSON, Lola Kate B. 2 DOCTORS DR 29605 #045-01-1984 L1987 **PD** *020 †19,55

CLAYTON, Lisa Tan. 1350 CLEVELAND ST 29607 #021-01-1991 L2000 **PD** *020 †55

CLAYTON, Mark Christopher. 200 PATEWOOD DR, STE A200 29615 #021-01-1992 L2000 **PD DBP** *020 †55

CLAYTON, Robt Morris, Jr. 10 ENTERPRISE BLVD, STE 201 29615 #036-05-1974 L1976 **OTO HNS** *020 †45

CLINCH, Marian Barton. 701 GROVE RD 29605 #665-04-2005 L2005 **FP** *012

COBB, William Sinton, IV. 2104 WOODRUFF RD, SURGERY 29607 #012-01-1998 L2002 **GS** *040 †85

COCHRANE, Leonard James. 200 PATEWOOD DR, BLDG B 29615 #045-01-1985 L1991 **PUD IM** *020 †20

COFER, Benton Edwards. 801 GROVE RD, DEPT. OF NEONATOLOGY 29605 #012-01-2000 L2001 **PD** *100 †55

COHEN, Amy Elizabeth. 701 GROVE RD, DEPT INTERNAL MEDICINE 29605 #036-08-2005 L2005 **IM** *012

COLE, Emily Milner. 701 GROVE RD, ATTN: MEDICAL STAFF OFC 29605 #045-01-2006 L2006 **PD** *012

COLEMAN, Wm Armstrong. 48 CROSS PARK CT 29605 #045-01-1978 L1979 **GYN** *020 †30

COLLINS, Arvie Cecil, III. 701 GROVE RD, ATTN: MEDICAL STAFF OFC 29605 #045-01-2006 L2006 **OBG** *012

COLLINS, Bradley G. 701 GROVE RD, FAMILY MEDICINE/SPORTS MED 29605 #020-02-2007 L2007 **FP** *012

COLLINS, Clark S. 605A ARLINGTON AVE 29601 #035-01-1951 L1959 **OTO** *071

COMPTON, Gregrey Alan. ■ 29605 #001-02-1995 L1995 **FM** *020 †18

CONSOLI, Rachael Joan M. ■ 29605 #048-05-1995 L2005 **OBG** *012 †18

COOK, Leroy Kenneth, Jr. 890 W FARIS RD, STE 330 29605 #045-04-1984 L1985 **OBG** *020 †30

COOK, Mark Harvey. 1 DOCTORS DR 29605 #018-03-1981 L1989 **OPH** *020 †35

COOMBES, Jos Dennis North. 1 SAINT FRANCIS DR 29601 #836-02-1964 L1978 **NEP IM** *020 †20

COOPER, John Allen. 1210 W FARIS RD, GREENVILLE RADIOLOGY PA 29605 #045-01-1983 L1984 **DR** *020 †80

COOTER, Michael Stephen. 200 PATEWOOD DR, STE B400 29615 #036-05-1993 L1998 **OTO** *020 †45

CORLETTE, Adrian P, Sr. 1 SAINT FRANCIS DR 29601 #036-08-1992 L1995 **EM** *020

CORNETT, Victor Eugene. 701 GROVE RD 29605 #051-01-1956 L1969 **TS VS** *071 †85,90

CORNETT, Wendy Renee. 701 GROVE RD, MUSC - DEPT OF SURGERY - D 29605 #038-41-1996 L1997 **GS** *020 †85

COURTER, Bradley Jay. 701 GROVE RD, DEPT OF EMERGENCY MEDICINE 29605 #017-20-1986 L1989 **EM** *020 †16

COUSAR, Geo Richard, Jr. 515 W BUTLER RD, STE A 29607 #036-07-1960 L1966 **OPH** *020 †35

COWLEY, Alfred Ronald. 1210 W FARIS RD 29605 #021-06-1977 L1981 **DR VIR** *020 †80

COX, Eugene Cary. ■ 29601 #045-01-1958 L1958 **DMP PTH** *071 †50

COX, Nancy Ann. 701 GROVE RD, BALCONY STE 4 29605 #012-22-2007 L2007 **MPD** *012

COX, Ralph Eugene, Jr. 215 HALTON RD 29607 #045-01-1963 L1963 **FM** *071 †18

CRAIG, William Rhett, III. 111 DOCTORS DR 29605 #045-01-1974 L1974 **IM** *020 †20

CRAWFORD, Patricia Ann. 81 POINTE CIR 29615 #045-01-1981 L1982 **IM** *020

CRAWLEY, Stuart Winston. 10 ENTERPRISE BLVD 29615 #045-01-1986 L1987 **AN** *020 †05 ‡

CREAMER, Jacquelyn Amber. 890 W FARIS RD, GREENVILLE HOSP SYSTEM 29605 #012-01-2007 **OBG** *012

CROMER, Hope Page. 27 MEMORICAL MEDICAL DR 29605 #045-01-1996 L2001 **CHP P** *020

CRONENBERG, Lauren Lee. 701 GROVE RD, ATTN: MEDICAL EDU. STAFF O 29605 #001-06-2006 L2006 **OBG** *012

CROOKS, Richard Hughey. ■ 29609 #045-01-1962 L1962 **D** *071 †15

CROSBY, William Oscar, III. 701 GROVE RD 29605 #045-01-1979 **IM** *020 †20

CROSSWELL, Howland Earle. 900 W FARIS RD, PEDIATRIC HEMATOLOGY / ONC 29605 #045-01-1997 L2000 **PD** *020 †55

CROSSWELL, Mary R. 701 GROVE RD, BALCONY STE #4 29605 #020-02-1999 L2002 **PD** *020 †55 ‡

CROWLEY, Michael Leon. 200 PATEWOOD DR, STE B200 29615 #047-05-1974 L1984 **GE IM** *020 †20

CRUMPLER, John Benj. 701 GROVE RD 29605 #045-01-1983 L1984 **EM** *020 †16

CULCLASURE, James Wise, Jr. 601 HALTON RD 29607 #045-04-1997 L2004 **OPH** *020 †35

CULL, David Lawrence. 890 W FARIS RD STE 580 29605 #048-04-1985 L1997 **GS** *020 †85

CULUMOVIC, Patrick Joseph. 701 GROVE RD 29605 #050-02-1996 L2001 **CRS** *020 †85,10

CUNNINGHAM, Dixon Courson. 1130 GROVE RD, NEUROLOGY ASSOC OF 29605 #036-05-1993 L2001 **N** *020 †75

CURRAN, Margaret Yap. 3 SAINT FRANCIS DR, STE 400 29601 #033-05-1997 L1999 **RHU** *020 †20

CURRAN, William Daniel. 200 PATEWOOD DR, BLDG B 29615 #012-01-1998 L1999 **PCC** *100 †20

DACUS, John Valentine. 890 W FARIS RD, STE 470 29605 #045-01-1970 L1971 **MFM OBG** *040 †30

DANCEL, Lizleah Drapete. 701 GROVE RD, BALCONY STE 4 29605 #051-04-2007 L2007 **PD** *012

DANIEL-SAUNDER, Joanne F. 305 TANNER RD, WEST END MEDICAL ALLIANCE 29607 #566-01-1991 L1999 **IM** *020 †20

DARBY, Lisa Weaver. 701 GROVE RD, GREENVILLE HOSPITAL SYSTEM 29605 #045-04-2003 L2004 **MPD** *020 †20

DARBY, William Madison. 131 COMMONWEALTH DR, STE 210 29615 #045-04-2000 L2001 **PD** *020 †55

DAVES, Glen Gordon. 317 SAINT FRANCIS DR, STE 150 29601 #045-01-1973 L1974 **GE IM** *020 †20

DAVID, Hamer Everett, Jr. 1210 W FARIS RD 29605 #012-05-1976 L1978 **DR** *020 †80

DAVIDS, Jon Robt. 950 W FARIS RD 29605 #024-01-1985 L1993 **OP HS** *020 †40

DAVIDS, Louise Grant. 30 MEMORIAL MEDICAL DR, CENTER FOR PEDIATRIC MEDIC 29605 #036-01-1987 L1994 **PD** *020 †55

DAVIS, Aaron H, Jr. 21 ABERDEEN DR #036-05-1946 L1949 **GP** *071

DAVIS, Barry Rodgers. 890 W FARIS RD STE 550 29605 #045-01-1986 L1987 **TS** *020 †85,90

DAVIS, Edward Newman. 124 MALLARD ST 29601 #045-01-1959 L1959 **P GP** *020

DAVIS, John Woodrow, Jr. 3510 AUGUSTA RD, OUT-PATIENT CLINIC 29605 #036-05-1970 L1974 **P** *020

DAVIS, Staci Diane. 701 GROVE RD, GREENVILLE HOSPITAL SUSTEM 29605 #047-20-2003 L2004 **AN** *012

DAVIT, Rajesh Kumar. 701 GROVE RD 29605 #665-02-2002 L2005 **FP** *012

DEBLOOM, James Robert, II. 300 ASHBY PARK LN 29607 #041-02-2001 L2006 **DS** *020 †15

DEETER, William Taylor, III. 1210 W FARIS RD 29605 #051-01-1985 L1992 **VIR DR** *020 †80

DE HART, Henry Sykes. 314 HILLSBOROUGH DR #036-07-1967 L1971 **U** *020 †95

DE LOACH, Perry Buckner. 124 VERDAE BLVD, STE 204 29607 #045-01-1974 L1977 **OBG** *020 †30

DE LOACHE, William R. 701 GROVE RD 29605 #047-05-1943 L1949 **PD** *071 †55

DENNIS, Hugh Milner. 317 SAINT FRANCIS DR # 120 29601 #021-01-1975 L2004 **TS** *020 †85,90

DE OCAMPO, Anna C C. 29 N ACADEMY ST 29601 #748-20-1992 L1999 **PD** *020 †55

DE PINA, Manuel Antonio. 701 GROVE RD, EMERGENCY DEPARTMENT 29605 #045-01-1997 L1999 **FM EM** *020 †18

DE ROSA, Joseph Warren. 12 ARBORLAND WAY 29615 #038-40-1996 L1999 **FM** *020 †18

DESAI, Bijal Nayan. 701 GROVE RD, ATTN: MEDICAL EDU STAFF OF 29605 #422-01-2006 L2006 **IM** *012

DESAI, Kesha. 701 GROVE RD, GHS - INTERNAL MEDICINE 29605 #045-04-2007 L2007 **IM** *012

DESAI, Nayanbhai R. 800 PELHAM RD, NORTH HILLS MEDICAL CENTER 29615 #495-22-1969 L1977 **R DR** *020 †80

DEVANE, Aron Michael. 1210 W FARIS RD, GREENVILLE RADIOLOGY, PA 29605 #011-03-1997 L2003 **DR VIR** *020 †80

DIGIUSEPPE, Robert Michae. 701 GROVE RD, DEPT PEDIATRICS 29605 #045-01-2005 L2005 **PD** *012

DIKE, A Uchenna. 800 PELHAM RD, NORTH HILLS MEDICAL CENTER 29615 #539-06-1995 L2006 **IM** *020 †20

DILLINGHAM, Christopher L. 701 GROVE RD, GHS - ORTHOPAEDIC SURGERY 29605 #017-20-2004 L2004 **ORS** *012

DING, Shao-Zheng. ■ 29607 #243-32-1987 L2004 **FM** *020 †18

DIXON, James Kelly. ■ 29605 #024-01-1959 L1965 **IM** *071 †20

DODGE, Rhett Andrew. 1007 GROVE RD STE B 29605 #048-12-1998 L2003 **CCA** *020 †20

DOHERTY, Jonathan Regan. 1 SAINT FRANCIS DR, PALMETTO ANESTHESIA ASSOCI 29601 #023-07-2002 L2006 **AN** *100 †05

DOLINAR, Louis John. 701 GROVE RD 29605 #020-02-1976 L1996 **P IM** *020 †75

DONELSON, David M. 205 ENTERPRISE BLVD, STE 150 29615 #045-04-1981 L1982 **OPH** *020 †35

DREISBACH, John Ardo. 1809 WADE HAMPTON BLVD, STE 110 29609 #038-40-1946 L1964 **ORS OS** *072 †40

DRESKIN, Richard Burgas. 701 GROVE RD 29605 #045-01-1971 L1975 **ID CCP** *071 †50

DRURY, William Byers. 2 MAPLE TREE CT, STE A 29615 #017-20-1975 L1978 **FM** *020 †18

DUBOSE, Kimberly C. 890 W FARIS RD, STE 330 29605 #045-01-1999 L2003 **OBG** *020 †30

DUBOSE, Robert Milton, III. 111 DOCTORS DR 29605 #045-01-1999 L2003 **IM** *020 †20

DUNCAN, Charles Ross, Jr. 1 DOCTORS DR, CROSS CREEK MEDICAL 29605 #036-05-1963 L1967 **OPH** *071 †35

DUNCAN, Dale Lemoin. 900 W FARIS RD 29605 #045-01-1979 L1987 **RO** *020 †80

DUNCAN, James Levi. 1210 W FARIS RD 29605 #045-01-1973 L1975 **DR NM** *020 †80

DUNLAP, James A, Jr. 1210 W FARIS RD, GREENVILLE RADIOLOGY 29605 #045-01-1953 L1953 **R NM** *071 †80

DURHAM, Jack Curtis, Jr. 503 W BUTLER RD 29607 #045-01-1978 L1979 **FM** *020 †18

DYLIK, Jason. ■ 29615 #422-01-2002 L2006 **EM** *100 ‡

EARLE, Julius Richard, Jr. 701 GROVE RD, UMG DEPT OF PSYCH 29605 #654-01-1981 L1983 **P CHP** *020 †75

EARLE, Oliver Perry, IV. 1350 CLEVELAND ST 29607 #045-04-2000 L2002 **PD** *020 †55 ‡

EASLEY, Clarence M. ■ 29605 #047-06-1951 L1953 **OBG** *071 †30

EASLEY, Wm Kenneth, Jr. 101 S VENTURE DR 29615 #021-05-1970 L1981 **OTO** *020 †45

EASTON, Edward James, Jr. 1 SAINT FRANCIS DR 29601 #024-07-1969 L2001 **ORS DR** *020 †80,28

ECKSTEIN, William Louis. 6 OLD GROVE RD, 6 NORTH OLD GROVE ROAD 29605 #028-02-1962 L1971 **PS** *020 †65

EDENFIELD, William J. 3 BUTTERNUT DR, CAROLINAS-GROVE COMMONS 29605 #011-02-1992 L2003 **HO IM** *020 †20

EDGE, Kristy Lauren. 701 GROVE RD, ATTN: MEDICAL EDU 29605 #012-01-2006 L2006 **PD** *012

EDMONDS, Phillip Craig. 25 CREEKVIEW CT, PELHAM FAMILY PRACTICE 29615 #045-01-2002 L2003 **FM** *020 †18

EDWARDS, Alan Grant. 1 SAINT FRANCIS DR 29601 #038-40-1962 L1964 **GP** *020

EDWARDS, Alfred C, II. 124 MALLARD ST, GREENVILLE MENTAL HEALTH 29601 #045-04-1982 L1983 **P PFP** *030 †75

EDWARDS, Tonya Deneen. 304 ASHBY PARK LN 29607 #051-07-1990 L1991 **FM** *020 †18

EL-IBIARY, Shereef Yehia. 701 GROVE RD, GHS - INTERNAL MEDICINE RE 29605 #045-04-2007 L2007 **IM** *012

ELLINGTON, John Kent. 950 W FARIS RD, SHRINERS HOSPITAL FOR CHIL 29605 #036-05-2004 L2007 **ORS** *012

ELLISON, Roy J, Jr. 701 GROVE RD 29605 #045-01-1953 L1953 **P OS** *071

ERICKSON, Jay R. 2 DOCTORS DR 29605 #048-14-1992 L1996 **OBG** *020 †30

ERVIN, Laurie Nelson. ■ 29615 #045-01-1963 L1963 **GS TS** *071 †85

ESPEY, Frank Filmore. ■ 29601 #038-41-1945 L1954 **NS** *071 †25

EVANS, John Peter. 13 EDGEWOOD DR, OAKWOOD ORTHOPEDIC CLINIC 29605 #026-04-1971 L1980 **ORS HS** *062 †40

EVANS, John Steed. ■ 29605 #036-07-1958 L1964 **U** *071 †95

EVANS, Joseph Michael. 1007 GROVE RD, STE B 29605 #012-01-1980 L1983 **AN** *020 †05 ‡

EVERT, Michael Bernard. 1210 W FARIS RD 29605 #012-05-1986 L1990 **DR** *020 †80

EVINS, William Boyd, Jr. 2078A WOODRUFF RD 29607 #045-01-1960 L1960 **ORS OSM** *071 †40

FAILE, Eric James. 3909 S HIGHWAY 14 29615 #041-09-1991 L1992 **FM** *020 †18

FARIS, Henry Miles, Jr. 21 ABERDEEN DR 29605 #045-01-1967 L1967 **IM ID** *020 †20

FARLEY, Harlicia Edwina. 800 PELHAM RD, NORTH HILLS MEDICAL CENTER 29615 #045-01-1998 L2002 **FM** *020 †20

FARNSWORTH, Samuel Eric. 1210 W FARIS RD 29605 #047-06-1995 L2000 **DR** *020 †80

FASS, Steven J. 317 SAINT FRANCIS DR, STE 360 29601 #048-12-1985 L1986 **GS VS** *020 †85

FATIANOV, Tamara. 701 GROVE RD, RCP BUSINESS OFFICE 29605 #913-78-1975 L2002 **PM** *020 †60

FAVATA, Kelli Raynell. 701 GROVE RD 29605 #305-01-2007 L2007 **IM** *012

FERGUSON, Cara Seay. 701 GROVE RD, ATTN: MEDICAL EDU STAFF OF 29605 #045-04-2006 L2006 **IM** *012

FERGUSON, Catherine L. 200 ANDREWS ST, STE 100 29601 #051-04-1991 L1999 **RO** *020 †80

FERLAUTO, Jerry. ■ 29607 #561-01-1971 L1976 **PD NPM** *020 †55

FERLISI, Frank Jos. 701 GROVE RD, ATTN: EMERGENCY MEDICINE D 29605 #005-14-1984 L1987 **EM** *020 †16

FEROZE, Alexander G S. 701 GROVE RD, GREENVILLE HOSPITAL SYSTEM 29605 #759-01-1999 L2003 **FM** *100 †18

FERRARO, Frank John. 877 W FARIS RD, STE D 29605 #035-08-1996 L2003 **END** *020 †20

FERRELL, Frank Kipling. 8 HEATHER WAY 29605 #036-05-1971 L1974 **GS** *020

FESSLER, Ann Suddath. 800 PELHAM RD 29615 #045-01-1977 L1977 **FM** *075 †18

FIELD, Justin Samuel. ■ 29605 #021-01-2001 L2004 **ORS** *012

FIELDS, Carolyn Ruth D. 1028 N CHURCH ST 29601 #045-01-1982 L1983 **FM** *020 †18

FINHOLT, David Albert. 950 W FARIS RD 29605 #026-04-1975 L2001 **AN** *020 †55,05

FINN, William Francis, Jr. 701 GROVE RD, GREENVILLE HOSPITAL SYSTEM 29605 #036-08-1985 L1988 **EM** *030 †16

FISHER, Gerald E. ■ 29615 #017-20-1943 L1976 **FM OS** *071 †18

FITCH, Michael Jerome. 701 GROVE RD 29605 #036-08-2004 L2004 **FM** *020

FLANAGAN, William Francis. 8 MEMORIAL MEDICAL CT, STE 6 29605 #036-07-1985 L1991 **U** *020 †95

FORET, Jonathan Lynn. 701 GROVE RD, 2ND FLOOR SUPPORT TOWER 29605 #021-05-2007 L2007 **ORS** *012

FOSTER, Emily Ellen. 701 GROVE RD, GRNVL HOSP SYSTEM 29605 #045-04-2003 L2004 **CHN** *012 †55

FOWLER, James Lyman, III. 31 MEDICAL RIDGE DR, UPSTATE SURGICAL SPECIALIS 29605 #045-01-1995 L1998 **PS** *020 †65

FOX, Thomas Jos, Jr. 138 MILESTONE WAY, STE A 29615 #020-12-1983 L1987 **N IM** *020 †20,75

FOXWORTH, Elizabeth L. 701 GROVE RD, CHILDREN'S EMERGENCY CENTE 29605 #045-01-1988 L1989 **PD** *040 †55

FRALEY, Paul Richard. 701 GROVE RD 29605 #045-01-1984 L1988 **IM GS** *020 †20,16

FRANKLIN, Brett Matthew. 701 GROVE RD, DEPT OF ORTHOPEDIC SURG 29605 #001-06-2003 L2004 **ORS** *012

FRAZIER, Tonya Knox. 800 PELHAM RD 29615 #025-12-1993 L2004 **PD MDM** *020

FRENCH, Glenn Martin. 213 MILLS AVE 29605 #012-01-1987 L1988 **OBG** *020 †30

FRIDY, Wm Wallace, Jr. 21 ABERDEEN DR 29605 #045-01-1966 L1966 **IM PUD** *020 †20

FULCHER, John Hampton. 1210 W FARIS RD 29605 #045-01-1976 L1985 **DR** *020 †80

FULLER, Everett Poole. 135 COMMONWEALTH DR, STE 300 29615 #045-01-1981 L1982 **OBG** *020 †30

FULLER, James Michael. 200 PATEWOOD DR, BLDG B 29615 #051-04-1990 L1996 **CCM** *020 †20

FUNARIU, Ana Gratiana. 200 PATEWOOD DR, STE A14 29615 #781-03-1993 L1999 **RHU** *020

FURMAN, Joseph Earle. 701 GROVE RD 29605 #045-01-1946 L1946 **PD** *071 †55

FUSON, James Robt. 215 HALTON RD 29607 #011-04-1985 L2001 **FM** *020 †18

GABRIEL, Wayne Morris. 1007 GROVE RD, STE B 29605 #001-06-1997 L2003 **AN** *020 †05

GAIKWAD, Nitin P. 800 PELHAM RD, NORTH HILLS MEDICAL CTR 29615 #495-27-1983 L1995 **IM** *020 †20

GAILEY, Thompson A, Jr. 890 W FARIS RD, STE 470 29605 #012-01-1969 L1970 **OBG** *020 †30

GAINES, David Isaac. 317 SAINT FRANCIS DR, STE 340 29601 #001-02-2000 L2004 **GE** *020 ‡

GAINES, Edmund P, Jr. 205 ENTERPRISE BLVD # 350 29615 #036-05-1965 L1966 **FM** *071 †20

GALBRAITH, Penelope. 1210 W FARIS RD, GREENVILLE RADIOLOGY 29605 #917-23-1981 L1989 **DR** *020 †80

GALLMAN-KELLER, Tamela G. 890 W FARIS RD, STE 330 29605 #045-01-1991 L1992 **OBG** *020 †30

GALLOWAY, Lisa B. 125 COMMONWEALTH DR 29615 #020-02-1989 L1998 **EM** *020 †18

GALVARINO, Mario E. 27 MEMORIAL MEDICAL DR 29615 #132-01-1967 L1977 **P** *020 †75

GANDENBERGER, Kurt Lee. 6704 WHITE HORSE RD 29611 #539-06-1980 L1989 **EM FM** *020 †18

GARBER, Matthew David. 701 GROVE RD, GREENVILLE MEMORIAL, BALCO 29605 #011-04-1994 L1995 **PD** *020 †55

GARDNER, Ronald Craig. 800 PELHAM RD, NORTH HILLS MEDICAL CENTER 29615 #045-01-1982 L1984 **NM FM** *020 †18,80

GARDNER, Stephen Ray. 200 PATEWOOD DR, STE A350 29615 #021-05-1974 L1984 **NS** *020 †25

GARG, Ajay. 3510 AUGUSTA RD, VETERANS AFFAIRS OUTPATIEN 29605 #495-73-1990 L2007 **IM** *020 †20

GARNER, Barbara A. 1210 W FARIS RD 29605 #028-02-1985 L1991 **NM** *020 †80,28

GAUDERER, Michael W L. 890 W FARIS RD STE 440, MEM MED OFFICE BLDG DEPT P 29605 #187-03-1969 L1994 **PDS GS** *020 †85

GAULT, Dominic Bruno. 701 GROVE RD, GREENVILLE HOSPITAL SYSTEM 29605 #041-15-2000 L2006 **PD SME** *020 †55

GEER, Jos Spottswood, Jr. 2 DOCTORS DR 29605 #045-01-1977 L1978 **MG PD** *020 †55,19

GEORGE, Zachary Hale. 877B W FARIS RD, CONSULTANTS 29605 #017-20-1999 L2006 **IC** *020

GERAC, Jeffrey A. 701 GROVE RD, GHS - MEDICINE/PEDIATRICS 29605 #021-06-2004 L2004 **MPD** *012

GETTYS, Franklin Keith. ■ 29607 #045-04-2008 *012

GETTYS, Richard Henry, Jr. 890 W FARIS RD, STE 320 29605 #045-01-1980 L1987 **GS** *020 †85

GETZ, Steven Joseph. 1 SAINT FRANCIS DR, C/O PALMETTO ANESTHESIA AS 29601 #036-05-2003 L2007 **AN** *020

GIBSON, Thomas W. 950 W FARIS RD, SHRINER'S HOSPTIAL FOR CHI 29605 #041-77-1992, ▲ L2002 **ORS** *020 †40

GILBERT, Donald Roy. 2106 WOODRUFF RD 29607 #025-07-1988 L1992 **GS** *020 †85

GILDERSLEEVE, Merrill J. 21 ABERDEEN DR 29605 #025-01-1976 L1998 **IM** *020 †20

GILLESPIE, Erin Lynn. ■ 29605 #030-06-2007 L2007 **IM** *012

GILPIN, John Witherspoon. 1210 W FARIS RD 29605 #045-01-1986 L1990 **DR** *020 †80 ‡

GILPIN, Lewis Bailey. 1210 W FARIS RD 29605 #045-01-1991 L1994 **DR** *020 †80 ‡

GILROY, Kevin Michael. 701 GROVE RD, SUPPORT TOWER 5TH FLOOR 29605 #041-02-1999 L2001 **IM** *020

GIVEN, Jason Tyler. 701 GROVE RD, GHS - FAMILY/SPORTS MEDICI 29605 #665-01-2007 L2007 **FP** *012

GLASGOW, Lowrie Ralston. ■ 29605 #051-01-1972 L1972 **GE IM** *071 †20

GLUCK, William Larry. 3 BUTTERNUT DR, CAROLINAS-GROVE COMMONS 29605 #041-12-1979 L1986 **ON HEM** *020 †20

GOBEN, Christina M. 701 GROVE RD, ATTN: MEDICAL EDU STAFF OF 29605 #045-04-2006 L2006 **PD** *012

GODLEWSKI, Janelle. 20 MEDICAL RIDGE DR 29605 #019-02-2001 L2002 **PD** *020 †55

GODWIN, David Alan. 135 COMMONWEALTH DR, STE 300 29615 #045-04-1987 L1988 **OBG FM** *020 †30

GOETZ, David Randall. 890 W FARIS RD, STE 510 29605 #056-05-1976 L1981 **OTR** *040 †40

GOFORTH, Augustus J, Jr. 317 SAINT FRANCIS DR # 170 29601 #004-01-1942 L1949 **OTO A** *071

GOFORTH, Augustus J, III. 131 COMMONWEALTH DR, STE 290 29615 #045-01-1980 L1981 **OTO FPS** *020 †45

GOFORTH, Diane L. ■ 29615 #038-41-1978 L1988 **PDC PD** *020 †55

GOLD, Steven Jack. PO BOX 26916 29616 #024-07-1970 L1976 **IM IMG** *071 †20

GOLDEN, Jill Diane. 30 MEMORIAL MEDICAL DR, CTR FOR PEDIATRIC MEDICINE 29605 #654-01-1984 L1994 **PD** *040 †55

GOLDSMITH, John Andrew. 104 WAYLINE CT 29605 #012-22-2008 *012

GOODBAR, Tony Reid. 2094 WOODRUFF RD 29607 #045-01-1985 L1989 **CHP** *020 †75

GOODING, Julie Regal. 701 GROVE RD, DEPT PEDIATRICS 29605 #051-07-2005 L2005 **PD** *012

GRABARCZYK, Mark Allen. 1005 GROVE RD, UPSTATE CARDIOLOGY 29605 #045-04-1998 L2006 **IC** *020 †55

GRADDICK, Steven Lee. 111 DOCTORS DR 29605 #045-01-1987 L1988 **IM** *020 †20

GRAHAM, Anne Dawn M. ■ 29617 #021-01-1977 L2002 **MFM OBG** *071 †30

GRAHAM, Sutton Lewis, II. 615 HALTON RD STE 100 29607 #048-12-1983 L1984 **PS** *020 †85,65

GRAY, Linda M. 1210 W FARIS RD 29605 #016-45-1985 L1989 **DR** *020 †80

GREEN, James Franklin. 701 GROVE RD 29605 #045-01-2005 L2005 **GS** *012

GREENE, Bronwen S. 200 PATEWOOD DR, GREENVILLE 29615 #045-04-2001 L2002 **PD** *020 †55

GREENE, Charles William. 200 PATEWOOD DR STE B120 29615 #045-04-1994 L1995 **AI IM** *020 †20,03

GREENE, Melanie Mae. 200 PATEWOOD DR, STE A14 29615 #036-01-1994 L1995 **IM** *020 †20

GREENE, William Michael. 8 PORTOFINO CT 29609 #045-01-1991 L1996 **OTO** *020 †45

GREER, Richard Cox. 317 SAINT FRANCIS DR, STE 150 29601 #047-06-1973 L1980 **GE IM** *020 †20

GREGG, Kevin John. 701 GROVE RD 29605 #016-11-1983 L1994 **EM** *020 †16

GREIG, Phillip Carnegie. 373 HALTON RD, HALTON MED PLZ 29607 #048-12-1987 L1996 **OBG MFM** *020 †30

GRIER, Robert Calvin, Jr. 1 SAINT FRANCIS DR 29601 #047-05-1947 L1954 **ORS** *071 †40

GRIFFIN, Floyd F, Jr. ■ 29605 #045-01-1959 L1959 **GP OBG** *071

GRIFFIN, Paul P. 890 W FARIS RD STE 510 29605 #036-05-1953 L1990 **ORS** *020 †40

GRISHAM, Matthew Paul. 701 GROVE RD, GHS - PEDIATRICS 29605 #012-01-2007 L2007 **PD** *012

GROVER, Daniel Austin. 111 DOCTORS DR, INTERNAL MEDICINE ASSOCIAT 29605 #045-01-1993 L1997 **IM** *020 †20

GRUBBS, David Scott. 131 COMMONWEALTH DR, STE 200 29615 #028-02-1980 L1981 **FM OM** *040 †18

GRUBBS, Sarah Rider. ■ 29609 #045-01-1981 L1982 **PD** *075 †55

GUERRY, Meri. 8 MEMORIAL MEDICAL CT, STE 1 29605 #045-01-1991 L1996 **PTH BBK** *020 †50

GUIRAO, David Paul Mendoz. 130 MALLARD CT, NEW HORIZON FAMILY HEALTH 29601 #748-02-1997 L2005 **IM** *020 †20

GWINN, Jane Vance. 58 BEAR DR, CHILDRENS RESPIRATORY CTR 29605 #045-01-1981 L1982 **PDP PD** *012 †55

GWYN, Darryl Royce. 701 GROVE RD, DEPT OF PEDIATRICS 29605 #023-01-1989 L1995 **CCP** *020 †55

HALE, Tabetha Marie. 423 TOWNES ST 29601 #045-04-2007 L2007 **GS** *012

HALL, James Graham. 1126 GROVE RD, 1126 GROVE RD 29605 #036-01-1992 L2000 **OPH** *020

HAMBERIS, Steve John. 3909 S HIGHWAY 14 29615 #045-01-1990 L1991 **FM** *020 †18

HAMILTON, Cynthia J. 1700 WADE HAMPTON BLVD 29614 #048-02-1984 L1989 **PD** *075

HAMILTON, Ted. 52 BEAR DR, GREENVILLE UROLOGY 29605 #005-12-1973 L1974 **FM** *030 †18

HAMMOND, Lyn Horton. 25 CREEKVIEW CT 29615 #045-01-1973 L1975 **FM** *020 †18

HANCOCK, Thomas Gerald. 701 GROVE RD 29605 #012-01-1981 L1991 **AN** *020 †05

HANLIN, Robert Bruce. 877 W FARIS RD, CENTER FOR FAMILY MEDICINE 29605 #012-05-1984 L1994 **FM AM** *040 †18

HANNA, Jeffrey Wm. 1210 W FARIS RD 29605 #038-44-1987 L1992 **DR** *020 †80

HANNA, Katie Bell. 255 ENTERPRISE BLVD, URGENT TREATMENT CTR 29615 #045-04-1987 L1988 **FM** *020 †18

HANNA, Richard Wayne. 25 CREEKVIEW CT, PELHAM FAMILY PRACTICE P.A 29615 #045-01-1974 L1975 **FM** *020 †18

HANNER, Torrence G, Jr. ■ 29607 #045-01-1964 L1964 **R** *071 †80

HARBER, James Jasper, III. 701 GROVE RD, GREENVILLE HOSPITAL SYSTEM 29605 #012-22-1999 L2001 **IM** *020 †20 ‡

HARNER, Russell Edward. 1 SAINT FRANCIS DR 29601 #036-07-1965 L1972 **OPH** *071 †35

HARPER, C Wallace. 890 W FARIS RD, STE 220 29605 #045-01-1956 L1956 **IM** *072 †20

HARPER, Linda Joyce. ■ 29607 #047-07-1975 **FM** *074

HARRAH, Michael Floyd. 2A CLEVELAND CT 29607 #036-05-1973 L1974 **FM** *020 †18

HARRILL, John A, Jr. 125 COMMONWEALTH DR 29615 #045-01-1968 L1968 **DR** *020 †80

HARRIS, Falls Lewis. 1 SAINT FRANCIS DR 29601 #036-01-1960 L1964 **D** *020 †15

HARRIS, Jeff Williams. ■ 29604 #045-07-1952 L1952 **CRS GS** *071 †85,10

HARRIS, Wade Allen. 701 GROVE RD 29605 #001-02-1980 L1990 **CHP** *020 †75

HARTE, Edward Emerson. 125 COMMONWEALTH DR 29615 #045-01-2004 L2004 **AN** *020 †05

HARTLEY, Lawrence J, Jr. 111 DOCTORS DR 29605 #048-14-1978 L1986 **GE IM** *020 †20

HARTLEY, Michael Carlisle. 701 GROVE RD 29605 #012-22-2003 L2004 **GS** *012

HARTMAN, Laura Kinard. 701 GROVE RD, DEPT OB 29605 #045-01-2005 L2005 **OBG** *012

HARTMAN, Robert James. 701 GROVE RD, ATTN: MEDICAL STAFF OFC 29605 #045-04-2006 L2006 **PD** *012

HASWELL, Elizabeth S. ■ 29609 #036-05-1993 L1997 **OBG** *020 †30

HASWELL, James Beckham. ■ 29609 #019-02-1991 L1996 **DR** *020 †80

HAULE, Elaine Mary. 1 SAINT FRANCIS DR, BON SECOUR ST FRANCIS HLTH 29601 #028-34-1978 L1997 **EM** *020 †16 ‡

HAWKINS, William Smith. 1 SAINT FRANCIS DR 29601 #051-01-1941 L1949 **IM** *071

HAWTHORNE, Heather Talber. 701 GROVE RD, DEPT INTERNAL MEDICINE / P 29605 #004-01-2005 L2005 **MPD** *012

HAYDEN, Frank Richard, Jr. 1210 W FARIS RD 29605 #011-04-1986 L1992 **DR** *020 †80

HAYES, James Waynard. 900 W FARIS RD 29605 #045-01-1969 L1969 **PHO** *020 †55
HAYES, Lloyd Eugene. 200 PATEWOOD DR, BLDG B 29615 #045-01-1970 L1971
 PUD CCM *020 †20
HAYS, Christopher Scott. 701 GROVE RD, GHS - OB/GYN 29605 #041-78-2004, ▲ L2004
 OBG *012
HAZEN, Matthew Lewis. ■ 29609 #305-01-2006 L2007 **PD** *012
HEIDTMAN, Edward P, IV. 213 HALTON RD 29607 #011-03-1993 L1994 **OBG** *020 †30
HENDERSON, Joseph Houston. 877B W FARIS RD, CAROLINA CARDIOLOGY CONSUL 29605
 #012-01-1986 L1987 **CD** *020 †20
HENDERSON, Nancy A. 701 GROVE RD, MCC PEDS 29605 #036-05-1984 L1992
 PD ADL *020 †55
HENDERSON, Nathan Alan. 701 GROVE RD, GREENVILLE HOSP SYS 29605 #011-75-2006,
 ▲ L2006 **IM** *012
HIBBETS, Gregory L. 701 GROVE RD, ATTN: MEDICAL STAFF OFC 29605 #048-78-2006,
 ▲ L2006 **FP** *012
HICKS, Jim Fuller. 25 SWEETBRIAR RD, PROF PLAZA BLDG STE 2 A 29615 #045-01-1957 L1957
 PD *071 †55
HILL, Austin D. 701 GROVE RD, GHS -DEPT OF SURGERY 29605 #048-14-2007 L2007 **GS** *012
HILL, Caroline Jane. 701 GROVE RD, GHS - PEDIATRICS 29605 #045-01-2004 L2004
 DBP *012 †55
HILL, Geneva L. 3 SAINT FRANCIS DR, STE 400 29601 #020-12-1987 L1992 **RHU** *020 †20
HILL, Lawrence K, Jr. 8 MEMORIAL MEDICAL CT, STE 6 29605 #045-04-1981 L1987
 U RO *020 †95
HILL, Sybil Anne. 1350 CLEVELAND ST, CHILDRENS CLNC 29607 #012-05-1984 L1988
 PD *020 †55
HINDMAN, Matthew Noel. 701 GROVE RD 29605 #045-04-2002 L2003 **MPD** *020 †20,55
HINES, Wm Bentley, Jr. 1210 W FARIS RD 29605 #045-01-1967 L1967 **R NM** *020 †80,28
HIPPENSTEAL, Alan Robt. 701 GROVE RD, STE E 29605 #041-07-1992 L1996 **PM CN** *020 †60
HOCHSTETLER, Kemmley Hern. 130 MALLARD ST, NEW HORIZON FAMILY HEALTH 29601
 #038-44-2004 L2007 **FM** *020 †18
HOCHSTETLER, Marion R, Jr. 701 GROVE RD, GHS - SURGERY 29605 #038-44-2002 L2007
 VS *012 †85
HODGE, Philip Julius. 200 PATEWOOD DR, NEUROSURGICAL AND SPINE 29615
 #023-07-1996 L2002 **NS** *020
HOFFMAN, Gregory Ryan. ■ 29605 #045-04-2000 L2001 **EM** *020 †16
HOFFMAN, Michael Robt. 158 MILESTONE WAY 29615 #045-01-1975 L1977 **OBG OS** *020 †30
HOGAN, Toni Denise. 209 THREE BRIDGES RD 29611 #045-04-1995 L1999 **OBG** *020 †30
HOLCOMBE, Sarah Margaret. ■ 29615 #045-01-2008 *012
HOLDREN, Rebecca Elayne. 15 PARK CREEK DR, PAIN MANAGEMENT ASSOCIATES 29605
 #051-04-1995 L1999 **PM** *020 †60
HOLLINGER, Wayne Miller. 3 SAINT FRANCIS DR, STE 300 29601 #045-01-1979 L1980
 PUD IM *050 †20
HOLLIS, Lynwood Breeden. 35 INTERNATIONAL DR 29615 #045-01-1989 L1993 **N** *020 †75
HOLLOWAY, Kimberly Sue. 48 CROSS PARK CT 29605 #045-04-1997 L1999 **OBG** *020 †30
HOLT, Gregory Scott. 200 PATEWOOD DR, STE B200 29615 #016-11-1987 L1993 **GE** *020 †20
HOLT, J Williams, III. 200 PATEWOOD DR, STE B200 29615 #035-01-1971 L1977 **GE IM** *020 †20
HOPKINS, William Benj, III. 135 COMMONWEALTH DR, STE 250 29615 #012-05-1974 L1975
 OBG *020 †30
HOPP, Laszlo. 200 PATEWOOD DR, STE A200 29615 #473-01-1977 L2006 **PN PD** *020 †55
HORNE, Benjamin Shinn. 200 PATEWOOD DR STE A200, SUITE A200 29615
 #045-01-1983 L1984 **PDC** *020 †55
HORNSBY, Rae Lynne. 29 N ACADEMY ST, CTR FOR DEVELOPMENTAL SERV 29601
 #036-01-1990 L1996 **PD** *020 †55
HORTON, James Kyle. ■ 29617 #012-22-2003 L2004 **IM** *020 †20
HORTON, Miranda Mcculloch. 701 GROVE RD, DEPT INTERNAL MEDICINE 29605
 #045-04-2005 L2005 **IM** *012
HORTON, Samuel Redden. 8 MEMORIAL MEDICAL CT 29605 #045-01-1996 L1998
 PTH *020 †50
HORTON, William Hickson. 10 ENTERPRISE BLVD 29615 #045-04-1987 L1988 **AN** *020 †05
HOUMANN, Paul Erik. 10 ENTERPRISE BLVD 29615 #005-12-1980 L1984 **AN** *020 †05
HOWARD, Bradley Steven. 1 SAINT FRANCIS DR 29601 #045-04-1985 L1986 *020 ‡
HOWARD, Carley Michelle. 701 GROVE RD 29605 #045-01-2005 L2005 **PD** *012
HOWARD, Leroy Jos. 4200 E NORTH ST, 2 CENTER EAST 29615 #045-01-1967 L1967
 OPH *071 †35
HOWE, Henry Glenn. 33 PONDEROSA RD 29607 #045-01-1956 L1956 **OM IM** *030
HUDSON, Ivet Esperanza. 4200 E NORTH ST, STE 5 29615 #011-02-1996 L2000 **FM** *020
HUDSON, Jennifer A. 701 GROVE RD, GREENVILLE HOSPITAL SYSTEM 29605
 #045-01-1997 L1998 **PD** *020 †55
HUGGINS, Joy M. 701 GROVE RD 29605 #045-04-1995 L2000 **IM** *020 †20
HULL, Robert Warren. 712 GROVE RD, ARRHYTHMIA CONSULTANTS PA 29605
 #012-05-1984 L1994 **ICE CD** *020 †20
HUMENIUK, John Michael. 21 MEMORIAL MEDICAL DR 29605 #062-01-1977 L1982
 D DS *020 †15
HUNT, Catherine Eloy. 877 W FARIS RD, STE A 29605 #048-02-1995 L1996 **FM** *040 †18
HUNTER, James Elmo. 900 W FARIS RD, FL 3 29605 #045-01-1987 L1993 **OBG** *020 †30
HUNTINGTON, Forrest Kay. 317 SAINT FRANCIS DR # 340 29601 #035-45-1955 L1963
 GE IM *071 †20
HUTCHESON, Angela C S. 850 S PLEASANTBURG DR, STE 103 29607 #045-01-2001 L2002
 D DS *020 †15
HWANG, Jai Wung. 111 DOCTORS DR 29605 #012-01-2002 L2004 **IM** *020 †20
IDRIS, Ahmad. 317 SAINT FRANCIS DR, STE 150 29601 #875-01-1990 L2000 **GE** *020 †20
IRWIN, George L. 950 W FARIS RD 29605 #045-01-1952 L1952 **R** *071 †80
ISLAM, Nurul Mohammed. 3510 AUGUSTA RD, VA OUT PATIENT CLINIC 29605
 #160-06-1989 L2003 **FM** *020 †18 ‡
ISMAIL, Naseem Haji H. 701 GROVE RD, DEPT OF GERIATRICS 29605 #965-01-1988 L2004
 FM *020 †18
IVERSON, Kenneth Charles. 1700 WADE HAMPTON BLVD, BOX 40272 29614 #045-04-2007
 OTO *012
JACKSON, Mark Robt. 3 SAINT FRANCIS DR, STE 490 29601 #051-01-1985 L2003 **VS** *020 †85
JACOB, George M. ■ 29615 #045-04-2006 **P** *012
JACQUES, Daniel Mark. 109 DOCTORS DR 29605 #038-40-1994 L1995 **GS AS** *020 †85
JACQUES, Denise M. 200 PATEWOOD DR STE A120 29615 #045-04-1999 L2000 **PD** *020 †55
JAMES, Clyatt W, III. 701 GROVE RD STE B 29605 #012-01-1981 L1981 **AN** *020 †05
JANSE, Melissa Clark. 701 GROVE RD, GREENVILLE MEMORIAL HOSP 29605
 #012-01-1996 L1999 **EM** *020 †16
JARECKY, Thomas Wolfe. 209 PATEWOOD DR, STE 300 29615 #020-12-1986 L1990
 AN *020 †05

JENNINGS, James E, Jr. 35 INTERNATIONAL DR, PIEDMONT ORTHOPAEDIC ASSOC 29615
 #012-01-1981 L1982 **ORS** *020 †40
JERAY, Kyle James. 890 W FARIS RD STE 510 29605 #016-11-1992 L1993 **OTR** *020 †40
JERNIGAN, William Clark. 35 INTERNATIONAL DR 29615 #012-01-1981 L1982
 ORS GP *020 †40
JERVEY, Edward Darrell. 104 SIMPSON ST 29605 #036-07-1961 L1966 **OPH** *071 †35
JETT, William Edward. ■ 29615 #045-01-1956 L1956 **FM OM** *071 †18
JETTON, Robert Larry. 317 SAINT FRANCIS DR # 110 29601 #047-05-1965 L1973
 D DMP *020 †15
JINDAL, Meenu. 876 W FARIS RD 29605 #495-69-1997 L2005 **IM** *020 †20
JOELS, Kristen Leah. 701 GROVE RD, ATTN: INTERNAL MEDICINE / 29605 #047-20-1998 L2006
 IM *020 †20
JOHNSON, Anthony Pruett. 601 HALTON RD 29607 #048-13-1981 L1982 **PO OPH** *020 †35
JOHNSON, Endia Cherese. 701 GROVE RD 29605 #045-01-2005 L2005 **IM** *012
JOHNSON, Gregory Allen. 701 GROVE RD, GHS - MEDICINE/PEDIATRICS 29605
 #045-01-2004 L2004 **MPD** *012
JOHNSON, Jake Carson. 1007 GROVE RD, STE B 29605 #045-01-1979 L1986
 AN FM *020 †18,05
JOHNSON, James Gowen, IV. ■ 29605 #012-05-2006 **IM** *012
JOHNSON, James Gregory. 48 CROSS PARK CT 29605 #045-01-1975 L1976 **OBG** *020 †30
JOHNSON, John Kim. 200 PATEWOOD DR, NEUROSURGICAL AND SPINE 29615
 #025-07-1977 L1986 **NS NSP** *020 †25
JOHNSON, Josette J. 3 SAINT FRANCIS DR, STE 400 29601 #165-01-1983 L1988 **RHU** *020 †20
JOHNSON, Shannon Lee. 213 HALTON RD 29607 #045-01-1995 L1997 **OBG** *020 †30
JOHNSON, Shannon Nakia. 701 GROVE RD, INTERNAL MEDICINE DEPT 29605
 #045-01-2007 L2007 **IM** *012
JOHNSON, William Paul. 701 GROVE RD 29605 #045-04-2003 L2004 **IM** *020 †20
JOHNSTONE, Reid Fain. 48 CREEKVIEW CT 29615 #045-04-1997 L1998 **AI** *020 †20,03
JOHNSTONE, Rudolph Gordon. 48 CREEKVIEW CT 29615 #045-01-1986 L1987 **A** *020 †55,03
JONES, Alison Maria. 701 GROVE RD 29605 #045-01-1989 L1990 **PD PEM** *020 †55
JONES, Amy Eileen. 701 GROVE RD, BROWNELL CENTER 29605 #045-01-1994 L1999
 CHP *020 †75
JONES, Kenneth P. 800 PELHAM RD, NORTH HILLS MEDICAL CENTER 29615
 #047-07-1978 L1983 **FM** *020 †18
JONES, Lewis Earle. 81 POINTE CIR 29615 #045-01-1957 L1957 **FM** *020 †18
JONES, Wesley Branch. 701 GROVE RD, GHS - SURGERY 29605 #045-04-2004 L2004 **GS** *012
JONES, Wesley Christian. 701 GROVE RD, DEPT INTERNAL MEDICINE / P 29605
 #036-08-2003 L2005 **MPD** *020 †20
JONES, William Burrell. 800 PELHAM RD, N HILLS MED CTR 29615 #036-07-1954 L1963
 ORS AM *071 †40
JONES, William Esley. ■ 29615 #045-01-1955 L1956 **FM** *071 †18
JOUDEH, Thaer A. 3921 S HIGHWAY 14 STE A, SOUTHSIDE MEDICAL CTR, PA 29615
 #875-01-1988 L2000 **IM** *020 †20
JUE, Sue Joan. 200 PATEWOOD DR, STE A200 29615 #021-06-1988 L2003 **PD** *020 †55
KABAS, John Scott. 890 W FARIS RD STE 550, VASCULAR DISEASE 29605 #036-07-1985 L1994
 TS *020 †85,90
KAHLER, Julie Ann. 2 ROPER CORNERS CIR, CAROLINA MEDICAL CENTER 29615
 #045-01-1998 L1999 **FM** *020
KAISER, Gregg Matthew. 1126 GROVE RD 29605 #047-06-1989 L1997 **OPH** *020 †35
KAISER, Katherine Lacey. ■ 29605 #001-02-1992 L1998 **IM** *020
KAMATH, Prashanth Jayaram. 701 GROVE RD, DEPT INTERNAL MEDICINE 29605
 #045-04-2005 L2005 **IM** *012
KANOS, Charles C. 890 W FARIS RD, NEUROSURGICAL AND SPINE 29605 #047-06-1994 L2000
 NS *020 †25
KAO, Neil Lin. 1202 E BUTLER RD 29607 #016-11-1988 L2000 **AI** *020 †20,03
KAVOLUS, Christopher H. 35 INTERNATIONAL DR, PIEDMONT ORTHOPAEDIC ASSOC 29615
 #020-12-1984 L1990 **ORS** *020 †40
KEITH, Rebecca Anne. 213 HALTON RD 29607 #017-20-1991 L1996 **OBG** *020 †30
KELLETT, Michael Parris. 890 W FARIS RD, STE 330 29605 #045-01-1970 L1971 **OBG** *071 †30
KELLETT, Richard Stanley. ■ 29601 #045-01-1997 L2000 **AN** *020
KELLETT, William West, III. 890 W FARIS RD STE 330 29605 #045-01-1966 L1966 **OBG** *071 †30
KELLICUT, Dwight Clesson. 701 GROVE RD, DEPT VASCULAR SURGERY 29605
 #023-12-1999 L2005 **VS** *020 †85
KELLY, Carrie Clement. 701 GROVE RD, DEPT PEDIATRICS 29605 #012-01-2004 L2005 **PD** *012
KELLY, Desmond Peyton. 200 PATEWOOD DR, STE A200 29615 #836-02-1977 L1995
 PD *020 †55
KELLY, Jason Patrick. ■ 29615 #012-01-2001 L2007 **DR** *020 †80
KELLY, John Wm. 890 W FARIS RD, STE 520 29605 #027-01-1981 L1994 **ID IM** *020 †20
KELLY, Michael Wm. 317 SAINT FRANCIS DR, STE 150 29601 #045-01-1973 L1974
 GE IM *020 †20
KEMMERLIN, Richard Wayne. 1817 WOODRUFF RD 29607 #012-01-1976 L1977 **FM** *020 †18
KENDALL, Thomas William. 701 GROVE RD, GREENVILLE HOSPITAL SYSTEM 29605
 #045-04-2003 L2004 **GS** *012
KENDALL, Thomas Wm. 1817 WOODRUFF RD 29607 #012-01-1976 L1977 **FM** *020 †18
KENNEDY, Keiron Takahria. 701 GROVE RD, DEPT GENERAL SURGERY 29605
 #045-04-2005 L2005 **GS** *012
KENNEMORE, Douglas Ervin. 20 MEDICAL RIDGE DR 29605 #045-01-1957 L1957 **NS** *071 †25
KENNERLY, Byron Thomason. 1007 GROVE RD, STE B 29605 #012-01-1972 L1973 **AN** *020 †05
KENSELL, Ralph Franklin. 1 SAINT FRANCIS DR, ST. FRANCIS HOSPITAL 29601
 #045-01-1980 L2001 **EM FM** *020 †18,16
KHAN, Mohammad Aiyub. 3510 AUGUSTA RD, VA CLINIC 29605 #704-09-1966 L1993
 ID IM *020
KILGORE, Donald G, Jr. ■ 29605 #048-12-1949 L1956 **PTH BBK** *071 †50
KIM, John Phillip. 1007 GROVE RD, STE B 29605 #036-01-1989 L1994 **M** *020 †20
KIM, Suzy Linda. 200 PATEWOOD DR, STE B200 29615 #041-01-1987 L1998 **GE IM** *020 †20
KING, David G. 1210 W FARIS RD, GREENVILLE RADIOLOGY PA 29605 #047-06-1960 L1967
 DR *071 †80
KIRKLAND, Larry R, Jr. ■ 29607 #001-02-1991 L1996 **IM** *100
KIRKLAND, Levi Singleton. ■ 29605 #047-07-1954 L1954 **GS GP** *071
KISTLER, Kent Howard. 1130 GROVE RD, NEUROLOGY ASSOC OF 29605 #036-07-1979 L1984
 N *020 †75
KLOCKER, Todd Robert. 701 GROVE RD 29605 #305-01-2005 L2005 **IM** *012
KMONICEK, Joseph M. 877B W FARIS RD, CAROLINA CARDIOLOGY CONSUL 29605
 #041-02-1978 L1988 **IC CD** *020 †20
KNIGHT, Edward Bert. 200 PATEWOOD DR STE 480, PULMONARY DISEASE BLDG B 29615
 #045-01-1976 L1977 **PUD CCM** *020 †20

KNIGHT, Roland M. 710 GROVE RD 29605 #045-01-1952 L1952 ORS *020 †40

KNOX, Richard Fredrick. 1007 GROVE RD, # B 29605 #012-01-1982 L1986 AN CCA *020 †05

KOCH, Benjamin Schaeffer. 701 GROVE RD, ATTN: MEDICAL STAFF OFC 29605 #045-01-2006 L2006 ORS *012

KOFOED, Sharon Eury. 1 SAINT FRANCIS DR 29601 #001-02-1992 L1993 OBG *020 †30

KOONTZ, David Wayne. 111 DOCTORS DR 29605 #036-05-1998 L2001 IM *020 †20

KOPERA, Kevin Wm. 1020 GROVE RD, CTR HLTH OCC SVCS 29605 #035-06-1988 L1992 PM OM *020 †60

KOSCHNITZKI, Kenneth G. 801 GROVE RD, DEPT NEONATOLOGY 29605 #016-43-1991 L2005 NPM *020 †55

KRAEMER, Keith Frederick. 1007 GROVE RD STE B 29605 #047-06-1971 L1983 AN LM *020 †05,16

KRISHNIAH, B. 545 W BUTLER RD, MAULDIN MED ASSOC 29607 #495-09-1993 L1997 IM *020 †20

KRUGER, Elke Brigitte. 701 GROVE RD, GREENVILLE MEM MED CTR 29605 #409-21-1990 L1996 IM *020 †20

KUBIAK, Joseph S, Jr. 3 SAINT FRANCIS DR, STE 300 29601 #041-02-1984 L1991 PCC CCM *020 †20

KUHL, John Thomas. 850 S PLEASANTBURG DR, STE 103 29607 #030-06-2003 L2007 D *020 †15 ‡

KUKHAR, Ivan Bogdanovych. 701 GROVE RD 29605 #913-42-1999 L2007 GS *012

KURAKULA, Satya Sai K. 800 PELHAM RD, NORTH HILLS MEDICAL CENTER 29615 #495-65-1991 L2000 FM *020 †18

LACKEY, Wesley Grayson. 701 GROVE RD, 2ND FLOOR SUPPORT TOWER 29605 #017-20-2007 L2007 ORS *012

LACROIX, Robin Newton. 200 PATEWOOD DR, STE A200 29615 #045-04-1986 L1987 PD ID *020 †55

LACY, John Eric. ■ 29611 #045-04-2008 *012

LAFFITTE, Ralph M, Jr. 890 W FARIS RD, STE 330 29605 #045-01-1977 L1978 OBG *020 †30

LAGLEVA, Rafael Lucas. 1 SAINT FRANCIS DR, MEDICAL STAFF SERVICES 29601 #422-01-2000 L2003 IM *020 †20 ‡

LANCE, Tracy Lynette. 701 GROVE RD 29605 #004-01-1992 L1996 EM *020 †20

LANE, Stephen Fuller. 1007 GROVE RD, STE B 29605 #045-04-1989 L1993 AN *020 †05

LANE, Stuart Paul. 1007 GROVE RD, STE B 29605 #045-01-1984 L1986 AN *020 †05

LANGAN, Eugene Michael. 701 GROVE RD, DEPT OF SURGICAL EDUCATION 29605 #010-02-1987 L1994 VS *020 †85

LANTZ, Andrea Ellen. 62 BEAR DR 29605 #045-04-1995 L1996 AI *020 †55,03

LANTZ, Todd Robert. 124 VERDAE BLVD, STE 204 29607 #045-04-1994 L1995 OBG *020 †30

LAPEYROLERIE, Daryl Allyn. 200 PATEWOOD DR, BLDG B 29615 #010-03-1988 L1998 IM *020 †20

LARSON, Christina Leigh. 701 GROVE RD, GREENVILLE HOSPITAL SYSTEM 29605 #026-04-2000 L2002 PD *020 †55

LATHAM, Bruce Byron. 877 W FARIS RD, STE D 29605 #045-04-1987 L1988 END IM *020 †20

LATHAM, John Thos, Jr. 1 SAINT FRANCIS DR 29601 #047-05-1974 L1981 PTH *020 †50

LATHEM, James Ernest. 2 STRATTON PL 29615 #045-01-1959 L1959 U *071 †95

LATTIMORE, Ralph E, Jr. 213 HALTON RD 29607 #045-01-1980 L1983 OBG *020 †30

LAURENS, Richard Giles. 3 SAINT FRANCIS DR, STE 300 29601 #045-01-1977 L1978 CCM PUD *020 †20

LAWDAHL, Richard Bria. 1210 W FARIS RD 29605 #047-05-1982 L1988 DR VIR *020 †80

LAWLEY, Michael Greenwood. 950 W FARIS RD, ATTN: MEDICAL STAFF OFFICE 29605 #001-06-2003 L2006 ORS *012

LAWSON, Jeffrey Geldert. 3 SAINT FRANCIS DR, STE 400 29601 #047-06-1971 L1979 RHU IM *020 †20

LAWTON, Wesley W, Jr. 21 ABERDEEN DR 29605 #045-01-1968 L1968 IM IMG *020 †20

LE BEL, Joseph Stephen. 200 PATEWOOD DR STE B200 29615 #047-06-1995 L1996 GE *020 †20

LE BEL, Laura W. 135 COMMONWEALTH DR, STE 300 29615 #045-01-1997 L2002 OBG *020 †30

LEBLOND, Robert Edward. 1003 GROVE RD, STE E 29605 #020-02-1991 L2000 PM *020 †60

LE-CARTER, Diemphuong. ■ 29605 #005-18-2005 L2005 FP *012

LEDER, Steven T. 209 PATEWOOD DR, STE 300 29615 #051-04-1984 L2003 AN CCM *020 †05

LEE, Sylvester. 1210 W FARIS RD 29605 #011-03-1990 L1997 DR *020 †80

LEFFERT, Frederick H. 20 RED FOX CT 29615 #012-05-1966 L1980 A PD *020 †55,03

LEHMAN, Edward Lamar. 1 DOCTORS DR 29605 #012-01-1963 L1969 AN *020 †05

LELAND, Richard Griffin. 12 ARBORLAND WAY 29615 #045-01-1993 L1994 FM *020 †18

LERNER, Edwin Milton, II. 1 ALM WAY 29601 #024-01-1944 PTH AI *030 †50

LESHMAN, Jeffrey Sherwin. 701 GROVE RD 29605 #038-43-1982 L1985 EM *020 †16

LEWIS, Katherine T. 701 GROVE RD 29605 #056-06-1988 L1992 FM *020 †18

LEWIS, Tameika Fleming. 701 GROVE RD 29605 #045-01-2006 L2006 OBG *012

LI, David Sui-Ng. 130 MALLARD ST, NEW HORIZON FAMILY HEALTH 29601 #045-01-1990 L1991 IM *020 †20

LINDAMOOD, Ronald Paul. 701 GROVE RD, ATTN: MEDICAL STAFF OFC 29605 #012-22-2006 L2006 IM *012

LIPSEY, Allison Sentelle. 111 DOCTORS DR 29605 #045-01-1990 L1991 RHU *020 †20

LITTLEPAGE, Sella R, II. 200 PATEWOOD DR, # A350A 29615 #020-12-1970 L1976 NS *020 †25

LOGAN, Wm Carlson, Jr. 255 ENTERPRISE BLVD, STE 101 29615 #036-01-1992 L2002 IMG *020 †20

LOGING, James Ashley. 701 GROVE RD, 2ND FL BALCONY STE 29605 #045-01-2001 L2002 ORS *020

LOKEY, Jonathan S. 701 GROVE RD, GREENVILLE HOSPITAL SYSTEM 29605 #051-04-1993 L1994 OS *020 †85

LONG, Lesle Dean. 3505 PELHAM RD STE A, MULTI-SPECIALTY CARE 29615 #045-01-1993 L1994 IM *020 †20

LONG, Woodrow Wilson, Jr. 18 MEMORIAL MEDICAL DR 29605 #045-01-1966 L1966 U *020 †95 ‡

LOOKADOO, Stephen Eddie. 3911 S HIGHWAY 14 29615 #045-01-1995 L1997 PD *020 †55

LOVE, Sandra Renae. 701 GROVE RD, DEPT. OF INT. MED 29605 #045-04-1989 L1993 IM *020 †20

LOVELACE, Nellie Esther. 1 SAINT FRANCIS DR, BON SECOURS ST FRANCIS HOS 29601 #012-01-2004 L2004 FM *020

LOVINGER, Sarah Beth. 701 GROVE RD, GHS - INTERNAL MEDICINE 29605 #028-03-2007 L2007 IM *012

LOWE, Steven Craig. 1210 W FARIS RD 29605 #047-06-1995 L2003 DR *020 †80

LUCAS, Jon Francis. 200 PATEWOOD DR, STE A200 29615 #035-03-1999 L2001 PDC *020 †55

LUCAS, Lannon Eric. 701 GROVE RD, GHS-INTERNAL MEDICINE 29605 #051-07-2007 L2007 IM *012

LUCAS, Silas E. 35 INTERNATIONAL DR 29615 #045-01-1989 L1995 ORS OSS *020 †40

LUPO, Perry Irvine. 527 MILLS AVE STE 201 29605 #045-01-1975 P *020

LUTZ, Leon Noel, Jr. ■ 29615 #017-20-1971 L1976 FM OS *075 †18

LUTZ, Martin Edward. 100 MALLARD ST 29601 #038-40-1981 L1984 EM *020 †16

LYNAGH, Adele Susan. 1 SAINT FRANCIS DR, ST FRANCIS HOSPITAL - ANES 29601 #038-43-1991 L1991 AN *020 †05

LYSAK, Steven Zane. 1007 GROVE RD 29605 #038-41-1980 L1988 AN *020 †05

MAC CLENAHAN, Kristen L. 890 W FARIS RD, STE 330 29605 #036-05-2003 L2004 OBG *020

MACFIE, Jefferys Ashe, Jr. 890 W FARIS RD STE 320 29605 #036-01-1964 L1973 GS *020 †85

MAC LAUGHLAN, Shannon D. 701 GROVE RD, DEPT OF OB/GYN 29605 #011-03-2002 L2004 OBG *100

MAC NAUGHTON, Robt J, Jr. 1 SAINT FRANCIS DR 29601 #036-01-1969 L1977 GS *020 †85

MADDEN, William M. ■ 29615 #665-02-1947 L1955 CRS *071 †85

MADELINE, Lee Allen. 1210 W FARIS RD 29605 #047-05-1992 L1998 RNR *020 †80

MADURO, Lissette Perlita. 877 W FARIS RD 29605 #665-02-2003 L2006 FP *012

MAHESHWARI, Sunildat Devd. 701 GROVE RD, GHS - FAMILY / SPORTS MEDI 29605 #820-02-2006 L2007 FP *012

MAHON, Robert Gray, Jr. 10 ENTERPRISE BLVD, STE 201 29615 #045-01-1962 L1962 OTO A *020 †45

MALPASS, David Gregory. 200 PATEWOOD DR, STE A200 29615 #001-06-1988 L2001 PDC *020 †55

MALVERN, Lori. 130 MALLARD ST 29601 #045-04-1992 L1993 IM *030 †20

MAMRICK, Richard Allen. 1210 W FARIS RD 29605 #038-44-1992 L1999 DR *020 †80

MANLEY, Philip Edward, Jr. 701 GROVE RD, GREENVILLE HOSP SYSTEM 29605 #012-05-1995 L1998 PD *040 †18,55

MANLY, Basil, IV. ■ 29605 #045-01-1951 L1951 OPH *071 †35

MANN, Robert Gary. 1601 CEDAR LANE RD 29617 #045-01-1955 L1956 FM *071 †18

MANN, Thomas Chas. ■ 29615 #045-01-1955 L1955 GS *071 †85

MANN, Thomas Chas, Jr. 3 SAINT FRANCIS DR STE 4, SUITE 490 29601 #045-01-1986 L1987 GS *020 †85

MANNING, Benjamin Meyer. 701 GROVE RD, DEPARTMENT OF SURGERY 29605 #045-01-1999 L2001 CCS *020 †85

MANNING, William Kenneth. 2078A WOODRUFF RD 29607 #045-01-1967 L1967 ORS *071 †40

MANOS, Peter Geo. 10 ENTERPRISE BLVD 29615 #045-01-1957 L1957 FM *020 ‡

MARCHANT, Milford Howarth. 950 W FARIS RD, ATTN: MEDICAL STAFF OFFICE 29605 #023-01-2003 L2006 ORS *012

MARION, Chad Jonathon. 950 W FARIS RD, SHRINERS HOSPITAL FOR CHIL 29605 #025-12-2003 L2007 ORS *012

MARKOWITZ, Jonathan E. 200 PATEWOOD DR, STE A140 29615 #045-04-1995 L2005 PG PD *020 †55

MARSHALL, William Patrick. 3909 S HIGHWAY 14 29615 #047-06-1970 L1972 MDM *030 †18

MARTI, Luis Fernando. 200 PATEWOOD DR STE A200, PEDIATRIC SVCS 29615 #042-01-1977 L2006 PD *020 †55

MARTIN, Jennifer Pearl. 35 INTERNATIONAL DR 29615 #051-07-2001 L2006 APM PM *020 †60

MARTIN, Mary Thurman. 701 GROVE RD, ATTN: MEDICAL STAFF OFC 29605 #012-22-2006 L2006 PD *012

MASKELL, Thomas Henry. 2310 WADE HAMPTON BLVD 29615 #045-01-1984 L1985 *020

MASTERS, Bernard F, III. 1210 W FARIS RD 29605 #045-01-1995 L1996 DR NM *020 †28,80

MATHEWS, Rajv. 950 W FARIS RD 29605 #690-05-1988 L2000 AN *020 †05

MATHIAS, Gretchen William. 200 PATEWOOD DR, GREENVILLE 29615 #045-04-2004 L2004 PD *020 †55

MATHIAS, Reed Anderson. 2 ROPER CORNERS CIR, CAROLINA MEDICAL CENTER 29615 #012-22-2002 L2003 IM *020 †20

MATHIS, Mark Douglas. 1007 GROVE RD STE B 29605 #040-02-1987 L1991 AN *020 †05 ‡

MATTHEWS, John P, Jr. 200 PATEWOOD DR, STE A200 29615 #045-01-1960 L1960 PDC *040 †55

MATTHEWS, Samuel Sheridan. 310 MILLS AVE 29605 #051-01-1983 L1984 PS *020 †65

MATTISON, W Theodore, Jr. 715 GROVE RD, GREENVILLE MHC 29605 #045-01-1966 L1966 P IM *020 †20

MATTOX, Lisa Marie. 877 W FARIS RD, CENTER FOR FAMILY MEDICINE 29605 #047-07-1998 L2004 FM *020 †18

MAUGHON, Michael Josiah, Jr. 701 GROVE RD, ATTN: ACADEMIC SVCS 29605 #045-01-2006 L2006 ORS *012

MAURIDES, Peter Steve. 111 DOCTORS DR 29605 #045-01-1987 L1988 IM *020 †20

MAY, Harry Vincent, Jr. 135 COMMONWEALTH DR, STE 210 29615 #035-45-1972 L1976 OBG *020 †30

MAYHER, Brant Edgar. 11 PARK CREEK DR, PALMETTO UROLOGICAL ASSOCI 29605 #012-01-1995 L2001 U *020 †95

MAZANEC, Paul Anthony. 9 HAWTHORNE PARK CT, PIEDMONT GASTROENTEROLOGY 29615 #038-06-1985 L1988 GE IM *020 †20

MAZZOLI, Vanessa A. 213 HALTON RD 29607 #045-01-1990 L1991 OBG *020 †30

MCADORY, Jane Elizabeth. 701 GROVE RD, GHS - DEPT. OF OB/GYN 29605 #027-01-2007 L2007 OBG *012

MCADORY, Richard Stephen. 701 GROVE RD, GHS - SURGERY 29605 #027-01-2007 L2007 GS *012

MC ALISTER, Malcombe A. 4131A VARDRY RD 29601 #045-01-1965 L1965 GP *020

MC CABE, Michael Baxter. 877 W FARIS RD, FAMILY PRACTICE RESIDENCY 29605 #759-01-1998 L2003 FM *012

MC CAIN, Watt, Jr. 1350 CLEVELAND ST 29607 #045-01-1960 L1960 PD *020 †55

MC CALLA, Samuel Wayne. 200 MILLS AVE 29605 #045-01-1963 L1963 ORS *071 †40

MC CANN, Christa Rigel. 701 GROVE RD 29605 #011-02-2003 L2004 MPD *012

MC CARTER, Jackson Howard. 8 MEMORIAL MEDICAL CT, STE 1 29605 #041-12-1963 L1969 PTH HMP *012

MCCLURE, Scott Brennan. 701 GROVE RD 29605 #036-01-2005 L2005 ORS *012

MCCORMAC, Rupert James, IV. 155 BROZZINI CT, STE E 29615 #045-04-1999 L2000 P *020

MC CRAW, Rhett C, Jr. 200 PATEWOOD DR, BLDG B 29615 #045-01-1976 L1983 PUD IM *020 †20

MC CUTCHEON, John S. ■ 29607 #045-01-1953 L1953 AN PUD *071 †05

MC DONALD, Andrew Gibson. 111 DOCTORS DR 29605 #045-01-1994 L1997 IM *020 †20

MC DONALD, Tillman Wayne. 135 COMMONWEALTH DR, STE 300 29615 #021-05-1964 L1970 OBG *071 †30

MC EVOY, Colston F. 200 PATEWOOD DR, STE A140 29615 #051-01-1987 L2003 PG *020 †55

MC FADDEN, Betty Jean. 1 CALEDON CT STE B 29615 #045-04-1982 L1983 FM *020 †18

MCFADDEN, Cedrek Latroy. 701 GROVE RD, GHS - SURGERY 29605 #041-13-2004 L2004 GS *012

MCFADDEN, Thomas C, Jr. 29 ROCKY SLOPE RD, ADVANCED COSMETIC SURGERY 29607 #045-04-1989 L2001 PS *020 †85,65

MCGILL, Eric Small. 890 W FARIS RD, STE 320 29605 #045-04-1991 L1992 GS *020 †85
MC GOWIN, Joseph Kim, Jr. 9 HAWTHORNE PARK CT, PIEDMONT GASTROENTEROLOGY 29615 #027-01-1998 L2006 GE *100 †20
MC KELVEY, John Keith. 308 BEREA FOREST CIR 29617 #028-34-1979 L1993 AN PD *020 †55,05
MC KINLEY, Brian Patrick. 900 W FARIS RD 29605 #041-02-1993 L2003 GS *020 †85
MCKINNEY, Sandra. 209 WEATHERBY DR, PREMIER FAMILY MEDICINE 29615 #051-07-1990 L1997 FM *020 †18
MC KISSICK, Murray P. PO BOX 789, LIBERTY LIFE INS CO 29602 #036-05-1979 L1980 IM *030 ‡
MC LANE, Nick J. 317 SAINT FRANCIS DR # 330 29601 #011-04-1980 L1981 OPH *020 †35 ‡
MC LANE, Robert C. 29601 #045-01-1953 L1953 DR *071 †80
MCLAURIN, Brent Tindal. 1005 GROVE RD 29605 #045-04-1991 L1992 CD *020 †20
MC LAWHORN, Walter R, Jr. 29615 #045-01-1944 L1944 PHP *071
MC LEAR, Patrick Wm. 400 PATEWOOD DR, STE B400 29615 #025-01-1986 L1992 OTO *020 †45
MC MANUS, Christopher M. 1210 W FARIS RD 29605 #045-04-1993 L1999 VIR R *020 †80
MC PHAIL, James Wm. 800 PELHAM RD, 800 PELHAM ROAD 29615 #045-01-1981 L1982 OM FM *020 †18
MCPHERSON, Kerisea Samata. 1 SAINT FRANCIS DR, HOSPITALIST 29601 #665-02-2002 L2004 IM *020 †20
MEADOWS, Deborah. 200 PATEWOOD DR, STE A160 29615 #035-45-1975 L1980 RHU IM *020 †20
MEAKIN, Arthur Griffin. 701 GROVE RD 29605 #051-04-1948 L1955 DIA IM *071
MEHTA, Prasun Harsukh. ■ 29615 #048-13-1991 L1994 EM *020 †16
MEHTA, Priyadarshini. 15 SCOTTS MOOR 29615 #048-13-1991 L1994 IM *020 †20
MEINE, Elizabeth Khan. 130 MALLARD ST, NEW HORIZON FAMILY HEALTH 29601 #036-07-1998 L2006 PD *020 †55
MELBA, John Edward. 12 ARBORLAND WAY 29615 #045-01-1999 L2000 FM *020 †18
MELNYTSKYY, Ihor. ■ 29615 #913-86-1997 *100
MENSONE, James Caesare. 10 ENTERPRISE BLVD, STE 112 29615 #051-01-1974 L1975 FM *020 †18
MERCHANT, Amanda May. ■ 29605 #045-01-1990 L1999 DBP *012 †55
MERCHANT, Ayub A. 9 HAWTHORNE PARK CT 29615 #704-02-1983 L1991 GE *020 †20
MERCHANT, Gulzar A. 200 PATEWOOD DR, STE A14 29615 #704-25-1991 L1996 RHU *020 †20
MERCHANT, Vernon Evans. 1007 GROVE RD, STE B 29605 #045-01-1990 L1998 AN *020 †05
MERENICH, William Maurice. 103 S VENTURE DR 29615 #041-07-1987 L1995 DR *020 †80
MERRITT, William Mciver. 890 W FARIS RD STE 470, GREENVILLE HOSPITAL SYSTEM 29605 #045-04-2001 L2004 OBG *100
MERRIWETHER, Wesley G. 135 COMMONWEALTH DR, STE 120 29615 #001-02-1997 L1998 FSM *020 †18
MESSER, William Anthony. 215 HALTON RD 29607 #045-04-1995 L1996 FM *020 †18
METHERELL, James F. 135 COMMONWEALTH DR, STE 300 29615 #045-04-1998 L2000 OBG *020 †30
MEUNIER, Paul Andre. 28 MEDICAL RIDGE DR 29605 #041-02-1963 L1970 ORS OS *071 †40
MEYER, Armin Dietrich. 200 PATEWOOD DR, BLDG B 29615 #409-33-1994 L2004 PCC *020
MEYER, James E. ■ 29615 #035-03-1949 L1984 GP *072
MEYER, Leslie C. 950 W FARIS RD 29605 #045-05-1943 L1951 ORS *071 †40
MILAM, Steven Glenn. 306 HILLSBOROUGH DR 29615 #045-01-1985 L1990 DR *020 †80
MILLAGE, Aaron Robert. 701 GROVE RD, DEPT OF PEDIATRICS 29605 #012-01-2003 L2005 PD *100 †55
MILLER, Matthew Lloyd. 317 SAINT FRANCIS DR, STE 210 29601 #055-01-1987 L2000 D *020 †15
MILLON, Angela D. 701 GROVE RD, GREENVILLE MEM HOSP-PEDS 29605 #045-01-1989 L1997 PD *020 †55
MILLS, Benjie B. 890 W FARIS RD, STE 470 29605 #001-02-1992 L2000 OBG *020 †30
MINETTE, Christopher Erin. ■ 29615 #045-04-1998 L2001 DR *020 †80
MINETTE, Lawrence Joseph. 8 MEMORIAL MEDICAL CT 29605 #030-06-1969 L1976 PTH FOP *020 †50
MIRMIRAN-YAZDY, S Ali A. 111 DOCTORS DR 29605 #517-01-1979 L1995 GE *020 †20,50
MITCHELL, Kamari Demond. 701 GROVE RD, DEPT INTERNAL MEDICINE 29605 #036-08-2005 L2005 IM *012
MITTAL, Sushil Chander. 800 PELHAM RD, NORTH HILL MEDICAL CENTRE 29615 #495-03-1981 L1997 FM *020 †18 ‡
MITTELSTAEDT, Stephen Jam. 701 GROVE RD, ATTN: MEDICAL STAFF OFC 29605 #045-01-2006 L2006 GS *012
MOCCIA, Roger Donald. 3 SAINT FRANCIS DR 29601 #422-01-2000 L2007 VS *020 †85
MOHAMMAD, Ali Abdel Majid. 701 GROVE RD STE 5, HOSPITALIST 29605 #915-02-1972 L2008 IM CCM *020 †20
MONROE, James Robt, Jr. 701 GROVE RD 29605 #045-01-1986 L1987 U *020 †95
MONTJOY, Christopher S. 701 GROVE RD, GREENVILLE HOSPITAL SYSTEM 29605 #045-04-1997 L2000 IM *020 †20
MOON, Bryan Scott. 200 PATEWOOD DR, STE C100 29615 #011-03-1995 L1995 OMO *020 †40
MOORE, Joseph Carlisle. ■ 29601 #045-01-1947 L1947 GYN *071 †30
MOORE, Mark Tillman. 890 W FARIS RD, STE 330 29605 #045-01-1987 L1990 OBG *020 †30
MORALES, Augusto. 200 PATEWOOD DR, STE A200 29615 #176-03-1980 L1997 N PD *020 †55,75
MOREIRA, Heather Alexis. ■ 29607 #012-22-2006 L2006 MPD *012
MORGAN, Erinn Ryan. 701 GROVE RD, GHS- DEPT OF OB/GYN 29605 #047-06-2007 L2007 OBG *012
MORGAN, Jeffrey Lynn. 130 MALLARD ST, NEW HORIZON FAMILY HEALTH 29601 #047-20-2002 L2004 PD *020 †55
MORGAN, Robert Ray, Jr. 1007 GROVE RD STE B 29605 #012-01-1998 L2002 AN *020 †05
MORRIS, Michael James. 950 W FARIS RD, SHRINERS HOSPITAL FOR CHIL 29605 #041-02-2004 L2007 ORS *012
MORRIS, Winston B. 701 CONGAREE RD, DOCTORS CARE 29607 #045-01-1997 L1999 FM *020
MORSE, Bryan Clarence. 701 GROVE RD, GHS - SURGERY 29605 #045-04-2004 L2004 GS *012
MORSE, Jana Kaye. 130 MALLARD ST 29601 #045-01-1991 L1992 IM *020 †20
MORSE, Jessica Nevins. 701 GROVE RD, GHS - INTERNAL MEDICINE 29605 #045-04-2007 L2007 OBG *012
MOSES, Allison Whitney. 701 GROVE RD, GHS - OB/GYN 29605 #045-04-2007 L2007 OBG *012
MOUSSA, Mohamad Kazem. 701 GROVE RD 29605 #913-96-1999 L2005 FP *012
MULLEN, Chas Vincent, Jr. 3 SAINT FRANCIS DR, STE 300 29601 #045-01-1978 L1979 PUD IM *020 †20

MULLEN, Patrick Bowman. 3 CLEVELAND CT STE C, POINSETT PSYCH GRP 29607 #036-01-1974 L1978 P *020
MURARI, Yogesh. 135 COMMONWEALTH DR, STE 270 29615 #495-41-1982 L1996 IM *020 †20
MURPHY, David Wayne. 50 CROSS PARK CT 29605 #012-01-1986 L1996 IM *020 †18
MURPHY, Marshall Jackson. 1 SAINT FRANCIS DR, BON SECOURS - ST FRANCIS H 29601 #045-01-1989 L1993 AN *020 †05
MURPHY, Randall Lee, Jr. 701 GROVE RD, 2ND FLOOR SUPPORT TOWER 29605 #001-02-2007 L2007 ORS *012
MURTY, Preethi Vishnu. 701 GROVE RD 29605 #308-13-1999 L2002 NEP *012 †20
MYERS, Barnwell Rhett. 27 MEMORIAL MEDICAL DR 29605 #012-05-1973 L1978 P ADM *020 †75
MYERS, Charles Hammett. PO BOX 9159 29604 #010-01-1960 L1976 NEP IM *020
MYERS, Christopher Blake. 601 HALTON RD 29607 #045-01-1987 L1988 OPH *020 †35
MYERS, Michael Frank. 10 ENTERPRISE BLVD STE 2 29615 #045-01-1980 L1981 FM *020 †18
NAIDU, Raana Pratap. 21 ABERDEEN DR 29605 #409-07-1979 L2004 FM *020 †18
NANNARELLO, Joseph John. 701 GROVE RD 29605 #010-02-1941 L1954 P *072 †75
NASSIF, Fady F. 105 DOCTORS DR 29605 #605-02-1990 L2000 PCC *020 †20
NATARAJAN, Sundar. 10 MEMORIAL MEDICAL DR, GREENVILLE KIDNEY CENTER, 29605 #422-01-1998 L2003 IM NEP *020 †20
NEAL, Matthew Bradley. ■ 29605 #045-04-2008 *012
NELSON, Alfred Turner, Jr. 890 W FARIS RD, NEUROSURGICAL AND SPINE 29605 #012-05-1979 L1985 NS *020 †20
NELSON, Hae Kyong K. 200 PATEWOOD DR, GREENVILLE 29615 #045-04-1997 L1998 PD *020 †55
NESBIT, Andrea Denise. 701 GROVE RD, BALCONY STE 4 29605 #012-01-2007 L2007 PD *012
NETTER, Nancy Mann. 3505 PELHAM RD, STE A 29615 #045-04-1994 L1997 IM *020 †20
NEWELL, Robert Wm. 701 GROVE RD 29605 #036-01-1978 L1983 NPM PD *020 †55
NEWMAN, Steven Michael. 50 CROSS PARK CT 29605 #045-01-1993 L1994 FM *020 †18
NICHOLS, James B, Jr. 3911 S HIGHWAY 14 29615 #012-01-1995 L1996 PD *020 †55
NICHOLS, John Edwin, Jr. 17 CALEDON CT, STE C 29615 #012-01-1988 L1997 OBG *020 †30
NISONSON, Andrea Beth. 130 ROCKINGHAM RD 29607 #041-02-1990 L1994 AN *020 †05
NITHYA, Ramaswamy. 800 PELHAM RD, NORTH HILLS MEDICAL CENTER 29615 #495-59-1992 L2006 PD *020 †55
NIX, Thomas Edward. 31 SAINT FRANCIS DR 29601 #012-01-1978 L1982 OTO *020 †45
NOH, Maureen Youngshin. 701 GROVE RD, ATTN: MEDICAL STAFF OFC 29605 #036-01-2006 L2006 PM *012
NORMAND, Nate John. 701 GROVE RD, GREENVILLE HOSP SYS 29605 #422-01-1998 L2001 IM *020 †20
NOVIA, Dennis Edward. 10 ENTERPRISE BLVD 29615 #041-07-1981 L1986 AN *020 †05
NUTHALAPATY, Francis S. 890 W FARIS RD, STE 470 29605 #016-06-1998 L2005 MFM OBG *020
O'BOYLE, Michael J. 209 PATEWOOD DR, CAROLINA ORTHOPAEDIC 29615 #048-12-1992 L1998 ORS *020 †40
O'GRADY-IRWIN, Sheila. 111 DOCTORS DR 29605 #045-04-1989 L1993 IM *020 †20
OHNING, Bryan Lawrence. 701 GROVE RD, NEONATOLOGY DEPT G H S 29605 #038-06-1981 L1988 PD NPM *020 †55 ‡
O'KELLY, Amanda Gayle. 701 GROVE RD, GHS - INTERNAL MED/PEDIATR 29605 #045-04-2007 L2007 MPD *012
OLIVER, Bradley Thomas. 701 GROVE RD, ATTN: MEDICAL STAFF OFC 29605 #045-04-2006 L2006 IM *012
OLIVER, James Collis. 800 PELHAM RD 29615 #045-01-1984 L1985 FM *020 †18
OLIVER, Thomas Lanier. 200 PATEWOOD DR, STE A300 29615 #045-01-1981 L1982 NEP IM *020 †20
OLSON, David Geo. 1 SAINT FRANCIS DR, ST. FRANCIS HOSPITAL 29601 #021-01-1974 L1997 EM IM *020 †20
ORICK, Veronica Lynn. 1208 AUGUSTA ST 29605 #038-43-2000 L2003 FM *020 †18
OWENS, Lynn S. 2310 WADE HAMPTON BLVD, EXIGENT WADE HAMPTON 29615 #045-04-1993 L1994 FM *020 †18
OWENS, Peter Lawrence. 110 MANLY ST, PSYCHIATRY/PSYCHOTHERAPY 29601 #045-01-1975 L1976 P *020 †75
OWENS-SLOAN, Natalie Chri. 701 GROVE RD, 5TH FLOOR TERRACE 29605 #305-01-2004 L2007 IM *020
OXNER, Kathleen G. 1210 W FARIS RD 29605 #036-01-1976 L1992 DR *020 †80
PACE, Thomas Brantley. 209 PATEWOOD DR, CAROLINA ORTHOPAEDIC 29615 #027-01-1982 L1984 ORS *020 †40
PAGE, James Benson. 527 MILLS AVE STE 201 29605 #045-01-1973 L1974 P *020 †75
PALMER, Charles Benjamin, IV. 701 GROVE RD, GHS-OB/GYN 29605 #020-75-2007, ▲ L2007 OBG *012
PALMER, Karen W. 701 GROVE RD, GHS-INTERNAL MEDICINE DEPT 29605 #020-75-2007, ▲ L2007 *012
PALMER, Michael Jason. 701 GROVE RD, 2ND FLOOR SUPPORT TOWER 29605 #045-01-2004 L2004 ORS *012
PANDYA, Ragesh Dahyalal. 274 COMMONWEALTH DR, STE B 29615 #495-89-1983 L1995 OBG *020 †30
PARIMI, Sam B. 27 CREEKVIEW CT 29615 #495-70-1980 L1995 PM *020 †60
PARK, Julie Unmee. 5 WELSH COBB CT, DIVERSIFIED RADIOLOGY OF C 29615 #041-13-1993 L2007 VIR *020 †80
PARK, Sonny Yong. 701 GROVE RD, GREENVILLE HOSPITAL SYSTEM 29605 #654-01-2001 L2004 FM *100 †18
PARKE, Charles Edward. 1 SAINT FRANCIS DR 29601 #036-01-1988 L1993 R *020 †80 ‡
PARKER, Anne V. 200 PATEWOOD DR STE B180 29615 #028-03-1982 L1989 OPH *020 †35
PARKER, Beatrice Grove. 3510 AUGUSTA RD, OUTPATIENT CLINIC 29605 #306-01-1985 L1986 P PYG *020 †75
PARKER, Colleen M. 850 S PLEASANTBURG DR #103 29607 #048-02-1978 L1999 D DMP *020 †20,15
PARKER, Margaret E. 48 CROSS PARK CT 29605 #036-07-1980 L1995 PD OS *071 †55
PARKER, Roy Turnage. ■ 29605 #051-04-1944 L1944 OBG *071 †30
PARKER, Scott Malcolm. 8 MEMORIAL MEDICAL CT, STE 1 29605 #048-02-1978 L2000 PTH IM *020 †50
PARKINSON, Edwin Brown. 701 GROVE RD 29605 #041-02-1945 L1956 OBG *071 †30
PARNELL, Brent Ashley. 701 GROVE RD, MMOB STE 470 29605 #001-02-2004 L2004 OBG *020 †18
PARROTT, John Flick, Jr. ■ 29605 #047-05-2000 L2006 RNR *020 †80
PARSONS, Edmund Cole. 701 GROVE RD, THE BROWNELL CENTER 29605 #045-01-1981 L1982 P *020 †20
PARTI, Naveen Nath. 1210 W FARIS RD 29605 #012-05-1998 L2004 R RNR *020 †80
PASSINI, Amber Marie. 701 GROVE RD, ATTN: MEDICAL STAFF OFC 29605 #016-45-2006 L2006 FP *012

PATE, Virginia Walker. ■ 29605 #045-04-2008 *012

PATEL, Sudhirkumar C. 1208 AUGUSTA ST 29605 #495-23-1983 L1989 **IM** *020 †20

PATNAM, Raju. 545 W BUTLER RD, MAULDIN MEDICAL ASSOCIATES 29607 #495-04-1988 L2000 **FM** *020 †18

PATRICK, Alexander M. 81 POINTE CIR 29615 #045-01-1969 L1969 **GP** *020 †18

PATTEM, Sandhya. 545 W BUTLER RD, MAULDIN MEDICAL ASSOCIATES 29607 #495-65-2000 L2006 **FM** *020 †18

PATTERSON, Doreen Parrena. 701 GROVE RD, DEPT PEDIATRICS 29605 #012-01-2005 L2005 **PD** *012

PAUL, Joshua. 701 CONGAREE RD 29607 #045-01-1994 L1998 **FM** *020 †18

PAUL-KAGIRI, Rachelle. 10 FARRELL KIRK LN 29615 #045-01-1992 L1999 **OS EM** *020 †20,16

PAYLOR, John Hill, III. 35 INTERNATIONAL DR 29615 #045-01-1977 L1978 **ORS** *020 †40

PAYNE, John Frederick. 17 CALEDON CT STE C 29615 #045-01-1992 L2007 **OBG REN** *020 †30

PEABODY, Alan Moffat. 1212 HAYWOOD RD STE 200 29615 #010-02-1961 L1972 **NEP IM** *050

PEASE, John Caleb. ■ 29605 #017-20-1979 L1987 **IM** *020 †20

PENMETSA, Ravindranath. ■ 29607 #495-65-1982 L1989 **IM P** *020

PEREZ-HUERTA, Angel. ■ 29615 #649-01-1956 **NS** *071

PERLMAN, Scott Jeffrey. 1 SAINT FRANCIS DR, ST FRANCIS HEALTH SYSTEM 29601 #012-01-1996 L2000 **IM** *020 †20

PETERSON, Christopher M. 3B CLEVELAND CT, ON CLEVELAND 29607 #012-01-1997 L2006 **DS D** *020 †15

PETRO, George Joseph. 701 GROVE RD, GHSUMC INTERNAL MED 29605 #012-22-2005 L2005 **MPD** *012

PFENNING, Kara Joy. 701 GROVE RD 29605 #041-02-2006 L2006 **OBG** *012

PHILIP, Thomas Manon. 1600 AZALEA HILL DR, # 1410 29607 #422-01-1999 L2002 **IM** *020 †20

PHILLIPS, Joel Courtney. 28 MEDICAL RIDGE DR 29605 #012-01-1996 L1997 **D** *020 †15

PHILLIPS, John Gordon. 200 PATEWOOD DR, STE B400 29615 #016-43-1986 L1992 **OTO** *020 †45

PHILLIPS, Michael Stephen. 10 ENTERPRISE BLVD STE 208, ADVANCED EYE CARE UPSTATE 29615 #027-01-1984 L1985 **OPH** *020 †35

PIERCE, Clovis H. 800 PELHAM RD 29615 #047-05-1958 L1967 **OBG** *020 †20

PIERCE, Therman Dane, Jr. 1350 CLEVELAND ST 29607 #045-01-1974 L1976 **PD** *020 †55

PITTMAN, James Patrick. 1208 AUGUSTA ST 29605 #036-01-1962 L1975 **IM GE** *020 †20

POINSETTE, Leslie H. 317 TANNER RD 29607 #045-01-1998 L2001 **D** *020 †15

POINSETTE, Michael James. 3909 S HIGHWAY 14 29615 #045-01-1999 L2002 **FM** *020 †18

POLLEY, Kevin Arthur. 701 GROVE RD, GREENVILLE HOSPITAL SYSTEM 29605 #045-01-1991 L1996 **PD** *020 †55

POOL, Joseph Danl, Jr. 3911 S HIGHWAY 14 29615 #045-01-1980 L1983 **PD** *020 †55

POPE, David Hyatt. ■ 29615 #001-02-1961 L2008 **EM NTR** *020 †85

PORTER, Melvin Ernest, Jr. 3204 WHITE HORSE RD, STE D 29611 #045-01-1978 L1979 **FPG** *020 †18

POSTA, Alan George, Jr. 209 PATEWOOD DR, CAROLINA ORTHOPAEDIC 29615 #035-01-1990 L1996 **OSM** *020 †40

POTEAT, Tony Samuel, Jr. 111 DOCTORS DR 29605 #045-01-1996 L1999 **IM** *020 †20

POWERS, John S, Jr. 701 GROVE RD 29605 #047-06-1940 L1940 **IM CD** *071 †20

POWERS, John Stephen. 15 QUEEN ANN RD 29615 #036-05-1981 L1982 **FM** *020 †18

POWERS, Nancy Rice. 200 PATEWOOD DR, STE A200 29615 #036-05-1981 L1997 **PD** *020 †55

PRATT, Karen. 124 MALLARD ST 29601 #045-15-1984 L1994 **P PTH** *020 †75

PRICE, Caroline R. 10 ENTERPRISE BLVD, STE 107 29615 #038-43-1995 L2001 **D** *020 †15

PRICE, Shannon Levonne. 701 GROVE RD, ATTN: MEDICAL STAFF OFC 29605 #011-05-2006 L2006 **OBG** *012

PRINCELL, Mark H. 1 SAINT FRANCIS DR, C/O EMER DEPT 29601 #038-45-1985 L1986 **EM FM** *020 †18

PROBST, Louis Ernest. 30 PATEWOOD DR BLDG 1, STE 140 29615 #065-05-1990 L2003 **OPH** *020 †35

PRYOR, William Watkins. 701 GROVE RD 29605 #036-07-1947 L1955 **CD IM** *071 †20

PUCKETT, James Dean. 135 COMMONWEALTH DR, STE 300 29615 #036-05-1968 L1973 **OBG** *071 †30

PUGH, Walter Leonard. 2 ROPER CORNERS CIR, CAROLINA MEDICAL CENTER 29615 #036-05-1979 L1982 **IM** *020 †20

PULCINI, John Michael. 701 GROVE RD, DEPT PEDIATRICS 29605 #017-20-2005 L2005 **PD** *012

PULS, Larry Edwin. 900 W FARIS RD, CANCER CENTERS OF THE CARO 29605 #048-12-1985 L1994 **GO OBG** *020 †30

PUSKER, Steven Henri. 1007 GROVE RD, STE B 29605 #012-01-1984 L1988 **AN** *020 †05

QUALLS, Ted R. 701 GROVE RD, GREENVILLE HOSPITAL SYSTEM 29605 #048-14-2006 L2007 *012

QUINN, Brendon Michael. ■ 29607 #017-20-2002 L2007 **VS** *012 †85

RAHMANIYAN-KOUSHKAKI, M. 111 DOCTORS DR 29605 #584-01-1990 L2002 **END** *075 †20

RAMOS, Robert Troy. 877 W FARIS RD 29605 #045-04-1990 L1996 **FM** *020 †18

RANA, Neeta Wadhwa. 35 CREEKVIEW CT 29615 #496-07-1983 L1991 **OBG** *020 †30

RANCK, Allison B. 701 GROVE RD 29605 #012-22-2005 L2005 **PD** *012

RANDOL, Richard Lindell, II. 701 GROVE RD, GREENVILLE HOSP SYSTEM 29605 #012-01-2001 L2004 **FM EM** *020 †18

RANDOL, Tabitha M. 701 GROVE RD, GHS - PEDIATRICS 29605 #012-01-2004 L2004 **PD** *020 †18

RASHID, Mohammad. 701 GROVE RD 29605 #704-16-1980 L1995 **IM** *020 †20

RAVICHANDER, Pinjai R. 4210 E NORTH ST, HEMATOLOGY ONCOLOGY) 29615 #495-53-1981 L1993 **HO IM** *020 †20

RAY, Dana Raphael. 200 PATEWOOD DR, STE B460 29615 #045-01-1998 L2000 **IM** *020 †20

REED, James Anthony. 701 GROVE RD, DEPT OB 29605 #104-01-2005 L2005 **OBG** *012

REESE, David P. 413 VARDRY ST 53 29601 #045-01-1941 L1941 **GS GP** *071

REICH, John Adam. 701 GROVE RD, GHS-SURGERY DEPT 29605 #045-04-2007 L2007 **GS** *012

REID, Hubert Stanley. 209 PATEWOOD DR STE 200, CAROLINA ORTHOPAEDIC CENTE 29615 #045-01-1978 L1985 **OSS ORS** *020 †40 ‡

REID, James Douglas, III. 3 SAINT FRANCIS DR, STE 490 29601 #051-04-1989 L1998 **GS** *020 †85

REIFSCHNEIDER, Kent Lee. 701 GROVE RD 29605 #036-08-2001 L2003 **PDE** *020 †55

REINARZ, Stephen John. 1210 W FARIS RD 29605 #026-04-1980 L1986 **DR RNR** *020 †80

REINDL, David. 111 DOCTORS DR 29605 #422-01-1992 L2004 **GE** *020 †20

RENFRO, John F, III. 1126 GROVE RD, RETINA CONSULTANTS OF CARO 29605 #045-01-1988 L1994 **OPH** *020 †35

RENFRO, Suzanne D. ■ 29607 #045-01-1990 L1994 **AN** *020 †05

RENFROW, Jocelyn Rogers. 701 GROVE RD, MEDICAL STAFF OFC 29605 #045-01-2006 L2006 **IM** *012

REYNOLDS, Jarrod Antonio. 701 GROVE RD 29605 #012-21-2004 L2004 **MPD** *012

RHINESS, Debra Lyn. 701 GROVE RD, BALCONY STE 4 29605 #025-12-1995 L1996 **PD** *020 †55

RHODES, Tiffany L. 213 MILLS AVE 29605 #048-15-2001 L2004 **OBG** *100 †30

RICARDO, Raymond C. 701 GROVE RD 29605 #748-08-1986 L2001 **PTH** *030 †50

RICHARDS, Robert W, Jr. 246 ADLEY WAY 29607 #036-08-1988 L1993 **CHP** *020 †75

RICKOFF, Michael Ira. 9 HAWTHORNE PARK CT 29615 #012-05-1979 L1980 **GE** *020 †20

RIDDLE, Charles Dayton. 701 GROVE RD 29605 #045-01-1957 L1957 **ORS** *040 †40

RIDDLE, Sieglinde C. 701 GROVE RD, GREENVILLE HOSP SYS 29605 #045-01-1995 L2007 **DBP** *012 †55

RIDGEWAY, Stephen Randell. 35 INTERNATIONAL DR, ASSOCIATES, P.A. 29615 #045-01-1994 L1996 **ORS OAR** *020 †40

RIEFFEL, Clement N, Jr. ■ 29615 #021-05-1961 L1961 **PD** *071 †55

RILES, William Lewis. 9 HAWTHORNE PARK CT, DIVISION OF GASTROENTEROLO 29615 #045-01-1998 L2007 **IM** *020 †20

RINKLIFF, John Michael. 890 W FARIS RD STE 320, UNIVERSITY MEDICAL GRP-GEN 29605 #045-04-1992 L1993 **GS** *020 †85

RIPPON, Mary Bernadette. 200 PATEWOOD DR STE A14 29615 #028-34-1984 L1996 **OS GS** *020 †85

RISINGER, Killian Benj H. 317 SAINT FRANCIS DR # 360 29601 #045-01-1970 L1970 **GS** *020 †85

ROBBINS, Amy Eliason. 701 GROVE RD, GHS - DEPT OF MEDICINE 29605 #020-02-1997 L2004 **PM** *020 †60

ROBERTS, Donald C. 413 VARDRY ST STE 1A 29601 #036-05-1959 L1968 **TS GS** *020 †85,90

ROBINSON, Charles M. ■ 29601 #036-05-1952 L1952 **OM IM** *071

ROBINSON, Julius Ernest, Jr. 701 GROVE RD 29605 #045-01-1977 L1979 **PD CCP** *020 †55

ROESCH, Thomas Markus. 511 W BUTLER RD, LAUREL GYNOB INFERTILITY 29607 #047-05-1984 L1990 **OBG** *020 †30

ROETTGER, Richard Harold. 35 MEDICAL RIDGE DR 29605 #021-01-1982 L2002 **GS OS** *020 †85

ROGERS, Jimmie Shawn. 701 GROVE RD, GREENVILLE HOSPITAL SYSTEM 29605 #305-01-1998 L1999 **FM** *020

ROGERS, John Mark. 1210 W FARIS RD 29605 #045-01-1981 L1982 **DR** *020 †80

ROGERS, Richard Curtis. 2 DOCTORS DR 29605 #045-01-1980 L1985 **CG PD** *020 †55,19

ROGERS, Robert Marshall. 213 MILLS AVE 29605 #045-01-2001 L2004 **D** *020 †15

ROGERS, Wayne Glenn. 3B CLEVELAND CT 29607 #045-01-1972 L1973 **D** *020 †15

ROLETT, Ronald David. PO BOX 2507 29602 #869-02-1969 L1975 **PHP** *030

ROMANIUK, Gregory Michael. 701 GROVE RD 29605 #104-01-2005 L2006 **FP** *012

ROPER, Ted Jones. 255 ENTERPRISE BLVD, EASTSIDE MEDICAL IMAGING 29615 #045-01-1959 L1959 **DR NM** *071 †80,28

ROSS, Connie Gene. 1003 W PARKER RD 29617 #045-04-1985 L1986 **FM** *020 †18

ROTHMAN, Kimberly Kyker. ■ 29615 #020-12-2000 L2003 **AN** *020

ROTHMAN, Theodore Eric. 1007 GROVE RD, STE B 29605 #020-12-1999 L2007 **AN** *020 †05

ROUNDTREE, Shelia E. 3510 AUGUSTA RD, VA CLINIC 29605 #012-01-1998 L1999 **IM** *020 †20

ROWELL, John Russell, Jr. 35 INTERNATIONAL DR, PIEDMONT ORTHOPAEDIC ASSOC 29615 #023-01-1967 L1974 **ORS OSM** *020 †40

ROYALS, Daggett Orman. 27 QUAIL HILL DR, PIEDMONT ORTHOPAEDIC 29607 #045-01-1955 L1955 **HS ORS** *071 †40

RUBEL, Christopher James. 6704 WHITE HORSE RD 29611 #045-01-1992 L1993 **OS** *020

RUBENSTEIN, Donald Steven. 712 GROVE RD, ARRHYTHMIA CONSULTANTS PA 29605 #016-43-1987 L1997 **ICE CD** *020 †20

RUDISILL, Lawrence E, Jr. 1011 FRONTAGE RD 29615 #036-05-1980 L1988 **HS** *020 †40

RUGGIERI, Jeffrey M. 701 GROVE RD, 6TH FLOOR SUPPORT TOWER 29605 #305-01-1998 L2001 **NPM** *020 †55

RUOCCO, Martin Jos. 139 APPLEWOOD DR 29615 #035-15-1990 L1995 **DR** *020 †80

RUSSELL, Hamilton E, Jr. 3 SAINT FRANCIS DR, STE 480 29601 #045-01-1967 L1967 **GS VS** *020 †85

SABIN, Jorge Alejandro. ■ 29617 #308-03-1997 L2004 **UCM GP** *020

SAITO, Jean Kimi. 1809 WADE HAMPTON BLVD, STE 120 29609 #007-02-1976 L1979 **IM** *020 †85

SALDANHA, Rita Louis. 701 GROVE RD 29605 #495-28-1973 L1991 **NPM PD** *020 †55

SANDERS, John Ragan. 8 WEATHERBY DR, VICE PRESIDENT 29615 #021-01-1968 L1975 **ORS OSM** *071 †40

SANDIFER, William Green. 701 GROVE RD, INTERNAL MEDICINE - UNIV M 29605 #045-04-1989 L1992 **IM** *020 †20

SANTORUM, Jennifer Esther. 701 GROVE RD, BALCONY STE 4 29605 #045-04-2007 L2007 **PD** *012

SARMIENTO, Emmanuel U. 7 MEMORIAL MEDICAL DR 29605 #748-08-1986 L1993 **ALI PD** *020 †55,03

SARMIENTO, Ma Cheryl A. 305 TANNER RD 29607 #748-08-1986 L1994 **IM** *020 †20

SAUL, Jerome Philip. 701 GROVE RD 29605 #036-07-1982 L1998 **PD PDC** *020 †55

SAUL, Robert Anthony. 2 DOCTORS DR 29605 #007-02-1976 L1978 **MG PD** *020 †55,19

SAUNDERS, Hal Stuart. 1210 W FARIS RD 29605 #012-01-1991 L1998 **DR** *020 †80

SAUNDERS, Steve Philbert. 701 GROVE RD, GREENVILLE MEMORIAL HOSPIT 29605 #566-01-1991 L1999 **IM** *020 †20

SAXENA, Naveen R. 401 GUESS ST, STE 100 29605 #495-65-1982 L1993 **CD IM** *020 †20

SCHAMMEL, David Paul. 8 MEMORIAL MEDICAL CT 29605 #026-04-1991 L2000 **PTH** *020 †50

SCHER, Adam David. 701 GROVE RD, GHS - INTERNAL MEDICINE 29605 #305-01-2007 L2007 **IM** *012

SCHILLIZZI, William B. 701 GROVE RD, GREENVILLE HOSPITAL SYSTEM 29605 #033-06-1985 L1998 **IM** *020 †20

SCHLEIN, Bruce Maxwell. 8 MEMORIAL MEDICAL CT, STE 1 29605 #035-08-1963 L1973 **PTH PCP** *071 †50

SCHMIDT, Wm Frederick, III. 701 GROVE RD 29605 #036-07-1976 L1985 **PD PHO** *030 †55

SCHNEIDER, Christopher Ro. 701 GROVE RD, DEPT GENERAL SURGERY 29605 #038-41-2005 L2005 **GS** *012

SCHRANK, John Henry, Jr. 890 W FARIS RD, STE 520 29605 #033-06-1986 L1997 **ID IM** *020 †20

SCHWARTZ, Robert Glenn. 317 SAINT FRANCIS DR # 350 29601 #025-07-1981 L1984 **PMM** *020 †60 ‡

SCOPTEUOLO, Amanda Lee. 1210 W FARIS RD, GREENVILLE RADIOLOGY PA 29605 #035-47-1995 L2002 **DR** *020 †80

SCOTT, Thomas Rufus. 1130 GROVE RD 29605 #036-05-1958 L1967 **N** *071 †75

SEASE, Kerry K. 701 GROVE RD, DEPT OF PEDIATRICS 29605 #045-04-1998 L1999 **PD** *020 †55

SEIGLER, Robert Sanders. 701 GROVE RD 29605 #045-01-1982 L1983 **PD CCP** *020 †55

SELLMAN, Gary Kendall. 701 GROVE RD 29605 #045-01-1982 L1986 **FM** *020 †18

SHALLCROSS, David Lee. 1003 GROVE RD STE E 29605 #055-01-1986 L1990 **PM PMM** *020 †60

SHALLEY, Ann. 255 ENTERPRISE BLVD, MED ASSOCIATES OF GREENVIL 29615 #041-07-1978 L2004 **IMG IM** *020 †20 ‡

SHANBHAG, Gajanan R. 800 PELHAM RD 29615 #496-38-1960 L1983 **GS TS** *020 †85,90

SHARP, Lorra Marie. 701 GROVE RD 29605 #005-06-2005 L2005 **ORS** *012

SHAVER, Jonathan C. 701 GROVE RD, 2ND FLOOR SUPPORT TOWER 29605 #047-06-2003 L2004 **ORS** *012

SHAW, Harold E, Jr. 1 DOCTORS DR 29605 #045-01-1973 L1978 **OPH N** *020 †35 ‡

SHELLEY, Brian Wells. 601 HALTON RD 29607 #045-04-2002 L2006 **OPH** *020 †35

SHELLEY, Donald Winburn. 1 DOCTORS DR, JERVEY EYE GRP 29605 #036-05-1971 L1975 **OPH** *020 †35

SHENOUDA, Ihab Mouris Bot. 701 GROVE RD 29605 #915-04-1997 **GS** *012

SHEPARD, Maryann. 1350 CLEVELAND ST 29607 #035-08-1984 L1985 **PD** *020 †55

SHEPHERD, Jonathan Paul. 701 GROVE RD, GHS - OB/GYN 29605 #036-01-2004 L2004 **OBG** *012

SHERBERT, John David. 10 ENTERPRISE BLVD 29615 #045-01-1990 L1996 **AN** *020 †05

SHERBONDY, David Shane. 112 LOVETT DR 29607 #005-12-1996 L1997 **CHP** *020 †75

SHERMAN, Harry Card, Jr. 1007 GROVE RD, STE B 29605 #012-01-1988 L1992 **AN** *020 †05

SHIDHAYE, Namrata Madhav. 3443 PELHAM RD STE 200, MAULDIN MEDICAL ASSOCIATES 29615 #495-21-1990 L2004 **FM** *020 †18

SHIRKEY, Breann Lyn. 701 GROVE RD, GHS - PEDIATRICS 29605 #055-02-2004 L2004 **PD** *020 †55

SHORT, Marvin John. ■ 29611 #036-07-1962 L1973 **P** *020 †75

SHRESTHA, Shristi Purna L. 701 GROVE RD 29605 #820-02-2006 L2007 **FP** *012

SIEGEL, Jeffrey Allen. 317 SAINT FRANCIS DR # 130 29601 #047-06-1980 L1984 **IM** *020 †20

SIFFRI, Paul Charles. 200 PATEWOOD DR, STE C100 29615 #045-01-1999 L2003 **OAR OSM** *020 †40

SIGHTLER, James Harold. 701 GROVE RD 29605 #023-07-1968 L1971 **PD** *071 †55

SIKES, Harvey Allen. 213 HALTON RD, GREENVILLE E CTR WOMEN 29607 #001-06-1986 L1987 **OBG** *020 †30

SILLIMAN, James F. ■ 29605 #020-02-1982 L2008 **ORS** *020 †40

SIMMONDS, John Sherwood. 3510 AUGUSTA RD, GREENVILLE VA OUTPATIENT C 29605 #035-01-1963 L1968 **IM** *020 †20

SINOPOLI, Angelo. 200 PATEWOOD DR, BLDG B 29615 #045-01-1982 L1983 **PUD CCM** *040 †20

SKAGGS, Joanne Carol. 701 GROVE RD, GHS - DEPT OF INTERNAL MED 29605 #012-05-2007 L2007 **IM** *012

SKINNER, Paul Belton. 2803B OLD BUNCOMBE RD 29609 #045-01-1973 L1974 **FM** *020

SKINNER, Steven Albert. 2 DOCTORS DR 29605 #045-01-1979 L1980 **PD MG** *020 †55,19

SLYNKOVA, Katarine. 3 SAINT FRANCIS DR, STE 300 29601 #286-03-1996 L2007 **PCC** *100 †20

SMITH, Alan Wayne. 1007 GROVE RD STE B 29605 #045-04-1998 L2002 **AN** *020 †05 ‡

SMITH, Arthur L. 1190B HAYWOOD RD, UPSTATE NEUROLOGY PA 29615 #048-13-1991 L1999 **N** *020

SMITH, Charles Edward, Jr. 200 PATEWOOD DR, STE B400 29615 #045-01-1984 L1986 **OTO GS** *020 †45

SMITH, Dane Edward. 35 MEDICAL RIDGE DR 29605 #021-06-1984 L1985 **AS SO** *020 †85

SMITH, Daniel Gray. ■ 29601 #045-04-2008 *012

SMITH, Desmond Ernesto. 45 CREEKVIEW CT 29615 #035-47-1979 L1987 **IM VM** *020 †20

SMITH, Hugh P, Jr. ■ 29601 #041-01-1943 L1948 **R** *071 †20,80

SMITH, James David. 200 PATEWOOD DR, STE A10 29615 #045-01-1968 L1968 **OBG** *020 †30

SMITH, James Ronald. 11 PARK CREEK DR, PALMETTO UROLOGICAL ASSOCI 29605 #045-01-1983 L1991 **U** *020 †95

SMITH, Jeffrey Kent. 2094 WOODRUFF RD, WOODRUFF ROAD PROFESSIONAL 29607 #001-02-1986 L1987 **P** *020 †75 ‡

SMITH, Matthew Lester. 1 SAINT FRANCIS DR 29601 #045-04-1989 L1990 **OBG** *020 †30

SMITH, Rebecca Starr. 503 W BUTLER RD 29607 #045-04-1998 L2002 **FM** *020 †18 ‡

SMITH, Samuel Wilson, Jr. 701 GROVE RD, CANCER TREATMENT CENTER 29605 #041-01-1963 L1970 **HEM IM** *040 †20

SMITH, Trevor Keith. 1007 GROVE RD, STE B 29605 #012-01-1996 L2000 **AN** *020 †05

SMITHERMAN, James Adam. 701 GROVE RD, SURGERY EDUCATION 29605 #027-01-2005 L2005 **ORS** *012

SNAPE, Palmira M Silva. 877 W FARIS RD, CENTER FOR FAMILY MEDICINE 29605 #045-01-1964 L1964 **FM** *071 †18

SNOW, Bradley Michael. 701 GROVE RD, GREENVILLE HOSPITAL SYSTEM 29605 #001-02-2000 L2004 **GS** *100 †85

SNYDER, Bruce Allen. 890 W FARIS RD, STE 320 29605 #036-05-1977 L1987 **VS GS** *040 †85

SNYDER, Melody Jan. 701 CONGAREE RD 29607 #038-43-1996 L2006 **FM** *020 †18

SO, Richard Rosales. 701 GROVE RD, ATTN: MEDICAL STAFF OFC 29605 #748-01-2000 L2006 **PD** *100

SOKHANDAN, Mehrgan. 357 WOODRUFF RD 29607 #517-08-1979 L1995 **PUD** *020 †20

SONG, Seungjai Nancy. 200 PATEWOOD DR, GREENVILLE 29615 #012-01-1997 L1998 **PD** *020 †55

SOUSA, Jo A. 701 GROVE RD 29605 #048-15-1988 L1992 **EM** *020 †16

SOUTHERLIN, Krystal Danie. ■ 29615 #045-04-2008 *012

SPIRES, Timothy Davenport. 701 GROVE RD, 2ND FLOOR SUPPORT TOWER 29605 #048-14-2004 L2004 **ORS** *012

SPITZER, Gary. 65 INTERNATIONAL DR, CAROLINAS EASTSIDE 29615 #297-02-1967 L1998 **ON IM** *020 †20

SPIVEY, Judith. 317 SAINT FRANCIS DR, STE 150 29601 #036-08-1988 L1994 **GE** *020 †20

SRIVASTAVA, Vinita. 401 GUESS ST, STE 100 29605 #495-65-1991 L1996 **IM** *020 †20

STAFFORD, Jesse Ray. 8 MEMORIAL MEDICAL CT 29605 #001-02-1979 L1984 **PTH** *020 †50

STANBRO, Marcus Duane. 200 PATEWOOD DR STE A300 29615 #039-79-1989, ▲ L2002 **VM IM** *020

STASIKELIS, Peter Jos. 950 W FARIS RD, SHRINERS HOSPS CHILDREN 29605 #048-02-1986 L1991 **ORS OP** *020 †40

STEIN, Michael Albert. 890 W FARIS RD, STE 220 29605 #012-05-1966 L1991 **TRS GS** *071 †85

STEPHENS, Jeffrey James. 27 MEMORIAL MEDICAL DR 29605 #045-01-2001 L2003 **P** *020 †75

STEPHENSON, Colin Ruffin. 21 ABERDEEN DR 29605 #045-01-1972 L1973 **IM RHU** *020 †20

STEPHENSON, James E. 900 W FARIS RD 29605 #011-04-1980 **TS** *020 †85

STEPHENSON, Joejohn. 65 INTERNATIONAL DR, CAROLINAS EASTSIDE 29615 #045-01-1991 L2000 **HO** *020 †20

STEVENSON, Roger Eugene. 2 DOCTORS DR 29605 #036-05-1966 L1974 **OS PD** *020 †55,19

STIGALL, Beverly Garrison. 701 GROVE RD, ATTN: MED STAFF SERVICES D 29605 #036-01-1985 L1989 **IM EM** *020 †20

STODDARD, William Robert, Jr. 135 COMMONWEALTH DR, STE 210 29615 #045-01-1972 L1973 **OBG** *020 †30

STOEBER, Jeffrey Edward. 3911 S HIGHWAY 14 29615 #045-01-1985 L1988 **PD** *020 †55

STONE, David Gerald. 242 ADLEY WAY 29607 #045-04-1997 L1998 **PHL FM** *020 †18 ‡

STONE, Zachary Michael. 701 GROVE RD, ATTN: MEDICAL STAFF OFC 29605 #001-06-2006 L2006 **MPD** *012

STONER, Chyrel East. 135 COMMONWEALTH DR, STE 300 29615 #036-08-1987 L1988 **GYN** *020 †30

STROUD, Cary Ernest. 900 W FARIS RD 29605 #036-05-1969 L1973 **ON PD** *020 †55

SURKA, Azim Ebun. 200 PATEWOOD DR, BLDG B-480 29615 #045-04-2001 L2007 **PCC** *020

SUVAL, Marcia Wendy. 701 GROVE RD 29605 #035-46-1985 L2004 **P** *020 †75

SWANSON, Eric Shane. 701 GROVE RD 29605 #012-22-2004 L2004 **IM** *020 †20

SWANSON, Jennifer Fortier. ■ 29601 #045-04-2006 L2006 **IM** *012

TAH, Neal Chander. 877 W FARIS RD, GHS - CENTER FOR FAMILY ME 29605 #661-02-2006 L2007 **FP** *012

TANDON, Prayrana. 701 GROVE RD 29605 #495-34-2000 L2005 **FP** *012

TAYLOR, Cheryl Marie. 950 W FARIS RD, CRIPPLED CHILDREN/GREENVIL 29605 #023-07-1988 L1995 **AN** *020 †05

TAYLOR, John Pickens. 2094 WOODRUFF RD 29607 #045-01-1963 L1963 **P IM** *020 ‡

TAYLOR, Richard Garison. 2078A WOODRUFF RD 29607 #045-01-1972 L1973 **ORS** *020 †40

TAYLOR, Spence Mc Lean. 701 GROVE RD 29605 #045-01-1983 L1984 **GS** *020 †85

TAYLOR, Susan Lynn. 701 GROVE RD, GMH 29605 #012-22-2003 L2005 **PD** *100 †55

TEAGUE, Julius Lynn. 200 PATEWOOD DR, STE A200 29615 #012-05-1981 L2007 **UP U** *020 †95

TEAGUE, Leighton Douglas. 701 GROVE RD, DEPT OF INTERNAL MEDICINE 29605 #045-04-2001 L2003 **IM** *020 †20

TERRY, Lewis Newman, Jr. 900 W FARIS RD, CANCER TREATMENT CENTER 29605 #036-07-1962 L1971 **RO** *020 †80

THAKKER, Ganpat Gopalji. 1 SAINT FRANCIS DR 29601 #495-22-1973 L1976 **CD IM** *020 †20

THANDROYEN, Francis T. 105 DOCTORS DR, CARDIOVASCULAR ASSOC GREEN 29605 #836-05-1973 L1998 **CD** *050 †20

THIYAGARAJAH, Aathirayen. 200 PATEWOOD DR STE A350, PATEWOOD MED CAMPUS 29615 #220-03-1995 L2002 **PM PME** *020 †60

THOMAS, Celia Melinda. 710 CRESCENT AVE, 710 CRESCENT AVENUE 29601 #012-01-1982 L1983 **EM** *020 †16

THOMAS, Charles B, Jr. 535 W BUTLER RD STE C 29607 #045-01-1984 L1985 **ORS** *020 †40

THOMAS, Gail Elizabeth. 135 COMMONWEALTH DR, STE 230 29615 #016-11-1986 L2007 **SO GS** *020 †85

THOMASON, Dan M. 1210 W FARIS RD 29605 #045-01-1981 L1982 **DR** *020 †80

THOMASON, Michael A. 1210 W FARIS RD 29605 #012-01-1981 L1982 **DR** *020 †80

THOMPSON, Philip Carlton. 9 MILLS AVE 29605 #045-01-1976 L1977 **PD** *020 †55

THOMPSON, Robert Chas. PO BOX 2846 29602 #035-15-1942 L1977 **OM** *071 †70

THORNBURG, John Glenn. 1210 W FARIS RD 29605 #036-01-1969 L1970 **DR** *071 †80

TIDD, John Thos. ■ 29605 #041-01-1946 L1947 **PTH GP** *071 †50

TILLER, Thomas Lucas. 48 CREEKVIEW CT 29615 #045-01-1963 L1963 **AI PUD** *020 †55,03

TINSLEY, Woodrow Fike, Jr. ■ 29609 #045-01-1973 L1975 **EM AN** *074

TOBOLA, Allison Michelle. 701 GROVE RD 29605 #048-14-2004 L2007 **FM** *020 †18

TOLLISON, Michael Edwin. 35 INTERNATIONAL DR 29615 #045-01-1987 L1988 **ORS** *020 †40

TOTTEN, Larry Kent. 1210 W FARIS RD, MARY BLACK PHYSICIAN GROU 29605 #036-07-1964 L1970 **DR** *020 †80

TOUZIN, Nadege Tacha. 701 GROVE RD, ATTN: MEDICAL STAFF OFC 29605 #011-03-2006 L2006 **IM** *012

TOWLER, Michael Alan. 6 DOCTORS DR, CROSS CREEK MEDICAL PARK 29605 #051-01-1992 L1997 **GS** *020 †85

TRAN, Thanh Thi. 1 SAINT FRANCIS DR 29601 #045-01-1999 L2002 **IM** *020 †20

TRANTHAM, Harry England. 407 VARDRY ST 29601 #036-07-1961 L1967 **OPH** *020 †35

TRAURIG, Michael Jay. 540 OLD HOWELL RD 29615 #035-09-1991 L1995 **IM** *020 †20

TRAXLER, Lucy Brannon. ■ 29605 #045-04-2008 *012

TREAS, April Updike. 701 GROVE RD, GHS - INTERNAL MEDICINE 29605 #051-04-2004 L2004 **IM** *020 †20

TRIDICO, Anthony Joseph, Jr. 27 MEMORIAL MEDICAL DR 29605 #021-05-1996 L2003 **CHP** *020 †75

TRIEPEL, Caroline Rogers. 701 GROVE RD 29605 #051-01-1994 L2005 **HS** *020 †40

TROCHA, Steven Dietrich. 900 W FARIS RD, GREENVILLE MEM CANCER CTR 29605 #056-06-1994 L2003 **GS** *020 †85

TROTT, Millard Clinton. 701 GROVE RD 29605 #005-12-1973 L1998 **P** *020 †75

TUCKER, Michelle Leigh. 701 GROVE RD 29605 #036-01-2004 L2004 **OBG** *012

TUMMONS, Rebecca Concetta. 800 PELHAM RD 29615 #045-01-1987 L1990 **FM** *020 †18

TWEDT, Carrie Ann. 890 W FARIS RD STE 330, OF GASTROENTEROLOGY/HEPATO 29605 #055-02-1996 L1997 **OBG** *020 †30

TYSON, Elizabeth Suzanne. 701 GROVE RD, 4TH FLOOR BALCONY 29605 #045-01-1999 L2007 **PD** *020 †55

ULMER, James Stanley. 1 SAINT FRANCIS DR 29601 #045-01-1977 L1978 **AN EM** *020 †05

USADI, Moshe Edward. 130 MALLARD ST, NEW HORIZON FAMILY HEALTH 29601 #036-07-1995 L2003 **FM** *020 †18

USADI, Rebecca Shari. 890 W FARIS RD STE 470 29605 #036-07-1995 L2003 **OBG** *020 †30

UTECHT, Laure Ann. 200 PATEWOOD DR, STE A200 29615 #045-04-1997 L1999 **PD** *020 †55

VAIL, Richard Wm. 20 MEMORIAL MEDICAL DR 29605 #045-01-1988 L1989 **IM** *020 †20

VANDERWESTHUIZ, Lionel. ■ 29611 #012-01-2007 L2007 **GS** *012

VANDER WOOD, Jack M. 527 MILLS AVE STE 102 29605 #056-06-1951 L1956 **AN** *071 †05

VAN HALE, Harriet M. 850 S PLEASANTBURG DR, STE 103 29607 #045-01-1975 L1976 **D DMP** *020 †50,15

VAN HALE, Philip Corby. 8 MEMORIAL MEDICAL CT 29605 #047-05-1974 L1992 **PTH ON** *020 †50,20

VANN, John Randolph. 35 INTERNATIONAL DR, PIEDMONT ORTHOPAEDIC ASSOC 29615 #051-07-1980 L1981 **ORS OS** *020 †40

VANPELT, Christopher D. 1050 GROVE RD 29605 #055-01-2000 L2006 **ORS** *020

VAUGHAN, Donald Reid. 18 MEMORIAL MEDICAL DR 29605 #047-06-1975 L1980 **U** *020 †95

VOGEL, Evan Lars. 124 MALLARD ST 29601 #033-06-1990 L1993 **P** *020 †75

VON HOFE, Stanley Edward. 877 W FARIS RD STE D 29605 #047-05-1971 L1978 **IM END** *020 †20

VRY, John Lawrence. 1 SAINT FRANCIS DR 29601 #020-12-1970 L1976 **FM FPG** *020 †18

WAGGETT, Kenneth M. 701 GROVE RD 29605 #045-01-1950 L1950 **P GP** *071

WAGSTAFF, Daniel Lee. 701 GROVE RD, GREENVILLE HOSPITAL SYSTEM 29605 #654-01-2000 L2004 **IM** *020

WAGSTAFF, Rebecca L. 701 GROVE RD, GREENVILLE HOSPITAL SYSTEM 29605 #654-01-2001 L2004 **IM** *020

WALKER, Marshall Whitson. 701 GROVE RD, GREENVILLE HOSP SYS DPT PD 29605 #045-01-1988 L1994 **NPM PD** *020 †55

WALKER, Robert Ricardo. 701 GROVE RD, DEPT OF INTERNAL MEDICINE, 29605 #045-04-1996 L1997 IM *020 †20
WALLACE, James Edmundboyd. 12 ARBORLAND WAY 29615 #045-04-1986 L1987 FM EM *020 †18
WALLACE, James Gilbert. 31 MEDICAL RIDGE DR 29605 #036-01-1969 L2005 PS *020 †65
WALLER, Sharlisa Danielle. ▪ 29609 #012-22-2008 *012
WALVOORD, Stella Marie. 701 GROVE RD, DEPT OB 29605 #045-01-2005 L2005 OBG *012
WANG, David William. 950 W FARIS RD, SHRINERS HOSPITAL FOR CHIL 29605 #036-07-2003 L2007 ORS *012
WANG, Laura. 890 W FARIS RD, STE 470 29605 #016-06-1992 L2001 OBG *020 †30
WARD, Michael Eugene. 8 MEMORIAL MEDICAL CT 29605 #001-06-1988 L1990 FOP *020 †50
WASHBURN, Brian Harvey. 37 BRENDAN WAY 29615 #045-04-1987 L1988 PD *020 †55
WASHER, Joshua Daniel. 701 GROVE RD, GHS - DEPT OF SURGERY 29605 #045-04-2007 L2007 GS *012
WATERS, Robert Curtis. 10 ENTERPRISE BLVD, STE 201 29615 #045-01-1977 L1982 OTO GS *020 †45
WATSON, Theodore Albert. 701 ARLINGTON AVE 29601 #025-07-1960 L1961 OTO A *071 †45
WATSON-RAMIREZ, K Leigh. 701 GROVE RD, TOWER 5FL 29605 #023-07-1989 L1994 IM *040 †20
WEATHERS, William Travis. 200 PATEWOOD DR, STE A200 29615 #045-01-1965 L1970 PD *020 †55
WEBB, John Kilgo. ▪ 29615 #045-01-1937 L1984 GS FM *071 †85
WEBB, Keith Matthew. 701 GROVE RD, ATTN: MEDICAL STAFF OFC 29605 #039-01-2006 L2006 GS *012
WEBER, Sandra Lee. 877 W FARIS RD STE D 29605 #016-06-1989 L1996 END *050 †20
WEBSTER, David Hunt. ▪ 29607 #045-01-1965 GS VS *071 †85
WEEMS, Jerome John, Jr. 701 GROVE RD 29605 #047-06-1981 L1990 ID IM *020 †20
WEISE, Karen Yax. 701 GROVE RD, ATTN: ACADEMIC SVCS. 29605 #011-02-2006 L2006 FP *012
WELBORN, Josh Eric. 877 W FARIS RD, CTR FOR FAMILY MED 29605 #001-02-2007 L2007 FP *012
WELBORN, Julius W, III. 515 W BUTLER RD 29607 #045-01-1980 L1981 OPH *020 †35
WELCOME, Amy Zampi. 111 DOCTORS DR 29605 #035-15-1997 L2002 IM *020 †20
WELCOME, Brian Allen. 1 DOCTORS DR 29605 #035-15-1997 L2002 OPH *020 †35
WELLS, David Howard. 701 GROVE RD, GREENVILLE NEONATOLOGY 29605 #005-15-1970 L2005 NPM *020 †55
WESSEL, Edith Miriam C. 701 GROVE RD 29605 #045-01-1984 L1985 FM *020 †18
WEST, Charles Shirley, Jr. 317 TANNER RD 29607 #012-05-1969 L1970 D *020 †15
WEST, Linton Burnside, Jr. ▪ 29605 #047-05-1962 L1962 U *071 †95
WESTBERRY, David Elbert. 950 W FARIS RD, SHRINERS HOSPITALS FOR CHI 29605 #012-01-1995 L1997 ORS *020 †20
WESTMORELAND, Patricia Pe. 850 S PLEASANTBURG DR, STE 103 29607 #045-01-1971 L1972 D GP *020 †15
WESTMORELAND, Wm Thos. 880 S PLEASANTBURG DR, STE 4E 29607 #045-01-1973 L1982 P IM *071 †75
WESTON, Lawrence Tye. 712 GROVE RD, ARRHYTHMIA CONSULTANTS PA 29605 #023-12-1981 L2001 ICE CD *020 †20
WETENHALL, Daniel James. 1 SAINT FRANCIS DR 29601 #045-01-1982 L1983 EM *020
WHIGHAM, Martin Donald. 125 COMMONWEALTH DR 29615 #027-01-1984 L1990 AN *020 †05
WHITAKER, Thomas E. 701 GROVE RD 29605 #041-01-1948 L1948 R *071 †80
WHITE, Cory Rafe. 701 GROVE RD, DEPT OF INTERNAL MEDICINE 29605 #045-04-2003 L2004 END *012 †20
WHITE, Ira M. ▪ 29615 #028-79-1943, ▲ L1943 OTO FPS *071
WHITE, Jacob Patrick. 701 GROVE RD 29605 #045-01-1992 L2000 IM *020
WHITE, Virginia Anne. ▪ 29615 #011-04-1981 L1984 PTH *075 †50
WHITNEY, Laura Kathleen. 131 COMMONWEALTH DR, STE 310 29615 #045-01-2002 L2006 PD *020 †55
WICKSTROM, Glenda C. ▪ 29615 #038-44-1991 L1992 IM IMG *020 †20
WIENKE, Jeffrey Ryan. 1210 W FARIS RD 29605 #055-01-1999 L2006 DR MSR *020 †80
WILCOX, Jeannette Louise. 65 INTERNATIONAL DR, CAROLINAS EASTSIDE 29615 #017-20-1986 L1991 RO FM *020 †80 ‡
WILHOIT, Randall David. 1007 GROVE RD, STE B 29605 #012-05-1983 L1991 AN *020 †05
WILKINSON, George R, Jr. 3510 AUGUSTA RD 29605 #023-07-1949 L1956 CD IM *020 †20
WILLIAMS, Bart David, III. 39 BRENDAN WAY 29615 #001-02-1992 L1998 OS FPS *040 ‡
WILLIAMS, Chas David, III. 1210 W FARIS RD 29605 #036-05-1981 L1985 DR NR *020 †80
WILLIAMS, John E. 200 PATEWOOD DR 29615 #047-06-1976 L2006 PD *020 †55 ‡
WILLIAMS, Patrick Fisher. 1007 GROVE RD, STE B 29605 #045-04-1998 L2001 AN *020 †05
WILLIAMS, Timothy Harold. 317 SAINT FRANCIS DR, STE 120 29601 #045-04-1992 L1993 TS *020 †85,90
WILLIS, Matthew Parker. 950 W FARIS RD 29605 #047-06-2004 L2007 ORS *012
WILSON, Freddie Ernest. 357 WOODRUFF RD 29607 #012-01-1964 SME PUD *072 †20
WILSON, John D, Jr. 701 GROVE RD, GHS - EMERGENCY MEDICINE 29605 #045-01-1988 L1989 PD *020 †55
WILSON, Joseph Brian. 950 W FARIS RD, SHRINERS HOSPITAL FOR CHIL 29605 #023-01-2000 L2006 ORS *012
WILSON, Pamela Kay. 701 GROVE RD, GHS UNIVERSITY MEDICAL CEN 29605 #045-04-1988 L1989 IM *020 †20
WILSON, Robert Alexander. 4200 E NORTH ST, STE 16 29615 #045-01-1972 L1980 PS OTO *020 †45
WINCHESTER, Catherine San. 877 W FARIS RD 29605 #036-01-2006 L2006 FP *012
WITTSTEIN, Jocelyn Ross. 950 W FARIS RD, SHRINERS HOSPITAL FOR CHIL 29605 #036-08-2004 L2007 ORS *012
WOLFF, Charles Michael. 8 MEMORIAL MEDICAL CT, STE 1 29605 #047-05-1975 L1979 PTH PCP *020 †50 ‡
WOLIN, Mitchell. 7 POINTE CIR 29615 #035-03-1983 L1988 OPH OS *020 †35
WONDRACEK, Sharon Emanuel. 701 GROVE RD, GHSUMC INTERNAL MED PED. 29605 #036-08-2005 L2005 MPD *012
WOOD, Michael Jos. 124 MALLARD ST, GREENVILLE MENTAL HEALTH 29601 #041-01-1984 L1987 CHP P *020 †75
WOODLIEF, Rebecca Sue. ▪ 29607 #051-04-2006 L2006 PD *012
WORSHAM, John Wesley. 15 ROE RD, POWERSVILLE MEDICAL PARK 29611 #045-01-1974 L1976 FM *020 †18
WORSTER, Miranda Lynn. 701 GROVE RD, BALCONY STE 4 29605 #045-04-2007 L2007 PD *020 †20
WORTHINGTON, David Bryan. 111 DOCTORS DR, INTERNAL MEDICINE ASSOCS 29605 #045-01-1987 L1995 IM *020 †20

WREN, Tonya N.P.. 1809 WADE HAMPTON BLVD 29609 #305-01-2002 L2006 FM *020 †18
WRIGHT, Christopher. 890 W FARIS RD, STE 550 29605 #033-06-1987 L1995 TS *020 †85,90
WRIGHT, Jonathan Patrick. 1007 GROVE RD STE B 29605 #012-01-1996 L2002 AN *020 †05
WYATT, Margaret Louise. 4A CLEVELAND CT 29607 #045-01-1961 L1962 PD *020
WYLIE, Wm Lindsay, Jr. 3911 S HIGHWAY 14 29615 #045-01-1979 L1980 PD *020 †55
WYNN, Paula Mignon. 701 GROVE RD 29605 #036-05-1979 L1980 OPH *020 †35
YARBOROUGH, Claude S. 200 PATEWOOD DR, STE B200 29615 #045-01-1984 L1985 GE IM *020 †20
YOON, Inho. 1007 GROVE RD, STE B 29605 #045-01-1981 AN *020 †05
YORK, John Walter. 890 W FARIS RD STE 32 29605 #036-08-1995 L1997 VS *020 †85
YOUKEY, Jerry Ray. 701 GROVE RD, GREENVILLE HOSP SYSTEM 29605 #056-06-1974 L1998 VS *030 †55
YOUNG, Dale Alexander. 701 GROVE RD 29605 #422-01-2005 L2005 IM *012
YOUNG, James Leland, Jr. 14 EDGEWOOD DR 29605 #045-01-1967 L1973 CD *071 †20
YOUNG, James Rogers. 3 SAINT FRANCIS DR, STE 480 29601 #036-05-1981 L1988 GS *020 †20
YOUNG, Marcela V. 3505 PELHAM RD, STE A 29615 #132-01-1980 L1988 IM *020
YOUNG, Thomas Oliver. 890 W FARIS RD, STE 320 29605 #045-01-1975 L1979 GS *020 †85
YOUNT, Sarah Elizabeth. 701 GROVE RD, BALCONY STE 4 29605 #045-04-2007 L2007 PD *012
YU, Henry T. 203 MILLS AVE, CAROLINA NEPHROLOGY 29605 #748-02-1986 L2006 NEP IM *020 †20 ‡
YUKO, Ronald Thos. 131 COMMONWEALTH DR, STE 290 29615 #036-05-1980 L1994 OTO EM *020 †45
ZANDER, Richard Evan. 9 HAWTHORNE PARK CT 29615 #021-05-1974 L1980 GE IM *020 †20
ZHAO, Charlene. 701 GROVE RD, HOSPITALIST OFFICE 29605 #243-47-1988 L2002 IM *020 †20
ZHOU-WANG, Meng. 701 GROVE RD, NEUROLOGY DEPT 29605 #243-45-1982 L2007 N *020 †75
ZIMMERMAN, Sam Riley, III. 205 ENTERPRISE BLVD STE 14 29615 #045-01-1965 N *071 †75
ZURENKO, Michael David. 65 INTERNATIONAL DR, CAROLINAS EASTSIDE 29615 #035-15-1985 L1993 RO *020 †80
ZWEIGORON, Rachael Thomas. ▪ 29605 #045-01-2006 PD *012

GREENWOOD — GREENWOOD

ACOSTA, Carlos Alberto. 155 ACADEMY AVE 29646 #056-06-2007 L2007 FP *012
ALBRECHT, Carlos Alfredo. 421 EPTING AVE 29646 #737-09-1993 L2006 CD *020 †20
AL-MUBASLAT, Ahmad Nabil. 104 LINER DR, PIEDMONT INTERNAL MEDICINE 29646 #575-01-1997 L2005 END IM *020 †20
ALTHOFF, Jennifer Pavela. 155 ACADEMY AVE 29646 #056-06-2005 L2005 FP *012
AUSTIN, Timothy Laxson. 210 WELLS AVE 29646 #045-04-2001 L2001 OPH *020 †35
AYERS, Russ Robert. 155 ACADEMY AVE 29646 #012-01-2007 L2007 FP *012
BAKER, Roy Phillip. 102 KATIE CT 29646 #045-01-1978 L1979 OBG *020 †30
BAKER, Stanley C. ▪ 29649 #045-01-1952 L1952 GS TS *071 †85
BARRACA, Claben Rey Maypa. 600 MONUMENT ST, STE 224 29646 #748-15-1992 L2004 P *020
BARTZ, Mark Alan. 1506 SPRING ST 29646 #017-20-1985 L1986 FM *020 †18
BATES, Phillips L. 1110 MARSHALL RD 29646 #035-45-1946 L1954 U *071 †95
BAZAN, Gus Zayas. 101 ACADEMY AVE, ANESTHESIOLOGY OF 29647 #045-01-1989 L1990 AN PMM *020 †05
BELCHER, James Hudson. 155 ACADEMY AVE 29646 #020-12-2006 L2006 FP *012
BELINSKI, Jodi Lynne. 155 ACADEMY AVE 29646 #665-01-2006 L2006 FP *012
BISHOP, Theresa Sullivan. 600 MONUMENT ST, STE 224 29646 #024-05-1989 L2000 P *020 †75
BLAIR, Joshua C. 155 ACADEMY AVE 29646 #654-01-2006 L2006 FM *100
BLEY, Roger Frederick. 121 PARTRIDGE RD 29649 #047-06-1967 L1973 DR NM *020 †80,28
BOBO, Charles Bailey. 210 WELLS AVE 29646 #045-01-1962 L1962 OPH *020 †35
BOYLSTON, James Alan. 303 W ALEXANDER AVE, STE K 29646 #036-07-1969 L1991 PTH HMP *020 †20
BRADFORD, Sarah Mae Nunez. 155 ACADEMY AVE, SELF REG HEALTHCARE 29646 #045-04-2007 L2007 FP *012
BRIDGES, David Scott. 311 MAIN ST 29646 #045-01-1992 L1995 FM *020 †18
BRUYERE, Charles Franklin. 464B HERITAGE WEST CT, HWY 72 NW BYPASS 29649 #039-01-1994 L1998 FM *020
BURCH, Barbara. 303 W ALEXANDER AVE, STE K 29646 #045-04-1993 L1998 PCP PTH *020 †50
BURDETTE, Marvin G, Jr. 210 WELLS AVE 29646 #011-03-1972 L1979 OPH *020 †35
BURDETTE, Marvin Garten. 210 WELLS AVE 29646 #051-04-1946 L1946 GS *071 †85
BURNETT, Samuel Thos. 104 LINER DR 29646 #045-01-1990 L1994 IM *020 †20
CAIN, Bibb Randall. 528 MONUMENT ST, RM B-12 29646 #045-01-1984 L1987 FM EM *020 †18
CARSON, Kevin Wright. 501 EPTING AVE 29646 #051-04-1995 L1996 GS *020 †85
CARTER, Richard Mitchell. ▪ 29649 #045-01-1957 L1957 OTO *071 †45
CASEY, Bryan Hodges. 102 ROCKCREEK BLVD, EXPRESS MEDICAL CARE 29649 #028-78-2001, ▲ L2006 FM *020 †18
CATHCART, John Harris, III. 102 GREGOR MENDEL CIR, LAKELANDS ORTHOPAEDIC 29646 #045-01-1989 L1994 ORS *020 †40
CAVANAGH, Christina Ann. 155 ACADEMY AVE, MONTGOMERY CENTER 29646 #011-03-2007 L2007 FP *012
CHAMPAIGNE, Neena L. 101 GREGOR MENDEL CIR, GREENWOOD GENETIC CENTER 29646 #048-02-1999 L2008 MG *100 †55,19
CHASTAIN, Luis T. 155 ACADEMY AVE 29646 #045-01-2005 L2005 FP *012
CHRISTIAN, Richard Morton. 102 GREGOR MENDEL CIR, LAKELANDS ORTHOPAEDIC 29646 #045-01-1986 L1987 ORS *050 †40
CLARKE, Walter Henry. 311 MAIN ST 29646 #016-11-1959 L1960 FM *020 †18
COBB, Orr Mc Clentic, Jr. 104 LINER DR 29646 #045-01-1970 L1971 PUD IM *020 †20
COLBY, Charles Fisk. 1156 EDGEFIELD ST, P O BOX 906ST 29646 #035-09-1975 L1980 DR VIR *020 †80
COLLINS, Jackie Lee. 1325 SPRING ST 29646 #055-01-1967 L1974 ATP CLP *071 †50
COMPTON, John De Vore. 1325 SPRING ST 29646 #045-01-1961 L1961 OPH *071 †35
CONE, George Preston, Jr. 115 OVERLAND DR, GREENWOOD INTERNAL 29646 #045-01-1969 L1969 IM ON *020 †20
COOK, James Bruce. 1325 SPRING ST 29646 #012-01-1987 L1988 FM *020 †18 ‡
CROITORU, Mihai. 421 EPTING AVE 29646 #781-01-1993 L2004 CD *020 †20
CULMER, David Andrew. 311 MAIN ST 29646 #012-01-1998 L1999 FM *020 †18
CURRY, Michelle M. 1325 SPRING ST, SELF REGIONAL HEALTHCARE 29646 #007-02-1990 L2002 EM *020 †16

DARBY, William Felder, Jr. 210 WELLS AVE 29646 #045-01-1992 L1993 **OPH** *020 †35
DAVIS, Clayton Houston. 155 ACADEMY AVE 29646 #045-01-2006 L2006 **FP** *012
DAVIS, Daphne Jennifer. 155 ACADEMY AVE 29646 #045-04-1993 L1994 **FM** *020 †18
DEAN, Jeffery Alan. 101 ACADEMY AVE, ANESTHESIOLOGY OF 29647 #012-01-1982 L1985 **AN** *020 †05
DEAN, Jeffrey Steven. 206 ELIZABETH AVE 29646 #048-12-1995 L1997 **GS** *020
DEMENT, Samuel Houston. 1325 SPRING ST, DEPT PATH SELF REGIONAL 29646 #047-05-1982 L1992 **PTH** *020 †50 ‡
DIBENEDETTO, Robert James. 101 ACADEMY AVE, ANESTHESIOLOGY OF 29647 #012-05-1989 L1993 **AN** *020 †05
DIVILBISS, Daniel David. 155 ACADEMY AVE 29646 #019-02-2005 L2005 **FP** *012
DOUD, Dennis Jacob. 435 EPTING AVE 29646 #030-05-1975 L1979 **D** *020
DUVALL, Alexander Valance. 155 ACADEMY AVE 29646 #045-04-2005 L2005 **FP** *012
EBERT, Alfred Ralph. 1547 PARKWAY STE 100, GREENWOOD MENTAL HEALTH CE 29646 #038-41-1990 L1993 **P** *020 †75
ELLENBERG, Bryan Keith. 1228 HIGHWAY 72 W, PIEDMONT HEALTH GROUP LLC 29649 #045-04-1993 L1994 **FM** *020 †18
ERGLE, John Mark. 1228 HIGHWAY 72 W, PIEDMONT HEALTH GROUP LLC 29649 #045-04-1994 L1996 **FM** *020 †18
FELDER, Jimmell Racquel. 113 LINER DR 29646 #045-01-2003 L2005 **PD** *100 †55
FEOLE, Glenn Louis. 113 LINER DR, GREENWOOD COMMUNITY CHILDR 29646 #038-41-1982 L2003 **PD** *020 †55
FERGUSON, Fred Bert, Jr. 1128 SPRING ST 29646 #012-01-1970 L1980 **GS** *050 †80
FORET, Ryan Thomas. 155 ACADEMY AVE 29646 #021-05-2006 L2006 **FP** *012
FRIEZ, Cara A. 1228 HIGHWAY 72 W, PIEDMONT HEALTH GROUP LLC 29649 #037-01-1995 L1998 **FM** *020 †18
FUNKE, Anderson B. 116 VENTURE CT 29649 #023-12-1988 L1989 **FM** *020 †18 ‡
FUNKE, John, III. 1325 SPRING ST 29646 #045-01-1983 L1984 **RO** *020 †80
FUQUA, Kevin Ray. 101 ACADEMY AVE, ANESTHESIOLOGY OF 29647 #045-01-1990 L1999 **AN** *020 †05
FUQUA, Linda Lee. 410 EPTING AVE, PIEDMONT HEALTH GROUP, LLC 29646 #045-01-1990 L1999 **PD** *020 †55
GALLMAN, Heather Smith. 410 EPTING AVE, PIEDMONT HEALTH GROUP, LLC 29646 #045-04-1991 L1994 **PD** *020 †55
GALLMAN, Todd Albert. 105 VINECREST CT, STE 600 29646 #045-04-1991 L1994 **FM** *020 †18
GALLOWAY, Jerry Edward. 202 OVERLAND DR, GALLOWAY REG EYE CENTER 29646 #045-01-1980 L1981 **OPH** *020 †35
GARRETT, Joshua Leon. 155 ACADEMY AVE, MONTGOMERY CTR FOR FAMILY 29646 #012-01-2004 L2004 **FM** *020 †18
GILMER, Allan Lee. 155 ACADEMY AVE 29646 #012-01-2002 L2003 **FM** *020 †18
GITU, Alfred Chege. 155 ACADEMY AVE 29646 #577-01-1994 L2003 **FM** *040 †18
GIVENS, Gregory Cadman. 1325 SPRING ST, PRMH - EMERGENCY MEDICINE 29646 #045-04-2004 L2004 **EM** *100
GOFORTH, Gary Alan. 155 ACADEMY AVE 29646 #047-05-1980 L1994 **FM AM** *040 †18
GOLDSTEIN, Dorian Lee. 102 KATIE CT 29646 #012-01-1978 L1979 **OBG** *020 †30
GOODWIN, Richard H, Jr. 210 WELLS AVE, GREENWOOD EYE CLINIC PA 29646 #041-02-1970 L1974 **OPH** *071 †35
GOWANS, Amanda Boswell. 600 MONUMENT ST # 224 29646 #045-04-2003 L2004 **CHP** *012
GRAHAM, Jed Alan. 1226 SPRING ST, GREENWOOD FAMILY PRACTICE 29646 #305-01-1999 L2003 **FM FPG** *020 †18
GRAHAM, Richard Bartow. 1325 SPRING ST, AT SELF REGIONAL 29646 #036-08-2004 L2007 **EM** *020
GRAVES, Lesslie Anna. 155 ACADEMY AVE 29646 #045-01-2007 L2007 **FP** *012
GUARESCHI, Claudio. 303 W ALEXANDER AVE, STE E 29646 #561-17-1992 L2001 **TS** *020 †85,90
HALL, Charles Luther. GREENWOOD MILLS 29646 #045-01-1967 L1967 **OM** *071
HALL, Russell David. 104 LINER DR, PIEDMONT INTERNAL MEDICINE 29646 #036-01-1990 L1993 **IM** *020 †20
HANNA, Sameh Ragaie Makka. 116 TIFTON DR E 29649 #915-02-1998 L2005 **IM** *100
HANOVER, Tod Martin. 160 ACADEMY AVE, GREENWOOD SURGICAL ASSOCIA 29646 #047-06-1988 L1989 **VS** *100 †85
HANS, Clarence L, Jr. ■ 29646 #038-06-1945 L1945 **OPH** *071 †35
HARDIN, Debra Sue. 1547 PARKWAY, STE 200 29646 #020-12-1982 L1983 **P CHP** *020
HARRISON, John D. 1110 MARSHALL RD, # 3001 29646 #023-07-1943 L1946 **GP GS** *071
HARWELL, Derek Scott. 101 ACADEMY AVE, ANESTHESIOLOGY OF 29647 #012-01-1976 L1981 **AN** *020 †05
HATCHER, Harvey Floyd. 155 ACADEMY AVE 29646 #045-01-1982 L1983 **FM** *040 †18
HATFIELD, Asa Q, Jr. 501 EPTING AVE 29646 #045-01-1984 L1985 **FM** *020 †18
HENDERSON, Grover C, III. GREENWOOD MED CTR 29646 #045-01-1976 L1977 **D** *020 †15
HICKS, John Trimmer. 303 W ALEXANDER AVE, STE G1 29646 #035-01-1972 L1990 **RHU IM** *020 †20
HILL, Joseph Benjamin. 1506 SPRING ST, FAM PHYS OF GREENWOOD 29646 #045-04-1995 L1996 **FM** *020 †18
HINDMAN, James T, Jr. 1325 SPRING ST 29646 #045-01-1984 L1985 **AN** *020
HOLLOWAY, William Osce. 160 ACADEMY AVE 29646 #045-01-1963 L1963 **VS GS** *071 †85
HOLMAN, John Wannamaker. 104 LINER DR 29646 #012-05-1981 L1986 **IM ID** *020 †20
HOLMES, Steven Larry. 116 VENTURE CT 29649 #045-01-1986 L1987 **FM** *020 †18
HUBBARD, William Fred, Jr. 101 ACADEMY AVE, ANESTHESIOLOGY OF 29647 #045-01-1992 L1996 **AN** *020 †05
HUGHES, Cecily S. 410 EPTING AVE, PIEDMONT HEALTH GROUP LLC 29646 #045-04-1994 L1998 **PD** *020 †55
HUNLEY, Marion B, Jr. 1325 SPRING ST 29646 #012-01-1984 L1989 **DR** *020 †80
HUNTON, Richard E. ■ 29649 #010-01-1952 L1954 **FM** *071 †18
ISENHOWER, William David. 1015 SPRING ST, ASSOCIATES, PA 29646 #036-01-1984 L1993 **OTO GS** *020 †45
JAMES, Walter Ennis, III. 421 EPTING AVE, PIEDMONT CARDIOLOGY ASSOC 29646 #045-01-1976 L1979 **CD IM** *020 †20
JEFFERY, Kathleen M. 160 ACADEMY AVE 29646 #038-40-1992 L2002 **GS** *020 †85
JENKINS, John Marshall. 155 ACADEMY AVE 29646 #012-01-2006 L2006 **FP** *012
JOHN, Chacko. 1325 SPRING ST 29646 #495-80-1982 L1993 **NPM** *020 †55
JOHNS, Martin Gerald. 155 ACADEMY AVE 29646 #041-13-2005 L2005 **FP** *012
KILBURN, Michael Peter B. 303 W ALEXANDER AVE STE C 29646 #068-01-1991 L1999 **NS FM** *020 †25
KIM, Paul Eukyung. 421 EPTING AVE, PIEDMONT CARDIOLOGY ASSPCO 29646 #048-04-1994 L2002 **IC** *020 †20
KING, John Allan. 102 GREGOR MENDEL CIR, LAKELANDS ORTHOPAEDIC 29646 #045-01-1985 L1990 **HS** *020 †40
KING, Karissa Rae. ■ 29649 #045-04-2008 *012
KITCHENS, Tammy Edwards. 1325 SPRING ST 29646 #011-03-1999 L2004 **DR** *020 †80
KITCHENS, Wm Claude, Jr. 1156 EDGEFIELD ST 29646 #012-01-1970 L1974 **DR** *071 †80
KLAUBER, William A, Jr. 1325 SPRING ST 29646 #045-01-1943 L1943 **R** *071 †80
KNOX, Christopher Cameron. 1325 SPRING ST 29646 #045-04-1997 L1997 **DR** *020 †80
KONSEK, John David. 160 ACADEMY AVE 29646 #056-06-1992 L1999 **GS** *020 †85
KRISHNA KUMAR, Gayathri. 155 ACADEMY AVE 29646 #496-22-2003 L2006 **FP** *012
KUMAR, Shekar Pillai. 421 EPTING AVE 29646 #495-16-1991 L2007 **IC** *020 †20
LAJOS, Thomas Zoltan. ■ 29649 #473-03-1956 L2004 **TS** *071 †85,90
LAL, Sumeer. 303 W ALEXANDER AVE, STE C 29646 #068-01-1991 L2004 **NS** *020 †25
LANFORD, Robin Morgan. 315 W ALEXANDER AVE 29646 #045-01-1989 L1991 **GP FM** *020
LAWRENCE, Robert Thomas. 155 ACADEMY AVE, MONTGOMERY CENTER/FAMILY M 29646 #054-04-2003 L2004 **FM** *020 †18
LEE, Kerry T. 101 ACADEMY AVE, ANESTHESIOLOGY OF 29647 #023-12-1990 L1997 **AN** *020 †05
LEWIS, Benj Franklin, Jr. 2809 AIRPORT RD, LEATH CORRECTIONAL INST 29649 #020-12-1980 L1981 **EM** *020 †16,18
LEWIS, Daniel Scott. 155 ACADEMY AVE, MONTGOMERY CTR FOR FAMILY 29646 #047-20-2004 L2004 **FSM** *012 †18
LEWIS, Edward A. 1325 SPRING ST 29646 #048-14-1984 L1985 **AN** *020 †05
LEWIS, Raymond Everett. 104 LINER DR, PIEDMONT INTERNAL MEDICINE 29646 #045-01-1982 L1993 **IM PUD** *020 †20
LINNERTZ, Carrie Ann. 155 ACADEMY AVE 29646 #016-45-2007 L2007 **FP** *012
LOGAN, Joseph Willis. 214 COWHEAD CREEK RD 29646 #012-01-1972 L1977 **EM IM** *020 †20
LOGAN, Matthew Tolbert. 1325 SPRING ST, DEPT OF E.R. 29646 #045-04-2001 L2002 **EM** *020 †16
LYNCH, Jonathan Paul. 155 ACADEMY AVE 29646 #012-22-2005 L2005 **FP** *012
LYNCH, Kendra Thomaston. 155 ACADEMY AVE 29646 #012-22-2005 L2005 **FP** *012
MACEDA, Melissa Perez. 600 MONUMENT ST STE 224, SUITE 224 29646 #748-01-1990 L1999 **P** *020
MADDOX, Donald Jerome. 1325 SPRING ST, SELF REGIONAL HEALTHCARE 29646 #012-01-1994 L1999 **EM** *020 †16
MAGRUDER, Christopher H. 1325 SPRING ST 29646 #021-01-1958 L1963 **PTH** *071 †50
MALLOW, William Olin. 1325 SPRING ST 29646 #055-01-1989 L1992 **EM** *020 †16
MANALICH, Carlos Manuel. 115 OVERLAND DR, GREENWOOD INTERNAL 29646 #011-04-1991 L1994 **IM** *020 †20
MAPPIN, Francis Gregory. 303 W ALEXANDER AVE STE E 29646 #036-07-1979 L1993 **GS OS** *030 †85
MARSHALL, Terry A. 1325 SPRING ST 29646 #047-06-1976 L1980 **NPM PD** *020 †55
MARTIN, Rebecca Brightly. 115 OVERLAND DR, GREENWOOD INTERNAL 29646 #016-42-1999 L2002 **IM** *020 †20
MC ALHANY, John W, Jr. 1325 SPRING ST 29646 #045-01-1992 L1996 **DR** *020 †80
MC GINNIS, Lincoln Mathew. 104 LINER DR 29646 #027-01-2002 L2003 **IM** *020 †20
MC KINNEY, John Roland. ALEXANDER STREET, GREENWOOD MEDICAL CENTER 29646 #012-01-1954 L1958 **IM** *020
MC LEOD, Darryl Lynn. 303 W ALEXANDER AVE, STE K 29646 #011-04-1984 L1989 **PTH** *020 †50
METZNER-SADURSKI, Joanna. 1325 SPRING ST, SELF REGIONAL HEALTHCARE 29646 #759-04-1992 L1999 **HO** *020 †20
MILLER, George Thos, Jr. 1325 SPRING ST 29646 #012-01-1965 L1970 **AN** *071 †05
MOBLEY, Edward Mims. 115 OVERLAND DR 29646 #045-01-1955 L1955 **IM CD** *071 †20
MONDA, Clifford Ahmad. 115 ACADEMY AVE, CAROLINA REHABILITATION AS 29646 #055-75-1999, ▲ L2003 **PM** *020 †60 ‡
MOSELEY, Willie Bradford. 1325 SPRING ST 29646 #045-01-1968 L1968 **P** *020
MULKEY, Arnold Peel. 109 LINER DR, GREENWOOD UROLOGICAL 29646 #012-01-1966 L1975 **U** *071 †95
MURPHY, Dennis Wayne. 105 VINECREST CT, STE 600 29646 #011-02-1981 L1982 **FM** *020 †18
NYARA TOMOR, Michael Kuya. 155 ACADEMY AVE 29646 #848-02-1995 L2007 **FP** *012
PARHAM, Kenneth Jackson. 1325 SPRING ST 29646 #045-01-1958 L1958 **OBG** *071 †30
PARRAMORE, Herman W. 109 LINER DR 29646 #012-01-1990 L1995 **U** *020 †95
PARRAMORE, James Brantley. 160 ACADEMY AVE 29646 #012-01-1993 L2002 **VS** *020 †85
PATRICK, Joseph Pearson. 155 ACADEMY AVE 29646 #045-04-2007 L2007 **FP** *012
PEREZ, Leah Dorothea P. 600 MONUMENT ST, STE 224 29646 #748-01-1991 L2000 **P** *020 †75
PEREZ, Pablo Ermelo, Jr. 155 ACADEMY AVE 29646 #748-01-1991 L2001 **FM FSM** *020 †18
PIKE, Daniel Ray. ■ 29649 #020-02-2008 *012
POLLY, Dawn Renee. 113 LINER DR 29646 #038-43-2003 L2006 **PD** *020 †55
POWELL, Douglas Franklin. 102 GREGOR MENDEL CIR, LAKELANDS ORTHOPAEDIC 29646 #012-01-1981 L2001 **ORS** *020 †40
PRICE, Wiley Norman, Jr. 1123 SPRING ST 29646 #021-05-1946 L1952 **IM** *020
PRITCHARD, Lyle L. 155 ACADEMY AVE 29646 #045-01-1988 L1989 **PD** *020 †55
PRITCHARD, Thomas Mc Coy. 421 EPTING AVE, PIEDMONT CARDIO ASSOC 29646 #001-02-1983 L1984 **CD IM** *020 †20
RAMPEY, Aubrey Ruth. 155 ACADEMY AVE 29646 #045-01-2007 L2007 **FP** *012
RAMSEUR, William Lee, Jr. 104 LINER DR 29646 #036-05-1971 L1978 **ON IM** *020 †20
RAPP, Edward Jos, II. 105 VINECREST CT, PREMIER SURGICAL SERVICES 29646 #010-02-1985 L1994 **GS OS** *020 †85
REAMS, Joshua Hendry. 155 ACADEMY AVE 29646 #012-22-2003 L2004 **FM** *020 †18
REINHARDT, Brian Allen. 155 ACADEMY AVE 29646 #045-01-2007 L2007 **FP** *012
REINHARDT, Randall L. DEPT OF EMERGENCY MEDICINE, SELF MEMORIAL HOSPITAL 29646 #028-34-1993 L1994 **EM** *020 †16
RICE, William T. 1325 SPRING ST 29646 #036-05-1953 L1956 **AN** *071
RICHARDSON, Melissa Kay. 115 ACADEMY AVE, CAROLINA REHABILITATION AS 29646 #036-08-1993 L1999 **PM** *020 †60
ROBIRDS, David Mark. 115 OVERLAND DR, GREENWOOD INTERNAL MEDICIN 29646 #028-34-1978 L1991 **IM NEP** *020 †20
ROOS, Julia Kirsten. 155 ACADEMY AVE, MONTGOMERY CTR FOR FAMILY 29646 #036-05-1999 L2000 **FM** *020 †18
RUSSELL, Kimberly Esh. 115 OVERLAND DR, GREENWOOD INTERNAL 29646 #041-14-1993 L1997 **IM** *020 †20
RUST, Kevin Randolph. 1015 SPRING ST, GREENWOOD ENT ASSOCIATES P 29646 #036-01-1991 L1996 **OTO** *020 †45
SAHLSTROM, Christopher Ja. 155 ACADEMY AVE 29646 #054-04-2005 L2005 **FP** *012
SCOTT, John Riser. 1325 SPRING ST 29646 #045-01-1955 L1955 **ORS** *071 †40
SEALY, David Probst. 155 ACADEMY AVE 29646 #036-07-1979 L1980 **FM** *020 †18
SEYMOUR, Clint Thurmond. 1325 SPRING ST 29646 #045-04-2001 L2003 **FM** *020 †18
SHINGLER, John M, III. 101 ACADEMY AVE, ANESTHESIOLOGY OF 29647 #045-01-1982 L1983 **AN** *020 †05

■ = Address Information Privacy Protected

SIDA, Wayne Brian. 303 W ALEXANDER AVE, P O BOX 1136 29646 #012-22-1992 L1996 N *020 †75

SIMONS, Locke Eugene. 313 MAIN ST 29646 #001-06-1996 L1997 FM *020 †18

SMITH, Horace Gratin. 155 ACADEMY AVE 29646 #045-01-1981 L1982 PD *020 †55

SMITH, James Henry. 303 W ALEXANDER AVE STE A 29646 #012-01-1958 L1958 IM CD *020

SMITH, Scott Wm. 102 ROCKCREEK BLVD 29649 #012-01-1991 L1992 FM *020 †18

SONI, Sureshchandra. 1111 EDGEFIELD ST 29646 #495-20-1965 L1977 N *020 †75

SPRUILL, Robert Ottis. 155 ACADEMY AVE, DEPT.- FAMILY PRACTICE 29646 #012-01-2004 L2004 FM *020 †18

STEVENSON, Travis Brown. ■ 29649 #045-01-1955 L1955 GS OS *071 †85

STEWART, Robert Lee. ■ 29646 #038-06-1967 L1974 GS *071 †85

STOKES, James Kenneth. 115 OVERLAND DR, GREENWOOD INTERNAL 29646 #045-01-1964 L1964 IM NEP *020 †20

SUGDEN, Mark Francis. ■ 29649 #051-07-1994 L1994 FM AN *075

SUNDERMANN, John Morgan. 303 W ALEXANDER AVE, STE K 29646 #004-01-1982 L2007 PTH PCP *050

TARASIDIS, Gregory. 1015 SPRING ST, CENTER 29646 #012-05-1991 L1998 OTO HNS *020 †45

TATE, Stephen Merritt. ■ 29646 #055-01-2003 L2007 OPH *020

TAYLOR, Scarlet Raymond. 155 ACADEMY AVE, MONTGOMERY CTR FOR FAMILY 29646 #045-04-2004 L2004 FM *020 †18

TEED, Susan Kellogg. 101 ACADEMY AVE, ANESTHESIOLOGY OF 29647 #045-01-1992 L1996 IM *020 †05

TENNIS, John Michael. 1736 S MAIN ST 29646 #045-01-1981 L1982 PHP PD *030 †55

THOMAS, Jeffrey Bernard. 160 ACADEMY AVE 29646 #020-02-1997 L2006 GS *020 †85

THOMAS, Jeffrey Boyd. 160 ACADEMY AVE 29646 #007-02-2006 IM *012

TILLER, Robert Joel. 155 ACADEMY AVE 29646 #017-20-1994 L1996 FM *020 †18

TIMMS, Anthony R. 102 GREGOR MENDEL CIR, LAKELANDS ORTHOPAEDIC 29646 #045-01-1986 L1987 ORS *040 †40

TINKLER, Stuart Alexander. 1325 SPRING ST 29646 #045-01-1992 L1993 DR *020 †80,28

TINKLER, William P. 1325 SPRING ST 29646 #047-05-1951 L1960 R NM *071 †80

TODD, Chandler Berry. 313 MAIN ST, UPTOWN FAMILY PRACTICE 29646 #045-01-2004 L2004 FM *020 †18

TODD, Robert William. 408 W ALEXANDER AVE, HOSPICE CARE OF THE PIEDMO 29646 #045-01-1982 L1983 FM *020 †18

TOZZI, Jerett Donald. 108 BYPASS 225 29646 #016-11-1994 L1997 EM *020 †16

TRENT, Howard Edgar, III. ■ 29646 #051-01-1971 L1977 PD PDA *071 †55

TURNER, Allan Pearson. 115 OVERLAND DR, GREENWOOD INTERNAL 29646 #045-01-1998 L2003 NEP *020 †20

TURNER, Wm Preston, III. 109 LINER DR 29646 #045-01-1980 L1982 U *020 †95

VANSWOL, Mark Alan. 155 ACADEMY AVE 29646 #045-01-1995 L1996 FM *020 †18

VAUGHN, Kenneth. 1325 SPRING ST 29646 #048-14-1990 L1993 EM *020 †16

VAUGHN, Ted Roy. 305 W ALEXANDER AVE # A 29646 #001-06-1983 L1984 PS HS *030 †65

VELAPPAN, Priya. 421 EPTING AVE 29646 #495-31-1999 L2007 IC *100 †20

VELKY, Paul Jos. 101 ACADEMY AVE, ANESTHESIOLOGY OF 29647 #045-01-1988 L1993 AN *020 †05

VICIAN, Elena. 1325 SPRING ST, ATTN: ONCOLOGY DEPT. 29646 #286-03-1971 L2006 ON *020 †20

VILLAREAL, Rollo Pebenito. 421 EPTING AVE, PIEDMONT CARDIOLOGY 29646 #748-02-1994 L2003 ICE *020 †20

WARNER, Bret James. 105 VINECREST CT 29646 #036-08-1992 L1996 N *020 †75

WARNER, William Reece. 101 ACADEMY AVE, ANESTHESIOLOGY OF 29647 #012-01-1976 L1977 AN *020

WHITESIDE, William Keisle. 155 ACADEMY AVE 29646 #045-01-2006 L2006 FP *012

WHITLEY, Vernon Charlton. 113 LINER DR 29646 #012-01-1994 L1996 PD *020 †55

WIGGINS, Ashley Copeland. 155 ACADEMY AVE, MONTGOMERY CTR FOR FAMILY 29646 #045-01-2004 L2004 FM *020 †18

WILES, Lindsay Michelle. 155 ACADEMY AVE 29646 #028-03-2003 L2004 FM *020 †18

WILLARD, Oliver Thos. 105 VINECREST CT, STE 600 29646 #045-01-1976 FM *020 †18

WILLIAMS, Kenneth Preston. 303 W ALEXANDER AVE STE D2 29646 #036-08-1992 P *020

WISE, Ronald Sloan. 1157 SPRING ST 29646 #045-01-1962 GS *020 †85

WOOD, William Earl. 1547 PARKWAY, STE 200 29646 #051-01-1963 L1963 P *071

ZELLER, Timothy Aaron. 155 ACADEMY AVE 29646 #017-20-2006 L2006 FP *012

GREER — GREENVILLE

BALLARD, Thomas Victor. 406 MEMORIAL DRIVE EXT, C/O MOUNTAIN VIEW FAMILY P 29651 #045-01-1976 L1977 FM *020 †18

BALOTIN, Robert Jay. 102 TUSCANY WAY, EAGLE EYE RADIOLOGY PA 29650 #035-09-1988 L2003 R *020 †80

BERTOLLO, Suzanne Marie. ■ 29650 #011-03-1995 L2007 EM *020 †16

BHATIA, Renu. ■ 29650 #496-07-1990 L2004 P *020 †75

BOZEMAN, Elizabeth W. 2755 S HIGHWAY 14, STE 2050 29650 #045-01-1989 L1990 U *020 †95

BRUNSON, Jack Wade, Jr. 398 THE PKWY 29650 #045-01-1979 L1980 EM FM *020 †18

BYARS, William David. 406 MEMORIAL DRIVE EXT 29651 #045-01-1977 L1979 FM *020 †18

CAMPBELL, Victor Clyde. ■ 29651 #045-01-1968 L1968 ORS *071 †40

CASTRIOTTA, Ralph J, Jr. 2700 E PHILLIPS RD 29650 #045-01-1986 L1987 P *020 †75

CHAPPELL, Michael Chase. 322 MEMORIAL DR 29650 #045-01-1989 L1990 FM *020 †18

CHEA, Elizabeth Anton. 501 MEMORIAL DR EXT 29651 #045-01-1996 L1999 PD *020 †55

CHERRY, Stephen Ross. 2755 S HIGHWAY 14, STE 1200H 29650 #048-12-1978 L2005 CD IM *020 †20

CHORNESS, Marjorie A. 89 SONIA DR, BLOSSOM OG GYN & INFERTLTY 29650 #056-06-1988 L1994 OBG *020 †30

CIRCLE, David Alan. 306 THORNBLADE BLVD 29650 #012-01-1999 L2002 EM *020 †16

CLARY, Jeffrey Neal. 2755 S HIGHWAY 14, STE 1200H 29650 #045-01-1997 L2000 IM *020 †20

COCHRAN, Robert Anderson. 2755 S HIGHWAY 14, STE 2500 29650 #045-01-1978 L1979 GS SO *020 †85

COLLINS, Aaron Matthew. 306 THORNBLADE BLVD, CAROLINA EMERGENCY MEDICIN 29650 #045-04-2003 L2006 EM *020 †16

CORDAS, Daniel Isadore. 501B MEMORIAL DRIVE EXT 29651 #050-02-1997 L2003 OSM *020

COWART, James David. 318 MEMORIAL DR 29650 #001-02-1997 L2001 OBG *020 †30

CROCKETT, Jay Anton. 108 W CHURCH ST 29650 #035-15-1992 L1998 GS *020 †85,10

CURRAN, Susan Michelle. ■ 29646 #045-01-2002 L2004 IM *020

DELAHUNTY, Nigel Patrick. 318 MEMORIAL DR 29650 #033-06-1991 L1995 OBG *020 †30

DEMOSS, Mark Andrew. 501 MEMORIAL DRIVE EXT, # C 29651 #055-02-1990 L1998 PD *020 †55

DEVANE, Courtney Hagler. 2755 S HIGHWAY 14, STE 1200H 29650 #045-01-1997 L2003 IM *020 †20

DE VORE, Robert Douglas. 420 THE PKWY, STE C 29650 #012-01-1979 L1981 U *020 †95

DORCHAK, Joseph Raymond. 2755 S HIGHWAY 14 29650 #038-41-1963 L1971 CD IM *020 †20

EATON, Coy Lynn. 2755 S HIGHWAY 14, STE 1200H 29650 #020-12-1984 L1985 IM *020 †20

EICKMAN, Francis M. 2755 S HIGHWAY 14 29650 #012-05-1978 L1984 CD *020 †20

EISON, Thomas Bennett. 2755 S HIGHWAY 14, STE 2100 29650 #045-01-1968 L1968 ORS *020 †40

ELLIS, Adrienne Charlene. 2755 S HIGHWAY 14, STE 1200F 29650 #045-01-2003 L2007 OBG *020

ELLISON, William Travis. 554 MEMORIAL DRIVE EXT, STE B 29651 #045-01-1977 L1980 IM *020 †20

FELDER, Jesse T, III. 306 THORNBLADE BLVD, GREENVILLE HOSPITAL SYSTEM 29650 #048-13-1997 L1998 EM *020 †16

FLANDERS, Raymond Wilson. 501 MEMORIAL DR EXT 29651 #048-04-1971 L1975 PD *020 †55

FLEMING, Harold Edward. 2755 S HIGHWAY 14, STE 1200H 29650 #045-01-1965 L1965 CD IM *020 †20

FLEMING, Nicholas Fred. 2755 S HIGHWAY 14, STE 1200H 29650 #024-01-1996 L1999 IM *020 †20

FOWLER, Ashley. 2755 S HIGHWAY 14, STE 2250 29650 #045-04-2003 L2007 OBG *020

GAFFNEY, Clyde Monroe, III. 101 LATOUR WAY 29650 #036-01-1964 L1964 U *071 †95

GALLAGHER, John Jos. 2755 S HIGHWAY 14 29650 #010-02-1968 L1989 CD IM *071 †20

GHANDNOOSH, Azizollah. 111 MEMORIAL DR, PEDIATRIC CTR 29650 #517-06-1978 L1996 PD *020 †55

GIEP, Bang Nguyen. 2755 S HIGHWAY 14, STE 2250 29650 #045-01-1991 L1995 OBG *020 †30

GIEP, Hoang Nguyen. 2755 S HIGHWAY 14, STE 2250 29650 #045-01-1999 L2003 OBG *020 †30

GIEP, Nguyen Ngoc. 2755 S HIGHWAY 14 29650 #840-01-1960 L1979 OBG *071 †30

GILMORE, Wm Dennis, Jr. ■ 29650 #045-01-1960 L1960 PD *071

GOCOCO, Kim O. 313 MEMORIAL DR, CAROLINAS GREER 29650 #748-01-1984 L1992 IM HO *020 †20

GRUBBS, Raymond Van. 556 MEMORIAL DR EXT STE A 29651 #045-01-1971 L1972 GS *071 †85

GUPTA, Navneet. ■ 29650 #495-45-1994 L2004 PM *020 †60

HAGER, Jennifer Ann. ■ 29650 #041-02-1999 L2004 FSM *020 †18

HALLA, James Thos. 2755 S HIGHWAY 14, STE 1200H 29650 #048-02-1970 L2003 RHU *020 †20

HAUSLADEN, Edward Henry. 554 MEMORIAL DRIVE EXT # C, GREER PEDIATRIC CLINIC 29651 #028-34-1984 L1991 PD *020 †55

HEALY, Grant Fletcher. 552 MEMORIAL DRIVE EXT 29651 #036-05-1976 L1986 NEP IC *020 †20

HEERDT, Mark E. ■ 29650 #035-06-1951 L1952 AN *071 †05

HEITMAN, Kurt F. 100 PHYSICIANS DR 29650 #048-12-1983 L1991 OPH *020 †35

HELMRICH, George A. 318 MEMORIAL DR 29650 #045-04-1990 L1994 OBG *020 †30

HELTON, William Barnett. 318 MEMORIAL DR 29650 #047-06-1956 L1962 GYN P *071 †30

HENRY, William John, III. 554 MEMORIAL DRIVE EXT, STE B 29651 #045-01-1983 L1984 IM *020 †20

HESTER, Benjamin Anderson. 322 MEMORIAL DR 29650 #045-01-1994 L1996 FM *020 †18

HILLMAN, Milton Henry. ■ 29650 #041-02-1956 L1957 OPH LM *071 †35

HIREMATH, Yoganand J. 2755 S HIGHWAY 14, STE 1200H 29650 #028-46-1989 L2004 CD *020 †20

HOUSER, James Jos. ■ 29651 #041-02-1964 L1972 IM *075

HUDSON, David Lee. 406 MEMORIAL DRIVE EXT 29651 #025-01-1994 L1995 FM *020 †18

HUELLMANTEL, Alan B, Jr. 58 PARKWAY COMMONS WAY 29650 #025-01-1972 L1977 END *020 †20

HUEY, Barry Lamar. 2755 S HIGHWAY 14 29650 #045-01-1981 L1987 CD *020 †20

HUNTER, Karen Ruth. 554 MEMORIAL DRIVE EXT, STE B 29651 #045-01-1991 L1992 IM *020 †20

IKE, David Geo. 2755 S HIGHWAY 14 29650 #012-01-1984 L1990 CD IM *020 †20

JANULIS, Alexander T. ■ 29650 #035-09-1953 L1973 GP GS *071 †85

JOHNSON, Sandra Christine. 111A BERRY AVE STE 2, NEW HORIZON FAMILY HEALTH 29651 #024-05-2006 EM *012

JONES, Douglas H. 2755 S HIGHWAY 14, STE 1200 29650 #045-04-1996 L2006 IM D *020 †20

KELLER, Kevin Metz. 301 THE PKWY, UPSTATE PLASTIC SURGERY 29650 #045-01-1991 L1992 PS *020 †65

KELLETT, Barto Paul. 230 W WADE HAMPTON BLVD, DOCTORS CARE 29650 #045-01-1977 L1978 FM *020 †18

KEMBLE, Mark Allen. 1107 W POINSETT ST 29650 #045-01-1990 L1991 FM *020 †18

KEY, James Bartlette. 554 MEMORIAL DRIVE EXT # C 29651 #045-01-1974 L1975 PD *020 †55

KHALID, Humaira. 554 MEMORIAL DRIVE EXT, STE B 29651 #704-01-1998 L2005 IM *020 †20

KIBLER, Larry Earl. 2755 S HIGHWAY 14 29650 #045-01-1973 L1974 CD IM *040 †20

KLIMAS, Victor Algis. 552 MEMORIAL DRIVE EXT 29651 #038-40-1979 L1992 NEP IM *020 †20

KOOISTRA, Carol Marie. 2755 S HIGHWAY 14, STE 1200H 29650 #051-01-1982 L1987 N *020 †75

LAWRENCE, Kenneth G, Jr. 406 MEMORIAL DRIVE EXT 29651 #045-01-1976 L1977 FM *020 †18

LAWSON, J Rutledge. 220 EXECUTIVE DR, 220 EXECUTIVE DR GREER SC2 29651 #045-01-1960 L1960 PD ADL *020 †55

LEEDY, Erin Brock. ■ 29650 #048-15-2008 *012

LETTIERI, John Thos. 2755 S HIGHWAY 14 29650 #039-05-1982 L1990 PS *020 †85,65

LEVENSON, Amy Beth. 220 EXECUTIVE DR, PIEDMONT MENTAL HEALTH 29651 #007-02-1987 L2002 CHP P *020 †75

LIJEWSKI, Mark Allen. 2755 S HIGHWAY 14 29650 #051-04-1989 L1997 IM *020 †20

LONERGAN, Keith Thomas. 556 MEMORIAL DR EXT STE D 29651 #041-14-1994 L2007 OSM *020 †40

LOPER, Raymond Harvey, Jr. ■ 29650 #045-01-1976 L1977 FM *020

LOPEZ, Alejandro N. 2755 S HIGHWAY 14 29650 #051-01-1990 L1999 CD *020 †20 ‡

LOVETT, James Emmett, III. 301 THE PKWY 29650 #035-01-1987 L2001 PS *020 †85,65

LYNCH, Michelle Sanders. 501 MEMORIAL DR EXT 29651 #045-01-1994 L1997 PD *020 †55

MACDONALD, Robert Glen. 2755 S HIGHWAY 14, STE 1200H 29650 #064-01-1978 L2004 CD *020

MALETIC, Vladimir. 38 PARKWAY COMMONS WAY 29650 #957-02-1981 L1994 CHP P *020 †75

MALMSTROM, Laurie Lynn. 306 THORNBLADE BLVD, CAROLINA EMERG MED PA 29650 #020-02-1993 L1999 EM PD *020 †16,55

MAUR, Gurpreet Singh. 501 MEMORIAL DRIVE EXT 29651 #495-55-1975 L1995 IM *020 †20

MAYES, Kate Barrett. 2755 S HIGHWAY 14, STE 1200H 29650 #045-01-2003 L2004 IM *020 †20

MC GUIRT, John K. ■ 29650 #045-01-1989 L1997 **IM** *071 †20
MEWBORN, Kevin John. 306 THORNBLADE BLVD, PA 29650 #045-04-1999 L2002 **EM** *020 †16
MILAS, John Michael. 554 MEMORIAL DRIVE EXT, STE B 29651 #051-07-1984 L1985 **IM** *020 †20
MILLS, Richard Thomas. 306 THORNBLADE BLVD, CAROLINA EMERGENCY MEDICIN 29650 #305-01-2004 L2004 **FM** *020
MONTAGNE, Thomas Marcel. 2755 S HIGHWAY 14 29650 #050-02-1987 L1999 **IM GE** *020 †20
NABORS, Dina Sharpe. 306 THORNBLADE BLVD, CAROLINA EMERGENCY MEDICIN 29650 #045-04-2001 L2003 **FM** *020 †20
OGATA, Sandra Cristina. 111A BERRY AVE 29651 #187-41-1996 L2007 **FM** *020 †18
OSTEEN, Frank Bernard. ■ 29650 #036-05-1967 L1978 **D GP** *071 †15
OWENS, Douglas C. 108 W CHURCH ST 29650 #045-01-1960 L1960 **GP OS** *071
PALADUGU, Raja R. 150 D ST 29651 #495-50-1987 L1997 **IM** *020 †20
PARKER, Linda Schwab. 501 MEMORIAL DR EXT 29651 #045-01-1981 L1982 **PD** *020 †55
PATEL, Pulin. 306 THORNBLADE BLVD 29650 #305-01-2001 L2004 **FM** *020 †18
PEARLMAN, Howard Wayne. ■ 29650 #025-07-1975 L1987 **FM EM** *020 †18
PEEPLES, Paul Wiggins. 322 MEMORIAL DR 29650 #045-01-1954 L1954 **GP OS** *071
PERVEZ, Nafees. ■ 29650 #704-06-1966 L1993 **ATP PCP** *030 †50
PFEIFFER, Kristen Kay. 2755 S HIGHWAY 14 29650 #045-01-1993 L1995 **CD** *020 †20
PILCH, John Francis. 150 D ST 29651 #010-02-1988 L1993 **N** *020 †75
QUATTLEBAUM, Cecil. ■ 29650 #045-01-1965 L1965 **GYN** *071 †30
RAFF, James Chaney. 319 S BUNCOMBE RD 29650 #051-04-1969 L1987 **PD** *020 †55
RAISSI-FARD, Hajar. 111 MEMORIAL DR, PEDIATRIC CTR 29650 #517-01-1984 L1996 **PD** *020 †55
RAJU, Mudunuri V. 150 D ST, SPARTANBURG REGIONAL MED. 29651 #495-11-1989 L1999 **IM** *020 †20
RAJU, Vegesena Prudhvi. ■ 29650 #495-58-1964 L1974 **EM** *020 †16
REGAL, Wendy Rene. 306 THORNBLADE BLVD, SYNERGY MEDICAL EDUCATION 29650 #048-13-1997 L2007 **EM** *020 †16
REX, James C, Jr. 108 W CHURCH ST 29650 #041-12-1985 L1991 **CRS** *020 †85,10
RIETH, Douglas James. 2755 S HIGHWAY 14, STE 1200H 29650 #047-05-1993 L1994 **IM** *020 †20
ROBBINS, James Alexander. 108 W CHURCH ST 29650 #021-01-1978 L1980 **CRS** *020 †10,85
ROCHESTER, Angel Alisha. 306 THORNBLADE BLVD, CAROLINA EMERGENCY PHYSICI 29650 #045-01-2003 L2006 **EM** *020 †16
RODAK, David James. 2755 S HIGHWAY 14 29650 #055-01-1987 L1996 **CD IM** *020 †20
ROTHMAN, Elizabeth Ann. 301 THE PKWY 29650 #020-12-1996 L2002 **PS** *020 †65
ROWLAND, Wade Russell. ■ 29651 #036-01-1959 L1972 **IM IMG** *072 †20
SAINDON, Lee Jackson. 398 THE PKWY, AT THORNBLADE 29650 #020-12-1982 L1983 **FM** *020 †18
SANCHEZ, Sergio Alfred. 2700 E PHILLIPS RD 29650 #187-15-1992 L2005 **P** *020
SCHANEN, Giles Martin. ■ 29650 #048-02-1959 L1968 **OBG** *071 †30
SHAIKH, Huneiza Yusuf. ■ 29650 #305-01-1999 L2006 **FM** *020 †18 ‡
SHUGART, Henry Edward. 2755 S HIGHWAY 14, STE 1200H 29650 #036-05-1994 L1995 **IM** *020 †20
SMYRE, Herbert Lee. ■ 29651 #036-01-1966 L1971 **PD** *071 †55
SNELL, Philip Arden. 410 MEMORIAL DRIVE EXT 29651 #035-03-1964 L1973 **FM AM** *020 †18
SRINIVASAN, Ajai. 2755 S HIGHWAY 14, STE 2500 29650 #045-01-1996 L1997 **PS** *020 †85
SRIVASTAVA, Nalin Kumar. 2755 S HIGHWAY 14 29650 #012-01-1988 L1995 **CD** *020 †20
STAFFORD, Warren K. 113B BERRY AVE 29651 #041-13-1986 L2003 **FM OBS** *020 †18
STOKES, Douglas Weeks, Jr. 100 PHYSICIANS DR 29650 #045-01-1988 L1993 **OPH** *020 †35
STORY, James R. 2755 S HIGHWAY 14 29650 #012-01-1974 L1981 **CD IM** *020 †20
STOUDEMAYER, Tullious C. 322 MEMORIAL DR 29650 #045-04-1984 L1987 **FM** *020 †18
SUBER, Walter John, Jr. 2755 S HIGHWAY 14 STE 2150, FOOTHILLS PLASTIC SURGERY 29650 #045-01-1993 L1999 **PS** *020
SULLIVAN, Francis S. 164 BELLAMY CLOSE 29651 #051-01-1949 L1954 **IM IMG** *020 †20
SUMEREL, William Bruce. ■ 29650 #045-01-1971 L1973 **DR** *071
TANKERSLEY, Susan March. ■ 29650 #045-01-1983 L1985 **AN** *075 †05
THURSTON, Brian Caldwell. ■ 29650 #048-15-2008 *012
TRAN, Duc Hoang. 150 D ST 29651 #305-01-1998 L2002 **IM** *020 †20
VAN SLOOTEN, Dale Allen. 313 MEMORIAL DR 29650 #035-06-1971 L1985 **GS** *062 †85
VAUGHT, Richard Loren. ■ 29650 #017-20-1958 L1958 **U UP** *071 †95
VIGLIANCO, Michelle Rene. 2755 S HIGHWAY 14 29650 #055-01-2000 L2006 **PD** *020 †55
VINSON, Linda Ann. ■ 29650 #045-01-1988 L1989 **IM** *020
WALKER, Theron Otis. ■ 29650 #045-01-1948 L1948 **GP** *071
WALTON, John Edmond. 402 MEMORIAL DRIVE EXT 29650 #011-03-1967 L1972 **U** *020 †95
WARD, Mark Edward. 2755 S HIGHWAY 14, STE 1200H 29650 #045-01-1996 L1997 **IM AI** *020 †20
WEIR, Richard Mark. 2755 S HIGHWAY 14 STE 2400 29650 #045-01-1982 L1987 **OTO** *020 †45
WELBORN, Norman P, Jr. ■ 29650 #045-01-1963 L1964 **FM P** *072
WENTZKY, Jos Harold, Jr. 600 N MAIN ST STE B, GREER SURGICAL ASSOCIATES 29650 #045-01-1980 L1985 **GS TS** *020 †85
WHITE, Janette E. 100 PHYSICIANS DR 29650 #065-06-1989 L1999 **OPH** *020 †35
WHITEHEAD, Douglas Wayne. 1107 W POINSETT ST 29650 #045-01-1990 L1992 **FM** *020 †18
WHITLOCK, Norris Walter. 420 THE PKWY, STE C 29650 #045-01-1973 L1979 **U** *020 †95
WHITTAKER, Jack Riley. 406 MEMORIAL DRIVE EXT 29651 #045-01-1962 L1967 **FM OS** *071 †18
WILKENFELD, Byron Eli. 2700 E PHILLIPS RD 29650 #048-14-1973 L1974 **P** *072
WILKINS, Thomas Leroy. ■ 29650 #045-01-1993 L1996 **EM** *020 †16
WILLIAMS, Bradley B. 100 PHYSICIANS DR 29650 #045-01-1981 L1984 **OPH** *020 †35
WISCHHUSEN, Lisa L. 220 EXECUTIVE DR, PIEDMONT CTR FOR MENTAL HE 29651 #045-04-1998 L1999 **P** *020 †75
WOLFORD, John Leland, Jr. 2755 S HIGHWAY 14, STE 1200H 29650 #047-05-1980 L1999 **GE IM** *020 †20
WOODS, Auburn, III. 2755 S HIGHWAY 14 29650 #045-01-1973 **GS** *020 †85
WOOLLEN, Claude D. 2755 S HIGHWAY 14, STE 2500 29650 #045-01-1991 L1992 **GS** *020 †85
ZEIGLER, Mark Roy. 1107 W POINSETT ST 29650, GREER FAMILY MEDICINE 29650 #055-02-1995 L1996 **FM OBG** *020 †18

HAMPTON — HAMPTON

BLOING, Robert David. 403 SHAW DR 29924 #422-01-1991 L1996 **AN PME** *020 †05
PULASKI, Count, Jr. PO BOX 207, 965 LURAY HWY 29924 #045-01-1960 L1960 **GP GS** *020 †18
REED, Edward Donald, Sr. 200 ELM ST E 29924 #045-01-1998 L2000 **IM** *020

VEGA, Luis. 408 JACKSON AVE E, HAMPTON PEDIATRICS FAMILY 29924 #024-05-1999 L2002 **FM** *020 †18
VEGA, Rosita Maria. 410 JACKSON AVE E 29924 #024-05-1997 L2006 **PD** *020
WELCKER, Glenn Wesley. 305 ELM ST W, HAMPTON FAMILY PRACTICE 29924 #045-04-1991 L1992 **FM** *020 †18

HANAHAN — BERKELEY

CATON, Kirt Ancil. 1254 YEAMANS HALL RD 29410 #045-01-1998 L2001 **FM** *020 †18
COKER, Jason Bryan. ■ 29410 #045-01-2008 *012
DAVIS, Susan Royal. ■ 29410 #035-06-1981 L1985 **OM GP** *020 †70
FLEMING, James Bernard. ■ 29410 #045-01-2008 *012
HAMILTON, Lin Holloway. 46 SORENTO BLVD 29410 #051-01-1974 L1978 **EM** *071 †16
HARVEY, Virgil. 1254 YEAMANS HALL RD 29410 #045-01-1959 L1959 **FM** *071 †18
MOORE, Merlyn G. ■ 29410 #748-02-1977 L1991 **OBG** *020 †30
SPENCER, Deborah Vinson. ■ 29410 #045-01-2006 L2006 **PTH** *012

HARDEEVILLE — JASPER

ANTON, Robert Chas. 1000 MEDICAL CENTER DR, COASTAL CAROLINA MEDICAL C 29927 #055-02-1989 L2006 **DR** *020 †80
BELL, John Luis. 1010 MEDICAL CENTER DR, STE 130 29927 #132-05-1993 L2000 **NEP** *020 †20
BOGUSH, Kimber Frosty. 1000 MEDICAL CENTER DR, ATTN: MEDICAL STAFF OFFICE 29927 #041-15-2003 L2006 **EM** *020 †16
BRUST, David Gardiner. 1000 MEDICAL CENTER DR 29927 #051-07-2002 L2006 **EM** *100
BURNAUGH, Robert Lester. 1010 MEDICAL CENTER DR, STE 100 29927 #012-01-1996 L2004 **PUD SME** *020 †20
CARLEO, Alexandra Marie. 1000 MEDICAL CENTER DR, COASTAL CAROLINA MEDICAL C 29927 #051-07-2003 L2004 **EM** *100 †16
CASEY, Terrence Eugene. HARDEEVILLE CENTER, OB/GYN WELLNESS CENTER 29927 #038-41-1963 L1963 **OBG OS** *071 †20
CLARK-COOLIDGE, Carol. 300 NEW RIVER PKWY STE 36, COOLIDGE PLASTIC SURG 29927 #028-46-1985 L1992 **PS** *020 †65
CRISOLOGO, John Michael. 1010 MEDICAL CENTER DR, STE 130 29927 #038-41-1997 L2003 **GE** *020 †20
DERRICK, Fletcher C, III. 1010 MEDICAL CENTER DR, STE 130 29927 #045-01-1993 L1996 **IM** *020 †20
EVANS, Randall Brian. 1010 MEDICAL CENTER DR, STE 100 29927 #034-01-1990 L1997 **PUD PCC** *020 †20
FLEXON, Phillip Billings. ■ 29927 #038-06-1984 L1996 **OTO HNS** *020 †45
GARSKE, Jeffrey Thos. 1010 MEDICAL CENTER DR, STE 240 29927 #056-05-1976 L2002 **ORS** *020 †40
HARPER, Melinda Carol. 420 NEW RIVER PKWY 29927 #047-06-1996 L1998 **FM** *020 †18
JOHNSON, Todd Eric. 420 NEW RIVER PKWY 29927 #038-40-1996 L1997 **FM** *020 †18
KHAN, Wasil. ■ 29927 #045-01-2000 L2005 **AI** *020 †20,03
LIGON, Deborah Gail. 8 STINEY RD 29927 #024-07-1980 L1983 **IM** *020 †20
NUNAMAKER, Jacob L, IV. 1010 MEDICAL CENTER DR, STE 130 29927 #045-01-1994 L1995 **CD** *020 †20
PARKER, John Ellis. 300 NEW RIVER PKWY, STE 16 29927 #045-01-1965 L1965 **GS** *020 †85
REUBEN, Jeffery Mark. 1010 MEDICAL CENTER DR, STE 130 29927 #023-07-1994 L2000 **OSS** *020 †40
RHODIN, Thor Robert. 1010 MEDICAL CENTER DR, STE 130 29927 #035-03-1978 L1994 **OSM GS** *020 †20,40
RUIZ, Michael Anthony. 1000 MEDICAL CENTER DR, COASTAL CAROLINA MEDICAL C 29927 #012-01-2001 L2005 **IM** *020 †20
STODDARD, Leland C, Jr. 1010 MEDICAL CENTER DR, STE 130 29927 #045-01-1979 L1980 **ORS** *020 †40
UZOCHUKWU, Lawrence N. 1000 MEDICAL CENTER DR, RADIOLOGY 29927 #038-06-1999 L2006 **DR** *020 †80
WILLIAMS, Denise Kym. 1000 MEDICAL CENTER DR 29927 #018-03-1988 L2007 **EM** *020 †16

HARTSVILLE — DARLINGTON

ACAYLAR, Joseph Villanuev. 1268 S 4TH ST, STE A, PO BOX 909 29550 #748-01-1999 L2007 **FM** *020 †18
AMBROSE, Michael F. 206 SWIFT CREEK RD 29550 #016-11-1997 L2002 **FM** *020 †18
AREEPHANTHU, Abraham. 701 MEDICAL PARK DR 29550 #020-02-1994 L1995 **FM** *020 †18
BALI, Arvind J. 206 SWIFT CREEK RD 29550 #495-45-1988 L2005 **CD** *020 †20
BALI, Suparna. ■ 29550 #496-07-1991 L1999 **IM** *072
BALLINGTON, Karen Louise. 206 SWIFT CREEK RD 29550 #045-01-1978 L1979 **IM CD** *020 †20
BALVICH, James C. 1304 W BOBO NEWSOM HWY 29550 #016-43-1978 L1997 **IM** *020 †20
BANNISTER, Carroll Brooks. 704 MEDICAL PARK DR, HARTSVILLE SURGICAL 29550 #045-01-1972 L1976 **GS GYN** *020 †85
BAXLEY, Luke Davis. 214 S 2ND ST 29550 #045-04-1982 L1983 **FM** *020 †18
BAXLEY, Luke Davis, Jr. 29550 #045-01-2008 *012
BELL, Thomas James, Jr. 1304 W BOBO NEWSOM HWY 29550 #045-01-1969 L1969 **FM** *020 †18
BEST, Darryl B. 1268 S 4TH ST 29550 #045-01-1989 L1995 **IM** *020 †20
BUDHRAM, Solomon. 708 MEDICAL PARK DR, MORPHIS PEDIATRIC GROUP 29550 #422-01-1997 L2005 **PD** *020 †55
BULLARD, Robert E, Jr. 701 MEDICAL PARK DR, STE 304 29550 #045-01-1983 L1984 **IM** *020 †20
CHAPMAN, Raymond Mcintosh. 701 MEDICAL PARK DR, STE 304 29550 #045-04-1985 L1987 **IM** *020 †20
CHRISTOPHER, Kaye Romayne. 701 MEDICAL PARK DR, STE 203 29550 #035-09-1992 L2001 **NEP IM** *020 †20
COOLER, Arthur Watson. 1304 W BOBO NEWSOM HWY 29550 #012-01-1991 L1992 **GS** *020 †85
COOPER, Emanuiel. 1268 S 4TH ST, STE A 29550 #051-07-1997 L2000 **FM** *020 †18
COWARD, Paul Alderman. 1268 S 4TH ST, STE B 29550 #045-01-1969 L1969 **PD** *020 †55 ‡
CRAWFORD, Kristopher R. 1304 W BOBO NEWSOM HWY 29550 #045-01-2001 L2001 **FM** *020

CULYER, Virginia Gail. ■ 29550 #045-01-2008 *012

DAMERON, Jason Richard. 704 MEDICAL PARK DR, HARTSVILLE SURGICAL CENTER 29550 #036-08-2000 L2003 **GS** *100 †85

DANIEL, Scott Henry. 206 SWIFT CREEK RD 29550 #045-04-1992 L1993 **OBG** *020 †30

DANZEY, Toya Janeane. 216 S 2ND ST 29550 #038-45-1989 L1993 **OBG** *020 †30

DAVIS, Charles Maurice. 1304 W BOBO NEWSOM HWY, RADIOLOGY DEPARTMENT 29550 #045-01-1969 L1969 **DR** *020 †80

DIXON, Woodward Rion. 411 BYERLY AVE 29550 #649-07-1972 L1975 **FM GS** *071 †18

ELDER, Robert L. 206 SWIFT CREEK RD, THE MEDICAL GROUP 29550 #020-02-1994 L1995 **FM OM** *020 †18

EVANS, Kenneth C. 515 E CAROLINA AVE 29550 #045-01-1981 L1982 **FM** *020 †18

FREEMAN, Tony A. 214 S 2ND ST 29550 #020-02-2001 L2003 **FM** *020 †18

HARLESS, Michael. 701 MEDICAL PARK DR, STE 301 29550 #020-02-1994 L1995 **FM** *020 †18

HARPER, Greta M. 101 N 2ND ST 29550 #048-14-1992 L1998 **FM** *020 †18

HASSLER, Terence Wm. 700 MEDICAL PARK DR 29550 #010-02-1982 L1993 **ORS GS** *020

KOHN, Jean D. 1304 W BOBO NEWSOM HWY 29550 #030-05-1987 L1988 **FM** *020

KRUEGER, Kenneth Wm. 1901 W CAROLINA AVE, # 134 29550 #048-04-1942 L1949 **IM IMG** *072 †20

LONG, William Hampton, III. 701 MEDICAL PARK DR, STE 305 29550 #045-04-2001 L2002 **FM** *020 †18

MINCHEFF, Thomas Vanko. 704 MEDICAL PARK DR, HARTSVILLE SURGICAL 29550 #409-16-1979 L1993 **GS** *020 †85

MITCHELL, Benjamin Thos. 1268 S 4TH ST, STE A 29550 #045-01-1992 L1993 **FM** *020 †18

MORPHIS, Elizabeth J. 708 MEDICAL PARK DR 29550 #045-01-1992 L1993 **PD** *020 †55

MORPHIS, James Oscar. 708 MEDICAL PARK DR 29550 #036-07-1958 L1964 **PD** *020 †55

MOYD, Pickens Kinard. 528 E CAROLINA AVE 29550 #045-01-1956 L1956 **GS GYN** *071 †85

NICKLES, Melvin Bond, Jr. 206 SWIFT CREEK RD 29550 #045-01-1959 L1959 **GP OM** *030

OVANNA-BUDHRAM, Joni Sue. 708 MEDICAL PARK DR, MORPHIS PEDIACTRIC GROUP 29550 #035-15-1997 L2005 **PD** *020 †55

POSANG, Paveena. 701 MEDICAL PARK DR, STE 205 29550 #055-01-1995 L2006 **FM** *020 †18

QUAYE, Emmanuel Otu. 701 MEDICAL PARK DR, STE 304 29550 #012-05-1990 L2002 **IM** *020 †20

QUAYE, Michelle Suzanne. 206 SWIFT CREEK RD 29550 #012-21-1994 L2002 **OBG** *020

REGAN, Sally Webb. 1304 W BOBO NEWSOM HWY 29550 #045-04-1989 L1996 **DR** *020 †80

REYNOLDS, Susan Du Barry. 206 SWIFT CREEK RD 29550 #045-01-1985 L1987 **IM** *020 †20

ROBINSON, Leroy F. 206 SWIFT CREEK RD 29550 #045-04-1990 L1991 **OBG** *020 †30

ROPP, John Conway, III. 701 MEDICAL PARK DR, STE 305 29550 #045-04-2001 L2002 **FM** *020 †18

STEWART, Charles Ray. 701 MEDICAL PARK DR, STE 108 29550 #021-01-1977 L2008 **N P** *020 †75

STOKES, Hunter Rhoad, Sr. 202 S 2ND ST 29550 #045-01-1963 L1963 **OPH** *071 †35

SURKA, Aqil Ebun. 701 MEDICAL PARK DR, STE 207 29550 #045-04-1996 L2000 **PD** *020 †55

THIELEN, Thomas Edward. 701 MEDICAL PARK DR, STE 207 29550 #045-01-2003 L2006 **PD** *020 †55

WARD, Tresha Taylor. 1268 S 4TH ST, STE A 29550 #023-01-1993 L1997 **FM** *020 †18

WHEELER, Harold Neil. 1304 W BOBO NEWSOM HWY 29550 #045-01-1969 L1969 **PTH** *062 †50

WOODBERRY, William H. 701 MEDICAL PARK DR, STE 301 29550 #045-01-1986 L1987 **IM** *020 †20

HEMINGWAY - GEORGETOWN

MUNGER, Christopher Wyley. 456 N MAIN ST 29554 #035-01-2000 L2003 **FM** *020 †18

VANDERGRIFF, Joseph Vance. 456 N MAIN ST 29554 #047-06-1996 L2000 **FM** *020 †18

HILTON HEAD ISLAND - BEAUFORT

ALBERTINI, Robert E. ■ 29928 #010-02-1967 L1968 **PUD IM** *030 †20

AMONITTI, George Jos, Jr. 15 NORTHRIDGE DR 29926 #010-03-1964 L1997 **OBG PD** *072 †30

ANDERSON, Brian Nathanael. 22 BETHEA DR 29926 #016-45-1989 L1993 **FM FSM** *020 †18

ANDERSON, Richard H. ■ 29928 #041-13-1966 L1967 **P IM** *075

ANTON, Charles Jos, Jr. 15 NORTHRIDGE DR 29926 #028-34-1963 L1963 **R** *071 †80

AQUINO, Luann. 15 NORTHRIDGE DR 29926 #012-01-1996 L2000 **IM** *020 †20

ASHWORTH, Charles V, Jr. 15 NORTHRIDGE DR 29926 #051-04-1960 L1995 **GP PD** *071 †18

AUDET, Jeanne D Amlicke. ■ 29926 #023-01-1946 L1947 **GP PM** *071 †18

AUDET, Robert J. ■ 29926 #023-01-1946 L1947 **GP OBS** *071 †18

AURANDT, Henry Norris. ■ 29926 #041-13-1968 L1969 **OBG** *071 †30

AUSBAND, John Rufus. LAMOTTE CLINIC 29928 #036-05-1943 L1975 **OTO** *020 †45

AUTRY, Ernest D. 25 HOSPITAL CENTER BLVD 29926 #012-01-1975 L2007 **OBG PD** *020 †55,30

BALINSKI, Thaddeus A. ■ 29926 #035-08-1952 L1954 **IM** *071

BARTELS, George Merrill. ■ 29926 #020-02-1960 L1961 **OBG** *071 †30

BASS, Jack C. ■ 29928 #028-02-1952 L1952 **PD** *071 †55

BATSON, John Preston, III. ■ 29928 #045-04-1999 L2001 **PD PSM** *020 †55

BEAHM, Walter Clarence. 15 NORTHRIDGE DR 29926 #038-40-1955 L1957 **FM OM** *071 †18

BEATTY, Doris Gay. 15 NORTHRIDGE DR 29926 #016-11-1955 L1956 **IM** *071

BELL, Hubert Harvey. 15 NORTHRIDGE DR 29926 #019-02-1962 L1963 **CD OS** *071 †20

BELL, Louis David. 23 MAIN ST STE 101, COASTAL GASTRNTRLGY 29926 #041-13-1978 L2002 **GE IM** *020 †20

BELLER, Thomas C. 25 HOSPITAL CENTER BLVD, MEDICAL PAVILION BLDG-STE 29926 #011-02-1998 L2004 **AI** *020 †20,03

BENZ, Harry Glackin. ■ 29928 #041-12-1948 L1949 **AN OS** *071 †05

BERNEY, John Wm. 15 NORTHRIDGE DR 29926 #018-03-1955 L1956 **R** *071 †80

BERRIGAN, Maureen Moosbru. ■ 29926 #012-05-1999 L2005 **PD** *020 †55

BERRIGAN, Thomas Jos. 25 HOSPITAL CENTER BLVD 29926 #035-15-1959 L1975 **R** *020 †80

BERRIGAN, Timothy Joseph. 25 HOSPITAL CENTER BLVD, CENTER DEPT OF RADIOLOGY 29926 #045-01-1997 L2003 **DR** *020 †80

BERTRAND, Charles Arthur. 25 HOSPITAL CENTER BLVD 29926 #035-08-1948 L1993 **CD** *071 †20

BILLINGS, David Elmer. ■ 29926 #040-02-1960 L1993 **OBG** *071 †30

BIRK, Robert E. ■ 29926 #035-45-1952 L1953 **RHU** *071 †20

BISHOP, Joseph Roy. 220 PEMBROKE DR 29926 #004-01-1993 L1994 **OPH** *020 †35

BISHOP, Kellie A Chandler. 19 BOW CIR STE A 29928 #004-01-1993 L1994 **P** *071 †75

BLACK, Joseph Wm. 25 HOSPITAL CENTER BLVD, HILTON HEAD REG MED CTR 29926 #036-05-1959 L1963 **PTH** *020 †50

BLAKE, Charles Richard. 224 PEMBROKE DR 29926 #001-02-2000 L2007 **PLI CHP** *020 †35

BLAZEK, William Vincent. 15 NORTHRIDGE DR 29926 #056-06-1958 L1959 **CD IM** *071 †20

BLESSITT, Kristi Lynn. ■ 29926 #027-01-2000 L2000 **OBG** *020 †30

BLUSEWICZ, Tracy Ann. 60 MAIN ST, UNIT C 29926 #010-02-1996 L2004 **OBG** *020 †30

BOGART, Keith Chas. ■ 29928 #038-40-1961 L1961 **N PM** *071 †75

BOKAT, Robert Bruce. 15 NORTHRIDGE DR 29926 #023-01-1962 L1986 **PD** *071 †55

BOLDT, Henry Andrew. ■ 29928 #025-01-1954 L1955 **OPH** *071 †35

BORELLI, Laura Cosimi. 15 BEAR ISLAND RD 29926 #034-01-1987 L1988 **PD PEM** *020 †55

BOTTNER, Randy Kyle. 8 HOSPITAL CTR BLVD # 130 29926 #010-01-1981 L1992 **CD IC** *020 †20

BOUSQUET, Franklyn P, Jr. ■ 29928 #024-07-1947 L1954 **OPH** *071 †35

BOWEN, Frank Winslow, Jr. 15 NORTHRIDGE DR, VOLUNTEERS IN MED 29926 #041-09-1969 L2000 **PD MDM** *030 †55

BOWMAN, David Harvey. ■ 29928 #041-12-1963 L1964 **OPH** *071 †35

BRADNAN, Alfred Andrew. ■ 29926 #038-40-1968 L1981 **P** *072 †75

BRAND, Alfredo Jorge. 25 HOSPITAL CENTER CMNS, STE 200 29926 #935-07-1976 L1991 **D** *020 †15

BREEN, James Langhorne. 15 NORTHRIDGE DR 29926 #016-06-1952 L1953 **OBG PTH** *071 †30

BRIAN, William John. 25 HOSPITAL CENTER BLVD 29926 #019-02-1971 L1999 **AN** *020 †05

BRIDGES, Thomas Howard. ■ 29926 #036-01-1965 L1991 **EM** *020 †16

BRINKMAN, Carl Alexander. 15 NORTHRIDGE DR 29926 #008-01-1957 L1962 **NS** *071 †25

BROECKER, Anna M Hardy. ■ 29926 #065-01-1962 L1968 **DMP ATP** *071 †50

BROSMAN, David Alan. 11 HOSPITAL CENTER CMNS, STE 100 29926 #051-04-1982 L1991 **AN IM** *020 †20,05

BROWN, Robert Larry. ■ 29926 #041-14-1972 L1973 **ID IM** *030

BUCHANAN, Charles Stuart. ■ 29928 #038-06-1963 L1998 **D DMP** *071 †15

BUCHHOLTZ, Thomas Walter. ■ 29926 #035-20-1969 L1976 **GS** *020 †85

BULLOCK, Ronald Ernest. 19 SHELTER COVE LN, STE 301 WATERSEDGE BLDG. 29928 #018-03-1963 L1983 **P N** *020 †75

BUNDY, A Thomas. 15 HOSPITAL CENTER BLVD, STE 1 29926 #055-01-1986 L1989 **D DS** *020 †15 ‡

CAMPI, Geralyn Mary. 25 HOSPITAL CENTER BLVD 29926 #041-09-1988 L1996 **IM** *020 †20

CANFIELD, John Jos, Jr. 15 NORTHRIDGE DR 29926 #010-02-1966 L1972 **ORS** *020 †40

CAREK, Donald John. 15 NORTHRIDGE DR 29926 #056-06-1956 L1976 **CHP P** *071 †75

CARGILL, Brett Jeffrey. 18 N CALIBOGUE CAY RD 29928 #045-04-1996 L1998 **EM** *020 †16

CARUSO, Peter V. ■ 29928 #055-01-1971 L1975 **DR R** *071 †80 ‡

CHALSON, Richard James. 15 NORTHRIDGE DR, VOLUNTEERS IN MEDICINE CLI 29926 #561-17-1971 L2005 **OBG** *020 †30

CHINDRIS, Ana Maria. ■ 29928 #781-03-1996 L2007 **IM** *100 †20

CITRON, Neil Nathan. ■ 29926 #035-15-1957 L1977 **GS** *071 †85

CLARK, Ernest James. ■ 29926 #028-02-1948 L1948 **IM AM** *071 †20

CLODFELTER, Robert. 25 HOSPITAL CENTER BLVD, HILTON HEAD MEDICAL CENTER 29926 #011-04-1980 L1997 **EM** *020 †16

COWAN, William Raymond. ■ 29926 #036-05-1957 L1986 **PTH AM** *072 †50

CROCKER, Keith Mc Lean. 15 NORTHRIDGE DR 29926 #067-01-1948 L1963 *050

CROSS, Harold Dick. 15 NORTHRIDGE DR 29926 #008-01-1957 L1998 **EM FM** *071

CUMMINGS, Robert V. ■ 29928 #041-09-1966 L1995 **OBG** *030 †30

CURRIE, Richard Jay. 15 NORTHRIDGE DR 29926 #041-02-1962 L1997 **U** *020 †95

DAL SANTO, Gianfranco. ■ 29928 #561-11-1950 L1961 **AN IM** *071 †05

DANDREA, Lori Ann. ■ 29928 #011-03-1989 L1991 **PD** *020 †55

DANIELS, Wheeler Thayer. 15 NORTHRIDGE DR 29926 #041-13-1964 L1970 **ORS** *071 †40

DE LORENZO, Michael. 15 NORTHRIDGE DR 29926 #561-01-1959 L1963 **PD** *071 †55

DERMAN, Herbert. 15 NORTHRIDGE DR 29928 #021-05-1943 L1943 **CLP PTH** *071 †50

DE VOE, James F. 4 BARKSDALE CT 29926 #847-05-1973 L1991 **AN EM** *020 †16,05

DICKENSHEETS, James G. ■ 29926 #041-02-1944 L1973 **IM PUD** *071 †20

DICKSON, Kenneth Beatty. ■ 29928 #065-01-1955 L1961 **PTH OS** *071 †50

DOLAN, John Albert. ■ 29926 #010-01-1961 L1966 **ORS** *071 †40

DOLAN, John Thos. 15 NORTHRIDGE DR 29926 #028-34-1954 L1954 **GS TS** *072 †85

DORSNER, David Edward. 157 WILLIAM HILTON PKWY 29926 #028-34-1976 L1983 **EM** *020

DRUCKER, Morris H. ■ 29926 #035-15-1971 L1993 **TS VS** *071 †85,90

DUVALL, Charles Patton. ■ 29926 #035-45-1962 L1967 **IM ON** *071 †20

EGGERS, James Donahue. 15 NORTHRIDGE DR 29926 #016-43-1961 L1962 **OBG END** *071 †30

ELIASOPH, James L. ■ 29926 #035-19-1949 L1950 **U** *071 †95

EMERY, Chas Bartlett, Jr. 92 MAIN ST, WHOOPING CRANE WAY 29926 #025-01-1956 L1986 **ORS** *071 †40

ENDLER, Gerhard Carl. 15 NORTHRIDGE DR 29926 #154-07-1953 L1964 **OS AN** *071 †05

ENGELMAN, Karl. ■ 29928 #024-01-1959 L1995 **IM CD** *071 †20

ENGLAND, Kent Boyd. ■ 29928 #041-02-1975 L1984 **FM** *020 †18

ERAS, Philip. 15 NORTHRIDGE DR 29926 #035-08-1960 L1961 **GE** *020 †20

FAILOR, Harlan John. ■ 29926 #056-05-1954 L1955 **IM ON** *071 †20

FARR, Kenneth Danl. 220 PEMBROKE DR STE 100 29926 #001-02-1992 L1993 **OPH** *020 †35

FELLNER, Donald Weber. PO BOX 7928 29938 #011-03-1961 L1968 **ORS** *072 †40

FELTON, Lester M. ■ 29928 #035-20-1952 L1987 **U** *071 †95

FESCHE, Paul Hudson. ■ 29928 #023-01-1965 L1965 **GYN** *072 †30

FIELD, James B. 15 NORTHRIDGE DR 29926 #024-01-1951 L1986 **END** *071 †20

FLEGEL, Ernest Edward. ■ 29938 #041-02-1965 L1966 **IM CD** *020 †20

FORNARI, Gabriel Chas. ■ 29928 #055-01-1977 L2002 **EM FM** *075 †16,18

FRIEDMAN, Richard M. 15 NORTHRIDGE DR 29926 #035-08-1960 L1961 **GS OS** *071 †85

FROST, William Warren. PO BOX 22988 29925 #047-06-1972 L1973 **PM FM** *071 ‡

GASSER, Walter Eugene. 25 HOSPITAL CENTER BLVD 29926 #038-41-1964 L2007 **IM** *020 †20

GAUBY, Van Alan. 25 HOSPITAL CENTER BLVD, HILTON HEAD REGIONAL MED C 29926 #038-45-1988 L2002 **EM FM** *020 †18,16 ‡

GAVIN, J Robert, Jr. 460 WILLIAM HILTON PKWY, GAVIN ORTHOPAEDICS 29926 #010-02-1984 L2004 **ORS** *020 †40 ‡

GELL, James W. 15 NORTHRIDGE DR 29926 #025-01-1949 L1950 **OBG** *071 †30

GIGANTE, James Francis. 35 BILL FRIES DR 29926 #016-42-1994 L2002 **IM** *020 †20

GILBREATH, Michael Joseph. 35 BILL FRIES DR STE F, ISLAND MEDICAL PLZ 29926 #016-11-1993 L1999 **GE IM** *020 †20

GLEITSMANN, Kenneth Yorke. 220 PEMBROKE DR STE 100 29926 #020-12-1978 L1985 **OPH** *071 †35

GOETZE, Lynn Marie. 25 HOSPITAL CENTER BLVD 29926 #422-01-1988 L2001 **FM** *020 †18

GOLDBERG, Ira B. ■ 29926 #165-04-1968 L1982 **IM CD** *020 †20

GOMBOA-BERTRAND, Maria E. ■ 29928 #132-02-1949 L1968 **P** *020 †75

■ = Address Information Privacy Protected

GOODMAN, Joseph Louis. 6 BRANFORD LN, BEAUFORT NAVAL HOSPITAL 29926 #065-09-1960 L1966 IM *071

GOODRICH, Richard Keith. ■ 29926 #038-41-1958 L1992 GYN PHP *071 †30

GORMAN, Ann Elizabeth. 100 EXCHANGE ST STE 200 29926 #038-40-1990 L1993 OBG *020 †30

GORMAN, Arthur Allan. ■ 29928 #025-07-1968 L1996 EM *020 †16

GREENBERG, David C. 15 NORTHRIDGE DR 29926 #035-15-1959 L1961 ORS *071 †40

GREENLEE, Robert L. ■ 29926 #010-01-1949 L1950 P CHP *071 †75

GRIFFIN, John Hugh. ■ 29928 #041-02-1948 L1949 R *071

GRIZ, John. 15 NORTHRIDGE DR 29926 #025-07-1959 L1981 ORS *071 †40

GUPTA, Atul Mohan. 12 WILD AZALEA LN 29926 #038-45-1999 L2003 EM *020

GWOZDZ, Christina Sawyer. 4101 MAIN ST STE F 29926 #035-20-1984 L1989 OTO *020 †45

GWOZDZ, Glenn Peter. 25 HOSPITAL CENTER BLVD, STE 103 29926 #035-20-1984 L1989 GE IM *020 †20

HAM, O Emerson, Jr. 8 HOSPITAL CENTER BLVD, STE 110 29926 #012-05-1964 L1964 N *071 †75

HANNEGAN, Michael West. 29926 #028-03-1960 L1960 PTH OS *020 †50

HANSCOM, Donald Richard. 15 NORTHRIDGE DR 29926 #051-01-1977 L1999 GYN *071 †30

HARRIS, Kathleen M. 15 NORTHRIDGE DR 29926 #041-07-1964 L1965 DR *071 †80

HARRISON, George Irwin. ■ 29926 #869-05-1956 L1959 OTO *071

HART, Frank Laurren. 460 WILLIAM HILTON PKWY 29926 #039-01-1973 L1984 IM *020 †20

HAWKINS, J Henry. ■ 29926 #023-01-1956 L1956 OM *071

HAYES, John T. ■ 29928 #025-01-1951 L1952 ORS *071 †40

HAYNER, Robert. ■ 29926 #038-41-1955 L1955 NS *020 †25

HEALY, Michael Jos. ■ 29926 #028-34-1948 L1950 ADM P *071 †80

HEBBLE, William Mack. 15 NORTHRIDGE DR 29926 #016-11-1960 L1967 ORS *071 †40

HELLMAN, Barry Harvey. 15 NORTHRIDGE DR 29926 #041-02-1960 L1986 CD IM *020 †20

HEUS, E Geo. 15 NORTHRIDGE DR 29926 #035-06-1943 L1947 GYN *071 †30

HEWES, Robert Chas. 3 MATHEWS CT 29926 #005-12-1976 L1998 DR CD *020 †80

HEYBOER, Donald Jay. ■ 29926 #025-01-1959 L1980 AN *071 †03

HICKEY, Joseph Thos. 30 NEW ORLEANS RD, THE HICKEY CENTER 29928 #035-09-1977 L1994 IM *020 †20

HINES, Dixie Jones. ■ 29926 #045-01-1983 L1986 PM *020 †60

HOLLAND, Wesley Rex. HILTON HEAD HOSPITAL 29928 #005-12-1979 L1984 DR *075 †80

HOPSON, Clark Nelson. 15 LAFAYETTE PL STE E 29926 #035-20-1970 L1972 ORS *020 †40

HOULIHAN, Robert Kenneth. 15 NORTHRIDGE DR 29926 #035-09-1954 L1956 GS *071 †85

HUMPHREY, Edward Wm. ■ 29926 #026-04-1952 L1952 GS TS *071 †85,90

HUSSONG, Richard Lee, Jr. 25 HOSPITAL CENTER CMNS, BLDG 25 29926 #038-41-1993 L2002 GS *020 †85

JASON, Janine Maria. ■ 29928 #024-01-1975 L1977 PHP ID *050 †55

JINKINS, Roger Eugene. ■ 29928 #016-11-1963 L1984 R *020 †80

JOHNSON, Joel M, III. 93 MAIN ST, MAIN ST MEDICAL PC 29926 #024-07-1974 L1995 EM FM *020 †85

JOHNSON, Joel Mandus, Jr. 93 MAIN ST 29926 #024-07-1945 L1988 GP GS *071

JOHNSON, Wayne Eric. 843 WILLIAM HILTON PKWY, ASSOCS 29928 #008-02-1994 L1996 FM *020 †18

JORDAN, Patrick Michael. 1038 WILLIAM HILTON PKWY, UNIT#C & D 29928 #010-02-1983 L1990 EM *020 †16

JUKOFSKY, S Lawrence. ■ 29926 #035-09-1948 L1978 OPH *071 †35

KALAN, Jay Mitchel. 8 HOSPITAL CENTER BLVD, SAVANNAH CARDIOLOGY 29926 #051-04-1983 L2000 CD IC *020 †20

KASTL, David Gene. 25 HOSPITAL CENTER BLVD, MEDICAL PAVILION 29926 #039-01-1973 L2006 TS *020 †85,90

KAUP, Michael Robt. 25 HOSPITAL CENTER BLVD 29926 #038-43-1988 L1992 EM *020 †16

KENNARD, John Wm. 15 NORTHRIDGE DR 29926 #036-05-1956 L1956 DR R *071 †80

KIMBALL, Sanford Garson. 157 WM HILTON PKWY, CROSS ISLAND MEDICAL CENTE 29926 #011-02-1958 L1999 IM CD *020

KING, Robert Lynn. ■ 29928 #041-12-1956 L1957 OBG *072 †30

KIRTLEY, William R. ■ 29926 #016-06-1941 L1978 OS IM *071

KLEYN, Kenneth Allen. 15 NORTHRIDGE DR 29926 #025-01-1959 L1960 GS GE *072 †85

KOHLI, Harvinder. 25 HOSPITAL CENTER BLVD 29926 #495-03-1979 L1991 N *020 †75

KOPENHAVER, Donald Bausch. 15 NORTHRIDGE DR 29926 #041-01-1958 L1998 GYN *071 †30

KORHAMMER, Alan F. 15 NORTHRIDGE DR 29926 #035-01-1960 L1964 OBG *020 †30

KRAMER, Richard Spencer. ■ 29938 #036-07-1962 L1962 NS *050 †25

KRISHNA, Raju Prasad. 222 PEMBROKE DR, BLDG C 29926 #012-05-1993 L2002 AN *020 †05

LATTIMER, Gary Lee. ■ 29926 #041-13-1966 L2003 ID IM *071 †20 ‡

LAUGHLIN, Robert Abel. 15 BILL FRIES DR, STE E ISLAND MEDICAL PLZ 29926 #041-12-1968 L1978 PS GS *020 †85,65

LAWTON, Mark Anthony. 1 HOSPITAL CENTER CMNS, HILTON HEAD HEART, P.A. 29926 #012-22-1988 L2003 CD *020 †20

LAZOREK, Michael Michael. 15 NORTHRIDGE DR 29926 #035-08-1957 L1958 R *071 †80

LEFF, Peter Brynan. 15 NORTHRIDGE DR, VOLUNTEER IN MEDICINE CLIN 29926 #051-04-1967 L1967 GE IM *071 †20

LENNS, Thomas Paul. 460 WILLIAM HILTON PKWY 29926 #041-09-1978 L1989 IM *020 †20

LETSON, Holton Chas. ■ 29926 #030-05-1948 L1948 OPH *071 †35

LEVIN, Richard Marvin. PO BOX 3184 29928 #016-11-1961 L1962 AN PD *071 †05

LEWIN, Julian R. ■ 29926 #007-02-1938 L1938 R *071 †80

LI, Lewis Loo-Yi. ■ 29928 #242-09-1936 L1956 PTH *020 †50

LI, Ronald. ■ 29926 #035-01-1968 L1998 U *020 †95

LIEBESKIND, David Hyman. ■ 29926 #561-01-1970 L2006 PM *071 †60

LIGHTFOOT, William P. ■ 29926 #010-03-1946 L1947 GS *071 †30

LINDNER, Joseph, Jr. ■ 29926 #038-41-1955 L1955 IM *071

LIVERETT, Leon Mc Neely. ■ 29928 #017-20-1945 L1949 GYN OBS *071 †30

LONG, Paul Mc Crary. 460 WILLIAM HILTON PKWY 29926 #016-42-1973 L1976 IM *020 †20

LOON, Nicholas Robt. 25 HOSPITAL CENTER BLVD, STE 104 MEDICAL PAV 29926 #539-03-1971 L1992 NEP END *020 †20

LOVE, Glenn Neil. 35 BILL FRIES DR, STE H 29926 #036-01-1965 L1976 OBG *020 †30

LUCAS, Charles T. 25 HOSPITAL CENTER BLVD 29926 #020-02-1966 L1993 PTH *020 †50

MAC CABE, Jonathan Edward. 8 HOSPITAL CENTER BLVD, SAVANNAH CARDIOLOGY 29926 #047-06-1999 L2006 CD *100 †20

MACKAY, Sinclair Ross. ■ 29928 #035-09-1957 L1976 ORS *071 †40

MAHANNAH, Harry Arthur. 800 MAIN ST, STE 210C 29926 #018-03-1962 L2000 CHP P *020 †75

MAIRS, Daniel A. 15 NORTHRIDGE DR 29926 #036-07-1950 L1950 GYN *071 †30

MAROCCO, Paul Pasco. 74 GOVERNORS RD 29928 #561-01-1965 L1974 AN *020

MARSHALL, George Wm. ■ 29926 #019-02-1970 L1971 OBG *020 †30

MASCOLO, Maria Cozzi. 23 MAIN ST, STE 202 29926 #051-01-1996 L1996 PCC SME *020 †20

MATTHEWS, Marilyn Lee. ■ 29926 #026-04-1969 L1970 NM *071

MAURER, David Edward. 23 MAIN ST STE 201, HILTON HEAD ENT/SINUS CENT 29926 #012-05-1990 L2000 OTO *020 †45

MAYES, Michael Patrick. 25 HOSPITAL CENTER BLVD 29926 #041-13-1994 L1997 IM *020 †20

MAYNE, John Cleland. ■ 29928 #010-01-1952 L1983 OBG *071 †30

MC CONNELL, Jack B. ■ 29926 #047-06-1949 L1949 R *071

MC LAIN, Wm Campbell, Jr. ■ 29928 #036-07-1942 L1946 EM IM *020 †20

MC LEAN, Roderick Allen. 15 NORTHRIDGE DR 29926 #035-15-1945 L1948 OS OBG *071

MC LENDON, Harold Leslie. 15 NORTHRIDGE DR 29926 #012-05-1954 L1954 GYN *020 †20

MIHELIC, Nicholas Edward. 35 BILL FRIES DR, ISLAND MEDICAL PLAZA, BLD 29926 #041-14-1973 L1992 ORS *020 †40

MIKITA, John James. 15 NORTHRIDGE DR 29926 #055-01-1968 L1969 R *071 †80

MITCHELL, Paul Raymond. 222 PEMBROKE DR 29926 #038-75-1998, ▲ L2002 AN *020

MOGIL, Robert Allen. ■ 29926 #041-09-1964 L1965 U *020 †95

MORALES-RODRIQUEZ, Hector. ■ 29926 #649-01-1954 L1983 GS *071 †85

MUEHLBERGER, James Jos. ■ 29926 #030-06-1960 L1963 PD *071

MULNER, Ronald Paul. 25 HOSPITAL CENTER BLVD 29926 #012-01-1990 L2002 AN *020 †05

MURPHY, James Francis. 15 NORTHRIDGE DR 29926 #035-08-1964 L1967 NEP IM *020 †20

MURRELL, David W. ■ 29926 #016-11-1949 L1950 GP *071

NEESE, Harry Glenn, Jr. ■ 29926 #041-13-1944 L1976 FM *071

NELSON, David Lee. 15 NORTHRIDGE DR 29926 #028-02-1963 L1963 GS *071 †18,85

NELSON, Harry Monroe, Jr. 15 NORTHRIDGE DR 29926 #025-07-1957 L1958 TS GS *071 †85

NORTH, Patricia Ann. 35 BILL FRIES DR 29926 #038-44-1985 L1996 IM *020 †20

O'MALLEY, Donald Francis, Jr. ■ 29928 #010-01-1962 L1976 ORS *071 †40

PALATCHI, Albert Sharaff. 15 NORTHRIDGE DR 29926 #649-01-1953 L1984 TS *071 †85,90

PALMA, L D. ■ 29926 #748-08-1962 L1970 U *020 †95

PARIS, Mark Frazer. 6 N OCEAN POINT PL 29928 #047-06-1966 L1986 GS *071 †85

PASCAL, Robert R. 3 ANGLERS POND CT 29926 #035-01-1962 L2001 ATP *071 †50

PEREZ, Gaston O. 15 NORTHRIDGE DR 29926 #308-12-1988 L1995 FM *020 †18

PEREZ, Manuel Jose. 25 HOSPITAL CTR, STE 302 29926 #010-02-1988 L2002 U EM *020 †95

PETTY, William Isaac, II. 460 WILLIAM HILTON PKWY 29926 #045-01-1996 L1997 IM *020 †20

PHILIP, James Louis. ■ 29926 #035-01-1961 L1963 OBG *071 †30

PLATT, Michael Anthony. 25 HOSPITAL CENTER BLVD 29926 #003-01-1971 L1981 IM *020 †20

PLOTKIN, Chester L. 15 NORTHRIDGE DR 29926 #035-08-1952 L1956 IM *020 †20

PLZAK, Louis Frank. 8 HOSPITAL CENTER BLVD, COASTAL CAROINA UROLOGY GR 29926 #016-02-1996 L2002 U *020 †95

POLEY, Brooks Jos. 15 NORTHRIDGE DR 29926 #030-05-1959 L2005 OPH *071 †35

PORTER, Mary Judith. 23 MAIN ST, STE 202 29926 #038-41-1988 L1999 PUD *020 †20

POSTLEWAITE, David S. 15 NORTHRIDGE DR 29926 #038-40-1967 L1967 PS HS *071 †65

PRATT, Lee Harold. 15 NORTHRIDGE DR 29926 #055-01-1971 L1971 N *071 †75

PRICE, Joanne Louise. 100 EXCHANGE ST, WOMEN'S HEALTHCARE ASSOCIA 29926 #004-01-2003 L2007 OBG *020

RABB, Forte Calloway. ■ 29926 #012-01-1966 L2005 D *020 †15

REDLER, Bruce. ■ 29926 #016-06-1978 L1984 OPH *071 †35

RENO, Joseph David. ■ 29926 #047-02-1957 L1958 OM GP *071

RENSHAW, Thomas Saml. 379 FORT HOWELL DR, STE 500 29926 #038-40-1966 L1995 ORS OP *071 †40

RICHARDSON, Norman Selby. ■ 29928 #045-01-1957 L1957 FM *071

RILEY, James A. 15 NORTHRIDGE DR 29926 #008-01-1951 L1955 IM *071 †20

RILEY, James Chas. 15 NORTHRIDGE DR 29926 #041-13-1967 L1974 GE IM *020

ROEHRIG, C Burns. ■ 29926 #023-01-1949 L1954 IM DIA *071 †20

ROSENBAUM-BLOOM, Laura S. 19 BOW CIR, STE A 29928 #038-41-1982 L2001 P *020 †75

RZECZYCKI, Thomas Paul. 25 HOSPITAL CTR BLVD, STE 306 MEDICAL PAVILLION 29926 #008-02-1993 L1998 GS *020 †85

SACK, Jonathan L. 2 MARSHLAND RD, HILTON HEAD HLTH WELLNESS 29926 #836-01-1974 L1996 FM *020 †18

SAKATI, Isam Awni. 15 NORTHRIDGE DR 29926 #605-01-1960 L1997 U *071 †95

SALERNO, Peter John. 35 BILL FRIES DR, ISLAND MED PLZ BLDG 1 29926 #422-01-1983 L1999 PD *020 †55

SAMBERG, L Carl. ■ 29926 #025-07-1959 L1960 OP OSS *071 †40

SCHAROLD, Timothy Andrew. 460 WILLIAM HILTON PKWY 29926 #038-45-1987 L2003 IM IMG *020 †20

SCHILLING, Fred J, Jr. ■ 29926 #035-08-1942 L1985 CD IM *020 †20

SCHMIDT, Werner A. ■ 29926 #407-05-1951 PA *071

SCHROETER, Gerald Anthony. 15 NORTHRIDGE DR 29926 #065-09-1961 L1963 N *071 †75

SCIONTI, Stephen Michael. 8 HOSPITAL CENTER BLVD, STE 150 29926 #008-02-1984 L1991 U *020 †95

SERRA, Catherine G. ■ 29926 #035-09-1950 L1951 PD *071 †55

SHARP, John Calvin, Jr. 8 HOSPITAL CENTER BLVD, SAVANNAH CARDIOLOGY 29926 #045-01-1994 L1997 CD *020 †20

SHEARBURN, Edwin W, Jr. ■ 29928 #030-05-1936 L1975 GS *071 †85

SHERWOOD, Bozeman Keith. 58 SHELTER COVE LN, STE L 29928 #012-01-1983 L1993 EM OS *020 †16

SHOSS, Milton. ■ 29926 #048-04-1946 L1986 R NM *071 †80,28

SIDKY-AFIFI, Mahmoud. ■ 29928 #035-04-1954 L1958 GS *071 †85

SITTERSON, Beecher W. PO BOX 2155 29925 #024-01-1943 L1943 OM IM *071 †20

SMITH, Kenneth Eugene. 460 WILLIAM HILTON PKWY, STE H 29926 #007-02-1970 L2002 GYN GP *020 †30

SMITH, William Royall, Jr. ■ 29926 #038-06-1955 L1955 FM *071 †18

SNOWMAN, Patrick Joseph. ■ 29926 #041-07-1996 L2004 EM *020 †16

SOARES, Robert Louis, Jr. 25 HOSPITAL CENTER CMNS, STE 100 29926 #028-02-1992 L1998 GS *020 †85

SOIFER, Edgar Henry. 15 NORTHRIDGE DR 29926 #035-19-1957 L1958 U *071 †95

SPRAGUE, Bruce Leighton. ■ 29938 #041-01-1964 L1967 ORS *071 †40

SRIVASTAVA, Ravindra P. 22 BETHEA DR, HILTON HEAD PSYCHIATRIC CL 29926 #495-05-1985 L2003 P *020 †75

STEHR, Christian Herman. 24 AVALON WAY, 15 INDIGO RUN DRIVE 29926 #016-43-1967 L1969 AN PME *071 †05 ‡

STEPHENS, Pete Louis. ■ 29926 #051-04-1962 L1963 EM *071

STETZ, Carl Adelbert. 15 NORTHRIDGE DR 29926 #033-05-1965 OBG *071 †30

STEVENS, Jason Henry. 15 NORTHRIDGE DR 29926 #035-06-1959 L1962 EM *071 †35

STRAYER, Luther M, III. 15 NORTHRIDGE DR 29926 #035-01-1961 L1962 OSS ORS *071 †40

STRICKLAND, Alva Lawton. 15 NORTHRIDGE DR 29926 #045-01-1961 L1961 PD END *071 †55

STUPAR, Ronald Kent. ■ 29926 #055-01-1966 L1967 **R NM** *071 †80,28

SUH, Daniel Youchan. 8 HOSPITAL CENTER BLVD, NEUROLOGICAL INSTITUTE 29926 #038-41-1995 L2004 **NS** *020 †25

SUNDERLIN, Frederick, Jr. 15 NORTHRIDGE DR 29926 #041-13-1974 L1975 **END IM** *020 †20

TALLMAN, John Eric. 222 PEMBROKE DR, BLDG C 29926 #023-12-1998 L2005 **AN** *020 †05

THIELE, Robert O. ■ 29928 #028-78-1958, ▲ L1958 **GP** *071

THOMAS, Gary Walsh. 45 HOSPITAL CENTER CMNS, HOSPITAL MEDICAL PAVILION 29926 #045-01-1987 L1988 **ON** *020 †20

THOMPSON, Ervin Magnus. 19 SHELTER COVE LN, WATERS EDGE BLDG, STE 204 29928 #047-05-1972 L2006 **P** *030 †75

THORSEN, Wm Borge, Jr. ■ 29928 #051-01-1960 L1960 **GE IM** *071 †20

TOBIN, Joseph Peter. 25 HOSPITAL CENTER BLVD 29926 #010-02-1991 L1997 **ORS** *020 †40

TOPOROFF, George Sherman. 15 NORTHRIDGE DR 29926 #041-01-1955 L1963 **PD** *071 †55

TORRES-ROZOF, Lydia C. 93 MAIN ST, MAIN STREET MEDICAL 29926 #025-07-1992 L2005 **FM** *020 †18

TRHLIK, Nancy Marie. ■ 29928 #038-40-1972 L1975 **EM IM** *071 †20,16

TROTTER, Benjamin Robt. 35 BILL FRIES DR 29926 #045-01-1977 L1980 **IM** *020 †20

VANDERPOOL, Gerald Eugene. 25 HOSPITAL CENTER BLVD 29926 #020-02-1965 L1980 **A PDA** *071 †55,03

VANDERSLICE, Richard, Jr. 25 HOSPITAL CTR BLVD, STE 302 29926 #010-02-1990 L1996 **U** *020 †95

VON HOLLE, Frank E. 15 NORTHRIDGE DR 29926 #038-41-1953 L1953 **FM** *071 †18

WALLAND, Debra Keefe. 100 EXCHANGE ST, STE 200 29926 #045-48-1990 L1999 **OBG** *020 †30

WALSH, James Aloysius. ■ 29928 #041-02-1961 L1962 **R NM** *020 †80,28 ‡

WEISENBERGER, Brockton L. ■ 29928 #017-20-1957 L1957 **OM** *071 †70

WEISS, Paul E. ■ 29928 #025-01-1973 L2002 **NR DR** *071 †80,28

WESTMAAS, William John. 19 SHELTER COVE LN STE 204 29928 #025-01-1948 L1981 **P** *020 †75

WHITE, Stephen Robt. ■ 29926 #012-05-1968 L1994 **GS** *020 †85

WILLIAMS, John Robt. ■ 29926 #035-08-1944 L1947 **GP U** *071

WOLF, James Stuart. ■ 29926 #016-11-1961 L1966 **GS** *071 †85

WOOD, George Thos, III. 1555 FORDING ISLAND RD, STE C1 29926 #036-01-1959 L1975 **FM GS** *020 †85

YORK, Charles Clifford. ■ 29928 #047-06-1958 L1959 **R** *071 †80

YOUNG, Joseph Michael. ■ 29928 #649-01-1960 L1963 **IM OM** *071

ZITELLO, Philip J. 222 PEMBROKE DR BLDG C 29926 #038-44-1983 L1997 **AN PMM** *020 †05

HODGES – GREENWOOD

FOWLER, William Edward. 3410 COKESBURY RD, PIEDMONT FAMILY MEDICINE 29653 #036-08-1990 L1991 **FM** *020 †18

RILEY, Eustace David, IV. 3410 COKESBURY RD, PIEDMONT HEALTH GROUP LLC 29653 #001-02-1991 L1992 **FM** *020 †18

STONE, Camilla Robin. 3410 COKESBURY RD, PIEDMONT HEALTH GROUP LLC 29653 #012-01-1990 L1991 **FM** *020 †18

HOLLY HILL – ORANGEBURG

ARIAS, Andres Julio. ■ 29059 #308-02-1991 L2000 **PUD** *020 †20

BULL, Steven Farrell. PO BOX 188 29059 #045-01-1978 L1979 **FM** *020 †18

CULBERTSON, Frank L. 738 STATE ST 29059 #045-01-1951 L1951 **GP** *071

HILL, Holly Ann. 932 HOLLY, HOLLY HILL HEALTH CENTER 29059 #036-01-1987 *074

RHAME, Robt Whitfield, Jr. 1475 BUNCH FORD RD 29059 #045-01-1979 L1980 **FM** *020 †18

WAY, Charles Franklin. 922 HOLLY ST 29059 #045-01-1985 L1986 **FM** *020 †18

HOLLYWOOD – CHARLESTON

POWELL, Adam William. ■ 29449 #045-01-2008 *012

SMYTHE, Gwendolyn Swiggum. ■ 29449 #056-05-1952 L1955 **GP** *071

SMYTHE, Lowell J. ■ 29449 #056-05-1951 L1975 **PTH** *071 †50

HONEA PATH – ANDERSON

JENKINS, Marion Kent. 21 S SHIRLEY AVE 29654 #045-01-1998 L1999 **FM** *020 †18

SMITH, James Adam. 21 S SHIRLEY AVE 29654 #045-01-1981 L1982 **FM** *020 †18

INDIAN LAND – LANCASTER

THOMAS, William Lee. 7580 CHARLOTTE HWY, INDIAN LAND PRIMARY CARE 29707 #045-01-1971 L1972 **FM** *020 †18

INMAN – SPARTANBURG

CHILDES, Jeffrey Lee. 219 WATERFORD DR, MARY BLACK HOSPITAL 29349 #017-20-1987 L2005 **AN** *020 †05

DINA, Joy Ellen. 12230 ASHEVILLE HWY 29349 #051-04-1996 L1997 **FM** *020 †18

ESPOSITO, Patrick John. 12230 ASHEVILLE HWY 29349 #055-02-1986 L1987 **FM** *020 †18

FISHER, William Matthew. ■ 29349 #045-04-2005 **P** *012

GODENICK, Constance E. 12230 ASHEVILLE HWY 29349 #005-12-1982 L1989 **FM** *071 †18

ROP, Timothy Jon. 12230 ASHEVILLE HWY 29349 #025-12-1997 L1998 **FM** *020 †18

TAYLOR, Benjamin Thos. ■ 29349 #012-05-1966 L1973 **FM** *020 †18

IRMO – RICHLAND

ALDERSON, M Todd. 1 WELLNESS BLVD 29063 #017-20-1995 L2004 **CD** *020 †20

BEARD, John T, II. 1 WELLNESS BLVD 29063 #045-04-1982 L1983 **CD** *020 †20

BELL, Myron. 1 WELLNESS BLVD 29063 #035-01-1987 L1993 **CD IM** *020 †20

BERAHO, Joseph Byamugisha. ■ 29063 #905-01-1987 L2000 **IM** *020 †20

BRIDGERS, David Keith. 7430 COLLEGE ST 29063 #045-04-1997 L2002 **IM** *020

BROWNING, Rosalie E. 7430 COLLEGE ST 29063 #045-01-1979 L1980 **IM** *020 †20

BUTTERFIELD, Lee Owens. 1 WELLNESS BLVD 29063 #045-01-1987 L1993 **CD** *020 †20

DASGUPTA, Himadri. 1 WELLNESS BLVD 29063 #495-32-1986 L2000 **CD** *020 †20

DELPHIA, Robert E, Jr. 1 WELLNESS BLVD 29063 #019-02-1983 L1987 **CD** *020 †20

DEVLIN, Charlie Wayne. 1 WELLNESS BLVD 29063 #041-02-1984 L1985 **CD IM** *020 †20

DOPPALAPUDI, Uday Kiran. 7320 COLLEGE ST, UNIT 101 29063 #496-24-1995 L2003 **IM** *020

DOUGHERTY, Glen Noble, Jr. 1 WELLNESS BLVD 29063 #045-04-2000 L2006 **CD** *020 †20

EDELSON, Richard Adam. 1 WELLNESS BLVD 29063 #051-04-1991 L1998 **IM CD** *020 †20

EPPS, William Burton, Jr. 1 WELLNESS BLVD 29063 #038-06-1971 L1974 **CD IM** *020 †20

FOSTER, Michael Cameron. 1 WELLNESS BLVD 29063 #017-20-1980 L1986 **CD IM** *020 †20

FRAVEL, William James, Jr. 1846 DUTCH FORK RD 29063 #045-04-1993 **FM** *020 †18

GABRIEL, Joseph Nishan. 1 WELLNESS BLVD, STE 200 29063 #056-06-1999 L2000 **IM** *020 †20

GOTTIPATY, Venkateshwa K. 1 WELLNESS BLVD 29063 #012-05-1989 L2001 **CD** *020 †20

GRAINGER, Terry Aubrey. 1 WELLNESS BLVD 29063 #045-01-1987 L1993 **CD** *020 †20

GUNTER, Donald Nelson. PO BOX 1547 29063 #045-01-1974 L1976 **N IM** *020 †75

GURAM, Surbjinder Singh. 1 WELLNESS BLVD, STE 200 29063 #045-04-1983 L1984 **IM** *020 †20

HALL, Patrick Xavier. 1 WELLNESS BLVD 29063 #051-01-1983 L2001 **CD IM** *020 †20

HARDEN, Laurie Michell. ■ 29063 #011-04-2007 L2007 **P** *012

HARRISON, Rodney Vaughn. 1 WELLNESS BLVD 29063 #045-04-1991 L1992 **CD** *020 †20

HITE, Louis Carey. 7430 COLLEGE ST 29063 #045-01-1973 L1977 **IM FM** *020 †20,18

HONIG, Philip Chas. 1 WELLNESS BLVD, STE 200 29063 #048-04-1980 L1983 **GP** *072

IMPERIAL, Eva Angelie. 1 WELLNESS BLVD, STE 203 29063 #045-04-2000 L2001 **FM** *020 †18

KHOURY, Leon Jos, Jr. 1 WELLNESS BLVD 29063 #045-04-1985 L1986 **CD IM** *020 †20

KHOURY, Norma Marie. 1 WELLNESS BLVD 29063 #045-01-1983 L1984 **CD IM** *020 †20

KIGER, Robert Gary. 1 WELLNESS BLVD 29063 #047-05-1958 L1963 **CD IM** *020 †20

LEONCAVALLO, Anthony Jose. ■ 29063 #045-01-2008 *012

LIDE, Lanneau Durant. 1 WELLNESS BLVD 29063 #045-01-1976 L1981 **IC CD** *020 †20

LONE, Bashir Ahmad. 1 WELLNESS BLVD 29063 #495-51-1986 L2003 **CD IM** *020 †20 ‡

MAYSURIA, Himaxi Maganlal. 1 WELLNESS BLVD 29063 #368-01-1988 L1999 **CD** *020 †20

MC KAY, Scott Alexander. 1846 DUTCH FORK RD, RICHLAND MEMORIAL HOSPITAL 29063 #025-07-1996 L1997 **FM** *020 †18

METZ, Aleta Marie. ■ 29063 #045-04-2007 L2007 **P** *012

METZGER, Wayne Thompson. ■ 29063 #045-01-1973 L1975 **END IM** *050 †20

MILLS-FLOYD, Theresa R. 7437 COLLEGE ST STE 101, PALMETTO COSMETIC PROCEDUR 29063 #045-04-1999 L2001 **IM** *020 †20

MINHAS, Balbir Singh. 1 WELLNESS BLVD, STE 110 29063 #495-03-1980 L1998 **IM GE** *020 †20

MOATS, Leslie Mcarthur. 144 COVE CT 29063 #045-04-1996 L1997 **EM** *020 †16

MORTON, Samatha Steingold. ■ 29063 #036-08-2002 L2006 **OBG** *020

NICHOLS, Heather Ruthann. ■ 29063 #017-20-2007 L2007 **PD** *012

O'LEARY, Melinda Lengel. 7936 BROAD RIVER RD 29063 #047-05-1992 L1998 **PD** *020 †55

ORLANDINI, Mark Louis. 1 WELLNESS BLVD 29063 #016-11-1977 L1987 **CD IM** *020 †20

PATRICK, Elizabeth Lebel. 7430 COLLEGE ST, THREE RIVERS MEDICAL ASSOC 29063 #041-01-1993 L2002 **IM EM** *020 †20

PENMETSA, Ram G. 1 WELLNESS BLVD 29063 #495-45-1983 L2002 **CD IM** *020 †20

RENNER, Richard G. ■ 29063 #036-07-1944 L1947 **GP** *071

RICE, James R. 224 BONUCK RD, SAME 29063 #020-02-1965 L1969 **P** *020 †75

RICHARDSON, James Huger. 1 WELLNESS BLVD 29063 #045-01-1978 L1984 **CD** *020 †20

ROBINSON, Donald H. ■ 29063 #041-09-1945 L1965 **OM LM** *072 †70

SANTROCK, Robert Dale. 1013 LAKE MURRAY BLVD 29063 #055-01-1997 L2005 **ORS** *020 †40

SOLTYS, Mary Karen. 108 GLEN RIDGE CT 29063 #016-45-1980 L2001 **P** *020 †75

STEUDE, Philip Gregory. 1036 KINLEY RD 29063 #020-12-1972 L1975 **P CHP** *020 †75 ‡

STINGONE, Marc. ■ 29063 #033-05-1998 L2006 **GS** *100

WHELESS, James Elijah. ■ 29063 #036-05-1954 L1954 **IM** *071 †20

WHITAKER, Robert Tye. 7936 BROAD RIVER RD 29063 #045-04-1995 L1996 **PD** *020 †55

WILE, Charles Henry. ■ 29063 #010-01-1975 L1989 **EM** *020 †18

ZIMMERMANN, Paul A. 1 WELLNESS BLVD 29063 #035-15-1988 L2003 **CD** *020 †20

ISLE OF PALMS – CHARLESTON

ANDERSON, Robert M. ■ 29451 #045-01-1973 L1974 **OM GP** *020 †70

ARIAS-PANDEY, Ana Isabel. ■ 29451 #045-01-2008 *012

ARMSTRONG, Brian Athan. 17 23RD AVE 29451 #028-02-1988 L2008 **CD IM** *020 †20

BAIRD, John Mc Cowan. ■ 29451 #020-02-1953 L1954 **EM GP** *071 †18

BAKER, Elizabeth Lynne H. 52 MORGANS COVE DR, P O BOX 304 29451 #045-04-1986 L1988 **PD** *020 †55

DAVIDSON, Joseph. 13 LINKSIDE CT 29451 #026-04-1960 L1960 **DR NM** *071 †80

ELLIOTT, Larry Paul. ■ 29451 #047-06-1957 L1973 **CD DR** *030 †80

GOLDMAN, Juliet. ■ 29451 #011-04-1996 L2000 **P** *020

GRAZIANO, Joel R. ■ 29451 #035-06-1966 L1969 **ORS** *020 †40

HARROD, David Bidwell. ■ 29451 #024-01-1957 L1962 **GS** *071

JAMES, Joseph Davis. ■ 29451 #045-01-1954 L1954 **GP** *071

JOHNSON, Thomas Clayton. 200 PALM BLVD, IRAD, INC 29451 #012-01-1991 L1991 **DR** *020 †80

KIGER, James Robert. ■ 29451 #041-12-2006 L2006 **PD** *012

MALANEY, Kathleen Ruth. 1202 PALM BLVD STE A 29451 #041-07-1971 L1986 **EM FM** *020 †16,18

MANN, Douglas Lowell. 31 SAND DOLLAR DR, C/O DR GARY FINK 29451 #041-13-1979 L1986 **IM CD** *050 †20

MC ALHANY, Joseph C, Jr. 609 OCEAN BLVD 29451 #036-05-1966 L1969 **GS** *020 †85

MIMS, Schuyler Kathleen. ■ 29451 #045-01-2005 L2005 **PD** *012

NASO, Stephen J, Jr. ■ 29451 #561-20-1960 L1964 **HS GS** *071 †85

NELSON, James Hissom, Jr. ■ 29451 #035-19-1954 L2002 **OBG** *071 †30

NELSON, Noreen Architetto. ■ 29451 #024-05-1988 L2001 **OBG** *040 †30

NUCKOLS, William Andy. 16 EDGEWATER ALY 29451 #051-04-1970 L1995 **FM** *020 †18 ‡

PIENING, Ralph Bernard. ■ 29451 #028-34-1984 L1985 **EM IM** *020 †20

QUEENER, Carl Edward. 3 SANDWEDGE LN 29451 #020-02-1994 L1997 **EM** *020 †16

RANEY, Laurence Hunter. 28 42ND AVE 29451 #011-03-1983 L1984 **EM** *020 †16

REINHART, Gretchen Anne. ■ 29451 #041-12-2006 L2006 **OBG** *012

SCHACHTER, Jerome Miles. 1104 WILD DUNES OCEAN CLB 29451 #036-07-1956 L1956 **NS** *071 †25

SMITH, Mildred M R. ■ 29451 #041-13-1954 L1955 **OBG GS** *075
STEWART, Courtney Eileen. ■ 29451 #045-01-2007 L2007 **TY** *012
UHDE, Thomas Whitley. ■ 29451 #020-02-1975 L1976 **P PA** *050 †75
WOHLTMANN, Hulda J. ■ 29451 #045-01-1949 L1976 **DIA OS** *071 †55
YARBROUGH, Joseph Coleman. ■ 29451 #045-01-1959 L1963 **OPH** *071 †35

IVA — ANDERSON

CAYELLI, Stephen Daniel. PO BOX 267, 331 ANTREVILLE HWY 29655 #051-07-1995 L1998
FM *020 †18

JACKSON — AIKEN

WESTON, Paul D. 214 ATOMIC RD 29831 #010-03-1946 L1952 **AS GS** *020

JEFFERSON — CHESTERFIELD

GIBSON, Michael Jeremiah. 409 E CHURCH ST, SANDHILLS MEDICAL FOUNDATI 29718
#045-04-1993 L2000 **GPM GP** *020
OLATOSI, Akinwale O. 409 E CHURCH ST, SANDHILLS MEDICAL FOUNDATI 29718
#690-01-1989 L2001 **IM** *020 †20
POTLA, Madhu Sudhanrao. PO BOX 249, 409 E CHURCH ST 29718 #495-21-1981 L2004
FM *100 †18
QUADIR, Zafar Abdul. 409 E CHURCH ST, SANDHILLS MEDICAL FOUNDATI 29718
#496-38-1998 L2005 **PD** *020 †55

JOANNA — LAURENS

ARSCOTT, Allan Gordon. 102 N MAIN ST 29351 #065-01-1954 L1965 **AN** *020

JOHNS ISLAND — CHARLESTON

ABBAS, Jonathan Asif. ■ 29455 #012-01-2007 L2007 **IM** *012
AGUSTA, Victor Emanuel. ■ 29455 #035-45-1966 L1986 **U** *071 †95
ALLEN, James Crawford. ■ 29455 #023-07-1955 L1982 **IM ID** *030 †20
ANGERMEIER, Eric William. ■ 29455 #045-01-2007 L2007 **ORS** *012
BENSONHAVER, Charles L. ■ 29455 #005-12-1965 L2003 **P** *020 †75
BENZEL, John E. ■ 29455 #041-01-1959 L1960 **HEM** *071 †20
BERQUE, Stephen Michael. ■ 29455 #035-08-1960 **GE IM** *071 †20
BILKLEY, Evelyn O. ■ 29455 #012-01-2005 L2005 **IM** *012
BRATTON, Charles F. ■ 29455 #036-01-1994 L2005 **GS** *050
BRODERICK, Gearin E. 5497 STONOVIEW DR F 29455 #045-01-1988 L1997 **AN** *020 †05 ‡
BROWNE, Richard Thos. 12 KIAWAH BEACH DR 29455 #025-07-1963 L1964 **R NR** *071 †80
CORLEY, Malcolm Osbourne. 5079 CORAL REEF DR, COASTAL PLAINS PHYSICIANS 29455
#045-01-1968 L1968 **DR** *020 †80
COULTER, Benjamin Lee. ■ 29455 #036-05-2008 *012
DANIELS, William Creed. ■ 29455 #038-41-1969 L1970 **ORS** *071 †40
DICK, Andrew Edwin. ■ 29455 #016-11-2005 L2005 **AN** *012
ELIZABETH, Sharon. ■ 29455 #012-22-1991 L1992 **FM** *074 †18
EVANS, Monica Nicole. ■ 29455 #028-34-2004 L2004 **OPH** *012
FRENCH, John Wesley. ■ 29455 #045-01-2007 L2007 **GS** *012
GAYNOR, William B. ■ 29455 #041-13-1952 L1980 **PTH** *071 †50
GLEATON, Douglas Harold. ■ 29455 #045-01-2007 L2007 **GS** *012
GOMEZ DELGADO DE LA FLOR, . ■ 29455 #737-06-2001 L2006 **PCC** *012
GRAM, Cameron Mclean. ■ 29455 #036-08-2004 L2004 **PD** *012
GRIFFIN, E David. ■ 29455 #016-11-1952 L1953 **PD** *071 †55
KENNEDY, Shannon Anne. ■ 29455 #031-01-2002 L2004 **MPD** *100 †20
LENA, Jonathan Ross. ■ 29455 #051-07-2008 *012
LOBO, Valerie Marie. ■ 29455 #495-17-1973 L1976 **FM EM** *020
MALINOVSKY, Michael R. 130 GARDNERS CIR, STE 126 29455 #028-02-1969 L1992
IM *020 †20
MISHRA, Seema Lynn. 395 GREEN WINGED TEAL RD 29455 #045-04-1993 L2003 **FM** *020 †18
NAAS, Peter Alex. ■ 29455 #020-02-2007 L2007 **IM** *012
OBERHEU, Kenneth Harry. ■ 29455 #056-05-1961 L2001 **TS** *071 †85,90
PASTIS, Maritsa Cosmides. ■ 29455 #055-01-1966 L1967 **PD ON** *071 †55
PASTIS, Nicholas James. ■ 29455 #038-41-1965 L1966 **IM CD** *071 †20
PILLERS, Amanda Marie. ■ 29455 #016-11-2005 L2005 **GS** *012
SCHULTZ, Elizabeth Fraser. ■ 29455 #035-45-1997 L1999 **BBK** *100 †50
SEIGNIOUS, David Wayne. 3312 MAYBANK HWY, STE A 29455 #045-01-1984 L1987
IM *020 †20
SEMMENS, James P. ■ 29455 #056-06-1943 L1971 **OBG OS** *072 †30
SHAPIRO, Harvey Harris. 2837 AUGUST RD 29455 #010-01-1973 L1979 **P** *020 †75
SHEPPE, Natalee Marie. ■ 29455 #045-01-2007 L2007 **PD** *012
SPENO, Leo Anthony. ■ 29455 #007-02-1962 L1993 **PD** *071 †55
STEWART, Scott Richard. ■ 29455 #025-12-2006 L2006 **AN** *012
VAN DERWERKER, Greg A. ■ 29455 #012-05-1977 L1982 **PTH** *071 †50
WARREN, Michael Forrester. 3312 MAYBANK HWY STE B 29455 #045-01-1984 L1989
D GS *020
YACOB, Usama Abdul-Razak. ■ 29455 #528-01-1958 L1972 **GP CLP** *020 †50
ZAMORA, Benjamin Ocampo. 3629 LOGGERHEAD CT, SEABROOK ISLAND 29455
#748-01-1959 L1970 **GS** *020 †85
ZHADKEVICH, Alexei. ■ 29455 #045-01-2008 *012

JOHNSONVILLE — FLORENCE

FAILE, Kenneth Mitchell. 355 S GEORGETOWN HWY, MC LEOD FAMILY MEDICINE CT 29555
#045-01-1996 L1997 **FM** *020 †18
MOON, David Wm. 625 S GEORGETOWN HWY 29555 #045-01-1979 L1980 **FM** *020 †18

JOHNSTON — EDGEFIELD

GARRISON, James Saml. ■ 29832 #045-01-1943 L1944 **FM** *071
MORGAN, Walter Hugh. 801 MOBLEY ST 29832 #045-01-1977 L1978 **FM** *071 †18

KERSHAW — LANCASTER

ANDERSON, Grover Lindsay. ■ 29067 #045-01-1960 **NS** *071 †25
BLACKWELL, Danny Reese. ■ 29067 #045-01-1957 L1957 **OM FM** *020
BREWER, John Mickle, Jr. 206 S MATSON ST # 208 29067 #036-07-1954 L1967 **D A** *020
KOON, James Fletcher. 206 S MATSON ST, SUMMERTON FAMILY MEDICINE 29067
#045-01-1989 L1996 **FM** *020 †18
ZEEDICK, John Francis I. 4151 OLD GEORGETOWN RD W 29067 #041-12-1954 L1983
AN PUD *020 †05 ‡

KIAWAH ISLAND — CHARLESTON

BOOK, Michael Raymond. 5480 SEA FOREST DR 29455 #036-07-1989 L1995 **FM** *020 †18
BYER, James Fred. 3 SUNDOWN BND 29455 #055-01-1974 L1976 **IM** *020 †20
GREAVES, Robert Clive. 1226 PINE SISKIN CT, GREENSLAKE COTTAGES 29455
#045-01-1997 L2005 **EM** *020 †16
KINSEY, Norman Frank. ■ 29455 #045-01-1959 L1959 **R DR** *020
SMALLEY, J Bryan. ■ 29455 #047-06-1959 L1960 **ORS** *071 †40
VREEDE, Anton A. ■ 29455 #660-01-1957 L1960 **VS GS** *071 †85

KINGSTREE — WILLIAMSBURG

ALLEN, Raymond Keels. 512 NELSON BLVD, STE 200 29556 #045-01-1982 L1983 **FM** *020 †18
BONAPARTE, Joel Winston. 520 THURGOOD MARSHALL HWY, STE B 29556
#412-02-1993 L2001 **NPM** *020 †55
CARSON, Mildred Frances. 520 THURGOOD MARSHALL HWY, STE B 29556
#020-02-2003 L2006 **PD** *100
FLOYD, Harry Wells. 500 THURGOOD MARSHALL HWY 29556 #045-01-1968 L1968 **GP** *020
GADEGBEKU, Polycarp K. 505 THURGOOD MARSHALL HWY 29556 #165-04-1967 L1984
FM *020
LAMPKIN, Emmett Michael. 310 E MAIN ST 29556 #045-01-1977 L1978 **P** *020 †75
MOORE, Blake Harrison. 500 THURGOOD MARSHALL HWY, STES A-C 29556
#033-05-1990 L2000 **GS** *020 †85
MUNFORD, Loreli. 520 THURGOOD MARSHALL HWY, BLACK RIVER HEALTH 29556
#025-07-2001 L2009 **MPD** *100
OBEIDOU, Bashar. 500 NELSON BLVD 29556 #875-01-1996 L2003 **IM** *020 †20
RIMKUS, Gilbertas. 402 NELSON BLVD, STE 100 29556 #913-49-1993 L2002 **GS** *020 †85
SPRINGLE, Kevin Anthony. 520 THURGOOD MARSHALL HWY, STE B 29556
#045-01-2000 L2001 **PD** *020 †55
TOWNSEND, Jessica Damienn. 520 THURGOOD MARSHALL HWY, STE B 29556
#045-01-2004 L2004 **FM** *020 †18
TREFNY, Frank Albert. 500 THURGOOD MARSHALL HWY, STE H 29556 #051-04-1964 L1974
FM PTH *020 †50

LADSON — DORCHESTER

COKER, Mark Anthony. 3601 LADSON RD, STE 100 29456 #045-01-1979 L1980 **ICE** *020 †20
DIMITROVA-KOUTLEVA, Dobrin. ■ 29456 #036-01-2005 L2006 **DR** *012
FAABERG, Jeffrey Evan. 549 COLLEGE PARK RD STE D, CROWFIELD PAIN CENTER 29456
#026-04-1980 L1991 **AN PMM** *020 †05
KENNEDY, Chris Lane. 3601 LADSON RD, STE 100 29456 #045-04-1992 L1999 **CD** *020 †20
MATAOSKY, Mark Allen. 3601 LADSON RD STE 100 29456 #010-02-1990 L2004 **CD** *020 †20
SIKORSKI, Cynthia Susan. 201 LOBLOLLY CIR 29456 #041-02-1994 L2002 **IM** *020 †20
TALLENT, Cynthia Lee. ■ 29456 #045-01-2007 **OBG** *012
VON LEHE, Diedreich P, Jr. 3601 LADSON RD, STE 100 29456 #045-01-1966 L1966
CD *020 †20

LAKE CITY — FLORENCE

ASKINS, Stephen Wofford. 258 N RON MCNAIR BLVD, LAKE CITY COMMUNITY HOSPIT 29560
#045-01-2003 L2004 **FM** *020 †18
ATKINSON, Ernest M. 325 MERCY ST, PEE DEE FAMILY PRACTICE 29560 #045-01-1990 L1991
FM *020 †18
BROWN, Morris Edward, III. 901 N MATTHEWS RD, LAKE CITY FAMILY MEDICINE, 29560
#051-07-1991 L1994 **FM** *020 †18
DE CAMPS, Daniel Edward. 325 MERCY ST, PEE DEE FAMILY PRACTICE 29560
#045-01-1982 L1983 **FM** *020 †18
ELLIS, Richard Kevin. 330 MERCY ST, PALMETTO PRIMARY CARE 29560 #045-01-1998 L1999
FM *020 †18
FAM, Nabil Abdalla. 324 MERCY ST 29560 #915-02-1969 L1977 **GS** *020
FOWLER, Marion S, Jr. 101 JOHN ST 29560 #051-04-1963 L1965 **GP** *020
FOWLER, Marion S, III. 101 JOHN ST, LAKE CITY MEDICAL CLINIC 29560
#045-01-1982 L1983 *020
GHERAIBEH, Jafer Naser. 258 N RON MCNAIR BLVD 29560 #915-03-1971 L1981
ORS *020 †40 ‡
GRAHAM, Toney, Jr. 29560 #035-01-1976 L1978 **PD FM** *020
GRIGGS, William Clark. 258 N RON MCNAIR BLVD, CAROLINAS HOSP SYS 29560
#045-01-1984 L1985 **FM EM** *020 †18
LAMB, Benjamin Wade. 330 MERCY ST 29560 #045-04-2000 L2001 **FM** *020 †18 ‡
MIMS, Albert Durant. 325 MERCY ST, PEE DEE FAMILY PRACTICE 29560 #045-01-1978 L1979
FM *020 †18
SINGH, Navdeep K. 276 N RON MCNAIR BLVD 29560 #496-01-1995 L2000 **FM** *020 †18
THOMY, James Jos. 210 LAKE DALE AVE BOX 1346 29560 #045-01-1975 **EM FM** *020
WALTMANN, Brian Keith. 217 DOGWOOD LN 29560 #045-01-1979 L1980 **AN PME** *020 †05

LAMAR – DARLINGTON

CARMICHAEL, Martin F. 105 N RAILROAD AVE 29069 #045-01-1983 L1984 **FM** *020 †18
GRIFFIN, Sidney Till. PO BOX 305 29069 #045-01-1959 L1959 **FM** *020 †18
WHITAKER, Halford Snyder. 641 CYPRESS CEMETARY RD 29069 #047-06-1956 L1957
  FM FPG *020 †16,18,55

LANCASTER – LANCASTER

AKHTAR, Muhammad Ishtiaq. 838 W MEETING ST, ASSOCIATES AT MEDICAL 29720
  #704-16-1991 L2006 **N** *020 †75 ‡
AMBATI, Saritha. 901 W MEETING ST, STE 205 29720 #495-21-1999 L2005 **PD** *020
AMIN, Vimal P. 834 W MEETING ST, STE G 29720 #495-23-1982 L1999 **GE** *020 †20
ANSARI, Amir Zia. 800 W MEETING ST 29720 #016-42-2000 L2003 **FM** *020 ‡
BAKER, Kenneth John. 1025 W MEETING ST STE 204 29720 #051-04-1984 L2006
  OBG NTR *020 †30
BELL, Ella Cooper. ■ 29721 #041-07-1947 L1949 **IM** *071 †20
BIOLETTI, John James. 141 SHERWOOD CIR 29720 #023-07-1954 L1955 **OBG** *020 †30
BLACK, Kristin Shannon. 820 W MEETING ST, NEW DAY FAMILY PRACTICE 29720
  #035-47-1998 L2001 **FM** *020 †18 ‡
BOSTICK, Anthony Lawrence. 800 W MEETING ST 29720 #010-03-1990 L1994 **EM** *020 †16
BOYKIN, James Alexander. 405 E GAY ST 29720 #010-03-1960 L1963 **FM GP** *071
CARROLL, Thomas Beville, III. 800 W MEETING ST 29720 #045-01-1964 L1964 **R** *071 †80
CATOE, Sandra V Clyburn. PO BOX 817, LANCASTER HEALTH DEPT 29721 #045-01-1963 L1963
  PHP *030 †55
CIMINELLI, Mark Anthony. 1029 W MEETING ST, CAROLINA HEART SPECIALIST 29720
  #422-01-1982 L1997 **CD IM** *020 †20
CORNELIUS, Deanna Guith. 1906 HIGHWAY 521 BYP S, CATAWBA COMM MENTAL
  HEALTH 29720 #056-06-1988 L1989 **P** *020 †75
CRUZ, Carmina Congco. 838 W MEETING ST, STE A 29720 #748-02-1990 L1998 **PN** *020 †55
DAVID, George Lamply, Jr. 1033 W MEETING ST 29720 #045-01-1959 L1959 **GS TS** *020 †85
DAYRIT, Francis M. 834 W MEETING ST, STE H 29720 #748-02-1990 L1998 **PCC** *020 †20
DUKE, William Waters. 800 W MEETING ST 29720 #041-01-1961 L1961 **FM** *020 †18,20
EDWARDS, Robert Malcolm. 1240 COLONIAL COMMONS CT 29720 #045-04-1984 L1988
  OPH *020 †35 ‡
ELLIS, Emily Ann. 1228 COLONIAL COMMONS CT 29720 #045-01-2001 L2002 **FM** *020
EZELL, Terry Hugh. 1077A W MEETING ST, CAROLINA UROLOGY CENTER 29720
  #045-01-1990 L1995 **U** *020 †95
FITZPATRICK, Robt Edward. 800 W MEETING ST 29720 #012-01-1976 L1980 **DR** *020 †80
FRIEDRICH, Thomas Charles. 1228 COLONIAL COMMONS CT 29720 #017-20-1979 L1994
  ORS *020 †40
FURSE, James Ardis, Jr. 1228 COLONIAL COMMONS CT, BARNETT FAMILY PRACTICE
  GR 29720 #045-01-1971 L1973 **FM AM** *020 †18
GOINS, Wendell A. 1010 N WOODLAND DR 29720 #010-03-1979 L1994 **GS CCS** *020 †18,85
GREEN, Christine D. 838 W MEETING ST, STE A 29720 #028-46-1995 L1998 **PD** *020 †55
GRUHN, William Bryant. 1228 COLONIAL COMMONS CT, CAROLINA BONE & JOINT, PA 29720
  #032-01-1974 L1979 **RHU IM** *020 †20
HELWIG, Jane T. 1025 W MEETING ST STE 204 29720 #036-01-1992 L2006 **OBG** *020 †30
HOLCOMBE, Kevin Westray. 800 W MEETING ST, SPRINGS MEMORIAL HOSPITAL 29720
  #011-03-1998 L1999 **EM FM** *020 †18
HORTON, James P, Jr. ■ 29720 #045-01-1953 L1953 **GP** *071
JAMES, W Scott. 1201 COLONIAL COMMONS CT 29720 #036-07-1957 L1957 **PD** *071 †55
JOHNSON, R Duren, Jr. 800 W MEETING ST 29720 #045-01-1976 L1977 **PTH** *020 †50 ‡
JONES, Carson R. ■ 29720 #048-02-1949 L1956 **R** *020
KASHYAP, Sona Shrikant. 834 W MEETING ST, STE B 29720 #495-76-1998 L2004 **END** *020 †20
KHAN, Muhammad Haroon. 800 W MEETING ST, SPRINGS MEMORIAL HOSPITAL 29720
  #704-09-1997 L2007 **IM** *020 †20
KHANDEKAR, Suresh. 834 W MEETING ST, STE G 29720 #495-34-1978 L2006 **IM** *020 †20
KIMBRELL, Fred Michael. 201 W MEETING ST, STE A 29720 #045-01-1975 **IM** *020 †20
KNIGHT, Marvin Eugene. 201 W MEETING ST STE A, PALMETTO TRICOUNTY INTERNA 29720
  #045-01-2004 L2006 **IM** *020 †20
KUMAR, Amrendra. 1130 HIGHWAY 9 BYP W 29720 #495-15-1997 L2006 **FM** *020 †18
KWON, Anthony Jun. 1228 COLONIAL COMMONS CT 29720 #051-01-2000 L2004 **ORS** *020
LALLA, Sunil Vishin. 1033 W MEETING ST 29720 #012-05-1988 L1995 **GS** *020 †85
LANGDON, Mark Ross. 800 W MEETING ST 29720 #045-01-1975 L1976 **R** *020 †80
LE ROY, Albert Grady, Jr. 1077A W MEETING ST 29720 #012-01-1965 L1973 **U** *020 †95
LEWIS, William David. ■ 29720 #041-09-1957 L1983 **AN OS** *020 †05
LIU, James Kuoli. 1228 COLONIAL COMMONS CT, STE 500 29720 #021-06-1996 L2003
  CD *020 †20
LIVINGSTON, Wilbur D, Jr. 1077A W MEETING ST, CAROLINA UROLOGY CENTER 29720
  #045-01-1975 L1981 **U** *020 †95
MAGURA, Christian Eugen. 1077A W MEETING ST, CAROLINA UROLOGY CENTER 29720
  #020-12-1977 L1978 **U EM** *020 †95
MANDELL, Howard. 838 W MEETING ST, ASSOCIATES AT MEDICAL 29720 #062-01-1981 L1992
  N *020 †75
MANTE, Ebenezer Yaw Obeng. 834 W MEETING ST STE C, MANTE PEDIATRICS 29720
  #412-01-1997 L2007 **PD** *020 †55
MATTHEWS, Curtis J, Jr. 1077A W MEETING ST, CAROLINA UROLOGY CENTER 29720
  #047-06-1986 L1991 **U** *020 †95
MC DOW, William L. 800 W MEETING ST 29720 #045-01-1951 L1951 **GP** *071
MORENO-HUSSEY, Sandra K. 838 W MEETING ST STE A 29720 #748-11-1991 L2002 **PD** *020
MORRIS, William Arthur. 1228 COLONIAL COMMONS CT 29720 #021-06-1989 L1992
  FM *020 †18
NANTAIS, Robert P. 1228 COLONIAL COMMONS CT 29720 #025-07-1987 L2007 **ORS** *020 †40
NATHWANI, Niyati Anand. 902 W MEETING ST, CAROLINA BLOOD & CANCER CA 29720
  #496-38-2000 L2006 **HEM** *100
NEUMAN, J Christopher. 800 W MEETING ST 29720 #051-04-1992 L1998 **EM** *020 †20,16
NUSZ, Kevin John. 1240 COLONIAL COMMONS CT, THE EYE & LASER CENTER 29720
  #023-07-2002 L2007 **OPH** *020
PALMER, David Bartow. ■ 29720 #035-01-1954 L1973 **P** *071 †75
PERERA, Menerig Nimal. 838 W MEETING ST, STE H 29720 #220-01-1976 L1997 **FM** *020
ROBERTS, James Wayne. 1228 COLONIAL COMMONS CT, STE 500 29720 #035-01-1984 L1998
  CD *020 †20

SCOTT, Todd Andrew. 1240 COLONIAL COMMONS CT, LANCASTER EYE CLINIC, P.A. 29720
  #038-43-1991 L1995 **OPH** *020 †35 ‡
SHAH, Amit. 201 W MEETING ST STE A 29720 #495-76-1984 L1998 **ON** *020 †20
SHAH, Deepak B. 1029 W MEETING ST, CAROLINA HEART SPECIALISTS 29720
  #495-23-1979 L1996 **CD IM** *020 †20
SHAH, Jay Nareshchandra. 800 W MEETING ST 29720 #495-76-1996 L2005 **IM** *020 †20 ‡
SHAH, Vipul B. 1029 W MEETING ST, CAROLINA HEART SPECIALIST 29720 #495-23-1984 L2003
  IC CD *020 †20
SHUGOLL, Richard Alan. 1228 COLONIAL COMMONS CT, STE 500 29720 #010-02-1984 L1990
  CD IM *020 †20
SLOTA, Paul Andrew. 1029 W MEETING ST, CAROLINA HEART SPECIALIST 29720
  #041-02-1988 L1996 **IC CD** *020 †20
SMITH, Christopher Atkins. 1228 COLONIAL COMMONS CT 29720 #010-02-1996 L1999
  FM *020 †18
STILL, Roy Allen. ■ 29720 #045-01-1971 L1972 **FM** *071 †18
STORY, Frances Ann. 1240 COLONIAL COMMONS CT 29720 #036-05-1978 L2004
  OPH *020 †35 ‡
STORY, John Walter. 209 S WYLIE ST 29720 #036-05-1978 L1979 **OPH** *020 †35
THOMPSON, Bobby G, Jr. 800 W MEETING ST 29720 #045-01-1990 L1991 **PTH** *020 †50
TIEDT, Douglas. 1370 W MEETING ST 29720 #011-04-1980 L1987 **OBG** *020 †30 ‡
TOWNSEND, Richard Eugene. 838 W MEETING ST STE F, PALMETTO PREFERRED
  OB/GYN 29720 #038-41-1973 L1985 **OBG FM** *020 †18,30 ‡
UMEH, Uchenna Lizmay. 901 W MEETING ST STE 205, CHILDREN FIRST MED CTR 29720
  #690-03-1991 L1999 **PD** *020 †55
VANCLEEFF, Sander. 1228 COLONIAL COMMONS CT, STE 500 29720 #041-02-1990 L1993
  CD *020 †20
VELASCO TRUJILLO, Juan Ca. 800 W MEETING ST, SPRINGS MEMORIAL HOSPITAL 29720
  #264-08-1998 L2007 **IM** *020 †20
WASHINGTON, Edward Martin. 1228 COLONIAL COMMONS CT 29720 #035-09-1976 L1994
  FM OS *020 †05,18
WEAVER, Tommy Lawrence. 800 W MEETING ST 29720 #045-01-1979 L1982
  DR FM *020 †18,80
WEBSTER, Julie Scott. 800 W MEETING ST 29720 #012-01-1992 L1997 **DR** *020 †80
WESCOAT, Richard Yeadon. 800 W MEETING ST 29720 #045-01-1947 **FM** *071 †18
WILLIAMSON, Christie R. 1906 HIGHWAY 521 BYP S, LANCASTER MHC 29720
  #045-04-1994 L1997 **P** *020 †75
WOODBURY, Lee Vernon. ■ 29720 #045-01-1977 L1981 **IM** *030
WOZNIAK, Robert. 834 W MEETING ST, STE B 29720 #759-01-1989 L1999 **END** *020 †20
WRIGHT, David Kenneth. 1077A W MEETING ST, CAROLINA UROLOGY CENTER 29720
  #012-01-1993 L1994 **U** *020 †95
ZHANG, Quanwei. 838 W MEETING ST, ASSOCIATES AT MEDICAL 29720 #243-70-1985 L2006
  CN *020 †75

LANDRUM – SPARTANBURG

BRATTON, Jack Lee. ■ 29356 #017-20-1960 L1960 **OM CD** *071
BRIDGES, Kimberly Lynn. 133 N HOWARD AVE 29356 #045-04-1986 L1987 **FM** *020 †18
BUCHANAN, Paul. ■ 29356 #017-20-1956 L1957 **AM** *071
COLLINS, Chester C, Jr. ■ 29356 #023-01-1965 L1969 **PD** *071 †55
DASHIELL, Thos Irwin, Jr. 1504 E RUTHERFORD ST, BLUE RIDGE MEDICAL ASSOCIA 29356
  #045-01-1981 L1986 **EM FM** *020 †16,18 ‡
DE WOLF, June E. ■ 29356 #016-11-1951 L1953 **GP** *071
GRIST, James Donald. 108 W RUTHERFORD ST, LANDRUM FMLY HLTH CARE CTR 29356
  #012-01-1974 L1975 **FM** *020 †18
MC CUEN, William Garrison. 409 HIGHWAY 101 29356 #036-05-1954 L1955 **IM GP** *020
PADGETT, Edwin Allen. 133 N HOWARD AVE 29356 #045-04-1996 L1997 **FM** *020 †18
ROZEMA, Theodore C. 1000 E RUTHERFORD ST 29356 #016-06-1960 L1963 **GPM GP** *020
STALTER, Galen Sherl. 719 S HOWARD AVE 29356 #017-20-1973 L1974 **EM** *020
STARLING, Wanda J. 1014 S BLACKSTOCK RD 29356 #045-01-1987 L1988 **FM** *020 †18

LATTA – DILLON

GEORGE, Percy Adams. ■ 29565 #045-01-1970 L1984 **IM** *071 †20
HARTER, Loren Donald. 108A E MAIN ST, COMMUNITY MEDICAL CENTER O 29565
  #041-09-1986 L2003 **FM ADL** *020 †18

LAURENS – LAURENS

BROWN, Cecil Yates. 314 W FARLEY AVE 29360 #045-01-1972 L1973 **FM** *020 †18 ‡
BROWNLEE, Catherine J. 209 LUCAS AVE 29360 #045-01-1987 L1988 **FM** *020 †18
CARLES, Javier Enrique. 106 PARKVIEW DR, LAURENS FAMILY PRACTICE 29360
  #045-04-1998 L2001 **FM** *020 †18
ECLAVEA, Paul Borja. ■ 29360 #016-42-1991 L1997 **AN** *020 †05
LOVE, George Newton. ■ 29360 #017-20-1939 L1939 **AN** *071 †05
NEW, Kimberly Diane. ■ 29360 #012-22-1999 L2003 **OBG** *020 †30

LEESVILLE – LEXINGTON

CROUT, Linda J. 338 E COLUMBIA AVE STE E, RIDGE PEDIATRIC AND ADOLES 29070
  #045-04-1985 L1986 **PD** *020 †55 ‡
DUNBAR, Cp. PO BOX 3608, 608 E COLUMBIA AVE 29070 #045-04-1983 L1984 **FM** *020 †18
GUNTER, Gariane. ■ 29070 #045-04-2006 L2006 **P** *012
HOSSLER, Janice Roberts. 338 E COLUMBIA AVE, STE C 29070 #036-01-1984 L1985
  FM *020 †18
RISINGER, Patricia Lucas. 6614 AUGUSTA HWY, THE PEDIATRIC CARE CTR LLC 29070
  #045-01-1997 L1999 **PD** *020 †55
SPEAKS, William R. 336 E COLUMBIA AVE 29070 #045-01-1951 L1951 **GP** *071

LEXINGTON – LEXINGTON

BATES, Lillie Edwards. 346 W BUTLER ST, LEXINGTON PEDIATRICS PRACT 29072
  #045-01-1990 L1991 **PD** *020 †55

BECKHAM, David R, Jr. ■ 29071 #045-01-1962 L1962 **AN** *071

BENNETT, William Neville. ■ 29072 #045-01-1964 **GP EM** *020

BLACK, Wayne Stephen. 2525 AUGUSTA HWY 29072 #045-01-1973 L1974 **GP** *020

BLEDSOE, Horace Wm, Jr. 811 W MAIN ST, STE 207 29072 #045-01-1977 L1978 **FM** *020 †18

BOLET, Celso Goicoechea. ■ 29072 #847-06-1972 L1977 **P** *020 †55

BOST, Misty Price. 811 W MAIN ST #020-02-2004 L2004 **IM** *020 †20

BOUKNIGHT, Anna Lee. 157 CORLEY MILL RD 29072 #048-14-1994 L2000 **OTO** *020 †45

BOYER, Stacie Jill. 811 W MAIN ST, STE 207 29072 #036-08-1997 L2004 **FM** *020 †18

BRAGDON, William H, Jr. 104 EVERLEIGH CT 29072 #045-04-1991 L1993 **P GP** *020 †75

BREARLEY, William Dubose. 811 W MAIN ST, STE 204 29072 #045-01-1976 L1977 **FM** *020 †18

CARROLL, Vernon Scott. ■ 29072 #045-04-1993 L1994 **EM** *020 †18

CARTER, Dee H. 214 OLD CHAPIN RD 29072 #045-04-1997 L1998 **FM** *020 †18

CHAUHAN, Jaswinder Tony. 811 W MAIN ST, LCHSD, INC. DBA LMC LEXING 29072 #665-02-2000 L2004 **FM** *020 †18

CHERRY, Merrie Anna. 212 PALMETTO PARK BLVD 29072 #017-20-1996 L2000 **P** *075

CHILLAG, Kim John. 4721A SUNSET BLVD 29072 #055-01-1979 L1985 **ORS OS** *020 †40

CLEMENZ, Frederick Wayne. 334 OLD CHAPIN RD, # 2 29072 #017-20-1960 L1969 **GS AM** *020 †85

COHEN, Dennis Allen. 1316 N LAKE DR, ADOLESCENCE MEDICINE 29072 #038-40-1970 L1975 **PD** *020 †55

COPE, Bruce Kevin. 4568 SUNSET BLVD 29072 #045-04-1997 L1998 **PD** *020 †55

CROSSWELL, Hal Holland. 100 PALMETTO PARK BLVD 29072 #045-01-1992 L1995 **OPH** *020

DACUS, William Scott. 122 POWELL DR 29072 #051-01-1986 L1987 **FM** *020 †18

DE LEON, Merry Ann. ■ 29072 #038-45-1994 L2003 **P** *020 †75

DEWAR, James Baker. 1404 W MAIN ST, STE A 29072 #045-04-1996 L1997 **PD** *020 †55

DURKIN, Martin Walter. 304 CAROLA LN 29072 #005-12-1973 L1986 **N PHP** *020 †75,70

ELTON, Donald Robt. 108 PALMETTO PARK BLVD, STE C 29072 #045-01-1987 L1988 **PUD IM** *020

ESPINOZA, Paul Manuel. 4721 SUNSET BLVD, STE D 29072 #045-04-1997 L1998 **PHL FM** *020 †18

EVANS, Victor Shaw, III. 305 PALMETTO PARK BLVD 29072 #045-01-1992 L1997 **CHP** *020 †75

FELMLY, William Tallman. 4721A SUNSET BLVD 29072 #045-01-1991 L1992 **ORS GS** *020 †40

FELTON, Richard J. 811 W MAIN ST, STE 206 29072 #039-01-1986 L1992 **GS** *020 †85

FLOCKE, Kathleen Michelle. 247 COLUMBIA AVE 29072 #035-03-2002 L2003 **FM** *020 †18

FULTON, David Brian. 4721A SUNSET BLVD 29072 #038-41-1993 L1999 **HS** *020 †40

GARDE, Vasant L R. 408 TWO NOTCH RD 29073 #495-34-1961 L1981 **GS VS** *020 †85

GILES, William Carey. 157 CORLEY MILL RD 29072 #045-01-1987 L1988 **PDO FPS** *020 †45

GOING, Jacquelyn Almeda. 157 CORLEY MILL RD 29072 #021-01-1976 L1977 **OTO** *020 †45

GOLAY, John Edward. 811 W MAIN ST STE 207 29072 #055-01-1977 L1979 **FM** *020 †18

GREEN, James Leo, Jr. ■ 29072 #036-07-1964 L1972 **PM** *071 †60

GRUBBS, James Aaron. ■ 29072 #045-01-2008 †012

GUYTON, Richard Kyle. 448 OLD CHEROKEE RD, PRMH - PEDIATRICS 29072 #045-01-2004 L2004 **PD** *100 †55

HAHN, Dora Edith. ■ 29073 #004-01-1971 L1972 **P** *020

HARMON, Charles Wm. 723 S LAKE DR 29072 #045-01-1972 L1973 **GS** *020 †85

HATFIELD, Sonya Renee. 1404 W MAIN ST, STE A 29072 #045-04-1998 L2000 **PD** *020 †55

HAYES, Julian. 116 SCOTLAND DR, STRAND REGIONAL SPECIALTY 29072 #012-01-1981 L1986 **N** *020

HERPST, Sally Louise. 811 W MAIN ST 29072 #041-02-1978 L1992 **EM OM** *020 †16

HILL, Frank Costigan. 157 CORLEY MILL RD 29072 #007-01-1983 L1984 **NO** *020 †45

HOLMES, S Wendell, Jr. 4721A SUNSET BLVD 29072 #045-04-1991 L1992 **ORS** *020 †40

HUGHES, Paul James. 412 KENWOOD DR 29072 #041-09-1984 L1985 **FM** *062 †18

JOHNSON, Carl Allen. 108 PALMETTO PARK BLVD, STE C 29072 #045-01-1975 L1984 **D DS** *020 †55,15

JONES, Robert Omega. ■ 29072 #045-01-1986 L2004 **PTH** *020 †50

KANITKAR, Kunal Datta. 340 W BUTLER ST 29072 #047-05-2000 L2000 **OPH** *020 †35

KEEFE, Leslie Dargan. 811 W MAIN ST, STE 204 29072 #045-04-2001 L2003 **FM** *020

KEISLER, Mark Sanford. 340 W BUTLER ST 29072 #045-01-1983 L1989 **OPH** *020 †35

KING, Jonathan D. 157 CORLEY MILL RD 29072 #011-03-1988 L1997 **OTO HNS** *020 †45

KINGERY, David Redding. 811 W MAIN ST 29072 #011-03-1980 L2003 **OSM ORS** *020 †40

KISTENEFF, Elvira. ■ 29071 #043-01-1982 L1989 **IM** *020 †20

KORMAN, William Taylor. 122 POWELL DR 29072 #045-01-2000 L2001 **FM** *020 †18

LAMB, David Hinkle. 811 E MAIN ST 29072 #001-02-1983 L1989 **U** *020 †95

LAMBERT, Elizabeth Sargen. ■ 29073 #045-04-2004 L2004 **OBG** *012

LOBEL, Keith Douglas. 5535 PLATT SPRINGS RD, LEXINGTON FAMILY PRACTICE 29073 #045-01-2000 L2001 **FM** *020 †18

LOCKE, Mark Douglas. 4721A SUNSET BLVD 29072 #038-06-1991 L1997 **ORS** *020 †40

LUBEROFF, Douglas Edward. 109 VISTA OAKS DR, # C 29072 #001-02-1976 L1979 **PD** *020 †55

LUNDVALL, Kathleen M. ■ 29072 #020-02-1990 L1993 **P** *020 †75

LYLE, David Pledger. 122 POWELL DR 29072 #036-05-1977 L1978 **FM IMG** *020 †18

MANLEY, Edwin, Jr. ■ 29072 #036-05-2007 †012

MARTIN, Henry. 122 POWELL DR 29072 #045-01-1973 L1975 **FM** *020 †18

MATHIAS, Elizabeth Fisher. 811 W MAIN ST, STE 209 29072 #045-04-1996 L1997 **IM** *020 †20

MC BRIDE, Jan Lynn. 811 W MAIN ST, LEXINGTON MEDICAL CENTER 29072 #011-03-1984 L2005 **FM** *020 †18 ‡

MC CARTT, Leah Marie. 305 PALMETTO PARK BLVD, CHILD AND ADOLESCENT SERVI 29072 #045-04-1996 L1997 **CHP** *020 †75

MC CORD, Carl William. 811 W MAIN ST, LEXINGTON MEDICAL CENTER U 29072 #045-01-1995 L1996 **FM** *020 †18

MC FADDEN, Earl B, Jr. 4721A SUNSET BLVD 29072 #045-01-1982 L1983 **ORS HS** *020 †40

MC KAY, John Gregory. 206 CIRCLEVIEW DR 29072 #020-12-1982 L1987 **NPM PD** *020 †55 ‡

MILLWOOD, Charles Edward. 4721 SUNSET BLVD, STE D 29072 #045-04-1998 L2000 **FM** *020 †18

MODZELEWSKI, Joseph R, Jr. ■ 29072 #045-04-1992 L1997 **PTH** *020 †50

MUSTIAN, Vernon Martin. ■ 29072 #036-05-1958 L1962 **N** *020

NAIRN, Dana Mairi. 811 W MAIN ST, STE 209 29072 #045-04-1998 L1999 **IM** *020 †20

NOOJIN, Frank K, III. 4721A SUNSET BLVD 29072 #001-02-1994 L2000 **ORS** *020 †40

O'MALLEY, Aran Marino. 4721A SUNSET BLVD 29072 #045-01-2001 L2007 **ORS** *020

PAKSIMA, Suzanne Leigh. 811 W MAIN ST, LEXINGTON URGENT CARE 29072 #035-15-1993 L1996 **FM** *020 †18

PATEL, Neel Ramesh. 108 PALMETTO PARK BLVD, STE D 29072 #665-02-2000 L2006 **CD** *020 †20

POTTS, William Arthur. ■ 29073 #035-06-1944 L1973 **GYN** *071 †30

PRESNAL, Bradley P. 4721A SUNSET BLVD 29072 #048-16-1988 L1989 **ORS** *020 †40

REYNOLDS, Dwight Raymond. 346 W BUTLER ST, LEXINGTON PEDIATRIC PRACTI 29072 #045-04-1981 L1987 **PD** *020 †55

REYNOLDS, Freddie. 811 S LAKE DR 29072 #021-01-1975 L1982 **OBG** *020 †30

RHINE, Philip Dale. 811 W MAIN ST, STE 207 29072 #045-01-1975 L1981 **FM** *020 †18

RIDER, John A. 1316 N LAKE DR, ADOLESCENCE MEDICINE 29072 #035-06-1970 L1975 **PD** *020 †55

SAUNDERS, John Lance. 247 COLUMBIA AVE 29072 #045-01-1984 L1985 **GP FM** *020

SHAHBAHRAMI, Paul Benson. 225 PRESQUE ISLE RD 29072 #017-20-1996 L1999 **EM** *020 †16

SHALKHAM, Kevin Quinlan. 5535 PLATT SPRINGS RD, LFP WHITE KNOLL 29073 #045-01-2002 L2006 **FM** *020 †18

SHEALY, Carl Jonathon. 811 W MAIN ST, STE 204 29072 #045-01-1989 L1990 **FM** *020 †18

SMITHSON, Stacy Lee. 1404 W MAIN ST, LAKE MURRAY OBGYN 29072 #016-11-1994 L1995 **OBG** *020 †30

SOTO, Carlos Andres. 811 W MAIN ST, LEXINGTON MEDICAL CTR-LEXI 29072 #264-05-1999 L2004 **FM** *020 †18

STEWART, Joseph Vincent. ■ 29072 #014-01-1977 L1995 **EM** *020 †16

STOTZER, Michael. 811 E MAIN ST 29072 #016-11-1998 L2004 **U** *020 †95

STOUT, D Michael. 109 VISTA OAKS DR, STE C 29072 #043-01-1980 L1981 **EM** *020 †16

TAYLOR, Marcia Lynn. 811 W MAIN ST, LEXINGTON MED CTR 29072 #045-04-2000 L2001 **FM** *020 †18

TAYLOR, Virginia Madison. ■ 29073 #045-04-2006 L2007 **IM** *012

THOMAS, Christie Pees. 4568 SUNSET BLVD 29072 #045-01-2001 L2002 **PD** *020 †55

TIMMONS, James M. ■ 29073 #036-07-1942 L1946 **OTO** *071 †45

TOOL, Susan Jeanne. 346 W BUTLER ST 29072 #045-01-1986 L1987 **PD** *020 †55

TORRI, John Chas. ■ 29072 #045-01-1976 L1977 **P** *100

TRUESDALE, Bruce Henry. 811 E MAIN ST 29072 #045-01-1971 L1972 **U** *020 †95

WADDELL, Bonnie B. 4568 SUNSET BLVD 29072 #045-04-1996 L1997 **PD** *020 †55

WALTERS, John Roy. 340 W BUTLER ST 29072 #045-04-1984 L1988 **OPH AM** *020 †35

WELCH, Michelle Deann. 5315 SUNSET BLVD STE A, DERMATOLOGY OF LEXINGTON 29072 #047-20-1996 L2004 **D DS** *020 †15

WENNER, Allen Richard. 4711 SUNSET BLVD 29072 #036-01-1974 L1976 **FM** *020 †18

WILLARD, Thomas Brian. 811 E MAIN ST 29072 #036-01-1998 L2004 **U** *020 †95

WILLIAMS, James O, Jr. 4711 SUNSET BLVD 29072 #045-04-1988 L1989 **FM** *020 †18

WILSON, Jenna Lynn. ■ 29073 #001-02-2007 L2007 **EM** *012

WOODY, Edward Arthur. 157 CORLEY MILL RD, STE 510 29072 #012-01-1978 L1983 **OTO GP** *020 †45

WRIGHT, Thomas Hamilton. ■ 29072 #041-13-1978 L1983 **GS** *020 †85

LIBERTY – PICKENS

CARNSEW, Lori Robin. 300 W FRONT ST 29657 #025-07-1997 L1999 **FM OBS** *020 †18 ‡

LITTLE MOUNTAIN – NEWBERRY

WHITE, Michael Jay. 99 N MILL ST 29075 #055-02-1999 L2002 **FM** *020 †18

LITTLE RIVER – HORRY

AL-JARAKI, Omar. 3361 HIGHWAY 9 E 29566 #875-01-1980 L1988 **IM** *100

BAUERLE, Wayne Bryan. 4237 RIVER HILLS DR, STRAND ORTHOPAEDIC 29566 #041-02-1991 L1997 **OSS** *020 †40

BERLEY, George Edward. 1300 HIGHWAY 17, WALKER URGENT AND FAMILY C 29566 #023-01-1974 L1996 **EM IM** *020

BIBB, Robert Douglas. 4000 HIGHWAY 9 E, STE 215 29566 #045-01-1979 L1980 **D** *020 †15

BLAKER, Alan Michael. 4000 HIGHWAY 9 E, STE 255 29566 #023-01-1984 L1990 **CD IM** *020 †20

BLUE, April Lou. 3361 HIGHWAY 9 E 29566 #036-01-2002 L2003 **FM** *020 †18

BROWN, Michael Hunter. 4000 HIGHWAY 9 E, CAROLINA RADIOLOGY 29566 #041-12-2000 L2002 **DR** *020 †80

BUSSE, Charles Peter. 4303 LIVE OAK DR 29566 #034-01-1989 L1990 **UCM FM** *020 †18

BUTLER, James Clark. 4237 RIVER HILLS DR, STRAND ORTHOPAEDIC 29566 #045-01-1990 L1995 **ORS** *020 †40

CALLIHAN, Steven Michael. 4237 RIVER HILLS DR, STRAND ORTHOPAEDIC 29566 #035-15-1979 L1984 **ORS** *020 †40

CARLSON, John Emil. 4237 RIVER HILLS DR, STE 150 29566 #026-04-1983 L2001 **IMG IM** *020 †18

CHRISTENSEN, Tom Allan. 4000 HIGHWAY 9 E 29566 #030-05-1982 L1996 **FM** *020 †18

COHEN, Paul Sydney. PO BOX 547, 4303 LIVE OAK DR 29566 #041-02-1972 L1991 **PUD CCM** *020 †20

CORNEJO, Juan Antonio. 4303 LIVE OAK DR 29566 #132-05-1969 L1976 **OBG** *020 †30

CRANE, Scott Jay. 4000 HIGHWAY 9 E, CAROLINA RADIOLOGY 29566 #017-20-1986 L1991 **DR** *020 †80

CROUCH, Timothy Ellis. 4000 HIGHWAY 9 E, STE 240 29566 #045-01-1995 L1999 **AI** *020 †20,03

DALY, John Joseph, Jr. 4000 HIGHWAY 9 E, CAROLINA RADIOLOGY 29566 #045-01-1992 L1993 **DR** *020 †80,28

DANIELS, Frederick W, IV. 4326 BALDWIN AVE 29566 #045-01-1987 L1989 **PD** *020 †55

DE GROOD, Robert Louis. 4000 HIGHWAY 9 E, STE 205 29566 #654-01-1986 L1994 **GS** *020 †85

DELLINGER, Clyde James. 4303 LIVE OAK DR, LITTLE RIVER MEDICAL CENTE 29566 #036-07-1961 L1973 **FM FPG** *020 †18

DERRICK, Russell Lamar. 4000 HIGHWAY 9 E, CAROLINA RADIOLOGY 29566 #045-01-1995 L1997 **DR** *020 †80

DOUGLAS, Danny. 4000 HIGHWAY 9 E, STE 240 29566 #028-34-1982 L1999 **IM** *020 †20,03

FORTMAN, Brian James. 4000 HIGHWAY 9 E, CAROLINA RADIOLOGY 29566 #035-06-1996 L2002 **RNR** *020 †80

GUHA, Prabal Kumar. 4000 HIGHWAY 9 E, STE 255 29566 #495-45-1992 L2003 **CD** *020 †20

HEWITT, J Carlisle. 4000 HIGHWAY 9 E, CAROLINA RADIOLOGY 29566 #045-01-1958 L1958 **R NM** *071 †80,28

IMBEAU, Stephen Alan. 4000 HIGHWAY 9 E, STE 240 29566 #005-02-1973 L1980 **AI IM** *020 †20,03

INSIGNARES, Luis Donaldo. 4303 LIVE OAK DR 29566 #045-01-1998 L2001 **FM** *020 †18

JARRETT, Joe Nelson, Jr. 4237 RIVER HILLS DR, STRAND ORTHOPAEDIC 29566 #055-01-1975 L1980 **ORS** *020 †40

JUBERG, Breton Chester. 4000 HIGHWAY 9 E, SEACOAST MEDICAL CENTER 29566 #038-45-1989 L2002 **OBG** *020 †30

KELLEY, Elizabeth Ann. 4000 HIGHWAY 9 E, CAROLINA RADIOLOGY 29566 #032-01-1998 L2004 **DR** *020 †80

KING, Amy Lynn. 4237 RIVER HILLS DR, STE 110 29566 #016-01-1997 L2001 **OBG** *020 †30

KUPERMAN, Paul Makoto. 4000 HIGHWAY 9 E, CAROLINA RADIOLOGY 29566 #056-06-1998 L2004 **DR** *020 †80

LACKEY, Jeffrey Scott. 4000 HIGHWAY 9 E, CAROLINA RADIOLOGY 29566 #045-01-1993 L1999 **DR** *020 †80

LEAK, Robert Simon. 4237 RIVER HILLS DR, STRAND ORTHOPAEDIC 29566 #039-01-1996 L2002 **ORS** *020 †40

LEASK, Gavin Mark. 4000 HIGHWAY 9 E, STE 255 29566 #836-01-1988 L1997 **CD** *020 †20

LEE, James Tillman, Jr. 4000 HIGHWAY 9 E, STE 255 29566 #045-01-1988 L1994 **CD IC** *020 †20

MARTIN, Ben Jos. 4237 RIVER HILLS DR, STE 110 29566 #020-02-1973 L1977 **OBG IM** *020 †30

MATUTE, Reynaldo. 4303 LIVE OAK DR 29566 #308-11-1987 L2005 **NEP** *020 †20

MENCKEN, Gregory Scott. 4000 HIGHWAY 9 E, CAROLINA RADIOLOGY 29566 #045-01-1993 L1994 **DR** *020 †80

MERRITT, James Osmond, III. 4237 RIVER HILLS DR, STE 110 29566 #045-01-1971 L1972 **OBG** *020 †30

MERRITT, James Osmond, IV. 4237 RIVER HILLS DR, STRAND ORTHOPAEDIC 29566 #045-01-2000 L2002 **ORS** *020

MERRITT, Jennifer Holland. 4237 RIVER HILLS DR, STE 100 29566 #045-01-2001 L2003 **OPH** *020 †35

MILKO, John Edward. 4000 HIGHWAY 9 E, SEACOAST MEDICAL CENTER 29566 #036-01-1996 L1999 **EM** *020 †18

MOUNT, Lisa E. 4237 RIVER HILLS DR, STE 150 29566 #045-01-1990 L1998 **IM IMG** *020 †20 ‡

OM, Anil. 4000 HIGHWAY 9 E, STE 255 29566 #495-47-1982 L1994 **PD** *020 †20

PETERS, Michael David. 4000 HIGHWAY 9 E, STE 270 29566 #035-08-1996 L2006 **OTO** *020 †45

PIRTTIMA, Steven Todd. 4000 HIGHWAY 9 E, CAROLINA RADIOLOGY 29566 #011-03-1998 L2004 **DR** *020 †80

POOLE, Trevor Ward. 4000 HIGHWAY 9 E, STE 205 29566 #055-01-1995 L2002 **GS** *020 †85

RAZOOK, John Michael. 4000 HIGHWAY 9 E, CAROLINA RADIOLOGY 29566 #039-01-1994 L1999 **RNR** *020 †80

RIKE, Gary Lee. 4000 HIGHWAY 9 E, CAROLINA RADIOLOGY 29566 #018-03-1981 L1985 **DR** *020 †80 ‡

RUBINTON, Paul Scott. 4000 HIGHWAY 9 E, SEACOAST MEDICAL CENTER 29566 #041-02-1998 L1999 **FM** *020 †18

SEDLAK, Stephen P. ■ 29566 #056-06-1949 L1950 **R DR** *071 †80

SHELLEY, Billie Edgar, Jr. 4000 HIGHWAY 9 E, CAROLINA RADIOLOGY 29566 #045-01-1979 L1980 **R** *020 †80

STONE, Harry David, Jr. 4000 HIGHWAY 9 E, STE 240 29566 #045-04-1992 L1997 **AI** *020 †20,03

STOUGHTON, Thomas Leroy. 4000 HIGHWAY 9 E, STE 255 29566 #041-13-1983 L1992 **CD IM** *020 †20

TEW, Joshua Brian. 4000 HIGHWAY 9 E, CAROLINA RADIOLOGY 29566 #045-04-1994 L2000 **DR** *020 †80

VERDIN, Thomas Marion, III. 4303 LIVE OAK DR 29566 #045-01-1968 L1968 **PD** *020 †55

WALKER, Rogers Smith. 1300 HIGHWAY 17 29566 #045-01-1979 L1980 **EM** *020 †16

WARD, Richard William. 4237 RIVER HILLS DR, STRAND ORTHOPAEDIC 29566 #055-01-1975 L1981 **ORS** *020 †40

WEIMER, Carl E, Jr. 4000 HIGHWAY 9 E, STE 215 29566 #055-01-1982 L1983 **D FM** *020 †18,15

WILLIAMS, Eston E, Jr. 4000 HIGHWAY 9 E 29566 #045-01-1963 L1994 **FM** *020 †18

WISS, Joan M. 4000 HIGHWAY 9 E, STE 215 29566 #051-07-1991 L1996 **D** *020 †15

WOODARD, William L, Jr. 4000 HIGHWAY 9 E, CAROLINA RADIOLOGY 29566 #045-01-1992 L1997 **RNR** *020 †80

ZDYBEL, Paul James. 4000 HIGHWAY 9 E, CAROLINA RADIOLOGY 29566 #025-12-1984 L1991 **DR R** *062 †80

LOBECO — BEAUFORT

LEWIN, Albert Read. 58 MORGON ROAD 29931 #045-01-1976 L1982 **OTO NO** *074 †45

LODGE — COLLETON

JONES, Edward Marshall. ■ 29082 #036-07-1961 L1970 **PTH** *020 †50

LORIS — HORRY

BARRETT, Gary Jos. 3109 CASEY ST 29569 #041-07-1979 L1980 **IM** *020 †20

BELLAMY, Fred Wm. 3655 MITCHELL ST 29569 #045-01-1987 L1988 **AN** *020 †05

CHOYAH, Natasha Angeli. 3204 CASEY ST, FAMILY HEALTH CENTER 29569 #894-01-1996 L2002 **FM** *020 †18

CODY, Rebecca Diane. 3008 BAYBORO ST 29569 #027-01-1996 L2001 **ON** *020 †20

COLLINS, Raymond Craig. 3655 MITCHELL ST, LORIS HEALTHCARE SYSTEM 29569 #019-02-1976 L1999 **AN** *020 †05

COX, Brandon Ray. ■ 29569 #045-01-2006 *012

CRAIGIE, James New. 3655 MITCHELL ST 29569 #010-01-1957 L1962 **GS** *071

GOLDBERG, Renwick Neal. 3008 BAYBORO ST 29569 #165-03-1975 L1984 **ON HEM** *020 †20

GRACE, Fady Sabry Shafeek. 3655 MITCHELL ST, LORIS HOSPITAL 29569 #915-04-1999 L2007 **IM** *020 †20

GRUBB, Stephen Dale. 3655 MITCHELL ST, LORIS COMM. HOSPITAL - FAM 29569 #028-02-1975 L1976 **FM FPG** *020 †18

HARKINS, Keith George. 3418 CASEY ST, SOUTHERN MEDICAL ASSOCIATE 29569 #010-02-1995 L1999 **MPD PD** *020 †20

LOGAN, Alexander C, III. 3655 MITCHELL ST, BOX 690001 29569 #045-01-1988 L1989 **PTH** *020 †50

LUDLOW, Donald N, Jr. 3109 CASEY ST, SEASHORE PEDIATRICS 29569 #041-09-1983 L2002 **PD PDP** *020 †55

MAHAJAN, Neeraj. 3008 BAYBORO ST 29569 #495-51-1994 L2005 **HO IM** *020 †20 ‡

MCCAULEY, Chris Stephen. 3617 CASEY ST 29569 #055-01-1990 L1994 **OBG** *020 †30

MESSINA, Joseph F. 3655 MITCHELL ST 29569 #035-75-2000, ▲ L2003 **IM** *020 †20

MILLS, Timothy Chuck. 3418 CASEY ST 29569 #036-08-1986 L1989 **FM** *020 †18

MOORE, Lane Ingram. 3327 CASEY ST, TRI COUNTY SURGERY, LLC 29569 #012-01-1988 L2000 **GS** *020 †85

PALOMARES, Bernabe P. 3655 MITCHELL ST 29569 #748-07-1966 L1977 **GS TS** *020

PALOMARES, Elba B. 3655 MITCHELL ST 29569 #748-07-1966 L1977 **PTH PCP** *071

PAUDEL, Vijay. 3008 BAYBORO ST, ASSOCIATED MED SPECIALISTS 29569 #016-11-1995 L2000 **HO** *020 †20 ‡

PELSTRING, Mark Fredrick. 3418 CASEY ST 29569 #020-02-1974 L1997 **FM ADM** *020 †18

PHILLIPS, Susan S. 3655 MITCHELL ST, DEPT OF PATHOLOGY 29569 #036-05-1989 L1991 **PTH** *020 †50

PO, Christopher L. 3418 CASEY ST 29569 #748-08-1983 L1996 **IM** *020 †20

RIEDY, Mark. 3439 CASEY ST, CARILION ROANKE MEMORIAL H 29569 #045-04-1994 L2001 **PCC** *020 †20

SEJAN, Andrew Joseph. 3418 CASEY ST 29569 #048-13-1982 L1991 **FM** *020 †18

STEINMAN, James A. 3655 MITCHELL ST, LORIS HEALTHCARE 29569 #422-01-1981 L2002 **FM EM** *020 †18

WRIGHT, James Francis. 3655 MITCHELL ST, LORIS COMMUNITY HOSPITAL 29569 #021-01-1979 L1992 **EM FM** *020 †18

ZIFF, Robert Alan. 3655 MITCHELL ST 29569 #033-06-1978 L1985 **OBG** *071 †30 ‡

LUGOFF — KERSHAW

BALOGUN, Olajide Anthony. 1165 HIGHWAY 1 S 29078 #690-14-1989 L1998 **MPD** *020 †20,55

BAXLEY, Elaine Boyd. 1060 HIGHWAY 1 S 29078 #045-04-1984 L1985 **EM OM** *020 †16

BRAZELL, Rebecca Naomi. ■ 29078 #045-04-2004 L2008 **OBG** *012

BROOKS, Alice Joyce. 116 STANDARD WAREHOUSE RD 29078 #025-07-1986 L1988 **FM** *020

CONNELL, Foy Douglas. ■ 29078 #045-04-1992 L1993 **FM** *020 †18

DYCE, Orville Hugh. 1165 HIGHWAY 1 S, STE 300 29078 #041-01-1997 L2005 **OTO** *020 †45

GUNNLAUGSSON, Chad Bjorn. 1165 HIGHWAY 1 S, STE 300 29078 #036-01-1998 L2006 **OTO** *020 †45

JOSEPH, Thomas Chester. 1165 HIGHWAY 1 S 29078 #045-01-1972 L1975 **PD** *020 †55

KAHLER, Guy Beyer. 1060 HIGHWAY 1 S 29078 #045-01-1981 L1985 **EM** *020 †18

KRAEMER, Todd Michael. 1165 HIGHWAY 1 S, STE 500 29078 #305-01-2003 L2007 **OBG** *020

OLIVER, Joel R, Jr. 1060 HIGHWAY 1 S 29078 #045-01-1988 L1989 **FM** *020 †18

PUCHALSKI, Robert. 1165 HIGHWAY 1 S, STE 300 29078 #028-02-1997 L2002 **OTO A** *020

SELLERS, Christine B. 1165 HIGHWAY 1 S 29078 #045-01-1994 L1996 **PD** *020 †55

SMITH, Roy Edgar. 116 STANDARD WAREHOUSE RD 29078 #045-01-1989 L1990 **FM** *020 †18

VIDRINE, David Macy. 1165 HIGHWAY 1 S, STE 300 29078 #021-05-2001 L2007 **OTO** *020 †45

LYMAN — SPARTANBURG

FACHADO, Manuel, Jr. 12315 GREENVILLE HWY 29365 #028-78-1993, ▲ L2005 **FM EM** *020

SOMANI, Jagdish Prasad. ■ 29365 #495-74-1968 L2005 **IM P** *020 ‡

LYNCHBURG — LEE

OLIVER, Benjamin Mondsie. 91 MAIN ST 29080 #045-01-1937 L1937 **GP** *071

MANNING — CLARENDON

ADLER, Roger Elliot. 319 S CHURCH ST, MAILING: P O BOX 82 29102 #660-01-1971 L1983 **CHP P** *075 †75

ALDRICH, William Council. 50 E HOSPITAL ST, STE 2 29102 #045-01-1987 L1988 **FM PTH** *020 †18

BACHUS-KEITH, Beryl L. ■ 29102 #021-01-1981 L1992 **PD** *020 †55

CARTER, Lucretia Ann. 12 W SOUTH ST 29102 #010-03-2001 L2004 **PD** *020 †55

COKER, Clarence Epps, Jr. 22 BOZARD ST, BOX 137 29102 #045-01-1965 L1965 **FM** *020 †18

DAVIS, Yvonne Jeanette. ■ 29102 #011-02-1994 L2007 **IM** *020 †20

DE CASTRO, Teresita O. 215 COMMERCE ST, CLARENDON COUNTY MENTAL HE 29102 #748-07-1961 L2004 **CHP** *020

DOMINICI, Raymond Henry. 20 E HOSPITAL ST 29102 #041-09-1965 L1984 **GS GE** *020 †85

EAGERTON, Robert S, Jr. 200 E HOSPITAL ST 29102 #045-01-1982 L1983 **FM** *020 †18

EGBONIM, Donatus M. 12 W SOUTH ST 29102 #690-01-1982 L1998 **IM** *020 †20

FLANIGAN, Clarence, Jr. PO BOX 550 29102 #012-01-1975 L1979 **FM** *020

GAINES, David Charles. 50 E HOSPITAL ST, STE 4 29102 #012-22-1993 L2000 **FM** *020 †18

GARMA, Reynald B. 12 W SOUTH ST 29102 #748-07-1987 L1996 **PD** *020 †55

HARRISON, George Eric. ■ 29102 #012-21-1998 L2001 **FM** *020 †18

HOEVENAAR, Nancy H. 1024 HERIOTT ST, SANTEE WATEREE CMHC 29102 #038-41-1986 L1987 **P** *020 †75

HOLMAN, Dawn Michelle. 20 E HOSPITAL ST 29102 #041-07-1995 L2006 **GS** *020

JOHNSON, Gerald Kenneth. ■ 29102 #045-01-1980 L1981 **FM** *020 †18

JONES, George Rou, Jr. 107 SUNSET DR 29102 #045-01-1977 L1977 **FM** *020 †18 ‡

KEITH, Edward Cyprian, Jr. 15 E HOSPITAL ST 29102 #045-01-1979 L1987 **FM** *020 †18

KENNEDY, Karel Ralph. ■ 29102 #010-03-1971 L1981 **CD IM** *020 †20

KOON, David Thos. 50 E HOSPITAL ST, STE 4 29102 #045-01-1990 L1997 **FM** *020 †18

MEIER, Gerald Frank. ■ 29102 #025-01-1962 L1983 **NS** *071 †25

MITCHELL, Charles Ray. 517 SUNSET DR 29102 #055-02-1994 L2002 **FM** *020 †18

MOORE, Dorwin Tillman. 1014 PROFESSIONAL CT, STE 1014 29102 #045-04-1988 L1992 **OBG** *020 †30

MOORE, John Marion. 538 SUNSET DR 29102 #045-01-1971 L1972 **PD** *020 †55

ORVIN, Donna Clair. 215 COMMERCE ST 29102 #010-01-1977 L2004 **P** *020 †75

RIDGEWAY, Robert L, III. 21 E HOSPITAL ST, PALMETTO WOMEN'S HEALTHCAR 29102 #045-04-1988 L1989 **OBG** *020 †30

SY, Ramon Proctan. PO BOX 280, 15 E HOSPITAL ST 29102 #748-25-1987 L1998 **CD** *020 †20

THOMPSON, Catherine E. 10 W HOSPITAL ST, EAST CLARENDON MEDICAL CEN 29102 #028-78-1998, ▲ L2004 *020

TOLLISON, Steven Bradley. 21 E HOSPITAL ST, PALMETTO WOMENS HEALTHCARE 29102 #045-04-1984 L2001 **OBG** *020

VENGEROWSKY, Oleg Y. ■ 29102 #913-04-1986 L2000 **AN** *05

WHEELER, Deborah Louise. 12 W SOUTH ST 29102 #045-01-1998 L2002 **MPD** *020

WILLIAMS, Marva Denise. 5202 CYPRESS POINTE 29102 #654-01-1994 L2000 **FM** *020 †18

WOODBURY, David Matthew. 50 E HOSPITAL ST, STE 6 29102 #056-06-1994 L2005 **ORS** *020 †40

WOODHAM, James Wm, Jr. ■ 29102 #016-43-1978 L1994 **GS EM** *020 †85

MARION – MARION

ABINSAY, Alvin Carin. 1115 N MAIN ST, P O DRAWER 1030 29571 #748-01-1991 L1996 **IM** *020 †20

BERRY, James B, Jr. 1115 N MAIN ST, PO DRAWER 1030 29571 #036-07-1950 L1951 **IM FM** *071

BURKE, Valerie. 1324 N MAIN ST, MARION COUNTY WOMENS CARE 29571 #035-47-1981 L1996 **OBG** *020 †30

CAMPBELL, Treadwell. 1108 N MAIN ST 29571 #047-07-1985 L1988 **FM** *020 †18

CLARK, Thomas B, Jr. ■ 29571 #045-01-1951 L1951 **FM** *071 †18

COLEMAN, Hugh V. PO BOX 1070 29571 #045-01-1952 L1952 **GS ORS** *071 †85

FOWLER, Donald Harrison. 1106 LOMBARDY ST 29571 #048-12-1957 L1973 **FM FPG** *020

GOPALAKRISHNAN, P. 1108 N MAIN ST 29571 #495-53-1964 L1976 **GS TS** *020 †90,85 ‡

KITCHENS, Darriel G. 210 E DOZIER ST 29571 #012-01-1951 L1957 **IM** *020

KLAUBER, Thomas Onley. 1108 N MAIN ST 29571 #045-01-1978 L1981 **DR NM** *020 †80

MC RAE, Charles Wm. 302 OLIVER ST, P O BOX 669 29571 #012-05-1963 L1970 **DR NM** *020 †80

QUERUBIN, Alexander U. ■ 29571 #748-01-1965 L1981 **GS** *020

SUGGS, James Lewis. 1108 N MAIN ST 29571 #045-01-1959 L1959 **IM FM** *020

VYGE, Robert Gerard. 1115 N MAIN ST 29571 #539-06-1995 L2000 **IM** *020 †20

WU, Der Sun. 1328 N MAIN ST 29571 #244-04-1969 L1971 **OBG** *020 †30

WU, Der Yang. HWY 501, DONALD S WU MD PA 29571 #244-02-1967 L1976 **GP HS** *020

MAULDIN – GREENVILLE

BARILOVITS, Michael. ■ 29662 #045-04-2003 L2004 **P** *020

BAXI, Hareshchandra T. 309 W BUTLER RD 29662 #495-48-1975 L1987 **PD** *020 †55

BONABON, Marie Rose Valde. 309 W BUTLER RD 29662 #748-08-1987 L2003 **PD** *020

BRANNON, Heather Lynn. 309 W BUTLER RD, NORTH HILLS MEDICAL CENTER 29662 #023-12-1993 L2005 **FM** *020 †18

CARPENTER, Richard H. PO BOX 1182, 6 WINCHESTER CT 29662 #045-04-1983 L1984 **PTH** *020 †50

DECLERCK, Paul A C. 309 W BUTLER RD 29662 #165-06-1975 L2004 **FM** *075

EARLES, Melissa Marie. ■ 29662 #056-06-2008 *012

GADDY, Russell Gene. 10 WINCHESTER CT, WINCHESTER FAMILY MEDICINE 29662 #045-01-1974 L1976 **PDR FPG** *020 †18

JOSHI, Nomita. 213 E BUTLER RD, STE C1 29662 #496-10-1977 L1995 **IM** *020 †20

PRZYBYLA, Adam Gregory. ■ 29662 #045-04-2008 *012

WELLS, Evangeline F Hyder. PO BOX 279 29662 #047-06-1952 L1952 **GP OS** *071

WELLS, Walter Martin. 11 JENKINS ST, P O BOX 279 29662 #047-06-1952 L1952 **GP OS** *071

WILLETT, David Prater. 5B OWENS LN 29662 #047-20-1983 L1984 **FM** *075 †18

MC BEE – CHESTERFIELD

SIEGMANN, James Ray. 645 S 7TH ST 29101 #007-02-1973 L1980 **EM** *020 †18

MC CLELLANVILLE – CHARLESTON

BOWENS, Henry, Jr. PO BOX 608, 1189 TIBWIN RD 29458 #045-01-1980 L1981 **FM** *020 †18

DANIELS, Alfred John. 1189 TIBWIN RD, ST JAMES-SANTEE FAMILY HLT 29458 #035-46-1968 L2005 **FM** *020 †18

FULCHER, James Edwin. 631 VENNING ST, SCOTIA AND VENNING 29458 #045-01-1970 L1971 **FM** *020 †18

MORRISON, Richard Leland. ■ 29458 #045-01-1961 L1961 **GP** *071

PETERSON, Jill Marie. 1189 TIBWIN RD 29458 #025-07-1995 L2003 **FM** *020 †18

MC COLL – MARLBORO

MOORE, George Gibson, Jr. 225 S MAIN ST 29570 #045-01-1969 L1969 **GP** *020 †18

MC CORMICK – MCCORMICK

FLOYD, Gene Eric, Jr. 219A N MINE ST 29835 #045-04-1994 L1996 **FM** *020 †18 ‡

FLOYD, Michelle Gooch. 219A N MINE ST 29835 #045-04-1994 L1996 **FM** *020 †18

GILBERT, James W. 219 N MINE ST 29835 #048-12-1952 L1971 **FM FOP** *072

KELLETT, Robert Jason. 219A N MINE ST, MCCORMICK FAMILY & DENTAL 29835 #045-04-2001 L2007 **FM** *100 †18

MC REE, John Browning. 386 REDEMPTION WAY, MCCORMICK CORRECTIONAL INS 29899 #045-01-1977 L1978 **FM FSM** *020 †18

MEGGETT – CHARLESTON

CHARIKER, Fredda Glenn. ■ 29449 #045-01-1977 L1978 **AN** *074 †05

MONCKS CORNER – BERKELEY

ACCETTA, Christopher R. 401 N LIVE OAK DR, LOW COUNTRY WOMENS 29461 #035-09-1984 L1991 **OBG** *020 †30

BOUNDS, Charles Wilson. 2061 HIGHWAY 52 29461 #051-01-1976 L1979 **FM** *020 †18

CAMPBELL, Jeanne Marie. 730 STONEY LANDING RD, STE 200 29461 #011-02-1982 L1985 **IM FM** *020 †20

CLAYTON, Christine. 109 W MAIN ST, CHILDREN'S CARE CLINIC 29461 #045-01-1995 L1998 **PD** *020 †55

EDWARDS, Melinda E. 403 STONEY LANDING RD, BERKELEY COMM. MENTAL HEAL 29461 #045-01-1997 L2002 **P** *020

ETIKERENTSE, Temisan L. 110 EXECUTIVE PKWY 29461 #690-02-1991 L1998 **IM** *020 †20

FLOYD, Meredith Diane. 401 N LIVE OAK DR 29461 #045-01-1996 L2000 **FM** *020 †18 ‡

FREEDMAN, Glenn Elliot. 730 STONEY LANDING RD 29461 #033-06-1980 L1997 **EM** *020 †16

GERBER, Patricia Sue. 401 N LIVE OAK DR 29461 #056-05-1976 L2002 **AI RHU** *020 †55,03

GERDING, Lori Ann. 403 STONEY LANDING RD 29461 #030-05-1996 L1997 **P** *020 †75

GIBBS, Rose Delores. 106 W MAIN ST, BERKLEY MEDICAL CENTER 29461 #045-01-1973 L1974 **IM ID** *020

GIVENS, Ronnie M, II. 401 N LIVE OAK DR, LOW COUNTRY WOMENS 29461 #045-01-1995 L1999 **OBG** *020 †30

HUNTER, Christine Johnson. 401 N LIVE OAK DR, LOW COUNTRY WOMENS 29461 #045-01-1993 L1997 **OBG** *020 †30

JONES, Edward Johnson, III. 401 N LIVE OAK DR, STE A 29461 #045-01-1996 L2000 **MPD** *020 †20,55

MOORE, Jos Carlisle, Jr. 730 STONEY LANDING RD, STE 200 29461 #045-01-1975 L1978 **PD** *020 †55

MURPHY, Thomas Robert. 401 N LIVE OAK DR 29461 #016-43-2000 L2006 **AI** *020 †55,03

POTTS, Carl Richard. 730 STONEY LANDING RD, ROPER ST FRANCIS MED CTR 29461 #045-01-1988 L1989 **EM** *020 †16

REEVES, William Miles, III. 401 N LIVE OAK DR, LOW COUNTRY WOMENS 29461 #045-01-1991 L1992 **OBG** *020 †30

ROBBINS, Paul Irvin. 117 E MAIN ST, OASIS CHRISTIAN COUNSELING 29461 #045-01-1997 L1998 **P** *020 †75

SANTI, Jeffrey Ramond. 2061 HIGHWAY 52, BERKELEY FAMILY PRACTICE 29461 #018-03-1995 L2001 **FM** *020 †18

SCHAEFER, Marcus L. 255 N HIGHWAY 52 STE 8, INDUSTRIAL MEDICAL CENTER 29461 #010-02-1975 L1998 **OM OS** *020 †30

SCHAFFER, Frederick M. 401 N LIVE OAK DR 29461 #035-08-1981 L2002 **AI PD** *020 †03,55

SCHWARTZBERG, Heather S. 401 N LIVE OAK DR, LOW COUNTRY WOMENS 29461 #012-01-2000 L2004 **OBG** *020

SKASKIW, Anna. 110 EXECUTIVE PKWY, HOPER CLINIC 29461 #654-01-2002 L2004 **PD** *020

SWICORD, John Howard. 1020 OLD HIGHWAY 52, HWY 52 OFFICE 29461 #045-01-1972 L1973 **GP** *071

THOMAS, Stephanie Gail. 403 STONEY LANDING RD, BERKELEY MENTAL HEALTH CEN 29461 #045-01-1994 L1998 **P** *020 †75

WEST, Joseph Raleigh, Jr. 730 STONEY LANDING RD, STE 200 29461 #045-01-1980 L1981 **PD** *020 †55

WOODFIELD, Scott Latimer. 730 STONEY LANDING RD 29461 #035-03-1990 L1998 **CD VS** *020 †20

MOORE – SPARTANBURG

BEARDEN, R Chester, Jr. ■ 29369 #045-01-1978 L1979 **EM** *020

ORGLER, Gordon K. 1775 LIGHTWOOD KNOT RD 29369 #030-06-1973 L1978 **OM** *071 †70

RONAN, David Michael. ■ 29369 #036-08-2004 L2007 **EM** *020

VLASS, Kelly E. ■ 29369 #012-01-2008 *012

MOUNT PLEASANT – CHARLESTON

ABIDE, Ashley Elizabeth. ■ 29464 #027-01-2007 L2007 **IM** *012

ABOU-KHALIL, Bassam. ■ 29464 #045-01-1987 L1991 **TS** *071 †85,90

ADELMAN, Judd Brone. 123 REVOLUTION DR 29464 #011-04-1997 L2003 **GE** *020 †20 ‡

AHLBERG, Tara Lynn. ■ 29464 #045-01-2008 *012

AIKEN, Albert Farmer. ■ 29464 #045-01-1963 L1963 **N IM** *071 †75

AIKEN, Jill C. 1210 CHUCK DAWLEY BLVD, SANDLAPPER PEDIATRICS 29464 #045-01-1995 L1996 **PD** *020 †55

ALEXANDER, John Robert, Jr. 180 WINGO WAY, STE 106 29464 #045-01-1998 L2004 **PM** *020 †60

ALLEN, Robert Johnson, Jr. ■ 29464 #045-01-2007 *012

ANDERSON, William S, III. 570 LONG POINT RD, STE 250 29464 #051-07-1982 L1983 **FM** *020 †18

ANIS, Munazza. ■ 29466 #704-06-1995 L2006 **AR** *020 †80

ANNIBALE, David Jos. 1200 JOHNNIE DODDS BLVD 29464 #041-07-1982 L1989 **NPM PD** *020 †55

ARLA, Julio Ernesto. ■ 29466 #132-01-1956 L1972 **P OS** *071

ARMSTRONG, Dena Carver. 250 MATHIS FERRY RD, STE 101 29464 #036-08-1999 L2004 **P** *020

ARNOLD, Andrew Taylor. 1200 JOHNNIE DODDS BLVD 29464 #045-01-1973 L1975 **ORS** *020 †40

ASH, Rima. ■ 29464 #011-03-2004 L2004 **N** *012

ATHAR, Saima. ■ 29466 #409-21-1998 L2003 **N SME** *100 †75

AYIKU, Henry Buenor. ■ 29464 #412-01-1995 L2003 **NEP** *100 †30

AYMOND, James Kirk. 594 LONE TREE DR 29464 #021-06-1986 L1992 **ORS** *020 †40

BAIRD, David Rogerson. 180 WINGO WAY, STE 308 29464 #045-01-1986 L1991 **GS** *020 †85

BAIRD, Michal Lucile. 570 LONG POINT RD, STE 100 29464 #045-01-1978 L1982 **EM** *020 †16

BANKS, James Leroy, Jr. ■ 29464 #023-01-1953 L1954 **GP** *071

BARBOSA, Sofia Isabel. ■ 29464 #036-05-1992 L2004 **IM** *020 †20

BARON, Paul Lawrence. 1200 JOHNNIE DODDS BLVD 29464 #024-05-1982 L1990 **SO GS** *020 †85

BECK, Lynn Hellebusch. 1952 LONG GROVE DR, STE 202 29464 #028-34-2002 L2003 **PD** *020 †55

BELLIL, Dalila Farida. 1067 CLIFFWOOD DR, CHARLESTON FAMILY MEDICINE 29464 #125-01-1974 L1996 **FM** *020 †18

BLALOCK, Cynthia Anne. 1405 BEN SAWYER BLVD 29464 #012-05-1992 L2000 **EM** *020 †16

BOENSCH, Frank N, Jr. ■ 29464 #045-01-1962 L1962 **OBG** *020 †30

BOLUS, Kathy Siegfried. 1208 TWO ISLAND CT 29466 #045-01-1988 L1990 **NEP** *020 †20

BONIFACE, Mary Elizabeth. ■ 29464 #045-01-1979 L1980 **IM** *100

BONNER, John Calvin. ■ 29464 #045-01-1943 L1943 **PD** *071 †55

BONNER, Walter Morse. 890 JOHNNIE DODDS BLVD, STE 2A 29464 #045-01-1955 L1955 RHU IM *020 †20

BOSMAN, Calvin Jonathan. ■ 29464 #025-12-2005 L2005 P *012

BOTELHO, Tina Marie. 180 WINGO WAY, STE 306 29464 #045-01-2001 L2004 IM *020 †20

BOUDET, Robert Allen. ■ 29464 #011-03-1962 L1984 GS IMG *030

BOWERS, Kimberly Shealy. ■ 29464 #045-01-2003 L2004 CHP *012

BRADFORD, Susanne M. 1400 HOSPITAL DR 29464 #025-07-1995 L2003 OBG *020 †30

BRESCIA, Frank Jos. 900 BOWMAN RD STE 103, MED UNIV SC, DIV HEMATOLO 29464 #033-05-1968 L1998 HO IM *030 †20

BREWERTON, Tim D. 216 SCOTT ST 29464 #021-01-1978 L1987 P CHP *020 †75

BRODERICK-CANTWELL, John. 300 W COLEMAN BLVD, STE 201A 29464 #025-01-1987 L2006 P CHP *020 †75

BROOKS, Walter Ely. ■ 29464 #045-01-1944 L1944 U *071 †95

BROWN, Alton Grady, Jr. 180 WINGO WAY, STE 308 29464 #045-01-1968 L1971 GS PN *020 †85

BROWN, Eugene G, III. 180 WINGO WAY, STE 103 29464 #036-08-1995 L1996 OTO *020 †45

BROWN, Yates Russell. ■ 29464 #021-01-2002 L2004 P *100 †75

BRYAN, Andrea Maria. ■ 29464 #045-01-2006 L2006 IM *012

BRYAN, George Sloan, III. 3074 HIGHWAY 17 N, DOCTORS CARE 29466 #050-02-1983 L1986 EM *020 †16

BURNHAM, William Douglas. 3074 HIGHWAY 17 N, DOCTOR'S CARE PARK WEST 29466 #041-02-1979 L1984 FM *020 †18

BYRD, Edward Bernard. ■ 29466 #010-01-1965 L2000 NS *020 †25

BYRNE, Ryan Robert. ■ 29464 #056-05-2007 L2007 P *012

CALDWELL, Kenneth Madison. 594 LONE TREE DR 29464 #045-01-1983 L1989 GS ORS *020 †40

CAMP, Ernest Ramsay. ■ 29464 #045-01-1997 L2007 GS *020 †85

CARSWELL, James Joseph, IV. 1300 HOSPITAL DR, STE 130 29464 #012-01-1998 L2004 PCC *020 †20

CAVE, Courtney Lynn. ■ 29464 #045-01-2007 L2007 IM *012

CHARIKER, Edd Price. 1241 WOODLAND AVE, PALMETTO CARDIOVASCULAR AN 29464 #045-01-1971 L1972 TS *020 †85,90

CHAUDHARY, Uzair B. 900 BOWMAN RD, STE 103 29464 #704-25-1992 L2000 HO *020 †20

CLARKE, Joseph Capt. ■ 29464 #045-01-2008 †012

COBB, Charles E. ■ 29464 #048-02-1953 L1953 U *071 †95

COHEN TODD, Mark. ■ 29464 #429-02-1992 PCC *012

COLEMAN, Thomas Hamrick. ■ 29464 #045-01-2008 *012

CONE, Christy Lynn. 710 JOHNNIE DODDS BLVD, STE 315 29464 #045-01-1996 L2004 FM *020 †18

COOK, Taylor Irving. ■ 29466 #050-02-1964 L1968 OS GS *030

CORBETT, Lara Lou. 1300 HOSPITAL DR, STE 270 29464 #045-01-1994 L1998 OBG *020 †30

COSCO, Frederick Edward. 1241 WOODLAND AVE, CHARLESTON RADIOLOGISTS, P 29464 #010-02-1974 L1992 DR *020 †20,80

COURSEY, Richard L. ■ 29464 #048-02-2006 L2007 DR *012

CRAIG, Mary Hart. ■ 29464 #045-01-2001 L2004 PYG *100 †75

CRANE, Roland Francis, Jr. ■ 29464 #048-04-1955 L1976 PM *020 †60

CRANNY, Jennifer Ruth. 1241 WOODLAND AVE 29464 #048-14-1995 L2005 DR *020 †80

CRUDEN, Thomas Bernard. 1049B ANNA KNAPP BLVD 29464 #048-04-1974 L1975 FPG *020 †18

CRYMES, Lynn Wimbish. 1300 HOSPITAL DR STE 27, STE 270 29464 #045-01-1995 L1997 OBG *020 †30

CUTHBERTSON, Rand James. 1241 WOODLAND AVE 29464 #010-01-1980 L2000 DR *020 †80

DALU, David Ziad. 1200 JOHNNIE DODDS BLVD, EMERGENCY DEPT 29464 #028-03-1996 L2005 EM *020 †16

DANI, Genta. ■ 29464 #120-01-1994 L2007 GS *012

DANIEL, Rodney Stephen. 268 ALEXANDRA DR, UNIT 3 29464 #011-02-2003 L2006 RHU *012 †20

DATTA, Susan Marie. 180 WINGO WAY, STE 306 29464 #045-01-2004 L2004 IM *020 †20

DAVIDSON, Lesly Salgado. 852 LOWCOUNTRY BLVD, STE 102 29464 #051-07-1993 L1994 D *020 †15

DAVIS-SEAGLE, Kimberly L. 897 VON KOLNITZ RD, MT PLEASANT INTERNAL MEDIC 29464 #045-01-1990 L1993 IM *020 †20

DEBROY, Sumita Kumari. 1208 TWO ISLAND CT, PARKWOOD PEDIATRICS 29466 #019-02-2003 L2006 PD *020

DE MARCO, James Robert. 180 WINGO WAY STE 301 29464 #045-01-1993 L1996 ORS OSM *020 †16,40

DEUSKAR, Sudan. 1241 WOODLAND AVE 29464 #495-01-1968 L1997 DR VIR *020 †80

DEVINE, Denise Hays. 570 LONG POINT RD 29464 #020-02-1996 L1997 OBG *020 †30

DILLON, Alison Elizabeth. 570 LONG POINT RD 29464 #036-05-1991 L1992 OBG *020 †30

DODDS, Colin Anthony. 1241 WOODLAND AVE, CHARLESTON RADIOLOGISTS 29464 #033-05-1998 L2004 VIR *020 †80

DODDS, Janine Mele. 1241 WOODLAND AVE, CHARLESTON RADIOLOGISTS 29464 #033-05-1998 L2004 DR *100 †80

DONALDSON, Jonathan T. 180 WINGO WAY, STE 304 29464 #024-05-1986 L1992 U *020 †95

DUNN, Ted Alan. 570 LONG POINT RD, STE 150 29464 #045-01-1985 L1986 EM *020 †18

EDENS, Clarence Jan. ■ 29464 #012-05-1963 L1969 P *020 †75

EDWARDS, Scott Michael. 679 OLDE SALT RUN, ANESTHESIA SERVICES OF CHA 29464 #025-07-1993 L1994 AN *020 †05

EGLEN, Rebecca Brown. 3400 SALTERBECK CT, STE 101 29466 #017-20-1990 L1997 PD *020 †55

EMMEL, John E. 1049B ANNA KNAPP BLVD 29464 #043-01-1977 L1978 FM FPG *020 †18 ‡

EMOVON, Osemwegie E. 1028 EWALL ST 29464 #690-06-1985 L2001 NEP IM *020 †20

ENGLE, James Coleman. ■ 29464 #012-05-1956 L1956 TS *071 †85,90

ERNST, John M J. 594 LONE TREE DR 29464 #035-45-1979 L1984 HS ORS *020 †40

ERVIN, Ann Harriott. ■ 29464 #045-01-2005 L2006 D *012

ESTES, William James. 767 JOHNNIE DODDS BLVD 29464 #018-03-1996 L2000 ORS *020 †40

EUDY, Grant Evan. 266 W COLEMAN BLVD STE 101, MAIZE CTR FOR DERMATOPATH 29464 #001-02-1999 L2005 PTH DMP *020 †50

FAIREY, Frank Strait, Jr. 180 WINGO WAY, STE 207 29464 #045-01-1971 L1972 FM *020 †18

FAULSTICH, Michael E. ■ 29466 #036-07-1991 L1996 DR NM *020 †80

FELLER, Mitchell Dean. 900 BOWMAN RD, STE 203 29464 #041-01-1977 L1978 FM *020 †18

FETZER, Donald Dudley. ■ 29464 #048-41-1995 L1955 PD *071 †55

FITZGERALD, Richard H, Jr. ■ 29464 #028-34-1970 L1979 ON *071 †20,80

FLETCHER, John Du Pre, Jr. ■ 29464 #045-01-1966 L1966 GP IMG *030

FLOWERS, Robert Boyd. 570 LONG POINT RD 29464 #027-01-1975 L1977 OBG *020 †30

FOGLE, Alan Wren. 180 WINGO WAY, STE 304 29464 #045-01-1979 L1980 U *020 †95

FOLK, James Wm, Jr. ■ 29464 #045-01-1965 L1965 P *071 †75

FOLSE, Sherry Dear. 1121 PARK WEST BLVD, STE B # 183 29466 #027-01-1986 L2006 DR *020 †80

FORCINA, Matthew Scott. ■ 29464 #041-13-2001 L2007 ICE *012

FORD, Angel Meredith. ■ 29466 #045-01-2007 L2007 AN *012

FORDHAM, Morgan Taylor, Jr. ■ 29464 #036-05-2008 *012

FOWLER, Susan Marie. 309 WINGO WAY, STE 101 29464 #045-01-2002 L2005 PD *020 †55

FRAIN, Bryan Henry. 180 WINGO WAY, STE 204 29464 #021-01-1996 L1997 ICE *020 †20

FRANKLIN, Nicole Yvonne. ■ 29466 #055-02-2007 L2007 P *012

FRASCIELLO, Lauren Maria. 570 LONG POINT RD 29464 #045-01-1993 OBG *020 †30

FRIED, Dennis Alan. 1230 HOSPITAL DR STE A, CHARLESTON COLON RECTAL CL 29464 #045-01-1973 L1974 CRS GS *020 †10,85

FRIEDMAN, Harvey Dan. 1241 WOODLAND AVE 29464 #033-05-1971 L1975 DR *020 †80

FRITSCHLE, Andrea Marie. ■ 29464 #011-03-2006 L2006 P *012

FUNCIK, Thomas. 1280 JOHNNIE DODDS BLVD, UNIT 101 29464 #036-01-1989 L1990 FPS OTO *020 †45

FURSE, Cory Michael. ■ 29464 #039-01-2001 L2006 PAN *100 †05

FYLSTRA, Leigh Rachele. ■ 29464 #045-01-2006 P *012

GABEL, Harold D. ■ 29466 #020-02-1966 L1981 OBG PHP *071 †30

GAGLIONE, Joseph Ignatius. 1241 WOODLAND AVE 29464 #038-43-1993 L2000 GP DR *020 †80

GAROVICH, Michael Chas. 1241 WOODLAND AVE 29464 #038-40-1977 L1987 DR RNR *020 †20,80

GASKINS, John Dewayne. ■ 29464 #045-01-1987 L1988 EM *020 †16

GEIER, Carl David. 1241 WOODLAND AVE 29464 #047-06-1975 L1991 R *020 †55,80

GEIER, Carl David, Jr. ■ 29464 #045-01-1999 L2005 OSM ORS *020

GEIER, Christian Smith. 1280 JOHNNIE DODDS BLVD, UNIT 200 29464 #036-08-1996 L1997 OBG *020 †30

GEILFUSS, Charles J, Jr. 1600 FRANKE DR, APT 203 29464 #045-01-1950 L1950 R DR *071 †80

GENEZ, Beverly Jean. 1136 BOWMAN RD, DISC IMAGING 29464 #038-45-1981 L1989 DR GP *020 †80

GERMAIN, Marguerite Ann. 612 SEACOAST PKWY 29464 #023-01-1993 L2000 D *020 †15

GHEGAN, Joanna Chandler. 900 BOWMAN RD STE 304 29464 #012-01-2003 L2004 PD *020

GIGLIO, Pierre. ■ 29466 #627-01-1993 L2006 CN *020 †75

GILMORE, Waddell H, III. 180 WINGO WAY, STE 301 29464 #045-01-1979 L1980 ORS *020 †40

GOLTRA, David D, Jr. PO BOX 176 29465 #038-40-1982 L1990 DR *020 †80,16

GOODALE, Fairfield, Jr. ■ 29464 #038-06-1950 L1950 OS PTH *071 †50

GOODNIGHT, Peter Delove. ■ 29464 #045-01-2006 L2006 AN *012

GORDON, James Hardy. ■ 29464 #012-01-2004 L2004 AN *012

GORSTEIN, David Seth. ■ 29464 #035-19-1983 L1989 DR *071

GOUNDER, Divya Govindasam. ■ 29464 #038-43-2005 L2005 P *012

GRADY, John Leo. 1705 BEAUCASTEL RD 29464 #041-13-1973 L1985 OPH *020 †35

GRAF, Carol Mullinax. 1012 ANNA KNAPP BLVD 29464 #045-01-1972 L1973 P *071

GRAHAM, Charles Dudley. 180 WINGO WAY, STE 205 29464 #020-02-1982 L1983 ON HEM *020 †20

GRAHAM, John Mc Kay, Jr. 594 LONE TREE DR 29464 #045-01-1985 L1986 ORS *020 †40

GRAHAM, William Mclaurin. 1952 LONG GROVE DR, STE 202 29464 #045-01-1991 L1996 PD *020 †55

GREENSLIT, Mark Leif. 1241 WOODLAND AVE 29464 #045-04-1989 L1996 DR *020 †80

GREER, Charles Frederick. 1241 WOODLAND AVE 29464 #045-01-1980 L1981 VIR DR *020 †80

GREGORIE, Rebecca Jane. 570 LONG POINT RD 29464 #045-01-1987 L1991 OBG *020 †30

GRICE, Charlene M. 735 JOHNNIE DODDS BLVD, STE 102 29464 #045-01-1987 L1988 OPH *020 †35

GRICE, George Danl, III. 180 WINGO WAY, STE 308 29464 #045-01-1987 L1989 GS *020 †85

GROB, Curt Harold. ■ 29464 #045-01-2005 L2005 *020

GROSS, John Darren. 1705 BEAUCASTEL RD, MT PLEASANT OPHTHALMOLOGY, 29464 #047-20-1998 L2007 OPH *020 †80

GUNSELMAN, Ryan Joseph. ■ 29464 #038-41-2006 L2006 GS *012

GUNTER, Prentis Richard. 2165 COUNTRY MANOR DR 29466 #045-01-1971 L1972 P *071 †75

HAGERTY, Richard Curry. 1300 HOSPITAL DR, STE 260 29464 #036-07-1976 L1984 PS *020 †85,65

HAHM, Thomas. 900 BOWMAN RD, STE 101 29464 #012-05-1995 L2004 PS CFS *020 †85,65

HALL, Rayna Kneuper. 2723 CODDELL CT 29466 #051-07-1985 L1991 ON HEM *020 †20

HALL, Stanley Christopher. 180 WINGO WAY, STE 304 29464 #051-04-1993 L1999 U *020 †95

HALLABA, Reda Saadallah. 1031 HIGHWAY 41, STE 100 29466 #915-03-1999 L2006 EM *020 †16

HALLMARK, Karen Hill. 1400 HOSPITAL DR 29464 #045-01-1987 L1999 OBG *020 †30

HAND, Lisa Dorn. 519 LIVE OAK DR 29464 #036-08-1987 L1988 P *020 †75

HAND, William Robert. ■ 29466 #028-34-2007 L2007 AN *012

HARDIN, Lilia Vanessa. ■ 29464 #047-06-2005 L2005 DR *012

HARPER, Frank Edward. 890 JOHNNIE DODDS BLVD, STE 2A 29464 #045-01-1975 L1978 RHU IM *040 †20

HARTWELL, Karen Jane. ■ 29464 #035-15-1983 L2006 ADP *020 †75

HARVEY, Tracy Scott. 1300 HOSPITAL DR, STE 260 29464 #051-04-1985 L1986 PS *020 †85,65

HENDRIX, Marilyn Roberts. 173 N PLAZA CT 29464 #039-01-1982 L1983 DR *020 †80

HENSEL, John Michael, Jr. 570 LONG POINT RD STE 240 29464 #019-02-1994 L1996 PS GS *020 †65

HERPEL, Laura Bogan. ■ 29466 #045-04-1999 L2007 PCC *100 †20

HERRING, Neill Mc Phail. 1041 JOHNNIE DODDS BLVD, STE 5A 29464 #036-05-1996 L1999 PD *020 †55

HOLCOMB, Edward S. ■ 29464 #035-20-1943 L1947 IM PUD *071 †20

HOLDEN, Kenton Roy. PO BOX 1047 29465 #051-04-1968 L1990 PD CHN *050 †55

HOLGATE, Richard Cecil. 1340 OLD GEORGETOWN RD 29464 #065-01-1965 L1989 IM OS *020

HOLLADAY, Charles Stephen. 180 WINGO WAY, STE 205 29464 #045-01-1995 L1996 HO *020 †20

HOLLOWELL, Joseph Gurney. ■ 29464 #045-01-1956 L1956 PD PHP *030 †55

HOLTZCLAW, Priscilla W. 570 LONG POINT RD, STE 250 29464 #045-01-2003 L2004 FM *020 †18

HOOD, John Bell. ■ 29464 #020-02-1970 L1974 DR *020 †80

HOPE, Cynthia Lee. 1012 ANNA KNAPP EXT 29464 #045-01-1992 L1993 P *020 †75

HORTON, Ira Boyce. ■ 29464 #045-01-1957 L1957 OS FM *071 †18

HOY, Mark Jeffrey. 1280 JOHNNIE DODDS BLVD, UNIT 205 29464 #041-13-1987 L1992 OTO *020 †45

HUGHES, Thomas Sanders. 913 BOWMAN RD B 29464 #045-01-1992 L1997 N *020 †75

HUNT, Louis David. ■ 29464 #008-01-1961 L1966 **U** *020 †95

HUNT, Noel Mcreynolds. 409 COLEMAN BLVD, STE 1A 29464 #047-05-1989 L1993 **P** *020 †75

HUTCHISON, Patricia Lee. 55 HOPETOWN RD, CHARLESTON PEDIATRICS 29464 #045-01-1992 L1995 **PD** *020 †55

INMAN, Amy Elizabeth. 214 LITTLE PALM LOOP 29464 #045-01-1993 L1994 **AN** *020 †05

JACOBSON, Michael Adam. ■ 29464 #041-02-2004 L2005 **D** *012

JONES, Christopher John. 222 W COLEMAN BLVD 29464 #020-12-1991 L1992 **CHP** *020

JONES, Mary Susan. 897 VON KOLNITZ RD, MT PLEASANT INTERNAL MEDIC 29464 #051-04-1982 L1983 **IM** *020 †20

JOSEPH, Mary Teresa. 1300 HOSPITAL DR, LOWCOUNTRY OBGYN 29464 #045-01-1992 L1993 **OBG** *020 †30

JOYNER, Jeffrey Ritchie. 1300 HOSPITAL DR, STE 300 29464 #016-11-1981 L1987 **GE** *020 †20

KAU, Elizabeth Ellen. 29464 #047-05-1997 L1997 **IM** *020 †20

KEENAN, Kevin. E COOPER COMM HOSP 29464 #051-01-1983 L1984 **EM** *020 †16

KELLETT, James Wimberly. ■ 29464 #045-01-1968 L1968 **U** *071 †95

KERRIGAN, Susan J. 29464 #051-04-1991 L1996 **OBG OS** *074 †30

KHAN, Reshma. ■ 29466 #495-49-1995 L2007 **OBG** *020 †30

KHOURY, Norman Paul. 1240 HIGHWAY 17 BYP 29464 #045-01-1975 L1977 **GS** *020 †85

KINARD, Fredrick Wm. ■ 29464 #047-06-1945 L1947 **OS** *071

KING, C Casey Harvey. ■ 29464 #045-01-2008 †012 ‡

KIRK, Robert Frank. ■ 29464 #047-06-1952 L1973 **GYN OBG** *071 †30

KLEIN, Matthew Holland. ■ 29464 #010-01-2002 L2005 **CD** *012 †20

KLINE, Elizabeth Miller. 1300 HOSPITAL DR, STE 360 29464 #020-12-1995 L2002 **TS GS** *020 †85,90

KLINE, Richard M, Jr. 1300 HOSPITAL DR, STE 120 29464 #045-01-1984 L1984 **GS** *020 †85,65

KOOLA, Jejo David. ■ 29464 #045-01-2006 *012

KOSNIK, Libby Marie. ■ 29464 #038-44-2007 L2007 **GS** *012

KRAAS, Jonathan Richard. ■ 29466 #036-05-2002 L2005 **DR** *012 †28

KUBINSKI, Dennis John. 180 WINGO WAY, STE 304 29464 #036-01-2000 L2005 **U** *020 †95

KULZE, Ann Gregorie. 246 MATHIS FERRY RD, STE 100 29464 #045-01-1988 L1989 **IM** *020

LABAROWSKI, Gretchen Anne. 900 BOWMAN RD, STE 103 29464 #045-01-1997 L1998 **HO** *020 †20

LACOMBE, Michael John. ■ 29464 #012-01-2002 L2007 **VIR** *012 †80

LANGLEY, John W. 1041 JOHNNIE DODDS BLVD, STE 5A 29464 #041-02-1951 L1953 **FM** *071 †18

LANGLEY, William John. 1200 JOHNNIE DODDS BLVD 29464 #051-01-1975 L1978 **PD** *020 †55

LAUGHLIN, Caryn Aimee. ■ 29464 #038-43-2008 *012

LEMAN, Robert Burton. 1200 JOHNNIE DODDS BLVD 29464 #004-01-1976 L1977 **CD ICE** *040 †12

LENTSCH, Kristi Mccauley. ■ 29464 #020-02-2006 L2007 **P** *012

LEVI, James Stuart. ■ 29466 #045-01-1967 L1967 **P** *071 †55

LEWIS, Bracken Clay. ■ 29464 #020-02-2006 L2006 **IM** *012

LEWIS, Evelyn Christopher. ■ 29464 #020-12-2004 L2004 **NEP** *012 †20

LEWIS, Margaret Ruffin. ■ 29465 #045-01-2008 *012

LINKER, Paul Sanders. 156 BOWMAN RD UNIT 105, COOPER RIVER PEDIATRICS 29464 #045-01-1996 L1999 **PD** *020 †55

LOWERY, Robert Booth. 767 JOHNNIE DODDS BLVD 29464 #045-01-1986 L1991 **ORS** *020 †40

LYDIARD, R Bruce. 1440 BEN SAWYER BLVD, STE 1101 29464 #026-04-1977 L1983 **P PA** *050 †75

LYNCH, William Harold. 1230 HOSPITAL DR STE A, 1230 HOSPITAL DRIVE 29464 #010-02-1988 L2004 **TS** *020 †90,85

MAIZE, John Christopher. 266 W COLEMAN BLVD, STE 101 29464 #025-01-1968 L1980 **D DMP** *020 †15

MAIZE, John Christopher, Jr. 266 W COLEMAN BLVD STE 101 29464 #045-01-1997 L2001 **DMP D** *020 †15 ‡

MAJESKI, James Anthony. 900 BOWMAN RD STE 100 29464 #045-01-1974 L1982 **GS VS** *020 †85 ‡

MALLIN, Robert. 1200 JOHNNIE DODDS BLVD 29464 #045-04-1981 L1996 **FM ADM** *040 †18

MARSH, William H. 1300 HOSPITAL DR, STE 300 29464 #036-01-1977 L1980 **IM** *020 †20

MASSEY, Caroline Coleman. ■ 29466 #027-01-2006 L2006 **PTH** *012

MASSEY, Matthew Bradley. ■ 29466 #027-01-2004 L2006 **ORS** *012

MASTERS, Kimberly F. 1101 BOWMAN RD 29464 #045-01-1995 L1996 **OBG** *020

MATARIA, Mohammad Rasmi. ■ 29466 #528-02-2002 L2007 **NEP** *012 †20

MATHER, Thomas Roscoe. 242 MATHIS FERRY RD, STE 100 29464 #017-20-1983 L1984 **OPH** *020 †35

MAYS, Anna Elizabeth. 1220 HOSPITAL DR, LOWCOUNTRY ADULT & SR. HLT 29464 #045-01-2004 L2004 **IM** *020 †20

MCARTHUR, Patrick David. 1001 ANNA KNAPP EXT 29464 #045-01-1990 L1991 **CHP** *020 †75

MC CALL, Isabella Fairey. 913 BOWMAN RD 29464 #045-01-1991 L1994 **PD** *020 †55

MCCLURE, Jeremiah Ramos. ■ 29464 #012-22-2008 *012

MC CROSSON, John Joseph. 594 LONE TREE DR 29464 #045-01-1994 L1995 **ORS** *020 †40

MC DONALD, John Woodbury. 1208 TWO ISLAND CT, EAST COOPER INTERNAL MED 29466 #045-01-1992 L1996 **IM** *020 †20

MC GILLICUDDY, John W. ■ 29464 #025-01-1998 L2005 **GS** *100

MC GUE, John Gregory. 1241 WOODLAND AVE, CHARLESTON RADIOLOGISTS PA 29464 #017-20-1991 L2003 **R** *020 †80

MC KINNEY, James Edward. ■ 29464 #045-01-1992 L1993 **CHP** *020 †75

MC LAUGHLIN, John F, Jr. ■ 29464 #045-01-1946 L1946 **FM OM** *071 †18

MC LAUGHLIN, Mark Alan. 913 BOWMAN RD, MARK MCLAUGHLIN 29464 #041-02-1976 L1987 **FM** *020 †18

MC NAB, James Fyffe, Jr. 216 BENNETT ST, MEDICAL STAFF DEPT 29464 #012-01-1977 L2006 **RO** *020 †80

MC PHERSON, Rebecca Jane. ■ 29464 #050-02-1992 L1993 **NPM** *020 †55

MEACHER, David Edward. 631 JOHNNIE DODDS BLVD 29464 #045-01-1980 L1989 **EM IM** *016

MERRILL, Keith. 767 JOHNNIE DODDS BLVD 29464 #016-06-1980 L1991 **ORS** *020 †40

MICHAEL, Fred A. 1145 SIX MILE RD 29466 #017-20-1992 L1993 **FM EM** *020 †18 ‡

MICHAELSEN, Douglas L. 180 WINGO WAY, STE 205 29464 #036-05-1996 L1997 **HO** *020 †20

MIKOLAJCZYK, Michael G. 180 WINGO WAY, STE 306 29464 #045-01-1991 L1992 **IM** *020 †20

MILLER, Edwin H. ■ 29466 #045-01-1952 L1952 **AN** *071

MILLING, Deborah Marie. 1012 ANNA KNAPP EXT 29464 #045-04-1987 L1988 **P** *020

MILLS, Richard Ernest. 180 WINGO WAY, STE 306 29464 #011-02-1985 L1986 **IM** *020 †20

MITCHELL, John Albert. 1300 HOSPITAL DR, STE 130 29464 #047-06-1986 L1995 **PUD SME** *020 †20

MITHOEFER, Michael C. 208 SCOTT ST 29464 #045-01-1977 L1981 **P IM** *020 †20,16,75

MITTELBRONN, Matthew A. 999 LAKE HUNTER CIR, STE B 29464 #021-05-2002 L2008 **D** *020

MITTELBRONN, Michele Ann. 999 LAKE HUNTER CIR, STE B 29464 #011-03-1997 L2001 **D** *020 †15

MOODY, Lara W. ■ 29464 #045-01-2008 *012

MORGAN, Rex Shad. 1220 HOSPITAL DR 29464 #001-06-2001 L2002 **IMG** *020

MORROW, David Lendrum. 767 JOHNNIE DODDS BLVD 29464 #045-01-1994 L1997 **ORS** *020 †40

MULLANEY, Joseph Martin. 1241 WOODLAND AVE 29464 #051-04-1992 L1997 **VIR DR** *020 †80

MULLER, Erica Lee. 1280 JOHNNIE DODDS BLVD, UNIT 300 29464 #048-13-2000 L2004 **D** *020

MULLER, Matthew Scott. 514 FERRY ST, HYPERBARIC MED 29464 #048-02-2002 L2005 **EM** *012

MULLINAX, Lee Ashley. 1200 JOHNNIE DODDS BLVD, MT PLEASANT ANES ASSOC 29464 #045-01-2001 L2006 **AN** *020 †05

MURPHY, Brendan Burke. 1439 STUART ENGALS BLVD, STE 100 29464 #011-04-1997 L2006 **CRS** *100 †85

MURPHY, Maria Margarita. 1439 STUART ENGALS BLVD, STE 100 29464 #264-10-1996 L2006 **GS** *020 †85,10

NAWABI, Mohammad Daud. 900 BOWMAN RD STE 103, LOWCOUNTRY HEMATOL & ONCOL 29464 #045-01-1992 L1995 **HO** *020 †20

NETHERTON, Mark Douglas. 1092 JOHNNIE DODDS BLVD, STE A2 29464 #045-01-1991 L1992 **AN** *020 †05

NETZLER, Peter Cliff. ■ 29464 #045-01-2006 L2006 **IM** *012

NICHOLSON, John Alexander. 3400 SALTERBECK CT, STE 102 29466 #012-01-1984 L1991 **PM** *020 †60

NIELSEN, Odd S. ■ 29464 #024-05-1947 L1949 **DR LM** *071

NOBLE, Shannon Mitchum. 309 WINGO WAY STE 101, SEASIDE PEDIATRICS 29464 #045-01-1997 L2006 **PD** *020 †55

NORTON, Heather Rae. ■ 29464 #011-02-2007 L2007 *012

NOVOTNY, Christopher A. ■ 29466 #036-05-2002 L2007 **PTH** *100

O'BRIEN, Sabrina Gail. ■ 29466 #020-12-1995 L1996 **GP N** *020

O'DAY, David Geo. 1280 JOHNNIE DODDS BLVD, UNIT 100 29464 #010-02-1985 L1996 **OPH** *020 †35

O'DELL, Robert Furman. 180 WINGO WAY STE 206 29464 #045-01-1970 L1971 **ON IM** *020 †20

OHLSON, Blake Lamonte. 594 LONE TREE DR 29464 #038-06-2001 L2004 **OFA** *020

OTTINGER, William Stanley. 570 LONG POINT RD 29464 #045-01-1994 L1995 **OBG** *020 †30

OWENS, Stuart Cameron. 767 JOHNNIE DODDS BLVD 29464 #045-01-1981 L1983 **OTO HNS** *071 †45

PAPADOPOULOS, Demetrios A. 900 BOWMAN RD, STE 203 29464 #036-07-1975 L1978 **FM** *020 †18

PAPPAS, Theodore M. 1435 STUART ENGALS BLVD 29464 #045-01-1989 L1992 **FM** *020 †18

PARKER, Telfair Hodgson. 180 WINGO WAY, STE 308 29464 #045-01-1973 L1976 **GS** *020 †85

PATEL, Ashwin Viren. ■ 29466 #045-01-2008 *012

PATTON, Grant Wm. 1200 JOHNNIE DODDS BLVD 29464 #016-06-1965 L1971 **OBG** *020 †30

PAUL, John R, Jr. 751 JOHNNIE DODDS BLVD 29464 #045-01-1942 L1942 **PD** *071 †55

PAWLIK, Joseph Wojciech. 1031 HIGHWAY 41, STE 100 29466 #025-01-1995 L2005 **EM** *020

PELIC, Christine Marie. ■ 29466 #038-43-2001 L2003 **P** *100 †75

PHILLIPS, Misha Janelle. ■ 29464 #055-01-2007 L2007 **FP** *012

PHILLIPS, William E, II. 1241 WOODLAND AVE 29464 #011-04-1992 L1997 **VIR** *020 †80

PIASKOWSKI, Ronald Alan. 1241 WOODLAND AVE 29464 #045-01-1988 L1997 **RNR** *020 †20

PILLAI, Ranjini. 570 LONG POINT RD, STE 230 29464 #495-63-1986 L1996 **IM ON** *020 †20

PLATZ, Elizabeth Ann. 1100 LEGENDS CLUB DR 29466 #045-01-2003 L2004 **OBG** *020

POUND, Toya Diann. 1280 JOHNNIE DODDS BLVD 29464 #045-01-1996 L1998 **OBG** *020 †30

POWELL, Sandra Lynn. 1041 JOHNNIE DODDS BLVD, STE 5A 29464 #045-01-1980 L1981 **PD** *020 †55

PRICE, James Lester, Jr. 594 LONE TREE DR 29464 #045-01-1979 L1985 **HS ORS** *020 †40

PRITCHETT, John Travis. 409 COLEMAN BLVD STE 1A 29464 #023-07-1988 L1992 **P** *020 †75

PRUITT, Mark Cleveland. 1665 LAUDA DR 29464 #045-04-2003 L2004 **AN** *012

PUCKETTE, Thomas Childs. 1241 WOODLAND AVE 29464 #045-01-1989 L1995 **DR** *020 †80

PURVES, J Todd. ■ 29464 #016-11-2000 **U** *100

QUICKERY, Kerrie Renee. ■ 29464 #017-20-2003 L2007 **PTH** *020 †50

RAIZES, Elliot G. ■ 29464 #016-06-1981 L1985 **ID IM** *020 †20

RAMAN, Sripriya. ■ 29466 #495-59-2001 L2006 **PD** *012

RAMBO, William Milton. 48 RIALTO RD 29464 #041-01-1958 L1961 **GS** *071 †85

RAWLS, James Turlington. 1200 JOHNNIE DODDS BLVD, DEPT OF ANESTH E COOPER RG 29464 #045-01-1992 L1993 **AN** *020 †05

REED, Frederick Edgar, Jr. 890 JOHNNIE DODDS BLVD, # 3 29464 #045-01-1969 L1969 **ORS** *020 †40

RHETT, Edmund, Jr. 1300 HOSPITAL DR STE 270, LOW COUNTRY OB & GYN 29464 #012-01-1974 L1977 **OBG** *020 †30

ROBSON, John Robert Keith. ■ 29466 #917-04-1948 L1979 *071

ROGERSON, Phyllis Wright. 1400 HOSPITAL DR 29464 #036-05-1987 L1988 **OBG** *020 †30

ROSE, Kelly L. ■ 29464 #045-01-2005 L2005 **PTH** *012

ROUSH, Thomas Fretz. 1106 CHUCK DAWLEY BLVD, STE 200 29464 #038-41-2001 L2004 **ORS** *012

ROWE, John R. 180 WINGO WAY STE 207, EAST COOPER FAMILY PRACTIC 29464 #045-01-1968 L1968 **FM** *020

ROWE, John Roger, Jr. 913 BOWMAN RD, EAST COOPER FAMILY PRACTIC 29464 #045-01-1998 L2001 **FM** *020 †18

RUBANO, Judith E. 1208 TWO ISLAND CT 29466 #048-15-1990 L1991 **IM** *020 †20

RUBEY, Robert Neal. 271 BAYVIEW DR 29464 #007-02-1988 L1989 **P** *020 †75

SAADEH, Kris. 46 EASTLAKE RD 29464 #012-05-1995 L1996 **DR NM** *020 †80,28

SAITO, Angela Marie. 1000 JOHNNIE DODDS BLVD, STE 103-175 29464 #045-01-1992 L1993 **FM** *020 †18

SCHAEFER, John J. ■ 29466 #055-01-1988 L1990 **AN** *040 †05

SCHAFFER, Richard S, Jr. 710 JOHNNIE DODDS BLVD, STE 315 29464 #048-02-1995 L2004 **FM** *020 †18

SCHIMENTI, Marilyn. ■ 29464 #024-05-1980 L1983 **GP N** *020

SCHMIDT, William Gert, Jr. 900 BOWMAN RD, STE 103 29464 #036-05-1994 L1995 **IM** *020 †20

SCHNORR, John Anthony, Jr. 1200 JOHNNIE DODDS BLVD 29464 #003-01-1994 L2001 **OBG REN** *020 †30

SCHULMAN, Paul Leon. ■ 29466 #035-08-1958 L1966 **HEM ON** *071 †20

SCOTT, Sheri Lynn. 156 BOWMAN RD, UNIT 105 29464 #011-04-1993 L1994 **PD** *020 †55

SCOTT, Valerie Ann. 570 LONG POINT RD, SUITE150 29464 #012-05-1984 L1985 **FM FPG** *020 †18

SEYMOUR, Elwood Quitman. ■ 29464 #045-01-1955 L1956 **R** *071 †80

SHABBIR, Munira. ■ 29464 #704-26-2001 L2007 **HO** *012 †20
SHAMBLIN, Clayton Joel. ■ 29464 #055-01-2006 L2006 **IM** *012
SHARPE, Elizabeth D. 721 LONG POINT RD, GLAUCOMA CONSULTANTS 29464 #012-01-1980 L1981 **OPH** *020 †35
SHILLITO, Judy Ann. 631 JOHNNIE DODDS BLVD 29464 #025-01-1986 L1987 **FM** *020 †18
SHORT, Jeffrey Keith. 1241 WOODLAND AVE, DIAGNOSTIC RADIOLOGY OF 29464 #045-01-1988 L2000 **VIR** *020 †80
SIMMONS, Carol Lynn. ■ 29466 #055-01-1986 L1988 **OBG** *020 †30
SIMMONS, G Millard, Jr. ■ 29466 #050-02-1966 L1968 **OBG MFM** *071 †30
SINGLETON, Stephanie Dare. 1375 HOSPITAL DR, SOUTHEASTERN FERTILITY CEN 29464 #012-22-1999 L2006 **OBG** *020
SKEENS, Heather Michelle. ■ 29464 #055-02-2002 L2008 **OPH** *020
SKINNER, Bruce Stuart. ■ 29464 #561-07-1981 L1986 **IM** *020
SLOAN, Alexander Matthew. ■ 29464 #041-01-1948 L1953 **U** *071
SMITH, Andrew Robert. ■ 29464 #045-01-2007 L2007 **IM** *012
SMITH, David Kevin. 1300 HOSPITAL DR STE 250 29464 #045-01-1977 L1978 **GYN EM** *020 †30
SMITH, W Sean. 1241 WOODLAND AVE 29464 #038-41-1983 L1997 **DR GP** *020 †80
SMITH-PHILLIPS, Stephanie. 1280 JOHNNIE DODDS BLVD, UNIT 300 29464 #036-07-1980 L1982 **D** *020 †15
SOKOL, Allen B. ■ 29464 #045-01-1953 L1953 **PD** *071 †55
SORRELL, John Foster. 1200 JOHNNIE DODDS BLVD 29464 #012-01-1982 L1983 **EM** *020 †16
STAFFORD, Sam, III. 1280 JOHNNIE DODDS BLVD, UNIT 300 29464 #045-01-1971 L1977 **D PD** *020 †55,15
STALLWORTH, William King. ■ 29464 #021-01-1959 L1963 **GYN** *071 †30
STEELE, Jennifer Anne. 1280 JOHNNIE DODDS BLVD, UNIT 300 29464 #051-04-1997 L2004 **D** *020 †55,15 ‡
STEICHEN, John David. 1341 OLD GEORGETOWN RD, STE A 29464 #024-01-1985 L1997 **NS** *020 †25 ‡
STEINBERG, Robert Michael. 1000 JOHNNIE DODDS BLVD, STE 103-330 29464 #045-01-1977 L1984 **DR** *020 †80
STEWART, Scott Hastings. ■ 29466 #041-13-1993 L1999 **IM** *020 †20
STITH, Suzanne Jaskwhich. 852 LOWCOUNTRY BLVD, STE 102 29464 #045-01-1995 L1996 **D DMP** *020 †15
STONE, Stephen Preston. ■ 29464 #051-01-1981 L1982 **EM** *020 †20
STRASSBURG, David Alan. ■ 29466 #050-02-1968 L1973 **PD** *071 †55
STROUD, William Hugh, Jr. 1240 HOSPITAL DR 29464 #045-01-1973 L1976 **GS VS** *020 †85
STROUT, Cynthia Becher. 1156 BOWMAN RD, UNIT 102 29464 #017-20-1985 L1993 **FM** *020 †18
STUBBS, Hal Session. ■ 29466 #021-01-1955 L1955 **U** *071 †95
STURDIVANT, John Lacy. ■ 29464 #001-02-1996 L2000 **CD** *020 †20
SULLIVAN, Brigid Eileen. ■ 29464 #045-01-2008 *012
SURANYI, Pal. ■ 29466 #473-03-2000 L2007 *100
SUWANRSUME, Harit. ■ 29464 #891-01-1992 L2002 **HO** *100 †20
SWEET, Raymond Chas. 144 N PLAZA CT 29464 #045-01-1973 L1996 **NS** *020 †25
TAGGART, James David. 1241 WOODLAND AVE 29464 #041-01-1971 L1980 **DR** *020 †80
TANGEMAN, Cayce Cole. 3070 HIGHWAY 17 N, STE 201 29466 #045-04-2001 L2002 **FM** *020 †18
TAPERT, Michael Jos. 1300 HOSPITAL DR, STE 370 29464 #025-01-1976 L1981 **OPH** *071 †35
TAYLOR, Joan Wynn. 3070 HIGHWAY 17 N 29466 #045-01-1984 L1985 **GP** *020
TAYLOR, Steven James. 1150 HUNGRYNECK BLVD STE C, 337 29464 #035-01-1972 L1973 **EM FM** *071 †18,16
TERRY, Delinda Harden. 1400 HOSPITAL DR 29464 #012-01-1979 L1980 **OBG** *020 †30
TEUTON, Michael Eugene. 1121 PARK WEST BLVD, STE B 29466 #045-01-1978 L1979 **OM OBG** *020
THOMAS, Karen Walters. 180 WINGO WAY STE 307 29464 #045-01-1995 L1996 **IM** *020
THOMAS, Theresa Joan. 1210 CHUCK DAWLEY BLVD 29464 #005-11-1987 L1994 **PD** *020 †55
THOMPSON, Chas Murry, Jr. 900 BOWMAN RD STE 304 29464 #045-01-1977 L2005 **PD** *020 †55
THOMPSON, Christine C. 1200 JOHNNIE DODDS BLVD 29464 #045-01-1986 L1987 **AN** *020 †05
THOMPSON, Jos Du Rant, Jr. 594 LONE TREE DR 29464 #045-01-1965 L1965 **ORS** *020 †40
THOMPSON, Joseph Jenkins. ■ 29464 #045-01-2007 L2007 **IM** *012
THOMPSON, Robert Scott. 897 VON KOLNITZ RD, MT PLEASANT INTERNAL MEDIC 29464 #048-12-1987 L1994 **IM** *020 †20
TOUNTAS, Chris Peter. 180 WINGO WAY, STE 106 29464 #023-01-1963 L1992 **ORS HS** *020 †40
TUTUIAN, Radu-Ioan I. ■ 29466 #781-01-1997 L2003 **GE** *100 †20
TYLER, Jane Leslie. 570 LONG POINT RD, METABOLIC MEDICAL CENTER 29464 #010-02-1978 L1979 **NM** *020 †20,28
UNDERWOOD, Paul Benj. 1280 JOHNNIE DODDS BLVD 29464 #045-01-1959 L1959 **ON OBG** *030 †30
UPTON, Laurie Beth. ■ 29466 #051-07-2007 L2007 **FP** *012
VANA, Matthew Robert. ■ 29466 #051-07-2007 L2007 **IM** *012
VAUGHAN, G Dennis, III. 1551 BEN SAWYER BLVD, UNIT 46 29464 #051-01-1973 L1980 **TS VS** *071 †85,90
VELA, Stacie Ann. ■ 29466 #038-40-2002 L2004 **GE** *012 †20
VERMA, Nitin. ■ 29464 #495-72-2001 L2006 **HO** *012 †20
VIECHNICKI, Tara Marie. 1705 BEAUCASTEL RD 29464 #041-15-1999 L2003 **GE** *020 †35
VOGEL, Steven Lee. 1241 WOODLAND AVE 29464 #024-05-1977 L1984 **DR IM** *020 †20,80
VOGT, Martin Vincent. ■ 29464 #020-12-1986 L1988 **AN** *020 †05
VOLKMAN, Fred Marty. ■ 29466 #016-01-1981 L1981 **PD** *030 †55
VON LEHE, John Andrew. 3400 SALTERBECK CT, STE A 29466 #045-01-2000 L2001 *020 †18 ‡
VORIES, Michael William. 498 WANDO PARK BLVD, STE 400 29464 #020-12-1996 L2003 **PME** *020 †18
VROMAN, Deanna D. 1280 JOHNNIE DODDS BLVD, EAST COOPER MED SPEC ASSOC 29464 #023-01-1995 L1996 **IM** *020 †20
WALLEN, Romita Lal. 2168 TALL GRASS CIR 29466 #045-01-2000 L2003 **FM** *020 †18
WARBURTON, Keeling Alfred. ■ 29464 #051-07-1963 L1996 **OBG** *071 †30
WARD, James Granbery, Jr. 121 PITT ST 29464 #045-01-1966 L1966 **PD PTH** *020 ‡
WARD, John Wesley, III. 631 JOHNNIE DODDS BLVD 29464 #036-05-1977 L2001 **IM** *020 †20
WARNER, Amy Stogner. 1400 HOSPITAL DR 29464 #045-01-1982 L2002 **OBG** *020 †30
WARNER, Amy Sue. 1400 HOSPITAL DR 29464 #035-09-1985 L1987 **IM** *020 †20
WEAVER, John Edward. 735 JOHNNIE DODDS BLVD, MUSC STORM EYE CLINIC 29464 #045-01-1978 L1989 **OPH** *020 †35

WEAVER, Robert Charles. 1041 JOHNNIE DODDS BLVD, STE 5A 29464 #045-01-1987 L1990 **PD** *020 †55
WEINHEIMER, Charles A, III. 1200 JOHNNIE DODDS BLVD 29464 #045-01-1991 L1992 **AN** *020 †05
WERSHING, Julie M. ■ 29464 #010-02-1958 L1990 **PD PDC** *071 †55
WEST, Henry Cowardin. 180 WINGO WAY, STE 308 29464 #045-01-1985 L1990 **GS VS** *020 †85
WHITE, Debra Ann. 1001 ANNA KNAPP EXT 29464 #045-01-1984 L1985 **P** *020 †75
WHITE, Janet O. 309 WINGO WAY STE 101, SEASIDE PEDIATRICS PA 29464 #054-04-1992 L1993 **PD** *020 †55
WIETERS, Thomas Russell. 3070 N HIGHWAY 17, STE 202 29466 #045-01-1979 L1981 **PHL GS** *070
WILCOX, Kandis G. 1000 JOHNNIE DODDS BLVD, STE 103 29464 #045-01-1999 L2003 **P** *020
WILL, Heather Michelle. ■ 29466 #051-07-2004 L2006 **NPM** *012 †55
WILLIAMS, Heidi Dollenber. 999 LAKE HUNTER CIR, STE D 29464 #010-01-1996 L2002 **PS** *020 †65
WILLIAMS, Monica Ann. ■ 29464 #012-21-2007 L2007 **AN** *012
WILLIAMSON, Bridget T. 1280 JOHNNIE DODDS BLVD, UNIT 200 29464 #045-01-2001 L2004 **OBG** *100
WILLIAMSON, Hubert Oliver. ■ 29464 #045-01-1956 L1961 **GYN REN** *072 †30
WILSON, William Earl. 900 BOWMAN RD STE 203 29464 #028-03-1975 **FM** *020 †18
WINGFIELD, William, Jr. 321 WINGO WAY, STE 102 29464 #045-01-1970 **IM PA** *020 †20
WITHERSPOON, Samuel M, Jr. ■ 29464 #045-01-1952 AN *071 †05
WOLF, Alicia E. ■ 29464 #048-12-1988 L1990 **PD** *020
WOLMAN, Maggie Giblin. ■ 29464 #045-01-2002 L2006 **OBG** *020
WRIGHT, Louis Dixon, Jr. 753 JOHNNIE DODDS BLVD 29464 #045-01-1960 L1961 **PTH** *071 †50
WRISTON, Gretchen Ann. ■ 29464 #045-01-2000 L2007 **DR** *100 †80
WURTHMANN, Polly Ann. 1200 JOHNNIE DODDS BLVD 29464 #045-01-1993 L1996 **AN** *020 †05
YANTIS, Paul Lester, III. 1300 HOSPITAL DR, STE 300 29464 #012-01-1976 L1977 **GE** *020 †20
YOUNG, Jeremy Wm Rory. 1341 OLD GEORGETOWN RD # C 29464 #917-21-1973 L1993 **DR** *050
ZACCAGNI, Hayden John. ■ 29466 #048-13-2006 L2006 **PD** *012
ZHANG, Linsheng. ■ 29464 #243-94-1986 L2007 **PTH** *012
ZIMLICH, Kimberly Sansbur. 309 WINGO WAY, STE 101 29464 #045-01-1992 L1993 **PD** *020 †55

MULLINS – MARION

BAHAN, Marc Gaylord. 2835 E HIGHWAY 76, STE 7 29574 #045-01-1994 L1997 **PD** *020 †55
CARROLL, Mark Wm. 2829 E HIGHWAY 76 29574 #422-01-1985 L2002 **EM PD** *020 †16
DAWANI, Parmanand J. 518C S MAIN ST 29574 #704-02-1962 L1976 **IM CD** *071 †20
FLOYD, Iris Marie. 2845 E HIGHWAY 76 STE 5B, TOTAL FAMILY CARE 29574 #305-01-2002 L2003 **FM** *020 †18
GANGI, Glenn Ross. 2835 E HIGHWAY 76, STE 3 29574 #035-46-1982 L1994 **U GS** *020 †95
GARNER, James S, Jr. 3032 E HIGHWAY 76 29574 #045-01-1946 L1946 **FM** *020 †18
GARNER, James Saml, IV. 3032 E HIGHWAY 76 29574 #045-01-1976 L1977 **FM** *020 †18
GASKIN, Hugh C, III. 3032 E HIGHWAY 76 29574 #045-01-1982 L1987 **OPH** *020 †35
GRUDZINSKI, Andrew Robert. 2835 E HIGHWAY 76 STE 3 29574 #016-42-1993 L1999 **U** *020 †95
HOOKS, Rosanne Jordan. 1004 S MAIN ST 29574 #051-04-1981 L1982 **FM** *020
LIBBY, John Pershing, II. 2829 E HIGHWAY 76 29574 #003-01-1980 L1999 **EM GS** *020 †16
MATHISUTHAN, Gangatharan. 511 S MAIN ST 29574 #495-95-1989 L1996 **IM** *020 †20
MENON, Preeth Achuthan. 511 S MAIN ST 29574 #495-18-1992 L2001 **NEP** *020 †20
MINCEY, Kenneth Hudson. 2835 E HIGHWAY 76 STE 5 29574 #045-01-1981 L1982 **GS VS** *020 †85
MULLINS, Julie Ann. ■ 29574 #055-75-2002, ▲ L2004 **OBG** *020
MURRAY, Ernest E. 2845 E HIGHWAY 76, STE 3 29574 #132-01-1965 L1978 **OBG** *020 †30 ‡
ODOM, John Newberry. 3032 E HIGHWAY 76 29574 #045-01-1991 L1992 **FM** *020 †18
RAO, Vege Rama Krishna. 2845 E HIGHWAY 76, STE 4 29574 #495-50-1970 L1978 **PD** *020 †55
REGEC, Stephen Paul. 2845 E HIGHWAY 76, STE 3 29574 #035-08-1974 L2007 **OBG** *020 †30
ROBERTS, Mark Dozier. 2845 E HIGHWAY 76 STE 5-A, DEPT PEDIATRICS 29574 #045-01-2003 L2006 **PD** *020 †55
ROSS, Mark Jay. 3032 E HIGHWAY 76 29574 #010-02-1977 L1984 **OPH** *020 †20,35
SMITH, Stuart Alva. 2829 E HIGHWAY 76 29574 #051-01-1978 L2002 **EM FM** *020 †16,18
STOKES, Hunter Rhoad, Jr. 3032 E HIGHWAY 76 29574 #045-01-1987 L1991 **IM** *020 †35
THOURANI, Harichand. 511 S MAIN ST 29574 #704-08-1963 L1976 **IM** *020
YOUNG, Eric Saml. 2835 E HIGHWAY 76, STE 5 29574 #045-04-1992 L2001 **GS** *020 †85
ZAKHOUR, Isam Jamil. 3032 E HIGHWAY 76 29574 #605-01-1976 L1982 **OPH** *020 †35
ZAVELL, Peter Jos. 2829 E HIGHWAY 76 29574 #048-14-1992 L1998 **EM** *020 †16

MURRELLS INLET – HORRY

AKTUG, Bulent Kamil. 694 JAMESTOWN DR 29576 #902-03-1956 L1982 **P** *020
ALFONSO, Mayra I. ■ 29576 #042-02-1992 L2000 **PM** *020
ANDERSON, David R. 2150 S WACCAMAW DR, GEORGETOWN MEMORIAL HOSPIT 29576 #045-01-1989 L2002 **DR** *020 †80
ANGUELOV, Ivo Valentinov. 675 WACHESAW RD, UNIT A 29576 #198-01-1990 L2000 **IM** *020 †20
ANGUELOVA, Dora L. 675 WACHESAW RD UNIT A 29576 #198-01-1989 L2001 **IM** *020 †20
BINDNER, Cynthia Givens. 4017 HIGHWAY 17 29576 #039-01-1988 L1992 **OBG** *020 †30
CHAMBERS, Thomas John. 4367 RIVERWOOD DR, UNIT 120 29576 #018-03-1990 L1996 **ORS OSM** *020 †40
CHASTAIN, Doyle Edward. ■ 29576 #011-02-1960 L1978 **IM** *071 †20
CREMER, Steven Marc. 4367 RIVERWOOD DR UNIT 130 29576 #045-01-1978 L1982 **FM** *020 †18 ‡
DOERING, Charles J. 4055 HIGHWAY 17, COASTAL EYE GROUP PC 29576 #035-08-1998 L2006 **OPH** *020 †35
ELLIS, Michael Holland. 912 INLET SQUARE DR 29576 #045-01-1978 L1979 **GS VS** *020 †85
EPPERSON, William Jackson. 912 INLET SQUARE DR 29576 #045-04-1984 L1985 **FM** *020 †18
EPSTEIN, Aaron M. 912 INLET SQUARE DR 29576 #045-01-1992 L1999 **GS** *020
EVERMAN, David Glenn. 4367 RIVERWOOD DR, UNIT 120 29576 #045-01-1998 L2002 **ORS** *020
FAIREY, William Fletcher. 4070 HIGHWAY 17 29576 #045-01-1965 L1965 **PTH** *030 †50

FARINA, Angel. ■ 29576 #132-01-1951 L1962 **FM** *071 †18
FISHER-JANES, Shelia. 2926 S HIGHWAY 17 29576 #045-01-1984 L1985 **FM** *020
GAMMEL, Joseph John. 4070 HIGHWAY 17 29576 #024-07-1997 L2000 **EM** *020 †16
GAMMON, William Reed. 912 INLET SQUARE DR, INLET MEDICAL ASSOCIATES 29576 #018-03-1993 L1998 **FM** *020 †18
GAUL, R Wharton. ■ 29576 #041-01-1953 L1953 **ORS** *071 †40
GERBER, Christine Stanley. 4017 HIGHWAY 17 29576 #041-02-1988 L1997 **OBG** *020 †30
GIDDENS, Eugene M. 4367 RIVERWOOD DR, UNIT 120 29576 #045-01-1989 L1990 **NS** *020 †25
HARMON, Gerald Edward. 4070 HIGHWAY 17 29576 #045-01-1976 L1978 **FM AM** *020 †18 ‡
HARVEY, Stephen Andrew. ■ 29576 #045-01-1986 L1989 **EM** *020 †18
HAZELTON, John Ronald. 4055 HIGHWAY 17, COASTAL EYE GROUP PC 29576 #033-05-1997 L2002 **OPH** *020 †35
HUBACH, Karl Stacy. 4367 RIVERWOOD DR, UNIT 240 29576 #010-01-1990 L1994 **FM GYN** *020 †18
KIMPTON, Robert Erskine. 2347 S HIGHWAY 17, MED PLUS 29576 #305-01-1999 L2003 **FM** *020 †18
KING, Scott Kenneth. 4070 HIGHWAY 17 29576 #016-42-1996 L2002 **EM** *020 †16
MASELLI, Lisa Renee. 4017 HIGHWAY 17 29576 #055-02-1996 L2000 **OBG** *020 †30
MAY, Charles Raysor, III. 380 PARSONAGE LN 29576 #045-01-1962 L1962 **AN** *071
MC CAFFREY, Michael. 4367 RIVERWOOD DR, UNIT 120 29576 #422-01-1988 L1996 **N** *020 †75
MOSS, Gene Thomas, Jr. 4055 HIGHWAY 17, COASTAL EYE GROUP PC 29576 #011-04-1999 L2001 **OPH** *020 †35
OWENS, Charles Haynes. ■ 29576 #036-01-1954 L1960 **OBG** *071
PARSLEY, Betsy Allen. ■ 29576 #036-05-1969 L1969 **PD** *071 †55
PLY, Jonathan J. 3911 HIGHWAY 17 29576 #023-12-1986 L1993 **OPH** *020 †35
RATZ, Michael James. 4070 HIGHWAY 17 29576 #759-01-2003 L2007 **MPD** *100 †20
RICHMOND, Gayle Ann. 4017 HIGHWAY 17 29576 #045-01-1983 L1985 **OBG** *020 †30
SANDOZ, George. 4367 RIVERWOOD DR, UNIT 120 29576 #132-09-1986 L1998 **OPH** *020 †75,35
SASSER, Paul Long. 912 INLET SQUARE DR 29576 #045-01-1986 L1987 **GS VS** *020 †85
SCHEXNAYDER, Jerry A, Jr. 4367 RIVERWOOD DR, UNIT 120 29576 #035-01-1990 L1996 **ORS OSM** *020 †40
SILBIGER, Stephen Alan. 4070 HIGHWAY 17 29576 #035-15-1972 L2000 **IM** *020 †20
STALVEY, Harold D. ■ 29576 #047-05-1947 L1974 **P PYA** *071 †75
TALBERT, Oliver Rhett. ■ 29576 #045-01-1945 L1945 **N DR** *071 †75
TEW, Jessica Deysach. ■ 29576 #045-04-1995 L1996 **PD** *020 †55
TUREK, James E. 2347 S HIGHWAY 17, MED PLUS 29576 #023-12-1987 L1988 **GP OM** *020
WADUD, Rubina. 9250B HWY 17 BYP, SOUTHEAST MEDICAL ASSCS, L 29576 #160-02-1984 L1999 **IM** *020 †20
WHITEHEAD, Robert Thos. 4070 HIGHWAY 17 29576 #045-01-1986 L1987 **DR** *020 †80

MYRTLE BEACH – HORRY

ABELL, Becky Anne. ■ 29579 #045-01-2007 **EM** *012
ADLER, Brian Keith. 1945 GLENNS BAY RD 29575 #422-01-1981 L1984 **IM** *075 †20
ALVAREZ, Victor Manuel. 5046 HIGHWAY 17 BYP S, STE 100 29588 #264-13-1995 L2008 **IMG** *020 †18
ANDREWS, Stephen Francis. 4708 OLEANDER DR 29577 #041-77-2000, ▲ L2005 **RO** *100
ATKINSON, David Owen. 809 82ND PKWY 29572 #012-05-2001 L2001 **AN** *020 †05
BAENS, Mariapaz Carolina. 4615 OLEANDER DR, STE 201A 29577 #045-04-1989 L1990 **IM** *020 †20
BARBIERI, Susan Caroline. 809 82ND PKWY, OCEAN AMBULATORY SURGERY C 29572 #045-01-1990 L1996 **AN** *020 †05
BARDEN, Anne Goodman. ■ 29572 #036-05-1993 *100
BARR, Lynn Diane. 4615 OLEANDER DR, STE 201A 29577 #041-13-1994 L2003 **EM** *030 †16
BASS, Robert Steven. 4708 OLEANDER DR 29577 #047-05-1985 L1987 **RO** *020 †80
BELCHER, Kenneth Lee. 809 82ND PKWY 29572 #055-01-2003 L2006 **IM** *020 †20
BELDEN, Terry Alexander. 831 82ND PKWY 29572 #038-43-1986 L1987 **FM** *020 †18 ‡
BENZ, Francis Matthew. 909 MEDICAL CIR 29572 #051-07-2000 L2002 **N** *020 ‡
BINARD, Marc Paul. 4615 OLEANDER DR 29577 #051-07-1983 L1987 **IM** *020 †20
BITTING, George Alan. 1301 48TH AVE N 29577 #665-01-1999 L2004 **PM** *020
BOATWRIGHT, Stephen Earle. 1301 48TH AVE N 29577 #045-01-1984 L1985 **AN IM** *020 †18,05
BOGACHE, William Kent. 823 82ND PKWY, GRAND STRAND UROLOGY LLP 29572 #045-01-1983 L1988 **U** *020 †95
BOROWICZ, Mark Richard. 845 82ND PKWY, SURGICAL ASSOCIATES OF 29572 #036-05-1990 L1991 **VS** *020 †85
BORST, Christopher A. 1220 21ST AVE N 29577 #010-02-1975 L1979 **EM** *020 †18
BRANNON, James Elliott. 809 82ND PKWY 29572 #012-01-1985 L2003 **AN** *020 †05
BROOKS, Hiram Brownlee. 5050 HIGHWAY 17 BYP S 29588 #038-40-1999 L2002 **EM** *020 †16
BROWN, Franchesca Dawn. 10838 KINGS RD, OCEAN SANDS PEDIATRICS, LL 29572 #036-07-1998 L2005 **PD** *020
BRYAN, Foster Curtis, II. 809 82ND PKWY 29572 #012-05-1988 L1999 **TS** *020 †85,90 ‡
BUNN, Paul David. 945 82ND PKWY, CAROLINA HEALTH SPECIALIST 29572 #038-40-1965 L1984 **IM** *020 †20
BUTLER, Harvey Eugene, Jr. 945 82ND PKWY, STE 3 29572 #045-01-1961 L1961 **CD IM** *020 †20
CAMERANSI, Benjamin Geo. 809 82ND PKWY 29572 #305-01-1995 L1999 **AN** *020 †05
CAMPBELL, Penelope Anne. 8120 ROURK ST 29572 #020-12-2001 L2004 **PD** *020 †55
CARR, Timothy John. 5050 HIGHWAY 17 BYP S 29588 #038-41-1988 L2005 **EM** *020 †16
CHARITY, Pamela Lynn. 1120 GLENNS BAY RD, STE 101 29575 #041-09-1992 L1998 **IM** *071 †20
CHARLES, John Austin. 5050 HIGHWAY 17 BYP S 29588 #010-01-1983 L1989 **EM** *020 †16
CHENGAPPA, Kambeyanda M. ■ 29577 #495-33-1964 L1972 **GS** *020 †85
CICCARELLI, Joan Lee. ■ 29572 #036-05-1993 L1996 **PD** *020 †55
CONAWAY, Douglas Camden. 945 82ND PKWY 29572 #048-04-1975 L1997 **RHU** *020 †20
CONVALECER, Jose William. 1153 MONTICELLO DR 29577 #748-01-1999 L2006 **IM** *100 †20
COOPER, Paul Norman. ■ 29577 #041-13-1955 L1956 **AN** *071 †05
CORNELL, Timothy Thomas. 945 82ND PKWY, STE 3 29572 #016-45-1995 L1996 **CCP** *100 †55
CORNNELL, Timothy Joseph. 809 82ND PKWY 29572 #011-02-1991 L1997 **GE HEP** *020 †20
COZART, Ralph Foster. 1021 MEDICAL CIR, STE 230 29572 #045-01-1991 L1998 **PS** *020 †65
CUNNINGHAM, Calhoun Dove. 915 MEDICAL CIR, OTOLARYNGOLOGY ASSOCIATES 29572 #045-01-1966 L1966 **OTO FPS** *020 †45
DAVEY, James E. ■ 29575 #048-13-2001 L2003 **FM** *020 †18
DAVEY, Joseph James. 4591 SOCASTEE BLVD, CAROLINA HEALTH SPECIALIST 29588 #048-12-1970 L1989 **FM OM** *020 †18 ‡
DAVIS, William Hampton. 7616 DRIFTWOOD DR 29572 #036-05-1965 L1971 **U** *062 †95
DEHART, Kenneth Lee. 5050 HIGHWAY 17 BYP S 29588 #017-20-1979 L1986 **EM** *020 †16
DE SALVO, Matthew. 5050 HIGHWAY 17 BYP S 29588 #038-44-1999 L2004 **EM** *020 †16
DEVENYI, Zoltan J. 921 MEDICAL CIR 29572 #473-01-1978 L1986 **GE IM** *020 †20
DICKINSON, Lewis Garrett. 845 82ND PKWY, SURGICAL ASSOCIATES OF 29572 #045-01-1995 L2001 **GS** *020 †85
DINEEN, Kevin Michael. 906 MEDICAL CIR 29572 #010-02-1997 L1998 **PCC** *020 †20
EAGERTON, Donald Chas. 945 82ND PKWY, STE 2 29572 #045-01-1989 L1992 **END** *020 †20
EMRAN, Mohammad A Haque. 1301 48TH AVE N, STE B 29577 #160-02-1984 L1998 **IM** *020 †20
FAHY, Richard A. 3381 PHILLIS BLVD, MYRTLE BEACH PRIMARY CARE 29577 #539-06-1968 L1970 **P** *020 †75
FAM, Hany Youssef Helmy. 8120 ROURK ST 29572 #915-02-1989 L1999 **PD** *020 †55
FAVARO, Mary K Asperheim. 7724 N KINGS HWY 29572 #056-05-1969 L1971 **FM PD** *071 †55
FINKLEA, John Furman. 155 PINE TREE LN, BRIARCLIFF ACRES 29572 #045-01-1958 L1958 **OM PHP** *071 †55,70
FLINT, Lloyd Donne. ■ 29572 #008-01-1941 L1983 **U** *071 †95
FLOYD, James Leon, Jr. 1410 S KINGS HWY, DUNES URGENT MEDICAL CARE 29577 #045-01-1980 L1981 **FM EM** *020 †18
FOUSHEE, Tasha Deirdre. 228 SHOREWARD DR 29579 #012-01-1998 L2006 **DR** *020 †80
GOETOWSKI, Paul Greg. 4708 OLEANDER DR, CAROLINA REG CANCER CTR 29577 #030-05-1984 L1991 **RO** *020 †80
GOH, Kimberley Bingchu. 4610 OLEANDER DR, STE 101 29577 #020-02-1984 L1991 **PS GS** *020 †65,85
GOLDEN, Thaddeus Whitmore. 906 MEDICAL CIR 29572 #041-02-1995 L2003 **PCC** *020 †20
GOLDEN, Tracey. 1021 MEDICAL CIR, STE 220 29572 #041-13-1994 L2003 **OBG** *020 †30
GOUDIE, James Scott. 4615 OLEANDER DR, CAROLINA HEALTH SPECIALIST 29577 #019-02-2000 L2007 **EM** *020
GRAHAM, James F, Jr. 5046 HWY 17 BYP S STE 100, SOUTH STRAND SENIOR HEALTH 29588 #036-05-1965 L1969 **ADM FM** *020
GREENE, William R. 823 82ND PKWY 29572 #035-15-1971 L1978 **U** *071 †95
HAUET, Anne Maureen. 945 82ND PKWY, STE 3 29572 #051-04-1997 L1998 **CD** *020 †20
HEIMBERGER, Eric. 3515 CADUCEUS DR, AZALEA LAKES 29588 #010-02-1992 L1997 **ORS** *020 †40
HERNANDEZ, Jorge D. 1021 MEDICAL CIR, STE 200 29572 #021-01-1979 L2001 **AN PME** *075
HESS, George Wm, Jr. 811 N OCEAN BLVD 29577 #025-01-1968 L1974 **OTO** *020 †45
HOLLINGSWORTH, Scott Alan. 809 82ND PKWY, GRAND STRAND REGIONAL MED 29572 #017-20-1994 L1996 **IM** *020 †20
HOLT, Lawrence Byerly, Jr. 8121 ROURK ST, 8121 ROURK ST 29572 #036-07-1977 L1982 **ON HEM** *020 †20 ‡
HONG, David Hampton. 141 MCDONALD CT 29588 #027-01-1996 L1999 **IM** *020 †20
HONICK, Murray Glenn. 4722 HWY 17 BYP S, STRAND PSYCHIATRIC ASSOCS, 29588 #051-07-1982 L1992 **P CHP** *020 †75
HOPKINS, Melanie Alesa. 809 82ND PKWY, DIAGNOSTIC PATHOLOGY AT 29572 #045-01-1990 L1991 **PTH PCP** *020 †50
HORSTEMEYER, Derek Lee. 809 82ND PKWY 29572 #047-05-1988 L1999 **AN CCA** *020 †05
HOUGHTON, Kenneth S, Jr. 809 82ND PKWY, DEPT OF ANESTHESIA 29572 #051-04-1992 L1999 **AN** *020 †05 ‡
HUBERTY, Chad Roger. 945 82ND PKWY, STE 2 29572 #056-06-2000 L2004 **FM** *020 †18
HUNTER, Timothy Michael. 4591 SOCASTEE BLVD, CAROLINA HEALTH SPECIALIST 29588 #010-01-1990 L1996 **IM** *020
HUSSEY, Richard H, III. 4573 OLEANDER DR 29577 #045-01-1995 L1997 **D** *020 †15
HYLER, Paul Jason. 4615 OLEANDER DR, STE 201A 29577 #045-04-2000 L2003 **IM** *020 †20
INFANTE, Jorge L. 5050 HIGHWAY 17 BYP S 29588 #011-02-2002 L2005 **EM** *020 †16
JACKSON, Michael Delano. 4701 OLEANDER DR STE C, MYRTLE BEACH MEDICAL CENTE 29577 #033-05-1988 L1998 **GP** *075
JACKSON, William Arthur. 945 82ND PKWY, STE 3 29572 #045-01-1998 L1999 **CD** *020 †20
JARRETT, Joe Nelson. ■ 29572 #041-01-1939 L1941 **FM** *071 †18
JENKINS, Joseph Matthew. 4615 OLEANDER DR, STE 103 29577 #051-01-1993 L1995 **EM** *020 †16
JOHNSON, Hooper Du Bois. ■ 29572 #036-05-1953 L1980 **EM PS** *071
JONES, Genevieve. 4022 POSTAL WAY, CHARLESTON PAIN & REHAB. C 29579 #041-13-1975 L1981 **FM** *020 †18
JONES, Zaundra Lavette. ■ 29579 #055-01-2001 L2004 **FM** *100 †18
JORDAN, John Niles. 1410 S KINGS HWY 29577 #045-01-1983 L1986 **IM** *020 †20
KANAMORI, Cesar Ivan. 809 82ND PKWY 29572 #051-04-1994 L2003 **IM** *020 †20
KANG, Changho Greg. 3029 NEWCASTLE LOOP, PAIN, SPINE & SPORTS MEDIC 29588 #011-03-1991 L1998 **PM PMM** *020 †60
KARAVAN, Mark Phillip. 945 82ND PKWY, STE 3 29572 #045-01-1985 L1987 **CD IM** *020 †20
KARCIC, Edin. 5046 HWY 17 BYP S, STE 100 29588 #957-08-1986 L2001 **IMG** *020 †20
KEE, David Bryan, Jr. 8170 ROURK ST 29572 #012-05-1980 L1989 **NS** *020 †25
KHOKHAR, Belal Siddique. 4615 OLEANDER DR, CAROLINA HEALTH SPECIALIST 29577 #665-01-2003 L2007 **IM** *020 †20
KING, Donald C. 809 82ND PKWY 29572 #048-04-1993 L2002 **IM** *071 †20
KING, Erika Rochelle. 4615 OLEANDER DR, STE 201A 29577 #018-03-1997 L2001 **IM** *020 †20
KING, John Everett. 4722 HIGHWAY 17 BYP S, KING INTERNAL MEDICINE PC 29588 #422-01-1983 L1993 **IM** *020
KIRKPATRICK, Helena. 1021 MEDICAL CIR, STE 220 29572 #005-14-1981 L1998 **OBG** *020 †30
KOPLEN, Julian Arthur. ■ 29575 #051-01-1957 L1957 **IM** *020 †20
KRZYZANIAK, Kenneth E. 823 82ND PKWY, GRAND STRAND UROLOGY LLP 29572 #017-20-1975 L1981 **U** *020 †95
KUPERMAN, Jennifer. ■ 29572 #025-07-1999 L2004 **IM** *020 †20
KYREAGES, Constantine G. ■ 29575 #041-13-1951 L1952 **GS** *071
LALE, Erol. 5046 HWY 17 BYP S, STE 206 29588 #409-24-1992 L2004 **CD** *020 †20
LAMM, Renee Ruth. 3025 NEWCASTLE LOOP 29588 #051-07-1982 L1992 **ADP P** *020 †18,75 ‡
LARK, Jarratt David. 5050 HIGHWAY 17 BYP S 29588 #047-05-1988 L1992 **EM** *020 †16
LEE, Wendy Wangling. 909 MEDICAL CIR, CAROLINA RHEUMATOLOGY & NE 29572 #748-10-1989 L1997 **RHU** *020 †20
LEIBMAN, Daniel. 209 80TH AVE N 29572 #041-13-1987 L2000 **PUD** *020 †20
LEMMEL, David Franklin. 4615 OLEANDER DR, CAROLINA HEALTH SPECIALIST 29577 #016-11-2003 L2006 **EM** *020
LEUNG, John Wingpui. 1294 RIVER OAKS DR 6-0 29579 #025-12-1993 L2000 **AN** *020 ‡
LICHTMANN, Manfred W. ■ 29579 #041-02-1963 **AN** *071 †05
LINDABERRY, Jeffrey Samue. 108 FINNEGAN CT, CAROLINA FOREST 29579 #018-75-2000, ▲ L2003 **FM** *020 †18

■ = Address Information Privacy Protected

MAGGIONCALDA, Joseph A. 809 82ND PKWY 29572 #041-13-1984 L1997 **AN CCM** *020 †05 ‡
MANCUSO, Lisa Marie. 1301 48TH AVE N 29577 #041-07-1998 L2003 **APM** *020 †05
MARCINKOWSKA, Ewa Beata. 1752 HIGHWAY 501 29577 #759-08-1988 L2003 **FM** *020 †18
MARKLEY, Karyn C. 1021 MEDICAL CIR, STE 220 29572 #041-02-1994 L1998 **OBG** *020 †30
MARTEL, Thomas John. 5050 HIGHWAY 17 BYP S 29588 #051-04-1987 L1991 **EM** *020 †16
MAYHEW, Scott Kenneth. 5050 HIGHWAY 17 BYP S 29588 #025-07-2000 L2003 **EM** *020
MC GANN, Desmond Martin. 7724 N KINGS HWY 29572 #539-02-1952 L1980 **GP** *071
MC INTYRE, Alex Brian. 933 MEDICAL CIR 29572 #020-02-1978 L1985 **TS VS** *020 †85,90
MC IVER, Winston Dowd, Jr. 4615 OLEANDER DR 29577 #047-07-1997 L2000 **FM** *020
MC KAY, Lauchlan. 421 79TH AVE N 29572 #035-01-1973 L1979 **FM** *020
MCNAIR, Rebecca B. 4591 SOCASTEE BLVD 29588 #045-04-2002 L2003 **FM** *020 †18
MEZA, Yenney Enrique. 5050 HIGHWAY 17 BYP S 29588 #270-02-2000 L2007 **EM** *020
MIKOL, Edward John. 3515 CADUCEUS DR STE B 29588 #010-01-1990 L1996 **ORS OSM** *020 †40
MILANO, Charles Thos. 3792 CAGNEY LN 29577 #035-47-1977 L2002 **GYN LM** *020 †30
MITCHELL, John Scott. 108 FINNEGAN CT 29579 #051-01-1972 L1973 **FM** *020 †18
MOCK, James Nelson. 4615 OLEANDER DR, STE 201A 29577 #036-01-1988 L1993 **EM OM** *020 †16
MOLNAR, John Thos, Jr. 5050 HIGHWAY 17 BYP S 29588 #038-41-1984 L1988 **EM** *020 †16
MOLTER, Darron Jos. 809 82ND PKWY 29572 #033-05-1987 L1995 **FM** *020 †18
MOORE, Terence Neal. 4708 OLEANDER DR, CAROLINA REG CANCER CTR 29577 #036-07-1968 L1975 **RO** *071 †80 ‡
MOSHOURES, Victoria E. 929 MEDICAL CIR 29572 #422-01-1995 L1998 **IM** *020 †20
NELSON, Tracy Dawn. 1021 MEDICAL CIR, STE 220 29572 #008-01-1990 L1998 **OBG** *020 †30
NEWLIN, Elizabeth W. 5001 N KINGS HWY, STE 205A 29577 #045-01-2001 L2003 **CHP** *020 †75
NICHOLSON, George Bryan, Jr. 845 82ND PKWY, SURGICAL ASSOCIATES OF 29572 #045-01-1979 L1980 **GS** *020 †85
NORMAN, Fred Paul. 7751 N KINGS HWY STE A, NORTHWOOD PLAZA 29572 #045-01-1972 L1974 **NTR FSM** *020
O'CONNOR, William Joseph. 7724 N KINGS HWY, LITTLE RIVER MEDICAL CENTE 29572 #045-01-1998 L1999 **FM** *020 †18 ‡
OSMAN, Richard Chas. 915 MEDICAL CIR, OTOLARYNGOLOGY ASSOCIATES 29572 #016-11-1987 L1999 **OTO** *020 †45
OVERBECK, Michael Case. 5050 HIGHWAY 17 BYP S 29588 #025-01-2000 L2004 **EM** *020 †16
PARAB, Minoti Vilas. 945 82ND PKWY, STE 2 29572 #539-04-2000 L2005 **FM** *020
PARANADA, Kathleen Sumisi. ■ 29579 #748-01-1999 L2006 **ID** *020 †20
PEL, Daravuth. 3381 PHILLIS BLVD, MYRTLE BEACH PRIMARY CARE 29577 #306-01-1993 L2001 **IM** *020 †20
PELTON-FREEMAN, Lisa W. 1203 48TH AVE N, HEALTH CARE PARTNERS 29577 #045-01-1992 L1994 **N** *020
PETERS, David Clark. 809 82ND PKWY, ATTN:ANESTHESIA DEPT 29572 #023-12-1992 L2002 **AN PAN** *020 †05
PETRUSICK, Thomas Wm. 8120 ROURK ST 29572 #045-01-1973 L1974 **PD ADL** *020 †55
PHILLIPS, Stephen Jervais. 8609 MONTAGUE LN 29588 #036-01-1998 L2004 **OPH** *020 †35
PIRTTIMA, Tatiana Ivanova. ■ 29577 #011-03-1999 L2008 **R** *074 †80
POLEN, Thomas Allen. 845 82ND PKWY, SURGICAL ASSOCIATES OF 29572 #047-06-1971 L1978 **GS** *020 †85
POLICH, Vyekoslav Marko. 4701 OLEANDER DR, STE C 29577 #957-02-1962 L1976 **EM PS** *020
PROCTOR, E Le Roy, Jr. 809 82ND PKWY, DIAGNOSTIC PATHOLOGY AT 29572 #045-01-1978 L1981 **PTH FOP** *020 †50
PROCTOR, Edward Le Roy. 809 82ND PKWY, DIAGNOSTIC PATHOLOGY AT 29572 #045-01-1947 L1947 **GS** *071 †85
PURVIS, Robert Scott. 5046 HIGHWAY 17 BYP S, STE 203 29588 #041-13-1987 L1995 **D** *020 †20,15
QUIRKE, Thomas Edmond. 917 MEDICAL CIR, WACCAMAW DERMATOLOGY & PLA 29572 #033-05-1990 L2000 **PS** *020 †85,65
RAMIREZ, Maria Elena. ■ 29588 #024-05-1994 L1998 **IM** *020 †20
RATHBUN, John E. 4701 OLEANDER DR STE B 29577 #422-01-1988 L1991 **IM** *020
REGOLI, Robert Louis. ■ 29577 #065-09-1966 L1967 **FM** *071
RETALIS, Philip Paul. 906 MEDICAL CIR 29572 #033-05-1990 L1991 **PCC** *020 †20
REY, Francisco J. 904 MEDICAL CIR 29572 #308-01-1982 L1991 **IM** *020 †20
RINI, Salvatore Anthony. 905 MEDICAL CIR 29572 #035-09-1965 L1972 **OBG PS** *075 †30
RIVES, Thomas Scott. 809 82ND PKWY 29572 #030-05-1985 L1990 **EM** *020 †16
ROBERTS, Brian Jefferson. 823 82ND PKWY, GRAND STRAND UROLOGY LLP 29572 #051-01-1992 L1998 **U** *020 †95
ROBERTS, Christine K. 4378 OLEANDER DR, GYNECOLOGY SPECIALISTS 29577 #051-01-1992 L1998 **OBG** *020 †30
ROEDER, Carol Henderson. 4615 OLEANDER DR, STE 201A 29577 #035-03-1995 L2000 **EM** *020 †16
ROSNER, Daniel Lerner. 915 MEDICAL CIR, OTOLARYNGOLOGY ASSOCIATES 29572 #045-01-1990 L1991 **OTO** *020 †45
ROTZ, Clifford T, Jr. ■ 29572 #041-02-1957 L1977 **DR** *071 †80
ROYAL, Gail Millette. 401 79TH AVE N, COASTAL EYE GROUP PC 29572 #023-01-1988 L1993 **OPH** *020 †35
RUDIES, Therese. ■ 29572 #407-21-1952 L1965 *071
SABBAGH, Michel J. ■ 29579 #045-01-2006 L2006 **GS** *012
SCHECKER, Mark H. 3516 CADUCEUS DR 29588 #035-08-1984 L1995 **AI IM** *020 †20,03
SCHMITT, Richard Alan. 5050 HIGHWAY 17 BYP S 29588 #051-04-1984 L1987 **EM** *020 †16
SCHWARTZ, Steve Wendelin. ■ 29577 #036-07-1981 L1982 **FM** *074 †18
SENN, Eric Randall. 5050 HIGHWAY 17 BYP S 29588 #047-05-1988 L1992 **EM** *020 †16
SHAH, Naishaj. 831 82ND PKWY, MYRTLE BEACH FAMILY MEDICI 29572 #654-01-2003 L2007 **FM** *020 †18
SHELVER, Lyle Norman. 809 82ND PKWY, GRAND STRAND REGIONAL MED 29572 #051-04-1988 L1995 **IM** *020 †20
SHORE, Neal D. 823 82ND PKWY, GRAND STRAND UROLOGY LLP 29572 #036-07-1983 L1994 **U** *020 †95
SHULER, Daniel Lloyd. 8120 ROURK ST, ADOLESCENT MEDICINE 29572 #045-01-1998 L1999 **PD** *020 †55
SLOAN, Frank Keenan, Jr. 401 79TH AVE N, COASTAL EYE GROUP PC 29572 #045-01-1981 L1982 **OPH** *020 †35
SMITH, Dean A. 831 82ND PKWY 29572 #041-09-1982 L1998 **IM** *020 †20
SMITH, Erin Elizabeth. 8120 ROURK ST, GRAND STRAND PEDIATRICS & 29572 #026-08-2003 L2007 **PD** *100 †55
SMITH, Ryan Wesley. 809 82ND PKWY 29572 #026-08-2003 L2007 **AN** *020
SMOLENSKI, Allen Edwin. 1408 MCMASTER DR, ALLEN E SMOLENSKI MD/PC 29575 #038-06-1998 L2001 **EM** *020 †16
SONG, Young Sug. PO BOX 1885 29578 #033-06-1997 L1999 **DR** *020 †80
SPIELVOGEL, Kenneth H. 1021 MEDICAL CIR, STE 250 29572 #010-01-1997 L2001 **OBG** *020 †30
STANCUT, Pavel Mihail. 945 82ND PKWY 29572 #781-01-1972 L2002 **NEP** *020 †20
STATON, Marshall A. ■ 29578 #045-01-1973 L1975 **P** *020 †75
SUSEC, Otto Charles, Jr. 5050 HIGHWAY 17 BYP S 29588 #038-40-1994 L1996 **EM** *020 †16
TANGEMAN, Linda Marie. 141 MCDONALD CT 29588 #045-01-1996 L1999 **IM** *020 †20
TARBERT, Charles Edward. 5050 HIGHWAY 17 BYP S 29588 #038-44-2000 L2004 **EM** *020
TARBERT, Lisa Marie. 809 82ND PKWY 29572 #038-44-2000 L2004 **MPD** *020
TERCHEK, Melissa Joan. 909 MEDICAL CIR 29572 #422-01-1997 L2003 **IM RHU** *020 †20
THOMPSON, Clarence R. 3381 PHILLIS BLVD, MYRTLE BEACH PRIMARY CARE 29577 #047-07-1973 L1986 **IM** *020 †20
THOMPSON, Joel Richard. 945 82ND PKWY 29572 #055-01-1973 L1978 **GE IM** *020 †20
THRASHER, James W, Jr. 1113 48TH AVE N, STE 117 29577 #051-04-1965 L1984 **P PFP** *020 †75
TIMMERMAN, Janet Loretta. 1120 GLENNS BAY RD, STE 101 29575 #047-05-1988 L1992 **IM** *020 †20
TIPTON, Reuben Ryder. 900 MEDICAL CIR 29572 #047-06-1974 L1980 **OPH** *020 †35
TOONE, C Doyne. ■ 29572 #054-04-1957 L1975 **FM GP** *071
TRASK, Joseph Lake. 945 82ND PKWY, ASSOCS OF MYRTLE BEACH, PA 29572 #045-01-1983 L1986 **CD IM** *020 †20
TRASK, Neil Webster, III. 945 82ND PKWY STE 3, ASSOCIATION OF MYRTLE BEAC 29572 #036-07-1977 L1978 **CD IM** *020 †20
TRULUCK, David Bowen. 945 82ND PKWY STE 3, ASSOCS OF MYRTLE BEACH, PA 29572 #045-01-1989 L1996 **CD** *020 †20
TUNIS, Scott Wm. 350 HILTON RD, STE 100 29572 #051-01-1981 L1982 **OPH** *020 †35
TWINING, Jon Mitchell. 909 MEDICAL CIR 29572 #017-20-1995 L2005 **RHU** *020 †20
VAN EPPS, Susan F. 417 79TH AVE N 29572 #045-01-1982 L1983 **N** *020 †16
VILLANI, Angelo Jos, Jr. 98 CLUB DR 29572 #051-04-1967 L1973 **OBG** *020 †30
VISLOCKY, Ronald Francis. 4915 N OCEAN BLVD, STE 201A 29577 #308-11-1986 L1991 **IM IMG** *071
VUKOV, Gary Arthur. 945 82ND PKWY 29572 #036-05-1982 L1985 **GE IM** *020 †20
VU-MOLASCHI, Tatiana L. 1021 MEDICAL CIR, STE 250 29572 #422-01-2001 L2005 **OBG** *020
WAGNER, Jess Bruce. 3381 PHILLIS BLVD, MYRTLE BCH VA PRIMARY CARE 29577 #033-05-1976 L2006 **FM** *020 †18
WALLS, Charles Thos, Jr. 809 82ND PKWY, DIAGNOSTIC PATHOLOGY AT 29572 #020-02-1981 L1982 **CLP** *020 †50
WATSON, Jerry Ernest, II. 945 82ND PKWY, STE 3 29572 #048-14-1989 L1990 **CD** *020 †20
WEINSTEIN, Frederic. ■ 29572 #023-01-1971 L1971 **P CHP** *075 †75
WENZ, Kenneth Jaan. 944 MEDICAL CIR, COASTAL INTERVENTIONAL PAI 29572 #035-06-1990 L1994 **AN** *020 †05
WHITAKER, Thomas A. 900 MEDICAL CIR 29572 #047-06-1970 L1971 **OPH** *020 †35 ‡
WHITE, Steven Kelly. 1275 21ST AVE N 29577 #045-01-1979 L1982 **PS HS** *020 †65,85
WILKOSZEWSKI, Artur. 7724 N KINGS HWY 29572 #759-03-1986 L1998 **FM** *020 †18
WILLIAMS, Asbury Hamilton. 4591 SOCASTEE BLVD 29588 #045-01-1963 **FM** *020 †18
WILLIAMS, Luther R, Jr. 4573 OLEANDER DR 29577 #051-04-1973 L1980 **D** *020 †15
WILLIAMS, Todd Edward. 4708 OLEANDER DR 29577 #045-01-1987 L1988 **RO** *020 †80
WUNDER, Richard John. 809 82ND PKWY 29572 #041-07-1989 L1996 **VIR** *020 †80
YOUNG, Richard Wm. 823 82ND PKWY, GRAND STRAND UROLOGY LLP 29572 #010-02-1987 L1993 **U GS** *020 †95
ZELLER, Julie Ann. 5050 HIGHWAY 17 BYP S 29588 #038-41-2004 L2007 **EM** *020

NEWBERRY - NEWBERRY

ALFORD, Earl Curry. 2669 KINARD ST 29108 #045-01-1959 L1959 **GS TS** *020 †85
BAKER, Mary Edwina. 1905 MAIN ST 29108 #045-01-1978 L1979 **OBG** *020 †30
BERNARDO, Darly Moore. 1830 PONDFIELD RD, STE A 29108 #045-01-1989 L1992 **FM** *020 †18
BERNARDO, Michael Jerome. 1830 PONDFIELD RD, STE A 29108 #035-20-1989 L1992 **FM** *020 †18
BRADBERRY, Thomas Freeman. ■ 29108 #012-01-1993 L1995 **IM** *020
BROWN, John Williamson. 2541 EVANS ST, STE 100 29108 #036-07-1961 L1966 **GS TS** *020 †85,90 ‡
CHAPMAN, Terence Neil. 2305 HARRINGTON ST 29108 #016-01-1995 L2007 **U** *020 †95
DALE, Jonathan Brooks. 1830 PONDFIELD RD, STE A 29108 #005-12-1998 L1999 **FM OBS** *020 †18
DAVIS, Kevin Wesley. 2541 EVANS ST, STE 100 29108 #036-05-1998 L2006 **GS** *100 †85
DAVIS, Mark Andrew. 2033 MEDICAL PARK DR 29108 #011-02-1977 L1981 **IM** *020 †20
EPTING, Elmer Eugene, Jr. 2562 KINARD ST 29108 #045-01-1967 L1967 **FM** *020
FICHTNER, Kurt Alfred. 2669 KINARD ST, (ATTN: ADMIN. DEPT.) 29108 #043-01-1983 L2000 **TS GS** *020 †85,90
GARCIA, Jorge Oswaldo. 2531 EVANS ST, STE B 29108 #737-01-1993 L2000 **FM** *020 †18
GARVIN, Keene Jackson. 2669 KINARD ST 29108 #011-02-1975 **FOP** *100
GODOY, Franco Bernard. 2531 EVANS ST, STE A 29108 #737-01-1995 L2003 **FM** *100 †18
GODOY, Gisella. 2531 EVANS ST, STE A 29108 #737-01-1995 L2003 **FM** *100 †18
GREEN, John Walter. 2562 KINARD ST 29108 #051-01-1977 L1978 **FM** *020 †18
HOLADAY, Duncan Allen. 2669 KINARD ST 29108 #051-04-1992 L1994 **GP** *020
HOLTZER, Karl Wm. 145 EXECUTIVE DR, PEDIATRICS OF NEWBERRY 29108 #041-02-1991 L2004 **PD** *020 †55
HUGHES, Everett Mc Querns. 2201 MAIN ST 29108 #045-01-1962 L1962 **R** *020 †80
HUNT, Corey Dale. 2525 KINARD ST 29108 #054-04-1988 L1989 **FM** *020 †18
LIVINGSTON, Robert E, III. 2306 HARRINGTON ST, P O BOX 130 29108 #045-01-1965 L1965 **OPH** *020 †35
LONG, Elmer Gordon. 2525 KINARD ST 29108 #045-01-1970 L1971 **FM** *020 †18
MASON, Helen Ringer. 2043 MEDICAL PARK DR, NEWBERRY CTY MNTL HLTH 29108 #045-01-1963 L1963 **P** *020
MASSI, Daniel Spong. ■ 29108 #654-01-1997 L1999 **PTH** *020
MATZINGER, Steven Alfred. 2541 EVANS ST, STE 100 29108 #038-43-1996 L2001 **GS** *020 †85
PAYSINGER, Alan Johnstone. 2033 MEDICAL PARK DR 29108 #045-01-2003 L2004 **IM** *020 †20
ROSS, Janice M E. 185 EXECUTIVE DR, NEWBERRY PATHOLOGY ASSOCS 29108 #035-15-1972 L1997 **PTH FOP** *020 †50
SCATES, Kyle Wayne. 2032 MEDICAL PARK DR 29108 #025-07-1992 L2002 **OTO** *020 †45
SEXTON, Joel Steven. 185 EXECUTIVE DR 29108 #045-01-1968 L1968 **PTH FOP** *020 †50
THOMPSON, John Meredith. 2033 MEDICAL PARK DR 29108 #010-01-1974 L1975 **IM** *020 †20

■ = Address Information Privacy Protected

TOLAN, Merritt Ashley. 2669 KINARD ST 29108 #045-01-1992 L1993 **AN** *020 †05

NINETY SIX – GREENWOOD

BRYANT, R Michael. 103 LITTLE MOUNTAIN RD, PIEDMONT HEALTH GROUP LLC 29666 #045-01-1989 L1991 **FM FSM** *020 †18

MEARNS, Robert David. ■ 29666 #045-04-1988 L1989 **EM** *030 †16

MUFUKA, Douglas Garikai. ■ 29666 #035-15-1973 L1974 **NEP MPD** *020 †20

ROBINSON, Dan Wesley, Jr. 103 LITTLE MOUNTAIN RD, PIEDMONT HEALTH GROUP LLC 29666 #012-01-1988 L1989 **FM EM** *020 †18

NORTH – ORANGEBURG

BRAVO FERNANDEZ, Enrique. ■ 29112 #023-07-1942 L1963 **N** *071 †75

NORTH AUGUSTA – AIKEN

AHLMAN, Mark Allan. ■ 29841 #012-01-2008 *012

AVANT, Cameron Clinton. ■ 29841 #012-01-2000 L2001 **PTH PCP** *100 †50

BAREFIELD, Tracy Robin. 105 E HUGH ST 29841 #012-01-1993 L2007 **FM** *020 †18

BEDINGFIELD, Wade R, Jr. ■ 29841 #012-01-1948 L1958 **IM** *071

BIGGER, John Franklin, Jr. ■ 29841 #028-02-1964 L1964 **OPH** *071 †35

BRODER, Jeffrey Neal. 1201 WEST AVE 29841 #035-09-1983 L1990 **GP OM** *020

BRYANT, Lindsay Elizabeth. ■ 29841 #045-04-2008 *012

BUCHANAN, Ralph Wm. ■ 29841 #012-01-1973 L1975 **FM** *020 †18

BURKHALTER, William H, III. 959 CAMPBELLTON DR 29841 #045-01-1999 L1999 **FP** *012

BURNETTE, Teresa June. ■ 29841 #001-06-2006 **IM** *012

CHALKER, Thomas Lee. ■ 29841 #012-01-1996 L1998 **FM** *100

CHAMPAGNE, Jason Paul. ■ 29860 #021-05-2006 **OTO** *012

CREWS, Lindsay King. ■ 29860 #012-01-2006 **AN** *012

DE VORE, Margaret Bowen. ■ 29841 #045-01-1955 L1955 **AN** *071 †05

DUBOSE, Jacqueline. ■ 29841 #012-01-2006 **FP** *012

EDWARDS, T Keith. ■ 29860 #036-05-1955 L1955 **GYN** *071 †30

GEORGE, Nicole S M. ■ 29860 #038-44-2002 L2005 **PD** *100 †55

GETZ, April Kelley. ■ 29841 #045-04-2005 L2007 **FP** *012

GOLDSMITH, Tiffany Kateas. ■ 29860 #045-04-2005 **OBG** *012

HUDGENS, Jeannette Louise. ■ 29841 #012-01-2005 **D** *012

IHNEN, Menard C. ■ 29841 #016-11-1946 L1972 **PTH NM** *071 †50,28

JACKSON, Lana Liane. ■ 29841 #027-01-2002 L2005 **OTO** *100

JACOB, Kristina Ashley. ■ 29860 #048-15-2005 L2008 **OBG** *012

JACOB, Richard Keith. ■ 29860 #048-15-2005 L2007 **GS** *012

JADICK, Richard H. ■ 29860 #035-75-1997, ▲ L1999 **U** *012

JESTER, David Matthew. 105 E HUGH ST 29841 #036-08-1992 L2005 **FM** *020 †18

KANG, Larry. ■ 29860 #039-01-2005 L2008 **FP** *012

KAUFFMANN, Amanda Lotz. ■ 29841 #012-01-2007 L2007 **PD** *012 †18

LAMBERT, Jerry Alan. 105 E HUGH ST 29841 #012-01-1997 L2006 **FM** *020 †18

LYON, Matthew Lankford. ■ 29841 #012-01-1999 L2006 **EM** *020 †16 ‡

MATTHEWS, Amanda E. ■ 29841 #012-01-2008 *012

MULLER-ROHLAND, Jean. ■ 29860 #045-04-1976 L1976 **PM** *071 †60 ‡

NATTIER, Bryce Andrew. ■ 29860 #016-11-2006 **GS** *012

OLIVER, Alyce Marie. ■ 29841 #001-02-2002 L2002 **RHU** *020 †20

SHAH, Sagar Rajendrakum. ■ 29841 #011-02-2003 L2004 **U** *012

SHEHEEN, Stephen Wayne. ■ 29841 #045-01-1987 L1990 **IM** *020

SLOAN, Allen Lee. 1168 W MARTINTOWN RD 29841 #012-01-1987 L1989 **AN** *020 †05

STAMPER, Elizabeth A. ■ 29841 #018-75-2007, ▲ **OBG** *012

STEADMAN, Richard A. ■ 29841 #045-01-1955 L1955 **GP** *071

SUYKERBUYK, Robert Adrian. 105 E HUGH ST 29841 #025-12-1997 L2004 **FM** *020 †18

THURMOND, John Wm, III. 309 WEST AVE 29841 #045-01-1975 L1976 **GP** *020

VELKY, John Robt. 309 WEST AVE, FAMILY PHYSICAN OF NORTH A 29841 #045-01-1985 L1986 **FM** *020 †18

WANG, David Chinsing. ■ 29860 #011-02-2007 **NS** *012

WARREN, Jeremy Aaron. ■ 29841 #012-01-2004 L2004 **GS** *012

WILLIAMS, John L. ■ 29860 #012-01-1961 L1961 **NS** *071 †25

WILSON, Melanie Renee. ■ 29841 #012-01-2007 **OTO** *012

YOST, Wayne Russell. 509 W MARTINTOWN RD 29841 #045-01-1973 L1976 **FM** *020

YOUNG, Bronwyn Louis, II. ■ 29841 #036-05-2008 *012

ZIMMERMAN, David Wayne. ■ 29841 #012-01-2007 **FP** *012

NORTH CHARLESTON – CHARLESTON

ALLEN, Timothy Graham. 2880 TRICOM ST, SPORTS MEDICINE 29406 #007-02-1991 L2003 **ORS HS** *020 †40

BACK, Jerry Glenn. 9221 UNIVERSITY BLVD, # 102 29406 #305-01-1987 L2008 **IM DIA** *020 †20 ‡

BAKER, Fletcher Keels. PO BOX 190029 29419 #045-01-1972 L1973 **P** *020

BAKSHI, Satbir Singh. 3600 RIVERS AVE 29405 #495-29-1965 **ORS U** *020

BALL, Robert Thomson, Jr. 4050 BRIDGE VIEW DR, STE 600 29405 #045-01-1970 L1975 **ID PHP** *020 †20

BARNETT, Harry James. ■ 29406 #016-42-1941 L1941 **FM IMG** *071

BENSON, Richard D, Jr. 3815 FABER PLACE DR 29405 #045-04-1984 L1985 **IM** *071 †20

BERENDT, Jason Eric. 3955 FABER PLACE DR, STE 202 29405 #045-01-2001 L2002 **IM** *020

BIANCO, Joseph Raymond. 7750 NORTHWOODS BLVD 29406 #038-40-1992 L1995 **EM** *020 †16

BIELSKY, Stephen Walter. 2687 LAKE PARK DR, SPECIALISTS 29406 #012-05-1974 L1979 **U** *020 †95

BOYLSTON, Colleen Jane. 2713 DANTZLER DR, SWEETGRASS PEDIATRICS 29406 #030-06-1999 L2001 **PD** *020 †55

BRAWMAN MINTZER, Olga. 5900 CORE AVE STE 203 29406 #550-01-1985 L1991 **P** *020 †75

BROOKER, R Christopher. 2880 TRICOM ST, SPORTS MEDICINE 29406 #045-01-2000 L2002 **HS** *020 ‡

BROWDER, Richard Wayne. 3815 FABER PLACE DR 29405 #036-01-1991 L1997 **NEP CCM** *020 †20

BROWN, Carroll Smith. 9326 MEDICAL PLAZA DR, STE B 29406 #045-01-1973 L1975 **AN** *071 †05

BROWN, John H. 9181 MEDCOM ST 29406 #422-01-1997 L2002 **PM** *020

BUCHANAN, Mark Gary. 2687 LAKE PARK DR, SPECIALISTS 29406 #047-06-1996 L1997 **U** *020 †95

BULGER, Rose M. 3600 RIVERS AVE 29405 #019-02-1984 L1996 **FM** *020 †18

BYRNE, Michael Cunningham. 2316 COSGROVE AVE, TRIDENT NEPHROLOGY 29405 #027-01-1994 L1999 **NEP** *020 †20

CALANDRA, Joseph John. 9100 MEDCOM ST 29406 #035-09-1982 L1989 **ORS HS** *020 †40

CANNICK, Leander. 3600 RIVERS AVE, NAVAL HOSPITAL 29405 #045-01-2003 2008 *020

CASE, Christine Anne. 9221 UNIVERSITY BLVD, STE 2E 29406 #045-04-1982 L1983 **OBG** *020 †30

CATALDO, Kari Piper. 9298 MEDICAL PLAZA DR 29406 #016-11-2001 L2003 **FM** *020 †18

CATHEY, Sara S. 3520 W MONTAGUE AVE, STE 104 29418 #055-02-1997 L1998 **MG PD** *020 †19,55

CHANDLER, Christopher D. 3600 RIVERS AVE 29405 #055-01-2001 L2002 **OBG** *100 †30

CHATELLIER, Charles. 2781 TRICOM ST 29406 #021-05-1969 L1975 **PD** *071 †55

CONNOLLY, James Frederick. 3625 W MONTAGUE AVE 29418 #065-09-1955 L1979 **OM GS** *071 †18

COOK, William Roy. 2845 TRICOM ST 29406 #045-01-1970 L1971 **IM PUD** *020 †20

COPSES, Constantine Peter. 2713 DANTZLER DR, MUSC - GRADUATE MED EDU 29406 #045-01-2004 L2004 **PD** *020

CROUCH, William E, III. 2600 ELMS PLANTATION BLVD 29406 #035-01-1969 L1975 **IM CD** *020 †20

CURTIS, Gary Michael. 9225 UNIV BLVD STE C 29406 #045-01-1978 L1978 **GE** *020 †20

DACUS, Elizabeth Norene. 9279 MEDICAL PLAZA DR # A 29406 #045-01-2002 L2006 **OBG** *020

D'AGOSTINO, Janet Lynn. 9330 MEDICAL PLAZA DR, COASTAL INPATIENT PHYSICIA 29406 #041-77-2004, ▲ L2004 **FM** *100 †18

DAY, Richard Philip. 9213 UNIVERSITY BLVD STE A 29406 #065-10-1979 L1980 **OBG** *020 †30

DEVRIES, Jon Peter. 9100 MEDCOM ST, & ORTHOPAEDIC CENTER 29406 #020-12-1994 L2001 **HS** *020 †40

DODDS, Kenneth Arnold. 3815 FABER PLACE DR 29405 #045-01-1974 L1976 **NEP IM** *020 †20

DONATO, Henry. 2171 ASHLEY PHOSPHAT RD #C 29406 #045-01-1945 L1945 **GS TS** *020 †85

DROHAN, Paul Shattuck. 3600 RIVERS AVE, NAVAL HOSP, CODE 02MD.2 29405 #010-01-1967 L1972 **OTO** *020 †45

DZIERZKO-TROJANOWSKA, Mari. 9237 UNIVERSITY BLVD, VAMC 29406 #759-10-1978 L1996 **IM** *020 †20

EDWARDS, William Milnes. 2860 TRICOM ST 29406 #045-01-1970 L1975 **RHU IM** *020 †20

EFFIONG, Charles. 3973B RIVERS AVE, FRANKLIN C. FETTER FAMILY 29405 #690-01-1984 L1997 **IM** *020 †20

ELLYN, John Chas. 9217 UNIVERSITY BLVD, STE 1B 29406 #010-01-1981 L1982 **OPH** *020 †35

ETHERIDGE, J Bruce. 2781 TRICOM ST 29406 #036-05-1996 L1998 **PD** *020 †55

FAISON, Warachal Eileen. 5900 CORE AVE STE 203, MUSC ALZHEIMER'S RESEARCH 29406 #036-01-1996 L2004 **PYG** *020

FIEDLER, Mark Dee. 9213 UNIVERSITY BLVD STE C, PALMETTO GEN SURG P 29406 #017-20-1981 L1986 **GS** *020 †85

FINK, Gary Eliot. 2860 TRICOM ST STE A 29406 #041-02-1981 L1985 **RHU IM** *020 †20

FIORINI, Jennifer Hall. 9221 UNIVERSITY BLVD, STE 102 29406 #045-01-2000 L2004 **GS** *020

FLOREZ, David Anthony. 2671 ELMS PLANTATION BLVD 29406 #038-41-1997 L2002 **GE** *020 †20

FRANKLIN, Samuel Clay, Jr. 3815 FABER PLACE DR 29405 #036-01-1991 L1997 **NEP** *020 †20

GOODEAR, Gregory C. 2671 ELMS PLANTATION BLVD, TRIDENT GASTROENTEROLOGY A 29406 #042-02-1999 L2005 **GE** *020 †20

GORDON, Richard M. 2891 TRICOM ST STE B 29406 #045-01-1989 L1993 **PM** *020 †60

GRAY, Timothy Kenney. 2831 TRICOM ST, CAROLINA ENDOCRINE ASSOCS, 29406 #023-01-1965 L1991 **END IM** *020 †20

GRISHAM, Andre D. 9221 UNIVERSITY BLVD, STE 102 29406 #020-12-1999 L2006 **GS** *020 †85

GUTIERREZ, Miguel Andres. 3600 RIVERS AVE, NAVAL HOSPITAL CODE 09MD.2 29405 #023-12-2002 L2003 *020

HALL, Jeffrey Stuart. 9221 UNIVERSITY BLVD, STE D 29406 #001-02-1992 L1996 **OS FPS** *020

HANDSHOE, David Keith. 9150 MEDCOM ST, CRITICAL CARE 29406 #027-01-1984 L1993 **PUD CCM** *020 †20

HANGER, Kenneth Hall, Jr. 4969 CENTRE POINTE DR, STE 100 29418 #023-01-1977 L1978 **CD** *020 †20

HARRIS, Joshua David. 8740 RIVERS AVE, MEDICAL UNIVERSITY OF SC- 29406 #041-15-2005 L2005 **AN** *100

HEPBURN, Lloyd Earl, Jr. 2179 ASHLEY PHOSPHAT RD #B 29406 #005-11-1990 L1995 **IM** *020 †20

HERIOT, Lucius Wells. 9313 MEDICAL PLAZA DR, CHARLESTON RADIOLOGISTS PA 29406 #045-01-1959 L1959 **R** *071 †80

HOOVER, Ruth D. 9181 MEDCOM ST 29406 #041-07-1989 L1993 **PM** *020 †60

HURSEY, Archibald W, Jr. 5290 RIVERS AVE, STE 101 29406 #045-01-1962 L1962 **OM FM** *071 †18

INMAN, John Gardner. 3600 RIVERS AVE, ATTN: CREDENTIAL OFFICE 29405 #045-01-1993 L1994 **FM** *020 †18

JACKSON, Allen B, Jr. 2175 ASHLEY PHOSPHATE RD, STE D 29406 #045-01-1986 L1987 **IM IMG** *020

JACOBS, Jon Robt. 9213 UNIVERSITY BLVD STE D 29406 #045-01-1977 L1983 **GS VS** *020 †85

JANG, Jessica Turner. 2781 TRICOM ST 29406 #055-02-2002 L2006 **PD** *100

JARRETT, Jennifer Moore. 2713 DANTZLER DR 29406 #036-08-2001 L2003 **PD** *020 †55

JAVED, Ghazala Bashir. 2791 TRICOM ST 29406 #704-02-1981 L1989 **CD IM** *020 †20

JENKINS, James Edward. 3300 W MONTAGUE AVE, STE A 29418 #045-01-1979 L1980 **P** *020 †75

JENKINS-ALFORD, Eleanor R. 3973 RIVERS AVE 29405 #045-01-1991 L1992 **FM** *020 †18

JOHNSON, Eric. 3600 RIVERS AVE, ATTN: CREDENTIAL OFFICE 29405 #047-07-1994 L1996 **OBG** *020 †30

KALIA, Jitander Nath. ■ 29406 #495-03-1960 L1976 **PD** *020

KAPLAN, Allen Phillip. 9165 UNIVERSITY BLVD, CENTERS OF CHARLESTON, P.A 29406 #035-08-1965 L1997 **IM AI** *020,03

KERRIGAN, Kevin Robt. 3600 RIVERS AVE, ATTN: CREDENTIAL OFFICE 29405 #011-04-1975 L1999 **GS** *020 †85

KHOURY, George Hasham. 9275 MEDICAL PLAZA DR # B 29406 #045-01-1980 **NS** *020 †25

KOLEHMA, Kerri Alexis. 3185 AZALEA DR, COASTAL PHYSICAL MEDICINE 29405 #036-01-1996 L1997 **PM** *020 †60

KOLENDER, Mark Harris. 2741 SPEISSEGGER DR, STE 205 29405 #045-01-1981 L1982 **PD** *071 †55

KUPFERMAN, Seth Paul. 9100 MEDCOM ST 29406 #035-46-1984 L1990 **ORS FSM** *020 †40

LAKE, Robert Scott. 3870 LEEDS AVE STE 101 29405 #021-01-1998 L2001 **IM** *020 †20

LANGDALE, Emory L. 1250 REMOUNT RD 29406 #045-01-1953 L1953 **PM OM** *072 †60

LECLERCQ, Anne Hawk. 8992 UNIVERSITY BLVD, STE 200 29406 #051-01-2003 L2004 **D** *020 †15

LEGERTON, Clarence W, III. 2860 TRICOM ST, LOWCOUNTRY RHEUMATOLOGY 29406 #045-01-1986 L1992 **RHU** *020 †20

LEMBO, Nancy R. 9225 UNIVERSITY BLVD, STE E1 29406 #035-75-1993, ▲ L2005 **PRS PME** *020 †60

LEMON, Henry Martyn. 2070 NORTHBROOK BLVD, STE A20 29406 #045-01-1996 L2000 **PD** *020 †55

LEONARDI, Michael Lane. 2781 TRICOM ST 29406 #045-01-1997 L1998 **PD** *020 †55

LOPEZ, Lisa Bryce. 2713 DANTZLER DR, P O BOX 250333 29406 #012-01-2003 L2004 **PD** *020 †55

LOWE, Philip Kenneth. 2781 TRICOM ST 29406 #045-04-2004 L2004 **PD** *020 †55

LOWRY, Morgan Anisa. 9217 UNIVERSITY BLVD, STE C-1-D 29406 #041-13-1998 L2002 **IM** *020 †20

LYONS, Michael Joseph. 3520 W MONTAGUE AVE, STE 104 29418 #024-07-1997 L2005 **PD** *020 †19,55

MACHADO, Gaston G, Jr. 8740 RIVERS AVE 29406 #048-02-1986 L1987 **EM** *020 †16

MARTIN, James Thomas, Jr. 9213 UNIVERSITY BLVD STE A 29406 #045-01-1979 L1980 **OBG** *020 †30

MARWICK, Robert A. 9229 UNIVERSITY BLVD, STE E 29406 #021-01-1970 L1973 **OTO HNS** *020 †45

MATTHEWS, Andrea Michelle. 9298 MEDICAL PLAZA DR, TRIDENT FAMILY MED-RESIDEN 29406 #045-01-2007 L2007 **FP** *012

MC ADAMS, Douglas Swan. 7750 NORTHWOODS BLVD 29406 #045-01-1975 L1977 **EM** *020 †16

MCINTYRE, Matthew Griffin. ■ 29418 #001-06-2006 L2006 **U** *012

MC MAHON, Edmund Brown. 3600 RIVERS AVE 29405 #050-02-1954 L1976 **GYN** *072 †30

MEYER, Robert James. 3600 RIVERS AVE, ATTN: CREDENTIAL OFFICIE 29405 #012-01-1999 L2007 **IM** *020 †20

MILLER, Karl Scott. 9150 MEDCOM ST, CRITICAL CARE 29406 #047-07-1980 L1981 **PUD CCM** *020 †20

MINSON, George Eaves. 2845 TRICOM ST 29406 #051-01-1977 L1980 **IM ON** *020 †20

MINTZER, Jacobo Enrique. 5900 CORE AVE, STE 203 29406 #132-01-1979 L1992 **P PYG** *040 †75

MITCHELL, James C, III. 9221 MEDICAL PLAZA DR 29406 #045-01-1960 L1960 **OS GS** *071

MOSELEY, Walton Strozier. 3815 FABER PLACE DR 29405 #036-07-1990 L1999 **NEP IM** *020 †20

MURDAUGH, Marvin S, Jr. 4600 GOER DR, STE 205 29406 #045-01-1969 L1969 **FM** *020 †18

NAQUIN, Mark David. 8085 RIVERS AVE 29406 #021-05-1982 L1987 **AN** *020 †05

NAYLOR, Peter Wm. 9229 UNIVERSITY BLVD, STE F2B 29406 #042-03-1991 L1995 **P** *020 †75

NEW, Marc Dean. 2671 ELMS PLANTATION BLVD 29406 #045-01-1988 L1998 **GE IM** *020 †20

NOLAN, Joseph Edward. 9267 MEDICAL PLAZA DR # G, TRIDENT INSTITUTE OF MEDIC 29406 #045-01-1996 L1997 **APM** *020 †05

NORDBY, Jennifer Ann. 2781 TRICOM ST, PALMETTO PEDIATRICS 29406 #035-06-1993 L2008 **PD** *020 †55

OKONOFUA, Eni C. 5390 DORCHESTER RD, PROVENS MED CTR INC 29418 #690-06-1983 L1999 **IM** *020 †20

ORR, Paula E. 5319 PARKSHIRE WAY, CHARLESTON WOMENS WELLNESS 29418 #025-07-1994 L1998 **OBG** *020 †30

PAGAN, Noemi Raquel. 2550 ELMS CENTRE RD, PALMETTO PRIMARY CARE PHYS 29406 #045-01-2002 L2006 **OBG** *100 †18

PATEL, Shailesh Maneklal. 2880 TRICOM ST, SPORTS MEDICINE 29406 #045-04-2002 L2007 **PM** *100 †60

PETERSON, Michael Alan. ■ 29406 #016-11-2006 L2006 **IM** *012

PRATT, John Mc Gill. 2690 LAKE PARK DR 29406 #045-01-1973 L1974 **AN** *020 †05

PRIDE, Eric Thomas. 3815 FABER PLACE DR 29405 #045-01-1999 L2001 **NEP** *020 †20

PRINGLE, Robert A. 4969 CENTRE POINTE DR, STE 100 29418 #045-01-1944 L1944 **IM** *071

PRINGLE, Robert Alexander. 4969 CENTRE POINTE DR, # 100 29418 #045-01-1981 L1984 **CD IM** *020 †20

PRUITT, Anna Cecilia. 3800 FABER PLACE DR 29405 #045-01-1994 L1997 **PD** *020 †55

RAMSAY, Alexander Wm. 2687 LAKE PARK DR, SPECIALISTS 29406 #045-01-1978 L1979 **U EM** *020 †95

REARDEN, Gail Lashun. 2075 EAGLE LANDING BLVD 29406 #045-01-2001 L2007 **IMG** *020

RISSING, Michael Scott. 9298 MEDICAL PLAZA DR, UNIVERSITY FAMILY MEDICINE 29406 #045-04-2007 L2007 **TY** *012

ROSSI, Michael John. 8740 RIVERS AVE, DOCTORS CARE 29406 #045-01-2004 L2006 **GS** *020

ROWLETT, William Taylor. ■ 29418 #020-02-2005 L2006 **DR** *012

RUCKER, John Michael. 9150 MEDCOM ST, CRITICAL CARE 29406 #028-46-1991 L2002 **PCC** *020 †20

SAAVEDRA, George G. 9181 MEDCOM ST 29406 #748-08-1987 L1997 **FM PM** *020 †60

SAUNDERS, Donald Eugene. 4969 CENTRE POINTE DR, STE 100 29418 #045-04-1986 L1994 **CD IM** *020 †20

SCHAFFER, James William. 3600 RIVERS AVE, ADULT HEALTH CLINIC 29405 #036-07-1994 L1996 **FM** *020 †18

SCHULLER, Kevin C. ■ 29406 #055-01-2006 L2006 **P** *012

SCHWERIN, Daniel Lawrence. ■ 29406 #045-01-2007 L2007 **GS** *012

SENOKOZLIEFF, Molly E. 9213 UNIVERSITY BLVD STE A 29406 #038-40-2000 L2004 **OBG** *020

SERGEV, Orlin T. 2831 TRICOM ST, CAROLINA ENDOCRINE ASSOCIA 29406 #473-01-1984 L2006 **IM END** *020 †20

SLAPPY, Ashley Lyn. 3600 RIVERS AVE, NAVAL HOSPITAL-GEN SURGERY 29405 #012-05-2000 L2006 **GS** *020 †85

SLAUGHTER, Sharvette J. 3973 RIVERS AVE, LOW COUNTRY PEDS 29405 #045-01-1995 L1998 **PD** *020 †55

SLOTT, Edwin F, Jr. 9229 UNIVERSITY BLVD, FC2 29406 #012-01-1991 L1994 **EM** *020 †16

SMEAR, John Lee. 2831 TRICOM ST STE B 29406 #038-41-1997 L2006 **GS** *020 †85

SMITH, Jacob Edward. ■ 29406 #004-01-2006 L2006 **OTO** *012

SMITH, Michael Alan. 2845 TRICOM ST 29406 #035-01-1995 L2000 **IM** *020 †20

SNYDER, Todd Louis. 2671 ELMS PLANTATION BLVD 29406 #422-01-1996 L2002 **GE** *020 †20

SPENCER, Jack Christopher. 8740 RIVERS AVE 29406 #047-20-1994 L2000 **EM** *020 †16

SPIERS, Jon Phillip. 9221 UNIVERSITY BLVD, STE 102 29406 #047-06-1988 L2006 **TS VS** *020 †85,90

SQUIRES, Gregory Thomas. 2831 TRICOM ST STE B, TIDEWATER SURGICAL GROUP, 29406 #045-01-1993 L1999 **GS** *020 †85

STEM, Eric Steven. 9100 MEDCOM ST 29406 #036-01-1993 L2003 **OAR OS** *020 †40

STEWART, Alexander Edward. 3600 RIVERS AVE, CHARLESTON SC 29405 #023-12-1995 L2004 **OTO** *020 †45

STOVALL, Don Owen, Jr. 2880 TRICOM ST, SPORTS MEDICINE 29406 #012-01-1991 L1997 **ORS** *020 †40

STROUD, Nancy Burgess. 9279 MEDICAL PLAZA DR # A 29406 #024-07-1982 L1983 **OBG** *020 †30

TERRANOVA, Wm Anthony. 2683 LAKE PARK DR 29406 #035-47-1973 L1986 **PS IM** *020 †20,65

TODD-HOUSTON, Gwendolyn F. 3973 RIVERS AVE 29405 #036-01-1978 L1987 **PD** *020 †55

TRACEY, Kevin Thos. ■ 29418 #041-02-1973 L1976 **IM** *100 †20

TROUCHE, Perry Edwin. 9229 UNIVERSITY BLVD STE F 29406 #045-01-1977 L1979 **P EM** *020 †75

TUNNEY, Francis Xavier. 7519 RIVERS AVE, PATIENT ONE MEDICAL CENTER 29406 #023-01-1986 L1994 **IM** *020 †20

UPADHYAYA, Vidya H. 2151 ASHLEY PHOSPHATE RD, STE B 29406 #496-38-1993 L1999 **P** *020 †75

VALLEJO, Victor Alexis. 9330 MEDICAL PLAZA DR, COASTAL INPATIENT PHYSICIA 29406 #047-06-2001 L2006 **IM** *020

VANDEGRIFT, Tara Nicole. 9313 MEDICAL PLAZA DR, STE 202 29406 #041-02-1999 L2002 **FM** *020 †18

VAUGHAN, Joel Fuller. 1670 DRYDOCK AVE, BLDG 10-A 29405 #045-01-2002 L2003 **MPD** *020 †20,55

WALKER, Flournoy C, III. 7301 RIVERS AVE STE 140 29406 #045-01-1975 L1976 **FM** *020

WALSH, Lyle Glenn. 2845 TRICOM ST, LOW COUNTY INTERNAL MED 29406 #045-01-1997 L1998 **IM** *020 †20

WARREN, George. 9217 UNIVERSITY BLVD, STE C1A 29406 #045-01-1962 L1962 **PUD** *071 †20

WARREN, George Farris. 2880 TRICOM ST, SPORTS MEDICINE 29406 #020-02-1970 L1976 **ORS** *020 †40

WEATHERSBY, Benjamin B. 3815 FABER PLACE DR 29405 #001-02-1998 L2003 **IM** *020 †20

WEISSGLASS, Barry L. 4600 GOER DR, STE 205 29406 #035-19-1979 L1980 **OM FM** *020 †70,18

WEST, Edward Hackett. 2781 TRICOM ST 29406 #045-01-1970 **PD** *020 †55

WHIRRETT, Brian Raymond. 9330 MEDICAL PLAZA DR, PALMETTO PRIMARY CARE PHYS 29406 #045-04-2000 L2001 **FM** *100 †18

WIDENHOUSE, Brian Glenn. 2801 TRICOM ST, PALMETTO PLASTIC SURGERY 29406 #036-08-1991 L1998 **PS** *020 †65

WILSON, William Ernest. 9100 MEDCOM ST 29406 #045-01-1989 L1995 **ORS** *020 †40

WINDLER, Gary Evan. 9100 MEDCOM ST 29406 #021-01-1982 L1989 **ORS OSM** *020 †40

YALLAPRAGADA, Shyam S R. 2811 TRICOM ST 29406 #495-57-1974 L1980 **PUD IM** *020 †20

ZIMLICH, Richard Halpin. 2880 TRICOM ST, SPORTS MEDICINE 29406 #020-02-1992 L1993 **ORS** *020 †40

ZINKOWSKI, Ernest Leon. 8780 RIVERS AVE, STE 200B 29406 #045-01-1969 L1969 **OM EM** *071

NORTH CHARLESTON – DORCHESTER

BUCKLER, Leroy Benj. ■ 29420 #023-01-1971 L1971 **PTH** *020 †50

CALLAGHAN, Timothy Joseph. 7510 NORTHFOREST DR, COEM 29420 #665-01-2000 L2004 **FM** *020 †18

DAVIS, John Lorraine, III. ■ 29420 #036-01-1969 L1969 **OPH** *020 †35

EDWARDS, Matthew Jonathan. 5325 APPIAN WAY 29420 #036-05-1995 L2002 **FM** *020 †18

ERDEM, Can Caglar. ■ 29420 #902-19-1997 L2006 **FM** *100

GIST, Mikki Amber. ■ 29420 #045-01-2008 *012

HALLABA, Radwan Saadallah. 5401 NETHERBY RD, STE 1201 29420 #045-01-1994 L2004 **EM** *020 †16

HANKIN, Lawrence G. ■ 29420 #035-08-1968 L2006 **FM** *020 †95,18

HETZ, Robert K. ■ 29420 #041-77-1976, ▲ L1977 **GP** *071

KOEHN, Douglas Allen. ■ 29420 #017-20-1968 L1968 **EM** *020

KONIVER, Craig Colman. 5401 NETHERBY RD, STE 101 29420 #041-02-2000 L2003 **FM** *020 †18

KONIVER, Laura Elizabeth. 5401 NETHERBY RD, STE 101 29420 #041-02-2000 L2005 *100

LIEBERMAN, Allan Danl. 7510 NORTHFOREST DR 29420 #016-42-1960 L1966 **OM AI** *020 †55

LIM, Alan Saruca. 8919 E FAIRWAY WOODS DR 29420 #045-01-1985 L1987 **FM EM** *020 †18

ORVIN, George Henry. 7515 NORTHSIDE DR STE 200 29420 #045-01-1946 L1946 **CHP** *072 †75

REDWINE, John Mark. 5325 APPIAN WAY 29420 #045-01-1986 L1987 **FM** *020 †18

RHEE, Woo Hyuk. 8636 TIMBERMARSH LN 29420 #583-10-1967 L1977 **PM FPG** *071

SISODIA, Madhvi. ■ 29420 #496-07-1966 L1975 **FM EM** *020 †18

YEARWOOD, Kirtley A D. ■ 29420 #004-01-1993 L2006 **FOP** *012 ‡

NORTH MYRTLE BEACH – HORRY

AMIGO, Isidro Jesus. ■ 29582 #275-01-1960 L1966 **GS GP** *071

BASILY, Kamal Sedky. 3816 HIGHWAY 17 S 29582 #330-04-1955 L1971 **GS** *020

BRAUN, Anton. ■ 29582 #407-10-1969 L1974 **AN** *071 †05

CARROLL, James Raymond. 2021 N MYRTLE POINT BLVD, STE 102 29582 #045-01-1980 L1981 **FM** *020 †18 ‡

HILZ, Mark David. 1714 HIGHWAY 17 S, DOCTORS CARE 29582 #038-41-1981 L1987 **GP** *020

MALLOW, L Suzanne. 1714 HIGHWAY 17 S 29582 #045-01-1983 L1986 **GP** *071

MERRILL, Corinne Louise. ■ 29582 #051-07-1993 L1994 **FM** *020 †18

NIXON, Nicholas Foy, Jr. 908 SEA MOUNTAIN HWY 29582 #045-01-1965 L1965 **GP** *020

POOLE, Georgina Aya-Ay. ■ 29582 #055-01-1995 L2005 **GP** *062

RAMSBOTTOM, J Garnett, Jr. 86 CEDAR AVE 29582 #045-01-1978 L1979 **FM** *020 †18

RAMSBOTTOM, John G. 86 CEDAR AVE 29582 #036-07-1943 L1948 **FM OBG** *071

ROBERTSON, James Marion. ■ 29582 #021-01-1977 L1977 **N** *020 †75

ROBINSON, James Paton. ■ 29582 #051-04-1975 L2002 **P** *020 †75

ROBINSON, James Waymond. ■ 29582 #047-07-1960 L1965 **IM** *071

SCOTT, Brian Stephen. 1714 HIGHWAY 17 S 29582 #048-02-1983 L1989 **GP GS** *020

SUTHERLAND, Deborah S. 1714 HIGHWAY 17 S 29582 #051-04-1988 L1992 **IM** *020

TROYA, Eduardo. ■ 29582 #869-05-1966 L1972 **OTO** *075

WHIDBY, Elma Denise. 2021 N MYRTLE POINT BLVD, STE 101 29582 #045-04-1992 L1993 **IM** *020 †20

WOOD, W Kimsey. 319 56TH AVE N 29582 #045-01-1957 L1958 **FM** *071 †18

NORWAY – ORANGEBURG

BAIR, Thomas Richard. ■ 29113 #045-04-2001 L2002 **FM** *020

OKATIE – BEAUFORT

BAYER, Joel Stephen. ■ 29909 #041-02-1964 L1965 **GS CRS** *071 †85
BINEGAR, Garry Neil. ■ 29909 #038-41-1966 L1966 **OPH** *071 †35 ‡
CUMMINGS, Scott Wm. 40 OKATIE CENTER BLVD, STE 100 29909 #048-13-1988 L2005 **IM EM** *020 †20
HASS, Robert Jos. ■ 29909 #024-05-1988 L2007 **GS** *020 †05
HORRY, Malcolm Holmes. ■ 29909 #036-05-1982 L1990 **FM** *020 †18
LA MOTTE, Peter. ■ 29909 #010-01-1955 L1971 **ORS OS** *071 †40
LOWE, Lance Steven. 40 OKATIE CENTER BLVD, STE 205 29909 #018-03-1998 L2001 **PD** *020 †55
MARSHALL, Bryan Edward. ■ 29909 #352-05-1959 L1968 **AN PUD** *071 †05
MEIER, Walter Chas. ■ 29909 #011-02-1971 L1995 **OPH** *071 †35
O'BRIEN, William A. ■ 29909 #539-04-1952 L1968 **R** *071 †05,80
SALYER, Alicia Avery. 40 OKATIE CENTER BLVD, STE 205 29909 #045-04-1999 L2002 **PD** *020
SMITH, Brendan Edward. 40 OKATIE CENTER BLVD, STE 350 29909 #045-01-1989 L2000 **PS** *020 †55
STUCKEY, Henry J, II. ■ 29909 #045-01-1961 L1966 **IM CD** *071 †20
THOMAS, Annette Marie. 40 OKATIE CENTER BLVD, STE 205 29909 #045-04-1983 L1984 **PD** *020 †55
VISCARDI, Anthony Peter. ■ 29909 #033-05-1968 L1969 **OBG** *020 †30 ‡
WRIGHT, Barry E. ■ 29909 #016-02-1973 L1991 **OPH OS** *071 †35

OLANTA – FLORENCE

MATTHEWS, Josiah Simpson. 103 PARK AVE 29114 #045-01-1957 L1957 **GP** *071
WELCH, Priscilla Lorine. 103 PARK AVE 29114 #045-01-1987 L1988 **FM** *020 †18

ORANGEBURG – ORANGEBURG

ABDALLA, Jehad Saleh. 1511 CAROLINA AVE 29115 #875-03-1994 L2004 **IM** *020 †20
ACKERMAN, Raymond Edward. 2323 SAINT MATTHEWS RD 29118 #045-01-1954 L1954 **P** *020 †75
ADAMS, Stuart Thos. 3000 SAINT MATTHEWS RD, ORANGEBURG & CALHOUN COUNT 29118 #020-12-1979 L1980 **EM** *020
AKINTUNDE, Oluyemisi Olut. 3310 MAGNOLIA ST, FAMILY HEALTH CENTERS INC 29115 #690-08-1989 L2004 **PD** *020 †55
ALGOOD, Denise Dixon. 655 LAUREL ST, ORANGEBURG MEDICAL CENTER 29115 #025-12-1989 L1990 **PHP OM** *020 †70
AL-HATOU, Moh'D Ibrahim. 2850 PELHAM CT 29118 #875-03-1993 L2002 **N** *020 †20
ALVA, Rakesh Vishwanath. 1133 COOK RD, ORANGEBURG LUNG ASSOC 29118 #496-38-1997 L2004 **PCC SME** *020 †20
AMOAH-APRAKU, Bismarck. 3310 MAGNOLIA ST, FAMILY HEALTH CENTER 29115 #412-01-1987 L2000 **IM** *020 †20
ANSLEY, John Fitzgerald. 1175 COOK RD, STE 230 29118 #035-20-1994 L2000 **OTO** *020 †45
ARANA, Julia Garrett. 3000 SAINT MATTHEWS RD, & CALHOUN COUNTIES 29118 #028-34-1997 L2007 **PD** *020 †20
AUGUSTINE, George. 1133 COOK RD 29118 #495-44-1983 L1993 **PCC IM** *020 †20
AVOSSO, Daniel Louis. 3000 SAINT MATTHEWS RD, TRMC - EMERGENCY MEDICINE 29118 #035-06-2001 L2004 **EM** *020 †16
BABB, Julius Wistar, III. 1175 COOK RD STE 320, MEDICAL ARTS CENTER 29118 #045-01-1972 L1974 **GS CD** *020 †85
BAGASRA, Omar. ■ 29118 #649-33-1985 **PTH ALI** *050
BAIR, James Richard. 3310 MAGNOLIA ST 29115 #016-11-1958 L1994 **OBG** *020 †30
BANISH, W Paul. 1175 COOK RD, STE 320 29118 #048-12-1991 L1997 **GS** *020 †85
BLALOCK, David B. 1695 CAROLINA AVE 29115 #038-40-1991 L1994 **IM** *020 †20
BRUNSON, Chris Y. 1161 COOK RD, MABRY CENTER FOR CANCER CA 29118 #010-03-1986 L1992 **ON HEM** *020 †20
BRUNSON, James H, Jr. 1170 BOULEVARD ST, STE A 29115 #045-01-1974 L1976 **FM EM** *020 †18 ‡
BUCHANAN, William Yongue. 1728 VILLAGE PARK DR 29118 #045-01-1968 L1968 **DR** *020 †80
BUGARIN, Felicitas Cruz. 2319 SAINT MATTHEWS RD, ORANGEBURG AREA MENTAL HEA 29118 #748-08-1963 L1977 **P CHP** *020 ‡
CAMPBELL, Linda June. 3310 MAGNOLIA ST, CAROLINAS CENTER FOR MEDIC 29115 #045-01-1988 L1989 **IM** *020 †20
CASSONE, Rocco Douglas. 1175 COOK RD STE 230 29118 #050-02-1973 L1977 **OTO A** *020 †45
CASTRO, George Enrique. 1137 COOK RD 29118 #035-09-1980 L1992 **CD IM** *020 †20
CAUGHMAN, Marion Roddey. 940 HOLLY ST NE 29115 #045-01-1954 L1954 **PD** *071 †55
CHEN, David. 1175 COOK RD STE 325 29118 #385-04-1967 L1976 **OBG** *020 †30
CHEN, David Chih. 1175 COOK RD STE 325, MED ARTS CTR 29118 #010-01-1995 L1997 **EM** *020 †16
CHERN, Chang-Ming Joseph. 1175 COOK RD STE 325, ORANGEBURG OBG 29118 #244-08-1982 L1994 *100
COLLE, Gregg Jos. 1719 VILLAGE PARK DR 29118 #030-06-1985 L1994 **D** *020 †15
CONNELLY, Karen Lackey. 940 HOLLY ST NE 29115 #045-01-1989 L1990 **PD** *020 †55
CONNOR, Susan Kearse. 1175 COOK RD 29118 #045-01-1994 L1997 **OBG** *072 †30
COULTER, Franklin C. 941 SUMMERS AVE NE 29115 #016-11-1978 L1981 **FM** *020 †18
CRAIG, Lucius, III. 1175 COOK RD, STE 215 29118 #021-05-2000 L2006 **ORS** *020
CROPPER, Leland Dunn, Jr. 1728 VILLAGE PARK DR 29118 #041-02-1973 L1974 **DR VIR** *020 †80
DAWKINS, Lamar W, Jr. 1097A COOK RD 29118 #045-04-1988 L1989 **IM** *020 †20
DEGEN, Jerome Barlow. 1175 COOK RD NE # NO-305 29118 #045-01-1973 L1974 **OBG** *020
DELANEY, Gary Allen. 1175 COOK RD STE 125, MEDICAL ARTS CTR 29118 #020-12-1975 L1978 **AN PME** *020
DISHER, Spencer C, Jr. 196 CENTRE ST 29115 #047-07-1960 L1963 **IM FM** *020
DROISEN, Benjamin. 3000 SAINT MATTHEWS RD, THE REGIONAL MEDICAL CENTE 29118 #035-48-2002 L2003 **EM** *020 †16

DURHAM, John Henry. 1175 COOK RD, STE 115 29118 #041-02-1996 L2003 **NEP** *020 †20
EDINGER, James R. ■ 29118 #018-75-1976, ▲ L1981 **DR** *071 †80
ELLIS, Mona. 1289 BOULEVARD ST 29115 #011-04-1988 L1990 **FM** *020 †18
EMANUEL, Guy Mac. ■ 29115 #035-10-1983 L1987 **PD IM** *020 †20,55
FANT, John Alexander. 3000 SAINT MATTHEWS RD, TRMC DEPT OF PATHOLOGY 29118 #045-04-1983 L1994 **PTH** *020 †50
FEINMAN, Mitchell C. 1768 VILLAGE PARK DR 29118 #305-01-1986 L1996 **RHU IM** *020 †20
FRIERSON, Henry F. 1175 COOK RD NE, STE 210 29118 #045-01-1951 L1951 **GS** *071 †85
FUNDERBURK, M S, Jr. 870 HOLLY ST, MEDICAL ARTS CENTER 29115 #045-01-1966 L1966 **GS** *020 †85
GEHRY, Eugene L, Jr. 3310 MAGNOLIA ST, FAMILY HLTH CTR 29115 #045-01-1952 L1952 **GP OS** *071
GENEIDY, Ayman Abdel A. 1184 ORANGEBURG MALL CIR 29115 #915-03-1992 L2004 **NEP** *020 †20
GILLESPIE, David Warren. 1175 COOK RD 29118 #045-01-1980 L1983 **OBG** *020 †30
GIRGIS, Sobhi Anis. ■ 29118 #915-03-1963 L1981 **EM GO** *075 †18 ‡
GONZALEZ-CUERVO, Alberto. 2323 SAINT MATTHEWS RD 29118 #042-02-1987 L1991 **P** *020
GREENE, Michael Keith. 3000 SAINT MATTHEWS RD, ATTN: HOSPITALIST 29118 #021-05-2002 L2006 **MPD** *020 †20,55
GROSS, Rachael E. 1727 VILLAGE PARK DR, GROSS FAMILY PRACTICE 29118 #011-75-1998, ▲ L2001 **FM** *020
GUE, Bertrand Victor. 970 HOLLY ST NE 29115 #045-01-1959 L1959 **IM** *071 †20
GUPTA, Avinash. 2227 SAINT MATTHEWS RD 29118 #495-69-1989 L2000 **AN** *020 †05
HAMMAD, Abdullah E. 1175 COOK RD, STE 115 29118 #875-01-1996 L2003 **NEP** *020 †20
HANE, Francis Simons. 3000 SAINT MATTHEWS RD, ORANGEBURG CALHOUN REGI HO 29118 #045-01-1978 L1979 **FM** *020 †18
HARE, Ester Rose. 1291 GLEN GLORIA ST 29118 #008-02-1990 L1992 **IM** *020 †20
HARGRAVE, Ronald Paul. 3000 SAINT MATTHEWS RD, ORANGEBURG & CALHOUN COUNT 29118 #036-01-1924 L1985 **EM OM** *020 †16
HAWN, Catherine Johnson. 1188 BERKELEY DR 29118 #045-04-2001 L2002 **IM** *020
HAY, Michael Scott. 1175 COOK RD, STE 310 29118 #045-01-1975 L1980 **U** *020 †95
HEATH, Gossie Colette. 3000 SAINT MATTHEWS RD 29118 #010-03-1983 L1987 **MPD PD** *020 †55,20
HENDRIX, Joe Douglass, Sr. 1559 CAROLINA AVE 29115 #422-01-1988 L1999 **CHP** *020
HILL, Michael Andre. 1175 COOK RD STE 320, P O BOX 1505 29118 #011-03-1994 L2000 **GS** *020 †85
HORGER, Richard Culler. CAROLINA AVE 29115 #045-01-1942 L1942 **GYN** *072
HUGHES, Charles Haskell. 1175 COOK RD STE 215, ORTHOPAEDIC SPECIALISTS OF 29118 #045-01-1985 L1986 **ORS** *020 †40
HUTTO, John Oxford. 3000 SAINT MATTHEWS RD 29118 #045-04-1984 L1985 **CD IM** *020 †20
JOHNSON, Clarence Birnie. 1595 CAROLINA AVE 29115 #045-01-1957 L1957 **IM** *071 †20
JOHNSON, Jack Frank, Jr. 1190 SUMMERS AVE 29115 #045-01-1970 L1971 **OPH** *020 †35
JOLLES, Alan Mark. 125 EXPRESS LN 29118 #012-01-1991 L1994 **FM** *020 †18
JUNEJA, Anil K. 2851 PELHAM CT 29118 #495-69-1982 L1991 **P** *020 †75
KENDALL, Brian William. 3000 SAINT MATTHEWS RD, THE REGIONAL MEDICAL CENTE 29118 #016-02-1998 L2002 **MPD** *020
KENNEDY, Arthur Kobina. 3310 MAGNOLIA ST 29115 #412-01-1991 L1998 **FM OS** *020 †18
KILGORE, Charles Julius. 3310 MAGNOLIA ST 29115 #045-01-1980 **PD** *020 †55
KING, Samuel Van. 2664 SAINT MATTHEWS RD 29118 #045-04-1992 L1993 **CD** *020
KIROL, Bernard Geo. 1732 VILLAGE PARK DR 29118 #020-12-1988 L1995 **ORS OSM** *020 †40
KONDAPANENI, Usha Grani. 655 LAUREL ST 29115 #495-58-1986 L1994 **IM** *020 †20
KRZYSTON, Mark Jos. 1175 COOK RD STE 225 29118 #422-01-1981 L1986 **CD** *020 †20
LAWSIN, Rosen Jamandre. 477 DANTZLER ST, NORTHEAST PSYCHIATRIC ASSO 29115 #748-10-1966 L1975 **P CHP** *020
LIAO, Shixiong. 3000 SAINT MATTHEWS RD, TRMC DEPT OF PATHOLOGY 29118 #243-16-1987 L2002 **PTH PCP** *020 †50
LORD, Lori Price. 3000 SAINT MATTHEWS RD, THE REGIONAL MEDICAL CENTE 29118 #045-04-1998 L2004 **IM** *020 †20
LOUIS, Willie Blease. 3000 SAINT MATTHEWS RD 29118 #045-01-1974 L1975 **FM** *020
LOVELACE, Dallas W, III. 1728 VILLAGE PARK DR 29118 #045-01-1966 L1966 **R** *020 †80
MACPHERSON, Teresa Dawn. 940 HOLLY ST 29115 #045-01-1987 L1988 **PD** *020 †55
MARRO, James Paul. 1175 COOK RD, STE 215 29118 #035-09-1988 L1997 **ORS** *020 †40
MC CARRON, David Peter. 3000 SAINT MATTHEWS RD, THE REGIONAL MEDICAL CENTE 29118 #048-14-1990 L1996 **IM** *040 †20
MC CULLOUGH, Henry Edward. 970 HOLLY ST 29115 #045-01-1965 L1965 **CD IM** *020 †20
MC GANNON, Mark Colman. 1190 SUMMERS AVE 29115 #038-40-1974 L1978 **OPH** *020 †35
MERRIMAN, Hugh Gross, III. 1161 COOK RD, THE MABRY CANCER CENTER 29118 #045-01-1976 L1979 **RO FM** *020 †18,80
MIMS, William Walton, Jr. 1175 COOK RD NE STE 310, MEDICAL ARTS BLDG 29118 #045-01-1966 L1966 **U** *020 †95
MOLE, Hughlet W. 653 LAKE EDISTO RD 29118 #045-01-1952 L1952 **OBG** *020 †30
MONTGOMERY, Stefan Lamar. 2850 PELHAM CT 29118 #045-04-2000 L2004 **FSM** *020 †18 ‡
MOUSTAFA, Moustafa A. 1184 ORANGEBURG MALL CIR 29115 #915-02-1980 L1995 **NEP IM** *020 †20
MURALI, Narayanachar S. 1131 COOK RD 29118 #495-33-1982 L1994 **GE IM** *020 †20
MYERS, Jocelyn Annette. 1709 VILLAGE PARK DR 29118 #035-48-1996 L2004 **END IM** *020 †20
NAHIGIAN, Kevin K. 1732 VILLAGE PARK DR 29118 #010-02-1990 L1997 **ORS** *020 †40
NASSRI, Mohammad Said. 1175 COOK RD STE 115 29118 #915-03-1972 L1980 **NEP IM** *020 †20
NELSON, Elizabeth Thompso. 3000 SAINT MATTHEWS RD, DEPT OF INTERNAL MEDICINE 29118 #010-03-2002 L2007 **IM** *100
NELSON, Matthew Koma. 1175 COOK RD, STE 215 29118 #010-03-2002 L2007 **ORS** *020
OUTZ, Charles Wendell, Jr. 3000 SAINT MATTHEWS RD, EMERGENCY DEPARTMENT 29118 #045-01-2001 L2003 **EM** *020
PATTERSON, Steven G. 1728 VILLAGE PARK DR 29118 #045-01-1980 L1984 **DR** *020 †80
PENDARVIS, Bennie C, Jr. 940 HOLLY ST 29115 #045-01-1966 L1966 **PD** *020 †55
PRICE, Neil C. 2306 RIVERBANK DR, # 127 29118 #045-01-1942 **U** *071
RAINE, Charles Herbert. 1760 VILLAGE PARK DR, DIABETES CONTROL CTR 29118 #047-07-1961 L1989 **IM DIA** *020
REAVES, Alvin Leo, III. 3000 SAINT MATTHEWS RD 29118 #051-04-1998 L2003 **IM** *020 †20
RHENEY, John W, Jr. 940 HOLLY ST NE 29115 #045-01-1951 L1951 **PD** *020 †55
RHOADES, Sidney Freeman. 3000 SAINT MATTHEWS RD, DEPT OF INTERNAL MEDICINE 29118 #038-44-2003 L2006 **IM** *100 †20
RICHARDSON, Richard. 1175 COOK RD, STE 110 29118 #045-01-1977 L1978 **OBG** *020 †30
RIDDLE, Patricia Ellen. 1101 COOK RD 29118 #308-03-1981 L1997 **FM** *020 †18

■ = Address Information Privacy Protected

RIVERA, Jose Antonio. 2323 SAINT MATTHEWS RD 29118 #306-01-1991 **FM PME** *020
ROBINSON, Rita M Jones. 1767 VILLAGE PARK DR, ORANGEBURG VA PRIMARY CARE 29118 #041-07-1975 L2006 **ON HEM** *020 †20
SALLEY, Lawton Harris. 970 HOLLY ST 29115 #045-01-1961 L1961 **IM** *020
SAMIES, John Hunter. 1511 CAROLINA AVE 29115 #041-09-1980 L1997 **ID IM** *020 †20
SANDERS, Michael David. 3000 SAINT MATTHEWS RD, NORTH FAMILY MEDICINE 29118 #654-01-1990 L1995 **FM** *020 †18
SAN-MARINA, Andrei. 1767 VILLAGE PARK DR, ORANGEBURG VA OUTPATIENT C 29118 #654-01-1995 L1998 **IM** *020 †20 ‡
SCHULZE, Steven Curtis. 3000 SAINT MATTHEWS RD, THE REGIONAL MEDICAL CENTE 29118 #051-01-2000 L2003 **EM** *016
SHETH, Pravina B. 2319 SAINT MATTHEWS RD 29118 #495-22-1971 L1976 **P** *020 †75
SHIPPEY, John Edgar, Jr. 3000 SAINT MATTHEWS RD, TRMC 29118 #011-03-1967 L1975 **PTH** *020 †50
SHULER, Vann Beth Myers. 1205 HUTTO ST NE 29118 #045-01-1978 L1979 **FM** *020 †18
SINGH, Harnek. 3310 MAGNOLIA ST, FAMILY HEALTH CENTER INC 29115 #495-21-1990 L2004 **IM** *020 †20
SINGLETON, Monnie Que. 1773 VILLAGE PARK DR 29118 #005-06-1983 L1989 **GP** *020 †18
SISTRUNK, Delores. ■ 29118 #010-03-1979 L1983 **UM** *100
SMITH, Hugh E. ■ 29116 #045-01-1950 L1950 **GYN** *071 †30
SMOAK, Randolph Duncan. 1175 COOK RD STE 320 29118 #045-01-1959 L1959 **GS OS** *062 †85
SMOAK, Robert Luther. 1739 VILLAGE PARK DR 29118 #045-01-1980 L1981 **FM PM** *020 †18
STEPHENS, Sandra Janee. 3310 MAGNOLIA ST, FAMILY HEALTHCENTER 29115 #035-09-1988 L1992 **PD** *020
STERLING, Richard Elliot. 2221 SAINT MATTHEWS RD 29118 #041-13-1988 L1989 **OTO** *020 †45
THACKSTON, Lawrence P, Jr. ■ 29115 #045-01-1957 L1957 **U** *071
VANDENBERG, Todd Leon. 1747 VILLAGE PARK DR, PALMETTO UROLOGY, PA 29118 #021-01-1993 L1999 **U** *020 †95
VAUGHAN, Robert E. 1728 VILLAGE PARK DR 29118 #005-12-1990 L1999 **DR** *020 †80
WANGEH, Joseph Kwesi. 3000 SAINT MATTHEWS RD 29118 #412-01-1994 L2004 **PD** *020 ‡
WANNAMAKER, Braxton B. 1145 BOULEVARD ST 29115 #045-01-1966 L1966 **OS N** *020 †75
WANNAMAKER, Wm Capers. ■ 29115 #045-01-1952 **OS** *075
WATERS, Stephanie Renee. 3310 MAGNOLIA ST, P O BOX 1806 29115 #041-09-1995 L1996 **PD** *020
WATKINS, Patricia Naomi. 2319 SAINT MATTHEWS RD, ORANGEBURG AREA MENTAL HEA 29118 #012-01-1979 L1985 **P** *020 †75
WEATHERS, Everette Arden. 1175 COOK RD, STE 320 29118 #045-01-1966 **GS** *020 †85
WEIGLE, Gordon Reese, II. 1717 VILLAGE PARK DR 29118 #045-01-1977 L2004 **FM EM** *020 †18
WELLS, James Leroy, Jr. 1595 CAROLINA ST 29115 #045-01-1971 L2005 **CD** *020 †20
WHEELER, Dennis Alfred. 3000 SAINT MATTHEWS RD, OF ORANGEBURG 29118 #054-04-1973 L2003 **EM** *016
WHITE, James Y. 909 SUMMERS AVE, FAMILY PHYSICIANS GROUP, P 29115 #045-01-1952 L2005 **FM** *020
WILLIAMS, Betty Jean. ■ 29115 #045-01-1979 *100
WILLIAMSON, James Ric. 1175 COOK RD STE 145 29118 #048-04-1978 L1980 **OBG EM** *020 †30
WILSON, Beverley Deloris. 1750 VILLAGE PARK DR, WILSON PEDIATRICS INC 29118 #045-01-1989 L1992 **PD** *020 †55
YATES, Clifton. 133 CENTRE ST NE 29115 #010-03-1980 L1981 **FM EM** *020
YOUMANS, Cynthia Pauline. 3310 MAGNOLIA ST, FAMILY HEALTH CENTER 29115 #012-01-1989 L1999 **GPM** *020 †70
ZHANG, Daoling. 1190 SUMMERS AVE 29115 #021-05-1997 L2002 **OPH** *020 †35

PACOLET – SPARTANBURG

BANNON, Richard Bruce. 391 GLENN SPRINGS RD, FOOTHILLS FAMILY MEDICINE 29372 #020-12-1973 L1974 **FM** *020 †18
BISHOP, Preston Eddie. 7221 S PINE ST 29372 #045-04-1998 L1999 **EM FM** *020 †18
FOWLER, Jimmy Dean, Jr. 7221 S PINE ST 29372 #045-04-1991 L1992 **FM** *020 †18
MILES, Mark Lancaster. 391 GLENN SPRINGS RD, FOOTHILLS FAMILY MEDICINE 29372 #045-01-1993 L1997 **FM** *020 †18

PAGELAND – CHESTERFIELD

BLAKENEY, Billy Carson. 703 S HICKORY ST 29728 #045-01-1967 L1967 **GP** *020
BUTLER, George A. 301 N VAN L MUNGO BLVD, PAGELAND FAMILY MEDICINE 29728 #566-01-1995 L2005 **FM** *020 †18
UWENSUYI-EDOSOMWAN, F. 905 N PEARL ST 29728 #690-06-1987 L1997 **IM** *020 †20

PAMPLICO – FLORENCE

DONATO, Eduardo A, Jr. 953 S PAMPLICO HWY, COLEMAN FAMILY PRACTICE 29583 #748-01-1991 L1998 **IM** *020 †20
WEATHERFORD, James Lucian. ■ 29583 #045-01-1955 **GP EM** *020 †16

PAULINE – SPARTANBURG

DENNIS, James Dickerson. ■ 29374 #045-01-1961 L1961 **EM** *020

PAWLEYS ISLAND – GEORGETOWN

ANGLEMYER, Bradley Lamar. ■ 29585 #036-01-2003 L2006 **EM** *020 †16
ARMONIO, Jose G, Jr. 14319 OCEAN HWY 29585 #748-20-1984 L1996 **IM** *020
BODIE, Uriah H, Jr. ■ 29585 #045-01-1951 L1951 **DR NM** *071 †80,28
BOURJEILY, Nabil Abdallah. ■ 29585 #038-44-2003 L2007 **IM** *020 †20
BRUMFIELD, Edward Scott. 9699 OCEAN HWY, WACCAMAW MEDICAL CENTER 29585 #055-02-1996 L2003 **FM FPG** *020 †18

CHANDLER, Thomas Marvin. 9653 OCEAN HWY, ASSOCIATES 29585 #422-01-1995 L2000 **PUD** *020 †20
CLOSE, Katherine Anne. 116 BASKERVILL DR, MAILING ADDRESS: BOX 1740 29585 #045-04-1988 L1989 **P** *020 †20
COKER, Clarence Epps. 9696 OCEAN HWY 29585 #045-04-1996 L1999 **FM** *020 †18
CONGDON, Gerald Francis. 13089 OCEAN HWY, UNIT D4 29585 #063-01-1995 L1997 **FM** *020 †18 ‡
DALISAY, Rebecca G. ■ 29585 #748-11-1966 L1982 **P** *020
DALY, Roswald B. ■ 29585 #036-05-1946 L1947 **GP** *071
DE HAAS, Anthony Huub. ■ 29585 #036-08-1994 L1999 **GS** *020 †85
DEVLIN, Mitchell. 9653 OCEAN HWY, ASSOCIATES 29585 #041-77-1995, ▲ L2002 **IC CD** *020
DIAZ, Victor Manuel. 9653 OCEAN HWY, ASSOCIATES 29585 #042-01-1990 L1998 **CD IC** *020 †20
DUFFEY, Benjamin Morrison. 14866 OCEAN HWY, LITCHFIELD MEDICAL CENTER 29585 #051-07-1993 L1996 **EM** *020 †20
FELKEL, David James. 90 WATSON WAY 29585 #045-01-1974 L1975 **EM GP** *020
FUGARO, Francis Gerard. ■ 29585 #561-01-1966 L1979 **GP EM** *071
GIBSON, James Adell. ■ 29585 #024-01-1954 L1994 **P CHP** *020 †75
GOERZ, Stephen Douglas. ■ 29585 #028-03-1996 L2000 **AN** *020
GRINMAN, Mark. 9653 OCEAN HWY, ASSOCIATES 29585 #913-69-1985 L1998 **N** *020 †75
GROMULTS, Jos Michael, Jr. ■ 29585 #035-19-1958 L1959 **IM** *071 †20
HARD, Edward Merrill. ■ 29585 #035-45-1948 L1948 **OS IM** *071 †20
HASELTINE, David Kent. 64 BUSINESS CENTER DR, GEORGETOWN INT MED & PED P 29585 #047-06-2000 L2004 **IM PD** *020 ‡
HEIMBERGER, Caroline. 354 RICE MILL DR, MARION ORTHOPEDICS & OB-GY 29585 #045-01-1992 L1997 **OBG** *020 †30
HENTZ, James Paget. 112 ANCIENT MARINER LN 29585 #045-01-1962 L1962 **GS** *020 †85
IJEM, John Kalu. 9653 OCEAN HWY, ASSOCIATES 29585 #031-06-2001 L2001 **CD** *020 †20
JONES, Robert O. 718 ALL SAINTS LOOP 29585 #016-06-1953 L1959 **R NR** *020 †80
KELLY, Larry Wade. 64 BUSINESS CENTER DR, GEORGETOWN INTERNAL MED & 29585 #036-07-1993 L1998 **MPD** *020 †55,20
KEMP, Faron James. ■ 29585 #038-40-1990 L1995 **IM PD** *020 †55,20
KILUK, Kenneth Ignatius. ■ 29585 #025-07-1964 L1965 **NS** *020 †25
KRAMER, John Willis. 120 BASKERVILL DR, SMITH CLINIC 29585 #025-01-1955 L1993 **GS** *072 †85
LIEBERMAN, Ariane Ulrich. 9653 OCEAN HWY, ASSOCIATES 29585 #308-11-1986 L1995 **CD IM** *020 †20
LIEBERMAN, Craig. 9653 OCEAN HWY, ASSOCIATES 29585 #041-13-1988 L1994 **CD** *020 †20
MARSHALL, John Edwin. PO BOX 1740 29585 #041-09-1954 L1955 **GP** *071
MAYEAUX, Eugene V, II. 86 SHOREBIRD LOOP, PALMETTO EMER PHYSICIANS 29585 #021-06-1994 L1997 **EM** *020 †16
MC COY, Roy Maxie. ■ 29585 #045-01-1962 L1962 **U** *071 †95
MYERS, Stephanie Marie. ■ 29585 #055-02-1997 L2005 **GP** *100
NICOL, Scott Andrew. 64 BUSINESS CENTER DR 29585 #020-02-1995 L1999 **MPD** *020 †20,55
OPPENHEIM, Joseph Mc Coy. ■ 29585 #016-06-1948 L1986 **GS** *071 †85
PAINCHAUD, Lionel A. ■ 29585 #068-01-1961 L1980 **DR** *071 †80
PETERSON, Edward Nohl, II. ■ 29585 #026-04-1954 L2002 **GS OM** *030 †30
PRINCIPE, James Michael. 64 BUSINESS CENTER DR, GEORGETOWN INTERNAL MEDICI 29585 #033-05-1988 L1992 **IM PD** *020 †20,55
RATLIFFE, Joseph Michael. ■ 29585 #051-01-2003 L2006 **EM** *020 †16
ROSENBERG, Jason Charles. PO BOX 2069 29585 #045-04-1999 L2004 **N** *075
SCHINDLER, Reinhardt Hans. 1135 BLUE STEM DR, UNIT 28B 29585 #869-07-1973 L2003 **OPH IM** *071 †35
SMOYER, Ronald Lee. ■ 29585 #041-02-1974 L1996 **FM NTR** *020 †18
STORTZ, Michael James. ■ 29585 #016-43-1959 L1974 **AN** *020
STOVER, John Matthews, Jr. ■ 29585 #045-01-1997 L2001 **EM** *020 †16
THOMAS, David George. 141 ROSE LAUREL CT 29585 #030-06-1999 L2000 **AN** *020 †05
THOMPSON, Needham Jos, Jr. PO BOX 1740, SMITH CLINIC AT BASKERVILL 29585 #045-01-1968 L1968 **PHP IM** *071 †70
YOUNG, Desmond J. 9653 OCEAN HWY, ASSOCIATES 29585 #028-46-2000 L2006 **PCC** *020 †20

PEAK – NEWBERRY

FERGUSON, John Herbert. 32 RIVER ST 29122 #045-01-1981 L1982 **FM** *020 †18
PINNER, Carroll A, III. 101 RIVER ST 29122 #036-05-1971 L1972 **FM** *020 †18

PELZER – ANDERSON

KOONTZ, Daniel Allen. 323 LEBBY ST 29669 #045-01-1982 L1983 **FM** *020 †18

PENDLETON – ANDERSON

COOPER, Herbert Press, Jr. 220 E MAIN ST 29670 #045-01-1967 L1967 **FM** *020 †18
HELLAMS, James Wm. 101 SHIRLEY ST 29670 #045-01-1956 L1956 **GP** *020
SMITH, Stacy Lee. 101 SHIRLEY ST 29670 #012-01-1998 L1999 **FM** *020 †18
WALKER, James H, III. 5304 HIGHWAY 76 29670 #045-01-1981 L1982 **FM** *020 †18

PICKENS – PICKENS

BEASLEY, Virginia Leigh. 200 MCDANIEL AVE 29671 #012-01-1984 L1985 **FM** *020 †18
BROWN, Heather Ann. ■ 29671 #045-04-2008 *012
CALDWELL, James Clifton. 123 WG ACKER DR 29671 #045-01-1990 L1991 **FM** *020 †18
CHAILLE, Matilda Nemenzo. 314 W MAIN ST, PICKENS MENTAL HTLH CLNC 29671 #748-11-1962 L1979 **P** *020
CURRY, Charles Richard. 837 PENDLETON ST 29671 #045-01-1992 L1993 **FM** *020 †18
DAHLHAUSEN, Daniel James. 123 ACKER DR 29671 #038-45-1985 L2002 **FM** *020 †18
DILLARD, Michael Lawrence. 123 ACKER DR 29671 #045-01-1986 L1989 **EM IM** *020 †20
DONALD, Michael Earl. 123 W G ACKER DR 29671 #045-01-1972 L1973 **FM DS** *020
DUNNE, Thomas Patrick. 314 W MAIN ST, PICKENS CO. MENTAL HEALTH 29671 #035-15-1967 L1980 **DR P** *020 †75

FRANCIS, William Wells. #2 MEDICAL PARK DRIVE 29671 #036-05-1961 L1962 **FM OS** *071 †18
HAMMOND, Mary Corrinne. 865 PENDLETON ST, P O BOX 1059 29671 #012-01-1974 L1976 **FM** *020 †18
HOLCOMBE, Jake King. 123 W G ACKER DR 29671 #045-01-1959 L1959 **GP OBG** *020
MAHANES, James Rudolph. 123 W G ACKER DR 29671 #051-01-1965 L1974 **GS** *020 †85
MARSH, Byron Patterson. 123 MEDICAL PARK DR STE C 29671 #051-04-1974 L1996 **ORS** *020 †40
MAULDIN, David Wayman. #2 MEDICAL PARK DRIVE 29671 #045-01-1957 L1957 **FM OS** *071 †18
PATERSON, Eileen. ■ 29671 #041-07-1965 L1966 **RO NM** *071 †80,28
PERRY, Ronald Edward. 123 ACKER DR, CANNON MEMORIAL HOSPITAL 29671 #012-01-2000 L2004 **UCM** *020
PERSON, Robert Goodwin. 123 WG ACKER DR STE B 29671 #012-01-1983 L2003 **FM EM** *020 †18
SUTTER, Lloyd Geo. 1593 REECE MILL RD 29671 #005-12-1973 L1975 **GS PD** *020 †85
WAGGETT, Kathy Marie. 314 W MAIN ST, PICKENS MENTAL HEALTH CLIN 29671 #045-01-1980 L1983 **P CHP** *020 ‡

PIEDMONT — GREENVILLE

BRUCE, Jackson Bernard. 115 BEATTIE PARK RD 29673 #012-01-1989 L1994 **FM** *020 †18
DE VAULT, William Leonard. PO BOX 51354 29673 #036-05-1983 L1984 **ORS** *020 †40
EDWARDS, Anne C. 3150 HIGHWAY 153, FOOTHILLS ORTHOPEDICS & SP 29673 #045-04-1993 L1994 **ORS** *020
GARAND, Joseph Thos. 115 BEATTIE PARK RD 29673 #045-01-1987 L1988 **FM** *020 †18
GARDNER, Don Leslie. ■ 29673 #028-79-1963, ▲ L1964 **GP AI** *071
KAZAGLIS, Jon C. ■ 29673 #308-07-1983 L1995 **P** *020
LEE, Daniel Eaton. 3150 HIGHWAY 153, FOOTHILLS ORTHOPAEDIC & SP 29673 #045-01-1988 L1989 **ORS OSM** *020 †40
SANDERS, Patricia Sue. 112 COMMONS BLVD 29673 #045-01-1984 L1985 **PD** *020 †55
SLOAN, John Lindsay, Jr. 115 BEATTIE PARK RD 29673 #045-01-1987 L1988 **FM FPG** *020 †18
TREEN, Ben Marcus. 107 CLAIR DR 29673 #045-01-1982 L1988 **D IM** *020 †15 ‡
WALPOLE, Horace Ed, Jr. 103 CLAIR DR, STE F 29673 #045-01-1991 L1998 **IM DIA** *020
WILEY, Dana Lee. 102 COMMONS BLVD, # C 29673 #025-07-1986 L1994 **P** *075

POMARIA — NEWBERRY

LILLIEWOOD, Eugene Wade. ■ 29126 #047-07-1962 L1969 **OBG** *071 †30

PORT ROYAL — BEAUFORT

BRYANT, Cynthia Jean. 1845 N PARIS AVE 29935 #056-06-2000 L2006 **RO** *020
DAWSON, Rosalind Dianna. 1320 RIBAUT RD, BEAUFORT-JASPER COMP HEALT 29935 #047-07-1982 L1991 **IM** *020 †55,20
FAUST, Jeffrey Neal. 1320 RIBAUT RD 29935 #028-03-2002 L2004 **PD** *020 †55
GAINES, Benjamin E. 1320 RIBAUT RD 29935 #010-03-1983 L2004 **OBG** *020 †30
HALL, James Martin. 1680B RIBAUT RD, KEYSERLING CANCER CENTER 29935 #056-06-1967 L2004 **ON HEM** *020 †20
MC GOWN, Henry Curtis. 1510 RIBAUT RD 29935 #047-06-1955 L1968 **EM** *072 †85
MC LENDON, Baxter F, III. P, BEAUFORT EYE CLNC 29935 #045-01-1970 L1972 **OPH** *020 †35 ‡
POLKEY, Faith Lawrence. 1320 RIBAUT RD 29935 #023-07-1997 L2002 **PD GPM** *020 †55,70
RICHARDSON, Eddie, Jr. 1320 RIBAUT RD, PORT ROYAL MEDICAL CENTER 29935 #012-21-1999 L2003 **FM** *020 †18
SIMMONS, James Earl. 1875 N PARIS AVE 29935 #041-12-1996 L1999 **PD** *020 †55
WEEMS, David Hale. 1680B RIBAUT RD, KEYSERLING CANCER CENTER 29935 #011-03-1982 L1989 **RO** *020 †80

PROSPERITY — NEWBERRY

MC DONALD, Alexander J, IV. ■ 29127 #045-04-2002 L2006 **P** *020 †75
SIDENBERG, Barry Stuart. 957 CIRCLE H WOODS RD 29127 #025-01-1966 L1990 **GS OS** *020 †85
SMITH, Robert Morris. 3445 SC HIGHWAY 391 29127 #422-01-1997 L2000 **FM** *020 †18

RAVENEL — CHARLESTON

AKOM, Francis. 5920 SAVANNAH HWY, RAVENEL OB/GYN & PRIMARY C 29470 #412-01-1989 L1997 **OBG** *020 †30
JOYCE, Hazel. ■ 29470 #539-06-1973 L1975 **RO** *071 †80

REMBERT — SUMTER

WANGENSTEEN, Stephen L. ■ 29128 #024-01-1958 L1995 **GS CD** *071 †85

RICHBURG — CHESTER

YOUSEFIAN, Mehrdad. 3248 EDGELAND HWY 29729 #409-25-1982 L1986 **IM** *020 †20

RIDGELAND — JASPER

BENNETT, J M, Jr. 1504 GRAYS HWY 29936 #045-01-1957 L1957 **FM AS** *071 †18
BEY, Annette. 721 N OKATIE HWY 170 29936 #010-03-1984 L1989 **OBG** *020 †30
BROWN, Donald Francis. ■ 29936 #035-09-1959 **U** *071 †95
ESQUIVEL, Hector F. 1506 GRAYS HWY STE B, P O BOX 1528 29936 #264-05-1964 L1983 **GS GP** *020 †85 ‡
ETHERIDGE, Tricia Lynn. PO BOX 999 29936 #045-01-1996 L1997 **FM** *020 †18

HOBBS, David Refior. 109 W SMITH ST, FAMILY HLTH CARE/RIDGELAND 29936 #055-01-1964 L1970 **IM RHU** *020 †20
KUMJIAN, Dana Arshag. 28 RICE POND RD, RIVERWALK BUSINESS PARK 29936 #011-03-1985 L1996 **NEP IM** *020 †20
MC ELVEEN, Cecil Tyrone. ■ 29936 #045-01-1994 L1995 **FM** *020 †18
MC GOWN, Steven Taylor. 721 N OKATIE HWY, BEAUFORT-JASPER-HAMPTON CO 29936 #045-01-1997 L2003 **FM** *020
RODRIGUEZ-MALDONADO, Jose. ■ 29936 #935-02-1994 L2003 **PCC** *100 †20
SLACHTA, Gregory Andrew. ■ 29936 #041-02-1968 L1987 **U** *071 †95
VUTHIGANON, Chatchaval. PO BOX 1266 29936 #891-02-1972 L1983 **GS** *020
VUTHIGANON, Jantana. PO BOX 1266 29936 #891-02-1975 L1984 **PD** *020
WHITE, Donald Anderson. PO BOX 357 29936 #012-05-1976 L1977 **PTH** *075
WHITE, Peter Francis. 49 BROWNS COVE RD, STE 6 29936 #023-07-1983 L1990 **PTH DMP** *020 †50

RIDGEVILLE — DORCHESTER

BRYANT, Yolanda. ■ 29472 #045-01-2004 **FM** *100

RIDGEWAY — FAIRFIELD

ANDREO, Larry Kenneth. ■ 29130 #020-12-1990 L1996 **OPH** *020 †35

ROCK HILL — YORK

AASSAR, Ole Sami. 197 PIEDMONT BLVD, STE 110 29732 #008-01-1991 L2001 **VIR** *020 †80
ABRAMS, Mark Jeffrey. 222 S HERLONG AVE 29732 #036-01-1992 L1997 **OTO FPS** *020 †45
ADAMS, John Carlisle. 197 PIEDMONT BLVD, STE 110 29732 #036-01-1982 L1984 **DR** *020 †80
ADAMSON, Tim Eugene. 175 AMENDMENT AVE STE 104, SPINE ASSOCIATES 29732 #047-05-1985 L1997 **NS** *020 †25
ADEOLA, Tolulola Omololu. 1609 CONSTITUTION BLVD 29732 #690-01-1990 L2003 **IM** *020 †20
ADLAKHA, Arun. 124 GLENWOOD DR, CAROLINA PULMONARY PHYSICI 29732 #495-08-1980 L1998 **PUD CCM** *020 †20
AGISIM, Deborah Gould. 197 PIEDMONT BLVD, STE 110 29732 #035-46-1997 L2003 **DR** *020 †80
AKINYELU, Akingbade A. 1462 CONSTITUTION BLVD, CORNERSTONE CLINIC 29732 #690-01-1994 L2003 **IM** *020 †20
ALEXANDER, Michael R. 101 SEDGEWOOD DR 29732 #422-01-1994 L1998 **CHP** *020
ALEXANDER, Robert Mc Aule. 1601 EBENEZER RD 29732 #036-05-1978 L1979 **PD GP** *020 †55 ‡
ALFORD, Todd Michael. 410 S HERLONG AVE, STE 105 29732 #011-03-1990 L2005 **PFP** *020 †75
ALLEYNE, William Franklyn. 124 GLENWOOD DR 29732 #035-19-1983 L1999 **PUD CCM** *020 †20
ALLINGER, James Augustus. 222 S HERLONG AVE, ROCK HILL ANESTHESIA ASSOC 29732 #012-01-1993 L1998 **AN** *020 †05
ALPERT, Eric David. 197 PIEDMONT BLVD, STE 110 29732 #036-07-1971 L1971 **R** *020 †80
AMATO, Victor Michael. 1380 EBENEZER RD, STE E 29732 #033-05-1982 L2002 **GE IM** *020 †20
ANANDPURA, Parag S. 2633 CELANESE RD 29732 #038-44-1994 L1997 **FM** *020 †18
ANDERSEN, Brian Lee. 2930 BROOKRIDGE DR 29732 #047-05-1979 L1980 **DR** *020 †80
ANDERSON, Bryan Keith. 1565 EBENEZER RD 29732 #045-04-1984 L1987 **OPH** *020 †35 ‡
ANDERSON, Hal C. 1601 EBENEZER RD BOX 3460 29732 #045-01-1962 L1962 **PD** *071 †55
ANTONACCI, Vittorio Paolo. 197 PIEDMONT BLVD, STE 110 29732 #035-08-1995 L2001 **VIR** *020 †80
AYODELE, Ayotunde K. 1538 HEALTH CARE DR 29732 #010-03-1981 L2000 **PD** *020 †55
BABINSKI, Joseph Stephen. 101 SEDGEWOOD DR, NEW HOPE CAROLINAS 29732 #036-08-1983 L1988 **CHP P** *020 †75
BADALYAN, Grigor. ■ 29730 #913-38-1998 L2007 **PUD** *100 †20
BADALYAN, Rupal. ■ 29730 #055-01-2002 L2008 **MPD** *020 †55
BAKER, Robert Wayne. 222 S HERLONG AVE, DEPT ANEST 29732 #045-04-1988 L1989 **AN** *020 †05
BAKI, Talal Tarek. 196 CARDIOLOGY DR, WAKE FOREST UNIV SCHL OF M 29732 #605-01-1991 L2003 **CD** *020 †20
BARRON, George Talbert, Jr. 2633 CELANESE RD 29732 #045-04-1991 L1997 **FM** *020 †18
BARTEL, Larry Dan. 1565 EBENEZER RD, ROCK HILL EYE CLINIC 29732 #017-20-1967 L1975 **OPH** *020 †35 ‡
BEDRICK, James Jos. 724 ARDEN LN, STE 120 29732 #036-01-1977 L1988 **OPH OS** *020 †35
BELLANFONTE, Lisa Natalie. 2450 INDIA HOOK RD STE B 29732 #010-03-2003 L2007 **IM** *020 †20
BELLAVIA, Ross Joseph. 197 PIEDMONT BLVD, STE 110 29732 #035-06-1995 L2001 **VIR** *020 †80
BELONI, Andrew John. 197 PIEDMONT BLVD, STE 110 29732 #033-06-1978 L1980 **DR** *020 †80
BENSKY, Andrew Scott. 197 PIEDMONT BLVD, STE 111 29732 #035-15-1986 L2001 **PDC PD** *020 †55
BHANDARI, Surendar. 222 S HERLONG AVE, SC INPATIENT MEDICINE ASSO 29732 #495-74-2013 L2005 **IM** *020 †20
BHOOTHAPURI, Ramesh. 1584 CONSTITUTION BLVD, STE 02 29732 #495-04-1988 L2001 **NEP** *020 †20
BILLMAN, Mark Thomas. 372 S HERLONG AVE 29732 #041-07-1997 L2000 **OS** *020
BIXENMAN, William Robt. 1584 CONSTITUTION BLVD, STE 02 29732 #017-20-1980 L1988 **NEP CCM** *020 †20
BLOTNICK, Charles Adam. 724 ARDEN LN, STE 120 29732 #050-02-1992 L1999 **OPH** *020 †35
BOBO, William Earl. 228 S HERLONG AVE, ROCK HILL RADIATION THERAP 29732 #012-05-1997 L2002 **RO** *020 †80
BONHAM, George Griffith. ■ 29732 #036-01-1967 L1972 **PD** *020 †55
BOULWARE, John Hugh, II. 222 S HERLONG AVE 29732 #045-01-1965 L1965 **GP** *071
BRANT, Charles Harry. ■ 29730 #051-04-1946 L1946 **PD** *071 †55
BUMGARNER, Elizabeth Jane. 724 ARDEN LN STE 100 29732 #036-01-2002 L2005 **PD** *020
BURACK, David Allan. 744 ARDEN LN, STE 225 29732 #047-05-1983 L1990 **RHU IM** *020 †20
BURRI, Stuart Heinrich. 228 S HERLONG AVE 29732 #012-05-1995 L1999 **RO** *020 †80
CAHANAP-MERCADO, Sonia. ■ 29732 #748-10-1978 L2000 **NPM PD** *020 †55

CAMPBELL, Margaret F. 1236 EBENEZER RD, STE 200 29732 #036-01-1989 L2005 IM *020 †20
CAPPS, John Lawton. 1430 EBENEZER RD, STE 101 29732 #036-07-1985 L1986 IM *020 †20
CARTER, Lois J. 1330 INDIA HOOK RD # 313 29732 #038-06-1950 L1966 PTH CLP *071 †50
CEDARHOLM, John C. 197 PIEDMONT BLVD, STE 111 29732 #016-06-1982 L1989
   CD IM *020 †20
CHACONAS, Christina Marie. 197 PIEDMONT BLVD, STE 110 29732 #010-02-1991 L1999
   DR *020 †80
CHANG, Peter C. 197 PIEDMONT BLVD, STE 110 29732 #244-04-1988 L2002 DR *020 †80
CHARLES, James Craig. 222 S HERLONG AVE 29732 #036-01-1988 L2001 ID *020 †20
CHOUDHURY, Anju. 1612 EBENEZER RD STE 101 29732 #495-18-1987 L1994 IM *020
CLEMENTE, Jonathan D. 197 PIEDMONT BLVD, STE 110 29732 #035-47-1995 L2002
   RNR *020 †80
CLONINGER, Timothy Earl. 228 S HERLONG AVE, ROCK HILL RADIATION THERAP 29732
   #036-01-1966 L1988 RO *020 †80
COLEMAN, Stanley Roger. 250 PIEDMONT BLVD, CATAWBA FAMILY CENTER 29732
   #036-01-1994 L1996 CHP *020 †75
COLL, Jennifer Marie. 197 PIEDMONT BLVD, STE 110 29732 #023-01-2001 L2007 DR *020 †80
COPPLE, Hal E, Jr. 2450 INDIA HOOK RD, PALMETTO PEDIATRICS 29732 #030-05-1978 L1996
   PD PN *020 †55
CORDARO, Joseph V. ■ 29732 #010-02-1951 L1957 IM CD *071 †20
CORUM, Lisa Leigh. 1435 EBENEZER RD, ROCK HILL FAMILY PRACTICE 29732
   #020-02-1995 L1996 FM *020 †18
COUMAS, James Michael. 197 PIEDMONT BLVD, STE 110 29732 #024-16-1981 L1985
   DR *020 †80
COX, Jeffrey Neal. 175 AMENDMENT AVE STE 103 29732 #036-05-1988 L1989 IM *020 †20
CRAIN, Corey Knox. 200 S HERLONG AVE STE G 29732 #045-01-1979 L1985 GS *020 †85 ‡
CRAWFORD, Chris Russell. 1721 EBENEZER RD STE 205 29732 #045-01-1983 L1984
   PS HS *020 †65
CREAGH, Chas Edward, Jr. 124 GLENWOOD DR, CAROLINA PULMONARY PHYSICI 29732
   #047-06-1966 L1983 PUD IM *020 †20
CRIMALDI, Anthony Joseph. 228 S HERLONG AVE 29732 #025-07-2000 L2005 RO *020 †80
CRIMALDI, Sona. 197 PIEDMONT BLVD, STE 110 29732 #041-07-1994 L2007 DR *072 †80
DAS, Sushil Kumar. 1787 EBENEZER RD 29732 #495-39-1976 L1996 IM *020
DE FILIPP, Gary Jos. 197 PIEDMONT BLVD, STE 110 29732 #035-20-1976 L1999 DR *020 †80
DENENBERG, Michael Bryan. 154 AMENDMENT AVE, STE 103 29732 #016-42-1989 L2000
   PCC *020 †20
DOLINE, Robert Morris. 228 S HERLONG AVE 29732 #051-07-1987 L2000 RO *020 †80
DOUGLAS, Thomas Henry. 1780 MEDICAL PARK DR 29732 #051-01-1989 L1999 U AM *020 †95
DUFF, Denise Emilie. 197 PIEDMONT BLVD, STE 110 29732 #050-02-1974 L1976 DR *020 †80
DWIVEDI, Tarunendu S. 1721 EBENEZER RD, STE 265 29732 #495-92-1986 L2004 CHP *020
EDGERTON, Thomas Arthur. 200 S HERLONG AVE STE E1 29732 #036-05-1981 L1992
   TS CD *020 †85,90
EISENBERG, Carl Jesse. 197 PIEDMONT BLVD, STE 110 29732 #035-08-1975 L1999 R *020 †80
EKUNSANMI, Bamidele A. 1609 CONSTITUTION BLVD, BOX 36291 29732 #690-06-1985 L1998
   IM ON *020 †20
ELLIOTT, Charles Martin. 197 PIEDMONT BLVD, STE 111 29732 #051-04-1970 L1989
   CD *020 †20
ELSHIHABI, Said. 175 AMENDMENT AVE, STE 104 29732 #048-13-2000 L2006 NS *100
ESPINAL, Alex Rolando. 1578 CONSTITUTION BLVD 1, PALMETTO SURG LLCV 29732
   #038-44-1994 L1999 GS VS *020 †85
EVANS, William Martin. 1665 HERLONG CT, STE B 29732 #012-01-2001 L2004 APM *020 †05
FASSLER, John Edward. 1436 RIVERCHASE BLVD 29732 #038-40-1991 L1997 NEP *020 †20
FEDOR, John Michael. 197 PIEDMONT BLVD, STE 111 29732 #036-07-1976 L1989
   CD IM *020 †20
FOUNTAIN, Helen V. 222 S HERLONG AVE, PIEDMONT MED CTR 29732 #917-02-1972 L2001
   NPM OS *020 †55 ‡
FOWLER, Amy Marie. 200 S HERLONG AVE, STE A 29732 #036-01-1998 L2002 OPH *020 †35
FRANK, Theodore Alan. 197 PIEDMONT BLVD, STE 111 29732 #041-01-1992 L1999
   CD *020 †20
FRASER, Robert W, III. 228 S HERLONG AVE 29732 #041-01-1975 L1988 RO *020 †80
FRITZ, Jonathan Paul. 1565 EBENEZER RD 29732 #005-12-2000 L2003 OPH *020 †35
FULMER, Robert Verley. 2633 CELANESE RD 29732 #045-04-1985 L1986 FM *020 †18
GAZZUOLO, Debra Jean. 311 GLENWOOD DR 29732 #028-02-1993 L2002 IM *020 †20
GETTELFINGER, Dennis M. 200 S HERLONG AVE, STE H 29732 #017-20-1972 L1982
   N *020 †75
GILCHRIST, Steven Lee. 2670 MILLS PARK DR 29732 #036-08-2004 L2007 FM *020 †18
GIRARD, Donna Jean. 228 S HERLONG AVE 29732 #011-03-1986 L1990 R *020 †80
GIRAULT, Gisele J. 410 S HERLONG AVE, STE 103-104 29732 #019-02-1990 L2002
   APM *020 †05
GODBOLD, Antonya W. 281 ROLLING RIDGE RD 29730 #045-04-1996 L2002 PD *020 †55
GOODBAR, Robert Clemans. 1601 EBENEZER RD, BOX 3460 29732 #045-01-1980 L1981
   PD *020 †55 ‡
GOPALI, Santosh R. 2670 MILLS PARK DR 29732 #495-33-1993 L2002 IM *020 †20
GOR, Asutosh S. 1583 HEALTH CARE DR 29732 #495-22-1991 L2003 HO *020 †20
GOUZENNE, Stacey R. 222 S HERLONG AVE, PIEDMONT MEDICAL CENTER 29732
   #048-02-1992 L2002 EM *020 †16
GRAHAM, Lalonda Monique. 1131 SALUDA ST 29730 #038-45-2002 L2003 FM *020 †18
GRAY, Roberta Milton S. ■ 29730 #036-01-1972 L2006 PN PD *020 †55
GREGORY, Wm Eugene, Jr. 134 PROFESSIONAL PARK DR 29732 #012-01-1966 L1974
   ORS *071 †40
GREWAL, Sandeep Singh Atm. 430 S HERLONG AVE, STE 104 29732 #495-48-1997 L2004
   IM *020 †20
GROMET, Matthew. 197 PIEDMONT BLVD, STE 110 29732 #035-48-1979 L1980 DR R *020 †80
GUILFORD, William Bonner. 197 PIEDMONT BLVD, STE 110 29732 #036-01-1973 L1973
   DR *020 †80
GULYAS, Clara Elisabeth. 222 S HERLONG AVE 29732 #038-43-1981 L1986 EM *020 †16
GUNTER, Richard Glenn. 1435 EBENEZER RD, ROCK HILL FAMILY PRACTICE 29732
   #045-01-1987 L1994 FM *020 †18
HAAKE, Michael Robert. 228 S HERLONG AVE 29732 #017-20-1980 L1989 RO IM *020 †20,80
HABER, Robert Hugh. 197 PIEDMONT BLVD, STE 111 29732 #035-47-1983 L1989
   IM CD *020 †20
HALES, Erika Rhushaun. 2450 INDIA HOOK RD 29732 #033-05-2004 L2008 PE *012
HALING, Joel Andrew. 222 HERLONG AVE 29732 #035-09-1992 L1997 EM *020 †16
HALL, Donald Gammon. 225 S HERLONG AVE, PIEDMONT OFF BLDG ONE STE 29732
   #011-03-1965 L1984 CD IM *020 †20
HANSEN, Douglas Brownell. 2450 INDIA HOOK RD, PALMETTO PEDIATRICS 29732
   #036-01-1989 L1992 PD *020 †55

HARBURY, Olin Laurence. 197 PIEDMONT BLVD, STE 110 29732 #036-07-1985 L1998
   DR *020 †80
HARR, Charles Dulaney. 200 S HERLONG AVE STE E 29732 #036-05-1983 L1995
   TS *020 †85,90
HART, Craig Franklin. PO BOX 4016, YORK PATHOLOGY ASSOCIATES 29732
   #036-01-2002 L2007 PTH *100 †50
HART, Darlington I. 1462 CONSTITUTION BLVD, CORNERSTONE CLINIC 29732
   #690-02-1990 L1998 IM *020 †20
HARTLEY, William Stuart. 197 PIEDMONT BLVD, STE 110 29732 #036-01-1987 L1988
   DR *020 †80
HAYNIE, Justin Fletcher. 197 PIEDMONT BLVD, STE 111 29732 #036-05-1998 L2005
   IC *020 †20
HEDLUND, Joel Axel. 197 PIEDMONT BLVD, STE 110 29732 #033-06-1998 L2000 R *020 †80
HELTON, Ann. 166 DOTSON ST 29732 #020-12-1980 L1993 P *075 †75
HENDRIX, Kimberly B. 197 PIEDMONT BLVD, STE 110 29732 #045-04-1987 L1988 DR *020 †80
HERLONG, James Rene. 197 PIEDMONT BLVD, STE 111 29732 #036-07-1989 L2006
   PDC *020 †55
HERNDON, Wm Mauney, Jr. 197 PIEDMONT BLVD, STE 111 29732 #036-01-1981 L2000
   CD IM *020 †20
HICKLIN, Cloud Hardin. 166 DOTSON ST 29732 #045-01-1962 L1962 IM *071
HICKLIN, Harry Eugene, III. 197 PIEDMONT BLVD, STE 111 29732 #422-01-1985 L1988
   CD *020 †20
HICKLIN, Jonathan Cloud. 1565 EBENEZER RD, ROCK HILL EYE CENTER 29732
   #045-01-1991 L1995 OPH *020 †35
HILDEBRAND, Hartwell Z. 2633 CELANESE RD, CMG - SHILAND 29732 #045-01-1957 L1957
   FM *071 †18
HINDEL, Peter Paul. 197 PIEDMONT BLVD, STE 110 29732 #038-44-1983 L1998 DR *020 †80
HOBGOOD, Kelly Redden. 250 PIEDMONT BLVD, CATAWBA FAMILY CENTER 29732
   #036-08-1992 L1994 CHP P *020 †75
HOITINK, John C. 311 GLENWOOD DR 29732 #038-40-1994 L1998 IM *020 †20
HOOTEN, Mark Taylor. 222 S HERLONG AVE, P.A., AMI PIEDMONT MEDICAL 29732
   #036-01-1990 L1994 AN *020 †05
HOWARD, Brian Adrian. 197 PIEDMONT BLVD, STE 110 29732 #775-01-1980 L1998
   DR *020 †80
HOWARD, John Dale. 197 PIEDMONT BLVD, STE 110 29732 #017-20-1985 L1998 DR *020 †80
HRKAL, Miloslav Milan. 2450 INDIA HOOK RD 29732 #286-07-1982 L1996 PD *020 †55
HSU, Rhea. 311 GLENWOOD DR 29732 #001-02-1994 L1997 IM *020 †20
HSU, Tah-Hsiung. 410 S HERLONG AVE 29732 #001-02-1966 L2003 END IM *020 †20
HULL, William Martin, Jr. 1565 EBENEZER RD, ROCK HILL EYE CLINIC PA 29732
   #036-07-1963 L1969 OPH *071 †35
HUNEYCUTT, Joel B. 222 S HERLONG AVE 29732 #024-01-1952 L1966 GYN *071 †30
IULIANO, Stephen Thomas. 197 PIEDMONT BLVD, STE 111 29732 #024-16-1995 L2004
   CD *020 †20
JABEN, Scott Leonard. 200 S HERLONG AVE, STE A 29732 #011-02-1977 L1987 OPH *020 †35
JACKSON, William Alfred. 2633 CELANESE RD 29732 #045-01-1981 L1993 FM *020 †18
JENKINS, Everett Earl. 222 S HERLONG AVE, YORK PATHOLOGY ASSOCIATES 29732
   #036-01-1973 L1977 PTH FOP *020 †50
JENKINS, Matthew D. 311 GLENWOOD DR 29732 #001-02-1994 L1997 IM *020 †20
JOHNSON, Eric Gordon. 2670 MILLS PARK DR 29732 #041-02-1977 L1980 FM ADM *020 †18
JOHNSON, Matthew E. ■ 29732 #041-02-1949 L1975 P FM *072 †75
JOHNSON, Thomas Vincent. 197 PIEDMONT BLVD, STE 111 29732 #012-05-1988 L1994
   CD *020 †20
JONES, Jeremy York. 197 PIEDMONT BLVD, STE 110 29732 #012-01-1996 L2007 RNR *020 †80
KEDAR, Rajesh Hari. 2670 MILLS PARK DR 29732 #038-43-1993 L1996 IM *020
KEDAR, Sudesh Hari. 222 HERLONG AVE 29732 #038-44-1994 L1998 EM *020 †16
KEELY, David Fulmer, III. 546 S CHERRY RD 29732 #036-05-1976 L1977 PHP FM *030 †18
KELLEY, Michael John. 197 PIEDMONT BLVD, STE 110 29732 #028-02-1969 L1999
   DR NM *020 †80
KELLEY, Thomas Francis. 197 PIEDMONT BLVD, STE 111 29732 #036-08-1983 L1989
   CD IM *020 †20
KELLY, Michael Ryan. 197 PIEDMONT BLVD, STE 110 29732 #018-03-1992 L1992 AN *020 †05
KELLY, Timothy John. 1565 EBENEZER RD, STE 110 29732 #025-01-1987 L2007
   OTO HNS *020 †45 ‡
KERR, Vicky Elmira. 1632 EBENEZER RD 29732 #010-01-1974 L1980 FM *020 †18
KIRSCH, Mark. 228 S HERLONG AVE 29732 #836-01-1969 L1990 RO *020 †80
KISER, Frank Wesley. 606 LAKE CLUB DR 29732 #038-06-1954 L1957 IM *072
KODZAI, William George, Jr. 197 PIEDMONT BLVD, STE 110 29732 #036-08-1995 L2003
   NM *020 †80
KOTTURI, Vijendra Babu. 222 S HERLONG AVE, PIEDMONT MEDICAL CENTER 29732
   #496-01-2003 L2007 IM *020 †20
KOURI, Edward Wm. 197 PIEDMONT BLVD, STE 110 29732 #036-01-1968 L1968 DR *020 †80
KRAVATH, Peter Edward. 197 PIEDMONT BLVD, STE 110 29732 #035-08-1993 L2000
   PDR *020 †80
LANE, David Richey. 420 S HERLONG AVE, STE 103 29732 #028-03-2001 L2004 D *020 †15
LANKFORD, Scott Patrick. 228 S HERLONG AVE 29732 #023-01-1993 L1998 RO *020 †80
LASSITER, Fred Darden. 197 PIEDMONT BLVD, STE 111 29732 #051-04-1994 L2001
   NM *020 †80,28
LAUGHLIN, Kenneth Michael. ■ 29732 #021-01-1965 L1971 OPH *071
LAVELLE, Michael Todd. 197 PIEDMONT BLVD, STE 110 29732 #038-06-1994 L2002
   DR *020 †80
LEE, James Earl, Jr. 452 LAKESHORE PKWY, STE 105 29730 #047-07-2002 L2004 PFP *020
LEE, John Wesley, Jr. 222 HERLONG AVE 29732 #011-03-1979 L1996 FM *020 †18
LEMMON, Francis M, Jr. 237 S HERLONG AVE 29732 #045-01-1964 L1964 GYN *020 †30
LEPINE, Eugene Michel. 1533 EBENEZER RD 29732 #041-01-1966 L1974 D *020 †15 ‡
LESSLIE, Robert Denton. 1393 CELANESE RD, RIVERVIEW MEDICAL CENTER 29732
   #045-01-1976 L1977 EM *020 †70,16 ‡
LIANG, Mark Joseph. 228 S HERLONG AVE 29732 #012-01-1982 L1988 RO *020 †80
LINDEMANN, Robert Cliffor. 2450 INDIA HOOK RD 29732 #017-20-1977 L1980 IM DIA *020 †20
LINDSAY, Nikita. 1601 EBENEZER RD 29732 #036-08-2000 L2004 PD *020 †55
MACHOWSKI, Roman J. 222 S HERLONG AVE, PIEDMONT MEDICAL CENTER 29732
   #759-07-1952 L1973 P *071
MACK, Yvonne. 228 S HERLONG AVE 29732 #036-05-1988 L1988 RO *020 †80
MAIA, Jose Frederico. ■ 29732 #187-06-1956 R *071
MANCUSO, Marc Angelo. 197 PIEDMONT BLVD, STE 110 29732 #024-16-2001 L2007
   PDR *020 †80
MARFO, Magdalene. 222 S HERLONG AVE, PIEDMONT MEDICAL CENTER 29732
   #412-01-1993 L2005 IM *020 †20

MARION, Malcolm L, III. 1435 EBENEZER RD, ROCK HILL FAMILY PRACTICE 29732 #045-01-1977 L1978 **FM** *020 †18

MARTIN, Stephen Ryan. 2633 CELANESE RD 29732 #055-01-1990 L1991 **FM** *020 †18

MASSEY, William Mcnair. 197 PIEDMONT BLVD, STE 111 29732 #036-05-1990 L1993 **CD** *020 †20

MAYNARD, James Lewis. 222 S HERLONG AVE, YORK PATHOLOGY ASSOCIATES 29732 #036-01-1973 L1975 **PTH** *020 †50

MC CALL, Bradley Todd. 228 S HERLONG AVE 29732 #012-01-1988 L1996 **RO** *020 †80

MC CASKILL, Quimby Edward. 1601 EBENEZER RD 29732 #035-03-2000 L2007 **PD** *020 †55

MC COY, Richard Lee. 360 S HERLONG AVE STE A 29732 #036-05-1974 L1980 **PD** *020 †55

MC GINNIS, Barry Douglas. 197 PIEDMONT BLVD, STE 110 29732 #025-01-1979 L1999 **DR** *020 †80

MC MAHON, Sandra E. 2450 INDIA HOOK RD, STE B 29732 #035-19-1979 L1997 **IM** *020 †20

MC MEEKIN, Hayne D. 2400 W MAIN ST, THE SALUDA CENTER 29732 #045-01-1973 L1977 **P** *020 †75

MC NAIR, C Scott. 1393 CELANESE RD 29732 #045-04-1993 L2002 **FM GP** *020 †60

MEAKIN, Charles James, III. 228 S HERLONG AVE 29732 #038-41-1985 L1994 **RO** *020 †80

MEHTA, Urvashi H.. 222 S HERLONG AVE, PIEDMONT MEDICAL CENTER 29732 #495-22-1996 L2005 **IM** *020 †20

MENKHAUS, Peter James. 118 PROFESSIONAL PARK DR, CENTER FOR ORTHOPEDIC SURG 29732 #038-41-1991 L1992 **AN** *020 †05

MILLER, Fred Harland. 2450 INDIA HOOK RD, STE B 29732 #041-02-1975 L1995 **IM** *020 †20

MITRO, Gregory Charles. 228 S HERLONG AVE 29732 #041-14-1995 L2001 **RO** *020 †80

MITTL, Robert Louis, Jr. 197 PIEDMONT BLVD, STE 110 29732 #028-02-1985 L1998 **RNR DR** *020 †20,80

MOORE, Arl Van, Jr. 197 PIEDMONT BLVD, STE 110 29732 #004-01-1974 L1998 **DR VIR** *020 †80

MUNIZ, Felix R. 1665 HERLONG CT, STE B 29732 #042-01-1992 L2005 **AN PME** *020 †05

MUNSON, Catherine Laura. 1590 CONSTITUTION BLVD 1 29732 #036-01-1988 L1992 **P** *020 †75

MURPHREE, Timothy Michael. 1795 DR FRANK GASTON BLVD 29732 #042-02-1987 L1991 **N** *020 †60

MUSIALOWSKI, Richard, Jr. 197 PIEDMONT BLVD, STE 110 29732 #035-06-1991 L2001 **CD IM** *020 †20

NAIDU, Sashi. 1583 HEALTH CARE DR 29732 #035-15-1999 L2005 **IM** *020 †20

NAIR, Jyothi Narayanan. 225 S HERLONG AVE, STE 250 29732 #495-31-1998 L2007 **PD** *020 †55

NAYLOR, Irvin Hart, Jr. 197 PIEDMONT BLVD, STE 111 29732 #020-02-1989 L1996 **CD** *020 †20

NEELY, Edward Michael. 1393 CELANESE RD 29732 #045-07-1998 L2001 **FM** *020 †20

NELSON, David Brian. 410 S HERLONG AVE, STE 101 29732 #016-42-1997 L2001 **OPH** *020 †35

NETZLER, Clifford Kenneth. 2450 INDIA HOOK RD STE B, HILL 29732 #038-41-1978 L1981 **IM** *020 †20

NICHOLS, Alan Milton. ■ 29732 #035-15-1976 L1977 **GE IM** *020 †20

NWE, Myo Marlar. 430 S HERLONG AVE, STE 104 29732 #209-01-1994 L2003 **M** *100 †20

OEHME, Stephen Frederick. 1435 EBENEZER RD, ROCK HILL FAMILY PRACTICE 29732 #019-02-1989 L1996 **FM** *020 †18

OKONNEH, Henry Ashimedua. 430 S HERLONG AVE, STE 103 29732 #690-02-1984 L1999 **AN** *020,05

OLIVER, James Henry, III. 197 PIEDMONT BLVD, STE 110 29732 #012-01-1985 L2000 **DR** *020 †80

ONASANYA, Alaba Abiodun. 205 PIEDMONT BLVD, VETERANS AFFAIRS CLINIC 29732 #690-02-1993 L2002 **IM** *020 †20

PADULA, Gina Rose. 101 SEDGEWOOD DR, STE 164 29732 #035-03-1991 L2006 **CHP** *020 †75

PARSONS, David S. 200 S HERLONG AVE, STE A 29732 #048-14-1977 L1998 **HNS PD** *020 †55,45 ‡

PARSONS, Gregory Stokes. 1565 EBENEZER RD 29732 #025-07-1982 L1988 **OTO A** *020 †45

PATEL, Archita Ajitbhai. 222 S HERLONG AVE, PIEDMONT MEDICAL CENTER 29732 #495-76-1994 L2001 **HOS IM** *020 †20

PATEL, Kashyap Bhogilal. 1583 HEALTH CARE DR, CAROLINA BLOOD AND CANCER 29732 #495-76-1984 L2002 **HO** *020 †20

PATEL, Rajeshkumar M. 724 ARDEN LN, STE 100 29732 #011-04-1996 L2002 **PD** *020 †55

PATEL, Shilpesh Shantilal. 196 CARDIOLOGY DR, CAROLINA CARDIOLOGY ASSOCI 29732 #023-07-1990 L1998 **CD** *020 †20

PELLEI, David Dante. 197 PIEDMONT BLVD, STE 110 29732 #051-04-1995 L2000 **DR** *020 †80

PENNINGTON, Amanda Marie. 2633 CELANESE RD 29732 #045-01-1991 L1998 **FM** *020 †18

PETERSON, Eric Wayne. 1584 CONSTITUTION BLVD, STE 02 29732 #056-06-1984 L1995 **NEP PD** *020 †20

PLUNKETT, Steven Rockwell. 228 S HERLONG AVE 29732 #012-01-1978 L1988 **RO** *020 †80

POMEROY, Mary Carolyn. 197 PIEDMONT BLVD, STE 110 29732 #027-01-1975 L1975 **DR** *020 †80

POPE, Brian Owen. 2633 CELANESE RD, ANMED HEALTH-FAMILY PRACTI 29732 #045-04-2004 L2004 **FP** *012 †18

PROCTOR, William Franklin. 197 PIEDMONT BLVD, STE 110 29732 #051-04-1970 L2005 **DR** *020 †80

RAIBLE, Robert Joseph, Jr. 197 PIEDMONT BLVD, STE 110 29732 #041-12-1995 L2000 **DR** *020 †80

RAMESHBABU, Alagusivakumar. 1612 EBENEZER RD, METRO MED ASSOC 29732 #495-95-1992 L2003 **IM** *020 †20

RAYMOND, Glenn A. 360 S HERLONG AVE 29732 #048-02-1992 L2000 **OBG** *020 †30

REDDING, Mark Peter. 175 AMENDMENT AVE, STE 104 29732 #038-41-1990 L2000 **NS** *020 †25

REDDY, Bhaskar Rallapalli. 196 CARDIOLOGY DR, CAROLINA CARDIOLOGY ASSOCI 29732 #495-62-1987 L1998 **CD** *020 †20

REVELL, Walter Jones, Jr. 200 S HERLONG AVE STE G 29732 #012-01-1974 L1982 **GS** *020 †85

REVELL, William S. 222 S HERLONG AVE 29732 #012-01-1982 L1982 **OBG EM** *020 †30

REYNOLDS, Cynthia Renee. 1131 SALUDA ST, CENTER, P.O. BOX 29 29730 #011-03-2000 L2003 **FM** *020 †20

RHOE, Jandrette Atayae. 2670 MILLS PARK DR 29732 #025-12-1998 L2001 **FM** *020 †18

RICHTER, Richard Lester. 200 S HERLONG AVE STE C, ANESTH ASSOC OF RICK HILL 29732 #036-05-1991 L1993 **AN PME** *020 †05

ROBBINS, Amy. 222 S HERLONG AVE, PIEDMONT MEDICAL CENTER 29732 #036-01-1991 L1997 **AN** *020 †05

ROOF, Kevin Scott. 228 S HERLONG AVE 29732 #036-01-1999 L2004 **RO** *020 †80

ROSE, Geoffrey Andrew. 197 PIEDMONT BLVD, STE 111 29732 #041-01-1988 L1996 **IM** *020 †20

ROWELL, Deanna Rathel. 1601 EBENEZER RD, ROCK HILL PEDIATRICS 29732 #045-01-1996 L2002 **PD** *020 †55

RUTLEDGE, Rion Mc Kissick. 2633 CELANESE RD 29732 #045-01-1963 L1963 **FM** *071 †18

SAMAAN, Maged Guirguis. 193 LONGSIGHT LN, APT 306 29730 #915-03-1988 L2008 **CCM** *020 †20

SAMIY, Nasrollah. 724 ARDEN LN STE 220 29732 #024-05-1991 L1997 **OPH** *020 †35

SAMPLE, Jerry Jordan. 2633 CELANESE RD 29732 #045-01-1968 L1968 **FM** *020 †18

SCHLAM, Bertrand Wax. 197 PIEDMONT BLVD, STE 110 29732 #041-09-1982 L1997 **DR** *020 †80

SCHNEIDER, Andrew Martin. 197 PIEDMONT BLVD, STE 110 29732 #036-07-1994 L2005 **VIR** *020 †80

SCHWARZ, Daniel Leland. 197 PIEDMONT BLVD, STE 110 29732 #008-01-1988 L1999 **DR EM** *020 †80

SCOTT, Shirley Kate. 154 AMENDMENT AVE, STE 104 29732 #047-06-1992 L2003 **GS** *020 †85

SCOVILLE, Robert Mabry. 134 PROFESSIONAL PARK DR 29732 #045-01-1964 L1964 **ORS** *020 †40

SEYMORE, Cathy Hawkins. 228 S HERLONG AVE 29732 #045-01-1982 L1987 **RO** *020 †80

SEYMORE, Russell Jeffrey. 2275 INDIA HOOK RD, HOSPICE & COMMUNITY CARE 29732 #045-01-1982 L1987 **AM** *020 †05

SHAH, Gaurang Chandughai. 225 S HERLONG AVE STE 250 29732 #495-23-1981 L2000 **NPM** *020 †55

SHAH, Jagdish Vallabhdas. 166 DOTSON ST, CATAWBA MENTAL HEALTH CENT 29732 #495-48-1982 L1994 **P** *020 †75

SHAH, Nirav Pravin. 197 PIEDMONT BLVD, STE 110 29732 #033-05-1997 L1997 **NR DR** *020 †80

SHARMA, Rajiv Kumar. 197 PIEDMONT BLVD, STE 110 29732 #026-04-1989 L2002 **PDR** *020 †80

SHAW, Dale Russell. 197 PIEDMONT BLVD, STE 110 29732 #036-07-1973 L1973 **DR AR** *020 †80 ‡

SHAW, Jan. 2025 EBENEZER RD, # 0 29732 #048-02-1975 L1980 **N PD** *020 †55

SICK, Brandon Roger. 2633 CELANESE RD, SHILAND FAMILY MEDICINE 29732 #035-03-1993 L1994 **FM** *020 †18

SIMMONS, Jeffrey James. ■ 29732 #048-15-2002 L2006 **OMF** *020

SIMON, Daniel J. 724 ARDEN LN, STE 120 29732 #035-08-2002 L2006 **OPH** *020 †35

SIMPSON, Thomas Herbert. 372 S HERLONG AVE, ORAL&MAXILLO FACL SUR CTR 29732 #001-02-1989 L1991 **OMF FPS** *020

SINCLAIR, Pamela R. 225 S HERLONG AVE, STE 201 29732 #041-09-1986 L1992 **HO ON** *020 †20

SOBEL, Amy H. 197 PIEDMONT BLVD, STE 110 29732 #041-09-1993 L2000 **DR** *020 †80

SPEIGHT, Otis Donnell. 222 S HERLONG AVE 29732 #036-01-1985 L1992 **EM IM** *020 †16

STACY-HUMPHRIES, Robyn L. 197 PIEDMONT BLVD, STE 110 29732 #036-01-1986 L2006 **DR** *020 †80

STADTLANDER, Kevin Sean. 197 PIEDMONT BLVD, STE 110 29732 #041-13-1991 L1998 **VIR DR** *020 †80

START, Robert John. 222 S HERLONG AVE 29732 #025-01-1990 L1999 **AN** *020 †05

STEELE, Walter Judson. 197 PIEDMONT BLVD, STE 110 29732 #036-01-1980 L1987 **R** *020 †80

STEIN, Jeffrey Paul. 197 PIEDMONT BLVD, STE 110 29732 #035-47-1997 L2004 **DR** *020 †80

STEPHENSON, Christopher G. 197 PIEDMONT BLVD, STE 111 29732 #422-01-1997 L2004 **CD** *020 †20

STEVENSON, John Saml. 197 PIEDMONT BLVD, STE 110 29732 #036-05-1967 L1967 **R NM** *020 †28,80

STRAIT, William F, III. 1721 EBENEZER RD STE 145 29732 #045-01-1953 L1953 **GYN** *071 †30

SWEET, Robert Michael. 311 PENDLETON ST, COSMETIC & RECONSTRVE ASSC 29730 #045-01-1976 L1997 **PS OTO** *020 †45,65

TAFARI, Gashaw Tedla. 1131 SALUDA ST 29730 #366-01-1983 L1997 **PD** *020 †55

TALARICO, Carmen L. 197 PIEDMONT BLVD, STE 110 29732 #038-40-1979 L1998 **PDR DR** *020 †80

TAORMINA, Martin. 1721 EBENEZER RD, STE 115 29732 #048-15-1990 L2003 **VS GS** *020 †85

THOMAS, Robert Earl, Jr. 222 S HERLONG AVE, YORK PATHOLOGY ASSOCIATES 29732 #045-01-1995 L1996 **PTH** *020 †50

THORP, James W. 222 S HERLONG AVE, PEDIATRIX MEDICAL GROUP 29732 #010-02-1975 L2004 **NPM PD** *020 †55 ‡

TIEDEMAN, Walter Probst. 1721 EBENEZER RD 7 29732 #045-01-1963 L1963 **GS** *071 †85

TIMONY, Tracy Marie. 311 GLENWOOD DR, CAROLINA MED CONSLTS 29732 #033-05-1987 L1991 **IM** *020 †20

TRAUTMANN, Thomas Gary. 228 S HERLONG AVE 29732 #038-41-1979 L1999 **RO ON** *020 †20,80

TRUESDALE, Dorenda G. 2633 CELANESE RD, SHILAND FAMILY MEDICINE 29732 #045-04-2000 L2001 **FM** *020 †18

TUCKER, Charles Leonard. 724 ARDEN LN, STE 220 29732 #045-01-1998 L2005 **OPH** *020 †35 ‡

TUTTLE, Nicholas Hamner. 1435 EBENEZER RD, ROCK HILL FAMILY PRACTICE 29732 #045-01-1982 L1983 **FM** *020 †18

ULLRICH, Christopher G. 197 PIEDMONT BLVD, STE 110 29732 #035-15-1976 L2000 **DR NRN** *020 †80

VALITE, Delfin F. 1156 EBENEZER RD 29732 #748-01-1990 L2002 **P** *020

VILLAMOR, Randolph V C. 311 GLENWOOD DR, CAROLINA MEDICAL CONSULTAN 29732 #748-11-1992 L2003 **IM** *020 †20

VUJICIC, Ratko. 197 PIEDMONT BLVD, STE 214 29732 #957-01-1989 L2003 **APM** *100 †05

WALLACE, Terry Wayne. 197 PIEDMONT BLVD, STE 110 29732 #036-01-1982 L1998 **DR NM** *020 †80

WARD, William Brien, Jr. ■ 29732 #045-01-1954 L1954 **R NM** *071 †80,28

WARLICK, William Byrd, Jr. 228 S HERLONG AVE 29732 #012-01-1994 L2002 **RO** *020 †80

WELSH, James Duncan. 1583 HEALTH CARE DR 29732 #021-05-1982 L1987 **ON HEM** *020 †20 ‡

WERTHMULLER, William C. 197 PIEDMONT BLVD, STE 110 29732 #051-04-1985 L1999 **DR** *020 †80

WHITE, George Huggin. 1435 EBENEZER RD, ROCK HILL FAMILY PRACTICE 29732 #045-01-1976 L1979 **FM** *020 †18

WHITE, Michael James. 222 S HERLONG AVE, PIEDMONT MEDICAL CENTER-EM 29732 #035-06-2000 L2007 **EM** *020 †16

WHITE, Richard Eric. 1563 HEALTH CARE DR 29732 #028-03-1997 L2003 **D** *020 †15

WIERCISIEWSKI, David R. 175 AMENDMENT AVE, STE 104 29732 #041-12-1989 L2005 **PM** *020 †60

WILSON, Brian Claud. 197 S HERLONG AVE 29732 #030-05-1984 L1990 **HNS** *020 †45 ‡

WILSON, Bryan Hadley. 197 PIEDMONT BLVD, STE 111 29732 #036-07-1980 L1989 **IM CD** *020 †20

■ = Address Information Privacy Protected

WILSON, Robert, Jr. 200 S HERLONG AVE STE A 29732 #045-01-1962 L1967 **OTO** *020 †45
WISSING, Joel Allen. 197 PIEDMONT BLVD, STE 110 29732 #001-02-1973 L1975 **DR GP** *020 †80
WOODALL, Timothy Gerrard. 1563 HEALTH CARE DR 29732 #045-01-1997 L2001 **D** *020 †15
WORDEN, Almarose Cooke. ■ 29732 #016-06-1951 L1955 **GP** *071
ZOLLINGER, Richard Wm. II. 200 S HERLONG AVE, STE E1 29732 #016-42-1978 L1989 **TS** *020 †85,90

ROEBUCK – SPARTANBURG

GENTRY, Carla Franklin. 5229 HIGHWAY 221, MARY BLACK FAM MED-DORMAN 29376 #047-06-1986 L1987 **FM OM** *020 †18
MACKENZIE, Allen Hugh. ■ 29376 #021-01-1955 L1960 **RHU PPR** *071

ROUND O – COLLETON

DODD, William Kennedy. ■ 29474 #045-01-1963 L1963 **FM** *071

RUBY – CHESTERFIELD

VALVERDE, Michael. 130 MARKET STREET 29741 #319-01-1948 L1963 **GP AN** *020

RUFFIN – COLLETON

BOLESKI, Paul Henry. ■ 29475 #016-42-1980 L1981 **EM FM** *071

SAINT GEORGE – DORCHESTER

DANTZLER, James Hart. 5664 MEMORIAL BLVD 29477 #045-01-1994 L1996 **FM** *020 †18
EVANS, Scott Chadwick. 202 RIDGE ST 29477 #045-01-2002 L2006 **FM** *100 †18
JORDAN, Cecil B. II. 109 DUKES ST 29477 #045-01-1983 L1984 **FM** *020 †18
SIMPSON, Dana Leigh. 202 RIDGE ST 29477 #036-01-1995 L1999 **FM** *020 †18
WATSON, Eric James. 202 GAVIN ST 29477 #036-08-1985 L1986 **IM** *020
WIMBERLY, Christopher W. 202 RIDGE ST 29477 #045-01-2000 L2001 **FM** *020 †18
WIMBERLY, Clarence Wm. Jr. 202 RIDGE ST 29477 #045-01-1969 **FM** *020 †18

SAINT HELENA ISLAND – BEAUFORT

CHRISTIAN, Richard Morton. ■ 29920 #047-05-1942 L1950 **IM** *072 †20
COLEMAN, William Mc Lin. ■ 29920 #012-01-1964 L1964 **ORS** *071 †40
COLLINGS, Harold, Jr. ■ 29920 #024-01-1949 L1962 **N** *071 †75
DAVY, John Robt. ■ 29920 #041-13-1958 L1959 **IM PHP** *071
DUNN, Adolphus Wm. ■ 29920 #036-07-1945 L1945 **ORS** *071 †40
GOETTLE, James W. ■ 29920 #038-41-1953 L1991 **FM** *071 †18
HORRAX, Trudeau M. ■ 29920 #041-13-1946 L1958 **OM U** *071 †95
JACKSON, William A. 1348 ROWLAND DR 29920 #021-01-1990 L1991 **DR** *020 †80
JANECKA, Ivo. ■ 29920 #286-02-1965 L1969 **HNS PS** *020 †45,65
LITTON, Linda Jane Taft. ■ 29920 #035-08-1962 L1967 **AN** *071 †05
REESE, Evan Chas. Jr. ■ 29920 #041-01-1967 L1968 **ORS** *071 †40
TOCHAROEN, Ahraya. 41 BALL PARK RD 29920 #891-02-1963 L1983 **PD EM** *020 †55,18
VIGUERA, Marcos Gilberto. ■ 29920 #847-01-1960 L1969 **AN** *071 †05
VIGUERA, Maria Luisa. ■ 29920 #847-01-1960 L1970 **GP OS** *071
WEIDNER, Larry Wayne. ■ 29920 #039-01-1963 L1963 **OPH AM** *071 †35

SAINT MATTHEWS – CALHOUN

ROWE, Robert William. 558 CHESTNUT ST, ST MATTHEWS FAM HLTH CTR 29135 #045-01-2002 L2005 **FM** *020 †18
STONE, Terrell Lee. PO BOX 638, 415 HARRY C RAYSOR DR 29135 #045-04-1986 L1987 **FM** *020 †18

SAINT STEPHEN – BERKELEY

BROWN, Sarah Holleman. 137 CEDAR DR, BOX 280 29479 #045-01-1992 L1994 **FM** *020 †18
SCHUMANN, Samuel O. 104 FUNK AVE, P.A. P.O. BOX 549 29479 #045-01-1953 L1953 **FM** *071 †18
SCHUMANN, Samuel O, Jr. 104 FUNK AVE 29479 #045-01-1986 L1987 **FM** *020 †18

SALEM – OCONEE

ALERRE, Ricardo Unabia. ■ 29676 #748-01-1955 L1981 **GS** *071
BOECKMAN, Clifford R. ■ 29676 #056-06-1954 L1990 **GS** *071 †85
CARNEY, John R. ■ 29676 #025-01-1945 L1946 **FM** *071 †18
CARRINGTON, Kenneth W. ■ 29676 #041-01-1954 L1959 **NS** *071 †25
CHAMBERLAIN, Donald S. ■ 29676 #016-06-1960 L1985 **R NR** *071 †80
DANIELS, Daniel Bell. ■ 29676 #017-20-1971 L1971 **TS** *020 †85,90
DRUKKER, Bruce Highstone. 616 N FLAGSHIP DR, BRUCE H DRUKKER MD 29676 #035-20-1959 L1996 **GYN GO** *071 †30
HOLZMAN, Gerald Bruce. ■ 29676 #005-11-1957 L1959 **OBG** *071 †30
HOTCHKISS, Dwight Jordan. ■ 29676 #041-01-1954 L1955 **ON HEM** *071 †20
PARKER, Irene Talley. 1002 W PINNACLE DR, LAUREL MEDICAL GROUP, PA 29676 #011-02-1985 L2001 **GE HEP** *020
PLUMMER, William D. 1002 W PINNACLE DR, LAUREL MEDICAL GROUP, PA 29676 #023-12-1980 L1999 **IM CD** *020 †20
SCHLUETER, John Jos. 19 LASH UP LN 29676 #038-41-1956 L1956 **R** *071 †80

SALTERS – WILLIAMSBURG

DOMINICI, Raymond Henry, Jr. ■ 29590 #045-01-1999 **IM** *100

SALUDA – SALUDA

GRATE, Deborah Johnson. 219 GREENWOOD HWY 29138 #045-01-1982 L1985 **FM** *020 †18
MOORE, Eugene Alman. 261 WALLACE RD 29138 #045-01-1965 L1965 **GS GP** *020
RILEY, Ralph Nichols. 501 W BUTLER AVE 29138 #045-04-1982 L1983 **FM** *020 †18
SAWYER, William Cone. 102 R L SAWYER MD DR, SALUDA FAMILY MEDICINE, PA 29138 #045-01-1991 L1992 **FM** *020 †18
SMITH, John Michael, Jr. ■ 29138 #045-01-1963 **P** *074

SANTEE – ORANGEBURG

WESTPHAL, Milton C. ■ 29142 #041-01-1951 L1952 **GE PD** *040 †55
WILLIAMS, Teresa Ann. 111 JOHN LAWSON AVE, EXPRESS HLTH CARE OF TRMC- 29142 #045-01-1998 L1999 **GPM GP** *020 †70

SEABROOK ISLAND – CHARLESTON

COOK, C Barrie. ■ 29455 #010-01-1948 L1950 **NM PTH** *071 †50,28
DAVIDSON, Jonathan Robt T. ■ 29455 #917-30-1967 L1973 **P** *020 †75
KING, Gerald Wesley. 3147 MARSHGATE LN, AB7332961 29455 #045-01-1966 L1966 **ON IM** *071 †20
PFEILSTICKER, Jeanne C. ■ 29455 #041-13-1975 L1977 **OS GYN** *075 †18
SANDERS, Joe Maxwell, Jr. ■ 29455 #045-01-1967 L1967 **PD ADL** *030 †55
VAN HEERDEN, Jonathan A. ■ 29455 #836-02-1961 L1970 **GS** *071 †85

SENECA – OCONEE

ACRES, George Steven. 109 OMNI DR, STE A 29672 #017-20-1977 L1982 **NEP IM** *020 †20
ADAMS, Francis Bowen. 298 MEMORIAL DR 29672 #012-05-1948 L1954 **FM** *071 †18
ALAM, Safdar. 111 CARTER PARK DR, STE A 29678 #045-01-1988 L1991 **FM** *020 †18
ALAM, Tauqueer S. 109 CARTER PARK DR STE 3A, KEOWEE PRIMARY CARE 29678 #495-01-1992 L1996 **IM** *020
ALBER, Thomas John. 298 MEMORIAL DR 29672 #045-01-1991 L2004 **PD** *020 †55
ANDERSON, Bonnie Bates. 298 MEMORIAL DR, OCONEE MEMORIAL HOSPITAL 29672 #011-02-1982 L2001 **R** *020 †80
AXSON, Frank Adams. 11092 N RADIO STATION RD, OCONEE INTERNAL MEDICINE 29678 #045-01-1970 L1973 **IM** *020 †20 ‡
AXSON, William Alan. 298 MEMORIAL DR 29672 #045-01-1976 L1980 **OPH** *020
BAEHR, Ralph Henry. ■ 29672 #016-06-1959 L1960 **R** *071 †80
BARDEN, Kathryn Davison. 298 MEMORIAL DR, OCONEE MEMORIAL HOSPITAL 29672 #045-01-1987 L1988 **EM** *020 †16
BATTLE, Earl Peters. 298 MEMORIAL DR 29672 #047-07-1955 L1976 **FM** *075
BECKER, Kenneth H. 109 OMNI DR, # B 29672 #305-01-1984 L2003 **FM** *020 †18 ‡
BOOKER, Christina A. 298 MEMORIAL DR 29672 #045-01-1998 L1999 **FM** *020 †18
BOOKER, Edward Henry, Sr. 298 MEMORIAL DR 29672 #045-01-1978 L1979 **FM** *020
BOWMAN, Larry Stanley. 10630 CLEMSON BLVD 29678 #045-01-1974 L1977 **ORS EM** *020 †40
BROCKWAY, Ronnie Allan. 215 STORK WAY, OCONEE OB/GYN ASSOCIATES, 29678 #001-02-1978 L1979 **OBG** *020 †30
BROWN, Timothy Ross. 10630 CLEMSON BLVD, HAND SURGERY CENTER PA 29678 #045-04-1990 L1991 **HS** *020 †40
BROWN, William Scott. 10630 CLEMSON BLVD 29678 #045-01-2000 L2005 **ORS** *020 †40
BRUCE, George Ray. 301 MEMORIAL DR, STE A 29672 #045-01-1966 L1966 **ORS** *020 †40
BRUCE, Lorraine Ann. 207 MAIN ST, SENECA PEDIATRICS 29678 #041-14-1986 L1987 **PD** *020 †55
BUSH, David James. 131 LILA DOYLE DR, CAROLINAS SENECA 29672 #018-03-1967 L2003 **RO** *020 †80
CABANERO, Juan Jose A. 704 N PINE ST 29678 #748-10-1986 L2003 **CD** *020 †20
CAPELL, Robert Donald. 290 APPLEWOOD CENTER PL #G 29678 #045-01-1967 L1967 **FM R** *075 †18
CARPENTER, Jimmie Harold. 867 WHITWORTH CIR 29672 #021-01-1958 L1959 **FM OBG** *071
CARRICK, Christina Rodger. 298 MEMORIAL DR, OCONEE MEM HOSP LAB 29672 #011-04-2000 L2002 **PTH** *020 †50
CHANDRAN, Ravi Theerthaka. 107 OMNI DR STE A 29672 #495-16-1991 L2002 **CCM** *020 †20
CHILES, Bill Robt. 298 MEMORIAL DR, OCONEE MEMORIAL HOSPITAL 29672 #001-02-1989 L1992 **EM** *020 †16
CONDUA-TILLMAN, Kakra. 107 E NORTH 1ST ST, GOLDEN CORNER INTERNAL MED 29678 #412-02-1988 L1996 **IM** *020 †20
CRIPPEN, Donald Arthur. 112 SURGICAL BLVD 29672 #048-04-1947 L1970 **GS** *072 †85
CROMER, Gregory Earle. 298 MEMORIAL DR, OCONEE MEMORIAL HOSPITAL 29672 #045-01-1996 L2001 **OS** *020 †16
CROWE, Anthony Todd. 10630 CLEMSON BLVD 29678 #045-01-1990 L1991 **AN** *020 †05
DEAN, Jordan Arthur, Jr. 207 MAIN ST 29678 #012-05-1970 L1981 **PD** *020 †55
DILLMAN, Mitchell Foy. 11082 N RADIO STATION RD, SENECA MEDICAL ASSOCIATES 29678 #012-05-1988 L1989 **FM** *020 †18
DIMASHKIEH, Haytham H. 298 MEMORIAL DR, OCONEE MEMORIAL HOSPITAL 29672 #605-01-1998 L2005 **PCP** *020 †50
DOBSON, Dean Mac Millan. 100 OMNI DR, # B 29672 #036-05-1968 L1973 **U** *071 †95
DOUD, Thomas Myles. 1059 BY PASS 123, MOUNTAINVIEW MEDICAL IMAGI 29678 #048-15-1986 L1987 **DR** *020 †80
DUFFY, Aimee Christina. 215 STORK WAY 29678 #048-13-2003 L2004 **FM OBS** *020 †18
ECKERT, Gordon Lee. 215 STORK WAY 29678 #056-05-1957 L1981 **OBG** *020 †18
ENDERS, Gregory Louis. 298 MEMORIAL DR 29672 #038-40-1993 L2001 **AN** *020 †05
EVANS, Thomas Edwin. 11082 N RADIO STATION RD, SENECA MEDICAL ASSOCIATES 29678 #012-05-1987 L1998 **FM** *040 †18
FEISTE, James Edward. 10706 CLEMSON BLVD 29678 #025-01-1994 L2003 **PD** *020 †55
FIORENTINO, Carmine. 298 MEMORIAL DR 29672 #561-10-1987 L1996 **IM** *020 †20
FOX, Karen Rose. 414 OLD CLEMSON HWY, UPSTATE ENT ASSOCS, PA 29672 #422-01-1985 L1992 **P** *020

GEIST, Robert Miller, IV. ■ 29672 #045-01-2004 L2007 **FM** *100

GILBERT, Osceola Pinckney. 112 SURGICAL BLVD, # A 29672 #045-01-1974 L1983 **GS** *020 †85

GIL-STEWART, Beatriz E. 298 MEMORIAL DR 29672 #011-75-1995, ▲ L2002 **FM** *020 †18

GULLY, Carey Molin. 457B BY PASS 123 29678 #045-01-2003 L2004 **PD AMF** *020

HANAHAN, James Ross, Jr. 12016 N RADIO STATION RD, OCONEE FAMILY PRATICE,PA 29678 #012-01-1975 L1976 **FM** *020

HANKS, Roy Kyle. ■ 29678 #036-07-2004 *100

HARDY, James. 1059 BY PASS 123 29678 #011-02-1988 L1994 **DR** *020 †80

HASSAN, Raza. 704 N PINE ST 29678 #704-01-1986 L1998 **CD** *020 †20

HICKLIN, Osmand Alexander. 1059 BY PASS 123, MOUNTAINVIEW MEDICAL IMAGI 29672 #045-01-1989 L1990 **DR NM** *020 †80

HOLDEN, Daniel James. 103 OMNI DR, STE A 29672 #065-09-1976 L2008 **RHU IM** *020 †20

HUGHES, Michael L. 107 OMNI DR STE B 29672 #048-02-1994 L2003 **GS** *020 †85

HUMMEL, Laura Elizabeth. 11082 N RADIO STATION RD, COUNTY MEM HOSP-FP 29678 #055-01-2000 L2006 **FP** *012

HUNTER, John Dane. 131 LILA DOYLE DR, CAROLINAS SENECA 29672 #036-07-1976 L2001 **ON HEM** *020 †20 ‡

JAMES, Joseph Burkett. 135 PROFESSIONAL PARK DR 29678 #036-05-1972 L1976 **ORS** *020 †40

JOHANNES, Patrick Michael. 298 MEMORIAL DR, OCONEE MEMORIAL HOSPITAL 29672 #025-07-1988 L1992 **EM** *020 †16

JORDAN, Arthur Elbert, Jr. 457A BY PASS 123 29678 #045-01-1974 L1976 **OS N** *020

KIDD, Joel Kenneth. 867 WHITWORTH CIR 29672 #045-01-1993 L1996 **FM** *020 †18

KWOFIE, Peter Kennedy. 115 EAGLES NEST DR, STE B 29678 #412-01-1989 L2000 **ID** *020 †20

LEAP, Keith Edwin. 298 MEMORIAL DR, OCONEE MEMORIAL HOSPITAL 29672 #055-01-1990 L1993 **EM** *020 †16

LEE, William Harrell. 210 N PINE ST, OCONEE PEDIATRICS 29678 #012-05-1954 L1962 **PD** *071 †55

LEMMON, Robert Pressman. 106 RAM CAT ALY 29678 #036-01-1993 L1994 **FM** *020 †18

LESLIE, Howard Miles. 298 MEMORIAL DR, OCONEE MEMORIAL HOSPITAL 29672 #001-02-1988 L1991 **EM** *020 †16

LEVINER, John Lindsay, Jr. ■ 29672 #045-01-1968 L1968 **CD IM** *071 †20

LLIBRE, Jose Danilo. ■ 29672 #308-01-1962 L1968 **PTH** *020 †50

MANSOUR, Abbas Hamzeh. 125 PROFESSIONAL PARK DR 29678 #575-01-1993 L2004 **PUD** *020 †20

MARSHALL, Kenneth Alan. 102 OMNI DR STE B, OMH CTR COMPREHSVE PAIN 29672 #041-01-1982 L2003 **AN PME** *020 20,05 ‡

MARTIN, John William. 298 MEMORIAL DR, OCONEE MEMORIAL HOSPITAL 29672 #045-01-2000 L2004 **AN** *020 †05

MARTIN, Steven Lee. 10630 CLEMSON BLVD 29678 #051-04-1984 L1994 **ORS** *020 †40

MARTIN, Susan Thrasher. 298 MEMORIAL DR 29672 #025-07-1986 L1991 **PTH** *020 †50

MASSIOS, Scott C. 530 BY PASS 123 29678 #035-46-1992 L2000 **OPH** *020 †35

MATHEW, Roshan Kuzhiveli. 298 MEMORIAL DR, BLUE RIDGE EMERGENCY PHYSI 29672 #665-02-2002 L2003 **FM** *020 †18

MC ALPINE, Cathryn Ruby. 109 CARTER PARK DR STE 3 29678 #047-05-1982 L1994 **IM** *020 †20

MC ALPINE, Robert G, Jr. 100 OMNI DR, STE B 29672 #036-05-1981 L1994 **U** *020 †95

MC CALLUM, Patrick Sean. 10630 CLEMSON BLVD 29678 #011-03-1989 L1995 **OSM ORS** *040

MCCOLLOUGH, Brian Anthony. 11082 N RADIO STATION RD, SENECA LAKES FAMILY MEDICI 29678 #654-01-2002 L2005 **FP** *012

MC GEORGE, James C. 10630 CLEMSON BLVD 29678 #561-01-1978 L1989 **ORS** *020 †40

MC GUFF, Miles D. 298 MEMORIAL DR, OCONEE MEMORIAL HOSPITAL 29672 #048-13-1989 L1995 **EM** *020 †16

MC MILLAN, Marion R, III. 457A BY PASS 123 STE 2 29678 #024-07-1980 L1991 **AN IM** *020 20,05

MCNEELY, Lacey Pounder. 298 MEMORIAL DR, OCONEE MEMORIAL HOSPITAL 29672 #045-04-2003 L2004 **IM** *020 †20

MCPHERSON, Timothy Joe. 298 MEMORIAL DR, OCONEE MEMORIAL HOSPITAL 29672 #055-02-2001 L2007 **FM** *020 †18

MEEDER, Lee Douglas. 298 MEMORIAL DR 29672 #016-11-1983 L1989 **AN** *020 †05

MENDES, Tarina Marlene. 207 MAIN ST, SENECA PEDIATRIC ENDOCRINO 29678 #051-01-1981 L1992 **PDE** *020 †55

MEYERS, Jaymi Sylvan. 105 OMNI DR STE C, KEWOEE FAMILY MED 29672 #018-03-1994 L1996 **FM** *020 †18

MILES, Robert Lyle. 298 MEMORIAL DR 29672 #051-04-1956 L1985 **DR OS** *071 †80

MILLER, John Franklin. 11082 N RADIO STATION RD, SENECA MEDICAL ASSOCIATES 29678 #045-01-1978 L1979 **FM** *020 †18

MIRZA, Absar Ahmad. 109 OMNI DR, STE A 29672 #704-02-1995 L2002 **NEP** *020 †20

MOSES, Leslie Teets. 298 MEMORIAL DR 29672 #039-01-1989 L2007 **IM** *020 †20

NAFZIGER, James Allen. 111 CARTER PARK DR, STE A 29678 #051-04-1988 L2007 **FM** *020 †18

O'ROURKE, Mark Allen. 131 LILA DOYLE DR, CAROLINAS SENECA 29672 #005-14-1982 L1990 **HO PLM** *020 †20

PAEZ, Raul. ■ 29678 #726-01-1962 L1988 **P** *020 †75

PALUZZI, Michael Wm. ■ 29672 #041-02-1986 L1998 **GS** *020 †85

PARKER, Jonathan David. 215 STORK WAY 29678 #045-04-1999 L2000 **OBG** *020 †30

PARRINO, Michael P H. 298 MEMORIAL DR 29672 #021-01-1968 L1981 **PD PDI** *020 †55

PATE, Eula Howell. 115 CARTER PARK DR 29678 #012-01-1965 L1971 **GP** *020

PIERCE, Mark Alan. 10630 CLEMSON BLVD, STE 100 29678 #016-01-2002 L2007 **ORS** *020

PIRKLE, Vance Newton. 215 STORK WAY 29678 #012-01-1997 L2007 **OBG** *020 †30

POLEYNARD, Blake C. 298 MEMORIAL DR 29672 #021-06-1987 L1997 **DR** *020 †80,18

PRUITT, James Robt. 298 MEMORIAL DR 29672 #045-01-1960 L1960 **PTH EM** *020 †50

RAMPEY, Stanley Alfred. 11082 N RADIO STATION RD, SENECA MEDICAL ASSOCIATES 29678 #045-01-1977 L1978 **FM** *020 †18

RAO, Frank G. 414 OLD CLEMSON HWY 29672 #041-09-1986 L1992 **OTO** *020 †45

REDMOND, Brian James. 10630 CLEMSON BLVD 29678 #056-05-1992 L2002 **OSM** *020 †40

REEVES, Douglas Allen, Jr. 10630 CLEMSON BLVD 29678 #045-01-1996 L1997 **FSM FM** *020 †18

REIS, James Robert. 301 MEMORIAL DR, STE G 29672 #038-45-2001 L2003 **IM** *020

RICALDE, Orlando A. 103 OMNI DR, STE B 29672 #048-14-1983 L1996 **N** *020 †75

RICHMOND, Wm Bruce, II. 10630 CLEMSON BLVD, STE 100 29678 #045-01-1989 L1999 **ORS** *020 †40

ROGOFF, Frederick David. 109 OMNI DR, STE A 29672 #038-06-1974 L1980 **NEP IM** *020 †20

ROPER, John A, Jr. ■ 29678 #041-13-1951 L1966 **FM GS** *020

ROPER, Ruth E Atkinson. ■ 29678 #041-13-1953 L1973 **OBG** *074

RUSHE, Todd Saml. 298 MEMORIAL DR, DEPARTMENT OF RADIOLOGY 29672 #045-04-1988 L2002 **DR** *020 †80

RUSS-BARBER, Stephanie L. 207 MAIN ST, SENECA PEDS. 29678 #012-01-1999 L2005 **PD** *020 †55

SCHANDL, Cynthia. 298 MEMORIAL DR 29672 #045-01-1999 L2001 **PTH FOP** *020 †50

SCHIMMEL, Nelson H. ■ 29672 #041-02-1948 L1950 **IM GP** *071

SHABANEH, Baha Eddin Araf. 704 N PINE ST 29678 #575-01-1996 L2004 **CD** *100 †20

SHERRILL, Jerry Frank, Jr. 103 OMNI DR, STE B 29672 #001-02-1991 L1993 **N** *020 †75

SHULER, Carol Wannamaker. 112 SURGICAL BLVD, STE B 29672 #045-01-1984 L1985 **OBG** *020 †30

SHULER, Conrad K, II. 11082 N RADIO STATION RD, SENECA MEDICAL ASSOCIATES 29678 #045-01-1981 L1982 **FM** *020 †18

SILVA, Monica E. 109 OMNI DR STE A, P O BOX 1647 29672 #737-06-1993 L2000 **PD PDI** *020 †55

SMITH, Daniel Mouzon, Jr. 106 RAM CAT ALY, PRACTICE, PA 29678 #045-01-1994 L1995 **FM** *020 †18

SMITH, Michael Timothy. 298 MEMORIAL DR 29672 #055-01-1972 L1993 **PTH NP** *040 †50

SOLER, Alexandro Travieso. 501 ROCHESTER HWY, STE D 29672 #025-07-1978 L1997 **GS VS** *020 †85

STEWART, Frank A. 210 N PINE ST 29678 #011-75-1994, ▲ L2001 **PD** *020 †55

SUGAR, Darryl Matthew. 135 PROFESSIONAL PARK DR 29678 #056-06-1977 L2000 **NEP** *020 †20

TEBALT, Michael Joseph. 298 MEMORIAL DR, AT OCONEE MEMORIAL HOSPITA 29672 #045-01-2002 L2004 **AN** *020 †05

THOMPSON, Paul Eugene, Jr. 12 BOARDWALK PL 29678 #041-09-1978 L1992 **GE IM** *020 †20

TOLMOS, Jorge. 100 OMNI DR, STE A 29672 #737-06-1992 L2000 **GS SO** *020 †85

TYLER, Bradford A. 16 ACCOUNTANTS CIR, P O BOX 834 29678 #048-02-1994 L2001 **GS** *020 †85

UDALL, John Brian. 298 MEMORIAL DR, DEPT OF RADIOLOGY 29672 #027-01-1986 L2001 **DR** *020 †80

UDEN, David Elliott. 704 N PINE ST 29678 #067-01-1962 L1991 **CD** *071 †20

WALLS, Jay David. 131 LILA DOYLE DR, CAROLINAS SENECA 29672 #047-06-1986 L1994 **ON HEM** *020 †20

WORTHINGTON, John Everett. 298 MEMORIAL DR, OCONEE MEMORIAL HOSPITAL 29672 #012-01-1992 L1995 **EM** *020 †16

WRIGHT, Daniel Lloyd. 298 MEMORIAL DR, OCONEE MEMORIAL HOSPITAL 29672 #045-04-1992 L1993 **AN** *020 †05

SHAW AIR FORCE BASE – SUMTER

AHEARN, Gianna Raquel. ■ 29152 #023-12-1993 L1995 **PD** *020 †55

ALMIRON, Rene Juan. ■ 29152 #726-01-1968 L1976 **IM END** *020

CASTLE-OH, Sandra Leigh. 431 MEADOWLARK ST, 20 MEDICAL GROUP 29152 #023-12-2003 L2005 **FM** *020 †18

FUNKE, Bryan Jay. ■ 29152 #023-12-1985 L1986 **GPM** *020 †70

MCREE, Necia Marie. 431 MEADOWLARK ST, 20TH MEDICAL GROUP 29152 #023-12-2004 L2005 **U** *012

MEEKS, Evan Roy. 431 MEADOWLARK ST 29152 #023-12-1996 L1997 **PD** *020 †55

SCHIEVENIN, Jeffrey Alan. 431 MEADOWLARK ST, 20 MDG/SGHC 29152 #025-01-1986 L1988 **FM EM** *020 †18

TRIGG, David Russell. 431 MEADOWLARK ST, 20TH MEDICAL GROUP 29152 #048-13-1994 L1995 **OM** *100 †18,70

WALDROP, Joel Stephen. 431 MEADOWLARK ST, 20 MDG/SGHC 29152 #045-04-2001 L2007 **EM AM** *020 †16

SHELDON – BEAUFORT

BERNE, Freeman Albert. 29941 #036-07-1964 L1967 **DR** *071

MANN, Carroll Lamb, III. 29941 #036-01-1963 L1963 **NS** *071

WOOD, Dennis A. 29941 #056-05-1977 L1980 **PTH** *071 †50

SIMPSONVILLE – GREENVILLE

ALLEN, Gary Wm. 104 RIVER WALK BLVD 29681 #012-05-1966 L1988 **AN** *020 †05

ANDERSON, Donald Edward. 2607 WOODRUFF RD STE E, PMB 104 29681 #041-09-1980 L1995 **FM** *020 †18

APPLEBY, Gayle White. ■ 29681 #045-01-1983 L1990 **ATP CLP** *020 †50

ARMSTRONG, Charlton P, III. 1340 HIGHWAY 14, GREENVILLE UROLOGY 29681 #045-01-1970 L1977 **U** *020 †95

BAILEY, Jonathan Scott. 727 SE MAIN ST, GREENVILLE OB GYN 29681 #024-01-1996 L1998 **OBG** *020 ‡

BAILEY, Jonathon Quin. 727 SE MAIN ST, GREENVILLE OB GYN 29681 #020-12-1997 L2001 **OBG** *020 †30

BANNEN, William James, Jr. ■ 29681 #023-01-1946 L1954 **FM** *071

BELVIN, Everett L, II. 408 SE MAIN ST 29681 #047-05-1995 L1998 **PD** *020 †55

BERGLIND, Larry Allan. 1338 HIGHWAY 14 29681 #045-01-1988 L1989 **FM** *020 †18

BITTRICK, Jon Michael. 719A SE MAIN ST, STE 360 29681 #045-04-1994 L2001 **IC CD** *020 †20

BLACKSTONE, Connie J. 727 SE MAIN ST STE 300, STONEVIEW INTERNAL MEDICIN 29681 #045-01-1990 L1991 **IM** *020

BLACKSTONE, Marcus Edward. 419 SE MAIN ST, STONEVIEW INTERNAL MEDICIN 29681 #045-04-1995 L1996 **IM** *020

BLANKS, Harold P, III. 719A SE MAIN ST, CONSULTANTS 29681 #047-05-1992 L2004 **CD** *020 †20

BOHN, Aaron Jay. ■ 29681 #056-06-1991 L1992 **AN** *020 †05

BROKER, Robert Edward. 717 SE MAIN ST 29681 #012-01-1984 L1985 **FM** *020 †18

CASTEL, Regina A. 210 E TRADE ST 29681 #654-01-1988 L2001 **P** *020

CATES, Banks Raleigh, III. 729 SE MAIN ST 29681 #869-07-1977 L1979 **IM** *020 †20

CEBE, John E. 727 SE MAIN ST, STE 360 29681 #045-01-1982 L1983 **CD IM** *020 †20

CHAMP, Jerry D. 719A SE MAIN ST, CONSULTANTS 29681 #041-12-1985 L1997 **CD** *020 †20

CHANDLER, Archie H, III. 719A SE MAIN ST, CONSULTANTS 29681 #045-04-1991 L1997 **CD** *020 †20

CHASEDUNN-ROARK, Jennifer. 727 SE MAIN ST, GREENVILLE OB GYN 29681 #045-01-1996 L1998 **OBG** *020 †30

CHEEK, Patricia Lorena. 16 POWDERHORN RD 29681 #036-05-1984 L1990 **NEP IM** *020 †20
CIVILETTO, Steven E. 674 FAIRVIEW RD 29680 #048-04-1975 L2000 **OPH** *020 †35
COLKER, Jack Eric. ■ 29681 #016-43-1987 L1995 **EM PD** *020 †20,55
CRADDOCK, Jeffrey Chas. 628 NE MAIN ST, STE 2 29681 #045-01-1992 L1996 **P ADM** *020
DEMOSTHENES, Lauren. 727 SE MAIN ST, GREENVILLE OB GYN 29681 #045-01-1981 L1982 **OBG** *020 †30
DESAI, Geera Nayan. 20 POWDERHORN RD 29681 #495-22-1970 L1976 **P** *020
DILLON, Paul Edward, Jr. 1336 HIGHWAY 14, SIMPSONVILLE FAMILY MED PA 29681 #045-01-1991 L1992 **FM** *020 †18
DOBSON, Scott Robert. 211 BATESVILLE RD 29681 #045-01-2003 L2004 **PD** *020 †55
DOLL, Josh Ryan. 719A SE MAIN ST, CONSULTANTS 29681 #017-20-2000 L2003 **IC** *020 †20
DUNCAN, Rhonda Jeanne. 719A SE MAIN ST, CONSULTANTS 29681 #045-01-1992 L1993 **CD** *020 †20
EASTERLING, Adam Ray. 674 FAIRVIEW RD, JERVEY EYE GROUP, PA 29680 #045-04-2002 L2007 **OPH** *020
EBERLY, Arthur Lee, III. 719A SE MAIN ST, CONSULTANTS 29681 #045-04-1989 L1996 **CD IM** *020 †20
EL-IBIARY, Seham Youssef. ■ 29681 #330-02-1969 L1995 **IM** *020 †20 ‡
ELLIS, Jennifer T. PO BOX 1177 29681 #005-18-2000 L2003 **FM** *100 †18
ELLISON, Floyd Edwin, Jr. 727 SE MAIN ST, GREENVILLE OB GYN 29681 #045-01-1964 L1964 **OBG** *020 †30
EVANS, Cheryl L. 104 W GEORGIA RD A 29681 #048-12-1992 L2002 **PD** *020
FAILE, Barbara Alma. 727 SE MAIN ST, STE 360 29681 #045-04-1992 L1999 **CD** *020 †20
FREEMAN, Lawrence Wm. 727 SE MAIN ST, STE 360 29681 #045-01-1977 L1978 **CD IM** *020 †20
FREEMAN, Ned David. 727 SE MAIN ST, STE 360 29681 #045-01-1984 L1985 **CD** *020 †20
GIAMBALVO, Linda Lee. 1338 HIGHWAY 14 29681 #045-04-1992 L1993 **FM** *020 †18
GOULD, Stanley Leo. ■ 29681 #012-05-1955 L1959 **GYN** *075
GOWER, Roger Huntington. 727 SE MAIN ST, GREENVILLE OB GYN 29681 #045-01-1977 L1978 **OBG** *020 †30
GUTIERREZ, Bernardo A. ■ 29681 #264-04-1972 L2004 **IM** *020 †20
HAMILTON, Thos Elson, II. 1340 HIGHWAY 14, GREENVILLE UROLOGY 29681 #045-01-1991 L1992 **U** *020 †95
HARPER, Nancy Elizabeth. ■ 29681 #045-01-2004 L2004 **OBG** *012
HEAD, Douglas Scott. 727 SE MAIN ST, STE 360 29681 #045-04-1982 L1985 **CD IM** *020 †20
HEIDT, Francis E, III. ■ 29681 #045-04-1991 L1995 **FM** *020 †18
HOFFERT, Kurt Alfred. ■ 29681 #045-04-1996 L2000 **EM** *020 †16
HOLMES, Melisa Marian. ■ 29681 #012-01-1989 L1993 **OBG** *020 †30
HUTCHINS, Earl Wayne. 35 RAY E TALLEY CT 29680 #012-01-1975 L1981 **FM** *020 †18
JACOBS, David Calhoun. 20 POWDERHORN RD 29681 #045-01-1975 L1978 **P** *020 †75
JOHNSON, Gretchen Heidt. PO BOX 1177, 717 SE MAIN ST 29681 #012-22-1989 L1993 **FM** *020 †18
JOHNSON, Steven De Vann. 727 SE MAIN ST, STE 360 29681 #012-05-1978 L1997 **CD EM** *020 †20,16
JONES, Stephen Mcalister. 211 BATESVILLE RD, PARKSIDE PEDIATRICS 29681 #055-02-2004 L2004 **PD** *020 †55
KENDRICK, William Cary. 16 POWDERHORN RD 29681 #045-01-1973 L1978 **IM NEP** *020 †20
LEEKE, Terrell Thos. 103 FAIRVIEW RD 29681 #045-01-1978 L1979 **FM** *020
LINDSAY, Sara Mc Cleave. ■ 29681 #045-01-1980 L1981 **FM EM** *071 †18
LOPEZ, Alberto. 1336 HIGHWAY 14, SIMPSONVILLE FAMILY MED PA 29681 #007-02-1991 L1995 **FM** *020 †18
LO PRESTI, Gaetano A. ■ 29680 #024-07-1951 L1952 **IM PM** *071
MAGNUSSON, Jessica Rose. ■ 29681 #001-02-2006 L2006 **PD** *012
MALONE, Thomas Arthur. 224 NE MAIN ST 29681 #045-01-1981 L1982 **FM OS** *020 †18
MATHERS, Michael S. 1340 HIGHWAY 14, GREENVILLE UROLOGY 29681 #010-02-1970 L1978 **U** *020 †95
MC CRAW, Andrew Shell. 404 SE MAIN ST, MCCRAW FAMILY MEDICINE 29681 #045-01-1996 L1997 **FM** *020 †18
MC DANIELS, Myron Brent. ■ 29681 #051-07-1995 L1998 **PD** *020
MCDERMOTT, Julie R. 419 SE MAIN ST, STE 200 29681 #045-01-1991 L1992 **FM** *020 †18
MEINE, Trip James. 719A SE MAIN ST, CONSULTANTS 29681 #036-07-1998 L2005 **IC** *020 †20
MILFORD, Morgan Todd, Jr. 727 SE MAIN ST, STE 130 29681 #036-05-1971 L1972 **GS** *020 †85
MOLL, Justin Steven. 211 BATESVILLE RD, PARKSIDE PED 29681 #036-01-2002 L2003 **PD** *020 †55
MORGAN, Sara Elizabeth. ■ 29680 #012-22-2008 *012
OLDSON, Teressa Mae. ■ 29681 #036-08-1993 L1994 **FM EM** *020 †18
PARKS, Stephen Emerson. 35 RAY E TALLEY CT 29680 #045-01-1981 L1982 **EM** *020 †16
PAYNE, Michael Woodlief. 727 SE MAIN ST, STE 360 29681 #020-02-1975 L1982 **CD IM** *020 †20
POMPEY, Michael O. ■ 29681 #011-04-1980 L1981 **IM** *020
PRESSLY, Jennings Gillem. 729 SE MAIN ST 29681 #045-01-1973 L1975 **R** *020 †80 ‡
PRICE, Stephen Wayne. 727 SE MAIN ST, GREENVILLE OB GYN 29681 #045-04-1991 L1992 **OBG** *020 †30
PUDI, Krishna Kumar. 110A HOSPITAL DR 29681 #198-01-1985 L1997 **IM** *020 †20
RAHEJA, Arvin. 210 LADEAN CT, WOMENS HEALTHCARE 29680 #016-01-1978 L1982 **OBG** *020 †30
RICE, James David. 1340 HIGHWAY 14, GREENVILLE UROLOGY 29681 #045-01-1984 L1985 **U GS** *020 †95
RICHARDSON, James Furman. 729 SE MAIN ST 29681 #045-01-1960 L1960 **FM** *020
ROSS, Charles Douglas. 727 SE MAIN ST, STE 360 29681 #012-05-1968 L1975 **CD** *020 †20
RUPP, Michael Robert. 408 SE MAIN ST, CHILDRENS MEDICAL CENTER 29681 #045-01-1995 L1998 **PD** *020 †55
SAN, Gregory Winston. 727 SE MAIN ST, STE 360 29681 #011-04-1979 L1980 **CD** *020 †20
SIACHOS, Arthur Thomas. 727 SE MAIN ST, STE 360 29681 #045-04-1997 L2000 **CD** *020 †20
SILKINER, David Carter. 729 SE MAIN ST 29681 #012-05-1983 L1984 **FM** *020 †18
SIMPSON, Brad Marshall. 727 SE MAIN ST, STE 360 29681 #045-01-1983 L1984 **CD IM** *020 †20
SMITH, Christopher H. 727 SE MAIN ST, STE 360 29681 #045-04-1997 L2004 **IC** *020 †20
STAMM, Michael Dean. 727 SE MAIN ST, GREENVILLE OB GYN 29681 #011-04-1982 L1983 **OBG** *020 †30
SURABHI, Satish Kumar. 719A SE MAIN ST, CONSULTANTS 29681 #495-21-1991 L2003 **IM** *020 †20
TAYLOR, Rosa Del Carmen. 1336 HIGHWAY 14 29681 #649-40-1988 L2000 **FM** *020 †18
TAYLOR, William David. 20 POWDERHORN RD, PIEDMONT CENTER FOR MENTAL 29681 #047-06-1981 L1990 **P** *030 †75
TAYLOR, William Johnston. 1338 HIGHWAY 14 29681 #012-01-1984 L1985 **FM IM** *020 †18

TROUTMAN, Eric Holt. 727 SE MAIN ST, GREENVILLE OB GYN 29681 #036-05-1984 L1985 **OBG** *020 †30
TSAI, Willy Cheng. 727 SE MAIN ST, STE 360 29681 #023-01-2001 L2006 **NEP IM** *020 †20
VAZ, Gerald Dev. ■ 29681 #496-38-1998 L2001 **CD** *020 †20
VINES, Margo Ann. 20 POWDERHORN RD, SIMPSONVILLE MHC 29681 #041-07-1975 L1980 **EM** *020 †20
WATERS, Keith Hopkins. 103 FAIRVIEW POINTE DR 29681 #045-01-1977 L1978 **GP EM** *020
WATSON, Derek Scott. 727 SE MAIN ST, STE 130 29681 #047-05-1992 L1997 **GS** *020 †85
WHITE, Mark Timothy. 1338 HIGHWAY 14, HOLLY TREE FAMILY PRACTICE 29681 #045-01-1989 L1990 **FM** *020 †18
WHITEHEAD, Kathrine Jebia. 6 THORNLESS CT 29680 #305-01-1996 L2003 **FM** *020 †18
WHITTENBERG, Chas Wallace. 408 SE MAIN ST 29681 #045-01-1977 L1978 **PD** *020 †55
WILLIAMS, Morris E, Jr. 727 SE MAIN ST, STE 360 29681 #036-01-1968 L1971 **CD IM** *020 †20
WORTHINGTON, John Walter. 719A SE MAIN ST, CONSULTANTS 29681 #012-05-1972 L1980 **CD IM** *020 †20
WRIGHT, Lynn Purcell. 2607 WOODRUFF RD STE E 29681 #045-04-1992 L1993 **P** *020 †75

SOCIETY HILL – DARLINGTON

BARKER, Gary Allen. PO BOX 239 29593 #018-03-1981 L1982 **FM** *020 †18
MOYD, Pickens Kinard, Jr. 737 S MAIN ST, ROSA LEE GERALD CTR 29593 #045-04-1985 L1986 **FM** *020 †18
SMITH, Stephen Leslie. 737 S MAIN ST, ROSA LEE GERALD CTR 29593 #051-04-1989 L1992 **FM** *020 †18

SPARTANBURG – SPARTANBURG

ABRAMOVITCH, Anna Irene. 101 E WOOD ST, SPARTANBURG REGIONAL HLTHC 29303 #047-05-2005 L2005 **DR** *012
ADAMS, Frederick F. 105 TRADD ST 29301 #045-01-1972 L1979 **IM NEP** *020 †20
ADAMS, Jennifer Jayne. PO BOX 4026, 101 E WOOD ST 29305 #045-01-1999 L2004 **DR** *020 †80
ALDAY, Michael Alan. 101 E WOOD ST 29303 #012-01-1981 L1982 **OM** *020 †70
ALEXANDER, Wellesley E. 101 E WOOD ST, SRMC INPATIENT MEDICINE 29303 #010-03-2002 L2005 **IM** *020 †20
ALLAN, Richmond Prater. 1690 SKYLYN DR STE 300, PIEDMONT INT MED 29307 #023-01-1985 L2003 **IM IMG** *020 †20
ALLEN, Mitchell Hurst, Jr. 853 N CHURCH ST, STE 620 29303 #036-05-1964 L1976 **GE IM** *020 †20
ALLRED, Thomas Frederick. 1700 SKYLYN DR 29307 #045-01-1987 L1988 **NPM PD** *020 †55
AL-SAWAF, Mazen. ■ 29302 #875-01-1978 L1984 **CD AN** *020 †18
ANDERSON, Joseph Thos. 1690 SKYLYN DR, STE 200 29307 #045-04-1989 L1990 **ORS** *020 †40
ANTOSH, Stanley. 101 E WOOD ST, DEPT OF ANESTHESIOLOGY 29303 #035-08-1984 L1989 **AN PME** *020 †05
APPIAH, Kofi Asante. 322 N PINE ST 29302 #412-01-1993 L2007 **NEP IM** *020 †20 ‡
ARLAUSKAS, Victoria Anne. 2995 REIDVILLE RD, STE 210 29301 #041-02-1995 L2001 **IM** *020 †20
ARNETT, Marion Lee, Jr. 391 SERPENTINE DR, STE 500 29303 #045-01-1974 L1975 **U** *020 †95
ARNETT, Robert Michael. 475 HEYWOOD AVE, WOMAN'S CLINIC, PA 29307 #045-01-1987 L1988 **OBG** *020 †30
ARNOLD, Ernest W, Jr. 1330 BOILING SPRINGS RD, STE 2500 29303 #036-05-1974 L1978 **IM** *020 †20
ASHLEY, Thomas Louis. 853 N CHURCH ST, STE 500 29303 #025-07-1983 L1995 **GS CRS** *040 †85
ATKINSON, Elizabeth S. 101 E WOOD ST, SPARTANBURG REGIONAL MEDIC 29303 #047-05-2002 L2005 **EM** *020 †16
AYAAY, Jerome Benitez. 853 N CHURCH ST STE 510, FAMILY PRACTICE 29303 #055-02-2004 L2004 **FM** *020 †18
BABUSHKINA, Victoria. 100 E WOOD ST STE 401, SPARTANBURG INTERNAL MEDIC 29303 #913-15-1978 L1999 **IM** *020 †20
BAGENHOLM, Allyson Christ. 853 N CHURCH ST, STE 510 29303 #130-02-2007 L2008 *012
BAGHDADY, Brian Harold. 101 E WOOD ST, RADIOLOGICAL ASSOCIATES 29303 #045-01-1993 L1999 **VIR** *020 †80
BAILES, George Steven. 105 POWELL MILL RD 29301 #045-01-1981 L1982 **FM** *020 †18
BAILEY, Amy Elizabeth. 853 N CHURCH ST STE 51 29303 #012-22-2007 L2007 **FP** *012
BAILEY, Crystal Gail. 853 N CHURCH ST STE 10 29303 #012-22-1994 L2005 **FP** *012
BAIROSSI, Nicole. 101 E WOOD ST, SPARTANBURG REGIONAL HLTHC 29303 #665-01-2002 L2002 **GS** *020
BARRINEAU, Devonne Domeni. 101 E WOOD ST, ATTN - MEDICAL EDUCATION 29303 #045-04-2006 L2006 **GS** *012
BARROW, Hugh Will, Jr. 853 N CHURCH ST 29303 #001-02-1974 L1975 **OBG** *020 †30
BARTEL, Frank Octave. ■ 29302 #045-01-1955 L1955 **PD** *071 †55
BARUCH, Amy Christine. 1700 SKYLYN DR 29307 #003-01-1999 L2006 **PTH** *030 †50
BARWICK, Lori Waldrop. 250 DEWEY AVE 29303 #045-01-1998 L2001 **P CHP** *020
BASS, George Liston, Jr. 1690 SKYLYN DR, STE 300 29307 #045-01-1963 L1963 **IM** *020 †20
BASS, Robert Bruce, Jr. 1 DOCTORS PARK DR 29307 #045-01-1975 L1990 **U** *020 †95
BAUGHMAN, Otis Lee. 853 N CHURCH ST STE 510, CTR FOR FAMILY MEDICINE 29303 #045-01-1977 L1978 **FM** *030 †18
BEAN, Howard Carlisle, Jr. 1690 SKYLYN DR, CAROLINA FAMILY 29307 #045-01-1977 L1978 **FM** *020 †18
BEASLEY, Joseph Ocran. ■ 29307 #045-01-1955 L1955 **OPH** *071 †35
BEAVERS, Troy Lee. 1686 SKYLYN DR 29307 #001-02-1992 L1999 **PD** *020 †55
BEETS, Joseph Wm. 11 DOCTORS PARK DR, STE 240 29307 #039-01-1991 L1999 **GE** *020 †20
BENSON, Ashley Beasley. 853 N CHURCH ST, STE 720 29303 #045-01-1998 L2001 **OBG** *020 †30
BERRY, David Pinckney. 1330 BOILING SPRINGS RD, STE 2400 29303 #045-01-1975 L1976 **OPH** *050 †35
BERRY, Roy Herbert. 1686 SKYLYN DR, STE 201 29307 #045-01-1973 L1975 **PD** *020 †55
BESHEARS, Kyra. 541 FLOYD RD, CAROLINA NEUROLOGY 29307 #035-46-1995 L2003 **N** *020 †75
BHATT, Manojkumar Ana. 157 S PINE ST, ANESTHESIA ASSOCIATES PA 29302 #495-23-1971 L1977 **AN** *020 †05

BIANCO, Salvatore. 101 E WOOD ST 29303 #035-06-1996 L1997 **FM** *020 †18

BIJOOR, Nivedita Santosh. 101 E WOOD ST 29303 #496-44-1998 L2004 **FM** *020 †18 ‡

BIJOOR, Santosh Mohan. 100 E WOOD ST, STE 401 29303 #496-25-1991 L1997 **CCM** *020 †20

BINGHAM, Natalie Dawn. 853 N CHURCH ST, STE 700 29303 #021-05-2001 L2003 **OBG** *100 †30

BLAIR, Brian Keith. 1650 SKYLYN DR, STE 200 29307 #045-01-2002 L2006 **ORS** *020

BLAKE, Stephen David. 1686 SKYLYN DR, STE 201 29307 #020-12-2000 L2004 **PD** *020 †55 ‡

BLESTEL, George Ambrose, Jr. 1690 SKYLYN DR, STE 140 29307 #021-05-1980 L1986 **CRS GS** *020 †10,85

BOGGS, Steven Dale. 101 E WOOD ST, SPARTANBURG REGIONAL MED C 29303 #016-02-1983 L1990 **AN** *020 †05

BOLLOM, Timothy Scott. 1690 SKYLYN DR, STE 230 29307 #026-04-1998 L2004 **OSM** *020 †40

BONAMINIO, Anthony. 101 E WOOD ST 29303 #038-40-1992 L1999 **IM** *020 †20

BOTTSFORD, John E, Jr. 385 SERPENTINE DR, STE B 29303 #005-12-1965 L1974 **VS PHL** *020 †85

BOUKNIGHT, Patricia Jean. 853 N CHURCH ST, STE 510 29303 #045-04-1994 L1995 **FM** *020 †18

BOWERS, Charles Edward. 120 DILLON DR, CAROLINAS SPARTANBURG 29307 #759-01-1985 L1999 **HO** *020 †20

BOWLING, Andrew Euel. 853 N CHURCH ST STE 510, RESIDENCY PROGRAM 29303 #045-04-2006 L2006 **FP** *012

BOYD, Wallace Wyman. 1690 SKYLYN DR, STE 200 29307 #045-01-1967 L1967 **ORS** *020 †40

BOYLAN, Joel Patrick. 101 E WOOD ST 29303 #038-43-1988 L1989 **AN** *020 †05

BOYLE, Ginger. 853 N CHURCH ST, STE 510 29303 #051-04-1996 L2004 **FM** *020 †18

BOZEMAN, Gary Douglas. 1690 SKYLYN DR 29307 #004-01-1989 L1991 **U** *020 †95

BRAUN, Peter Douglas. 101 E WOOD ST 29303 #048-14-1999 L2006 **EM** *020

BRENDA, Derek Steven. 101 E WOOD ST, SPARTANBURG REGIONAL 29303 #055-01-2007 L2007 **GS** *012

BREWINGTON, Chloe P. 101 E WOOD ST, SPARTANBURG REGIONAL HOSPI 29303 #045-01-1981 L1982 **FM** *020 †18

BRITANISKY, Robert Gregg. 1690 SKYLYN DR 29307 #012-01-1989 L1997 **U** *020 †95

BROOKS, John Herbert. 2375 E MAIN ST, STE A204 29307 #055-01-1973 L1980 **A** *020

BROWN, James Edward, IV. 100 E WOOD ST 29303 #001-02-1974 L1978 **IM ID** *020 †20

BURCHFIELD, John Robt. 1700 SKYLYN DR 29307 #045-01-1990 L1994 **AN** *020

BURKE, Stephanie Kameron. 853 N CHURCH ST, STE 510 29303 #012-01-2004 L2004 **FM** *020 †18

BURKS, Robert Tucker. 1700 SKYLYN DR, MARY BLACK HOSPITAL 29307 #045-01-1987 L2000 **PTH** *020 †50

BURNIKEL, Brian Geo. 1690 SKYLYN DR, STE 200 29307 #018-03-1990 L1995 **ORS** *020 †40

BURNS, William Walker. 147 OAKWOOD AVE 29302 #045-01-1972 L1973 **PD** *071 †55

BUTEHORN, Henry F, Jr. 1330 BOILING SPRINGS RD, SPARTANBURG EAR NOSE & T 29303 #045-01-1969 L1969 **OTO** *020 †45

BUTEHORN, Henry Frederick. 1330 BOILING SPRINGS RD, STE 1400 29303 #045-01-1998 L2004 **OTO** *020 †45

BUTTINO, Louis, Jr. 1686 SKYLYN DR, STE 102 29307 #048-04-1975 L2000 **OBG MFM** *020 †30

BYRD, Richard Guerrant. 606 PERRIN DR 29307 #020-02-1977 L1978 **EM** *020 †20,16,18

BYRD, Sheri Carter. 101 E WOOD ST 29303 #045-01-1992 L1993 **PD SME** *020 †55

CALDWELL, John A. 1700 SKYLYN DR 29307 #048-14-1993 L2000 **DMP** *020 †50

CALTON, Wm Cuyler, Jr. 101 E WOOD ST 29303 #036-07-1988 L2000 **VS** *020 †85

CAMP, Ernest, III. PO BOX 4128, 16 DRAYTON CT 29305 #012-05-1968 L1973 **GS** *020 †85

CAMPBELL, Bayard Bryon. 1071 BOILING SPRINGS RD, ASSOCIATES, P.A. 29303 #051-07-1986 L1992 **NS** *020 †25

CANNON, Matthew David. 853 N CHURCH ST STE 510, RESIDENCY PROGRAM 29303 #055-75-2005, ▲ L2006 **FP** *012

CARNEY, Michelle C. 101 E WOOD ST, SPARTANBURG REG MED CTR 29303 #012-05-1991 L1996 **ID** *020 †20

CASSAS, Kyle James. 1690 SKYLYN DR, STE 200 29307 #031-01-1997 L2004 **FSM** *020 †18

CASTON, John Christopher. 1330 BOILING SPRINGS RD 29303 #045-01-1971 L1972 **P** *020 †75

CASWELL, Robert John, II. 123 DILLON DR, WOMENS RADIOLOGY CTR 29307 #025-01-1969 L1979 **DR** *071 †80

CATHCART, Edward Reaver. 853 N CHURCH ST 29303 #045-01-1959 L1959 **OBG** *020 †30

CATHCART, John H, Jr. 250 DEWEY AVE, SPARTANBURG AREA MENTAL HE 29303 #045-01-1959 L1959 **GYN** *020 †30

CEBALLOS, Raul, Jr. 684 N PINE ST 29303 #042-01-1985 L1999 **DR RNR** *062 †80

CHAMPION, Francis Parker. ■ 29302 #045-01-1955 L1956 **OM OS** *071 †18

CHAPMAN, Darren Craig. ■ 29301 #020-12-1988 L2001 **GS** *020 †85

CHAUHAN, Anil Kumar. 101 E WOOD ST 29303 #654-01-2002 L2002 **IM** *020 †20

CHAVEZ, Marcelino I. 101 E WOOD ST 29303 #737-01-1951 L1967 **NS** *071

CHITTUM, Christopher J. 1075 BOILING SPRINGS RD, SPARTANBURG NEUROSURGICAL 29303 #038-43-1998 L1999 **NS** *020 ‡

CHRISTENSEN, Gregory S. 480 N CHURCH ST 29303 #045-01-1989 L1994 **OPH** *020 †35

CLARK, John Douglas. 2030 N CHURCH STREET PL 29303 #047-06-1985 L1997 **PUD** *020 †20

COBB, Kelly Ann. 1686 SKYLYN DR 29307 #045-04-1998 L2002 **OBG** *020 †30

COLE, Eric Lynn. 130 DILLON DR 29307 #045-04-2003 L2004 **FM** *020 †18

COLE, Jack Martin. 2995 REIDVILLE RD, STE 210 29301 #036-01-1988 L1992 **IM** *020 †20

COLEY, Scott Alan. 120 HEYWOOD AVE, DRS WESTMORELAND HICKLIN 29302 #045-01-1992 L1993 **FM** *020 †18

COLLINGS, Thomas A, Jr. 324 N PINE ST 29302 #045-01-1985 L1990 **N** *020 †75

COLLINGS, Thomas Albert. ■ 29302 #045-01-1954 L1954 **PD GP** *071

CONN, Richard Lee. 391 SERPENTINE DR 29303 #024-01-1962 L1969 **GS VS** *020 †85

CONTRERAS-GROVE, Patricia. 1089 BOILING SPRINGS RD, UPSTATE PEDIATRIC PULMONAR 29303 #308-02-1990 L2005 **PDP** *020 †55

COOK, David Albert. 245 E BLACKSTOCK RD, STE B 29301 #012-01-1976 L1977 **FM** *020 †30

COOK, Paul H. 390 E HENRY ST, STE 103 29302 #036-07-1951 L1959 **D** *020 †15

CORNETT, Benjamin Cole. 101 E WOOD ST, SPARTANBURG REGIONAL MED C 29303 #011-04-2007 L2007 **TY** *012

CORSON, Deborah Anne. 101 E WOOD ST, SPARTANBURG REGIONAL MED C 29303 #036-01-2007 L2007 **TY** *012

CRAFT, Jeffrey Marshall. 100 E WOOD ST 29303 #045-04-1985 L1988 **IM** *020 †20

CUPSTID, Henry Griffin. 1700 SKYLYN DR 29307 #045-04-1983 L1984 **FM** *020 †18

CURRAN, Colin Patrick. 380 SERPENTINE DR, STE 200 29303 #033-05-1997 L1998 **HO** *020 †20

CZUBA, Karen Margaret. 8311 WARREN H ABERNTHY HWY 29301 #012-01-1992 L1994 **FM** *020 †18

DAIGLE, Andrew Philip. 101 E WOOD ST, ATTN: MEDICAL STAFF SERVIC 29303 #021-05-1986 L1987 **PLM EM** *020 †18

DALEY, Bradley Lee, Jr. 1330 BOILING SPRINGS RD, STE 1300 29303 #045-01-1985 L1991 **PD** *020 †55

DALEY, Luci Wannamaker. 1330 BOILING SPRINGS RD, STE 1300 29303 #045-01-1985 L1991 **PD** *020 †55

DARR, Emily Ann. 101 E WOOD ST, SPARTANBURG REGIONAL MED C 29303 #045-01-2007 L2007 **TY** *012

DAVENPORT, Pamela N. 100 E WOOD ST 29303 #045-04-1986 L1990 **IM IMG** *020 †20

DAVIS, Brandon Scott. 100 E WOOD ST, PHYSICIAN BULIDING STE 401 29303 #045-01-2001 L2002 **IM** *020

DAVIS, Dean Eldon. 853 N CHURCH ST 29303 #036-08-1984 L1988 **OBG** *020 †30

DAVIS, William Mc Alhany. ■ 29302 #045-01-1962 L1962 **PCP PTH** *071 †50

DECRISTOFARO, Claire. 101 DORMAN CENTRE DR, STE C # 126 29301 #035-46-1979 L1995 **FM GP** *020 ‡

DEFRIECE, Joshua Chad. 853 N CHURCH ST, STE 510 29303 #051-04-2007 L2007 **FP** *012

DEL SAVIO, Beth C. 2020 N CHURCH STREET PL 29303 #036-05-1994 L1998 **D** *020 †15

DENLER, Arnold L, Jr. 144 ROMAINE DR, P O BOX 4217 29307 #649-14-1970 L1972 **FM PHP** *020 †18

DEPRA, Roger Christopher. 853 N CHURCH ST, STE 510 29303 #305-01-2006 L2006 **FP** *012

DEVORE, Karen Abele. 490 FLOYD RD, DEVORE DERMATOLOGY, PA 29307 #012-01-1988 L1992 **D DMP** *020 †15

DEVORE, William Geo. 101 E WOOD ST, ANESTHESIOLOGY DEPT 29303 #012-01-1988 L1992 **AN** *020 †05

DILLE, Brice Barber. 479 HEYWOOD AVE, PALMETTO EYE AND LASER CEN 29307 #012-01-2001 L2005 **OPH** *020 †35

DING, Weirong Connie. 101 E WOOD ST 29303 #045-01-2001 L2001 **AN** *100 †05

DOMERS, Theresa Ann. 101 E WOOD ST 29303 #038-45-1995 L2002 **EM** *020 †16

DORLON, Robert Edwin, Jr. 391 SERPENTINE DR STE 240 29303 #011-02-1975 L1985 **IM RHU** *020 †20

DORNA, Manuel Antonio. ■ 29303 #042-03-1996 L1997 **FM** *020 †18

DORNER, Matthew James. 853 N CHURCH ST STE 510 29303 #016-43-2005 L2005 **FP** *012

DOUGLASS, Walter James. 853 N CHURCH ST, STE 620 29303 #045-01-1973 L1976 **GE** *020 †20

DOWLING, Kyran. ■ 29302 #001-06-1981 L2005 **VIR GS** *020 †80

DUNCAN, James L. 1700 SKYLYN DR 29307 #012-01-1944 L1947 **FM AN** *072 †18

DUNLAP, John Collins. 599 E MAIN ST 29302 #045-01-1960 L1960 **P CHP** *020

DUNLAVEY, Elizabeth S. 2020 N CHURCH STREET PL 29303 #045-01-1995 L1996 **D** *020 †15

DUNN, James Dewey. 324B N PINE ST, JAMES DUNN SURGICAL CLINIC 29302 #047-06-1986 L1993 **GS CRS** *020 †85,10

DY, Caroline Ang. 101 E WOOD ST, SRMC DEPT OF PEDIATRIC NUT 29303 #748-01-1992 L1999 **PD** *020 †55

EARLY, Ira Gordon, Jr. 1241 BOILING SPRINGS RD 29303 #036-01-1987 L1996 **OM PTX** *020 †70

EASTIN, Emory L. 1686 SKYLYN DR, STE 101 29307 #048-12-1992 L2006 **OBG** *020 †30

EBRAHIM, Muhammad Y. 322 N PINE ST 29302 #704-02-1991 L1999 **IM NEP** *020 †20

EFIRD, Meica Maria. 101 E WOOD ST, NICU OFFICE 29303 #036-01-1996 L2006 **NPM** *020 †55

ELHASSANI, Sami Baqir. 1700 SKYLYN DR 29307 #528-01-1959 L1976 **NPM PD** *020 †55

ELLIS, Paul Timothy. 391 SERPENTINE DR 29303 #038-45-1989 L1995 **GS U** *020 †95

ELSTON, William Chas. 1700 SKYLYN DR 29307 #028-34-1959 L1964 **GS TS** *020 †85

ESCE, Phillip George. 1075 BOILING SPRINGS RD, SPARTANBURG NEUROSURGICAL 29303 #035-45-1996 L1999 **NS** *020 †25

ESLAMI, Said. 138 DILLON DR STE A 29307 #517-01-1970 L1977 **R** *020 †80

ESMAEILI, Ehsan. 101 E WOOD ST 29303 #130-02-2007 L2007 **GS** *012

ESSMAN, James Andrew. 391 SERPENTINE DR STE 440 29303 #038-41-1983 L1992 **ORS** *020 †40

EVANS, Hilary James. 2995 REIDVILLE RD 29301 #036-05-1988 L2005 **IM** *020 †20

EVANS, Jack Allen, Jr. ■ 29307 #012-01-1962 L1967 **U** *020 †95

FALCON, Daniel Aaron. 391 SERPENTINE DR, STE 440 29303 #035-47-1992 L1999 **HS** *020 †85 ‡

FARLEY, Frank Giles. ■ 29307 #035-15-1945 L1972 **OS GS** *030 †85

FARR, Gist Henry, Jr. 1700 SKYLYN DR 29307 #045-01-1967 L1967 **PTH** *062 †50 ‡

FEATHERSTON, John Smith. 333 MANSFIELD DRIVE 29302 #010-01-1946 L1962 **R** *071 †80

FEDALEI, Albert Geo. 11 DOCTORS PARK DR 29307 #023-01-1988 L1997 **GE** *020 †20

FINCH, Max Cortez, Jr. 1690 SKYLYN DR, RM 123 29307 #047-06-1996 L2000 **IM** *020 †20

FINCH, Susan. 1690 SKYLYN DR STE 300, PIEDMONT INTERNAL MEDICINE 29307 #047-06-1996 L2000 **IM** *020 †20

FISGUS, C Wayne. 1 MANDALA LN 29303 #035-06-1966 L1972 **OBG** *020 †30

FLANDRY, Robert Edward. 1075 BOILING SPRINGS RD, SPARTANBURG NEUROSURGICAL 29303 #021-01-1974 L1983 **NS** *020 †25

FOGARTY, Charles Michael. 2030 N CHURCH STREET PL 29303 #035-45-1970 L1978 **PUD CCM** *020 †20

FOLK, Jason W. 1690 SKYLYN DR, STE 200 29307 #048-12-1996 L2005 **OSM** *020 †40

FOSTER, John Allan. 1330 BOILING SPRINGS RD, STE 1400 29303 #045-01-1985 L1987 **OTO OS** *020 †45

FOWLER, John Brian. 100 E WOOD ST 29303 #045-01-1995 L1997 **GS** *020 †20

FRANCE, H Gordon, Jr. 853 N CHURCH ST, STE 620 29303 #055-01-1980 L1985 **GE** *020 †20

FREEDMAN, Arthur Morris. 101 E WOOD ST 29303 #035-08-1983 L2001 **VIR DR** *020 †80

FRESH, Lane Eric. 101 E WOOD ST 29303 #036-05-1996 L2003 **EM** *020 †16

FRITSCHE, Melissa D. 853 N CHURCH ST, STE 510 29303 #012-01-2006 L2007 **GS** *012

FROST, Edward Harold, Jr. 151 E WOOD ST 29303 #045-01-1976 L1979 **EM** *020 †18

FULMER, J Sidney. 101 E WOOD ST 29303 #012-05-1957 L1964 **GYN** *020 †30 ‡

GABEL, Dorotea Mony. 100 E WOOD ST 29303 #781-01-1995 L2002 **IM** *020 †20

GAINES, Michael Delan. 1650 SKYLYN DR STE 200 29307 #012-01-2002 L2007 **ORS** *100

GALT, Thomas Teasley. ■ 29303 #045-01-1954 L1954 **AN** *075

GANDHI, Mukesh Manilal. 101 E WOOD ST 29303 #495-22-1984 L1990 **IM** *020 †20

GARBER, Lance Matthews. 101 E WOOD ST 29303 #039-01-2003 L2003 **DR** *012

GARRELL, Robin Felice. 101 E WOOD ST, ATTN: DEPT OF MEDICAL EDU 29303 #045-01-1999 L2006 **IM** *020 †20

GARRELL, Stephen Lloyd. 128 DILLON DR 29307 #035-01-1967 L1977 **NEP IM** *020 †20

GARY, Thomas Dillard. 853 N CHURCH ST STE 510 29303 #012-22-2005 L2005 **FP** *012

GAULT, Paige Meacham. 853 N CHURCH ST, STE 720C 29303 #011-03-2000 L2006 **END** *020 †20

GEARY, Stephen Paul. 1690 SKYLYN DR, STE 200 29307 #021-05-1987 L1997 **ORS** *020 †40

GELDERS, William Keith. ■ 29307 #045-01-1986 L1988 **FM** *020 †18

GEMMELL, John Paul. 2995 REIDVILLE RD, STE 210 29301 #047-20-1983 L1984 **IM** *020 †20

GILL, Sanjitpal Singh. 1690 SKYLYN DR, STE 200 29307 #024-05-1998 L2004 **OSS OSM** *020 †40

GLACE, Charles Lawrence. 2995 REIDVILLE RD STE 260 29301 #654-01-1984 L1987 **FM** *020 †18

GLENN, George Chester, III. 1686 SKYLYN DR, STE 201 29307 #047-06-1986 L1987 **PD** *020 †55

GO, Robin Ong. 98 WILLOW LN 29307 #748-02-1986 L1996 **AI PD** *020 †55,03

GODENICK, Mark Todd. 853 N CHURCH ST STE 510 29303 #005-12-1982 L1989 **FM GPM** *040 †70,18

GODFREY, Earl Hampton. 101 E WOOD ST 29303 #045-01-1959 L1959 **N** *071 †75

GONDA, Frank Emilio. 2212 OLD FURNACE RD 29316 #045-04-1982 L1983 **FM** *020 †18

GOODEN, Justin Lee. 101 E WOOD ST, SPARTANBURG REG HLTHCARE C 29303 #019-02-2004 L2004 **GS** *100

GOODLETT, Robert Field. 853 N CHURCH ST, OBSTETRICS AND GYNECOLOGY 29303 #045-01-1994 L1995 **OBG** *020 †30

GORDON, Katherine E. 853 N CHURCH ST STE 510 29303 #045-01-1997 L1998 **FM** *020 †18

GRAHAM, Jack Mc Queen. 225 E WOOD ST 29303 #045-01-1954 L1954 **U** *071 †95

GRAHAM, John Randolph. 428 OLD IRON WORKS RD 29302 #045-04-1988 L1993 **DR NM** *020 †80

GRAVELY, Vonda Kay. 358 SERPENTINE DR 29303 #045-04-1998 L1999 **PYG** *020 †75

GREEN, James F. 1330 BOILING SPRINGS RD, STE 2300 29303 #045-01-1962 L1962 **GS CD** *020 †85

GREWAL, Reetu. 853 N CHURCH ST, STE 510 29303 #033-06-2005 L2005 **FP** *012

GRIESHOP, Theodore Jos. 100 E WOOD ST STE 302 29303 #038-40-1987 L1990 **ID IM** *020 †20

GRIFFIN, Patricia Caye. 101 E WOOD ST, SRMC 29303 #045-01-1989 L1994 **RO** *020 †80

GRIFFIN, Tommy Brewer. 2020 NORTH CHURCH PLACE 29303 #041-01-1961 L1970 **D OM** *071 †15

GUDGER, Jeffrey Neil. 1700 SKYLYN DR, MARY BLACK HOSPITAL 29307 #665-02-2004 L2004 **IM** *020

GWIN, Todd David. 1330 BOILING SPRINGS RD, STE 2400 29303 #028-46-1986 L1989 **OPH** *020 †35

HAAS, Robert Junius. 479 HEYWOOD AVE 29307 #045-01-1967 L1967 **OPH** *020 †35

HAASIS, John Christian. 1330 BOILING SPRINGS RD, STE 2700 29303 #041-07-1992 L1997 **APM** *020 †05

HABIB, Magdy A. 1702 SKYLYN DR - DOCTOR'S 29307 #330-04-1965 L1976 **PS** *020

HADDAD, George Charles, Jr. 1686 SKYLYN DR, # 201 29307 #045-01-1994 L1996 **PD** *020 †55

HADDAD, Robert Gerges. 101 E WOOD ST, SPARTANBURG REGL MED CTR 29303 #605-03-1997 L2006 **IM** *020 †20

HAGGERTY, Christopher Jay. 1330 BOILING SPRINGS RD, STE 2400 29303 #055-01-1999 L2001 **OPH** *020 †35

HAMILTON, William Hugh, Jr. ■ 29307 #045-01-1944 L1944 **IM PUD** *071

HAMMOND, Gaines Wardlaw. 11 DOCTORS PARK DR, STE 220 29307 #045-01-1974 L1980 **U** *020 †95

HANEY, John Thomas. 853 N CHURCH ST STE 510 29303 #020-12-2005 L2005 **FP** *012

HANNA, Charles Benj. ■ 29302 #045-01-1944 L1944 **GS OS** *030 †85

HANNA, Richard Tinsley. 750 S CHURCH ST 29306 #045-01-1976 L1977 **FM P** *020 †18

HANSPARD, Kenya. 101 E WOOD ST 29303 #025-07-1998 L2003 **IM** *020 †20

HARDIN, Brandi D. 475 HEYWOOD AVE 29307 #045-01-1999 L2000 **OBG** *020 †30

HARPE, Katrina Nicole. 853 N CHURCH ST, STE 510 29303 #051-07-2006 L2006 **FP** *012

HAWKINS, Richard James. 1690 SKYLYN DR, STE 200 29307 #065-06-1969 L2004 **ORS OSM** *020 †40

HEAVRIN, Lawrence Allen. 25 DOCTORS PARK DR, STE 103 29307 #045-01-1960 L1960 **FM** *020 †18

HEDDEN, Julius Clyde, Jr. 1690 SKYLYN DR, CAROLINA FAMILY 29307 #045-01-1972 L1973 **FM** *020 †18

HELLAMS, Robert Michael. 101 E WOOD ST 29303 #045-04-1995 L1996 **FM** *020 †18

HENDERSON, Barry Branyon. 740 OAK GROVE RD 29301 #045-01-1978 L1979 **GP** *020

HENSLEY, Justin Paul. 101 E WOOD ST, SPARTANBURG REGIONAL MED C 29303 #047-20-2007 L2007 **GS** *012

HICKLIN, David Mark. 120 HEYWOOD AVE, DRS WESTMORELAND HICKLIN 29302 #036-05-1977 L1982 **FM** *020 †18

HIGGINS, Eric Benjamin. 101 E WOOD ST, REGIONAL HEALTHCAR 29303 #012-01-2006 L2006 **TY** *012

HILL, William Henry. 101 E WOOD ST 29303 #020-02-1977 L1978 **EM FM** *020 †18

HILSMAN, Susan Olson. 101 E WOOD ST 29303 #045-04-1987 L1988 **FM** *020 †18

HINES, Robert Stephen. 1776 SKYLYN DR 29307 #045-01-1987 L1993 **FM** *020 †18

HIRD, Robert Barry. 853 N CHURCH ST, STE 500 29303 #025-07-1991 L1993 **GS** *020 †85

HOBBS, Royal Albert. 100 E WOOD ST 29303 #065-01-1979 L1999 **PS HS** *020 †65

HODGE, Gameel Byron. 8311 GREENVILLE HWY, REGIONAL OCCUPATIONAL HEAL 29301 #047-05-1942 L1947 **GS TS** *071 †85

HOLBROOK, John Farrell. 101 E WOOD ST 29303 #047-06-2005 L2005 **DR** *012

HOLMES, Michael Wood. 479 HEYWOOD AVE, PALMETTO EYE & LASER CENTE 29307 #045-01-1969 L1969 **OPH** *020 †35

HOLT, David Arnold. 853 N CHURCH ST, STE 720 29303 #012-01-1976 L1977 **IM RHU** *040 †20

HOMMEL, Kenneth Herbert. 8311 GREENVILLE HWY, REGIONAL OCCUPATIONAL HEAL 29301 #012-01-1987 L1998 **OM** *020 †70

HOOPER, Kari Kathleen. 101 E WOOD ST, REGIONAL HEALTHCAR 29303 #039-01-2007 L2007 **GS** *012

HORNBUCKLE, Hobson Wayne. 101 E WOOD ST, DEPARTMENT OF ANESTHESIA 29303 #012-05-1992 L2001 **AN** *020 †05

HOUSTON, Robert Eric. 853 N CHURCH ST, STE 510 29303 #030-06-1980 L1981 **FM FPG** *040 †18 ‡

HOWARD, Leslie W, Jr. ■ 29307 #045-01-1960 L1960 **IM CD** *071 †20

HUDGENS, William Robt. 147 OAKWOOD AVE 29302 #045-01-1957 L1957 **PD** *071 †55

HUDSON, James Wallace. 853 N CHURCH ST STE 510 29303 #045-01-1997 L1998 **FM** *020 †18

HULL, Gerald Wm, III. 391 SERPENTINE DR STE 500 29303 #011-03-1992 L1993 **U SO** *020 †95

HUMAR, Thomas Borut. 720 N PINE ST 29303 #050-02-1981 L1988 **AN** *020 †05 ‡

HURST, Lawrence Ronald. 397 SERPENTINE DR, STE A 29303 #036-07-1957 L1964 **OTO** *020 †45

HUTTO, Celedor. 853 N CHURCH ST STE 510, MED PROGRAM 29303 #012-22-2006 L2006 **FP** *012

IAGULLI, Kristen Marie. 853 N CHURCH ST STE 510, MED PROGRAM 29303 #054-04-2007 L2007 **FP** *012

JACKO, Joseph Gerard. 1650 SKYLYN DR, STE 200 29307 #038-40-1986 L2006 **ISM** *020 †20

JACKSON, Robert Edward. 105 POWELL MILL RD 29301 #045-01-1981 L1982 **FM** *020 †18

JAKUBCHAK, James Jos. 125 DILLON DR 29307 #041-13-1971 L1977 **OPH IM** *020 †35

JAMES, Hugh T. 100 E WOOD ST, STE 301 29303 #045-01-1989 L1991 **GS** *020 †85

JAMES, William A. 1330 BOILING SPRINGS RD, STE 2400 29303 #035-01-1965 L1989 **OPH** *071 †35

JAMES, William Frank, Jr. 475 HEYWOOD AVE, WOMAN'S CLINIC, PA 29307 #045-01-1976 L1977 **OBG** *020 †30

JARRELL, April Lea. 1686 SKYLYN DR, STE 101 29307 #055-01-1997 L2002 **OBG** *020 †30

JAWORSKI, Michelle A. 1690 SKYLYN DR, STE 200 29307 #038-44-1998 L2004 **FM FSM** *020 †18

JEFFORDS, Joseph V. 100 E WOOD ST, STE 301 29303 #045-01-1952 L1952 **GS TS** *071 †85,90

JOEFIELD, Jermaine Angela. 853 N CHURCH ST STE 51 29303 #422-01-2004 L2005 **FP** *012

JOHNS, Ralph Hagood. 451 E SAINT JOHN ST 29302 #045-01-1973 L1993 **PD** *020 †55

JOHNSON, James O. 475 HEYWOOD AVE, WOMAN'S CLINIC P.A 29307 #020-02-1967 L1972 **GYN** *020 †30

JOHNSON, John Wilcox. 157 S PINE ST 29302 #047-06-1971 L1989 **AN GP** *020 †05

JOHNSON, Terry Duane. 105 POWELL MILL RD 29301 #016-43-1974 L1975 **FM** *020 †18

JOSEPH, Renju Thomas. 1330 BOILING SPRINGS RD, STE 2700 29303 #305-01-2001 L2005 **PM** *020 †60

JOSEY, Julian Cleon, Jr. 101 E WOOD ST, GIBBS REG CAN CTR/REG HLT 29303 #036-05-1964 L1970 **RO** *020 †80

JOYCE, William Terence. 101 E WOOD ST 29303 #045-01-1992 L1997 **DR** *020 †80,28

JUAN, Emerson Alfonso. 101 E WOOD ST, SRMC - REG EMERGENCY CTR 29303 #011-75-2004, ▲ L2007 **EM** *020

JUMAQUIO, Lynnette Fombue. 750 S CHURCH ST 29306 #748-02-1999 L2004 **IM IMG** *020

JURS, Dennis Gregg. 101 E WOOD ST, SPARTANBURG REGIONAL MEDIC 29303 #045-01-1978 L1994 **PD** *020 †55

KANA, Stephen Michael. 303 E WOOD ST, OF SPARTANBURG LLC 29303 #010-02-1986 L1994 **ORS** *020 †40

KATEMBA, Edward Leons. 853 N CHURCH ST STE 510 29303 #622-01-1997 L2004 **FM** *020 †18

KATZ, Aaron Steven. 2020 N CHURCH STREET PL 29303 #035-03-1994 L1999 **D** *020 †15

KAUR, Poonaminder. 853 N CHURCH ST, STE 510 29303 #495-03-1996 L2005 **FP** *012

KAVANAGH, Joseph Andrew. 101 E WOOD ST 29303 #018-03-1983 L1987 **DR** *020 †80

KAVANAGH, Julie Ann. 101 E WOOD ST 29303 #018-03-1983 L1987 **PD PDI** *020 †55

KEITH, John E. 303 E WOOD ST, ORTH SPECLTS OF SPARTANBRG 29303 #041-01-1951 L1957 **ORS** *020 †40

KEITH, John Edmond, Jr. 303 E WOOD ST 29303 #045-01-1979 L1985 **OS HS** *020 †40

KELLER, Darwin William. 1075 BOILING SPRINGS RD, SPARTANBURG NEUROSURGICAL 29303 #045-01-1965 L1965 **NS** *020 †25

KELLEY, Henry Grace. 101 E WOOD ST 29303 #045-01-1956 L1956 **CD TS** *071 †85,90

KELLY, Ann Jeannette. 853 N CHURCH ST, STE 700 29303 #021-01-1970 L1987 **OBG** *020 †30

KERFOOT, William Warren. 391 SERPENTINE DR 29303 #011-04-1985 L1994 **U** *020 †95

KETCHEN, Carol Ann. 1686 SKYLYN DR # 201 29307 #020-12-1986 L1990 **OBG** *020 †30

KHAN, Phillip David. 101 E WOOD ST 29303 #036-08-2004 L2005 **GS** *012

KIDWAI, Asif Salah. 1330 BOILING SPRINGS RD, STE 1300 29303 #045-01-1995 L1999 **PD** *020 †55

KIESAU, Kyle Frank. 1 DOCTORS PARK DR 29307 #051-04-1967 L1973 **OBG** *020 †30

KILMAN, Mark David. 101 E WOOD ST, DEPT OF GENERAL SURGERY 29303 #422-01-2004 L2004 **GS** *100

KINARD, Harry Wilson. 391 SERPENTINE DR, STE 500 29303 #045-01-1978 L1983 **U** *020 †95

KINSMAN, Julie Marie. 853 N CHURCH ST, STE 510 29303 #045-04-2003 L2004 **FM** *020 †18

KISSENBERTH, Michael John. 1690 SKYLYN DR, STE 200 29307 #045-01-1993 L2004 **ORS** *020 †40

KNIPFER, Mark Allen. 1250 JOHN B WHITE SR BLVD, FAMILY PHYSICIANS OF 29306 #012-01-1978 L1979 **FM** *020 †18

KNOY, Kathryn W. 100 E WOOD ST 29303 #045-01-1974 L1976 **NEP** *020 †20

KONZ, Ladia Maria. 101 E WOOD ST 29303 #025-07-2001 L2004 **EM** *020 †16

KOSER, Andras. 101 E WOOD ST, DEPT OF IN-PATIENT MEDICIN 29303 #913-70-1981 L1997 **IM** *020 †20

KOVACS, Suzanne Denise. 1690 SKYLYN DR, STE 300 29307 #035-09-1994 L1998 **IM** *020 †20

KRAMER, Ari David. 101 E WOOD ST, STE 301 29303 #305-01-1997 L2002 **GS** *020 †85

KRUPP, Ryan Jeffrey. 1650 SKYLYN DR, STE 200 29307 #020-02-2002 L2007 **OSM ORS** *020

KUCABA, Walter D. 8311 WARREN H ABERNTHY HWY, WESTSIDE MINOR CARE 29301 #041-77-1998, ▲ L2000 **FM** *100 †18

KUPEYAN, Kristen Ann. 853 N CHURCH ST, SPARTANBURG FAMILY MEDICIN 29303 #104-01-2004 L2004 **FM** *020 †18

KURKJIAN, Joseph Karnig. ■ 29307 #012-01-2000 L2006 **NR** *100 †80

LAGOS, Jaime Andres. 98 WILLOW LN, FOOTHILLS ALLERGY & ASTHMA 29307 #011-04-2001 L2007 **AI** *020 †55

LAMM, Ronald Max. 205 N PINE ST 29302 #012-05-1963 L1974 **OPH** *071 †35

LANE, Tameka Kimesung. 101 E WOOD ST, SPARTANBURG REGIONAL MED C 29303 #045-01-2004 L2004 **D** *012

LANFORD, Cecil Floyd. 25 DOCTORS PARK DR, STE 201 29307 #045-01-1960 L1960 **OBG** *071 †30

LAPHAM, Rosanna Lorena. 1700 SKYLYN DR 29307 #048-02-1987 L1998 **PTH** *020 †50 ‡

LEGARDA, Maris Stella. 853 N CHURCH ST STE 640, REGIONAL FAM NEUROLOGY 29303 #748-16-1982 L1997 **CHN PD** *020 †75,55

LEPAGE, Angelina Joann. 1066C ASHEVILLE HWY 29303 #023-12-1982 L1994 **AI PD** *020 †55,03

LEPAGE, Paul Anthony. 853 N CHURCH ST, STE 500 29303 #023-12-1982 L1994 **GS** *020 †85

LEVINE, Beth Ellen. 362 N PINE ST 29302 #055-01-1984 L1988 **AN** *020 †05

LEVY, Arden Lynn. 98 WILLOW LN 29307 #012-01-1989 L1994 **AI** *020 †55,03

LEYLAND, Steven Anthony. 225 E WOOD ST 29303 #038-45-1981 L1989 **TS VS** *020 †85,90

LIPTAK, Justine Catherine. 853 N CHURCH ST STE 510 29303 #759-01-2004 L2004 **FM** *020

LITTLE, Mark Dickson. 101 E WOOD ST 29303 #045-01-2003 L2003 **DR** *012

LITTLEFIELD, Ronald H. 319 N PINE ST 29302 #045-01-1971 L1972 **IM CD** *020

LIU, Jonathan Jay. 853 N CHURCH ST, STE 510 29303 #036-08-2004 L2005 **FP** *012

LLEWELYN, Helen R E. ■ 29302 #023-01-1937 L1958 **PHP** *071

LLEWELYN, Timothy Scott. 100 E WOOD ST 29303 #045-01-1981 L1982 **IM** *020 †20

LOMBARDOZZI, Christopher. 101 E WOOD ST, DEPT OF EMERGENCY MEDICINE 29303 #016-01-1994 L2004 **OS** *020 †16,55

LOMBARDOZZI, Kristine. 853 N CHURCH ST, STE 500 29303 #026-04-1995 L2004 **GS** *020 †85

LOPEZ-SANDRIN, Mayte. 100 E WOOD ST STE 101 29303 #011-02-2000 L2005 **END** *020 †20

LOUKA, Hany Helmy. 101 E WOOD ST 29303 #915-02-1971 L1980 **AN** *020 †05

LOVETT, Warren Clay. 101 E WOOD ST 29303 #005-12-1959 L1965 **FM** *040 †18

LOWRY, William Brownlee. 1700 SKYLYN DR 29307 #045-01-1968 L1968 **PTH** *020 †50

LUDKOWSKI, Michael John. 101 E WOOD ST, PO BOX 4026 29303 #016-11-1993 L2006 **VIR DR** *020 †80

■ = Address Information Privacy Protected

LUGO, Raul Nelson. 1071 BOILING SPRINGS RD #035-09-1979 L2004 **GS SO** *075 †85 ‡

LURIE, Michael Vincent. 853 N CHURCH ST STE 510 29303 #036-08-2000 L2006 **FM** *100

LYLES, Clarence Cross. ■ 29302 #045-01-1945 L1945 **PD** *020 †55

MACHIMADA, Muthamma Jeeva. 1770 SKYLYN DR 29307 #496-34-1997 L2005 **RHU** *100 ‡

MAHAFFEY, Shelley Hammett. 8311 WARREN H ABERNTHY HWY, PALMETTO PEDIATRICS 29301 #045-01-1998 L2001 **PD** *020 †55

MAHONEY, Philip, Jr. 8311 WARREN H ABERNTHY HWY 29301 #038-43-2003 L2004 **FM** *020 †18

MAINMAN, David Blair. ■ 29307 #056-06-1989 L1993 **OBG** *020 †30

MALHAN, Deepak C. 2995 REIDVILLE RD, MARY BLACK URGENT CARE 29301 #495-17-1986 L2006 **FM** *020 †18 ‡

MANGANNAN, Vijayananmaran. 299 E PEARL ST 29303 #495-04-1976 L1996 **IM PD** *020 †55,20

MANKINEN, Richard William. 101 E WOOD ST, SPARTANBURG REGIONAL MED C 29303 #036-01-2007 L2007 **TY** *012

MARGALIT, Gal Gustav. 1230 JOHN B WHITE BLVD, P O BOX 41 29306 #917-29-1979 L1983 **GP PM** *020

MARIK, Susan Adams. 853 N CHURCH ST 29303 #004-01-1990 L2000 **OBG** *020 †30

MARTIN, Mark A. 218 E BLACKSTOCK RD 29301 #050-02-1990 L1996 **FM** *020 †18

MATHIS, Richard Kaye. 2830 REIDVILLE RD #005-14-1969 L1970 **PD GE** *020 †55

MAYFIELD, Michael T. 390 E HENRY ST, MAYFIELD FAM PRACT STE 206 29302 #045-01-1979 L1980 **FM** *020 †18

MAYFIELD, Ronald Keith. 100 E WOOD ST, STE 101 29303 #055-01-1975 L1978 **DIA END** *030 †20

MC CALL, Jane. 101 E WOOD ST 29303 #041-02-1980 L1981 **EM** *020 †16

MC CARLEY, Frances Mixson. 2306 CHESNEE HWY STE 10 29303 #045-01-1986 L1987 **FM** *020 †18

MCCARTHY, Christopher Rob. 853 N CHURCH ST, STE 510 29303 #011-04-2004 L2004 **FM** *020 †18

MCCARTY, Curtis Lee. 101 E WOOD ST, DEPT OF GENERAL SURGERY 29303 #661-02-2004 L2004 **PTH** *012

MC CLURE, Donald Hutson. 303 E WOOD ST 29303 #016-06-1966 L1973 **ORS** *020 †40

MC CORKLE, Cavert Keith. 1075 BOILING SPRINGS RD, SPARTANBURG NEUROSURGICAL 29303 #045-01-1972 L1979 **NS** *020 †25

MC CULLOCH, John Hathorn. 101 E WOOD ST 29303 #016-11-1966 L1974 **ON GS** *020 †85

MC DONALD, Robert E, Jr. 853 N CHURCH ST, STE 510 29304 #047-06-1984 L1985 **FM** *020 †18

MC ELHANEY, Austin R, Jr. 1330 BOILING SPRINGS RD, N GROVE MED PARK STE 1200 29303 #045-01-1980 L1982 **FM IMG** *020 †18

MC GEE, Angela Terase. 169 HALL ST, BARNET PARK FAMILY MEDICIN 29302 #056-06-1999 L2003 **FM** *020 †18

MC GEE, Lawrence S, III. 322 N PINE ST 29302 #396-24-1989 L1995 **IM NEP** *020 †20

MC HENRY, Timothy Patrick. 1690 SKYLYN DR, STE 200 29307 #035-19-1991 L2005 **OTR** *020 †40

MCKINNEY, Troy Festus, Jr. 157 S PINE ST 29302 #036-05-1990 L1994 **AN** *020 †05

MC LEOD, Lizabeth Ann. 1686 SKYLYN DR, STE 201 29307 #045-01-1989 L1990 **PD** *020 †55

MC LEOD, Thomas Allen. 1071 BOILING SPRINGS RD 29303 #011-02-1975 L1976 **GS** *020 †85

MC ROBBIE, Patricia. 120 HEYWOOD AVE, DRS WESTMORELAND HICKLIN 29302 #919-02-1975 L1994 **FM FPG** *020 †18

MEDLOCK, Melvin Du Bose. 130 DILLON DR 29307 #045-01-1958 L1958 **FM OS** *020 †18

MEETZE, Daniel Boyd. 301 N PINE ST, NETWORK GERIATRIC SERVICES 29302 #045-01-1997 L2001 **IM IMG** *020 †20

MEMON, Mohammed Amin. 100 E WOOD ST STE 200 29303 #704-08-1986 L2000 **P PYG** *020 †75

MENDOZA, Rico Vicente I. 2030 N CHURCH STREET PL 29303 #748-01-1990 L2002 **PCC SME** *020 †20

MENENDEZ-CALDWELL, Ann. 601 W MAIN ST 29301 #048-14-1993 L2000 **CHP** *020 †75

MILLER, Stanley Danl. 1690 SKYLYN DR, STE 300 29307 #654-01-1984 L1998 **ID IM** *020 †20

MILLER-COX, Debra L. 101 E WOOD ST, SPARTANBURG REGIONAL HLTH 29303 #035-46-1994 L2003 **ID** *020 †20

MILLICAN, Joseph Ronald. 101 E WOOD ST, SPARTANBURG REG HEALTHCARE 29303 #012-01-2003 L2004 **GS** *012

MILLS, Jennifer Hershberg. 101 E WOOD ST, SPARTANBURG REGIONAL MED C 29303 #045-01-2007 L2007 **TY** *012

MIMS, William Walton, III. 1700 SKYLYN DR 29307 #045-01-1991 L1992 **PTH** *020 †50

MIRONER, Yevgeny. 1330 BOILING SPRINGS RD, STE 2700 29303 #913-15-1980 L1996 **AN** *020 †05

MISTR, Ernest Noel. 101 E WOOD ST, DIV MED EDUCATION 29303 #051-04-1967 L1994 **PD NPM** *040 †55

MITCHELL, Robert Eugene. ■ 29307 #025-01-1966 L1973 **R** *071 †80

MOBLEY, Joseph Emory. ■ 29303 #001-02-2000 L2005 **CD** *020 †20

MOLINA, Jules Gomez. 853 N CHURCH ST, STE 510 29303 #308-03-1999 L2004 **P** *012

MONAGHAN, Suzanne Bruckel. 147 OAKWOOD AVE 29302 #038-40-1981 L1984 **PD** *020 †55

MONITTO, Drew Carl. 101 E WOOD ST, ASSOCIATES PA 29303 #036-01-1991 L1998 **RO** *020 †20,80

MONSON, Mark Donald. PO BOX 4026 29305 #036-01-1978 L1985 **DR PD** *020 †55,80

MOODY, Harold W. 101 E WOOD ST 29303 #005-12-1953 L1953 **GP** *071 †18

MOORE, Daniel Lee. 2375 E MAIN ST, STE A311 29307 #036-05-1963 L1976 **OS CHP** *020 †55

MORAN, Charles Thos. 101 E WOOD ST 29303 #045-01-1986 L2000 **AN PME** *020 †05

MORETZ, Laura M. 170 CAMELOT DR 29301 #012-01-1981 L1982 **GP** *020

MORETZ, Richard Emil. 1690 SKYLYN DR, STE 140 29307 #012-01-1977 L1978 **GS EM** *020 †85

MORRIS, William Albert. 100 E WOOD ST STE 301 29303 #012-01-1961 L1968 **GS** *071 †85

MORRISON, James Jeffrey. 218 E BLACKSTOCK RD, DOCTORS CARE - EAST BLACKS 29301 #012-01-1983 L1984 **FM** *020 †18

MORROW, Charles Eugene, Jr. 101 E WOOD ST, DEPT SURG 29303 #045-04-1993 L1994 **CCS** *020 †85

MOSSBURG, Albert Jurdan. 853 N CHURCH ST, STE 620 29303 #045-01-1991 L1992 **GE** *020 †20

MOURTADA, Husam. 8311 WARREN H ABERNTHY HWY, REGIONAL PHYSIATRY 29301 #875-02-1988 L2004 **PM** *020 †60

MURDOCK, Charles Bruce. 126 DILLON DR 29307 #036-07-1979 L1985 **NEP IM** *020 †20

NASH, Erin Nicole. 853 N CHURCH ST 29303 #045-04-2006 L2006 **FP** *012

NEIDENBACH, Peter John. 1410B JOHN B WHITE SR BLVD 29306 #045-01-1991 L1993 **D** *072 †15 ‡

NELSON, Eric Chas. 1330 BOILING SPRINGS RD 29303 #036-05-1972 L1979 **ON HEM** *020 †20

NELSON, John William. 1700 SKYLYN DR, MARY BLACK HOSPITAL 29307 #012-01-1961 L1986 **PTH** *020 †50

NETTLES, Harry Heyward. 1686 SKYLYN DR, STE 201 29307 #045-01-1966 L1966 **PD** *020 †55

NEWMAN, Jeffrey Miles. ■ 29302 #045-01-1990 L1995 **DR** *020 †80

NEWMAN, Sarah Elizabeth. ■ 29302 #047-06-1992 L1996 **MPD IM** *020 †20,55

NGUYEN, Christophe L. 1330 BOILING SPRINGS RD, STE 2300 29303 #048-04-1997 L2000 **GS** *100 †85

NGUYEN, Cuong Duy. 101 E WOOD ST, SPARTANBURG REGIONAL HLTHC 29303 #012-01-2002 L2004 **GS** *020 †85

NGUYEN, My-Anh Thi. 853 N CHURCH ST STE 510, DEPT OF FAMILY MEDICINE 29303 #305-01-2000 L2004 **FP** *020 †18

NGUYEN, Trudy Thuy. 101 E WOOD ST 29303 #665-01-2002 L2005 **FM** *100

NGUYEN-DUY, Tuan. 101 E WOOD ST 29303 #035-46-1982 L1991 **TS VS** *020 †90,85

NICHOLS, Carol D Sanders. 541 FLOYD RD 29307 #045-01-1972 L1973 **N** *020

NICHOLS, John Thos, Jr. 1686 SKYLYN DR, STE 101 29307 #045-01-1972 L1973 **OBG** *020 †30

NICHOLSON, David Wm. 479 HEYWOOD AVE, PALMETTO EYE & LASER CENTE 29307 #045-01-1969 L1969 **OPH** *020 †35

NIXON, William Harold. 391 SERPENTINE DR, STE 500 29303 #012-01-1961 L1972 **U** *020 †95

NNAJI, Ifeoma. 853 N CHURCH ST STE 510, MED PROGRAM 29303 #012-21-2006 L2006 **FP** *012

NOBLES, Michelle Bruce. ■ 29306 #045-01-1999 L2003 **FM** *020 †18

NORTON, Eric. 130 DILLON DR, FAMILY MEDICAL CENTER 29307 #045-01-1993 L1996 **FM** *020 †18

NOWATKA, Thomas Christian. 130 DILLON DR 29307 #020-12-1999 L2000 **FM** *020 †18

OGBEBOR, Christian Efosa. 853 N CHURCH ST STE 510, RESIDENCY PROGRAM 29303 #661-02-2006 L2006 **FP** *012

ORR, Richard Kenneth. 101 E WOOD ST, CARE SYS DEPT OF MED EDUCA 29303 #011-04-1977 L1999 **GS ON** *020 †85

ORSECK, Michael James. 391 SERPENTINE DR, STE 250 29303 #305-01-1998 L2001 **PS GS** *020 †85,65

PACENTINE, Gregory G. 1700 SKYLYN DR, MARY BLACK MEMORIAL HOSPIT 29307 #018-75-1990, ▲ L2001 **AN** *020 †05

PADGETT, James Earl. PO BOX 4217 29305 #045-01-1955 L1955 **PHP** *030 †55

PANCZYK, Eliza. 101 E WOOD ST 29303 #003-01-2006 L2006 **GS** *100

PARES, Gonzalo. 243 E BLACKSTOCK RD, STE 6 29301 #042-03-1988 L1995 **N** *020 †75

PARNES, Neil Hamilton. 101 E WOOD ST, SRMC 29303 #047-05-1978 L1982 **DR** *020 †80

PARRA, Marcia Leonor. 1330 BOILING SPRINGS RD, STE 1300 29303 #012-05-1997 L2004 **PD** *020 †55

PATEL, Pranay R. 3020 REIDVILLE RD, STE B 29301 #495-37-1990 L1999 **IM** *020 †20

PATEL, Viral Suresh. 853 N CHURCH ST STE 510, DEPT OF GENERAL SURGERY 29303 #047-07-2003 L2004 **GS** *012

PATTERSON, Christopher J. 301 N PINE ST, NETWORK GERIATRIC SVCS PA 29302 #056-05-1985 L1998 **IMG PLM** *020 †20

PATTERSON, John Albert. 123 DILLON DR, WOMENS RADIOLOGY CTR 29307 #036-05-1965 L1969 **R DR** *071 †80

PEEK, Sharon Kay. 101 E WOOD ST, DEPT OF ANESTHESIA 29303 #012-05-1982 L1990 **AN PD** *020 †05

PENNEBAKER, Richard S. 167 PIERPONT AVE 29303 #045-01-1983 L1986 **PD** *020 †55

PEREYO, Roberto Jose. 475 HEYWOOD AVE, WOMAN'S CLINIC PA 29307 #045-01-2001 L2004 **OBG** *020

PERKINS, Jennifer Lane. 853 N CHURCH ST, STE 510 29303 #047-06-2007 L2007 **FP** *012

PETTIS, Vastyne T Whaley. 131 DUNBAR ST 29306 #047-07-1949 L1952 **GP OBG** *071

PHAN, Phong Thanh. ■ 29303 #016-42-2003 L2006 **IM** *012

PHILLIPS, Stephen Anthony. 101 E WOOD ST, SPARTANBURG REGIONAL 29303 #001-02-2007 L2007 **GS** *012

PICKENS, Charles Andrew. 100 E WOOD ST 29303 #047-05-1975 L1979 **GE IM** *020 †20

POLSELLI, Ryan Joseph. 101 E WOOD ST, SPARTANBURG REGIONAL MEDIC 29303 #011-04-2006 L2006 **DR** *012

POOLE, Mack Collier. 130 DILLON DR 29307 #045-01-1959 L1959 **FM** *020 †18

PORTER, Deborah. 180 W WOODGLEN RD 29301 #051-04-1983 L2000 **AN** *020 †05

PORTER, Jan Leslie. 170 CAMELOT DR, STE A 29301 #036-07-1980 L1982 **FM** *020 †18

POTEAT, Robert Neal. 311 E MAIN ST 29302 #045-01-1965 L1965 **AN** *020

POWELL, William Sullivan. 250 DEWEY AVE 29303 #045-01-1965 L1965 **P** *020 †75

PRATT, Samuel Benj, III. 1410B JOHN B WHITE SR BLVD 29306 #045-01-1966 L1966 **D** *071 †15

PRESSLY, James Patterson. 1330 BOILING SPRINGS RD, STE 2400 29303 #045-01-1968 L1968 **OPH AM** *020 †35

PRESTON, April Ames. ■ 29302 #038-44-1984 L1985 **PDR** *071 †80

PRICE, Chad Thomas. 1650 SKYLYN DR, STE 200 29307 #047-06-2002 L2007 **ORS** *020

PRICE, Joey Stone. 1410B JOHN B WHITE SR BLVD 29306 #047-06-2002 L2007 **D** *020 †15

PRICE, William Foster. 100 E WOOD ST, STE 401 29303 #036-07-1962 L1968 **END IM** *071 †20

PRIGGE, Michelle Lynn. 1686 SKYLYN DR, STE 201 29307 #055-01-1999 L2001 **PD** *020 †55

PRYOR, Michael Brooks. 1690 SKYLYN DR 29307 #045-01-1997 L2007 **U** *020 †95

RAINER, Robert Oscar. 1700 SKYLYN DR, MARY BLACK HOSPITAL 29307 #045-01-1988 L1997 **PTH** *020 †50

RANA, Yashbir Singh. 2995 REIDVILLE RD, MARY BLACK URGENT CARE 29301 #495-67-1991 L1992 **EM OM** *020 †70

RATZLAFF, Alvin Jos. 250 DEWEY AVE, SPARTANBURG AREA MENTAL HE 29303 #005-12-1954 L1979 **P** *020 †75

RAUCH, Gary Don. 101 E WOOD ST 29303 #034-01-1993 L1999 **FM** *020 †18 ‡

RAY, Barbara Cantrell. 1060 N CHURCH ST, DOCTOR'S CARE 29303 #047-06-1989 L1990 **FM** *020 †18

REEL, Tod Rainsford. 1330 BOILING SPRINGS RD, STE 1200 29303 #045-01-1987 L1988 **FM** *020 †18

REICHERT, William Walter. 1690 SKYLYN DR STE 300 29307 #035-01-1969 L1973 **PUD IM** *020 †20

REID, Samuel Dolphus, Jr. 100 E WOOD ST 29303 #045-01-1965 L1965 **CD IM** *020 †20

REINHARDT, Richard B, Jr. 100 E WOOD ST, STE 301 29303 #045-04-1994 L1996 **GS** *020 †85

REYNOLDS, Stuart F. 1091 BOILING SPRINGS RD 29303 #060-01-1996 L2000 **EM FM** *020

RIDNER, Courtney Webb. 101 E WOOD ST, DEPT. GENERAL SURGERY 29303 #047-20-2004 L2004 **GS** *020

RIEDINGER, Meghan Elizabe. 853 N CHURCH ST STE 510, RESIDENCY PROGRAM 29303 #011-04-2005 L2007 **FP** *012

RIEHLE, Robert A, Jr. 101 E WOOD ST 29303 #035-01-1973 L2001 **U** *030 †95

RINALDO, Frank E, Jr. 157 S PINE ST 29302 #012-05-1988 L1989 **AN** *020 †05,20

RINALDO, Susan Smith. 171 W WOODGLEN RD 29301 #036-05-1983 L1988 **CHP P** *020 †75

RINGEL, Robert A. 362 N PINE ST, NEUROLOGY CENTERS OF THE C 29302 #055-01-1982 L1988 **N** *020 †75

RITCHIE, Henry Skeen. ■ 29302 #051-01-1961 L1975 **P** *075

ROBINSON, Thomas Little. 1690 SKYLYN DR, STE 300 29307 #036-05-1973 L1976 **IM** *020 †20

RODRIGO, Juan Jose. 1690 SKYLYN DR, STE 200 29307 #005-02-1968 L2004 **ORS** *020 †40

RODY, Richard Brent. 101 E WOOD ST, DEPT OF EMERGENCY MEDICINE 29303 #039-01-1987 L2006 **EM IM** *020 †16

ROEL, Lawrence Edmund. 735 E MAIN ST 29302 #041-01-1985 L1989 **OPH** *020 †35

ROSINSKI, Elisa Ann. 8311 WARREN H ABERNTHY HWY, WESTSIDE URGENT CARE 29301 #025-12-1997 **FM** *020 †18

ROSS, Joseph Paul, III. 100 E WOOD ST, STE 301 29303 #045-01-1994 L1996 **GS** *020 †85

ROTH, Katherine Rae. 853 N CHURCH ST STE 510, MED PROGRAM 29303 #025-07-2007 L2007 **FP** *012

ROTHEMICH, Brian Earl. 101 E WOOD ST, SPARTANBURG REGIONAL MED C 29303 #033-05-1976 L1977 **EM** *020 †16,18

ROY, Micah Jordan. 101 E WOOD ST, SRMC - EMERGENCY DEPT. 29303 #035-45-2001 L2004 **EM** *020 †16

RUCKER, Christopher D. 1330 BOILING SPRINGS RD, STE 1400 29303 #051-01-1984 L1999 **OTO GS** *020 †45

RYAN, Forrest Peter, Jr. 101 E WOOD ST 29303 #047-06-1979 L1985 **DR PTH** *020 †50,80

SAAD, Juliette Saad. 100 WILLOW LN, STE A 29307 #025-07-1983 L1996 **N** *020

SAHHAR, Hanna Samaan. 101 E WOOD ST, ATTN: MEDICAL STAFF OFC. 29303 #528-02-1994 L2005 **CCP** *100 †55

SAMPSON, Craig Hirsch. 853 N CHURCH ST, STE 510 29303 #012-01-2006 L2006 **FP** *012

SANCHEZ, Anthony Andres. 303 E WOOD ST 29303 #047-05-1990 L1992 **ORS AM** *020 †40

SANDERS, Stacie Denise. 101 E WOOD ST 29303 #020-02-1999 L2007 **AN** *020 †05

SANSBURY, Paul A, III. 101 E WOOD ST, SPARTANBURG REGIONAL MED C 29303 #045-01-1980 L1981 **EM** *020 †16,18

SANTOS, Ottao Azambuja. PO BOX 4583, STE B 29305 #187-11-1957 L1972 **PS** *075 †85

SARTOR, Claude C. ■ 29307 #045-01-1949 L1949 **PD** *071 †55

SCHNEIDER LONG, Ursula. 101 E WOOD ST 29303 #016-06-1978 L1982 **AN** *030 †05

SCHUTZ, Leonard. 1455 E MAIN ST, STE 103 29307 #038-40-1962 L1996 **HEM ON** *020 †20

SCOTT, Glenn Lawrence. 1700 SKYLYN DR 29307 #021-01-1965 L1973 **ORS** *020 †40

SCOTT, John Russell. 853 N CHURCH ST STE 720, 853 NORTH CHURCH ST STE 72 29303 #001-02-1967 L1974 **GYN** *020 †30 ‡

SCOVELL, John F. 1650 SKYLYN DR, STE 200 29307 #048-15-2002 L2007 **ORS** *020

SEASE, Wayne Franklin, Jr. 1690 SKYLYN DR, STE 200 29307 #045-04-1998 L1999 **FSM** *020 †18

SEASTRUNK, James Saml. 1241 BOILING SPRINGS RD 29303 #045-01-1965 L1965 **OSM** *020 †40

SEPMEYER, Jacob Alan. ■ 29302 #047-05-2008 *012

SEREQUE, Peter Arnold. 853 N CHURCH ST, STE 700 29303 #038-41-1968 L1974 **OBG** *020 †30 ‡

SHAH, Amishi Yogesh. 358 SERPENTINE DR 29303 #045-04-1999 L2000 **P** *020 †75

SHAIKH, Imranullah. 101 E WOOD ST, MEDICAL STAFF OFFICE 29303 #308-13-1999 L2005 **HOS IM** *020 †20

SHANBHAG, Ashish Gajanan. 1060 N CHURCH ST 29303 #045-01-1993 L1997 **PM** *020 †60

SHANTHA, D T. 101 E WOOD ST 29303 #495-99-1992 L1997 **AN** *020 †05

SHARON, Elliott Arnold. 101 E WOOD ST 29303 #305-01-2006 L2007 **FP** *012

SHEALY, Michael James. 101 E WOOD ST, SPARTANBURG REGIONAL HEALT 29303 #045-01-2005 L2005 **GS** *100

SHEALY, Roger Dale. 2224 OLD FURNACE RD 29316 #045-01-1973 L1974 **FM** *020 †18

SHERARD, Gordon Brown, III. 1686 SKYLYN DR 29307 #045-01-1997 L2002 **OBG** *020 †30

SHINGLER, John M, Jr. 101 E WOOD ST 29303 #045-01-1954 L1954 **AN** *071

SHIRLEY, Brayton Robert. 1650 SKYLYN DR STE 200 29307 #045-01-1999 L2000 **ORS** *100 †40

SIMMONS, John Walton. PO BOX 8627 29305 #012-01-1968 L1969 **FM** *020 †18

SIMMONS, Neal Benj. 1690 SKYLYN DR, STE 350 29307 #012-01-1983 L1985 **DR** *020 †80

SIMON, Ifekan-Shango E E. 853 N CHURCH ST, STE 510 29303 #012-01-1994 L2001 **FM** *020 †18

SINGLETARY, Frank Joe. 101 E WOOD ST 29303 #045-01-1974 L1976 **EM FM** *020 †18,16

SINGLETON, Steven Brian. 1650 SKYLYN DR STE 200, CAROLINAS 29307 #048-12-1991 L2003 **ORS** *020 †40

SLAUGHTER, Chad Christoph. 101 E WOOD ST, SRHC - SURGICAL EDUCATION 29303 #422-01-2005 L2005 **IM** *012

SMILEY, Althea Jeffers. 101 E WOOD ST, ANESTHESIA DEPARTMENT 29303 #036-01-1980 L1989 **AN** *020 †05

SMITH, Bradford William. 101 E WOOD ST, DEPARTMENT OF INPATIENT ME 29303 #654-01-1998 L2001 **IM** *020 †20

SMITH, David Conan, II. 101 E WOOD ST, ATTN: EMERG. DEPT. 29303 #010-03-2002 L2008 **EM** *020

SMITH, Donna Payne. 8311 WARREN H ABERNTHY HWY 29301 #045-01-1990 L1991 **PD** *020 †55

SMITH, Eugene Freeman. 250 DEWEY AVE 29303 #045-01-1977 L1978 **P** *020 †75 ‡

SMITH, T Ravenel. 1700 SKYLYN DR 29307 #045-01-1974 L1975 **FM** *020 †18

SMITH, Wilson Pedrick, Jr. 2030 N CHURCH STREET PL 29303 #055-01-1976 L1981 **PUD IM** *020 †20

SOVENYHAZY, Gabor. 11 DOCTORS PARK DR STE 210 29307 #035-08-1975 L1980 **CRS GS** *020 †10

SPILKER, Thomas Craig. ■ 29307 #047-05-1978 L1985 **EM** *020 †16

STEWART, Randall Steve. 2995 REIDVILLE RD, MARY BLACK MEMORIAL HOSP 29301 #045-01-1981 L1983 **EM** *020

STOKES, David Kershaw, Jr. 101 E WOOD ST 29303 #045-01-1957 L1957 **FM FPG** *071 †18

STOPPENHAGEN, David Ray. 101 E WOOD ST, P O BOX 4026 29303 #017-20-1989 L1999 **DR** *020 †80

STRESING, Harland Albert. 391 SERPENTINE DR, STE 500 29303 #045-01-1970 L1971 **U** *020 †95

SUBRAMANIAM, Subhashini C. 126 DILLON DR, FOOTHILLS NEPHROLOGY 29307 #495-04-1997 L2005 **NEP** *020

SWANN, Lisa Ann. 101 E WOOD ST, EMERGENCY DEPARTMENT 29303 #045-01-1983 L1984 **EM FM** *020 †18,16

SWENSEN, Frederick C. 1690 SKYLYN DR STE 10 29307 #049-01-1966 L1979 **PS** *020 †65

SZWAPA, Mary Elizabeth. 100 E WOOD ST STE 202 29303 #025-07-1992 L1996 **OBG** *020

TABAMO, Rowena E J. 541 FLOYD RD, CAROLINA NEUROLOGY 29307 #748-02-1994 L2006 **N** *020 †75

TAN, Ann Marie C. ■ 29301 #748-02-1991 L1996 **PDE** *020 †55

TARAZI, Sylvia Shawqi B. 385 SERPENTINE DR STE A 29303 #915-02-1968 L1984 **GS** *020 †85

TATE, John Thompson. 1690 SKYLYN DR, STE 140 29307 #012-05-1974 L1979 **AS GS** *020 †85

TAYLOR, Deborah Jo. 853 N CHURCH ST, STE 510 29303 #055-01-2004 L2005 **FP** *012

TAYLOR, Lee Brown. 1250 JOHN B WHITE SR BLVD, FAMILY PHYSICIANS OF 29306 #045-01-1978 L1979 **FM** *020 †18

TAYLOR, Robert Hutchinson. 391 E HENRY ST 29302 #045-01-1954 L1954 **FM OM** *071 †18

TESSENEER, Ralph Athen, III. 130 DILLON DR 29307 #020-02-1977 L1978 **FM** *020 †18

THIBODEAUX, Laurie J. 1700 SKYLYN DR, MARY BLACK INPATIENT PHYSI 29307 #028-78-2002, ▲ L2004 **IM** *020 †20

THOMAS, Aydrian Leshawn. 101 E WOOD ST 29303 #045-01-2000 L2002 **FM** *020 †18

THOMAS, Stephen James. 101 E WOOD ST 29303 #012-01-2002 L2003 **FM** *100 †18

TILLER, Wendell H. 110 DILLON DR 29307 #036-05-1945 L1946 **ORS** *071 †40

TOLAN, Stefan John. 1690 SKYLYN DR, STE 200 29307 #045-01-1992 L1993 **ORS** *020 †40

TOLER, Aaron Mc Lain. 1686 SKYLYN DR 29307 #001-02-1994 L1998 **OBG** *020 †30

TOLER, Kimberly Frazier. 1686 SKYLYN DR 29307 #001-02-1994 L1998 **OBG** *020 †30

TOLLISON, Ronald Mark. 1330 BOILING SPRINGS RD, STE 2700 29303 #045-01-1980 L1981 **FM** *020 †18

TRACY, Kevin Patrick. 1770 SKYLYN DR 29307 #051-04-1981 L1990 **RHU IM** *020 †20

TROTT, David Chas. 8311 WH ABERNATHY HWY, REGIONAL OCCUPATIONAL HLTH 29301 #005-12-1978 L2006 **OM GPM** *020 †70 ‡

TYSON, Adam Beckett. 101 E WOOD ST, SRMC-REGIONAL OB/GYN SERVI 29303 #045-01-1998 L1998 **OBG** *020 †30

UTLEY, Joella Faye. 101 E WOOD ST 29303 #028-02-1967 L1984 **RO** *020 †80

UY, Imelda Perez. 101 E WOOD ST 29303 #748-08-1990 L2001 **NPM PD** *020 †55

VALAINIS, Gregory Thomas. 101 E WOOD ST, CENTER 29303 #051-04-1980 L1989 **ID IM** *020 †20

VARN, Mary Milhous. 233 E BLACKSTOCK RD, STE F 29301 #045-01-1990 L1992 **OPH PO** *020 †35

VAUGHN, Kenneth W, Jr. 101 E WOOD ST 29303 #024-05-1964 L1966 **IM** *020 †20

VELLANKI, Anu Prasad. 101 E WOOD ST 29303 #495-58-1991 L1998 **IM** *020 †20

VENIEGAS, Cheryl R.. 853 N CHURCH ST, STE 510 29303 #748-08-2002 L2004 **FP** *012

VERMILLION, Stephen T. 853 N CHURCH ST, STE 610 29303 #051-04-1993 L1994 **OBG** *020 †30

VISK, Mark Douglas. 303 E WOOD ST 29303 #018-03-1981 L1986 **ORS EM** *020 †40

VU, Thuy L. 101 E WOOD ST, SPARTANBURG REGIONAL MED. 29303 #045-01-2007 L2007 **TY** *012

WAGNER, Jeffrey Mark. 98 WILLOW LN, DBA FOOTHILL ALLERGY 29307 #041-09-1986 L1992 **IM** *020 †20,03

WALTON, Everette Jos, Jr. 101 E WOOD ST 29303 #036-01-1970 L1983 **END IM** *020 †20

WARE, Larry Lamar. 1776 SKYLYN DR 29307 #045-04-1989 L1991 **GS** *020 †18

WARREN, Edward Shaw. 301 N PINE ST, NETWORK GERIATRIC SERVICES 29302 #036-05-1975 L2000 **FPG PLM** *020 †18

WARREN, Grantham Dewitt. 853 N CHURCH ST 29303 #036-08-2000 L2004 **OBG** *020 ‡

WARREN, Petra K. 101 E WOOD ST 29303 #036-05-1975 L2000 **FM** *020 †18

WARREN, Thomas Linson. 101 E WOOD ST, ANESTHESIA DEPT 29303 #055-01-1978 L1988 **AN CCM** *020 †05

WATKINS, Michael Roland. 100 E WOOD ST, STE 202 29303 #012-05-1979 L1995 **OBG** *040 †30

WATSON, Kandra Williams. ■ 29306 #045-01-1997 L2001 **FM** *020 †18

WATTS, Garrison Grier, Jr. 951 E MAIN ST 29302 #045-01-1962 L1968 **CD IM** *020 †20

WEAVER, Paul Douglas. 1700 SKYLYN DR 29307 #012-01-1983 L1984 **IM** *020 †20

WEBB, Omri Kenneth, III. 170 CAMELOT DR, STE A 29301 #045-04-1985 L1986 **FM** *020 †18

WEBB, Richard Clark. ■ 29301 #045-01-2007 *012

WEBB, Shannon Claye. 853 N CHURCH ST, STE 510 29303 #001-02-2000 L2001 **FM** *020 †18

WEBER, Marc Edward. 1330 BOILING SPRINGS RD, STE 1300 29303 #047-06-1974 L2006 **PD** *020 †55,16

WEEKS, James Patrick. 1690 SKYLYN DR STE 250 29307 #041-09-1981 L1985 **OPH** *020 †35

WEIR, Alexander F, Jr. 148 DILLON DR 29307 #036-05-1953 L1960 **OTO OS** *071 †45

WEIR, David Frank. 148 DILLON DR 29307 #036-05-1977 L1982 **OTO HNS** *020 †45

WELLS, Kenneth Wayne. 943 N CHURCH ST 29303 #045-01-1972 **P** *020 †75

WESSEL, Thomas Jacob, Jr. 101 E WOOD ST 29303 #045-01-1983 L1984 **FM** *040 †18

WESSINGER, John Mark. 101 E WOOD ST 29303 #045-04-2002 L2002 **VIR** *012

WESSINGER, Philip Heyward. 1690 SKYLYN DR, STE 200 29307 #045-01-1988 L1993 **ORS GS** *020 †40

WESTMORELAND, Thomas Wade. 120 HEYWOOD AVE, STE 200 29302 #045-01-1976 **FM** *020 †18

WESTON, Laurel Andrea. 250 DEWEY AVE 29303 #045-01-1978 L1979 **P CHP** *020 †75

WHITAKER, James Whitney. 101 E WOOD ST, SPARTANBURG REGIONAL MED C 29303 #012-01-2007 L2007 **GS** *012

WHITE, Larry Butler. 1686 SKYLYN DR, STE 101 29307 #045-01-1968 **OBG** *020 †30

WHITMORE, Robert Lester. 101 E WOOD ST, FAMILY MEDICINE 29303 #045-04-2005 L2005 **FP** *012

WHITNEY, Roy Bradford, Jr. 301 N PINE ST, NETWORK GERIATRIC SERVICES 29302 #045-01-1981 L1986 **FPG FM** *071 †18

WICKER, David Lamar. 101 E WOOD ST, SPARTANBURG REGIONAL HEALT 29303 #012-01-2005 L2005 **DR** *012

WIEDER, John Richard. 170 CAMELOT DR, STE A 29301 #045-01-1974 **GP** *020

WILEY, David Huey. 1650 SKYLYN DR, STE 200 29307 #038-44-2002 L2007 **ORS** *020

WILLIAMS, Clifton L, Jr. 1690 SKYLYN DR, STE 100 - BOX 11 29307 #045-01-1980 L1981 **U** *020 †95

WILLIAMS, Julian. 1330 BOILING SPRINGS RD, STE 2500 29303 #045-01-1954 **IM CD** *071

WILSON, James Matthew. 101 E WOOD ST, SRHC - SURGICAL EDUCATION 29303 #051-01-2005 L2005 **GS** *012

WINKELER, Brett Michael. 853 N CHURCH ST STE 510 29303 #016-11-2005 L2005 **FP** *012

WOLFE, Ricky David. ■ 29302 #045-01-1987 L1988 **PTH** *020 †50 ‡

WOLPE, Sarah June. 853 N CHURCH ST, STE 510 29303 #045-01-2004 L2004 **FM** *020 †18

WOOD, Brian Richard. 101 E WOOD ST, PEDIATRIX MED GRP 29303 #308-07-1983 L2004 **NPM PD** *020 †55

WOOD, Robert Michael. 1690 SKYLYN DR, STE 200 29307 #041-12-1974 L1986 **ORS PM** *020 †40

WOOD, Samuel K. 120 DILLON DR 29307 #048-12-1996 L2006 **HO** *020 †20

WOOD, Tyrone Keith. 285 KESWICK FARM RD, MARY BLACK MEMORIAL HOSPIT 29302 #045-01-1977 L1978 **AN** *020 †05

WOOTTON, Robert Daniel. ■ 29307 #025-07-1962 L1963 **PD** *071 †55

WREN, John David. 1700 SKYLYN DR 29307 #045-01-1979 L1980 **PTH FOP** *020 †50

WYLAND, Douglas John. 1690 SKYLYN DR, STE 200 29307 #036-01-1995 L2005 **OSM** *020 †40

YEE, Kim Hont Aramburo. 120 DILLON DR, CAROLINAS SPARTANBURG 29307 #748-01-1986 L2000 **HO** *020 †20

YELTON, John Richard. 101 E WOOD ST, MEDICAL STAFF 29303 #045-04-1996 L2004 **PD** *020 †55

■ = Address Information Privacy Protected

YOON, Heesuk Richard. 101 E WOOD ST 29303 #048-15-2006 L2006 **GS** *012
YOST, Stephen Arthur. 1250 REIDVILLE RD 29306 #045-01-1979 L1980 **FM** *020 †18
ZHADKEVICH, Michael M. 101 E WOOD ST 29303 #913-15-1983 L1999 **TS** *020 †85,90
ZOLLINGER, Pamela Lee. ■ 29304 #045-04-2008 *012

SULLIVANS ISLAND — CHARLESTON

AIMAR, Charles E. PO BOX 91, 2724 MIDDLE ST 29482 #045-01-1953 L1953 **GP** *071
ANDEREGG, Katherine Ann. ■ 29482 #045-01-1984 L2000 **PTH OS** *020 †50
BRADHAM, Eloise Daniel. 3109 ION AVE 29482 #045-01-1986 L1987 **AN** *020 †05
COLLIE, Cynthia Elaine. 306 STATION 22 1/2 ST 29482 #045-01-1988 L1992 **OPH** *020
CONDON, Emily Yarbrough. 306 STATION 22 1/2 ST 29482 #036-07-1979 L1983 **FM** *020 †18
DURST, George Gardner, Jr. 306 STATION 22 1/2 ST 29482 #045-01-1966 L1966 **GP** *020 †18
DURST, Kay. 306 STATION 22 1/2 ST 29482 #045-01-1998 L2008 **FM** *020 †18
EDGAR, Berdine Muirna. ■ 29482 #045-01-2007 *012
GOODMAN, Michael Moses. ■ 29482 #036-08-2005 L2007 **IM** *012
HANN, Maureen Ann. 306 STATION 22 1/2 ST 29482 #008-02-1988 L1991 **FM** *020 †18
INABINET, Geo Marion, Jr. 332 IZLAR ST, 332 IZLAR STREET 29482 #045-01-1980 L1981 **AN** *020 †05
LEPPARD, William Mciver. ■ 29482 #045-01-2007 L2007 **GS** *012
LYLES, Lori. 1651 ATLANTIC AVE 29482 #045-01-1988 L1989 **OBG** *020 †30
RUTLEDGE, Rochelle Cohen. 306 STATION 22 1/2 ST 29482 #035-47-1978 L1979 **FM** *020 †18
WILLIAMS, Norton L. ■ 29482 #024-07-1940 L1942 **P** *075 †75

SUMMERTON — CLARENDON

KELLER, Eugene W, Jr. 14 MOOD DR 29148 #045-01-1951 L1951 **GP** *071
SHEELY, Lowry Lindsey. ■ 29148 #021-01-1955 L1955 **AN** *071 †05

SUMMERVILLE — DORCHESTER

ADEAGBO, Bamidele Adekunl. ■ 29485 #690-08-1991 L2005 **PTH** *100
ANDERSON, William Robt. 105B HARTH PL 29485 #045-01-1983 L1987 **IM GE** *020 †20
BAGGETT, David Jay. 299 MIDLAND PKWY # A 29485 #045-01-1977 L1978 **FM** *020 †18
BERNARD, Darlene Carolyn. 75 SPRINGVIEW LN, WOMENS HEALTH PARTNERS 29485 #023-01-1989 L2007 **OBG** *020 †30
BOLSTER, David Eric. 201 OAKBROOK LN, PALMETTO INTERNAL 29485 #036-07-1988 L1993 **IM** *020 †20
BRASSEUX, Stephen Joseph. ■ 29485 #021-05-2006 L2006 **P** *012
BRYANS, William Owen. 295 MIDLAND PKWY, ANESTHESIA DEPT 29485 #012-01-1980 L1982 **AN** *075 †05
BURGER, Jan Hendrik. 299 MIDLAND PKWY A, DORCHESTER MEDICAL ASSOCS 29485 #836-03-1997 L2004 **FM** *100 †18
CANFIELD, Michael Ellison. 87 SPRINGVIEW LN 29485 #001-06-1983 L1995 **FM AM** *020 †18 ‡
CARRUTHERS, Mary W. 295 MIDLAND PKWY, SUMMERVILLE MEDICAL CENTER 29485 #045-01-1998 L2003 **EM** *020 †16
CASTELLONE, David Louis. 213 W 4TH NORTH ST, PALMETTO PRIMARY CARE PHYS 29483 #050-02-1982 L1983 **FM** *020 †18
CHISHOLM, Frederick F, Jr. 206 W RICHARDSON AVE STE B 29483 #045-01-1971 L1976 **PD** *020 †55
COOK, Beth A. 75 SPRINGVIEW LN 29485 #055-01-1998 L2002 **OBG** *020
COOLER, Henry Paul. 320 MIDLAND PKWY, STE A 29485 #045-01-1967 L1967 **OPH** *020 †35 ‡
COX, Joel Robt, Jr. 93A SPRINGVIEW LN, SPORTS MEDICINE 29485 #045-01-1968 L1968 **ORS** *020 †40
CROCKER, Susan Spivey. 225 MIDLAND PKWY, THE PINES TREATMENT CENTER 29485 #045-01-1978 L1979 **CHP PD** *020
DAS, Bijoy Chandra. 295 MIDLAND PKWY 29485 #495-13-1963 L1979 **GE IM** *020
DEBERRY, Skye Nicole. 213 W 4TH NORTH ST 29485 #045-01-1997 L2001 **FM** *020 †18
DIETRICH, Amy R. 312 MIDLAND PKWY 29485 #028-34-2000 L2004 **PD** *020 †55
DOTSON, Kurtis Wilson. ■ 29485 #036-05-2006 L2006 **PD** *012
ENGELMAN, Dendy Elizabeth. ■ 29483 #045-01-2004 L2005 **D** *012
ENGELMAN, Otis Edward, Jr. 299 MIDLAND PKWY 29485 #045-01-1972 L1977 **FM** *020 †18
ESTOCK, Nicole Jeanine. 202 BENTONS LODGE RD, OAKBROOK PEDIATRICS, PA 29485 #041-15-1999 L2002 **PD** *020 †55
EWENS, Joseph Danl. 90 SPRINGVIEW LN 29485 #005-06-1990 L1999 **FM** *020 †18
FENWICK, Jerry Lynn. ■ 29483 #051-07-1988 L1996 **EM** *020 †16
GETTLIFFE, Cyril Dudley. ■ 29485 #836-01-1942 L1975 **GP** *071
GLASER, Anthony Nicholas. 602 N MAIN ST 29483 #654-01-1995 L1998 **FM** *020 †18
GREEN, George C, Jr. ■ 29483 #016-11-1952 L1953 **GP OM** *020
GROSSMAN, Colby Harold. 201 OAKBROOK LN, PALMETTO INTERNAL 29485 #045-01-1983 L1985 **IM** *020 †20
GUANZON, Leocadio Antonio. ■ 29483 #748-07-1955 L1967 **GP** *074
GULLATT, Theodore, III. ■ 29485 #045-01-1996 L2003 *020 †18
HARBACH, Gregory Paul. 5124 TINSTON CT 29485 #031-01-1994 L2003 **ORS** *100 †40
HARRIS, Craig Dyer. 130 E 3RD NORTH ST 29483 #045-04-1992 L1993 **PM** *020
HOLBROOK, Julius C. PO BOX 964 29484 #045-12-1952 L1969 **FM** *075
HOWE, John Keith, Jr. 1710 TROLLEY RD 29485 #041-02-1964 L1982 **PD AM** *071 †55
HUTCHINS, Joshua Corneliu. 700 N PINE ST, ANMED HEALTH-FAMILY PRACTI 29483 #422-01-2004 L2004 **FM** *020 †18
IBEN, Glenn Allan. ■ 29485 #041-12-1976 L1981 **FM** *020 †18
JASKWHICH, David Harrison. 93A SPRINGVIEW LN, SPORTS MEDICINE 29485 #045-01-1996 L2002 **OSM ORS** *020 †40
JENKINS, Shantae James. ■ 29485 #045-01-2007 L2007 **IM** *012
JORDAN, Robert Chas. 208 E 2ND NORTH ST, LOMAX-JORDAN EAR NOSE & TH 29483 #045-01-1980 L1981 **OTO** *020 †45
KATZ, Barry Stephen. 213 W 4TH NORTH ST 29483 #045-01-1995 L1997 **FM** *020 †18
KEARSE, Henry Lewis, III. 103 HARTH PL # B 29485 #045-01-1981 L1987 **D PD** *020 †15
KELLER, Brian Keith. 300 W 4TH NORTH ST 29483 #020-12-1994 L1995 **FM AN** *020 †18
KIM, Sola. 295 MIDLAND PKWY 29485 #045-01-1989 L1990 **PUD CCM** *020
LAFOND, Jeffrey Marc. 295 MIDLAND PKWY 29485 #045-01-1990 L1991 **GS** *020 †85
LAM, Michael Alan. 109 BURTON AVE STE E, CARDIOLOGY CARE OF SC LLC 29485 #012-01-1976 L1983 **CD IM** *020 †20

LEIGHTON, George A, Jr. 404 N PINE ST 29483 #038-40-1956 L1975 **IM ON** *020
LENES, Steven John. 9995 JAMISON RD, COASTAL CENTER 29485 #012-05-1986 L1987 **FM** *020 †18
LEVENTHAL, Walter. 299 MIDLAND PKWY # A 29485 #836-02-1973 L1978 **FM** *020 †18
LITTLE, Mark. 102 HARTH PL, MIDLAND PARKWAY 29485 #045-01-2001 L2003 **FM** *020 †18
LITTLE, Mary Elizabeth. 102 HARTH PL, HARTH PLACE FAMILY MEDICIN 29485 #539-05-1977 L1995 **FM** *020 †18
LOMAX, William Roger. 208 E 2ND NORTH ST 29483 #011-02-1968 L1974 **FPS OTO** *020 †45
LORANTH, G Victor. ■ 29485 #649-14-1980 L1981 **GS** *020
MALLIN, Kimberly Sue Alde. 602 N MAIN ST, FLOWERTOWN FAMILY PHYSICIA 29483 #036-08-1988 L2004 **FM** *020 †18
MANDEL, Lloyd Bernard. 295 MIDLAND PKWY 29485 #035-15-1967 L1980 **GS** *020 †85
MC CALL, Mark Jeffrey. 312 MIDLAND PKWY 29485 #047-06-1975 L1982 **PD** *020 †55
MC COY, James J. 93A SPRINGVIEW LN, SPORTS MEDICINE 29485 #035-06-1971 L1978 **ORS OSM** *020 †40
MONTOYA, Sara Blakely. 507 N LAUREL ST, PALMETTO PRIMARY CARE PHYS 29483 #045-01-1987 L1988 **FM** *020 †18
MORRIS, William Henry, Jr. 404 N PINE ST 29483 #045-01-1972 L1973 **GP** *020
MULROY, Constance Marie. 75 SPRINGVIEW LN, WOMENS HEALTH PARTNERS 29485 #036-05-1994 L2002 **OBG** *020 †30
O'CONNOR, Stephen Joseph. 295 MIDLAND PKWY, DEPT OF EMERGENCY MEDICINE 29485 #011-03-1998 L2004 **EM** *020 †16
OSBON, Timothy Barton. 295 MIDLAND PKWY, SUMMERVILLE MEDICAL CENTER 29485 #045-01-2002 L2004 **EM** *020 †16
OUZTS, Katharyn Butts. 295 MIDLAND PKWY 29485 #012-01-1973 L1975 **CHP P** *020 †75
PARKER, Edward C, Jr. 10160 DORCHESTER RD 29485 #021-01-1954 L1975 **GP PD** *071 †55
PELZER, Leslie Hubbard. 295 MIDLAND PKWY, SUMMERVILLE MEDICAL CENTER 29485 #045-01-1988 L1990 **EM FM** *020 †18
PENCE, John Wm. 1815 OLD TROLLEY RD, UNIT 111 29485 #047-06-1975 L1980 **PD** *020 †55
PRICE, William David. 133 E 1ST NORTH ST STE 3 29483 #036-07-1966 L1969 **OPH** *020 †35
PUTNEY, Floyd Witt. ■ 29483 #045-01-1973 L1975 **OBG** *071 †30
RAMSHUR, Scott Jarrett. 410 N MAIN ST, DOCTOR'S CARE - SUMMERVILL 29483 #012-01-2004 L2006 **FM** *100 †18
RIDDELL, Gladys May. ■ 29485 #919-01-1953 L1976 **PHP PD** *030 †55
ROBERTSON, Heather Ann. ■ 29485 #048-14-2003 L2005 **OBG** *020
ROBINSON, Russell Lloyd. ■ 29483 #045-01-1987 L1991 **IM** *071 †20
SABOM, Michael Shay. 10160 DORCHESTER RD 29485 #012-05-2000 L2004 **FM** *020 †18
SCHWAB, Lea T. 312 MIDLAND PKWY, SUMMERVILLE PEDIATRICS 29485 #047-06-1996 L1999 **PD** *020 †55
SCOTT, Roxane W. 106 SPRINGVIEW LN, SC DEPT OF MENTAL HEALTH 29485 #045-01-1997 L1999 **P** *020 †75
SIAS, Charles Robt. 435 N CEDAR ST 29483 #035-45-1941 L1971 **FM** *040 †18
SMITH, Burwell Riddick. 105 HARTH PL # A 29485 #045-01-1967 L1967 **PS GS** *020
SMITH, David Paul. 133 E 1ST NORTH ST STE 2 29483 #045-01-1986 L1989 **FM** *020 †18
SMITH, Walter E, Jr. 1525 OLD TROLLEY RD STE D, PMB 301 29485 #045-01-1984 L2002 **FM OS** *020 †18
SPEARMAN, James David. 93A SPRINGVIEW LN, SPORTS MEDICINE 29485 #045-01-1983 L1992 **ORS OSM** *020 †40
SUTTON, Kyrsten E. 75 SPRINGVIEW LN 29485 #010-02-1996 L2000 **OBG** *020 †30
TRAWICK, Wanda Moseley. ■ 29483 #021-05-1956 L1956 **OS** *074
WALSH, Norman Sinkler. 435 N CEDAR ST 29483 #045-01-1961 L1961 **GS** *071 †85
WARREN, Gerald Clemmie. 87 SPRINGVIEW LN, # A 29485 #045-01-1985 L1991 **GS VS** *020 †85
WAY, Granville Smith. 213 W 4TH NORTH 29483 #045-01-1954 L1954 **FM** *071
WEINSTEIN, Eric Steven. 402 BELLERIVE LN, ERIC S. WEINSTEIN MD 29483 #033-06-1987 L1993 **EM** *020 †16
WOOD, Samuel Earl. ■ 29483 #012-01-1967 L1968 **DR NM** *071 †80
WOOD, Vanessa Leigh. 709 TROLLEY RD 29485 #051-07-1999 L2003 **P** *020
YOUNGER, Deborah Ann. 295 MIDLAND PKWY 29485 #654-01-1987 L1990 **EM** *020 †18
ZELLNER, Eric Eugene. ■ 29485 #041-14-1974 L1975 **FM EM** *020 †16,18

SUMTER — SUMTER

ABBOTT, John Julian. 129 N WASHINGTON ST 29150 #045-01-1973 L1974 **IM** *020 †20
ALAN, Carol B. 1278 N LAFAYETTE DR 29150 #023-07-1997 L2001 **OBG** *020 †30
AMPHAN, Choncharoen. 129 N WASHINGTON ST 29150 #891-07-1991 L2003 **IM NEP** *020 †20
ANDERSON, Einar Wulfsberg. 129 N WASHINGTON ST 29150 #024-01-1968 L1983 **EM FM** *020 ‡
ANDERSON, Pauline M. 115 N SUMTER ST STE 110, OBGYN ASSOCIATES OF SUMTER 29150 #539-04-1971 L1986 **OBG** *020 †30
ANDREWS, Charles H, Jr. ■ 29150 #045-01-1943 L1943 **GS** *071
ANGUS, Floyd Lancelot. 540 PHYSICIANS LN 29150 #045-04-1997 L1998 **GE** *020 †20
ARSCOTT, Melissa Kennon. 237 CHURCH ST 29150 #045-01-1995 L1998 **PD** *020 †55
ATKISON, James Arthur. 208 W HAMPTON AVE 29150 #045-01-1982 L1994 **A PD** *020 †55,03
AYCOCK, Geo Calhoun, Jr. 295 LAKEWOOD DR 29150 #045-01-1978 L1981 **FM** *020 †18
BAILEY, Tracey Denise. 129 N WASHINGTON ST 29150 #047-20-1994 L1999 **EM** *020 †16
BARROW, Tawana Annette. 215 N MAGNOLIA ST, SANTEE WATEREE MHC 29150 #012-05-1997 L2001 **P** *020
BAY, John R. 2475 BROAD ST 29150 #038-06-1953 L1982 **IM FM** *071 †18
BELIN, Eric Jawaski. ■ 29150 #045-01-2004 **ORS** *012
BERMUDEZ, Jennifer Jane. 129 N WASHINGTON ST 29150 #038-40-2000 L2000 **P** *020 †75
BIBEAU, Guy Robt. 129 N WASHINGTON ST 29150 #045-01-1987 L1992 **FM** *020 †18
BLACK, Samuel Arthur. 129 N WASHINGTON ST 29150 #045-01-1968 L1968 **PM** *020 †40
BLANCHARD, Mary E. ■ 29150 #045-01-1952 L1952 **OBG** *071 †30
BLAND, Robert Purdy. 129 N WASHINGTON ST 29150 #023-07-1957 L1965 **OPH** *071 †35
BOHANON, Caroline Ann. ■ 29150 #005-19-1976 L1977 **DR** *020 †80
BRADFORD, Linwood Gray. 738 W LIBERTY ST STE B 29150 #045-01-1965 L1965 **D** *020
BRANDT, Philip Hansford. 244 CHURCH ST 29150 #051-04-1968 L1970 **IM** *020
BRANT, Russell Victor. 250 W WESMARK BLVD 29150 #017-20-1976 L1979 **EM** *020 †20
BRINGS, Hans Anthony. 115 N SUMTER ST, STE 300 29150 #023-12-1985 L2005 **VS GS** *020
BRITTON, John J. 115 N SUMTER ST, STE 200 29150 #045-01-1962 L1962 **GYN** *020 †30
BROWN, David Eugene, Jr. 365 W WESMARK BLVD 29150 #045-01-1973 L1975 **OPH** *071 †35
BRUNER, Allan Preston. 11 W CALHOUN ST 29150 #045-01-1957 L1957 **GP OS** *071

BRYANT, Earl Wood. 237 CHURCH ST 29150 #020-12-1970 L1979 PD *020 †55
BYRD, Eric Ravenel. ■ 29150 #045-01-1976 L1977 OM GP *020
CAIN, James Ravenel, III. 635 W WESMARK BLVD 29150 #045-01-1976 L1977 NEP IM *020 †20
CAMPBELL, Julius E, Jr. 220 BROAD ST 29150 #045-01-1951 L1951 FM EM *020
CANNON, Jimmie Dale, Jr. 540 PHYSICIANS LN 29150 #045-01-1987 L1990 CD PUD *020 †20
CLANTON, Garrett Martin. 129 N WASHINGTON ST 29150 #016-11-1994 L1997 EM *020 †16
CLOWNEY, Billy Wayne. 1105 N LAFAYETTE DR, SANTEE HEMATOLOGY ONCOLOGY 29150 #020-12-1988 L1990 ON HEM *020 †20
COMPTON, Arland Hasty. 430 N MAIN ST 29150 #045-01-1972 L1976 FM *020 †18
COOK, Galen Bruce. PO BOX 1628 29151 #028-02-1955 L1977 GS ON *071 †85
CORBIN, Saml Jacques, Jr. 18 BARNETTE DR 29150 #045-01-1967 L1967 GP *020
CRABBE, Linda Swain. 1215 ALICE DR 29150 #045-01-1982 L1992 PD *020 †55
CRABBE, Mark Mac Gregor. 115 N SUMTER ST 29150 #045-01-1982 L1992 GS TS *020 †85
CUCE, Frank Louis. ■ 29150 #018-75-1992, ▲ L2006 ORS *020
CULBERTSON, Gary Randall. 18 MILLER RD 29150 #048-14-1984 L1994 PS GS *020 †85,65 ‡
CUNNINGHAM, Kent Newton. 540 PHYSICIANS LN 29150 #016-11-1988 L1989 GE IM *020 †20
DAVIS, Harry A, Jr. ■ 29150 #041-02-1944 L1946 OM GP *071
DAVIS, Marion H, Jr. ■ 29150 #045-04-1990 L1991 FM *020 †18
DENNIS, Ronnie Wayne. 319 N MAIN ST, WOMENS HLTHCARE OF SUMTER 29150 #045-04-1984 L1988 OBG *020 †30
DENNY, Richard Lee. 1278 N LAFAYETTE DR, SUMTER FAMILY HEALTH CENTE 29150 #036-05-1971 L1972 PTH *020 †18
DICKERSON, Gene Franklin. 115 N SUMTER ST 29150 #020-12-1977 L1982 GS *020 †85
DILTS, George Scot. 129 N WASHINGTON ST 29150 #038-43-1994 L1997 EM *020 †16
DINKINS, Teresa Lynn. 237 CHURCH ST 29150 #045-04-1998 L1999 PD *020 †55
DRAKEFORD, Michael Keith. 595 W WESMARK BLVD 29150 #045-01-1982 L1983 ORS *020 †40
DU BOSE, Edward M, Jr. 240 CHURCH ST 29150 #045-01-1972 L1975 FM EM *020 †18
DUBOSE, Macdonald Mayes. 240 CHURCH ST 29150 #045-04-2000 L2001 FPG *020 †18
DUFFY, Edward W. 130 N WASHINGTON ST 29150 #045-01-1989 L1992 RO *020 †80
DU RANT, James M, Jr. 237 CHURCH ST 29150 #045-01-1976 L1977 PD *020 †55
ELLETT, James Wiley. 115 N SUMTER ST, STE 300 29150 #036-07-1973 L1975 GS TS *020 †85
EVANGELISTI, Paul Andrew. 100 N SUMTER ST, STE 400 29150 #035-15-1991 L2001 OTO *020 †45
FINLEY, Philip Alan. 129 N WASHINGTON ST, TUOMEY REGIONAL MED CTR 29150 #051-01-1977 L1978 PTH *020 †50
FITES, Brandon Sean. 100 N SUMTER ST, STE 200 29150 #017-20-2000 L2006 OSM *100
FITES, Terri Lynn. 129 N WASHINGTON ST 29150 #017-20-2002 L2006 FM *020 †18
FLEMING, John Russell, Jr. 115 N SUMTER ST STE 315 29150 #020-12-1996 L1999 FM *020 †18
FORD, Danny Howard. 100 N SUMTER ST, STE 200 29150 #004-01-1993 L1998 ORS *020 †40
GEE, James Eugene. 1215 ALICE DR 29150 #012-05-1965 L1970 ORS *020 †40
GIVENS, Lea Burnett. 244 CHURCH ST 29150 #036-05-1952 L1959 IM *020 †20
GOODSON, James Arthur, III. 365 W WESMARK BLVD 29150 #045-04-1993 L1997 OPH *020 †35
GRAY, Auston Hawkins, Jr. 1250 WILSON HALL RD, SUMTER PSYCHIATRY ASSOCIAT 29150 #012-01-1995 L1997 P *020
GRUNSKY, Mitchell Robert. 325 BROAD ST, STE 100 29150 #045-04-2001 L2004 FM *100
HAYNIE, William Ransom. ■ 29150 #045-01-1960 L1960 R *071 †80
HEPFER, Thomas Willard. 115 N SUMTER ST, STE 200 29150 #045-01-1974 L1976 OBG *020 †30
HIOTT, James Capers. 6 BARNETTE DR 29150 #045-01-1964 L1964 OTO *071 †45
INGRAM, James Roper. 738 W LIBERTY ST STE A 29150 #045-01-1974 L1976 FM FPG *020 †18
JACKSON, Jerry Eugene. 410 W WESMARK BLVD 29150 #045-01-1968 L1968 U *071 †95
JACOCKS, Charles West, IV. 540 PHYSICIANS LN 29150 #047-05-1986 L1988 IM CD *020 †20
JACOCKS, Mitchell Wells. 540 PHYSICIANS LN 29150 #045-04-1992 L1999 ICE CD *020 †20
JORDAN, Harry Alton, Jr. 115 N SUMTER ST, STE 115 29150 #045-01-1990 L1991 IM *020 †20
JUDY, Carrie Anne. ■ 29150 #041-14-2002 L2004 FM *020 †18
JUSTICE, David Alan. 215 N MAGNOLIA ST 29150 #045-04-1991 L1992 P *020 †75
KAMATH, Jayaram Kaup. 129 N WASHINGTON ST 29150 #495-37-1964 L2005 GS *020 †85
KAY, James Edward. 129 N WASHINGTON ST 29150 #045-01-1967 L1967 AN GP *020 †05
KEY, Timothy Lane. 237 CHURCH ST 29150 #045-01-1985 L1986 PD *020 †55
KINCADE, Tessa Annell. 115 N SUMTER ST, STE 200 29150 #027-01-1996 L2000 OBG *020 †30
KING, Gregory Alan. 365 W WESMARK BLVD 29150 #047-06-1993 L2002 OPH *020 †35
KING, William Anthony. 533 OXFORD ST 29150 #023-01-1963 L1969 P *020
KORANLOO, Kamran Zargham. 764 W LIBERTY ST, STE 3 29150 #517-05-1995 L2002 AN PME *020
LATHAM, Eliz Hood Boykin. ■ 29150 #045-01-1950 L1963 PD *071 †55
LATHAM, Helen Demos. 115 N SUMTER ST, STE 200 29150 #045-01-1988 L1989 OBG *020 †30
LATHAM, Phillip Lane, Jr. 325 BROAD ST STE 200 29150 #045-01-1988 L1989 D *020 †15
LAUZON, Steven Charles. 115 N SUMTER ST 29150 #305-01-1998 L2006 GS *020 †85
LECHER, Brian Robert. 3440 DECLARATION BLVD, FASTER CARE, INC. 29154 #028-79-1999, ▲ L2003 EM *020
LEE, Robert Edward. 410 W WESMARK BLVD 29150 #025-01-1968 L1978 U *020 †95
LEONARD, Jason Michael. 325 BROAD ST 29150 #020-02-2004 L2004 FM *020 †18
LEVI, W Mitchell, III. 129 N WASHINGTON ST, TUOMEY REG MED CENTER 29150 #045-01-1992 L1993 AN *020 †05
LEVI, Wendell Mitchell. 129 N WASHINGTON ST 29150 #045-01-1954 L1954 GS TS *071 †85
LI, Yongxin. 635 W WESMARK BLVD, SUMTER MEDICAL SPECIALISTS 29150 #243-77-1982 L1998 IM *020 †20
LILAVIVAT, Usah. 635 W WESMARK BLVD 29150 #891-02-1970 L1981 DIA END *020 †20
LONG, Charles Wm. 291 KEELS RD 29154 #004-01-1976 L1977 CHP P *020 †75
LOVICE, David Brian. 100 N SUMTER ST, STE 400 29150 #051-07-1992 L1998 FPS OTO *020 †45
LOWDER, Clayton Ralph, III. 325 BROAD ST, STE 100 29150 #045-04-1993 L1994 FM *020 †18
MADSEN, Jill Mitchell. ■ 29150 #018-03-1991 L1992 PTH *020 †50
MAHR, Christopher Michael. 1278 N LAFAYETTE DR 29150 #654-01-2002 L2005 FM *020 †18
MARDESICH, Patrick M. 698A BULTMAN DR, CAROLINA EYE CARE SUMTER 29150 #005-06-1991 L2001 OPH *020 †35
MC COLLOUGH, Wilmot S, III. 129 N WASHINGTON ST 29150 #045-01-1981 L1982 IM *020 †20
MC DOWELL, Robert Ernest. ■ 29150 #045-01-1957 L1957 OM *071
MC DUFFIE, Scott Ramsey. 540 PHYSICIANS LN 29150 #036-01-1991 L1996 GE *020 †20
MCFADDIN, Ansel Rose, III. 115 N SUMTER ST, STE 115 29150 #045-01-1990 L1991 IM *020 †20
MEASE, Michael Richard. 129 N WASHINGTON ST 29150 #041-01-1995 L2000 DR *020 †80
MESHEL, Ellyn Schreibman. 129 N WASHINGTON ST, TUOMEY HOSPITAL - EMERGENC 29150 #016-42-1990 L2006 EM IM *020 †20
MEYERS, Edward Julian. 3440 DECLARATION BLVD, FASTER CARE 29154 #038-44-1999 L2006 EM *020 †16
MITCHINER, John M. 237 CHURCH ST 29150 #048-02-1994 L1996 PD *020 †55
MOSES, Henry Phillips. 115 N SUMTER ST 29150 #012-05-1980 L1989 GS *020 †85
MOSS, Charles Eugene. 410 W WESMARK BLVD 29150 #021-01-1979 L1993 U *020 †95
MUNIZ, Luis E. 129 N WASHINGTON ST 29150 #042-01-1980 L1985 EM GP *020
OGUNFOWORA, Ayodele A. 215 N MAGNOLIA ST, PO BOX 1946 29150 #690-01-1989 L1999 P *020
OKEKE, Alfred E. 635 W WESMARK BLVD 29150 #690-04-1987 L2000 END *020 †20
OKEREKE, Ugochukwu N. 325 W LIBERTY ST 29150 #690-04-1990 L2000 IM *020 †20
PANNELL, Tammy Elizabeth. 129 N WASHINGTON ST 29150 #045-01-1987 L1992 IM *020 †20
PANNELL, Timothy Len. 129 N WASHINGTON ST 29150 #045-01-1987 L1991 DR *020 †80
PARKER, Gilbert E, Jr. 129 N WASHINGTON ST 29150 #045-01-1989 L1994 DR *020 †80
PATEL, Narendra Chhota. ■ 29150 #495-46-1984 L1997 IM *020 †20
PATRICK, Richard Thomas. 129 N WASHINGTON ST, TOUMEY MEDICAL CENTER 29150 #045-01-1995 L1998 DR VIR *020 †80
PETER, Carl Wehr, Jr. ■ 29153 #308-11-1984 L1989 FM *075 †18
PINILLA, Osmar Adolfo. 129 N WASHINGTON ST 29150 #847-04-1967 L1974 PTH *020 †50
PINTO, Vijay Paul. 410 W WESMARK BLVD 29150 #041-13-1999 L2005 U *100 †95
POMMERENKE, Forrest A. 1215 ALICE DR 29150 #019-02-1975 L2001 IM *020 †70
POWELL, Jesse W, Jr. 129 N WASHINGTON ST 29150 #036-05-1999 L2000 HMP *020 †50
RABON, Catherine Ezell. 129 N WASHINGTON ST 29150 #045-01-1996 L1998 IM *020 †20
RASUL, Muhammad Fayyaz. 220 BROAD ST, DOCTOR'S CARE 29150 #704-01-1987 L1997 PDC *020 †55
REESE, Cynthia S. 115 N SUMTER ST, STE 315 29150 #012-01-1983 L2002 FM *020 †18
REYNOLDS, Andrew James. 244 CHURCH ST 29150 #045-01-1996 L2002 IM *020 †20
RHAME, John M. ■ 29150 #045-01-1944 L1944 GP *071
RHYNE, Linda Hunter. 250 W WESMARK BLVD, INDUSTRIAL MEDICINE & WELL 29150 #045-01-1979 L1980 EM *020 †16
RIDDLE, Samuel Marvin, III. 115 N SUMTER ST, STE 200 29150 #045-01-1978 L1986 OBG *020 †30
ROSEFIELD, Martin K, Jr. 129 N WASHINGTON ST 29150 #045-01-1964 L1964 R NM *020 †80
ROWE, John Elliott, III. 237 CHURCH ST 29150 #045-01-1961 L1961 PD *020 †55
SINEATH, Marvin Hubert, Jr. 1450 CROWNDALE DR, 20TH MEDICAL GROUP 29150 #045-01-2003 L2005 FM *020 †18
SKINNER, Ada Kathleen. ■ 29153 #038-40-1969 L1990 EM *020 †16 ‡
SMITH, George Murrell. 115 N SUMTER ST, STE 200 29150 #045-01-1972 L1973 OBG *020 †30
SMITH, Laurie Nicholas. ■ 29150 #045-01-1960 L1960 AN *071
SMITH, Triz Van. ■ 29150 #045-04-2003 L2004 OBG *020
STANFORD, Jon Lawrence. 115 N SUMTER ST 29150 #038-40-1996 L2003 GS CCS *020 †85
STAVROU, William Strat. 540 PHYSICIANS LN 29150 #045-01-1975 L1976 CD IM *020 †20
STEWART, Ike Christopher. 220 BROAD ST, TUOMEY HOSPITAL 29150 #041-14-2002 L2005 FM *020 †18
STODDARD, Hugh Toland. 244 CHURCH ST 29150 #036-05-1972 L1975 IM *020
STROEBEL, Kurt Thrall. 115 N SUMTER ST, STE 110 29150 #038-40-1989 L1995 ORS OSM *020 †40
STURGIS, Nelson H, III. 1278 N LAFAYETTE DR, SUMTER FAM HLTH CTR 29150 #050-02-1968 L1992 PD AM *020 †55
SUCHINDA, Pusadee. 635 W WESMARK BLVD 29150 #891-02-1970 L1981 NEP IM *020 †20
TANTAWANICHPISAL, D. 129 N WASHINGTON ST 29150 #891-07-1990 L2003 IM *020 †20
THOMAS, Derek Raphael. 213 W HAMPTON AVE 29150 #010-03-1991 L1997 CD *020 †20
ULRICH, Robert F. 308 W WESMARK BLVD, SOUTHEAST NEUROLOGY 29150 #048-78-1998, ▲ L2005 N *020 †75
WAGNER, Timothy Ronald. 595 W WESMARK BLVD 29150 #041-13-1975 L1979 ORS *020 †40
WALL, Richard Arthur, Jr. 115 N SUMTER ST, STE 315 29150 #045-01-2003 L2004 FM *100 †18
WANG, Deli. 1105 N LAFAYETTE DR, STE B 29150 #243-43-1983 L1999 FM END *020 †70
WARRICK, Michael Todd. 129 N WASHINGTON ST, C/O SUMTER PAIN & SPINE, L 29150 #045-01-2002 L2007 APM *020 †05
WARRICK, Pressley W. ■ 29150 #045-01-2003 L2007 CHP *012
WASHINGTON, Lorone C. 129 N WASHINGTON ST, TUOMEY HEALTH CARE - EMERG 29150 #045-04-2002 L2005 EM *100 †16
WATKINS, William Curtis. 105 N MAGNOLIA ST, WATEREE DISTRICT OFFICE 29150 #045-01-1957 L1957 PD *071 †55
WHALEY, David Glenn, Jr. 325 BROAD ST, STE 100 29150 #036-01-1996 L1997 FM *020 †18
WHETSELL, Carl Gene. 237 CHURCH ST 29150 #045-01-1985 L1986 PD *020 †55
WHITE, Charles Herman, Jr. 540 PHYSICIANS LN 29150 #045-01-1976 L1979 PUD IM *020 †20
WHITE, Marshall Allyn. 312 BROAD ST, SUMTER NEUROLOGY & PAIN MG 29150 #045-04-1986 L1987 N *020 †75
WILLIAMS, Barney Levy, Jr. 115 N SUMTER ST, STE 200 29150 #045-01-1962 L1962 OBG *020 †30
WILLIAMS, Brenda Chapman. 448 N MAIN ST 29150 #012-01-1978 L1979 GP *020
WILLIAMS, David C. 20TH MEDICAL GROUP, SHAW AFB 29150 #012-01-1970 L1991 GS *020 †85
WILLIAMS, Joseph Cecil. 448 N MAIN ST 29150 #012-01-1977 L1979 IM IMG *020 †20
WILLIAMS, Theophilus, III. 540 PHYSICIANS LN 29150 #045-01-1975 GE IM *071 †20
WILSON, Timothy Mark. 630 PORTSMOUTH DR 29150 #012-01-1988 L1995 AN *020 †05
YOUNG, William Frederick. 237 CHURCH ST 29150 #041-01-1954 L1954 PD *071 †55

SUNSET - PICKENS

MILLER, Carter F, Jr. 802 TOP RIDGE DR 29685 #047-06-1958 L1959 PTH CLP *071 †50
ROGERS, Sherry Hammond. ■ 29685 #035-15-1969 L1970 A NTR *020 †18 ‡

SURFSIDE BEACH - HORRY

BALDRIDGE, Paul Lincoln. 1120 GLENNS BAY RD, STE 120 29575 #041-12-1984 L1988 PD *020 †55
BESTIC, Philip B. 1120 GLENNS BAY RD STE 101 29575 #654-01-1990 L1994 IM *020 †20
CARLAN, Susanne Stanley. PO BOX 5037 29587 #036-05-1967 L1967 FM *074
DENTON, John Fredric. 1600 HIGHWAY 17 N 29575 #051-04-1959 L1983 OM GP *071

EGGART, Jeff Lionel. 1945 GLENNS BAY RD 29575 #021-06-1978 L1980 **OBG** *020 †30
GAUTHIER, Mark Allan. 1600 HIGHWAY 17 N 29575 #030-05-1988 L1991 **EM** *020 †16
HUGHES, James Chalmers. 1600 HIGHWAY 17 N, STE 310 29575 #045-01-1957 L1957 **GP GS** *071 †85
HUGHES, James Richard. 1600 HIGHWAY 17 N 29575 #308-11-1983 L1996 **EM FM** *020 †18
MOORE, Kristin Emily. 1120 GLENNS BAY RD, STE 120 29575 #001-02-1995 L1997 **PD** *020 †55
MUNTEAN, Dan. 1413 HIGHWAY 17 N, PRIMARY MEDICAL ASSOCIATES 29575 #781-04-1994 L2006 **FM** *020 †18
O'BRIEN, Mary E. ■ 29575 #024-16-1980 L1982 **IM** *020 †20
RATLIFF, John M, Jr. ■ 29575 #051-04-1943 L1943 **R** *071 †80
SMITH, Ronnie Dale. 1600 HIGHWAY 17 N, DOCTORS CARE SURFSIDE 29575 #036-01-1978 L1980 **GP GS** *020
TOMLINSON, Alfred Jess. 1120 GLENNS BAY RD STE 106 29575 #035-08-1982 L1986 **OPH** *020 †35
VEST, James Marvin. PO BOX 14340 29587 #025-12-1984 L1987 **FM** *020 †18
WOOD, Ivey Francis, Jr. ■ 29575 #045-01-1972 L1973 **GP** *071

SWANSEA — LEXINGTON

BLIZZARD, Dale. 935 W 2ND ST, LEXINGTON MED CNTR SWANSEA 29160 #045-04-1997 L1999 **FM** *020 †18 ‡
CLEMENZ, Layne Richard. 935 W 2ND ST 29160 #045-01-1984 L1985 **DR** *020 †80
DAVIS, Clarence S, III. 935 W 2ND ST 29160 #045-01-1981 L1982 **DR** *020 †80
EDENFIELD, William Perry. 935 W 2ND ST 29160 #045-01-1994 L1996 **DR** *020 †80
HAMBY, Lon Powell. 935 W 2ND ST 29160 #001-02-1976 L1980 **DR** *020 †80
HAYNES, John William. 935 W 2ND ST 29160 #025-07-1977 L1984 **DR R** *020 †80
HOOD, Charles Guy. 935 W 2ND ST 29160 #045-04-1987 L1991 **DR** *020 †80
HUDSON, Edwin Robt. 935 W 2ND ST 29160 #047-20-1987 L1997 **DR** *020 †80
KNIGHT, David Neal. 935 W 2ND ST 29160 #012-05-1994 L1999 **VIR R** *020 †80
MC CARTY, Christopher T. 935 W 2ND ST 29160 #038-41-1995 L2000 **RNR** *020 †80
MC GUIRE, Keith Alan. 935 W 2ND ST 29160 #021-01-1993 L2003 **DR** *020 †80
MORGAN, Patrick Montague. 935 W SECOND ST 29160 #422-01-1995 L1998 **FM** *020 †18
PATEL, Rajantiben N. 935 W 2ND ST, AT SWANSEA 29160 #045-01-1991 L1994 **IM** *020
PERTILE, Ariel Alejandro. 935 W 2ND ST 29160 #045-04-2000 L2006 **AR** *020 †80
PIA, Edwin Potes. 935 W 2ND ST 29160 #055-01-1995 L1996 **DR** *020 †80
SIROTY-SMITH, Beth Michel. 935 W 2ND ST 29160 #023-01-1990 L1995 **DR** *020 †80
THOMAS, Albert Patrick. 935 W 2ND ST 29160 #045-01-1955 L1955 **OBG OS** *071
WHITEHEAD, James D, Jr. 935 W 2ND ST 29160 #045-01-1968 L1968 **DR** *020 †80

TAYLORS — GREENVILLE

ANDERSON, Albert Severin. 3110 WADE HAMPTON BLVD, 19 GALLERY CENTRE 29687 #035-09-1955 L1973 **A NTR** *071
EBERLY, John Brewer. 4501 OLD SPARTANBURG RD 29687 #045-04-1989 L1990 **FM** *020 †18
FEW, Brian Keith. 4501 OLD SPARTANBURG RD, STE 9 29687 #045-04-1997 L1998 **PD** *020 †55
HARRIS, Roslyn Hayes. 3551 RUTHERFORD RD 29687 #051-04-1994 L1996 **FM** *020 †18
HUNT, Laura A Foster. 3551A RUTHERFORD RD 29687 #045-01-1994 L1996 **FM EM** *020 †18
MAGES, Roy Anthony. 4501 OLD SPARTANBURG RD, STE 9 29687 #047-06-2001 L2003 **PD** *020 †55
MEARES, Cecil H, Jr. ■ 29687 #039-01-1952 L1952 **GS TS** *071 †85
NORVELL, Marisa Smith. ■ 29687 #020-02-1996 L1998 **FM** *075 †18
OTUBU, Oritsetimeyin E. 2801 WADE HAMPTON BLVD, STE 115 29687 #041-07-1996 L1997 **FM** *020 †18
RUGHANI, Govind N. 56 SAINT MARK RD, PEACE MEDICAL CENTER 29687 #495-20-1978 L1992 **IM** *020 †20
SCHULTZ, Carolyn Gardner. 4501 OLD SPARTANBURG RD, STE 9 29687 #045-01-1999 L2000 **PD** *020 †55
SMITH, Kevin Stewart. 400 W MAIN ST, TAYLORS FAMILY PRACTICE 29687 #047-05-1982 L1991 **GS** *020
ZEAGER, Michael Eugene. 3551 RUTHERFORD RD 29687 #045-01-1979 L1980 **FM** *020 †18

TEGA CAY — YORK

MATEO, Guillermo. 7126 TOPSAIL CIR 29708 #016-02-1948 L1954 **IM** *020

TIMMONSVILLE — FLORENCE

JACKSON-DOZIER, Focell I. 755 E SMITH ST 29161 #045-01-1995 L1996 **FM** *020 †18

TOWNVILLE — ANDERSON

DOBBINS, William Lee. 450 FRED DOBBINS RD 29689 #045-01-1973 L1974 **EM** *020 †16
GOODWIN, Ben A. ■ 29689 #048-12-1949 L1950 **P** *071 †75

TRAVELERS REST — GREENVILLE

CADDELL, Titus Danl. 907 N MAIN ST, NORTH GREENVILLE MED CTR 29690 #045-01-1984 L1985 **FM** *020 †18
COLEMAN, Stanley I, Jr. 9 MCELHANEY RD 29690 #045-01-1984 L1985 **FM** *020 †18
ECARMA, Romeo Abella. ■ 29690 #748-09-1961 *100
ENRIGHT, Gretchen Lorig. 1 HAVENWOOD LN, SPRINGBROOK HOSPITAL 29690 #038-45-1986 L1992 **CHP P** *020 ‡
GETTYS, James Boulware. 9 MCELHANEY RD 29690 #045-01-2000 L2003 **FM** *020 †18
GOLD, Fred Martin. ■ 29690 #024-07-1961 L1965 **U** *020 †95
HOLLIDAY, John H. ■ 29690 #045-01-1950 L1950 **FM** *071 †18
KING, Fitzwilliam W. 406 N POINSETT HWY, TRAVELERS REST FAMILY CARE 29690 #041-14-1971 L1974 **FM AM** *020 †18
LEE, Christy Michelle. ■ 29690 #045-01-2008 *012
LUCAS, John Thos. ■ 29690 #045-01-1974 L1975 **NS** *071 †25

MC CARRELL, Landrum I, Jr. 9 MCELHANEY RD 29690 #045-01-1981 L1982 **FM** *020 †18
MINA, Albert Charles. 406 N POINSETT HWY, TRAVELERS REST FAMILY CARE 29690 #045-01-1995 L2001 **FM** *020 †18
PADALIYA, Bimal Bhupatrai. ■ 29690 #047-05-2006 L2006 **IM** *012
STAMLER, Arthur A. ■ 29690 #045-01-1949 L1968 **PD** *071 †55
STEPHENS, Julie G. 406 N POINSETT HWY 29690 #045-01-2001 L2004 **FM** *020 †18
STINE, Harold Emerson. ■ 29690 #017-20-1966 L1966 **DR** *020 †80

TURBEVILLE — CLARENDON

BURGESS, Clinton. ■ 29162 #030-05-1987 L1990 **GP** *075
SMITH, Kate Elizabeth. PO BOX 206, 944 SMITH ST 29162 #045-01-1963 L1963 **FM** *020 †18

UNION — UNION

ALL, Wanda Richardson. ■ 29379 #045-04-1985 L1986 **PD** *020 †55
BARKER, Frederick W. 407 W SOUTH ST STE B, CAROLINAS HEALTH ASSOCIATE 29379 #055-01-1981 L2007 **GS** *020 †85
BEARDEN, James D, III. 407 W SOUTH ST 29379 #045-01-1969 L1969 **ON HO** *020 †20
BUTLER, Margot Blaidsell. 407 W SOUTH ST, ADOLESCENT MEDICINE 29379 #051-07-1994 L1999 **PD** *020 †55
CARTER, James Wm. 322 W SOUTH ST 29379 #012-01-1986 L1988 **FM** *020 †18
CLARK, Terence Mather. 322 W SOUTH ST 29379 #035-06-1971 L1978 **DR GYN** *020 †80
COOKE, Alisahah Janell. ■ 29379 #038-45-2004 L2007 **FM** *020 †18
CRUMLIN, Lindsey Eugene. 319 W SOUTH ST 29379 #023-07-1983 L2003 **GS** *020 †85
DARAMOLA, John Bamidele. 1005 THOMPSON BLVD 29379 #690-01-1995 L2002 **IM** *020 †20
DUA, Anterpreet Singh. 322 W SOUTH ST, WALLACE THOMSON HOSPITAL 29379 #495-29-1991 L2004 **AN** *020 †05
FIELDER, Gerald Dexter. 127 E MAIN ST 29379 #004-01-1952 L1953 **FM** *020 †18
FLOOD, Matthew John. 801 W MAIN ST 29379 #045-04-1991 L1992 **FM OBS** *020 †18
HAMES, Boyd L. 429 E MAIN ST 29379 #045-01-1951 L1951 **FM** *071 †18
HOBBS, La Floyd H, Jr. 167 AUSTIN RD, TIME AWAY MEDSPA 29379 #036-01-1974 L1984 **OBG** *020 †30
JAMES, William Stanford. ■ 29379 #045-01-1959 L1959 **DR** *071 †80
KEITH, David Martin. 429 E MAIN ST 29379 #045-01-1976 L1977 **FM** *020 †18
KINCHELOE, Robert Lee, Jr. 100 BEVERLY DR 29379 #041-12-1967 L1996 **ORS** *020 †40
LUTZ, Robert Brian. 720 S DUNCAN BYP 29379 #005-12-1982 L2007 **OBG** *020 †30
MACATUNO, Edifel Nacu. 407 W SOUTH ST, ADOLESCENT MEDICINE 29379 #748-08-1988 L2003 **PD** *020 †55
MCWHORTER, Christopher Ro. 429 E MAIN ST 29379 #422-01-2001 L2004 **FM** *020 †18
MILLER, W Lance. 322 W SOUTH ST 29379 #023-01-1995 L1996 **FM** *020 †18
PRICE, Ronald Wayne. 322 W SOUTH ST 29379 #045-01-1983 L1985 **IM** *020 †20
SANFORD, Harold W. 322 W SOUTH ST 29379 #045-01-1965 L1965 **DR** *020 †80
SINGH, Harmohan. 322 W SOUTH ST, WALLACE THOMPSON HOSPITAL 29379 #495-43-1988 L2001 **IM** *020 †20
STOCKINGER, Helen M. 1005 THOMPSON BLVD 29379 #045-04-1985 L1988 **IM** *020 †20
SWITZER, Paul K, Jr. PO BOX 603 29379 #045-01-1941 L1941 **IM** *071 †20
WASHINGTON, Tonya Renee. 801 W MAIN ST, THE CENTER FOR FAMILY HLTH 29379 #047-07-1997 L2001 **FM** *020 †18
WENTZ, Robert Merritt. 429 E MAIN ST, P O BOX 70 29379 #021-01-1963 L1963 **GP** *020 †18
WHITT, Suzanne Balliett. 322 W SOUTH ST 29379 #045-04-1988 L1989 **FM** *020 †18
WIGGINS, James Thos. 2502 SANTUCK HWY 29379 #045-01-1960 **PD** *071
WILSON, James Robt. 322 W SOUTH ST 29379 #045-01-1954 L1955 **EM GS** *072 †85,90
YANNETTI, Robert Anthony. 408 N DUNCAN BYP, STE L 29379 #045-01-1982 L1985 **IM** *020 †20
YIRENKYI, Emmanuel Awuku. 1005 THOMPSON BLVD, CAROLINA INTERNAL MEDICINE 29379 #275-01-1995 L2007 **IM** *020

VANCE — ORANGEBURG

BROADHEAD, Alfred Wright. 10280 OLD HWY 6, COMMUNITY MEDICAL CENTER 29163 #067-01-1970 L1994 **FM** *071 †18

VARNVILLE — HAMPTON

ARMSTRONG, Brent Alan. 595 W CAROLINA AVE 29944 #045-01-2000 L2001 **EM** *020 †18
BOWER, Philip Jeffrey. 595 W CAROLINA AVE, COASTAL PLAINS PHYSICIAN 29944 #023-07-1961 L2001 **CD IM** *020 †20
CERAME, Mario Anthony. 595 W CAROLINA AVE, COASTAL PLAINS PHYSICIAN A 29944 #561-17-1982 L2008 **GS VS** *020 †85
CORDERO-PORRAS, Carlos A. 595 W CAROLINA AVE, COASTAL PLAINS PHYSICIAN 29944 #935-02-1994 L2002 **IM** *020
KORECKIJ, Theodore. 595 W CAROLINA AVE, COASTAL PLAINS PHYSICIAN 29944 #008-02-1976 L2007 **ORS** *020 †40 ‡
MONTENEGRO, Carlos Eloy. 595 W CAROLINA AVE, COASTAL PLAINS PHYSICIAN 29944 #319-01-1988 L2002 **GS VS** *020 †85
ROMAN, Horatius. 595 W CAROLINA AVE, COASTAL PLAINS PHYSICIAN 29944 #781-01-1983 L2003 **AN CCA** *020 †05
SHEALY, Neal Luther. 503 W CAROLINA AVE 29944 #045-01-1979 L1980 **FM** *020 †18
TEMPLETON, Archibald W. 595 W CAROLINA AVE 29944 #030-05-1957 L1981 **R** *071 †80
WARREN, Edward, III. 595 W CAROLINA AVE 29944 #045-01-1974 L1976 **DR** *072 †80
WELDON, Harvey W. ■ 29944 #041-13-1951 L1978 **GS CRS** *071 †85

WADMALAW ISLAND — CHARLESTON

ANDERSON, Kenneth A. ■ 29487 #045-01-1993 L1997 **AN** *020 †05
BEALE, Mark Douglas. 6670 BEARS BLUFF RD 29487 #051-07-1989 L1991 **P** *020 †75
KOUTEN, Joseph Wm, Jr. ■ 29487 #041-09-1961 L1994 **ORS** *020 †40
MAYER, John Alan. ■ 29487 #020-02-1966 L1967 **R GP** *071
RICHBOURG, Miller N. ■ 29487 #045-01-1956 L1956 **AN** *071
RUTLAND, Eugene D, Jr. ■ 29487 #047-06-1960 L1978 **PTH CLP** *071 †50

■ = Address Information Privacy Protected

WALHALLA – OCONEE

BRODOFF, Bernard Noah. 103 WHITETAIL DR, P O BOX 529 29691 #035-19-1946 L1991 **CD IM** *020 †20
COCHRAN, James Walter N. 111 N EARLE ST 29691 #045-04-1990 L1991 **FM** *020 †18
DARBY, Wm Strother, Jr. 103 WHITETAIL DR, HIGHWAY 28 29691 #045-01-1974 L1976 **GP** *020

WALTERBORO – COLLETON

ACKERMAN, Riddick. 400 CONSTANCE ST 29488 #045-04-1982 L1983 **OBG** *020 †30
ALANIS, Mark Christopher. 501 ROBERTSON BLVD, COLLETON MEDICAL CENTER 29488 #048-13-2003 L2007 **OBG** *100
ARRAS, Milton John, Jr. PO BOX 1123 29488 #027-01-1964 L1999 **PTH CLP** *075 †50
BAUMGART, Judy Rebecca. 304 MEDICAL PARK DR 29488 #005-14-1972 L2003 **AN** *020 †05
BIGGERS, John Frank, III. 124 MEDICAL PARK DR 29488 #045-01-1971 L1972 **IM MDM** *020 †20
BLUBAUGH, Michael L. 461 SPRUCE ST 29488 #048-02-1996 L1997 **IM** *020 †20
BOATWRIGHT, John Garlandp. 459 SPRUCE ST, CAROLINA EYE CARE 29488 #051-01-1985 L1986 **OPH** *020 †35
BRAME, Robert Griffin, Jr. 459 SPRUCE ST, CAROLINA EYE CARE 29488 #036-07-1982 L1984 **OPH FM** *020 †35
BRANDLI, David William. 302 MEDICAL PARK DR, STE 207 29488 #041-14-1997 L2003 **UP** *020 †95
BRIDGES, Emily Dodd. 406 ROBERTSON BLVD, LOWCOUNTRY FAMILY MEDICINE 29488 #045-01-1987 L1992 **FM ATP** *020 †18
CALCUTT, Andrew Fenters. 901 ROBERTSON BLVD 29488 #045-01-1990 L1998 **GS SO** *020 †85
CALCUTT, Vonda Gilgen. 16 NORTHSIDE DR, LOW CNTRY CTR-DIAB & ENDCL 29488 #045-01-1991 L1998 **END IM** *020 †20
CANNON, Trent Edward. 400 CONSTANCE ST 29488 #036-05-1979 L1980 **OBG** *020 †30
CARNOHAN, Peter Scott. 415 ROBERTSON BLVD STE B 29488 #045-01-2000 L2001 **IM** *020 †20 ‡
CHIODO, Albino A. 103 REBECCA LN 29488 #065-01-1991 L1997 **OTO** *020
CREEL, John Glen. 447 SPRUCE ST 29488 #045-01-1999 L2000 **FM** *020 †18 ‡
DE MARCO, Lucinda. 501 ROBERTSON BLVD, PEDIATRICS 29488 #305-01-1985 L2007 **PD** *020 †55
DUKES, Robert Raymond. 501 ROBERTSON BLVD 29488 #036-08-1989 L1994 **AN** *020 †05
ERWIN, Luke Latimer. ■ 29488 #045-01-1956 L1956 **GP** *071
FENDER, William E, Jr. 501 ROBERTSON BLVD 29488 #045-01-1952 L1952 **GS GP** *071
FERVIL, Marie-Yolene. 461 SPRUCE ST, ATTN: CREDENTIALING DEPT. 29488 #011-02-1997 L2005 **IM** *020 †20
FLOWERS, Joseph Francis. 107 CHURCH ST 29488 #045-01-1961 L1961 **FM GS** *020 †18 ‡
GERSBACH, Jeffrey Clark. 501 ROBERTSON BLVD 29488 #051-04-1984 L1990 **EM** *020
GOULDING, Frederick James. 302 MEDICAL PARK DR, STE 207 29488 #017-20-1971 L1976 **U** *020 †95
GRABOWSKI, Kathleen Ann. 600 PADGETT LOOP 29488 #045-01-1994 L1995 **IM** *020
GRANT, Cheryl Antionette. 416 ROBERTSON BLVD STE D, EDISTO PEDIATRICS 29488 #045-01-2001 L2004 **PD** *020 †55
GRANT, Paul Murray. 459 SPRUCE ST, CAROLINA EYE CARE 29488 #041-12-1969 L1975 **OPH** *020 †35
GREGORY, Jonathan Mark. 415 ROBERTSON BLVD STE C, COLLETON HEART CENTER 29488 #025-01-1968 L2000 **CD IM** *020 †20
HAYNES, Wm Walter, Jr. 415 ROBERTSON BLVD, STE D 29488 #045-01-1976 L1977 **FM OS** *020 †18
HERRING, Paul Malcolm. 459 SPRUCE ST, CAROLINA EYE CARE 29488 #045-01-1990 L1996 **OPH** *020 †35
HILL, Otis Monroe, Jr. ■ 29488 #045-01-1963 L1963 **PD GP** *072 †55
HIOTT, David Weston. 107 CHURCH ST 29488 #045-01-1973 L1974 **FM** *071 †18
HOLMAN, Hildegard Hsieh. 501 ROBERTSON BLVD 29488 #036-05-1990 L1997 **EM** *020 †16
HOLMAN, Jeffrey Andrew. ■ 29488 #048-12-1987 L1997 **ORS OSM** *020 †40
HUNT, Rexford Hugh. PO BOX 800 29488 #045-01-1954 L1954 **GS TS** *071
JOHNSTON, John B. 107 CHURCH ST 29488 #045-01-1971 L1972 **FM OBG** *020
KINARD, John Albert, Jr. 124 MEDICAL PARK DR 29488 #045-01-1965 L1965 **GS TS** *020 †85
KRAMER, Jeffrey Rae. 873 ROBERTSON BLVD 29488 #045-01-1994 L1996 **IM** *020 †20
KUMAR, Sanjay. 461 SPRUCE ST 29488 #495-69-1984 L1993 **IM NEP** *020 †20
LEE, Barry Lorenzo. 811 CARN ST 29488 #023-01-1980 L1983 **IM** *020
LEWIS, Daniel Ethan. 501 ROBERTSON BLVD, EMERGENCY DEPT. 29488 #038-44-2001 L2006 **EM** *020 †16
MC CASKILL, George Lee. 501 ROBERTSON BLVD, COLLETON MEDICAL CENTER 29488 #039-01-1997 L2007 **FM** *020 †18
MLYNARCZYK, Francis Adam. ■ 29488 #041-02-1966 L1992 **OTO GS** *071 †45
NEWLAND, Thomas Jordan. 459 SPRUCE ST, CAROLINA EYE CARE 29488 #045-01-1992 L1994 **OPH PS** *020 †35
NWAEKWU, Ifeanyi Ifeoma. 211 EDDIE CHASTEEN DR, HOPE CLINIC 29488 #690-02-1999 L2001 **IM** *020 †20
PINOSKY, Mark. 501 ROBERTSON BLVD 29488 #045-01-1989 L1993 **AN** *020 †05 ‡
PLOCH, Nelson R. 302 MEDICAL PARK DR, STE 207 29488 #048-15-1987 L1994 **U** *020 †95
PRITCHETT, Frances. 103 MEDICAL PARK DR 29488 #001-02-1960 L1961 **OPH FM** *020
RAKES-STEPHENS, Kimberly. 501 ROBERTSON BLVD 29488 #047-20-1994 L1995 **IM** *020 †20
RENCKEN, Gunther. 107 CHURCH ST 29488 #012-01-2000 L2003 **FM** *020 †18
REUTHER, Robert George. 459 SPRUCE ST, CAROLINA EYE CARE 29488 #021-05-1997 L2003 **OPH** *020 †35
SEAB-TETRICK, Kelly B. 501 ROBERTSON BLVD, COLLETON MEDICAL CENTER 29488 #422-01-1997 L2001 **AN** *020 †05 ‡
SMITH, Michael Ralph. 107 CHURCH ST 29488 #012-01-2000 L2004 **FM** *020 †18 ‡
SPARANO, Robert John, Jr. 501 ROBERTSON BLVD, EXPRESS MEDICAL CARE 29488 #035-08-1980 L1994 **EM** *020 †16
STIEGLER, Karl Davin. 120 MEDICAL PARK DR, COASTAL CAROLINA SURGICAL 29488 #021-01-1997 L2002 **GS** *020 †85
STOKES, Curtis Dean. 107 CHURCH ST, WALTERBORO MEDICAL CENTER 29488 #023-01-1988 L1997 **FM** *020
THOMAS, Robert L. 300 RUBY ST 29488 #495-31-1986 L1994 **PCC SME** *020 †20
TRAYLOR, Roy Allen, Jr. 302 MEDICAL PARK DR, STE 207 29488 #045-01-1970 L1971 **U** *071 †95

YAPA, Dayanandanie V. 501 ROBERTSON BLVD, COLLETON MEDICAL CENTER 29488 #220-03-1991 L2002 **AN** *020 †05

WARE SHOALS – LAURENS

CLARKE, Samuel Lindsey. 157B S GREENWOOD AVE 29692 #045-01-1996 L1999 **FM** *020 †18
MCGEE, Ashley Charles. 157 S GREENWOOD AVE, STE B 29692 #045-01-2004 L2004 **FM** *100 †18
PENDERGRASS, Samuel D, III. 85 S GREENWOOD AVE 29692 #045-01-1975 L1976 **FM** *020
ROBINSON, Hugh Coleman. 157 S GREENWOOD AVE B, MEDICINE 29692 #045-04-1997 L1998 **FM** *020 †18

WARRENVILLE – AIKEN

CAMPBELL, Nicholas Paul. ■ 29851 #012-01-2006 L2006 **IM** *012
GOLDFEDDER, Phillip. ■ 29851 #035-09-1962 L1964 **NS PD** *071

WATERLOO – LAURENS

CHAN, Kam Wei. 17124 HIGHWAY 72 W 29384 #045-01-1998 L1999 **FM** *020 †18

WELLFORD – SPARTANBURG

HARRIS, Robert B, Jr. 102A ASTOR ST 29385 #045-01-1980 L1984 **FM** *020 †18
NEFF, George J, Jr. 102 ASTOR ST 29385 #020-12-1971 L1972 **FM** *020 †18

WEST COLUMBIA – LEXINGTON

AITCHISON, Paul Morgan. 2997 SUNSET BLVD 29169 #045-04-1995 L2000 **DR** *020 †80
ALFORD, Hampton Seebert. 2728 SUNSET BLVD 29169 #045-01-1987 L1988 **IM** *020 †20
ARMSTRONG, William Roger. 2720 SUNSET BLVD 29169 #025-01-1969 L1978 **PTH HMP** *020 †50
ARROYO, Julio C. 206 MEDICAL CIR, STE 2A 29169 #042-01-1971 L1978 **ID IM** *020 †20
ASAAD, Shonda Michelle. 2728 SUNSET BLVD, STE 402 29169 #055-01-1996 L2004 **IM** *020 †20
ASHLEY, James Park. 2720 SUNSET BLVD 29169 #045-01-1965 L1965 **DR NM** *071 †80,28
BARKER, Alice Arnim. 300 W DUNBAR RD, OCCUPATIONAL HEALTH 29170 #045-01-2000 L2007 **GPM** *100 †70
BARTLEY, John Harrison. 2720 SUNSET BLVD, LEXINGTON MEDICAL CENTER - 29169 #012-01-1998 L2008 **NPM** *040 †55
BARWICK, Ethredge Myron. 2728 SUNSET BLVD, STE 104 29169 #045-04-1990 L1991 **GS** *020 †85
BAUGH, John Kevin. 120 HOSPITAL DR W 29169 #045-04-1990 L1991 **CD** *020 †20
BELDING, Robert Henry. 2989 SUNSET BLVD 29169 #045-01-1973 L1975 **ORS OFA** *020 †40
BENEDICT, James Porter. 2720 SUNSET BLVD 29169 #305-01-2003 L2007 **IM** *100
BENNETT, John Neyle. 2720 SUNSET BLVD 29169 #045-01-1963 L1963 **OBG** *071
BLACK, John Geist. 146 HOSPITAL DR N, STE 530 29169 #045-01-1976 L1977 **IM** *020 †20
BOGART, Walter Lovell. 110 MEDICAL LN E STE 160 29169 #048-04-1980 L1988 **OPH OS** *020 †35
BOGUSKI, Lee Jos. 2720 SUNSET BLVD, EMERGENCY DEPT 29169 #038-43-1981 L1983 **EM** *020 †16
BOOZER, Harriet Lynn. 2720 SUNSET BLVD, LEXINGTON MEDICAL CENTER 29169 #045-04-1999 L2002 **IM** *020 †16
BOYCE, Kyle David. ■ 29170 #045-04-2008 *012
BOYD, Scott Burton. 2728 SUNSET BLVD, STE 106 29169 #045-01-1990 L1996 **NS** *020 †25
BOYER, Matison Leo. 110 MEDICAL LN E, STE 220 29169 #016-42-1996 L2002 **ORS** *020 †40
BRADHAM, M Eloise Adcock. 1709 MOBILE AVE 29170 #045-01-1959 L1959 **OS AN** *030
BRADLEY, Mary Eleanor. ■ 29169 #041-14-1999 L2002 **PD** *020 †55
BRIGHTBILL, Keith Eric. 2728 SUNSET BLVD, STE 310 29169 #038-40-2002 L2007 **U** *020
BROWN, Edwin Roman. 146 HOSPITAL DR N, ASSOCIATES AT LEXINGTON 29169 #051-07-1990 L1992 **IM** *020 †20
BRYANT, Aubrey Alan. 2720 SUNSET BLVD 29169 #045-04-1993 L1994 **EM** *020 †16
BRYANT-MOBLEY, Phyllis M. 1904 SUNSET BLVD STE D 29169 #045-04-1997 L1999 **CHP** *020 †75
BULLARD, Ponce D, Jr. 2728 SUNSET BLVD, STE 202 29169 #047-05-1968 L1974 **OBG** *020 †30 ‡
BUTTERFIELD, Patrick T J. 160 MEDICAL CIR, FL 1 29169 #038-40-1969 L2005 **CHP P** *020 †75
CARLIN, Charles Brett. 115 HOSPITAL DR W 29169 #045-01-1991 L1999 **PS** *020 †85,65
CARTER, John Baxter. 2720 SUNSET BLVD 29169 #026-04-1969 L1974 **ATP CLP** *020 †50 ‡
CATE, Vasa Wm. 131 SUMMERPLACE DR 29169 #045-01-1970 L1973 **GE IM** *071 †20
CHAPPLE, Iva Thigpen. 421 HULON LN 29169 #045-04-1988 L1989 **AN APM** *020 †05
CHISHOM, Patrice Gibson. 500 N 12TH ST 29169 #045-01-1994 L1996 **PD** *020 †55
COLEMAN, Dewitt Mcintyre. 103 MIDLANDS CT, THE MIDLANDS 29169 #045-01-2000 L2005 **AI** *020 †20,03
CONSTABLE, Deanna Lynn. 110 MEDICAL LN E, STE 225 29169 #038-41-1988 L1989 **ORS OTR** *020 †40 ‡
COOPER, Stuart Leonard. 111 MEDICAL LN E 29169 #036-01-1991 L1994 **IM** *020 †20
CRUMP, Michael Todd. 2720 SUNSET BLVD, EMERG DEPT 29169 #045-04-1998 L1999 **EM** *020 †16
DANIEL, Beverly W. 2720 SUNSET BLVD 29169 #045-01-1984 L1985 **PTH** *020 †50
DAVIDSON, Daniel R. 300 W DUNBAR RD 29170 #048-14-1982 L2005 **GPM FM** *020 †18,70
DAVIS, Daniel W, Jr. 110 MEDICAL LN E, STE 230 29169 #036-07-1949 L1958 **TS** *071 †85
DE WITT, John Howard. 160 MEDICAL CIR, FIRST FLOOR 29169 #045-04-1984 L1987 **P** *020 †75
DODDS, Cheryl C. 1904 SUNSET BLVD STE D 29169 #045-04-1993 L1994 **CHP P** *020 †75
DODDS, Douglas Alan, II. 206 MEDICAL CIR, STE 1B 29169 #045-04-1993 L1994 **PD** *020 †55
DONATO, Andrew Robt. 2720 SUNSET BLVD 29169 #041-09-1992 L1993 **EM** *020 †16
DRYE, Randall Gregory. 2728 SUNSET BLVD, SUITE 106, LEXINGTON MED P 29169 #047-20-1989 L1996 **NS** *020
DUNN, John Robt, III. 3316 PLATT SPRINGS RD 29170 #045-01-1978 L1979 **FM** *020 †18

DUNOVANT, William A, Jr. 111 MEDICAL LN E, LEXINGTON COUNTY HEALTH SV 29169 #045-01-2001 L2004 **IM** *020
DUNOVANT, Wm Anderson. 120 MEDICAL LN E, DBA LEXINGTON MEDICAL ASSO 29169 #045-01-1965 L1965 **IM** *020 †20
EBERDT, Edward Chas. 2720 SUNSET BLVD, IRMO CAMPUS 29169 #040-02-1959 L1995 **OM IM** *071
ESTES, James Edward. 2728 SUNSET BLVD STE 201, LEXINGTON MEDICAL PARK 29169 #045-04-1989 L1993 **OBG** *020 †30 ‡
EZEKIEL, Mark Patrick. 2720 SUNSET BLVD, RADIATION ONCOLOGY 29169 #045-01-1995 L1999 **DR** *020 †80
FABER, Theodore. 110 MEDICAL LN E, STE 230 29169 #012-01-1985 L1989 **N** *020 †75
FELDMAN, Barry Jay. 120 HOSPITAL DR W, LEXINGTON HEART CLINIC, LL 29169 #024-07-1983 L1993 **CD IM** *020 †20
FELDMAN, Jennifer Anne. 120 HOSPITAL DR W, LEXINGTON HEART CLINIC, LL 29169 #143-05-1981 L1995 **CD IM** *020
FISHER, John H, Jr. 3314 PLATT SPRINGS RD 29170 #045-04-1990 L1996 **FM** *020 †18
FITZGIBBON, Rodney. 2720 SUNSET BLVD 29169 #004-01-1955 L1964 **OBG OS** *071 †30
FOWLES, Dorothy Whaley. 1904 SUNSET BLVD STE D 29169 #045-04-1988 L1989 **CHP** *020 †75
FRIERSON, Wesley Harry. 2720 SUNSET BLVD, PRMH - EMERGENCY MEDICINE 29169 #045-04-2004 L2004 **EM** *100
GAJEWSKI, Stacy Janeen. 3630 SUNSET BLVD 29169 #019-02-1989 L1994 **FM** *020 †18
GALBRAITH, Dennis James. 2720 SUNSET BLVD 29169 #025-01-1978 L1984 **OPH PS** *071 †35
GALE, Ian Sanford. PO BOX 5341 29171 #041-13-1965 L1969 **P GP** *075
GALLERY, Geo Patrick, Jr. 2728 SUNSET BLVD STE 201, LEXINGTON MEDICAL PARK 29169 #045-01-1980 L1981 **OBG** *020 †30
GALPHIN, Gwendolyn C. 2728 SUNSET BLVD 29169 #020-12-1986 L1987 **IM** *020 †20 ‡
GARMAN, Cynthia S. 1721 CHARLESTON HWY 29169 #012-01-1978 L1979 **P CHP** *020 †75
GIVENS, James D. 2728 SUNSET BLVD, STE 308 29169 #047-05-1977 L1978 **GS** *020 †85
GOODSON, Charles Thos. 2311 SUNSET BLVD, BARIATRIC MEDICAL CLINIC 29169 #045-01-1963 L1963 **GS IMG** *020
GRIGGS, Roger Kevin. 3314 PLATT SPRINGS RD 29170 #045-04-1996 L1996 **FM** *020 †18
GUNTER, Arthur Rhett. 2720 SUNSET BLVD 29169 #012-05-1944 L1976 **IM GE** *020
GUNTER, Brett C. 2728 SUNSET BLVD, STE 106 29169 #001-02-1991 L1999 **NS** *020 †25
GUNTER, Tracy Dianne. 2900 SUNSET BLVD 29169 #045-04-1990 L1992 **CHP** *050 †75
HA, David Jefferson. 111 MEDICAL LN E, MCI HOSPITALISTS 29169 #012-01-1995 L1999 **IM** *020 †20
HALBERT, Amy Renee. 2720 SUNSET BLVD, LMC-EMERGENCY MEDICINE 29169 #048-14-2003 L2004 **EM** *100 †16
HALL, Thomas Richard. 2720 SUNSET BLVD, LEXINGTON MEDICAL CENTER 29169 #045-01-1983 L1984 **FM** *020 †18
HAM, Charles Helmoth. 130 HOSPITAL DR N, LEXINGTON COURTY COMMUNITY 29169 #045-01-1963 L1963 **P GP** *020 †75
HARRIS, Michael Paul. 3314 PLATT SPRINGS RD 29170 #045-04-1983 L1984 **FM** *020 †18
HAYES, Steven Ted. 2720 SUNSET BLVD, LEXINGTON MEDICAL CENTER 29169 #035-03-1993 L1996 **EM** *020 †16
HEALEY, Jill B. 2720 SUNSET BLVD, LEXINGTON MEDICAL CENTER 29169 #005-12-1997 L1998 **EM** *020 †16
HEINZELMANN, Eric James. 131 SUMMERPLACE DR 29169 #001-06-1987 L1991 **GE IM** *020 †20
HICKS, James Allan, Jr. 3314 PLATT SPRINGS RD 29170 #045-04-1990 L1991 **FM** *020 †18
HOLBROOK, Thomas J, Jr. 2728 SUNSET BLVD, STE 106 29169 #055-01-1981 L1987 **NS** *020 †25
HUTCHESON, J Kelby. 421 HULON LN 29169 #045-01-2001 L2002 **APM** *020 †05
HYDE, Alexander P. ■ 29171 #024-05-1952 L1985 **P** *071
IHRIG, Jacqueline Ellen. ■ 29169 #035-06-1957 L1978 **D** *071
JOHNSON, Elbert Neil, Jr. ■ 29169 #036-05-1947 L1955 **IM** *071 †20
JOHNSON, T Ruth Smith. ■ 29169 #036-05-1948 L1954 **PD** *071
JONES, Allyson Innocenti. 2728 SUNSET BLVD, STE 308 29169 #045-01-2002 L2006 **OBG** *020
JONES, Charles Cabell. 1709 MOBILE AVE, SC VOCTNL REHAB DISBLTY 29170 #045-01-1967 L1967 **GE IM** *030 †20
KEETON, Janis Elizabeth. 2728 SUNSET BLVD, STE 308 29169 #045-04-1999 L2000 **OBG** *020
KINARD, Carl O'Dell. 160 MEDICAL CIR, FL 1 29169 #045-01-1973 L1983 **P** *020 †75
KIRKLEY, William Hughlett. 3221 SUNSET BLVD 29169 #012-05-1974 L1981 **ORS** *020 †40
KLETT, Eric Leighton. 110 MEDICAL LN E, STE 140 29169 #045-01-1999 L2000 **END IM** *020 †20
KLETT, Nicole Wertz. 110 MEDICAL LN E STE 140 29169 #045-01-1999 L2000 **RHU IM** *020 †20
KLUTZOW, Friedrich W. ■ 29171 #660-04-1951 L1954 **PTH NP** *062 †50
KOLI, Vijay Avinash. 3020 SUNSET BLVD, STE 101 29169 #045-01-1995 L1998 **IM** *020 †20
KONDUROS, Gregory James. 3314 PLATT SPRINGS RD 29170 #045-04-1987 L1988 **FM** *020 †18
KORRAPATI, Vijaya. 2728 SUNSET BLVD, STE 402 29169 #495-50-1993 L2000 **ON IM** *020 †20
KRUSLING, David Edward. 2720 SUNSET BLVD, LEXINGTON MEDICAL CENTER 29169 #038-41-2002 L2003 **EM** *100 †16
KUKLA, Robert Dale. 2807 SHADBLOW LN 29170 #038-40-1974 L1986 **PM** *075 †60
KULBERSH, David Louis. 2728 SUNSET BLVD STE 201, LEXINGTON MEDICAL PARK 29169 #012-01-1976 L1980 **GYN** *020 †30
LAL, Asheesh. 2728 SUNSET BLVD, STE 402 29169 #496-09-1991 L1996 **HO** *020 †20
LANGLEY, Adrian Doran. 2720 SUNSET BLVD, LMC - EMERGENCY MEDICINE 29169 #045-04-2002 L2005 **EM** *020 †16
LAWSON, Richard Mc Lean. 131 SUMMERPLACE DR 29169 #045-01-1980 L1981 **GE IM** *020 †20
LAZARO, John Michael. 2728 SUNSET BLVD 29169 #055-02-1992 L1993 **IM** *020 †20
LEE, David Kyoung. 3221 SUNSET BLVD, CAROLINA ORTHOPAEDIC & SPO 29169 #035-15-1996 L1997 **ORS** *020 †40
LENCKE, Mark Kasson. 110 MEDICAL LN E, STE 130 29169 #012-01-1991 L1995 **N** *020 †75
LEONE CAMPO, Andres Felix. ■ 29169 #319-01-2001 L2004 **IMG FM** *020 †18 ‡
LEVIN, Philip Allan. 3020 SUNSET BLVD STE 105, MIDLANDS OB/GYN LLC 29169 #050-02-1971 L1977 **OBG** *020 †30
LIBBEY, Jeffrey Scott. 2728 SUNSET BLVD STE 403, LEXINGTON MEDICAL PARK 29169 #016-42-1992 L1999 **GS** *020 †85
LOHR, Jeffrey Allen. 2720 SUNSET BLVD, LEXINGTON MEDICAL CENTER 29169 #038-41-2001 L2004 **EM** *020 †16
LORICK, Hugh Thos, Jr. 3240 SUNSET BLVD 29169 #045-01-1970 L1971 **GP** *020
MAC LEAN, Lloyd Ronald. 139 SUMMERPLACE DR 29169 #065-05-1959 L1981 **U** *071 †95
MADDEN, Steven Allan. 2728 SUNSET BLVD, STE 204 29169 #011-04-1976 L1985 **ON HMP** *020 †20
MANDANAS, Rizalino M. 2720 SUNSET BLVD 29169 #748-01-1960 L1976 **IM** *020 †20
MARKHAM, Roy Douglass. 103 MIDLANDS CT 29169 #047-05-1978 L1988 **A PDA** *020 †55,03
MARKOWITZ, Jay Michael. 3020 SUNSET BLVD 29169 #041-13-1970 L1974 **IM** *020 †20
MARKOWITZ, Michael B. 103 SALUDA RIDGE CT 29169 #045-04-2003 L2004 **IM** *020 †20
MASTERS, Kim James. 200 ERMINE RD 29170 #024-01-1972 L1990 **CHP P** *020 †75 ‡
MATHIAS, John H, Jr. ■ 29169 #045-01-1951 L1951 **GP** *071
MC CORQUODALE, Kristine E. 206 MEDICAL CIR, STE 1B 29169 #045-04-1993 L1999 **PD** *020 †55
MC ELVEEN, Frederick, Jr. 105 HOSPITAL DR W 29169 #045-01-1969 L1969 **D** *020 †15
MC FADDEN, Earl B. 110 MEDICAL LN E, STE 225 29169 #023-01-1951 L1969 **P** *071
MC GOWN, Andrew. 110 MEDICAL LN E, STE 220 29169 #045-01-1995 L1995 *020
MC INTOSH, James Calvin. 110 MEDICAL LN E, STE 220 29169 #045-01-1989 L1990 **ORS** *020 †40
MC MASTER, Kitt Rion, III. 2720 SUNSET BLVD, DEPT. OF PATHOLOGY 29169 #045-01-1975 L1978 **PTH** *020 †50
MERZ, David Chas. 169 MEDICAL CIR, STE C 29169 #023-07-1983 L2006 **ID IM** *020 †20
MOFFATT, Elizabeth Jayne. 2720 SUNSET BLVD, 2720 SUNSET BLVD 29169 #047-20-1990 L1997 **PTH PCP** *020 †50
MONTEITH, Ragin Clarkson. 500 N 12TH ST, BROOKLAND PEDIATRICS 29169 #041-01-2001 L2004 **PD** *020 †55
MOORE, William M, Jr. 2728 SUNSET BLVD STE 403, LEXINGTON MEDICAL PARK 29169 #045-04-1983 L1984 **VS GS** *020 †85
MORGAN, Alan Richmond. 110 MEDICAL LN E, STE 130 29169 #012-01-2003 L2007 **N** *020
MORRIS, David C. 3630 SUNSET BLVD 29169 #036-07-1978 L1979 **FM** *020 †18
MORROW, Richard Craig. 2728 SUNSET BLVD, STE 301 29169 #001-02-1974 L1998 **U** *020 †95
MOTTO, John Matthew. 169A MEDICAL CIR 29169 #018-03-1982 L1994 **PLM PHP** *020
MURRAY, Richard Pierce. 146 HOSPITAL DR N, ASSOCIATES AT LEXINGTON 29169 #045-01-1979 L1980 **IM** *020 †20
MYATICH, Ronald George. 2728 SUNSET BLVD STE 403, LEXINGTON MEDICAL PARK 29169 #036-01-1994 L1999 **GS** *020 †85
NELSON, Larry Wayne. 160 MEDICAL CIR, FIRST FLOOR 29169 #020-02-1973 L1974 **P** *020 †75
NEWELL, Rebecca Tyson. 2720 SUNSET BLVD, DEPT OF RADIOLOGY 29169 #045-01-1984 L1985 **DR NM** *020 †80
NIESTAT, Herbert B. 110 MEDICAL LN E, STE 225 29169 #016-06-1960 L1967 **ORS HS** *071 †40
NORTON, Terry Odell. 2728 SUNSET BLVD STE 403, LEXINGTON MEDICAL PARK 1 29169 #045-04-1990 L1996 **GS** *020 †85
O'MEARA, Sean. 2720 SUNSET BLVD, DEPT OF EMERGENCY MEDICINE 29169 #012-01-1994 L1997 **EM** *020 †16
OWINGS, Ralph Seer, Jr. 110 MEDICAL LN E STE 225 29169 #021-01-1962 L1969 **ORS** *020 †40
PAKALNIS, Victoria S. 139 SUMMERPLACE DR 29169 #011-03-1984 L1990 **NS** *020 †25
PARKER, Charles Howard. 146 HOSPITAL DR N, ASSOCIATES AT LEXINGTON 29169 #041-13-1996 L2000 **IM** *020 †20
PATEL, Subhash. ■ 29169 #495-23-1970 L1981 **ORS HS** *071 †40
PATTERSON, Cassandra. 146 HOSPITAL DR N, STE 350 29169 #654-01-2003 L2004 **IM** *020
PEREZ, Mieke Janel. 2720 SUNSET BLVD, LEXINGTON MEDICAL CENTER 29169 #019-02-1998 L2002 **IM** *020 †20
PHAN, Huong Thi. 111 MEDICAL LN E, WEST COLUMBIA INTERNAL MED 29169 #045-01-1992 L1994 **IM** *020 †20
PLYLER, William Elliott, Jr. 2728 SUNSET BLVD STE 201, LEXINGTON MEDICAL PARK 29169 #045-01-1980 L1981 **OBG** *020 †30
POWERS, Brent Michael. 146 HOSPITAL DR N STE 530, INTERNAL MEDICINE ASSOCIAT 29169 #036-05-2001 L2004 **IM** *020
PRESBERG, Jan Deborah. 1904 SUNSET BLVD STE D 29169 #051-04-1990 L2001 **CHP** *020 †75
PRESSLEY, Lucius C, Jr. ■ 29169 #045-01-1961 L1961 **P** *071 †75
PRUITT, James Luther, Jr. 500 N 12TH ST 29169 #045-01-1979 L1983 **FM PD** *020 †55
RAMBO, William M, Jr. 132 SUNSET CT 29169 #045-01-1988 L1994 **NS** *020 †25
RAST, Charles Lewis, Jr. ■ 29169 #023-07-1947 L1947 **CD IM** *071 †20
RAVITA, John Salvatore. 2720 SUNSET BLVD 29169 #012-01-1972 L1976 **RO FM** *020 †18,80
RAWL, Eva Jane. 2728 SUNSET BLVD, STE 106 29169 #045-01-1987 L1989 **AN** *020 †05
RENTZ, Simms Hunter. ■ 29169 #045-01-1956 L1956 **GP** *020 †18
ROGERS, Gilbert Lawrence. 146 HOSPITAL DR N, STE 350 29169 #045-01-1983 L1990 **IM** *020 †20
ROUSE, Scott Tyler. 2720 SUNSET BLVD, LEXINGTON MEDICAL CENTER 29169 #008-02-2002 L2005 **EM** *020 †16
ROUTHIER, Denise Diane. 2720 SUNSET BLVD, DEPT. OF E.R. 29169 #025-07-2003 L2006 **FSM** *100 †16
SALEEBY, Samuel Gabe. 131 SUMMERPLACE DR 29169 #045-04-1986 L1987 **GE IM** *020 †20
SCHABERG, John William. 2720 SUNSET BLVD 29169 #036-01-1993 L1997 **GE IM** *020 †20
SCHWAB, Stephen Richard. 2720 SUNSET BLVD, EMERGENCY DEPT. 29169 #045-01-1993 L1996 **EM** *020
SCHWARZ, Eugene Francis. 107 HOSPITAL DR W 29169 #561-01-1976 L1981 **CD** *020 †20
SCOTT-DEMONBREUN, C. 111 MEDICAL LN E, WEST COLUMBIA INTERNAL MED 29169 #001-02-1987 L1991 **IM** *020 †20
SEABROOK, March Edings. 131 SUMMERPLACE DR 29169 #045-04-1986 L1987 **GE IM** *020 †20 ‡
SEAWRIGHT, Tanya Arlene. 3020 SUNSET BLVD, STE 101 29169 #045-04-2000 L2001 **IM** *020 ‡
SHARMA, Sunil. 3231 SUNSET BLVD STE F, COLUMBIA LUNG & SLEEP 29169 #495-45-1993 L2005 **PCC** *100 †20
SHAW, Ervin Bartow, Jr. 2720 SUNSET BLVD DPT PATH, LEXINGTON MEDICAL CTR 29169 #045-01-1970 L1971 **PTH FOP** *020 †50
SHENNAN, James Russell. 2720 SUNSET BLVD, DEPT. OF EMERGENCY MEDICIN 29169 #045-04-2003 L2006 **EM** *020
SHIPLEY, Chas Frederick. 2728 SUNSET BLVD, STE 106 29169 #045-01-1979 L1981 **OBG** *020 †30
SHULER, Wesley Heyward. 2720 SUNSET BLVD 29169 #045-01-1974 L1976 **EM** *020 †16,18
SHULER-SHALKHAM, Anna H. 2720 SUNSET BLVD 29169 #045-01-2002 L2006 **EM** *100 †16
SIMPSON, Deborah Brock. 2720 SUNSET BLVD, LEXINGTON MEDICAL CENTER 29169 #045-04-1992 L1993 **EM** *020 †16
SINHA, Kaushal Kishore P. 110 MEDICAL LN E STE 120 29169 #495-15-1966 L1980 **ORS** *020
SKINNER, Valerie Ann. 2728 SUNSET BLVD, STE 201 29169 #045-04-1997 L1999 **OBG** *020 †30
SMITH, Geo Washington, Jr. ■ 29169 #016-01-1940 L1948 **R** *071 †80
SMITH, James Allen, III. ■ 29169 #012-05-1960 L1981 **U** *020
SMITH, Paul Douglas. 2728 SUNSET BLVD, STE 104 29169 #012-05-1990 L1991 **GS** *020 †85
STALLARD, David J, Jr. 2728 SUNSET BLVD, STE 201 29169 #047-05-1991 L1999 **OBG** *020 †30

STEPTOE, Kirk Raymond. 146 HOSPITAL DR N, ASSOCIATES AT LEXINGTON 29169 #045-01-1986 L1988 **IM** *020 †20

STORICK, Steven Barry. 132 SUNSET CT, COLUMBIA NEUROSURGICAL ASS 29169 #045-01-1988 L1992 **AN** *020 †05

STRICKLAND, Glen Fleming. 2728 SUNSET BLVD, STE 403 29169 #004-01-1984 L1985 **PS GS** *020 †85

STROHECKER, William J. ■ 29169 #045-01-1953 L1953 **EM AM** *071

SUAREZ, Randall Steven. 146 HOSPITAL DR N, STE 140 29169 #045-04-1981 L1982 **ORS** *020 †40

SWEAZY, Scott Merritt. 111 HOSPITAL DR W 29169 #019-02-1988 L1995 **U** *020 †95

THOMPSON, Frederick B. 2728 SUNSET BLVD, STE 201 29169 #012-01-1970 L1977 **GYN** *020 †30

THOMPSON, Katherine C. 105 HOSPITAL DR W 29169 #045-01-1989 L1992 **D** *020 †15

TOBIN, Joseph A. 1174 GUNTER CIR 29169 #045-01-1949 L1949 **IM A** *071

TYLER, John Mark. 720 CHARLESTON HWY 29169 #045-04-1996 L2000 **FM** *020 †18

VASUDEVA, Rajeev. 131 SUMMERPLACE DR 29169 #495-03-1980 L1989 **GE IM** *040 †20

VISMARA, Vince Michael. 120 HOSPITAL DR W, LEXINGTON HEART CLINIC 29169 #028-34-1997 L2007 **CD** *020 †20

WALKER, Bryan Lawrance. 134 MEDICAL LN E 29169 #045-01-1965 L1965 **IM** *100

WATKINS, Robert S. ■ 29169 #045-01-1947 L1947 **OM** *072

WATKINS, Stephen Lee. 2720 SUNSET BLVD, LEXINGTON MED CTR 29169 #045-04-1982 L1983 **IM** *040 †20

WHITE, Carl Alexander. 146 HOSPITAL DR N, ASSOCIATES AT LEXINGTON 29169 #045-01-1968 **IM** *020 ‡

WILCOX, Miriam A. 2728 SUNSET BLVD STE 201, LEXINGTON MEDICAL PARK 29169 #045-01-1987 L1988 **OBG** *020 †30

WILLIAMS, Joseph R. 3020 SUNSET BLVD, STE 106 29169 #305-01-1992 L1995 **IM** *020

XU, Xiao-Meng. 2720 SUNSET BLVD, DEPARTMENT OF PATHOLOGY 29169 #243-16-1987 L1999 **PTH** *020 †50

YOUNG, Foster Harold, Jr. 1628 JAMAICA DR 29169 #036-05-1968 **PD PHP** *030

YOUNG, Frank Watson. 3020 SUNSET BLVD, CAROLINA AVIATION MEDICINE 29169 #045-01-1959 L2008 **OTO AM** *020

ZGLESZEWSKI, Timothy M. 206 MEDICAL CIR STE 2A, PALMETTO SPINE & SPORTS ME 29169 #041-13-1994 L2002 **PM PMM** *020 †60

WEST UNION — OCONEE

BOOKER, Edward Henry, Jr. ■ 29696 #045-01-1998 L1999 **FM** *020 †18

WESTMINSTER — OCONEE

CAMPBELL, George Wm. 111 W MAIN ST, FOOTHILLS FAMILY MEDICINE 29693 #045-01-1981 L1984 **FM** *020 †18

WILLIAMSTON — ANDERSON

ABERNATHY, Mabra Glenn. 900 GREENVILLE DR, # B 29697 #045-01-1978 L1979 **FM** *020 †18

CARR, Wesley Allen, Jr. 313 WILLIAMS ST 29697 #012-01-1978 L1986 **N** *020

DIBALA-WRIGHT, Anne C. 900 GREENVILLE DR 29697 #048-12-1975 L1987 **P ADP** *020 †18,75

DORTON, Peter John. 16 ROBERTS BLVD, ANMED FAMILY MEDICINE ASSO 29697 #036-08-1996 L1998 **FM** *020 †18

ROSS, Russell Alan. 520 MOUNTAIN VIEW RD, CANNON MEMORIAL HOSPITAL 29697 #045-04-1995 L1996 **FM** *020

WILLISTON — BARNWELL

GANTT, Aubrey D. ■ 29853 #045-01-1946 L1946 **FM** *071

WINNSBORO — FAIRFIELD

BABCOCK, Cheyenne. 56 US HWY 321 BYP N, JOHN A MARTIN PRIMARY HEAL 29180 #054-04-1998 L2001 **FM** *020 †18

BARNETT, Steven Keith. 880 W MOULTRIE ST 29180 #008-02-1995 L1998 **FM** *020 †18

BENNETT, Lawrence Kirk. 1136 KINCAID BRIDGE RD, STE A 29180 #045-01-2003 L2004 **FM** *020

DELAINE, Brenna B. 1136 KINCAID BRIDGE RD, STE A 29180 #047-07-1989 L1992 **IM** *020 †20

GADDY, Roger Arnold. 880 W MOULTRIE ST 29180 #045-01-1976 L1977 **FM** *020 †18

KUDCHADKAR, Anil Janardan. 880 W MOULTRIE ST STE 100 29180 #495-82-1968 L1981 **GS CD** *020 †85

KUDCHADKAR, Shubhalaxmi A. 880 W MOULTRIE ST STE 100 29180 #496-15-1972 L1982 **PD ADL** *020 ‡

MAZYCK, Carol Hinchman. HWY 321 BY PASS 29180 #005-12-1982 L1991 **R** *071 †80

MC ELMURRAY, Chas Tyner. 56 US HIGHWAY 321 BYP N 29180 #045-01-1981 L1982 **FM** *020 †18

PATRICK, Harmon Fairey. 880 W MOULTRIE ST 29180 #045-01-1977 L1978 **FM** *020 †18

PATRICK, Margaret Gasque. 219 N CONGRESS ST 29180 #045-01-1982 L1983 **GP** *020

SAWATZKY, Robert John. 318 S CONGRESS ST 29180 #068-01-1984 L1989 **FM** *020

SCHLUETER, Eric Marcus. 1136 KINCAID BRIDGE RD # A, PALMETTO FAM PRIM HTLH CR 29180 #038-06-1997 L1999 **FM** *020 †18

STUCK, Deborah. ■ 29180 #041-01-1982 L1989 **FM** *020 †18

WOODRUFF — SPARTANBURG

BYRD, Edwin Oscar, III. 220 IRBY ST 29388 #045-01-1992 L1993 **FM** *020 †18

GRAGG, James Muriel. 511 CROSS ANCHOR RD 29388 #045-04-1993 L1994 **FM** *020 †18

JAMES, J Elwyn. 100 MEDICAL CENTER DR 29388 #027-01-1974 L1975 **GS** *020 †85

POTDAR, Meenu. 511 CROSS ANCHOR RD, SHANBHAG MEDICAL ASSOCIATE 29388 #496-02-1992 L2004 **ADL** *100 †55 ‡

SHANBHAG, Pramila Gajanan. ■ 29388 #495-01-1967 L1983 **FM GYN** *020

SOMMERVILLE, Jennifer Lyn. ■ 29388 #005-12-2004 L2004 **PD** *020 †55

WILLMOT, Michael Henry. 100 MEDICAL CENTER DR 29388 #027-01-1975 L1980 **GS** *020 †85

WORKMAN, Belton James, Jr. ■ 29388 #045-01-1948 L1948 **GS** *071 †85

YONGES ISLAND — CHARLESTON

MEYER, Renee Page. 4277 HIGHWAY 165 29449 #016-43-1979 L1981 **IM** *020 †20

PAGE, Traute L. ■ 29449 #407-16-1946 L1951 **OS** *071

YORK — YORK

HAMILTON, Lee Michael. ■ 29745 #025-12-1978 L1979 **FM** *020 †18

HARDIE, James A. ■ 29745 #038-40-1948 L1949 **FM** *071 †18

HAYES, Terry Frederick. 1190 FILBERT HWY, PIEDMONT WEST 29745 #039-01-1980 L1981 **EM OM** *020 †16

HIOTT, Greer F, Jr. ■ 29745 #036-05-1951 L1952 **FM** *071 †18

JOHN, Trent Everard. 815 E LIBERTY ST 29745 #422-01-2003 L2007 **PD** *100

SINK, Bryan Lindsey. 1190 FILBERT HWY STE 110, PIEDMONT WEST URGENT CARE 29745 #051-04-1980 L1981 **EM OM** *020 †16

ABERDEEN – BROWN

ADAMS, John Alexander. 201 S LLOYD ST, PHYSICIANS PLAZA #270 57401 #035-47-1991 L1994 **IM** *020 †20

AGUILAR, Melchor Julia. 305 S STATE ST, AVERA, ST LUKES HOSPITAL 57401 #748-11-1971 L2000 **DR** *062

ALEXANDER, Larry Chas. 305 S STATE ST 57401 #016-45-1981 L1991 **PTH** *075 †50

ALTMAN, Stanley B. 305 S STATE ST 57401 #018-03-1967 L1973 **OPH** *071

ANDERSON, Esther E. ■ 57401 #017-20-1948 L1948 **PD** *071 †55

ASENCIO, Alida. 1440 15TH AVE NW, AVERA UNITED CLINIC 57401 #042-01-1979 L2003 **PD** *020

BACHMAYER, Jay Dee. 3015 3RD AVE SE 57401 #018-03-1975 L1978 **IM** *020 †20

BERRY, Scott Harrison. 310 S PENNSYLVANIA ST, ASSOCIATES OF ABERDEEN 57401 #046-01-1981 L1983 **OBG GYN** *020 †30

BOCK, Jeffrey Scott. 815 1ST AVE SE STE 104 57401 #046-01-1991 L1994 **FM** *020 †18

BORKE, Mark Wayne. 305 S STATE ST, AVERA ST. LUKES C/O MED ST 57401 #018-03-1967 L1977 **FM** *020 †18,16

BORMES, John Michael. 310 8TH AVE NW 57401 #046-01-1990 L1994 **OPH** *020 †35

BORN, Tage Elizabeth. 310 S PENNSYLVANIA ST, ASSOCIATES OF ABERDEEN 57401 #046-01-1990 L1994 **OBG** *020 †30 ‡

BROADHURST, Kennon E. 1117 18TH AVE NE 57401 #047-07-1963 L1971 **TS CD** *071 †85

BROWN, Robert H. 305 S STATE ST 57401 #068-01-1977 L1981 **FM** *020

BUNKER, Thomas Geo. 201 S LLOYD ST # 666 57401 #041-13-1960 L1965 **OTO** *020 †45

BURNS, Howard Wm. 305 S STATE ST, AVERA ST. LUKES HOSPITAL 57401 #041-13-1976 L1979 **EM ETX** *020 †16

BURT, Roy Gene. 305 S STATE ST 57401 #037-01-1979 L1983 **PTH** *020 †50

CARLSON, Gregg Willard. 310 S PENNSYLVANIA ST, ASSOCIATES OF ABERDEEN 57401 #046-01-1983 L1987 **OBG** *020 †30

CHANG, Joe Ping. 305 S STATE ST 57401 #385-03-1953 L1970 **IM** *020

CHAUDHARY, Shahid Sattar. 3015 6TH AVE SE, STE 10 57401 #704-01-1997 L2003 **NEP** *020 †20

CIHAK, Robert Alan. 201 S LLOYD ST 57401 #036-07-1993 L1999 **OTO** *020 †45

CONKLIN, Richard James. 1400 15TH AVE NW 57401 #047-05-1983 L1989 **ON HEM** *020 †20

D'SOUZA, Edward Paul. 405 8TH AVE NW, STE 2 57401 #496-38-1960 L1974 **GS CD** *020

DYE, Sara Kay. 115 4TH AVE SE, USPHS-IHS 57401 #032-01-1975 L1995 **GS** *020

ECKRICH, Jerome A, Jr. 209 S LLOYD ST, STE E105 57401 #056-06-1958 L1964 **U UP** *020 †95

ECKRICH, Paul C. 201 S LLOYD ST STE E105 57401 #046-01-1987 L1992 **U** *020 †95

FALK, Alex Anthoney. 305 S STATE ST 57401 #046-01-1983 L1984 **GP EM** *020

FRITZ, John Robt. 305 S STATE ST 57401 #046-01-1983 L1986 **IM** *020 †20

GERBER, Bernard Chas. 201 S LLOYD ST STE 204 57401 #016-06-1953 L1960 **GS** *071 †85

GERBER, Jean Louise. 201 S LLOYD ST STE E204 57401 #016-06-1981 L1986 **GS** *020 †85

GIRIDHAR, Sanjeevi. 628 CIRCLE DR 57401 #495-04-1976 L1983 **P** *020 †75 ‡

HARBERT, Thomas Gerald. 201 S LLOYD ST, STE 110 57401 #030-05-1991 L1999 **ORS** *020 †40

HARLOW, Mark Chas. 201 S LLOYD ST, STE 110 57401 #028-02-1968 L1976 **ORS** *020 †40

HERNBERG, Ingrid Sara Bir. 3015 3RD AVE SE 57401 #374-01-1991 L2006 **FM** *020

HOLKESVIK, Reid Edgar. 3015 3RD AVE SE 57401 #005-14-1979 L1983 **FM** *020 †18

HOVLAND, James Iver. 616 8TH AVE SE, BROWN COUNTY 57401 #019-02-1960 L1964 **GYN** *071

IWERKS, Bryce John. 310 S PENN ST, STE 201 57401 #046-01-1991 L1996 **GS** *020 †85

JAWAID, Georgia Santos. ■ 57402 #748-01-1972 L2007 **PD** *020 †55

JUNDT, Kim Wayne. 815 1ST AVE SE, STE 104 57401 #046-01-1991 L1997 **FM** *020 †18

KESSLER, Robert Alfred. ■ 57401 #046-01-2008 *012

KHAN, Navaid Ahmed. 201 S LLOYD ST, STE E3021 57401 #704-02-1991 L2002 **P** *020 †75

KIMBLER, Carl Mc Camey. ■ 57401 #030-05-1994 L1997 **GS** *020

KLEIN, Dale Joseph. 701 8TH AVE NW, STE C 57401 #305-01-1997 L2001 **AN** *020 †05

KNAPP, Michael J. 815 1ST AVE SE, STE 104 57401 #018-75-2004, ▲ L2007 **FM** *100

KOM, Carlton Jos. 215 9TH AVE SE APT A 57401 #041-13-1966 L1973 **U** *071

KOSSE, Karl-Heinz Kurt. ■ 57401 #407-33-3156 L1964 **U ADM** *071 †95

LANDES, Fred Sims. 305 S STATE ST 57401 #010-03-1974 L1997 **AN CD** *030 †05 ‡

LECHNER, Thomas R. 3015 3RD AVE SE 57401 #654-01-1988 L1997 **FM** *020 †18

LENTER, Leslie Harold. 305 S STATE ST, DEPT OF RADIOLOGY 57401 #033-05-1981 L2003 **DR PD** *020 †80

LEON, Paul Roy. ■ 57401 #026-04-1954 L1961 **DR RO** *071 †80

LUNDELL, Caroline Jeanne. PO BOX 4450 57402 #028-02-1975 L1995 **DR** *020 †80

LUZIER, Thomas Langworthy. 201 S LLOYD ST, STE W190 57401 #019-02-1974 L1983 **A PDA** *020 †55,03

LYNCH, Patrick Henry. 1620 N HARRISON ST 57401 #539-04-1976 L1991 **N** *020 †75

MACIAS, Enrique G. 201 S LLOYD ST, STE E206 57401 #649-03-1965 L2007 **PD ID** *020 †55

MAYO, Chester Wilson P. 701 8TH AVE NW, STE E 57401 #026-04-1986 L1992 **ORS** *075 †40

MAYO, Julie Mc Donnell. 3015 3RD AVE SE, STE 120 57401 #005-76-1985, ▲ L1992 **PD** *020 †55

MENDOZA, Enrique Flores. 305 S STATE ST, ST LUKES HOSPITAL 57401 #748-01-1974 L1986 **RO** *020

MEZA, Eduardo Enrique. 1400 15TH AVE NW 57401 #264-02-1984 L2002 **CHP P** *020 †75

MILLER, Elaine. 115 4TH AVE SE, STE 309 57401 #048-16-1983 L1994 **CHP P** *030 †55,75 ‡

MILROY, Thomas W. ABERDEEN INDIAN HLTH SERV, FEDERAL BLDG 57401 #062-01-1945 L1949 **OBG PHP** *071

MOGEN, Mark Philip. 815 1ST AVE SE STE 104 57401 #046-01-1982 L1983 **FM** *020 †18

MOORE, Gary Floyd. 201 S LLOYD ST, STE 106 57401 #030-05-1979 L1999 **OTO** *020 †45

MUKERJI, Sanjay. 201 S LLOYD ST STE W230 57401 #495-36-1986 L2001 **PS HS** *020 †85,65

MYRMOE, Arlin M. 201 S LLOYD ST, STE E104 57401 #046-01-1978 L1981 **IM** *020 †20

NORUZIAN, Masoud. ■ 57401 #517-03-1990 L2007 **PD** *020

ODLAND, Winston Bryant. HWY 281 N & 15 AV NW 57401 #046-01-1979 L1983 **OTO** *071

PETERS, Stephen Ross. 305 S STATE ST 57401 #026-04-1987 L1996 **GP** *020 †80

PIETZ, Russell Chas. 815 1ST AVE SE 57401 #046-01-1989 L1996 **EM FM** *020 †18

PURINTUN, Scott Julian. 305 S STATE ST 57401 #046-01-1984 L1985 **IM** *020 †20

RAMIG, Susan Wynne. 305 S STATE ST, AVERA ST LUKES 57401 #030-05-1976 L1983 **AN** *020 †05

REDMOND, Steven Thos. 3015 3RD AVE SE, ABERDEEN ADVANCED CARE AMS 57401 #026-04-1986 L1994 **FM OM** *020 †18

REDMOND, Warren John. 201 S LLOYD ST 57401 #048-14-1973 L1982 **D** *020 †15

ROVANG, Ronald D. 201 S LLOYD ST 57401 #046-01-1984 L1994 **IM** *020 †20

SALMANZADEH, Saeedeh. ■ 57401 #517-20-2000 L2007 **PD** *020 †55

SCHMIDT, Shawna Marie. ■ 57401 #046-01-2003 L2007 **AN** *020

SIEGMUND, Sheryl Ann. 305 S STATE ST, AVERA ST LUKES HOSP 57401 #030-05-1991 L1997 **DR** *020 †80

SMALL, Donna M. 3015 3RD AVE SE 57401 #046-01-1988 L1993 **FM** *020 †18

SMOOK, Shirlene Knudtson. 3015 3RD AVE SE, UNITED CLINIC 57401 #046-01-1994 L2000 **FM** *020 †18

STEHLY, Christine Ann. 310 S PENNSYLVANIA ST, ASSOCIATES OF ABERDEEN 57401 #046-01-1997 L2001 **OBG** *020 †30

SUURMEYER, Robert Dale. 201 S LLOYD ST, STE E101 57401 #046-01-1980 L1984 **IM GE** *020 †20

TAYLOR, William R. ■ 57401 #036-05-1951 L1958 **IM** *071 †20

THORPE, Dusty James. ■ 57401 #046-01-2008 L2008 *012

TOONKEL, Leonard Manuel. 305 S STATE ST 57401 #011-02-1975 L2008 **RO** *020 †80

VASSAR, John Scott. 701 8TH AVE NW, DAKOTA PLAINS SURGERY CENT 57401 #028-34-1985 L2006 **AN** *020 †05

VICK, Martin Gregory. 301 S STATE ST, AVERA ST LUKES HOSPITAL 57401 #026-04-1981 L1989 **AN** *020 †05

VIDOLOFF, John Clarence. 201 S LLOYD ST, STE W130 57401 #016-43-1966 L1989 **PM** *020 †60

VONK, Jack Barnet. 305 S STATE ST, AVERA ST LUKES HOSPITAL 57401 #055-01-1992 L2004 **DR** *020 †80

WACHS, David Michael. 815 1ST AVE SE STE 104 57401 #046-01-1981 L1985 **FM** *020 †18

WATERMAN, Timothy Roy. 201 S LLOYD ST 57401 #046-01-1989 L1992 **IM** *020 †20

WEEKLY, James Mathew. 201 S LLOYD ST, STE E106 57401 #030-05-1991 L1997 **OTO** *020 †45

WERTH, Roger Wayne. 310 S PENNSYLVANIA ST, STE 201 57401 #046-01-1982 L1987 **GS** *020 †85

WESTBROOK, Heloise Demoin. 815 1ST AVE SE, PAIN MANAGEMENT CLINIC 57401 #016-42-1994 L2001 **APM** *020

WISCHMEIER, Curt Alan. 310 8TH AVE NW STE 507 57401 #030-05-1976 L1978 **OPH IM** *020

ZHANG, Zhi Gang. 305 S STATE ST 57401 #243-72-1984 L1999 **IM EM** *020 †20

ZVEJNIEKS, Karlis. ■ 57401 #407-24-1948 L1957 **GP** *020

ARMOUR – DOUGLAS

HAGGE, Regg Allen. 708 8TH ST, PRAIRIE HEALTH CLINIC 57313 #030-05-1998 L2005 **FM** *020 †18

MONFORE, James Edward. ■ 57313 #026-04-1961 L1962 **GP EM** *071

BELLE FOURCHE – BUTTE

ASPER, Richard C. ■ 57717 #046-01-1984 L1986 **IM** *020

BREEDEN, Virgil, Jr. 2200 13TH AVE 57717 #308-06-1980 L1983 **GP** *020

HARRIS, Suzanne Kay. 1409 5TH AVE, QUEEN CITY MEDICAL CTR 57717 #305-01-2001 L2006 **FM** *020 †18

HOGEN, Dale Arthur. 2200 13TH AVE, BELLE FOURCHE MEDICAL 57717 #046-01-1977 L1981 **GP** *020

SWENSON, Casey Tad. 2200 13TH AVE, MEDICAL CLINIC 57717 #028-02-2003 L2006 **FM** *020 †18

BERESFORD – UNION

CARLISLE, Christopher J. 600 W CEDAR ST 57004 #048-13-1982 L1983 **PTH** *020

FERRELL, Michael Rene. 600 W CEDAR ST 57004 #007-02-1952 L1960 **IM PUD** *071

GRACE-CRUZ, Elizabeth Ann. ■ 57004 #025-12-1997 L2007 **CHP** *012

NELSON, Donald Edward. ■ 57004 #016-02-1963 L1967 **PTH HEM** *071 †50

BIG STONE CITY – GRANT

WYATT, Ronald Orren. ■ 57216 #048-12-1965 L1966 **ORS** *071 †40

BLACK HAWK – MEADE

HOGUE, Michael E. 6500 RIES RD 57718 #037-01-1982 L1983 **FM** *030 †18

KLOPFENSTEIN, David Alan. ■ 57718 #054-04-1980 L1997 **DR FM** *020 †80,18

BOWDLE – EDMUNDS

LUMNITZ, Janice S. ■ 57428 #035-46-1970 L2000 **FM** *020

BRANDON – MINNEHAHA

BRIGGS, Richard Gerard. 1101 E HOLLY BLVD 57005 #046-01-1992 L1996 **FM** *020 †18

CHESTER, Darren D. 1101 E HOLLY BLVD 57005 #046-01-1995 L1998 **FM** *020 †18

HERMANSON, John M. 2501 E ASPEN BLVD 57005 #030-06-1945 L1948 **GP** *071

HOIME, Shannon Dionne. 57005 #023-12-1997 L2007 **PD** *020 †55

MC ELROY, Michelle Lisa. 1101 E HOLLY BLVD 57005 #046-01-2001 L2004 **FM** *020 †18

RASMUSSEN, Larry Dean. ■ 57005 #046-01-2002 L2005 **P** *020

VAN ES, Nicolas Jon. 1200 E HOLLY BLVD 57005 #018-03-2000 L2006 **FM** *020 †18

BROOKINGS – BROOKINGS

BENSON, Gail Max. 407 22ND AVE, ORTHOPEDIC INSTITUTE 57006 #016-06-1967 L1974 **ORS GP** *020 †40

BIEN, Matt Neil. 400 22ND AVE, BROOKINGS MEDICAL CLINIC 57006 #046-01-1996 L2000 **MPD** *020 †20,55 ‡

CECIL, Daniel P. 400 22ND AVE 57006 #046-01-1989 L1992 **IM** *020 †20

DITMORE, Rosanne Y. ■ 57006 #572-27-1943 *071

ELAPROLU, Kishore. 400 22ND AVE 57006 #495-58-1998 L2006 **IM** *020 †20

FILLER, Elliott Wayne. 922 22ND AVE S, SIOUX VALLEY CLINIC-BROOKI 57006 #037-01-1988 L1991 **FM OS** *020 †18

GUDVANGEN, Richard Jay. 400 22ND AVE 57006 #048-13-1987 L1999 **OBG** *020 †30

HIEB, Richard Scott. 400 22ND AVE 57006 #030-05-1983 L1984 **FM** *020 †18

HIEB, Wilbert E. ■ 57006 #028-02-1944 L1948 **GP** *071

HOLM, Richard Powell. 400 22ND AVE, BROOKINGS MEDICAL CLNC 57006 #012-05-1975 L1981 **IM IMG** *020 †20 ‡

JOHNSON, Thomas Charles. 400 22ND AVE 57006 #041-01-1967 L1974 **IM PTH** *071 †50,20

KNUDTSON, Kenneth John. 2311 YORKSHIRE DR, YORKSHIRE EYE CLNC 57006 #046-01-1995 L2001 **OPH** *020 †35

LOOBY, Peter Anthony. 407 22ND AVE, ORTHOPEDIC INSTITUTE 57006 #028-02-1990 L1996 **ORS OSM** *020 †40

LUSHBOUGH, Bruce Calvert. 300 22ND AVE 57006 #041-02-1958 L1961 **FM AM** *071 †18

MOLLER, Christopher J. ■ 57006 #016-06-1960 L1961 **OTO** *071 †45

MURUNGA, Eric Mwenda. 400 22ND AVE 57006 #577-01-1998 L2007 **IM** *020 †20

OLSON, Jennifer Lea. 922 22ND AVE S, SANFORD CLINIC BROOKINGS 57006 #026-04-2000 L2006 **FM** *020 †18

PARK, Chanjin. 400 22ND AVE, AVERA BROOKINGS MEDICAL CL 57006 #583-02-1970 L2002 **GS** *020 †85

RAMSAY, John David. 400 22ND AVE 57006 #039-01-1974 L1979 **ORS AM** *020 †40

RIETZ, Robert R. 400 22ND AVE 57006 #030-06-1979 L1983 **OTO PDO** *020 †45

RODEGHIERO JOHNSTON, D. 400 22ND AVE, AVERA BROOKINGS MEDICAL CL 57006 #018-03-1995 L1998 **FM** *020 †18

SAXENA, Satish Chandra. 400 22ND AVE 57006 #495-41-1965 L1981 **IM** *071 †20

SERGEEV, Tatiana B. 400 22ND AVE, AVERA BROOKINGS MEDICAL C 57006 #913-15-1979 L1999 **PD** *020 †55

SMITH, Sarah Jen. 400 22ND AVE 57006 #030-05-2001 L2004 **FM** *020 ‡

TAN, Jennifer Siy. 922 22ND AVE S, SIOUX VALLEY CLINIC BROOKI 57006 #748-01-2000 L2006 **FM** *020 †18

TESCH, Ronold Ralph. 2311 YORKSHIRE DR 57006 #030-05-1967 L1974 **OPH** *020

TURNER, Gerald Lee. 400 22ND AVE 57006 #046-01-1984 L1987 **IM PD** *020 †20,55

VANDE KOP, Rebecca Sue. 400 22ND AVE 57006 #046-01-2001 L2004 **FM** *020 †18

VENUGOPAL, M. 400 22ND AVE 57006 #495-16-1964 L1981 **GS** *020 †85

WAKE, Richard Arnold. 400 22ND AVE, BROOKINGS CLNC 57006 #026-04-1974 L1977 **FM** *020 †18

WALERY, Jim F. 400 22ND AVE, AVERA BROOKINGS MEDICAL CL 57006 #046-01-1992 L1995 **FM EM** *020 †18

WARREN, Merritt Gregg. 400 22ND AVE, AVERA BROOKINGS MED CLNC 57006 #030-05-1979 L1980 **FM** *020 †18

YOUNGREN, Linda Sterup. 400 22ND AVE, BROOKINGS MED CLINIC 57006 #046-01-1996 L2004 **FM** *020 †18

CANTON – LINCOLN

DEVICK, Margaret Rosanne. 400 N HIAWATHA DR, CANTON-INWOOD HOSPITAL CAM 57013 #046-01-1981 L1982 **FM** *020 †18 ‡

HAIGH, Charles Peter. 400 N HIAWATHA DR 57013 #759-12-2003 L2006 **FM** *020 †18

HENNIES, Cathy S. 400 N HIAWATHA DR, CANTON FAMIY PHYSICIANS 57013 #046-01-1996 L1999 **FM** *020 †18

REGIER, Eugene Roy. 1010 E 2ND ST, KEYSTONE TREATMENT CENTER 57013 #030-05-1965 L1966 **FM GP** *020 †18 ‡

CHAMBERLAIN – BRULE

BROWN, Marden Lee. 112 W 16TH AVE, COMMUNITY CLINIC 57325 #030-05-1980 L1993 **FM** *020 †18

GIEBINK, Patricia Kay. 300 S BYRON BLVD 57325 #046-01-1987 L1991 **OBG** *020 †30

HOLLAND, Lambert Wm. 114 S MAIN ST, CHAMBERLAIN CLINIC PA 57325 #030-06-1944 L1946 **FM AS** *071 †18

HUNT, Ralph Edward. 400 S BYRON BLVD, CHAMBERLAIN SPECIALTY CLIN 57325 #019-02-1965 L1994 **GS TS** *071 †85

JONES, John Boyd. 300 S BYRON BLVD 57325 #046-01-1979 L1980 **FM** *020 †18

LERITZ, Arthur Francis. ■ 57325 #030-06-1970 L1971 **P** *075 †75

RODRIGUEZ, Diana Maria. ■ 57325 #649-14-2002 L2004 **GP** *020

SANGER, Travis Matthew. 300 S BYRON BLVD 57325 #030-05-2001 L2006 **FM** *020 †18

TOBIN, Gregg Moran. 300 S BYRON BLVD 57325 #046-01-1978 L1979 **GS** *020 †85

VISINTINE, John Francis, III. 300 S BYRON BLVD 57325 #038-43-1997 L2004 **OBG** *012 †30

WILLCUTTS, Morton D, Jr. 300 S BYRON BLVD, POB BOX 640 57325 #017-20-1955 L1994 **CD IM** *071 †20

CLEAR LAKE – DEUEL

ADAJAR, Alejandro A. 701 3RD AVE S, COMMUNITY HEALTH CLINIC 57226 #748-01-1955 L1977 **GP EM** *020

SMITH, Terrance Herbert. 701 3RD AVE S 57226 #046-01-1992 L1998 **IM** *020

VOSSLER, Mark Anthony. 47241 180TH ST, MEDICAL EMERGENCY DOCTORS 57226 #046-01-1988 L1991 **IM** *020 †20

COLOME – TRIPP

CLARK, Andrew Neil. 308 MAIN ST 57528 #018-03-1987 L1990 **FM** *020 †18

EVEN, Lisa Ann. 308 MAIN ST 57528 #046-01-1999 L2002 **FM** *020 †18

KAFKA, Richard Lee. 308 MAIN ST 57528 #046-01-1987 L1990 **FM** *020 †18

MALM, John Arthur. 308 MAIN ST 57528 #040-02-1975 L1976 **FM** *020 †18

NEMER, Raymond Gene. 308 MAIN ST 57528 #030-06-1959 L1962 **FM GP** *020 †18

CONDE – SPINK

FAHRENWALD, Myron E. ■ 57434 #028-02-1960 L1961 **EM** *071

CUSTER – CUSTER

FALKENBURG, Joy Marie. 1041 MONTGOMERY ST, CUSTER REGIONAL MEDICAL CL 57730 #046-01-2000 L2003 **FM** *020 †18

GRABER, Terry Michael. 1041 MONTGOMERY ST, CLINIC 57730 #016-11-1987 L1991 **FM** *020 †18

HANSON, George Robt. 1039 MONTGOMERY ST BOX 272 57730 #007-02-1948 L1982 **DR OS** *071 †80

NITSCHELM, Robert David. 1041 MONTGOMERY ST 57730 #040-02-1995 L1998 **FM** *020 †18

WICKS, Dennis R. 25224 HOLIDAY TRL 57730 #047-06-1967 L1975 **FM GS** *020

DAKOTA DUNES – UNION

ANDERSON, Robert Ernest. 705 N SIOUX POINT RD, STE 100 57049 #026-04-1983 L1994 **GS** *020 †85

BLOCK, Craig Alan. 455 N SIOUX POINT RD 57049 #018-03-2002 L2007 **U** *020

BRUENING, Beth M Kollars. 101 TOWER RD, STE 300 57049 #030-05-1987 L1992 **OPH** *020 †35 ‡

CARLTON, Gary Roger. 705 N SIOUX POINT RD, STE 100 57049 #030-05-1972 L1994 **GS PDS** *020 †85

COOK, John E. 600 N SIOUX POINT RD 57049 #056-06-1978 L1994 **AN PME** *020

DAFFER, Michelle Lee. 705 N SIOUX POINT RD # 100, MIDLANDS CLINIC, P.C. 57049 #030-06-2000 L2004 **D** *020 †15

DANNER, Kristine Thayer. 345 W STEAMBOAT DR, STE 300 57049 #056-06-1993 L1994 **FM** *020 †18 ‡

EMERSON, Raymond Lee. 575 N SIOUX POINT RD 57049 #018-03-1972 L2005 **ORS** *020 †40

GUNN, Roger Albertus. 350 W ANCHOR DR STE 200, DUNES MEDICAL LABS. 57049 #030-05-1972 L1995 **PTH CLP** *020 †50

IRELAND, Jennifer Kay. 575 N SIOUX POINT RD 57049 #018-03-1999 L2004 **N** *020

JOHNSON, Paul Eric. 705 N SIOUX POINT RD, STE 100 57049 #030-06-1977 L1995 **GS TRS** *020 †85

JOHNSON, Todd Christopher. 600 N SIOUX POINT RD, SIOUXLAND SURGERY CENTER 57049 #046-01-1992 L1996 **AN** *020 †05

KHAIRALLA, Tareq Suleiman. ■ 57049 #575-01-1999 L2007 **IM** *100 †20

KNEIB, Timothy Gerard. 455 N SIOUX POINT RD, SIOUXLAND UROLOGY ASSOCIAT 57049 #019-02-1992 L1998 **U** *020 †95

MC CARTHY, Gregory Edward. 600 N SIOUX POINT RD 57049 #308-11-1986 L1987 **OM IM** *020 †70,20

OPHEIM, Kathryn Debra. 345 W STEAMBOAT DR, STE 3 57049 #026-04-1981 L1989 **FM** *020 †18

PAULSRUD, David Gerhardt. 575 N SIOUX POINT RD 57049 #018-03-1959 L1960 **ORS** *020 †40

PERSAUD, Michael V. 101 TOWER RD STE 105 57049 #018-75-1978, ▲ L1992 **GE** *020

PIERRET SCHENK, Nancy Jo. 345 W STEAMBOAT DR, STE 300 57049 #046-01-1996 L2002 **FM** *020 †18

POWERS, Robert E. 600 N SIOUX POINT RD, SIOUXLAND SURGERY CENTER 57049 #016-01-1982 L1998 **PS GS** *020 †65

PURVES, Garth Barrie. 575 N SIOUX POINT RD 57049 #068-01-1967 L1996 **NS** *071 †25

QALBANI, Askar Ali. 350 W ANCHOR DR, STE 200 57049 #704-08-1970 L1995 **PTH** *020 †50

QALBANI, Fahima Askar. 612 N SIOUX POINT RD, STE 500 57049 #704-08-1970 L1980 **DR** *020 †80

RATINO, Richard Michael. 600 N SIOUX POINT RD, BOX 982 57049 #030-06-1969 L1994 **OBG** *020 †30

REMER-GILLETTE, Lisa. 345 W STEAMBOAT DR, STE 300 57049 #030-05-1989 L2002 **FM** *020 †18

TAN, Caridad Chua. 600 N SIOUX POINT RD 57049 #748-21-1984 L1999 **NEP IM** *020 †20

VOLLSTEDT, Keith Alan. 612 N SIOUX POINT RD, STE 400 57049 #018-03-1987 L1993 **GS VS** *020 †85

WOLPERT, Michael Leo. 612 N SIOUX POINT RD, STE 400 57049 #030-06-1975 L1994 **GS** *020 †85

WOLPERT, Paul William. 612 N SIOUX POINT RD, STE 400 57049 #030-06-1966 L1994 **GS** *020 †85

ZIMMERMAN, Robert Graham. 600 N SIOUX POINT RD 57049 #038-40-1970 L1997 **AN** *020 †05

DE SMET – KINGSBURY

BELL, George Robt. 115 2ND ST SE, BELL MEDICAL SERVICES PA 57231 #030-05-1953 L1954 **FM** *071 †18

BERG, John Andrew. 801 3RD ST SW, BELL MEDICAL SERVICES 57231 #046-01-1994 L1997 **FM** *020 †18

BINAMIRA, Andrew Sainz. 801 3RD ST SW, BELL MEDICAL SERVICE 57231 #748-11-1992 L1999 **IM** *020 †20

KARLEN, Louis Wm. KINGSBURY COUNTY, 111 2ND SE AVE 57231 #019-02-1964 L1965 **GP RHU** *020

MOSQUEDA, Ruth Garciano. 801 3RD ST SW, BELL MEDICAL SERVICE 57231 #748-11-1992 L2001 **IM** *020 †20

DEADWOOD – LAWRENCE

ANDERSON, Allen B, Jr. 61 CHARLES ST 57732 #030-05-1959 L1961 **GP AN** *071

CASEY, James H. PO BOX 162 57732 #056-06-1951 L1952 **GS TS** *071 †85,90

FAHRNI, John Howard. ■ 57732 #018-03-1963 L1979 **AM GP** *075 †70

GROEGER, Thomas John. 71 CHARLES ST, MEDICAL CLINIC 57732 #007-02-1986 L1989 **FM** *020 †18

HOLLOWAY, James J. 71 CHARLES ST, LEAD-DEADWOOD REGIONAL MED 57732 #017-20-1979 L1992 **IM PHP** *020 †20

HOLZ, Lynne Ann. 71 CHARLES ST, BLACK HILLS MEDICAL CLINIC 57732 #030-05-1985 L2003 **FM** *020 †18

KELLEY, Donald Howard. ■ 57732 #048-04-1966 L1972 **PTH** *071 †50

MINTON, Timothy Patrick. 88 CHARLES ST 57732 #046-01-1980 L1985 **OPH** *020 †35

OFFICER, Todd M. 71 CHARLES ST, MEDICAL CLINIC 57732 #037-01-2004 L2007 **FM** *020 †18

RODRIGUEZ, Edwin Jose. 71 CHARLES ST 57732 #305-01-2000 L2004 **FM** *020 †18

■ = Address Information Privacy Protected

SAYLER, Elizabeth Jubitz. 71 CHARLES ST, MEDICAL CLINIC 57732 #054-04-1996 L1999 IM *020 †20 ‡

TJADEN DIEM, Karen S. 71 CHARLES ST, BLACK HILLS MED CLNC 57732 #046-01-1998 L2001 FM *020 †18

VOGELE, Kenneth Allen. 61 CHARLES ST 57732 #030-05-1969 L1975 GE IM *071 †20

WYCKOFF, Sonja B. 71 CHARLES ST 57732 #005-15-1971 L1990 GYN *071 †30

EAGLE BUTTE – DEWEY

GRAY, Scharazard Lee. ■ 57625 #041-12-1991 L1991 FM *100 †18

LIN, Rong-Gong. MAIN ST 57625 #243-50-1966 L1973 PD PHP *020 ‡

UPELL, Margaret Louise. ■ 57625 #025-07-1984 L1998 FM *020 †18

ELK POINT – UNION

MULLER, Merle Henry. 204 E MAIN ST, BOX 798 57025 #016-45-1982 L1992 FM FPG *040 †18

ELLSWORTH AIR FORCE BASE – MEADE

COSTELLO, Amy Ackerman. 2900 DOOLITTLE DR, 28TH MEDICAL GROUP/ACC 57706 #023-12-2001 L2001 PD *020 †55

GOODHOPE, Michael Chris. 2900 DOOLITTLE DR, 28TH MEDICAL GROUP (ACC) 57706 #028-79-2000, ▲ L2008 OMM *020

GULIUZZA, Randy Jean. 2900 DOOLITTLE DR STE 1M0, ATTN: CREDENTIAL OFFICE 57706 #026-04-1996 L1997 GPM *020 †70

LAVALLEE, Philip James. ■ 57706 #032-01-1991 L1994 DR *020 †70

ROHDE, Christopher Scott. 2900 DOOLITTLE DR, 28TH MEDICAL GROUP (ACC) 57706 #046-01-1995 L1998 FM *020 †18

WALTZ, Julie Kay. ■ 57706 #026-04-1992 L1996 PD *100 †55

EMERY – HUTCHINSON

BARNHILL, Floyd R, Jr. ■ 57332 #047-06-1961 L1961 OTO HNS *020 †45

TAYLOR, David Douglas. ■ 57332 #018-03-1997 L1997 FM *020 †18

ESTELLINE – HAMLIN

HESBY, Joel Harris. ■ 57234 #026-04-1978 L1979 FM *020 †18

SVEC, Linda Pearle P. 47024 SD HIGHWAY 28 # 14 57234 #046-01-1992 L1995 FM *020 †18

EUREKA – MCPHERSON

ALANDY, Antonio Mora. C AVENUE & 9TH ST 57437 #748-01-1974 L1991 GP *020

ALANDY, Maria Luz. PO BOX 37, 508 10TH ST 57437 #748-01-1973 L1991 FOP PTH *071 †50

FAULKTON – FAULK

ANDERSON, Sylvia Marie. ■ 57438 #046-01-2003 L2006 FM *100 †18

FLANDREAU – MOODY

FISK, Robert G. ■ 57028 #016-11-1951 L1952 GP *071

FORT MEADE – MEADE

BRENNAN, Thomas Jos. 113 COMANCHE RD, VAMC 57741 #025-12-1990 L1995 FM *020 †18

BUCHANAN, James P. 113 COMANCHE RD 57741 #028-34-1985 L1995 IMG IM *030 †20

DAVIES, Michael Lester. 113 COMANCHE RD 57741 #046-01-1984 L1985 IM *030 †20

ELSAYED, Mona. 113 COMANCHE RD 57741 #915-03-1989 L2002 IM *020 †20

FAUSTINO, Pablo Andaya. 113 COMANCHE RD 57741 #748-01-1956 L1970 GP *020

FINN, John Jos, Jr. 113 COMANCHE RD 57741 #030-06-1965 L1970 FM *071 †18

FISCHER, Lana Kay. 113 COMANCHE RD, FT MEADE VA HOSPITAL 57741 #047-05-1990 L1998 IM *020 †20

FOSSUM, Reed Merrit. 113 COMANCHE RD, FT MEADE VA HOSPITAL 57741 #028-34-1990 L1998 IM *020 †20

GOFF, Steven Kyle. 113 COMANCHE RD 57741 #056-05-1969 L1989 PM *020 †60

GOODMAN, Margaret Anne. ■ 57741 #037-01-1997 L1998 FM *020 †18

GWINN, Charles Bentley. 113 COMANCHE RD 57741 #025-01-1954 L1961 GS *071 †85

HERRIN, Gerald Rexford. 113 COMANCHE RD, VA BLACK HILLS HEALTHCARE 57741 #040-02-1963 L1968 ORS *071 †40

JEWITT, Thomas Lee. 113 COMANCHE RD 57741 #046-01-1977 L1980 P *020 †75

KOFOED, Lial Lee. 113 COMANCHE RD, MHS-4-FM 57741 #054-04-1977 L1992 P ADP *020 †75

KOVALIK, Simon Geo. 113 COMANCHE RD, VA BLACK HILLS HLTH CARE 57741 #041-01-1975 L1978 VS GS *020 †85

KUMAR, Ashok. 113 COMANCHE RD, VA FORT MEADE 57741 #495-94-1977 L1992 IM CCM *020 †20

LARSON, Rodney D. 113 COMANCHE RD, FT. MEADE VAMC 57741 #025-12-1986 L1991 FM *020 †18

LA SUER, Douglas L. ■ 57741 #046-01-1994 L1998 PD *020 †55

MARGARET, Heather. PO BOX 198, QUARTERS 13 MCKERZIE CIRCL 57741 #041-07-1995 L2002 FM *020 †18

MASSOPUST, Steven A. 113 COMANCHE RD, BLACK HILLS HEALTH CARE SY 57741 #026-04-1976 L1979 FM EM *020 †16,18

MEYER, Larry Alan. 113 COMANCHE RD 57741 #030-06-1975 L1982 U EM *020 †95

MOREHOUSE, Paul David. 113 COMANCHE RD 57741 #019-02-1978 L1979 GS *020 †85

OTT, Gary Robt. ■ 57741 #020-02-1975 L1976 IM ID *020

PETERSON, Kenneth B. 113 COMANCHE RD, VA. BLACK HILLS HLTH CARE 57741 #046-01-1980 L1985 FM *020 †18

SUYAMA, Eji. ■ 57741 #016-02-1950 L1952 GS *020 †85

VOSLER, Robert Melvin. 113 COMANCHE RD 57741 #046-01-1981 L1984 IM *020 †20

FORT PIERRE – STANLEY

SWANSON, Charles L. 124 PORT NA HAVEN ST, STANLEY COUNTY 57532 #016-06-1949 L1950 FM GS *071

FORT THOMPSON – BUFFALO

MC FEE, John Lewis. ■ 57339 #030-05-1967 L1974 GP *020 ‡

FREEMAN – HUTCHINSON

EPP, Dennis Lee. ■ 57029 #016-06-1954 L1957 GP *072 †18

KAUFMAN, Irvin Ivan. 408 S WIPF ST 57029 #038-41-1947 L1949 GP *071

KIRTON, Kenneth Terrell. 804 S WALNUT ST 57029 #046-01-1989 L1992 FM *020 †18

RIES, Dennis Dean. 804 S WALNUT ST, BOX 900 57029 #048-13-1972 L1973 FM *020 †18

GARRETSON – MINNEHAHA

BOHLMEYER, Teresa J. ■ 57030 #048-02-1989 L2003 PTH *020 †50

CULEY, Shawn Robt. 980 4TH ST 57030 #046-01-1989 L1992 FM *020 †18

HEGGE, Kassy Arnette. ■ 57030 #046-01-2008 L2008 *012

HERBER, Matt Edward. 980 4TH ST 57030 #030-06-1999 L2002 FM *020 †18

KROME, Lori Ann. 980 4TH ST 57030 #046-01-1989 L1992 FM *020 †18

LARSON, Valerie Ann. 980 4TH ST 57030 #018-03-1992 L2001 FM *020 †18

PRASEK, Joseph Paul. 980 4TH ST 57030 #046-01-2000 L2003 FM *020 †18

GAYVILLE – YANKTON

LIKNESS, Micah Marshall. ■ 57031 #046-01-2008 *012

GETTYSBURG – POTTER

YECHA, David James. ■ 57442 #026-04-1975 L1976 FM *020 †18

GREGORY – GREGORY

GREINEDER, Juergen. 400 PARK AVE 57533 #407-16-1964 L1994 GS TS *020 †85,90

HARRISBURG – LINCOLN

FLIGGE, Pastel Anne. ■ 57032 #046-01-2008 *012

HERMOSA – PENNINGTON

BELTZ, Melvin Evens. ■ 57744 #005-12-1945 L1980 GP *071

BLOWER, Donald Vernon. HC 89, BOX 185S 57744 #005-12-1959 L2002 GP EM *020

FOSTER, Ray Lyon. 13815 BATTLE CREEK RD 57744 #836-02-1959 L2004 ORS PM *071 †40

OLIVER, Michael Leonard. ■ 57744 #005-19-1994 L2006 PD *020 †55

HILL CITY – PENNINGTON

CARSON-STRNAD, Amy E. ■ 57745 #011-04-1993 L1996 PD *020 †55

HOT SPRINGS – FALL RIVER

AKHTAR, Hasan. ■ 57747 #704-01-1966 L1992 IM NEP *071

BEDEAU, Grover Wm, Jr. 500 N 5TH ST, VA MED CTR 57747 #010-01-1962 L1994 GS *020 †85

BENDER, Barry Donell. 209 N 16TH ST, EMERGENCY DEPARTMENT 57747 #037-01-1988 L2005 EM *020 †16

BIEVER, Edward Eugene. ■ 57747 #030-05-1958 L1959 GP *071

BRADBURY, Christine L. 500 N 5TH ST, RM D214 57747 #051-07-1991 L2006 U *020 †95

CHANDLER, Elizabeth J. 500 N 5TH ST 57747 #055-02-2002 L2004 PM *100

DYER, Jasper Lee. 500 N 5TH ST 57747 #030-05-1954 L1974 P GP *020 †75

FETTERS, Barbara Ruth. 500 N 5TH ST 57747 #056-05-1981 L1982 FM *020 †18

HASSARD, George H. 27257 WIND CAVE RD 57747 #019-02-1952 L1987 PM *071 †60

HOOK, William Franklin. ■ 57747 #041-02-1961 L1979 R NM *020 †80,28

JACOBSON, Theodore R. 145 N 16TH ST, MEDICAL ASSOCIATES 57747 #030-05-1951 L1952 FM *071 †18

LOPEZ, Alberto Santos. ■ 57747 #748-01-1955 L1973 FM GS *071

MC DOWELL, Richard Lee. 500 N 5TH ST 57747 #028-34-1966 L1997 PTH CLP *062 †50

MITCHEL, Pat Wm. 209 N 16TH ST, FALL RIVER HEALTH SERVICES 57747 #046-01-1989 L2004 FM *020 †18

MUNTZ, Keith Stickler. ■ 57747 #038-06-1955 L1994 IM *071 †20

NEDVED, Lonnie Joe. 11835 SUNDANCE DR 57747 #030-06-1981 L1991 OBG *020 †30

NORLIN, Rolf Amund. 500 N 5TH ST, BLACK HILLS HEALTH CARE SY 57747 #046-01-1995 L1998 FM *020 †18

NORRIS, Marvin G. ■ 57747 #017-20-1952 L1976 FM *071 †18

PENFOLD, Richard Lee. 500 N 5TH ST 57747 #019-02-1956 L1963 FM *020

PICKETT, Conrad Laverne. ■ 57747 #035-15-1960 L1961 P *071 †75

POLCYN, Robert Eugene. 500 N 5TH ST 57747 #016-43-1960 L1994 GP R *071 †80,28

RAO, Vyasanakere S. 500 N 5TH ST 57747 #495-09-1962 L1990 **GS** *020 †85
RAYMOND, Arthur John. 209 N 16TH ST 57747 #037-01-1990 L1994 **FM** *020 †18
SCHWARZENBACH, John Reed. 500 N 5TH ST 57747 #048-02-1971 L1999 **IM** *062 †20
STEELE, David Allen. 105 N RIVER ST, BLACK HILLS FAMILY HEALTH 57747 #046-01-1997 L2006 **FM** *020 †18
STRAUSER, Garry David. 500 N 5TH ST, VA BLACK HILLS HLTH CARE 57747 #003-01-1974 L2000 **DR** *020 †80
WELLS, John Maurice. 500 N 5TH ST, VETERANS HOSPITAL 57747 #005-02-1980 L1984 **DR NM** *020

HOVEN – POTTER

RAMIREZ, Dionisio R, Jr. ■ 57450 #748-01-1960 L1990 **GP** *020

HURON – BEADLE

ANDERSON, James A. 172 4TH ST SE 57350 #030-05-1951 L1952 **GP** *071
BECKER, Michael Norton. 142 3RD ST SE 57350 #048-15-1976 L1994 **OBG** *020 †30
BELYEA, Mark Edmund. 172 4TH ST SE 57350 #037-01-1979 L1982 **FM** *020 †18
BLESSINGER, Karl Joseph. 172 4TH ST SE 57350 #017-20-1993 L1998 **PTH** *020 †50
COLE, James Ford. 530 IOWA AVE SE, STE 107 57350 #016-06-1968 L1997 **ORS GS** *020 †40
FRISCO, Donald Jerome. 1301 DAKOTA AVE S 57350 #056-05-1994 L1998 **PM** *020 †60
HAATVEDT, Cy Bennett. 172 4TH ST SE 57350 #026-04-1982 L1994 **GS** *020 †85
HOHM, Paul H. 455 KANSAS AVE SE 57350 #016-02-1943 L1946 **GP GS** *071
HOHM, Robert Carey. 455 KANSAS AVE SE, TSCHETTER-HOHM CLINIC 57350 #039-01-1973 L1974 **IM** *020
HUET, William Guillermo M. ■ 57350 #649-01-1953 L1961 **R NM** *071 †80
KURCH, Julie Ann. ■ 57350 #583-02-1958 L1967 **AN** *020
LAUSTERER, Jack Keith. 111 4TH ST SE, HURON CLINIC 57350 #030-05-1967 L1997 **FM** *020
LOEWEN, Nathan H. 433 KANSAS AVE SE STE L 57350 #019-02-1985 L1992 **FM OBS** *020 †18
MC KENNEY, Janice M. 111 4TH ST SE 57350 #065-05-1975 L1993 *020
MILLER, Linda Ann. 172 4TH ST SE, HURON REGIONAL MED CTR 57350 #032-01-1991 L2003 **GS** *020
MINER, William John. 455 KANSAS AVE SE, TSCHETTER & HOHM CLINIC, P 57350 #046-01-2004 L2007 **IM** *020
NICHOLAS, George Alfred. 530 IOWA AVE SE STE 106 57350 #026-04-1974 L1976 **GP** *020
PARK, Choong-Geun. 1552 DAKOTA AVE S 57350 #583-02-1959 L1995 **P** *071 †75
REED, Mary J. 172 4TH ST SE STE 401, THE REED CLINIC 57350 #048-12-1987 L1998 **GS CCS** *020 †85
REED, Richard Henry. 22147 404TH AVE 57350 #023-01-1966 L1993 **GS** *020 †85
REYNEN, Matthew Carl. 1301 DAKOTA AVE S 57350 #046-01-1991 L1996 **ORS OSS** *020 †40
SCHWAIGER, Jim. 904 COLORADO AVE SW 57350 #048-13-1990 L1998 **DR** *020 †80
SNEDEN, John Patrick. 118 3RD ST SE 57350 #046-01-1994 L1997 **IM** *020 †20
TRUH, Lois Ilean. 807 DAKOTA AVE S 57350 #026-08-1986 L1991 **FM OBS** *020 †18
WHEELER, Jeffrey Sebring. 111 4TH ST SE, HURON CLINIC FOUNDATION, L 57350 #039-01-1976 L1980 **IM** *020 †16,20
WIEDEL, Gregory Louis. 455 KANSAS AVE SE, TSCHETTER & HOHM CLINIC, P 57350 #030-06-1992 L1995 **IM** *020 †20
WOLFGRAM, Danny Allan. 1301 DAKOTA AVE S 57350 #026-04-1990 L2005 **FM FSM** *020 †18

IPSWICH – EDMUNDS

CHAVIER, Juan Ramon. 110 5TH AVE 57451 #308-01-1957 L1965 **PD** *071
HART, Harvey J. 110 5TH AVE 57451 #068-01-1970 L1980 **FM** *072

IRENE – YANKTON

MASON, Marianne T. ■ 57037 #026-04-1987 L2005 **OBG** *075 †30

JEFFERSON – UNION

GITTER, Richard. ■ 57038 #021-01-1992 L1993 **TS CD** *020 †85,90

KEYSTONE – PENNINGTON

LEONARD, Kenneth Ordell. 410 OLD CEMETERY RD 57751 #030-05-1954 L1968 **OPH GP** *071

KYLE – SHANNON

RESER, Juliana M. ■ 57752 #019-02-1975 L1992 **FM** *020 †18
TRAN, Khiem T. PO BOX 540 57752 #025-07-1994 L1995 **IM GP** *020 †20

LEAD – LAWRENCE

FINNEY, Lawrence Willard. ■ 57754 #018-03-1972 L1973 **FM** *071 †18

LEMMON – PERKINS

HOERAUF, Kent Rodney. 401 6TH AVE W, UNITED CLINIC LEMMON 57638 #037-01-1981 L1984 **IM IMG** *020 †20
JOYCE, John Patrick. 401 6TH AVE W, LEMMON CLINIC 57638 #037-01-1978 L1981 **FM** *020 †18
WILLOUGHBY, Brian G. 401 6TH AVE W, LEMMON CLINIC 57638 #028-34-1981 L1994 **IM** *020 †20

LENNOX – LINCOLN

FARMER, Joel David. ■ 57039 #046-01-2007 L2008 **TY** *012

LETCHER – SANBORN

MC NARY, Robert Eugene. PO BOX 187 57359 #048-14-1977 L1977 **GP** *075

MADISON – LAKE

ALLRED, Reid James. ■ 57042 #049-01-1971 L1972 **EM OM** *020 †18,16
BEECHER, Mary Jane. 903 N WASHINGTON AVE 57042 #046-01-1984 L1985 **FM** *020 †18
BELATTI, Richard Geo. 57042 #030-06-1956 L1959 **AN** *071
CHAMALES, Ingrid Andenas. 917 N WASHINGTON AVE 57042 #046-01-1987 L1996 **OBG** *020 †30
GOEBEL, Christina. 903 N WASHINGTON AVE 57042 #409-25-1993 L2003 **FM** *020 †18
HEILMAN, Bernard Francis. 220 NE 9TH ST 57042 #046-01-1980 L1983 **FM** *020 †18
JENNINGS, Laurel Jean. 917 N WASHINGTON AVE 57042 #046-01-2001 L2004 **FM** *020
NIELSEN, James Leroy. 903 N WASHINGTON AVE 57042 #024-07-1975 L1977 **FM** *020 †18
SAMPLE, Richard Gordon. 903 N WASHINGTON AVE 57042 #046-01-1978 L1979 **FM FPG** *020 †18
TIESZEN, Arden James. ■ 57042 #041-12-1961 L1962 **GP IM** *071 †18
WETZBARGER, Wayne Allen. 903 N WASHINGTON AVE 57042 #046-01-1981 L1982 **IM** *020 †20

MARTIN – BENNETT

BUTTERBRODT, Mark Pearson. ■ 57551 #026-04-1977 L1984 **PD** *020 †55

MECKLING – CLAY

FREEBURG, Erica Nichole. ■ 57069 #046-01-2008 L2008 *012

MENNO – HUTCHINSON

WALTNER, Lonnie Lee. 301 S HIGH ST 57045 #030-05-1965 L1966 **FM** *071 †18

MILBANK – GRANT

BJORDAHL, Kevin Leroy. 901 E VIRGIL AVE, CENTER-PRIMARY CARE 57252 #046-01-1982 L1984 **FM** *020 †18
CARPENTER, Paul Lynn. 901 E VIRGIL AVE, AREA HOSPITAL 57252 #026-04-1974 L1980 **CD** *020 †20
GEHRING, Stephen Hubbuch. 901 E VIRGIL AVE 57252 #020-12-1967 L1975 **U** *071 †95
HENRICHS, Christine E. 901 E VIRGIL AVE, CENTER-PRIMARY CARE 57252 #016-11-2000 L2001 **FM** *020 †18
JIBBEN, Celeste Marie. 233 E 2ND AVE 57252 #030-06-1992 L2003 **FM** *020 †18
MC DONALD, Bradley Allwin. 14724 480TH AVE, GLACIER MEDICAL SERVICES, 57252 #026-04-1992 L1998 **FM** *020 †18
REYNEN, Peter Jay. 901 E VIRGIL AVE, CENTER-PRIMARY CARE 57252 #046-01-1994 L1997 **FM** *020 †18
VANADURONGVAN, Kanya. 901 E VIRGIL AVE, CENTER-PRIMARY CARE 57252 #891-02-1970 L1979 **GP GS** *020
VANADURONGVAN, Vichit. 901 E VIRGIL AVE, CENTER-PRIMARY CARE 57252 #891-02-1967 L1978 **GS FM** *020 †85
VAN PEURSEM, Nanci Joy. 803 E MILBANK AVE 57252 #046-01-1997 L2000 **FM** *020 †18 ‡
WEBB, Crispin John, II. 803 E MILBANK AVE, AVERA MILBANK MEDICAL CTR 57252 #046-01-1999 L2002 **FM** *020 †18

MILLER – HAND

HUBER, Joel Bruce. 300 W 5TH ST, AVERA HAND CO CLINIC, PA 57362 #039-01-1977 L1980 **FM** *020 †18
SCHROEDER, Stephan Donlin. 300 W 5TH ST, AVERA HAND COUNTY CLINIC 57362 #026-04-1977 L1980 **FM** *020 †18 ‡
TURNER, Michelle A. 300 W 5TH ST 57362 #046-01-1994 L2001 **FM** *020 †18

MINA – EDMUNDS

KIMMEL, Douglas Jay. ■ 57451 #016-11-1975 L1995 **DR** *020

MITCHELL – DAVISON

ANDERSEN, Calvin Frank. 2200 N KIMBALL ST, STE 700 57301 #026-04-1969 L1974 **DR NM** *020 †80
ANDERSON, Ronald David. 2200 N KIMBALL ST STE 850 57301 #046-01-1984 L1988 **OBG** *020 †30
ARNOLD, Christine Jean. ■ 57301 #054-04-2000 L2003 **PD** *020 †55
BECKER, Phillip John. 525 N FOSTER ST 57301 #030-06-1992 L2000 **AN PME** *020 †05
BERRY, Jack Thos. ■ 57301 #005-06-1956 L1961 **FM** *071 †18
BHAT, Dileep Sadashiv. 2200 N KIMBALL ST, STE 900 57301 #495-22-1973 L1982 **U** *020 †95
BIEBERLY, Frank G, Jr. 525 N FOSTER ST 57301 #046-01-1979 L1982 **IM** *020 †20
BIRKENKAMP, Ray Thos. 305 N SANBORN BLVD 57301 #016-45-1977 L1979 **OPH** *020 †35 ‡
BUHLER, Carey Clay. 2200 N KIMBALL ST STE 700, JAMES VALLEY IMAGING LTD 57301 #046-01-1982 L1988 **DR VIR** *020 †80
CAMPBELL, Theresa Mae. 2250 N KIMBALL ST 57301 #046-01-1991 L1995 **FM** *020 †18
CARLSON, Walter Oscar. 1204 S BURR ST, ORTHOPEDIC INSTITUTE 57301 #026-04-1977 L1982 **ORS** *020 †40
CHRISTENSEN, Martin J. 818 W HAVENS AVE 57301 #046-01-1980 L1985 **FM** *020 †18
CHRISTIANSON, Heather P. 1200 E 6TH AVE, PEDIATRICS PLUS 57301 #046-01-1996 L1999 **PD** *020 †55
DELANEY, William A, Jr. ■ 57301 #030-06-1942 L1943 **GS OS** *071

DICK, Stephen James. 605 N FOSTER ST 57301 #649-28-1980 L1985 **RO** *020 †80
DOOHEN, Mark Thos. 525 N FOSTER ST, AVERA QUEEN OF PEACE 57301 #046-01-1987 L1988 **FM** *020 †18
FERRIE, Derek James. 2200 N KIMBALL ST STE 300 57301 #046-01-1997 L2000 **IM** *020 †20
FOUNTAIN, Karen Schueler. 605 N FOSTER ST 57301 #023-01-1972 L2006 **RO** *020 †80
GERLACH, Michael Dennis. 818 W HAVENS AVE, MITCHELL CLINIC, LTD 57301 #046-01-1998 L2001 **FM** *020 †18
HALEY, Michael Dennis. 2250 N KIMBALL ST 57301 #041-07-1974 L1975 **GS** *020 †85
HALEY, Michael Shawn. 525 N FOSTER ST 57301 #422-01-1998 L2002 **AN** *020 †05
HOLUM, Douglas Maynard. 818 W HAVENS AVE 57301 #026-04-1985 L1992 **FM** *020 †18
HOWE, Jerome Kent. 2250 N KIMBALL ST 57301 #030-05-1976 L1981 **GS** *020 †85
KRAUSE, Michael Ross. 625 N FOSTER ST STE 10 57301 #018-75-1998, ▲ L2003 **OBG** *020
LARIMER, Alan Mc Clelland. 1222 E 7TH AVE 57301 #036-07-1964 L1997 **ORS** *020 †40
LELAND, Dennis G. 2250 N KIMBALL ST 57301 #026-04-1987 L1992 **GS FM** *020 †85
MALTERS, David Thos. 2250 N KIMBALL ST 57301 #046-01-1983 L1984 **IM IMG** *020 †20
MALTERS, Patricia Brown. 2200 N KIMBALL ST, STE 800 57301 #046-01-1983 L1984 **IM** *020
MARGALLO, Lucio N. 1115 E 5TH AVE 57301 #748-01-1970 L1978 **IM** *020
MC KENZIE, Matthew James. 1204 S BURR ST, ORTHOPEDIC INSTITUTE 57301 #046-01-1991 L1996 **ORS** *020 †40
MC WHIRTER, Robert Ernest. 525 N FOSTER ST 57301 #056-06-1972 L1985 **ORS EM** *020 †40
MEANEY, Trevor Andrew. 2200 N KIMBALL ST, STE 400 57301 #046-01-1993 L2001 **FM** *020 †18
OLEGARIO, Jonathan Cacere. 120 W 6TH AVE 57301 #748-10-1999 L2005 **IM** *020 †20
RASMUSSEN, Paul Hunter. 818 W HAVENS AVE 57301 #026-08-1983 L1990 **FM** *020 †18
REYNOLDS, Andrew Young. 2200 N KIMBALL ST, STE 200 57301 #030-05-1999 L2004 **GS** *020 †85
SKOREY, Richard Joseph. 525 N FOSTER ST 57301 #231-04-1992 L1999 **P CHP** *020 †75
SNORTUM, Robert Allen. 525 N FOSTER ST, AVERA QUEEN OF PEACE HOSPI 57301 #026-04-1979 L1990 **FM AM** *020 †18
TEGETHOFF, Jennifer Lee. 1200 E 6TH AVE, PEDIATRICS PLUS 57301 #046-01-2001 L2004 **PD** *020 †55
TJARKS, Brian Dean. 625 N FOSTER ST, STE 209 57301 #046-01-1986 L1989 **FM** *020 †18
VANERDEWYK, John Martin. 525 N FOSTER ST 57301 #046-01-1988 L1992 **AN** *020 †05
VAN ERT, Gary Paul. 525 N FOSTER ST 57301 #030-05-1979 L1980 **FM** *020 †18
VISANI, Sandro. 2200 N KIMBALL ST 57301 #561-01-1967 L1979 **U** *071 †95
WAGNER, Rick J. 2200 N KIMBALL ST, STE 200 57301 #046-01-1990 L1997 **GS VS** *020
WARRAICH, Jamshed Asif. 2200 N KIMBALL ST STE 300 57301 #704-01-1999 L2006 **IM** *020 †20
WEATHERILL, Donald W. 818 W HAVENS AVE 57301 #030-06-1953 L1954 **GS GP** *071
WHEELER, Tamara Sue. 525 N FOSTER ST, JAMES VALLEY IMAGING 57301 #030-05-1995 L2000 **DR** *020 †80

MOBRIDGE – WALWORTH

CSAKI, Bela. 1401 10TH AVE W, MOBRIDGE MEDICAL CLINIC 57601 #407-10-1963 L2007 **TS VS** *071
DUCHENEAUX, Colette A. 1309 10TH AVE W, MOBRIDGE MEDICAL CLINIC 57601 #037-01-1999 L2002 **FM** *020 †18
HENDERSON, Travis Bruce. 1309 10TH AVE W, MOBRIDGE MEDICAL CLINIC 57601 #046-01-1997 L2000 **IM** *020 †20
LINDE, Leonard Melvin. ■ 57601 #039-01-1956 L1963 **FM** *020
MALMBERG, Kenric Dana. 1401 10TH AVE W 57601 #037-01-2004 L2007 **FM** *100 †18
MANTONE, James Keith. 1415 E GRAND XING 57601 #035-06-1993 L2003 **ORS OFA** *020 †40
REISTER, Jami Marie. PO BOX 520, 1309 10TH AVE W 57601 #046-01-2000 L2003 **FM** *020 †18
REISTER, Randolph James. PO BOX 520, 1309 10TH AVE W 57601 #046-01-1999 L2003 **IM** *100 †20
WUNDER, James Francis. ■ 57601 #026-04-1964 L1965 **R FM** *072 †80

MONTROSE – MCCOOK

SHAEFFER, James Howard. ■ 57048 #056-06-1955 L1960 **FM GP** *071

NEMO – LAWRENCE

HOUSER, Robert Lewis, Jr. ■ 57759 #030-06-1994 L1997 **IM** *020 †20
SEAMAN, Maynard Maurice. ■ 57759 #048-04-1956 L1959 **GP GS** *071

NORTH SIOUX CITY – UNION

BANKS, Brenda Jean. ■ 57049 #035-01-2008 L2008 *012
CHOW, Min-Hwa. ■ 57049 #305-01-1987 L2006 **NEP IM** *020 †20
DODDABELE, Sudarshan. ■ 57049 #495-35-1990 L1994 **HEM** *020 †20
FARRELL, Curtiss Dean. 612 N SIOUX POINT RD # 100 57049 #030-05-1983 L1992 **FM** *020 †18
FISHER, Frederick C. 600 N SIOUX POINT RD 57049 #025-12-1992 L1996 **AN** *020 †05
KEANE, Kenneth Martin. 57049 #030-06-1946 L1949 **ORS** *071 †40
KENNY, Thomas Joseph, IV. 101 TOWER RD, STE 120 57049 #046-01-1994 L2002 **OTO HNS** *020 †45
MENSCH, Christie Marie. ■ 57049 #030-06-2001 L2001 **FM** *100 †18
POWELL, Sarah Pertzborn. 101 TOWER RD, STE 120 57049 #018-03-2000 L2007 **OTO** *020 †45

PARKSTON – HUTCHINSON

BRINK, Darin Ray. 401 W GLYNN DR, AVERA ST BENDICT CRHC 57366 #046-01-1995 L1998 **FM** *020 †18
HONKE, Richard W, Jr. 401 W GLYNN DR 57366 #016-45-1975 L1978 **FM** *020 †18
MONSON, Charles David. 502 W FIR ST 57366 #030-05-1959 L1961 **GP** *071
PORTER, Maynard H. ■ 57366 #030-05-1950 L1951 **FM GS** *071
PROCHASKA, Douglas Ray. ■ 57366 #030-05-1985 L1992 **FM** *020 †18
VANDERPOL, Antoinette J. 401 W GLYNN DR, AVERA ST BENEDICT CRHC 57366 #046-01-1997 L2000 **FM** *020 †18

WICKERSHAM, Jason Wayne. 401 W GLYNN DR, AVERA ST BENEDICT HEALTH C 57366 #046-01-2001 L2004 **FM** *020

PEEVER – ROBERTS

WARHOL, Peter Joseph. ■ 57257 #026-04-2000 L2003 **CHP** *020 †75

PHILIP – HAAKON

HOLMAN, David Allen. 505 W PINE ST, PHILLIP CLINIC 57567 #037-01-1996 L1999 **FM** *020 †18
KLOPPER, Coenraad C. 503 W PINE ST 57567 #836-01-1979 L1991 *020

PIERRE – HUGHES

ABRAHAM, Prema. 801 E SIOUX AVE 57501 #004-01-1989 L1995 **OPH** *020 †35
ALLISON, Marty. 800 E DAKOTA AVE, AT ST MARYS HEALTHCARE 57501 #030-05-1995 L1998 **PD** *020 †55
ALLISON, Robert Louis. 800 E DAKOTA AVE, AT ST MARYS HEALTHCARE 57501 #030-05-1994 L1998 **IM** *020 †20
BAACK, Michelle Leigh. 800 E DAKOTA AVE, AT ST MARYS HEALTHCARE 57501 #046-01-1995 L1999 **PD** *020 †55
BARTHOLOMEW, Kenneth A. 800 E DAKOTA AVE, AT ST MARYS HEALTHCARE 57501 #049-01-1976 L1978 **GP** *020
BECKER, Eldon Ray. 800 E DAKOTA AVE, AT ST MARYS HEALTHCARE 57501 #037-01-1983 L1989 **GS** *020 †85
CHICOINE, Noel Denis. 640 E SIOUX AVE, SANFORD CLINIC DAKOTA PLAI 57501 #046-01-1981 L1985 **FM** *020 †18
DIRKS, Monte Steven. 801 E SIOUX AVE 57501 #023-12-1984 L1986 **OPH** *020 †35
HANISCH, Denise S. 800 E DAKOTA AVE, CAPITAL CITY PHYSICIANS, L 57501 #046-01-1994 L1997 **FM** *020 ‡
HARTFIEL, David Allen. 100 MAC LN, LLP 57501 #654-01-2000 L2005 **OBG** *020
HOFFSTEN, Phillip Ernest. 800 E DAKOTA AVE, AT ST MARYS HEALTHCARE 57501 #028-02-1965 L1979 **NEP** *020 †20
HOLLAND, Mikel Dean. 800 E DAKOTA AVE 57501 #046-01-1993 L1996 **FM** *020 †18
HUBER, Thomas John. 640 E SIOUX AVE, SANFORD CLNC-DAKOTA PLAINS 57501 #046-01-1977 L1978 **FM** *020
JERDE, O Myron. 615 E 4TH ST, SOUTH DAKOTA DEPT. OF HEAL 57501 #007-02-1964 L1968 **IM IMG** *071 †20
KHAWAJA, Imran Rashid. 800 E DAKOTA AVE, AT ST MARYS HEALTHCARE 57501 #704-01-1997 L2005 **IM** *020 †20
LINDBLOOM, Buron Otto. 100 MAC LN 57501 #017-20-1955 L1957 **FM OBG** *020 †18
LINN, Bernard James. 1601 N HARRISON AVE, LINN MEDICAL CLINIC 57501 #046-01-1983 L1986 **IM** *020 †20
MINDER, Jim L. 800 E DAKOTA AVE, AT ST MARYS HEALTHCARE 57501 #654-01-1988 L1993 **OBG** *020 †30
MONFORE, Barry Scott. 800 E DAKOTA AVE, MISSOURI VALLEY RADIOLOGY, 57501 #046-01-1992 L1997 **DR** *020 †80
NIELSON, Shelley Leigh. 800 E DAKOTA AVE, AT ST MARYS HEALTHCARE 57501 #048-12-1990 L2001 **OBG** *020 †30
NIXON, Robert Brian. 801 E SIOUX AVE 57501 #060-01-1977 L1985 **OPH** *020 †35
PESCE, Ulises Jorge. 803 E DAKOTA AVE 57501 #132-01-1970 L1981 **P** *020
PLUMAGE, Darrell Wade. 1601 N HARRISON AVE STE 6, LINN MEDICAL CLINIC 57501 #046-01-1995 L1998 **IM** *020 †20
POCHOP, Cindi Jo Marek. 800 E DAKOTA AVE, AT ST MARYS HEALTHCARE 57501 #046-01-1991 L1994 **IM** *020
RICHARDSON, Michael Todd. 800 E DAKOTA AVE, AT ST MARYS HEALTHCARE 57501 #046-01-1989 L1994 **FM** *020 †18
SANCHEZ, Gonzalo. 800 E DAKOTA AVE, AT ST MARYS HEALTHCARE 57501 #649-18-1962 L1974 **NS** *075 †25
SANCHEZ, Gonzalo Henry. 800 E DAKOTA AVE, AT ST MARYS HEALTHCARE 57501 #019-02-1998 L2003 **ORS** *020 †40
SPEARS, Barbara E Krumm. 111 S HURON AVE, PIERRE CLINIC PC 57501 #048-12-1959 L1960 **FM** *071 †18
STOUT, Stephen Young. 800 E DAKOTA AVE, AT ST MARYS HEALTHCARE 57501 #046-01-1980 L1985 **ORS** *020 †40
VILLA, Joseph Simon. 100 MAC LN 57501 #046-01-1989 L1999 **FM** *020 †18
VIZCARRA, Dale Elizabeth. 800 E DAKOTA AVE, AT ST MARYS HEALTHCARE 57501 #005-12-1989 L1992 **IM** *020 †18
VIZCARRA, Rodney T. 800 E DAKOTA AVE, AT ST MARYS HEALTHCARE 57501 #005-12-1984 L1992 **GS** *020 †85
WERTHMANN, Hubert Erwin. ■ 57501 #407-16-1948 L1959 **R** *071 †80
ZAKAHI, Raymond J. 772 E DAKOTA AVE, MEDICAL ASSOCIATES CLINIC 57501 #649-02-1957 L1961 **FM** *071 †18
ZIMMERMAN, Paul Lawrence. 801 E SIOUX AVE 57501 #040-02-1984 L2002 **OPH OS** *020 †35

PINE RIDGE – SHANNON

BERRY, Barbara Jean. PO BOX 1201, PHS/IHS PINE RIDGE 57770 #030-05-1972 L1991 **NPM** *074 †55
BORDEN, James Brooks. PO BOX 3031 57770 #040-02-1963 L1974 **GS GP** *020 †85
DELGADO-CANAS, Frankie. PO BOX 6004 57770 #308-06-1985 L1992 **FM** *020 †18
MURDOCK, David Keith. PO BOX 1201 57770 #025-07-1967 L1970 **PD PDI** *020
NIETO, Charles Michael. PO BOX 5010 57770 #035-01-1999 L2000 **HEM** *020
ROOKS, Sandra Kay. PO BOX 1201 57770 #047-05-1986 L1994 **PD** *020 †55
SUMNERS, Rory Christopher. PO BOX 1201, PINE RIDGE HOSP 57770 #035-09-1990 L1991 **FM** *020 †18
WEBER, S Patrick. HWY 18 57770 #037-01-1982 L1983 **PD ADL** *020

PLATTE – CHARLES MIX

BENTZ, Jerome Wayne. PO BOX 818, 601 E 7TH ST 57369 #046-01-1980 L1983 **FM FPG** *020 †18

KALDA, Ellison Franklin. 601 E 7TH ST 57369 #041-13-1947 L1949 **GP** *071

SCHMIESING, Michael Dale. PO BOX 818, PLATTE FAMILY MED CLINIC 57369 #030-06-1999 L2004 **FM** *020 †18

RAPID CITY – PENNINGTON

AHMAD, Sarfraz. 2805 5TH ST STE 100 57701 #704-21-1995 L2007 **GE** *020 †20

AHRLIN, Hollis Le Roy, Jr. ■ 57701 #056-05-1969 L1970 **ORS** *071 †40

AKERSON, Robert David. 353 FAIRMONT BLVD 57701 #026-04-1978 L1984 **PTH FOP** *020 †50

ALDRICH, Marc Nathan. 353 FAIRMONT BLVD 57701 #046-01-1983 L1992 **IM** *020 †20

ALLEN, Bruce Harris. 2800 JACKSON BLVD BOX 9153, PENNINGTON COUNTY 57702 #041-13-1957 L1958 **OTO** *072 †45

ALLEN, Richard Bruce. 2805 5TH ST 57701 #046-01-1990 L1998 **AN** *020 †05

ALLEN, Robert Glenn, Jr. 353 FAIRMONT BLVD 57701 #021-01-1975 L1981 **OS AM** *030 †05

ANDERSON, Dale Robt. 101 MINNESOTA ST, STE 210 57701 #005-12-1971 L1985 **ORS HS** *020 †40

ANDERSON, Eric Thomas. ■ 57701 #046-01-2008 *012

ANDERSON, Trevor Ryan. ■ 57701 #046-01-2006 **FP** *012

AUTHIER, Noe. 353 FAIRMONT BLVD 57701 #030-05-1961 L1962 **OPH** *075

AWAN, Saba Naureen. ■ 57702 #067-01-2006 **FP** *012

BABB, Terrence Elliott. 640 FLORMANN ST 57701 #051-07-1985 L2008 **OBG FM** *020 †30,18 ‡

BABBITT, Nancy Hutchins. 2620 JACKSON BLVD, STE C 57702 #046-01-1996 L1999 **FM** *020 †18

BACHWICH, Dale Richard. 2820 MT RUSHMORE RD, RAPID CITY MEDICAL CENTER, 57701 #025-01-1984 L1997 **GE HEP** *020 †20

BADE, Priscilla Faith. 640 FLORMANN ST STE 210 57701 #028-02-1987 L1993 **IMG IM** *020 †20

BAILEY, Stephen Patrick. 2805 5TH ST 57701 #003-01-1971 L1984 **AN IM** *020 †20,05

BALLARD, Mark Clifford. 101 MINNESOTA ST, STE 230 57701 #046-01-1993 L2000 **OBG** *020 †30

BAREIS, Reuben Julius A. 353 FAIRMONT BLVD, # 100 57701 #007-02-1952 L1957 **LM IMG** *071 †20

BARLOW, John Ford. 2805 5TH ST STE 210 57701 #024-01-1958 L1965 **PTH NM** *071 †50,28

BARRETT, Kathryn Ann. 740 SHERIDAN LAKE RD, STE B 57702 #046-01-1989 L1993 **FM** *020 †18

BARTSCH, David Carl. 353 FAIRMONT BLVD 57701 #016-06-1969 L1997 **ON IM** *020 †20

BAXTER, Brian Rik. 2929 5TH ST 57701 #034-01-1993 L2002 **DR** *020 †80

BAXTER, Ronald N. 2929 5TH ST 57701 #016-06-1992 L1998 **DR** *020 †80

BEASLEY, Richard Lee. 1600 MOUNTAIN VIEW RD 57702 #046-01-1989 L1994 **IM** *020

BECKER, Lois Jean. 502 E MONROE ST 57701 #016-06-1987 L1995 **FM** *020 †18

BEDINGFIELD, John R, Jr. 2820 MOUNT RUSHMORE RD 57701 #045-01-1967 L1978 **GS VS** *020 †85

BEHRENS, Clayton Leo. 353 FAIRMONT BLVD 57701 #041-13-1943 L1947 **GS GP** *071 †85

BELL, Eldon Earl. ■ 57702 #054-04-1960 L1969 **GPM AM** *071 †70

BELSAAS, Rebecca Lynn. 2929 5TH ST 57701 #046-01-1982 L1986 **DR** *020 †80

BENDT, Jeffrey Lynn. 2820 MOUNT RUSHMORE RD 57701 #046-01-1985 L1989 **OBG** *020 †30

BENN, Steven. 2905 5TH ST 57701 #396-21-1980 L1995 **NPM PD** *020 †55

BERGERON, Dale Alfred. 353 FAIRMONT BLVD 57701 #026-04-1955 L1970 **NM IM** *071 †20,28

BERGLUND, Eric F. 2040 W MAIN ST STE 210, # 1022 57702 #048-12-1983 L2004 **HEM IM** *020 †20

BERKEBILE, Dale Eugene. 1717 W BLVD 57701 #017-20-1962 L1969 **ORS** *071 †40

BERNARD, Gail Ann. 2201 JACKSON BLVD, STE 102 57702 #046-01-1996 L2000 **OPH** *020 †35

BERNHARD, Shana Strand. 677 CATHEDRAL DR 57701 #030-06-2001 L2005 **OBG** *020 †30

BERRY, Jeanne Marie. 3625 5TH ST STE 202, INTERNAL MEDICINE GERIATRI 57701 #046-01-1989 L1992 **IM** *020 †20

BESHARA, Marcia Jean. 2820 MT RUSHMORE RD, RAPID CITY MEDICAL CENTER 57701 #026-04-1997 L2001 **OBG** *020 †30

BEYER, Eugene Franklin. ■ 57702 #026-04-1948 L1955 **D** *071 †15

BIRCH, Fredric Martin. 640 FLORMANN ST, NEPHROLOGY 57701 #016-11-1978 L1981 **NEP IM** *020 †20

BLACKLER, Edmund Lloyd. ■ 57701 #046-01-2008 L2008 *012

BLICKENSDERFER, E D. 2805 5TH ST 57701 #037-01-1989 L1993 **OS** *020 †05

BLOEMENDAAL, Robert David. ■ 57701 #041-02-1958 L1959 **PTH** *071 †50

BOCHNA, Gary Stephen. 2820 MT RUSHMORE RD, RAPID CITY MEDICAL CENTER 57701 #056-06-1982 L1987 **GE IM** *020 †20

BODDICKER, Marc Eric. 705 COLUMBUS ST, ADVANCED DERM CTR 57701 #018-03-1980 L1984 **D CS** *020 †15 ‡

BORMES, Paul Andrew. 353 FAIRMONT BLVD 57701 #046-01-1986 L1991 **AN** *020 †05

BOWMAN, James Delmar. 640 FLORMANN ST, INTERNAL MEDICINE 57701 #046-01-1992 L1995 **IM** *020 †20

BRADLEY, Nathan Alan. ■ 57701 #046-01-2008 L2008 *012

BRIGHT, Douglas Alan. 502 E MONROE ST 57701 #018-03-1973 L1993 **FM** *040 †18

BRINK, Joel Michael. ■ 57703 #046-01-2008 *012

BROOKS, Patricia. ■ 57702 #046-01-2007 **FP** *012

BRYSON, Keith Gibson. 640 FLORMANN ST, STE 300 57701 #012-01-1978 L2006 **U** *020 †95

BUEHNER, Marvin Eldon. 677 CATHEDRAL DR, BLACK HILLS OB GYN LLP 57701 #048-04-1983 L1993 **OBG FM** *020 †18,30

BUNNELL, Susan Lynn. 2920 SHERIDAN LAKE RD 57702 #007-02-1977 L2005 **CHP P** *020 †18,75

BURGESS, Robert Carl. 2820 MT RUSHMORE RD, RAPID CITY MEDICAL CTR LLP 57701 #018-03-1989 L2001 **OTO** *020 †45

BURKHOLDER, Dayton Dee. ■ 57702 #041-01-1958 L2006 **GP** *020 †18

BURNAP, Donald Webster. 550 N 5TH ST STE 301 57701 #005-14-1966 L1972 **P** *071 †75

BURNETT, Raymond G. 677 CATHEDRAL DR 57701 #016-11-1962 L1968 **GYN EM** *071 †30

BUTZ, Gerald Warner. 710 SAINT ANNE ST 57701 #048-04-1973 L1978 **U** *020 †95

CALHOON, Stephen Lee. 353 FAIRMONT BLVD, RAPID CITY REG HOSP 57701 #024-01-1974 L1981 **PUD CCM** *020 †20

CAMERON, Douglas E. ■ 57702 #007-02-1950 L1952 **GS LM** *072 †85

CARLSON, Gary Loy. 353 FAIRMONT BLVD 57701 #007-02-1971 L1976 **OTO PS** *020 †45

CARVER, Richard F. 7236 JORDAN DR, STE 100A 57702 #035-15-1963 L1992 **PS GS** *020 †65

CAVANAUGH, Dennis Jos. ■ 57702 #030-06-1974 L1979 **GS NM** *020 †85,28

CHIBA, Masaru. 2805 5TH ST STE 100 57701 #572-01-1988 L2007 **PCC** *020 †20

CHRISTENSEN, Michael W. 677 CATHEDRAL DR STE 200 57701 #028-02-1986 L1990 **OBG** *020 †30

CHRISTENSEN, Rochelle M. 677 CATHEDRAL DR STE 200 57701 #030-06-1993 L1997 **OBG** *020 †30

CHRISTIANSEN, Gary Lee. 710 SAINT ANNE ST 57701 #034-01-1987 L1995 **U GS** *020 †85,95

CLARK, Leroy Allen. 3200 CANYON LAKE DR, SIOUX SAN IHS 57702 #026-04-1998 L2002 **FM** *020 †18

COLTHARP, Stephen Plunket. ■ 57702 #042-02-2007 **FP** *012

CORNFORD, Raymond Chas. 353 FAIRMONT BLVD 57701 #056-05-1963 L1964 **D A** *071

CWACH, Heather Gay. 2929 5TH ST, STE 240 57701 #046-01-1995 L2001 **N** *020 †75

DAVY, James M. ■ 57709 #018-75-1977, ▲ L1978 **EM GP** *020

DEGEN, Katherine Anne. ■ 57703 #046-01-2008 *012

DE MARS, Patrick Dennis. 5021 IRELAND PL 57702 #026-04-1981 L2003 **AN PD** *020 †55,05

DEMETRIOU, James Peter. 502 E MONROE ST 57701 #028-34-2002 L2005 **FM** *020 †18

DEN HARTOG, Bryan Dale. 7220 S HIGHWAY 16 57702 #018-03-1985 L1995 **ORS** *020 †40

DENKER, Thomas Lee. 2805 5TH ST 57701 #305-01-1998 L2003 *020 †05

DEWALD, Allan Lee. 716 QUINCY ST, RADIOLOGY ASSOCIATES 57701 #026-04-1964 L1965 **R** *071 †80

DIAMOND, Kenneth Chas. 703 QUINCY ST STE 1 57701 #031-01-1990 L1995 **FM** *020 †18

DICK, Stephen Duane. 353 FAIRMONT BLVD 57701 #005-12-1985 L1990 **EM** *020 †16

DICKSON, Daryl S. 3625 5TH ST 57701 #046-01-1978 L1988 **GP** *020

DIEHL, Amanda Nichole. 640 FLORMANN ST, PEDIATRICS 57701 #030-06-1996 L2000 **PD** *020

DIEHL, Anthony Scott. 677 CATHEDRAL DR 57701 #030-06-1993 L2000 **OBG** *020 †30

DIETRICH, Christopher T. 1136 JACKSON BLVD 57702 #046-01-2001 L2005 **PM** *020 †60

DIRKS, Michael Steven. ■ 57701 #023-12-2006 L2008 **GS** *012

DROVDAL, Cynthia Susan. 502 E MONROE ST 57701 #046-01-2002 L2005 **FM** *100

DRUMMOND, Ronald Geo. 353 FAIRMONT BLVD, CANCER CARE INSTITUTE 57701 #030-06-1968 L1975 **RO R** *071 †80

DUCHENE, Clark Charles. 7220 S HIGHWAY 16 57702 #048-12-1998 L2004 **OSM** *020 †40

DURR, Samuel Jos. 4150 5TH ST, CARDIOLOGY ASSOCS PC 57701 #030-06-1983 L1988 **CD IM** *020 †20

D'URSO, Michael Philip. 4150 5TH ST 57701 #030-06-1989 L1996 **CD** *020 †20

DURST, Robert Andrew, Jr. 2929 5TH ST 57701 #018-03-1979 L1992 **DR** *020 †80

DVORAK, Derrick William. ■ 57701 #046-01-2002 L2002 **FP** *012

DZINTARS, Egon Felix. 717 SAINT FRANCIS ST, MEDICAL ARTS CLNC 57701 #038-40-1983 L1986 **FM** *020 †18

DZINTARS, Paul Felix. ■ 57702 #407-24-1948 L1955 **FM** *071

EASTMO, Eric Stener. 353 FAIRMONT BLVD 57701 #030-06-1999 L2004 **RO** *020 †80

EATON, D Bruce. 2820 MOUNT RUSHMORE RD 57701 #026-04-1989 L1997 **IM** *020 †20

EBBERT, Larry Paul. 353 FAIRMONT BLVD 57701 #038-40-1969 L1975 **ON HEM** *020 †20

ECCARIUS, Scott Grant. 631 SAINT ANNE ST, STE 103 57701 #046-01-1987 L1991 **OPH** *020 †35

EDELEN, Rachel Christine. 640 FLORMANN ST, ENDOCRINOLOGY 57701 #046-01-1997 L2000 **PDE PD** *020 †55

EIDE, Brook Matthew. 353 FAIRMONT BLVD 57701 #046-01-2005 L2005 **EM** *012

ELIASON, Susan L. 2805 5TH ST STE 210 57701 #046-01-1993 L1998 **PTH DMP** *020 †50

ELSTON, John T. 353 FAIRMONT BLVD 57701 #018-03-1945 L1955 **PTH** *071 †50

ELSTON, Michael Philip. 529 KANSAS CITY ST, STE 200 57701 #046-01-1986 L1991 **FM** *040 †18

ENGELBRECHT, James Allen. 7220 S HIGHWAY 16 57702 #018-03-1975 L1980 **RHU IM** *020 †20

EVANS, Bradley James. 600 DAKOTA DR 57702 #046-01-1988 L1988 **OPH** *020 †35

EVANS, Bruce Allan. 600 DAKOTA DR 57702 #046-01-1984 L1992 **GP EM** *020

FALKENBURG, Joleen Elaine. 502 E MONROE ST 57701 #046-01-2003 L2006 **FM** *020 †18

FERRAZ, Francisco Marconi. 353 FAIRMONT BLVD, ATTN: SHELLY BINNEBOSE 57701 #187-07-1975 L2008 **NS N** *020 †25

FERRELL, Robert Lee. 2820 MOUNT RUSHMORE RD, RAPID CITY MEDICAL CTR 57701 #055-01-1965 L1973 **OTO** *020 †45

FERRIER, Lewis Norman. 4150 5TH ST 57701 #060-02-1979 L1996 **CD IM** *020

FINLEY, Robert Cameron. 2929 5TH ST, STE 240 57701 #046-01-1983 L1987 **N** *020 †75

FINLEY, Victoria Kosters. 2820 MOUNT RUSHMORE RD 57701 #046-01-1981 L1987 **D** *020 †15

FISHER, Anne Krier. 353 FAIRMONT BLVD 57701 #018-03-1988 L1994 **EM** *020 †16

FLYNN, Leo P. 2929 5TH ST 57701 #046-01-1998 L2004 **DR** *020 †80

FRANZ, Daniel Peter. 3810 JACKSON BLVD 57702 #007-02-1984 L1987 **FM** *020 †18

FRAZER, Paul Daniel. 915 MOUNTAIN VIEW RD, RAPID CITY REGIONAL WEST 57702 #020-12-1978 L1979 **P** *071 †75

FREDERICKSON, Helen L. 677 CATHEDRAL DR, BLACKHILLS OBGYN 57701 #007-02-1979 L2000 **GO GYN** *020 †30

FREI, Virginia Lynn. 3200 CANYON LAKE DR 57702 #016-02-1981 L1987 **FM** *020 †18

FREIMARK, Lyle G. ■ 57702 #025-01-1952 L1961 **GS VS** *071 †85

FROMM, Christopher Karl. 6950 PRESTWICK RD 57702 #046-01-2000 L2004 **FM** *020 †18

FROMM, David Sterling. 2820 MT RUSHMORE RD, RAPID CITY MEDICAL CENTER, 57701 #046-01-2002 L2007 **GS** *020

FROMM, Deborah Lynn. 717 SAINT FRANCIS ST 57701 #046-01-1998 L2001 **FM** *020 †18

FROMM, Harold Edward. 353 FAIRMONT BLVD 57701 #016-06-1957 L1965 **GS** *071 †85

FROST, Harold Lester. 353 FAIRMONT BLVD 57701 #025-07-1953 L1960 **PTH** *071 †50

FROST, James Alexander. 2805 5TH ST, STE 210 57701 #046-01-1983 L1985 **PTH IM** *020 †50

FROST, Steven Gerard. 2805 5TH ST 57701 #046-01-1991 L1996 **APM** *020 †05

FROST, Timothy Robt. 353 FAIRMONT BLVD, CITY REGIONAL 57701 #046-01-1984 L1988 **DR R** *020 †80

GARRY, Mark Thomas. 353 FAIRMONT BLVD 57701 #012-05-1994 L2002 **P** *020 †75

GIBSON, Joan Elaine. ■ 57702 #035-08-1991 L2004 **PD** *020 †55

GILBERT, James Alan, Jr. 353 FAIRMONT BLVD, RAPID CITY EMERGENCY SERVI 57701 #034-01-1989 L1999 **EM** *020 †16

GILL, Timothy Jon. 7220 S HIGHWAY 16 57702 #034-01-1976 L1981 **ORS** *020 †40

GOBLE, Kimberly Jo. 2805 5TH ST, STE 210 57701 #046-01-1997 L2002 **PTH HMP** *020 †50

GODBE, David Hampton. 2820 MOUNT RUSHMORE RD, RAPID CITY MEDICAL CENTER 57701 #016-43-1988 L2003 **GS VS** *020 †85

GORDON, Robert Thos. 4150 5TH ST 57701 #016-06-1972 L2003 **CD TS** *020 †85,90

GREEN, Justin Lane. 2820 MT RUSHMORE RD, DEPT OF SURGERY 57701 #019-02-1994 L1999 **GS** *020 †85

GROOTE, Curtis Arthur. 2100 7TH ST 57701 #018-03-1965 L1972 **OTO** *071 †45

GROSS, Eric Malcolm. 640 FLORMANN ST, REGIONAL MEDICAL CLINIC 57701 #019-02-1993 L2007 **OTO** *020 †45

GUNDERSON, Dale Eugene. 629 QUINCY ST 57701 #048-12-1976 L1981 **OTO** *071 †45

GUZMAN, Manuel Alfredo. ■ 57702 #935-01-1971 L1977 **ID IM** *050

GUZMAN, Manuel Cruz. 3200 CANYON LAKE DR 57702 #748-07-1960 L1982 *020

HAAS, Stephen Nelson. 640 FLORMANN ST, ENDOCRINOLOGY 57701 #026-06-1967 L1972 **END IM** *071 †20

8360

■ = Address Information Privacy Protected

HABBE, Donald Mark. 2805 5TH ST, STE 210 57701 #046-01-1984 L1989 **PTH FOP** *020 †50
HABBE, Thomas Geo. 2929 5TH ST 57701 #007-02-1989 L2000 **VIR** *020 †80
HALL, Courtland J. 216 ANAMARIA DR 57701 #010-01-1975 L1989 **AN** *020 †05
HALL, Julianna Heller. ■ 57702 #010-01-1976 L1991 **PTH** *020 †50
HAMLYN, Harry Ward. 915 MOUNTAIN VIEW RD 57702 #005-06-1985 L1995 **P** *020 †75
HANNA, Chad Brooks. 353 FAIRMONT BLVD, RAPID CITY REGIONAL HOSPIT 57701 #046-01-1993 L1998 **IM** *020 †20
HANSEN, Craig Knute. 2620 JACKSON BLVD STE C 57702 #046-01-1979 L1980 **FM** *020 †18
HANSEN, James Jesse. ■ 57701 #016-06-1967 L1997 **PTH** *072 †50
HANSON, Charles Eric. 2805 5TH ST 57701 #046-01-1985 L1989 **AN** *020 †05
HANSON, Thomas James. 3501 5TH ST, REG MED CLNC 57701 #039-01-1970 L2007 **END IM** *020 †20
HARLOW, Mark Louis. 7220 S HIGHWAY 16 57702 #056-06-1986 L1992 **ORS** *020 †40
HARRISON, Geniel. 502 E MONROE ST 57701 #037-01-2005 L2007 **FP** *012
HART, Charles Edward. 353 FAIRMONT BLVD, ADMIN RAPID CITY REG HOSP 57701 #026-04-1975 L1983 **EM FM** *030 †18,16
HATA, Steven Kenichi. 2929 5TH ST, STE 240 57701 #014-01-1978 L1986 **N** *020 †75
HAWLEY, Dustin. ■ 57702 #046-01-2008 *012
HEILMAN, K John. 4150 5TH ST 57701 #028-34-1980 L2006 **CD IM** *020 †20
HEINTZ, Douglas Jon. 2507 THAMES CIR 57702 #026-04-1971 L1988 **GP** *020
HENDERSON, Jeffrey Allen. 701 SAINT JOSEPH ST, STE 204 57701 #005-18-1989 L1993 **IM** *020 †20
HEPNAR, Gerald John. 353 FAIRMONT BLVD 57701 #016-43-1988 L2004 **IM** *020 †20
HERBST, John Wesley. 504 E MONROE ST, OF THE BLACK HILLS 57701 #018-03-1976 L1982 **IM** *030 †20
HERCULES, Costas. ■ 57702 #035-45-1969 L1973 **P OS** *020
HERLIHY, John Jos. 2820 MT RUSHMORE RD, RAPID CITY MEDICAL CENTER, 57701 #039-01-1978 L1982 **OPH** *020 †35
HERMANN, Harland Thos. ■ 57702 #030-05-1943 L1964 **P N** *072 †75
HERR, Victoria Ann. 2805 5TH ST STE 210 57701 #007-02-1987 L1993 **PTH PCP** *020 †50
HEWITT, John Mc Leod. 716 QUINCY ST 57701 #016-11-1947 L1958 **R** *071 †80
HICKS, Terry Ray. 2525 W MAIN ST STE 209 57702 #001-06-1978 L1979 **P** *020 †75
HILL, Briana M. 2820 MT RUSHMORE RD, RAPID CITY MEDICAL CENTER, 57701 #023-12-1986 L2006 **D** *020 †15
HILL, John Thomas, Jr. 353 FAIRMONT BLVD, EMERGENCY DEPT. 57701 #021-05-1995 L2000 **EM** *020 †16
HOFFMANN, Jay Walter. 640 FLORMANN ST, INTERNAL MEDICINE 57701 #046-01-1982 L1983 **IM** *020
HOFMANN, Alfred Robt. 353 FAIRMONT BLVD 57701 #016-06-1960 L1965 **AN** *071 †05
HOFMANN, Daniel Peter. 4215 CORRAL DR 57702 #056-06-1987 L1999 **EM** *020 †16
HONKE, Sandra Jane. 353 FAIRMONT BLVD 57701 #016-06-1976 L2001 **EM** *020 †16
HOWARD, William James. 2820 MOUNT RUSHMORE RD 57701 #007-02-1968 L1975 **IM CCM** *071 †20
HUSEMAN, Joseph Anthony. ■ 57703 #023-12-2004 L2005 **GS** *020
IVERSON, Gregory Joel. 353 FAIRMONT BLVD, RAPID CITY REGIONAL HOSP 57701 #026-04-1975 L1978 **EM** *020 †18,16
JAMES, Edward Herman. ■ 57702 #068-01-1957 L1973 **NS** *071
JANSS, Gerti Jimeno. 1828 W KANSAS CITY ST, BOX 57709 57702 #847-01-1956 L1973 **A IM** *020 †16
JANSS, William Bruce. 1828 W KANSAS CITY ST, WILLIAM B JANSS & GERTI J 57702 #018-03-1955 L1994 **IM P** *020
JOHNSON, Dave Robt. 101 E MINNESOTA ST, STE 260 57701 #046-01-1980 L1984 **IM** *030 †20
JOHNSON, David Arthur. 3810 JACKSON BLVD, SIDE 57702 #030-06-1986 L1997 **FM** *020 †18
JOHNSON, Paul Steven. 353 FAIRMONT BLVD 57701 #030-05-1974 L1992 **ON IM** *020 †20
JOHNSON, Robert Kabrud. ■ 57701 #035-45-1957 L1963 **IM** *071
JONES, Christine Ann. 2929 5TH ST, STE 230 57701 #026-04-1995 L2000 **RHU** *020 †20
JOUBERT, Marie. ■ 57701 #067-02-1964 L1992 **N** *071
KADRMAS, Michael Wayne. 7220 S HIGHWAY 16, BLACK HILLS ORTHO & SPINE 57702 #054-04-1994 L2004 **ORS** *020 †40
KEEGAN, James Michael. 353 FAIRMONT BLVD, ADMINISTRATION 57701 #012-05-1977 L1990 **ID IM** *020 †20
KELTS, Eric Alan. 2929 5TH ST, STE 240 57701 #046-01-1996 L2005 **OPH N** *020 †75
KELTS, Keith Alan. 2929 5TH ST, STE 240 57701 #035-45-1971 L1979 **N CHN** *020 †55,75
KIRANE, Harshal Devidas. ■ 57701 #048-12-2007 **FP** *012
KNIGHT, Douglas Graham. ■ 57702 #026-04-1974 L1975 **ADM P** *020 †18
KNOWLES-SMITH, Peter. 1702 E HIGHWAY 44 57703 #671-01-1956 L1975 **FM GP** *020 †18
KNUTSEN, Roger Steven. 717 MEADE ST 57701 #046-01-1981 L1986 **D IM** *020 †20,15 ‡
KOCH, Sherri Danelle. 3625 5TH ST 57701 #026-04-1995 L1998 **FM** *020 †18 ‡
KOVARIK, Joseph Allen. ■ 57702 #030-06-1960 L1967 **U** *020 †95
KOVARIK, Richard A. ■ 57701 #030-06-1952 L1959 **OBG** *071 †30
KOVARIK, Stephen Matthew. 2905 5TH ST 57701 #016-02-1981 L1986 **NPM PD** *020 †55
KOVARIK, Wenzel James. 353 FAIRMONT BLVD 57701 #030-06-1962 L1963 **FM** *071 †18
KOWAL, Vera Olya. 7660 CINNAMON RIDGE DR, BLACK HILLS LASIK CENTER 57702 #025-01-1989 L1997 **OPH** *020 †35
KRAFKA, Thomas Lee. 2929 5TH ST 57701 #048-02-1970 L1976 **DR GP** *020 †80
KULLBOM, James Byron. ■ 57702 #030-05-1969 L1970 **ORS** *020 †40
KUMAR, Kaushalya Ashok. ■ 57701 #495-94-1977 L1993 **P** *074
KUNZ, James Arthur. 716 QUINCY ST 57701 #026-04-1961 L1966 **R** *071 †80
LAMPERT, Arthur Arno, Jr. ■ 57702 #041-13-1968 L1969 **FM** *075
LASSEGARD, John J. 504 E MONROE ST, OF THE BLACK HILLS 57701 #046-01-1988 L1991 **FM** *020 †18 ‡
LAWLOR, Brett David. 1136 JACKSON BLVD, STE 3 57702 #046-01-1992 L1997 **PM** *020 †60
LEHMANN, Douglas Dixon. ■ 57702 #016-11-1989 L1999 **OS** *020 †20,55
LEMBKE, Jeanie Marie. 717 SAINT FRANCIS ST, MEDICAL ARTS CLINIC 57701 #046-01-1996 L1999 **FM** *020 †18
LOOBY, John Edward. 353 FAIRMONT BLVD, DEPT OF INTERNAL MEDICINE 57701 #046-01-1994 L1997 **IM** *020 †20
LOOS, Charles Michael. 3810 JACKSON BLVD, WESTSIDE FAMILY PRACTICE 57702 #030-06-1963 L1966 **FM** *071
LORD, Charles Jerald. 419 QUINCY ST 57701 #048-15-1974 L1977 **P** *020
LUND, Kari Ann. 504 E MONROE ST, OF THE BLACK HILLS 57701 #046-01-1997 L2000 **FM** *020 †18
MACLACHLAN, Robert D. 653 TEXAS ST 57701 #068-01-1993 L2002 **N** *020 †75
MANGULIS, George J. 353 FAIRMONT BLVD 57701 #407-21-1948 L1955 **FM FPG** *071
MANLOVE, Stephen Paul. 636 SAINT ANNE ST STE 100 57701 #026-04-1982 L1987 **P IM** *020 †20,75
MANNING, Kelly Wade. ■ 57702 #049-01-1994 L2001 **EM** *020 †16
MARIETTA, Dean Roy. 2805 5TH ST 57701 #030-06-1994 L2001 **AN** *020 †05
MARRS, Jeffrey Scott. 7220 S HIGHWAY 16 57702 #026-08-1997 L2002 **ORS** *020 †40
MATHEWS, Michael John. 2333 CHANCERY LN 57702 #046-01-1980 L1981 **EM IM** *020 †16
MAXWELL, Marius. 4141 5TH ST 57701 #917-03-1985 L2003 **NS GS** *020
MAY, Jennifer Kay. 353 FAIRMONT BLVD 57701 #046-01-1999 L2005 **RHU** *020 †20
MC CAFFERTY, James Duff. 2805 5TH ST, PULMONOLOGY 57701 #030-05-1981 L1992 **PUD CCM** *020 †20
MC GUIGAN, Patrick M. ■ 57702 #016-11-1959 L1974 **GS AM** *071 †85
MC GUIRE, Michael Patrick. 2820 MT RUSHMORE RD, RAPID CITY MEDICAL CENTER, 57701 #054-04-1984 L1993 **GE IM** *020 †20
MILESTONE, Julian. ■ 57701 #005-11-1955 L1956 **FM GP** *071
MILLEA, Roger P. 2805 5TH ST 57701 #018-03-1953 L1960 **U** *071 †95
MILLER, Stephan James. 353 FAIRMONT BLVD, DEPT. OF EMERGENCY MEDICIN 57701 #046-01-1999 L2006 **EM** *020 †16
MILLS, Craig Gilman. 2929 5TH ST, STE 240 57701 #019-02-1990 L1998 **PM PME** *020 †60
MORSE, James Arthur. ■ 57701 #030-05-1957 L1992 **GP EM** *071 †85
MORTIMER, Sam L. 2905 5TH ST 57701 #054-04-1972 L1976 **PD** *020 †55
NABWANGU, James Francis. 2805 5TH ST STE 100 57701 #023-07-1967 L2001 **NS** *020 †25
NESBIT, Dennis Elliott. 2929 5TH ST 57701 #049-01-1978 L1982 **DR** *020 †80
NESBIT, Troy Michael. 2805 5TH ST 57701 #049-01-2001 L2007 **AN** *020 †05
NEU, Norman Dean. ■ 57701 #048-12-1970 L1975 **OBG** *020 †30
NEZ, Patricia Ann. ■ 57702 #008-01-2000 *100
NIEMANN, Nicole Cristina. 717 SAINT FRANCIS ST 57701 #046-01-2002 L2005 **FM** *100
NOBACK, Keith Allan. 502 E MONROE ST 57701 #016-01-1996 L1996 **FM** *020 †18
NORD, Allen Evans. 717 SAINT FRANCIS ST 57701 #026-04-1974 L1980 **FM** *020 †18 ‡
O'DAY, Wyatt James. 353 FAIRMONT BLVD, RAPID CITY REGIONAL HOSPIT 57701 #046-01-2000 L2003 **EM** *020
OGUNREMI, Ayodele Oluwole. 640 FLORMANN ST, NEPHROLOGY 57701 #690-08-1991 L2001 **NEP** *020 †20 ‡
OLIVER, Christopher Lee. ■ 57702 #046-01-2001 L2002 **OTO** *012
OLIVER, Donald Errett. 2905 5TH ST 57701 #024-07-1975 L1980 **PD** *020 †55
ORECCHIA, Paul Mario. 4150 5TH ST 57701 #005-02-1976 L2004 **TS GS** *020 †85,90
OSTERMANN, Kelli Marie. 640 FLORMANN ST, MEDICAL ASSOCIATES OF THE 57701 #037-01-1996 L1998 **PD MPD** *020 †55
PANSEGRAU, Donald Griffin. ■ 57701 #018-03-1963 L2001 **CD IM** *071 †20
PAPENDICK, Lew Wayne. 7220 S HIGHWAY 16 57702 #046-01-1984 L1989 **ORS** *020 †40
PARYS, Stephen Chas. 2905 5TH ST 57701 #030-06-1989 L2003 **PD** *020 †55
PETEREIT, Daniel Grant. 353 FAIRMONT BLVD 57701 #046-01-1989 L1999 **RO** *020 †80
PETUKHOVA, Marina. 2820 MT RUSHMORE RD, RAPID CITY MEDICAL CENTER, 57701 #913-13-1981 L1999 **IM** *020 †20
PIERCE, Raymond Leonard. 101 E MINNESOTA ST, STE 260 57701 #016-01-1987 L2001 **IM** *020 †20
POLING, Tamara Lyn. 2820 MOUNT RUSHMORE RD 57701 #046-01-1990 L1994 **D** *020 †15
PRESTON, Robert Chas. 408 KNOLLWOOD DR 57701 #046-01-1983 L1985 **GP IM** *020
PURDY, Drew Alan. 4150 5TH ST 57701 #046-01-1982 L1984 **CD IM** *020 †20
RAFEEQ, Bushra. ■ 57702 #704-21-1995 L2008 **NEP** *100 †20
RAFFERTY, Michael Charles. 2006 MOUNT RUSHMORE RD 57701 #046-01-1995 L2006 **FM** *020 †18
RAWSON, Daniel Young. 2805 5TH ST, PULMONOLOGY 57701 #012-05-1975 L1996 **PUD CCM** *020 †20
RAYMOND, Julie Todd. 640 FLORMANN ST, GENERAL SURGERY 57701 #041-09-1989 L1994 **GS** *020 †85
RAYMOND, Louis Chas. 640 FLORMANN ST, NEPHROLOGY 57701 #041-09-1989 L1994 **NEP** *020 †20
REISS, Adam Scott. 502 E MONROE ST 57701 #056-06-2002 L2005 **FM** *020
RENKA, Richard Pierce. 528 QUINCY ST 57701 #048-04-1974 L1977 **P** *020
RICE, Stuart Glen. 4141 5TH ST 57701 #056-06-1987 L2000 **NS** *020 †25
ROCK, Gene Fredrick. ■ 57701 #019-02-1967 L1969 **R** *074
ROSARIO, Elmo Jos. 2805 5TH ST, PULMONOLOGY 57701 #048-04-1973 L1979 **PUD IM** *050 †20
RUD, James Amos. ■ 57702 #030-05-1959 L1966 **PTH** *072 †50
RUSSELL, Richard John. 2805 5TH ST 57701 #050-02-1991 L1998 **AN** *020 †05
SABOW, John David. ■ 57701 #041-02-1967 L1972 **N** *020 †75
SAFFELL, Greg Dale. 2929 5TH ST 57701 #028-34-1989 L2002 **DR** *020 †80
SANDVIK, David Eugene. 640 FLORMANN ST, STE 210 57701 #048-12-1976 L1979 **IMG IM** *020 †20
SANMARTIN, Jorge Enrique. 4150 5TH ST 57701 #030-06-1966 L1978 **CD IM** *071 †20
SCHABAUER, Alexander M. 4150 5TH ST 57701 #016-06-1989 L1996 **CD** *020 †20
SCHABAUER, Ernest A. ■ 57709 #154-07-1951 L1959 **IM GS** *071 †18
SCHAEFER, Gerald Bradley. 2905 5TH ST, BLACK HILLS PEDIATRICS 57701 #039-01-1982 L2002 **OS PDE** *050 †55,19
SCHAEFFER, Jamie S. 2820 MT RUSHMORE RD, C/O RAPID CITY MEDICAL CEN 57701 #037-01-2004 L2007 **FM** *020 †18
SCHATZ, Sarah Lynn. 502 E MONROE ST 57701 #037-01-2005 L2007 **FP** *012
SCHAUER, Bobbie Ann. 353 FAIRMONT BLVD, RAPID CITY EMERGENCY SERVI 57701 #026-04-1998 L2002 **EM** *020 †16
SCHINDLER, Jay Jenson. 2805 5TH ST, NEUROSURGERY 57701 #008-01-1996 L2004 **NS** *020 †25
SCHLEUSENER, Jeffrey T. 2805 5TH ST, STE 210 57701 #046-01-1990 L1995 **PTH** *020 †50
SCHLEUSENER, Rand Lee. 7220 S HIGHWAY 16 57702 #030-05-1986 L1997 **ORS** *020 †40
SCHMAGEL, Pamela Ann. 101 E MINNESOTA ST, STE 230 57701 #046-01-1993 L2005 **OBG** *020 †30
SCHROEDER, Mark Thos. 353 FAIRMONT BLVD 57701 #032-01-1988 L1992 **HO** *020 †20
SCHUTZ, Robert J. 3615 5TH ST STE 101 57701 #030-06-1986 L1993 **PS GS** *020 †85,65
SCOTT, Lycia Anne. 2820 MT RUSHMORE RD, RAPID CITY MED CTR 57701 #056-06-1999 L2003 **D** *020 †15
SEAMAN, David. ■ 57701 #041-13-1954 L1964 **OPH** *071 †35
SEJVAR, Joseph Peter. 716 QUINCY ST 57701 #019-02-1964 L1967 **R** *071 †80
SELJESKOG, Edward Louis. 4141 5TH ST 57701 #026-04-1959 L1973 **NS** *020 †25
SHAEFER, Janet Eleanor. 2929 5TH ST 57701 #008-01-1984 L2001 **DR IM** *020 †20,80
SHINING, H Streeter. 640 FLORMANN ST 57701 #018-03-1958 L1965 **IM CD** *071 †20
SIBERT, Mary Ann. ■ 57702 #001-02-1975 L1994 **P** *020
SILVIO PICARDI, Edward J. 101 MINNESOTA ST, STE 220 57701 #041-09-1983 L1989 **GS VS** *020 †85

SIMMONS, Lynn Harvey. 2905 5TH ST 57701 #030-06-1985 L1992 **PD** *020 †55
SIMMONS, Matt Edward. 2929 5TH ST, STE 240 57701 #030-06-1985 L1992 **N** *020 †75
SKALESKI, Stephen Anthony. ■ 57701 #033-06-1993 L1996 **FM** *020 †18
SLAMA, David Dean. 717 SAINT FRANCIS ST 57701 #012-05-1975 L1977 **GS VS** *020 †85
SLINGSBY, John Geoffrey. 240 MINNESOTA ST 57701 #012-05-1976 L1982 **OPH** *020 †35
SMITH, Brian Douglas. 502 E MONROE ST, RCRH FM RESIDENCY CLINIC 57701 #007-02-1995 L2004 **FM** *020 †18
SMITH, Gregory Lamonte. 353 FAIRMONT BLVD, RAPID CITY REGIONAL HOSPIT 57701 #056-06-1993 L2003 **IM** *020 †20
SNELLING, Dustin Michael. ■ 57701 #030-05-2004 L2004 **FM** *020 †18
SPAHN, Martin Stefan. 504 E MONROE ST, OF THE BLACK HILLS 57701 #409-10-1985 L1991 **PD** *020 †55
SPANGLER, John Grover. 2905 5TH ST 57701 #030-05-1970 L1994 **PDC PD** *020 †55
STACY, Kelly Ann. 640 FLORMANN ST, INTERNAL MEDICINE 57701 #422-01-2000 L2004 **IM** *020
STAM, John. ■ 57701 #016-11-1943 L1975 **PD** *071
STATZ, Michael John. 2820 MOUNT RUSHMORE RD 57701 #030-06-1984 L1989 **GS VS** *020 †85
STELZLE, Robert Conrad. 101 E MINNESOTA ST, STE 240 57701 #028-34-1992 L2001 **AI** *020 †20,03
STENBERG, Jon Russell. 2929 5TH ST 57701 #026-04-1977 L1991 **DR NR** *020 †80 ‡
STEPHENS, Valerie Dee. 2820 MOUNT RUSHMORE RD, RAPID CITY MEDICAL CENTER, 57701 #046-01-1997 L2005 **GE** *020 †20
STEPHENSON, Patricia Jo. 353 FAIRMONT BLVD 57701 #046-01-1998 L2001 **FM** *020 †18
STOCK, Lorelee L. 3200 CANYON LAKE DR 57702 #046-01-1995 L1999 **FM** *020 †18
STOCKLAND, Darcey Jo. 101 E MINNESOTA ST, STE 260 57701 #046-01-2004 L2007 **FM** *020
STOCKS, Steven Craig. 640 FLORMANN ST, INTERNAL MEDICINE 57701 #007-02-1975 L1980 **IM** *020
STONE, Kurt Ander. 502 E MONROE ST, HEALTH-FAMILY MEDICINE 57701 #056-05-1977 L1993 **FM** *020 †18
STONE, Richard Howard. ■ 57702 #056-06-1963 L1968 **R** *062 †80
STORM, Jeremy C. ■ 57701 #018-75-2005, ▲ **FP** *012
STRAND, Ray Douglas. 1600 MOUNTAIN VIEW RD, STE 108 57702 #007-02-1971 L1972 **FM** *020
STRONG, Lori Ann. 2905 5TH ST, NEONATOLOGY, LLP 57701 #046-01-1987 L1990 **PD** *020 †55
SUROIU, Ana-Maria. ■ 57701 #003-01-2007 **FP** *012
SUTLIFF, Willis Copley. 2905 5TH ST, NEONATOLOGY 57701 #007-02-1968 L1978 **PD PHP** *020 †55
SWISHER, Lowell Philip. ■ 57702 #030-05-1956 L1957 **GP** *071 †18
TACKETT, Daniel Martin. 353 FAIRMONT BLVD 57701 #039-01-1983 L1987 **RO** *020 †80
TEIXEIRA, Jose Mauricio. 4150 5TH ST 57701 #770-02-1978 L1990 **CD ICE** *020 †20
TENGLIN, Richard Chas. 353 FAIRMONT BLVD, ONCOLOGY ASSOCIATES 57701 #023-12-1983 L2003 **ON** *020 †20
TERRASAS, Greg Scott. 508 6TH ST STE 201, DEPT OF ANESTHESIA 57701 #034-01-1983 L2000 **AN** *020 †05
TEUBER, Larry Lee. 4141 5TH ST 57701 #046-01-1985 L1991 **NS** *020 †25
THATCHER, Ruth Elizabeth. 502 E MONROE ST, HEALTH-FAMILY MEDICINE 57701 #046-01-1995 L1998 **FM** *040 †18
THEISSEN, Hubert Herbert. ■ 57701 #056-06-1947 L1955 **OBG** *071 †30
TIBBLES, Patrick Matthew. 353 FAIRMONT BLVD 57701 #010-02-1990 L1998 **EM** *020 †16
TILLOTSON, Loyal Gogstad. 2820 MOUNT RUSHMORE RD, RAPID CITY MED CTR 57701 #024-01-1985 L2000 **GE IM** *020 †20
TRAUB, Douglas Michael. 2820 MOUNT RUSHMORE RD 57701 #046-01-1980 L1981 **IM** *020 †20
TSCHETTER, William Ralph. 717 SAINT FRANCIS ST 57701 #016-06-1970 L1971 **FM** *020 †18
TSCHIDA, Brian Elliot. 2929 5TH ST, STE 240 57701 #026-04-1976 L1990 **N SME** *020 †75
TUMA, Joseph Leo. 4150 5TH ST 57701 #030-05-1998 L2006 **CD** *030 †20
VAN DAM, Scott Donovan. ■ 57701 #026-08-2005 L2007 *100
VANDERGON, Dirk Denier. 2805 5TH ST, CARDIOLOGY & CARDIAC 57701 #003-01-1980 L2002 **CD IM** *020 †20
VAN ETTEN, Donald D. 3810 JACKSON BLVD 57702 #018-03-1960 L1979 **GS GP** *071 †85
VAUGHN-WHITLEY, Kelly E. 343 QUINCY ST, STE 104 57701 #030-06-1986 L1992 **CD IC** *020 †20
WALDER, James Spaulding. 4150 5TH ST 57701 #016-11-1971 L2002 **CD IM** *020 †20
WALDO, Carolyn. 3200 CANYON LAKE DR, RAPID CITY IHS HOSPITAL 57702 #028-46-1993 L1993 **FM EM** *020 †20
WALLER, Wm Chambers, Jr. 2805 5TH ST 57701 #001-02-1985 L1996 **U GS** *020 †95
WALTMAN, Steven Edward. 2201 JACKSON BLVD, STE 102 57702 #046-01-1979 L1983 **FM** *020 †18
WANGSNESS, Christopher Er. ■ 57701 #046-01-2007 **FP** *012
WATT, Tim J. 4141 5TH ST 57701 #019-02-1985 L2002 **NS OSS** *020 †25
WEAVER, Cynthia Anderson. 2820 MOUNT RUSHMORE RD, RAPID CITY MEDICAL CTR. LL 57701 #046-01-1984 L1989 **RHU IM** *020 †20
WECHSLER, Sidney Edward. 5650 UNA DEL DR 57702 #035-08-1958 L1976 **OBG** *071 †30
WEHRKAMP, Larry Lloyd. 640 FLORMANN ST, REGIONAL MEDICAL CLINIC 57701 #012-05-1974 L1975 **GS** *020 †85
WEISENSEE, Laurie Anne. 1136 JACKSON BLVD 57702 #046-01-1992 L1996 **N** *020 †75
WELSH, Gary Lee. 2820 MOUNT RUSHMORE RD 57701 #048-13-1970 L1971 **GP** *020 †18
WESSEL, Alvin Eugene, Jr. 2201 JACKSON BLVD, STE 102 57702 #046-01-1980 L1984 **FM** *020 †18
WHIPPLE, Joy Rene. 2805 5TH ST 57701 #305-01-1998 L2003 **AN** *020 †05
WHITE, Russell Andrew. 640 FLORMANN ST, STREET # 400 57701 #051-04-1983 L2008 **OBG** *020 †30
WHITNEY, David Bryan. 2905 5TH ST 57701 #046-01-1991 L1994 **PD** *020 †55
WHITNEY, John Turstine. 4925 RAVEN CIR, ALPENA REGIONAL MEDICAL CE 57702 #046-01-1979 L2005 **NEP IM** *020 †20
WIDNER, Lauren Rae. ■ 57702 #046-01-1980 L1998 **PD CCP** *062 †55
WISNIEWSKI, Stephen John. ■ 57702 #026-04-2002 L2007 **PM PRS** *020 †60
WITTENBERG, Gregory Paul. 2820 MOUNT RUSHMORE RD 57701 #046-01-1994 L1999 **D** *020 †15 ‡
WORTEL, Heidi May. 3200 CANYON LAKE DR, INDIAN HEALTH SERVICE 57702 #030-06-1987 L2002 **P** *020 †75
WRIGHT, Paul Louis. 240 MINNESOTA ST 57701 #016-06-1973 L1977 **OPH** *020 †35
YACKLEY, James V. 353 FAIRMONT BLVD 57701 #030-06-1943 L1949 **GP** *071

YAMADA, Andrew Ryuji. 2805 5TH ST STE 220 57701 #016-06-1965 L1976 **U** *071 †95
YOUNG, Vassilia D. 7236 JORDAN DR STE 101 57702 #056-05-1991 L1996 **D** *020 †15
ZAVITZ, William Read. 2929 5TH ST 57701 #007-02-1985 L1990 **RNR DR** *020 †80
ZIELIKE, Carol Marie. 717 SAINT FRANCIS ST 57701 #046-01-1979 L1980 **FM** *020 †18
ZINELDIN, Amadeldin. 2805 5TH ST, CARDIOLOGY & CARDIAC 57701 #915-03-1989 L2002 **CD** *020 †20

REDFIELD – SPINK

BERG, Sterling. 709 W 1ST ST, BERG MEDICAL CLINIC 57469 #030-05-1953 L1954 **GP** *071
CABACAR, Joselito M. 111 W 10TH AVE 57469 #748-10-1993 L1999 **NEP** *020 †20
MORRIS, Mary Irene. 1010 W 1ST ST, REDFIELD CLINIC 57469 #046-01-1992 L1995 **FM** *020 †18 ‡
MORRISON, Kristine Kay. 1010 W 1ST ST 57469 #046-01-1995 L2006 **FM** *020 †18
OWENS, Matthew Peter. 1010 W 1ST ST, REDFIELD CLINIC 57469 #046-01-1993 L1997 **FM** *020 †18
PATTERSON, David M. 37454 SD HIGHWAY 26 57469 #062-01-1952 L1955 **FM OS** *071
PERRY, Edmond Jos. SPINK COUNTY 57469 #016-11-1943 L1946 **OS GP** *071
SANDERS, Mary Elizabeth. SPINK COUNTY 57469 #016-06-1943 L1947 **IM** *071 †20
SULA, Dennis Sayong. 1010 W 1ST ST 57469 #748-02-1999 L2006 **ID** *020

ROSEBUD – TODD

APONTE SINGALA, Charles G. PO BOX 400, PHS ROSEBUD I 57570 #649-14-1987 L1991 *020
BARTOLOMEI, Luis A. ■ 57570 #847-04-1969 L1972 **OBG** *020
PARKER, Valerie Adoree. ■ 57570 #035-08-1987 L1993 **IM** *030
REIFEL, Lucy Maria. ■ 57570 #005-02-1975 L1980 **PD** *020
REUMAN, Peter Douglass. PO BOX 450, INDIAN HEALTH SVC HOSP 57570 #016-02-1973 L1974 **PDI** *050 †55

ROSHOLT – ROBERTS

KASS, Joseph. 116 E MAIN ST 57260 #473-03-1952 L1960 **FM GS** *020 †18

SALEM – MCCOOK

BILLION, Stephen Paul. 740 S HILL ST 57058 #046-01-1982 L1985 **IM** *020 †20

SCOTLAND – BON HOMME

BARTLING, Melissa Jo. 610 BILLARS ST 57059 #046-01-2003 L2006 **FM** *020 †18
RAMOS, Manuel Donato. 1391 1ST ST 57059 #748-08-1961 L1973 **GS GP** *020 †85

SELBY – WALWORTH

OTTENBACHER, John Carl. ■ 57472 #046-01-1980 L1981 **GP** *020

SIOUX FALLS – LINCOLN

ADAM-BURCHILL, Paula M. 6110 S MINNESOTA AVE 57108 #046-01-1990 L1993 **FM** *020 †18
AKINS, Robert Arthur. 5000 S MINNESOTA AVE, STE 100 57108 #004-01-1982 L1997 **OTO** *020 †45
ALVINE, Allison Gilhousen. 4400 W 69TH ST STE 1500, UNIVERSITY OF SOUTH DAKOTA 57108 #019-02-1997 **P** *100
AMIOTTE, Lisa Carol. 4400 W 69TH ST, STE 1500 57108 #046-01-2000 L2004 **P** *020
ANDREONE, Peter Anthony. 4520 W 69TH ST 57108 #005-14-1981 L1992 **TS** *020 †85,90
BACHARACH, John Michael. 4520 W 69TH ST 57108 #056-05-1986 L1995 **CD IM** *020 †20
BEAN, David Wm. 4400 W 69TH ST STE 1500 57108 #026-04-1960 L1977 **P PFP** *020 †75
BHATARA, Vinod Sagar. 4400 W 69TH ST 57108 #495-36-1969 L1979 **P CHP** *020 †75
BHATIA, Ruchi. ■ 57108 #495-45-2000 L2007 **IM** *020 †20
BHATIA, Vishal. ■ 57108 #495-36-1997 L2006 **END** *020 †20
BHAVSAR, Kalpeshkumar Bhi. ■ 57108 #495-89-1992 **P** *012
BLOW, Jerry John. 101 W 69TH ST, STE 103 57108 #046-01-1989 L1993 **PM OM** *020 †20
BOSWORTH, Annette Marie. 5019 S WESTERN AVE STE 200 57108 #046-01-1998 L2007 **IM** *020 †20
CHESTER-ADAM, Heather K. 4400 W 69TH ST STE 1500 57108 #046-01-2002 L2006 **P** *100
CHURCH, Bill Grant. ■ 57108 #018-03-1947 L1956 **NS** *071
CINK, Paul Arthur. 2315 W 57TH 57108 #048-04-1984 L1990 **OTO HNS** *020 †45
CRANDELL, Michael Peter. 5300 S BROADBAND LN # 300 57108 #050-02-1976 L1980 **FM** *030
D'ALMADA-REMEDIOS, A H. ■ 57108 #067-01-1953 L1963 **PTH FOP** *071 †50
DAVIDSON, Christopher M. 4400 W 69TH ST, STE 1500 57108 #046-01-2003 L2005 **P** *100
DEL MONTE, Wm Raymond. 4400 W 69TH ST, STE 1500 57108 #030-06-1987 L1995 **CHP** *020 †75
DONELAN, Kent Joseph. ■ 57108 #046-01-2006 **PTH** *012
DOSADO, Jose Marius D. 2208 W SLEIGH CREEK TRL 57108 #748-11-1987 L2004 **NPM** *020 †55
ELLIS, Zach Mitchum. ■ 57108 #017-20-1987 L1988 **PTH** *020 †85,50
ERICKSON, David Kenneth. 3900 W AVERA DR, STE 200 57108 #046-01-1983 L1986 **FM** *030 †18
ERIE, John Kenneth. 4500 W 69TH ST 57108 #026-04-1988 L1998 **AN** *020 †05
ERMER, David John. 200 W SPY GLASS DR 57108 #030-05-1990 L2000 **CHP** *040 †75
FAUSCH, Mark David. 4520 W 69TH ST, NORTH CENTRAL HEART 57108 #026-04-1979 L1997 **CD IM** *020 †20
FLICKEMA, Dawn Amy. 1910 W 69TH ST, MCGREEVY CLINIC -69TH 57108 #046-01-1994 L1997 **FM** *020 †18
FLORA, George C. ■ 57108 #041-13-1950 L1953 **N** *071 †75
FLYNN, Sarah Ann. 4400 W 69TH ST, STE 1500 57108 #046-01-1998 L2003 **CHP** *020 †75
FLYNN, Valerie Evonne. ■ 57108 #046-01-2007 **TY** *012

FROST, Donald Morgan. 3408 W RALPH ROGERS RD 306 57108 #016-06-1955 L1958 GP GS *071 †18

FULLER, William Clark. 4400 W 69TH ST STE 1500 57108 #030-05-1972 L1975 P *040 †75 ‡

GAECKLE, Charles Thos. 4520 W 69TH ST 57108 #046-01-1979 L1983 CD *020 †20

GEORGIEV, Oleg P. 2333 W 57TH ST, STE 101 57108 #198-01-1983 L2000 IM NEP *020 †20

GNANASEKHARAN, Meena. ■ 57108 #495-04-1995 L2007 CHP *100 †75

GORDON, Mark Richard. 4520 W 69TH ST 57108 #026-04-1989 L1995 CD *020 †20

GREENE, Stacia Lee. 6110 S MINNESOTA AVE 57108 #046-01-1995 L1999 FM *020 †18

GREENFIELD, Duane L. ■ 57108 #023-01-1946 L1952 U *071

HAJAL, Rizan Assaad. 2315 W 57TH ST, PULMONARY & SLEEP CONSULTA 57108 #605-02-1995 L2002 PCC *020 †20

HAMMER, Bryan John. 6601 S MINNESOTA AVE 57108 #046-01-1988 L1993 OPH *020 †35

HANSEN, Lornell E, II. 5011 S LOUISE AVE, CENTER OF FAMILY MED 57108 #046-01-1994 L2000 FM *020 †18 ‡

HARLOW, Michael Charles. 4400 W 69TH ST, STE 1500 57108 #046-01-2003 L2007 P *012

HEDGES, Craig. 2315 W 57TH ST 57108 #046-01-1983 L1992 OTO *020 †45

HEIER, Jeffrey Roy. ■ 57108 #046-01-1994 L1999 IM *020 †20

HELVIG, Bethany Susan. 2315 W 57TH ST 57108 #046-01-1988 L1998 OTO *020 †45

HERBSTER, Stacey Lynn. 4400 W 69TH ST STE 1500 57108 #046-01-1994 L1999 P *020 †75

HIBBARD, Michael David. 4520 W 69TH ST 57108 #026-04-1985 L1992 CD IM *020 †20

HOHM, Byron Theodore. 6601 S MINNESOTA AVE 57108 #048-12-1976 L1979 OPH OS *020 †35

HOWARD, Richard James. 6301 S MINNESOTA AVE, STE 300 57108 #056-06-1982 L1990 PS GS *020 †65

HRUBY, Bradley Edward. 6110 S MINNESOTA AVE, FAMILY PRACTICE PHYSICIANS 57108 #046-01-2001 L2004 FM *020 †18

HURLEY, Dominic Vincent. 1905 W 57TH ST, STE 1 57108 #046-01-1982 L1987 CD *020 †20

ISAACSON, Thomas Chris. 4520 W 69TH ST, NORTH CENTRAL HEART INSTIT 57108 #016-11-1987 L2000 CD *020 †20

JAGRAM, Nalini Ravidai. ■ 57108 #759-06-2005 FP *012

JAMISON, Darla Dawn. 4500 W 69TH ST 57108 #046-01-1992 L1995 IM *020 †20

JASSIM, Hassanain Ali. ■ 57108 #046-01-2008 L2012

JENSEN, Nicoline Violet. ■ 57108 #049-01-1995 L2007 IM *020 †20

JENSEN, Richard Alex. 2333 W 57TH ST 57108 #046-01-1989 L1995 NEP CCM *020 †20

JERSTAD, Kelly Michele. 4950 S MINNESOTA AVE 57108 #010-01-1998 L2003 D *020 †15

JOHNSON, Jana Bernice. 116 W 69TH ST 57108 #026-08-1999 L2003 D *020 †15

KANNAN, Hari Dasan. 5120 S WESTERN AVE, STE 104 57108 #495-37-1980 L1991 P *020

KNUDSON, Donald Henry. 6110 S MINNESOTA AVE 57108 #028-02-1973 L1978 GS *020 †85

KNUTSON, Brian Dennis. 116 W 69TH ST, STE 100 57108 #046-01-1996 L2000 D *020 †15

KNUTSON, Dennis Dorf. ■ 57108 #046-04-1966 L1975 D DMP *020 †15 ‡

KOOB, Kenneth Gene. ■ 57108 #018-03-1968 L1974 N *071 †75

LARSEN, Laura. 2315 W 57TH ST 57108 #025-07-1980 L1984 OTO *020 †45

LEACH, Christi Lorraine. 4400 W 69TH ST, STE 1500 57108 #046-01-2005 P *012

LITTLE, Phillip Edward. ■ 57108 #025-07-1978 L1979 NEP IM *020 †20

LUTHER, Jeffrey Lynn. 5027 S BUR OAK PL, WORK FORCE OCCPTNL & MED 57108 #046-01-1991 L1994 OM IM *020 †20

MALONE, Matthew T. 4400 W 69TH ST, STE 1500 57108 #018-75-2001, ▲ L2006 PYG *100 †75

MALSAM, Eric John. ■ 57108 #046-01-2005 IM *012

MANTHEY, Darren Allen. ■ 57108 #026-04-2002 L2005 EM *020 †16

MAZURCZAK, Wioleta Elzbie. ■ 57108 #759-10-1984 L2007 CHP *100 †75

MCCRACKEN, Rachel A. ■ 57108 #917-08-1988 L2000 P *020 †50,75

MC GRANN, James R. 4950 S MINNESOTA AVE 57108 #046-01-1978 L1982 D DS *020 †15

MC HALE, Michael S. 3720 W 69TH ST, MCHALE INSTITUTE 57108 #030-05-1980 L1986 HO HEM *020 †20

MOENCH, Jerry Lee. 4520 W 69TH ST, NORTH CENTRAL HEART INSTIT 57108 #026-04-1979 L1984 CD IM *020 †20

MOHAMA, Riyad E. 4520 W 69TH ST 57108 #875-01-1977 L1991 ICE IM *020 †20

MOHLER, Charles Wm. 6601 S MINNESOTA AVE 57108 #038-06-1973 L1980 OPH *020 †35

MON, Didima C. ■ 57108 #024-01-1994 L2006 PD *020 †55

NAGELHOUT, David Allen. 4520 W 69TH ST 57108 #046-01-1983 L1990 CD IM *020 †20

NAIR, Preetha. 6501 S CONNIE AVE, APT 120 57108 #495-44-2002 IM *012

NELSON, Amy Lynn. 6110 S MINNESOTA AVE 57108 #046-01-2000 L2003 FM *020 †18

NEMEH, Mazen N. 2333 W 57TH ST 57108 #875-01-1985 L1999 NEP *020 †20

OFSTEIN, Lewis Craig. 4520 W 69TH ST 57108 #018-03-1974 L1980 TS *020 †85,90

OLIPHANT, John Rhodes. 5024 S BUR OAK PL, STE 114 57108 #048-14-1973 L1996 PS OTO *020 †45,65

OLSON, Douglas Jeffrey. ■ 57108 #046-01-2006 L2008 FP *012

OLSON, Michael Lee. 6110 S MINNESOTA AVE 57108 #026-04-1975 L1980 FM *020 †18

OSMUNDSON, Gregory David. 6601 S MINNESOTA AVE 57108 #046-01-1994 L1999 OPH *020 †35

OWENS, Leycester, Jr. 4520 W 69TH ST 57108 #051-04-1969 L1980 TS *071 †85,90

PAA, Christopher James. ■ 57108 #030-06-1995 L2001 CD *020 †20

PAPPAS, Anastasios Angelo. 47488 85TH ST 57108 #046-01-1994 L1998 D *020 †15

PATEL, Ankit Shankarbhai. ■ 57108 #495-99-2004 L2005 IM *012

PAY, Douglas Knight. 116 W 69TH ST, AVERA DERMATOLOGY & LASER 57108 #041-01-1962 L1965 D DMP *020 †15

PAYER, Joshua Wade. ■ 57108 #422-01-2002 L2006 FM *100

PETERSON, Judith Rovno. 5023 S BUR OAK PL, SODAK REHAB 57108 #035-20-1986 L2003 PM PME *020 †60

PLUCKER, Milton W. ■ 57108 #030-05-1951 L1952 IM GP *071

RAIDOO, Bharathi Mahendri. ■ 57108 #836-05-1981 L2007 P *012

RAIDOO, Deshandra Munsamy. ■ 57108 #836-02-1985 L2007 P *012

REINERS, Michael Noble. 4400 W 69TH ST, STE 1500 57108 #046-01-1991 L1995 FM *020 †18

REYNOLDS, James Robt. 4520 W 69TH ST, NORTH CENTRAL HEART 57108 #023-07-1969 L1970 TS *020 †85,90

REYNOLDS, Tommy Ray. 4520 W 69TH ST 57108 #046-01-1984 L1992 TS CD *020 †85,90

RIDDER, Glenn Ambrose. 6110 S MINNESOTA AVE 57108 #030-05-1985 L1991 FM *020 †18

SAHL, William Jay, Jr. ■ 57108 #026-04-1970 L1993 D DMP *020 †15

SARBACKER, Sarah K Short. 4950 S MINNESOTA AVE 57108 #037-01-1993 L1997 D DS *020 †15

SCHELLPFEFFER, Donald A. 4500 W 69TH ST 57108 #046-01-1978 L1981 AN *020

SCHNEIDER, Scott Anthony. 4400 W 69TH ST STE 500 57108 #046-01-1988 L1993 CHP P *020 †75

SCHRIEVER, Jennifer Ann. 6110 S MINNESOTA AVE 57108 #046-01-2000 L2003 FM *020 †18 ‡

SCHULTZ, Richard Douglas. ■ 57108 #040-02-1959 L1966 PTH DMP *071 †50

SCHUMACHER, Bretta May. ■ 57108 #046-01-2008 *012

SCOTT, Kenneth Mark. 2315 W 57TH ST 57108 #061-01-1991 L2006 OTO *020 †45

SEURER, Joseph James. ■ 57108 #046-01-2008 *012

SHETH, Manish Vallabhdas. 4400 W 69TH ST, STE 1500 57108 #495-89-1993 L2003 P *020 †75

SINGARAM, Chandar. 1905 W 57TH ST STE 2, MIDWEST MED CARE PC 57108 #495-04-1984 L2001 GE *020

SMITH, Robert Maclean. 4301 W 57TH ST, STE 160 57108 #016-43-1980 L1988 AI IM *020,03

SOUNDY, Timothy James. 4400 W 69TH ST, STE 1500 57108 #030-05-1987 L1992 CHP *020 †75

STANLEY, Matthew B. 4400 W 69TH ST STE 1500, UNIVERSITY PSYCHIATRY ASSO 57108 #018-75-1991, ▲ L1995 P *020 †75

STOLTZ, Charles Roger. 5105 S RIVER PARK PL, SIOUX VALLEY CLINIC 57108 #048-13-1970 L1976 OBG *020 †30

THOMAS, Eric Richard. 6601 S MINNESOTA AVE 57108 #046-01-2001 L2006 OPH *100 †35

THOMPSON, Arliss Norman. 4500 W 69TH ST, HEART HOSPITAL OF SD 57108 #040-02-1988 L1991 NM *020 †28,20

TODD, Daniel Warren. 2315 W 57TH ST 57108 #037-01-1994 L2002 OTO A *020 †45

TSCHETTER, Richard T. 6601 S MINNESOTA AVE 57108 #023-07-1961 L1968 OPH *020 †35

TUFTY, Geoffrey Thos. 6601 S MINNESOTA AVE 57108 #046-01-1992 L1997 OPH *020 †35

VACA, Anthony Michael. 4400 W 69TH ST, STE 500 57108 #046-01-1988 L1992 P OS *020 †75

VAKARELSKA, Rossitza T. 4500 W 69TH ST, ATTN: EM DEPT 57108 #198-01-1988 L1999 IM EM *020 †20

VAN KALSBEEK, Carilyn. 1910 W 69TH ST 57108 #046-01-1994 L1997 FM *020 †18 ‡

VIK, Tamara Lynn. 4400 W 69TH ST, STE 1500 57108 #046-01-2000 L2004 CHP *100 †75

VONK, Galen Neil. 4520 W 69TH ST 57108 #046-01-1983 L1989 CD IM *020 †20

WAGNER, Loyd R. ■ 57108 #030-05-1950 L1966 PTH NM *071 †50,28

WALLACE, Caryn Marie. 6110 S MINNESOTA AVE 57108 #046-01-1995 L1998 FM *020 †18

WATT, Bruce A, Jr. 4520 W 69TH ST, NORTH CENTRAL HEART 57108 #030-06-1984 L1985 CD *020 †20

WEATHERILL, Jay Edward. 4400 W 69TH ST STE 15 57108 #046-01-2002 L2006 P *020

WEGNER, Karl Heinrich. ■ 57108 #024-01-1959 L1962 PTH *071 †50

WEST, David Russell. 6601 S MINNESOTA AVE 57108 #039-01-1985 L1989 OPH *020 †35

WHITE, Ty Anthony. 4500 W 69TH ST 57108 #046-01-1999 L2003 AN *020 †05

WILSON, Nancy Luechtefeld. 4400 W 69TH ST STE 1500 57108 #007-02-1977 L2001 P PTH *020 †50,75

WOOLHISER, Kimberly Dawn. 3720 W 69TH ST 57108 #046-01-1992 L1995 OPH *020 †20

SIOUX FALLS – MINNEHAHA

AAMLID, Brian Craig. 1210 W 18TH ST, STE G01 57104 #026-04-1985 L1990 ORS *020 †40

AARONSON, Michael Lee. 1001 E 21ST ST STE 300 57105 #008-02-1996 L2002 NEP *020 †20

ABU-GHAZALEH, Samir. 2812 S LOUISE AVE 57106 #915-04-1969 L1981 OBG GO *020 †30 ‡

ALAM, M Rabiul. 911 E 20TH ST, DISEASE SPECIALISTS PC 57105 #160-02-1987 L2002 ID *020 †20

ALHANOUN, Elias. 1305 W 18TH ST, S.V.C. HOSPITALIST PROGRAM 57105 #875-01-2002 L2006 IM *100 †20

ALLANKU, Sarat. 2501 W 22ND ST, UNIV OF SD SCH OF MED 57105 #495-65-1999 IM *012

ALLARD, Brandon Lee. 1310 W 22ND 57105 #026-04-1997 L2004 END *020 †20

ALPERS, Josie Ruth. 1417 S MINNESOTA AVE, MEDICAL X-RAY CENTER 57105 #038-06-1995 L2001 DR *020 †80

ALVINE, Franklin Gustave. 2908 E 26TH ST 57103 #054-04-1964 L1972 ORS *020 †40

ALVINE, Gregory Franklin. 2908 E 26TH ST 57103 #018-03-1991 L1997 ORS *020 †40

AMBAYI, Rudo. 2501 W 22ND ST 57105 #775-01-1997 IM *012

AMUNDSON, E Paul. 2600 W 49TH ST, BOX 7406 57105 #017-20-1989 L1992 MDM FM *062 †18 ‡

AMUNDSON, Loren Hugh. 1621 S MINNESOTA AVE, NON-PAR 57105 #056-05-1956 L1959 FM *071 †18

ANDERSON, Courtney Wm. 115 E 11TH ST 57104 #016-06-1958 L1959 AM FM *071

ANDERSON, David Scott. 1200 S EUCLID AVE, STE 110 57105 #046-01-2004 L2007 FM *020

ANDERSON, Keith Allan. 1305 W 18TH ST, P O BOX 5134 57105 #037-01-1981 L1982 PTH BBK *020 †50

ANDERSON, Susan Marie. 1310 W 22ND ST 57105 #046-01-1997 L2000 FM *020 †18 ‡

ANDRUS, Milan S. 1201 S EUCLID AVE, MB 2 STE G04 57105 #010-02-1973 L1996 R NR *020 †80

ANEL, Roberto Cornelio L. 1115 E 20TH ST, CTR FOR FAMILY MEDICINE 57105 #748-02-1996 L2007 FM *020 †18

ARNESON, Wallace A. 1305 W 18TH ST 57105 #024-01-1941 L1946 GS *071 †85

ARVIND, Kasaragod B. 911 E 20TH ST, CRITICAL CARE AND 57105 #495-04-1988 L1999 CCP *020 †55

ASFORA, Wilson Theophhilo. 1210 W 18TH ST STE 104 57104 #187-07-1977 L1991 NS *020 †25

ASPAAS, Paul Kenneth, Jr. 1201 S EUCLID AVE, STE 610 57105 #024-01-1972 L1974 IM *030 †20

ASSAM, Sam. 1210 W 18TH ST, STE 104 57104 #026-04-1956 L1980 NS *020 †25

ASSAM, Susan Finley. 1210 W 18TH ST, STE G01 57104 #046-01-1987 L1991 PM IM *020 †60

ASSIMACOPOULOS, A. 911 E 20TH ST, DISEASE SPECIALISTS PC 57105 #046-04-1991 L2001 ID *020 †20

ASSIMACOPOULOS, Costas A. ■ 57106 #026-04-1960 L1969 GS OS *071 †85

ATCHISON, Scott Robert. 1305 W 18TH ST 57105 #026-08-1980 L1989 AN PME *020 †05

AUGSPURGER, Ken Douglas. 1621 S MINNESOTA AVE 57105 #046-01-1977 L1982 OPH *020 †35

AWADALLAH, Sami Mohammed. 1305 W 18TH ST 57105 #575-01-1982 L1991 PDC PD *020 †55

AYTEKIN, Betul. 2501 W 22ND ST 57105 #902-01-1999 IM *100

AZAM, Arif. 1000 E 21ST ST STE 4100, C/O PHYSICIANS LABORATORY 57105 #704-02-1966 L2002 PTH NM *020 †50,28

BAHNSON, Berne B. 1001 E 21ST ST 57105 #026-04-1980 L1987 N *020

BAKA, Joseph Jeffrey. 1417 S MINNESOTA AVE 57105 #041-02-1986 L1993 RNR *020 †80

BAKER, Bradley Scott. 1210 W 18TH ST 57105 #046-01-1995 L2001 ORS *020 †40

BAKER, Scott Lawson. 911 E 20TH ST, INSTITUTE OF SOUTH DAKOTA 57105 #046-01-2000 L2005 GS *020 †85

BALOUN, Brett Daniel. ■ 57105 #046-01-2004 L2004 IM *100

BANDETTINI, Francis C. 2500 W 49TH ST, STE 206 57105 #018-75-1987, ▲ L1992 P *020

BARKER, James Michael. 300 N DAKOTA AVE, STE 117 57104 #026-04-1976 L2002 **IM GP** *020 †20

BARKER, John Dennis, Jr. 1001 E 21ST ST, STE 501 57105 #026-04-1968 L1977 **GE IM** *020 †20

BARNESS, Bryan Lee. 1305 W 18TH ST, 3561 S SPENCER BLVD 57105 #046-01-1990 L1996 **DR** *020 †80

BARNETT, George Louis. 1200 S 7TH AVE 57105 #030-06-1947 L1948 **GP** *071

BARTH, Richard John. 1310 W 22ND ST 57105 #016-43-1978 L1989 **END DIA** *020 †20

BASAPPA, Rishika. PO BOX 5046, VAMC SIOUX FALLS 57117 #496-35-1999 **IM** *012

BAUER, Barry Charles. 1201 S EUCLID AVE, STE 307 57105 #046-01-1982 L1985 **PD** *020 †55

BAUMGARTEN, Keith Michael. 810 E 23RD ST, ORTHOPEDIC INSTITUTE 57105 #023-07-1999 L2005 **OSM** *020 †40

BEAN, David Wm, Jr. 1417 S MINNESOTA AVE, MEDICAL X-RAY CENTER 57105 #046-01-1985 L1987 **DR** *020 †80

BEHREND, Robert Dale. 1201 S EUCLID AVE, STE 510 57105 #046-01-1989 L1992 **IM** *020 †20

BELL, Douglas Giltner. 1305 W 18TH ST 57105 #046-01-1984 L1988 **AN** *020 †05

BELL, Maria Caroline. 1500 W 22ND ST, STE 102 57105 #046-01-1988 L2000 **OBG** *020 †30

BELL, William Frederic. 1210 W 18TH ST, STE G01 57104 #016-06-1977 L1997 **ORS EM** *020 †40

BENSON, Kevin David. 1201 S EUCLID AVE STE 510, SANFORD CLN 57105 #046-01-1995 L1999 **OBG** *020 †30

BENSON, Margaret Ann. 4405 E 26TH ST 57103 #046-01-1984 L1986 **FM** *020 †18

BERG, Mary Gene. 4405 E 26TH ST 57103 #030-06-2002 L2007 **FM** *100 †18

BERNARDO, Rosaleah V. 1305 W 18TH ST, SANFORD'S CHILDREN'S SPECI 57105 #748-01-1987 L1996 **CCP** *020 †55

BESHAI, Emad Farid. 1100 E 21ST ST, STE 400 57105 #915-09-1981 L1997 **IM IMG** *020 †20

BIEGLER, Lyle Wayne. 1115 E 20TH ST, CENTER FOR FAMILY MEDICINE 57105 #026-04-2004 L2007 **FM** *020 †18

BILLION, John Jos. ■ 57105 #016-43-1964 L1968 **ORS** *071 †40

BISHOP, Donald Thos. 800 E 21ST ST, C/O EICU AVERA MCKENNAN 57105 #007-02-1974 L1988 **CD CCM** *050 †20

BLAKE, Jerome Martin. 1305 W 18TH ST, SPECIALTY CLINIC 57105 #048-13-1973 L1977 **OS PDP** *020 †55

BLUE, Daniel Walter. 1305 W 18TH ST 57105 #046-01-1986 L1987 **FM** *030 †18

BOADE, Werner Allan. 109 S PETRO AVE 57107 #030-05-1966 L1971 **NM PTH** *020 †50,28

BOETEL, Thomas Matthew. 1210 W 18TH ST 57104 #016-76-2000, ▲ L2008 **PM PRS** *020 †60 ‡

BOICE, John Leland. ■ 57105 #035-45-1973 L1992 **IM IMG** *040 †20 ‡

BOTTOLFSON, Diane Marie. 2501 W 22ND ST, VA. MEDICAL CENTER 57105 #046-01-1990 L1998 **AN** *020 †05

BOWDEN, Ann Margaret. ■ 57103 #046-01-2008 *012

BOYENS, Scott L. 3401 W 49TH ST 57106 #046-01-1995 L1998 **FM** *020 †18

BRAITHWAITE, Thomas M. 800 E 21ST ST 57105 #046-01-1982 L1985 **IM** *020 †20

BRANDENBURG, Verdayne Ray. 2701 S KIWANIS AVE 57105 #046-01-1978 L1979 **FM** *020 †18

BRECHTELSBAUER, David A. 1115 E 20TH ST 57105 #025-01-1973 L1985 **FM FPG** *040 †18

BREIT, James Anthony. 911 E 20TH ST STE 602, SOUTH DAKOTA, LTD 57105 #046-01-1998 L2005 **PS** *020 †85,65

BRENNAN, Brian Alfred. 2701 S KIWANIS AVE, SIOUX VALLEY CLINIC 57105 #033-05-1985 L2006 **AI PD** *020 †55,03

BRESKE, Colleen Joan. 6000 W 41ST ST 57106 #046-01-1988 L1993 **FM** *020 †18

BREVIK, Alan Kermit. 1305 W 18TH ST 57105 #048-04-1963 L1989 **P ADP** *020 †75

BREWER, Marshall Lee. 320 E ASPEN CIR 57105 #005-12-1968 L1987 **OS DR** *020 †18,80

BRIGGS, Ashley Brooke. 1500 W 22ND ST STE 301, SANFORD WOMEN'S HEALTH 57105 #046-01-2000 L2005 **OBG** *020 †30

BRODERSON, Stephanie O. 4405 E 26TH ST, STE 1 57103 #046-01-1995 L1999 **FM** *020 †18

BROOKS, Steven David. 2501 W 22ND ST, SIOUX FALLS VA MEDICAL CTR 57105 #046-01-1986 L1987 **IM** *020 †20

BROWN, Christie Lynn. ■ 57106 #046-01-2008 *012

BROWN, Michael Jerome. 4405 E 26TH ST, SANFORD CLINIC 57103 #048-13-1970 L1971 **GP** *020 †18

BRUNING, Kara Coleman. 1200 S 7TH AVE 57105 #030-05-2003 L2006 **PD** *020 †55

BRUNNER, William Clinton. 1310 W 22ND ST, SANFORD CLINIC 57105 #046-01-2002 L2006 **D** *020 †15

BUBAK, Mark Edward. 2200 W 49TH ST STE 104 57105 #046-01-1986 L1992 **AI IM** *020 †20,03

BUNCH, Bonnie Lynn. 1305 W 18TH ST, SPECIALTY CLINIC 57105 #035-48-1990 L1997 **CHN** *020 †75,55

BUNGER, Patricia Jane. 2404 S GRINNELL AVE, AVERA UNIV PSY ASSOCIATES 57106 #030-05-1970 L1976 **ADL PDE** *020

BURDGE, Kelly Kathleen. 1001 E 21ST ST STE 300 57105 #038-45-1999 L2004 **IM NEP** *020 †20,55

BURGERS, James Walter. 1200 S 7TH AVE, MCGREEVY CLINICS 57105 #046-01-1980 L1984 **FM OBS** *075 †18

BURKHART, Thomas Jay. 2501 W 22ND ST, VAMC 57105 #026-04-1973 L1976 **IM** *020 †20

BURNS, Edith Marie Alcorn. ■ 57117 #005-12-1945 L1947 **GP OBG** *071

BURRISH, Gene Frank. 1310 W 22ND ST 57105 #026-04-1978 L1979 **D** *071 †15

BYNUM, Gaither Daniel. 2601 S MINNESOTA AVE, # 105-304 57105 #034-01-1972 L1994 **EM GP** *050 †70

CAMP, Samuel Thomas. ■ 57105 #046-01-2007 *012

CARDA, Chad James. 1115 E 20TH ST, CTR FOR FAMILY MEDICINE 57105 #654-01-2005 L2007 **FP** *012

CARLSON, Carrie J. 6000 W 41ST ST 57106 #018-75-1998, ▲ L2001 **FM** *020 †18

CARLSON, Craig Leigh. 1100 E 26TH ST 57105 #046-01-1982 L1985 **AN** *020 †05

CARROLL, Nancy Linda. 4405 E 26TH ST 57103 #026-04-1978 L1983 **PD** *020 †55

CASEY, Matthew Ray. 1417 S MINNESOTA AVE 57105 #018-03-2000 L2006 **VIR** *020 †80

CAUWELS, Jeremy Michael. 1305 W 18TH ST, SIOUX VALLEY HOSPITAL 57105 #018-03-2002 L2006 **IM** *100 †20

CAVANAUGH, D Susan. 2000 S SUMMIT AVE 57105 #046-01-1999 L2003 **P** *020 †75

CHAKUNTA, Umesh Chander R. 2501 W 22ND ST 57105 #496-42-2001 **P** *012

CHALMERS, James H. ■ 57105 #026-04-1942 L1978 **IM** *071

CHEATHAM, Anna Draughn. 1305 W 18TH ST, SPECIALTY CLINIC 57105 #012-01-1990 L2006 **NPM** *020 †55

CHEATHAM, Robert Wycliffe. 1305 W 18TH ST, SPECIALTY CLINIC 57105 #012-22-1999 L2006 **NPM** *100 †55

CHINN, Alison Faye. 1100 E 21ST ST, STE 400 57105 #026-04-2002 L2005 **IM** *100 †20

CHO, Myung Joo. 3934 S WESTERN AVE, MIDWEST PAIN & REHAB CLNC 57105 #583-08-1977 L1986 **PM PME** *020 †60

CHONTOS, Andrew John. ■ 57105 #007-02-1995 L1998 **GS** *020 †85

CHOUDHRY, Sabina. 1417 S MINNESOTA AVE 57105 #496-07-1989 L2001 **DR** *020 †80

CHOUDHRY, Vikrant. PO BOX 5046, VA MED CTR 57117 #495-08-1984 L1994 **ORS** *020

CHRISTENSON, Nicole Ann. ■ 57103 #046-01-2002 L2007 **CHP** *012

CHRISTOPHERSON, Thomas J. 1305 W 18TH ST 57105 #046-01-1988 L1992 **AN** *020 †05

CINK, Thomas M. 1417 S MINNESOTA AVE 57105 #046-01-1977 L1981 **OS DR** *020 †80

CLARK, Edward Thos. 2701 S KIWANIS AVE 57105 #026-04-1976 L1977 **FM** *020 †18

CLIFFORD, Gail Lisa. 1305 W 18TH ST 57105 #035-09-1991 L2005 **HOS IM** *020 †20 ‡

COBB-GERHART, Victoria R. ■ 57106 #018-03-1974 L1991 **P** *020

COCHRAN, Steven Dee. 2812 S LOUISE AVE 57106 #005-12-1980 L2001 **CHP P** *020 †75

COLE, Shelley Janelle. 1500 W 22ND ST, STE 301 57105 #046-01-1993 L1998 **OBG** *020 †30

CROSBY, Daniel L. 1417 S MINNESOTA AVE 57105 #030-05-1984 L1999 **RNR VIR** *071 †80

CURD, Richard Blake. 810 E 23RD ST 57105 #028-46-1991 L2001 **HS** *020 †40

CZARNECKI, Edward John. 1417 S MINNESOTA AVE 57105 #025-01-1990 L1996 **RNR** *020 †80

DAGHER, Hikmat Nicolas. 1100 E 21ST ST, STE 601 57105 #605-02-1997 L2004 **PCC** *020 †20

DAHL, Robert Keith. 911 E 20TH ST, STE 501 57105 #030-06-1977 L1987 **VS GS** *020 †85

DARABI, Kamran. ■ 57104 #409-22-2000 L2008 **HO** *012

D'ASCOLI, Peter T. 6511 W 41ST ST, PLANNED PARENTHOOD OF MN/S 57106 #010-03-1978 L1997 **OBG** *020 †30

DAVID, Gerard Roque. 1201 S EUCLID AVE, STE 401 57105 #748-01-1993 L2006 **IM** *020 †20

DAVID, Raymund Edward R. 1001 E 21ST ST STE 10 57105 #748-01-1993 L2004 **N** *020

DAVIS, Cynthia. 414 W 18TH ST, INDEPENDENT WOMEN'S CARE, 57104 #011-03-1992 L1999 **OBG** *020 †30

DAY, Richard Paul. 7220 W 41ST ST, SANFORD FAMILY MEDICINE 57106 #046-01-1981 L1982 **FM** *020 †18

DE BACA, Monica Elizabeth. 1000 E 21ST ST 57105 #132-07-1990 L2006 **PTH** *020 †50

DE CLARK, Robert Peter. 1417 S MINNESOTA AVE 57105 #025-01-1964 L1970 **R** *020 †80

DEGEN, Jessica Marie. ■ 57105 #046-01-2008 *012

DEHAAN, Douglas Robt. 7220 W 41ST ST, SANFORD FAMILY MEDICINE 57106 #046-01-1986 L1987 **FM** *020 †18

DEJONG, Paul William. ■ 57110 #016-11-2006 L2007 **FP** *012

DE VRIES, Brian Lee. 1100 E 26TH ST, ANESTHESIOLOGY ASSOCIATES, 57105 #046-01-2000 L2004 **AN** *020 †05

DEWALD, Dean Allen. 1100 E 26TH ST, ANESTHESIOLOGY ASSOCS INC 57105 #046-01-2003 L2007 **AN** *100

DIB, Elie Ghassoub. 1020 W 18TH ST, CLINIC-ONCOLOGY 57104 #605-03-1999 L2006 **HO** *020 †20

DIERKS, Scott John. 1200 S 7TH AVE 57105 #046-01-2003 L2006 **FM** *020 †18

DILL, James Ellis. 2601 S MINNESOTA AVE, STE 105 57105 #051-01-1967 L2001 **GE** *020 †20

DILLON, Bonnie Johnson. 2501 W 22ND ST, SIOUIX FALLS VAM & ROC 57105 #046-01-1995 L1998 **FM** *020 †18

DILLON, Jeanne Catherine. 800 E 21ST ST, AVERA MCKENNAN HOSP 57105 #051-07-1991 L2002 **IM** *020 †20

DIMAILIG, Anna Belinda Sa. ■ 57106 #748-01-1993 L2006 **PD** *020

DIMITRIEVICH, Elizabeth. 625 W 18TH ST 57105 #917-24-1986 L1991 **OBG** *020 †30

DOLE, Arthur Sidney, Jr. ■ 57104 #038-41-1945 L1945 **U** *071 †95

DONELAN, Craig William. 1305 W 18TH ST 57105 #046-01-2002 L2006 **AN** *020 †05

DONELAN, Timothy Paul. 3401 W 49TH ST 57106 #046-01-1991 L1994 **FM** *020 †18

DOSCH, Wade Edward. 1200 S 7TH AVE, MCGREEVY CLINIC 57105 #046-01-1992 L1999 **GS** *020 †85

DRIVER, Shelley D. 1305 W 18TH ST, SIOUX VALLEY HOSPITAL 57105 #030-06-2001 L2004 **EM** *020 †16

DRYMALSKI, Mark Wayne. 1100 E 21ST ST STE 401, AVERA MCKENNAN REHAB ASSOC 57105 #046-01-2003 L2007 **PM** *020

DUDYCHA, Benjamin William. ■ 57105 #048-02-2007 *012

DUFFEK, Susan Marie. 1417 S MINNESOTA AVE 57105 #046-01-1992 L1997 **DR** *020 †80

DURSO, John Vincent. 2501 W 22ND ST # 116C, SIOUX FALLS VA MED CTR 57105 #030-05-1988 L1995 **P** *020

DZINTARS, Valdis Andrew. 1417 S MINNESOTA AVE 57105 #041-13-1972 L1979 **R** *020 †80

EASTON, Jessie K M. 3936 S WESTERN AVE 57105 #060-01-1957 L1979 **PM** *071 †60

ECKHOFF, Philip James, Jr. 1210 W 18TH ST, SANFORD-RHEUMTLGHY STE 201 57104 #026-04-1978 L1989 **RHU IM** *020 †20

ECKLUND, Scott Wayne. 600 N SYCAMORE AVE 57110 #046-01-1983 L1984 **FM** *020 †18

EICH, Shari Lee. 1200 S 7TH AVE 57105 #046-01-2004 L2007 **PD** *020 †55

EID, Wael Emad. 2501 W 22ND ST 57105 #915-03-1990 L2004 **END IM** *020

EIDSNESS, Luann Marie. 1400 W 22ND ST, SANFORD SCHOOL OF MED 57105 #046-01-1987 L1990 **IM PLM** *030 †20

EKSTRUM, Jacqueline Kaye. ■ 57105 #021-01-1997 L1997 **FM** *074

ELIAS, Abdallah Frederic. 1115 E 20TH ST, CTR FOR FAMILY MED 57105 #409-05-1995 **FP** *012

ELKINS, Bruce Alden. 4928 N CLIFF AVE 57104 #056-05-1993 L2004 **OM** *020 †70

ELLERBUSCH, David Allan. 600 N SYCAMORE AVE, FAMILY MEDICINE 4TH & SYCA 57110 #046-01-1983 L1984 **FM** *020 †18

ELLIOTT, Michael Keith. 1200 S 7TH AVE 57105 #037-01-1997 L2002 **PD** *020 †55

ELLIS, Lisa Lafollette. 1500 W 22ND ST, STE 301 57105 #051-04-2001 L2004 **IM** *020

ELSON, David Lee. 1000 E 21ST ST STE 2000, AVERA MEDICAL ONCOLOGY & H 57105 #018-03-1975 L1980 **ON IM** *020 †20

ENGLISH, Gilbert Loyal. 1200 S 7TH AVE 57105 #030-06-1968 L1977 **OBG** *020 †30

ENSBERG, Dorence Lester. 2700 W OAK ST, MINNEHAHA COUNTY 57105 #023-07-1946 L1955 **GS** *075 †85

ENTWISTLE, Frederick R. CENTRAL PLAINS CLINIC MAIN 57105 #041-13-1957 L1966 **ORS PM** *071 †40,60

EPHGRAVE, Pamela Marie. 1201 S EUCLID AVE, STE 301 57105 #016-43-1978 L1992 **OBG** *020 †30

ERICKSON, Kirsten Ruth. 1417 S MINNESOTA AVE 57105 #026-04-1982 L1984 **RO** *020 †80

ERICKSON, Mark C. 1305 W 18TH ST 57105 #046-01-1999 L2004 **IM** *020 †20

EVANS, David Charles. 1305 W 18TH ST 57105 #046-01-1995 L1998 **IM** *020 †85,20

FAITHE, Margaret Emerson. ■ 57104 #038-06-1954 L1955 **FM** *071 †18

FAMESTAD, Gary Leonard. 1417 S MINNESOTA AVE 57105 #046-01-1983 L1987 **DR** *020 †80

FANCIULLO, Joseph John. 810 E 23RD ST, ORTHOPEDIC INSTITUTE 57105 #030-05-1992 L1997 **RHU** *020 †20

FARB, Harry Franklin. 1305 W 18TH ST 57105 #005-14-1969 L2007 **MFM OBG** *020 †30

FARNHAM, Richard Jay. 101 W 37TH ST STE 111, C/O FARNHAM FORENSIC MED 57105 #035-08-1973 L1997 **OM LM** *020

FARRITOR, Michael Edward. 4405 E 26TH ST, SIOUX VALLEY CLINIC EAST 57103 #030-05-1979 L1980 **FM** *020 †18

■ = Address Information Privacy Protected

FEISTNER LEUNING, Heide L. 6000 W 41ST ST, MCGREEVY CLINIC WEST 57106 #026-04-1999 L2002 **FM** *020 †18

FENG, Xuesheng. 1210 W 18TH ST, STE 101 57104 #243-32-1988 L2007 **N** *100

FENNER, Randall Scott. ■ 57105 #046-01-2008 *012

FENTON, Lawrence Jules. 1305 W 18TH ST 57105 #038-41-1966 L1978 **NPM** *020 †55

FIEGEN, Michael Max. 1201 S EUCLID AVE, STE 510 57105 #038-40-1983 L1987 **OBG** *020 †30

FINCH, Sudhir Eugene. 911 E 20TH ST, CRITICAL CARE AND 57105 #033-05-1987 L2004 **CCP PD** *020 †20,55

FJELSTAD KJELSTRUP, Diane. ■ 57106 #037-01-2003 L2007 **CHP** *012

FLANAGAN, David Michael. 1200 S 7TH AVE 57105 #007-02-1990 L2003 **GS** *020 †85

FLETCHER, Harold James. 4603 S TECHLINK CIR 57106 #026-04-1967 L1968 **FM** *072 †18

FLOHR, Charles Edwin. 1417 S MINNESOTA AVE 57105 #030-05-1977 L1980 **DR NR** *020 †80

FLOM, Jon Orrin. 1305 W 18TH ST 57105 #026-04-1966 L1980 **PD** *020 †55

FLORIO, Kathryn I. 1210 W 18TH ST, STE 101 57104 #035-75-1993, ▲ L2000 **N** *020 †75

FLUHARTY, Colleen Louise. 800 E 21ST ST, AVERA MCKENNAN HOSPTIAL E. 57105 #030-06-1997 L2007 **PD** *020 †16,55

FOLEY, Stephen Thos. 2701 S KIWANIS AVE, SANFORD CLINIC FAMILY MEDI 57105 #046-01-1984 L1985 **FM FSM** *020 †18

FOX, Mark Warren. 1100 E 21ST ST, STE 210 57105 #005-02-1987 L1997 **NS** *020 †25

FREEMAN, Jerome Wm. 1210 W 18TH ST, STE 203 57104 #049-01-1974 L1979 **N IM** *020 †20,75

FRIEDMAN, Jared Anthony. 800 E 21ST ST, AVERA MCKENNAN HOSPITAL 57105 #046-01-2002 L2005 **EM** *020 †16

FRIESS, Richard Wm. 1201 S EUCLID AVE, STE 303 57105 #018-03-1966 L1967 **FM OM** *020 †18

FRIEZ, Matthew H. ■ 57105 #048-14-2005 **PTH** *012

FROEMMING, Sheila Marie. 1115 E 20TH ST, CENTER FOR FAMILY MEDICINE 57105 #026-04-2003 L2005 **FM** *100 †18

FULLERTON, Thomas Edward. 1200 S 7TH AVE 57105 #046-01-1987 L1993 **GS** *020 †85

FUNK, Allen Edward. 1201 S EUCLID AVE, STE 510 57105 #046-01-1988 L1998 **IM** *020 †20

FYSTRO, Kristin Joy. ■ 57106 #046-01-2008 *012

GAMMETER, William Bryce. ■ 57106 #046-01-2006 **P** *012

GARDNER, Bruce Allen. ■ 57106 #026-08-2008 *012

GASPARI, Jack Christopher. 1305 W 18TH ST, ANESTHESIA DEPT 57105 #038-43-1993 L1998 **AN** *020 †05

GEIS, Michael C. 1305 W 18TH ST 57105 #026-04-1995 L2007 **PTH** *020 †50

GEIS, Tara Willette. 1115 E 20TH ST, CENTER FOR FAMILY MEDICINE 57105 #026-04-1997 L2007 **FM FPG** *020 †18

GEISE, Douglas Howard. 4405 E 26TH ST, STE 1 57103 #046-01-1984 L1985 **FM** *020 †18

GEISE, Gregory L. 1305 W 18TH ST, SVC HOSPITALIST PROGRAM 57105 #048-04-1985 L1993 **IM** *020 †20

GIEBINK, Robert Rodger. 1305 W 18TH ST 57105 #026-04-1943 L1953 **ORS** *071 †40

GILBERT, Jorge Alberto. 1201 S EUCLID AVE, STE 104 57105 #319-04-1989 L2001 **GE** *020 †20

GILL, J S. PO BOX 5046, VA MED CTR # 112 57117 #495-03-1965 L1975 **GS TRS** *020 †85

GILLETT, Michael D. 1200 S EUCLID AVE, SPECIALISTS CHARTERED 57105 #048-13-2000 L2006 **U** *020 †95

GIOIA, Frank R. 911 E 20TH ST, CRITICAL CARE AND 57105 #005-19-1976 L1999 **PD CCP** *030 †55

GLATT, Dennis James. 1508 W 22ND ST, STE 101 57105 #046-01-1997 L2002 **GS TRS** *020 †85

GRADY, Robert Ernest, Jr. 1305 W 18TH ST 57105 #036-05-1991 L2000 **AN** *020 †05

GRAHAM, Donald Bryant. 1508 W 22ND ST STE 101, S C SURGICAL ASSOCS 57105 #026-04-1972 L1978 **GS** *020 †85

GREEN, Marc Allan. 1310 W 22ND ST, SANFORD CLINIC 57105 #026-04-1979 L1983 **D** *020 †15

GREENE, Denise Dawn. 1115 E 20TH ST 57105 #046-01-1993 L1994 **FM** *020 †18

GREENE, Derek Scott. 3400 S SOUTHEASTERN AVE, MCGREEVY CLINIC SOUTHEASTE 57103 #046-01-1995 L1998 **FM** *020 †18

GREGG, John Bailey. ■ 57105 #018-03-1946 L1953 **PHP OTO** *071 †45 ‡

GREGG, Mark Wayne. 1100 E 21ST ST, STE 506 57105 #046-01-1986 L1990 **N** *020 †75

GREGORY, Christopher. 1417 S MINNESOTA AVE 57105 #023-07-1985 L2003 **DR NM** *020 †80,28

GRIFFIN, John Farror. 1417 S MINNESOTA AVE 57105 #046-01-1984 L1986 **RO IM** *020 †20,80

GUL, Samina. 1115 E 20TH ST, CTR FOR FAMILY MEDICINE 57105 #704-24-1989 **FM** *100

GUNNARSON, Richard Eugene. ■ 57105 #056-05-1963 L1964 **OTO** *071 †45

GUPTA, Ashutosh. 300 N DAKOTA AVE STE 1170 57104 #495-13-1985 L2004 **PDE** *020 †55

GUTCH, Charley F. ■ 57104 #018-03-1943 L1947 **IM NEP** *071 †20

GUTNIK, Leonard Mark. 1100 E 21ST ST STE 400, AVERA DOCTORS PLAZA 2 57105 #016-06-1976 L1980 **IM** *020 †20

HAFT, Geoffrey Frederick. 1210 W 18TH ST STE G01 57104 #040-02-1999 L2005 **ORS OP** *020 †40

HAIDER, Kamal-Uddin. 1000 E 21ST ST, STE 1200 57105 #704-02-1991 L2002 **HO** *020 †20

HAJEK, Catherine Anne. ■ 57103 #046-01-2008 *012

HALLIGAN, Christine Shann. 810 E 23RD ST, ORTHOPEDIC INSTITUTE 57105 #028-46-1999 L2006 **RHU** *020 †20

HALMA, Gary Allan. 1305 W 18TH ST 57105 #005-18-1982 L1986 **AN** *020 †05

HANNA, Hany Emile. 2501 W 22ND ST, ROYAL JOHNSON MEM HOSP 57105 #915-05-1982 L1998 **IM FM** *020 †20

HANNA, Marwan Daoud. 1000 E 21ST ST, STE 3100 57105 #875-01-1975 L1984 **PHO** *020 †55

HANSEN, John Alan, Jr. 1210 W 18TH ST, STE LL04 57104 #030-05-1979 L1990 **PMM** *020 †70

HANSEN, Keith Allen. 1500 W 22ND ST, STE 301 57105 #028-02-1983 L1998 **REN OBG** *020 †30

HANSEN, Mark Chandler. ■ 57106 #046-01-2008 *012

HARDIE, Richard Dean. 1201 S EUCLID AVE, STE 407 57105 #046-01-1978 L1985 **PUD IM** *020 †20

HARMS, Robert Wm. 132 N DAKOTA AVE 57104 #030-05-1976 L1977 **EM FM** *020 †16,18

HARRIS, Frederick Lewis. 911 E 20TH ST, STE 300 57105 #048-04-1976 L1983 **GS CCS** *020 †85 ‡

HARRIS, Mary Helen R. 1305 W 18TH ST 57105 #048-04-1976 L1983 **EM** *020 †16

HART, Randi Wayne. 1417 S MINNESOTA AVE, MEDICAL X-RAY 57105 #056-06-1982 L2007 **R** *020 †80

HARTMANN, Alfred Erich. 1000 E 21ST ST 57105 #030-05-1968 L1974 **CLP PTH** *020 †50

HARTZELL, Allan James. 1200 S EUCLID AVE STE 312 57105 #026-04-1962 L1973 **U** *071 †95

HARVISON, Gregg Arden. 1200 S 7TH AVE 57105 #046-01-1994 L1997 **FM** *020 †18

HASSEBROEK-JOHNSON, J. 1500 W 22ND ST, STE 301 57105 #018-03-1994 L1998 **OBG** *020 †30

HEARNS, Valerie Lynne. 1200 S EUCLID AVE, STE 104 57105 #041-13-1985 L1992 **FM** *020 †18

HECKMANN, Robert Edwin. 4405 E 26TH ST, SIOUX VALLEY CLINIC EAST 57103 #026-08-1995 L1998 **FM** *020 †18

HEDDLESTON, Leslie Norman. 1001 E 21ST ST STE 401, AVERA MATERNAL FETAL MEDIC 57105 #055-02-1981 L1994 **OBG** *020 †30

HEILING, Karen Jean. 1200 S 7TH AVE 57105 #026-04-1987 L1990 **FM** *020 †18

HEIN, Barry Drew. 1305 W 18TH ST 57105 #007-02-2000 L2005 **AN** *100 †05

HEINEMANN, Daniel Joseph. 1305 W 18TH ST, SANFORD HEALTH 57105 #046-01-1981 L1982 **FM** *030 †18

HELD, William Eric. 4405 E 26TH ST 57103 #026-04-1977 L1984 **FM** *020 †18

HELGAAS, Steffen Andrew. ■ 57107 #026-04-1968 L1973 **FM** *020 †18

HELGESON, Matthew Scott. 1417 S MINNESOTA AVE 57105 #018-03-1997 L2007 **DR** *020 †80

HENRY, Scott. 1201 S EUCLID AVE 57105 #016-11-1988 L1992 **PD** *020 †55

HERMANSON, Evan Nord. 810 E 23RD ST, ORTHOPEDIC INSTITUTE 57105 #030-05-2001 L2007 **OSM** *020

HERMANSON, Kristin Leigh. 1500 W 22ND ST STE 301, SANFORD WOMENS HEALTH 57105 #030-05-2001 L2007 **OBG** *020 †30

HESS, Benjamin Andrew. ■ 57106 #026-04-2006 L2007 **FP** *012

HICKEY, David Craven. 1305 W 18TH ST 57105 #048-12-1977 L2001 **R NM** *020 †80,28

HIEB, Gregory Dean. 1305 W 18TH ST 57105 #046-01-1999 L2005 **AN** *100 †05

HILL, Cristina Alison. ■ 57104 #046-01-2001 L2007 **GE** *100

HOF, Jem Jerome. 2501 W 22ND ST, P O BOX 5046 57105 #046-01-1986 L1987 **PM PMM** *020 †60

HOFER, Catherine M. 1100 E 21ST ST 57105 #016-06-1989 L1992 **PD** *020 †55

HOFER, Darlys Roy. 1200 S EUCLID AVE, SPECIALISTS CHARTERED 57105 #046-01-1984 L1991 **U** *020 †95

HOFFMAN, Wendell Walter. 1201 S EUCLID AVE, STE 401 57105 #046-01-1979 L1986 **ID IM** *020 †20

HONG, Song Yun. 2501 W 22ND ST, UNIV OF SD SCH OF MED 57105 #583-09-2001 L2007 **IM** *100

HORN, Jessica Ann. 1115 E 20TH ST, CTR FOR FAMILY MEDICINE 57105 #046-01-2005 **FP** *012

HORNER, Emily Jean. ■ 57103 #046-01-2008 *012

HORNER, William James. 1305 W 18TH ST 57105 #026-04-1980 L1982 **AN** *020

HORNING, James Ross. 2501 W 22ND ST, BOX 5046 57105 #046-01-1977 L1979 **IM GP** *040 †20

HOSEN, Richard Stanford. 1100 E 21ST ST 57105 #021-01-1957 L1960 **PD** *071 †55

HOSKINS, John Howard. 1200 S EUCLID AVE 57105 #041-13-1961 L1963 **U** *071 †95

HOVERSTEN, David Lincoln. 1320 S MINNESOTA AVE, STE 100 57105 #007-02-1973 L1981 **ORS** *020 †40

HOWARD, Thomas Christophe. ■ 57105 #046-01-2008 *012

HOXTELL, Eugene Orville. 1201 S EUCLID AVE 57105 #026-04-1969 L1976 **D DMP** *071 †15

HUBER, Lu Yu. 2501 W 22ND ST 57105 #243-63-1993 **IM** *012

HUBER, Mark Ryan. 1000 E 21ST ST STE 2000, AVERA CANCER INST 57105 #012-01-1999 L2005 **HO** *020 †20

HUCKINS, Scott John. 1200 S 7TH AVE, MCGREEVY CLINIC AVERA 57105 #046-01-1981 L1982 **IM** *020 †20

HUMPHREYS, Donald Wayne. 1400 W 22ND ST, INTERNAL MEDICINE 57105 #028-02-1963 L1976 **ID IM** *040 †20

HUNTINGTON, Mark Kenneth. 1115 E 20TH ST, CENTER FOR FAMILY MED 57105 #025-12-1995 L2006 **FM** *020 †18 ‡

HUOT, Samuel Wm. 1305 W 18TH ST 57105 #026-04-1979 L1981 **FM A** *020 †18

HURD, Jason Lee. 1210 W 18TH ST STE G01, SANFORD ORTHO & SPORTS MED 57104 #016-06-2001 L2007 **ORS** *020

HURLEY, Christopher M. 1201 S EUCLID AVE, STE 104 57105 #016-43-1989 L1994 **GE** *020 †20

HURLEY, Timothy E. 1201 S EUCLID AVE STE 510, INTERNAL MEDICINE 57105 #016-43-1978 L1981 **PHL IM** *020 †20

HUSSAIN, Rif At. 1500 W 22ND ST STE 104 57105 #704-09-1966 L1975 **PS** *020 †65

HUSSER, Casey Scott. 1305 W 18TH ST 57105 #026-08-1999 L2006 **AN** *100 †05

HUTCHENS, Kate Elizabeth. ■ 57105 #030-05-2005 L2007 **FP** *012

HYLAND, Lowell James. 2200 W 49TH ST, STE 104 57105 #026-04-1962 L1973 **A IM** *071 †03

INAMDAR, Shashita Ramsinh. 1621 S MINNESOTA AVE, SIOUX VALLEY CLC PSYCH 57105 #495-23-1993 L2004 **CHP** *020 †75

ISRAEL, Michael. ■ 57105 #050-02-1964 L1969 **PTH** *071 †50

JAMOUS, Fady Ghassan. 300 N DAKOTA AVE STE 117 57104 #605-01-1999 L2005 **PCC** *100 †20

JAQUA, Richard Allen. 1305 W 18TH ST, SIOUX VALLEY HOSPITAL 57105 #024-01-1965 L1970 **PTH NM** *071 †50,28

JASSIM, Ali Dakhil. 1305 W 18TH ST 57105 #528-02-1978 L1992 **PTH ON** *020 †50

JEFFREYS, Sana. 1020 W 18TH ST, CLINIC-ONCOLOGY 57104 #422-01-1998 L2007 **HO** *020 †20

JENKINS, Jeffrey James. 2701 S KIWANIS AVE, SANFORD CLINIC FAMILY MEDI 57105 #030-06-2000 L2002 **FM** *020 †18

JENSEN, Ricky C. 1310 W 22ND ST, SANFORD CLINIC 57105 #049-01-1993 L2006 **OTO** *020 †45

JERSTAD, John Peter. 800 E 21ST ST 57105 #046-01-1988 L1991 **IM** *020 †20

JOHNSON, Christopher Ryan. ■ 57103 #046-01-2006 L2006 **AN** *012

JOHNSON, Julie A. 1100 W 41ST ST 57105 #025-07-1988 L1997 **PM** *020 †60

JOHNSON, Mark Wm. 1305 W 18TH ST 57105 #046-01-1986 L1991 **PTH HMP** *020 †50

JOHNSON, Melissa K. 1508 W 22ND ST, STE 101 57105 #046-01-2001 L2006 **GS** *020

JOHNSON, Michael Marlton. 1305 W 18TH ST 57105 #046-01-1998 L2002 **AN** *020

JOHNSON, Peter David. 1210 W 18TH ST STE 103, SANFORD CLINIC NORTH CENTE 57104 #046-01-1989 L1996 **PM SCI** *020 †60

JOHNSON, Robert Carl. 1200 S EUCLID AVE, SPECIALISTS CHARTERED 57105 #024-05-1972 L1977 **U** *020 †95

JOHNSON, Virginia P. 1305 W 18TH ST, G804 ANN BERDAHL HALL 57105 #748-01-1961 L1971 **CG CCG** *071 †19

JONES, Charles Saml. 3801 S ELMWOOD AVE, JONES EYE CLINIC 57105 #010-03-1960 L1978 **OS** *075

JONES, Christopher Lee. 1115 E 20TH ST 57105 #046-01-2005 **FP** *012

JONSSON, Orvar Thor. 1305 W 18TH ST 57105 #484-01-1998 L2006 **CD** *100

JULIUS, Steven Craig. 2501 W 22ND ST, CHIEF OF STAFF OFFICE 57105 #034-01-1982 L1984 **N** *020 †75

KALDA, Ellison Franklin, II. 911 E 20TH ST, INSTITUTE OF SOUTH DAKOTA 57105 #046-01-1977 L1982 **GS** *020 †85

KALLEMEYN, Brenda Kay. 1200 S 7TH AVE 57105 #046-01-2002 L2006 **OBG** *020

KALO, Jeffrey S. 2908 E 26TH ST 57103 #028-79-1988, ▲ L2003 **ORS** *020

KANGLEY, Daniel Jos. 2701 S MINNESOTA AVE, STE 3 57105 #037-01-1976 L1977 **EM** *020 †16

KAPASKA, David L. 800 E 21ST ST, AVERA MCKENNAN HOSP 57105 #018-75-1986, ▲ L1999 **FM** *030 †18 ‡

KAPOOR, Aarti G. 1200 S 7TH AVE 57105 #496-07-1987 L2002 IM *020 †20

KAPOOR, Shiv Shashi. 800 E 21ST ST, AVERA MCKENNAN HOSPITAL 57105 #495-45-1986 L2001 NPM *020 †55

KARL, Stephen R. 1001 E 21ST ST, STE 12 57105 #035-20-1974 L1992 PDS *020 †85

KARMAZIN, Alexander. 1305 W 18TH ST, SANFORD CHILDRENS SPEC CLN 57105 #028-46-1997 L2007 PDE *020 †55 ‡

KARU, Heather Lyn. 1500 W 22ND ST, STE 104 57105 #046-01-1999 L2006 PS *020

KASEM, Hussien Heshmat Mo. 2501 W 22ND ST 57105 #915-02-1998 IM *100

KASINATHAN, Sriranjani. 1115 E 20TH ST, CTR FOR FAMILY MEDICINE 57105 #495-59-1982 L2005 FM *020 †18

KAUFMAN, Jay Stuart. 1001 E 21ST ST 57105 #056-06-1975 L1996 CD IM *020 †20

KAUFMANN, Anthony Michael. 1305 W 18TH ST 57105 #062-01-1987 L2002 *020

KEIL, James Edwin. 1305 W 18TH ST 57105 #019-02-1970 L2001 FM P *020 ‡

KELLY, Patrick Wayne. 1305 W 18TH ST, SIOUX VALLEY CLINIC-VASCUL 57105 #046-01-1998 L2003 VS *020 †85

KEMP, Earl David. 1115 E 20TH ST, CENTER FOR FAMILY MED 57105 #018-03-1972 L1973 FM PHP *040 †18

KENDRICK, David Donald. ■ 57103 #010-03-1959 L1970 GP U *074

KENNELLY, Daniel James. 517 W 20TH ST 57105 #056-06-1965 L1972 P *020 †75

KEPPEN, Laura Ann. 1305 W 18TH ST 57105 #046-01-1979 L1990 PDE *020 †55,19

KEPPEN, Michael D. 1020 W 18TH ST, CLINIC-ONCOLOGY 57104 #046-01-1978 L1990 HEM ON *020

KERR, James Douglas. 1305 W 18TH ST 57105 #048-15-1984 L1988 FM EM *020 †18

KHAN, Imran Ahmed. PO BOX 5046, VAMC SIOUX FALLS 57117 #704-02-2004 IM *012

KHAN, Mohammed Akram. 1305 W 18TH ST, USD SCHOOL OF MEDICINE 57105 #704-01-1987 L2001 NPM *020 †55

KHURANA, Aman. 1305 W 18TH ST 57105 #495-34-1997 L2003 IM *020

KIDMAN, Brian Keith. 2701 S MINNESOTA AVE, DESTINY FAMILY MEDICAL CLI 57105 #048-15-1985 L1986 FM *020 †18

KIETZMANN, Paul Michael. 1115 E 20TH ST 57105 #026-04-2005 L2007 FP *012

KIHNE, Michael Jos. 1417 S MINNESOTA AVE 57105 #030-05-1978 L1990 DR *020 †80

KING, Gregory Paul, Jr. ■ 57104 #046-01-2007 TY *012

KLEIN, Jennifer Lynn. 600 N SYCAMORE AVE 57110 #046-01-1999 L2002 FM *020 †18

KLEIN, Richard Lewis. 1201 S EUCLID AVE, STE 301 57105 #028-34-1971 L2000 U *020 †95

KLEINSASSER, Bradley Jay. ■ 57103 #046-01-1990 L1995 CHP *020 †75

KOCH, Michael Royduane. 1305 W 18TH ST 57105 #046-01-1986 L1988 PTH *020 †50

KOELEWYN, Jason Robert. ■ 57106 #005-12-2005 L2007 FP *012

KOOIMA, Rick A. 1200 S 7TH AVE 57105 #018-03-1990 L1998 PD *020 †55

KOSIAK, Donald John, Jr. ■ 57106 #037-01-2001 L2004 EM *020 †16

KOVALESKI, David Hugh. 1001 E 21ST ST, STE 300 57105 #046-01-1999 L2004 NEP *020 †20

KRIE, Amy Kathryn. 1000 E 21ST ST STE 2000, AVERA CANCER INST 57105 #018-03-2001 L2006 ON *020

KUCHANGI, Vasanthumar C. 2501 W 22ND ST, MED 57105 #495-33-1986 L1998 IM *020 †20

KUNKEL, Shirley Yeh. ■ 57105 #028-02-1979 L1989 OBG *074 †30

KUNKEL, Steve Edward. ■ 57105 #028-02-1979 L1989 AN *020 †05

KURTENBACH, Chad A. ■ 57106 #026-04-2007 #012

KUSMAK, Jacob Michael. ■ 57106 #046-01-2007 TY *012

KUTAYLI, Farid. 1001 E 21ST ST, GROUND FLOOR 57105 #605-01-1970 L1990 PDC *020

LAKSTIGALA, Peters E. 607 S DAKOTA AVE 57104 #407-15-1948 L1952 GP AM *071 †18

LAL, Yasir. PO BOX 5046, VAMC SIOUX FALLS 57117 #704-21-2002 IM *012

LAMFERS, Randall Ben. 1201 S EUCLID AVE, STE 510 57105 #028-03-2002 L2006 IM *020 †20

LANDEEN, Laurie B. 1500 W 22ND ST, STE 301 57105 #010-02-1988 L1996 OBG *020 †30 ‡

LANG, Terry Allen. 1201 S EUCLID AVE, STE 407 57105 #030-05-1975 L1978 PD *020 †55

LANKHORST, Barry John. 2501 W 22ND ST, SVC-TRANSPLANT/NEPHROLOGY 57105 #048-15-1974 L1981 NEP IM *050 †20

LAPKA, Beth. 1305 W 18TH ST, SIOUX VALLEY HOSPITAL 57105 #028-46-1998 L2001 EM *020 †16

LAPP, Robert Towner. ■ 57105 #046-01-2008 *012

LARSEN, David Allen. 1200 S 7TH AVE 57105 #056-05-1985 L1986 FM *020 †18

LARSON, Eric Allan. 1201 S EUCLID AVE, STE 510 57105 #046-01-1996 L2000 IM *020 †20

LARSON, Tricia Lynn. 1200 S 7TH AVE 57105 #046-01-2002 L2005 FM *020

LAUDENSCHLAGER, Mark Davi. ■ 57106 #046-01-2007 PTH *012

LAVENDER, John Gould. ■ 57105 #030-05-1943 L1943 GP *071

LAWLER, Patrick Jos. 1100 E 26TH ST, STE 1 57105 #030-06-1988 L1992 AN *020 †05

LEE, Richard Walker. 1305 W 18TH ST, CREIGHTON UNIVERSITY-GME 57105 #030-06-1999 L2006 VS *020

LEEBURTON, Timothy J. 1210 W 18TH ST STE G01, SVC-VANDEMARK ORTHO 57104 #016-01-1998 L2004 HS *020 †40

LEITHEISER, Jamie Lynn. 1305 W 18TH ST 57105 #046-01-1996 L2002 EM *020 †16

LEMASTER, Larry Alan. 1200 S 7TH AVE 57105 #046-01-1978 L2007 FM *020 †18

LEONARD, Lorraine Marie. 1305 W 18TH ST, SIOUX VALLEY HOSPTIAL/ER 57105 #046-01-1991 L1994 IM *020 †20

LI, Faqian. 1100 E 21ST ST, CARDIOVASC RES INST #700 57105 #243-65-1983 L2005 PTH *050 †20

LINDEMANN, Janet Corinne. 1200 S EUCLID AVE STE 104, SANFORD CLINIC USD PHYSICI 57105 #056-06-1980 L1997 FM *020 †18

LIU, Editha Abelardo. 1200 S 7TH AVE 57105 #748-02-1996 L2005 IM *020 †20

LOBBEZOO, Luanne Joy. 3700 S WESTERN AVE # 775 57105 #025-12-1985 L1986 EM *020 †16

LOCKWOOD, Scott A. 1100 E 26TH ST, STE 1 57105 #046-01-1988 L1992 AN *020 †05

LONGO, Charles Anthony. 911 E 20TH ST, STE 500 57105 #018-03-1998 L2003 END *020 †20

LOOBY, Thomas Lawrence. 1500 W 22ND ST, STE 301 57105 #025-01-1966 L1972 OBG *020 †30

LORENZEN, Kim Marlan. 1000 E 21ST ST 57105 #046-01-1983 L1988 PTH FOP *020 †50 ‡

LOUW, Deon Francois. ■ 57101 #836-02-1983 L2001 N *100

LOVRIEN, Fred Clinton. 1305 W 18TH ST 57105 #018-03-1973 L1978 END IM *020 †20,28

LUEBKE, Marlys L Schulz. 1305 W 18TH ST 57105 #046-01-1986 L1987 FM *020 †18

LUNDIN, Rosa Ella. 2300 S DAKOTA AVE, CENTER FOR FAMLIY MEDICINE 57105 #030-05-2001 L2004 FM *020 †18

LUNN, Robert Jay. 1305 W 18TH ST 57105 #048-04-1985 L1996 AN *020 †05

MABEE, Lee Maitland, Jr. 1201 S EUCLID AVE STE 206 57105 #012-05-1976 L1980 OBG *020 †30

MADISON, Dean Loren. 1500 W 22ND ST, STE 301 57105 #018-03-1971 L1977 OBG *020 †30

MADSEN, Melanie Sue. 1305 W 18TH ST 57105 #030-01-1992 L2002 CCP *020 †55

MAGIDSON, Melvin Allan. ■ 57103 #016-11-1966 L1983 DR *020 †80

MAGNUSON, Gregory Lynn. 1201 S EUCLID AVE, STE 201 57105 #030-05-1973 L1976 FM *020 †18

MAILLOUX, Carolyn. ■ 57103 #028-46-1984 L2000 OM EM *020 †70

MAILLOUX, Edward Robert. 4405 E 26TH ST, SIOUX VALLEY CLINIC 57103 #028-34-1993 L2000 PD *020 †55

MALLEK, John Anthony. 1210 W 18TH ST, STE 201 57104 #016-43-1978 L1992 RHU IM *020 †20

MAMSA, Muhammad Faisal. 2501 W 22ND ST 57105 #704-02-1995 P *100

MARCKSTADT, Gary Steven. 4405 E 26TH ST, SIOUX VALLEY CLINIC 57103 #654-01-1998 L2007 FM *020 †85

MARESH, James Everett. 1508 W 22ND ST, STE 101 57105 #007-02-1972 L2000 GS *020 †85

MAROUN, Christiane. 800 E 21ST ST 57105 #605-02-1989 L1994 PD *020 †55

MASILAMANI, Stanley Saul. 1001 E 21ST ST, STE 501 57105 #495-27-1959 L2004 IM GE *020 †20

MASKA, Leann Beth. ■ 57106 #046-01-2007 IM *012

MASTERSON, Thomas Edward. 1417 S MINNESOTA AVE 57105 #026-04-1975 L1981 R OS *020 †18,80

MATOS, Eugenio. 1210 W 18TH ST, STE 101 57104 #308-02-1976 L1995 N CN *020 †75

MAXWELL, Clare Louise. 1001 E 21ST ST, STE 200 57105 #422-01-2002 L2007 P *100

MAZURCZAK, Miroslaw A. 1020 W 18TH ST, SANFORD CANCER CENTER ONCO 57104 #759-10-1988 L1998 IM HO *020 †20

MC CAUL, Kelly George. 1000 E 21ST ST STE 1200, AVERA HEMATOLOGY AND TRANS 57105 #065-05-1992 L2000 IM *020 †20

MC GRAW, Steven Charles. 1417 S MINNESOTA AVE 57105 #046-01-1997 L2002 RO *020 †80

MC GREEVY, Patrick S. 1200 S 7TH AVE 57105 #030-06-1962 L1969 GS *020 †85

MC KAY, Jennifer Marie. 1200 S 7TH AVE 57105 #046-01-2000 L2003 IM *020 †20 ‡

MCKAY, Julie Ann. 1201 S EUCLID AVE, STE G04 57105 #037-01-1988 L1995 DR *020 †80

MC KAY, Kimberlee Ann. 1200 S 7TH AVE 57105 #046-01-2000 L2006 OBG *020 †30

MC LAUGHLIN, Julie Ann. ■ 57105 #047-05-1984 L1997 IM *020 †20

MC MENAMY, Kandi Burton. 800 E 21ST ST 57105 #028-34-1986 L1993 NPM PD *020 †55

MC MILLIN, John Michael. 1320 S MINNESOTA AVE 57105 #026-04-1965 L1977 END IM *020 †20

MC NAMEE, Turi Ann. 800 E 21ST ST, AVERA MCKENNAN HOSPITAL 57105 #016-02-1996 L2002 IM *020 †20

MC NAUGHTON, Clifford A. 1700 S SHAFER DR 57110 #046-01-1995 L2000 P *020

MC SHERRY, Marc Stanley. 1305 W 18TH ST, DEPT OF EMERGENCY MEDICIN 57105 #026-04-2002 L2005 EM *020 †16

MEIERHENRY, Mary E. 414 W 18TH ST, INDEPENDENT WOMEN'S CARE P 57104 #046-01-1992 L1999 OBG *020 †30

MELANSON, Tina Marie. 1001 E 21ST ST, STE 300 57105 #046-01-1997 L2002 NEP *020

MENON, Kozhikode Veetil N. 1001 E 21ST ST, STE 303 57105 #495-94-1988 L2007 GE *020

METZ, Timothy John. 1100 E 26TH ST 57105 #046-01-1991 L2000 AN *020 †05

MEYER, Angela Marie. 3400 S SOUTHEASTERN AVE 57103 #046-01-2000 L2003 FM *020 †18

MEYER, Jason Lars. ■ 57104 #046-01-2004 PTH *012

MEYER, Jeff Dayle. 3401 W 49TH ST, SANFORD FAMILY MEDICINE 57106 #046-01-1995 L2005 FM *020 †18

MEYER, Robert David. 1200 S EUCLID AVE, STE 210 57105 #046-01-1983 L1989 GE IM *020

MEYER, Vaughn Henry. 911 E 20TH ST STE 602 57105 #037-01-1976 L1984 PS *020 †65,85

MILANOVICH, Samuel Jacob. BOX 1172 AUGUSTANA COLLEGE 57197 #037-01-2006 PD *012

MILES, Carol Beth. 1100 E 21ST ST, STE 506 57105 #046-01-1991 L1995 N *020 †75

MILLER, L Patrick. 911 E 20TH ST, STE 602 57105 #016-02-1979 L1996 PS FPS *020 †65

MILLER, Nathan James. ■ 57103 #046-01-2008 *012

MILLER, Steven Eric. 1305 W 18TH ST 57105 #030-06-1991 L2001 CD *020 †20

MOBLEY, Elijah. 1001 E 21ST ST, STE 301 57105 #047-07-1993 L2005 GS *020 †85

MONTEAU, Lance. ■ 57104 #046-01-2007 IM *012

MOOSE, Courtney Jo. 3400 S SOUTHEASTERN AVE 57103 #046-01-2002 L2005 FM *020 †18

MORK, Michael R. 3700 S WESTPORT AVE, # 1852 57106 #012-05-1977 L1978 AM *071 †70

MORSE, Peter Hodges. 1701 S MINNESOTA AVE, GREAT PLAINS EYE CLC LTD 57105 #016-02-1963 L1993 OPH *020 †35

MOUSSEAU, Francine L. ■ 57106 #046-01-2006 IM *012

MUDUNDI, Ashok Kumar. 2501 W 22ND ST, DEPT. OF VA AFFAIRS 57105 #495-37-2000 L2007 IM *020 †20 ‡

MUNCE, David Blaine. 1100 E 26TH ST, ANESTHESIA ASSC INC 57105 #046-01-1992 L2001 AN *020 †05

MUNSON, David Paul. 1305 W 18TH ST 57105 #026-04-1969 L1973 NPM PD *020 †55

MURPHY, Karla Kenefick. 1000 E 21ST ST 57105 #046-01-1982 L1986 PTH *020 †50

MURRAY, Jeffrey Allan. 1201 S EUCLID AVE, STE 104 57105 #046-01-1982 L1987 GE *020 †20

MURTHY, Madhu Kiran Holen. ■ 57106 #496-35-2000 L2006 ID *012 †20

MUTCH, Milton Gardner. 1500 W 22ND ST, STE 301 57105 #026-04-1955 L1959 OBG *071 †30

MUTHU, Krishnakumar R.. ■ 57105 #496-45-1998 L2007 IM *020

MYO, Nay. 1400 W 22ND ST, USD HEALTH SCIENCE CTR 57105 #209-01-1990 IM *100

NANTON, Stephen Errol. 300 N DAKOTA AVE STE 1170 57104 #422-01-1998 L2005 PG *020 †55,20

NAPOLITANO, Christine. 800 E 21ST ST 57105 #035-75-2000, ▲ L2006 PCC *020 †20

NAUGHTON, Gregory. ■ 57105 #030-06-1963 L1969 IM *071 †20

NAZIR, Jawad. 911 E 20TH ST, DISEASE SPEACIALISTS PC 57105 #704-01-1993 L2003 ID *020 †20

NEIDICH, Gary Archer. 1305 W 18TH ST, SPECIALTY CLINIC 57105 #043-01-1978 L1983 PG *020 †55

NELIMARK, Robert Allen. 1020 W 18TH ST, CLINIC-ONCOLOGY 57104 #016-43-1973 L1982 ON IM *020 †20

NELSON, Candice Louise. 4405 E 26TH ST 57103 #037-01-1998 L2001 PD *020 †55

NELSON, David Christopher. 1201 S EUCLID AVE STE 510, MEDICAL BLDG 2 57105 #046-01-1991 L1994 IM *020

NELSON, Earl Goodwin. 1913 S SHAW AVE 57106 #016-06-1961 L1962 GP *020

NELSON, Jenny Schultz. ■ 57107 #046-01-2008 *012

NELSON, Patrick Arthur. 1417 S MINNESOTA AVE, MEDICAL X-RAY CENTRE AVENU 57105 #037-01-1986 L1992 DR *020 †80

NELSON, Richard A. 1200 S 7TH AVE 57105 #001-02-1976 L1977 IM *020 †20

NELSON, Robert Eugene. 1100 E 21ST ST, CENTRAL PLAINS CLINIC LTD 57105 #028-02-1946 L1955 GS TS *071 †85

NEMEH, Rand Khouri. 911 EAST 21TH ST, #401 57105 #037-01-1992 P *012

NIAZ, Saleha S. 1400 W 22ND ST, INTERNAL MEDICINE RESIDENT 57105 #704-02-2004 IM *012

NICE, Richard Fay. 1500 W 22ND ST, SUITE 102/TWIN OAKS 57105 #016-06-1962 L1970 ORS *071 †40

NOBLE, Jason William. ■ 57106 #046-01-2007 **TY** *012
NOLD, Joan Lee. 1305 W 18TH ST 57105 #046-01-1998 L2001 **NPM** *020 †55
NORD, Wesley John. 1115 E 20TH ST 57105 #026-04-1975 L1982 **FM IM** *040 †20,18
NORDSTROM, Donald Gene. 1417 S MINNESOTA AVE 57105 #018-03-1973 L1978 **RO** *020 †80
NURI, Humayun. 2501 W 22ND ST 57105 #665-01-2005 **IM** *012
NUSSBAUM, David Kent. 1200 S 7TH AVE 57105 #046-01-1982 L1984 **IM** *020 †20
NYKAMP, Verlyn Jon. 1500 W 22ND ST STE 105 57105 #026-04-1990 L1999 **TS VS** *020 †85,90
OAKLAND, James Alan. ■ 57105 #051-04-1976 L1977 **FM FSM** *071 †18
O'BRIEN, Charles Patrick. 1305 W 18TH ST, BOX 5039 57105 #030-06-1970 L1980 **CD** *020 †20
O'BRIEN, Peter John. 1508 W 22ND ST STE 101, SANFORD CLN SURG ASSOCS 57105 #030-06-1968 L1974 **GS** *020 †85
O'CONNELL, Kevin John. 911 E 20TH ST, INSTITUTE 57105 #033-05-1968 L2000 **U** *020 †95 ‡
OHRT, David Walter. 1305 W 18TH ST 57105 #004-01-1977 L1979 **PTH** *020 †50
OLEJNIK, Waclaw. ■ 57106 #165-02-1954 L1980 **GP P** *071
OLSON, Bradley Lee. 1100 E 26TH ST, STE 1 57105 #046-01-1989 L1994 **AN** *020 †05
OLSON, James Paul. 1305 W 18TH ST 57105 #046-01-1990 L1999 **CD** *020 †20
OLSON, Steven Paul. 1000 E 21ST ST 57105 #018-03-1981 L1985 **PTH NM** *020 †50,28 ‡
ONG, Tuyen Binh. 2501 W 22ND ST 57105 #917-28-1998 **IM** *100
OPHEIM, Warren Louis. 4407 S TOWNPARK PL, MINNEHAHA COUNTY 57105 #041-13-1945 L1948 **GP** *071
OPHEIM, Warren O V. 1100 E 21ST ST, STE 506 57105 #026-04-1973 L1977 **N** *020 †75
OPPENHEIMER, Mark Jeffrey. 3926 S WESTERN AVE, OPPENHEIMER ENDOCRNLGY 57105 #026-04-1981 L1989 **IM END** *020 †20 ‡
ORMAND, Joann Eileen. 1201 S EUCLID AVE, STE 104 57105 #026-04-1984 L2004 **GE IM** *020 †20
O'SHEA, Timothy Thos. 2501 W 22ND ST 57105 #048-04-1976 L1992 **IM** *020 †20
OSTBY, Jason Raymond. 2501 W 22ND ST 57105 #046-01-1981 L1984 **FM** *020 †18
OTRADOVEC-GAETZE, Jane. 1001 E 21ST ST, CLINICS 57105 #028-03-1976 L1986 **OBG** *020 †30
PALMER, Bradley Lane. 7220 W 41ST ST, SANFORD FAMILY MEDICINE 57106 #046-01-1999 L2002 **FM** *020 †18
PARAMESWARAN, Ramakrishnan. 800 E 21ST ST 57105 #495-04-1989 L2003 *020
PARDY, Matthew Terrence. 1000 E 21ST ST, STE 1000 57105 #046-01-1998 L2004 **RNR** *020 †80
PARDY, Paula K. 1001 E 21ST ST STE 401, OBGYN ASSOCS-AVERA HLTH 57105 #046-01-1998 L2004 **OBG** *020 †30
PARRY, Rodney Russell. 1310 W 22ND ST 57105 #056-05-1969 L1976 **PUD IM** *040 †20
PASEK, Edward A. 2701 S 2ND AVE, MINNEHAHA COUNTY 57105 #026-04-1949 L1958 **OPH** *071 †35
PATEL, Darshana Yogendra. 1400 W 22ND ST, INTERNAL MEDICINE RESIDENT 57105 #305-01-2006 **IM** *012
PAUL, K-Lynn. 5800 W KAREN DR 57106 #026-04-1967 L1986 **P** *071 †75
PAULSON, Brad Alan. 1417 S MINNESOTA AVE 57105 #046-01-1988 L1993 **DR** *020 †80
PAVLIS, Clay Joseph. 1001 E 21ST ST 57105 #046-01-2003 L2005 **P** *020
PAYNE, Harlan Adner. 1100 E 21ST ST, STE 506 57105 #011-03-1972 L1978 **N** *020 †20,75
PEDERSON, Kim Alan. 1200 S 7TH AVE 57105 #046-01-1981 L1982 **FM** *020 †18
PEERY, Curtis Lynn. 1508 W 22ND ST, STE 101 57105 #046-01-1996 L2003 **GS** *020 †85
PEIK, Donald John. ■ 57103 #026-04-1946 L1951 **R** *071 †80
PEKAS, Michael Wayne. 4701 W RESEARCH DR, STE 102 57107 #019-02-1968 L1972 **OPH** *030 †35
PETEREIT, Martin Frank. ■ 57103 #030-05-1959 L1966 **R** *071 †80
PETERS, Patricia A. 1200 S 7TH AVE 57105 #046-01-1980 L1981 **FM** *020 †18
PETERSEN, Kara Linda. 800 E 21ST ST 57105 #046-01-2001 L2006 **RHU** *020
PETERSON, Karl Gregory. 1305 W 18TH ST, P O BOX 5134 57105 #005-15-1974 L1982 **PTH CLP** *062 †50
PETERSON, Scott Norman. ■ 57106 #046-01-2007 **FP** *012
PETRASKO, Marian. 1305 W 18TH ST 57105 #286-13-1983 L2004 **CD IC** *020 †20
PILAPIL, Elene Sell. 1200 S 7TH AVE, MCGREEVY CLINIC AVERA 57105 #748-11-2000 L2007 **IM** *020 †20
PITT-HART, Barry Thomas. 1212 S EUCLID AVE 57105 #352-06-1959 L1966 **PTH** *071 †50
PLAGA, Bradley Ray. 810 E 23RD ST, ORTHOPEDIC INSTITUTE 57105 #023-12-1984 L1996 **ORS** *020 †40
PLUMMER, Richard Lee. 800 E 21ST ST 57105 #046-01-1980 L1981 **FM** *020 †18
PORTER, Richard Irving. 2801 S KIWANIS AVE, STE 200 57105 #028-02-1963 L1964 **IM FM** *020 †18
PRADHAN, Neeta Padmakar. 2501 W 22ND ST, UNIV OF SD SCH OF MED 57105 #495-62-1994 *100
PRAKASH, Preethi. ■ 57105 #496-39-2004 **IM** *012
PRESTBO, Aaron Alton. 1115 E 20TH ST, CENTER FOR FAMILY MEDICINE 57105 #046-01-2005 L2007 **FP** *012
PRESTBO, Leah Lorraine. ■ 57105 #046-01-2007 **FP** *012
PROUSE, Bruce Ray. 1000 E 21ST ST 57105 #046-01-1990 L1998 **PTH** *020 †20,50
PUTNAM, Wesley Duane. 1305 W 18TH ST 57105 #048-12-1970 L1971 **PTH HMP** *020 †50
PUUMALA, Michael Ricard. 1100 E 21ST ST, STE 610 57105 #026-08-1990 L1996 **NS** *020 †25
RABENBERG, Rita Mae. 1201 S EUCLID AVE, STE 307 57105 #046-01-1987 L1990 **PD** *020 †55
RABIE, Yasser Mohamed Mok. 2501 W 22ND ST 57105 #915-02-1994 L2007 **PUD** *020 †20
RAJ, Jayapriya Darshini. 2501 W 22ND ST 57105 #496-20-1998 **IM** *012
RANDALL, Bradley Bruce. 1305 W 18TH ST 57105 #018-03-1975 L1981 **PTH FOP** *020 †50 ‡
RANDOL, James Russell. 1201 S EUCLID AVE, STE G04 57105 #054-04-1969 L2003 **DR** *072 †80
RECTOR, Mark Allen. 3401 W 49TH ST 57106 #046-01-1999 L2002 **FM** *020 †18
REDDY, Gaddum Pavan. 911 E 20TH ST, STE 800 57105 #048-15-1999 L2002 **GS** *020 †85
REDING, Arthur P. ■ 57103 #030-06-1934 L1935 **FM** *071
REED, Richard Clarkin. 1310 W 22ND ST 57105 #041-01-1965 L1980 **RO IM** *020
REILAND-SMITH, Juliann M. 1508 W 22ND ST STE 101, SANFORD SURG ASSOCS 57105 #046-01-1992 L1999 **GS** *020 †85
REINSCHMIDT, John Patrick. 1210 W 18TH ST, LOWER LEVEL RADIOLOGY 57104 #046-01-1996 L2004 **DR** *020 †80
RENNER, Leonard Mark. 4305 S LOUISE AVE, STE 101A 57106 #046-01-1989 L1993 **P** *020 †75
REUTER, Suzanne D. 1305 W 18TH ST, SANFORD CHILDRENS SPECIALT 57105 #046-01-2000 L2006 **NPM** *100 †55
REYNEN, Paul Donald. 1210 W 18TH ST, STE G01 57104 #046-01-1986 L1992 **ORS** *020 †40
REYNOLDS, Kathy Lou. 911 E 20TH ST, CRITICAL CARE AND 57105 #026-04-1978 L2000 **PD** *020 †55
RICE, Amber. 1500 W 22ND ST STE 301, SANFORD CLINIC WOMEN'S HEA 57105 #040-02-2000 L2006 **OBG** *020
RICHARDS, George A. 2501 W 22ND ST 57105 #649-14-1970 L1974 **P** *020
RICHARDSON, James Lloyd. 625 W 18TH ST 57105 #046-01-1988 L1991 **FM** *020 †18
RIDGWAY, Tim Morrow. 1201 S EUCLID AVE, STE 104 57105 #046-01-1984 L1991 **GE IM** *020 †20
RIFE, Daryl Craig. 1417 S MINNESOTA AVE 57105 #030-05-1976 L1984 **DR** *075 †80
RIPPERDA, Thomas John. 1100 E 21ST ST, STE 401 57105 #046-01-1999 L2003 **PM** *020 †60
ROBBINS, John Kenton. 1200 S EUCLID AVE, SPECIALISTS CHARTERED 57105 #048-14-1978 L1984 **U** *020 †95
ROBINSON, Michael Oren. 1000 E 21ST ST, STE 2000 57105 #030-05-1976 L1983 **ON IM** *020 †20
RODIG, Mark Dodd. 3400 S SOUTHEASTERN AVE 57103 #046-01-1987 L1990 **FM** *020 †18
RODMAN, Peter Kleven. 810 E 23RD ST, ORTHOPEDIC INSTITUTE 57105 #026-04-1973 L1974 **ORS** *020 †40
ROGERS, Samuel E. 800 E 21ST ST, BOX 5045 57105 #035-03-1975 L1999 **NPM ADL** *020 †55
ROHR, Susan M. 1201 S EUCLID AVE, STE 407 57105 #038-75-1998, ▲ L2005 **PCC** *100 †20
ROJAS-ESPAILLAT, Luis A. 300 N DAKOTA AVE STE 117, AVERA DOWNTOWN CTR 57104 #308-02-1998 L2007 **OBG** *100
ROLFSMEYER, Eric Scott. 1201 S EUCLID AVE STE 104, SURGICAL ASSOCIATES LTD 57105 #030-05-1976 L1983 **CRS** *020 †10,85
ROSEN, Yuan Chen. 1305 W 18TH ST 57105 #016-42-2001 L2008 **NEP** *020 †20
ROSINSKY, David Edward. 1200 S EUCLID AVE, SPECIALISTS CHARTERED 57105 #019-02-1991 L1997 **U** *020 †95
ROSSING, David Robt. 1305 W 18TH ST 57105 #048-12-1975 L1980 **IM PCC** *040 †20
ROSSING, Ronald Mark. 900 E 54TH ST N STE 200, SIOUX VLY CLC OCCPTNL MED 57104 #016-06-1972 L1973 **OM GP** *020 †70
ROSSING, William Osmund. ■ 57105 #016-06-1959 L1962 **IM** *071 †20 ‡
ROSSING, William Robt. 1100 E 21ST ST, STE 506 57105 #046-01-1990 L1994 **N** *020 †75
ROST, Michael Clark. 2301 W RUSSELL ST 57104 #026-04-1964 L1971 **AN** *071 †05
RYAN, John J. 2501 W 22ND ST, VA MEDICAL CENTER 57105 #539-06-1977 L1991 **GS** *020 †85
RYCKMAN, Jon Gregory. 1305 W 18TH ST, PO BOX 5039 57105 #041-02-2001 L2008 **GS** *100 †85
RYDBERG, Mitchell Lester. 2501 W 22ND ST 57105 #026-04-1979 L1980 **FM** *020 †18
SAGE, Robert James. ■ 57103 #046-01-2007 **TY** *012
SAHIBZADA, Asad Ahmad. 2501 W 22ND ST 57105 #704-09-2003 **IM** *012
SAHIBZADA, Waheed Ahmad. ■ 57105 #704-09-1966 L1977 **IM** *020 †20
SALL, John Chas. ■ 57105 #046-01-1977 L1982 **U** *020 †95
SALMELA, Steven Ray. 1100 E 21ST ST, CENTRAL PLAINS CLINIC, LTD 57105 #026-04-1970 L1977 **OTO GP** *020 †45
SALMON, Don Raoul. ■ 57106 #047-06-1962 L1963 **AN** *020
SALVI, Satish B. 1201 S EUCLID AVE, KIDNEY AND HTN CARE 57105 #495-17-1985 L2007 **NEP** *020 †20
SAMUEL, Justin Varghese. 1115 E 20TH ST, CTR FOR FAMILY MEDICINE 57105 #495-37-2000 L2007 **FM** *020 †18
SANCHEZ, Jorge D. 1001 E 21ST ST STE 10, AVERA DOCTORS PLAZA 1 57105 #649-14-1980 L1993 **CHN** *020
SANCHEZ, Veronica T. 1310 W 22ND ST, UNIVERSITY PHYSICIANS CLIN 57105 #308-03-1984 L1993 **IM ID** *020 †20
SANDERS, Malcolm Stuart. 1305 W 18TH ST, ANESTHESIA DEPT 57105 #056-06-1991 L2001 **AN** *020 †20,05
SANDERSON, Everett W. ■ 57104 #048-04-1949 L1955 **IM** *071 †20
SANTELLA, Robert Nicholas. 1001 E 21ST ST, STE 300 57105 #030-06-1983 L1993 **NEP IM** *020 †20
SCHAFER, Larry Wm. 1001 E 21ST ST STE 501 57105 #046-01-1979 L1984 **GE IM** *040 †20
SCHECHTER, Marc Joel. 200 E 10TH ST, BOX 5126 57104 #033-05-1981 L1997 **TS** *020 †85,90
SCHELLPFEFFER, Ryan S. 1100 E 26TH ST, ANES ASSOCS INC 57105 #010-02-2002 L2006 **AN** *020 †05
SCHLAGEL, David Andrew. ■ 57110 #056-06-2002 L2002 **PYG** *020
SCHLAGER, Barbara Anne. 1417 S MINNESOTA AVE, MEDICAL XRAY CTR 57105 #041-07-1973 L2006 **RO** *020 †80 ‡
SCHMIDT, Troy D. 1201 S EUCLID AVE, STE 104 57105 #048-12-1997 L2006 **GE** *020 †20
SCHNEEKLOTH, Kathleen Sch. 1417 S MINNESOTA AVE, MEDICAL X-RAY CENTER, PC 57105 #030-06-1989 L2002 **IM** *020 †80
SCHRADER, Kari Jo. 6000 W 41ST ST 57106 #046-01-2003 L2006 **FM** *100 †18
SCHROEDER, Greg Michael. 1100 E 26TH ST, ANESTHESIOLOGY ASSOCIATES 57105 #046-01-1982 L1983 **AN** *020 †05
SCHROEDER, Michael Ray. 1100 E 26TH ST, STE 1 57105 #046-01-1988 L1992 **AN** *020 †05
SCHULTZ, Thomas Aaron. 1201 S EUCLID AVE, SIOUX VALLEY CLINIC 57105 #036-05-1971 L1983 **NM** *020 †20
SCHULZ, Bruce Henry. 600 N SYCAMORE AVE, SANFORD CLINIC 57110 #046-01-1997 L2000 **FM** *020 †18
SCHWARTZ, Carmen Marie. ■ 57106 #046-01-2008 *012
SCOTT, Jodi Lynn. 1001 E 21ST ST, CLINICS 57105 #046-01-1998 L2004 **OBG** *020 †30
SEGELEON, Joseph Edward. 1305 W 18TH ST, SIOUX VALLEY HOSPITAL 57105 #038-40-1988 L1997 **CCP** *020 †55
SEGER, Yvonne Beth. 1200 S 7TH AVE 57105 #046-01-1987 L1991 **OBG** *020 †30
SEIDEL, Robert Ray. 7220 W 41ST ST, SANFORD FAMILY MEDICINE 57106 #046-01-1977 L1978 **FM** *020 †18
SEKERAMAYI, Maggie. 2501 W 22ND ST, UNIV OF SD SCH OF MED 57105 #775-01-1995 L2007 **IM** *020 †20
SETHI, Surendra. 1305 W 18TH ST 57105 #495-19-1960 L1975 **CD IM** *020
SETLIFF, Reuben Carroll. 2709 E 26TH ST 57103 #004-01-1964 L1995 **OTO** *020 †45
SHAFER, Charles Warren. 521 N MAIN AVE 57104 #030-05-1986 L1987 **FM** *020 †18
SHAMOUN, Dany Karam. 1001 E 21ST ST, STE 501 57105 #605-01-1994 L2003 **GE** *020 †20
SHERLOCK, John Lyman. 1417 S MINNESOTA AVE 57105 #030-06-1972 L1995 **R EM** *020 †80
SHIELDS, David Arnold. 1310 W 22ND ST, SANFORD CLINIC 57105 #018-03-1975 L1990 **D** *020
SHRESTHA, Saroj. 2501 W 22ND ST 57105 #672-01-2000 **IM** *012
SIDDIQUE, Shahzad Khan. 2501 W 22ND ST, UNIV OF SD SCH OF MED 57105 #704-24-1999 L2008 **IM** *012
SIECZKOWSKI, Lisa M. 1200 S 7TH AVE, MCGREEVY CLINIC 57105 #030-05-2000 L2003 **PD** *020 †55
SIERRA, Anthony Alfred. 1500 W 22ND ST, STE 301 57105 #319-03-1984 L2006 **OBG** *020 †30
SILVIDI, Julius Anthony. 911 E 20TH ST, STE 400 57105 #038-44-1981 L1990 **NS** *020 †25
SIMMONS, Jerry Lee. 1305 W 18TH ST 57105 #038-40-1967 L1981 **PTH GP** *020 †50 ‡
SIMPKINS, Janell Lynn. 1305 W 18TH ST, SIOUX VALLEY HOSPITAL 57105 #046-01-1991 L1994 **IM** *020 †20
SINGH, Rajesh. 1621 S MINNESOTA AVE, SIOUX VALLEY CLINIC-UNIV P 57105 #495-90-1993 L2000 **P** *020 †75

■ = Address Information Privacy Protected

SIOREK, Lidia Stefania. 2501 W 22ND ST, MED 57105 #759-10-1980 L1998 **IM** *020 †20
SIOREK, Marek Jakub. ■ 57105 #046-01-2008 *012
SITTNER, Larry Lee. 1200 S EUCLID AVE, STE 104 57105 #030-05-1968 L1972 **FM GP** *020 ‡
SKOW, Brian Steven. 800 E 21ST ST, AVERA MCKENNAN HOSPITAL 57105 #037-01-1999 L2003 **EM** *020 †16
SKRETVEDT, John Paul. ■ 57106 #037-01-2007 *012
SLATTERY, Mary Theresa. 1310 W 22ND ST 57105 #030-06-1974 L1976 **IM** *071 †20
SMITH, Craig M. 810 E 23RD ST, ORTHOPEDIC INSTITUTE 57105 #037-01-1992 L1995 **FM FSM** *020 †18 ‡
SMITH, Janet E. 1610 S MINNESOTA AVE, STE 1 57105 #018-03-1981 L1992 **U EM** *020 †95
SMITH, R David. 911 E 20TH ST, CRITICAL CARE AND 57105 #038-40-1995 L2005 **PEM PD** *020 †55
SMITH, Sandra Barbara. 1200 S 7TH AVE 57105 #026-04-1990 L1993 **FM** *020 †20
SMITHSON, William Anthony. 1000 E 21ST ST, STE 3100 57105 #036-05-1967 L1983 **PHO** *020 †55
SMYER, Theodore Franklin. 1305 W 18TH ST, SANFORD HOSPITAL 57105 #004-01-1978 L1998 **EM** *020 †16
SNEED, Diane Coppock. 1000 E 21ST ST 57105 #046-01-1985 L1990 **PTH** *020 †50
SNOW, Dawn. 2701 S KIWANIS AVE, SANFORD CLINIC FAMILY MEDI 57105 #046-01-1996 L1999 **FM** *020 †18
SOLARES, Andrew Miguel. 800 E 21ST ST 57105 #038-41-2001 L2004 **EM** *020 †18
SORENSEN, Todd Allen. 3401 W 49TH ST, SVC FAMILY MEDICINE 57106 #046-01-1997 L2000 **FM** *020 †18
SOYE, Andrew I. 1417 S MINNESOTA AVE 57105 #917-09-1977 L1982 **DR** *020 †80
SPENCER, Nali. 1305 W 18TH ST, C/O SANFORD USD MEDICAL CE 57105 #704-25-1998 L2007 **IM** *100 †20 ‡
SPENCER, Suzannah Harding. 1115 E 20TH ST, CENTER FOR FAMILY MED 57107 #038-41-1980 L1992 **FM** *075 †18
SPREHE, Michael Robert. 1305 W 18TH ST, SPECIALTY CLINIC 57105 #021-05-1996 L2006 **PHO** *020 †20,55
STAMATO, Theresa M. 1305 W 18TH ST, SPECIALTY CLINIC 57105 #035-15-1988 L2000 **PDC** *020 †55
STARS, Lorenzo Lee. 1200 S 7TH AVE, MCGREEVY CLNC AVERA 57105 #046-01-1989 L1993 **IM** *020 †20
STASSEN, Michael Dean. 1200 S 7TH AVE 57105 #026-04-1976 L1977 **FM** *020 †18
STEERS, Jeffery Lee. 1001 E 21ST ST, STE 301 57105 #019-02-1985 L2006 **TTS AS** *020 †85
STENSLAND, Vernon Hans. 1310 W 22ND ST 57105 #016-06-1970 L1971 **OTO** *020 †45
STENSON, Jeffrey Lein. 1200 S 7TH AVE, MCGREEVY CLINIC 57105 #025-07-1995 L2001 **FM** *020 †20
STETHEM, Nicole Lynn. 800 E 21ST ST, AVERA MCKENNAN HOSPITAL 57105 #046-01-2002 L2005 **EM** *020 †16
STEVENS, Dennis Chas. 1305 W 18TH ST 57105 #017-20-1974 L1980 **NPM PD** *020 †55
STOKKA, Cameron Lee. 1417 S MINNESOTA AVE 57105 #048-04-1976 L1990 **DR** *020 †80
STONE, Jonathan Dwight. 1100 E 21ST ST, STE 410 57105 #038-40-1983 L2003 **PM** *020 †60
STOUT, Linda Apperley. 1305 W 18TH ST, SPECIALTY CLINIC 57105 #048-13-1995 L2001 **PD PHO** *020 †55
STRAND, David A. 911 E 20TH ST, INSTITUTE OF SOUTH DAKOTA 57105 #037-01-1989 L1995 **GS TRS** *020 †85
STROM, Kevin Bruce. 1100 E 26TH ST, 1100 E 26TH ST 57105 #005-12-1992 L2001 **AN** *020 †05
STYS, Adam T. 1305 W 18TH ST 57105 #759-03-1992 L1998 **IC** *020 †20
STYS, Tomasz Piotr. 1305 W 18TH ST 57105 #759-03-1994 L2004 **IC** *020 †20
SULAIMAN, Raed Ata. 1000 E 21ST ST 57105 #875-03-1988 L1997 **PTH PCP** *020 †50 ‡
SULANC, Ebru. 300 N DAKOTA AVE STE 117, AVERA DOWNTOWN CTR 57104 #902-07-1997 L2004 **END IM** *020 †20 ‡
SUTHERLAND, Garnette. 1500 W 22ND ST 57105 #062-01-1978 *100
SWANSON, David Allan. 1000 E 21ST ST STE 4100 57105 #046-01-2000 L2003 **NM** *020 †28
SWANSON, Priscilla Marie. 620 S MAIN AVE 57105 #046-05-1963 L1971 **D** *071 †14
TALLEY, Robert Cochran. 1400 W 22ND ST, HEALTH SCIENCE CTR 57105 #016-02-1962 L1976 **IM CD** *040 †20
TAM, Guy Eugene. ■ 57105 #018-03-1965 L1968 **FM OM** *071 †18
TAMS, Kimberlee. 1305 W 18TH ST 57105 #046-01-2000 L2005 **PTH** *062 †50
TAN, Raymund R. 2501 W 22ND ST, UNIV OF SD SCH OF MED 57105 #748-09-2001 **CHP** *012
TANNER, Philip Edwin. 1201 S EUCLID AVE, STE 104 57105 #026-04-1989 L2005 **GE** *020 †20
TAYLOR, Donald Eugene. ■ 57101 #026-04-1945 L1947 **P** *071 †75
TAYLOR, Garrett Ross. 800 E 21ST ST, AVERA-MCKENNAN HOSPITAL 57105 #007-02-2000 L2003 **EM** *020
TENDLER, Alison Renae. 1310 W 22ND ST FL 2, SANFORD CLINIC - VANCE THO 57105 #046-01-2001 L2006 **OPH** *020 †35
TENNANT, Edward Eugene. 1417 S MINNESOTA AVE, MEDICAL X-RAY CENTER 57105 #056-05-1948 L1986 **RO NM** *071 †80 ‡
TERMAAT, Jill Christine. ■ 57103 #046-01-2008 *012
TETZLAFF, Thomas Ross. 911 E 20TH ST, CRITICAL CARE AND 57105 #016-06-1972 L2000 **PD ID** *020 †55
THAEMERT, Bradley Clark. 911 E 20TH ST, INSTITUTE OF SOUTH DAKOTA 57105 #026-04-1993 L1998 **GS** *020 †85
THAKKAR, Jitendra Ravindr. 1305 W 18TH ST, SIOUX VALLEY HOSPITAL 57105 #496-41-1997 L2003 **IM** *020 †20
THANEL, Fredric Harold. 1115 E 20TH ST, CTR FOR FAMILY MED 57105 #030-06-1975 L1993 **FM** *020 †18
THOMAS, Melvin Walter. 2501 W 22ND ST 57105 #051-07-1976 L1977 **IM** *030 †20
THOMPSON, Tracey Brown. 800 E 21ST ST, AVERRA MCKENNAN HOSPITAL 57105 #036-07-1982 L2000 **PD** *020 †55
THOMPSON, Vance Michael. 1310 W 22ND ST 57105 #046-01-1986 L1997 **OPH** *050 †35
TIBBITTS, George Michael. 1400 W 22ND ST, SCH OF MED OFF OF DEAN 57105 #010-02-1975 L1993 **FM FPG** *040 †18 ‡
TIESZEN, Jerel Edward. 1201 S EUCLID AVE, STE 510 57105 #024-07-1977 L1981 **IM** *020 †20
TIMMERMAN, Gary Lee. 1508 W 22ND ST, STE 101 57105 #028-02-1984 L1989 **GS** *020 †85
TJARKS, Mary Renee. 1200 S 7TH AVE 57105 #036-08-1996 L2002 **OBG** *020 †30
TOBIN, Michael Douglas. 1200 S 7TH AVE 57105 #030-06-1977 L1981 **IM** *020 †20
TOLENTINO, Addison R. 1000 E 21ST ST STE 2000 57105 #748-02-1994 L2004 **HO** *020 †20
TRAVERS, Henry. 1000 E 21ST ST 57105 #041-14-1971 L1988 **PTH BBK** *020 †50
TRAVNICEK, John Michael. 800 E 21ST ST, AVERA MCKENNAN HOSPITAL ER 57105 #046-01-2003 L2006 **EM** *020 †16
TSCHETTER, Loren Keith. 1020 W 18TH ST, CLINIC-ONCOLOGY 57104 #019-02-1968 L1969 **ON HEM** *020 †20

TYNAN, Daniel Gerard. 1100 E 21ST ST, STE 600 57105 #016-11-1986 L2000 **NS** *020 †25
UKEN, Patsy Ann. 1210 W 18TH ST 57104 #046-01-1981 L1984 **DR** *020 †80
ULLAH, Sana. PO BOX 5046, VAMC SIOUX FALLS 57117 #704-04-2001 **IM** *012
UNDAVALLI, Sathiraju. ■ 57106 #495-58-1998 **IM** *012
USATII, Anatolie Anatolie. 1201 S EUCLID AVE STE 201, SANFORD TRANSPLANT CTR 57105 #913-50-1993 L2006 **GS TTS** *020 †85
UTHE, Craig Joel. 3401 W 49TH ST 57106 #046-01-1986 L1991 **FM** *020 †18
VALENTINE, Verle Dean. 1210 W 18TH ST, SIOUX VALLEY CLINIC 57104 #046-01-1994 L1998 **FM FSM** *020 †18
VAN BALEN, Clayton Gerald. 900 E 54TH ST N, STE 200 57104 #046-01-1979 L1980 **OM FM** *020 †70,18
VAN BEEK, Michelle Linnae. 4405 E 26TH ST 57103 #018-03-2001 L2005 **PD** *020 †55
VAN DEMARK, Robt Eugene, Jr. 1210 W 18TH ST, STE G01 57104 #024-07-1976 L1979 **ORS** *020 †40
VANDEN BOSCH, Mick E. 1621 S MINNESOTA AVE, SVC-OPHTH/OPTOM 57105 #018-03-1989 L2006 **OPH** *020 †35
VANDER WOUDE, John Cecil. 1500 W 22ND ST STE 105 57105 #028-02-1978 L1987 **TS VS** *020 †90,85
VANDER WOUDE, Larry B. 2701 S KIWANIS AVE, SANFORD CLINIC - WEST 57105 #046-01-1977 L1980 **FM** *020 †18
VANGERPEN, Shawn David. 1001 E 21ST ST, USD PYSCHIATRY 57105 #046-01-2003 L2007 **CHP** *012
VASA, Aaron A. ■ 57103 #046-01-2008 *012
VASKA, Kevin James. 1727 S CLEVELAND AVE, SIOUX FALLS CARDIOVSCLR 57103 #046-01-1982 L1984 **CD IM** *020 †20
VELOIRA, Wilfredo Garcia. 1001 E 21ST ST, STE 10 57105 #748-20-1994 L2002 **PDP** *020 †55
VERMA, Suneet. 1200 S 7TH AVE, MCGREEVY CLINIC AVERA 57105 #496-09-1993 L2004 **IM** *020 †20 ‡
VINAYEK, Namita. 1305 W 18TH ST, SIOUX VALLEY HOSP SD 57105 #496-07-2001 L2005 **IM** *020 †20
VIOLA, Lisa Corinne. 1100 E 21ST ST, STE 506 57105 #035-75-1997, ▲ L2002 **N CN** *020 †75
VOGT, H Bruce. 1200 S EUCLID AVE, STE 104 57105 #030-05-1974 L1975 **FM** *030 †18
VOGT, Regina Kay. ■ 57107 #046-01-1995 L1996 **FM** *075 †18
VOLIN, Verlynne V. ■ 57105 #050-02-1943 L1948 **GP OBG** *071 †18
WAHL, Naomi L. 1001 E 21ST ST, CLINICS 57105 #028-02-1981 L1997 **OBG** *020 †30
WALDBY, Gail Ellen. 2501 W 22ND ST 57105 #019-02-1977 L1995 **GS** *020 †85
WALKER, Timothy Lee. 1210 W 18TH ST STE G01, SVC-VANDEMARK ORTHO 57104 #017-20-1998 L2004 **ORS** *020 †40
WALLACE, James Wm. 1305 W 18TH ST, SPECIALTY CLINIC 57105 #048-02-1986 L1992 **PDP PD** *020 †55
WALTON, Jerry Le Roi. 1100 E 21ST ST, STE 600 57105 #048-12-1964 L1965 **FM** *030 †18
WALTZ, William Frederick. 1305 W 18TH ST, SANFORD CHILDREN'S HOSPITA 57105 #026-04-1993 L2002 **PDC** *020 †55
WALZ, Amanda Marie. ■ 57110 #026-04-2008 *012
WATSON, Mary Elizabeth. 1115 E 20TH ST, CENTER FOR FAMILY MEDICINE 57105 #046-01-1986 L1987 **FM** *040 †18
WATTS, Jonathan David. 2908 E 26TH ST, ORHTOPAEDIC CONSULTANTS 57103 #026-04-2000 L2005 **ORS** *020 †40
WEBER, William Neils. ■ 57101 #056-06-1965 L1966 **DR** *020 †80
WEGRZYNOWICZ, Edward S. 1305 W 18TH ST 57105 #026-04-1980 L1997 **AN** *020 †05
WEINACHT, Donna Jean. 1201 S EUCLID AVE STE 307, SVC - PEDIATRIC SPECIALIST 57105 #046-01-1996 L1999 **PD** *020 †55
WEINER, Robin Sue. 1310 W 22ND ST, SANFORD CLINIC 57105 #046-01-2002 L2006 **D** *020 †15
WELLMAN, Bryan John. 1210 W 18TH ST STE 104, SIOUX FALLS NEUROSURGICAL 57104 #041-01-1993 L2002 **NS** *020 †25
WELLMAN, Lawrence Raymond. 1305 W 18TH ST, USD SCH OF MEB DEPT OF PED 57105 #020-12-1970 L1978 **PD NPM** *020 †55
WELTER, Randal Lee. 1417 S MINNESOTA AVE 57105 #046-01-1984 L1990 **DR** *020 †80
WENDT, James Brian. 2501 W 22ND ST, SIOUX FALLS VA MEDICAL CEN 57105 #016-43-1994 L1994 **IMG** *020 †20
WENGER, Robert S. 1200 S 7TH AVE 57105 #030-05-1976 L1993 **FM** *020 †18
WHALEY, David John. ■ 57106 #046-01-2008 *012
WHEELER, Kirke Holland. 1508 W 22ND ST, STE 101 57105 #046-01-1979 L1991 **GS** *020 †85
WHITE, Thomas Clement. 1701 S MINNESOTA AVE 57105 #026-04-1968 L1975 **OPH** *020 †35
WHITTLE, Kevin David. 2501 W 22ND ST, VAMC 57105 #046-01-1982 L1985 **IM** *020 †20
WIERDA, Allison. 1500 W 22ND ST, STE 301 57105 #016-06-1997 L2001 **OBG** *020 †30
WIERDA, Daryl Ray. 1417 S MINNESOTA AVE 57105 #018-03-1968 L1974 **DR PDR** *020 †80
WILDE, James Robt. 1115 E 20TH ST, CTR FOR FAMILY MED 57105 #056-05-1988 L2000 **FM** *040 †18
WILDE, Michael Charles. 1201 S EUCLID AVE, STE 510 57105 #046-01-1998 L2001 **IM** *020 †20
WILSON, Thomas Milton. 2701 S KIWANIS AVE 57105 #047-06-1957 L1980 **AI PD** *020 †55
WINGERT, Donald Jos. 911 E 20TH ST STE 800, INSTITUTE OF SOUTH DAKOTA 57105 #046-01-1982 L1987 **GS TS** *020 †85
WINGERT, Marvin Edward. 800 E 21ST ST 57105 #056-06-1958 L1959 **GP** *020
WINSKUNAS, Philip Felix. ■ 57110 #016-43-1963 L1993 **TS GS** *020 †85,90
WIRTZ, Patricia Suzanne. 800 E 21ST ST 57105 #048-15-1974 L1981 **OBG** *020 †30
WITTE, Deborah Ann. ■ 57110 #030-05-1994 L1999 **PTH** *020 †50
WITTE, Matthew Nolan. 1200 S EUCLID AVE, SPECIALISTS CHARTERED 57105 #030-05-1994 L2003 **U** *020 †95
WITZKE, David John. 911 E 20TH ST STE 602 57105 #026-08-1977 L1984 **PS GS** *020 †65,85
XU, Min. 2501 W 22ND ST 57105 #243-52-1999 **IM** *012
YEAGER, Terry Douglas. 1000 E 21ST ST STE 1000 57105 #028-02-1988 L2000 **VIR** *020 †80
YOKAN, Nicholas Jos. 1309 S DUNDEE DR, VAN DEMARK ORTHO SPECIALIS 57106 #023-12-1990 L2002 **ORS OSM** *020 †40
YU, John C. 1201 S EUCLID AVE, STE 407 57105 #748-01-1988 L2000 **PUD CCM** *020 †20
ZAMULKO, Alla Oleksiivna. 1200 S 7TH AVE, MCGREEVY CLINIC 57105 #913-89-1985 L2001 **IM** *020 †20 ‡
ZAWADA, Edward Thaddeus. 1001 E 21ST ST, STE 300 57105 #016-43-1973 L1983 **NEP CCM** *020 †20
ZEIGLER, Candace Nelson. 1201 S EUCLID AVE, STE 510 57105 #046-01-1991 L1994 **IM** *020 †20
ZEIGLER, David Wayne. 1201 S EUCLID AVE, STE 510 57105 #046-01-1995 L1998 **IM** *020 †20
ZIEBARTH, Joel Armin. 1305 W 18TH ST 57105 #046-01-1990 L1999 **PTH** *020 †50
ZIMPRICH, Todd Alan. 1100 E 21ST ST, STE 506 57105 #021-05-1997 L2002 **CN** *020 †75
ZOELLNER, Timothy Melvin. 810 E 23RD ST, ORTHOPEDIC INSTITUTE 57105 #056-06-1982 L1987 **ORS** *020 †40

ZYLSTRA, Aaron Mark. 1201 S EUCLID AVE, STE 307 57105 #018-03-2000 L2003 **PD** *020 †55

SISSETON – ROBERTS

CRAWFORD, Lois Ann. ■ 57262 #046-01-1998 L2001 **FM** *020 †18
ERDRICH, Angela Mary. ■ 57262 #032-01-1994 L1994 **PD** *020 †55
KIENHOLZ, Judy C. 205 ORCHARD DR 57262 #037-01-1985 L1987 **FM** *020 †18
MAGAT, Alfonso Flores, Jr. ■ 57262 #748-07-1965 L1968 **GS GP** *071
MITCHELL, Lou Ann. 100 LAKE TRAVERSE AV 57262 #018-03-1981 L1982 **FM** *020 †18
OEY, David Liang Tie. 205 ORCHARD DR 57262 #409-16-1967 L1976 *020
PATEL, Sandeep Devendra. PO BOX 58 57262 #023-07-1994 L1994 **PD** *020 †55
PETERSON, Linda Rae. 205 ORCHARD DR 57262 #046-01-1978 L1982 **OBG AN** *020 †30
STAUB, David Winfield. 205 ORCHARD DR 57262 #054-04-1973 L1976 **FM** *020 †18
SWINEY, Jennifer Rose. ■ 57262 #028-03-1973 L1974 **IM** *020 †20

SPEARFISH – LAWRENCE

ALTSTIEL, Terry Lee. 1316 N 10TH ST 57783 #046-01-1980 L1981 **GS** *020 †85
ANDERSON, Jeffrey Lee. 1440 N MAIN ST, EMERGENCY DEPT 57783 #046-01-1992 L1995 **FM** *020 †18
ANDERSON, Wayne Julius. 550 E COLORADO BLVD 57783 #046-01-1981 L1983 **FM OM** *020 †70,18
BAILEY, Lee Burton. 2479 E COLORADO BLVD, MEDICAL CLINIC EAST 57783 #046-01-2000 L2003 **FM** *020 †18 ‡
BOGARD, Jay Douglas. 1316 N 10TH ST 57783 #046-01-1998 L2002 **FM** *020 †18
BOYER, David Walter. 550 E COLORADO BLVD 57783 #035-20-1969 L1974 **ORS** *020 †40
BRADY, Forrest Sherwood. 2479 E COLORADO BLVD, MEDICAL CLINIC EAST 57783 #030-06-1977 L1978 **FM** *020 †18
CHURCH, Ann. 130 YANKEE ST 57783 #046-01-1986 L1990 **OBG** *020 †30
DOLL, Ranae Ann. 2479 E COLORADO BLVD, MEDICAL CLINIC EAST 57783 #037-01-1996 L2005 **PD IM** *020 †20,55
ECKRICH, Sheila Barnett. ■ 57783 #025-12-1987 L1992 **IM** *020 †20
FINKBEINER, Scott Alan. 1316 N 10TH ST 57783 #030-06-1995 L1998 **IM** *020 †20
GILBERT, Freeman J. ■ 57783 #005-12-1942 L1944 **IM** *071
GIUSEFFI, Steven A. 1445 NORTH AVE, SPEARFISH REGIONAL MED CLI 57783 #038-41-1980 L1985 **GS GE** *020 †85
GIUSEFFI, Steven Adam. ■ 57783 #025-01-2008 *012
GOLLIHER, Warren Norman. 1445 NORTH AVE 57783 #019-02-1964 L1965 **FM** *071 †18
HAYES, Craig Richard. 1420 N 10TH ST 57783 #024-07-1975 L1976 **GP** *071
HEWITT, Gregory Dale. 1316 N 10TH ST 57783 #030-06-1975 L1987 **FM** *020 †18
HIGGINS, Jack Wayne. ■ 57783 #017-20-1964 **FM FPG** *071 †18 ‡
HILL, Regan R. 2479 E COLORADO BLVD, MEDICAL CLINIC EAST 57783 #037-01-2002 L2006 **OBG** *020
HORRELL, Eugene Dale. ■ 57783 #041-13-1957 L1963 **HS GS** *071 †40
KEIM, Richard Lee. 1316 N 10TH ST 57783 #030-06-1983 L2003 **IM** *030 †20
KNUDSON, Jason Lynn. 1316 N 10TH ST 57783 #046-01-2001 L2004 **FM** *020 †18
KNUDSON, Rebecca Lynn. 1316 N 10TH ST 57783 #046-01-2002 L2005 **FM** *100 †18
KULLERD, Deborah A. 1316 N 10TH ST 57783 #048-13-1989 L1994 **FM** *020 †18
LANG, David Harlan. 550 E COLORADO BLVD 57783 #056-06-1985 L1993 **ORS** *020 †40
LEWIS, Jane Catherine. 1016 S 35TH ST 57783 #046-01-1989 L2002 **OSM** *020 †40
LITTLE, Richard Mark. 1316 N 10TH ST 57783 #026-04-1991 L1997 **ORS** *020 †40
LUSTIG, Karl Anton. 1440 N MAIN ST 57783 #033-05-1963 L1992 **R GP** *072 †80
MAROUSEK, Melvin A. 1420 N 10TH ST 57783 #016-11-1952 L1953 **FM** *072
MC ADOO, Gregg Lyn. 1316 N 10TH ST 57783 #030-06-1993 L2001 **OBG** *020 †30 ‡
MCADOO, Mary Catherine. 1316 N 10TH ST 57783 #030-06-1995 L2001 **PD** *020 †55
MC BRIDE, Alexander M. 1445 NORTH AVE STE 2 57783 #016-06-1963 L1992 **U** *071 †95
MC LAUGHLIN, Ruth M. ■ 57783 #046-01-1978 L1979 **GP** *071
MILLER, Pamela Jean. 1420 N 10TH ST, QUEEN CITY MEDICAL GROUP 57783 #039-79-2002, ▲ L2005 **IM** *020 †20
O'CONNOR, Brian Lee. 2479 E COLORADO BLVD, MEDICAL CLINIC EAST 57783 #046-01-2000 L2003 **FM** *020 †18
POTTS, Donald Mark. 1440 N MAIN ST 57783 #046-01-1981 L1984 **FM** *020 †18
QUIGLEY, Dean R. 1316 N 10TH ST 57783 #037-01-1993 L2001 **GS** *020 †85
ROBERTS, Bob Hubert. 1420 N 10TH ST 57783 #056-06-1966 L1982 **IM GE** *071
SCHLEEHAUF, Karen Marie. 6625 PENDO RD, MASSA BERRY CLINIC 57783 #033-06-1986 L2004 **GS** *020 †85
SIGMOND, Eric Roy. 1420 N 10TH ST, QUEEN CITY MEDICAL CENTER 57783 #016-43-1978 L2004 **ORS OAR** *020 †40
SMITH, Barry Allen. 736 ELK RUN RD 57783 #024-07-1975 L1991 **FM EM** *020
STAMPE, Angela Rae. 1445 NORTH AVE STE 2 57783 #046-01-1986 L1994 **PD** *020 †55
SWISHER, Jonathan Paul. ■ 57783 #046-01-2008 *012
SWISHER, Paul Lowell. 19768 HUNTER RD, REEBE RANCH 57783 #046-01-1983 L1984 **GP** *020
TUDOR, Robert Bruce. ■ 57783 #026-04-1938 L1938 **PD GE** *071 †55
VOSLER, Steven Thos. 1445 NORTH AVE, SPEARFISH REGIONAL MEDICAL 57783 #026-04-1976 L1980 **FM** *020 †18
WITT, Heather Anne. 2479 E COLORADO BLVD, MEDICAL CLINIC EAST 57783 #019-02-2000 L2004 **OBG** *020
WRIGHT, Darin Lane. 1445 NORTH AVE 57783 #005-18-1991 L2006 **OTO** *020 †45

STURGIS – MEADE

ATKINSON, Seann M. 890 LAZELLE ST, MEDICAL CLINIC 57785 #018-75-2001, ▲ L2004 **FM** *020 †18
BLUM, Mark Frederick. ■ 57785 #030-05-1961 L1961 **GS** *020 †85
FIELDS, Billy Leroy. 890 LAZELLE ST 57785 #039-01-1975 L1989 **OBG** *071 †30
FROMM, Stuart Edward. 949 HARMON ST 57785 #046-01-1990 L1996 **ORS OSM** *020 †40
HERMANN, Harland Thomas, Jr. 890 LAZELLE ST, MEDICAL CLINIC 57785 #046-01-1984 L1985 **FM** *072 †18
JONES, William E. PO BOX 756 57785 #018-03-1946 L1950 **IM** *020
KLAR, Werner. ■ 57785 #286-02-1945 L1958 **GP** *071
LEWIS, Charles A. 890 LAZELLE ST, MEDICAL CLINIC 57785 #028-79-1978, ▲ L1984 **FM** *072

PREYS, Michael C. 1247 SHERMAN ST, BLACK HILLS FAMILY PRACTIC 57785 #016-01-1990 L1993 **FM** *020 †18
STOCK, Constance A. 890 LAZELLE ST, MEDICAL CLINIC 57785 #046-01-1994 L2005 **FM** *020 †18

TIMBER LAKE – DEWEY

KRAFT, Richard Louis. HC 64, BOX 164 57656 #046-01-1984 L1996 **FM** *020 †18

TYNDALL – BON HOMME

FOLEY, Robert John. 410 BROADWAY 57066 #030-05-1947 L1952 **FM** *071
SALOUM, Herbert Al. ■ 57066 #030-05-1972 L1973 **FM** *020 †18
WALLINGA, Melvin Lynn. 410 E 16TH AVE 57066 #018-03-1981 L2002 **FM** *020 †18

UTICA – YANKTON

FLEVARES, James William. ■ 57067 #046-01-1990 L1994 **P** *020

VALLEY SPRINGS – MINNEHAHA

JENSEN, Kristin Adele. ■ 57068 #041-09-1984 L1988 **EM** *020 †16

VERMILLION – CLAY

ANDRE, Kent D. ■ 57069 #046-01-2004 **P** *012
CORNELISEN, Mathew Alan. 414 E CLARK ST, UNIV OF SD SCH OF MED 57069 #046-01-2000 *100
ESCOBAR, Fernando Alfonso. 20 S PLUM ST, SIOUX VALLEY VERMILLION CL 57069 #649-06-1974 L2002 **GS** *020 †85
JOHNSON, Daniel Chas. 20 S PLUM ST 57069 #046-01-1981 L1991 **ORS** *020 †40
KITTO, C. ■ 57069 #030-05-1979 L1982 **PD** *020
LAMB, Riley Aaron. ■ 57069 #046-01-2008 *012
LINDAHL, Josette. 414 E CLARK ST, SCHOOL OF MEDICINE 57069 #046-01-2000 L2004 **P** *020
MORTINSEN, Roy Lane. 20 S PLUM ST, SIOUX VALLEY VERMILLION CL 57069 #046-01-1999 L2002 **FM** *020 †18 ‡
NELSEN, Courtney Elizabet. ■ 57069 #046-01-2008 *012
OLSON, Mary Jo. 20 S PLUM ST, SIOUX VLY VERMILLION MED C 57069 #046-01-1997 L2000 **FM** *020 †18
OLSON, Thomas Harry. 1330 E MAIN ST, BOX 277 57069 #051-07-1976 L1977 **GP** *020
REZAC, Annette Lee. ■ 57069 #046-01-2008 *012
STEVENS, Julie Clare. 101 S PLUM ST 57069 #039-01-1976 L1980 **PD** *020 †55
TARVER, Daniel David. ■ 57069 #046-01-2008 *012
THRONSON, Hillary Lea. ■ 57069 #046-01-2008 *012
WALKER, Vicki Louise. 20 S PLUM ST, SIOUX VALLEY VERMILLION CA 57069 #046-01-1997 L2000 **FM** *020 †18

VIBORG – TURNER

FAITHE, Rose F. 315 N WASHINGTON ST 57070 #030-05-1964 L1964 **FM** *071 †18
HAGIWARA, Yuya. 315 N WASHINGTON ST, PIONEER MEMORIAL HOSP 57070 #572-79-2004 L2006 **FM** *020 †18
MARK, Curtis Leo. 29312 SD HIGHWAY 19 57070 #007-02-1970 L1973 **FM** *020 †18
NELSEN, Marcia Kay. 45125 291ST ST 57070 #046-01-1982 L1984 **ORS** *020
SHAH, Syed A R. PO BOX 337 57070 #704-02-1990 L1995 **IM** *020 †20

WAGNER – CHARLES MIX

BUBAK, Gary Alan. 517 3RD ST SW 57380 #026-04-1978 L1983 **IM** *020
DESSOUKI, Ahmed Hassan. 517 3RD ST SW 57380 #915-02-2002 L2007 **FM** *020 †18
ESPLUND, Gretchen Marie. 111 WASHINGTON AVE NW, PO 490 57380 #023-12-1997 L2002 **FM** *020 †18
NIEBEL, Donald Bruce. 111 WASHINGTON AVE NW, US PUBLIC HEALTH SERVICE 57380 #046-01-1983 L1996 **FM** *020 †18

WALKER – CORSON

MESSINGER, David W. ■ 57659 #028-78-1961, ▲ L2007 **GP** *072

WATERTOWN – CODINGTON

ALLEN, Stanley W, Jr. ■ 57201 #016-06-1952 L1953 **FM** *071 †18
AMBUR, Richard Frederick. 401 9TH AVE NW, PRAIRIE LAKES HEALTHCARE S 57201 #054-04-1961 L1997 **ORS** *020 †40
ARGABRITE, John Wm. ■ 57201 #016-11-1945 L1948 **A** *020
BERGSBAKEN, Jeffrey Owen. 401 9TH AVE NW, PRAIRIE LAKES HOSP & CARE C 57201 #026-04-1992 L2004 **AN** *020 †18
BISHOP, William Keith. 401 9TH AVE NW 57201 #038-06-1969 L2001 **DR** *020 †80
BOBZIEN, Wm Frederick. 401 9TH AVE NW, PRAIRIE LAKES HLTH CARE SY 57201 #010-02-1969 L2004 **ON HEM** *020 †20
BRINDLE, Jeffrey Steven. 1201 MICKELSON DR 57201 #016-42-1981 L1985 **RO** *020 †80
CALMAC, Roxana. 901 4TH ST NW 57201 #781-01-1999 L2006 **IM** *020 †20
CARLSON, David Truman. 506 1ST AVE SE, SE 57201 #046-01-1981 L1982 **FM PTH** *020 †50,18
CARTER, Roger Louis. 901 4TH ST NW 57201 #046-01-1981 L1985 **GS** *020 †85
CHRISTENSEN, Alan Richard. 901 4TH ST NW 57201 #046-01-1997 L2005 **GS** *020 †85
CLARK, Teralynn Sue. 1201 MICKELSON DR 57201 #030-05-1990 L1997 **AN** *020 †05

CRANK, Robert Neal. 901 4TH ST NW 57201 #028-34-1978 L1986 **DR NR** *020 †80
CRISMON, Craig Eugene. 1201 MICKELSON DR 57201 #046-01-1990 L1993 **PD** *020 †55
DEIGERT, Fred A. 401 9TH AVE NW, THERAPEUTIC RADIOLOGY PSC 57201 #028-34-1964 L1986 **RO LM** *020 †80
DE SAUTEL, Mark Gregory. 901 4TH ST NW 57201 #018-03-1991 L1997 **OTO** *020 †45
DEVINE, William Wayne. 901 4TH ST NW 57201 #034-01-1994 L1998 **FM** *020 †18
DINGSOR, David John. 1201 MICKELSON DR, STE 2 57201 #046-01-2002 L2006 **AN** *020
DRAGICH, Debbie A. 401 9TH AVE NW 57201 #056-06-1987 L2000 **AN** *020 †05
ELSHAMI, Ashraf Ahmed. 901 4TH ST NW 57201 #041-13-1989 L1996 **PUD** *020 †20
FLAHERTY, Daniel Jos. 506 1ST AVE SE, BROWN CLINIC 57201 #037-01-1991 L1996 **OBG** *020 †30
GEIER, Allison Joy. 506 1ST AVE NE 57201 #046-01-2004 L2007 **FM** *020
GERRISH, Catherine Carter. 1201 MICKELSON DR 57201 #046-01-1978 L1983 **IM** *020 †20
GERRISH, Edwin Shewman. 1201 MICKELSON DR 57201 #046-01-1978 L1983 **GS** *020 †85
GIEBINK, Robert Wm. 401 9TH AVE NW 57201 #046-01-1992 L1996 **P** *020
GOEPFERT, Mary. ■ 57201 #026-04-1952 L1983 **P IM** *020 †20
HANSON, Bernie H P. 705 14TH AVE NE 57201 #026-04-1962 L1972 **OPH** *020 †35
HAWTHORNE, Catherine G. 401 9TH AVE NW, PRAIRIE LAKES HEALTHCARE 57201 #050-02-1973 L2004 **ORS PM** *020 †40
HOEKMAN, Allen Lee. 901 4TH ST NW 57201 #046-01-1979 L1981 **PD** *074
JOHNSON, Jeffrey Allen. 901 4TH ST NW 57201 #046-01-1993 L1999 **FM** *020 †18
JOHNSON, Kenneth Mcdonald. 901 4TH ST NW 57201 #030-05-1982 L1983 **FM** *020 †18
JONES, James Alan. 401 9TH AVE NW 57201 #046-01-1982 L1983 **OBG** *020 †30
KARU, Andrew Paul Kimaku. 506 1ST AVE SE 57201 #577-02-1997 L2005 **IM** *020 †20
KIMAKU, Emily Kananu Ruka. 506 1ST AVE SE, BROWN CLINIC, P.L.L.P. 57201 #577-02-1997 L2007 **IM** *020 †20
LABESKY, James Wm, Jr. 506 1ST AVE SE, BROWN CLINIC P.L.L.P 57201 #046-01-1991 L1994 **IM** *020 †20
LARSON, Gregory Ronald. 1201 MICKELSON DR 57201 #046-01-1990 L1993 **FM** *020 †18
LARSON, James Chas. 511 14TH AVE NE, BROWN CLINIC-NORTHRIDGE 57201 #016-06-1959 L1961 **GS** *071
LARSON, Paul Myron. 401 9TH AVE NW 57201 #007-02-1966 L1967 **U** *071 †95
LAWRENCE, Alan Anthony. 506 1ST AVE SE, BROWN CLINIC 57201 #041-13-1990 L1995 **GS** *020 †85
LEADABRAND, Catherine A. 1201 MICKELSON DR 57201 #030-05-1995 L1999 **IM** *020 †20
LENSSEN, Stacie Anne. 1201 MICKELSON DR 57201 #026-04-2000 L2003 **FM** *020 †18
LIKNESS, Clark Wayne. 1201 MICKELSON DR 57201 #046-01-1978 L1979 **FM** *020 †18 ‡
LUNARDI, Ivaldo Artemio. 401 9TH AVE NW, PRAIRIE LAKE HEALTHCARE SY 57201 #025-01-1978 L2007 **CD EM** *020
LUNDIEN, Matthew Carl. 901 4TH ST NW 57201 #027-01-1995 L2002 **PDP** *020 †55
MC AREAVEY, Jonathan M. 511 14TH AVE NE 57201 #046-01-2001 L2004 **FM** *020 †18
MEYER, Robert J. ■ 57201 #026-04-1951 L1973 **R GP** *071 †80
MILLER, Charles Jos. 901 4TH ST NW 57201 #016-43-1986 L1998 **NS** *020 †25
MORAN, Michael John. 705 14TH AVE NE 57201 #046-01-1995 L1999 **OPH** *020 †35
NEVINS, Kerry Francis. 401 9TH AVE NW, PRAIRIE LAKES HEALTHCARE 57201 #035-09-1968 L2005 **ORS** *020 †40
NIPE, Hollis Dean. 1201 MICKELSON DR 57201 #046-01-1985 L1986 **IM IMG** *020 †20
PATHAN, Karamullah Khan. 1201 MICKELSON DR 57201 #704-08-1978 L2001 **U** *020 †95
PENGILLY, Rebecca L. 901 4TH ST NW 57201 #037-01-1999 L2002 **FM** *020 †18
PHAM, Scott. 901 4TH ST NW 57201 #026-04-1993 L2003 **ICE** *020 †20
PIERRET, Tracy John. 901 4TH ST NW 57201 #046-01-2003 L2006 **PD** *020 †55
REIFFENBERGER, Daniel H. 1201 MICKELSON DR 57201 #046-01-1991 L1994 **FM** *020 †18
REIFFENBERGER, Sarah A. 506 1ST AVE SE, BROWN CLINIC 57201 #046-01-1991 L1994 **FM** *020 †18
RETTERATH, Patrick L. 1512 4TH ST NE 57201 #037-01-1985 L1989 **AN IM** *020 †05
RIEBER, Gerald Michael. 1201 MICKELSON DR, STE 1 57201 #026-04-1997 L2002 **ORS** *020 †40
RITTMANN, John Edgar. 1201 MICKELSON DR 57201 #028-02-1962 L1973 **FM** *071 †18
ROSETH, Calvin Al. 901 4TH ST NW 57201 #046-01-1985 L1988 **IM** *020
RUBEN, Richard. 1201 MICKELSON DR 57201 #748-10-1987 L2004 **ON** *020 †20
SANDELL, Richard Jon. 401 9TH AVE NW 57201 #016-11-1969 L2006 **ORS** *020 †40
SCHULTZ, Gregory Alan. 901 4TH ST NW 57201 #026-04-1978 L1985 **VS** *020 †85
SCHWARTZ, John Christian. 506 1ST AVE SE 57201 #028-34-1978 L1991 **NM** *020 †28,80
SHIVES, Aaron Burl. 1201 MICKELSON DR 57201 #046-01-1986 L1987 **FM FSM** *020 †18
SNYDER, Wayne Earle. 1225 4TH ST NE, SNYDER EYE CLINIC 57201 #046-01-1981 L1984 **OPH** *020 †35
SOLBERG, Lloyd Eugene. 901 4TH ST NW 57201 #016-06-1974 L1979 **CD IC** *020 †20
SPIES, Heather Nicole. 901 4TH ST NW 57201 #046-01-2002 L2006 **OBG** *020
STESKA, Stephen Jos. 401 9TH AVE NW, PRAIRIE LAKES HEALTHACARE 57201 #028-34-1976 L1988 **DR** *020 †80
STRANSKY, John J. 401 9TH AVE NW 57201 #026-04-1949 L1950 **OS GS** *071 †18
THOMAS, David Arlo. 901 4TH ST NW 57201 #007-02-1978 L1988 **PUD IM** *020 †20
TRACY, Gerald Eugene. 200 19TH ST SE 57201 #030-06-1955 L1957 **PD GP** *071
VENER, Michael John. 1201 MICKELSON DR STE 1 57201 #026-04-1989 L1995 **ORS** *020 †40
WEGNER, Edward Lyle. 1201 MICKELSON DR 57201 #046-01-1980 L1982 **PTH** *020 †18,50
WHITCROFT, Ian A. 200 E HIGHLAND BLVD 57201 #917-06-1979 L1997 **FM** *020 †15
WILDE, Kim Levi. 1201 MICKELSON DR 57201 #046-01-1977 L1980 **IM IMG** *020
WRAGE, Theodore Julius. 506 1ST AVE SE 57201 #016-06-1955 L1956 **FM** *071 †18

WEBSTER – DAY

BLOOM, Alan Ray. 101 PEABODY DR 57274 #046-01-1985 L1986 **FM** *020 †18 ‡
GRAVLEY, Elizabeth Jean. 1401 W 1ST ST 57274 #026-04-1995 L1998 **FM** *020 †18
NELSON, Lawrence Fredrick. 1401 W 1ST ST 57274 #016-11-1967 L1971 **GP** *020 †18

WESSINGTON SPRINGS – JERAULD

DEAN, Roscoe E, Jr. ■ 57382 #041-13-1943 L1946 **FM** *072
DEAN, Thomas Michael. 602 1ST ST NE, STE 1 57382 #035-45-1972 L1978 **FM** *020 †18
LIM, Lance Sia. 602 1ST ST NE STE 1, JERAULD COUNTY CLINIC 57382 #748-11-1992 L2002 **SCI** *020

WHITEWOOD – LAWRENCE

JOHNSON, Jorge Howard. ■ 57793 #007-02-1963 L1984 **NS** *071

WINNER – TRIPP

BERG, Tony Lynn. 825 E 8TH ST BOX 110, MEDICAL ARTS BLDG 57580 #001-02-1978 L1979 **FM** *020 †18
CARPENTER, Mary Susan. 825 E 8TH ST 57580 #046-01-1981 L1984 **FM** *020 †18 ‡
HAFNER, Daniel James. 1436 E 10TH ST 57580 #024-01-1970 L1976 **OPH** *020 †35
HENDERSON, Anora Dawn. 825 E 8TH ST 57580 #046-01-2000 L2003 **FM** *020 †18
HOLLAND, Kristen Lee. 1436 E 10TH ST, STE 2 57580 #046-01-1994 L1998 **FM** *020 †18
KOSINA, Thomas Michael. 825 E 8TH ST 57580 #018-03-1975 L1988 **GS** *020
MARTS, Teresa Ann. 825 E 8TH ST 57580 #046-01-1997 L2000 **FM** *020 †18
PINTER, Jeffrey David. ■ 57580 #046-01-1990 L1993 **FM** *020 †18

WORTHING – LINCOLN

BESS, Michael Allen. 27873 SD HIGHWAY 115 57077 #026-04-1974 L1981 **GS** *020 †85

YANKTON – YANKTON

AANNING, Harald Larsen. 501 SUMMIT ST 57078 #030-05-1976 L1983 **GS** *020 †85
ABBOTT, David Joel. 409 SUMMIT ST, STE 3200 57078 #030-06-1996 L2002 **OTO** *020 †45
ADAMS, Curtis Milton. 501 SUMMIT ST 57078 #026-04-1976 L1979 **OBG** *020 †30
ALSGAARD, Hartley Chas. PO BOX 7600 57078 #046-01-1980 L1991 **P** *020 †75
APPELWICK, James E. 1104 W 8TH ST 57078 #046-01-1971 L1973 **GS** *020 †85
BARNES, David John. 1104 W 8TH ST, YANKTON MEDICAL CLINIC, P. 57078 #046-01-1982 L1985 **FM** *020 †18
BOUDREAU, Joseph Raymond. 1000 W 4TH ST, YANKTON UROLOG SURG PROF 57078 #064-01-1982 L1997 **U** *020
BOYD, Rock Francis. 1100 DOUGLAS AVE, FEDERAL PRISON CAMP 57078 #046-01-1982 L1983 **FM OS** *020
BRADY, John Warren. 1104 W 8TH ST 57078 #046-01-1989 L1996 **FM** *020 †18
BRAY, Kevin Bruce. 1104 W 8TH ST, YANKTON MED CLINIC 57078 #046-01-1988 L1993 **OBG** *020 †30
BUTTOLPH, Thomas Bryan. 501 SUMMIT ST, AVERA SACRED HEART HOSP 57078 #023-12-1993 L2004 **PTH** *020 †50
CALLAHAN, Robert A. 1104 W 8TH ST 57078 #008-01-1971 L2006 **ORS OSS** *020 †40
CAMMOCK, Charles Danl. 1000 W 4TH ST STE 1, AVERA SACRED HEART HOSPITA 57078 #033-06-1985 L1999 **AN GS** *020 †05
CAMMOCK, Leona Marie. 1104 W 8TH ST 57078 #033-05-1985 L1994 **FM** *020 †18
CHANG, Kwang Uk. 1101 BROADWAY AVE, ORTHOPEDIC INSTITUTE 57078 #011-03-1987 L2001 **PM** *020 †60
COHEN, William Edward. 1719 BROADWAY AVE STE F, AMERICAN PAIN RELIEF 57078 #748-01-1981 L1999 **PME PMM** *020
COLLISON, Patrick Jos. 1104 W 8TH ST, YANKTON MEDICAL CLINIC 57078 #018-03-1977 L1995 **OTO** *020 †45
DEJONG, Brenda Marie. 1104 W 8TH ST 57078 #046-01-1992 L1995 **FM** *020 †18
DENDINGER, William James. 1104 W 8TH ST 57078 #007-02-1974 L1976 **FM** *020 †18
EIDSNESS, Will Robert. ■ 57078 #046-01-2002 L2007 **DR** *020 †80
ERICKSON, Gregory Scott. 501 SUMMIT ST 57078 #046-01-1986 L1990 **EM IM** *020
FANTA, Susan Elizabeth. 1104 W 8TH ST 57078 #030-05-1993 L1996 **IM** *020 †20
FARVER, Max Lynn. 1104 W 8TH ST, YANKTON MEDICAL CLINIC 57078 #030-05-1983 L1984 **ON HEM** *020 †20
FERRELL, Robert Thornton. 1104 W 8TH ST, YANKTON MED CLINICTAL 57078 #046-01-1983 L1984 **OBG** *020 †30
FOURNIER, George R, Jr. 1104 W 8TH ST, YANKTON MEDICAL CLINIC PC 57078 #048-02-1980 L2003 **U ON** *020 †95
FRANK, John Jos, Jr. 1104 W 8TH ST 57078 #046-01-1981 L1982 **IM** *020 †20
GAUGER, David Wm. 501 SUMMIT ST, SACRED HEART HOSPITAL 57078 #018-03-1969 L1987 **PTH** *020 †50
GILMORE, Howard Thos. 1000 W 4TH ST, U.S.D. SCHOOL OF MEDICINE 57078 #018-03-1970 L1971 **OBG** *020 †30
GUTNIK, Steve Howard. 1104 W 8TH ST 57078 #037-01-1979 L1984 **GE** *020 †20
HALVERSON, Kenneth. 1104 W 8TH ST, YANKTON MEDICAL CLINIC 57078 #026-04-1959 L1964 **GS** *071 †85
HANSEN, Travis David. 3515 BROADWAY AVE, UKCMC-GME 57078 #046-01-2000 L2005 **CHP ADP** *020 †75
HANSEN-WAID, Keri Ann. 1104 W 8TH ST 57078 #030-05-1984 L1985 **PUD IM** *020 †20
HEIN, Michael Scott. 1104 W 8TH ST, YANKTON MEDICAL CLINIC 57078 #046-01-1995 L2001 **IM** *020 †20
HEISINGER, Randolph W. 1104 W 8TH ST 57078 #048-13-1971 L1973 **PD** *020 †55
HICKS, Daniel Jos. 1028 WALNUT ST 57078 #046-01-1987 L1994 **P** *020 †75
HILTUNEN, Scott Jerome. 501 SUMMIT ST, DEPT OF EMERGENCY 57078 #046-01-1990 L1993 **IM** *020 †20
HOCHSTEIN, Mary Lee. ■ 57078 #046-01-2001 L2007 **HO** *020
HOLZWARTH, David R. 1104 W 8TH ST 57078 #016-06-1962 L1963 **GYN** *071 †30
HUBNER, Jay Wm. 1104 W 8TH ST 57078 #048-12-1968 L1971 **IM** *020 †20
HURLEY, Willard Chas. 1104 W 8TH ST 57078 #046-01-1985 L1991 **CD IM** *020 †20
ISBURG, Carroll Dale. 1104 W 8TH ST 57078 #030-05-1970 L1973 **N CHN** *020 †55
JAMESON, George Malcolm. 1104 W 8TH ST, YANKTON MEDICAL CLINIC PC 57078 #041-13-1954 L1955 **GP OS** *071
JAVUREK, Anthony Jay. 43384 WHITETAIL DR 57078 #007-02-1970 L1971 **EM FM** *020 †16,18
JOHNSON, Mitchell C. 1101 BROADWAY AVE, ORTHOPEDIC INSTITUTE 57078 #028-78-1997, ▲ L2003 **ORS** *020
KING, Dwight F. 1104 W 8TH ST 57078 #654-01-1991 L1999 **N P** *020 †75
KING, Patrick Holt. 415 W 3RD ST 57078 #028-02-1979 L1983 **OPH** *020 †35
KOLBERG, Amy Michelle. 1104 W 8TH ST 57078 #046-01-1999 L2003 **OBG** *020 †30
KRELL, Matthew David. 1104 W 8TH ST 57078 #046-01-1997 L2000 **PD** *020 †55
KROHN, David Clark. 1104 W 8TH ST, YANKTON MED CLNC PC 57078 #030-05-1973 L1992 **FM** *020 †18

■ = Address Information Privacy Protected

LARSON, Barrett Paul, II. ■ 57078 #046-01-2008 *012

LARSON, Dawn Marie. 1104 W 8TH ST, P O BOX 706 57078 #030-05-1996 L1999 **PD** *020 †55 ‡

LEON, Lawrence Michael. 314 WALNUT ST 57078 #046-01-1991 L1995 **DR** *020 †80

LIUDAHL, Jeffrey Jon. 409 SUMMIT ST, STE 2800 57078 #046-01-1981 L1982 **OTO HNS** *020 †45

MABEE, Mark Judson. 1104 W 8TH ST, YANKTON MEDICAL CLINIC 57078 #046-01-1988 L1992 **FM** *020 †18

MC VAY, Michael Rutan. 1104 W 8TH ST 57078 #024-07-1972 L1978 **CD IM** *020 †20

MEGARD, Daniel J. 1104 W 8TH ST, YANKTON MEDICAL CLINIC P.C 57078 #046-01-1988 L1991 **IM** *020 †20

MESSNER, Frank David. 314 WALNUT ST BOX 650 57078 #007-02-1968 L1974 **DR RO** *020 †80

MIKKELSEN, Beth A. 1104 W 8TH ST 57078 #026-08-1983 L1986 **IM** *020 †20

MILLER, Lisa Ann. 409 SUMMIT ST, STE 3400 57078 #046-01-2001 L2006 **GS** *020 †85

MILLER, M Kathy. 501 SUMMIT ST 57078 #028-78-1992, ▲ L1996 **PD** *020

MILROY, Mary Jeannine. 1104 W 8TH ST, YANKTON MEDICAL CLINIC 57078 #046-01-1981 L1984 **GS** *020 †85

NEILSON, Doug Donald. 1000 W 4TH ST STE 1 57078 #068-01-1976 L1996 **ORS** *020

NEUBAUER, Jo Marie. 610 BROADWAY AVE 57078 #046-01-1980 L1982 **EM** *020 †16

NEUMAYR, Robert J. 1104 W 8TH ST, YANKTON MEDICAL CLINIC 57078 #049-01-1975 L1978 **IM IMG** *020 †20

NOWAK, Bonnie Ellen. 1104 W 8TH ST 57078 #046-01-2001 L2004 **IM** *020

PETER, Beverly Kennon. ■ 57078 #051-01-1930 L1933 **OTO OPH** *071 †45

PETERSON, Michael Evan. 501 SUMMIT ST, AVERA SACRED HEART HOSPITA 57078 #035-20-1985 L2001 **RO IM** *020 †20,80

PIETILA, Michael Paul. 1104 W 8TH ST 57078 #046-01-2000 L2006 **PCC** *020 †20

POSCH, Thomas Joel. 314 WALNUT ST, YANKTON RADIOLOGY 57078 #026-04-1990 L2001 **DR** *020 †80

POTAS, David Gene. 501 SUMMIT ST 57078 #046-01-1981 L1984 **AN PUD** *020 †05

PTACEK, Mark John. 501 SUMMIT ST, AVERA SACRED HEART 57078 #030-05-1984 L2001 **FM** *020 †18

RADACK, Morris Lee. 1104 W 8TH ST 57078 #054-04-1962 L1966 **IM GP** *071

RAFFERTY, Kelly Rae. 1000 W 4TH ST STE 15, OF YANTON, PROF. LLC 57078 #046-01-1994 L1997 **FM** *020 †18

RAGNARSSON, Thorir Sturla. 1104 W 8TH ST 57078 #484-01-1978 L1997 **NS** *020 †25

RANNEY, Brooks. 1104 W 8TH ST, YANKTON MEDICAL CLINIC PC 57078 #016-06-1941 L1948 **GYN** *071 †30

REANEY, Duane B. 501 SUMMIT ST 57078 #016-06-1948 L1949 **GP OBG** *071

REIFENRATH, Bruce Harold. 1000 W 4TH ST, STE 13 57078 #018-03-1993 L2006 **AN** *020 †05

RHOADES, Marques Everett. 1104 W 8TH ST 57078 #048-04-1965 L1966 **ORS PM** *030 †40

RUGGLES, James Geo. 501 SUMMIT ST, SACRED HEART HOSPITAL 57078 #019-02-1957 L1981 **PTH CLP** *020 †50

SAOI, Nicasio B. 811 BELFAST ST, YANKTON COUNTY 57078 #748-01-1953 L1963 **U** *071

SCHNEIDER, Rudy Jay. 1000 W 4TH ST, STE 6 57078 #030-05-2000 L2000 **GS** *020

SCHURRER, Michael Edwin. 501 SUMMIT ST 57078 #046-01-1984 L1999 **NM** *020 †20,28

SEARS, Gregory Scott. 1000 W 4TH ST, STE 6 57078 #030-05-1974 L1986 **HNS GS** *020

SEIBEL, Stanford Gale. 1104 W 8TH ST, YANKTON MEDICAL CLINIC, P. 57078 #019-02-1973 L2000 **ORS** *020

SERCK, Luke Christopher. ■ 57078 #046-01-2002 L2007 **GS** *020 †85

SOMEPALLI, Ramesh Babu. PO BOX 7600 57078 #495-50-1979 L1986 **P** *020 †75

STANAGE, Willis F. 1104 W 8TH ST, YANKTON MEDICAL CLINIC PC 57078 #030-05-1951 L1953 **PD** *071 †55

STERNQUIST, John Chas. 1104 W 8TH ST, YANKTON MEDICAL CLINIC, P. 57078 #026-04-1973 L1980 **GS** *020 †85

SUGA, Robert Carlton. 1101 BROADWAY AVE, ORTHOPEDIC INSTITUTE 57078 #046-01-1981 L1986 **ORS** *020 †40

THOMPSON, Robert Francis. 1104 W 8TH ST 57078 #025-01-1948 L1955 **HEM ON** *071 †20

TRAIL, Kynan Charles. 1000 W 4TH ST STE 7 57078 #030-05-1995 L2000 **GS** *020 †85

TUAN, Chung-Hao. ■ 57078 #385-03-1962 L1973 **P** *071 †75

VAIDYA, Abhay. 1104 W 8TH ST, YANKTON MEDICAL CLINIC 57078 #496-38-1973 L2006 **DR GP** *020 †80

VAN GERPEN, Sandra Moore. ■ 57078 #046-01-1980 L1982 **OBG** *071 †70

WATSON, Eric Scott. 1101 BROADWAY AVE, ORTHOPEDIC INSTITUTE 57078 #030-06-1995 L2004 **ORS** *020 †40

WEILAND, Kevin John. 2611 MULBERRY ST 57078 #046-01-1992 L1996 **IM** *020 †20

WIGGS, James Wm. 1104 W 8TH ST 57078 #017-20-1963 L1986 **N** *071

WILLCOCKSON, John Robert. PO BOX 819 57078 #016-06-1968 L1970 **OPH** *071 †35

WILLCOCKSON, Thos Harden. ■ 57078 #030-05-1942 L1950 **OPH** *071 †35

WITHROW, David Wesley. 501 SUMMIT ST 57078 #046-01-1990 L1993 **PD** *020 †55

YELVERTON, Chas Clinton. 1104 W 8TH ST 57078 #046-01-1980 L1990 **FM FPG** *020 †18

ADAMS – ROBERTSON

ABUBUCKER, Shabeer. ■ 37010 #012-01-2003 L2007 **P** *020
CRONK, Daniel Robert, Jr. ■ 37010 #030-05-2001 L2002 **GS** *020
STRANGE, Charles Edwin. ■ 37010 #047-06-1963 L1963 **GP** *071 †18

ADAMSVILLE – MCNAIRY

BAXTER, James Daniel. 726 E MAIN ST 38310 #039-01-1977 L2004 **OBG** *020 †30
EASON, William Andrew. 347 E MAIN ST 38310 #047-06-1989 L1990 **FM** *020 †18
KING, James D. 347 E MAIN ST 38310 #047-06-1982 L1982 **FM** *020 †18
MC CARVER, Brian Monroe. 347 E MAIN ST 38310 #047-06-2001 L2002 **FM** *020 †18
SMELSER, Michael Harding. 345 US HIGHWAY 64 38310 #047-06-1974 L1975 **IM** *020 †20
VINSON, John William. 345 US HIGHWAY 64 38310 #047-06-1996 L1997 **FM** *020 †18

ALAMO – CROCKETT

IDEMUDIA, Uyi-Oghosa. 281 CLIMER LOOP N, STE 4 38001 #473-04-2001 L2005 **IM** *020 †20
MONTOYA CHAVEZ, Jaime Edg. 281 CLIMER LOOP N, STE 4 38001 #341-01-1996 L2006 **IM** *020
OBI, Emmanuel Izuchukwu. 281 CLIMER LOOP N, STE 4 38001 #690-03-1985 L1996 **IM** *020 †20
OBI, Patricia Renee. 281 CLIMER LOOP N, STE 4 38001 #041-13-1984 L1987 **CD IM** *020 †20
RHEAR, Raymond Wayne. 59 S BELLS ST, CROCKETTE MED CLC INC 38001 #047-06-1971 L1973 **FM FPG** *020 †18 ‡
TILLMAN, Ronald Clyde. 157 N BELLS ST 38001 #047-06-1979 L1980 **FM** *020 †18
VIDES DE MONTOYA, Joaquina. 281 CLIMER LOOP N, STE 4 38001 #341-03-1999 L2006 **IM** *020

ALCOA – BLOUNT

ATCHLEY, Neal William. 266 JOULE ST 37701 #047-06-1994 L1997 **FM** *020 †18
BARTLEY, Nancy Gail. 266 JOULE ST 37701 #047-20-1992 L1994 **FM** *020 †18
BASILE, James Anthony. 220 ASSOCIATES BLVD, SPRINGBROOK 37701 #035-46-1978 L1995 **PS OM** *020 †85
BEARD, Marvin Robison. 266 JOULE ST 37701 #047-06-1971 L1971 **RHU IM** *020 †20
BEST, Jennifer Lynn. 266 JOULE ST 37701 #047-20-2003 L2004 **IM** *020 †20
BISHOP, Britton Keith. 230 ASSOCIATES BLVD, AT SPRINGBROOK 37701 #051-04-1994 L2002 **FM** *020 †18
BOOHER, Robert Wm. 232 ASSOCIATES BLVD 37701 #047-06-1974 L1974 **PD ADM** *020 †55
BRUNO-DELAMATA, Kimberly. 266 JOULE ST, EAST TENNESSEE MEDICAL GRO 37701 #055-01-1994 L2000 **IM** *020
CASH, Heather Kenerly. 232 ASSOCIATES BLVD 37701 #047-20-2001 L2003 **PD** *020 †55
COBB, Diana Lea. 281 CUSICK RD 37701 #047-06-2001 L2002 **FM** *020 †18
COLLINS, Tommy E, Jr. 232 ASSOCIATES BLVD 37701 #047-06-1988 L1991 **PD** *020 †55
CROSS, Thea Williams. 266 JOULE ST 37701 #047-20-1999 L2003 **N** *020 †75
DIRMEYER, Andrew Carter. 266 JOULE ST, EAST TENNESSEE MEDICAL GRO 37701 #047-06-1987 L1988 **FM** *020 †18
FERGUSON, Rodney Ryan. 266 JOULE ST, EAST TENNESSEE MEDICAL GRO 37701 #011-03-2003 L2006 **FM** *020 †18
GALLAGHER, Michael Paul. 266 JOULE ST 37701 #011-04-1978 L1983 **CD IM** *020 †20
GIBBS, Elmer Rickey. 266 JOULE ST 37701 #012-22-1993 L2001 **GS** *020 †85
GILLEY, Sarah Mason. 232 ASSOCIATES BLVD 37701 #047-06-1986 L1987 **IM** *020 †55
HEINY, Jerome J. 266 JOULE ST, EAST TENNESSEE MEDICAL GRO 37701 #047-06-1976 L1977 **FM** *020 †18
HOOKER, Henry Clay. 266 JOULE ST, EAST TENNESSEE MEDICAL GRO 37701 #041-07-1992 L1999 **N** *020 †75
HUET, Rocio A. 281 CUSICK RD 37701 #025-01-1981 L1983 **IM** *020 †20
INGRAM, John Jackson, III. 266 JOULE ST, EAST TENNESSEE MEDICAL GRO 37701 #047-06-1971 L1972 **IM** *020
IVEY, Jessica Mc Cullough. 244 S CALDERWOOD ST, STE C2 37701 #012-01-1998 L2000 **IM** *020 †20 ‡
KELSEY, Stanley Scott. 266 JOULE ST, EAST TENNESSEE MEDICAL GRO 37701 #047-06-1989 L1992 **GS** *020 †85
KIRPEKAR, Komal H. 266 JOULE ST, E. TENNESSEE MEDICAL GROUP 37701 #495-03-1989 L1995 **IM** *020 †20
KUHL, Roy Edwin, Jr. 266 JOULE ST, EAST TENNESSEE MEDICAL GRO 37701 #038-44-1995 L2002 **FM** *020 †18
LA FOUNTAIN, Elisa Jane. 266 JOULE ST 37701 #028-78-2003, ▲ L2006 **IM** *020 †20
LARSEN, George Keefe. 244 S CALDERWOOD ST, STE C-2 37701 #012-01-1979 L1996 **GP FPG** *071
LEAIRD, Alma Kimberly. 266 JOULE ST, EAST TENNESSEE MEDICAL GROU 37701 #045-01-1988 L2001 **RHU** *020 †20
MAHONEY, Patricia K. 244 S CALDERWOOD ST 37701 #051-07-1991 L2002 **IM** *020 †20
MANDRELL, Joe Thos. 266 JOULE ST, EAST TENNESSEE MEDICAL GRO 37701 #047-06-1972 L1973 **FM** *020 †18
MILHOLLIN, James L, Jr. 266 JOULE ST, EAST TENNESSEE MEDICAL GRO 37701 #047-20-2000 L2001 **IM** *020 †20
MONLA-HASSAN, Jaber M. 266 JOULE ST, EAST TENNESSEE MEDICAL GRO 37701 #875-02-1985 L2004 **PCC** *020 †20
MOORE, William Roger. 266 JOULE ST 37701 #038-40-1975 L1980 **IM EM** *020 †20
NEELY, E Robt. 220 ASSOCIATES BLVD 37701 #047-06-1959 L1960 **OM EM** *071 †55
PAYNE, Joseph Duane. 241 E WATT ST 37701 #047-20-1999 L2000 **IM** *020
PITTENGER, John Wm. 266 JOULE ST 37701 #047-06-1975 L1976 **FM** *020 †18
RADOFF, Fredric Martin. 266 JOULE ST 37701 #033-05-1976 L1989 **N SME** *020 †75
RAHN, Charles Lawrence. 266 JOULE ST, KNOXVILLE EMERGENCY PHYSIC 37701 #047-06-1984 L1988 **EM FM** *020 †18,16
REISS, Michael Shirey. 232 ASSOCIATES BLVD, KNOXVILLE PEDIATRIC ASSOC. 37701 #008-02-1997 L2000 **PD** *020 †55
REISSER, John Randolph. 266 JOULE ST 37701 #047-06-1984 L1987 **GS** *020 †85
RIEGEL, Darryl Louis. 266 JOULE ST 37701 #010-01-1990 L2000 **FM** *020 †18
ROBERTS, Bruce Taylor. 266 JOULE ST 37701 #051-04-1973 L1993 **PUD IM** *020 †20

ROOKE, John David. 117 GILL ST 37701 #047-06-1991 L1994 **FM** *020 †18
SALAZAR-CATRON, Teresa M. 266 JOULE ST 37701 #047-20-2000 L2001 **FPG** *020 †18
SARKAR, Pradip Kumar. 235 S CALDERWOOD ST 37701 #020-02-1975 L1979 **EM** *071
SCHEIB, Jeffrey Steven. 266 JOULE ST, EAST TENNESSEE MEDICAL GRO 37701 #038-43-1982 L1989 **RHU IM** *040 †20
SCOTT, Peter Ridsdel. 266 JOULE ST, EAST TENNESSEE MEDICAL GRO 37701 #047-06-1998 L2005 **IM** *020 †20
SHAMBLIN, Christopher Sco. 266 JOULE ST, EAST TENNESSEE MEDICAL GRO 37701 #654-01-2000 L2004 *020
SMUCKLER, Alan Lee. 266 JOULE ST 37701 #010-02-1977 L1983 **CD IM** *020 †20
SOMMERVILLE, Lewis C, Jr. 266 JOULE ST 37701 #005-12-1977 L1982 **PUD IM** *020
THURSTON, Timothy Wm. 232 ASSOCIATES BLVD 37701 #047-06-1971 L1972 **PD** *020 †55
TILLEY, Rachel Ellen. ■ 37701 #004-01-2007 **OBG** *012
UNKEFER, Robert Paul. 266 JOULE ST 37701 #048-04-1997 L2001 **DS D** *020 †15
VINES, William David. 266 JOULE ST, E. TENNESSEE MEDICAL GROUP 37701 #047-06-1992 L1995 **FM** *020 †18
WELLS, James David. 220 ASSOCIATES BLVD, PITT COUNTY MEM HOSP// REG 37701 #047-20-1982 L1987 **PM OM** *020 †60,70
WERNER, Wally Mark. 266 JOULE ST, EAST TENNESSEE MEDICAL GRO 37701 #021-05-1986 L1992 **IM AM** *020
WIGHT, Clinton Alan. 230 ASSOCIATES BLVD, AT SPRINGBROOK 37701 #047-20-2001 L2004 **FM** *020 †18

ALEXANDRIA – DEKALB

BRYAN, Thornton Embry, III. 400 E PUBLIC SQ 37012 #020-02-1993 L1996 **FM** *020 †18
COOPER, Steven Wright. 400 E PUBLIC SQ 37012 #047-06-1996 L1997 **FM** *020 †18
CRIPPS, Hugh Don. 400 E PUBLIC SQ 37012 #047-06-1970 L1971 **FM** *020 †18
DARRAH, David Edward. 400 E PUBLIC SQ 37012 #047-06-1969 L1969 **FM** *071 †18
HOOPER, Doug Gibbons. 400 E PUBLIC SQ 37012 #047-06-1983 L1984 **FM** *020 †18
SHERWOOD, William Hanford. 400 E PUBLIC SQ 37012 #038-41-1993 L1996 **FM** *020 †18

ANDERSONVILLE – ANDERSON

EKLUND, Robert Harold. 715 MILL CREEK RD 37705 #047-06-1978 L1980 **GP** *020
STEEL, Burton Byron. ■ 37705 #035-19-1946 L1948 **P PYA** *071

ANTIOCH – DAVIDSON

AINA-BABALOLA, Adejoke F. 2031 ANTIOCH PIKE 37013 #690-01-1994 L2000 **IMG** *020 †20
AKINPELU, Olayinka Alade. 5170 HICKORY HOLLOW PKWY, APT 242 37013 #198-01-1992 **IM** *012
BAMIGBOYE, Babajide A. 2031 ANTIOCH PIKE 37013 #690-05-1979 L1986 **IM** *020 †20
BRITT, Earl Bernard, Jr. ■ 37013 #047-07-2008 *012
BROWN, Rebekah Flowers. ■ 37013 #004-01-2003 L2003 **PD** *100 †55
COLLINS, Marlise R L. ■ 37013 #047-07-1978 L1987 **D PD** *020 †55,15
DEIHIM-PANAH, Mohammad A. ■ 37013 #517-01-1967 L1975 **OBG** *020 †30
DELK, Aubrey Michael. ■ 37013 #047-06-2006 L2008 **EM** *012
ERICKSON, Cyrus Conrad, III. 5801 CROSSINGS BLVD 37013 #021-01-1998 L2004 **PMM AN** *012
FABIE, Anastacia Espanol. ■ 37013 #748-02-1948 L1985 **IM IMG** *071
FRANKLIN, Michael Wallace. ■ 37013 #047-07-2002 L2007 **P** *100
HEIM, Helen L. ■ 37013 #041-07-1950 L1951 **GP** *071
HIGH, Lucius Eddie. ■ 37013 #047-07-1969 L1972 **OBG** *075
HORTON, Angela Michelle. ■ 37013 #047-06-2006 L2006 **IM** *012
HUGHES, Chris G. ■ 37013 #017-20-2005 L2007 **AN** *012
HUIZINGA, Mary Margaret. 1052 BLUE MOUNTAIN LN 37013 #047-05-2003 L2005 **IM** *020 †20
ITHARAT, Prat. ■ 37013 #035-15-2004 L2004 **OPH** *012
JARRETT, Marco Alfred. ■ 37013 #047-07-2006 **OBG** *012
KHAN, Mehmood Hassan. ■ 37013 #704-29-2002 L2008 **IM** *012
LADSON, James Wilbur. 5801 CROSSINGS BLVD 37013 #047-07-1984 L1993 **AN EM** *020 †05
LEE, Kevin Jerraine. ■ 37013 #036-01-2003 **OBG** *012
LEONE, William H. 5811 CROSSINGS BLVD, TENNESSEE PAIN SURGERY CEN 37013 #422-01-1992 L1997 **AN** *012
LOHRASBI, Riaz. ■ 37013 #654-01-1996 **CHP** *020
MC QUEEN, Sylvia Maria. 608 MOUNT HOOD DR 37013 #047-07-1992 L1994 **IM** *020 †20
MILLER, Timothy Harold. 5801 CROSSINGS BLVD, THE PAIN MANAGEMENT GROUP 37013 #020-02-2000 L2002 **APM** *100 †05
OKAFOR, Obiajulu Chukwudi. 1906 HICKORY HIGHLANDS DR 37013 #690-04-1992 L2003 **OBG** *012
OLAGUNDOYE, Damaris Moren. ■ 37013 #047-07-2004 **OBG** *012
OLINGER, Jason Bradley. ■ 37013 #046-01-2005 L2007 **AN** *012
OWENS, Susan J. 5801 CROSSINGS BLVD 37013 #047-06-1984 L1985 **AN** *020 †05
PASSYN, Julia Beall. ■ 37013 #001-06-2002 L2004 **END** *012
RAMOS, Andres A. 724 VANGUARD PL 37013 #264-01-1951 L1971 **EM GP** *071
ROSS, Carolyn Kenia. ■ 37013 #047-07-2008 *012
RUGLESS, Keith Adrian. ■ 37013 #030-05-1993 **CHP** *100
RUSSELL, Bradley W. ■ 37013 #048-12-2005 L2006 **EM** *012
SIMPKINS, Katherine Wynne. ■ 37013 #038-44-2004 L2007 **AN** *012
SLATTERY, Stephen Ormond. ■ 37013 #046-01-2005 L2007 **AN** *012
SMITH, Terrence Allen. 7220 SANTEELAH WAY 37013 #038-45-1997 L2000 **GE** *020
SULLIVAN, Kenneth Wayne. 5801 CROSSINGS BLVD, THE PAIN MANAGEMENT GROUP 37013 #021-06-1983 L1995 **FM ADM** *020 †18
TIMS-COOK, Zandraetta L. ■ 37013 #035-20-2005 L2007 **IM** *012
TOOR, Harbinder Singh. ■ 37013 #495-03-1980 L1996 **NM** *020
URBAN, Steven Allen. 5801 CROSSINGS BLVD 37013 #035-09-1994 L1999 **PM** *020 †60
VORKPOR, Sam Gbutue. ■ 37013 #610-01-1989 **FP** *012
WEBB, Leland Harding. ■ 37013 #025-07-2006 **GS** *012
WILLOUGHBY, Lionel F. 2717 MURFREESBORO PIKE 37013 #047-07-1973 L1976 **PD A** *072
WILSON, Katie Elizabeth. ■ 37013 #036-05-2004 **CHP** *012
ZAFAR, Blal Ahmed. 2929 OLD FRANKLIN RD 37013 #308-13-2000 L2003 **IM** *020 †20
ZIEBER, Sarah Rebecca. ■ 37013 #038-41-2002 L2002 **PHO** *012 †55

ARDMORE – GILES

ALEJANDRINO, Angelina I. 31151 COMMERCIAL DR 38449 #748-21-1991 L1998
IM GP *020 †20

ARLINGTON – SHELBY

ENYENIHI, Henry Nubung. 11121 HIGHWAY 70, STE 101 38002 #308-10-1987 L1997
IM *020 †20

HUBBARD, Mark Adam. ■ 38002 #017-20-2005 L2008 IM *100

IVERSON, Kenneth Jay. ■ 38002 #026-04-1986 L1989 FM *020 †18

KEMP, Timothy L. 9755 HIGHWAY 64 STE 101 38002 #048-13-1992 L1993 EM AN *020

LAKIN, Karen Niimi. ■ 38002 #036-08-1993 L1995 PD *020 †55

MOTIWALA, Mohammed Munir. 11293 MEMPHIS ARLINGTON RD, ARLINGTON DEV CTR 38002
#308-10-1984 L1997 IM *020 †20

MYERS, Jennifer Lynn. ■ 38002 #038-44-1993 L1994 FM *020 †18

NGUYEN, Tuan Anh Ngoc. ■ 38002 #305-01-2003 L2008 FM *100

O'NEAL, Carla Louise. ■ 38002 #025-01-2000 L2001 EM *020

SALEEM, Muhammad. 11293 MEMPHIS ARLINGTON RD, ARLINGTON DEVELOPMENTAL
CE 38002 #704-02-1979 L1995 IM *020 †20

SARGENT, Susie Jane. 9160 HIGHWAY 64, STE 12 38002 #047-06-1982 L1984 ID IM *040 †20

SHELBY, Hannah Lee. ■ 38002 #047-06-2004 L2008 MPD *012

SHEPPARD, Theresa Marie. ■ 38002 #016-45-2007 PD *012

ARRINGTON – WILLIAMSON

POOLE, James Talmadge. ■ 37014 #654-01-1995 L1999 IM *020 †20

ASHLAND CITY – CHEATHAM

ALEXANDER, Dave Almon, Jr. 313 N MAIN ST 37015 #047-05-1976 L1979 ORS HS *020 †40

ANDERSON, James Reginald. 313 N MAIN ST 37015 #001-02-1983 L1984 FM *020 †18

BALDWIN, James Marvin. 313 N MAIN ST, BOX 536 37015 #020-02-1963 L1967 FM *020

BARTEK, John Gregory. 313 N MAIN ST 37015 #025-01-1977 L1987 DR *071 †80

BERGER, Brian Lee. 313 N MAIN ST 37015 #036-05-1983 L1992 FM *020 †80

BERGER, Kurt V. 313 N MAIN ST 37015 #048-12-1984 L1989 DR R *020 †80

BROWN, Scott Duff. 342 FREY ST 37015 #041-13-1986 L1996 FM OM *020 †18

DOTY, Robert D. 1800 CHEATHAM DAM RD 37015 #047-06-1976 L1978 EM GP *020 †80

DUKE, Billy Lee, II. 102 BOYD ST 37015 #047-06-1986 L2001 OBG *020 †30

GOODIN, Ellis Len. 313 N MAIN ST 37015 #047-06-1975 L1976 DR *020 †80

GRAY, Scott David. 313 N MAIN ST 37015 #041-12-1991 L1997 FM *020 †80

GREEN, Eric Brent. 313 N MAIN ST 37015 #001-06-2001 L2007 *020 †80

HOFFMAN, Christopher D. 313 N MAIN ST, SYCAMORE VALLEY MED GRP 37015
#012-01-1988 L1996 FM *020 †18

HORNSBY-ODOI, Suzette A. 104 FREY ST, STE 100 37015 #412-02-1992 L2005
MPD *020 †20,55

JOBE, Jeffrey Scott. 313 N MAIN ST, SYCAMOREVALLEY MEDICAL GRO 37015
#305-01-2001 L2004 FM *020 †18

KING, John David. 313 N MAIN ST 37015 #047-06-1988 L1991 DR *020 †80

LASSITER, Gregory L. 313 N MAIN ST 37015 #047-06-1995 L2000 RNR *020 †80

LUNDY, Jeffrey Dean. 313 N MAIN STE 100 37015 #017-20-1982 L1985 FM *020 †18

MALLORY, James Davis. ■ 37015 #036-07-1958 L1963 P *020 †75

MASSIE, James Daniel. 313 N MAIN ST 37015 #047-06-2000 L2005 RNR *020 †80

MONTESI, Scott Anthony. 313 N MAIN ST 37015 #030-06-1983 L1984 R *020 †80 ‡

NG, Christopher Cheukho. 313 N MAIN ST 37015 #036-01-1984 L1990 DR *062 †80 ‡

PARKER, Keith Randall. 313 N MAIN ST 37015 #047-06-1988 L1998 VIR *020 †80

PRIEST, Edward Mc Call. 313 N MAIN ST 37015 #047-06-1974 L1974 DR IM *020 †20,80

RHEA, Robert Eugene. 202 N MAIN ST STE 9 37015 #039-05-1986 L1987 FM *020 †18 ‡

SCHOFIELD, Carl N. 313 N MAIN ST 37015 #021-06-1983 L2007 DR *020 †80

SHOEMAKER, Benjamin Edgar. 202 N MAIN ST 37015 #047-02-1986 L1987 FM *020 †18

SMITH, Gregory Dean. 313 N MAIN ST 37015 #047-05-1985 L1988 DR *020 †80

TEPPER, Patricia Ann. 313 N MAIN ST 37015 #047-05-1981 L2006 DR *020 †80 ‡

WELLS, Robert Allan. ■ 37015 #020-02-2005 L2007 AN *012

ATHENS – MCMINN

BERRY, Debra Martin. 135 N MEADOWS DR, STE 300 37303 #047-06-1995 L1998 PD *020 †55

BERRY, Timothy Bryan. 740 TELL ST, STE 300 37303 #047-06-1995 L1998 FM *020 †18

BIBILEISHVILI, Eteri. 711 COOK DR, STE 210 37303 #913-23-1990 L2007 N *020 †75

BLEDSOE, Robert Eugene. 817 COOK DR 37303 #036-07-1981 L1983 OBG *020 †30

BOULOS, Paul Tymour. 1031 W MADISON AVE, NEUROSURGERY & SPINE 37303
#041-02-2000 L2006 NS *100

BOWERS, William Richard. 719 COOK DR, POST OFFICE BOX 906 37303 #017-20-1973 L1975
FM *020 †18

BREEDEN, Kimberly T. 705 COOK DR STE 203, COVENANT PEDIATRICS 37303
#019-02-1986 L1989 PD *020 †55

BROWN, John Preston. ■ 37303 #047-06-1996 L2001 GS *085

BURROUGHS, Wallace F, II. 1031 W MADISON AVE, STE 70 37303 #047-06-1975 L1976
FM EM *020 †18

BYRD, David Leland. 307 MAPLE ST 37303 #047-20-1988 L1989 FM *020 †18

BYRD, Jenny Marion. 711 COOK DR, STE 100 37303 #047-20-1988 L1989 FM *020 †18

CARTER, Johnnie Clarence. 705 COOK DR, STE 202 37303 #047-06-1986 L1989 FM *020 †18

CHILDRESS, David Ryan. 711 COOK DR, STE 100 37303 #047-06-1997 L2004 FM *020 †18

COX, Charles Boggess. 503 W MADISON AVE 37303 #047-06-1983 L1988 GS *020 †85

DAVIS, William Mayfield. PO BOX 568 37371 #047-06-1954 L1954 GP GS *020

DE FREITAS, Eric Allan. 135 N MEADOWS DR 37303 #045-01-1984 L1992 OBG *020 †30

DENTON, Stephen Lewis. 406 W MADISON AVE, P O BOX 1208 37303 #047-06-1971 L1972
EM GP *075

DRURY, William John. 705 COOK DR STE 201 37303 #030-06-1979 L1987 ORS *020 †40

DUNHAM, Rodney. 2324 CONGRESS PKWY S 37303 #047-06-1982 L1983 FM *020

FLOCK, Travis Lee. 711 COOK DR, STE 110 37303 #021-06-1994 L1997 IM *020 †20

FOREE, William Edwin, Jr. 100 W WASHINGTON AVE 37303 #047-06-1955 L1956
U FOP *062 †95

GOPINATHAN, Saji K. 119 EPPERSON ST 37303 #495-31-1994 L2000 PD *020 †55

GOULD, Richard Chas. ■ 37303 #020-12-1983 L2000 AN *020

GRIFFITH, Shelley F. 719 COOK DR STE 103, BOX 1875 37303 #047-06-1970 L1971
OBG *020 †30

HAHN, Michael Wayne. 135 N MEADOWS DR STE B 37303 #021-05-1982 L1994 OBG *020 †30

HARDISON, Cary Don. ■ 37303 #047-06-1964 L1964 EM GP *020 †16

HAUGE, David Hans. 1031 W MADISON AVE, NEUROSURGERY & SPINE 37303
#055-01-1984 L1990 NS *020 †25

HEWGLEY, Robert G, Jr. 1114 W MADISON AVE 37303 #047-06-1981 L1982 DR EM *020

HEWGLEY, Robert Gardner. 1114 W MADISON AVE 37303 #047-06-1954 L1954 CD IM *071

HOLLIDAY, Harold Joseph. 1005 W MADISON AVE 37303 #047-06-1973 L1974 GS NTR *020

JACKSON, Stephen Wm. 1031 W MADISON AVE 37303 #047-06-1984 L1986 U *020 †95

JONES, Milnor. 1114 W MADISON AVE 37303 #047-05-1948 L1948 GS *071 †85

LAUTERBACH, Joseph C. 817 COOK DR 37303 #047-06-2001 L2005 OBG *020 †30

LAYMAN, Thomas Stuart. 719 COOK DR, STE 110 37303 #047-06-1989 L1991 GS *020 †85

LEMINGS, Stephen. 1114 W MADISON AVE, HCA ATHENS REGIONAL ME 37303
#047-06-1977 L1977 DR *020

LOAIZA, Augusto. 1304 DECATUR PIKE 37303 #319-01-1955 L1989 OPH GP *071

MARTIN, Clyde Sidney. 119 EPPERSON ST 37303 #012-01-1979 L1980 U *020 †95

MAYNARD, Christopher Lee. 1031 W MADISON AVE, STE 70 37303 #020-12-1986 L1990
IM *020 †20

MC INTIRE, Edward Melton. 1031 W MADISON AVE 37303 #004-01-1992 L1997 U *020 †95

MC KENZIE, John Carl. 117 EPPERSON ST 37303 #048-04-1959 L1961 GYN *071 †30

MOON, Leah Nicole. 1118 COOSA ST 37303 #047-20-1999 L2002 IM *020 †20

MORRIS, William Gourrier. 1805 ELMHURST DR 37303 #021-05-1965 L1975
GP A *071 †55,03,18

NICHOLS, Lorenzo Dudley. 705 COOK DR STE 203, ATHENS ORTHOPEDICS & SPORT 37303
#047-06-1992 L2003 ORS *020

OSBORN, Carl Quinn. 705 COOK DR, STE 201 37303 #039-01-1977 L2003 ORS *020 †40

RAGLAND, Joel Bryan. 1031 W MADISON AVE, NEUROSURGERY & SPINE 37303
#004-01-1988 L1994 NS *020 †25

RAMSEY, Donald Franklin. 2808 DECATUR PIKE, C/O HOMESTEAD INN WEST, #1 37303
#047-06-1985 L1986 EM FM *020 ‡

ROGERS, Lynda Knight. ■ 37303 #047-20-1991 L1995 DR *020 †80

RUCKER, Walter Winfield. 500 DECATUR PIKE 37303 #020-02-1993 L1997 FM *020 †18

SCHWIGER, Paul A, Jr. 719 COOK DR, STE 104 37303 #047-06-1976 L1977 ORS *020 †40

SHARPE, Charles Richard. 1031 W MADISON AVE, STE 70 37303 #422-01-1986 L1989
IM *020 †20

SLOWEY, Iris G Snider. 817 COOK DR 37303 #047-06-1967 L1968 PD *020 †55

SLOWEY, James Fergus, III. 817 COOK DR 37303 #047-06-1968 L1970 OBG *020 †30

SUMIDA, Michael Patrick. 719 COOK DR, STE 110 MEDICAL MALL 37303 #020-12-1994 L1995
GS *020 †85

TROTTER, Robert Wm. ■ 37371 #047-06-1954 L1954 GS *071 †85

TURNBOUGH, Vickie A. 711 COOK DR STE 110, MED ASSOC OF ATHENS 37303
#020-12-1990 L1994 IM *020

VARGAS, Eugenio Fortunato. 1031 W MADISON AVE, NEUROSURGERY & SPINE 37303
#649-40-1983 L1990 NS *020 †25

WATTERS, Donald Howard. 711 COOK DR, STE 200 37303 #047-06-1981 L1982 GP *020

WILLIAMS, Michael Tyelar. 404 S WHITE ST 37303 #047-20-2002 L2003 FM *020 †18

ATOKA – TIPTON

BORJA, Jherico Pineda. ■ 38004 #748-01-2000 L2004 EM FM *020 †18

DEMENT, Roy Moore. 11180 HIGHWAY 51 S, STE 3 38004 #047-06-1974 L1974 GS *020 †85

BARTLETT – SHELBY

ALEXANDER, Michelle Inez. 6555 STAGE RD, #1 THE FAMILY CARE GROUP 38134
#047-07-1997 L2000 FM *020 †18

ALLEN, Gisele Renea. 6555 STAGE RD, STE 1 38134 #047-06-1997 L2000 FM *020 †18

ASSFOURA, Rana. 6385 STAGE RD # 2 38134 #875-01-1995 L2004 FP *020 †18

BALDERAMA, Hermino B. 2743 SUMMER OAKS DR, BARTLETT RALEIGH INTERNAL 38134
#748-01-1979 L1989 IM *020

BASTNAGEL, William R. 6332 DAYBREAK DR 38135 #047-06-1982 L1983 IM NEP *020 †20

BEAVER, Terinell. 6570 SUMMER OAKS CV 38134 #047-06-1983 L1984 IMG IM *020 †20

BENAIM, Elisa I. 8025 STAGE HILLS BLVD 38133 #935-07-1987 L1995 PD *020 †55

BORING, James Howard. 6045 WILLOUGHBY OAK LN 38135 #047-06-1965 L1965
FM AM *071 †18

BOURLAND, Robert Leon, Jr. 2926 KATE BOND RD, STE 201 38133 #047-06-1966 L1967
ORS *020 †40

CHEN, Quan. 2986 KATE BOND RD, ST FRANCIS HOSPITAL 38133 #243-46-1988 L2002
RO *020 †80

CHOUDHRI, Saleem Akhtar. 8383 WOLF LAKE DR 38133 #704-06-1966 L1997 FM *020

DE FRANCO, Joseph Anthony. 7400 STAGE RD 38133 #041-13-1977 L1984 GYN OBS *020

DEWITT, Cheryl Denise. ■ 38135 #047-06-2007 FP *012

EANES, Eric Scott. ■ 38135 #055-02-1990 L1991 FM *062 †18

ELIAS, Said E. 2986 KATE BOND RD, MEDICAL STAFF OFFICE 38133 #875-01-1986 L1997
IM *020 †18

ELLIOTT, Aaron Michael. ■ 38135 #038-43-2004 L2007 DR *012

FALEYE, Olugbenga. 6637 SUMMER KNOLL CIR, STE 101 38134 #690-08-1991 L1998
IM *020 †20

GERLACH, Paul A. 2963 ELMORE PARK RD 38134 #047-06-1981 L1982 CD IM *020 †20

GILLESS, Jerry Paul. ■ 38134 #047-06-2006 IM *012

GREAR, Benjamin Joplin. ■ 38134 #047-06-2007 ORS *012

HENRICKSEN, Jared William. 3592 SKYLIGHT DR E, 3592 SKYLIGHT DRIVE 38135
#056-06-2002 L2005 CCP *012 †55

HERMAN, Jean Tucker. ■ 38135 #047-06-1963 L1964 N IM *072

HILER, Lloyd. ■ 38135 #018-03-1965 L1972 GS *074 †85

HOLLEY, Jerry Morgan. 6570 SUMMER OAKS CV 38134 #027-01-1986 L1990 FM *020 †20

HYATT, Terri Lyn. 2996 KATE BOND RD, STE 405 38133 #021-06-1986 L1989 FM *020 †18

JARAMILLO, Juan R. 3173 KIRBY WHITTEN RD, STE 104 38134 #264-13-1989 L1998
CHP *020 †75

KWOK, Warren. 6570 STAGE RD, STE 120 38134 #062-01-1993 L1995 **UCM FM** *020
LACASSE, Alexandre. ■ 38133 #665-01-2003 L2007 **ID** *012 †20
LATIF, Kashif A. 2996 KATE BOND RD, STE 413 38133 #704-25-1990 L1995 **IM** *020 †20
LAWSON, Robert Edward. ■ 38135 #047-06-1941 L1941 **AN** *071 †05
LAZAR, Edward Harry. 6750 STAGE RD # 160 38134 #047-06-1967 L1971 **OBG** *020 †30
LEMONDS, Mike Edward. 6570 SUMMER OAKS CV 38134 #047-06-1984 L1985 **IM** *020 †20
LYMAN, Erik Mackinnon. ■ 38135 #038-40-2006 **OTO** *012
MAY, Monique Danielle. 2996 KATE BOND RD, STE 401 38133 #041-13-1996 L2005
 FM *020 †18
MILLER, Robert Glenn. 2996 KATE BOND RD STE 405 38133 #047-20-1987 L1988 **FM** *100 †18
MONAGHAN, Thomas Walker. 5705 STAGE RD, STE 212 38134 #036-05-1960 L1975
 RO DR *071 †80
MONTGOMERY, James C. 8025 STAGE HILLS BLVD 38133 #001-02-1994 L1997 **PD** *020 †55
MUNN, Charles Wilson. 6570 SUMMER OAKS CV 38134 #047-06-1980 L1981 **IM** *020 †20
NAIMEY-SOUSS, Nahem A. 6600 STAGE RD STE 126206 38134 #308-11-1986 L1994 **IM** *020
NOLLNER, Robert Michael. 3091 KIRBY WHITTEN RD 38134 #047-06-1982 L1983
 EM FM *020 †18
NORTON, Brian D. ■ 38133 #004-01-2008 *012
OWEN, Keith Bennett. 8025 STAGE HILLS BLVD 38133 #051-01-1998 L2002 **PD** *020 †55
PATTERSON, Michael Alan. 3189 KIRBY WHITTEN RD, STE 105 38134 #011-03-1983 L1986
 P EM *020
PORTER, William Richard. 2743 SUMMER OAKS DR 38134 #047-06-1973 L1974 **IM** *020
QURESH, Mohammad N. 2996 KATE BOND RD, STE 413 38133 #704-01-1996 L2003
 END IM *020 †20
SAEED, Salman. 6570 STAGE RD STE 202 38134 #704-02-1988 L1996 **N CN** *020
SARGENT, John P. ■ 38135 #041-02-1950 L1951 **GS GP** *071
SCOTT, Hugh Barrett. 8025 STAGE HILLS BLVD 38133 #047-06-1989 L1992 **PD** *020 †55
SMITH, Eric Lemuel. 3173 KIRBY WHITTEN RD, STE 104 38134 #047-06-1995 L1999 **P** *020
SONPATKI, Anant Kamalakar. 8919 BRISTOL PARK CIR 38133 #306-01-1998 L2004
 IMG *020 †18
TURNER, James Ethridge. 6570 STAGE RD STE 140 38134 #020-02-1976 L1980 **D IG** *020 †15
UNGAB, Ramon Tom. 2851 STAGE CENTER DR, VERZOSA & UNGAB INTE MED 38134
 #748-10-1984 L1997 **IM** *020
VERZOSA, Samuel Tadiar. 2851 STAGE CENTER DR 38134 #748-07-1982 L1987 **IM** *020
VICKERY, John David. ■ 38135 #047-06-2007 **IM** *012
VILLANUEVA, Randy Joseph. 6637 SUMMER KNOLL CIR 38134 #748-01-1999 L2005
 IM *020 †20
WOLTERS, William Clay. 3173 KIRBY WHITTEN RD, STE 104 38134 #047-06-1995 L1996
 P *020 †75
WONG, Joseph Kenneth. 3091 KIRBY WHITTEN RD 38134 #027-01-1986 L1989 **FM** *020 †18
WOODS, James Ray. 3173 KIRBY WHITTEN RD, STE 104 38134 #047-06-1991 L1992
 P EM *020 †75
YUSUF, Harar Abdulahi. 6637 SUMMER KNOLL CIR, STE 101 38134 #366-03-1991 L2007
 IM *020 †20

BAXTER – PUTNAM

LEFTWICH, Lanny Michael, Jr. 526 1ST AVE N 38544 #047-06-1997 L2001 **P** *020 †75
RAYALA, Christopher Zagui. 319 BROAD ST, POBOX 175 38544 #748-02-2000 L2005
 FM *020 †18

BEAN STATION – GRAINGER

SIDDIQI, Amanullah. 1285 HIGHWAY 11W 37708 #704-02-1989 L1995 **IM** *020 †20

BEERSHEBA SPRINGS – GRUNDY

KEMMERLY, Paul Courtland. ■ 37305 #039-01-1958 L1966 **AN** *071 †05

BELL BUCKLE – BEDFORD

CAMPBELL, Earl Roy, Jr. PO BOX 309, 204 MATT DR 37020 #021-01-1954 L1959 **ORS** *071 †40
MC CABE, Bridget Kathleen. PO BOX 5013, 206 FOLLIN LN 37020 #024-01-2001 L2005
 PD *100

BELLEVUE – DAVIDSON

POMEROY, Howard Clifton. 7643 HIGHWAY 70 S, BELLEVUE FAMILY PRACTICE 37221
 #047-06-1959 L1959 **GP PD** *071

BELLS – CROCKETT

FREEMAN, John Dungan. ■ 38006 #047-06-1966 L1979 **EM FM** *020 †18
UGBAJA, Felix Chukwudi. 4944 COLLEGE ST 38006 #308-03-1989 L1999 **IM** *020 †20

BENTON – POLK

PAGAN, Patricia Ann. 108 LIFESTYLE WAY 37307 #005-12-1975 L2001 **FM** *020 †18

BIRCHWOOD – HAMILTON

LICCIARDELLO, Jere T W. ■ 37308 #024-07-1977 L2003 **ON HEM** *071 †20 ‡

BLAINE – GRAINGER

ROBBINS, Sherry Lynn. 180 EMORY RD 37709 #047-20-1989 L1990 **FM** *020 †18

BLOUNTVILLE – SULLIVAN

ARENAS, Apollo Manlapig. ■ 37617 #748-01-1976 L1982 **N** *020 †75
BOONSUE, Aarom. ■ 37617 #891-01-1951 L1964 **FM** *071 †18
HICKS, Joshua Aaron. ■ 37617 #036-05-2008 *012
MCDUFFIE, Everett Ellison. 200 DECK LN UNIT 1001, 200 DECK LANE 37617
 #654-01-2000 L2006 **P** *012
UKAEGBU, Chibuzo Onyeze. ■ 37617 #690-12-1996 L2005 **FP** *012

BLUFF CITY – SULLIVAN

AGUAS, Elena Y. 229 HIGHWAY 19 E 37618 #748-11-1980 L1995 **IM** *020 †20
BROWN, George Richard. 549 MILLER HOLLOW RD 37618 #035-45-1983 L1994 **P** *020 †75
MCFARLAND, Neil. ■ 37618 #038-43-2002 L2006 **FM** *020
MOHLER, Troy Randolph. ■ 37618 #051-01-2005 L2006 **FP** *012

BOLIVAR – HARDEMAN

BARHAM, Harvey Haywood. 649 W MCNEAL ST, STE B 38008 #047-06-1955 L1956 **FM** *071
CABRERA-ALONSO, Juliana. 629 NUCKOLLS RD, P O BOX 720 38008 #726-01-1994 L2006
 FM *100 †18
CHANDEL, Vijaya K. 11100 HIGHWAY 64, WESTERN MENTAL HLTH INSTIT 38008
 #495-20-1968 L1982 **CHP P** *020
DUNAVANT, Robert Wayne. 407 W LAFAYETTE ST 38008 #047-06-1974 L1974
 FM GP *020 †18 ‡
FROST, Charles Lester. 407 W LAFAYETTE ST 38008 #047-06-1959 L1960 **GP** *071
GUIA, Priscila Cabrera. HWY 64 WEST 38008 #748-01-1955 L1972 **P GP** *071
ILOH, Emmanuel Chuka. 622 NUCKOLLS RD, NEW PRIME CARE CLINIC 38008
 #690-04-1988 L2004 **IM** *020 †20
KING, Louis Douglass. ■ 38008 #047-06-1975 L1975 **CHP P** *020 †75
LINDER, Hilary Francis. 11100 HIGHWAY 64, WESTERN MENTAL HEALTH INST 38008
 #028-34-1960 L1966 **P** *020 †75
LOGAN, Elizabeth. ■ 38008 #039-01-2004 L2005 **FM** *020 †18
LOGAN, Jason Alton. ■ 38008 #047-06-2002 L2003 **FM EM** *020 †18
NICOL, Sylvester Desmond. 640 NUCKOLLS RD 38008 #917-03-1991 L1998 **IM** *071 †20
ONYIUKE, Ijeoma Catherine. PO BOX 479, 622 NUCKOLLS RD 38008 #690-04-1992 L2004
 IM *100
PAKKALA, Nithyananda Y. 630 NUCKOLLS RD 38008 #495-09-1969 L1976 **GP** *020
PATEL, Pravin J. 407 W LAFAYETTE ST 38008 #495-23-1978 L1983 **IM** *020 †20
RICH, Anthony Michael. 10710 OLD HIGHWAY 64 38008 #025-01-1967 L1992 **CHP P** *020 †75
ROBBINS, Jeffrey Mark. 11100 HIGHWAY 64, INSTITUTE 38008 #056-05-1970 L2000 **P** *020 †75
SUARA, Rahaman Olatunji. 650 NUCKOLLS RD 38008 #690-01-1986 L2001 **PD PDI** *020 †55
SURENDER, Ennu. 11100 HWY 64TH WEST 38008 #495-21-1962 L1981 **CHP** *020
VARNER, James Wm. 11100 HIGHWAY 64, WESTERN MENTAL HEALTH INST 38008
 #001-02-1974 L1980 **P ADM** *030 †75

BON AQUA – HICKMAN

BRADY, Emilie Camille. ■ 37025 #047-06-2007 **TY** *012

BRADFORD – GIBSON

CAMPBELL, Thomas King. 216 E MAIN ST, POST OFFICE BOX 100 38316 #005-15-1962 L1975
 FM AN *071 †18

BRENTWOOD – WILLIAMSON

AARON, Mark Freeman. 1195 OLD HICKORY BLVD, HEART GROUP PLLC 37027
 #036-07-1992 L2000 **CD** *020 †20
ADKINS, Richard Kermit. 7105 CROSSROADS BLVD, BLVD. SUITE105 37027
 #011-03-1984 L1986 **AN EM** *020 †05
AKKINENI, Gopichand. PO BOX 2584 37024 #495-57-1974 **FM** *020
ALBERHASKY, Mark Thomas. 5301 VIRGINIA WAY, ASSOCIATED PATHOLOGISTS 37027
 #020-02-1979 L1985 **PTH FOP** *020 †50 ‡
ALBERHASKY, Robert Carlis. 5301 VIRGINIA WAY, ASSOCIATED PATHOLOGISTS 37027
 #020-02-1976 L2004 **PTH** *020 †50 ‡
ANDERSON, Ansel Glen, III. ■ 37027 #027-01-1988 L2005 **EM** *020 †16
ANDERSON, John Latimer. ■ 37027 #422-01-1981 L1985 **EM** *071 †16
ANDERSON, Michael David. 1587 RED OAK LN 37027 #012-01-2002 L2005 **EM** *020 †16
ANDRADE, William Geo. ■ 37027 #036-07-1972 L1979 **EM PD** *020
ARCHER, Clark Edward. 2316 TINNEY PL 37027 #047-06-1997 L2000 **EM** *020 †16
ARKAVA, Todd Eric. 2049 VALLEY BROOK DR 37027 #016-06-2000 L2003 **EM** *020
ARNOLD, Fredrick S. 330 FRANKLIN RD, STE 135A-123 37027 #047-06-1970 L1970
 AN *020 †05
ATKINS, Robert Michael. 9142 SADDLEBOW DR 37027 #023-07-1978 L2001 **MDM P** *030 †75
ATKINSON, James Byron. 6312 NOEL DR 37027 #047-05-1981 L1982 **PTH CD** *020 †50
AWH, Mark Hunchul. 103 POWELL CT, STE 350 37027 #027-01-1988 L1993 **DR** *020 †80
BABU, Narayanareddy S. 1195 OLD HICKORY BLVD, HEART GROUP PLLC 37027
 #495-09-1973 L1977 **CD** *020 †20
BAKER, James Haywood, II. 1195 OLD HICKORY BLVD, HEART GROUP PLLC 37027
 #024-01-1987 L1994 **CD** *020 †20
BANNYKH, Galina Ivanovna. 201 SUMMIT VIEW DR STE 100 37027 #913-61-1988 L2004
 PTH *020 †50
BATTLES, Oscar Eugene. 5301 VIRGINIA WAY, ASSOCIATED PATHOLOGISTS 37027
 #001-06-1990 L1992 **PCP ATP** *020 †50 ‡
BAXTER, Jere W. 5301 VIRGINIA WAY STE 32, SKYLINE MEDICAL CENTER 37027
 #047-06-1976 L1977 **PTH** *020 †50 ‡
BELIHAR, Robert Patrick. 105 WESTWOOD PL STE 350, LIFESIGNS OF THE SOUTH 37027
 #049-01-1969 L1978 **AM OPH** *020 †35,70
BENNETT, Marc Logan. ■ 37027 #023-07-2000 L2007 **OTO** *100 †45

BINHLAM, John Q. 10 CADILLAC DR, STE 120 37027 #020-02-1990 L1993 **D IM** *020 †20,15

BODEN, Donna J. 5301 VIRGINIA WAY, ASSOCIATED PATHOLOGISTS 37027 #048-14-1987 L2001 **PTH** *020 †50 ‡

BODIN, Christopher Jude. 1113 HAVERHILL DR 37027 #021-05-1992 L2006 **DR** *020 †80

BOMAR-DAVIS, Sara L. ■ 37027 #047-07-1998 L2006 **DR** *020

BONDURANT, Jennifer Elyse. 5056 THOROUGHBRED LN, MARYLAND FARMS PEDIATRICS 37027 #047-06-1997 L1999 **PD** *020 †55

BOORGU, Kartik. 9025 OVERLOOK BLVD, STE 200 37027 #001-02-1996 L1998 **VIR** *020 †80

BRUNER, Kathy Sanders. 5301 VIRGINIA WAY, ASSOCIATED PATHOLOGISTS 37027 #020-02-1998 L1999 **PTH** *100 ‡

BUCHANAN, Richard Durr. 5301 VIRGINIA WAY STE 320 37027 #047-05-1961 L1961 **PTH** *071 †50

BULLOCK, Bradley Neil. 1607 WESTGATE CIR, STE 200 37027 #011-03-1993 L1995 **MPD** *020 †55,20

BURCH, Roy Perry, Jr. 343 FRANKLIN RD 37027 #047-06-1987 L1989 **OBG** *020 †30

BURDETT, Pamela Hay. 8 CADILLAC DR, STE 200 37027 #035-45-1989 L2003 **DR** *020 †80

BURGESS, Earle Frederick. ■ 37027 #012-01-2002 L2004 **HO** *012 †20

BUTTERFIELD, Martha Jean. 343 FRANKLIN RD, STE 203 37027 #047-05-1987 L1989 **AI** *020 †20,03

CACHIA, Richard Michael. 5301 VIRGINIA WAY, ASSOCIATED PATHOLOGISTS 37027 #627-01-1973 L1978 **PTH** *020 †50 ‡

CARROLL, John Francis. 8 CADILLAC DR STE 200 37027 #041-13-1998 L2007 **DR** *020 †80

CARTER, Cleo. 4821 MANASSAS DR 37027 #047-07-1982 L1983 **FM** *020 †30

CARUSO, Keith Allen. 9005 OVERLOOK BLVD 37027 #035-20-1990 L1999 **P PFP** *020 †75

CASEY, Terence Thomas. 5301 VIRGINIA WAY, ASSOCIATED PATHOLOGISTS 37027 #021-01-1981 L1987 **PTH** *020 †50

CHAND, Eric Matthew. 5301 VIRGINIA WAY, ASSOCIATED PATHOLOGISTS 37027 #654-01-1988 L2002 **PCP** *020 ‡

CHANG, David Keydai. 1616 WESTGATE CIR, STE 210 37027 #045-01-1993 L1995 **ADP P** *020 †75

CHATTERJEE, Molly Syamali. 1195 OLD HICKORY BLVD #202, HARPETH MED CTR 37027 #495-02-1965 L1994 **OBG MFM** *020 †30

CHENG, Po-Chak Japheth. ■ 37027 #244-04-1975 **GPM** *100

CINCERE, Brandon Alexande. ■ 37027 #047-06-2006 **ORS** *012

CLARK, William Bennett. ■ 37027 #051-04-2004 L2007 **HO** *012

CLYMER, Mark Allen. 1800 MALLORY LN STE A-3 37027 #018-03-1990 L1993 **FPS OTO** *020 †45

COLLIER, Ronald Derek. ■ 37027 #010-03-2005 **GS** *100

COLLINS, Merri. 95 SEABOARD LN, # 201 37027 #047-06-1996 L2000 **MPD** *020 †20,55

CONNOR, Dan Ellis. 3 MARYLAND FARMS, ASSOCIATED PATHOLOGISTS 37027 #047-05-1976 L1977 **PTH** *020 †50

CONNOR, Laura Nelle. ■ 37027 #047-05-1979 L1979 *075

COPELAND, Lanny Ross. 103 POWELL CT 37027 #020-02-1971 L1972 **FM EM** *030 †18

COTHREN, Frederec B. 200 WINNERS CIR S 37027 #005-12-1942 L1942 **GP** *071

CRAWFORD, Alvin S. ■ 37027 #010-02-1949 L1960 **PTH** *071 †50

DANIEL, Gerald Owen. ■ 37027 #036-05-1965 L1969 **R** *020 †80

DAVIS, Ben Weldon. 5301 VIRGINIA WAY, ASSOCIATED PATHOLOGISTS 37027 #004-01-1977 L1979 **OS** *030 †50 ‡

DAVIS, Monica Leigh. 1195 OLD HICKORY BLVD, STE 103 37027 #047-07-1995 L2000 **FM** *020 †18

DEMARQUE, Charles D. 5133 GRAND OAK WAY 37027 #048-14-1990 L1995 **FM** *020 †30

DENNEY, Mary Butterfield. 343 FRANKLIN RD, STE 203 37027 #047-05-1987 L1989 **IM** *030 †20

DILLARD, Samuel Henry, Jr. 5301 VIRGINIA WAY, STE 320 37027 #047-05-1967 L1974 **CLP PTH** *020 †50 ‡

DJAZAB, Aminollah. ■ 37027 #517-01-1957 **GS OBG** *100

DODD, Kathleen Murray. ■ 37027 #027-01-1988 L1994 **EM** *020 †16

DOZIER, J Emmett, Jr. 215 CENTERVIEW DR STE 204 37027 #047-05-1965 L1965 **CHP P** *020 †75

DRAUGHN, Jeffrey Danl. 343 FRANKLIN RD, STE 108 37027 #027-01-1988 L1992 **OBG** *020 †30

DUNCAN, Thomas Clyde. ■ 37024 #047-06-1966 L1966 **EM FM** *071 †18 ‡

DUNN, David B. 1720 GENERAL GEORGE PTN DR, 2ND FL 37027 #048-13-1985 L1994 **VS GS** *062 †85

DUNN, Paula H. ■ 37027 #021-05-1996 L1997 **FM** *020 †18

DUNNINGTON, James E, Jr. 5301 VIRGINIA WAY, ASSOCIATED PATHOLOGISTS 37027 #051-01-1980 L1981 **PTH HMP** *020 †50 ‡

DURRANI, Muhammad Hayat. ■ 37027 #704-09-1993 L2006 *100

EDMONDSON, William Daniel. 1607 WESTGATE CIR 37027 #047-06-1993 L1995 **MPD** *020 †55,20

EFOBI, Anthony Udokwu. ■ 37024 #308-03-1987 L2006 **IM** *020 †20

EISENSTEIN, Warren J. 5301 VIRGINIA WAY, ASSOCIATED PATHOLOGISTS 37027 #016-42-1979 L1983 **PTH** *020 †50 ‡

ERICKSON, Douglas Jos. 5301 VIRGINIA WAY, ASSOCIATED PATHOLOGISTS 37027 #036-07-1978 L1979 **PTH** *020 †50 ‡

FAHEEM, Sabahat. 6057 BRENTWOOD CHASE DR 37027 #704-06-1988 L2006 **P** *100

FARMER, Madeline E. ■ 37024 #047-07-1984 L1985 **P** *020 †75

FARTHING, William Howell. 5301 VIRGINIA WAY, ASSOCIATED PATHOLOGISTS 37027 #051-04-1989 L2004 **PTH** *020 †50 ‡

FERRISS, David Meadow, Jr. 105 CONTINENTAL PL, QUORUM HLTH RESOURCES INC 37027 #021-01-1976 L1977 **GPM FM** *030 †70,18

FLEET, William Floyd. ■ 37027 #047-05-1958 L1958 **PD** *071 †55

FLEMING, Philip Edward. 5409 MARYLAND WAY STE 115 37027 #001-02-1979 L1982 **PS HS** *020 †65

FORSTER, Anthony C. ■ 37027 #024-01-1996 **PTH** *100

FRAZIER, John W, Jr. ■ 37027 #047-05-1938 L1938 **IM** *071

FREED, Charles Roger, Jr. 8 CADILLAC DR STE 410 37027 #649-14-1983 L2000 **P CHP** *020 †75

FREEMAN, Lee Mc Cullough. 5056 THOROUGHBRED LN 37027 #047-06-1982 L1986 **PD** *020 †55

FREMONT, Richard D. ■ 37027 #035-15-2001 L2005 **PCC** *012

FRISBIE, Brent Keith. ■ 37027 #047-05-2003 L2006 **DR** *012

GAINES, Donald Lee. ■ 37027 #047-06-1958 L1959 **OSS OS** *071 †40

GALUTEN, Alvin Beryl. 649 LOGWOOD BRIAR CIR 37027 #012-05-1981 L1992 **DR** *071 †80

GHIASSI, Mahan. ■ 37027 #047-05-2007 **GS** *012

GIBBS, Jerry Lee. 5301 VIRGINIA WAY, ASSOCIATED PATHOLOGISTS 37027 #047-05-1966 L1983 **PTH CLP** *020 †50 ‡

GIBSON, David Wayne. 1195 OLD HICKORY BLVD, HEART GROUP PLLC 37027 #003-01-1991 L1992 **CD** *020 †20

GILLIAM, Larry Austin. 7100 COMMERCE WAY, STE 180 37027 #005-12-1971 L1993 **EM** *071 †16

GOLDFARB, Mark Steven. 1195 OLD HICKORY BLVD, HEART GROUP PLLC 37027 #010-01-1979 L1986 **CD IM** *020 †20

GRAHAM, Larry Gill. 5301 VIRGINIA WAY, STE 320 37027 #039-01-1967 L1975 **PTH** *020 †50 ‡

GRAVES, Dante James. 1195 OLD HICKORY BLVD, HEART GROUP PLLC 37027 #020-02-1988 L1994 **CD** *020 †20

GRAY, Roland Wm. 216 CENTERVIEW DR, STE 304 37027 #047-06-1972 L1973 **ADM PD** *020 †55

GREEN, Sharon Fetterman. ■ 37027 #001-06-2001 L2007 **IM** *062 †20

HAIN, Ann-Marie E. 5056 THOROUGHBRED LN 37027 #012-01-1996 L1999 **PD** *020 †55

HALL, Graves Scott. 5301 VIRGINIA WAY, ASSOCIATED PATHOLOGISTS 37027 #001-06-1988 L2005 **PTH PCP** *020 †50 ‡

HAMILTON, Rodney Mack. 5111 MARYLAND WAY STE 301, BRENTWOOD PEDIATRICS PLLC 37027 #047-06-1999 L2002 **PD** *020 †55

HANDTE, Robert E. ■ 37027 #035-09-1953 L1978 **AN** *071 †05

HARBISON, Mary Alice. 105 WESTWOOD PL, STE 350 37027 #047-05-1983 L1990 **ID IM** *020 †20

HARBOLDT, Samuel Lowell. 5301 VIRGINIA WAY, ASSOCIATED PATHOLOGISTS 37027 #005-12-1985 L1998 **PTH** *020 †50 ‡

HARLESS, Dean Mikal. 1030 GRACELAWN DR 37027 #038-41-1980 L1993 **AN** *020 †20,05

HASSON-GRISWOLD, Holly A. 330 FRANKLIN RD, STE 135A 37027 #001-02-1991 L1992 **PTH DMP** *020 †50

HILDRETH, James E. ■ 37027 #023-07-1987 **PA** *100

HILL, Fontaine Sallis, Jr. ■ 37027 #047-06-1977 L1980 **TS** *020 †85,90

HINES, Tiffany Elder. 1607 WESTGATE CIR 37027 #001-06-1995 L1997 **IM PD** *020 †20,55

HINSON, James Mc Call, Jr. ■ 37027 #047-05-1976 L1977 **PUD** *020 †20

HOBBS, Susan L. ■ 37027 #023-07-1997 **P** *100

HOFF, Catherine Ruth. ■ 37027 #023-07-1986 L1989 **NPM PD** *074 †55

HONIG, Allen. ■ 37027 #005-06-1974 L1994 **EM AN** *020 †16

ISAACSON, Frederick M. ■ 37027 #035-08-1970 L1997 **DR NR** *020 †80

JAHANGIR, Mohammad. ■ 37027 #517-04-1969 **GPM** *100

JANTZ, Jennifer Kathryn. ■ 37027 #047-20-2008 *012

JARAMILLO, Michael David. ■ 37027 #034-01-1979 L2005 **PTH** *020 †50 ‡

JERKINS, Gary Welch. 343 FRANKLIN RD, STE 204 37027 #047-06-1977 L1978 **OPH** *020 †35

JOHNSON, Calvin John. ■ 37027 #016-06-1961 L1997 **ORS** *071 †40

JOHNSON, Mark Lanier. 278 FRANKLIN RD, STE 150 37027 #001-02-1981 L1990 **U** *020 †95

JONES, John Donald. 5301 VIRGINIA WAY, STE 350 37027 #005-06-1965 L1977 **PTH** *071 †50

JULIAO, Saul A. ■ 37027 #264-01-1991 L1994 **OM** *072 †70

KAMAL, Jawaid. ■ 37027 #704-16-1983 L1995 **NEP FM** *020 †20

KATKURI, Kirthi Reddy. ■ 37027 #047-07-2005 **OBG** *012

KAUSHAL, Rajneesh Kumar. ■ 37027 #495-29-1984 **OS** *030

KEFFER, James Edward. 782 OLD HICKORY BLVD, STE 201 37027 #001-02-2001 L2006 **MPD** *020 †20,55

KELDIE, Carl James. 105 WESTPARK DR, STE 200 37027 #011-04-1978 L2001 **EM** *020 †16

KEMP, Wilson Evans, Jr. 1195 OLD HICKORY BLVD, HEART GROUP PLLC 37027 #036-01-1991 L1993 **CD IM** *020 †20

KIRCHBERG, Roy William. 5301 VIRGINIA WAY, ASSOCIATED PATHOLOGISTS 37027 #036-01-1960 L1969 **PTH** *020 †50 ‡

KNOX-CARTER, Glenda Dale. 5046 THOROUGHBRED LN 37027 #047-07-1986 L1986 **IM** *020

KRAVTSOV, Vladimir D. 9208 HERITAGE DR, DIATECH ONCOLOGY LLC 37027 #913-22-1977 L2003 **HMP** *020 †50

LAMAR, Lucius M. ■ 37027 #021-01-1959 L1965 **D** *071 †15

LAUGHLIN, Lawrence Paul. ■ 37027 #016-06-1962 L1967 **ORS OTR** *071 †40

LEBOW, Richard Lindsey. ■ 37027 #048-14-2004 **NS** *012

LEE, Ronald Vincent. 201 SUMMIT VIEW DR STE 100 37027 #011-03-1994 L2003 **PTH HMP** *020 †50

LENNINGTON, Wayne Jacob. 5301 VIRGINIA WAY, ASSOCIATED PATHOLOGISTS 37027 #017-20-1987 L1989 **PTH** *040 †50

LIGHT, Richard Theodore. ■ 37027 #047-05-1961 L1961 **PHP** *071

LISKE, Angela J. ■ 37027 #038-45-1992 L2000 **FM** *020 †18

LODGE, Jeffrey Sands. 7105 CROSSROADS BLVD, STE 105 37027 #036-05-1989 L1995 **OBG** *020 †30

LOEPPKE, Ronald Ray. ■ 37027 #019-02-1979 L2000 **OM OS** *030 †70

LONG, Brian Robert. ■ 37027 #047-05-2000 L2007 **CD** *100 †20

LUTZAK, K Stephen. ■ 37027 #065-06-1989 L1992 **EM** *020 †18

MALTZ, Brad Edward. 832 PISGAH PARK 37027 #011-02-2003 L2005 **GE** *012 †20

MANALO, Ronald Salazar. ■ 37024 #047-07-2008 *012

MARTINEZ, Erlinda O A. ■ 37027 #748-10-1965 L1972 **OS PD** *020

MAY, Estelle Eargle. 5301 VIRGINIA WAY, STE 320 37027 #045-01-1979 L1987 **ATP NP** *020 †50 ‡

MCCOY, Carrie Campbell. ■ 37027 #047-05-2008 *012

MC COY, Jeff C, Jr. 6414 WATERFORD DR 37027 #010-03-1974 L1994 **R** *040 †80

MC DANIEL, William Robt. 343 FRANKLIN RD, STE 202 37027 #051-01-1976 L1982 **D** *020 †15

MC DONALD, Shannon C. 317 SEVEN SPRINGS WAY, STE 104 37027 #031-01-1995 L2005 **FM** *020 †18

MC LEAN, John Laughlin. ■ 37027 #001-06-1988 L2003 **AN** *020 †05

MC MURRAY, Brian Royal. 9400 COXBORO DR 37027 #038-41-1978 L1992 **EM IM** *020 †20,16

MEHTA, Hemal Vinod. 1805 WILLIAMSON CT 37027 #305-01-1999 L2004 **PM** *020 †60

MEHTA, Ragini B. 9259 CHEVOIT DR, 9259 CHEVOIT DRIVE 37027 #495-76-1980 L1995 **AN** *020 †05

MEYER, Allen Frederick. 2 MARYLAND FARMS STE 240 37027 #024-01-1972 L1987 **FM IM** *020 †18

MILLER, Brian Geo. ■ 37027 #028-02-1975 L1988 **CLP HEM** *075 †50

MILLER, Randolph Arthur. 676 OLD ORCHARD RD 37027 #041-12-1976 L1994 **IM** *050 †20

MISHRA, Smita. ■ 37027 #495-85-1992 L2007 **FM** *020

MISHU, Mona Kirma. ■ 37027 #528-01-1957 L1972 **PTH** *020 †18

MITCHELL, Debra M. 201 SUMMIT VIEW DR, STE 100 37027 #566-01-1986 L2003 **PTH** *020 †50

MOOLMAN, Karin Coetzee. 343 FRANKLIN RD 37027 #836-04-1986 L1997 **FM** *020 †18

MOORE, Marc Aaron. ■ 37027 #020-02-2005 L2008 **OPH** *012

MOREL, Gabriela T. 343 FRANKLIN RD, STE 210 37027 #047-05-1994 L1997 **PD** *020 †55

MOSS, Charles Albert, III. 95 SEABOARD LN, # 201 37027 #001-02-1987 L1990 **PD** *020 †55

MOTSENBOCKER, Erik Byron. 364 CHILDE HAROLDS CIR, TEAM HEALTH 37027 #048-02-2003 L2006 **EM** *020

MURRAY, Robert Craig, Jr. 5315 MCGAVOCK RD 37027 #012-05-1981 L1984 **AN** *020 †05 ‡

NELSON, Eugene Harris. 5301 VIRGINIA WAY, ASSOCIATED PATHOLOGISTS 37027 #047-05-1987 L1989 **PTH** *020 †50 ‡

NWOFIA, John Chije. 1805 WILLIAMSON CT 37027 #690-02-1987 L1998 **PM PMM** *020 †60

NWOZO, Madubueza U. ■ 37027 #690-04-1996 L2003 **IM** *020 †20

OLAFSSON, Bjarki. 1195 OLD HICKORY BLVD, HEART GROUP PLLC 37027 #484-01-1979 L1985 **CD** *020 †20

OLLAPALLY, Elsie P. 5301 VIRGINIA WAY, ASSOCIATED PATHOLOGISTS 37027 #495-52-1974 L1982 **PTH** *020 †50 ‡

ORUCEVIC, Amila. 5301 VIRGINIA WAY, ASSOCIATED PATHOLOGISTS 37027 #957-08-1983 L2007 **PTH** *020 †50 ‡

PANKOWSKY, Dan A. 201 SUMMIT VIEW DR STE 100, CYTOMETRY ASSOC INC 37027 #048-14-1984 L1997 **PTH HMP** *020 †50

PAPIEZ, Joseph Steven. 201 SUMMIT VIEW DR 37027 #017-20-1995 L2001 **PTH** *020 †50

PAPUCHIS, Trudy. 5301 VIRGINIA WAY, ASSOCIATED PATHOLOGISTS 37027 #047-07-1984 L1989 **PTH** *020 †50 ‡

PARVEEN, Talat. 5301 VIRGINIA WAY, ASSOCIATED PATHOLOGISTS 37027 #704-06-1975 L1998 **PTH** *074 †50 ‡

PEARCE, Douglas James. 1195 OLD HICKORY BLVD, HEART GROUP PLLC 37027 #012-01-1985 L1996 **CD IM** *020 †20

PERERA, N Ranmali Anne. ■ 37027 #422-01-1991 L1995 **IM** *020 †20

PIECH, Kenneth Stowell. 5301 VIRGINIA WAY, ASSOCIATED PATHOLOGISTS 37027 #036-07-1975 L2005 **PTH** *030 †50 ‡

PIERCE, Edgar H, Jr. 5301 VIRGINIA WAY, ASSOCIATED PATHOLOGISTS 37027 #047-06-1974 L1974 **PTH CLP** *020 †50 ‡

POCHAMPALLY, Kalpana Rao. ■ 37027 #495-21-1998 L2005 **IM** *020 †20

POE, Larry Bernard. 8 CADILLAC DR, STE 200 37027 #036-01-1981 L2006 **R** *020 †55,80

POTTS, James Lafayette. ■ 37027 #047-07-1967 L1994 **CD IM** *020 †20

POWELL, Dan Stanfield. ■ 37027 #036-08-1999 L2003 **EM FM** *020 †18

PRAKASH, Andani Siddappa. ■ 37027 #495-33-1970 L1982 **PM** *020 †60

READUS, Valarie Faye. ■ 37027 #047-06-1996 L1999 **IM** *020

RICE, Jeffrey Jack. ■ 37027 #036-07-1992 L1994 **DR** *062

RICHARD, Robin E. ■ 37027 #047-07-1987 L1993 **OM** *020 †70

RIETZ, Heather Marguerite. 5301 VIRGINIA WAY, ASSOCIATED PATHOLOGISTS 37027 #047-05-1994 L2000 **HMP** *020 †50 ‡

RILEY, Debra Smith. ■ 37027 #020-12-1983 L1994 **IM** *020 †20

ROBERTSON, Eliza Ellis. ■ 37027 #055-02-2005 **N** *012

ROCHESTER, Richard Earle. 5123 VIRGINIA WAY, STE C11 37027 #047-05-1984 L1988 **P** *020 †75

ROSS, Tony Lynn. 343 FRANKLIN RD, STE 101 37027 #020-02-1982 L1985 **FM** *020 †18

ROWAN, Julie Jeter. ■ 37027 #047-06-2001 **IM** *100

RUOFF, Jennifer Mai. ■ 37027 #005-06-2003 L2007 **OBG** *100

RUPP, Sara Jo. 1451 GREEN HILL BLVD, . 37027 #048-02-1991 L1999 **DR** *020 †80

SACKS, Eugene Ira. ■ 37027 #033-05-1970 L1984 **EM GS** *075 †85

SAMUDRALA, Sreedhar. 1195 OLD HICKORY BLVD, STE 103 37027 #025-07-1997 L2002 **FM** *020 †18

SANTORO, Frank Leonard. ■ 37027 #038-40-1986 **PA** *030

SATTARI BAHRI, Nader. 9776 JUPITER FOREST DR 37027 #517-23-2001 **IM** *012

SAVANI, Bipin Nagjibhai. ■ 37027 #495-22-1989 L2007 **HEM** *100 †20

SCHATZ, Mary Pullig. 3 MARYLAND FARMS, ASSOCIATED PATHOLOGISTS 37027 #047-05-1969 L1969 **PTH PM** *020 †50 ‡

SCHOENHARD, John Andrew. ■ 37027 #047-05-2004 L2006 **CD** *012

SCOTT, Frank Hal. 343 FRANKLIN RD, STE 204 37027 #047-05-1992 L1996 **OPH** *020 †35

SCOTT, Veronica Jean. ■ 37027 #035-46-1973 L1988 **IMG IM** *050

SCOVEL, Clark Allen. 330 FRANKLIN RD, STE 135A-123 37027 #026-04-1993 L1999 **CCA** *020 †05

SCOVILLE, George S, Jr. 1195 OLD HICKORY BLVD, HEART GROUP PLLC 37027 #047-06-1978 L1979 **CD IM** *020 †20

SEIBERT, Louis Edward. 5301 VIRGINIA WAY, STE 320 37027 #012-01-1982 L2000 **ATP** *020 †50 ‡

SEKULOVSKI, Bill Gorgi. 104 EASTPARK DR, STE 102 37027 #957-04-1989 L2007 **FM** *020 †18

SHAMSUDDIN, Abdul K. 5301 VIRGINIA WAY, ASSOCIATED PATHOLOGISTS 37027 #495-31-1963 L1971 **GP EM** *071 †50 ‡

SHARIFI, Mahnoosh. ■ 37027 #047-05-2007 L2007 **PD** *012

SHUPE, David Ralston W. ■ 37027 #041-12-1943 L1960 **P** *071

SIDANI, Mohamad Anis. ■ 37027 #605-01-1984 L2006 **FM FPG** *020 †18

SILVERNAGEL, Sean Wyatt. 5301 VIRGINIA WAY, ASSOCIATED PATHOLOGISTS 37027 #020-02-1995 L2000 **PTH** *020 †50 ‡

SIMS, Jill Andrea. 5111 MARYLAND WAY, STE 310 37027 #012-01-1991 L1994 **PD** *020 †55

SINARD, Dorothy B. ■ 37027 #025-01-1991 L1994 **PD** *074 †55

SINGH, Kavita. 1607 WESTGATE CIR, ST. 200 37027 #043-01-2002 L2007 **MPD** *020 †20,55

SLAY, Jerry Lee. ■ 37027 #047-06-1978 L1980 **P ADP** *020 †75

SLEMMER, J Ross. 5301 VIRGINIA WAY, ASSOCIATED PATHOLOGISTS 37027 #041-02-1986 L2005 **PTH PCP** *020 †50 ‡

SLONECKER, William Thos. 95 SEABOARD LN, # 201 37027 #047-06-1958 L1959 **PD** *071

SMITH, Robert Maxwell. 5046 THOROUGHBRED LN 37027 #041-77-1961, ▲ L1999 **CD IM** *020

SMITH, Roger Fielding. ■ 37027 #025-01-1946 L1948 **GS VS** *071 †85

SMITH, Samuel Arnold. 5301 VIRGINIA WAY, ASSOCIATED PATHOLOGISTS 37027 #020-02-1973 L1978 **PTH** *030 †50 ‡

SNEARLY, William Norman. 8 CADILLAC DR, STE 200 37027 #035-15-1986 L2004 **DR** *020 †80

SOLDO, Catherine R. 5301 VIRGINIA WAY, ASSOCIATED PATHOLOGISTS 37027 #020-12-1990 L1996 **PTH** *020 †50 ‡

SON, Ae Kyoung Kim. 5111 MARYLAND WAY, STE 304 37027 #583-08-1975 L1978 **IM** *020

SORKIN, Hardy Leigh. ■ 37027 #041-07-1972 L2006 **NEP IM** *030 †20 ‡

STADNICK, Michael Edward. 8 CADILLAC DR, STE 200 37027 #012-01-1987 L1998 **DR** *020 †80

STAGGS, Stephen Michael. 343 FRANKLIN RD 37027 #047-06-1978 L1979 **OBG** *020 †30

STARMER, John Malotte. ■ 37027 #035-06-1995 L1999 **IM** *100

STEWART-RAMAGE, Phyleen. 5034 THOROUGHBRED LN, STE D 37027 #047-05-1991 L1992 **CHP** *020 †75

STOVALL, Isaac Henry. ■ 37027 #012-21-1989 L1990 **GS** *020

STROUP, David G. ■ 37027 #047-05-1948 L1948 **OBG** *071 †30

SUN, Jianping. 8115 ISABELLA DR, STE 8 37027 #243-29-1982 L2001 **AN PMM** *020

SUTTON, Harold Saml. ■ 37027 #047-06-1959 L1973 **GYN** *071

SWARR, Peter James. 1607 WESTGATE CIR, STE 200 37027 #050-02-1999 L2001 **MPD** *100 †55,20

SZCZARKOWSKI, Wlodzimierz. 201 SUMMIT VIEW DR STE 10 37027 #759-01-1982 L1996 **HMP** *020

TABER, Richard Potter. ■ 37027 #035-45-1948 L1954 **PD** *071

TALLENT, Marion Beverly. 1025 BEECH TREE LN, MARION B TALLENT 37027 #055-01-1968 L1975 **EM** *020 †85 ‡

TANG, Yi-Wei. ■ 37027 #243-16-1982 **MM** *100

TANNENBAUM, Jerome S. 5200 VIRGINIA WAY 37027 #047-05-1976 L1976 **NEP IM** *030 †20

TATE MOORE, Tiffanie Lavo. ■ 37027 #047-07-2000 L2007 **OBG** *020

TAYLOR, Dean Gates. 3 MARYLAND FARMS, ASSOCIATED PATHOLOGISTS 37027 #041-01-1965 L1972 **PTH** *020 †50 ‡

TAYLOR, Rebecca J. 343 FRANKLIN RD, STE 204 37027 #027-01-1996 L1997 **OPH** *020 †35

TEMPLETON, John Waggoner. 5301 VIRGINIA WAY, ASSOCIATED PATHOLOGISTS 37027 #047-06-1965 L1966 **PTH** *062 †50 ‡

TEODOROVIC, Dusan S. ■ 37027 #957-02-1985 L1994 **IM EM** *071

THATI, Arunadevi Amara. ■ 37027 #495-57-1980 L2002 **FM** *020 †18

THOMASON, Ronald Wayne. 201 SUMMIT VIEW DR 37027 #047-06-1990 L1990 **PTH** *020 †50

THOMISON, John B. 5301 VIRGINIA WAY, # 320 37027 #047-05-1944 L1944 **ATP** *071 †50

THOMISON, John Brown, Jr. 5301 VIRGINIA WAY, ASSOCIATED PATHOLOGISTS 37027 #047-05-1974 L1978 **PTH** *020 †50 ‡

THOMISON, Rena M. 5301 VIRGINIA WAY, ASSOCIATED PATHOLOGISTS 37027 #001-02-1977 L1978 **PTH** *020 †50 ‡

THOMPSON, Afua Yesi. ■ 37027 #020-02-2005 L2005 **DR** *012

TURNER, James Herbert. ■ 37027 #004-01-1952 L1991 **P** *020

VANDERPOOL, David Martin. 5409 MARYLAND WAY STE 11 37027 #048-15-1987 L1992 **GS VS** *020 †85

VARNADO, Carol Elizabeth. 6910 MOORES LN 37027 #422-01-1986 L2006 **FM** *020 †18 ‡

VASTBINDER, Earl Edward. ■ 37027 #038-40-1961 L1976 **ADL PD** *071 †55

WAHID, Zia U. ■ 37027 #704-01-1984 L1989 **P** *020 †75

WAHL, Robert Wilhelm. 5301 VIRGINIA WAY, ASSOCIATED PATHOLOGISTS 37027 #019-02-1968 L1975 **PTH PCP** *020 †50 ‡

WALPOLE, Howard T, Jr. 1195 OLD HICKORY BLVD, HEART GROUP PLLC 37027 #012-01-1981 L1983 **CD** *020 †20

WARNER, Harrison F. 5301 VIRGINIA WAY, ASSOCIATED PATHOLOGISTS 37027 #047-05-1994 L2006 **DMP** *020 †50 ‡

WEARNER, Neal Elwood. 5301 VIRGINIA WAY, ASSOCIATED PATHOLOGISTS 37027 #005-12-1973 L1986 **PTH** *062 †50 ‡

WEEKS, Libby Ann. ■ 37027 #020-02-1992 L1993 **P** *020 †75

WEI, Jian. ■ 37027 #243-69-1986 L2004 **FM** *020 †18

WELCH, Derek Christopher. 5301 VIRGINIA WAY, ASSOCIATED PATHOLOGISTS 37027 #047-05-2000 L2002 **PTH** *020 †50 ‡

WHITFIELD, Thos C Rye, Jr. 343 FRANKLIN RD 37027 #047-06-1977 L1977 **GP** *020 †16

WILLIAMS, Bryan Jeffrey. ■ 37027 #028-03-2003 L2005 **PCC** *012 †20

WILLIAMS, Carmen Denise. 105 WESTPARK DR STE 200 37027 #047-07-1994 L1998 **IM** *020

WILLIAMS, Patricia. 343 FRANKLIN RD STE 210 37027 #035-06-1993 L1999 **PD** *020 †55

WILSON, Ronald Eugene. 343 FRANKLIN RD, STE 200 37027 #047-05-1981 L1982 **N** *020 †75

WOLFE-SIDBERRY, Nancy A. 5046 THOROUGHBRED LN 37027 #047-07-1985 L1986 **FM** *020 †18 ‡

WRAY, Everett Bassett, II. 1195 OLD HICKORY BLVD, HEART GROUP PLLC 37027 #055-01-1972 L2000 **CD IM** *020 †20

WRIGHT, Amy Elizabeth. 5301 VIRGINIA WAY, ASSOCIATED PATHOLOGISTS 37027 #047-05-1995 L1997 **PTH FOP** *062 †50 ‡

YESUS, Yohannes Wolde. 5301 VIRGINIA WAY, STE 320 37027 #366-01-1968 L2000 **PTH HEM** *020 †50 ‡

YOUNG, Pampee. ■ 37027 #048-12-1998 L2003 **PTH** *100 †50

ZENKER, Mark Andrew. 1195 OLD HICKORY BLVD, HEART GROUP PLLC 37027 #016-45-1989 L1990 **IM CD** *020 †20

ZIEBEL, Dana Suzanne. ■ 37027 #035-15-1981 L1981 **OBG** *020 †30

BRIGHTON – TIPTON

ARMOUR, Karen Ann. 39 W WOODLAWN AVE 38011 #028-46-1988 L1990 **PHP** *020 †18

COOK, Buffy Jay. 7615 HIGHWAY 51 S 38011 #047-06-1998 L1999 **FM** *020 †18

CRAIG, Michael Scott. 1880 OLD HIGHWAY 51 S, STE C 38011 #047-06-1996 L1997 **FM** *020 †18

JONES, Clay Voyne. 39 W WOODLAWN AVE, STE 200 38011 #047-06-1975 L1975 **GS** *020

BRISTOL – SULLIVAN

ADAMS, Wesley Frazier. 2901 W STATE ST 37620 #012-01-1974 L1978 **OBG** *020

AGUIRRE, Dennis Manuel. 3183 W STATE ST, MANAGEMENT CENTER 37620 #049-01-1975 L1982 **AN** *020 †05

ALTMAN, Benjamin. 1 MEDICAL PARK BLVD, MEDICAL CTR 37620 #035-15-1989 L1995 **FM** *020 †18

AMIN, Fazia. 1 MEDICAL PARK BLVD, STE 350W 37620 #704-21-1996 L2002 **IM** *100 †20

ARNOLD, Walter Davis, Jr. 210 MEMORIAL DR, HEALING HANDS HEALTH CENTE 37620 #036-07-1994 L2006 **IM** *020 †20

ASTIN, William David. 308 8TH ST 37620 #422-01-1988 L1992 **FM** *020 †18

AUSTIN, Rebekah Crump. 1 MEDICAL PARK BLVD 37620 #036-05-1998 L2004 **NS** *020

BAILEY, Lawrence Delmore. 1 MEDICAL PARK BLVD 37620 #051-04-1983 L1990 **GE IM** *020 †20

BANDEIAN, John J, Jr. 3169 W STATE ST 37620 #024-01-1973 L1980 **GS** *020 †85,65

BARKER, Randall Forrest. 1 MEDICAL PARK BLVD 37620 #047-06-1991 L1993 **DR** *020 †80

BARNEWOLT, Brien Alfred. 1 MEDICAL PARK BLVD 37620 #016-06-1987 L1988 **EM** *020 †16

BARON, Michael B. 271 MEDICAL PARK BLVD 37620 #035-06-1971 L1996 **PUD CCM** *020 †20

BASHAM, Christopher M. 1 MEDICAL PARK BLVD 37620 #051-01-1999 L1999 **FM** *020 †18

BATTLE, James Wayne, III. 225 MIDWAY MEDICAL PARK 37620 #047-20-2002 L2007 **OPH** *100

BEASEY, Matthew Dean. 271 MEDICAL PARK BLVD, P.C. 37620 #020-12-1994 L2000 **END** *020 †20,55

BECH PEDERSEN, Charlotte. 208 MEDICAL PARK BLVD, ETSU FAMILY PHYSICIANS OF 37620 #297-01-2001 L2005 **FM** *100

BECHTEL, Jack T, Jr. 1 MEDICAL PARK BLVD 37620 #012-05-1974 L1980 **PTH** *020 †50

BECKNER, David C. 1 MEDICAL PARK BLVD, CARDIOVASCULAR ASSOCIATES 37620 #055-01-1991 L1999 **IM** *020 †20

■ = Address Information Privacy Protected

BEESON, Broadus Monroe. 28 MIDWAY ST 37620 #036-05-1977 L1983 **FM OM** *020 †18

BHARTI, Rachna. ■ 37620 #496-07-2003 L2005 **FP** *012

BIBLE, Michael W. 271 MEDICAL PARK BLVD 37620 #047-06-1976 L1976 **RHU IM** *020 †20 ‡

BIRKITT, Glenn H, Jr. 249 MIDWAY ST 37620 #051-04-1985 L1990 **GS** *020 †85

BLANTON, Frank S, Jr. ■ 37620 #051-01-1952 L1960 **GS TS** *071 †85

BLANTON, Robert Hamilton. 350 BLOUNTVILLE HWY, STE 201 37620 #051-04-1989 L1992 **GS** *020 †85

BLOW, Alton Jos, Jr. 271 MEDICAL PARK BLVD 37620 #050-02-1979 L2004 **ON HEM** *020 †20

BLOW, Joanne Prusiecki. 201 FOREST HILLS DR, HOLSTON MEDICAL GROUP, PC 37620 #048-14-1988 L2004 **PD** *020 †55

BOLICK, Charles Arthur. 240 MEDICAL PARK BLVD, STE 3000 37620 #036-01-1987 L1994 **FM** *020 †18

BORSCH, Mark Andrew. 1 MEDICAL PARK BLVD, CARDIOVASCULAR ASSOCIATES 37620 #038-40-1981 L1996 **CD IC** *020 †20

BOWLING, Gretchen Hawkins. ■ 37620 #048-15-2007 **FP** *012

BOWMAN, James Howard. 1 MEDICAL PARK BLVD, STE 200 37620 #047-06-1975 L1975 **IM** *020 †20

BOYLE, Gary Clayton. 2901 W STATE ST 37620 #051-01-1975 L1979 **OBG** *020

BRADLEY, Michael Barton. 3185 W STATE ST, STE 2010 37620 #017-20-1993 L1997 **OPH** *020 †35

BRASFIELD, Jimmy C. 320 BRISTOL WEST BLVD, # 2 37620 #047-06-1976 L1976 **NS** *020 †55,25

BRINKLEY, Billy Booth. 1 MEDICAL PARK BLVD 37620 #047-06-1947 L1947 **OBS** *071

BROCKMYRE, Andrew Peter. 240 MEDICAL PARK BLVD, STE 3000 37620 #025-12-1994 L1997 **FM** *020 †18

BROGLIO, Anthony Lee. 350 BLOUNTVILLE HWY, ASSOCIATES P C 37620 #038-06-1968 L1977 **U** *020 †95

BROWN, Andrew Nathan. 208 MEDICAL PARK BLVD, OF BRIS 37620 #422-01-2004 **FM** *100 †18

BUNNING, Jeffrey William. 3185 W STATE ST STE 2010, MOUNTAIN EMPIRE EYE PHYSIC 37620 #055-01-2000 L2004 **OPH** *020 †35

BURKE, Stephen Matthew. 240 MEDICAL PARK BLVD, STE 3000 37620 #041-02-1998 L2005 **FM** *020 †18

BURRESS, Jonathan. 1 MEDICAL PARK BLVD, STE 458W 37620 #055-75-2000, ▲ L2006 **CD** *020 †20

BURT, Jacquelyn Clark. ■ 37620 #027-01-1987 L1996 **FM** *020 †18

BURT, James Travis. 1 MEDICAL PARK BLVD, STE 400E 37620 #027-01-1987 L1995 **NS** *020 †18

BUTTERWORTH, Jackson, Jr. 350 BLOUNTVILLE HWY, STE 105 37620 #012-01-1964 L1971 **U** *020 †95

BYERS, John Gordon, Jr. 1 MEDICAL PARK BLVD, 5TH FL 37620 #051-04-1968 L1977 **PUD CCM** *071 †20

CALCOTE, Claude Mc Ghee. 249 MIDWAY MEDICAL PARK 37620 #012-05-1961 L1968 **GS** *071 †85

CARNELL, Alan Gene. 235 MEDICAL PARK BLVD 37620 #011-04-1984 L2000 **GE IM** *020 †20

CASSEDY, Kelly James. 3053 W STATE ST 37620 #038-41-1987 L1992 **DR** *020 †80

CASSETTA, Brian Damian. 1 MEDICAL PARK BLVD, STE 200E 37620 #010-02-1981 L1984 **IM FM** *020 †20

CHANDLER, John M, Jr. 1 MEDICAL PARK BLVD, STE 300 37620 #047-06-1976 L1977 **ORS** *020 †40

CLARITY, Gregory Edward. 208 MEDICAL PARK BLVD 37620 #047-20-1993 L1994 **FM** *040 †18

CLAYBROOK, Harry Phillip. 350 STEELES RD 37620 #047-06-1996 L1999 **MPD** *020 †20,55

COOGAN, Joan C. 1918 W STATE ST 37620 #016-11-1971 L1988 **PTH BBK** *071 †50

CORRELL, Geoffrey Grattan. 308 8TH ST 37620 #045-04-1994 L1995 **FM** *020 †18 ‡

COUCH, Chad Tillman. 350 BLOUNTVILLE HWY, ASSOCIATES P C 37620 #012-01-1989 L2000 **U** *020 †95

COWAN, Bennett Young. 28 MIDWAY ST, MICHAEL W BIBLE MD 37620 #024-01-1945 L1951 **IM** *071

CRABTREE, Amanda Marie. ■ 37620 #047-20-2005 L2008 **FP** *012

CRAWFORD, Robert Gunn. 208 MEDICAL PARK BLVD, ETSU FAMILY PHY OF BRISTOL 37620 #654-01-1999 L2003 **FM** *100

CROSS, Andrew Monroe, Jr. 1 MEDICAL PARK BLVD, CARDIOVASCULAR ASSOCIATES 37620 #035-08-1987 L2006 **CD** *020 †20

CULP, John Stephen. 208 MEDICAL PARK BLVD 37620 #001-02-1980 L1986 **FM FPG** *040 †18

DAVIS, Alan Dean. 1 MEDICAL PARK BLVD 37620 #047-06-1975 L1980 **PO** *035

DEWEY, Carol Ann. 522 ALABAMA ST, WELLSPRING 37620 #047-06-1975 L1976 **FM EM** *071 †16,18 ‡

DIZON, Louis R. 1 MEDICAL PARK BLVD 37620 #748-10-1991 L2001 **PM** *020

EARLY, James Lawrence. ■ 37621 #047-06-1971 L1971 **IM** *071

EMORY, Theresa Swain. 1 MEDICAL PARK BLVD 37620 #051-07-1989 L1999 **PTH** *020 †50

ESTES, Terrell Carroll. 1 MEDICAL PARK BLVD 37620 #036-05-1971 L1977 **DR** *020 †80

FAZEL, Farid. 208 MEDICAL PARK BLVD 37620 #517-05-1994 L2004 **FM** *100

FEIERABEND, Raymond H, Jr. 208 MEDICAL PARK BLVD, ETSU FAM PHYS OF BRISTOL 37620 #021-01-1975 L1978 **FM** *040 †18

FERGUSON, Jere Wayne. 1 MEDICAL PARK BLVD 37620 #047-06-1973 L1973 **PTH** *020 †50

FINCH, Shannon Michael. 240 MEDICAL PARK BLVD, STE 3000 37620 #045-01-1998 L1999 **FM** *020 †18

FINCHER, John Albert, Jr. 3053 W STATE ST 37620 #001-02-1974 L1977 **RO** *020 †80

FLEENOR, Michael Ralph. 260 MIDWAY MEDICAL PARK, STE 100 37620 #051-04-1979 L1988 **ORS** *020 †40

FLETCHER, Terry Michael. 3053 W STATE ST 37620 #012-01-1993 L2004 **DR** *100 †55,80

FORREST, Terry L. 1 MEDICAL PARK BLVD 37620 #017-20-1986 L1997 **CD IM** *020 †20

FOSTER, Richard Warren. 1 MEDICAL PARK BLVD 37620 #051-07-1980 L1987 **DR** *020 †80

FRY, Stephen Wm. 1 MEDICAL PARK BLVD 37620 #038-40-1987 L1996 **GE** *020 †20

GALLOWAY, Roger Fowler. 1 MEDICAL PARK BLVD, STE 150W 37620 #047-06-1973 L1974 **OM** *020

GANGWER, Matthew Morgan. 28 MIDWAY ST, BRISTOL FAMILY MEDICAL CEN 37620 #055-01-1982 L1989 **FM** *020 †18 ‡

GANTT, Pickens Allison. 1 MEDICAL PARK BLVD 37620 #012-01-1973 L1981 **GYN REN** *020 †30

GARCHAR, Susan. 240 MEDICAL PARK BLVD, STE 3600 37620 #038-44-1988 L1997 **IM** *020 †20

GENTRY, Richard Ryan. 3053 W STATE ST, BLUE RIDGE RADIOLOGY PC 37620 #045-01-1979 L1992 **DR** *020 †80

GERLOCK, Gregory Alan. 1 MEDICAL PARK BLVD, BRISTOL REGIONAL MED CTR 37620 #012-01-1989 L1990 **FM** *020 †18

GIBBON, Bruce Nelson. 1 MEDICAL PARK BLVD, BRISTOL REGIONAL MEDICAL C 37620 #047-20-1992 L1994 **EM** *020 †16

GINTHER, Jeffrey Paul. 246 MIDWAY MEDICAL PARK 37620 #051-04-1978 L1979 **FM FPG** *020 †18

GLASGOW, Robert Morris. 260 MIDWAY ST STE 2G 37620 #047-06-1955 L1956 **D** *071 †15

GOLDSTEIN, Marilyn Jean. 1 MEDICAL PARK BLVD 37620 #017-20-1988 L1998 **AN** *020 †05

GORRELL, Alan Louis. 1 MEDICAL PARK BLVD # 208E 37620 #020-12-1972 L1980 **OBG** *020 †30

GREEAR, Fred Bonham, Jr. 1 MEDICAL PARK BLVD, STE 200E 37620 #051-01-1961 L1967 **IM** *020 †20

GREEN, Douglass Woodson. 1 MEDICAL PARK BLVD, STE 450W 37620 #051-04-1979 L1984 **NEP IM** *020 †20

GREEN, John Adair. 1 MEDICAL PARK BLVD, STE 450W 37620 #051-04-1975 L1978 **IM** *020 †20

GREEN, Thomas Walton, Jr. 1 MEDICAL PARK BLVD, STE 450W 37620 #051-04-1971 L1976 **IM** *020 †20

GREEN, Waverly S, Jr. 1 MEDICAL PARK BLVD STE 4 37620 #023-07-1950 L1959 **IM** *071

GREENE, Thomas Conley. 350 BLOUNTVILLE HWY, STE 201 37620 #047-06-1974 L1975 **GS** *020 †85

GRENVIK, Stefan Jan. 3183 W STATE ST, MANAGEMENT CENTER 37620 #041-12-1989 L1993 **AN PME** *020 †05

GRIFFITH, John Gregory. 350 BLOUNTVILLE HWY, ASSOCIATES P C 37620 #039-01-1988 L1994 **IM** *020 †95

GRUNSTRA, Bernard Paul. 350 STEELES RD 37620 #011-03-1985 L1991 **IM PD** *020 †20,55

GUADAGNOLI, Donald A. 663 HIGHWAY 126 STE 1, HIGHLANDS WELLMONT HLTH NE 37620 #010-01-1982 L2002 **OBG MDM** *030 †30

GWALTNEY, David Nelson. 1 MEDICAL PARK BLVD, STE 250W 37620 #004-01-1978 L1984 **GS VS** *020 †85

HALL, Jonathan Craig. 1 MEDICAL PARK BLVD 37620 #012-01-2001 L2005 **OBG** *020

HANOR, Steven Richard. 1 MEDICAL PARK BLVD, STE 200E 37620 #047-05-1980 L1983 **IM** *020 †20

HARKLEROAD, Alfred L, II. 240 MEDICAL PARK BLVD, STE 3800 37620 #047-06-1980 L1980 **FM** *020 †18

HARMON, Deana Lynn. 350 STEELES RD, UNIT ONE 37620 #055-75-2003, ▲ L2007 *020

HARRIS, Erin Elizabeth. ■ 37620 #047-20-2004 L2006 **FM** *020 †18

HARRIS, Kelley Brantley. 1 MEDICAL PARK BLVD, STE 450W 37620 #047-20-1991 L1992 **FM** *020 †18

HARRIS, Wesley Jackson. 249 MIDWAY MEDICAL PARK 37620 #048-12-1980 L1983 **OBG GS** *020 †30

HAWKINS, Andrew Frost. 1 MEDICAL PARK BLVD 37620 #047-06-1991 L2002 **MPD EM** *020 †55,20

HAYES, Joseph Steven. 1220 VOLUNTEER PKWY, MED ONE 37620 #045-01-1972 L1975 **EM FM** *020 †18

HEDDERICH, Ronald L. 1 MEDICAL PARK BLVD 37620 #048-12-1987 L1998 **AN** *020 †05

HINES, Ethan William. 208 MEDICAL PARK BLVD, OF BRIS 37620 #025-07-2007 FP *012

HOFFER, Phillip Franklin. 133 QUEENSGATE, 1 MEDICAL PARK BLVD 37620 #045-01-1974 L1982 **AN CCM** *020 †05

HOFFNUNG, Jack Meyer. 1 MEDICAL PARK BLVD 37620 #047-05-1979 L1984 **R** *020 †80

HOVIOUS, John R, III. 245 MIDWAY MEDICAL PARK, STE 200 37620 #047-06-1979 L1981 **PD** *020 †55

HUTCHISON, John E, Jr. 1 MEDICAL PARK BLVD 37620 #039-05-1984 L1989 **DR** *020 †80

IQBAL, Sharjeel. 208 MEDICAL PARK BLVD 37620 #704-04-2002 L2005 **FP** *012

ISTFAN, Pierre. 1 MEDICAL PARK BLVD, CARDIOVASCULAR ASSOCIATES 37620 #055-02-1985 L1991 **CD IC** *020 †20 ‡

JACKSON, George Hagan. 3183 W STATE ST, STE 1201 37620 #020-02-1992 L1996 **N** *020 †75

JAYNE, J Lawrence, Jr. 350 BLOUNTVILLE HWY, BRISTOL SURGICAL CENTER IN 37620 #047-06-1973 L1973 **AN PME** *020 †05

JEWELL, Neal Anthony. 1 MEDICAL PARK BLVD, STE 300E 37620 #028-34-1968 L1982 **ORS** *020 †40

JOHNSON, John Clifford. 225 MIDWAY MEDICAL PARK 37620 #047-05-1969 L1969 **OPH** *020 †35

JOHNSTONE, William Henry. 3053 W STATE ST 37620 #020-02-1978 L1983 **DR** *020 †80

KARIMPOUR, Farshad. 208 MEDICAL PARK BLVD, ETSU FAMILY PHYSICIANS OF 37620 #517-12-2001 L2007 **FP** *012

KENNEDY, Christopher John. 1 MEDICAL PARK BLVD, CARDIOVASCULAR ASSOCIATES 37620 #016-42-1979 L1987 **CD IM** *020 †20

KITTS, Thomas Alan. 1 MEDICAL PARK BLVD 37620 #047-06-1976 L1978 *020

KNICKERBOCKER, Fred Ray. 260 MIDWAY ST STE 100 37620 #012-01-1972 L1977 **ORS** *020 †40

KOPITZKE, Steven Dale. 1220 VOLUNTEER PKWY 37620 #005-12-1980 L1984 **FM CCM** *020

KURRE, Joseph H, Jr. 249 MIDWAY MEDICAL PARK, SURGICAL ASSOC, PC 37620 #020-02-1969 L1974 **GS** *020 †85

LADY, Michael Byron. 1220 VOLUNTEER PKWY 37620 #047-06-1975 L1976 **GP EM** *020

LAPIS, James Lawrence. 235 MEDICAL PARK BLVD 37620 #048-12-1973 L1978 **GE** *020 †20

LEVINE, Jeffrey. 235 MEDICAL PARK BLVD 37620 #035-15-1987 L1999 **GE** *020 †20

LINK, Nelson Edward. 350 BLOUNTVILLE HWY, STE 205 37620 #051-01-1963 L1971 **FPS PS** *071 †45

LITTON, Frederick Mitchel. 2124 VOLUNTEER PKWY, STE B 37620 #051-04-1974 L2004 **FM** *020 †18

LIZARRALDE, German. 271 MEDICAL PARK BLVD 37620 #264-04-1959 L2005 **IM END** *020 †28,20

LOONEY, Jeffrey Ray. 350 STEELES RD, UNIT ONE 37620 #047-06-1994 L1997 **OBG** *020 †30

LORIA, Elvira Loueres. 1 MEDICAL PARK BLVD, STE 450W 37620 #748-01-1976 L2000 **NEP PTH** *020 †50,20

LORIO, Morgan Packard. 240 MEDICAL PARK BLVD, STE 2700 37620 #021-06-1988 L2001 **ORS HS** *020 †40

LUNA, James Andrew. 1 MEDICAL PARK BLVD 37620 #047-06-1991 L1992 **EM** *020 †16

LYNCH, Joanne C Miller. 947 VOLUNTEER PKWY 37620 #047-06-1958 L1963 **GP** *071

MACFARLANE, Robert Iain. ■ 37620 #665-01-2003 L2006 **AN** *020

MAGGARD, Brian Lee. 208 MEDICAL PARK BLVD 37620 #051-01-1997 L1999 **FM** *020 †18

MAI, Jonathan Vinh. ■ 37620 #050-02-2002 L2006 **DR** *020 †80

MAKRES, Thomas Duncan. 320 STEELES RD 37620 #047-06-1974 L1976 **PD** *020 †55

MANCINI, Jean Marie. 1 MEDICAL PARK BLVD, STE 450W 37620 #047-20-2001 L2004 **IM** *020

MARSHALL, John Morgan. 1 MEDICAL PARK BLVD, STE 400E 37620 #020-02-1987 L1991 **PM** *020 †60

MARTIN, Frederick Allen. 350 STEELES RD 37620 #047-06-1989 L2001 **FM** *020 †18

MC CARTT, Alan Noe. 225 MIDWAY MEDICAL PARK 37620 #047-06-1982 L1983 **OPH** *020 †35

MC CLINTIC, Eugene C. 249 MIDWAY MEDICAL PARK 37620 #001-02-1988 L1993 **GS** *020 †85
MC ILWAIN, Wm Anthony. 7 S BRIARCLIFF RD 37620 #047-06-1974 L1974 **ORS OSS** *020 †40
MC KAY, Robert Douglas. 3183 W STATE ST, MANAGEMENT CENTER 37620 #041-02-1972 L1990 **AN CCM** *020 †05
MC MURRAY, John Mark. 3053 W STATE ST 37620 #027-01-1980 L1982 **DR** *020 †80
MC QUEARY, Jeffrey Allen. 350 STEELES RD, UNIT ONE 37620 #005-12-1992 L1996 **OBG** *020 †30
MC SHARRY, Roger John. 271 MEDICAL PARK BLVD 37620 #024-07-1984 L1996 **PCC CCM** *020 †20
MENDREK, Mitchell James. 1 MEDICAL PARK BLVD 37620 #001-02-2001 L2006 **DR** *020 †80
MERCER, Timothy E. 350 BLOUNTVILLE HWY 37620 #005-12-1985 L2006 **AN** *020 †05
MILLER, Calvin Lewis. 249 MIDWAY MEDICAL PARK 37620 #051-01-1970 L1985 **OPH** *020 †35 ‡
MITORAJ, Thomas Edward. 212 MIDWAY ST 37620 #020-02-1988 L1991 **PD** *020 †55
MONTEITH, Linda Gail. 1 MEDICAL PARK BLVD 37620 #036-08-1991 L1994 **EM** *020 †16
MOONEY, Neil Francis. 2320 VOLUNTEER PKWY 37620 #028-34-1962 L1966 **GP OM** *030
MOORE, Jason Brent. 208 MEDICAL PARK BLVD, ETSU FAMILY PHYSICIANS/BRI 37620 #038-40-1999 L2002 **FM** *020 †18
MOORE, Sharon Wyatt. 1241 VOLUNTEER PKWY, STE 950 37620 #047-05-1985 L1987 **PHM IM** *050
MORGAN, Steven Wesley. 3183 W STATE ST, STE 1201 37620 #051-04-1973 L1981 **N P** *075
MORIN, David Jos. 1958 W STATE ST 37620 #050-02-1984 L1987 **IM** *020 †20
MORRISON, Philip Hapworth. ■ 37620 #051-04-1960 L1965 **GP GPM** *075
MUELLER, Robert Alan. 1 MEDICAL PARK BLVD, STE 150W 37620 #045-01-1981 L1983 **OM EM** *020 †18,16
MULLINS, Danny Arthur. 1 MEDICAL PARK BLVD, STE 300E 37620 #051-01-1993 L2007 **ORS** *020 †40
NEAL, Gary Wayne. 260 MIDWAY MEDICAL PARK, STE 2G 37620 #047-06-1982 L1985 **IM** *062 †20
NEALE, John Carlysle, III. 26 MIDWAY ST 37620 #047-06-1962 L1962 **P** *071 †70
NELSON, Shawn Keith. 3183 W STATE ST, STE 1201 37620 #056-06-1996 L2000 **N** *020 †75
NICLEY, Floyd Edward. 1 MEDICAL PARK BLVD, STE 200 37620 #047-06-1955 L1955 **IM** *071
NILSON, Nicole Marie. ■ 37620 #007-02-2002 L2007 **PTH** *100 †50
ODUM, Brett Carter. 240 MEDICAL PARK BLVD, STE 3000 37620 #051-01-2000 L2003 **FM** *020 †18
OLDS, Shelby Gilmer. 350 STEELES RD 37620 #047-20-2000 L2003 **MPD** *020
OLMSTED, Mary Catherine. 207 ROSCOMMON DR 37620 #021-06-1983 L1983 **P** *020 †75
ORCHARD, Kenneth Alan. 350 CARLTON RD 37620 #033-05-1990 L1996 *020
OVERBAY, Mark Richard. 308 8TH ST, MIDTOWN MEDICAL CENTER 37620 #047-20-1990 L1993 **FM** *020 †18
OWENS, Dia Patrice. 208 MEDICAL PARK BLVD 37620 #047-20-2002 L2004 **FM** *020 †18
PATEL, Ashvin Ambalal. 26 MIDWAY ST 37620 #045-23-1972 L1982 **P** *020 †75
PATTON, Suzanne Elizabeth. 271 MEDICAL PARK BLVD 37620 #036-07-1988 L2005 **HO IM** *020 †20
PENNY, Richard Mortimer. 1 MEDICAL PARK BLVD 37620 #020-12-1972 L1988 **AN** *020 †05
PETERS, Jennifer Carlita. 208 MEDICAL PARK BLVD, ETSU FAMILY PHYSICIANS OF 37620 #422-01-2003 L2003 **FM** *020
POWELL, Stephanie Johnson. 1 MEDICAL PARK BLVD, STE 450W 37620 #027-01-1995 L1998 **IM** *020 †20
POWERS, Matthew L. ■ 37621 #048-13-1984 L2007 **DR MSR** *020 †80
ROLEN, Alvin Curry. 249 MIDWAY MEDICAL PARK 37620 #047-06-1958 L1968 **OBG** *071 †30
ROWELL, Michael Dwayne. 350 BLOUNTVILLE HWY, STE 201 37620 #038-45-1986 L1991 **GS VS** *020 †85
RUDD, Eugene Gregory. PO BOX 7500 37621 #045-01-1977 L1997 **OBG** *030 †30
RUSSELL, David Paul. 1 MEDICAL PARK BLVD 37620 #047-06-1986 L1988 **OBG** *020
SAMUEL, Dennis C, Jr. 350 STEELES RD, UNIT 1 37620 #051-04-1992 L1996 **OBG** *020 †30
SCHARFSTEIN, Benjamin S. 350 BLOUNTVILLE HWY, STE 201 37620 #047-06-1998 L2000 **GS VS** *020 †85
SCHERMER, William John. 3183 W STATE ST, STE 1102 37620 #051-04-1976 L1982 **D IM** *020 †15
SCHRENKER, James Hollies. 240 MEDICAL PARK BLVD, STE 3800 37620 #017-20-1993 L1994 **FM** *020 †18
SCRUGGS, Katherine Lynn. 350 STEELES RD, UNIT ONE 37620 #051-04-1992 L1997 **OBG** *020 †30
SHAHBAZI, Michael Farzin. 225 MIDWAY MEDICAL PARK 37620 #047-06-1985 L1985 **OPH** *020 †35
SHELTON, Karen Eller. 1 MEDICAL PARK BLVD 37620 #051-01-1993 L1997 **OBG** *020 †30
SHERRILL, John Doke, III. 607 HOLSTON AVE 37620 #001-06-1984 L1986 **FM** *020 †18
SIKORA, Frank Steven. 1 MEDICAL PARK BLVD, STE 204E 37620 #038-40-1958 L1963 **AN CD** *071 †05
SMITH, William David. 3183 W STATE ST, MANAGEMENT CENTER 37620 #055-01-1982 L1986 **AN PME** *020 †05
SPARKS, David Alan. 1 MEDICAL PARK BLVD 37620 #004-01-1982 L2002 **R NRN** *020 †80
SPEAR, John Michael. 235 MEDICAL PARK BLVD 37620 #011-03-1979 L1982 **GE IM** *020 †20
SPILLETT, Andrew Patrick. 3053 W STATE ST 37620 #025-07-1993 L2003 **DR** *020 †80
STANLEY, Gail Lynn. 1 MEDICAL PARK BLVD, WELLMONT INFECTIOUS DISEAS 37620 #001-02-1983 L1989 **ID IM** *020 †20
STEVENS, David Lynn. PO BOX 7500 37621 #020-02-1977 L1996 **FM** *020 †18
STRADER, L Dow. ■ 37620 #016-11-1958 L1977 **TS GS** *071 †85,90
STRELETZ, Patricia M C. 208 MEDICAL PARK BLVD 37620 #041-02-1970 L1974 **OS** *074
SUH, Pyung J. 1220 VOLUNTEER PKWY 37620 #583-01-1992 L1995 **FM** *020 †18
SWANK, Melissa Jane. ■ 37620 #041-07-1992 *075
SWEITZER, Donald Edward. 350 BLOUNTVILLE HWY, STE 205 37620 #012-01-1983 L1992 **PS GS** *020 †85,65
TAGERT, Bert Edwin. 1 MEDICAL PARK BLVD # 300E, OFFICE PLAZA 37620 #011-03-1985 L1988 **OAR OSM** *020 †40
TESTERMAN, John Robt. 240 MEDICAL PARK BLVD, STE 2700 37620 #012-01-1979 L1995 **ORS** *020 †40
THOMAS, Lynette Elizabeth. 1 MEDICAL PARK BLVD 37620 #047-07-2000 L2000 **IM** *020 †20
THOMPSON, David Eugene. 1 MEDICAL PARK BLVD, STE 200E 37620 #036-05-1986 L1988 **IM** *020 †20
THOMPSON, Linda Ruth. 115 EASTSIDE DR, LRT CONSULTING LLC 37620 #051-01-1966 L1982 **P** *020 †75
THORNSBERRY, Michael Dean. ■ 37620 #028-03-1983 L1995 **OPH** *020 †18
TOWNSEND, Thos Edward, Jr. 208 MEDICAL PARK BLVD, DBA ETSU FAMILY 37620 #004-01-1973 L1991 **FM** *020 †18

TURNER, Kenneth E, Sr. 1 MEDICAL PARK BLVD, BRISTOL REG MED CTR 37620 #047-20-1992 L1995 **EM** *020 †16
VALLEY, Marc Alan. 3183 W STATE ST STE 1101, CENTER 37620 #005-12-1984 L2004 **PME PMM** *020 †05
VANN, Robert Lee. ■ 37620 #036-05-1945 L1973 **PD** *071 †55
WALLEN, Neil. 933 HIGHWAY 126 37620 #011-03-1985 L1987 **A IM** *020 †20,03
WAYNE, Stephen Leon. 3183 W STATE ST, STE 1201 37620 #001-02-1993 L1998 **N OS** *020 †75
WEIR, William Strickland. 3183 W STATE ST, STE 1201 37620 #016-06-1963 L1990 **N IM** *071 †75
WHILES, Rick James. 240 MEDICAL PARK BLVD, STE 3600 37620 #038-43-1996 L2002 **MPD** *020,55
WHISNANT, William Howard. 1 MEDICAL PARK BLVD 37620 #036-01-1973 L1974 **R DR** *020 †80
WHITMAN, Thomas Lisle. 1 MEDICAL PARK BLVD, OFFICE PLAZA, 300-E 37620 #051-01-1994 L2000 **ORS** *020 †40
WIKE, Sidney Alfred. 249 MIDWAY MEDICAL PARK 37620 #036-05-1960 L1964 **OPH** *071 †35
WIKE, Sudie Doggett. ■ 37620 #036-05-1960 L1964 **OS** *050
WILLIAMS, Douglas P. 3183 W STATE ST, STE 1201 37620 #038-44-1982 L1990 **N IM** *020 †20,75
WILLIAMS, John Frederic. 1 MEDICAL PARK BLVD STE 20 37620 #422-01-1997 L2000 **IM** *020 †20
WILLIAMS, Ronald Lee. 240 MEDICAL PARK BLVD, STE 3800 37620 #047-06-1981 L1984 **FM** *020 †18,16
WILSON, Earl Keith. 3183 W STATE ST, STE 1201 37620 #051-04-1976 L1981 **N** *020 †75
WIREMAN, Jonathan Ward. 1 MEDICAL PARK BLVD 37620 #020-12-1990 L1993 **EM** *020 †16
WOOD, Matthew W, Jr. 1 MEDICAL PARK BLVD, STE 400 37620 #047-06-1976 L1977 **NS** *020 †25
WOODARD, John Mark. 1 MEDICAL PARK BLVD, DEPT. OF EMERGENCY MED. 37620 #047-20-1992 L1995 **EM** *020 †16
WRIGHT, Kent Steven. 1 MEDICAL PARK BLVD, EMERGENCY DEPARTMENT 37620 #047-20-1996 L2001 **EM** *020 †16
ZAIDI, Sarfraz Ali. 1 MEDICAL PARK BLVD, CARDIOVASCULAR ASSOCIATES 37620 #704-01-1958 L1976 **CD IM** *020
ZICKLER, Roderick Paul. 350 BLOUNTVILLE HWY, STE 205-BRISTOL PROF. PARK 37620 #035-45-1985 L1996 **PS** *020 †65

BROWNSVILLE – HAYWOOD

BROOKS, Leonard Jos. 405 N DUPREE AVE 38012 #016-06-1955 L1970 **PHP OBG** *075
CARRERA, Rogelio L. 2545 N WASHINGTON AVE 38012 #847-04-1978 L1986 **FM EM** *020 †18
DOWLING, Clarey Reginald. 2569 N WASHINGTON AVE 38012 #064-01-1979 L1980 **FM** *020 †05
FLEENOR, John David. 2545 N WASHINGTON AVE, HAYWOOD PARK COMMUNITY HOS 38012 #047-06-1996 L1999 **IM** *020
GANDHI, Raja R. 2545 N WASHINGTON AVE, ATTN: GINGER SLOAN 38012 #495-85-1991 L2001 **IM** *020 †20
GLISSON, Jack James. 2545 N WASHINGTON AVE 38012 #305-01-1988 L1991 **IM PUD** *020 †20
HALE, Bobby Dee. ■ 38012 #047-06-1960 L1960 **PHP** *071
HARDISTER, Robert Edward. ■ 38012 #047-06-2006 **GS** *012
HINTON, Charles Leslie. 2454 N WASHINGTON AVE, ATTN: MEDICAL STAFF OFFICE 38012 #048-13-1986 L1993 **FM** *020 †18
MITCHELL, Robert Lee. 2545 N WASHINGTON AVE, MEDICAL STAFF OFFICE 38012 #047-06-1981 L1988 **PTH GP** *020 ‡
NWOKOLO, Ejikeme Uchenna. 1215 E COLLEGE ST, FIRSTCARE MEDICAL CENTER 38012 #690-04-1992 L2006 **IM** *020
ORUMA, David. 2545 N WASHINGTON AVE 38012 #690-03-1984 L2004 **IM** *020 †20
SPENCER, Donald Ray. 107 N LAFAYETTE AVE, SPENC CLNC 38012 #004-01-1970 L1975 **FM** *020
WALKER, Tracie Annette. 1215 E COLLEGE ST 38012 #047-06-1999 L2001 **IM** *020 †20
WHITE, Jerald Wayne. 2565 N WASHINGTON AVE 38012 #047-06-1972 L1974 **FM** *020
WILBURN-WREN, Kristie R. 2555 N WASHINGTON AVE, CENTER 38012 #047-20-1995 L2005 **OBG** *020 †30
ZANATY, Mostafa Kamel. 2545 N WASHINGTON AVE 38012 #915-02-1959 L1977 **FM** *071

BUCHANAN – HENRY

JONES, Joe Paul. ■ 38222 #047-06-1956 L1961 **AN** *071

BULLS GAP – GREENE

DOMAN, Mark Richard. PO BOX 188, BULLS GAP MED CTR 37711 #047-20-1985 L1991 **IM** *020 †20

BURNS – DICKSON

ELSON, Melvin Leslie. 4081 HIGHWAY 96 37029 #036-07-1969 L1971 **D** *020 †15
SMITH, Murray Wilton. 999 GIRL SCOUT RD 37029 #047-05-1963 L1969 **ADM IM** *020 †20

BUTLER – JOHNSON

HINDMAN, Michael Clark. ■ 37640 #016-11-1973 L1977 **CD IM** *020 †20

BYRDSTOWN – PICKETT

BEATY, Kenneth Dale. 8401 HIGHWAY 111, YRDSTOWN MEDICAL CENTER 38549 #047-06-1999 L2001 **FM** *020 †18 ‡
JORDAN, Charles E, III. 8401 HIGHWAY 111 38549 #038-40-1966 L1973 **OTO HNS** *020 †45 ‡
KING, Matthew Joel. 8401 HIGHWAY 111 38549 #047-06-1996 L2004 **MPD** *020 †20,55
KRETH, Timothy Kerwin. 8401 HIGHWAY 111 38549 #004-01-1980 L1982 **CD** *020 †20
MASON, Larry Michael. 8401 HIGHWAY 111 38549 #020-12-1973 L1982 *020

MC KINNEY, James D. 8401 HIGHWAY 111 38549 #001-02-1981 L1992 ORS *020 †40
SHAFFER, Jori Lynne. 8401 HIGHWAY 111, BYRDSTOWN MEDICAL CENTER 38549
#047-06-1998 L2000 MPD *020 †55,20

CAMDEN – BENTON

BERRY, Kenneth Dwayne. 30 E MAIN ST 38320 #047-06-2000 L2001 FM *020 †18 ‡
BOURNE, Robert Irl. 101 HOSPITAL DR 38320 #047-06-1955 L1956 GP *020
BUTTERWORTH, Joseph S. ■ 38320 #047-05-1952 L1952 GS AM *071
CARNEY, William Raymond. 175 HOSPITAL DR, CAMDEN GENERAL HOSPITAL 38320
#047-06-1999 L2000 FM *020 †18
HOLLINGSWORTH, Jason L. 186 HOSPITAL DR 38320 #047-07-1981 L1981 FM *020 †18 ‡
HORTON, Robert Leslie. ■ 38320 #047-06-1945 L1946 GP GS *071
VITUALLA, Agustin Varron. 135 HOSPITAL DR, BENTON MEDICAL CLINIC 38320
#748-11-1972 L1986 GS EM *020

CARTHAGE – SMITH

BARRIAULT, Ronald J. 158 HOSPITAL DR 37030 #064-01-1968 L1995 FM OM *020
BERNARDO, Wilfrido D L P. 130 LEBANON HWY, STE B 37030 #748-08-1969 L1978 GP *020
CRAFT, Alissa Anne. ■ 37030 #047-06-2002 L2006 OPH *020
DUCHASTEL, Paul Alexander. 104 ERVIN DR 37030 #067-04-1967 L1997 FM *071
DUKE, Roger Mackey. 107 HEALTH CARE DR, BLDG 3 37030 #047-20-1985 L1985
FM *030 †18 ‡
FARRAR, Henry Cheirs. 130 LEBANON HWY, STE B 37030 #047-06-1954 L1954 GS GP *085
JONES, Ernest Jos. 133 HOSPITAL DR, STE 200 37030 #047-07-1971 L1995 FM *020 †18
LAWRENCE, Thomas La Verne. 130 LEBANON HWY 37030 #038-40-1973 L1978
OTO FPS *020 †45
LYLES, Wm Dewayne, Jr. 74 LEBANON HWY 37030 #047-07-1984 L1986 FM *020
PETTY, David Gordon. 608 JACKSON AVE 37030 #047-05-1982 L1983 RHU *020 †20
ROY, Robert Gordon. 259 DIXON SPRINGS HWY, TANGLEWOOD MEDICAL CENTER 37030
#064-01-1982 L1999 GP EM *020
SMITH, Bowdoin Grayson. 9 MAGGART CIR 37030 #028-79-1986, ▲ L1987 GP *020
SMITH, Sammy Mac. 160 HOSPITAL DR 37030 #021-05-1970 L1978 ORS *072
TURNER, Larry Lowell. 130 LEBANON HWY, STE B 37030 #028-34-1969 L1978
GP NTR *020 †85
VAN ARSDELL, Roger Clay. 158 HOSPITAL DR, SMITH COUNTY MEMORIAL HOSP 37030
#005-12-1960 L1973 EM GS *020 †85,16
VEENSTRA, Jacob. 131 HOSPITAL DR STE 1000 37030 #065-06-1971 L1995 GP *020
WEST, Richard Joe. 133 HOSPITAL DR STE 600 37030 #047-06-1982 L1982 GS *020 †85

CEDAR GROVE – CARROLL

SMILEY, Karen J. 490 MURPHY TOWER RD 38321 #047-07-1983 L1986 FM P *075

CEDAR HILL – ROBERTSON

BEAIRD GAINES, Lillian D. ■ 37032 #047-07-1992 L1996 MPD *020 †20,55

CELINA – CLAY

CARDONA, Aristides. 100 MCARTHUR AVE 38551 #035-15-1951 L1958 GP GS *071 †85
MAURICIO, Roberto S. 102 OLD JEFFERSON ST, CLAY COUNTY CLINIC 38551
#748-01-1941 L1951 R *071 †80
RUANTO, Arturo Natada. 112 DONALDSON AVE 38551 #748-08-1969 L1981 GP GS *020
SHERFEY, Mark Anthony. 100 OLD JEFFERSON ST, NORTH 38551 #305-01-1986 L1989
GP IM *020

CENTERVILLE – HICKMAN

BUTSCH, April Christina. 135 E SWAN ST 37033 #001-02-1997 L2004 DR *020 †80
COLEMAN, Robert M. 135 E SWAN ST 37033 #020-02-1941 L1951 R *071 †80
DANIEL, Eslick Ewing. 135 E SWAN ST 37033 #047-06-1967 L1968 ORS *071 †40
DURAKIEWICZ, Marek. 135 E SWAN ST 37033 #759-06-1988 L1999 IM EM *020 †20
EAKIN, Eliane Festa. 135 E SWAN ST 37033 #187-04-1987 L2003 PD PDP *020 †55 ‡
HUTCHENS, Zachary Mc Vey. 150 E SWAN ST 37033 #654-01-1985 L1990 FM *020 †18
LEON, William. 135 E SWAN ST 37033 #649-38-1983 L1990 PME *020
SAFAR, Elyas. 150 E SWAN ST 37033 #875-02-1997 L2004 IM IMG *020 †20 ‡
SATPATHY, Anup Kumar. 135 E SWAN ST, FAMILY HEALTH CLINIC 37033 #495-13-1978 L1990
FM *020
SEXTON, John T. 150 E SWAN ST 37033 #654-01-1985 L1990 FM *020 †18
WOJCICKI, Walter Edward. 135 E SWAN ST 37033 #047-05-1995 L1997 DR *020 †80

CHAPEL HILL – MARSHALL

NEWCOMB, Devi Merchant. 4696 NASHVILLE HWY 37034 #048-02-1996 L2004 FM *020 †18

CHARLESTON – BRADLEY

CALDWELL, Hugh R, Jr. ■ 37310 #027-01-1982 L1985 FM *020 †18
DUNN, Gregory Neil. ■ 37310 #047-06-2006 L2008 AN *012

CHATTANOOGA – HAMILTON

ABDU, Adio Ishmael. 979 E 3RD ST, STE C720 37403 #045-01-1998 L2007 OBG *012 †18
ABRAMS, Jody Gottlieb. 5715 CORNELISON RD, BLDG 6600 37411 #021-06-2002 L2007
IM *100

ACKELL, Adele Barbara. 721 GLENWOOD DR STE W467 37404 #038-40-1982 L1989
N *020 †75
ADAIR, Charles David. 979 E 3RD ST, STE C825 37403 #055-02-1990 L1997
OBG MFM *020 †30 ‡
ADAMS, Carol Jean. 979 E 3RD ST STE 601, MEDICAL CENTER PLAZA NORTH 37403
#036-07-1985 L1989 OBG ADL *020 †30
ADAMS, Don Edward. 979 E 3RD ST, STE C620 37403 #047-06-2001 L2004 IM *020 †20
ADAMS, John Sindos, Sr. 929 SPRING CREEK RD, STE 104 37412 #021-01-1987 L1995
OBG *020 †30
ADAMS, Stephen Mark. 1100 E 3RD ST 37403 #047-06-1994 L1997 FM *040 †18
ADEWALE, Abimbola O. 7011 SHALLOWFORD RD 37421 #690-02-1978 L1995 IM *020 †20
ADEWALE, Olusina O. 7011 SHALLOWFORD RD, STE 101 37421 #690-02-1983 L1996 PD *020
ADKINS, John F, Jr. 975 E 3RD ST 37403 #012-01-1983 L1988 AN *020 †05
AIKEN, Michael Mc Keehan. 1 UNION SQ STE 816, KRYSTAL BLDG 37402 #047-06-1979 L1980
EM *075
AKIN, Edgar Danl. 1201 CARTER ST STE A 37402 #047-06-1956 L1957 GS OM *020
AKPAM, Emem Jessica Edet. ■ 37421 #047-07-2008 *012
AL-AMIN, Ihssan. 4719 BRAINERD RD, STE C 37411 #047-07-1984 L1990 IM *020
ALAY, Rohini. 1720 GUNBARREL RD, STE 108 37421 #495-33-1993 L1999 IM *020 †20
ALBRITTON, John Thos. 924 SPRING CREEK RD 37412 #047-06-1960 L1964 AN *071
ALBURY, Michele Yolande. 921 E 3RD ST, CHATTANOOGA-HAMILTON COUNT 37403
#024-07-1989 L1994 GPM *020 †55
ALCANTARA, Karin Lee. 1755 GUNBARREL RD, STE 300 37421 #008-02-1991 L2001
PD *020 †55
ALI, Mohsin. 601 CUMBERLAND ST 37404 #704-25-1996 L2006 P CHP *020 †75
ALISAGO, Andres S, Jr. 7694 E BRAINERD RD 37421 #748-08-1961 L1970 AN PUD *071 †05
ALISAGO, Hilda Navera. ■ 37421 #748-08-1962 L1971 IM *071
ALLAN, Michael Christian. 2341 MCCALLIE AVE 37404 #047-06-2000 L2002 CD *020 †20
ALLEN, Alicia Renee. ■ 37412 #047-06-2008 *012
ALLEN, George Edward, Jr. 2333 MCCALLIE AVE 37404 #047-06-1962 L1962
EM FM *071 †16,18 ‡
ALVAREZ, David Manuel. 979 E 3RD ST, STE C620 37403 #308-03-1994 L1999 IM *020 †20
ALVAREZ, Richard Glen. 725 GLENWOOD DR STE 884 37404 #047-06-1975 L1975
ORS *020 †40
AL ZEER-KHALIFEH, Siham K. 6918 SHALLOWFORD RD, STE 201 37421 #575-01-1997 L2004
PD *020 †55
AMIL, Shazia Taherali. 921 E 3RD ST # 400, DIV OF INTERNAL MEDICINE 37403 #496-30-1997
IM *012
ANAMEKWE, Kenechim Anyanw. 921 E 3RD ST # 400 37403 #690-04-1998 IM *012
ANDERSON, Mark David. 725 GLENWOOD DR STE E484, INFECT DIS PHYS OF CHATTAN 37404
#021-01-1986 L1995 ID IM *020 †20
ANDERSON, Steven Randle. 2339 MCCALLIE AVE, STE 200 37404 #047-06-1982 L1983
OPH EM *020 †30
ANFIELD, Robert Newman. 1 FOUNTAIN SQ 3W 37402 #017-20-1979 L1998 OM *020 †18
ANOWER, Mohammad Nurul. 921 E 3RD ST # 400 37403 #160-02-1997 IM *012
APPAREDDY, Vijayalakshmi. 6918 SHALLOWFORD RD, STE 200 37421 #495-21-1982 L1992
P CHP *020 †75
APPEL, Michael. ■ 37402 #035-01-1992 L1994 AN *020 †05
APYAN, Paul Misak. 979 E 3RD ST 37403 #056-05-1980 L1981 ORS OTR *020 †40
ARANT, Billy Sunday, Jr. 910 BLACKFORD ST 37403 #045-01-1965 L1973 PN PD *020 †55
ARMSTRONG, David Lynn. 725 GLENWOOD DR, STE E588 37404 #047-06-2002 L2007
OTO *020
ARNOLD, Coleman Lee. 2108 E 3RD ST, STE 200 37404 #047-06-1972 L1972 GS *020 †85 ‡
ARNOLD, Joshua David. ■ 37405 #020-02-2004 GS *012
ARNOLD, Justin Mchenry. ■ 37405 #047-06-2005 ORS *012
ARRINGTON, Terry Lee. 975 E 3RD ST, ERLANGER HOSPITAL 37403 #012-01-2004 L2005
ORS *012
ARROWSMITH, Edward Riker. 605 GLENWOOD DR, STE 200 37404 #047-05-1992 L1995
HO *020 †20
ASHCRAFT, Delmon E, Jr. 929 SPRING CREEK RD, STE 10 37412 #027-01-1993 L1997
OBG *020 †30
ATKINS, Jeffery Vaughn. 975 E 3RD ST 37403 #047-06-1981 L1982 EM IM *020 †20
ATKINSON, Joseph Sprott. 605 GLENWOOD DR STE 300 37404 #047-05-1968 L1974
IM *020 †20
AUSTIN, Brett Leroy. 1949 GUNBARREL RD, ATRIUM IMAGING CENTER 37421
#012-01-1983 L1992 DR NM *020 †28,80
AUSTIN, Steven Kenneth. 2515 DESALES AVE, STE 205 37404 #047-06-1990 L1991
CD IM *020 †20
AVERY, Joel Eugene. 2339 MCCALLIE AVE, STE 200 37404 #001-02-1965 L1974
CD TS *071 †85,90
AZZOUZ, Rami. 910 BLACKFORD ST, PEDIATRIX MEDICAL GROUP 37403 #875-01-1994 L2003
NPM *020 †55
BAGAMERY, Matthew Edward. 979 E 3RD ST, STE C0630 37403 #025-01-1982 L1995
GE IM *020 †20
BAKER, Jennie Mae. ■ 37406 #047-06-2006 PD *012
BAKSHI, Sanatkumar V. ■ 37421 #495-22-1953 L1977 IM *020 †20
BALABANOVA, Liliya V. 960 E 3RD ST, STE 200 37404 #913-05-1985 L2008 IM *012
BALL, Gregory Neil. 1755 GUNBARREL RD, STE 203 37421 #012-01-1993 L1994
AN PME *020 †05
BALLARD, William Timothy. 2333 MCCALLIE AVE 37404 #038-41-1990 L1996
ORS OSM *020 †40
BALSER, Jeffrey Scott. 2341 MCCALLIE AVE STE 402 37404 #012-01-1988 L1992 AN *020 †05
BALSER, Robin Schwartz. 910 BLACKFORD ST 37403 #012-01-1988 L1992 PD *020 †55
BANKS, Samuel Louis. 6141 SHALLOWFORD RD 37421 #012-01-1967 L1973 D *020 †15
BANKS, Woodruff Asbury. 562 MEM MED BLDG 37404 #047-06-1955 L1956 GS *071 †85
BANNOR, Philip Ababio. 960 E 3RD ST, STE 512 37403 #056-06-1997 L2001 IM *020 †20
BARDONER, James Bradley. 975 E 3RD ST, ERLANGER MED CTR 37403 #308-07-1983 L1990
EM *020 †16
BAREDDY, Swarna Kumari. 3309 CUMMINGS HWY, STE A 37419 #495-62-1974 L1979
FM *020 †18
BAREDDY, Venkata R R. 2341 MCCALLIE AVE, STE 402, P.O. BOX 3549 37404
#495-62-1969 L1975 AN *020 †05
BARKER, David Muecke. 2341 MCCALLIE AVE, STE 302 37404 #047-06-1999 L2003
OBG *020 †30
BARKER, Donald Edgar. 979 E 3RD ST, STE 320 37403 #047-06-1975 L1975 CCS GS *040 †85
BARNES, David Robt. 1755 GUNBARREL RD, STE 301 37421 #047-06-1972 L1973
OTO HNS *020 †45

BARNES, Gary Thos. 1501 RIVERSIDE DR, WORKFORCE CORPORATE HEALTH 37406 #021-05-1984 L1987 **OM EM** *020
BARNETT, Robert M, III. 2108 E 3RD ST, STE 200 37404 #047-06-1976 L1976 **GS CRS** *020 †85
BARRON, Noel D, Jr. 2525 DESALES AVE 37404 #047-06-1984 L1987 **AN** *020 †05
BARRON, Robin Anne. 979 E 3RD ST, PHYSICIANSSUITE 1001 37403 #021-06-1991 L1994 **IM** *020 †20
BARTLETT, David Douglas. 2341 MCCALLIE AVE, STE 402, P.O. BOX 3549 37404 #048-04-1982 L1986 **AN** *020 †05
BATANGHARI, Budianto T. ■ 37415 #028-02-1988 L1989 **PDE MDM** *030 †55
BAUTISTA, Juancho C. 2333 MCCALLIE AVE 37404 #748-01-1965 L1971 **AN GP** *071
BAXTER, Blaise William. 975 E 3RD ST, DEPT RAD 37403 #064-01-1988 L1999 **R** *020 †80
BEAHM, Thomas Marion. 1949 GUNBARREL RD STE 100 37421 #019-02-1976 L1983 **PS GS** *020 †85,65 ‡
BEAN, Marilyn Louise. 2525 DESALES AVE 37404 #021-01-1991 L2000 **AN** *020 †05
BEAN, Mary Laura. 632 MORRISON SPRINGS RD, STE 201-202 37415 #027-01-1982 L1983 **FM FPG** *020 †18
BEASLEY, Glenn Allen. 2333 MCCALLIE AVE 37404 #047-06-1987 L1990 **FM FSM** *020 †18 ‡
BECHARD, Douglas Leandre. 5746 MARLIN RD STE 500, DIV OF MEDICAL AFFAIRS 37411 #005-12-1972 L1977 **ID IM** *030 †20
BEELER, Synthia Cook. 7446 SHALLOWFORD RD, STE 200 37421 #001-06-1997 L1998 **FM** *020 †18
BELL, Calvin Arthur. 1614 GUNBARREL RD, STE 101 37421 #036-01-1985 L1988 **CD IM** *020 †20
BELL, Gary L. 910 BLACKFORD ST 37403 #047-06-1982 L1984 **NPM PD** *020 †55
BELL, Todd Douglas. 2415 MCCALLIE AVE 37404 #001-02-1996 L2002 **ORS** *020
BENSON, Suzanne E. 2412 MCCALLIE AVE 37404 #048-13-1991 L1995 **PM** *020 †60
BERTSCH, Britney Anne. 921 E 3RD ST # 400 37403 #422-01-2007 **PD** *012
BESING, John Wm. 2337 MCCALLIE AVE, STE 307 37404 #308-07-1981 L1983 **IM** *075 †20
BHAKTA, Manoobhai G. 910 BLACKFORD ST 37403 #775-01-1975 L1980 **PHO** *020 †55
BHAT, Sushma. 921 E 3RD ST # 400, DEPT OF INTERNAL MEDICINE 37403 #495-17-1999 **IM** *012
BHATIA, Anil Kumar. 1334 MACKEY BRANCH DR, # A 37421 #496-09-1976 L1987 **END IM** *020
BHATTARAI, Nimesh. 921 E 3RD ST # 400 37403 #672-07-2004 **IM** *012
BICKEL, John Thos. 2525 DESALES AVE, PATHOLOGY SERVICES, BOX 36 37404 #028-03-1978 L2004 **PTH** *020 †50
BIERLY, John Robt. 1949 GUNBARREL RD STE 220 37421 #035-20-1986 L1999 **OPH** *020 †35
BIRCH, Lorna May. 2525 DESALES AVE 37404 #035-48-1997 L2004 **IMG** *020 †20
BIRD, Joseph Simmons, Jr. 979 E 3RD ST, STE C725 37403 #047-20-1990 L1991 **REN GYN** *020 †30 ‡
BISESE, John Herbert, II. 601 DODDS AVE 37404 #051-07-1980 L1999 **DR RNR** *020 †80
BISHOP, Christianne. 1100 E 3RD ST, UNIVERSITY OF TENNESSEE DE 37403 #030-06-1998 L2006 **FP** *012
BLAKE, Charles Alan. 979 E 3RD ST 37403 #005-12-1963 L1975 **AN PUD** *071
BLAKE, William Woods. 975 E 3RD ST, BOX 159 37403 #047-06-1975 L1975 **NPM PD** *020 †55
BLALOCK, Travis Wayne. ■ 37405 #012-22-2007 **GS** *012
BLALOCK, William Eldridge. 1614 GUNBARREL RD # 101, CARDIOVASCULAR CARE CENTER 37421 #036-05-1988 L1991 **CD IM** *020 †20
BLANKENBAKER, Ronald Gail. 615 MCCALLIE AVE, 50 FOUNDERS HALL, DEPT 580 37403 #017-20-1968 L1968 **MDM FM** *071 †18
BLEVINS, Phillip Atchley. 975 E 3RD ST, DEPT. OF MEDICAL AFFAIRS 37403 #047-06-1998 L2001 **OS** *020 †16
BOAZ, Lonnie R, III. 960 E 3RD ST STE 101 37403 #010-03-1983 L1986 **GE IM** *071
BOAZ, Valerie Aurellia. 921 E 3RD ST, DEPT 37403 #028-34-1983 L1986 **IM** *020
BOEHM, Peter Eric. 1010 E 3RD ST, STE 202 37403 #047-06-1970 L1972 **NS N** *020 †25
BOEHM, Walter Michael. 1010 E 3RD ST, STE 202 37403 #035-19-1966 L1972 **NS** *020 †25
BOISER, Anita Madria. 709 WALNUT ST 37402 #748-08-1963 L1979 **AN** *020
BOLDT, John Wesley, Jr. 2205 MCCALLIE AVE, FL 5 37404 #047-05-1982 L1994 **CCM PUD** *020 †20
BONVALLET, Todd Cecil. 979 E 3RD ST, STE C225 37403 #005-06-1991 L1997 **ORS** *020 †40
BOOKOUT, Mark Wm. 632 MORRISON SPRINGS RD, STE 300 37415 #047-06-1978 L1978 **OTO A** *020 †45
BOROUGHS, Eileen Young. ■ 37421 #047-06-2002 L2004 **FM** *020 †18
BOROUGHS, Jon Brooks. ■ 37421 #047-20-2007 **PD** *012
BOSTANJIAN, David. 979 E 3RD ST STE 401 37403 #913-58-1983 L2006 **FM** *020
BOWDEN, Harvey D. 1935 AMBERLEY TRL 37421 #047-06-1976 L1977 **EM OBG** *020
BOWERS, David Neil. 2333 MCCALLIE AVE 37404 #005-12-1978 L1996 **FM PM** *020 †60
BOWERS, Elizabeth M. 929 SPRING CREEK RD, STE 10 37412 #028-78-1999, ▲ L2003 **OBG** *020
BOWERS, Jemison O, Jr. ■ 37415 #001-02-1965 L1969 **OPH** *072 †35
BOWERS, Joseph Lee. 8489 E BRAINERD RD 37421 #649-14-1993 L1996 **FM** *020 †18
BOWERS, Patrick Joseph, Jr. 725 GLENWOOD DR, STE 892 37404 #012-01-1996 L2001 **OPH** *020 †35
BOWERS, Richard. 929 SPRING CREEK RD, STE 10 37412 #028-78-1973, ▲ L1973 **OBG** *020 †30
BOWERS, Robert Eugene. 725 GLENWOOD DR, STE E588 37404 #005-12-1961 L1973 **OTO** *071 †45
BOXELL, John Frederick. 1949 GUNBARREL RD, STE 230 37421 #017-20-1965 L1970 **OTO** *071 †45
BOYD, Stacy Dean. 979 E 3RD ST, STE C725 37403 #012-01-1991 L1993 **OBG** *020 †30
BRACKETT, Richard Wayne. 6145 SHALLOWFORD RD, STE 102 37421 #047-06-1985 L1985 **RHU IM** *020 †20
BRACKETT, Stephen Ronald. ■ 37402 #001-02-2006 **GS** *012
BREEN, John Michael. 979 E 3RD ST, STE C725 37403 #748-10-1982 L1990 **GYN** *020 †30
BREMER, Joel Lewis. 632 MORRISON SPRINGS RD, STE 300 37415 #025-07-1976 L1982 **PD** *020
BREWER, Randall J. ■ 37421 #047-06-1976 L1977 **P** *020 †75
BRICE, Charles Terry. 979 E 3RD ST, STE 801 37403 #020-02-1974 L1975 **GS GP** *020
BRIEN, Thomas Philip. 2525 DESALES AVE, P O BOX 3637 37404 #035-45-1992 L2000 **PTH** *020 †50
BRIERY, Christian Michael. 979 E 3RD ST, STE C825 37403 #021-06-1999 L2006 **OBG** *020
BRINN, Kenneth Alan. 975 E 3RD ST 37403 #038-41-1989 L1999 **RNR** *020 †80
BRIT, Michael. 979 E 3RD ST, STE B805 37403 #913-15-1989 L2003 **RHU** *020 †20
BROADSTONE, Paul Alvin. 979 E 3RD ST, STE C225 37403 #047-06-1973 L1974 **OSS ORS** *020 †40
BROCKER, Gerald K, Jr. 975 E 3RD ST 37403 #047-06-1979 L1992 **AN PD** *020 †55,05
BRODY, Kirk Warren. 2341 MCCALLIE AVE STE 302 37404 #047-06-1993 L1997 **OBG** *020 †30
BROOKS, Thomas Jefferson. 3300 WILCOX BLVD, FAMILY HEALTH SERVICES 37411 #047-07-1978 L1981 **OBG** *020 †30
BROOKSBANK, Ronald Chas. 961 SPRING CREEK RD 37412 #065-06-1963 L1978 **FM EM** *020
BROWN, Hugh Pearce. 979 E 3RD ST, STE C220 37403 #047-06-1965 L1966 **ORS OP** *020 †40
BROWN, James Wm. 975 E 3RD ST, DEPT OF ANESTHESIA 37403 #001-02-1988 L1990 **AN** *020 †05
BROWN, Thomas Walter, III. 2707 CITICO AVE 37406 #021-05-1983 L1989 **ORS GS** *020 †40
BROYLES, Jennifer Sue. 1100 E 3RD ST 37403 #305-01-2003 L2007 **FM** *020 †18
BRUCE, Gregory Keith. 2501 CITICO AVE 37404 #012-05-1998 L2005 **ICE CD** *020 †20
BRUCE, Jeremy Reginald. ■ 37415 #012-01-2007 **ORS** *012
BRUCE, William David. 1809 GUNBARREL RD, SURGEONS, P.C. SUITE 101 37421 #001-02-1992 L1995 **ORS** *020 †40
BRUNNER, Bridget Suzanne. 979 E 3RD ST, STE C720 37403 #001-02-2003 L2005 **OBG** *020
BRUNS, Thomas Benj. 910 BLACKFORD ST, TC THOMPSON CHILDREN'S HOS 37403 #046-01-1990 L1991 **PEM** *020 †55
BRYAN, Calvin Patrick. PO BOX 2459 37409 #047-06-1972 L1973 **GP** *020
BRYANT, Max Vincent. 725 GLENWOOD DR STE E882 37404 #045-01-1973 L1984 **PD PUD** *020 †55
BUCHNER, Edward F, III. 112 LEE PARKWAY DR, STE 103 37421 #047-06-1954 L1954 **IM** *071
BUCHNER, William Francis. ■ 37416 #047-06-1958 L1958 **GS** *071 †85
BULATAO, Imelda Santiago. ■ 37421 #748-08-1980 L2006 **PTH DMP** *020 †50
BURKHOLDER, Hans C. ■ 37405 #035-19-2003 **GS** *012
BURKICH, Robert A. 707 SIGNAL MOUNTAIN RD, CONVENIENT CARE 37405 #305-01-1987 L1996 **GP** *020
BURNS, Randel Phillip. 979 E 3RD ST, STE 320 37403 #047-06-1966 L1967 **GS ORS** *020 †85
BUTLER, Gloria. 100 MOCCASIN BEND RD, MOCCASIN BEND MNT HLTH INS 37405 #025-07-1978 L1997 **IM** *020 †20
BUTTRAM, William R, Jr. 2525 DESALES AVE 37404 #012-05-1944 L1949 **IM OS** *072
BUTTRAM, William Rees. 2525 DESALES AVE 37404 #047-06-1970 L1971 **DR** *071 †80
BYKOV, Yury. ■ 37421 #041-13-2003 L2003 **ORS** *012
CABLE, Thomas Allen. 975 E 3RD ST 37403 #011-03-1976 L1995 **FM** *020 †18
CAINE, Winston P, Jr. 979 E 3RD ST, STE C620 37403 #023-07-1963 L1969 **HEM IM** *020 †20
CALDWELL, Gary Blaine. 2341 MCCALLIE AVE, STE 402 37404 #027-01-1965 L1970 **AN** *071
CALHOUN, Calvin Lee, Jr. 975 E 3RD ST 37403 #047-07-1975 L1978 **IM** *020
CALLAHAN, Robert Bennett. MOCCASIN BEND RD 37405 #056-06-1955 L1979 **CHP OS** *020
CAMPBELL, Brent. 921 E 3RD ST # 400, DEPT FM 37403 #041-78-2007, ▲ **FP** *012
CAMPBELL, William O'Neal. ■ 37416 #047-06-1962 L1962 **OM FM** *071
CANAVAN, Amy Langham. 910 BLACKFORD ST, DEPARTMENT OF PEDIATRICS 37403 #012-01-2000 L2002 **PD** *020 †55
CANNON, Allison Ann. 721 GLENWOOD DR, 462 W 37404 #047-20-1998 L2001 **IM** *020
CANNON, Don Allen. 721 GLENWOOD DR STE W462 37404 #047-06-1960 L1963 **GP IM** *020
CARLOS, Rodolfo A. MOCCASEN BEND PSYCH HOSP 37405 #748-08-1964 **P** *030
CARR, Michael Grady. 979 E 3RD ST, STE 320 37403 #020-02-1974 L1981 **PDS** *040 †85
CARRICO, Brian C. ■ 37421 #020-02-2007 **GS** *012
CARROLL, Richard John. 725 GLENWOOD DR, STE E882 37404 #016-06-1994 L2001 **PD** *020 †55
CARTER, James Wesley. ■ 37421 #047-06-2007 **TY** *012
CARTER, Louise Elenore. 1755 GUNBARREL RD, STE 202 37421 #047-07-1944 L1946 **FM** *071
CARTER, Mary Elizabeth. 1949 GUNBARREL RD, STE 285 37421 #001-06-1986 L1990 **PD** *020 †55
CARTER, Susanna Ellen. ■ 37405 #001-02-2007 **OBG** *012
CATHRO, David Methven. ■ 37405 #803-03-1954 L1997 **PDE ADL** *071 †55
CATTERTON, Wm Zachary. 910 BLACKFORD ST 37403 #051-04-1971 L1976 **IMG OP** *040 †55
CAUGHRAN, Bennett W. ■ 37416 #047-05-1953 L1953 **ORS** *020 †40
CAUGHRAN, Donald G. 601 DODDS AVE 37404 #047-06-1976 L1977 **DR PDR** *020 †80
CAUGHRAN, Martha. 2525 DESALES AVE 37404 #047-06-1976 L1977 **DR** *020 †80
CAUSO, Ricardo Federico. 6131 SHALLOWFORD RD, STE 103 37421 #308-07-1982 L1989 **PD NDP** *020 †55
CHAFFIN, David C, Jr. 1720 GUNBARREL RD, STE 400 37421 #047-06-1997 L2000 **AI** *020 †55,03 ‡
CHAMBERLAIN, Donald H. 1000 E 3RD ST, STE 201 37403 #030-06-1984 L1998 **GO OBG** *020 †30
CHAMBERLAIN, Morrow, II. 725 GLENWOOD DR, MEMORIAL MEDICAL BLDG EAST 37404 #047-06-1970 L1970 **OTO** *020 †45
CHAMBLESS, Kurt Miller. 2415 MCCALLIE AVE 37404 #012-01-1982 L1987 **ORS** *071 †40
CHAMPION, Deann K. 725 GLENWOOD DR, STE E487 37404 #005-12-1997 L2000 **EM** *020 †16
CHANDER, Ravi S. 979 E 3DR ST, STE 1210 37403 #495-04-1985 L1998 **N OS** *020 †75
CHANDLER, Luther F, Jr. 1651 GUNBARREL RD, GALEN MEDICAL GROUP EAST 37421 #001-02-1982 L1985 **IM** *020 †20
CHANDRA, Channappa. 725 GLENWOOD DR STE E580 37404 #495-09-1965 L1979 **ORS EM** *020 †40
CHARAPATA, Chad Michael. 979 E 3RD ST, GALEN MEDICAL GROUP PC 37403 #025-07-2000 L2002 **GE** *020 †20
CHASE, Christopher W. 2337 MCCALLIE AVE, STE 303 37404 #047-20-1992 L1993 **PS GS** *020 †85,65
CHATTIN, Ami Heather. 2333 MCCALLIE AVE, 4TH FL 37404 #047-20-1999 L2002 **IM** *100 †20
CHEN, Nancy. ■ 37402 #024-05-1994 L1994 **APM** *020 †05
CHERRY, Collin Glenn. 725 GLENWOOD DR, STE EAST 480 37404 #047-06-1985 L1986 **IM** *020 †20
CHIEN, Lawrence Tien-Tso. 725 GLENWOOD DR STE 786 37404 #385-03-1962 L1975 **CHN PD** *020 †55,75
CHILDS, Kent Danl. 1651 GUNBARREL RD, GALEN MEDICAL GROUP 37421 #047-20-1992 L1995 **OBG** *020 †30
CHIPMAN, Donald Dyrone, Jr. 2339 MCCALLIE AVE, PARKRIDGE MED CTR STE 309 37404 #001-02-2000 L2006 **APM AN** *100 †05
CHOBOT, Edwin F, Jr. 2709 CITICO AVE 37406 #047-06-1953 L1954 **NS OS** *071
CHOI, Suni. ■ 37421 #583-03-1950 L1975 **PD HEM** *071
CHOPRA, Joginder Gurbux. 5600 LAKE RESORT TER # 406 37415 #495-01-1954 L1967 **PD NTR** *071 †55
CHOWDHURY, Aparna Saha. 921 E 3RD ST # 400 37403 #160-02-2001 **IM** *012
CHUTHAI, Surachart. 1100 E 3RD ST, DEPT OF FAMILY MEDICINE 37403 #143-11-2003 **FP** *012
CLARK, C Robt. 975 E 3RD ST 37403 #036-05-1955 L1960 **ORS OS** *071 †40
CLARK, Robert Baker. ■ 37415 #047-06-1954 L1955 **PD** *071 †55
CLAXTON, Rita Renee. 3300 WILCOX BLVD 37411 #047-20-1991 L1996 **HO** *020 †20
CLEAVELAND, Clifton Rance. 960 E 3RD ST, STE 200 37403 #023-07-1964 L1970 **IM** *071 †20

■ = Address Information Privacy Protected

CLEMENTS, Joel Benj. 1755 GUNBARREL RD, STE 203 37421 #047-06-1968 L1969 **GS** *020 †85

CLOSE, David Kendall. 961 SPRING CREEK RD 37412 #001-06-1986 L1989 **FM** *020 †18

CLOSE, Elizabeth Denby. ■ 37415 #047-06-2007 **FP** *012

COBB, Clara Martine. 975 E 3RD ST 37403 #020-12-1982 L1983 **PTH PCP** *062 †50

COCKERHAM, William Todd. 2108 E 3RD ST, STE 200 37404 #004-01-1998 L2004 **GS** *020 †85

CODDINGTON, Robert Chas. 975 E 3RD ST 37403 #017-20-1956 L1966 **OP OSM** *020 †40

COFER, Joseph Broaddus. 2108 E 3RD ST, STE 200 37404 #047-06-1978 L1979 **GS TTS** *020 †85

COHEN, Jonathan Stuart. 6216 AIRPARK DR 37421 #036-01-1985 L1989 **P** *020 †75

COLES, Robert A, Jr. 725 GLENWOOD DR, STE E487 37404 #012-01-1988 L1992 **FM** *020 †18

COLLINS, David Newton. 725 GLENWOOD DR, STE 690 E MEM MED BLDG 37404 #047-06-1977 L1978 **GE** *020 †20 ‡

COLLINS, John Richard. 2525 DESALES AVE 37404 #047-05-1956 L1956 **GE IM** *020 †20

COLLINS, Sabrina Lee. 7490 ZIEGLER RD 37421 #047-06-1999 L2003 **OBG** *020

COLLINS, Sonya Rose. 975 E 3RD ST BOX 159, PEDIATRIX MEDICAL GROUP 37403 #048-13-1994 L2002 **PDC** *020 †55

CONN, Eric Hadley. 2501 CITICO AVE 37404 #036-07-1976 L1982 **CD** *020 †20

CONNELL, Bernard Patrick. 910 BLACKFORD ST, T.C. THOMPSON CHILDREN'S H 37403 #028-03-1979 L1997 **PEM PD** *020 †55

COOPER, Earnest Hugh, Jr. ■ 37415 #047-06-1977 L1977 **GS EM** *071

COPELAND, Mark Edward. 975 E 3RD ST, ERLANGER MEDICAL CENTER 37403 #047-06-1989 L1993 **EM** *020 †16

COREY, James Hicks, Jr. 1755 GUNBARREL RD STE 300 37421 #051-01-1947 L1957 **PD** *071 †55

CORNEA, Ana. 2205 MCCALLIE AVE 37404 #781-03-1995 L2003 **END** *020 †20

CORNEA, Paul. 725 GLENWOOD DR, STE 48 37404 #781-03-1995 L2003 **ID** *020 †20

CORNELL, Allyson Neeley. 632 MORRISON SPRINGS RD, STE 202 37415 #047-06-2001 L2003 **FM** *020 †18

COULTER, Steven Lee. 801 PINE ST 37402 #039-01-1977 L1997 **IM** *030 †20 ‡

COUNCIL, Susan. 1 SISKIN PLZ 37403 #020-02-1985 L2001 **PM SCI** *020 †60

COURTS, Marc Vincent. 910 BLACKFORD ST, ERLANGER HOSPITAL 37403 #055-02-2005 L2008 **PD** *012

COX, Sue Clarke. ■ 37415 #047-06-1950 L1951 **FM** *071 †18

COX, Tonia R Richardson. 632 MORRISON SPRINGS RD, STE 300 37415 #047-06-2001 L2006 **PD** *020 †55

CRAVEN, Patrick Bates. 100 MOCCASIN BEND RD 37405 #047-06-1972 L1973 *040

CROFT, Chasen Ashley. ■ 37421 #048-02-2003 **GS** *012

CROMIE, Marc William. 6624 LEE HWY, CHATTANOOGA ALLERGY CLINIC 37421 #012-01-1995 L1999 **AI** *020 †55,03

CRUMP, Charles Athey, Jr. 2205 MCCALLIE AVE 37404 #047-20-1993 L1994 **IM** *020 †20

CUI, Xiaoying. 2339 MCCALLIE AVE STE 401 37404 #243-72-1988 L2004 **P** *100 †75

CUNNINGHAM, Jalila. ■ 37412 #047-07-2001 L2003 **IM** *020 †20

CURREY, Thomas Woodruff. 979 E 3RD ST 37403 #047-06-1963 L1964 **ORS** *040 †40

CURRIN, Samuel Marion. 725 GLENWOOD DR, STE E780 37404 #045-01-1984 L1991 **U** *020 †95

CURTIS, Donald Arthur. 425 CUMBERLAND ST, STE 110 37404 #026-04-1997 L2004 **FPG** *020 †18

CURTIS, E Carroll. 1 FOUNTAIN SQ STE 1 37402 #047-06-1964 L1964 **OM** *030 †70

CURTIS, Thomas H. ■ 37412 #047-06-1949 L1949 **OBG OS** *071 †30

CYLEMAN, Nabil Nader K. 960 E 3RD ST, STE 400 37403 #915-05-1981 L1994 **IM** *020 †20

DAGHLIAN, Bedros Dikran. 975 E 3RD ST 37403 #528-01-1960 L1978 **AN** *020

DAMSHALA, Nalini K. 340 N HOLTZCLAW AVE 37404 #495-21-1976 L1991 **PD** *020

DANIEL, Davey Benjamin. ■ 37415 #023-07-1999 L2005 **HO** *020 †20

DANIELL, Malcolm Butler. 2525 DESALES AVE 37404 #048-04-1960 L1974 **TS** *071 †85,90

DART, Benjamin Wall, IV. 979 E 3RD ST, STE 320 37403 #021-05-1999 L2003 **GS** *020 †85

DAUNOY, Mary Elizabeth. 103 JORDAN DR, STE 8 37421 #001-06-1993 L2000 **PD** *020 †55

DAVIS, Allan Eric. 7155 LEE HWY, STE 600 37421 #065-09-1975 L1980 **D** *020 †15

DAVIS, James Phillip, Jr. 2525 DESALES AVE 37404 #047-05-1979 L1982 **AN** *020 †05

DAVIS, James Wilson. 975 E 3RD ST 37403 #021-01-1946 L1949 **PS** *071 †65

DAVIS, Jimmy B. ■ 37405 #047-06-1959 L1960 **FM** *020 †18

DAVIS, Thomas Edward. 1 SISKIN PLZ, ASSOCIATES 37403 #012-05-1998 L2002 **PM** *020 †60

DAVIT, Alexander Joseph. 979 E 3RD ST STE 401 37403 #036-05-2000 L2006 **PS** *012 †85

DEMOS, Robert G. ■ 37405 #047-06-1944 L1944 **GYN OBG** *071 †30

DE PASQUALE, Stephen E. 979 E 3RD ST, STE C725 37403 #033-06-1993 L2001 **GO** *020 †30

DE ROSE, Norina Escribano. ■ 37421 #231-01-1964 L1983 **DR NM** *071

DESBIENS, Norman Adrien. PO BOX 94, 375 E 3RD ST 37401 #024-01-1972 L1997 **IM IMG** *040 †18,20

DE STEFANO, Joseph A, Jr. 2525 DESALES AVE 37404 #045-04-1993 L2004 **IM** *020 †20

DE VANE, Jo Mitchell. 910 BLACKFORD ST 37403 #047-06-1977 L1979 **PD** *020 †55

DEVERSA, Peter Roger. 975 E 3RD ST BOX 251, UNIVERSITY HOSPITALISTS 37403 #047-06-1996 L1997 **ID** *020 †20

DEVLIN, Thomas Glenn. 721 GLENWOOD DR STE W467 37404 #048-04-1991 L1996 **N** *020 †75

DEVOID, David Eugene. 979 E 3RD ST, GALEN MEDICAL GROUP PC 37403 #048-04-1987 L1996 **PD PG** *020 †55

DIETZEN, Charles David. 4411 OAKWOOD DR, P O BOX 19269 37416 #047-06-1975 L1976 **CRS GS** *020 †10,85

DIGGS, Jacqulyn Mayre. 540 MCCALLIE AVE, STATE OF TENNESSEE DEPT.HE 37402 #048-02-1977 L1996 **OBG GPM** *020

DILWORTH, James Patrick. 725 GLENWOOD DR STE E780 37404 #047-06-1985 L1986 **U** *020 †95

DI STEFANO, Deborah R. 1801 GUNBARREL RD 37421 #056-06-1976 L1982 **OPH** *020 †35

DODSON, David Bryan. 2525 DESALES AVE, HOSPITALIST DEPT 37404 #047-05-1976 L1978 **IM** *020 †20

DONALDSON, Richard B. 725 GLENWOOD DR STE E580 37404 #035-20-1942 L1949 **ORS** *071 †40

DONESKY, Barry Wm. 1624 GUNBARREL RD 37421 #005-12-1987 L1994 **REN GYN** *020 †30

DONOWITZ, Arlene Joan. 605 GLENWOOD DR STE 404 37404 #010-01-1980 L1988 **IM** *020 †20

DORIZAS, John Angelo. 1755 GUNBARREL RD, STE 102 37421 #001-02-1999 L2004 **ORS** *100

DOUGLAS, Michael. 1720 GUNBARREL RD 37421 #047-06-1976 L1977 **IM** *020 †20

DOWLEN, Steven Harris. 605 GLENWOOD DR STE 300 37404 #047-05-1980 L1983 **IM** *020 †20

DRAKE, James Robt. 961 SPRING CREEK RD 37412 #047-05-1954 L1954 **IM** *020

DRAKE, Robert Agnew. 961 SPRING CREEK RD 37412 #065-01-1968 L1983 **FM EM** *020

DRESSLER, Stanley Jay. 2341 MCCALLIE AVE STE 302 37404 #047-06-1958 L1963 **GYN** *071 †30

DRINNON, William Danl. 1751 GUNBARREL RD, STE 100 37421 #047-06-1989 L1992 **IM** *020 †20

DUBECKBROOKS, Annesofie K. 2333 MCCALLIE AVE 37404 #024-16-1988 L1996 **IM** *020 †20

DUFF, Siobhan Alaine. 961 SPRING CREEK RD 37412 #063-01-1992 L1994 **FM** *020 †18

DUFFIELD, Deborah Sue. 4411 OAKWOOD DR, P O BOX 19269 37416 #021-05-1993 L1994 **IM** *020 †20

DUFFY, Mary Alexis. 1 FOUNTAIN SQ, UNUMPROVIDENT 37402 #047-06-1980 L1980 **OM FM** *030 †18 ‡

DUNBAR-DAVIES, Winnifred. 960 E 3RD ST, STE 418 37403 #004-01-1991 L1995 **FM** *020 †18

DUNCAN, Deanna Viola. 2700 PARKWOOD AVE, HOSPICE OF CHATTANOOGA 37404 #001-02-1995 L1997 **FM** *020 †18

DUNN, Terence Sean. 2339 MCCALLIE AVE, STE 309 37404 #012-05-1987 L2006 **PM** *020

DU PLOOY, Johannes J. 3739 HIXSON PIKE 37415 #836-03-1992 L2000 **IM** *020 †20

DURHAM, James Herbert. 2333 MCCALLIE AVE, PARKRIDGE MEDICAL CTR 37404 #012-01-1987 L1990 **IM** *020 †20

DUTTA, Gautam. 921 E 3RD ST # 400 37403 #160-02-1994 **IM** *012

DUVOISIN, Peter Marc. 2410 MCCALLIE AVE, DIAGNOSTIC CENTER 37404 #036-07-1960 L1966 **CD IM** *071 †20

DYER, William Carl, Jr. 2339 MCCALLIE AVE, STE 402 37404 #047-05-1965 L1965 **ORS** *020 †40

EASON, Patricia Ann. 910 BLACKFORD ST 37403 #047-07-1980 L1985 **PD** *074

ECKER, Robert Beard. 1720 GUNBARREL RD, STE 400 37421 #054-04-2002 L2006 **D DS** *020 †15

EGLY, Jonathan Andrew. 921 E 3RD ST # 400 37403 #422-01-2007 **OBG** *012

ELETR, Abdulhafiz M. 979 E 3RD ST, ERLANGER PROF. PLAZASUITE1 37403 #012-01-2002 L2005 **N** *020

ELG, Steven A. 721 GLENWOOD DR, STE 560 37404 #054-04-1985 L2000 **ON** *020 †30

ELIAS, Caroline Kirk. 3898 HIXSON PIKE 37415 #047-06-1990 L1994 **OPH** *020 †35

ELIAS, David Brian. 605 GLENWOOD DR, STE 300 37404 #047-06-1987 L1988 **IM** *020 †20

ELLIS, Eric Robt. 2525 DESALES AVE, STE 200 37404 #036-05-1985 L1989 **RO** *020 †80

ELLISON, David F S. 975 E 3RD ST, DEPT. OF ANESTHESIA 37403 #028-78-1981, ▲ L1987 **AN** *020 †05

ELROD, Bruce A. ■ 37421 #001-02-1947 L1957 **PTH** *071 †50

ENJETI, Suresh. 979 E 3RD ST, STE B-1201 37403 #495-65-1970 L1984 **PUD CCM** *020 †20

ENZENAUER, Raymond Jos. 979 E 3RD ST, STE B-805 37403 #028-03-1984 L2001 **RHU IM** *020 ‡

EPPIHIMER, Brandon Michae. ■ 37411 #012-01-2005 L2007 **FP** *012

EPPS, Jesse Miller, III. 2525 DESALES AVE 37404 #001-02-1991 L2003 **AN** *020 †05

ERDOES, Luke Stephan. 2108 E 3RD ST, STE 200 37404 #024-07-1984 L2000 **VS GS** *020 †85

ESELGROTH, Stephan F. 975 E 3RD ST, # 379 37403 #003-01-1998 L2002 **PM PRS** *020 †60

ESHETE, Belay Tessema. 150 DEBRA RD, BLDG 6200 37411 #366-01-1983 L2002 **IM** *020 †20

ESTEP, Dennis Paul. 403 SPRING CREEK RD 37411 #654-01-1981 L1985 **PD** *020

ESTES, Amy Johnston. ■ 37405 #038-40-2007 **TY** *012

EVANS, Charles Armstrong. 2333 MCCALLIE AVE, DEPT OF PATHOLOGY 37404 #038-41-1979 L1985 **PTH** *020 †50

EVANS, John Thos. 1000 E 3RD ST 37403 #036-01-1956 L1960 **OTO** *071 †45

EVANS, Lindsay Carol. ■ 37411 #001-02-2006 **GS** *012

EYSSEN, James Edward. 2337 MCCALLIE AVE, STE 303 37404 #047-06-1970 L1971 **PS GS** *020 †65

FAHR, Michael Edward. ■ 37415 #021-05-2003 **GS** *012

FAHS, Jeffrey James. 600 N HOLTZCLAW AVE, STE 100 37404 #003-01-1978 L2000 **P N** *020 †75

FAIN, Guy Franklin, III. 941 SPRING CREEK RD, PARKRIDGE EAST HOSPITAL 37412 #036-05-1980 L1983 **FM EM** *020 †18

FALINSKI, Boleslaus Alan. 2525 DESALES AVE 37404 #016-43-1985 L1993 **AN** *020 †05 ‡

FANNIN, Quentin L. 3712 RINGGOLD RD # 315 37412 #020-12-1982 L1987 **FM** *020 †18

FARBER, Sharon Nancy. 721 GLENWOOD DR, STE W467 37404 #028-02-1983 L1987 **N** *020 †75

FARMER, Tony Randall. ■ 37411 #012-22-2006 **PD** *100

FEINTUCH, Theodore Ard. 1030 E 4TH ST 37403 #047-05-1964 L1964 **ATP CLP** *020 †50,28

FELIX, Arnaud Pierre. 1751 GUNBARREL RD, STE 302 37421 #038-40-1993 L2002 **IM** *020 †20

FELIX, Cherise Marie. ■ 37405 #047-20-2004 L2006 **OBG** *012

FELLOWES, Sarah Gale. 2525 DESALES AVE, MEMORIAL HEALTH CARE SYSTE 37404 #010-02-1984 L2005 **IM** *020 †20

FERGUSON, Kevin R. 2200 MORRIS HILL RD 37421 #048-02-1985 L1990 **P CHP** *020 †75

FERNANDEZ ACOSTA, Carlos. 921 E 3RD ST # 400 37403 #264-01-1993 **GS** *012

FESMIRE, Francis Miller. 975 E 3RD ST, ER DEPT 37403 #047-05-1985 L1988 **EM** *020 †16

FEW, Tiffany. 1751 GUNBARREL RD, STE 101 37421 #012-05-1997 L2005 **OBG** *020 †30

FEW, Walter Lee, III. 1614 GUNBARREL RD 37421 #023-07-1997 L2005 **CD** *100 †20

FINDLEY, William Blaine. 1404 DODDS AVE 37404 #047-06-1964 L1965 **FM GP** *020 †18

FINNEGAN, Martin Melrose. 1710 GUNBARREL RD 37421 #067-01-1990 L2001 **DR** *020 †80

FISCHER, Desmond Lawrence. 1301 MCCALLIE AVE 37404 #065-09-1980 L1987 **R** *020 †80

FISHER, Danl Franklin, Jr. 2108 E 3RD ST, STE 200 37404 #047-06-1975 L1976 **VS GS** *020 †85

FOLEY, Patrick Henry. 2337 MCCALLIE AVE STE 407 37404 #011-02-1990 L1996 **U** *020 †95

FOLKENING, James Edmund. 2341 MCCALLIE AVE STE 306 37404 #017-20-1974 L1983 **IM** *020 †20

FONG, Eugene Glenn. 2333 MCCALLIE AVE, DEPT OF PATHOLOGY 37404 #008-01-1978 L1988 **CLP ATP** *020 †50

FORD, Augustus C. 921 E 3RD ST 37403 #005-12-1944 L1946 **PHP FM** *071 †18

FORTIER, Diane. 961 SPRING CREEK RD 37412 #067-04-1983 L1997 **FM** *020 †18

FRANKLIN, Donald. 979 E 3RD ST, STE B-1111 37403 #012-01-1985 L1986 **NEP** *020 †20

FRANKLIN, John David. 979 E 3RD ST STE 4002 37403 #047-06-1966 L1967 **PS GS** *020 †85,65

FRANKLIN, Selmon T, III. 2205 MCCALLIE AVE, DIAGNOSTIC CENTER 37404 #047-06-1982 L1982 **IM** *020 †20

FREEMAN, Mark Gregory. 725 GLENWOOD DR, STE E580 37404 #051-01-2000 L2003 **ORS** *020

FRIDDELL, Roy Anthony. 725 GLENWOOD DR STE E882, PEDIATRIC DIAGNOSTIC ASSOC 37404 #048-13-1993 L1997 **PD** *020 †55

FRIESEN, Kerry Douglas. 7405 SHALLOWFORD RD, STE 270 37421 #065-05-1991 L1995 **IM** *020 †20

FROMM, Richard Friedrich. 1949 GUNBARREL RD, STE 250 37421 #012-01-1991 L1993 **GS** *020 †85

FRYE, Augustus H, Jr. 721 GLENWOOD DR, 470 MEMORIAL MED BLDG WEST 37404 #023-01-1943 L1960 **ORS OS** *071 †40

FUNDERBURK, Randall L. 979 E 3RD ST 37403 #047-06-1979 L1980 **OPH** *020 †35

■ = Address Information Privacy Protected

FURR, Joe Corry. ■ 37405 #027-01-2008 *012
FURR, Robert Scott. 1604 GUNBARREL RD, CHATTANOOGA WOMEN'S LASER 37421 #305-01-2001 L2005 **OBG** *020
GAINES, Joan Schubert. ■ 37421 #048-13-1975 L1976 **GP EM** *074
GALBRAITH, John N. 975 E 3RD ST 37403 #004-01-1970 L1980 **DR** *071 †80
GALEN, Norman Richard. 979 E 3RD ST, STE A-450 37403 #021-01-1968 L2005 **U** *020 †95
GALLAGHER, Michael R. 1010 E 3RD ST, STE 202 37403 #041-02-1987 L1995 **NS GS** *020 †25
GALLOWAY, Andrea Kaye. 2341 MCCALLIE AVE, STE 302 37404 #047-06-1996 L1997 **OBG** *020 †30
GANDHI, Jitendra. 2205 MCCALLIE AVE, STE 502 37404 #496-38-1976 L1983 **ON HEM** *020 †20
GARCIA, Karla Lisbeth. 910 BLACKFORD ST, DEPT OF PEDIATRICS 37403 #011-02-1990 L1995 **PD** *020 †55
GAURAV, Kumar. 921 E 3RD ST # 400 37403 #496-09-2004 L2006 **IM** *012
GAZALEH, Shawn. ■ 37416 #418-01-1970 L1975 **EM IM** *020 †16
GBADEBO, Tokunbo David. 1614 GUNBARREL RD 37421 #012-05-1994 L1999 **ICE CD** *020 †20
GEDDAM, Padmavathi. 601 CUMBERLAND ST 37404 #496-01-1994 L2004 **P** *020
GEER, Michael Reynaud. 960 E 3RD ST, STE 408 37403 #036-07-1975 L1985 **CD IM** *020 †20
GEFTER, Jeffrey Wm. 979 E 3RD ST, STE G20 37403 #011-03-1975 L1982 **RO** *020 †80
GEFTER, Monica Aviva Lehr. 979 E 3RD ST, STE 1001 37403 #011-03-1977 L1982 **IM** *040 †20 ‡
GESUALDI, Gary Paul. ■ 37411 #016-42-1983 L1996 **FM** *020
GHAMGOSAR, Farrokh. 1200 DODSON AVE 37406 #517-08-1979 L1997 **FM** *020 †18
GILBERT, Mark Alan. 975 E 3RD ST, ER DEPT 37403 #011-04-1985 L1988 **EM** *020 †16
GINTHER, Stuart Gordon. 979 E 3RD ST, STE B1111 37403 #036-05-2001 L2006 **NEP** *020
GODUCO, Roberto S. 100 MOCCASIN BEND RD 37405 #748-07-1953 **P** *020
GOLDER, Stephen Langdon. 2333 MCCALLIE AVE, SARAH CANNON CANCER CENTER 37404 #011-03-1977 L2002 **RO** *020 †80
GOLDING, John Vincent, III. 1614 GUNBARREL RD 37421 #047-07-1997 L2004 **IC** *020 †20
GOLDING, Monique H. 5600 BRAINERD RD, # H-100 37411 #047-07-1997 L2004 **FM** *020 †18
GOOD, Matthew Williamson. 910 BLACKFORD ST, DEPT EM 37403 #051-04-1999 L2002 **PD** *020 †55
GOODMAN, Michael Wm. 979 E 3RD ST STE C0630 37403 #017-20-1974 L1984 **GE IM** *020 †20
GOTHARD, Al Walton. 605 GLENWOOD DR STE 404 37404 #030-05-1959 L1963 **IM** *071 †20
GRACY, Ronald A, II. 941 SPRING CREEK RD 37412 #012-01-1990 L1993 **IM** *020 †20
GRAHAM, Frank B, III. ■ 37405 #012-01-1945 L1952 **GS** *071 †85
GRAHAM, Gordon Drexel. 2501 CITICO AVE 37404 #011-03-1977 L1992 **CD NM** *020 †20,28
GRANT, William Hurley. ■ 37421 #033-05-1964 L1965 **P OS** *030 †75
GRATIAS, Eric James. 910 BLACKFORD ST, PEDIATRIC HEM/ONC 37403 #036-05-1998 L2004 **PHO** *020 †55
GREEN, William Roy. 300 ASHLAND TER 37415 #047-06-1943 L1950 **PD** *071 †55
GREENE, Devon Andrew. ■ 37415 #012-01-2007 **PD** *012
GREER, Jack Ewell. 725 GLENWOOD DR, STE E588 37404 #047-06-1993 L1994 **OTO** *020 †45
GREER, Michael Spencer. 2108 E 3RD ST, STE 200 37404 #047-06-1978 L1979 **VS GS** *020 †85
GREER, William C. 7405 SHALLOWFORD RD, STE 160 37421 #047-06-1961 L1962 **P** *071
GREGG, Fred Marshall, III. 725 GLENWOOD DR STE E782 37404 #047-06-1978 L1979 **OPH** *071 †35
GREGORY, Oliver Lee. 2200 MORRIS HILL RD 37421 #047-06-1988 L1989 **P CHP** *020 †75
GRIGGS, Lane Brooks. 1751 GUNBARREL RD, STE 200 37421 #021-01-1984 L1992 **GYN REN** *020 †30
GRIGORIAN, Marina. 921 E 3RD ST # 400, UNIV TN COLL MED-CHATTANOO 37403 #913-38-1988 L2007 **IM** *100
GRIMSLEY, Mark S. ■ 37406 #001-02-1981 L1981 **FM** *020 †18
GRISSOM, Wallace Doyle. ■ 37421 #047-06-1961 L1962 **ORS** *071 †40
GROSS, Andrew Harry. 100 MOCCASIN BEND RD, INSTITUTE 37405 #036-01-1987 L1993 **P** *020 †75
GROTEFENDT, Kent Alan. 4626 HIGHWAY 58 37416 #016-45-1994 L1995 **FM** *020 †18
GRUVER, Carol Lynn. 2205 MCCALLIE AVE, DIAGNOSTIC CENTER 37404 #041-13-1984 L1996 **CD IM** *020 †20
GRUWELL, Mark Louis. 2525 DESALES AVE 37404 #019-02-1984 L1987 **AN** *020 †05
GUAN, David Hongrong. 961 SPRING CREEK RD 37412 #243-52-1984 L2001 **PCC** *020 †20
GUMNICK, Jane Frances. 100 MOCCASIN BEND RD, INSTITUTE 37405 #048-04-1995 L2001 **P** *020 †75
GUNTER, John Paul, Jr. 979 E 3RD ST, STE C520 37403 #047-06-1985 L1986 **PUD CCM** *020 †20
GUNTER, Timothy Allen. 1755 GUNBARREL RD, STE 300 37421 #045-04-1983 L1984 **PD PEM** *020 †55
GUPTA, Nishant. 921 E 3RD ST # 400 37403 #496-09-2006 **IM** *012
GUPTA, Rohit Kumar. 2300 E 3RD ST, STE B 37404 #012-01-1999 L2004 **NEP** *020 †20
GUPTA, Shobha Karwan. 420 BELL AVE 37405 #495-21-1971 L1998 **P** *020
GWIN, John L, Jr. 979 E 3RD ST, STE 300 37403 #008-01-1984 L1993 **SO ON** *020 †85
HADGU, Akberet Beyene. 921 E 3RD ST # 400 37403 #366-01-1997 **IM** *012
HAGOOD, Robert B, Jr. ■ 37416 #028-02-1941 L1956 **P** *071 †75
HALFORD, Wesley Chad. 921 E 3RD ST # 400, DEPT OF INTERNAL MEDICINE 37403 #143-11-2003 **IM** *012
HALL, David Raymond. 2525 DESALES AVE, POB 3549 37404 #012-01-1991 L1995 **AN** *020 †05
HALL, Marvin Neal. 910 BLACKFORD ST 37403 #012-05-1987 L1994 **CCP PD** *020 †55
HAMILTON, John W. 975 E 3RD ST, ANES. CONSULTANTS EXCHANGE 37403 #028-79-2001, ▲ L2005 **AN** *020 †05
HAMILTON, Robert Ezra, III. 975 E 3RD ST, ATT: DEPT OF EMERG. MED. 37403 #027-01-1997 L2000 **EM** *020 †16
HAMMOCK, Mary Cannon. 725 GLENWOOD DR, STE EAST480 37404 #047-06-1981 L1982 **IM** *020 †20
HAMMOND, John D. ■ 37421 #047-07-1983 L1983 **IM** *020 †20
HAMMOND, Sabrina W. 975 E 3RD ST 37403 #047-07-1983 L1984 **IM** *020 †20
HAN, Yuchun. 1626 GUNBARREL RD 37421 #243-10-1986 L2001 **N PME** *020
HARLESS, Renee Rice. 725 GLENWOOD DR STE E490 37404 #047-06-1986 L1987 **FM** *020 †18
HARNSBERGER, Benjamin Dan. 2205 MCCALLIE AVE, 2205 MCCALLIE AVE 37404 #012-05-1968 L1974 **PUD IM** *020 †20
HARNSBERGER, Daniel Scott. 2341 MCCALLIE AVE STE 302, PARKRIDGE PROFESSIONAL PLA 37404 #047-06-1999 L2003 **OBG** *020 †30
HARRIS, Charles Dennis. 2158 NORTHGATE PRK LN #104 37415 #047-06-1975 L1978 **FM** *020
HARRIS, Cindy Tang. 1651 GUNBARREL RD, STE 302 37421 #047-06-2000 L2002 **PD** *020 †55
HARTKOPF, Alyson Padgett. 2507 MCCALLIE AVE 37404 #045-01-1999 L2006 **PD** *020
HARTLEY, William Todd. 2415 MCCALLIE AVE, ORTHOPAEDICS 37404 #051-04-1992 L2004 **ORS** *020 †40
HASHWAY, Thomas, Jr. 1 FOUNTAIN SQ 37402 #035-45-1972 L2000 **CD IM** *030 †20
HAUN, Julie H. 935 SPRING CREEK RD, STE 100 37412 #047-06-2000 L2001 **FM** *020 †18
HAVRON, William Samuel. ■ 37421 #047-06-2003 **CCS** *012
HAWKEN, Kristi Anne. ■ 37405 #047-20-2006 **OBG** *012
HAWKINS, Charles W. 979 E 3RD ST, PLAZA UROLOGY GROUP 37403 #023-01-1946 L1952 **U** *071 †95
HAWKINS, Stephen Smith. 960 E 3RD ST, GROUP 37403 #036-01-1974 L1975 **ID IM** *020 †20
HAYES, Cauley Wilbur, Jr. 979 E 3RD ST STE C-920 37403 #047-05-1961 L1968 **HS PS** *020 †85,65 ‡
HAYES, Thomas Eugene. 721 GLENWOOD DR, STE W562 37404 #047-06-1961 L1961 **GS** *071 †85
HAYS, Leonard J, III. 2525 DESALES AVE 37404 #020-12-1982 L1993 **IM CD** *020 †20 ‡
HAYS, Mark Douglas. 910 BLACKFORD ST, T.C. THOMPSON CHILDREN'S H 37403 #045-01-1982 L2000 **PDC PD** *020 †55
HEAD, Harold David. 2108 E 3RD ST STE 300, THORACIC & VASCULAR SURGEO 37404 #036-07-1970 L1994 **TS GS** *020 †90,85
HEADRICK, James Robt, Jr. 2108 E 3RD ST, STE 300 37404 #047-06-1991 L1992 **TS** *020 †90,85
HEDDEN, James W. 4626 HIGHWAY 58 37416 #047-06-1959 L1960 **FM** *020 †18
HEIDEMANN, Nicole Leigh. ■ 37405 #012-01-2003 L2007 **OBG** *100
HEINSOHN, Mark Edward. 605 GLENWOOD DR, STE 404 37404 #047-05-1981 L1993 **IM** *050 †20
HEISSER, Randy Robt. 2337 MCCALLIE AVE, STE 307 37404 #021-06-1991 L1995 **FM** *020 †18
HEITHOLD, Pamela Marcena. 7550 GOODWIN RD 37421 #047-06-1993 L1994 **PD** *020 †55
HENDRICKS, Paul M. 725 GLENWOOD DR, STE E487 37404 #011-03-1981 L1993 **EM FM** *020 †18
HENRY, Warren B. ■ 37415 #021-01-1947 L1948 **PUD IM** *071
HENSON, Paul Edward, III. 725 GLENWOOD DR, STE E780 37404 #012-01-1992 L1997 **U** *020 †95
HERMAN, Leslie Dawn. 975 E 3RD ST, PO BOX 94 37403 #047-05-1997 L1998 **IM** *020 †20
HERMANN, Bruce F. 921 E 3RD ST # 400, DEPT PS 37403 #048-15-2002 L2003 **PS** *012
HEROLD, Steven Edward. 910 BLACKFORD ST 37403 #012-01-1999 L2005 **PDC** *100 †55
HERRICK, C Neil. 979 E 3RD ST, STE C720 37403 #016-06-1958 L1984 **REN GYN** *040 †30
HESSLER, Richard Bernard. 975 E 3RD ST, ERLANGER MEDICAL CENTER, P 37403 #050-02-1989 L2006 **PTH** *020 †50 ‡
HEYWOOD, Humphrey B, III. 979 E 3RD ST, STE C220 37403 #012-05-1960 L1967 **ORS** *071 †40
HIGDON, Kent Kihyet. 979 E 3RD ST, STE 401 37403 #027-01-2002 L2008 **GS** *012
HILDRETH, Amy Nicole. ■ 37411 #045-04-2002 L2008 **GS** *012
HILL, Hal Eugene. 725 GLENWOOD DR, SUITE E484 MEDICAL BUILDIN 37404 #051-01-1987 L1992 **ID** *020 †20
HILL, John Scott. 2525 DESALES AVE 37404 #012-01-1989 L1993 **AN** *020 †05
HILL, Robert Anthony. 1 FOUNTAIN SQ 37402 #027-01-1989 L1997 **FM** *020 †18
HILLWIG, Robert Jos. 700 E 3RD ST 37403 #041-12-1989 L1997 **PTH** *020 †50
HINA, Holly Ann. 929 SPRING CREEK RD, STE 102 37412 #020-12-1979 L1985 **OBG** *020 †30
HINE, Matthew Martin. ■ 37405 #048-02-1987 L1988 **OM GPM** *020 †70
HOBACK, James Wm, Jr. 979 E 3RD ST, STE C0925 37403 #047-05-1974 L1980 **CD** *020 †20
HODGES, Fred Barry, III. 979 E 3RD ST 37403 #012-01-1970 L2006 **ORS** *020 †40
HOFFMANN, Paul Erich. 1010 E 3RD ST, STE 202 37403 #047-06-1996 L1998 **PM** *020 †60
HOFFMANN, Paul Wilfried. 1 SISKIN PLZ 37403 #005-02-1964 L1971 **OTO AM** *020 †45
HOLLAND, Derek Weldon. 605 GLENWOOD DR, STE 200 37404 #028-02-2000 L2004 **HO** *020 †20
HOLLIE, Michael Carrell. 1720 GUNBARREL RD STE 400 37421 #005-12-1985 L1986 **AI PD** *020 †55,03
HOLMES, Terry Floyd. 100 MOCCASIN BEND RD, INSTITUTE 37405 #048-04-1974 L1994 **P OM** *020 †70,75
HOLSEY, Tanja Anderson. 1651 GUNBARREL RD, GALEN MEDICAL GROUP EAST 37421 #012-01-1991 L1994 **IM** *020 †20
HOLT, Brant Grover. 979 E 3RD ST, STE B1111 37403 #047-06-1999 L2000 **NEP** *020 †20
HONG, Moon Wha. 2525 DESALES AVE 37404 #583-03-1964 L1973 **PTH** *020 †50
HOOPER, Charles Mc Dowell. ■ 37411 #012-05-1941 L1946 **OBG** *071
HOPPE, Rudolph August. 904 BRYNWOOD DR 37415 #012-05-1944 L1946 **GP GYN** *062
HORGER, David Collins. 979 E 3RD ST, STE A450 37403 #045-01-1999 L2006 **U** *020 †95
HORN, Jeffrey Steven. ■ 37421 #045-01-2004 **GS** *012
HORNE, Adam Charles. ■ 37411 #001-02-2005 L2008 **PD** *012
HORNE, Tanya M. 1 FOUNTAIN SQ 37402 #012-21-1989 L2000 **FM** *030 †18
HOUSE, John Clinton. 2337 MCCALLIE AVE, STE 407 37404 #012-05-2001 L2006 **GS** *020 †95
HOWARD, Larry Donald. 7405 SHALLOWFORD RD, STE 280 37421 #047-20-1991 L1992 **IM IMG** *020
HUBBARD, Willie M. 3300 WILCOX BLVD, FAMILY HEALTH SERVICES 37411 #047-07-1978 L1981 **PD** *020 †55
HUBBERT, David Edmond. 2333 MCCALLIE AVE 37404 #047-06-1977 L1978 **EM** *020 †16
HUDDLESTON, Charles L, II. 1 SISKIN PLZ 37403 #047-06-1987 L1991 **PM** *020 †60
HUFF, Janara J. 910 BLACKFORD ST, PEDIATRIC INFEC DISEASE 37403 #047-06-1977 L1978 **PDI PD** *040 †55
HUFFMAN, David Michael. 823 MCCALLIE AVE, CONSULTANTS 37403 #036-01-1982 L1989 **DIA END** *020 †20
HUGHES, Alan David. 1720 GUNBARREL RD, STE 306 37421 #033-05-1970 L1980 **NM PTH** *020 †50,28 ‡
HUGHES, Charles Paul. 979 E 3RD ST, S C520 37403 #038-06-1964 L1983 **N** *020 †75
HUMBLE, Michael Brian. ■ 37415 #047-05-2000 L2002 **IM** *012
HUMPERT, Edward Leslie. ■ 37404 #010-02-1967 L2005 **MDM GS** *030 †85
HUMPHREYS, Steven Craig. 2415 MCCALLIE AVE, CHATTANOOGA ORTHOPAEDIC GR 37404 #016-43-1990 L1996 **OSS** *020 †40
HUNNICUTT, John W. 700 E 3RD ST, BLOOD ASSURANCE 37403 #048-13-1988 L1991 **PTH** *020 †50
HUNT, Darren James. ■ 37405 #012-22-2007 **GS** *012
HUNT, Kathleen Stewart. ■ 37405 #047-05-1994 L2003 **PD** *020 †55
HUSBAND, Betty Jean. 1501 RIVERSIDE DR, STE 120 37406 #027-01-1995 L1998 **IM** *020
HUSE, Robert Dale. ■ 37421 #005-12-1965 L1996 **R** *020 †80
HUTCHINSON, Amanda Justin. ■ 37402 #047-06-2007 **OBG** *012
HUTSON, Rodney Kent, Jr. 975 E 3RD ST, ERLANGER HEALTH SYSTEM 37403 #048-04-1991 L1995 **RNR** *020 †80
INCE, Christopher Werner. ■ 37403 #041-15-2002 L2006 **APM** *020 †05

INGALLS, Brian Edward. 725 GLENWOOD DR, STE E487 37404 #016-45-1987 L1991 FM *020 †18

INGRAM, Dale Clifford. 979 E 3RD ST 37403 #011-03-1981 L1982 ORS OSM *020 †40

JACKSON, Patricia Suzanne. 403 MCBRIEN RD 37412 #020-12-1982 L1987 FM *020 †18

JACOBS, Harvey A. ■ 37421 #869-02-1957 L1991 OPH *071 †35

JACOBSON, Edward L. 5600 BRAINERD RD, # H-100 37411 #065-01-1978 L1996 FM *020 †18

JACOBSON, Stephen Grant. 1 FOUNTAIN SQ, UNUM PROVIDENT 37402 #040-02-1976 L1991 OM IM *030 †20,70

JACOBSON, Tatiana Borisov. 921 E 3RD ST # 400 37403 #913-67-1984 IM *012

JAMES, Dabney. 2525 DESALES AVE 37404 #047-06-1976 L1977 IM *020 †20

JEMISON, David M. 1755 GUNBARREL RD, STE 302 37421 #047-06-1983 L1984 HS ORS *020 †40

JENKINS, Oliver W, Jr. 910 BLACKFORD ST 37403 #012-01-1967 L1970 PD *020 †55

JENNINGS, Mark O. 6400 LEE HWY 37421 #048-02-1990 L1999 CHP P *020 †75

JENNINGS, Richard Hunter. 721 GLENWOOD DR STE 471 37404 #012-05-1982 L1988 GS CCS *020 †85

JEONG, Christine Marie. 975 E 3RD ST, ER DEPT 37403 #041-07-1994 L1999 EM *020 †16

JEONG, Yune-Gill. 2205 MCCALLIE AVE, 2205 MCALLIE AVE 37404 #583-06-1970 L1978 PUD IM *020 †20

JOELS, Charles Scott. 979 E 3RD ST STE 300, ATTN: PHOEBE SMITH 37403 #020-12-2000 L2006 VS *012 †85

JOHNSON, Brian Dean. 975 E 3RD ST, ANESTHESIA DEPT 37403 #005-12-1983 L1990 AN *020 †05

JOHNSON, Bruce Wheeler. 4626 HIGHWAY 58 37416 #012-01-1981 L1996 FM EM *020 †18

JOHNSON, Darrell Ray. 605 GLENWOOD DR STE 200 37404 #020-02-1989 L1992 ON HEM *020 †20

JOHNSON, Deborah Jean. 105 LEE PARKWAY DR, STE A 37421 #033-05-1983 L1985 PD *020 †55

JOHNSON, J Paul, Jr. 2333 MCCALLIE AVE 37404 #047-05-1951 L1951 GYN OBS *071

JOHNSON, Natalie Inge. 1100 E 3RD ST, STE G100 37403 #021-06-1998 L2002 IMG *020 †20

JOHNSON, Sonya Lashawn. 251 N LYERLY ST, STE 300 37404 #047-07-1996 L1999 FM *020 †18

JOLLEY, James Edward, II. 2415 MCCALLIE AVE 37404 #048-06-1998 L1999 OSS *020 †40

JOLLEY, Kellie Amanda. 725 GLENWOOD DR, EAST SUITE 486 37404 #047-06-1995 L1998 IM *020 †20

JONAKIN, Steven Kenneth. 840 LAWSON ST 37415 #047-06-1981 L1981 DR *020 †80

JONES, Monica Maria. 975 E 3RD ST 37403 #017-20-1980 L1990 AN *020 †05

JONES, Roger Carrol. 960 E 3RD ST, STE 200 37403 #047-05-1977 L1978 IM *020 †20

JONES, Russell Allen. 605 GLENWOOD DR, STE 200 37404 #012-05-1965 L1975 ON HEM *020 †20

JOSEPH, Amanda Grounds. 921 E 3RD ST # 400 37403 #654-01-2006 PD *012

JOSEPH, Jason Michael. 921 E 3RD ST # 400 37403 #654-01-2006 OBG *012

JOVEN-LABRADOR, Irene. ■ 37416 #748-02-1965 L1972 IM CD *012

JUMP, Jeffrey Scott. 1100 E 3RD ST, STE G100 37403 #038-40-1990 L1996 FM *020 †18

JUNG, Wee Jin. 929 SPRING CREEK RD, STE 206 37412 #012-01-1999 L2002 PD *020 †55

JURGENS, Liezelle. 725 GLENWOOD DR, STE E788 37404 #836-03-1992 L2000 IM *020 †20

KAAKO, Ahmad. 501 E 3RD ST # 400, DEPT MED 37403 #875-02-2005 IM *012

KADRIE, Hytham Ali. 721 GLENWOOD DR STE W467 37404 #065-06-1972 L1976 N *020 †75

KADRIE, Tareck Alec. 721 GLENWOOD DR, STE 467-W 37404 #047-06-1998 L2003 N *020 †75

KALLA, Brian Michael. 1 SISKIN PLZ 37404 #047-14-1991 L1999 PM PMM *020 †60

KALRA, Yuvraj. 921 E 3RD ST # 400 37403 #496-59-2005 PD *012

KAPLAN, Bruce Alfred. 1322 DODDS AVE 37404 #011-02-1983 L1990 N *020 †75

KAPLAN, Hyman M. 6624 LEE HWY 37403 #012-01-1968 L1975 A IM *020 †20,03

KAPLAN, Paul A. 2525 DESALES AVE, P O BOX 3637 37402 #028-79-2002, ▲ L2006 PTH *100 †50

KAZIMI, Farzaneh. 975 E 3RD ST, DEPT OF RADIOLOGY 37403 #048-14-1991 L2001 DR *020 †80

KEEGAN, Patrick Francis. 910 BLACKFORD ST, TC THOMPSON CHILDREN'S HOS 37403 #027-01-1983 L1992 PD CCM *020 †55

KELLEY, Joseph Earl, Jr. 979 E 3RD ST, STE 320 37403 #047-20-1986 L1989 PDS UP *020 †85

KEMMERER, Scott Rolston. 5959 SHALLOWFORD RD, STE 575 37421 #005-12-1992 L2001 VIR *020 †80

KEMP, William J. 632 MORRISON SPRINGS RD, STE 101 37415 #047-06-1984 L1984 FM *020 †18

KENNEDY, Charles David. 2333 MCCALLIE AVE 37404 #047-06-1962 L1962 IM AM *071

KENNEDY, Denis. 6216 AIRPARK DR 37421 #539-03-1965 L1995 P *020 †75

KENNEDY, James Woodfin. 979 E 3RD ST, STE C920 37403 #001-02-1989 L1997 PS HS *020 †65

KENNEDY, Lizbeth Ann. 975 E 3RD ST, BOX 159 37403 #011-03-1983 L1990 NPM PD *020 †55

KENNEDY, Steven Clark. 961 SPRING CREEK RD, FL 2 37412 #047-06-1981 L2003 GS *020 †85

KENT, Craig Hunter. 715 GEORGIA AVE 37402 #012-01-1986 L1991 GS *020 †85

KERN, Richard Lee, Jr. 1010 E 3RD ST, STE 202 37403 #036-08-1996 L2002 NS *020

KHAN, Shabaz A. 901 CHANNEL VIEW LN 37415 #704-16-1990 L1996 IM *020 †20

KIDWELL, Christopher Wayn, Jr. ■ 37415 #047-20-2007 FP *012

KIM, Wayne Yongwon. 960 E 3RD ST STE 526 37403 #583-01-1963 L1978 P PYG *020 †75 ‡

KIMSEY, Charles W. 1000 E 3RD ST 37403 #047-06-1952 L1952 RO R *020 †80

KIMSEY, Frank Chas. 605 GLENWOOD DR, STE 208 37404 #047-06-1989 L1990 RO *020 †80

KINER, Dirk William. 979 E 3RD ST 37403 #025-07-2001 L2007 ORS *020

KING, David Anthony. 1618 GUNBARREL RD, STE 101 37421 #012-05-1998 L2002 GS *020 †85

KING, Frank Knox, Jr. 3202 AMNICOLA HWY 37406 #047-06-1980 L1985 FOP *062

KING, Walter Hughey, Jr. 2339 MCCALLIE AVE STE 201 37404 #047-06-1969 L1970 ORS *020 †40

KINGSMAN, Kilton Deroy. 601 DODDS AVE, DIAGNOSTIC IMAGING CONSULT 37404 #012-01-1981 L2004 DR *020 †80

KIPIKASA, Joseph Henry. 979 E 3RD ST, STE C825 37403 #041-07-1989 L1995 MFM OBG *020 †30

KIRBY, Charles Anthony. 5715 CORNELISON RD, #6600 BLDG 37411 #047-06-1977 L1978 OPH OS *020 †35

KLYACHMAN, Helen. 3309 CUMMINGS HWY STE A 37419 #035-01-2002 L2005 *020 †18

KNIGHT, Frank H. 1000 E 3RD ST STE 302 37403 #028-03-1971 L1984 DR *020 †80

KNIGHTS, Donald Arthur. 100 MOCCASIN BEND RD 37405 #917-24-1951 P *020

KNOWLES, Paul Douglas. 910 BLACKFORD ST 37403 #051-07-1981 L1998 CHN SME *020 †55,75

KODSI, Matthew Heath. 721 GLENWOOD DR, STE 467 37404 #005-18-1997 L2002 N FM *020 †75

KORN, William Kyle. 725 GLENWOOD DR, STE E487 37404 #001-06-1998 L2000 FM *020 †18

KORNER, Harold. 100 MOCCASIN BEND RD 37405 #039-01-1949 L1977 P CHP *071

KORT, Arthur A. 2501 CITICO AVE 37404 #035-19-1978 L1993 CD IM *020 †20

KOSANOVICH, Michael. 1030 E 4TH ST 37403 #017-20-1959 L1967 PTH *071 †50

KRAUSE, Richard Alan. 6035 SHALLOWFORD RD, STE 109 37421 #041-13-1972 L1977 GE IM *020 †20

KREEK, Andrew Edmund. ■ 37405 #041-13-1996 L2002 RNR *020 †80

KROUSKOP, Andrew Carter. 1 SISKIN PLZ 37403 #041-13-1977 L2002 PM *020 †60

KUETER, Daniel Baltz. 1010 E 3RD ST, STE 202 37403 #004-01-2000 L2006 NS *100

KUNDA, Prabha Annapurna. 2341 MCCALLIE AVE, RIVER CITY MEDICAL 37404 #495-70-1975 L1983 IM *020 †20

KUNDA, Sarma R. 975 E 3RD ST, DEPARTMENT OF ANESTHESIA 37403 #495-50-1971 L1980 AN *020 †05

KUTZNER, Waldemar. 2525 DESALES AVE 37404 #005-12-1964 L1972 GP *072

KUZUCU, Ethem Yildirim. ■ 37405 #902-01-1954 L1971 AN *071 †05

LABRADOR, Daniel P, Jr. 725 GLENWOOD DR STE E888 37404 #748-02-1965 L1972 PS *020 †65

LAMAN, Douglas Lewis. 910 BLACKFORD ST 37403 #047-06-1994 L1996 PG *020 †55

LANADE, Raphael Dada. 100 MOCCASIN BEND RD, MOCCASIN BEND MENTAL HLTH 37405 #913-48-1985 L1999 IM EM *020 †20

LANHAM, Gary Robt. 2333 MCCALLIE AVE, DEPT OF PATHOLOGY 37404 #047-06-1979 L1981 PTH *020 †50

LANSFORD, Frederick D, Jr. ■ 37415 #047-06-1956 L1957 FM GP *071 †18

LANTZ, H Jos. 1755 GUNBARREL RD, STE 301 37421 #038-40-1975 L1990 OTO FPS *020 †45 ‡

LARAMORE, John Wade. 605 GLENWOOD DR, STE 404 37404 #012-05-1973 L1976 IM *020 †20

LARSON, Tamarin Candis. 2288 GUNBARREL RD, PMB 111-241 37405 #005-12-1988 L1989 P *020 †75

LARSON, Tim Vernon. 6216 AIRPARK DR 37421 #056-06-1988 L1997 P *020 †75

LAU, Serena Winglin. 2341 MCCALLIE AVE, STE 402 37404 #047-05-1992 L1996 AN *020 †05

LAWLEY, Janet Mc Reynolds. 100 E 37TH ST 37410 #001-06-2003 L2006 PD *020 †55

LAWRENCE, Harry Martin. 1042 E 3RD ST, STE 102 37403 #047-06-1956 L1957 OPH *020 †35

LAWRENCE, Paul Arthur. 1720 GUNBARREL RD 37421 #045-04-1992 L1995 IM *020 †20

LAWSON, Tamunosaki E. 2339 MCCALLIE AVE, STE 401 37404 #654-01-1983 L1992 P *020 †75

LAWWILL, Stewart, Jr. 302 NORTHGATE MALL 37415 #047-05-1950 L1950 OPH *071 †35

LEDBETTER, Joel Craig. 910 BLACKFORD ST 37403 #001-02-1976 L1984 PUD OS *020 †55

LEDFORD, Calvin Saml. 979 E 3RD ST, STE C0925 37403 #045-04-1992 L2006 IC *020 †20

LEE, Angela Ching-Ying. 921 E 3RD ST 37403 #462-01-1987 L1994 OBG *100

LEE, Jason. ■ 37421 #012-01-2003 L2007 IM *020

LEE, Kent Alan. 1100 E 3RD ST 37403 #047-06-1993 L1995 FM *020 †18

LEECH, Mark Hatley. 1616 GUNBARREL RD, STE 103 37421 #012-01-1986 L1987 PS *020 †85,65

LENAZ, Maria P. 801 PINE ST, BLUE CROSS BLUE SHIELD OF 37402 #422-01-1982 L2008 OBG *020 †30

LENZ, Dean Lawrence. 1300 CLEVELAND AVE 37404 #017-20-1999 L2004 U *020 †95

LESAR, Christopher James. 2108 E 3RD ST, STE 200 37404 #038-43-1995 L2003 VS *020 †85

LEVIN, Todd Andrew. 6624 LEE HWY 37421 #012-01-2001 L2005 AI *020 †55,03

LEWIS, Allen David. 960 E 3RD ST STE 514 37403 #012-05-1965 L1972 D *020 †15

LEWIS, Jay Frederick. 1030 E 4TH ST 37403 #047-05-1958 L1958 PTH *020 †50

LI, Hai-Yan. 921 E 3RD ST # 400 37403 #243-13-1987 TY *012

LIENING, Douglas Alan. 1755 GUNBARREL RD, STE 204 37421 #023-12-1985 L2005 NO OTO *020 †45

LIGON, Jeff Jackson. 6141 SHALLOWFORD RD 37421 #047-06-1994 L1999 D *020 †20,15

LILLY, Mari Lynn. 901 MOUNTAIN CREEK RD, STE 200 37405 #055-01-1980 L1981 P *020 †75

LINDBLAD, Carl Axel Edwin. 1402A STRATMAN CIR 37421 #649-14-1975 L1980 EM *020

LIU, Chung-Yuen. 1604 GUNBARREL RD 37421 #244-04-1970 L1976 GYN *020 †30

LODGE-SHERWOOD, Em. 2501 MILNE ST 37406 #047-06-1957 L1957 PHP *030

LONG, Ira Morris. 5715 CORNELISON RD, BLDG 6600 37411 #047-05-1948 L1948 OPH *072 †35

LONGER, Charles F. 975 E 3RD ST 37403 #023-12-1981 L1986 ID IM *020 †20

LOPEZ, Julana D. ■ 37421 #005-12-2006 *012

LORD, Edward Frederick. 5600 BRAINERD RD, # H-100 37411 #065-01-1982 L1997 FM *020 †18

LOVE, Michael Allan. 1614 GUNBARREL RD 37421 #016-01-1972 L1978 CD IM *020 †20

LOWE, John Richard. 100 MOCCASIN BEND RD 37405 #004-01-1974 L1995 P *020 †75

LOWERY-SMITH, Lisa Ann. 910 BLACKFORD ST 37403 #001-06-1987 L1993 NPM *020 †55

LOWY, Sam Jos. 420 BELL AVE 37405 #048-02-1975 L1982 P *020 †75

LUCE, Kevin Peter. 979 E 3RD ST 37403 #054-04-2003 L2004 IM *020 †20

LUNDY, Mc Kinley S. 931 SPRING CREEK RD, STE 200 37412 #028-78-1979, ▲ L1980 OM IM *020 †20,70

LUSK, Christy Auburn. ■ 37421 #001-02-2006 PD *012

LYNN, Richard Monroe. 601 DODDS AVE 37404 #045-01-1980 L1987 DR *020 †80

MABRY, Elizabeth Danzig. 1210 PREMIER DR, STE #110, THE POINTE 37421 #005-19-1992 L1996 OPH *020 †35

MAC GUIRE, William B, Jr. ■ 37404 #035-01-1941 L1948 IM *071 †20

MACKLER, Donald Franklin. 721 GLENWOOD DR STE 552 37404 #010-02-1973 L1978 GE IM *020 †20

MAGILL, Robert Matthew. 2508 CROSS WINDS LN 37421 #047-06-1998 L1999 IM *020 †20

MAJEED, Shahul Hameed A. ■ 37416 #020-01-1966 L1981 GYN *072 †30

MAKDSI, Fadi. 921 E 3RD ST # 400, DEPT OF INTERNAL MEDICINE 37403 #875-01-2004 IM *012

MAKHIJANI, Sumeet Narende. ■ 37406 #047-06-2005 PS *012

MALHOTRA, Jagadish C. ■ 37415 #704-07-1940 L1973 P GP *072

MANDA, Winfred. 1949 GUNBARREL RD STE 230 37421 #913-48-1986 L2004 IM PCC *020 †20 ‡

MANKIN, Shannon Mc Callie. 935 SPRING CREEK RD 37412 #047-06-1998 L2001 IM *020 †20

MANN, Hillman Kemp. 921 E 3RD ST DEPT ROTAT 37403 #047-06-1988 L1989 *075

MANTON, James Scott. 2339 MCCALLIE AVE STE 402 37404 #047-06-1993 L1995 L1996 GE *020 †20

MANZARI, Nicholas J, Jr. 801 PINE ST, BLUECROSS BLUESHIELD OF TN 37402 #654-01-1986 L2000 EM IM *020 †20

MARIANI, Mario E. 3739 HIXSON PIKE, HIXSON PIKE MEDICAL CENTER 37415 #561-25-1991 L1997 IM PD *020 †20

MARSH, Clarence Bruce. ■ 37415 #047-06-1958 L1960 GE *071 †20

MARSHALL, John Willis. 2333 MCCALLIE AVE 37404 #020-12-1993 L1998 FM *020 †18 ‡

MARSHALL, Robert Nelson, Jr. 910 BLACKFORD ST 37403 #036-07-1967 L1990 PDE PD *020 †55

MARSHALL, Willis H, Jr. 420 BELL AVE 37405 #017-20-1961 L1974 **P N** *020

MARTI, Jonathen Joseph. ■ 37404 #012-22-2006 **GS** *012

MARTIN, Dorothy Jeannette. 910 BLACKFORD ST 37403 #047-06-1968 L1969 **PD** *040 †55

MARTIN, Laura Westbrook. 975 E 3RD ST, ANESTHESIOLOGY CONSULTANTS 37403 #047-06-1986 L1989 **AN** *020 †05

MARTIN, Martin S. 935 SPRING CREEK RD, STE 100 37412 #781-01-1966 L1993 **CD IM** *020 †20

MARTIN, Stephen Lee. 2108 E 3RD ST, STE 300 37404 #047-06-1985 L1990 **TS VS** *020 †85,90

MASSOUD, Hossein. 910 BLACKFORD ST 37403 #517-06-1956 L1970 **PD** *020 †55

MASTEY, Robert Danl. 1949 GUNBARREL RD STE 125 37421 #033-06-1989 L1996 **HS OS** *020

MATHENY, Gary L, II. 1 FOUNTAIN SQ 37402 #055-01-1984 L1999 **ORS** *020 †40 ‡

MAURONER, Richard F. 2200 MORRIS HILL RD 37421 #021-06-1983 L2004 **P** *020 †75

MAXWELL, Robert Allen. 979 E 3RD ST, STE 320 37403 #051-04-1992 L1997 **CCS** *020 †85

MC CALLIE, David P. 2501 CITICO AVE, STE 300 37404 #041-01-1946 L1949 **IM** *071 *020

MC CALLIE, Jack Bass. 725 GLENWOOD DR, STE E480 37404 #047-05-1984 L1987 **IM** *020 †20

MC CARLEY, John David. 2300 E 3RD ST STE B 37404 #056-05-1995 L1996 **NEP IM** *020 †20

MC CLARTY, Stacey Jack. 975 E 3RD ST, DEPT OF ANESTHESIA 37403 #005-12-2003 L2006 **AN** *020

MC CRAVEY, John Wells. 979 E 3RD ST, A0540 37403 #047-06-1974 L1975 **ON IM** *020 †20

MC DONALD, June Seaton. ■ 37419 #919-05-1961 L1972 **IM FM** *071

MC DOUGAL, John Small. 605 LINDSAY ST 37403 #027-01-1971 L1974 **P** *020

MC ELHENEY, Norman Earl. 1949 GUNBARREL RD, STE 270 37421 #012-01-1985 L1991 **ORS OSM** *020 †40

MCFARLIN, Elizabeth Louis. ■ 37403 #047-20-2008 *012

MC GAULEY, John Raymond. ■ 37419 #047-06-1969 L1970 **EM GS** *071 †16

MC GEE, H Lynn. 725 GLENWOOD DR STE 788 37404 #047-06-1977 L1978 **IM** *020 †20

MC GINTY, Patrick Brandon. 2205 MCCALLIE AVE 37404 #012-22-2003 L2005 **IM** *020

MC GRAW, Ralph, Jr. 975 E 3RD ST 37403 #036-07-1964 L1969 **NS** *071 †25

MC GUIRE, Susan Kay. 6400 LEE HWY 37421 #020-12-1976 L1981 **CHP** *020 †75 ‡

MC KELLAR, Sally Marie. 975 E 3RD ST, DEPT OF ANESTHESIA 37403 #036-05-1981 L1988 **AN** *020 †05

MC KENZIE, Randolph A, Jr. ■ 37405 #047-06-1983 L1983 **OTO NO** *020 †45

MCKEOWN, John. 2337 MCCALLIE AVE, STE 307 37404 #012-01-1976 L1997 **FM** *020 †16

MC KINNEY, James E. ■ 37405 #041-02-1948 L1952 **GP** *071

MC KOY, Robert Curtis. 979 E 3RD ST, STE B808 37403 #036-01-1982 L1988 **CD IM** *020 †20

MC LEAN, Susan W J. 929 SPRING CREEK RD, STE 206 37412 #036-07-1975 L1977 **PD N** *020

MCLELLAND, Patricia E. 1651 GUNBARREL RD, GALEN MEDICAL GROUP 37421 #047-05-1994 L2003 **OBG** *020 †30

MC NAMARA, Ryan Scott. 2333 MCCALLIE AVE, SUMMIT MEDICAL GROUP 37404 #001-02-1998 L2001 **IM** *020 †20

MC NEILL, Thomas Pinckney. ■ 37421 #020-02-1961 L1974 **R NM** *071 †80

MEADOWS, William E, III. 2021 HAMILTON PLACE BLVD, STE G 37421 #047-06-1982 L1982 **UCM FM** *020 †16

MEGISON, Donald Philip. 1010 E 3RD ST, STE 202 37403 #021-06-1983 L1989 **NS GS** *020 †25

MEHTA, Rohitash. 921 E 3RD ST # 400 37403 #496-09-2004 **IM** *012

MEJIA, Vicente Alonso. 979 E 3RD ST, STE 320 37403 #264-06-1995 L2003 **GS** *020 †85

MELVIN, Terry Ann. 4413 OAKWOOD DR, PRIMATIVE CARE SERVICE 37416 #024-07-1984 L1991 **PLM IMG** *020

MEMON, Naveed Hassan. 2341 MCCALLIE AVE, STE 403 37404 #704-25-1996 L2006 **FM** *020 †20

MERCADO, Avelino Velasco. 2339 MCCALLIE AVE, STE 403 37404 #748-08-1962 L1972 **GS TS** *020 †85

MERCADO, Elizabeth B. ■ 37404 #748-02-1963 L1972 **P IM** *071

MEREDITH, Gary Eugene. 725 GLENWOOD DR STE E882, MEMORIAL MEDICAL BLDG EAST 37404 #047-05-1974 L1976 **PD** *020 †55

METCALFE, James Kenneth. 3202 AMNICOLA HWY, ASSOCIATED PATHOLOGISTS 37406 #143-01-1972 L1987 **PTH PCP** *052 †50

MEYER, Barbara L. 975 E 3RD ST, EMERGENCY DEPARTMENT 37403 #048-13-1983 L1987 **EM** *020 †16

MEYERS, Larry Jos. ■ 37405 #004-01-1985 L1989 **AN** *020 †05

MILLER, John Edwin. 1949 GUNBARREL RD STE 150 37421 #020-12-1988 L1989 **OPH** *020 †35

MILLER, Karl Eugene. 1100 E 3RD ST 37403 #038-43-1980 L1996 **FM** *020 †18

MILLER, Thomas Paul. 2339 MCCALLIE AVE, STE 309 37404 #048-13-1975 L1978 **AN** *020 †05

MILLS, Don Gilbert. 440 N HOLTZCLAW AVE 37404 #005-12-1968 L1969 **DR RO** *020 †80

MILLS, Gary Eugene. 1751 GUNBARREL RD, STE 100 37421 #048-04-1973 L1982 **OBG** *020 †30

MILLS, Joyce Dunston. ■ 37421 #005-12-1980 L2007 **PTH** *020

MILLS, Marvin Leon. 975 E 3RD ST 37403 #047-06-1972 L1972 **CD IM** *020 †20

MILLS, Robert J. 2501 CITICO AVE, CARDIOVASCULAR GROUP, PC 37404 #010-02-1976 L1995 **CD** *040 †20

MINGUS, Robert Paul. 2525 DESALES AVE 37404 #045-01-1991 L2005 **AN** *020 †05

MINTON, Joseph Walker. 725 GLENWOOD DR, STE E487 37404 #047-20-1986 L1989 **EM** *020 †18

MIRANDA, Paul Anthony. 725 GLENWOOD DR, STE E487 37404 #001-06-1998 L2000 **FM** *020 †18

MITCHELL, Jerry Wayne, Jr. 941 SPRING CREEK RD 37412 #047-06-1972 L1977 **DR** *020 †80

MITCHELL, Kathleen C. 1751 GUNBARREL RD, STE 100 37421 #005-12-1990 L1997 **OBG** *020 †30

MOCANU, Brindusa Ioana. 921 E 3RD ST # 400 37403 #781-03-1996 **IM** *012

MOLLOY, Ronald Lynn. 112 LEE PARKWAY DR, STE 103 37421 #047-06-1967 L1968 **PD** *020 †55

MONROE, F Bruce. ■ 37402 #016-02-1940 L1942 **GS** *071 †85

MONROE, Van Stephen, Jr. 979 E 3RD ST, STE C0925 37403 #011-04-1993 L2002 **CD** *020 †20

MONTREY, Jill Suzanne. ■ 37415 #028-03-1979 L1980 **GS** *071 †85

MOODY, Richard Dwight. 961 SPRING CREEK RD 37412 #005-12-1994 L2002 **FM** *020 †18

MOORE, Christopher T. 318 WALNUT ST, RESEARCH ALLIANCE FOR WELL 37403 #047-06-1987 L1990 **FM** *020 †18

MOORE, Richard Alan. 979 E 3RD ST, STE 320 37403 #041-13-1987 L2002 **CRS GS** *020 †85,10

MORGAN, John Ronald. 910 BLACKFORD ST 37403 #047-05-1966 L1968 **PDC PD** *071 †55

MORONEY, David Matthew. 801 PINE ST, # 4G 37402 #021-07-1974 L1976 **PD** *020 †55

MORRISON, Richard Clarke. 605 GLENWOOD DR STE 405 37404 #047-06-1977 L1978 **TS** *020 †85,90

MORRISON, Richard Louis. 921 E 3RD ST # 400, DIV OF INTERNAL MEDICINE 37403 #654-01-2005 L2007 **IM** *012

MOSES, Wendell Meredith S. 910 BLACKFORD ST, T.C. THOMPSON CHILDREN'S H 37403 #005-12-1982 L2002 **OP** *020 †40

MOSS, William Joel. 1000 E 3RD ST, STE 202 37403 #047-06-1971 L1972 **OBG** *020 †30

MOTTO, Joseph A. 4355 HIGHWAY 58, 58 COMMONS 37416 #035-47-1978 L1982 **OTO A** *020 †45

MOUNIR, Deyaa. 2525 DESALES AVE, MEMORIAL HOSPITALISTS 37404 #915-02-1997 L2005 **IM** *020 †20 ‡

MOYER, Karen Marie. 921 E 3RD ST 37403 #308-11-1985 L1990 **IM** *020 †20

MULLADY, Thomas Francis. 2333 MCCALLIE AVE 37404 #023-07-1955 L1962 **IM** *020

MUNIR, Muhammad Amjad. 2337 MCCALLIE AVE, STE 307 37404 #704-16-1986 L1998 **FM PM** *020 †60

MUNSON-JACKSON, Julie C. 7446 SHALLOWFORD RD, STE 103 37421 #047-20-2003 L2005 **FM** *020 †18

MURPHY, Joshua Dean. ■ 37421 #047-06-2003 L2005 **GS** *100

MURRAY, Mark Garry. ■ 37411 #001-06-2005 L2008 **PD** *012

MURRAY, R Smith. 725 GLENWOOD DR STE E484 37404 #047-06-1960 L1961 **U** *020 †95

MUSGRAVE, David Michael. 2525 DESALES AVE 37404 #047-06-1988 L1989 **AN** *020 †05

MUTTER, Mitchell Luke. 979 E 3RD ST, STE C0925 37403 #047-06-1972 L1972 **CD IM** *030 †20

MYERS, Stuart Ira. 2108 E 3RD ST, STE 200 37404 #028-02-1976 L2006 **VS GS** *020 †85

NAGLE, Lawrence Steven. 979 E 3RD ST, UNIV. ONCOLOGY HEMATO LOGY 37403 #041-09-1976 L1987 **HO ON** *020 †20 ‡

NAKAMURA, Fujie. 900 MCCALLIE AVE 37403 #572-27-1944 L1960 **AN IM** *020

NASEER, Kaukab. 632 MORRISON SPRINGS RD, STE 300 37415 #704-01-1986 L1996 **PD** *020 †55

NASH, John Patrick. 1809 GUNBARREL RD, STE 101 37421 #024-01-1990 L1995 **ORS OSM** *020 †40

NATHAN, Marvin Myer. ■ 37412 #012-01-1947 L1951 **FM** *071

NAYEEM, Mohammed Abdul. 975 E 3RD ST, MEDICAL AFFAIRS OFFICE 37403 #495-21-1963 L1978 **FM EM** *020 †18 ‡

NEGUS, Brian Hartwell. 2501 CITICO AVE, THE CHATTANOOGA HEART INST 37404 #012-01-1988 L1999 **CD** *020 †20

NEHLAWI, Mohammed M. 975 E 3RD ST 37403 #875-01-1980 L1988 **END IM** *020 †20

NEWMAN, Copper Kiser. 1651 GUNBARREL RD, GALEN MEDICAL GROUP 37421 #047-06-2000 L2003 **OBG** *020

NEWMAN, Glenn Allen. 725 GLENWOOD DR, STE EAST480 37404 #001-02-1982 L1983 **IM** *020 †20

NEWTON, Philip Thos, Jr. 3812 TENNESSEE AVE 37409 #001-02-1969 L1974 **GP** *020

NICOLA, Paula Chrstine. 1042 E 3RD ST 37403 #001-06-2002 L2003 **OPH** *020

NIEVES-GONZALEZ, Alfredo. 1755 GUNBARREL RD STE 202, THE PELVIC PAIN & RECONST 37421 #308-03-1981 L1992 **GYN PME** *020 †30

NIPP, Ralph Elgin. 2339 MCCALLIE AVE, STE 200 37404 #047-06-1967 L1968 **CD TS** *020 †85,90

NOONAN, David Vance. 725 GLENWOOD DR STE 880 37404 #010-01-1969 L1979 **AN** *020 †05

NOWOTARSKI, Peter James. 979 E 3RD ST 37403 #047-06-02-1988 L1998 **ORS** *020 †40

NUNALLY, Bessie A Ingram. 975 E 3RD ST 37403 #012-05-1991 L1993 **IM** *020 †20

NUNALLY, James T, Jr. 251 N LYERLY ST, STE 300 37404 #001-02-1985 L1987 **OBG OBS** *020 †30

ODEM, Carroll Gilbert. ■ 37421 #047-20-1991 L1993 **IM** *020 †20

ODOM, Alan Clifton. 2415 MCCALLIE AVE 37404 #047-06-1973 L1974 **ORS** *020 †40

OELLERICH, William Fritz. 2501 CITICO AVE 37404 #047-06-1993 L2001 **CD IM** *020 †20

OH, Sai Hwan. 2412 MCCALLIE AVE 37404 #583-02-1967 L1989 **PM** *062 †60

O'NEAL, David Medford. 680 S CREST RD 37404 #047-06-1957 L1958 **ORS** *071 †40

OOMMEN, Annie Anchanattu. ■ 37421 #010-03-2005 **GS** *012

ORDONEZ, Jorge Enrique. 1755 GUNBARREL RD, STE 205 37421 #264-04-1970 L1983 **OBG** *020 †30

ORDONEZ, Luis J. 100 MOCCASIN BEND RD 37405 #264-04-1960 L1970 **GP EM** *071

ORIA, Jose Rodriguez. ■ 37415 #275-01-1939 L1981 **IM** *071

ORME, Terence James. 8644 E BRAINERD RD, STE B2/3 37421 #040-02-1968 L1987 **UCM FM** *020

ORQUIA, Carl Michael. 4626 HIGHWAY 58 37416 #005-12-1996 L1999 **FM** *020 †18

OSBORN, James Michael. 979 E 3RD ST, STE C0225 37403 #005-12-1991 L2000 **ORS** *020 †40

OSCAR, George Robinson. 2341 MCCALLIE AVE STE 402, PARKRIDGE PLAZA 3 37404 #012-05-1995 L1999 **AN** *020 †05

OXENHANDLER, Ronald W. 2525 DESALES AVE #MEMORIAL, P O BOX 3637 37404 #028-03-1972 L1984 **PTH** *020 †50

OZAWA, T Ted. 100 MOCCASIN BEND RD, MOCCASIN BEND MENTAL HLTH 37405 #572-05-1969 L1982 **IM NEP** *020 †20

OZBORN, George Michael. 3739 HIXSON PIKE 37415 #027-01-1974 L1976 **IM** *020 †20

PAGE, Cari Beth. 4802 14TH AVE, PAGE FAMILY PRACTICE, INC 37407 #047-06-1997 L2000 **FM** *020 †18

PAIK, Henry Ki. 2341 MCCALLIE AVE, STE 406 37404 #024-05-1989 L1996 **GE IM** *020 †20

PALMER, Chadwick Marshall. ■ 37411 #012-01-2005 **FP** *012

PANCAKE, Bruce David. 1736 GUNBARREL RD 37421 #047-06-1979 L1987 **OTO HNS** *020 †45

PANDA, Mukta. 975 E 3RD ST 37403 #496-15-1986 L1998 **IM** *020 †20

PANDA, Niladri Shekhar. 929 SPRING CREEK RD 37412 #496-15-1979 L1993 **IM CD** *020 †20

PANDIT, Lotika. 425 CUMBERLAND ST, SERVICES 37404 #495-18-1989 L1998 **IMG** *020 †20

PAPILLION, Paul Warner. 979 E 3RD ST STE 401, DEPARTMENT OF SURGERY 37403 #021-06-2005 L2007 **GS** *012

PARHAM, Bernard Lee. 3475 BRAINERD RD B, OPTIMA HEALTH CENTER PC 37411 #001-02-1988 L1991 **IM EM** *020 †20

PARIKH, Anuj Anil. 975 E 3RD ST, DEPT OF 37403 #041-02-2002 L2005 **EM** *100 †16

PARK, Won Bae. 100 MOCCASIN BEND RD, MOCCASIN BEND HOSPITAL 37405 #583-10-1968 L1979 **P** *020

PARKER, Christine Wright. 1200 GROVE STREET CT, WESTSIDE CLINIC 37402 #047-06-1982 L1983 **IM MDM** *020

PARKER, William Jason. 975 E 3RD ST BOX 15, PEDIATRIX MEDICAL GROUP 37403 #047-06-2003 L2006 **PD** *020

PARKS, Eric Daniel. 1100 E 3RD ST, DEPT OF FAMILY MEDICINE 37403 #047-20-2005 L2007 **FP** *012

PARSONS, Mark Kevin. 910 BLACKFORD ST, TC THOMPSON CHILDRES HOSP 37403 #047-05-1981 L1986 **PDC** *020 †55

PATEL, Chirag M. 979 E 3RD ST, GALEN MEDICAL GROUP PC 37403 #495-23-1996 L2003 **IM HEP** *020 †20

PATEL, Hareshkumar D. 975 E 3RD ST, DEPT OF ANESTHESIOLOGY 37403 #495-23-1978 L1988 **AN** *020 †05

PATEL, Manisha V. 979 E 3RD ST, STE 601 37403 #001-02-2000 L2006 **OBG** *020 †30

PATEL, Shetul Ishverbhai. ■ 37421 #654-01-2006 **PD** *012
PATEL, Vijaykumar P. 725 GLENWOOD DR S-582E 37404 #495-17-1982 L1990 **GE IM** *020 †20
PATEL, Yogini Hariprasad. 1755 GUNBARREL RD, STE 102 37421 #495-23-1979 L1993 **IM** *020 †20
PATIL, Vinit D. 975 E 3RD ST 37403 #056-06-1980 L1983 **AN** *020 †05
PAYNE, Catherine L. 9107 HUNDLEY RD 37416 #047-07-2000 L2001 **IM** *020
PAYNE, Stanley Ross. 975 E 3RD ST 37403 #021-01-1957 L1969 **ORS PS** *071 †40
PAYNTER, Steven William. 1949 GUNBARREL RD, STE 250 37421 #012-01-1983 L1984 **GS SO** *020 †85
PEARCE, Christy Friday. ■ 37421 #001-02-2005 L2007 **OBG** *012
PEARCE, Richard Garfield. 979 E 3RD ST, STE C225 37403 #047-06-1984 L1984 **ORS OSS** *020 †40
PEREZ, Martin Allen. 975 E 3RD ST 37403 #047-06-1958 L1959 **DR** *020 †80
PERKINS, Thornton Delos. 979 E 3RD ST STE 1203 37403 #017-20-1965 L1973 **ORS** *071 †40
PERRIN, Millard Foy. 1755 GUNBARREL RD, STE 300 37421 #047-06-1957 L1957 **PD PDC** *071 †55
PERRY, Gershon Y. 979 E 3RD ST STE A350, ACC 37403 #550-03-1980 L1994 **ICE CD** *020 †20
PESCE, Richard Rocco. 2501 CITICO AVE 37404 #035-03-1976 L1995 **PUD CCM** *020 †20
PETARRA, Steven Douglas. 2525 DESALES AVE 37404 #041-02-1991 L1999 **AN** *020 †05
PETERS, Richard Andrew. 1751 GUNBARREL RD, STE 100 37421 #036-01-1989 L1992 **IM** *020 †20
PETERSON, Edward Andrew. 1949 GUNBARREL RD, STE 220 37421 #049-01-1998 L2002 **OPH** *020 †35
PETERSON, Mark Wm. 2120 NORTHGATE PRK LN #201 37415 #016-06-1974 L1978 **P ADM** *020 †75
PETERSON, Robert Allen. 2205 MCCALLIE AVE 37404 #047-06-1993 L1996 **IM** *072 †20
PETERSON, Thomas Roy. 975 E 3RD ST, DEPT. OF ANESTHESIA 37403 #047-20-1983 L1987 **AN OS** *020 †05
PETERSON, Walter A, Jr. 320 N MARKET ST 37405 #047-06-1958 L1959 **GP** *020
PHELPS, John Y, III. 1604 GUNBARREL RD, CHATTANOOGA WOMEN'S LASER 37421 #010-02-1988 L2000 **OBG REN** *020 †30
PHILIPPOSE, Jawahar M. 725 GLENWOOD DR, STE E488 37404 #495-37-1974 L2003 **IM** *020 †20
PHILLIPS, David James. 979 E 3RD ST, STE C0620 37403 #012-01-1993 L1995 **IM** *020 †20
PHLEGAR, Robert Francis. 975 E 3RD ST 37403 #047-06-1970 L1971 **DR GP** *071 †80
PICKARD, Clay Mitchell. 744 MCCALLIE AVE, STE 427 37403 #020-02-1982 L1990 **D** *020 †15
PINE, Kathryn Dodd. 500 DODDS AVE 37404 #021-05-2005 L2008 **PD** *012
PITTMAN, Heather Carmen. ■ 37421 #665-01-2004 L2007 **PD** *100
PLUCKER, Samuel Milton. ■ 37421 #047-20-2007 **FP** *012
POCHEDLY, Carl Eugene. 910 BLACKFORD ST, CHILDRENS HOSPITAL 37403 #038-06-1956 L1985 **PHO PD** *050 †55
POLLOCK, Philip Gary. 2525 DESALES AVE, MEMORIAL HOSPITAL 37404 #028-03-1972 L1977 **PTH** *020 †50
POMERANCE, Glenn Noel. 2030 HAMILTON PLACE BLVD, STE 140 37421 #035-01-1974 L1984 **OPH** *020
PONCE-PORTUGAL, Jaime. 1949 GUNBARREL RD, STE 250 37421 #649-52-1990 L2002 **GS** *020 †85
POOLE, Christopher Vell. 979 E 3RD ST, STE B-1111 37403 #001-06-1998 L2003 **NEP** *020 †20
PORTERA, Charles Anthony. 721 GLENWOOD DR, STE 460 37404 #027-01-1964 L1971 **GYN ON** *020 †30
PORTERA, Chas Anthony, Jr. 721 GLENWOOD DR, MEMORIAL MED BLDG STE 471 37404 #047-06-1991 L1994 **SO** *020 †85
PORTERA, Joseph C. 1751 GUNBARREL RD, STE 200 37421 #035-03-1991 L1994 **OBG** *020 †30
POTDAR, Anilkumar. 150 DEBRA RD, VA OUTPATIENT CLINIC 37411 #495-21-1968 L1976 **P CHP** *020 †75
POTEET-JOHNSON, Deborah J. ■ 37421 #047-06-1985 L1985 **ADL PD** *072 †55
POTLURI, Prabhu Kumar. 2525 DESALES AVE 37404 #036-05-1994 L1998 **AN** *020 †05
PRATER, Christopher D. 2229 OLAN MILLS DR 37421 #047-06-1973 L1974 **FM ADM** *020 †18
PRATER-BIVINS, Linda Kay. 1949 GUNBARREL RD STE 2 37421 #011-03-1983 L1990 **EM FM** *020 †18
PRICE, Julian Paul. ■ 37415 #012-01-2005 L2007 **ORS** *012
PRITCHETT, Valerie Robin. ■ 37415 #047-06-2004 L2006 **OBG** *012
PUCKETT, Walter. 975 E 3RD ST, CARDIAC SERVICES 37403 #047-05-1955 L1956 **CD IM** *020 †20
QUILLIAN, Joe Anne. 2337 MCCALLIE AVE, 106 PARKRIDGE PROFESSIONAL 37404 #047-06-1954 L1954 **IM** *020
QUINN, James Gilbert. 601 DODDS AVE 37404 #012-01-1966 L1968 **R** *020 †80
RADER, Galine B. 4355 HIGHWAY 58, STE 101 37416 #913-67-1981 L2003 **FM** *020 †18 ‡
RADER, Melissa Michelle. ■ 37415 #012-01-2006 **GS** *012
RADER, Richard Alan. 615 DERBY ST 37404 #422-01-1983 **IM FM** *030
RADPOUR, Christopher Jon. 975 E 3RD ST 37403 #047-06-1998 L2001 **OBG** *020 †30
RAFULS, William Anthony. 9317 SHADOW POINT CIR 37421 #308-03-1980 L2001 **P PYG** *020 †75 ‡
RAHMAN, Abu Ahmed Zahidur. 921 E 3RD ST # 400, DIV OF INTERNAL MEDICINE 37403 #160-02-1999 **IM** *012
RAMSAY, Philip Turner. ■ 37415 #012-22-2004 **GS** *012
RANKINE, David Andrew. 979 E 3RD ST, STE 1210 37403 #063-01-1984 L1995 **N OS** *030 †75
RATLIFF-DANIEL, Brooke E. 605 GLENWOOD DR, STE 200 37404 #047-06-1998 L2005 **HO** *020 †20
RAWLINGS, Maurice S, Sr. 3815 ROSSVILLE BLVD, AVENTIS BIO LABS INC 37407 #010-01-1947 L1954 **CD IM** *071 †20
RAWLINGS, Maurice S, Jr. 605 GLENWOOD DR, STE 103 37404 #036-05-1976 L1976 **GS OS** *020 †85
RAWLINGS, Peter Carey. 725 GLENWOOD DR, STE E882 37404 #047-05-1979 L1981 **PD** *020 †55
RAY, Bobby Lull, Jr. 2525 DESALES AVE 37404 #047-20-1994 L1998 **AN** *020 †05
RAYBECK, Michael Jos. 1111 MARKET ST FL W 37402 #021-01-1971 L2004 **GS CRS** *030 †85
REDD, David Craig. 2339 MCCALLIE AVE, STE 403 37404 #047-06-1987 L1997 **GS** *020 †85
REDDY, Sudhakar K. 975 E 3RD ST 37403 #495-70-1971 L1980 **AN** *020 †05
REDEKER, Mark Dole. ■ 37415 #041-09-1996 **PD** *100
REDISH, Martin Harry. 2525 DESALES AVE 37404 #017-20-1980 L1985 **ORS** *020 †40
REEVES, Emily Juanita. 1751 GUNBARREL RD, STE 200 37421 #041-14-1995 L1999 **OBG** *020
REEVES, Michael Leo. 725 GLENWOOD DR, E688 37404 #036-05-1975 L1989 **DIA END** *020 †20
REYNOLDS, F Hall, II. 6141 SHALLOWFORD RD 37421 #047-06-1978 L1979 **D IM** *020 †20
REYNOLDS, John Robert. 979 E 3RD ST STE 900 37403 #030-06-1956 L1966 **PS** *020 †65
REYNOLDS, Thomas Michael. 1801 GUNBARREL RD, NOVA MED SURGERY CENTER 37421 #047-06-1984 L1985 **OPH** *020 †35
RHOTON, Alexander. 1725 MCCALLIE AVE 37404 #047-06-1962 L1963 **GS GP** *071
RHYNE, Patrick Norwood. 605 GLENWOOD DR, STE 300 MEMORIAL PLAZA 37404 #001-02-1998 L2001 **IM** *020 †20
RICE, Cynthia Jean. PO BOX 3278 37404 #020-02-1982 L1990 **RO** *071 †80
RICE, David Watson. 605 GLENWOOD DR STE 212 37404 #001-02-1994 L1998 **RO GS** *020 †80
RICE, Megan Amelia. ■ 37405 #012-01-2008 *012
RICH, John Stephen. 979 E 3RD ST, STE C728 37403 #047-06-1974 L1975 **OBG** *020 †30
RICH, Stephen Allen. ■ 37421 #047-06-2002 L2007 **GS** *012
RICHARDS, Theodore David. 2341 MCCALLIE AVE 37404 #047-06-1978 L1985 **CD IM** *020 †20
RICHARDSON, Arlene Jamell. ■ 37405 #047-06-2007 **TY** *012
RICHARDSON, James M, Jr. 7550 GOODWIN RD 37421 #027-01-1983 L1985 **PD** *020
RICHMOND, James Pierce, Jr. 932 SPRING CREEK RD 37412 #020-02-1977 L1983 **OPH** *020 †35
RIGGAN, Brandon Eugene. ■ 37421 #047-06-2005 L2007 **OBG** *012
RIMER, Thomas Richard. 601 DODDS AVE, DIAGNOSTIC IMAGINC CONS 37404 #047-06-1985 L1991 **DR** *020 †80
RINCON, Marielisa. 910 BLACKFORD ST, T.C. THOMPSON CHILDREN'S H 37403 #935-03-1998 L2005 **PDE** *100 †55
RISLEY, Jon Holland. 150 DEBRA RD 37411 #036-05-1991 L2006 **FM** *020 †18
RISSLING, Deloris E. 975 E 3RD ST 37403 #041-07-1964 L1968 **DR R** *072 †80
RITTENBERRY, Andrew B, Jr. 2108 E 3RD ST, STE 200 37404 #047-06-1969 L1970 **GS** *020 †85
RIZVI, Naushaba Hasan. 2205 MCCALLIE AVE, CHATTANOOGA MEDICAL ASSOCI 37404 #704-16-1988 L1997 **IM** *020 †20
RIZVI, Syed Farhan M. 2341 MCCALLIE AVE, STE 406 37404 #704-16-1991 L1999 **IM** *020 †20
ROACH, Kyle Vance. 2341 MCCALLIE AVE, STE 402 37404 #045-01-1996 L2000 **AN** *020 †05
ROBERTS, William Eggers. 979 E 3RD ST, STE C-825 37403 #001-02-1974 L2007 **MFM OBG** *020 †30
ROBERTSON, Jason Andrew. 2415 MCCALLIE AVE 37404 #047-20-2003 L2005 **FSM** *020 †18
ROBERTSON, Phillip Barry. 621 E 11TH ST 37403 #306-01-1984 L1989 **PD** *020 †55
ROBINSON, Neal Adams. ■ 37421 #004-01-1963 L1984 **FM OM** *071 †18
ROBISON, Michelle Yu. 2030 HAMILTON PLACE BLVD, STE 140 37421 #012-05-1991 L1996 **OPH** *020 †35
ROCKHOLT, English Allison. ■ 37411 #047-06-2006 **OBG** *012
RODELA, Elaina D. 975 E 3RD ST 37403 #048-13-2000 L2003 **IM** *020
RODGERS, Virginia Norton. 1949 GUNBARREL RD, STE 285 37421 #047-06-1985 L1987 **PD** *020 †55
RODNEY, Kelly Macmillan. ■ 37405 #047-06-2006 L2008 **FP** *012
ROE, Stephen Michael. 979 E 3RD ST STE 300 37403 #036-05-1986 L1989 **GS** *020 †85
ROGERS, Alfred Perkins. 975 E 3RD ST 37403 #047-06-1952 L1952 **GS OM** *072 †85
ROGERS, Marilyn J. 632 MORRISON SPRINGS RD, ERLANDER NORTH ED 37415 #047-06-1976 L1976 **EM** *020 †16
ROHRER, Jane Lively. 1651 GUNBARREL RD, GALEN MEDICAL GROUP 37421 #047-06-1979 L1979 **OBG FM** *072 †18
ROSE, Lance Mitchell. ■ 37416 #047-20-1992 **P** *100
ROSE, Walter Burr. 721 GLENWOOD DR, STE W550 37404 #047-06-1984 L1985 **GS** *020 †85
ROSS, Brenda Jane. 705 BARTON AVE 37405 #047-06-1992 L1993 **FM EM** *020
ROUNDTREE, Silverrene. ■ 37401 #026-04-1975 L1976 **FM GP** *075 †18
ROWE, William Edward. 961 SPRING CREEK RD, FL 2 37412 #045-01-1959 L1960 **GS** *071
ROWLAND, Jack Meridith. 929 SPRING CREEK RD # 202 37412 #048-04-1994 L2000 **OBG** *020 †30
ROYAL, James Richard. ■ 37421 #047-06-1957 L1958 **FM** *071 †18
RUDOLPH, Charles Todd. ■ 37421 #048-15-1995 L1999 **FM** *020 †18
RUFFNER, B Winfred, Jr. 979 E 3RD ST, STE 1001-B 37403 #036-07-1964 L1976 **MDM IM** *030 †20
RUIZ, David Enrique. 1100 E 3RD ST, UT COLLEGE OF MED CHATTANO 37403 #005-12-1984 L1987 **FM** *040 †18
RUSSELL, William Lee. 979 E 3RD ST STE 401 37403 #004-01-1968 L1976 **GS VS** *020 †85
RUTLEDGE, Jack Flanagan. 961 SPRING CREEK RD, FL 2 37412 #001-06-1985 L1988 **GS VS** *020 †85
RYAN, Eugene Healy. 2205 MCCALLIE AVE, DIAGNOSTIC CENTER 37404 #012-01-1990 L1996 **IM AM** *020 †20 ‡
RYBOLT, Ann Harris. 960 E 3RD ST, STE 208 UNIV MED ASSOC 37403 #012-05-1980 L1981 **IM IMG** *040 †20
SADOWITZ, Richard H. 2341 MCCALLIE AVE, PLAZA III STE 400 37404 #011-02-1987 L1994 **GE HEP** *020 †20
SAHAJ, David Alan. 1300 CLEVELAND AVE 37404 #051-07-1988 L1993 **GS U** *020 †95
SALAZAR, Oscar Daniel. 975 E 3RD ST, ERLANGER HOSP/DEPT ANESTH 37403 #649-14-1982 L2002 **AN PD** *020 †05
SALERNO, David Michael. 2501 CITICO AVE, CHATTANOOGA HEART INSTITUT 37404 #035-03-1974 L1993 **CD IM** *020 †20
SANABRIA, Luis Alejandro. 7446 SHALLOWFORD RD, STE 103 37421 #264-11-1998 L2006 **PD** *020
SANDERS, Brett Stanford. 2415 MCCALLIE AVE 37404 #047-06-2000 L2006 **ORS** *020 ‡
SANDERS, Virginia M. 910 BLACKFORD ST, T.C. THOMPSON CHILDREN'S H 37403 #047-06-2001 L2005 **PEM** *100 †55
SANTOS, Benjamin G. PO BOX 5254 37406 #748-07-1953 L1965 **AN** *071
SARGENT, Larry A. 979 E 3RD ST, STE C-920 37403 #012-05-1977 L1987 **PS CFS** *020 †65
SCANLAND, Jeanne A. 975 E 3RD ST 37403 #047-06-1982 L1986 **PS GS** *020 †85,65
SCHATZMAN, Nathan K. 2525 DESALES AVE 37404 #048-04-1989 L1993 **AN** *020 †05
SCHEINBERG, Marty. 1300 CLEVELAND AVE 37404 #047-06-1976 L1977 **U** *020 †95
SCHERER, Kurt Friedrich. ■ 37421 #011-03-2008 *012
SCHLABACH, Larry Lee. 979 E 3RD ST, STE A0540 37403 #038-45-1987 L1988 **ON** *020 †20
SCHMITS, G Michael. 2120 NORTHGATE PRK LN #201 37415 #038-40-1974 L1979 **CHP P** *020 †75
SCHMITT, Colleen Maclin. 979 E 3RD ST, GALEN MEDICAL GROUP PC 37403 #001-06-1986 L1994 **GE IM** *020 †20
SCHUBERT, Daniel C. 979 E 3RD ST, STE C720 37403 #021-06-1998 L2005 **OBG** *020 †30
SCHUBERT, Eric Douglas. 2525 DESALES AVE 37404 #035-06-1991 L1997 **PTH** *020 †50
SCHUTTE, Warren Patrick. 921 E 3RD ST # 400, DEPT PS 37403 #030-05-2002 L2007 **PS** *012 †85
SCOTT, Edgar Leonard, Jr. 1300 E 3RD ST 37404 #047-07-1955 L1964 **GS** *020
SCREWS, Jeremy Clark. 910 BLACKFORD ST 37403 #027-01-2001 L2003 **PG** *020 †55
SEABERG, David Chas. 960 E 3RD ST STE 100, OFFICE OF THE DEAN 37403 #026-04-1987 L2007 **EM** *030 †16

■ = Address Information Privacy Protected

SEAL, Molly Elaine Rogers. 1210 PREMIER DR, STE 100 37421 #048-12-1965 L1969 OPH *020 †35

SEIFER, Frederic Douglas. 632 MORRISON SPRINGS RD, STE 202 37415 #016-06-1982 L1988 PUD *020 †20

SEITERS, George Z. 1000 E 3RD ST STE 101 37403 #051-01-1967 L1977 ORS *020 †40

SELVA, Dennis Anthony. 975 E 3RD ST, PEDIATRIC EMERGENCY DEPT 37403 #027-01-1983 L2000 PD *020 †55

SELZER, Jerrold Lee. 3739 HIXSON PIKE 37415 #017-20-1977 L1978 IM *020 †20

SENDELE, Robert Leo. 979 E 3RD ST, STE A-0450 37403 #056-06-1976 L1983 OS *071 †40

SENTEF, Joseph, Jr. 6740 LEE HWY 37421 #027-01-1982 L1983 FM *020 †18

SEPP, Howard William. ■ 37405 #038-45-2006 PD *012

SHAFI, Arif. 409 DODDS AVE, PEDIATRICS ON DODDS 37404 #704-16-1990 L1995 PD *020 †55

SHAH, Indravadan K. 2339 MCCALLIE AVE STE 203 37404 #495-22-1973 L1984 RHU IM *020 †20

SHAH, Nikhil Suresh. 961 SPRING CREEK RD, STE 300 37412 #495-57-1981 L2002 GE IM *020 †20

SHAH, Umbar. ■ 37421 #704-25-1996 L2002 PD *020 †55

SHAH, Viren Jashvantlal. 2333 MCCALLIE AVE, PARKRIDGE MED CTR HOSPITAL 37404 #495-22-1998 L2004 IM *100 †20

SHAMAS, Azhar Min Ul. 921 E 3RD ST # 400, DEPT OF INTERNAL MED 37403 #704-21-2000 IM *012

SHAMMAS, Carlos Rafic. 2333 MCCALLIE AVE #654-01-1999 L2004 EM FM *020 †18

SHANDER, Gregg Stuart. 2501 CITICO AVE 37404 #041-12-1990 L1998 ICE *020 †20

SHANTHAVEERAPPA, Harsha N. 2205 MCCALLIE AVE 37404 #495-33-1995 L2002 PUD *020 †20

SHARMA, Naina. 1200 DODSON AVE 37406 #495-98-1995 L2002 FM *020 †18

SHARP, Sanford Collins. 2525 DESALES AVE, PATHOLOGY & LABORAT'Y MEDI 37404 #047-05-1988 L1992 PTH *020 †50

SHAW, Jacqueline Denise. 3300 WILCOX BLVD 37411 #017-20-1982 L1989 PD *020

SHELDON, Scott Andrew. 425 CUMBERLAND ST, STE 110 37404 #012-22-1998 L2002 IM *020 †20

SHENOUDA, Adel Nemr. 1520 RIVER VIEW OAKS RD 37405 #915-02-1963 L1975 NEP IM *020 †20

SHEPHERD, Brian Shane. 975 E 3RD ST, DEPARTMENT OF ANESTHESIA 37403 #020-02-2004 L2008 AN *012

SHERARD, Jerome Arnold. 340 N HOLTZCLAW AVE 37404 #041-02-1981 L1984 PD *020 †55

SHERMAN, Seth Brian. 100 MARKET ST, UNIT 404 37402 #035-08-1978 L2005 DR *020 †80

SHERRELL, James Wm. 2341 MCCALLIE AVE, PLAZA III, STE #304 37404 #047-06-1970 L1971 GYN REN *020 †20

SHERWOOD, Allen Thompson. 1755 GUNBARREL RD, STE 200 ERLANGER EAST 37421 #047-06-1985 L1987 FM EM *020 †18

SHIKOH, Alan Furhung. 721 GLENWOOD DR, STE W473 37404 #047-05-1991 L1995 GE IM *020 †20

SHIN, Chung Song. 100 MOCCASIN BEND RD 37405 #583-02-1960 L1977 P *071

SHIRE, James Robt. 6151 SHALLOWFORD RD, STE 101 37421 #038-43-1981 L1997 PSH CS *020 †45

SHOME, Brenda Gaye. 979 E 3RD ST, STE C520 37403 #047-06-1995 L1998 END *020 †20

SHORT, Kenneth Bruce. 1809 GUNBARREL RD, STE 101 37421 #047-06-1988 L1993 ORS *020 †40

SHUCK, Edwin Haywood, Jr. 975 E 3RD ST 37403 #047-06-1954 L1955 CRS *020

SHUCK, Edwin Haywood, III. 2341 MCCALLIE AVE, PLAZA 3, SUITE 305 37404 #028-02-1973 L1979 CRS GS *020 †10,85

SHULL, Anne Grotheer. ■ 37405 #005-12-1972 L2007 FM *020 †18

SHULL, John Albert. 929 SPRING CREEK RD, STE 203 37412 #005-12-1974 L1976 OBG *020

SIMMONS, Christina Marie. ■ 37421 #047-20-2006 PD *012

SIMMS, Cassandra Goins. 6400 LEE HWY 37421 #020-12-1999 L2004 CHP *020

SIMMS, Martin David. 1710 GUNBARREL RD, D/B/A CHATTANOOGA IMAGING 37421 #062-01-1989 L1996 *020 †80

SIMPSON, Aduke L. ■ 37415 #016-45-2007 GS *012

SIMPSON, Howard T. ■ 37405 #047-06-1951 L1951 P *071 †75

SIMPSON, Janelle D. 1100 E 3RD ST 37403 #064-01-1998 L2001 *020 †18

SINGH, Amar. 979 E 3RD ST STE A-450 37403 #035-15-2000 L2007 U *100 ‡

SISKO, Frank Edward. 2341 MCCALLIE AVE, PLZ 3 PARKRIDGE STE 402 37404 #047-06-1974 L1975 AN *020 †05

SIZEMORE, James Michael. 960 E 3RD ST, GROUP 37403 #047-06-1998 L2005 ID *020 †20

SLEDGE, Joseph Walter, III. 2339 MCCALLIE AVE, PLAZA II, SUITE 204 37404 #001-02-1978 L1993 CD IM *020 †20

SMALL, Suzanne C. 725 GLENWOOD DR, STE E487 37404 #047-06-1990 L1996 IM *020 †20

SMALLEY, Chad Carlton. 2415 MCCALLIE AVE 37404 #047-06-2000 L2006 ORS *020

SMITH, Allison Joy. ■ 37409 #012-01-2005 FP *012

SMITH, Angela. 7550 GOODWIN RD 37421 #001-06-1993 L1996 PD *020 †55

SMITH, Archibald Y, III. 2300 MCCALLIE AVE 37404 #047-06-1952 L1952 FM OS *071 †18

SMITH, Bill Moore. 1200 PINEVILLE RD 37405 #047-06-1987 L1990 FM FSM *020 †18

SMITH, Daniel Ray. 2205 MCCALLIE AVE, FL 5 37404 #012-01-1988 L1994 PUD PCC *020 †20

SMITH, Daniel Ray. 1032 MCCALLIE AVE 37404 #036-01-1988 L1994 PUD *020 †20

SMITH, Gary Danl. 2525 DESALES AVE 37404 #048-02-1982 L1985 AN *020 †05

SMITH, Josh Macdougald. 979 E 3RD ST 37403 #012-01-1983 L1984 PD *020 †20

SMITH, Lisa Ann. 979 E 3RD ST, STE 401B 37403 #041-09-1993 L2001 PDS GS *020 †85

SMITH, Michael Hall. 979 E 3RD ST, STE C725 37403 #045-04-1995 L1997 OBG *020 †30

SMITH, Philip Wright. 979 E 3RD ST, STE 320 37403 #047-20-1990 L1996 CCS *020 †85

SMITH, Richard Stephen. ■ 37415 #005-02-1960 L1961 OBG *071

SMITH, Samuel Morgan. 975 E 3RD ST, ERLANGER MEDICAL CENTER 37403 #001-06-1990 L1991 AN *071 †05

SMITH, Stewart Phillip. 1949 GUNBARREL RD, STE 285 37421 #047-05-1942 L1942 PD *071 †55

SMITH, Terry Walker. 979 E 3RD ST, STE 1203 37403 #047-06-1983 L1984 FM *020 †18

SNELL, Kenneth Bryant. ■ 37402 #024-05-1959 L1963 DR *071 †80

SNYDER, Paul Edgar, Jr. 725 GLENWOOD DR, STE E486 37404 #047-06-1966 L1974 OBG *071 †30

SOLOMON, Allen L. 6216 AIRPARK DR 37421 #047-06-1982 L1983 P *020 †75

SOM, Sibaji. 979 E 3RD ST, STE 240 37403 #495-38-1980 L1993 IM PCC *020 †20

SOTERES, Pete Spiros. 2333 MCCALLIE AVE 37404 #001-02-1964 L1972 PUD IM *071 †20

SOUFLERIS, Adam James. 960 E 3RD ST, GROUP 37403 #001-02-1986 L1993 ID *040 †20

SOUFLERIS, Nickie K. 113 STRINGER ST, STE A 37405 #001-02-1986 L1993 P *020 †75

SOWELL, Richard Forrest. 605 GLENWOOD DR, STE 300 37404 #045-01-1995 L1998 IM *020 †20

SPALDING, Robert Tucker. 551 OAK ST 37403 #047-05-1956 L1958 P CHP *020 †75

SPIEKERMANN, Luke Ezra. 3739 HIXSON PIKE 37415 #010-02-1978 L1992 EM GP *020 †16

SPROUSE, Larry Richard. 2108 E 3RD ST, STE 200 37404 #047-06-1996 L2001 VS *020 †85

STAFFORD, Florence E. 2507 MCCALLIE AVE 37404 #036-05-1950 L1953 PD *071 †55

STAFFORD, Ralph Wayne, Jr. 979 E 3RD ST, STE B1111 37403 #654-01-1999 L2002 NEP *100 †20

STALLINGS, Shawn Patrick. 979 E 3RD ST, STE C825 37403 #020-02-1996 L2002 OBG MFM *020 †20

STANDRIDGE, John Brendle. 1100 E 3RD ST 37403 #047-06-1974 L1975 FM FPG *040 †18

STANFIELD, James Edward. ■ 37421 #039-01-2003 L2007 IM *100

STANLEY, John Danl. 2108 E 3RD ST, STE 200 37404 #017-20-1988 L1994 GS *020 †85,10

STAPLETON, Lee Brown. 150 DEBRA RD, CHATTANOOGA OUTPATIENT CLI 37411 #422-01-1997 L2000 FM *020

STATON, Brent Davis. 921 E 3RD ST # 400, DEPT OF FAMILY MEDICINE 37403 #143-11-2003 FP *012

STATON, Lisa Jones. 975 E 3RD ST BOX 94, UT COLLEGE OF MEDICINE 37403 #036-08-1995 L2006 IM *020 †20

STECIW, Ann. 2525 DESALES AVE, MEMORIAL HOSPITAL 37404 #011-02-1989 L2007 CCM *020 †20

STEELE, Mark Alan. 1651 GUNBARREL RD, GALEN MEDICAL GROUP 37421 #047-06-1984 L1985 OBG *020 †30

STEGALL, Stephanie A. 929 SPRING CREEK RD # 206 37412 #012-05-1995 L1998 PD *020 †55

STEM, William Allison. ■ 37405 #047-06-1936 L1937 GPM *071

STERNBERGH, W Chas A, Jr. 1010 E 3RD ST 37403 #036-07-1965 L1973 NS *071 †25

STEVENS, Cathy Ann. 910 BLACKFORD ST DEPT PD, T C THOMPSON HOSPITAL 37403 #047-06-1982 L1984 CG PD *020 †55,19

STIPANOV, Michael Anthony. 605 GLENWOOD DR, STE 200 37404 #011-03-1993 L1995 HO *020 †20

STOCK, Alex Victor. 1100 E 3RD ST 37403 #047-06-2005 L2007 FP *012

STOHLER, Dennis Lee. 2415 MCCALLIE AVE 37404 #047-06-1971 L1972 ORS *071

STONE, John Logan. 979 E 3RD ST STE C235 37403 #024-16-1987 L1993 OPH *020 †35

STONE, Larry Dumas. 725 GLENWOOD DR, STE E487 37404 #047-06-1973 L1973 EM *020 †16

STRAIT, Timothy A. 1010 E 3RD ST, STE 202 37403 #047-06-1977 L1978 NS *020 †25 ‡

STRANG, William Howard. 961 SPRING CREEK RD 37412 #065-01-1963 L1995 FM *071 †18

STRATIENKO, Alexander A. 1032 MCCALLIE AVE, STE 200 37403 #041-13-1983 L1993 CD IM *020 †20

STRELNIKOVA, Natalie S. ■ 37411 #047-06-2006 IM *012

STRICKLAND, Adrien Kathry. 921 E 3RD ST # 400, DEPT MED 37403 #012-01-2006 IM *012

STRIKER, William Kendall. 1501 RIVERSIDE DR 37406 #036-05-1965 L1970 PTH *071 †50

STROUD, Mary E Thompson. ■ 37404 #004-01-1952 L1963 P *071

STROUP, Rebekah Kay. ■ 37421 #020-12-2008 *012

STUBBLEFIELD, Steven B. 2515 DESALES AVE, STE 205 37404 #047-06-1980 L1980 IM CD *020 †20

SUBTIRELU, Mihail Marius. 910 BLACKFORD ST, PEDIATRIC NEPHROLOGY, T.C. 37403 #781-01-1986 L2004 PN *100 †55

SUD, Avinash M. 1301 MCCALLIE AVE, CHATTANOOGA OUTPATIENT CTR 37404 #047-06-1986 L1999 RNR NM *020 †28,80

SUGGS, Charles L, Jr. 975 E 3RD ST 37403 #047-05-1942 L1942 GYN *071 †30

SULTAN, Zara. 6918 SHALLOWFORD RD, STE 201 37421 #704-25-1998 L2006 PD *020 †55 ‡

SUMMERS, Jonathan Allen. 1100 E 3RD ST, UT FAMILY PRACTICE CENTER 37403 #001-06-2004 L2006 FM *020 †18

SUPAN, Angelina A. 601 CUMBERLAND ST 37404 #748-07-1964 L1975 P *020

SURENDERANATH, Nisha K. 910 BLACKFORD ST, DEPT OF PEDS 37403 #495-44-1993 L2007 PD PDC *100 †55

SUTTERFIELD, William C. 1949 GUNBARREL RD, STE 250 37421 #039-01-1995 L1997 GS *020 †85

SUTTON, Joel Trent. 9107 HUNDLEY RD 37416 #047-06-2000 L2001 IM *100 †20

SWEARINGEN, Mary Lynn. 2333 MCCALLIE AVE, DEPT OF PATHOLOGY 37404 #047-06-1981 L1990 PTH PCP *020 †50

SZCZUKOWSKI, Myron J. ■ 37411 #028-34-1949 L1967 DR *071 †80

TALBERT, Timothy Mchaney. 2341 MCCALLIE AVE 37404 #047-06-1988 L1989 ICE *020 †20

TALBOTT, Gregory Alan. 910 BLACKFORD ST, T.C. THOMPSON CHILDREN'S H 37403 #036-07-1988 L1998 AN *020 †55

TALLENT, Phillip Gabriel. 632 MORRISON SPRINGS RD, STE 202 37415 #012-22-2002 L2007 N SMI *020 †75

TAPP, John Edward, II. 2205 MCCALLIE AVE, DIAGNOSTIC CENTER 37404 #047-06-2000 L2001 IM *020 †20

TAYLOR, Robert Creston. 1 FOUNTAIN SQ, UNUMPROVIDENT CORP 2W210 37402 #047-06-1967 L1968 EM OM *030

TAYLOR, Thomas Edward. ■ 37412 #047-06-1958 L1962 OTO AI *071 †45

TEJANI, Sushila N. 975 E 3RD ST 37403 #496-38-1972 L1979 AN *020 †05

TEMLOCK, Arthur Aaron. 2341 MCCALLIE AVE, PARK RIDGE PLZ 3 STE 402 37404 #039-01-1976 L1979 AN *020 †05

TEW, W Michael. 979 E 3RD ST 37403 #539-06-1983 L1994 ORS OSM *020

THEL, Mark Chas. 2501 CITICO AVE, INSTITUTE 37404 #010-02-1986 L2000 CD IM *020 †20

THOMAS, Bradley Winston. ■ 37405 #036-05-2005 GS *012

THOMAS, Ronishia Daria. 979 E 3RD ST, STE C720 37403 #021-01-2004 L2007 OBG *012

THOMAS, Steven Michael. 632 MORRISON SPRINGS RD, SUITE 202, ERLANGER NORTH 37415 #047-06-1975 L1976 OPH *020 †35

THOMAS, Victor James. 975 E 3RD ST, PEDIATRIC MEDICAL GROUP 37403 #011-03-1983 L1989 NPM *020 †55

THOMASSON, Joseph Richard, III. ■ 37406 #047-20-2007 GS *012

THOMPSON, Lloyd W. 3222 WILCOX BLVD 37411 #047-07-1950 L1954 GS *071

TIGAR, Michael C. 1651 GUNBARREL RD 37421 #047-06-1997 L2000 PD *020 †55

TIN, Pe Than. 930 OAK ST 37403 #209-01-1966 L1978 OPH *020 †35

TINDNI, Arshdeep. 921 E 3RD ST # 400 37403 #496-09-2005 IM *012

TIPPS, Jeffrey Elliott. 601 DODDS AVE, DIAGNOSTIC IMAGING CONSULT 37404 #047-06-1996 L2003 DR *100 †80

TODD, Matthew Justin. 975 E 3RD ST BOX 251, CHATTANOOGA 37403 #012-01-2000 L2002 IM *020 †20

TODD, Nivin Shihata. 1755 GUNBARREL RD, SUITE205 37421 #012-22-1997 L1998 OBG *020 †30

TOLOSA, Drago. 910 BLACKFORD ST, T.C. THOMPSON'S CHILDREN H 37403 #308-03-1982 L1995 GE *020 †20

TOMPKINS, Ronald Wayne. 2333 MCCALLIE AVE 37404 #021-06-1990 L1999 FM *020 †18

TOOLSIE, Ronald. 7836 MAGNOLIA LAKE DR 37421 #917-08-1984 L1991 PTH *020 †50 ‡

TORRES, Carlos. 979 E 3RD ST, STE C825 37403 #047-06-1999 L2001 **OBG** *020 †30
TRASK, Shawn Daniel. 910 BLACKFORD ST 37403 #027-01-1987 L1990 **PD** *020 †55
TRUBEY, Cameron Lee. ■ 37421 #005-12-2007 **FP** *012
TRUELOVE, Steven Mark. 2525 DESALES AVE 37404 #047-20-1991 L1995 **AN** *020 †05
TUN, Katherine Mui. 2507 MCCALLIE AVE 37404 #016-45-1996 L1999 **PD** *020 †55
TURNER, Elizabeth Stone. 979 E 3RD ST, STE B805 37403 #047-20-1996 L1999 **RHU** *020 †20
TVEITE, Molly Helen. ■ 37415 #020-02-2007 **IM** *012
TWIEST, Melvin Wayne. 975 E 3RD ST, ERLANGER HEALTH SYSTEMS 37403 #025-01-1970 L2001 **MDM GS** *030 †85
ULIN, Louis. 960 E 3RD ST 37403 #041-09-1939 L1946 **GS** *072
USON, Glicerio Marinas. 100 MOCCASIN BEND RD 37405 #748-07-1955 **GP OS** *100
UTADEJ, Banchob. 2333 MCCALLIE AVE 37404 #891-01-1961 L1975 **PTH** *071
VALLE, Alvaro Alejandro. 2108 E 3RD ST, STE 200 37404 #682-01-1978 L1989 **SO GS** *020 †85
VANCE, Minnie Ratliff. 2507 MCCALLIE AVE 37404 #047-06-1949 L1953 **PD** *020 †55
VANDERBILT, Douglas Lee. 1949 GUNBARREL RD STE 255 37421 #047-06-1972 L1973 **GS** *020 †85
VARGAS, Efren. 100 E 37TH ST, SOUTHSIDE COMMUNITY HEALTH 37410 #319-03-1978 L1996 **IM** *020 †20
VARNELL, Jessie Lanett. 601 DODDS AVE 37404 #001-06-1982 L2001 **DR** *020 †80
VAUGHN, Barry Richard. 935 SPRING CREEK RD, STE 200 37412 #047-20-1990 L1996 **ORS** *020 †40
VECHINSKI, Thomas Osberg. 601 DODDS AVE 37404 #056-05-1961 L1978 **R** *020 †80
VEMURI, Sameer. 1 SISKIN PLZ, SISKIN SPINE & REHABILITAT 37403 #654-01-1999 L2005 **PM** *100 †60
VENTRA, Pamela Christine. ■ 37416 #005-18-1984 L1996 **GP** *020
VERNON, Andrew Norbert. 1032 MCCALLIE AVE 37403 #039-01-1985 L1993 **PCC IM** *020 †20
VIETH, Roger Gordon. ■ 37405 #036-07-1959 L1966 **NS** *020 †25
VIRANI, Subhash. 1720 GUNBARREL RD 37421 #035-09-1995 L1998 **IM** *020 †20
VIRTUCIO, Rolen C. TVA 201 EDNEY BLDG 37401 #748-07-1957 **GS** *071
VISSER, Jeffrey David. 725 GLENWOOD DR, STE E487 37404 #018-03-1990 L1995 **EM FM** *020 †18
VOELZKE, Will Rowland. 605 GLENWOOD DR, STE 200 37404 #048-04-2002 L2008 **HO** *012 †20
VON CANON, Charles Hunter. 1755 GUNBARREL RD, STE 300 37421 #047-06-1962 L1963 **PD PDA** *072
VON WERSSOWETZ, A J. 2337 MCCALLIE AVE, STE 303 37404 #047-06-1972 L1973 **PS** *020 †65
VOYCHEHOVSKI, Tomasz H. 632 MORRISON SPRINGS RD, STE 300 37415 #759-06-1968 L1992 **PD ID** *020 †55
WAGG, Christopher Anthony. 725 GLENWOOD DR, STE E487 37404 #064-01-1980 L1997 **EM GP** *020 †18
WALDROP, Jimmy Lee, Jr. ■ 37415 #012-01-2000 L2004 **PS** *012 †85
WALKER, Russell Lee. 1720 GUNBARREL RD, STE 400 37421 #047-06-1991 L1993 **AI PD** *020 †03,55 ‡
WALLACE, Kenneth Arthur. ■ 37415 #025-07-1989 L1992 **EM PD** *020 †16
WARREN, William Powers. 2501 CITICO AVE 37404 #024-01-1996 L2003 **CD** *020 †20
WATERS, Clyde Cleveland. 929 SPRING CREEK RD, STE 202 37412 #047-06-1978 L1979 **OBG** *020
WATLINGTON, Joseph Thos. 3555 BROAD ST 37409 #047-06-1979 L1980 **NEP** *020 †20
WATSON, George R. 601 DODDS AVE, DIAGNOSTIC IMAGING CONSULT 37404 #016-01-1986 L2004 **NM** *020 †80,28
WEBB, Deborah Lee. ■ 37421 #010-01-1983 L2007 **IM GP** *020 †20
WENDT, David John. 2501 CITICO AVE 37404 #025-07-1982 L1994 **ICE CD** *020 †20
WENG, Jen-Tsoh. 975 E 3RD ST 37403 #244-03-1968 L1983 **AN** *020 †05
WENTLAND, Paul Douglas. 1 FOUNTAIN SQ # 4S-426, C/O UNUM PROVIDENT CORP 37402 #005-12-1985 L2005 **IM** *062 †20
WERLE, Zachary R. ■ 37411 #028-78-2005, ▲ L2007 **FP** *012
WESSELS, Izak Frederick. 7405 SHALLOWFORD RD 37421 #836-01-1973 L1995 **OPH** *020 †35 ‡
WHARTON, David Reed. 975 E 3RD ST, ERLANGER MEDICAL CENTER 37403 #012-01-1982 L1986 **EM** *020 †16
WHEELOCK, Argil Jerry. 756 GLENWOOD DR STE E-484, MEMORIAL MED BLDG EAST 37404 #047-06-1971 L1972 **U** *020 †95
WHITAKER, Cassandra Denis. 929 SPRING CREEK RD, STE 202 37412 #001-06-1990 L2004 **OBG** *020 †30
WHITE, Gregory P. 1755 GUNBARREL RD, STE 206 37421 #047-07-1985 L1987 **PM PMM** *020 †60
WHITE, James Eugene. 7446 SHALLOWFORD RD, STE 205 37421 #012-01-1990 L1992 **GS VIR** *020 †85
WHITE, Jay Perry. 1651 GUNBARREL RD, GALEN MEDICAL GROUP 37421 #047-06-1989 L1990 **OBG** *072 †30
WHITEFIELD, Julia Sabine. 910 BLACKFORD ST, EMERGENCY DEPT. 37403 #409-32-1983 L2002 **PD** *020 †55
WILCOX, Kirk Alexander. 2158 NORTHGATE PARK LN, STE 104 37415 #005-12-1991 L1994 **FM** *020 †18
WILLIAMS, Chanda Yvette. ■ 37421 #047-20-2006 **PTH** *012
WILLIAMS, Robert Henry. 605 GLENWOOD DR STE 300 37404 #047-05-1974 L1979 **IM** *020 †20 ‡
WILLIAMS, Terry Lee. 975 E 3RD ST BOX 121 37403 #055-75-2004, ▲ L2006 **OBG** *012
WILLINGHAM, Winborn B, Jr. 960 E 3RD ST STE 1 37403 #047-06-1964 L1964 **U** *071 †95
WINICK, Kathryn Annette. 921 E 3RD ST # 400, DEPT OF OB/GYN 37403 #305-01-2006 **OBG** *012
WISEMAN, Ralph Steven. 2339 MCCALLIE AVE, STE 309 37404 #036-01-1987 L1991 **AN** *020 †05
WITHERSPOON, Laura Ellen. 2205 MCCALLIE AVE, STE 102 37404 #047-05-1985 L1994 **GS** *020 †85
WOLFE, Lynlee Marie. 921 E 3RD ST # 400, CHATTANOOGA DEPT OF OB/GYN 37403 #422-01-2005 **OBG** *012
WONG, Herbert Man-Yin. 1604 GUNBARREL RD, CHATTANOOGA WOMEN'S LASER 37421 #065-01-1998 L2003 **OBG** *012
WOOD, John Cromwell. 979 E 3RD ST, STE C0620 37403 #025-12-1983 L2001 **IM CD** *020 †20
WOOD, Michael John. 605 GLENWOOD DR, STE 404 37404 #048-12-1982 L2003 **IM** *020 †20
WORTHINGTON, Julian Mack. 1100 E 3RD ST 37403 #048-02-1975 L1980 **FM** *020 †18
WRIGHT, Kinsman E, Jr. 2501 CITICO AVE 37404 #024-01-1964 L1977 **CD IM** *020 †20
YALAVARTHY, Umesh Chowdar. 921 E 3RD ST # 400, DEPT OF MED 37403 #495-50-2001 **IM** *012

YAP, Dolorosa B. 100 MOCCASIN BEND RD, MBMHI 37405 #748-09-1966 L1981 **P** *020
YAP, Richard Litonjua. ■ 37421 #748-02-1995 L2003 **IM** *020 †20
YATES, Munford R, III. 979 E 3RD ST, STE 520 37403 #051-04-1994 L2000 **GE** *020
YETTER, Christopher Ross. 2525 DESALES AVE 37404 #041-12-1984 L1986 **AN** *020 †05
YIUM, Jackson Joe. 979 E 3RD ST, STE B1111 37403 #048-02-1962 L1973 **NEP IM** *071 †20
YOOD, Steven Henry. 725 GLENWOOD DR 37404 #047-05-1985 L1989 **IM** *075
YOUNG, Christopher Edward. 975 E 3RD ST, ERLANGER MEDICAL CENTER 37403 #010-02-1985 L1986 **AN** *020 †05
YOUNG, George G. ■ 37404 #012-01-1938 L1946 **GS** *071 †85
YOUNG, Lawrence I. 2525 DESALES AVE 37404 #036-01-1975 L1978 **AN** *020 †05
YOUNG, William M. 725 GLENWOOD DR, STE E780 37404 #047-06-1995 L2001 **U** *020 †95
YOUNGER, Robt Edward, III. 1720 GUNBARREL RD, STE 400 37421 #047-06-1980 L1980 **AI** *020 †55,03
ZEIGLER, Donald Keith. 5959 SHALLOWFORD RD, STE 539 37421 #038-45-1999 L2001 **FM** *020 †18
ZELLNER, James Lawrence. 2108 E 3RD ST, STE 300 37404 #038-41-1986 L2000 **TS** *020 †85,90
ZHANG, Xuhan. 709 WALNUT ST 37402 #243-16-1985 L1999 **IM** *020 †20
ZURAWICK, Jason George. 910 BLACKFORD ST 37403 #047-20-2005 L2008 **PD** *012

CHRISTIANA – RUTHERFORD

ARNOLD, Edward Stanley. ■ 37037 #047-05-1977 L1978 **P** *071 †75
MARLIN, Raleigh Wm. ■ 37037 #654-01-1986 L1991 **FM** *020 †18

CHUCKEY – GREENE

MESSINGER, Lindsay H. ■ 37641 #005-12-1991 L1995 **DR** *020 †80

CHURCH HILL – HAWKINS

MANOLE, Viorel D. 406 E MAIN BLVD 37642 #781-01-1984 L2000 **IM** *020 †20
MIRMOHAMADSADEGHI, Seyed. 115 GARLAND AVE, KINGSPORT MEDICAL ASSOCIAT 37642 #902-05-1993 L2005 **IM** *020 †20
PIERSON, Henry Earl. ■ 37642 #047-06-1958 L1987 **GP DR** *020
ROBERSON, Travis Hubert. 115 GARLAND AVE 37642 #047-06-1956 L1957 **GP** *071
SCHILLING, David Erwin. 406 E MAIN BLVD 37642 #016-06-1976 L1977 **FM** *020 †18
SKELTON, Barbara Johnston. ■ 37642 #047-20-1985 L1992 **PD PHP** *020 †55

CLAIRFIELD – CLAIBORNE

CORTEZ, Ma Luzvida J S. PO BOX 67, 5663 HIGHWAY 90 37715 #748-02-1987 L1995 **IM NEP** *020 †20

CLARKSVILLE – MONTGOMERY

AARON, John. 2147 WILMA RUDOLPH BLVD, PREMIER MEDICAL GROUP PC 37040 #495-04-1988 L2007 **IM IMG** *020 †20
ALBAN, Paul Thomas. ■ 37043 #025-07-2002 L2005 **PD** *020 †55
ANDERSON, Jeffrey Van. 1850 BUSINESS PARK DR, STE 110A 37040 #021-06-1992 L1996 **OBG** *020 †30
ANSELL, Jacqueline Rose. 219 DUNBAR CAVE RD STE B, CENTER, PLC 37043 #064-01-1989 L2006 **N** *020 †75
AQUINO, Barbara Ann C. 311 LANDRUM PL, STE A500 37043 #748-01-1978 L1996 **PD** *020 †55
AQUINO, Ramon Jongo. 201 DOVER RD, N CLARKSVILLE MED CTR 37042 #748-10-1974 L1983 **GP** *020
ARANCIBIA, Marcos A. 330 PAGEANT LN, MONTGOMERY COUNTY HEALTH D 37040 #231-01-1972 L1996 **FM** *020 †18
BAGGETT, Henry Wesley. 1731 MEMORIAL DR, STE 108 37043 #047-06-1983 L1986 **AN** *020 †05
BARTON, Stephen John. 1824 MEMORIAL DR 37043 #012-01-1992 L1996 **OBG** *020 †30
BARVICK, Edward James. ■ 37042 #041-12-1968 L2005 **AN CD** *020 †05
BEAZLEY, William C. 121 HILLCREST DR, HEALTHSOUTH SURGERY CENTER 37043 #047-06-1977 L1980 **ORS** *020 †40
BELLENGER, James F. 625 N RIVERSIDE DR 37040 #016-06-1960 L1961 **FM** *075
BENDT, Robert Richard. 105 USSERY RD 37043 #047-05-1976 L1983 **OBG EM** *020 †30 ‡
BENITEZ, Maria Corazon V. 482 WARFIELD BLVD 37043 #748-10-1989 L1998 **PD** *020 †55
BETHI, Vidya Rekha. 331 LANDRUM PL 37043 #495-57-1988 L1995 **AN PME** *020 †05
BIRNBAUM, David Bruce. 1832 MEMORIAL DR 37043 #012-01-1986 L1995 **OPH** *020 †35
BOLAR, Randall Jay. 1731 MADISON ST, STE 105 37043 #038-45-1983 L2001 **GS** *020 †85
BOYD, Alton Reuther. 1811 MEMORIAL CIR 37043 #047-06-1966 L1966 **GP** *071 †18
BRADLEY, Joel Fontaine. 1771 MADISON ST 37043 #036-05-1977 L1984 **PD** *020 †55
BRANDON, Gilbert T, Jr. 1740 MEMORIAL DR, PREMIER MEDICAL GROUP 37043 #047-06-1981 L1982 **OTO** *020 †45
BRANTLEY, Damon Wiley. 311 LANDRUM PL, STE 100 37043 #023-01-1992 L2007 **GS** *020 †85
BROY, Charles Christopher. ■ 37042 #025-12-2004 L2006 **IM** *020 †20
BURNS, Olen Bradley. 2277C WILMA RUDOLPH BLVD 37040 #048-16-2005 L2007 **GS** *100
BURT, Rodney Levan. 1731 MEMORIAL DR, TENNESSEE SUIT 37043 #047-07-1996 L2006 **AN** *020 †05
BUSH, Joel Gregory. 1850 BUSINESS PARK DR, STE 110A 37040 #047-06-1971 L1972 **IM** *020 †20
CARRIGAN, Vernon M. 1850 BUSINESS PARK DR, STE 110A 37040 #047-06-1976 L1977 **IM** *020 †20
CHA, Paul Sangyong. 1731 MEMORIAL DR STE 201 37043 #583-01-1975 L1985 **ON HEM** *020 †20
CHANG, Timothy Tinyau. ■ 37040 #014-01-1994 **ORS** *020
CHARNOCK, Ginny Cash. 2320 WILMA RUDOLPH BLVD 37040 #036-01-1985 L1989 **DR** *020 †80
CLARDY, George Thos, Jr. 215 8TH ST 37040 #025-12-1974 L2003 **FM** *020 †18
CLARDY, John Thos. 215 8TH ST, JT CLARDY SR & GT CLARDY J 37040 #025-12-1974 L1998 **FM IM** *020 †18

■ = Address Information Privacy Protected

COLE, Herbert Rowland. ■ 37043 #047-06-1958 L1990 **AN** *071

COLLINS, Gwynetta Maria. 482 WARFIELD BLVD 37043 #001-06-1998 L2001 **PD** *020 †55

COLON, Nadja Christina. ■ 37042 #047-05-2008 *012

CRAWFORD, Darcey Bittner. 1771 MADISON ST 37043 #016-02-1999 L2005 **EM** *020 †16

CRAWFORD, Donald A, II. 1824 MEMORIAL DR 37043 #047-06-1984 L1984 **OBG** *020 †30

CREEKMORE, Harry Stone. 226 UFFELMAN DR 37043 #021-01-1973 L1988 **PS** *020 †85,65

CRUZ, Cristina Reyes. 1731 MEMORIAL DR, STE 209 37043 #748-01-1988 L1996 **PD** *020 †55

CUNNINGHAM, Thomas M, Jr. 1731 MEMORIAL DR STE 202 37043 #047-06-1970 L1970 **U** *020 †95

DAUGHERTY, Micki Jacks. ■ 37043 #012-05-1979 L1994 **DR** *074 †80

DAUGHERTY, Stephen F. 1731 MEMORIAL DR STE 101, PHYSICIANS OFFICE BLDG 37043 #012-05-1979 L1992 **VS GS** *020 †85

DEAN, Scott Wynn, III. ■ 37043 #047-20-2000 L2003 **AN** *020 †05

DE JESUS, Maria. ■ 37042 #038-06-2002 **OBG** *020

DEPENBROCK, Patrick John. ■ 37043 #036-05-2002 L2004 **FM** *020 †18

DESRUISSEAU, Richard Paul. 2831 WILMA RUDOLPH BLVD, PREMIER MEDICAL GROUP 37040 #305-01-2000 L2006 **DR** *100 †80

DE VRIES, William Henry. 141 HILLCREST DR 37043 #010-01-1989 L1998 **OS** *020 †40

DUFFIN, Timothy Kevin. 1762B MEMORIAL DR 37043 #010-02-1988 L1995 **U** *020 †95

DYER, Joseph Eugene. ■ 37042 #019-02-1976 L2005 **PTH FOP** *020 †50

ELLIS, Jennifer Lowe. 1606 HAYNES ST, MONTGOMERY COUNTY HEALTH D 37043 #047-05-1989 L1996 **PHP** *074 †70

ELLIS, Randall Edward. 222 CHEROKEE TRL 37043 #047-05-1989 L1995 **EM** *020 †16,18

ENDSLEY, John Kenton. 311 LANDRUM PL, STE 100 37043 #047-06-1990 L1992 **NEP** *020 †20

ENGLER, David Gregory. 482 WARFIELD BLVD, CENTENNIAL PEDS, PC 37043 #016-11-1994 L2003 **PD** *020 †55

FADARE, Olubayo Olatunde. ■ 37040 #690-01-1995 L2007 **FM** *100

FAN, Qing Ivy. 1771 MADISON ST 37043 #243-47-1987 L2005 **IM** *020 †20

FANDRE, Sarah P. ■ 37043 #048-16-2005 L2007 **AN** *012

FAUST, Larry Mc Neill. 482 WARFIELD BLVD, CENTENNIAL PEDIATRICS 37043 #047-06-1973 L1973 **PD** *020 †55

FITCH, Charles Patrick. 1731 MEMORIAL DR, STE 100 37043 #023-01-1987 L1995 **OPH** *020 †35

FLEIG, Lisa Marie. ■ 37043 #025-12-1990 L1997 **OBG** *020 †30

FLINT, Joseph Leroy. ■ 37042 #038-43-2001 L2001 **PD** *020

GALAPON, Derrick Brent. 273 DOVER RD 37042 #023-12-1988 L1991 **GS** *020 †85

GANNAWAY, Richard Philip. 1731 MEMORIAL DR, STE 100 37043 #047-06-1987 L1988 **OPH** *020 †35

GILL, Charlotte Ann. ■ 37043 #020-12-1994 L2000 **PTH** *020 †50

GLASSELL, Edwin Crane. 132 HILLCREST DR 37043 #021-05-1979 L1987 **GE IM** *020 †20

GONZALEZ, Luz Emilia. ■ 37043 #737-01-1974 L2005 **FM** *020

GOODCHILD, Carl William, III. ■ 37040 #035-47-1998 L2007 **FM** *020 †18

GRABENSTEIN, Thomas Geo. 330 PAGEANT LN 37040 #047-06-1977 L1979 **FM** *020 †18

GRABENSTEIN, Wm Philip. 1822 MEMORIAL DR 37043 #047-06-1985 L1987 **FM** *020 †18

GULLETT, David Laird. 434 FRANKLIN ST 37040 #020-12-1964 L1968 **IM** *020

HALL, Billy T. 1771 MADISON ST 37043 #047-06-1953 L1953 **AN** *020 †05

HALL, Denver Ray, Jr. 1731 MEMORIAL DR, STE 108 GATEWAY ANESTHESIA 37043 #047-06-1995 L1999 **AN** *020 †05

HAMPTON, James Edward. 1606 HAYNES ST, MONTGOMERY COUNTY 37043 #047-06-1954 L1955 **IM OS** *071 †20

HANEY, Aaron Wesley. ■ 37042 #017-20-2002 L2003 **P** *020

HANKENSON, Richard Ralph. 311 LANDRUM PL, STE 100 37043 #018-03-1969 L1993 **ON HEM** *020 †20

HARRIS, Troy Daniel. 1771 MADISON ST 37043 #005-12-1996 L2001 **EM** *020 †16

HARRIS-FORD, Laurie. 2199 MEMORIAL DR 37043 #001-02-1989 L1991 **PD** *020 †55

HEFNER, Jonathan Allister. 135 WESTFIELD CT 37040 #025-12-2000 L2003 **IM** *020

HERMAN, Sanford Harvey. 1771 MADISON ST 37043 #654-01-1982 L2002 **EM GS** *020

HERZOG, Joshua Paul. ■ 37043 #023-12-2001 L2006 **ORS** *020

HONG, Doug U. 2320 WILMA RUDOLPH BLVD 37040 #583-01-1966 L1975 **DR NM** *020 †80

HUANG, Thomas. 1771 MADISON ST, GATEWAY MEDICAL CTR 37043 #023-12-1994 L2005 **NPM** *020 †55

HUDSON, Robert Wood. 1856 MEMORIAL DR 37043 #047-06-1977 L1978 **GP** *020

HUDSON, William David, III. 1856 MEMORIAL DR 37043 #047-06-1971 L1972 **GS** *020

HUFFMAN, Donald Wade. 2831 WILMA RUDOLPH BLVD, PREMIER MEDICAL GROUP 37040 #004-01-1988 L1996 **FM OM** *020 †18

HUFFMAN, William Raymond. 1771 MADISON ST 37043 #047-06-1972 L1972 **EM GP** *020 †16

JAMES, Leonard Haynes. ■ 37040 #024-07-1984 L1989 **IM** *020

JARVIS, Christopher Gary. ■ 37043 #023-12-1997 L1998 **FSM** *100 †18

JOHNSON, Beverly Clark. 123 CENTER POINTE DR, COVENANT FAMILY PRACTICE 37040 #001-06-1991 L1996 **FM** *020 †18

JOHNSON, Constance Joan. 311 LANDRUM PL STE B4 37043 #023-01-1982 L1998 **N OS** *020 †75

JOHNSTON, David Gordon. 2199 MEMORIAL DR 37043 #047-06-1999 L2001 **PD** *020 †55

JOHNSTON, Jennifer E. 1824 MEMORIAL DR 37043 #047-06-1999 L2003 **OBG** *020

KADAKIA, Jatin Kirtanlal. 311 LANDRUM PL STE 70, CLARKSVILLE PLMONARY CRITI 37043 #495-96-1982 L1994 **PUD PCC** *020 †20

KASPER, Robert Edward. 2831 WILMA RUDOLPH BLVD 37040 #038-40-1984 L1992 **FM** *020 †18

KELLY, Earl Lee. 1731 MEMORIAL DR, STE 110 37043 #047-07-1983 L1986 **FM** *020 †18

KELSEY, Doris S. ■ 37040 #047-05-1962 L1962 **ID PD** *071 †55

KENNEDY, Howard R. 1771 MADISON ST 37043 #047-06-1951 L1951 **OPH** *071

KENT, Stephen W. 2302 MADISON ST, DBA: DOCTORSCARE-SANGO 37043 #047-06-1982 L1982 **EM OM** *020 †70,16

KERR, Glenn Jamieson. ■ 37043 #023-12-1999 L2007 *020 †40

KERR, Julie Sumner. ■ 37043 #023-12-2000 L2001 **OTO** *020 †45

KING, Kevin Michael. 3008 NEPSA CT 37040 #023-12-1998 L2004 **EM** *020 †16

KING, Melody O. ■ 37042 #048-15-2002 L2007 **IM** *020 †20

KING, Shawn Melissa. 2831 WILMA RUDOLPH BLVD 37040 #048-12-1994 L2001 **FM** *020 †18

KLOEK, Jan Garrett. ■ 37043 #035-03-1962 L1968 **P CHP** *075

KOEHN, Robert C, Jr. ■ 37043 #047-06-1951 L1951 **OBG** *071 †30

KORIVI, Giriprasadarao. 2831 WILMA RUDOLPH BLVD 37040 #495-37-1998 L2003 **FM** *020 †18

KORIVI, Jyotsna Padmaja. PO BOX 3799, 2831 WILMA RUDOLPH BLVD 37043 #495-21-1998 L2006 **FM** *020 †18 ‡

KURITA, George Isao, Jr. 1812 HAYNES ST 37043 #048-12-1972 L1977 **D** *020 †15

LARKINS, Gary Landon. 1824 MEMORIAL DR 37043 #047-06-1980 L1981 **OBG EM** *020 †30

LEDBETTER, Buford Brown. 1731 MEMORIAL DR, STE 203 37043 #047-06-1974 L1975 **OBG** *020 †30

LEE, George Shou-Cheng. 2285 RUDOLPHTOWN RD, STE 200 37043 #047-05-2002 L2006 **OMF FPS** *020

LEMOINE, Fritz F. 1731 MEMORIAL DR STE 103 37043 #440-01-1954 L1970 **GS OS** *071

LIMBAUGH, James Wilson. 1716 MEMORIAL DR BOX 3098 37043 #047-06-1956 L1957 **R** *071 †80

LIND, Roger Chas, Jr. 2320 WILMA RUDOLPH BLVD 37040 #027-01-1981 L1982 **DR** *020 †80

LOWE, Reginald Shaw. 1731 MEMORIAL DR, STE 100 37043 #021-01-1959 L1969 **OPH** *020 †35

LU, George Eric. 2831 WILMA RUDOLPH BLVD 37040 #016-01-1999 L2002 **FM** *020 †18

LYLE, William Green. ■ 37043 #047-05-1944 L1944 **IM** *071

MADAELIL, Philip Thomas. 1731 MEMORIAL DR, STE 205 37043 #495-59-1981 L1998 **CD IM** *020 †20

MAHOOD, Arif. ■ 37042 #704-01-1961 L1971 **OBG** *020 †30

MANNING, Greta Charisse. 2831 WILMA RUDOLPH BLVD 37040 #025-01-1995 L2002 **FM** *020 †18

MARCHBANK, Steven Gary. 482 WARFIELD BLVD 37043 #028-03-1996 L2003 **PD** *020

MAXWELL, Lisa Michelle. ■ 37042 #023-12-1999 L2000 **GS** *020 †85

MC CAMPBELL, Frank G. 659C PROVIDENCE BLVD 37042 #047-06-1956 L1957 **GYN** *071 †30

MC CLURE, Christopher C. 1731 MEMORIAL DR, STE 205 37043 #047-06-1985 L1990 **CD IM** *020 †20

MC CULLOUGH, John Scott. 1771 MADISON ST, LABORATORY 37043 #001-02-1987 L2000 **PTH** *020 †50

MC GEE, William Anthony. 1731 MEMORIAL DR, STE 209 37043 #021-06-1987 L2005 **TS VS** *020 †85,90

MC GRAIL, Mark Allen. 2831 WILMA RUDOLPH BLVD 37040 #023-12-1993 L1998 **OS** *020 †18

MC GREGGOR, Douglass. ■ 37042 #005-17-1962 L1977 **GP** *071

MC HOOD, Craig H. ■ 37043 #023-12-1998 L1998 **FM** *020 †18

MC INTOSH, Wm Douglas. 1850 BUSINESS PARK DR, STE 110A 37040 #047-20-1989 L1993 **OBG** *020 †30

MERIWETHER, Betty Ann. ■ 37043 #047-06-1959 L1960 **OBG** *071 †30

MEZA, Carol Anne. 330 PAGEANT LN, DEPARTMENT 37040 #023-12-1994 L2003 **GS** *020

MIKICKI, Barbara. 560 FIRE STATION RD 37043 #759-12-1980 L1995 **P** *020

MILAM, Jacqueline Denise. 1850 BUSINESS PARK DR, STE 110A 37040 #020-02-1990 L1991 **IM** *020 †20

MILES, Joseph Wm, Jr. 1771 MADISON ST 37043 #047-06-1970 L1970 **U** *020 †95

MILLER, Daniel Rea. 2831 WILMA RUDOLPH BLVD 37040 #023-12-1993 L1994 **FM** *020 †18 ‡

MISHRA, Pradip K. 311 LANDRUM PL, STE 600 37043 #496-14-1980 L1997 **CD** *020 †20

MOORE, Donald Alvin, Jr. 304 NEW PROVIDENCE BLVD 37042 #005-12-2000 L2004 **AN** *020 †05

MOORE, Echo Megan. 511 8TH ST, GRAYSON & ASSOCIATES, PC 37040 #020-02-2000 L2008 **P** *020 †75

MOORE, Marion Robertson. ■ 37043 #047-06-1950 L1950 **P** *071

MOORE, William Robertson. 1771 MADISON ST 37043 #047-05-1982 L1985 **PD** *020 †55

MUIZNIEKS, Mark Alexander. 1771 MADISON ST 37043 #047-06-2003 L2005 **EM** *020 †16

NAWATHE, Chandrakanta D. 311 LANDRUM PL 37043 #495-27-1980 L1997 **IM** *020 †20

ORUSA, Samson K. 261 STONECROSSING DR 37042 #690-06-1988 L1996 **IM** *020 †20

OSBORN, David James. ■ 37043 #041-02-2001 L2008 **U** *020

PAASCHE, Robert Evan. 1771 MADISON ST 37043 #038-43-2001 L2005 **EM** *020 †16

PARKER, Robert Brannon. 1100 TED A CROZIER SR BLVD 37043 #047-05-1978 L1997 **IM** *020 †20

PATEL, Anil Chhotubhai. 280 WARFIELD BLVD 37043 #965-01-1982 L1986 **GE IM** *020 †20

PATEL, Bharatkumar R. 2150 WILMA RUDOLPH BLVD, STE 6 37040 #495-89-1990 L1995 **IM** *020 †20

PEACHER, Terry Gene. 1854 MEMORIAL DR 37043 #047-06-1966 L1975 **P CHP** *020 †75

PEASE, Francis Barber, Jr. 537 POND APPLE RD 37043 #024-01-1971 L1995 **GS** *020 †85

PEDIGO, William Joel. 2199 MEMORIAL DR 37043 #047-06-1974 L1974 **PD** *020 †55

PERALES, Angel U. 1731 MEMORIAL DR, STE 200 37043 #649-14-1976 L1980 **AN** *071

PERCELAY, Stephen Howard. 2320 WILMA RUDOLPH BLVD 37040 #048-12-1989 L1993 **DR** *020 †80

PETERSON, Keith Douglas. 1771 MADISON ST 37043 #047-06-1971 L1972 **U GS** *020 †95

PFAFFENBACH, Andrew Craig. 2246 JASMINE DR 37043 #056-05-1997 L2004 **IM** *020

PHILIP, Annie. ■ 37043 #495-17-1983 L1989 **PD AI** *020 †55

PIERSON, Lisa Michelle. ■ 37043 #023-12-1994 L1997 **OBG** *020 †30

PODELL, Barry David. ■ 37040 #035-19-1953 L1954 **OBG** *071 †30

PRABHU, Satish Dayananda. 1728 MEMORIAL DR 37043 #495-37-1983 L1995 **PD PN** *020 †55

PRIETO, Rafael L. 1750C MEMORIAL DR 37043 #048-02-1995 L2006 **PM** *020 †60

PRINE, William Wesley, Jr. 2199 MEMORIAL DR 37043 #027-01-1971 L1973 **PD** *020 †55

PRITCHETT, Elizabeth E. 800 TINY TOWN RD 37042 #035-15-1981 L1990 **CHP** *020 †75

RICHARDS, Randolph M. 542 POND APPLE RD 37043 #047-06-1989 L1990 **OTO** *020 †45

RICHARDSON, Donald Ray. 1740 MEMORIAL DR STE 1 37043 #047-06-1963 L1963 **OTO** *020 †45

RIESTRA, Jorge Casanova. 105 USSERY RD 37043 #020-12-1983 L1989 **OBG** *020 †30

RITZER, Theodore Frank. 311 LANDRUM PL, STE C-500 37043 #649-33-1980 L1991 **CD IM** *020 †20

ROADS, Timothy R. 2199 MEMORIAL DR 37043 #017-20-1978 L1985 **PD** *020 †55

ROBERTS, Joy G. ■ 37042 #023-07-1991 L1997 **P** *100

SALCEDO, Pedro I. 311 LANDRUM PL, STE 200 37043 #748-10-1985 L1996 **IM** *020 †20

SALEH, Adel S. 235 MED PARK DR, STE B 37043 #915-04-1978 L1991 **NEP IM** *020 †20

SANDERS, Scott Jeffrey. 273 DOVER RD, GRIFFIN CENTER 37042 #003-01-1994 L2000 **GS** *020 †85

SAWYER, Kimberly Driscoll. PO BOX 3799, 1832 MEMORIAL DR 37043 #011-03-1997 L2005 **OBG** *020 †30

SCHOONOVER, Edwin Dale. 1731 MEMORIAL DR, STE 110 37043 #048-13-1980 L1986 **FM AM** *020 †18

SCHULTZ, Stephanie Lynn. 2199 MEMORIAL DR 37043 #041-01-1995 L2001 **PD** *020 †55

SELASSIE, Daniel Haile. ■ 37042 #041-02-1997 L2000 **IM** *020 †18,20

SHAH, Jigar Kanubhai. ■ 37043 #038-41-1999 L2005 **HO** *020 †20

SHAH, Ramnik B. ■ 37043 #495-22-1962 L1985 **P GP** *020 ‡

SHIELDS, John Douglas. 1608 HAYNES ST, ATT: SUPPLY 37043 #047-05-1995 L2004 **EM** *020 †16

SHIELDS, Tammy Ketch. 1771 MADISON ST 37043 #047-05-1995 L2004 **EM** *020 †16

SILE, Helen. 1771 MADISON ST, GATEWAY HEALTH SYSTEM 37043 #041-12-1998 L1999 **IM** *020 †20

■ = Address Information Privacy Protected

SILER, Rita Anne. ■ 37043 #047-05-1963 L1963 **AN** *071 †30
SILVEY, Gary Lynn. 1771 MADISON ST, PO BOX 3160 37043 #020-02-1970 L1976 **PTH** *050 †50
SMITH, James Roy. 344 PEARTREE DR 37043 #047-06-1962 L1963 **IM** *072 †20
STACK, Kathryn E. 1731 MEMORIAL DR, STE 200 37043 #035-09-1992 L1997 **AN** *020 †05
STANTON, John Louis. 331 LANDRUM PL 37043 #048-04-1980 L1996 **ORS** *020 †40
STARKWEATHER, Keith D. 331 LANDRUM PL 37043 #005-14-1991 L1996 **ORS** *020 †40
STARNES, Danl Livingston. 2320 WILMA RUDOLPH BLVD 37040 #047-06-1978 L1979 **R VIR** *020 †80
STEELE, Malcolm Aubrey. 1771 MADISON ST 37043 #023-01-1978 L1987 **IM** *020 †20,16
STEELY, William M. 1731 MEMORIAL DR, STE 105 37043 #020-02-1982 L1988 **GS TS** *020 †85
SZCZEPANSKI, Michael Paul. ■ 37043 #023-12-2003 L2005 **EM** *020 †16
TAYLOR, Stephens Davis. 273 DOVER RD 37042 #027-01-1982 L1983 **VS GS** *020 †85
TEDDY, Virginia A P. 2535 MADISON ST, STE D 37043 #047-06-1988 L1990 **P** *020 †75
TIFFAULT, Gerard Rock. ■ 37043 #035-10-1996 L1999 **EM** *020 †16
TRAN, Hung Viet. ■ 37043 #005-06-2003 L2006 **EM** *020 †16
TSAMBASSIS, Nicholas A. 127 DEAN DR, RIVERSIDE MEDICAL ASSOC 37040 #305-01-1985 L1989 **IM PD** *020 †55,20
VANDIVEER, Carol. PO BOX 30429, 1891 OLD TRENTON RD 37040 #047-06-1975 L1975 **P** *020 †75
VASENKO, Eileen Marie. ■ 37043 #023-12-1991 L2007 **FM** *020 †18 ‡
VERMILLION, Roy James. ■ 37043 #047-06-1961 L1962 **GS** *071 †85
WERNER, Alan Meyer. 273 DOVER RD 37042 #041-12-1991 L1998 **GS VS** *020 †85
WEST, Michael Scott. 2151 WILMA RUDOLPH BLVD, COVENANT FAMILY PRACTICE 37040 #047-06-1998 L1999 **IM** *020 †20 ‡
WHITE, Steve Aulton. 1811 MEMORIAL CIR 37043 #047-06-1981 L1982 **IM** *020 †20
WILLIAMS, David B. 251 HILLCREST DR 37043 #047-06-1980 L1981 **IM** *020 †20
WILSON, Frank. ■ 37043 #047-06-1961 L1967 **OBG** *071 †30
WILSON, Jeffrey Craig. 810 WEATHERBY DR 37043 #038-40-1984 L2000 **AN GS** *020 †05
WITTER, Douglas Alan. 291 CLEAR SKY CT, STE B 37043 #011-04-1994 L2007 **FM** *020 †18
WOODS, Kelly Wayne. 1771 MADISON ST 37043 #041-07-1995 L1998 **EM** *020 †16
WRIGHT, John Fay, Jr. 1731 MEMORIAL DR, STE 200 37043 #047-06-1962 L1962 **AN** *071 †05

CLEVELAND – BRADLEY

ABDELRAZEK, Nermean M. 2301 N OCOEE ST, STE A 37311 #047-06-1997 L2001 **OBG** *020
ALDRICH, William T. 2305 CHAMBLISS AVE NW 37311 #005-12-1947 L1975 **IM** *071 †20
ANDERSON, David Scott. 1860 EXECUTIVE PARK NW, STE B 37312 #036-05-1973 L1979 **IM EM** *020 †20
APPLING, John Morgan. 2850 WESTSIDE DR NW, STE G 37312 #051-04-1959 L1962 **PD PHP** *020 †55
BARAT, Guy Raymond. ■ 37312 #038-40-1979 L2006 **DR NM** *020 †80
BEASLEY, Robert A. 102 DUNHILL PL NW, ORTHOPAEDICS 37311 #047-06-1977 L1978 **ORS** *020 †40
BETTS, Dennis Allen. 1060 PEERLESS XING NW, CROSSING DRIVE 37312 #047-06-1993 L1997 **MPD** *020 †55
BIVENS, Jennifer Margaret. 2850 WESTSIDE DR NW STE G 37312 #047-20-1995 L1998 **PD** *020 †55
BLANK, Nancy M. 2415 CHAMBLISS AVE NW, CLEVELAND EYE CLINIC 37311 #047-06-1982 L1984 **OPH** *020 †35
BOWERS, Andrea Joy. 2305 CHAMBLISS AVE NW 37311 #047-20-1995 L2006 **IM** *020
BOWERS, William David. 2301 N OCOEE ST, STE B 37311 #017-20-1977 L1982 **GS** *020 †85
BREETZKE, Cecil Brian. 1420 FRITZ ST SE 37323 #051-01-1989 L2003 **FM** *020 †18
BROWN, Raymond Sean. 1065 PEERLESS XING NW 37312 #012-01-1996 L2000 **PM** *020
BRYAN, John Milton. 2295 CHAMBLISS AVE NW, KYLE BRYAN AND JACKSON 37311 #047-06-1956 L1956 **U** *071 †95
BUCHNER, William F, Jr. 2850 OCOEE ST N, STE C 37312 #047-06-1983 L1989 **GE IM** *020 †20
BUCHWALTER, Cheryl Lynn. 2301 N OCOEE ST 37311 #038-06-1996 L2007 **OBG** *020 †30
BYERS, Glen Marsh. 2850 WESTSIDE DR NW 37312 #025-07-1966 L1973 **OTO** *020 †45
BYRD, Jack Pool. 2414 CHAMBLISS AVE NW 37312 #036-01-1976 L1983 **OTO** *020 †45
CATANESE, Marlene Johnson. 2305 CHAMBLISS AVE NW 37311 #011-04-1984 L1988 **IM** *020 †20
CHAFFIN, David Curtis. ■ 37312 #047-06-1972 L1972 **DR** *020 †80 ‡
CHAMBERLAIN, Nathan E. 2253 CHAMBLISS AVE NW, STE 200 37311 #001-12-1996 L1997 **NEP** *020 †20
CHAMBERS, John Wallace. 55 25TH ST NW 37311 #047-06-1969 L1969 **OBG** *020 †30
CHASTAIN, Allan Chalmer. 2850 WESTSIDE DR NW, STE D 37312 #047-06-1975 L1976 **FM** *020
CHASTAIN, Chalmer, Jr. 2850 WESTSIDE DR NW 37312 #047-06-1953 L1953 **GP** *071
CHASTAIN, Garvin Kent. 1060 PEERLESS XING NW, STE 200 37312 #047-06-1982 L1985 **IM CD** *020 †20
CHEUNG, Tobun Toby. 2305 CHAMBLISS AVE NW, BRADLEY MEMORIAL HOSPITAL 37311 #038-41-1999 L2002 **NEP** *020 †20 ‡
CHHAJWANI, Balram L. 915 CLINGAN RIDGE DR NW 37312 #495-23-1975 L1988 **NEP IM** *020 †20
CLAIRMONT, Albert A, Jr. 2700 WESTSIDE DR NW, STE 301 37312 #051-04-1967 L2003 **OTO HNS** *020 †45
CLARK, Marc Lewis. 110 DUNHILL PL NW STE B, BLUE RIDGE GASTROENTEROLOG 37311 #045-01-1986 L1986 **GE HEP** *020 †20 ‡
COLEMAN, Ronald Sherman. 343 LEATHA LN NW 37312 #038-43-1978 L1983 **GS VS** *071
COLLINS, Larry Coy. 2370 N OCOEE ST 37311 #012-01-1972 L1979 **DR** *020 †80
COOMBS, Janet Haas. 2253 CHAMBLISS AVE NW #100 37311 #047-20-1992 L1997 **GS** *020 †85
COOPER, Floyd Childs. 2765 EXECUTIVE PARK NW, STE 1 37312 #047-06-1957 L1957 **P** *075 †75
COYLE, Brian Eugene. 1060 PEERLESS XING NW, STE 100 37312 #039-05-1989 L1996 **PD** *020 †55
CRABB, Joseph Thos. 114 STUART RD NE, STE 191 37312 #005-12-1978 L1981 **AN** *020
CRABTREE, Barry Dewayne. 1060 PEERLESS XING NW 37312 #047-06-1993 L1996 **PD** *020 †55
DALE, Elizabeth Louise. ■ 37312 #047-05-2006 **GS** *012
DAUBNER, Elizabeth Allen. 4625 N LEE HWY 37312 #011-04-1984 L1986 **GP OM** *020
DAUBNER, Michael A. 201 DOOLEY ST SE 37311 #011-04-1982 L1986 **IM MDM** *020 †20
DE VANE, Jerry A. 435 25TH ST NW, CLEVELAND PEDIATRICS 37311 #047-06-1977 L1978 **EM IM** *020 †20,16

DRESKIN, Stephen V. 2700 WESTSIDE DR NW, STE 306 37312 #024-07-1990 L1994 **APM AN** *020 †05
DUGAN, Philip Jerald. 2620 PEERLESS RD NW, CLEVELAND REGIONAL CANCER 37312 #028-34-1963 L1975 **RO R** *020 †80
DUNCAN, Eddie Norris. 2415 CHAMBLISS AVE NW, CLEVELAND EYE CLINIC 37311 #047-06-1968 L1968 **OPH** *020 †35
ERMER, Susan Arlene. 435 25TH ST NW, CLEVELAND PEDIATRICS PC 37311 #047-06-1989 L2005 **PD** *020 †55
FAERBER, Bruce William. 2415 CHAMBLISS AVE NW 37311 #028-03-1988 L1991 **OPH** *020 †35
FALL, Adam Emery. 2253 CHAMBLISS AVE NW, STE 101 37311 #038-44-1993 L2001 **IM** *020 †20
FARRUKH, Kamran. 2700 WESTSIDE DR NW, STE 200 37312 #704-01-1989 L1997 **IM** *020 †20
FERNANDO, Felicito Emil. 435 25TH ST NW, CLEVELAND PEDIATRICS PC 37311 #047-06-1988 L1991 **PD** *020 †55
FINLEY, Julia Pierce. 1060 PEERLESS XING NW, STE 200 37312 #047-06-1992 L1993 **IM** *020 †20
FISHER, Susan Goodman. 1995 KEITH ST NW 37311 #020-02-1985 L1992 **IM FM** *020 †20 ‡
FORD, Dennis Clifford. 2020 KEITH ST NW STE C, FORD CTR FOR PAIN MNGMNT 37311 #047-06-1979 L1979 **PME FM** *020 †05,18
FRAUWIRTH, Neal Howard. 2800 WESTSIDE DR NW, INTEGRATED PAIN MANAGEMENT 37312 #011-04-1995 L2007 **PM** *020 †60
GALPHIN, Claude Mabry. 2253 CHAMBLISS AVE NW, STE 200 37311 #045-01-1980 L1997 **NEP IM** *020 †20
GANGAVARAPU, Sarath B. 2765 EXECUTIVE PARK NW, STE 1 37312 #495-50-1980 L1985 **P** *020 †75
GIBSON, Donald Baker. 2325 OAKLAND DR NW 37311 #045-01-1965 L1966 **FM** *020
GILSON, Troy Danl. 940 S OCOEE ST 37311 #047-06-1988 L1989 **P** *020 †75
GLYNN, Martin Anthony. 2650 EXECUTIVE PARK NW, STE 2 37312 #539-05-1969 L1996 **FM** *020
GOLDMAN, Maurice Saml. 2850 WESTSIDE DR NW STE K 37312 #012-05-1958 L1977 **CD PUD** *071 †20
GONCALVES, Rod Manuel. 2301 N OCOEE ST, STE B 37311 #016-06-1991 L2001 **GS** *020 †85
GREWAL, Mandeep Singh. 2253 CHAMBLISS AVE NW, STE 200 37311 #577-01-1985 L1995 **NEP** *020 †20
HAMILTON, Howard Kenton. 2305 CHAMBLISS AVE NW 37311 #012-01-1973 L1974 **DR** *071 †80
HANNIFIN, James Francis. 2305 CHAMBLISS AVE NW 37311 #047-06-1978 L1979 **AN EM** *020 †20,05
HARRIS, Cynthia Mcintyre. 2417 CHAMBLISS AVE NW, OASIS GYN & OB 37311 #001-06-2000 L2004 **OBG** *020 ‡
HARTING, Don Chas. 2200 CHAMBLISS AVE NW 37311 #047-06-1975 L1975 **D** *020 †15 ‡
HAYES, Susan Hope. 1060 PEERLESS XING NW, GALEN MEDICAL GROUP EAST 37312 #001-02-1985 L1988 **PD** *020 †55
HAYS, William Augustus. 2850 WESTSIDE DR NW 37312 #422-01-1987 L1990 **FM** *020 †18
HELTON, David Keith. 1060 PEERLESS XING NW, GALEN MEDICAL GROUP EAST 37312 #047-20-1991 L1992 **MPD** *020 †20
HESS, Amy Marie. ■ 37312 #047-06-2008 *012
HOOPS, Michael Lee. 597 CHURCH ST NE 37311 #016-11-1989 L1994 **PS HS** *020 †65
HUEBSCHMAN, Jon Clark. 1060 PEERLESS XING NW, STE 200 37312 #017-20-1984 L1987 **IM** *020 †20
HUGHES, Charles Richard. ■ 37312 #047-06-1959 L1961 **PD** *071 †55
HUNTER, Laura Annette. 2301 N OCOEE ST, LIFECIRCLE WOMENS HLTHCARE 37311 #021-06-2001 L2005 **OBG** *020
IBRAHIMBACHA, Ahmad M. 110 DUNHILL PL NW 37311 #875-02-1982 L2002 **PCC** *020 †20
INANKUR, Yuksel Abidin. 435 25TH ST NW 37311 #902-03-1956 L1998 **PD A** *071
JACK, Joani Barnes. 1060 PEERLESS XING NW, GALEN MEDICAL GROUP EAST 37312 #047-06-1991 L1993 **PD** *020 †55
JAGGERS, John Sterrette. 110 DUNHILL PL NW 37311 #047-06-1982 L1983 **PUD CCM** *020 †20
JARRETT, Jeffrey Ross. 2800 WESTSIDE DR NW 37312 #012-01-1985 L1994 **CD IM** *020 †20
JOHNSON, Daniel V. 102 DUNHILL PL NW, ORTHOPAEDICS 37311 #026-04-1976 L1984 **ORS EM** *020 †40
JOHNSON, Kavin J. 55 BEN DR NW, THE CLEVELAND CLINIC OF TN 37311 #010-03-1981 L1991 **IM DIA** *020
KELLY, Wayne. 435 25TH ST NW, CLEVELAND PEDIATRICS PC 37311 #047-06-1995 L1997 **PD** *020 †55
KEMKAR, Ajitkumar. 2625 EXECUTIVE PARK NW 37312 #495-99-1981 L1995 **IM** *020
KILLEN, Larry Ray. 2370 N OCOEE ST 37311 #047-06-1967 L1990 **R** *020 †80
KIM, Stephen S. ■ 37312 #583-03-1963 L1979 **FM GS** *071
KIMBALL, Cecil Harry. 4135 FRITZ ST SE 37323 #047-06-1948 L1956 **DR** *071 †80
KNABB, James Louis. 2301 N OCOEE ST 37311 #011-02-1979 L1985 **GS** *020
KNIGHT, Cecil D. 1494 STUART RD NE, P O BOX 3360 37312 #047-06-1976 L1976 **FM EM** *020 †18
KRUEGER, Sylvia Lynne. 353 WORTH ST NW, MEDICAL ONCOLOGY 37311 #047-06-1977 L1978 **ON HEM** *020 †20
KYLE, Clyde Alexander. 2295 CHAMBLISS AVE NW, KYLE BRYAN & JACKSON MD'S 37311 #047-06-1958 L1958 **U** *075 †95
LACKEY, Herbert L, Jr. 2370 N OCOEE ST 37311 #047-06-1990 L1993 **DR** *020 †80
LIU, Niansen. 3555 KEITH ST NW, STE 102 37312 #243-63-1985 L2002 **P** *020
LOWRY, Philip Dale. 2080 CHAMBLISS AVE NW # 1, P O BOX 3090 37311 #047-20-1995 L1996 **AN** *020
MALAKHOV, Aleksander I. 2305 CHAMBLISS AVE NW 37311 #913-04-1975 L2002 **IM** *020 †20
MARCUM, James Lewis. 400 BERYWOOD TRL NW, STE A 37312 #048-13-1991 L1998 **CD** *020 †20
MARCUM, Robert Francis. 110 DUNHILL PL NW 37311 #045-01-1982 L1990 **PUD IM** *020 †20
MARQUEZ, Obadias. 1060 PEERLESS XING NW, STE 200 37312 #048-38-1993 L2005 **IM** *020
MAZZA, Gerard K. 2725 KEITH ST NW 37312 #011-04-1981 L1984 **FM EM** *020 †18
MAZZOLINI, Joe Michael. 2850 WESTSIDE DR NW, STE D 37312 #039-01-1977 L1987 **FM** *020 †18
MC ALLISTER, Jonathan D, II. ■ 37311 #047-06-1996 L1997 **IM** *020 †20
MC CARLEY, Kenneth Hugh. 137 25TH ST NE 37311 #012-01-1988 L1996 **OTO** *020 †45
MCGUIRE, Thomas William. 2415 CHAMBLISS AVE NW, CLEVELAND EYE CLINIC INC 37311 #038-45-1990 L1992 **OPH** *020 †35
MC KENZIE, Mark M. 1060 PEERLESS XING NW, PEERLESS MEDICAL GROUP 37312 #038-43-2000 L2002 **IM** *020
MC KINNEY, David Wendell. 2305 CHAMBLISS AVE NW 37311 #027-01-1991 L1996 **AN** *020 †05

■ = Address Information Privacy Protected

MILLER, Roger Dale. 2370 N OCOEE ST 37311 #047-20-1985 L1991 **DR IM** *020 †80

MITCHELL, Brian C. 400 BERYWOOD TRL NW, STE A 37312 #047-06-1998 L2003 **CD** *020 †20

MITCHELL, Hays. ■ 37312 #047-06-1952 L1952 **PD** *071 †55

MORGAN, Ann Marie. 55 25TH ST NW, STE A 37311 #023-12-1984 L1995 **OBG FM** *030 †18,30

MU, Xiao C. 2305 CHAMBLISS AVE NW, DEPT. OF PATHOLOGY 37311 #243-45-1988 L2003 **PTH** *020 †50 ‡

MULLIN, Christopher Noel. 2301 N OCOEE ST, LIFE CIRCLE WOMEN'S HEALTH 37311 #047-06-1993 L1997 **OBG** *020 †30

MURPHY, Billy Howard. 435 25TH ST NW, CLEVELAND PEDIATRICS PC 37311 #047-20-1982 L1985 **PD** *020 †55

MURPHY, John Allen. 605 FOREST LN NE 37312 #027-01-1967 L1972 **PD GP** *020 †55

MUTHS, Frederick August. 2080 CHAMBLISS AVE NW # 1, CLEVLD ANESTH INC POB 3090 37311 #001-01-1969 1973 **AN PME** *071 †05

MYERS, Christine Beville. 2305 CHAMBLISS AVE NW 37311 #017-20-1995 L2006 **MPD** *020 †20,55

NEWMAN, Jerry Glynn, Jr. 2650 EXECUTIVE PARK NW, STE 3 37312 #047-06-1996 L2005 **PFP** *020 †75

NEWTON, Nicholas. ■ 37312 #025-07-1963 L1977 **U** *071 †95

NIAZ, Faiz. 2810 WESTSIDE DR NW STE H, COMP NEURO SVCS EAST TN 37312 #704-02-1984 L1998 **CN** *020 †75

PARKINSON, John Dee. 2800 WESTSIDE DR NW 37312 #047-06-1962 L1969 **P EM** *020 ‡

PATEL, Nilesh Chiman. 2253 CHAMBLISS AVE NW, STE 200 37311 #001-06-2001 L2006 **NEP** *020

PERRY, Michelle Yvonne. 2417 CHAMBLISS AVE NW, OASIS GYNECOLOGY & OBSTETR 37311 #047-06-1999 L2002 **OBG** *020

PIERCE, E Harris. 2305 CHAMBLISS AVE NW 37311 #012-05-1949 L1959 **GS OS** *071 †85

POWELL, John Manley. 2301 N OCOEE ST 37311 #047-06-1964 L1965 **OBG** *020 †30

POWERS, Joseph Keenan. 400 BERYWOOD TRL NW, STE A 37312 #035-08-1989 L1995 **CD** *020 †20

RAHBE, Samir. 2825 WESTSIDE DR NW 37312 #561-03-1976 L1990 **IM** *020

ROBINSON, Donald Edwin. 1860 EXECUTIVE PARK NW, STE B 37312 #047-06-1974 L1974 **IM** *020 †20

ROMANIUK, Alexander G. 2700 WESTSIDE DR NW, STE 200 37312 #060-01-1973 L1997 **GP** *020

RUMBLE, Michael Turner. 2700 WESTSIDE DR NW, STE 301 37312 #012-05-1984 L1992 **GS** *020 †85 ‡

SAMUEL, Aaron Doss. ■ 37312 #495-16-1963 L1995 **GS CD** *020 †85,90

SANDERSON, Stephanie Mill. 1060 PEERLESS XING NW, STE 100 37312 #047-20-1991 L2000 **PD** *020 †55

SAN MIGUEL, David E. 2305 CHAMBLISS AVE NW 37311 #016-76-1991, ▲ L2001 **AN** *020 †05

SCHNARS, Beth Ann. 2305 CHAMBLISS AVE NW 37311 #047-01-1991 L1993 **IM** *020 †20

SEEKINS, Jayne M. 2305 CHAMBLISS AVE NW, DEPT OF RADIOLOGY 37311 #022-75-2001, ▲ L2006 **PDR** *100 †80

SHARIFF, Aslam Ahmed. ■ 37312 #495-99-1979 L2003 **FM** *020 †18

SHEIKH, Azhar S. 2650 EXECUTIVE PARK NW, STE 2 37312 #704-21-1986 L1996 **IM** *020 †20

SHOEMAKER, Kenneth E. 2535 GEORGETOWN RD NW 37311 #047-06-1946 L1949 **P** *071

SHUSTER, Larry David. 1060 PEERLESS XING NW, CROSSING DRIVE 37312 #047-06-1982 L1983 **GE IM** *020 †20

SIMS, Harrison G, III. 2620 WESTSIDE DR NW 37312 #036-01-1994 L2002 **FM** *020 †18

SIMS, Jerome P. 2600 EXECUTIVE PARK NW 37312 #047-06-1951 L1951 **GP** *071

SMITH, William Hoyt. 1060 PEERLESS XING NW, GALEN MEDICAL GROUP EAST 37312 #028-34-1997 L2001 **MPD** *020 †20,55

SNODDY, Janet Elizabeth. 1881 PARTRIDGE RD NW 37312 #047-06-1980 L1981 **OM IM** *020 †20,70

SNOWMAN, Brenda Anne. 55 25TH ST NW, STE B 37311 #024-07-1984 L1992 **OBG** *020 †30

SPRAGGINS, Yolanda R. 1060 PEERLESS XING NW, GALEN MEDICAL GROUP EAST 37312 #036-07-1994 L1997 **PD** *020 †55

STANBERY, Wm Cecil, II. 424 BERYWOOD TRL NW 37312 #047-06-1985 L1987 **FM** *020 †18

STETSON, Robert Alan. 2650 EXECUTIVE PARK NW, STE 3 37312 #011-03-1996 L2007 **PFP** *020 †75

STONE, James Patterson. 102 DUNHILL PL NW, ORTHOPAEDICS 37311 #051-01-1978 L1984 **ORS** *020 †40

STREKO, Ronald Richard. 1060 PEERLESS XING NW, GALEN MEDICAL GROUP EAST 37312 #033-05-1993 L1997 **MPD PD** *020 †55,20

SULTAN, Gulshan Ara. 1600 CLINGAN RIDGE DR NW 37312 #160-02-1970 L1984 **P** *020

SWAN, Lawrence Carl. 2620 WESTSIDE DR NW 37312 #047-20-1985 L1988 **FM** *020 †18

TAYLOR, Owen Cameron. 1060 PEERLESS XING NW, STE 200 37312 #016-45-1976 L1978 **IM FM** *020 ‡

THACKER, Christopher C. 2800 WESTSIDE DR NW 37312 #012-05-1995 L2001 **U** *020 †95

THURMAN, James Robt. 75 BEN DR NW, BRADLEY MED CENTER 37312 #047-06-1956 L1956 **GYN** *071 †30

TILSON, Forrest Blaine. 1060 PEERLESS XING NW, CROSSING DRIVE 37312 #047-06-1979 L1980 **IM** *020

TIN, Than Zaw Win. 2305 CHAMBLISS AVE NW, BRADLEY MEMORIAL HOSPITAL 37311 #422-01-1998 L2003 **IM** *020 †20

TOMCZYK, Maria Jadwiga. 2810 WESTSIDE DR NW, STE H 37312 #759-10-1973 L1997 **FM** *020 †18

TORRENCE, James Madison. 499 PAUL HUFF PKWY NW, BRADLEY COUNTY EMS 37312 #047-06-1996 L1999 **EM** *020 †16

UGWUEZE, Eze Chidinma. 2305 CHAMBLISS AVE NW, P O BOX 3060 37311 #913-92-1995 L2003 **IM** *020 †20

VANCE, Daniel Brevard, IV. 1060 PEERLESS XING NW, STE 200 37312 #047-06-1979 L1980 **IM** *020 †20

VINCENT, Bennie Ray, Jr. 2305 CHAMBLISS AVE NW 37311 #005-12-2000 L2006 **AN** *020

VIROSTEK, Lisa June. 2620 PEERLESS RD NW 37312 #047-06-1992 L1996 **RO** *020 †80

VISER, Timothy Allen. 2800 WESTSIDE DR NW 37312 #036-01-1980 L1991 **OTO** *020 †45

VOYTIK, Gary Joseph. 2700 WESTSIDE DR NW # 103 37312 #041-77-1991, ▲ L1996 **ORS** *020

WALKER, Ramsey Oneal. 4625 N LEE HWY, THE EMPLOYEE CENTER 37312 #047-07-1992 L1993 **GPM** *020

WENGER, Eston Keith. 2253 CHAMBLISS AVE NW, STE 100 37311 #038-41-2001 L2007 **GS** *020 †85

WHITE, James E. 2292 CHAMBLISS AVE NW, STE F 37311 #671-01-1984 **PTH** *100

WINTERER, Joerg G. 2305 CHAMBLISS AVE NW 37311 #024-01-1967 L1987 **PD GS** *020 †55

YOUNGER, Clyde P, Jr. 102 DUNHILL PL NW, SOUTHEAST TN ORTHO 37311 #047-06-1969 L1971 **ORS** *071 †40

ZEMICHAEL, Dawit. 1855 EXECUTIVE PARK NW 37312 #654-01-1991 L1999 **P** *020

CLINTON – ANDERSON

ASHLEY, Christopher Paul. 2130 N CHARLES G SVRS BLVD 37716 #047-07-1993 L1997 **PM** *020 †60

BOWLES, Mark Gregory. 710 N MAIN ST, STE B 37716 #047-06-1989 L1990 **U** *020 †95

CARTER, Charles Philip. 1115 N CHARLES G SVRS BLVD, STE 41 37716 #047-06-1977 L1984 **EM GP** *020

CHOATE, Philip Ross. ■ 37716 #004-01-1960 *075

CULBERT, William Howard. 102 S CHARLES G SEVRS BLVD 37716 #047-20-1996 L1999 **FM** *020 †18

DAUGHERTY, John Thomas. 110 EXECUTIVE PARK DR, MCNEELEY FAMILY CLINIC 37716 #047-06-1988 L1991 **FM** *020 †18

DEE, Jonathan Daniel. 1107 N CHARLES G SVRS BLVD, STE 101 37716 #047-20-2004 L2007 **FM** *020 †18

GOANS, Ronald Earl. ■ 37716 #010-01-1983 L1983 **OM** *062 †70

HARREL, Elizabeth Myers. 110 EXECUTIVE PARK DR 37716 #003-01-1994 L1997 **FM** *020 †18

HICKS, William Mc Kindree. 2130 N CHARLES G SVRS BLVD, STE 4 37716 #047-06-1960 L1960 **PD OS** *020 †55

KING, Renee Annmarie. ■ 37716 #047-06-2003 L2006 **EM** *100

MACKAY, Michael Alan. 2130 N CHARLES G SVRS BLVD 37716 #025-07-1992 L1997 **ORS** *020 †40

MALAGON, Jose Julio. 102 S CHARLES G SEVRS BLVD 37716 #935-02-1988 L1995 **FM** *020 †18

MAY, Wendy Noelle. 102 S CHARLES G SEVRS BLVD, CLINTON FAMILY PHYSICIANS 37716 #047-20-2002 L2003 **FM** *020 †18

MCCOLL, Daphne Maples. 2130 N CHARLES G SVRS BLVD, STE 4 37716 #047-06-1997 L2000 **PD** *020 †55

MC MAHON, Cletus Jos. 2130 N CHARLES G SVRS BLVD 37716 #047-06-1974 L1975 **ORS** *020 †40

MC NEELEY, Edward Trent. 110 EXECUTIVE PARK DR 37716 #047-06-1978 L1978 **FM** *020 †18

MC NEELEY, Howard Bensley. 110 EXECUTIVE PARK DR 37716 #047-06-1978 L1979 **FM** *020 †18

O'CONNOR, Laurence Thos. 710 N MAIN ST, STE B 37716 #035-20-1992 L1997 **U** *020 †95

PIRKLE, Jacob Konrad. ■ 37716 #047-20-2007 **TY** *012

POSMAN, Clifford Lewis. 2130 N CHARLES G SVRS BLVD, STE 4 37716 #025-12-1980 L1986 **ORS** *020 †40

SAYRE, Warren Brooks. 1107 N CHARLES G SVRS BLVD, CLINTON 37716 #055-02-1999 L2002 **FM** *020 †18

SLOAN, James Collier. 710 N MAIN ST, STE B 37716 #047-05-1997 L2003 **U** *020 †95

THAKUR, Manisha Shrihari. 102 S CHARLES G SEVRS BLVD, CLINTON FAMILY PHYSICIANS 37716 #495-15-1992 L1998 **FM** *020 †18

VAZ, Godfrey R. 710 N MAIN ST, STE A 37716 #025-12-1987 L1991 **PHP IM** *020

COALMONT – GRUNDY

HELFMAN, Laura Lee. 297 SUNSET VISTA RD 37313 #041-07-1985 L1994 **EM PEM** *020 †16

COLLEGEDALE – HAMILTON

ALLEN, Linda Diane. 5623 MAIN ST 37363 #047-06-1981 L1982 **IM** *020 †20

DODD, Warren Duane. ■ 37315 #016-11-1962 L1963 **FM** *075 †18

FULLER, Forrest La Verne. PO BOX 416, 11231 BLAIR RD 37315 #005-12-1961 L1972 **OBG** *071 †30

HILL, Lucinda Sue. ■ 37315 #005-12-1983 L2004 **EM** *020

HOWARD, Ronald Maurice. ■ 37363 #005-15-1977 L1978 **PD** *075 †55,16

JENSEN, Robert Lloyd. 5206 SILVER LN 37315 #005-12-1964 L1969 **EM** *020

SIDDALL, Donley Dee. 5504 BARRINGTON CIRCLE 37315 #005-12-1970 L1974 **RHU IM** *020

THORESEN, F Douglas. ■ 37363 #005-12-1959 L1982 **FM OBS** *072 †18

TILSTRA, John Louis. ■ 37315 #005-12-1964 L1965 **AN GP** *071

COLLIERVILLE – SHELBY

AUSTIN, Susan Marguerite. 1458 W POPLAR AVE STE 200 38017 #047-06-1989 L1995 **ORS OP** *020 †40

BAILEY, Iris Williams. PO BOX 398 38027 #047-20-2000 L2002 **IM** *020 †20

BALLARD, Robert C. 151 N MAIN ST 38017 #047-06-1972 L1972 **FM** *020

BAYMILLER, Niloofar. ■ 38017 #154-07-1994 L2002 **NEP** *020 †20

BENTLEY, Steven Garold. 5190 ROWEN OAK RD 38017 #016-01-1990 L1999 **PCC** *020 †20

BETAPUDI, Bindu. ■ 38017 #495-62-1997 L2005 **IM** *100 †20

BETT-BELLEAU, Christine E. 126 US HIGHWAY 72 E 38017 #016-11-1997 L1999 **FM** *020 †18

BOLFING, Mary Frances. ■ 38017 #028-34-1992 L2007 **PD** *020 †55

BRAHMADEVI, Sowmya. 1500 W POPLAR AVE, STE 308 38017 #495-57-1997 L2003 **IM** *100 †19

BREWER, Raymond Michael. 790 W POPLAR AVE, STE 1 38017 #047-06-1986 L1987 **FM** *020 †18

BRYANT, Shelly Laine. ■ 38017 #004-01-2001 L2007 **AN** *020 †05

BURBECK, Joy Carol. 1500 W POPLAR AVE, PC 38017 #047-06-1993 L1995 **PCC PUD** *020 †20

BURNS, Tina K. 400 MARKET BLVD STE 101, THE FAM PHYS GRP 38017 #027-01-1984 L1985 **FM** *020 †18

CABE, Annabelle D. ■ 38017 #748-01-1985 L1993 **FM** *020 †18 ‡

COLLINS, Ross E, Jr. 311 POPLAR VIEW LN W 38017 #047-06-1984 L1985 **CHP P** *020 †75

CRAWFORD, John Danl. 790 W POPLAR AVE 38017 #047-06-1978 L1979 **FM OM** *020 †18

CROCKARELL, John Reams. 1500 W POPLAR AVE, STE 301 38017 #047-06-1965 L1965 **NS** *071 †25

CUNNINGHAM, Roger Jones. 1500 W POPLAR AVE, STE 302 38017 #018-03-1960 L1972 **CD IM** *071

CURLEE, Patrick Matthew. 1458 W POPLAR AVE, STE 100 38017 #036-08-1994 L1999 **ORS** *020 †40

DIRMEYER, Phillip Hays. 3508 E TAPLOW WAY 38017 #047-06-1959 L1960 **FM EM** *071 †18

DOCKERY, John Dee. 1500 W POPLAR AVE, # 301 38017 #012-05-2002 L2005 **PM** *020 †60

DUNCAN, Thane Edward. 400 MARKET BLVD 38017 #036-05-1987 L1988 **OTO** *020 †45

DUNN, David. ■ 38017 #047-06-1970 L1970 **IM PUD** *020

FARMER, Rachel Iva. 790 W POPLAR AVE, STE 1 38017 #047-06-1988 L1991 **FM** *020 †18

FESMIRE, William Murray. 120 CRESCENT DR 38017 #047-06-1984 L1986 **PD** *020 †55

FETTERMAN, Bruce Leroy. 1500 W POPLAR AVE 38017 #012-01-1990 L1997 **OTO NO** *020 †45

FINDLEY, Dwayne Denis. 126 US HIGHWAY 72 E, FAMILY MEDICAL GROUP 38017 #016-42-1984 L1986 **FM OM** *020 †18

FREEMAN, Barney Lynn. 1500 W POPLAR AVE, STE 301 38017 #045-01-1973 L1975 **ORS** *020 †40

GARDNER, James Eric. ■ 38017 #047-06-1996 L2001 **VS** *020 †85

GERARD, Dava Felice. ■ 38017 #005-18-1972 L2007 **GS** *020 †85

GUERRA, Eric R. 1500 W POPLAR AVE, STE 302 38017 #649-14-1990 L1997 **CD** *020 †20

GUINTER, Robert H. 120 CRESCENT DR 38017 #035-45-1973 L1984 **PD** *020 †55

HAGEMANN, Margarethe H. ■ 38017 #056-06-1971 L1972 **OS** *030 †20

HANISSIAN, Ara James. 1125 SCHILLING BLVD E, STE 105 38017 #047-06-1993 L1997 **MPD** *020 †55,20

HANISSIAN, Gina Marie. 1500 W POPLAR AVE, # 309 38017 #047-06-1995 L1999 **MPD** *020 †55,20

HASTINGS, Margaret C. ■ 38017 #047-06-2000 L2003 **NEP** *012 †20,55

HAYDEN, John Wm, Jr. ■ 38017 #025-01-1974 L1991 **EM FM** *071 †18,16

HAYES, Wayland J, III. 120 CRESCENT DR 38017 #047-06-1984 L1987 **PD** *020 †55

HOWARD, Cassandra D. ■ 38017 #056-06-1998 L1999 **MPD** *020

INGRAHAM, Carol Jane. 642 W POPLAR AVE 38017 #021-01-1992 L1994 **OBG** *020 †30

JEFFERS, Raymond Clarence. 526 HALLE PARK DR, COLLIERVILLE MEDICAL 38017 #004-01-1986 L1995 **IM** *020 †20

JONES, George Pierce, Jr. 934 TURNBERRY CV 38017 #047-06-1944 L1945 **FM AM** *071

KANE, Javier R. ■ 38017 #649-52-1986 L1992 **PD PHO** *020 †55

KAVOUSSI, Harold Peter. 336 POPLAR VIEW PKWY STE 1 38017 #047-07-1979 L1979 **OPH** *020

LAMBRECHT, Lauren Elizabe. ■ 38017 #047-06-2007 **OBG** *012

LUTTRELL, Mark Gore. 865 W POPLAR AVE, MEMPHIS MENTAL HEALTH INST 38017 #654-01-1986 L1993 **P IMG** *020

MAKAPUGAY, Fidel D, III. 491 W POPLAR AVE, FAMILY MEDICINE PARTNERS 38017 #748-08-1986 L1990 **FM** *020 †18

MANIKTAHLA, Kanwal Nain. ■ 38017 #495-29-1964 L1983 **U** *020 †95

MC CALLUM, Lee Wilkes. 400 MARKET BLVD, STE 101 38017 #047-06-1985 L1986 **FM** *020 †18

MC CORMACK, Harold Arthur. 250 ASHLEY HALL CT 38017 #047-06-1962 L1963 **R GP** *071 †80

MC EAHERN, Robert Jos. ■ 38017 #007-02-1959 L1960 **GP** *071 †18

MC GREGOR, David Kenji. ■ 38017 #028-02-1997 L2005 **HMP** *020 †50

MOOREHEAD, Si Fried, Jr. ■ 38017 #047-06-1946 L1955 **ORS** *071 †40

NEWMAN, Grant Thomas. 120 CRESCENT DR, PEDIATRICS EAST 38017 #047-06-1997 L1999 **PD** *020 †55

OKOYE, Ambrose C. ■ 38017 #690-04-1984 **EM** *100

OPIE, Joseph Chas. 2028 W POPLAR AVE STE 108 38017 #026-04-1981 L1992 **OBG** *020 †30

ORAEDU, Kingsley Ogonna. 1764 LISSON LN 38017 #690-02-1983 L1999 **OBG** *020 †30

OUTLAN, John Edward. 491 W POPLAR AVE 38017 #047-06-1957 L1957 **FM** *071 †18

PALMIERI-SEVIER, Ana K. 1458 W POPLAR AVE, STE 200 38017 #047-06-1994 L1997 **ORS OSM** *020 †40

PERKINS, Charles Lee. ■ 38017 #047-06-2001 L2005 **DR** *020 †80

PLUMMER, Andrea Meah. ■ 38017 #035-03-2006 **PD** *012

PUSHPANSHU, Pushpanshu. ■ 38017 #496-14-1990 L1998 **IMG** *020 †20

RAYDER, Robert N. 1636 COTON HALL CV 38017 #047-06-1997 L1999 **MPD** *020 †20,55

RICHARDSON, David R. 1500 W POPLAR AVE, # 301 38017 #047-20-1999 L2005 **ORS** *020 †40

SCARVEY, Lisa D. ■ 38017 #048-02-1986 L2005 **PN** *020 †55

SCHRINER, Robert Wm. 1500 W POPLAR AVE, PC 38017 #047-06-1986 L1992 **SME PUD** *020 †20

SIDHU, Savira. 328 POPLAR VIEW LN E, EAST #2 38017 #495-08-1980 L1994 **P** *020 †75

SOMOGYI, Christopher Todd. ■ 38017 #047-06-2000 L2005 **DR** *020 †80

STAMPS, Henry Baines. 526 HALLE PARK DR, COLLIERVILLE MEDICAL 38017 #004-01-1991 L1997 **IM** *020 †20

STENTZ, David Lee. 400 MARKET BLVD, STE 100 38017 #047-06-1974 L1974 **OBG** *020

STINNETT, Sarah Elizabeth. ■ 38017 #047-06-2008 *012

STOEV, Tzvetko George. 526 HALLE PARK DR, COLLIERVILLE MEDICAL 38017 #198-01-1984 L1997 **IM** *020 †20

TETRAULT, Gregory Alan. ■ 38017 #035-08-1983 L2003 **PCH CLP** *020 †50

THOMPSON, Tommy Clay. 1500 W POPLAR AVE, STE 309 38017 #048-02-1974 L1981 **U EM** *020 †95

THRASHER, Barton Borg. 1500 W POPLAR AVE, EMERGENCY DEPARTMENT 38017 #047-06-1990 L1994 **EM** *020 †16

VENKATARAMAN, Jayalakshmi. 2028 W POPLAR AVE STE 112, COLLIERVILLE PEDIATRICS,LL 38017 #690-05-1986 L2004 **PD** *020 †55

VLASAK, Mark C. 1164 W POPLAR AVE 38017 #048-14-1983 L1986 **IM** *020

WALLS, Kevin Michael. ■ 38027 #047-06-2008 *012

WEITZMAN, David Mark. ■ 38017 #166-02-1999 **GP** *050

WILLIAMS, Paul Parker. 335 POPLAR VIEW LN E, # 1 38017 #055-01-1975 L2004 **FM EM** *020 †18,16

WOODBURY, Michael John. 875 W POPLAR AVE, STE 5 38017 #016-02-1992 L1996 **D** *020 †15

ZAMAN, Kazi Aftabuz. ■ 38017 #495-02-2002 L2007 **IM** *020 †20

COLLINWOOD — WAYNE

MAGAS, David Mandresa. HIGHWAY 13 SOUTH 38450 #649-14-1978 L1987 **FM** *020

COLUMBIA — MAURY

ADAMS, Jeffrey Thos. 1050 N JAMES CAMPBELL BLVD, STE 200 38401 #047-06-1986 L1991 **ORS OSM** *020 †40

ALBANNA, Suzanne E. 1224 TROTWOOD AVE 38401 #051-04-1994 L1999 **EM** *020 †16

ANDREWS, Claudia Sainz. 1222 TROTWOOD AVE, STE 101 38401 #028-02-1972 L1976 **PD** *020 †55

ATNIP, Charles Dalton. 1116 W 7TH ST 38401 #047-06-1988 L1992 **OPH** *020 †35

BAIN, Robert Aaron. 1224 TROTWOOD AVE 38401 #047-06-1982 L1983 **FM** *020 †18

BALI, Indu. 1394 HATCHER LN 38401 #308-11-1985 L1999 **NEP** *020 †20

BALL, Charles A. 854 W JAMES CAMPBELL BLVD, STE 101 38401 #047-06-1976 L1977 **FM** *020 †18

BARR, Ralph Ivan. 801 SCHOOL ST, CENTERSTONE 38401 #047-05-1972 L1974 **P** *020 †75 ‡

BART, Belinda Kaye. 1600 NASHVILLE HWY, STE 104 38401 #047-07-1995 L1999 **FM** *020 †18

BENNETT, Julian Adoteyg. ■ 38402 #047-07-1999 L2007 **MPD EM** *020 †20,55

BENNY, Edcheril Varkey. 854 W JAMES CAMPBELL BLVD, STE 205 38401 #495-37-1973 L1998 **FM** *020 †75

BERRY, Sidney A, III. ■ 38401 #047-05-1969 L1969 **OBG** *020 †30

BERSCHEID, Russell James. 1218 TROTWOOD AVE, AMBULATORY CARE CTR 38401 #068-01-1986 L1996 **FM** *020

BOWERS, Gregory R. 1510 HATCHER LN STE 1 38401 #028-46-1983 L1999 **AN AM** *020 †05

BRAMLETT, Charles Bruce. 1602 HATCHER LN 38401 #047-06-1991 L1993 **PTH** *020 †50

BREIWA, Leslie Marief. 1114 W 7TH ST, THE HARTLAND INTERNAL MED 38401 #020-02-1990 L2008 **IM** *020 †20

BRENNAN, Rhonda Kay. ■ 38401 #055-01-1977 L1979 **P** *075

BREWER, John Marcus. 609 MAYES PL 38401 #027-01-1989 L1992 **EM FM** *020 †18

BREWER, Michael Eric. 1224 TROTWOOD AVE 38401 #001-02-2004 **U** *012

BREWER, William Wesley. 1224 TROTWOOD AVE 38401 #047-06-1997 L2005 **VIR** *100 †80

BRITT, Laurence T, Jr. 1224 TROTWOOD AVE, MAURY REGIONAL HOSPITAL 38401 #047-06-1994 L1995 **MPD** *020 †20,55

BROADWAY, Carol Hicks. 1222 TROTWOOD AVE, STE 101 38401 #047-06-1988 L1991 **PD IM** *020 †20,55

BROWN, Jerry Mark. 1224 TROTWOOD AVE, MAURY REGIONAL HOSP 38401 #047-06-1975 L1975 **NM IM** *040 †20,28,80

BROWN, John Preston Watts. 808 HATCHER LN 38401 #047-06-1966 L1966 **GS** *020 †85

BULLARD, Guinevere. 808 JENLAND DR, MIDDLE TN WOMEN'S GROUP 38401 #038-06-1996 L2003 **OBG** *020 †30

BUTLER, James Blair. 1224 TROTWOOD AVE, MAURY REGIONAL HOSPITAL 38401 #036-01-1988 L1991 **DR VIR** *020 †80

CASPARIS, Anthony Drake. RR 8 BOX 225 38401 #047-06-1961 L1961 **OTO** *075

CASTIELLO, Alexander. 1602 HATCHER LN 38401 #011-04-1994 L2005 **PTH** *020 †50

CHAMBERLAIN, Neil Oliver. 1114 W 7TH ST 38401 #005-14-1957 L2001 **U** *020 †95

CHANEY, Martin Mc Kinley. 1224 TROTWOOD AVE 38401 #001-06-1994 L2002 **MPD PD** *020 †20,55

CHOKSI, Amit Arvind. 1222 TROTWOOD AVE 38401 #495-17-1977 L1985 **GE IM** *020 †20

CHUCK, Frank J. 1121 TROTWOOD AVE, STE 10 38401 #035-03-1990 L1995 **OBG** *020 †30

CHUNN, Kevin Anderson. 1224 TROTWOOD AVE 38401 #001-06-1986 L1987 **EM** *020 †20

CLIFFORD, Rufus Rudolph. 1222 TROTWOOD AVE, STE 101 38401 #047-06-1959 L1959 **PD** *020 †55

CORBIN, Shaun Carlisle. 1222 TROTWOOD AVE, STE 503 38401 #012-05-1993 L1998 **OTO** *020 †45

CRYAR, Anthony Keith. 854 W JAMES CAMPBELL BLVD, STE 304 38401 #001-02-1982 L2006 **END IM** *020 †20

DAKE, Thomas Scott. 854 W JAMES CAMPBELL BLVD, STE 101 38401 #047-06-1967 L1972 **FM** *020 †18

DANIELS, David Allen. 1224 TROTWOOD AVE 38401 #004-01-1976 L1979 **EM** *020

DAVIS, Karen Fisher. 808 JENLAND DR 38401 #047-06-1986 L1989 **OBG** *020 †30

DAVIS, Lakeisha Renee. ■ 38401 #023-12-1998 L1999 **OTO** *020

DAVIS, Patricia Clifford. 1222 TROTWOOD AVE, STE 101 38401 #047-06-1965 L1974 **DBP PD** *020 †55

DE HAVEN, Howard Travis. 1602 HATCHER LN 38401 #020-02-1957 L1993 **PTH** *020 †50

DENNEY, Thomas Wade. 1600 NASHVILLE HWY, STE 101 38401 #047-06-1986 L1988 **PD** *020 †55

DIRR, Louise Dobbs. 1222 TROTWOOD AVE, STE 302 38401 #036-05-1987 L1992 **N** *020 †75

DOMM, Albert C. 1602 HATCHER LN 38401 #001-06-1978 L2001 **PTH** *020 †50

DORNFELD-FINKE, Jean M. ■ 38401 #026-04-1988 L1992 **PTH** *020 †50

DUNCAN, Thomas Ray. 1510 HATCHER LN, STE 1 38401 #047-06-1958 L1961 **R OS** *020 †80 ‡

ERTNER, Robert A. 1224 TROTWOOD AVE, EMORY UNIVERSITY HOSPITAL 38401 #048-15-2000 L2007 **AN** *020 †05

FARMER, Tom. 854 W JAMES CAMPBELL BLVD, STE 101 38401 #038-06-1986 L1995 **FM** *020 †18

FERRELL, Harold Wiley. 1602 HATCHER LN 38401 #048-02-1964 L1971 **PTH** *020 †50

FITTS, James Morgan, Jr. 1407 HATCHER LN 38401 #047-06-1963 L1964 **U** *020 †95

FOX, Beth Ann. 1224 TROTWOOD AVE, MAURY REGIONAL HOSPITAL 38401 #047-20-1998 L1999 **FM** *020 †18 ‡

FRANTZ, Gretchen Mary. 1602 HATCHER LN 38401 #045-01-1976 L1989 **PTH** *020 †50

FREELS, Jon Lee. 1222 TROTWOOD AVE, STE 605 38401 #003-01-1998 L2004 **PCC** *020 †20

FREELS, Liane Katherine. 1222 TROTWOOD AVE STE 101 38401 #003-01-1998 L2004 **PD** *020 †55

FULKS, Kenneth Dwayne. 1224 TROTWOOD AVE 38401 #047-20-1985 L1989 **PS FPS** *020 †65

FUQUA, William G. PO BOX 149 38402 #047-05-1949 L1949 **CD IM** *071

GARDNER, Benny Alto. 854 W JAMES CAMPBELL BLVD, STE 404 38401 #001-02-1980 L1987 **IM EM** *020 †20

GENTRY, Shawn Nathan. 1600 NASHVILLE HWY, STE 104 38401 #047-06-1996 L1997 **FM** *020 †18

GIBSON, L Danielle. 1602 HATCHER LN 38401 #001-06-1997 L2002 **PTH** *062 †50

GILBERT, Rodney Bradley. 3404 HAWKS RIDGE RD, 1224 TROTWOOD AVE 38401 #001-02-1989 L2000 **AN** *020 †05

GILL, James Robert. 1224 TROTWOOD AVE 38401 #047-20-2000 L2003 **EM** *020 †16

GILMORE, Robin Lee. 1222 TROTWOOD AVE, STE 302 38401 #038-40-1975 L1980 **N SME** *040 †75

GOLDSMITH, Deborah Lynn. 854 W JAMES CAMPBELL BLVD, STE 303-FERTILITY MGMT 38401 #007-02-1990 L2003 **IM ID** *020 †20

GORSKI, Marie Jane. 854 W JAMES CAMPBELL BLVD, STE 305 38401 #016-11-1992 L2000 **GS** *020 †85

GRAY, Susan Thos. 1394 HATCHER LN 38401 #047-06-1981 L1984 **GYN** *020 †30

GRIPPO, James David. ■ 38401 #047-05-2001 L2007 **DR** *100 †80

HARGROVE, Joel T. 820 HATCHER LN, VANDERBILT COOL SPRINGS 38401 #047-06-1960 L1960 **GYN** *020 †30

HARMON, Roy Franklin. RR 7 38401 #047-06-1969 L1969 **GS** *020 †85

HARRIS, Gaylon Lee. 1114 W 7TH ST, CORE PHYSICIANS AT 38401 #047-06-1991 L1991 **IM** *020 †20

HARTMAN, Patrick Erwin. ■ 38401 #047-06-1964 L1964 **GYN** *071 †30

HAYS, Danny. 1222 TROTWOOD AVE, STE 305 38401 #048-13-1982 L1991 **OBG** *020 †30

HEARD, George Jernigan, Jr. 1190 SEQUOYA TRL 38401 #047-06-1980 L1981 **DR** *020 †80

HEFFINGTON, Stephen H. 1222 TROTWOOD AVE, STE 207 38401 #047-06-1998 L2004 **U** *020 †95

■ = Address Information Privacy Protected

HEIBIG, Jacques. 1220 TROTWOOD AVE, STE 401 38401 #396-31-1975 L1996 **CD IM** *020 †20
HELM, Harry Clay. ■ 38401 #047-05-1940 L1940 **GP** *071
HENDERSON, Daryl Scott. 1224 TROTWOOD AVE, STE 280 38401 #005-02-1990 L2003 **DR** *020 †80
HIGH, Ben Greer. 854 W JAMES CAMPBELL BLVD, STE 204 38401 #047-06-1981 L1983 **FM** *020 †18
HINSON, Mark Sidney. 1222 TROTWOOD AVE STE 211, MID-SOUTH SURGEONS PLLC 38401 #047-06-1993 L1998 **GS** *020 †85
HOLLISTER, Robert Morris. 180 BEAR CREEK PIKE, STE B 38401 #035-01-1954 L1964 **IM CD** *020 †20
HUBER, Thomas J. ■ 38401 #264-04-1970 L1977 **ORS** *020 †40
HUNT, Karen Lynnette. 1224 TROTWOOD AVE 38401 #047-20-1991 L1994 **IM** *020
IVERSEN, Erik John. 854 W JAMES CAMPBELL BLVD, ASSOCIATES, INC. 38401 #016-06-1997 L2003 **PCC** *020 †20
JACOBSON, Alan Irwin. 1602 HATCHER LN 38401 #051-01-1966 L1992 **PTH** *020 †50
JAMESON, Chet H, III. 1222 TROTWOOD AVE 38401 #039-01-1978 L1998 **ON HEM** *020 †20
JERNIGAN, William Norman. 1224 TROTWOOD AVE 38401 #047-05-1956 L1956 **AN PD** *071 †55
JOHNSON, Cheryl Anderson. ■ 38401 #012-01-1999 L2006 **MPD** *020 †20,55
JONES, Helen Greene. 1224 TROTWOOD AVE 38401 #047-05-1950 L1950 **P** *020
JONES, Norman E. 1114 W 7TH ST, CORE PHYSICIANS AT 38401 #047-07-1981 L1996 **DR** *020 †80
JOYNES, Angela L. 1301 HATCHER LN 38401 #064-01-1987 L1995 **FM** *020 †18
JUSTICE, Larry Todd. 1220 TROTWOOD AVE, STE 401 38401 #020-12-2000 L2005 **IC** *020 †20
KANTH, Hrishi Madisetty. 1114 W 7TH ST, CORE PHYSICIANS AT 38401 #055-01-2002 L2006 **MPD** *100 †20
KASLOW, Michael. 1222 TROTWOOD AVE, STE 302 38401 #028-34-1969 L1984 **OPH** *020 †35
KELLEY, James Brinkley. 854 W JAMES CAMPBELL BLVD, STE 101 38401 #047-06-1971 L1972 **FM** *071 †18
KENNEDY, Richard Douglas. 854 W JAMES CAMPBELL BLVD, STE 301 38401 #047-06-1997 L2000 **FM** *020 †18
KHIM, Anthony Dayhwae. 1407 HATCHER LN 38401 #016-06-1986 L1996 **U** *020 †95
KIM, Charles S. 1050 N JAMES CAMPBELL BLVD, STE 200 38401 #004-01-2002 L2006 **PM** *020 †60
KING, James Claude. 1116 W 7TH ST 38401 #047-06-1955 L1955 **OPH LM** *020 †35,45
KOOMEN, John Chapin. 801 SCHOOL ST 38401 #036-01-1979 L1980 **P CHP** *020 †75
KURTZ, Bryan Richard. 854 W JAMES CAMPBELL BLVD, STE 203 38401 #047-06-1987 L1989 **OBG** *020 †30
KUYKENDALL, Saml James, III. 1203 TROTWOOD AVE 38401 #047-05-1976 **OBG** *020 †30
LANDON, Tiffany P. 1600 NASHVILLE HWY, STE 101 38401 #016-42-1994 L2001 **PD** *020 †55
LANGA, Ambrose M. PO BOX 1078 38402 #286-03-1947 L1954 **GS** *071 †85
LAY, Allyn Monroe. ■ 38401 #047-06-1961 L1962 **OPH** *071 †35
LEACH, James Wendell. 842 HATCHER LN 38401 #047-06-1975 L1975 **OBG** *020 †30
LEE, Suellen C. 6011 TROTWOOD AVE, STE C 38401 #001-02-1976 L1982 **NEP IM** *072
LIVINGSTON, Jeffrey F. 1224 TROTWOOD AVE, MAURY REGIONAL HOSPITAL 38401 #020-02-1996 L1999 **EM** *020 †16
LORD, Teri Michele. 1224 TROTWOOD AVE, MAURY REG HOSP 38401 #001-06-1993 L1997 **MPD PD** *020 †55,20
MAHONEY, Robert Jeffrey. 1224 TROTWOOD AVE, MAURY REGIONAL HOSPITAL 38401 #047-06-1997 L2001 **DR** *020 †80
MALLIPEDDI, Dayaker Reddy. 1222 TROTWOOD AVE STE 501 38401 #495-57-1988 L2000 **GE IM** *020 †20
MANN, Anuradha P. 1114 W 7TH ST, CORE PHYSICIANS AT 38401 #495-33-1991 L1998 **IM** *020 †20
MAQUILING, Kevin Michael. 1220 TROTWOOD AVE, STE 401 38401 #016-01-1991 L2002 **CD IC** *020 †20
MARSHALL, James Howard. 1114 W 7TH ST, CORE PHYSICIANS AT 38401 #047-06-1984 L1985 **U** *020 †95
MARTIN, Betsy Harris. ■ 38401 #047-06-1986 L1990 **DR** *020 †80
MC CALL, Scott William. 1050 N JAMES CAMPBELL BLVD, STE 200 38401 #047-06-2001 L2005 **ORS** *020
MC CLURE, Robert Wallace. 1222 TROTWOOD AVE 38401 #047-05-1986 L1989 **GE IM** *020 †20
MERRELL, James Lowell. 1224 TROTWOOD AVE 38401 #047-20-1993 L1994 **AN** *020 †05
MESSENGER, Mark Herschel. 1222 TROTWOOD AVE, AVE STE#603SICI 38401 #020-02-1993 L1998 **HO** *020 †20
MILLER, Clay R. 1224 TROTWOOD AVE 38401 #047-05-1943 L1943 **GP** *071
MONROE, Linda Peacher. 854 W JAMES CAMPBELL BLVD, STE 301 38401 #027-01-1986 L1987 **IM** *020 †20
MOORE, Joseph Clinton. 1602 HATCHER LN 38401 #038-45-1983 L1992 **PTH PCP** *020 †50
MOORE, Kenneth Lynn. 1223 1/2 TROTWOOD AVE, MID-TENNESSEE BONE & JOINT 38401 #047-06-1967 L1968 **ORS** *071 †40
MYLES, Clifford Martin. 725 S JAMES CAMPBELL BLVD 38401 #030-05-1988 L1998 **AN** *020 †05
NADDY, Gibran Badie. 1114 W 7TH ST, CORE PHYSICIANS AT 38401 #047-06-1996 L1999 **OS** *020 †20
O'BRIEN, Kevin Michael. 1224 TROTWOOD AVE 38401 #561-01-1971 L1974 **NEP IM** *020
OLSON, John Richard. 1602 HATCHER LN 38401 #056-05-1965 L1972 **PTH OS** *020 †50
OVERTON, Mary Elizabeth. 1222 TROTWOOD AVE, STE 101 38401 #047-06-1977 L1979 **PD** *020 †55
OXLEY, Daniel Davidson. 854 W JAMES CAMPBELL BLVD, STE 202 38401 #047-06-1991 L1999 **GS** *020 †85
PAREY, Stephen Edwin. 1222 TROTWOOD AVE, STE 503 38401 #021-01-1982 L1987 **OTO HNS** *020 †45
PARROTT, Earl Quinton. 1140 CARTHELL RD 38401 #047-06-1974 L1976 **P** *020
PATE, Joseph Edward. 1224 TROTWOOD AVE 38401 #047-06-1991 L1995 **DR** *020 †80
PEACHEY, Matthew Reed. ■ 38401 #047-05-2006 **MPD** *012
PEARSON, Jack Teryle. 1602 HATCHER LN 38401 #047-06-1983 L1984 **PTH** *020 †50
PERRYMAN, Paul Edward. 854 W JAMES CAMPBELL BLVD, STE 103 38401 #047-06-1989 L1990 **IM** *020 †20 ‡
PETTIT, Jonathan Reid. 1050 N JAMES CAMPBELL BLVD, STE 200 38401 #020-12-2001 L2005 **ORS** *020
PHILLIPS, Lisa Ann. 808 JENLAND DR 38401 #010-02-1995 L1999 **OBG** *020 †30
PIERCY, Kenneth Todd. 1220 TROTWOOD AVE, MED OFFICE BLDG STE 211 38401 #036-08-1998 L2006 **VS** *020 †85
PODGORSKI, Gary Thomas. 1224 TROTWOOD AVE, MAURY REGIONAL HOSPITAL 38401 #036-01-1983 L1984 **DR** *020 †80

POLING, Rodney Allen. 1222 TROTWOOD AVE STE 309 38401 #019-02-1983 L1989 **P PYG** *020 †75 ‡
QUINN, Thomas Edward, Jr. 1222 TROTWOOD AVE, STE 605 38401 #047-05-1994 L1995 **CCM** *020 †20,55
RAYBURN, Jennifer Taylor. ■ 38401 #047-06-2007 **IM** *012
RAYBURN, Martin Richard T. 1411 HATCHER LN 38401 #047-06-1958 L1958 **D** *020 †15
REDDY, Srikar Sunki. 1222 TROTWOOD AVE, STE 501 38401 #001-02-1991 L1996 **GE** *020 †20
REED, Shawn Lawrence. 1114 W 7TH ST, CORE PHYSICIANS AT 38401 #038-06-1995 L1998 **IM** *020 †20
REVILL, Jeffrey John. 1530 CENTER STAR RD 38401 #047-20-2001 L2003 **FM** *020 †18
RICHARDSON, James W, Jr. 1224 TROTWOOD AVE 231 38401 #047-06-1978 L1979 **GS VS** *020 †85
RICHARDSON, Michael David. 1224 TROTWOOD AVE 38401 #047-20-1989 L1991 **IM** *020 †20
RINEHART, Darrel Ray. 1114 W 7TH ST, CORE PHYSICIANS AT 38401 #017-20-1981 L1984 **IM** *020 †20
ROBINSON, Wm Allison, II. 1114 W 7TH ST, CORE PHYSICIANS AT 38401 #047-06-1969 L1970 **IM** *020 †20
RODRIGUEZ-VIERA, Emilio J. 1114 W 7TH ST, CORE PHYSICIANS AT 38401 #010-01-1969 L1991 **OS RHU** *020 †20
ROSENTHAL, Marc David. 1609 ROSEWOOD DR 38401 #011-02-1999 L2003 **OTO** *100 †45
SATTAH, Michael Vithaya. 1224 TROTWOOD AVE 38401 #012-05-1998 L2003 **RO** *020 †80
SEAGO, Mark Andrew. 1224 TROTWOOD AVE, MAURY REGIONAL HOSPITAL 38401 #021-05-1997 L2001 **MPD** *020 †20,55
SEVERE, Rebecca Sue. 1224 TROTWOOD AVE, MAURY REGIONAL HOSPITAL 38401 #018-03-2001 L2005 **END** *020 †20,55
SHACKELFORD, David Monroe. 1224 TROTWOOD AVE 38401 #051-04-1997 L2006 **DR** *020 †80
SIMMONS, John Oursler. 1114 W 7TH ST, CORE PHYSICIANS AT 38401 #001-02-1978 L1989 **IM** *020 †20
SIMMONS, Stephen Pierce. 1707 GROVE ST 38401 #047-05-1974 L1977 **IM** *020 †20
SISK, Andrew Webb. 1224 TROTWOOD AVE 38401 #047-06-1971 L1971 **GS VS** *020 †85
SKARZYNSKI, Daniel John. 1220 TROTWOOD AVE STE 401 38401 #016-06-1985 L2002 **CD IM** *020 †20
SMITH, Anthony Leon. 1222 TROTWOOD AVE, STE 101 38401 #047-06-1986 L1987 **PD** *020 †55
SMITH, Lang. 1216 TROTWOOD AVE 38401 #028-03-1978 L1982 **FM EM** *020 †18
STRICKLAND, Raymond Chas. 1224 TROTWOOD AVE 38401 #047-05-1976 L1977 **GE IM** *020 †20
SUTTER, William Buckley. 1224 TROTWOOD AVE, MAURY REGIONAL HOSPITAL 38401 #047-05-1990 L1992 **DR** *020 †80
TAYLOR, Kelley Leah. ■ 38402 #001-02-2002 L2007 **PTH** *100 †20
THOMPSON, Robt Guerin, Jr. 1222 TROTWOOD AVE STE 101, MAURY COUNTY HOSP MED BLDG 38401 #047-06-1972 L1973 **PD** *020 †55
THOMPSON, Tadd Thane. 1218 TROTWOOD AVE 38401 #036-05-1998 L2001 **FM** *020 †18
TOBAN, M Moataz. 1222 TROTWOOD AVE STE 601 38401 #915-04-1970 L1983 **PUD IM** *020 †20
TURNER, David M. 1224 TROTWOOD AVE 38401 #068-01-1984 L1995 **FM** *020
VAN VEEN, William Jan. 1222 MEDICAL CENTER DR, MAURY COUNTY MENTAL HEALTH 38401 #033-05-1960 L1998 **P** *071 †75
VINSON, Janice Marie. 1220 TROTWOOD AVE, STE 401 38401 #047-06-1984 L1990 **CD IM** *020 †20
VIRE, Clarence Gordon. 109 BLYTHEWOOD DR 38401 #020-12-1975 L1985 **D DMP** *020 †18,15
WALLWORK, James Caleb. 1223 HATCHER LN, WORKERS HEALTH 38401 #047-05-1965 L1965 **EM** *020
WALTERS, Patricia Rose. 1224 TROTWOOD AVE 38401 #020-12-1988 L1992 **AN** *020 †05
WHITE, Thomas Ray. 1224 TROTWOOD AVE 38401 #047-06-1960 L1960 **AN** *030 †05
WHITTEN, Therese Lynn. 808 JENLAND DR 38401 #040-02-1986 L1988 **OBG** *020 †30
WIESMAN, Harold J, Jr. 1300 TROTWOOD AVE, C/O COLUMBIA ORTHOPEDIC CL 38401 #047-05-1969 L1977 **ORS** *020 †40
WILKES, James Wallace, Jr. ■ 38401 #035-20-1948 L1952 **OPH** *071 †35
WOODLEY, Steven Edward. 1222 TROTWOOD AVE, STE 603 38401 #001-06-1989 L1994 **ON** *020 †20
WORTHMAN, John Frederick. 1222 TROTWOOD AVE STE 603 38401 #019-02-1974 L1986 **ON HEM** *020 †20
YOUNG, Thomas Kay, Jr. EXPERIMENT STA LN 38401 #047-06-1940 L1940 **GS** *020 †85
ZOLKIEWICZ, Michael R. 1401 HATCHER LN 38401 #020-02-1990 L2003 **NEP** *020 †20

CONCORD — KNOX

DEES, Donald Ray. ■ 37922 #047-06-1959 L1959 **R** *071 †80

COOKEVILLE — PUTNAM

ADAMS, Robert R. ■ 38501 #023-12-1982 L1984 **PYG P** *071 †75
AGBENOHEVI, Rexford Yao. 315 N WASHINGTON AVE, STE 109 38501 #412-01-1985 L2000 **IM** *020 †20
ANDERSON, Roy Randell. 201 W 5TH ST 38501 #047-06-1971 L1972 **IM** *020 †20
ARAIM, Leheb Hisham. 228 W 4TH ST, STE 301 38501 #012-01-1998 L2006 **TS** *012 †85,90
ARNSTINE, Jeffrey B. PO BOX 3437 38502 #010-03-1968 L1990 **CD IM** *020
AUSTIN, Lori Lynn. 128 N WHITNEY AVE 38501 #047-20-1997 L2000 **IM** *020 †20
BALEEIRO, Carlos Eduardo. 145 W 4TH ST, SPECIALISTS SUITE 102 38501 #187-01-1995 L2003 **PCC** *020 †20
BARNARD, Vaughn Noel. 340 N CEDAR AVE 38501 #047-06-1972 L1972 **GS** *020 †85
BARNES, Sam Taylor. 404 N HICKORY AVE 38501 #047-06-1961 L1962 **ORS** *071 †40
BATSON, James Howard. 345 W BROAD ST, ASSOCIATES 38501 #047-20-1996 L1998 **PD** *020 †55
BERTRAM, Katherine Alice. 128 N WHITNEY AVE 38501 #047-05-1986 L1998 **IM IMG** *020 †20
BERTRAM, Philip Darold. 128 N WHITNEY AVE 38501 #047-06-1968 L1969 **GE** *020 †20
BOLTON, Matthew Michael. 142 W 5TH ST, ATTN: VOLUNTEER MEDICAL GR 38501 #047-06-1988 L1991 **FM** *020 †18
BOYD, Michael Ray. 470 LAUREL PARK CIR 38501 #047-05-1975 L1975 *020
BREMER, Joyce Faye. 128 N WHITNEY AVE 38501 #047-06-1981 L1981 **GE IM** *020 †20
BREWINGTON, Stacy David. 228 4TH AVE 38506 #047-06-1997 L1998 **IC** *100 †20

BREYER, James Leonard. 345 W BROAD ST 38501 #016-11-1965 L1969 **PD** *071

BUSH, Gladys Ann. 1200 S WILLOW AVE 38506 #047-07-1984 L1984 **CHP** *020 †75

BUTLER, Walter B. 100 W 4TH ST 38501 #047-06-1997 L2005 **AN** *100 †05

BYRNE, Gregory Luce, Jr. 142 W 5TH ST 38501 #001-06-1979 L1984 **FM** *020 †18

CAIN, William Travis. 100 W 4TH ST, STE 250 38501 #422-01-1999 L2004 **AI** *020 †20,03

CASAL, Michael Palma. 1080 NEAL ST, STE 200 38501 #005-19-1994 L2000 **OBG** *020 †30

CASE, Robert Alexander. 228 4TH AVE 38506 #047-06-1988 L1992 **CD IM** *020 †20

CATES, James W. 1120 SAMS ST, SATELLITE MED 38506 #047-07-1985 L1986 **EM** *020 †18

CHAKRABARTY, Satya. 435 N CEDAR AVE 38501 #495-13-1985 L1997 **PD** *020 †55

CHAPMAN, Gerald Todd. 228 W 4TH ST, STE 301 38501 #001-06-1991 L1996 **TS** *020 †90,85

CLARK, Richard Gary. 142 W 5TH ST 38501 #047-06-1977 L1978 **IM** *020 †20,16

CLEMONS, Steven La Roy. 142 W 5TH ST, COOKEVILLE REGIONAL MEDICA 38501 #047-07-1993 L2003 **AN** *100 †05

CLIMACO, Christopher D. 758 S WILLOW AVE 38501 #748-11-1985 L1995 **PDC** *020 †55

COLLINS, Timothy J. 115 N PEACHTREE AVE 38501 #055-01-1989 L1992 **PTH** *020 †50

COLLINS, Timothy Ray. 254 W 7TH ST, . 38501 #047-06-1992 L1993 **U** *020 †95

CONNELLY, Lauretta Anne. 109 W 6TH ST 38501 #919-05-1972 L1997 **OBG** *020 †30 ‡

COONCE, Daniel F. 315 N WASHINGTON AVE, STE 209 38501 #047-06-1976 L1976 **DR AM** *020 †80

COPELAND, Scott Anthony. 203 N CEDAR AVE STE A 38501 #047-20-1989 L1990 **GS VS** *020 †85

CRABTREE, John Dennie. 224 N OAK AVE 38501 #047-06-1961 L1966 **GS GP** *071

CROSIER, Jefferson Ward. 221 N OAK AVE 38501 #047-06-1972 L1973 **GE IM** *020 †20

CROWE, Lee Ray, Jr. 128 N WHITNEY AVE 38501 #047-06-1971 L1972 **IM NEP** *020 †20

DALTON, Anthony Peter. 377 SHORT ST, STE B 38501 #030-06-1975 L1998 **ORS** *075 †40

DE BERRY, James T. 1200 S WILLOW AVE, PLATEAU MENTAL HEALTH CTR 38506 #047-06-1944 L1944 **GP FM** *071 †18

DERRYBERRY, Walter E. 317 N HICKORY AVE 38501 #047-06-1959 L1960 **OBG** *071 †30

DOMINGUEZ, Rosalia R. 1200 S WILLOW AVE, PLATEAU MENTAL HEALTH CENT 38506 #748-07-1975 L1996 **P** *020

DONOVAN, Daniel Hatheway. 105 CHERRY AVE 38501 #012-05-1982 L1987 **N P** *020 †75

DOUGLAS, Dale Everett. 340 N CEDAR AVE 38501 #047-06-1972 L1973 **GS** *020 †85

DURVASULA, Viswa Bharathi. 509 N CEDAR AVE, PERSONAL GROWTH & LEARNING 38501 #495-21-1982 L1989 **P** *020 †75

EPLEY, John Martin. 100 W 4TH ST, STE 200 38501 #047-06-1980 L1980 **OPH** *020 †35

ESKANDER, Gamal Sadek. 1150 PERIMETER PARK DR # B, PERIMETER MED CARE 38501 #915-02-1979 L1988 **FM GPM** *020 †70,18

FERGUSON, Edrick Jordan. ■ 38501 #047-06-1993 L1994 **DR** *020 †80

FLATT, Steven Glen. 1101 NEAL ST 38501 #047-06-1988 L1989 **FM EM** *020 †18

FLYNN, Timothy J. 201 W 5TH ST 38501 #047-06-1985 L1986 **IM** *020 †20

FOUNTAIN, Chip Hayward. 1135 S WALNUT AVE 38501 #048-15-1999 L2003 **P** *071

FOURNET, Timothy Scott. 228 4TH AVE 38506 #021-06-1989 L1990 **CD** *020 †20

FOX, Eric Gregory. 428 N WILLOW AVE, NORTH WILLOW FAM MED LLC 38501 #020-02-1988 L1993 **FM EM** *020

FRANKLIN, Lloyd Douglas. 345 W BROAD ST, ASSOCIATES 38501 #001-02-1980 L1983 **PD** *020 †55

GAW, Randy Alan. 315 N WASHINGTON AVE, STE 204 38501 #047-06-1984 L1984 **N IM** *020 †75

GELFAND, Stephen Gerard. 145 W 4TH ST, STE 103 38501 #035-03-1968 L1974 **RHU IM** *020 †20

GENTRY, Chet Mason. 142 W 5TH ST 38501 #025-12-1988 L1992 **FM** *020 †18

GENTRY, Richard Harold. 112 N WALNUT AVE 38501 #045-01-1973 L1996 **D IM** *020 †20,15

GERNDT, Brian Gregory. 203 N CEDAR AVE, STE A 38501 #056-05-1994 L1999 **VS GS** *020 †85

GERNT, Paige Renee. 317 N HICKORY AVE 38501 #047-06-1996 L2005 **OBG** *020 †30

GLASGOW, Samuel Mc Pheete. 115 N PEACHTREE AVE 38501 #021-01-1981 L1986 **PTH** *020 †50

GLEASON, Jeffrey James. 317 N HICKORY AVE 38501 #019-02-1989 L1992 **OBG** *020 †30

GOFF, Katherine W. 142 W 5TH ST 38501 #047-06-1962 L1962 **EM GP** *020 †18

GORYL, Stephen V. 320 N OAK AVE 38501 #025-07-1968 L1976 **U OM** *020 †95

GOTCHER, Jane Wright. 1101 NEAL ST 38501 #047-06-1991 L1993 **FM** *020 †18

GRAY, James Chas. 200 W 10TH ST, TENNESSEE DEPARTMENT OF HE 38501 #012-01-1976 L1977 **OBG PHP** *020 †30

GRIFFIN, Chad Aubrey. 142 W 5TH ST 38501 #047-06-1995 L1996 **FM OBS** *020 †18

GRISHAM, Donald W. 315 N WASHINGTON AVE, STE 175 38501 #047-06-1982 L1983 **IM** *020 †20

GRISOLANO, James M, Jr. 100 W 4TH ST, STE 200 38501 #016-11-1981 L1985 **OPH** *020 †35

GUILLORY, Dale Joseph. 100 W 4TH ST, STE 200 38501 #021-06-1990 L1994 **PS** *020 †65

HALL, Richard Scott. 112 N WALNUT AVE 38501 #047-05-1984 L1987 **D** *020 †15

HALL, Robert Glenn. 115 N PEACHTREE AVE 38501 #047-06-1975 L1975 **PTH** *020

HASSLER, Lloyd Ray. 350 S LOWE AVE STE A, 1223 LOCUST GROVE ROAD 38501 #047-06-1974 L1975 **OS PHP** *071

HENSEL, Albert Earl, III. 220 N OAK AVE 38501 #021-05-1979 L1989 **A AI** *020 †20

HENSON, David James. 315 N WASHINGTON AVE STE 2 38501 #033-05-1979 L1998 **PUD CCM** *020 †20

HENSON, Lorrie Lynne. 145 W 4TH ST, STE 103 38501 #047-06-1999 L2005 **GE** *020 †20

HOLLMANN, Carl M. 404 N HICKORY AVE 38501 #047-05-1981 L1982 **ORS** *020 †40

HUDSON, Toney Britton. 1245 E SPRING ST, STE G 38501 #047-06-1972 L1973 **IM OM** *020 †20

HUMPHREY, William Merritt. 315 N WASHINGTON AVE, STE 209 38501 #047-06-1967 L1969 **DR** *020 †80 ‡

IVEY, George Louis, III. 340 N CEDAR AVE 38501 #012-05-1980 L1982 **GS VS** *020

JACKSON, John M, Jr. 404 N HICKORY AVE 38501 #012-05-1970 L1978 **ORS** *071 †40

JACQUIN, Paul Nicholas. 142 W 5TH ST 38501 #016-11-1970 L1995 **ON HEM** *020 †20

JENKINS, Thomas Arthur. 445 N CEDAR AVE, COOKEVILLE PRIMARY CARE AS 38501 #047-06-1971 L1971 **FM** *020 †18

JESTUS, Joseph Allan. 145 W 4TH ST STE 201 38501 #016-11-1991 L1997 **NS** *020 †25

JOHNS, Charise Bowman. 142 W 5TH ST, VOLUNTEER MEDICAL GROUP 38501 #038-45-1996 L2001 **EM** *020 †16

JOHNSON, Bruce Dewayne. ■ 38501 #005-12-1986 L2006 **AN** *020 †05

JOHNSON, Ron Lanier. 142 W 5TH ST 38501 #047-07-2002 L2005 **IM** *020

JOHNSON, Welburne De Witt. 142 W 5TH ST, CYNTHIA 38501 #016-06-1980 L1985 **EM FM** *020 †18

JONES, Clarence Lee, Jr. 222 N OAK AVE 38501 #047-06-1963 L1963 **FM AN** *020 †18

KANE, Douglas Winthrop. 145 W 4TH ST, STE 102 38501 #051-04-1986 L1987 **PUD CCM** *020 †20

KINCAID, Robert Samuel. 115 N PEACHTREE AVE 38501 #047-06-1975 L1976 **PTH** *020 †50

KLEIN, Karl Jeffrey. ■ 38501 #020-12-1970 L1985 **OBG** *071 †30

LANDRY, Robert Harrison. 100 W 4TH ST 38501 #021-06-1987 L1995 **AN** *020 †05

LANIER, James L, Jr. 142 W 5TH ST, ER DEPT 38501 #021-06-1984 L1988 **FM** *020 †18

LE FRANC, Raymond Elishe. 438 N WHITNEY AVE STE 1 38501 #264-02-1995 L2005 **IMG** *020 †20 ‡

LENHART, Michael Blaine. 228 W 4TH ST, STE 200 38501 #051-04-1988 L1995 **CD IM** *020 †20

LIMBACHER, John Paul. 315 N WASHINGTON AVE, STE 209 38501 #047-06-1974 L1974 **DR** *020 †80

LONG, Mary Caroline. 345 W BROAD ST, ASSOCIATES 38501 #047-07-2003 L2006 **PD** *020

LOVE, Stewart Tannahill R. ■ 38501 #064-01-1955 L1982 **AN PME** *071

LOVETT, Roderick Wilson. 100 W 4TH ST 38501 #048-02-1998 L2001 **AN PME** *020 †05

LYNN, Kenny W. 210 N CEDAR AVE 38501 #047-06-1976 L1977 **FM** *020 †18

MACDONALD, Lorraine Alice. 315 N WASHINGTON AVE, STE 102 38501 #065-10-1986 L1993 **IM CCM** *020

MALTMAN, Craig J. 652 N CEDAR AVE 38501 #065-05-1987 L1995 **FM** *020 †18

MC ALEXANDER, Donald Lee. 438 N WHITNEY AVE, STE 2 38501 #012-01-1981 L2008 **IM** *020 †20

MC CARTER, Jeffrey Harmon. 203 N CEDAR AVE STE A, MIDDLE TN SURGICAL SPECIAL 38501 #047-20-1998 L2001 **GS** *020 †85

MC MAHON, Yvonne. 142 W 5TH ST 38501 #047-05-1982 L1987 **PD PN** *020 †55

MEAD, George Olaf. 315 N WASHINGTON AVE, STE 103 38501 #047-06-1986 L1987 **DR** *020 †80

MENDIRATTA, Anju. 146 S WILLOW AVE, STE A 38501 #496-20-1998 L2005 **NEP** *020 †20

MILLER, Dalia. 438 N WHITNEY AVE, STE 3 38501 #913-49-1981 L2005 **N SME** *020 †75

MILLER, Richard Chas. 110 W MAIN ST 38506 #047-06-1987 L1988 **FM** *075 †18

MINCHEY, John William. 142 W 5TH ST, VOLUNTEER MEDICAL GRP 38501 #047-06-1974 L1975 **EM FM** *020 †18,16

MITCHELL, Thom R. 142 W 5TH ST 38501 #035-20-1984 L1987 **EM IM** *020 †20 ‡

MOORE, Jeffrey Stuart. 203 N CEDAR AVE 38501 #047-06-2003 L2008 **GS** *012

MOORE, Lee Stuart. 320 N OAK AVE 38501 #047-06-1983 L1984 **U** *020 †95

MOSS, Walter Dickson, III. 115 N PEACHTREE AVE 38501 #036-01-1969 L1984 **PTH** *020 †50

NABORS, Cheryl Lynn. ■ 38501 #001-02-2001 L2004 **IM** *020

NELL, James Edward. 142 W 5TH ST 38501 #020-12-1980 L1994 **FM EM** *020 †18,16

NOLAN, Jason Scott. 115 N PEACHTREE AVE 38501 #047-06-2002 L2006 **PTH** *100

OVERHOLT, Robert Marion. 100 W 4TH ST, STE 250 38501 #047-06-1962 L1963 **A IM** *020 †20,03

PANZER, James David. ■ 38502 #011-03-1963 L1975 **D PS** *071

PIERCE, Mark Arden. 142 W 5TH ST 38501 #016-45-1980 L1990 **ID IM** *050 †20

PIPPIN, Michael Stephen. 317 N HICKORY AVE 38501 #047-06-1980 L1980 **OBG** *020 †30

RAMOS, Maria Teresa S. 758 S WILLOW AVE 38501 #748-01-1990 L2006 **PD** *020 †55

RANA, Anjana. ■ 38501 #495-55-1974 L2007 **IM** *020

RANA, Brij Bhushan M. 866 E 10TH ST 38501 #495-76-1973 L1996 **IM** *020 †20

RECKREY, Gloria. ■ 38501 #023-01-1988 L1992 **PM** *071 †60

REYNOLDS, Gary Alan. 228 W 4TH ST STE 200 38501 #048-12-1980 L2004 **CD IM** *020 †20

RICHARDS, James Darryl. 652 N CEDAR AVE 38501 #047-06-1989 L1990 **FM** *020 †18

ROBERTS, Gregory Joseph. 142 W 5TH ST 38501 #047-06-1999 L2002 **ORS** *020 †40

RODRIGUEZ CRUZ, Leonardo. 145 W 4TH ST, SPINAL SURGERY, PLLC 38501 #035-01-1988 L2000 **NS** *020 †25

SAMUEL, Brian. 142 W 5TH ST, CRMC ED - VOLUNTEER MEDICA 38501 #010-03-1981 L1990 **EM** *020

SAUER, Curtis Michael. ■ 38501 #024-07-1968 L1984 **N IM** *075 †75

SEITZINGER, David Bradley. 100 W 3RD ST STE B 38501 #038-40-1981 L1992 **IM IMG** *020 †20

SHARMA, Pardeep Kumar. 146 S WILLOW AVE STE A 38501 #305-01-1999 L2005 **FPG** *020 †18 ‡

SHAW, James Wm. 137 W 2ND ST 38501 #047-06-1968 L1968 **OBG GP** *071 †30

SIDRYS, Algis Petras. 142 W 5TH ST 38501 #016-43-1980 L1996 **RO HO** *020 †20,80

SISKO, Stephen Joseph. 100 W 4TH ST STE 310 38501 #047-06-1989 L1993 **AN** *020 †05

SMITH, Sullivan Kay. 142 W 5TH ST 38501 #047-06-1986 L1987 **FM** *020 †18

STARKWEATHER, George A, III. 100 W 4TH ST 38501 #039-01-1980 L1995 **AN END** *020 †20,05

STOUT, Jeffrey Bunker. 228 4TH AVE 38506 #047-06-1988 L1989 **CD** *020 †20

STRANGE, Danny Jay. 142 W 5TH ST 38501 #021-06-1989 L1993 **AN** *020 †05

STUBER, Harry Leslie. 503 N CEDAR AVE 38501 #048-13-1972 L1978 **GYN** *020 †30

TALLEY, Rockey Cliff. ■ 38501 #039-01-1984 L2000 **IM** *020 †20

TALMAGE, James Byron. 1245 E SPRING ST, COOKEVILLE, SUITE G 38501 #038-40-1972 L1979 **OM EM** *020 †40,16

TANSIL, Donald Wayne. 200 W 10TH ST, TENNESSEE DEPT OF HEALTH 38501 #047-06-1966 L1966 **GP PHP** *020

TAYLOR, William Snodgrass. 866 E 10TH ST 38501 #047-06-1953 L1953 **FM** *071

TOKARUK, Joseph. 109 W 6TH ST 38501 #065-01-1972 L1997 **IM END** *020 †20

TOLBERT, Audrey Karen. 142 W 5TH ST 38501 #047-06-1996 L1999 **IM** *020 †20

TREECE, Leslie Mooney. 345 W BROAD ST, ASSOCIATES 38501 #001-06-1998 L2001 **PD** *020 †55

TREECE, Robert Neil. 345 W BROAD ST 38501 #001-06-1997 L1999 **PD** *020 †55

VERMEESCH, Marilyn Kay. 1120 SAMS ST 38506 #025-07-1993 L2002 **MPD** *020 †55,20

VOSSEL, Louis F, Jr. 200 W 10TH ST, UPPER CUMBERLAND REG 38501 #047-06-1971 L1971 **IM PUD** *062 †20

WAGGONER, Brian Scott. 315 N WASHINGTON AVE, STE 102 38501 #028-02-1994 L1995 **IM** *020 †20

WARE, William F. 200 W 10TH ST, DEPARTMENT OF HEALTH 38501 #020-02-1967 L1995 **GYN** *020 †30

WHEELHOUSE, Walter W, Jr. 315 N WASHINGTON AVE, STE 201 38501 #047-05-1974 L1975 **ORS OSM** *020 †40

WHITEAKER, Lisa. 315 N WASHINGTON AVE, STE 150 38501 #001-02-1990 L1997 **D IM** *020 †20,55,15

WILLIAMS, Claude M. ■ 38501 #047-06-1949 L1950 **DR NM** *071 †80

WILLIAMS, Claude Manly. PO BOX 719 38503 #041-02-1956 L1957 **GYN** *071 †30

WILLIAMS, Richard Irvin. 142 W 5TH ST 38501 #017-20-1989 L1995 **OSM ORS** *020 †40

WILSON, Robert Lewis, Jr. 228 W 4TH ST, STE 301 38501 #036-05-1987 L1992 **CD** *020 †90,85

WOMACK, Charles Theodore. 320 N OAK AVE 38501 #021-01-1970 L1975 **U** *020 †95

WOOD, Kenneth W. 652 N CEDAR AVE, NORTH CEDAR MEDICAL CENTER 38501 #047-06-1996 L1997 **IM** *020 †20

COPPERHILL - POLK

ADLER, Margaret J. STATE HWY 68 37317 #041-09-1982 L1999 **FM BBK** *020

■ = Address Information Privacy Protected

ADLER, Richard. ■ 37317 #041-09-1976 L1999 IM *020
CHOROST, David Ian. 136 DEAL HILL RD, P O BOX 568 37317 #039-05-1989 L1993 P *020 †75
PINGA, Emelito R. PO BOX 179, 316 OLIVER RD 37317 #748-01-1970 L2002 IM ON *020
SIDDIQUI, Mahmood Abdul Q. STATE HWY 68 37317 #704-02-1987 L1995 IM *020 †20
TREON, Stephen Marshall. 111 OCOEE ST 37317 #041-12-1986 L1993 RHU *020
UHLIK, Allen Stephen. STATE HWY 68 37317 #011-02-1975 L1992 IM EM *020 †20
WOOD, Frank Henderson. STATE HWY 68 37317 #047-06-1983 L1983 FM EM *020
ZACHARY, Warner C, Jr. P O DRAWER Z 37317 #047-06-1952 L1953 OM *020

CORDOVA – SHELBY

ABUTINEH, Mohammed I. 9145 RANDLE VALLEY DR, ADULT PRIMARY CARE OF MEMP 38018 #056-06-1994 L1997 IM *020 †20
ADAMS, Melissa Binder. 8110 WALNUT RUN RD, PEDIATRICS EAST, INC 38018 #021-05-1996 L2007 PD *020 †55
AGUILLARD, Susan Mack. 8110 WALNUT RUN RD 38018 #021-06-1984 L1988 PD *020 †55
AHMED, Shameela Neaz. ■ 38018 #704-02-1993 L2002 CN *020 †75
AL-ABSI, Ahmed Ibrahim. ■ 38016 #575-01-1998 NEP *012 †20
ALISSANDRATOS, Jane Kirk. 540 TRINITY CREEK CV 38018 #047-06-1979 L1980 RHU *020 †20
ALLISON, David William. ■ 38018 #047-06-2007 TY *012
ALTABBAA, Ahmad H. 7550 CHAPEL RIDGE DR 38016 #875-01-1988 L1996 IM *020 †20 ‡
ANDERSHOCK, Christopher J. 1585 PISGAH RD 38016 #028-03-1994 L2002 EM *020 †16
ARKIN, Charles Richard. 540 TRINITY CREEK CV 38018 #047-06-1964 L1964 RHU IM *020 †20
ARMONA, Miguel Angel. ■ 38016 #275-01-1943 L1973 OS GP *071
ARNOLD, Thomas Winn. 8000 CENTERVIEW PKWY, STE 300 38018 #047-06-1983 L1984 N *020 †75
ASH, Judy Duxbury. 540 TRINITY CREEK CV 38018 #047-06-1986 L1990 RHU IM *020 †20
ATWOOD, Sue C. 2442 EAGLERIDGE LN 38016 #047-06-1957 L1957 CHP *071 †75
BANDEALY, Amin A. ■ 38018 #704-02-1986 L1995 IM *020 †20
BELLOTT, Arthur L, III. 134 TIMBER CREEK DR, STE 100 38018 #396-28-1983 L1985 IM *020 †20
BETESH, Elliott Leon. 584 N GERMANTOWN PKWY, STE 103 38018 #010-01-1983 L1994 OBG *020 †30
BILLS, John M, Jr. 1660 BONNIE LN, STE 105 38016 #047-06-1989 L1990 EM *020 †20
BLACK, Audria K. 8000 CENTERVIEW PKWY, STE 104 38018 #047-20-1997 L2002 CHP *020 †75
BLACK, John T. 8134 COUNTRY VILLAGE DR 38016 #047-06-1982 L1982 P *020 †75
BOATRIGHT, Michael David. 540 TRINITY CREEK CV 38018 #047-06-2000 L2003 RHU *020 †20
BOYD, Jeffrey Kenneth. ■ 38016 #027-01-2005 L2008 DR *012
BRITTON, Ernest Loring. 58 TIMBER CREEK DR 38018 #047-06-1970 L1970 P *020
BROWN, Roland Romarr. ■ 38016 #004-01-2003 L2006 FM *020 †18
BURNS, Gloria Ann. ■ 38018 #010-03-1995 L2000 FM *020 †18
BUSBEE, Matthew Lloyd. ■ 38016 #001-02-2004 L2006 ORS *012
BYRD, Kenneth Norris. 315 S WALNUT BEND RD 38018 #012-01-1979 L1987 OBG *020
CANNON, Tyler Austin. ■ 38018 #047-06-2008 *012
CARROLL, Jerry Scott. ■ 38018 #045-01-2005 L2008 IM *020
CHAKRAVERTY, Bhabani P. ■ 38016 #495-02-1959 L1995 ORS *071 †40
CHEEKS, Morris Edward. 8949 ROWLEY CV 38016 #010-03-1989 L1992 FM *020 †18
CHOUDHRI, Fiaz Ahmad. ■ 38018 #704-04-1960 L1971 N *020 †25
CHU, Thomas. 520 TRINITY CREEK CV 38018 #047-06-1984 L1985 DS *020 †20,15
COLE, Frederick Lawrence. 8045 CLUB PKWY 38016 #027-01-1973 L1975 IM DR *020
CRADDOCK, Culver Carter. ■ 38016 #047-06-1959 L1959 R *071
CRAIG, John Michael. ■ 38016 #047-06-2002 L2008 VS *012
CRUPIE, Marc Jos. 1025 CORDOVA STATION AVE 38018 #047-06-1984 L1984 FM GPM *020 ‡
CUNNINGHAM, Deborah K. ■ 38016 #047-20-1998 L2002 GS *020 †85
CYRAN, Katherine Frances. ■ 38016 #017-20-2005 PD *100
DANNULL, Kimberly Ann. ■ 38018 #004-01-2004 L2006 *100
DAVIS, Ashley Jaquay. ■ 38016 #020-02-2007 PD *012
DAWOUD, Samir Riad. 2384 CARROLLWOOD LN 38016 #915-02-1960 L1984 ORS *071 †40
DELLINGER, Caryl Ann. ■ 38018 #012-01-1996 L1997 N *100
DILLON, Karen Ashmore. ■ 38016 #027-01-2006 MPD *012
DOUGHERTY, Laura Waikart. 9005 RIVERWOOD FARMS PKWY 38016 #047-06-1981 L1982 IM *020 †20 AI *100 †20,03
EDWARDS, Mark Steven. 8138 COUNTRY VILLAGE DR 38016 #047-06-1981 L1982 IM *020 †20
ESTEPP, Jeremie Heath. ■ 38018 #055-02-2006 PD *012
ESTEPP, Rye Ellen. ■ 38018 #055-02-2006 OBG *012
FEILD, James Rodney. 234 GERMANTOWN BEND CV 38018 #047-06-1957 L1957 NS N *020 †25
FREY, Jamie Lynn. ■ 38018 #030-06-2006 D *012
GALLAHER, Preston Carr. ■ 38016 #047-06-2007 IM *012
GEHRES, Stephanie Boyd. ■ 38018 #047-06-2005 MPD *012
GRIFFIN, Monica Lewis. ■ 38018 #047-06-2005 L2007 FP *012
HALE, Steven Shea. ■ 38018 #021-01-2004 L2006 ORS *012
HESTON, Jerry Dale. 1135 CULLY RD 38018 #011-04-1981 L1983 CHP *020 †75,55
HIGGINBOTHAM, Robert T. 8110 WALNUT RUN RD 38018 #051-01-1998 L2001 PD *020 †55
HIGLEY, Geo Brainard, Jr. ■ 38018 #047-06-1955 L1956 ORS *071 †40
HUFF, Donnie Wayne. ■ 38016 #047-06-2003 L2006 DR *012
HUSSAIN, Shazia M. 8110 WALNUT RUN RD, C/O PEDS EAST INC 38018 #704-25-1990 L1994 PD *020 †55
JACKSON, Charolette Tamar. ■ 38016 #004-01-2007 FP *012
JENKINS, Gregory Keith. 8138 COUNTRY VILLAGE DR 38016 #027-01-1986 L1989 IM *020 †20
JONES, Adisa J. ■ 38018 #043-01-2006 IM *012
JUSTICE, Clarence Allen. 6938 SCOFIELD CV 38018 #027-01-2002 L2005 GE *012 †55,20
KASSER, Christine L. 320 S WALNUT BEND RD, STE 5 38018 #019-02-1981 L1988 ADM ID *020 †20
KENDALL-SMITH, Genevia. 320 S WALNUT BEND RD, STE 2 38018 #027-01-1989 L1991 P *020 †75
KENDRICK, William Riley. 275 S WALNUT BEND RD, STE 102 38018 #004-01-1969 L1972 AN *020 †05
KENNEDY, Irma Stewart. ■ 38016 #011-02-1964 L1968 P LM *030
KHAN, Fauzia. 8095 MACON RD, STE 109 38018 #704-09-1982 L1991 IM *020 †20
KHAN, Khurshid Ahmad K. 8407 TRONDHEIM DR, DIV OF ENDOCRINOLOGY 38018 #704-01-1990 L2007 END *020 †20

KHAN, Raja Baqa Ullah. 8000 CENTERVIEW PKWY, STE 300 38018 #704-01-1985 L2001 OS IM *020 †75
KING, Fred Ernest. 1025 CORDOVA STATION AVE 38018 #004-01-1979 L1979 AN *020 †05
KLUG, Dean Anthony. 8090 WALNUT RUN RD 38018 #004-01-1988 L1989 OTO PDO *020 †45
KOTTAPURAM, Manesh Thomas. ■ 38018 #495-63-1998 L2005 CD *012 †20
KUDUMULA, Ravi. ■ 38018 #496-31-1999 NPM *012
LAMB, Nancy L. 764 WALNUT KNOLL LN, STE 102 38018 #048-04-1990 L2005 SME N *020 †75
LARKIN, Charles Newton. 8110 WALNUT RUN RD 38018 #047-06-1974 L1975 PD *020 †55
LEE, Marsha V. 8110 CORDOVA RD STE 111 38016 #654-01-1989 L1994 IM *020 †20
LOFTON, William Bradley. 8066 WALNUT RUN RD, STE 200 38018 #047-06-1999 L2001 IM *020 †20
LOPEZ VIZCARRA, Marco Ant. ■ 38018 #737-05-1993 N *012
LOWREY, Jeffrey Harris. 8045 CLUB PKWY 38016 #004-01-1980 L1981 UCM ADM *020
LUTON, Edgar Frank. ■ 38016 #047-06-1944 L1945 NEP IM *071 †20
MC COMB, Randy Glen. 151 FOREST HILL IRENE RD S 38018 #004-01-1984 L1992 EM *020 †16
MC CORDIC, Ross Emerson. ■ 38016 #039-05-1988 L1993 PD *020 †55
MCNEELEY, Michael Fielden. ■ 38016 #047-06-2008 *012
MERIGIAN, Kevin Sam. 8200 OLD DEXTER RD, STE 103 38016 #025-12-1982 L1991 OS EM *016
MIDDLETON, Susan Kay. ■ 38016 #034-01-2003 PD *020
MILLER, Marvin Tyrone. 8066 WALNUT RUN RD, STE 200 38018 #047-06-1993 L1995 IM *020 †20
MILLER, Richard D. 274 S WALNUT BEND RD, STE 102 38018 #012-01-1957 L1966 U *071 †20
MITCHELL, Christopher W. ■ 38018 #047-06-2002 L2007 CN *100 †75
MITCHELL, Lauren Sue. 8110 WALNUT RUN RD, PEDIATRICS EAST 38018 #021-05-1997 L1999 PDI *020 †75
MULLINIX, Derek Russell. ■ 38018 #047-20-2001 L2004 FM *100 †18
MULLINS, Calvin Jeffrey. 8110 CORDOVA RD, STE 111 38016 #047-06-1989 L1991 FM *020 †18
MURPHY, Michael Patrick. ■ 38018 #047-20-2004 L2005 DR *012
MYA, Min Min. 8477 KINGS TRAIL DR, DEPARTMENT OF MEDICINE 38016 #209-01-1994 L2005 IM *020 †20
NAIDU, Srikanth Injeti. 8090 WALNUT RUN RD 38018 #001-02-1998 L2000 OTO *020 †45 ‡
NAROTAM, Sanjay Kumar. ■ 38016 #039-01-2003 L2006 DR *012
NEASE, Hilbert Howard, III. 8138 COUNTRY VILLAGE DR 38016 #047-06-1986 L1990 IM *020 †20
NEWMAN, Justin Robert. ■ 38018 #047-06-2008 *012
NORWOOD, Jeremy Scott. ■ 38016 #047-06-2006 U *012
O'CAIN, Peggy Ann. ■ 38018 #021-05-1998 L2006 CCP *100 †55
O'CARROLL, Kelly Farrell. ■ 38018 #021-06-2004 L2008 MPD *012
O'CARROLL, Peter J, III. ■ 38018 #047-06-2004 N *012
ODIFE, Amechi Valentine. ■ 38016 #047-06-2004 L2005 PD *012
O'SULLIVAN, Patrick Josep. 8000 CENTERVIEW PKWY, STE 300 38018 #539-03-1964 L1972 N *020 †20
PABBATHI, Sabitha Reddy. ■ 38016 #495-21-2004 IM *012
PANG, Jim, Jr. 8134 COUNTRY VILLAGE DR, STE 102 38018 #004-01-1977 L1987 P *020 †75
PATTERSON, Carrie Watson. ■ 38018 #047-06-2005 U *012
PERKINS, Nicholson B, Jr. 9772 WOODLAND VIEW LN 38018 #047-06-1987 L1991 AN *020 †05
PHELPS, Gregory Lance, Jr. ■ 38018 #047-06-2008 *012
PHILLIPS, Jerry Clyde. 1440 HOUSTON LEVEE RD, RADIOLOGY 38018 #047-06-1960 L1961 R *020 †80
PITTMAN, Beau Bryan. 8066 WALNUT RUN RD, STE 200 38018 #047-06-1987 L1988 IM *020 †20
RAINS, Boyce Manrin, III. 8090 WALNUT RUN RD 38018 #012-05-1975 L1976 OTO PDO *020 †45
RAJU, Jampana. 8936 RIVER PINE DR 38016 #495-72-1990 L2003 PD *020 †55
RAMSAY, Kelinda Peoples. ■ 38016 #047-06-2005 IM *012
RAO, Ashok Bangalore. 58 TIMBER CREEK DR 38018 #495-33-1974 L1979 P PYG *020 †75
REISS, Louis Henry. 8045 CLUB PKWY 38016 #038-40-1973 L1999 FM *020 †18
ROANE, Jourdan Archibald. 300 S WALNUT BEND RD, STE 6 38018 #047-05-1956 L1956 PDA PD *071 †55,03
ROTHROCK, Perry Clyde, III. 8055 CLUB PKWY 38016 #004-01-1990 L2003 FM *020 †18
RUTLEDGE, Julie Lynn. ■ 38016 #038-43-2005 L2006 IM *100
SAINO, James B. 1172 VICKERY LN 38016 #047-06-1977 L1978 PD *020 †55
SARLONE, Christine Marie. ■ 38018 #028-46-2005 PD *012
SCHRADER, Lawrence F. 927 CORDOVA STATION AVE 38018 #005-02-1983 L1997 ORS *020 †40
SEGAL, Robert Henry. 8000 CENTERVIEW PKWY, STE 300 38018 #047-06-1983 L1985 N *020 †75
SHIVRAM, Mara Giriappa. ■ 38016 #495-33-1969 L1995 IM *020
SIMS, Thomas Leslie. ■ 38018 #045-01-2003 GS *012
SLATON, Johnny J, Jr. ■ 38088 #012-01-1982 GP *020
SMITH, Hayden Blake. ■ 38018 #047-06-2006 FP *012
SMITH, Leah Nichole. ■ 38016 #047-06-2007 MPD *012
SMITH, Leslie Eugene, Jr. 1540 APPLING CARE LN # 100 38016 #047-06-1986 L1993 CHP P *020 †75
SMITH, William Edward. ■ 38016 #047-06-2006 OBG *012
SNAPP, Sharon Marie. 1172 VICKERY LN 38016 #047-06-2000 L2003 PD *020 †55 ‡
SOLOMITO, Vincent Lee. ■ 38018 #047-06-1966 L1967 R *071 †80
SPENCER, Jason Bradley. ■ 38016 #047-06-2008 *012
SPRABERY, Aubrey Trevelin. 540 TRINITY CREEK CV 38018 #027-01-1987 L1990 RHU *020 †20
STANCIL, Stephen Paul. ■ 38016 #047-20-2005 PD *012
STEIN, Lee. 8000 CENTERVIEW PKWY, STE 300 38018 #012-01-1981 L1985 N *020 †75
STEPP, William Price, Sr. 8110 WALNUT RUN RD 38018 #047-06-1943 L1944 PD *071 †55
STEWART, Wm Clark, Jr. 8066 WALNUT RUN RD, STE 200 38018 #047-06-1988 L1989 IM *020 †20
TAMEEZ, Iffat. ■ 38018 #704-16-1991 L2005 FM *020 †18
TESFAU, Simon Haileselass. ■ 38018 #366-01-1989 L2006 IM *020 †20
THOMPSON, Robert Lowell. ■ 38018 #047-06-2008 *012
THRELKELD, William Cleage. 8110 WALNUT RUN RD 38018 #047-06-1954 L1955 PD *020 †55
TORNGREN, Travis Roy. ■ 38018 #031-01-2007 ORS *012
VANKAYALAPATI, Sri V P. ■ 38016 #495-70-1987 L1996 NPM *100 †55
VANPOPPEL, Mark Daniel. ■ 38016 #017-20-2006 GS *012
VASU, Renga I. 8000 CENTERVIEW PKWY, STE 300 38018 #495-42-1973 L1984 N *020 †75
VICENCIO, Carmencita C. ■ 38018 #748-24-1992 L2007 CHP *012

VIDAL, Alex. ■ 38018 #042-03-2001 L2007 **CD** *012 †20
WALKER, Robert Ab. 8110 WALNUT RUN RD 38018 #047-06-1971 L1971 **PD** *020 †55
WALZER, Yair. 640 N GERMANTOWN PKWY, STE 200 38018 #067-01-1976 L1982 **U** *020 †95
WARE, Julie Lynne. ■ 38018 #048-04-1981 L2004 **PD** *020 †55
WEBB, Christopher Guy. ■ 38018 #004-01-2003 L2007 **PTH** *100 †50
WEBB, Oscar Dean. ■ 38016 #008-02-1998 L2001 **IM** *100
WILLARD, Tiffany Marie. ■ 38016 #019-02-2002 L2002 **CCS** *012
WINGATE, Robert Lee, Jr. 2813 MORNING WOODS DR 38016 #045-01-1961 L1982 **IM IMG** *071
WOODARD, Jean Pratz. ■ 38016 #036-01-1992 L1993 **P** *020
WOODBURY, George Robt. 8143 WALNUT GROVE RD 38018 #016-02-1987 L1988 **D** *020 †15 ‡
WRIGHT, David Bruce. 8066 WALNUT RUN RD, STE 200 38018 #011-04-1979 L1981 **IM** *020 †20
WRIGHT, Monica. 1665 BONNIE LN, STE 101 38018 #045-01-1996 L1999 **PD** *020
ZIEBARTH, David Matthew. 1172 VICKERY LN 38016 #046-01-1985 L1992 **PD** *020 †55

CORNERSVILLE – MARSHALL

TAYLOR, Richard Clark. ■ 37047 #007-02-1971 L1995 **ORS** *020 †40

CORRYTON – KNOX

CLAPP, Lindy Suzanne. ■ 37721 #047-06-2004 **FP** *012
DAVIS, James Allen. 7419 PLEASANT VALLEY RD 37721 #017-20-1997 L2004 **IM** *020 †20
HAMILTON, Benjamin Craig. ■ 37721 #305-01-2005 L2007 **FP** *012
LAMSEN, Leonard Nadong. ■ 37721 #025-07-2007 **FP** *012
MCGAHA, Charles Brandon. ■ 37721 #047-06-2006 **AN** *012
TRENT, Anthony Heath. ■ 37721 #055-02-2004 L2007 **FM** *100

COTTONTOWN – SUMNER

HELDZINGER, Derek. ■ 37048 #836-04-1987 *100

COUNCE – HARDIN

PETERS, Joseph Alan. 8917 HIGHWAY 57 38326 #001-02-1980 L1981 **FM** *020

COVINGTON – TIPTON

ALEXANDER, Warren Alison. 1995 HIGHWAY 51 S 38019 #047-06-1961 L1961 **FM D** *071
ATRIHAM, Adan Ramirez. 1995 HIGHWAY 51 S, EMERGENCY DEPARTMENT 38019 #649-38-1996 L2004 **EM FM** *020 †18
BABIN, Richard Weyro. 1830 HIGHWAY 51 S 38019 #005-14-1969 L1983 **OTO** *040 †45
BEASLEY, Deborah L. 1998 HIGHWAY 51 S, COVINGTON PEDIATRICS 38019 #028-79-1990, ▲ L1994 **PD** *020
BEASLEY, Jimmie Lee. 1998 HIGHWAY 51 S 38019 #047-06-1973 L1974 **NPM PD** *020
BOLTON, Travis Leon. 728 W SHERROD AVE 38019 #047-06-1960 L1961 **GS GP** *020
BROFFITT, Samuel Lee. 1995 HIGHWAY 51 S 38019 #047-06-1978 L1981 **FM** *020 †18
CARUTHERS, Thomas J, Jr. 1995 HIGHWAY 51 S, STE 112 38019 #047-07-1992 L1997 **OBG** *020 †30
CHANDA, Jayasree. 1830 HIGHWAY 51 S 38019 #495-39-1987 L1997 **FM OBG** *020 †18 ‡
CHEATHAM, Chas Phillips. 1995 HIGHWAY 51 S 38019 #047-06-1958 L1958 **DR** *020 †80
COLEMAN, Charlotte D. 4700 MUELLER BRASS RD 38019 #047-07-1992 L1994 **FM** *020 †18
CROWN, Loren Arthur. 1999 HIGHWAY 51 S, UT FAMILY PRACTICE TIPTON 38019 #028-02-1972 L1975 **FM EM** *020 †18
DEDWYLDER, Wilkins W, Jr. ■ 38019 #027-01-1978 L1979 **EM** *020 †18
DEOGAYGAY, Bernadette A. 2047 HIGHWAY 51 S, MID SOUTH NEPHROLOGY 38019 #748-20-1988 L2004 **NEP IM** *020 †20
FRANKEL, Don. 1995 HIGHWAY 51 S STE 109, COMPREHENSIVE HLTH CARE 38019 #035-03-1998 L2001 **FM** *020 †18
GOEWEY, Stephen Kenneth. 1995 HIGHWAY 51 S 38019 #422-01-1996 L2004 **FM** *020 †18
GUERRANT, Richard Putney. 1995 HIGHWAY 51 S 38019 #020-12-1983 L1984 **IM** *020
HO, Jiunn Hour. 1995 HIGHWAY 51 S, STE 201 38019 #244-01-1970 L1977 **GYN** *020 †30
JACKSON, William Clay. 1995 HIGHWAY 51 S, STE 109 38019 #047-06-1998 L1999 **FM** *020 †18
JANOVICH, John Richard. 1995 HIGHWAY 51 S STE 102 38019 #047-06-1967 L1968 **ORS GS** *075 ‡
JOHNSON, Samuel T. 1995 HIGHWAY 51 S, 507 38019 #047-07-1976 L1978 **FM** *020 †18
JONAS, Karl Crawford, Jr. 1995 HIGHWAY 51 S, STE 204 38019 #539-06-1975 L1985 **GS** *020 †85
KULUBYA, Patrick Serwano. 2047 HIGHWAY 51 S, MID SOUTH NEPHROLOGY 38019 #905-01-1991 L2003 **NEP** *020 †20
LARKIN, John Kenneth. 1995 HIGHWAY 51 S 38019 #035-46-1992 L2005 **IM** *020 †20
MARTIN, James William. 1995 HIGHWAY 51 S, STE 105 38019 #047-20-1998 L2000 **FM** *020 †18
MARTIN, Marysue. 1995 HIGHWAY 51 S 38019 #011-03-2003 L2006 **FM** *100 †18
MAXWELL, Zachary Thornton. 899 HIGHWAY 51 S 38019 #047-06-2002 L2003 **FM** *100 †18
MILLER, Alvin James, Jr. 1995 HIGHWAY 51 S 38019 #047-20-1995 L2000 **IM** *020
MIRZA, Abbas. 1999 HIGHWAY 51 S 38019 #704-02-1996 L2004 **FM** *020 †18
O'CONNOR, Maurine Bishop. 120 S MUNFORD ST, THE WEST CLINIC, P.C. 38019 #001-06-1986 L2004 **HO** *020 †20
POTTER, Angela Paige. 1995 HIGHWAY 51 S 38019 #047-06-1999 L2002 **FM** *020 †18
RHODES, Charles Thos, Jr. 1997 HIGHWAY 51 S 38019 #047-06-1963 L1974 **CHP P** *020
RUIZ, Julio Pablo. 2047 HIGHWAY 51 S, MID SOUTH NEPHROLOGY 38019 #308-02-1985 L1994 **NEP IM** *020 †20
SAMAHA, Joseph K. 1995 HIGHWAY 51 S, STE 208 38019 #047-06-1976 L1977 **CD IM** *020 †20
TEACH, Guy Victor. 1995 HIGHWAY 51 S, STE 206 38019 #654-01-1995 L2008 **IM** *020 †20
UGORJI, Nneoma A. 1995 HIGHWAY 51 S, STE 108 38019 #690-04-1982 L2004 **PD** *020 †55
VIPRAKASIT, Dejo. 1995 HIGHWAY 51 S, STE 104 38019 #891-01-1970 L1978 **U** *020 †95
VIPRAKASIT, Suttiwara. 1995 HIGHWAY 51 S, STE 104 38019 #891-02-1970 L1978 **AN** *020

COWAN – FRANKLIN

SOMMERSCHIELD, Stephen S. PO BOX 422, 203 MONTGOMERY ST 37318 #025-12-2002 L2005 **FM** *020 †18

CROSSVILLE – CUMBERLAND

ALJAMAL, Eyad Khamis. 320 S MAIN ST 38555-528-01-1975 L2000 **IM** *020 †20 ‡
BARNAWELL, James Ross. PO BOX 667 38557 #047-06-1970 L1975 **PTH** *020 †50
BAYLOSIS, Roberto B. 421 S MAIN ST, CUMBERLAND MEDICAL CENTER 38555 #748-01-1969 L1978 **EM GP** *020 †16
BEDELL, Paul Frank. ■ 38558 #017-20-1963 L1963 **GP AM** *071 †70
BELL, Christopher M. 1645 S MAIN ST, STE 101 38555 #021-01-1973 L1974 **GS GP** *020 †85
BERMAN, Robert Joseph. 3496 N MAIN ST 38555 #047-06-1997 L2000 **PD** *020 †55
BERMAN, Suzanne Kathleen. 3234 MILLER AVE, STE 210 38555 #047-06-1998 L2000 **PD** *020 †55
BILBREY, Richard Lee. 36 4TH ST 38555 #047-06-1965 L1965 **R** *020
BISE, Stanley Lawrence. 96 HAYES ST STE 201, HAYES STREET PROF BLDG 38555 #047-06-1973 L1973 **OTO FPS** *020 †45
BOBCZYNSKI, Wilhelmina E. ■ 38558 #025-07-1937 L1937 **OS** *071
BOWERS, Marvin A, III. 194 CLEVELAND ST 38555 #046-01-1982 L1991 **FM** *100 †18
BRADEN, James M. ■ 38555 #039-01-1975 L1976 **ORS** *020
BROWN, Barry Joseph. 36 4TH ST 38555 #047-07-1976 L1978 **DR EM** *020 †80
BUCHANAN, Ernest Grover, IV. 1645 S MAIN ST, STE 101 38555 #047-06-1997 L1998 **FM** *020 †18
CALLIS, James Taylor. ■ 38572 #047-06-1954 L1954 **GP** *071
CAMPBELL, David Edward. ■ 38555 #047-06-1967 L1967 **GS GP** *071 †85
CARLTON, H Stacey Bowman. 1645 S MAIN ST, STE 101 38555 #047-20-1993 L1994 **FM** *020 †18
CARPENTER, Douglas R, Jr. 100 LANTANA RD STE 202 38555 #047-06-1985 L1986 **FM** *020 †18
CATRON, Connie. 3496 N MAIN ST 38555 #007-02-1987 L2003 **FM** *020 †18
CHAKKAR, Tiiu Maavere. ■ 38558 #363-01-1931 **GP** *071
CHUNG, Stephen Sangwon. 421 S MAIN ST 38555 #005-12-1991 L1997 **N** *020 †75
CLAYPOOL, Kimberly M. 49 CLEVELAND ST, STE 240 38555 #047-06-1991 L1992 **OBG** *020 †30 ‡
CLAYTON, Thomas Edward. 1645 S MAIN ST, STE 101 38555 #042-01-1979 L1982 **IM** *020 †20
COOKE, Robert S, Jr. ■ 38558 #004-01-1949 L1949 **PTH CLP** *071 †50
CRAVENS, R Gene. 29 E STANLEY ST 38555 #047-06-1950 L1950 **GP GS** *020
DEATHERAGE, Philip M. ■ 38555 #041-01-1951 L1974 **OS** *020
DRABIK-NOWAK, Renata A. 57 W ADAMS ST, PLATEAU INTERNAL MEDICINE 38555 #759-03-1989 L1998 **IM** *020 †20
DUER, Carl Thos. 100 LANTANA RD, STE 202 38555 #047-06-1964 L1964 **GP** *071
DURHAM, Beatrice L. 108 HAYES ST, PHYSICIANS ASSOCIATES 38555 #047-06-1976 L1976 **IM GP** *071 †20
ERVIN, Paul A, Jr. 208 LANTANA ROAD 38555 #047-06-1945 L1945 **GS GP** *071
FOX, Mark Alan. 100 LANTANA RD, PA 38555 #047-06-1986 L1987 **GS** *020 †85
GALLOWAY, Michael Stewart. 57 FAIRFIELD BLVD 38558 #047-06-1991 L1993 **OPH** *020 †35
GALOS, Richard Scott. 100 LANTANA RD, PA 38555 #035-03-1984 L2006 **OTO** *020 †45
GARDNER, Herbert Colby. ■ 38558 #047-06-1953 L1954 **R** *071 †80
GARLAND, Russell Tyson. 49 CLEVELAND ST, STE 300 38555 #036-08-1986 L2003 **ORS** *020 †40
GUTHRIE, Fred Ashley. ■ 38572 #047-06-1963 L1964 **IM** *020 †20,16
HALL, Danny Ray. 131 S WEBB AVE, CUMBERLAND COUNTY HEALTH 38555 #047-06-1970 L1971 **FM** *030 †18
HALLMARK, Ferris Eugene. 122 MEADOWVIEW DR 38558 #047-07-1970 L1990 **GS** *020
HAMILTON, Richard D. ■ 38555 #048-04-1950 L1950 **NS** *071 †25
HARRISON, Celia H. 421 S MAIN ST 38555 #001-02-1988 L1989 **EM FM** *020 †18
HEADRICK, Mary Margaret. 100 LANTANA RD, PA 38555 #047-06-1983 L1984 **IM** *020 †20
HEIKAL, Mohamed Osama Ahm. 49 CLEVELAND ST, STE 210 38555 #915-02-1998 L2007 **PUD CCM** *020
HENDRIXSON, Mark Neal. 53 N MAIN ST, STE 106 38555 #047-06-1990 L1991 **HO** *020 †20
HIJAZI, Fadi Ahmad. ■ 38571 #605-01-1994 L2006 **NEP** *100 †20
HIJAZI, Rabih Ahmad. 49 CLEVELAND ST 38555 #605-01-1998 L2005 **END** *020 †20
HILL, Shelby Lynn. 49 CLEVELAND ST STE 200 38555 #011-02-2002 L2006 **OBG** *020
IVEY, Donathan M. 100 LANTANA RD, PA 38555 #047-06-1976 L1976 **GS GYN** *020 †85
IVEY, R Donathan. 811 S MAIN ST 38555 #047-06-1945 L1945 **NS GS** *071
JAMIESON, John Geo. ■ 38558 #028-34-1943 L1946 **GP** *071
JOHNSON, James Selva. 421 S MAIN ST, PRIMARY CARE CENTER 38555 #027-01-1995 L1998 **FM** *020 †18
JONES, David Thos. ■ 38558 #038-40-1967 L1967 **EM GS** *071 †85
JONES, Lisa P. 194 CLEVELAND ST, WOOD MEDICAL CLINIC/SSC, P 38555 #047-20-1996 L1997 **FM** *020 †18
JOSEPH, Gnanaraj. 49 CLEVELAND ST, STE 230 38555 #495-66-1993 L2004 **PCC** *020 †20
JUAREZ, Sara Bertha. 133 HAYES ST 38555 #649-13-2002 L2007 **IM** *020 †20
KABASAKAL, Ayca. 133 HAYES ST 38555 #902-09-1992 L2002 **IM** *020 †20
KANAGASEGAR, Sivalingam. 49 CLEVELAND ST, STE 350 38555 #220-02-1985 L2001 **IM RHU** *020
KIMBRELL, Keith Mc Coy. 561 WEBB LOOP 38572 #020-02-1983 L1984 **DR** *020 †80
KOUCHEKI, Mohammad Hassan. 40 ELMO DR 38555 #517-01-1973 L1979 **PD** *020 †55
KRISKOVICH, Mark Douglas. 96 HAYES ST, STE 201 38555 #048-04-1993 L2002 **OTO** *020 †45
LANZILLO, Joseph Heinrich. 421 S MAIN ST, CMC REGIONAL CANCER CENTER 38555 #011-03-1982 L2005 **RO** *020 †80 ‡
LEE, Mark Keith. 100 LANTANA RD, PA 38555 #027-01-1986 L1987 **IM** *020 †20
LINDSAY, Jack Wasson. 421 S MAIN ST, CUMBERLAND MED CTR-X RAY 38555 #047-06-1961 L1961 **R** *020 †80
LISTER, Kenneth Ray. 116 BROWN AVE 38555 #047-06-1972 L1973 **AN** *020 †05
LITCHFORD, David Williams. 33 W ADAMS ST 38555 #047-06-1972 L1973 **OPH** *020 †35
LOONEY, John Guy. 1130 CLINT LOWE RD, CUMBERLAND MOUNTAIN FARM 38572 #048-12-1969 L1987 **CHP P** *020 †75 ‡
MAK, Ernest Mung-Yuk. 49 CLEVELAND ST, STE 330 38555 #005-02-1972 L2006 **OBG** *020 †30
MANSUR, Izzuddin. 49 CLEVELAND ST, STE 220 38555 #605-01-1979 L1998 **U PDS** *020 †95
MANTILLA, Guillermo Alber. 133 HAYES ST 38555 #264-04-1997 L2007 **IM** *020 †20

MARASIGAN, Francisco S. 421 S MAIN ST, CAMBERLAND MEDICAL CENTER 38555 #748-01-1989 L1997 **IM** *020 †20
MARTIN, Richard G, Jr. 133 HAYES ST 38555 #048-14-1981 L1997 **GS** *040 †85
MENDEZ-MARTINEZ, Oscar En. ■ 38571 #935-03-1998 L2005 **CN** *020 †75
MILLER, David R. ■ 38558 #038-40-1961 L1989 **GS** *071 †85
MONAGHAN, Thomas Gavan. 314 ROMA DR 38555 #065-09-1959 L1978 **U** *071
MOON, Young Ja. 322 S MAIN ST, STE 101 38555 #308-11-1985 L1999 **ON IM** *020 †20
MORRIS, Gary Nelson. 100 LANTANA RD 38555 #027-01-1975 L1979 **IM** *020 †20
MORRISON, Kendall A. 29 TAYLOR AVE, STE 101 38555 #035-03-1992 L2003 **D** *020 †15
NICHOLS, Robert Eugene. 100 LANTANA RD, PA 38555 #047-06-1984 L1985 **IM** *020 †20
OLAECHEA, Reinaldo A. 133 HAYES ST 38555 #847-04-1967 L1971 **GS GP** *020 ‡
OSTEEN, Robert Wm. 116 BROWN AVE 38555 #047-06-1990 L1992 **AN** *105
PATTERSON, Larry E. 15 IRIS LN 38555 #047-06-1984 L1985 **OPH** *020 †35
PAULK, James Flood. ■ 38558 #001-02-1964 L1965 **FM PD** *020 †18
PEASLEE, Kimberly S. 1645 S MAIN ST STE 101 38555 #047-20-1993 L1994 **IM** *020 †20
PERRIGAN, Michael Dale. 448 W ADAMS ST 38555 #047-06-1982 L1986 **GYN** *020 †30
PETTY, Elizabeth Mitchell. 100 LANTANA RD STE 202, 100 LANTANA ROAD 38555 #047-06-1990 L1993 **IM** *020 †20
PICK, Susan Norris. 116 BROWN AVE, SPECIALTY SURGERY CENTER 38555 #048-13-1989 L1992 **ORS** *020 †40
PINEDA, Lilibeth. 41 WEST AVE STE 204 38555 #748-02-1985 L1999 **PCC** *020 †20
PITTS, David Wilson. 58 W FIRST ST 38555 #047-06-1990 L1991 **OBG** *020 †30
PRIBANICH, Steven, III. 100 LANTANA RD, PA 38555 #055-02-1991 L2000 **FM FSM** *020 †18
RAFFEL, Bruce Corwyn. 100 LANTANA RD, PA 38555 #027-01-1977 L1987 **PS OTO** *020 †45,65
REED, Christine Louise. ■ 38558 #051-07-2004 L2007 **PD** *100 †55
REED, Larry Dewayne. 811 S MAIN ST 38555 #047-06-1973 L1974 **FM** *020
REGAN, Robert Leu. ■ 38558 #010-02-1947 L1949 **GYN** *071 †30
REISS, Norman. ■ 38558 #041-13-1954 L1955 **OBG** *071 †30
SATYANARAYAN, Viswesvar. 811 S MAIN ST 38555 #047-06-1991 L1992 **FM** *020
SHERRILL, John Branson. 100 LANTANA RD, PA 38555 #047-06-1986 L1989 **IM** *020 †20
SIDRYS, Debbee S. 421 S MAIN ST 38555 #041-09-1981 L1997 **IM NEP** *020
SIMPSON, Jon Alan. 118 BROWN AVE, STE 103 38555 #016-43-1984 L1989 **ORS** *020 †40
SPITLER, Timothy Michael. 100 LANTANA RD, PA 38555 #012-01-1994 L1995 **IM** *020 †20
STALLWORTH, James M. 421 S MAIN ST 38555 #021-01-1990 L1995 **DR** *020 †80
STOUT, Bill Dean. ■ 38558 #047-06-1958 L1962 **OS CD** *071 †20
STUBBS, Maria V. 421 S MAIN ST 38555 #019-02-1994 L2006 **IM** *020 †20
TABOR, David Carter. 49 CLEVELAND ST, STE 340 38555 #051-04-1976 L1983 **ON IM** *020 †20
TAVALLAEE, Mehran Monazam. 133 HAYES ST 38555 #517-04-1999 L2007 **IM** *020
THOMPSON, Bill. 36 4TH ST 38555 #047-06-1979 L1980 **DR GP** *020 †80
VILLARUZ, Vianney E. 100 LANTANA RD, PA 38555 #748-02-1987 L1995 **CD** *020 †20
WAGNER, Barry S. 811 S MAIN ST 38555 #028-79-1981, ▲ L1982 **EM** *020 †16
WALLACE, Joe Kenneth. ■ 38555 #047-06-1958 L1958 **FM** *071 †18
WALLNER, Jill Margaret. 2193 N MAIN ST STE 101 38555 #028-34-1990 L1995 **GP PHP** *020
WHITMILL, Jonanna Gibbs. 100 LANTANA RD, PA 38555 #047-20-1998 L1999 **IM** *020 †20
WIKERT, Gary Allan. ■ 38555 #012-01-1977 L2000 **U** *020 †95
WILSON, Garland Anthony. 100 LANTANA RD, STE 202 38555 #047-06-2000 L2002 **FM** *020 †18 ‡
WOJCIK, James Francis. 118 QUAIL HOLLOW CT 38555 #047-20-1985 L1986 **EM IM** *020 †20
WOOD, Robert Hancock, Jr. ■ 38571 #047-06-1969 L1970 **FM** *071 †18
YATTO, Robert Paul. 96 HAYES ST STE 102 38555 #561-01-1975 L1999 **GE** *020 †20
ZEINO, Merhaf. 99 DOOLEY ST 38555 #875-02-1981 L2003 **NEP** *020 †20

DANDRIDGE – JEFFERSON

BOGGAN, Joel Curtis. ■ 37725 #036-07-2008 *012
CONNER, Patricia Jean. 3885 HIGHWAY 411 37725 #047-20-2005 L2006 **FM** *020 †18
DILLARD, Donna R. 118 E MEETING ST 37725 #047-20-1993 L1998 **FM** *020 †18
DONALDSON, Barbara Hasty. JEFFERSON CO HLTH DEPT 130 37725 #047-06-1951 L1958 **PHP** *071
EATON, Allison Michelle. ■ 37725 #045-04-2003 L2007 **OBG** *020
FOSTER, James Wm. 1026 HIGHWAY 92 S, DANDRIDGE FAMILY PRACTICE 37725 #020-02-1985 L1988 **IM EM** *020
GARBARINO, Angelo J, Jr. 1026 HIGHWAY 92 S, DANDRIDGE FAMILY PRACTICE 37725 #047-06-1970 L1971 **FM** *020 †18
GREENE, Jeffrey Carlin. 118 E MEETING ST 37725 #020-12-1992 L1995 **FM** *020 †18
HOOD, Michael T. 1026 HIGHWAY 92 S, DANDRIDGE FAMILY PRACTICE 37725 #047-06-1977 L1978 **FM** *020 †18
HOWARD, Jessie Eugene. ■ 37725 #047-06-1956 L1957 **OBG** *071
KICKLITER, David. 1026 HIGHWAY 92 S, DANDRIDGE FAMILY PRACTICE 37725 #047-06-1985 L1987 **FM** *020 †18
MC CONNELL, David Houston. 1026 HIGHWAY 92 S, DANDRIDGE FAMILY PRACTICE 37725 #047-06-1965 L1966 **FM OS** *020 †18 ‡
SWANSON, Rual Clark. 118 E MEETING ST 37725 #665-01-1999 L2004 **FM** *020 †18 ‡
TAYLOR, Deanna Faye. ■ 37725 #047-06-2002 L2007 **NM** *012 †80

DAYTON – RHEA

BACON, Stuart Peter. 7794 RHEA COUNTY HWY # 101 37321 #047-06-1974 L1975 **FM GE** *020 †18
BLACK, David Henning. ■ 37321 #045-01-1974 **OS** *030
BOVINE, Thomas Patrick. 7794 RHEA COUNTY HWY, STE 104 37321 #047-06-1980 L1983 **FM** *020 †18
BROCK, Howard Robert. 1436 RAILROAD ST 37321 #306-01-1995 L2003 **FM** *020 †18
CREWS, Alan L. 163 WALNUT GROVE CHURCH RD 37321 #047-06-1982 L1983 **IM** *020 †20
GRAHAM, David L. ■ 37321 #649-14-1972 **IM** *020
HORTON, Christopher R. 163 WALNUT GROVE CHURCH RD, STE 103 37321 #047-06-1999 L2000 **FM** *020 †18
JOHNSON, Edward Downey. 188 16TH AVE, STE 104 37321 #041-01-1961 L1981 **OS OM** *020
NELSON, James Donovan. 149 WALNUT GROVE CHURCH RD 37321 #031-01-1981 L1984 **PD** *020 †55
TANTIHACHAI, Sithipol. 7794 RHEA COUNTY HWY, STE 102 37321 #244-04-1972 L1981 **GS** *020 †85
WADE, Mervin Alvin. PO BOX 809, K PLAZA 37321 #060-01-1957 L1975 **FM AN** *071

DECATUR – MEIGS

ROBERTS, Rodney Shane. 398 N MAIN ST 37322 #047-20-1991 L1992 **FM** *020 †18
SINHA, Manvesh N. 305 RIVER RD 37322 #495-33-1992 L1996 **IM** *020 †20
SLUSHER, Donald Howard. HUNTER BEND ROAD 37322 #038-41-1963 L1986 **NM DR** *071 †28

DECATURVILLE – DECATUR

REDDY, Ramesh Keesara. 187 W MAIN ST 38329 #495-65-1973 L1980 **IM** *020 †20

DECHERD – FRANKLIN

HOOD, Dewey Woodrow. PO BOX 232 37324 #047-06-1958 L1959 **GP OBG** *020
WILLIAMS, Jennie Lynn. 2006 DECHERD BLVD 37324 #422-01-1986 L1990 **FM** *020 †18 ‡

DICKSON – DICKSON

ALEXANDER, Jean Kay. 113 HIGHWAY 70 E 37055 #038-40-1983 L1984 **AI** *020
AL-SOUB, Mohammad A. 113 HIGHWAY 70 E 37055 #575-01-1987 L2004 **PCC** *020 †20
ANDERSON, Stanley Martin. 101 NATCHEZ PARK DR 37055 #047-06-1966 L1967 **DR R** *020 †80
ASAD, Muhammad. 113 HIGHWAY 70 E 37055 #704-04-1992 L2002 **CD** *020 †20
BELL, Walter A, III. 2005 HWY 46 S 37055 #047-06-1978 L1978 **IM** *020 †20
BLAZER, David Julius. 113 HIGHWAY 70 E 37055 #561-06-1980 L1994 **CD IM** *020 †20
CHAMBERS, David Earl. 113 HWY 70 E, DICKSON MEDICAL GROUP 37055 #001-06-1986 L1992 **CD IM** *020 †20
CHEROLIS, Julie Dark. 111 HIGHWAY 70 E, DEPT. OF SURGERY 37055 #047-06-2001 L2006 **AN** *100
CLOSE, Louis Ward. 112 HIGHWAY 70 E 37055 #047-05-1973 L1976 **OPH** *020 †35
COLE, Cecil Richard. ■ 37055 #021-01-1957 L1957 **GP** *020 †18
COLE, Michael Eugene. 116 HIGHWAY 70 E STE 2 37055 #047-06-2004 L2008 **OBG** *012
COLLINS, Clyde Edward. 758 HIGHWAY 46 S, HORIZON MEDICAL GROUP 37055 #012-05-1972 L1978 **FM OM** *020 †18
DINKINS, Juan Stacy. 113 HIGHWAY 70 E, DICKSON MEDICAL ASSOCIATES 37055 #025-76-1998, ▲ L2004 **FM** *020
DONG-AS, Maria Fernando. 113 HIGHWAY 70 E, DICKSON MEDICAL ASSOCIATES 37055 #748-16-1989 L2005 **CN** *020 †75
DRINNEN, Daniel Brooks. 113 HIGHWAY 70 E 37055 #047-06-1965 L1965 **FM** *020 †18
GORDON, Jeffery Saml. 114 HWY 70 E, STE 5 37055 #021-01-1972 L1978 **PD PHP** *020 †55
GORZNY, Jan M. 113 HWY 70 E, ASSOCIATES PC 37055 #035-06-1974 L1984 **ORS** *020 †40
GRIFFITTS, Rebekah Earle. 113 HIGHWAY 70 E 37055 #047-06-1965 L1966 **EM** *020 †16
HAWKINS, Kenneth Ernest. 160 HWY 70 E, UNIT 4, OLD TOWN CT 37055 #047-06-1992 L1997 **DR** *020 †80
HAWKINS, Michael Darren. 111 HIGHWAY 70 E STE H, DICKSON, PLLC 37055 #012-05-1991 L1995 **OBG** *020 †30
HAYES, Phillip Walton. 301 E COLLEGE ST 37055 #047-06-1968 L1970 **IM GE** *071 †20
HUERTA MERCADO, Gustavo. 704 E COLLEGE ST 37055 #649-01-1976 L1991 **GS** *020 †85
HUFFNAGLE, Milford James. 113 HIGHWAY 70 E, DICKSON MED ASSOC 37055 #041-02-1989 L1996 **FM** *020 †18
HUFFNAGLE, Vera Hentosh. 113 HIGHWAY 70 E 37055 #041-02-1989 L1996 **N** *020 †75
JACKSON, Robert Stewart. 113 HIGHWAY 70 E, DICKSON MEDICAL ASSOCIATES 37055 #047-06-1973 L1974 **IM** *020 †20
LAWSON, Jerold Oliver. 113 HIGHWAY 70 E, DBA HORIZON MEDICAL GROUP 37055 #047-07-1973 L1988 **IM** *020
LUCAS, Dolores Jocelyn. 113 HIGHWAY 70 E, DICKSON MEDICAL ASSOCIATES 37055 #035-19-1994 L1998 **D** *020 †15
LUDEMANN, John Wm. 111 HIGHWAY 70 E 37055 #067-01-1959 L1996 **OBG** *071 †30
LUPLOW, Rolland E, II. 758 HWY 46 S 37055 #047-06-1984 L1984 **FM** *020 †18
MAHAN, Marcille. 114 HWY 70 E, STE 5 37055 #021-01-1973 L1978 **PD** *071 †55
MANI, Venk. 113 HIGHWAY 70 E 37055 #495-53-1967 L1994 **PTH DMP** *020 †50,28
MC CLURE, Daniel Joe. 114 HWY 70 E STE 4 37055 #047-06-1994 L1995 **IM** *020 †35
MC NEAL, Mary Kathryn. 110 MATHIS DR STE 104 37055 #020-02-1998 L2001 **PD** *020 †55
MILLS, Van Frank. 758 HIGHWAY 46 S, DICKSON MEDICAL ASSOCIATES 37055 #422-01-1985 L1988 **FM** *020 †18
MORSE, John C W. 113 HIGHWAY 70 E, DICKSON MEDICAL ASSOCIATES 37055 #422-01-1985 L1988 **FM** *020 †18
ORGAIN, Robert Wm. 758 HWY 46 S 37055 #047-06-1977 L1977 **FM** *020 †18
PAVULURI, Vijaya Lakshmi. 721 HIGHWAY 46 S 37055 #495-50-1989 L1998 **P** *020 †75
PERRIGIN, Julie Ferguson. 219 CHURCH ST, DICKSON MEDICAL ASSOCIATES 37055 #047-06-1999 L2002 **FM** *020 †18
PREBUS, Sol Allen. 111 HWY 70 E, HORIZON MEDICAL CENTER 37055 #038-06-1994 L2001 **IM** *020 †20
PRIYADARSHI, Anumeet. 256 BEASLEY DR 37055 #496-21-1991 L2006 **NEP** *020 †20
REDDY, Yekolla M. 111 HIGHWAY 70 E 37055 #495-70-1989 L2002 **EM** *020 †18 ‡
ROSS, David Lamar. 113 HIGHWAY 70 E 37055 #047-06-2000 L2003 **IM** *020 †20
ROSS, Kerry Wayne. 113 HIGHWAY 70 E 37055 #047-06-1998 L1999 **MPD** *020 †55,20
ROTH, James Matthew. 111 HWY 70 E, 2ND FLOOR, STE 3 37055 #056-06-1999 L2004 **OTO** *020 †45 ‡
SALYER, John R. 113 HIGHWAY 70 E 37055 #047-06-1976 L1976 **FM** *020 †18
SAVELL, Truitt Anthony. 445 HENSLEE DR 37055 #038-06-2004 L2004 **GS** *100
SIEGIEN, Jolanta. 111 HWY 70 E, HORIZON MEDICAL CENTER 37055 #759-11-1990 L2000 **IM** *020 †20
SMITH, Bobby Joel. 729 MARSHALL STUART DR, CCHS 37055 #047-06-1958 L1959 **OM FM** *071 †18
SMITH, Ernest Ross, Jr. 113 HIGHWAY 70 E, DICKSON MEDICAL ASSOCIATES 37055 #017-20-1991 L1999 **U** *020 †95
SPENCER, J Vennard. 301 W END AVE 37055 #054-04-1979 L1993 **FM PD** *020 †18
SPIGEL, Stuart Chas. 103 NATCHEZ PARK DR, STE 103 37055 #035-06-1968 L1975 **ON HEM** *020 †20
STEPHENS, Walter Earnest, III. 113 HIGHWAY 70 E, DICKSON MED ASSOC 37055 #047-06-1998 L1998 **FM** *020 †18
SWANSON, Roger Thos. 111 HIGHWAY 70 E 37055 #047-05-1969 L1969 **DR NM** *020 †80

THUAN, Robert Pham Ngoc. 113 HIGHWAY 70 E, HORIZON MEDICAL GROUP 37055 #941-01-1970 L1977 **GS** *020

WHITFIELD, April Linn. 116 HIGHWAY 70 E, STE 2 37055 #025-12-2001 L2005 **OBG** *020 †30

WISER, Eldred Houck. 113 HIGHWAY 70 E 37055 #047-06-1965 L1966 **GS** *020 †85

WOOLRIDGE, Thomas J, III. 301 W END AVE 37055 #047-07-1978 L1980 **FM** *040 †18

ZURAWEK, Tomasz A. 766 HWY 46 S 37055 #759-03-1987 L1997 **IM PUD** *020 †20

DONELSON — DAVIDSON

ARNOLD, Rosalia Valeriana. ■ 37214 #275-01-1945 L1973 **GP** *071

DOVER — STEWART

BIRNEY, Paul Kenneth. ■ 37058 #038-40-1975 L2005 **FM** *071 †18

DURRETT, Dawson Winfield. 1020 MOORE RD, GATEWAY MEDICAL CLINIC 37058 #047-06-1958 L1958 **GS** *020 †85

LEA, Gary Hobart. 1020 MOORE RD 37058 #038-40-1976 L1995 **GP** *020

LEE, Robert Henry. 1020 MOORE RD 37058 #028-03-1965 L1966 **FM** *020 †18

DRESDEN — WEAKLEY

BERNARD, Clement F. 130 E LOCUST ST 38225 #041-09-1988 L1997 **CD** *020 †20

COOPER, Mark Anthony. 130 E LOCUST ST 38225 #047-20-1994 L1997 **IM** *020

YOGESH, Kumar Patel. 130 E LOCUST ST 38225 #495-23-1983 L1990 **IM PUD** *020 †20

DUCKTOWN — POLK

LEE, William Reece. MAIN ST 37326 #048-04-1957 L1958 **GP OS** *071

DUNLAP — SEQUATCHIE

DANIEL, Debora Carole. 16931 RANKIN AVE, NORTH VALLEY MEDICAL PLAZA 37327 #047-20-1987 L1994 **FM** *020 †18

GRAVES, Charles Guy, Jr. 8 CATES RD 37327 #005-12-1953 L1955 **FM** *071 †18

NELSON, Roger T. 8 CATES RD 37327 #005-12-1945 L1983 **GS TS** *072 †85,90 ‡

WAGNER, James Landis. 16062 RANKIN AVE 37327 #047-06-1986 L1987 **IM** *020 †20

DYERSBURG — DYER

ALLISON, Jack R. 400 E TICKLE ST 38024 #047-06-1975 L1976 **DR** *020 †80

ASLAM, Tanveer. 1950 COOK ST, STE D 38024 #704-01-1991 L2000 **PCC** *020 †20

ATEGBOLE, Olusegun Victor. 400 E TICKLE ST, 24 HR ON PHYSICIAN 38024 #690-01-1988 L2003 **IM** *020 †20

BABA, Rauf M. 1950 COOK ST, HIGHWAY 51 BY PASS 38024 #495-51-1994 L2002 **END** *020 †20

BARTON, Melissa. PO BOX 846 38025 #001-02-1980 L2004 **HS PS** *020 †65

BARTON, Stephen Nye. 400 E TICKLE ST, MEDICAL STAFF OFFICE 38024 #026-04-1973 L2006 **P GPM** *020 †70,75

BINDRA, Gurpal Singh. 1716 PARR AVE STE B 38024 #495-73-1986 L1991 **OTO** *020 †45

BRUNSON, Bernie Lee. 1716 PARR AVE STE F 38024 #020-02-1988 L2001 **GS** *020 †85

CANNON, Jesse J, Jr. 1130 US HIGHWY 51 BYP W #1 38024 #047-06-1976 L1977 **IM** *020 †20

CAPE, Richard Chas. 401 E TICKLE ST, CAPE SURGERY CENTER 38024 #047-06-1989 L1991 **OPH** *020 †35

CASEY-BOLDEN, Monique C. 1716 PARR AVE, STE D 38024 #047-20-1999 L2001 **FM** *020 †18

CAYLOR, James August. 503 E TICKLE ST 38024 #047-06-1985 L1987 **GS** *020 †85

CHOUEIRY, Mona Adib. 1501 BRAYTON AVE 38024 #605-03-1990 L1997 **PD** *020 †55

CRINER, Roger Dale. 400 E TICKLE ST, DRMC EMERGENCY DEPT 38024 #654-01-2003 L2006 **EM FM** *020 †18 ‡

DALATI, Fakhri. 400 E TICKLE ST, DYERSBURG RMC 38024 #875-02-1996 L2004 **IM** *020 †20

DAVID, Mary Stuart. 1535 PARR AVE, WOMEN'S CLINIC OF DYERSBUR 38024 #047-06-1979 L1979 **OBG GYN** *020 †30

EL-ABBOUD EL-KHEDER, Anass. 400 E TICKLE ST, ATTN: DEBRA MARBURRY, INTE 38024 #875-02-1995 L2005 **CCM** *020 †20

EVANS, Thomas Paul. 400 E TICKLE ST, DYERSBURG REGIONAL MEDICAL 38024 #001-02-1995 L1999 **MPD** *020 †20,55

FELDHOUSE, Doreen Eleanor. 1716 PARR AVE, STE D 38024 #041-12-1984 L1994 **FM PHP** *020 †18 ‡

FERNANDES, Deborah Maria. 1501 BRAYTON AVE 38024 #473-02-1996 L2001 **PD** *020 †55

FISCHL, Henry Jos. ■ 38024 #028-34-1963 L1984 **OBG** *075

FITTS, William Elton. 1700 WOODLAWN AVE, MED SOUTH HEALTH CARE, P.C 38024 #028-02-1979 L1989 **OBG** *020 †30

FLOWITT, Catherine Jean. 400 E TICKLE ST 38024 #065-01-1981 L1998 **FM** *020 †18

FREEMAN, Gordon Redfern. 503 E TICKLE ST, OTOLARYNGOLOGY CNSLNTS 38024 #007-02-1952 L1976 **OTO HNS** *071 †45

FRIEDERICH, Jeffrey Allen. 291 QUAIL HOLLOW DR, DIRECTOR OF ANESTHESIA 38024 #039-01-1990 L1995 **CCA PME** *020 †05

GREEN, Daniel Parker, Jr. 305 E TICKLE ST 38024 #047-06-1967 L1968 **IM IMG** *020 †20

GUTHRIE, David Porter. 1716 PARR AVE, STE C 38024 #047-06-1987 L1988 **IM** *020 †20

HARRINGTON, Robert Lee. 108 E COURT ST 38024 #047-06-1959 L1959 **OBG** *071 †20

HARROD, Charles Scott. 1700 WOODLAWN AVE 38024 #038-40-1978 L2006 **IM** *020 †20 ‡

HAYNES, Douglas B, Jr. 1700 WOODLAWN AVE 38024 #047-06-1961 L1961 **IM HEM** *020

HUFF, Carl Wayne. 1855 US HIGHWAY 51 BYP N, STE B 38024 #047-06-1969 L1970 **ORS** *020 †40,70

INCLAN, Aurelio Peter. 400 E TICKLE ST 38024 #275-01-1943 L1968 **PTH** *071 †50

ISAACS, Randy Ray. 1700 WOODLAWN AVE 38024 #016-11-1992 L1999 **PD** *020 †55

JAIN, Angeli. ■ 38024 #495-37-2001 L2006 **FM** *020

JERNIGAN, Jerry Marshall. 350 E PARKVIEW ST 38024 #047-05-1961 L1961 **OPH** *020

JOHNSON, Darren Lemar. 116 HIGHWAY 70 E 38024 #047-06-2003 L2004 **FM** *020 †18

JOHNSON, Eloiett. 315 E TICKLE ST 38024 #047-06-1962 L1962 **OBG** *071

JOYNER, Johnny B. 315 E TICKLE ST, WOMENS CLINIC 38024 #047-06-1982 L1982 **OBG** *020 †30

KERR, Robert Thompson. ■ 38024 #004-01-1944 L1949 **GS** *071

KING, Elton Aaron. 315 E TICKLE ST 38024 #047-06-1959 L1963 **OBG** *071 †30

KUMAR, Rakesh Muthu. 400 E TICKLE ST, 24ON PHYSICIANS, P.C. 38024 #495-33-1996 L2006 **IMG** *020 †20

LAING, Ian Robert. 1716 PARR AVE 38024 #060-01-1967 L1994 **U** *071

LEGAN, John Keith. ■ 38024 #028-03-1958 L1958 **GS GP** *071 †85

LEGAN, John Marcus. 400 E TICKLE ST, DYERSBURG REGIONAL MEDICAL 38024 #028-03-1985 L1993 **R** *020 †80

LEPEJIAN, Garine Antranik. 1501 BRAYTON AVE, PEDIATRIC ASSOCIATES, PC 38024 #575-01-1996 L2006 **PD** *020 †55

LOMAS, Russell W. 1067 VENDALL RD 38024 #048-12-1988 L1990 **GE** *020 †20

LOOPER, Fred Buford. 305 W COURT ST 38024 #047-06-1961 L1961 **R RO** *071 †80

LOVE, Beverly Ray. 315 E TICKLE ST, BEVERLY LOVE, MD 38024 #035-45-1976 L2005 **OBG** *020 †30 ‡

LUNDY, James Harold. 715 COUNCIL RD, POB 501 38024 #027-01-1983 L1984 **AN EM** *020

MACHRA, Gurpreet Singh. ■ 38024 #495-51-1994 L2005 **IM** *100 †20

MAGEE, Robert W. 1700 WOODLAWN AVE 38024 #047-07-1977 L1978 **FM** *020 †18

MALONEY, Kenneth Roscoe. 1700 WOODLAWN AVE, MED SOUTH 38024 #047-06-1975 L1976 **D** *020

MC KEE, William Neil. 1716 PARR AVE STE C, CENTER FOR ADULT HEALTHCAR 38024 #047-06-1988 L1989 **IM PUD** *020 †20

MC KENZIE, Debra Kay. 509 LAKE RD, STE 4 38024 #017-20-1991 L2003 **OBG** *020 †30

MELLO, Vickie B. 400 E TICKLE ST 38024 #025-76-1999, ▲ L2004 **OBG** *020

MELTON, Stevens Doyle. 1700 WOODLAWN AVE 38024 #047-06-1981 L1982 **PD EM** *020 †55

MOCKRIN, Lee David. 1700 WOODLAWN AVE 38024 #016-06-1969 L2001 **PD OS** *020 †55

MONNIG, Jack Anthony. 575 E TICKLE ST, DYERSBURG UROLOGY CLINIC 38024 #047-06-1972 L1972 **U** *095

MOORE, Olyn Fred, III. 503 E TICKLE ST 38024 #047-06-1979 L1979 **GS** *020 †85

MULAY, Ramakant M. 1575 PARR AVE 38024 #495-56-1974 L1986 **NEP IM** *020 †20

NABHAN, Said I. 710 US HIGHWAY 51 BYP W, PMB 770 38024 #605-01-1991 L1997 **GE** *020 †20

NAIFEH, James Edward, Jr. 400 E TICKLE ST 38024 #422-01-1983 L1987 **FM EM** *020 †18

NOONAN, James Rothwell. 400 E TICKLE ST, DYERSBURG REG MED CTR 38024 #047-06-1964 L1964 **IM IMG** *030 †20

NORD, Keith Douglas. 640 US HIGHWAY 51 BYP E, STE D 38024 #023-12-1983 L1995 **ORS** *020 †40

OYEFESO, Olumide. ■ 38024 #690-06-1998 L2007 **PD** *020 †55

PALACIOS, Esteban J. 400 E TICKLE ST 38024 #275-01-1955 L1980 **PTH** *071 †50

PREWITT, Darrion Jewayne. 503 E TICKLE ST, PREWITT MEDICAL CARE, P.C. 38024 #047-20-1991 L1995 **IM** *020 †20

PUZDRAKIEWICZ, Michelle L. 1700 WOODLAWN AVE 38024 #021-01-1997 L2007 **PD** *020 †55

RAO, Mohan Padamannur. 1700 WOODLAWN AVE 38024 #495-52-1978 L1995 **NEP** *020 †20

REYNOLDS, James Ralph. ■ 38024 #047-06-1964 L1964 **IM NPM** *071 †20

RODRIGUEZ CONESA, Yvonne. 1716 PARR AVE, STE D 38024 #042-01-1985 L2005 **FM** *020 †20

SCARA, Russell Gardener. 400 E TICKLE ST 38024 #027-01-1982 L1982 **AN** *020 †05

SMITH, James Herman. 215 ELM AVE, DEPT. OF CORRECTIONS 38024 #047-06-1964 L1964 **IM GP** *020

SWETNAM, Jeffrey Alle. 420 WILKINSON DR, RIVERSIDE SURGERY CENTER 38024 #028-46-1982 L1991 **GS VS** *020 †85

THOMPSON, Thomas Reece. 400 E TICKLE ST, DYERSBURG REGIONAL MEDICAL 38024 #047-06-1970 L1971 **DR NM** *020 †80

THORNTON, W I, Jr. ■ 38024 #047-06-1951 L1951 **GP** *071

WATSON, Lydia Viola. ■ 38024 #047-06-1937 L1937 **GP** *071

WOLFE, James Hardy. 400 E TICKLE ST, METHODIST HEALTHCARE 38024 #027-01-1978 L1982 **DR** *020 †80

WOODS, Arthur Hopkins, Jr. 350 E PARKVIEW ST 38024 #004-01-1969 L1976 **OPH** *020 †35

WOODS, Roger Larry. 400 E TICKLE ST, ATTN; MEDICAL STAFF OFFICE 38024 #028-03-1994 L1995 **FM** *020 †18

YOUSUF, Mohammad. 1950 COOK ST, STE D 38024 #704-02-1982 L1998 **IM** *020 †20

EADS — FAYETTE

AKERS, Phillip Vaughn. ■ 38028 #047-06-1970 L1971 **IM AM** *020 †20

CARBONE, Raymond Anthony. ■ 38028 #010-02-1962 L1965 **IM CD** *071

HARRAWAY, Carolyn Loraine. ■ 38028 #018-03-1993 L2007 **OBG** *020 †18,30

HOWARD, Nicholas Wendell. ■ 38028 #047-06-1972 L1973 **R** *020

LAWRENCE, Jesse Alvah. ■ 38028 #047-06-1960 L1961 **N** *071 †75

WILCOX, William David. 365 S HOUSTON LEVEE RD 38028 #047-06-1981 L1982 **EM GP** *020 †16

EAGLEVILLE — RUTHERFORD

MILLER, David Thos. ■ 37060 #030-05-1975 L1999 **PTH** *020 †50

PARKER, James Phillip. ■ 37060 #016-45-1995 L1997 **IM** *020

EAST RIDGE — HAMILTON

BICKERS, Philip Gordon. 403 MCBRIEN RD 37412 #036-05-1970 L1976 **FM** *020 †18

CATTERTON, Jane Spence. 941 SPRING CREEK RD 37412 #051-04-1973 L1976 **PD** *020 †55

MORRISON, Teresa Ann. ■ 37412 #001-06-1991 L1993 **PD** *020 †55

PAYNE, Doyce Gene. 941 SPRING CREEK RD 37412 #011-03-1978 L1982 **OBG** *020 †30

PROSTKO, Michael C. 1508 TOMBRAS AVE, IN GOOD HEALTH 37412 #037-01-1998 L2003 **IM** *020 †20

THORNER, Donald Romaine. 929 SPRING CREEK RD, STE 101 37412 #065-06-1952 L1978 **FM EM** *071

WALKER, Meeca. 929 SPRING CREEK RD, STE 201 37412 #047-07-1999 L2003 **OBG** *020

ELIZABETHTON — CARTER

ADAMS, Joseph Anthony. ■ 37643 #012-01-2004 L2007 **PD** *020 †55

ALBRACHT, Douglas A. 1503 W ELK AVE, STE 2 37643 #048-78-1992, ▲ L2007 **ORS** *020

ALLEN, Elizabeth. ■ 37644 #047-06-1958 L1958 **P CHP** *075 †55

BALAICUIS, Charles Wm. 407 HUDSON DR, P O BOX 194 37643 #041-02-1960 L1989 **CHP PYA** *030

BASSAL, Aly Aly Hassan. 104 ROGOSIN DR, P O BOX 640 37643 #915-02-1968 L1982 **GS GP** *020 †85

BREMER, Jonathan S. 1503 W ELK AVE, STE 8 37643 #016-11-1981 L1983 **IM** *020 †20

BRONSON, Sylvester Martin. ■ 37643 #869-01-1953 L1960 **R** *072 †80

BURIK, Nicholas P. 185 HUDSON DR W TOWN SQ 37643 #286-02-1950 L1976 **GP GS** *071

CAUDLE, Scott O'Krina. 1503 W ELK AVE, STE 1 37643 #047-06-1977 L1981 **GS** *020 †85

CHAMBERS, Gary Randall. 709 POWDER BRANCH RD 37643 #036-05-1964 L1967 **ORS** *071 †40

CLARK, Vivian Mercado. 1503 W ELK AVE, STE 5 37643 #748-10-1985 L2004 **IM** *020 †20

CRITZ, George Theodore. ■ 37643 #038-06-1948 L1982 **A PD** *071 †55

CRUZ, Teodorico P, Jr. 208 ROGOSIN DR, CARTER CO EMORIAL HOSP 37643 #748-01-1965 L1972 **GP GS** *020

DAVENPORT, James Lee. 306 PINE HILL RD 37643 #047-20-1998 L2000 **FM** *020 †18

DAVENPORT, Michelle L. 306 PINE HILL RD 37643 #047-20-1998 L2002 **MPD** *020 †55,20

DIGBY, Justin David. 1503 W ELK AVE STE 8, ASSOC 37643 #039-01-1997 L2000 **GS** *100 †85

DUNN, Julie Ann. 1501 W ELK AVE 37643 #047-20-1991 L1994 **GS TRS** *020 †85

FENNER, David Kenneth. 1505 W ELK AVE, STE 2 37643 #047-06-1972 L1973 **IM GE** *050 †20

GALLOWAY, Richard Eugene. 1501 W ELK AVE 37643 #047-06-1962 L1967 **FM** *071 †18

GASTINEAU, Jerry Lee. 1501 W ELK AVE 37643 #017-20-1969 L1972 **FM** *072 †18

GREEN, John David. 1505 W ELK AVE, STE 1 37643 #047-20-1990 L1995 **OBG** *020 †30

HARDIN, David Ross. 106 ROGOSIN DR, ELIZABETH SURGERY CENTER, 37643 #047-06-1986 L1987 **ORS** *020 †40,

HECHT, David Scott. 1503 W ELK AVE STE 6 37643 #033-06-1996 L2001 **GS** *020 †85

HECHT, Rachel M. 1937 W ELK AVE 37643 #021-05-1997 L2001 **PD** *020 †55

HERRIN, Charles Bomar. 1501 W ELK AVE, SYCAMORE SHOALS HOSPITAL 37643 #047-05-1978 L1979 **EM** *020

HIREMAGALUR, Shobha R. 1505 W ELK AVE, STE 3 37643 #495-49-1985 L1993 **CD IM** *020 †20

IBRAHIM, Atef Abdellatif. ■ 37643 #330-04-1964 L1977 **GS FM** *020 †85

KITCHENS, Tammy Lin. 1503 W ELK AVE STE 12, RIVERSIDE PEDIATRICS 37643 #019-02-1992 L1999 **PD** *020 †20

LAING, Brent David. 1505 W ELK AVE STE 1 37643 #065-10-1979 L1984 **OBG GYN** *020 †30

LOYD, Stephen Douglas. 1503 W ELK AVE STE 3, DEPT OF INTERNAL MEDICINE 37643 #047-20-1999 L2000 **IM** *020 †20

MAY, Andrew Stephen. 923 W G ST 37643 #047-06-1983 L1985 **FM** *020 †18

MAY, David Paul. 923 W G ST 37643 #047-06-1987 L1988 **AN** *020 †05

MAY, Floyd Earl. 922 W G ST 37643 #047-06-1956 L1956 **AN** *071 †05

MAY, Joseph Carl. 923 W G ST, THE MAY CLINIC 37643 #047-06-1961 L1962 **GP OBG** *020

MAY, Winifred Joyce Cobb. 207 RIDGECREST DR 37643 #047-06-1956 L1956 **GP AN** *071

MORAN, Paul Edward, III. 314 ROGOSIN DR, FIRST ASSIST URGENT CARE 37643 #041-13-1987 L1988 **FM** *020 †18

NELSON, Robert Barry. 1503 W ELK AVE STE 3 37643 #016-06-1965 L1997 **ORS** *020 †40

O'KELLY, Karen Ruth. ■ 37643 #047-20-2003 L2006 **MP** *012

PACK, Sheryl Denise. 305 LAWSON AVE 37643 #004-01-1998 L1999 **FM** *020 †18

PARIS, Claire D. 1503 W ELK AVE STE 8 37643 #422-01-1998 L2003 **IM** *020 †20

PAUL, Daniel Joseph. 145 JUDGE DON LEWIS BLVD, # 7 37643 #038-44-1993 L1994 **FM** *020 †18

PERRY, Edgar Eugene. 401 HUDSON DR, STE 3 37643 #047-06-1961 L1961 **OBG GP** *020 †18

REECE, Richard Randolph. ■ 37643 #047-06-1977 L1978 **DR** *020 †80

SCHUBERT, Robert Luther. 1000 W G ST 37643 #038-43-1995 L1996 **FM** *020 †18

SHIPLEY, James Micales. 305 LAWSON AVE 37643 #047-20-1998 L2001 **FM** *020 †18

SHOLES, Christopher W. 1505 W ELK AVE, STE 3 37643 #047-06-1979 L1986 **CD IM** *020 †20 ‡

STAMBOVSKY, Marshall K. 403 E G ST, CARTER CO HEALTH DEPT. 37643 #422-01-1989 L1993 **FM EM** *020 †20

STEWART, Robert Lynn, Jr. 922 W G ST 37643 #020-12-1987 L1989 **AN** *020 †05

TANNER, Catherine Keffer. 1505 W ELK AVE, STE 2 37643 #012-22-1991 L1993 **FM** *020 †18

TUBERTY, Peter Michael. 1503 W ELK AVE STE 8 37643 #047-20-2000 L2003 **FM** *020 †18

WALTER, Robert E. 1505 W ELK AVE, STE 2 37643 #012-01-1977 L1982 **IM** *020 †20

WHITAKER, Todd Anthony. 1900 W ELK AVE 37643 #020-12-1994 L1996 **IM** *020 †20

ENGLEWOOD – MCMINN

WINEBARGER, Kristel Wyn. 321 W ATHENS ST 37329 #047-20-1997 L2003 **FM** *020 †18

ERIN – HOUSTON

BRANSON, James William. 4895 E MAIN ST 37061 #065-01-1967 L1995 **GS** *020

CHAMBERS, Erin Emrich. 302 E MAIN ST 37061 #047-06-2002 L2004 **FM** *020 †18

LANDIS, Mark Allen. 4891 E MAIN ST 37061 #047-20-1991 L1997 **FM** *020 †18

LIGON, Douglas Wister. 15 N BOONE ST, STE C 37061 #047-06-1968 L1969 **FM D** *020 †18 ‡

MARTIN, Daniel Ernest. 4891 E MAIN ST 37061 #047-05-1976 L1979 **FM** *020

ERWIN – UNICOI

BIEBERLY, Joseph Edward. 630 ONEEGA LN, STE A 37650 #019-02-1979 L1980 **IM** *020

CAMPBELL, Diane. ■ 37650 #047-20-1991 L1993 **FM** *020 †18

COLINGER, Judd Walton, Jr. 105 GAY ST, P O BOX 399 37650 #047-06-1974 L1974 **GP** *020

DUNWORTH, Robert Geo. 800 S MOHAWK DR, STE C 37650 #041-12-1976 L1991 **GYN** *020 †30

FERNANDO, Linden Cedric. 100 GREENWAY CIR 37650 #654-01-1983 L1987 **FM** *020 †18

FORE, Edward Johnson. 361 OKOLONA DR 37650 #045-01-1993 L1995 **GS** *020 †85

HARRIS, Michael Alan. 218 N MAIN AVE 37650 #047-06-1962 L1987 **P AM** *071 †75

HYDER, Nat Edens, Jr. 1826 N MAIN AVE 37650 #047-06-1954 L1954 **FM** *020 †18

JOHNSON, Thomas Ray. 630 ONEEGA LN, STE D 37650 #035-15-1987 L2000 **ON** *020 †20

MC CARLEY, Jill Dinwiddie. ■ 37650 #047-20-1999 L2008 **CHP** *020 †75

MC MICHEN, John Wayne. 1826 N MAIN AVE 37650 #012-01-1991 L1994 **FM** *020 †18

MOUGHON, Gordon Wyche. 630 ONEEGA LN 37650 #047-05-1977 L1980 **IM** *020 †20

PLEMMONS, Rita E Treanor. 1826 N MAIN AVE 37650 #036-01-1992 L1999 **FM** *020 †18 ‡

QUARLES, Glenn Richard. 100 GREENWAY CIR, UNICOI COUNTY MEMORIAL HOS 37650 #045-01-1982 L1996 **EM** *020 †20

SLONAKER, Daniel Andrew. 1001 N MAIN AVE, P O BOX 499 37650 #047-06-1979 L1979 **IM** *020

TRZIL, Kenneth Paul. 100 GREENWAY CIR 37650 #047-06-1987 L1988 **IM** *020

WEGMAN, Frank Todd. ■ 37650 #665-01-2000 L2003 **FM** *020

ESTILL SPRINGS – FRANKLIN

BOYANTON, Lia C. ■ 37330 #649-14-1984 L1987 **FM** *020 †18

BOYANTON, Walter J, III. 300 S MAIN ST 37330 #649-14-1984 L1986 **FM** *020 †18

D'ANGELO, Laura J. 416 S MAIN ST 37330 #036-01-1981 L1987 **P** *020 †75

JURICH, Nicholas Roger. ■ 37330 #020-12-1970 L2006 **FM** *020 †18

ETOWAH – MCMINN

CLEVELAND, James Franklin. 886 HIGHWAY 411 N 37331 #047-06-1956 L1956 **GP** *020

COLLINS, Timothy James. 305 GRADY RD, STE B 37331 #041-02-1992 L1998 **FM** *020 †18

DURKIN, James Brendan. 305 GRADY RD, STE A 37331 #041-09-1978 L2002 **FM** *020 †20

GRADY, John Louellean. 886 HIGHWAY 411 N 37331 #030-02-1960 L1977 **GP OS** *020

KHAN, Ghazali A. 886 HIGHWAY 411 N 37331 #704-02-1984 L1994 **NEP** *020 †20

LEE, Yung Gil. 318 GRADY RD, GIL LEE YUNG MD 37331 #583-04-1966 L1973 **GS** *020

MEIER, Monica Therese. 250 GRADY RD 37331 #056-02-2000 L2002 **FM** *020 †18

MEYER, Charles Thos. 886 HIGHWAY 411 N 37331 #038-41-1973 L1989 **ORS** *020

OLSEN, Samuel John, II. 301 GRADY RD 37331 #047-20-2001 L2005 **FSM ISM** *020 †20

RILEY, Joel Craig, II. 886 HIGHWAY 411 N 37331 #001-02-1989 L1992 **IM** *020 †20

ROBERTS, Edward Vann. 886 HIGHWAY 411 N 37331 #047-06-1969 L1985 **EM OS** *020

RODGERS, Stephen Ross. 250 GRADY RD, P O BOX 671 37331 #047-06-1980 L1981 **FM EM** *020 †18

SONI, Harish Babulal. 109 GRADY RD STE B 37331 #495-23-1968 L1975 **GS** *020 ‡

SONI, Renuka Harish. 109 GRADY RD 37331 #495-76-1969 L1976 **PD** *071

WATTERS, Russell Brandon. PO BOX 325 37331 #047-06-1989 L1992 **IM** *020 †20

WILLIAMS, Thomas Wolford. 886 HIGHWAY 411 N 37331 #028-02-1954 L1964 **FM** *071 †18

FAIRFIELD GLADE – CUMBERLAND

LORD, Kurtland H. ■ 38555 #024-05-1949 L1953 **U** *071 †95

FAIRVIEW – WILLIAMSON

BIRCHER, Ana Maria. ■ 37062 #132-01-1982 L2007 *062 †19

CHALLA, Mydhili. ■ 37062 #495-62-1999 L2006 **IM** *100 †20

CHAPDELAINE, Perry A, Jr. 7111 SWEETGUM RD 37062 #047-07-1989 L1990 **PHP GPM** *030 †70

PETERSON, Marsha Jane. ■ 37062 #054-04-1992 L2007 **IM** *020 †05

SPICER, Paul James. ■ 37062 #047-07-2004 L2004 **DR** *012

VITOLA, Joao V. ■ 37062 #187-08-1991 L1996 **NM** *020 †28

ZIMMER, John Fredrick. ■ 37062 #017-20-1964 L1964 **PD AM** *062 †55

FALL BRANCH – GREENE

DEARMAN, Henry B. ■ 37656 #047-06-1946 L1962 **P** *071

PIERCE, Deidre Alane Murr. ■ 37656 #047-20-2008 *012

FARRAGUT – KNOX

KEANE, Robert Anthony. ■ 37934 #654-01-1995 L2007 **FM** *020 †18

SCOTT, Susan Choo. 11416 GRIGSBY CHAPEL RD 37934 #047-06-1998 L2007 **PD** *020 †55

FAYETTEVILLE – LINCOLN

ASHBY, Sam Michael. 804 WILLIAM D JONES BLVD 37334 #047-05-1973 L1977 **GP** *020

ASKINS, Andrea Cole. ■ 37334 #047-06-2006 **PD** *012

BARNES, Larry Wayne. 2330 THORNTON TAYLOR PKWY, STE A 37334 #047-06-1983 L1985 **FM FPG** *020 †18

BASU, Ashish Kumar. 2330 THORNTON TAYLOR PKWY, STE B 37334 #495-53-1983 L1995 **CD IM** *020 †20

BURNS, Charles Randall. 2330 THORNTON TAYLOR PKWY, STE B 37334 #001-06-1982 L2005 **IM** *020 †20

CASH, Gordon Henry. 2330 THORNTON TAYLOR PKWY, STE B 37334 #012-05-1981 L1986 **CD** *020 †20

CHENG, Shichi. 2330 THORNTON TAYLOR PKWY, STE 37334 #016-02-1992 L2004 **CD** *020 †20

COBB, Rudy Theodore. 305 COLLEGE ST W 37334 #047-06-1978 L1979 **GS** *020 †85

DINERMAN, Jay Lawrence. 2330 THORNTON TAYLOR PKWY, STE B 37334 #011-03-1987 L2005 **ICE** *020 †20

DRENNING, David Humphrey. 2330 THORNTON TAYLOR PKWY, STE B 37334 #047-06-1986 L1987 **IM** *020 †20

EDWARDS, William Ables. 108 MEDICAL CENTER BLVD, STE G-50 37334 #047-06-1998 L1999 **FM** *020 †18

GAFFORD, Christopher E. 108 MEDICAL CENTER BLVD, STE G50 37334 #047-06-1993 L1994 **FM** *020 †18

GESSLER, Carl John, Jr. 2330 THORNTON TAYLOR PKWY, STE B 37334 #004-01-1981 L1991 **CD IM** *050 †20

GRAY, James Alfred. 108 MEDICAL CENTER BLVD, STE G50 37334 #047-20-1998 L1999 **FM** *020 †18

GREEN, L Margaret. ■ 37334 #047-06-1946 L1946 **PD** *071 †55

GROARK, Sean Patrick. 2330 THORNTON TAYLOR PKWY, STE B 37334 #023-07-1989 L1990 **CD IM** *020 †20

HARTLEY, John Thos, III. 2330 THORNTON TAYLOR PKWY, STE B 37334 #011-03-1981 L1991 **CD IM** *020 †20

HAUGHT, Walter Herbert. 2330 THORNTON TAYLOR PKWY, STE B 37334 #038-40-1989 L2003 **CD IM** *020 †20

HUGHES, William David. 108 MEDICAL CTR BLVD G5 37334 #001-02-1997 L2000 **FM** *020 †18

HUNTER, Vernon Ross, Jr. 2330 THORNTON TAYLOR PKWY, STE B 37334 #001-02-1990 L2003 **CD** *020 †20

JEFFERSON, Kelley Vincent. 207 ELK AVE S, FAYETTEVILLE MEDICAL 37334 #047-06-1999 L2003 **MPD** *020 †20,55

JEFFRES, Earl Mc Ilwain. 37334 #001-02-1961 L1991 **ORS** *071

JONES, William R. 207 ELK AVE S, FAYETTEVILLE MEDICAL 37334 #047-06-1976 L1976 **FM** *020 †20

KHAN, Muhammad Asim. 2330 THORNTON TAYLOR PKWY, STE B 37334 #704-02-1990 L1998 **CD** *020 †20

KRASNOW, Joshua Michael. 2330 THORNTON TAYLOR PKWY, STE B 37334 #024-16-1998 L1999 **IC CD** *020 †20

LANEY, Phillip Leonard. 2330 THORNTON TAYLOR PKWY, STE B 37334 #001-02-1986 L1996 **CD** *020 †20

MC CAULEY, David Richard. 207 ELK AVE S, FAYETTEVILLE MEDICAL 37334 #047-06-1973 L1974 **FM** *020 †18

MORRISON, Theresa T. 10 ELDAD RD 37334 #001-02-1983 L1986 **FM** *020 †18

MURPHY, James Danl. 2330 THORNTON TAYLOR PKWY, STE B 37334 #016-42-1988 L2004 **CD** *020 †20

NEWTON, Norris Lynn. ■ 37334 #039-01-1956 L1997 **OPH** *020 †35

NORDYKE, Mark Dwight. 108 MEDICAL CENTER BLVD, STE 100 37334 #048-02-1982 L2007 **ORS** *020

NORMAN, Steven Ennis. 4140 THORNTON TAYLOR PKWY, EASTSIDE MEDICAL 37334 #047-20-1996 L1997 **FM** *020 †18

NORSKOV, William R, Jr. 65 ORCHARD HILL RD 37334 #005-12-1981 L1983 **FM** *020 †18

OLIVE, Dennis Lee. 106 MEDICAL CENTER BLVD 37334 #001-02-1981 L1997 **RO ON** *020

PACE, Stacey. ■ 37334 #047-20-1996 L1999 **FM** *020 †20

PATEL, Yashwant P. 207 ELK AVE S, FAYETTEVILLE MEDICAL 37334 #495-23-1970 L1976 **IM GE** *020 †20

PLUNKETT, Mark Allen. 108 MEDICAL CENTER BLVD, STE 150 37334 #001-02-1997 L2006 **OBG** *020

RALSTON, Joseph F, Jr. 207 ELK AVE S, FAYETTEVILLE MEDICAL 37334 #047-06-1980 L1981 **IM** *020 †20 ‡

RIDNER, Michael Lloyd. 2330 THORNTON TAYLOR PKWY, STE B 37334 #039-01-1982 L1991 **IM CD** *020 †20

ROBBINS, William Calvin. 2330 THORNTON TAYLOR PKWY, STE B 37334 #012-05-1984 L1987 **CD IC** *020 †20

SAIN, Paul David. 207 ELK AVE S, FAYETTEVILLE MEDICAL 37334 #047-06-1994 L1997 **FM** *020 †18

SHELLEDY, Linda Marie. 207 ELK AVE S 37334 #001-02-2003 L2006 **FM** *020

SIAW, Michael. 1797 WILSON PKWY 37334 #005-12-1964 L1993 **ORS** *071

SMITH, Stephanie Woodward. 108 MEDICAL CENTER BLVD, # G-50 37334 #047-06-1994 L1995 **FM** *020 †18

SOLIMAN, George M. 2330 THORNTON TAYLOR PKWY, STE B 37334 #011-03-1997 L1999 **IC** *020 †20

SPEARS, William Kyle. 207 ELK AVE S, FAYETTEVILLE MEDICAL 37334 #047-06-1985 L1986 **PD** *020 †55

STRICKLAND, Warren Lee. 2330 THORNTON TAYLOR PKWY, STE B 37334 #004-01-1984 L2004 **CD NM** *020 †20

VASQUEZ, Alejandro. 2330 THORNTON TAYLOR PKWY, STE B 37334 #429-02-1994 L1998 **CD IC** *020 †20 ‡

VELASQUEZ, Enrique Martin. 2330 THORNTON TAYLOR PKWY, STE B 37334 #649-14-1997 L2001 **CD** *020 †20

WILLIAMS, Jerry Brent. 2330 THORNTON TAYLOR PKWY, STE B 37334 #654-01-1983 L1987 **CD PUD** *020 †20

WILLIAMS, Karen Marie. 106 MEDICAL CENTER BLVD 37334 #047-06-1999 L2002 **FM** *020 †18 ‡

YOUNG, William Mc Kinney. ■ 37334 #047-06-1960 L1961 **PD OS** *071 †55

FRANKLIN – WILLIAMSON

ABBATE, Matthew John. 2105 EDWARD CURD LN, VANDERBILT MED GROUP-FRANK 37067 #024-07-1991 L1994 **IM** *020 †20

ABELL, Lora Marie. 840 CRESCENT CENTRE DR, STE 300 37067 #020-02-1982 L1983 **FM** *030 †18 ‡

ADKINS, Thomas Green. 206 BEDFORD WAY 37064 #036-05-1979 L1984 **AN** *020 †05

AGBEIBOR, Catrell O. 1324 W MAIN ST, WILLIAMSON MEDICAL CENTER 37064 #036-01-1995 L2001 **FM** *020 †18

AISAGBONHI, Omonigho Augu. ■ 37067 #047-05-2008 *012

ALBERTSON, Norman L. 508 AUTUMN SPRINGS CT, STE 2B 37067 #048-13-1991 L1994 **PD** *020 †55

ALLEN, Gregg Philip. 730 COOL SPRINGS BLVD, STE 800 37067 #041-02-1978 L1995 **FM EM** *030 †16,18 ‡

AL-MASHHARAWI, Issam Maso. ■ 37067 #495-37-1997 L2004 **IM** *020 †20

ANDERSON, Richard Michael. 100 COVEY DR, STE 104 37067 #047-06-1973 L1974 **GP** *020 †20

ANDREWS, E James, Jr. 730 COOL SPRINGS BLVD, STE 800 37067 #011-03-1966 L2001 **DR NR** *020 †80

ARTHUR, Scott Thomas. 206 BEDFORD WAY, BONE & JOINT CLINIC 37064 #047-06-2000 L2006 **ORS** *100

ASHMORE, Timothy Elbert. ■ 37069 #021-05-1997 L1999 **FM** *020 †18

AXTON, Paul Warren. 37064 #047-07-1972 L1972 **ORS** *020

BARTSOKAS, Tom Wirth. 206 BEDFORD WAY, BONE & JOINT CLINIC 37064 #016-45-1984 L1994 **FSM FM** *020 †18

BASTIAN, Samuel Ray. 2339 HILLSBORO RD 37069 #047-06-1989 L1990 **IM PD** *020 †55,20

BASYE, Shelly Ummel. 37064 #047-06-2005 L2008 **MPD** *012

BAUDENBACHER, Petra Maria. ■ 37069 #047-05-2004 *100

BAUTISTA, John Theodore. 206 BEDFORD WAY 37064 #025-01-1988 L2007 **AN** *020 †05

BAXTER, Malcolm Everett. 2009 MALLORY LN, STE 200 37067 #027-01-1990 L1995 **ORS** *020 †40

BELL, Denise Price. ■ 37064 #047-07-1980 L1980 **IM** *071

BELL, John Henry. 2020 FIELDSTONE PKWY, STE 900 # 212 37069 #036-07-1958 L1963 **ORS** *071 †40

BELL, William Bryan. 2001 MALLORY LN STE 303 37067 #020-12-1988 L1996 **P** *020 †75

BELL, William L, Jr. ■ 37067 #005-11-1984 L1989 **EM** *020 †16

BELLEAU, Joseph Terrence. 1909 MALLORY LN STE 300 37067 #016-11-1997 L1999 **AI MPD** *020 †20,55,03

BENNIE, Jeffrey Barker. 206 BEDFORD WAY 37064 #028-02-1987 L1991 **AN** *020 †05

BENNIE, Jonathan Edward. 206 BEDFORD WAY 37064 #047-06-1992 L1996 **AN** *020 †05

BENNIE, Kelly R. 4085 MALLORY LN, STE 204 37067 #047-06-1994 L1997 **PD** *020 †55

BENNING, Thomas Richard. 206 BEDFORD WAY 37064 #047-06-1970 L1976 **AN FM** *020 †05

BERGERON, Kimberly C. 100 COVEY DR, STE 210 37067 #027-01-1993 L1998 **AI** *020 †03,55

BESHARIAN, Chas Michael. 206 BEDFORD WAY 37064 #012-05-1979 L1984 **AN PD** *020 †55,05

BEST, Anthony Paul. 206 BEDFORD WAY 37064 #020-12-1985 L1991 **AN IM** *020 †05

BETHURUM, Alva Jefferson. 100 COVEY DR, STE 201 37067 #047-06-1968 L1969 **GS VS** *020 †85

BHATT, Vivak Suryakant. 919 MURFREESBORO RD 37064 #305-01-1999 L2002 **FM** *020 †18

BISHOP, Michael Robt. 730 COOL SPRINGS BLVD, STE 800 37067 #047-05-1975 L1975 **GYN** *071 †30

BOOKER, Benjamin Franklin. 1650 MURFREESBORO RD, STE 202 37067 #047-06-1990 L1994 **GP** *020

BRANSTETTER, Danny Ross. ■ 37067 #047-06-2004 L2007 **ID** *012 †20

BRATTON, David Moffatt. 206 BEDFORD WAY, BONE & JOINT CLINIC 37064 #047-06-1975 L1976 **ORS** *020 †20

BRILL, Aaron Bertrand. ■ 37069 #049-01-1956 L1965 **NM** *030 †28

BROOKS, Arthur Scott. 570 BAKERS BRIDGE AVE 37067 #047-06-1981 L1984 **PD** *020 †55

BROWN, Douglas Victor. 206 BEDFORD WAY 37064 #016-02-1989 L2007 **AN** *020 †05

BROWNING, Sharon. 740 COOL SPRINGS BLVD, STE 110 37067 #654-01-1997 L2004 **FM** *020 †18 ‡

BUCK, Allen Wesley. 206 BEDFORD WAY 37064 #020-02-1976 L1981 **AN** *050 †05

BUCKNER, George S, Jr. 730 COOL SPRINGS BLVD, STE 800 37067 #021-05-1967 L2006 **ORS** *030 †40

BUECHEL, Paul Cyril. 4323 S CAROTHERS RD # 608 37064 #035-15-1991 L2000 **N** *020 †75

BURCH, Wilmot C, Jr. 740 COOL SPRINGS BLVD, STE 210 37067 #021-05-1984 L1987 **IM** *020 †20

BURGESS, Bernard L, Jr. 100 COVEY DR, STE 201 37067 #047-20-1988 L1994 **GS** *020 †85

BURNS, David Alvin. 109 HOLIDAY CT, STE A4 37067 #020-02-1986 L1988 **CHP P** *020

BURRICHTER, Calvin Arthur. 206 BEDFORD WAY 37064 #011-03-1988 L1992 **AN** *020 †05

BYERS, Jeffrey David. 919 MURFREESBORO RD, VANDERBILT MEDICAL GROUP 37064 #036-07-1992 L1996 **D** *020 †15

CAIN, John W, II. 2020 FIELDSTONE PKWY, STE 900 37069 #047-20-1984 L1985 **P** *020 †75

CALENDINE, Cory Layne. ■ 37067 #047-06-2001 L2004 **ORS** *020

CALISI, Cynthia Renee. 2339 HILLSBORO RD STE 100 37069 #020-02-1999 L2003 **MPD** *020 †20,55

CANTRELL, Stephen B. ■ 37064 #047-05-1991 L2006 **GS** *100

CAPOBIANCO, Faust Joseph. ■ 37064 #005-15-1962 L1992 **GP** *071

CAPRIO, Francis John. 1909 MALLORY LN, STE 110 37067 #023-07-1992 L1995 **IM** *020 †20

CARLISLE, Vicki P. ■ 37067 #001-02-1992 L1994 **IM** *020 †20

CARR, Thomas Joseph, Jr. 570 BAKERS BRIDGE AVE 37067 #016-43-1996 L1998 **PD** *020 †55

CARROLL, Nicole Summerour. ■ 37064 #036-08-2006 **OBG** *012

CAUDILL, Max Tillman. 100 COVEY DR, STE 105 37067 #047-06-1988 L1994 **GE** *020 †20

CAVALLO, Martyn John. 206 BEDFORD WAY 37064 #036-01-1990 L1995 **AN** *020 †05

CHALAL, Richard Lee. ■ 37069 #041-09-1976 L1978 **IM ADM** *020

CHAMBERS, John W, Jr. 570 BAKERS BRIDGE AVE 37067 #047-06-1995 L1998 **PD** *020 †55

CHAUDHURI, Kanika. ■ 37067 #495-24-1961 L1981 **PD** *071

CISTOLA, Carol Lynn. 2000 MALLORY LN, STE 130-370 37067 #041-07-1975 L1993 **OBG** *020 †30

CLARK, Howard Daniel. 377 RIVERSIDE DR, STE 202 37064 #024-01-2000 L2003 *020

CLARK, Jameel Tamir. ■ 37064 #036-05-2008 *012

CLARKE, Lois E. 4319 CAROTHERS PKWY, STE 202 37067 #063-01-1975 L1978 **FM** *071

CLEMMONS, Samuel Clay. ■ 37067 #001-06-1992 L1994 **AN** *020

CLIFFORD, Christopher H. 324 COOL SPRINGS BLVD 37067 #047-06-1994 L1996 **FM PME** *020

COGGESHALL, Jack Warren. 2105 EDWARD CURD LN, STE B1 37067 #017-20-1979 L1983 **PUD IM** *020 †20

COLLETTI, Richard Adrian. ■ 37064 #035-06-2001 L2006 **CHP** *020

COLLINS, David Reid. 4085 MALLORY LN STE 204 37067 #047-06-1997 L2000 **PD** *020 †55

COLLINS, Ouida Marcia. 125 COOL SPRINGS BLVD, STE 100 37067 #047-07-1998 L2003 **FM** *020 †18

COOK, Jeffrey Wade. 3310 ASPEN GROVE DR, STE 102 37067 #047-06-1987 L1991 **ORS** *020 †40

COOK, William Gregory. 3310 ASPEN GROVE DR, FRANKLIN ORTHO & SPORTS 37067 #047-06-1984 L1989 **ORS** *020 †40

COOK, William N. ■ 37069 #047-06-1936 L1936 **GP GPM** *071 †70

COOPER, George Jackson. 4321 CAROTHERS PKWY, WILLIAMSON MEDICAL CENTER 37067 #027-01-1991 L1995 **EM** *020 †16

COUDEN, Allison. 570 BAKERS BRIDGE AVE 37067 #047-06-1996 L2002 **PD** *020 †55

CRAWFORD, Walter M, Jr. 206 BEDFORD WAY 37064 #047-06-1983 L1984 **AN IM** *020 †20,05

CRETELLA, Joseph P. 730 COOL SPRINGS BLVD, STE 800 37067 #033-06-1986 L2005 **DR R** *020 †80

CURTIS, Shannon Ray. 206 BEDFORD WAY 37064 #047-06-1964 L1965 **ORS OS** *071 †40

DALTON, John Charles. 206 BEDFORD WAY 37064 #005-12-1983 L1986 **AN** *020 †05

D'AMICO, Stephen Jasper. 2001 MALLORY LN, STE 302 37067 #308-07-1983 L1987 **IM IMG** *020

DASARI, Sriram. 1909 MALLORY LN, STE 303 37067 #035-08-1996 L2003 **U** *020 †95

DASH, Lamarr Antonio. 100 COVEY DR STE 307, PHYSICIANS PLAZA 37067 #035-08-1973 L1981 **OBG** *020 †30

DAVIS, Evelyn Jeffries. ■ 37067 #020-12-1973 L1976 **OS AN** *071

DEHMLOW, Pamela Gail. 730 COOL SPRINGS BLVD, STE 800 37067 #016-42-1984 L1987 **FM** *020 †18

DENDY, Jeffrey Michael. ■ 37067 #047-05-2000 L2002 **CD** *100 †20

DENNIS, Kevin Odell. 2000 MALLORY LN, STE 130-256 37067 #047-07-1999 L2003 **FM** *020

DENTZ, Barbara B. ■ 37069 #025-01-1991 L1999 **PD** *074 †55

DENTZ, Mark Edwin. 206 BEDFORD WAY 37064 #025-01-1989 L1995 **AN** *020 †05

DEVENNEY, John Edward. 730 COOL SPRINGS BLVD, STE 800 37067 #041-09-1971 L2005 DR NM *020 †28,80

DHILLON, Rennee Nagra. 1325 W MAIN ST, STE A 37064 #495-43-1995 L2004 FM *020 †18

DIDIER, Irina A. 2105 EDWARD CURD LN, COUNTY 37067 #913-32-1987 L2005 FM *020 †18 ‡

DODSON, William Alfred. 1136 BUCKINGHAM CIR 37064 #054-04-1979 L2004 PM *020 †60

DOUGLAS, Glenn Craig. 2001 MALLORY LN STE 100, VANDERBILT RHEUMATOLOGY 37067 #047-20-1998 L2002 RHU *020 †2 ‡

DOWNEY, William Lee. 1909 MALLORY LN, STE 302 37067 #047-05-1963 L1963 OTO *071 †45

DOYLE, Deborah Rose. ■ 37064 #016-02-1977 L1980 RHU IM *071 †20

DYKES, Katherine Anne. 4155 CAROTHERS PKWY 37067 #047-06-1988 L1991 OBG *020 †30

EAST, Christopher Jon. 206 BEDFORD WAY 37064 #035-06-1995 L1999 AN *020 †05

EBLEN, Abby C. ■ 37069 #047-06-1992 L2002 OBG *020 †30

EICHHOLZ, Amy Klostermann. 4323 CAROTHERS PKWY, STE 203 37067 #028-34-2000 L2006 OBG *020 †30

ELLINGTON, Lynn Noel. 4323 CAROTHERS PKWY, STE 208 37067 #047-05-1992 L1996 OBG *020 †30

ERICKSEN, Alan Steven. 1836 OLD NATCHEZ TRCE 37069 #033-05-1984 L2002 DR NM *020 †80

EVINS, Starling Claude. 100 COVEY DR, STE 207 37067 #020-12-1970 L1978 U *020 †95

FACCIA, John. 1345 W MAIN ST 37064 #065-06-1975 L1980 PME UCM *020

FALBO, Francis Joseph, III. 324 COOL SPRINGS BLVD 37067 #055-01-1995 L1998 FM *020 †18

FARNHAM, Lisa M Hackworth. 2105 EDWARD CURD LN, VANDERBILT MEDICAL CENTER 37067 #047-05-1994 L1998 IM *020 †20

FAULKNER, Scott Lee. 600 AYLESFORD LN 37069 #023-07-1969 L2007 TS VS *020 †85,90

FELCH, James Walton. 100 COVEY DR STE 107, MIDDLE TN 37067 #047-05-1977 L1978 OPH IM *020 †35 ‡

FERRELL, Claude Lee, III. 206 BEDFORD WAY 37064 #047-06-1989 L1993 AN PME *020 †05

FERRELL, Michael Craig. 206 BEDFORD WAY, BONE & JOINT CLINIC 37064 #021-01-1974 L1977 ORS *020 †40

FICHTEL, Jill Crowell. 740 COOL SPRINGS BLVD, STE 200 37067 #047-06-2001 L2004 D *020 †15

FISCUS, Michelle Dorothy. 508 AUTUMN SPRINGS CT, STE 2B 37067 #017-20-1994 L1997 PD *020 †55

FLACK, English Chapman. ■ 37069 #045-01-2007 PD *012

FLEXNER, John Morris. 324 COOL SPRINGS BLVD, DIV OF HEMATOLOGY 37067 #023-07-1954 L1960 HEM ON *020

FORREST, Patrick Anthony. 206 BEDFORD WAY 37064 #001-02-1994 L1999 AN CD *020 †05

FRANK, Beverly Ann. 1909 MALLORY LN, STE 201 37067 #041-12-1992 L1996 PD *020 †55

FRANKLIN, Jerry Malvin. 4323 CAROTHERS PKWY # 400 37067 #047-06-1977 L1978 CD IC *020 †20

FRANKLIN, Shelley Fleet. 740 COOL SPRINGS BLVD, STE 200 37067 #012-01-2000 L2005 D *020 †15

FRIEDMAN, Wallace Louis. 206 BEDFORD WAY 37064 #836-02-1982 L1990 AN IM *020 †05

FURMAN, John Robert. ■ 37067 #035-03-1962 L1970 U *071 †95

GAILANI, Salman Dia. ■ 37067 #528-01-1949 L1961 ON HEM *071 †20

GAMMENTHALER, Sammy A. 730 COOL SPRINGS BLVD, STE 800 37067 #005-12-1975 L2006 CD IM *020 †20

GARNER, Daniel Creston. 730 COOL SPRINGS BLVD, STE 800 37067 #023-12-1987 L2002 RO AM *020 †80

GARVIN, Ronald M. ■ 37068 #020-02-1965 L1966 OS *020

GENCA, Erol. 206 BEDFORD WAY 37064 #902-10-1962 L1972 AN *020 †05

GILES, Robert H, Jr. ■ 37067 #051-01-1941 L1948 OBG *071

GLENN, Renee La Vonne. 1915 COLUMBIA AVE 37064 #047-07-1982 L1983 P *020

GORE, James Edward. 2001 MALLORY LN, STE 100 37067 #020-12-1999 L2004 RHU *020 †20

GORE, Johnny E. ■ 37067 #047-06-1976 L1977 PD *030 †55

GORMAN, Thomas Mitchell. 4321 CAROTHERS PKWY 37067 #047-06-1990 L1992 EM FM *020 †18

HAGEN, Ronald Albert. WILLIAMSON MEDICAL CTR, EMER DEPT 37064 #005-12-1978 L1979 EM *020 †16

HALFORD, William Danl. 4321 CAROTHERS PKWY 37067 #047-06-1985 L1986 FM *020 †18

HAMADA, Tara N. 112 9TH AVE S, CEDAR MEDICAL GROUP, P.C. 37064 #047-06-1995 L1999 MPD *020 †20,55

HARDMAN, Norman Chandler. ■ 37069 #012-01-1985 L1994 IM *020 †20

HARTLEY, Mark F. ■ 37064 #047-06-1952 L1974 GP *071

HASSAN, John Matthew. 1909 MALLORY LN, STE 303 37067 #047-05-2001 L2004 U *020 †95

HATCHER, Elizabeth Alliso. ■ 37064 #047-06-2008 *012

HAWKINS, Anne B. 4085 MALLORY LN, STE 204 37067 #047-06-1992 L1997 PD *020 †55

HAYS, Michael Wallace. 206 BEDFORD WAY 37064 #047-06-1987 L1991 AN *020 †05

HENDRIX, Julie Ann. 4323 CAROTHERS PKWY, STE 403 37067 #038-44-1989 L1999 END *020 †20

HENSLEY, Elaine R. ■ 37069 #020-12-1986 L1990 CHP FM *020 †18,75

HOLLIS, David Olyn. ■ 37069 #047-06-1978 L1978 IM *020 †20

HOLLY, Howard Rhea. 1711 NEW HIGHWAY 96 W 37064 #047-06-1984 L1985 AN EM *020 †05

HOLT, Mark Manning. 4323 CAROTHERS PKWY, STE 400 37067 #042-02-1998 L2000 CD *020 †20

HOOD, Molly Ramona. 570 BAKERS BRIDGE AVE 37067 #047-06-1999 L2003 MPD *020 †20,55

HOOVER, Howell P, Jr. CARTER'S CREEK PIKE 37064 #047-06-1961 L1962 FM GP *075 †18

HOROZOV, Nikolay Petrov. 508 CASTLEBURY CT 37064 #198-03-1989 L2006 ADP *100

HUBER, Todd Christopher. 100 COVEY DR STE 303 37067 #047-05-1999 L2004 OTO *020 †45

HUESMANN, Louis C. ■ 37069 #017-20-1959 L1999 ORS *020 †40

HUNTER, Samuel Forrester. 101 FORREST CROSSING BLVD, STE 103 37064 #048-02-1991 L1997 N NRN *020 †75

HUTCHESON, Robt Henry, Jr. 4321 CAROTHERS PKWY 37067 #047-06-1955 L1955 PD *020 †55,70

IDZIKOWSKI, Maryann M. ■ 37067 #025-12-1989 L1996 PD *020

JACOBSON, Ned Robert. ■ 37064 #016-01-1985 L1990 AN *020 †05

JAMISON, Dale Henry, Jr. 206 BEDFORD WAY 37064 #047-06-1985 L1986 FM *020 †18,05

JANTZ, Thomas Augustus. 4323 CAROTHERS PKWY, STE 400 37067 #041-12-1970 L1971 IM CD *020 †20

JESSOP, Aaron Craig. ■ 37067 #030-05-2006 NM *012

JOHN, James Thos, Jr. 2001 MALLORY LN, STE 100 37067 #036-01-1969 L1972 RHU BBK *020 †20

JOHNSON, Douglas Scott. ■ 37064 #047-05-2006 IM *012

JOHNSON, Louis L. ■ 37064 #001-02-1953 L1956 OPH *071 †35

JONES, Phillip Ritchie. 206 BEDFORD WAY 37064 #047-05-1978 L1979 AN *020 †05

JONES-JACKSON, Laurie Bet. ■ 37067 #001-02-1996 L2007 DR NM *020 †28

KALB, Daniel Bennett. 4091 MALLORY LN, STE 118 37067 #035-48-1990 L2005 FM *020 †18

KANDEL, Laurence Bruce. ■ 37067 #021-01-1982 L1996 U *020 †95

KARLEKAR, Mohana B. ■ 37067 #035-48-1990 IM PD *040 †20

KEELER, Jodi H. ■ 37067 #035-48-1989 L1992 PD *020 †55

KEELER, Stephen Leonard. ■ 37067 #035-48-1989 L1995 AI *020 †20,03

KEHLER, Jeffrey William. 206 BEDFORD WAY 37064 #045-01-1987 L1991 AN *020 †05

KENDRICK, Will Davis. 206 BEDFORD WAY 37064 #036-05-1987 L1991 AN *020 †05

KENNEDY, James Stephen. 919 MURFREESBORO RD 37064 #047-06-1979 L1980 IM MDM *030 †20

KETCH, Robert B. 730 COOL SPRINGS BLVD, STE 800 37067 #048-14-1986 L2006 DR NM *040 †80

KETCHUM, Jennifer Michell. ■ 37067 #047-20-2008 *012

KIDD, Jennifer Kay. 206 BEDFORD WAY 37064 #045-01-1980 L1983 AN *020

KILLMAN, Kathryn R. 206 BEDFORD WAY 37064 #004-01-1977 L1983 AN *020 †05

KING, Jeffrey Luis. 206 BEDFORD WAY 37064 #047-06-1985 L1989 AN *020 †05

KLEKAMP, John Wm. 206 BEDFORD WAY, BONE & JOINT CLINIC 37064 #012-22-1990 L1992 ORS *020 †40

KRAKAUER, Maria Christine. ■ 37069 #051-07-2004 L2007 MPD *012

KRAKAUER, Mark Mendel. ■ 37069 #051-07-2004 L2007 MPD *012

KROMER, Christopher Lee. ■ 37069 #012-01-1997 L2002 GP *020

LAMB, William Charles. 206 BEDFORD WAY 37064 #047-06-1992 L1994 AN *020 †05

LANE, Richard Geoffrey. 2105 EDWARD CURD LN, VMG FRANKLIN 37067 #047-06-1973 L1973 IM IMG *020 †20 ‡

LANGFORD, Michael D. 133 HOLIDAY CT, STE 204 37067 #047-06-1981 L1984 AN FM *020 †18,05

LANGSTON, Sheron Joan. 100 COVEY DR, STE 304 37067 #055-02-1992 L1993 MPD PD *020 †55,20

LATOUR, Dana Lechman. 740 COOL SPRINGS BLVD SU 37067 #047-06-1977 L1978 D *020 †15

LATOUR, Paul Andre. 740 COOL SPRINGS BLVD, STE 200 37067 #047-06-1977 L1978 D IM *020 †20

LAYTON, Robert Glenn. 730 COOL SPRINGS BLVD, MEDSOLUTIONS INC 37067 #024-05-1972 L2004 DR *030 †80

LEBLEU, Todd Howle. 206 BEDFORD WAY 37064 #012-05-1989 L1993 AN *020 †05

LEE, Anthony Joel. ■ 37064 #047-06-1958 L1959 GP *020

LEE, Mark Andrew. 1909 MALLORY LN STE 201, CHILDREN'S CLINIC 37067 #001-02-1994 L1996 PD *020 †55

LEINER, Christina Marie. ■ 37067 #305-01-2003 L2007 PD *020 †55

LE QUIRE, Virgil S. ■ 37069 #047-05-1946 L1946 PTH CD *071

LEVAN, Karen Renee. ■ 37069 #012-05-1988 L1995 PUD *020 †20

LEVENTHAL, Marc Stephen. ■ 37069 #023-01-1961 L1961 PS GS *071 †85

LIM, Rene Michael. 4321 CAROTHERS PKWY, PHYSICIANS HOSPITALIST 37067 #748-19-1999 L2003 IM *020 †20

LIPSON, Paul Jay. 206 BEDFORD WAY 37064 #020-02-1986 L1990 AN *020 †05

LOCKE, Joel Raymon. 100 COVEY DR STE 207 37067 #047-06-1980 L1981 U *020 †95

LONERGAN, Daniel Freeburg. ■ 37067 #028-34-2006 AN *012

MAC CORD, Christopher S. PO BOX 192 37065 #023-01-1995 L1997 EM GP *020

MALLIPEDDI, Madhavi. 1915 COLUMBIA AVE 37064 #495-65-1991 L1999 PYG *020 †75

MANSON, James Edward. 133 HOLIDAY CT, STE 204 37067 #047-06-1972 L1972 AN *020

MARABLE, Charles Trenton. 2001 MALLORY LN STE 202 37067 #004-01-1991 L1999 FM *020 †20

MARTIN, David Scott. 4323 CAROTHERS PKWY # 608 37067 #023-07-1989 L1995 PS HS *020 †65

MC CAIN, Kristina Kokubun. 4155 CAROTHERS PKWY 37067 #047-05-1987 L1990 OBG *020 †30

MC CALL, Herbert Travis. ■ 37064 #047-06-1959 L1959 OBG *071

MC CONNELL, Charity E. 740 COOL SPRINGS BLVD, STE 200 37067 #045-04-1996 L2000 D *020 †15

MC CROSKEY, Debbie Jean. 919 MURFREESBORO RD, FRANKLIN 37064 #019-02-1989 L1992 IM *020 †20

MC CURRY, Paul Michael. 730 COOL SPRINGS BLVD, STE 800 37067 #047-20-1996 L1997 AN *020 †05

MC GEHEE, James Bartley. 4323 S CAROTHERS RD, STE 600 37064 #047-05-2001 L2006 ORS OSM *100

MC GINLEY, James Henry. 2339 HILLSBORO RD 37069 #012-05-1975 L1976 IM EM *020 †20,16

MEKO, Jennifer Bupp. 730 COOL SPRINGS BLVD #800, MED SOLUTIONS INC 37067 #023-07-1991 L2001 TS *030 †85,90

MELKIN, Stephen Pellar. 1006 HARWICK DR 37067 #035-09-1966 L1972 OBG *020 †30

MENEELY, Raymond Leroy. 570 BAKERS BRIDGE AVE 37067 #041-12-1973 L1977 PD *020 †55

MENZIE, James Warren. 206 BEDFORD WAY 37064 #047-05-1976 L1976 AN *020 †05

MERIWETHER, Curtiz Dwayne. ■ 37067 #042-07-1980 L2004 OBG *020 †30

MILHOUA, Paul Maurice. ■ 37067 #035-08-2001 L2007 U *020

MILLER, Michael Peter. 100 COVEY DR STE 210, ALL SEASONS ALLERGY & ASTH 37067 #056-06-1975 L1976 AI IM *020 †20,03

MILLER, Philip Graydon. 4155 CAROTHERS PKWY 37067 #047-06-1972 L1972 OBG *020 †30

MITCHELL, Larry Morris. 1487 SNEED RD W 37069 #027-01-1963 L1987 IM GE *020 †20

MOESSNER, Harold F. 1909 MALLORY LN STE 308 37067 #626-04-1971 L1987 A *020 †55,03

MOORE, John Reagan. 1909 MALLORY LN STE 104 37067 #002-07-1987 L1998 PS *020 †65

MOORE-CALDWELL, Sharon Y. 112 9TH AVE S, MERCY CHILDREN'S CLINIC 37064 #041-12-1990 L1992 IM PD *020 †55

MOSELEY, Kimberly Ann. 2105 EDWARD CURD LN, 102 37067 #051-07-1996 L2004 GS *020 †85

MOSS, Joe, Jr. 100 COVEY DR, FRANKLIN MEDICAL CLINIC 37067 #047-06-1966 L1970 PD N *075 †55

MOWERY, Gregory Alan. 2001 MALLORY LN STE 105 37067 #005-12-1991 L1993 OTO *020 †45

MOYNIHAN, Patricia C Cook. ■ 37067 #027-01-1965 L1991 PDS *020

MULLALY, Alison Clare. 4155 CAROTHERS PKWY 37067 #047-06-1997 L1998 OBG *020 †30

MYERS, Jennifer Braden. 4085 MALLORY LN, STE 204 37064 #047-06-1997 L2000 PD *020 †55

NAEEM, Mohammed Athar. ■ 37069 #047-07-2007 L2007 IM *012

NAGY, Huba. 4319 CAROTHERS PKWY, STE 202 37067 #063-01-1975 L1978 FM OBS *071

NETHERTON, Cynthia Lu. 4155 CAROTHERS PKWY 37067 #004-01-1978 L1981 GYN *020 †30

NETTERVILLE, John Thos. 2001 MALLORY LN, STE 300 37067 #047-06-1977 L1978 PD ADL *020 †55

NIMMAGADDA, Srinivas. ■ 37064 #654-01-1998 L2006 FM *020 †18

NIMS, Tracy Askew. 4323 CAROTHERS PKWY, STE 203 37067 #047-05-1989 L2003 OBG *020 †30

NORTON, Douglas Edward. 206 BEDFORD WAY 37064 #047-06-1984 L1985 AN *020 †05

NORVELL, John Michael. 400 SUGARTREE LN, STE 100 37064 #048-14-2000 L2004 IM *100 †20,03

NYQUIST, Steven Richard. 354 COOL SPRINGS BLVD, STE 105 37067 #019-02-1974 L1977 P OS *020 †75

OMOHUNDRO, John Moten, III. 100 COVEY DR, STE 107 37067 #047-06-1962 L1964 OPH *071 †35

OSBURN, Nancy Elizabeth. 4155 CAROTHERS PKWY 37067 #047-06-2002 L2006 OBG *020

OVERHOLT, John Patrick. 400 SUGARTREE LN, STE 100 37064 #047-06-1995 L1998 PCC *020 †20

OWEN, Robert Carroll. 740 COOL SPRINGS BLVD, STE 140 37067 #047-06-1961 L1961 OTO A *020 †45

OZENNE, Joseph Bernard. 740 COOL SPRINGS BLVD, STE 120 37067 #047-20-1996 L1999 IM *020 †20

PARSONS, Paul David. 206 BEDFORD WAY, BONE & JOINT CLINIC 37064 #047-06-1978 L1979 ORS *020 †40

PAST, Wallace Lyle, Jr. ■ 37064 #020-02-1985 L1986 FM IM *075

PAUL, Barbara Rose. 4000 MERIDIAN BLVD, CHS 37067 #005-11-1984 L2008 IM *030 †20

PEABODY, Allen Monroe. ■ 37069 #012-21-2007 PD *012

PELEROSSI, Mark Francis. 206 BEDFORD WAY 37064 #035-03-1985 L1992 AN IM *020 †05

PENA, Julie Marie. 200 COOL SPRINGS BLVD 37067 #016-06-1993 L2000 D *020 †15

PENNINGTON, Frank R. ■ 37064 #047-06-1976 L1976 OTO FPS *020

PEPPERS, Jennifer Lee. 100 COVEY DR STE 201, PHYSICIANS PLZ 37067 #021-01-1994 L1999 GS *020 †85

PEREZ, Andres. ■ 37068 #042-03-1981 L1988 EM OM *020

PERRY, Frank A, Jr. 819 LEGENDS GLEN CT 37069 #047-07-1976 L1978 IM ADM *020 †20

PETCU, David Julius. 206 BEDFORD WAY 37064 #041-01-1988 L1992 AN *020 †05

PHARRIS, Larry James. 1909 MALLORY LN, STE 200 37067 #047-06-1994 L1997 IM *020 †20

PHILLIPS, James Eugene. ■ 37069 #047-06-1993 L2000 PHP GP *071

PORCH, Phillip Pullen, Jr. ■ 37067 #047-05-1955 L1956 U *071 †95

POSTHUMA, Millard. ■ 37064 #025-01-1942 L1943 GS CRS *071 †85

POWELL, James Edward, Jr. 2105 EDWARD CURD LN 37067 #001-02-1991 L1995 IM PD *020,55

PRICE, John Duncan. 206 BEDFORD WAY 37064 #027-01-1978 L1983 AN IM *020 †05

PRITCHETT, Erin Gaw. 1909 MALLORY LN STE 301 37067 #048-15-1995 L1996 IM *020 †20

PRUDOFF, Adam James. 2105 EDWARD CURD LN, STE B4 37067 #041-09-1998 L2004 CD *020 †20

PUGH, Joe Robt. ■ 37064 #020-12-1967 L2007 R *020 †80

PULLIAM, Cary Watson. 100 COVEY DR STE 204 37067 #047-05-1979 L1984 VS GS *020 †85

RAGLE, Steven Paul. 86 PEARL ST 37064 #020-12-2001 L2004 EM *020 †16

REHM, Richard Dean. ■ 37069 #048-12-1972 L1973 OM FM *030 †18

REID, William Kirkpatrick. 4323 CAROTHERS PKWY # 409 37067 #036-01-1981 L1990 HEM ON *020 †20

RENFRO, Roy James. 2001 MALLORY LN, STE 203 37067 #047-06-1956 L1956 GS *071 †85

RICH, Austin T. 206 BEDFORD WAY 37064 #048-13-2002 L2004 AN *020 †05

RIEDEL, Robert David. 206 BEDFORD WAY 37064 #047-05-1985 L1989 AN *020 †05

ROBERTS, Philip Lee. 1239 BROADMOOR CIR 37067 #001-02-1985 L1992 GS *020

ROBERTS, Richard Lowell. ■ 37067 #018-03-1987 L2003 PTH *020

ROBINSON, Christine Genel. ■ 37069 #047-05-2004 *100

ROBINSON, Steven Carl. ■ 37069 #047-05-1998 L2001 IM *020 †20

RODES, W Dyer, II. 206 BEDFORD WAY 37064 #051-01-1986 L1991 AN GS *020 †05

ROTHMAN, Brian Samuel. ■ 37064 #038-41-2000 L2007 AN *020 †05

ROTKER, Iris W. ■ 37069 #035-03-1988 L2002 IM *020 †20

RUDGE, Bradley K. 9040 CAROTHERS PKWY, STE A205 37067 #047-06-1982 L1984 GP OM *020

RUNYON-HASS, Arthur. 206 BEDFORD WAY 37064 #016-02-1987 L1991 AN *020 †05

RUPERT, Matthew Paul. 2009 MALLORY LN STE 250, INTERVENTIONAL PAIN MANAGE 37067 #048-12-2000 L2007 APM *020 †05

RUSSELL, Henry Paul. 2105 EDWARD CURD LN, VANDERBILT MEDICAL GROUP 37067 #047-06-1978 L1986 GS TS *020 †85

RUSSELL, Jon Andrew. 4321 CAROTHERS PKWY 37067 #047-20-2001 L2004 EM *020 †16

SANTI, Stephen Farris. 206 BEDFORD WAY 37064 #047-06-1989 L1993 AN *020 †05

SCARBOROUGH, Norman Avery. 730 COOL SPRINGS BLVD, STE 800 37067 #027-01-1983 L1998 DR FM *020 †80

SCHMIDT, John Woodward. 37064 #030-05-2003 L2007 PD *100 †55

SCHOTTLAND, John Robt. 730 COOL SPRINGS BLVD, STE 800 37067 #005-06-1966 L2003 N *030 †75 ‡

SCHROEDER, David Wm. ■ 37064 #021-01-1990 L1997 EM *020 †16

SCOTT, John Douglas. 2105 EDWARD CURD LN 37067 #047-06-1996 L1998 MPD *020 †20,55

SCOTT, Kim Puckett. 4323 CAROTHERS PKWY, STE 208 37067 #047-06-1995 L1999 OBG *020 †30

SEARS, Kenneth Lewis, Jr. 206 BEDFORD WAY 37064 #038-41-1983 L1986 AN *020 †05

SEARS, Peter Joseph. ■ 37064 #305-01-2002 L2008 FM *020 †18

SEEMAN, Cynthia Lee. 4091 MALLORY LN, STE 118 37064 #047-07-2003 L2006 FM *020 †18

SEIBERT, John Whaley. 341 COOL SPRINGS BLVD, STE 130 37064 #004-01-2001 L2007 OTO *100 †45

SEITZ, Paul Albert. 206 BEDFORD WAY 37064 #016-02-1982 L1992 AN OS *020,05

SHANKLE, Steven B. 206 BEDFORD WAY 37064 #047-06-1991 L1995 AN *020 †05

SHAW, Amy Elizabeth. 1909 MALLORY LN, STE 200 37067 #047-05-2001 L2006 END *020

SHAW, Mark Raymond. 3310 ASPEN GROVE DR, STE 203 37067 #030-06-1993 L1998 RNR *020 †80

SHURNEY, Dexter Wayne. 701 COOL SPRINGS BLVD 37067 #010-03-1983 L1984 PHP GPM *030 †70

SIEGEL, Marc Neal. 206 BEDFORD WAY 37064 #048-13-1985 L1989 AN IM *020 †05

SIERRA-ANDERSON, Rigoberto. ■ 37069 #012-01-2004 L2006 AN *012

SILAS, Steven Lee. 2105 EDWARD CURD LN, STE B1 37067 #021-05-1987 L2003 PUD CCM *020 †20

SLANDZICKI, Alex James. 2001 MALLORY LN, STE 100 37067 #038-40-1993 L1998 FM *020 †18

SLAVIK, John Raymond. 206 BEDFORD WAY 37064 #048-12-1981 L1989 AN *020 †05

SMAJSTRLA, Shiloh Suzan. ■ 37069 #011-03-2004 OBG *012

SOTUNDE, Babatunde S. 112 9TH AVE S 37064 #690-01-1988 L1999 PD *020 †55

SPERRING, Steven Jeffrey. 206 BEDFORD WAY 37064 #917-23-1978 L1988 AN *020 †05

SPOONER, John. ■ 37064 #003-01-2001 L2007 NS *012

STABILE, Michael Jerome. 206 BEDFORD WAY 37064 #033-05-1980 L1987 AN CCM *020 †05

STAFFORD, Jacqueline. 4155 CAROTHERS PKWY 37067 #047-06-1991 L1994 OBG *020 †30

STARK, Chris Tom. 206 BEDFORD WAY, BONE & JOINT CLINIC 37064 #056-06-1989 L1994 ORS *040

STEIGELFEST, Eli. 2001 MALLORY LN, STE 100 37067 #035-46-1995 L2001 RHU *020 †20

STILWELL, Charles Albert, Jr. 342 COOL SPRINGS BLVD #203 37067 #047-05-1975 L1977 PD *020 †55

STINNETT, Shannon E. 324 COOL SPRINGS BLVD 37067 #047-06-2001 L2006 HO *100

STRANGE, Glen Julian, Jr. 206 BEDFORD WAY 37064 #047-06-1983 L1984 AN *020 †05

STULTS, Richard Franklin. 3045 TROTTERS LN 37067 #018-03-1983 L1991 DR *020 †80

SUMMIT, John Blair. 1007 SCRAMBLERS KNOB 37069 #047-06-1995 L1998 PS *020 †65

SUPPINGER, Amy Marie. 100 COVEY DR, STE 103 37067 #012-05-2000 L2003 IM *020 †20

SUPPINGER, Jeffrey Andrew. 100 COVEY DR, STE 103 37067 #012-05-2000 L2003 FM *020 †18

SUTTER, Michael John. 206 BEDFORD WAY 37064 #020-12-1984 L1991 AN IM *020 †05

SWANK, Darrell Wm. ■ 37067 #037-01-1986 L2005 PTH *020 †50

TAN, Jean L. 1909 MALLORY LN, STE 305 37067 #748-10-1991 L2001 IM *072 †20

TATE, Steven M. 2001 MALLORY LN STE 30 37067 #047-06-1976 L1977 PDA AI *020 †55

THOMAS, Jane Marshall. 206 BEDFORD WAY 37064 #017-20-1985 L1991 AN *020 †05

THOMAS, Paul Austin. 4321 CAROTHERS PKWY 37067 #047-06-1983 L1985 ORS *020 †40

THOMAS, Thomas Colwell. 206 BEDFORD WAY 37064 #049-01-1984 L1989 AN PME *020 †05

THOMAS, Thomas K. 1909 MALLORY LN STE 108 37067 #036-05-1995 L1999 OBG *020 †30

THOMSEN, William B. ■ 37067 #047-06-1976 L1977 AN *071 †05

TISSOT, William David. 100 COVEY DR, STE 207 37067 #038-43-2000 L2006 U *020 †95

TOWNSEND, Phyllis L. 570 BAKERS BRIDGE AVE 37067 #035-20-1988 L1996 PD *020 †55

URBANEK, Anthony P. 1909 MALLORY LN 37067 #047-05-1979 L1980 FPS *020

VACHON, Claude Andre. 206 BEDFORD WAY 37064 #012-01-1999 L2005 AN *020 †05

VEHEC, Amy Elizabeth. 112 9TH AVE S 37064 #017-20-2001 L2004 PD *020 †20

VOUTSINAS, Lynne. 730 COOL SPRINGS BLVD, STE 800 37067 #035-09-1983 L2005 DR RNR *030 †80

WATKE, Christopher Mark. 206 BEDFORD WAY 37064 #036-07-1993 L1998 AN *020 †05

WATKINS, Steven L. 2009 MALLORY LN STE 220 37067 #055-01-1985 L1989 OBG *075 †30

WEBSTER, Leonard Gleen. 5064 ABINGTON RIDGE LN 37067 #047-07-1998 L2003 IM *020

WEIKERT, Daniel Scott. 100 COVEY DR, STE 107 37067 #047-05-1991 L1994 OPH *020 †35

WEIL, Howard Lee. 206 BEDFORD WAY 37064 #047-06-1985 L1986 AN *020 †05

WHITE, David J. 1909 MALLORY LN, STE 201 37067 #048-13-1995 L1999 PD *020 †05

WHITE, Houston Wayne. 206 BEDFORD WAY 37064 #047-20-1986 L1986 AN *020 †05

WILLIAMS, Freeland Le Roy. ■ 37069 #011-02-1979 L2007 FM *020 †18

WILLIAMS, Linda Morgan. 321 BILLINGSLY CT, STE 20 37067 #038-45-1994 L2000 IM *020 †20

WILLIAMS, Wayne Patrick. 4155 CAROTHERS PKWY 37067 #047-06-1967 L1971 OBG *020 †30

WILLIARD, Kenny Francis. 206 BEDFORD WAY 37064 #036-01-1978 L1983 AN *020 †05

WILLIS, Larry Gale. 206 BEDFORD WAY 37064 #047-05-1968 L1970 AN *020 †05

WILLOUGHBY, Joseph Leeper. 1311 W MAIN ST 37064 #047-06-1957 L1958 FM IM *020 †18 ‡

WILSON, Woodrow Ray. 4321 CAROTHERS PKWY 37067 #020-02-1977 L1984 EM *071 †16

WINEK, David Kent. 206 BEDFORD WAY 37064 #020-02-1983 L1988 AN *020 †05

WITT, William Stephen. ■ 37069 #047-07-1975 L1976 R IM *020 †80

WOHL, Thomas. 3326 ASPEN GROVE DR, STE 200 37067 #038-41-1988 L1997 OPH *020 †35

WOLLAS, George Williamjos. ■ 37064 #047-06-2005 L2008 FP *012

WOODALL, Cynthia Kay. 4155 CAROTHERS PKWY, FRANKLIN WOMENS CENTER 37067 #047-06-1996 L2006 OBG *020 †30

WRIGHT, Sharon Carpenter. 1909 MALLORY LN, STE 110 37067 #047-06-1995 L1998 IM *020 †20

WURTH, Todd Ray. 206 BEDFORD WAY, BONE & JOINT CLINIC 37064 #020-02-1998 L2003 ORS *020 †40

YATES, David Robert. 5310 INDIAN VALLEY RD 37064 #035-15-1963 L1968 PTH PCP *030 †50

YATES, Hodon Kendle. 206 BEDFORD WAY 37064 #047-05-1993 L1998 AN PME *020 †05

YONEYAMA, Tad. 2339 HILLSBORO RD 37069 #051-04-1994 L1997 MPD PD *020 †20,55

YORK, Douglas Clifton. 2001 MALLORY LN, STE 304 37067 #047-06-1972 L1972 GS GE *020

ZARABI, Manuchehr. ■ 37064 #517-06-1958 L1984 R *020 †80

FRIENDSHIP – CROCKETT

CONNELL, Joseph Donald. ■ 38034 #047-06-1956 L1956 PD *071

FRIENDSVILLE – BLOUNT

HATHAWAY, Joseph Chas, Jr. ■ 37737 #054-04-1957 L1967 PTH *020 †50

MITCHELL, Donald Eugene. ■ 37737 #047-06-1966 L1967 ORS *071 †40

GAINESBORO – JACKSON

BALDWIN, Mary E. 415 E GORE AVE 38562 #012-22-1987 L1988 FM *020 †18

DUDNEY, Elijah Morgan. 402 E GORE AVE 38562 #047-06-1952 L1953 GP GS *071

DYCUS, Douglas Clark. 316 N MURRAY ST, ATTN: JACKSON CO AMBU. SVC 38562 #047-06-1989 L1990 IM *020 †20

GARINGAN, Evangelito C. 620 HOSPITAL DR 38562 #748-07-1960 L1980 P *020

JOHNSON, Jack S. 515 CRESTVIEW DR 38562 #047-06-1953 L1954 GP GS *072

KREWER, Philip G. ■ 38562 #005-06-1995 L2000 ORS *020

GALLATIN – SUMNER

AHSAN, Jawaid. 253 W MAIN ST 37066 #160-02-1982 L2003 N *020

ARONS, Murray Mathew. 555 HARTSVILLE PIKE 37066 #033-05-1991 L1993 PCC *020 †20

AUGUST, Leila Marie. 608 COMMONS DR, STE A 37066 #001-02-1999 L2002 FM *020 †18

BACON, John Wayne. 300 STEAM PLANT RD, STE 210 37066 #040-02-1978 L2001 ORS *020

BATTAD, Hermogenes P D. 300 STEAM PLANT RD, STE 300 37066 #748-20-1991 L2004 PUD *020 †20

BENNETT, Leslie F. 555 HARTSVILLE PIKE 37066 #047-20-1996 L1999 PD *020 †55

BENNETT, Richard Alan. 890 N BLUEJAY WAY, PATIENT PARTNERS SURGERY C 37066 #020-02-1998 L2002 OBG *020

BENNETT, Stephen Vincent. 300 STEAM PLANT RD, STE 300 37066 #047-20-1996 L1999 **FM** *020 †18
BLACKSHEAR, Joseph R. ■ 37066 #036-05-1947 L1954 **GS** *072
BROWN, Lisa Beth. 300 STEAM PLANT RD, STE 300 37066 #046-01-1998 L2005 **FM** *020 †18
BROWN, Lloyd Tynte. 555 HARTSVILLE PIKE 37066 #047-06-1966 L1967 **FM** *020 †18
BURRUS, Roger Grady. 555 HARTSVILLE PIKE 37066 #047-06-1987 L1990 **GS** *071 †85
CALDWELL, William Rudolph. 555 HARTSVILLE PIKE 37066 #039-01-1975 L1986 **OBG** *020 †30
CAREY, Jack Willard, Jr. 555 HARTSVILLE PIKE 37066 #047-06-1975 L1976 **GP** *020
CARR, Charles Morgan. ■ 37066 #047-05-1965 L1965 **FM** *040 †18
CARTER, Thomas Foster. 555 HARTSVILLE PIKE 37066 #047-06-1958 L1958 **FM** *020
CARTER, Thomas Mark. 300 STEAM PLANT RD, STE 240 37066 #012-01-1992 L1996 **AN** *020 †05
CASE, Kenneth Ryon, Jr. 300 STEAM PLANT RD, STE 260 37066 #005-12-1967 L1969 **FM IM** *020 †18
COLE, James Escoe, II. 728 NASHVILLE PIKE 37066 #047-20-1987 L1988 **IM** *020
COLLINS, Robert D. 555 HARTSVILLE PIKE 37066 #047-05-1951 L1951 **PTH** *020 †50
COOK, Joann. 648 HARTSVILLE PIKE, GALLATIN CHILDREN'S CLINIC 37066 #047-05-1997 L1999 **PD** *020 †55
COWDEN, Charles Marshall. 555 HARTSVILLE PIKE 37066 #047-06-1956 L1957 **GS EM** *072 ‡
COX, Joe David. 300 STEAM PLANT RD, STE 300 37066 #047-06-1961 L1965 **FM** *020
DAVIS, William Gerald. 555 HARTSVILLE PIKE 37066 #020-02-1979 L1984 **VS GS** *020 †85
DILL, Andrew Brendan. 300 STEAM PLANT RD, STE 300 37066 #045-01-1999 L2007 **FM** *020 †18
ELAZAR, Don. 214 E MAIN ST, STE 200 37066 #048-02-1990 L2001 **P** *020 †18,75
EMERSON, Charles Whitley. 692 SAINT BLAISE RD 37066 #027-01-1994 L1999 **GPM** *020
EVANS, Jonathan G. 555 HARTSVILLE PIKE 37066 #048-02-1988 L1993 **PUD IM** *075 †20
FAITH, William Thos. 300 STEAM PLANT RD, STE 300 37066 #020-02-1977 L1988 **PUD IM** *020 †20
FALOUJI, Wiaam M. 555 HARTSVILLE PIKE 37066 #704-02-1981 L1999 **CN** *020 †35
FINDLEY, Christopher Chad. 555 HARTSVILLE PIKE 37066 #011-04-2002 L2006 **EM** *020
GAUTSCH, Thomas L. 555 HARTSVILLE PIKE 37066 #023-07-1989 L1995 **ORS** *020 †40
GILLESPIE, James Robt. 555 HARTSVILLE PIKE 37066 #038-40-1985 L1991 **GE IM** *020 †20
GRAHAM, Ralph B. ■ 37066 #048-12-1985 L2006 **AN** *020 †05
GREEN, Michael Edward. 854 LONE OAK DR 37066 #004-01-1990 L1994 **OPH** *020 †35
GUHA, Subir. 555 HARTSVILLE PIKE 37066 #566-01-1989 L1997 **FM** *020 †18
GUPTA, Seema. ■ 37066 #496-09-1995 L2004 **GPM** *012
HARTMAN, Bert Allen. 332 SUMNER HALL DR, CENTERSTONE 37066 #047-06-1998 L2003 **P** *020 †75
HILL, Ted W. 556 HARTSVILLE PIKE, STE 200 37066 #047-06-1976 L1976 **IM** *071 †20
HOLLIS, Jeffrey Dixon. 300 STEAM PLANT RD, STE 470 37066 #422-01-1999 L2003 **GS** *020 †85
HOOPER, Halden Wayne. 555 HARTSVILLE PIKE 37066 #047-06-1953 L1954 **FM** *071 †18
HOOPER, Halden Wayne, Jr. 300 STEAM PLANT RD, STE 300 37066 #047-05-1980 L1983 **FM** *020 †18
HUDGINS, James M. ■ 37066 #047-06-1953 L1953 **FM** *072 †18
KESSLER, Thomas Melvin. ■ 37066 #038-40-1973 L1993 **FM** *071 †18
KING, Alton S, Jr. 300 STEAM PLANT RD STE 300 37066 #047-06-1976 L1976 **IM** *020 †20
KNECHT, Janice Marie. ■ 37066 #005-12-1981 L1986 **DR** *020
KNOX, George Phillip, III. 555 HARTSVILLE PIKE 37066 #047-06-1986 L1986 **EM IM** *020
KOCH, Brian Edward. 300 STEAM PLANT RD, STE 470 37066 #038-40-1998 L2004 **OSM** *020 †40
LAU, Henry Stacy. 300 STEAM PLANT RD, STE 300 37066 #047-06-2000 L2002 **FM** *020 †18
LAWHORN, David Wood. 555 HARTSVILLE PIKE 37066 #047-06-1988 L1988 **EM** *020 †16
LAYMAN, Douglas Chas. 612 HARTSVILLE PIKE 37066 #016-11-1956 L1957 **AN** *071 †05
LEE, Jung Ho. 555 HARTSVILLE PIKE 37066 #035-06-1991 L2001 **CD** *020 †20
LEE, Michael Kearny. 300 STEAM PLANT RD, STE 430 37066 #005-06-1987 L1999 **OTO** *020 †45
LIFFERTH, Geoffrey D. 555 HARTSVILLE PIKE, SUMNER REGIONAL MEDICAL CE 37066 #047-06-1997 L2002 **EM** *020 †16
LILLY, James Aaron. 510 E MAIN ST 37066 #055-01-1964 L1973 **OPH** *071
LITTLE, William Robert. 555 HARTSVILLE PIKE 37066 #021-05-1993 L1995 **EM** *020 †16
MACCONNELL, Clayton Mann. 300 STEAM PLANT RD, STE 300 37066 #048-15-1985 L1986 **FM** *020 †18
MANAYAN, Rex Chang. 323 STEAM PLANT RD 37066 #024-07-1991 L2007 **GS** *020 †85
MASSEY, William Roe. ■ 37066 #047-06-1959 L1961 **R** *071
MAZUREK, David Gregory. 300 STEAM PLANT RD, STE 300 37066 #011-04-1990 L2005 **IM** *020 †20
MC DANIEL, Robert Earl. 300 STEAM PLANT RD STE 30 37066 #047-06-1981 L1981 **FM** *020 †18
MEWBOURNE, Rodney Brandon. 323 STEAM PLANT RD, SUMNER SURGICAL ASSOCIATES 37066 #001-02-2002 L2007 **GS** *020 †85
NORTON, Charles Glenn. ■ 37066 #047-06-1965 L1969 **ORS** *020 †40
PHILLIPS, Robert Dabney. 437 E MAIN ST, GALLATIN WOMEN'S CENTER, P 37066 #001-02-1971 L1995 **OBG** *020 †30
PINKSTON, John Ray. 464 BAY POINT DR 37066 #047-06-1991 L1993 **EM IM** *020 †20,16
REICHERT, Paige Huber. 555 HARTSVILLE PIKE, SUMNER WOUND CARE 37066 #001-02-1996 L2003 **IM OS** *020 †20
ROBERTSON, Sheila Winnis. ■ 37066 #649-14-1975 L1980 *071
RUARK, Chas Sanford, Jr. 555 HARTSVILLE PIKE 37066 #001-02-1974 L1977 **EM** *020 †16
RUTLAND, Todd Eric. 300 STEAM PLANT RD, STE 300 37066 #020-12-2001 L2005 **N** *020
SANDERS, Clarence Ramey. 316 E MAIN ST 37066 #047-06-1961 L1961 **FM** *071 †18
SIMONTON, Ralph W, Jr. 555 HARTSVILLE PIKE 37066 #047-06-1949 L1950 **GP** *071
SMITH, Carlenda Monique. ■ 37066 #047-20-2007 **PD** *012
SPENCER, Chas Norman, Jr. 648 HARTSVILLE PIKE, GALLATIN CHILDREN'S CLINIC 37066 #047-05-1976 L1977 **PD** *020 †55
STEWART, William David. 316 E MAIN ST, SANDERS MEDICAL GROUP 37066 #047-06-1959 L1960 **GS** *020 †85
STROUP, Steven L. 555 HARTSVILLE PIKE 37066 #016-11-1968 L1974 **RO** *020 †80
THOMPSON, John King. 555 HARTSVILLE PIKE 37066 #047-06-1973 L1973 **GS** *020 †85
TRUBIA, Joseph Robt, Jr. 300 STEAM PLANT RD, STE 420 37066 #041-13-1980 L2003 **ORS** *020 †40
UHL, Mark Dennis. 300 STEAM PLANT RD, STE 300 37066 #018-03-1987 L1994 **GE** *020 †20
WATSON, Marshall Tredway. 300 STEAM PLANT RD, PLLC SUITE 470 37066 #016-42-1998 L2005 **NS** *100
WESLEY, Raymond J. 555 HARTSVILLE PIKE 37066 #020-02-1968 L1977 **D DS** *020
WILLIS, Robert Arthur. 300 STEAM PLANT RD, STE 300 37066 #036-01-1983 L1988 **OTO** *020 †45
WRIGHT, Donald Arthur. 300 STEAM PLANT RD STE 30 37066 #047-06-1963 L1968 **IM RHU** *020

GATLINBURG – SEVIER

BROOKS, R Christopher. 107 PARK HEADQUARTERS RD, GREAT SMOKY MTNS NATL PARK 37738 #047-06-1981 L1981 **EM** *020 †16
COCHRAN, Leon Henry. 1754 HIDDEN HILLS RD, STE H-108 37738 #047-06-1961 L1962 **IM OM** *020 †20
DEW, Richard Allan. ■ 37738 #047-06-1965 L1966 **FM** *020 †18
FORREST, Paul Dorsey. ■ 37738 #021-01-1965 L1965 **NS** *071 †25
MAUGHON, Robert Mickey. 1015 E PARKWAY 37738 #047-06-1984 L1985 **GP** *020
MOORE, Vickie S. 815 E PARKWAY, STE 7 37738 #020-02-1978 L1982 **FM** *020
MORRIS, Robert Wilford. ■ 37738 #047-06-1953 L1954 **GS** *072
MORRIS, Thomas Wm. ■ 37738 #012-01-1973 L1975 **FM** *020 †18

GEORGETOWN – MEIGS

MILLER, Jeffrey Lynn. 542 KINCANNON LN NW 37336 #665-01-1998 L2002 **FM** *020 †18

GERMANTOWN – SHELBY

ADAMS, John Robt. ■ 38138 #047-06-1964 L1964 **U** *071 †95
ADAMS, John Robt, Jr. 1325 WOLF PARK DR, STE 102 38138 #047-06-1985 L1985 **U** *020 †95
ADKINS, Henry Leigh. 7705 POPLAR AVE, BLDG B 38138 #016-11-1954 L1958 **GYN** *071 †30
AHMAD, Masood. ■ 38139 #704-21-1987 L2001 **P** *020 ‡
AKINS, Charles Dormer. 1900 EXETER RD STE 210 38138 #047-06-1973 L1974 **AN GP** *020 †05
ALBERS, William Eric. 1400 S GERMANTOWN RD 38138 #038-06-1977 L2005 **ORS** *020 †40
ALRUFAIE, Zeena M. ■ 38139 #047-06-2007 **PD** *012
ALSTON, George Phillip. 7655 POPLAR AVE, STE 225 38138 #047-06-1978 L1978 **GS OS** *020 †85
ANDERSON, Keith G. 7460 WOLF RIVER BLVD 38138 #047-06-1984 L1985 **IC CD** *020 †20
ANDERSON, Lanetta. 7705 POPLAR AVE, STE B150 38138 #023-07-1992 L1996 **OBG** *020 †30
ARONOFF, Phillip Michael. 2120 EXETER RD, STE 130 38138 #048-12-1983 L1983 **IM** *020 †20
AYCOCK, Richard Stephen. 8000 WOLF RIVER BLVD, STE 200 38138 #048-02-1980 L1982 **GE IM** *020 †20
BAILEY, James Wesley. 1900 EXETER RD, STE 210 38138 #027-01-1972 L1980 **AN** *020 †05
BAKSHI, Madhurita. ■ 38139 #496-14-1998 L2005 **IM** *071 †20
BARAZI, Hassana. ■ 38138 #055-02-2006 L2006 **DR** *012
BARCLAY, Kimberly Ann. ■ 38138 #048-12-2004 L2007 **PD** *020 †55
BARTAKKE, Swaroopa V. ■ 38138 #496-39-1996 L2006 **END** *012 †20
BARTUSCH, Scott Linton. 1900 EXETER RD STE 210 38138 #047-06-1991 L1992 **AN** *020 †05
BASKIN, Reed Carl. 7945 WOLF RIVER BLVD, STE 300 38138 #047-06-1966 L1967 **ON HEM** *020 †20
BAUM, Alex Ernesto. 8000 WOLF RIVER BLVD, STE 200 38138 #935-01-1992 L2006 **GE** *020 †20
BAYMILLER, Scott E P. 7945 WOLF RIVER BLVD 38138 #047-06-1996 L2002 **P** *020 †75
BEATUS, Benj Louis, Jr. 1928 CLARINGTON DR 38138 #047-06-1960 L1962 **P** *020 †75
BEATY, James Harold. 1400 S GERMANTOWN RD 38138 #047-06-1976 L1978 **ORS** *020 †40
BECKFORD, Neal S. 7655 POPLAR AVE 38138 #010-03-1980 L1985 **OTO** *020 †45
BENOIT, David Allen. 1900 EXETER RD, STE 210 38138 #048-14-1995 L1999 **AN** *020 †05
BENTON, Mary Elizabeth. 7705 POPLAR AVE 38138 #047-06-1995 L1998 **PD** *020 †55
BERRY, Michael Paul. 1385 W BRIERBROOK RD, STE 1 38138 #004-01-1990 L2002 **GS** *020 †85
BERTORINI M, Tulio E. 7655 POPLAR AVE, STE 385 38138 #737-01-1970 L1977 **N** *020 †75
BHATNAGAR, Sneh Arati. 7691 POPLAR AVE, METHODIST HOSPITAL 38138 #495-47-1974 L1990 **PD** *020
BISHOP, Laura J. 7705 POPLAR AVE, STE 330 38138 #047-06-1997 L2001 **OBG** *020 †30
BISWAS, Ajit Kumar. 1900 EXETER RD, STE 210 38138 #160-05-1969 L1976 **AN** *020 †05
BOCK, Gerald Warren. 8573 CORDES CIR 38139 #038-43-1982 L1992 **GPM AM** *020 †18
BOMAR, John Cornelios, Jr. 6750 POPLAR AVE, STE 620 38138 #047-06-1993 L1994 **P OM** *100
BONNER, Courtney Lynn. ■ 38139 #047-06-2008 *012
BOOTH, Georgia Annita. ■ 38138 #038-06-1979 L1979 **GP** *074
BOSTON, Barry. 7945 WOLF RIVER BLVD, STE 300 38138 #021-05-1971 L1976 **ON HEM** *020 †20
BOULOS, Susie. ■ 38139 #915-04-1985 L1996 **IM** *020 †20
BRONSTEIN, Michael S. 7705 POPLAR AVE 38138 #047-06-1976 L1976 **OBG** *020 †30
BROOKS, Christie Nicole. 7945 WOLF RIVER BLVD 38138 #047-06-1998 L1999 **CHP** *020 †75
BROWN, Ann Dail. 7690 WOLF RIVER CIR, FOUNDATION MED GRP PLLC 38138 #047-06-1978 L1980 **IM PD** *020 †20
BROWN, Rufus Milton. ■ 38138 #047-06-1961 L1978 **GP GS** *071
BRUNT, Charles Hal. 1384 CORDOVA CV STE 1 38138 #021-01-1966 L1975 **CHP P** *020 †75
BUADI, Francis Kwadwo A. 7945 WOLF RIVER BLVD, STE 300 38138 #412-02-1991 L2004 **HO** *020 †20
BUCY, William Wesson. 2162 JUDICIAL DR 38138 #027-01-1985 L1986 **FM** *020 †18 ‡
BURROW, William Booker. ■ 38138 #047-06-1959 L1959 **GP** *071
CABALLERO, Hugo A. 1920 KIRBY PKWY, STE 202 38138 #048-16-1987 L1990 **FM** *020 †18
CAMPANA, Dario. ■ 38139 #561-20-1980 L2007 *100
CAMPFIELD, Brett Allan. ■ 38138 #007-02-2002 L2002 **FM** *100
CANNON, Bland Wilson. 6685 POPLAR AVE, STE 200 38138 #016-06-1945 L1950 **NS** *071 †25
CARNEY, Judi Lynn. 7705 POPLAR AVE 38138 #051-01-1994 L1996 **OBG** *020 †30
CARTER, Belvia Ann. 7705 POPLAR AVE, STE B150 38138 #027-01-1978 L1982 **OBG AN** *020 †30
CARTER, Peter Whitney. 8000 WOLF RIVER BLVD, STE 100 38138 #047-06-1983 L1984 **HO ON** *020 †20
CASTELLAW, Mark Allan. 8040 WOLF RIVER BLVD 38138 #047-06-1981 L1982 **IM** *020 †20
CATTAU, Edward L, Jr. 8000 WOLF RIVER BLVD, STE 200 38138 #036-01-1976 L1990 **GE IM** *020 †20
CHANIN, Louis Ross. 2120 EXETER RD, STE 250 38138 #041-77-1979, ▲ L1989 **OTO GS** *020 †45

■ = Address Information Privacy Protected

CHAUHAN, Dinesh N. 2129 S GERMANTOWN RD 38138 #495-22-1965 L1979 **AN** *062
CHEATHAM, Charles F. 3620 FOREST HILL RD 38138 #047-06-1990 L1993 **FM** *020 †18
CHEEMA, Farah. ■ 38138 #704-21-1996 L2004 **PCC** *100 †20
CHIDESTER, Catherine Ann. 1355 W BRIERBROOK RD 38138 #047-06-2004 L2007 **PD** *020 †55
CHRISTIAN, Aimee Magnant. 1255 S GERMANTOWN RD 38138 #051-04-1986 L1988 **PD** *020 †55
CHURCHWELL, Luella Grigg. 1335 CORDOVA CV 38138 #047-06-1986 L1988 **D** *020 †20,15
CHURCHWELL, Mary Ashley. 1335 CORDOVA CV 38138 #047-06-1984 L1986 **D** *020 †15
CLARK, Dwight Witt, Jr. 7205 WOLF RIVER BLVD, STE 201 38138 #047-06-1964 L1965 **CD** *020 †20
CLARK, Kenneth David. ■ 38139 #047-06-1999 L2005 **P** *020
COCKE, Edwin W, Jr. 7945 WOLF RIVER BLVD 38138 #047-06-1943 L1943 **HNS OTO** *071 †45
COLE, Kristina Ann. 7705 POPLAR AVE BLDG B, STE 110 38138 #023-01-2001 L2001 **PHO** *100 †30,55
COLLADO, Orlando Acosta, Jr. ■ 38138 #748-20-2005 **FP** *012
CONRAD, Lynn Wilson. 1325 WOLF PARK DR, STE 102 38138 #047-06-1969 L1969 **U** *020 †95
COOPER, Charlie Walter. 1900 EXETER RD, STE 210 38138 #027-01-1959 L1965 **AN** *020 †05
COX, Sam Jones, III. 7705 POPLAR AVE, ALLIANCE PC 38138 #027-01-1974 L1980 **OBG** *020
CRAVEN, William Fielding. 1920 KIRBY PKWY, STE 100 38138 #027-01-1981 L1987 **FM** *020 †18
CRENSHAW, Andrew H, Jr. 1400 S GERMANTOWN RD 38138 #047-06-1982 L1983 **ORS** *020 †40
CRENSHAW, Thomas H. 7705 POPLAR AVE, STE 330 38138 #047-06-1982 L1984 **GYN OBS** *020 †30
CURLEE, Lida Mesa. ■ 38139 #264-10-1993 L2006 **IM** *100 †20
DAHER, Fadi. ■ 38138 #875-01-1998 L2007 **NEP** *100
DALSANIA, Jivanlal C. 8657 DOGWOOD OAKS CV 38139 #495-48-1972 L1986 **AN** *020 †05
DALTON, Franklin Palmer. ■ 38139 #036-07-1960 L1960 **CD IM** *020
DAVIS, Edward Charles. 2002 EXETER RD 38138 #047-20-1993 L1994 **PD** *020 †55
DEATON, William Jerry. ■ 38138 #047-06-1957 L1957 **U** *071
DE LAMERENS, Maite. 1255 S GERMANTOWN RD, MEMPHIS PEDIATRICS 38138 #011-02-1985 L1987 **PD** *020 †55
DELLINGER, Janet W. 1255 S GERMANTOWN RD, MEMPHIS PEDIATRICS 38138 #047-06-1986 L1988 **PD** *020 †55
DERWEESH, Ithaar Hadier. 7945 WOLF RIVER BLVD 38138 #016-02-1995 L2005 **U** *020 †95
DEWEESE, Melvin Wayne. ■ 38138 #020-02-1957 L1958 **OPH** *071 †35
DICK, Charlotte. 1255 S GERMANTOWN RD, MEMPHIS PEDIATRICS 38138 #016-11-1988 L2000 **PD** *020 †55
DICK, Maroun Tannous. 7705 POPLAR AVE 38138 #605-01-1986 L1989 **N CN** *020 †75
DONATO, Heather O'Cain. 7705 POPLAR AVE STE 110 38138 #047-06-1996 L1998 **OBG** *020 †30
DORROH, Charles Wm. 1900 EXETER RD, STE 210 38138 #028-03-1981 L1985 **AN FM** *020 †18,05
DRAGUTSKY, Michael S. 1324 WOLF PARK DR 38138 #048-16-1982 L1982 **GE HEP** *020 †20
DRUMMOND, Charles Duncan. ■ 38138 #024-05-1959 L1961 **PTH** *071 †50
DUBAL, Nilesh Vallabhdas. 1381 S GERMANTOWN RD 38138 #036-05-1992 L2003 **RO** *020 †20,80
DUGGIRALA, Vijaya Lakshmi. 1900 EXETER RD, STE 210 38138 #495-62-1974 L1980 **AN** *020 †05
DULANEY, Bettyjo. 7705 POPLAR AVE, ALLIANCE PC 38138 #041-15-2001 L2005 **OBG** *020 †30
DULANEY-HURLEY, Mary M. 7514 CORPORATE CENTER DR 38138 #047-06-1993 L1997 **MPD** *020 †55,20
DURHAM, Anna Maria. 7705 POPLAR AVE, STE 230 38138 #047-06-1992 L1995 **PD** *020 †55
EASTMEAD, Donald Jos. 7645 WOLF RIVER CIR 38138 #048-12-1978 L1987 **PD N** *020 †55
EBAUGH, Lynn. 7640 WOLF RIVER CIR, 2ND FL 38138 #001-06-1988 L1990 **NEP** *020 †20
EDWARDS, Lelon Opal, Jr. 2004 EXETER RD, STE 6T 38138 #047-06-1981 L1983 **PD** *020 †55
EDWARDS, Neil Bonham. 7945 WOLF RIVER BLVD 38138 #041-13-1965 L1979 **P** *030 †75
EFIRD, Walter G, III. 1329 CORDOVA CV 38138 #021-01-1983 L1983 **PS GS** *020 †65,85
EL-GHANDOUR, Omar. 7945 WOLF RIVER BLVD, STE 140 38138 #605-01-1992 L2002 **RO** *020 †80
ELLIS, Richard A. 7655 POPLAR AVE 38138 #047-06-1984 L1985 **GS** *020 †85
EPSTEIN, Eugene U. ■ 38138 #047-06-1951 L1951 **PD FM** *071 †55
ESCUE, Ashley Brawley. 3085 FOUNTAINSIDE DR, STE 202 38138 #004-01-1998 L2003 **AI** *020 †55,03 ‡
EVANS, Christine Hardin. 1920 KIRBY PKWY, STE 202 38138 #047-06-1999 L2003 **FM** *020
FANNING, David Wilson. 1900 EXETER RD, STE 210 38138 #047-20-1982 L1983 **AN** *020
FAQUIN, Cornell Chas. ■ 38138 #047-06-1958 L1958 **FM OBG** *075 †18
FAROOQ, Farees Taqiuddin. ■ 38139 #047-06-2000 L2007 **GE** *100 †20
FARRAR, Thomas Crowell. 2102 JOHNSON RD 38139 #047-06-1977 L1978 **EM** *020 †16
FERRELL, Thaddeus Hagan. 7730 WOLF RIVER BLVD, STE 112 38138 #027-01-1969 L1973 **PS** *020 †65
FOLEY, Lynn M. 2195 WEST ST 38138 #005-14-1981 L1994 **D** *020 †15
FOX, Thomas Grovenor. ■ 38138 #047-06-1979 L1983 **R** *020
FRANKLIN, Edward Arthur. 2215 WEST ST 38138 #047-06-1991 L1992 **IM** *020 †20
FREDERICK, Randall Carl. 8000 WOLF RIVER BLVD, STE 200 38138 #047-06-1979 L1981 **GE IM** *020 †20
FREELAND, Lynda Jo. 7690 WOLF RIVER CIR, FOUNDATION MEDICAL GROUP, 38138 #047-06-1981 L1983 **IM** *020 †20
FRIEDMAN, Roy Joseph, II. ■ 38183 #036-01-2004 L2007 **FM** *020 †18
FUNDERBURG, William R, Jr. 1900 EXETER RD, STE 210 38138 #001-02-1990 L1999 **AN** *020 †05
GAILLARD, Ian Trevor. ■ 38138 #010-03-2002 L2003 **IM** *100
GAIRHAN, Charles Hurd. 1900 EXETER RD, STE 210 38138 #004-01-1992 L2002 **AN** *020 †05
GALLANT, Donald Marvin. ■ 38183 #021-01-1955 L2005 **P** *071 †75
GESHKE, Terrence Edward. 7705 POPLAR AVE 38138 #047-06-1967 L1969 **PD** *020 †55
GIBSON, Roger O. 1374 CORDOVA CV, STE 102 38138 #047-06-1976 L1977 **IM** *020 †20
GIESCHEN, Holger Louis. 1381 S GERMANTOWN RD 38138 #409-12-1986 L1998 **RO IM** *020 †80
GINDT, Henry Sylvain. 2095 EXETER RD STE 80 38138 #165-04-1973 L1977 **AN FM** *020 †05
GORLINE, William James. 1900 EXETER RD, STE 210 38138 #028-34-1973 L1977 **AN** *020
GRAVENOR, Shirley T. ■ 38139 #067-01-1983 L2000 *020
GRAVES, Lester Rose. 7705 POPLAR AVE, ALLIANCE PC 38138 #047-06-1954 L1954 **GYN** *020 †30
GREENWELL, Thomas David. 7705 POPLAR AVE 38138 #047-06-1980 L1980 **OBG EM** *020 †30
GRIFFIN, Daniel Eugene. 1310 WOLF PARK DR 38138 #047-06-1970 L1971 **GE** *020 †20
GRIFFITH, Allison W. ■ 38138 #047-20-2000 L2007 **PD** *020 †55
GRIZZARD, Henry Thompson. 7205 WOLF RIVER BLVD, STE 100 38138 #047-06-1961 L1962 **OPH** *020 †35
GROGAN, Fred Turley. 7205 WOLF RIVER BLVD, STE 200 38138 #047-06-1954 L1954 **AI** *072 †55,03
GUBIN, Steven Sydney. 8060 WOLF RIVER BLVD 38138 #047-06-1985 L1991 **CD IM** *020 †20
GULLA, Shannon Miller. ■ 38139 #047-06-2003 L2007 **DR** *012
GUYTON, James Lawrence. 1400 S GERMANTOWN RD, CAMPBELL CLINIC 38138 #024-01-1985 L1991 **OS ORS** *020 †40
HACKMAN, Bela Bernat. 7460 WOLF RIVER BLVD, THE SUTHERLAND CARDIOLOGY 38138 #047-06-1978 L1981 **CD IM** *020 †20
HAMBY, Donald Lynn. 7705 POPLAR AVE 38138 #047-06-1979 L1979 **OBG** *020 †30
HANISSIAN, Aram S. 2101 MERCHANTS ROW, STE 3 38138 #605-01-1958 L1970 **RHU PDA** *020 †55,03
HANISSIAN, Gregory A. 2101 MERCHANTS ROW, STE 3 38138 #001-02-1991 L1993 **AI PDA** *020 †55,03
HAQUE, Nasir Mainul. 7645 WOLF RIVER CIR # 202 38138 #160-01-1985 L1995 **IM** *020 †20
HARKESS, James Wilson. 1400 S GERMANTOWN RD 38138 #012-01-1982 L1984 **ORS** *020 †40
HAYES, Burton Lucas. 7945 WOLF RIVER BLVD, STE 120 38138 #004-01-1994 L1995 **MPD** *020 †20,55
HERRING, Paula Ann. 2339 FOREST HILL IRENE RD, DEPT OF MED AFFAIRS 38139 #047-06-1998 L2001 **RHU** *040 †20
HERRING, William Taul. ■ 38138 #004-01-1964 L1971 **IM** *020
HICKEY, Homer David, Jr. 1325 WOLF PARK DR, STE 102 38138 #047-06-1966 L1966 **U** *020 †95
HILL, Brandon Deemond. 7205 WOLF RIVER BLVD, STE 200 38138 #012-21-1999 L2002 **AI** *020 †20,03 ‡
HOEHN, Robert Gardell. 1384 CORDOVA CV, STE 1 38138 #047-06-1989 L1990 **CHP** *020 †75
HOLLABAUGH, Robert S, Jr. 1325 WOLF PARK DR, STE 102 38138 #047-06-1992 L1998 **U** *020 †95
HOLLOWAY, David Hoyt, Jr. 8060 WOLF RIVER BLVD 38138 #047-06-1961 L1962 **CD IM** *020 †20
HOLMES, John Pierce. 7119 STOUT RD 38138 #047-05-1957 L1957 **OPH** *071 †35
HOOD, Stephen Thos. 1900 EXETER RD, STE 210 38138 #027-01-1967 L1971 **AN** *020 †05
HOOVER, Tyron Christian. ■ 38138 #048-12-1995 L1998 **PTH** *020 †50
HOPKINS, Jack Tackett, Jr. 7460 WOLF RIVER BLVD, SUTHERLAND CARDIOLOGY CLIN 38138 #047-05-1974 L1979 **CD** *020 †20
HUFF, Christopher Morris. ■ 38139 #047-06-2006 **IM** *012
HUGHES, Thomas Arthur. 7945 WOLF RIVER BLVD 38138 #028-02-1975 L1987 **IM END** *050 †20
INABA, Hiroto. ■ 38138 #572-34-1991 L2003 **PHO** *100 †55
ISHIKAWA, Susan Naomi. 1400 S GERMANTOWN RD 38138 #041-02-1992 L1998 **ORS OFA** *020 †40
JABBOUR, J T. 7645 WOLF RIVER CIR, STE 100 38138 #047-06-1951 L1952 **CHN PD** *020 †55
JACKSON, Terrence L. 8000 WOLF RIVER BLVD, STE 200 38138 #028-46-1994 L2000 **GE** *020 †20
JAHANZEB, Mohammad. 7945 WOLF RIVER BLVD, STE 140 38138 #704-01-1986 L2002 **ON HEM** *020 †20
JAMES, Hal Pearson. ■ 38138 #047-06-1944 L1945 **OBG** *071 †30
JANKOV, Aleksandar. 7710 WOLF RIVER CIR, THE JONES CLINIC 38138 #957-07-1990 L2002 **IM** *020 †20
JERKINS, Gerald Ray. 1920 KIRBY PKWY, STE 100 38138 #047-06-1973 L1974 **UP** *020 †95
JOBE, Mark Tilden. 1400 S GERMANTOWN RD 38138 #051-04-1981 L1987 **ORS GP** *020 †40
JOHNS, Alethea Susanne. ■ 38138 #047-06-2004 L2007 **PD** *100 †55
JOHNS, Cameila D'Silva. ■ 38139 #506-13-1993 L2004 **PTH** *020 †50
JOHNSON, Eric Edward. 8060 WOLF RIVER BLVD 38138 #038-44-1986 L1994 **ICE CD** *020 †20
JOHNSON, Ronald Jackson. 7910 WOLF RIVER BLVD 38138 #027-01-1973 L1977 **PS HNS** *020 †85,65 ‡
JONES, Bradley Kelvin. 7705 POPLAR AVE 38138 #047-06-1993 L1995 **PD** *020 †55
JONES, Clyde Michael. 7710 WOLF RIVER CIR 38138 #001-02-1974 L1995 **HO ON** *020 †20
JONES, R Luby. ■ 38139 #047-06-1950 L1950 **GS** *071 †85
JONES, Rushelle Alicia. ■ 38139 #047-06-2001 L2005 **OBG** *020 †30
JORDAN, Richard James. 8040 WOLF RIVER BLVD, STE 200 38138 #047-06-1981 L1982 **IM** *020 †20
KALSI, Carle Crane. 7691 POPLAR AVE 38138 #048-02-1997 L1999 **MPD EM** *020 †55
KAPLAN, Stanley Baruch. 7945 WOLF RIVER BLVD 38138 #047-06-1954 L1956 **RHU IM** *020 †20
KEEGAN, Mary Leigh. 7705 POPLAR AVE, STE 220 38138 #047-06-1986 L1987 **OBG** *020 †30
KERLAN, Jeffrey Eliot. 8060 WOLF RIVER BLVD 38138 #047-06-1998 L2005 **CD** *020 †20
KHAN, Ghazala Parvez. ■ 38139 #704-06-1983 L2006 **FM** *100 †18
KIER, John H. ■ 38183 #036-07-1950 L1954 **GE IM** *071 †20
KING, Truman Franklin. 7705 POPLAR AVE, STE 220 38138 #001-02-1982 L1983 **OBG** *020 †30
KIRK, Helen Renee. 1781 MALABAR DR 38138 #055-01-1996 L2000 **PCC** *020 †20
KLEMIS, James Edward. 8060 WOLF RIVER BLVD 38138 #012-01-1997 L1999 **IC** *100 †20
KLOEK, Scott Mitchell. 7705 POPLAR AVE 38138 #047-06-1992 L1994 **PD** *020 †55
KNEFATI, Mohamed Z. ■ 38139 #875-02-1979 L1992 **N** *020
KNIGHT, William Harold. 7655 POPLAR AVE, STE 250 38138 #039-01-1978 L1980 **ORS** *020 †40
KNOWLES, Felicia M. 7645 WOLF RIVER CIR, PEDIATRIC NEUROLOGY, PA 38138 #047-06-1997 L2000 **PD** *020 †55
KOSS, Katherine Jennifer. ■ 38138 #010-02-2006 L2007 **PD** *012
KRAUS, Alan Jeffrey. 2120 EXETER RD STE 100 38138 #047-06-1982 L1983 **PME AN** *020 †05
KUMAR, Vishad. 7655 POPLAR AVE, STE 385 38138 #495-05-1988 L1998 **N** *020 †75
KUTTEH, Carol Countryman. ■ 38139 #039-01-1987 L1996 **OBG** *040 †30
LABOY, Miguel A. ■ 38138 #042-02-1999 L2007 **FOP** *020 †50
LACHICA, Roberto Danilo. 7945 WOLF RIVER BLVD, STE 290 38138 #016-02-1992 L1998 **PS** *020 †65
LANDAU, Reed Stephen. 1900 EXETER RD, STE 210 38138 #047-06-1985 L1989 **AN** *020 †05
LANDY, Stephen Hall. 7655 POPLAR AVE, STE 385 38138 #047-06-1982 L1982 **N** *020 †75
LANGSDON, Phillip Royal. 7499 POPLAR PIKE, CENTER, LLC 38138 #004-01-1980 L1986 **FPS** *020 †45
LARIMER, Perry James. 1325 WOLF PARK DR, STE 102 38138 #047-06-1971 L1972 **U** *020 †95
LASTER, Angela Gailey. 1900 EXETER RD, STE 210 38138 #047-06-1997 L2003 **AN** *020 †05
LAURENCE, Gregory N. 2195 WEST ST, LAURENCE FAM PRACT OBS 38138 #048-14-1992 L1993 **FM OBS** *020 †18
LAVELLE, David Glen. 1400 S GERMANTOWN RD 38138 #047-06-1979 L1979 **ORS OAR** *020 †40

■ = Address Information Privacy Protected

LAZAROV, Stuart J. 1900 EXETER RD, STE 210 38138 #047-06-1987 L1992 **AN** *020 †05
LEE-SIGLER, Judith Rae. 2120 EXETER RD, STE 130 38138 #041-13-1986 L2005 **PM** *020 †60
LENDEL, Irina G. ■ 38138 #064-01-2000 L2007 **END** *100 †20
LENDEL, Vasili A. ■ 38138 #064-01-2000 L2007 **CD** *100 †20
LEVENTHAL, Marvin R. 7655 POPLAR AVE, STE 250 38138 #047-06-1981 L1982 **ORS OSM** *020 †40
LEVINSON, Michael Jay. 8000 WOLF RIVER BLVD, STE 200 38138 #047-06-1968 L1973 **GE** *020 †20
LEWIS, Myron. 8000 WOLF RIVER BLVD, STE 200 38138 #035-01-1963 L1964 **GE IM** *020 †20
LIEBERMAN, Phillip Louis. 7205 WOLF RIVER BLVD, STE 200 38138 #047-06-1965 L1966 **IM A** *020 †20,03
LIGHT, William Harry. 7715 WOLF RIVER BLVD 38138 #047-06-1979 L1981 **IM** *020 †20
LIMAN, Andrew Dede. 7945 WOLF RIVER BLVD, STE 140 38138 #506-01-1983 L2005 **HO** *020 †20
LINDSAY, Herbert Lamar. 1900 EXETER RD, STE 210 38138 #027-01-1990 L1994 **AN IM** *020
LING, Frank Wen-Yung. 7800 WOLF TRAIL CV 38138 #048-12-1974 L1977 **OBG** *020 †30
LITCH, Melvin, Jr. 7945 WOLF RIVER BLVD, STE 240 38138 #036-07-1959 L1965 **OPH** *020 †35
LITZOW, James Troy. 7460 WOLF RIVER BLVD, STE 101 38138 #056-06-1987 L1998 **ICE CD** *020 †20
LIVERMORE, George R, Jr. ■ 38138 #024-01-1943 L1951 **GS** *071 †85
LONG, Diane M. 7705 POPLAR AVE, STE 330 38138 #047-06-1982 L1984 **OBG** *020 †30
LONG, Thomas Edward. 7675 WOLF RIVER CIR, STE 202 38138 #047-06-1973 L1974 **OTO** *020 †45
LUTTERMAN, Joel. 7945 WOLF RIVER BLVD 38138 #024-05-1991 L2003 **PDC** *020 †55
LYNCH, Michael Hardy. 7655 POPLAR AVE, STE 250 38138 #021-05-1968 L1977 **ORS** *020 †40
LYNN, Ronald B. 7645 WOLF RIVER CIR, STE 100 38138 #039-01-1976 L1979 **N** *020 †75
MAC DONALD, Charles B. 7945 WOLF RIVER BLVD 38138 #064-01-1984 L1999 **OTO** *020 †45
MADDUX, Holt Benjamin. 1325 WOLF PARK DR, STE 102 38138 #047-06-1977 L1978 **U GS** *020 †95
MAGDOVITZ, Nouth Chanmani. ■ 38138 #047-06-2005 **PD** *012
MAGUIRE, James K. 2621 HACKS CROSS RD 38138 #021-05-1952 L1959 **GS GP** *020
MANUGIAN, Arsen H. 7655 POPLAR AVE, STE 250 38138 #919-02-1972 L1977 **ORS** *020 †40
MARTIN, Dan F. ■ 38138 #048-12-2004 **GS** *012
MARTIN, Daniel Clyde. 7945 WOLF RIVER BLVD, STE 320 38138 #012-05-1972 L1977 **REN OBG** *020 †30
MAYERS, William Winfrey. ■ 38138 #047-06-1958 L1960 **U** *020 †95
MAYZELL, George Grant. 7691 POPLAR AVE, GERMANTOWN HOSPITAL 38138 #033-05-1982 L2007 **IM IMG** *020 †20
MC CAFFERTY, Linda Raye. 7655 POPLAR AVE STE 350 38138 #001-02-1984 L1987 **IM** *020
MC CLOY, Randolph M. 1324 WOLF PARK DR 38138 #047-06-1961 L1961 **GE** *020 †20
MC COURT, Carol Jo. 1900 EXETER RD, STE 210 38138 #004-01-1995 L1999 **AN** *020
MC GEE, Roger Lynn. ■ 38138 #047-06-2003 **GS** *012
MC GREW, Frank A, III. 8060 WOLF RIVER BLVD 38138 #038-06-1970 L1976 **CD IM** *020 †20
MC LEMORE, Thomas E, Jr. 2018 S GERMANTOWN RD 38138 #012-01-1953 L1969 **IM OS** *071 †20
MC SWAIN, Harold Michael. 1325 WOLF PARK DR, STE 102 38138 #047-06-1977 L1977 **U** *020 †95
MEHR, Sonal Modhvadia. ■ 38139 #028-34-2005 **IM** *012
MERRITT, Lauren Neal. 1900 EXETER RD, STE 210 38138 #047-06-1984 L1985 **AN** *020 †05
MESTEMACHER, Christine S. 7705 POPLAR AVE, STE 110 38138 #047-06-1993 L1995 **OBG** *020 †30
MEYER, David. 7205 WOLF RIVER BLVD, STE 10 38138 #047-06-1962 L1962 **OPH** *020 †35
MIHALKO, Marc Jeffrey. 1400 S GERMANTOWN RD 38138 #047-06-1998 L2002 **ORS** *020 †40
MILLER, Kristin M. 7705 POPLAR AVE, STE 220 38138 #028-03-1991 L1995 **OBG** *020 †30
MILLER, Mark Page. 7655 POPLAR AVE STE 230 38138 #027-01-1983 L1984 **GS** *020 †85
MILLER, Vernon Arthur. 1900 KIRBY PKWY, STE 100 38138 #047-06-1993 L1994 **GP AN** *020
MINHAS, Sohail Azam. 7945 WOLF RIVER BLVD, STE 300 38138 #704-20-1985 L1997 **ON HEM** *020 †20
MIRRO, Betty J. 3085 FOUNTAINSIDE DR, STE 202 38138 #047-06-1985 L1987 **AI PD** *020 †55,03
MOGAN, Edward Nenon. ■ 38138 #047-06-1956 L1958 **PD** *071 †55
MONTGOMERY, Van Alexander. ■ 38139 #047-06-2003 **DR** *012
MOOLCHANDANI, Rajendra K. 1900 EXETER RD, STE 210 38138 #495-30-1982 L1992 **AN** *020 †05
MORRIS, John Thomas, III. 7640 WOLF RIVER CIR, EAST MEMPHIS NEPHROLOGY 38138 #047-06-1995 L1997 **NEP** *020 †20
MORRIS, Van Karlyle, II. ■ 38138 #047-06-2008 *012
MORRIS, William Randolph. 7945 WOLF RIVER BLVD 38138 #047-06-1964 L1965 **OPH** *040 †35
MORRISON, Michael Burch. 1900 EXETER RD, STE 210 38138 #027-01-1986 L1987 **AN** *020 †05
MORROW, Jennifer Sae. 8060 WOLF RIVER BLVD 38138 #047-06-1998 L2004 **CD** *020 †20
MOSKOP, Robert Jay, Jr. 1900 EXETER RD, STE 210 38138 #047-06-1989 L1993 **AN** *020 †05
MOUCHON, Ward Paul. ■ 38138 #005-12-1957 L1958 **ORS HS** *071 †40
MOWRY, Robert W. ■ 38138 #023-07-1946 L1960 **ATP** *071 †50
MUIR, Edward Simmons. 2136 EXETER RD, STE 103 38138 #027-01-1986 L1987 **ON HEM** *020 †20
MULLINS, Brent Anthony. 7710 WOLF RIVER CIR, JONES CLINIC 38138 #047-06-1985 L1988 **ON** *020 †20
NATARAJAN, Monika. 7645 WOLF RIVER CIR, MID-SOUTH PHYSICIANS 38138 #495-32-1995 L2001 **IM** *020 †20
NATARAJAN, Shiva S. 7645 WOLF RIVER CIR 38138 #495-32-1991 L2000 **N** *020 †75
NATH, Rajneesh. 7945 WOLF RIVER BLVD, STE 140 38138 #495-14-1985 L2005 **ON HO** *020 †20
NIX, Thomas Lynn. 2018 S GERMANTOWN RD 38138 #004-01-2006 L2007 **GP** *012
NORMAN, Robert Sidney. 6816 HIGHWAY 72 38138 #047-06-1952 L1953 **GPM IM** *071 †20
O'BRIEN, Barbara Cape. 7645 WOLF RIVER CIR 38138 #047-06-1986 L1987 **N** *020 †75
OKAMOTO, Yasuhiro. ■ 38138 #572-52-1990 **PHO** *100
ORTIZ, Juan Antonio. ■ 38138 #042-02-2000 L2002 **GS** *020 †85
OSAROGIAGBON, Raymond U. 7945 WOLF RIVER BLVD, STE 140 38138 #690-01-1988 L2004 **HO** *020 †20
OSTROW, Bridget Flavin. 7776 FARMINGTON BLVD, P O BOX 383213 38138 #028-34-1981 L1988 **VS GS** *020 †85
OSTROW, Louis Barry. 6750 POPLAR AVE, STE 210 38138 #035-09-1982 L1988 **TS** *020 †85,90
OTTEN, Daniel Edmond. 8060 WOLF RIVER BLVD 38138 #047-05-2000 L2007 **CD** *020 †20
OVERBY, Steven Todd. 8040 WOLF RIVER BLVD, STE 200 38138 #027-01-1996 L1998 **IM** *020 †20
OWENS, James Harvey. 7655 POPLAR AVE 38138 #047-06-1972 L1973 **GS** *020
PARIKH, Sonali Salil. ■ 38139 #495-83-1992 L2003 **IM** *020 †20
PARIKH, Viraj Kaushik. ■ 38139 #047-06-2003 L2007 **DR** *012
PASLAWSKI, Wlodzimierz. ■ 38183 #759-04-1954 L1980 **AN** *020
PATEL, Phalgun J. 1900 EXETER RD, STE 210 38138 #495-49-1991 L2000 **AN** *020
PATIL, Avinash Shivaputra. ■ 38139 #047-06-2006 **OBG** *012
PATTERSON, Chas Richard. ■ 38139 #047-06-1978 L1980 **GS** *020 †85
PATTERSON, Kyle Sperry. 7705 POPLAR AVE, STE 110 38138 #047-06-2001 L2003 **OBG** *020
PAULLUS, Rodney Alan. ■ 38138 #047-06-2008 *012
PEARSON, Richard M. 1325 WOLF PARK DR, STE 102 38138 #047-06-1971 L1972 **U** *020 †95
PEDIGO, Phillip Adler. 2100 EXETER RD 38138 #047-06-1959 L1959 **GS** *020 †85
PETRI, Jan Holley. 7945 WOLF RIVER BLVD # 220 38138 #047-06-1985 L1986 **OTO GS** *020 †45
PHILLIPS, Owen Patterson. 7945 WOLF RIVER BLVD 38138 #027-01-1980 L1989 **OBG** *020 †19,30
PHOTOPULOS, Guy. 2100 EXETER RD, WEST CLINIC 38138 #016-11-1967 L1978 **OBG GO** *020 †30
PICKENS, John Houston. 7705 POPLAR AVE, STE 330 38138 #047-06-1981 L1990 **OBG** *020 †30
PILLAI, Rekha. 7655 POPLAR AVE, STE 385 38138 #495-54-1979 L1982 **N CN** *020 †75
POMYKALA, Lora Alison. 8040 WOLF RIVER BLVD, STE 200 38138 #047-06-2001 L2004 **IM** *020
PORTER, Jolie Garcia. 7690 WOLF RIVER CIR 38138 #021-06-1990 L1996 **IM** *020 †20
PRIDE-BOONE, Janice B. 1255 S GERMANTOWN RD 38138 #024-01-1981 L2006 **PD** *020 †55
PRZEPIORKA, Donna. 1684 WILLISSHIRE LN 38139 #016-11-1980 L2002 **ON HEM** *050 †20
PYUN, Hak He. ■ 38138 #583-08-1960 L1972 **PD** *071
QUIROZ, Antonio C. 7460 WOLF RIVER BLVD, STE 101 38138 #748-01-1955 L2001 **CD IM** *020 †20
RATLIFF, Thomas Warren. 7945 WOLF RIVER BLVD, STE 300 38138 #048-12-1987 L1999 **ON HEM** *020 †20
RAZA, Ali. ■ 38138 #704-21-2000 L2007 **DR** *012
REED, Cheston Murray, Jr. 7705 POPLAR AVE, ALLIANCE PC 38138 #047-06-1976 L1976 **OBG** *020 †30
REED, Patrice Cowan. 1255 S GERMANTOWN RD, MEMPHIS PEDIATRICS 38138 #047-06-1988 L1996 **PD** *020 †55
RENTROP, William Emil. 1900 KIRBY PKWY 38138 #047-06-1947 L1956 **GP GS** *071
RICHARDSON, Brenda Jean. 7205 WOLF RIVER BLVD, STE 201 38138 #001-02-1986 L1987 **CD IM** *020
RICHARDSON, Elbert Greer. 1400 S GERMANTOWN RD 38138 #047-06-1967 L1975 **ORS** *020 †40
RINKER, Lillian Hamilton. 1381 S GERMANTOWN RD 38138 #036-05-1992 L1997 **RO** *020 †80
RISELING, Elizabeth M. 7705 POPLAR AVE BLDG B 38138 #047-06-1993 L1994 **OBG** *020 †30
RIVERA, Carlos Eric. 1400 S GERMANTOWN RD 38138 #042-01-1996 L2002 **PM PME** *020 †60
ROGINSKY, Rina Rosa. 7705 POPLAR AVE 38138 #038-40-2002 L2007 **OBG** *020 †30
ROUSELLE, Dionne Marie. 7705 POPLAR AVE, STE B150 38138 #041-01-1994 L1998 **OBG** *020
RUSSO, William Louis. 8060 WOLF RIVER BLVD 38138 #047-06-1970 L1971 **CD IM** *020 †20
RUSTOM, Amal. ■ 38139 #047-06-1994 L1995 **IM** *020 †20
RYAN-TODD, Margaret Mary. ■ 38139 #539-04-1970 L1987 **PM** *020 †60
SAINI, Tejinder Singh. 2546 WOODHURST CV, 2546 WOODHURST COVE 38139 #495-29-1979 L1984 **P** *020 †75
SALLEE, David Christopher. ■ 38139 #028-34-2001 L2004 **DR** *020 †80
SALMAN, Raed. ■ 38139 #875-03-1999 L2007 *100
SAMANT, Sandeep. 7945 WOLF RIVER BLVD 38138 #495-36-1987 L1999 **OTO** *020
SAMUEL, Vincent R. 1900 EXETER RD, STE 210 38138 #308-11-1985 L1996 **AN** *020 †05
SAMUELS, Alan Danl. 1324 WOLF PARK DR 38138 #038-06-1966 L1973 **GE IM** *020 †20
SANFORD, Jack Carter, Jr. 7705 POPLAR AVE, ALLIANCE PC 38138 #047-06-1962 L1962 **OBG OS** *020 †30 ‡
SANFORD, Martha Helene. 7691 POPLAR AVE, METHODIST HOSP GERMANTOWN 38138 #047-06-1997 L1999 **IM** *020 †20
SAWYER, Jeffrey Raymond. 1400 S GERMANTOWN RD, CAMPBELL CLINIC 38138 #035-45-1993 L1997 **ORS OP** *020 †40
SCHAEFFER, Sandeford J. ■ 38138 #047-06-1950 L1950 **FM** *071
SCHNEIDER, Michael A. 1335 CORDOVA CV 38138 #047-06-1988 L1989 **D** *020 †15
SCOTT, Dawn Heather. 7691 POPLAR AVE 38138 #030-06-1999 L2001 **PD** *020 †55
SCRUGGS, Jerry Lawrence. 1900 EXETER RD, STE 210 38138 #654-01-1981 L1984 **AN** *020 †05
SHALA, Bashar A. 7655 POPLAR AVE, STE 140 38138 #875-02-1990 L1995 **CD** *020 †20
SHAPIRO, Norman D. ■ 38139 #047-06-1949 L1950 **FM** *020 †05
SHAPPLEY, Wm Vance, Jr. 7705 POPLAR AVE, STE 310B 38138 #047-06-1966 L1967 **U** *020 †95
SHEIKH, Ghazanfar Ali. ■ 38138 #704-01-1970 L1977 **PD** *020 †55
SHELTON, Thomas Berkeley. 1325 WOLF PARK DR, STE 102 38138 #047-06-1981 L1982 **U** *020 †95
SHEPHARD, Claudette Jones. 7945 WOLF RIVER BLVD 38138 #005-12-1987 L1991 **OBG** *020 †30
SHIRWANY, Uzma Khanum. 1771 DICKENS CV 38139 #704-04-1995 L2002 **IM** *020 †20
SHURLEY, William Robt, III. 1900 EXETER RD, STE 210 38138 #027-01-1978 L1983 **AN EM** *020 †05
SIEGEL, Jerome Seymour. 7715 WOLF RIVER BLVD 38138 #047-06-1961 L1961 **CD IM** *020 †20 ‡
SINGH, Rajeev. ■ 38139 #913-18-1994 L2006 **EM** *020 †18
SLEDGE, James Mark. 7945 WOLF RIVER BLVD, STE 290 38138 #422-01-1997 L2003 **PS** *020 †85
SMITH, Kirby Lee. 8000 WOLF RIVER BLVD, STE 100 38138 #047-06-1964 L1965 **ON HEM** *020
SMITH, Matthew C. ■ 38139 #047-06-2002 L2003 *100
SMITH, W Chapman. 7945 WOLF RIVER BLVD 38138 #045-01-1969 L1973 **DR** *020 †80
SNIDER, Charles Van. 7705 POPLAR AVE 38138 #004-01-1962 L1966 **PD PSM** *020 †55
SOKOLOFF, Bret Robert. 7655 POPLAR AVE, STE 250 38138 #041-02-1996 L2001 **ORS** *020 †40 ‡
SPENCE, David Daniel. ■ 38139 #047-06-2006 **ORS** *012
SPIERS, Kathleen D. 7945 WOLF RIVER BLVD, STE 300 38138 #047-06-1988 L1991 **ON** *020 †20
SPIOTTA, Larry Brooks. 8060 WOLF RIVER BLVD 38138 #047-06-1973 L1974 **CD IM** *020 †20
SRINIVASAN, Ashok. ■ 38138 #495-45-1985 L1993 **PDI** *012 †55
STEPHENS, Raj K. 1900 EXETER RD, STE 210 38138 #495-42-1974 L1981 **AN** *020 †05
STERN, Bradley Jonathan. 7705 POPLAR AVE, STE 220 38138 #047-06-1997 L1998 **OBG** *020
STEWART, David G. 7460 WOLF RIVER BLVD, STE 101 38138 #047-06-1984 L1990 **CD IM** *020 †20

■ = Address Information Privacy Protected

STINSON, William David. 7705 POPLAR AVE, ALLIANCE PC 38138 #047-06-1994 L1998 **OBG** *020 †30
STOCKS, Rosemary Sutton. 7945 WOLF RIVER BLVD 38138 #036-08-1988 L1993 **OTO** *020 †45
STOCKSTILL, Todd F. 1381 S GERMANTOWN RD 38138 #051-04-1986 L1995 **RO** *020 †80
STOVALL, Thomas Gregory. 7800 WOLF TRAIL CV, WOMEN'S HEALTH SPECIALISTS 38138 #047-06-1983 L1983 **GYN OBS** *020 †30
STROINIGG, Nora. ■ 38138 #038-43-2008 *012
STROM, Ted Stephen. ■ 38138 #016-02-1988 L1998 **PTH** *020 †50
STUBBLEFIELD, Calvin F. ■ 38138 #051-01-1948 L1962 **IM** *071
SULLIVANT, Henry Paul. 7705 POPLAR AVE, STE 330 38138 #027-01-1979 L1983 **OBG** *020 †30
SUMMITT, Margaret Zavada. 7800 WOLF TRAIL CV, WOMEN'S HEALTH SPECIALISTS 38138 #047-06-1986 L1989 **OBG GS** *020 †30
SUMMITT, Robt Layman, Jr. 7800 WOLF TRAIL CV 38138 #047-06-1983 L1984 **OBG U** *020 †30
SWEENEY, Mary Peg. 2726 FOX HILL CIR E 38139 #010-02-1987 L1992 **PD** *020 †55
SZATKOWSKI, Arie. 8000 WOLF RIVER BLVD, STERN CARDIOVASCULAR CENTE 38138 #035-20-1997 L2003 **CD** *020 †20
TAYLOR, Herbert A, III. 7705 POPLAR AVE 38138 #047-06-1963 L1963 **OBG** *020 †30
TAYLOR, Martha Neumann. 7690 WOLF RIVER CIR 38138 #047-06-1982 L1983 **IM** *020 †20
TEMPLETON, Terry Paul. 2120 EXETER RD STE 210 38138 #047-06-1973 L1973 **OTO A** *020 †45
THOMAS, James. ■ 38138 #047-06-2008 *012
THOMPSON, Barry Franklin. 2326 WICKERSHAM CV 38139 #005-06-1978 L1983 **N** *071 †75
THOMPSON, Bryan Francis. 8000 WOLF RIVER BLVD, STE 200 38138 #001-06-1998 L2003 **GE** *020 †20
THOMPSON, Natascha Stone. 7945 WOLF RIVER BLVD 38138 #047-06-1998 L2000 **MPD** *020 †55,20
THOMPSON, Paul Andrew. 8040 WOLF RIVER BLVD, STE 200 38138 #047-06-1960 L1961 **IM** *020
TICHY, Jill Rene. ■ 38138 #047-06-2007 **IM** *012
TODD, Danielle Marie. ■ 38139 #047-06-2006 **P** *012
TODD, Tanja Lu House. 7516 CAPITAL DR 38138 #047-06-1979 L1979 **OBG** *020 †30
TOWNE, Thomas Carter. 8000 WOLF RIVER BLVD, STE 200 38138 #047-06-1977 L1977 **GE IM** *020 †20
TOWNSEND, Arthur M, III. ■ 38138 #010-03-1962 L1973 **OBG** *071
TOWNSEND, Arthur M, IV. 7655 POPLAR AVE STE 140, ASSOC OB/GYN PC 38138 #030-05-1990 L1994 **OBG** *020 †30
TSUJI, Soichi. 7840 GROVE CT W, APT 204 38138 #572-31-1992 L2007 *100
TURNER, Jan Lewis. 8060 WOLF RIVER BLVD 38138 #020-02-1971 L1978 **CD IM** *071 †20
TYEHIMBA, Arthur. 7655 POPLAR AVE 38138 #033-06-1980 L2001 **OTO GS** *020
UPSHAW, Jefferson Davis. 8000 WOLF RIVER BLVD, STE 100 38138 #023-07-1954 L1961 **HEM IM** *071 †20
VASIREDDY, Sailendra. 7945 WOLF RIVER BLVD # 300 38138 #496-21-1999 L2006 **HO** *020 ‡
VINCENT, John Robt. 8573 CORDES CIR 38139 #016-06-1954 L1955 **AM HS** *020 †65
VOGT, Val Y. 7800 WOLF TRAIL CV, WOMEN'S HEALTH SPECIALISTS 38138 #016-01-1990 L1997 **OBG** *020 †30
WAGGONER, Stephen Michael. 7655 POPLAR AVE, STE 250 38138 #047-20-1989 L1994 **ORS OSS** *020 †40
WAGH, Ajay Arun. ■ 38138 #047-06-2007 L2007 **IM** *012
WAKE, Robert Wm. 7945 WOLF RIVER BLVD, STE 350 38138 #047-06-1985 L1986 **U** *020 †95
WALDRUP, Phillip Dewayne. 1374 CORDOVA CV, STE 102 38138 #047-06-1995 L1996 **IM** *020 †20
WALL, Barry Michael. ■ 38138 #047-06-1980 L1981 **NEP IM** *030 †20
WALLACE, Robert Doyle. 7945 WOLF RIVER BLVD 38138 #041-02-1984 L1996 **PS CFS** *020 †45,65
WALSH, John Thos. 1900 EXETER RD, STE 210 38138 #047-06-1982 L1986 **AN** *020 †05
WARNER, William C, Jr. 1400 S GERMANTOWN RD 38138 #021-01-1983 L1989 **ORS OP** *020 †40
WARR, Alston Graham. 7715 WOLF RIVER BLVD 38138 #047-06-1993 L1995 **MPD** *020 †55,20
WEATHERALL, Jeffrey S. 1900 EXETER RD, STE 210 38138 #047-06-1999 L2001 **AN** *100 †05 ‡
WEBB, Roderick C, Jr. 7294 MONT BLANC DR 38138 #047-06-1972 L1974 **DR** *020 †80
WEBBER, Ben Porter. 1900 EXETER RD, STE 210 38138 #047-06-1971 L1972 **AN** *020 †05
WEEMS, Thomas Doyle. 1365 S GERMANTOWN RD 38138 #047-06-1963 L1964 **NS** *020 †25
WEIR, Alva Bowen, Jr. ■ 38138 #047-06-1945 L1946 **IM** *071 †20
WEIR, Alva Bowen, III. 7820 WALKING HORSE CIR 38138 #047-06-1975 L1975 **HEM ON** *020 †20
WEISS, Steven Jay. 1900 EXETER RD, STE 210 38138 #011-02-1983 L1999 **AN** *020 †05
WENER, Steven Irvin. 8040 WOLF RIVER BLVD, STE 200 38138 #047-06-1997 L2000 **IM** *020 †20
WENNEMARK, James R. ■ 38139 #018-03-1953 L1966 **NM IM** *071 †28
WETZEL, Glenn T. 7945 WOLF RIVER BLVD 38138 #005-18-1985 L2004 **PDC PD** *020 †55
WHITEHEAD, Peter Yates. 7705 POPLAR AVE 38138 #027-01-1988 L2004 **PD** *020 †55
WHITEHEAD, William Jerry. 1900 KIRBY PKWY, STE 201 38138 #047-06-1959 L1970 **D** *020 †15
WHITTEN, A Elizabeth. 1900 EXETER RD, STE 210 38138 #187-01-1977 L1998 **AN** *020 †05
WILDER, William Wiggins. ■ 38138 #047-06-1946 L1947 **OPH** *071 †35
WILLIAMS, Keith Dawson. 1400 S GERMANTOWN RD 38138 #048-12-1986 L1991 **OSS ORS** *020 †40
WOMACK, Catherine R. 7945 WOLF RIVER BLVD 38138 #047-06-1995 L1998 **IM** *020 †20
WOOD, Thomas Oval. 7945 WOLF RIVER BLVD, STE 240 38138 #047-06-1965 L1965 **OPH** *020 †35
WRIGHT, Becky Buckley. 1900 EXETER RD, STE 210 38138 #047-06-1987 L1992 **AN** *020 †05
WRIGHT, Dana John. 8040 WOLF RIVER BLVD, STE 200 38138 #001-02-1975 L1979 **IM** *020
WRUBLE, Gary Allan. 8000 WOLF RIVER BLVD, STE 200 38138 #047-06-1990 L1995 **GE** *020 †20
YALAMANCHILI, Ramesh. ■ 38138 #305-01-2001 L2005 **IM** *100
YUKON, Charles Laurence. 1355 W BRIERBROOK RD 38138 #047-06-1992 L1995 **PD** *020 †55
YUKON, Gordon. 1355 W BRIERBROOK RD 38138 #047-06-1971 L1974 **PD** *020
YUNUS, Furhan. 7945 WOLF RIVER BLVD, STE 300 38138 #704-01-1985 L1995 **HO IM** *020 †20
ZAMAN, Khaleda. ■ 38139 #160-02-1980 L1991 **IM** *020
ZHANG, Yanlong. ■ 38139 #243-47-1987 L2004 **DMP** *020 †50

GOODLETTSVILLE – DAVIDSON

ADETUNJI, Felix Dapo. 815 WREN RD, BEHAVIORAL HEALTH CENTER 37072 #306-01-1993 L2000 **P** *020 †75
ALARCON, John Jos. 3024 BUSINESS PARK CIR 37072 #012-01-1986 L1991 **RNR PDR** *020 †80
ANDERSON, M Anne F. 450 PROFESSIONAL PARK DR 37072 #047-05-1996 L1999 **OBG** *020
AREVALOS, Enrique Romo. 3024 BUSINESS PARK CIR 37072 #048-12-1980 L1992 **DR GS** *020 †80
ATHAR, Zillur Rahman. 803 MEADOWLARK LN 37072 #704-03-1959 L1972 **P** *020
BAITES, John Edwin, Jr. 740 CONFERENCE DR, P O BOX 710 37072 #001-02-1976 L1982 **FM** *020 †18
BLOUNT, Steven Michael. 3024 BUSINESS PARK CIR 37072 #047-20-1989 L1991 **DR** *020 †80
BOSKIND, Cynthia Louanne. 740 CONFERENCE DR, P O BOX 710 37072 #005-12-1998 L2000 **FM** *020 †18
BOTSKO, James John. 740 CONFERENCE DR 37072 #038-40-1986 L2003 **FM** *020 †18
BROWN, Pamela Elaine. ■ 37072 #047-07-1982 L1982 **IM** *071
BURCHAM, Robert Stanley. 3024 BUSINESS PARK CIR 37072 #012-01-2000 L2003 **DR** *100 †80
BUSH, Steven Brian. 3024 BUSINESS PARK CIR 37072 #047-06-1991 L1993 **DR** *020 †80
CALENDINE, Chad Logan. 3024 BUSINESS PARK CIR 37072 #047-06-1998 L2004 **DR** *020 †80
CIAN, Michael Curtis. 3024 BUSINESS PARK CIR 37072 #035-09-1996 L1998 **DR** *020 †80
CLAUDEL, Christopher Drew. 201 BLUEBIRD DR, RIVERGATE DERMOTOLOGY 37072 #021-06-1994 L1999 **D DS** *020 †15
COUDEN, Michael Robert. 3024 BUSINESS PARK CIR 37072 #047-06-1996 L2002 **DR** *020 †80
COWDEN, Robert Wilson, Jr. 3050 BUSINESS PARK CIR, STE 101 37072 #001-02-1974 L1980 **OTO PS** *020 †45
CUNNEELY, Kevin P. 3024 BUSINESS PARK CIR, ADVANCED DIAGNOSTIC IMAG 37072 #048-13-2001 L2007 **DR** *100 †80
DARWIN, Brett Wayne. 740 CONFERENCE DR 37072 #001-06-1986 L1987 **IM** *020 †20
EIDSON, Timothy H. 807 MEADOWLARK LN 37072 #047-06-1996 L2000 **PD** *020 †55
EL-ALAYLI, Hani. 3024 BUSINESS PARK CIR, ANESTHESIA SERVICE ASSOCIA 37072 #915-04-1987 L2001 **AN** *020 †05
ELLIS, Michael Conrad. 3024 BUSINESS PARK CIR 37072 #048-12-1978 L1978 **DR NM** *020 †80,28
ENAYAT, Samim. ■ 37072 #047-06-2008 *012
FAKHRUDDIN, A K M. 803 MEADOWLARK LN 37072 #704-03-1959 L1972 **P** *020 †75
FINLAY, Christopher Lewis. 900 CONFERENCE DR, COVENANT FAMILY PRACTICE 37072 #062-01-1995 L2003 **FM** *020
FONTENOT, Nigel Mark. 103 BRAXTON PARK CT 37072 #047-06-1988 L1990 **IM** *020
FRIDAY, Jack Michael. 3024 BUSINESS PARK CIR 37072 #036-01-1988 L1994 **DR** *020 †80
GORDON, Jonathan Paul. 3024 BUSINESS PARK CIR 37072 #051-04-2000 L2007 **RNR** *020 †80
HAMMERMAN, Stephen L. 601 S MAIN ST 37072 #067-01-1969 L1991 **FM OBG** *020 †18
HARDING, James Steven. ■ 37072 #020-02-1980 L1991 **AN** *072 †05
HARNEY, Iantha Lucille. 3024 BUSINESS PARK CIR 37072 #039-01-2000 L2006 **DR** *020 †80
HASTIE, James Sutton. ■ 37072 #016-11-1959 L1962 **FM** *071 †18
HILL, Warren Thos. 500A LONG HOLLOW PIKE, DIAGNOSTIC 37072 #047-06-1960 L1961 **EM GP** *020
HILL, William Harold. PO BOX 249 37070 #045-01-1958 L1964 **DR NM** *020 †80
HIMMELFARB, Elliot Harvey. 3024 BUSINESS PARK CIR 37072 #035-08-1966 L1973 **DR** *020 †80
HOUNTRAS, Dean Michael. 3024 BUSINESS PARK CIR, PHYDATA, LLC 37072 #025-12-1987 L2005 **DR** *020 †80
HUDA, Shahana. 815 WREN RD, RIVERGATE PSYCH CTR 37072 #160-04-1983 L2006 **P** *020
HUGGETT, Jeffrey Michael. 3024 BUSINESS PARK CIR 37072 #025-07-1997 L2003 **DR** *020 †80
HUMPHREY, Stephen Paul. 3024 BUSINESS PARK CIR 37072 #047-06-1975 L1975 **R EM** *020 †80
JAHAN, Mohammed S. 815 WREN RD 37072 #160-01-1978 L1988 **P GPM** *020 †75
JOHNSON, Anita L. 102 PARK CT 37072 #047-07-1987 L1991 **AN IM** *020 †05
KINKEL, Donald Merrill. 3024 BUSINESS PARK CIR 37072 #056-05-1957 L1980 **AN** *071 †05 ‡
LANZ, Elwin C. ■ 37072 #005-12-1953 L1968 **OPH** *071 †35
LEVITT, Michael J. 3024 BUSINESS PARK CIR 37072 #012-05-1977 L1982 **DR** *020 †80
LIM, Robert T, Jr. 900 CONFERENCE DR, COVENANT FAMILY PRACTICE 37072 #748-11-1987 L1998 **FM** *020 †18
LODEN, James Carlton. 907 RIVERGATE PKWY, STE C2020 37072 #047-06-1992 L1995 **OPH** *020 †35
LUBOW, Lawrence D. 3024 BUSINESS PARK CIR 37072 #035-06-1971 L1979 **DR NM** *020 †80
MACCURDY, Joe Milton, Jr. 3024 BUSINESS PARK CIR 37072 #021-05-1990 L1996 **VIR** *020 †80
MAZZELLA, John Louis. 3024 BUSINESS PARK CIR 37072 #055-01-1997 L2005 **RNR** *020 †80
METZMAN, Michael Scott. 3024 BUSINESS PARK CIR 37072 #041-09-1982 L1991 **DR** *020 †80
MILLER, Ted Jonathan. 740 CONFERENCE DR, P O BOX 710 37072 #047-05-1982 L1986 **FM** *020 †18
MILLER, Thomas Buford. 500A LONG HOLLOW PIKE 37072 #047-06-1971 L1972 **IM** *020 †20
NAU, Paul Christopher. 3024 BUSINESS PARK CIR 37072 #020-02-1980 L1988 **DR NM** *020 †80
PEARSON, Robin Sorrow. 807 MEADOWLARK LN 37072 #047-06-1991 L1994 **PD** *020 †55
PIERCE, Elizabeth Payne. 313B BLUEBIRD DR 37072 #051-04-1978 L1979 **PD** *020 †55
RYU, Chi Yol. 500 PROFESSIONAL PARK DR 37072 #583-02-1958 L1977 **DR** *071 †80
SETLER LOGAN, Nona Marie. 861 LORETTA DR 37072 #047-07-1984 L2000 **FM** *020 †18
SHARMA, Vineet. 3024 BUSINESS PARK CIR 37072 #047-06-2000 L2006 **DR** *100 †80
SHAW, Alfred Eddie. 210 CIMA DR, AGAPEE SURGICAL ASSOCIATES 37072 #610-01-1980 L1989 **GS** *020 †85
SOBLE, Marc Gregory. 3024 BUSINESS PARK CIR 37072 #010-02-1985 L2002 **DR** *020 †80
SPELLMAN, Michael James. 3024 BUSINESS PARK CIR 37072 #028-34-1994 L2003 **RNR** *020 †80
THEKKERUMBIL, Vijaya R. ■ 37072 #495-09-1973 L2001 **IM** *020
THOMPSON, Julia. 807 MEADOWLARK LN 37072 #039-01-1981 L1984 **PD** *020 †55
THOMPSON, Keith Shannon. 807 MEADOWLARK LN 37072 #047-06-1994 L1997 **PD** *020 †55
THORSTAD, Brett Lee. 3024 BUSINESS PARK CIR 37072 #001-02-1986 L1993 **RNR** *020 †80
TUMBLETY, Joseph P. ■ 37072 #035-09-1953 L1985 **R OS** *075 †80
UDDIN, Azeza Bano. ■ 37072 #047-07-2005 L2007 **P** *012
WATTS, David Reed. 3024 BUSINESS PARK CIR 37072 #047-06-1978 L1986 **DR** *020 †80
WHITE, Joan Weber. 807 MEADOWLARK LN 37072 #051-04-1986 L1988 **PD** *020 †55
WILSON, Robert Alan. 900 CONFERENCE DR, COVENANT FAMILY PRACTICE 37072 #017-20-2000 L2003 **FM** *020 †18 ‡
WUNDER, Daniel Jay. 3024 BUSINESS PARK CIR 37072 #046-01-1990 L1992 **VIR** *020 †80
YABUT, Edmond P. 200 BUFFALO RUN 37072 #748-02-1990 L1995 **MPD** *020 †55,20

GORDONSVILLE – SMITH

HILL, Keith Regen. ■ 38563 #665-01-2000 L2003 **FM** *020 †18 ‡

■ = Address Information Privacy Protected

MOSS, Angela Sue. 126 JMZ DR, GORDONSVILLE CLNC 38563 #047-20-1999 L2001
FM EM *020 †18

GRAND JUNCTION – HARDEMAN

EDWARDS, Nicholas Henry. ■ 38039 #047-06-1956 L1956 FM AN *072

GRAY – WASHINGTON

BOGGS, Bruce Daniel. 203 GRAY COMMONS CIR 37615 #047-20-2003 L2004 FM *020 †18
CLARK, Guy Delano. ■ 37615 #047-20-1988 L1989 IM *020
COATES, Griffin Ray. 1210 OLDE OAKS DR 37615 #047-06-1981 L1982 TS *020 †85,90
COMBS, Stephen Paul. 2103 FOREST DR 37615 #047-20-1992 L1995 PD CCP *020 †55 ‡
GARITANO, William Warren. ■ 37615 #869-01-1963 L1969 CHP P *071 †75
KIRK, Kevin Patrick. 405 ROY MARTIN RD, STE 104 37615 #036-07-1994 L2006 IM *020 †20
LANDESS, Christopher A. 143 SUN CHASE CT 37615 #047-20-1998 L1999 GS *020 †18
LIVESAY, Tommy Dale. ■ 37615 #047-20-2008 *012
MERRILL, Jeffrey Ronald. 203 GRAY COMMONS CIR, FIRST ASSIST URGENT CARE 37615
#051-04-1988 L1998 FM FSM *020 †18
PALMER, Elizabeth Brezina. ■ 37615 #047-20-2008 *012
PROCTER, Carol. 114 KING DR 37615 #047-20-2000 L2002 IM *100
SHILLING, Kimberly Lynn. ■ 37615 #048-02-2006 GS *012
SMITH, Jeanne Lynne. ■ 37615 #047-20-2005 P *012
WALLEN, Ellen B. ■ 37615 #047-20-1989 L1989 FOP *020 †50 ‡

GREENBACK – LOUDON

BENNE, Michael Geo, Jr. ■ 37742 #017-20-1964 L2000 EM *020 †16
DEEAN, Ibeyaima D. ■ 37742 #495-37-1972 L1987 P *020

GREENBRIER – ROBERTSON

FLORENDO, Randy Estacion. 2354 HIGHWAY 41 S 37073 #748-01-1983 L1999
MPD PD *020 †20,55
LEWIS, William Michael. 2557 HIGHWAY 41 S 37073 #047-06-1973 L1974 FM *020 †18
SIMMONS, Alan Joseph. ■ 37073 #020-02-2007 AN *012
SPARKS, David Parker. 2557 HIGHWAY 41 S 37073 #047-20-1988 L1988 FM *020 †18

GREENEVILLE – GREENE

AASHEIM, Richard John. 438 E VANN RD, MEDICAL GROUP OF 37743 #005-12-1973 L1976
FM *020 †18
ADAMS, Phillip Steven. 229 N IRISH ST 37745 #047-06-1975 L1975 GP *020
AHMED, Munir. PO BOX 910, GREEN VALLEY DEVELOPMENTAL 37744 #160-02-1982 L1996
IM *020 †20
AIKEN, Marc Alan. 1406 TUSCULUM BLVD, STE 1000 37745 #027-01-1983 L1988 ORS *020 †40
ASHE, Walter Dee. 221 N MAIN ST 37745 #047-06-1971 L1972 PD *020 †55
ASPLEY, Donald Bruce. 1744 E ANDREW JOHNSON HWY 37745 #020-02-1961 L1969
OM FM *030
AUSTIN, Joseph Wm. 803 E CHURCH ST, MEDICINE 37745 #047-06-1975 L1976 IM *020 †20
AUSTIN, Maynard Wade. 803 E CHURCH ST, MEDICINE 37745 #047-06-1967 L1969 IM *020 †20
BAKSHI, Mandeep Singh. 1404 TUSCULUM BLVD, STE 2200 37745 #495-03-1989 L2004
PUD *100 †20
BARNES, Lloyd Rogers. 1410 TUSCULUM BLVD # 1800 37745 #047-06-1971 L1972
OBG *020 †30
BARTON, Deborah Daye. 438 E VANN RD STE 100 37743 #047-06-1980 L1981 PM LM *020 †60
BECKNER, Thos Folsom, III. 803 E CHURCH ST, MEDICINE 37745 #047-06-1971 L1972
IM IMG *020 †20
BERRY, Robert Street. 1231 TUSCULUM BLVD 37745 #036-01-1989 L1996 EM IM *020 †20
BONFARDIN, Brian Robert. 616 E CHURCH ST, STE A 37745 #047-20-1990 L1991 P *020 †75
BOYS, John Carlton. 1420 TUSCULUM BLVD 37745 #045-01-1982 L1993 RO PLM *020 †80
BRECKENRIDGE, Rufus G. 109 E CHURCH ST 37745 #012-01-1984 L1992 FM *020 †18
BRIDGES, William Robt. 438 E VANN RD, MEDICAL GROUP OF 37743 #005-12-1988 L1994
GS VS *020 †85
BROCK, Julian S. ■ 37745 #036-07-1951 L1952 R *071
BROWN, Thomas Lloyd. 801 E CHURCH ST 37745 #047-06-1998 L2001 OPH *020 †35
CARTER, Jason Bryant. 1404 TUSCULUM BLVD, STE 2000 37745 #047-20-1997 L2006
U *020 †95
CHANG, Ann Celine. 1420 TUSCULUM BLVD, LAUGHLIN HOSPITAL (ER) 37745
#047-20-1995 L1996 IM *020 †20
CHAPMAN, Walter Clay, Jr. 1012 COOLIDGE ST 37743 #051-01-1965 L1972 ORS OS *020 †40
CLEMENS, Elizabeth Anna. 1420 TUSCULUM BLVD, LAUGHLIN MEM HOSP 37745
#047-20-1989 L1991 EM IM *020 †20
COBBLE, Douglas Catron. 221 N MAIN ST 37745 #047-06-1973 L1974 PD PSM *020 †55
COLE, Ronald Arthur. 895 E ANDREW JOHNSON HWY 37745 #047-06-1974 L1974
FM IMG *020
DAUERTY, Charles V R. ■ 37743 #041-02-1953 AN EM *071 †05
DE TROYE, Robert John. 1406 TUSCULUM BLVD, STE 1000 37745 #056-05-1986 L1992
ORS *020 †40
DIEBOLD, William Casper. 401 TAKOMA AVE, TAKOMA BEHAVIORAL HLTH 37743
#020-02-1991 L1995 P *020 †75
DIEZ D'AUX, Robert. 228 N MAIN ST, GREENEVILLE 37745 #067-01-1973 L1983
FM OM *020 †18
DUNCAN, Richard White. 1406 TUSCULUM BLVD, STE 1000 37745 #027-01-1988 L1994
OSS ORS *020 †40
DYER, Crystal Shanelle. ■ 37743 #047-20-2006 L2007 FP *012
EASTERLY, James F, Jr. ■ 37745 #047-06-1966 L1971 R *071 †80
ELLENBURG, Luke L. ■ 37745 #047-05-1941 L1941 GP PD *071 †55
ELLENBURG, Luke Lamar, Jr. 801 E CHURCH ST 37745 #047-05-1975 L1977 OPH *020 †35
FILKA, Marianne E. 401 TAKOMA AVE 37743 #036-05-1984 L1987 FM *020 †18
FLEISHER, Joel Barry. ■ 37743 #011-02-1965 L1993 GS *071 †85

FLOHR, Robert Stephen. 1410 TUSCULUM BLVD, STE 1700 37745 #047-06-1971 L1972
GS *020 †85
FOWLER, Todd Alan. 1406 TUSCULUM BLVD, STE 1000 37745 #048-13-1989 L1993
FSM *020 †18
FREEMAN, John Leon, Jr. 1012 COOLIDGE ST 37743 #021-01-1970 L1980 ORS *020 †40
GILES, Stanley Allen. 428 E VANN RD 37743 #005-12-1966 L1980 PD *020 †55
GRANT, Joseph Durham. 1406 TUSCULUM BLVD, STE 1000 37745 #048-14-1979 L2000
ORS EM *020 †40 ‡
HARTSELL, Michael H. 314 TUSCULUM BLVD, GREENEVILLE FAM PRACTICE 37745
#047-06-1978 L1980 FM *020 †18 ‡
HAWTHORNE, Jo Lynn. 1021 COOLIDGE ST 37743 #012-01-1987 L1991 OBG *020 †30
HENARD, Donald Claude. 1420 TUSCULUM BLVD 37745 #047-06-1966 L1966
ORS HS *071 †40
HENSON, Donald L, Jr. 401 HOLSTON DR 37743 #036-08-1988 L1991 P *020 †75
HILL, Clint Patrick. 1406 TUSCULUM BLVD, STE 1000 37745 #047-20-2001 L2006 ORS *100
HOLLADAY, Connie J. PO BOX 1030 37744 #047-06-1983 L1984 IMG *020 †20
HOPPE, Gordon Paul. 1021 COOLIDGE ST 37743 #005-12-1966 L1972 FM *071 †18
HORNER, Nathan P. 109 E CHURCH ST 37745 #047-06-1942 L1942 GP *071
JAFFE, Michael Scott. 401 TAKOMA AVE 37743 #047-15-1993 L1999 EM *020 †18
KEEBLER, Ben Jennings. 906 TUSCULUM BLVD 37745 #047-06-1954 L1954 GP *071
KOHNE, Raymond Ernest. ■ 37743 #005-12-1992 L1997 VIR *020 †80
KRETCHMAR, Arthur L. ■ 37743 #025-07-1947 FM *100
LOCKLEAR, Robert Wayne, Sr. 438 E VANN RD, MEDICAL GROUP OF 37743
#036-07-1998 L2002 IM *020 †20
MARCELO, Bernardino D. 580 VAN HILL RD, BAILEYTON MEDICAL CENTER 37745
#748-07-1955 L1987 FM EM *071
MARINO, Philip A. 1113 TUSCULUM BLVD, # 394 37745 #036-07-1983 L1996 DR VIR *020 †80
MARSA, Gordon Lee. 438 E VANN RD, MEDICAL GROUP OF 37743 #836-02-1964 L1980
GE IM *020 †20
MARTY, Aurora Trivino. 1508 VALIANT DR 37744 #748-01-1964 L1983 PD *020
MASON, Walter Lawrence. 801 E MCKEE ST, LAUGHLIN HEALTH CARE CTR 37743
#047-06-1957 L1957 GS *020 †85
MATHIESEN, K Marlin. 4850 E ANDREW JOHNSON HWY, GREENE VALLEY
DEVELOPMENT 37745 #005-12-1964 L1974 PUD IM *020 †20
MC CORD, Elizabeth Couch. 895 E ANDREW JOHNSON HWY 37745 #051-04-1988 L1996
FM *020 †18
MC CRORY, Allison Lee. 1410 TUSCULUM BLVD, STE 2500 37745 #021-05-1999 L2004
OTO *020 †45
MC KINNEY, James Ray. 438 E VANN RD, MEDICAL GROUP OF 37743 #005-12-1959 L1960
GP GS *020 †18
MC QUAIN, Mark Thos. 1406 TUSCULUM BLVD, STE 1000 37745 #038-40-1986 L1992
PM *030 †60
MCRAE, Karen Jane. 1406 TUSCULUM BLVD, STE 1000 37745 #047-06-1991 L1997
ORS *020 †40
MENZ, Michael Jos. 438 E VANN RD, # 301 37743 #051-01-1989 L1994 ORS *020 †40
METCALF, Dee Lamar, III. 1410 TUSCULUM BLVD, STE 2000 37745 #047-06-1969 L1969 R *071
MICHAELS, Robin R. 4850 E ANDREW JOHNSON HWY, CENTER, P O BOX 910 37745
#040-02-1974 L1993 GP PD *020 †55
MORELOCK, Brooks Graham. 1406 TUSCULUM BLVD, MEDICINE ASSOCIATES 37745
#047-20-1996 L1998 IM *020 †20
MORGAN, James P. 401 TAKOMA AVE 37743 #047-20-1998 L1999 FM *020 †18
MYERS, Frederick James. 438 E VANN RD, MEDICAL GROUP OF 37743 #005-12-1969 L1978
GS *020 †85
NASH, Roland Wade. 401 TAKOMA AVE 37743 #047-20-2000 L2001 FM *020 †18
NELSON, Harry Chas, III. 1021 COOLIDGE ST, STE 2 37743 #005-12-1973 L1988 OBG *020 †30
NELSON, Lynda Marlene K. ■ 37743 #005-12-1973 L1988 AN *075 †05
OAKLEY, Jaime Gabriel. 228 N MAIN ST, GREENEVILLE 37745 #047-20-2001 L2003
FM *020 †18
ODELL, Michael James. 438 E VANN RD, MEDICAL GROUP OF 37743 #005-12-1964 L1967
FM *020 †18
PAMILLA, Jeanne Rose. 1410 TUSCULUM BLVD STE 250, LAUGHLIN MEMORIAL
HOSPITAL 37745 #041-07-1968 L1996 ORS OP *020 †40
PATEL, Dharmen J. 1410 TUSCULUM BLVD, STE 2200 37745 #495-76-1990 L2002
IM HO *020 †20
PATTERSON, Mark David. 1410 TUSCULUM BLVD, STE 1700 37745 #047-06-1990 L1992
GS VS *020 †85
PECTOL, Richard W, Jr. 1012 COOLIDGE ST 37743 #047-20-1994 L1999 ORS *020 †40
PERRY, Charles Stephen. 438 E VANN RD, STE 100 37743 #027-01-1983 L2002 PD *020 †55
REARDON, Peter A. 1410 TUSCULUM BLVD 37745 #065-09-1978 L1983 OBG *020 †30
REID, Lawrence Henry. 1404 TUSCULUM BLVD 37745 #047-06-1970 L1971 D *020 †15
REVIERE, Calvin Barton. ■ 37745 #047-06-1953 L1953 DR R *071 †80
REYNOLDS, Drew Howard. ■ 37745 #047-06-2006 GS *012
ROBERTS, Andy Alfred. 109 E CHURCH ST 37745 #047-06-1989 L1995 FM *020 †18
RODGERS, James Steven. 803 E CHURCH ST, MEDICINE 37745 #047-06-1968 L1969
CD IM *020 †20
SAGADRACA, Remy Cadiz. 401 TAKOMA AVE 37743 #005-12-1973 L1990 EM *020 †16
SANDERS, Neal Ray. 228 N MAIN ST 37745 #047-06-1966 L1966 EM FM *071 †55
SCHNELL, Martin N, Jr. 401 TAKOMA AVE, EMERGENCY DEPARTMENT 37743
#036-08-1987 L2002 EM *020 †18
SCOTT, William Jos. 803 E CHURCH ST, MEDICINE 37745 #012-05-1983 L1986 IM *020 †20
SEN, Anindya Kumar. 1406 TUSCULUM BLVD # 2000 37745 #495-45-1972 L1991
ON HEM *020 †20
SHAW, John Louis. 438 E VANN RD, MEDICAL GROUP OF 37743 #005-12-1964 L1965
FM *020 †18
SMALL, Karin Leanne. 1021 COOLIDGE ST STE 2 37743 #025-07-2002 L2006 OBG *020
SMEAD, William J. 801 E CHURCH ST 37745 #004-01-1970 L1978 OPH *020 †35
SMITH, Elliott Benj. 1406 TUSCULUM BLVD, STE 2003 37745 #047-20-1983 L1984
IM *020 †20 ‡
SOUTHERLAND, Crystal Mae. 343 VIKING PL 37745 #047-20-1996 L1997 IM *071
STEWART, Gregory Lee. 1406 TUSCULUM BLVD, STE 1000 37745 #047-05-1998 L2003
ORS *020 †40
STONE, Coy Barton. 109 E CHURCH ST 37745 #047-06-1978 L1981 AM *020 †18
STRANGE, Ernest B. 701 PROFESSIONAL PLAZA DR 37745 #047-06-1976 L1977 FM *020 †18
STRIMER, Robt Merrill, Jr. 1410 TUSCULUM BLVD, STE 1000 37745 #038-06-1969 L1976
U *071 †95
SULLIVAN, Timothy J, Jr. 122 VILLAGE DR, BEHAVRL HLTH OF GREENVLE 37745
#308-03-1983 L1987 P PTH *020 ‡

■ = Address Information Privacy Protected

SUSONG, Kenneth Clark. 110 SPENCER ST 37745 #047-06-1959 L1960 **GP** *020

SVENDSEN, Claes Ulvar. 438 E VANN RD, MEDICAL GROUP OF 37743 #005-12-1997 L2000
FM *020 †18

SWARNER, Orville Ward, Jr. ■ 37743 #005-12-1965 L1966 **PD NPM** *050 †55

SWENSON, James Alan. 1410 TUSCULUM BLVD, STE 1200 37745 #028-34-1984 L1995
GE IM *020 †20

THACKER, William Carl. 1420 TUSCULUM BLVD 37745 #047-06-1961 L1961 **PTH** *071 †50

THOMAS, Robert Donald. 401 TAKOMA AVE 37743 #836-02-1985 L1999 **DR** *020 †80

THWING, Philip Tolleson. 400 Y ST, PHILIP THWING MD 37745 #036-01-1988 L1995
FM *020 †18

TIMMS, G Douglass. 11045 NEWPORT HWY 37743 #005-12-1960 L1999 **AN** *020

TOPPENBERG, Kevin Scott. 1410 TUSCULUM BLVD, STE 2600 37745 #005-12-1994 L1998
FM *020 †18

TOPPENBERG, Marcia Dee. 1410 TUSCULUM BLVD, STE 2600 37745 #005-12-1994 L1998
FM *020 †18

TUROFF, Jonathan Andrew. 1410 TUSCULUM BLVD, STE 2800 37745 #035-09-1995 L2006
N *020 †75

URBAN, Laura Leigh. 801 E CHURCH ST 37745 #047-20-1994 L1999 **OPH** *020 †35 ‡

VINES, Gregory Franklin. 401 TAKOMA AVE 37743 #047-20-2002 L2004 **FM** *100 †18

VINSANT, George O'Neal. 1406 TUSCULUM BLVD, STE 2001 37745 #047-06-1983 L1987
TRS GS *020 †85

WEBSTER, Thomas Moore. 223 N MAIN ST 37745 #010-01-1964 L1975 **ORS** *020 †40

WOODS, Sonja Bryan. 314 TUSCULUM BLVD, PRACTICE ASSOCIATES 37745
#047-20-2000 L2003 **FM** *020 †18 ‡

YEARWOOD, Kenneth Deaver. PO BOX 910 37744 #047-06-1966 L1970 **GP PD** *020

ZOOK, Kimi Hmar. 1021 COOLIDGE ST 37743 #495-27-1991 L2001 **IM** *020 †20

GREENFIELD — WEAKLEY

EDWARDS-DAVIDSON, Lesa K. 230 N FRONT ST 38230 #047-06-1987 L1989 **FM** *020 †18

SMITH, O K, Jr. 801 S MERIDIAN ST 38230 #047-06-1963 L1964 **GP** *020

HALLS — LAUDERDALE

ROBBINS, Billy Gerald. 201 S FRONT ST, MEDSOUTH HEALTHCARE, PC 38040
#047-06-1969 L1970 **FM** *020 †18

SRIVASTAVA, Pankaj. 104 E MAIN ST 38040 #495-36-1997 L2001 **IM CD** *020 †20

TUCKER, William Henry. 201 S FRONT ST 38040 #047-06-1960 L1961 **FM** *020 †18

HAMPTON — CARTER

BOWIE, Richard Roy. 437 HIGHWAY 321 37658 #051-04-1972 L1984 **GS GP** *020 †85

CARAVELLO, Peter Michael. 437 HIGHWAY 321 37658 #041-02-1971 L1981 **IM CD** *020 †20

GALLAHER, Richard G. 437 HIGHWAY 321 37658 #047-06-1976 L1977 **PD** *020 †55

HOPLAND, Arnold Orvin. 437 HIGHWAY 321 37658 #056-05-1979 L1980 **GP** *020

HOPLAND, Jeffrey Arnold. 437 HIGHWAY 321 37658 #047-20-1995 L1996 **FM** *020 †18

HOPLAND, Kenneth Marvin. 437 HIGHWAY 321 37658 #047-20-2002 L2003 **FM** *020 †18

KUMAR, Pullatikurthi L. 437 HIGHWAY 321 37658 #495-11-1964 L1993 **PD** *020

MAY, Scott Edmond. 437 HIGHWAY 321 37658 #047-06-1983 L1984 **OBG** *020 †30

HARRIMAN — ROANE

ABO-AUDA, Wael Saleem. 525 DEVONIA ST STE B, EAST TENNESSEE HEART CONSU 37748
#495-37-1996 L2002 **CD** *020 †20

AHLER, Albert Julian. 412 DEVONIA ST 37748 #047-06-1958 L1959 **R NR** *071

BARRY, Frederick J. 525 DEVONIA ST, STE A 37748 #038-40-1968 L1976 **CD IM** *071 †20

BELITZ, John Conard, IV. 408 N ROANE ST, STE 100 37748 #047-06-2002 L2005
MPD *020,55

BENNETT, William Earl. 415 DEVONIA ST 37748 #011-03-1978 L1981 **IM** *020 †20 ‡

BINGHAM, Terry Marshall. 412 DEVONIA ST 37748 #047-06-1976 L1977 **GS** *020 †85

BOYE, Harry Geo, Jr. 415 DEVONIA ST # 1 37748 #047-06-1979 L1979 **GS** *020

BROWNING, Thomas Anthony. 2497 S ROANE ST, STE 110 37748 #047-06-1985 L1986
OPH *020 †35

DAVIS, Randal Lee. 412 DEVONIA ST 37748 #665-01-2002 L2005 **FM** *020 †18

DENTON, Randy Lee, Jr. 408 N ROANE ST, STE 100 37748 #047-06-1991 L1992
MPD IM *020 †20,55

DODGE, Herbert Shubert. 412 DEVONIA ST 37748 #047-06-1964 L1964 **ORS** *071 †40

FOOTE, Clary P. 2319 S ROANE ST 37748 #064-01-1974 L1979 **GP FM** *020

GORNISIEWICZ, Elzbieta E. 408 N ROANE ST 37748 #759-03-1989 L2002 **CN** *020

HALAMA, James Scott. 525 DEVONIA ST, STE A 37748 #047-20-1991 L1992 **CD** *020 †20

HELLMANN, Robert S, Jr. 413 DEVONIA ST 37748 #047-06-1965 L1966 **FM** *020

JOST, Richard Raymond. 412 DEVONIA ST 37748 #047-06-1964 L1964 **FM EM** *071

KAROLCZAK, Pawel Gregorz. PO BOX 489, 412 DEVONIA ST 37748 #759-09-1991 L1998
PCC *020 †20

KIRILUK, Randy Mark. 412 DEVONIA ST 37748 #047-06-1987 L1988 **FM PD** *020 †18 ‡

LATHAM, Kent Emerson. 718 MORGAN AVE 37748 #047-06-1973 L1974 **IM** *020

LAWSON, W M, Jr. 525 DEVONIA ST, STE A 37748 #047-06-1982 L1987 **CD IM** *020 †20

LAY, Kristan M. 412 DEVONIA ST 37748 #035-47-1994 L1999 **PTH** *020 †50

LY, Hao Anh. 421 DEVONIA ST 37748 #010-02-1994 L1997 **IM** *072

LYNCH, James Edward. 408 N ROANE ST 37748 #021-01-1982 L1986 **N OS** *020 †75

MATTHIESSEN, Patrick M. 408 N ROANE ST 37748 #020-02-1998 L2002 **N** *020 †75

MCLAUGHLIN, Victor W. 525 DEVONIA ST, STE A 37748 #047-06-1965 L1968 **CD** *020

MC MILLIN, Rodney Moore. 408 N ROANE ST STE 100 37748 #047-06-1978 L1979
FM *020 †18

MICHEL, James R. 525 DEVONIA ST, STE A 37748 #026-04-1972 L1986 **CD IM** *020 †20

NADROUS, Hassan Fouad. 415 DEVONIA ST 37748 #875-03-1993 L2004 **PCC** *020 †20

PANELO, Arnel Hernandez. 412 DEVONIA ST, ROANE MEDICAL CTR 37748 #748-01-1990 L1998
IM *020 †20

PRICE, Robert Eugene. 1798 ROANE STATE HWY 37748 #047-20-1985 L1991 **OPH OS** *020 †35

RAGSDALE, Timothy F. 2497 S ROANE ST 37748 #047-06-1995 L2000 **OTO** *020 †45

RORIE, Mark A. 525 DEVONIA ST, STE A 37748 #027-01-1995 L2001 **CD** *020 †20

SHARMA, Mukesh K. 525 DEVONIA ST, STE A 37748 #495-08-1978 L1993 **CD IM** *020 †20

SILLS, E Scott. ■ 37748 #047-06-1992 L1993 **REN** *020 †30 ‡

SULLIVAN, Robert S. 138 HEIDLE RD 37748 #028-34-1975 L1995 **IM** *020 †20

TEAGUE, Stephen Michael. 525 DEVONIA ST, STE A 37748 #016-11-1977 L2000
CD IM *020 †20

TEDDER, Miriam B. 525 DEVONIA ST STE A 37748 #047-06-1976 L1976 **FM** *020 †18 ‡

VALEDON, Jose Gaspar. 408 N ROANE ST 37748 #042-02-1987 L1992 **N** *020 †75

WALLACE, Marty G. 415 DEVONIA ST 37748 #308-11-1987 L1993 **FM** *020 †18

WATERS, David Barton. 319 DEVONIA ST 37748 #047-06-1985 L1991 **VS GS** *020 †85

WHITTAKER, Karen Letha. 412 DEVONIA ST 37748 #011-04-1991 L2001 **IM** *020 †20

WILSON, Robert J. 408 N ROANE ST, STE 100 37748 #048-13-1997 L1998 **FM** *020 †18

WITTKE, Paul Edward. 1798 ROANE STATE HWY 37748 #025-07-1962 L1973 **OPH** *020 †35

HARRISON — HAMILTON

FREEDA, Austen Elizabeth. 7010 ANTLER LN 37341 #047-20-1999 L2002 **IM** *020 †20

HAYES, Douglas Scott. ■ 37341 #047-06-1997 L2002 **DR** *020 †80

NAIK, Janak Harshad. 6800 HARRISON PARK DR, HARRISON MEDICAL CENTER 37341
#047-06-1994 L1998 **FM** *020 †18

POLLARD, Nancy B. ■ 37341 #016-45-1987 L1990 **PD** *020

RODIER, Sophia Maureen. 8106 ISLAND POINT DR 37341 #012-21-1997 L2003 **FM** *020 †18

TURNER, Sharlinda B. ■ 37341 #047-06-1976 L1976 **PHP PD** *075 †70

HARROGATE — CLAIBORNE

AHMED, Bilal. 6144 CUMBERLAND GAP PKWY, STE 1 37752 #704-01-1993 L2002 **P** *020 †75

AYRES, Thomas M, Jr. 169 WESTMORELAND ST 37752 #021-01-1984 L1990 **CD IM** *050 †20

COBB, Leah Shannon. ■ 37752 #020-12-2002 L2004 **CHP** *020

DAY, George Louis. 170 BEECH ST, STE 1 37752 #047-06-1958 L1959 **FM GP** *020

DE VORE, Russell F, III. 389 FORGE RIDGE RD, BAKER CANCER CENTER 37752
#055-01-1984 L1987 **ON IM** *020 †20

DILWORTH, Lee Robt. 169 WESTMORELAND ST 37752 #038-41-1980 L1986 **CD** *020 †20

EKER, Deniz. 6144 CUMBERLAND GAP PKWY, STE 1 37752 #902-07-1994 L2002 **CHP** *020 †75

ELLIS, Roy Caldwell, Jr. ■ 37752 #047-06-1962 L1962 **FM** *020 †18

KRISLE, George Menees, III. 169 WESTMORELAND ST 37752 #012-05-1970 L1977
CD *020 †20

RAO, Ramesh Kadekoppal. 389 FORGE RIDGE RD, BAKER CANCER TREATMENT CTR 37752
#495-09-1970 L1991 **RO** *020 †80

RASMUSSEN, Kenneth Edward. ■ 37752 #023-01-1961 L1963 **EM GS** *071

SLUTZKER, Daniel Michael. 169 WESTMORELAND ST 37752 #038-40-1982 L1988 **CD** *020 †20

SMITH, Joseph Saml, III. 169 WESTMORELAND ST 37752 #045-01-1978 L1985 **CD IM** *020 †20

WOOD, David Emerson. 169 WESTMORELAND ST 37752 #048-14-1997 L2004 **CD IC** *020 †20

HARTFORD — COCKE

BROTHERTON, Deana Rymer. 4261 BIG CREEK RD 37753 #047-20-1997 L1998 **FM** *020 †18

SANDERS, Pamela Joy. 4261 BIG CREEK RD 37753 #047-06-2002 L2005 **FM OBS** *020 †18

HARTSVILLE — TROUSDALE

KELLEY, Ira N. ■ 37074 #004-01-1952 L1953 **GP** *071

REED, Floyd. 213 BROADWAY 37074 #047-06-1975 L1981 **GP** *020

SAMSON, Bienvenido T. 755 MCMURRY BLVD E 37074 #748-10-1964 L1993 **OS GP** *020

HELENWOOD — SCOTT

THOMPSON, Steven Joshua. ■ 37755 #047-06-2004 L2007 **IM** *020 †20

HENDERSON — CHESTER

CREECH, Erika Hazard. 208 NORTH AVE, THE JACKSON CLINIC PA 38340 #047-06-1992 L1993
FM *020 †18

FRIX, Carey Wallace. 116 W MAIN ST 38340 #047-06-1998 L2000 **FM** *020 †18

JENNINGS, Nicole M. 116 W MAIN ST 38340 #047-06-1998 L2001 **IM** *020 †20

SCHWARTZ, Paul Edward. 1306 US HIGHWAY 45 N 38340 #048-02-1980 L1980
FM OM *020 †18

HENDERSONVILLE — SUMNER

ALEXANDER, John Oscar, III. 1012 MARGARET DR 37075 #047-06-1977 L1978
FM EM *020 †18

ALGEO, James H, Jr. 131 RIVIERA DR 37075 #041-02-1979 L1996 **NM IM** *020 †20,80,28

ALI, Mohammad Farooq. 353 NEW SHACKLE ISLAND RD, STE 201A 37075 #704-21-1997 L2006
RHU *020

ANANDAIAH, K M. 107 IMPERIAL BLVD STE 11, ADULT CARDIOLOGIST PC 37075
#495-09-1964 L1979 **CD IM** *020 †20

ANDERSON, James P. 353 NEW SHACKLE ISLAND RD, STE 202A 37075 #055-01-1984 L1990
N P *020 †75

ARNEY, Timothy L. 355 NEW SHACKLE ISLAND RD, ANESTHESIA SERVICES ASSOCI 37075
#654-01-1987 L1991 **EM AN** *020 †05

AZIZ, Basit. 919 W MAIN ST STE L5 37075 #704-21-1971 L1979 **IM** *020

BARDEN, Leroy Flippen, III. 127 HAVEN ST, THE HAVEN CLINIC 37075 #047-06-1973 L1974
GP *020

BOLLIG, Stephen Louis. 625 E MAIN ST, STE 4 37075 #038-43-1981 L1994 **FM** *020 †18

BOSKIND, Andrew Sidney. 107 IMPERIAL BLVD, STE 3 37075 #005-12-1965 L1973 **GS** *020 †85

BRANSON, Brett Cameron. 353 NEW SHACKLE ISLAND RD, STE 341C 37075
#005-12-1982 L1995 **OBG** *020 †30

BURCH, Christina Marshall. 353 NEW SHACKLE ISLAND RD, STE 202A 37075 #010-02-1985 L2001 **N IM** *020 †75

BURKS, Helen Crawford. 353 NEW SHACKLE ISLAND RD, STE 106A 37075 #005-12-1962 L1969 **PD** *020

CALLISTER, Tracy Quayle. 353 NEW SHACKLE ISLAND RD, STE 300C 37075 #005-14-1979 L1984 **CD IM** *020 †20

CARMACK, James H, Jr. 105 GLEN OAK BLVD STE 100 37075 #047-06-1972 L1975 **IM** *020

CHAFFIN, Goodloe S, Jr. 353 NEW SHACKLE ISLAND RD, WELLNESS GROUP 37075 #047-05-1975 L1976 **FM** *020 †18

CORMIER, Kylie Marie. 105 GLEN OAK BLVD STE 102 37075 #021-05-2003 L2007 **PD** *020 †55

CRUZ, Helion Wilfredo. 353 NEW SHACKLE ISLAND RD, STE 202A 37075 #042-01-1996 L2000 **N** *020 †75

CURTIS, Terry Randall. 353 NEW SHACKLE ISLAND RD, STE 141C 37075 #308-07-1982 L1986 **FM** *020 †18

DALLAS, Anthony V, Jr. 353 NEW SHACKLE ISLAND RD, STE 141C 37075 #020-12-1979 L1986 **FM** *020 †18

DAUGHERTY, Paul Sherdell. 101 MAPLE DR N, STE F 37075 #005-12-1975 L1979 **IM** *020 †20

DAUPHIN, Pascal Andre. 170D E MAIN ST, STE 113 37075 #005-01-1998 L2003 **END** *020 †20

DEMOVILLE, Raymond B. 107 GLEN OAK BLVD SU 37075 #023-12-1986 L2000 **OTO** *020 †45

DIAZ, Michael Carlos. 105 GLEN OAK BLVD STE 200 37075 #038-06-1979 L1985 **GE IM** *020 †20

ENAYAT, Nigar A. 353 NEW SHACKLE ISLAND RD, STE 140C 37075 #118-02-1978 L1995 **IM** *020 †20

ERVIN, Warren Dixon. 100 SPRINGHOUSE CT, STE 100 37075 #036-07-1980 L1983 **PD** *020 †55

FLATT, John Adam. ■ 37075 #047-06-2003 L2006 **CHN** *012

FLEMING, Herbon H. 353 NEW SHACKLE ISLAND RD, # 12 37075 #047-07-1985 L1991 **PUD CCM** *020 †20

FOGOLIN, Robert Paul. 353 NEW SHACKLE ISLAND RD, STE 226B 37075 #005-15-1992 L1997 **ORS** *020 †40

FRENCHMAN, Khushru H. 107 IMPERIAL BLVD, STE 15 37075 #495-37-1968 L1979 **PS** *020

FRENCHMAN, Rita Khushru. 107 IMPERIAL BLVD STE 15 37075 #496-38-1969 L1979 **AN** *020

GASKINS, Fay M Rice. ■ 37075 #047-05-1956 L1969 **P** *071

GHABOUR, Mary Mourad Helm. 100 BLUEGRASS COMMONS BLVD 37075 #915-07-1987 *100

HAN, Jung Hee Lee. 353 NEW SHACKLE ISLAND RD, STE 110A 37075 #583-03-1972 L1977 **P N** *020 †75

HANDE, Scott Alan. 353 NEW SHACKLE ISLAND RD, STE 249C 37075 #047-05-2000 L2008 **IM** *100 †20

HARRISON, Duane Edson. 353 NEW SHACKLE ISLAND RD 37075 #047-07-1983 L1984 **IM EM** *020

HATTAWAY, Kevin Todd. 353 NEW SHACKLE ISLAND RD, STE 123B 37075 #021-06-1995 L1998 **FM** *020 †18

HITCHMAN, James Kenneth. 355 NEW SHACKLE ISLAND RD 37075 #047-06-1971 L1972 **DR** *020 †20

HUBBELL, Richard L. 129 HAVEN ST, STE B 37075 #047-05-1990 L1993 **AN** *020 †05

HUCKABY, Janice Butcher. 102 BEAUMONT CT 37075 #055-02-1988 L1998 **OBG** *020 †30

HUDSON, David Randall. 100 SPRINGHOUSE CT, STE 100 37075 #047-05-1993 L1996 **PD** *020 †55

ISOM, Joel Terrance. ■ 37075 #047-07-2003 L2007 **IM** *100

JANSSEN, Angelisa. ■ 37077 #036-01-1999 L2002 **FM** *020 †18

JEWETT, David Geo. 107 IMPERIAL BLVD, STE 4 37075 #005-12-1971 L1977 **OBG** *020 †30

JOHNSON, Marshall R, Jr. 355 NEW SHACKLE ISLAND RD, HENDERSONVILLE MEDICAL CEN 37075 #047-06-12-1994 L2003 **IM** *020 †20

JOHNSON, William Stephen. 166 E MAIN ST 37075 #305-01-1983 L1999 **PD** *020 †55

JONES, Jeffrey Alan. 353 NEW SHACKLE ISLAND RD, STE 244C 37075 #048-15-1999 L2007 **PS** *020 †85

KABTIMER, Hailu T. 919 W MAIN ST M-3, LAKE VIEW TERRACE 37075 #366-01-1986 L1998 **IM** *020 †20

KARLEKAR, Saagar B. 105 GLEN OAK BLVD, STE 102 37075 #422-01-1997 L2004 **PD** *020 †55

KNECHT, Craig Lee. 353 NEW SHACKLE ISLAND RD, STE 101A 37075 #005-12-1982 L1986 **OBG** *020 †30

KRAFT, William Lee. 112 N GOVERNORS CV 37075 #005-14-1982 L2002 **DR IM** *020 †80

KROLL, Peter Brian. 353 NEW SHACKLE ISLAND RD, STE 219B 37075 #005-12-1997 L2002 **AN** *020 †05

LADD, James Truble. ■ 37075 #005-12-1954 L1955 **GP** *071

LAMBERT, Denny Ray. 131 INDIAN LAKE RD, MODERN MEDICAL PSYCHIATRY 37075 #047-20-1988 L1988 **P GP** *075

LANDSBERG, Robert Paul. 353 NEW SHACKLE ISLAND RD, STE 110 37075 #065-01-1979 L1993 **ORS** *020 †40

LEAVITT, Paul Jason. 353 NEW SHACKLE ISLAND RD, STE 103 37075 #665-01-1998 L2005 **FM** *020 †18

LIPPOLIS, Nicholas John. 353 NEW SHACKLE ISLAND RD, STE 300C 37075 #654-01-1986 L1995 **CD IM** *020 †20

LITTLE, Shannon Leeson. 109 HAZEL PATH 37075 #047-06-1989 L1992 **CHP** *020 †75

LITTLE, Walter Francis. 107 GLEN OAK BLVD 37075 #047-06-1987 L1992 **U** *020 †95

MACMASTER, Jennifer. 100 SPRINGHOUSE CT, STE 100 37075 #038-45-1996 L1999 **PD** *020 †55

MAGOUN, Joseph Ratcliff. 353 NEW SHACKLE ISLND RD D 37075 #021-05-1995 L1996 **FM** *020 †18

MC CLURE-BARNES, Laura. 353 NEW SHACKLE ISLAND RD, STE 204 37075 #047-06-1997 L1999 **HO** *020 †20

MC CONNELL, Conn Michael. 351 NEW SHACKLE ISLAND RD 37075 #047-05-1970 L1979 **GP** *020 †85

MENDOZA, Daniel. 101 MAPLE DR N 37075 #649-01-1957 L1972 **PD OS** *020

MIDDLETON, John Berry. ■ 37075 #021-05-1975 L1988 **FM** *020 †18

MILLS, Leo Kendrick. 353 NEW SHACKLE ISLAND RD, STE 300C 37075 #024-01-1985 L2004 **CD** *020 †20

MILLSPAUGH, John B. 353 NEW SHACKLE ISLAND RD, STE 128B 37075 #001-06-1995 L2002 **FM** *020 †18

MONTAGUE, Jennifer Lynn. 107 GLEN OAK BLVD, STE 200 37075 #025-01-2001 L2004 **FM** *100 †18

MOORE, Jennifer Elaine. 100 SPRINGHOUSE CT, STE 100 37075 #036-01-1992 L1995 **PD** *020 †20

MOTZ, Gregg Andrew. 353 NEW SHACKLE ISLAND RD, MEDICINE PLC SUITE 240C 37075 #038-40-1995 L2002 **ORS** *020 †40

MURPHY, George Jos, III. 353 NEW SHACKLE ISLAND RD, STE 101A 37075 #005-12-1971 L1977 **OBG** *020 †30

NARAIN, Vivek. 107 GLEN OAK BLVD, STE 100 37075 #038-44-1996 L2002 **U** *020 †95

NASON, William Brent. 353 NEW SHACKLE ISLAND RD, STE 224B 37075 #047-20-1992 L1996 **OBG** *020 †30

NESTOR, Nell Elizabeth. 353 NEW SHACKLE ISLAND RD, STE 140C 37075 #047-06-1978 L1978 **FM** *020 †18

NEWSOM, David L. 107 IMPERIAL BLVD STE 8 37075 #039-01-1986 L1990 **OPH** *020 †35

NORTH, Kenneth Timothy. 130 IMPERIAL BLVD 37075 #047-06-1970 L1970 **PD EM** *020 †55

OBIANYO, Ifeanyi Obi. 353 NEW SHACKLE ISLAND RD, STE 206A 37075 #047-07-1984 L1988 **IM** *020 †20

PO, Giog Sing Tan. ■ 37075 #748-01-1963 L1973 **GP GS** *071 †85

RICE, Ronnie Neal. 353 NEW SHACKLE ISLAND RD, STE 221B 37075 #047-05-1972 L1974 **GYN GS** *020 †30

RUSSO, Donald Jos. 353 NEW SHACKLE ISLAND RD, STE 110A 37075 #035-08-1979 L1985 **CD** *020 †20

RYAN, Michael Nixon. ■ 37075 #047-06-1970 L1971 **OBG** *071

SHELL, William Alfred, Jr. 353 NEW SHACKLE ISLAND RD, STE 148 37075 #047-06-1981 L1982 **ORS** *020 †40

SIEGEL, Jane Meredith. 353 NEW SHACKLE ISLAND RD, STE 148 37075 #047-05-1988 L1994 **HS ORS** *020 †40

SMITH, Peter Keith. 107 IMPERIAL BLVD STE 3 37075 #001-02-1983 L1989 **GS** *020 †85

SOUTHWELL, Clyde O'Brien. 353 NEW SHACKLE ISLAND RD 37075 #008-02-1999 L2007 **PCC** *020 †20

SPICER, Robert James. ■ 37075 #047-07-2005 **PM** *012

STAHMANN, Fred Dale. ■ 37075 #016-06-1967 L1971 **TS** *020 †85,90

STEIER, Jill. 353 NEW SHACKLE ISLAND RD, STE 221B 37075 #051-04-1986 L1988 **OBG** *020 †30

STEWART, John Alan. 353 NEW SHACKLE ISLAND RD, STE 107-A 37075 #047-20-1991 L1996 **FM** *020 †50,18

STONE, Jeffrey Lee. 107 IMPERIAL BLVD STE 3 37075 #011-02-1977 L1993 **GS VS** *020 †85

STOWERS, Stewart Frazier. 353 NEW SHACKLE ISLAND RD, STE 148 37075 #036-07-1981 L1989 **ORS OSM** *020 †40

STUART, Brian James. 353 NEW SHACKLE ISLAND RD, WELLNESS GROUP 37075 #028-34-2000 L2006 **FM** *020 †18 ‡

STUART, Denise Francis. 105 GLEN OAK BLVD, STE 102 37075 #028-34-2001 L2006 **PD** *020 †55

TAYLOR, Joseph Gifford. 353 NEW SHACKLE ISLAND RD, STE 140C 37075 #036-05-1982 L1985 **FM** *020 †18

TINCHER, Matthew Roach. 100 BENTREE CT 37075 #038-41-1998 L2001 **EM** *020 †16

TIZARD, Gary Tiffany. 107 IMPERIAL BLVD, STE 5 37075 #048-04-1970 L1980 **IM** *075 †20

VALENTINO, Roxanne Marie. ■ 37075 #038-40-2000 L2007 **SME CN** *020 †75

WEBB, Robert Thos. 107 GLEN OAK BLVD, STE 100 37075 #004-01-1975 L1980 **U** *020 †95

WIGGLETON, Catherine Oels. ■ 37075 #047-05-2006 **PD** *012

WILHITE, Joe Lynn. 355 NEW SHACKLE ISLAND RD 37075 #047-06-1959 L1962 **TS EM** *020

WILSON, Tadron Lavonda. ■ 37075 #047-07-1998 L2002 **IM** *020 †20

WOLFE, Jimmy Vernon. 353 NEW SHACKLE ISLAND RD, STE 202A 37075 #055-02-1984 L1992 **N** *020 †75

WOODS, Ashley F. 353 NEW SHACKLE ISLAND RD, WELLNESS GROUP 37075 #047-07-1995 L1998 **FM** *020 †18

WYATT, Kenneth Noel. 105 GLEN OAK BLVD, STE 102 37075 #025-12-1979 L1984 **PD** *020 †55

WYATT, Susan Dianne. 353 NEW SHACKLE ISLAND RD, STE 247C 37075 #047-07-1988 L1989 **FM** *020 †18

YUILL, John Matthew. 353 NEW SHACKLE ISLAND RD, STE 141C 37075 #020-12-2000 L2002 **MPD** *020 †20,55

HENNING – LAUDERDALE

SANDLER, Paula Margery. 480 GREEN CHAPEL RD 38041 #035-06-1989 L1998 **PTH** *100 †95

HENRY – HENRY

NIENABER, Kirk Anthony. ■ 38231 #038-41-1992 L1993 **FM** *072 †18

HERMITAGE – DAVIDSON

BAHNER, Roderick Iren, Jr. 5655 FRIST BLVD, SUMMIT MEDICAL CENTER 37076 #023-07-1997 L2003 **EM** *020 †16

BAKER, Michael Thos. 5651 FRIST BLVD, STE 603 37076 #047-06-1990 L1993 **CD** *020 †20

BARNES, Maurice Clarke, Jr. 5651 1ST BLVD STE 214 37076 #019-02-1975 L1980 **GE IM** *020 †20

BARON, Christopher M. ■ 37076 #048-13-2005 **DR** *012

BAUCOM, William E, III. 5653 FRIST BLVD 37076 #047-06-1982 L1983 **IM** *020 †20

BEATTY, Brian C. 5651 FRIST BLVD 37076 #010-01-1982 L1986 **OBG** *020 †30

BECKHAM, Michael Thos. 3901 CENTRAL PIKE, STE 257 37076 #047-06-1991 L1993 **IM** *020 †20

BENNETT, Jeremy Michael. ■ 37076 #047-07-2008 *012

BERTEAU, Craig David. 5651 FRIST BLVD, STE 712 37076 #021-05-1991 L1995 **N** *020 †75

BIRDWELL, Ben Jason. 5653 FRIST BLVD 37076 #047-06-1961 L1962 **IM** *071

BLUHM, Renata Elizabeth. 5655 FRIST BLVD 37076 #016-11-1977 L1988 **IM OM** *020 †20,70

BODNER, Stanley Jacob. 3515 CENTRAL PIKE 37076 #047-06-1967 L1971 **IM ID** *020 †20

BRYANT, Grady Lee, Jr. 5045 OLD HICKORY BLVD, STE 200 37076 #047-05-1992 L1995 **OTO** *020 †45

BRYWCZYNSKI, Jeremy Josep. ■ 37076 #038-45-2004 L2006 **EM** *100

BUCKMAN, David Dale. 5655 FRIST BLVD, EMERGENCY DEPARTMENT 37076 #005-12-1975 L1988 **EM OM** *020 †18,16

BUNTIN, Denise Melia. 4755 ANDREW JACKSON PKWY 37076 #047-06-1979 L1979 **D** *020 †15

BURNS, Gerald Robt. 4050 ANDREW JACKSON PKWY 37076 #047-06-1966 L1967 **GS** *020 †85

CADENA, Alberto. 5653 FRIST BLVD STE 333 37076 #047-07-1995 L1999 **OBG** *020 †30

CHALKO, Alexander J, III. 5653 FRIST BLVD STE 331 37076 #051-01-1978 L1995 **P** *020 †75

CHAUVIN, John Rene. 5653 FRIST BLVD, STE 230 37076 #010-02-1978 L1982 **IM** *020 †20

CRUMBO, Donald Slider. 5651 FRIST BLVD, STE 603 37076 #047-05-1971 L1981 **CD IM** *020 †20

DEMIRJIAN, Kenneth Allan. 5045 OLD HICKORY BLVD, STE 200 37076 #001-02-1987 L1990 **FM** *020 †18

DILLAHA, Larry Michael. 403 N CAMERON CT 37076 #047-06-1992 L1993 **FM** *020
DIMICK, Robert Marshall. 5651 FRIST BLVD, STE 500 37076 #001-02-1984 L1994 **OSS ORS** *020 †40
DINELLA, Thomas John. 5653 FRIST BLVD 37076 #001-02-1990 L1995 **IM** *020 †20
DINKINS, Edward Jeffrey. 5653 FRIST BLVD STE 630 37076 #045-01-2003 L2005 **IM** *020 †20
DOAK, William Melville. 3901 CENTRAL PIKE, STE 251 37076 #047-06-1956 L1957 **PD** *071 †55
DUBE, Walter William. 5651 FRIST BLVD, STE 400 37076 #047-20-1997 L2001 **ORS OSM** *020 †40
DUTTON, William Patterson. 5651 FRIST BLVD, STE 616 37076 #047-06-1965 L1968 **U** *020 †95
EBY, James Wilder. ■ 37076 #005-12-2002 L2007 **PM** *100 †60
ELALAYLI, Tarek Galal. 5651 FRIST BLVD, STE 409 37076 #025-07-1994 L1999 **ORS** *020 †40
ELROD, James Thos, Jr. 5653 FRIST BLVD 37076 #047-06-1983 L1984 **IM** *020 †20
ENAYAT, Abdul Shukoor. 5651 FRIST BLVD, STE 704 37076 #118-02-1969 L1986 **IM** *020 †20
ESBENSHADE, Aaron M, Jr. 5651 FRIST BLVD STE 408 37076 #011-03-1976 L1978 **PUD** *020 †20
EZELL, Meredith Ann. 5653 FRIST BLVD 37076 #047-06-1982 L1983 **OPH** *020 †35
EZELL, Roy Clay. 5653 FRIST BLVD 37076 #047-06-1955 L1955 **OPH** *071 †35 ‡
FAIRBANK, Elizabeth H. 5651 FRIST BLVD, STE 200 37076 #035-09-1997 L2000 **PD** *020 †55
FEHRMAN, Terri Lynne. 105 BONNABROOK DR STE 202 37076 #016-45-1980 L1982 **P** *020
FELTS, Stephen Karey. 5653 FRIST BLVD, STE 531 37076 #027-01-1968 L1974 **ID IM** *020 †20
FERNANDEZ, Luis Guillermo. 5653 FRIST BLVD 37076 #011-02-1997 L2002 **IM** *020 †20
FORTUNE, David Scott. 3901 CENTRAL PIKE STE 351 37076 #047-05-1993 L1997 **OTO A** *020 †45
FRAZIER, Kendra Evelyn. ■ 37076 #047-07-2008 *012
FRIDDELL, Thomas James. 5045 OLD HICKORY BLVD, STE 200 37076 #047-06-1963 L1964 **GP** *020 †18
GABOY, Narciso C. 1312 CENTRAL CT 37076 #748-01-1969 L1981 **P** *020
GASTON, Robert B. 3939 CENTRAL PIKE, ATTN: RHIANNON 37076 #047-06-1951 L1951 **FM** *071
GASTON, Robert Bernard. 3939 CENTRAL PIKE, STE 100 37076 #047-06-1972 L1977 **FM** *020 †18
GATES, William Gene. 5410 OLD HICKORY BLVD 37076 #021-06-1989 L1993 **OPH** *020 †35
GNAU, Charles Ronald. ■ 37076 #041-02-1964 L1965 **GP EM** *071
GOODMAN, Bruce Randolph. 5651 FRIST BLVD STE 201 37076 #047-05-1982 L1983 **OBG** *020 †30
GREAVES, Mark Kessler. 5655 FRIST BLVD, SUMMIT MEDICAL CENTER 37076 #017-20-1980 L1990 **EM** *020 †16
GUILLERMIN, John Philip. PO BOX 86 37076 #047-06-1971 L1972 **NS** *071
GUPTA, Navin. 5651 FRIST BLVD, STE 603 37076 #035-19-1992 L1994 **IC VIR** *020 †20
GUTH, Robert Wm. 4777 ANDREW JACKSON PKWY 37076 #016-01-1984 L1988 **FM** *020 †18
HAMBY, Mindi Bein. 3939 CENTRAL PIKE, STE 100 37076 #038-40-1996 L2002 **FM** *020 †18
HAMILTON, Kevin Michael. 5651 FRIST BLVD 37076 #001-02-1993 L1997 **OBG** *020 †30
HARROM, Heidi Lou. ■ 37076 #005-12-2001 L2007 **PYG** *020
HIRANYA-GOWDA, C K. 3901 CENTRAL PIKE, STE 351 37076 #495-29-1960 L1971 **OTO** *020 †45
HOOVER, Bradley Whitt. 5655 FRIST BLVD 37076 #047-06-1989 L1990 **EM** *020 †16
HUFF, John Gregory. 5655 FRIST BLVD 37076 #047-05-1977 L1978 **DR EM** *020 †80 ‡
HUMPHREYS, Jerry K. 4733 ANDREW JACKSON PKWY 37076 #047-05-1962 L1962 **PTH** *071 †50 ‡
HURT, Joseph Edward. 5653 FRIST BLVD, STE 730 37076 #047-06-1953 L1953 **IM** *071 †20
INTERLANDI, John Wm. 5651 FRIST BLVD, STE 208 37076 #047-05-1976 L1979 **END IM** *020 †20
ISAAC, Victor William. 5651 FRIST BLVD STE 712, NEUROMUSCULAR REHABILITATI 37076 #915-03-1989 L2005 **PM** *020 †60
JAMES, G Whit. 5651 FRIST BLVD, STE 309 37076 #036-05-1987 L1993 **GE** *020 †20
JASELSKIS, Thomas Peter. 3901 CENTRAL PIKE, STE 352 37076 #016-45-1989 L1990 **FM** *020 †18
KALRA, Manisha. 3939 CENTRAL PIKE, STE 100 37076 #495-47-1994 L2006 **FM** *020 †18 ‡
KAMINSKY, Sean Bryant. 5651 FRIST BLVD, STE 500 37076 #012-05-1994 L2000 **ORS** *020 †40
KENNON, Roy Stanley. ■ 37076 #047-06-1981 L1982 **OM LM** *030 †70
KING, Edward Lee. 3939 CENTRAL PIKE, SUMMIT FAMILY PRACTICE CAR 37076 #047-06-1974 L1975 **GP EM** *020
KINNEY, Steven Ross. 244 JACKSON MEADOWS DR 37076 #047-06-1980 L1980 **FM** *020 †18
KRUSE, John J. 5651 FRIST BLVD, SUITE702 37076 #021-05-1993 L1999 **NS OSS** *020 †25
LADOUCEUR, Michael Steven. 5653 FRIST BLVD, STE 731 37076 #026-04-1986 L1999 **ORS** *020 †40
LANDON, Thomas Harold. 5651 FRIST BLVD, STE 616 37076 #016-42-1994 L2001 **U** *020 †95
LAYA, Lisa M. 3515 CENTRAL PIKE 37076 #748-02-1987 L1995 **ID** *020 †20
LAZAS, Donald Joseph, Jr. 5651 FRIST BLVD, STE 309 37076 #010-01-1988 L1997 **GE** *020 †20
LE, Son Diep. 5651 FRIST BLVD, STE 712 37076 #016-42-1995 L2001 **PM** *020 †60
LEE, Sue Jungsook. 5651 FRIST BLVD, STE 309 37076 #012-05-1985 L1993 **GE** *020 †20
LENNING, Leslie Garth. 5655 FRIST BLVD 37076 #001-02-1999 L2001 **EM** *020 †16
LIEN, David Yuder. 5655 FRIST BLVD 37076 #024-07-1996 L1999 **EM** *020 †16
LIM, Noel Pung. 5651 FRIST BLVD STE 308 37076 #748-11-1993 L2002 **N CN** *020 ‡
LIVINGSTON, David. 5114 OLD HICKORY BLVD, FAMILY MEDICAL CENTER 37076 #048-02-1986 L1992 **FM** *020 †18
LOCH-DONAHUE, Janet Marie. 5655 FRIST BLVD, EMERG DEPT 37076 #012-05-1989 L1995 **EM** *020 †16
LOVELESS, James Alva, Jr. 5651 FRIST BLVD, STE 716 37076 #047-06-1970 L1970 **U GS** *020 †95
LUMAR, Alanna Marie. ■ 37076 #047-07-2003 **FM** *100
LYNCH, James Michael. 5655 FRIST BLVD 37076 #065-01-1976 L1982 **EM** *020 †16
MAJOR, John Scott. 3939 CENTRAL PIKE, STE 100 37076 #047-06-1997 L1999 **FM** *020 †18 ‡
MC GUIRE, Philip Michael. 5655 FRIST BLVD 37076 #047-05-1992 L2001 **DR** *020 †80
MC GUIRE, Sueann. 5653 FRIST BLVD, STE 339 37076 #016-45-1995 L1999 **OBG** *020 †30
MCWEENEY, Dennis Todd. ■ 37076 #003-75-2003, ▲ L2006 **OBG** *020
MEHTA, Archana Kochar. 5651 FRIST BLVD STE 414 37076 #495-55-1992 L2003 **IM** *020 †20
MEHTA, Ashok Kumar. 5651 FRIST BLVD, STE 414 37076 #495-55-1989 L2003 **IM** *020 †20
MERTENS, Michael John. 5045 OLD HICKORY BLVD, STE 200 37076 #047-06-1997 L1998 **FM** *020 †18
MEYER, Alvin Henry, Jr. 5651 FRIST BLVD STE 509 37076 #021-05-1967 L1973 **D DMP** *020 †15
MILLER, Lisa Davone. 5114 OLD HICKORY BLVD, STE 201 37076 #047-07-1997 L2001 **IM** *020
MISHRA, Sushri. 5651 FRIST BLVD, STE 415 37076 #305-01-1999 L2002 **FM** *020 †18
MONTGOMERY, Deborah G. 5653 FRIST BLVD 37076 #016-01-1979 L1982 **IM IMG** *020 †20
MULAISHO, Chilango. 5653 FRIST BLVD, STE 330 37076 #539-06-1970 L1999 **IM END** *020 †20
MURABITO, Frank J. 5655 FRIST BLVD 37076 #047-05-1981 L1983 **EM** *030 †16
MURPHY, Kent R. 5653 FRIST BLVD, STE 231 37076 #023-12-1984 L1994 **OTO GS** *020 †45
NOVAK, Vincent Paul. 5651 FRIST BLVD, STE 500 37076 #023-01-2000 L2008 **HS** *020 ‡
OQUIST, Niki Lee. 705 WILL PL 37076 #001-06-1987 L1992 **PD** *040 †55
PAK, Richard Young. 3939 CENTRAL PIKE, STE 100 37076 #001-06-2002 L2005 **FM** *020 †18
PALONEN, Katri Pauliina. 5653 FRIST BLVD, STE 630 37076 #001-02-2000 L2006 **IM** *040 †20 ‡
PARANJAPE, Yeshawant. 4733 ANDREW JACKSON PKWY 37076 #495-33-1963 L1980 **OPH P** *020 †35
PARDUE, Travis Kirk. 5653 FRIST BLVD STE 236 37076 #654-01-1988 L1993 **IM** *020 †20
PATEL, Mitul Kanti. 5651 FRIST BLVD, STE 409 37076 #038-44-1998 L2003 **ORS** *020 †40
PATIL, Sushil Raj. 5651 FRIST BLVD STE 309 37076 #047-06-1995 L1998 **GE** *020 †20
PIERCE, Vinton Douglas. 5651 FRIST BLVD STE 500 37076 #007-02-1982 L1991 **ORS** *020 †40
PINKARD, John F. 5651 FRIST BLVD STE 709 37076 #047-06-1984 L1985 **TS VS** *020 †85,90
PORTER, Bennet Allen, Jr. ■ 37076 #010-01-1953 L1957 **FM** *071 †18
RAMANNA, M V. ■ 37076 #495-09-1958 *100
RAMOS, Michael P. 5651 FRIST BLVD 37076 #748-01-1990 L2001 **PCC** *020 †20
REID, Michael Lynn. 5651 FRIST BLVD STE 500 37076 #004-01-1975 L1985 **ORS OSM** *020 †40
RENTUZA, Ronald Chu. ■ 37076 #748-11-1993 L2004 **IM** *020 †20
RIVAS, Alejandro Alberto. 4779 ANDREW JACKSON PKWY 37076 #649-01-1970 L1977 **GS** *020 †85
ROSDEUTSCHER, John David. 5651 FRIST BLVD 37076 #047-05-1991 L1998 **PS OTO** *020 †45,65 ‡
ROSDEUTSCHER, Kimberly J. 5651 FRIST BLVD, STE 200 37076 #038-41-1994 L1998 **PD** *020 †55
ROUCH, Carl Linnaeus. 5651 FRIST BLVD, STE 603 37076 #017-20-1994 L2002 **IC** *020 †20
RUARK, Deborah J Stewart. 4733 ANDREW JACKSON PKWY 37076 #047-05-1975 L1976 **OPH** *071 †35
SCOTT, Brian Mark. 5653 FRIST BLVD 37076 #001-02-2000 L2003 **IM** *020 †20
SHARPE, Bryan Campbell. 5655 FRIST BLVD 37076 #047-06-1985 L1987 **EM AM** *020 †16
SHIPPEN, William Driver. 5655 FRIST BLVD 37076 #004-01-1978 L1981 **EM A** *020 †16
SMITH, David William. 5655 FRIST BLVD 37076 #047-06-1983 L1984 **AN** *020 †05
SRINIVAS, Naveen. 5653 FRIST BLVD, STE 237 37076 #495-33-1970 L1982 **OBS** *020 †30
STEGER, Christina W. 5651 FRIST BLVD STE 200 37076 #028-46-1979 L1983 **PD** *020 †55
TEDESCO, James Vincent. 5653 FRIST BLVD 37076 #010-02-1999 L2002 **IM** *020 †20
THOMAS, Michael Carey. 5651 FRIST BLVD, STE 709 37076 #047-06-1981 L1982 **GS VS** *020 †85
THOMPSON, Carolyn Crump. 5651 FRIST BLVD, STE 505 37076 #047-06-1993 L1997 **OBG** *020 †30
VAFAI, Parvin. 5651 FRIST BLVD STE 200 37076 #517-04-1973 L1992 **PD** *020 †55
VAZQUEZ, Ernesto. 3939 CENTRAL PIKE, STE 100 37076 #048-12-2000 L2003 **FM** *020 †18
VERVERIS, John J. 5651 FRIST BLVD, STE 603 37076 #028-34-1987 L1995 **IM CD** *020 †20
WADLINGTON, William B. 5045 OLD HICKORY BLVD, STE 200 37076 #047-05-1952 L1952 **PD N** *071 †55
WALKER, Lottie Ann. 5655 FRIST BLVD 37076 #047-06-1994 L1999 **P** *020 †75
WALLACE, Cynthia L. 4777 ANDREW JACKSON PKWY, STE 2 37076 #047-06-1996 L1998 **FM** *020 †18
WARD, Bryan Kendale. ■ 37076 #047-06-2000 L2002 **IM** *020 †20
WATSON, Keith Fitzroy. 5651 FRIST BLVD, STE 701 37076 #566-01-1986 L2002 **NEP** *020 †20
WESTERMEIER, Thomas G. ■ 37076 #396-01-1980 L1994 **PTH** *020 †50
WHITSITT, Jeffrey Scott. ■ 37076 #039-05-1988 **IM** *020
WILLIAMS, Jana Montice. 233 JACKSON MEADOWS DR 37076 #047-07-1988 L1991 **P** *020
WILLIAMS, Joan Thompson. 5651 FRIST BLVD 37076 #047-06-1971 L1972 **DR OS** *020 †80
WILLIAMS, Robin. 5651 FRIST BLVD, STE 601 37076 #023-01-1989 L1994 **GS** *020 †85
WILLIAMS, Thomas Ashurst. 5651 FRIST BLVD, STE 603 37076 #047-20-1998 L2001 **CD** *100 †20
WITHERSPOON, Christi A. 5653 FRIST BLVD 37076 #047-20-1998 L2000 **IM** *020 †20
WITTERS, Gregory D. 4777 ANDREW JACKSON PKWY, STE 101 37076 #020-12-1974 L1978 **FM** *020 †18
YOUNG, Joshua Olsen. 5410 OLD HICKORY BLVD, SUMMIT EYE ASSOC 37076 #012-01-2003 L2006 **OPH** *020
ZHOU, Shan-Ren. 5651 FRIST BLVD, STE 308 37076 #243-49-1978 L1998 **N** *020 †75

HILLSBORO – COFFEE

DANIEL, David Alan. ■ 37342 #017-20-1990 L1992 **AN** *020 †05

HIXSON – HAMILTON

ALIMURKA, Krystyna Tamara. 1039 EXECUTIVE DR STE 102 37343 #065-01-1974 L1978 **AI IM** *020 †20,03
ASBURY, Brandon Shane. ■ 37343 #047-06-2005 **ORS** *012
BERGLUND, Robert Kent. 2051 HAMILL RD, STE 2000 37343 #048-04-1973 L1977 **CD IM** *020 †20
BHUSHAN, Sumeet Jagdish. 2051 HAMILL RD, GALEN NORTH 37343 #012-01-1997 L1998 **GE** *020 †20
BHUSHAN, Susan Denice. 1017 EXECUTIVE DR, STE 101 37343 #048-02-1997 L1998 **IM** *020 †20
BLOOM, Deidre Ann. 1008 RING RD, # B 37343 #005-06-1993 L1996 **PD** *020 †55
BOISER, Aristides L. ■ 37343 #748-09-1967 L1977 **AN** *020
BOLTON, James Patrick. 4843 HIXSON PIKE, STE C 37343 #001-06-1985 L1987 **OBG** *020 †30
BRANNON, Carolyn C. 1039 EXECUTIVE DR, GALEN MEDICAL GROUP 37343 #028-46-1985 L2002 **PD** *020 †55
BRIMI, John Benj. 2051B HAMILL RD, STE 210 37343 #047-06-1971 L1971 **OPH** *020
BURTON, Edward Miles. 2070 HAMILL RD 37343 #011-03-1971 L1976 **PDR** *020 †55,80
CALDWELL, Thomas Conrad. 2051B HAMILL RD, STE 201 37343 #001-02-1982 L1987 **U GS** *020 †95
CARROLL, Corina F. 4519 HIXSON PIKE 37343 #935-07-1988 L1994 **PD** *020 †55
CATLIN, Roger Wm. 1012 EXECUTIVE DR 37343 #007-02-1971 L1980 **PME AN** *020 †05
CHROSTOWSKI, John Henry. 2051B HAMILL RD STE 3000 37343 #024-07-1991 L1996 **ORS** *020 †40
COFFMAN, Roger Allen, Jr. 4519 HIXSON PIKE 37343 #012-01-1999 L2002 **PD** *020 †55
COHN, Ross Allen. ■ 37343 #010-01-2002 L2007 **U** *020
CONSTANTINESCU, Daniel E. 2051B HAMILL RD, STE 301 37343 #781-01-1957 L1995 **CD IM** *071 †20

COOK, Thomas Andrew. 2051B HAMILL RD, STE 204 37343 #012-05-1978 L1979 **IM** *020 †20

COVI, Karin Marie. 2051B HAMILL RD, STE 301A 37343 #005-12-1985 L1990 **EM** *020 †16

DAHRLING, Bruce E, II. 5022 OLD GODSEY LN, STE 7 37343 #023-07-1965 L1972 **OPH PTH** *020 †35

DALTON, Howell B, Jr. 2051B HAMILL RD STE 203 37343 #495-37-1982 L1987 **IM** *020

DAVIS, Larry Wendell. 4843 HIXSON PIKE, STE C 37343 #021-05-1966 L1969 **GYN GO** *071 †30

DAVIS, Timothy P. 1039 EXECUTIVE DR, GALEN MEDICAL GROUP 37343 #047-06-1976 L1976 **PD EM** *020 †55

DICKINSON, Elizabeth B. 2051 HAMILL RD, STE 400A 37343 #020-12-1972 L1973 **OBG** *020 †30

DONALDSON, Richard Wm. 2051B HAMILL RD, STE 210 37343 #047-06-1970 L1970 **ORS** *020 †40

DOTY, Jesse Forbes. ■ 37343 #047-06-2007 **ORS** *012

DOWELL, William Curtis. 2051B HAMILL RD STE 103 37343 #047-06-1958 L1958 **IM** *020

DUVALL, Daniel J. ■ 37343 #010-02-1981 L1991 **EM PD** *020 †55,16

DUVALL, Mary Michela. ■ 37343 #045-01-1989 L1994 **IM** *020 †20

DWYER, William Knowles. 2051 HAMILL RD 37343 #047-06-1960 L1961 **GS** *071 †85

EGELI, Lale Suzan. 1035 EXECUTIVE DR, STE 105 37343 #012-05-2001 L2006 **RHU** *020

ELDRIDGE, Frank R. 4519 HIXSON PIKE 37343 #047-06-1966 L1966 **PD** *020

FENNEWALD, Clarence L. 4513 HIXSON PIKE, STE 101 HIXSON COMMONS 37343 #028-03-1976 L1980 **D** *020 †15

FOREMAN, Chas Steel, Jr. ■ 37343 #047-07-1978 L1979 **OBG** *040 †30

FORSTEN, Ernest Alvin. 2051B HAMILL RD, STE 301 37343 #047-06-1960 L1961 **GP GS** *020 †18

FOWLER, Todd Everett. 1724 HAMILL RD STE 102, OASIS PARK BLDG I 37343 #025-01-1991 L1997 **OTO** *020 †45

GALINDEZ, Elaine Griffin. 2051B HAMILL RD, STE 103 37343 #047-06-1982 L1983 **ON** *020 †20

GIBSON, Larry. 2051B HAMILL RD STE 301 37343 #017-20-1982 L1989 **N OS** *020 †75

GOODLAD, James K. ■ 37343 #021-01-1953 L1971 **OS** *071

GOSS, Laura Michelle. ■ 37343 #047-06-2005 L2008 **PD** *012

GRUBB, Amanda Leigh. ■ 37343 #047-06-2006 **IM** *012

HARVEY, Hathaway K. 1724 HAMILL RD STE 102, OASIS PARK BLDG I 37343 #017-20-1965 L1970 **OTO HNS** *020 †45

HICKS, Biram Clyde. 2051 HAMILL RD, MEMORIAL NORTH PARK HOSPIT 37343 #028-03-1980 L1980 **ID** *040 †20

HOBGOOD, Donna Kay. 4843 HIXSON PIKE, STE C 37343 #012-01-1984 L1986 **OBG** *020 †30

HORTON, Marshall L, III. 2051 HAMILL RD, GALEN NORTH 37343 #027-01-1979 L1988 **GE IM** *020 †20

HUFFSTUTTER, Jos Eugene. 1035 EXECUTIVE DR, STE 105 37343 #047-06-1978 L1984 **RHU** *020 †20

HUGGINS-FELIX, Sharon G. 6303 MARINA POINTE CIR, HIXSON 37343 #012-21-1992 L2002 **EM** *020

HUNT, Noel Clarence. 2051 HAMILL RD, STE 2000 37343 #047-05-1961 L1961 **CD IM** *020 †20

HUNT, Peter Mc Lain. 1724 HAMILL RD STE 102, OASIS PARK BLDG I 37343 #047-05-1994 L2001 **OTO** *020 †45

INNES, Christopher Ian. 2051A HAMILL RD 37343 #047-06-2003 L2005 **OBG** *020

JOHNSON, William Frank, Jr. 1013 EXECUTIVE DR, STE 103 37343 #047-06-1969 L1969 **GS** *020 †85

JOHNSTON, John T. 2070 HAMILL RD 37343 #016-43-1980 L1987 **DR** *020 †80

JONES, Andrew Roy. 2051 HAMILL RD, STE 400A 37343 #047-06-1986 L1990 **OBG** *020 †30

JONES, Gerald Isom. 2051 HAMILL RD, STE 400A 37343 #047-06-1958 L1959 **OBG** *071 †30

KENNEDY, John Henry. 2051B HAMILL RD STE 102 37343 #020-02-1975 L1976 **IM FM** *020

KRECKER, Martin Thos. 5022 OLD GODSEY LN, STE 10 37343 #001-06-1990 L1997 **GS CRS** *020 †85

KRUMMERT, Brett Alan. ■ 37343 #012-01-2008 *012

KYLE, Clyde Alexander, III. 2070 HAMILL RD 37343 #047-06-1986 L1988 **DR** *020 †80

LAND, Roger Lynn. 2051B HAMILL RD, STE 101 37343 #012-01-1988 L1990 **GS** *020 †85

LEFLER, Lee Murriel. 2070 HAMILL RD 37343 #012-01-1997 L1998 **DR** *020 †80

LOWRY, Patricia Ann. 2070 HAMILL RD 37343 #028-34-1978 L2006 **PDR DR** *020 †80

LOYD, James Alan. 2070 HAMILL RD 37343 #048-04-1978 L1983 **DR** *020 †80

MANCE, Cornelius J. 2051B HAMILL RD, STE 301B 37343 #047-06-1973 L1974 **N** *020 †20,75

MARTIN, James Austin. 2070 HAMILL RD 37343 #047-06-1953 L1959 **DR** *020 †80

MARTIN, Maria. 1013 EXECUTIVE DR, STE 101 37343 #781-01-1966 L1993 **FM** *020 †18

MATTHEWS, William Edwin. 5022 OLD GODSEY LN, STE 8 37343 #045-01-1971 L1980 **ORS** *040 †40

MAY, Marian G. 4519 HIXSON PIKE 37343 #011-04-1977 L1980 **PD** *020 †55

MAY, Steven L. 4519 HIXSON PIKE 37343 #011-04-1977 L1980 **PD** *020 †55

MC DONALD, Mary Katherine. 5211 HIGHWAY 153, STE M 37343 #005-18-1992 L1996 **PM PMM** *020 †60

MC DONALD, Preston Arnold. ■ 37343 #001-06-1977 L1999 **EM FM** *020 †18

MC LEAN, George Wallace. 2051B HAMILL RD, STE 401 37343 #036-07-1973 L1976 **END IM** *020 †20

MC MAHAN, Becky Sue. 4519 HIXSON PIKE 37343 #027-01-1983 L1986 **PD** *020

MEHTA, Tejal Vijay. 2051 HAMILL RD STE 30, PROFESSIONAL BUILDING 37343 #012-01-2002 L2006 **IM** *020 †20

MENA, Michael Christopher. 2051B HAMILL RD, STE 403 37343 #048-04-1978 L1987 **GS** *020 †85

MILLER, Phyllis A Edwards. 4843 HIXSON PIKE STE C 37343 #047-06-1972 L1972 **GYN** *020 †30

MITCHELL, Allen Myers. 2051 HAMILL RD 37343 #038-40-1975 L1981 **DR** *020 †80

MOORE, Benjamin Charles. ■ 37343 #027-01-2008 *012

MOSES, Thomas Edward. 2051 HAMILL RD 37343 #011-02-1972 L1978 **ORS** *020 †40

MULLER, John Scott, Jr. 2051 HAMILL RD, STE C0620 37343 #047-05-1996 L1999 **IM** *020 †20

MUNDAY, Tona. 2070 HAMILL RD 37343 #036-01-1989 L1999 **RNR** *020 †80

NEALL, David Lawrence. 4519 HIXSON PIKE 37343 #001-02-1981 L1986 **PD** *040 †55

NUNES, John Orel. 2070 HAMILL RD 37343 #011-04-2000 L2006 **DR** *020 †80

O'CONNELL, James Jos. 2051B HAMILL RD, STE 301 37343 #018-03-1972 L1995 **FM ADM** *020 †18 ‡

PALLAS, William Chas. 5251 HIGHWAY 153 # C # 158 37343 #035-08-1944 L1954 **GYN** *071 †30

PARKHURST, Walter Douglas. 2051 HAMILL RD, GALEN NORTH 37343 #051-04-1974 L1978 **IM IMG** *020 †20

PATY, John Garland, Jr. 1035 EXECUTIVE DR, STE 105 37343 #047-06-1966 L1967 **RHU** *020 †20

PAUL, Larry H. 2070 HAMILL RD 37343 #025-07-1974 L1981 **DR** *020 †80

QUARFORDT, Steven Daniel. 2070 HAMILL RD 37343 #036-08-1994 L2002 **VIR** *020 †80

RAGON, William Stansul, Jr. ■ 37343 #047-06-2006 **ORS** *012

RAMSEY, Millard Wray. 2051A HAMILL RD, STE 400 37343 #027-01-1963 L1969 **OBG** *071 †30

RAVEE, Mani. ■ 37343 #495-94-1989 L2006 **PCC** *100

RAYERS, Philip Robert. 927 SHERRY CIR 37343 #047-06-2002 L2004 **IM** *020 †20

REDDY, Amardeep K. ■ 37343 #028-78-2006, ▲ L2007 *012

SALT, Nicholas Joseph. 2051 HAMILL RD 37343 #917-29-1978 L1995 **FM IM** *020 †18

SAMUEL, Sandy. ■ 37343 #661-03-2005 **PD** *012

SCOTT, Wayne Thos. 2051 HAMILL RD, GALEN NORTH 37343 #001-02-1983 L1984 **IM** *020 †20

SEMAN, Charles Frederick. ■ 37343 #012-01-1962 L1970 **PD** *071 †55

SHAH, Chetan Dineshbhai. 2051 HAMILL RD 37343 #495-23-1992 L1999 **IM** *020 †20

SHUCK, Susan Mary. 2051 HAMILL RD, STE 400A 37343 #012-01-1990 L1993 **OBG** *020 †30

SHUMAKER, Nita Wall. 1039 EXECUTIVE DR, GALEN MEDICAL GROUP 37343 #036-08-1989 L2000 **PD** *020 †55

SIENKNECHT, Chas Willson. 1035 EXECUTIVE DR, STE 105 37343 #047-06-1967 L1975 **RHU IM** *020 †20

SIMPSON, Mark T. 4513 HIXSON PIKE, THE WELLNESS CLINIC STE102 37343 #047-06-1982 L1989 **FM OM** *020 †18

SPITALNY, Neil Howard. 5022 OLD GODSEY LN, STE 2 37343 #035-03-1979 L1984 **ORS** *020 †40

STANKO, James Alexander. 2051B HAMILL RD STE 204, GALEN NORTH 37343 #065-01-1973 L1978 **IM** *020 †20

ST CHARLES, Christopher S. 1724 HAMILL RD STE 102, OASIS PARK BUILDING I 37343 #047-06-1987 L1992 **OTO GS** *020 †45

SUMIDA, Mark Sean. 2051B HAMILL RD STE 107 37343 #020-12-1988 L1989 **ORS** *020 †40

SUSONG, Charles R. 2051B HAMILL RD STE 301 37343 #047-06-1976 L1976 **D IM** *020 †20,15

SWINDELL, Stanley Mark. 2051 HAMILL RD 37343 #047-06-1987 L1988 **EM IM** *020 †20

TALLEY, Mark Andrew. 2070 HAMILL RD 37343 #039-01-1982 L1987 **R VIR** *020 †80

THOMPSON, Bruce Todd. 4490 HIXSON PIKE 37343 #001-06-1991 L1995 **FM** *020 †18

TRUELOVE, Laura Thompson. 1039 EXECUTIVE DR, GALEN MEDICAL GROUP 37343 #055-01-1994 L1997 **PD** *020 †55

VERVILLE, Gregory Lorne. 2070 HAMILL RD 37343 #062-01-1989 L2006 **DR** *020 †80

WANG, Anne Chinghuey. 4843 HIXSON PIKE STE C 37343 #047-06-1997 L2004 **OBG** *020 †30

WATERS, Ronald Douglas, Jr. ■ 37343 #001-02-1999 L2007 **DR** *100 †80

WEATHERBY, Brian A. ■ 37343 #045-01-2003 L2005 **ORS** *012

WILEY, Benjamin Wayne. 1039 EXECUTIVE DR, GALEN MEDICAL GROUP 37343 #020-12-1997 L2001 **PD** *020 †55

WILLIAMSON, Ivey. 2051 HAMILL RD, GALEN NORTH 37343 #001-02-1992 L1998 **IM** *020 †20

WOOD, Robert Moodie. 4519 HIXSON PIKE 37343 #048-04-1982 L1997 **PD** *020 †55

YAMADA, Donovan Lyle. 2070 HAMILL RD 37343 #005-12-2000 L2006 **VIR** *020 †80

HOHENWALD – LEWIS

ALFREDSON, David Gordon. 621 W MAIN ST 38462 #016-43-1976 L1981 **DR GP** *020

ANAND, Veena. 621 W MAIN ST, ANAND CLINIC 38462 #495-36-1967 L1973 **IM GP** *020

ANAND, Virender. 621 W MAIN ST, ANAND CLINIC 38462 #495-36-1966 L1973 **GS GP** *020 †85

HEFFINGTON, Charles A, Jr. 200B W LINDEN AVE 38462 #047-06-1966 L1967 **ORS HS** *020

HENSLEY, Joseph Shelby. 507 W MAIN ST 38462 #047-06-1983 L1984 **FM** *020 †18

NINER, Paul Jos, III. 621 W MAIN ST, THE ANAND CLINIC 38462 #010-12-1986 L1988 **GP** *020

HORNSBY – HARDEMAN

BLACKWELL, Samuel Jos, Jr. ■ 38044 #047-06-1964 L1965 **CD** *071 †20

HUMBOLDT – GIBSON

ARINZE, Festus N. 3565 CHERE CAROL RD 38343 #690-04-1989 L2002 **IM** *020 †20

BARKER, Robert Crowe. 3519 CHERE CAROL RD 38343 #047-06-1962 L1962 **FM** *020

BURLESON, David Glen. 3525 CHERE CAROL RD, JACKSON UROLOGICAL ASSOC 38343 #039-01-1985 L1990 **U GS** *020 †95

CHIOCO, Ernesto P. 701 MEDICAL PARK DR, PURIHIN CLINIC PC 38343 #748-08-1982 L2001 **IM IMG** *020 †20

COUCH, Billy Lanier. 306 FOREST DR 38343 #047-06-1959 L1959 **FM ID** *071 †18 ‡

CRENSHAW, Thomas Malcolm. 1634 E MAIN ST 38343 #047-06-1964 L1964 **FM** *020 †18

CURLIN, John Paschal. ■ 38343 #004-01-1965 L1973 **GYN** *071 †30

DIETZ, Bernhard Eric. 701 MEDICAL PARK DR 38343 #041-02-1984 L1996 **FM** *020 †18

DIEUDONNE, Gina Marie. 1804 E MAIN ST, RAINBOW PEDIATRIC, P.C. 38343 #016-11-1989 L2007 **PD** *020 †55

DUNLAP, Warner Benj. 1629 E MAIN ST, P O BOX 424 38343 #047-06-1968 L1968 **PD** *020

HARRISON, Nelson C, Jr. ■ 38343 #047-06-1969 L1970 **EM** *071 †18

HOWARD, Raymond Collier. 3525 CHERE CAROL RD, JACKSON UROLOGICAL ASSOC 38343 #047-06-1990 L1992 **U** *020 †95

JAMES, David Franklin. 3525 CHERE CAROL RD, HUMBOLDT GENERAL HOSPITAL 38343 #047-06-1989 L1990 **FM** *020 †18

KIRBY, Keith Harmon. 3568 CHERE CAROL RD, JACKSON CLINIC OF HUMBOLDT 38343 #047-06-1989 L1990 **FM** *020 †18

MADRID, Dulce Flor E. 3568 CHERE CAROL RD, HUMBOLDT 38343 #748-01-1991 L1998 **FM** *020 †18

MURPHY, Richard Louis. 3535 CHERE CAROL RD 38343 #047-06-1981 L1982 **FM** *020 †18

PETERS, Jerry Dean. 3525 CHERE CAROL RD, HUMBOLDT GENERAL HOSPITAL 38343 #048-04-1964 L1984 **EM FM** *071 †18,16

PRESSON, Matthew B. ■ 38343 #028-78-2006, ▲ L2008 **FP** *012

ROUTON, William Robt. 3535 CHERE CAROL RD 38343 #047-06-1973 L1973 **GS** *020 †85

SWAIM, Cynthia Raines. 3568 CHERE CAROL RD, HUMBOLDT 38343 #047-20-1998 L1999 **FM** *020 †18

UTLEY, Jennifer Elizabeth. 3525 CHERE CAROL RD 38343 #047-06-1995 L1997 **FM** *020 †18

WILLIAMS, Lynnette P. ■ 38343 #047-07-1986 L1992 **IM** *020

YANCEY-ALLEN, Beryl G. 3511 CHERE CAROL RD 38343 #047-07-1987 L1989 **FM** *020

YEATES, Sheran Arden. 1804 E MAIN ST 38343 #305-01-1990 L1997 **FM** *020 †18

HUNTINGDON – CARROLL

ATKINS, Jerry Franklin. 641 RB WILSON DR, R. B. WILSON MEDICAL CENTE 38344 #047-06-1963 L1963 **FM OS** *020 †18

BLANKENSHIP, John Lee. 641 RB WILSON DR, STE D 38344 #047-06-2000 L2002 **FM** *020 †18

BORDERS, Trent Wade. 631 RB WILSON DR HU 38344 #047-06-2002 L2006 **DR** *020 †80

CALFEE, Michael David. 641 RB WILSON DR, STE L 38344 #047-06-1995 L2000 **ORS** *020 †40

CARTER, Lee Marvin. 641 RB WILSON DR STE F 38344 #047-06-1991 L1992 **FM** *020 †18 ‡

CARTY, Calphor Stanford. 641 RB WILSON DR, STE J 38344 #036-05-1991 L2004 **GS** *020 †85

CRAN-CARTY, Wendy. 631 RB WILSON DR STE 4, CARROLL COUNTY ANESTH 38344 #036-05-1995 L2004 **AN IM** *020

DHAR, Ujjwal. 50 STONE RIDGE CV 38344 #160-06-1990 L2003 **ID** *100 †20

HAMPTON, Toby Andrew. 600 RB WILSON DR 38344 #047-20-2002 L2003 **FM** *020 †18

PORTIS, Bill Scott. 641 RB WILSON DR 38344 #047-06-1972 L1973 **EM FM** *020 †20

REITER, Amanda Moore. 20719 E MAIN ST, HUNTINGDON 38344 #047-06-1993 L1994 **FM** *020 †18

SALAZAR, Sergio A. 50 STONE RIDGE CV 38344 #654-01-1988 L1991 **IM** *020 †20

WHEATLEY, Kevin Joe. 631 RB WILSON DR 38344 #047-20-1991 L1992 **FM** *020 †18

WILLIAMSON, James Stephen. 641 RB WILSON DR, STE G 38344 #047-06-1974 L1975 **FM** *020 †20

WINSTON, Robert Lee. 631 RB WILSON DR 38344 #047-07-1976 L1977 **IM EM** *020 †20

HUNTSVILLE – SCOTT

DAVIDSON, Dirk C. 125 LITTON COVERED BRDG RD 37756 #055-01-1984 L1991 **IM** *020 †20

MOREHEAD, Vernon Tupper. 344 COURT ST, SCOTT CTY HLTH DEPT 37756 #047-06-1971 L1972 **OBG PHP** *020 †30

SMITH, Timothy Dwayne. 950 BAKER HWY UNIT 4, GRACE PRIMARY CARE 37756 #047-20-1995 L1996 **FM** *020 †18 ‡

WOLFE, Larry E. 2974 BAKER HWY 37756 #047-06-1977 L1981 **FM** *020

INDIAN MOUND – STEWART

ROBY, Justin David. 108 MILLER DR 37079 #023-12-1992 L1993 **FM** *020 †18

JACKSBORO – CAMPBELL

CAMPBELL, Philip Darby. 2523 JACKSBORO PIKE 37757 #021-01-1981 L1985 **OPH** *020 †35

CUNNINGHAM, Leslie B. 2523 JACKSBORO PIKE 37757 #027-01-1982 L1991 **OPH PD** *020 †55,35

HAUN, Louis Eugene, Jr. 2523 JACKSBORO PIKE 37757 #047-06-1964 L1965 **OPH** *020 †35

ISHAM, Charles Aubrey. 163 PERKINS LN, AUBREY ISHAM JR MD 37757 #047-06-1980 L1981 **IM IMG** *020 †20

NARULA, Gurpreet K. 2503 JACKSBORO PIKE 37757 #495-45-1988 L1995 **IM** *020 †20

NARULA, Harjeet. 2503 JACKSBORO PIKE 37757 #495-69-1984 L1995 **IM** *020 †20

TAYLOR, Christopher Tobin. 2523 JACKSBORO PIKE 37757 #048-01-1992 L1997 **OPH** *020 †35

JACKSON – MADISON

ADKINS, William Bradford. 244 COATSLAND DR 38301 #047-06-1992 L1996 **OBG** *020 †30

AELION, Jacob Asher. 371 N PARKWAY STE 400 38305 #550-02-1978 L1989 **RHU IM** *020 †20

AGBETOYIN, Adeyinka. 17 CENTRE PLAZA DR, DELTA CONVENIENT CARE 38305 #913-32-1989 L2002 **CD** *020 †20

AHMAD, Omar. 708 W FOREST AVE 38301 #704-02-1990 L1997 **HO** *020 †20

AHMED, Khwaja Asif. 616 W FOREST AVE 38301 #704-25-1997 L2007 **OTO** *020

AKIN, Jay D. ■ 38305 #048-13-2005 L2007 **FP** *012

ALEX, Susan. 16 MURRAY GUARD DR 38305 #495-31-1976 L1997 **NEP IM** *020 †20

ALEXANDER, Clyde Vinson. PO BOX 3459 38303 #036-07-1959 L1964 **R VIR** *071 †80

ALLEN, Misty Yow. 294 SUMMAR DR, UTFP RESIDENCY PROGRAM 38301 #047-06-2005 L2006 **FM** *020 †18

ALPEROVICH, Alexander. 327 SUMMAR DR, APEX CARDIOLOGY 38301 #913-96-1982 L2008 **CD** *020 †20

AMPOMAH, John Kweku. ■ 38305 #412-01-1999 L2007 **IM** *100 †20

ANDERSON, Charles B. 708 W FOREST AVE, JACKSON COUNTY GEN HOSP 38301 #047-06-1984 L1985 **AN** *020

ANDERSON, Mary E Neal. 2863 HIGHWAY 45 BYP, NORTH JACKSON 38305 #047-06-1992 L1996 **MPD** *020 †20,55

ANSAH, Martinson Asiedu. ■ 38305 #305-01-2000 L2007 **IM** *020 †20

ANTIQUE, Daisy Tan. 708 W FOREST AVE, GENERAL HOSPITAL 38301 #748-01-1981 L2005 **IM** *020 †20

ANTIQUE, Julie Tan. 708 W FOREST AVE, JACKSON MADISON COUNTY GEN 38301 #748-01-1991 L2004 **IM** *020 †20

ANTWI, Ernest K. 14 WEATHERFORD SQ 38305 #913-92-1981 L2001 **END** *020 †20

ANTWINE, Harold Melville. 24 PHYSICIANS DR 38305 #021-01-1991 L1998 **ORS** *020 †40

APPLE, Jeffrey M. 395 HOSPITAL BLVD, JACKSON SURGICAL 38305 #048-13-1997 L2007 **VS** *020 †85

APPLETON, James Roy, Jr. 616 W FOREST AVE 38301 #047-06-1962 L1962 **U** *020

APPLETON, James Roy, III. 708 W FOREST AVE 38301 #047-20-1995 L1997 **FM** *020 †20

APPLETON, Melissa Anne. 616 W FOREST AVE, UNIVERSITY OF TENNESSEE 38301 #047-06-1985 L1986 **IM** *020 †20

AQUINO, Myrna T. 804 N PARKWAY 38305 #748-01-1964 L1990 **PD** *071 †55

ASMAR, Salomon Narciso. 616 W FOREST AVE, JACKSON CLINIC, P.A. 38301 #042-01-1977 L2001 **IM HEM** *050 †20

ATKINS, Keith Lantrip. 176 W UNIVERSITY PKWY, STE C 38305 #047-06-1992 L1995 **IM** *020 †20

BADA, Samuel Olaniyi. 1673 N ROYAL ST 38301 #590-01-1990 L2000 **IM** *020 †20

BAKER, John Wm. ■ 38301 #047-06-1990 L1996 **CD** *020 †20

BALL, John Jeffrey. 2863 HIGHWAY 45 BYP, NORTH JACKSON 38305 #027-01-1988 L1992 **OBG** *020 †30

BALLARD, Thomas Kelly. 418 E BALTIMORE ST, T K BALLARD 38301 #047-06-1984 L1985 **FM** *020 †18

BANEZ, Monico P. 708 W FOREST AVE, 8W 38301 #748-01-1988 L2001 **IM** *020 †20

BANKS, Marshall Denny. 616 W FOREST AVE 38301 #047-06-1991 L1994 **IM** *020 †20

BARKER, James Harris. 619 SKYLINE DR 38301 #047-06-1962 L1964 **OTO PS** *020 †45

BARNES, James Walter, Jr. 45 PHYSICIANS DR, THE UROLOGY CLINIC PA 38305 #047-06-1968 L1969 **U** *071

BARNETT, Hugh Glenn, II. 614 SKYLINE DR 38301 #021-01-1968 L1976 **NS** *020 †25

BARNETT, Robert J. ■ 38301 #021-01-1944 L1957 **ORS** *020 †40

BATEMAN, Mark Roy. 668 SKYLINE DR 38301 #047-20-1985 L1987 **OPH** *020 †35

BAYLOR, Edward Means, III. 1747 N ROYAL ST 38305 #047-07-1981 L1984 **GP** *020

BEARB, Michael Edwin. 810 W FOREST AVE 38305 #048-12-1984 L1993 **AN PME** *020 †05

BERGQUIST, Stephen G. 616 W FOREST AVE 38301 #654-01-1986 L1997 **IM RO** *020

BINGHAM, Ronald Craig. ■ 38305 #021-06-1985 L1989 **PM OM** *020 †60

BLAISS, Michael Steven. 587 SKYLINE DR, STE B 38301 #047-06-1976 L1977 **A PDA** *020 †55,03

BLAKE, Jeremy Todd. 264 COATSLAND DR 38301 #004-01-1996 L1999 **PD** *020 †55

BLANKENSHIP, Joe David. 1203 VANN DR 38305 #047-06-1977 L1978 **CD** *020 †20

BOND, Elias King, Jr. 708 W FOREST AVE, GENERAL HOSPITAL 38301 #047-06-1968 L1969 **P** *020

BOOTH, Jack H. 708 W FOREST AVE 38301 #048-02-1949 L1958 **ORS** *071 †40

BOWEN, Wendy Elizabeth. 616 W FOREST AVE 38301 #027-01-1996 L1999 **PD** *020 †55

BOXELL-DUCKWORTH, Sandra. 72 PHYSICIANS DR 38305 #011-04-1992 L2001 **OBG** *020 †30

BOYAPATI, Madhav. 244 COATSLAND DR, WOMAN'S CLINIC, P.A. 38301 #047-05-1996 L2000 **OBG** *020 †30

BOYD, Roderick Rene. 686 W FOREST AVE STE A5 38301 #047-07-1990 L1999 **GS** *020 †85

BROOKS, Nathaniel, II. 8 STONEBRIDGE BLVD, STE J 38305 #038-45-1985 L1994 **FM** *020

BROUSSARD, Heath Jude. 616 W FOREST AVE 38305 #021-05-1994 L1999 **GS** *020 †85

BROWN, Jane Warne. ■ 38305 #047-06-1968 L1970 **DR** *020

BROWN, Joe Lawrence, II. 616 W FOREST AVE, THE JACKSON CLINIC, PA 38301 #047-06-1969 L1970 **DR** *020

BRUEGGEMAN, Michael Wayne. 614 SKYLINE DR 38301 #016-11-1980 L1981 **N** *020 †75

BRUNO, Gregory Carl. 708 W FOREST AVE 38301 #035-19-1998 L2003 **DR** *020 †80

BRYAN, William David. 2859 US HIGHWAY 45 BYP 38305 #047-06-1986 L1987 **FM** *020 †18

BURTON, Mark Preston. 708 W FOREST AVE 38301 #023-12-1992 L2004 **PTH** *020 †50

CARRAHER, John B. 28 MEDICAL CENTER DR, JACKSON UROLOGICAL 38301 #047-06-1993 L1994 **U** *020 †95

CARRUTH, Cynthia Denise. 367 HOSPITAL BLVD 38305 #047-06-1975 L1977 **PTH** *020 †50

CARRUTH, James Clark. 96 PHYSICIANS DR 38305 #047-20-1990 L1995 **PCC** *020 †20

CARRUTH, Larry Wayne. PO BOX 3841 38303 #047-06-1975 L1975 **PUD IM** *020 †20

CARTER, Michael Allen. ■ 38301 #047-06-2007 **FP** *012

CAUDILL, Robert Paul, Jr. 708 W FOREST AVE 38301 #047-06-1963 L1963 **AM** *020 †70

CHANDLER, Pamela Alford. ■ 38301 #047-06-1972 **PTH** *075

CHARY, Kandala Ram. 16 MURRAY GUARD DR 38305 #495-65-1973 L1980 **NEP IM** *020 †20

CHERRY, Christopher Jason. 616 W FOREST AVE, JACKSON CLINIC, PA 38301 #047-06-1996 L1998 **CD** *020 †20

CHIKE, Aleruchi Yvonne. 616 W FOREST AVE 38301 #690-12-1994 L2005 **IM** *020 †20

CLOWERS-WEBB, Holly E. 87 MURRAY GUARD DR, PLASTICS 38305 #001-02-1998 L2002 **D** *020 †15

COBB, R Michael. 24 PHYSICIANS DR 38305 #047-06-1978 L1979 **ORS OSM** *020 †40

CODJOE, Karen Kaufman. 295 SUMMAR DR, WEST TENNESSEE REGIONAL HE 38301 #047-06-1978 L1979 **PD** *020 †55

COLEMAN, Joseph Curtis. 708 W FOREST AVE 38301 #020-02-1989 L1996 **HMP** *020 †50

COLEMAN, Marilyn Joy L. 2863 HIGHWAY 45 BYP 38305 #047-06-2001 L2007 **PD** *020 †55

COLLIER, Stephen Edward. 616 W FOREST AVE 38301 #001-02-1995 L2006 **IM** *020 †20

CONNER, Shavetta Demetria. 295 SUMMAR DR, WEST TN REGIOAL HLTH DEPT. 38301 #047-07-1991 L1993 **GPM** *020 †70

CORDAHI, Ghassan J. 207 STONEBRIDGE BLVD 38305 #605-02-1992 L2000 **OPH** *020 †35

CORRELL, Donald Chas. 708 W FOREST AVE 38301 #047-02-1981 L1986 **IM** *020 †16

COX, Charles Wm. 708 W FOREST AVE 38301 #047-06-1960 L1960 **OTO A** *071 †45

CRAIG, Carol S. ■ 38305 #047-06-1984 L1990 **CD IM** *071 †20

CRAIG, James Thomas, Jr. 616 W FOREST AVE 38301 #047-06-1962 L1963 **ORS** *020 †40

CRAIG, Sterling Ruffin. 2817 N HIGHLAND AVE, STE A 38305 #047-06-1965 L1966 **D** *020 †15

CRANE, Patricia Gail. 295 SUMMAR DR, STATE DEPT. OF HEALTH-WTRO 38301 #047-06-1990 L1991 **FM** *020 †18

CRENSHAW, James H, Jr. 616 W FOREST AVE 38301 #047-06-1986 L1987 **CD** *020 †20

CRENSHAW, James Harris. 616 W FOREST AVE, JACKSON CLINIC PRO ASSN 38301 #047-06-1956 L1956 **FM** *071 †18

CROCKER, Edward F. 395 HOSPITAL BLVD 38305 #047-06-1951 L1952 **GS TS** *071 †85

CROCKER, John Driver. 708 W FOREST AVE 38301 #047-06-1976 L1980 **VIR R** *020 †80

CROSSETT, Janice Moyers. ■ 38305 #047-06-1983 L1989 **DR** *071 †80

CROSSETT, Timothy Ray. 708 W FOREST AVE, GENERAL HOSPITAL 38301 #047-06-1983 L1989 **DR IM** *020 †80

CUNNINGHAM, Louis E. 48 MEDICAL CENTER DR 38301 #047-07-1979 L1980 **IM CD** *020 †20

CURRIE, Dean Paul. 395 HOSPITAL BLVD, JACKSON SURGICAL 38305 #047-06-1985 L1990 **GS** *020 †85

CURWEN, Davidson Clive. 262 CARRIAGE HOUSE DR 38305 #005-14-1988 L1992 **PM** *020 †60

DAMIAN, Perry Salvador. ■ 38305 #047-07-2004 L2007 **FP** *012

DAVIS-THARPE, Vernessa. 655 LEXINGTON AVE 38301 #010-03-1985 L1991 **PD** *020 †55

DE COSTA, Brian R. 367 HOSPITAL BLVD 38305 #065-01-1997 L2002 **DR** *020 †80

DEE, Maria Sandra V. 616 W FOREST AVE 38301 #047-01-1987 L1999 **IC** *020 †20

DEJARNATT, Alan Carter. 587 SKYLINE DR, STE B 38301 #047-06-1986 L1989 **AI** *020 †20,03

DEMING, Woodie Monroe. 130 STONEBRIDGE BLVD, STE A 38305 #047-06-1975 L1976 **CD EM** *020

DE RUITER, Peter Louis. ■ 38305 #027-01-1957 L1965 **P OS** *071

DE SIO, Marcus Antonio. 1044 GREYSTONE SQ, MEDICAL STAFF OFFICE 38305 #748-19-1984 L1998 **N IM** *020

DIFFEE, James Jones, III. 2863 HIGHWAY 45 BYP, NORTH JACKSON 38305 #047-06-1978 L1979 **IM** *020 †20

DINKINS, Ruth Eleanor. 708 W FOREST AVE 38301 #047-06-1963 L1964 **D AN** *071

DI PUMA, Laura L. 44 FOREST CV 38301 #023-12-1983 L1995 **OPH** *020 †35

DONNELL, James Harold. 648 W FOREST AVE, THE JACKSON CLINIC 38301 #047-06-1962 L1963 **FM GP** *071 †18

DONNELLY, Tara Kim. 2863 HIGHWAY 45 BYP, NORTH JACKSON 38305 #047-06-2001 L2004 **PD** *100

DOTSON, Delores Chantel. 294 SUMMAR DR, UNIVERSITY OF TENNESSEE, JA 38301 #047-06-2004 L2008 **FP** *012

DOUGLAS, Kelvin Lynn. ■ 38301 #016-42-1983 L1995 **IM** *020

DRAPER, Jeremy Michael. ■ 38305 #047-06-2008 *012

DRIVER, Clarence. ■ 38305 #047-06-1952 L1952 **U** *071 †45

DUNNEBACKE, Robert Hudson. 587 SKYLINE DR, STE B 38301 #047-06-1977 L1978 **IM** *020 †20

■ = Address Information Privacy Protected

DU VAL, John Wm. 616 W FOREST AVE 38301 #051-04-1976 L1982 **GE IM** *020 †20
EDWARDS, George T. 395 HOSPITAL BLVD 38305 #047-06-1976 L1976 **GS** *020 †85
EGAN, James Edward. 616 W FOREST AVE 38301 #028-03-1978 L1999 **GE IM** *020 †20
ELDRIDGE, Lolly Houston. 2859 HIGHWAY 45 BYP 38305 #047-06-2004 L2008 **OBG** *012
ELLIS, Ira Keith. 294 SUMMAR DR 38301 #047-06-2002 L2003 **FM** *040 †18
ELLIS, James L, Jr. 52 EMERALD LAKE DR 38305 #047-06-1984 L1985 **DR** *020 †80
ELLIS, Thomas Warren. 616 W FOREST AVE 38301 #047-06-1972 L1973 **PUD IM** *020 †20
EMISON, Tony R. 804 N PARKWAY 38305 #047-20-1984 L1984 **FM** *030 †18 ‡
EPPS, J Michael. 244 COATSLAND DR 38301 #001-06-1978 L1979 **OBG** *020 †30
EVERETT, John Everton. 24 PHYSICIANS DR 38305 #047-06-1971 L1972 **ORS** *020 †40
EWOH, Charles Egbo. 2777 N HIGHLAND AVE, EZE CLINIC PC 38305 #690-06-1997 L2004 **IM** *020
EZE, Gift Egbon. 2777 N HIGHLAND AVE 38305 #308-11-1992 L1996 **IM EM** *020 †20
FEICK, Steven Wade. 708 W FOREST AVE 38301 #026-04-1996 L2003 **DR** *020 †80
FIGUEROA, Estuardo. 708 W FOREST AVE, PEDIATRIC SPECIALTY INC 38301 #429-01-1993 L2006 **PD NPM** *020 †55
FIGUEROA, Mario. ■ 38305 #429-01-1997 L2005 **FM** *100 †18
FINAN, Eugene Michael. 110 E FOREST AVE 38301 #004-01-1976 L1994 **OBG** *020 †30
FINNEN, Neil Patrick. 569 SKYLINE DR, STE 200 38301 #034-01-1992 L2000 **OPH** *020 †35 ‡
FORD, Charles Davis. 367 HOSPITAL BLVD 38305 #049-01-1984 L2004 **EM** *020 †16
FOSTER, Charles Stephen. 708 W FOREST AVE 38301 #047-06-1970 L1971 **PTH** *071 †50
FRANCISCO, Susan Marie. 616 W FOREST AVE 38301 #047-06-1986 L1987 **NEP IM** *020 †20
FRANZEN, Dirk Geo. 172 W UNIVERSITY PKWY, STE A 38305 #011-02-1983 L1995 **NS** *020 †25
FREEMAN, Charles M. 708 W FOREST AVE, JACKSON COUNTY GEN HOSP 38301 #028-78-1982, ▲ L1987 **AN** *020 †05
GALDINO, Gregory Michael. ■ 38305 #036-07-1996 L2007 **GS** *020 †80
GARDNER, Peter Thomas. ■ 38301 #047-06-1993 L2006 **FP** *012
GAREY, David Lee. 2859 US HIGHWAY 45 BYP 38305 #047-06-1985 L1986 **FM EM** *020 †18
GEORGIOU, Anastasios L. 708 W FOREST AVE, JACKSON MADISON HOSP DEPT 38301 #005-06-1988 L1993 **RO** *020 †80
GHODADRA, Trushit M. 708 W FOREST AVE 38301 #012-01-1999 L2005 **DR** *020 †80
GIAMPAPA, Christopher Sam. 708 W FOREST AVE 38301 #047-06-1992 L1993 **PTH** *020 †50
GILROY, Robert Johnson. 616 W FOREST AVE 38301 #033-05-1984 L1987 **PUD CCM** *020 †20
GINGOLD, Glenn Adam. 1804 HIGHWAY 45 BYP, THIRD FLOOR 38305 #011-02-1975 L2001 **FM EM** *020
GO, Josefina Dee. 708 W FOREST AVE, DIVISION OF NEONATOLOGY 38301 #748-01-1988 L2004 **PD** *020 †55
GO, Victor Velez, Jr. ■ 38305 #748-01-1987 L2007 **FM** *100
GOOCH, Clarence Terry. 8 MEDICAL CENTER DR 38301 #047-07-1976 L1980 **OBG** *020
GOODWIN, Stephen Chester. 31 PHYSICIANS DR 38305 #308-11-1985 L1988 **IM** *020 ‡
GORBET, Lauri A. 708 W FOREST AVE, JACKSON COUNTY GEN HOSP 38301 #004-01-1990 L1994 **AN** *020 †05
GRAHAM, Matthew Timothy. 708 W FOREST AVE, GENERAL HOSPITAL 38301 #045-01-1993 L1995 **VIR** *020 †80
GRAY, Jean Paul. 244 COATSLAND DR 38301 #021-05-1988 L1990 **OBG** *020 †30
GRAY, Kevin Gerard. 587 SKYLINE DR, STE B 38301 #047-06-1988 L1989 **IM** *020
GREEN, Diane Elaine. 706 W FOREST AVE 38301 #047-06-1980 L1981 **PTH** *020 †50
GREEN, John Allen. 105 STONEBROOK PL STE F 38305 #021-05-1962 L1970 **R NM** *020
GREENE, Catherine Morton. 135 STONEBRIDGE BLVD 38305 #047-06-1977 L1979 **P** *020 †75
GRIMBALL, Arthur. 329 COATSLAND DR 38301 #045-01-1978 L1990 **TS CD** *020 †85,90
GRISSOM, Hilary Carol. 668 SKYLINE DR 38301 #047-06-2004 L2008 **OPH** *012
GUIDI, John Flanagan. 295 SUMMAR DR 38301 #047-06-1990 L1992 **FM** *020 †18
GUYTON, Joseph L. 27 BRENTSHIRE SQ, STE A 38305 #047-06-1950 L1967 **P** *072
HAGE-KORBAN, Elie Emile. ■ 38305 #605-01-1997 L2002 **CD** *020 †20
HAGER, Dana Dee. 616 W FOREST AVE 38301 #035-19-1987 L1994 **PUD CCM** *020 †20
HAMILTON, Karen Trenace. 367 HOSPITAL BLVD 38305 #047-07-2002 L2006 **OBG** *020
HAMMOND, Jere Devan. 2863 HIGHWAY 45 BYP, JACKSON CLINIC 38305 #047-06-1977 L1978 **IM** *020 †20
HAMMOND, Stephen Dumas. 2863 HIGHWAY 45 BYP, NORTH JACKSON 38305 #047-06-1974 L1975 **OBG** *020 †30
HAMMOND, Stephen Dumas, Jr. 2863 HIGHWAY 45 BYP 38305 #047-06-2002 L2006 **OPH** *100
HARMON, Harvey Carl. 616 W FOREST AVE 38301 #047-06-1971 L1971 **GS** *020 †85
HARPER, Andrea Marshall. 244 COATSLAND DR 38301 #048-14-2003 L2007 **OBG** *020
HARRIS, Joe Mark. 170 WILLOW GREEN DR OR 38305 #027-01-1983 L1998 **EM** *020 †18
HASHIM, Ahmed Shamsal D. 17 CENTRE PLAZA DR 38305 #528-01-1992 L2007 **IC** *020 †20
HATCHER, Donald B. 294 SUMMAR DR, FAMILY MEDICINE RESIDENCY 38301 #028-78-2006, ▲ L2008 **FP** *012
HAWKINS, Wesley Norbert. 11 WYNDCHASE DR 38305 #047-06-1999 L2002 **FM** *020 †18
HAWKS, Charles Franklin. 1203 VANN DR, CARE SOUTH CLINIC, PC 38305 #012-21-1989 L1995 **PUD IM** *075
HAYDEN, Timothy W. 31 HUGHES DR, NORTHSIDE MEDICAL CLINIC 38305 #047-06-1983 L1984 **FM** *020 †18
HAYES, Jason Thaddeous. 655 LEXINGTON AVE, EAST JACKSON FAMILY MEDICA 38301 #047-07-2004 L2007 **IM** *020 †20
HAYS, Edwin Carlton, Jr. 2863 HIGHWAY 45 BYP, NORTH JACKSON 38305 #047-06-1995 L1999 **MPD IM** *020 †20,55
HAZLEHURST, George Edward. 620 SKYLINE DR 38301 #047-06-1954 L1954 **GS GE** *071 †85
HEAD, Thomas Channing. 614 SKYLINE DR 38301 #001-02-1989 L1994 **N CN** *020 †75
HEINLY, Tammy L. 587 SKYLINE DR, STE B 38301 #028-46-1993 L1994 **MPD** *020 †20,55,03
HERTZ, Charles Schaeffer, Jr. 708 W FOREST AVE 38301 #041-01-1976 L1981 **GE IM** *020 †20
HIGGS, Bobby Clark. ■ 38305 #047-06-1956 L1956 **PD** *020 †55
HIGGS, Cyrus Henry, Jr. ■ 38305 #047-06-1954 L1967 **P IM** *020
HILL, Tori Samantha. ■ 38305 #047-06-2007 **FP** *012
HOCKADAY, Edward E, Jr. 616 W FOREST AVE 38301 #047-06-1987 L1988 **AN** *071 †05
HOELDTKE, Kim C. ■ 38305 #036-05-1992 L2006 **PD** *020 †55
HOELDTKE, Nathan John. 708 W FOREST AVE, MID SOUTH PERINATAL ASSOC 38301 #054-04-1989 L2003 **OBG MFM** *020 †30
HOLLIS, Robert A. 27 MEDICAL CENTER DR 38301 #048-12-1988 L1993 **GE IM** *020 †20
HOMBERG, Eric Jon. 367 HOSPITAL BLVD 38305 #047-06-1990 L1991 **AN GP** *020 †05
HONEYCUTT, Daniel Lee. 2863 HIGHWAY 45 BYP, NORTH JACKSON 38305 #047-06-1979 L1979 **IM** *020 †20
HOPKINS, Sharon Dellinger. 648 W FOREST AVE, JACKSON CLINIC 38301 #047-06-1978 L1989 **FM** *040 †18
HOPPERS, James Wm, Jr. 616 W FOREST AVE 38301 #047-06-1979 L1979 **PD** *020 †55
HOPPERS, Melanie. 648 W FOREST AVE 38301 #047-06-1993 L1994 **IM MPD** *020 †20,55
HORNSBY, Robert Jerald. 24 PHYSICIANS DR 38305 #047-06-1961 L1965 **ORS** *071 †40
HOUSE, Ben Fred. 666 SKYLINE DR 38301 #001-02-1956 L1963 **OPH** *071 †35
HOUSEWORTH, Stephen Wayne. 569 SKYLINE DR, STE 100 38301 #012-05-1980 L2007 **ORS** *020 †40
HOUSTON, Benny Cortez. 616 W FOREST AVE 38301 #047-20-1989 L1990 **FM** *020 †18
HOWERTON, Kimberly Ann. 294 SUMMAR DR, CLINIC/UNIV OF TENNESSEE 38301 #047-06-1997 L1999 **FM OBS** *020 †18
HUFF, Gregory Eugene. 708 W FOREST AVE, INDEPENDENT HOSPITAL 38301 #047-07-1997 L2005 **IM** *020
HULM, Dennis Alfred. 708 W FOREST AVE, DEPT OF RADIOLOGY 38301 #046-01-1996 L2003 **DR** *020 †80
HUMPHREYS, T J. ■ 38305 #047-06-1964 L1964 **EM FM** *071 †20
HUTCHISON, Jason Todd. 24 PHYSICIANS DR 38305 #047-06-1998 L2002 **ORS** *020 †40
HUTCHISON, Timothy Neal. 708 W FOREST AVE, JACKSON COUNTY GEN HOSP 38301 #047-06-1989 L1993 **AN** *020 †05
HYRE, Charles Edwin. 657 SKYLINE DR, MID SOUTH SURGERY ASSOCIAT 38301 #038-40-1993 L1999 **GS VS** *020 †85
IBACH, Michael Brett. 27 MEDICAL CENTER DR 38301 #011-04-1989 L1995 **GE** *020 †20
INMAN, Dustin Price. 1893 S HIGHLAND AVE, SOUTH JACKSON 38301 #047-06-2001 L2003 **FM** *020 †18
IRVINE, William David. 1000 VANN DR STE A 38305 #047-06-1987 L1993 **OPH** *020 †35
ISAEFF, Shawn Dale. 708 W FOREST AVE, JACKSON-MADISON CTY GEN HO 38301 #005-12-1994 L2000 **VIR** *020 †80
JAIN, Prathmesh. 569 SKYLINE DR, STE 100 38301 #495-36-2003 L2007 *100
JAMIESON, Pamela Ann. 708 W FOREST AVE 38301 #047-06-1974 L1976 **R** *020 †80
JAYAKUMAR, Mabbu P. 168 W UNIVERSITY PKWY # C, CARDIO CARE 38305 #495-35-1967 L1993 **IM CD** *020 †20
JENKINS, John Mark. 2863 HIGHWAY 45 BYP, NORTH JACKSON 38305 #020-02-1978 L1981 **IM** *020 †20
JOGLEKAR, Kanchan Shirish. 31 MURRAY GUARD DR 38305 #495-17-1976 L1991 **PD** *020 †55
JOGLEKAR, Shirish Shankar. 26 STONECREEK CIR STE B 38305 #495-01-1973 L1991 **NEP IM** *020 †20
JOHNSON, Jennifer Caylene. 616 W FOREST AVE 38301 #047-06-1964 L1965 **IM CD** *030 †20
JOHNSON, Larry David. 24 PHYSICIANS DR 38305 #047-06-1985 L1986 **ORS** *020 †40
JOHNSON ANYANWU, Allyson. ■ 38305 #025-12-2003 L2005 **EM** *100 †16
JOHNSTON, Stephen Edward. ■ 38308 #047-06-1990 L1993 **EM** *020 †16
JONES, Kent Lewis. 616 W FOREST AVE 38301 #020-12-1974 L1979 **GS TRS** *020
JONES, Robert Mcneilly, II. 27 MEDICAL CENTER DR 38301 #047-06-1986 L1987 **D** *020 †15
JORDAN, Frank Edwin. 160 W UNIVERSITY PKWY # C 38305 #047-06-1982 L1983 **AN IM** *020 †20,05
JOSHI, Mahendra Kumar. 16 MURRAY GUARD DR STE B, JOSHI CLINIC, MD, PA 38305 #495-30-1978 L1998 **IM** *020 †20
JOVES, Froilan Borja. ■ 38305 #422-01-2002 L2006 **IM** *100
JOYNER, June Carole. 708 W FOREST AVE 38301 #047-06-1981 L1983 **NPM PD** *020 †55
KARAMI-SICHANI, Mohamad R. 50 BENT CREEK LN, ADVANCED PSYCHIATRIC SERVI 38305 #308-11-1984 L1996 **P** *020
KAUFMAN, Dwight Crawford. 616 W FOREST AVE 38301 #004-01-1979 L1995 **ON IM** *050 †20
KENDALL, John Allen. ■ 38301 #047-06-1963 L1963 **IM** *071
KHAMAPIRAD, T Sunny. 609 SKYLINE DR 38301 #048-04-1997 L2003 **OPH** *020 †35
KIRKLAND, Ronald Hayden. 616 W FOREST AVE 38301 #047-06-1977 L1979 **OTO HNS** *020 †45
KOERNER, Paul Daniel. 322 HOSPITAL BLVD 38305 #047-20-1994 L1999 **RO** *020 †80
KOONCE, Duval Holtzclaw. 708 W FOREST AVE 38301 #036-07-1946 L1955 **IM CD** *071 †20
KOONCE, Edward Duval. 587 SKYLINE DR 38301 #047-06-1982 L1983 **IM** *020 †20
KOVALIC, Jeffrey John. 708 W FOREST AVE 38301 #056-06-1986 L1991 **RO** *020 †80
LA FONT, Donald Sharp. ■ 38301 #047-06-1964 L1964 **PD** *020 †55
LAIRD, David Michael. 395 HOSPITAL BLVD, JACKSON SURGICAL 38305 #012-05-1993 L1998 **GS** *020 †85
LAM, Michael Gerald. 616 W FOREST AVE 38301 #010-02-1999 L2002 **AN** *020 †05 ‡
LANGDON, James A. 616 W FOREST AVE 38301 #047-06-1950 L1950 **GYN** *071 †30
LANTER, James Kenneth. 19 SECURITY DR 38305 #047-06-1985 L1991 **ORS HS** *020 †40
LARSEN, David Malcolm. 31 HUGHES DR, NORTHSIDE MEDICAL CLINIC 38305 #036-01-1975 L1976 **FM** *020 †18
LAWRENCE, Bethany Jane. 681 SKYLINE DR, HEALTH AND HEALING CLINIC 38301 #020-02-1997 L2004 **IM** *020 †20
LAWRENCE, Peter Griffin. 28 MEDICAL CENTER DR, JACKSON UROLOGICAL 38301 #020-02-1998 L2004 **U** *020 †95
LENTS, Russell Stefan. 616 W FOREST AVE, JACKSON CLINIC P.A. 38301 #047-06-1983 L1983 **OPH** *020 †35
LEVERNIER, James Edwin. ■ 38301 #026-04-1968 L1984 **PD** *071 †55
LEWIS, Christopher Lee. 1893 S HIGHLAND AVE, SOUTH JACKSON 38301 #038-45-1999 L2000 **EM** *020 †18
LEWIS, Donald Ray. 512 ROLAND AVE, WOMANS CLINIC A PRO ASSN 38301 #004-01-1962 L1966 **GYN** *071 †30
LONDINO, Elizabeth S. 31 HUGHES DR, NORTHSIDE MEDICAL CLINIC 38305 #028-03-1993 L2001 **FM** *020 †18
LUI, Henry. 327 SUMMAR DR 38301 #005-19-1978 L1996 **CD** *020 †20
LUNDY, Michael Mahoney. 367 HOSPITAL BLVD, REGIONAL HOSPITAL 38305 #021-01-1974 L1993 **DR NM** *020 †28,80 ‡
MACMILLAN, Robert Duncan, Jr. 294 SUMMAR DR, UT FAMILY PRACTICE 38301 #047-06-2006 L2008 **FP** *012
MAHAJAN, Natasha C. 616 W FOREST AVE, THE JACKSON CLINIC, P.A. 38301 #496-07-1992 L1998 **IM** *020 †20
MAHALATI, Kamran. 616 W FOREST AVE 38301 #902-05-1991 L2005 **GS** *020 †85
MAHAYNI, Mohamad Amer. 367 HOSPITAL BLVD 38305 #875-01-1987 L2002 **CD IM** *020 †20
MAHR, Nicholas. 17 CENTRE PLAZA DR 38305 #422-01-1986 L2003 **CD** *020 †20
MALEY, Bruce Benj. 264 COATSLAND DR 38301 #047-06-1970 L1971 **PD** *020 †55
MANDLE, Robert Bennie. 616 W FOREST AVE 38301 #047-06-1955 L1956 **IM** *071 †20
MANNING, James Louis. 1893 S HIGHLAND AVE, SOUTH JACKSON 38301 #047-06-1978 L1979 **FM** *020 †18
MARIENCHECK, Maria Chiara. 87 MURRAY GUARD DR, PLASTICS 38305 #028-02-1994 L2000 **D** *020 †15
MARKEL, Thomas Owen. 708 W FOREST AVE 38301 #005-02-1989 L2006 **RNR** *020 †80
MARTIN, Laurence Francis. 37 SANDSTONE CIR 38305 #060-01-1976 *100
MARTIN, Lawrence F. 37 SANDSTONE CIR, JACKSON PEDIATRIC CENTER 38305 #055-01-1974 L1996 **IM** *020

■ = Address Information Privacy Protected

MARTINDALE, Michael Lynn. 616 W FOREST AVE 38301 #047-06-1988 L1989 **AN** *020

MATTHEWS, John Townsend. 329 COATSLAND DR 38301 #055-01-1974 L1983 **TS** *020 †85,90

MC BRIDE, Gary Lyn. 1893 S HIGHLAND AVE, SOUTH JACKSON 38301 #036-08-1993 L1995 **MPD** *020 †20,55

MCCARTNEY, Jeff Paul. 174 MURRAY GUARD DR, JACKSON PULMONARY CARE PA 38305 #047-06-1990 L1991 **PCC IM** *020 †20

MC CRUDDEN, Brian Edward. 367 HOSPITAL BLVD 38305 #065-06-1965 L1978 **DR NM** *020

MCDANIEL, Brock Gregory. 708 W FOREST AVE 38301 #056-06-1997 L2002 **DR NM** *020 †80,28

MC GUIRE, William L. 708 W FOREST AVE 38301 #047-06-1978 L1979 **EM IM** *020 †16

MC INTOSH, John Edward. 1869 HIGHWAY 45 BYP 38305 #047-06-1961 L1965 **P PA** *020 †75

MC IVER, Harold Thomas. 708 W FOREST AVE 38301 #047-06-1946 L1946 **OTO OPH** *071 †45

MCKEE, Alice R. 8 STONEBRIDGE BLVD, STE J 38305 #038-41-1988 L1996 **FM** *020 †18

MC KENZIE, Donna Gail. 238 SUMMAR DR, PATHWAYS 38301 #047-20-1998 L2000 **P** *020

MC KNIGHT, Donald T, Jr. 28 MEDICAL CENTER DR, JACKSON UROLOGICAL 38301 #047-06-1987 L1992 **U** *020 †95

MENACHEM, Allan Michael. 9 PHYSICIANS DR 38305 #561-01-1972 L2005 **GE** *020 †20

MERIWETHER, John Henning. 616 W FOREST AVE, THE JACKSON CLINIC 38301 #047-06-1985 L1990 **U** *020 †95

MICETICH, Keith A. 72 PHYSICIANS DR 38305 #060-01-1983 L1994 **OBG** *020

MIDDLETON, Augustus L. JACKSN MADSON CO GEN HOSP 38301 #035-01-1959 L1963 **PTH** *020 †50

MILLER, Holly Raass. 2863 HIGHWAY 45 BYP, NORTH JACKSON 38305 #016-43-2002 L2006 **OBG** *100

MILLER, Jesse Alfred. 708 W FOREST AVE 38301 #047-06-1955 L1955 **PD** *071 †55

MILLER, Tommy Lee, III. 48 MEDICAL CENTER DR 38301 #047-06-1998 L2006 **IC** *100 †20

MISULIS, Karl Edward. 614 SKYLINE DR 38301 #047-05-1982 L1984 **N** *020 †75

MITCHELL, Gregg E. 294 SUMMAR DR, FAMILY PRACTICE CENTER 38301 #047-06-1994 L1995 **FM** *020 †18

MORAGNE, Sidney. 238 SUMMAR DR, PATHWAYS OF TENNESSEE INC. 38301 #010-03-1985 L2003 **P** *020 †75

MORTON, Morris Lamont. 51 BOYD DR 38305 #047-07-2000 L2004 **FM** *020

MOSHER, Keith Alden, Jr. 367 HOSPITAL BLVD, BOX 3310 38305 #047-06-1992 L1993 **FM** *020 †18

MUELLER, Alfred J. ■ 38301 #047-06-1952 L1952 **PHP GPM** *030

MUIR, Eric Wyatt. 2863 HIGHWAY 45 BYP, NORTH JACKSON 38305 #027-01-1986 L1986 **FM** *020 †18

MURRAY, Pamela Denise. 708 W FOREST AVE 38301 #047-06-1988 L1991 **IM** *020 †20

MYHR, Lamb Bolton. 616 W FOREST AVE 38301 #047-05-1941 L1941 **IM IMG** *071 †20

NAIK, Ami Kanti. 27 MEDICAL CENTER DR 38301 #047-06-2002 L2007 **GE** *012 †20

NEBLETT, John Wallace, Jr. 1040 GREYSTONE SQ, WEST TN NEUROSURGICAL CLIN 38305 #047-05-1977 L1978 **NS** *020 †25

NEEL, Sean Torin. 668 SKYLINE DR, EYE CLINIC P.C. 38301 #017-20-1995 L1999 **OPH** *020 †35

NEUDECKER, Roy M. ■ 38305 #047-06-1940 L1940 **PHP** *071

NGUYEN, Jason Tan. ■ 38301 #047-06-2005 **MPD** *012

NICKELSON, Connie L. ■ 38305 #012-22-1996 L2004 **IM** *020

NORSWORTHY, Thomas Philip. 708 W FOREST AVE 38301 #027-01-1982 L1991 **FM** *020 †18

OBERG, Richard Alan. 706 W FOREST AVE 38301 #047-06-1981 L1981 **PTH** *020 †50

ODEH, Osayawe Nosayaba. 616 W FOREST AVE 38301 #690-06-1995 L2006 **IM** *020 †20

ODHAV, Satish. 371 N PARKWAY, STE 400 38305 #836-01-1986 L1990 **RHU IM** *020 †20

OLERU, Chima Obioma. 616 W FOREST AVE, JACKSON CLINIC, PA 38301 #690-04-1990 L2005 **NEP** *020 †20

OSAYAMWEN, Michael O. 616 W FOREST AVE 38301 #047-06-1996 L1999 **CD** *020 †20

OWENS, Scott E. 2863 HIGHWAY 45 BYP, NORTH JACKSON 38305 #047-06-1984 L1986 **PD** *020 †55

PAKIS, George. ■ 38301 #004-01-1954 L1959 **GYN** *071 †30

PALMER, Edmund Tansil, Jr. 294 SUMMAR DR 38301 #047-06-1975 L1976 **IM** *040 †20

PANOVEC, Parker Kevin. 294 SUMMAR DR 38301 #047-06-1991 L1994 **FM** *020 †18

PATEL, Kandarp B. 1203 VANN DR, 34 WILLOW GREEN DRIVE 38305 #495-23-1992 L1999 **CD** *020 †20

PAYNE, James Allen. 616 W FOREST AVE, DEPT MED 38301 #047-06-1987 L1988 **IM PD** *020 †20,55

PEARCE, David Armstrong. 24 PHYSICIANS DR 38305 #010-02-1995 L2004 **ORS OSM** *020 †40

PECHACEK, Alan X. 616 W FOREST AVE 38301 #018-03-1967 L1991 **ORS** *020 †40

PERCHIK, Joel Evan. ■ 38305 #012-05-1989 L1990 **DR** *020 †80

PERCIVAL, Hisman Habili. 635 OIL WELL RD 38305 #026-04-1990 L1994 **GS** *020 †85

PERMENTER, William Dale. 322 HOSPITAL BLVD, CANCER CARE CENTER OF JACK 38305 #047-20-1985 L1986 **RO** *020 †80

PHILLIPS, Tony Nelson. 616 W FOREST AVE, JACKSON CLINIC, PA 38301 #047-06-1983 L1983 **CD** *020 †20

PHOTIADIS, James. 810 W FOREST AVE 38301 #055-01-1985 L2006 **AN FM** *020 †05,18

PIERCE, Wm Franklin, IV. 616 W FOREST AVE 38301 #047-06-1991 L1992 **OBG** *020 †30

PIERCEY, Lisa Michelle. 2863 HIGHWAY 45 BYP, NORTH JACKSON 38305 #047-20-2002 L2003 **PD** *020 †55

POOLE, Charles Thomas. 131 TUCKER ST STE 5 38301 #004-01-1989 L1993 **AN** *020 †05

PRESTON, William Anderson. 616 W FOREST AVE, THE JACKSON CLINIC 38301 #047-05-1998 L2003 **OTO** *020 †45

PRICE, James Alfred, Jr. 668 SKYLINE DR 38301 #004-01-1962 L1969 **OPH** *071 †35

PRIESTER, Wm Bradford. 609 SKYLINE DR 38301 #047-06-1991 L1992 **OPH** *020 †35

PRINCE, Edna Jacqueline. 256 VANN DR STE C, THE WALK-IN CLINIC, INC. 38305 #036-01-1980 L1986 **GP** *020

PROCTOR, Evanna Salone. 616 W FOREST AVE, THE JACKSON CLINIC 38301 #041-07-1994 L1997 **IM** *020

PUCEK, Kelly Dwayne. 24 PHYSICIANS DR, WEST TN BONE/JOINT CLINIC 38305 #004-01-1992 L1998 **ORS** *020 †40

QUADEER, Abdulrahman. ■ 38305 #048-02-2001 L2007 **VIR** *020 †80

RAGON, Joseph Lee. 1893 S HIGHLAND AVE, SOUTH JACKSON 38301 #047-06-1985 L1986 **FM** *020 †18

RAINEY, Debra Lee. 708 W FOREST AVE, JACKSON-MADISON COUNTY GEN 38301 #001-02-1988 L1994 **IM ID** *020 †20

RAMDAS, Swaroopa. 16 MURRAY GUARD DR 38305 #496-20-1992 L2004 **FM** *020 ‡

REDDY, Avinash Dubbaka. 294 SUMMAR DR 38301 #047-20-1997 L2002 **OBG** *040 †18

REESE, Eugene P, Jr. 367 HOSPITAL BLVD 38305 #020-02-1967 L1979 **ON HEM** *020 †20

REVELLE, Michael Allen. 708 W FOREST AVE 38301 #047-06-1999 L2000 **EM** *020 †18

RHENEY, Molly Mc Lemore. 244 COATSLAND DR 38301 #047-06-1984 L1987 **OBG** *020 †30

ROBBINS, Melissa Annette. 294 SUMMAR DR 38301 #047-06-2005 L2007 **FP** *012

ROBBINS, Russell Hugh. 2863 HIGHWAY 45 BYP, NORTH JACKSON 38305 #047-06-1964 L1965 **IM ID** *020

ROBERTS, David E. 708 W FOREST AVE, GENERAL HOSPITAL 38301 #047-06-1976 L1977 **FM FPG** *030 †18

ROBERTS, Jerry L. 379 HOSPITAL BLVD, STE 101 38305 #047-06-1984 L1984 **TS VS** *020 †85,90

RODRIGUEZ, Mary-Anne. 648 W FOREST AVE 38301 #748-01-1990 L1997 **FM** *020 †18

ROGERS, Lisa W. 2863 HIGHWAY 45 BYP, NORTH JACKSON 38305 #047-06-1987 L1991 **OBG** *020 †30

ROTHROCK, Alan Curtis. 616 W FOREST AVE 38301 #047-20-2002 L2006 **IM** *100 †20

ROTHROCK, Rebecca A. 2863 HIGHWAY 45 BYP, NORTH JACKSON 38305 #047-20-2002 L2006 **OBG** *020

ROWLAND, Joseph Perry. 614 SKYLINE DR 38301 #047-06-1959 L1959 **NS OS** *020 †25

ROY, Ryan Allen. 244 COATSLAND DR 38301 #047-06-2002 L2005 **OBG** *020

SARIDAKIS, Michael Andrew. 379 HOSPITAL BLVD, JACKSON REGIONAL SURGERY 38305 #016-42-1988 L1997 **GS** *020 †85

SARKAR, Shyamal. 170 MURRAY GUARD DR 38305 #496-08-1980 L1998 **NEP IM** *020 †20

SCHLAMP, Allen Lee. 708 W FOREST AVE, GENERAL HOSPITAL 38301 #047-05-1968 L1971 **DR** *020 †80

SCHMIDT, Roy Arturo. 37 MURRAY GUARD DR 38305 #005-12-1984 L1992 **PME AN** *020 †05

SCOTT, Augustus Barnett. 395 HOSPITAL BLVD 38305 #047-06-1959 L1960 **GS** *071 †85

SELF, Amelia Goolsby. 264 COATSLAND DR 38301 #047-20-1991 L1995 **PD** *020 †55

SELF, David Leslie, Jr. 264 COATSLAND DR 38301 #047-20-1991 L1995 **PD** *020 †55

SHAW, Elizabeth Ann. 294 SUMMAR DR, FAMILY PRACTICE CENTER 38301 #065-10-1981 L1992 **FM** *040 †18

SHAW, John Lyle. 616 W FOREST AVE 38301 #047-06-1972 L1973 **U** *020 †95

SHELLABARGER, Benjamin Ru. 294 SUMMAR DR 38301 #047-06-2004 L2006 **FP** *012

SHEPPARD, Lee Calvin. 670 SKYLINE DR 38301 #028-34-1959 L1967 **PTH** *071 †50

SHORT, R Mark. 616 W FOREST AVE 38301 #041-09-1984 L1991 **IM** *020 †20

SHUTE, Anne Marie. 7 WINDWOOD HILL DRIVE 38305 #047-05-1969 L1970 **GS IM** *020 †20,85

SICKLE, David Michael. 616 W FOREST AVE 38301 #038-06-1999 L2007 **ORS** *020 †40

SIMS, Paul Jeffrey. 708 W FOREST AVE 38301 #020-02-1991 L2000 **BBK** *020 †50

SIOSON, Conrado B. 587 SKYLINE DR, STE B 38301 #748-01-1988 L1995 **IM** *020 †20

SIOSON-AHERRERA, Priscilla. 708 W FOREST AVE, JACKSON MADISON CNTY HOSP 38301 #748-02-1983 L1988 **ID IM** *020 †20

SMIGIELSKI, Michael J. 616 W FOREST AVE 38301 #056-06-1982 L2003 **ORS OAR** *020 †40

SMITH, Adam Michael. 24 PHYSICIANS DR 38305 #020-12-1998 L2004 **OAR** *020 †40

SMITH, Clyde Earl. 708 W FOREST AVE 38301 #047-06-1974 L1974 **ON HEM** *020 †20

SMITH, Crystal Antrease. ■ 38305 #047-06-2007 **FP** *012

SMITH, Harris L. 708 W FOREST AVE 38301 #047-06-1951 L1952 **CHP P** *071 †55

SMITH, Paul Jonathan. 587 SKYLINE DR 38301 #047-06-1989 L1992 **IM** *020 †20

SMITH, Robert Jos. ■ 38305 #047-06-1955 L1955 **ORS** *071 †40

SMITH, Theresa Troutt. 264 COATSLAND DR 38301 #047-06-1989 L1992 **PD** *020 †55 ‡

SNYDER, Kimberly Jean. 294 SUMMAR DR 38301 #047-06-2005 L2007 **FP** *012

SOLL, David John. 244 COATSLAND DR 38301 #018-03-1989 L2002 **OBG FM** *020 †30,18 ‡

SOUDER, Bob Tyler. 9 PHYSICIANS DR, DDC SURGERY CENTER 38305 #047-06-1974 L1974 **GE IM** *020 †20

SPALDING, Alanson R, III. 329 COATSLAND DR 38301 #039-01-1971 L1972 **TS** *020 †85,90

SPARROW, John Gregory. 2863 HIGHWAY 45 BYP, NORTH JACKSON 38305 #027-01-1982 L1994 **PS HS** *020 †65

STEPHENSON, Robert Cherry. PO BOX 3430 38303 #047-06-1975 L1976 **EM** *020 †16

STEPP, William Price, Jr. 2863 HIGHWAY 45 BYP, NORTH JACKSON 38305 #047-06-1973 L1973 **PD** *020 †55

STEWART, Earl Lee. 2815 N HIGHLAND AVE, STE C 38305 #027-01-1981 L1998 **IMG** *020

STEWART, Leslie Douglas. 616 W FOREST AVE, THE JACKSON CLINIC PA 38301 #045-01-1983 L2005 **VS GS** *020 †85

STONECIPHER, Lowell F. 24 PHYSICIANS DR 38305 #021-01-1966 L1973 **ORS** *020 †40

STORY, William Chas. ■ 38305 #004-01-1955 L1978 **IM OM** *071 †70

STUDTMANN, Karl Eric. 619 SKYLINE DR 38301 #047-06-1994 L1999 **OTO** *020 †45

SULLIVAN, Jason Murray. 668 SKYLINE DR 38301 #047-06-1995 L1999 **OPH** *020 †35

SUTTON, Herbert Lee. 686 W FOREST AVE STE A5, JMCGH-TRAUMA SERVICES 38301 #047-07-1984 L1998 **GS TRS** *020 †85

SWAIM, Mark Wendell. 45 PHYSICIANS DR 38305 #036-07-1990 L2002 **GE** *020 †20

SWEO, Timothy David. 569 SKYLINE DR, STE 100 38301 #048-02-1989 L1994 **ORS** *020

SWINDLE, James Tyler. 244 COATSLAND DR 38301 #004-01-1967 L1972 **OBG** *020 †30

TAYLOR, Jackie Lynn. 367 HOSPITAL BLVD 38305 #047-06-1987 L1988 **EM** *020 †18

TAYLOR, Mechelle Evette. 655 LEXINGTON AVE 38301 #047-07-1998 L2003 **FM** *020 †18

TAYLOR, Ronald. 616 W FOREST AVE 38301 #051-04-1982 L1983 **IM PUD** *020 †20

TEAGUE, Todd Alan. 2863 HIGHWAY 45 BYP, JACKSON CLINIC, PA 38305 #047-06-1993 L1996 **IM** *020 †20

TEER, Wm Patrick Brown. 27 MEDICAL CENTER DR 38301 #047-06-1992 L1994 **D** *020 †20,15

THOMAS, George Emanuel. 9 PHYSICIANS DR 38305 #001-02-1968 L1976 **GS** *020 †85

THORNE, Steven Ray. 616 W FOREST AVE 38301 #030-06-1988 L1994 **GS** *020 †85

TORSTRICK, Robt Frederick. 616 W FOREST AVE 38301 #020-02-1973 L1980 **HS ORS** *020 †40

TOWNES-BOUGARD, Tracy A. 616 W FOREST AVE 38301 #027-01-1999 L2005 **NEP** *020 †20

TOYOS, Rolando. 569 SKYLINE DR, STE 200 38301 #016-11-1994 L1998 **OPH** *020 †35

TRUEX, S Allen. RR 5 38305 #047-05-1942 L1942 **GYN OS** *071

TURNER, Robert Dale. 102 MURRAY GUARD DR, G54 38305 #004-01-1987 L2000 **FM** *020

TURNER, William Richard. ■ 38305 #035-47-1988 L1994 **FM AN** *072

TYGART, Bryan Phillip. 616 W FOREST AVE, THE JACKSON CLINIC 38301 #004-01-1997 L2000 **IM** *020 †20

UNDERWOOD, David Wayne. 668 SKYLINE DR 38301 #004-01-1984 L1989 **OPH EM** *020 †35

URETSKY, Harvey Richard. 72 PHYSICIANS DR 38305 #060-01-1970 L1995 **OBG** *020

VALDIVIA, Remy Antonio. 3363 N HIGHLAND AVE 38305 #016-11-1999 L2003 **PM** *020 †60

VEGORS, Robert Alan. 616 W FOREST AVE 38301 #023-01-1975 L1981 **IM** *075 †20

VILLARREAL, David. 395 HOSPITAL BLVD, JACKSON SURGICAL 38305 #048-13-1989 L1995 **GS VS** *020 †85

VRANEY, George Alvin. 176 W UNIVERSITY PKWY 38305 #056-06-1969 L2003 **PUD CCM** *020 †20

WADE, Kenneth Lynn. 367 HOSPITAL BLVD, DEPT ANESTH 38305 #004-01-1999 L2005 **AN** *020 †05

WAGNER, Richard Kent. 708 W FOREST AVE, MID-SOUTH PERINATAL ASSOCI 38301 #016-11-1990 L2000 **MFM OBG** *020 †30

■ = Address Information Privacy Protected

WAINSCOTT, William Keith. 619 SKYLINE DR 38301 #047-06-1981 L1982 **OTO** *020 †45
WALKER, Armie Walls. 8 MEDICAL CENTER DR 38301 #027-01-1986 L1998 **OBG** *020
WALKER, Brian N. 27 MEDICAL CENTER DR, NORTH MS HEMATOLOGY & ONCO 38301 #028-78-2000, ▲ L2008 **HO** *020 †20
WALLACE-WILDING, Kellie L. 294 SUMMAR DR 38301 #047-06-2005 L2006 **FP** *012
WARDLOW, Bethany Ann. ■ 38305 #047-06-2007 **FP** *012
WARMBROD, James G, Jr. 616 W FOREST AVE 38301 #047-06-1967 L1970 **ORS** *020 †40
WARREN, Kenneth Russel Wm. 31 PHYSICIANS DR, STE 1 38305 #068-01-1968 L1979 **FM** *020 †18
WASHINGTON, Terry L. ■ 38305 #047-20-2002 **FP** *012
WEAVER, Steven Glenn. 1893 S HIGHLAND AVE, SOUTH JACKSON 38301 #047-06-1989 L1996 **IM EM** *020 †20
WEBB, Bradley Michael. 616 W FOREST AVE 38301 #001-02-1998 L2002 **IM** *020 †20
WEBB, Jimmy Franklin. 244 COATSLAND DR 38301 #047-06-1961 L1962 **GYN** *071 †30
WELLES, Edward Hunter, III. 708 W FOREST AVE 38301 #047-06-1970 L1970 **DR** *020 †80
WELSCH, Christopher T. 2863 HIGHWAY 45 BYP, NORTH JACKSON 38305 #016-06-1992 L1999 **OBG** *020 †30
WHITBY, Rodney Scott. 616 W FOREST AVE 38301 #047-06-1991 L1993 **PD IM** *020 †20,55
WHITE, John Sharkey, II. 1893 S HIGHLAND AVE, SOUTH JACKSON 38301 #047-06-1997 L1998 **UCM** *020 †18
WILLIAMS, Allen N, Jr. 1104 N PARKWAY 38305 #047-06-1952 L1952 **GP** *071
WILLIAMS, Lane Edward. 72 PHYSICIANS DR 38305 #016-11-1990 L2005 **OBG** *020 †30
WILLIAMS, Philip Gray. 1605 S HIGHLAND AVE, THE TUCKER CLINIC 38301 #047-06-1952 L1953 **FM GS** *071 †18
WILLIAMS, William Keith. 2863 HIGHWAY 45 BYP, NORTH JACKSON 38305 #047-06-1981 L1982 **OBG** *020 †30
WILLIAMSON, Felix E, III. 706 W FOREST AVE 38301 #047-06-1982 L1983 **PTH** *020 †50
WILLIS, William Arthur. ■ 38305 #047-06-1994 L1995 **FM** *020 †18
WILLOUGHBY, Mitchell. ■ 38305 #047-06-2007 **FP** *012
WILSON, Donald Allen. 2863 HIGHWAY 45 BYP, NORTH JACKSON 38305 #047-06-1986 L1987 **OBG** *020 †30
WINGATE, Harry Lynnwood. 367 HOSPITAL BLVD, REGIONAL HOSPITAL OF JACKS 38305 #012-01-1988 L2005 **EM** *020
WITHERINGTON, James B, III. 616 W FOREST AVE, THE JACKSON CLINIC PROF AS 38301 #021-06-1977 L1977 **IM** *020 †20
WITTBER, Glynn Marie. 2863 HIGHWAY 45 BYP, NORTH JACKSON 38305 #047-06-1994 L1998 **FM** *020 †18
WOOD, Tommy Albert. 616 W FOREST AVE 38301 #027-01-2001 L2007 **PCC** *020
WOODS, John Bryan. 207B STONEBRIDGE BLVD 38305 #047-06-1990 L1991 **IM** *020 †20
WOODS, William Hugh, Jr. 2863 HIGHWAY 45 BYP, NORTH JACKSON 38305 #047-06-1980 L1981 **PD** *020 †18,55
WREN, Kelvin. 174 MURRAY GUARD DR, STE D 38305 #010-03-1999 L2005 **GPM** *020 †70
WRIGHT, Garth Bradford. 569 SKYLINE DR STE 10, SPORTS, ORTHOPEDICS & SPIN 38301 #054-04-1984 L1999 **ORS OSM** *020 †40
WRIGHT, Lucius F, III. 616 W FOREST AVE 38301 #001-02-1974 L1975 **NEP** *020 †20
WRIGHT, Rosilin Knight. 648 W FOREST AVE, JACKSON CLINIC, P.A. 38301 #047-06-1998 L1999 **FM** *020 †18
YARBRO, Edward Scott. 28 MEDICAL CENTER DR, JACKSON UROLOGICAL 38301 #051-01-1982 L1988 **U** *020 †20
YARBRO, Harold Ray. ■ 38301 #051-01-1949 L1957 **IM** *071
YELLEN, Marshall Ross. 10 LYNOAK CV 38305 #035-19-1988 L1997 **PS HS** *020 †65,85

JAMESTOWN – FENTRESS

ALLRED, Baley Fred. PO BOX 40 38556 #047-06-1952 L1952 **GP GS** *071
ALLRED, Jonathan David. PO BOX 1168, 234 W CENTRAL AVE 38556 #047-20-1988 L1991 **IM PD** *020 †20
CARROLL, Ramon Leonard. PO BOX 1350 38556 #047-06-1967 L1967 **GS ADM** *075 †85
CLAPP, Mark Allen. 101 S DUNCAN ST 38556 #047-06-1986 L1987 **FM OBS** *020 †18
GRIGSBY, David Alan. ■ 38556 #047-06-1972 L1973 **GS** *020 †85
HONARVAR, Samad. 114 N DUNCAN ST, STE 2 38556 #517-05-1967 L2006 **OTO** *020 †45
JOSHI, Dilip Nilkanth. PO BOX 849 38556 #496-38-1971 L1979 **FM EM** *020 †16
KHAN, Matloob Ahmad. 114A N DUNCAN ST 38556 #704-09-1964 L1999 **GS** *020 †40
PATIBANDLA, Vijaya Kumar. 114 N DUNCAN ST, STE 1 38556 #495-57-1974 L2007 **IM** *020 †20
PAYANT, Joseph Aaron. ■ 38556 #047-06-1993 L1994 **EM** *020 †18
SEWELL, Christopher S. PO BOX 1320, 238 W CENTRAL AVE 38556 #047-20-1995 L1996 **FM** *020 †18
SMITH, Jack Calvin. HWY 52 W 38556 #047-06-1956 L1956 **GP** *072
SMITH, Richard D. PO BOX 98 38556 #047-06-1976 L1977 **IM** *020 †20
WEISSINGER, Mark Gerald. 114 N DUNCAN ST, PO BOX 607 38556 #046-01-1990 L1994 **OBG** *020 †30

JASPER – MARION

BARNETT, Frances H. 980 HIGHWAY 28 STE 104 37347 #001-02-1976 L1983 **FM** *020 †18
BOECK, Karin Anne. 980 HIGHWAY 28, STE 101 37347 #047-06-1996 L1997 **FM** *020 †18
CHAVARRIA-AGUILAR, Marco. 980 HIGHWAY 28, STE 205 37347 #012-22-1999 L2004 **GS** *020
DESJARLAIS, Scott Eugene. 980 HIGHWAY 28, STE 100 37347 #046-01-1991 L1993 **GP** *020
EASON, Marvin Lewis. 1000 HIGHWAY 28 37347 #047-07-1978 L1980 **EM** *020
HOWE, Charles Michael. 980 HIGHWAY 28, STE 204 37347 #047-06-1966 L1972 **OBG GYN** *020 †30
HUA, Vin-Paul. 1000 HIGHWAY 28 37347 #244-03-1962 L1978 **GP** *020
IJAZ, Sajeel. 980 HIGHWAY 28, STE 201 37347 #704-21-1983 L1997 **IM** *020 †20
JUSTO, Rory Dial. 980 HIGHWAY 28 37347 #748-07-1984 L1999 **IM** *020 †20
LEONARD, Dennis Joe. 4665 MAIN ST, STE 2 37347 #039-01-1982 L1996 **FM FSM** *020 †18
LEVINE, Richard Lawrence. 980 HIGHWAY 28, STE 201 37347 #056-06-1966 L2006 **U** *020 †95
MALLIK, Gagan Chand. ■ 37347 #495-38-1962 L2006 **OTO** *020 †45
MANANYAN, Conrad C. 1000 HIGHWAY 28 37347 #022-75-1991, ▲ L1999 **GS** *020
MILLER, Frank Jolles. 300 WESTFIELD PL 37347 #036-01-1975 L1980 **NEP** *020 †20
PATE, Linda Marie. 980 HIGHWAY 28, STE 205 37347 #047-06-1993 L1999 **GS** *020 †85
PATEL, Ashish Vijay. 1000 HIGHWAY 28 37347 #047-20-2002 L2004 **FM EM** *020 †18
PHILYAW, Kathy Renee. 980 HIGHWAY 28, STE 408 37347 #047-06-1995 L1998 **PD** *020 †55
SNYDER, Stephen Lockard. 1000 HIGHWAY 28, GRANDVIEW MEDICAL CENTER 37347 #047-06-1973 L1980 **IM** *020 †20

VANRENTERGHEM, Rena Ann. 980 HIGHWAY 28, STE 202 37347 #025-12-1993 L1998 **OBG** *020 †30
WILLIS, Marshall Ray. 1000 HIGHWAY 28 37347 #051-01-1964 L1978 **DR NM** *020 †80

JEFFERSON CITY – JEFFERSON

ANDERSON, Craig Cole. 120 HOSPITAL DR, STE 250 37760 #020-12-1979 L1987 **OBS GYN** *020 †30
BUKOVITZ, Mary Elizabeth. 657 E BROADWAY BLVD 37760 #047-06-1967 L1968 **PD** *020 †55
BYRD, Leann M. 120 HOSPITAL DR, STE 260 37760 #047-20-1999 L2001 **FM** *020 †18
CARTER, Richard Blair, Jr. 120 HOSPITAL DR, TENNESSEE VALLEY MEDICAL G 37760 #048-04-2003 L2007 **MPD** *020 †20,55
CLARK, Peter Larson. 120 HOSPITAL DR, STE 250 37760 #020-12-1983 L1987 **OBG** *020 †30
DARBY, Dewayne Paschall. 1810 BISHOP AVE, STE A 37760 #047-06-1977 L1978 **FM** *020 †18
DAVENPORT, Mark Rogers. 110 HOSPITAL DR 37760 #654-01-1983 L1995 **AN** *020
ELLIS, Frank Shannon. 120 HOSPITAL DR, STE 250 37760 #047-06-1984 L1985 **OBG** *020 †30
FIELDS, Regina Jellicorse. ■ 37760 #047-06-2007 **FP** *012
GANTTE, Stephen Campbell. 120 HOSPITAL DR 37760 #047-20-1999 L2001 **IM** *020 †20
GREENE, James Chad. 490 N HIGHWAY 92 37760 #047-06-2007 *012
GRENKOSKI, Mark Edwin. 110 HOSPITAL DR 37760 #025-12-1988 L2000 **FM** *020 †18
HARRIS, William Boatwright. 120 HOSPITAL DR, STE 250 37760 #422-01-1988 L1991 **OBG** *020 †30
HINDS, Spencer Walton. 120 HOSPITAL DR STE 110, JEFFERSON HEART CONSULTANT 37760 #054-04-1985 L2007 **CD IM** *020 †20
HUGHES, Michael Webb. 120 HOSPITAL DR, STE 230 37760 #012-22-1998 L1999 **CHP** *020
KIRBY, John Austin. 120 HOSPITAL DR, GROUP 37760 #012-05-1997 L2001 **MPD** *020 †20,55 ‡
KNIGHT, Penny Lynn. 120 HOSPITAL DR, STE 250 37760 #047-06-1995 L1999 **OBG** *020 †30
LANGTON, Joanne Elizabeth. 657 E BROADWAY BLVD STE C, HEALTHSTAR PHYSICIANS 37760 #143-05-1993 L2002 **END IM** *020 †20
LOPEZ-ROMERO, Jose. 110 HOSPITAL DR, ST. MARY'S JEFFERSON MEMOR 37760 #847-04-1975 L2006 **AN PME** *020 †05
LUBAS, Janet W. 1413 RUSSELL AVE 37760 #012-01-1991 L1994 **IM** *020 †20
MANLEY, Emmett S, III. 120 HOSPITAL DR STE 260 37760 #047-06-1986 L1987 **FM** *020 †18
MC GRAW, John Jay. 120 HOSPITAL DR STE 120 37760 #027-01-1978 L2003 **ORS GP** *020 †40
MC NABNEY, David Patrick. 1810 BISHOP AVE STE A 37760 #017-20-1995 L2002 **FM** *020 †18
MILLIGAN, Leslie Walton. 1810 BISHOP AVE STE C 37760 #047-06-1971 L1972 **GS** *020 †85
MORRIS, Steven Allen. 120 HOSPITAL DR 37760 #047-06-1969 L1970 **U** *020 †95
MUNCY, Estle Pershing. 1428 RUSSELL AVE, ESTLE P MUNCY 37760 #047-06-1943 L1944 **IM** *071
PATTON, Lance Stephen. 120 HOSPITAL DR, GROUP 37760 #047-06-1981 L1984 **PD IM** *020 †20,55
POWELL, Laura Anne. 657 E BROADWAY BLVD 37760 #033-06-1994 L1997 **PD** *020 †55
PURDOM, Laura Lee. ■ 37760 #047-20-2005 L2006 **FP** *012
RAMSEY, Bill Wilson. 120 HOSPITAL DR, GROUP 37760 #047-06-1986 L1987 **PD** *020 †20,55
SALANSKY, Renee Abbott. 657 E BROADWAY BLVD 37760 #047-20-1994 L1997 **PD** *020 †55
SEMMER, John Richard. 120 HOSPITAL DR, STE 250 37760 #047-06-1968 L1969 **OBG** *020 †30
TOFFOLETTO, Larry Michael. 657 E BROADWAY BLVD 37760 #047-06-1986 L1992 **PD** *020 †55 ‡
WILKINSON, John William. 657 E BROADWAY BLVD 37760 #017-20-2000 L2003 **PD** *020 †55 ‡
WILLBANKS, David Verner. 657 E BROADWAY BLVD 37760 #047-06-1966 L1968 **PD** *020 †55
WORLEY, Clyde Walter. 120 HOSPITAL DR STE 130, GROUP 37760 #047-20-2000 L2004 **MPD** *020
ZIRKLE, John Wm. 120 HOSPITAL DR, TENNESSEE VALLEY MED GROUP 37760 #036-01-1970 L1971 **IM HEM** *071 †20 ‡

JELLICO – CAMPBELL

CHOUDHURY, Ruhul Ahmed. 188 HOSPITAL LN, STE 1 37762 #160-06-1980 L1998 **IM** *020 †20
ESCALANTE, David Alberto. 292 N MAIN ST 37762 #649-38-1987 L1994 **END IM** *020 †20
GULLETT, Heidi L Duff. ■ 37762 #038-45-2004 L2007 **FM** *100 †18
GULLETT, Travis Colin. 188 HOSPITAL LN, OREGON HEALTH SCIENCE UNIV 37762 #038-41-2004 L2007 **FM** *020
HARTMAN, Ronald Dennis. 188 HOSPITAL LN, JELLICO COMMUNITY 37762 #005-12-1969 L1977 **FM** *072 †18
KABIR, Mohammed Humayun. 188 HOSPITAL LN STE 1 37762 #160-06-1980 L1994 **CCM** *020
MC RAY, David Eugene. 550 SUNSET TRL, INDIAN MTN CLINIC POB 30 37762 #016-06-1986 L1989 **FM** *020 †18
NYUNT, Tun. 188 HOSPITAL LN, JELLICO COMMUNITY HOSPITAL 37762 #209-01-1988 L2005 **IM** *020
RAFALSKI, Matthew E. 107 S MAIN ST, DAYSPRING FAMILY HEALTH CT 37762 #023-07-1996 L1997 **FM** *020 †20
VILA, Raul Javier. ■ 37762 #264-09-1998 L2008 **IM** *020 †20
WILKENS, Charles Henry. 188 HOSPITAL LN, JELLICO COMMUNITY 37762 #005-12-1965 L1974 **GS** *020
WILKENS, Gregory Charles. 131 HOSPITAL LN, JELLICO COMMUNITY 37762 #005-12-1994 L2001 **GS** *100
WILKENS, Todd Henry. 188 HOSPITAL LN, JELLICO COMMUNITY 37762 #005-12-1993 L1995 **VS** *020 †85

JOELTON – DAVIDSON

DRAKE, Wonder P. ■ 37080 #047-05-1994 L1999 **ID** *100 †20

JOHNSON CITY – WASHINGTON

ABBOUD, Lucien Naji. ■ 37604 #605-03-2002 **CD** *012 †20
ABDEL NOUR, Souheil. PO BOX 70571 37614 #605-03-2006 **IM** *012
ABDELWAHAB, Ayman M. 325 N STATE OF FRANKLIN RD 37604 #915-09-1986 L2001 **PG** *020 †55
ABKES, Bruce Alan. 215 E WATAUGA AVE, EAR NOSE & THROAT ASSOC 37601 #018-03-1999 L2006 **OTO** *020

■ = Address Information Privacy Protected

ABU-ERREISH, Nasser G. 119 BOONE RIDGE DR STE 201, IPC OF TENNESSEE 37615 #575-01-1994 L2005 **ON** *012 †20

ABU-SHAHIN, Fadi Ismail. PO BOX 70571 37614 #575-01-2004 **IM** *012

ABU-ZEITOON, Rawan Ghazi. PO BOX 70571 37614 #575-01-2004 **IM** *012

ACHARYA, Deep Sarvadaman. ■ 37604 #495-23-2000 **FP** *012

ADEBONOJO, Festus O. 325 N STATE OF FRANKLIN RD 37604 #008-01-1960 L1984 NTR PD *050 †55

AHMAD, Elizabeth Ann. 830 JOHNSON AVE, # 1 37604 #305-01-2000 L2003 **P** *020 ‡

AHMAD, Irshad Ali. 830 JOHNSON AVE 37604 #704-01-1966 L1975 **FM OM** *020 †70 ‡

AHMED, Zubair. PO BOX 70571 37614 #704-04-2002 **IM** *100

AKHAVON, Fariba. PO BOX 70571 37614 #517-01-1996 **FP** *012

ALBALBISSI, Kais Adli. ■ 37604 #575-02-2002 L2007 **CD** *012 †20

AL-GARATLI, Ali. 607 BAXTER ST 37601 #875-01-1988 L1999 **P** *020 †75

AL HASAN, Muhanad Abdella. PO BOX 70571, PULM CRITICAL CARE MED 37614 #575-01-2000 L2008 **PCC IM** *012 †20

ALI, Mohamed F. 401 PRINCETON RD 37601 #915-02-1978 L1984 **EM FM** *075 †18

ALI, Muhammad. PO BOX 70571 37614 #704-15-2001 L2007 **FP** *012

ALISON, Harold Wayne. 2408 SUSANNAH ST STE 1 37601 #047-06-1968 L1969 **CD IM** *020 †20

ALISON, Judaun. 325 N STATE OF FRANKLIN RD, 3RD FL 37604 #047-20-1989 L1993 OPH *020 †35

ALLEN, Charles Edward. 1 PROFESSIONAL PARK DR, STE 21 37604 #047-06-1954 L1955 **IM CD** *071 †20

ALLEN, Robert Clark. 1416 S ROAN ST 37601 #047-06-1973 L1974 **IM** *020 †20

ALLEN, Suzanne Charlotte. 400 N STATE OF FRANKLIN RD, JOHNSON CITY MED CTR HOSP 37604 #028-03-1980 L1987 **EM** *020 †16

ALLEY, Christopher Lee. ■ 37601 #047-20-2008 *012

AMBREEN, Farhana. PO BOX 70571 37614 #704-02-1999 L2007 **FP** *012

ANAND, Aashish. PO BOX 70571 37614 #495-36-1999 **IM** *012

ANAND, Rajani. 325 N STATE OF FRANKLIN RD 37604 #495-09-1983 L1991 **PDC** *020 †55

ANDERS, Michael Hilbert. 1019 W OAKLAND AVE, STE 1 37604 #047-20-1987 L2004 FM *040 †18

ANDERSON, James Lee. ■ 37604 #005-12-1977 L1982 **PHP** *030 †50,70

ANTHONY, Marianne Rhodes. 1301 SUNSET DR, STE 3 37604 #004-01-1991 L1999 PDR *020 †80

ARGERSON, John Nicholas. 101 MED TECH PKWY, STE 402 37604 #051-04-1986 L1988 **OM FM** *020 †18

ARMENTROUT, Amy Lynn. 1 PROFESSIONAL PARK DR, STE 21 37604 #001-06-2000 L2005 **IM** *020 †20

ASBERRY, Don Eugene. ■ 37604 #047-20-2006 **PTH** *012

ASHBURN, Robert. 1114 SUNSET DR, STE 4 37604 #048-02-1990 L1994 **AN** *020 †05

ASMAR, Philip Elias. 1113 SUNSET DR 37604 #012-01-1996 L2003 **OTO** *020 †05

AUSTIN, Charles N. ■ 37604 #036-07-1951 L1960 **DR** *071 †80

AWAN, Monam Bashir. 917 W WALNUT ST 37604 #704-01-2003 L2007 **FP** *012

AZIMA, Borzou. 2911 ROYAL TROON, SYCAMORE SHOALS HOSPITAL 37604 #047-20-1990 L1993 **GS** *020

AZZAZY, Nora Nadia. ■ 37604 #047-20-2008 *012

BACKOFEN, Joanne E. 203 E WATAUGA AVE 37601 #035-20-1976 L1993 **AN PAN** *020 †55,05

BAGHERI, Michael. ■ 37601 #517-08-2000 **CD** *012 †20

BAGNELL, Philip C. 325 N STATE OF FRANKLIN RD, UNIV PHYSICIANS - PEDIATRI 37604 #064-01-1968 L1991 **PD PG** *030 †55

BAILEY, Elizabeth Dowell. ■ 37601 #047-06-1954 L1969 **PD** *071

BAJAJ, Jaya Suresh. ■ 37604 #495-83-1998 L2006 **FP** *012

BAKER, David Alan. 912 MILLERCREST DR 37604 #020-02-1979 L1990 **TS** *020 †85,90

BARABOUTI, Dimitra. ■ 37601 #418-01-1995 L2003 **GS CRS** *020 †85,10

BARBARITO, Nancy Gower. 1 PROFESSIONAL PARK DR, BLDG 1 37604 #047-20-1995 L1996 **FM** *020 †18

BARBIAN, Peter J. 101 MED TECH PKWY, STE 405 37604 #056-06-1995 L2005 **PD** *020 †55

BARDHAN, Upasana. PO BOX 70571 37614 #496-59-1999 **IM** *012

BARKLOW, Thomas Alan. PO BOX 70571 37614 #305-01-2003 L2003 **PTH** *012

BARNES, Charles Edward. 1 PROFESSIONAL PARK DR #21 37604 #011-03-1990 L1996 **ORS** *020 †40

BARROW, Heather Michelle. ■ 37604 #047-20-2008 *012

BARWICK, Michael Cook. ■ 37604 #047-06-1972 L1972 **ORS** *020 †40

BATTLE, Gay Kirchner. ■ 37604 #001-02-1971 L1973 **FM AN** *020 †05,18

BATTLE, James Wayne, Jr. 325 N STATE OF FRANKLIN RD, DEPT SURG 37604 #036-01-1965 L1973 **GS** *020 †85

BAYARD, Max Mcmurray, III. 917 W WALNUT ST 37604 #047-20-1991 L1992 **FM** *020 †18

BEAIRD, David A. 300 W WATAUGA AVE, JOHNSON CITY UROLOGICAL 37604 #048-02-1995 L1999 **U** *020 †95 ‡

BEAVER, Walter Richard. 310 N STATE OF FRANKLIN RD, STE 101 37604 #047-06-1967 L1975 **ORS** *020 †40

BECKER, Vincent Gerard. 1301 SUNSET DR, STE 3 37604 #047-20-1993 L2001 **DR** *020 †80

BELANGER, Arthur Wm. 3500 BONDWOOD CIR, MOUNTAIN HOME VETERANS 37604 #025-12-1977 L1994 **FM** *020 †18

BELKNAP, Jeffry Alan. 401 E MAIN ST 37601 #045-01-1970 L1975 **CD IM** *020 †20

BENDFELDT, Fernando. 101 MED TECH PKWY, STE 407 37604 #429-01-1969 L1988 **P** *020 †75

BENSON, Paul Michael. 1009 N STATE OF FRANKLN RD 37604 #021-01-1978 L2004 **D** *020 †15

BENTON, Sally Suzanne. ■ 37604 #047-20-2007 **P** *012

BERRY, Boyce Monroe, Jr. 615 N STATE OF FRANKLIN RD 37604 #045-01-1966 L1972 **PD** *020 †55

BERTOTTI, Marian Lee. 1 PROFESSIONAL PARK DR 37604 #654-01-1983 L1986 **FM OBG** *020 †18

BESSOM, Matthew Ryan. ■ 37604 #047-20-2008 *012

BHAGAT, Anoop. ■ 37601 #836-07-2000 **MP** *012

BHARTI, Des Raj. 325 N STATE OF FRANKLIN RD 37604 #495-77-1973 L1990 **NPM PD** *020 †55

BILLIPS, Polly Olinger. 405 ROY MARTIN RD, STE 104 37615 #051-01-1992 L1998 **FM** *020 †18

BIRUR, Badari. PO BOX 70571 37614 #495-72-2000 **P** *012

BISCHOFF, Paul A. 1 PROFESSIONAL PARK DR, STE 21 37604 #048-04-1986 L1989 **PD** *020 †55

BISHOP, Marilyn Ann. 200 MED TECH PKWY STE 108, MEDWORKS YOUR HLTH ADV 37604 #063-01-1978 L1991 **PD** *020 †70

BLACKMORE, Ron Lee. 1 PROFESSIONAL PARK DR, STE 21 37604 #028-03-1993 L1999 **FM** *020 †18

BLAIK, Ziad. 105 WOODLAWN DR 37604 #915-02-1981 L1987 **N** *020 †75

BLANKENSHIP, Lisa Dawn. ■ 37604 #021-01-1997 L1998 **PM** *020 †60

BLOM, James Gerrit. 400 N STATE OF FRANKLIN RD 37604 #012-05-1991 L2002 **RO** *020 †80

BOATENG, Lydia Alberta K.. PO BOX 70571 37614 #412-02-2002 **PD** *012

BONTA, Bedford Withers. 203 E WATAUGA AVE 37601 #041-01-1969 L1993 **PD NPM** *020 †55

BOREL, Terry C. 403 N STATE OF FRANKLIN RD, WOODRIDGE HOSP 37604 #019-02-1978 L1986 **P** *020 †75 ‡

BORTHWICK, Thomas Richard. 310 N STATE OF FRANKLIN RD, STE 202 37604 #041-02-1971 L1980 **GE IM** *020 †20

BOSWELL, Bill Nelson. 508 PRINCETON RD, STE 104 37601 #047-20-1982 L1984 **U** *020 †95

BOU MALHAB, Nisrine Gerge. PO BOX 70571, E TN U-J H QUILLEN COLL ME 37614 #605-03-2003 **IM** *012

BOUTROS, Gamal Sami A. 2412 SUSANNAH ST STE 3 37601 #915-02-1982 L1996 **N PD** *020 †75,55

BOX, Stephen Tom. 408 N STATE OF FRANKLIN RD 37604 #027-01-1982 L1986 **OBG** *020 †30

BOYD, Kendall H. 401 PRINCETON RD 37601 #422-01-1986 L1989 **IM** *020 †20

BRAHMBHATT, Hetal K. 500 LONGVIEW DR 37604 #495-76-1991 L1999 **P** *020 †75,20

BRAHMBHATT, Vipul Rameshc. 119 BOONE RIDGE DR, STE 201 37615 #495-22-2001 L2005 **CD** *012 †20

BRANTNER, Jim N. 302 WESLEY ST, STE 3 37601 #012-05-1977 L1993 **PS GS** *012

BRIDGFORTH, Wm Adams, Jr. 615 N STATE OF FRANKLIN RD 37604 #047-06-1974 L1975 **PD** *020 †55

BROOKS, Sandra Craft. 400 N STATE OF FRANKLIN RD, DEPT OF PATHOLOGY 37604 #047-20-1988 L1989 **PTH** *020 †50

BROWDER, Isaac Wm. 325 N STATE OF FRANKLIN RD 37604 #021-01-1971 L1990 **GS TRS** *020 †85

BROWN, Aaron Christopher. 221 SHADOWOOD DR, EAST TENNESSEE ANESTHESIA 37604 #036-05-1998 L2002 **AN** *020 †03

BROWN, Dana Steven. 3114 BROWNS MILL RD 37604 #047-06-1987 L1988 **FM** *020 †18

BROWN, Earl Jos. BLDG 52 VA CAMPUS 37605 #021-06-1981 L1987 **PTH** *020 †50

BROWN, Janet Derouen. 325 N STATE OF FRANKLIN RD 37604 #021-06-1982 L1987 OPH *020 †35

BROWN, Joseph Roger, Jr. 1114 SUNSET DR, STE 4 37604 #051-01-1979 L1992 **AN** *020 †55,05

BROWN, Paul Edward, Jr. 219 PRINCETON RD, STE 200 37601 #051-04-1969 L1976 **IM CD** *020 †20

BROWNELL, Morton E, Jr. ■ 37604 #019-02-1942 L1951 **OPH OTO** *071 †45

BUCKNER, Adrian Chad. ■ 37601 #047-20-2002 L2004 **MP** *012

BUDD, Duane Coleman. 315 N STATE OF FRANKLIN RD 37604 #047-06-1960 L1961 **FM** *071 †18

BULLMAN, Michelle Sue. 615 N STATE OF FRANKLIN RD 37604 #036-08-2003 L2006 **PD** *020 †55

BURNETTE, Harold Winston. ■ 37604 #051-04-1961 L1970 **U** *071 †95

BURNS, Kevin Devany. ■ 37604 #047-20-2008 *012

CANCELLARO, Louis Anthony. 325 N STATE OF FRANKLIN RD 37604 #036-07-1965 L1979 **P** *071 †75 ‡

CARLSEN, Jeff Owen. 110 MED TECH PKWY, STE 1 37604 #049-01-1999 L2000 **OPH** *020 †35

CARR, Henry Austin. 1301 SUNSET DR, STE 3 37604 #047-05-1967 L1967 **DR** *020 †80

CARRILLO, Amy Davis. 2 PROFESSIONAL PARK DR, STE 21 37604 #020-75-2004, ▲ L2008 **OBG** *012

CARY, Matthew Glen. 219 PRINCETON RD 37601 #028-02-1989 L1993 **IM** *020 †20

CHAKRABORTY, Kanishka. PO BOX 70571 37614 #495-02-2002 **IM** *012

CHAMPNEY, Gregory Christo. ■ 37601 #047-20-2005 **GS** *012

CHAMPNEY, Heather Naomi. ■ 37601 #047-20-2006 **PD** *012

CHANG, Mark Wansoo. 2408 SUSANNAH ST STE 1 37601 #035-01-1987 L1997 **CD** *020 †20

CHARAF, Edriss Ali. PO BOX 70571, E TN U-J H QUILLEN COLL ME 37614 #605-03-2004 **IM** *012

CHASTAIN, David Otto. 325 N STATE OF FRANKLIN RD 37604 #027-01-1978 L2001 **ADL** *020 †55

CHAUDHARY, Humera Bashir. ■ 37604 #704-06-1987 L2005 **PTH PCP** *062

CHAUDHRY, Muna Faisal. PO BOX 70571 37614 #704-06-1988 L2006 **FP** *012

CHEEK, Samuel Burch, Jr. 400 N STATE OF FRANKLIN RD 37604 #047-20-1993 L1998 **OM EM** *062

CHILAKALA, Sandeep Kumar. PO BOX 70571 37614 #495-62-2004 **PD** *012

CHINNAREDDY, Prasanthy. PO BOX 70578 37614 #496-34-2002 L2008 **PD** *012

CHISHOLM, Joel Patrick. ■ 37604 #036-08-2008 *012

CHO, Moon Kyung. PO BOX 70571 37614 #583-09-1990 L2007 **IM** *100 †20

CHUNG, Sue Yong. 1301 SUNSET DR STE 3 37604 #016-06-1982 L1990 **DR NM** *020 †28,80

CHURCHILL, John Alvord. ■ 37601 #041-01-1945 L1983 **N CHN** *072 †75

CLARK, Jill Elisabeth. ■ 37604 #047-20-2003 **GS** *012

CLARK, Robert L. 110 MED TECH PKWY 37604 #035-45-1962 L1971 **OPH** *020 †35

CLARK, Stephen Wesley. PO BOX 70571 37614 #047-06-2005 **IM** *100

CLARK, Terrence Peter. 403 N STATE OF FRANKLIN RD 37604 #048-04-1973 L2001 **CHP P** *040 †75

CLEMONS, Donald Eugene. 1009 N STATE OF FRANKLN RD 37604 #021-05-1971 L1986 **D DMP** *020 †15

CLEMONS, Robert John. 1009 N STATE OF FRANKLIN RD 37604 #047-20-1998 L2001 **D** *020 †15

CLEVELAND, Leland Chas. 401 PRINCETON RD 37601 #045-01-1992 L2001 **FM** *020 †18

COBBLE, Anita Diane. 325 N STATE OF FRANKLIN RD 37604 #047-20-1993 L1998 **GS** *020 †85

COLE, Charles Pittman. 310 N STATE OF FRANKLIN RD, STE 303 37604 #047-06-1970 L1970 **PUD SME** *020 †20

COLETTI, Cynthia Mae. 1019 W OAKLAND AVE, STE 1 37604 #041-01-1988 L1999 **FM** *020 †18

COLONNA, Alexander L. 1735 W STATE OF FRANKLN RD, STE 5 37604 #045-01-2002 L2007 **GS** *012

COLVETT, Kyle Todd. 400 N STATE OF FRANKLIN RD 37604 #047-20-1992 L1996 **RO GS** *020 †80

COLYAR, Lee A. 2514 WESLEY ST, STE 102 37601 #422-01-1990 L1996 **FM** *020 †18

COMBS, Landon Shane. 2103 FOREST DR, STE 5 37615 #047-20-1994 L1997 **PD** *020 †55

CONE, William Joseph. 203 E WATAUGA AVE, MEDICAL CENTER OB-GYN PC 37601 #012-01-1962 L1968 **OBG** *020 †30

COOGAN, Philip Shields. 400 N STATE OF FRANKLIN RD 37604 #028-34-1962 L1978 **ATP** *071 †50

COOK, Keith Ray. 219 PRINCETON RD 37601 #047-20-1995 L1996 **IM** *020 †20

COOPER, Scott Bryson. ■ 37604 #016-06-1982 L1990 **IM** *020 †20

COPELAND, Billy Harold, II. 219 PRINCETON RD 37601 #047-20-2003 L2005 **IM** *020 †20

COPELAND, Rebecca Jean. 325 N STATE OF FRANKLIN RD 37604 #047-06-1982 L1983 **IM** *020 †20

COSBY, Lewis F., Jr. ■ 37604 #051-01-1943 L1948 **PD** *071 †55

COSTA, Amanda Guedes De M. PO BOX 70571 37614 #187-07-2003 **IM** *012

COSTA, Ricardo Lima Barro. PO BOX 70571, E TN U-J H QUILLEN COLL ME 37614 #187-07-2004 **IM** *012

COSTELLO, Patrick N. 400 N STATE OF FRANKLIN RD 37604 #539-04-1992 L1999 **PTH** *020 †50

COTT, Craig John. PO BOX 70567, ETSU 37614 #045-01-1990 L2002 **P** *020

COTTRELL, James Wm. 1114 SUNSET DR STE 4 37604 #038-40-1975 L1992 **AN PUD** *020 †05

COUNTS, Marc Dalmond. 2408 SUSANNAH ST, STE 1 37601 #047-20-1998 L1999 **CD** *020 †20

CRISOSTOMO, Conchitina. ■ 37604 #748-01-1995 L2006 **NEP** *020 †20

CROCKETT, Douglas Harman. 203 E WATAUGA AVE 37601 #051-01-1948 L1960 **OPH** *071 †35

CROWDER, Brenda Jane. 2 PROFESSIONAL PARK DR, STE 21 37604 #017-20-1983 L1987 **GYN** *020 †30

CRUMPLER, Tammy North. 1301 SUNSET DR 37604 #047-20-1996 L2000 **DR** *020 †80

CUPP, Horace Ballard, Jr. ■ 37601 #036-07-1955 L1964 **NS** *071 †25

CUTSHALL, Kenneth Edward. 701 MED TECH PKWY, STE 400 37604 #047-06-1987 L1988 **GS** *085

DACKS, Laura Michelle. ■ 37604 #011-05-2005 **GS** *012

DARAKYAN, Brian Henry. PO BOX 70571 37614 #270-03-2002 **FP** *012

DARLING, Ian Andrew. 1114 SUNSET DR, STE 4 37604 #047-20-1989 L1993 **AN** *020 †05

DARRAJ, Kathrin Farah. ■ 37614 #047-20-2005 **IM** *012

DARROW, Joseph Chas., Jr. ■ 37604 #033-05-1977 L1978 **HS ORS** *020 †40

DAVID, Daniel Jos. 917 W WALNUT ST, FAMILY MEDICINE ASSOCIATES 37604 #051-01-1978 L1985 **FM ADM** *040 †18

DELL, Kevin David. 325 N STATE OF FRANKLIN RD, ETSU DEPT OF INTERNAL MEDI 37604 #051-07-2002 L2005 **IM** *050 †20

DEMAY, Jessica M. 325 N STATE OF FRANKLIN RD, DEPT OF OB/GYN 37604 #016-11-1994 L2001 **OBG** *020 †30

DENGLER, John Martin. 105 WOODLAWN DR, TRI STATE MOUNTAIN 37604 #025-12-1986 L1991 **N CN** *020 †75

DENHAM, James Wesley. ■ 37601 #021-05-2002 L2005 **PTH** *012

DESHMUKH, Kiran. 2002 MILLBROOK DR 37604 #495-28-1973 L1983 **AN** *020 †05

DE VOE, William Michael. 325 N STATE OF FRANKLIN RD 37604 #038-40-1977 L1992 **NPM** *020 †55

DE VOS, Elaine Lee. 400 N STATE OF FRANKLIN RD, JOHNSON CITY MEDICAL CENTE 37604 #041-14-1992 L1996 **PM** *020 †60

DEVOS, Keith Joseph. 105 WOODLAWN DR 37604 #041-14-1991 L1996 **N** *020 †75

DE WIT, Albertine. 310 N STATE OF FRANKLIN RD, STE 201 37604 #660-01-1973 L1981 **RHU IM** *020 †20

DHAIMAT, Ammar Oqlah. PO BOX 70571, E TN U-J H QUILLEN COLL ME 37614 #575-01-1997 **IM** *100

DHALIWAL, Avtar Singh. 3606 HONEYWOOD DR 37604 #495-29-1965 L1976 **PS FPS** *020 †65

DHALIWAL, Manjit Kaur. 37604 #495-03-1970 L1984 **PM P** *100

DIAZ-MIRANDA, Constantino. ■ 37604 #308-03-1982 L1991 **PUD PTH** *020

DIAZ VALDES, Sergio Alfon. PO BOX 70571, E TN U-J H QUILLEN COLL ME 37614 #429-02-1998 **IM** *012

DONAHUE, Donald Clark. 1301 SUNSET DR, STE 3 37604 #017-20-1981 L1987 **RO** *020 †80

DONOVAN, Brian Patrick. 119 BOONE RIDGE DR, STE 201 37615 #027-01-1982 L1989 **IM** *020 †20

DONOVAN, Joan Elizabeth. 325 N STATE OF FRANKLIN RD 37604 #038-43-1984 L1988 **OPH** *020 †35

DONOVAN, Mark Lowell. 1 PROFESSIONAL PARK DR # 1 37604 #038-43-1984 L1988 **PD** *020 †55

DOSSETT, Burgin E., Jr. 400 N STATE OF FRANKLIN RD 37604 #047-06-1953 L1953 **IM** *020

DOUGLAS, John Elwood. ■ 37615 #023-07-1963 L1980 **CD IM** *071 †20

DOVE, Amanda Alvada. ■ 37604 #047-20-2008 *012

DOWNS, Christopher Jos. 408 N STATE OF FRANKLIN RD, STE 24 37604 #047-20-1989 L1990 **CD** *020 †20

DRAKE, Janet Gail. 325 N STATE OF FRANKLIN RD, ETSU CANCER CENTER 37604 #011-03-1992 L1999 **OBG** *020 †30

DREY, Chad Aaron. 408 N STATE OF FRANKLIN RD, STE 32 37604 #012-22-2003 L2007 **OBG** *020

DUBE, Michael Norman. ■ 37601 #047-20-1995 L1996 **IM** *020

DUGGAL, Sonia. PO BOX 70571, E TN U-J H QUILLEN COLL ME 37614 #495-90-2000 **FP** *012

DULEBOHN, Scott Carmody. 408 N STATE OF FRANKLIN RD, STE 42 37604 #028-03-1989 L2000 **NS GS** *025

DUNCAN, Natalie Renee. ■ 37604 #047-20-2003 L2007 **GS** *012

DUNKELBERGER, Brian H. 203 E WATAUGA AVE, STE 1 37601 #047-06-1967 L1968 **OBG GP** *020 †30

DUNN, Jason Lamar. 37601 #012-22-2004 L2007 **GS** *012

DYER, Allen R. 325 N STATE OF FRANKLIN RD 37604 #036-07-1972 L1992 **P** *030 †75

DYKES, James Thomas. 219 PRINCETON RD 37601 #047-20-1992 L1993 **IM** *020 †20

EASON, Martin Phan. ■ 37601 #003-01-1987 L2005 **AN** *020 †05

EBEO, Celso Taburnal. 310 N STATE OF FRANKLIN RD, STE 303 37604 #748-11-1995 L2007 **PCC** *020 †20

EBERHART, Anne Helen. 325 N ST FRANKLIN RD 37604 #047-20-1999 L2003 **OPH** *020 †35

EDENFIELD, Mark Emmett. 401 PRINCETON RD 37601 #047-06-1982 L1982 **AN** *020 †05

EDENS, Fred R. ■ 37604 #051-04-1951 L1953 **D** *071 †15

EL-ABBASSI, Adel Mohamad. PO BOX 70571, E TN U-J H QUILLEN COLL ME 37614 #605-04-2001 **IM** *012

EL-ANDARY, Nada Nabih. ■ 37604 #605-04-2002 **IM** *012

EL-BAZOUNI, Hadi Elias. PO BOX 70571 37614 #605-03-2000 L2006 **IM** *100 †20

ELDEEB, Maha Abdalbaki. E TN U-J QUILLEN COL OF M, DEPT PED 37614 #915-02-1985 **PD** *100

ELFAKIH, Assem Anis. PO BOX 70571 37614 #913-13-1999 L2007 **IM** *020 †20

EL KHOURY, Raymonda Raymo. PO BOX 70571 37614 #605-03-2006 **IM** *012

EL KHOURY ANTOUN, Georges. PO BOX 70571 37614 #605-03-2006 **IM** *012

ELLIOTT, Richard Levere. 400 N STATE OF FRANKLIN RD 37604 #017-20-1962 L1975 **U** *071

EL MINAOUI, Wael Khaled. PO BOX 70571, E TN U-J H QUILLEN COLL ME 37614 #605-04-2003 **IM** *012

EL-SAGHBINI, Fady Elias. ■ 37604 #605-03-2002 **ID** *012 †20

EL-SHINNAWY, Ihab Hussein. ■ 37604 #915-04-1995 L2005 **PTH** *100 †50

ENCK, Robert Edwin. PO BOX 70622, VAMC BLDG 1 37614 #041-09-1971 L2007 **ON HEM** *020 †20

ERNSPIKER, Erich Lee. ■ 37604 #020-02-2003 **GS** *012

ERNST, Mary Lou. E TENN ST PO BOX 19930A 37601 #041-13-1962 **D** *100

ESTES, Michelle Renee. 1 PROFESSIONAL PARK DR, STE 21 37604 #047-20-2003 L2005 **PD** *020 †55

EVANS, James Robt. 2 PROFESSIONAL PARK DR, STE 11 37604 #028-34-1983 L1987 **GS VS** *020 †85

FAIRCHILD, Gary A. 138 FAIRLAWN DR 37601 #422-01-1981 L1985 **OM EM** *020 †20,70

FAMOYIN, Charles O. 310 N STATE OF FRANKLIN RD, STE 401 37604 #690-01-1992 L2006 **IM HO** *020 †20

FARMER, Margaret F. 1 PROFESSIONAL PARK DR, STE 21 37604 #036-01-1992 L1996 **PD** *020 †55

FARROW, Jeff Richard. 310 N STATE OF FRANKLIN RD, STE 303 37604 #034-01-1985 L1990 **PUD** *020 †20

FENLEY, John David. 302 SUNSET DR STE 105 37604 #047-20-1987 L1989 **P** *020 †75

FIELDS, Cheryl Lynn. ■ 37604 #020-02-1984 L1997 **ID PUD** *020 †20

FISH, Charles Abraham. 615 N STATE OF FRANKLIN RD 37604 #038-41-1968 L1973 **PD** *020 †55

FLETCHER, Brandon Scott. PO BOX 70571 37614 #654-01-2006 **FP** *012

FLORESGUERRA, Carlos A. 325 N STATE OF FRANKLIN RD, SURGERY SUITE 37604 #132-07-1982 L1994 **GS** *020 †85

FOLEY, Charles E. 310 N STATE OF FRANKLIN RD, HIGHLAND PLASTIC SURG PLLC 37604 #008-02-1996 L2004 **PS** *020 †85

FORBUSH, Frank A. 1 PROFESSIONAL PARK DR, BLDG 1 37604 #047-06-1982 L1983 **IM** *020 †16,20

FORESTER, David Lionel. 209 E UNAKA AVE, THE FORESTER CLINIC, P.C. 37601 #051-01-1986 L2000 **P ADM** *020 †20

FOULK, Brooke Anne. ■ 37604 #047-20-2006 **OBG** *012

FRANKO, John Patrick. 917 W WALNUT ST, JOHNSON CITY 37604 #051-01-1982 L2007 **FM** *040 †18

FREEMON, David Noble. 219 PRINCETON RD 37601 #047-06-1973 L1973 **IM** *020 †20

FRIZZELL, Peter Graham. 325 N STATE OF FRANKLIN RD, ETSU DEPT OG PSYCHIATRY 37604 #047-20-1991 L1992 **P** *020 †75

FULLAGAR, Timothy Michael. 310 N STATE OF FRANKLIN RD, STE 103 37604 #051-04-1986 L2006 **NS** *020 †20

GADADHAR, Harsha. ■ 37601 #496-22-2000 L2006 **ON** *012 †20

GAGE, Jodi Burton. 615 N STATE OF FRANKLIN RD 37604 #047-20-1998 L2001 **PD** *020 †55

GAGE, Kathleen A. ■ 37601 #011-03-1979 L1985 **IM ID** *071

GAGE, Trevor Jason. 615 N STATE OF FRANKLIN RD 37604 #047-20-1999 L2002 **PD** *020

GALLEMORE, Gail Hurd. 325 N STATE OF FRANKLIN RD 37604 #036-07-1977 L1980 **PLM PDI** *020 †55

GANGADHARAN, Venkataramana. PO BOX 70571 37614 #496-23-2006 **IM** *012

GANOTE, Charles Edgar. EAST TENNESSEE STATE UNIV, DEPT PATH 37601 #047-05-1965 L1965 **PTH GE** *050

GARCIA, Israel Dikit. 311 PRINCETON RD, STE 7 37601 #748-01-1993 L2003 **CD** *020 †20

GARCIA, Maria Castillo. PO BOX 70571, E TN U-J H QUILLEN COLL ME 37614 #748-10-1993 L2004 **IM** *100 †20

GARDNER, Timothy Lee. 1009 N ST FRANKLIN RD, TRI-CITIES SKIN AND CANCER 37604 #051-01-1993 L2003 **D DMP** *015

GARRETT, Wm Allan, Jr. 917 W WALNUT ST 37604 #045-01-1987 L2003 **FM** *020 †18

GARRIDO, Jose Antonio. 119 BOONE RIDGE DR, STE 201 37615 #042-01-1989 L2005 **GE AN** *020

GEBKA, Ann Maria. 325 N STATE OF FRANKLIN RD, 1ST FL 37604 #011-02-2000 L2004 **OBG** *020 †30 ‡

GERAYLI, Fereshteh. 917 W WALNUT ST, ETSU FAMILY MEDICINE ASSOC 37604 #517-04-1981 L2004 **FM** *020 †18 ‡

GETAZ, Emile Paul. 119 BOONE RIDGE DR, STE 201 37615 #836-02-1968 L1980 **ON HEM** *050 †20

GHAFFAR, Umbar. PO BOX 70571 37614 #704-20-2004 **IM** *012

GIBSON, James Warren. 1301 SUNSET DR, STE 3 37604 #047-06-1957 L1958 **R** *020 †80

GIBSON, Mary Jane. 219 PRINCETON RD, STE 200 37601 #047-06-1987 L1988 **IM** *020

GILBERT, Anna Broome. 219 PRINCETON RD 37601 #047-20-2002 L2004 **IM** *100

GILBERT, Wayne Paul. 3201 BRISTOL HWY, STE 7 37601 #039-01-1979 L1992 **EM** *020 †16

GILL, Thomas W. 1 PROFESSIONAL PARK DR, STE 21 37604 #048-04-1987 L1992 **PD** *020 †55

GILLESPIE, Christopher L. 101 MED TECH PKWY STE 305, PHYSICIANS, PC 37604 #047-06-1974 L1974 **IM** *020 †20

GIRISH, Mirle R. 310 N STATE OF FRANKLIN RD, STE 303 37604 #495-37-1989 L2001 **PCC** *020 †20

GODFREY, James Hodge. NORTHSIDE HOSP 37601 #021-01-1965 L1975 **PTH** *020 †50

GOENKA, Puneet. 310 N STATE OF FRANKLIN RD, STE 202 37604 #495-03-1988 L1995 **GE IM** *020 †20

GOENKA, Seema. ■ 37604 #495-30-1992 L1999 **FM** *020 †18

GOLI, Anil Kumar. ■ 37604 #496-01-1995 L2002 **ICE** *012 †20

GOLI, Sujatha A. 310 N STATE OF FRANKLIN RD, STE 303 37604 #495-21-1997 L2002 **PCC** *020 †20

GOPALAGOWDA, Bhavya Hanum. PO BOX 70571 37614 #496-20-2000 **IM** *012

GORMAN, Paul Wm. 2335 KNOB CREEK RD 37604 #048-02-1984 L1990 **ORS** *020 †40

GOSEY, Michael Louis. 119 BOONE RIDGE DR, STE 2503 37615 #023-01-1986 L2003 **IM** *020 †20

GOSS, James Alan. 1 PROFESSIONAL PARK DR #21 37604 #051-04-1992 L1997 **ORS** *020 †40

GOULDING, Clarence E, III. 401 PRINCETON RD 37601 #036-05-1982 L1984 **EM OM** *020 †16,18

GRAHAM, Mary Frances Lyon. ■ 37602 #016-11-1951 L1952 **PHP PD** *030

GRANGER, James Archibald. 810 XANADU CT 37604 #035-45-1961 L1981 **CHP P** *071 †75

GRANT, Daniel Ryan. ■ 37604 #047-20-2008 *012

GREEN, Bobby M. ■ 37604 #047-06-1976 L1980 **P CHP** *020

GREENWOOD, Kenneth K. 607 BAXTER ST 37601 #422-01-1989 L1997 **P** *020

GRINDSTAFF, Robert E. 1270 MILLIGAN HWY 37601 #047-06-1983 L1984 **FM PME** *020 †18

GROBOVSKY, Laura Vanini. ■ 37604 #047-20-1993 L1995 **ON HO** *071

GROSSERODE, Michael Jay. 1 PROFESSIONAL PARK DR, STE 21 37604 #004-01-1991 L1995 **IM** *020 †20

GROSSMAN, Joshua Bernard. ■ 37604 #028-02-1965 L1976 **IM CD** *020 †20

GUBLER, Robert Jay. ■ 37604 #010-01-1967 L1978 **DR** *071 †20

GUHA, Bhuvana. 325 N STATE OF FRANKLIN RD 37604 #495-66-1989 L1996 **IM** *020 †20

GUINN, Alison Dawn. 3114 BROWNS MILL RD 37604 #047-20-2004 L2005 **FM** *100 †18

GUNTER, Kelly Parks. 1301 SUNSET DR, STE 3 37604 #047-07-1988 L1989 **DR** *020 †80

HADDADIN, Tariq Ziad. 2 PROFESSIONAL PARK DR #15 37604 #575-01-1996 L2005 **IC CD** *020 †20

HAIRE, Craig Michael. 105 W PINE ST 37604 #047-20-1988 L1990 **GP** *020

HALDER, Ranjay. ■ 37601 #306-01-2003 **P** *012
HALEY, Tony O'Neal. 701 MED TECH PKWY, STE 400 37604 #012-01-1982 L1984
  GS VS †85
HALL, Anjeanette Kittrell. ■ 37615 #047-20-2005 **FP** *012
HALL, Apryl Meshea Parks. PO BOX 70578, DEPT OF PEDIATRICS 37614 #047-20-2005 L2008
  PD *012
HALL, Ben David. ■ 37601 #047-06-1947 L1947 **IM NM** *071 †20
HALL, Stephanie. ■ 37601 #012-05-1981 L1990 **P** *012 †20,70
HALSTEAD, George Oliver. ■ 37602 #045-01-2005 **FM** *100
HAMATI, Fawwaz Ibrahim. 311 PRINCETON RD STE 7 37601 #654-01-1985 L1991
  CD IM *020 †20 ‡
HAMEL, Steven Callan. 408 N ST FRANKLIN RD, MED CTR OFFICE BLDG STE 42 37604
  #048-12-1979 L1985 **NS** *020 †25
HAMM, Robert Walter. PO BOX 70571 37614 #305-01-2006 **P** *012
HAMMONS, Zachary Alfred. ■ 37604 #047-20-2008 *012
HANSEN, James Wendell. 219 PRINCETON RD 37601 #030-06-1986 L1999 **PUD IM** *020 †20
HANSEN, Shannon Leigh. ■ 37614 #047-20-2008 *012
HANSEN, Shoko. 219 PRINCETON RD, PLLC DBA JOHNSON CITY INT 37601
  #030-06-1988 L2001 **IM** *020
HARKER, Anita Kenkarey. PO BOX 70571 37614 #495-21-1991 **IM** *012
HARRIS, Arthur Sale. 215 E WATAUGA AVE 37601 #004-01-1967 L1975 **OTO** *020 †45
HART, Lora Lee. ■ 37601 #047-20-2006 **MP** *012
HARTLEY, Frederick Chas. 203 E WATAUGA AVE, STE 1 37601 #048-04-1972 L1978
  OBG *020 †20
HATCHER, Glen Homer, Jr. 1301 SUNSET DR, STE 3 37604 #047-20-1991 L1995 **DR** *020 †80
HATJIOANNOU, Jason. 219 PRINCETON RD 37601 #654-01-1984 L1987 **IM** *020 †20
HAWS, Claude Carterhelm. 1301 SUNSET DR, STE 3 37604 #047-06-1972 L1972 **DR** *020 †80
HAYEL-MOGHADAM, Kamran. PO BOX 70571 37614 #517-19-2000 **P** *012
HAYNES, Daniel F. 325 N STATE OF FRANKLIN RD, THIRD FLOOR 37604 #021-01-1985 L1994
  PS *020 †85,65
HELOU, Jihad Said. ■ 37604 #605-02-1997 **CD** *100 †20
HEMPHILL, Christopher B. 315 N STATE OF FRANKLIN RD, BLDG 1 37604 #047-06-1973 L1974
  IM PUD *020 †20
HENDRICK, John Preston. ■ 37601 #051-04-1982 L1989 **P PYG** *020 †75
HENRY, Philip Dominique. 2 PROFESSIONAL PARK DR, STE 15 37604 #869-02-1960 L2004
  CD VM *050 †20
HERD, John Kenneth. 310 N STATE OF FRANKLIN RD, STE 303 37604 #035-20-1954 L1978
  RHU PD *071 †55
HERRIN, Steve Johnson. 1109 SOUTHWEST AVE 37604 #047-06-1978 L1979
  GPM PHP *100 †75,70
HILLMAN, Charles Harlan. 325 N STATE OF FRANKLIN RD, 1ST FL 37604 #036-07-1953 L1959
  GYN *071 †30
HINES, Robt Stickley, Jr. 408 N STATE OF FRANKLIN RD, STE 42 37604 #047-06-1966 L1967
  NS *071 †25
HINTON, Jeffrey Taylor. 2 PROFESSIONAL PARK DR, STE 21 37604 #020-12-1984 L1994
  OBG *020 †30
HODGE, Michael James. 2333 KNOB CREEK RD STE 16 37604 #047-06-1988 L1993
  GS *020 †85
HOFUNG, Brian C. 119 E KING ST 37601 #011-02-1996 L1999 **IM** *020 †20
HOLLADAY, Rodney L. 119 BOONE RIDGE DR, STE 201 37615 #047-06-1982 L1982
  IM IMG *020 †20
HOLLIER, Paul Anthony. 403 PRINCETON RD, STE 5 37601 #048-13-1976 L1982
  GP VS *020 †85
HOLMES, Sheri Holmes. ■ 37604 #047-20-2001 L2005 **OBG** *100 †30
HOLT, James David. 917 W WALNUT ST, DEPT FP 37604 #023-01-1982 L2001 **FM FPG** *040 †18
HOOKS, Mary Alicia. 325 N STATE OF FRANKLIN RD 37604 #041-01-1989 L1996 **GS** *020 †85
HOOVER, Randy Wayne. 401 PRINCETON RD 37601 #047-20-2000 L2003 **IM** *020 †20
HOPKINS, Steven Paul. 11 PROFESSIONAL PARK DR, BLDG 2 37604 #055-01-1993 L2001
  VS *020 †85
HOSKERE, Girendra V. 325 N STATE OF FRANKLIN RD, DEPT OF INTERNAL MEDICINE 37604
  #495-37-1994 L1999 **PCC** *012 †20
HOUCK, Kelly Suzanne. ■ 37604 #047-20-2002 L2004 **OS** *020 †20
HOUGHTON, Rodney Adam. 607 BAXTER ST 37601 #048-13-1976 L1998 **P CHP** *020 †75
HOWELL, Mark Allan. 215 E WATAUGA AVE 37601 #047-06-1976 L1977 **OTO FPS** *020 †45
HUANG, Y Annette. 105 WOODLAWN DR, TRI STATE MOUNTAIN 37604 #243-16-1985 L2003
  N *020 †75 ‡
HUDDLESTON, Charles T. 214 W UNAKA AVE 37604 #047-20-2001 L2004 **GS** *012
HUDDLESTON, Thomas Lamont. 400 N STATE OF FRANKLIN RD 37604 #047-06-1984 L1984
  ORS *020 †40
HUDDLESTON, William Scott. ■ 37604 #047-20-2008 *012
HUDSON, Larry David. 1021 W OAKLAND AVE STE 102 37604 #012-01-1975 L1980
  D *020 †20,15
HUSSEIN, Rezhan Hama Ali. ■ 37604 #528-02-1992 L2006 **ID IM** *100 †20 ‡
HUTCHINS, Christina Renee. 3114 BROWNS MILL RD 37604 #047-06-1990 L1991 **FM** *020 †18
IALAMOVA-TOUNTCHEVA, Dimka. 119 BOONE RIDGE DR, STE 201 37615 #198-03-1982 L2004
  IM *100 †20
IBRAHIM, Joseph A. ■ 37601 #047-20-2003 **CCS** *100
IBRAHIM, Lamis Wahid. PO BOX 70571, E TN U-J H QUILLEN COLL ME 37614 #605-04-2003
  IM *012
INGRAM, Charles T, Jr. 1114 SUNSET DR, STE 4 37604 #012-05-1977 L1994 **AN** *020 †05
IQBAL, Maryam. PO BOX 70571 37614 #704-21-2003 **FP** *012
ISLAM, Md. Aticul. ■ 37614 #160-08-1997 L2007 **ID** *012 †20
ISMAIL, Hassan M. 325 N STATE OF FRANKLIN RD, ETSU DEPT OF INT MED 2FL 37604
  #875-01-1988 L2001 **IM** *020 †20
ITARO, Gabriel Ochuko. PO BOX 15100A, DEPT MED 37614 #047-20-1990 L1993 **N** *100
JACOME VILLAMAR, Francisco. PO BOX 70571 37614 #319-08-2003 **GS** *012
JAIN, Sangeeta Jitender. PO BOX 18601, STATE UNIVERSITY 37614 #038-40-2007 **IM** *012
JEFFERS, Steven Wayne. PO BOX 70571 37614 #306-02-2006 **P** *012
JELOVSEK, Fred Robt. 400 N STATE OF FRANKLIN RD 37604 #025-01-1969 L1991
  OBG *020 †30 ‡
JENIGIRI, Bharat. ■ 37604 #495-37-2002 L2006 **IM** *100 †20
JENNINGS, Charles Edward. ■ 37604 #047-07-1980 L1981 **U** *020 †95
JERNIGAN, Perry David. 1301 SUNSET DR STE B 37604 #047-20-1993 L1998 **VIR** *020 †80
JERNIGAN, Thomas Watson. 408 N STATE OF FRANKLIN RD, STE 32 37604
  #055-01-1975 L1979 **GYN** *020 †30
JOHN, Jayashree Sunil. ■ 37601 #495-28-1984 **P** *012

JOHN, Sunil. 119 BOONE RIDGE DR, STE 201 37615 #495-28-1984 L2004 **IM** *020 †20
JOHNSON, Frank P, Jr. 203 E WATAUGA AVE 37601 #047-06-1983 L1984 **IM** *020
JOHNSON, James Nolen. ■ 37604 #047-06-1957 L1957 **EM FM** *071 †18
JOHNSTON, Chambless Rand, III. PO BOX 70571, E TN U-J H QUILLEN COLL ME 37614
  #654-01-2006 **IM** *012
JONES, Chandra Renee. 325 N STATE OF FRANKLIN RD 37604 #012-21-1993 L2007 **OBG** *020
JONES, David Wayne. 508 PRINCETON RD, STE 104 37601 #047-06-1970 L1971 **U** *020 †95
JONES, Jon Wm, Jr. 2 PROFESSIONAL PARK DR, STE 13 37604 #012-01-1986 L2005
  GS *020 †85
JONES, Phillip Wayne. 403 PRINCETON RD STE 9 37601 #001-02-1997 L2000 **AI** *020 †20,03
JORDAN, Louis Collier, Jr. 2408 SUSANNAH ST, STE 1 37604 #012-01-1976 L1978
  CD IM *020 †20
JOSHI, Deepak. ■ 37601 #495-03-1985 L2007 **MP** *012
JOURNAGIN, Andrea Monique. ■ 37604 #047-20-2005 **OBG** *012
KADAM, Rajesh Shivaji. ■ 37601 #496-38-1991 L2007 **MP** *012
KADARI, Rajendra. ■ 37604 #047-06-42-2004 **IM** *012
KALLADA, Sahla. PO BOX 70571, E TN U-J H QUILLEN COLL ME 37614 #495-44-2002 **PD** *012
KALRA, Sumit. PO BOX 70571, E TN U-J H QUILLEN COLL ME 37614 #495-90-2000 **IM** *012
KALWINSKY, David Knowlton. QUILLEN COLLEGE OF MED, E TN STATE UNIV 37614
  #041-01-1973 L1977 **PHO PD** *040 †55
KAROU, Fadi. PO BOX 70571 37614 #875-02-2004 **IM** *012
KASASBEH, Ehab Saleh. PO BOX 70571, E TN U-J H QUILLEN COLL ME 37614
  #575-01-2001 L2007 **CD** *012 †20
KATRAGUNTA, Neelima. PO BOX 70571, E TN U-J H QUILLEN COLL ME 37614
  #495-73-2003 L2006 **GS** *012
KATRAS, Anthony. 325 N STATE OF FRANKLIN RD, THIRD FLOOR 37604 #047-20-1984 L1985
  VS GS *020
KAUFFMAN, William M. ■ 37601 #020-12-1981 L1990 **PDR** *020 †80
KAUR, Tarandeep. PO BOX 70571 37614 #495-03-2003 **FP** *012
KEHLER, George Bela, II. ■ 37604 #047-20-1991 L1992 **AN** *020
KEITER, Mary Beth Fudge. ■ 37601 #036-01-1972 L1972 **PD OS** *074 †55
KEITER, Robert Harvey. ■ 37601 #036-01-1967 L1994 **P ADP** *071 †55
KEITH, Robby Lee. 119 BOONE RIDGE DR, SUTIE 201 37615 #055-01-2002 L2006
  PCC *012 †20
KELLER, Jessica L. PO BOX 70569 37614 #020-75-2007, ▲ **OBG** *012
KELLEY, Paul R. 2313 SILVERDALE DR, STE B 37601 #045-04-1982 L1990 **P** *020 †75
KERLEY, Mei-Fung. 112 BARBERRY RD, 37 YORKTOWNE SQUARE 37604 #047-20-1992 L1993
  IM *020 †20
KERNY, Ben John, Jr. PO BOX 70571 37614 #473-01-2003 **FP** *012
KFOURY, Lara Wahib. PO BOX 70571, E TN U-J H QUILLEN COLL ME 37614 #605-03-2004
  IM *012
KHAN, Ahmed Abdullah. 311 PRINCETON RD 37601 #495-57-1974 L1981 **CD ICE** *020 †20 ‡
KHARALKAR, Shweta. PO BOX 70571 37614 #495-83-2003 L2007 **FP** *012
KILGUS, Mark Duane. 403 N STATE OF FRANKLIN RD 37604 #045-04-1989 L2002
  CHP *020 †20
KIMBROUGH, Barbara Joan O. 325 N STATE OF FRANKLIN RD 37604 #026-08-1976 L1980
  OPH *020 †35
KIMBROUGH, Stephen M. 105 WOODLAWN DR, TRI STATE MOUNTAIN 37604
  #026-08-1976 L1980 **N CN** *020 †75 ‡
KINCAID, William Ralph. 310 N STAT OF FRNKLN #401 37604 #055-01-1972 L1976
  ON HEM *020 †20
KINDLE, Joy Je Nean. 1301 SUNSET DR, STE 3 37604 #047-20-1996 L1998 **DR** *020 †80
KING, John Chadwick. 400 N STATE OF FRANKLIN RD 37604 #051-01-1987 L1992
  PTH *020 †50
KING, Kelly Noel. ■ 37601 #047-20-2006 L2007 **P** *012
KING, Michelle Renee. 525 N STATE OF FRANKLIN RD, STE B-12 FRANKLIN MED PARK 37604
  #020-12-1995 L2001 **P** *020 †75
KLOPFENSTEIN, Kathryn J. ■ 37614 #003-01-1987 L2006 **PHO PD** *020 †55
KLOSTERMAN, Lance Alan. 1301 SUNSET DR STE 3, MOUNTAIN EMPIRE RADIOLOGY 37604
  #038-41-1999 L2002 **DR** *020 †80
KLUGEWICZ, Christopher J. 2333 KNOB CREEK RD, STE 12 37604 #038-41-1991 L2007
  ICE *020 †20
KNIGHT, Theron Turner. 325 N STATE OF FRANKLIN RD, UNIVERSITY PHYSICIANS PRAC 37604
  #020-02-1959 L1997 **GS** *040 †85
KOLSKI, John Mark. ■ 37604 #016-45-1994 L1994 **U** *020
KOSSEIFI, Semaan Georges. PO BOX 70571 37614 #605-03-2002 L2007 **PCC** *012 †20
KOTULLA, Jerry Arthur. 1114 SUNSET DR, STE 4 37604 #016-11-1985 L1999 **AN** *020 †05
KRAMER, Paul Ronald, Jr. ■ 37615 #051-04-1991 L2007 **OBG** *020 †30
KRAMER, Valerie Marie. ■ 37604 #047-20-2008 *012
KRISHNAN, Koyamangalath. ■ 37614 #495-59-1979 L1998 **IM ON** *020 †20
KRISHNAPPA, Ritesha Shant. DEPT OF PSY & BHVRL SCIENC, ETSU 37614 #496-33-2002
  MP *012
KRISHNASWAMY, Guha. 325 N STATE OF FRANKLIN RD 37604 #495-04-1983 L1988
  IM *020 †20,03
KROZSER, Agnes G. 400 N STATE OF FRANKLIN RD, FIRST FL 37604 #654-01-1986 L1990
  ON HEM *020 †20
KULKARNI, Kailash Pradip. PO BOX 70571 37614 #495-89-2004 **IM** *012
KULKARNI, Vinee Vijay. PO BOX 70571 37614 #495-31-2002 L2005 **FP** *012
LAIWALA, Vaishanavi Chait. PO BOX 70571 37614 #495-89-2004 **IM** *012
LAJOIE, Dawn Renee. ■ 37601 #047-20-2008 **PTH** *012
LAMB, Millard Ray. 310 N STATE OF FRANKLIN RD, STE 401 37604 #047-20-1982 L1983
  HO IM *020 †20
LANG, Ellen Harley. 1416 S ROAN ST 37601 #047-20-2001 L2003 **FM** *020 †18
LANG, Forrest Jos. 403 N STATE OF FRANKLIN RD 37604 #041-09-1971 L1984
  FM PD *020 †55,18
LANGAH, Rumman Abbas Khan. PO BOX 70571 37614 #704-01-2000 L2007 **NM** *012 †20
LAPHAM, Craig Allen. 105 WOODLAWN DR, TRI STATE MOUNTAIN 37604 #041-09-1984 L1988
  N *020 †75 ‡
LARSEN, Geoffrey Arthur. ■ 37604 #036-05-1966 L1968 **GS** *071 †85
LATIMER, Linda. 400 N STATE OF FRANKLIN RD 37604 #047-20-1995 L1998 **PTH** *020 †50
LAURAIN, Alan R. ■ 37604 #028-02-1949 L1954 **PTH** *071 †50
LAWSON, Elizabeth Ann. 3 PROFESSIONAL PARK DR, STE 31 37604 #047-06-1980 L1981
  GS *020 †85
LECRAW, Deborah Edwards. 101 MED TECH PKWY, STE 305 37604 #012-01-1993 L1996
  MPD *020 †20,55
LEDES, Christopher R. 615 N STATE OF FRANKLIN RD, JOHNSON CITY PEDIATRICS 37604
  #047-20-1995 L1998 **PD** *020 †55

LEE, Cheng Vang. PO BOX 70571 37614 #305-01-2000 **FP** *012

LEE, Joseph Robert. 525 N STATE OF FRANKLIN RD, STE 9 37604 #041-13-1998 L2006 **GS** *100 †85

LEFEMINE, Armand A. 16 CARRIAGE CT 37604 #024-01-1952 L1978 **TS** *071 †85,90

LEHWALD, Lenora Moore. 325 N STATE OF FRANKLIN RD, ETSU PHYSICIANS AND ASSOCI 37604 #045-04-2001 L2006 **CHN** *100 †75

LEICHT, Stuart Seth. 325 N STATE OF FRANKLIN RD 37604 #012-05-1978 L1986 **D IM** *020 †20,15

LEWIS, James Vincent. ■ 37601 #056-06-1964 L1971 **CCM GS** *071 †85

LEWIS, Samuel Vaden. 408 N STATE OF FRANKLIN RD 37604 #047-06-1983 L1984 **OBG** *020 †30

LICUP, Nerissa Libardo. PO BOX 70571 37614 #748-01-2004 **IM** *012

LIEW, Victor. ■ 37601 #462-01-1997 **GS** *012

LIMA, Raquel Furtado. 1825 W LAKEVIEW DR, APT D135 37601 #187-16-2006 **IM** *012

LINVILLE, Mark David, Jr. ■ 37604 #047-20-2000 L2005 **GP** *100

LIVINGSTON, Rebekah Ann. ■ 37601 #047-20-2007 **FP** *012

LOCKETT, Mark Alan. 325 N ST FRANKLIN RD, ETSU PHYSICIANS & ASSOCIAT 37604 #045-01-1994 L2001 **GS** *020 †85

LOWE, Charles E, III. 325 N STATE OF FRANKLIN RD, ROAD 37604 #020-02-2000 L2003 **AI** *020 †55,03

LOWERY, April Dawn. ■ 37601 #047-20-2004 L2006 **PD** *012

LU, Qun. ■ 37614 #243-71-1992 **BBK** *100

LUBSEY PENN, Erika Simone. ■ 37601 #047-20-2008 *012

LURA, Theresa Fish. 325 N STATE OF FRANKLIN RD, UNIVERSITY PHYSICIANS 37604 #047-20-1984 L1988 **PTH PCP** *040 †50

LURIE, David Phillip. 106 WOODLAWN DR 37604 #016-45-1976 L1981 **RHU IM** *020 †20

MAATOUK, Jamal Gerges. PO BOX 70571, E TN U-J H QUILLEN COLL ME 37614 #605-03-2001 **IM** *012

MACMILLAN, Patrick Joseph. ■ 37615 #305-01-2004 L2007 **MP** *012

MADHOK, Ashish Brij. 926 W OAKLAND AVE, STE 206 37604 #496-38-1996 L2005 **PDC PD** *020 †55

MAHBOOB, Rashid. ■ 37601 #704-02-1998 L2005 **IM** *100 †20

MAHONEY, James Cooper. 408 N STATE OF FRANKLIN RD, STE 23 37604 #047-06-1965 L1966 **GS** *020 †85

MALAK, Emad Fouad Massoud. ■ 37604 #915-03-2000 **IM** *012

MALETICH, Robert Theodore. ■ 37604 #017-20-1957 L1957 **OBG** *071 †30

MALIK, Shahram. PO BOX 70571 37614 #704-21-2002 L2007 **FP** *012

MANALO, Nora Nery. 1114 SUNSET DR, STE 4 37604 #748-10-1965 L1980 **AN IM** *071

MANAOIS-LIQUETE, Maria Th. 403 N STATE OF FRANKLIN RD 37604 #748-16-1994 L2005 **P** *020

MANGINELLI, Stephanie C. 2514 WESLEY ST, STE 102 37601 #047-20-1993 L1994 **FM** *020 †18

MANN, Herman Felix. ■ 37604 #286-13-1998 **IM** *100 †20

MANNEM, Sai Prasanna. PO BOX 70571 37614 #495-70-2003 **IM** *012

MARINO, Anna V.. PO BOX 70571, E TN U-J H QUILLEN COLL ME 37614 #913-13-2001 **IM** *012

MARSH, Camile. PO BOX 70571 37614 #028-78-2005, ▲ **OBG** *012

MARSHALL, Kenneth Edwin. 400 N STATE OF FRANKLIN RD, MOUNTAIN STATES HLTH ALLIA 37604 #020-12-1986 L2003 **FM** *030 †18

MARTIN, Deborah Warwick. ■ 37604 #007-02-2003 L2007 **FM** *100

MARTIN, Ricardo S, Jr. 401 E MAIN ST, MEDICAL ARTS BLDG 37601 #748-01-1962 L1971 **FM GS** *020 †18

MARWEDE, W Peter. ■ 37604 #023-01-1975 L1977 **PM** *100

MASSELLO, Thomas Payne. ■ 37615 #024-05-1970 L1971 **GS VS** *020 †85

MASSEY, Samuel Oliver, III. 1301 SUNSET DR, STE 3 37604 #027-01-1989 L1999 **RNR** *020 †80

MATHES, W T.. 215 E WATAUGA AVE 37601 #047-06-1945 L1946 **OTO** *072 †45

MATHEWS, Christopher Mark. 310 N STATE OF FRANKLIN RD, STE 202 37604 #011-02-2000 L2003 **GE** *020 †20

MATTAR, Costy Salim. ■ 37604 #605-03-2001 L2007 **CD** *012 †20

MAY, Angela Earlene. 1 PROFESSIONAL PARK DR, STE 21 37604 #047-20-1986 L1990 **IM** *020 †20

MAY, Grover Earl. 408 N STATE OF FRANKLIN RD 37604 #047-20-1992 L1994 **OBG** *020 †30

MCCLAIN, Morgan Wade. PO BOX 70571 37614 #654-01-2007 L2007 **FP** *012

MCCOWAN, Rebecca C. PO BOX 70569 37614 #020-75-2007, ▲ **OBG** *012

MC COY, Daniel W. 1 PROFESSIONAL PARK DR 37604 #045-01-1989 L1997 **TS** *020 †85,90

MC CREARY, Albert B. 325 N STATE OF FRANKLIN RD 37604 #047-06-1952 L1952 **GYN** *071 †30

MCCURLEY, Beth Anna. PO BOX 70571, E TN U-J H QUILLEN COLL ME 37614 #422-01-2006 **IM** *012

MC DAVID, Richard Keith. 3114 BROWNS MILL RD 37604 #045-01-1993 L1995 **FM** *020 †18

MC ELROY, Aubrey D, Jr. 2406 SUSANNAH ST 37601 #047-06-1988 L1994 **FM** *020 †18

MCELROY, Clinton Edgar. ■ 37615 #012-05-2007 **PTH** *012

MC FARLAND, Drew P, IV. 917 W WALNUT ST 37604 #047-20-1995 L1996 **FM** *020 †18

MCGINLEY, Daniel Baulch. ■ 37604 #047-20-2008 L2008 *012

MC GINNIS, Thomas Bryan. 300 W WATAUGA AVE, JOHNSON CITY UROLOGICAL 37604 #004-01-1969 L1976 **U PD** *020 †95

MC GOWAN, Judson Chase. 2410 SUSANNAH ST, WATAUGA ORTHOPAEDICS 37601 #010-01-1978 L1983 **ORS** *020 †40

MC GOWAN, Winford R, Jr. 3629 HONEYWOOD DR, 310 N STATE OF FRANKLIN RD 37604 #047-06-1969 L1970 **GE IM** *020 †20

MCLAIN, Scott David. 917 W WALNUT ST 37604 #654-01-2000 L2005 **FM** *020 †18

MC LAUGHLIN, Dean E. 3114 BROWNS MILL RD 37604 #016-11-1946 L1997 **FPG** *071 †18

MCLAUGHLIN, Marion D. 3114 BROWNS MILL RD, CITY 37604 #308-11-1985 L1993 **FM** *020 †18 ‡

MC VEIGH, J Randall. ■ 37601 #028-03-1990 L2001 **AN** *020 †05

MECHLEB, Wissam Khattar. PO BOX 70571, E TN U-J H QUILLEN COLL ME 37614 #605-02-2005 **IM** *012

MEDINA, Jocelyn Adele. 1301 SUNSET DR, STE 3 37604 #011-02-2001 L2006 **DR** *020 †80

MEHTA, Ashok Vallavdas. 926 W OAKLAND AVE STE 206 37604 #495-23-1973 L1986 **PDC PD** *020 †55

MEHTA, Jayantilal B. 310 N STATE OF FRANKLIN RD, STE 303 37604 #495-23-1968 L1977 **PUD IM** *020 †20

MEHTA, Rahul. PO BOX 70571, E TN U-J H QUILLEN COLL ME 37614 #495-47-2001 **IM** *012

MEJIA, Jose Luis. 2 WINDSOR CT 37604 #319-01-1994 L2005 **GS** *020 †85

MERRICK, Raymond Danl. 408 N STATE OF FRANKLIN RD, STE 24 37604 #020-12-1985 L1987 **CD IMG** *020

MERRIFIELD, Angela S. 1 PROFESSIONAL PARK DR, STE 21 37604 #036-08-1993 L1995 **FM** *020 †18 ‡

MERRIFIELD, David Leslie. 2811 W MARKET ST, DOCTOR'S CARE 37604 #036-08-1993 L1995 **FM** *020 †18

MESSERSCHMIDT, William H. 325 N STATE OF FRANKLIN RD, 3RD FL 37604 #041-02-1979 L1988 **TS** *020 †90,85

METTETAL, Ray Wallace, Jr. ■ 37601 #047-06-1977 L1977 **N NS** *020 †16,75

MICHAEL, Mini Ann. PO BOX 70571, E TN U-J H QUILLEN COLL ME 37614 #495-63-2001 **IM** *012

MICHAL, Mary Lenoir. 302 WESLEY ST STE 10, MICHAL CHILD DEVLPMNT CTR 37601 #047-05-1960 L1960 **PD CPP** *072

MILLER, Christopher Willi. PO BOX 70571 37614 #187-17-2005 **IM** *012

MILLER, John Mc Clellan. 2 PROFESSIONAL PARK DR, STE 21 37604 #047-06-1964 **GYN** *020 †30

MILLER, Merry Noel. 325 N STATE OF FRANKLIN RD, DEPT PSYCH 37604 #047-06-1983 L1995 **P** *030 †75

MILLER, Valerie Jane. 408 N STATE OF FRANKLIN RD 37604 #047-20-1985 *100

MILLS, Ralph Lee. 310 N STATE OF FRANKLIN RD, STE 101 37604 #047-20-1984 L1984 **FM FSM** *020 †18

MISENAR, Garik Traverse. ■ 37615 #027-01-2002 L2005 **EM** *020 †16

MISNER, Gavin Isaac. ■ 37604 #012-01-2006 **GS** *012

MODICA, Louis Andrew. 325 N STATE OF FRANKLIN RD 37604 #035-08-1980 L1984 **OTO** *020 †45

MOFFATT, Lawrence Strong. 415 N STATE OF FRANKLIN RD 37604 #047-06-1955 L1955 **PHP OBG** *030

MOHON, Ricky Thos. 325 N STATE OF FRANKLIN RD 37604 #047-06-1981 L1985 **PD** *020 †20,55

MONDERER, Rachel. 1 PROFESSIONAL PARK DR, STE 21 37604 #023-07-1988 L1991 **IM** *020 †20

MONTENEGRO, Franklin R. 310 N STATE OF FRANKLIN RD, STE 201 37604 #737-01-1972 L1981 **END IM** *020 †20

MOORMAN, Jonathan P. PO BOX 70622, INTERNAL ME 37614 #051-01-1991 L2000 **ID** *020 †20

MORELOCK, Christina Johan. ■ 37604 #047-20-2007 **IM** *012

MORGAN, Calvin Vere, Jr. 408 N STATE OF FRANKLIN RD 37604 #036-07-1962 L1971 **GS CD** *071 †85

MORGAN, Vickie Gay. ■ 37601 #665-01-2005 L2008 **IM** *012

MOSS, Casey Nelson. 37 CHEROKEE RIDGE CT 37604 #047-20-2004 L2006 **PD** *020 †55

MOULTON, David F, II. 219 PRINCETON RD STE 200, JOHNSON CITY INT MED ASS P 37601 #038-41-1985 L1990 **IM** *020 †20

MULLERSMAN, Jerald Eric. ■ 37601 #011-03-1986 L1993 **CLP BBK** *050 †20

MUNSHI, Firoz Bashirahmed. ■ 37601 #495-22-1996 L2007 **P** *012

MURILLO, Liliana. PO BOX 70571 37614 #132-04-1997 **MP** *012

MYERS, James Wesley. 203 E WATAUGA AVE 37604 #005-08-1985 L1986 **ID IM** *020 †20

NANDA KUMAR, Vijay Kumar. ■ 37601 #496-31-2000 L2006 **FP** *012

NARAMORE, Lee Ellen. 403 N STATE OF FRANKLIN RD 37604 #047-20-1988 L1990 **P** *020 †75

NASR, Georgina Melhem. PO BOX 70571 37614 #605-03-2006 **IM** *012

NASRALLAH, Sami Nabil. PO BOX 70571, E TN U-J H QUILLEN COLL ME 37614 #575-02-2003 **IM** *012

NASSOUR, Dima Nassour. PO BOX 70571, E TN U-J H QUILLEN COLL ME 37614 #605-03-2003 **IM** *012

NATHAN, Rohini. 917 W WALNUT ST 37604 #496-39-1989 L2007 **FP** *012

NAZAROV, Vitaly. ■ 37604 #913-15-1989 L2005 **IM** *020 †20

NEGI, Smita Indrasingh. PO BOX 70571 37614 #495-23-1998 **IM** *012

NELLUTLA, Subbalakshmi. PO BOX 70571 37614 #495-31-1993 **P** *100

NERREN, Bryan Keith. 219 PRINCETON RD 37601 #047-06-1996 L1999 **IM** *020 †20

NEUBERT, Richard Eugene. ■ 37604 #047-20-1999 L2006 **EM** *020 †16

NORRIS, Laura R. ■ 37604 #047-20-2003 **IM** *020

NORWOOD, Donald Barry, Jr. ■ 37615 #004-01-2000 L2006 **DR** *020 †80

NWOSU, Uchenna C. 325 N STATE OF FRANKLIN RD, ETSU COLLEGE OF MEDICINE 37604 #024-05-1968 L1990 **OBG** *050 †30

OH, Emmy Lissa Paguirigan. PO BOX 70571, E TN U-J H QUILLEN COLL ME 37614 #748-01-2003 **IM** *012

O'LEARY, Roland Timothy. ■ 37604 #021-05-1988 L2003 **FM** *020 †18

OLIVE, Kenneth Everett. 325 N STATE OF FRANKLIN RD 37604 #036-08-1982 L1989 **IM IMG** *020 †20

OLSEN, Martin Elmer. 325 N STATE OF FRANKLIN RD 37604 #038-43-1985 L1990 **OBG FM** *020 †18,30

OLSEN, Natalie M. ■ 37601 #038-43-1985 L1989 **FM** *020 †18

ONGTENGCO, Edgar Alan. 1019 W OAKLAND AVE 37604 #025-07-1989 L1995 **IM** *020 †20

ORTIZ, Vincente. PO BOX 70571, E TN U-J H QUILLEN COLL ME 37614 #422-01-2004 **GS** *012

OSBORNE, James Baisden. ■ 37604 #012-01-2007 **GS** *012

OSBORNE, Leroy Robt. ■ 37604 #3727 37602 #028-78-1987, ▲ L1989 **AN** *020 †05

OSSORIO, Miguel Antonio. ■ 37604 #935-05-1979 L1997 **PUD CCM** *020 †20

PALMER, Rufus Paul. ■ 37604 #038-06-1960 L1969 **GS** *071 †85

PANDIAN, Shantha Grace. ■ 37604 #495-37-1995 L2000 **P** *020 †75

PANG, Changlee Seo. PO BOX 70571, E TN U-J H QUILLEN COLL ME 37614 #583-12-1999 L2007 **PTH** *012

PANICKAVEETIL, Reena Paul. PO BOX 70571 37614 #496-29-1993 L2007 **IM** *100 †20

PANINI, Aruna S. 325 N STATE OF FRANKLIN RD, # 2FL 37604 #007-02-1992 L1996 **FM** *020 †18

PANUS, Leslie Ann. 107 WOODLAWN DR 37604 #001-06-1983 L1995 **IM NEP** *020 †20

PARDUE, Janice Brittany. ■ 37604 #047-20-2008 *012

PARKS, Matt Allen. 400 SUNSET DR APT C12 37604 #047-20-2001 L2003 **IM** *100

PARR, Reagan Royse. 3 PROFESSIONAL PARK DR, STE 21 37604 #039-01-1994 L2005 **ORS** *020 †40

PARTAIN, Cynthia Polhemus. 401 E MAIN ST 37601 #047-02-1992 L1993 **FM** *020 †18

PATEL, Alpesh Bhagubhai. PO BOX 70571, E TN U-J H QUILLEN COLL ME 37614 #495-22-2003 **IM** *012

PATEL, Falguniben Arvindb. PO BOX 70571, E TN U-J H QUILLEN COLL ME 37614 #495-22-2001 **IM** *012

PATEL, Hiren Bharatbhai. ■ 37604 #495-76-1997 L2003 **ID** *100 †20 ‡

PATEL, Mayur Chandrakant. PO BOX 70571, E TN U-J H QUILLEN COLL ME 37614 #496-30-1999 L2008 **PCC** *012 †20

PATEL, Parasbhai Dashrath. 119 BOONE RIDGE DR, STE 201 37615 #495-22-1996 L2005 **ID** *012 †20

PATEL, Rakesh Bhagwandas. 900 BUFFALO ST 37604 #759-06-2000 L2006 **IM** *012

PATEL, Sudhirkumar Vinodc. ■ 37604 #047-20-2001 L2007 **IM** *020 †20

PATEL, Tarak Vipinchandra. ■ 37601 #496-61-2003 L2008 **IM** *012

PATIBANDLA, Kiran. 219 PRINCETON RD 37601 #496-23-2001 L2005 **IM** *020 †20

PATTABIRAMAN, Vivekananda. PO BOX 70571, E TN U-J H QUILLEN COLL ME 37614 #496-39-1996 **IM** *012

PAUL, Timir Kumar. ■ 37604 #160-02-1997 **IM** *012

PEARSON, James M. 1 PROFESSIONAL PARK DR 37604 #047-06-1976 L1977 **PD** *020 †55

PEARSON, Michael Zachary. 1 PROFESSIONAL PARK DR, STE 21 37604 #047-06-2003 L2006 **IM** *020 †20

PEIRIS, M Alan. 325 N STATE OF FRANKLIN RD 37604 #917-20-1977 L1994 **END DIA** *040 †20

PELLETIER, Michael Jean. 203 E WATAUGA AVE, STE 1 37601 #047-06-1991 L1995 **OBG** *020 †30

PENNINGTON, Connie Jo. 1321 SUNSET DR, STE 22 37604 #051-07-1995 L1998 **CRS** *020 †85,10

PENNINGTON, D Glenn. 325 N STATE OF FRANKLIN RD, EAST TN STATE UNIV 37604 #027-01-1966 L1997 **TS GS** *020 †85,90

PERRY, Scott Daniel. ■ 37604 #047-20-2008 *012

PERRY, Thomas Clayton. 105 WOODLAWN DR, TRI-STATE MOUNTAIN NEUROLO 37604 #654-01-2002 L2007 **N** *020

PETERSON, Steve Leroy. 1009 N STATE OF FRANKLIN RD 37604 #045-01-1998 L2005 **OTO PSH** *020 †45

PHILIP, Ranjit. PO BOX 70571 37614 #495-37-2005 **PD** *012

PICAZA, Jose Ernesto. 1301 SUNSET DR, STE 3 37604 #308-11-1986 L1989 **DR** *020 †18,80

PICKLER, Eva Carol. 2 PROFESSIONAL PARK DR #21 37604 #024-05-1998 L2002 **OBG** *020 †30

PICKSTOCK, Janet Gail. 119 BOONE RIDGE DR, STE 201 37615 #047-07-1996 L2000 **IM** *020 †20

PIERCE, Stephanie Renee. ■ 37604 #047-20-2008 *012

PILLINGER, Lynn Elizabeth. ■ 37604 #045-01-1977 L1981 **IM** *020 †20

PLATT, John P. ■ 37604 #012-05-1942 L1952 **GS** *071 †85

POLKAMPALLI, Nandakishore. PO BOX 70571 37614 #495-65-2004 **FP** *012

POLLITTE, Jonathan Lee. 203 BROYLES ST STE 301, ACCUMED MEDICAL SERVICES C 37601 #047-20-1999 L2000 **IM** *020 †20

PONDER, Michael Alan. 408 N STATE OF FRANKLIN RD, STE 24 37604 #036-08-1988 L1989 **CD** *020 †20

PORET, Harvey Andrew, III. 310 N STATE OF FRANKLIN RD, STE 101 37604 #021-05-1988 L1996 **TS** *020 †85,90

POWERS, Rebecca Ruby. 325 N STATE OF FRANKLIN RD, GROUND FLOOR 37604 #039-01-1997 L2000 **PD** *020 †55

PRISCO TEIXEIRA, Otto H. 926 W OAKLAND AVE STE 2 37604 #187-01-1964 L2000 **PDC PD** *020 †55

PRUDHOMME, Bryan James. 615 N STATE OF FRANKLIN RD 37604 #047-20-2004 L2007 **PD** *020

PUGH, Alan Hixson. 1114 SUNSET DR, STE 4 37604 #047-06-1982 L1983 **AN IM** *020 †05

PUGH, Barbara Pate. 101 MED TECH PKWY, STE 405 37604 #047-06-1982 L1985 **PD** *020 †55

PUMARIEGA, Andres Julio. E TN STATE UNIV BOX 70567, JAMES H QUILLEN COL MED 37614 #011-02-1976 L1980 **CHP P** *030 †75

PUNYASAVATSUT, Natavut. 325 N STATE OF FRANKLIN RD, EAST TENNESSEE STATE UNIV 37604 #891-01-1991 L2003 **PDE** *020 †55

PURSWANI, Krish S. 119 E KING ST, STE 208 37601 #016-11-1991 L2007 **FM** *020 †18

PUTHUVEL, Shaji Justus. ■ 37601 #495-37-1999 **P** *012

QAYUM, Salman. ■ 37601 #704-09-1994 L2005 **DR** *020 †80

QUARLES MILLS, Debra Lynn. 325 N STATE OF FRANKLIN RD, GROUND LEVEL 37604 #047-20-1993 L1995 **PD** *020 †55

QUINN, Donald. 119 BOONE RIDGE DR, STE 201 37615 #654-01-1988 L1992 **IM** *020 †20

RABON, Randal Jos. 110 MED TECH PKWY, STE 1 37604 #038-44-1981 L1986 **OPH** *020 †35

RADCHUK, Olena. ■ 37604 #913-13-2003 **IM** *012

RADFORD, James Michael. ■ 37604 #047-20-1990 L1993 **P** *020 †75

RAHMAN, Zia Ur. ■ 37604 #704-01-2001 L2008 **FP** *012

RAINEY, Elisabet Ellen. ■ 37604 #045-04-2004 **P** *012

RAMAKRISHNAN, Karthik. PO BOX 70571 37614 #496-23-2002 L2005 **IM** *100 †20

RAMSEY, David Earl, Jr. 403 N STATE OF FRANKLIN RD 37604 #047-20-1985 L1989 **P** *020

RAMSEY, Glynda Jo Fox. 1301 SUNSET DR, STE 3 37604 #047-20-1985 L1989 **R** *020 †80

RAMU, Vijay Kumar. ■ 37604 #495-33-1995 L2002 **CD** *012 †20

RANNICK, Gilbert A. 1019 W OAKLAND AVE, STE 1 37604 #036-07-1949 L1956 **GS** *071 †85

RASCH, Robert W. ■ 37604 #016-06-1951 L1979 **OS** *071

REAGAN, David Ralph. ■ 37604 #047-05-1985 L1987 **IM** *020 †20

REDDY, Vedire Vijaysen. ■ 37614 #665-01-2006 **FP** *012

REEVES, Robert D. 926 W OAKLAND AVE, STE 222 37604 #047-06-1977 L1978 **EM SME** *020 †16

REYNANTE, Jeffrey Alfred. PO BOX 70571 37614 #748-10-2000 **P** *012

RICE, Mark John. 1114 SUNSET DR, STE 4 37604 #056-05-1982 L1990 **AN** *020 †05

RICHESIN, Samuel Douglas. ■ 37604 #047-20-2008 *012

RIKHYE, Somi. ■ 37604 #422-01-2005 **IM** *012

ROBBINS, Margaret Shippen. 302 SUNSET DR STE 106 37604 #047-20-1988 L1989 **P** **IM** *020 †75

ROBERTSON, John Fletcher. 701 MED TECH PKWY, STE 400 37604 #020-02-1997 L2002 **GS** *020 †85

ROBERTSON, Julie Smith. 400 N STATE OF FRANKLIN RD 37604 #020-02-1997 L2001 **PTH** *020 †50

ROBINS, Guy Winston. 1 PROFESSIONAL PARK DR, STE 21 37604 #003-01-1990 L1996 **FM** *020 †18

RODRIGUEZ, Juan F. ■ 37604 #308-01-1988 L1999 **PYG** *020

ROE, David Philip. 203 E WATAUGA AVE 37604 #047-06-1970 L1971 **OBG** *020 †30

ROGERS, Mailien R. ■ 37604 #055-75-2006, ▲ **IM** *012

ROJAS, Carlos E. ■ 37601 #264-04-1982 L2005 **FP** *012

ROLEN, Richard Louis. 219 PRINCETON RD STE 200, JOHNSON CITY INT MED ASSOC 37601 #047-06-1985 L1986 **IM** *020 †20

ROLLER, Kimberly Dean. PO BOX 70571, E TN U-J H QUILLEN COLL ME 37614 #305-01-2006 L2008 **FP** *012

ROLLINS, Edward Sterling. 401 PRINCETON RD 37601 #028-02-1984 L1990 **VIR R** *020 †80

ROLLINS, Susan Davidson. 2400 SUSANNAH ST STE A 37601 #028-02-1984 L1990 **PTH** *020 †50

ROSS, Daniel W. ■ 37601 #047-20-2000 L2003 **FM** *100 †18

ROSS, Harold Eugene. ■ 37604 #045-01-1961 L1984 **DR** *071 †80

ROSS, James Arthur. 226 CHICKASAW ST 37604 #422-01-1983 L1985 **IM EM** *020

RUSH, Daniel Scott. 325 N STATE OF FRANKLIN RD, THIRD FLOOR 37604 #020-12-1976 L1997 **VS GS** *020 †85

SAAD, Mustafa Mahmoud. ■ 37604 #575-01-1996 L2005 **ID** *100 †20

SABA, Nakhle Saadallah. PO BOX 70571, E TN U-J H QUILLEN COLL ME 37614 #605-03-2005 **IM** *012

SARKER, Sharmeen. PO BOX 70571 37614 #160-03-1992 L2007 **FP** *012

SARKODIE, Olga Leonidovna. 325 N STATE OF FRANKLIN RD 37604 #913-32-1990 L2008 **OBG** *012

SARUBBI, Felix A, Jr. 325 N STATE OF FRANKLIN RD 37604 #035-19-1969 L1987 **ID IM** *020 †20

SCARBERRY, Jerel Devere. ■ 37601 #047-20-2005 L2007 **PD** *012

SCHAFER, Liudmila Nikolae. PO BOX 70571 37614 #913-43-1996 **IM** *012

SCHETZINA, Karen E. 325 N STATE OF FRANKLIN RD 37604 #036-01-1997 L2003 **PD** *020 †55

SCHMALZRIED, Craig D. 1 PROFESSIONAL PARK DR, STE 21 37604 #048-15-1998 L2003 **FM** *020 †18

SCHMIDT, Lawrence Wendell. 310 N STATE OF FRANKLIN RD, STE 202 37604 #047-06-1974 L1980 **GE IM** *020 †20

SCHNELL, Thomas Geo. 403 ELM ST 37601 #026-04-1976 L1977 **IM** *020 †20

SCHNELL, Thomas Richard. 403 ELM ST 37601 #038-43-1983 L1997 **IM** *020 †20

SCHOLL, George Kenneth. 400 N STATE OF FRANKLIN RD 37604 #047-06-1937 L1937 **GP** *071

SCHOONDYKE, Jeffrey Wayne. 408 N STATE OF FRANKLIN RD, STE 24 37604 #422-01-1999 L2002 **CD** *100 †20

SCHUELLER, William Alan. 1026 SOMERSET DR, P O BOX 6105 37604 #038-06-1966 L1975 **D** *071 †15

SCHWEITZER, Janice B. 917 W WALNUT ST, FAMILY MEDICINE ASSOCIATES 37604 #028-46-1979 L1985 **FM** *020 †18

SCHWEITZER, John B. ■ 37615 #028-02-1978 L1985 **NP ATP** *050 †50

SCHWIND, Robert James. 1114 SUNSET DR, STE 4 37604 #012-01-1988 L1992 **AN** *020 †05

SELMAN, Bruce Richard. 325 N STATE OF FRANKLIN RD, ETSU 37604 #056-05-1995 L2005 **OBG** *020 †30

SENTELL, Marcia Mathes. 408 N STATE OF FRANKLIN RD 37604 #047-20-1985 L1989 **OBG** *020 †30

SHAH, Chirag Gopaldas. PO BOX 70571 37614 #496-41-2000 **P** *012

SHAH, Mayank Piyushkumar. PO BOX 70571, E TN U-J H QUILLEN COLL ME 37614 #495-76-1998 L2008 **IM** *012

SHAH, Pramod Anupchand. 2231 GRANITE CT 37604 #496-38-1972 L1985 **P PYG** *020 †75

SHAHBAZI, Nasser. ■ 37601 #517-01-1947 L1970 **GS** *071 †85

SHAMS, Wael Elsaied. DEPT OF IM DIV ID, JAMES H QUILLEN COLL MED 37614 #915-03-1991 L2004 **ID IM** *040 †20

SHARMA, Dinesh. PO BOX 70571 37614 #496-09-2004 **IM** *012

SHEPARD, Frank Michael. 325 N STATE OF FRANKLIN RD, GROUND LEVEL 37604 #047-05-1959 L1959 **PD ADL** *071 †55

SHEPS, David Saml. 325 N STATE OF FRANKLIN RD 37604 #036-01-1969 L1997 **CD IM** *050 †20

SHILAD, Sabrina. ■ 37601 #047-20-2005 **GS** *012

SHIN, Sonyo. PO BOX 70571, EAST TN STATE UNIV 37604 #583-08-1998 L2006 **ON** *012

SHINGLETON, Gerald Coburn. ■ 37604 #036-07-1950 L1952 **FM** *075

SHORMAN, Mahmoud Adnan. ■ 37604 #575-02-1996 **IM** *100 †20

SHULRUFF, Steven Michael. 325 N STATE OF FRANKLIN RD 37604 #047-05-1977 L2007 **CHP** *020 †75

SHURBAJI, Muhammad S. PO BOX 70568, DEPT OF PATHOLOGY 37614 #605-01-1984 L1990 **PTH PCP** *020 †50

SIBLEY, David Anthony. 400 N STATE OF FRANKLIN RD, JOHNSON CITY MED CNTR 37604 #051-01-1984 L1989 **PTH BBK** *020 †50

SIBLEY, Denise Swink. 403 PRINCETON RD 37601 #051-01-1986 L1989 **IM** *020 †20

SLAUGHTER, Frederick D. 110 MED TECH PKWY 37604 #047-06-1963 L1964 **OPH** *071 †35

SMALLIGAN, Roger D. 325 N STATE OF FRANKLIN RD 37604 #023-07-1987 L1991 **IM PD** *020 †20,55

SMITH, Daniel Scott. ■ 37604 #047-20-2008 *012

SMITH, John Kelly, Jr. 707 N MOUNTAIN VIEW CIR 37601 #035-20-1960 L1980 **ID AI** *040 †20,03

SMITH, Stephen James. 1 PROFESSIONAL PARK DR, STE 18 37604 #021-05-1986 L1992 **HO** *020 †20

SMITH, Steven Michael. 2 PROFESSIONAL PARK DR 37604 #047-20-1985 L1992 **CD IM** *020

SMITH, Wayne Odell. ■ 37601 #047-20-2007 **IM** *012

SNIDER, Ralph Danl. 400 N STATE OF FRANKLIN RD, RM 2746 37604 #038-40-1990 L2006 **CCM** *020 †20

SOIKE, David Richard. 400 N STATE OF FRANKLIN RD, JOHNSON CITY MED CENTER HO 37604 #038-43-1979 L1984 **PTH** *020 †50

SPADY, Michael Leo. 213 STERLING SPRINGS DR 37604 #041-01-1982 L1988 **PM** *020 †60

SPANNUTH, Clarence L. 107 WOODLAWN DR 37604 #041-14-1973 L1975 **NEP** *020 †20

SPIRES, Ross Richard. PO BOX 70569 37614 #020-75-2006, ▲ **OBG** *012

SPITZNAS, Andrew Lincoln. ■ 37615 #041-07-1994 L2004 **P** *020 †75

SRINATH, Manoj. 203 E WATAUGA AVE 37601 #495-33-1990 L2001 **GE** *020 †20

STANIFER, Bryan Payne. ■ 37604 #047-20-2008 *012

STANTON, Paul Eugene, Jr. 325 N STATE OF FRANKLIN RD 37604 #012-01-1969 L1985 **VS** *071 †85

STARR, Dennis Martin. ■ 37604 #047-20-2008 *012

STEEN, Marian E. ■ 37604 #047-07-1978 L1981 **P IM** *020 †20

STEFFNER, Edward Benj. 403 PRINCETON RD 37601 #047-06-1957 L1957 **FM** *071

STEPHENSON, David Wayne. ■ 37604 #047-20-2006 **AN** *012

STERN, Harold Patrick. 203 E WATAUGA AVE 37601 #038-06-1974 L1999 **PD CHP** *020 †55 ‡

STONE, Matthew Lloyd. ■ 37604 #047-20-2008 *012

STOOTS, Connie R. ■ 37604 #047-20-2007 L2007 **FP** *012

STOSS, Thomas David. ■ 37615 #020-12-2006 L2008 **P** *012

STUART, Charles Albert. 325 N STATE OF FRANKLIN RD 37604 #035-06-1971 L2001 **END IM** *030 †20

SUBBA RAO, Goli Venkata. ■ 37604 #495-50-1969 L1996 **ORS** *020

SUN, Fang. PO BOX 70568, EAST TENNEESEE STE UNIV 37614 #243-45-1986 L2005 **PTH** *100

SUNDARAM, Aiswarya. PO BOX 70571, E TN U-J H QUILLEN COLL ME 37614 #495-04-2003 **IM** *012

SWEET, Jo Gordon. 415 N STATE OF FRANKLIN RD 37604 #047-06-1965 L1966 **IM OS** *020 †20

SWEET, Kevin Donald. 219 PRINCETON RD 37601 #010-02-1998 L2001 **IM** *020 †20

TAASAN, Vicente Cabahug. ■ 37604 #748-02-1975 L1984 **DR IM** *020 †28

TALLAPU REDDY, Sreedhar R. ■ 37604 #495-21-1998 L2006 **GS FP** *012 †18

TALLEY-HORNE, Jill Renee. 408 N STATE OF FRANKLIN RD 37604 #047-20-1993 L1995 **OBG** *020 †30

TANNER, Wade Sheppard. 118 W SPRINGBROOK DR 37604 #012-22-1990 L1991 **FM** *020 †18

TAYLOR, Grant David. 300 W WATAUGA AVE, JOHNSON CITY UROLOGICAL 37604 #048-14-2000 L2005 **U** *020 †95

TAYLOR, Robert Alexander. 310 N STATE OF FRANKLIN RD, STE 303 37604 #012-01-1982 L1987 **PUD CCM** *020 †20

TAYLOR, Tamarro Lynn. 1 PROFESSIONAL PARK DR, STE 18 37604 #051-04-1992 L2005 HO *020 †20

TAYLOR, Tedford Steve. 1 PROFESSIONAL PARK DR, STE 21 37604 #047-06-1974 L1975 PD *020 †55

TCHOU, Sheng. 411 PRINCETON RD, SUIE 101 37601 #243-16-1970 L1992 PM PMM *020 †60

TEMPLETON, Mia Lyn. ■ 37604 #045-01-1993 L2001 AN *020 †05

TERAN, Gerson Ariel. PO BOX 70571 37614 #649-18-1995 IM *012

TEROVA, Sotiraq. 119 BOONE RIDGE DR, STE 201 37615 #120-01-1999 L2006 IM *020 †20

TEW, Beverly Ellen. PO BOX 70571 37614 #021-01-2004 L2004 GS *012

THATCHER, Samuel Seldon. 408 N STATE OF FRANKLIN RD, STE 31 37604 #055-01-1981 L1988 REN GYN *020 †30

THOMAS, Eapen. 408 N STATE OF FRANKLIN RD, STE 23 37604 #495-27-1961 L1979 GE IM *020 †20

THOMPSON, Anne S. 1 PROFESSIONAL PARK DR, STE 21 37604 #027-01-1988 L2001 FM *100 †18

THUR DE KOOS, Paul. 3 PROFESSIONAL PARK DR, STE 31 37604 #132-01-1969 L1980 GS *071 †85

TINO, Michael Dandridge. 119 BOONE RIDGE DR, STE 201 37615 #665-01-2000 L2005 FM *020 ‡

TOLAN, Daniel Lee. ■ 37601 #036-05-1985 L2004 FM GS *020 †18

TONGCO, Wayne P. 300 W WATAUGA AVE, JOHNSON CITY UROLOGICAL 37604 #048-13-1996 L2002 U *020 †95

TOROK, Peter Gregory. ■ 37604 #023-12-1988 L2007 OPH *020 †18

TORRES-GUILLON, Reinaldo. 1114 SUNSET DR, TANTS, P.C., PO BOX 1070 37604 #041-13-1990 L2001 AN *020 †05

TRENT, Carol Glenn, Jr. 3 PROFESSIONAL PARK DR, STE 21 37604 #025-07-1978 L2003 ORS IM *020 †40

TUDIVER, Fraser Gerald. 917 W WALNUT ST, JOHNSON CITY FAMILY MEDICI 37604 #063-01-1973 L2002 FM *020 †20

TUELL, Dawn S. 325 N STATE OF FRANKLIN RD, ETSU PEDIATRICS 37604 #047-20-2001 L2004 PD *020 †55

TUSCANO, Thomson Baptista. PO BOX 70571 37614 #496-44-2003 FP *012

UDOEYOP, Udoeyop Walter. 119 BOONE RIDGE DR STE 20, C/O INPATIENT MEDICAL SERV 37615 #690-01-1980 L2002 IM *020 †20

VADLAMUDI, Raja Sekhar. PO BOX 70571, E TN U-J H QUILLEN COLL ME 37614 #495-62-2000 L2007 IM *020 †20

VALDEZ FIGUEROA, Gerson D. PO BOX 70571 37614 #341-01-2003 IM *012

VANDIVER, Clayton J, Jr. ■ 37601 #041-01-1949 L1957 AN *071 †05

VAN WINKLE, Jmes D. ■ 37601 #047-20-2006 GS *012

VASHIST, Amit. PO BOX 70571 37614 #495-83-2001 MP *012

VAYNBERG, Luiza. ■ 37604 #913-50-1984 PTH *100

VELILLA, Rowena E. ■ 37601 #748-01-1990 L2003 HMP *100

VIKAS, Praveen. ■ 37604 #495-76-2002 IM *012

VILLENEUVE, Paul Charles. 104 KEELAND DR, EAST TENNESSEE PSYCHIATRY 37615 #047-20-1996 L2001 CHP P *020 †75

VOTAW, May L Korteling. EAST TENNESSEE STATE UNIV, DEPT OF INTERNAL MEDICINE 37601 #025-01-1956 L1978 IM ON *071 †20

VYAS, Bavna B. PO BOX 70571, E TN U-J H QUILLEN COLL ME 37614 #496-23-2005 IM *012

VYAS, Harsha. PO BOX 70571 37614 #495-37-2000 L2007 HO *012 †20

VYAS, Umesh Kumar. PO BOX 70571, DEPT OF PSYCHIATRY 37614 #496-03-1989 P *012

WADDEY, Jaclyn Marie. ■ 37604 #047-20-2008 *012

WADZINSKI, James Daniel. 1021 W OAKLAND AVE, STE 301 37604 #665-01-2004 L2007 IM *020 †18

WAGNER, Charles Kim. 203 E WATAUGA AVE 37601 #021-05-1999 L2003 AN *020 †05

WALKER, Robert Wayne. 119 BOONE RIDGE DR, STE 201 37615 #017-20-1982 L2005 IM *020 †20

WALKER, William Alan. 310 N STATE OF FRANKLIN RD, STE 101 37604 #011-04-1981 L1982 TS *020 †85,90

WALTERS, David N. 325 N ST FRANKLIN RD 37604 #012-01-1977 L1989 GS CCM *030 †85

WALTERS, Phil Vernon. 110 MED TECH PKWY, STE 1 37604 #047-06-1960 L1961 OPH *020 †35

WALTON, Joseph Albert, Jr. 2301 GRANITE DR 37604 #011-03-1960 L1993 CD IM *071 †20 ‡

WANG, Wenli. 917 W WALNUT ST 37604 #243-36-1991 L2007 FP *012

WARD, Luther Edward. ■ 37615 #021-01-2005 GS *012

WARREN, Hannah Alice. ■ 37604 #047-20-2008 *012

WASON, William Martin. 325 N STATE OF FRANKLIN RD 37604 #016-02-1974 L2004 RHU IM *020 †20 ‡

WATSON, Scotty Dale. 2333 KNOB CREEK RD 37604 #004-01-1983 L1989 GS OS *020 †85

WATTAD, Ahmad Abdullatif. 325 N STATE OF FRANKLIN RD 37604 #561-11-1977 L1990 PN PD *020 †55

WEAVER, Oscar M, Jr. ■ 37604 #041-02-1948 L1975 R EM *020 †80,28

WEBB, Clinton Steve. 211 W WATAUGA AVE 37604 #047-06-1970 L1970 FM *020 †18

WEBB, Jason Michael. ■ 37604 #047-20-2004 L2007 GS *012

WEINGART, Rebecca Lynn. 3333 BERKSHIRE CIR 37604 #010-01-1987 L1996 IM *020 †20

WELCH, David Brent. 310 N STATE OF FRANKLIN RD, STE 202 37604 #047-06-1984 L1985 GE IM *020 †20

WHITAKER, Jack Harry. 408 N STATE OF FRANKLIN RD, STE 24 37604 #047-20-1989 L1990 CD *020 †20

WHITSON, Dale Eugene. 3114 BROWNS MILL RD 37604 #047-20-1984 L1985 FM *020 †18

WHITTEN, Eliza Joyce. ■ 37604 #047-20-2008 *012

WIEGAND, Clifford Frank. 107 WOODLAWN DR 37604 #038-43-1975 L1987 NEP IM *020 †20

WILES, David Alan. 310 N STATE OF FRANKLIN RD, CENTER SUITE 103 37604 #021-01-1991 L1996 NS *020 †25

WILEY, William Arthur, Jr. 112 E MYRTLE AVE, STE 506 37601 #047-06-1956 L1956 P *020

WILKINSON, Mark Julian. 2685 BOONES CREEK RD, STE 104 37615 #033-05-1993 L1995 EM FM *020 †18

WILLIAMS, G Alex, III. 400 N STATE OF FRANKLIN RD 37604 #047-06-1973 L1974 ORS *020 †40

WILLIAMS, Henry Jackson. 7 LLEWELLYN WOOD 37601 #047-06-1965 L1965 ORS *020 †40

WILLIAMS, Marcus G. 4 PHILLIP CT 37604 #010-03-1979 L1989 GS *020 †85,90

WILLIAMS, Mark Arnold. 219 PRINCETON RD, STE 200 37601 #047-06-1992 L1993 IM *020 †20

WILSON, David M. 400 N STATE OF FRANKLIN RD 37604 #047-06-1976 L1977 OPH *071 †35

WILSON, Gary Glenn. 1114 SUNSET DR STE 4, P O BOX 1070 37604 #012-01-1990 L1994 AN *020 †05

WILSON, George Dean. 400 N STATE OF FRANKLIN RD 37604 #036-01-1972 L1978 N *071 †75

WILSON, James Marion. 300 W WALNUT ST 37604 #012-01-1967 L1975 U *071 †95

WILSON, Jimmy Lester. 917 W WALNUT ST, DBA KINGSPORT FAMILY 37604 #028-03-1970 L1995 FM FPG *071 †18

WINTON, George Beverly. 1009 N STATE OF FRANKLN RD 37604 #045-01-1978 L1987 D DS *020 †15

WIREMAN, Jill W. 615 N STATE OF FRANKLIN RD 37604 #020-12-1990 L1993 PD *020 †55

WISDOM-SCHEPERS, Jennifer. ■ 37601 #047-20-2003 L2004 P *020

WOFFORD, Charles Parker. ■ 37601 #041-01-1936 L1939 A IM *071 †20

WOLFORT, Sean Francis. 325 N STATE OF FRANKLIN RD, ETSU SURGERY 37604 #051-01-1990 L1999 PS HS *020 †65 ‡

WOOD, James Fowle. 215 E WATAUGA AVE 37601 #047-06-1966 L1973 OTO *020 †45

WOOD, R Harber. 101 MED TECH PKWY, STE 305 37604 #004-01-1993 L1997 IM *020 †20

WOODSIDE, Jack Richard, Jr. 917 W WALNUT ST, COLLEGE OF MEDICINE 37604 #041-02-1977 L1986 FM ADM *040 †05,18

WOOLDRIDGE, Thomas Major. 1301 SUNSET DR STE 3, MOUNTAIN EMPIRE RADIOLOGY 37604 #048-13-2000 L2006 MSR *020 †80

WOOTEN, Daniel Jerry, Jr. ■ 37604 #047-07-1965 L1967 AN CCA *040

WYCHE-BASHOR, Donna. 308 SUNSET DR STE 1 37604 #047-20-1986 L1989 AI *020 †20

WYKOFF, Randolph Forbes. ■ 37615 #021-01-1981 L2007 PD GPM *030 †55,70

YACOUB, George Hosni Rafi. PO BOX 70571 37614 #915-04-2000 ON *012 †20

YAO, Zhi Qiang. ■ 37604 #243-95-1985 L2008 ID *012

YEH, David John. 408 N STATE OF FRANKLIN RD, STE 42 37604 #012-01-1998 L2005 NS *020 †25

YOHANNAN, Thomas Munnu. PO BOX 70571 37614 #495-31-2003 PD *012

YONG, Junesik Nuri. 301 E MAIN ST STE 2 37601 #583-02-1952 L1982 P *020 †75

YOUNESS, Houssein Abbass. PO BOX 70571 37614 #605-03-2001 L2005 PCC *012 †20

YOUNG, Amy Broyles. 110 MED TECH PKWY, STE 1 37604 #047-20-1989 L1993 OPH *020 †35

YOUNG, Mark F. 310 N STATE OF FRANKLIN RD, STE 202 37604 #047-20-1985 L1987 IM AN *020 †20

YOUNGBERG, George Anthony. 112 E MYRTLE AVE # 2 37601 #016-06-1977 L1980 PTH *040 †50

YOUSSEF, Dima Ahmad. PO BOX 70571, E TN U-J H QUILLEN COLL ME 37614 #605-03-2004 IM *012

ZAHEER, Ambreen. PO BOX 70571 37614 #704-27-1999 L2007 FM *100

ZAIETTA, Gabriel Alberto. PO BOX 70571 37614 #132-04-1997 IM *012

ZAJONC, Timothy P, Jr. 215 E WATAUGA AVE 37601 #048-12-1995 L2001 OTO *020 †45

ZAKARIA, Wael N. MOUNTAIN HOME VAMC 37604 #575-01-1983 L1995 IM HOS *020 †20

ZEPEDA, Fernando Arturo. 1114 SUNSET DR, STE 4 37604 #047-20-1993 L1997 AN *020 †05

ZOGHBI, Christiane Samir. PO BOX 70571 37614 #605-03-2004 L2008 IM *012

JONESBOROUGH – WASHINGTON

ADAMS, Shane Mc Callum. ■ 37659 #020-12-1994 L1995 FM *020 †18

BENSON, Paul Vincentin. ■ 37659 #038-43-1999 L2006 HMP *100 †50

BROWN, Seth Allen. ■ 37659 #047-20-2008 *012

CESARE, Charles David, Jr. ■ 37659 #027-01-2007 OBG *012

CLARK, Stephen Dennis. ■ 37659 #047-20-2005 L2007 IM *012

CORNWELL, Kevin Scott. ■ 37659 #047-20-2003 L2006 PCC *012 †20

DOANE, David G. 1509 MILL SPRINGS RD 37659 #024-07-1946 L1981 FM *071 †18

DRALLE, William Michael. 475 CHARLIE HICKS RD, RURAL ROUTE # 8 37659 #016-11-1969 L1978 PUD IM *020 †20 ‡

GIBSON, Stephanie. ■ 37659 #001-06-2006 OBG *012

GREENE, Marcella June. ■ 37659 #047-20-2004 GS *012

HALEY, Hillary Ann. ■ 37659 #047-20-2005 OBG *100

HAMM, Emile Victor. ■ 37659 #165-04-1970 L1986 IM CD *071

HERRELL, Howard Ernest. ■ 37659 #047-20-2004 L2007 OBG *012

JAIN, Vinay. ■ 37659 #495-45-1997 L2006 RNR *100 †80

JEWETT, Michael Eric. 806 E JACKSON BLVD, STE 8 37659 #023-12-1993 L2002 FM *020 †18

KENDRICK, John Brian. ■ 37659 #004-01-2007 GS *012

KENNEDY, William Ennis. 115 W MAIN ST 37659 #012-05-1965 L1972 ORS LM *062 †40

KIGER, Tammy Leigh. ■ 37659 #036-08-2000 L2006 IM *020

LAMBERT-DRWIEGA, April M. ■ 37659 #055-75-2004, ▲ L2007 IM *012

MAY, Joe Harold. ■ 37659 #047-20-2003 L2005 IM *020 †20

MC CORMICK, Wm Frederick. 120 NILES WHEELOCK RD 37659 #047-06-1955 L1956 FOP NP *071 †50 ‡

MEEKS, Edwin A. ■ 37659 #047-05-1950 L1950 PD *071 †55

MERRILL, Lloyd Kent. ■ 37659 #017-20-1968 L1973 MDM OBG *071 †30

MOORE, Norman Charles. ■ 37659 #918-01-1964 L2006 P CN *030 †75

PAPAS, Konstantino A. ■ 37659 #036-01-1997 L2003 IM *020 †20

PINYARD, Joseph Vincent. 114 W JACKSON BLVD 37659 #047-20-1996 L1997 FM *020 †18

SEMCHYSHYN, Stefan. ■ 37659 #065-05-1971 L1995 OBG MFM *020 †30

SHARISH, Rebecca S. 415 BOONES CREEK RD 37659 #038-44-1984 L1987 FM *020 †18

STEAGALD, Melinda Gail. ■ 37659 #047-20-2004 L2006 GS *012

STEWART, William Ross. 263 SUNNY SLOPES DR 37659 #038-06-1941 L1941 GP GS *071

STRAIN, Stephen Frederick. 415 BOONES CREEK RD 37659 #047-20-1999 L2001 FM *075 †18

TROXLER, Joyce Anne. ■ 37659 #047-20-2005 L2007 FP *012

VILLANUEVA, Brian Lee. ■ 37659 #047-20-2004 L2005 GS *012

WADZINSKI, Eve Lillian. ■ 37659 #047-20-2006 L2008 PD *012

WEAVER, Kenneth. 1103 E JACKSON BLVD, STE 1 37659 #036-01-1960 L1978 OBG *030 †30

WHITE, Norman Eugene. ■ 37659 #020-02-1959 L1969 PTH *071 †50

KINGSPORT – SULLIVAN

ABOUAMARA, Mouna. 4 SHERIDAN SQ STE 200 37660 #655-03-1987 L2003 *020 †20

ADDINGTON, Darryl Stephen. 2524 ESSEX DR 37660 #047-06-1971 L1971 IM OM *030 †20

ADELSON, Gary Lee. 130 W RAVINE RD 37660 #005-18-1976 L1981 PTH *020 †50

AHMAD, Abrar. 2002 BROOKSIDE DR, STE 102 37660 #704-01-1996 L2005 NEP *020 †20

AIKEN, Allison Marie. 201 CASSELL DR 37660 #041-12-2005 L2007 FP *012

ALLEY, Edmond Lynn. ■ 37660 #047-06-1955 L1955 AN *071 †05

ALLEY, Mark Webster. 135 W RAVINE RD, STE 5-B 37660 #047-05-1986 L1989 AN *020 †05

ALWANI, Anita Atmaram. 2204 PAVILION DR, STE 200 37660 #495-17-1991 L2002 PCC *020 †20

ANANTHULA, Parvati D. 2033 MEADOWVIEW LN, STE 200 37660 #024-05-2000 L2002 FM *020 †18

ANANTHULA, Srinivas. 2204 PAVILION DR, STE 200 37660 #495-57-1999 L2005 IM *100 †20

ANDERSON, Joy Kohne. 130 W RAVINE RD, STE 3A 37660 #048-13-2002 L2006 OBG *020

AUSTIN, Arthur Rhett. 2000 BROOKSIDE DR, DEPT OF RADIOLOGY 37660 #001-06-1988 L1993 DR EM *020 †80

BACON, Michael Lynn. 130 W RAVINE RD 37660 #047-06-1983 L1992 EM *020 †16

BAKER, Richard Dudley. 2412 N JOHN B DENNIS HWY 37660 #047-06-1968 L1969 OPH *020

BALES, Donald W, Sr. 202 W RAVINE DR, DONALD W BALES MD PC 37660 #047-06-1946 L1946 IM *071 †20

BANKS, Jerry Burton, II. 737 E SEVIER AVE 37660 #036-08-1992 L2000 FM *020 †18

BAREFOOT, Karen. 105 W PARK DR 37660 #036-08-1987 L1995 FM *020 †18

BATES, Chad Everett. ■ 37664 #051-07-2004 L2008 FM *020 †18

BAUMRUCKER, Steven James. 111 W STONE DR 37660 #036-01-1986 L1988 FM PLM *020 †18

BECKER, Mary Elizabeth. 2204 PAVILION DR, STE 212 37660 #035-45-1981 L1995 FM *020 †18

BECKNER, James Patrick. 130 W RAVINE RD, STE 3A 37660 #055-01-1997 L2001 OBG *020 †30

BEINE, Kathleen Barksdale. ■ 37664 #020-12-1978 L1989 FM *040 †18

BELAGODE, Vinaya S. 130 W RAVINE RD 37660 #496-22-1990 L1997 IM *020 †20

BELL, William Mc Kinley. 2205 PAVILION DR, STE 201 37660 #045-01-1972 L1980 RHU IM *020 †20

BENDECK, Carl Eric. 2000 BROOKSIDE DR, THIRD FLOOR 37660 #012-05-1983 L1996 IM GP *020 †20

BERRY, John Franklin. 2050 MEADOWVIEW PKWY, CARDIOVASCULAR ASSOCIATES 37660 #011-03-1994 L2006 CD *020 †20

BERTUSO, John Richard. 2050 MEADOWVIEW PKWY, CARDIOVASCULAR ASSOCIATES 37660 #016-45-1980 L1988 CD IM *020 †20

BESTERMANN, W H, Jr. 2033 MEADOWVIEW LN, STE 110 37660 #036-05-1973 L2007 VM IM *020 †20

BICE, Charles Robert. 135 W RAVINE RD, STE 2-C 37660 #047-06-1973 L1974 OPH *020 †35

BIEBER, Jeffry Dwayne. 3 SHERIDAN SQ, ARTHRITIS ASSOCIATES OF KI 37660 #047-20-1998 L2001 RHU IM *020 †20

BLACKWELDER, Reid Bruce. 201 CASSELL DR 37660 #012-05-1984 L1992 FM *040 †18

BLACKWELL, Gerald Grant. 2050 MEADOWVIEW PKWY, CARDIOVASCULAR ASSOCIATES 37660 #055-02-1983 L1995 CD IM *020 †20 ‡

BLAND, Susan M. ■ 37660 #010-01-1969 L1985 IM GPM *020 †20,70

BLAZIER, John Kent. 2033 MEADOWVIEW LN, STE 200 37660 #047-06-1960 L1963 PD *020

BLEVINS, Ballard Houston. ■ 37664 #047-06-1957 L1973 FM OS *071

BLICKENSTAFF, Theron. 709 CLANDON DR 37660 #038-41-1970 L1983 OM *030 †70

BOCHIS, Melania. 4 SHERIDAN SQ, STE 200 37660 #047-20-1999 L2002 IM *020

BOGGAN, Michael Dahyl. 111 W STONE DR, STE 100 37660 #012-01-1967 L1990 TS *020 †85

BOICIUC, Mircea Raducu. 2204 PAVILION DR, STE 200 37660 #781-01-1989 L2005 IM *020 †20

BOOKOUT, James M. 2205 PAVILION DR, STE 201 37660 #047-06-1976 L1976 IM *020 †20

BOOZE, George Wm. 1916 BROOKSIDE DR 37660 #051-01-1967 L1973 IM END *020 †20

BOWDEN, James Alexander. 1657 E STONE DR, # 231 37660 #063-01-1984 L2007 FM *030 †18

BOWER, Anthony D. 201 CASSELL DR 37660 #035-03-1951 L1982 FM *020 †18

BOYD, Arthur Morgan. 105 W PARK DR 37660 #047-06-1972 L1972 FM GS *020 †18

BOYLE, J William, III. 2002 BROOKSIDE DR, STE 300 37660 #005-12-1974 L1987 GYN EM *020 †30

BRANDON, Richard Lynmore. 101 PROFESSIONL PRK PVT DR 37663 #045-01-1983 L1986 FM *020 †18

BRAZEE, Jason H. 135 W RAVINE RD, STE 5-A 37660 #025-12-1976 L1977 IM *020 †20

BRAZEE, Louise J. 135 W RAVINE RD, STE 5-A 37660 #025-12-1976 L1977 GP *020

BREEDING, Samuel D. 563 E MAIN ST 37660 #051-04-1977 L1984 OM FM *020 †70,18

BROCK, Howard Thomas. 914 BROAD ST, SURGICAL ASSOCIATES OF 37660 #012-05-1971 L1978 GS *020 †85

BROOKSHIRE, Paul F, Jr. ■ 37660 #012-05-1942 L1955 OTO *071 †45

BROWN, Andrew Nathaniel. ■ 37660 #035-45-1965 L2007 PHP PD *020 †55

BROWN, Henry James. 130 W RAVINE RD 37660 #047-06-1944 IM OS *072

BRYANT, Erin Elizabeth. 201 CASSELL DR 37660 #047-07-2001 L2003 FM *020 †18

BULLE, Thomas Michael. 2050 MEADOWVIEW PKWY, CARDIOVASCULAR ASSOCIATES 37660 #035-03-1978 L1989 CD *020 †20 ‡

BURLESON, James Henry. 2000 BROOKSIDE DR, INDIAN PATH MEDICAL CTR 37660 #047-20-1988 L1989 EM FM *020 †18

BURMEISTER, Douglas Glen. ■ 37660 #056-06-1954 L1961 D *071 †15

BUSH, Gary Edward. 130 W RAVINE RD 37660 #654-01-1984 L1987 IM *020 †20

BUTLER, Steven Craig. 2002 BROOKSIDE DR, STE 102 37660 #016-02-1982 L1991 NEP OBG *020 †20

BYRD, Keith Harold. 130 W RAVINE RD 37660 #020-02-1965 L1970 EM GP *020

CAMERON, Donald Alexander. ■ 37663 #065-01-1951 L1977 FM *040

CAMPBELL, Keith Sean. 914 BROAD ST, SURGICAL ASSOCIATES OF 37660 #047-06-1995 L1997 GS VS *020 †85

CARROLL, Daniel Dwight. 177 W SEVIER AVE 37660 #047-20-1988 L1989 FM *020 †18

CARTER, Locke Yancey. 130 W RAVINE RD 37660 #012-05-1962 L1968 IM CD *020 †20

CARTER, Richard Saml. 135 W RAVINE RD STE 5-B 37660 #047-06-1969 L1970 AN *020 †05

CARVER, Mark Edward. 135 W RAVINE RD, STE B 37660 #047-06-1990 L1991 AN *020 †05

CASEY, Gary Q. 105 W PARK DR 37660 #047-06-1977 L1978 FM *020 †18

CHADWICK, Frank Beasley, Jr. 135 W RAVINE RD, STE 5-B 37660 #047-06-1999 L2003 AN *020 †05

CHAMBERLIN, Marian L. 4 SHERIDAN SQ, STE 200 37660 #025-12-1978 L1981 IM *020 †20

CHAPMAN, John Lynn. 135 W RAVINE RD, STE 2-C 37660 #036-05-1979 L1983 OPH *020 †35

CHARTIER, Gilbert John. ■ 37664 #025-07-1964 L1977 OM GPM *020

CHATRA, Shubha. 2000 BROOKSIDE DR, RM 321 37660 #495-35-1995 L2002 IM *020 †20

CHIRCULESCU, Camelia. 146 W PARK DR, STE 9G 37660 #781-04-1995 L2005 IM *100 †20

CLARK, Warner L. 2000 BROOKSIDE DR 37660 #047-06-1949 L1950 FM *071 †18

CLINES, Nancy E. 1201 N WILCOX DR 37660 #451-01-1988 L1995 PD *020 †55

COEN, Scott Douglas. 130 W RAVINE RD, C LAGUARDIA PHILLIP CANCER 37660 #055-01-1998 L2003 RO *020 †80

COLQUITT, Landon A. 130 W RAVINE RD 37660 #048-14-1981 L1989 PTH ATP *072 †50

CONWAY, Melanie. 4507 TIMBERLAKE LN 37664 #004-01-1994 L2002 P *020 †75

COOPER, Joe Byron. 130 W RAVINE RD 37660 #047-06-1961 L1961 R *071 †80

CORRADINO, Gregory. 999 EXECUTIVE PARK BLVD, STE 102 37660 #051-01-1982 L1992 NS *020 †25 ‡

COUCH, David Allan. 2412 N JOHN B DENNIS HWY 37660 #012-22-1997 L2001 OPH *020 †35

COWDEN, David Anthony. 2204 PAVILION DR, STE 200 37660 #039-01-1969 L1976 OTO *020 †45

CRAVEN, Bickley. 201 CASSELL DR 37660 #047-06-1982 L1985 FM *040 †18 ‡

CRAWFORD, Amylyn L. 737 E SEVIER AVE 37660 #047-20-2001 L2003 FM *020 †18

CREASY, John David. 130 W RAVINE RD 37660 #001-02-1994 L1999 VIR *020 †80

CROUCH, David Norman. 111 W STONE DR 37660 #016-43-1991 L2007 FM *020 †18

CROWDER, Jack Roberts. 2002 BROOKSIDE DR, STE 300 37660 #047-06-1967 L1971 OBG *020 †30

CUMMINGS, Howard Lee, Jr. 2412 N JOHN B DENNIS HWY 37660 #048-12-1987 L1998 OPH IM *020 †35

DA SILVA, Marco Antonio C. 111 W STONE DR, STE 300 37660 #187-02-1979 L2002 HO HEM *020 †20 ‡

DAVIDSON, Melanie Rosario. 2205 PAVILION DR, STE 201 37660 #005-12-2000 L2003 CD *020 †20

DE FLUITER, Elizabeth B. 2205 PAVILION DR, STE 105 37660 #047-20-2000 L2005 GS *020 †85

DEKIC-DJORDJEVIC, Zvjezdan. 1025 KENDRICK CREEK RD 37663 #957-08-1985 L2003 FM *020 †18

DELWADIA, Andy D. 2204 PAVILION DR, STE 212 37660 #495-23-1979 L1983 IM *020 †20

DEVENS, William E. 130 W RAVINE RD 37660 #011-04-1986 L1989 EM *020 †16

DEW, Michael Stuart. 2012 BROOKSIDE DR STE 8, BLUE RIDGE NEUROLOGYASSOCI 37660 #010-02-1986 L1995 N *020 †75

DICKERSON, Danl Lawrence. 105 W PARK DR 37660 #047-06-1974 L1974 FM *020 †18

DIMITROV, Marin Vasilev. 130 W RAVINE RD 37660 #198-02-1973 L1996 IM *020 †20

DIXON, Mark Cameron. 135 W RAVINE RD, STE 5-B 37660 #047-06-1989 L1990 AN *020 †05

DOELL, Robert John. 130 W RAVINE RD 37660 #484-01-1980 L1985 AN *020 †05 ‡

DOTY, Robert D. 130 W RAVINE RD 37660 #023-07-1943 L1952 GS *071 †85

DOYLE, Charlene A. 130 W RAVINE RD 37660 #047-20-1992 L1996 EM *020 †16

DYER, William Mills, Jr. 100 N EASTMAN RD 37660 #028-02-1965 L1975 OM AM *071 †70

EASTRIDGE, Wesley Vance. 1105 W STONE DR 37660 #012-05-1983 L1986 FM *020 †18

EHRENFRIED, John Albert. 914 BROAD ST, SURGICAL ASSOCIATES OF 37660 #030-05-1991 L2000 SO GS *020 †85

EHRENFRIED, Lorna K. 2706 KINGSLAND CT, . 37660 #048-02-1994 L2000 AN *020 †05

ELDERBROCK, Wm Burley. 201 CASSELL DR, CENTER 37660 #038-40-1957 L1993 FM *071 †18

EMERSON, William Kenneth. 130 W RAVINE RD 37660 #001-02-1978 L1979 GP *075

EMERY, Mark Watson. 111 W STONE DR, STE 100 37660 #048-02-1984 L1989 PCC *020 †20

EVERHART, Anthony Todd. 2204 PAVILION DR, STE 200 37660 #047-20-1996 L2002 IM *020 †20

EXUM, William Allen. ■ 37660 #036-07-1941 L1945 IM *071

FALCONER, Randall Jos. 1728 N EASTMAN RD, STE 1A 37664 #016-45-1982 L1988 OTO *020 †45

FEIT, Richard Allan. ■ 37660 #035-03-1975 L1982 TS *040 †85,90

FENYVES, Jeffrey Paul. 10461 WALLACE ALLEY ST, TRI-CITIES ENDOSCOPY CENTE 37663 #036-05-1985 L1991 IM GE *020 †20

FERRIS, James Michael. ■ 37663 #048-15-2007 PTH *012

FIFE, Robert Dean. 4105 FORT HENRY DR STE 207, C/O PREMIER ANESTH SVCS PC 37663 #047-06-1981 L1985 AN *020 †05

FISCHER, Francis H, Jr. 111 W STONE DR, STE 200 37660 #048-13-1974 L1975 PD *020 †55

FISCHER, Judith J P. 2002 BROOKSIDE DR, STE 200 37660 #048-13-1975 L1976 OBG EM *020 †30

FLANARY, Frank Sevier. 400 MANOR DR 37660 #051-04-1948 L1950 PD *071

FLORA, Don Atlee. ■ 37660 #047-06-1959 L1959 D *071

FOGG, Darlene Elizabeth. 135 W RAVINE RD, STE 1-A 37660 #011-02-1997 L2001 OBG *020 †30

FONTAINE, Darryl. 135 W RAVINE RD STE 5-B 37660 #021-06-1985 L1989 AN *020 †05

FORT, Richard Lee. 1936 BROOKSIDE DR STE A 37660 #051-01-1977 L1982 P *020

FOSTER, Larry J. 111 W STONE DR, STE 1 37660 #047-06-1970 L1980 PUD SME *020 †20

FOWLER, Scott Raymond. 117 W SEVIER AVE, STE 200 37660 #012-01-1989 L1999 OBG *020

FRANCE, Jeffery Jay. 2202 N JOHN B DENNIS HWY, STE 1 37660 #047-06-1998 L2003 ORS *020 †40

FRANCISCO, Mary Patricia. 111 W STONE DR, STE 200 37660 #047-20-1988 L1996 PD PG *020 †20,55

FRANKLIN, John Leonard. 2204 PAVILION DR, STE 200 37660 #011-03-1994 L2005 ORS *020 †40

FRANZUS, David Harold. 121 E RAVINE RD, STE 700 37660 #047-20-1983 L1984 IMG IM *020 †20

FREEMAN, Kristin Michelle. ■ 37660 #020-02-2006 L2007 FP *012

FUNKE, Robert Harold. 121 E RAVINE RD, STE 400 37660 #021-01-1979 L1985 FM *020 †18

GAINES, Robin Annette. ■ 37660 #036-08-2005 PD *100

GALE, Peter Foster. 130 W RAVINE RD, DEPT OF LAB MED HOLSTON MD 37660 #026-04-1976 L1984 PTH HMP *020 †50

GALL, Stanley Adolph, Jr. 2050 MEADOWVIEW PKWY, CARDIOVASCULAR ASSOCIATES 37660 #036-07-1987 L2004 TS VS *020 †85,90

GARFIELD, Claude R. ■ 37660 #051-01-1950 L1972 IM *072 †20

GARRETT, Arthur Randolph. 2212 N JOHN B DENNIS PKWY, INDIAN PATH PEDIATRICS 37660 #001-06-1977 L1983 PD EM *020 †55

GARRIOTT, David Kent. 1105 W STONE DR, FRIENDS IN NEED HEALTH CEN 37660 #047-06-1969 L1970 N *071 †75

GARZA, Jose Enrique. 2204 PAVILION DR, STE 200 37660 #048-14-2004 L2007 IM *020

GASH, Denny Lynn. 2050 MEADOWVIEW PKWY #020-12-1983 L1989 CD IM *020 †20

GENDRON, Richard Maurice. 2033 MEADOWVIEW LN, STE 200 37660 #050-02-1970 L1978 PD GP *020 †55

GINN, David Roy. 4 SHERIDAN SQ, STE 200 37660 #026-04-1979 L1982 IM *020 †20

GOH, Kenton Binghock. 130 W RAVINE RD 37660 #020-12-1990 L1993 EM *020 †16

GOLDSTEIN, Jack Stanley. 121 E RAVINE RD, MTN REGN INTERNL MEDCN PLC 37660 #306-01-1983 L1987 IM *040 †20

GONCE, Joel Dwight. 2204 PAVILION DR, STE 200 37660 #047-06-1975 L1975 FM *020 †18

GONZALEZ, George Danl. 914 BROAD ST, SURGICAL ASSOCIATES OF 37660 #027-01-1980 L1989 VS GS *020 †85

GREEN, Steven Morris. 201 CASSELL DR 37660 #012-01-1985 L1987 FM *075

GREENE, Charles David. 135 W RAVINE RD, STE 5-B 37660 #047-06-1982 L1983 AN *020

GREENE, Elmer Albert. TN EASTMAN CO BOX 1975 37662 #047-06-1956 L1956 OM OS *030 †70

GREENFIELD, D Tyler. 2050 MEADOWVIEW PKWY, THE HEART CTR 37660 #048-12-1984 L1997 TS PCS *020 †85,90 ‡

GREWAL, Raman Singh. 1045 UNION ST 37660 #035-09-2000 L2001 AN *020 †05

GREWAL, Ranjit Singh. 201 CASSELL DR 37660 #104-01-2003 FM *100

GRIFFIN, Edward Alan. 2205 PAVILION DR, STE 201 37660 #021-06-1983 L1985 IM *020 †20

GRIFFIN, William Cecil, Jr. 2300 W STONE DR 37660 #047-06-1969 L1969 D PD *020 †55,15

GRIFFITH, Mark Wm. 130 W RAVINE RD 37660 #041-13-1983 L1988 **ORS** *020 †40

GRIGSBY, William Paul. 2204 PAVILION DR, STE 115 37660 #051-04-1956 L1967 **GS** *020 †85

GRIMES, Marcus C. 10368 WALLACE ALLEY ST #18, HIGHLANDS PATHOLOGY CNSLTS 37663 #018-03-1980 L1984 **PTH PCP** *020 †50

GROCE, Ann. 135 W RAVINE RD STE 5-B 37660 #036-01-1972 L1980 **AN** *020 †05

GROVER, Bruce Scott. 1920 BROOKSIDE DR, STE 2 37660 #051-04-1982 L1990 **PUD IM** *020 †20

GUNN, Joseph Michael. 2412 N JOHN B DENNIS HWY 37660 #047-06-1985 L1986 **OPH** *020 †35

GUPTA, Sudershan. 201 CASSELL DR 37660 #495-17-1997 L2005 **FM** *020

HALL, John Richard. 134 W PARK DR, TRAUMA SERVICE 37660 #003-01-1977 L1995 **CCS TRS** *040 †85

HANEY, Anthony Wade. 2050 MEADOWVIEW PKWY, CARDIOVASCULAR ASSOCIATES 37660 #039-01-2000 L2006 **CD** *020 †20

HARMAN, Eric Wayne. 1002 EXECUTIVE PARK BLVD 37660 #047-20-1998 L1999 **FM** *020 †18

HARRIS, Robert Mitchell. 121 E RAVINE RD, STE 200 37660 #051-01-1987 L2006 **ORS TRS** *020 †40

HARRISON, William, Jr. ■ 37664 #008-01-1942 L1952 **PTH CLP** *071 †50

HARTMAN, Lawrence P. 135 W RAVINE RD, STE 4-A 37660 #011-04-1977 L2002 **NS AM** *020 †25

HEIBA, Ibrahim Mohammed. ■ 37664 #915-03-1981 L2002 **OM GPM** *020 †70

HEISE, John G. 2033 MEADOWVIEW LN, STE 200 37660 #011-02-1986 L1994 **ADL PD** *020 †55

HELMS, Kimberly M. 130 W RAVINE RD 37660 #047-20-1999 L2004 **PTH** *100 †50

HEREFORD, John Robt. 2002 BROOKSIDE DR, STE 300 37660 #020-02-1979 L1984 **OBG** *020 †30

HERMAN, James Robert. 822 BROAD ST, UROLOGY ASSOCIATES OF 37660 #007-02-1993 L2001 **U** *020 †95

HERNANDEZ, Gustavo E. 1920 BROOKSIDE DR, STE 9 37660 #264-01-1958 L1973 **R** *071 †80

HICKS, Mack Lynn, III. 121 E RAVINE RD, STE 400 37660 #047-06-1983 L1983 **FM** *020 †18

HINTON, Philip John. 2205 PAVILION DR, STE 105 37660 #056-07-1971 L1979 **GS** *020 †85

HIXSON, Clair S. 2050 MEADOWVIEW PKWY, THE HEART CENTER 37660 #049-01-1979 L1991 **CD IM** *020 ‡

HIXSON, Constance T. 201 CASSELL DR, EAST TN STATE UNIV DEPT FP 37660 #049-01-1979 L1991 **FM** *040 †18

HODGES, Stanley Melvin. 2000 BROOKSIDE DR, THIRD FLOOR 37660 #012-22-1992 L2001 **IM** *020 †20

HOLLANDSWORTH, James J. 4848 FORT HENRY DR 37663 #055-01-1990 L1995 **FM** *020 †18

HOLT, Steven Michael. 2204 PAVILION DR, STE 200 37660 #036-05-1994 L2000 **GS** *020 †85

HOMOKY, Carri Beth Grimes. 2300 W STONE DR, DERMATOLOGY ASSOCIATES 37660 #028-46-1990 L1999 **D** *020 †15

HOMOKY, Douglas Edward. 135 W RAVINE RD, STE 3-A 37660 #028-46-1990 L1999 **GE** *020 †20

HONEYCUTT, Jeffrey W. 2000 BROOKSIDE DR 37660 #051-07-1989 L2006 **DR** *020 †80

HOPE, Lapsley Grant, Jr. 130 W RAVINE RD 37660 #308-03-1981 L1984 **IM** *020 †20

HUBBS, Doris Taam. 1105 W STONE DR, FRIENDS IN NEED HEALTH CEN 37660 #020-02-1988 L1989 **IM** *020 †20

HUDDLESTON, Sam W, Jr. 2002 BROOKSIDE DR STE 201 37660 #047-06-1983 L1983 **GS** *020 †65

HUDSON, Wm Dudley, III. 130 W RAVINE RD 37660 #004-01-1976 L1977 **EM** *020 †16

HUNT, Jeffrey Thos. 2204 PAVILION DR, STE 200 37660 #030-06-1992 L1998 **OTO** *020 †45

HUNT, Kimberley A. 111 W STONE DR, STE 200 37660 #011-04-1994 L1998 **PD** *075 †55

HUNTER, Ronald Wilson. 2020 BROOKSIDE DR, STE 29 37660 #025-07-1976 L1976 **FM** *020 †18

ICK, Kurt Alexander. 1932 BROOKSIDE DR, KINGSPORT UROLOGY GROUP 37660 #019-02-1992 L1997 **U** *020 †95

JACKSON, Lisa Suzanne. ■ 37663 #036-08-2004 L2005 **FM** *100 †04

JAIN, Rekha. 1920 BROOKSIDE DR, STE 3 37660 #496-07-1997 L2006 **DR** *100

JARJOURA, Chadi Milad. 117 W SEVIER AVE, STE 200 37660 #605-02-1992 L2006 **OBG IM** *020 †30

JARVIS, Roy Joe. ■ 37663 #047-06-1952 L1952 **PD** *072 †55

JEANSONNE, Gregory Edmund. 2202 N JOHN B DENNIS HWY, STE 100 37660 #021-05-2001 L2005 **ORS** *020

JEANSONNE, Susan Watts. 111 W STONE DR, STE 200 37660 #021-05-1999 L2005 **PD** *020 †55

JENKINS, Mark Coleman. 2212 N JOHN B DENNIS HWY, STE D 37660 #020-12-1983 L1990 **FM** *020 †18

JERNIGAN, Robert H. 130 W RAVINE RD 37660 #021-01-1950 L1956 L1956 **IM** *071 †20

JIJON, Francisco Xavier. 146 W PARK DR, STE 9B 37660 #319-01-1982 L1990 **NPM PD** *020 †55

JOLLEY, Broughton D. 135 W RAVINE RD, STE 5-B 37660 #047-20-1990 L1991 **AN** *020 †05

JONES, Gregory Kevin. 2050 MEADOWVIEW PKWY, CARDIOVASCULAR ASSOCIATES 37660 #005-14-1988 L2002 **CD** *020 †20

JONES, Jason Andrew. ■ 37664 #047-20-2007 *012

JONES, Lesley Ann. 2012 BROOKSIDE DR, STE 6 37660 #051-04-1990 L1993 **FM** *020 †18

JONES, Malcolm Mc Kinley. 2000 BROOKSIDE RD 37660 #047-06-1958 L1958 **GP OS** *071

JONES, Robert Clark. ■ 37660 #024-01-1943 L1952 **U** *071 †95

JONES, Samuel Riddle. 146 W PARK DR, STE 9D 37660 #047-06-1962 L1963 **OBG** *071 †30

JONES, Warren Lee. 4848 FORT HENRY DR 37663 #036-01-1985 L1988 **FM** *020 †18

KADEKAR, Sitaram Gururao. 2050 MEADOWVIEW PKWY, CARDIOVASCULAR ASSOCIATES 37660 #496-38-1963 L2005 **CD AMI** *020 †20

KAO, Lidia L. 2002 BROOKSIDE DR, STE 300 37660 #048-02-1982 L1992 **OBG** *020 †30

KAPPA, Jeffrey Ray. 914 BROAD ST, SURGICAL ASSOCIATES OF 37660 #036-07-1981 L1988 **GS VS** *020 †85

KAPPA, Rosanne Denise. 135 W RAVINE RD, STE 1-A 37660 #036-07-1981 L1989 **OBG** *074 †30

KAZMIER, W Jan. 2995 FORT HENRY DR, STE 100 37664 #759-09-1969 L1986 **AI IM** *020 ‡

KEENE, Charlotte S. 2002 BROOKSIDE DR STE 300 37660 #001-02-1986 L1990 **OBG** *020 †30 ‡

KEITH, Robert Earl. TENN EASTMAN CO BOX 511 37662 #047-06-1956 L1956 **OM** *030 †70

KIDWELL, Eugene Raymond, Jr. 1920 BROOKSIDE DR, INDIAN PATH PROF BLD 37660 #055-01-1977 L1981 **P** *020 †75

KLINAR, Daniel Franklyn. 2202 N JOHN B DENNIS HWY, STE 100 37660 #045-01-1985 L1988 **ORS** *020 †40

KNAPP, Richard Meriwether. 2995 FORT HENRY DR, ASSOC PATH PLC STE 300 37664 #039-05-1984 L2000 **PTH** *050 ‡

KOMMAREDDI, Vijaya Kumar. ■ 37660 #495-57-1967 L2007 **IM** *020 †20

KRAMER, Robert Keith. 2050 MEADOWVIEW PKWY, CARDIOVASCULAR ASSOCIATES 37660 #036-08-1993 L1999 **CD** *020 †20 ‡

KRCAL, Otakar. 914 BROAD ST, STE 3A 37660 #035-48-2002 L2007 **N** *100 †75

KREIN, Steven Walter. 2204 PAVILION DR, STE 200 37660 #054-04-1979 L1989 **ORS** *020 †40

KRISHNAMOORTHY, S. 1901 BROOKSIDE DR, STE 105 37660 #495-16-1967 L1977 **GP** *072

KUTTY, Ittamveetil N. 1920 BROOKSIDE DR, STE 14 37660 #495-44-1967 L1985 **CHP P** *020 †75 ‡

LADLEY, Herbert De Ross. 2050 MEADOWVIEW PKWY, CARDIOVASCULAR ASSOCIATES 37660 #051-07-1977 L1984 **CD IM** *020 †20

LAIL, Sharon E. 146 W PARK DR STE 9B 37660 #051-04-1977 L1983 **NPM PD** *020 †55

LANE, David Lee. 130 W RAVINE RD 37660 #051-01-1976 L1979 **FM** *020 †18

LATEEF, Shoaib Sultan. 2204 PAVILION DR, STE 200 37660 #308-13-1998 L2002 **IM** *020 †20

LAURO, Frank Louis. ■ 37660 #561-01-1969 L1970 **RO** *075 †80

LAWHON, Reet Thomas, IV. 135 W RAVINE RD, STE 5-B 37660 #021-06-1999 L2001 **AN** *020 †05

LEE, Robert Chapman. 1029 E SULLIVAN ST, HOLSTON MEDICAL GROUP 37660 #027-01-1978 L1982 **FM EM** *020 †18 ‡

LEGAULT, Laurent Joseph. 1944 BROOKSIDE DR, APPALACHIAN ORTHOPAEDIC AS 37660 #065-09-1980 L1995 **ORS** *020 †40

LEPSCH, Thomas C. 130 W RAVINE RD 37660 #026-08-1983 L1987 **DR** *020 †80

LEWIS, Anthony Evan. 1936 BROOKSIDE DR, STE D 37660 #011-02-1989 L1993 **IM** *020 †20

LEWIS, Donald Herbert. 2033 MEADOWVIEW LN, STE 200 37660 #047-06-1979 L1981 **PD NPM** *020 †55

LEY, Joseph A. 111 W STONE DR, STE 200 37660 #048-14-1982 L1985 **PD ADL** *020 †55

LINDBERG, Douglas James. 201 CASSELL DR 37660 #016-43-2003 L2006 **FM** *040 †18

LITCHFIELD, Peter Michael. ■ 37664 #047-20-2007 **GS** *012

LITTLE, James Peter. 212 E MARKET ST, SOUTHERN REHABILITATION GR 37660 #025-07-1977 L1984 **PM EM** *030 †60

LITTLEJOHN, Jimmy Rodney. 822 BROAD ST, UROLOGY ASSOCIATES OF 37660 #011-04-1977 L1997 **U** *020 †95

LONDON, Jerry Frank. 135 W RAVINE RD, STE 3-A 37660 #047-06-1984 L1990 **GE IM** *030 †20

LOUTHAN, James David. 2033 MEADOWVIEW LN, STE 200 37660 #017-20-1992 L1999 **IM** *020 †20

LOVELACE, Donald Ray. 2002 BROOKSIDE DR, STE 300 37660 #020-02-1978 L1982 **OBG** *020 †30

LOVELESS, Howard Wm, Jr. 2204 PAVILION DR, STE 200 37660 #047-06-1981 L1982 **OTO EM** *020 †45

LYMBERIS, Marvin Edward B. 2000 BROOKSIDE DR 37660 #036-07-1977 L1981 **R** *020 †80

MAC DONALD, R Scott. 914 BROAD ST, ASSOCIATED NEUROLOGISTS 37660 #016-11-1979 L1983 **N** *020 †75

MADER, Russell David. 2300 W STONE DR 37660 #045-01-1991 L1998 **D** *020 †15

MADHOK, Shailee A. 2995 FORT HENRY DR, STE 100 37664 #496-38-1996 L2005 **AI** *020 †55,03

MAKI, Anton, Jr. 948 MEADOW LN, ID MICRO, LLC 37663 #063-01-1980 L2003 **ID MM** *020 †20

MARCUM, Gregory Carl. 130 W RAVINE RD 37660 #047-20-1987 L1988 **EM FM** *020 †18

MARLOW, Amy Whorton. 2033 MEADOWVIEW LN, STE 200 37660 #011-03-1993 L2004 **PD** *020 †55

MARTIN, Christopher G. 146 W PARK DR, NEONATOLOGY ASSOCIATES P 37660 #005-19-1976 L1995 **NPM PD** *020 †55

MARTIN, Michael Richard. ■ 37664 #018-03-1995 L2005 **P** *020

MASTERS, James Edward. 4105 FORT HENRY DR, STE 207 37663 #047-20-1990 L1991 **AN** *020 †05

MATHEWS, Mack R, III. 130 W RAVINE RD, ONCOLOGY 37660 #020-02-1976 L1985 **HO IM** *020 †16,20

MATTHEWS, Christopher V. 101 PROFESSIONL PRK PVT DR 37663 #021-05-1980 L1994 **FM** *020 †18

MAY, Byron Clay. 130 W RAVINE RD, WELLMONT/HOLSTON VALLEY HO 37660 #021-01-1990 L2000 **RO** *020 †80

MAYNARD, Scott Eric. 135 W RAVINE RD STE 5-B 37660 #055-02-2002 L2006 **AN** *020 †05

MAZIARZ, David Michael. 2050 MEADOWVIEW PKWY, CARDIOVASCULAR ASSOCIATES, 37660 #033-05-1999 L2007 **GS** *100 †85

MC BRIDE, Charles Edward. 2204 PAVILION DR, STE 200 37660 #045-01-1996 L2007 **FM** *020 †18

MC DONOUGH, John R. PO BOX 511, TENN EASTMAN CO 37662 #051-04-1952 L1955 **OM** *030 †70

MC ELROY, Edwin A, Jr. 111 W STONE DR, STE 300 37660 #001-06-1991 L2000 **HO** *020 †20

MC GINN, Debra Lee. ■ 37660 #047-05-1982 L1987 **PTH** *020 †50

MC GUIRE, James Eldridge. 2204 PAVILION DR, STE 209 37660 #047-06-1963 L1963 **OBG** *071 †30

MC LAUGHLIN, Randy Keith. 1916 BROOKSIDE DR 37660 #047-06-1977 L1977 **IM** *020 †20

MC MAHAN, William Jerry. 2033 MEADOWVIEW LN, STE 200 37660 #021-05-1965 L1971 **PD** *020

MCQUIRTER, Ivy G. 2202 N JOHN B DENNIS HWY, STE 204 37660 #010-03-2000 L2003 **IM** *020

MELNIK, Evelyn A Hearl. 146 W PARK DR, STE 9B 37660 #055-01-1971 L1998 **NPM** *020 †55

MELVIN, Barbara M. 2971 FORT HENRY DR 37664 #027-01-1985 L1990 **PD** *020 †55

METZGER, David C. 2050 MEADOWVIEW PKWY, CARDIOVASCULAR ASSOCIATES 37660 #055-02-1992 L1999 **CD** *020 †20

MEYERS, Cary Howard. 2050 MEADOWVIEW PKWY, CARDIOVASCULAR ASSOCIATES 37660 #016-02-1988 L2003 **TS CD** *020 †85,90

MICHALIK, Richard Edmund. 2050 MEADOWVIEW PKWY 37660 #041-12-1974 L1985 **TS** *030 †85,90

MICHALS, Herbert James. 4241 SULLIVAN GARDENS DR 37660 #005-12-1958 L1976 **GPM FM** *071

MILLER, Bradley Willis. 1920 BROOKSIDE DR, STE 9 37660 #030-05-1983 L1988 **R EM** *020 †80

MILLER, Bruce Milton. 2202 N JOHN B DENNIS HWY, STE 100 37660 #016-42-1996 L2005 **ORS** *020 †40

MILLER, Gregory Houston. 2205 PAVILION DR, STE 201 37660 #051-04-1991 L1997 **CD IM** *020 †20

MILLER, Jerry Lee. 2323 N JOHN B DENNIS HWY, HOLSTON MEDICAL GROUP 37660 #051-04-1965 L1966 **FM** *020 †18

MILLER, Lee Hutter. ■ 37660 #041-01-1947 L1969 **OM IM** *072 †70

MILLER, Lucinda. 111 W STONE DR, STE 100 37660 #016-42-1997 L2005 **PCC** *020 †20

MILLER, Nicole Magnant. 111 W STONE DR, STE 200 37660 #051-04-1992 L1997 **PD** *020 †55

MISHKIN, Fredric Ronald. 135 W RAVINE RD STE 3-A 37660 #017-20-1975 L1989 **GE IM** *020 †20

MITCHELL, Christopher Ray. 117 W SEVIER AVE, STE 200 37660 #047-20-1996 L2005 OBG *020 †30

MITRI, Ghaith. 2204 PAVILION DR, STE 212 37660 #875-01-1995 L2001 RHU *020 †20

MIZE, Howard, Jr. 2202 N JOHN B DENNIS HWY, STE 100 37660 #020-02-1969 L1977 ORS HS *040 †40

MOFFET, Eric David. 1920 BROOKSIDE DR, STE 12 37660 #051-04-1986 L1990 P *020 †75 ‡

MOORE, John H, III. ■ 37664 #041-12-1953 L1959 GYN *071 †30

MORAES, Manoel Ary, Jr. 111 W STONE DR, STE 300 37660 #187-02-1981 L2005 HEM ON *020 †20

MORAWSKI, Emily Jane. 2204 PAVILION DR, STE 200 37660 #051-07-1999 L2002 FM *020 †18

MORIN, Jean E. 102 E RAVINE RD, DIAGNOSTIC LEARNING CENTER 37660 #067-03-1961 GS *020 †85,90

MORIN, Joseph Raoul. 698 CLINCHFIELD ST 37660 #051-04-1971 L1979 PD OS *020 †55

MORRIS, Alton J. 3 SHERIDAN SQ 37660 #021-05-1951 L1979 RHU IG *020 †20

MORRIS, Lawrence Ray. 2008 BROOKSIDE DR, STE 102 37660 #055-01-1969 L1975 END IM *071 †20

MOSES, John Lawrence. 111 W STONE DR, STE 300 37660 #001-06-1991 L1994 PD *020 †55

MOSRIE, Azett Jimmie. 1920 BROOKSIDE DR 37660 #051-04-1962 L1968 OPH *071 †35

MURTHY, Jayanth. ■ 37660 #495-33-1992 L1997 IM *020 †20

MURTHY, Ravindra Narayana. ■ 37660 #495-37-1982 L2003 GE *020 †20

MUSIL, Clinton A, Jr. 2001 STONEBROOK PL 37660 #047-20-1992 L1997 P PD *020 †55,75

NAGARAJAN, Ranjani. 130 W RAVINE RD 37660 #496-01-1984 L1992 IM *020 †20

NICHOLS, James B, Jr. ■ 37660 #047-06-1951 L1951 NS *071 †25

NORTHROP, Robert Clayton. 914 BROAD ST, SURGICAL ASSOCIATES OF 37660 #047-06-1996 L2002 GS VS *020 †85

NORTHROP, Robert Edwards. 111 W STONE DR 37660 #047-06-1962 L1962 PD *071

NORTON, Richard Chas. 37664 #005-12-1986 L1987 EM FM *075 †18

NUNLEY, Diana Lynn. 4 SHERIDAN SQ, STE 200 37660 #047-20-1983 L1986 ID IM *020 †20

NYE, Terry Randall. 1916 BROOKSIDE DR, BROOKSIDE MEDICAL GROUP 37660 #007-02-1990 L2003 IM *020 †20

O'BRIEN, Susan Nettleton. 201 CASSELL DR 37660 #016-43-1998 L2000 FM *020 †18

OLNEY, La Verne Edward. 1932 BROOKSIDE DR 37660 #018-03-1970 L1978 U *071 †95

OSTERHUS, David Robert. 2204 PAVILION DR 37660 #038-41-1998 L2004 OTO *020 †45

OTCHERE-BOATENG, Yaw. ■ 37660 #412-01-1989 L2006 IM *100 †20

OWEN, C Richard. ■ 37664 #041-09-1956 L1966 AN GP *071

PALATNIKOV-WOOD, Yelena. 2204 PAVILION DR, STE 110 37660 #005-06-1998 L2004 IM *020 †20

PARK, Jason C-H. 2204 PAVILION DR, STE 210 37660 #025-07-2002 L2007 ORS *020

PARRA ARISTIZABAL, Jose M. 201 CASSELL DR 37660 #264-06-1991 FP *012

PARSONS, Jeremy Craig. 201 CASSELL DR 37660 #020-02-2005 L2007 FP *012

PASTRICK, Gregory Harold. 1 SHERIDAN SQ, STE 200 37660 #001-02-1993 L1999 PS HS *020 †65

PATTON, Charley Mack. 822 BROAD ST 37660 #047-06-1966 L1967 U *020 †95

PATTON, Robert Carroll. ■ 37664 #051-04-1968 L1975 GE *071 †20

PAYNE, Charles E. 1932 BROOKSIDE DR 37660 #025-01-1953 L1954 P *071 †75

PAYNE, Charles Edward. 1932 BROOKSIDE DR, KINGSPORT UROLOGY GROUP 37660 #023-12-1989 L2001 U *020 †95

PENDOLA, Christopher A. 914 BROAD ST, STE 3A 37660 #041-06-1992 L1996 N *020 †75

PERDUE, John Marvin, Sr. ■ 37663 #036-05-1965 L1966 GP EM *071

PHILLIPS, James Benajah. ■ 37664 #047-05-1968 L1973 ORS *071 †40

PHILLIPS, James Curtis. 130 W RAVINE RD 37660 #047-06-1982 L1983 DR *020 †80

PHILLIPS, Monte Wayne. ■ 37664 #047-06-1960 L1961 GS OS *020 †85

PINELL, Octavio J. 2002 BROOKSIDE DR, STE 200 37660 #048-04-1982 L1986 OBG *020 †30

PLATT, William Marshall. 117 W SEVIER AVE, STE 120 37660 #047-06-1986 L1990 PM *020 †60

PLATZER, Peter Benham. 2004 AMERICAN WAY, STE 207 37660 #010-02-1977 L1997 FM *020 †18

POITRAST, Bruce James. 200 S WILCOX DR 37660 #050-02-1967 L2000 OM P *030 †75,70

POORTENGA-PHILLIPS, C. 1029 E SULLIVAN ST, HOLSTON MEDICAL GROUP 37660 #016-11-1983 L1986 FM *020 †18

PORTER, Keith Geo. 1936 BROOKSIDE DR, STE C 37660 #035-09-1992 L2002 IM *020 †20

PROVANCE, Paul Thomas. 2033 MEADOWVIEW LN, STE 200 37660 #038-45-2002 L2006 IM *020 †20

PUCKETT, Terry Lee. 536 E MAIN ST 37660 #047-06-1986 L1987 AM UCM *020 †70

PUGH, Thomas Floyd, Jr. 130 W RAVINE RD 37660 #047-06-1981 L1982 DR RNR *020 †80

RAFF, John Bourke. 2202 N JOHN B DENNIS HWY, STE 100 37660 #025-01-1980 L1994 OSS ORS *020 †40

RAJOO, Shari Kisten. 111 W STONE DR, STE 120 37660 #422-01-2001 L2007 FM *020 †18

RAO, Arun P. 2050 MEADOWVIEW PKWY, CARDIOVASCULAR ASOCIATES 37660 #495-19-1985 L2001 CD ICE *020 †20

RASH, James Patrick. 2300 W STONE DR 37660 #051-04-1983 L1989 D *020 †15

RASHEED, Atif. 201 CASSELL DR 37660 #704-21-2001 L2006 FP *012

REDDICK, Lovett Pratt. 2008 BROOKSIDE DR, STE 202 37660 #036-05-1970 L1979 PS HS *020 †85,65

REED, John S. 130 W RAVINE RD 37660 #024-01-1940 L1941 GS *071

REED, Michael Forsythe. ■ 37664 #047-06-1975 L1976 PTH *071 †50

REED, Richard Kyle. 1916 BROOKSIDE DR 37660 #035-17-1975 IM *020 †20

REEVES, Donny Luprice. 4 SHERIDAN SQ 37660 #049-01-2000 L2004 OPH *020 †35

REEVES, Woodrow W, Jr. 1932 BROOKSIDE DR, KINGSPORT UROLOGY GROUP 37660 #036-01-1983 L1988 U *020 †95

REIFF, Deborah Waters. 2204 PAVILION DR, STE 200 37660 #047-06-1977 L1978 FM *020

REIFF, Robert H, Jr. 2002 BROOKSIDE DR, STE 300 37660 #047-06-1977 L1978 OBG *020 †30 ‡

RENFRO, Clay Arlen. 4848 FORT HENRY DR 37663 #047-06-1961 L1962 FM *071 †18

RICHARDSON-COX, Barbara. 2002 BROOKSIDE DR, STE 300 37660 #005-02-1990 L1994 OBG *020 †30 ‡

RIDGEWAY, Nathan Alvah. 1105 W STONE DR, FRIENDS IN NEED HEALTH CTR 37660 #036-07-1957 L1963 IM *020 †20

RIGGINS, Matthew Paul. 2000 BROOKSIDE DR, INDIAN PATH MEDICAL CENTER 37660 #422-01-1986 L1991 EM *020 †18

RIGGINS, Patrick Jon. 2202 N JOHN B DENNIS HWY, STE 100 37660 #011-02-1989 L1995 ORS *020 †40

ROGERS, Malcolm E. ■ 37660 #047-06-1948 L1950 GS *071 †85

ROGERS, Robert Andrew. 1567 N EASTMAN RD 37660 #047-06-1987 L1992 GS *020 †85

ROGERS, Thomas Edward. 1567 N EASTMAN RD, HOLSTON MEDICAL GROUP, PC 37664 #047-20-1984 L1986 FM *020 †18

ROSE, Douglas Jeffrey. 201 CASSELL DR 37660 #041-02-1995 L2002 FM *040 †18

ROSSER, Robert Alan. 111 W STONE DR STE 100 37660 #011-04-1975 L1980 PUD IM *020 †20

SAGO, Joni Glavan. 2300 W STONE DR 37660 #023-07-1997 L2003 D *020 †20,15

SAHA, Pabitra Kumar. 2050 MEADOWVIEW PKWY, CARDIOVASCULAR ASOCIATES, 37660 #160-02-1984 L2007 CD PD *020 †20

SAHA, Tapasi C. 2002 BROOKSIDE DR, STE 102 37660 #160-04-1988 L2007 NEP *020 †20

SALCEDO, Julio A. 130 W RAVINE RD 37660 #726-01-1953 L1969 PTH *071 †50

SALLUZZO, Richard Francis. 1905 AMERICAN WAY, WELLMONT HEALTH SYSTEM 37660 #024-07-1978 L2004 EM *020 †20,16

SALYER, Alicia Wright. 111 W STONE DR, STE 200 37660 #020-12-1997 L2001 PD *020 †55

SARGENT, Jeffery Dale. 1905 AMERICAN WAY 37660 #051-04-1979 L1984 PUD *020 †20

SAUNDERS, Robert Danl. 130 W RAVINE RD, STE 3A 37660 #047-20-1989 L1993 OBG REN *020 †30

SCHMITZ, Evan Denis. 201 CASSELL DR 37660 #654-01-2003 L2005 IM *012

SCHWARTZ, Eric Mark. 2204 PAVILION DR STE 200, HOLSTON MEDICAL GROUP 37660 #035-48-1993 L1997 IM *020 †20

SCHWOB, Timothy Edward. 1101 E STONE DR, STE 2 37660 #305-01-1983 L1986 EM *020 †18

SEATON, Anthony Dean. 135 W RAVINE RD, STE 2-C 37660 #036-05-1992 L1996 OPH *020 †35

SEWELL, David Huff. ■ 37660 #021-01-1964 TS *071 †85,90

SHAH, Aruna Rangarajan. 2033 MEADOWVIEW LN, STE 200 37660 #422-01-2001 L2004 FM *020 †18

SHAH, Nalinchandra G. 1516 BRIDGEWATER LN, P O BOX 3490 37660 #495-22-1962 L1984 A PTH *020 †50

SHAH, Vishant Pramod. 2033 MEADOWVIEW LN, STE 200 37660 #047-06-2001 L2003 IM *020

SHAIKH, Mohammed Arif. 111 W STONE DR, STE 100 37660 #495-22-1996 L2002 PCC *020 †20

SHEHZAD, Nazia Iqbal. 201 CASSELL DR 37660 #704-21-2001 L2005 FP *012

SHIPSTONE, Asheesh. 111 W STONE DR, STE 300 37660 #495-30-1982 L1995 HO *020 †20

SHOCKLEY, Lisa Louise. 135 W RAVINE RD, STE 5-B 37660 #036-01-1983 L1992 PD CCM *020 †55,05

SHONE, Dallas Norman. 2204 PAVILION DR, STE 200 37660 #836-02-1983 L1994 GE IM *075 †20

SHOOK, Josh. 2033 MEADOWVIEW LN, STE 200 37660 #034-01-1998 L2001 PD *020 †55

SIDES, Paul J. 130 W RAVINE RD 37660 #036-07-1974 L1978 CLP ATP *020 †50

SIFFRING, Corydon Walter. 130 W RAVINE RD 37660 #001-06-1986 L2006 TRS CCS *020 †20

SILVIA, Kenneth Addison, II. 2000 BROOKSIDE DR 37660 #050-02-1996 L2004 APM *020 †05

SIMPSON, Harland Douglas. 135 W RAVINE RD, STE 5-B 37660 #047-20-1989 L1996 AN PME *020 †05

SINER, John Robt. 130 W RAVINE RD 37660 #045-01-1983 L1988 DR *040 †80

SINGH, Jasjot Paul. 1335 E CENTER ST, STE 1 37664 #495-12-1993 L2002 IM *020 †20

SINGH, Vijay Raj. ■ 37660 #495-93-1995 L2004 FM *020 †18

SKINNER, Wendell Lawrence. ■ 37664 #047-06-1961 L1961 GS *071 †85

SLOCUM, Carl Wm. 2204 PAVILION DR 37660 #030-06-1965 L1975 OTO *020 †45

SMIDDY, Jospeh Franklin. 1920 BROOKSIDE DR, STE 2 37660 #051-01-1967 L1973 PUD *020 †20

SMITH, Elizabeth Cain. 521 LAKEWOOD RD 37660 #011-03-1990 L1993 PD *020 †55

SMITH, Eric K. 135 W RAVINE RD, STE 2-C 37660 #048-04-1985 L1989 OPH *020 †35

SMITH, Galen Richard. 2202 N JOHN B DENNIS HWY, STE 1 37660 #021-05-1976 L1980 ORS *020 †40

SMITH, Ken W. 2 SHERIDAN SQ STE 200 37660 #012-05-1982 L1989 NS *020 †25

SMITH, Lyle R. ■ 37660 #035-20-1951 L1953 FM *071 †18

SMITH, Ronald Steven. 1920 BROOKSIDE DR STE 12 37660 #036-05-1977 L1981 P *020 †75

SMITH, Warren Young. ■ 37664 #012-05-1955 L1956 FM *071 †18

SMITH, Whitaker Michael. 1002 EXECUTIVE PARK BLVD 37660 #020-12-1988 L1999 FM *020 †18

SMYTH, Timothy Scott. 2020 BROOKSIDE DR, STE 21 37660 #036-01-1986 L1993 AN PME *020 †05

SOBEL, Abraham Isaac. 102 E RAVINE RD 37660 #051-01-1959 L1967 GYN *071 †30

SOHN, Richard Hong. 2204 PAVILION DR, STE 200 37660 #305-01-2001 L2006 IM *100

SOLOMON, Dale Edward. 1916 BROOKSIDE DR 37660 #047-06-1970 L1970 IM CD *020 †20

SOLOMON, Joseph Alpheus. ■ 37663 #051-04-1947 L1975 FM *071 †18

SOMIAH, Sachdev. 2000 BROOKSIDE DR, PSYCHIC UNIT 37660 #496-22-1988 L2005 P *020

SPIVEY, Patrick H, III. 4623 FORT HENRY DR 37663 #047-20-1982 L1985 EM *020 †16

SPRINGER, Doug John. 135 W RAVINE RD, STE 7-A 37660 #060-02-1973 L1978 GE IM *020 †20

STANSKI, Cheryl Ann. 2204 PAVILION DR, STE 200 37660 #021-01-1996 L2001 GS *020 †85

STEPHENS, Thomas Eric. 737 E SEVIER AVE, KINGSPORT MEDICAL CENTER 37660 #036-01-1998 L2005 FM *020 †18

STIRMAN, Edward M. 2204 PAVILION DR, STE 200 37660 #048-12-1975 L1978 FM *020 †18

STRANG, Robert Tudor, Sr. 2202 N JOHN B DENNIS HWY, STE 100 37660 #024-01-1946 L1953 ORS OS *071 †40

STRANG, Robert Tudor, Jr. 2202 N JOHN B DENNIS HWY, STE 100 37660 #047-06-1975 L1979 ORS *020 †40

SULKOWSKI, Viktor Peter. ■ 37660 #035-09-1971 L1977 AN GP *071 †05

SULLIVAN, Hugh Milton. 822 BROAD ST, UROLOGY ASSOCIATES OF 37660 #047-06-1968 L1972 U *020 †95

SULLIVAN, Michael Jude. 2204 PAVILION DR 37660 #035-47-1979 L1984 GE *020 †20

SUMMERS, Jeffrey Alan. 4 SHERIDAN SQ, STE 200 37660 #048-40-1982 L2000 IM *020 †20

SUMMERS, Robert Mark. 130 W RAVINE RD 37660 #047-20-2001 L2004 EM *020 †16

SYKES, Ted Ford. 120 W RAVINE RD 37660 #021-01-1967 L1974 ORS *071 †40

TASKER, John James Jos. 1303 E CENTER ST 37664 #065-06-1969 L1986 GYN GP *020

TAYLOR, William Riley. 2012 BROOKSIDE DR, STE 8 37660 #001-02-1978 L2001 ON HEM *020 †20

TEGELER, Monica Lynn. 201 CASSELL DR 37660 #028-34-2005 L2007 FP *012

TESTERMAN, Geo Milum, Jr. 134 W PARK DR, WELLMONT HOLSTON VALLEY 37660 #047-06-1978 L1980 CCS GE *020 †85

THIBAULT, Lenita Helen. 135 W RAVINE RD, STE 1-A 37660 #047-05-1984 L1991 OBG *020 †30

THOMAS, Chadwick Van. 2300 W STONE DR 37660 #045-01-1998 L2000 GS *020 †85

THOMAS, Lissy. 2002 BROOKSIDE DR, STE 102 37660 #495-63-1986 L1998 NEP *020 †20

THOMAS, Thomas V. 2204 PAVILION DR, STE 200 37660 #028-02-1992 L2001 GS VS *020 †85

THOTTIYIL, Anu Chacko. 201 CASSELL DR 37660 #308-13-2001 L2006 FP *012

TOCHEV, Tihomir Ivanov. 1501 E STONE DR, PROCARE 37660 #198-01-1989 L1998 FM *020 †18

TORRES, Camilo. 130 W RAVINE RD, EMERGENCY DEPARTMENT 37660 #049-01-2002 L2004 EM *020 †16

TOYNE, Susanne Marguerite. 111 W STONE DR, STE 120 37660 #045-01-1986 L1987 FM *020 †18

TUMKUR, Deepika A. 201 CASSELL DR 37660 #495-98-1999 L2006 **FM** *100 †18

TURNER, Harrison Douglas. 2050 MEADOWVIEW PKWY, CARDIOVASCULAR ASSOCIATES 37660 #047-05-1971 L1972 **CD NC** *020 †20 ‡

VAN DER WESTHUIZEN, Gert. 130 W RAVINE RD 37660 #836-03-1986 L2002 **NR** *020 †80,28

VAUGHN, Jeff Roland. 2204 PAVILION DR, STE 200 37660 #051-04-1985 L1987 **FM** *020 †18

VINCENT, Bruce Stewart. 177 W SEVIER AVE 37660 #011-04-1987 L1996 **FM** *020 †18

VU, Duc Qui. 2002 BROOKSIDE DR, STE 102 37660 #048-13-1987 L1992 **NEP IM** *020 †20

WADEWITZ, Peter. 1932 BROOKSIDE DR 37660 #041-02-1960 L1971 **U** *071 †95

WARD, Sameh Abou. 2020 BROOKSIDE DR, STE 21 37660 #915-04-1990 L1999 **APM AN** *020 †05

WARSY, Adil Kabir. 4 SHERIDAN SQ 37660 #704-08-1990 L2004 **IM** *020 †20

WATSON, Rodney Joe. 2212 N JOHN B DENNIS HWY 37660 #004-01-1982 L1995 **PD** *020 †55

WESTERFIELD, Larry Haynes. 130 W RAVINE RD 37660 #020-12-1967 L1977 **DR NM** *020 †80,28

WESTMORELAND, Dennis G. 2000 BROOKSIDE DR 37660 #047-06-1969 L1970 **OS** *071 †80

WHITE, J Johnny. 2204 PAVILION DR, STE 200 37660 #021-05-1984 L1985 **IM** *020 †20

WHITE, Judith Lorio. 2033 MEADOWVIEW LN, STE 200 37660 #021-05-1984 L1985 **IM** *020 †20

WHITE, Sean Patrick. 2002 BROOKSIDE DR, STE 300 37660 #036-08-1991 L2002 **OBG** *020 †30 ‡

WHITT, Hiram Jackson. ■ 37660 #051-01-1960 L1961 **GP** *071

WILCOXSON, Lesley Taylor. 1008 STAGSHAW LN 37660 #016-43-1988 L2002 **GS** *020 †85

WILLIAMS, Robert Herman. 1916 BROOKSIDE DR, BROOKSIDE MEDICAL CENTER 37660 #047-06-1967 L1967 **IM CD** *020 †20

WILLIAMS, Timothy Michael. 135 W RAVINE RD, STE 5-B 37660 #047-20-1986 L1989 **AN** *020 †05

WILLIAMS, William Turney. 2020 BROOKSIDE DR, STE 21 37660 #028-02-1979 L1988 **AN** *020 †05

WINDES, Lois Hildegarde. 2204 PAVILION DR, STE 212 37660 #035-45-1981 L1986 **FM** *020 †18

WINEGAR, James Bryston. 111 W STONE DR, STE 200 37660 #051-04-1978 L1981 **FM** *020 †18

WINSOR, Michael Jon. 914 BROAD ST 37660 #056-05-1971 L1975 **N** *071

WITHROW, Mark Lee. 2002 BROOKSIDE DR, STE 200 37660 #046-01-1991 L1994 **OBG** *020 †30

WRIGHT, Douglas Alan. 914 BROAD ST, STE 3A 37660 #038-40-1993 L2000 **N** *020 †75

WYKER, Arthur Townsend. 822 BROAD ST, UROLOGY ASSOCIATES OF 37660 #035-20-1977 L1982 **U** *020 †95

WYSOR, Michael Sanders. 5400 FORT HENRY DR, STE 10 MT CASTLE MED CARE 37663 #035-47-1992 L1994 **P** *020

YALLOURAKIS, Stephen J. 2008 BROOKSIDE DR, STE 201 37660 #047-05-1989 L1993 **FPS HNS** *020

YOST, Tony Edward. 4307 FORT HENRY DR STE B, A NEW IMAGE WEIGHT LOSS CL 37663 #047-20-1994 L1995 **EM FM** *020 †18 ‡

YOUNG-SIMPSON, Leigh Anne. 146 W PARK DR STE 9G 37660 #047-20-1990 L1996 **IM** *020 †20

ZAHNKE, Kim Patrick. 2000 BROOKSIDE DR 37660 #496-23-2002 L2005 **IM** *100 †20

ZEIGER, Curtis Nelson. 2012 BROOKSIDE DR, STE 8 37660 #048-12-1983 L1989 **N CN** *020

KINGSTON – ROANE

BEARD, Alice C Anderson. 136 E CUMBERLAND ST 37763 #004-01-1954 L1955 **PHP** *020

BODUCH, Thomas. 314 E SPRING ST 37763 #050-02-1979 L1982 **FM** *020

CUNNINGHAM, Elbert C. ■ 37763 #047-06-1959 L1959 **FM** *071 †18

DEWAR, Douglas Scott. 820 W RACE ST 37763 #038-40-1974 L1990 **FM EM** *020 †18

LADD, Hugh Evans. ■ 37763 #047-06-1938 L1938 **GPM OM** *071

REDMON, Eric Matthew. 143 BRADFORD VILLAGE WAY 37763 #036-05-1999 L2000 **FM** *020 †18

WILLETT, Dwight Haynes. 820 W RACE ST 37763 #047-06-1977 L1977 **GP** *020

WOODS, John Franklin. 900 WATERFORD PL 37763 #047-06-1971 L1972 **GP** *020

ZNIDER, John Frederick. 814 N KENTUCKY ST 37763 #005-15-1969 L1997 **ORS** *020 †40

KINGSTON SPRINGS – CHEATHAM

BROOKS, Arthur L. RTE S HARPETH RD 37082 #047-05-1952 L1952 **ORS OS** *071 †40

MC MAHAN, John Wellington. 1645 CRAGGIE HOPE RD 37082 #047-05-1964 L1965 **OPH** *020

MERRITT, Louise Clark. ■ 37082 #047-20-1994 L2002 **P** *020

KNOXVILLE – KNOX

AABY, Gene Victor. 9333 PARK WEST BLVD 37923 #005-12-1955 L1975 **TS** *071 †85,90

ABRAMS, Jeffrey Howard. 2018 W CLINCH AVE 37916 #016-06-1993 L2002 **PD PEM** *020 †55

ABU-HATAB, Mazen A. 8044 RAY MEARS BLVD # 116 37919 #584-01-1983 L1997 **NEP IM** *020 †20

ACKER, John Howard. 1940 ALCOA HWY, STE E310 37920 #047-06-1978 L1980 **CD** *020 †20

ACUFF, William Jos. 101 E BLOUNT AVE, STE 200 37920 #047-06-1956 L1964 **CRS** *071 †85

ADAMS, Arthur Franklin. 210 FORT SANDERS WEST BLVD 37922 #012-05-1983 L1987 **DR** *020 †80

ADAMS, Charles Edward, III. ■ 37923 #047-20-1989 L1990 **FM** *020 †18

ADAMS, David Graham. 1924 ALCOA HWY, STE U109 37920 #065-01-1977 L1984 **AN** *020 †05

ADAMS, George Andrew. ■ 37920 #047-06-2008 *012

ADAMS, John Stewart. 1915 WHITE AVE, KIDC KNOXVILLE INFECTIOUS 37916 #036-01-1981 L1988 **ID IM** *020 †20

ADAMS, Terry Lee. 10810 PARKSIDE DR STE 305 37934 #047-06-1981 L1981 **GS VS** *020 †85

ADDONIZIO, Steven James. 2001 LAUREL AVE, STE N304 37916 #047-06-1981 L1985 **DR** *020 †80

ADKINS, David Alan. 1120 E WEISGARBER RD, CONSULTANTS 37909 #020-12-1998 L2004 **PCC** *020

ADLER, Michael Bentley. 2001 LAUREL AVE N304, HERITAGE RADIOLOGY 37916 #035-15-1997 L2003 **DR** *020 †80

AGHEL, Essam M Nasar. 4042 SEQUOYAH AVE 37919 #613-02-1992 L2005 **EM IM** *020 †20

AHMED, Syed Mubashar. 2027 N BROADWAY ST 37917 #496-01-1990 L1997 **IM** *020 †20 ‡

AIKENS, Christopher H. 1112 E WEISGARBER RD, STE 201 37909 #047-06-1995 L2007 **DR** *020 †80

AINGE, George R. 2001 LAUREL AVE, STE N304 37916 #014-01-1984 L2006 **DR** *020 †80

AKERS, Donald L, Jr. ■ 37922 #047-06-1984 L1985 **VS GS** *020 †85

AKHTAR, Syed Mohammad R. 1930 ALCOA HWY, PEDIATRIC CONSULTANTS INC 37920 #704-02-1988 L1997 **PD** *020 †55

AKIN, Hobart Earl. 1924 ALCOA HWY, BOX U11 37920 #047-06-1975 L1976 **GS** *020 †85

ALEXANDER, Andrea Mariah. ■ 37923 #001-02-2007 **GS** *012

ALEXANDER, James Sidney. 9111 CROSS PARK DR, STE D200 37923 #047-06-1984 L1987 **P** *020 †75

ALEXANDER, Pierce Cooper. 1225 E WEISGARBER RD, GROUP SUITE 200 37909 #047-06-1988 L1991 **IM FM** *020 †20

ALI, Yaqub. 2001 LAUREL AVE STE 202 37916 #495-51-1986 L2000 **NEP** *020 †20

AL KHOURY, Salwa Fahed. 1400 DUTCH VALLEY DR, CHILDRENS PRIMARY CARE CEN 37918 #875-01-1990 L2001 **PD** *020 †55

ALLAN, J Davis, Jr. 930 E EMERALD AVE, ASSOCIATES 37917 #016-02-1979 L1994 **ID IM** *020 †20

ALLEN, Amber Janelle. 1431 CENTERPOINT BLVD 37932 #027-01-2000 L2008 **EM** *020 †16

ALLEN, Anton M, Jr. 1924 ALCOA HWY 37920 #051-04-1981 L1994 **R** *020 †80

ALLEN, Deborah Jeanne. 11808 KINGSTON PIKE, FARRAGUT 37934 #051-04-1981 L1994 **IM** *020 †20

ALLEN, Jonathon Christoph. 1901 W CLINCH AVE 37916 #017-20-2004 L2007 **EM** *020 †20

ALLEN, Robert Brock. 1900 N WINSTON RD STE 300, C/O TEAM HELTH 37919 #004-01-1983 L2003 **FM** *020 †18

ALLEY, James Stephen. 10810 PARKSIDE DR, STE 305 37934 #047-06-1982 L1982 **IM** *020 †20 ‡

ALLEY, Robert Curtis. 930 E EMERALD AVE, ASSOCIATES 37917 #047-20-1986 L1990 **IM** *020 †20

ALLSOP, Bruce Neal. 220 FORT SANDERS WEST BLVD, STE 101 37922 #047-06-1987 L1990 **FM** *020 †18

ALLUM, Kenneth M, III. 1704 JOHNNY MAJORS DR 37996 #047-06-1998 L1999 **FSM** *020 †18

AL-MUQBEL, Kusai Marouf. ■ 37923 #875-01-1995 L2001 **NM** *100 †20,28

ALSHARIF, Samar Mohamed. 1924 ALCOA HWY 37920 #047-06-2002 L2004 **IM** *020 †20

AL-TAWIL, Youhanna Said. 2100 W CLINCH AVE, STE 510 37916 #875-01-1984 L2001 **PG PD** *020 †55

ALTERMAN, Daniel Mark. ■ 37912 #036-08-2005 **GS** *012

AMBROSE, Paul Seabrook. 9349 PARK WEST BLVD, STE 105 37923 #047-05-1970 L1970 **OPH** *020 †35

AMBROSIA, John. 1704 JOHNNY MAJORS DR 37996 #016-43-1980 L1986 **HS** *020 †40

AMORTEGUI GONZALEZ, Jose. 1924 ALCOA HWY, UNIV TN GRAD SCH OF MED 37920 #264-16-1997 **GS** *012

ANDERSON, Alan Eldon. 2100 W CLINCH AVE STE 430, SURGERY GROUP, PLLC 37916 #038-41-1966 L1986 **PDS GS** *020 †55,85

ANDERSON, Elizabeth Wiser. 6311 KINGSTON PIKE, STE 2100E 37919 #047-06-1999 L2005 **DMP** *020 †15

ANDERSON, Ilse Janell. 1930 ALCOA HWY STE 435, UT GENETICS UT MEDICAL CEN 37920 #035-09-1985 L1991 **CG PD** *020 †19,55

ANDERSON, Mark Donald. 1928 ALCOA HWY, STE 100B 37920 #047-05-1984 L1989 **GE IM** *020 †20

ANDERSON, Mark Eugene. 1930 ALCOA HWY, STE 145 37920 #016-11-1981 L1986 **NPM** *020 †55

ANDERSON, Nicholas Gray. 1124 E WEISGARBER RD # 207, SOUTHEASTERN RETINA ASSOC. 37909 #047-06-1999 L2005 **OPH** *020 †35

ANDERSON, Thomas Irving. 2060 LAKESIDE CENTRE WAY, NORTHSHORE 37922 #025-07-1973 L1974 **FM** *020 †18

ANDREW, Samuel Edwards. 324 DOMINION CIR 37934 #047-06-1940 L1941 **EM GS** *071 †85

ANDREWS, Edmund B. PO BOX 6837 37914 #025-01-1953 L1961 **PS** *020 †65

ANDREWS, Ellen. 2018 W CLINCH AVE, KNOXVILLE NEONATAL ASSOCIA 37916 #047-07-1985 L1985 **NPM PD** *020 †55

ANDREWS, George Andreas. 1420 CENTERPOINT BLVD 37932 #035-47-1978 L2003 **CD IM** *030 †20 ‡

ANGE, Charles Gilmer. 1928 ALCOA HWY, STE 324 37920 #036-05-1967 L1973 **OPH** *020 †35

ANGE, David Westley. 900 E OAK HILL AVE 37917 #036-01-1968 L1975 **RO** *071 †80

ANGEL, Carlos Alberto. 2100 W CLINCH AVE, STE 430 37916 #264-10-1980 L2006 **PDS PD** *020

ANGEL, Cathryn. 1323 SALUDA RD 37922 #026-04-1988 L2004 **NPM** *020 †55

ANNAND, David W. 140 CAPITOL DR, ALLIANCE OF EAST 37922 #036-05-1982 L1989 **AN** *020 †05

ANTONUCCI, Richard Angelo. 726 HAMPTON ROADS DR 37934 #035-47-1980 L1986 **ON HEM** *020 †20

APOSTOAEI, Daniela. ■ 37922 #781-01-1990 L2002 **AN** *020 †05

ARJONA, Jose Luis. 1431 CENTERPOINT BLVD #100, TEAM HLTH TELERDLGY 37932 #042-03-1984 L1986 **DR PD** *020 †80

ARMFIELD, Richard Locke. 140 CAPITOL DR, ALLIANCE OF EAST 37922 #024-01-1989 L1998 **AN** *020 †05

ARNETT, John D, III. 10810 PARKSIDE DR, CONSULTANTS PC 37934 #047-07-1983 L1983 **CD** *020 †20

ARNOLD, Sara Lynn. 137 E BLOUNT AVE 37920 #040-02-1999 L2003 **AN** *020 †05 ‡

ARTAR, Ali Onur. 9947 SMOKEY RIDGE WAY 37931 #902-03-1986 L2005 **CHP** *020 †75

ARWOOD, Don Calvin. 1915 WHITE AVE, RADIATION ONCOLOGY DEPARTM 37916 #047-20-1984 L1988 **RO** *071 †80

ARWOOD, Jana Michel. 4905 GUINN RD 37931 #047-20-1984 L1988 **P** *020 †75

AVERY, Bebe Anne Bass. 5810 KINGSTON PIKE 37919 #047-06-1955 L1960 **GYN** *071

AVERY, Robert Bruce. 1114 E WEISGARBER RD STE A 37909 #047-06-1962 L1962 **HO HEM** *020 †20

AVERY, Shirley Bannister. 1114 E WEISGARBER RD, STE A 37909 #047-06-1962 L1963 **A** *071 †55,03

AYCINENA GOICOLEA, Jose F. 1924 ALCOA HWY 37920 #429-02-2002 **GS** *012

AYO, Raye-Anne B. 116 CONCORD RD, STE 100 37934 #021-05-2001 L2002 **FM** *020 †18

AZZAZY, Hossam Salah. ■ 37934 #047-06-2002 L2006 **PTH** *100

BADDOUR, George Robt, Jr. 11440 PARKSIDE DR, STE 110 37934 #047-06-1978 L1979 **ORS** *020 †40

BAGLEY, Warren Poore. 1924 ALCOA HWY, STE U109 37920 #048-13-1977 L1989 **AN OTO** *020 †05

BAILEY, William Kevin. 112 HOTEL RD 37918 #047-06-1986 L1990 **PM** *020 †60

BAINS, Jujhar Singh. 1924 ALCOA HWY, UT. GRADUATE SCHOOL OF MED 37920 #038-41-2005 **IM** *100

BAIRD, Michael Allen. 501 20TH ST, STE 606 37916 #047-06-1986 L1990 **AN** *020 †05

BAKER, Brooke Leigh. ■ 37921 #021-06-2006 L2007 **GS** *100

BAKER, Daniel Austin. 930 E EMERALD AVE, STE 512 37917 #047-06-2001 L2006 **DR** *100 †80

BAKER, Evelynn Ruth. 100 TECH CENTER DR, PEDIATRIC CONSULTANTS INC 37912 #001-02-1998 L2001 **PD** *020 †55

BAKER, James Wm. 101 E BLOUNT AVE, BAPTIST MED TWR STE 200 37920 #038-41-1982 L1989 **CRS** *020 †85,10

BAKER, Kelly Lynn. 501 20TH ST, FORT SANDERS 37916 #047-20-1997 L2000 **FM** *020 †18

BAKER, Leslie Katherine. 1932 ALCOA HWY, STE 160 37920 #047-06-1992 L1997 **OTO** †45

BAKER, Martin Ross, Jr. 7671 N SHORE DR 37919 #047-06-1960 L1965 **ORS** *071 †40

BAKER, Paul Douglas. 140 CAPITOL DR, ALLIANCE OF EAST 37922 #017-20-1972 L1983 **AN** *020 †05

BAKER, Tammy Ewayne. 2013 HIGHLAND AVE 37916 #020-12-1989 L1992 **OBG** *020 †30

BALDRIDGE, Ruth Ellen. 1924 ALCOA HWY, STE U67 37920 #055-02-1992 L1995 **FM** *040 †18

BALDWIN, Shawn Allan. 101 E BLOUNT AVE, CONSULTANTS PC 37920 #048-13-2000 L2007 **ICE** *020 †20

BANICK, Paul David. 200 E BLOUNT AVE, STE 200 37920 #010-02-1989 L1997 **PUD CCM** *020 †20

BANKSTON, Floyd N. ■ 37919 #047-06-1945 L1945 **OBG OS** *071 †30

BARBEE, Jacob Paul. 1924 ALCOA HWY, SCH OF 37920 #422-01-2004 **FP** *012

BARBER, Joseph Richard. 1924 ALCOA HWY, BOX U109 37920 #036-05-2006 **AN** *012

BARD, Calvin M. 11440 PARKSIDE DR, STE 302 37934 #048-12-1991 L1996 **IM** *020 †20

BARKER, Rachel Marguerite. 1924 ALCOA HWY, SCH OF 37920 #045-01-2003 L2003 **DR** *012

BARKER, Rosanne S. 1368 PAPERMILL POINTE WAY 37909 #047-20-1981 L1986 **SME** *020

BARNES, Kristy Lee. 1928 ALCOA HWY STE 2 37920 #047-06-1998 L2003 **IM P** *020 †20,75

BARNES, Norman Alan. 626 BERNARD AVE, DRD KNOXVILLE MEDICAL CLIN 37921 #047-06-1972 L1973 **GP EM** *020

BARNES, Robert Luther. 11416 GRIGSBY CHAPEL RD, STE 104 37934 #036-01-1972 L1975 **PD** *020 †55

BARNETT, Charles Franklin. 2160 LAKESIDE CENTRE WAY, STE 250 37922 #047-06-1975 L1976 **IM CMG** *050 †20

BAROCAS, Morris. 10810 PARKSIDE DR, STE 306 37934 #035-08-1982 L2002 **GE IM** *020 †20

BARRETT, Lynn. 930 E EMERALD AVE, STE 512 37917 #036-07-1984 L1989 **DR** *020 †80

BARRON, Freddie Thos. 9352 PARK WEST BLVD 37923 #047-06-1975 L1976 **PS GS** *020 †85,65

BARRON, Marjorie B. OAK HILL AVE, ST MARYS HOSP ER 37917 #027-01-1980 L1986 **EM** *020 †16

BARRON, Stephen Thos. 4117 E EMORY RD, STE 6011 37938 #004-01-1977 L1978 **FM** *020 †18

BARROW, Brent Alan. 2001 LAUREL AVE, STE N304 37916 #047-06-1990 L1995 **VIR** *020 †80

BARTENFELD, Emily Anne. ■ 37918 #012-01-2008 *012

BASILE, Phanel. 1900 N WINSTON RD STE 603 37919 #440-01-1976 L1983 **IM** *020

BASS, Ellen Sofia. 7150 SIR ARTHUR WAY, 601 ELMWOOD AVENUE 37919 #010-02-1992 L2006 **PD** *020 †55

BASS, James Kirk. 1930 ALCOA HWY, STE 145 37920 #045-04-2000 L2007 **NPM** *100 †55 ‡

BATCHELOR, Douglas M. ■ 37922 #047-06-1979 L1980 **EM FM** *020 †18,16

BATT, Margaret Anne. 9352 PARK WEST BLVD 37923 #046-01-1991 L1993 **PTH** *020 †50

BEALS, David H. 1120 E WEISGARBER RD, STE 104 37909 #051-04-1981 L1982 **PUD CCM** *020 †20

BEAMER, Wilson Carter. 501 20TH ST STE 606 37916 #051-04-1978 L1985 **AN EM** *020 †16,05

BEASLEY, Alfred Durant. 1924 ALCOA HWY # U-28 37920 #047-06-1959 L1959 **IM CD** *072 †20

BEAVER, Mary-Es Anderson. 930 E EMERALD AVE, STE 720 37917 #048-14-1995 L2005 **OTO** *020 †45

BEAVER, Richard Leigh. 1932 ALCOA HWY, STE 360 37920 #048-14-1997 L2005 **ORS** *020 †40

BECKER, Paul Lawrence. 1704 JOHNNY MAJORS DR 37996 #047-06-1994 L1999 **OSM** *020 †40

BECKER, Stephanie Smith. 9330 PARK WEST BLVD, STE 402 37923 #047-06-1996 L1999 **IM** *020 †20

BECKER, Stephen Mayes. 120 SUBURBAN RD, STE 102 37923 #047-05-1974 L2006 **FM** *020 †18

BEELER, Thomas Craig. 1704 JOHNNY MAJORS DR 37996 #047-06-1975 L1975 **ORS** *020 †40

BELL, James Bowers. 137 E BLOUNT AVE 37920 #047-06-1961 L1961 **FM** *071 †18

BELL, John Lawrence. 1934 ALCOA HWY, MEDICAL BUILDING D STE #4 37920 #001-02-1980 L1988 **GS OS** *020 †85

BELLINGRATH, Leonard, Jr. 2060 LAKESIDE CENTRE WAY, NORTHSHORE 37922 #004-01-1984 L1984 TW 7022 *020 †18

BELLNER, Lisa A. 9352 PARK WEST BLVD 37923 #035-46-1989 L2001 **PM** *020 †60

BELT, Robert. 1440 KNIGHTSBRIDGE DR, P O BOX 10228 37922 #048-02-1990 L2000 **ICE** *020 †20

BENEDICT, Walter Hanford. 137 E BLOUNT AVE 37920 #025-01-1946 L1952 **OPH** *071 †35

BENHAYON, Jack. 939 EMERALD AVE, STE 610 37917 #041-14-1976 L1981 **NEP IM** *020 †20 ‡

BENITEZ, Juan. 9349 PARK WEST BLVD, STE 101 37923 #042-01-1982 L2003 **IM** *020 †20

BENNETT, Camilla Collins. 200 FORT SANDERS WEST BLVD, MOB 1, SUITE 107 37922 #026-04-1989 L1995 **FM** *020 †20

BENNETT, Freddie James. 2908 TAZEWELL PIKE, STE A 37918 #025-07-1983 L1995 **FM** *020 ‡

BENTLEY, Amy Elizabeth. 930 E EMERALD AVE, ASSOCIATES 37917 #047-06-1993 L1995 **MPD** *020 †55,20

BENTON, James Carl. 4741 BROADWAY ST 37918 #047-06-1959 L1965 **PD** *071

BERGIA, Berta M. 9333 PARK WEST BLVD, STE 108 37923 #847-04-1981 L1987 **N OS** *020 †75 ‡

BERMAN, Barry Scott. 1451 DOWELL SPRINGS BLVD 37909 #011-04-1988 L2007 **ON HEM** *020 †20

BERNARD, Michael Prentice. 200 E BLOUNT AVE, STE 101 37920 #048-12-1993 L1996 **IM** *020 †20

BERTOLI, Carol L. 1928 ALCOA HWY, PHYS OFFICE BLDG 1 37920 #041-09-1981 L1993 **DR** *020 †80

BESOZZI, Myrwood Chas. 1940 ALCOA HWY, STE E310 37920 #011-02-1970 L1986 **CD IM** *050 †20,28

BETCHER, Russell Anderson. 1704 JOHNNY MAJORS DR 37996 #027-01-1992 L1997 **ORS** *020 †40 ‡

BEUERLEIN, Frank Joseph. 501 20TH ST, STE G3 37916 #047-06-1987 L1987 **PTH PCP** *020 †50

BEUERLEIN, John Thomas. 1924 ALCOA HWY, KNOXVILLE INPATIENT PHYSIC 37920 #047-06-1995 L1999 **MPD HOS** *020 †20,55 ‡

BEVAN, Charles Albert, III. ■ 37923 #045-04-2007 **TY** *012

BEVELHIMER, Ann Stuart. 3114 ALCOA HWY, LAKEMOOR FAMILY PHYS 37920 #038-45-1984 L1985 **FM** *020 †18

BHANDARI, Ashok. 200 E BLOUNT AVE STE 504 37920 #495-45-1981 L1997 **IM** *020 †20

BHANDARI, Punam. 200 FORT SANDERS WEST BLVD, M O B # 1 SUITE 304 37922 #495-53-1982 L1997 **IM** *020 †20

BIDAWID, Helen Susan. 1900 N WINSTON RD, STE 300 37919 #654-01-1988 L1998 **FM** *020 †18

BIELAK, Kenneth Michael. 1924 ALCOA HWY 37920 #025-12-1986 L1993 **FM FSM** *040 †18

BIGGS, Monte Bruce. 1932 ALCOA HWY, STE 570 37920 #047-06-1966 L1966 **IM** *020

BILBREY, Brett Shannon. 4117 E EMORY RD 37938 #047-20-2001 L2003 **FM** *020 †18

BINDRIM, Steven John. 11440 PARKSIDE DR 37934 #035-09-1988 L2005 **GE** *020 †20

BING, Paul Daniel. ■ 37909 #047-06-1998 L1999 **IM** *020 †20

BIRDWELL, David Allen. 501 20TH ST STE G3 37916 #047-06-1969 L1969 **CLP PP** *020 †50

BISHOFBERGER, Thomas Edwi. ■ 37918 #654-01-2002 L2006 **GS** *100

BISHOP, Archer W, Jr. 501 19TH ST, STE 600 37916 #047-06-1968 L1968 **ORS** *071 †40

BISHOP, Harry Louis. 101 E BLOUNT AVE, CONSULTANTS PC 37920 #035-47-1976 L1981 **CD IM** *020 †20

BISHOP, Jan. 332 RUSSFIELD DR 37934 #041-01-1978 L1991 **PE** *020 †55

BIVINS, Jeremiah Nathanie. ■ 37922 #047-06-2008 *012

BLACHE, Natalie Louise. ■ 37921 #021-05-2005 **OBG** *012

BLACK, Joe W. 4741 N BROADWAY ST, DRS BLACK & BENTON PSC 37918 #047-06-1984 L1987 **PD** *020 †55

BLACK, Joe Wm, Jr. 4005 FOUNTAIN VALLEY DR 37918 #047-06-1957 L1958 **PD** *071 †55

BLACK, Monica L Field. 4741 BROADWAY ST 37918 #047-06-1984 L1987 **PD** *020 †55

BLACK, Paul Clifford. 1924 ALCOA HWY U-67, UNIV OF TENNESSEE GRADUATE 37920 #654-01-2005 **FP** *012

BLACK, William Donald. 939 EMERALD AVE, STE 610 37917 #047-06-1967 L1968 **NEP IM** *020 †20

BLACK, William John. 9050 EXECUTIVE PARK DR C 37923 #561-07-1982 L1984 **OM IM** *020 †20,70 ‡

BLACK, William Lawrence. 9355 PARK WEST BLVD 37923 #036-01-1960 L1980 **CD IM** *071

BLACKY, Albert Robt. 9330 PARK WEST BLVD, CONSULTANTS PC 37923 #040-02-1981 L1996 **CD IM** *020 †20

BLAINE, Robert A, Sr. 1900 N WINSTON RD, SOUTHEASTERN EMER PHYS 37919 #047-06-1982 L1983 **EM** *020 †16

BLAIR, Kelly Samuel. 1608 SAINT PETERSBURG RD 37922 #016-01-1994 L1997 **VS** *020 †85

BLAKE, Gregory Harold. 1924 ALCOA HWY, STE U67 37920 #048-12-1977 L1999 **FM** *030 †18

BLAKE, Hu Al. 1924 ALCOA HWY 37920 #041-02-1946 L1957 **TS GS** *071 †85,90

BLAKE, John R, Jr. 4306 ASHEVILLE HWY 37914 #047-20-1984 L1985 **FM** *020 †18

BLAKE, Lynn French. 1601 AILOR AVE, MEDIC REGIONAL BLOOD CTR 37921 #047-06-1958 L1958 **PTH BBK** *030 †50

BLAKE, Michael C. 2018 W CLINCH AVE 37916 #036-01-1993 L1997 **PHO** *020 †55

BLAKELEY, Russell Reed. 900 E OAK HILL AVE, CONSULTANTS PC 37917 #048-13-1982 L1985 **CD IM** *020 †20

BLAKEMORE, Nadia Michelle. ■ 37918 #047-06-2007 L2007 **AN** *012

BLEVINS, Cameron Terrill. 11416 GRIGSBY CHAPEL RD, STE 104 37934 #001-02-1995 L1998 **PD** *020 †55

BLOSSOM, Gerald Lee. 12005 BUTTERNUT LN 37934 #017-20-1970 L1980 **PEM PD** *020 †55

BLUE, Melinda Huey. 210 FORT SANDERS WEST BLVD 37922 #047-06-1985 L1987 **DR** *020 †80

BODENHEIMER, Marc Alan. 2020 KAY ST 37920 #028-02-1994 L1996 **OPH** *020 †35

BOGGAN, Kelly Hicks. 140 DAMERON AVE 37921 #047-01-1990 L1993 **PD** *020 †20

BOGGS, Kimberley Still. 401 CATHERINE MCAULEY WAY, STE 5212 37919 #051-04-1980 L1984 **PD** *020

BOLIN, William Rogers. 12837 LEBEL RD 37934 #047-06-1978 L1979 **IM** *020 †20

BONET AYENDEZ, Miguel A. ■ 37922 #847-02-1970 L1973 **P** *020

BONNYMAN, Brian Andrew. 9625 KROGER PARK DR, STE 500 37922 #012-05-1990 L1993 **FM** *020 †18

BOPPANA, Srinivas. 900 E OAK HILL AVE, DEPT RADIATION ONCOLOGY 37917 #055-02-1997 L2003 **RO** *020 †80

BORRELLI, G Scott. 2001 LAUREL AVE, STE 206 37916 #051-04-1993 L1999 **NEP** *020 †20

BORUFF, Jeffrey Scott. 9330 PARK WEST BLVD, STE 402 37923 #047-06-1994 L1997 **IM** *020 †20

BOUCHILLON, Samuel Keith. ■ 37923 #047-06-1973 L1974 **AN** *075

BOYCE, Stephen Glenn. 200 FORT SANDERS WEST BLVD, BLDG 1 37922 #048-12-1987 L1992 **GS** *020 †85

BOYER, Richard P. 501 19TH ST, STE 607 37916 #048-13-1992 L1998 **NS** *020 †25

BRABSON, Leonard Allison. 1924 ALCOA HWY 37920 #047-06-1973 L1973 **OBG** *020 †30

BRADLEY, Stephanie. ■ 37921 #036-08-2003 L2003 **GS** *012

BRADSHER, Jacob T, Jr. ■ 37917 #036-07-1944 L1953 **TS** *071 †85

BRAILEY, Richard F. 1901 W CLINCH AVE 37916 #038-06-1954 L1957 **AN** *071 †05

BRAKEBILL, Larry Chas. 930 E EMERALD AVE, ASSOCIATES 37917 #047-06-1984 L1984 **IM** *020 †20

BRAKOVEC, Joseph Warren. ■ 37933 #028-34-1959 L1959 **GS** *071 †85

BRANCA, Paul Richard. 1940 ALCOA HWY, STE E210 37920 #011-02-1994 L1997 **PCC** *020 †20

BRANDON, Miriam Waters. 930 E EMERALD AVE, ASSOCIATES 37917 #047-06-2000 L2002 **IM** *020 †20

BRANDT, Kurt Fredrick. 9017 CROSS PARK DR, STE 200 37923 #051-04-1984 L1993 **PD** *020 †20

BRANSON, Aubra David. BLOUNT PROFESSIONAL BLDG 37920 #047-06-1956 L1957 **U** *071 †95

BREAZEALE, Earl E, Jr. 2068 LAKESIDE CENTRE WAY 37922 #047-06-1990 L1995 **PS** *020 †85,65

BREAZEALE, Richard Ion. 1124 E WEISGARBER RD, STE 207 37909 #047-06-1994 L1999 **OPH** *020 †35

BREMER, Richard Louis, II. 211 E BLOUNT AVE STE 507 37920 #035-06-1998 L2004 **IM** *020 †20

BREMER, Yvonne. 2100 W CLINCH AVE, STE 210 37916 #035-06-1998 L2004 **PDC** *020 †55

BRESEE, Stuart James. 1940 ALCOA HWY, STE E310 37920 #012-05-1982 L1985 **CD** *020 †20

BREWER, Gregory Vaughn. 10810 PARKSIDE DR, CONSULTANTS PC 37934 #048-13-1986 L1993 **CD** *020 †20

BRICE, Scott Workman. 2201 W CLINCH AVE 37916 #045-04-1998 L2006 **PD** *020 †55

BRIDGES, Arnold D, Jr. 1900 N WINSTON RD, STE 300 37919 #027-01-1983 L1989 **EM IM** *020 †20

BRIDGES, Matthew David. 101 E BLOUNT AVE STE 65 37920 #041-09-1995 L2002 **GS** *020 †85

BRIDGES, William Scott. 939 EMERALD AVE, STE 901 37917 #020-12-1991 L1995 **N** *020 †75

BRIG, Raymond. 101 E BLOUNT AVE STE 610 37920 #035-09-1987 L1993 **HO** *020 †20

BRIGGS, Richard Miller. 101 E BLOUNT AVE, STE 800 37920 #020-12-1978 L1992 **CD TS** *020 †85,90

■ = Address Information Privacy Protected

BRINKMANN, Jennifer Hodge. 9625 KROGER PARK DR, SHORE MEDICAL PLAZA 37922 #047-06-1999 L2001 **MPD** *020 †20

BRINKMANN, Kevin Carl. 2018 W CLINCH AVE, EAST TENNESSEE CHILD HOSP 37916 #047-06-1998 L2000 **CCP** *020 †55

BRINNER, Richard Allan. 501 19TH ST, STE 501 37916 #021-01-1973 L1979 **GS VS** *020 †85

BRITT, James C. 210 FORT SANDERS WEST BLVD 37922 #027-01-1967 L1973 **DR** *071 †80

BROADY, Joseph Leroy. 137 E BLOUNT AVE 37920 #047-06-1964 L1964 **PTH GP** *020 †50

BROADY, Roy Cox. 501 19TH ST, STE 701 37916 #047-06-1993 L1997 **OBG** *020 †30

BROCK, Karen Reno. 433 SEVIER AVE, STE 109 37920 #045-01-1980 L1989 **DR** *020 †80

BRODELL, George Kline. 501 20TH ST, STE 601 37916 #038-06-1984 L2005 **CD IM** *020 †20

BROOKSBANK, Roger Alan. 1431 CENTERPOINT BLVD, STE 100 37932 #047-06-1988 L1989 **EM** *020 †18

BROOME, Monroe Alan. 10820 PARKSIDE DR 37934 #047-06-1983 L1984 **DR IM** *020 †80

BROOME, William Smith, III. 4410 VALLEY VIEW DR 37917 #047-06-1981 L1982 **FM** *020 †18

BROTT, Walter Howard. 1928 ALCOA HWY, PRO F #300 37920 #019-02-1959 L1982 **TS** *020 †85,90

BROUSSARD, Jeffrey Kent. 140 CAPITOL DR, ALLIANCE OF EAST 37922 #021-05-1994 L1995 **AN** *020 †05

BROWDER, Joe H, II. 220 FORT SANDERS WEST BLVD, STE 308 37922 #047-06-1982 L1982 **PME** *020 †05

BROWDER, John Franklin. 1928 ALCOA HWY, PHYS OFC BLDG 1 STE 209 37920 #047-06-1989 L1994 **D** *020

BROWN, Gary Kenna. 1900 N WINSTON RD STE 300, C/O SEP-LEZLIE RANEY 37919 #422-01-1997 L2000 **PD** *020 †55

BROWN, Jeffrey Brent. 9330 PARK WEST BLVD, STE 302 37923 #047-06-1990 L1992 **OBG** *020 †30

BROWN, Jeffrey Ian. 2001 LAUREL AVE, STE N603 37916 #038-43-1981 L1988 **GE IM** *020 †20

BROWN, Leonard Wilkins. 11201 W POINT DR, STE 103 37934 #047-06-1980 L1984 **OTO HNS** *020 †45

BROWN, Lytle, IV. 9430 PARK WEST BLVD, STE 310 37923 #047-06-1981 L1982 **GS** *020 †85

BRUMIT, James Mark. 2001 LAUREL AVE, STE N304 37916 #047-20-1997 L2003 **VIR** *020 †80

BRUNER, Joseph Paul. 501 19TH ST, STE 304 37916 #030-05-1979 L1990 **OBG MFM** *020 †30

BRUNSON, Michael Dean. 1120 E WEISGARBER RD, CONSULTANTS 37909 #047-06-1992 L1995 **PUD IM** *020

BRYAN, Ronald Wm. 9330 PARK WEST BLVD, STE 103 37923 #037-01-1977 L1981 **N** *020

BUCHANAN, James Kevin. 11201 W POINT DR, STE 102 37934 #047-20-1994 L1996 **FM** *020 †18

BUCHANAN, Martha Lynn. 140 DAMERON AVE 37917 #047-20-1993 L1996 **FM** *020 †18

BUCHHEIT, John Q, IV. 2018 W CLINCH AVE, KNOXVILLE NEONATAL ASSOC. 37916 #047-06-1988 L1994 **NPM** *020 †55

BUCKINGHAM, Lisa Caroline. ■ 37923 #047-06-2006 **OBG** *012

BUFKIN, Bradley L. 9314 PARK WEST BLVD, STE 302 37923 #048-04-1990 L1999 **TS** *020 †90,85

BULLEN, Gurpreet Dhindsa. 1124 E WEISGARBER RD, STE 200 37909 #047-20-1990 L1994 **PD** *020 †55

BULLEN, Michael Edward. 10810 PARKSIDE DR, STE 100 37934 #047-20-1990 L1994 **OBG** *020 †30

BUONOCORE, Edward. 1924 ALCOA HWY, DEPT RADIOL UNIV TENN MED 37920 #035-08-1956 L1966 **R AN** *071 †80

BURGIN, James Berry. 11130 KINGSTON PIKE, STE 1-167 37934 #047-06-1978 L1979 **IM** *020 †20

BURKHART, James M. 2001 LAUREL AVE, STE 601 37916 #047-06-1958 L1960 **ORS HS** *020 †40

BURKHART, John Mclain. 900 E OAK HILL AVE 37917 #047-06-1974 L1974 **FM** *071 †18

BURKHART, William Lindsey. 103 MIDLAKE DR, PHYSICIANS 37918 #047-06-1982 L1983 **FM** *020 †18 ‡

BURNETTE, Tara Moulton. 1924 ALCOA HWY U-113, UNIV OF TN MEDICAL CTR 37920 #047-06-1983 L1986 **NPM PD** *020 †55

BURNHAM, Cynthia Leigh. ■ 37922 #047-06-2004 **GS** *012

BURNS, Edward B, Jr. 501 19TH ST, STE 600 37916 #051-04-1980 L1989 **ORS HS** *020 †40

BURNS, James Luther, Jr. 324 N PARK 40 BLVD, OF EAST TENNESSEE 37923 #047-06-1981 L1981 **RHU IM** *020 †20

BURNS, Jodi Ann. ■ 37918 #028-34-2007 **OBG** *012

BURNSIDE, Sharon Renee. 6906 KINGSTON PIKE STE 200 37919 #020-02-1992 L1996 **P** *020 †75

BUSHKELL, Lawrence Lee. 200 FORT SANDERS WEST BLVD, BLDG 1 37922 #017-20-1970 L1981 **D DMP** *020 †15 ‡

BUSHORE, John Thos. 7211 WELLINGTON DR, DEANE HILL 37919 #047-06-1970 L1971 **FM** *020 †18

BUSTAMANTE, Danl Richard. 1924 ALCOA HWY, STE U109 37920 #047-06-1986 L1987 **AN** *020 †05

BUTCHER, M Bain. 8350 KINGSTON PIKE 37919 #038-41-1995 L2005 **FM** *020 †18

BUTLER, Kelly Marie. ■ 37919 #051-01-1998 L2000 **PE** *020 †55

BYRD, Ricky Ray. 3403 TAZEWELL PIKE, STE 102 37918 #047-20-1997 L1998 **IM** *020

BYRD, Shannon Lyn. 1120 E WEISGARBER RD, CONSULTANTS 37909 #021-01-1992 L1998 **CCM** *020 †20

BYRD, William Geo. 4529 ASHEVILLE HWY 37914 #047-06-1954 L1954 **PD** *071 †55

CABRERA, Anthony. 1924 ALCOA HWY, BOX 56 37920 #748-02-1992 L2006 **IM** *020 †20

CADIGAN, Rosalind M. 9330 PARK WEST BLVD # 502, OB/GYN PROF OF EAST TN PC 37923 #063-01-1996 L1997 **OBG** *020 †30

CALHOUN, Douglas Newton. 1704 JOHNNY MAJORS DR 37996 #047-06-1999 L2001 **HS** *020 †40

CAMERON, Jason Robert. 930 E EMERALD AVE, STE 512 37917 #047-07-1999 L2001 **VIR** *020 †80

CAMERON, Katherine Medley. 9330 PARK WEST BLVD 37923 #047-06-2002 L2007 **U** *020

CAMPBELL, John E, Jr. 1124 E WEISGARBER RD # 100 37909 #047-06-1946 L1947 **OPH** *071 †55

CAMPBELL, Keith Earl. 11440 PARKSIDE DR, STE 205 37934 #047-20-1996 L2003 **FM** *020 †18

CAMPBELL, Kevin Sean. 7503 N SHORE DR 37919 #047-06-1999 L2002 **FM** *020 †18

CAMPBELL, Lori Margaret. ■ 37930 #014-01-1983 L1989 **FM** *020 †18

CAMPBELL, Mary Palmer. 2018 W CLINCH AVE 37916 #047-06-1986 L1990 **PD** *020 †55

CAMPBELL, Morris Dean. 2001 LAUREL AVE STE 105 37916 #020-12-1973 L1973 **GYN** *020 †30

CAMPBELL, Peter Jos. 1450 DOWELL SPRINGS BLVD 37909 #917-26-1977 L1987 **END** *020 †20

CAMPBELL, Willard Brandt. 4713 PAPERMILL DR, STE 100 37909 #012-05-1987 L1992 **GS VS** *020 †85

CAPPS, Robert James. 4707 PAPERMILL DR, STE 200 37909 #028-02-1978 L1983 **RHU** *020 †20

CARDENAS, Rodolfo Mario. 1900 N WINSTON RD STE 60 37919 #649-14-1981 L2004 **IM** *020

CARDER, John Randolph. 2018 W CLINCH AVE, EAST TENNESEE CHILDREN'S H 37916 #051-04-1991 L1998 **PD** *020 †55

CARLSON, Carl Sanford, Jr. 501 19TH ST, STE 600 37916 #047-06-1975 L1976 **ORS** *020 †40

CARLSON, Eric R. 1930 ALCOA HWY STE 335, UNIV OF TENN MED CTR-OMFS 37920 #011-02-2000 L2004 **OMF HNS** *040

CARPENTER, Corey Micah. 3817 MARINA VIEW LN, HOME 37920 #012-01-2004 L2008 **AN** *012

CARPENTER, Kenneth B. 9352 PARK WEST BLVD 37923 #047-06-1960 L1961 **P OS** *071 †75

CARRINGER, Michael Wallin. 1924 ALCOA HWY, SCH OF 37920 #654-01-2006 **IM** *012

CARROLL, John D. 2587 WILLOW POINT WAY 37931 #654-01-2001 L2004 **IM** *020

CARTER, Christopher G. 1900 N WINSTON RD, STE 309 37919 #016-02-1991 L1992 **AN** *020 †05

CARTER, Martha W. 6501 DEANE HILL DR, MEDMANPROFESSIONALS 37919 #047-06-1991 L1992 **AN** *020 †05

CARTER, Paul Michael. 801 N WEISGARBER RD, STE 200 37909 #047-06-1991 L1992 **AI** *020 †03,20

CASEY, Michael Thomas, Jr. 9430 PARK WEST BLVD, STE 130 37923 #047-06-1994 L2000 **ORS** *020 †40

CASH, Jennifer Erin. 1924 ALCOA HWY 37920 #305-01-2005 **FP** *012

CASON, Peter Lee. ■ 37929 #039-01-1960 L1969 **EM** *071

CASSADA, David C. 1924 ALCOA HWY, BOX U11 37920 #051-01-1994 L1996 **VS** *020 †85

CASTANEDA, Victoria L. 2018 W CLINCH AVE, EAST TENNESSEE CHILDREN'S 37916 #748-02-1979 L1993 **PHO PD** *020 †55

CATES, Harold Eugene, Jr. 9340 PARK WEST BLVD, STE 130 37923 #047-06-1985 L1991 **ORS OAR** *020 †40

CATNEY, Kevin Guy. 1431 CENTERPOINT BLVD, STE 100 37932 #035-15-1993 L2005 **EM FM** *020 †18

CATRON, Donald Gibson. 201 N WEISGARBER RD 37919 #047-06-1964 L1965 **P AN** *071 †75

CAUBLE, Danl Webster, III. 1901 W CLINCH AVE 37916 #047-06-1971 L1972 **IM GP** *020

CAUDLE, Michael Ray. 1924 ALCOA HWY, BOX 94 37920 #036-05-1977 L1982 **OBG** *030 †20

CEARLOCK, Michael Brad. ■ 37923 #104-01-2004 L2007 **FP** *012

CHACKO, George. 1924 ALCOA HWY 37920 #495-08-1973 L1995 **NM CD** *020 †28

CHAMBERS, Robert Todd. 1208 MERCHANT DR 37912 #055-02-1990 L1992 **FM** *020 †18

CHASTAIN, Sharon Norwood. 600 ARTHUR ST 37921 #001-02-1987 L1991 **P** *020 †75

CHAUDHURI, Udit. 9333 PARK WEST BLVD 37923 #047-06-1981 L1982 **IM** *020 †20

CHAVEZ, Jack Jose. 1924 ALCOA HWY, STE U109 37920 #023-12-1989 L1999 **AN** *020 †05

CHEBIB, Mohamad Fawaz. ■ 37931 #875-01-1988 **FM** *100

CHEN, Chang Wen. 10430 LOVELL CENTER DR 37922 #001-06-1993 L1995 **FM** *020

CHERRY, Ronald Robt. 12020 BROADWOOD DR 37934 #051-04-1978 L1981 **PUD IM** *020 †20

CHESNEY, John Tucker. 1924 ALCOA HWY, DEPT OF ANESTHESIA V-109 37920 #047-06-1964 L1964 **AN** *071 †05

CHILDS, Joseph Franklin. 6224 CRESWELL DR 37919 #048-02-1980 L1988 **CCP PEM** *020 †55

CHILES, Melissa Cole. 501 20TH ST, STE G3 37916 #047-06-1999 L2004 **PTH** *020 †50

CHILES, Walter W, III. 101 E BLOUNT AVE, KNOXVILLE UROLOGY CLC PC 37920 #047-06-1999 L2005 **U** *020 †95

CHILIAN, Peter Christian. 10820 PARKSIDE DR 37934 #007-02-1973 L2003 **AN** *020 †05

CHIRONNA, Robert Lawrence. 1901 W CLINCH AVE, STE 301 37916 #035-09-1977 L1985 **PM IM** *020 †60

CHOBANIAN, Sarkis John. 11440 PARKSIDE DR 37934 #041-12-1977 L1987 **GE IM** *020 †20

CHRISTENBERRY, Henry E. 1318 W CLINCH AVE 37916 #047-06-1935 L1935 **OTO** *071 †45

CHRISTENBERRY, K W, Jr. 1318 W CLINCH AVE 37916 #047-06-1966 L1966 **OTO** *020 †45

CHRISTENSEN, Lise Marie. 2018 W CLINCH AVE, CHILDREN'S HOSPITAL 37916 #056-05-1985 L1995 **PD PE** *020 †55

CHRISTIAN, Brett A. ■ 37909 #049-01-2004 L2008 **DR** *012

CHRISTIANO, Jose Q. ■ 37921 #187-31-1997 **GS** *012

CHRISTIANSEN, Deborah J. 9017 CROSS PARK DR, STE 200 37923 #047-20-1984 L1987 **PD** *020 †55

CHRONIS, Alex Geo. 3324 CIRCLE PARK 37996 #047-06-1965 L1965 **GP P** *020 †75

CHUN, Joseph Tongkyun. 1930 ALCOA HWY STE 235 37920 #051-04-1985 L1992 **GS** *020 †65

CLADERA, Dustin Byrnes. 1924 ALCOA HWY, SCH OF 37920 #025-12-2006 **IM** *012

CLADERA, Edward, Jr. ■ 37909 #025-12-2007 **IM** *012

CLAIBORNE, Chester F. ■ 37923 #047-06-1966 L1974 **GP OS** *020

CLANTON, Colin Riley. ■ 37919 #012-01-2005 **AN** *012

CLARK, Charles Nelson. 10215 KINGSTON PIKE 37922 #306-01-1994 L1997 **IM** *020 †20

CLARK, Jack C, Jr. 103 MIDLAKE DR, PHYSICIANS 37918 #047-06-1991 L1992 **FM** *020 †18

CLARK, Jack Crowley. 1900 N WINSTON RD, STE 500 37919 #047-06-1961 L1961 **DR NR** *020 †80

CLAUSSEN, Peter Valenine. 6501 DEANE HILL DR 37919 #047-06-1995 L1997 **DR** *020 †80

CLOUD, Mark W. 4117 E EMORY RD 37938 #047-06-1994 L1995 **FM** *020 †18

CLOUD, William Wiley. 900 E OAK HILL AVE, ST MARYS WOUND HEALING CTR 37917 #047-06-1969 L1970 **FM** *020 †18

COFER, Kenneth Fleming. 930 E EMERALD AVE, STE 615 37917 #047-06-1989 L1996 **GO GYN** *020 †30

COFER, Robert Harrison. ■ 37918 #047-06-1955 L1956 **IM** *071 †20

COFFEY, Richard Lawrence. 1120 E WEISGARBER RD, GROUP 37909 #011-02-1998 L2001 **IM** *020 †20

COHEN, Shannon. ■ 37919 #047-06-1997 L2001 **PD** *020 †55

COHN, Richard Allan. 101 E BLOUNT AVE 37920 #048-02-1977 L1982 **IM** *020 †20

COLE, Stephen Andrew. ■ 37923 #047-06-1999 L2002 **FM** *100

COLE, William Clifford, II. 1120 E WEISGARBER RD, CONSULTANTS 37909 #047-20-1996 L1997 **PUD** *020 †20

COLLIER, Brian Keith. 11440 PARKSIDE DR, STE 302 37934 #038-45-1989 L1991 **IM** *020 †20

COLLIER, Michael Shawn. 11808 KINGSTON PIKE, FARRAGUT 37934 #047-06-1997 L1999 **IM** *020 †20

COLLIER, Robert Hoyal, Jr. 900 E OAK HILL AVE, WHC ST MARYS MED CTR 37917 #047-06-1963 L1963 **GS VS** *020 †85

COLLINS, Jason Patrick. 110 N CAMPBELL STATION RD, STE 104 37934 #047-06-1998 L1999 **FM** *020 †18

COLLINS, Mary Patricia. 9349 PARK WEST BLVD # 105 37923 #038-45-1983 L1989 **OPH** *020 †35

COLWELL, Strant Thompson. 1924 ALCOA HWY 37920 #047-20-2004 L2008 **FP** *012

COMAS, Frank Vilanova. 1924 ALCOA HWY 37920 #847-01-1949 L1970 **RO** *071 †80

COMBS, Craig Michael. ■ 37923 #021-05-2004 L2008 **AN** *012

CONGLETON, Lee, III. 9330 PARK WEST BLVD 37923 #047-06-1985 L1990 **U GS** *020 †95
CONLEY, Dean Raymond. 9349 PARK WEST BLVD, STE 202 37923 #030-05-1968 L1975 **GE** *020 †20
CONLEY, Jane R. 1346 DOWELL SPRINGS BLVD 37909 #028-34-1994 L1999 **AI** *020 †03,55
CONNIN, R Scott. ■ 37932 #038-43-1984 L1999 **DR** *020 †80
CONNORS, Cara Chloe. 1924 ALCOA HWY 37920 #654-01-2004 L2007 **FM** *020 †18
CONNORS, Jerard Michael. 2018 W CLINCH AVE 37916 #051-04-1992 L1998 **PD** *020 †55
CONREY, Brian Richard. ■ 37918 #011-02-2003 L2007 **AN** *020
COOK, L Nichols. 2020 KAY ST 37920 #001-06-1986 L1993 **OPH** *020 †35
COOK, Lane Marshall. 4428 SUTHERLAND AVE, P O BOX 10187 37919 #021-06-1977 L1983 **P** *020 †75
COOLEY, Caroline E. 1120 E WEISGARBER RD, GROUP 37909 #048-02-1976 L1983 **NEP IM** *020 †20
COONES, Charles Matthew. ■ 37932 #047-06-2008 *012
COOPER, Gary Leon. 501 20TH ST, STE G3 37916 #047-20-1984 L1986 **PTH PCP** *062 †50
COOPER, James Alvin. 1924 ALCOA HWY 37920 #661-02-2005 **FM** *100
COOPER, John Franklin. 501 20TH ST, FORT SANDERS 37916 #047-05-1985 L1991 **IM** *020 †20
COOPER, John Harrison, Jr. 1932 ALCOA HWY 37920 #047-06-1972 L1973 **IM** *020
COPAS, Pleas Reed, Jr. 10810 PARKSIDE DR, STE 108 37934 #047-06-1976 L1977 **OBG** *020 †30
COPELAND, Christopher S. 501 20TH ST, OF EAST TN 37916 #047-06-1982 L1983 **AN** *020 †05
COPLEY, Patricia Deann. 1120 E WEISGARBER RD, CONSULTANTS 37909 #047-20-1996 L2000 **PCC** *020 †18,20
CORRALES, Alberto G. 1932 ALCOA HWY 37920 #016-42-2002 L2007 **PM** *100
COSBY, Otis, Jr. ■ 37922 #047-07-1989 L1991 **GPM** *020 †70
COTTAM, Korin Gourley. 501 19TH ST, STE 501 37916 #047-06-1995 L1999 **OBG** *020 †30
COTTON, Hollis J, Jr. 9333 PARK WEST BLVD 37923 #027-01-1992 L1997 **IM** *020 †20
COUGHLIN, Dennis, Jr. 501 19TH ST, STE 600 37916 #047-06-1953 L1953 **ORS** *071 †40
COVINO, Brian Mark. 1704 JOHNNY MAJORS DR 37996 #010-02-1986 L1993 **ORS OAR** *020 †40
COX, Christopher Ramsey. 7541 CROSSWOOD BLVD, FAMILY PRACTICE 37924 #047-06-1994 L1998 **MPD PD** *020 †55
COX, David Allan. 900 E OAK HILL AVE, CONSULTANTS PC 37917 #036-07-1982 L1988 **CD IM** *020 †20
COX, James Kyle, Jr. 10820 PARKSIDE DR 37934 #047-06-1988 L1989 **DR** *020 †80
COX, James W, Jr. 1940 ALCOA HWY, STE E310 37920 #047-06-1984 L1985 **ICE CD** *020 †20
COX, William Eric. 1924 ALCOA HWY, BOX U-109 37920 #047-06-2000 L2003 **AN** *020 †05
CRAFT, Robert Mitchell. 1924 ALCOA HWY, STE U109 37920 #047-06-1988 L1990 **AN** *020 †05
CRAIG, Frances M. 1900 N WINSTON RD STE 300, EMERGENCY PHYSICIAN 37919 #048-13-1992 L2003 **PD PE** *020 †16
CRAIG, James P. 501 20TH ST, STE G3 37916 #011-04-1977 L1984 **PTH** *020 †50
CRAIG, Michael Chapman. 1128 E WEISGARBER RD 37909 #038-40-1997 L2001 **PM SCI** *020 †60
CRAMOLINI, Gordon Mark. 2018 W CLINCH AVE 37916 #005-11-1978 L1996 **AN CCP** *020 †05,55
CRAWFORD, David Scott. 5908 LYONS VIEW PIKE 37919 #035-06-1995 L2002 **P** *020 †75
CRAWFORD, Jacqueline Sue. 10810 PARKSIDE DR, STE G15 37934 #005-18-1992 L1998 **N** *020 †75
CRAWFORD, John Jay. 260 FORT SANDERS WEST BLVD, STE 200 37922 #047-05-1993 L1994 **ORS** *020 †40
CRAWLEY, Robert Allen. 1515 SAINT MARY ST 37917 #047-06-1974 L1975 **OTO HNS** *020 †45
CRIST, Jeffrey Robt. 9349 PARK WEST BLVD, STE 101 37923 #016-02-1978 L1990 **GE IM** *020 †20
CROCKER, Robert Orr. ■ 37923 #036-05-1982 L1984 **IM** *020 †20
CROSS, Stephanie B. 10810 PARKSIDE DR, STE 108 37934 #047-06-1988 L1991 **OBG** *020 †30
CROWDER, William Wilson. 8524 KINGSTON PIKE 37919 #047-06-1958 L1960 **IM** *071 †20
CRUMLEY, Joe C. ■ 37920 #047-06-1949 L1950 **ORS** *071 †40
CUEVAS, Clarisa Esther. 2100 W CLINCH AVE STE 510 37916 #042-01-1980 L1991 **PG** *020 †55
CULHANE, Donna Kathryn. 930 E EMERALD AVE, STE 512 37917 #030-05-1991 L1998 **DR** *020 †80
CUNNINGHAM, Richard B, Jr. 9430 PARK WEST BLVD, STE 130 37923 #051-04-1990 L2000 **ORS OSM** *020 †40
CURFMAN, Wayne Corbet. 600 ARTHUR ST 37921 #048-12-1975 L1978 **P** *020 †75
CURNOW, Randall Thomas, Jr. 1225 E WEISGARBER RD, STE 200 37909 #051-01-1994 L2008 **IM** *020 †20
CURRIER, Ryan Patrick. ■ 37917 #019-02-2005 **DR** *012
CURTIN, Francis Gregory. 930 E EMERALD AVE, STE 512 37917 #024-07-1987 L1996 **DR** *020 †80
DABBS, Randal L. 1900 N WINSTON RD STE 300 37919 #047-06-1976 L1977 **EM FM** *020 †18,16
DAIGLE, Rodd Louis. 1431 CENTERPOINT BLVD, STE 100 37932 #021-05-2000 L2003 **EM** *020 †16
DALEY, Brian James. 1932 ALCOA HWY STE 27 37920 #021-01-1986 L1996 **GS TRS** *020 †85 ‡
DAMRON, Douglas Len. 1901 W CLINCH AVE 37916 #039-01-1985 L2000 **IM** *020 †20
DAR, Ayesha S. 2018 WESTERN AVE 37921 #704-01-1992 L2004 **PD** *020 †55
DAVENPORT, Larry E. 7328 MIDDLEBROOK PIKE 37909 #306-01-1986 L1989 **FM** *020 †18
DAVIDSON, Clifford Marc. 11541 KINGSTON PIKE 37934 #001-02-1986 L1993 **IM NM** *020 †28,20
DAVIDSON, Elvyn V. 710 CHERRY ST NE 37914 #047-07-1953 L1959 **GP** *071
DAVIDSON, Evelyne Monique. 710 N CHERRY ST 37914 #047-20-1987 L1990 **IM GP** *020
DAVIES, Glenn Thomas. 1128 E WEISGARBER RD, KNOXVILLE ORTHOPEDIC CLINI 37909 #143-05-1989 **OSM** *100
DAVIS, Gayle Leanne. ■ 37919 #036-05-1991 L1994 **P** *020 †75
DAVIS, Leila Katherine. 9352 PARK WEST BLVD 37923 #047-06-1990 L1993 **IM PD** *020 †55,20
DAVIS, Lloyd Cleveland. 601 HALL OF FAME DR 37915 #012-01-1955 L1956 **FM** *071
DAVIS, Martin. 9330 PARK WEST BLVD, STE 302 37923 #047-06-1944 L1944 **OBG** *020 †30
DAVIS, Robert Scott. 9333 PARK WEST BLVD, STE 104 37923 #021-05-1983 L1993 **NS** *020 †25
DAVIS, Stephen Craig. 9330 PARK WEST BLVD, STE 302 37923 #021-01-1984 L1988 **OBG** *020 †30
DAVIS, Tamara Faye. ■ 37917 #051-04-2001 L2004 **FM** *020 †18
DAWSON, John T. 930 E EMERALD AVE STE 510 37917 #012-01-1985 L1990 **OPH** *020 †35
D'CRUZ, Paul Ivan. 1230 ARBORBROOKE DR 37922 #012-01-1995 L1999 **P** *020 †75
DE BOER, Michael H. 10820 PARKSIDE DR 37934 #048-02-1988 L1989 **EM FM** *020 †18
DE FIORE, Joseph Chas, Jr. 1704 JOHNNY MAJORS DR 37996 #016-43-1963 L1972 **ORS HS** *030 †40

DEGNAN, Jonathan Nelson. 501 19TH ST STE 601 37916 #021-01-1985 L1990 **ORS OSM** *020
DE GUZMAN, Abigail B. 1924 ALCOA HWY 37920 #003-75-2007, ▲ **IM** *012
DEICHERT, Robert Geo. 8350 KINGSTON PIKE 37919 #041-09-1965 L1991 **OM GP** *020
DE LEESE, Joseph Saml. 101 E BLOUNT AVE, CONSULTANTS PC 37920 #038-41-1969 L1979 **CD IM** *020 †20
DELL, Jeffrey Russell. 9430 PARK WEST BLVD STE 3, TOWER PARKWEST 37923 #026-04-1992 L1993 **OBG** *020 †30
DE LOZIER, Alton O, Jr. ■ 37923 #047-06-1944 L1945 **GYN OS** *071 †30
DE LOZIER, Hugh Helton. 210 FORT SANDERS WEST BLVD 37922 #036-08-1983 L1988 **DR PD** *020 †80
DE LOZIER, Joseph B. 1490 TOURAINE PL, P O BOX 52164 37919 #047-06-1953 L1954 **GP** *020
DEMERS, Robert G. PO BOX 22573 37933 #010-02-1964 L1983 **P** *071 †75
DENNENY, Elise. 101 E BLOUNT AVE, STE G10 37920 #016-01-1981 L1987 **OTO FPS** *020 †45 ‡
DENNENY, James C, III. 101 E BLOUNT AVE, STE G10 37920 #039-01-1979 L1986 **OTO HNS** *020 †45
DEO, Sonali Prakash. ■ 37922 #496-25-1999 L2007 **FM** *020 †18
DEPERSIO, Richard John. 1932 ALCOA HWY, STE 160 37920 #047-06-1974 1975 **OTO** *020 †45
DEPEW, James Bradford. ■ 37919 #051-04-2008 *012
DE PUE, Ray V, Jr. 1901 W CLINCH AVE 37916 #047-06-1946 L1950 **OTO** *071
DEVAULT, Randall Maynard. 7217 W CHERMONT CIR 37918 #047-06-2000 L2004 **AN** *020 †05
DE VEGA, Armando Fernando. ■ 37934 #275-01-1955 L1963 **PTH FOP** *071 †50
DEVRNJA, Robert F. ■ 37922 #649-14-1977 L1988 **EM FOP** *075
DHYANCHAND, Charles J. 9625 KROGER PARK DR, STE 500 37922 #016-01-1995 L1996 **FM** *020 †18
DIAZ, Edgar. 1924 ALCOA HWY, SCHOOL O 37920 #016-11-2006 **IM** *012
DICKSON, Mitchell Alan. 501 20TH ST STE 606, ANESTHESIA MEDICAL ALLIANC 37916 #047-06-1983 L1988 **AN** *020 †05
DICKSON, Robert K. 205 BATTLE FRONT TRL 37934 #047-06-1982 L1985 **PD PEM** *020 †55
DIDDLE, Albert W. ■ 37909 #008-01-1936 L1948 **GYN** *071 †30
DIETER, Raymond Andrew. 1924 ALCOA HWY 37920 #047-06-1942-1990 L1991 **TS** *020 †85,90
DI FRANCO, Anthony. 1900 N WINSTON RD, STE 300 37919 #308-07-1983 L1987 **FM** *020 †18
DIGBY, Myles Christopher. ■ 37931 #021-05-2003 L2007 **DR** *012
DILL, Stephen Hurley. 501 20TH ST, STE 110 37916 #047-06-1972 1972 **CD IM** *020 †20
DILLON, Mary Bolton. ■ 37934 #038-41-1988 L2003 **PM** *020 †60
DI MEO, Michael Jos. 10810 PARKSIDE DR 37934 #024-07-1973 L2006 **PUD IM** *020 †20
DINH, Duythu Phan. 939 E EMERALD AVE STE 801 37917 #051-07-1999 L2004 **OBG** *020 †30
DIRUZZO, Cassy Lynn. ■ 37918 #048-13-2006 **DR** *012
DIRUZZO, Jonathan S. ■ 37918 #048-13-2006 **AN** *012
DITTRICH, Lee Baxter. 1928 ALCOA HWY, STE 209 37920 #036-05-1998 L2002 **D** *020 †15
DIVITO, Anthony Richard. ■ 37923 #038-40-2004 L2005 **DR** *012
DOBBINS, William Todd. 1924 ALCOA HWY 37920 #047-06-1956 L1956 **PD END** *071 †55
DODD, Susan Price. 10810 PARKSIDE DR, STE 108 37934 #047-06-1983 L1984 **OBG** *020 †30
DOERS, Jesse Thos. 1120 E WEISGARBER RD, CONSULTANTS 37909 #056-05-1985 L1995 **PUD CCM** *020 †20
DOGGWEILER, Regula. 1928 ALCOA HWY, STE 222 37920 #561-06-1991 *100
DOIRON, Clint Thos. 101 E BLOUNT AVE, CONSULTANTS PC 37920 #048-02-1976 L1983 **CD IM** *020 †20
DONAUER, Robert M. ■ 37919 #035-01-1947 L1984 **IM CD** *020
DOODY, Michael C. 220 FORT SANDERS WEST BLVD, STE 106 37922 #048-04-1980 L1987 **REN GYN** *020 †30
D'OOGE, Benjamin Wayne. 1900 N WINSTON RD, STE 300 37919 #023-12-1982 L1993 **EM AM** *030 †16
DOOLEY, Patrick Mcdermott. 501 20TH ST, STE 606 37916 #047-06-1983 L1984 **AN** *020 †05
DOPPELT, Matthew B. 101 E BLOUNT AVE, STE 820 37920 #011-75-1997, ▲ L2003 **D** *020
DORSEY, Larry. 2911 ESSARY DR 37918 #047-06-1957 L1958 **IM** *020
DOTY, Thomas W, III. 1450 DOWELL SPRINGS BLVD 37909 #047-06-1984 L1991 **END IM** *020 †70
DOUGHERTY, John Henry. 939 EMERALD AVE, STE 907 37917 #047-06-1973 L1973 **N IM** *020 †75
DOUGHERTY, Robert Edward. ■ 37917 #047-06-1958 L1958 **OBG** *071 †30
DOUGLAS, Jeffrey Lee. 1915 WHITE AVE, STE 601 37916 #047-06-1986 L1996 **ID IM** *020 †20 ‡
DOUGLASS, Andrew Martin. 1344 DOWELL SPRINGS BLVD, EAST TENNESSEE VEIN CLINIC 37909 #047-06-1989 L1991 **PHL FM** *020 †18
DOUMAS, Damianos Thomas. 1900 N WINSTON RD STE 500, TEAMHEALTH RADIOLOGY SERVI 37918 #418-02-1962 L1971 **R** *020 †80
DOVER, Norris Lee. 501 20TH ST, STE 606 37916 #036-08-1982 L1986 **AN OBG** *020 †05
DOVGAN, Daniel Jakob. 210 FORT SANDERS WEST BLVD 37922 #030-06-1989 L1995 **DR** *020 †80
DOWELL-GRAVATT, Margaret. ■ 37916 #026-04-1945 L1968 **GP PD** *071 †55
DOWNEY, Jon Patrick. 2027 N BROADWAY ST 37917 #047-06-1969 L2002 **FM OS** *020 †18
DOWRAY, Ramesh. ■ 37919 #495-33-1968 L1995 **OM GP** *020 †80,70
DRINNEN, Jeffrey Wade. 103 MIDLAKE DR, PHYSICIANS 37918 #047-06-1991 L1992 **FM** *020 †18
DRINNEN, Thos Brabson, Jr. 5300 MOUNTAINCREST DR 37918 #047-06-1961 L1961 **FM** *020 †18
DRYZER, Scott R. 1120 E WEISGARBER RD, CONSULTANTS 37909 #048-12-1987 L2001 **PUD CCM** *020 †20
DU BOIS, Dale David. 1431 CENTERPOINT BLVD, STE 100 37932 #030-06-1999 L2006 **MPD** *020 †55
DUCKLES, Nancy Ellen. 9048 HEMINGWAY GROVE CIR 37922 #035-45-1988 L1995 **AN** *020 †05
DUDNEY, Tina M. 1940 ALCOA HWY, STE E210 37920 #047-06-1988 L1990 **PUD** *020 †20
DUDRICK, Paul Stanley. 501 19TH ST STE 501 37916 #028-34-1988 L1997 **SO GS** *020 †85
DUKES, Robert Allen. 1900 N WINSTON RD, STE 603 37919 #047-06-1981 L1982 **EM** *030 †18
DUNCAN, Lisa Diane. 1924 ALCOA HWY, DRAWER U-108 37920 #047-20-1996 L2001 **PTH** *020 †50
DUNCAN, Orville Jack. ■ 37922 #047-06-1962 L1969 **AN** *071
DUNCAN, Raphael H, Jr. 9352 PARK WEST BLVD 37923 #047-06-1947 L1947 **FM** *071
DURBIN, David Cameron. 930 E EMERALD AVE, ASSOCIATES 37917 #003-01-1991 L1994 **IM** *020 †20
DURST, Debra Renee. ■ 37922 #038-40-1995 L2003 **EM** *020 †16
DUZAN, Daniel Rudolph. 1900 N WINSTON RD, STE 300 37919 #038-44-1998 L1999 **MPD** *020 †20
DYER, Michael Lewis. 501 20TH ST, STE G3 37916 #047-06-1979 L1980 **PTH** *030 †50

EADDY, John Albert. 1924 ALCOA HWY, STE U67 37920 #023-01-1969 L1971 **FM DIA** *040 †18

EAKES, David Lamar. 100 TECH CENTER DR, PEDIATRIC CONSULTANTS INC 37912 #027-01-1983 L1995 **PD** *055

EAPEN, Saji. 1114 E WEISGARBER RD 37909 #495-63-1992 L2006 **HO** *020 †20

EASTERLY, Jeffery Lee. 7211 WELLINGTON DR, CLINIC 37919 #047-20-1999 L2000 **FM** *020 †18

EASTHAM, Jerome F. ■ 37919 #047-06-1973 L1973 **IM** *020

EBENEZER, C S Albert. 2001 LAUREL AVE, STE 604 37916 #495-04-1964 L1972 **ON HEM** *020

EBERENZ, Wayne Michael. 930 E EMERALD AVE, STE 512 37917 #041-01-1990 L1997 **DR** *020 †80

EBERTS, Thomas Joseph. 5301 RIVERBRIAR RD, LABORATORY 37919 #017-20-1975 L1991 **PTH** *020 †50 ‡

ECKARD, Alexis Ann. 1924 ALCOA HWY U-67 37920 #654-01-2004 L2007 **FM** *100 †18

ECKARD, William David. ■ 37920 #012-22-2004 L2007 **AN** *012

EDGE, Diane Leslie. 930 E EMERALD AVE 37917 #032-01-1982 L1989 **DR** *020 †80

EDGLEY, Heather Gayle. ■ 37922 #048-12-1991 L1996 **PD** *020 †55

EDMUNDS, Kathleen O. 930 E EMERALD AVE, OB/GYN SPECIALISTS OF 37917 #051-01-1988 L1995 **OBG** *020 †30

EDMUNDS, Meade Castleton. 11440 PARKSIDE DR 37934 #051-01-1988 L1995 **GE** *020 †20

EDROSOLANO, Reynaldo G. ■ 37920 #748-08-1975 **PTH** *100

EDWARDS, David Franklin. 400 TORRINGTON CT 37934 #051-07-1996 L2004 **FM** *020 †18

EDWARDS, Sarah Marie. P.O. BOX 16327 37996 #047-20-2006 **EM** *012

EGNER, Benjamin James. ■ 37912 #048-15-2004 L2008 **DR** *012

EIDELWEIN, Alexandra P. 2100 W CLINCH AVE, STE 510 37916 #187-23-1993 L2005 **PG** *020 †55

EILERMAN, Michael Stuart. 11440 PARKSIDE DR 37934 #038-41-1987 L1993 **ORS** *020 †40

ELAM, Curtis Jay. 2001 LAUREL AVE STE G4 37916 #047-06-1985 L1990 **OBG** *020 †30

EL CHEMEITELLI, Samer A. ■ 37922 #605-01-1995 L2006 **PCC** *100 †20

ELDER, Robert Frank. 1928 ALCOA HWY, STE 300 37920 #047-06-2004 L1985 **OBG** *020 †30

ELKINS, Sandra Kay. 1924 ALCOA HWY 37920 #047-06-1987 L1994 **FOP ATP** *020 †50

ELLENBURG, Donald T. 2121 HIGHLAND AVE 37916 #047-06-1976 L1977 **PDA AI** *020 †55,03

ELLIOTT, Michael Byron. 140 CAPITOL DR, ALLIANCE OF EAST 37922 #051-01-1975 L1980 **AN** *020 †05

ELLIS, Carol. 11160 KINGSTON PIKE, STE 700 37934 #041-01-1978 L1980 **CD IM** *075 †20

ELLIS, Carrie Diane. ■ 37924 #028-78-2005, ▲ L2007 **FP** *012

ELLIS, Edward Stephen. ■ 37919 #047-06-1979 L1979 **IM OM** *020 †20

ELY, Daniel S. 11440 PARKSIDE DR, STE 302 37934 #049-01-1983 L1984 **IM** *020 †20

EMANUEL, Peter Geo. 2001 LAUREL AVE, STE N304 37916 #001-02-1992 L1997 **DR VIR** *020 †80

EMBRY, Jerry J. 7632 GLEASON DR 37919 #001-02-1961 L1968 **P** *020 †75

EMERY, Turner Paul. ■ 37919 #011-03-2005 **GS** *100

EMMETT, Kim Robinson. 11440 PARKSIDE DR, STE 302 37934 #020-12-1987 L1999 **IMG** *020

ENDERSON, Blaine Lynn. 1932 ALCOA HWY STE 270, UNIV GENERAL SURGEONS PC 37920 #046-01-1980 L1987 **TRS GS** *020 †85

ENGLAND, Benjamin David. 1924 ALCOA HWY U-67, SCH OF 37920 #047-20-2006 **FP** *012

ENGLAND, Welborn David. 11201 W POINT DR, STE 102 37934 #047-06-1978 L1979 **FM** *020 †18

EPPERT, Alex James. ■ 37919 #017-20-2004 L2007 **EM** *020

EPPS, Jerry Lynn. 1924 ALCOA HWY, STE U109 37920 #012-01-1980 L1987 **AN** *020 †05

ERGEN, Frederick Julian. 900 E OAK HILL AVE, C/O ST MARYS EMERG DEPT 37917 #047-06-1979 L1979 **EM IM** *020 †20

ERICKSON, Cara L. ■ 37919 #048-13-2006 L2006 **AN** *012

ERICKSON, Richard James. 501 20TH ST, 4TH FL 37916 #023-01-1958 L1960 **FM** *071 †18

ERPENBACH, John Ernest. 9031 CROSS PARK DR, DEPT OF VETERANS AFFAIRS C 37923 #047-06-1975 L1976 **FM AN** *020 †05,18

ERPENBACH, Jonathan David. ■ 37922 #047-06-2005 L2006 **GS** *020

ERWIN, Paul Campbell. 1522 CHEROKEE TRL, TENNESSEE DEPT OF HEALTH 37920 #001-02-1983 L1984 **OS IM** *020 †20,70

ESTES, Ronald John. 1120 E WEISGARBER RD, CONSULTANTS 37909 #011-04-1984 L1986 **IM PCC** *020 †20

ETEZADI-AMOLI, Saeed. 10810 PARKSIDE DR, STE 305 37934 #517-01-1978 L1984 **IM** *020 †20

EVANCHO, Andrew Michael. 930 E EMERALD AVE, STE 512 37917 #041-14-1984 L1991 **R** *020 †80

EVANS, Virginia Jean. ■ 37920 #056-06-2007 **OBG** *012

EVERETT, Jeffrey Earl. 1940 ALCOA HWY, STE E260 37920 #038-40-1989 L2007 **TS** *020 †90,85

EVITT, Emily Frances. 9330 PARK WEST BLVD, PARKWEST OB/GYN 37923 #047-06-1999 L2003 **OBG** *020 †30

FAGET, Reinaldo. 4639 NEWCOM AVE 37919 #275-01-1956 L1975 **P GP** *071

FAHOUM, Antoine Sadik. ■ 37922 #875-01-1980 **PTH** *100

FAISAL, Mohammed R. 1900 N WINSTON RD, STE 300 37919 #704-01-1990 L2002 **IM** *020 †20

FARDON, David Favreau. 1704 JOHNNY MAJORS DR 37996 #019-02-1964 L1970 **ORS** *020 †40

FARR, George W. 501 20TH ST, STE 606, AMAET 37916 #047-06-1994 L1998 **AN** *020 †05

FEASTER, Samuel Haynie. 210 FORT SANDERS WEST BLVD 37922 #036-01-1985 L1991 **DR** *020 †80

FEEHAN, Tammy T. 2018 WESTERN AVE 37921 #047-06-1993 L1995 **PD** *020 †55

FELD, Neil. 1718 SAINT MARY ST, STE A 37917 #561-01-1978 L1984 **NPM OS** *020 †55

FERGUSON, James Vogt, Jr. 501 20TH ST, FORT SANDERS 37916 #047-06-1975 L1976 **IM IMG** *020

FERGUSON, Steve Guy. 1901 W CLINCH AVE # 301 37916 #051-07-1981 L1988 **PM** *020 †60

FIELDS, Larry Michael. 930 E EMERALD AVE, STE 614 37917 #047-20-1997 L2001 **OBG** *020 †30

FILCHOCK, Joanne Victoria. 110 N CAMPBELL STATION RD 37934 #047-06-1980 L1981 **FM** *020 †18

FILLION, Michelle Marie. ■ 37922 #038-41-2007 **GS** *012

FILSTON, Howard Church. 1924 ALCOA HWY, UNIV OF TENN MED CTR/KNOXV 37920 #038-06-1962 L1990 **PDS GS** *071 †85

FINELLI, Robert Edward. 9314 PARK WEST BLVD 37923 #038-40-1974 L1976 **NS** *071 †25

FITZGIBBON, James Francis. 1924 ALCOA HWY, DEPT PATH 37920 #539-02-1982 L1994 **PTH** *020 †10

FLORIAN, Anthony Louis. 7503 N SHORE DR, NORTHSHORE FAMILY PHYSICIA 37919 #045-01-1986 L1987 **FM** *020 †18

FLOWERS, Michael Brian. 1120 E WEISGARBER RD, GROUP 37909 #012-22-1996 L2002 **IM** *020 †20

FLYNN, Michael Richard. 1924 ALCOA HWY, STE U109 37920 #051-04-1987 L1990 **AN CCA** *020 †05

FOGLE, Wayne D. 11416 GRIGSBY CHAPEL RD, STE 104 37934 #036-01-1976 L1982 **PD** *020 †55

FOKENS, Jeffrey Hendrick. 1431 CENTERPOINT BLVD, TEAM HEALTH 37932 #047-06-1972 L1972 **FM PG** *020

FORD, Ronald Andrew. 2018 W CLINCH AVE 37916 #036-05-1992 L1994 **PEM OS** *020 †55

FORSBERG, David Anderson. 210 FORT SANDERS WEST BLVD 37922 #036-07-1986 L1991 **R** *030 †20

FORSEE, Amy Elizabeth. 7503 N SHORE DR 37919 #001-06-1997 L1998 **FM** *020 †18

FORSTMANN, Carrie Leigh. 1924 ALCOA HWY, DEPT MED 37920 #051-04-2007 **TY** *012

FORTICH, Jairo Alfredo. 1431 CENTERPOINT BLVD, STE 100 37932 #654-01-1997 L2005 **FM** *020 †18

FORTNER, Kimberly Bailey. 1928 ALCOA HWY, MEDICAL BLDG. B SUITE 300 37920 #012-05-2001 L2005 **OBG** *020 †30

FOSTER, Malcolm Tennyson. 101 E BLOUNT AVE, CONSULTANTS PC 37920 #036-05-1991 L2001 **CD IM** *020 †20

FOSTER, William Edwin. ■ 37934 #047-06-1964 L1964 **ORS** *071 †40

FOUST, Ashley Susan. ■ 37919 #047-06-2004 L2007 **PD** *100 †55

FOWLER, Carol Lynne. 2100 W CLINCH AVE, STE 430 37916 #021-05-1979 L2006 **PDS GS** *020 †85

FOWLER, Daniel Petermazei. ■ 37920 #047-06-2008 *012

FOX, Daniel Robt. 1924 ALCOA HWY 37920 #047-06-1987 L1988 **DR** *020 †80

FOX, James E. 234 MORRELL RD # 304 37919 #047-06-1994 L1998 **PM** *020 †60

FRAME, Barry Dean. 930 E EMERALD AVE STE 719 37917 #021-01-1971 L1976 **TS** *020 †85,90

FRANKE, Glenn Henry. ■ 37919 #016-06-1953 L1997 **IM** *071 †20

FRANKLIN, Stephen R. 930 E EMERALD AVE, STE 711 37917 #047-06-1982 L1982 **OPH EM** *020 †35

FRAZIER, Jonathan Russell. 5001 MALONEYVILLE RD 37918 #047-06-1997 L1998 **AN** *020 †05

FRAZIER, Timothy Cockrum. 2121 HIGHLAND AVE 37916 #047-20-1988 L1994 **AI PD** *020 †55,03

FREEBERG, Susan E. 109 SUBURBAN RD STE C101 37923 #047-06-1988 L1992 **D** *020 †15

FREEMAN, Coy. 9330 PARK WEST BLVD 37923 #039-01-1967 L1975 **U** *020 †95

FREEMAN, Karen Vincent. 9017 CROSS PARK DR, STE 200 37923 #047-06-1990 L1993 **PD** *020 †55

FREEMAN, Michael Benton. 1924 ALCOA HWY, BOX U-11 37920 #012-01-1980 L1987 **VS GS** *020 †85

FRIEDMAN, Wayne Henry. 1924 ALCOA HWY, DEPT OF OB/GYN; BOX U-27 37920 #021-01-2001 L2006 **OBG** *020 †30

FROMKE, Michael D. 930 E EMERALD AVE, KNOXVILLE, PLLC SUITE 611 37917 #047-06-1990 L2000 **NS** *020 †25

FRY, Bruce B. 1704 JOHNNY MAJORS DR 37996 #028-78-1997, ▲ L2001 **PM** *020 †60 ‡

FRY, Mellon Alma, Jr. ■ 37934 #047-06-1961 L1961 **R OS** *071 †80

FU, Yitong. 1924 ALCOA HWY, DEPT OF GENERAL SURGERY 37920 #243-46-1985 **NM** *012

FUNG, Ka Kin. ■ 37923 #045-04-2005 L2008 **IM** *012

FUQUA, Jeffery L. 501 20TH ST, STE 606 37916 #047-06-1990 L1991 **AN** *020 †05

FUXA, Jorge Guillermo. ■ 37920 #275-01-1947 L1973 **GP** *071

GAINES, Thomas Edward. 1940 ALCOA HWY STE E-26 37920 #054-04-1979 L1990 **TS GS** *020 †85,90

GALDUN, John Patrick. 501 20TH ST, STE 606 37916 #051-04-1984 L1993 **AN EM** *020 †16,05

GALE, Christine Linda. 9430 PARK WEST BLVD, GENERATIONS OB GYN PC 37923 #047-06-1985 L1986 **OBG** *020 †30

GALLAHER, Tom Tracey. 6700 BAUM DR STE 1, KNOXVILLE 37919 #047-06-1990 L2001 **PS** *020 †85,65

GALLIAN, Richard S. ■ 37932 #021-06-2004 L2007 **IM** *020

GALLIVAN, Wm Francis, Jr. 501 19TH ST, STE 600 37916 #035-06-1948 L1953 **ORS** *020 †40

GALLOWAY, Alan Keith. 137 E BLOUNT AVE, KNOXVILLE ASSOCIATED 37920 #047-06-1984 L1988 **PTH PCP** *020 †50

GAMMELTOFT, Karsten. 2100 W CLINCH AVE, STE 210 37916 #297-01-1984 L1989 **CHN PD** *020 †75

GARDNER, Amber Lea. 1704 JOHNNY MAJORS DR 37996 #012-01-2002 L2006 **PSM** *020

GARDNER, Katherine R. 1924 ALCOA HWY, STE U109 37920 #047-06-1991 L1992 **CCA** *020 †05

GARDNER, William Henry. ■ 37919 #047-06-1946 L1946 **GYN** *071 †30

GARRETT, Albert S, Jr. ■ 37923 #047-06-1959 L1960 **OM IM** *071 †70

GASH, Judson Roy. 1924 ALCOA HWY 37920 #045-04-1990 L1997 **DR** *020 †80

GAYLORD, Mark Shannon. 1930 ALCOA HWY, STE 145 37920 #047-06-1978 L1979 **NPM** *020 †55

GEBROW, Martin. 900 E OAK HILL AVE, FL 4 37917 #020-12-1964 L1981 **P** *020 †20

GEIBIG, Erik Eugene. 433 SEVIER AVE 37920 #038-44-2001 L2004 **EM** *020 †16

GENTRY, Robert Elliott. 9330 PARK WEST BLVD, CONSULTANTS PC 37923 #036-07-1976 L1978 **CD** *020 †20

GENTRY, Robert Homer. 1240 OLD WEISGARBER RD 37909 #048-02-1956 L1960 **P** *020

GENTRY, Tucker James. 501 20TH ST, STE 606 37916 #047-20-2000 L2004 **AN** *020

GEORGE, Courtney C. 1932 ALCOA HWY, BLDG C 37920 #036-05-1995 L1998 **IM** *020 †20

GERKIN, David George. 1928 ALCOA HWY, STE 324 37920 #017-20-1962 L1971 **OPH MDM** *071 †35

GHARAVI, Hesamm Elmi. 9430 PARK WEST BLVD, STE 120 37923 #021-05-1997 L2004 **HO** *020 †20

GHONIEM, Ayman Ali. 1900 N WINSTON RD, STE 500 37919 #915-03-1990 L2004 **DR** *020 †80

GIBSON, Carl Eugene. FT SANDERS PROF BD STE 606 37916 #047-06-1959 L1959 **AN** *020 †05

GIBSON, John Thos. ■ 37912 #047-06-1957 L1977 **PD** *071

GIBSON, Richard Lee. 1928 ALCOA HWY STE G50, VOLUNTEER RESEARCH GRP 37920 #020-12-1970 L1976 **P** *020 †20,75

GILBERT, Verne Ephraim. 211 E BLOUNT AVE 37920 #023-01-1957 L1970 **IM ID** *071 †20

GILBERTSON, Robert B. FT SANDERS PROF BD STE 404 37916 #047-06-1951 L1952 **IM** *071 †20

GILLESPIE, Carla La Juan. 1120 E WEISGARBER RD, GROUP 37909 #047-20-1991 L1992 **IM** *020 †20

GILLESPIE, James T, Jr. 6906 KINGSTON PIKE STE 200 37919 #051-01-1981 L1985 **P ADP** *020 †75

GILLESPIE, Richard Allen. ■ 37920 #047-06-1959 L1960 **AN OS** *071 †05

GIMBEL, J Rod. 9330 PARK WEST BLVD, CONSULTANTS PC 37923 #056-05-1988 L1996 **ICE CD** *020 †20

GITSCHLAG, Gary Norman. 2100 W CLINCH AVE, STE 400 37916 #025-07-1976 L1982 **OPH PO** *020 †35

GLASS, Sharon M. 1901 W CLINCH AVE, STE 301 37916 #048-13-1984 L1989 **PM** *020 †60

GLATT, Herbert Jeffrey. 1928 ALCOA HWY, STE 324 37920 #036-07-1983 L1989 **OPH** *020 †35
GLEAVES, James Everett. 200 E BLOUNT AVE STE 503 37920 #047-06-1974 L1975 **FM** *020 †18
GLOVER, Abner M, Jr. ■ 37919 #047-06-1951 L1951 **GS PDS** *071 †85
GLOVER, Abner Michael. 501 20TH ST STE 50 37916 #047-06-1979 L1985 **CRS** *020 †85,10
GLOVER, Gregory Lyle. 10810 PARKSIDE DR, STE 100 37934 #001-02-1982 L1989 **OBG** *020 †30
GLOVER, Richard Allan. 1341 BRANTON BLVD, STE 102 37922 #047-06-1989 L1991 **PD** *020 †55
GODBOLD, Michael David. 1924 ALCOA HWY, UNIV OF TN # U114 37920 #012-05-2007 **TY** *012
GODFREY, Carl Edgar. 4529 ASHEVILLE HWY 37914 #047-06-1963 1964 **PD** *071
GODWIN, Charles Wayne. 501 19TH ST STE 701 37916 #048-02-1965 L1972 **OBG** *071 †30
GOKLANEY, Anil Kumar. 433 SEVIER AVE 37920 #047-05-2000 L2004 **EM** *020 †16 ‡
GOLD, John Frederick. ■ 37902 #012-01-2007 **TY** *012
GOLDMAN, David G. 3403 TAZEWELL PIKE, STE 101 37918 #048-12-1987 L1991 **IM** *020
GOLDMAN, Mitchell Howard. 1924 ALCOA HWY 37920 #024-01-1970 L1984 **VS TTS** *020 †85
GOLDSTEIN, Jonas Henry. 1924 ALCOA HWY, CENTER AT KNOXVILLE, DEPT 37920 #012-05-1991 L2003 **RNR** *020 †80
GOOD, Edward Frederick M. 9333 PARK WEST BLVD 37923 #047-20-1987 L1988 **IM** *020
GOOGE, Joseph Morris, Jr. 1225 E WEISGARBER RD, STE S380 37909 #047-06-1978 L1979 **OPH** *020 †35
GOOGE, Paul Buntyn. 315 ERIN DR 37919 #047-06-1983 L1984 **DMP ATP** *020 †50
GORNISIEWICZ, Marcin T. 4707 PAPERMILL DR, STE 200 37909 #759-03-1989 L2002 **RHU** *020 †20
GOSSAGE, David Layton. 458 OAKHURST DR 37919 #047-06-1986 L1997 **AI PD** *050 †55,03
GOUFFON, Charles Allen. 939 EMERALD AVE, STE 510 37917 #047-06-1965 L1966 **ORS** *071 †40
GOULD, Howard Richard. 5401 KINGSTON PIKE, STE 310 TWELVE OAKS EXECUT 37919 #035-08-1956 L1984 **R NM** *071 †80,28
GOYETTE, Richert Edgar. 9724 KINGSTON PIKE, STE 1404 37922 #048-04-1971 L1999 **HO IM** *020 †50
GRABEEL, Conrad Lindsay. 1924 ALCOA HWY 37920 #047-06-1952 L1953 **P** *071
GRAHAM, Garth Prinsloo. 2001 LAUREL AVE, STE N304 37916 #012-05-1998 L2003 **DR R** *020 †80
GRAHAM, Larry David. 1 COLONY PARK STE 200, 4709 PAPERMILL RD 37909 #047-06-1990 L1992 **GS** *020 †85
GRAHAM, Randal O. 501 19TH ST, STE 501 37916 #048-12-1982 L1987 **GS VS** *020 †85
GRANDAS, Oscar H. ■ 37920 #264-01-1986 L2004 **VS** *020 †85
GRANDE, Kimberly K. 10215 KINGSTON PIKE, STE 200 37922 #030-05-1994 L2000 **D** *020 †15
GRANT, Audrey Louise. 1900 N WINSTON RD, STE 300 37919 #045-01-1981 L1984 **EM IM** *020 †20
GRAPSKI, Richard Thos. 1915 WHITE AVE, THOMPSON ONCOLOGY GROUP 37916 #016-43-1978 L1997 **ON HEM** *020 †20
GRAVES, Joe Alan. 2100 W CLINCH AVE, STE 330 37916 #048-13-1986 L1992 **OTO** *020 †45
GRAY, Frank Benton. 1128 E WEISGARBER RD 37909 #036-01-1969 L1977 **ORS** *071 †40
GRAY, Jack Kenneth, Jr. 5908 LYONS VIEW PIKE, LAKESHORE MENTAL HEALTH IN 37919 #305-01-1984 L1989 **P** *020
GRAY, Keith Demond. 1934 ALCOA HWY, BLDG D 37920 #036-05-1998 L2001 **GS** *020 †85
GRAY, Nathan Adam. 11808 KINGSTON PIKE, FARRAGUT 37934 #047-06-2000 L2002 **IM** *020 †20 ‡
GREEN, James Regan. 211 E BLOUNT AVE, STE 507 37920 #047-06-1975 L1975 **EM** *020 †16
GREEN, Linda K. 101 E BLOUNT AVE STE G10, BAPTIST MED TOWERS 37920 #048-02-1984 L1988 **D** *020 †15
GREEN, Ralph Michael. 220 FORT SANDERS WEST BLVD, STE 101 37922 #047-06-1992 L1996 **MPD PD** *020 †20,55
GREENE, Richard W. 5733 WOODLEAF DR 37912 #047-06-1978 L1979 **PTH** *020 †55,19
GREER, David Michael. 318 ERIN DR, STE 6 37919 #027-01-1988 L1989 **CHP P** *020 †75
GREGG, Spencer Duncan. 1818 ANDY HOLT AVE, STUDENT HEALTH SERVICE 37996 #047-06-1989 L1990 **IM** *020 †20
GREGORIOU, Panos Geo. ■ 37923 #051-04-1956 L1956 **OS GP** *071
GRELLO, Fred Wm, Jr. ■ 37922 #010-02-1987 L1995 **PD** *020 †55
GRIFFIN, Tchad F. 4435 VALLEY VIEW DR 37917 #045-04-1990 L1992 **FM** *020 †18
GRIFFITH, Robert Carl. 6311 KINGSTON PIKE, STE 22E 37919 #021-01-1973 L1977 **D** *020 †15
GRINDSTAFF, Alan Dorn. 1924 ALCOA HWY 37920 #047-20-1994 L1999 **PTH** *020 †50
GRISHKIN, Brent Anthony. 1940 ALCOA HWY STE E260 37920 #041-14-1973 L1996 **CD TS** *020 †85,90
GROSSMAN, Allan Marc. 1451 DOWELL SPRINGS BLVD 37909 #035-08-1975 L1981 **ON HEM** *020
GUE, Crystal Levette. 4005 FOUNTAIN VALLEY DR, STE 350 37918 #055-02-1990 L1993 **IM** *020 †20
GUGLIELMO, Christopher Ge. ■ 37917 #047-06-2004 **DR** *012
GULATI, Sangeeta. 1928 ALCOA HWY, STE 100B 37920 #047-20-1994 L2002 **GE** *020 †20
HAASE, Theodore F, Jr. ■ 37931 #047-06-1951 L1951 **R** *071 †80
HACKER, Jeremy Paul. ■ 37919 #017-20-2006 L2006 **AN** *012
HADDAD, Elias Victor. ■ 37922 #047-06-2002 L2005 **CD** *012 †20
HAGOOD, Lewis R, Jr. 2000 RIVER SOUND DR 37922 #047-06-1984 L1985 **IM** *062 †20
HALE, Darin Louis. 1924 ALCOA HWY 37920 #047-06-2002 L2007 **FM** *020
HALE, Meredith Danielle. 1924 ALCOA HWY U-67, UNIV OF TENNESSEE GRAD SCH 37920 #661-02-2006 **FP** *012
HALL, Don Jennings. 10810 PARKSIDE DR, STE 200 37934 #036-05-1971 L1979 **GO OBS** *020 †30
HALL, Glen Edward. 1120 E WEISGARBER RD, GROUP 37909 #047-06-2000 L2003 **IM** *020 †20
HALL, Robert Edmund. 2020 KAY ST 37920 #047-06-1963 L1967 **OPH** *035
HALL, Vaughan Dabney. 220 FORT SANDERS WEST BLVD, STE 101 37922 #051-01-1982 L1997 **FM** *020 †18
HAMILTON, Leo Haydon. ■ 37919 #001-02-2000 L2003 **PHO** *100 †55
HAMILTON, Steven Wesley. 9352 PARK WEST BLVD 37923 #020-12-1995 L1999 **APM AN** *020 †05
HAMMETT, Jay. 4711 CENTERLINE DR 37917 #045-01-1984 L1987 **GPM** *020 †18
HAMPTON, Amber Garland. ■ 37922 #047-20-2006 L2006 **GS** *100
HAMPTON, Bert Allan. 10219 KINGSTON PIKE, STE 100 37922 #047-06-1975 L1976 **PUD IM** *020 †20
HANCOCK, David Allen. 2725 E JOHN SEVIER HWY 37914 #047-06-1989 L1990 **ORS** *020
HANEY-WEAVER, Jerrie C. 939 E EMERALD AVE, STE 612 37917 #047-20-2002 L2006 **OBG** *020
HANNA, Samia Rizk. ■ 37919 #330-04-1969 L1981 **PTH CLP** *074

HANNA, Wahid Tewfik. 1924 ALCOA HWY BOX U-, RESEARCH CENTER AND HOSPIT 37920 #330-04-1969 L1980 **ON HEM** *020
HAQ, Jamshed U. 137 E BLOUNT AVE, KNOXVILLE ASSOCIATED 37920 #704-01-1960 L1974 **PTH OS** *020 †50 ‡
HARB, Joseph W. ■ 37919 #047-06-1960 L1967 **IM** *071 †20
HARGROVE, R Leslie. 5908 LYONS VIEW PIKE, LAKESHORE MENTAL HEALTH IN 37919 #041-01-1961 L1971 **GE IM** *030 †20
HARMON, William Neal. 9625 KROGER PARK DR, STE 450 37922 #055-01-1994 L1997 **IM** *020 †20
HARNED, Robert Glenn. 5908 LYONS VIEW PIKE 37919 #036-05-1986 L2004 **P** *020 †75
HARP, Daryl Louis. 210 FORT SANDERS WEST BLVD 37922 #048-02-1980 L1988 **DR** *020 †80
HARPER, John Michael. 9330 PARK WEST BLVD, STE 202 37923 #036-01-1973 L2001 **CD** *020 †20
HARPER, Kenneth Allen. 9349 PARK WEST BLVD # 107 37923 #012-01-1963 L1973 **PS HNS** *020 †65
HARRIS, David Jos, Jr. 1928 ALCOA HWY, STE 324 37920 #047-06-1978 L1984 **OPH** *020 †35
HARRIS, Denise M. 1932 ALCOA HWY, STE 460 37920 #028-78-1992, ▲ L2000 **NEP** *020 †20
HARRIS, Gayla Sue. 9301 PARK WEST BLVD, STE A 37923 #016-11-1986 L1993 **OBG** *020 †30
HARRIS, Lewis W, Jr. 1932 ALCOA HWY, STE 255 37920 #051-01-1982 L1995 **NS GS** *020 †25
HARRISON, James Thos. 8712 ASHEVILLE HWY, O.H.S. EAST KNOXVILLE CLIN 37924 #035-09-1982 L1990 **GS** *020 †85
HARRISON, John E B. 9430 PARK WEST BLVD, STE 130 37923 #062-01-1973 L1985 **ORS** *020 †40
HARRISON, William Edward. 1930 ALCOA HWY, PEDIATRIC CONSULTANTS INC 37920 #047-06-1971 L1972 **PD** *020
HART, Tadhg Michael. 11808 KINGSTON PIKE, FARRAGUT 37934 #048-13-1987 L1991 **FM** *020 †18
HARTLINE, Randal Garnett. 814 E WOODLAND AVE, KNOXVILLE, P.C. 37917 #012-01-1983 L1988 **OBG** *020 †30
HARVILLE, Lacy Edward, III. 2001 LAUREL AVE, STE 401 37916 #047-06-1985 L1992 **TS** *020 †85,90
HASANADKA, Thimmappayya. 5908 LYONS VIEW PIKE, LAKESHORE MENTAL HEALTH IN 37919 #495-09-1966 L2003 **P GP** *020 †75
HASKINS, Thomas G, III. 103 MIDLAKE DR, PHYSICIANS 37918 #047-06-1995 L1996 **FM** *020 †18
HASSELL, David Frank. 103 MIDLAKE DR, CLINIC 37918 #001-06-1980 L1981 **FM** *020 †18 ‡
HATCHER, Paul Arthur. 1932 ALCOA HWY C475 37920 #036-07-1983 L1991 **U GS** *020 †95
HAUFE, Frank J. 1818 ANDY HOLT AVE, 900 VOLUNTEER BLVD 37916 #016-06-1949 L1971 **GP** *020
HAWKINS, Jimmy Lynn. 200 FORT SANDERS WEST BLVD, INTERNAL MEDICINE 37922 #047-20-2001 L2004 **IM** *020
HAYMAN, Kenneth H, Jr. 1900 N WINSTON RD, STE 300 37919 #027-01-1983 L1983 **EM** *020
HAYS, James Martin. ■ 37923 #047-06-1956 L1959 **GPM GP** *071
HAYS, James Martin, Jr. 501 19TH ST STE 602 37916 #047-06-1981 L1981 **OBG ADL** *020 †30
HEADRICK, Jennifer Lynn. ■ 37919 #047-06-2006 **IM** *012
HECHT, Jeffrey S. 1932 ALCOA HWY, BLDG C 37920 #025-01-1979 L1982 **PM FM** *030 †60
HEGERICH, David Jonathan. ■ 37918 #012-01-2004 **IM** *012
HEISER, Don Richard. 9330 PARK WEST BLVD 37923 #016-11-1968 L1975 **U** *072 †95
HELMS, Van Edward. 9352 PARK WEST BLVD 37923 #047-06-1977 L1978 **EM** *020 †16
HELSEL, Robert Alan. 1940 ALCOA HWY STE 260 37920 #023-01-1969 L1988 **TS GS** *020 †85,90
HEMBREE, Douglas Kirby. 1932 ALCOA HWY, STE 570 37920 #047-06-1972 L1973 **IM** *020 †20
HEMPHILL, James Louis. 501 20TH ST STE G1, FT. SANDERS PROFESSIONAL B 37916 #027-01-1965 L19█ **OBG** *020 †30
HENDERSON, Kendric Knoll. 939 EMERALD AVE STE 907, KNOXVILLE NEUROLOGY CLINIC 37917 #017-20-1996 L2002 **CN** *020 †20,75
HENDERSON, Richard Winn. 2721 WHITTLE SPRINGS RD 37917 #001-02-1972 L1976 **ADM OS** *075 †18,16
HENDRICK, Sophia J. 814 E WOODLAND AVE 37917 #048-14-1982 L1987 **D** *020 †15 ‡
HENNESSY, Mark Donald. 1924 ALCOA HWY, DEPT OB 37920 #016-11-1986 L1992 **OBG** *020 †30
HENRY, Bertram Rowe. 214 S PETERS RD, STE 101 37923 #021-05-1967 L1973 **N** *020 †75
HENRY, Kevin Eugene. 433 SEVIER AVE 37920 #038-44-2000 L2003 **EM** *020 †16
HENSCHEN, Bruce Lowell. 1120 E WEISGARBER RD, CONSULTANTS 37909 #036-08-1982 L1987 **PUD PCC** *020 †20
HERMAN-GORRONDONA, Maria. 1120 E WEISGARBER RD, GROUP 37909 #429-02-1992 L2000 **IM** *020 †20
HERRELL, Evann Max. 1924 ALCOA HWY U-67, UNIVERSITY FAMILEY PHYSCIA 37920 #020-75-2003, ▲ L2004 **FM** *020 †20
HERRON, Lisa Michelle. 11416 GRIGSBY CHAPEL RD, STE 104 37934 #038-43-1998 L2003 **PD** *020 †20
HERTZOG, Michael S. 6501 DEANE HILL DR 37919 #001-02-1981 L1989 **DR** *020 †80
HETRICK, Thomas Henry. 7715 OAK RIDGE HWY 37931 #027-01-1974 L1975 **FM** *020 †18 ‡
HEWGLEY, Isham C. ■ 37934 #047-06-1984 L1986 **IM** *020 †20
HICKS, Howard K, Jr. 1924 ALCOA HWY, DEPT RAD 37920 #047-06-1974 L1975 **DR** *020 †80
HICKS, James Stacy. 1300 OLD WEISGARBER RD 37909 #045-01-1985 L1994 **FM** *020 †18
HICKS, Kimberly Griffin. 2018 W CLINCH AVE 37916 #047-06-1997 L2000 **PD** *020 †55
HIGGINBOTHAM, Raymond Alb. ■ 37909 #047-06-2007 **GS** *012
HIGGINS, Thomas Grant. 501 20TH ST, STE 303 37916 #041-12-1980 L1985 **N** *020 †75
HIGLEY, Thomas Meade. ■ 37918 #047-06-2004 **AN** *012
HILL, David Edwin. 2100 W CLINCH AVE, STE 120 37916 #047-06-1980 L1980 **UP** *020 †95
HILL, Hubert Cawood. 4711 CENTERLINE DR, ST. MARY'S EAST TOWNE 37917 #047-06-1947 L1948 **GP** *071
HILL, Jason Andrew. 1924 ALCOA HWY, SCH OF 37920 #047-06-2006 **DR** *012
HILL, Matthew Richard. 2018 W CLINCH AVE, EAST TENNESSEE CHILDRENS H 37916 #047-20-1990 L1999 **CCP PD** *020 †55
HILL, Michael Winslow. 10810 PARKSIDE DR, MEDICINE 37934 #001-06-1983 L1990 **DR** *020 †20,80
HILLMAN, David Carl. 2001 LAUREL AVE, STE 304 37916 #011-02-1960 L1987 **R NM** *071 †80,28
HILSENBECK, John Robt. 1924 ALCOA HWY, DEPT OF PATHOLOGY 37920 #011-02-1972 L1978 **ATP PTH** *030 †50
HIMEBAUGH, Karen Sue. 930 E EMERALD AVE, STE 615 37917 #047-06-1985 L1989 **OBG** *020 †30
HIMELRIGHT, Inga Marie. 6305 KINGSTON PIKE, BLUECROSS BLUESHIELD OF TN 37919 #011-04-1986 L1991 **ID** *020 †20

HINRICHS, Milbrey. ■ 37918 #047-06-1944 L1945 **PUD** *071
HIRSH, Jeffrey Brian. 1940 ALCOA HWY, STE E310 37920 #033-05-1995 L2002 **CD** *020 †20
HITCHCOCK, Danielle Kryst. ■ 37912 #048-15-2004 L2008 **OBG** *012
HOADLEY, Stephen D. 101 E BLOUNT AVE, CONSULTANTS PC 37920 #051-04-1977 L1988 **CD IM** *020 †20
HODGES, Patrick James. 1718 SAINT MARY ST 37917 #048-14-1985 L1989 **NPM** *020 †55
HODGES, Teri L. 1818 ANDY HOLT BLVD, UT STUDENT HEALTH SERVICES 37996 #047-06-1984 L1991 **ID IM** *020 †20
HOGAN, Julie Maree. ■ 37920 #047-06-2007 L2007 **IM** *012
HOGAN, William Mitchell. 1432 HICKEY RD, P O BOX 31649 37932 #001-02-1970 L1982 **P** *020 †75
HOIG, Oliver Ellsworth. 2018 W CLINCH AVE 37916 #030-05-1996 L2005 **AN** *020 †05,55
HOLBROOK, Deann Richele. 1900 N WINSTON RD, TEAM HLTH 37919 #047-20-1997 L2000 **PD** *020 †55
HOLLAND, Douglas Edward. 433 SEVIER AVE 37920 #047-06-1987 L1990 **IM** *020 †16
HOLLAND, Mark E. 9000 EXECUTIVE PARK DR, STE C200 37923 #047-06-1992 L1995 **IM FM** *020 †20
HOLLAND, Reuben Wright. ■ 37918 #047-06-1957 L1958 **GP OM** *020 †70
HOLLAND, Wm Arthur, Jr. 1900 N WINSTON RD, STE 300 37919 #047-20-1986 L1986 **FM** *020
HOLLOWAY, Brian G. 1704 JOHNNY MAJORS DR 37996 #041-13-1992 L1998 **ORS** *020 †40
HOLLOWAY, Kathleen Anne. 9017 CROSS PARK DR, STE 200 37923 #041-13-1992 L1998 **PD** *020 †55
HOLMES, Albert Keisling. 2020 KAY ST 37920 #047-06-1981 L1982 **OPH** *020 †35
HOLMES, Gregory Milton. 6501 DEANE HILL DR, MARYVILLE ANESTHESIOLOGIST 37919 #001-06-1980 L1982 **AN** *020
HOLMES, Lewis Henry, III. 939 EMERALD AVE, STE 610 37917 #045-01-2001 L2006 **NEP** *020 †20
HOLMES, Matthew Kyle. 1924 ALCOA HWY U-67, SCH OF 37920 #051-04-2006 **FP** *012
HOLMES, William Sanner. 210 FORT SANDERS WEST BLVD 37922 #047-20-1984 L1988 **DR** *030 †80
HOLST, Lorin Glen. 1932 ALCOA HWY, MEDICAL BLDG C, SUITE 570 37920 #016-11-1982 L2001 **IM** *075 †20
HOLT, Edwin Michael. 11440 PARKSIDE DR 37934 #047-06-1983 L1983 **ORS** *020 †40
HOLT, Jaclyn Beth. ■ 37924 #020-12-2004 L2008 **OBG** *012
HOOKMAN, Lawrence David. 939 EMERALD AVE, STE 505 37917 #048-12-1981 L1988 **CD IM** *020 †20
HOOPER, Fred Jos. 400 COMMERCE AVE 37902 #047-06-1947 L1947 **OM** *030
HOOPER, Mary Elizabeth. ■ 37919 #047-06-2004 L2007 **IM** *020
HORTON, Bennett Franklin. ■ 37909 #012-01-1953 L1955 **AN** *071 †05
HORTON, William Don. 1515 SAINT MARY ST, STE 200 37917 #047-06-1983 L1988 **OTO HNS** *020 †45
HOSKING, Michael Patrick. 1924 ALCOA HWY, STE U109 37920 #056-06-1985 L1993 **AN** *020 †05
HOSKINS, John Brandon. 1924 ALCOA HWY, UT. GRADUATE SCHOOL OF MED 37920 #047-20-2007 **IM** *012
HOSKINS, John Chas. 1225 E WEISGARBER RD, STE S380 37909 #047-06-1971 L1976 **OPH** *020 †35
HOUSER, Kris D. 214 S PETERS RD, STE 101 37923 #020-02-1987 L1992 **P** *020 †75
HOUSER, Molly Virginia. ■ 37914 #047-20-2004 L2008 **OBG** *012
HOVIS, Rachel Wright. ■ 37922 #047-06-2001 L2005 **IM** *020 †20
HOVIS, William David. 10810 PARKSIDE DR, STE 209 37934 #047-05-1993 L1994 **ORS OSM** *020 †40
HOVIS, William Marvin. 10810 PARKSIDE DR, STE 209 37934 #047-06-1966 L1967 **ORS OSM** *020 †40
HOWARD, Anne Frances. 224 S PETERS RD, STE 105 37923 #047-05-1997 L2003 **PD** *020 †55
HOWARD, Bobby Clayton. 1924 ALCOA HWY, 6-SOUTH 37920 #001-02-1993 L2007 **OBG** *020 †30
HOWARD, Cecil B. 1924 ALCOA HWY 37920 #047-05-1953 L1953 **PD** *071 †55
HOWARD, John Lawrence, II. 11201 W POINT DR, STE 103 37934 #047-05-1997 L2003 **OTO** *020 †45
HOWARD, Lewis Thos. 9031 CROSS PARK DR 37923 #047-06-1954 L1954 **GP GS** *071
HOWARD, Robert G. 2018 W CLINCH AVE 37916 #020-02-1966 L1976 **PD AM** *020
HOWE, William Curtis. 9241 PARK WEST BLVD, BLDG A 37923 #047-05-1992 L1996 **GS** *100
HOWICK, John Robt, Jr. 2018 W CLINCH AVE 37916 #001-02-1975 L1977 **NPM** *020 †55
HOWLADER, Anjuman Ara. 1924 ALCOA HWY, UNIV OF TENNESSEE GRAD SCH 37920 #160-02-1998 **IM** *012
HOYT, Robert Harrison, Jr. 4320 BALL CAMP PIKE 37921 #041-09-1979 L1984 **IM** *020 †20
HUANG, Laykoon Tan. 108 W INSKIP DR STE B 37912 #047-05-1975 L1975 **GP OM** *020 †70
HUANG, Po C. 900 W BAXTER AVE 37921 #244-06-1971 L1981 **GP UCM** *020
HUBBARD, Elizabeth W. 1924 ALCOA HWY 37920 #045-01-1986 L1990 **PTH** *020 †50
HUBNER, Karl Franz. 1924 ALCOA HWY 46, UNIV OF TENN HOSPITAL 37920 #407-10-1959 L1973 **NM OS** *071 †28 ‡
HUDDLESTON, Charles Irvin. 1928 ALCOA HWY, BLDG B 37920 #047-06-1966 L1967 **D GP** *020 †15
HUDSON, Arnold R, Jr. ■ 37922 #005-12-1967 L1976 **PUD IM** *071 †20
HUDSON, Kathleen T. 1924 ALCOA HWY 37920 #021-06-1989 L1990 **DR** *020 †80
HUFF, Dawn Maree. 5413 COVE ISLAND RD 37919 #047-06-1986 L1993 **PD** *020 †55
HUGHES, Brian Ward. 211 E BLOUNT AVE STE 507, THE HOSPITALIST GROUP 37920 #001-02-2000 L2004 **HOS IM** *020 †20 ‡
HUGHES, Jarvis Leland, Jr. 11551 KINGSTON PIKE 37934 #047-06-1976 L1977 **FM** *020 †18
HULL, Elizabeth Jane. 433 SEVIER AVE 37920 #017-20-2000 L2003 **EM** *020 †16
HUNTER, Teri L. 1018 ORCHID DR 37912 #047-20-2000 L2003 **FM** *020
HUNTSINGER, David Russell. 1940 ALCOA HWY, STE E310 37920 #021-01-1997 L2000 **CD IM** *020 †20
HUNTSINGER, Susan N. 1934 ALCOA HWY STE 474 37920 #021-01-1997 L2000 **HO IM** *020 †20
HURD, Aaron Michael. 1924 ALCOA HWY 37920 #422-01-2005 **GS** *012
HURST, Fred Alan. 4117 E EMORY RD 37938 #047-06-1973 L1973 **FM** *020 †18 ‡
HURST, James Wilson. 4117 E EMORY RD 37938 #047-06-2003 L2005 **IM** *020 †20
HUSKEY, Larry Cecil. 4117 E EMORY RD 37938 #047-06-1971 L1972 **FM** *020 †18
HUSSAIN, Mohammad Islam. 320 N PARK 40 BLVD STE B 37923 #915-04-1984 L1996 **N PM** *020
HUSSAIN, Zakir. 1120 E WEISGARBER RD, GROUP 37909 #704-02-1996 L2004 **PTH** *020 †20
HUSSAINI, Amir A A A. 10263 KINGSTON PIKE 37922 #704-02-1986 L2002 **P** *020
HUTCHINS, Stephen Fleming. 140 CAPITOL DR, ALLIANCE OF EAST 37922 #047-06-1974 L1975 **AN** *020 †05
HUTSON, Charles Combs. 200 E BLOUNT AVE STE 505 37920 #047-06-1954 L1954 **OTO** *020
HYATT, Hugh Crockett. 501 19TH ST STE 501, PREMIER SURG ASSOCS 37916 #047-06-1967 L1968 **GS VIR** *020 †85
IBACH, Daniel M. 9711 SHERRILL BLVD, STE 201 37932 #047-06-1994 L1997 **HO** *020 †20
IBRAHIM, Malik Abd A. 501 20TH ST, STE 503 37916 #528-04-1984 L2006 **CN** *100
INGRAHAM, Robert Quinn, Jr. 1932 ALCOA HWY, STE 255 37920 #021-01-1995 L2002 **NS** *020
INGRAM, Amanda Davis. ■ 37920 #047-06-2007 **TY** *012
IQBAL, Farzana. 200 E BLOUNT AVE, STE 502 37920 #704-02-1982 L2004 **IM** *020 †20
IQBAL, Muhammed. 2001 LAUREL AVE, STE 603 37916 #160-01-1984 L1997 **GE** *020 †20
IRWIN, John Bruce. 12328 BLUFF SHORE DR, P O BOX 30678 37922 #047-06-1975 L1975 **EM** *020 †16
ISON, Matthew Wallace. ■ 37938 #047-06-2008 *012
ISRAEL, Daniel. 5908 LYONS VIEW PIKE, LAKESHORE MENTAL HEALTH 37919 #495-27-1962 L1984 **PD EM** *020 †55
IVENS, Mark Young. 2020 KAY ST 37920 #047-06-1978 L1979 **OPH** *020 †35
IVY, Robert E, II. 1128 E WEISGARBER RD 37909 #047-05-1988 L1994 **ORS** *020
JACK, Laura Ellen. 1924 ALCOA HWY, DEPT IM 37920 #031-01-2007 **IM** *012
JACKSON, Becky Lynn. 9625 KROGER PARK DR, STE 400 37922 #038-40-1986 L1993 **IM** *020 †20
JACKSON, Kyoo. ■ 37931 #047-20-2008 *012
JACKSON, Mark Williams. 2001 LAUREL AVE, STE 603 37916 #028-03-1985 L1996 **GE IM** *020 †20
JACKSON, Rebecca T. 10215 KINGSTON PIKE 37922 #012-01-1991 L1996 **IM** *020 †20
JACKSON, Steve Judson. 3217 GARDEN DR 37918 #649-14-1981 L1993 **IM** *020 †18
JACOB, Pradeep Kumar. 1924 ALCOA HWY 37920 #001-02-1990 L2001 **RNR** *020 †80,28
JACOB, Sanjivini Vishwas. ■ 37922 #495-98-1988 L1996 **PCP** *075
JACOBS, Jeffry Alan. 600 ARTHUR ST 37921 #034-01-1999 L2004 **CHP P** *020 †75
JAFER, Jemal Hashim. ■ 37919 #848-01-1991 L2004 *020 †18
JAIN, Pradumna S. 3105 ESSARY DR 37918 #308-11-1985 L1995 **CHP** *020 †75
JAVIER, Maria Corazon B. 100 TECH CENTER DR, PEDIATRIC CONSULTANTS INC 37912 #748-22-1984 L1998 **PD** *020 †55
JEFFRIES, Glenn Edward. 11440 PARKSIDE DR 37934 #047-06-1974 L1975 **ORS** *020 †40
JENKINS, Basia. 501 20TH ST STE 606 37916 #025-07-1976 L1978 **AN PME** *020 †05
JENKINS, Chad Anthony. 1924 ALCOA HWY, SCH OF 37920 #038-40-2006 **AN** *012
JENKINS, Fred Ellis. ■ 37920 #047-06-1944 L1953 **GP** *071
JENNINGS, Jeffory G. 2100 W CLINCH AVE, STE 210 37916 #047-06-1976 L1983 **PDC PD** *020 †55
JENTILET, Douglas Adam. 1431 CENTERPOINT BLVD #100, TEAM HEALTH 37932 #017-20-1999 L2006 **EM** *020 †16
JERDEN, David Carle, Jr. 1120 E WEISGARBER RD, GROUP 37909 #047-06-1998 L1999 **IM** *020 †20
JERNIGAN, Thomas Lee. 1120 E WEISGARBER RD, GROUP 37909 #047-06-1993 L1995 **IM** *020 †20
JETHANANDANI, Arun. 1841 REGENTS PARK RD 37922 #495-53-1982 L1989 **P** *020
JETHANANDANI, Vijay. 900 E OAK HILL AVE, 1ST MARION 37917 #495-53-1981 L1989 **PYG P** *020 †75
JOBSON, Kenneth Owens. 7610 GLEASON DR, STE 302 37919 #012-05-1968 L1978 **P** *020 †75
JOCHER, Camilla Aemiliana. 1930 ALCOA HWY, PEDIATRIC CONSULTANTS INC 37920 #016-11-1981 L1990 **PD** *020 †55
JOFFE, Ralf. 522 TREYBURN DR 37934 #005-76-1987, ▲ L1999 **EM FM** *020 †16
JOHN, Cyriac. 10820 PARKSIDE DR 37934 #047-06-1993 L2004 **APM** *020 †05
JOHN, Sunil Mani. 101 E BLOUNT AVE STE 740 37920 #047-06-1990 L1993 **IM** *020 †20
JOHNSON, Hughes. ■ 37934 #047-06-1940 L1941 **D** *071 †15
JOHNSON, Jeffrey Hurst. 1940 ALCOA HWY, STE E310 37920 #047-06-1988 L1989 **CD** *020 †20
JOHNSON, Jerry Richard. ■ 37922 #047-06-1960 L1960 **GYN** *071 †30
JOHNSON, Joe Breese. ■ 37919 #047-06-1952 L1952 **R** *071 †80
JOHNSON, Joe Breese, Jr. 1112 E WEISGARBER RD, STE 201 37909 #047-06-1981 L1983 **DR** *020 †80
JOHNSON, Joseph Lee. 320 N CEDAR BLUFF RD, STE 330 37923 #043-01-1996 L1999 **IM** *020 †20
JOHNSON, Michele Marie. 626 BERNARD AVE, DRD KNOXVILLE MEDICAL CLIN 37921 #021-05-1990 L2006 **IM ID** *020 †20
JOHNSON, Paul Harriss. 1704 JOHNNY MAJORS DR 37996 #016-06-1989 L1995 **ORS** *020 †40
JOHNSON, William Larry. 2001 LAUREL AVE, STE 402 37916 #047-06-1982 L1993 **ORS OSM** *020 †40
JOHNSON, Wm Reeves, Jr. 501 20TH ST, FORT SANDERS 37916 #001-02-1983 L1988 **FM** *020 †18
JOHNSTON, Cheri Conley. 9625 KROGER PARK DR, STE 500 37922 #020-02-1985 L1986 **FM** *020 †18
JOHNSTON, Jeffrey Scott. 1924 ALCOA HWY 37920 #020-02-2001 L2003 **FOP** *020 †50
JONES, Billy Paul. ■ 37919 #047-06-1997 L2000 **PD** *020 †55
JONES, Cheryl Ashley. 1924 ALCOA HWY U-67, SCH OF 37920 #654-01-2006 **FP** *012
JONES, Donald Ennis. 6501 DEANE HILL DR 37919 #048-04-1979 L1990 **OS** *020 †05
JONES, Edwin Clay. 9031 CROSS PARK DR, VA OUTPATIENT CLINIC 37923 #047-07-2000 L2004 **P** *020
JONES, Francis S. 1924 ALCOA HWY, UNIVERSITY HOSPITAL 37920 #024-05-1946 L1954 **PTH BBK** *071 †50
JONES, Jonathan Eli. 1924 ALCOA HWY U-67, SCH OF 37920 #047-06-2006 L2008 **FM** *100
JONES, Thomas Matthew. ■ 37917 #027-01-2007 **GS** *012
JORDON, Mark Steven. 211 E BLOUNT AVE, STE 507 37920 #025-07-1980 L1988 **AN** *020 †05
JOURDAN, Paul Leon. ■ 37924 #047-06-1959 L1960 **GP** *071
JULIUS, Clark Eldon. 1928 ALCOA HWY, STE 209 37920 #018-03-1965 L1971 **D** *071 †15
JUNG, Glenn Edward. 210 FORT SANDERS WEST BLVD 37922 #011-03-1990 L1995 **DR** *020 †80
KABBANI, Samir Al. 9430 PARK WEST BLVD, STE 350 37923 #875-01-1979 L1987 **N PMM** *020 ‡
KAHN, Edward Keith. 10321 KINGSTON PIKE 37922 #011-02-1982 L1994 **ORS OSS** *020 †40
KAMMONA, Hussein Alwan. 1900 N WINSTON RD STE 300, TEAM HEALTH 37919 #528-04-1984 L1998 **IM PD** *020 †20,55
KANG-ROTONDO, Cynthia H. 814 E WOODLAND AVE, DERMATOLOGY SPLST PLLC 37917 #043-01-1985 L1991 **D** *020 †15
KAPLAN, Mary Gretchen. 501 19TH ST, STE 701 37916 #047-06-1974 L1974 **OBG** *050 †30
KASERMAN, Fred Brown. 9430 PARK WEST BLVD, STE 240 37923 #047-06-1969 L1970 **PS OS** *020 †65
KATTINE, Anthony Albert. 1924 ALCOA HWY DEPT PATH 37920 #021-05-1957 L1966 **PTH** *071 †50

■ = Address Information Privacy Protected

KAUFMAN, Nesreen Hanna. ■ 37934 #422-01-2001 L2006 **GS** *100

KAUFMAN, Paul Emmett. 550 W MAIN ST, STE 600 37902 #035-03-1976 L1979 **EM** *020 †16

KEENAN, Jeffrey Alan. 10810 PARKSIDE DR, STE 304 37934 #041-02-1983 L1987 **REN OBG** *020 †30 ‡

KELLETT, Philip Benson. 2018 W CLINCH AVE 37916 #917-05-1973 L1978 **PD AN** *100 †05

KEMP, Ernest Brian. 1915 WHITE AVE, KIDC KNOXVILLE INFECTIOUS 37916 #038-43-1985 L1995 **ID** *020 †20

KENDALL, Ross S. 4709 PAPERMILL DR, BLDG 1 37909 #035-06-1972 L2000 **PD PG** *020 †55

KENNEDY, Alfred P, Jr. 2100 W CLINCH AVE, STE 430 37916 #041-09-1990 L2004 **PDS GS** *020 †85

KENNEDY, James Jos. 101 E BLOUNT AVE, STE 820 37920 #047-06-1985 L1990 **P** *020 †75

KENNEDY, Michael B. 501 20TH ST, STE 101 37916 #047-06-1984 L1985 **IM EM** *020 †20

KENT, Mark Gregory. 101 E BLOUNT AVE STE 600, BAPTIST MED TOWER 37920 #001-02-1995 L2001 **GS** *020 †85

KEOUGH, George Carey. 900 E OAK HILL AVE, STE 500 CENTRAL ANNEX 37917 #011-04-1992 L2001 **D** *020 †15

KERLEY, Harold Eugene. ■ 37919 #047-06-1965 L1966 **R** *071

KERNS, Ross Eric. 9430 PARK WEST BLVD, STE 120 37923 #047-20-1984 L1990 **HEM ON** *020 †20

KERSEY, Brant Gregory. 601 GOVERNOR JOHN SEVR HWY 37920 #012-01-1999 L2002 **FM** *020 †18

KERSEY, Pamela Leanne. 601 GOVERNOR JOHN SEVR HWY 37920 #012-01-1999 L2002 **FM** *020 †18 ‡

KESSLER, Kathryn Paige. 10810 PARKSIDE, STE 108 37934 #055-01-1999 L2003 **OBG** *020

KESTERSON, Gregg H D. 501 20TH ST, FORT SANDERS 37916 #047-06-1983 L1986 **IM** *020 †20

KESTERSON, John E. 1924 ALCOA HWY 37920 #047-05-1943 L1943 **GS** *071 †85

KHALIL, Mazen Younis. 1934 ALCOA HWY, MED BLD D STE 472 37920 #875-03-1994 L2006 **HO** *020 ‡

KHAN, Mujeeb Hasan. 137 E BLOUNT AVE 37920 #704-01-1977 L2001 **P** *020 †75 ‡

KHANNA, Manju. 224 S PETERS RD STE 208 37923 #495-12-1971 L1995 **P** *020

KILLEFFER, Fred Ayres. 1924 ALCOA HWY 37920 #047-06-1958 L1959 **NS** *020 †25

KILLEFFER, James A. 1932 ALCOA HWY STE 470 37920 #047-06-1991 L1997 **NS** *020 †25

KIM, Edward David. 1928 ALCOA HWY, STE 222 37920 #016-06-1989 L1999 **U** *020 †95

KIM, Hea Za. 5809 LYONS VIEW PIKE, LAKE MENTAL HEALTH INST 37919 #583-08-1969 L2006 **P** *071

KIM, Kimberly. 1431 CENTERPOINT BLVD, STE 100 37932 #047-07-2002 L2005 **PD** *020 †55

KIM, Yoo Keun. 6207 CHAPMAN HWY 37920 #583-01-1974 L1981 **IM ON** *020

KIMBALL, Jimmy C. 4529 ASHEVILLE HWY 37914 #048-15-1975 L1981 **PD EM** *55

KIMBLE, James Robt. 2020 KAY ST 37920 #048-02-1976 L1983 **OPH** *020 †35

KINCAID, Geoffrey Carl. 200 FORT SANDERS WEST BLVD, STE 301 37922 #038-41-1974 L1977 **GYN** *020 †30

KING, Bernadette Tan. 1928 ALCOA HWY 37920 #047-06-1986 L1990 **DR** *020 †80

KING, Dennis R. ■ 37922 #308-11-1986 L1994 **FM** *071 †18

KING, Franklin Gregory. 501 20TH ST, STE 606 37916 #047-06-1986 L1990 **AN** *020 †05 ‡

KING, Jack Donald, Jr. 1826 AILOR AVE 37921 #047-06-1971 L1972 **FM OM** *020 †20

KING, Jeffry Thos. 1915 WHITE AVE, KIDC KNOXVILLE INFECTIOUS 37916 #048-12-1981 L1986 **ID IM** *020 †20

KING, Mariano Lo. ■ 37923 #748-01-1954 L1977 **GP** *071

KING, Roy. 315 ERIN DR 37919 #836-01-1988 L1998 **DMP** *020 †50

KINZY, Judith Daniel. 4005 FOUNTAIN VALLEY DR, HALLS MED PLZ 37918 #051-07-1990 L1993 **IM** *020 †20

KIRBY, James Thomas, Jr. 9333 PARK WEST BLVD 37923 #047-06-1998 L2001 **IM** *020 †20

KIRK, Clifford C, Jr. 213 SAINT ANDREWS DR 37934 #047-06-1963 L1963 **R** *020 †80

KIRZEDER, Daniel James. ■ 37912 #826-04-2004 L2008 **DR** *012

KLARICH, Rena Teri. ■ 37919 #047-06-1990 L1993 **OBG** *020 †30

KLEIN, Carl John. 1104 MERCHANT DR 37912 #016-11-1974 L1975 **FM** *020

KLEIN, Frederick Abraham. 1928 ALCOA HWY, STE 127 37920 #016-43-1974 L1986 **U** *020 †95

KLENCK, Chris Allen. 1704 JOHNNY MAJORS DR 37996 #017-20-2001 L2006 **FSM** *020 †20,55

KLETO, Demosthenes Dean. 9123 CROSS PARK DR BLDG 2, STE 100 37923 #047-06-1979 L1980 **PS HS** *020 †65

KLIEFOTH, A Bernhard, III. 718 WESTBOROUGH RD 37909 #048-02-1970 L1981 **NS N** *020 †25

KLIGERMAN, Sidney. ■ 37931 #016-11-1940 L1940 **PYA P** *071 †75

KLIPPLE, Gary Lee. 1932 ALCOA HWY, STE 550 37920 #047-06-1970 L1971 **RHU IM** *020 †20

KNIGHT, Marion B, Jr. ■ 37934 #011-02-1962 L1975 **OS** *075

KNIGHT, Steven Patrick. 1924 ALCOA HWY 37920 #047-06-1998 L2002 **DR** *020 †80

KNOWLING, Robert Edward. ■ 37927 #047-06-1959 L1960 **PS** *071 †65

KODOTH, Sangeetha Mohan. 1346 DOWELL SPRINGS BLVD 37909 #495-44-1992 L2001 **AI PD** *020 †03,55

KOENIG, Thomas Martin. 11808 KINGSTON PIKE # 190 37934 #041-09-1986 L1992 **ORS OSM** *020 †40

KOLLER, Darwin Martin. 1900 N WINSTON RD, STE 300 37919 #051-07-1999 L2005 **PEM** *100 †55

KONOMOS, William. 501 20TH ST, STE G3 37916 #038-40-1994 L2003 **PTH** *020 †50

KORNREICH, Martin Allen. 37914 #011-03-1965 L1973 **ORS** *071 †40

KOSENTKA, Anna Ewa. 2100 W CLINCH AVE 37916 #759-08-1979 L2005 **PD** *100

KOZLOWSKI, Kamilia. 6307 LONAS DR 37909 #025-07-1976 L1982 **R OS** *020 †80

KRAMER, Troy Donald. 1120 E WEISGARBER RD, STE 201 37909 #021-06-1991 L2007 **PCC** *020 †20

KRAUSS, Stephen. 1924 ALCOA HWY MEM RES CTR 37920 #041-01-1958 L1970 **ON HEM** *071 †20

KROPILAK, Michael D. 501 19TH ST STE 501 37916 #041-09-1982 L1988 **GS VS** *020 †85

KUBOTA, Thomas Tomi. 2001 LAUREL AVE, STE NG3 37916 #016-02-1974 L1986 **ON** *020 †20

KUCHIBOTLA, Gayathri. 1120 E WEISGARBER RD, GROUP 37909 #496-24-1994 L2000 **CD** *012 †20

KUMAR, Arvind. 5908 LYONS VIEW PIKE, LAKESHORE MENTAL HEALTH IN 37919 #495-29-1974 L1992 **P** *020

KURTZ, Jenifer A. 2027 N BROADWAY ST 37917 #048-04-1995 L1999 **IMG** *020 †20

KVAMME, Peter. 1924 ALCOA HWY 37920 #021-01-1992 L2001 **VIR** *020 †80

LACEY, John Wm, III. 1520 CHEROKEE TRL, STE 200 37920 #047-06-1973 L1974 **IM** *020

LACHARITE, Claude Anding. ■ 37934 #020-12-1999 L2002 **PCC** *020

LAING, Geoffrey Glynn. 1924 ALCOA HWY 37920 #048-02-2001 L2007 **DR** *100 †80

LAING, William Gavin. 2001 LAUREL AVE, STE 110 37916 #047-06-1955 L1955 **GE IM** *071 †20

LALL, Ameeta. 2018 W CLINCH AVE 37916 #047-20-2000 L2003 **PD** *020 †55 ‡

LANGDON, James Russell. 1924 ALCOA HWY, STE U109 37920 #047-06-1978 L1984 **AN IM** *020 †05

LANGFORD, Chas Thos, Jr. 909 WEATHERLY HILLS BLVD 37934 #047-06-1966 L1967 **NEP IM** *071

LARMEE, Donald Edward. 1124 E WEISGARBER RD # 200 37909 #020-02-1965 L1971 **PD** *020 †55

LARSON, Ramsey G. 1900 N WINSTON RD, STE 603 37919 #043-01-1992 L1995 **FM** *020 †18

LATTIMORE, Keri Anne. 1930 ALCOA HWY, STE 145 37920 #012-01-2000 L2007 **NPM** *100 †55

LAUG, Dennis Geo. 11220 W POINT DR 37934 #025-07-1970 L1977 **PD** *020 †55

LAW, John Lynn. 11416 GRIGSBY CHAPEL RD, FARRAGUT 37934 #422-01-1983 L1990 **FM** *020 †18

LAW, Nancy Pendleton. CHATEAUGAY RD 37923 #051-04-1948 L1962 **OS** *074

LAW, William M, Sr. 1924 ALCOA HWY 37920 #051-04-1948 L1956 **END IM** *071 †20

LAW, William M, Jr. 1450 DOWELL SPRINGS BLVD 37909 #047-06-1976 L1977 **END IM** *020 †20

LAWRENCE, Karl Everette. 7328 MIDDLEBROOK PIKE, WESTBROOK MEDICAL CENTER, 37909 #047-06-1995 L1998 **IM** *020

LAWSON, Christy Marie. 1924 ALCOA HWY, SCH OF 37920 #012-01-2005 **GS** *012

LAZARUS, Stephen Mark. 801 N WEISGARBER RD # 500 37909 #021-01-1975 L1980 **PS** *020 †85,65

LE, Thuc Thibich. ■ 37918 #047-06-2005 **AN** *012

LEAHY, Michael Douglas. 930 E EMERALD AVE, ASSOCIATES 37917 #047-06-1973 L1974 **IM** *020 †20

LE BEL, J Serge. 1928 ALCOA HWY, J SERGE LEBEL MD PC 37920 #065-09-1966 L1972 **GE** *071

LEBOW, Michael Hart. ■ 37919 #051-01-2001 L2002 **VS** *012 †85

LE BUFFE, Francis Peter. 939 EMERALD AVE, STE 608 37917 #023-07-1971 L1993 **P** *020 †75

LEE, Jay David. 11440 PARKSIDE DR 37934 #047-20-1987 L1993 **GE** *020 †20

LEE, Patricia Wasik. ■ 37919 #047-20-1987 L1993 **PUD** *020

LEE, Richard Thos. 101 E BLOUNT AVE, PLLC SUITE 610 37920 #047-06-1988 L1994 **ON** *020 †20

LEE, William Luke. 433 SEVIER AVE, RIVERMONT 37920 #047-06-1989 L1993 **EM** *020 †16

LE FORCE, Bruce Ryan. 220 FORT SANDERS WEST BLVD, STE 300 37922 #020-02-1985 L1998 **N CN** *020 †75

LEISY, Marlyn Ann. 9430 PARK WEST BLVD, GENERATIONS OB GYN PC 37923 #047-06-1977 L1978 **OBG** *020 †20

LEMBERSKY, Robert Bruce. 712 WESTBOROUGH RD 37909 #016-02-1989 L1995 **AN** *012 †55

LEMENSE, Gregory Paul. 2001 LAUREL AVE, STE 101 37916 #047-06-1989 L1990 **PUD CCM** *020 †20

LEONARD, Joe H. 2001 LAUREL AVE 37916 #047-06-1952 L1952 **IM NEP** *071

LEPAGE, James Robt. 1924 ALCOA HWY 37920 #583-09-1963 L1987 **VIR DR** *071

LESTER, Thomas Edward. ■ 37920 #047-06-1962 L1963 **PD** *071 †50

LE TARD, Francis X, Jr. 10265 KINGSTON PIKE STE C 37922 #021-05-1973 L1981 **PS** *020

LETT, James Chancey. ■ 37922 #047-06-1955 L1955 **GS** *071 †85

LETT, Michael Foster. 11730 KINGSTON PIKE 37934 #047-06-1979 L1979 **OPH** *020 †35

LEWIS, Gloria Lovelace. 140 CAPITOL DR, ALLIANCE OF EAST 37922 #012-01-1977 L1984 **AN IM** *020 †05

LEWIS, Robert A. 501 20TH ST, STE 202 37916 #047-06-1952 L1952 **D** *020 †15

LEWIS, Ryan Christopher. 1924 ALCOA HWY U-67, UNIV OF TENNESSEE GRADUATE 37920 #654-01-2005 L2008 **FP** *012

LIANEKHAMMY, Phonesavane. ■ 37912 #020-02-2004 **IM** *012

LIAW, Kevin. ■ 37922 #047-05-2008 *012

LIETZKE, Christiana Marie. 1431 CENTERPOINT BLVD, STE 100 37932 #047-06-2002 L2003 **MPD** *020 †20,55

LIGHTER, Donald Eugene. 2120 RIVER SOUND DR 37922 #028-34-1973 L1983 **PD** *030 †55

LIN, Jennyu Jeff. 11416 GRIGSBY CHAPEL RD, STE 104 37934 #001-02-1995 L2005 **PD** *020 †20

LINCOLN, Thomas A. ■ 37934 #026-04-1950 L1951 **OM** *071 †70

LINDSAY, James H, Jr. 2908 TAZEWELL PIKE, STE A-D 37918 #045-01-1980 L1985 **GYN** *020 †30

LINDSAY, Robert Lynn. 6501 DEANE HILL DR 37919 #047-06-1991 L1992 **DR EM** *020 †80

LINDSAY, William Corwin. 101 E BLOUNT AVE, CONSULTANTS PC 37920 #012-01-1981 L1989 **ICE CD** *020

LINDSTROM, Grant M. 9352 PARK WEST BLVD 37923 #037-01-1990 L1995 **PTH** *020 †50

LINE, Felix Glen. ■ 37919 #047-06-1944 L1945 **PD** *071 †55

LINE, Mary Lee Pittman. ■ 37919 #047-06-1944 L1945 **PHP** *071

LINN, Brian Keith. ■ 37920 #004-01-2004 L2007 **FM** *020 †18

LINN, David Christian. 522 SERENITY LN 37934 #048-04-1995 L2002 **EM** *020 †16

LISCHER, Garrett Henry. 101 E BLOUNT AVE, STE 100 37920 #048-12-1998 L2003 **U** *020 †95

LITTLE, John Perry. 2100 W CLINCH AVE, STE 410 37916 #047-06-1992 L1998 **PDO OTO** *020 †45

LITTLEFIELD, Thomas Ralph. 11808 KINGSTON PIKE, FARRAGUT 37934 #047-06-1977 L1979 **PUD IM** *020 †20

LIU, Joseph Chensin. 1940 ALCOA HWY, STE E310 37920 #016-06-1990 L2000 **CD IM** *020 †20

LOAIZA, Sergio. 220 FORT SANDERS WEST BLVD, STE 300 37922 #264-01-1986 L2000 **CN** *020 †75

LONG, Henry Heath. ■ 37919 #047-06-1953 L1953 **PD PDC** *071 †55

LORCH, Vichien. 1930 ALCOA HWY, STE 145 37920 #891-02-1965 L1980 **NPM** *020 †55 ‡

LORINO, Stephen Peter. 900 E OAK HILL AVE 37917 #047-20-1995 L1998 **IM** *020 †20

LOVELACE, Randy Scott. 200 E BLOUNT AVE, STE 200 37920 #036-08-1996 L2003 **PCC** *020 †20

LOWREY, Daniel B. ■ 37931 #028-02-1950 L1950 **OPH** *071 †35

LOWRY, Randolph Murphree. 200 FORT SANDERS WEST BLVD, STE 302 37922 #047-06-1977 L1979 **GP** *075 †20

LOWRY, Thomas Henry. 224 S PETERS RD, STE 105 37923 #047-06-1966 L1969 **PD** *020 †55

LOZZIO, Carmen Bertucci. 1930 ALCOA HWY, STE 435 37920 #132-01-1955 L1975 **OS PD** *019

LUALLEN, Jennifer Jane. ■ 37912 #047-06-1982 L1982 **PHP** *020 †55

LUCAS, Jay H. 10810 PARKSIDE DR, STE 310 37934 #047-01-1994 L2002 **PS** *020 †65

LUCAS, Melinda Ann. 1924 ALCOA HWY, DEPT OF PEDS EMERG MED 37920 #047-06-1981 L1984 **CCP PEM** *020 †55 ‡

LUCHSINGER, Scott Trent. 1120 E WEISGARBER RD, CONSULTANTS 37909 #056-06-1987 L1997 **PUD** *020 †20

LUNA, Joe Louis. 137 E BLOUNT AVE, SPCH & HEARING GRD FLR 37920 #047-06-1959 L1959 **ORS** *071 †40

LUNDERS, William Geo. 1900 N WINSTON RD, STE 300 37919 #046-01-1979 L2005 **FM** *020 †16

LUNDGRIN, Daryl Brent. 9303 PARK WEST BLVD 37923 #039-01-1977 L1994 **PTH HMP** *020 †50

LUTTRELL, Arvell Stanley. 9330 PARK WEST BLVD, STE 507 37923 #047-06-1965 L1965 P PYA *020 †75

LUTTRELL, Kelli Renee. 1924 ALCOA HWY 37920 #011-75-2005, ▲ OBG *012

LYNCH, Penny Beth. 140 CAPITOL DR, ALLIANCE OF EAST 37922 #047-06-1983 L1984 AN *020 †05

LYNE, James Evans. 4253 HOLLOWAY DR 37919 #047-05-1987 L1990 GP *020

LYNN, Kristie. 5908 LYONS VIEW PIKE, LAKE SHORE MENTAL HEALTH 37919 #047-06-1972 L1973 FM P *020 †18

LYNNES, Howard Malcolm. ■ 37922 #060-01-1954 L1979 GP NR *075

MACHEN, Charles Wm. 224 S PETERS RD, STE 105 37923 #021-05-1974 L1995 PD ADL *020 †55

MACK, John W, Jr. 1940 ALCOA HWY, STE E260 37920 #051-04-1972 L1985 TS *020 †85,90

MACK, Lamar Octavius. 1924 ALCOA HWY, SCH OF 37920 #036-01-2006 GS *012

MACLEAN, Ronald Neil. 1930 ALCOA HWY, STE 435 37920 #132-01-1948 L1980 OS PD *071 †19

MAC NAUGHTON, Jon Mark. 10810 PARKSIDE DR, STE 109 37934 #047-06-1987 L1992 ORS *020 †40

MADDOX, John Roberts, Jr. 2100 W CLINCH AVE, STE 430 37916 #047-06-1958 L1958 PDS *071 †85

MADIGAN, Luke. 1704 JOHNNY MAJORS DR 37996 #041-02-2001 L2007 ORS *020

MADIGAN, Robert Regis. 1704 JOHNNY MAJORS DR 37996 #041-02-1967 L1974 ORS *020 †40

MAGGART, Michael Lynn. 101 E BLOUNT AVE, STE 800 37920 #047-05-1978 L1983 TS *020 †85,90

MAGUIRE, James K, Jr. 1704 JOHNNY MAJORS DR 37996 #047-06-1983 L1984 ORS *020 †40

MALAD, Salman. 9430 PARK WEST BLVD, STE 120 37923 #905-02-2000 L2007 HO *020

MALIK, Shahid Ahmed. 2018 W CLINCH AVE, PED HEM/ONCPO BOX 15010 37916 #704-02-1984 L1993 PD PHO *020 †55

MALIYEKKEL, Ittoop T. 5908 LYONS VIEW PIKE 37919 #495-52-1970 L1982 P *020 ‡

MANCEBO, Gerald Louis. 930 E EMERALD AVE, ASSOCIATES 37917 #048-15-1979 L1983 IM DIA *020 †20

MANCINI, Gregory John. 1924 ALCOA HWY, BOX U-11 37920 #012-22-2000 L2006 GS *020 †85 ‡

MANCINI, Matthew Lawrence. 1924 ALCOA HWY, STE 240 37920 #012-22-1994 L1999 GS *020 †85

MANN, Julianne. 1818 ANDY HOLT AVE 37916 #045-01-1980 L1981 IM PHP *020

MANNING, David Bryan. 600 ARTHUR ST 37921 #038-40-1987 L1991 P PYG *020 †75

MANNING, Richard Oliver. 313 CONCORD ST, VOLUNTEER WOMENS MED CLNC 37919 #036-05-1972 L1979 GYN OS *020 †30

MANNING, Rickey Dean. 4117 E EMORY RD 37938 #047-20-1988 L1990 FM *020 †18

MAPES, Donald Lee. BAPTIST PROFESSIONAL BLDG, PRIMARY CARE ASSOCIATES 37920 #005-12-1961 L1993 FM *071 †18

MAPLES, Maria Ellen. ■ 37920 #047-06-2007 IM *012

MARCY, John Saml. 9430 PARK WEST BLVD, STE 130 37923 #047-06-1968 L1969 ORS *020 †40

MARDINI, Antoin Hanna. 10215 KINGSTON PIKE 37922 #306-01-1991 L1995 IM *020

MARGULIES, Aaron Bledsoe. 6307 LONAS DR, CENTER 37909 #016-11-1993 L1997 GS *020 †85

MARIETTA, Stephen Louis. 9330 PARK WEST BLVD, CONSULTANTS PC 37923 #030-06-1979 L1985 CD IM *020 †20

MARLOW, Douglas James. 200 E BLOUNT AVE, STE 101 37920 #038-43-1994 L2001 IM *020 †20

MARTIN, David Allen. 10810 PARKSIDE DR, STE 200 37934 #017-20-1984 L1995 GO OBG *020 †30

MARTIN, Jonathan Gerald. 211 E BLOUNT AVE, STE 507 37920 #047-20-1999 L2003 FM *020 †18

MARTIN, Robert Owen. 101 E BLOUNT AVE, CONSULTANTS PC 37920 #010-02-1977 L1984 CD IM *020 †20

MARTINOLICH, Kevin M. 1940 ALCOA HWY, STE E210 37920 #035-03-1991 L1999 PCC *020 †20

MASCIOLI, Charles Jos. 1431 CENTERPOINT BLVD, STE 100 37932 #048-14-1984 L2005 IM *020 †20

MASSINGALE, Harold Lynn. 1900 N WINSTON RD, STE 300 37919 #047-06-1977 L1977 EM OS *100 †16

MASTER, Charles P. 1900 N WINSTON RD, STE 500 37919 #035-09-1996 L1998 DR *020

MASTERS, Steven Bradley. 103 MIDLAKE DR, PHYSICIANS 37918 #047-06-1983 L1984 FM *020 †18

MATHES, Catherine Lee. 200 FORT SANDERS WEST BLVD, MOB 1, STE 304 37922 #047-06-1990 L1993 IM *020 †20

MATHEWS, Carl Leslie. ■ 37934 #004-01-1966 L1974 CLP PTH *071 †50

MATHIEN, Gregory Mark. 1704 JOHNNY MAJORS DR 37996 #035-15-1986 L1991 ORS GS *020 †40

MAVES, Barry Victor. 11440 PARKSIDE DR 37934 #025-07-1980 L1986 GE IM *020 †20

MAY, Charles Randall. 1111 N NORTHSHORE DR 5490 37919 #020-02-1985 L1994 P *020 †75

MAY, Lonnie C, Jr. 433 SEVIER AVE 37920 #047-06-1950 L1950 EM OS *071

MAYNARD, Samuel Louis. 930 E EMERALD AVE, STE 512 37917 #047-06-1995 L2000 DR *020 †80

MAYS, Richard Harold. 7209 CHAPMAN HWY 37920 #020-12-1984 L1985 FM *020 †18

MC ALLISTER, Nancy Eileen. ■ 37918 #047-20-1984 PTH *071

MCBRIDE, Richard R. 900 E OAK HILL AVE, CONSULTANTS PC 37917 #654-01-1989 L2004 CD *020 †20

MC CACHREN, S Spence, Jr. 1915 WHITE AVE, THOMPSON ONCOLOGY 37916 #036-07-1978 L1994 ON HEM *050 †20

MC CALL, Chas Louis, Jr. 2001 LAUREL AVE, STE N304 37916 #021-06-1980 L1984 DR *020 †80 ‡

MC CALLEN, Perry Boies. 501 20TH ST 37916 #047-06-1960 L1968 OTO *071 †45

MCCALLISTER, Matthew Char. ■ 37932 #047-06-2008 *012

MC CAMMON, Curtis P. ■ 37919 #041-13-1949 L1950 PHP *071 †70

MCCAMMON, Daniel Kevin. 1450 DOWELL SPRINGS BLVD 37909 #047-06-1987 L1989 END *020 †20

MC CAULEY, Lowell L, Jr. 930 E EMERALD AVE, STE 515 37917 #020-02-1984 L1989 OBG *020 †30

MC CLARY, Lowell Reece. ■ 37909 #020-02-1959 L1960 MDM *071

MCCOLL, Mark Benton. 220 FORT SANDERS WEST BLVD, STE 101 37922 #047-06-2002 L2006 MPD *100 †20,55

MC COLLUM, Lionel Dean. 9430 PARK WEST BLVD, GENERATIONS OB GYN PC 37923 #047-06-1979 L1979 OBG *020 †30

MC COLLUM, Michael J. 11440 PARKSIDE DR 37934 #047-20-1993 L1998 ORS *020 †40

MCCONVILLE, Patrick Owen. ■ 37922 #021-01-2005 AN *012

MC CORMACK, Michael T. 1940 ALCOA HWY STE E210, KNOXVILLE PULMONARY GROUP 37920 #005-06-1984 L1995 IM *020 †20

MC COY, Kyle W. 900 E OAK HILL AVE, CONSULTANTS PC 37917 #048-12-1988 L1994 IM CD *020 †20

MC COY, William John, III. 1124 E WEISGARBER RD, EAST TN EYE CARE ASSOCS PC 37909 #047-06-1955 L1956 OPH *071 †35

MC CROSKEY, Marye Lois. 1924 ALCOA HWY 37920 #051-04-1986 L1988 FM *020 †18

MC DONALD, Thomas Wm. 220 FORT SANDERS WEST BLVD, STE 202 37922 #020-02-1971 L1986 GO OBG *020 †30

MCDONALD, William Wayne. 9711 SHERRILL BLVD 37932 #012-05-1985 L1995 RO *020 †80

MC DOWELL, Philip Gene, Jr. 11440 PARKSIDE DR 37934 #047-06-2002 L2007 ORS *020

MC GINN, Larry Dean. ■ 37923 #019-02-1968 L1974 AN GP *020 †05

MC GINNIS, Carroll Wm. 1208 MERCHANT DR 37912 #047-06-1962 L1962 GP *075

MC GOLDRICK, Justin B. 1900 N WINSTON RD, STE 300 37919 #021-01-1998 L2001 EM *020 †16

MC GUIRE, Jean Nicholas. ■ 37920 #035-09-2004 AN *012

MC HARGUE, Donna. 10810 PARKSIDE DR, MEDICINE 37934 #001-06-1983 L1990 IM EM *020

MCKEETHREN, Carla Gipson. 1930 ALCOA HWY, PEDIATRIC CONSULTANTS INC 37920 #047-06-1975 L1976 PD *020 †55

MC KENZIE, Donald Keith. 3301 TAZEWELL PIKE 37918 #047-06-1975 L1976 IM IMG *020 †20

MC KENZIE, Jerome F. 9333 PARK WEST BLVD, STE 210 37923 #047-06-1973 L1974 IM *020

MC KEOWN, Frank R. 9430 PARK WEST BLVD, GENERATIONS OB GYN PC 37923 #048-04-1995 L1997 OBG *020 †30

MC KINNEY, Marion Berry. ■ 37922 #047-06-1942 L1942 OM *071

MC KISSICK, William Rober. 930 E EMERALD AVE, STE 512 37917 #047-06-1971 L1971 DR *020 †80 ‡

MC LEAN, Alan Robb. ■ 37918 #017-20-2002 L2005 EM *100 †16

MC LEAN, Frederick Miller. 2001 LAUREL AVE, STE N304 37916 #045-04-1989 L1995 RNR R *020 †80

MC LEES, Steven Alan. 10810 PARKSIDE DR, STE 108 37934 #045-01-1990 L1993 OBG *020 †30

MC LEMORE, Laurie Ann. 315 GILL AVE, INTERFAITH HEALTH CLINIC 37917 #028-03-1994 L2003 FM *020 †18

MC MICHAEL, Jeffrey Allen. 1300 OLD WEISGARBER RD 37909 #047-20-1990 L1993 FM *020 †18

MC MILLAN, Cynthia E S. ■ 37934 #036-01-1969 L1971 PD *071 †55

MC MILLAN, Tod Alan. 1124 E WEISGARBER RD, STE 207 37909 #047-20-1990 L1997 OPH *020 †35

MC NEELEY, Samuel Gene. 900 E OAK HILL AVE 37917 #047-06-1945 L1945 GP *071

MC NIEL, Frank Harmon. 420 BEARDEN RD 37919 #005-12-1965 L1985 FM PMM *020

MC NIEL, Janet L Snow. 420 BEARDEN RD 37919 #005-12-1967 L1985 GP *020

MC PEAKE, Wm Thos, III. 1704 JOHNNY MAJORS DR 37996 #047-06-1975 L1976 OFA *020 †40

MC PHERSON, Garth Douglas. 320 NANCY LYNN LANE 7-C, DEPARTMENT 888303 37995 #051-04-1987 L2000 DR *020 †80

MC WHIRTER, Dewey Young. 137 E BLOUNT AVE, BAPTIST SLEEP CENTER 37920 #045-01-2002 L2007 SME N *020 †75

MEHTA, Ravi S. 10810 PARKSIDE DR, CONSULTANTS PC 37934 #495-73-1987 L2000 CD *020 †20

MEISENHEIMER, Stephen L. 200 E BLOUNT AVE, STE 403 37920 #020-02-1979 L1979 FM *020 †18

MERCER, Charles Wayne. ■ 37919 #020-02-1960 L1969 CD IM *071 †20

MERWIN, William Hemsley, Jr. 101 E BLOUNT AVE, STE 500 37920 #036-01-1981 L1990 OTO NO *020 †45

MESERVY, Clifford James. 2001 LAUREL AVE, STE N304 37916 #025-07-1981 L1986 PDR DR *020 †80

MESSENGER, Brigitte M. ■ 37909 #055-01-2007 TY *012

MEYER, Angela Marie. 103 MIDLAKE DR, PHYSICIANS 37918 #050-02-1996 L1997 FM *020 †18

MEYER, Joseph Thurmond. 137 E BLOUNT AVE 37920 #012-01-1990 L1996 RO *020 †20,80

MEYERS, Anthony L. 1928 ALCOA HWY, BLDG B 37920 #012-01-1974 L1977 D *020 †15

MEYETTE, Philip Frank. 200 E BLOUNT AVE, STE 401 37920 #422-01-2003 L2006 FM *020 †18

MIALE, Thomas David. ■ 37950 #041-12-1969 L1988 PHO PLM *020 †55 ‡

MICHAEL, Phillip Brooks. 11230 KINGSTON PIKE 37934 #047-06-1984 L1984 OPH *020

MICHELSON, Barry Ira. 101 E BLOUNT AVE, CONSULTANTS PC 37920 #011-02-1984 L1992 CD IM *020 †20

MIDIS, Gregory Panos. 501 19TH ST STE 501, PREMIER SURGICAL ASSOCIATE 37916 #051-01-1987 L1997 CRS *020 †10,85

MIHELIC, Fabian Matthew. 1924 ALCOA HWY, STE U67 37920 #016-43-1982 L2000 FM GS *020 †18

MILEUSNIC, Darinka. 1924 ALCOA HWY, U71 37920 #957-05-1986 L2002 FOP ATP *062 †50

MILLARD, Bobby Joe. 1924 ALCOA HWY 37920 #047-06-1966 L1971 AN *071

MILLARD, Robert Joseph. 7101 SHADYLAND DR 37919 #047-06-2002 L2005 AN *020 †05

MILLER, Christopher Alan. 2100 W CLINCH AVE STE 440 37916 #008-02-1979 L1986 CHN N *020 †55,75

MILLER, Daniel Jjezzard. 8723 COURTYARD WAY, P O BOX 30313 37931 #017-20-2004 L2007 AN *100

MILLER, James Alexander. 1120 E WEISGARBER RD, GROUP 37909 #051-04-2003 L2007 IM *100 †20

MILLER, James Howard, Jr. 1225 E WEISGARBER RD, STE S380 37909 #047-05-1985 L1985 OPH OS *020 †35

MILLER, James Kevin. ■ 37922 #047-06-2002 L2006 PAN *100 †05

MILLER, Joshua A. 501 19TH ST, STE 601 37916 #048-16-2000 L2005 NS *020

MILLER, Michael M. 1114 E WEISGARBER RD 37909 #016-06-1972 L1978 AI IM *020 †20,03

MILLER, Stephen Stanley. 1934 ALCOA HWY 37920 #016-11-1995 L2002 HO *020

MILLER, Thomas Robt. 1932 ALCOA HWY, STE 460 37920 #023-07-1972 L1978 NEP *020 †20

MILLIGAN, John Leslie. 1924 ALCOA HWY, DEPT OF GENERAL SURGERY 37920 #422-01-2004 GS *012

MILLWOOD, Roger Howell. 433 SEVIER AVE 37920 #012-01-1978 L1987 EM *020 †16

MILSAPS, Reagan Nicole. ■ 37921 #047-06-2005 OBG *012

MINARDO, Joseph David. 900 E OAK HILL AVE, CONSULTANTS PC 37917 #038-06-1981 L1987 CD IM *020 †20

MINTEER, William Jeffrey. 900 E OAK HILL AVE, CONSULTANTS PC 37917 #041-14-1978 L1988 CD IM *020 †20

MIR, Muhammad Qasim Salar. 1924 ALCOA HWY BOX 11, GRADUATE SCHO 37920 #704-01-2001 IM *012

MIRANI, Haresh Kanayalal. PO BOX 3730 37927 #495-17-1979 L1983 **FM OS** *020 †18
MIRE, Anwar Dean. 200 E BLOUNT AVE STE 401 37920 #047-06-1982 L1985 **FM FPG** *020 †18
MISRA, Eva. 116 GLENLEIGH CT 37934 #308-13-1999 L2005 **IM** *020
MISTRY, Savita N. 2018 WESTERN AVE, 140 DAMERON AVE 37921 #409-21-1986 L1995 **IM** *020 †20
MITCHELL, Foy B, Sr. 2001 LAUREL AVE, MITCHELL & PITARD 37916 #047-06-1949 L1949 **PD** *071
MITCHELL, Foy Burton, Jr. 2001 LAUREL AVE, STE NG-2 37916 #047-06-1976 L1977 **OTO** *020 †45
MITCHELL, Michael Earl. 200 FORT SANDERS WEST BLVD, MOB 1, STE 304 37922 #012-01-1982 L1987 **PUD IM** *020 †20
MITCHELL, Michael Shawn. 12607 BARNSTABLE LN 37922 #047-06-1989 L1990 **FM** *020 †18
MITCHELL, Phillip Raymond. 501 20TH ST, STE 606 37916 #836-02-1980 L1989 **AN PME** *020 †05
MIX, William John. 1924 ALCOA HWY, BOX U11 37920 #012-22-2002 **VS** *012 †85
MIXON, William Robt. 1818 ANDY HOLT 37996 #047-06-1982 L1984 **IM** *020 †20
MOBLEY, Edward Colin. 1924 ALCOA HWY, STE U109 37920 #047-20-1991 L1992 **AN** *020 †05
MOBLEY, Jack Murphy. FT SANDERS PROF BLDG 606 37916 #047-06-1955 L1962 **AN** *071 †05
MOBLEY, Joe Dick. ■ 37919 #047-06-2005 **U** *012
MOBLEY, Pamela Peterson. 1924 ALCOA HWY, STE U109 37920 #047-20-1994 L1995 **AN** *020 †05
MOCK, Allen Ray. ■ 37923 #021-05-2005 **PTH** *012
MOFFAT, L Ellen. 501 19TH ST, STE 701 37916 #047-06-1999 L2003 **OBG** *020
MOFFETT, Steven Ray. 930 E EMERALD AVE, STE 612 37917 #017-20-1978 L1979 **OBG** *020 †30
MOFFITT, Gregory Allen. 1450 DOWELL SPRINGS BLVD 37909 #020-02-1997 L2004 **END** *020 †20
MOHIUDDIN, Mohmmed Azam. 1924 ALCOA HWY U-67, SCH OF 37920 #020-12-2005 **FP** *012
MOHR, Patricia Ann. 1930 ALCOA HWY, PEDIATRIC CONSULTANTS INC 37920 #016-01-1966 L1987 **PD OS** *020 †55
MOLONY, William Lawrence. 6501 DEANE HILL DR 37919 #021-01-1980 L1984 **DR** *020 †75,80
MONTGOMERY, Charles E, II. 501 20TH ST STE 606, OF EAST TENNESSEE 37916 #047-06-1992 L1995 **AN** *020 †05
MONTGOMERY, John Lee, Jr. 1932 ALCOA HWY, UNIVERSITY EYE SURGEONS 37920 #047-06-1960 L1961 **OPH** *071 †35
MONTGOMERY, Joseph Tucker. 11726 KINGSTON PIKE 37934 #047-06-1972 L1972 **LM EM** *062
MONTGOMERY, Robert Neal. 9333 PARK WEST BLVD 37923 #047-06-1973 L1974 **IM** *020 †20
MOON, Joseph Benjamine. 1924 ALCOA HWY, VFP 37920 #047-06-1961 L1961 **FM** *071 †18
MOORE, Amanda Terry. 1120 E WEISGARBER RD, STE 104 37909 #027-01-2004 L2007 **IM** *020 †20
MOORE, Eddie Stanley. 1930 ALCOA HWY, STE 145 37920 #047-07-1961 L1988 **NEP PD** *030 †55
MOORE, Lee D. ■ 37923 #048-16-2006 **OBG** *012
MOORE, Merrill Dennis, Jr. 433 SEVIER AVE, RIVERMONT 37920 #047-05-1959 L1959 **EM** *071 †85,16
MOORE, Robert Saylor, Sr. 2001 LAUREL AVE, FORT SANDERS RADIOLOGY PG 37916 #047-06-1962 L1962 **R OS** *071 †80
MOOSS, Suneetha. 1044 HAMILTON RIDGE LN 37922 #016-11-1995 L2002 **PD** *020 †55
MOOSS, Vasudevan C. ■ 37922 #495-37-1965 L1975 **PD** *020 †55
MORALES, Landy Michael. 1924 ALCOA HWY, SCH OF 37920 #011-02-2004 L2008 **IM** *100
MOREHEAD, Lance. 9303 PARK WEST BLVD, PARKWEST 37923 #047-06-1975 L1976 **FM** *020 †20
MORENO, Francisco Gustavo. 501 20TH ST STE 201 37916 #021-05-1976 L1977 **OTO** *020 †45
MORGAN, Julie Trouy. 2018 W CLINCH AVE, BOX 15010 37916 #047-06-1996 L1999 **PD** *020 †55
MORGAN, Rebecca Lynn. 1818 ANDY HOLT AVE 37916 #001-06-1991 L1996 **FM FSM** *020 †18
MORGAN, Tommy Edmonds. 501 19TH ST STE 701 37916 #047-06-1972 L1972 **GO GYN** *020 †30
MORGAN, Travis Eugene. 900 E OAK HILL AVE 37917 #047-06-1952 L1953 **U** *071 †95
MORIN, Garnetta Ioana. 1924 ALCOA HWY 37920 #021-05-1991 L1996 **DR** *020 †80
MORRIS, Kimberly Lynn. 1924 ALCOA HWY, BOX U114 37920 #047-20-1988 L1990 **IM** *040 †20
MORRIS, Steve Allen. 1924 ALCOA HWY, ANESTHESIOLOGY DEPARTMENT 37920 #047-06-1977 L1977 **AN OS** *020 †05
MORTON, Anthony Wayne. 501 20TH ST, FORT SANDERS 37916 #047-06-1983 L1984 **IM** *020 †20
MORVANT, Elise Marie. PO BOX 15010, 2018 CLINCH AVE 37901 #021-05-1987 L2001 **AN** *020 †05,55
MOSLEY, Jennifer Lee. 1120 E WEISGARBER RD, GROUP 37909 #027-01-2002 L2004 **IM** *020 †20
MOSRIE, Brian Todd. 103 MIDLAKE DR, PHYSICIANS 37918 #045-04-1995 L1996 **FM** *020 †18
MOSS, Heather Katherine. 939 EMERALD AVE, STE 901 37917 #047-06-1997 L2004 **OBG** *020 †30
MOUNGER, Emerson Jay. 1932 ALCOA HWY, STE 475C 37920 #047-06-1963 L1963 **U** *020 †95
MOZINGO, Jennifer A. 1900 N WINSTON RD, STE 300 37920 #047-20-1998 L2004 **EM** *020 †16
MUGEMUZI, Jules Kitongo. 1924 ALCOA HWY BOX 56, KNOXVILLE INPATIENT PHYSIC 37920 #305-01-2003 L2007 **IM** *020 †20
MULDONG, Ben David. ■ 37919 #748-07-1959 L1975 **GP CLP** *071 †50
MUMFORD, Mark S. 210 FORT SANDERS WEST BLVD, OUTPATIENT SURGERY CENTER 37922 #020-02-1978 L1981 **AN** *020 †20
MUMPOWER, Kenneth Todd. ■ 37934 #047-20-1992 L1993 **FM** *020 †18
MUNTEANU, Dragos M. 1120 E WEISGARBER RD, GROUP 37909 #781-01-1995 L2000 **IM** *020 †20
MUNTEANU, Ileana G. 1120 E WEISGARBER RD, GROUP 37909 #781-01-1995 L2001 **IM** *020 †20
MURCHISON, John F, Jr. 2020 KAY ST 37920 #047-06-1986 L1993 **OPH OS** *020 †35
MURFF, Ronald Earle. 1300 OLD WEISGARBER RD 37909 #001-06-1979 L1990 **FM** *020 †18
MURPHY, Jean Radovich. 9303 PARK WEST BLVD, PARKWEST 37923 #047-20-1992 L1993 **FM** *020 †18
MURRAY, Edward Lee, Jr. 939 EMERALD AVE STE 705 37917 #047-06-1969 L1970 **GS VS** *071 †85
MURRAY, Mark Bradley. 1924 ALCOA HWY, STE U109 37920 #001-06-2000 L2004 **AN** *020 †05
MURRAY, Michael Craig. 133 S CENTRAL ST, # 201 37902 #047-20-2005 L2007 **IM** *012
MURRAY-JACKSON, Marlo Eve. ■ 37912 #005-12-2004 L2007 **IM** *020
MYERS, Craig. 9430 PARK WEST BLVD, GENERATIONS OB GYN PC 37923 #047-06-1994 L1995 **OBG** *020 †30

MYERS, James David. 1924 ALCOA HWY, UNIV OF TENNESSEE HOSP 37920 #047-06-1953 L1953 **GYN** *071 †30
MYERS, Sanford Kent. 8861 KINGSTON PIKE 37923 #649-14-1982 L1985 **FM EM** *020 †18
NADAUD, Matthew Clifford. 1704 JOHNNY MAJORS DR 37996 #038-43-1995 L2001 **ORS** *020 †40
NAGARAJAN, Vijay Raj. 1924 ALCOA HWY, SCH OF 37920 #495-11-2002 **IM** *012
NAGARSHETH, Khanjan Haris. 1924 ALCOA HWY 37920 #422-01-2006 **GS** *012
NAGUIB, Sameh Samy. 2587 WILLOW POINT WAY 37931 #915-04-1982 L2004 **IM** *020
NAGY, Sandor. 1924 ALCOA HWY, U-38 37920 #473-04-1989 L2004 **NPM** *020 †55
NAIR, Sudha Raghavan. 1932 ALCOA HWY STE 150, WOMEN'S CARE GROUP, PC 37920 #495-96-1994 L2003 **OBG** *020
NALLE, Louden. 2018 W CLINCH AVE, EAST TENNESSEE CHILDREN'S 37916 #017-20-1974 L1984 **NPM PD** *020 †55
NAMEY, Thomas Curtis. 200 E BLOUNT AVE, STE 300 37920 #028-02-1973 L1988 **RHU IM** *020 †28
NAPIER, Shelly Victoria. 9625 KROGER PARK DR, STE 500 37922 #003-01-1991 L1994 **FM** *020 †18
NARAMORE, George Harold. 6716 CREEKHEAD DR 37909 #047-20-1987 L1988 **P** *020 †55
NARRO, John Patrick. 1924 ALCOA HWY U-114, UNIV OF TENN MED CTR 37920 #048-14-1985 L1999 **ID IM** *020 †20
NATELSON, Stephen Ellis. 2001 LAUREL AVE STE 103 37916 #035-45-1963 L1972 **NS** *020 †25
NEAL, Christine Parker. 814 E WOODLAND AVE, KNOXVILLE 37917 #056-05-1989 L2003 **P** *012 †30
NEFF, John Carl. 1924 ALCOA HWY 37920 #028-34-1963 L1984 **PTH CLP** *020 †50
NELSON, Bill M. 401 CATHERINE MCAULEY WAY, # 6201 37919 #016-02-1952 L1956 **PTH NM** *071 †50
NELSON, Henry Sperry. 1930 ALCOA HWY, PEDIATRIC CONSULTANTS INC 37920 #047-05-1945 L1945 **EM GS** *071
NELSON, Henry Sperry, Jr. 1924 ALCOA HWY, BOX U-11 37920 #047-06-1971 L1972 **GS TRS** *020 †85
NELSON, Jeffrey P. 501 20TH ST, STE 503 37916 #048-15-2000 L2005 **N** *020 †75
NELSON, Mark Louis. 140 CAPITOL DR, ALLIANCE OF EAST 37922 #026-08-1977 L1984 **AN** *020 †05
NELSON, Melissa Haenisch. ■ 37922 #001-02-1986 L1993 **CHP P** *020 †75
NEW, Daniel Loris. 2018 W CLINCH AVE, EAST TENNESSEE CHILDRENS H 37916 #035-20-1988 L1999 **PD** *020 †55
NEWMAN, George Edward. 324 N PARK 40 BLVD, # B 37923 #021-01-1994 L1999 **NEP** *020 †20
NEWTON, Cynthia Naramore. 1932 ALCOA HWY, STE 570 37920 #047-20-1991 L1992 **IM** *020 †20
NEWTON, Kristy Lee. 930 E EMERALD AVE 37917 #017-20-1978 L1980 **OBG DR** *020 †30
NGUYEN, Noi Bill. 1120 E WEISGARBER RD, GROUP 37909 #654-01-2003 L2006 **IM** *020 †20
NICELY, Eric Roger. 9330 PARK WEST BLVD 37923 #047-06-1985 L1989 **U** *020 †95
NICHOLS, Christa Dawn. 501 20TH ST, STE G3 37916 #047-20-1995 L2002 **DMP** *020 †50
NICHOLS, Dale Ellen. 930 E EMERALD AVE, STE 512 37917 #036-01-1984 L1986 **DR** *020 †80
NICHOLS, Phillip L, II. 1120 E WEISGARBER RD STE 2, CONSULTANTS 37909 #047-20-1995 L2003 **PCC** *020 †20
NICHOLS, Trent Lee. 1924 ALCOA HWY, INPATIENT PHYSICIANS 37920 #047-06-1986 L1987 **IM** *020 †20
NICHOLSON, Brenda P. 101 E BLOUNT AVE, STE 610 37920 #038-45-1992 L1995 **HO** *020 †20
NICKELS, David Andrew. 2100 W CLINCH AVE, STE 140 37916 #016-02-1985 L1995 **PDE** *020 †55
NICKLOES, Todd A. 1932 ALCOA HWY STE 270, UNIV GENERAL SURGEONS PC 37920 #038-75-1993, ▲ L1999 **GS CCS** *020
NIETHAMMER, John George. 6501 DEANE HILL DR 37919 #047-06-1987 L1988 **DR** *020 †80
NODIT, Laurentia. 501 20TH ST, STE G3 37916 #781-04-1994 L2006 **PTH** *100
NOE, Jacob Aaron. ■ 37923 #047-06-2005 **DR** *012
NOONAN, Holly Elizabeth. 2001 HIGHLAND AVE, GREAT EXPECTATIONS 37916 #047-06-1997 L2001 **OBG** *020 †30
NORRIS, David Michael. 2001 LAUREL AVE, STE N304 37916 #047-06-1989 L1995 **DR** *020 †80
NORWOOD, Daphne Maureen. 4005 FOUNTAIN VALLEY DR, STE 350 37918 #033-06-1993 L1996 **IM** *020 †20
NUNLEY, Lori Blake. 2018 W CLINCH AVE, E TN CHILDRENS HOSP 37916 #047-20-1988 L1989 **PEM** *020 †55
OBENOUR, Richard A. 1924 ALCOA HWY, DEPT OF MEDICINE, U-114 37920 #047-06-1955 L1955 **PUD** *040 †20 ‡
O'BRIEN, Patrick. 1924 ALCOA HWY, BOX 43 37920 #045-01-1982 L1988 **EM** *020 †16
O'CONNOR, Charles Maurice. 801 N WEISGARBER RD # 100 37909 #011-04-1985 L1990 **GE IM** *020 †20
OGDEN, Harry K. 801 VANOSDALE RD 37909 #047-06-1949 L1949 **FM** *071 †18
OGRODOWSKI, James L. 9301 PARK WEST BLVD, STE 2 37923 #056-05-1986 L1992 **NEP IM** *020 †20
O'HARA, James Mc Vey. ■ 37934 #011-02-1964 L1981 **PTH** *072 †50
OJEDA, Gabriel Angel. 9303 PARK WEST BLVD, GABRIEL A OJEDA MD 37923 #308-07-1982 L1990 **CD OS** *020 †20
O'KELLEY, Kenneth R. 9430 PARK WEST BLVD, GENERATIONS OB GYN PC 37923 #047-06-1985 L1987 **OBG** *020 †30
OKUMURA, Michael T. 5401 KINGSTON PIKE, BOX 11764 37919 #025-07-2000 L2006 **AN** *020
OLATIDOYE, Constance M. 913 HAYSLOPE DR, STE B-400 37919 #036-01-1994 L2000 **P** *020
OLLIS, Jeffery Allen, II. ■ 37931 #036-05-2008 *012
OOMMEN, Bindhu. 1924 ALCOA HWY, SCH OF 37920 #048-15-2006 **GS** *012
OROS, William Robert. 11440 PARKSIDE DR 37934 #038-43-1997 L2003 **ORS** *020 †40
ORTHOEFER, Carl Scott. 1120 E WEISGARBER RD, GROUP 37909 #047-06-1997 L1999 **IM** *020 †20
OSBORNE, Warren Ross. ■ 37920 #047-06-1960 L1960 **GP** *071
OTIS, Michael Vaughn. 7211 WELLINGTON DR, DEANE HILL 37919 #047-06-1969 L1970 **FM OBG** *020 †18
O'TOOLE, James Thomas, Jr. ■ 37931 #305-01-1999 L2002 **AN** *020
OVERHOLT, Bergein F. 11440 PARKSIDE DR STE 100, THE ENDOSCOPY CENTER WEST 37934 #047-06-1961 L1961 **GE** *050 †20
OVERHOLT, Meredith Taylor. 10215 KINGSTON PIKE # 200 37922 #048-04-1991 L1997 **D** *020 †15
OVERHOLT, Samuel Mark. 9430 PARK WEST BLVD STE 3 37923 #048-04-1991 L1996 **OTO** *020 †45
OWEN, John D. 501 19TH ST STE 509 37916 #047-06-1976 L1976 **OBG** *020 †30
OWENS, Tony Lamar, Jr. 1924 ALCOA HWY, SCH OF 37920 #045-01-2006 **AN** *012

■ = Address Information Privacy Protected

ÖZDIL, Turan. ■ 37922 #902-01-1950 L1966 **AN GS** *071 †05
ÖZMENT, Jason Mark. 10820 PARKSIDE DR 37934 #021-01-1995 L1998 **DR** *020 †80
PACK, Ronald Lynn. 9333 PARK WEST BLVD, STE 201 37923 #047-06-1972 L1972
IM NTR *020 †20
PADGETT, Lisa Bucca. 1124 E WEISGARBER RD, KNOXVLE PEDIATRIC STE 200 37909
#047-06-1989 L1992 **PEM PD** *020 †55
PAGE, Casey Jay. 1450 DOWELL SPRINGS BLVD 37909 #028-03-1985 L1990 **END IM** *020 †20
PAGE, Robert Norman. 315 ERIN DR 37919 #004-01-1996 L2000 **PTH DMP** *062 †50
PAGE, Robert Stephen. 9031 CROSS PARK DR, KNOXVILLE VA. OUTPATIENT C 37923
#010-01-1996 L2002 **FM** *020 †18
PAINE, Raymond Lee, Jr. 9401 PARK WEST BLVD 37923 #025-01-1964 L1979 **P** *020 †75 ‡
PAIS, Ray Carl. 2018 W CLINCH AVE, EAST TENNESSEE CHILDREN'S 37916
#016-11-1983 L1991 **PHO PD** *020 †55
PALATINUS, Joseph. 9332 PARK WEST BLVD, PARKWEST HOSP EMGY DEPT 37923
#011-03-1969 L1974 **EM OM** *020 †16
PALMER, Cedric Morris, Jr. ■ 37918 #047-07-2004 L2007 **FM** *020
PANELLA, Timothy John. 1934 ALCOA HWY, STE 474 37920 #047-06-1983 L1991
ON HEM *020 †20
PAPPANO, Dante Allen. ■ 37919 #028-02-1992 L2006 **PE** *020 †55
PARDUE, Jeanann P. 2018 W CLINCH AVE, E TENN CHILDREN'S HOSP 37916
#047-06-1986 L1988 **PD** *020 †55
PARDUE, Randy Thos. 220 FORT SANDERS WEST BLVD, STE 101 37922 #047-06-1987 L1990
FM *020 †18
PARIKH, Kalpesh D. 10820 PARKSIDE DR 37934 #495-22-1984 L1989 **IM** *020 †20 ‡
PARK, Christy Chunghae. ■ 37922 #047-06-1995 L2007 **RHU IM** *020 †20
PARK, Soung-Ho. 2018 W CLINCH AVE 37916 #583-03-1973 L1981 **PD** *020 †55
PARKER, Brian David. 9330 PARK WEST BLVD 37923 #048-16-1999 L2005 **U** *020 †95
PARKER, Donald Wayne. 7541 CROSSWOOD BLVD, FAMILY PRACTICE 37924
#047-06-1993 L1995 **FM** *020 †18
PARKER, Heath A. 1431 CENTERPOINT BLVD, STE 100 37932 #028-78-1996, ▲ L2003
MPD EM *020 †20,55
PARROTT, James Ancil. 917 WEATHERLY HILLS BLVD, 917 WEATHERLY HILLS BLVD. 37934
#020-12-1965 L1969 **DR** *020 †80 ‡
PASSARELLO, Michael J. 501 20TH ST, FORT SANDERS 37916 #020-12-1984 L1987
IM *020 †20
PATEL, Amit Mahendra. 2018 W CLINCH AVE 37916 #047-06-2002 L2005 **PD** *020 †55
PATEL, Nilesh Shantilal. 900 E OAK HILL AVE, DEPARTMENT OF RADIATION ON 37917
#048-04-2002 L2007 **RO** *020
PATIL, Vijay R. 2001 LAUREL AVE, STE 201 37916 #495-09-1965 L1976 **TS PUD** *020
PATTERSON, Lori. 2018 W CLINCH AVE 37916 #016-06-1983 L1989 **PDI PD** *020 †55
PATTERSON, Reese Williams. 137 E BLOUNT AVE 37920 #047-06-1948 L1948 **OPH** *071 †35
PATTESON, Stephen K. 1924 ALCOA HWY, STE U109 37920 #051-07-1984 L1985 **AN** *020 †05
PAUL, Andrews. 1120 E WEISGARBER RD, CONSULTANTS 37909 #495-63-1990 L2003
PCC SME *020 †20
PAULAUSKAS, Dovile. 600 ARTHUR ST 37921 #913-96-1985 L2004 **CHP** *020 †75
PAULSEN, William Allen. 1932 ALCOA HWY STE 450 37920 #056-05-1964 L1970 **N** *020 †75
PEACE, Christie Eve. 501 19TH ST, STE 406 37916 #047-06-1992 L1996 **OBG** *020
PEAGLER, Charles G. 433 E. HILLVALE 37919 #012-01-1952 L1959 **TS** *071 †85,90
PEARCE, Robert Ernest. 2825 BELLA VISTA LN 37914 #045-01-1978 L1981 **AN** *020 †05
PEARMAN, Bradley Leon. 1928 ALCOA HWY, STE 324 37920 #045-04-1993 L1999
OPH *020 †35
PEARMAN, Cynthia Mc Clain. 1924 ALCOA HWY, STE U67 37920 #047-06-1986 L2000
FM *040 †18
PEARSON, Don Ray, Jr. 1924 ALCOA HWY, STE U109 37920 #047-06-1978 L1979 **AN** *020 †05
PEDIGO, Randall Eric. 1924 ALCOA HWY 37920 #047-06-1974 L1975 **GS FOP** *075 †85
PEEDEN, Joseph Noble, Jr. 1124 E WEISGARBER RD 37909 #047-06-1975 L1978
PD CG *020 †55,19
PEEDEN, Paula S Zarbock. 939 EMERALD AVE STE 805 37917 #047-06-1984 L1987
OBG *020 †30
PEEKE, Jeffrey Wilson. 1924 ALCOA HWY, RADIOLOGISTS 37920 #005-12-2001 L2007
DR *020 †80
PEELER, Molly Mcpeake. 501 19TH ST STE 701 37916 #047-06-1984 L1985 **OBG** *020 †30
PERALES, Marymer Patricia. 1900 N WINSTON RD, STE 300 37919 #005-12-1998 L2004
PD *020
PEREIRA, Derek John. 1924 ALCOA HWY 37920 #308-13-2004 **IM** *012
PERKINS, Phillip Eugene. ■ 37934 #025-01-1963 L1964 **NR DR** *071 †80
PERKINS, Stephen Lee. 1124 E WEISGARBER RD, STE 207 37909 #036-07-1995 L2002
OPH *020 †35
PERRA, Lenette H. 5541 CLINTON HWY 37912 #409-16-1991 L1996 **IM** *020 †20
PERRY, Gregory James. 2018 WESTERN AVE 37921 #047-05-1991 L1995 **P** *020 †75
PERRY, Leslie David. 1341 BRANTON BLVD STE 10 37922 #011-04-1994 L1997 **PD** *020 †55
PETERS, Todd Michael. 1208 MERCHANT DR 37912 #047-06-2000 L2001 **FM** *020 †18
PETERSON, Paul Carl. 900 E OAK HILL AVE 37917 #025-07-1990 L1996 **NS** *020 †25
PETRUZZI, Peter Tobias, Jr. 6501 DEANE HILL DR, RADIOLOGY IMAGING ASSOC OF 37919
#001-06-1998 L2004 **DR** *020 †80
PETTY, Albert M. 1924 ALCOA HWY, STE 106 37920 #011-04-1980 L1987 **RO** *020 †80
PETTY, Cathy E. 1320 OLD WEISGARBER RD 37909 #011-04-1980 L1987 **AN** *020 †05
PETTY, David G. ■ 37922 #047-05-1950 L1950 **GP** *071
PFLANZE, William Ted. 1924 ALCOA HWY 37920 #047-06-1978 L1979 **DR** *020 †80
PHAM, Loc Ba. 501 20TH ST STE 606 37916 #047-06-1996 L2000 **AN** *020 †05
PHARAOH, James Daniel. 1120 E WEISGARBER RD, CONSULTANTS 37909
#011-04-1985 L1991 **PUD CCM** *020 †20
PHELPS, Gregory Lange. 900 E OAK HILL AVE, ST. MARY'S MEDICAL CENTER 37917
#045-01-1979 L1995 **FM OM** *030 †70,18
PHELPS, Preston V, Jr. 501 20TH ST STE 205 37916 #047-06-1968 L1968 **IM** *020 †20
PHELPS, Richard Wm. 501 20TH ST STE 205 37916 #047-06-1974 L1975 **IM** *020 †20
PHILIPS, Annie Helen. ■ 37922 #495-08-1974 L1992 **DR** *100
PHILLIPS, Michael David. 433 SEVIER AVE 37920 #047-06-1978 L1979 **EM** *020 †16
PHILLIPS, Nancy Lynn. 4005 FOUNTAIN VALLEY DR 37918 #012-05-1996 L1999 **PD** *020 †55 ‡
PICKENS, Ryan Baird. 1924 ALCOA HWY, UNIV OF TENNESSEE MED CTR 37920 #020-02-2006
U *012
PIENKOWSKI, Marek M. 7417 KINGSTON PIKE STE 101 37919 #759-03-1969 L1984
AI IM *020 ‡
PIERCE, John Mark. 10215 KINGSTON PIKE 37922 #027-01-1984 L1986 **IM EM** *020 †20
PIERCE, Steven Faulkner. 2001 LAUREL AVE, STE 105 37916 #047-06-1975 L1976
GYN *020 †30

PIERSON, Farrell Dee. 9333 PARK WEST BLVD, STE 103 37923 #004-01-1987 L1997
CD *020 †20
PIMENTEL, Francis J. 1900 N WINSTON RD STE 300 37919 #042-01-1972 L1994 **EM** *075
PINZON, Elmer Guillermo. 1932 ALCOA HWY, STE 580 37920 #041-09-1994 L2001
PM OM *020 †60 ‡
PITTMAN, Laurence Matthew. ■ 37922 #055-02-2008 *012
PLACE, James Gilbert. 2001 LAUREL AVE STE 304 37916 #047-06-1969 L1970 **DR** *020 †80
POEHLEIN, Richard Eric. 7328 MIDDLEBROOK PIKE 37909 #047-06-1970 L1971
GP PD *020 †55
POLLACK, Robert Alan. 101 E BLOUNT AVE 37920 #011-04-1988 L2000 **GE IM** *020 †20
POLLARD, Thomas R. 101 E BLOUNT AVE, STE 800 37920 #048-13-1989 L1996 **TS** *020 †85,90
POLLOCK, Christopher W. 9314 PARK WEST BLVD, STE 400 37923 #047-06-1997 L2003
VS *020 †85
PONDER, Robert David. 6700 BAUM DR, STE ONE 37919 #020-12-1988 L1993 **AI** *020 †55,03
POOL, Michael L. 9401 PARK WEST BLVD 37923 #036-01-1977 L1980 **P** *020 †75 ‡
PORTER, F Raymond. 801 N WEISGARBER RD # 100 37909 #047-05-1973 L1975 **GE** *020 †20
POTEET, Tony Vencen. 5310 BALL CAMP PIKE 37921 #654-01-1987 L1990 **FM EM** *020 †18
POWERS, Laura Beth. 939 E EMERALD AVE, STE 907 37917 #012-05-1976 L1982
N IM *071 †20,75
POWERS, William Philip. 200 E BLOUNT AVE, STE 200 37920 #020-12-1982 L1983
PUD CCM *062 †20
POWERS, Wilson Lee. 7733 OAK RIDGE HWY 37931 #047-06-1978 L1979 **PD** *020 †55
POWERS, Wilson Watkins. 1924 ALCOA HWY 37920 #047-06-1945 L1946 **IM** *071 †20
PRATT, Mark Edward. 1431 CENTERPOINT BLVD, STE 100 37932 #047-06-1999 L2003
EM *020 †16
PRATT, Martha Ann. 1431 CENTERPOINT BLVD, STE 100 37932 #047-06-1999 L2003
EM *020 †16
PRENSHAW, Eric R, III. 1818 ANDY HOLT AVE 37916 #027-01-1980 L1981 **PD ADL** *020 †55
PRESS, Hejung. 2001 LAUREL AVE, STE N304 37916 #012-05-1995 L2000 **NM** *020 †80
PRESSWOOD, James Jackson. 10820 PARKSIDE DR 37934 #047-06-1970 L1971 **AN** *020 †05
PRIMKA, Edward John, III. 900 E EMERALD AVE, STE 705 37917 #036-01-1992 L2001
D *020 †15
PRIMKA, Lynda Rozas. ■ 37922 #036-01-1992 L2002 **FM** *020 †18
PRINCE, Blake Michael. 501 20TH ST STE 606, AMAET 37916 #047-06-2002 L2005 **AN** *020 †05
PRINCE, John Martin, Jr. 1120 E WEISGARBER RD, CONSULTANTS 37909 #051-04-1980 L1992
PUD *020 †20
PRINCE, Mark Dickson. 9333 PARK WEST BLVD, CEDAR BLUFF MEDICAL ARTS B 37923
#047-06-1973 L1974 **IM** *020 †20
PRINCE, Steven Ryland. 1120 E WEISGARBER RD, STE 104 37909 #051-07-1981 L1995
IM *020 †20
PRINCE, Thomas Chafer, Jr. 2001 LAUREL AVE STE 405 37916 #047-06-1947 L1947
GS TS *020 †85,90
PRINZ, Stephen Chas. 2018 W CLINCH AVE 37916 #047-06-1972 L1973 **NPM PD** *020 †55
PRITCHARD, Brenda N. 501 20TH ST, STE G3 37916 #027-01-1985 L1990 **PTH OS** *020 †50
PRITCHER, Gerald Marquis. 1208 MERCHANT DR 37912 #012-01-1980 L1980 **FM** *020 †18
PRUETT, Billy Dean. 501 20TH ST, STE 205 37916 #047-06-1999 L2002 **IM** *020
PRYOR, Kenneth Harold. 930 E EMERALD AVE, STE 512 37917 #012-05-1987 L1989
DR *020 †80
PULIDO-SORIANO, Gina. 1120 E WEISGARBER RD, GROUP 37909 #035-46-2002 L2005
IM *020 †20
PULLEN, Charles Scott. ■ 37934 #004-01-1995 L1998 **IM** *020 †20
PUMPHREY, Cherra Faye. 1924 ALCOA HWY, SCH OF 37920 #011-04-2005 **IM** *012
PURKEY, Janet Laster. 11440 PARKSIDE DR, STE 302 37934 #047-06-1987 L1990 **IM** *020 †20
PURVIS, John T. ■ 37919 #047-06-1953 L1954 **NS** *071 †25
QUEEN, Jeffrey Scott. 2108 W CLINCH AVE 37916 #045-04-1984 L1989
PAN CCP *020 †05,55 ‡
RAAB, Gregory Ernest. 1704 JOHNNY MAJORS DR 37996 #005-12-2001 L2006 **ORS** *020
RADER, Gregg Martin. 7210 OAK RIDGE HWY 37931 #047-06-1986 L1989 **IM** *020 †20
RADER, Karen T. 9330 PARK WEST BLVD, STE 402 37923 #047-06-1986 L1989 **IM** *020 †20
RAGSDALE, John Wilson. ■ 37934 #041-02-2006 L2007 **MPD** *012
RAHMAN, Obaidur. ■ 37922 #047-06-2006 **IM** *012
RAMSEY, Christopher Eric. 9330 PARK WEST BLVD 37923 #038-43-1997 L2002 **U** *020 †95
RANGE, James Jacob. ■ 37920 #023-01-1943 L1944 **R** *071
RANGNEKAR, Nitin J. 10810 PARKSIDE DR, STE 305 37934 #495-97-1985 L2007 **GS** *020 †85
RANKIN, David Michael. 200 E BLOUNT AVE, STE 101 37920 #047-06-1978 L1978 **IM** *020 †20
RAPER, D. 1900 N WINSTON RD STE 300, TEAM HEALTH 37919 #036-01-1979 L2001
EM GP *020 †16
RAPPE, Matthew Alan. 1704 JOHNNY MAJORS DR 37996 #047-06-2001 L2006 **OSM** *020
RASNAKE, Mark Steven. ■ 37922 #047-06-1998 L2000 **ID** *020 †20
RATCLIFF, Steven Matthew. ■ 37938 #048-16-1999 L2004 **FM** *020
RATHFOOT, Christopher J. 1932 ALCOA HWY, STE 160 37920 #025-12-1992 L1993
OTO PS *020 †45
RAULSTON, Kenneth L, Jr. 930 E EMERALD AVE STE 711 37917 #047-06-1962 L1963
OPH *020 †35
RAY, Thomas Lafayette. 1901 W CLINCH AVE 37916 #047-06-1948 L1948 **OM** *020
REATH, David Brooke. 109 NORTHSHORE DR, STE 101 37919 #048-12-1979 L1986
PS *020 †85,65
REDDY, Geetha Paturu. 1924 ALCOA HWY U-67, SCH OF 37920 #047-07-2007 **FP** *012
REDMAN, Ryan Lowell. 2018 W CLINCH AVE 37916 #026-04-1999 L2006 **PEM** *020 †55
REDMOND, Jeff Steven. ■ 37909 #021-05-2003 L2006 **DR** *012
REED, Brian Keith. 1924 ALCOA HWY, SCH OF 37920 #047-06-2003 **GS** *012
REED, Steve Wilson. 101 E BLOUNT AVE, CONSULTANTS PC 37920 #047-06-1975 L1975
CD IC *020 †20
REESE, Kenneth Chas. 200 E BLOUNT AVE, KENNETH C REESE MD 37920 #012-01-1986 L1992
IM *020 †20
REGEN, Edwin Scott. ■ 37922 #047-20-2000 L2002 **AN** *020 †05
REGESTER, Rolland F, Jr. 1932 ALCOA HWY STE 460 37920 #047-05-1960 L1961
NEP IM *071 †20
REICHERT, Matthew Michael. 1225 E WEISGARBER RD, STE 200 37909 #016-45-2002 L2008
PCC *012 †20
REID, Elizabeth Ann. 2018 WESTERN AVE 37921 #012-01-1991 L1998 **P** *020
REID, William Augustus. 2321 COVE FIELD RD 37919 #047-07-1970 L1978 **FM** *020
REID, William Stuart. 1924 ALCOA HWY, STE 280 37920 #003-01-1971 L1979 **NS** *020 †25
REYNOLDS, Charles Wilson. 9330 PARK WEST BLVD 37923 #047-06-1977 L1982 **U** *020 †95
REYNOLDS, Diane M. 140 CAPITOL DR, ALLIANCE OF EAST 37922 #047-06-1997 L2001
AN *020 †05

REYNOLDS, John Moses, IV. 2701 KINGSTON PIKE 37919 #028-02-1995 L2001 **ORS** *020 †40

RHEA, Russel Whiteside. 9625 KROGER PARK DR, PEDIATRIC CONSULTANTS INC 37922 #047-07-1990 L1993 **PEM PD** *020 †55

RICE, Robert Alan. 7009 KINGSTON PIKE 37919 #047-06-1975 L1975 **IM** *020

RICE, Todd Mitchell. 433 SEVIER AVE 37920 #021-06-1989 L1993 **EM** *020 †16

RICH, Joseph Edward. 9217 PARK WEST BLVD, STE E1 37923 #409-21-1974 L1995 **OBG PHP** *020 †30 ‡

RICHARDS, Paul De. 2018 W CLINCH AVE 37916 #036-05-1944 L1944 **PD** *071 †55

RICHARDSON, John Michael. 210 FORT SANDERS WEST BLVD 37922 #047-20-1989 L1992 **DR** *020 †80

RIDEN, David Jay. 2100 W CLINCH AVE, STE 130 37916 #038-06-1989 L1999 **UP U** *040 †95

RIDENHOUR, Kevin Patrick. 9430 PARK WEST BLVD, STE 120 37923 #036-08-1994 L2004 **HO** *020 †20

RIDER, Steven Patrick. 1932 ALCOA HWY, STE 350 37920 #017-20-2000 L2005 **CN** *020 †75

RIFF, Eduardo Jose. 2100 W CLINCH AVE, STE 220 37916 #054-04-1977 L2000 **PDP PD** *020 †55

RIGGINS, Billy Newell. 3827 HOLSTON DR 37914 #047-06-1962 L1962 **GP AM** *020

RIMER, Ronald Lee. 9017 CROSS PARK DR, STE 200 37923 #047-06-1972 L1973 **PD** *020 †55

RIST, Toivo E. 939 EMERALD AVE, STE 705 37917 #012-01-1970 L1977 **D** *020 †15

RISTEV, Goran. ■ 37932 #038-40-2003 L2006 **IM** *020 †20

RITTGERS, Aaron L. 1120 E WEISGARBER RD, GROUP 37909 #012-22-1998 L2001 **IM** *020 †20

RIVERS, James Benj, Jr. 501 20TH ST, FORT SANDERS 37916 #047-06-1992 L1993 **IM** *020 †20

ROATEN, Jeffrey Brent. 2100 W CLINCH AVE STE 430, EAST TENNESSEE PEDIATRIC S 37916 #047-06-2001 L2008 **PDS** *012 †55

ROBERTS, Anne Sanchez. 1924 ALCOA HWY, STE U67 37920 #047-06-1968 L1972 **OM AM** *020 †70

ROBERTS, James G. 10810 PARKSIDE DR, STE 309 37934 #020-02-1994 L2003 **VS GS** *020 †85

ROBERTS, Jeffrey Ralph. 140 CAPITOL DR, ALLIANCE OF EAST 37922 #038-41-1985 L1989 **AN** *020 †05

ROBERTS, Kimberly Anne. 10820 PARKSIDE DR 37934 #004-01-2000 L2002 **OBG** *020

ROBERTS, Roxsann Lee. ■ 37923 #048-13-2003 L2007 **DR** *012

ROBERTS, Sidney C, III. 2001 LAUREL AVE, VISTA RADIOLOGY 37916 #047-06-1993 L2000 **PDR DR** *020 †80

ROBERTS, Stephen Michael. 1900 N WINSTON RD, STE 300 37919 #038-45-1985 L1996 **EM** *020 †18

ROBERTS, Susan B. 1124 E WEISGARBER RD, STE 200 37909 #047-06-1993 L1995 **PD** *020 †55

ROBERTSON, Candace Apple. 10820 PARKSIDE DR 37934 #036-05-1991 L1995 **AN** *020 †05

ROBERTSON, John Burr, Jr. 10241 KINGSTON PIKE, SUITES 1 AND 2 37922 #047-06-1986 L1991 **CHP P** *020 †75

ROBINSON, Grover C, IV. 930 E EMERALD AVE STE 510, MED & SURG OF THE EYE 37917 #051-04-2002 L2006 **OPH** *020 †35

ROBINSON, Jeffrey William. 9333 PARK WEST BLVD 37923 #422-01-1996 L1999 **IM** *020

ROBINSON, Kip Daron. 1924 ALCOA HWY, DEPARTMENT OF ANESTHESIOLO 37920 #023-12-1994 L2004 **AN** *100 †20

ROBINSON, Patricia. ■ 37920 #017-20-1989 L1991 **GE IM** *020 †20

ROBINSON, Richard Walter. 603 W MAIN ST, STE 303 37902 #035-03-1962 L1973 **GP FPG** *020

ROBINSON, William Dan. 2761 SULLINS ST 37919 #047-06-1982 L1984 **AN** *020 †05

ROBINSON, Wm Bruce, III. 9333 PARK WEST BLVD 37923 #047-06-1979 L1979 **IM** *020

ROCHESTER, John Crawford. 224 S PETERS RD, STE 105 37923 #001-02-1959 L1964 **PD** *020 †20

RODGERS, John C, Jr. 8820 COVE POINT LN 37922 #012-01-1968 L1973 **P** *020 †75

RODGERS, Larry Edwin. 100 TECH CENTER DR, PEDIATRIC CONSULTANTS INC 37912 #047-06-1974 L1975 **PD** *020 †55

RODRIQUEZ, Humberto. 1928 ALCOA HWY, BLDG B 37920 #737-05-1972 L1987 **OBG PD** *020 †55,30 ‡

RODWELL, Charles Geo. 224 S PETERS RD, STE 200 37923 #759-03-1974 L1992 **P** *020

ROESCH, Jeffrey Martin. 2001 LAUREL AVE, STE N304 37916 #023-07-1989 L1996 **VIR R** *020 †80

ROGERS, Bret Alan. ■ 37934 #041-02-2001 L2007 **IM** *100

ROGERS, John Sims. 2100 W CLINCH AVE, STE 220 37916 #048-04-1976 L1993 **PUD PD** *020 †55

ROGERS, Maricarmen Malago. 1924 ALCOA HWY, STE U67 37920 #264-10-1977 L1990 **PN PD** *020 †55

ROGERS, William Klar. 1901 W CLINCH AVE 37916 #035-45-1945 L1952 **TS** *071 †85,90

ROLLHAUSER, Carlos A. 1928 ALCOA HWY, STE 100B 37920 #132-02-1987 L2002 **GE** *020 †20

ROMANS, Allan Maurice. 1900 N WINSTON RD, STE 300 37919 #047-06-1978 L1979 **EM** *020 †16

ROPER, Marygwyn Sansom. 2100 W CLINCH AVE STE 140 37916 #045-01-1997 L2002 **PDE** *020 †55

ROQUE, Joey Edward M. 1901 W CLINCH AVE, STE 301 37916 #748-10-1991 L2006 **PM** *020 †60

ROSE, Richard Contee. 501 20TH ST, FORT SANDERS 37916 #012-05-1975 L1982 **IM ID** *020 †20

ROSENBAUM, Allan Moris. 1515 SAINT MARY ST, STE 200 37917 #016-11-1993 L2003 **OTO** *020 †45

ROSENBLOOM, Scott Avin. 10820 PARKSIDE DR 37934 #041-09-1980 L1991 **DR RNR** *020 †80

ROSINE, Amy Rebecca. 103 MIDLAKE DR, PHYSICIANS 37918 #047-06-1998 L1999 **FM** *020 †18

ROSSOW, David James. ■ 37909 #025-07-2005 L2005 **DR** *012

ROTONDO, Russell Elias. 900 E OAK HILL AVE, CONSULTANTS PC 37917 #043-01-1985 L1991 **CD IM** *020 †20

ROULIER, Gayle Ellen. 2001 LAUREL AVE, STE N304 37916 #025-07-1991 L1996 **DR** *020 †80

ROUSSIS, Periclis. 501 19TH ST STE 304 37916 #308-07-1982 L1988 **OBG MFM** *020 †30

ROWE, Buford Edward. 939 EMERALD AVE STE 910 37917 #055-01-1969 L1974 **AN** *071

ROWE, Cecil Darrell. 501 20TH ST, STE 606 37916 #047-06-1961 L1961 **AN** *020 †05

ROYER, John Mark. 10820 PARKSIDE DR 37934 #047-06-1981 L1985 **DR** *020 †80

RUBY, Rubinder Singh. ■ 37922 #495-03-1997 L2008 **CD** *012

RUDRAPATNA SREENIVASA MURT, ■. 37918 #495-99-2001 L2007 **IM** *020 †20

RUEDA, Maria Fernanda. 11416 GRIGSBY CHAPEL RD, STE 100 37934 #264-18-1994 L2004 **D** *020 ‡

RUEFF, David Anthony. ■ 37931 #047-06-1964 L1964 **GYN** *071 †30

RULE, Jack Andrew. 2020 KAY ST 37920 #047-06-1963 L1963 **OPH** *071 †35

RULE, Kenneth Andrew. 1924 ALCOA HWY, UT MEMORIAL HOSPITAL 37920 #047-06-1981 L1985 **DR** *020 †80

RUSH, Janet T. 100 TECH CENTER DR, PEDIATRIC CONSULTANTS - NO 37912 #017-20-1970 L1983 **PD** *071 †55

RUSSELL, Cecil E, Jr. ■ 37912 #047-06-1965 L1965 **GP** *071

RUSSELL, Gerald Thos. 11201 W POINT DR, STE 102 37934 #047-06-1979 L1980 **FM** *020 †18

RUSSELL, Kimberly Ann. 1120 E WEISGARBER RD, CONSULTANTS 37909 #047-06-1995 L2002 **PCC** *020 †20

RUSSELL, Robert Claude. 1924 ALCOA HWY 37920 #047-06-1966 L1969 **IM** *020

RUSSELL, Stephen Aubry. 211 E BLOUNT AVE, STE 507 37920 #047-06-1978 L1979 **EM** *020 †16

RUTHERFORD, Charles E, Jr. 1928 ALCOA HWY, STE 222 37920 #012-05-1970 L1973 **GS** *020

RUTHERFORD, Kyle Otis. ■ 37938 #047-06-1954 L1954 **R** *071 †80

RUTLEDGE, Charles David. 4711 CENTERLINE DR 37917 #047-20-1987 L1988 **FM** *020 †18

RYLANDS, John Craig. 2060 LAKESIDE CENTRE WAY, NORTHSHORE 37922 #016-11-1974 L1975 **FM** *020 †18 ‡

SAIN, Robert Lynn. 9430 PARK WEST BLVD, STE 310 37923 #047-06-1967 L1968 **GS** *071 †85

SALAITA, Murad Ghaleb. 3055 KINGSTON PIKE 37919 #055-01-2001 L2003 **IM** *020

SALES, Kathleen A C. 4905 GUINN RD 37931 #047-05-1972 L1981 **P** *020

SALTER, Victor Eugene. 2001 LAUREL AVE STE 101 37916 #027-01-1977 L1978 **PUD IM** *020

SAMPLES, Karen Leigh. ■ 37921 #001-02-2007 *012

SANCES, Richard Anthony. 501 20TH ST, STE G3 37916 #051-01-1994 L1998 **PP** *020 †55,50

SANDBERG, Ronald Kenneth. 1515 SAINT MARY ST 37917 #041-02-1965 L1972 **OTO** *020 †45

SANDERS, James Mitchell. ■ 37909 #021-06-2007 **GS** *012

SANDERS, Jerry Earl. 501 19TH ST, STE 406 37916 #047-06-1972 L1973 **GYN** *030 †30

SANDERS, John Townsend. 1431 CENTERPOINT BLVD, STE 100 37932 #036-08-2000 L2007 **PN** *012 †55

SANDERS, Steven Allen. 9314 PARK WEST BLVD STE 20, NEUROSURGERY & SPINE 37923 #047-06-1985 L1992 **NS** *020 †25

SANNER, Harry Joel. 2018 W CLINCH AVE 37916 #005-12-1978 L1988 **PAN PD** *020 †55,05

SANTEE, Robert H, II. 2001 LAUREL AVE, STE N304 37916 #048-12-1984 L1989 **DR** *075 †80

SANTORO, Thomas Delaney. ■ 37934 #036-05-2007 L2007 **TY** *012

SARKAR, Diana Dee. ■ 37919 #038-43-1976 L1980 **EM** *020 †16

SARLO, Robert A. 6911 ASHEVILLE HWY 37924 #035-47-1983 L1995 **GP OBG** *020 †18

SAUMELL, Syria Hassan. 9031 CROSS PARK DR, CLINIC 37923 #308-03-1987 L2000 **FM** *020 †18

SAUNDERS, Eric Jacob. ■ 37922 #012-01-2002 L2006 **AN** *020 †05

SAUTER, Kent. 1932 ALCOA HWY, STE 470 37920 #001-06-1989 L2004 **NS** *020 †25

SAWYER, Christopher Edwin. 211 E BLOUNT AVE STE 3, BLOUNT PROF BLDG 37920 #047-06-1977 L1978 **FM** *020 †18

SCAPEROTH, Daniel D. 1915 WHITE AVE, DEPT OF RAD/ONC 37916 #047-06-1990 L1994 **RO** *020 †80

SCARIANO, Jack Emile, Jr. 300 PROSPERITY RD, STE 103 37923 #021-05-1975 L1978 **N PMM** *020 †75

SCHADY, Deborah Ann. ■ 37918 #045-01-2005 **PTH** *012

SCHEUNEMAN, Tricia L. 1900 N WINSTON RD, STE 300 37919 #005-12-2002 L2005 **FM** *020 †18

SCHIOPESCU, Irina. ■ 37934 #781-01-1996 L2004 **ID** *020

SCHLACTUS, Jeffrey Lloyd. 1120 E WEISGARBER RD # 102 37909 #035-03-1981 L1986 **AI PD** *020 †55,03

SCHMID, James Dempster. 1930 ALCOA HWY, STE 145 37920 #047-06-1977 L1978 **NPM PD** *020 †55

SCHNEIDER, Paul Damian. 2018 W CLINCH AVE, EAST TENNESSEE CHILDREN'S 37916 #001-02-1994 L2000 **PD PEM** *020 †55

SCHNEIDER, William James. 801 N WEISGARBER RD, STE 500 37909 #047-05-1970 L1977 **GS** *020 †85,65

SCHRIVER, Elise Emery. 1940 ALCOA HWY, STE E210 37920 #047-06-1983 L1986 **PUD CCM** *020 †20

SCHROCK, Nathan Eric. 101 E BLOUNT AVE, STE 610 37920 #027-01-1997 L2003 **HO** *020 †20

SCHROEDER, Charles David. 9330 PARK WEST BLVD, STE 502 37923 #001-02-1992 L1996 **OBG** *020 †30

SCHUCHMANN, Geo Frederick. 1924 ALCOA HWY, BOX U11 37920 #030-06-1963 L1983 **TS GS** *071 †85,90

SCHUCHMANN, George D. 2001 LAUREL AVE STE 204, NEWLAND PROF. BLGD 37916 #018-03-1983 L1989 **GS** *020 †85

SCHUELER, Victor J. 5908 LYONS VIEW PIKE, LAKESHORE MNTL HLTH INSTIT 37919 #048-12-1990 L1994 **P** *020 †75

SCHUMAKER, Robert D. 101 E BLOUNT AVE, STE 610 37920 #048-12-1994 L1999 **HO** *020 †20

SCHWARZ, Susan Jane. 9330 PARK WEST BLVD, STE 302 37923 #045-04-1987 L1991 **OBG** *020 †30

SCOGGINS, Thomas Hancock. 12530 COMBLAIN RD 37934 #005-12-1999 L2002 **EM** *020 †16

SCOTT, John Christopher. 1940 ALCOA HWY, STE E310 37920 #047-06-1979 L1980 **CD** *020 †20

SCOTT, John David. 1930 ALCOA HWY, STE 240 37920 #047-06-2001 L2007 **GS** *100

SEALE, David Randal. 6800 BAUM DR, HEALTH 37919 #047-06-1991 L1999 **PYG P** *020 †75

SEALS, James Lee. 501 20TH ST, STE 204 37916 #047-06-1983 L1984 **OTO EM** *020 †45

SEALS, Roy Lee. 9430 PARK WEST BLVD, STE 330 37923 #047-06-1961 L1961 **OTO** *071 †45

SEARS, Cameron Johnson. 1704 JOHNNY MAJORS DR 37996 #035-45-1988 L1995 **ORS** *020 †40

SEATON, Douglas York. 501 20TH ST, STE 606 37916 #047-06-1974 L1975 **AN** *020 †05

SEELEY, Robert Craig. 1901 W CLINCH AVE, FORT SANDERS REGIONAL MED 37916 #060-01-1994 L1999 **FM** *020 †18

SEGARS, James Hugh. 2001 LAUREL AVE STE 604 37916 #012-01-1955 L1956 **OBG** *071 †30

SEIFERT, Phillip Jay. 900 E OAK HILL AVE, EMERGENCY DEPT 37917 #035-03-1990 L1995 **IM** *020 †20

SELLERS, David Matthew. 200 E BLOUNT AVE, STE 201 37920 #012-01-1991 L1997 **PCC** *020 †20

SENTER, Riley Stone. 8861 KINGSTON PIKE, COMPLETE FAMILY CARE PLLC 37923 #051-04-1974 L1975 **IM** *020 †20

SERRELL, Paul Burt. 1932 ALCOA HWY STE 460 37920 #024-01-1971 L1976 **NEP IM** *020 †20

SEVILLA, Evelyn Alcantara. 9217 PARK WEST BLVD, STE A3 37923 #748-10-1979 L1987 **N IM** *020

SEWELL, Daniel Wm. 1924 ALCOA HWY, STE U109 37920 #056-06-1991 L1997 **AN** *020 †05

SEXTON, Andrew Michael. 1924 ALCOA HWY, BOX 56 37920 #047-06-1999 L2002 **OS** *020 †20

SEXTON, Curtis Cecil. 615 S GAY ST STE 300, 2 CENTRE SQ 37902 #047-06-1962 L1963 **FM AM** *030 †18

SEXTON, David Herron. ■ 37934 #047-06-1960 L1961 **OM IM** *020

SEYMOUR, Digby Gordon. ■ 37909 #056-05-1948 L1953 **AN** *071 †05

SHACKLETT, George E. 1924 ALCOA HWY, DEPT FP U 67 37920 #047-06-1952 L1952 **FM** *071 †18

SHAFI, Mohammad Javeed. 2001 LAUREL AVE, STE 203 37916 #704-02-1991 L1999 **NEP** *020 †20

SHAHBAZI, Shirin Smith. 930 E EMERALD AVE, STE 713 37917 #047-20-1984 L1988 **OBG** *020 †20

SHAMIYEH, James Edward. 1940 ALCOA HWY, STE E210 37920 #047-06-1998 L2005 **PCC** *020 †20

SHANKS, James F, Jr. 620 GLEN WILLOW DR, METHODIST MED CTR OF OAK R 37934 #047-06-1987 L1990 **AN IM** *020 †05

SHATTUCK, Deaver Timothy. ■ 37919 #047-06-1992 L1996 **IM** *020 †20

SHAW, Cathryn Johnson. ■ 37919 #027-01-2005 **DR** *012

SHAW, Kenneth Neil. ■ 37932 #056-06-1988 L1991 **FM** *020

SHEEN, Fu Jen. 4700 WESTERN AVE 37921 #244-05-1974 L1980 **GP** *071

SHEEN, Yuh Jen. 4700 WESTERN AVE, STE 104 37921 #244-01-1975 L1980 **GP PM** *020

SHEETS, Kristen P. 2018 W CLINCH AVE, EAST TENN CHILDRENS HOSP 37916 #045-01-2002 L2005 **PD** *020 †30

SHEKHAT, Nanji Mahidas. 600 ARTHUR ST 37921 #495-48-1972 L1979 **P** *020

SHELL, William N. ■ 37919 #047-06-1953 L1954 **P** *020

SHERRER, Daniel Matthew. ■ 37919 #001-02-2004 **AN** *012

SHERRILL, S Beth. 9333 PARK WEST BLVD, STE 204 37923 #047-06-1979 L1980 **IM GP** *020 †20

SHINE, Donna Lynn. 501 19TH ST, STE 701 TRUSTEES TOWER 37916 #016-11-1981 L1986 **OBG** *020 †30

SHIRK, James Owen. 10810 PARKSIDE DR, STE 108 37934 #047-20-1990 L1994 **OBG** *020 †30

SHOWALTER, John C. 1120 E WEISGARBER RD, GROUP 37909 #019-02-1997 L2000 **IM** *020 †20

SHULTS, Stephanie Renee. 2072 LAKESIDE CENTRE WAY 37922 #047-06-1991 L1993 **PD** *020 †55

SHUMWAY, David Lucius. 2911 TAZEWELL PIKE, # 304 37918 #016-11-1975 L1998 **EM** *020 †16

SHUPP, David Lynn. 1928 ALCOA HWY 37920 #041-14-1980 L1989 **D DS** *020 †20,15

SHURE, Merton Allyn. 1810 AILOR AVE, STE 2 37921 #012-05-1953 L1997 **ORS** *071

SHUTT, Robert Douglas. 4410 VALLEY VIEW DR 37917 #023-12-1988 L2001 **FM** *020 †18

SIDDIQI, Naseemul Haq. 2001 LAUREL AVE STE N202 37916 #495-45-1967 L1977 **NEP IM** *020

SIDDIQUI, Hafeezul H. 5908 LYONS VIEW PIKE, LAKE SHORE MENTAL INST 37919 #495-54-1971 L1984 **GP ADM** *020

SIDDIQUI, Sabina. ■ 37922 #047-06-2004 **GS** *012

SIENKNECHT, E Chas, Jr. 1901 W CLINCH AVE 37916 #047-06-1939 L1940 **IM** *071 †20

SILASI, Ovidiu-Gabriel. 1120 E WEISGARBER RD, STE 104 37909 #781-04-1995 L2002 **IM** *020 †20

SILMON, Robert Wayne. ■ 37934 #422-01-2002 **FP** *012

SILVER, Harold Steven. 9000 EXECUTIVE PARK DR, STE A250 37923 #047-06-1975 L1976 **GE IM** *020 †20

SIM, Jea Wook. 101 GLENLEIGH CT, DOCTOR'S CARE WEST 37934 #583-12-1973 L1981 **OBG GP** *020

SIMMONS, John Douglas. 930 E EMERALD AVE, STE 512 37917 #038-06-1977 L1983 **R** *020 †80

SIMMONS, Rebecca Crowe. ■ 37922 #047-06-1981 L1982 **P** *020

SIMMONS, Reynald Thos. 729 HAMPTON ROADS DR 37934 #021-05-1976 L1986 **IM** *020 †16

SIMONS, Jon Ruric. ■ 37919 #047-06-1963 L1964 **R NM** *071 †80,28 ‡

SIMPSON, Bert Edward. 5908 LYONS VIEW PIKE 37919 #019-02-1985 L2003 **P** *020 †75

SIMPSON, Joseph Edward. 1924 ALCOA HWY, STE U109 37920 #004-01-1988 L1989 **AN** *020 †05

SINGER, Andrew Michael. 2121 HIGHLAND AVE, UNIVERSITY OF MICHIGAN 37916 #017-20-1998 L2007 **AI** *020 †55,03

SINGH, Ashutosh. 2001 LAUREL AVE, STE 202 37916 #495-12-1994 L2004 **NEP** *020 †20

SINGH, Meharban. 1924 ALCOA HWY, UNIVERSITY OF TENNESSEE 37920 #496-21-1996 L2004 **HO** *020 †20

SIZEMORE, Kenny Ross. 324 N PARK 40 BLVD, OF EAST TENNESSEE 37923 #001-02-1986 L1992 **RHU IM** *020 †20

SLUTZKER, Albert David. 2001 LAUREL AVE STE 101 37916 #038-45-1983 L1989 **PUD CCM** *020 †20

SMALL, Robert Ray. 7000 MAYNARDVILLE HWY 37918 #025-07-1965 L1975 **GP FM** *071

SMITH, Allen Carmichael. 2001 LAUREL AVE, SUITE 101 NEWLAND PROF BLD 37916 #012-01-1992 L2002 **PUD CCM** *020 †20

SMITH, Andrew Louis. 220 FORT SANDERS WEST BLVD, STE 101 37922 #050-02-1986 L2000 **IM** *020 †18

SMITH, Arthur Audie. 1924 ALCOA HWY, STE U109 37920 #027-01-1984 L1985 **AN** *040 †05

SMITH, Audra B. 101 GLENLEIGH CT 37934 #020-02-1950 L1950 **FM** *020

SMITH, Audrey Marcelle. 101 GLENLEIGH CT, DOCTOR'S CARE 37934 #047-20-1995 L1996 **FM** *020 †18

SMITH, Bradford Whitney. 1924 ALCOA HWY 37920 #047-06-1973 L1974 **EM** *020 †16

SMITH, Bruce Alan. 5201 KINGSTON PIKE # 317 37919 #004-01-1976 L1980 **AN** *020 †05

SMITH, Daniel Edward, Jr. 1818 ANDY HOLT AVE 37916 #047-05-1987 L1992 **P CHP** *020 †75

SMITH, Darin Scott. 2020 KAY ST 37920 #036-07-1994 L1998 **OPH** *020 †35

SMITH, Dean Preston. 2100 W CLINCH AVE STE 120 37916 #048-14-1987 L1988 **UP U** *020 †95

SMITH, Dustin Welles. ■ 37932 #047-06-2004 **GS** *012

SMITH, Edith Faye. 1346 PAPERMILL POINTE WAY 37909 #010-03-1977 L1993 **AN FM** *020 †05

SMITH, Gary Thos. 1924 ALCOA HWY, DEPARTMENT OF RADIOLOGY 37920 #048-12-1983 L1984 **NM IM** *020 †20,28

SMITH, George Walton, Jr. 501 19TH ST STE 701 37916 #047-06-1986 L1990 **OBG** *020 †30

SMITH, Herbert X. 1431 CENTERPOINT BLVD, STE 100 37932 #045-01-1981 L1983 **EM** *020 †16

SMITH, Lou Mahala. 1932 ALCOA HWY STE 270, UNIV GENERAL SURGEONS PC 37920 #001-06-1985 L1997 **CCS** *020 †20

SMITH, Louis Asbury. 9333 PARK WEST BLVD 37923 #047-06-1981 L1982 **IM** *020 †20

SMITH, Mark Larry. ■ 37920 #001-02-2006 L2008 **IM** *012

SMITH, Marvin Montgomery. ■ 37912 #047-20-2006 **DR** *012

SMITH, Richard S. 1932 ALCOA HWY, STE 360 37920 #047-06-1984 L1990 **ORS HS** *040 †40

SMITH, Robert Deaton. 433 SEVIER AVE 37920 #051-01-1973 L1982 **EM** *020 †16

SMITH, Robert Grant. 260 FORT SANDERS WEST BLVD, KNOXVILLE ORTHOPEDIC CLINI 37922 #047-06-2001 L2007 **ORS** *100

SMITH, Robert Lloyd. 930 E EMERALD AVE, STE 514 37917 #047-06-1968 L1972 **DR VIR** *071 †80

SMITH, Ronald Allen. 1900 N WINSTON RD, STE 300 37919 #005-12-1972 L2004 **FM EM** *020 †18

SMITH, Russell Joe. 1924 ALCOA HWY 37920 #047-20-1985 L1986 **ID IM** *020 †20

SMITH, Scott Tracy. 1932 ALCOA HWY STE 360, UNIV. ORTHOPAEDIC SURGEONS 37920 #018-03-1991 L1997 **ORS** *020 †40

SMITH, Stephanie Dawn. 3846 KEOWEE AVE 37919 #047-06-1999 L2003 **AN** *020 †05

SMITH, Steven James. 9430 PARK WEST BLVD, STE 110 37923 #047-06-1982 L1983 **PS HNS** *020 †45,65

SMITHEY, Brandon Eric. ■ 37922 #047-20-1998 L2000 **PCP** *020 †20

SMOAK, Guy Lynwood, IV. 1924 ALCOA HWY, STE U67 37920 #045-04-1986 L1987 **FM** *020 †18

SNIDOW, John Jos. 1924 ALCOA HWY 37920 #055-02-1985 L2004 **R** *020 †80

SNOW, David Lloyd. 10263 KINGSTON PIKE 37922 #047-20-1987 L1990 **P** *020

SNYDER, Edward Duncan. ■ 37934 #047-06-1953 L1954 **GS GP** *071 †85

SNYDER, William Earl, Jr. 1932 ALCOA HWY, STE 255 37920 #017-20-1993 L1999 **NS ORS** *020 †25

SOLLA, Julio Antonio. 1930 ALCOA HWY STE 240 37920 #033-05-1980 L1993 **CRS GS** *020 †85,10

SOLOMON, Alan. 1924 ALCOA HWY 37920 #036-07-1957 L1966 **ON HEM** *050 †20

SOLOMON, Dennis Ray. 9017 CROSS PARK DR, STE 200 37923 #047-06-1996 L1999 **PD** *020 †55

SOLOMON, Marianne K. 9330 PARK WEST BLVD, STE 402 37923 #047-06-1996 L1999 **IM** *020 †20

SOSS, Sheldon Barry. 1515 SAINT MARY ST 37917 #041-02-1964 L1972 **OTO** *071 †45

SOWELL, Jonathan Webster. 1928 ALCOA HWY, STE 324 37920 #047-06-1977 L1977 **OPH** *075 †35

SPALDING, Steven Lee. 1924 ALCOA HWY, STE U67 37920 #020-12-1988 L1993 **FM** *020 †75,18

SPARROW, Martha Gates. 1400 DUTCH VALLEY DR 37918 #021-05-1974 L1992 **PD** *020 †55

SPENCER, Edwin Earl, Jr. 1704 JOHNNY MAJORS DR 37996 #036-07-1996 L2002 **ORS** *020 †40

SPENCER, Linda Sue. 1114 E WEISGARBER RD, STE A 37909 #037-01-1986 L1997 **ON IM** *020 †20

SPIEGELMAN, Gary Allen. 9330 PARK WEST BLVD # 307 37923 #011-02-1987 L1992 **GE IM** *020 †20

SPRINGER, Michael Andrew. 6700 BAUM DR, STE ONE 37919 #021-05-1987 L1990 **AI** *020 †55,03

SRILATHA, Chilukuri. 1924 ALCOA HWY 37920 #495-21-1994 L2002 **IM** *020 †20

SRINARAYANA, Hanumaiah. ■ 37934 #495-33-1968 L1981 **AN** *075

STAAB, David Bernard. 1817 SILVER CLOUD LN, PREMIER SURGICAL ASSOCIATE 37909 #030-05-1985 L2001 **GS** *020 †85 ‡

STAACK, Jeffrey Blair. 234 MORRELL RD 37919 #018-03-2003 **AN** *012

STAFFORD, Gary Lee. 1431 CENTERPOINT BLVD, STE 100 37932 #001-02-1994 L1995 **EM FM** *020 †18

STAFFORD, James Marshall. 2001 LAUREL AVE, STE N304 37916 #016-42-2000 L2001 **DR** *020 †80

STALEY, John Robt, Jr. 1431 CENTERPOINT BLVD 37932 #047-06-1980 L1980 **EM** *030

STALLINGS, Ted Richard. 9333 PARK WEST BLVD, SUMMIT MEDICAL GROUP, PLLC 37923 #047-20-1985 L1986 **OM EM** *020

STALLWORTH, John Park. 10820 PARKSIDE DR 37934 #021-01-1994 L1995 **DR** *020 †80

STALLWORTH, William Park. 137 E BLOUNT AVE 37920 #021-01-1959 L1967 **R NM** *071 †80,28

STANCHER, John Adolph. 1928 ALCOA HWY, STE 100B 37920 #025-07-1982 L1991 **GE IM** *020 †20

STANLEY, Lowell D, Jr. 1932 ALCOA HWY, STE 280 37920 #020-12-1982 L1988 **NS** *020 †25

STATHACOS, Eustace James. 9031 CROSS PARK DR 37923 #036-01-1957 L1957 **P** *020 †75

STAUBER, Christian Lee. 1120 E WEISGARBER RD, CONSULTANTS 37909 #020-12-1986 L1993 **PUD** *020 †20

STERLING, Steven Lloyd. 2607 KINGSTON PIKE 37919 #047-06-1986 L1987 **OPH** *020 †35

STEVENS, Amy Barger. 1924 ALCOA HWY, STE U67 37920 #047-06-1995 L1996 **FM** *020 †18

STEVENS, Jeffrey Lawrence. 4117 E EMORY RD 37938 #047-06-1997 L2000 **FM** *020 †18

STEVENS, Scott Lawrence. 1924 ALCOA HWY, BOX U-11 37920 #049-01-1984 L1989 **GS** *020 †85

STEVENSON, Aaron William. ■ 37921 #036-05-2004 L2007 **DR** *012

STEWART, Adam Frederick. ■ 37918 #047-06-2007 **GS** *012

STEWART, Wm Richard Carl. 1826 AILOR AVE 37921 #047-06-1979 L1981 **OM GP** *020 †70

STILES, James H, Jr. 1124 E WEISGARBER RD, STILES LARMEE BARNES FOGLE 37909 #021-01-1951 L1954 **PD** *071

STIRNEMANN, Jeffrey Alton. 1900 N WINSTON RD STE 300, ATTN: MINSOUTH 37919 #047-07-1997 L1998 **GS** *020

STOTT, Roger W. ■ 37919 #047-06-1976 L1977 **IM** *020

STRAVINO, Vincent Joseph. 1924 ALCOA HWY, BOX 56 37920 #041-09-1995 L1997 **IM** *020 †20

STREVELS, Stephen Morris. 1924 ALCOA HWY, STE U109 37920 #020-02-1995 L1996 **AN** *020 †05

STRIPE, Sonia Renee. ■ 37932 #038-43-2005 L2005 **AN** *012

STRNAD, Bradley Thomas. 1924 ALCOA HWY 37920 #038-41-1996 L2002 **VIR** *020 †80

STROBEL, Cory Thos. 2100 W CLINCH AVE STE 230 37916 #030-05-1973 L1984 **PG NTR** *020 †55

STURGEON, Rodney Emmett. 4117 E EMORY RD 37938 #051-07-2003 L2007 **FM** *020 †18

SUD, Pamela R. 10108 EL PINAR DR 37922 #422-01-1993 L1996 **PCC** *020 †20

SUGANTHARAJ, Andrew D. 8861 KINGSTON PIKE, COMPLETE FAMILY CARE OF KN 37923 #047-20-1992 L1994 **IM** *020

SUGANTHARAJ, Christiana R. ■ 37950 #495-27-1956 L1975 **GYN** *020 †30

SULLIVAN, Thomas Alan, Jr. 1940 ALCOA HWY, STE E210 37920 #036-07-1965 L1973 **PUD IM** *020 †20

SULLIVAN, William Ross. 2020 KAY ST 37920 #041-01-1967 L1974 **OPH** *020 †35

SUMMERS, Barbara Jean. 9017 CROSS PARK DR, STE 200 37923 #047-06-1998 L2000 **PD** *020 †55

SUMMERS, Jeffrey Scott. 6612 MAYNARDVILLE HWY 37918 #047-06-1992 L1995 **IM** *020 †20

SUNDAHL, C Gerald. 1928 ALCOA HWY STE 2 37920 #035-01-1964 L1972 **CD FM** *071 †20

SURESH, Urath. 1932 ALCOA HWY, STE 460 37920 #495-44-1985 L2001 **NEP** *020 †20

SUTPHIN, Daniel David. ■ 37920 #047-06-2004 **GS** *012

SUVARNAMMA, Hanumaiah. 1718 SAINT MARY ST, STE A 37917 #495-33-1973 L1983 **PD NPM** *020 †55 ‡

SWABE, Gregory Lee. 1124 E WEISGARBER RD, STE 200 37909 #047-20-1982 L1986 **PD** *020 †55

SWAFFORD, Craig Steven. 1924 ALCOA HWY 37920 #047-06-2003 L2005 **GS** *012

SWANGER, Stephen James. 501 20TH ST, STE G3 37916 #036-08-1991 L1997 **PCP** *020 †50

SWANSON, George Alden. 1431 CENTERPOINT BLVD, STE 100 37932 #047-06-1996 L1997 **AN** *020 †05

SWILLEY, Jeffrey Austin. 10810 PARKSIDE DR, STE 305 37934 #305-01-1988 L1996 **IM** *020 †20

TAFFEL, Bruce Henry. 6305 KINGSTON PIKE, BLUECROSS BLUESHIELD OF TN 37919 #035-19-1973 L1999 **OBG** *020 †30

TAHIR, Omar Zahoor. 1924 ALCOA HWY, SCH OF 37920 #286-13-2005 L2006 **GS** *012

TAJEN, Nejat Mansur. 120 HUXLEY RD, STE 103 37922 #902-01-1960 L1991 **GS PME** *020 †85

TAKEMURA, Yousuke. 1924 ALCOA HWY 37920 #572-76-1988 L1993 **FM** *020 †18

TANG, Vincent Cuong Duc. ■ 37938 #654-01-2001 L2002 **FM** *020 †18

TAN-JAUREGUI, Alarice A. 2018 W CLINCH AVE, EAST TENNESSEE CHILDREN'S 37916 #048-16-2000 L2004 **PD** *020

TAO, Ting Yin. ■ 37922 #028-02-2008 *012

TAPIADOR, Carmen Diez. 2100 W CLINCH AVE, STE 140 37916 #748-10-1993 L2002 **PDE** *020 †55

TARR, Jack Howard. 1320 OLD WEISGARBER RD, FAMILYCARE SPECIALISTS PC 37909 #047-06-1975 L1978 **FM** *020 †18

TARVERS, Richard Crawley. 10820 PARKSIDE DR 37934 #033-06-1987 L2003 **AN** *030 †05

TATE, Morris Lee, Jr. 501 20TH ST STE 606, AMAET 37916 #047-06-1978 L1978 **AN EM** *020 †05

TATUM, Robert King. 939 EMERALD AVE, STE 805 37917 #036-07-1979 L1983 **OBG** *020 †30

TAUXE, Edward L. ■ 37919 #047-06-1952 L1952 **ORS** *071 †40

TAYLOR, Dana Ann. 1932 ALCOA HWY STE 270, UNIV GENERAL SURGEONS PC 37920 #305-01-1998 L2003 **CCS** *020 †85

TAYLOR, James Walter. 1930 ALCOA HWY, "STE 235, MED BLDG A" 37920 #023-07-1967 L1977 **PS** *020 †85,65

TAYLOR, Nancy Lynne. 930 E EMERALD AVE, ASSOCIATES 37917 #047-06-1988 L1990 **IM** *020 †20

TEAGARDEN, Dana Delores. 10810 PARKSIDE DR, STE 200 37934 #018-75-1997, ▲ L2003 **OBG** *020 †20

TEASTER, David Sean. 4005 FOUNTAIN VALLEY DR 37918 #047-06-1995 L1998 **PD** *020 †55

TEMPLETON, Steven Allen. 9050 EXECUTIVE PARK DR C 37923 #047-06-1983 L1984 **EM FM** *020 †18

TENNISON, Clifton R, Jr. 600 ARTHUR ST 37921 #021-01-1979 L1983 **P** *020 †75

TERNAY, John Andrew. 900 E OAK HILL AVE, CONSULTANTS PC 37917 #035-15-1999 L2006 **CD** *020 †20

TERRY, William Ferrell. 2201 W CLINCH AVE 37916 #035-01-1974 L1979 **PD PHO** *020 †55

TESTERMAN, Mary Chris. 1704 JOHNNY MAJORS DR 37996 #051-04-1990 L1997 **ORS** *020 †40

THOMAS, Daniel Martin. ■ 37920 #047-06-1944 L1944 **OM PDA** *071 †55

THOMAS, Gary Lynn. 9303 PARK WEST BLVD, PARKWEST 37923 #047-06-1975 L1975 **FM** *020 †18

THOMAS, Timothy Darrell. 2020 KAY ST, STE 300B 37920 #047-06-1985 L1990 **N** *020 †75

THOMPSON, Robt Gordon, II. 101 E BLOUNT AVE, STE 740 37920 #045-01-1981 L1982 **IM** *020 †20

THURMAN, Robert Daniel. 1924 ALCOA HWY, SCH OF 37920 #047-06-2006 **DR** *012

TIGNER, Bryan Jonathan. 9430 PARK WEST BLVD, STE 330 37923 #047-06-2001 L2006 **OTO** *020 †45

TIPTON, Samuel Ridley, Jr. 1818 ANDY HOLT AVE., STUDENT HEALTH CENTER 37996 #047-06-1968 L1969 **IM FM** *020 †18

TITTLE, Joe Evan. ■ 37909 #047-06-1954 L1954 **ORS** *071 †40

TO, Loan Quynh. ■ 37921 #047-20-2008 *012

TOLHURST, George Frederic. 6501 DEANE HILL DR, LE CONTE RADIOLOGY, P.C. 37919 #005-12-1973 L1982 **R** *020 †80

TOMKINSON, Elsie Vannatta. ■ 37918 #035-08-1950 L1963 **R FM** *071 †80,18

TOMPKINS, Forrest Glenn. ■ 37923 #041-13-1956 L1978 **GYN OS** *071 †30

TOMPKINS, James Paul. 1924 ALCOA HWY 37920 #047-20-2006 L2008 **FM** *100

TONEY, Lee Egbert, III. 2060 LAKESIDE CENTRE WAY, NORTHSHORE 37922 #021-05-1976 L1982 **EM FM** *020 †18,16

TOWNE, Randall Douglas. 101 E BLOUNT AVE, CONSULTANTS PC 37920 #495-37-1982 L1989 **CD IM** *020 †20

TOYOHARA, Hiroshi. 101 E BLOUNT AVE, BAPTIST MED TWR STE 800 37920 #572-16-1966 L1975 **TS** *071 †85,90

TRAINER, Nadine M. 1025 CHILDRENS WAY 37922 #035-20-1980 L1993 **PM PD** *020 †55,60

TRAYLOR, Thomas Reid. 930 E EMERALD AVE, STE 614 37917 #001-06-1977 L1981 **OBG** *020 †30

TREASURE, Charles Bland. 900 E OAK HILL AVE, CONSULTANTS PC 37917 #023-07-1984 L1996 **CD IM** *020 †20

TREECE, Yvonne Perle. 10810 PARKSIDE DR, STE 108 37934 #047-20-2003 L2007 **OBG** *012

TRENT, Lucian Williams. ■ 37919 #047-06-1944 L1946 **GS OS** *071 †85

TROUT, Monroe Eugene. ■ 37919 #041-01-1957 L1958 **PA LM** *071

TROWELL, Shannon Heath. 1924 ALCOA HWY, SCH OF 37920 #654-01-2006 **GS** *012

TRUAN, James Armand. ■ 37918 #016-06-1961 L1962 **GP** *071

TRUDELL, Randall Gerald. 1932 ALCOA HWY, STE 350 37920 #035-45-1979 L1985 **N CN** *020 †75

TRUPOVNIEKS, Janis. ■ 37922 #407-07-1950 L1979 **GP** *071

TSALTAS, Theodore T. 939 E EMERALD AVE STE 805 37917 #028-02-1983 L1997 **OBG** *020 †30

TUCKER, Jason David. ■ 37922 #055-02-2008 *012

TUMMERS, Alexander Michae. ■ 37923 #047-20-2006 **GS** *012

TURHAL, Nazim Serdar. 1114 E WEISGARBER RD, STE A 37909 #902-07-1989 L2000 **HO** *020 †20

TURNER, Cannon Elliott. 501 20TH ST STE 606 37916 #047-06-2002 L2006 **AN** *020 †05

TURNER, Dean Montgomery. 2001 LAUREL AVE STE N404 37916 #047-06-1983 L1984 **OBG** *020 †30

TURNER, James Espy. 501 20TH ST, STE 404 37916 #047-06-1957 L1959 **RHU IM** *071

TURNER, John Chas. 1924 ALCOA HWY 37920 #065-10-1977 L1980 **EM FM** *020 †70,16,18

TURNER, Mark Dudley. 2001 LAUREL AVE, STE 402 37916 #023-12-1982 L1984 **ORS OP** *020 †40

TURNEY, Asher Abebe. PO BOX 30698, 1900 WINSTON RD SUITE 379 37930 #047-07-2002 L2005 **NS** *100

TUTOR, David Kent. 2725 ASBURY RD, STE 103 37914 #047-06-1989 L1990 **IM** *020 †20

TYLER, William Alexander. 501 19TH ST STE 607 37916 #047-06-1967 L1976 **NS** *071 †25

UNDERWOOD, Michael Donald. 9333 PARK WEST BLVD # 103 37923 #047-06-1973 L1974 **CD** *020

UPADHYAYA, Nirmala Bhatt. 1924 ALCOA HWY, STE 303 37920 #495-62-1974 L1989 **OBG IG** *020 †30 ‡

URI, Bobbie Gwen. 930 E EMERALD AVE, STE 512 37917 #038-06-1979 L1987 **DR NM** *020 †80,28

URI, Margaret. 930 E EMERALD AVE, STE 512 37917 #038-06-1977 L1983 **R** *020 †80

UZZLE, Jeffrey Alan. 10321 KINGSTON PIKE 37922 #020-12-1987 L1991 **PM** *020 †60 ‡

VALET, Amy Suzannah. ■ 37919 #047-05-2006 **IM** *012

VAN ARSDELL, Kent Howard. 9217 PARK WEST BLVD, STE C3 37923 #005-12-1987 L1994 **IM** *020 †20

VANCE, Matthew Burris. 1924 ALCOA HWY, STE U109 37920 #047-20-1999 L2002 **APM** *020 †05

VANMETER, Stuart Ellis. 1924 ALCOA HWY 37920 #045-01-1986 L1989 **PTH PCP** *020 †50

VANNOY, John Fredrick. 930 E EMERALD AVE, ASSOCIATES 37917 #047-20-1987 L1988 **IM** *020 †20

VAN ZYL, Julia Richards. ■ 37922 #654-01-2001 L2004 **IM** *020 †20

VASQUEZ, Rhodora B. 939 EMERALD AVE, STE 610 37917 #748-11-1983 L1987 **NEP** *020 †20

VASTINE, David Alan. 2725 ASBURY RD, STE 103 37914 #038-41-2002 L2005 **IM** *020

VAZIRANI, Priyadarshani M. ■ 37932 #496-36-2001 L2005 **NM** *020 †20,28

VEKASI, William Howard. 10820 PARKSIDE DR 37934 #025-12-1984 L1987 **AN** *020 †05

VELASCO, Claude R. 1924 ALCOA HWY 37920 #005-11-1983 L1993 **PTH HMP** *020 †50

VICK, George Wilson. 817 E OLDHAM AVE 37917 #055-01-1979 L1983 **OBG** *020 †30

VICKERS, Marvin Haber, Jr. 9430 PARK WEST BLVD, STE 310 37923 #047-05-1968 L1975 **GS VS** *020 †85

VINSANT, Christopher L. 140 CAPITOL DR, ALLIANCE OF EAST 37922 #047-06-1977 L1977 **PMM AN** *020 †05

VONDERAU, Peter Edward, V. 10810 PARKSIDE DR, STE 209 37934 #038-45-2002 L2006 **PM** *020 †60

VOSS, Corey Robert. 1431 CENTERPOINT BLVD, STE 100 37932 #025-07-2000 L2003 **EM** *020 †16

WADDELL, Nicholas Ryan. ■ 37922 #017-20-2006 L2007 **DR** *012

WADE, Dwight Robt, Jr. 1225 E WEISGARBER RD, STE N200 37909 #047-06-1964 L1965 **IM CD** *020 †20

WADE, Matthew Joel. 1924 ALCOA HWY, UNIV OF TENNESSEE GRAD SCH 37920 #305-01-2005 **IM** *012

WAKEFIELD, Paul Henry. 1208 MERCHANT DR 37912 #047-06-1987 L1988 **FM** *020 †18

WALKER, Bruce Edwin. ■ 37920 #047-06-1961 L1961 **OBG** *071 †30

WALKER, Kelley Denise. 10241 KINGSTON PIKE STE 2 37922 #047-06-1986 L1991 **P ADP** *020 †75

WALKER, Norma Bragg. 2018 W CLINCH AVE 37916 #047-06-1952 L1953 **PD OS** *071 †55

WALKER, Rebecca Allison. 9330 PARK WEST BLVD, STE 100 37923 #047-06-1993 L1997 **OBG** *020 †30

WALKER-FILLMORE, Janice M. 501 20TH ST, STE 606 37916 #047-06-1983 L1984 **AN IM** *020 †20,05

WALL, James Wheland. 9017 CROSS PARK DR, STE 200 37923 #048-04-1962 L1965 **PD** *020 †55

WALLACE, Febe Iris. 2018 WESTERN AVE 37921 #036-07-1981 L1992 **IM PD** *020 †20,55

WALLACE, Sidney L. 1704 JOHNNY MAJORS DR 37996 #047-06-1949 L1950 **ORS OSS** *020 †40

WALLIS, Donald Edwin. BAPTIST PROFESSIONAL BLDG 37920 #047-06-1956 L1958 **GS AM** *071

WALSH, Daniel W. 930 E EMERALD AVE, STE 512 37917 #041-13-1991 L2001 **DR** *020 †80

WALTERS, William James. 101 E BLOUNT AVE, STE 650 37920 #047-06-1978 L1979 **GS TRS** *020 †85

WALTON, Clifford L, Jr. ■ 37919 #012-05-1945 L1951 **R DR** *071 †80

WALTON, Norman Clifford. 1924 ALCOA HWY, DEPARTMENT OF MEDICINE 37920 #035-15-1974 L1989 **IM** *020 †20,75

WARE, Robert Edwin. 101 E BLOUNT AVE STE 800 37920 #012-05-1966 L1976 **TS** *071 †85,90

WARNER, Douglas Keith. 3711 RIVER TRACE LN 37920 #038-40-1994 L1997 **EM** *020 †16

WARREN, Caleb Todd. 211 E BLOUNT AVE, STE 3 37920 #056-06-1995 L1997 **FM** *020 †18

WARRICK, Jay Henderson. 4707 PAPERMILL DR, STE 200 37909 #036-08-1986 L1991 **RHU** *020 †20

WARSINSKI, Ivy Marie. 210 FORT SANDERS WEST BLVD 37922 #025-12-1984 L1991 **DR** *071 †80

WASHER, John Elliott. 140 DAMERON AVE, KNOX CO HEALTH DEPT 37917 #047-06-1972 L1973 **PD** *020 †20

WATERS, William Bedford. 1928 ALCOA HWY, STE 222 37920 #047-05-1974 L2000 **U** *020 †95

WATSON, David Theodore. 200 E BLOUNT AVE STE 502 37920 #047-06-1962 L1962 **GP PHP** *020 †18 ‡

WATSON, John David. ■ 37919 #039-01-1993 L2000 **EM** *020 †16

WATSON, Paul Morris. 10517 KINGSTON PIKE, STE C 37922 #005-12-1959 L1974 **FM** *071 †18

WATSON, Phillip Michael. 4306 ASHEVILLE HWY 37914 #039-05-1986 L1992 **FM** *020 †18

WATTS, Glenn Ferrell. 1932 ALCOA HWY, STE 150 37920 #047-06-1955 L1956 **OBG OS** *071 †30

WEBB, Susan Elaine. 9330 PARK WEST BLVD, STE 409 37923 #047-20-1993 L1997 **OBG** *020 †30

WEBB, William Keating. 1120 E WEISGARBER RD, STE 201 37909 #047-06-1973 L1974 **PUD IM** *020 †20

WEBBER, George Robt. 6307 LONAS DR 37909 #047-06-1967 L1971 **GS AM** *020 †85

WEGRYN, Scott Anthony. 2001 LAUREL AVE, STE 304 37916 #038-43-1987 L1993 **DR VIR** *020

WEINSTEIN, Miriam Lynn. 2001 LAUREL AVE STE 404, NEWLAND PROFESSIONAL BLDG 37916 #021-05-1973 L1994 **PM OS** *020 †60

WEISS, Amanda Joy. ■ 37931 #056-06-2005 **FP** *012

WEISS, Mitchell Howard. 9314 PARK WEST BLVD, STE 300 37923 #023-01-1984 L2003 **CD IM** *020 †20

WELLS, Karen J. 1818 ANOY HOLT AVE, U.T. KNOXVILLE STUDENT HEA 37996 #047-05-1990 L1997 **IM** *020 †20

WENDER, Charles M. 1932 ALCOA HWY, 260 U.T. PHYSICIANS BLDG 37920 #047-06-1959 L1960 **CD** *071 †20

WERDERITCH, Frank M. 1900 N WINSTON RD, STE 603 37919 #016-11-1990 L1991 **IM** *020 †20

WEST, Michael Hart. 1208 MERCHANT RD 37912 #047-20-1988 L1989 **FM** *020 †18

WETZEL, Raun Joseph. 1924 ALCOA HWY, # U114 37920 #027-01-2007 **TY** *012

WHEATLEY, Donald Gregory. 2020 KAY ST, STE 300B 37920 #047-06-1993 L1993 **N** *020 †75

WHITE, Keith C. ■ 37922 #048-04-1949 L1999 **OBG** *071 †30

WHITE, Perry Merrill, III. 10321 KINGSTON PIKE 37922 #012-01-1979 L1995 **OSS ORS** *020 †40

WHITE, Robert Franklin. 501 20TH ST STE 606 37916 #020-12-1981 L1985 **AN** *020 †05

WHITE, Wesley Matthew. ■ 37919 #047-06-2004 **U** *012

WHITEHEAD, Bennie Wm. 12631 BARNSTABLE LN 37922 #047-20-1986 L1987 **FM** *020 †18
WHITLOW, Jeffrey Eugene. 6622 CHAPMAN HWY 37920 #020-02-1984 L1993 **IM** *075
WHITSON, Michael Lee. 501 20TH ST, STE G3 37916 #047-06-1974 L1975 **PTH** *020 †50
WHITTED, Anthony Douglas. 1050 1/2 OGLEWOOD AVE 37917 #047-06-2006 **IM** *012
WHITTLE, Robert Bruce. 137 E BLOUNT AVE 37920 #047-06-1955 L1955 **FM GS** *020 †18
WIGGER, Tessa Ehlers. ■ 37924 #001-06-2008 *012
WIKE, James Seymour, Jr. 140 CAPITOL DR, ALLIANCE OF EAST 37922 #001-06-1990 1991
    AN PME *020 †05
WILDER, Charles Clinton. 1120 E WEISGARBER RD, STE 104 37909 #047-20-1997 L2000
    IM *020 †20
WILHOITE, Scott Louis. 9349 PARK WEST BLVD, STE 202 37923 #047-06-1986 L1987
    GE *020 †20
WILLBORN, Katherine Anne. ■ 37931 #048-14-2007 **GS** *012
WILLIAMS, Charles Hughes, Jr. 140 CAPITOL DR, ALLIANCE OF EAST 37922
    #305-01-1985 L1988 **AN IM** *020,05
WILLIAMS, Ginger Ann. 9314 PARK WEST BLVD, STE 404 37923 #047-20-2000 L2004
    OBG *020 ‡
WILLIAMS, James Robt. 5201 N BROADWAY ST 37918 #047-06-1964 L1964 **AN** *075
WILLIAMS, John B. 1450 DOWELL SPRINGS BLVD 37909 #048-12-1987 L1993 **IM** *020 †20
WILLIAMS, John P, III. 210 FORT SANDERS WEST BLVD 37922 #001-06-1989 L1996
    PDR *020 †80
WILLIAMS, John R, Jr. 2018 W CLINCH AVE 37916 #048-16-1989 L1994 **PD PEM** *020 †55
WILLIAMS, Juli Denise. 11440 PARKSIDE DR, STE 302 37934 #001-02-1990 L2005 **IM** *020 †20
WILLIAMS, Kathrine Danell. 1924 ALCOA HWY, DEPT M 37920 #047-20-2007 **IM** *012
WILLIAMS, Keary Robert, Jr. 9430 PARK WEST BLVD, STE 310 37923 #051-01-2000 L2006
    GS *100 †85
WILLIAMS, Lane Porter. 930 E EMERALD AVE, STE 512 37917 #047-06-1985 L1986
    DR *020 †20
WILLIAMS, Muriel Lester. 9031 CROSS PARK DR, VA OUTPATIENT CLINIC 37923
    #047-06-1957 L1957 **FM** *020 †18
WILLIAMS, Richard Eugene. 101 E BLOUNT AVE, STE 800 37920 #045-01-1971 L1983
    TS *071 †85
WILLIAMSON, Perry J. ■ 37922 #047-06-1950 L1950 **OBG** *020 †30
WILLIAR, Sara Bertha. 4428 SUTHERLAND AVE 37919 #041-01-1982 L1986 **P** *020 †75
WILLIFORD, William Nelson. 930 E EMERALD AVE STE 510 37917 #047-06-1970 L1971
    OPH *020 †35
WILLILAMS, Sommer Dea. ■ 37934 #654-01-2003 L2006 **IM** *020
WILLINGHAM, Richard B. 8350 KINGSTON PIKE 37919 #041-01-1949 L1955 **PD** *071 †55
WILLIS, Randall Matthew. ■ 37909 #060-01-1976 L1982 **FM EM** *075 †16
WILSON, David Douglas. 1924 ALCOA HWY, DEPT PTH 37920 #047-06-1973 L1974
    PTH HMP *020 †50
WILSON, Robin Terrell. 137 E BLOUNT AVE, KNOXVILLE ASSOCIATED 37920
    #047-06-1982 L1983 **PTH** *020 †50
WILSON, Stephen Glenn, Jr. 9352 PARK WEST BLVD 37923 #036-01-1954 L1961 **PTH** *071 †50
WILSON, Timothy Scott. 9430 PARK WEST BLVD, STE 240 37923 #047-06-1990 L1998
    PS *020 †65
WINN, Donna Marie. 4707 PAPERMILL DR, STE 200 37909 #017-20-1973 L1979
    RHU IM *020 †20
WIRTHWEIN, Darren Paul. 501 20TH ST, STE G3 37916 #017-20-1995 L2002 **PTH** *020 †50
WIRTHWEIN, Elizabeth. 2100 W CLINCH AVE, ETCH STE 140 37916 #016-43-1997 L2004
    PDE PEM *020 †55
WISEMAN, Brian Frederick. 939 E EMERALD AVE, STE 907 37917 #016-45-1998 L2005
    CN *020 †75
WISNIEWSKI, Joseph Marion. 6700 BAUM DR, STE ONE 37919 #047-06-1994 L1997
    AI *020 †20,55,03
WISNIEWSKI, Quynh Vu. 4529 ASHEVILLE HWY, BOYS & GIRLS PEDIATRICS 37914
    #028-46-1994 L1997 **PD** *020 †55
WOJTANOWSKI, Robert. 1900 N WINSTON RD, P O BOX 30707 37919 #759-08-1982 L1997
    FM *020 †18
WOLFE, John Frederick. 4707 PAPERMILL DR, STE 200 37909 #036-01-1972 L1979
    RHU IM *020 †20
WOOD, Armand Charles. 2060 LAKESIDE CENTRE WAY, NORTHSHORE 37922
    #047-20-1995 L1998 **FM** *020 †18
WOOD, George Harden, III. 12300 S NORTHSHORE DR 37922 #021-01-1957 L1965 **R** *020 †80
WOODWARD, Britton Keith. 2001 LAUREL AVE, STE N304 37916 #047-06-1996 L1997
    DR *020 †80
WOODWORTH, Bruce Edward. 1932 ALCOA HWY, STE C475 37920 #047-20-1983 L2006
    U *020 †95
WOOLDRIDGE, William Henry. 828 W WOODCHASE RD 37934 #027-01-1971 L1982
    NPM PD *020 †55
WOOTEN, Bobby D. 930 E EMERALD AVE, ASSOCIATES 37917 #047-06-1982 L1982
    IM *020 †20
WOOTEN, Paul T. 1924 ALCOA HWY, UNIV OF TENN HOSP 37920 #047-06-1959 L1960
    VIR *071 †80
WORDEN, James P. ■ 37920 #047-06-1946 L1947 **IM** *071 †20
WORKMAN, Edward Alva. 110 PERIMETER PARK RD # C 37922 #045-01-1988 L1988
    PMM P *020 †75
WORLEY, Thomas Parks, III. 1120 E WEISGARBER RD, GROUP 37909 #047-20-2000 L2003
    IM *020 †20
WORTHAM, Dale Cralle. 1940 ALCOA HWY, STE E310 37920 #048-04-1974 L1994
    CD IM *020 †20
WORTHINGTON, Winston Hall. 9352 PARK WEST BLVD 37923 #047-06-1971 L1974 **FM** *020 †20
WRAY, Sibyl Eisenmann. 10810 PARKSIDE DR, STE G15 37934 #036-05-1994 L1999 **N** *020 †75
WRIGHT, Kelly. 1930 ALCOA HWY, STE 145 37920 #035-45-1976 L1990 **NPM PD** *020 †55
WRIGHT, Matthew Joshua. 1924 ALCOA HWY, GRADUATE SCHOOL OF MEDICIN 37920
    #012-01-2005 L2006 **AN** *020
WU, Chuen-Shiong. ■ 37923 #385-02-1962 L1979 **GP FM** *020 †55
WUNDERLICH, Caryn C. 6307 LONAS DR, KNOXVILLE BREAST CENTER 37909
    #016-02-1982 L1995 **R** *020 †80
YANG, Ceeccy. 9314 PARK WEST BLVD, STE 400 37923 #021-06-1998 L2000 **OBG** *020 †30
YANK, Glenn R. 601 HALL OF FAME DR 37915 #047-06-2000 **P** *030 †75
YARBERRY, Otha Horace, Jr. 137 E BLOUNT AVE 37920 #047-06-1953 L1954 **AN** *071
YARBROUGH, Demetria Lasha. ■ 37917 #051-07-2005 **IM** *012
YATES, James Douglas. 1940 ALCOA HWY, STE E310 37920 #025-01-1964 L1974
    CD IM *020 †20
YATES, Raymond Bernard. 5635 SUMMITRIDGE LN 37921 #021-05-1966 L1972 **R GP** *020

YATTEAU, Ronald Francis. 101 E BLOUNT AVE, CONSULTANTS PC 37920 #051-04-1966 L1974
    CD IC *020 †20
YEN, Deanna Rose. 11416 GRIGSBY CHAPEL RD, STE 104 37934 #047-05-1993 L1996
    PD *020 †55
YLITALO, Ashley Dawn. 1300 OLD WEISGARBER RD 37909 #039-01-2001 L2003 **FM** *020 †18
YOUMANS, William Tinsley. 900 E OAK HILL AVE 37917 #047-05-1961 L1961 **ORS** *020 †40
YOUNG, Jay Alger. 1901 W CLINCH AVE 37916 #056-05-1989 L1996 **CRS** *020 †85,10
YOUNG, Margaret Ann. 1818 ANDY HOLT AVENUE, U.T. STUDENT HEALTH CENTER 37996
    #038-06-1984 L1989 **IM** *020 †20
YOUNG, Richard Michael. 101 E BLOUNT AVE, STE 430 37920 #010-02-1994 L2004
    VS *020 †85
YOUNG, Thomas Lanzi. 1928 ALCOA HWY STE 105 37920 #047-06-1979 L1980 **GE IM** *020 †20
YOUNG, Vernon Hutton. 501 20TH ST STE 303 37916 #047-06-1954 L1954 **ORS** *071 †40
YU, James Zheng. 524 SUNDANCER RD 37934 #063-01-1998 L2002 **IM** *020 †20
ZACHARY, Eugene G. ■ 37919 #047-06-1950 L1950 **GP** *071
ZEE, Paulus. 2510 HAMMOND LN 37912 #660-01-1954 L1963 **PD NTR** *020 †55
ZEZULAK, Ashley Carole. ■ 37902 #654-01-2005 **PTH** *012
ZIBAS, Lou Anne. 1120 E WEISGARBER RD, GROUP 37909 #047-20-1992 L1996 **IM** *020 †20
ZIBAS, Walter Michael. 1120 E WEISGARBER RD, GROUP 37909 #047-20-1992 L1996
    IM *020 †20
ZIMO, Deborah Amanda. 611 22ND ST, CHILDRENS PRIMARY CARE CTR 37916
    #016-06-1980 L1995 **PD** *020 †55
ZIRKLE, Charles Rankin. ■ 37919 #047-05-1941 L1941 **GS** *071 †85
ZIRKLE, George Andrew, Jr. 612 CHEROKEE BLVD 37919 #051-04-1945 L1950 **PD A** *071 †55
ZIRKLE, Peter Kevin. 501 19TH ST, STE 501 37916 #047-05-1978 L1979 **VS GS** *020 †85
ZITE, Nikki Beth. 1928 ALCOA HWY, STE 300 37920 #016-01-1998 L2003 **OBG** *020
ZOHARY, Hossam Ali. 211 E BLOUNT AVE STE 507, THE HOSPITALIST GROUP 37920
    #915-03-1994 L2007 **IM EM** *020 †20 ‡

KODAK – SEVIER

HICKMAN, James H, Jr. ■ 37764 #041-01-1945 L1948 **OM** *071 †20
MACGREGOR, Alexander H. ■ 37764 #803-09-1956 L1983 **OBG PA** *071
PARSONS, Roy Burlew, Jr. ■ 37764 #005-12-1957 L1972 **EM AN** *071

LA FOLLETTE – CAMPBELL

BAKER, Charles Thomas. 109 INDEPENDENCE LN, STE 200 37766 #047-06-2003 L2006
    IM *020
BALJEPALLY, Rajagopal M. 109 INDEPENDENCE LN, STE 500 37766 #495-65-1989 L1999
    CD *020 †20
BECK, Roswell Nathaniel. 704 E CENTRAL AVE, PYSICIANS MEDICAL CLINIC 37766
    #047-07-1972 L1984 **NM DR** *075 †28
BRITTO, Errol John. 919 E CENTRAL AVE, STE 201 37766 #495-52-1981 L2001 **GS SO** *020 †85
BROWNSTEIN, Richard Earl. 919 E CENTRAL AVE 37766 #041-02-1976 L1992 **GE** *020 †20
BUCK, Andrea Carol. 905 E CENTRAL AVE, LAFOLLETTE 37766 #012-22-1998 L2001
    IM *020 †20
CLINE, Elijah Grady, Jr. 110 EAST AVE 37766 #047-06-1970 L1971 **EM FM** *020 †18
COHEN, Thomas Leonard. LAFOLLETTE MED CTR RAD DEP 37766 #047-06-1971 L1973
    DR *020 †80
CRUTCHFIELD, James Donald. 945 W CENTRAL AVE 37766 #047-06-1954 L1954
    GS GP *071 †85
DHANDAPANI, Murugesen. 2146 JACKSBORO PIKE, STE C 37766 #495-94-1989 L2000
    FM *020 †18
DONAHOE, Kenneth Todd. 905 E CENTRAL AVE, COUNTY 37766 #038-43-2003 L2005
    FM *020 †18
FARRIS, James Clarence. 109 INDEPENDENCE LN, STE 200 37766 #047-06-1963 L1964
    IM *020 †20
FERNANDES, Ingrid W F. 502 W CENTRAL AVE 37766 #473-02-1998 L2004 **IMG** *020 †20
HALL, Ronald Daker, III. 919 E CENTRAL AVE STE 101B, PHYSICIANS OFFICE BLDG 37766
    #047-06-1970 L1971 **FM EM** *020
HASNAIN, Shahid. 109 INDEPENDENCE LN, PEDIATRIC CONSULTANTS INC 37766
    #704-02-1989 L1998 **PD** *020 †55
HILTY, Robert Butler. ■ 37766 #038-40-1964 L1994 **OBG** *071 †30
HOOD, Melissa Anne. 511 W CENTRAL AVE, STE 3 37766 #045-04-1998 L2001 **PD** *020 †55
ISBER, Jamal. 511 W CENTRAL AVE, STE II 37766 #875-01-1983 L1994 **PUD** *020 †20
JERNIGAN, John Forrest. 303 E CENTRAL AVE 37766 #047-06-1968 L1975 **OTO** *071 †45
MANSOUR, Elie. 919 E CENTRAL AVE, STE 103 37766 #875-01-1980 L1991 **IM PUD** *020 †20
OCULAM, Aleona A Alsay. 109 INDEPENDENCE LN, STE 200 37766 #748-11-1992 L2001
    IM *020 †20
SEARGEANT, Lee Jess, Jr. 307 E CENTRAL AVE 37766 #047-06-1941 L1942 **GP** *071
WOOD, Burgin Henry. 905 E CENTRAL AVE 37766 #047-06-1952 L1953 **FM GP** *071 †85

LA VERGNE – RUTHERFORD

AKATUE, Richmond A.. ■ 37086 #198-01-1992 L2005 **IM** *020 †20
BONNAIRE, Harry Jos. 5242 MURFREESBORO RD 37086 #440-01-1979 L1990 **FM GS** *020 †18
CHIHOMBORI, Arikana C. 5242 MURFREESBORO RD 37086 #047-07-1986 L1990 **GS** *020 †18
JORDAN, Helen. ■ 37086 #047-06-2000 *100
QUAO, Nii Saban. 5242 MURFREESBORO RD 37086 #008-01-1976 L1977 **IM** *020
SMITH, Richard Benton. 5227 MURFREESBORO RD, STE 101 37086 #047-07-1973 L1983
    GP OBG *020
SWAUNCY, Moses Andre. 6001 JACKSON SQUARE BLVD, STE 100 37086 #047-07-2001 L2004
    FM *020 †18
TURPIN, Buford Paul, Jr. 5227 MURFREESBORO RD, STE 101 37086 #047-06-1971 L1971
    IM END *020

LAFAYETTE – MACON

BASTIN, Timothy Roger. 204 HIGHWAY 52 BYP W 37083 #001-06-1982 L1985 **IM** *020 †20
CHUNN, Stanley Allan. 200 HIGHWAY 52 BYP W 37083 #001-06-1982 L1985 **IM GPM** *020 †20

EZUTEH, Donald Otiari. 209 COLLEGE ST, ALPHA MEDICAL ASSOCIATES 37083 #690-06-1993 L2005 **IM** *020 †20

FROEDGE, Evert M. ■ 37083 #020-02-1949 L1951 **GP** *071

GRUMMON, Robt Auchincloss. 427 HIGHWAY 52 BYP W 37083 #008-01-1963 L1985 **GS GP** *071 †85,10

HENCEY, Jennifer Yost. 204 MEDICAL DR 37083 #047-05-1988 L2003 **DR** *020 †80

HUNT, Philip W. 420 COLLEGE ST, STE A 37083 #048-02-1992 L1994 **FM** *020 †18

ILIA, Hanna Chamuon. 207 W LOCUST ST 37083 #781-04-1991 L1998 **FM** *020 †18

KRAMER, Michael K. 204 MEDICAL DR 37083 #025-01-1991 L2006 **DR** *020 †80

MAYER, Jan A. 907 SYCAMORE ST 37083 #017-20-1976 L1976 **P** *075 †75

MORAN-HASSAN, Henry. 204 MEDICAL DR 37083 #187-73-1983 L1998 **DR** *020 †28,80

NABORS, Glenn F, Jr. 204 MEDICAL DR 37083 #047-06-1989 L1990 **RNR** *020 †80

ODUNUSI, Olufemi Odubola. 209 COLLEGE ST, ALPHA MEDICAL ASSOICATES I 37083 #654-01-1985 L1993 **IM** *020 †20

RILEY, Steven Todd. 205 N LOCUST ST 37083 #028-03-1992 L1997 **EM** *020 †16,55

RUDNY, Kevin. 204 MEDICAL DR 37083 #016-11-1998 L2004 **DR** *020 †80

RUNDUS, Victoria R. 205 N LOCUST ST 37083 #048-13-1999 L2002 **PD** *020 †55

SUDHEENDRA, Ramegowda. 207 W LOCUST ST, FAMILY CARE CENTER 37083 #496-39-1986 L2002 **IM** *020 †20

TODD, Malyn Alfred. 204 MEDICAL DR 37083 #047-06-1968 L1970 **DR** *071 †80

LAKE CITY – ANDERSON

NEAL, Wilmer Lewis. PO BOX 696, 514 N MAIN ST 37769 #017-20-1961 L1972 **P** *071

SMITH, Tamra Lee. 110 INDUSTRIAL PARK LN, LAKE CITY FAMILY PHYS 37769 #047-06-1994 L1995 **FM** *020 †18

LAKELAND – SHELBY

ALSAFWAH, Shadwan Fawzee. 9820 QUEBEC LN, CARDIOLOGY FELLOWSHIP PROG 38002 #875-01-1991 L2004 **CD** *012 †20

AMOS, Cynthia Lynne. ■ 38002 #047-07-1992 L1993 **CHP** *020 †75

BALDI, Tiffany Michelle. ■ 38002 #047-06-2007 **TY** *012

BEIS, Russell David. 9160 HIGHWAY 64, STE 12 38002 #047-06-1983 L1984 **IM** *020

DAVIS, Omar Rashad. 4385 MONTELEONE WAY 38002 #047-06-2000 L2002 **NEP** *100 †20

MC LARTY, Alexander M. ■ 38002 #005-12-1953 L1954 **FM GP** *071 †18

LANCASTER – SMITH

RICHARDS, Richard D. ■ 38569 #025-01-1951 L1952 **OPH** *071 †35

LAWRENCEBURG – LAWRENCE

ALDRICH, Sheila Kay. 1605 S LOCUST AVE, STE 101 38464 #038-41-1993 L2007 **PD** *020 †55

ATIYAH, Raja Ata. 1321 S LOCUST AVE 38464 #605-01-1980 L2005 **HNS OTO** *020 †45

BENEFIELD, Thomas Scott. 1607 S LOCUST AVE 38464 #047-06-1996 L1999 **PD** *020 †55

BERRY-BROWN, Frances Ann. 233 E GAINES ST 38464 #047-20-1986 L1987 **IM** *020 †20

BOONE, John Mc Namara, Jr. 2121 N LOCUST AVE, STE 7 38464 #027-01-1991 L1994 **FM** *020 †18

BOYD, Michael A. 1329 S LOCUST AVE 38464 #001-06-1987 L1993 **GS** *020 †85

BUSBY, Micky Lynn. 317 W GAINES ST 38464 #047-06-1978 L1978 **IM** *020 †20

CROWDER, Virgil Holt, Jr. ■ 38464 #047-06-1960 L1961 **GS** *071 †85

DOBIAS, Matthew C. 110 WEAKLEY CREEK RD 38464 #016-42-1983 L1986 **FM** *020 †18

ELMES, Cornelis Millard. 1323 S LOCUST AVE, P O BOX 1054 38464 #016-06-1998 L2006 **ORS** *020 †40

EVERETT, Leon Eldon. 184 PROSSER RD 38464 #064-01-1978 L1981 **FM** *020

FITE, Joe R, Jr. 416 W GAINES ST, LAWRENCE COUNTY AMBULANCE 38464 #047-06-1982 L1982 **FM** *020 †18

FONTENOT, William Lindsey. 1323 S LOCUST AVE 38464 #048-13-1994 L2008 **ORS** *020

HENDERSON, Norman Leroy. ■ 38464 #005-12-1956 L1959 **FM** *071 †18

HINES, Gregory Alan. 1607 S LOCUST AVE 38464 #665-01-1997 L2003 **FM OBS** *020 †18 ‡

HUNTER, Alton Lee, Jr. 2352 SPRINGER RD 38464 #047-06-1992 L1994 **ORS** *020 †40

JOSEPH, Claire. 1605 S LOCUST AVE, STE 201 38464 #308-07-1982 L2005 **N** *020

KELLY, Charles Eugene, II. 192 PROSSER RD 38464 #019-02-1984 L2005 **GE IM** *020

KERSULIS, Gregory Anton. 124 S COLUMBIA AVE, P O BOX 558 38464 #005-19-1986 L2000 **N** *020

KHATRI, Haresh Hotchand. 1607 S LOCUST AVE 38464 #495-23-1974 L1985 **IM** *020 †20

LOVE, Charles V. 246 PULASKI ST 38464 #047-06-1988 L1989 **FM** *020 †18

MC DONALD, James Vincenzo. 183 PROSSER RD 38464 #016-43-1990 L2005 **GPM** *012 †55

MEDIATE, Penny S. 1605 S LOCUST AVE, STE 102 38464 #047-06-1991 L1994 **FM** *020 †18

MULLENIX, Jason Bryan. ■ 38464 #047-06-2001 L2005 **OBG** *020

PARRISH, Villard L. ■ 38464 #047-06-1949 L1950 **FM** *071

POWERS, Richard Reams, Jr. 129 N LOCUST AVE, STE A 38464 #047-06-1997 L1998 **FM EM** *020 †18

SHAH, Jayraj Chandrakant. 1607 S LOCUST AVE 38464 #495-23-1976 L1980 **IM** *020 †20

STALEY, Homer Lee. 104 N LOCUST AVE 38464 #047-06-1973 L1974 **FM** *020 †18

SUTHERLAND, W Shaen. 369 BRINK ST 38464 #005-12-1957 L1958 **GP** *071

TOLAR, Bill Keith. 183 PROSSER RD 38464 #047-06-1991 L1993 **PD** *020 †55

WARREN, Elbert Graham. 1605 S LOCUST AVE, STE 200 38464 #048-02-1983 L2002 **OBG** *020 †30

WILSON, Clayton Don. 1009 N LOCUST AVE, STE 1 38464 #025-07-1975 L1989 **FM** *020 †18

LEBANON – WILSON

ABBEY, Paul A. 1616 W MAIN ST, STE 300 37087 #024-07-1981 L1991 **ORS** *020 †40

ANDERSON, Kenneth W. 417A HARDING DR 37087 #047-06-1980 L1980 **IM FM** *020 †30,18

BABE, Kenneth Stewart, Jr. 1409 W BADDOUR PKWY 37087 #047-05-1991 L1997 **AI** *020 †20,03

BACHSTEIN, James Michael. 112 BABB DR, JAMES M. BACHSTEIN, MD & A 37087 #038-41-1989 L1995 **FM** *020 †18

BAKER, Thomas Scott. 1616 W MAIN ST, STE 300 37087 #020-02-1995 L1999 **PM PMM** *020 †60

BONE, Robert Carver. 404 CASTLE HEIGHTS AVE # E 37087 #047-05-1962 L1962 **GS FM** *020 †55,85

BOWLES, Fred Kirk. 1670 W MAIN ST, STE 100 37087 #047-05-1992 L1994 **OPH** *020 †35

BRADSHAW, James C, Jr. 1409D W BADDOUR PKWY 37087 #047-06-1960 L1961 **FM** *020 †18

BRASFIELD, Barry Wendell. 102 HARTMAN DR, STE G PMB 352 37087 #047-20-1985 L1990 **AN MDM** *020 †05

BRYANT, Joe Frank. 200 E SPRING ST 37087 #047-06-1955 L1955 **GP GS** *020

BUCKLER, Thomas Allen. ■ 37090 #047-06-1988 L1989 *075

BURTON-SHANNON, Clarinda. 1420 W BADDOUR PKWY, STE 230 37087 #047-07-1984 L1985 **OBG** *020

BUTCHER, John Laurence. 1411 W BADDOUR PKWY, UNIV MED CTR EMGY DEPT 37087 #034-01-1990 L1996 **EM GPM** *020 †70

CADENA-CUCTA, Guillermo. 1411 W BADDOUR PKWY 37087 #264-01-1960 L1974 **OBG R** *020

CLAYCOMB, Stephen Harmon. 1405 W BADDOUR PKWY, STE 101 37087 #004-01-1989 L1992 **PD** *020 †55

COLE, Donald Alexander. 100 PHYSICIANS WAY, STE 330 37090 #051-04-1980 L1996 **GE IM** *020 †20

COLLINS, Tamara Jean. 404F CASTLE HEIGHTS AVE 37087 #020-02-1998 L2002 **IM** *020

DEDICK, Paul Eugene. 123 N GREENWOOD ST 37087 #010-01-1976 L1988 **R VIR** *062 †80

DEPPEN, Cathy Alice. 1432 W MAIN ST 37087 #047-06-1994 L1998 **OBG** *020 †30

DOVE, Francis Bernard, Jr. 716 CASTLE HEIGHTS CT, # B 37087 #036-05-1967 L1991 **RHU IM** *020 †20

DOW, Frederick T, III. 1419 W BADDOUR PKWY 37087 #001-06-1984 L1990 **PUD IM** *020 †20

EVANS, Randolph R. 1670 W MAIN ST STE 100 37087 #038-40-1983 L1988 **OPH EM** *020 †35

FERGUSON, Morris Dean. 1409 W BADDOUR PKWY 37087 #047-06-1956 L1957 **FM** *072 †18

FRUIN, Alex Brent. 100 PHYSICIANS WAY, STE 330 37090 #047-05-1998 L2005 **GS** *020 †85

GALLANT, Gary Geo. 1420 W BADDOUR PKWY, STE 210 37087 #064-01-1979 L1982 *020

GIBSON, Russell Eugene. 1417A W BADDOUR PKWY, UNIVERSITY OF MICHIGAN 37087 #020-12-2000 L2007 **PD** *100 †55

GILL, Charles Mc Clelland. 1421 W BADDOUR PKWY 37087 #047-06-1984 L1989 **U** *020 †95

GREGORY, Kelly Gentry. 2188 WEST MAIN STREET 37087 #047-06-1956 L1957 **AM OM** *071 †70

GRIME, Harvey H. ■ 37087 #047-06-1959 L1960 **R** *071 †80

HALCOMB, Rhonda Telette. 1432 W MAIN ST 37087 #001-02-1993 L2000 **OBG** *020 †30

HUGHEY, Brian Walker. 715B CASTLE HEIGHTS CT 37087 #021-01-1988 L1988 **IM** *020 †20

HUNTER, Melanie Dolores. ■ 37087 #024-05-1984 L2007 **FM** *020 †18

JABUSCH, Lisa Marie. 1432 W MAIN ST 37087 #028-34-1986 L2004 **OBG** *020 †30

JANTZ, Robert Jos. 706 CADET CT 37087 #041-13-1981 L1988 **FM** *020 †18

JOHNSON, Roy Phillip. 936 MURFREESBORO RD, MTOEM 37090 #047-07-1990 L1991 **OM** *020 †70

JORDAN, Charles Andrew. 201C SIGNATURE PL 37087 #047-06-1987 L1989 **PD** *020 †55

KAUFFMAN, Christopher P. 1616 W MAIN ST STE 300, . 37087 #035-08-1993 L2004 **OSS OTR** *020 †40

KEARNEY, Kathleen. 1423 W BADDOUR PKWY 37087 #012-01-1990 L2002 **CD** *020 †20

KEHINDE, Modupe O. 1424 W BADDOUR PKWY, STE H 37087 #690-01-1983 L2005 **PCC** *020 †20

KOWAL, Thomas Alfred. 102 HARTMAN DR, STE H 37087 #025-07-1995 L1998 **GP GS** *020

LANNING, Chas Bedford, Jr. 1421 W BADDOUR PKWY, STE B 37087 #047-06-1981 L1982 **OBG EM** *020 †30

LETT, Earl Dwayne. 1417A W BADDOUR PKWY 37087 #047-06-1988 L1994 **PS** *020 †85,65

LEVECK, Mary Ann. ■ 37087 #020-02-1976 L1977 **OBS EM** *071

LIN, Susie I-Ching. 1420 W BADDOUR PKWY, STE 220 37087 #047-05-2001 L2004 **GS** *020

LITTMAN, Margaret C Sopko. ■ 37087 #038-06-1947 L1947 **PTH** *071 †50

LITTMAN, William John. 1419 W BADDOUR PKWY 37087 #016-11-1982 L1987 **CD IM** *020 †20

LONG, William Stephen. 1405 W BADDOUR PKWY, STE 104 37087 #027-01-1984 L1995 **PME** *020

LUCK, David Wayne. 322 N MAPLE ST 37087 #047-20-1995 L1998 **FSM** *020 †18

MARK, Deborah Wen-Yee. 115 WINWOOD DR, STE 105 37087 #041-07-1997 L2007 **PD** *020

MATHEWS, Jeffrey Allen. 1405 W BADDOUR PKWY, # 102B 37087 #047-06-1994 L1996 **GS** *020 †85

MCCULLOUGH, Carol Hope. 1432 W MAIN ST 37087 #047-06-1990 L1994 **OBG** *020 †30

MC KINNEY, Roger Earl. 1407 W BADDOUR PKWY 37087 #047-06-1977 L1979 **FM** *020 †18

MITCHELL, Charles Austin. 206B BABB DR 37087 #047-06-2000 L2003 **IM** *020 †20

MITCHELL, Charles Austin. 206 BABB DR # B 37087 #047-06-1970 L1971 **D PD** *020 †55

MITCHELL, E Kay S. 1421 W BADDOUR PKWY, STE B 37087 #045-01-1974 L1989 **OBG** *020

MOORE, Michael Patrick. 1616 W MAIN ST, STE 200 37087 #051-07-1981 L1990 **PM OS** *020 †60

MOORE, Ralph B. ■ 37087 #005-12-1953 L1953 **GP** *071

MORRIS, James Wayne. 1405 W BADDOUR PKWY, STE 100 37087 #047-06-1972 L1973 **GS** *020 †85

NEELY, Stephen Minick. 1616 W MAIN ST, STE 200 37087 #051-01-1973 L1980 **ORS** *020 †40

NIXON, John Alexander. 1412 W BADDOUR PKWY 37087 #047-07-1973 L1980 **PTH** *020 †16

NOACK, Stephanie P. ■ 37087 #011-03-1994 L2000 **AN** *020 †05

NUESSLE, Donald W. 1441 W BADDOUR PKWY, UMC EMERGENCY DEPT 37087 #011-02-1984 L1992 **EM PD** *020 †20,55

O'QUINN, Bancroft, Jr. 1405 W BADDOUR PKWY, STE 106 37087 #028-02-1981 L1987 **OTO HNS** *020

PAWLOWSKI, Yvonne. 201 SIGNATURE PL, STE C 37087 #759-09-1973 L1990 **PD** *020 †55

PETHKAR, Vijay. 1419 W BADDOUR PKWY 37087 #495-21-1985 L1999 **PUD** *020 †20

PETTY, Damon Hayes. 1616 W MAIN ST, STE 300 37087 #051-07-1996 L2002 **OSM** *020 †40

PEYTON, James David. 115 WINWOOD DR STE 205 37087 #047-06-1998 L2000 **HO** *020 †20

PEYTON, Richard Randolph. 1411 W BADDOUR PKWY, CANCER CARE CENTER 37087 #036-05-1967 L1979 **RO OBG** *020 †30,80

PICKETT, Alton Wayne. 437 PARK AVE 37087 #047-07-1971 L1974 **OBG** *020

ROBERTSON, George William. 1407 W BADDOUR PKWY 37087 #047-06-1997 L1999 **MPD** *020 †20,55

ROBERTSON, George Wm. 1407 W BADDOUR PKWY 37087 #047-06-1967 L1967 **GS PD** *020 †85

ROUNDTREE, Alan Wayne. 1421B W BADDOUR PKWY, WOMEN'S HEALTH CENTER PC 37087 #039-01-1979 L1986 **OBG** *020 †30

ROY, John Chas. ■ 37087 #035-19-1954 L1956 **ORS** *071 †40

SAVELL, Vernon David, Jr. ■ 37087 #027-01-1978 L1989 **PD** *020 †55

SHAH, Rahil Devendra. 417 HARDING DR, STE D 37087 #654-01-1999 L2005 **GE** *020 †20

SMITH, Basil Eugene. 1616 W MAIN ST, DOW, SOBIEK & HUENE ORTHOP 37087 #051-04-1982 L2005 **OSM ORS** *020 †40

SORRELS, Hardie V, III. 715B CASTLE HEIGHTS CT 37087 #047-06-1986 L1987 **IM** *020 †20

SY, Bernard Tan. 1407 W BADDOUR PKWY 37087 #027-01-2003 L2007 **MPD** *020 †20,55

TATE, John Louis. 206A BABB DR 37087 #021-06-1979 L1991 **OTO FPS** *020 †45

TAYLOR, Billy James. 838 MILL RD, MILL ROAD 37090 #047-07-1972 L1978 **OBG** *020 †30

TERRY, Roy Clarence. 1616 W MAIN ST, STE 203 37087 #036-01-1989 L1994 **ORS** *020 †40

THORNHILL, Timothy Wyatt. 1411 W BADDOUR PKWY 37087 #047-06-1982 L1984 **AN** *020

VERNON, Crystal Nolen. 1029 W MAIN ST STE M, TENNESSEE CHILDREN'S HEALT 37087 #047-06-2003 L2006 **PD** *100 †55

WARREN, Larimore Colvett. 1405 W BADDOUR PKWY, STE 104 37087 #047-06-1977 L1983 **GS VS** *020 †85

WEST, Willard Mahlon. 1425 W BADDOUR PKWY 37087 #047-06-1975 L1976 **IM** *020 †20

WIGGINS, Bernard Alfred. 1029 W MAIN ST STE M 37087 #051-01-1970 L1975 **PD** *020 †55

WIGGINS, Charles Alfonsa. 1007 CARTHAGE HWY, 1420 BADDOUR PARKWAY SUITE 37087 #047-07-1969 L1971 **IMG GP** *020

WOODS, Robert Cameron. 1423 W BADDOUR PKWY 37087 #051-04-1988 L1993 **CD** *020 †20

LENOIR CITY – LOUDON

ARNOLD, Henry Grady, Jr. 576 FORT LODN MDCL CNTR DR, STE 207 37772 #047-06-1968 L1969 **OTO** *020 †45

AYERS, David Russell. 423 MEDICAL PARK DR, STE 100 37772 #055-02-1985 L2007 **FM** *020 †18

BACHUS, Robert Wm K. 423 MEDICAL PARK DR, HEALTH 37772 #011-03-1992 L1997 **P** *020 †75

BURDETTE, James Ashby. 1559 HIGHLAND PARK DR 37772 #047-06-1952 L1953 **FM** *071 †18

CAMPBELL, John Wilson. 576 FORT LODN MDCL CNTR DR, STE 207 37772 #047-06-1953 L1953 **OTO** *072

CHROSTOWSKI, Mary L. 2771 HIGHWAY 11 E, STE 5 37772 #305-01-1986 L1996 **IM** *020

CUMMINGS, Barry Frank. 221 WATERFORD CIR 37772 #047-06-1984 L1984 **IM EM** *020

DEEAN, Arunkumar D. 207 MYERS RD 37771 #495-37-1975 L1982 **OBG** *020 †30

DILTZ, Emily Ann. 423 MEDICAL PARK DR 37772 #024-07-1981 L1995 **CD IM** *020 †20

EASON, John Henry, Jr. 1018 HIGHWAY 321 N 37771 #047-06-1985 L1991 **GS VS** *020 †85

FRIEND, Mary E. 423 MEDICAL PARK DR, STE 200 37772 #048-13-1987 L1990 **PD** *020 †55

GREGORY, Gladys Regina. 423 MEDICAL PARK DR, HEALTH 37772 #036-08-1990 L2001 **P** *020 †75

GUYTON, James Roy. ■ 37772 #021-01-1955 L1962 **R** *071 †80

HAHN, Jan T. 501 ADESSA PKWY, STE A150 37771 #035-47-1977 L1984 **FM** *020 †18

HOLMES, Howard Gene. 780 HIGHWAY 321 N, 780 HWY 321 N SUITE 8 37771 #422-01-1983 L1986 **EM IM** *020

JAMES, Tina Tan. 550 FORT LODN MDCL CNTR DR, CENTER DRIVE 37772 #048-15-1997 L2002 **DR** *020

JOHNSON, Clifford Q, Jr. 576 FORT LODN MDCL CNTR DR, STE 207 37772 #047-06-1972 L1973 **OTO** *020 †45

KNIGHT, Steven Bartley. 550 FORT LODN MDCL CNTR DR, FT LOUDON MED CTR IMAGING 37772 #047-20-1992 L1993 **DR NM** *020 †80,28

MACLELLAN, Andrew James. 423 MEDICAL PARK DR, STE 400B 37772 #023-12-1988 L2004 **ORS** *020 †40

MARTYN, Robert Peter. 423 MEDICAL PARK DR 37772 #025-12-1986 L1992 **CD IM** *020 †20

MISTRY, Nareshbhai R. 689 MEDICAL PARK DR, STE 101 37772 #495-89-1983 L1995 **CD IM** *020 †20

MOKAL, Albert Jos. 550 FORT LODN MDCL CNTR DR, FT LOUDON MED CTR 37772 #011-02-1963 L1968 **R** *071 †82 ‡

MORSE, James Andrew. 1018 HIGHWAY 321 N, MEDICAL CENTER 37771 #038-41-1989 L1997 **FM** *020 †18

MORTON, Randall Taylor. 1018 HIGHWAY 321 N, MEDICAL CENTER 37771 #047-20-1983 L1989 **FM OM** *020 †18

PATRIC, Kenneth Ward, Jr. 785 HIGHWAY 321 N, STE 24 37771 #035-45-1976 L1996 **FM** *030 †18

PATTERSON, Joan B. 423 MEDICAL PARK DR, STE 100 37772 #003-01-2004 L2006 **FP** *012

POLLARD, Mark T. 785 HIGHWAY 321 N, STE 24 37771 #016-45-1986 L1990 **FM** *020 †18

PREMJI, Moez R. 308 E BROADWAY ST, LENOIR MEDICAL CLINIC 37771 #704-25-1989 L2004 **IM** *020 †20

REDDY, Ramani M. 689 MEDICAL PARK DR, STE 301 37772 #495-16-1986 L1996 **IM** *020 †20

RIMER, Lloyd James. 785 HIGHWAY 321 N, STE 24 37771 #047-06-1982 L1984 **IM** *020 †20

ROTHWELL, Joseph Michael. 576 FORT LODN MDCL CNTR DR, STE 101 37772 #045-01-1985 L1993 **GS VS** *020 †85

SANABRIA, John D. 460 MEDICAL PARK DR, STE 103 37772 #306-01-1993 L1996 **FM** *020 †18

SEALS, Michael Taite. 576 FORT LODN MDCL CNTR DR, STE 207 37772 #047-06-1986 L1988 **OTO** *020 †45

SEXTON, David Glenn. 576 FORT LODN MDCL CNTR DR, STE 207 37772 #047-06-1981 L1981 **OTO** *020 †45

SHEA, Walter Carlton. ■ 37772 #047-06-1956 L1956 **GP** *071

SHETH, Milan Nareshbhai. 689 MEDICAL PARK DR, STE 301 37772 #495-22-1985 L1995 **IM** *020 †20

STANLEY, Richard Edmund. 423 MEDICAL PARK DR # 100, PRIMARY CARE ASSOCS 37772 #005-12-1974 L1979 **FM** *020 †18

SUD, Leela Bhavnani. 423 MEDICAL PARK DR, HEALTH 37772 #495-01-1952 L1974 **P FM** *020

SURANYI, Emese M. 423 MEDICAL PARK DR, STE 100 37772 #041-09-1996 L2000 **D** *020 †15

SWICEGOOD, Kathy Diane. 423 MEDICAL PARK DR # 100, PRIMARY CARE ASSSOCS 37772 #047-06-1998 L2001 **FM** *020 †18

WALTER, Gail-Marie K. 1018 HIGHWAY 321 N, MEDICAL CENTER 37771 #045-04-1988 L1989 **FM** *020 †18

WARD, Albert N. ■ 37772 #047-06-1951 L1951 **OM** *071 †70

WHITAKER, Lee Carl. 785 HIGHWAY 321 N, STE 24 37771 #024-05-1990 L2001 **FM PHP** *020 †18 ‡

WILLIAMS, Saundra Annette. 785 HIGHWAY 321 N, STE 24 37771 #041-13-1985 L1988 **IM** *020

LEOMA – LAWRENCE

ECKHART, Milton D. ■ 38468 #048-04-1994 L1995 **N** *100

LEWISBURG – MARSHALL

BONE, George. 1080 N ELLINGTON PKWY 37091 #917-04-1966 L1985 **GS** *020

BURROW, Ted Dylan. 529 W COMMERCE ST 37091 #047-06-1992 L1994 **IM** *020 †20

DELAPLANE, Robert Warren. 451 CORNERSVILLE RD 37091 #030-05-1955 L1983 **GP GPM** *071

GILES, Wesley Heath. ■ 37091 #047-06-2005 **GS** *012

GIST, William Edward. 1090 N ELLINGTON PKWY, # 101 37091 #038-41-1988 L2006 **OBG OS** *020 †30 ‡

GORDON, Timothy Edward. 1080 N ELLINGTON PKWY 37091 #047-06-1984 L1985 **OPH** *020 †35

LEWIS, Melvin Glenn. 110 FREEMAN DR 37091 #047-06-1974 L1975 **FM** *020 †18

MC CRACKEN, Dennis P. 1080 W ELLINGTON PKWY 37091 #020-12-1986 L1992 **GP** *020

MURPHY, Mark Anthony. ■ 37091 #033-05-1983 L1992 **AN** *020 †05

NASH, Timothy Alan. 1090 N ELLINGTON PKWY, STE 102 37091 #047-06-1985 L1986 **IM** *020 †20

PHELPS, Kenneth J, Jr. 304 W CHURCH ST 37091 #047-06-1972 L1973 **FM IM** *020 †18

SHACKELFORD, Claude E. 1090 N ELLINGTON PKWY, STE 102 37091 #001-02-2000 L2003 **FM** *020 †18 ‡

VON ALMEN, Jos Franklin. 113 W EWING ST, P O BOX 1492 37091 #047-06-1959 L1959 **FM PD** *020 †18

WADE, Joseph Fredrick. 1080 N ELLINGTON PKWY 37091 #001-02-1989 L1994 **ORS OSS** *020 †40

WERNER, Denise Lynn. 1090 N ELLINGTON PKWY, STE 102 37091 #016-45-1996 L2000 **MPD** *020 †20,55

LEXINGTON – HENDERSON

BRATTON, Christopher Hall. 90 BENWOOD AVE 38351 #047-06-1978 L1978 **GS** *020

DAVIS, Daniel Alfred. ■ 38351 #047-06-1991 L1993 **EM** *020 †16

DAVIS, Joe Harris. ■ 38351 #047-05-1965 L1966 **PHP FM** *071 †70

DAVIS, Pansy H. ■ 38351 #047-06-1991 L1994 **PD** *020 †55

FLETCHER, Walter Frizzell. 250 BOSWELL ST, FAMILY PHYSICIANS OF 38351 #047-06-1993 L1994 **FM** *020 †18 ‡

HENDERSON, Reggie Allan. 250 BOSWELL ST, FAMILY PHYSICIANS OF 38351 #004-01-1979 L1979 **FM** *020 †18

HERRON, Bruce Emerson. 14 HOSPITAL DR 38351 #047-05-1969 L1975 **OPH** *020 †35

HORNE, Karen Elaine. 14 HOSPITAL DR 38351 #047-06-2006 **OBG** *012

LENTZ, Jonathan David. 9486 HIGHWAY 412 W 38351 #047-06-1996 L1999 **PD** *020 †55

MAYORGA, Luis L. ■ 38351 #231-01-1968 L1980 **GS** *020

MC DONALD, Thomas C. 270 W CHURCH ST, STE D 38351 #047-06-1991 L1992 **IM** *020

MC KEE, Heather Marie. 185 BOSWELL ST 38351 #039-01-1996 L1998 **IM** *020 †20

MUNISWAMY, Harish. 185 BOSWELL ST 38351 #496-34-1998 L2006 **IM** *100 †20

RAJA, Kallaiah M. 200 W CHURCH ST, MEDICAL STAFF OFFICE 38351 #495-09-1961 L1971 **IM PD** *020 †55

RAMER, Warren Carlton, Jr. 250 BOSWELL ST, FAMILY PHYSICIANS OF LEXIN 38351 #047-06-1969 L1970 **GP** *020 †18 ‡

SADLER, Scott Michael. 250 BOSWELL ST, FAMILY PHYSICIANS OF 38351 #047-06-1996 L1998 **FM** *020 †18

STRIPLING, Jack Clements. 21 W CHURCH ST, STRIPLING CLINIC 38351 #047-06-1955 L1955 **FM** *071

STROUP, Kevin Hallum. 270 W CHURCH ST STE A, LEXINGTON FAMILY CARE 38351 #047-06-1991 L1992 **FM EM** *020 †18

WHITE, Charles Wesley. 250 BOSWELL ST, FAMILY PHYSICIANS OF 38351 #047-06-1962 L1962 **FM** *020 †18

WHITE, Charles Wesley, Jr. 250 BOSWELL ST, FAMILY PHYSICIANS OF 38351 #047-06-1990 L1991 **FM** *020 †18 ‡

LIMESTONE – GREENE

CLARK, James Warner. 105 LIMESTONE RURITAN RD, LIMESTONE MED CTR POB 217 37681 #654-01-1981 L1984 **FM** *020 †18

LINDEN – PERRY

AVERETT, Andrew Knox. 2718 SQUIRREL HOLLOW DR 37096 #047-06-1989 L1991 **FM** *020

AVERETT, Stephen Lee. 2718 SQUIRREL HOLLOW DR 37096 #047-06-1978 L1979 **IM EM** *020 †20

LIVINGSTON – OVERTON

CLEMENTS, Barton Matthew. 310 OAK ST 38570 #047-06-1986 L1987 **GS** *020 †85

CLOUGH, John Robt. 5751 BRADFORD HICKS DR, PRIORITY CARE CLINIC 38570 #005-12-1982 L1985 **FM OBG** *020 †18

COLBURN, Kenneth Lee. 315 OAK ST 38570 #005-12-1980 L1991 **FM** *020 †18

COPELAND, Jessie Lee, Jr. 315 OAK ST 38570 #047-06-1995 L1998 **MPD PD** *020

COX, Michael T. 500 W MAIN ST 38570 #020-12-1981 L1984 **IM IMG** *020 †20

CRUTCHFIELD, Edward H. 1010 JOHN T POINDEXTER DR, OVERTON COUNTY JAIL 38570 #020-02-1994 L1996 **EM** *020 †18 ‡

FIELDS, Richard Dean. 315 OAK ST 38570 #041-13-1973 L1986 **GS** *020 †85

FROMKE, Vincent Lind. 500 W MAIN ST, LIVINGSTON CLINIC 38570 #028-34-1958 L1994 **IM HEM** *020

GASPAR, Matthew Jos. ■ 38570 #049-01-1978 L1997 **OS** *020 †18

HIX, Amy Spears. 529 MEDICAL DR 38570 #047-06-1998 L2002 **FM OBS** *020 †18

JAIN, Pushpendra Kumar. 1061 W MAIN ST 38570 #495-73-1977 L1985 **GP EM** *020

JONES, Albert A, III. 315 OAK ST, ATTN: RADIOLOGYDEPARTMENT 38570 #047-06-1982 L1982 **DR** *020

LANGENBERG, Katherine R. ■ 38570 #047-06-1997 L2000 **PD** *020 †55

LANGENBERG, Mark Taylor. 500 W MAIN ST 38570 #047-06-1997 L2001 **MPD** *020 †20,55

MC LERRAN, Samantha E. 500 W MAIN ST 38570 #047-07-2001 L2004 **FM** *020 †18

NOWELL, Mark Dewayne. 310 OAK ST 38570 #027-01-2000 L2002 **GS** *020 †85

ORSBURN, D Elizabeth. 406 W 1ST ST STE A 38570 #020-02-1998 L2005 **PM** *100
QUARLES, Will Grundy. ■ 38570 #047-06-1958 L1958 **GP** *071
ROE, Jack Michael. 315 OAK ST 38570 #047-06-1958 L1958 **GP AN** *071
SMITH, Trueman David. 529 MEDICAL DR, STE B 38570 #064-01-1982 L1994 **FM** *020
TERRY, Silas David, Jr. 700 W MAIN ST 38570 #005-06-1995 L1999 **OBG** *020 †30
TITUS, William Pearce. 1061 W MAIN ST 38570 #047-06-1971 L1972 **FM** *020 †18
TURNBULL, John Matthew. 502 W MAIN ST 38570 #047-05-1995 L2000 **ORS** *020 †40

LOOKOUT MOUNTAIN – HAMILTON

BUTLER, Jeffery Miles. ■ 37350 #012-22-2006 **GS** *012
GILLEY, Edwin Wayne. ■ 37350 #051-01-1948 L1953 **IM** *071 †20
GOLDER, Barbara Harty. ■ 37350 #011-03-1977 L2005 **PTH OS** *020 †50
HOPPER, Richard Edmund. ■ 37350 #047-06-1966 L1967 **DR** *071 †80
LIGON, Elizabeth Libby. ■ 37350 #047-06-1995 L1999 **AN** *020 †05
MC DONALD, Charles D, Jr. 406 W BROW RD 37350 #012-01-1963 L1970 **CD IM** *071 †20
MC DONALD, Martha W. ■ 37350 #041-07-1963 L1967 **EM IM** *071 †28
TUCK, Benjamin Calvin. ■ 37350 #001-02-2007 **GS** *012
VISCOMI, Vincent Andrew. 1000 SCENIC HWY 37350 #041-02-1981 L1989 **SME PUD** *020 †20

LORETTO – LAWRENCE

GOODEMOTE, Kimberly Ann. 106 S MILITARY ST 38469 #010-02-1997 L2001 **FM** *020 †18
METHVIN, Ray Elwin. 206 S MILITARY ST, PO 160 38469 #047-06-1954 L1954 **GP** *071
SCHANTZ, Matthew Edward. 206 S MILITARY ST, STE 1 38469 #017-20-1999 L2002 **FM** *020 †18

LOUDON – LOUDON

ABCEDE, Pio S. ■ 37774 #748-07-1954 L1969 **AN OS** *100
ACKER, James Joseph. ■ 37774 #047-06-1956 L1956 **CD IM** *071 †20
COUDEN, Trevert Lester. ■ 37774 #016-02-1958 L1959 **ORS** *071 †40
COX, James B. ■ 37774 #041-02-1951 L1956 **PS** *071 †65
GUIDER, James Perry. 616 WARD AVE 37774 #047-06-1977 L1980 **PD** *020 †55
HARRISON, Samuel A. 901 GROVE ST 37774 #047-06-1948 L1949 **GP GS** *071
KYKER, Paul Gail, Jr. ■ 37774 #047-06-1960 L1961 **PD** *071 †55
PATEL, Bipinchandra M. 111 CLYDE ST, INTERNAL MEDICINE ASSOCIAT 37774 #495-37-1983 L1993 **IM** *020 †20
PERSHING, Stephen Douglas. 111 CLYDE ST 37774 #047-06-1974 L1977 **IM** *020
RAHMAN, Ayaz Mohammad. ■ 37774 #028-46-2004 **IM** *012
RAHMAN, Mohammad Razaur. 111 CLYDE ST 37774 #704-02-1974 L1981 **IM** *020 †20
RITZENTHALER, David Otto. ■ 37774 #056-05-1964 L1996 **OPH** *071 †35
RUDOLPH, Burton M. 901 GROVE ST 37774 #041-02-1953 L1964 **IM AI** *020 †03,20
SCHAERER, Calvin Robert. 616 WARD AVE, LOUDON PED CLINIC 37774 #047-06-2001 L2004 **PD** *020 †55
STIMPSON, Peter Gagnon. 901 GROVE ST 37774 #047-06-1973 L1974 **GP** *020
ZAAR, Gregory Thos. ■ 37774 #047-06-1985 L1986 **IM GPM** *020 †20

LOUISVILLE – BLOUNT

AMEEL, Brian Albert. 2347 JONES BEND RD, HEALTH AT PENINSULA 37777 #025-12-1996 L2005 **P CHP** *020 †75
BREWER, Dan E. 2347 JONES BEND RD, HEALTH AT PENINSULA 37777 #036-05-1984 L1989 **FM FPG** *040 †18
COX, Daniel Lewis. 2347 JONES BEND RD, HEALTH AT PENINSULA 37777 #047-20-1984 L1987 **FM** *020 †18
DAVIS, Douglas Lee. 2347 JONES BEND RD, HEALTH AT PENINSULA 37777 #047-20-1985 L1985 **IM** *020 †20
DAVIS, Larry Eugene. 2347 JONES BEND RD, HEALTH AT PENINSULA 37777 #025-12-1973 L1986 **FM FSM** *020 †18
HARAF, Frank Jos. ■ 37777 #016-11-1970 L1976 **ON HEM** *071 †20
HOOKER, Michael Douglas. ■ 37777 #012-05-1984 L1989 **ORS** *020 †40
HUFFMAN, John Raymond. ■ 37777 #047-06-1963 L1963 **OTO** *071
KEEBLE, Donald Spencer. 2347 JONES BEND RD, HEALTH AT PENINSULA 37777 #048-02-1984 L1985 **FM** *020 †18
MARKHAM, Curtis Reid. 1214 TOPSIDE RD 37777 #012-01-1986 L1987 **AN** *020 †05
NASH, Barrington Nelson. 1921 TOPSIDE RD, PELLISSIPPI PRIMARY CARE 37777 #023-12-1988 L2004 **FM** *020 †18
RAMSEY, Melissa Hazlewood. 3224 MISER STATION RD 37777 #047-20-1995 L1999 **AN** *020 †05
SABRI, Safia M. 2347 JONES BEND RD, HEALTH AT PENINSULA 37777 #704-06-1983 L1999 **CHP P** *020 †75
SMITH, Darrell Laverne. 2347 JONES BEND RD, HEALTH AT PENINSULA 37777 #047-20-1985 L1986 **IM** *020 †20
STOCKTON, M David. 2347 JONES BEND RD, HEALTH AT PENINSULA 37777 #047-06-1978 L1978 **FM** *020 †70,18
VUYYURU, Shyamsunder P. 2347 JONES BEND RD, HEALTH AT PENINSULA 37777 #495-65-1990 L1998 **P** *020
WALLACE, Cynthia Juanita. ■ 37777 #012-22-2003 L2006 **PD** *100 †55
WALTER, Angela Sue. 1921 TOPSIDE RD, PELLISSIPPI PRIMARY CARE 37777 #038-43-2000 L2003 **FM** *020 †18 ‡

LYLES – HICKMAN

SZCZUKA, Anna. 5194 HIGHWAY 100 STE 107 37098 #759-11-1977 L1998 **IM** *020 †20

LYNCHBURG – MOORE

NESBETT, Billy Curtis. PO BOX 8219, 37 S MECHANIC ST 37352 #047-06-1964 L1964 **FM OS** *020

LYNNVILLE – GILES

HUDSON, James Irvin, Jr. ■ 38472 #023-07-1952 L2005 **PHP PD** *071 †55
SAVAGE, Steven Ross. 181 MILL ST 38472 #047-20-1987 L1988 **FM** *020 †18

MADISON – DAVIDSON

ASTA, Roy Oon. 510 HOSPITAL DR, STE 340 37115 #047-07-2001 L2004 **P** *020 †75
BRIGGS, Karen Tabitha. 620 GALLATIN RD S 37115 #020-12-1991 L1995 **P** *020 †75
BURNES, James Edmond. 607 W DUE WEST AVE 37115 #012-01-1960 L1964 **OPH** *071 †35
BURR, Robert Edward. ■ 37115 #047-05-1961 L1961 **PD** *030 †55
BYLAND, James Tod. 154 CUDE LN 37115 #020-12-1982 L1985 **AN** *020 †05
CASTELLANI, Sam. 500 LENTZ DR, STE 90 37115 #047-05-1969 L1989 **P** *040 †75
CHANNABASAPPA, Kodihalli. 607 W DUE WEST AVE # 122, STE 122 37115 #495-33-1963 L1977 **CD IM** *020 †20
CLASSEN, Jeannine Archer. 612 W DUE WEST AVE 37115 #039-01-1954 L1957 **AN OS** *071
COLGROVE, Eric Earl. 200 GLEAVES ST, STE A 37115 #047-05-1995 L1998 **PD** *020 †55
DICKERSON, Steven Reid. 647 MYATT DR 37115 #036-05-1992 L1996 **AN** *020 †05
DOVAN, Laura Miller. 200 GLEAVES ST 37115 #012-05-1997 L2000 **PD** *020 †55
DOZIER, Kenneth Cornel. 1210 BRIARVILLE RD, BLDGB 37115 #047-06-1971 L1972 **FM AM** *020 †18
DUFFY, Karen Barr. 1114 GALLATIN RD N 37115 #047-06-1973 L1973 **UCM EM** *020
DUNDON, Mary Catherine M. 200 GLEAVES ST STE A 37115 #047-05-1979 L1981 **PD** *020 †55
FADIGAN, Annette Barbara. 1210 BRIARVILLE RD, 200B 37115 #012-01-1990 L2000 **FM** *020 †18
FRAZIER, Ruth Ann. 500 HOSPITAL DR, ER DEPT 37115 #041-12-1984 L1995 **EM FM** *020 †18
FRY, Bradley Charles. 154 CUDE LN 37115 #056-05-1982 L1986 **AN** *020 †05
GELESKIE, Peter Thomas. 1210 BRIARVILLE RD, 200B 37115 #041-12-1993 L2000 **FM** *020 †18
GOLDBERG, David Stanton. 500 HOSPITAL DR 37115 #041-09-1982 L1992 **EM** *020 †20
GUPTON, Henry Lewis. 1719 GALLATIN PIKE N, CONCENTRA MEDICAL CENTERS 37115 #047-06-1986 L1989 **FM** *020 †18
HABIBIAN, Sara. 1210 BRIARVILLE RD, BLDG A 37115 #047-05-2002 L2006 **OBG** *020
HAGAN, George Bryant. ■ 37115 #047-06-1953 L1953 **IM** *071 †20
HALEY, Nancye Ruth. 500 HOSPITAL DR, ER DEPT 37115 #047-20-1983 L1986 **EM** *020
HALEY, Robert Leo, Jr. 612 W DUE WEST AVE 37115 #047-05-1960 L1960 **DR NM** *071 †80
HEAD, Hugh L, III. 154 CUDE LN 37115 #020-12-1984 L1987 **AN** *030 †05
HENSON, Alan Stuart. 510 HOSPITAL DR STE 100, BAPTIST MED PLZ 37115 #025-12-1977 L1983 **ORS OSM** *020
HUNLEY, Christine Weaver. 200 GLEAVES ST, # A 37115 #047-06-1992 L1996 **PD** *020 †55
JOHNSON, Mary Heather. 200 GLEAVES ST, # A 37115 #047-05-1994 L1997 **PD** *020 †55
JONES, Stephen Reid. ■ 37115 #047-07-2008 *012
JORDAN, John C. 1035 E OLD HICKORY BLVD 37115 #005-12-1973 L1992 **FM** *020 †18
KRISHNASASTRY, Chandra S. 510 HOSPITAL DR 37115 #495-33-1980 L1994 **P ADP** *020 †75
LEVOY, John Matthew. 510 HOSPITAL DR 37115 #005-12-1999 L2004 **AN** *020 †05 ‡
MARIASH, David. 100 RIVERCHASE BLVD, # 1007 37115 #048-12-1951 L1951 **PHP** *071 †85
MARTIN, Jei Florensari. 607 W DUE WEST AVE STE 102, DUE W FAMILY HLTH CARE 37115 #047-07-1996 L2000 **IM** *020
MARTZ, Holly Dyan. 510 HOSPITAL DR, STE 240 37115 #005-12-2003 L2005 **IM** *020 †20
MATHEWS, George Mathews. 600 MEDICAL PARK DR, STE 204 37115 #495-01-1979 L1991 **P** *020 †75
MILLER, James Olney, Jr. 1210 BRIARVILLE RD, BLDG A 37115 #047-06-1971 L1971 **OBG** *020 †30
MISHU, Dina Hanna. 200 GLEAVES ST STE A 37115 #306-01-1985 L1988 **PD** *020 †55
NAIR, Jaygopal. 200 GLEAVES ST, STE A 37115 #023-01-1997 L1999 **PD** *020 †55
NEUMANN, Bruce Russell. 1114 GALLATIN RD N, MADISON MINOR MEDICAL CLIN 37115 #026-04-1976 L1993 **EM FM** *020 †16,18
OBERMEIER, Stephen James. 154 CUDE LN 37115 #048-13-1978 L1985 **AN EM** *020 †05
PANOS, Andrew Judson. 500 HOSPITAL DR, ER DEPT 37115 #005-12-1975 L1977 **EM** *020
PATTERSON, Sara Fletcher. 200 GLEAVES ST, STE A 37115 #047-05-1997 L2000 **PD** *020 †55
PETTUS, Robert L, Jr. 612 W DUE WEST AVE 37115 #047-06-1951 L1952 **FM** *071 †18
PO, Divina Ong Tan. 1210 BRIARVILLE RD BLDG A 37115 #748-10-1964 L1973 **GYN** *020 †30
RANDOLPH, Alicia H. 1114 GALLATIN RD N 37115 #016-11-1991 L2001 **UCM** *020
RICE, Leonidas Edwin, Jr. 607 W DUE WEST AVE, STE 115 37115 #012-01-1979 L1981 **OPH** *020 †35
ROBINSON, Kenneth Arnold. ■ 37115 #047-07-2008 *012
ROBINSON, Kenneth Stanley. ■ 37115 #024-01-1979 L1982 **IM** *020 †20
ROBINSON, Patricia F. 200 GLEAVES ST, # A 37115 #041-14-1979 L1982 **PD** *020 †55
ROBINSON, Yvonne Demairs. 1210 BRIARVILLE RD, BLDG E 37115 #019-02-1999 L2004 **FM** *020 †18
SCHOOLEY, Barbara M. PO BOX 488 37116 #021-01-1989 L1994 **AN** *020
SILVA, Samuel. ■ 37115 #649-14-1978 *075
SMITH, Wm Orville Thos. 500 HOSPITAL DR 37115 #005-12-1967 L1972 **AN GP** *020 †05
SOLOMON, Haregewain H. 607 W DUE WEST AVE STE 113 37115 #366-01-1987 L2003 **IM** *020 †20
STEVENSON, Charles Bryce. ■ 37115 #047-05-2001 **NS** *012
STOUDER, Dennis Alan. 605 W DUE WEST AVE 37115 #017-20-1966 L1971 **IM NEP** *020
STRIEPE, Volker Ingo A. 154 CUDE LN 37115 #836-01-1980 L1990 **AN** *020 †05
STUYVESANT, Florence V N. ■ 37115 #005-12-1956 L1958 **AN** *071
STUYVESANT, V Wilfred. ■ 37115 #005-12-1956 L1971 **PTH** *071 †50
WALWYN, Lloyd Alexis. 1994 GALLATIN PIKE N, STE 305 37115 #010-03-1967 L1975 **ORS LM** *020 †40
WILKERSON, Emmett E. ■ 37115 #048-13-1996 L2006 **FM** *020 †18
WINTERS, Charles, Jr. 1037 E OLD HICKORY BLVD 37115 #047-06-1978 L1986 **IM** *020 †20
ZIELSKE, David Robt. 610 W DUE WEST AVE, UROLOGY ASSOCIATES 37115 #040-02-1983 L1989 **R EM** *071 †80
ZUA, Mene Sugage. 1308 BRIARVILLE RD 37115 #690-12-1986 L1995 **GE** *020 †20

MADISONVILLE – MONROE

BECK, Thomas Stanley, Jr. 520 COOK ST, CENTER 37354 #005-12-1996 L2007 **CHP** *020 †75
BEVERLEY, Tracey Darlene. 4233 HIGHWAY 411 37354 #020-12-1997 L2003 **FM** *020 †18
JETER, Julie W. 321 TELLICO ST S 37354 #047-06-1996 L1997 **FM** *020 †18
KANABAR, Hasmukh Vanmali. 167 WARREN ST 37354 #649-33-1985 L1995 **FM EM** *020 †18

■ = Address Information Privacy Protected

LOWRY, Frank H. ■ 37354 #047-06-1953 L1953 **FM** *071 †18
MC NEAL, Wesley Earl. 4233 HIGHWAY 411 37354 #005-12-1960 L1998 **FM** *071
NAMASIVAYAM, Karthi S. 520 COOK ST, STE I 37354 #495-35-1991 L2007 **P** *020 †75
RAMAN, Rajendra T. 4023 HIGHWAY 411, HEALTH FC 37354 #496-20-1991 L1999 **P CHP** *020 †75
SCHULTE, John Glenn. 520 COOK ST, CENTER 37354 #047-05-1988 L1992 **P** *020 †75

MANCHESTER – COFFEE

ANDERSON, Charles Earland. 481 INTERSTATE DR 37355 #060-01-1970 L1982 **EM GP** *020 ‡
BERRYMAN, Arthur Henry. ■ 37355 #048-02-1959 L1972 **GP** *100
BIRDWELL, Joel Stanley. 1001 MCARTHUR ST 37355 #047-06-1980 L1980 **DR** *020
BLAIR, Mark. 481 INTERSTATE DR 37355 #017-20-1994 L2000 **GS** *020 †85
BRYANT, Gary Barton. 1321 MCARTHUR ST STE B 37355 #005-12-1974 L1975 **FM** *020 †18 ‡
CHRISTOPHER, Neil E, Jr. 1001 MCARTHUR ST 37355 #001-02-1988 L1990 **IM** *020 †20
DAVIS, Glenn Alan. 1020 MCARTHUR ST 37355 #047-20-1984 L1985 **FM** *020 †18
HALSTEAD, William Dyrk. ■ 37355 #055-01-1982 L1983 **EM** *020
HARLOW, Susan Byers. 1405 HILLSBORO BLVD, HIGHLAND RIM MEDICAL ASSOC 37355 #004-01-1988 L1989 **IM** *020 †20
HARMUTH, Charles Robt. 2345 MURFREESBORO HWY 37355 #047-06-1978 L1979 **APM PM** *020 †30
HARRIS, George Andrew. ■ 37355 #030-05-1956 L1984 **GP P** *072
HENNINGS, Jacob Ryan. ■ 37355 #017-20-2008 *012
MABY, Sharon Lee. ■ 37355 #038-41-1973 L1978 **END PD** *040 †55
MAITRA, Sarbani. ■ 37355 #654-01-2006 *100
MILLMAN, Marshall Stuart. 2345 MURFREESBORO HWY 37355 #649-33-1981 L1993 **AN PMM** *020 †05
ROY, Francis. 119 E FORT ST 37355 #023-12-1991 L1993 **GP** *020
SALIBAY, Maria Dolores. 917 MCARTHUR ST, NEUROMETRICS 37355 #748-11-1979 L2003 **N** *020
SIVA, Anna A. ■ 37355 #919-02-1997 *100
SMITH, Milton. 119 E FORT ST 37355 #047-07-1984 L1986 **FM** *020
SPERKER, Erich R. 481 INTERSTATE DR 37355 #064-01-1981 L1995 **GP EM** *020
STROUD, Roland Ray, Jr. 450 INTERSTATE DR 37355 #027-01-1985 L2000 **FM** *020 †18
YANG, Harrison. 845 MCARTHUR ST STE D 37355 #244-01-1970 L1977 **CD IM** *020 †20
YOUNG, Coulter Smartt. ■ 37355 #047-06-1952 L1953 **FM** *071 †18
YU, Ja-Nan. 845 MCARTHUR ST STE A 37355 #385-02-1966 L1973 **GS** *020 †85

MARTIN – WEAKLEY

BEALE, Hobart H. PO BOX 67 38237 #047-06-1967 L1969 **FM FPG** *071 †18
BREWER, Susan Coker. 142 MOUNT PELIA RD 38237 #004-01-1985 L1988 **PD** *020
CARR, Kenneth Wm. 115 MOUNT PELIA RD 38237 #047-06-1975 L1975 **FM** *020 †18
DALVI, Anant Gajanan. 143 KENNEDY DR 38237 #496-44-1998 L2007 **PUD** *100
DUNCAN, Elizabeth Paige. 300 W PEACH ST 38237 #021-01-1992 L1996 **OBG** *020 †30
DUNCAN, William Lloyd. 300 W PEACH ST 38237 #047-06-1956 L1957 **GS** *071 †85
EASON, Darlene Dailey. ■ 38237 #047-05-1978 **PTH** *020
HASSAN, Randa Maher Abou. 300 W PEACH ST 38237 #915-03-1989 L2006 **OBG** *020
HINDS, Michael Wayne. 215 HAWKS RD, STE 6 38237 #047-06-1977 L1979 **IM** *020 †20
HOPLA, Anna Kristine. 117 KENNEDY DR, MARTIN MEDICAL CENTER 38237 #039-01-1980 L1994 **IM NEP** *020 †20
HOWARD, John D. ■ 38237 #047-06-1976 L1976 **EM** *020 †18
HUSSAIN, Ahmed. 143 KENNEDY DR 38237 #495-19-1963 L2008 **U** *020 †95
JONES, David Douglas. 143 KENNEDY DR 38237 #047-06-1977 L1979 **IM** *020
LUND, Peter John. 300 W PEACH ST 38237 #021-01-1990 L1996 **HS** *020 †40
LYERLY, Donald Newton. 142 MOUNT PELIA RD 38237 #047-06-1964 L1965 **ORS** *071 †40
OLIVER, David Allan. ■ 38237 #047-06-1970 L1974 **IM GP** *020 †20
PATEL, Nikhil Rameshbhai. 148 MOUNT PELIA RD 38237 #495-76-1985 L1989 **GE** *020 †20
PATEL, Vadankumar M. 457 HANNINGS LN 38237 #495-23-1982 L1994 **P** *020 †75
PATRICK, Robert Glynn. ■ 38237 #047-06-1959 L1959 **GP** *020
PORTER, Nathan F. 161 MOUNT PELIA ST 38237 #047-06-1948 L1949 **GP** *071
RAGSDALE, Keener B, III. 300 W PEACH ST 38237 #047-06-1980 L1981 **ORS GS** *020 †40
REBEIRO, Egbert. 143 KENNEDY DR, STE B 38237 #495-52-1971 L1980 **GS VS** *020 †85
SHORE, James William. 117 KENNEDY DR 38237 #047-06-1964 L1975 **FM** *020 †18
SHORE-LOWRY, Susan Denise. 117 KENNEDY DR, MARTIN MED CTR PC 38237 #047-20-1992 L1995 **FM** *020 †18
SONMEZTURK, Hasan Huseyin. 143 KENNEDY DR 38237 #902-19-1999 L2006 **N** *020 †75
SUTTON, Richard Otto, Jr. PO BOX 1006 38237 #047-06-1967 L1986 **ORS** *020 †40
THOMPSON, Keith Edward. 143 KENNEDY DR 38237 #038-41-1967 L2006 **GS TS** *020 †85,90 ‡
THOTA, Suresh. 143 KENNEDY DR 38237 #495-21-1993 L2005 **IM** *020
TREVATHAN, Robert D. ■ 38237 #047-06-1942 L1942 **P IM** *071 †20,75
YOUNG, Stephen Hoyt. 143 KENNEDY DR 38237 #048-02-1967 L2008 **CD IM** *020 †20

MARYVILLE – BLOUNT

ABERCROMBIE, John F. 907 E LAMAR ALEXANDER PKWY, EMERGENCY DEPT. 37804 #047-20-1996 L1999 **EM** *020 †16
ADHAM, Robert Edward. 275 CHEROKEE PROFESNL PARK 37804 #051-01-1984 L1993 **OTO FPS** *020 †45
ADLER, John Craige. PO BOX 5567 37802 #041-01-1948 L1956 **GP** *071
AGEE, Oliver King. 907 E LAMAR ALEXANDER PKWY 37804 #047-06-1947 L1947 **FPG** *020
ALMAND, Bond, III. 275 CHEROKEE PROFESNL PARK 37804 #047-05-2000 L2006 **OTO** *020 †45
BALLARD, Kimberly Ramsey. 270 BMH PHYSICINS OFC BLDG 37804 #051-04-1993 L2000 **OBG** *020 †30
BAXTER, Lori Ann. 616 SMITHVIEW DR 37803 #025-07-1987 L1991 **PD IM** *020 †55
BELL, William Kenneth. 827 E LAMAR ALEXANDER PKWY 37804 #047-06-1976 L1977 **ORS** *020 †40
BERTOLI, Robert Jos. 907 E LAMAR ALEXANDER PKWY 37804 #041-09-1981 L1993 **RO** *020 †80
BLANKS, Billy Harrell. ■ 37803 #047-06-1957 L1964 **R** *074 †80

BORCHERDING, Sara Lynn. ■ 37801 #047-06-2002 L2008 **IM** *100 †20
BOWEN, John H. 907 E LAMAR ALEXANDER PKWY 37804 #005-12-1949 L1950 **R** *071 †80
BRIGGS, James David. 215 BMH CANCER CTR 37804 #020-12-1986 L1987 **U GS** *020 †95
BROOKS, Charles, Jr. 1343 W HUNT RD 37801 #011-04-1984 L1985 **FM EM** *020 †18
BROWN, Edward Francis. 1706 E LAMAR ALEXANDR PKWY, BLOUNT GASTROENTEROLOGY 37804 #041-13-1977 L1988 **IM GE** *020 †20
BUDAYR, Mahdi Mohammad. 405 BMH PHYSICINS OFC BLDG 37804 #915-04-1979 L1996 **GS CRS** *020 †10,85
BURKHART, Patrick H. 1702 E LAMAR ALEXANDR PKWY 37804 #047-06-1976 L1977 **D** *020 †15
BURROUGHS, Joel Matthew. 116 CHANTILLY LN, GOOD SAMARITAN CLNC 37803 #051-04-1997 L2002 **FM** *020 †18
BUSSEY, Aaron Daniel. 907 E LAMAR ALEXANDER PKWY 37804 #048-14-1997 L2006 **END** *020 †20
CALDWELL, Benjamin H, Jr. PO BOX 5870 37802 #047-05-1960 L1960 **GYN** *071 †30
CALLAWAY, Henry A, Jr. ■ 37803 #047-05-1954 L1954 **GS TS** *071
CALLAWAY, James Miller. 907 E LAMAR ALEXANDER PKWY 37804 #047-05-1956 L1956 **GS VS** *071 †85
CALVERT, David Keith. 611 MORGANTON SQUARE DR, VANDERGRIFF FAMILY MEDICIN 37801 #055-02-1984 L1985 **FM** *020 †18
CAMPBELL, Michael Lyle. 827 E LAMAR ALEXANDER PKWY 37804 #045-01-1992 L2001 **ORS** *020 †40
CAPPS, Clyde Lee. ■ 37804 #047-06-1953 L1954 **AN** *075 †05
CAUGHRON, Justin Derek. ■ 37803 #047-06-2007 **TY** *012
CHRISTOFFERSON, James W. 907 E LAMAR ALEXANDER PKWY 37804 #056-06-1944 L1956 **AN** *071 †05
CLINE, Kim Hawkins. 111 STATION DR, KIM H CLINE MD 37804 #038-40-1981 L1983 **IM** *020 †20
CLINE, Richard Glen. 1706 E LAMAR ALEXANDR PKWY, BLOUNT GASTROENTEROLOGY 37804 #038-40-1976 L1983 **GE** *020 †20
COFFEY, Michael John. 1706 E LAMAR ALEXANDR PKWY, BLOUNT GASTROENTEROLOGY 37804 #033-05-1991 L1997 **GE** *020 †20
COLEMAN, Cheryl Engles. 763 E LAMAR ALEXANDER PKWY 37804 #047-20-1983 L1983 **AN** *020 †05
COLLINS, Kimberly Wilder. 270 BMH PHYSICINS OFC BLDG 37804 #047-06-1988 L1991 **OBG** *020 †30
COLQUITT, Mark Alan. 2012 CHILHOWEE MEDICL PARK 37804 #047-06-1985 L1990 **GS OS** *020 †85
COOLEY, Sarah F. ■ 37803 #012-01-1952 L1952 **PTH** *071 †50
COTTEN, Daniel Wayne. 907 E LAMAR ALEXANDER PKWY 37804 #047-06-1988 L1989 **DR** *020 †80
COWAN, John David. 907 E LAMAR ALEXANDER PKWY 37804 #047-06-1974 L1975 **ON** *020 †20
COX, David A. 2022 CHILHOWEE MEDICL PARK 37804 #047-06-1982 L1984 **IM** *020 †20
COYLE, Brent Richard. 907 E LAMAR ALEXANDER PKWY 37804 #026-04-1986 L1993 **P** *020 †75
CROWDER, Clay Gardner. 116 CHANTILLY LN 37803 #047-06-1962 L1963 **PD P** *020
DAMRON, Michael Todd. 907 E LAMAR ALEXANDER PKWY 37804 #038-41-1996 L1999 **PD** *020 †55
DAVID, Bertha Da Costa. 210 SIMMONS ST, CENTER 37801 #495-27-1967 L1980 **P** *020
DEE, Whitney Elizabeth. 414 GREENBELT DR, MARYVILLE PEDIATRIC GROUP 37804 #047-20-2004 L2007 **PD** *020 †55
DELASHMIT, James Richard. ■ 37803 #047-06-1973 L1973 **IM** *020 †20
DILIBERTI, Charles Peter. ■ 37803 #035-19-1952 L1954 **R RO** *071 †80
DURAND, Andre Mark. 720 FOOTHILLS MALL DR 37801 #047-05-1982 L1986 **FM** *075 †18
DURAND, Charles Gerard. 312 HIGH ST 37804 #005-11-1978 L1985 **RHU IM** *020 †20
ELMORE, Dale Bryant. 417 E LAMAR ALEXANDER PKWY 37804 #011-04-1978 L1982 **OBG** *020 †30
EVANS, Samuel Dixie. 907 E LAMAR ALEXANDER PKWY 37804 #045-01-1972 L1976 **OBG** *071 †30
FAGET, Otilia Miga. 210 SIMMONS ST, CENTER 37801 #132-01-1957 L1975 **P** *020
FINNEY, Raymond A, Jr. ■ 37803 #047-06-1964 L1964 **PTH** *071 †50
FLICKINGER, Jeff Ernest. 611 SMITHVIEW DR 37803 #047-05-1991 L1993 **U** *020 †95
FLICKINGER, Ted Lawrence. 611 SMITHVIEW DR 37803 #010-01-1954 L1960 **U** *071 †95
FOX, Lana Gayle. 616 SMITHVIEW DR 37803 #047-06-1995 L1997 **PD** *020 †55
FROULA, Paul Douglas. 622 SMITHVIEW DR, UNIVERSITY EYE SURGEONS 37803 #047-20-1988 L1992 **OPH** *020 †35
FUERTES, Melanie R. 1051 E LAMAR ALEXANDR PKWY 37804 #748-01-1998 L2002 **PYG** *020
GARST, Ronald Jos. ■ 37803 #039-01-1948 L1980 **ORS** *071 †40
GARZA, Nancy Frerichs. 425 BMH PHYSICINS OFC BLDG 37804 #047-20-2002 L2006 **OBG** *020
GASS, Gregory Lloyd. 627 SMITHVIEW DR 37803 #047-06-1984 L1985 **P** *020 †05,75
GIBSON, Ernest Russell. 129 MONTGOMERY LN 37803 #047-20-1986 L1987 **FM** *020 †18
GILLEY, Jerry Michael. 907 E LAMAR ALEXANDER PKWY 37804 #047-06-1988 L1992 **AN** *020 †05
GILLIAM, David Mark. 907 E LAMAR ALEXANDER PKWY 37804 #047-05-1988 L1997 **PTH** *020 †50
GOUDELOCK, Daniel Stevens. 627 SMITHVIEW DR 37803 #045-01-1964 L1979 **CHP P** *072
GREEN, Daniel Mogensen. 907 E LAMAR ALEXANDER PKWY 37804 #047-05-1981 L1989 **RO IM** *020 †20,80
GREEN, Mark Ellison. 907 E LAMAR ALEXANDER PKWY 37804 #047-06-1986 L1986 **IM** *020
GREENWOOD, Jeffrey Dixon. 659 MORGANTON SQUARE DR 37801 #051-01-1979 L1983 **P** *020 †75
GRIFFITH, Todd Robt. 907 E LAMAR ALEXANDER PKWY 37804 #041-13-1988 L1994 **ORS** *020 †40
HALL, Albert Thos. ■ 37803 #047-06-1947 L1947 **GP GS** *071
HATFIELD, Charles Newman. ■ 37803 #047-06-1965 L1966 **OM GP** *071
HATFIELD, Robert Wayne. 611 SMITHVIEW DR 37803 #012-01-1994 L1997 **U** *020 †95
HAUN, Alden Kirkpatrick. 628 SMITHVIEW DR, CAMPBELL, CUNNINGHAM, & TA 37803 #047-05-1997 L2000 **OPH** *020 †35
HEATH, Ty A. 907 E LAMAR ALEXANDER PKWY 37804 #048-13-2002 L2005 **AN** *020 †05
HITCH, James Parks, Jr. 611 SMITHVIEW DR 37803 #047-06-1969 L1970 **U** *020 †95
HOFFMAN, Cindy E. 414 GREENBELT DR, MARYVILLE PEDIATRIC GROUP 37804 #047-06-1997 L2000 **PD** *020 †55
HOFFMAN, Philip Knox. 162 BMH PHYSICINS OFC BLDG 37804 #047-20-1986 L1992 **CD IM** *020 †20

HUSAINY, Muhammad Nassooh. ■ 37803 #055-75-2007. ▲ **GS** *012
HYATT, Renee Joy. 116 CHANTILLY LN, GOOD SAMARITAN CLINIC 37803 #001-02-1982 L1991 **IM** *020 †20
ISBELL, Homer L, Jr. 907 E LAMAR ALEXANDER PKWY 37804 #047-06-1946 L1950 **AN FM** *071
JACKSON, Richard Evan. 683 MORGANTON SQUARE DR, OVERLOOK CENTER 37801 #016-45-1980 L1984 **P ADM** *020 †75 ‡
JARVIS, Stuart Craig. 1706 E LAMAR ALEXANDR PKWY, BLOUNT GASTROENTEROLOGY 37804 #036-07-1975 L1980 **GE IM** *020 †20
JOYNER, James Brian. 902 E LAMAR ALEXANDER PKWY, BLOUNT MEMORIAL HOSPITAL 37804 #047-20-1995 L1998 **EM** *020 †16
KAMPERMAN, Colin Lee. ■ 37803 #041-12-1955 L1972 **OM** *071 †70
KELMAN, Edward M. 133 W BROADWAY AVE 37801 #047-06-1949 L1949 **PTH GP** *072 †50
KHAN, Mohammad Khurram. ■ 37804 #047-06-2006 L2006 **RO** *012
KIEFER, Stephen K. 162 BMH PHYSICINS OFC BLDG 37804 #030-06-1976 L1983 **CD** *020 †20
KINTNER, Elgin P. ■ 37803 #017-20-1943 L1951 **PTH** *071 †50
KNOLL, David Andrew. 313 N HOUSTON ST 37801 #012-05-1993 L1996 **IM** *020 †20
LAPENAS, Anna H Entz. ■ 37804 #019-02-1941 L1942 **GP** *071
LAUGHMILLER, Roy W. ■ 37803 #010-01-1951 L1953 **PD** *071 †55
LE BRUN, Elizabeth D. 425 BMH PHYSICINS OFC BLDG 37804 #422-01-1984 L1991 **OBG** *020 †30
LONG, Carole Louise. 2036 CHILHOWEE MEDICL PARK 37804 #038-40-1985 L1994 **IM** *020 †20
LUHN, Gaelan Burns. 907 E LAMAR ALEXANDER PKWY 37804 #021-01-2000 L2005 **AN** *020 †05
MANDOJANA, Ricardo Marcos. 616 SMITHVIEW DR, MARYVILLE DERMATOLOGY ASSO 37803 #132-07-1968 L1988 **D DMP** *075 †50,15
MARMON, Kenneth Waldo. 108 CLYDE CIR 37804 #047-06-1962 L1962 **PD** *020 †55
MASON, Gary Merlin. 417 E LAMAR ALEXANDER PKWY 37804 #038-06-1982 L1996 **OBG** *020 †30
MC AMIS, John Carl, III. 270 BMH PHYSICINS OFC BLDG 37804 #047-06-1978 L1981 **OBG** *020 †30
MC CALL, Benny Gordon. 603 SMITHVIEW DR 37803 #047-06-1963 L1964 **IM** *071
MC CARTY, Matthew James. 1023 E LAMAR ALEXANDR PKWY 37804 #038-06-1988 L1998 **HO** *020 †20
MC DANIEL, Daryl Lee. 622 SMITHVIEW DR, UNIVERSITY EYE SURGEONS 37803 #012-01-1989 L1994 **OPH** *020 †35
MC KINNON, Norman A, Jr. ■ 37801 #021-01-1952 L1956 **GYN** *071 †20
METELKA, Richard Carl. 270 BMH PHYSICINS OFC BLDG 37804 #047-06-1981 L1981 **OBG** *020 †30
MILLER, Craig, Jr. 907 E LAMAR ALEXANDER PKWY 37804 #001-02-1987 L1994 **DR** *020 †80
MORGAN, Eric Arnold. 827 E LAMAR ALEXANDER PKWY, P.C. 37804 #055-02-1991 L1997 **ORS** *020,15
MORGAN, Patrick Lee. 270 BMH PHYSICINS OFC BLDG 37804 #001-02-1986 L1987 **OBG** *020 †30
MUSE, William Scott, Jr. 611 SMITHVIEW DR 37803 #047-06-1967 L1968 **U** *020 †95
MYNATT, Robert D. 2036 CHILHOWEE MEDICL PARK 37804 #047-06-1953 L1953 **U** *071 †95
MYNATT, Steven Robt. 1037 E LAMAR ALEXANDER PKWY 37804 #047-06-1980 L1980 **U** *020
NELSON, Jeffery Ernest. 907 E LAMAR ALEXANDER PKWY 37804 #036-05-1983 L1984 **IM EM** *020 †20
NILES, Robert I. ■ 37804 #016-43-1960 L1961 **ORS** *071 †40
OLANDER, Kenneth William. 622 SMITHVIEW DR, C/O MARYVILLE EYE CENTER 37803 #021-01-1976 L1997 **OPH** *020 †35 ‡
PENDERGRASS, Chas Allen. ■ 37803 #654-01-1987 L1989 **FM** *020
POPE, Mary Frances. 307 HIGH ST 37804 #004-01-1975 L1984 **P** *020 †75
POTTER, Robert Marion. 907 E LAMAR ALEXANDER PKWY 37804 #047-06-1983 L1987 **PTH** *020 †50
PRICE, Jerry Lee. 907 E LAMAR ALEXANDER PKWY 37804 #036-01-1990 L1994 **FM EM** *020 †18
PRINCE, Tidence Ln. 653 MORGANTON SQUARE DR, ALLERGY ASTH & SINUS CTR 37801 #047-06-1989 L1991 **AI** *020 †20,03
PROFFITT, James David, Jr. 129 MONTGOMERY LN 37803 #047-20-1989 L1993 **IM** *020 †20
PROFFITT, Robert David. 611 S WASHINGTON ST 37804 #047-06-1955 L1955 **FM PD** *020
PROFFITT, Wilma Coleman. 907 E LAMAR ALEXANDER PKWY 37804 #047-20-1988 L1994 **AN** *020,05
RAGSDALE, Anthony Gene. 1800 WILKINSON PIKE 37803 #047-06-1997 L2001 **AN** *020
RAPER, Charles Allen. 414 GREENBELT DR, MARYVILLE PEDIATRIC 37804 #047-06-1960 L1975 **PD** *020 †55
RAY, Jonathan Holcombe. 2012 CHILHOWEE MEDICL PARK 37804 #021-05-1981 L1988 **GS OS** *020 †85
ROBERTS, Jack T, Jr. 104 PARLIAMENT DR, JACK T ROBERTS MD 37804 #047-06-1976 L1976 **IM** *020 †20
ROSEMAN, Barry Joel. 405 BMH PHYSICIANS OFC BLG 37804 #056-06-1988 L1997 **SO GS** *020 †85
RUBRIGHT, Robert Lee. ■ 37803 #017-20-1955 L1970 **GP** *071
SAVELL, Richard Alan. ■ 37801 #027-01-1997 L2004 **IM** *020 †20
SAXON, David Henry. 907 E LAMAR ALEXANDER PKWY, EMERGENCY DEPARTMENT 37804 #005-12-1984 L1994 **EM** *020 †18
SENTELL, Kevin James. 907 E LAMAR ALEXANDER PKWY 37804 #017-20-1988 L1993 **DR** *020 †80
SHAFFER, George Wm. ■ 37803 #041-09-1947 L1948 **OS** *071
SHALABY, Ibrahim. 463 BLOUNT, PHYS OFFICE BLDG 37701 #915-07-1983 L1996 **IM** *020 †20
SHIMAZU, Colleen Nobuko. 653 MORGANSON SQUARE DR 37801 #014-01-1987 L2000 **D** *020 †20,15
SHIVERS, Selby Britt. 907 E LAMAR ALEXANDER PKWY 37804 #047-06-1985 L1987 **AN** *020 †05
SIDDIQUI, Farrukh A. 720 FOOTHILLS MALL DR 37801 #038-44-1998 L1999 **FM** *020 †18
SIGHTLER, Harold E. 907 E LAMAR ALEXANDER PKWY 37804 #045-04-1990 L1992 **CLP** *020 †50
SIMPSON, Oscar L, Jr. ■ 37803 #047-06-1951 L1952 **GP** *071
SLAWSKY, Lewis David. 615 SMITHVIEW DR 37803 #035-15-1987 L1994 **D AM** *020 †15
SMITH, Michael Frank. 627 SMITHVIEW DR 37803 #047-06-1979 L1981 **P** *020 †75
SOMMERVILLE, Lewis Cass, III. ■ 37804 #047-06-2007 L**012
SOUTHER, Susan Jane. 1001 W LAMAR ALEXANDR PKWY 37801 #047-06-1983 L1984 **CD IM** *020 †20
TAN, Hiediliza Y. 907 E LAMAR ALEXANDER PKWY, BOX 56 37804 #748-02-1990 L2002 **ID** *020 †20
TEAGUE, Michael D. 907 E LAMAR ALEXANDER PKWY 37804 #048-13-1990 L1991 **PTH** *020 †50

TERMINI, John Frank. ■ 37801 #021-05-2005 L2006 **AN** *012
THOMAS, Mark K. PO BOX 5479, 827 E LAMAR ALEXANDER PKW 37802 #048-14-1990 L1995 **ORS** *020 †40
THOMPSON, Bryan Brooks. 611 MORGANTON SQUARE DR 37801 #047-06-1981 L1982 **FM PD** *020 †18
TIENG, Edward Bob, Jr. 611 SMITHVIEW DR 37803 #035-47-1994 L2005 **U** *020 †95
TRAVER, Tracie Ann. 425 BMH PHYSICINS OFC BLDG 37804 #021-05-1993 L1997 **OBG** *020 †30
TREKELL, Melissa Emlyn. 1111 E LAMAR ALEXANDR PKWY 37804 #019-02-1978 L1986 **GS** *020 †30
TURNER, Julie Coltrin. 270 BMH PHYSICINS OFC BLDG 37804 #047-20-2000 L2002 **OBG** *020 †30
TURNER, Kevin Leonard. 611 MORGANTON SQUARE DR, VANDERGRIFF FAMILY MEDICIN 37801 #047-20-2000 L2002 **FM** *100 †18
VANDERGRIFF, Harris T. ■ 37803 #047-06-1944 L1944 **GP** *071
WAGNER, Carl Michael. 907 E LAMAR ALEXANDER PKWY 37804 #048-13-1979 L1989 **AN AS** *020 †05,18
WATKINS, Mark Darryl. 414 GREENBELT DR, STE 300 37804 #011-04-1984 L1991 **PD** *020 †55
WEATHERBEE, Taylor Carson. 1001 W LAMAR ALEXANDR PKWY 37801 #030-06-1976 L1984 **CD IM** *020 †20
WELLINGER, John R. ■ 37804 #869-05-1977 L1982 **GS TS** *020 †85
WHITE, Richard H. 687 MORGANTON SQUARE DR 37801 #047-06-1976 L1976 **FM** *020 †18
WHITMER, Kelley Kendall. ■ 37804 #047-20-2003 L2007 **DR** *012
WHITTLE, Herbert P, Jr. ■ 37803 #047-06-1945 L1945 **OM** *071 †18
WINSTEAD, Alison Virginia. ■ 37804 #036-05-2008 *012

MAYNARDVILLE – UNION

AHMAD, Mustafa. PO BOX 117, 300 MAIN ST 37807 #704-02-1990 L2000 **NEP** *020 †20
ARMSTRONG, Janice Dale. 2595 MAYNARDVILLE HWY 37807 #021-01-1975 L1977 **FM PD** *020 †18,55
BHIDYA, Mohammad. PO BOX 117, 300 MAIN ST 37807 #704-25-1989 L1994 **NEP** *020 †20
CHINTALAPUDI, Srinivasa. 149 DURHAM DR 37807 #495-50-1992 L1999 **ID** *020 †20
FARKHONDEH, Mahmoud. 2595 MAYNARDVILLE HWY 37807 #305-01-2001 L2004 **PD** *020 †55
IMTIAZ-RAZA-KHAN, Rafay. 149 DURHAM DR 37807 #704-02-1991 L1998 **AI** *020 †55
MONCIER, Hal Martin. 4330 MAYNARDVILLE HWY, P O BOX 279 37807 #047-20-1989 L1990 **FM** *020 †18
VENKATESH, Vivek Kalpathi. 4330 MAYNARDVILLE HWY 37807 #496-26-1992 L1999 **IM** *020 †20

MC DONALD – BRADLEY

CRUMPLER, Timothy Keith. ■ 37353 #001-02-1991 L1993 **IM** *020 †20
GRUNDSET, Harold Melvin. ■ 37353 #005-12-1955 L1958 **AN** *071 †05
SCHLEIFER, Kieth Randolf. 6019 CROOK CREST DR, THE DON CROOK BUILDING 37353 #005-12-1984 L1987 **FM** *020 †18 ‡
SHEARER, Robert Vernon. ■ 37353 #005-12-1943 L1943 **OPH** *071 †35

MC KENZIE – CARROLL

BHAT, Narayana. 161 HOSPITAL DR 38201 #495-35-1961 L1970 **GS P** *071 †85
BROWN, Thomas Eugene. 325 CHERRY AVE, BETHEL CLGE PA PROGRAM 38201 #056-05-1972 L1990 **GS AS** *071
BRYANT, Michael Lee. 161 HOSPITAL DR 38201 #011-03-1996 L2001 **FM** *020 †18
COLOTTA, Terry Andrew. 205A HOSPITAL DR 38201 #047-06-1991 L1992 **FM EM** *020 †18
HAMES, Joseph Robt. ■ 38201 #045-04-1982 L1993 **FM** *020 †18
HOLANCIN, John Robt. 132 HOSPITAL DR, KENZIE 38201 #064-01-1974 L1978 **FM EM** *020
LEMUS PARADA, Jesus. 161 HOSPITAL DR 38201 #649-01-1971 L1989 **EM GP** *020
MERRICK, Bryan Hale. 205A HOSPITAL DR, STE A 38201 #047-06-1981 L1984 **IM** *020 †20
PAGOAGA, Luis Fernando. 201 HOSPITAL DR, METHODIST HOSP 38201 #451-01-1990 L1997 **FM** *020 †18
POMPHREY, Robert J. 205A HOSPITAL DR, MCKENZIE MEDICAL CENTER 38201 #047-06-1992 L1997 **FM** *020 †18
RAY, Sidney Carroll. 161 HOSPITAL DR 38201 #047-06-1961 L1961 **FM** *071
SUMROK, Daniel D, Jr. 1894 CEDAR ST 38201 #055-02-1984 L1991 **FM P** *020 †18
WINKLER, Volker Gert. 205A HOSPITAL DR 38201 #065-06-1977 L1978 **GP** *020

MC MINNVILLE – WARREN

ARMS, Donald Mark. 207 OAK PARK 37110 #047-06-1991 L1997 **ORS** *020 †40
BIGBEE, Wallace Burns. 1589 SPARTA ST, STE 201 37110 #047-06-1956 L1957 **FM** *071 †18
BROCK, William Bradford. 145 HEALTH WAY, MIDDLE TENNESSEE SURGICAL 37110 #047-06-1988 L1989 **GS** *020 †85
BROOM, James Howell. 191 ANTHONY DR, TN 37111) 37110 #036-07-1979 L2000 **P** *020 †75
BURCK, Harry Edward, Jr. 1514 SPARTA ST, MC MINNVILLE MEDICAL 37110 #047-06-1975 L1975 **IM** *020 †20
CAMPBELL, Otis, Jr. 1550 SPARTA ST, STE 3 37110 #047-07-1986 L1988 **IM** *020 †20
CATEN, Joseph Lee. 140 VO TECH DR, STE 7 37110 #025-07-1964 L1968 **GP** *020
CHASTAIN, Bryan D. 155 HEALTH WAY, STE 1 37110 #048-02-1985 L1988 **FM OBG** *020 †18
COGER, William Allen. 1559 SPARTA ST 37110 #004-01-1970 L1991 **DR** *071
DAVIS, William Glenn. 220 N CHANCERY ST 37110 #047-06-1975 L1975 **OPH** *020 †35
DEL VALLE, Rene Carlos. 3085 SPARTA ST 37110 #011-02-1982 L1986 **OBG** *020 †30
FISHER, Joseph F. 120 OMNI DR 37110 #036-05-1948 L1950 **GP** *071
FOSTER, Linda Ann. 1589 SPARTA ST, STE 201 37110 #047-06-1983 L1984 **FM EM** *020 †18
GLOVER, Dannie Welden. 1514 SPARTA ST, MC MINNVILLE MEDICAL 37110 #047-06-1979 L1981 **FM** *020 †16,18
HAYNES, Douglas Brandt. 207 OAK PARK ST 37110 #047-06-1976 L1977 **ORS** *020 †40
HEKIMOGLU, Cetin. 140 VO TECH DR, STE 3 37110 #902-10-1989 L2006 **IM** *020 †20
HUANG, Allen Ming. 1560 SPARTA ST 37110 #024-05-1995 L1999 **IM IMG** *020 †20
JACOBS, Gordon J, Jr. 485 N CHANCERY ST 37110 #012-05-1971 L1978 **FM** *020 †18
JAMIESON, Mary J. 1589 SPARTA ST, STE 305 37110 #062-01-1981 L1997 **FM** *020 †18

JENKINS, Jimmy Ellis. 1514 SPARTA ST, MC MINNVILLE MEDICAL 37110 #047-06-1975 L1976 IM *020 †20

KEITH, Scott Harold. 1559 SPARTA ST, STE 301 37110 #018-03-1990 L1994 OTO FPS *020 †45

LANG, Eric Alan. 1589 SPARTA ST STE 100 37110 #011-02-1976 L2004 PUD IM *020 †20

LAWHON, Jeffrey Cory. 1589 SPARTA ST, STE 107 37110 #047-06-1992 L1998 GS *020 †85

LAYMAN, William D. 69 T E MCGEE RD 37110 #047-06-1982 L1983 R *020 †80

LUDWIG, Philip James. 1589 SPARTA ST, STE 106 37110 #028-34-1988 L1995 GS *020 †85

MAITRA, Badshah. 201 W MAIN ST, CUMBERLAND PSYCHIATRIC SER 37110 #495-73-1972 L1996 P *020

MARTIN, Jacob Alton, II. 1560 SPARTA ST 37110 #021-06-1978 L1980 GP OM *020 †70 ‡

MC ABEE, Wendell Vernon. 1560 SPARTA ST 37110 #047-06-1977 L1977 DR *020 †80

MORGAN, Charles Dwight. 1550 SPARTA ST, STE 4 37110 #047-06-1993 L1994 FM *020 †18

NUTHALAPATY, Suneetha S. 1589 SPARTA ST, STE 104 37110 #495-27-1994 L2005 PM *020 †60

PRASANNAKUMAR, Kodihalli. 1550 SPARTA ST, STE 4 37110 #495-33-1973 L1982 TS GS *020 †85

PURVIS, John Haigler. 1589 SPARTA ST, STE 203 37110 #047-06-1999 L2002 PD *020 †55

QUESTELL, Michael. 1589 SPARTA ST, STE 307 37110 #011-75-1998, ▲ L2007 FM *020 †18 ‡

RAEFSKY, Eric Lee. 1589 SPARTA ST, STE 306 37110 #041-13-1980 L1989 ON HEM *020 †20 ‡

RAGSDALE, Tommy Mac. 1514 SPARTA ST, MC MINNVILLE MEDICAL 37110 #047-06-1975 L1975 IM *020 †20

RAMPP, Randal Don. 1559 SPARTA ST 37110 #021-05-1990 L1995 HOS IM *020

REUTER, Rogina K. 1560 SPARTA ST 37110 #915-04-1976 L1998 PD *020 †55

SABO, Robert Pattison. 1550 SPARTA ST, MIDDLE TENNESSEE NEPHROLOG 37110 #041-09-1981 L2005 IM *020 †20

SPIVEY, Oscar Smith. 1550 SPARTA ST, STE 1 37110 #012-01-1979 L1980 U *020 †95

STEWART, Michael Todd. 1514 SPARTA ST, MC MINNVILLE MEDICAL 37110 #047-06-1995 L1998 FM *020 †18 ‡

TROOP, Joe Raymond, Jr. 1514 SPARTA ST, MC MINNVILLE MEDICAL 37110 #047-06-1966 L1966 FM *020 †18

WATLINGTON, David J. 153 VO TECH DR 37110 #048-15-1994 L1997 OBG *020 †30

WEBB, Glenn Todd. 120 OMNI DR 37110 #047-06-1991 L2001 P *020

WEEKS, Mark Timothy. 1559 SPARTA ST 37110 #047-20-1987 L1988 FM *020 †18

WILEY, Gregory S. 140 VO TECH DR 37110 #047-07-1984 L1985 IM FM *075

WOODLEE, Jimmie Dale. 155 HEALTH WAY, STE 2 37110 #047-20-1987 L1988 FM *020 †18

YESIL, Sadik. 140 VO TECH DR, STE 4 37110 #902-08-1989 L2004 N *020

ZWEMER, Rodger J. 207 OAK PARK DR 37110 #020-02-1976 L1994 ORS *020

MEDINA – GIBSON

MYATT, Jason Adam. ■ 38355 #047-20-2008 *012

MEDON – MADISON

BATCHELLOR, Janell J. ■ 38356 #011-03-1995 L2005 P *020 †75

CHIPMAN, Lauren Tucker. ■ 38356 #047-20-2007 PD *012

MEMPHIS – SHELBY

ABAZID, Bassem Abdulnaim. ■ 38103 #047-06-2008 *012

ABBASI, Bushra. ■ 38103 #704-16-2003 IM *012

ABDULLAH, Abdullah Nuri. ■ 38103 #047-06-2008 *012

ABOUSHALA, Nabil. 49 N DUNLAP ST 38103 #875-02-1983 L1985 PUD IM *020 †20

ABRAHAM, Scott Marvin. ■ 38120 #019-02-2004 L2006 ORS *012

ABU AL RUB, Fadee. 956 COURT AVE 38163 #875-01-2002 IM *012

ABUSHAER, Muhammad B. 5959 PARK AVE, CHEST PAIN CENTER 38119 #875-01-1987 L1998 IM *020 †20

ACCHIARDO, Sergio A. 920 MADISON AVE STE 200, UNIVERSITY OF TENNESSEE 38103 #231-01-1959 L1971 NEP *040 †20

ACKER, James David. 55 HUMPHREYS CTR, STE 100 38120 #012-01-1973 L1980 N DR *020 †80

ACREE, Martin Vernon. 1325 EASTMORELAND AVE, PEABODY FAMILY CARE 38104 #027-01-1985 L1986 FM *020 †20

ADAMOLEKUN, Bolanle M. 1211 UNION AVE STE 200 38104 #690-01-1979 L2004 CN *020 †75

ADAMS, Cecilia Dowsing. 1301 PRIMACY PKWY 38119 #027-01-1994 L1999 FM *020 †18

ADAMS, James Frank. 6305 HUMPHREYS BLVD # 205 38120 #001-02-1991 L1999 RO *020 †80

ADAMS, James W, II. 3960 KNIGHT ARNOLD RD, STE 215A 38118 #027-01-1984 L1985 IM *020 †20

ADAMS, Lorenzo H. ■ 38117 #047-06-1940 L1940 PS *071 †65

ADAMS, Robert Franklin. 6263 POPLAR AVE, STE 503 38119 #047-06-1963 L1964 RHU *050 †20

ADAMS, Robert Louis. 80 HUMPHREYS CTR, STE 100 38120 #047-06-1977 L1978 PS GS *020 †85,65

ADAMS-GRAVES, Patricia. 3 NORTH DUNLAP, UNIV OF TENNESSEE, MEMPHIS 38163 #020-02-1986 L1989 ON HEM *020 †20

ADAMS-HOLTZMAN, Lori Rae. 3876 NEW COVINGTON PIKE, PEDIATRIC ASSOCIATES PC 38128 #038-44-1987 L1999 PD *020 †55

ADDERSON, Elizabeth E. 332 N LAUDERDALE ST, RM E0854 MAILSTOP 320 38105 #060-01-1984 L1999 PD *050 †55

ADDINGTON, Milton Brent. 80 HUMPHREYS CTR, STE 202 38120 #047-06-1978 L1979 IC IM *020 †20

ADEBANJO, Olugbenga Alaba. 756 RIDGE LAKE BLVD, STE 228 38120 #690-01-1986 L2003 IM *020 †20

ADEBISI, Omoniyi Yakubu. 1301 PRIMACY PKWY, FAMILY MEDICINE, RESIDENCY 38119 #690-05-1992 L2004 FM *100

ADEDIPE, Olugbenga M. 1362 MISSISSIPPI BLVD 38106 #690-06-1983 L2003 PD *020 †55 ‡

ADELEYE, Olufemi Ojo. 899 MADISON AVE 38103 #690-02-1981 L1991 NEP IM *020 †20

ADIBOSHI, Augustine Osond. 956 COURT AVE 38163 #690-19-1998 P *012

ADLER, Justin C. 5959 PARK AVE 38119 #047-06-1976 L1976 PTH *020 †50

ADWELL, Charles Edward, Jr. 786 ESTATE PL, LE BONHEUR EAST SURGERY CE 38120 #047-06-1971 L1972 AN PD *020 †55

ADZOTOR, Kwasi Ellis S. ■ 38103 #412-01-1987 L2001 N *100 †20

AELION, Miriam. ■ 38120 #550-02-1978 L2000 *100

AFSHANI, Mansour. TENNESSEE MEMPHI, UNIVERSITY OF 38163 #517-05-1991 L2006 N *100

AFZAL, Muhammad Omer. 956 CT AVE, UNIV OF TN COLL OF MED 38163 #704-21-2002 IM *100

AGAPOS, Emmanuel Michael. ■ 38117 #021-05-1990 L1995 IM *020 †20

AGGARWAL, Ritu. 1301 PRIMACY PKWY 38119 #495-78-2003 FP *012

AGUILLARD, Robert Neal. 5050 POPLAR AVE, SPECIALISTS 38157 #021-06-1984 L1984 PUD IM *020 †20

AHMAD, Khurram. 956 CT AVE, UNIV OF TN COLL OF MED 38163 #704-01-2002 L2007 IM *100 †20

AHMAD, Zeeshan. 956 COURT AVE 38163 #704-04-2001 IM *012

AHMAD-SABRY, Mohammad-Haze. ■ 38134 #915-03-1993 L2005 AN *012

AHMED, Aliya. 1030 JEFFERSON AVE, MEDICAL CENTER 38104 #704-16-1988 L2004 FM *020 †18

AHMED, Elwaleed Ali. ■ 38105 #848-01-1999 L2005 ID *012 †20

AHMED, Javeria. 956 COURT AVE 38163 #704-25-1998 END *012 †20

AHMED, Saira. 1331 UNION AVE, STE 800 38104 #704-25-2000 HO *012 †20

AKBAR, Umar. 956 COURT AVE 38163 #704-21-2001 GS *012

AKBIK, Mohamad Jamil. 3960 KNIGHT ARNOLD RD 38118 #875-01-1972 L1978 GS VS *020 †85

AKERS, Howard Thos. ■ 38117 #047-06-1964 L1964 FM OM *071 †18

AKHIGBE, Churchill Arobon. 956 COURT AVE 38163 #690-02-1998 IM *012

AKINS, Derene Ellen. 66 N PAULINE ST STE 633 38105 #047-01-1978 L1980 IM *020 †20

AKINS, Steven Lee. 6005 PARK AVE, STE 500B 38119 #027-01-1977 L1980 CD IM *020 †20

ALBA, Geraldine. 1462 POPLAR AVE 38104 #021-06-2003 L2005 OBG *020

ALBAHLAWAN, Lama Mouhamad. ■ 38103 #605-01-1996 L2003 CCP *012 ‡

ALBRITTON, John Fortune. 7900 US HIGHWAY 64, GYNECOLOGY ASSOCIATES PC 38133 #047-06-1966 L1966 OBG *020 †30

ALDEA, Peter A. 6401 POPLAR AVE STE 360 38119 #035-01-1983 L1994 FM PS *020 †85,65

ALDRIDGE, Joszi Cheyenne. 956 COURT AVE 38163 #305-01-2007 GS *012

ALEMAN, Michael Abraham. ■ 38125 #047-05-1998 L2006 U *020 †95

ALEXANDER, Albert M, Jr. 6025 WALNUT GROVE RD # 304 38120 #047-06-1951 L1951 OBG OS *020 †30

ALGEA, William David. ■ 38103 #047-06-2008 *012

AL-HAMDA, Ahmad B. 777 WASHINGTON AVE, STE 110 38105 #875-01-1989 L2002 CHN *020 †75

ALI, Cina Joseph. ■ 38103 #047-06-2008 *012

ALI, Irfan. 1715 AARON BRENNER DR, STE 326 38120 #704-20-1989 L2000 P CHP *020

ALI, Meer Akbar. 956 COURT AVE 38163 #496-65-2004 IM *012

ALI, Sheharyar. 920 MADISON AVE., STE 300, UNIVERSITY OF TENNESSEE 38163 #704-01-1997 L2007 CD *012 †20

ALI, Zenab Ahmed. ■ 38103 #330-04-1961 L1978 N *071 †75

ALISHAHI, Yasmin. ■ 38103 #047-06-2006 IM *012

ALLAN, Katherine F. 100 N HUMPHREYS BLVD, WEST CLINIC, PC 38120 #047-06-2004 L2007 IM *100

ALLEN, David Mark. 135 N PAULINE ST 6TH FL, DEPARTMENT OF PSYCHIATRY 38105 #005-02-1974 L1991 P *020 †75

ALLEN, Jeffrey Warren. 1331 UNION AVE, DEPT OF MED/DIV HEMONC 38104 #035-03-2002 L2007 HO *012 †20

ALLEN, Joseph E. 6027 WALNUT GROVE RD, STE 401 38120 #047-06-1982 L1984 IM *020 †20

ALLEN, Lee. 1455 UNION AVE, MEMPHIS DERMATOLOGY 38104 #047-06-1965 L1965 D *020 †15

ALLEN, Ray M, Jr. 80 HUMPHREYS CTR STE 202, CARDIOLOGY SPECLTS 38120 #047-06-1982 L1983 CD IM *020 †20

ALLEN, Shawn Michael. ■ 38103 #047-06-2008 *012

ALLMON, J Michelle. 6005 PARK AVE STE 200, MEMPHIS MED SPECIALISTS 38119 #047-06-1999 L2001 IM *020 †20

ALLURI, Krishna Chaitanya. ■ 38120 #495-65-2002 L2007 HO *012 †20

ALMOAZEN, Lama. ■ 38135 #875-01-1994 *100

ALPERT, Bruce Stephen. 777 WASHINGTON AVE, STE P110 38105 #023-07-1973 L1984 PDC PD *050 †55

ALSHAYEB, Hala Mohammad. ■ 38103 #575-02-2003 IM *012

ALSHEIKH, Mohammed Hashem. 50 N DUNLAP ST, OF PEDI 38103 #528-01-1998 L2007 CCP *012 †55

ALSTON, James L. 6019 WALNUT GROVE RD 38120 #047-06-1946 L1947 GS *071 †85

AL-TAHER, Mohamad. 3173 KIRBY WHITTEN RD, STE 104 38134 #915-04-1994 L2006 P *020 †75

ALTURKMANI, Ragheed. ■ 38105 #875-01-2003 IM *012

ALVAREZ QUINTERO, Harold. 6046 KNIGHT ARNOLD ROD EXT, STE 101 38115 #264-16-1994 L2007 BBK *020

AMIN, Hassan. 956 CT AVE, UNIV OF TN COLL OF MED 38163 #704-01-2002 NEP *012 †20

AMIN AUR, Rhomes Joao. 332 N LAUDERDALE 38105 #187-08-1953 L1970 PHO *020 †55

AMISON, Terako Santara. 1030 JEFFERSON AVE, MEDICAL CENTER 614/116A 38104 #001-02-2001 L2004 P *100 †75

AMMINGER, Peter Brian. 322 N LAUDERDALE ST MS 210, DEPT OF RADIOLOGY 38105 #047-06-1997 L2003 DR *020

AMMONS, James Ray. ■ 38115 #047-06-1960 L1961 GP P *075

AMONETTE, Rex A. 1455 UNION AVE, MEMPHIS DERMATOLOGY 38104 #004-01-1966 L1969 DS D *020 †15

AMOO-LAMPTEY, Aubrey. 332 N LAUDERDALE ST, ST JUDE CHILDREN'S RESEARC 38105 #412-01-1988 L2001 IM PD *020 †20,55

ANDERSON, Cary. 3960 KNIGHT ARNOLD RD, STE 100 38118 #047-07-1979 L1981 P *020

ANDERSON, Gregory. 266 S FRONT ST, # 206 38103 #047-07-1992 L1994 IM *020

ANDERSON, Joe Pat. ■ 38120 #047-06-1957 L1957 FM *071 †18

ANDERSON, Martyne. 6019 WALNUT GROVE RD 38120 #047-06-1978 L1979 IM EM *020

ANDERSON, Otis, III. ■ 38115 #047-06-2005 P *012

ANDERSON, Toby Eric. 1301 PRIMACY PKWY 38119 #047-06-2002 L2003 FM *100 †18

ANDREW, Elizabeth Marie. 6615 KIRBY CENTER CV 38115 #035-19-1984 L1992 PD *020 †55

ANDREWS, Charles R. 6027 WALNUT GROVE RD, STE 212 38120 #047-06-1976 L1976 GS *020 †85

ANDREWS, James Mc Kay. 5050 POPLAR AVE, SPECIALISTS 38157 #047-06-1985 L1985 PUD CCM *020 †18

ANGEL, John Jos. 877 JEFFERSON AVE, RM 610 38103 #016-43-1966 L1979 AN OS *020 †05 ‡

ANGHELESCU, Doralina L. 332 N LAUDERDALE ST, ST. JUDE CHILDREN'S HOSPIT 38105 #781-01-1985 L1999 APM *020 †05

ANISHANSLIN, Donald N. 3205 CHEVAL DR 38125 #047-06-1956 L1956 D OS *071

ANTHONY, Courtney L, Jr. 777 WASHINGTON AVE, STE 215 38105 #016-06-1960 L1972 PDC PP *020 †55

ANTHONY, James Michael. 3688 N WATKINS ST 38127 #047-06-1984 L1984 EM *075

ANTHONY, Larry Wilson. 3960 KNIGHT ARNOLD RD, STE 302 38118 #047-07-1978 L1995 FM *100 ‡

APPELBAUM, Alan Henry. 1030 JEFFERSON AVE, MEMPHIS VAMC; RADIOLOGY DE 38104 #539-06-1986 L1989 DR NM *020 †80,28

ARCE, Veronica Maria. ■ 38103 #047-06-2008 *012

ARCOT, Kishore Kumar. 5220 PARK AVE, STE 210 38119 #495-21-1982 L2001 IM *020

ARDOIN, Shannon Edmonds. 6305 HUMPHREYS BLVD, MSIT 38120 #021-06-2002 L2003 DR *012

ARMSTEAD, Adam Mathew. ■ 38117 #011-04-2004 L2007 DR *012

ARMSTRONG, Gregory Thomas. 332 N LAUDERDALE ST, MAIL STOP 735 38105 #001-02-1999 L2006 PHO *100 †55

ARMSTRONG-MILLER, Marsha. 6215 HUMPHREYS BLVD, STE 100 38120 #025-07-1983 L1999 DR *020 †80

ARNAOUT, Maha K. 332 N LAUDERDALE ST 38105 #575-01-1987 L1993 PHO *020

ARNAUTOVIC, Kenan. 6325 HUMPHREYS BLVD, SEMMES-MURPHEY CLINIC 38120 #957-08-1984 L2002 NS *020 †25

ARNOLD, Anita Lynn. 100 N HUMPHREYS BLVD 38120 #047-06-1993 L1995 IM *071 †20

ARNOLD, Kevin Todd. ■ 38103 #047-06-2008 *012

ARNOLD, Sandra L. 50 N DUNLAP ST 38103 #065-01-1992 L2001 PDI *050 †55

ARNOLD, Valerie Kaplan. 711 JEFFERSON AVE, CHILD & ADOL PSYCHIATRY 38105 #001-02-1988 L1989 CHP P *040 †75

ARONOFF, Philip Melvin. 6286 BRIARCREST AVE, FL 2 38120 #021-01-1963 L1971 ORS *020 †40

ARRINDELL, Esmond L. 6215 HUMPHREYS BLVD # 310 38120 #566-01-1978 L1986 NPM *020 †55

ARRINDELL, Esmond Llewell, Jr. ■ 38103 #047-06-2008 *012

ARROYO DURAN, Maximiliano. DEPT OF MEDICINE, 920 MADISON AVE STE 300 38163 #270-02-1999 L2007 CD *020

ARTEH, Jihad Omer. 842 JEFFERSON, RM A601 38163 #575-01-2002 IM *012

ARTHUR, Adam Stephen. 6325 HUMPHREYS BLVD 38120 #051-01-1998 L2004 NS *020

ARUNA KUMAR, Vaddadi. 1755 KIRBY PKWY, STE 330 38120 #495-11-1973 L1987 AN *020 †05

ASIF SIDDIQUI, Omer Muham. 956 COURT AVE, MED EDU OFF 38163 #704-21-2002 IM *012

ASIM, Muhammad Ali. ■ 38103 #704-02-1993 L1996 GE *012 †20

ASKARI, Raza. 956 CT AVE, UNIV OF TN COLL OF MED 38163 #704-01-2002 L2008 IM *100

ASKINS, Kelly Marsh. 135 N PAULINE ST 38103 #047-06-1991 L1995 P *020 †75

ASLAM, Romila. 956 COURT AVE 38163 #704-21-1999 RHU *012 †20

ASSEFA, Kidane H. 825 RIDGE LAKE BLVD 38120 #035-08-1998 L2002 OPH *020

ATKINSON, Edward, III. 6401 POPLAR AVE, STE 100 38119 #048-02-1982 L1982 DR *020 †80

ATKINSON, Richard Agard. ■ 38125 #067-01-1958 L1971 AN *071 †05

ATWOOD, John Wesley. 930 MADISON AVE, STE C1 38103 #047-06-1958 L1959 DR *071 †80

AUCHUS, Alexander Patrick. 1211 UNION AVE, STE 200 38104 #028-02-1985 L2006 N IM *040 †75

AULT, Bettina Harman. 50 N DUNLAP ST, RM 301 38103 #047-06-1984 L1988 PN PD *020 †55

AUSTIN, John Lindsay. 6215 HUMPHREYS BLVD # 301 38120 #047-06-1975 L1976 OBG *020 †30

AUSTIN, John Roger. 6027 WALNUT GROVE RD, STE 401 38120 #027-01-1970 L1971 IM *020 †20

AVECILLAS, Jaime Fernando. 956 COURT AVE, RM H314 38103 #319-04-1994 L2005 PCC *020 †20

AVGERIS, John Andrew. 756 RIDGE LAKE BLVD # 120 38120 #047-06-1963 L1963 FM *020

AVILA, Reuben Wm. 6027 WALNUT GROVE RD, STE 201 38120 #041-13-1978 L1981 IM *020 †20

AWDEH, Mahir Ramiz. 3787 SUMMER AVE 38122 #605-01-1972 L1977 CD *020 †20

AWWAD, Reem. ■ 38138 #047-06-2008 *012

AYCOCK, William W, Jr. 7900 US HIGHWAY 64, GYNECOLOGY ASSOCIATES PC 38133 #654-01-1981 L1985 OBG *020

AYYAGARI, Venkatachalam. 2784 BARTLETT BLVD 38134 #495-17-1968 L1974 IM DIA *020

AYYASH, Marwan Abu. ■ 38116 #605-01-1971 L1977 PD *020 †55

AZADI, Ali. ■ 38163 #517-03-1999 L2008 OBG *012

AZAR, Frederick Martin. 1211 UNION AVE, STE 500 38104 #021-01-1989 L1995 ORS OSM *020 †40

AZIZ, Huma. ■ 38103 #704-02-2003 L2008 IM *012

AZMI, Syed Shehzad. 842 JEFFERSON AVE RM A601 38103 #704-01-2002 HO *012 †20

AZOUZ, Abdallah. 956 COURT AVE 38163 #125-01-1994 PTH *012

BABAR, Fatima. 956 COURT AVE 38163 #704-25-2003 IM *012

BABB, John Robert. 1030 JEFFERSON AVE, STE 510 38104 #019-02-2002 L2003 ORS *020

BABCOCK, Raven Melissa. ■ 38104 #047-06-2006 L2007 MPD *100

BABULA, Bruce Edward. 877 JEFFERSON AVE, STE 632 38103 #038-40-1973 L1991 AN *020 †05

BAGOUS, Wagdy Aziz. 877 JEFFERSON AVE, CHANDLER FG-040 38103 #915-02-1971 L1989 AN GP *020 †05

BAH, Mohammed Muctarru. 5959 PARK AVE 38119 #913-15-1995 L2003 FM *020 †18

BAHR, Michael Henry. 810 WASHINGTON AVE 38105 #047-06-2006 GS *012

BAILEY, James Earl, Jr. 66 N PAULINE ST, STE 381 38105 #001-02-1990 L1994 IM *020 †20

BAILEY, Lamar Edward. 842 JEFFERSON AVE # A601 38103 #001-06-1987 L1990 IM *020 †20

BAKER, Adam Walter. 1301 PRIMACY PKWY 38119 #047-06-2001 L2002 FM *020 †18

BAKER, Irvin Clayton. 2150 WHITNEY AVE, FRAYSER FAMILY COUNCELING 38127 #047-06-1967 L1973 P *020

BAKER, Justin N. 332 N LAUDERDALE ST, MS 260 38105 #048-13-2001 L2006 PD *100 †55

BAKER, Laurie Moling. 3725 CHAMPION HILLS DR, STE 2000 38125 #047-06-1987 L1988 FM *020 †18

BAKER, Suzanne Elaine. 1800 PYRAMID PL 38132 #028-46-1981 L1983 FM *050 †18

BALAS, George Ivan. 877 JEFFERSON AVE 38103 #041-01-1956 L1977 AN *071 †05

BALAZS, Louisa Maria. UNIV OF TN MEMPHIS, DEPT OF PATHOLOGY 38163 #473-03-1976 L1996 PTH *012 †18

BALDWIN, Heather Sehnert. UNIV OF TENNESSEE, DEPT OF PATHOLOGY RESIDENC 38163 #047-06-1997 L1998 PTH *012 †18

BALDWIN, Robert L. 5842 SUNNY MORNING DR 38141 #016-11-1967 L1980 EM IM *020

BALFOUR, Eric Lee. 6305 HUMPHREYS BLVD, STE 205 38120 #021-06-2000 L2005 RO *020 †80

BALL, Charles Wm, Jr. 1301 PRIMACY PKWY, UT FAMILY MEDICINE 38119 #004-01-1977 L2006 FM *020 †18

BALL, Robert Horace. 3141 DIRECTORS ROW, CONCENTRA MEDICAL CENTERS 38131 #047-06-1980 L1982 FM *020 †18

BALLARD, Steven Roy. ■ 38135 #023-12-2005 L2007 OPH *012

BALLENGER, Reid Peter L. 7900 US HIGHWAY 64, GYNECOLOGY ASSOCIATES PC 38133 #047-06-1962 L1967 GYN OS *020 †30

BALLOUK, Wesam Fuad. 956 CT AVE 38163 #875-01-1996 L2003 NEP *100 †20

BALTHROP, Paul Matthew. ■ 38117 #020-02-2007 ORS *012

BALTZ, Sandra Maria. 146 RIVERWALK PL 38103 #047-06-1991 L2002 P PYG *020 †75

BANAVALI, Shripad D. ■ 38103 #495-96-1985 PHO *100 †55

BANDURA, Jack Paul. 5959 PARK AVE, CHEST PAIN EMERGENCY CARE 38119 #047-06-1975 L1976 CD IM *020

BANERJEE, Amit. UT - DEPT. OF NEUROSURGERY, 847 MONROE AVENUE STE. 42 38163 #047-06-1999 L2005 NS *020

BANG, Hoi Jine. 6005 PARK AVE, STE 605 38119 #583-01-1964 L1976 AN *020 †05

BANI HANI, Samer Hisham H. 842 JEFFERSON AVE, RM A601 38103 #575-02-2003 IM *012

BANNISTER, Lea M. 7900 US HIGHWAY 64, GYNECOLOGY ASSOCIATES PC 38133 #047-06-1990 L1993 OBG *020

BANNISTER, Thomas Glenn. 55 HUMPHREYS CTR, BEN L BEATUS JR MD PC 38120 #047-06-1989 L1994 P *072

BARBER, Roy M. ■ 38115 #047-06-1949 IM P *071

BARFIELD, Raymond Carlton. 332 N LAUDERDALE ST 38105 #012-05-1993 L1999 PHO *020 †55

BARKOUDAH, Ebrahim. 842 JEFFERSON AVE, STE A601 38103 #875-01-2001 L2008 MPD *012

BARNES, Grover Wesley. 4250 FARONIA RD, FARONIA MEDICAL BLDG 38116 #026-04-1979 L1980 PD *072

BARNETT, Christopher S. 687 JEFFERSON AVE 38105 #047-06-2003 L2007 P *020

BARNETTE, Eugene. 814 JEFFERSON AVE 38105 #047-06-1957 L1958 PHP OBG *020

BARR, John Dean. 55 HUMPHREYS CTR, STE 100 38120 #051-01-1986 L2000 RNR *020 †80

BARRANCO, Luis Alfredo. 50 N DUNLAP ST 38103 #649-14-1999 L2004 AN *020 ‡

BARREDA GARCIA, Javier. ■ 38103 #429-02-2005 IM *012

BARRETT, Bret Joseph. ■ 38112 #021-06-2002 L2005 ID *012 †20

BARRETT, Fred Frank. 50 N DUNLAP ST, LEBONHEUR CHILDRENS MED CT 38103 #048-04-1961 L1978 PD ID *071 †55

BARRETT, Maryanna Lee. ■ 38118 #047-06-2005 L2005 OBG *012

BARRETT, William Mark. 1129 HALE RD 38116 #047-06-1996 L2002 PD *020 †55

BARRETT-TANGOREN, Tracy E. 3155 KIRBY WHITTEN RD 38134 #041-01-1989 L1991 PUD *020 †20

BARRIGA, Jose Antonio. 920 MADISON AVE STE 240 38103 #737-06-1998 L2003 GE *020 †20

BARRIGA-CALLE, J Eduardo. ■ 38116 #737-06-1967 L1971 GE IM *020

BARRON, John Morgan. 2232 WASHINGTON AVE 38104 #047-06-1952 L1953 IM *071

BARRUS, David Michael. ■ 38119 #024-07-1997 L2000 NPM *020 †55

BARTEK, Mary Kathryn. ■ 38103 #054-04-2007 PD *012

BARTLE, Samuel T. 1750 MADISON AVE, STE 450 38104 #001-06-1991 L1993 PEM PE *020 †55

BARTON, Ellen Huston. 1550 N PARKWAY 38112 #047-06-2006 DR *012

BARTON, Ginny Elisabeth. ■ 38103 #047-06-2007 OBG *012

BASCO, Eduardo Virtucio. 6005 PARK AVE, STE 500B 38119 #748-08-1986 L1999 CD *020 †20

BASKIN, Jacquelyn Lisa. ■ 38103 #035-46-2004 L2007 PD *100 †55

BASKIN, Joel Reed. ■ 38111 #047-06-2005 IM *100

BATES, Richard Greene. 1661 INTERNATIONAL DR, STE 350 38120 #047-06-1978 L1978 DR *020 †80

BATTAILE, Najiba A H. 2150 WHITNEY AVE 38127 #605-01-1962 L1970 CHP PD *020 †75

BATTIN, David Lynn. 5959 PARK AVE, SAINT FRANCIS HOSPITAL 38119 #019-02-2002 L2007 CD *012 †20

BATTLES, Michele Ann. 6401 POPLAR AVE, STE 340 38119 #011-04-1996 L2000 OPH *020

BATTLES, Odie Lee, Jr. 1314 PEABODY AVE 38104 #038-06-1987 L1993 OBG *020

BAUCH, Stephen Thomas. 3155 KIRBY WHITTEN RD 38134 #048-12-1998 L2000 PD *020 †55

BAYAT-MOKHTARI, Susan P. 825 RIDGE LAKE BLVD, STE 125 38120 #047-06-1994 L1996 AN *020 †05

BEALE, Howard Leo. 6060 PRIMACY PKWY, STE 200 38119 #047-06-1964 L1965 PS OPH *020 †35

BEAN, Albert Louis, Jr. 945 S COX ST 38104 #047-05-1994 L1998 EM *020 †16

BEARD, Gwen B. 1455 UNION AVE, MEMPHIS DERMATOLOGY 38104 #020-02-1994 L1997 D DS *020 †15

BEASLEY, Thomas Bass. ■ 38104 #047-06-2008 *012

BEASLEY, William B R. ■ 38117 #047-06-1949 L1949 PHP OBS *062

BEATUS, Mitchell Drew. 2701 UNION AVENUE EXT, STE 400 38112 #047-20-1989 L1995 ID *020

BECKER, Daniel Jay. 55 HUMPHREYS CTR, STE 100 38120 #047-06-1986 L1987 DR *020 †80

BEDWELL, Charles Leon. 1030 JEFFERSON AVE 38104 #047-06-1971 L1972 IM *020

BEE, Tiffany Kay. STE 213, 910 MADISON 38163 #046-01-1993 L2001 CCS *020 †85

BEEMAN, H Gail. 50 N DUNLAP ST, LEBONHEUR CHILDRENS HOSPIT 38103 #048-02-1978 L1981 PD *020 †55

BEHNKE, Ernest Schorr. ■ 38112 #047-06-2008 *012

BEHRMAN, Stephen Wheeler. G218, 956 COURT AVENUE 38163 #024-05-1987 L1997 GS *020 †85

BELGAUMI, Asim Fakhruddin. ■ 38103 #704-25-1989 L1997 PHO *020 †55

BELL, Darren J. 6401 POPLAR AVE, STE 190 38119 #048-16-2001 L2005 OPH *020 †35

BELL, Emmett Dixon, Jr. 1129 HALE RD 38116 #047-06-1953 L1953 PD PDC *072 †55

BELL, Rebecca Todd. ■ 38111 #047-06-2008 *012

BELLOTT, Arthur L, Jr. ■ 38117 #047-06-1945 L1946 CD IM *071

BELLUR, Bharathi Srinath. 1000 HAYNES ST 38114 #495-09-1972 L1989 PD *020 †55

BELLUR, Srinath N. 1211 UNION AVE, STE 400 38104 #495-37-1969 L1989 N SME *020 †75

BENAIM, Ely. 262 N DANNY THOMAS BLVD 38105 #935-07-1987 L1997 PHO PD *020 †55

BENITONE, Jerry Donald. 2144 MONROE AVE 38104 #016-11-1969 L1970 GS GP *020 †85

BENN, Sonia Marie. 100 N HUMPHREYS BLVD 38120 #047-06-1999 L2001 HO *020 †20

BENNETT, Gregory Daniel. 956 CT AVE, STE G228 38163 #048-12-2005 GS *012

BENOIT, Carolyn T. 50 N DUNLAP ST, DIVISION OF EMERGENCY MEDI 38103 #048-14-1995 L1998 PD *020

BENTON, Benj Frederick. ■ 38120 #047-06-1946 L1946 GS *071 †85

BERARD, Costan Wm. ■ 38117 #024-01-1959 L1980 PTH *100 †50

BERG, Karin Diane. ■ 38117 #050-02-1994 L2006 PTH *020 †50

BERGERON, Christian Blake. ■ 38103 #047-06-2007 PD *012

BERKENSTOCK, Oran Lee. 3109 WALNUT GROVE RD 38111 #047-06-1992 L1993 FM OBG *020 †18

BERNARD, Matthew Stephen. ■ 38120 #047-06-2005 ORS *012

BERNTSON, Gail K. 1030 JEFFERSON AVE # 11C-3 38104 #021-05-1998 L1999 IM *020 †20

BERRY, Allen Doug, III. 5959 PARK AVE 38119 #047-06-1979 L1983 PTH NP *020 †50

BERRY, J Demos. 1030 JEFFERSON AVE, VAMC # 11C 38104 #047-06-1984 L1985 PTH OS *020 †50

BERRY, Karen. 1715 AARON BRENNER DR, STE 326 38120 #047-06-1984 L1986 **P** *020 †75

BERT, Timothy Michael. ■ 38103 #016-43-2007 **ORS** *012

BESH, Stephen Andrew. 100 N HUMPHREYS BLVD 38120 #021-05-1990 L1993 **HO** *020 †20

BESHOAR, Daniel Francis. ■ 38128 #051-01-1992 *075

BESSER, Susan Levine. ■ 38120 #027-01-1981 L1987 **FM** *020 †18

BESSOFF, Joel Ira. ■ 38119 #024-07-1968 L2004 **GE** *040 †20

BEST, Jara Lavonda. 6215 HUMPHREYS BLVD, STE 300 38120 #047-06-2000 L2004 **PD** *020

BETHEA, Veronica Michelle. 1200 PEABODY AVE 38104 #047-07-1998 L2001 **IM** *020 †20

BEVILACQUA, Aldo Romano. 6019 WALNUT GROVE RD 38120 #187-12-1958 L1971 **P N** *071

BHATIA, Harmeet K. 956 COURT AVE, UNIV TN COLL OF MED 38103 #495-03-1980 **IM** *100

BHATTACHARYA, S T. ■ 38117 #047-06-2001 L2005 **OBG** *100

BHOJWANI, Deepa Shyam. ■ 38103 #496-21-1994 L2008 **PHO** *020 †55

BHUSNURMATH, Shefali Shiv. RESIDENCY PROGRAM, DEPT OF PATHOLOGY 38163 #495-98-2004 **PTH** *012

BICKERS, William Jesse. ■ 38117 #047-06-1961 L1962 **IM CD** *071 †20

BICKNELL, Bennett Wm. 1755 KIRBY PKWY, STE 330 38120 #047-06-1992 L1993 **AN** *020 †20

BIERMAN, Paul S. 80 HUMPHREYS CTR, STE 200 38120 #011-02-1991 L1996 **GE IM** *020 †20

BIKHAZI, George Bishara. 332 N LAUDERDALE ST, DEPT. OF ANESTHESIOLOGY MS 38105 #605-01-1971 L2001 **AN OS** *020

BILAL, Muhammad. 956 CT AVE, UNIV OF TN COLL OF MED 38163 #704-01-2004 **IM** *012

BILLMEIER, Gerard Jos, Jr. 6248 POPLAR AVE 38119 #047-06-1964 L1964 **PD** *071 †55

BIRDSONG, Emmitt Sidney, Jr. 3950 NEW COVINGTON PIKE, STE 2500 38128 #047-06-1954 L1954 **GS** *020 †85

BIRDSONG, Michael Sidney. 153 S REESE ST 38111 #047-06-1979 L1981 **N EM** *020

BISHOP, Hal Douglass. 1750 MADISON AVE, STE 400 38104 #047-06-1961 L1988 **ORS** *071 †40

BLACK, David Albritton. ■ 38112 #027-01-2007 **GS** *012

BLACK, Dennis Darrel. 777 WASHINGTON AVE, STE P110 38105 #047-06-1978 L1981 **PD** *020 †55

BLACKETT, Melrose Ingle. 1265 UNION AVE 38104 #028-02-1982 L1983 **OBG EM** *020 †30

BLAKELY, Laura Johnetta. 100 N HUMPHREYS BLVD 38120 #047-06-1998 L2004 **ON** *020 †20

BLAKELY, Martin Lee. 777 WASHINGTON AVE, STE 230 38105 #047-06-1989 L1990 **PDS GS** *020 †85

BLAKNEY, Eric Dewayne. 2725 KIRBY RD, STE 1 38119 #047-06-1997 L1998 **IM** *020 †20

BLALACK, Jeffrey A. 877 JEFFERSON AVE 38103 #047-06-1990 L1994 **AN** *040 †05

BLANKINSHIP, Joseph Patri, Jr. ■ 38120 #047-06-2008 *012

BLOCH-MENSCHIK, Melissa A. 6305 HUMPHREYS BLVD, STE 205 38120 #011-03-1999 L2005 **DR** *020 †80

BLOTNER, Adrian Brian. 6401 POPLAR AVE STE 316 38119 #021-05-1984 L2005 **P PMM** *020 †75

BLUMENFELD, Harry Bernard. 6005 PARK AVE, MEMPHIS MEDICAL 38119 #047-06-1958 L1959 **RHU IM** *020 †20

BLUMER, Dietrich Peter. 135 N PAULINE ST, UNIERSITY OF TENN MEMPHIS 38105 #869-07-1955 L1988 **P** *020 †20

BLYTHE, Joseph Alfred, III. 5050 POPLAR AVE 38157 #027-01-1967 L1972 **PUD CCM** *020 †20

BOALS, Christopher Adam. 1661 INTERNATIONAL DR, STE 350 38120 #047-06-1999 L2001 **DR** *020 †80

BOALS, James William, Jr. 6075 POPLAR AVE, STE 405 38119 #047-06-1995 L1998 **VIR** *020 †80

BOALS, James Wm. 1661 INTERNATIONAL DR, STE 350 38120 #047-06-1970 L1970 **R** *020 †80

BOALS, Jennifer Robertson. 1661 INTERNATIONAL DR, STE 350 38120 #047-06-1995 L1998 **DR** *020 †80

BOALS, Nino Bradberry. ■ 38126 #047-06-2004 L2005 **DR** *012

BOBO, Robert Thompson. 6005 PARK AVE, STE 430B 38119 #027-01-1967 L1974 **ORS** *020 †40

BOBO-MOSLEY, Loretta. 1734 MADISON AVE 38104 #047-06-1980 L1980 **IM** *020 †20

BOEHM, Peter Eric. 956 COURT AVE 38163 #539-04-2004 **GS** *100

BOGER, Robert Shelton. 3 N DUNLAP ST 38163 #024-01-1972 L2004 **NEP IM** *020 †20

BOOM, Alan Dexter. 1211 UNION AVE, STE 300 38104 #047-06-1985 L1989 **PTH** *020 †50

BOONE, Howard A. 6019 WALNUT GROVE RD 38120 #047-06-1944 L1944 **IM** *071 †20

BOONE, James Earl. 5575 POPLAR AVE, STE 320 38119 #047-06-1976 L1977 **IM** *071 †20

BOOP, Frederick Alan. 1211 UNION AVE, STE 200 38104 #004-01-1983 L1999 **NS NSP** *020 †25

BORS-KOEFOED, Roy. 6266 POPLAR AVE 38119 #165-06-1981 L2001 **MFM** *040 †30

BOSTON, Umar Sekoutoure. 50 N DUNLAP ST STE 2958, LEBONHEUR CHILDRENS 38103 #010-03-1995 L2006 **TS** *100 †85,90

BOSWELL, James Lionel. 6005 PARK AVE STE 809 38119 #027-01-1973 L1976 **IM CD** *020 †20

BOSWELL, Richard Lee. 5050 POPLAR AVE, STE 800 38157 #047-06-1970 L1972 **PUD CCM** *020 †20

BOTTA, Sisir. ■ 38103 #047-06-2008 *012

BOUDREAUX, Lynzie Elizabe. ■ 38103 #021-05-2007 **PD** *012

BOULDEN, Thomas Frazer. 50 N DUNLAP ST, LEBONHEUR CHILDREN'S MED C 38103 #004-01-1979 L1984 **DR PDR** *020 †40

BOURLAND, William Landess. 6286 BRIARCREST AVE, FL 2 38120 #047-06-1972 L1973 **HS ORS** *020 †40

BOUTTE, James Noble. U TN MEMPHIS/TN M ED PRG 38163 #021-05-1989 L1993 **AN** *020 †05

BOWDEN, Marcia Renee. 1652 MADISON AVE 38104 #004-01-1994 L1997 **IM** *020

BOWDEN, Phillip Rodney. 100 N HUMPHREYS CTR 38120 #047-06-1987 L1991 **GE IM** *020 †20

BOWEN, Ronnie Durrell. 4783 CHILDS DR 38116 #047-07-2002 L2004 **FM** *020

BOWMAN, Anthony Juan. 1211 UNION AVE S-865, INC. 38104 #649-14-1980 L2001 **ICE CD** *020 †20

BOWMAN, Benjamin David. ■ 38120 #047-06-2007 **MPD** *012

BOYANTON, Deborah D. 777 WASHINGTON AVE, STE P110 38105 #047-06-1990 L1993 **PD** *020 †55

BOYD, Allen Street, Jr. 6325 HUMPHREYS BLVD 38120 #047-06-1964 L1965 **NS** *020 †25

BOYD, Daniel Street. 1715 AARON BRENNER DR, STE 326 38120 #047-06-1990 L1991 **P** *020 †75

BOYKINS, Derayne. 877 JEFFERSON AVE 38103 #032-01-1988 L1992 **AN** *020

BOYLE, John William, IV. ■ 38103 #047-06-2003 L2007 **OPH** *100

BOYTE, Mary Brinson. ■ 38122 #047-06-2004 **GS** *012

BOZEMAN, Paula Moffett. 1755 KIRBY PKWY, STE 330 38120 #047-06-1982 L1983 **AN PUD** *020

BRADFORD, Marcia D. 602 W MITCHELL RD 38109 #043-01-1992 L1995 **IM** *020

BRADLEY, Robert Maynard. 1211 UNION AVE, STE 300 38104 #047-05-1989 L1995 **PTH BBK** *020 †50

BRADY, Boyer M. ■ 38117 #047-06-1951 L1956 **R NM** *071 †80,28

BRADY, Esther Batson. ■ 38117 #047-06-1951 L1951 **OS PHP** *071

BRADY, Michael Batson. 6005 PARK AVE, STE 101B 38119 #047-06-1981 L1984 **DR NR** *020 †20

BRAHMBHATT, Jamin Vinod. ■ 38103 #024-05-2007 **GS** *012

BRANDAO, Leonardo R. 332 N LAUDERDALE ST, ST JUDE CHILDRENS HOSP 38105 #187-04-1990 L2006 **PD** *100

BRANTLEY, James Hays. 5182 SANDERLIN AVE, SPECIALISTS 38117 #047-06-1981 L1981 **IM** *020 †20

BRASFIELD, Joyce Borup. 1325 EASTMORELAND AVE, PEABODY FAMILY CARE 38104 #047-06-1983 L1985 **IM OBG** *020

BRAZA, Mary Elizabeth. 1200 PEABODY AVE 38104 #056-05-1984 L1993 **FM** *020 †18

BREWER, Brian Lamont. 956 CT AVE, RM E222 38163 #047-07-2005 **GS** *012

BREWER, Michelle L. 777 WASHINGTON AVE, STE 410 38105 #047-06-1985 L1989 **N** *020 †75

BREWER, Susan Crouch. 1211 UNION AVE STE 340, DEPARTMENT OF MEDICINE 38104 #047-06-1990 L1993 **ID** *100 †20

BRIDGES, Ruth Anne. 6005 PARK AVE, STE 901 38119 #047-06-1978 L1979 **AN** *020 †05

BRINGMAN, Jay Joseph. 880 MADISON AVE, STE 3C 38103 #055-01-1998 L2003 **OBG** *020 †30

BRINT, Jeffrey Mark. 1030 JEFFERSON AVE 111-H1, VA MED CTR 38104 #011-04-1985 L1989 **IM ID** *020 †20

BRITT, Louis Goodno. 956 COURT AVE RM G210 38103 #047-06-1955 L1955 **GS** *071 †85

BROADWAY, Steven Jared. ■ 38103 #004-01-2005 **GS** *100

BROCATO, Brian E. ■ 38107 #005-76-2007, ▲ **OBG** *012

BRODY, Jonathan Geo. 1750 FRAYSER BLVD STE A 38127 #047-06-1983 L1985 **GP** *020

BROIDES, Arnon. 332 N LAUDERDALE ST, ST. JUDE CHILDREN'S RESEAR 38105 #550-04-1995 **AI** *100

BROMLEY, Howard Russ. 1030 JEFFERSON AVE, 1030 JEFFERSON AVENUE 38104 #011-02-1981 L2003 **AN CCM** *062 †05 ‡

BRONISCER, Alberto. 332 N LAUDERDALE ST 38105 #187-04-1989 L2002 **PHO** *020 †55

BRONSTEIN, Maury W. 6027 WALNUT GROVE RD, STE 103 38119 #047-06-1951 L1952 **CD IM** *020 ‡

BROOKS, Brown. ■ 38119 #047-06-1957 L1957 **GS** *071 †85

BROOKS, Maria T. 1388 MADISON AVE 38104 #047-06-1984 L1985 **DR NM** *020 †80

BROOKS, Todd Frederick. 220 S CLAYBROOK ST, STE 201 38104 #047-07-1980 L1981 **OBG** *020

BROPHY, John David. 1325 EASTMORELAND AVE, STE 370 38104 #012-01-1983 L1995 **NS** *020 †25

BROWN, Angie Jean. ■ 38119 #047-06-2003 L2005 **FM** *100 †18

BROWN, Charles H. 3960 KNIGHT ARNOLD RD, STE 400 38118 #047-06-1977 L1979 **FM** *020 †18

BROWN, Clyde Miller. 587 S BELVEDERE BLVD, T.M CARR MD, P.C. 38104 #027-01-1993 L1997 **GS EM** *020

BROWN, David Griffin. ■ 38117 #047-06-2006 **ORS** *012

BROWN, James Stephen. 50 N DUNLAP ST 38103 #047-06-1954 L1954 **PD** *071 †55

BROWN, Sarah L. ■ 38104 #048-02-1990 L1990 **IM** *020 †20

BROWNLEE, William Taylor. ■ 38103 #047-06-2007 **MPD** *012

BRYAN, Jennifer Adams. 956 CT AVE 38163 #047-06-2000 L2002 **FM** *100 †18

BRYANT, James Walter. 5220 PARK AVE, STE 100 38119 #047-06-1956 L1958 **FM** *020 †18

BUCHALTER, Robert. 6005 PARK AVE, STE 524B 38119 #047-06-1964 L1964 **P** *020 †75

BUCHANAN, Jack Willard, Jr. 1030 JEFFERSON AVE 38104 #020-12-1975 L1999 **IM** *050

BUCHIGNANI, John Shea. 55 HUMPHREYS CTR, STE 100 38120 #047-06-1965 L1965 **NM R** *020 †80,28

BUCKINGHAM, Steven C. 777 WASHINGTON AVE, STE P110 38105 #005-14-1993 L1996 **PD PDI** *020 †55

BUCKLEY, Madison H, Jr. 6005 PARK AVE, STE 101B 38119 #047-06-1962 L1962 **R OS** *020 †80

BUECHNER, David Edward. 1661 INTERNATIONAL DR, STE 350 38120 #047-06-1991 L1992 **RNR** *020 †80

BUGG, Michael Frederick. 6046 KNIGHT ARNOLD ROD EXT, STE 101 38115 #021-05-1988 L1992 **ATP CLP** *020 †50

BUGGS, Vernois. 3177 POPLAR AVE 38111 #047-07-1984 L1992 **IM GS** *020

BUGNITZ, Mark C. 50 N DUNLAP ST 4TH FL, LE BONHEUR CHILDREN'S HOSP 38103 #028-03-1982 L1987 **CCM PD** *020 †55

BUIE, Kimberly Ann. ■ 38122 #047-06-2007 **PD** *012

BUIJS, Marleen. 1121 UNION AVE 38104 #660-07-1991 L1997 **FM** *020 †18

BURANAPIYAWONG, Arkom. 6005 PARK AVE STE 905B 38119 #891-02-1968 L1978 **AN** *020 †05

BURCH, James Reginald, III. 1755 KIRBY PKWY, STE 330 38120 #047-06-1986 L1986 **AN IM** *020 †05

BURGHEN, George Andrew. 50 N DUNLAP ST 38103 #027-01-1964 L1971 **DIA PDE** *020 †55

BURGOYNE, Laura Lee-Anne. 332 N LAUDERDALE ST, ST JUDE CHILDREN'S RESEARC 38105 #143-11-1994 L2005 **AN** *050

BURKE, Larry Dale. 6025 WALNUT GROVE RD, STE 311 38120 #028-02-1972 L1977 **VS** *020 †85

BURKES, Walter Joe. ■ 38116 #047-07-1979 L1980 **IM** *075

BURKITT, Michael Joseph. ■ 38163 #047-06-2008 *012

BURKLE, George Henry, III. 1030 JEFFERSON AVE 38104 #047-06-1958 L1959 **GP** *071 †85

BURLEW, Brad Steven. 1211 UNION AVE STE 340, DEPARTMENT OF MEDICINE 38104 #016-06-1979 L1986 **CD** *040 †20

BURNETT, Chas Roland, Jr. 6025 WALNUT GROVE RD, STE 111 38120 #004-01-1977 L1982 **CD IM** *020 †20

BURNETT, John Arthur. 55 HUMPHREYS CTR 38120 #019-02-1984 L1998 **RO** *020 †80

BURNETT, Sharon L. ■ 38116 #056-06-1981 L1990 **OBG** *020

BURNS, Robert. 2714 UNION AVENUE EXT, STE 150 38112 #035-06-1983 L1986 **IMG IM** *020 †20

BURRUSS, George Lewis. 80 HUMPHREYS CTR, STE 100 38120 #047-06-1977 L1977 **PS** *020 †85,65

BURTON, William Duer. 1265 UNION AVE 38104 #025-01-1962 L1967 **PTH** *020 †50

BUSBY, David F. ■ 38122 #047-06-1949 L1949 **P PFP** *020 †75

BUSS, Nicholas Ian. ■ 38111 #047-06-2008 L2012 *012

BUTAWAN, Dominique Marie. ■ 38120 #047-06-2008 *012

BUTLER, Darel Anthony. 1264 WESLEY DR STE 209 38116 #005-02-1989 L1996 **N** *020 †75

BUTLER, Dorothy Ann Hicks. 1129 HALE RD 38116 #021-01-1965 L1970 **PD** *020 †55

BUTLER, Ray S. 6019 WALNUT GROVE RD 38120 #048-15-2002 L2005 **DR** *100 †80

BUTTRAM, John Grant, Jr. ■ 38104 #036-08-2002 L2008 **NS** *012

BUTTROSS, John Boustany. 1068 CRESTHAVEN RD STE 360 38119 #027-01-1981 L1983 **IM** *020 †20

BUTTS, Natasha Lynn. 1362 MISSISSIPPI BLVD 38106 #047-06-2002 L2004 **FM** *020 †18

BYRD, John Matthew. 5070 RALEIGH LAGRANGE RD B, COVINGTON PIKE ANIMAL HOSP 38134 #030-05-1998 L1999 **FM** *020 †18

BYRD, Kathryn Woods. 6515 POPLAR AVE STE 112 38119 #047-06-1988 L1990 **OPH PO** *020 †35

BYRD, William Gregory. 1301 PRIMACY PKWY 37501 #004-01-1999 L2004 **FM** *020 †18

CABANERO, Niceno Lavares. ■ 38125 #748-01-1954 L1980 **GP EM** *020

CABIGAO, Eduardo Consunji. 2221 POPLAR AVE, EMERGENCY PHYSICIAN 38104 #748-01-1979 L1990 **EM FM** *020 †18,16 ‡

CABIGAO, Olivia Ordona. 1755 KIRBY PKWY, STE 330 38120 #748-08-1978 L1991 **AN OS** *020

CABRERA, Antonio Gabriel. 50 N DUNLAP ST STE 2598 38103 #429-02-1998 L2006 **PDC** *100 †55

CAFFEY, Shed H, Jr. 5959 PARK AVE 38119 #012-05-1951 L1961 **PD** *075 †55

CAI, Songmin. 956 COURT AVE 38163 #243-54-1987 **FP** *012

CALDWELL, Felix Lehman. 1714 W MASSEY RD, LS OF MEMPHIS, PC DBA LIFE 38120 #047-06-1981 L1982 **IM** *020 †20

CALHOUN, Susan Valerie. 1030 JEFFERSON AVE, VETERANS ADMINISTRATION HO 38104 #010-03-1984 L1995 **AN** *020 †05

CALLIHAN, Thomas Ralph. 6046 KNIGHT ARNOLD ROD EXT, STE 101 38115 #010-01-1973 L1980 **PTH** *020 †50

CALLISON, Maston K. ■ 38117 #047-06-1939 L1940 **IM** *071 †20

CAMILLO, Francis Xavier. 1211 UNION AVE, STE 500 38104 #035-09-1992 L2001 **ORS OSS** *020 †40

CAMPBELL, Colin. 38117 #067-01-1953 L1961 **OS OBG** *071 †30

CAMPBELL, Patrick Kent. 332 N LAUDERDALE ST, DEPT HEMATOLOGY/ONCOLOGY 38105 #012-05-2002 L2007 **PHO** *012

CAMPBELL, Tommy Jay. 1068 CRESTHAVEN RD, STE 360 38119 #027-01-1983 L1983 **IM** *020 †20

CAMPOS, Paulo Cesar G. ■ 38111 #187-12-1992 L2002 **CD** *100 †20

CANADA, Robert Bradley. 2200 UNION AVE 38104 #047-06-1998 L1999 **NEP IM** *020 †20

CANALE, Dee James. 6325 HUMPHREYS BLVD 38120 #047-06-1955 L1956 **NS** *071 †25

CANAVAN, Natalia Vladimir. 956 COURT AVE 38163 #913-72-1994 **BBK** *100

CANCIO-BABU, Consolacion. 50 N DUNLAP ST 38103 #748-01-1971 L1980 **AN PAN** *020

CANIZA, Miguela A. 332 N LAUDERDALE ST, MAIL STOP 721 38105 #726-01-1983 L1997 **PD ID** *040 †55

CANNON, Idah Mary. 1264 WESLEY DR, FAMILY PRACTICE 38116 #021-01-1977 L1978 **FM GP** *020 †18

CAO, Yan. 956 COURT AVE 38163 #243-47-1989 L2007 **IM** *020 †20

CAPE, Charles Albert. 80 HUMPHREYS CTR, STE 320 38120 #036-05-1959 L1965 **N** *020 †75

CAPOOTH, Luther Wayne. ■ 38138 #047-06-1970 L1972 **EM** *020 †16

CARBONE, Laura Dolores. 1325 EASTMORELAND AVE, STE 365 38104 #056-06-1989 L1992 **RHU** *020 †20

CARDOSO, Sergio Steiner. UNIV OF TENN MED UNITS 38163 #187-03-1952 **PA ON** *100

CAREY, Jack Willard, III. ■ 38105 #047-06-2007 **MPD** *012

CARLOTA, Lupo T, Jr. 5180 PARK AVE, STE 175 38119 #748-01-1960 L1980 **P** *020

CARR, Silvana Barbosa. 956 COURT AVE, UNIV OF TN COLL MED 38163 #187-01-1993 L2004 **PDI** *012 ‡

CARRO, Manuel. 6325 HUMPHREYS BLVD 38120 #042-03-1987 L1991 **PM** *020 †60

CARROLL, Gregory S. 825 RIDGE LAKE BLVD 38120 #037-01-1990 L1995 **OPH EM** *020

CARRUTH, Paul Clay. 1661 INTERNATIONAL DR, STE 350 38120 #047-06-1992 L1993 **DR** *020 †80

CARSON, Rickey Reynolds. 3030 COVINGTON PIKE, STE 100 38128 #004-01-1974 L1982 **GP OBG** *020

CARTER, Bradley Paul. 3362 S 3RD ST, CHRIST COMMUNITY HEALTH 38109 #021-01-1997 L2002 **MPD** *020 †20,55

CARTER, Charles Leslie. 6263 POPLAR AVE, STE 1052 38119 #036-01-1985 L1988 **IM** *020 †20

CARTER, James E. 1444 E SHELBY DR, STE 317 38116 #047-07-1981 L1981 **PD** *020 †55

CARTER, Jerry Lee. ■ 38103 #047-02-1982 L1985 **EM** *020 †16

CARTER, Mary Carrigan. 332 N LAUDERDALE ST 38105 #001-02-1982 L1985 **PHO PD** *020 †55

CARTER, Russell Allan. 6029 WALNUT GROVE RD, STE 401 38120 #047-06-1988 L1990 **TS** *020 †90,85

CARTER, Sarah Anne. 4451 FAIRMEADOW RD 38117 #004-01-1965 L1983 **IM OS** *071 †20

CARTER, Ursula Nicole. 409 AYERS ST 38105 #016-43-2002 L2006 **OBG** *100

CARVEL, Lynn Tate. 5948 LAKE TIDE CV 38120 #004-01-1991 L1995 **DR** *020 †80

CASH, Darlene Kaye. 100 N HUMPHREYS BLVD, BOSTON CANCER GROUP/UTCI 38120 #047-06-1976 L1977 **HEM** *020

CASHION, Ernest L. 930 MADISON AVE, STE 600 38103 #004-01-1951 L1967 **NS** *071 †25

CAULEY, David Brian. 1300 WESLEY DR, EMERGENCY DEPT 38116 #004-01-1986 L1997 **FM** *020 †18

CAUSEY, Karima Taneishia. 8970 WINCHESTER RD 38125 #047-20-2004 L2007 **FM** *020 †18

CAZALAS, Christi Lee. ■ 38103 #001-06-2006 **MPD** *012

CHAI, Yaohui. 956 CT AVE, UNIV OF TN COLL OF MED 38163 #243-76-1986 **N** *012

CHAKRAVERTY, Tamal. 956 CT AVE 38163 #028-46-2000 **NP** *100

CHAN, Godfrey Chi-Fung. ■ 38105 #047-18-1985 L1985 **PHO** *100

CHANCE, Joseph Walker. 1755 KIRBY PKWY, STE 330 38120 #047-06-1983 L1984 **AN PMM** *020 †05

CHANCELLOR, Karen E. ■ 38112 #036-07-1985 L2004 **NP FOP** *050 †50

CHANDLER, Robert Gregory. 80 HUMPHREYS CTR # 10 38120 #047-06-1988 L1990 **PS** *020 †85,65

CHANDRASHEKARAN, Rama. ■ 38103 #038-45-2004 L2007 **PD** *020

CHAPMAN, Cathy Marie. 5210 POPLAR AVE, STE 150 38119 #016-02-1988 L1992 **RHU** *020 †20

CHAPMAN, Miriah Beth. ■ 38112 #017-20-2007 **OBG** *012

CHAPPELL, Benjamin Todd. ■ 38122 #047-06-2005 **OBG** *012

CHAPPELL, Fenwick W. 6019 WALNUT GROVE RD 38120 #047-06-1946 L1946 **EM GS** *071 †85

CHARI, Radha Samavedam. ■ 38103 #068-01-1988 L1993 **OBG** *020

CHASE, Adam Joseph. ■ 38111 #019-02-2005 L2007 **ORS** *012

CHASE, Nancy Ann. 805 ESTATE PL STE 1 38120 #035-08-1970 L1978 **PDC** *020 †55

CHAUDHARY, Asad Junaid. ■ 38103 #704-01-2002 L2008 **IM** *100

CHAUDHRY, Sufiyan Hafeez. 956 CT AVE, UNIV OF TN COLL OF MED 38163 #704-01-2003 **GE** *012 †20

CHAUHAN, Heather Pearson. 6215 HUMPHREYS BLVD, STE 500 38120 #047-06-2000 L2004 **OBG** *020 †20

CHAUM, Edward. 920 MADISON AVE, STE 915 38103 #035-20-1987 L2000 **OPH PD** *075 †35,55

CHAWLA, Anita Dey. 3960 KNIGHT ARNOLD RD, STE 316 38118 #496-07-1983 L2000 **IM** *020 †20

CHEEK, Richard Calvin. 1030 JEFFERSON AVE, STE 336 38104 #047-06-1964 L1965 **GS** *020 †85

CHEN, Aaron Edward. 1903 CRUMP AVE 38107 #048-02-1999 L2001 **PEM** *100 †20,55

CHEN, Feiyu. 6325 HUMPHREYS BLVD 38120 #243-77-1982 L1995 **N** *020

CHESNEY, Carolyn Leach M. 6046 KNIGHT ARNOLD ROD EXT, STE 101 38115 #047-05-1968 L1974 **HEM IM** *020 †20

CHESNEY, P Joan. 50 N DUNLAP ST, 4TH FL 38103 #067-01-1966 L1988 **ID PD** *050 †55

CHESNEY, Russell Wallace. 50 N DUNLAP ST 38103 #035-45-1968 L1988 **PN PD** *030 †55

CHESNEY, Thomas Mc Coll. 6046 KNIGHT ARNOLD ROD EXT, STE 101 38115 #047-05-1969 L1969 **PTH DMP** *020 †50 ‡

CHESSER, Allison Patricia. ■ 38126 #047-06-2008 *012

CHILDERS, Jennifer W. 1981 UNION AVE 38104 #047-06-1985 L1986 **D UM** *020 †15

CHILDRESS, Richard Dale. 5659 S REX RD 38119 #021-06-1999 L2004 **END** *020 †20

CHILDRESS, Rommel Gabriel. 1444 E SHELBY DR, STE 203 38116 #024-07-1974 L1979 **ORS** *020 †40

CHIN, Frank Tuin Wong, Jr. 5347 DUNNELLON AVE 38134 #011-03-1974 L1979 **FM PTH** *020

CHIN, Thomas Kiang. 777 WASHINGTON AVE, STE P215 38105 #025-01-1983 L1997 **PDC PD** *020 †55

CHISHOLM, Patricia Ann. 1028 CRESTHAVEN RD, STE 101 38119 #041-07-1995 L2005 **FM** *020 †18

CHISHTI, Waqas Ahmed. 956 CT AVE, UNIV OF TN COLL OF MED 38163 #704-01-1999 **PCC** *012 †20

CHISM, David Dewayne. ■ 38105 #047-06-2008 *012

CHO, Moon Jung. ■ 38133 #047-06-2006 L2006 **IM** *012

CHU, George. 6027 WALNUT GROVE RD, STE 206 38120 #047-06-1986 L1987 **IM** *020 †20

CHUANG, Howard Jyi-Juang. 3960 KNIGHT ARNOLD RD #321 38118 #244-04-1967 L1976 **IM CD** *020 †20

CICALA, Roger S. 6325 HUMPHREYS BLVD, SEMMES-MURPHY CLINIC 38120 #047-06-1982 L1982 L1982 **N** *020 †20

CLARIDGE, Jeffrey Arnold. 877 JEFFERSON AVE 38103 #035-45-1996 L2003 **CCS** *020 †85

CLARK, Aubrey A. ■ 38119 #048-14-2007 **PD** *012

CLARKE, Catherine Jane. 1325 EASTMORELAND AVE #101 38104 #047-06-1994 L1996 **IM** *040 †20

CLARKE, Dave Fitzgerald. 777 WASHINGTON AVE, STE P250 38105 #566-01-1994 L2005 **CHN** *020 †75

CLEIN, Paul David. 1715 AARON BRENNER DR, STE 326 38120 #012-01-1990 L1995 **CHP** *020 †75

CLEVELAND, Kerry O. 1211 UNION AVE, STE 340 38104 #027-01-1989 L1990 **ID IM** *020 †20

CLEVELAND, Kevin Bron. 1211 UNION AVE, STE 500 38104 #012-22-1996 L2001 **ORS** *020

COBURN, Thomas Preston. ■ 38122 #047-06-1965 L1966 **PDR NM** *020 †80

COCKROFT, Robert Lawrence. 1661 INTERNATIONAL DR, STE 350 38120 #047-06-1966 L1968 **R** *020 †80

COFFEE, Nefeteria. ■ 38126 #047-06-2008 *012

COHEN, Alan Jay. 5659 S REX RD, ENDOCRINE CLINIC P.C. 38119 #010-03-1979 L1984 **END DIA** *020

COHEN, Avrahm. 6005 PARK AVE STE 906 38119 #067-01-1975 L2006 **CD IM** *020 †20 ‡

COHEN, Lawrence Louis. 5959 PARK AVE 38119 #047-06-1947 L1947 **A OTO** *071 †45 ‡

COLE, Francis Hammond, Jr. 1265 UNION AVE 38104 #047-06-1968 L1969 **TS GS** *020 †85,90

COLE, Kristi M. 6215 HUMPHREYS BLVD, STE 200 38120 #047-06-1995 L1998 **OBG** *020

COLE, Robert Jeffrey. 6286 BRIARCREST AVE, FL 2 38120 #047-05-1989 L1990 **ORS HS** *020 †40

COLE, Steve. 1750 MADISON AVE 38104 #005-11-1983 L1984 **AI IM** *020 †20,03

COLE, William Leon. 20 DUDLEY ST STE 702-B 38103 #017-20-1966 L1970 **AN** *020 †05

COLEMAN, Alexander Chisol. ■ 38111 #045-01-2006 **ORS** *012

COLLINS, Blaine C. ■ 38122 #047-06-1942 L1942 **GS GP** *071

COLLINS, Etheldreda L. 1265 UNION AVE, METHODIST UNIV ER 38104 #047-20-1993 L1994 **IM** *020 †20 ‡

COLLINS, Frank H. 5959 PARK AVE 38119 #047-06-1951 L1951 **GP** *072

COLVIN, Hugh Frederick, Jr. ■ 38104 #051-04-2003 L2006 **EM** *020

CONLEY, Mary Ellen. 332 N LAUDERDALE ST 38105 #005-18-1975 L1988 **PD IG** *050 †55

CONNELLY, Stephanie Ann. UNIVERSITY OF TENNESSEE, 66 N PAULINE #633 38163 #025-12-1996 L2002 **IM** *020 †20,70

CONNER, David Terrance. ■ 38112 #047-06-2004 **GS** *100

CONOLEY, Jack A. ■ 38111 #048-12-2004 L2006 **ORS** *012

CONRAD, John Robert. ■ 38103 #422-01-2000 L2005 **GS** *100

COO, Audrey W. 2225 UNION AVE STE 100 38104 #748-10-1984 L1997 **NEP IM** *020 †20

COOKE, Charles Robt. 1030 JEFFERSON AVE, VA MED CTR DEPT NEP # 111B 38104 #023-07-1954 L1987 **NEP IM** *020 †20

COOPER, Gbaqyee Emmanuel. 956 CT AVE, UNIV OF TN COLL OF MED 38163 #305-01-2004 L2006 **IM** *012

COOPER, Lauren Roberts. ■ 38122 #047-06-2008 *012

COORS, George A. 3980 NEW COVINGTON PIKE, STE 304 38128 #047-06-1944 L1944 **GS GP** *071 †85

CORBETT, Cathy Elizabeth. 1211 UNION AVE STE 340, DEPARTMENT OF MEDICINE 38104 #047-06-1980 L1981 **IM ID** *020 †20 ‡

CORBETT, Charles Melvin. 4137 KIRBY PKWY 38115 #027-01-1983 L2003 **GP** *020 †18

CORLEY, Holly Liane. ■ 38107 #021-06-2006 **MPD** *012

CORNELIUS, Leland Raeburn. 7655 POPLAR AVE, STE 130 38138 #047-06-1963 L1975 **FM** *020 †18

COUCH, Charles Edward, Sr. 1301 PRIMACY PKWY 37501 #047-06-1964 L1965 **OBG** *071 †30

COUNCE, Michael Forbes. 7900 US HIGHWAY 64, GYNECOLOGY ASSOCIATES PC 38133 #047-06-1988 L1990 **OBG** *020 †30

COURINGTON, Doris Payne. ■ 38112 #005-06-1961 L1977 **ATP** *071 †50

COVALT, Michelle Angie. ■ 38111 #025-12-2006 **OBG** *012

COWAN, George Sheppard M, Jr. ■ 38112 #803-01-1964 L1982 **GS OS** *071 †85

COWAN, James L. 6073 MT MORIAH RD EXT, STE 23 38115 #047-07-1987 L1990 **PD** *020

COWLES, Stefan Jos. 6005 PARK AVE, STE 101B 38119 #047-06-1983 L1984 **DR NM** *020 †80

COX, Clair Edward. 956 COURT AVE RM F208, DEPT OF UROLOGY UNIV OF TE 38163 #025-01-1958 L1972 **U** *030 †95

COX, Katharine S. 6019 WALNUT GROVE RD 38120 #064-01-1976 L1995 **PEM PD** *020 †55

COX, M Lillian. 1030 JEFFERSON AVE 38104 #047-06-1960 L1960 **IM CD** *071 †20

CRAVEN, Robert Andrew. ■ 38103 #047-06-2008 *012

CRAVEN, Rufus Edgar. 899 MADISON AVE 38103 #047-06-1953 L1953 **PS** *071 †65

CRAYCROFT, Laurie Bay. ■ 38104 #020-02-2002 L2005 **EM** *020 †16

CREASY, Steven Randall. 8342 CHAMPIONSHIP DR # 304 38125 #027-01-2001 L2005 **EM** *020 †16

CREEL, Nathan Joseph. ■ 38103 #047-06-2008 *012

CREMER, Michael Alan. 1030 JEFFERSON AVE, VA MEDICAL CTR III 38104 #016-11-1969 L1973 RHU IM *050 †20

CRENSHAW, Shrearest M. 6005 PARK AVE, STE 704 38119 #016-45-2000 L2005 FM *020 †18

CRENSHAW, William David. 1211 UNION AVE STE 510 38104 #021-05-2004 L2006 ORS *012

CRESON, Thomas Kyle. 3960 KNIGHT ARNOLD RD, STE 106 38118 #047-06-1955 L1955 IM HO *071 †20

CREWS, John Thomas. 5084 OLD SUMMER RD 38122 #047-06-1962 L1962 IM *020

CRIBBS, Richard Ronald. 951 COURT AVE 38103 #047-06-1965 L1965 P *020

CRISLER, Crista Loretta. 7900 US HIGHWAY 64, GYNECOLOGY ASSOCIATES PC 38133 #047-06-1990 L1992 OBG *020 †30

CRISLER, Herman A, Jr. 5660 MOUNT MORIAH RD 38115 #047-06-1962 L1962 PD GP *020 †55

CRISMARU, Ciprian. ■ 38163 #781-07-1997 L2004 FM *020 †18

CROCE, Martin Alexander. 956 CT, RM E 226 38163 #047-06-1983 L1984 GS TRS *030 †85

CRONE, Robert Andrew. 1755 KIRBY PKWY, STE 330 38120 #047-06-1986 L1987 AN *020 †05

CROSBY, Glenn Allen, II. 6027 WALNUT GROVE RD, STE 409 38120 #047-06-1989 L1996 NS *020 †25

CROSBY, Virgil Glenn. 6027 WALNUT GROVE RD # 114 38120 #047-06-1958 L1959 TS *071 †85,90

CROSS, Cynthia Denise. 6019 WALNUT GROVE RD 38120 #047-06-1989 L1992 PD EM *020 †55

CROSTHWAIT, Edward L, Jr. 1910 MADISON AVE, # 83 38104 #047-06-1969 L1969 GP *020

CRUTCHER, Nancy. 5390 ESTATE OFFICE DR 38119 #047-06-1980 L1982 D *020 †15

CRUTHIRDS, Terry Park. ■ 38120 #047-06-1954 L1955 PTH *071 †50

CRUZ, Dinia Ticar. 2574 FRAYSER BLVD 38127 #748-01-1974 L1981 PD *020

CRUZ, Eduardo Vargas. 2795 APPLING RD, STE 111 38133 #748-10-1974 L1981 PM *020

CULBRETH, Angela Michelle. 6005 PARK AVE, STE 310 38119 #047-06-2001 L2003 FM *020 †18

CULPEPPER, Carolyn Ann. 220 OVERTON AVE 38105 #047-06-1965 L1965 PTH CLP *062 †50

CUMMINGS, Judd Edward. 1211 UNION AVE, STE 510 38104 #030-06-2002 L2004 ORS *100

CUNNINGHAM, Dale Preston. 6325 HUMPHREYS BLVD 38120 #047-06-1986 L1989 PM *020 †60

CUNNINGHAM, David Lane. 1211 UNION AVE, STE 220 38104 #047-06-1961 L1961 NS *020 †25

CUNNINGHAM, Edwin D, Jr. 1755 KIRBY PKWY, STE 330 38120 #047-06-1980 L1983 AN *020 †05

CUNNINGHAM, John Michael. 332 N LAUDERDALE ST # BMT 38105 #539-04-1982 L1995 PD HO *020

CUNNINGHAM, Melody J. 332 N LAUDERDALE ST, RESEARCH HOSPITAL 38105 #024-16-1994 L2006 PHO PD *020 †55

CUOZZO, Francis Patrick. ■ 38117 #047-06-2005 GS *012

CURD, Karen Keen. 1030 JEFFERSON AVE, VA MEDICAL CENTER 111C 38104 #045-01-1982 L1984 IM *020 †20

CURLE, Ray Eugene. ■ 38111 #047-06-1955 L1956 AN *071 †05

CURREY, Thomas Arthur. 1900 KIRBY PKWY, STE 100B 38138 #047-06-1958 L1958 OPH *020 †35 ‡

CURTIS, Karen Louella. 1265 UNION AVE 38104 #047-06-1980 L1980 IM *020

CUSHMAN, William Chandler. 1030 JEFFERSON AVE # 111Q, VA MC 38104 #027-01-1974 L1974 IM *050 †20

CUSICK, Michael Christoph. ■ 38104 #021-05-2008 *012

CYPRIANO, Monica. ■ 38111 #187-12-1989 PHO *100

CYRUS, Carlos Byron. 4539 WINCHESTER RD STE 3 38118 #041-14-1998 L2004 PM *020 †60

DABNEY, Cynthia A. 187 S GOODLETT ST 38117 #047-06-1968 L1976 RO DR *020 †20

DA CUNHA, Carl Maclin. 1715 AARON BRENNER DR, STE 326 38120 #187-15-1980 L1989 P *020 †75

DAGOGO-JACK, Samuel E. 956 COURT AVE, ROOM D334 38163 #690-01-1978 L2001 IM END *020 †20

DAHL, Julia. 660 JEFFERSON AVE 38105 #040-02-1995 L2004 PTH OS *020 †50

DALAL, Ajay. 6005 PARK AVE, STE 500B 38119 #917-14-1992 L2002 CD *020 †20

DALAL, Apurva R. 1264 WESLEY DR, STE 502 38116 #495-01-1987 L2000 ORS *020 †40

DALE, James B. 66 N PAULINE ST 38103 #047-06-1977 L1982 IM *020

DANCY, Andrew J, Jr. 701 E MALLORY AVE, RIVER CITY MEDICAL GROUP 38106 #047-07-1965 L1966 PD OS *071

DANFORD, Jill Mchenry. ■ 38104 #047-06-2008 *012

DANG, Gerald Triminhhuy. 995 S YATES RD, STE 1 38119 #021-01-2002 L2007 U *020

DANG, Paul Huu. 3725 CHAMPION HILLS DR 38125 #047-06-1993 L1995 IM *020

DANIEL, Chalmers B, Jr. 5182 SANDERLIN AVE, SPECIALISTS 38117 #047-06-1973 L1974 IM *020

DANIEL, James Howard, Jr. 1265 UNION AVE, STE 135 38104 #045-01-2007 TY *012

DANIEL, Sima Anna. 3362 S 3RD ST, CLINIC 38109 #041-07-1996 L2000 FM *020 †18

DANISH, Robert Kenneth. 806 ESTATE PL 38120 #041-09-1969 L1999 PDE PD *020 †55

DANLEY, Beverly D. 5959 PARK AVE 38119 #047-06-1979 L1986 CD IM *020 †20

DARGIE, Tripp A. ■ 38119 #047-06-1997 L1998 EM PD *020 †20,55

DARHOWER, Adrienne M. 176 S BELLEVUE BLVD, STE 502 38104 #048-12-2000 L2003 EM *100 †20

DAS, Shibendra Nath. 5959 PARK AVE 38119 #704-03-1961 L1970 AN *020 †05 ‡

DASAREE, Lakshmi K. 6005 PARK AVE, STE 720B 38119 #495-21-1988 L1998 IM GE *020 †20

DATTA, Vivekananda. 956 COURT AVE 38163 #495-41-1993 PTH *012

DAUSMAN, Jason Darrell. 2953 BROAD AVE, CHRIST COMMUNITY HEALTH SE 38112 #021-01-2000 L2005 MPD *020

DAVE, Raj C. 4901 RALEIGH COMMON DR, OF MEMPHIS INC 38128 #495-17-1984 L1993 CD IM *020 †20

DAVENPORT, William Brett. ■ 38111 #047-06-2007 OBG *012

DAVIDOFF, Andrew Michael. 332 N LAUDERDALE ST, ST JUDE CHILDREN'S RESEARC 38105 #041-01-1987 L1997 PDS *020 †85

DAVILA, Rene. 920 MADISON AVENUE, STE 240 38163 #041-01-1992 L1999 GE IM *020 †20

DAVIS, Bonnie Lee. ■ 38117 #047-06-1973 L1973 R *020 †80

DAVIS, Brandy Alexis. 956 CT AVE 38163 #004-01-2000 L2003 FM *100 †18 ‡

DAVIS, Clarence, Jr. 1407 UNION AVE, STE 200 38104 #047-07-1989 L1990 IM *030 †20

DAVIS, Edward Ritch. 1211 UNION AVE 38104 #047-06-1985 L1986 IM *020 †20

DAVIS, Jesse Theo, Jr. 995 S YATES RD, STE 1 38119 #027-01-1963 L1970 TS *020 †85,90

DAVIS, Michael Turone. ■ 38119 #036-08-2003 L2006 ORS *012

DAVIS, Randall Andrew. 1388 MADISON AVE 38104 #047-06-1988 L1989 DR NR *020 †80

DAVIS, Richard C, Jr. SUITE 300, 920 MADISON AVE. 38163 #035-01-1974 L2000 CD IM *040 †20

DAVIS, Valerie Anne. 1698 BELVEDERE CT 38104 #030-05-2000 L2002 PEM *012 †55 ‡

DAW, Najat Shafik. 332 N LAUDERDALE ST, ST JUDE CHLDRNS RSCH HOSP 38105 #605-01-1988 L1996 PHO *020 †55

D'CRUZ, Ivan Anthony. 1030 JEFFERSON AVE, VA MED CTR 38104 #495-17-1961 L1995 CD IM *020

DEAN, Patrick Jos. 150 COLLINS ST 38112 #010-02-1979 L1983 PTH *020 †50 ‡

DEARMOND, Gregory M. ■ 38104 #048-13-2002 L2007 GS *012

DEATON, Paul Rumble. 5050 POPLAR AVE, SPECIALISTS 38157 #047-06-1987 L1993 PUD *020

DE BIASE, Norberto Jorge. ■ 38119 #132-01-1966 L1978 TS *020 †85

DE FLUMERE, Charlotte A. 1715 AARON BRENNER DR, STE 326 38120 #045-01-1988 L1989 IM ADM *020 †20

DE LA OSSA, Margarita M. ■ 38103 #264-04-1995 L2006 HMP *100 †50

DELGADO, Eduardo Enrique. ■ 38103 #270-02-2000 L2001 PHO *012 †55

DELK, Sam. 176 BELLEVUE BLVD S-505 38104 #047-07-1971 L1973 FM GS *020 †85

DELLINGER, Hubert L, Jr. 6248 POPLAR AVE 38119 #047-06-1957 L1958 PD ADL *071 †55

DE LOS SANTOS, Noel Mores. 777 WASHINGTON AVE, STE P110 38105 #027-01-1997 L2002 PD *020 †55

DE LUCA KARABELL, Ana Hel. 956 CT AVE, UNIV OF TN COLL OF MED 38163 #935-01-1993 L2008 PD *012

DEMPSEY, Buckley Kinard. 5959 PARK AVE 38119 #047-06-1969 L1970 CD IM *071 †20

DEMPSEY, Buckley Kinard, Jr. 842 JEFFERSON AVE A601 38103 #047-06-2006 MPD *012

DENBO, Jason William. 956 CT AVE, SUITE G228 38163 #017-20-2007 GS *012

DENEKA, David Alan. 6286 BRIARCREST AVE, FL 2 38119 #047-05-1991 L1997 ORS OSM *020 †40

DENEKE, Milton D. 790 MADISON SUITE 218 38163 #047-06-1946 L1949 OS GP *071

DENTON, Norman Clifford. 930 MADISON AVENUE 38163 #004-01-1998 L2006 OPH *020

DESAI, Nita Sanjay. 3628 SUMMER AVE 38122 #495-89-1979 L1987 P *020 †55

DE SAUSSURE, R L, Jr. ■ 38111 #051-01-1942 L1950 NS *071 †25

DESHAIES, Roger Lee. 3980 NEW COVINGTON PIKE, STE 308 38128 #047-06-1974 L1974 OPH *020 †35

DE SHAZO, Michael Henry. 6325 HUMPHREYS BLVD 38120 #021-01-1972 L1972 N *020 †75

DESHMUKH, Prajwal Ashok. 956 COURT AVE 38163 #496-19-2000 IM *012

DESSALINES, Duclos. ■ 38115 #649-26-1997 L2005 PDE *012

DEVINCENZO, John Peter. 50 N DUNLAP ST, 4TH FL CFRC, LBCMC 38103 #047-05-1988 L1995 PDI *040 †55

DEWANE, Jos Christopher. 6246 POPLAR AVE 38119 #047-06-1979 L1979 OBG *020 †30

DEWEY, William Chapman. 1087 ALICE AVE 38106 #047-06-1996 L2002 P *020 †55

DE WIRE, Mariko Dawn. ■ 38104 #038-45-2004 L2007 PHO *012

DHANIREDDY, Rama Subba R. 853 JEFFERSON AVE RM 201, UNIF OF TN HLH SCIENCE CTR 38163 #495-62-1975 L2005 NPM PD *030 †55

DHAR, Archana Vishal. 50 N DUNLAP ST, LEBONHEUR CHILDRENS MEDICA 38103 #495-22-1993 L2008 CCP *012 †55

DIAZ, Claro Faustino. 1325 EASTMORELAND AVE, STE 460 38104 #021-05-1988 L1995 CD *020 †20

DI BLASIO, Christopher Ja. 956 COURT AVE 38163 #422-01-2002 U *012

DICKSON, Paxton Vandiver. ■ 38112 #047-06-2002 GS *012

DIDIER, Scott David. 55 HUMPHREYS CTR, STE 100 38120 #021-06-2001 L2004 RNR *020 †80

DIEHL, Jennifer Ann. 956 COURT AVE 38163 #665-02-2005 FP *012

DIGAETANO, Dolores Maria. 6401 POPLAR AVE, STE 420 38119 #047-06-1978 L1980 P *020 †75 ‡

DILAWARI, Raza Ali. 1325 EASTMORELAND AVE 38104 #704-01-1968 L1976 GS SO *020 †85

DILL, Christopher Parish. ■ 38104 #047-20-2007 MPD *012

DILLARD, Erika Alicia. ■ 38104 #047-06-2008 *012

DIRGHANGI, Banani. 2500 PERES AVE 38108 #495-38-1977 L1983 PD *020 †55

DIRGHANGI, Jayanta Kumar. 6005 PARK AVE STE 825B 38119 #495-38-1973 L1980 OBG *020 †30

DISHMON, Dwight Anthony. ■ 38122 #047-06-2002 L2004 CD *012 †20

DISMUKES, James Richard. 6025 WALNUT GROVE RD, STE 417 38120 #035-09-1993 L1996 IM *020 †20

DOBIE, William Lewis, Jr. 6305 HUMPHREYS BLVD, STE 205 38120 #048-13-2003 L2006 DR *012

DOBSON, John M. 220 S CLAYBROOK ST, STE 300 38104 #047-06-1960 L1964 R NM *071 †80

DOHAN, Francis Curtis, Jr. 930 MADISON AVE, STE 500 38163 #024-01-1961 L1985 NP *062 †50

DOME, Jeffrey Stuart. 332 N LAUDERDALE ST, ST JUDE CHILD RESEARCH HOS 38105 #041-01-1991 L1997 PD PHO *020 †55

DONATO, Federico Victorio. MEMPHIS MENTAL HEALTH INST 38128 #748-01-1994 *100

DONEPUDI, Sreekrishna Kan. ■ 38120 #033-05-2004 GS *012

DONLON, Richard N. 3362 S 3RD ST 38109 #021-05-1990 L1993 IM PD *020 †55,20

DONOVAN, Francis Daniel. 1661 INTERNATIONAL DR, STE 350 38120 #047-06-2000 L2003 DR *020 †80

DONOVAN, Timothy Bohn. 1661 INTERNATIONAL DR, STE 350 38120 #047-06-1993 L1995 DR *020 †80

DORIAN, John Bernard. 66 N PAULINE ST STE 633 38105 #047-06-1952 L1952 FM *071 †18

DORKO, Craig Steven. 842 JEFFERSON AVE RM 607, UNIVERSITY OF TENNESSEE 38103 #047-06-1987 L1988 IM *020 †20

DOROS, Leslie Ann. ■ 38107 #045-01-2004 PD *012

DORRITY, Michael Alan. 1265 UNION AVE 38104 #047-06-1978 L1978 GS EM *020

DOTSON, Jimmie Lee. ■ 38125 #047-06-2005 L2007 IM *012

DOUGLAS, Dane Edward. 6401 POPLAR AVE STE 402 38119 #047-20-1989 L1991 PDC PD *020 †55

DOUGLASS, Roy A, Jr. 66 N PAULINE ST STE 633 38105 #047-05-1946 L1946 OBG *072 †30

DOUTHITT, Paul Michael. 1300 WESLEY DR, METHODIST SOUTH HOSPITAL 38116 #007-02-1977 L1981 PD *020 †55

DOWELL, Stanley Wayne. 1325 EASTMORELAND AVE #245, EASTMORELAND INTERNAL MEDI 38104 #047-07-1983 L1987 IM *020

DOWLING, Carrie Louise. 7865 EDUCATORS LN, STE 300 38133 #047-06-1989 L1992 GP GYN *020

DOWLING, David Joseph. 6286 BRIARCREST, FL 2 38120 #047-06-1995 L1999 PRS PMM *020 †60

DOWNING, James Robt. 332 N LAUDERDALE ST 38105 #025-01-1981 L1986 ATP *012

DOWNS, John Mc Call. 707 W BROOKHAVEN CIR 38117 #047-06-1965 L1966 P *050 †75

DRAKE, Arnold Mannas. 6025 WALNUT GROVE RD STE 6 38120 #047-06-1959 L1960 GE IM *020 †20

DRAKE, Sabra Fredfreeda. 3965 S MENDENHALL RD 38115 #047-06-1987 L1988 IM *020 †20

DRAPER, Jacqueline Yvonne. 5959 PARK AVE 38119 #001-02-1992 L1996 AN *020 †05

DRESHER, Brad Dean. 1211 UNION AVE, STE 510 38104 #019-02-2001 L2001 **ORS** *020
DRESS, Matthew Alan. 930 MADISON AVE FL 5, DEPT OF PATHOLOGY 38103 #047-06-2004 L2008 **PTH** *012
DREWRY, Richard Danl, Jr. 350 N HUMPHREYS BLVD 4TH, BAPTIST MEMORIAL HCC 38120 #047-06-1965 L1966 **OPH** *071 †35
DREWRY, William Rice. 756 RIDGE LAKE BLVD, STE 120 38120 #047-06-1986 L1988 **FM AM** *020 †18
DUBERSTEIN, Larry Edwin. 3068 COVINGTON PIKE STE 1 38128 #038-41-1967 L1975 **OTO HNS** *020 †45
DUBOIS, Benjamin Caleb. 956 CT AVE, STE G228 38163 #048-13-2006 **GS** *012
DUCKWORTH, John Kelly. 930 MADISON AVE 5TH FL, DEPT OF PATH & LAB MED 38163 #047-06-1956 L1956 **PTH MDM** *030 †50
DUCKWORTH, Nancy C H. ■ 38104 #047-06-1966 L1970 **P** *071
DUGDALE, Marion. 842 JEFFERSON AVE, RM A607 38103 #024-01-1954 L1961 **HEM IM** *040 †20
DUKE, Don De Windle. ■ 38119 #047-06-1961 L1961 **GS** *071
DUKE, Robert A. 6401 POPLAR AVE, STE 100 38119 #047-06-1981 L1982 **DR NR** *020 †80
DULANEY, Allison Leslie. ■ 38104 #047-06-2008 *012
DUNAVANT, William David. 6027 WALNUT GROVE RD # 118 38120 #027-01-1996 L2001 **GS** *020 †85
DUNAVANT, William David. 6027 WALNUT GROVE RD 38120 #047-06-1974 L1975 **GS AS** *072 †85
DUNAWAY, Dan Alexander. 5210 POPLAR AVE STE 100 38119 #012-05-1961 L1966 **D** *020 †15
DUNCAN, James T, Jr. ■ 38112 #047-06-1951 L1951 **GS OM** *071 †85
DUNCAN, Kristen Taylor. 6401 POPLAR AVE, STE 340 38119 #021-06-2002 L2006 **OPH** *100
DUNCAN, Vernita Gray. 951 COURT AVE 38103 #047-07-1981 L1982 **GP GPM** *020
DUNCAN-CODY, Barbara. 1174 POPLAR AVE 38105 #047-07-1980 L1984 **OBG** *020
DUNNAVANT, Floyd Daniel. ■ 38105 #047-06-2008 *012
DUNTSCH, Christopher D. ■ 38104 #047-06-2002 **NS** *012
DURAND, April Lynn. 6305 HUMPHREYS BLVD, STE 205 38120 #011-02-2003 L2004 **IM** *100
DURBIN, Constance E. 711 JEFFERSON AVE RM 137, PSYCHIATRY 38105 #047-06-1983 L1984 **CHP P** *040 †75
DURRANI, Ehsan-Ullah Khan. ■ 38175 #704-04-1993 L2004 **N** *020 †20
DUSA, Narcisa Adina. 3950 NEW COVINGTON PIKE 38128 #781-05-1992 L2004 **IM** *020
DUSZAK, Richard, Jr. 55 HUMPHREYS CTR, STE 100 38120 #041-14-1989 L2006 **VIR DR** *020 †80
DWEIK, Husni W. 877 JEFFERSON AVE 38103 #781-03-1983 L2006 **AN** *020 †05
DYER, Andrew Wakefield. ■ 38104 #047-06-2004 L2007 **DR** *012
EASON, James David. 1265 UNION AVE 38104 #047-06-1987 L1989 **TTS GS** *020 †85
EAST, Mary Ruth. ■ 38104 #047-06-2006 L2006 **PD** *012
EBER, Paul Richard. 3950 NEW COVINGTON PIKE, STE 340 38128 #017-20-1988 L1990 **U** *020 †95
EBERLE, Louis V, III. 6263 POPLAR AVE, STE 1052 38119 #047-06-1986 L1987 **PUD** *020 †20
EBERLE, Tammy Leah. ■ 38112 #047-06-1999 L2006 **IM** *100
EBY, Patricia Lynn. 6401 POPLAR AVE STE 120 38119 #028-02-1982 L1994 **PS GS** *020 †85,65
ECHOLS, James Robert. 909 RIDGEWAY LOOP RD, PASSONS EYE CENTER, PLLC 38120 #047-06-2004 L2008 **OPH** *012
ECKERLE, Dara Lee. ■ 38103 #047-06-2008 *012
EDDY, Lisa Marie. 687 JEFFERSON AVE # 8 38105 #047-06-2003 L2006 **FM** *100 †18
EDELSON, Michael L. 6570 STAGE RD, OB/GYN PHYS GRP OF MEMPHIS 38134 #047-06-1984 L1985 **OBG** *020 †30
EDGERLY, Donald Wm. 2986 KATE BOND RD, ST FRANCIS HOSPITAL-BARTLE 38133 #011-04-1985 L1994 **EM FM** *020 †18
EDMONSON, Allen S. ■ 38112 #047-06-1953 L1953 **OSS ORS** *071 †40
EDWARDS, Nona Lee S. 853 JEFFERSON AVE RM 102 38103 #016-11-1980 L2001 **OBG** *020 †30
EGERMAN, Robert Scott. STE E102, 853 JEFFERSON AVENUE 38163 #001-02-1987 L1993 **MFM IM** *020 †20,30
EGGERS, Frank M, II. 55 HUMPHREYS CTR, STE 100 38120 #047-05-1971 L1981 **DR RNR** *020 †80
EGIDI, Maria Francesca. 920 MADISON AVE STE 200, UNIV OF TENNESSEE 38103 #561-03-1981 L1997 *020
EICHHOLZ, Janet Lillian. ■ 38128 #047-06-2008 *012
EINHAUS, Stephanie L. 6325 HUMPHREYS BLVD 38120 #011-03-1989 L1994 **NS NSP** *020 †25
EISEMAN, Robert Martin. 920 ESTATE DR STE 3 38119 #047-06-1987 L1989 **PD** *020 †55
EISENBERG, Alan David. 55 HUMPHREYS CTR, STE 100 38120 #033-06-1984 L1991 **RNR DR** *020 †80
ELAHI, Hafiz Awais. 956 COURT AVE 38163 #704-20-1989 L2007 **N** *100
ELAM, Marshall Byron, III. 1030 JEFFERSON AVE 38104 #047-06-1979 L1981 **CD IM** *050 †20
ELDER, Agnes Domantay. ■ 38105 #748-01-1981 **P** *012
ELFERVIG, John Lars. 5146 STAGE RD, STE 101 38134 #021-05-1972 L1976 **OPH** *020 †35
EL-GAMAL, Amr Ahmed. 956 COURT AVE, UNIV OF TENNESSEE 38103 #915-03-1995 L2002 **PCC** *012 †20
ELIAS, David Wadie. 1211 UNION AVE STE 510, CAMPBELL CLINIC FOUNDATION 38104 #021-06-2001 L2003 **ORS** *020
ELLICHMAN, Jonathan Joe. 1325 EASTMORELAND AVE, STE 220 38104 #654-01-1999 L2007 **TS** *020
ELLIOTT, Rodney Gorhman. 995 S YATES RD, STE 1 38119 #051-04-1961 L1969 **U** *020 †95
ELLIS, Donald Thomas, II. 50 N DUNLAP ST, ER DEPT 38103 #023-01-2000 L2003 **PEM** *012 †55
ELLIS, Garrettson Smith. 6025 WALNUT GROVE RD, STE 508 38120 #023-01-1998 L2004 **PCC** *020 †20
ELLIS, James V. 1661 INTERNATIONAL DR, STE 350 38120 #047-06-1976 L1981 **DR** *040 †80
ELLIS, John Wm, III. 6215 HUMPHREYS BLVD # 300 38120 #047-06-1981 L1983 **PD** *020 †55
ELLISON, David William. 332 N LAUDERDALE ST, DEPT OF PATHOLOGY MS #250 38105 #917-03-1981 L2006 **NP** *100
ELLZEY, John A. 55 HUMPHREYS CTR, STE 100 38120 #047-06-1996 L2002 **DR** *020 †80
ELMORE, Thomas Dees. 853 JEFFERSON AVE RM E102, DEPT OB/GYN 38103 #047-06-1978 L1979 **OBG** *020 †30
EL SHAZLY, Mounir Ahmed Y. 877 JEFFERSON AVE 38103 #915-03-1973 L1990 **AN** *020 †05
EMERSON, Donald Stewart. 1661 INTERNATIONAL DR, STE 350 38120 #024-07-1979 L1985 **DR** *020 †80
EMERSON, Patrick Fording. ■ 38103 #047-06-2008 *012
EMERY, Derek John. 930 MADISON AVE, STE 364 38103 #060-02-1986 L1997 *020
EMMETT, John Roy. 6133 POPLAR PIKE 38119 #010-01-1970 L1976 **OTO** *020 †45
EMMETT, Katrina Pauline. ■ 38111 #048-12-2005 **GS** *012
ENGBRETSON, John Wayne. 2953 BROAD AVE 38112 #001-06-2000 L2007 **FM** *020 †18
ENGBRETSON, Laura Lynne. 6215 HUMPHREYS BLVD, STE 208 38120 #001-02-2003 L2007 **OBG** *020
ENGELBERG, Jerry. 6325 HUMPHREYS BLVD 38120 #047-06-1965 L1965 **NS** *020 †25 ‡
ENGLISH, Boyce K. 777 WASHINGTON AVE, STE P110 38105 #048-04-1982 L1989 **ID PD** *020 †55
ENNIS, Richard Lyn. 6005 PARK AVE, STE 430B 38119 #047-06-1971 L1971 **ORS** *020 †40
ENSOR, James Kelly. 6005 PARK AVE, STE 900B 38119 #047-06-1975 L1976 **IM** *020 †20
ENTMAN, Howard. 877 JEFFERSON AVE 38103 #047-06-1990 L1991 **DR** *020
ENZENAUER, Robert Wm. 930 MADISON AVE #470, HAMILTON EYE INSTITUTE 38163 #028-03-1979 L1998 **OPH AM** *030 †55,70,35
EPPEL, Stephen M. 995 S YATES RD STE 1, SOUTHEAST UROLOGY NETWORK 38119 #836-01-1975 L1988 **U** *020 †95
ERBELE, Krista Eileen. 2953 BROAD AVE 38112 #021-01-2001 L2005 **FM** *020 †18
ERBELE, Phillip Wayne. 2953 BROAD AVE 38112 #021-01-2001 L2005 **PD** *020 †55
ERKULWATER, Samard. VET ADMIN HOSP NEUR SER 38104 #891-02-1965 L1978 **N IM** *020 †75
ERMANN, Joerg. 956 CT AVE, UNIV OF TN COLL OF MED 38163 #408-14-1994 L2006 **RHU** *012 †20
ERNST, Thomas Lynn. 50 N DUNLAP ST 38103 #021-05-1974 L1982 **AN** *020 †05
ESBENSHADE, Adam John. 687 JEFFERSON AVE 38105 #047-06-2004 **PHO** *012
ESCUE, James Eric. 531 ALEXANDER ST 38111 #047-06-2000 L2002 **CCP** *020
ESHUN, John Kraku. 332 N LAUDERDALE ST 38105 #275-01-1988 L1999 **PG** *020 †55
EUBANKS, James Wallace. 777 WASHINGTON AVE, STE P230 38105 #027-01-1994 L1996 **PDS** *020 †85
EVANS, Allison Ashby. 2000 N PARKWAY BOX 1378 38112 #020-02-2006 **PD** *012
EVANS, Benjamin Franklin. 1264 WESLEY DR STE 206, PRIMUS MEDICAL GROUP 38116 #047-07-1984 L1989 **IM** *020
EVERSON, Freddie Lee. 1750 MADISON AVE, STE 400 38104 #027-01-1978 L1994 **FM** *020 †18
EZEKIEL-BRAIDE, Young D. 1069 MCEVERS RD 38111 #047-07-1992 L1997 **IM** *020
FABIAN, Timothy Chas. 880 MADISON AVE 38103 #016-43-1974 L1980 **GS** *020 †85
FAHEY, Christian Seavers. 3980 NEW COVINGTON PIKE, STE 204 38128 #033-06-1996 L2004 **HS ORS** *020 †40
FAHHOUM, Joseph S. 899 MADISON AVE 38103 #875-01-1981 L1993 **AI EM** *020 †20,03
FALVEY, William Davis. ■ 38104 #048-12-1973 L1974 **EM** *030 †16
FANCHER, William Henry. 6141 WALNUT GROVE RD, STE 200 38120 #048-04-1956 L1962 **AN** *071 †05
FANG, David Pingchyuan. 1661 INTERNATIONAL DR, STE 350 38120 #039-01-1998 L2002 **VIR** *020 †80
FARA, Lisa F A. ■ 38111 #422-01-1982 L1984 **FM** *020 †18
FARLEY, Harold G. ■ 38105 #047-06-1951 L1952 **GP** *071
FARMER, Ivan Godfrey. 1725 ASH ST, P O BOX 80130 38108 #047-06-1974 L1975 **IM** *020
FARMER, Michael Reinhart. 1661 INTERNATIONAL DR, STE 350 38120 #020-02-2002 L2007 **RO** *020
FARMER, Richard Guerard. 1355 LYNNFIELD RD STE 159 38119 #047-06-1960 L1960 **P ADP** *040 †75
FAROOQ, Aamer. ■ 38103 #704-04-2003 **IM** *012
FAROOQUI, Nabeel Nazir. 956 CT AVE, UNIV OF TN COLL OF MED 38163 #704-01-2002 **IM** *012
FAROOQUI, Saleem Owais. ■ 38103 #704-25-2001 L2006 **DR** *012
FARST, Douglas Edson. 1030 JEFFERSON AVE, VAMC-GENL INTL MEDICINE 38104 #047-06-1983 L1984 **IM IMG** *020 †20
FAULKNER, Lee Edwin. 3960 KNIGHT ARNOLD RD, STE 215 38118 #047-20-1990 L1996 **CD** *020
FAULKNER, Wm Lawrence. 6005 PARK AVE, STE 704 38119 #047-06-1969 L1970 **IM** *020 †20
FAYNER, Yuri. ■ 38120 #047-06-2006 L2008 **DR** *012
FEAGIN, Oscar Thos. 6423 SHELBY VIEW DR, STE 103 38134 #023-07-1964 L1969 **IM IMG** *071 †20
FEARNOW, Daniel Seth. 658 N PERKINS RD 38122 #047-06-1978 L1981 **FM** *020 †18
FEDERICO, Sara Michele. 332 N LAUDERDALE ST, DEPT HEMATOLOGY/ONCOLOGY 38105 #051-04-2003 L2006 **PHO** *012 †55
FELER, Claudio Andres. 6325 HUMPHREYS BLVD 38120 #020-02-1984 L1986 **NS N** *020 †25
FENAUGHTY, Francis John. ■ 38125 #035-03-1981 L1986 **EM** *020 †16
FENG, Jessie Yuanqi. 956 COURT AVE 38163 #243-77-1994 **IM** *012
FERGUSON, Christopher A. 3980 NEW COVINGTON PIKE, STE 200 38128 #027-01-2002 L2007 **ORS** *020
FERGUSON, John Mitchell. 50 N DUNLAP ST, NEONATAL ICU 38103 #047-06-1975 L1975 **NPM PD** *020 †55
FERGUSON, Thomas Charles. 3809 COVINGTON PIKE 38135 #047-06-1996 L1997 **IM** *020 †20
FERNANDEZ, Joss Dean. 920 MADISON AVE, SUITE C50, UNIVERISTY OF TENNESSEE MEM 38163 #051-01-2000 L2005 **VS** *020 †85 ‡
FERNANDEZ, Julius. 6325 HUMPHREYS BLVD 38120 #024-07-1999 L2004 **NS** *020
FIDLER, William Jonas. ■ 38111 #010-01-1965 L1978 **ATP PCP** *071 †50
FIEDLER, Frederick Adolph. 6263 POPLAR AVE STE 1052 38119 #047-06-1985 L1986 **IM HO** *020 †20
FIELDS, Kenneth I. 80 HUMPHREYS CTR, STE 200 38120 #035-46-1991 L1999 **IM** *020 †20
FIGUEREDO-CARDENAS, G. 6063 MT MORIAH RD EXT, STE 4 38115 #935-07-1988 L1999 **FM** *020 †18
FILIPCIC, Ramune. 3091 KIRBY WHITTEN RD 38134 #913-49-1997 L2001 **FM** *020 †18
FINK, Robert David. 5668 S REX RD, # 103 38119 #047-06-1967 L1968 **P ADM** *020
FINKS, Abraham Lloyd. 1265 UNION AVE, DEPT OF MEDICAL EDUCATION 38104 #422-01-1998 L2001 **IM** *020 †20
FINN, Cary Martin. 6025 WALNUT GROVE RD, STE 301 38120 #047-20-1986 L1988 **IM** *020 †20
FINNERN, James Fredrick. 3610 WYTHE RD 38135 #047-06-1980 L1989 **AN** *020 †05
FISCHER, Julia Fern. ■ 38111 #047-06-2008 *012
FISCHER, Peter Edmund. ■ 38103 #038-41-2004 **GS** *012
FISHER, Joseph Newton. 920 MADISON AVE STE 300 38163 #048-12-1955 L1974 **END IM** *040 †20,55
FISHER, Kayla Lyn. 865 POPLAR AVE, MEMPHIS MENTAL HEALTH INST 38105 #019-02-1991 L2005 **CHP** *020 †75
FISHER, Kristopher Reed. ■ 38104 #038-43-2005 **D** *012
FISHER, Scott Randon. ■ 38117 #054-04-1979 L1981 **AN** *075
FITCH, Charles Walter. 49 N DUNLAP ST 38103 #047-06-1953 L1954 **NPM PDC** *040 †55
FLANAGAN, William H. 6025 WALNUT GROVE RD, ST 111 38120 #004-01-1970 L1977 **CD** *020 †20
FLECKENSTEIN, James M. 66 N PAULINE ST STE 633 38105 #028-34-1985 L1998 **ID** *020 †20
FLECKENSTEIN, Jaquelyn F. 920 MADISON AVE STE 240, UNIVERSITY OF TENNESSEE 38103 #028-34-1985 L1997 **IM** *020 †20

■ = Address Information Privacy Protected

FLEMING, Elizabeth Ann. ■ 38103 #047-06-2008 *012
FLEMING, Gina Dolores. ■ 38103 #047-06-2002 L2005 **IM** *020 †20
FLEMING, Irvin Durant. 2996 KATE BOND RD, STE 309 38133 #047-06-1955 L1956
  GS SO *071 †85
FLEMING, James Christian. STE 100, 930 MADISON AVENUE 38163 #047-06-1974 L1975
  OPH OS *020 †85
FLEMING, Julian Glenn. ■ 38119 #047-06-1961 L1961 **IM CD** *020
FLEMING, Martin Douglas. 6029 WALNUT GROVE RD, STE 404 38120 #047-06-1986 L1993
  GS SO *020 †85
FLEMING, Richard M. 1388 MADISON AVE 38104 #047-06-1983 L1984 **IM** *020 †80
FLINN, Carl Edwin. 773 ESTATE PL 38120 #047-06-1980 L1980 **OPH** *020 †35 ‡
FLINN, George Shea, Jr. 188 S BELLEVUE BLVD, STE 222 38104 #047-06-1969 L1969
  R NM *020 †80,28 ‡
FLIPPIN, Dane H. 756 RIDGE LAKE BLVD, STE 120 38120 #004-01-1995 L1998 **FM** *020 †18
FLORENDO, Noel Tadiar. 1211 UNION AVE, STE 300 38104 #047-06-1974 L1975
  ATP PTH *020 †50
FLORENDO, Purificacion T. 273 RIVER COMMONS CIR W CW 38120 #748-02-1946 L1971
  GYN *071
FLORES, Ana Lucia. 6029 WALNUT GROVE RD, STE 101 38120 #041-14-1997 L2001 **OPH** *020
FLORES-PERKINS, Silva P. 2860 COVINGTON PIKE 38128 #649-52-1992 L2005 **PD** *020 †55
FLOWERS, Bobby Franklin. 20 DUDLEY ST 38103 #047-06-1967 L1968 **GP OS** *020 †85
FLY, William Randolph. 2986 KATE BOND RD, STE 301 38133 #047-06-1983 L1984
  ORS *020 †40
FLYNN, Patricia Michele. 322 N LAUDERDALE ST 38105 #021-05-1981 L1984 **ID PD** *050 †55 ‡
FOLEY, Kevin Thos. 1211 UNION AVE, STE 200 38104 #045-14-1979 L1992 **NS** *020 †25
FOLSE, Timothy Edmonds. 332 N LAUDERDALE ST, MAIL STOP 375 38105 #027-01-1985 L1987
  FM *020 †18
FOLZ, Tamara Paskowitz. 6248 POPLAR AVE 38119 #047-06-1997 L1999 **PD** *020 †55
FONER, Max. 361 N 3RD ST 38105 #047-06-1960 L1960 **GP LM** *020
FONG, Terry. 899 MADISON AVE 38103 #891-02-1968 L1974 **AN CD** *020
FORD, Mary Nell. 1200 PEABODY AVE 38104 #023-07-1992 L1995 **IM** *020 †20
FORD, Tasha J. 842 JEFFERSON AVE STE A645 38103 #036-01-1994 L1999 **MPD** *020 †20
FORNARI, Gianluigi Aloisi. ■ 38135 #048-15-2004 L2007 **DR** *012
FORSYTHE, Camilla Rose. 50 N DUNLAP ST, ER DEPT 38103 #068-01-1981 L1995 **PD** *040 †55
FORSYTHE, Raquel Maria. 175 RIVER BRIDGE LN # 302 38103 #035-48-1997 L2003
  CCS *020 †85
FORTENBERRY, Tamra N. ■ 38163 #047-06-2004 **OBG** *012
FORTNER, Thomas Milford. ■ 38111 #001-06-1977 **PS** *020
FOSNAUGH, Adam Warren. 1211 UNION AVE STE 5 38104 #038-40-2002 L2007 **OSM** *012
FOSTER, Monique Aaron. ■ 38103 #051-07-2007 **PD** *012
FOUNTAIN, Francis F, Jr. 388 S PAULINE ST 38104 #047-06-1962 L1962 **PUD** *020 †20
FOUST, James Darryl. ■ 38122 #422-01-1995 L1998 **FM** *071
FOWLER, Blakley Atkins. ■ 38103 #027-01-2004 **PD** *012
FOWLER, Brian Thomas. ■ 38120 #051-01-2008 **DR** *012
FOWLER, John W. 184 COLONIAL RD 38117 #047-06-1977 L1978 **IM** *020 †20
FOWLER, Tommy Shaw. 1661 INTERNATIONAL DR, STE 350 38120 #047-06-1977 L1978
  R EM *020 †80
FOWLER, Tracy Elizabeth. ■ 38112 #048-13-2001 L2004 **PD** *020
FOX, Michael M. 3960 KNIGHT ARNOLD RD, STE 206 38118 #035-09-1977 L2002
  GS CRS *020 †85,10
FOX, Roy Cecil. 5050 POPLAR AVE, SPECIALISTS 38157 #027-01-1985 L1985
  PUD CCM *040 †20
FOX, Teresa O. 920 MADISON AVE, STE 1018 38103 #047-06-1985 L1985 **AN** *071 †05
FRANCIS, Hugh. 6005 PARK AVE STE 821B 38119 #047-06-1954 L1954 **GS** *020
FRANCIS, Hugh, III. 6029 WALNUT GROVE RD, STE 404 38120 #047-05-1984 L1985
  VS GS *020 †85
FRANCISCO, Jerry Thos. ■ 38119 #047-06-1955 L1955 **FOP PTH** *071 †50
FRANKLIN, Edgar R. 3980 NEW COVINGTON PIKE, STE 310 38128 #047-06-1960 L1960
  OTO A *020 †45
FRANKUM, Charles Eugene. ■ 38120 #004-01-1961 L1966 **GS** *071 †85
FRANZ, Gregory B. ■ 38119 #035-45-2000 L2005 **HO** *012
FRANZ-STEPNIAKOWSKA, J B. 1058 E RAINES RD 38116 #759-03-1984 L2002 **IM** *020 †20
FREDERICK, Carla Anne. ■ 38104 #035-06-2005 **MPD** *012
FREE, Lovely Arzetta. 6920 WINCHESTER RD 38115 #047-06-1962 L1962 **EM FM** *071
FREEMAN, Dawrell Jayette. 210 JACKSON AVE, STE 405 38105 #047-07-1990 L1994 **P** *020
FREEMAN, James F D. 6485 POPLAR AVE 38119 #047-06-1990 L1991 **OPH** *020 †35
FREEMAN, Jerre Minor. 6485 POPLAR AVE 38119 #047-06-1963 L1963 **OPH** *020 †35
FREEMAN, John Macklin. 6485 POPLAR AVE 38119 #047-06-1999 L2002 **OPH** *020
FREEMAN, Kimberly Willey. ■ 38119 #047-06-1999 L2002 **IM** *100
FREIRE, Amado Xavier. 956 CT AVE RM H314, UNIV OF TN HSC 38163 #319-03-1979 L1999
  IM PCC *020 †20
FRIEDMAN, Harry. 50 HUMPHREYS CTR, STE 32 38120 #047-06-1964 L1965 **NS** *020 †25
FRITZSCHE, James Lealand. 5959 PARK AVE 38119 #308-07-1982 L1986 **FM** *020 †18
FRIZZELL, Noel K. 6215 HUMPHREYS BLVD, STE 300 38120 #047-06-1977 L1980 **PD** *020 †55
FROST, Christopher M. 2647 LAURELCREST DR 38133 #012-01-1998 L1999 **MPD** *020 †20,55
FRYLING, Brent Alan. 3362 S 3RD ST, CLINIC, INC. 38109 #041-13-1996 L2002 **FM** *020 †18
FULTON, Prentice Grady. ■ 38112 #047-06-1956 L1957 **OM** *020
FULTON, Stephen Parker. 777 WASHINGTON AVE, STE 110 38105 #047-06-2003 L2005
  PD HOS *020 †55
FUNDERBURK, Amy E. 6263 POPLAR AVE STE 1052 38119 #047-06-1997 L1999 **IM** *020 †20
FUNG, Kenneth Hokyin. 6401 POPLAR AVE STE 190, CHARLES RETINA INSTITUTE P 38119
  #036-08-2003 L2007 **OPH** *100
FURMAN, Wayne Lee. ■ 38134 #038-40-1979 L1983 **PHO** *020 †55
FURR, Philip Marvin. 920 MADISON AVE STE 605 38103 #027-01-1980 L1984 **OPH** *020
GADE, Ramani. 1030 JEFFERSON AVE, SCI UNIT 38104 #495-10-1989 L1998 **PMM** *020
GAJJAR, Amar Jayant. 332 N LAUDERDALE ST # 260, DETP OF ONCOLOGY 38105
  #495-01-1982 L1989 **PD PHO** *020 †20
GAJKOWSKI, Errin Marie. ■ 38111 #048-14-2004 **PD** *012
GALJOUR, George Christoph. ■ 38103 #027-01-2006 **ORS** *012
GALLASPY, Glenn Todd. 853 JEFFERSON AVE, E 102 ROUT CENTER FOR WOME 38103
  #001-02-2004 L2006 **OBG** *012
GALLIMORE, George Wm, Jr. 55 HUMPHREYS CTR, STE 100 38120 #047-06-1981 L1982
  DR *020 †80
GALYEAN, James Rufus, III. 188 S BELLEVUE BLVD # 405 38104 #027-01-1963 L1978
  CD *020 †20

GALYON, James Theodore. 6005 PARK AVE, STE 309 38119 #047-06-1953 L1954
  ORS *020 †40
GAMMILL, Stephen Lane. 6305 HUMPHREYS BLVD, STE 205 38120 #027-01-1962 L1973
  DR *071 †80
GANDHI, Malay Suresh. 956 CT AVE, UNIV OF TN COLL OF MED 38163 #495-23-2003 L2007
  CD *012 †20
GANDHI, Manhar C. 360 E EH CRUMP BLVD 38126 #495-89-1972 L1979 **PD** *020 †55
GANGULI, Sanjay Kumar. 956 CT AVE, UNIV OF TN COLL OF MED 38163 #495-32-1980 **FM** *100
GANGULI, Santosh Kumar. 920 MADISON AVE, STE 810 38103 #495-38-1959 L1975 **U** *020 †95
GANT, Linda Long. ■ 38184 #047-06-1984 L1985 **ATP** *071 †50
GARBARINI, Joseph C, Jr. ■ 38117 #047-06-1949 L1950 **FM OS** *020
GARCIA KUTZBACH, Abraham. 1734 MADISON AVE 38104 #429-01-1966 L1970
  IM RHU *020 †20
GARDNER, John Harvey. 1455 UNION AVE, MEMPHIS DERMATOLOGY 38104
  #047-06-1970 L1970 **D** *020 †15
GARNER, Dewey Duane, Jr. 55 HUMPHREYS CTR, STE 100 38120 #027-01-1991 L1995
  DR *020 †80
GARRETT, Harvey E, Jr. 6029 WALNUT GROVE RD, STE 401 38120 #047-05-1979 L1986
  TS VS *020 †85,90
GARRETT, Kevin Michael. ■ 38104 #047-06-2004 L2007 **DR** *012
GARRETT, Lanetria Wynette. 1325 EASTMORELAND AVE # 10 38104 #047-06-2002 L2006
  IM *100
GARRETT, Richard Henry. 6005 PARK AVE 38119 #047-06-1963 L1963 **GYN** *071
GARRETT, Tiffani Renae. ■ 38116 #047-06-2008 *012
GARRIS, Robert Berry. ■ 38104 #045-01-2003 L2007 **DR** *012
GARRISON, Janice Lou. 80 HUMPHREYS CTR, STE 202 38120 #047-06-1981 L1982
  CD IM *020 †20
GATES, Jay Alan. 150 COLLINS ST, GI PATHOLOGY PLLC 38112 #008-01-1986 L2006
  PTH *020 †50 ‡
GAUR, Aditya Harikrishna. 332 N LAUDERDALE ST, TRANSLATIONAL TRIALS UNIT 38105
  #495-89-1994 L2004 **PDI** *020 †55
GAVRIZI, Yanco N. 1835 UNION AVE STE 315 38104 #781-01-1978 L1997 **CHP** *020
GAYCKEN, Bettina Anne Mar. ■ 38104 #047-06-2004 L2008 **DR** *012
GAYDEN, Evelyn Wilkerson. 6215 HUMPHREYS BLVD, STE 100 38120 #048-04-1982 L1983
  R DR *020 †80
GAYDEN, John Overton. 7900 US HIGHWAY 64, GYNECOLOGY ASSOCIATES PC 38133
  #047-06-1971 L1973 **OBG** *020
GEATER, Barbara. 2245 S LAUDERDALE ST 38106 #047-06-1993 L1996 **FM FSM** *020 †18 ‡
GEHI, Mohan M. 6005 PARK AVE STE 900B, PLLC 38119 #496-38-1972 L1976 **IM P** *020 †75,20
GEIGER, Janet Dang. 5050 SANDERLIN AVE 38117 #048-01-1990 L1999 **PD** *020 †55
GEIGER, Terrence Lee. 332 N LAUDERDALE ST 38105 #008-01-1993 L1999 **PTH** *020 †50
GELFAND, Michael. 1211 UNION AVE STE 340, UNIVERSITY OF TENNESSEE 38104
  #048-12-1977 L1988 **ID IM** *020 †20
GEORGE, Beena Rebecca. 6005 PARK AVE STE 306 38119 #001-02-1982 L1993 **PD** *020 †55
GEORGE, David Lewis. 5050 POPLAR AVE, STE 1528 38157 #012-05-1983 L1989
  ID IM *020 †20
GEORGE, Jojy Mattackal. ■ 38114 #048-13-2004 **GS** *012
GEORGE, Phillip. 50 N DUNLAP ST 38103 #035-20-1956 L1964 **PUD PD** *071 †55
GERALD, Barry Elmo. 865 JEFFERSON F150C, DEPT OF RADIOLOGY 38163
  #027-01-1958 L1968 **R RNR** *020 †80
GERBERI, Michael Adamtodd. 1265 UNION AVE, STE 135 38104 #016-45-2007 **TY** *012
GERTH, David Jesse, Jr. ■ 38103 #047-06-2007 **OTO** *012
GETTELFINGER, Thomas C. 6485 POPLAR AVE 38119 #024-01-1966 L1976 **OPH** *020 †35
GHANEM, Najeeb Suliman. 956 COURT AVE 38163 #575-01-1995 **VIR** *100
GHAWJI, Maher. 6027 WALNUT GROVE RD, STE 307 38120 #875-01-1983 L1992 **IM** *020 †20
GIBBS, Hettie S Wall. 661 MADISON AVE STE 803 #010-03-1972 L1981 **IM IMG** *020
GIBBS, Mark Bennett. ■ 38119 #048-02-2005 **ORS** *012
GIBBS, Richard B. 1215 POPLAR AVE 38104 #047-07-1969 L1971 **D GP** *020 †15
GIBSON, Benjamin Ryan. 2996 KATE BOND RD, STE 309 38133 #038-41-2006 L2006 **GS** *012
GIBSON, David Benjamin. ■ 38103 #047-06-2000 L2005 **GS** *020 †85
GIBSON, Francis D, Jr. ■ 38119 #012-05-1940 L1967 **IM SCI** *012
GIBSON, Jeffrey B. 6005 PARK AVE 38119 #047-06-1995 L1998 **TS** *020 †85,90
GIBSON, Lisa Carothers. 3155 KIRBY WHITTEN RD 38134 #047-06-1995 L1998 **PD** *020 †55
GIBSON, William Cary. 6005 PARK AVE STE 821B 38104 #047-06-2000 L2006 **GS** *020
GIDDENS, Gus Aric. 6215 HUMPHREYS BLVD # 401, MEMPHIS OB GYN 38120
  #012-05-1991 L1992 **OBG** *020 †30
GIDDENS, Mary Andrea. 7900 US HIGHWAY 64, GYNECOLOGY ASSOCIATES PC 38133
  #004-01-1989 L1993 **OBG** *020 †30
GIEL, Thomas Vincent. ■ 38111 #047-06-2005 L2008 **ORS** *012
GIEM, Andrew David. ■ 38103 #005-12-2004 **U** *012
GIGER, Jerri Lynn. 1129 HALE RD 38116 #047-06-1991 L1994 **PD** *020 †55
GILLESPIE, Timothy Graham. 6615 KIRBY CENTER CV 38115 #047-06-1984 L1986 **PD** *020 †55
GILLETTE, S L, Jr. ■ 38117 #047-06-1972 L1972 **EM AM** *030 †16
GILLILAND, Charles Arthur. ■ 38111 #047-06-2005 **DR** *012
GILLILAND, Lawrence Lea. ■ 38111 #047-06-2005 **DR** *012
GILMORE, Barry Gene. 50 N DUNLAP ST, ER DEPT 38103 #004-01-1992 L1998
  PD PEM *012 †55
GINN, Bobby H. ■ 38120 #047-06-1951 L1951 **EM GS** *071 †85
GIOIA, D Frederick. 210 JACKSON AVE # 212 38105 #869-04-1951 L1956 **NS** *071 †25
GIPSON, Stephen L. 6005 PARK AVE, STE 510 38119 #422-01-1982 L1983 **AN** *020
GIRALDO, Elias A. UNIV OF TN HLTH SCIENCE CT, 855 MONROE AVE ROOM 415 38163
  #737-01-1990 L2002 **N** *040 †75
GISH, Matthew Jaye. ■ 38111 #019-02-2004 L2005 **DR** *012
GISH, Sarah Lewis. 956 COURT AVE, MEDICINE EDUCATION OFF 38163 #019-02-2004
  MPD *012
GIVENS, Cheryl Denise. ■ 38111 #047-06-2008 *012
GIVENS, Preston Grant. 7685 WINCHESTER RD, STE 100 38125 #047-06-1996 L1997
  FM *020 †18
GIVENS, Vanessa M. 1301 PRIMACY PKWY 38119 #047-06-1996 L2001 **OBG** *020 †30
GLASS, Anna Elizabeth. ■ 38104 #047-06-2008 *012
GLAZER, Louis. 825 RIDGE LAKE BLVD # 125 38120 #561-01-1969 L1972 **AN** *020
GLENN, Martha Elizabeth. 6215 HUMPHREYS BLVD, STE 100 38120 #048-02-1979 L1998
  ID IM *020 †20
GLOTZBACH, Raymond E. 5959 PARK AVE 38119 #047-06-1976 L1977 **PTH IM** *020 †20,50
GLOVER, Suzanne Elizabeth. ■ 38104 #047-06-2007 **PD** *012

GODAMBE, Sandip Ashok. 50 N DUNLAP ST, ER DEPT 38103 #028-02-1995 L1999 **PE** *020 †55
GODSEY, William Cole. 3960 KNIGHT ARNOLD RD, STE 303 38118 #047-06-1958 L1959 **P** *071 †75
GOINGS, John Herbertrud, Jr. ■ 38111 #047-06-2008 **OS DR** *020 †80
GOLD, Robert Eric. 865 JEFFERSON F150 CHANDLE, UNIVERSITY OF TENNESSEE 38163 #062-01-1966 L1977 **OS DR** *020 †80
GOLDEN, Emmel B, Jr. 6025 WALNUT GROVE RD, PC 38120 #047-06-1975 L1976 **PUD CCM** *020 †20
GOLDIN, Melvin Lester. 6401 POPLAR AVE STE 318 38119 #027-01-1975 L1977 **P CHP** *020 †75 ‡
GOLLAMUDI, Subba Rao. 825 RIDGE LAKE BLVD 38120 #008-01-1987 L1991 **OPH** *020 †35 ‡
GOMEZ, Isabel Garralon. ■ 38163 #047-06-2004 **OBG** *012
GONYEA, Edward Francis. 1030 JEFFERSON AVE 38104 #010-02-1957 L1974 **N OPH** *071 †75
GOOCH, Jerry Burton. 6029 WALNUT GROVE RD, STE 401 38120 #047-06-1969 L1970 **TS** *020 †85,90
GOODIN, Geoffrey S. ■ 38111 #047-06-2004 L2004 **DR** *012
GOODMAN, Jack A. 4515 POPLAR AVE, STE 426 38117 #047-06-1981 L1982 **AN PME** *020 †05
GOODMAN, Ralph Conrad. 6027 WALNUT GROVE RD, STE 307 38120 #047-06-1974 L1975 **END** *020 †20
GOODWIN, Autumn Joi. NEWBORN CTR, 853 JEFFERSON/2ND FL 38163 #010-03-2004 **NPM** *012 †55
GOODWIN, Henry North, Jr. 956 CT AVE 38163 #012-01-1996 L2002 **U** *020 †95
GOODWIN, Kayla Danae. ■ 38103 #047-06-2008 *012
GOORHA, Salil. 1331 UNION AVE, STE 800 38104 #047-06-2000 L2003 **HO** *012 †20
GORDON, Lawrence Wooten. 6005 PARK AVE, STE 624B 38119 #047-06-1988 L1989 **OPH** *020 †35
GORDON, Richard Jos. 5200 PARK AVE, STE 102 38119 #023-01-1989 L2004 **CD IM** *020 †20
GOREN, Marshall Phillip. 332 N LAUDERDALE ST # 318 38105 #025-01-1978 L1981 **CLP** *050 †50
GORMAN, Mary Elizabeth. ■ 38104 #016-11-2004 **OTO** *012
GOSHORN, Neumon Taylor. 80 HUMPHREYS CTR, STE 100 38120 #027-01-1980 L1988 **PS GS** *020 †85,65
GOSMANOV, Aidar. 894 UNION AVE, UNIV OF TN HEALTH CENTER 38103 #913-03-1997 **IM** *012
GOSMANOVA, Elvira Olegovn. 956 CT AVE, UNIV OF TN COLL OF MED 38163 #913-03-1997 **NEP** *012 †20
GOSSETT, Gail J. 1331 UNION AVE, STE 900 38104 #047-07-1978 L1981 **PD** *020 †55
GOSWAMI, Anil Kumar. ■ 38111 #495-47-1976 L2003 **IM** *020 †20
GOTTEN, Nicholas, Jr. 6019 WALNUT GROVE RD 38120 #047-06-1965 L1965 **IM RHU** *020 ‡
GRAHAM, Belinda Kaye. ■ 38103 #047-07-2006 **IM** *012
GRAHAM, Robert Matthew. 1223 ISLE VIEW DR 38103 #047-06-2006 **IM** *012
GRANDBERRY, Deidrea L. ■ 38119 #047-06-2000 L2004 **OBG** *020
GRANESE, Jacqueline Mary. UNIV OF TENNESSEE, DEPT OF PATHOLOGY RESIDENC 38163 #422-01-2000 L2007 **DMP** *012
GRANT, Natarsha Denine. 176 S BELLEVUE BLVD, STE 502 38104 #045-01-2002 L2006 **NEP** *020 †20
GRAVES, Thomas Houston. 1265 UNION AVE, STE 135 38104 #027-01-2007 **TY** *012
GRAVES, William Alan. 1661 INTERNATIONAL DR, STE 350 38120 #027-01-1994 L1997 **NR** *020 †80
GRAY, Richard Ian. ■ 38104 #047-06-2005 **DR** *012
GRAY, Roberta. PO BOX 750187 38175 #047-07-1977 L1985 **PD** *020
GRAY, Thomas Lynn. 5154 STAGE RD STE 101 38134 #047-06-1977 L1978 **OBG** *020 †30
GRAYSON, Jackie Catrina. 1301 PRIMACY PKWY, PRACTICE CTR 38119 #021-05-2005 L2008 **FP** *012
GREEN, Christie Ann. 920 MADISON AVE STE 200, UNIVERSITY OF TENNESSEE 38103 #047-06-1995 L1999 **NEP** *020 †20,55
GREEN, Christopher Brian. 2725 KIRBY RD STE 1 38119 #047-06-1991 L1993 **IM** *020 †20
GREEN, James Butler, Jr. ■ 38120 #047-06-1961 L1961 **GS** *071 †85
GREEN, Jeffrey Williams. 6005 PARK AVE, STE 101B 38119 #047-06-1996 L1997 **DR** *020 †80
GREEN, Joseph Barnet. 1030 JEFFERSON AVE 38104 #041-02-1954 L1955 **N CHN** *050 †75
GREEN, Phillip Edward. 6005 PARK AVE, STE 502 38119 #004-01-1984 L1987 **AN EM** *020 †05
GREENBERG, David Eric. ■ 38122 #021-01-2005 **DR** *012
GREENBERGER, Mark David. 530 OAK COURT DR STE 1 38117 #012-05-1994 L1996 **U** *020 †95
GREENE, Elton Benjamin. 1265 UNION AVE, STE 135 38104 #047-06-2007 **TY** *012
GREENE, James Allen. 135 N PAULINE ST, STE 122 38105 #047-06-1963 L1969 **P PYG** *071 †18
GREENE, Michael Renato. ■ 38119 #008-02-2000 L2002 **HO** *100 †20
GREENE, Robert W, Jr. 220 S CLAYBROOK ST STE 500 38104 #047-06-1985 L1989 **PM** *020 †60
GREER, Sarah Catherine. ■ 38111 #020-02-2004 L2007 **D** *012
GREGORY, Arthur Wynns. 451 LINDEN AVE 38126 #036-01-1958 L1984 **IM NEP** *020 †20
GREGORY, Justin Michael. ■ 38103 #047-06-2008 *012
GRIFFIN, Benjamin David. 3739 WAYNOKA AVE 38111 #047-06-2002 L2005 **RNR** *012 †80
GRIFFIN, John Patrick. 956 COURT AVE RM H314, DIV OF PULM & CRITCL CARE 38103 #016-43-1958 L1967 **PUD IM** *020 †20
GRIFFIN, Latonya Danielle. ■ 38103 #001-06-2006 **PD** *012
GRIFFITH, Laura Ellen. ■ 38103 #047-06-2006 L2007 **P** *012
GRIMALDI, John A R, Jr. 135 N PAULINE ST 38105 #047-05-1978 L2007 **P** *020 †75
GRIMMIG, Jana E. 427 LINDEN AVE, MIDTOWN MENTAL HEALTH CTR 38126 #286-02-1962 L1981 **P** *020 †75
GRISE, Jerry Wade. 220 S CLAYBROOK ST, STE 300 38104 #047-06-1956 L1957 **DR** *071 †80
GROBMYER, Albert Jos, III. 3175 LENOX PARK BLVD, STE 309 38115 #047-06-1962 L1963 **GS** *071 †85
GROSHART, Kenneth Dean. 6019 WALNUT GROVE RD 38120 #047-06-1972 L1973 **PTH IM** *020 †20,50
GROSHART, Mary Ellen. ■ 38111 #047-06-2008 *012
GROSS, Lawrence Baker. 1325 EASTMORELAND AVE, STE 150 38104 #004-01-1986 L1989 **EM** *020 †18 ‡
GROSSMAN, Ronald K. 1127 UNION AVE 38104 #020-02-1967 L1976 **AN** *020 †05
GUERRA, Guerraumberto J. 5959 PARK AVE 38119 #187-03-1970 L1974 **CD OS** *020 †20
GUERRA, Sonia-Maria O. 6005 PARK AVE STE 902 38119 #187-03-1970 L1974 **END IM** *020 †20
GUEVARA, Benjamin Gray. ■ 38111 #021-05-2005 **ORS** *012
GUGGISBERG, Wilhelm Rodol. 956 COURT AVE 38163 #935-01-1992 **PTH** *100
GUILLORY, Karen L. 50 N DUNLAP ST 3RD FL, CENTER 38103 #048-02-1989 L2005 **CCP** †55
GUMIDYALA, Krishna Venkat. ■ 38111 #016-11-2004 L2006 **ORS** *012

GUPTA, Malini. 956 COURT AVE 38163 #539-02-2003 **IM** *012
GUPTA, Ramesh Chandra. 6005 PARK AVE STE 409 38119 #495-36-1965 L1982 **IG** *020
GUPTA, Vanita. ■ 38119 #016-42-2003 L2006 **FM** *100 †18
GUYTON, Thomas Scott. 1755 KIRBY PKWY, STE 330 38120 #024-01-1987 L1996 **AN** *020 †05
HABASHY, Hany M. 1325 EASTMORELAND AVE, STE 335 38104 #915-03-1978 L1995 **IM** *020 †20
HABERMAN, Brent Kester. 956 COURT AVE, RESIDENT EDUCATION 38163 #028-34-2005 **PD** *012
HABIB, Muhammad Jawad. 956 COURT AVE 38163 #704-04-1999 **IM** *012
HADDAD, Hassan. 776 MOUNT MORIAH RD, STE 4 38117 #875-02-1988 L2000 **NEP IM** *020 †20
HAIDER ZAIDI, Syed Shumil. 956 CT AVE, UNIV OF TN COLL OF MED 38163 #704-16-2004 **IM** *012
HAIK, Barrett Geo. 930 MADISON AVE, STE 100 38163 #021-05-1976 L1995 **OPH** *020 †35
HAJGHASSEMAL, Mehrdokht. ■ 38139 #517-01-1966 L1975 **AN** *071
HAJJAR, Mohammad Anas. 956 COURT AVE 38163 #875-02-2000 L2007 **IM** *020
HAKIM, Hana Mohamad Aly. ■ 38134 #605-01-2000 **PDI** *012 †55
HAKIMIAN, Arman. ■ 38120 #047-06-2008 *012
HALE, Gregory Alan. 332 N LAUDERDALE ST, DEPT HEMATOL-ONCOL 38105 #055-02-1990 L1999 **PHO** *020 †55
HALFORD, Hollis H, III. 1661 INTERNATIONAL DR, STE 350 38120 #047-06-1979 L1979 **DR** *020 †20
HALFORD, Jack Richard. 717 S WHITE STATION RD 38117 #047-06-1953 L1954 **GP** *071 †18
HALL, Christopher James. 3980 NEW COVINGTON PIKE, STE 310 38128 #047-06-1998 L2004 **OTO** ‡
HALL, Johnnie Cameron. 6046 KNIGHT ARNOLD ROD EXT, TRUMBULL LABORATORIES 38115 #047-06-1984 L1985 **ATP CLP** *020 †50
HALL, Tiffany Tijuana. 3725 CHAMPION HILLS DR, DR. #2000 38125 #047-06-1998 L2002 **MPD** *020 †20,55
HALLE, Margaret J A. ■ 38117 #038-41-1946 L1952 **OPH** *071 †35
HAMILTON, Derrick Rush. 50 N DUNLAP ST, MED CTR 38103 #043-01-2001 L2004 **PD** *020 †55
HAMILTON, Emily Thos. 50 N DUNLAP ST 38115 #047-06-1975 L1975 **PD** *020 †55
HAMILTON, Fred Hadley, III. 6005 PARK AVE, STE 101B 38119 #047-06-1972 1972 **DR NM** *020 †80
HAMILTON, Ralph Frederick. 6238 POPLAR AVE 38119 #047-06-1976 L1977 **OPH** *020 †35
HAMILTON, Ralph S. 930 MADISON AVE, STE 230 38103 #047-06-1952 L1952 **OPH** *020 †35
HAMLETT, James M, III. 6215 HUMPHREYS BLVD # 310, EAST MEMPHIS NEONATOLOGY 38120 #047-06-1967 L1970 **NPM PD** *020 †55
HAMMETT, Jessica. ■ 38104 #047-06-2008 *012
HAMMOND, Alan Richard. 1325 EASTMORELAND AVE, STE 410 38104 #023-07-2002 L2003 **DR** *100 †20
HAMMOND, Douglas Alan. 6005 PARK AVE STE 905B 38119 #001-02-1991 L1997 **GS** *020 †85
HAMMOND, Mark L. 6263 POPLAR AVE, STE 1052 38119 #047-06-1983 L1984 **IM** *020 †20
HAMNER, John Blair. ■ 38103 #021-06-2003 **GS** *012
HAMPTON, Lloydetta S. 602 W MITCHELL RD 38109 #047-06-1997 L1999 **PD** *020 †55
HAMZE, Omar Oussama. 176 S BELLEVUE BLVD, STE 502 38104 #605-01-1997 L2004 **IM** *012
HANDGRETINGER, Rupert. 332 N LAUDERDALE ST, D-2058 STOP 321 38105 #407-19-1989 L2000 **HO TTS** *012
HANDORF, Charles Russell. 1211 UNION AVE STE 300 38104 #047-06-1977 L1977 **ATP CLP** *020 †50
HANKINS, Jane Silva. 332 N LAUDERDALE ST MS 7, ST. JUDE CHILDREN'S RES HO 38105 #187-02-1993 L2005 **PHO** *020 †55
HANNA, Debra Lee. 711 JEFFERSON AVE 38105 #028-46-1980 L1996 **PD** *020 †55
HANNA, Sabrina Ann. 853 JEFFERSON AVE, RM E102 38103 #045-04-2001 L2005 **OBG** *020
HANSEN, Dale Eugene. 1661 INTERNATIONAL DR, STE 350 38120 #011-02-1981 L1988 **DR** *020 †80
HANSON, Charles C. 5050 SANDERLIN AVE 38117 #047-06-1993 L1995 **PD** *020 †55
HARDISON, Robert Damion. 3030 COVINGTON PIKE, STE 100 38128 #021-06-1999 L2002 **FM** *020 †18
HARDT, Nancy Sisson. 66 N PAULINE ST STE 633 38105 #016-43-1977 L2002 **PTH OBG** *050,30
HARDY, Brenda Mozette. 1264 WESLEY DR, STE 103 38116 #047-06-1988 L1990 **OBG** *020 †20
HARDY, Dawn Yumi. ■ 38120 #047-06-2008 *012
HARDY, F Oliver. 4520 ELVIS PRESLEY BLVD 38116 #018-03-1975 L1979 **GS OS** *020
HARE, Marion E. 50 N DUNLAP ST 4TH FL, U T MEDICAL GROUP, INC 38103 #047-06-1989 L1992 **PD** *020 †55
HARPER, Julie Golden. 7900 US HIGHWAY 64, GYNECOLOGY ASSOCIATES PC 38133 #047-06-1999 L2003 **OBG** *020 †30
HARRELL, Ethel Ashton. ■ 38107 #047-06-1957 L1958 **PD** *071 †55
HARRIMAN, Mark Steven. 4816 RIVERDALE RD 38141 #047-01-1979 L1989 **ORS** *020 †40
HARRINGTON, Adrienne Nico. ■ 38126 #047-06-2007 **IM** *012
HARRINGTON, Oscar B. 1325 EASTMORELAND AVE, STE 220 38104 #004-01-1953 L1964 **TS** *071 †85,90
HARRIS, Frederick Richard, Jr. ■ 38120 #047-06-2007 **IM** *012
HARRIS, John Joel. 6263 POPLAR AVE, STE 535 38119 #047-06-1963 L1964 **P ADM** *020
HARRIS, Kenneth Wayne. 3960 KNIGHT ARNOLD RD, STE 420 38118 #027-01-1984 L1995 **IM** *020
HARROD, Virginia Lynn. 332 N LAUDERDALE ST, DEPT HEMATOLOGY/ONCOLOGY 38105 #048-14-2001 L2006 **PD** *100
HARSHMAN, Heather Anne. 3362 S 3RD ST 38109 #021-05-2001 L2006 **FM OBS** *020 †18
HARTLINE, Brian Keith. 38111 #004-01-1994 **PD** *020
HARVEY, Stephen Thomas. ■ 38163 #047-06-2004 **AN** *012
HASKINS, Laura Bennis. ■ 38163 #047-06-2005 **OBG** *012
HATCH, Fred Erdman. 951 COURT AVE # 649D 38103 #047-06-1954 L1955 **NEP IM** *020
HAUSMANN, James Stanford. 1388 MADISON AVE 38104 #047-06-1995 L1999 **DR** *020 †80,28
HAWKINS, Harry Lee, Jr. 6005 PARK AVE # 426-B 38104 #047-06-1966 L1967 **GE IM** *020 †20
HAYDEN, Jane Ellen. 6215 HUMPHREYS BLVD, STE 310 38120 #047-20-1988 L1990 **NPM** *020 †55
HAYDEN, Leonard Alva. 3965 S MENDENHALL RD, STE 6 38115 #028-03-1967 L1995 **EM** *071
HAYDEN, Randall Todd. ■ 38103 #016-11-1989 L2000 **ATP MM** *020 †50
HAYDEN, Shawn Joseph. 48 S PRESCOTT ST 38111 #012-01-1997 L1998 **IM** *020 †20
HAYES, John Wm. 3000 GETWELL RD 38118 #047-06-1975 L1976 **FM** *020
HAYES, William Timothy. 5959 PARK AVE 38119 #047-06-1963 L1963 **PTH** *071 †50
HAYKAL, Mohamad Ayman. ■ 38105 #875-01-2005 **N** *012
HAYKAL, Radwan Faysal. 6263 POPLAR AVE STE 402 38119 #605-01-1975 L1977 **P** *020 †75 ‡

HAZLEHURST, Waring Mikell. 1755 KIRBY PKWY, STE 330 38120 #047-06-1984 L1985 **AN** *020 †05

HAZRATI, Simindokht. 5744 NANJACK CIR 38115 #517-01-1961 L1977 **AN** *020

HEAD, Thomas Glenn. 1265 UNION AVE 38104 #047-06-1962 L1963 **FM** *071 †18

HEADLEY, Arthur Stacey. 4571 COURT AVENUE RM H314, UNIVERSITY OF TENNESSEE 38163 #001-02-1987 L1989 **PUD CCM** *020 †20

HEALY, Regina Gadomski. 6215 HUMPHREYS BLVD 38120 #047-06-1992 L2000 **OBG** *020 †30

HECHING, Norman. 100 N HUMPHREYS BLVD 38120 #550-02-1981 L2006 **ON IM** *020 †20

HECHT, Alan. ■ 38115 #028-02-1953 L1957 **OM IM** *071

HECK, Michael James. 6286 BRIARCREST AVE, FL 2 38120 #021-06-1979 L1979 **ORS** *020 †40

HECOX, Celeste D. ■ 38111 #048-02-2006 **PD** *012

HECOX, Scott E. ■ 38111 #048-02-2006 **ORS** *012

HEDRICK, Donna Lynn. 899 MADISON AVE, DEPT PATHOL 38103 #047-06-1987 **PTH** *100

HEGEDUS, Steven Michael. 409 AYERS ST 38105 #038-45-2002 L2006 **IM** *020 †20

HEIMBERG, Murray. 951 COURT AVENUE RM D334, UNIVERSITY OF TENNESSEE 38163 #047-05-1959 L1959 **END PA** *020

HEINKEL, Oluwaseun. 1129 HALE RD 38116 #028-34-2003 L2005 **PD** *020

HEINS, Kristen Lynn. ■ 38117 #047-06-2008 *012

HELMS, Jody Benton. ■ 38135 #047-06-2004 **NS** *012

HELTON, Kathleen J. 332 N LAUDERDALE ST, DEPT OF DIAGNOSTIC IMAGING 38105 #047-06-1991 L1996 **RNR** *020 †80

HENDERSON, Ellena Lynn. 1325 EASTMORELAND AVE, STE 245 38104 #047-06-1998 L2004 **ID** *020 †20

HENDERSON, Haller S, III. ■ 38104 #047-06-1962 L1963 **GE CD** *075

HENDRICKS, Sean David. 825 RIDGE LAKE BLVD, STE 2 38120 #016-11-2001 L2007 **OPH** *100

HENDRIX, Ashley Allen. ■ 38104 #047-06-2008 *012

HENLEY, Russell Gray, III. 6005 PARK AVE, STE 510 38119 #047-06-1978 L1978 **GP** *020

HENRY, Anne Coker. ■ 38163 #047-06-2001 L2002 **DR** *020

HENWICK, Scott. ■ 38115 #061-01-1985 **PD** *020

HERMAN, Martin Isaac. 806 ESTATE PL, CENTER, LE BONHEUR EAST UR 38120 #023-01-1977 L1993 **EM PEM** *020 †15

HERNANDEZ, Jacinto Angel. 1428 MONROE AVE, BMA MEMPHIS 38104 #847-05-1974 L1979 **IM NEP** *020 †20

HERNDON, Bruce Wayne, Jr. 4299 ELVIS PRESLEY BLVD 38116 #047-06-1960 L1960 **OPH** *020 †35

HERNDON, Patricia C M. ■ 38120 #047-06-1961 L1970 **GP** *020

HERREN, Gil Edward. ■ 38122 #047-20-2001 L2003 **MPD** *020

HERRERA, Fernando A. 6005 PARK AVE STE 828B 38119 #649-04-1970 L1977 **TS CD** *020 †85,90

HERRINGTON, Clarence G, III. 6401 POPLAR AVE, STE 100 38119 #047-06-1998 L2003 **DR** *071 †80

HERROD, Henry Grady. 600 JEFFERSON AVE 38105 #001-02-1972 L1978 **PD PDA** *062 †55,03

HERTZ, Amy L. 5411 COLLINGWOOD CV 38120 #021-01-1987 L1990 **PEM** *020 †55

HESS, Paul Geo. 6025 WALNUT GROVE RD, STE 111 38120 #035-20-1972 L1977 **CD IM** *020 †20

HESS, Paul Laurence. ■ 38120 #012-05-2006 L2006 **IM** *012

HEYEN, Moriah Louise. ■ 38112 #028-34-2005 **PD** *012

HIATT, Roger Lew. 956 COURT/ ROOM D228., U.T. COLL OF MEDICINE 38163 #047-06-1958 L1958 **OPH** *071 †35

HICKS, Anthony Marcellus. 1955 S 3RD ST 38109 #025-12-1991 L1994 **IM** *040 †20

HICKS, John Mc Call. ■ 38111 #045-04-2003 L2006 **ORS** *012

HIDAJI, Faramarz Fred. 6252 POPLAR AVE, VISIONARY EYE CARE 38119 #047-06-1992 L2000 **OPH PO** *035

HIGDON, Dennis Alan. 1755 KIRBY PKWY, STE 330 38120 #047-06-1970 L1970 **AN AM** *020 †05

HIGGINS, Alexis Connor. 361 N 3RD ST, PROMEDICA CLINIC PC 38105 #045-01-1961 L1978 **PM** *020 †60

HIGGINS, Marybeth. 777 WASHINGTON AVE, STE 410 38105 #047-06-1993 L1996 **PD** *020 †55

HIGGINS, Megan Janette. ■ 38120 #047-20-2007 **PD** *012

HIGHTOWER, Denise Michele. 2900 KIRBY RD, STE 14 38119 #047-06-1998 L1999 **FM** *020 †20

HILL, Ericka Gunn. 956 CT AVE 38163 #012-21-1999 L2002 **FM** *020 †18

HILL, John Roy. 777 WASHINGTON AVE, STE 215 38105 #008-01-1968 L1969 **PD** *020 †55

HILL, Paul Bryan. 1715 AARON BRENNER DR, STE 326 38120 #047-06-1985 L1989 **P** *020 †75

HILL, Regan Frances. ■ 38104 #047-06-2004 **GS** *012

HILLEBERT, Susan Annette. 2860 COVINGTON PIKE 38128 #027-01-1985 L1988 **PD** *020 †55

HILSENBECK, Holly Lynne. 1211 UNION AVE, STE 300 38104 #047-06-2001 L2007 **PTH** *020 †50

HINES, Donna L. 409 AYERS ST 38105 #010-03-1995 L1998 **PD** *020 †55

HINES, Elbert Edwin, III. 6263 POPLAR AVE, STE 1052 38119 #047-06-1983 L1984 **FM FPG** *020 †18

HINES, Leonard Harvey. 6029 WALNUT GROVE RD, STE 404 38120 #047-06-1964 L1964 **GS** *020 †85

HITCHCOCK, Matthew Ray. ■ 38105 #047-06-2008 *012

HIXSON, Sherman Douglas. 777 WASHINGTON AVE, STE 230 38105 #047-06-1973 L1974 **PDS GS** *020 †85

HO, John. 956 COURT AVE, DEPT OF PEDIATRICS 38163 #047-06-2006 **PD** *012

HO, Ralph Tinghan. 6305 HUMPHREYS BLVD, STE 205 38120 #016-01-1995 L2001 **VIR** *020 †80

HOBBS, Melvin Lynn. ■ 38118 #047-07-1987 L1991 **OBG** *020

HODGES, Frederick T. 1264 WESLEY DR, STE 402 38116 #047-07-1995 L2000 **OBG** *020 †30

HODGES, John Mc Iver. 1325 EASTMORELAND AVE #450 38104 #047-06-1963 L1963 **OTO FPS** *020 †45

HODGKISS, Linda Cox. 1661 INTERNATIONAL DR, STE 350 38120 #047-20-1987 L1988 **DR** *020 †80

HODGKISS, Thomas Dalton. 100 N HUMPHREYS BLVD 38120 #047-06-1989 L1990 **DR** *020 †80

HOEHN, Mary Ellen. 930 MADISON AVE STE 400 38163 #047-06-1997 L2003 **OPH PO** *020

HOERMAN, Beth Anne. ■ 38120 #019-02-2004 **PD** *012 †55

HOFMANN, Marc Eugene. 6025 WALNUT GROVE RD, PC 38120 #305-01-1995 L1998 **PCC** *020

HOLBERT, James Marion, Jr. 6286 BRIARCREST AVE, STE 308 38120 #047-06-1970 L1970 **HEM IG** *020 †50,20

HOLCOMB, Lisa Gayle. ■ 38120 #047-06-2008 *012

HOLCOMB, Randall Lawrence. 6286 BRIARCREST AVE, FL 2 38120 #047-06-1978 L1979 **OSM** *020 †40

HOLCOMB, Thomas Jefferson. 1755 KIRBY PKWY, STE 330 38120 #047-06-1982 L1985 **AN** *020 †05

HOLLABAUGH, Robert Sterli. 777 WASHINGTON AVE, STE 230 38105 #047-06-1963 L1963 **PDS** *071 †85

HOLLAND, Nancy Elizabeth. 3876 NEW COVINGTON PIKE, PEDIATRIC ASSOCIATES PC 38128 #047-06-1969 L1970 **PD** *020

HOLLIDAY, James Newton. 4571 SUMMER AVE 38122 #036-07-1987 L1988 **OPH** *020 †35

HOLMAN, Benjamin Carllee. ■ 38111 #004-01-2006 **DR** *012

HOLMAN, Lester Clay. ■ 38104 #047-06-1965 L1966 **CHP P** *020

HOLMES, Perry Don. 711 W BROOKHAVEN CIR 38117 #047-06-1967 L1970 **IM** *020 †20

HOLT, Huey Thos, Jr. 388 S PAULINE ST 38104 #047-06-1987 L1989 **IM** *020 †20

HOLT, Lee Christopher. ■ 38104 #047-06-2007 **TY** *012

HOMSI, Riad. 80 HUMPHREYS CTR, STE 201 38120 #605-01-1986 L1994 **OBG** *020 †30

HONG, Julie Christine. ■ 38124 #028-03-2006 **MPD** *012

HOOVER, Jeffery Neal. 6027 WALNUT GROVE RD, STE 401 38120 #047-06-1981 L1983 **IM** *020

HOOVER, Robert Michael. 3362 S 3RD ST, CHRIST COMMUNITY HEALTH SV 38109 #005-15-1983 L1991 **FM** *020 †18

HOPPER, Karen Elizabeth. 3960 NEW COVINGTON PIKE, ADMINISTRATION 38128 #021-06-1979 L1982 **IM** *020 †20

HOPPER, Wm Clayton, Jr. ■ 38112 #027-01-1971 L1971 **ORS OSS** *071 †40

HORAN, Jeanne M Marcoux. 1030 JEFFERSON AVE 38104 #021-01-1949 L1961 **OS** *071 †55

HORN, Howard R. 877 JEFFERSON AVE 38103 #047-06-1964 L1964 **CD IM** *040 †20

HORNE, Arthur E. 6590 KIRBY CENTER CV, SUITE103 38115 #047-07-1951 L1951 **FM** *071 †18

HORRAS, Randy Joseph. 6305 HUMPHREYS BLVD, STE 205 38120 #004-01-1999 L2003 **DR** *020 †80

HORTON, Thomas Russell. 1462 POPLAR AVE, HEALTH 38104 #051-07-1998 L2002 **GYN** *020

HORWITZ, Edwin Mark. 332 N LAUDERDALE ST, RESEARCH HOSPITAL 38105 #017-20-1988 L1995 **PHO** *020 †55

HOU, Jeannie Whitshan. ■ 38125 #016-06-1996 L1997 **ON IM** *020 †20

HOUSHOLDER, Charles H. 5050 SANDERLIN 38117 #047-06-1939 L1940 **PD** *072 †55

HOWARD, David Alan. 1661 INTERNATIONAL DR, STE 350 38120 #047-06-1982 L1982 **PDR PD** *020 †55,80

HOWARD, Hector Smythe, Jr. 6027 WALNUT GROVE RD, NO 309 38120 #047-06-1954 L1961 **TS CD** *071 †85,90

HOWARD, Scott Charles. 332 N LAUDERDALE ST, INTERNATIONAL OUTREACH PRO 38105 #001-02-1994 L1995 **PHO** *020 †20,55

HOWELL, Joyce Elaine. 1325 EASTMORELAND AVE, STE 150 38104 #041-07-1958 L1958 **IM PD** *071

HOWSE, Robert Julian. 1265 UNION AVE 38104 #047-07-1962 L1966 **OBG** *020

HOWSER, John Patton. 3960 KNIGHT ARNOLD RD, STE 215E 38118 #047-06-1960 L1962 **NS** *020 †25

HUANG, Eunice Yueedean. 777 WASHINGTON AVE, STE 230 38105 #005-06-1997 L2006 **PDS** *020 †85

HUBBARD, Amy E. 3876 NEW COVINGTON PIKE, PEDIATRIC ASSOCIATES PC 38128 #012-01-1996 L1999 **PD** *020 †55

HUBBARD, Ronald Eugene. 6027 WALNUT GROVE RD, STE 411 38120 #004-01-1966 L1970 **OTO GS** *071 †45

HUBBERT, Charles Hughes. 6019 WALNUT GROVE RD 38120 #027-01-1963 L1966 **P IM** *020 †75,20,18

HUBER, Amy Amonette. 1455 UNION AVE, MEMPHIS DERMATOLOGY 38104 #047-06-1998 L2001 **D DS** *020 †15

HUBER, John Dominic. 1455 UNION AVE, MEMPHIS DERMATOLOGY 38104 #047-06-1997 L2001 **DS** *020 †15

HUCH, Kim Marie. 1030 JEFFERSON AVE # 111B, VAMC 38104 #047-06-1987 L1991 **NEP PD** *020 †55,20

HUDGINS, Channon Teria. UNIV OF TENNESSEE, DEPT OF OB/GYN 38163 #048-02-2004 L2004 **OBG** *012

HUDSON, Joseph S. 6325 HUMPHREYS BLVD 38120 #047-06-1964 L1965 **NS** *020 †25

HUDSON, Melissa Maria. 332 N LAUDERDALE ST, ST JUDE CHILDREN'S HOSPITA 38105 #048-14-1983 L1989 **PHO** *050 †55

HUDSON, Rickey H. 220 OVERTON AVE 38105 #047-07-1986 L1988 **FM** *020

HUFF, Garry Lynn. 6019 WALNUT GROVE RD 38120 #047-06-1975 L1976 **IM** *020 †20

HUFFMAN, John David. 266 S CLEVELAND ST, STE 104 38104 #038-40-1965 L1970 **PM** *020

HUGGINS, Arthur E, Jr. 1265 UNION AVE # NICU 38104 #047-06-1990 L1992 **IM** *020 †55,20

HUGHES, Allen Holt. 80 HUMPHREYS CTR, STE 100 38120 #047-06-1964 L1965 **PS** *020 †85,65

HUGHES, Stephanie E. ■ 38103 #021-06-2004 **U** *012

HUGHES, Walter Thompson. 332 N LAUDERDALE ST, HOSPITAL 38105 #047-06-1954 L1954 **PDI PD** *050 †55

HUGHEY, John Raymond. 1211 UNION AVE, STE 120 38104 #020-02-1976 L1977 **PUD** *020 †20

HUMBLE, Eric Allen. ■ 38103 #020-02-2000 L2003 **PS** *012

HUMPHREYS, Robert A. 5220 PARK AVE, STE 100 38119 #047-06-1976 L1976 **FM** *020 †18

HUNGERFORD, James Lucas. ■ 38103 #047-06-2008 *012

HUNT, Charles Austin. 1325 EASTMORELAND AVE, STE 220 38104 #017-20-1996 L2005 **TS** *020 †85,90

HUNT, James C. ■ 38115 #036-05-1953 L1978 **NEP IM** *071 †20

HURD, William Chas. 220 S CLAYBROOK ST STE 101 38104 #047-07-1980 L1982 **OPH** *020

HUSAIN, Arshad Iftekhar. 1331 UNION AVE, STE 800 38104 #495-17-1992 L2006 **HO** *012 †20

HUTCHINS, Charles Edward. 6075 POPLAR AVE STE 405, CORPORATION 38119 #047-06-1999 L2003 **NM** *020 †80

HUTCHINS, Eric Burton. 6075 POPLAR AVE STE 405, CORPORATION 38119 #047-06-1968 L1969 **OBG** *071 †30

HUTCHINS, Linda L. ■ 38112 #047-06-1968 L1969 **OBG** *071 †30

HUTCHINS, Sabrina Burns. 50 N DUNLAP ST, STE 309 38103 #047-06-2003 L2006 **PD** *100 †55

HYATT, John David. OF MED, UNIV OF TENNESSEE COLL 38163 #021-06-2002 L2003 **OPH** *012

HYDEN, John Carl. ■ 38133 #047-06-2005 L2008 **FP** *012

IANNACCONE, Alessandro. 930 MADISON AVE STE 731, UNIV OF TN HSC-OPH 38163 #561-17-1989 L1998 **OPH** *020

IANSMITH, David Hayden. 80 HUMPHREYS CTR, STE 202 38120 #047-06-1982 L1983 **CD** *020

IBRAHIM, Alia Ahmed. 1030 JEFFERSON AVE, VA MEDICAL CENTER 38104 #613-02-1991 L2006 **FM** *100 †18

IBRAHIM, Fadi. 150 COLLINS ST 38112 #875-02-1995 L2005 **PTH** *020

IGARASHI, Masanori. 777 WASHINGTON AVE P110 38105 #572-03-1967 L1979 **D ID** *020 †55,75

IJAMS, Joe Hartley. ■ 38111 #047-06-1950 L1951 **GP** *072

ILABACA, Patricio A. 6027 WALNUT GROVE RD # 114 38120 #231-01-1967 L1976 **TS VS** *020 †85,90

ILFELD, David Norman. 1030 JEFFERSON AVE 38104 #024-01-1973 L1986 **IG IM** *050 †20,03

IMSEIS, Raed E. 100 N HUMPHREYS BLVD 38120 #528-02-1987 L2002 **END** *020 †20

INDIRADEVI, Ayyagari. 6005 PARK AVE, STE 307 38119 #495-11-1959 L1978 **P CHP** *020 †75

INGRAM, Charles C. 1755 KIRBY PKWY, STE 330 38120 #025-01-1994 L1997 **AN** *020 †05
INGRAM, Kimberly Cherie. 842 JEFFERSON AVE A601 38103 #047-06-2006 **PD** *012
IONICA, Nicoleta. ■ 38105 #781-01-1997 L2007 **IM** *100 †20
ISMAIL, Mohammad Kashif. 1211 UNION AVE STE 340, UNIVERSITY OF TENNESSEE 38104 #704-02-1993 L2001 **GE** *020 †20
ISOM, Johnathan Milton. 5744 NANJACK CIR 38115 #056-06-1985 L1990 **AN** *020 †05
IVEY, Holly Britt. ■ 38107 #047-06-2008 *012
JACEWICZ, Michael. 855 MONROE AVE RM 415, DEPT OF NEUROLOGY UTHSC 38163 #038-06-1978 L1992 **N** *040 †75
JACKSON, Anna Martin. 956 COURT AVE BX 19A 38103 #018-03-1987 L1990 **FM** *020 †18
JACKSON, Anthony Wade. 892 COLGATE RD 38106 #047-07-1991 L1992 **CHP** *020
JACKSON, Barbara Kay. 66 N PAULINE ST STE 633 38105 #047-06-1981 L1983 **GE** *020 †20
JACKSON, Bryan Scott. 3950 NEW COVINGTON PIKE, STE 200 38128 #047-06-1999 L2004 **GS** *020 †85
JACKSON, Casey Gordon. 4095 AMERICAN WAY 38118 #010-02-2003 L2006 **IM** *020 †20
JACKSON, Julia Amanda. ■ 38104 #047-06-2008 *012
JACKSON, Meghan Dale. ■ 38104 #047-06-2004 L2007 **MPD** *012
JACKSON, Paul D. ■ 38104 #047-07-1976 L1979 **P** *020 ‡
JACKSON, Robert L. 6286 BRIARCREST AVE, STE 314 38120 #047-07-1978 L1979 **D** *020 †15 ‡
JACKSON, Tennye Rochelle. 3960 KNIGHT ARNOLD RD, STE 215D 38118 #047-07-1992 L1995 **FM** *020 †18
JACKSON, Thomas M. 6019 WALNUT GROVE RD 38120 #047-06-1945 L1945 **OTO A** *072 †45
JACOB, Glady. 956 COURT AVE 38163 #495-44-1996 L2007 **CN** *012
JACOBS, David Courtney. 1628 WHITEWATER RD 38117 #047-06-2000 L2003 **IM** *020 †20
JACOBS, Jonathan Daniel. ■ 38104 #038-45-2006 **PD** *012
JAFARI MEHR, Ali. 956 COURT AVE 38163 #517-01-2002 **IM** *012
JAHANGIR, Amir Ahmad. ■ 38104 #047-06-2003 L2007 **ORS** *012
JAIN, Manoj Kumar. 6027 WALNUT GROVE RD, STE 312 38120 #024-05-1989 L1995 **ID** *020 †20
JAIN, Sunita Kumari. 6019 WALNUT GROVE RD 38120 #033-05-1989 L1995 **PM** *020 †60
JAKUBOWSKI, Eric Michael. ■ 38103 #016-11-2004 **DR** *012
JALFON, Isaac Mitrani. 80 HUMPHREYS CTR STE 200, MEDICAL CENTER ENDOSCOPY G 38120 #048-13-1986 L1991 **GE IM** *020 †20
JAMAL, Yasser. 956 COURT AVE 38163 #704-01-2002 **IM** *012
JAMES, David H, Jr. 66 N PAULINE ST STE 633 38105 #047-05-1951 L1951 **PD** *071 †55
JAMES, Marvin Mc Kinnis. 4274 FARONIA RD STE 2 38116 #047-07-1977 L1982 **OBG** *020
JAMESON, Valerie Parrott. 50 N DUNLAP ST, DEPARTMENT OF PEDIATRICS, 38103 #021-01-1982 L1990 **PD** *040 †55
JAMESON, William Dean. 6286 BRIARCREST AVE, FL 2 38120 #021-01-1982 L1989 **ORS OFA** *020 †40
JANECEK, Martin. 956 CT AVE, UNIV OF TN COLL OF MED 38163 #286-13-1999 **IM** *100 †20
JARRED, Lois Katherine. 50 N DUNLAP ST 38103 #047-06-1962 L1963 **PD** *020
JARRELL, John Arthur. 956 CT AVE, STE G228 38163 #047-06-2004 **GS** *012
JASTER, James Howard. ■ 38104 #305-01-1987 L1995 **N** *020
JAUCHLER, Gerard W. 1265 UNION AVE 38104 #021-05-1952 L1975 **OBG OS** *071
JEAN-PIERRE, Antoine. 6005 PARK AVE STE 631B 38119 #440-01-1969 L1980 **P N** *020 †75
JEHA, Sima Shafik. 332 N LAUDERDALE ST, MAIL STOP 260 38105 #605-01-1983 L2003 **PHO** *020
JEMISON, Jeanne Stewart. ■ 38117 #047-06-1981 L1983 **PD** *020 †55
JENKINS, Jesse Jay, III. 332 N LAUDERDALE ST 38105 #023-07-1969 L1985 **ATP** *020 †50
JENKINS, Jon Calvin. 1211 UNION AVE, STE 330 38104 #047-06-1963 L1964 **R RO** *071 †80
JENKINS, Martin B. 3960 NEW COVINGTON PIKE, METHODIST HOSP NORTH 38128 #047-06-1983 L1984 **NPM PD** *020 †55 ‡
JENKINS, Michael Bruce. 853 JEFFERSON AVE, RM 201 38103 #036-01-1971 L1971 **VS TS** *020 †85
JENKINS, Willyn Taylor. 4245 CHERRY CENTER DR, STE 1 38118 #027-01-1984 L1989 **IM** *020
JENNINGS, David Keith. 1200 PEABODY AVE 38104 #047-06-1979 L1980 **IM** *020 †20
JENNINGS, George Russell. ■ 38133 #027-01-2000 L2000 **PS** *012 ‡
JERKINS, Brian Montgomery. ■ 38119 #047-06-2008 *012
JERNIGAN, Jefferey Robt. 877 JEFFERSON AVE, STE 633 38103 #047-06-1986 L1987 **AN PME** *020 †05
JHA, Ashwini Kumar. 2070 CARR AVE 38104 #047-06-2001 L2004 **NEP** *100
JHA, Sunil Kumar. 1325 EASTMORELAND AVE, STE 440 38104 #495-15-1983 L2001 **CD** *020 †20
JHAVERI, Urmila B. 360 E EH CRUMP BLVD 38126 #495-01-1966 L1978 **GP** *020
JIANG, Hong. 956 CT AVE 38163 #243-64-1986 L2005 **DMP** *100 †50
JOE, Penn Quork. 6215 HUMPHREYS BLVD STE 40 38120 #047-06-1980 L1981 **OBG** *020 †30
JOHN, Isaac. 6005 PARK AVE, STE 306 38119 #495-33-1973 L1987 **PD NPM** *020 †55
JOHNSON, Christopher Eric. 1703 BENDER RD 38116 #010-01-1986 L1987 **IM** *020 †20
JOHNSON, Eric Von. ■ 38117 #047-06-2004 L2007 **DR** *012
JOHNSON, Ethelyn Denise. 842 JEFFERSON AVE # A 645, UNIVERSITY OF TENNESSEE 38103 #056-06-1986 L2004 **EM** *020 †16
JOHNSON, Harry Durell. 3030 COVINGTON PIKE 38128 #047-06-1962 L1965 **PD OS** *020
JOHNSON, James Gibb. 877 JEFFERSON AVE 38103 #047-06-1963 L1963 **NEP IM** *071 †20
JOHNSON, James W, Jr. 6005 PARK AVE, STE 828B 38119 #047-06-1977 L1978 **CD** *020 †85,90
JOHNSON, Karen Chandler. 49 N DUNLAP ST 38103 #047-06-1985 L1987 **IM GPM** *020 †20,70
JOHNSON, Larry Holliday. 6215 HUMPHREYS BLVD, STE 301 38120 #047-06-1962 L1962 **OBG** *071 †30
JOHNSON, Michael Eugene. 956 COURT AVE BX 19A 38103 #039-01-1991 L1995 **GS** *020
JOHNSON, Rhonda Charlene. 4250 FARONIA RD 38116 #047-06-1999 L2003 **PD** *020 †55
JOHNSON, Richard Paul. 1030 JEFFERSON AVE 116A, 1030 JEFFERSON 116A 38104 #016-06-1972 L1990 **P** *030 †75
JOHNSON, Robert Alan. 100 N HUMPHREYS BLVD 38120 #028-34-1981 L1991 **HO HEM** *020 †20
JOHNSTON, Gina Ayerdis. 5959 PARK AVE 38119 #047-06-1991 L1996 **PTH** *020 †50
JOINER, Marie Lyons. ■ 38111 #047-06-2004 L2008 **MPD** *100
JONES, Anthony Wade. ■ 38105 #047-06-2008 *012
JONES, Bobby Wayne. ■ 38126 #004-01-1990 L1990 **NEP** *020 †20
JONES, Brinders. 1588 UNION AVE, HEALTH FIRST MEDICAL GROUP 38104 #056-06-1983 L1987 **PD** *020 †55
JONES, David Franklin. OF MED, UNIV OF TENNESSEE COLL 38163 #027-01-2006 **OPH** *012
JONES, Deborah Price. 50 N DUNLAP ST, RM 301 38103 #047-06-1983 L1986 **PN PD** *030 †55
JONES, Douglas Edgar. ■ 38117 #047-06-1984 L1987 **IM** *071 †20
JONES, Frederick Douglas. ■ 38116 #010-03-1974 L1975 **R** *020 †80
JONES, James Sidney, III. ■ 38116 #047-06-2007 L2007 **AN** *012
JONES, James Wesley. 1755 KIRBY PKWY, STE 330 38120 #047-06-1985 L1986 **AN** *020 †05
JONES, Matthew Keith. 1265 UNION AVE, STE 135 38104 #047-06-2007 **TY** *012
JONES, Olga. 956 COURT AVE 38163 #913-37-1995 **IM** *012
JONES, Quitman Warde. 1325 EASTMORELAND AVE, STE 260 38104 #047-06-1973 L1978 **GS** *020
JONES, Robert Riley. 3980 NEW COVINGTON PIKE, STE 204 38128 #047-06-1972 L1973 **ORS** *020 †40
JONES, Robin Doreen. 1265 UNION AVE, THOMAS 1 38104 #028-02-1983 L1988 **IM** *020 †20
JONES, Wesley Earl. 1264 WESLEY DR STE 303 38116 #035-01-1974 L1978 **IM GE** *020 ‡
JONES-MILLER, Rosemary. 4707 WOODRIDGE DR 38116 #047-07-1981 L1987 **FM** *020
JORDAN, Anne M. 930 MADISON AVE, STE 500 38163 #047-06-1982 L1986 **PTH** *020 †50
JORDAN, Oakley Carroll, Jr. 48 S PRESCOTT ST 38111 #020-02-1975 L1978 **IM** *020
JORDAN, Robert Greene, Jr. 711 JEFFERSON AVE 38105 #047-05-1943 L1944 **PD** *071 †55
JOSHI, Salil Sudhir. UNIV OF TENNESSEE, DEPT OF RADIOLOGY 38163 #496-36-1996 L2005 **VIR** *100
JOSHI, Surekha Salil. ■ 38103 #496-36-1996 **DR** *012
JOSHI, Vijaya Madhukar. 777 WASHINGTON AVE, STE P215 38105 #050-02-1986 L2004 **PDC** *020 †55
JOYNER, Royce Etienne. 1211 UNION AVE STE 300 38104 #047-05-1979 L1988 **PTH** *020 †50
JUDGE, Beth Amelia. 865 POPLAR AVE 38105 #026-04-1999 L2005 **P** *020 †75
JUKKOLA, Alina Frances. 49 N DUNLAP ST 38103 #047-06-1974 L1975 **PTH** *062 †50
JUSTICE, Penniford L. 1030 JEFFERSON AVE, VAMC SCI 128 38104 #010-03-1981 L1996 **SCI PM** *020 †60
KADARIA, Dipen. ■ 38105 #672-06-2004 **IM** *012
KALE, Santosh Sudhir. ■ 38103 #495-28-1999 **IM** *012
KALISH, Beatrice. ■ 38120 #035-19-1943 L1944 **D** *071 †15
KAMALOV, German Gennady. 956 CT AVE, UNIV OF TN COLL OF MED 38163 #913-38-1995 **IM** *012
KAMIN, Ehud Ron. 6027 WALNUT GROVE RD, STE 103 38120 #047-06-1993 L1994 **IM** *020 †20
KAMO, Alka. 6019 WALNUT GROVE RD 38120 #495-77-1992 L1998 **IM** *020 †20
KANAKAMEDALA, Bhanu V. 5861 QUINCE RD 38119 #496-01-1984 L1994 **AN IM** *020 †05
KANDALAFT, Victoria Ann. 193 E GOODWYN ST 38111 #028-46-1982 L1984 **AN** *020 †05
KANG, Andrew Ho. RM G326, 956 COURT AVENUE 38163 #024-01-1962 L1972 **RHU IM** *050 †20
KANG, Ellen Soo Sun Song. ■ 38120 #005-11-1955 L1972 **PD** *071 †55
KANNER, Elliott Makary. 930 MADISON AVE, STE 200 38103 #035-20-2001 L2006 **OPH** *020
KAPLAN, Edward Steven. ■ 38120 #035-01-1959 L1964 **NS** *071 †25
KAPLAN, Robert Joel. 1265 UNION AVE 38104 #047-06-1973 L1973 **D** *020 †15 ‡
KAPOOR, Gauri. 956 CT AVE 38163 #496-07-1986 **PHO** *100
KAPTIK, Steven Randall. ■ 38103 #047-05-2002 L2002 **GE** *012 †20
KARAMICHALIS, Ioannis M. ■ 38103 #917-09-1993 L2001 **TS** *012 †85
KARCIOGLU, Zeynel Abidin. 930 MADISON AVE, STE 470 38163 #902-05-1969 L2006 **OPH** *040 †50,35
KARI, Suresh. 1030 JEFFERSON AVE, VETERANS AFFAIRS MEDICAL C 38104 #047-06-1997 L1999 **IM EM** *020 †20
KARKERA, Mohandas Seena. 50 N DUNLAP ST, DEPARTMENT OF ANESTHESIOLO 38103 #496-38-1975 L1980 **AN** *020 †05
KARMEL, Douglas Lawrence. 6005 PARK AVE, MEMPHIS MEDICAL 38119 #035-09-1990 L1992 **IM** *020 †20
KARRI, Someswara R. 1211 UNION AVE, STE 150 38104 #495-58-1980 L2001 **CD IM** *020 †20
KASPER, Kenneth C, Jr. 1755 KIRBY PKWY, STE 330 38120 #048-13-1994 L1998 **AN** *020 †05
KASSIS, Laila Issa. 6385 STAGE RD, STE 2 38134 #407-32-1966 L1973 **PD RHU** *020 †55
KASTAN, Michael Barry. 332 N LAUDERDALE ST, ST. JUDE CHILDREN'S RSCH H 38105 #028-02-1984 L1998 **PD** *020 †55
KATHAWALA, Ahsan H. 1264 WESLEY DR STE 501, CRESCENT MED INC 38116 #495-74-1989 L1996 **IM** *020 †20
KATHAWALA, Arifa. 6005 PARK AVE, STE 905B 38119 #495-74-1989 L2001 **AN** *020 †05
KATHAWALA, Zulekha. 6005 PARK AVE, STE 900B 38119 #495-74-1987 L1997 **IM** *020 †20
KATZ, Gilbert Marvin. ■ 38116 #047-06-1964 L1964 **P** *020
KATZ, Paul Jay. 6401 POPLAR AVE, STE 400 38119 #047-06-1990 L1992 **IM** *020 †20
KAUFMAN, Joan Arlene. 1030 JEFFERSON AVE, VA MED CTR RAD ONC DPT 38104 #004-01-1978 L1995 **RO PD** *020 †80
KAUFMAN, Robert Alan. 848 ADAMS AVE DEPT RAD 38103 #016-02-1974 L1988 **R** *020 †80
KAUFMAN, Seth Ian. 100 N HUMPHREYS BLVD 38120 #067-01-1983 L1986 **PMM PLM** *020 †05
KAZEMI, Shoeleh. 956 COURT AVE 38163 #517-05-2001 **IM** *100
KAZMI, Asif Saeed. ■ 38103 #704-04-1999 L2008 **NEP** *012 †20
KE, Raymond Weehan. 80 HUMPHREYS CTR, STE 307 38120 #064-01-1986 L1992 **REN GYN** *020 †30
KEARNEY, Nicole Shuntell. 1270 ISLE POINTE DR 38103 #047-06-2004 L2006 **PD** *100
KEENE, Leslie Thompson. 6401 POPLAR AVE, STE 530 38119 #047-06-2002 L2006 **OBG** *020
KELLEY, Bobby Jerald. 50 HUMPHREYS CTR, STE 28 38120 #047-06-1963 L1964 **NEP IM** *020 †20
KELLY, Stephen Joseph. ■ 38103 #001-02-2004 L2007 **OPH** *012
KENNEDY, Adam Monroe. ■ 38111 #021-05-2007 **IM ORS** *012
KENNEDY, Albert Franklin. 6215 HUMPHREYS BLVD, STE 500 38120 #047-06-1986 L1987 **OBG** *020 †30
KENNEDY, Jennifer Lynne. ■ 38163 #047-06-2008 *012
KENNEDY, Kristy Roper. ■ 38111 #021-05-2007 **IM** *012
KENNEDY, Lisa. 5050 POPLAR AVE, SPECIALISTS 38157 #001-06-1988 L1989 **PUD IM** *020 †20
KENNEDY, Ross Donoho. 3181 POPLAR AVE, STE 200 38111 #054-04-1965 L1966 **PO** *020 †05
KENT, Robert Morris. 1755 KIRBY PKWY, STE 330 38120 #047-06-1987 L1988 **AN** *020 †05
KERLAN, Robert Ashley. 6005 PARK AVE, MEMPHIS MEDICAL 38119 #047-06-1969 L1969 **GE IM** *020 †20
KERR, Natalie Christine. UNIVERSITY OF TENNESSEE, 930 MADISON AVE, #470 38163 #011-03-1987 L1991 **OPH** *020 †35
KESTERSON, Georgina. 1755 KIRBY PKWY, STE 330 38120 #012-01-1986 L1995 **AN** *020 †05
KETCHERSIDE, William Jos. 1211 UNION AVE, METHODIST HEALTHCARE 38104 #016-02-1979 L2006 **OS NS** *071 †25
KHAJA, Ibrahim Ali. 956 COURT AVE 38163 #496-27-1997 L2006 **P** *100
KHALIQ, Fazila. 956 CT AVE, UNIV OF TN COLL OF MED 38163 #704-06-2003 **IM** *012
KHAN, Amna Bashir. ■ 38103 #704-01-2001 **END** *012 †20
KHAN, Asma. 4299 ELVIS PRESLEY BLVD 38116 #704-16-1979 L1999 **PD** *020
KHAN, Bilal Qamar. 956 COURT AVE 38163 #704-20-2002 **IM** *012

8454

■ = Address Information Privacy Protected

KHAN, Haroon Nasir. 6027 WALNUT GROVE RD, STE 312 38120 #704-02-1998 L2006 **ID** *020
KHAN, Khuram S. 956 COURT AVE, UNIV TN COLL MED 38103 #704-01-1987 **VIR** *100
KHAN, Mohammed Bahadur. 3960 KNIGHT ARNOLD RD, STE 110 38118 #305-01-1984 L1989 **IM NEP** *020
KHAN, Nabeel Hasan. ■ 38103 #704-01-1996 L2003 **IM GE** *020 †20
KHAN, Shahid Ishaq. 1211 UNION AVE STE 495 38104 #704-04-1981 L1997 **CD** *020 †20
KHAN, Shehma. ■ 38103 #496-35-2002 L2007 **PEM** *012
KHANDEKAR, A Alim. 1325 EASTMORELAND AVE, STE 220 38104 #704-03-1970 L1977 **TS** *020 †85,90
KHANDEKAR, Sayra Ahmed. ■ 38120 #021-01-2005 **IM** *100
KHANDEKAR, Sofia Haque. 1264 WESLEY DR STE 405 38116 #160-02-1970 L1977 **IM** *020 †20
KHANI, Munir Kamel. VET ADMIN HOSP, DEPT PSYCH 38104 #605-01-1974 L1977 **P** *100 †75
KHATTAK, Taslim Akhtar. 6005 PARK AVE, STE 433B 38119 #704-09-1984 L1997 **IM** *020 †20
KHURI, Radwan Rafik. 3150 LENOX PARK BLVD, STE 214 38115 #605-01-1978 L1980 **P ADM** *020 †75
KIEFER, Patsy. 1755 KIRBY PKWY, STE 330 38120 #047-06-1962 L1963 **AN** *071 †05
KILEDJIAN, Vartkes. 6005 PARK AVE, STE 1004B 38119 #605-01-1969 L1972 **GS** *020
KIM, Jeong-Hoon. 956 COURT AVE 38163 #583-02-1994 **IM FM** *100
KIM, Michael Paul. 956 CT AVE, RM E222 38163 #036-01-2005 **GS** *012
KIMBALL, Brent Young. ■ 38104 #035-01-2007 **GS** *012
KIMBALL, Noah Braden. ■ 38117 #047-06-1968 L1971 **AN** *071 †05
KIMZEY, Gary Wayne. 1755 KIRBY PKWY, STE 330 38120 #047-06-1977 L1979 **AN** *020
KINCADE, Matthew Clark. ■ 38103 #004-01-2003 L2008 **U** *012
KING, Charles Mack. ■ 38103 #004-01-1936 L1939 **OPH** *075 †35
KING, Cynthia Lynn. 814 JEFFERSON AVE, STE 221F 38105 #422-01-2002 L2007 **ID** *100 †20
KING, Stephen R. SUITE A212, 956 COURT AVENUE 38163 #048-12-1985 L1991 **PS OS** *020 †65
KING, William Scott, Jr. 6029 WALNUT GROVE RD, STE 404 38120 #047-06-1973 L1974 **VS OS** *020 †85
KINK, Rudy John. 50 N DUNLAP ST, MED CTR 38103 #016-11-2003 L2006 **PEM** *012 †55
KINNARD, Jennifer Jones. ■ 38120 #047-06-1972 L1972 **IM NEP** *071
KINNARD, Michael Smithson. 6005 PARK AVE, STE 906 38119 #047-06-1973 L1973 **CD** *020
KIRALY, Megan Faye. ■ 38103 #047-06-2008 *012
KIRKLAND, Frances Glasgow. ■ 38111 #047-06-2006 **D** *012
KIRKLEY, John Beauchamp. 814 JEFFERSON AVE, MEMPHIS & SHELBY CO HLTH D 38105 #004-01-1948 L1980 **GYN GP** *071 †30
KIRKPATRICK, Robert Dean. 1005 HARBOR AVE 38113 #047-06-1974 L1975 **OM FM** *020 †18
KISTLER, Sarah Ellen. 1030 JEFFERSON AVE, VA MEDICAL CENTER 38104 #041-02-1986 L2000 **IM** *020 †20
KITABCHI, Abbas Eqbal. 956 CT AVE STE D334 38163 #039-01-1965 L1968 **DIA END** *050 †20
KLINE, Robert Paul. 966 E RIVERWALK DR 38120 #047-06-1956 L1956 **GYN** *020 †30
KNAPP, Katherine Marie. 332 N LAUDERDALE ST MS 600, ST JUDE CHILD RES HOSP 38105 #004-01-1994 L2000 **PDI PD** *020 †55
KNECHT, Kenneth Richard. ■ 38105 #047-06-1997 L1998 **PD** *020 †55 ‡
KNEPPER, John Guyton. 50 N DUNLAP ST, ER DEPT 38103 #021-01-1968 L1990 **PD** *020 †55
KNIGHT, Cameron Dewayne. ■ 38103 #047-06-2005 **ORS** *012
KNIGHT, Janet L. 6401 POPLAR AVE STE 405 38119 #039-01-1980 L1985 **D** *020 †15
KNOTT, David Howard. 3960 KNIGHT ARNOLD RD #105 38118 #047-06-1963 L1964 **ADM FM** *020 †18 ‡
KNOX, Robert John. UNIV OF TN MEMPHIS, DEPT GASTRO 38163 #913-03-1977 **GE** *100
KOCH, Robert Walter. 899 MADISON AVE, EMERG DEPT 38103 #047-06-1983 L1985 **EM** *020
KOGAN, Alexander. 66 N PAULINE ST, STE 206 38105 #913-69-1971 L2000 **BBK** *020 †50
KOIRALA, Kanchan. ■ 38103 #495-67-1997 **PCC** *012 †20
KOLEYNI, Asghar. 6005 PARK AVE, STE 1007B 38119 #517-01-1962 L1973 **PS** *020
KOMOLAFE, Babatunde Oluwa. ■ 38115 #690-05-2005 **IM** *012
KONERU, Padmaja. 6215 HUMPHREYS BLVD, STE 310 38120 #495-21-1991 L2004 **NPM** *020 †55 ‡
KOPLON, Michael David. 6005 PARK AVE, MEMPHIS MEDICAL 38119 #001-02-1995 L2000 **IM** *020 †20
KORONES, Sheldon Bernarr. 853 JEFFERSON AVE, RM 201 38103 #047-06-1947 L1948 **NPM PD** *071 †55
KOSTOHRYZ, Francis Thos. ■ 38135 #048-02-1956 L1956 **R** *071
KOUMBOURLI-ECONOMIDES, Ag. 451 LINDEN AVE 38126 #418-01-1973 L1977 **PD PDA** *020 †55
KRAHN, Tim Henry. 6286 BRIARCREST AVE, FL 2 38120 #039-01-1987 L1989 **ORS** *020 †40
KRASIN, Audrey Leigh. 332 N LAUDERDALE ST, DEPT OF ANESTHESIOLOGY 38105 #048-14-1995 L2000 **PD** *020 †55
KRASIN, Matthew James. 332 N LAUDERDALE ST, ST. JUDE CHILDREN'S RES HO 38105 #048-02-1995 L2000 **RO** *020 †80
KRAUS, Alfred Paul. ■ 38163 #016-01-1941 L1953 **HEM IM** *071 †20
KRAUS, Alfred Paul, Jr. 49 N DUNLAP ST 38103 #047-06-1976 L1977 **IM** *020 †20
KRAUS, David Howard. 5959 PARK AVE 38119 #047-06-1978 L1979 **CD IM** *020 †20
KRAUS, Gordon Jerome. 6005 PARK AVE STE 728B 38119 #047-06-1980 L1981 **IM** *020 †20
KRAUS, Melvin M. 5959 PARK AVE 38119 #047-06-1952 L1954 **IM** *071
KRAUS, Robert Mark. 6005 PARK AVE STE 728B 38119 #047-06-1975 L1976 **IM** *020 †20
KRAUSS, Andrew Mark. 825 RIDGE LAKE BLVD, STE 2 38120 #010-01-1987 L1991 **OPH** *020 †35
KRIGER, Sidney Herman. 6401 POPLAR AVE, STE 340 38119 #047-06-1983 L1984 **OPH** *020 †35
KRISHNAMURTHI, Lakshmi. 4913 RALEIGH COMMON DR, STE 201 38128 #495-66-1989 L2000 **END** *020 †20
KRISLE, Joe Richard, Jr. 55 HUMPHREYS CTR, STE 100 38120 #047-06-1973 L1973 **DR** *020 †80
KRIWANEK, Kelly Lynn. 3803 SUNGROVE CIR E 38135 #028-02-1999 L2001 **PEM** *020 †55
KROLL, Donald Alan. 1030 JEFFERSON AVE, VA MEDICAL CENTER-MEMPHIS 38104 #025-01-1978 L1998 **AN** *050 †05
KRONENBERG, Joel Ivan. 920 ESTATE DR, STE 3 38119 #047-06-1975 L1976 **PD** *020
KUBE, David Arnold. 711 JEFFERSON AVE, UT BCDD 38105 #030-06-1985 L1994 **PD** *020 †55
KULINSKI, Robert Francis. 3787 SUMMER AVE 38122 #047-06-1988 L1990 **IM** *020
KULKARNI, Anand Laxman. 956 COURT AVE 38163 #495-83-1981 **PTH** *100
KULP, Roy, Jr. 6075 POPLAR AVE, STE 405 38119 #047-06-1972 L1973 **DR** *020 †80
KUMAR, Alok. 1265 UNION AVE, NEONATOLOGY, METHODIST HOS 38104 #047-06-2002 L2006 **OBG** *100
KUMAR, Aneel. 956 COURT AVE 38163 #704-16-2004 **IM** *012
KUN, Larry Emanuel. 332 N LAUDERDALE ST MS 220, ST JUDE CHILDS RESCH HOSP 38105 #041-02-1968 L1984 **RO** *020 †80
KUNG, Amy Lingan. ■ 38120 #047-06-2008 *012
KURT, Beth Anne. ■ 38111 #025-12-2001 L2005 **PHO** *012 †20,55
KUTTEH, William Hanna. 6225 HUMPHREYS BLVD 38120 #036-05-1985 L1996 **REN IG** *020 †30
KUYKENDALL, Lucy Elizabet. ■ 38103 #047-06-2008 *012
KY, Thai Vinh. 1030 JEFFERSON AVE 38104 #840-01-1964 L1982 **IM ID** *030 †20
KYLATHU, Ranjit Isaac. 50 N DUNLAP ST, LE BONHEUR CHILDREN'S HOSP 38103 #495-58-1982 L2005 **NPM** *100 †55
KYLE, Joseph Warren. ■ 38120 #047-06-1942 L1942 **IM CD** *071 †20
LACHINA, Frank Michael. 5959 PARK AVE 38119 #001-02-1972 L1998 **PD MDM** *075 †55 ‡
LACY, Susan Northen. 6401 POPLAR AVE, STE 530 38119 #023-07-1993 L1996 **OBG** *020 †30
LA GUARDIA, Stephen Paul. ■ 38117 #004-01-2002 L2006 **CD** *012 †20
LAINE, Agnes A. ■ 38122 #047-06-1951 L1951 **P ORS** *071
LAKE, Jason Edward. 1211 UNION AVE STE 510, CAMPBELL FOUNDATION 38104 #003-01-2004 L2006 **ORS** *012
LAMBERT, Jack William, III. ■ 38104 #047-06-2008 *012
LAMOTHE, Margarita. 5210 POPLAR AVE STE 200 38119 #847-04-1982 L1987 **ID** *020 †20
LAN, Zhi-Qiang. 6025 WALNUT GROVE RD, STE 111 38120 #243-16-1985 L2004 **CD** *020 †20
LANCASTER, Danny Joe. 1265 UNION AVE, METHODIST UNIVERSITY HOSPI 38104 #055-01-1976 L1985 **IM ID** *040 †20
LAND, Mack Alan. 5210 POPLAR AVE STE 2 38119 #047-06-1973 L1974 **ID IM** *020 †20
LANDRIGAN, John W, Jr. 5180 PARK AVE, STE 200 38119 #047-06-1972 L1973 **OBG** *020 †30
LANGHAM, Max R, Jr. 777 WASHINGTON AVE, STEP220 38105 #023-07-1981 L2005 **PDS** *020 †85
LANGSTON, James Wilson. 865 JEFFERSON AVE, UT RADIOLOGY 38163 #047-06-1968 L1969 **DR** *020 †80
LANINGHAM, Fred H, III. 332 N LAUDERDALE ST, MS 210 38105 #004-01-1991 L1997 **PDR** *020 †80
LANKFORD, Ann Tatum. 956 COURT AVE, DEPT OF PEDIATRICS 38163 #047-06-2005 L2008 **PD** *012
LANKFORD, Wm Alexander. 100 N HUMPHREYS BLVD, THE WEST CLINIC 38120 #047-06-1972 L1972 **R** *020 †80
LARAYA, Jose Ari G. 3860 NEW COVINGTON PIKE, PIKE 101 38128 #065-06-1995 L1997 **FM** *020 †18
LARKIN, John C, Jr. 814 JEFFERSON AVE 38105 #047-06-1942 L1943 **PUD IM** *020 †20
LARKIN, Julie Elizabeth. 1265 UNION AVE, STE 135 38104 #021-05-2007 **TY** *012
LARUE, Richard Wayne, Jr. ■ 38103 #047-06-2008 *012
LASATER, Olga Edwards. 1211 UNION AVE STE 300, DUCKWORTH PATHOLOGY GROUP 38104 #030-05-1980 L1986 **PTH** *020 †50
LASTER, Robert Eugene, Jr. 1661 INTERNATIONAL DR, STE 350 38120 #047-06-1970 L1973 **R** *020 †80
LATHRAM, Marvin W, Jr. 176 S BELLEVUE BLVD # 600 38104 #047-06-1942 L1948 **P** *071 †75
LAUGHLIN, Albert E, Jr. 6029 WALNUT GROVE RD, STE 404 38120 #047-06-1966 L1974 **GS VS** *020 †85
LAVARIAS, Santiago Pena. 3333 ELVIS PRESLEY BLVD, STE 101 38116 #748-01-1965 L1989 **GP PUD** *020
LAVELLE, Herman G, Jr. 899 MADISON AVE 38103 #047-06-1951 L1952 **OTO HNS** *071 †45
LAW, Peter Hinchang. ■ 38104 #047-06-2007 **IM** *012
LAWRENCE, Joseph Keith. 1264 WESLEY DR, STE 402 38116 #047-07-1980 L1985 **OBG** *020
LAWRENCE, Scott David. OF MED, UNIV OF TENNESSEE COLL 38163 #035-20-2005 L2005 **OPH** *012
LAWSON, Ronald David. 100 N HUMPHREYS BLVD 38120 #047-06-1973 L1974 **ON** *020 †20
LAZAR, Robert Stanley. 150 COLLINS ST 38112 #008-02-1979 L1992 **PTH** *020 †50
LAZAROWICZ, Michael Paul. ■ 38103 #047-06-2008 *012
LAZARUS, Edward Jay. 853 JEFFERSON AVE, ROUTE 102 38103 #021-05-1973 L2005 **OBG** *040 †30
LEAL, Gumersindo R. 3445 POPLAR AVE, STE 1 38111 #275-01-1954 L1994 **FM FPG** *020 †18 ‡
LEAL, Jorge F. ■ 38120 #649-01-1949 L1959 **U** *071 †95
LEDBETTER, Christopher Kl. ■ 38117 #021-05-2004 **U** *012
LEDERMAN, Henrique Manoel. ■ 38120 #187-12-1969 L1988 **DR** *020 †80
LEDOUX, Mark Steven. 855 MONROE AVE STE 415, UNIV OF TENN HLTH SCI CTR 38163 #021-05-1988 L1995 **N EM** *050 †75
LEE, Grace Younjung. 50 N DUNLAP ST RM 306-307, LE BONHEUR CHILDREN'S MED 38103 #035-47-1995 L2001 **MG PD** *020 †19,55
LEE, Jea Youl. 55 HUMPHREYS CTR STE 100, STE 100 38120 #583-10-1969 L2000 **RO** *020 †80
LEE, Kamela Devi. ■ 38103 #047-07-1991 L1993 **IM** *020
LEE, Ling Hong. 5791 SUMMER TREES DR 38134 #048-04-1958 L1963 **R** *071 †80
LEE, Michael Jerry. ■ 38120 #047-06-2008 *012
LEE, Paul, Jr. 100 N HUMPHREYS BLVD, STE 100 38120 #047-06-1978 L1979 **IM** *020 †20
LEGGETT, David Coleman. 1755 KIRBY PKWY, STE 330 38120 #021-01-1989 L1997 **AN** *020 †05
LEMMI, Helio. 350 N HUMPHREYS BLVD, # 38120 #187-04-1955 L1970 **N SME** *071
LEMMI, Michael Alan. 1661 INTERNATIONAL DR, STE 350 38120 #047-06-1983 L1984 **DR IM** *020 †80
LEMOND, Thomas Charles. ■ 38120 #047-06-2007 **TY** *012
LEMONS, Robert Stanley. 3109 WALNUT GROVE RD 38111 #047-07-2003 L2005 **IMG** *020 †18
LENDERMON, Laura Nell. 7685 WINCHESTER RD, MECHANIX SPORTS & OCCUP 38125 #047-06-1996 L1997 **FM FSM** *020 †18
LENHART, Laurie Ellen. ■ 38104 #001-06-2006 **PD** *012
LEPPERT, William Michael. 1755 KIRBY PKWY, STE 330 38120 #047-06-1981 L1982 **AN PAN** *020 †05
LESTER, Lanya L. ■ 38109 #047-06-1997 **PTH** *100
LESUEUR, Jeffrey Rayne. ■ 38135 #048-04-2007 **OTO** *012
LEUNG, Wing-Hang. 332 N LAUDERDALE ST C6006, ST JUDE CHILDREN'S RSRCH H 38105 #462-01-1988 L1999 **PD PHO** *020 †55
LEVENTHAL, Kris Ann. 4711 POPLAR AVE, STE 200 38117 #047-06-1995 L2000 **PD** *020 †55
LEVIE, Benton Bains. ■ 38120 #036-07-1969 L1994 **PD** *071 †55
LEVIN, Michael Carnes. 1211 UNION AVE STE 200, SEMMES-MURPHEY CLINIC 38104 #041-14-1988 L1997 **N** *020 †75
LEVINE, Paul George. ■ 38103 #035-08-1962 L1968 **PYA P** *071 †75
LEVITCH, Melvyn Abraham. 3960 KNIGHT ARNOLD RD 38118 #047-06-1959 L1959 **P** *020 †75
LEVY, Alan Louis. ■ 38120 #047-06-2004 L2008 **D** *012
LEVY, Joe Simon. 5575 POPLAR AVE, STE 708 38119 #047-06-1966 L1967 **A PD** *020 †55,03
LEW, Dukhee Betty. 848 ADAMS AVE DEPT PED 38103 #041-13-1980 L1986 **AI PD** *075 †55,03
LEWIS, Erin Nicole. ■ 38103 #047-20-2004 L2005 **AI** *012 †20

■ = Address Information Privacy Protected

LEWIS, James Bryant, Jr. 842 JEFFERSON AVE A608 38103 #023-07-1976 L1978 **IM** *040 †20
LEWIS, James Riddell. 6027 WALNUT GROVE RD # 103 38120 #027-01-1990 L1992 **IM** *020 †20
LI, Bo. 6215 HUMPHREYS BLVD, STE 208 38120 #038-41-1999 L2003 **OBG** *020 †30
LI, Bojia. ■ 38119 #047-06-2008 *012
LI, Sherri Xuan. UNIV OF TENNESSEE, DEPT OF OB/GYN 38163 #021-01-2002 L2004 **OBG** *020 †30
LI, Shuxin. 956 COURT AVE 38163 #243-47-1989 L2007 **IM** *012
LI, Yingjun. ■ 38103 #243-72-1995 L2007 **N** *100
LIEBERMAN, Gerald Jay. 80 HUMPHREYS CTR, STE 200 38120 #035-20-1978 L1983 **GE IM** *020 †20
LIMAN, Agnes K. 1030 JEFFERSON AVE, VAMC MEMPHIS 38104 #506-01-1983 L2005 **PCP ATP** *100 †50
LINDER, James Saml. 6029 WALNUT GROVE RD # 109 38120 #047-06-1992 L2000 **OPH** *020 †35
LINDERMUTH, J R. 6005 PARK AVE, STE 1002B 38119 #041-07-1975 L1980 **NS** *071
LINDSEY, Leticia Anne. ■ 38104 #027-01-2001 L2007 **FP** *012
LINDY, Peter Barnes. 2986 KATE BOND RD, STE 301 38133 #021-01-1989 L1994 **ORS** *020
LINN, John Edward. 1245 MADISON AVE 38104 #047-05-1980 L1984 **OPH** *020 †35
LINVILLE, Douglas A, III. 6005 PARK AVE, STE 400 38119 #028-46-1991 L2000 **OSS** *020 †40
LIPMAN, Craig Laurence. 55 HUMPHREYS CTR, STE 100 38120 #035-06-1989 L1996 **R NM** *020 †80,28
LIPSCOMB, Alys H. 220 S CLAYBROOK ST, STE 300 38104 #047-06-1945 L1945 **END IM** *071 †20,28
LIPSEY, George Gartley. 255 S PAULINE ST, MIDTOWN SURGERY CENTER 38104 #047-06-1966 L1971 **AN** *071
LIU, Eileen Ailing. 877 JEFFERSON AVE, CHANDLER 6TH FLOOR 38103 #243-22-1984 L2001 **AN** *020
LIVA, Maud Eva. ■ 38103 #021-01-2007 **OBG** *012
LIVESAY, Christopher H. 5681 QUINCE RD 38119 #010-01-1989 L1997 **AN** *020 †05
LIVINGSTON, Leon Otis. 6215 HUMPHREYS BLVD, STE 300 38120 #023-07-1995 L2001 **PD** *020 †55
LOCHEMES, John Jos. 3980 NEW COVINGTON PIKE, STE 200 38128 #056-06-1988 L1996 **ORS** *020 †40
LOCKRIDGE, Leandrea Crist. ■ 38107 #047-06-2008 *012
LOGUE, Alicia Josephine. ■ 38111 #001-06-2003 L2007 **GS** *012
LOGUE, Amanda Case. ■ 38117 #021-06-2005 L2008 **IM** *012
LOISEAU, Jean Claude. 1264 WESLEY DR STE 304 38116 #440-01-1972 L1998 **GS** *020 †85
LONERGAN, Robert Philip, III. 6005 PARK AVE, STE 608 38119 #051-01-1995 L2003 **ORS** *020 †40
LONG, Celeste Stokely. 6263 POPLAR AVE STE 1052 38119 #047-06-1989 L1991 **IM** *020 †20
LONG, James Anthony. ■ 38111 #012-22-2006 L2008 **DR** *012
LONG, Mary Elizabeth. UNIV OF TENNESSEE, DEPT OF OB/GYN 38163 #012-22-2006 **OBG** *012
LONG, Taura Laverne. 3694 WOOD GLADE LN 38116 #038-41-2008 *012
LONG, Timothy Edward. 8071 WINCHESTER RD 38125 #047-06-1989 L1991 **IM** *020 †20
LONG, William E. 220 S CLAYBROOK ST, STE 300 38104 #047-06-1951 L1952 **R** *071 †80
LONGJOHN, Mindy Kay. ■ 38103 #021-01-2002 L2004 **PEM** *012 †55
LORSBACH, Robert Brian. ■ 38103 #019-02-1994 L1999 **PTH** *020 †50
LOSKOVITZ, Lewis Irwin. 2018 S GERMANTOWN RD 38138 #047-06-1971 L1972 **GP FM** *020 †18
LOVE, Varna Mae Peyton. 6215 HUMPHREYS BLVD # 100 38120 #047-06-1953 L1960 **R** *020
LOVEJOY, George S. ■ 38115 #047-06-1943 L1943 **PD PHP** *071 †55
LOVELACE, Jerry Lee, Jr. 1488 MADISON AVE 38104 #047-06-2000 L2005 **IM** *020
LOVELL, Laverne Ray. 1325 EASTMORELAND AVE, STE 370 38104 #023-12-1986 L1990 **NS** *020 †25
LOVING, Martha A. ■ 38117 #047-06-1949 L1949 **GYN** *071 †30
LUCE, Edward Andrew. 80 HUMPHREYS CTR, STE 100 38120 #020-12-1965 L2004 **PS HS** *020 †65,85
LUNCEFORD, Travis Eugene. 7865 EDUCATORS LN, STE 300 38133 #021-01-1956 L1983 **FM** *020 †18
LUNSFORD, Kevin Michael. 3950 NEW COVINGTON PIKE, STE 200 38128 #012-01-1989 L1995 **GS** *020 †85
LUQMAN, Ashar. 956 CT AVE, UNIV OF TN COLL OF MED 38163 #704-21-2005 **IM** *012
LYDA, Mark Harry. 6046 KNIGHT ARNOLD ROD EXT, STE 101 38115 #040-02-1989 L1999 **HMP** *020 †50
LYN-BOSWELL, Carla G. 3030 COVINGTON PIKE, STE 100 38128 #308-03-1997 L2006 **FM** *100
LYNCH, Mary T. ■ 38119 #024-07-1950 L1953 **GP IM** *071
LYTLE, Nathaniel W. ■ 38111 #048-13-2007 L2007 **GS** *012
MABIE, Matthew Wheeler. 5050 POPLAR AVE, SPECIALISTS 38157 #012-01-1997 L1999 **PCC** *020
MABRY, Edward Hays, Jr. 6075 POPLAR AVE, STE 405 38119 #047-06-1972 L1973 **DR** *020 †80
MAC GAW, Douglas Merritt. 2860 COVINGTON PIKE 38128 #047-06-1970 L1971 **PD** *020
MACHIN, James Elliott. 55 HUMPHREYS CTR, STE 100 38120 #017-20-1978 L1981 **DR** *020 †80
MADASU, Ravi Kiran. 1265 UNION AVE, EMERGENCY DEPARTMENT 38104 #654-01-1999 L2002 **IM** *020 †20
MADDEN, Renee Marie. 332 N LAUDERDALE ST # 260 38105 #056-05-1995 L2005 **PD** *020 †55
MADLOCK, Lawrence Elliott. 1265 UNION AVE 38104 #048-04-1977 L1977 **IM** *020 †20
MADUBUONWU, Paul N. ■ 38119 #690-07-1982 **FM** *100
MADUSKA, Albert Lowell. 1755 KIRBY PKWY, STE 130 38120 #019-02-1965 L1971 **AN** *020 †05
MAGILL, H Lynn. 55 HUMPHREYS CTR, STE 100 38120 #016-01-1970 L1980 **NR PDR** *020 †80
MAGNOTTI, Louis Jude. ■ 38120 #033-05-1995 L2001 **GS** *020 †85
MAGSINO, Cesar H, Jr. 1211 UNION AVE STE 340, DEPARTMENT OF MEDICINE 38104 #748-07-1986 L2002 **END** *020 †20
MAHAN, Lisa June. 877 JEFFERSON AVE, FL 5 38103 #047-06-1997 L2001 **IM** *020 †20
MAJZLIK, Anna Christina. ■ 38111 #021-06-2004 L2006 **IM** *100 †20
MAKAPUGAY, Lydia M. 150 COLLINS ST 38112 #748-08-1986 L1993 **OS** *062 †50
MAKRES, Joseph Christophe. ■ 38104 #047-06-2008 *012
MALCOLM, John Bradley. ■ 38117 #051-04-2003 L2007 **U** *012
MALHOTRA, Mandeep Kaur. 1030 JEFFERSON AVE, VA MEDICAL CENTER 38104 #495-29-1999 L2002 **IM** *012
MALINOWSKA, Dorota M. 920 MADISON AVE, SUITE # 3 38163 #759-03-1992 L2007 **END** *012 †20
MALLARE, Johanna M T. 50 N DUNLAP ST 4TH FL, UNIVERSITY OF TENNESSEE 38103 #748-01-1991 L2003 **PDE** *020 †55
MALLETT, Veronica Thierry. 853 JEFFERSON STE E102, U OF TN HEALTH SCIENCE CTR 38163 #025-12-1983 L2005 **OBG** *020 †30

MALLOV, Joseph Stephan. 5659 S REX RD 38119 #016-02-1972 L2000 **IM END** *020 †20
MALONE, Patrick Kirkland. 409 AYERS ST 38105 #056-06-1986 L1988 **IM** *020 †20
MANCELL, Jimmie. ■ 38133 #047-06-1994 L1995 **IM** *075 †20
MANEJWALA, Fazal M. 7900 US HIGHWAY 64, GYNECOLOGY ASSOCIATES PC 38133 #041-12-1994 L1995 **OBG** *020 †30
MANGIANTE, Eugene C, Jr. 956 COURT AVE 38103 #047-06-1975 L1976 **TRS GS** *040 †85
MANJUNATH, Skantha Krupa. 956 CT AVE, UNIV OF TN COLL OF MED 38163 #495-21-2003 **IM** *012
MANKIN, John C. 5349 ESTATE OFFICE DR, STE 3 38119 #047-06-1951 L1951 **GS OS** *071 †85
MANNAN, Ghalib. 6027 WALNUT GROVE RD, STE 312 38120 #917-18-1992 L2001 **ID** *020 †20
MANSBACH, Chas Milton, II. 920 MADISON AVE STE 240 38163 #035-19-1963 L1986 **GE** *050 †20
MANSOOR, Simin. 956 CT AVE, UNIV OF TN COLL OF MED 38163 #704-02-2003 **N** *012
MANSOUR, Nawar E. 176 S BELLEVUE BLVD, STE 502 38104 #875-01-1989 L1994 **NEP** *020 †20
MARCHAND, Gregory Joseph. DEPT OF OB/GYN, UNIV OF TENNESSEE 38163 #306-01-2004 **OBG** *012
MARDIS, Marlah Hubbard. 1689 NONCONNAH BLVD, STE 105 38132 #012-21-1991 L1994 **FM** *020 †18
MARIENCHECK, William I, Jr. 5050 POPLAR AVE, SPECIALISTS 38157 #028-02-1994 L2000 **PCC** *020 †20
MARIENCHECK, William Irvi. 5050 POPLAR AVE, STE 800 38157 #047-06-1965 L1965 **PUD SME** *020 †20
MARINO, Christopher R. 1030 JEFFERSON AVE, VA MEDICAL CENTER 38104 #035-20-1982 L1995 **IM** *050 †20
MARKER, Howard Wm. 6005 PARK AVE, MEMPHIS MEDICAL 38119 #048-02-1958 L1962 **IM RHU** *020 †20
MARKS, Michael Edward. 55 HUMPHREYS CTR, STE 100 38120 #001-02-1982 L2002 **RO** *020 †80
MARLER, Donna Marie. 1200 PEABODY AVE 38104 #047-06-1991 L1993 **FM** *020 †18
MARON ALFARO, Gabriela Ma. 956 COURT AVE 38163 #341-03-2000 **PDI** *012
MARSHALL, Daniel Payne. 515 N HIGHLAND ST 38122 #047-06-1975 L1976 **GP GPM** *020
MARSHALL, Michael Ralph. 6225 HUMPHREYS BLVD, STE 301 38120 #047-06-1970 L1970 **OBG** *020 †30
MARTIN, Henry Frank, Jr. 3340 POPLAR AVE, STE 326 38111 #027-01-1976 L1977 **CD IM** *020 †20
MARTIN, Rodney Addison. 1286 PEABODY AVE 38104 #047-07-1986 L1988 **GS** *020 †85
MARTINEZ, Antonio. 1300 JEFFERSON AVE, PATHOLOGY SVC (113) 38104 #847-04-1968 L1992 **PTH** *020 †50
MARTINEZ, Caridad A. 332 N LAUDERDALE ST, DEPT HEMATOLOGY/ONCOLOGY 38105 #042-01-2001 L2004 **PD** *100 †55
MARTINEZ, Jesus Felix. 1211 UNION AVE STE 400 38104 #341-01-1993 L2007 **N** *020
MARX, Ann Pompe. 1000 BROOKFIELD RD, STE 100 38119 #016-42-1994 L2000 **PS** *020 †65
MASCIOLI, Anthony Andrew. 1211 UNION AVE STE 510, CAMPBELL FOUNDATION 38104 #035-08-2003 L2005 **ORS** *012
MASON, Katherine Anna. ■ 38117 #047-06-2006 **PD** *012
MASON, Kimberly W. 1211 UNION AVE, STE 300 38104 #047-06-1995 L1999 **PTH** *020
MASON, Mark Thomas. 3173 KIRBY WHITTEN RD, STE 104 38134 #047-06-1995 L1998 **P** *020 †75
MASSOUH, Rawad. ■ 38107 #875-01-2003 **FP** *012
MASTROFRANCESCO, Lois. 1661 INTERNATIONAL DR, STE 350 38120 #010-02-1983 L2007 **RO** *020 †80
MATHES, Gordon Lawrence. 6019 WALNUT GROVE RD 38120 #035-01-1948 L1949 **U** *071 †95
MATHEW, Alexander. 956 CT AVE, COLEMAN RM E228 38163 #001-02-1994 L2006 **CRS** *020 †85
MATHIS, Christopher Lynn. 6215 HUMPHREYS BLVD, STE 300 38120 #047-06-1989 L1992 **PD** *020 †55
MATTEWADA, Vijay Kishore. 3860 NEW COVINGTON PIKE, STE 101 38128 #495-57-1992 L2005 **FM** *020 †18
MATTHEWS, Alexander. 1301 PRIMACY PKWY, PRACTICE CTR 38119 #021-01-2007 **FP** *012
MATTINGLY, Jay Edward. 877 JEFFERSON AVE 38103 #047-06-1979 L1985 **AN** *020 †05
MAUCK, Benjamin Matthew. 956 COURT AVE, DEPT OF ORTHOPAEDIC SURGER 38163 #047-06-2006 **ORS** *012
MAUER, Alvin Marx. 3 DUNPLAP 38163 #018-03-1953 L1973 **ON HEM** *071 †55
MAXWELL, Angela Cherie. ■ 38187 #004-01-2008 *012
MAY, William Neil. 49 N DUNLAP ST 38103 #047-06-1971 L1977 **CHN N** *020 †55,75
MAYFIELD, Amber Meshell. ■ 38111 #021-06-2003 L2006 **PHO** *012 †55
MAYFIELD, Russell W. ■ 38104 #047-06-1950 L1950 **GP** *071 †18
MAYS, Kit Sanford. 55 HUMPHREYS CTR, STE 200 38104 #047-06-1972 L1973 **PME AN** *020
MAYS, Owita Renee. 6005 PARK AVE, MEMPHIS MEDICAL 38119 #047-06-1999 L2001 **IM** *020 †20
MAZUMDER, Shirin Asleha. ■ 38103 #016-01-2005 L2005 **IM** *012
MBEWE, Bernard Magereta. 3141 DIRECTORS ROW, CONCENTRA MEDICAL CENTERS 38131 #047-07-1989 L1994 **OM** *020 †70
MBURA, Jaffery Saidi. ■ 38177 #880-01-1977 **FM** *100
MCBRIDE, Erin Ruth. ■ 38104 #047-06-2008 *012
MCCABE, Michael Patrick. ■ 38104 #021-01-2006 **ORS** *012
MC CALLA, Mary Rainey. 1719 KIRBY PKWY 38120 #047-06-1981 L1982 **OTO FPS** *020 †45
MC CARVILLE, Mary E. 332 N LAUDERDAL ST #D-116A, DIAGNOSTIC IMAGING DEPT 38105 #018-03-1990 L1998 **DR** *020 †80
MCCLARTY, Philip Patrick. ■ 38103 #047-06-2008 *012
MC CLURE, James G. ■ 38111 #047-06-1947 L1947 **ORS** *071 †40
MCCOY, Dennis Dewayne. 6005 PARK AVE STE 802, PARKER PAIN & REHAB 38119 #305-01-2001 L2006 **APM** *020 †05
MCCOY, Elishae M. ■ 38111 #047-06-2008 *012
MC CULLERS, Jonathan A. 332 N LAUDERDALE ST, DEPT OF INFECTIOUS DISEASE 38105 #001-02-1993 L1996 **PD PDI** *020 †55
MC DANIEL, Carter Ennis. 6029 WALNUT GROVE RD, STE 404 38120 #047-06-1978 L1979 **GS VS** *020 †85
MC DONALD, Donald Lee. 915 UNIVERSITY ST 38107 #004-01-1993 L1996 **P** *020
MC DONALD, Mary Neumann. 6215 HUMPHREYS BLVD # 200 38120 #047-06-1983 L1984 **OBG** *020 †30
MC DONALD, Michael Baird. 6005 PARK AVE, STE 500B 38119 #047-06-1982 L1983 **CD IM** *020 †20
MC EACHERN, Robt Coleman. 5050 POPLAR AVE, SPECIALISTS 38157 #027-01-1992 L2002 **IM PUD** *020 †20

MC EWAN, Robert C, Jr. 756 RIDGE LAKE BLVD, STE 120 38120 #047-06-1964 L1965 **FM** *020 †18
MC FADDEN, Isaac Jos, II. ■ 38111 #045-01-1965 L1997 **P OS** *020 †75,05
MC FARLANE, Joshua J. 1331 UNION AVE, STE 800 38104 #048-12-2003 L2003 **HO** *012 †20
MC GEE, Jesse Edward. 4567 MILLBRANCH RD 38116 #018-03-1974 L1979 **CD IM** *020 †20
MC GEHEE, John Lucius. 5959 PARK AVE 38119 #047-06-1980 L1983 **SME PUD** *020 †20
MC GHEE, Brown Omar. 360 E EH CRUMP BLVD 38126 #056-05-1976 L1981 **GP GS** *020
MC GILL, Lora Jannette. 6401 POPLAR AVE, STE 420 38119 #021-01-1987 L1993 **N** *020 †75
MC GLOTHAN, Corey Shane. 1264 WESLEY DR, STE 402 38116 #001-02-1999 L2003 **OBG** *020
MCGLOTHAN, Kim Rudolph. ■ 38119 #047-06-2007 **IM** *012
MC GOWAN, Leslie Raines. 6027 WALNUT GROVE RD # 319 38120 #047-06-1981 L1982 **U** *020 †95
MC GRATH, Virginia. 6029 WALNUT GROVE RD, STE 404 38120 #047-06-1997 L2003 **GS** *020 †85
MCGREGOR, Amy. 777 WASHINGTON AVE, STE P240 38105 #028-02-1998 L2005 **CN** *020 †55,75
MC GREGOR, Lisa Macnabb. 332 N LAUDERDALE ST, ST. JUDE CHILDREN'S HOSPIT 38105 #023-07-1998 L2004 **PHO** *100 †55
MC GUKIN, Donald Richard. 66 N PAULINE ST, STE 300 38105 #422-01-1988 L1997 **FM** *020
MC HUGH, Peter Howard. 5659 S REX RD 38119 #036-01-2000 L2003 **END MPD** *020
MC INTIRE, Mary Ellen. 3284 WINDERLY CV 38125 #047-06-1985 L2002 **FM** *020
MC INTOSH, Cynthia. 951 COURT AVE 38103 #035-19-1977 L1990 **P CHP** *020
MC KAY, Roxane. 50 N DUNLAP ST STE 2598, LEBONHEUR CHILDREN'S MEDIC 38103 #016-02-1970 L2007 **GS TS** *020
MC KENZIE, Eugene Eaton. 3960 KNIGHT ARNOLD RD, STE 203 38118 #047-06-1959 L1960 **IM OS** *020
MC LAURIN, Eugene B. 6060 PRIMACY PKWY, STE 200 38119 #027-01-1973 L1974 **OPH** *020 †35 ‡
MC LENDON, Richard E. 1211 UNION AVE, STE 300 38104 #047-06-1976 L1978 **PTH** *020 †50 ‡
MC LEOD, Alan Jay. 55 HUMPHREYS CTR, STE 100 38120 #019-02-1978 L1991 **DR** *020 †80
MC MILLAN, David Arthur. 3960 NEW COVINGTON PIKE, METHODIST NORTH EMERGENCY 38128 #047-06-1982 L1984 **EM** *020
MC NAMARA, Gregory. ■ 38120 #042-04-1982 L1990 **AN IM** *020 †05
MC QUISTON, Elise T. 1265 UNION AVE 38104 #047-06-1944 L1944 **GP** *020
MC RAE, Marilyn. ■ 38117 #001-02-1969 L1974 **PD** *075 †55
MC VICAR, Kathryn Anne. 777 WASHINGTON AVE, STE 335 38105 #035-06-1996 L2007 **CHN** *020
MEANS, Seth Winston. ■ 38105 #047-06-2008 *012
MEDURI, G Umberto. RM H316, 956 COURT AVENUE 38163 #561-11-1977 L1988 **PUD CCM** *050 †20
MEFFORD, Amanda Taylor. ■ 38122 #020-12-2005 L2008 **PD** *012
MEHRAZIN, Reza. ■ 38103 #661-02-2006 **GS** *012
MEHTA, Amit. ■ 38103 #039-01-2005 **PD** *012
MENEES, James Keith. 695 BROOKHAVEN CIR 38117 #020-02-1980 L1981 **IM** *020
MENSAH, Daniel. ■ 38119 #409-21-1969 L1976 **OBG** *020 †30
MERIWETHER, Thomas W, III. 6019 WALNUT GROVE RD 38120 #047-06-1960 L1960 **IM ISM** *071 †20
METZGER, Monika. ■ 38103 #409-39-1994 L2005 **PHO** *100 †55
METZGER, William Edgar. 7685 WINCHESTER RD 38125 #047-06-1954 L1954 **FM** *020 †18
MEYER, Ira Keith. 687 JEFFERSON AVE 38105 #047-06-1981 L1981 **GS** *020
MEYER, Norman Lewis. STE E-102, 853 JEFFERSON AVE 38163 #047-06-1982 L1982 **OBG** *020 †30
MEZA, Elena Isabel. 6063 MT MORIAH RD EXT # 4 38115 #649-33-1986 L1992 **PD** *020 †55
MICHAEL, Christie Farris. 2941 ROBIN RD, UNIVERSITY OF TENNESSEE 38111 #047-06-1998 L2000 **AI** *020 †20,55,03
MICHAEL, Lattimore M, II. 6325 HUMPHREYS BLVD 38120 #047-06-1998 L1999 **NS** *100
MICHAEL, Ronald C. 3775 COVINGTON PIKE 38135 #495-47-1975 L1991 **GE IM** *020 †20
MICHAELS, Matthew G. 1068 CRESTHAVEN RD, STE 400 38119 #051-04-1992 L1996 **PM** *020 †60
MICHELSEN, Anette Erika. ■ 38111 #047-06-2007 **PD** *012
MIKOLAENKO, Ivan. 855 MONROE AVE. #415, UNIV OF TENNESSEE MEMPHIS 38163 #913-86-1992 L2007 **N** *012
MILBURN, Mark Andrew. 6286 BRIARCREST AVE, STE 300 38120 #045-01-1992 L1994 **OTO** *020 †45
MILES, Robert Millard. ■ 38111 #047-06-1943 L1943 **GS** *071 †85
MILEV, Dilyana Nencheva. 956 CT AVE, UNIV OF TN COLL OF MED 38163 #198-03-1993 **P** *012
MILFORD, Lee Watson, Jr. ■ 38115 #012-05-1946 L1954 **ORS** *071 †40
MILLER, Ashley B. 5050 SANDERLIN AVE, LAURELWOOD PEDIATRICS 38117 #047-06-1998 L2000 **PD** *020 †55
MILLER, Christopher D. 1325 EASTMORELAND AVE #101 38104 #030-05-1999 L2001 **GE** *100 †20
MILLER, Leona Arica. 3109 WALNUT GROVE RD 38111 #065-10-1988 L2003 **FM** *020 †18
MILLER, Logan Earl. 4707 WOODRIDGE DR 38116 #038-41-1981 L1986 **FM** *020 †18
MILLER, Stephen Thos. 1211 UNION AVE STE 721, METHODIST HEALTHCARE 38104 #023-07-1970 L1974 **IM IMG** *040 †20
MILLER, Thomas Iva. 6325 HUMPHREYS BLVD 38120 #027-01-1960 L1966 **NS** *071 †25
MILLIGAN, Kerry Lee. 3809 COVINGTON PIKE 38135 #047-06-1995 L1996 **IM** *020 †20
MILLS, Dan Clifford. ■ 38117 #005-12-1952 L1952 **GYN** *020 †30
MILLS, Mark Randall. 6305 HUMPHREYS BLVD, STE 205 38120 #027-01-2000 L2003 **IM** *020 †80
MILNOR, J Pervis, Jr. 20 DUDLEY ST STE 811B 38103 #047-06-1942 L1942 **IM CD** *071 †20
MILNOR, J Pervis, III. 920 ESTATE DR, STE 8 38119 #047-06-1974 L1976 **AN EM** *020 †05
MINARD, Gayle. SECOND FLOOR, 910 MADISON 38163 #038-41-1981 L1989 **TRS GS** *020 †85
MINK, Jennifer Dayle. 2860 COVINGTON PIKE 38128 #047-06-2002 L2005 **PD** *020
MINNIEAR, Timothy Dean. ■ 38103 #025-07-2003 L2005 **PDI** *012 †55
MINTZ, Philip Grayer. 8970 WINCHESTER RD 38125 #047-06-1978 L1980 **FM** *020 †18
MIR, Hassan Riaz. 1211 UNION AVE STE 510, CAMPBELL CLINIC FOUNDATION 38104 #055-01-2003 L2006 **ORS** *012
MIRRO, Joseph. 66 N PAULINE ST STE 633 38105 #041-13-1975 L1981 **PHO PD** *020 †55
MIRVIS, David Marc. 66 N PAULINA, STE 463 38163 #035-46-1970 L1975 **CD** *030 †20
MIRZA, Imran. ■ 38187 #704-16-1987 L2001 **IM PTH** *020 †20
MIRZA, Muhammad Mudassir. 956 COURT AVE 38163 #704-16-2003 **IM** *012
MISHRA, Ashutosh Kumar. 1264 WESLEY DR STE 405 38116 #495-15-1990 L2003 **IM** *020 †20
MISHRA, Shefali. 4829 KAYE RD 38117 #496-38-1996 L2004 **IM** *100
MITCHELL, Carol Jean. 6401 POPLAR AVE, STE 400 38119 #027-01-1983 L1984 **IM** *020 †20
MITCHELL, James Michael. 4325 STAGE RD 38128 #047-06-1971 L1971 **FM** *020
MITCHELL, Thomas Creighto. ■ 38104 #047-06-2006 L2006 **IM** *012
MITCHUM, James Richartz. 1661 INTERNATIONAL DR, STE 350 38120 #047-06-1985 L1986 **DR NM** *020 †80
MITCHUM, William Robson. 6075 POPLAR AVE, STE 405 38119 #047-06-1948 L1948 **R** *071 †80
MITELMAN, Olga. ■ 38120 #041-01-1997 **OPH** *100
MITTAL, Sanjeev Kumar. 6027 WALNUT GROVE RD, STE 402 38120 #496-09-1985 L2000 **IM** *020 †20
MITTLEMAN, Rachal Marie. ■ 38103 #038-43-2004 L2006 **MPD** *012
MIXON, Joseph Allan. 1910 MADISON AVE, BOX 512 38104 #047-06-1995 L1998 **IM** *020 †20
MIXON, Judy. 877 JEFFERSON AVE, 5TH FLOOR ADAMS BLDG 38103 #047-06-1996 L2001 **FM** *020 †18
MIYAIRI, Isao. 956 COURT AVE 38163 #572-20-1995 L2007 **PDI** *100 †55
MIZELLE, Eric Quentin. 3810 WINCHESTER RD 38118 #036-08-1998 L2004 **P** *020
MOFFATT, William Lee, III. 6005 PARK AVE, STE 309 38119 #047-06-1973 L1974 **ORS** *020 †40
MOHAMED, Omar Ahmed. 135 N PAULINE ST, 810 WASHINGTON 38105 #613-01-2001 **P** *012
MOHAN, Kamal Jit. ■ 38187 #495-03-1988 L2001 **IM** *020 †20
MOHAN, Veena. 6025 WALNUT GROVE RD # 311 38120 #495-90-1989 L2004 **IM** *020 †20
MOINUDDIN, Mohammed. 55 HUMPHREYS CTR, STE 100 38120 #495-21-1965 L1972 **NM IM** *020 †28,20 ‡
MOINUDDIN, Shamim. 6046 KNIGHT ARNOLD ROD EXT, STE 101 38115 #495-21-1967 L1974 **PTH PCP** *020 †50
MOISE, Claudia Leonard. 6401 POPLAR AVE STE 530, PENN MARC CENTRE 38119 #048-02-1980 L1982 **OBG** *020 †30 ‡
MONGER, Ralph Horace, Jr. 1264 WESLEY DR STE 607 38116 #047-06-1955 L1955 **U** *020 †95
MONROE, Justin. 6029 WALNUT GROVE RD, STE 404 38120 #047-06-1999 L2004 **CRS** *020 †85
MOODY, Laura O. 150 COLLINS ST 38112 #047-20-1995 L1999 **PTH** *020 †50
MOODY, Norma Marie. ■ 38103 #047-06-2002 **GS** *012
MOOLCHANDANI, Geeta R. 6584 POPLAR AVE, STE 130 38138 #495-17-1983 L1992 **AN** *020
MOORE, Angela A. 865 JEFFERSON AVE, UT MEDICAL GROUP 38163 #047-07-1988 L2002 **DR** *020 †80
MOORE, Dwight Melvyn. 1264 WESLEY DR, STE 402 38116 #047-06-1976 L1979 **OBG** *020
MOORE, Gina Michelle. 2953 BROAD AVE, INC. 38112 #047-07-2000 L2006 **MPD** *020
MOORE, James A. 7685 WINCHESTER RD 38125 #047-06-1953 L1953 **FM** *071 †18
MOORE, John Holland. ■ 38104 #012-01-2004 L2008 **MPD** *012
MOORE, Tammie Tucker. 1030 JEFFERSON AVE, 111AC 38104 #047-06-1995 L1998 **IM** *020 †20
MOORE, Yvonne Frank. 6401 POPLAR AVE STE 530 38119 #028-34-1980 L1981 **OBG** *020 †30
MORADA, Manuel Scarella. 3628 SUMMER AVE 38122 #748-07-1973 L1985 **CHP PD** *020
MORAFA, Olawale Adetayo. 1064 BREEDLOVE ST 38107 #690-01-1986 L2002 **FM** *020 †18 ‡
MORAN, Edward Richard, Jr. 2934 RIDGEWAY RD STE 102 38115 #047-06-1989 L1990 **AN** *020 †05
MORETTA, Anthony C. 50 N DUNLAP ST, LEBONHAR CHILDREN'S HOSPIT 38103 #047-06-1994 L2004 **PD** *020 †55
MORGAN, Jack Colbert. 6005 PARK AVE, STE 509 MED PSYCH ASSOC 38119 #021-01-1971 L1974 **P** *020
MORISY, Lee Richard. 6025 WALNUT GROVE RD, STE 201 38120 #016-42-1980 L1985 **GS CRS** *020 †85
MORRIS, Albert Walker, Jr. 1444 E SHELBY DR STE 205 38116 #010-03-1976 L1978 **DR** *020
MORRIS, Carrie Lynn. ■ 38163 #001-02-2003 L2007 **OPH** *100
MORRIS, Eugene Brannon. 332 N LAUDERDALE ST MS 2, ST. JUDE CHILDREN'S RES HO 38105 #012-01-1998 L2004 **CHN** *020 †55,75
MORRIS, Glenn Scott. 1200 PEABODY AVE 38104 #012-05-1983 L1986 **FM** *020 †18
MORRIS, Stephan Wade. 332 N LAUDERDALE ST, ST JUDE CHILDREN'S RESERCH 38105 #021-06-1980 L1989 **ON IM** *050 †20
MORRIS, Stephen David. 55 HUMPHREYS CTR, STE 100 38120 #047-20-1991 L1997 **RNR** *020 †80
MORRIS, Tamara Jewell. 50 N DUNLAP ST, MED CTR 38103 #001-02-2003 L2007 **PD** *020
MORRISON, R Ray. 332 N LAUDERDALE ST MS734, ST. JUDE CHILDREN'S RESEAR 38105 #030-05-1992 L2005 **PD CCP** *050 †55
MORRISON, Robert Edward. 880 MADISON AVE 38103 #017-20-1967 L1987 **IM ID** *020 †20
MORROW, Helen G. 814 JEFFERSON AVE, MEMPHIS & SHELBY CNTY HEAR 38105 #047-06-1976 L1976 **PD** *020 †55
MORTAZAVI, Hamid. 1211 UNION AVE, STE 400 38104 #517-25-2000 L2006 **N** *020
MOSAH, Michael Mesembe. 956 COURT AVE 38163 #217-01-1982 **FM** *100
MOSELEY, Micah Seth. ■ 38126 #047-06-2008 *012
MOSER, Davis D. 6075 POPLAR AVE, STE 405 38119 #047-06-1976 L1977 **R** *020 †80
MOSES, Linda Fay. 2500 PERES AVE 38108 #047-20-1988 L2001 **OBG** *020 †30
MOSHIER, William Hill. 4515 POPLAR AVE, WEST TN ANESTHESIOLOGISTS 38117 #038-40-1956 L1961 **AN** *071 †05
MOSKOVITZ, Randall J. 1325 EASTMORELAND AVE, STE 500 38104 #024-05-1975 L1978 **P PFP** *020 †75
MOSS, William Benj. 5846 DISTRIBUTION DR, MEMPHIS PATHOLOGY LAB 38141 #047-06-1963 L1964 **PTH** *020 †50
MOTAGHIAN, Faranak. 1129 HALE RD 38116 #517-05-1980 L1987 **PD** *020 †55
MOTLEY, Anne Marie. 1264 WESLEY DR, STE 201 38116 #030-06-1996 L2000 **IM** *020
MOTLEY, Thomas Earl, Jr. 1264 WESLEY DR 38116 #010-03-1990 L1996 **IM** *100
MOTLEY, Thomas Earl, II. 1265 UNION AVE 38104 #010-03-1965 L1971 **IM** *020
MOTLEY, Todd Seth. 1264 WESLEY DR, STE 606 38116 #047-06-1997 L1999 **IM** *020
MOUSSA ALEECH, Yasser. 956 CT AVE, H 314 38163 #875-01-1992 L2003 **PCC** *020 †20
MOUSTAFA, Salwa. 6779 NESHOBA RD, POST OFFICE BOX 17445 38120 #915-02-1970 L1979 **AN** *020
MROZ, Christine Teresa. 6005 PARK AVE STE 700 38119 #035-15-1972 L1978 **GS** *020 †85
MUHLBAUER, Michael Scott. 6325 HUMPHREYS BLVD 38120 #048-12-1981 L1987 **NS N** *020 †25
MUHLERT, Michael K. ■ 38111 #048-13-2004 L2007 **DR** *012
MUKATIRA, Shubi Razdan. ■ 38103 #017-20-2005 L2007 **P** *012
MUKHERJEE, Sourabh. 956 CT AVE, SUITE G228 38163 #012-21-2007 **GS** *012
MULLEN, Jesse Gael. 1265 UNION AVE 38104 #021-05-1958 L1974 **AN** *071 †05
MULLINAX, Clarice Weather. 3362 S 3RD ST, CHRIST COMMUNITY MED CLINI 38109 #056-06-1999 L2002 **FM** *020 †18
MULLINAX, William Gregory. 3362 S 3RD ST, CHRIST COMMUNITY MED CLINI 38109 #047-06-1999 L2002 **FM** *020 †18
MUNIR, Ahmad. 920 MADISON AVE STE 300, UNIVERSITY OF TENNESSEE 38103 #704-01-1994 L2004 **CD** *020 †20

MURCHISON, Laura A. 188 S BELLEVUE BLVD # 222 38104 #047-20-1999 L2004 *020 †80

MURILLO, Luis Carlos. ■ 38103 #649-30-1996 L2003 PCC *012 †20

MURPHY, James Garnett. 1000 BROOKFIELD RD, STE 100 38119 #027-01-1964 L1975 PS *020 †85,65

MURRAY, Evan Wm. 5220 PARK AVE, STE 210 38119 #047-20-1989 L1989 ID *020

MURRAY, Gary Lee. 7205 WOLF RIVER BLVD, STE 201 38138 #021-01-1974 L1976 CD IM *020 †20

MURRAY, Ian Farrell. 5190 PARK AVE 38119 #047-06-1969 L1970 R *020 †80

MURRAY, Ringland Smith. 80 HUMPHREYS CTR, STE 307 38120 #047-06-1999 L2006 OBG *020 †30

MURRAY, Stacey Frohn. 3155 KIRBY WHITTEN RD 38134 #027-01-1994 L1997 PD *020 †55

MURRELL, Sam Edwin, III. 6286 BRIARCREST AVE, FL 2 38120 #047-05-1991 L2000 OSS *020 †40

MURRMANN, Susan Ann. 6215 HUMPHREYS BLVD 38120 #016-42-1987 L1989 OBG *020 †30

MUSICANTE, Robin Friedman. 1455 UNION AVE, MEMPHIS DERMATOLOGY 38104 #047-06-1995 L1998 D *020 †15

MUSICANTE, Sergio A. 899 MADISON AVE 38103 #047-06-1995 L1996 IM EM *020 †20

MYA, Maung. 1265 UNION AVE STE 1SHE, TRANSPLANT CLINIC 38104 #209-01-1994 L2005 NEP *020 †20

MYERS, Adrianne Lee. 956 COURT AVE, UNIV OF TN COLL MED 38163 #028-34-2006 GS *012

MYERS, James Eric. ■ 38104 #047-06-2008 IM *012

MYERS, Linda Kay. 956 CT AVE RM B310, UNIV OF TENNESSEE 38163 #047-06-1978 L1979 FM PD *020 †55

MYERS, Lisa Marie. 6027 WALNUT GROVE RD # 307 38120 #047-06-1989 L1990 END IM *020 †20

MYERS, Richard Kelley. 1355 LYNNFIELD RD, STE B187 38119 #012-01-1997 L2004 FM *020 †18

MYERS, William Stanley. 999 REDDOCH CV 38119 #047-06-1960 L1961 AI *020 †03,20

NADEL, Alan Marc. 6005 PARK AVE STE 804 38119 #041-12-1968 L1975 N IM *020 †20,75

NAFICY, Sephre. ■ 38120 #010-02-1994 L1994 VS *012 †85

NAIDA, Abubakar Mohammed. 6005 PARK AVE, STE 306 38119 #690-03-1981 L2005 NPM *020 †20

NANNEY, Martha Plog. ■ 38117 #047-06-1987 L1988 P CHP *020

NAQVI, Shaider Abbas. 6005 PARK AVE, STE 605 38119 #704-16-1990 L1996 IM *020 †20

NARAN, Sage. 956 COURT AVE 38163 #661-02-2006 FP *012

NARAPAREDDY, Murty. 877 JEFFERSON AVE 38103 #495-11-1975 L1998 NEP *020 †20

NARRA, Sri Lakshmi. 956 CT AVE, UNIV OF TN COLL OF MED 38163 #495-21-2002 GE *012 †20

NASEER, Adnan. 920 MADISON AVE STE 200, UNIVERSITY OF TENNESSEE 38103 #704-01-1994 L2004 NEP *020 †20

NASH, John Paul. 62 S DUNLAP ST, STE 500 38103 #047-06-1956 L1957 GS *071 †85

NASSER, Wael. 956 COURT AVE 38163 #875-01-2002 IM *012

NATERA, Alejandro. ■ 38126 #047-06-2008 *012

NATHAN, Boomi Thiagarajan. 956 COURT AVE 38163 #305-01-2003 L2008 FM *020

NATIONS, Jeffrey De Witt. 7865 EDUCATORS LN, STE 300 38133 #027-01-1992 L2002 FM *020 †18

NAUERT, Timothy Craig. 55 HUMPHREYS CTR, STE 100 38120 #048-04-1980 L1987 RNR OS *020 †80

NAVID, Fariba. ■ 38112 #021-01-1989 L2002 PHO *020 †55

NAWAB, Qurrat-Ul-Ain. UNIV OF TENNESSEE, DIV OF PULMONARY DISEASES 38163 #704-25-1999 L2008 PCC *012

NAWAF, Kays. 6005 PARK AVE, STE 605 38119 #875-01-1971 L1978 AN PME *020 †05

NAWAZ, Fareha Ali. 156 CT AVE, UNIV OF TN COLL OF MED 38163 #704-02-1999 NEP *012 †20

NEAL, Matthew Thomas. ■ 38103 #047-06-2008 *012

NEAL, Michele E. 3135 POPLAR AVE 38111 #004-01-1993 L1996 FM *020 †18

NEARN, Andrew Buchman. ■ 38117 #047-06-2008 *012

NEBLETT, Paul David. 80 HUMPHREYS CTR 38120 #047-06-1996 L1997 OBG *020 †30

NEEDHAM, Lance Luker. ■ 38115 #047-05-2006 PTH *012

NEEHALL, David John. 956 CT AVE, UNIV OF TN COLL OF MED 38163 #894-01-1991 OBG *100

NEEL, Michael Danl. 6286 BRIARCREST AVE, FL 2 38120 #047-06-1989 L1994 ORS *020 †40

NEELY, Charles Lea, Jr. ■ 38117 #028-02-1954 L1954 ON IM *071 †20

NEILSON, Robert W, Jr. ■ 38104 #041-01-1950 L1955 TS GS *071 †85,90

NELSON, Damon Lee. ■ 38103 #046-01-2003 L2006 EM *020 †16

NELSON, John Shelton. ■ 38112 #047-06-2008 *012

NELSON, Richard Allan. 3238 PLAYERS CLUB CIR, ST 58 38125 #036-01-1971 L1994 PD GP *020 †55

NELSON, Susan Frink. 718 HARBOR BEND RD 38103 #048-14-1985 L1993 FM OBG *020 †18

NESHEIWAT, Joseph Paul. 842 JEFFERSON AVE A-601, UNIV TN COLL MED-INT MED 38103 #422-01-2003 L2006 RHU *012 †20

NESS, Marsha Jean. ■ 38120 #048-12-1984 L1993 PTH *020 †50

NETLAND, Peter Andreas. 930 MADISON AVE, STE 100 38103 #005-02-1987 L1996 OPH *020 †35

NEVITT, Matthew F. ■ 38117 #048-12-2005 L2007 ORS *012

NEWLAND, Anne Marie. 1030 JEFFERSON AVE 38104 #030-05-1993 L2000 MPD *020 †20,55

NEWMAN, Jason R. ■ 38111 #048-14-2003 L2006 MPD *100 †20

NEWMAN, Kevin Paul. 66 N PAULINE ST 38103 #047-07-1977 L1988 CD IM *020 †20

NEWMAN, Larry Bernard. 995 S YATES RD, STE 1 38119 #036-07-1969 L1973 U *020 †95

NEY, Paul Alexander. ■ 38117 #056-05-1982 L1992 HEM IM *020 †20

NEZAKATGOO, Nostratollah. 1265 UNION AVE STE S1012 38104 #517-05-1982 L2000 TTS *020

NGUYEN, Binh Yen. ■ 38133 #047-06-2005 IM *012

NGUYEN, Luc. ■ 38119 #047-06-2008 *012

NGUYEN, Man Huu. 956 MADISON AVE 38103 #941-01-1973 L1980 FM *020 †18

NGUYEN, Minh Duong. 1301 PRIMACY PKWY, PRACTICE CTR 38119 #041-09-1997 L1998 FP *012

NGUYEN, Tri Minh. 956 COURT AVE 38163 #305-01-2003 L2007 FM *020

NGUYEN, Trung Tan. 1301 PRIMACY PKWY 38119 #005-77-2004, ▲ L2005 OBG *012

NGUYEN, Trung Toan. 3030 COVINGTON PIKE STE 10 38128 #047-07-2003 L2005 FM *020

NGUYEN, Tuan Cao. ■ 38133 #047-06-2002 GS *012

NGUYEN, Viet Hoai. 956 CT AVE, SUITE G228 38163 #021-05-2007 GS *012

NIAKAN, Atossa. 1030 JEFFERSON AVE 38104 #517-01-1992 L1997 IM *020 †20

NICHOPOULOS, George C. ■ 38120 #047-05-1959 L1960 IM *071

NIELL, Harvey Barrett. 66 N PAULINE ST STE 633 38105 #047-06-1969 L1969 HEM ON *020 †20

NIENHUIS, Arthur Wesley. 332 N LAUDERDALE ST, RESEARCH HOSPITAL 38105 #005-14-1968 L1993 HEM *050 †20

NIMMAGADDA GANGULI, Sudha. 6263 POPLAR AVE, STE 503 38119 #495-99-2002 L2007 RHU *100

NOBLES, Eugene Rodman, Jr. ■ 38117 #024-01-1954 L1961 GS *071 †85

NOE, Horace Norman. 770 ESTATE PL 38120 #047-06-1969 L1970 UP GS *020 †95

NORMAN, Johnita K. 3876 NEW COVINGTON PIKE, PEDIATRIC ASSOCIATES PC 38128 #004-01-1990 L1993 PD *020

NORRIS, William Edgar. 956 CT AVE 38163 #047-07-1999 L2002 GE *012 †20

NORTHCROSS, Phillip R. 969 PEABODY AVE 38104 #047-07-1984 L1986 IM *020 †20

NOVAK, Keith Walter. 1030 JEFFERSON AVE 11C 38104 #047-06-1997 L2000 IM *020 †20

NOVICK, William Michael. 1750 MADISON AVE, STE 100 38104 #001-02-1981 L1993 TS GS *020 †85,90

NUNN, Stewart Lewis. ■ 38112 #047-06-1953 L1953 CD *020 †20

NUNTNARUMIT, Pracha. ■ 38107 #891-05-1986 NPM *100

NWOKEJI, Emmanuel Igweze. 3810 WINCHESTER RD 38118 #654-01-1983 L1989 P *020 †20

NYENWE, Ebenezer Azubuike. UNIV OF TENNESSEE, 956 COURT AVE RM D334 38163 #690-12-1989 L2007 END *100 †20

OBAJI, Suhail Mohamed. 6029 WALNUT GROVE RD, STE 301 38120 #875-02-1983 L1990 ON *020 †20

OBI-OKOYE, Nwannem U. 1045 MULLINS STATION RD 38134 #690-04-1988 L1997 IM *020 †20,55

O'BRIEN, Thomas Francis, Jr. 1211 UNION AVE, STE 300 38104 #047-06-1986 L1987 PTH *020 †50 ‡

O'CAIN, Debbie. 3725 CHAMPION HILLS DR, SOUTHWIND MEDICAL SPECIALI 38125 #027-01-1988 L1989 FM *020 †20

O'CONNELL, John F. 877 JEFFERSON 38163 #047-06-1976 L1977 IM *020 †20

O'CONNOR, Timothy John. 50 N DUNLAP ST, EMERGENCY DEPT. LEBONHEUR 38103 #001-06-1984 L2004 PD *020 †15

O'DEA, Douglas Lawrence. 4901 RALEIGH COMMON DR, STE 200 38128 #047-06-1985 L1987 IM *020 †20

ODOM, Lawrence Neil. UNIV OF TENNESSEE, DEPT OF OB/GYN 38163 #012-01-2006 OBG *012

O'DONNELL, James A, II. 50 N DUNLAP ST, ER DEPT 38103 #027-01-1978 L1986 PEM PD *020 †55

O'DONNELL, Thomas James. 930 MADISON STE 470, HAMILTON EYE INSTITUTE 38163 #047-06-1975 L1975 OPH *071 ‡

O'GILVIE, Chrishana L. ■ 38116 #020-02-2003 L2006 AI *012

OGLE, Evelyn Bassi. 1265 UNION AVE 38104 #047-06-1947 L1947 OS *071

OGLESBY, Claude Dunn. 6401 POPLAR AVE, STE 340 38119 #047-06-1956 L1957 OPH OS *071 †35

OKEON, Melvyn Mayer. 877 JEFFERSON AVE 38103 #047-06-1962 L1962 R *020 †80

OKPOR, Kenneth Azuka. 6025 WALNUT GROVE RD, PC 38120 #690-01-1992 L2003 PCC *020 †20

OKTAEI, Hooman. 7639 GLENFIELD CV 38133 #517-01-1992 L2003 END *020 †20

OLINGER, Rodney Glenn. 899 MADISON AVE 38103 #011-02-1977 L1983 NS *020 †25

OLIVER, Robert Perrin, Jr. ■ 38117 #047-06-1962 L1971 FM *071 †18

OLIVER, Thomas Adam. ■ 38104 #021-05-2006 GS *012

OMER, Imad. 5210 POPLAR AVE, STE 200 38119 #004-01-1995 L2002 ID *020 †20

ONCIU, Mihaela M. 332 N LAUDERDALE ST 38103 #781-01-1992 L2001 PTH *020 †50

OPTICAN, Robert Jos. 55 HUMPHREYS CTR, STE 100 38120 #028-02-1988 L1994 DR *020 †80

ORAEDU, Ijeoma Linda. 201 POPLAR AVE, SHELBY COUNTY CRIMINAL JUS 38103 #690-04-1992 L1999 IM *020 †20

ORLEANS-LINDSAY, Kodwo. 1417 MONROE AVE 38104 #412-01-1994 L2005 GE *100 †20

ORMSETH, Eric John. 6005 PARK AVE, STE 323B 38119 #021-01-1992 L2002 GE IM *020 †20

OSBORN, Frank David. 150 COLLINS ST 38112 #047-06-1992 L1993 PTH *020 †50

OSBORNE, Pamela T. 930 MADISON AVE, DEPT OF PATH 5TH FL 38163 #047-06-1976 L1976 PTH *020 †50

OST, Shelley Rae. ■ 38122 #047-06-2005 MPD *012

O'SULLIVAN, Erin Jean. ■ 38111 #016-45-2006 PTH *012

OSWAKS, Roy M. 6005 PARK AVE, LOWENBERG BLDG., STE 700 38119 #035-06-1971 L2003 GS *020 †85

OSWALD, William J. 1620 S WHITE STATION RD 38117 #047-06-1953 L1953 GP OS *072 †18

OTTO, Mario. ■ 38119 #409-19-1994 L2006 PD *012

OVERSTREET, Hugh Thos. 5374 ESTATE OFFICE DR, STE 2 38119 #027-01-1982 L1985 IM *020

OVERTON, Clayton Justus, III. 701 ROZELLE ST 38104 #021-05-1997 L2001 EM *020 †16

OWEN, Bethany. ■ 38117 #047-06-2004 IM *012

OWEN, Edmond Wanis. 3980 NEW COVINGTON PIKE, STE 101 38128 #048-04-1980 L1987 TS *020 †85,90

OWEN, Virginia. 55 HUMPHREYS CTR, STE 100 38120 #021-05-1988 L1993 DR NM *020 †80

OWENS, Curtis L. 3960 KNIGHT ARNOLD RD #200 38118 #047-06-1989 L1990 HO IM *020 †20

OWENS, Donald Davis. 6005 PARK AVE, STE 101B 38119 #047-06-1976 L1977 DR *020 †80 ‡

OWENS-WOODS, Carolyn. 1331 UNION AVE, STE 1250 38104 #047-06-1975 L1976 IM *075 †20

OWOSO, Moses Adekunle. 1067 E RAINES RD 38116 #690-01-1973 L2006 GS *020 †85

OZOIGBO, Valentine Chuks. 1620 S WHITE STATION RD 38117 #690-04-1994 L2005 FM *020 †18

PABA PRADA, Claudia Esthe. 1331 UNION AVE, STE 800 38104 #264-09-2000 L2004 HO *012 †20

PACKIANATHAN, Xavier Raje. DEPT OF RADIOLOGY, UNIV OF TENNESSEE 38163 #495-66-1999 L2007 VIR *012

PADGETT, Diana Marie. ■ 38103 #047-06-2003 L2007 PP *012 †50

PADMANABHAN NAIR, S. 1211 UNION AVE, STE 340 38104 #495-31-1990 L2000 GE *020 †20

PAGE, Roy Calvin. 3960 KNIGHT ARNOLD RD, STE 322 38118 #047-06-1955 L1956 ON *071 †85

PAGLIARULO, Anthony R. 333 S BELLEVUE BLVD 38104 #561-01-1978 L1993 IM *020

PAIDIPALLI, Babu Rao. 50 N DUNLAP ST 38103 #495-57-1973 L1979 AN *020 †05

PAIG, Camilo Ungab. 1030 JEFFERSON AVE 38104 #748-01-1965 L1976 RO *071 †80

PAIG, Maria Paz. 1755 KIRBY PKWY, STE 330 38120 #748-01-1964 L1976 AN IM *020

PAIPANANDIKER, Atmaram S. ■ 38112 #048-13-2002 L2007 RO *100

PALLERA, Arnel Molina. 100 N HUMPHREYS BLVD, THE WEST CLINIC, P.C. 38120 #047-06-1995 L1998 HO *020 †20,55

PALMER, Frederick Bristol. 711 JEFFERSON AVE, DEVELOPMENTAL DISABILITIES 38105 #035-45-1972 L1994 PD *040 †55

PALMER, Robert E, IV. 5791 SUMMER TREES DR 38134 #047-06-1962 L1962 RO *071 †80

PALMIERI, Genaro Miguel A. 100 N HUMPHREYS BLVD, STE 100 38120 #132-02-1956 L1974 END GP *020 †20

PANATTIL, Jain George. ■ 38105 #496-29-1991 NS *100

PANDEY, Soumya. ■ 38103 #495-30-1999 PTH *012

PANDURANGA, Jallepalli. 4274 FARONIA RD 38116 #495-50-1969 L1976 END DIA *020

PANG, Szekim. ■ 38104 #021-01-2007 FP *012

PAREKH, Sushma. ■ 38120 #495-01-1987 L2000 DR *020 †80

■ = Address Information Privacy Protected

PARIKH, Salil Prabhakar. 1661 INTERNATIONAL DR, STE 350 38120 #047-06-1993 L1998 DR *020 †80

PARK, Lynda Jane. 877 JEFFERSON AVE 38103 #047-06-1985 L1986 IM *020 †20

PARKER, Autry James, Jr. 6005 PARK AVE, STE 802 38119 #008-01-1988 L1992 PME AN *020 †05

PARMER, Joseph. 5959 PARK AVE 38119 #047-06-1950 L1953 PD *071 †55

PARKS, Frank Deluca. 1661 INTERNATIONAL DR, STE 350 38120 #047-06-1977 L1978 DR *020 †80

PARKS, Joseph William. 956 COURT AVE, UNIV OF TX COLL MED 38163 #012-22-2007 GS *012

PARKS, Rhonda Kaky. 8071 WINCHESTER RD 38125 #004-01-1993 L1998 FM *020 †18

PARRELLA, Mark Stephen. ■ 38103 #010-02-2002 L2007 ORS *100

PARRIS, Wesley Buell. ■ 38117 #047-06-2007 FP *012

PARSIOON, Fereidoon. 5673 S REX RD 38119 #517-05-1980 L1987 NS *020

PARTAL, Andreea Evelyn. 930 MADISON AVE STE 470, HAMILTON EYE INSTITUTE, UT 38103 #038-06-2000 L2004 OPH *020 †35

PARTEE, Brenda Demond. 1211 UNION AVE 38104 #047-07-1980 L1984 AN *020

PARTHASARATHY, Ranganatha. 55 HUMPHREYS CTR, STE 100 38120 #035-06-1990 L1999 IM *020 †80,28

PARVEY, Louis Swig. 6401 POPLAR AVE, STE 100 38119 #047-06-1968 L1969 PDR DR *020 †80

PASLEY, Monica Armstead. 1469 POPLAR AVE 38104 #012-22-2000 L2004 OBG *012

PASSONS, Gary Allen. 909 RIDGEWAY LOOP RD 38120 #047-06-1980 L1980 OPH *020 †35

PATCHEN, Jay. 3960 NEW COVINGTON PIKE 38128 #041-14-1981 L1983 IM *020 †20

PATCHEN, Mary J Ilsemann. 50 N DUNLAP ST, LEBONHEUR CHILDREN'S MEDCT 38103 #041-14-1981 L1985 PAN *012

PATE, Ann Scott. ■ 38103 #036-01-2005 PD *012

PATE, James W. 910 MADISON AVE, STE 525 38103 #012-01-1950 L1959 TS *072 †85,90

PATEL, Chandrakant Prakas. 2344 KETCHUM RD 38114 #306-01-1999 FP *012

PATEL, Jayesh Dipakbhai. 956 COURT AVE 38163 #495-22-2003 FP *012

PATEL, Mohanlal Ladhabhai. 6005 PARK AVE, STE 605 38119 #495-48-1972 L1979 AN *020 †05

PATEL, Nehali Dinesh. 332 N LAUDERDALE ST, DEPT OF INFECTIOUS DISEASE 38105 #011-02-1997 L2000 PD *030 †55

PATEL, Purvisha Jitendra. ■ 38103 #051-01-2002 L2007 D DS *100 †15

PATEL, Tejesh Surendra. ■ 38103 #917-35-2004 IM *012

PATEL, Vikul Vinodbhai. ■ 38103 #495-23-2001 NEP *012 †20

PATERSON, William Hunt. ■ 38103 #016-42-2005 ORS *012

PATIL, Mahadev Rachappa. 6005 PARK AVE, STE 605 38119 #495-35-1970 L1977 AN *020

PATTERSON, Anthony L. 910 MADISON AVE, RM 416 38103 #047-06-1982 L1986 U *030 †95

PATTERSON, James Kendrick. 4325 STAGE RD 38128 #047-06-1982 L1986 OBG *020 †30

PATTERSON, James O, III. 48 S PRESCOTT ST 38111 #047-06-1985 L1989 IM *020

PATTERSON, Jared James. 6286 BRIARCREST AVE, FL 2 38120 #021-06-2000 L2007 ORS *020

PATTERSON, Joseph Michael. 3000 GETWELL RD, DELTA MEDICAL HOSPITAL 38118 #001-06-1988 L1991 GS *020

PATTERSON, Kelly. 5050 POPLAR AVE, SPECIALISTS 38157 #047-06-1972 L1972 PUD IM *020 †20

PATTERSON, Rushton E, Jr. 4325 STAGE RD 38128 #047-06-1980 L1985 OBG *020 †30

PATTERSON, Russell H, III. 6215 HUMPHREYS BLVD, STE 505 38120 #047-06-1969 L1970 GS *020 †85

PATTON, Kurt Thoreau. 6046 KNIGHT ARNOLD ROD EXT, STE 101 38115 #047-06-2001 L2007 PTH *100 †50

PATTON, Ruth Cheney. ■ 38104 #047-06-2001 L2003 PD *020

PAUL, Annalee Lynn. ■ 38103 #028-46-2006 PD *012

PAUL, Raphael Nathan. ■ 38120 #038-41-1941 L1948 PDC PD *071 †55

PAULUS, Basil Mantas. 920 MADISON AVE, STE 300 38103 #035-03-2003 L2008 CD *012 †20

PAYDAR, Amir. ■ 38105 #047-06-2008 *012

PAYDAR, Kiarash. ■ 38103 #047-06-2008 *012

PAYNE, Kerry Daniel. ■ 38111 #012-22-2003 L2007 PTH *100 †50

PAYNE, Melvin P, III. 2996 KATE BOND RD, STE 309 38133 #047-06-1988 L1997 GS VS *020 †85

PAYNE, Paul Augustine. 2225 UNION AVE, STE 100 38104 #047-06-1972 L1972 NEP *071

PAYNE-JOHNSON, Ann Ilene. 3950 NEW COVINGTON PIKE, STE 130 38128 #306-01-2000 L2007 FM *100

PEACOCK, Dennis Alan. 687 JEFFERSON AVE 38105 #047-06-2004 L2006 MPD *012

PEAN, Carl Frederic. 3530 HICKORY HILL RD 38115 #308-12-1987 L1998 FM OBS *020 †18 ‡

PEARCE, Iris A. ■ 38133 #047-06-1950 L1951 IM *071

PEARSON, Cherryl Lamont. 2860 COVINGTON PIKE 38128 #047-07-1993 L1999 PD *020 †55

PEELER, David Wallace. 55 HUMPHREYS CTR, STE 100 38120 #047-06-1983 L1984 DR *020 †80

PEELER, Geo Huffman, III. 6027 WALNUT GROVE RD 38120 #047-06-1989 L1992 OBG *020 †30

PEGGS, Kiffany Janese. ■ 38103 #047-06-2008 *012

PELLACANI, Laureano. 643 SEMMES ST 38111 #847-01-1958 L1976 IM RHU *020

PELLETIER, Allen Lewis. 1301 PRIMACY PKWY 37501 #021-06-1983 L2000 FM *075 †18

PELZ, Frederick. 6005 PARK AVE, STE 900B 38119 #056-05-1977 L1979 IM IMG *020

PENDER, John Vincent, Jr. 3876 NEW COVINGTON PIKE, PEDIATRIC ASSOCIATES PC 38128 #047-06-1960 L1960 PD CHP *020 †55

PENDLEY, Bradford Daniel. ■ 38120 #047-06-2007 IM *012

PENDLEY, Cara Beth. ■ 38120 #047-06-2007 IM *012

PENG, Yun. 956 CT AVE, UNIV OF TN COLL OF MED 38163 #243-30-1986 PTH *100

PEPPERMAN, David Alan. 877 JEFFERSON AVE 38103 #021-05-1990 L1993 FM *020 †18

PEREIRAS, Lilia Ana. 332 N LAUDERDALE ST, MAIL STOP 130 DPET OF ANES 38105 #275-01-1985 L2004 PAN *020 †05

PEREZ, Angel Sixto. ■ 38103 #737-06-1991 N *012

PEREZ, Edward Anthony. 1211 UNION AVE, STE 500 38104 #016-01-1994 L2001 ORS *020 †40

PERKERSON, Jace Marshall. ■ 38126 #047-06-2008 *012

PERKINS, Freedom F, Jr. 777 WASHINGTON AVE, STE P250 38105 #048-02-1995 L2005 N PD *020 †75

PERKINS, Melanie Guia. 1030 JEFFERSON AVE, DEPT OF PSY #116A 38104 #047-07-1989 L1991 P *020 †75

PERKINSON, Brian Thomas. ■ 38111 #047-06-2007 ORS *012

PERRY, Edgar Emrich. 5050 SANDERLIN AVE 38117 #004-01-1966 L1972 PD *020 †55

PERRY, Judy Emrich. 5050 SANDERLIN AVE 38117 #047-06-1977 L1979 PD DR *071 †55

PERSHAD, Mrityunjay. 50 N DUNLAP ST, ER DEPT 38103 #496-38-1988 L1998 PD *020 †55

PERSONS, Derek Alan. 332 N LAUDERDALE ST, EXPERIMENTAL HEMATOLOGY 38105 #036-07-1991 L1996 HO *020 †20

PETRIDES, Alexander S. 951 COURT AVE RM 555D, UT MEDICAL GROUP 38103 #409-25-1982 L1993 *040

PETRINJAC-NENADIC, Rada. DEPARTMENT OF NEUROLOGY, UNIVERSITY OF TENNESSEE ME 38163 #957-02-1979 L2008 N *012

PFEIFFER, Ronald F. 855 MONROE AVE, DEPT OF NEUR UNIV OF TENN 38163 #030-05-1973 L1994 N *040 †75

PFLAUMER, Sean Merle. 1211 UNION AVE, STE 300 38104 #038-40-1994 L2001 PP *020 †50

PHAM, Nguyen Nguyen. ■ 38103 #028-46-2005 MPD *012

PHARIS, John Ray. 2150 WHITNEY AVE, FRAYSER FAMILY COUNSELING 38127 #047-06-1971 L1972 P *020

PHILIPS, Nancy Muir. 880 MADISON AVE, STE 3C 38103 #032-01-1979 L1980 OBG *020 †20

PHILLIPS, Gabriel Hooper. ■ 38104 #047-06-2007 GS *012

PHILLIPS, Samuel. ■ 38120 #021-01-1930 L1934 PD OS *075 †20

PHILLIPS, Travis. 899 MADISON AVE, ATTN GME 38103 #047-06-1997 L1999 IM *020 †20

PHILLIPS, William Earl. ■ 38128 #047-06-1964 L1965 PHP GPM *075

PIERCE, Andrew Scot. 6381 DAVIDSON CV 38119 #047-20-2000 L2003 MPD *020

PIERCE, Johnny Douglas. 777 WASHINGTON AVE, STE 240 38105 #010-03-1975 L1993 OTO *075

PIERINI, Jana Catherine. ■ 38104 #004-01-2006 L2007 FP *012

PILGRIM, Paula. 6401 POPLAR AVE, STE 530 38119 #047-06-1985 L1987 OBG *020 †30

PINSTEIN, Martin Lee. 6005 PARK AVE, STE 101B 38119 #047-07-1973 L1975 R *020 †80

PINTO, Fernando De Olivei. 956 COURT AVE 38163 #187-04-1997 PHO *100

PIPER, David Fredrick. 3238 PLAYERS CLUB CIR, 50 NORTH DUNLOP 38125 #021-06-1996 L1999 PD *020 †55

PITCOCK, James Allison. 899 MADISON AVE # 270, MIDSOUTH PATHOLOGY GROUP 38103 #028-02-1955 L1964 PTH *071 †50

PITTS, Wesley Mc Arthur, Jr. 1030 JEFFERSON AVE # 116A, VA HOSPITAL PSYCHIATRY SER 38104 #045-01-1975 L1985 P ADP *020 †75

PIVNICK, Eniko Karman. 806 ESTATE PL 38120 #473-01-1979 L1988 PD *020 †55,19

PLUNK, Nathan Hardin. ■ 38103 #047-06-2008 *012

POLK, Samuel Carlton, III. 1211 UNION AVE, STE 200 38104 #047-07-2000 L2006 APM *020

POLLACK, Joseph. 50 N DUNLAP ST, ER DEPT 38103 #913-32-1973 L1987 OS PD *020 †55

POLLY, Stuart Mc Grath. 877 JEFFERSON AVE, RM AG62 38103 #011-03-1968 L1990 IM ID *030 †20

PORPIGLIA, Andrea Susan. ■ 38104 #047-06-2008 *012

PORTER, Samuel Glenn. ■ 38134 #047-06-2008 *012

PORTERA, Stephen Gregory. 6215 HUMPHREYS BLVD, STE 110 38120 #021-01-1992 L1994 OBG *020 †30

PORTERFIELD, James Grady. 1211 UNION AVE STE 475 38104 #047-06-1974 L1975 ICE *020

POSEY, Michael Evans. 6005 PARK AVE, STE 900B 38119 #027-01-1975 L1978 IM GE *020

POSTLETHWAITE, Arnold E. 880 MADISON AVE 38103 #035-20-1966 L1985 RHU IM *050 †20

POTTER, William Arthur. 910 MADISON AVE, STE 608 38103 #047-06-1962 L1962 PUD IM *030

POURCYROUS, Massroor. 853 JEFFERSON AVE, RM 201 38103 #517-03-1975 L1985 NPM PD *050 †55

POURMOTABBED, Ghassem. 951 COURT AVENFUE ROOM 340, UNIVERSITY OF TN MEMPHIS 38163 #517-01-1970 L1989 IM *020 †20

POWELL, Benjamin Scott. ■ 38103 #047-06-2003 L2008 GS *012

POWELL, Timothy John. 6005 PARK AVE 38119 #047-06-1994 L1999 TS *020 †85,90

PRASAD, Bheerendra Ramann. 3836 PARK AVE, P O BOX 17962 38111 #047-07-2004 L2007 IM *020 †20

PRASAD, Rajeev. 777 WASHINGTON AVE, STE P-220 38105 #041-13-1995 L1997 PDS *020 †85

PRASAD, Sriranga V. 4250 FARONIA RD STE 4 38116 #495-70-1989 L1995 IM *020 †20

PRASAD, Sudha Rama. 3836 PARK AVE 38111 #495-33-1974 L1980 FM *020 †55

PRATHER, John Thomas. 1211 UNION AVE, STE 510 38104 #012-01-2005 ORS *012

PRATT, Christopher G, Jr. 135 N PAULINE ST 38105 #047-07-1971 L1977 P *020

PRATT, Edward Stephen. 1203 RIDGEWAY RD, STE 203 38119 #047-05-1981 L1982 OSS ORS *020 †40

PRATT, Thomas Halloran. 5169 WHEELIS DR 38117 #047-06-1978 L1979 OPH *020 †35

PRESBURY, Gerald Johnson. 777 WASHINGTON AVE, STE P110 38105 #041-13-1976 L1980 PHO PD *020 †55

PRICE, James Howard. 6141 WALNUT GROVE RD, STE 200 38120 #047-06-1954 L1954 AN *071 †05

PRICE, Kristy Lynn. 2861 BROAD AVE 38112 #047-06-2002 L2004 IM *020 †20

PRICE, Robert Allen. ■ 38128 #047-06-1965 L1966 NP ON *050 †50

PRIDGEN, Stephen Allen. 6025 WALNUT GROVE RD 38120 #047-06-1947 L1947 GS *071 †85

PRITCHARD, Frances E. 956 COURT AVE RM E226 38103 #047-06-1984 L1989 GS CCM *020 †85

PROCTOR, Bobby E. 956 COURT AVE 38163 #665-02-2004 L2008 FP *012

PROVIDENCE, Kathryn Azeli. 956 COURT AVE 38163 #422-01-2005 OBG *012

PRUETT, Michael Riddell. 6027 WALNUT GROVE RD, STE 206 38120 #047-06-1986 L1988 IM *020 †20

PU, Yongbing. ■ 38105 #243-03-1993 P *012

PUCHAEV, Michael. ■ 38120 #035-08-2004 L2007 IM *020

PUGAZHENTHI, Muthiah. ROOM H314, 956 COURT AVE, COLEMAN BLD 38163 #495-04-1987 L1999 PCC CCM *020 †20

PUI, Ching-Hon. 332 N LAUDERDALE AVE # 318 38105 #244-02-1976 L1978 PD PHO *020 †55

PULSINELLI, Wm Anthony. 6325 HUMPHREYS BLVD, SEMMES-MURPHEY CLINIC 38120 #049-01-1973 L1992 N *040 †75

PULUSANI, Deepika Reddy. 6005 PARK AVE, STE 511 38119 #495-21-1981 L1997 IM *020 †20

PURDY, Karen Adeline. 1325 EASTMORELAND AVE, PEABODY FAMILY CARE 38104 #021-06-1986 L1987 FM *020 †18

QUIGLEY, Karen Krobot. 80 HUMPHREYS CTR, STE 100 38120 #020-12-1979 L1985 PS GS *020 †85,65

QUINN, Peter Jos, III. 1265 UNION AVE 38104 #010-02-1964 L1972 U PDS *071 †95

QURESHI, Faiza. 1301 PRIMACY PKWY, UT, ST. FRANCIS HOSP 38119 #704-04-2002 FP *012

QURESHI, Shoaib. ■ 38163 #704-16-1999 L2006 FM *020

RABAA, Ehab. ■ 38103 #875-03-1992 L2006 PTH *100

RABINOVICH, Yekaterina. ■ 38103 #047-06-2003 L2007 DR *012

RADA, John Burton, III. 3950 NEW COVINGTON PIKE, STE 220 38128 #045-01-1977 L1979 OBG EM *020 †30

RAD POUR, Omid. 956 COURT AVE 38163 #517-04-2000 IM *012

RAGHAVAIAH, Nimmagadda V. 6005 PARK AVE # 826 38119 #495-11-1960 L1977 U *020 †95

RAGLAND, David Kenneth. 2860 COVINGTON PIKE 38128 #047-06-1970 L1972 PD *020

RAHIMI-SABER, Shahram. 1265 UNION AVE, METHODIST UNIV HOSP 38104 #517-06-1981 L2001 FM EM *020

RAHMAN, Mahfuzur. 3960 KNIGHT ARNOLD RD, STE 215C 38118 #704-03-1970 L1980 **IM** *020
RAHMANI, Shervin. 6005 PARK AVE, STE 728B 38119 #517-01-1988 L1999 **IM** *020 †20
RAINES, Edwin Allen. 1211 UNION AVE, STE 300 38104 #047-06-1971 L1972 **PTH DMP** *062 †50
RAJAN, Roy. ■ 38103 #041-13-2005 L2005 **OTO** *012
RAJASEKARAN, Surender. 332 N LAUDERDALE ST MS 7, ST. JUDE CHILDREN'S RES. H 38105 #690-14-1990 L2003 **CCP** *020 †55
RAMANATHAN, Jaya. 865 JEFFERSON AVE, # FG039 38103 #495-31-1968 L1979 **AN** *020 †05
RAMANATHAN, Kodangudi B. 1030 JEFFERSON AVE, # 111E1 38104 #495-53-1963 L1979 **CD IC** *020 †20
RAMEY, Danl Randolph, III. 6305 HUMPHREYS BLVD, STE 205 38120 #047-06-1963 L1963 **R** *020 †80
RAMIREZ, Armando. ■ 38117 #048-13-2007 **GS** *012
RANDALL, Milton Barry. 1211 UNION AVE, STE 250 38104 #036-01-1983 L1997 **PTH** *020 †50
RANDLE, Yvette Inita. 5142 STAGE RD, STE 100 38134 #004-01-1994 L1996 **FM** *020 †18
RANDOLPH, Bonnie Fry. 842 JEFFERSON AVE A645 38103 #047-20-2001 L2003 **MPD** *020 †20,55
RANDOLPH, Bruce Wendell. 3960 KNIGHT ARNOLD RD, STE 103 DELTA MED OFF BLDG 38118 #011-03-1984 L1996 **OM GPM** *020 †70
RANDOLPH, Donna Marie. 4274 FARONIA RD 38116 #038-43-1991 L1993 **OBG** *020
RANDOLPH, Patrick F. 853 JEFFERSON AVE RM 308 38103 #047-20-2002 L2005 **PD** *020
RANDOLPH, Paul D, Jr. 661 S PARKWAY E 38106 #038-43-1990 L1991 **OBG** *020
RANDOLPH, Paul Douglas. 661 N PARKWAY, RANDOLPH WOMEN'S CENTER 38105 #047-07-1959 L1966 **OBG** *020 †20
RANDOLPH, Sandra Boyland. 880 MADISON AVE 38103 #047-07-1993 L1995 **FM** *020 †18
RANGASWAMI, Bharathi. 451 LINDEN AVE 38126 #495-70-1969 L1981 **FM** *020 †18
RANGI, Navdip Singh. 1755 KIRBY PKWY, STE 330 38120 #047-06-1992 L1994 **AN** *020 †05
RAO, Bhaskar Narayan. 332 N LAUDERDALE ST, MS#721 38105 #495-33-1961 L1980 **PDS SO** *020 †20
RAO, Bina. 1030 JEFFERSON AVE, VA MEDICAL CENTER 38104 #495-33-1973 L1982 **DR** *020
RASBERRY, Ronnie Dale. 1211 UNION AVE STE 340, UNIVERSITY OF TENNESSEE 38104 #004-01-1969 L1994 **D** *020 †15
RASSOUL, Khalid Samir. 7948 WINCHESTER RD # 201 38125 #422-01-1994 L1999 **IM** *020 †20
RAWLINSON, William Thos. 6005 PARK AVE, STE 728B 38119 #001-02-1980 L1981 **IM END** *020 †20
RAWTANI, Pallavi Vijay. 910 MADISON AVE, STE 704 38103 #495-01-1967 L1977 **GP** *020
RAY, Mario Marquist. 842 JEFFERSON AVE A601 38103 #047-06-2003 L2005 **IM** *100 †20
RAY, Morris William. 6325 HUMPHREYS BLVD 38138 #047-06-1962 L1963 **NS** *071 †25
RAYMOND, Amos. ■ 38119 #047-06-2000 L2002 **IM** *020 †20
RAYUDU, Subbulaxmi Swamy. 7219 WINCHESTER RD 38125 #495-59-1979 L1986 **P** *020
RAZA, Syed Hasan. 956 CT AVE, UNIV OF TN COLL OF MED 38163 #704-01-2002 **IM** *012
RAZA, Syed Muhammad Mohsi. 956 COURT AVE 38163 #704-01-2004 **IM** *012
RAZZOUK, Bassem I. 332 N LAUDERDALE ST, ST JUDE CHILDRENS RES HOSP 38105 #605-01-1987 L1997 **PHO PD** *020 †55
REAVES, Edward Mc Cormick. 6027 WALNUT GROVE RD # 201 38120 #047-06-1962 L1962 **IM CD** *020
RECH, Cacilda Maria. 956 COURT AVE 38163 #187-01-1991 **PD** *012
REDDING, Alan Russell. ■ 38103 #012-01-2002 L2004 **AI** *012 †20
REDDY, Sunil S. 1056 E RAINES RD, SOUTH CLINIC 38116 #495-21-1986 L1993 **IM** *020 †20
REED, Damon Russell. 332 N LAUDERDALE ST, DEPT HEMATOLOGY/ONCOLOGY 38105 #038-06-2002 L2005 **PHO** *020
REED, Edward Wilson. 220 OVERTON AVE 38105 #047-07-1955 L1960 **GS** *071 †85
REED, Jarvis Dewayne. 100 N HUMPHREYS BLVD 38120 #047-06-1986 L1988 **ON** *020 †20
REED, Mark Edward. 100 N HUMPHREYS BLVD 38120 #047-06-1987 L1990 **OBG GO** *020 †30
REED, Mark L. 3789 COVINGTON PIKE 38135 #047-06-1976 L1976 **GP** *020
REED, Ralph Robt. ■ 38117 #021-01-1948 L1979 **IM** *071
REED, Sandra Joann. 1755 KIRBY PKWY, STE 330 38120 #047-07-1984 L1984 **AN** *020 †05
REGAN, William Bates. 5959 PARK AVE 38119 #021-06-1987 L1988 **IM** *020 †20
REID, David Hollis. 1755 KIRBY PKWY, STE 330 38120 #047-06-1988 L1989 **AN** *020 †05
REISMAN, Joel Allen. 5170 SANDERLIN AVE STE 204 38117 #047-06-1966 L1974 **P PFP** *062 †75
REISS, Ulrike Margret. 332 N LAUDERDALE ST MS 763, ST. JUDE CHILDREN'S RESEAR 38105 #409-10-1991 L2003 **PHO** *020 †55
REMSON, Ellsworth Jack. 1030 JEFFERSON AVE, VA HOSPITAL 38104 #021-05-1990 L1990 **PM LM** *020 †60
RENDTORFF, Robert C. ■ 38112 #023-07-1949 L1957 **PHP GPM** *071
RENTROP, Walter Anton. ■ 38117 #047-06-1947 L1947 **GP GS** *020
REYES, Avelino Galang. 3100 WALNUT GROVE RD 38111 #748-01-1952 L1985 **OS FPG** *020 †18
REYES, Nora V. 210 JACKSON AVE 38105 #748-01-1960 L1978 **P** *071 †75
REYNOLDS, Gary Lynn. 1000 BROOKFIELD RD, STE 100 38119 #047-06-1975 L1975 **PS GS** *020 †85
RIBEIRO, Raul Correa. 332 N LAUDERDALE ST, ST JUDE CHILDRENS HOSPITAL 38105 #187-08-1975 L1989 **PHO** *050 †55
RICE, Kevin Eric. 6238 POPLAR AVE 38119 #005-12-1992 L1993 **OPH** *020 †35
RICE, Steven Nicholas. 6005 PARK AVE, STE 626B 38119 #021-01-1976 L1976 **P** *020 †75
RICE, William Coleman. ■ 38111 #001-02-2006 L2007 **DR** *012
RICHARDSON, Michael S. 1030 JEFFERSON AVE 38104 #566-01-1974 L1982 **PUD CCM** *030 †20
RICHARDSON, Robert L, III. 1211 UNION AVE, STE 340 38104 #047-06-1991 L1994 **IM PLM** *020
RICHEY, Sylvia Sellers. 100 N HUMPHREYS BLVD 38120 #001-02-1997 L2000 **ON** *020 †20
RICHLI, William Rudolph. 100 N HUMPHREYS BLVD 38120 #005-12-1973 L1999 **DR** *020 †80
RICKMAN, Christopher E. 1661 INTERNATIONAL DR, STE 350 38120 #020-12-1988 L1990 **DR** *020 †80
RIDDLE, John Chas. 1030 JEFFERSON AVE 38104 #047-06-1975 L1976 **CD IM** *020 †20
RIEDLEY, Shannon Elaine. ■ 38104 #047-06-2007 **OBG** *012
RIELY, Caroline Armistead. 66 N PAULINE ST 38105 #035-01-1970 L1988 **IM** *020 †20
RIGGS, Rebecca Jane. ■ 38104 #047-06-2008 *012
RIGGS, Wm Webster, Jr. 55 HUMPHREYS CTR, STE 100 38120 #047-06-1958 L1958 **PDR R** *020 †80
RIIKOLA, Robert Wm. 1129 HALE RD 38116 #047-06-1968 L1970 **PD** *020 †55
RILEY, Angela Marie. 842 JEFFERSON AVE, STE A601 38103 #047-06-2002 L2005 **NEP** *012 †20
RILEY, Donald Clifford. ■ 38111 #047-06-1973 L1974 **DR NM** *071 †80
RING, John Coleman. 1 CHILDLREN PLAZA, CRITICLA CARE SERVICE 38103 #026-04-1977 L1990 **CCM PDC** *020 †55

RITTENBERRY, W Hunter. ■ 38104 #047-06-1997 L1998 **IM** *020 †20
RIVERA, Gaston Koeppen. 332 N LAUDERDALE ST 38105 #231-01-1967 L1973 **HEM PD** *050
RIZK, Tewfik Elias. 920 MADISON AVE STE 921 38103 #915-02-1964 L1981 **PM RHU** *020 †60
ROACH, John Michael. 550 CHALMERS RD 38120 #020-02-2000 L2003 **PD** *020 †55
ROBBINS, Edward T. 6027 WALNUT GROVE RD, STE 203 38120 #047-06-1976 L1978 **TS GS** *020 †85,90
ROBBINS, Samuel Gwin, Jr. 6005 PARK AVE 38119 #047-06-1971 L1974 **TS GS** *020 †85,90
ROBERGE, David. 332 N LAUDERDALE ST RM C20, ST. JUDE CHILLDREN'S RES H 38105 #067-02-1997 L2002 *020 †80
ROBERSON, Charles Daniel. 5229 LEXINGTON RD, ST FRANCIS HOSPITAL 38120 #047-06-1962 L1962 **GS EM** *020
ROBERSON, Jessica Romano. ■ 38107 #051-07-2002 L2005 **PHO** *012
ROBERTS, Jon Alan. 1661 INTERNATIONAL DR, STE 350 38120 #047-20-1990 L1991 **DR** *030 †80
ROBERTS, Kim C. 1661 INTERNATIONAL DR, STE 350 38120 #047-06-1993 L1996 **DR** *020 †80
ROBERTS, Larry K. 6005 PARK AVE, STE 101B 38119 #047-06-1976 L1977 **DR** *020 †80
ROBERTS, Matthew. ■ 38117 #047-06-2008 *012
ROBERTSON, James Thos. 847 MONROE AVE RM 427, DEPT NEURSURGY U OF TENN 38163 #047-06-1954 L1955 **NS** *020 †20
ROBERTSON, Kenneth Ray. 50 N DUNLAP ST, 1ST FLOOR ADMINISTRATION 38103 #047-06-1990 L1992 **PD** *020 †55
ROBINS, David Barry. 1211 UNION AVE, STE 300 38104 #836-01-1982 L1996 **PTH** *020 †50
ROBINSON, Aimee Claire. ■ 38104 #021-06-2006 **OBG** *012
ROBINSON, Lloyd Edward. 1785 NONCONNAH BLVD, STE 120 38132 #027-01-1979 L1981 **FM OM** *020 †18
ROBINSON, Marilyn Bearden. 50 N DUNLAP ST 38103 #027-01-1979 L1983 **NPM** *020 †55
ROBINSON, Todd Vincent. 920 MADISON AVE, UT MEDICAL GROUP INC 38103 #047-06-1992 L1994 **IM** *020
ROBINSON, Wiley Thos. 6263 POPLAR AVE, STE 1052 38119 #422-01-1984 L1987 **IM** *020
ROBISON, Lowell Benj, Jr. 6263 POPLAR AVE, STE 503 38119 #047-06-1965 L1967 **RHU IM** *020
RODGERS, Clifton, Jr. 5959 PARK AVE 38119 #047-07-1982 L1982 **FM** *020 †18
RODRIGUEZ, Miguel H. 2637 INVERARY CV 38119 #021-01-1989 L1990 **EM** *020 †16
RODRIGUEZ-GALINDO, Carlos. 332 N LAUDERDALE ST 38105 #847-12-1986 L1998 *020 †55
ROHMAN, Grant Thomas. ■ 38103 #047-20-2005 **GS** *012
ROHRER, Michael John. 1325 EASTMORELAND AVE #310 38104 #016-06-1981 L2006 **VS GS** *020 †85
ROJAS, Norberto. 1755 KIRBY PKWY, STE 330 38120 #748-01-1964 L1971 **AN** *020
ROJAS, Philip Andrew. 1755 KIRBY PKWY, STE 330 38120 #047-06-1995 L1999 **AN** *020 †05
ROMAN BERMUDEZ, Farid. 5659 S REX RD 38119 #264-05-1993 L2003 **END** *020 †20
ROMANO, Eric Michael. 956 COURT AVE, UNIV OF TN COLL OF MED 38163 #041-02-2000 **DR** *100
ROMINE, Lucas Brandon. ■ 38103 #047-06-2008 *012
RONEY, Ronald S. 6005 PARK AVE, STE 101B 38119 #047-06-1976 L1978 **DR RNR** *020 †80
ROSEBROCK, Richard E. ■ 38119 #048-14-2006 L2007 **DR** *012
ROSEN, Gerald Michael. 6019 WALNUT GROVE RD 38120 #035-45-1961 L1972 **AN** *071 †05
ROSENBERG, E William. 1211 UNION AVE, STE 340 38104 #041-01-1956 L1962 **D** *040 †15
ROSENBERG, Zachary. 5118 PARK AVE, STE 602 38117 #016-42-1966 L1975 **OTO** *020 †45
ROSS, Glenn Ray. ■ 38120 #035-08-1979 L1996 **DR** *020 †80
ROSS, Marco Aurelio. 1060 MADISON AVE, REGIONAL FORENSIC CENTER 38104 #021-01-1985 L2007 **FOP** *020 †85,50
ROTHSTEIN, Rodney D. 5885 RIDGEWAY CENTER PKWY, STE 104 38120 #039-01-1994 L1997 **AN** *020 †05
ROUTT, William Edward, Jr. 1661 INTERNATIONAL DR, STE 350 38120 #047-06-1977 L1978 **DR** *020 †80
ROUX, Jeffrey Jude. 1211 UNION AVE, STE 300 38104 #027-01-1999 L2005 **PCP** *100 †50
ROWLAND, Joseph Perry, Jr. 3960 NEW COVINGTON PIKE 38128 #047-20-1997 L2002 **OPH** *020 †35
ROY, Shane, III. 777 WASHINGTON AVE 38105 #047-06-1959 L1959 **NEP PD** *072 †55
RUBIN, Michael Andrew. 6644 SUMMER KNOLL CIR 38134 #035-47-1977 L1997 **IM CD** *020 †20
RUBNITZ, Jeffrey Ely. 332 N LAUDERDALE ST, ST. JUDE CHILDREN'S RSCH. 38105 #005-18-1988 L1995 **PHO** *020 †55
RUCH, Robert Milton. 6027 WALNUT GROVE RD, RUCH CLINIC PC 38120 #041-01-1947 L1950 **OBG** *071 †30
RUCKER, James D. 5220 PARK AVE, STE 100 38119 #047-06-1976 L1976 **EM OM** *020 †16,18
RUFFIN, Jessica Darice. 6401 POPLAR AVE STE 530 38119 #047-06-2000 L2004 **OBG** *020
RUIZ, Judith. 877 JEFFERSON AVE, DEPT OF ANESTH 38103 #005-18-1993 L1997 **AN** *020 †05
RUKHSANA BEIG, Khaleel. ■ 38124 #704-02-1980 L1988 **P** *020
RULEMAN, Chester Allan. 3980 NEW COVINGTON PIKE, STE 310 38128 #047-06-1973 L1973 **OTO** *020 †45
RUNYAN, John Wm, Jr. 66 N PAULINE ST STE 633 38105 #023-07-1947 L1960 **END GPM** *071 †20
RUSHING, George Van Dyck. 6799 GREAT OAKS RD, STE 250 38138 #047-06-1978 L1979 **IM** *020 †20 ‡
RUSSELL, John Murray, Jr. 4466 ELVIS PRESLEY BLVD 38116 #047-06-1952 L1952 **GP OM** *071
RUSSELL, Scott C. 66 N PAULINE ST # 381, UNIVERSITY OF TENNESSEE 38105 #047-06-1997 L1999 **MPD** *020
RUTLAND, James Henry, III. 6005 PARK AVE, STE 323B 38119 #001-02-1997 L1998 **GE** *020 †20
RYDER, Kathryn Marie. 1325 EASTMORELAND AVE #300 38104 #008-01-1992 L1998 **IM** *050 †20
RYE, Anna Kathryn. ■ 38107 #045-04-2002 L2004 **PDI** *012 †55
SABERI, Ali. ■ 38104 #473-03-2001 **IM** *012
SACHDEV, Jasgit Chugh. 1331 UNION AVE, DEPT OF MED/DIV HEMONC 38104 #495-43-2000 L2007 **HO** *100
SACHDEV, Mankanwal Singh. 920 MADISON, STE 240, DIVISION OF GASTROENTEROLO 38163 #495-43-1996 L2004 **GE** *012 †20
SACKS, Harold S. 6027 WALNUT GROVE RD, STE 307 38120 #836-02-1967 L1977 **END DIA** *020
SADLOW, Christina Ann. ■ 38117 #047-06-2001 L2004 **IM** *100
SAENZ, Jay Michael. 6005 PARK AVE, STE 608 38119 #004-01-2000 L2005 **ORS** *020
SAFLEY, Chas Franklin, Jr. 968 REDDOCH CV 38119 #047-06-1966 L1973 **D** *020 †15
SAHJPAUL, Ramesh Lal. 220 S CLAYBROOK ST, STE 600 38104 #065-01-1987 L1999 **NS** *100 †25

SAITIS, Diana Mihaela. ■ 38135 #781-03-1999 **OBG** *012
SAITO, Kaori. ■ 38117 #047-06-1995 L1998 **PTH** *012 †20
SAKAUYE, Kenneth Mark. 135 N PAULINE ST # 122, DEPARTMENT OF PSYCHIATRY 38105 #016-02-1974 L2006 **PYG P** *040 †75
SALAZAR, Jorge Alejandro. 1750 MADISON AVE, STE 300 38104 #047-06-1995 L2000 **VIR** *020 †80
SALAZAR CABRERA, Jorge E. 877 JEFFERSON AVE 38103 #737-06-1966 L1971 **DR** *020 †80
SALIM, Sarwat. STE 470, 930 MADISON AVENUE 38163 #035-08-1994 L2007 **OPH** *020 †35
SALTZMAN, Joel Arthur. 50 N DUNLAP ST 38103 #422-01-1982 L2004 **AN PD** *020 †05 ‡
SAMARA, Dafer Mahmoud. ■ 38103 #575-01-1998 **PCC** *012 †20
SAMSON, Jacques Edouard. 853 JEFFERSON AVE, DEPARTMENT OF OBSTETRICS/G 38103 #047-07-2002 L2007 **OBG** *020
SANCHEZ, Carl Thomas. 1755 KIRBY PKWY, STE 330 38120 #021-05-1993 L1994 **AN** *020 †05
SANDER, Craig Jay. 6215 HUMPHREYS BLVD # 310 38120 #035-08-1976 L1981 **NPM PD** *020 †55
SANDERS, B Jeff. 1755 KIRBY PKWY, STE 330 38120 #047-06-1990 L1991 **AN** *020 †05
SANDERS, Drew. 687 JEFFERSON AVE 38105 #047-06-2008 *012
SANDERS, Frederick D. 6005 PARK AVE, STE 510 38119 #036-05-1975 L1980 **GYN** *020 †30
SANDERS, Whitney Lovings. ■ 38104 #047-06-2007 **PD** *012
SANDLUND, John T, Jr. 332 N LAUDERDALE ST 38105 #038-40-1980 L1987 **PHO** *050 †55
SANDS, Christopher W. 1325 EASTMORELAND AVE, STE 101 38104 #047-06-1992 L1996 **IM** *020 †20
SANDS, Cynthia Stimbert. 3155 KIRBY WHITTEN RD 38134 #047-06-2001 L2004 **PD** *020 †55
SANDS, Michelle Green. 200 N PARKWAY 38105 #047-06-1993 L1997 **IM** *020 †20
SANFORD, David Marshall. 5959 PARK AVE 38119 #047-06-1966 L1967 **PM CD** *020
SANFORD, Robert Alexander. 6325 HUMPHREYS BLVD 38120 #004-01-1967 L1984 **NS** *020 †25
SANTANA, Victor Manuel. 332 N LAUDERDALE ST 38105 #042-01-1978 L1984 **PHO PD** *020 †55
SANTOSO, Joseph T. 100 N HUMPHREYS BLVD 38120 #005-19-1989 L2000 **GO OCC** *020 †30
SARKAR, Brojo Gopal. 5527 PECAN GROVE LN, STE 605 38120 #160-05-1972 L1979 **AN** *020
SAROGLOU, George John. ■ 38116 #418-01-1968 L1976 **ID IM** *050
SARRAJ, Mouhamd Bassel. ■ 38134 #875-01-1991 *100
SARVER, David Keith. 6005 PARK AVE 38119 #055-01-1972 L1979 **ID IM** *020 †20
SARWAR, Salman. 956 CT AVE, UNIV OF TN COLL OF MED 38163 #704-04-2001 **IM** *012
SATPATHY, Bighnesh. ■ 38103 #047-06-2008 *012
SAUCIER, Ashley B. ■ 38103 #021-06-2004 L2006 **PD** *020 †55
SAUNDERS, Brook Allen. 3384 HIGHLAND PARK PL 38111 #047-06-2001 L2006 **OBG** *020
SAUNDERS, Leah Carmen. ■ 38103 #047-06-2003 L2005 **OBG** *020
SAVARE, Arlillian Jones. 4707 WOODRIDGE DR 38116 #056-06-1983 L1987 **IM** *075
SAVCHENKO, Ilya. ■ 38120 #047-06-2008 *012
SAXTON, Grady L. 6055 PRIMACY PKWY, STE 125 38119 #047-07-1978 L1979 **CD IM** *020
SAYAGO DE ARAMBURU, Merced. ■ 38104 #048-15-2005 **OBG** *012
SCHABERG, Dennis Ray. 1211 UNION AVE, STE 340 38104 #028-03-1972 L1993 **ID IM** *040 †20
SCHAFFER, Donald Earl. ■ 38120 #035-06-1957 L1965 **P** *071 †75
SCHAFFER, Harry Ivan. 5641 NORMANDY AVE 38120 #047-06-1971 L1971 **AN** *020
SCHANZER, Mary Cathleen. 5350 POPLAR AVE STE 950 38119 #048-14-1981 L1989 **OPH** *020 †35 ‡
SCHAS, Daniel Francis. 4539 WINCHESTER RD, STE 1 38118 #047-06-1974 L1977 **OM** *020
SCHECHTMAN, Jay Chas. 1030 JEFFERSON AVE 38104 #010-03-1976 L1980 **IM** *020 †20
SCHENKEN, Elizabeth J. 135 N PAULINE ST, UNIVERSITY OF TENNESSEE DE 38105 #030-05-1994 L2003 **P** *020 †75
SCHETTLER, Betty J. 245 PANDORA ST 38117 #047-06-1951 L1951 **OBG** *071 †30
SCHETTLER, Wm Heymoore. 1755 KIRBY PKWY, STE 330 38120 #047-06-1961 L1962 **AN** *020
SCHLESINGER, Victor Adler. 6005 PARK AVE, STE 908 38119 #047-06-1963 L1963 **OTO** *020 †45
SCHNAPP, Moacir. 55 HUMPHREYS CTR, STE 200 38120 #187-04-1976 L1980 **N** *020
SCHNEIDER, Debra Ann. ■ 38163 #056-05-2006 **DR** *012
SCHNEIDER, Michael B. 6266 POPLAR AVE 38119 #030-05-1988 L1992 **OBG** *020 †30
SCHOETTLE, Glenn P, Jr. 1325 EASTMORELAND AVE, STE 220 38104 #047-06-1972 L1973 **TS CD** *075 †85,90
SCHOUMACHER, Robert Alan. 50 N DUNLAP ST, 3RD FL 38103 #047-05-1982 L1993 **PDP** *050 †55
SCHREIBER, Andrew Michael. ■ 38117 #036-08-2002 L2006 **HO** *012 †20
SCHROCK, Steven Daniel. 1301 PRIMACY PKWY, UT DEPT OF FAMILY MEDICINE 38119 #038-41-2001 L2007 **FM** *020 †18
SCHROEPPEL, Thomas John. 910 MADISON, 216, DEPT OF SURGERY 38163 #026-04-2000 L2006 **CCS** *100 †85 ‡
SCHULZ, Angela Marie. 3876 NEW COVINGTON PIKE 38128 #035-09-1977 L1985 **PD** *020 †55
SCHWARTZBERG, Lee Steven. 100 N HUMPHREYS BLVD 38120 #035-09-1980 L1987 **HEM ON** *020 †20
SCIMECA, Tyler Ross. ■ 38103 #048-12-2003 L2006 **DR** *012
SCOBEY, Eugene C, Jr. 5959 PARK AVE 38119 #047-06-1984 L1985 **IM EM** *020 †20
SCOTT, Benjamin F, III. 600 JEFFERSON AVE FL 4, BLUECROSS BLUESHIELD OF TN 38105 #004-01-1945 L1957 **TS** *071 †85,90
SCOTT, Daniel Joyner, III. 3960 NEW COVINGTON PIKE 38128 #047-06-1985 L1997 **FM EM** *020 †18
SCOTT, Edward Patton. 1040 MADISON AVE 38104 #027-01-1973 L1987 **BBK HEM** *030 †20
SCOTT, Edwin Lee. 1264 WESLEY DR, STE 405 38116 #047-06-1960 L1960 **IM** *071 †20
SCOTT, Joseph Manson. 6485 POPLAR AVE 38119 #047-06-1954 L1954 **OPH** *071 †35
SCOTT, Randall Lee. 17 WALNUT GROVE CT, UNIVERSITY OF TENNESSEE 38117 #047-06-1973 L1974 **R** *020 †80
SCOTT, Riddell Walcott. 5210 POPLAR AVE, STE 100 38119 #047-06-2002 L2005 **D** *020 †15
SCOTT, Robert E. 800 MADISON AVE 38103 #047-05-1967 L1989 **PTH CLP** *050 †50
SCRUGHAM, Jeffrey Alan. ■ 38122 #047-06-2005 L2006 **IM** *100
SEA, Tamika Louise. ■ 38111 #047-06-2008 *012
SEALE, James L. ■ 38116 #047-06-1945 L1945 **GYN** *072 †30
SEAY, Michael Bruce. 427 LINDEN AVE, MIDTOWN MENTAL HEALTH CENT 38126 #025-07-2000 L2004 **P** *020
SEBES, Jeno Imre. 865 JEFFERSON AVE STE F 38103 #047-06-1967 L1968 **R** *020 †80
SEECHARAN, Grace Amy. ■ 38105 #047-06-2008 *012
SEGAL, Anthony. 6005 PARK AVE STE 800 38119 #352-08-1963 L1973 **NS** *020 †25
SEGAL, Jack. 920 ESTATE DR, STE 3 38119 #047-06-1946 L1947 **PD** *020 †55
SEHGAL, Snehi. ■ 38103 #661-03-2004 **N** *012
SEIDENSTRICKER, Lynn Mari. ■ 38117 #016-45-2007 **PD** *012
SEILER, Steven John. 1211 UNION AVE, STE 510 38104 #048-13-2001 L2003 **HS** *020
SELEKTOR, Yelena Yevseyev. DEPT OF MED, 920 MADISON AVE STE 300 38163 #912-05-1999 L2007 **CD** *012 †20
SELLARS, John Robt. 6005 PARK AVE, STE 601 38119 #047-06-1966 L1967 **GS** *020 †85
SELLERS, Kenneth Dale. 49 N DUNLAP ST 38103 #047-06-1968 L1968 **GS** *020 †85
SELVIDGE, Sidney D D. 1661 INTERNATIONAL DR, STE 350 38120 #047-06-1999 L1999 **DR** *100 †80
SENTER, Anthony M. 2002 EXETER RD 38138 #047-06-1984 L1986 **PD** *020 †55
SEPULVEDA-CATINCHI, V S. 6215 HUMPHREYS BLVD, STE 300 38120 #039-01-1993 L1996 **PD** *020 †55
SEVIER, Georgette Rochell. 1129 HALE RD DEPT PD 38116 #047-06-1987 L1990 **PD** *020 †55
SEXTON, Ray Owen. PO BOX 770815 38177 #047-06-1964 L1965 **P** *071
SEXTON, Robert Graham. 601 WALNUT ST 38126 #047-06-2001 L2004 **DR** *100 †80
SEYAL, Adeel Rahim. 956 CT AVE, UNIV OF TN COLL OF MED 38163 #704-01-2004 **IM** *012
SEYMORE, Melvinie. 6060 PRIMACY PKWY STE 251 38119 #025-07-1983 L1987 **OBG** *020 †30
SEYMOUR, Lawrence D. 1325 EASTMORELAND AVE, STE 435 38104 #010-03-1961 L1968 **U** *020
SHAFIQUE, Rehan. 956 CT AVE, UNIV OF TN COLL OF MED 38163 #704-01-2003 **IM** *012
SHAH, Anant Vipin. 1755 KIRBY PKWY, STE 330 38120 #047-06-1991 L1995 **AN** *020 †05
SHAHBAZ, Atta Ur Rehman. 956 CT AVE, UNIV OF TN COLL OF MED 38163 #704-01-2003 **IM** *012
SHAHBAZ, Fatima. 956 COURT AVE 38163 #704-01-2003 **PD** *012
SHAIKH, Aftab Ahmed. 5959 PARK AVE 38119 #704-08-1972 L1998 **CD** *020 †20
SHAIKH, Fareed Raza. 6005 PARK AVE, STE 906 38119 #704-08-1997 L2007 **IC** *020 †20
SHAIKH, Khawar Mushtaq. 1211 UNION AVE STE 33 38104 #704-01-1997 L2005 **CD** *100 †20
SHANKLIN, Douglas Radford. 930 MADISON AVE STE 599 38163 #035-15-1955 L1983 **PTH OBG** *040 †50
SHANNON, Andrew Thomas. ■ 38107 #047-06-2006 **DR** *012
SHANNON, Kerwin Frank. 956 COURT AVE, #B219 DEPT OTOLARYN 38163 #143-03-1987 **OTO** *100
SHAPIRO, Marvin Louis. 1755 KIRBY PKWY, STE 330 38120 #047-06-1981 L1984 **AN** *020 †05
SHARFMAN, David Morris. 6005 PARK AVE, STE 900B 38119 #038-41-1978 L1983 **IM** *020 †20
SHARIF, Zain. 956 COURT AVE 38163 #704-16-2004 **IM** *012
SHARMA, Manika. ■ 38103 #047-06-2008 *012
SHARMA, Ruchika P.. 1301 PRIMACY PKWY 38119 #495-34-1994 L2005 **FM** *100 †18
SHARMA, Sharad Laxminarai. 956 COURT AVE STE E228 38136 #495-19-1994 *100
SHARP, Burt Martin. 874 UNION AVE, CROWE BUILING ROOM 115 38163 #038-41-1975 L1998 **END IM** *050 †20
SHAW, Fawwaz Ridwan. ■ 38125 #436-02-2005 L2007 **FP** *012
SHAW, Jonathan David. 410 N WILLETT ST 38112 #047-06-2001 L2002 **CHP** *020 †75
SHEA, John Jos, Jr. 6133 POPLAR PIKE 38119 #024-01-1947 L1953 **OTO** *020 †45
SHEA, John Jos, III. 6401 POPLAR AVE, STE 150 38119 #021-01-1980 L1985 **NO OTO** *020 †45
SHEA, Martin Coyle, Jr. 6286 BRIARCREST AVE, STE 300 38120 #047-06-1952 L1953 **OTO NO** *020 †45
SHEA, Paul Flanagan. 6133 POPLAR PIKE 38119 #021-01-1995 L2001 **OTO** *020 †60
SHEFFIELD, Nicole M. 1750 MADISON AVE, STE 280 38104 #020-02-1998 L2001 **PD** *020
SHELL, Dan Huff. 6209 POPLAR AVE, STE 200 38119 #027-01-1974 L1981 **PS** *020 †65
SHELSO, John Howard. 332 N LAUDERDALE ST 737 38105 #030-05-1986 L2002 **PDE** *020 †55
SHELTON, Brixey Randolph. 1661 INTERNATIONAL DR, STE 350 38120 #047-06-1977 L1977 **R** *020 †80
SHEN, Christopher Chihhsi. ■ 38104 #047-06-2005 **OPH** *012
SHENEP, Jerry Lynn. 332 N LAUDERDALE ST 38105 #047-05-1977 L1982 **PD PDI** *050 †55
SHERIDAN, Jerome Ney. 5959 PARK AVE, EMERGENCY RM. 38119 #048-12-1975 L1987 **RO** *020 †80
SHERMER, Mark. 6005 PARK AVE, STE 807 38119 #016-06-1992 L1997 **NEP IM** *020 †20
SHERR, Charles Jonathan. ■ 38117 #035-19-1972 **MM** *100
SHERWOOD, Scot Hamilton. 55 HUMPHREYS CTR, STE 100 38120 #047-06-2001 L2006 **DR** *100 †80
SHIER, Janice Marie. ■ 38119 #025-01-1994 L2006 **OBG** *020 †30
SHIFFMAN, Stephen Murray. 6005 PARK AVE, MEMPHIS MEDICAL 38119 #047-06-1972 L1972 **IM** *020
SHIH, Chieschin. ■ 38103 #010-01-2001 L2001 **PD** *100
SHILOAH, Shira. ■ 38103 #047-06-1999 L2004 **AN** *020 †05
SHIMEK, Cristina Maria. 1211 UNION AVE, STE 300 38104 #038-40-1994 L2001 **PTH DMP** *020 †50
SHIRES, Courtney Brooke. ■ 38103 #027-01-2006 **OTO** *012
SHIRES, Jay Gordon. ■ 38103 #047-06-2008 *012
SHIRLEY, William Cason. ■ 38117 #047-06-2008 *012
SHIRWANY, Arsalan Tariq. 1030 JEFFERSON AVE 111E1 38104 #704-01-1993 L2001 **CD** *020 †20
SHOKOUH-AMIRI, Mohammad H. ■ 38163 #297-01-1996 **PTH** *012
SHOOK, David Richard. ■ 38103 #023-07-2004 L2007 **PHO** *012 †55
SHOOK, Marshall Shannon. ■ 38120 #023-01-1998 L2007 **CD** *012 †20
SHOURI, Mohammad Reza. ■ 38105 #308-11-1986 *100
SHOWKAT, Arif. 920 MADISON AVE STE 200, UNIVERSITY OF TENNESSEE 38103 #160-02-1988 L2004 **NEP** *020 †20
SHRADER, Floyd Ray. 1684 POPLAR AVE, LIFELINE EMS 38104 #039-01-1969 L1990 **FM** *020 †18
SHULL, James Herbert. 2900 KIRBY RD, STE 1 38119 #016-06-1974 L1986 **GS** *020
SHUMAKE, Leslie Bowlin. 5959 PARK AVE 38119 #047-06-1956 L1964 **GS** *071
SIAL, Robina Ijaz. 956 CT AVE, UNIV OF TN COLL OF MED 38163 #305-01-2004 **FP** *012
SIDDIQ, Muhammad S. 1417 MONROE AVE 38104 #704-02-1988 L2001 **GE** *020 †20
SIEGEL, Barry Ross. 5050 POPLAR AVE STE 611 38157 #047-06-1982 L1984 **IM** *020 †20
SIEGEL, Joel Israel. 50 N DUNLAP ST, LEBONHEUR EMERGENCY DEPART 38103 #035-47-2004 L2006 **PD** *020 †55
SIEVERS, Richard Ervin. 6005 PARK AVE STE 624B 38119 #036-05-1978 L1981 **OPH** *020 †35
SIGEL, Kenneth Joel. ■ 38120 #047-06-1985 L1987 **N P** *100
SIKES, James C. 3809 COVINGTON PIKE 38135 #047-06-1976 L1976 **IM** *020 †20
SILBERBERG, Marc Steven. 6019 WALNUT GROVE RD 38120 #047-06-1982 L1983 **AN** *020 †05
SILLS, Allen Kent, Jr. 1211 UNION AVE, STE 200 38104 #023-07-1990 L1997 **NS** *020 †25
SILVERMAN, Michael N. 6005 PARK AVE, STE 908 38119 #047-06-1958 L1958 **R** *071 †80
SIMARD, Jean. 6005 PARK AVE, STE 430B 38119 #067-04-1984 L1991 **ORS** *020 †40
SIMHA, Samuel. 1028 CRESTHAVEN RD, STE 101 38119 #231-01-1976 L1992 **OBG** *020 †30
SIMMONS, Bryan Paul. 188 S BELLEVUE BLVD # 408 38104 #047-05-1976 L1984 **ID IM** *020 †20

■ = Address Information Privacy Protected
8461

SIMMONS, David Lee. 6005 PARK AVE, STE 200 38119 #047-06-1983 L1983 **IM CD** *020
SIMMONS, James C H. ■ 38117 #004-01-1951 L1960 **NS OS** *071 †25
SIMONSEN, Rebecca Via. ■ 38107 #020-12-2004 L2006 **OBG** *012
SIMPSON, Latanya Asenath. 6555 STAGE RD, STE 1 38134 #047-07-1997 L1999 **FM** *020 †18
SIMS, Clifford Wm. 910 MADISON AVE STE 906 38103 #047-07-1971 L1977 **OPH** *020
SIMS, Silvia Daina. 1129 HALE RD 38116 #045-01-2003 L2006 **PD** *020
SINCLAIR, Scott Evetts. 956 CT AVE., H316, UNIVERSITY OF TENNESSEE 38163 #048-12-1991 L2002 **PCC IM** *012
SINELNIKOV, Aleksandr. 956 CT AVE, UNIV OF TN COLL OF MED 38163 #913-04-1978 **PTH** *100
SINGH, Anjali. 3238 PLAYERS CLUB CIR, PEDIATRIC EMERGENCY SPECIA 38125 #495-01-1998 L2005 **PEM** *012
SINTON, Peter Marcus. 50 N DUNLAP ST, MED CTR 38103 #039-01-2003 L2007 **PD** *100
SIOSON-AYALA, Maria Virgi. 956 COURT AVE 38163 #748-01-1997 **FP** *012
SISK, Thomas David. 1068 CRESTHAVEN RD STE 400, ORTHOMEMPHIS, P.C. 38119 #047-06-1961 L1961 **ORS** *020 †40
SIVADON, Joanne. 6005 PARK AVE STE 426B 38119 #047-06-1964 L1964 **IM CD** *071
SKAGGS, Marvin Richard. 920 MADISON AVE STE 1018 38103 #048-02-1966 L1969 **AN** *071
SKAPEK, Stephen Xavier. 332 N LAUDERDALE ST 38105 #036-07-1988 L1999 **PD** *020 †55
SKINNER, Robt Barrett, Jr. 1211 UNION AVE, STE 340 38104 #048-02-1978 L1981 **D** *020 †15
SLADE, Joel Ronald. 877 JEFFERSON AVE 38103 #048-02-1982 L1992 **AN** *020 †05
SLADE, Whitney Thompson. 4901 RALEIGH COMMON DR, STE 200 38128 #047-06-1988 L1989 **IM** *020 †20
SLEDGE, Rebecca Denise. 877 JEFFERSON AVE, CHANDLER 6TH FLOOR 38103 #422-01-1997 L2002 **AN** *020
SLOAS, David Dale. 1407 UNION AVE, STE 1400 38104 #047-06-1981 L1981 **GE IM** *020 †20
SLOBOD, Karen S. 2463 MADISON AVE, ST JUDE CHILDREN'S RES HOS 38112 #067-01-1986 L1993 **PD ID** *012
SLOMINSKI, Andrzej T. 930 MADISON AVE, DEPT OF PATHOLOGY STE 599 38163 #759-07-1979 L2000 **PTH** *050 †50
SLUTSKY, Avron Abe. 6401 POPLAR AVE, STE 400 38119 #047-06-1958 L1958 **IM** *020 †20 ‡
SMARTT, Chantay Deres. 842 JEFFERSON AVE A645, DEPT OF EMERGENCY MEDICINE 38103 #047-06-1991 L1994 **IM** *020
SMILEY, Linda Marie. 100 N HUMPHREYS BLVD 38120 #047-06-1984 L1985 **OBG** *020 †30 ‡
SMITH, Annette Marie. ■ 38103 #055-02-1993 L2007 **ORS** *100
SMITH, Brian Samuel. ■ 38103 #047-20-2007 **IM** *012
SMITH, Carole Mc Cormick. 50 N DUNLAP ST, NICU 4TH FLOOR 38103 #047-06-1969 L1973 **PD OS** *020 †55
SMITH, Chas Michael, Jr. 6025 WALNUT GROVE RD, PC 38120 #047-06-1992 L1994 **PCC PUD** *020 †20
SMITH, Clark Boyne. 1301 PRIMACY PKWY 37501 #025-07-1957 L1993 **FM OBG** *071 †18
SMITH, Clyde Rufus, III. 3960 KNIGHT ARNOLD RD, STE 108 38118 #047-06-1979 L1985 **GP EM** *030 †16
SMITH, David Lamar. 4321 FAYETTE RD 38128 #047-06-1981 L1982 **IM** *020
SMITH, Garrison Berry. ■ 38103 #047-06-2007 **GS** *012
SMITH, James Lacey. 1211 UNION AVE STE 340, DEPARTMENT OF MEDICINE 38104 #048-04-1976 L1989 **GE IM** *020 †20
SMITH, Jay Daniel. 2859 VAN LEER DR, FAMILY PHYS GRP PC 38133 #047-06-2000 L2002 **FM** *020 †18 ‡
SMITH, Jerry Allen. ■ 38107 #036-01-1963 L1985 **ADL PD** *020 †55
SMITH, Joseph Andrew. ■ 38103 #047-06-2008 *012
SMITH, Leland Clayton. ■ 38122 #047-06-2005 **D** *012
SMITH, Lovell Bernard, Jr. 6027 WALNUT GROVE RD, STE 212 38120 #017-20-1998 L2005 **GS** *020
SMITH, Maurice Mell. 6325 HUMPHREYS BLVD 38120 #005-06-1988 L1994 **NS** *020
SMITH, Michael Landon. ■ 38103 #305-01-2007 **IM** *012
SMITH, O'Brian C. 49 N DUNLAP ST 38103 #056-06-1978 L1980 **FOP PTH** *020 †50
SMITH, Phillip Karl. 877 JEFFERSON 38163 #027-01-1990 L1991 **FM** *020 †18
SMITH, Rachael Elizabeth. ■ 38104 #047-06-2004 L2007 **MPD** *012
SMITH, Randelon Dondriell. ■ 38141 #047-06-2004 L2007 **IM** *020 †20
SMITH, Rebecca Helen. ■ 38103 #047-06-2008 *012
SMITH, Ricky Allen. 3980 NEW COVINGTON PIKE, STE 304 38128 #047-06-1983 L1984 **U GS** *020 †95
SMITH, Robert James. 1067 E RAINES RD 38116 #047-07-1955 L1965 **GS** *020 †85
SMITH, Roger Gordon. ■ 38139 #010-03-1997 L1983 **IM** *020
SMITH, Stacy. 6025 WALNUT GROVE RD STE 1, STE 111 38120 #005-06-1986 L2000 **CD IM** *020 †20
SMITH, Stanley Leon. 6027 WALNUT GROVE RD STE 1 38120 #047-06-1974 L1975 **GS** *020 †85
SMITH, Susan Jane. 1301 PRIMACY PKWY 38119 #012-05-1985 L2006 **FM** *020
SMITH, Vincent D. 6027 WALNUT GROVE RD STE 103 38120 #047-06-1975 L1975 **IM** *020 †20
SMITH, William Allen, Jr. 1264 WESLEY DR, STE 405 38116 #027-01-1987 L1988 **IM** *020 †18
SMITH-DEMPS, Carletta. 1030 JEFFERSON AVE, 111-C 38104 #011-03-1992 L1996 **EM** *020 †16
SMITHERS, Maureen Ann. 3950 NEW COVINGTON PIKE, STE 120 38128 #056-06-1987 L2004 **CD** *020 †20
SMOLIN, Matthew Richard. 4901 RALEIGH COMMON DR, STE 100 38128 #035-09-1984 L1994 **CD** *020 †20
SNADER, Brent Michael. 2861 BROAD AVE, CHRIST COMMUNITY HEALTH SV 38112 #047-05-2000 L2003 **MPD** *020 †20,55
SNELL, Stephen Reid. ■ 38103 #047-06-2008 *012
SNYDER, Dowen Ervin. 6325 HUMPHREYS BLVD, SEMMES-MURPHEY CLINIC 38120 #047-06-1963 L1965 **NS** *020 †25
SNYDER, Joy Lynn. ■ 38120 #047-06-1998 L2000 **IM** *020 †20
SNYDER, Linda J. 711 JEFFERSON AVE RM 178, UNIVERSITY OF TENNESSEE CO 38105 #047-06-1995 L1998 **CHP** *020 †75
SOBERMAN, Judith Ellen. 920 MADISON AVE STE 300, UNIV OF TENN HLTH SCI CTR 38103 #041-12-1982 L1988 **CD IM** *020 †20
SOLLEE, Arthur Neyle, Jr. 1211 UNION AVE STE 300, DUCKWORTH PATHOLGY GRP 38104 #047-06-1968 L1969 **PTH** *020 †20
SOLOMON, Solomon Sidney. 951 COURT AVE 38163 #035-45-1962 L1969 **END IM** *020 ‡
SOMER, Bradley Grant. 100 N HUMPHREYS BLVD 38120 #035-46-1996 L2002 **HO** *020 †20
SOMJEE, Nilofer. 2087 UNION AVE 38104 #704-25-1993 L1994 **FM** *020 †18
SORENSEN, Michael Jos. 6286 BRIARCREST AVE, FL 2 38120 #026-04-1986 L1998 **PM** *020 †60
SORENSON, Jeffrey M. 6325 HUMPHREYS BLVD 38120 #048-14-1995 L2002 **NS** *020 †25
SORRENTINO, Brian Phillip. 332 N LAUDERDALE ST 38105 #035-15-1985 L1998 **IM** *050 †20
SOSKEL, Norman Terry. 6005 PARK AVE STE 501 38119 #051-01-1974 L1984 **PUD IM** *020 †20

SOTO VIERA, Manuel E. 711 JEFFERSON AVE 38105 #396-01-1956 L1975 **PD** *030 †55
SOUDER, Marva Lanette. 6401 POPLAR AVE, STE 530 38119 #011-03-1981 L1988 **OBG** *020 †30
SOYINKA, Olufemi Emmanuel. ■ 38119 #690-06-1985 L2007 **FM** *100 †18
SPANN, David Christopher. 1755 KIRBY PKWY, STE 330 38120 #004-01-2001 L2004 **AN** *020 †05
SPEARMON, Larryl Chana. ■ 38111 #047-06-2003 L2007 **PD** *020
SPENCER, Gene David, Jr. 6046 KNIGHT ARNOLD ROD EXT 38115 #027-01-1987 L1992 **PTH** *020 †50
SPENCER, John David. 956 COURT AVE, RESIDENT EDUCATION 38163 #017-20-2005 **PD** *012
SPENCER, Judy. 6027 WALNUT GROVE RD, STE 307 38104 #047-06-1978 L1979 **END DIA** *020 †20
SPENTZAS, Thomas T. 50 N DUNLAP ST 38103 #418-01-1983 L2004 **CCP** *020 †55
SPIOTTA, Eugene Jos. 6005 PARK AVE, MEMPHIS MEDICAL 38119 #047-06-1948 L1949 **CD IM** *020 †20
SPIOTTA, Eugene Jos, Jr. 6005 PARK AVE, MEMPHIS MEDICAL 38119 #047-06-1973 L1974 **GE IM** *020 †20
SPOONER, Stephen Andrew. 50 N DUNLAP ST, MEMPHIS 4TH FLOOR CENTRAL 38103 #047-06-1988 L1989 **PD** *020 †55
SPRABERY, Laura Read. 842 JEFFERSON AVE STE A607 38103 #027-01-1987 L1992 **IM** *040 †20
SPRAKER, Holly Lynn. ■ 38107 #051-04-2003 L2006 **PHO** *012 †55
SPUNT, Sheri Lee. 332 N LAUDERDALE ST, ST JUDE CLDS RESEARCH HOSP 38105 #025-01-1992 L1998 **PHO** *050 †55
SRIVANNABOON, Kleebsabai. ■ 38119 #891-02-1993 L1998 **PHO** *100 †55
STACK, Michael Lee. 6215 HUMPHREYS BLVD STE 40 38120 #001-02-1995 L1996 **OBG** *020 †30
STAFFEL, Jon G. 6133 POPLAR PIKE 38119 #048-13-1985 L1998 **OTO FPS** *020 †45
STALLINGS, John Morris. 1265 UNION AVE # NICU 38104 #047-06-1974 L1974 **EM FM** *020 †18,16
STAMPER, James Jesse. 6005 PARK AVE, STE 500B 38119 #048-04-1988 L1995 **CD** *020 †20
STAMPS, James Kevin. 777 WASHINGTON AVE 38105 #047-06-2001 L2004 **PD** *020 †55
STANFORD, Carl Cooper. 5575 POPLAR AVE, STE 112 38119 #048-04-1946 L1951 **PD ADL** *071 †55
STANFORD, James Franklin. 5575 POPLAR AVE, STE 112 38119 #021-05-1961 L1966 **PD** *071 †55
STANLEY, Kevin Jon. 1211 UNION AVE, STE 510 38104 #035-06-2000 L2002 **OAR** *100
STANLEY, Thomas V, Jr. ■ 38120 #047-06-1953 L1953 **GS VS** *071 †85
STANTON, Ronald Andrew. ■ 38104 #047-06-2003 L2005 **DR** *012
STARACE, Gabriel Edward. ■ 38103 #047-06-2008 *012
STECKER, Ellen Jane. 5575 POPLAR AVE, STE 112 38119 #035-46-1987 L2006 **PD** *020 †55
STEGMAN, Marc Hadley. 2225 UNION AVE STE 100 38104 #047-06-1982 L1988 **NEP** *020 †20
STEIN, Preston Miles. ■ 38111 #060-02-1975 L1979 **PHO CCM** *020 †55
STEINER, Mitchell Shuster. 3 N DUNLAP ST, VAN VLEET BUILDING 38163 #047-06-1986 L1992 **U OS** *020 †95
STEINHAUER, Bruce Wm. 842 JEFFERSON AVE A607, UNIVERSITY OF TENNESSEE 38103 #024-01-1959 L1998 **IM** *030 †20
STEINMAN, Fred. 1755 KIRBY PKWY, STE 330 38120 #021-05-1984 L1990 **AN** *020
STENDER, Sarah Sandlin. 777 WASHINGTON AVE, STE P110 38105 #045-01-1979 L1980 **PD P** *020 †55
STENNES, Corey John. ■ 38103 #028-34-2008 *012
STEPHENS, Martha Anne. ■ 38117 #047-06-1964 L1984 **P** *020 †75
STEPNIAKOWSKI, Konrad T. 220 S CLAYBROOK ST, STE 314 38104 #759-03-1984 L2002 **NEP IM** *020 †20
STERN, Eugene Norman. 185 ALEXANDER ST 38111 #047-06-1968 L1969 **OPH** *071 †35
STERNBERG, Thomas Gerald. ■ 38103 #016-06-2000 L2007 **AI** *012 †55
STEVENSON, Robin Malcolm. 1000 BROOKFIELD RD, STE 100 38119 #047-06-1965 L1965 **PS GS** *020 †85,65
STEWART, Altha J. 111 S HIGHLAND ST # 180 38111 #041-13-1978 L1980 **P** *020
STEWART, Baker Lee. 1030 JEFFERSON AVE, VA MEDICAL CENTER 38104 #047-06-1998 L2000 **IM** *020 †20
STEWART, Gloria Corean. ■ 38119 #056-05-1979 L1982 **PD** *020 †18
STEWART, Sherrill Bryce. 6025 WALNUT GROVE RD # 612 38120 #047-06-1963 L1964 **PS GS** *020
ST GERMAIN, David Joseph. ■ 38104 #021-06-2003 L2006 **DR** *012
STICKLEY, Shaun Michael. 956 CT AVE, RM E222 38163 #038-41-2005 **GS** *012
STIDHAM, Gregory Lee. 50 N DUNLAP ST 38103 #038-43-1976 L1980 **PD OS** *020 †55
STILES, Allison Marie. 1325 EASTMORELAND AVE #585 38104 #038-41-1999 L2003 **MPD** *020 †20,55
STIPANUK, Gerald Steve. 201 POPLAR AVE, SHELBY COUNTY JAIL 38103 #016-11-1977 L1997 **IM FM** *020 †20
STOCKSTILL, Ronald Gene. 2986 KATE BOND RD 38133 #048-12-1972 L1982 **PTH** *020 †50
STOIKES, Nathaniel Floydn. ■ 38103 #016-01-2005 **GS** *012
STOKES, Dennis Clifton. 50 N DUNLAP ST, LE BONHEUR CHILDREN'S MEDI 38103 #020-12-1973 L1992 **PUD PD** *020 †55
STORGION, Stephanie Ann. 50 N DUNLAP ST 38103 #038-43-1982 L1987 **CCP PD** *020 †55
STOUT, Charity Dawn. ■ 38118 #047-06-1998 L2000 **AN** *100
STRECK, Christian J, Jr. 956 COURT AVE, SURGERY 38103 #036-05-1999 L2002 **PDS** *012 †85
STROCK, Sylvia Shepherd. 4634 PEPPERTREE LN 38117 #047-06-1975 L1975 **PS** *071
STRUBLE, David Lee. 6005 PARK AVE, STE 630B 38119 #047-06-1996 L2005 **P** *020 †75
STUART, John Marvin. 66 N PAULINE ST STE 633 38105 #047-06-1970 L1970 **RHU IM** *050 †20
STUCKEY-SCHROCK, Kimberly. 3030 COVINGTON PIKE # 100, MEDICOS PARA LA FAMILIA 38128 #038-45-2002 L2007 **FM** *020 †18
SUAREZ, Paola Juliana. 956 CT AVE, UNIV OF TN COLL OF MED 38163 #264-09-2000 L2007 **PD** *020 †55
SUBONG, Eric Neilpaulino. 825 RIDGE LAKE BLVD, STE 2 38120 #010-03-2002 L2006 **OPH** *020
SUBRAMANIAM, Poorna. 50 N DUNLAP ST, PEDIATRIC ANESTHESIOLOGY 38103 #495-17-1995 L2005 **PAN** *020 †55
SUDHEENDRAN, Prabhavathy. 4299 ELVIS PRESLEY BLVD 38116 #495-31-1974 L1981 **PD** *020 †55
SULLIVAN, Donald James. 4100 AUSTIN PEAY HWY 38128 #038-40-1988 L1994 **PM APM** *020 †60
SULLIVAN, Joseph Albert. 1325 EASTMORELAND AVE, STE 335 38104 #047-06-1963 L1963 **IM** *071 †45
SULTAN-ALI, Ibrahim A. 1267 HARBERT AVE, # 201 38104 #047-06-1999 L2003 **PCC** *020 †20
SUMMERS, Samuel Timothy. 5959 PARK AVE 38119 #047-06-1984 L1985 **FM** *020 †18

SUN, Zhiqiang. 956 COURT AVE 38163 #242-69-1985 **P** *012
SUNDARA, Ruth Nisha. 3362 S 3RD ST 38109 #047-06-2002 L2004 **IM** *020 †20
SUNEELA, Gottumukkala. 2743 SUMMER OAKS DR 38134 #495-99-1995 L2004 **FM** *020 †18
SURBROOK, Michelle Lynn. 842 JEFFERSON AVE, DEPT EM 38103 #047-06-1995 L1996 **IM** *020 †20
SUSONG, Jason Rodney. ■ 38107 #047-06-2008 *012
SUTHERLAND, Arthur J, III. ■ 38117 #047-06-1963 L1964 **CD IM** *071 †20
SUTTON, David Kristofer. ■ 38103 #036-01-2007 **TY** *012
SUTTON, Michelle Renee. 50 N DUNLAP ST, OF PEDI 38103 #017-20-1997 L1999 **CCP** *012
SWAFFORD, Greg Phillip. ■ 38133 #308-03-1981 L1989 **FM** *071
SWAIN, Donna Elaine. 1030 JEFFERSON AVE, VA HOSPITAL 38104 #047-06-1979 L1981 **DR** *020 †55,80
SWAMY, Alagiri P. 6005 PARK AVE, STE 1003B 38119 #495-04-1966 L1981 **NEP IM** *020 †20
SWAMY, Alagiri Palani. 956 COURT AVE 38163 #422-01-2003 **IM** *100
SWAMY, Usha. 1087 ALICE AVE 38106 #495-59-1990 L2000 **P** *020
SWANSON, Heather Renee. 3622 MIMOSA AVE 38111 #047-06-2001 **IM** *100
SWEETEN, Bianca Juselle. 3124 THOMAS ST 38127 #047-06-1997 L2000 **PD** *020 †55
SWIFT, Naomi. 2600 POPLAR AVE 38112 #047-07-1979 L1979 **IM** *020
SWYMN, Jeremy Paul. ■ 38103 #004-01-2003 L2005 **ORS** *012
SYLVESTRE, Pamela B. 1211 UNION AVE, STE 300 38104 #005-06-1995 L2001 **PTH** *020 †50
SZABO, Tibor Samdor. 4901 RALEIGH COMMON DR, OF MEMPHIS INC 38128 #473-02-1978 L1996 **CD** *020 †20

TABOR, Owen Britt. 6005 PARK AVE, STE 608 38119 #036-07-1963 L1970 **ORS** *020 †40
TABOR, Owen Britt, Jr. 6005 PARK AVE, STE 608 38119 #051-01-1993 L1999 **ORS** *020 †40
TADJALI, Azita K. M. 956 CT AVE, UNIV OF TN COLL OF MED 38163 #297-01-1997 **DR** *012
TAG, Arnold Ray. 3960 KNIGHT ARNOLD RD, STE 116 38118 #047-06-1975 L1975 **OTO UM** *012 †45
TAHIRAJ, Genti. ■ 38126 #047-06-2008 *012
TALATI, Ajay. 853 JEFFERSON AVE 38163 #495-76-1989 L1999 **NPM** *020 †55
TALBERT, Louis Gregory. 6027 WALNUT GROVE RD, STE 206 38120 #051-01-1984 L1985 **IM** *020 †20
TAMEEZ UD, Din. 176 S BELLEVUE BLVD, STE 502 38104 #704-02-1989 L1995 **NEP** *020 †20
TAMMAA, Maamoon. 956 CT AVE, UNIV OF TN COLL OF MED 38163 #875-01-1998 **MN** *012
TANENBAUM, Alan Harris. 760 E BROOKHAVEN CIR 38117 #047-06-1991 L1994 **D** *020 †15
TANENBAUM, Mark Harris. 760 E BROOKHAVEN CIR 38117 #011-02-1960 L1964 **D** *072 †15
TANJAPATKUL, Mongkol. 7516 CAPITAL DR 38138 #572-03-1969 L1974 **GS EM** *020 †85
TANNER, Dennis J. 956 COURT AVE, RESIDENT EDUCATION 38163 #043-01-2005 **PD** *012
TANNER, Paul Russell. 55 HUMPHREYS CTR, STE 100 38120 #047-07-1991 L1994 **DR** *020 †80
TAO, Stanley Lingwai. 825 RIDGE LAKE BLVD, STE 2 38120 #035-03-2002 L2006 **OPH** *100
TAQI, Muhammad Asif. ■ 38103 #704-02-2003 L2008 N *012
TARPEY, Jeffrey David. ■ 38112 #028-34-2005 **MPD** *012
TATE, Robert Pressly. 1265 UNION AVE 38104 #047-06-1972 L1980 **IM** *020
TAUER, Kurt Walter. 100 N HUMPHREYS BLVD, # 100 38120 #028-34-1980 L1980 **ON IM** *020 †20
TAVIN, Ellis. 80 HUMPHREYS CTR, STE 100 38120 #035-46-1987 L2006 **PS HS** *020 †45,65 ‡
TAYLOR, Eddie Lee. ■ 38112 #047-20-2004 L2007 **DR** *012
TAYLOR, Edwin Oscar. 5050 POPLAR AVE, SPECIALISTS 38157 #047-06-1973 L1974 **PUD CCM** *020 †20
TAYLOR, Emily Cristen. ■ 38104 #036-05-2007 **TY** *012
TAYLOR, John Chas. 6005 PARK AVE, STE 430B 38119 #047-06-1979 L1984 **ORS** *020 †40
TAYLOR, Ralph. 1750 MADISON AVE, STE 401 38104 #047-06-1981 L1982 **IM** *020 †20
TAYLOR, Shari Lyn. 150 COLLINS ST 38112 #030-05-1991 L1995 **PTH** *020 †50
TAYLOR, William Wood, Jr. 1755 KIRBY PKWY, STE 100 38120 #047-06-1966 L1969 **A IM** *020 †03
TEJWANI, Indurani. 6005 PARK AVE, STE 508 38119 #495-01-1966 L1971 **OBG** *020 †30
TENNANT, Paul Albert. ■ 38105 #047-06-2008 *012
TERHUNE, Ronald Lytle. 740 BARTLETT RD 38122 #047-06-1965 L1966 **GP** *020 †18
TERRELL, William, Jr. 1444 E SHELBY DR, STE 317 38116 #047-07-1972 L1973 **PD PHO** *020
TERRY, Kenny. 3810 WINCHESTER RD 38118 #047-06-2003 L2005 **P** *020
TETTELBACH, William H. 188 S BELLEVUE BLVD # 408, INFECTIOUS DISEASE ASSOC 38104 #047-06-1995 L2003 **ID IM** *020 †20
TETZELI, John Paul, Jr. 5659 S REX RD 38119 #011-02-1986 L1989 **END IM** *020 †20
THAKUR, Tapan Kumar. 1264 WESLEY DR STE 405 38116 #495-15-1991 L1998 **IM** *020 †20
THOMAS, Errol Mabon. 877 JEFFERSON AVE 38103 #047-06-2000 L2002 **IM** *020 †20
THOMAS, J R. 1030 JEFFERSON AVE 38104 #047-06-1951 L1951 **CD** *072 †50,20
THOMAS, James E, Jr. 6005 PARK AVE, STE 101B 38119 #047-06-1988 L1989 **DR** *020 †80
THOMAS, Jonathan Stephen. ■ 38107 #047-06-2008 *012
THOMAS, Lloyd Randolph. 55 HUMPHREYS CTR, STE 100 38120 #047-06-1974 L1974 **DR** *020 †80 ‡
THOMAS, Michael Chumley. 2208 JEFFERSON AVE 38104 #047-06-1967 L1967 **CRS EM** *072 †10
THOMAS, Nancy N. 853 JEFFERSON AVE 38103 #021-06-2004 L2008 **OBG** *012
THOMAS, Oswald H, III. 3789 COVINGTON PIKE, COVINGTON PIKE MEDICAL CLI 38135 #047-06-1984 L1985 **FM** *020 †18
THOMAS, Sheila Maria. 1301 PRIMACY PKWY 38119 #047-06-1990 L1992 **FM** *020 †18
THOMAS, Wendy Ann. 1661 INTERNATIONAL DR, STE 350 38120 #010-01-1994 L2005 **PDR** *020 †20
THOMASON, Fred Godwin. 5515 SHELBY OAKS DR 38134 #047-06-1978 L1979 **CHP P** *020 †75
THOMASSON, James David. ■ 38103 #047-06-2005 **DR** *012
THOMPSON, Allison Heather. 777 WASHINGTON AVE STE 215, PHYSICIANS OFFICE BLDG 38105 #039-01-2001 L2004 **PD** *040 †55
THOMPSON, Andre Christoph. 930 MADISON AVE STE 500, UNIV TN HSS DEPT PATHOLOGY 38163 #875-03-1995 L2007 **PTH** *012
THOMPSON, Gregory Lamar. 1755 KIRBY PKWY, STE 330 38120 #047-06-1989 L1993 **AN** *020 †05
THOMPSON, Jeffrey David. 3155 KIRBY WHITTEN RD 38134 #030-06-1999 L2001 **PD** *020 †55
THOMPSON, Jerome Walter. 910 MADISON AVE RM 430, DEPT OF OTOLARNGOLOGY 38163 #005-14-1976 L1994 **OTO PDO** *020 †45
THOMPSON, Kenneth Allan. 7900 US HIGHWAY 64, GYNECOLOGY ASSOCIATES PC 38133 #001-02-2002 L2006 **EM** *020 †16
THOMPSON, Roy Leland. 842 JEFFERSON AVE STE A 38103 #039-01-2001 L2004 **GE** *012
THOMPSON, Stanley Craig. 6019 WALNUT GROVE RD 38120 #047-06-1996 L1999 **EM** *020
THOMPSON, Terrence Lee. 5959 PARK AVE 38119 #047-06-1972 L1972 **R VIR** *020 †80
THORPE, E M. 853 JEFFERSON AVE, RM E102 38103 #047-07-1981 L1982 **OBG ID** *020 †30

THRELKELD, Michael Gavin. 5210 POPLAR AVE STE 200 38119 #047-06-1983 L1983 **ID IM** *020 †20
THRELKELD, Stephen Colin. 5210 POPLAR AVE, STE 200 38119 #001-02-1990 L1996 **ID** *020 †20
THURMAN, Francis Wayne. 6005 PARK AVE, STE 1011B 38119 #047-06-1974 L1975 **ON GP** *020 †30,20
THURMOND, Susan Gail. 850 POPLAR AVE, STE 200 38105 #047-06-1976 L1977 **N IM** *020 †20
TIAN, Gary. 100 N HUMPHREYS BLVD, WEST CLINIC PC 38120 #243-03-1996 L2003 **HO** *020 †20
TIBBS, Martha Katherine. 5959 PARK AVE 38119 #035-01-1992 L1997 **RO** *020 †80
TICHANSKY, David Samuel. 910 MADISON, 2ND FLOOR, UT MEDICAL GROUP 38163 #033-05-1996 L2004 **GS** *020 †85
TILLMANNS, Todd David. 100 N HUMPHREYS BLVD 38120 #030-06-1996 L2003 **OBG** *020 †30
TIMMONS, Shelly Diane. 6325 HUMPHREYS BLVD, SEMMES-MURPHEY CLINIC 38120 #016-11-1991 L1997 **NS** *020 †25
TINKER, Cory Ray. 7900 US HIGHWAY 64, GYNECOLOGY ASSOCIATES PC 38133 #047-06-1995 L1996 **OBG** *020 †30
TIPTON, Robert Eugene. 3876 NEW COVINGTON PIKE, PEDIATRIC ASSOCIATES PC 38128 #047-06-1968 L1969 **NPM PD** *020 †55,19
TOBIAS, Michael E. ■ 38103 #043-01-2000 L2007 **NS** *100
TOBIN, Marie Bernadette. 135 N PAULINE ST, FL 6 38105 #539-02-1982 L1995 **P** *020 †75
TOLE, John W. ■ 38104 #011-75-2003, ▲ L2007 **IM** *100
TOMBAZZI, Claudio Ruben. 920 MADISON AVENUE SUITE 2 38163 #935-08-1986 L2001 *020
TOMEH, Chafeek. ■ 38103 #056-06-2007 **OTO** *012
TONKIN, Allen Kenneth. 55 HUMPHREYS CTR, STE 100 38120 #020-02-1970 L1979 **R** *020 †80,28
TONKIN, Ina Lynn Dyer. 899 MADISON AVE 38103 #020-02-1970 L1979 **PDR VIR** *020 †80
TONKIN, Keith Allen. 6305 HUMPHREYS BLVD, STE 205 38120 #047-06-2003 L2004 **DR** *012
TOOMS, Robert Edwin. 910 MADISON AVE STE 600 38120 #047-06-1956 L1956 **ORS PM** *071 †40
TOSH, John Williams. 3590 THOMAS ST 38127 #047-06-1954 L1954 **GS** *071 †85
TOULIATOS, John Spero. 6286 BRIARCREST AVE, STE 300 38120 #047-06-1995 L2001 **OTO** *020 †45
TOWNSEND, Clara W. 6041 MT. MORIAH, SUITE 1 38115 #041-02-1980 L1983 **P** *020
TRAN, Tuan Minh. ■ 38107 #047-06-2006 **DR** *012
TRAUTMAN, Lucas Anthony. 135 N PAULINE ST 38105 #047-06-2003 L2006 **P** *012
TRAUTMAN, Robert J. 6005 PARK AVE, DERMATOLOGY CLINICS 38119 #038-06-1950 L1965 **GS** *071 †85
TRAUTMAN, Robert Jos, Jr. 6005 PARK AVE STE 1005B 38119 #021-05-1974 L1974 **D GP** *020 †15
TREW, Gary Franklin. 6025 WALNUT GROVE RD, PC 38120 #047-06-1972 L1972 **PUD IM** *020 †20 ‡
TRINH, Cuong. 2500 PERES AVE, 2500 PERES AVENUE 38108 #941-01-1965 L1981 **GP** *020 ‡
TSAI, Shen-Kou. 848 ADAMS AVE DEPT ANES 38103 #244-03-1972 **AN** *040
TSIU, Willie. 920 ESTATE DR STE 3 38119 #047-06-1983 L1985 **PD** *020 †55
TUFENKEJI, Haysam Taher. 332 N LAUDERDALE ST 38105 #528-02-1976 L1979 **ID PD** *050 †55
TULI, Malika. 6570 STAGE RD, STE 140 38134 #028-46-1996 L1998 **D** *020 †15
TULL, Lesli Ann. ■ 38119 #654-01-1999 L2004 **FOP** *012
TULLIS, Kenneth Frank. 5158 STAGE RD STE 120 38134 #047-05-1971 L1972 **P ADM** *020
TUOMANEN, Elaine Ingrid. 332 N LAUDERDALE ST, ST JUDES CHILDRENS HOSP 38105 #067-01-1976 L1997 **ID PD** *050 †55,16
TUPPER, Jonathan J. 1265 UNION AVE, (ATTN EMERGENCY DEPT) 38104 #047-06-1994 L1997 **IM** *020 †20
TURNER, George Randolph. 6029 WALNUT GROVE RD, STE 404 38120 #047-06-1960 L1961 **GS VS** *071 †85
TURNER, John M. ■ 38135 #016-11-1978 L1980 **FM ADM** *020
TURNER, Robert Emmett, III. 6019 WALNUT GROVE RD 38120 #047-06-1979 L1979 **IM EM** *020 †20,16
TUTOR, James Dudley. 777 WASHINGTON AVE, PHYSICIAN OFFICE BLDG 38105 #027-01-1983 L1985 **PDP** *020 †55
TWILLIE, Twyla Monette. 4131 KIRBY PKWY, STE 1 38115 #004-01-1988 L1991 **FM** *020 †18
TYNDALL, Miriam Leah. DEPT OF OB/GYN, UNIV OF TENNESSEE 38163 #654-01-2005 **OBG** *012
TYRER, A Roy, Jr. 220 S CLAYBROOK ST STE 103 38104 #005-12-1944 L1950 **NS** *071 †45
TZEN, Chin-Yuan. ■ 38103 #244-01-1981 L1996 **PTH** *020 †50
UMPIERREZ, Guillermo E. 66 N PAULINE ST 38105 #319-03-1979 L2000 **IM END** *020 †20
UPRETY, Prabin Raman. 956 COURT AVE 38163 #672-01-2003 **IM** *012
UPSHAW, James Jeremiah. 3950 NEW COVINGTON PIKE, STE 300 38128 #047-06-1964 L1965 **GE IM** *071
USDAN, David Aaron. 6005 PARK AVE STE 830B 38119 #047-06-1966 L1966 **OPH** *020 †35
UTKOV, Edmund S. ■ 38116 #869-05-1947 L1948 **GP** *071
UTLEY, Anne C. ■ 38117 #047-06-1964 L1964 **CHP P** *071 †75
VABNICK, Felice. 877 JEFFERSON AVE, CHANDLER BL 38103 #035-06-1995 L2001 **PAN** *020 †05
VADDADI, Lalitha. 2579 DOUGLASS AVE, HLTH CENTER 38114 #495-50-1975 L1988 **P** *020
VALAULIKAR, Ganpat S. ■ 38106 #495-15-1988 L2006 **GS** *100 †85,90
VALLANCE, Kelly Loren. ■ 38103 #021-01-2003 L2006 **PHO** *012 †55
VANALSTINE, David Alan. 1755 KIRBY PKWY, STE 330 38120 #005-19-1990 L1995 **AN PME** *020 †05
VANATTA, Jason Michael. 1265 UNION AVE, 10TH FL 38104 #041-15-2000 L2007 **GS TTS** *100 †85
VANDEVEN, Greg Eugene. 3960 KNIGHT ARNOLD RD #322 38118 #028-03-1987 L1995 **IM** *020 †20
VAN FOSSEN, Helen Key. ■ 38111 #021-05-1955 L1962 **GE IM** *071 †20
VANG, Meng C. 50 N DUNLAP ST 38103 #048-12-1990 L1998 **DR** *020 †80
VAN MIDDLESWORTH, Lester. 894 UNION AVE 38163 #047-06-1951 L1952 **IM** *071
VANNOR, Nicole Boss. ■ 38125 #047-06-2007 **MPD** *012
VAN VOORST, Steven J. 956 CT AVE, UNIV OF TENN DEPT OF SURG 38163 #017-20-1972 L1983 **GS VS** *050 †20
VAN WINKLE, Staci Adele. 3109 WALNUT GROVE RD 38111 #047-06-2002 L2005 **FM** *020 †18
VAN WYHE, Galen Glenn. 3950 NEW COVINGTON PIKE, STE 120 38128 #018-03-1978 L1996 **CD IM** *020 †20
VANZANT, Rebecca Lee. 1030 JEFFERSON AVE, 116-A 38104 #027-01-1981 L2003 **P IM** *020 †20,75
VARGO, Jacob Aaron. 1129 HALE RD, MEMPHIS CHILDREN'S CLINIC 38116 #047-06-2005 L2008 **PD** *012

VARMA, Anita Sudan. 135 N PAULINE ST, UNIVERISTY OF TN DEPT OF P 38105 #305-01-2001 L2005 **P** *100
VARNER, Claude F, Jr. 1265 UNION AVE # NICU 38104 #047-06-1966 L1967 **EM FM** *030 †18,16
VARTANIAN, Robert K. 150 COLLINS ST, GI PATHOLOGY PLLC 38112 #067-01-1991 L2004 **ATP** *020 †50
VASHI, Satyam Vikram. ■ 38105 #047-06-2008 *012
VAUGHN, Gregory Lenard. ■ 38103 #024-01-1991 L1993 **OPH** *071 †35
VAZIRI, Brent. ■ 38104 #047-06-2008 *012
VAZQUEZ ANAYA, Angelica B. ■ 38111 #820-02-2005 **P** *012
VELASQUEZ, Pedro Alejandr. 777 WASHINGTON AVE, STE P110 38105 #935-01-1984 L2001 *020
VENTURELLA, Samuel Carey. 956 COURT AVE 38163 #422-01-2007 **IM** *012
VERA, Santiago Rafael. 1265 UNION AVE # 1012S, DEPART OF SURGERY TRANSPLA 38104 #935-01-1975 L1979 **GS TTS** *040 †85
VERNER, Walter Eugene. 2960 AUSTIN PEAY HWY 38128 #047-06-1954 L1954 **GP** *071
VERNES, Reka. ■ 38163 #473-01-1995 **FM** *100
VERNON, Michael Lee. 1755 KIRBY PKWY, STE 330 38120 #047-06-1973 L1974 **AN** *071 †05
VERRIER, Carmel Sabine. 1331 UNION AVE STE 800 38104 #028-34-2001 L2007 **HO** *100
VERZOSA, Rogelio Cueto. ■ 38134 #748-01-1950 L1971 **P** *071 †75
VESSELS, Benjamin Eugene. ■ 38122 #020-02-2007 *012
VIEIRA, Francisco Otavio. ROOM B226, 956 COURT AVENUE 38163 #187-26-1981 L2004 *100
VIERON, Leonidas Nicholas. 6027 WALNUT GROVE RD, STE 103 38120 #047-06-1975 L1975 **IM** *020 †20
VIJ, Gaurav. ■ 38103 #495-45-2003 L2007 **IM** *020
VINCENT, Vedamanickom. CITY OF MEMPHIS HOSP PSYCH 38103 #495-42-1968 L1978 **P** *100
VIRK, Ejaz S. 135 N PAULINE ST # 6 38105 #704-21-1987 L1996 **P** *020 †75
VIRK, Zubia Ejaz. 1030 JEFFERSON AVE, VA MEDICAL CENTER 38104 #704-01-1994 L2001 **IM** *020 †20
VOELLER, Guy Russell. 50 HUMPHREYS CTR, STE 30 38120 #021-01-1982 L1982 **GS VS** *020 †85
VOGELFANGER, Roger Bruce. 6005 PARK AVE, STE 630B 38119 #047-05-1972 L1973 **P** *020 †75
VOLANAKIS, Emmanuel John. ■ 38107 #001-02-2001 L2004 **PHO** *012 †55
VON BUTTLAR, Norman. 1030 JEFFERSON AVE, 116A 38104 #409-25-1980 L1991 **CHP** *020 †75
VOOKLES, John Thorn. 1714 W MASSEY RD 38120 #047-06-1961 L1962 **IM** *020
VOSOGHI, Houman. ■ 38120 #035-06-2005 **OPH** *012
VU, Andrew Trong. 1755 KIRBY PKWY, STE 330 38120 #941-02-1974 L1981 **AN GP** *020 †05
VU, Duytoan Hoang. ■ 38119 #047-06-2008 *012
VU, Loi Thien. 6005 PARK AVE, STE 101B 38119 #030-05-1991 L1996 **DR** *020 †80
VU, Tolan Hoang. 2574 FRAYSER BLVD 38127 #941-01-1975 L1985 **FM CLP** *020 †18
WADE, David Everett. ■ 38117 #038-41-1959 L1966 **END IM** *020 †20
WADE, Mark Robt. 1200 PEABODY AVE 38104 #036-05-1981 L1999 **CD IM** *020 †20
WAHBA, Mervat Nasry. 1211 UNION AVE STE 200, SEMMES-MURPHEY CLINIC 38104 #915-02-1982 L2005 **N** *100 †75
WAHEED, Sarah. 1331 UNION AVE, DEPT OF MED/DIV HEMONC 38104 #704-01-1996 L2001 **HO** *020
WAHID, Samir M. 6071 APPLE TREE DR, STE 2 38115 #047-06-1985 L1986 **FM FPG** *020
WAHL, Joseph Wm. ■ 38115 #047-06-1957 L1958 **OS OPH** *071 †35
WAITE, Aaron Noble. OF MED, UNIV OF TENNESSEE COLL 38163 #049-01-2006 L2006 **OPH** *012
WALKER, Frances Carolyn. 188 S BELLEVUE BLVD # 417 38104 #020-02-1957 L1964 **IM** *020
WALKER, James Wakefield. 1030 JEFFERSON AVE 38104 #047-06-1953 L1953 **PS OS** *020 †65
WALKER, Larry Michaels. 4250 FARONIA RD, STE 4 38116 #017-20-1982 L1983 **FM** *020 †18
WALKER, Raymond Rogers. 1301 PRIMACY PKWY 37501 #047-06-1992 L1993 **FM** *040 †18
WALKER, Rebecca Hutt. 6263 POPLAR AVE, STE 1052 38119 #028-78-1997, ▲ L1999 **IM** *020 †20
WALKER, William W, Jr. 1030 JEFFERSON AVE 38104 #021-01-1953 L1960 **P** *071
WALL, Hershel Perry. 777 WASHINGTON AVE, STE P110 38105 #047-06-1960 L1960 **PD** *020 †55
WALL, Sherri Dawn. 858 MADISON AVE 38103 #036-01-1981 L1987 **PTH** *020 †50
WALLACE, Charles R, II. 1325 EASTMORELAND AVE, STE 425 38104 #010-03-1978 L1984 **U** *020
WALLACE, Michael C. 7685 WINCHESTER RD, STE 100 38125 #047-06-2000 L2002 **FM** *020 †18 ‡
WALLER, Benjamin Rush, III. 50 N DUNLAP ST 2ND FL, LEBONHEUR CHILDREN'S MED C 38103 #047-06-1987 L1989 **PDC** *020 †55
WALLER, Maurice Edward. ■ 38115 #047-06-1954 L1955 **GP** *071
WALLER, Robert Rex. ■ 38117 #047-06-1963 L1964 **OPH** *071 †35
WALLING, Robert Van. 777 WASHINGTON AVE, STE P110 38105 #047-06-1970 L1973 **PD OS** *072
WALN, Volha. 956 COURT AVE 38163 #913-33-1997 **IM** *012
WALSH, Michele Lynette. 3030 COVINGTON PIKE, STE 100 38128 #038-40-2004 L2007 **FM** *100 †18
WALSH, Penny Josephine. 899 MADISON AVE 38103 #048-13-1994 L2001 **PD** *020 †55
WALTERS, Cyrilyn Amarie. ■ 38103 #026-04-2007 **MPD** *012
WALTHER, Ray. 1211 UNION AVE, STE 350 38104 #001-02-1980 L1982 **IM** *020 †16
WALTON, Jarvis Dorell. ■ 38103 #047-06-2001 L2004 **NEP** *100
WALTON, R Christopher. 930 MADISON AVE STE 470, HAMILTON EYE INST 38163 #001-06-1986 L1995 **OPH** *020 †35
WANDERMAN, Richard Gordon. 6077 APPLE TREE DR, STE 5 38115 #035-08-1969 L1978 **PD A** *020 †55
WANDREY, Daniel Enoch. ■ 38111 #048-12-2006 **GS** *012
WANG, Benjamin Wei En. 956 COURT AVE., ROOM G326 38163 #065-01-1991 L2000 **RHU IM** *040 †20
WANG, Gordon. ■ 38120 #917-24-1988 L2005 **FM** *020 †18
WANG, Guan. 150 COLLINS ST 38112 #243-92-1986 L2000 **PTH** *100 †50
WANG, Haiqiu. 3109 WALNUT GROVE RD 38111 #243-03-1993 L2003 **FM** *020 †18
WANG, James Jinxing. 6005 PARK AVE, STE 202 38119 #243-67-1985 L1998 **N IM** *020 †75
WANG, Weihua. 6046 KNIGHT ARNOLD ROD EXT, STE 101 38115 #243-16-1982 L2003 **PCP PTH** *020 †50
WANG, Winfred Ching-Chung. 332 N LAUDERDALE ST 38105 #016-02-1967 L1979 **PHO** *050 †55
WARD, Forrest Chas. 6644 SUMMER KNOLL CIR 38134 #047-06-1984 L1985 **IM** *020
WARD, Jewell Catherine. 806 ESTATE PL 38120 #017-20-1971 L1979 **MG PD** *020 †19
WARD, John David. 6005 PARK AVE, STE 323B 38119 #047-06-1988 L1993 **GE IM** *020 †20
WARDLAW, Lee Lyle. ■ 38104 #027-01-1966 L1974 **GE IM** *071
WARE, John Rigdon. 1030 JEFFERSON AVE, VA MEDICAL CENTER 38104 #012-01-1977 L1990 **DR** *020 †20,80
WARE, Russell Earl. 332 N LAUDERDALE ST, HOSPITAL - MS 355 38105 #036-07-1983 L2004 **PHO PD** *020 †55
WARNER, Ronnie Mark. 6005 PARK AVE, STE 101B 38119 #021-06-1977 L1981 **DR** *020 †80
WARNER, Susan Linen. 6046 KNIGHT ARNOLD ROD EXT, STE 101 38115 #005-11-1981 L1993 **IM** *020 †20
WARR, James Andrew. 956 COURT AVE 38163 #422-01-2004 L2007 **FM** *020
WARR, Otis Sumter, III. 362 N WILLETT ST 38112 #047-06-1963 L1963 **CD IM** *020 †20
WARREN, Jeffery Steven. 3109 WALNUT GROVE RD 38111 #036-07-1982 L1988 **FM EM** *020 †18,16
WASHINGTON, Cherese D. 1030 JEFFERSON AVE, VA MEDICAL CENTER 38104 #027-01-1981 L1989 **IM** *020 †20
WASIM, Zainab. 1265 UNION AVE, METHODIST HSP-CENTRAL UNIT 38104 #704-06-1995 **IM** *100 †20
WATERS, Bradford. 66 N PAULINE ST STE 633 38105 #047-05-1982 L1984 **GE IM** *020 †20
WATKINS, Jeremy Paul. UNIV OF TENNESSEE HSC, DEPT OF OTOLARYNGOLOGY 38163 #021-05-2003 L2007 **OTO** *012
WATRIDGE, Clarence Boyett. 6325 HUMPHREYS BLVD 38120 #047-06-1975 L1976 **NS** *020 †25
WATSON, Andrew Todd. 1325 EASTMORELAND AVE # 4, SUTHERLAND CARDIOLOGY CLIN 38104 #654-01-1999 L2005 **CD** *020 †20
WATSON, Timotheus George. ■ 38116 #038-06-2006 L2006 **PD** *012
WATT, Mridula. ■ 38107 #047-06-2008 *012
WATTS, Marilyn P. 2900 KIRBY RD, STE 4 38119 #048-02-1995 L1998 **PD** *020 †55
WATTS, Susan Jane. ■ 38117 #047-06-1985 L1988 **PTH** *020 †50
WEATHERLY, Mark Willard. 1661 INTERNATIONAL DR, STE 350 38120 #047-06-1980 L1980 **DR** *020 †80
WEAVER, Jason Andrew. 956 CT AVE 38163 #028-34-2001 L2007 **NS** *100
WEAVER, Joseph. 3362 S 3RD ST, CHRIST COMMUNITY MEDICAL C 38109 #016-11-1996 L2000 **FM** *020 †18
WEBB, David Louis, Jr. ■ 38112 #047-06-2006 **GS** *012
WEBB, Luke Michael. 842 JEFFERSON AVE, STE A601 38103 #047-06-2002 L2004 **IM** *020 †20
WEBB, Trenia Lyn. UNIV OF TENNESSEE, DEPT OF OB/GYN 38163 #047-06-2003 L2007 **OBG** *020
WEBBER, Bruce Leonard. 6046 KNIGHT ARNOLD ROD EXT, STE 101 38115 #836-01-1965 L1979 **ATP** *020 †50
WEBER, Alvin Julian, III. 6075 POPLAR AVE, STE 405 38119 #047-06-1962 L1963 **DR NM** *071 †20,80,28
WEBER, Bill Carl. 1325 EASTMORELAND AVE, STE 335 38104 #047-06-1962 L1962 **IM** *071
WEBER, David Jay. 6019 WALNUT GROVE RD 38120 #035-20-1986 L1990 **FM PLM** *020 †18
WEBER, Karl Theodore. 8080 MADISON AVE, UNIVERSITY OF TENNESSEE 38163 #041-13-1968 L2000 **CD IM** *050 †20
WEBER, Philip Rowe. 6075 POPLAR AVE STE 405 38119 #047-06-1999 L2003 **VIR** *020 †80
WEEKS, Albert Earle. 6005 PARK AVE, STE 1000B 38119 #048-14-1983 L1989 **ON HEM** *020 †20
WEEKS, Eloise Estelle. ■ 38106 #047-06-2006 L2006 **P** *012
WEEKS, James Kelley, Jr. ■ 38117 #047-06-2003 L2004 **DR** *012
WEEMS, Joseph Lell. 6005 PARK AVE 38119 #047-06-1969 L1970 **OTO** *071 †45
WEI, Tie. ■ 38119 #243-36-1986 **FP** *012
WEIMAN, Darryl Seth. 1030 JEFFERSON AVE 38104 #028-34-1978 L1993 **GS TS** *020 †90,85
WEIMAR, James Dudley. UT - DEPT. OF NEUROSURGERY, 847 MONROE AVENUE STE. 42 38163 #047-06-2003 L2006 **NS** *012
WEINBERG, Joseph Arnold. 50 N DUNLAP ST, ER DEPT 38103 #024-01-1973 L1981 **PEM EM** *071 †55,16
WEINLEIN, John Charles. 1211 UNION AVE STE 51, CAMPBELL FOUNDATION 38104 #033-06-2004 L2006 **ORS** *012
WEINSTEIN, Joseph Seth. 4901 RALEIGH COMMON DR, OF MEMPHIS INC 38128 #028-03-1982 L1989 **CD IM** *020 †20
WEINTRAUB, Aliza Shulamit. ■ 38120 #041-15-2000 L2006 **RHU** *020
WEISS, Carl Barton. 6286 BRIARCREST AVE 38120 #035-08-1984 L2004 **ORS HS** *020 †40
WEISS, Kenneth Stephen. 6286 BRIARCREST AVE, FL 2 38120 #047-06-1995 L2001 **ORS** *020 †40
WEISS, Martin Jeffrey. 6027 WALNUT GROVE RD 38120 #047-20-1998 L1999 **IM** *020
WEISS, William Todd. 6027 WALNUT GROVE RD, STE 103 38120 #047-20-1990 L1991 **IM** *020 †20
WELCH, Susan Kathleen. 8025 STAGE HILLS BLVD 38133 #054-04-1984 L2006 **IM** *050 †55
WELDEN, Jonathan Galaz. 687 JEFFERSON AVE, # 13 38105 #047-06-2006 **OBG** *100
WELLS, Van Henry. 176 S BELLEVUE BLVD # 607 38104 #047-06-1961 L1961 **TS** *071 †85,90
WENZEL, Aaron James. 956 COURT AVE 38163 #305-01-2007 **FP** *012
WESBERRY, Jesse M, Jr. 2900 S PERKINS RD 38118 #047-06-1980 L1981 **OPH** *020 †35
WEST, Harold Maxell. 865 POPLAR AVE 38105 #047-06-1957 L1958 **P** *071 †75
WEST, James Mitchell. 1755 KIRBY PKWY, STE 330 38120 #047-06-1983 L1984 **AN** *020 †05
WEST, Thomas La Follette. 17 S ROSE RD 38117 #047-06-1965 L1965 **GS** *020 †85
WEST, William Hoath. 6019 WALNUT GROVE RD 38120 #023-07-1973 L1974 **ON IM** *071 †20
WESTBROOK, Rita Faye. 6019 WALNUT GROVE RD 38120 #001-02-1986 L1987 **PD PEM** *020 †20,55
WESTMORELAND, Daniel Kirk. 200 WAGNER PL, PH 105 38103 #047-06-1969 L1970 **R** *020 †80
WHEAT, Wendell Tillman. 6005 PARK AVE STE 601 38119 #047-06-1974 L1975 **GS** *020 †85
WHEELER, Benton M, III. 100 N HUMPHREYS BLVD, THE WEST CLINIC 38120 #012-01-1980 L1993 **HO HEM** *020 †20
WHEELER, Kristopher Scott. ■ 38103 #047-06-2008 *012
WHELESS, James Warren. 777 WASHINGTON AVE P250, PEDIATRIC NEUROLOGY 38105 #039-01-1982 L2005 **PD CHN** *020 †55,75
WHITAKER, Mark Alan. 85 N DANNY THOMAS BLVD 38103 #019-02-1977 L2005 **PD** *020 †55
WHITAKER, Toni Michele. 711 JEFFERSON AVE, UNIV OF TENN BOLING CENTER 38105 #047-06-1993 L1995 **PD** *020 †55
WHITE, Charles Edward. 5200 PARK AVE 38119 #047-06-1964 L1964 **PS** *071 †85,65
WHITE, Frank Louis. 1211 UNION AVE, STE 250 38104 #047-06-1969 L1969 **PTH CLP** *020 †50
WHITE, Thomas Jefferson. 1210 PEABODY AVE 38104 #047-06-1958 L1958 **IM** *071 †20
WHITE, Thos Jefferson, III. 49 N DUNLAP ST 38103 #047-06-1967 L1968 **DR** *071 †80
WHITE, William Guerin. 877 JEFFERSON AVE 38103 #051-01-1940 L1948 **PUD IM** *071
WHITINGTON, Gene L. 2670 UNION AVENUE EXT, EXT'D 1220 38112 #047-06-1953 L1955 **PG HEP** *020 †55

WHITLEY, Justin Matthew. ■ 38126 #047-06-2008 *012
WHITLOCK, Lawrence Wayne. 3725 CHAMPION HILLS DR, STE 2000 38125 #047-06-1972 L1973 **IM** *020
WHITNACK, Ellen. 1030 JEFFERSON AVE, UNIVERSITY OF TENNESSEE 38104 #038-41-1974 L1977 **IM** *020 †20
WHITNEY, Carolyn. 1955 S 3RD ST 38109 #047-07-1984 L1985 **PD** *020 †55
WHITTLE, Allison Paige. 1211 UNION AVE, STE 500 38104 #024-05-1986 L1991 **ORS OTR** *020 †40
WHITWORTH, John Ross. 806 ESTATE PL 38120 #047-06-1998 L2000 **PG** *020 †20,55
WICKMAN, John Raymond. 8485 US HIGHWAY 64, STE 101 38133 #047-06-1988 L1991 **FM GPM** *020 †18
WIEDERHOLD, Michael Sulli. ■ 38111 #004-01-2006 **PD** *012
WIENER, Isadore David. 38 N PAULINE ST 38105 #021-01-1941 L1948 **GYN** *071 †30
WIENER, Robert Alan. 6019 WALNUT GROVE RD 38120 #047-06-1972 L1973 **OBG** *071 †30
WILD, Kathleen Joanne. 687 JEFFERSON AVE 38105 #047-06-2008 *012
WILIMAS, Judith Ann. 332 N LAUDERDALE ST 38105 #025-07-1970 L1974 **HEM ON** *020 †55
WILKERSON, Benjamin Wade. ■ 38122 #027-01-2005 **DR** *012
WILKERSON, Dana Lea. ■ 38111 #047-06-2000 L2008 **U** *100
WILLIAMS, Beverly Jean. 920 MADISON AVE, RM 324 38103 #047-06-1969 L1969 **IM END** *020 †20
WILLIAMS, Dorothy Lucille. 350 N HUMPHREYS BLVD, # EAGLBLD2 38120 #047-06-1962 L1975 **PTH IM** *071
WILLIAMS, Ethelyn Juanita. 1331 UNION AVE STE 900 38104 #016-11-1967 L1972 **PD FM** *020 †55
WILLIAMS, Glenn. 5050 POPLAR AVE, SPECIALISTS 38157 #047-06-1984 L1985 **PUD PD** *020 †20,55
WILLIAMS, Glenn Blake. ■ 38104 #047-06-2004 **OTO** *012
WILLIAMS, Hugh Hermes. 220 S CLAYBROOK ST STE 314 38104 #566-01-1972 L1980 **IM NEP** *020 †20
WILLIAMS, James Scott. 50 N DUNLAP ST 38103 #048-14-1990 L1995 **DR** *020 †80
WILLIAMS, Jeffrey Lemoine. 6005 PARK AVE, STE 605 38119 #028-02-1997 L2002 *020 †05
WILLIAMS, Judith A J. 6215 HUMPHREYS BLVD # 301 38120 #047-06-1998 L2002 **OBG** *020 †30
WILLIAMS, Linkwood. 1265 UNION AVE 38104 #047-07-1960 L1964 **OBG GP** *071
WILLIAMS, Mark Alan. 770 ESTATE PL 38120 #012-01-1986 L1987 **UP** *020 †95
WILLIAMS, Michael Anthony. 2900 KIRBY RD STE 10 38119 #001-02-1996 L1998 **OS** *020
WILLIAMS, Richard Thomas. 332 N LAUDERDALE ST 38105 #143-05-1995 **PHO** *100
WILLIAMS, Susan Theresa. 150 COLLINS ST 38112 #016-45-1993 L1997 **PTH** *020 †50
WILLIAMS, Susannah Taylor. 38104 #001-02-2003 L2006 **P** *012
WILLIAMSON, Tena June. 2900 KIRBY RD, STE 14 38119 #047-06-1990 L1991 **FM** *020 †18
WILLS, Gordon Lee. ■ 38104 #047-06-1955 L1955 **GP OS** *071
WILLS, John Ross. ■ 38117 #047-06-1959 L1960 **GP OS** *071
WILONS, Michael David. 6025 WALNUT GROVE RD, PC 38120 #047-06-1972 L1973 **PUD OS** *071
WILROY, Robert Sidney, Jr. 777 WASHINGTON AVE, STE P110 38105 #047-06-1960 L1961 **OS PD** *071 †55,19
WILSON, Arthur James. 1211 UNION AVE, STE 300 38104 #041-13-1968 L1975 **PTH** *071 †50
WILSON, Darrel Lenard. 7948 WINCHESTER RD, STE 109 38125 #018-03-1991 L1999 **P EM** *020
WILSON, Donald Bruce. 188 S BELLEVUE BLVD # 405 38104 #047-06-1972 L1975 **CD OS** *020 †20
WILSON, Fred P, Jr. 1750 MADISON AVE, STE 400 38104 #047-06-1988 L1991 **IM** *020 †20
WILSON, Gina Simone. 3950 NEW COVINGTON PIKE, STE 220 38128 #047-07-2001 L2005 **OBG** *020
WILSON, Harry Williamson. 744 E BROOKHAVEN CIR, JOHN LANDRIGAN MD 38117 #047-06-1957 L1962 **OS OBG** *071
WILSON, James Alfred, III. 7900 US HIGHWAY 64, GYNECOLOGY ASSOCIATES PC 38133 #047-20-1986 L1990 **OBG** *020
WILSON, Lori Nicole. ■ 38104 #047-06-2008 *012
WILSON, Marjorie Pauline. ■ 38105 #047-06-2008 *012
WILSON, Matthew Walls. 930 MADISON AVE., STE. 470 38163 #012-05-1990 L1999 **OPH** *020 †35
WILSON, Raymond Edward. 1755 KIRBY PKWY, STE 330 38120 #047-06-1984 L1985 **AN** *020 †05
WIMBERLY, Latrina Yvette. 956 CT AVE 38163 #047-20-1999 L2002 **IM** *020
WINBERY, Stephen Loyd. 842 JEFFERSON AVE RMA645, EMERGENCY MEDICINE 38103 #021-05-1990 L1994 **IM PD** *062 †20
WINDHAM, Andrew Allen. 38125 #047-06-1945 L1956 **GS FM** *075
WINDHAM, Michael Courtney. ■ 38125 #016-11-2007 **IM** *012
WINESTONE, John Sloan. ■ 38120 #047-06-2003 **NS** *012
WINESTONE, Marie Isley. ■ 38120 #047-06-2007 **IM** *012
WINFREY, Cheryl Denise. ■ 38184 #047-20-1992 L1996 **FM** *020 †18
WINTON, John Crawford. ■ 38120 #047-01-2004 L2007 **MPD** *012
WISDOM, Randall Thos. 5366 MENDENHALL MALL 38115 #004-01-1970 L1993 **PTH** *020
WISE, Merrill Sheppard. 5050 POPLAR AVE, STE 300 38157 #047-06-1984 L2006 **CHN PD** *020 †55,55
WISSINGER, Daniel Hunt. 1203 RIDGEWAY RD, PARK PL CTR STE 201 38119 #005-12-1970 L1990 **OPH** *020 †35
WITHERINGTON, John M. 2915 TISHOMINGO LN 38111 #047-06-1982 L1983 **IM** *020 †20
WITHERSPOON, Frank G, Jr. 1455 UNION AVE, MEMPHIS DERMATOLOGY 38104 #047-06-1977 L1978 **DS D** *020 †15
WITT, Reginald Lyvonne. 1030 JEFFERSON AVE, VA MEDICAL CENTER 38104 #047-06-1996 L2002 **AN** *020
WITTE, Dexter H, III. 55 HUMPHREYS CTR, STE 100 38120 #047-06-1985 L1986 **DR** *020 †80
WOLF, Bradley Aaron. 6029 WALNUT GROVE RD, STE 401 38120 #047-06-1990 L1995 **TS** *020 †85,90
WOLF, Frederick Gregory. 6005 PARK AVE, STE 608 38119 #017-20-1993 L2002 **ORS** *020 †40
WOLF, Rodney Yale. 6029 WALNUT GROVE RD, STE 401 38120 #047-06-1961 L1961 **TS** *020 †85,90
WOLFE, Susan Elizabeth. 669 JEFFERSON AVE 38105 #021-05-1988 L1990 **IM** *020
WOMACK, Jamie Harris. ■ 38111 #045-01-2004 L2006 **P** *012
WOMACK, John Wesley. ■ 38111 #047-06-2002 L2007 **ORS** *100
WOMBACK, Kimberly Felicia. 5959 PARK AVE, EMERGENCY DEPARTMENT 38119 #047-06-2001 L2008 **EM** *020
WONG, Frank Sou-Him. 956 COURT AVE, RM B224 38103 #244-02-1967 L1993 **OTO** *020 †45
WONG, Peter Lap. 956 CT AVE, RM G228 38163 #010-02-2004 **GS** *012

WOOD, George Wm. 1211 UNION AVE, STE 500 38104 #041-09-1973 L1978 **ORS HS** *020 †40
WOOD, James Barker. 877 JEFFERSON AVE 38103 #051-01-1979 L1984 **DR** *050 †80
WOOD, Janice Carol. 6025 WALNUT GROVE RD, STE 201 38120 #001-02-1981 L1985 **GS** *020 †85
WOODALL, Charles Jackson. 7685 WINCHESTER RD, STE 100 38125 #027-01-1986 L1986 **FM** *020 †18
WOODALL, Diane Lynn. 1211 UNION AVE, STE 350 38104 #001-02-1975 L1988 **NPM PD** *020 †55
WOODALL, Jesse C, Jr. 6570 STAGE RD, STE 160 38134 #047-06-1964 L1964 **OBG** *020 †30
WOODALL, Melanie Landrum. 7685 WINCHESTER RD, STE 100 38125 #027-01-1986 L1986 **FM** *020 †18
WOODARD, Joseph Paul, Jr. 332 N LAUDERDALE ST, HSP INC., DEPT OF HEMATOLO 38105 #036-01-1992 L1999 **PD** *020 †55
WOODHOUSE, Catherine L. 2953 BROAD AVE, INC. 38112 #023-12-1995 L2006 **MPD** *020 †20,55
WOODMAN, George Ellis. 6027 WALNUT GROVE RD, STE 206 38120 #020-02-1992 L1998 **GS OS** *020 †85
WOODSIDE, Jeffrey Robt. 66 N PAULINE ST STE 633 38105 #040-02-1968 L1992 **U AM** *030 †95
WOOTEN, Richard Lindsey. 80 HUMPHREYS CTR, MEMPHIS CLNC INTERNL MEDCN 38120 #047-06-1947 L1948 **IM DIA** *071 †20
WORK, Richard Macnaughton. 3109 WALNUT GROVE RD 38111 #047-06-1984 L1987 **GP** *020
WORTHAM, George F, III. 7900 US HIGHWAY 64, GYNECOLOGY ASSOCIATES PC 38133 #047-06-1983 L1984 **OBG** *020 †30
WRIGHT, Harvey Banks, Jr. 6485 POPLAR AVE 38119 #027-01-1990 L1996 **OPH** *020 †35
WRIGHT, Karen Denise. 332 N LAUDERDALE ST, DEPT HEMATOLOGY/ONCOLOGY 38105 #041-13-2003 L2006 **PHO** *012 †55
WRIGHT, Lance Jefferson. 6325 HUMPHREYS BLVD 38120 #048-14-1986 L1993 **N** *020 †75
WRIGHT, Leonard D, Jr. 3980 NEW COVINGTON PIKE, STE 310 38128 #047-06-1959 L1963 **OTO** *020 †45
WRIGHT, Tony Lasonya. 50 N DUNLAP ST 38103 #047-07-1997 L1998 **MPD EM** *020 †55,20
WRUBLE, Lawrence David. 6019 WALNUT GROVE RD 38120 #047-06-1958 L1958 **GE OS** *020 †20
WU, Bo. 6005 PARK AVE, STE 605 38119 #243-72-1985 L2001 **AN** *020 †05
WYATT, Robert Jethro. 50 N DUNLAP ST, RM 301WPT 38120 #012-01-1973 L1984 **NEP PD** *050 †55
XAVIER, Frederico. ■ 38103 #187-30-1997 **PHO** *012 †55
XIE, Huiwen. 6046 KNIGHT ARNOLD ROD EXT, STE 101 38115 #243-76-1982 L2004 **PCP** *020 †50
XU, Ying. 4137 KIRBY PKWY STE 1 38115 #243-45-1989 L2003 **FM** *100 †18
YAFFE, Sherwin Abe. 4515 POPLAR AVE STE 322 38117 #047-06-1977 L1979 **P** *020 †75
YALIF, Asaf. ■ 38103 #033-06-2000 L2005 **PS** *012 †85
YAM, David Allen. ■ 38103 #047-06-2004 **NS** *012
YANG, Wanting. ■ 38105 #047-06-2007 **FP** *012
YANISHEVSKI, Svetlana. 5959 PARK AVE 38119 #913-05-1991 L1998 **PD** *020 †55 ‡
YARBROUGH, Robert Reed. 1661 INTERNATIONAL DR, STE 350 38120 #047-06-1978 L1979 **DR** *020 †80
YASEEN, Zaneb. ■ 38104 #047-06-2008 *012
YATACO, Jose Carlos. ROOM H314, 956 COURT AVENUE 38163 #737-06-1998 L2006 **PCC** *020 †20
YATES, Amy Ashford. ■ 38111 #021-06-2005 **PD** *012
YATES, Linda Kay. 920 MADISON AVE STE 407N 38103 #047-06-1973 L1974 **EM** *062 †16
YATES, Robert Louis. 85 N DANNY THOMAS BLVD, 2ND FL 38103 #004-01-1976 L1977 **OBG** *030 †30
YATSULA, Michael Anthony, Jr. ■ 38104 #047-06-2008 *012
YEH, Melissa Janet. ■ 38103 #047-06-2003 **NEP** *020 †20
YIM, Eric Tingkin. ■ 38111 #019-02-2006 **MPD** *012
YOO, Tai-June. UNIVERSITY OF TENNESSEE, 956 COURT AVE ROOM B318 38163 #583-02-1959 L1980 **AI IM** *050
YORK, Krista Anne. ■ 38120 #038-43-2003 L2006 **PD** *100 †55
YOSER, Seth Leigh. 2996 KATE BOND RD, STE 413 38133 #005-14-1988 L1994 **OPH** *020 †35
YOUNG, Jack G. 188 S BELLEVUE BLVD, STE 408 38104 #048-04-1940 L1947 **OBG GYN** *071
YOUNG, Lisa La Donna. 6005 PARK AVE, STE 500B 38119 #035-45-1989 L2004 **CD** *020 †20
YOUNG, Mark Scott. 6005 PARK AVE STE 728B, MEMPHIS INTERNAL MEDICINE 38119 #004-01-1982 L1985 **IM** *020 †20
YOUNGER, Carl Thos. 1000 HAYNES ST 38114 #047-06-1981 L1982 **GP** *020 ‡
YU, Fang. 956 COURT AVE 38163 #243-72-1997 **DR** *012
YUAN, Qing. 956 COURT AVE 38163 #243-46-1989 L2006 **IM** *020 †20
YUSUF, Usman. 332 N LAUDERDALE ST, HOSPITAL, DEPT OF HEMAT./O 38105 #690-03-1982 L2002 **PD PHO** *020
ZAFAR, Nadeem. 930 MADISON AVE, STE 500 38163 #704-02-1985 L2003 **PTH** *020 †50
ZAFARULLAH, Haris. ■ 38103 #704-26-2001 L2006 **CD** *012 †20
ZAFER, Ghany. 1755 KIRBY PKWY, STE 330 38120 #665-01-1997 L2001 **AN** *020
ZAIDI, Amna Ahmad. 956 COURT AVE 38163 #704-16-2003 **IM** *012
ZAIDI, Syeda Sadia. 956 CT AVE, UNIV OF TN COLL OF MED 38163 #704-02-2002 **IM** *012
ZALAMEA, Roderick Millan. 6305 HUMPHREYS BLVD # 205 38120 #047-06-2002 L2005 **DR** *100 †80
ZAMAN, Muhammad. 66 N PAULINE ST STE 633 38105 #160-02-1980 L1991 **PUD IM** *020 †20
ZANELLA, John. 877 JEFFERSON AVE, 615 CHANDLER BLDG 38103 #038-06-1974 L1979 **AN PD** *020 †05
ZARE, Fereshteh. 956 CT AVE, UNIV OF TN COLL OF MED 38163 #496-07-1983 **IM** *012
ZARZAUR, Ben Louis, Jr. 956 COURT AVENUE ROOM E228 38163 #001-02-1996 L1999 **CCS** *100 †85
ZBYTEK, Blazej. ■ 38107 #759-07-1999 **PTH** *012
ZENI, Phillip T, Jr. 55 HUMPHREYS CTR, STE 100 38120 #004-01-1994 L1999 **VIR** *020 †80 ‡
ZEPEDA OROZCO, Diana. 956 CT AVE, UNIV OF TN COLL OF MED 38163 #649-03-2005 L2008 **PD** *012
ZHANG, Jie. ■ 38103 #243-38-1983 L2006 **PP** *100 †50
ZHANG, Jing. 6046 KNIGHT ARNOLD ROD EXT, STE 101 38115 #243-58-1984 L2000 **PTH** *020 †50
ZHAO, Jun. ■ 38105 #243-95-1998 **IM** *012
ZIA, Ayhan Ahmed. DEPT OF MED, 920 MADISON AVE STE 300 38163 #704-22-1995 L2006 **CD** *012 †20
ZIA, Mona Azizi. 38103 #422-01-2002 L2007 **IM** *020 †20
ZOGLEMAN, Brice Jarod. ■ 38111 #019-02-2005 **MPD** *012
ZSOHAR, Jeffrey. ■ 38111 #048-14-2002 L2005 **MPD** *100 †20

■ = Address Information Privacy Protected

MIDDLETON – HARDEMAN

KAMSO-PRATT, Jimmy M. 100 CHICKADEE AVE 38052 #047-06-1993 L1994 **FM** *020 †18 ‡

MILAN – GIBSON

ANDRE, Patrick Nicholas. 6041 TELECOM DR 38358 #047-06-2000 L2002 **FM** *020 †18
APPLETON, Joe Allen. 4039 HIGHLAND ST, JACKSON CLINIC 38358 #047-06-1993 L1995
  IM *020 †20
APPLETON, Nicolas Burns. 4039 HIGHLAND ST 38358 #047-06-1985 L1987 **IM** *020 †20
MC ADOO, Michael Allen. 6041 TELECOM DR 38358 #047-06-1975 L1976 **FM** *020 †18 ‡
REEVES, Wade Park. 6041 TELECOM DR 38358 #047-06-1986 L1987 **FM** *020 †18
TOZER, Kenneth H, II. 4022 LIBERTY ST, BOX 758 38358 #005-12-1980 L1985 **GS VS** *020 †85
TWILLA, Ronald Guy. 4039 HIGHLAND ST 38358 #047-06-1974 L1975 **FM** *020 †18
WILSON, Jerry Paul. 6041 TELECOM DR 38358 #047-06-1992 L1993 **FM** *020 †18
YAKIN, David Eric. 4039 HIGHLAND ST 38358 #041-09-1992 L1997 **ORS** *020 †40

MILLINGTON – SHELBY

ALGEA, Janice Skinner. 8081 US HIGHWAY 51 N, JANICE S ALGEA MD 38053
  #047-06-1975 L1976 **PD** *020 †55
ALGEA, William Leroy, III. 1561 CUBA MILLINGTON RD 38053 #047-06-1975 L1975 **GP** *020
BAIG, Abdullah. 8081 US HIGHWAY 51 N 38053 #704-02-1989 L1998 **IM** *020 †20
BELL, Darl Vilbro. 8076 US HIGHWAY 51 N 38053 #021-06-1992 L1995 **IM** *020 †20
FLOYD, Jerry Ray. 7662 US HIGHWAY 51 N 38053 #306-01-1991 L1997 **FM** *020 †18
GOODE, Fletcher Howard. 4759 EASLEY ST 38053 #047-06-1956 L1957 **OPH** *020 †35
KARNEZIS, Chrisanthos. 4771 EASLEY ST STE 2 38053 #047-07-1976 L1978 **IM** *100
KROPF, Justin Kyle. ■ 38053 #047-06-2006 **U** *012
LA BARREARE, John C, Jr. 4785 CUBA MILLINGTON RD 38053 #047-06-1975 L1976
  GP PTH *020
LINDSEY, Regina Suzanne. 8222 US HIGHWAY 51 N 38053 #019-02-1986 L1987 **GP EM** *072
MATTHEWS, J Barret. 8998 BARRET RD, P O BOX 400 38053 #047-06-1976 L1977 **IM EM** *020
NORRIS, Dale Wayne. PO BOX 279, 4772 NAVY RD 38053 #047-06-1984 L1985 **EM** *020
RIVERA, Juan Pedro. ■ 38053 #034-01-1992 L2005 **N** *020 †75
SMOLENSKI, Lisabeth Ann. ■ 38053 #041-09-1982 L1985 **FM** *020 †18
TICKLE, Samuel Milton. ■ 38053 #047-06-1957 L1957 **PUD IM** *071

MILTON – RUTHERFORD

SPEARS, Joanetta Hopkins. ■ 37118 #020-02-1983 L1985 **GP** *020

MONTEAGLE – MARION

CHOUNZOM, Tenzing. 15 S CENTRAL AVE, MONTEAGLE INTERNAL MED 37356
  #495-45-1987 L1999 **IM** *020 †20
LESTER, James Peyton. 2023 CLIFFTOPS AVE 37356 #047-06-1948 L1948 **TS VS** *071 †85,90
MANGRU, Jagindra Nath. 15 S CENTRAL AVE, MONTEAGLE INT MED/RHEUM 37356
  #566-01-1996 L2004 **RHU IM** *020 †20

MONTEREY – PUTNAM

GOLDMAN, Lloyd Selig. ■ 38574 #038-06-1967 L1967 **ORS** *071 †40
HALL, Robert Crombie. ■ 38574 #025-01-1961 L1965 **OPH** *071 †35
SMITH, Charles Gray. 400 W CRAWFORD AVE 38574 #047-20-1984 L1984 **FM** *020 †18

MOORESBURG – HAWKINS

HANCOCK, John Theodore. 9505 HIGHWAY 11 W 37811 #005-12-1988 L1989 **IM** *020
PATEL, Bharat Zaver. 150 LORENE LN 37811 #495-01-1959 L1997 **GS EM** *020 †85

MORRIS CHAPEL – HARDIN

QUALLS, Jerry Franklin. 198 DONOHOO LN 38361 #047-06-1965 L1965 **PD OBS** *020

MORRISON – WARREN

BUTLER, Maurice Keith. ■ 37357 #005-12-1952 L1954 **GP** *071
HARRIS, Hoyt C. ■ 37357 #047-06-1946 L1946 **AS FM** *071 †18

MORRISTOWN – HAMBLEN

ABEL, Todd Bruce. 420 W MORRIS BLVD 37813 #005-12-1996 L2005 **NS** *020
ADAMS, Jeffrey Scott. 711 MCFARLAND ST 37814 #001-02-1998 L2003 **OTO** *020 †45
ADAMS, Linas Jonas. 615 W 7TH NORTH ST 37814 #649-14-1978 L1982 **GE IM** *020 †20
AHMED, Mohammed Imtiaz. 110 N HIGH ST 37814 #704-20-1992 L2002 **NEP IM** *020 †20
ALEXANDER, William King. ■ 37814 #047-06-1957 L1960 **GP GS** *071
ALLUM, Kenneth Manson, Jr. ■ 37814 #047-06-1965 L1969 **IM CD** *071 †20
AMADOR, Jose Garcia, Jr. 421 N HIGH ST 37814 #748-11-1963 L1974 **U** *072 †95
ANDERSON, John Marshall. 908 W 4TH NORTH ST, MORRISTOWN REG CANCER CTR 37814
  #003-01-1991 L2001 **RO** *020 †80
ANDREWS, Douglas Eugene. 726 MCFARLAND ST 37814 #051-04-1958 L1973 **AN** *071
ASHLEY, Holvor W. 726 MCFARLAND ST 37814 #654-01-1986 L1989 **PTH BBK** *062 †50
ASSADNIA, Shahin. 1751 W MORRIS BLVD, STE 4 37813 #051-04-1993 L2001 **VS** *020 †85
BACKWINKEL, Klaus D. 739 E 2ND NORTH ST 37814 #407-16-1953 L1960 **GS** *071 †85
BARHAM, James Eldred. 1447 W MORRIS BLVD 37813 #036-07-1974 L1992 **FM** *071 †18
BARROWCLOUGH, John Robt. 908 W 4TH NORTH ST 37814 #036-05-1983 L1986
  IM EM *020 †20

BELLAIRE, Mack J. 739 E 2ND NORTH ST, UNIT 398 37814 #056-06-1930 L1930 **GP** *071
BENAVIDES, Moses Benaiah. ■ 37813 #047-07-1999 L2005 **FM** *020
BLACK, Billy J, Jr. 609 MCFARLAND ST 37814 #048-13-2001 L2007 **OBG** *020
BLAKE, Cleland Conway. 850 W 3RD NORTH ST 37814 #047-06-1958 L1959 **PTH FOP** *072 †50
BOOKER, Bert Luther, Jr. 3027 BRANDYWINE CIR 37814 #047-06-1964 L1964 **R** *020
BOWERS, Patricia Lynn. ■ 37814 #001-02-1986 L1990 **AN** *020 †05
BRATSCH, Colleen Q. 525 MCFARLAND ST 37814 #041-77-1998, ▲ L2003 **OBG** *020 †30
BRATTON, Michael Wayne. 420 W MORRIS BLVD, STE D 37813 #047-06-1985 L1994
  ORS *020 †40
BUKEAVICH, Alfred Peter. ■ 37814 #041-01-1954 L1972 **OBG** *071 †30
BUNN, Raymond Clyde. 2609 W ANDREW JOHNSON HWY, WEIGHT LOSS MANAGEMENT
  CLI 37814 #047-06-1953 L1954 **FM** *071 †18
BURJA, Izabela T. 908 W 4TH NORTH ST 37814 #759-08-1982 L1994 **PTH** *020 †50
BURNETTE-VICK, Bonnie A. 420 MORRIS BLVD, HEALTH STAR PHYS 37813
  #047-20-1997 L1998 **FM** *020 †18
BYARLAY, Jean Ann. 1907 W MORRIS BLVD 37813 #035-45-1991 L1995 **D** *020 †15
CARDALI, Paul Benedetto. 420 W MORRIS BLVD, STE C 37813 #011-02-1997 L1999
  IM *020 †20
CARSON, John W. 735 MCFARLAND ST 37814 #021-01-1990 L2000 **OPH** *072 †35
CASEY, Terrance Charles. 5741 W ANDREW JOHNSON HWY 37814 #422-01-1998 L2005
  PYG *020
CHAVIN, Michael Alan. 1639 W MORRIS BLVD 37813 #016-01-1983 L2000 **AN PME** *020 †05
CHAWLA, Manoj. ■ 37814 #495-45-1991 L1996 **IM FM** *020 †20
CHRISTOPHER, Ronald G. 420 W MORRIS BLVD, STE D 37813 #051-04-1992 L2000
  ORS *020 †40
CINTRON, Evelyn. 705 N HIGH ST 37814 #042-02-1990 L1995 **IM** *020
CODY, Richard Francis, Jr. 420 W MORRIS BLVD, STE 400F 37813 #036-01-1990 L2007
  DR *020
COLLINSON, Kim A D. 619 W 7TH NORTH ST, STE F 37814 #012-01-1981 L1986 **OBG** *020
COOZE, Derek A. 420 W MORRIS BLVD, STE 400B 37813 #063-01-1985 L1986 **FM** *020
COX, Jason Erle. ■ 37814 #047-06-1997 L2000 **FM** *020 †18
CRAWFORD, David Paul. 1633 W MORRIS BLVD, STE B 37813 #045-01-1994 L2004
  GS *020 †85
CROWDER, Bennett L, II. 726 MCFARLAND ST 37814 #047-06-1961 L1962 **EM GS** *071 †85
DAMODARAN, Harikrishnan. ■ 37814 #495-31-1994 L2007 **IC** *100 †20
DE FELICE, Joseph Michael. 908 DRINNON DR 37814 #654-01-1984 L2008 **ON IM** *020 †20
DELAY, Eric Gardner. 908 W 4TH NORTH ST 37814 #001-06-2002 L2006 **MPD** *020 †20,55
DILLARD, Michael Leslie. 711 MCFARLAND ST 37814 #047-06-1993 L1997 **OTO** *020 †45
DOBBS, Tracy. 420 W MORRIS BLVD, STE 400C 37814 #028-46-1983 L1989 **HEM ON** *020 †20
DOLAPTCHIEV, Bojidar Boji. 220 N FAIRMONT AVE, CRESCENT MEDICAL PLLC 37814
  #198-01-1993 L2006 **FM** *020 †18
DRINNEN, Daniel Brooks. 1633 W MORRIS BLVD 37813 #047-06-1992 L1995 **GS** *020 †85
ELLIS, Michael Robert. 1907 W MORRIS BLVD, STE G 37813 #024-05-1999 L2005 **GE** *020 †20
FOSTER, Allen Ricardo. 222 BOWMAN ST, STE 3 37813 #010-03-1988 L1999 **AN** *020 †05
FULK, Charles Saml. 400 E ECONOMY RD, STE 8 37814 #036-05-1973 L1982 **D IM** *020 †20,15
GAVIN, Daniel James. 420 W MORRIS BLVD, STE 400C 37813 #016-11-1991 L2002
  PCC *020 †20
GEORGE, Charles F, Jr. 4645 EAJ HWY 37814 #047-06-1946 L1946 **ORS** *071
GEYER, Clarissa Salgado. 908 W 4TH NORTH ST, UNIVERSITY CANCER SPECIALI 37814
  #187-80-1989 L2001 **HO IM** *020 †20
GREENE, David Louis, Jr. ■ 37813 #047-06-1964 L1964 **P GP** *020
GRONEWALD, W Robert. ■ 37813 #016-02-1964 L1971 **IM DIA** *072
GUBATAN, Veronica Manaois. 305 N BELLWOOD RD 37814 #748-16-1994 L2001 **P** *020 †75
GUPTA, Rajeev. 1621 W MORRIS BLVD STE C 37813 #495-10-1989 L2001 **FM FPG** *020 †18
HANCOCK, Shannon P. 420 W MORRIS BLVD, STE 400B 37813 #048-04-1996 L2004
  FM *020 †18
HARMELING, Mark Peter. ■ 37814 #016-06-1958 L1994 **ORS** *020
HARRELL, Mark Jeffrey. 908 W 4TH NORTH ST, MORRISTOWN-HAMBLEN HOSPITA 37814
  #047-20-1990 L1996 **EM** *020 †16
HARRIS, Dennis Gibson. 420 W MORRIS BLVD, STE 130 37813 #047-20-1983 L1986
  PME OS *020 †05
HEINZ, Stephan M. 3378 OLD KENTUCKY RD 37814 #048-16-1995 L1996 **FM** *020 †18
HELMS, Crampton Harris. 908 W 4TH NORTH ST 37814 #067-01-1958 L1962 **GS** *020 †85
HORNER, John Calvin. 538 N 6TH NORTH ST 37814 #047-06-1982 L1982 **IM** *020 †20
HUNT, Robert Mc Phail, Jr. 830 W 4TH NORTH ST 37814 #047-06-1968 L1969 **GE IM** *020 †20
JACKSON, Lawrence Richard. ■ 37813 #047-06-1961 L1962 **GP** *072
JACQUES, Julie Ann. 1907 W MORRIS BLVD, STE G 37813 #011-75-1999, ▲ L2002 **N SME** *020
JAMISON, Robert Alan. 908 W 4TH NORTH ST 37814 #047-06-1979 L1980 **PD** *020 †55
JETT, Paul Lee. 420 W MORRIS BLVD, STE 130 37813 #020-02-2001 L2004 **PM** *020 †60
JOHNSON, David A. 500 MCFARLAND ST, STE D 37814 #065-09-1973 L1996 **FM** *020 †18 ‡
KAVANAGH, Eugene L. 703 MCFARLAND ST 37814 #035-09-1974 L1996 **U** *020
KERLEY, Eric Lynn. 420 W MORRIS BLVD, STE 400B 37813 #047-20-2001 L2004
  MPD *020 †20,55
KIM, Joo Taek. 1085 PANTHER CREEK RD 37814 #583-02-1960 L1977 **PTH** *071 †50
KINSER, John H. 850 MCBRIDE RD, BOX 627 37814 #047-06-1950 L1951 **GP ADM** *072
KISS, Stephen Clement. 420 W MORRIS BLVD STE 110, FMC MORRISTOWN 37813
  #047-06-1985 L1991 **NEP IM** *020 †20
KODALI, Swatantra Babu. 1104 W 4TH NORTH ST 37814 #495-50-1971 L1989 **P** *020 †75
KOUSER, Aqueel Mohamed. 420 W MORRIS BLVD, STE C 37814 #704-02-1991 L1996
  RHU *020 †20
KOUSER, Hina. 500 MCFARLAND ST, STE D 37814 #704-25-1992 L1998 **IM** *020 †20
LANE, Debra Ann. 405 MCFARLAND ST, MORRISTOWN FAMILY MEDICINE 37814
  #017-20-1997 L2005 **FM** *020 †18
LANE, Robert A. 420 W MORRIS BLVD, STE 400 37813 #065-10-1976 L1992 **GS AS** *020 †85
LEE, Thomas Warren. ■ 37813 #047-06-1984 L1990 **AN** *020 †05
LINDSEY, Charles Hugh. 735 MCFARLAND ST 37814 #047-06-1977 L1978 **OPH GP** *020 †35
LISH, Kelly Lagrand. 850 W 3RD NORTH ST, C/O PHYSICIANS MEDICAL LAB 37814
  #047-20-1987 L1998 **PTH** *020
LITTLE, Frank B, Jr. 711 MCFARLAND ST 37814 #036-05-1981 L1986 **OTO** *020 †45
LIVESAY, Jackie Allen, Jr. 908 W 4TH NORTH ST 37814 #047-20-1997 L1998 **IM** *020 †20
LOWRY, Orlanda R, III. 850 W 3RD NORTH ST 37814 #047-06-1964 L1964 **IM** *020 †20
LUMB, John C. 701 MCFARLAND ST 37814 #048-14-1989 L1999 **GS** *020 †85
MAHMOOD, Mubashir. 420 W MORRIS BLVD, STE C 37813 #704-20-1990 L2000
  END IM *020 †20
MANY, Angela S. 609 MCFARLAND ST 37814 #047-06-2000 L2005 **IM** *020 †30

MANY, Heath Richard. 1633 W MORRIS BLVD, STE B 37813 #047-06-2000 L2005 **GS** *020 †85
MARAN, Siva. 500 MCFARLAND ST, STE E 37814 #495-42-1967 L1992 **GE** *020 †20
MATHEWS, Kenneth Milton, Jr. 812 W 4TH NORTH ST 37814 #005-12-1975 L1980 **PM PHP** *020 †70
MATSON, Scott Daniel. 619 W 7TH NORTH ST, STE F 37814 #008-02-1996 L2002 **U** *020 †95
MC LEMORE, Wayne Laverne. 726 MCFARLAND ST 37814 #051-04-1975 L1980 **ORS** *020 †40
MC NEIL, David Wyatt. 735 MCFARLAND ST 37814 #047-06-1965 L1966 **OPH** *020
MEJIA, Ernesto. 500 MCFARLAND ST, STE B 37814 #341-01-1977 L1994 **PUD** *020 †20
MELLING, Blake Page. 5741 W ANDREW JOHNSON HWY 37814 #305-01-2000 L2003 **FM** *020 †18
MERRITT, O L. ■ 37814 #047-06-1954 L1955 **FM** *071 †18
MINAMI, Carl Masao. 726 MCFARLAND ST 37814 #014-01-1990 L2003 **PTH PCP** *020 †50
MOHAMED, Abdelrahman. 230 BOWMAN ST, STE C, HAMBLEN NEUROSCI CTR PC 37813 #848-01-1975 L1999 **N CN** *020 †55,75
NASEEM, Shoaib A. 420 W MORRIS BLVD, STE 400C 37813 #704-01-1987 L2000 **CD** *020 †20
NIX, Jeffrey Alan. 1633 W MORRIS BLVD, STE B 37813 #047-06-1995 L1999 **GS** *020 †85
PAGE, Wayne C. 1907 W MORRIS BLVD, STE A100 37813 #039-01-1976 L1992 **NR EM** *020 †18
PEREZ, Ivan. 709 MCFARLAND ST 37814 #308-03-1980 L1987 **N** *020
PERRY, Cindy Dee. 305 N BELLWOOD RD 37814 #047-07-1991 L1995 **P** *020
PERRY, Patricia E. ■ 37814 #919-02-1961 L1977 **DR PDR** *020 †80
PRATT, Eustacia L. 420 W MORRIS BLVD, STE 400A 37813 #047-20-1997 L1999 **FM** *020 †18
PRESUTTI, Henry Jos. PO BOX 1657 37816 #064-01-1956 L1978 **FM EM** *071
RADAWI, Joseph Sabry. ■ 37814 #654-01-2003 L2006 **FM** *020 †18
RAMAPRASAD, Sunil T. 705 MCFARLAND ST, MORRISTOWN HEART CONSULTAN 37814 #495-33-1986 L1995 **CD** *020 †20
RENNER, Omer Clyde, Jr. 331 W MAIN ST, HAMBLEN CTY HLTH DEPT 37814 #047-06-1960 L1961 **GS** *020 †85
RIDEN, Edie Denise. 420 W MORRIS BLVD, STE G 37813 #047-20-1998 L2000 **FM** *020
SACHDEV, Arvinder. 1907 W MORRIS BLVD, STE G 37813 #495-29-1969 L2004 **GE IM** *020 †20
SADLON, Justin George. 4209 CARNATION DR, 1932 ALCOA HOWY 37814 #047-20-1993 L1995 **IM** *020 †20
SAMS, Josiah Bailey. 901 W 4TH NORTH ST 37814 #047-06-1957 L1957 **R GP** *072 †80
SANDLAND, Helen. 619 W 7TH NORTH ST, STE F 37814 #063-01-1984 L2007 **OBG** *020 †30
SAUL, Charles Dudley, III. ■ 37814 #040-02-1963 L1965 **FM EM** *020 †18
SCHULZ, Marilyn Jane. 856 W 4TH NORTH ST 37814 #024-01-1982 L1989 **OBG** *020 †30
SHAHID, Saleh Rashid. 850 W 3RD NORTH ST, STE B 37814 #422-01-1997 L2001 **IM** *020 †20
SHELTON, Anne B. 609 MCFARLAND ST 37814 #035-09-1984 L1997 **OBG** *020 †30
SINHA, Neeraj. 726 MCFARLAND ST, C/O ROBYN ROBINSON/MED STA 37814 #495-36-2000 L2004 **IM** *020 †20 ‡
SLEETER, Donald Ray. 4417 BROCKLAND DR 37813 #020-02-2000 L2003 **EM** *020
SMITH, Devon Dane. 1621 W MORRIS BLVD, STE A 37813 #047-20-1989 L1990 **IM** *040 †20
SOBCZYNSKI, Valery Peter. 2348 W ANDREW JOHNSON HWY, # 498 37814 #005-15-1979 L1986 **DR MSR** *020
SUTHERLAND, Peter Michael. 420 W MORRIS BLVD, STE 400B 37813 #063-01-1992 L1995 **GP** *020
TAN, Michael Angelo. 854 W 7TH NORTH ST 37814 #748-01-1989 L2000 **IM** *020 †20
THOMPSON, Tom Chas. 1633 W MORRIS BLVD, STE B 37813 #047-06-1990 L1995 **GS** *020 †85
TOWNSEND, Andrew. 210 E ECONOMY RD 37814 #047-20-1993 L1996 **PD** *020 †55
WALKER, David Arden. 850 W 3RD NORTH ST STE B 37814 #018-03-1979 L1982 **IM** *020 †20
WEE ENG, Jose L. 709 MCFARLAND ST 37814 #748-08-1964 L1973 **GS GP** *071
WYSOR, Wanda June. ■ 37814 #422-01-1994 **P** *100
YARID, Frederick Rudolph. 823 MCFARLAND ST 37814 #025-01-1992 L1997 **FM** *020 †18
ZAIN, Harry Allie. 230 BOWMAN ST, STE B 37813 #039-01-1985 L1987 **OBG FM** *020 †18,30

MOSCOW – FAYETTE

OGLE, Luther Curtis. ■ 38057 #047-06-1977 L1978 **EM** *020

MOSHEIM – GREENE

ALTMAN, Jonathan Andrew. ■ 37818 #654-01-2001 L2006 **FM** *020 †18

MOUNT CARMEL – HAWKINS

PARSONS, Toni M. ■ 37645 #020-02-2005 *100

MOUNT JULIET – WILSON

AMARTEY, Patrick Kofi. ■ 37122 #036-01-1991 L1993 **AN** *020 †05
ANDERSON, James Chas. 2640 N MOUNT JULIET RD 37122 #047-05-1989 L1993 **PD** *020 †55
BOUTIN, Mario. 3500 N MOUNT JULIET RD, STE 201 37122 #067-02-1988 L1996 **FM** *020 †18
BYRD-GLOSTER, Angela L. ■ 37122 #011-04-1996 L2005 **PTH** *020 †50
CLARK, Richard Stroebe. 3584 N MT JULIET RD, DR.S DIET PROGRAM INC 37122 #005-06-1959 L1997 **GS NTR** *020 †20
GEORGE, James Alexander. ■ 37122 #067-01-1949 L1989 *100
HASELTON, Dana Jean. 5002 CROSSINGS CIR, STE 310 37122 #054-04-1995 L1999 **PD** *020 †55
HITCH, Wendy Lynne. 2640 N MOUNT JULIET RD 37122 #012-01-1998 L2001 **PD** *020 †55
HOLLIS, Lynna Gaye. ■ 37122 #047-20-1987 L1999 **P CHP** *020 †75
JOHNSTON, Margreete Gaye. 2640 N MOUNT JULIET RD 37122 #047-07-1979 L1985 **PD** *020 †55
JONES, Katherine W. 2620 N MT JULIET RD 37122 #047-06-1993 L1996 **FM** *020 †18
KAELIN, Charles Robt. 5002 CROSSINGS CIR, 2ND FL 37122 #020-02-1982 L1993 **ORS GS** *020 †40
KIRSHNER, Neil Edward. 2640 N MOUNT JULIET RD 37122 #047-20-1990 L1992 **PD** *020 †55
LAGUEUX, Marthe-Sophie. 4024 N MOUNT JULIET RD 37122 #067-02-1980 L1982 **FM GYN** *020
LETT, Donna Woodall. 2640 N MOUNT JULIET RD 37122 #047-06-1988 L1994 **PD** *020 †55
MC LEVAIN-WELLS, Karie A. 2640 N MOUNT JULIET RD 37122 #047-20-1996 L1999 **PD** *020 †55
MEHROTRA, Deepak. 2640 N MOUNT JULIET RD 37122 #027-01-1992 L1998 **PD** *020 †55

MURTI, Aparna Kuruganti. 3500 N MT JULIET RD, STE 201 37122 #047-06-2003 L2004 **FM** *020 †18
OLDHAM, Karen L. 5002 CROSSINGS CIR, URGENT CARE AT PROVIDENCE 37122 #038-44-1982 L1988 **OM EM** *020 †70 ‡
PARE, Bernard. 3500 N MT JULIET RD, STE 201 37122 #067-03-1979 L1982 **GP** *020
PRASAD, Pinki Kumari. ■ 37122 #665-02-2000 L2001 **PHO** *012 †55
SANES, Gilmore M, Jr. 1560 GUILL RD 37122 #041-12-1970 L1976 **OBG** *020 †30
SHEARER, Cameron A. 4024 N MOUNT JULIET RD 37122 #064-01-1983 L1984 **GP** *020
SHEPHERD, Kimbel David. 2640 N MT JULIET RD, CHILDRENS CLINIC EAST 37122 #027-01-1996 L2004 **PD** *020 †55
VASKO, Bryan Louis. 5002 CROSSINGS CIR, STE 340 37122 #012-01-1992 L2008 **IM** *020 †20
WHITE, Gregory Geo. 5002 CROSSINGS CIR, TENNESSEE SPORTS MEDICINE 37122 #021-01-1984 L1995 **ORS** *020 †40
YORK, James Jeffrey. 5002 CROSSINGS CIR, TN SPORTS MED & ORTHOPED 37122 #919-05-1991 L1999 **AN** *020

MOUNT PLEASANT – MAURY

COUCH, James C, III. 200 S CROSS BRIDGES RD 38474 #047-20-1993 L1994 **FM** *020 †18
WILLIAMS, Kelly Johanna. 200 S CROSS BRIDGES RD 38474 #038-41-2001 L2004 **FM** *020

MOUNTAIN CITY – JOHNSON

GIBSON, Donna Frances. 251 SPRUCEY LN 37683 #047-20-1987 L1988 **FM** *020 †18
KIMBRO, Michael Kerry. 1901 S SHADY ST, JOHNSON COUNTY MEDICAL GRO 37683 #036-05-1987 L1992 **FM** *020 †18
SHINE, James Wm. 1901 S SHADY ST 37683 #001-02-1986 L1996 **FM** *020 †18
SHINE, Susanne Mayer. 1901 S SHADY ST, JOHNSON COUNTY MED GRP 37683 #001-02-1987 L1996 **FM** *020 †18
SLUDER, Raina L. 377 COLD SPRINGS RD 37683 #305-01-1998 L2001 **FM** *020 †18
TARR, Donald F. 4200 COLD SPRINGS RD 37683 #005-16-1962 L1966 **FM** *020 †18
TRATHEN, William Thos. ■ 37683 #065-01-1964 L2005 **OBG** *071 †30
VERMILLION, Stanley E. 120 PIONEER VILLAGE DR, BMA OF MOUNTAIN CITY 37683 #019-02-1964 L1970 **IM NEP** *020 †20
WALTERS, Court Carroll. 224 S CHURCH ST BOX 670 37683 #036-01-1993 L1997 **FM** *020
WAMPLER, Fred W. ■ 37683 #051-04-1957 L1973 **GP** *071

MOUNTAIN HOME – WASHINGTON

BORISUK, Paul. SIDNEY & LAMONT ST 37684 #048-12-1967 L1984 **IM** *071
CAMPBELL, Teresa Allen. ■ 37684 #045-01-1984 L2000 **PTH FOP** *062 †50,18
FULTON, Lyman Avard. ■ 37684 #024-01-1944 L1958 **IM** *071 †20
GERBER, Carl Jos. SIDNEY & LAMONT ST 37684 #036-07-1967 L1967 **OS P** *030 †75
HAMDY, Ronald Charles. SIDNEY & LAMONT ST 37684 #915-03-1968 L1985 **IM IMG** *020
HAMMAD, Ahmad Najib. ■ 37684 #575-01-2000 L2008 **ON** *100 †20
HANSEN, Dianne Leslie. SIDNEY & LAMONT ST 37684 #018-16-1986 L1994 **P** *020 †75
KRISHNAN, Vinodini. PO BOX 4000, PRIME CARE CLINIC (11 PC) 37684 #496-38-1985 L2001 **IM** *020 †20
KUMAR, Pullatikurthi P. VA MEDICAL CTR, DEPT RAD 37684 #495-11-1966 L1993 **RO D** *020 †80
MELTON, Casey Wayne. PO BOX 4000, CTR 111-B 37684 #001-06-2002 L2004 **PCC** *012 †20
MIRANDA, Roger. VA MED CTR 37684 #847-04-1957 L1969 **GS** *020 †85
O'NEIL, Terrence Jay. PO BOX 4000, CORNER OF SYDNEY & LAMONT 37684 #005-18-1976 L2006 **NEP IM** *020 †20
OVERBAY, Barbara T King. VA MEDICAL CENTER #11A 37684 #047-20-1990 L1993 **IM** *020 †20
REKHA, G S. VA MEDICAL CENTER, 114-R RADIATION ONCOLOGY 37684 #495-11-1969 L1985 **RO** *020 †80 ‡
ROY, Thomas Michael. JAMES H QUILLEN VAMC 37684 #020-02-1973 L1997 **PUD IM** *020 †18,20
UMAKANTHA, Kaggal V. PO BOX 4000, VAMC, PMRS117 37684 #495-35-1965 L1975 **PM** *020 †60
WALLEN, Joseph Jeffrey. ADMISSION OFFICE, DEPT OF INTERN MED & 37684 #047-20-1989 L1990 **IM** *020 †20
WHITENER, Jacob Woodrow. PO BOX 4000, JAMES H. QUILLEN VA MED CT 37684 #036-05-1990 L2008 **P** *020 †75
ZUHLKE, Todd. ■ 37684 #056-05-2005 L2005 **GS** *012

MUNFORD – TIPTON

BOWER, Eric Alan. ■ 38058 #041-07-1988 L2007 **IM** *030 †20
CHAMBERS, George Wm, Jr. 56 E MAIN ST 38058 #025-07-1981 L1988 **IM** *020 †20
ELIAS, Walter, III. ■ 38058 #051-04-1985 L1989 **FM** *020 †18
MAY, Anne Schlafke. 99 DOCTORS DR, STE 700 38058 #047-20-1987 L1988 **FM** *020 †18
MAY, Jeffery Alan. 99 DOCTORS DR, STE 700 38058 #047-20-1987 L1988 **FM** *020 †18
SHIRAZEE, Syed Hassan. 76 DOCTORS DR, # A-B 38058 #704-02-1989 L1996 **PCC** *020 †20
WITHERINGTON, Albert S. 56 E MAIN ST 38058 #047-06-1938 L1938 **GP** *071
WOOLDRIDGE, Paul Douglas. ■ 38058 #047-06-2004 L2007 **DR** *012

MURFREESBORO – RUTHERFORD

ABBOTT, Kenneth H, II. 1001 N HIGHLAND AVE 37130 #005-12-1963 L1977 **DR NM** *071 †80 ‡
ABERNATHY, James Paul. 1004 N HIGHLAND AVE 37130 #047-06-1959 L1960 **GS** *071 †85
ACOSTA, Estrella. 3400 LEBANON RD, TENNESSEE VALLEY HEALTHCAR 37129 #748-02-1970 L1981 **P CHP** *020
AGGARWAL, Reita Nirankari. 625 N HIGHLAND AVE 37130 #047-06-1996 L1999 **IM** *020 †20
AGHEBAT-KHAIRY, Behrouz. 611 N HIGHLAND AVE 37130 #517-03-1972 L1989 **TS** *020 †28
AHAD, Khandakar Abdul. 3400 LEBANON RD, ALVIN C YORK VA MEDICAL CE 37129 #160-02-1972 L1997 **OPH** *020 †35
AKATUE, Olawumi. 3400 LEBANON RD, ALVIN C YORK VA MEDICAL CE 37129 #198-01-1995 L2006 **IM** *020 †20
AKIN, Gordon Clay. 3400 LEBANON RD, CARE SYSTEM 37129 #004-01-1983 L1986 **IM** *020 †20

AKIN, Harold Thos. 503 HIGHLAND TER, STE B 37130 #047-06-1970 L1971 **OPH** *020 †35
AKINS, Mark Attaway. 503 E BELL ST, STE 314 37130 #012-05-1989 L1995 **GS** *020 †85
AKMAL, Muhammad Mubeen. ■ 37129 #654-01-1993 L1998 **IM** *020 †20
ALEA, Jorge Antonio. ■ 37127 #012-01-1957 L1957 **GE** *071 †20
ALEXANDER, John Hutchins. ■ 37129 #007-02-1958 L1971 **GYN** *071 †30
ALLEN, Brady West. 400 N HIGHLAND AVE 37130 #051-01-2004 L2007 **EM** *020
ALLEN, James Thos. ■ 37129 #047-05-1942 L1942 **IM** *071
ANDERSON, Philip Bradley. 1134 DOW ST 37130 #047-05-1986 L1987 **P** *020 †75
ANDREWS, Susan Toy. 515 E BELL ST 37130 #047-05-1978 L1981 **FM** *020 †18
ANSARI, Ishrat J. 3400 LEBANON RD, ALVIN C YORK MEDICAL CTR 37129 #704-02-1984 L2001 **IMG** *020
ARNETT, Eugene B, III. ■ 37130 #020-02-1980 L1981 **AN** *074
AUER, Charles. 400 N HIGHLAND AVE 37130 #047-06-1982 L1983 **EM** *020 †16 ‡
AUSTIN, Stephen Brawner. ■ 37130 #036-05-1976 L1989 **IM** *020 †20
BAILEY, Joseph C. 511 MEMORIAL BLVD 37129 #047-05-1952 L1952 **OPH** *020 †35
BALI, Ajay Kumar. 3400 LEBANON RD, VETERAN ADMIN MED CTR 37129 #495-03-1972 L2000 **IM CD** *020 †20
BARRICK, Kecia Michelle. 1004 N HIGHLAND AVE, MURFREESBORO MED CLC 37130 #047-06-1995 L1996 **IM** *020 †20
BARTON, John H, Jr. 1020 N HIGHLAND AVE, STE A 37130 #036-05-1987 L1997 **ON** *072 †20
BASKIN, Laura Rebecca. 1004 N HIGHLAND AVE, MURFREESBORO MEDICAL CLINI 37130 #047-20-1997 L2002 **GS** *020 †85
BATES, Sandra Aileen. 3400 LEBANON RD 37129 #047-07-1972 L1977 **DR NM** *020
BEAIRD, David Anderson. 1004 N HIGHLAND AVE 37130 #047-06-1999 L2004 **GS** *020 †85
BEALL, Brook D. 400 N HIGHLAND AVE 37130 #043-01-2000 L2007 **EM** *020 †16
BEASLEY, Timothy Joe. 1004 N HIGHLAND AVE 37130 #047-06-1974 L1974 **OBG FM** *020 †18,30
BECKMAN, James C. 301 N UNIVERSITY ST, STE 106 37130 #047-06-1996 L1998 **FM** *020 †18
BECKMAN, Melinda Claire. ■ 37128 #047-06-2004 L2007 **PD** *020 †55
BEIER, Kevin Hugh. 400 N HIGHLAND AVE 37130 #051-01-1993 L2004 **EM** *020 †16
BELL, Michael W. 1725 MEDICAL CENTER PKWY, STE 300 37129 #060-02-1979 L1995 **D PTH** *020 †15,50
BELL, Richard Bryan. 610 E CLARK BLVD 37130 #047-06-1963 L1964 **OTO** *020 †45
BERGSTRESSER, Jack D. 406 W NORTHFIELD BLVD, NORTHFIELD FAMILY PRACTICE 37129 #028-78-1965, ▲ L2001 **GP** *071
BIGHAM, Virgil Lee, IV. 1004 N HIGHLAND AVE 37130 #027-01-1993 L1997 **PD** *020 †55
BLANKENSHIP, Brad Edwin. 2441 OLD FORT PKWY STE Q 37128 #047-06-1985 L1986 **GE IM** *020 †20
BOERNER, James Lee. 507 HIGHLAND TER 37130 #020-02-1977 L1981 **OBG** *020 †30
BOGUS, Devin Lydell. 1818 WARD DR 37129 #047-07-2001 L2005 **PD** *020
BOLES, Charles Brent. 301 N UNIVERSITY ST, STE 102 37130 #020-02-1992 L2004 **OBG** *020 †30
BOLIN, Marion Gilbert. 1020 N HIGHLAND AVE, STE A 37130 #012-01-1967 L1974 **RO R** *020 †80
BONDALAPATI, Sivaji Babu. 3400 LEBANON RD 37129 #495-58-1974 L1989 **P** *062 †75
BONNER, Kevin J, Jr. 400 N HIGHLAND AVE 37130 #064-01-1978 L1979 **EM** *020 †16
BOONE, Joseph Eddins, Jr. 1004 N HIGHLAND AVE 37130 #047-06-1978 L1980 **OPH** *020 †35
BOTSCHNER, Monika Karen. 910 SAINT ANDREWS DR # B7 37128 #409-16-1973 L1998 **FM FPG** *020 †18
BOUTROS, Nabil. 400 N HIGHLAND AVE 37130 #025-01-1997 L2006 **EM** *020 †16
BRADLEY, Donald H, Jr. 1004 N HIGHLAND AVE 37130 #048-15-1985 L1989 **OBG** *020 †30
BRANCH, Millicent Anne. 3400 LEBANON RD, THE VETERAN'S ADMINISTRATI 37129 #001-02-1991 L1997 **CHP** *020 †75
BRAY, Elizabeth Smith. 1004 N HIGHLAND AVE 37130 #047-20-1988 L1989 **IM** *020 †20
BRETON, Roland. 3400 LEBANON RD 37129 #440-01-1962 L1967 **R** *050 †80
BRILEY, Randall James. 400 N HIGHLAND AVE, MTMC-PATHOLOGY 37130 #021-06-1983 L1994 **PTH** *020 †50
BRITE, Charles Richard. ■ 37128 #047-06-1959 L1959 **DR NM** *071 †80
BROWN, Dan Adam. 1004 N HIGHLAND AVE, MURFREESBORO MEDICAL CLINI 37130 #012-01-1990 L1994 **AN EM** *020 †05
BROWN, Frederick F, Jr. ■ 37130 #047-06-1945 L1953 **NS** *071
BROWN, Mary Jane. 400 N HIGHLAND AVE 37130 #028-03-1980 L1986 **EM** *020 †18,16
BROWN, Walter Edward, Jr. 400 N HIGHLAND AVE 37130 #012-01-1964 L1972 **EM OBG** *071 †30
BROWN, William Andrew. 400 N HIGHLAND AVE 37130 #047-06-1978 L1979 **PD** *030 †55
BRUNETTO, Angeline Denise. 602 N WALNUT ST 37130 #047-20-1993 L1997 **EM** *020 †16
BUCKNER, Susan Harris. ■ 37129 #048-16-1987 L1988 **PD** *020 †55
BULLOCK, Sally Hill. 1004 N HIGHLAND AVE 37130 #004-01-1981 L1983 **IM** *020 †20
BUTLER, Henry King. 511 COUNCIL BLUFF PKWY 37127 #047-05-1963 L1963 **D** *020 †15
CADE, Wanda Bray. 1004 N HIGHLAND AVE, MURFREESBORO MEDICAL CLINI 37130 #027-01-1993 L1998 **PD** *020 †55
CAISSIE, Kenneth F. 400 N HIGHLAND AVE 37130 #047-06-1982 L1982 **AN** *020 †05
CAMPBELL, Jerry Neal. 1004 N HIGHLAND AVE 37130 #047-06-1965 L1966 **PD** *020 †55
CARTER, Dennis Charles. 211 HERITAGE PARK DR 37129 #047-07-1980 L1980 **FM** *020 †18
CARTER, James Taylor. 1004 N HIGHLAND AVE 37130 #048-12-1985 L1991 **GS** *020 †85
CARTER, Sam Frank, III. 1004 N HIGHLAND AVE 37130 #047-05-1970 L1970 **IM** *020 †20
CASTELLI, Joseph Warren. 1004 N HIGHLAND AVE 37130 #047-06-1997 L2000 **OBG** *020
CHALLA, Indira Devi. ■ 37129 #495-50-1981 L1996 **P** *020
CHANDLER, Charles Glenn. 1004 N HIGHLAND AVE 37130 #047-06-1980 L1982 **PD** *020 †55
CHANDRASHEKAR, Lingaiah. 1004 N HIGHLAND AVE 37130 #496-39-1989 L2005 **GE** *020 †20
CHATMAN, David Maurice. 1004 N HIGHLAND AVE 37130 #047-20-1989 L1996 **VS GS** *020 †85
CHERDAK, Danielle Sherri. 1004 N HIGHLAND AVE 37130 #035-46-2000 L2005 **CN** *100
CHESNEY, Brad Stuart. 1004 N HIGHLAND AVE 37130 #048-13-1997 L2000 **OBG** *020 †30
CHITALE, Nitin Arvind. 1127 DOW ST 37130 #495-89-1995 L2003 **IC** *020 †20
CHOUGULE, Prakash B. 1020 N HIGHLAND AVE, STE A 37130 #495-97-1979 L2007 **RO** *020 †80
CHUNDURU, Nageswara Rao. 528 N UNIVERSITY ST 37130 #495-58-1973 L1996 **FM** *020 †18
CLARK, Eric Walter. 1500 GREENLAND DR PO, MTSU STUDENT HEALTH 37132 #021-06-1995 L1996 **FM** *020 †18
CLARK, S Kathleen. 1132 DOW ST 37130 #047-20-1984 L1984 **D** *020 †15
CLEVELAND, Robert R. 1747 MEDICAL CENTER PKWY, STE 210 37129 #012-05-1977 L1982 **U** *020 †95
COBB, Jason Douglas. ■ 37128 #001-02-2005 L2007 **GS** *100
COHEN, Brad Robt. 1020 N HIGHLAND AVE, STE A 37130 #055-01-1983 L1995 **RO** *020 †80
COLEMAN, Jack Andrew. 1255 N HIGHLAND AVE 37130 #038-41-1979 L1985 **OTO** *020 †45
COLFAX, John Drew. 400 N HIGHLAND AVE 37130 #024-01-2004 L2007 **EM** *020
COLLIER, James Ronnie. 3400 LEBANON RD, MURFRESBORO CAMPUS 37129 #047-07-1972 L1994 **GS** *020 †85
COLLINS, Douglas Jerry. 1004 N HIGHLAND AVE 37130 #004-01-1991 L1994 **PD** *020 †55
COLLINS, George Harwood. ■ 37133 #005-19-1981 L1993 **AN** *020 †05
COOPER, Janice Lorraine. ■ 37133 #422-01-1994 L1995 **P** *100
COOPER, Robert Seth. 1020 N HIGHLAND AVE, STE A 37130 #021-05-1971 L1973 **HEM IM** *020 †20
CORLEW, Daniel Scott. ■ 37129 #012-05-1981 L1988 **PS GS** *020 †65,85 ‡
CRISP, Angela. 1832 WARD DR, STE 101 37129 #036-01-1986 L2006 **OPH** *020 †35
CUDDY, Stephen Richard. 1127 DOW ST 37130 #035-15-1979 L2001 **CD IM** *020 †20
CUMBERBATCH, Rudolph S. 3400 LEBANON RD 37129 #024-01-1959 L1997 **GS OS** *071 †85,90
DAME, Eric Arthur. ■ 37130 #011-04-2001 L2004 **DR** *100 †80
DAVIS, Gordon Bruce. 1818 WARD DR 37129 #030-06-1976 L2005 **PD** *020 †55
DAVISON, James Lindsay. 400 N HIGHLAND AVE 37130 #048-14-1979 L1981 **IM** *020 †20,16
DE ROCHE, Michael Edward. 503 E BELL ST, STE 304 37130 #036-05-1996 L2003 **OBG** *020 †30
DIAMOND, Paul Harvey. 3400 LEBANON RD 37129 #047-05-1958 L1958 **PUD IM** *071 †20
DI CORLETO, Peter Anthony. 1832 WARD DR STE 102 37129 #008-02-1979 L1996 **IM** *020 †20
DIERINGER, Nicholas James. 400 N HIGHLAND AVE, MTMC HOSP DEPT 37130 #047-06-2000 L2004 **IM** *020
DIXON, John Herman, Jr. 237 W NORTHFIELD BLVD, STE 101 37129 #047-05-1967 L1979 **PD OS** *020 †55
DODD, David T. ■ 37130 #047-06-1953 L1953 **ADM GS** *071 †85
DODEK, Marvin Irwin. ■ 37130 #041-09-1972 L1977 **GP** *020
DONAGHEY, Susana I. 1819 WARD DR STE 101 37129 #021-05-1996 L2006 **IM** *020 †20
DOOLEY, Tanzania Marie. 1725 MEDICAL CENTER PKWY, STE 210 37129 #047-07-1997 L2002 **MPD** *020 †20
DOSS, Habib H. 1020 N HIGHLAND AVE, STE A 37130 #915-02-1986 L2000 **IM HO** *020 †20
DRAY, Robert James, Jr. 301 N UNIVERSITY ST, STE 204 37130 #050-02-1979 L1981 **U UP** *020 †95 ‡
DROWOTA, Frank Russell. 400 N HIGHLAND AVE 37130 #047-05-1998 L2002 **OPH** *020 †35
DUDLEY, Bunyan Stephens. 1020 N HIGHLAND AVE, STE A 37130 #047-05-1977 L1979 **GO GYN** *020 †30
DUFFY, Jamira Niambi. 522B BRANDIES CIR STE 2, PREMIERE MEDICAL ASSOCIATE 37128 #041-12-2004 L2007 **FM** *020 †18
DUTT, Anjali. 3400 LEBANON RD 37129 #495-05-1955 **PTH** *020
DUTT, Asim Kumar. 3400 LEBANON RD 37129 #495-05-1952 L1985 **PUD IM** *020 †20
EASTHAM, Edward D. 237 W NORTHFIELD BLVD, STE 101 37129 #047-06-1982 L1990 **PD** *020 †55
ECKLES, George Love, Jr. 1602 W NORTHFIELD BLVD, PLLC SUITE 504 37129 #047-06-1973 L1973 **GS AS** *020 †85
EGLI, Eric Karl. 503 E BELL ST STE 212 37130 #047-06-1993 L1996 **IM** *020 †20
EVANS, James Frederick. 415 E BELL ST 37130 #050-02-1981 L2005 **FM** *020 †18
FAROOQUE, Ahmed Iqbal. 1830 HERITAGE PARK PLZ 37129 #160-02-1974 L1987 **P** *020 †75
FENTRESS, J Vance. ■ 37127 #047-05-1952 L1952 **IM** *071 †20
FLINN, Ian Winchester. 1020 N HIGHLAND AVE, STE A 37130 #023-07-1990 L2006 **ON** *020 †20
FOGERTY, Mary Dorothy. 3400 LEBANON RD, ALVIN C YORK VA MEDICAL CE 37129 #034-01-1992 L2003 **TS** *020 †85
FONGNALY, Vanpraseuth. ■ 37128 #047-06-2005 L2006 **AN** *012
FORD, Andrew Hunter. 1004 N HIGHLAND AVE 37130 #005-18-1989 L1999 **OTO** *020 †45
FORTUNATO, Stephen Jos. 503 E BELL ST, STE 304 37130 #038-41-1980 L1986 **MFM OBG** *020 †30
FOSTER, Jerry Michael. 1020 N HIGHLAND AVE, STE A 37130 #036-07-1979 L1982 **ON HEM** *020 †20
FUA, Diego C. ■ 37129 #748-07-1964 L1980 **GS** *020
FULFORD, Kevin Lee. 400 N HIGHLAND AVE, MIDDLE TN MED CTR 37130 #005-12-1997 L2001 **OBG** *020 †30
GALLOWAY, Russell Eugene. 400 N HIGHLAND AVE 37130 #047-05-1984 L1989 **EM** *020 †16
GALLOWAY, Sherry Jordan. 400 N HIGHLAND AVE 37130 #047-05-1984 L1989 **EM** *020 †16
GARNER, James Wm, Jr. 503 HIGHLAND TER STE D 37130 #047-06-1972 L1973 **IM OM** *020 †20
GARRISON, R James. ■ 37130 #047-05-1952 L1954 **PD** *071 †55
GIAN, Victor Gerard. 1020 N HIGHLAND AVE, STE A 37130 #041-12-1989 L1998 **ON** *020 †20
GOODMAN, Charles Edward, Jr. 320 E MAIN ST 37130 #028-02-1969 L1973 **D IM** *020 †20,15
GRAY, James Ronald, Jr. 1020 N HIGHLAND AVE, STE A 37130 #047-05-1986 L1994 **RO** *020 †80
GRECO, Frank Anthony. 1020 N HIGHLAND AVE, STE A 37130 #055-01-1972 L1976 **ON IM** *020 †20
GREEN, Carl Alexander. ■ 37130 #045-01-1977 L1995 **PUD** *050 †20
GREENBERG, Robert Charles. 1010 N HIGHLAND AVE 37130 #028-34-1993 L2003 **ORS** *020 †40
GRESHAM, Tina C. 1023 N HIGHLAND AVE 37130 #010-03-1987 L1993 **CD IM** *020 †20
GROSS, William Elsworth. 1004 N HIGHLAND AVE 37130 #051-01-1987 L1994 **OTO** *020 †45
HACKMAN, Robert Henry. 301 N UNIVERSITY ST 37130 #047-06-1961 L1962 **FM** *020 †18
HADGU, Yemane Beyene. 3400 LEBANON RD, ALVIN C. YORK VA HOSPITAL 37129 #366-01-1990 L2002 **IM** *020 †20
HAINSWORTH, John Danl. 1020 N HIGHLAND AVE, STE A 37130 #047-05-1976 L1977 **ON** *020 †20
HAMADA, Omar Louis. 1725 MEDICAL CENTER PKWY, STE 130 37129 #047-06-1993 L1994 **OBG FM** *020 †18
HANCOCK, Lloyd Douglas. 745 S CHURCH ST STE 501, PLLC 37130 #047-07-1990 L2002 **END** *020 †20
HARDY, Thomas Lee, Jr. 400 N HIGHLAND AVE 37130 #047-07-1990 L1997 **APM** *020 †05
HARRISON, Jeremy Brooks. 1004 N HIGHLAND AVE, MURFREESBORO MEDICAL CLINI 37130 #047-20-1996 L1997 **PD** *020 †55
HASTING-ADAMS, Tammy R. 1004 N HIGHLAND AVE 37130 #047-20-1997 L2001 **PD** *020 †55
HAY, Sam H, Sr. 200 W BURTON ST 37130 #047-05-1940 L1968 **R** *071 †80
HAZLEWOOD, Jeffrey Evans. 1725 MEDICAL CENTER PKWY, STE 210 37129 #047-06-1992 L1996 **PM PME** *020 †60
HAZLEY, Andrew J. 1009 N HIGHLAND AVE 37130 #047-07-1977 L1981 **GS** *020
HELTON, Thomas Michael. 1034 N HIGHLAND AVE, STE C 37130 #047-06-1997 L2000 **FM** *020 †18
HENDERSON, Wayne Zeno. 400 N HIGHLAND AVE 37130 #047-06-2002 L2006 **AN** *020 †05
HENSCHEL, Timothy Mark. 237 W NORTHFIELD BLVD, STE 101 37129 #056-06-1995 L1998 **PD** *020 †55

HERLEVIC, Michael Scott. 1004 N HIGHLAND AVE 37130 #305-01-2000 L2003 **IM** *020 †20
HESTER, George Stephen. 1927 MEMORIAL BLVD 37129 #047-06-1962 L1963 **IM** *020
HODGES, Barbara Gail. 517 HIGHLAND TER STE A, HEALTH CENTER 37130 #056-06-1993 L1997 **FM** *020 †18
HOFFMAN, Christine Marie. 301 N UNIVERSITY ST # 201 37130 #011-04-1993 L1998 **FM** *020 †18
HOOD, Roy L. 1004 N HIGHLAND AVE 37130 #047-06-1994 L1997 **GE** *020 †20
HOPKINS, George David. 130 S MAPLE ST 37130 #045-01-1976 L1979 **IM** *020 †20
HUDEK, Sabitha Sunderrao. 1417 MARK ALLEN LN 37129 #654-01-1982 L1990 **P** *020
HUDSON, David Lee. ■ 37129 #047-05-1967 L1971 **R** *071 †80
HUMPHREY, Robert Stephen. 1004 N HIGHLAND AVE 37130 #023-07-1986 L1991 **PUD PD** *020 †55
HUNT, David Edward. 1020 N HIGHLAND AVE, STE A 37130 #045-04-1990 L1996 **RO** *020 †80
HUTTON, Robert Meredith. 400 N HIGHLAND AVE 37130 #055-01-1976 L1980 **EM** *020 †16
INFANTE, Jeffrey Roger. 1020 N HIGHLAND AVE, STE A 37130 #011-03-1999 L2006 **ON** *100 †20
INGLE, Robert P, Jr. 1004 N HIGHLAND AVE 37130 #047-06-1982 L1983 **GE** *020 †20
JACKSON, Chad Michael. 1004 N HIGHLAND AVE 37130 #021-06-2001 L2006 **U** *020 †95
JACKSON, Paul Anthony. ■ 37130 #010-03-1991 L2004 **CD** *020 †20
JAMES, Joyline D.. ■ 37129 #422-01-1999 L2003 **IM** *020 †20
JANES, Rex Lee. 3400 LEBANON RD, ALVIN C YORK VA HOSPITAL 37129 #047-06-1977 L1977 **IM IG** *020 †20
JEKOT, William James. 1029 N HIGHLAND AVE 37130 #025-01-1975 L1980 **ORS** *020 †40
JIRUT, Paisal. 3400 LEBANON RD 37129 #891-01-1972 L1976 **PM** *020 †60
JOHNS, Oscar Thos. 525 N UNIVERSITY ST 37130 #047-06-1972 L1972 **ORS OSM** *020 †40
JOHNSON, Andrew Finley. 1108 SECOND STREET, MDFARLAND BLDGT 37132 #047-06-1965 L1990 **FM PD** *071
JOHNSON, David L. 509 HIGHLAND TER 37130 #047-06-1982 L1989 **FM** *020 †18
JOHNSON, Derek Keith. 1004 N HIGHLAND AVE 37130 #041-12-1995 L2006 **PD** *020 †55
JOHNSON, Ray Charles. 1041 N HIGHLAND AVE, MIDDLE TENNESSEE CENTER 37130 #047-07-1982 L1982 **PCC PUD** *020 †20
JOHNSON, Richard Wayne. 400 N HIGHLAND AVE 37130 #047-06-1997 L2000 **DR** *020 †80
JOHNSTON, Susan Elaine. 1004 N HIGHLAND AVE, MMC PEDIATRICS 37130 #027-01-1996 L2007 **PD** *020 †55
JONES, Dana Dement. 503 E BELL ST, WOMENS HEALTH SPECIALISTS 37130 #047-06-1996 L2000 **OBG** *020 †30
JONES, Joyce. 3400 LEBANON RD, VA MED CTR 37129 #026-08-1976 L2000 **IM** *030 †20,70
JORDAN, Michael Robt. 525 N UNIVERSITY ST 37130 #047-05-1988 L1991 **ORS** *020 †40
JOSOVITZ, Mark Steven. 726 S CHURCH ST 37130 #748-11-1982 L1987 **IM FM** *020 †20
KANE, Kerry Jean. 1004 N HIGHLAND AVE 37130 #047-06-1998 L2005 **IM** *020 †20
KARAM, Jyotheen Sukhmoy. 1020 N HIGHLAND AVE, STE C-2 37130 #495-36-1997 L2005 **NEP** *020 †20
KATTINE, Albert Anthony. 1004 N HIGHLAND AVE 37130 #021-05-1986 L1993 **D IM** *020 †15
KELLERMANN, Andrew Mcmill. ■ 37130 #028-78-2007, ▲ L2007 *012
KELTON, Jerry Michael. 1602 W NORTHFIELD BLVD, STE 504 37129 #047-06-1997 L2007 **GS** *012
KENDALL, Charles Norman. 3400 LEBANON RD, VA MEDICAL CENTER 37129 #005-12-1963 L1973 **R NM** *020 †80,28
KENDALL, Douglas Warren. 1024 N HIGHLAND AVE STE B 37130 #005-12-1965 L1967 **PTH** *020 †50
KENNEDY, Alan Paul. 3400 LEBANON RD, ALVIN C YORK VAMC III 37129 #021-06-1980 L1988 **HEM ON** *020 †20
KHATRI, Gajedra Kumar. 3400 LEBANON RD, ALVIN YORK VA HOSP 37129 #495-55-1968 L1997 **ID IM** *020 †20
KLUMPE, Marynelle J. 400 N HIGHLAND AVE 37130 #047-06-1987 L1993 **DR** *020 †80
KNIGHT, Joseph C. 400 N HIGHLAND AVE, MIDDLE TN MED CTR 37130 #047-06-1960 L1960 **IM CD** *071 †20
KNIGHT, Robert Tavel. 1034 N HIGHLAND AVE 37130 #047-06-1960 L1967 **U** *020
KNOX, Robert L. 1004 N HIGHLAND AVE 37130 #047-06-1951 L1952 **AN** *020 †05
KNOX, Robert Lee, Jr. 1004 N HIGHLAND AVE 37130 #047-06-1989 L1990 **GE** *020 †20
KOLLI, Murali Krishna. 507 N UNIVERSITY ST 37130 #001-02-1989 L1995 **CD** *020 †20
KONDAPAVULURU, S V. 528 N UNIVERSITY ST 37130 #495-58-1985 L1997 **P PYG** *020 †75
KOWALSKI, Kurtis Lorenz. 400 N HIGHLAND AVE 37130 #010-02-1997 L2004 **ORS** *020 †40
KUZUR, Michel Elias. 1020 N HIGHLAND AVE, STE A 37130 #605-01-1975 L1977 **ON IM** *020 †20
LAMAR, Ruth Elaine. 1020 N HIGHLAND AVE, STE A 37130 #047-06-1987 L1989 **ON** *020 †20
LANGWORTHY, Warren Orvel. 301 N UNIVERSITY ST # 207 37130 #027-01-1982 L1989 **FM EM** *020 †18
LA ROCHE, Elizabeth Read. 305 UPTOWN SQ 37129 #047-06-1980 L1984 **OBG** *020 †30
LEDBETTER, William Henry. 400 N HIGHLAND AVE 37130 #020-02-1979 L1985 **ORS** *020 †40
LE DOUX, Paul David. 400 N HIGHLAND AVE 37130 #047-06-1983 L1998 **AN CCM** *020 †05
LEE, Brian Kyung. 509 E BELL ST, STE 100 37130 #041-09-1994 L1998 **RO** *020 †80
LEE, David Granville. 400 N HIGHLAND AVE 37130 #047-06-1972 L1975 **EM** *020 †16
LEWIS, Charles Wingo. ■ 37130 #047-06-1956 L1956 **PD** *071 †55
LIEN, George Harrison. 503 E BELL ST, STE 300 37130 #023-07-1984 L1985 **NS GS** *020 †25
LIGGETT, William H, Jr. 1020 N HIGHLAND AVE, STE A 37130 #024-01-1991 L1999 **ON** *020 †20
LITTLE, Joseph Alexander. 237 W NORTHFIELD BLVD, STE 101 37129 #047-05-1977 L1979 **PD EM** *020 †55
LOGAN, Thomas Percival. 3400 LEBANON RD 37129 #047-07-1966 L1968 **P** *030 †75
LOMBARDI, Salvatore Jos. 503 E BELL ST, STE 304 37130 #649-02-1981 L1986 **MFM CHP** *020 †30
LOUTHAN, Frank Blonvil. 1041 N HIGHLAND AVE, MIDDLE TENNESSEE CENTER 37130 #047-06-1988 L1989 **PUD CCM** *020 †20
LOVELACE, Fred Royce. ■ 37133 #047-06-1959 L1959 **AN** *071
LOWE, Lisa Lynn. 1004 N HIGHLAND AVE 37130 #047-20-1984 L1987 **PD** *020 †55
LUINA-DIAZ, Ramon Rafael. ■ 37129 #030-06-1952 L1959 **R** *071
MACQUARRIE, Michael. 602 E CLARK BLVD 37130 #064-01-1986 L1994 **UCM GP** *020
MAHESHWARI, Seema. 3400 LEBANON RD, VA/TVHS/ACY (ALVIN C YORK 37129 #495-83-1989 L2007 **IM** *020 †20 ‡
MALLICK, Ranjit Singh. 3400 LEBANON RD 37129 #495-11-1961 L1989 **P PYG** *020 †75
MANDA, Ravindedr Reddy. 507 N UNIVERSITY ST, CARDIAC CENTER LLC 37130 #495-57-1990 L2003 **CD** *020 †20
MARIPURI, Dhana L. 3400 LEBANON RD 37129 #495-14-1972 L1977 **EM IM** *020 †20,16
MAXWELL, Elizabeth Jewell. 132 SAINT ANDREWS DR, STE D 37128 #308-03-1997 L2005 **FM** *100 †18
MCCABE, Craig F. 122 HERITAGE PARK DR, STE 100 37129 #045-01-1995 L1999 **OPH** *020 †35
MCCLURE, Robert Todd. 1020 N HIGHLAND AVE, STE A 37130 #038-41-1991 L1999 **RO** *020 †80
MC GEE, Caroline Campbell. 2139 CREEKWALK DR 37130 #047-06-1982 L1984 **FM EM** *020 †18
MC GOWAN, Kimberly. 503 E BELL ST, WOMENS HEALTH SPECIALISTS 37130 #038-43-1992 L1998 **OBG** *020 †30
MCGRIFF-CHATMAN, Yolando. 1004 N HIGHLAND AVE, MURFREESBORO MEDICAL CLINI 37130 #047-20-1989 L1996 **OBG** *020 †30
MC KAY, Chas Elford, III. 1020 N HIGHLAND AVE, STE A 37130 #036-05-1977 L1979 **ON IM** *020 †20
MCKINNEY, Matthew Stuart. ■ 37129 #036-07-2006 **IM** *012
MC KISSICK, Russell C. 1010 N HIGHLAND AVE 37130 #047-06-2001 L2006 **ORS** *100
MC KNIGHT, David Thos. 1004 N HIGHLAND AVE 37130 #047-06-1979 L1980 **OBG** *020 †30
MC PHERSON, Warren F. ■ 37130 #010-01-1966 L1968 **NS** *071 †25
MEADOWS, Natasha Dionne. 1450 BATTLEGROUND DR, TOTAL FAMILY CARE CLINIC 37129 #011-02-2001 L2005 **MPD** *020 †20
MEERS, Stanley Davis. 400 N HIGHLAND AVE 37130 #012-05-1979 L1989 **EM** *020 †20
MELSON, Melita Fae. 1004 N HIGHLAND AVE, MURFREESBORO MEDICAL CLINI 37130 #011-02-1996 L1999 **PD** *020 †55
MELUCH, Anthony Alan. 1020 N HIGHLAND AVE, STE A 37130 #038-40-1987 L1993 **HO IM** *020 †20
MENKE, Paul Gerard. 400 N HIGHLAND AVE 37130 #020-02-1988 L1992 **DR** *020 †80
MEYEROWITZ, Colin B. 1001 N HIGHLAND AVE 37130 #836-01-1987 L1995 **VIR** *020 †80
MICHAELSON, Richard D, Jr. 400 N HIGHLAND AVE, MIDDLE TENNESSEE MED CTR 37130 #045-01-1981 L1988 **PTH MDM** *020 †50
MILLER, Karen Frances. 100 W BURTON ST 37130 #021-05-1990 L1995 **OBG** *020 †30
MIRANDA, Fernando T. 1020 N HIGHLAND AVE, STE A 37130 #231-05-1973 L1978 **ON HEM** *020 †20
MOBLEY, Derrick Lamount. 3400 LEBANON RD 37129 #020-02-1980 L1987 **U** *020 †95
MOGALI, Shanthi. ■ 37129 #047-07-2005 **P** *012
MOGALI, Sobha Rani. ■ 37129 #495-58-1975 **P** *020
MOGALI, Sreenivasa Reddy. 3400 LEBANON RD, ALVIN C YORK MED CTR 37129 #495-62-1975 L1983 **P OS** *020 †75
MOORE, Sovana Rani. 400 N HIGHLAND AVE 37130 #047-05-2000 L2004 **OBG** *020 ‡
MORAD, Anna Whorton. 237 W NORTHFIELD BLVD 37129 #001-02-1997 L1999 **PD** *020 †55
MORAN, Michael Francis. 503 E BELL ST, STE 300 37130 #025-07-1988 L1990 **NS** *020 †25
MOSS, Mary Thomas. 503 E BELL ST, WOMENS HEALTH SPECIALISTS 37130 #047-06-1987 L1988 **OBG** *020 †30
MOSS, Max Lee, Jr. 400 N HIGHLAND AVE 37130 #047-06-1989 L1992 **DR** *020 †80
MUDIAM, Madhusudhan. 2035 ALEXANDER BLVD 37130 #495-21-1989 L1997 **P PFP** *020 †75
MUDUMBI, Saranyacharyulu. 528 N UNIVERSITY ST 37130 #495-50-1978 L1998 **P CHP** *020
MULLEN, Stanley Paul. 400 N HIGHLAND AVE 37130 #047-06-1982 L1982 **DR** *020 †80
MURPHY, Dorothy Snoddy. 3400 LEBANON RD 37129 #001-02-1983 L1987 **IM** *020 †20
MURPHY, Grady Fred, Jr. ■ 37129 #048-13-1982 L2005 **FM** *020 †18
MURPHY, Patrick Brian. 1020 N HIGHLAND AVE, STE A 37130 #047-06-1985 L1989 **IM** *020 †20
MURPHY, Wayne. 503 E BELL ST STE 212 37130 #047-05-1983 L1987 **IM** *020 †20
NARAYANASHASTRY, R. 527 N MAPLE ST, BELL FAMILY MEDICAL CENTER 37130 #495-33-1976 L1999 **GPM** *020
NARAYAN GOWDA, Ramesh. 1004 N HIGHLAND AVE, MURFREESBORO MED CLINIC 37130 #495-99-1983 L2001 **VS** *020 †85
NELSON, Ronald Andrew. 1725 MEDICAL CENTER PKWY, STE 300 37129 #047-05-1990 L1999 **D DS** *020 †15
NEWMAN, Leslie John, Jr. 1703 FIRST PL STE B 37129 #021-05-1988 L1993 **AI A** *020 †20,03
NGUYEN, My Thanh. 1020 N HIGHLAND AVE, STE A 37130 #025-07-1991 L1996 **RO** *020 †80
NIEBAUER, Marivi A. 1004 N HIGHLAND AVE, NEURO DEPT 37130 #020-02-2001 L2005 **N** *020 †75
NOAH, Melody P. 1725 MEDICAL CENTER PKWY, STE 220 37129 #047-06-1986 L1988 **IM** *020 †20
NOAH, William Holbrook. 1725 MEDICAL CENTER PKWY, STE 220 37129 #047-06-1986 L1988 **PCC SME** *020 †20
NUNNERY, James A, Jr. 1004 N HIGHLAND AVE 37130 #047-06-1970 L1971 **GS** *071 †85
ODOM, Eugene Porter. 2809 MIDDLE TENNESSEE BLVD 37130 #047-06-1940 L1940 **GP** *020
ODOM, Stephen Guy. 2809 MIDDLE TENNESSEE BLVD 37130 #047-06-1967 L1969 **GP IM** *020 †20
OURS, David Earl. 400 N HIGHLAND AVE 37130 #047-06-1982 L1982 **FM** *020 †18
OWEN, Ann Burleson. 400 N HIGHLAND AVE 37130 #004-01-1986 L1987 **DR** *020 †80
OWENS, Jeremy Wayne. ■ 37127 #305-01-2004 L2007 **P** *012
PARANJAPE, Arun R. 3400 LEBANON RD, DEPT OF ANESTHESIOLOGY 37129 #495-33-1963 L1978 **AN** *071
PARRISH, Richard E. 1041 N HIGHLAND AVE, MIDDLE TENNESSEE CENTER 37130 #047-06-1976 L1977 **PUD CCM** *020 †20
PARSH, Suman. 3400 LEBANON RD 37129 #495-37-1974 L1980 **PTH** *020 †50
PATEL, Rohit R. 1020 N HIGHLAND AVE, STE A 37130 #495-22-1989 L1997 **HO** *020 †20
PATEL, Utpal Pravin. 1004 N HIGHLAND AVE 37130 #047-06-1992 L1993 **IM** *020 †20
PATTON, Jeffrey Franklin. 1020 N HIGHLAND AVE, STE A 37130 #051-07-1988 L1996 **ON HEM** *020 †20
PAYNE, Steven James. 1015 N HIGHLAND AVE 37130 #020-02-1985 L1987 **IM** *020
PEACOCK, Nancy Walker. 1020 N HIGHLAND AVE, STE A 37130 #028-03-1988 L1995 **ON** *020 †20
PEARSON, John Gustaf. 1020 N HIGHLAND AVE, STE C-2 37130 #047-05-1977 L1978 **IM NEP** *020 †20
PENLEY, William Chas. 1020 N HIGHLAND AVE, STE A 37130 #036-05-1982 L1985 **ON IM** *020 †20
PERKINS, Lauren Nicole. ■ 37129 #047-06-2007 L2007 **PD** *012
PERLMUTTER, Martin Ira. 171 HERITAGE PARK DR 37129 #036-05-1977 L1980 **OPH** *020 †35 ‡
PERTILLER, Sheila Dennen. 3400 LEBANON RD, VA TN VALLEY HEALTH CARE 37129 #047-07-1998 L2003 **IM** *020 †20
PETERSON, Laleisha Moniqu. ■ 37130 #010-01-2008 *012
PIEPER, Samuel John Louis. 3400 LEBANON RD 37129 #048-04-1955 L1969 **P N** *020 †75
POAG, Kenneth Leslie. 400 N HIGHLAND AVE 37130 #047-06-1973 L1973 **IM** *071
POPE, Stan Lamar. 400 N HIGHLAND AVE 37130 #047-06-1999 L2002 **DR** *020 †80
PORTILLA, L Ivan. 2656 RIDEOUT LN 37128 #429-01-1985 L2002 **PUD IM** *020
PUCKETT, Dennis Chas. 400 N HIGHLAND AVE, MTMC HOSPITALIST SERVICES 37130 #047-06-1989 L1992 **IM** *020 †20
PUCKETT, Karen Jane. 305 UPTOWN SQ 37129 #047-06-1993 L1997 **OBG** *020 †30

■ = Address Information Privacy Protected

PUTATUNDA, Bhabendra Nath. 1024 N HIGHLAND AVE STE B 37130 #495-39-1981 L1991 **GE IM** *020 †20

PUTATUNDA, Shipra. 1024 N HIGHLAND AVE STE B 37130 #495-39-1984 L1994 **P** *020

QURESHI, Nadeem U. ■ 37129 #704-02-1989 L1994 **CCP** *020 †55

RAGGIO, Christopher H. 118 N CHURCH ST 37130 #027-01-2003 L2004 **P** *020

RAHMAN, Azizur. 511 MEMORIAL BLVD 37129 #704-04-1980 L1999 **OPH** *020

RAMESH, Arundati. 1004 N HIGHLAND AVE 37130 #495-33-1991 L1999 **IMG** *020 †20

RANSOM, Robert Geo. 400 N HIGHLAND AVE 37130 #020-02-1957 L1961 **IM** *071

RANZ, David O. 171 HERITAGE PARK DR 37129 #016-01-1978 L1986 **OPH EM** *020 †16,35

RASHID, Syed Akhtar. ■ 37129 #495-24-1955 L1968 **GP OS** *020

RAZZAQ, Asim. 1004 N HIGHLAND AVE 37129 #704-21-1989 L2006 **RHU IM** *020 †20

REDDY, Pranahitha C. 1417 MARK ALLEN LN 37129 #495-21-1985 L1996 **P** *020 †75

REED, Kristal Nichole. 37128 #047-07-2003 L2005 **IM** *020

REED, Robert Murphy. ■ 37129 #047-05-1954 L1954 **P** *071

RHEA, I Elizabeth Hay. ■ 37129 #047-06-1958 L1961 **R DR** *071 †80

RICHERSON, Dennis Ray. 400 N HIGHLAND AVE 37130 #020-12-1985 L1991 **AN** *020 †05

RICKARD, Randall Craig. 515 E BELL ST 37130 #036-07-1978 L1981 **FM** *020 †18

RICKARD, Susan Dorseyandr. ■ 37130 #047-05-2007 **MPD** *012

ROBERTS, Rebecca Jill. 3400 LEBANON RD 37129 #021-06-1993 L1994 **CHP** *020 †75

RODRIGUEZ, Raul. ■ 37130 #847-10-1961 L1967 *071

RONE, James Kellett. 1004 N HIGHLAND AVE, MURFREESBORO MED CLINIC, P 37130 #045-04-1987 L1998 **END IM** *020 †20

ROSENBLATT, Paul Allen. 1020 N HIGHLAND AVE, STE A 37130 #047-05-1977 L1979 **RO** *020 †80

ROSSER, Brent Andrew. 237 W NORTHFIELD BLVD, STE 101 37129 #047-06-2000 L2003 **PD** *020 †55

ROY, Salil. 3400 LEBANON RD 37129 #495-13-1959 L1973 **IM NEP** *020 †20

RUSZNAK, Csaba. 1703 FIRST PL STE B 37129 #473-04-1985 L2002 **IM** *020 †20,03

RYAN, Jeff Lee. 400 N HIGHLAND AVE 37130 #001-02-1997 L2003 **GS** *020 †85

RYDEN, Amanda M. 400 N HIGHLAND AVE 37130 #047-06-1999 L2002 **EM** *020 †16

SAHA, Ashok K. 3400 LEBANON RD, DEPT OF ANESTHESIOLOGY 37129 #160-02-1975 L2003 **AN PME** *020 †05

SAJID, Hussain Muhammad. 3400 LEBANON RD 37129 #704-02-1956 L1970 **N** *020 †75

SALEKIN, Choudhury M. ■ 37130 #160-02-1979 L1996 **N** *020

SARASWAT, Sudha. 615 N HIGHLAND AVE 37130 #496-38-1973 L1980 **PD** *020 †55

SARASWAT, Suresh Chandra. 611 N HIGHLAND AVE 37129 #496-02-1972 L1980 **CD IM** *020 †20

SARVARIA, Sunil. 517 HIGHLAND TER, STE B 37130 #496-09-1978 L1995 **GE** *020 †20

SAXENA, Rishi K. 1127 DOW ST 37130 #496-17-1980 L1994 **CD IM** *020 †20

SCOTT, Joseph Montgomery. 1004 N HIGHLAND AVE, PA 37130 #047-06-1997 L2000 **IM** *020 †20

SEIBERT, Michael E. 211 HERITAGE PARK DR 37129 #047-07-1990 L1995 **FM** *020 †18

SELLERS, David M. 1019 N HIGHLAND AVE 37130 #047-07-1994 L1995 **FM** *020 †18

SHACKLETT, William White. 818 E CLARK BLVD 37130 #047-06-1944 L1944 **GP IM** *071

SHAH, Navin Punjalal. 1004 N HIGHLAND AVE 37130 #495-23-1973 L1989 **DR** *020 †80

SHANNON, Kimberly B. 1004 N HIGHLAND AVE, MEDICAL CLINIC 37130 #047-06-1995 L1996 **IM** *020 †20

SHARMA, Susheel K. ■ 37130 #495-12-1977 L1991 **CD** *020 †20

SHEPARD, Theodore Geddes. 1004 N HIGHLAND AVE, MURFREESBORO MEDICAL CLINI 37130 #021-06-1985 L1992 **U** *020 †95

SHIBAYAMA, Libby Ann. 237 W NORTHFIELD BLVD, STE 101 37129 #016-11-2000 L2006 **PD** *020 †55

SHIH, Kent Conheng. 1020 N HIGHLAND AVE, STE A 37130 #047-05-1997 L1998 **ON** *020 †20

SHIPLEY, Dianna Dofka. 1020 N HIGHLAND AVE, STE A 37130 #055-02-1992 L1999 **IM HO** *020 †20

SHOWALTER, Patrick Rene. 1747 MEDICAL CENTER PKWY, STE 210 37129 #047-05-1996 L2002 **U** *020 †95

SIEGMANN, Adolf F H. 3400 LEBANON RD 37129 #409-15-1945 L1976 **P N** *071 †75

SIMMONS, Jory S. 1203 MEMORIAL BLVD 37130 #047-07-1979 L1985 **OM GP** *020

SIMPSON, Leigh Ann. ■ 37130 #047-06-2003 L2007 **OBG** *020

SINGH, Alvin. 448 E BURTON ST 37130 #047-07-1977 L1980 **OBG** *020.

SINGH, Ravi Prakash. 1830 HERITAGE PARK PLZ, MID SOUTH PSYCH ASSOC 37129 #496-03-1972 L1989 **P ADM** *020 †75

SIVA, Sadhish Kumar. 1004 N HIGHLAND AVE 37130 #041-13-1997 L2005 **VIR** *020 †80

SMITH, Bretton Carl. 400 N HIGHLAND AVE 37130 #048-14-1995 L1997 **DR** *020 †20

SMITH, Charles Dawes. 420 N UNIVERSITY ST 37130 #047-06-1956 L1957 **OBG OS** *071

SMITH, George Wilburt. 211 HERITAGE PARK DR 37129 #047-07-1975 L1977 **FM GPM** *030 †18

SPEER, Paul D, Sr. 503 E BELL ST, STE 304 37130 #021-06-1998 L2005 **OBG** *020

SPIGEL, David Robert. 1020 N HIGHLAND AVE, STE A 37130 #047-06-1996 L2003 **HO** *020 †20

SRIHARAN, Kalavally. 3400 LEBANON RD, ALVIN C. YORK VA MEDICAL C 37129 #220-02-1973 L1997 **IM** *020 †20

STARRETT, James Alan. 400 N HIGHLAND AVE 37130 #017-20-1966 L1970 **DR NM** *071 †80

STRICKLAND, J Ed. ■ 37129 #012-05-1945 L1949 **IM** *071

STUBBS, Marvin Augustus. 3400 LEBANON RD 37129 #047-07-1980 L1982 **IMG IM** *030 †20

SULKOWSKI, Thomas Edward. 301 N UNIVERSITY ST # 201 37130 #051-04-1987 L1990 **FM FSM** *020 †18

SWAFFORD, Carl Aaron, Jr. 400 N HIGHLAND AVE 37130 #047-06-1985 L1987 **AN IM** *020 †05

TANNER, Jenifer Lynne. 400 N HIGHLAND AVE 37130 #012-21-2004 L2006 **EM** *020

TAYLOR, Gregory Mark. 1004 N HIGHLAND AVE 37130 #047-06-1995 L1999 **OBG** *020 †80

TENPENNY, James W. ■ 37130 #047-06-1951 L1952 **P OBG** *071

TERRY, Gregory Bryan. 400 N HIGHLAND AVE 37130 #039-01-1994 L1996 **AN** *020 †05

THOMPSON, Dana Shelton. 1020 N HIGHLAND AVE, STE A 37130 #047-06-1988 L1991 **IM ON** *020 †20

THORBURN, Gerald Michael. 400 N HIGHLAND AVE 37130 #047-06-1995 L1999 **DR** *020 †80

TOLBERT, E C. 421 E BELL ST 37130 #047-06-1963 L1964 **GP P** *020

TOOMEY, Mitchell Alan. 1020 N HIGHLAND AVE, STE A 37130 #047-06-1984 L1985 **ON** *020 †20

TUGGLE, Lynn Kendell. 400 N HIGHLAND AVE 37130 #047-07-2002 L2005 **EM** *100 †16

TUMA, Robert Paul. ■ 37130 #016-06-1962 L1973 **OTO** *071 †45

UCHIYAMA, Tomoharu. ■ 37129 #036-01-2007 **IM** *012

VAN DYKE, Ann Elizabeth. ■ 37133 #043-01-1979 L1987 **P** *020 †75

VEERAMACHANENI, P V. 1818 WARD DR 37129 #495-11-1991 L1998 **PD** *020 †55

VENUGOPAL, Dharapuram S. 1211 HAZELWOOD ST # H11 37130 #495-94-1973 L1995 **IM** *020 †20

WADE, Frank Darrell. 211 HERITAGE PARK DR 37129 #047-07-1998 L2001 **FM** *020 †18

WALKER, Terri Lynn. 905 S CHURCH ST 37130 #012-21-1991 L1993 **OM GP** *030 †70

WARNER, Barton Wayne. 330 FOREST GLEN CIR, BARTON WARNER, MD 37128 #047-06-1975 L1975 **FM** *030 †18

WESTMORELAND, Morris W. 1602 W NORTHFIELD BLVD, PLLC SUITE 504 37129 #047-06-1978 L1979 **GS VS** *020 †85

WILLIAMS, Deborah Lynn. 1004 N HIGHLAND AVE 37130 #047-06-1987 L1992 **DR** *020

WILLIAMS, Kelly George. 1004 N HIGHLAND AVE 37130 #021-05-2000 L2004 **OBG** *020

WILLIAMS, Kenna Jane. 400 N HIGHLAND AVE 37130 #047-06-1986 L1990 **GS** *020 †20

WILLIAMS, Olin Olis. 400 N HIGHLAND AVE 37130 #047-06-1953 L1954 **GS TS** *071 †85

WILLIAMS, Patricia W. MTSU P.O. BOX 53, 329 KEATHLEY UNIVERSITY CE 37132 #020-12-1986 L1991 **P CHP** *020 †20

WILSON, Mark Christopher. 3400 LEBANON RD, ACY, VAMC, DEPT. OF MEDICI 37129 #010-03-1993 L2005 **IM** *020

WINTERS, Deborah Ann. 1102 DOW ST, RADIOLOGY & DIAGNOSTICS PL 37130 #005-12-1978 L1984 **DR** *020 †80

WITT, John Curtis. 1004 N HIGHLAND AVE, MURFRSBORO MED CTR 37130 #016-02-1990 L1999 **N CN** *020 †75

WITT, Terry James. 507 HIGHLAND TER 37130 #020-02-1969 L1975 **OBG** *020 †30

WOLF, Bruce Lee. 1045 N HIGHLAND AVE 37130 #020-02-1982 L1985 **AI IM** *020 †20,03

WOLOHON, Charles Thos. 1833 WARD DR STE 102 37129 #039-01-1974 L1993 **IM** *020 †20

WOODBERRY, Kerri Michelle. 1725 MEDICAL CENTER PKWY, STE 110 37129 #023-07-1989 L2003 **PS HS** *020 †85,65

WOODS, Dexter L, III. 400 N HIGHLAND AVE 37130 #047-06-1996 L2001 **EM** *020 †16

WOODS, Joan B. 3400 LEBANON RD, VA MEDICAL CENTER 37129 #016-02-1960 L1969 **P GP** *020 †75

WRIGHT, Andrew Maurice. 400 N HIGHLAND AVE 37130 #047-06-1989 L1993 **AN** *020 †05

YARDLEY, Denise Aysel. 1020 N HIGHLAND AVE, STE A 37130 #012-01-1988 L2000 **HO HEM** *020

YOUNG, Jesse Howard, Jr. 507 HIGHLAND TER 37130 #047-06-1953 L1954 **GYN** *071 †30

ZUBKUS, John David. 1020 N HIGHLAND AVE, STE A 37130 #048-12-1997 L2000 **HO** *020 †20 ‡

NASHVILLE – DAVIDSON

AARONSON, Oran Sacha. VUMC - DEPT OF NEUROSURGER, T-4224 MED CENTER NORTH 37232 #917-31-1997 L2004 **NS** *020 †25

AARONSON, Steven Pryce. 391 WALLACE RD 37211 #028-34-1987 L1991 **EM** *020 †16

ABARAY, Damon Michael. ■ 37209 #017-20-2004 L2007 **IM** *020 †20

ABBAS, Aamer. ■ 37209 #704-02-1996 L2002 **IC** *012 †20

ABBAS, Rashida Alyia. 1215 21ST AVE S 37232 #041-01-1996 L1999 **CD** *100 †20

ABDEL-RAHMAN, Fawzi Abdel. ■ 37205 #575-01-1995 **IM** *100 †20

ABEL, Ty William. 1301 22ND AVE N 37232 #003-01-2001 L2005 **PTH** *020 †50

ABLE, Antoinne Chiari. 1005 DR DB TODD JR BLVD, DEPT OF SURGERY 37208 #047-07-1989 L2001 **PM SCI** *020 †60

ABOU-KHALIL, Bassel Wm. A-0118 MCN, VANDERBILT NEUROLOGY - EPI 37232 #605-01-1978 L1988 **N CN** *020 †75

ABRAHAM, Robert Lucien. 2220 PIERCE AVE, VUMC, PRB, ROOM 383 37232 #012-01-2000 L2005 **CD** *100 †20

ABRAM, Mary Lou Combs. ■ 37205 #051-01-1958 L1971 **PTH** *030

ABRAM, Steven Ronald. 2011 MURPHY AVE, STE 301 37203 #016-43-1985 L1995 **NS GS** *020 †25

ABRAMO, Thomas James. 1301 22ND AVE N 37232 #047-07-1982 L1982 **PD EM** *020 †55

ABRAMSON, David Lewis. ■ 37215 #305-01-2002 L2006 **NS** *020

ABSI, Tarek Sami. 2971 TVC, 1301 22ND AVE SOUTH 37232 #605-01-1995 L2003 **TS** *020 †85,90

ABUMRAD, Naji N. 1301 22ND AVE N 37232 #605-01-1971 L1979 **GS SO** *030 †85

ACHARYA, Suresh Kumar. ■ 37217 #496-05-1978 L1988 **IM** *020

ACHEBE, Ebele Mary-Anne. 1005 D B TODD BLVD 37208 #690-04-2003 **IM** *012

ACOSTA, Paulo C. 3443 DICKERSON PIKE 37207 #748-10-1968 L1980 **N OPH** *020 †75

ACRA, Sari A. 2200 CHILDRENS WAY, RM 2510 37232 #605-01-1989 L1994 **PG** *020 †55

ACREE, Maurice Mason, Jr. 37220 #047-06-1961 L1962 **PTH CLP** *071 †50

ADAIR, Candace Bene. ■ 37209 #047-07-2006 **P** *012

ADAMS, Carlton Z, Jr. 1005 DR DB TODD JR BLVD 37208 #010-03-1983 L1988 **GS** *020 †85

ADAMS, Joshua Allen. ■ 37206 #047-06-2008 *012

ADAMS, Mark Chas. 2200 CHILDRENS WAY, 4102 DOCTOR'S OFFICE TOWER 37232 #047-05-1983 L1995 **UP GS** *040 †95

ADDLESTONE, Gail Lynn. 222 22ND AVE N STE 100 37203 #047-05-1997 L2000 **PD** *020 †55

ADDLESTONE, Ronald B. 210 25TH AVE N, STE 602 37203 #012-05-1968 L1974 **DR** *020 †80

ADELANI, Muyibat Adetoun. ■ 37217 #047-05-2008 L2008 *012

ADELEKUN, Olumayowa Adefu. 1005 DR DB TODD JR BLVD 37208 #690-18-2002 **IM** *012

ADELMAN, Marisa Rachel. ■ 37212 #051-01-2007 **OBG** *012

ADEWUMI, John Taiwo. 2201 MURPHY AVE, STE 220 37203 #654-01-1991 L2001 **GPM** *020

ADKINS, Heather Denise. ■ 37215 #020-02-2002 L2007 **N** *100 †75

ADKINS, Royce Terrell. 2011 MURPHY AVE, STE 200 37203 #048-04-1983 L1984 **OBG** *020 †30

ADKISSON, Douglas Wayne. ■ 37217 #047-05-2005 L2007 **CD** *012

ADLER, David Henry. ■ 37212 #051-04-2001 L2004 **CD** *012 †20

ADZOKPA, Selorm Amah. 1005 DR DB TODD JR BLVD, MEHARRY MED COLLEGE 37208 #198-01-1995 **IM** *012

AFTAB GUY, Deanna. 2200 CHILDRENS WAY, RM 2510 37232 #038-44-1991 L1999 **PDE** *020 †55

AGAN, Melissa Watson. CHILDREN'S HOSPTIAL, VANDERBILT 37232 #020-02-2005 **PD** *012

AGARWAL, Anita. 1301 22ND AVE N 37232 #495-37-1986 L1997 **OPH** *020 †35

AGBUNAG, Arnulfo Abat. 3443 DICKERSON PIKE, STE 340 37207 #748-01-1964 L1971 **GS AS** *020 †85

AGUIRRE, Rene Valiente. CTR N, D-3100 VANDERBILT MED 37232 #025-01-2004 L2007 **END** *012 †20

AHIABUIKE, Smithson Onyeb. 1005 DR DB TODD JR BLVD, MEHARRY MED COLLEGE 37208 #690-04-1990 **IM** *012

AHMAD, Farhaan Ali. CTR N, D-3100 VANDERBILT MED 37232 #028-46-2004 L2007 **IM** *020

AHMAD, Nadir. ■ 37221 #422-01-2000 L2007 **GS** *020

AHMAD, Rashid Mobin. 1215 21ST AVE S, STE 5209 37232 #035-01-1992 L2002 **GS** *020 †85,90

AHMED, Nazneen S. 330 WALLACE RD STE 100, CENTENNIAL PEDIATRICS 37211 #495-33-1985 L1999 **PD** *020 †55

AHN-SUNG, Yoo K. 1501 MURFREESBORO PIKE 37217 #583-03-1960 L1978 **PD IMG** *020

AJAYI, Oluwaseyi Olumide. 1005 D B TODD BLVD 37208 #690-02-2002 **IM** *012

AJMAL, Muhammad. 1310 24TH AVE S, VA MEDICAL CENTER DEPT OF 37212 #704-21-1991 L2004 **OAR** *020

AKAMAH, Joseph Atiah. 1005 DR DB TODD JR BLVD, YAABA MEDICAL SERVICES, SC 37208 #412-01-1993 L2007 **CD** *020 †20

AKHIGBE, Omoikhefe Gbemis. 37203 #047-07-2008 *012

AKHTER, Syed Moin. 1005 DR DB TODD JR BLVD, DEPT PSYCH 37208 #308-12-1991 **P** *012

AKIN, Judith Lynn. 2323 21ST AVE S, STE 201 37212 #004-01-1986 L1987 **P** *020 †75

AKINGBEMI, Olumide Makanj. 37203 #047-07-2008 *012

ALAO, David. ■ 37215 #690-01-1987 **GS** *100

ALBERS, Erin Lynn. ■ 37216 #051-01-2004 **PD** *100 †55

ALBERS, Sharon Elizabeth. 1005 DR DB TODD JR BLVD 37208 #011-04-1989 L2001 **D** *020 †15

ALBORNOZ ALARCON, Francisc. 1161 21ST AVE S 37232 #231-03-1990 **IC** *100

ALDERSON, Karli Jai. ■37221 #019-02-2002 L2007 **FM** *020 †18

ALDERSON, Thomas Whitney. ■37221 #019-02-2007 **IM** *012

ALEMKA, Foretia Denis. ■37212 #047-05-2008 *012

ALEXANDER, Paul Crayton. 2010 CHURCH ST, STE 320 37203 #047-07-1974 L1978 **IM** *020 †20

ALEXANDER, William F. 2400 PATTERSON ST, STE 101 37203 #036-01-1983 L1988 **GE IM** *020 †20

ALFERY, David Dwight. 110 29TH AVE N, STE 301 37203 #021-05-1976 L1980 **AN** *020 †05

ALFORD, Robert Henderson. 2300 PATTERSON ST, CENTENNIAL MC 37203 #047-05-1961 L1961 **IM ID** *030 †20

ALFORD, William Cutter, Jr. 4230 HARDING PIKE, STE 450 37205 #047-05-1955 L1955 **TS** *071 †85,90

ALGREN, John Travis. 1301 22ND AVE N 37232 #020-02-1975 L1998 **AN PME** *040 †55,05

AL-HENDY, Ayman A. 1005 DR DB TODD JR BLVD 37208 #915-09-1986 L2007 ***020 †30

ALI, Shahid. 1005 DR DB TODD JR BLVD 37208 #704-16-1980 L1999 **P** *020

ALI, Shahla. ■ 37211 #704-20-2001 **P** *012

ALI, Syed Asad. 1161 21ST AVE S, VANDERBILT UNIV SCH OF MED 37232 #704-25-2001 **PDI** *012 †55

ALI, Yasmine Subhi. MEDICINE, VAN, DIVISION OF CARDIOVASCULAR 37232 #047-05-2001 L2003 **CD** *012 ‡

ALKAYYALI, Fawwaz A. 388 HARDING PL 37211 #575-01-1990 L1995 **IM** *020 †20

ALLEN, Brian Frazer Scott. ■ 37215 #028-02-2006 **AN** *012

ALLEN, David Wayne. 2400 PATTERSON ST, STE 101 37203 #047-20-1989 L1993 **IM** *020 †20

ALLEN, George Sewell. RM T-4224 MCN, VANDERBILT UNIVERSITY MEDI 37232 #028-02-1967 L1984 **NS** *020 †25

ALLEN, Jeralyn Arnette. ■37205 #047-07-2006 **IM** *012

ALLEN, Joseph Hunter. ■37205 #028-02-1948 L1956 **R** *071 †80

ALLEN, Marguerite Theresa. CHILDREN'S HOSPITAL, VANDERBILT 37232 #012-05-2004 **PD** *020 †55

ALLEN, Newton Perkins, Jr. 4230 HARDING PIKE, STE 400 37205 #047-05-1986 L1987 **IM** *020 †20

ALLEN, Terry Reynolds. 2011 CHURCH ST, SUITE 404 PLAZA I 37203 #051-01-1966 L1975 **VS** *020 †20

ALLEN, Vaughan Arthur. 2214 ELLISTON PL, STE 200 37203 #041-13-1972 L1978 **NS** *075 †25

ALLISON, Fred, Jr. 2554 THE VANDERBILT CLINIC, VANDERBILT UNIV MED CTR 37232 #047-05-1946 L1946 **IM ID** *071 †20

ALLISON, Joe Gary. PO BOX 11627 37222 #047-06-1960 L1961 **OBG OS** *020

ALLOS, Suhail Hazim. 1301 22ND AVE N 37232 #528-02-1980 L1998 **GS** *020 †85

ALLRED, John Winfield, III. 1161 21ST AVE S, DEPT OF RADIOLOGY, ROOM CC 37232 #001-02-2000 L2005 **RNR** *020 †80

ALLRED, Nicole Alison. ■37209 #047-07-2008 *012

AL-OMARY, Malek H. 393 WALLACE RD STE 104 37211 #575-01-1990 L1995 **IM** *020 †20

ALPER, Benjamin J. 4230 HARDING RD STE 525 37205 #047-05-1949 L1949 **IM RHU** *071 †20

ALRAYAH, Haytham Alrayah. 1005 DR DB TODD JR BLVD 37208 #848-01-2001 **FP** *012

ALSENTZER, Laurel Vaden. 5819 OLD HARDING RD, STE 201 37205 #041-07-1987 L1990 **PD** *020 †55

ALSUP, Peggy Ann. ■ 37218 #010-03-1964 L1977 **PHP FM** *062 †18

ALTENBERN, Darrington P. 345 23RD AVE N, STE 209 37203 #047-05-1988 L1991 **OBG** *020 †20

ALTENBERN, Douglas C, Jr. 395 WALLACE RD STE 206B 37211 #047-05-1986 L1991 **U** *020 †95

ALTIERI, Lisa Ann. 2000 CHURCH ST 37236 #020-02-1985 L1989 **DR** *020 †80

ALVARADO-LAVIN, Rosa Vivi. 2220 PIERCE AVE, 397 PRB 37232 #649-13-1998 **PHO** *050 †55

ALVAREZ, Vincent Leo. 1801 W END AVE STE 1100 37203 #016-43-1972 L1973 **IM** *030 †20

ALVES, Patrice. ■37211 #035-01-1997 L2006 **IM** *020 †20

ALWAN, Nadia K.. 1005 DR DB TODD JR BLVD, OF PSYCH 37208 #528-01-1989 L2007 **P** *100

AMAEFUNA, Emeka Raymond. 1005 DR DB TODD JR BLVD 37208 #690-06-1988 **GPM** *100

AMDAHL, John Peter. ■37209 #026-04-2007 **EM** *012

AMIN, Adnan Saeed. 1601 23RD AVE S, STE 3105 37212 #704-21-2000 L2003 **CHP** *012

AMIN, Mahmoud Abdelazim. 1161 21ST AVE S DEPT ANES 37212 #330-02-1962 **AN** *020

AMIS, Lori Lee. 2201 MURPHY AVE, STE 201 37203 #047-06-1993 L1996 **PD** *020 †55

AMLICKE, James David. 2220 PIERCE AVE, 383 PRB 37232 #016-06-1988 L1992 **IC** *020 †20

AMMARELL, Robert Lynn. 2000 CHURCH ST 37236 #021-01-1977 L1978 **IM** *020 †20

ANAND, Vinita. 2021 CHURCH ST, STE 305 37203 #495-33-1978 L1984 **IM NEP** *020 †20

ANANTHAKRISHNAN, Madhumit. 1161 21ST AVE S 37232 #043-01-1998 L1999 **CCP** *012 †55

ANCELL, Kristin Kathleen. 21ST AVENUE SOUTH AND GARL 37232 #028-03-2005 L2007 **IM** *012

ANDERSON, Akashia V. ■37203 #047-07-2008 *012

ANDERSON, Arthur R, Jr. 2400 PATTERSON ST STE 30 37203 #047-05-1950 L1950 **IM** *071

ANDERSON, Brent Carroll. ■37215 #012-22-2001 L2003 **CD** *012

ANDERSON, Christian Noel. ■37203 #047-05-2007 *012

ANDERSON, Christopher Bur. ■37205 #016-06-2008 *012

ANDERSON, Edward Eugene. 4230 HARDING RD STE 901 37205 #047-05-1961 L1961 **CD** *071

ANDERSON, Edwin B. 2000 CHURCH ST 37236 #047-05-1945 L1945 **IM** *071

ANDERSON, Edwin B, Jr. 4230 HARDING RD STE 6 37205 #047-05-1973 L1974 **IM** *020 †20

ANDERSON, H R. ■37221 #047-06-1945 L1946 **PUD IM** *071

ANDERSON, Jeffrey Scott. ■37221 #017-20-2007 **P** *012

ANDERSON, John Eugene. 2400 PATTERSON ST, STE 101 37203 #047-05-1986 L1988 **IM** *020 †20

ANDERSON, Mark Daniel. ■37210 #001-02-2007 **IM** *012

ANDERSON, Ted Louis. 1161 21ST AVE S, DEPT OBG 37232 #047-05-1993 L1996 **GYN** *020 †30

ANDERSON, William Clyde. 2400 PATTERSON ST STE 400, THE FIRST CLNC PC 37203 #047-05-1959 L1959 **IM** *020 †20

ANDERSON, William Jos. 2000 CHURCH ST 37236 #047-05-1969 L1969 **GS TS** *020 †85,90

ANDERSON, Willie Thomas. 2400 PATTERSON ST, STE 216 37203 #017-20-1993 L2004 **CHN CN** *020 †75

ANDREOTTI, Rochelle F. 1301 22ND AVE N 37232 #011-03-1978 L2004 **R OBG** *020 †80

ANDREWS, Heather Lynn. 1008 HALCYON AVE, MD 37204 #021-01-1999 L2002 **IM** *020 †20

ANDREWS, Jeffrey C. 1301 22ND AVE N 37232 #065-01-1983 L2003 **OBG** *020

ANNO, Takafumi. 1161 21ST AVE S DEPT MED 37212 #572-47-1979 **IM** *100

ANSARI, Sikander Jaweed. 658 GRASSMERE PARK, ASSOCIATED PATHOLOGISTS IN 37211 #704-02-1984 L2003 **DMP** *020 †50 ‡

ANTEVIL, Jared Lee. ■37204 #051-01-1998 L1999 **TS** *012 †85

ANTEVIL, Karin Maurer. 2000 CHURCH ST 37236 #035-09-1998 L2007 **DR** *020 †80

APRILL, Brian Scott. 2400 PATTERSON ST, STE 101 37203 #028-02-1983 L2003 **END** *020 †20

ARAIN, Amir M. A-0118 MEDICAL CTR NO 37232 #704-02-1993 L2000 **N CN** *020 †75

ARENDALE, Charles Richard. ■37205 #048-04-1973 L1975 **R OPH** *020 †80

ARILDSEN, Mary A Thompson. 1301 22ND AVE N 37232 #041-01-1983 L1999 **HMP** *020 †50

ARILDSEN, Ronald Curtis. 1301 22ND AVE N 37232 #035-01-1981 L1991 **DR** *020 †80

ARMISTEAD, Lauren Michell. ■37203 #055-01-2005 **GS** *012

ARNDT, Frederick Vedder. 7TH FL. MEDICAL CENTER EAS 37232 #035-03-2003 L2005 **NEP** *012 †20

ARNESON, Francine Vanessa. ■37209 #047-05-2007 **IM** *012

ARNETT, Darrell G. 1916 CHURCH ST, CHURCH STREET CARE, PLLC 37203 #048-02-1983 L1984 **IM** *020 †20

ARNEY, Casey Clark. 30 BURTON HILLS BLVD STE 3 37215 #020-02-1988 L1989 **P PFP** *020 †20

ARNOLD, Donald Hayes. 1301 22ND AVE N 37232 #012-05-1979 L2002 **PD** *071 †55

ARNOLD, Larry Totty. 2611 W END AVE, STE 380 37203 #047-06-1961 L1962 **OBG** *020 †30

ARNS, Patricia Ann. 300 20TH AVE N, FL 7 37203 #035-47-1985 L1987 **IM PA** *020 †20

ARRINDELL, Everton Leroy. 2021 CHURCH ST, STE 606 37203 #018-03-1986 L1992 **OPH** *020 †35

ARRINDELL, Saundrett G. 1301 22ND AVE N 37232 #018-03-1986 L1992 **D** *071 †15

ARROWSMITH, Peter Noel. 210 25TH AVE N, STE 900 37203 #011-02-1973 L1974 **OPH EM** *020 †35

ARTEAGA, Carlos Luis. 1301 22ND AVE N 37232 #319-03-1979 L1989 **ON IM** *050 †20

ARTHUR, Catherine E. 2200 CHILDRENS WAY, RM 2510 37232 #047-07-1983 L1984 **PD GE** *020 †20

ARTHUR, Clarissa. 300 20TH AVE N, FL 9 37203 #012-21-1995 L1998 **FM** *020 †18

ARTHUR, Marisa Ezoma. ■37208 #047-07-2007 *012

ARTIME, Carlos Alejandro. ■ 37215 #048-04-2005 L2006 **AN** *012

ARUNACHALAM, Rangarajan. 395 WALLACE RD, STE B301 37211 #495-61-1988 L2005 **IC** *020 †20

ARZUBIAGA, Maria Del C. ■37215 #737-06-1981 L1988 **D** *020 †20,15

ASAF, Saeedah. 1211 21ST AVE S STE 701, VUMC, DEPT. OF ANESTHESIOL 37212 #704-20-1997 L2004 **PAN** *020 †20

ASARO, Alison Rene. 710 HART LANE, MID-CUMBERLAND REGIONAL OF 37247 #021-01-1999 L2001 **PD** *020 †55

ASAYAMA, Kohtaro. ■37205 #572-20-1975 **PD** *050

ASCHNER, Judy L. 1301 22ND AVE N 37232 #035-45-1981 L2004 **NPM PD** *050 †55

ASCHNER, Yael. ■37203 #047-05-2007 **IM** *012

ASGILL, Naett Ibironke. 1005 D B TODD BLVD, MEHARRY MED COLL 37208 #012-21-2007 **OBG** *012

ASHBY, Nathan Edward. 1211 22ND AVE N, STE 3255VUH 37232 #047-06-2003 L2005 **AN** *020

ASHER, Harvey. ■ 37221 #047-05-1965 L1965 **P ADM** *071 †75 ‡

ASHER, Jordan Ross. 4230 HARDING RD, STE 400 37205 #047-05-1990 L1991 **IM** *020 †20

ASLAM, Muhammad. ■ 37209 #047-04-1981 **GS** *100

ATHAVALE, Sanjay Manohar. OF OTOLAR, VANDERBILT UNIV DEPT 37232 #011-04-2007 **OTO** *012

ATKINSON, Cameron Theodor. ■37211 #047-05-2008 *012

ATKINSON, Douglas Burton. 2200 CHILDRENS WAY, CHILDREN'S HOSPITAL 37232 #012-01-2003 **CCP** *012 †55

ATKINSON, Ralph Creyton. 28 WHITE BRIDGE RD, STE 300 37205 #027-01-1985 L1991 **NEP IM** *071 †20

ATTOUSSI, Said. 476 HARDING PL, NASHVILLE FAMILY MEDICAL 37211 #125-03-1987 L1998 **IM** *020 †20

ATTWELL, Augustin R. 1301 22ND AVE N 37232 #048-12-1998 L2005 **IM** *020 †20

ATUBRA, Mary Elemawusime. ■ 37221 #412-02-1989 L2007 **PD** *020 †55

AULINO, Joseph Michael. 1301 22ND AVE N 37232 #051-04-1995 L2001 **RNR** *020 †80

AUNSPAUGH, Jennifer Patri. 1301 22ND AVE N 37232 #654-01-2000 L2004 **AN** *020 †05

AUSTIN, John Clayton. 2010 CHURCH ST, STE 736 37203 #039-01-1982 L1990 **TS** *020 †85,90

AUZENNE, Jean Armisha. ■37221 #021-01-2007 **P** *012

AVANT, George Ray. VANDERBILT MEDICAL CENTER, 1660 TVC 37232 #036-01-1967 L1972 **GE** *020 †20

AVERBUCH, Mark Stephen. 4230 HARDING RD STE 400 37205 #021-01-1973 L1973 **IM** *020 †20

AVERY, James Kelley. ■37215 #047-06-1948 L1949 **OS FM** *072 †18

AVILA, Francisco Orlando. 860 HILLHAVEN CT 37220 #047-20-1988 L1988 **FM** *020 †18

AWAD, Joseph Albert. 1030 MRB IV, VANDERBILT UNIVERSITY 37232 #028-02-1985 L1989 **GE IM** *040 †20

AWAZU, Midori. 1211 22ND AVE N 37232 #572-20-1977 L1988 **PN** *050

AWH, Carl Cholin. 2011 MURPHY AVE 37203 #027-01-1986 L1994 **OPH** *020 †35

AXT, Jason Ronald. ■37221 #038-44-2007 **GS** *012

AYAD, Michael Joseph. 1301 22ND AVE N 37232 #005-14-1998 L2005 **NS** *020

AYASH, Gerard Habib. 112 VILLAGE 37212 #605-01-1996 **P** *100

AYLOR, Sarah Brown. 250 25TH AVE N, STE 315 37203 #047-05-1983 L1984 **P** *020 †75

AZAR, Nabil John. 2311 PIERCE AVE STE 2214, DEPT OF NEUROLOGY 37232 #605-01-2000 L2005 **IM** *100 †75

BABAT, Lawrence Brett. 3443 DICKERSON PIKE, SPORTS MEDICINE SUITE 190 37207 #008-01-1995 L2002 **ORS** *020 †40

BABCOCK, Thomas Irving. ■37209 #001-02-2005 L2008 **EM** *012

BACHA, Fatimah Bte Chan. 1005 D B TODD BLVD 37208 #495-59-1998 **FP** *012

BACHRACH, Alan Frank. 3443 DICKERSON PIKE, STE 550 37207 #011-04-1987 L1989 **N** *020 †75

BACKLUND, Dana Catherine. ■37203 #036-01-2003 L2005 **HO** *012 †20

BACKUS, Elizabeth Maureen. 1916 PATTERSON ST 37203 #047-07-1958 L1965 **OBG OS** *071

BACON, William Louis. 6028 DEER TRCE 37211 #047-07-1962 L1994 **ORS HS** *020 †40

BADGER, Stephen Briant. ■ 37221 #056-06-2007 **AN** *012

BAER, Harry. BAPTIST MEDICAL PLAZA II 37203 #047-06-1954 L1954 **GYN** *071 †30

BAGAI, Kanika. 1301 22ND AVE N 37232 #495-45-1995 L2002 **CN** *020 †75

BAGGETT, Kelvin Antoine. ■ 37203 #036-08-1999 L2006 **IM** *020 †20

BAGGOTT, Nicole Olive. 3443 DICKERSON PIKE, STE 770 37207 #021-01-2000 L2004 **IM PD** *020 †20,55

BAHNER, Roderick Iren. 3443 DICKERSON PIKE, STE 370 37207 #047-07-1966 L1971 **PD** *020

BAILES, Elizabeth Jane. ■ 37205 #020-12-2002 L2005 **PD** *020 †55

BAILEY, Allan Harold. 2010 CHURCH ST STE 420 37203 #017-20-1980 L1986 **GE** *020 †20

BAKER, Jack Richard. 2000 CHURCH ST 37236 #020-12-1985 L1988 **DR** *020 †80 ‡

BAKER, Wendy Pais. 310 25TH AVE N, STE 201 37203 #047-06-1991 L1994 **PD** *020 †55

BAL, Deepinder Singh. 2400 PATTERSON ST, STE 101 37203 #495-73-1988 L1998 **IM** *020 †20

BALAGUER, Jorge. 1301 22ND AVE N 37232 #132-01-1985 L2004 **CD** *072

BALDWIN, Harold Scott. 1301 22ND AVE N 37232 #051-01-1981 L2002 **PDC PD** *020 †55

BALEEIRO, Jennifer Ann. 2220 PIERCE AVE, RM 397PRB 37232 #041-15-1999 L2005 **PHO** *100 †55

BALL, Stephen Kent. 1215 21ST AVE S, MCE - 5TH FLOOR- STE 5209 37232 #027-01-1987 L1995 **TS** *020 †85,90

BALL, Weselyn Lynette. 1500 21ST AVE S, STE 2200 37212 #012-05-1988 L2000 **P** *020 †75

BALLARD, Billy Ray. 1818 ALBION ST, 1005 DR D B TODD, JR, BLVD 37208 #047-07-1980 L1981 **ATP OS** *020 †50

BALLINGER, Jeanne Field. 4230 HARDING PIKE, STE 302 37205 #024-01-1977 L1982 **GS** *020 †85

BALSER, Jeffrey Raymond. 1301 22ND AVE N 37232 #047-05-1990 L1998 **CCA** *020 †05

BALUSEL, Maria Raducuta. ■ 37215 #781-01-1968 **IM GS** *020

BAMGBELU, Olukayode Adeol. 1005 DR DB TODD JR BLVD, MEHARRY MED COLLEGE 37208 #690-14-1994 **IM** *012

BANDY, Preston H. ■ 37205 #047-06-1946 L1946 **AN** *071 †05

BANERJEE, Arna. 1301 22ND AVE N 37232 #495-32-1994 L2002 **CCA** *020 †05

BANERJI, Anamika. ■ 37212 #047-05-2008 *012

BANGALORE VITTAL, Nandakum. ■ 37212 #496-39-2000 L2007 **CN** *012

BANNERMAN, Dana Ringgold. 2010 CHURCH ST STE 710 37203 #047-06-1999 L2000 **IM** *020 †20

BANNON, Krista Maureen. ■ 37217 #047-07-2008 *012

BANYARD, Derek Anthony. ■ 37209 #047-07-2008 *012

BAO, Philip. D-4314 MEDICAL CENTER NORT, VANDERBILT DEPT. OF SURGER 37232 #035-47-2000 L2003 **GS** *100 †85

BAO, Shichun. 1301 22ND AVE N 37232 #243-16-1989 L2002 **END** *100 †20 ‡

BARKIN, Shari Lynn. 2200 CHILDRENS WAY, 8246 DOP 37232 #038-41-1991 L2006 **PD** *050 †55

BARNES, Edward Kirk. 3443 DICKERSON PIKE, STE 760 37207 #047-06-1996 L1997 **HO** *020 †20

BARNES, Gregory Neal. 1301 22ND AVE N 37232 #020-12-1992 L2004 **CHN PD** *050 †55

BARNES, Jason Warren. ■ 37204 #016-11-2005 **PTH** *012

BARNES, Walter Lee, Jr. ■ 37211 #047-07-1977 L1981 **IM** *020

BARNETT, Donald Robt. 210 23RD AVE N, STE 302 37203 #055-01-1968 L1974 **OBG** *020 †30

BARNETT, John Earl. 7575 COCKRILL BEND BLVD, DEBERRY SPECIAL NEEDS FACI 37209 #048-12-1966 L2001 **IM ON** *020 †20

BARNETT, Paul Harold. 6134 MEDICAL CENTER EAST, CENTER 37232 #047-05-1958 L1958 **IM** *071 †20

BARNETT, Robert Burton. 2801 CHARLOTTE AVE, UROLOGY ASSOCIATES, P.C. 37209 #047-05-1969 L1969 **U** *020 †95

BAROCAS, Daniel Ari. 1161 21ST AVE S, A-1302 MEDICAL CENTER NORT 37232 #023-07-2001 L2007 **U** *100

BARON, Michael John. 2011 ASHWOOD AVE 37212 #021-01-1986 L1991 **P ADM** *020 †05,75

BARR, Frederick Earl. 1301 22ND AVE N 37232 #051-01-1988 L1994 **CCP** *020 †55

BARR, James Grant. 28 WHITE BRIDGE RD, STE 300 37205 #047-06-1985 L1987 **NEP IM** *020 †20

BARRAZA, Donald F. ■ 37220 #021-05-1953 L1953 **D OBG** *071 †30

BARRETT, Amanda Daviette. 300 20TH AVE N, STE 302 37203 #047-20-2004 L2008 **OBG** *012

BARRETT, Sterling Isaiah. 2400 PATTERSON ST, STE 400 37203 #025-01-1996 L2007 **IM** *020 †20

BARRETT, Tyler Warren. 1301 22ND AVE N 37232 #047-05-2001 L2005 **EM** *020 †16

BARRIER, Charles Harold. ■ 37203 #036-01-2007 **IM** *012

BARRIOS, Jo Anne. ■ 37221 #021-06-2006 **PTH** *012

BARTEK, Anne Prindiville. 1501 16TH AVE S 37212 #025-01-1979 L1987 **P PYA** *020 †75

BARTHOLOMEW, Kenneth E. 3443 DICKERSON PIKE # 590 37207 #005-12-1980 L1983 **APM** *020 †20

BARTLETT, Thomas Glenn. 4230 HARDING RD, STE 330 37205 #035-01-1988 L2007 **CD IM** *020 †20

BARTON, Daniel Frederick. 207 LAUDERDALE RD 37205 #047-06-1999 L2005 **CHP** *020 †75

BARTON, David. ■ 37205 #021-01-1962 L1970 **P** *071 †75

BARTON, David K. 4301 HILLSBORO PIKE, STE 220 37215 #035-45-1993 L1998 **P** *020 †75

BARWISE, John Allan. 1211 21ST AVE S, STE 526 37212 #775-01-1983 L1998 **AN CCA** *020 †05

BARWISE, Sharone Franco. 1310 24TH AVE S 37212 #836-02-1983 L1999 **P** *020 †75 ‡

BASHIR, Nasir Ahmad. G W HUBBARD HOSP 37208 #047-07-1975 **FM** *100

BASSETT, Heather May. ■ 37211 #048-02-2005 **IM** *012

BATCHELOR, Edwin Dale. 4220 HARDING RD, OFFICE OF MEDICAL AFFAIRS 37205 #047-05-1976 L1977 **OPH** *020 †35

BATEMAN, Mckay Harold. ■ 37221 #021-01-2005 L2007 **AN** *012

BATES, George Wm. 102 WOODMONT BLVD, STE 500 37205 #036-01-1965 L1972 **REN OBG** *020 †30

BATSON, Alicia Bond. 1215 21ST AVE S, VANDERBILT INT MED 7114 ME 37232 #047-06-1998 L2003 **IM** *020 †20,75

BATTLE, Elizabeth Jane. CHILDREN'S HOSPITAL, VANDERBILT 37232 #047-05-2004 L2007 **PD** *020 †55

BAUER, Todd Michael. ■ 37221 #016-43-2005 L2006 **IM** *012

BAUGH-PATTERSON, Dainia. 211 22ND AVE N, ASSOCIATES, P.C. 37203 #047-06-1994 L1999 **IM** *020 †20

BAUM, Robert. 2201 CHILDRENS WAY 37212 #038-41-1988 L1994 **PM OS** *020 †60

BAXTER, Elizabeth Ann. 2409 21ST AVE S, STE 104 37215 #047-05-1990 L1995 **P** *020 †20

BAXTER, Tammy Michelle. ■ 37221 #012-05-1999 L2003 **TS** *020

BAYER, D Scott. ■ 37215 #047-05-1933 L1933 **OBG** *071 †30

BAYSINGER, Curtis Landry. UNIVERSITY HOS, 4202 VANDERBILT 37232 #047-05-1978 L2003 **AN** *020 †05

BAZZEL, Grady Judson. 448 2ND AVE N, DAVIDSON COUNTY SHERIFF'S 37201 #001-06-1996 L1999 **FM** *020 †18

BEALL, Stephanie Ann. ■ 37211 #043-01-2006 **OBG** *100

BEAN, Xylina Deloris. 5141 RAVENS GLN 37211 #041-01-1973 L2006 **NPM PD** *040 †55

BEAUCHAMP, Robert Danl. 1301 22ND AVE N 37232 #048-02-1982 L1987 **GS SO** *020 †85

BECHER, Mark Wm. 1301 22ND AVE N 37232 #030-05-1988 L2004 **NP PTH** *020 †50

BECHTEL, Brett Francis. ■ 37212 #036-05-2007 **EM** *012

BECK, Barry W. 5802 NOLENSVILLE PIKE, STE 103 37211 #038-06-1997 L1999 **OS** *020

BECK, Charles Bernard. 3443 DICKERSON PIKE, STE G30 37207 #048-04-1960 L1966 **IM CD** *020 †20

BECK, William Clarence. ■ 37209 #021-01-2007 **GS** *012

BECKER, Samuel Scott. ■ 37205 #005-02-2002 L2007 **OTO** *100

BEECH, Derrick Jerome. 1035 14TH AVE N 37208 #051-04-1988 L1999 **GS** *020 †85

BEGTRUP, Robert Oscar. 1601 23RD AVE S 37212 #021-01-1966 L1983 **CHP P** *075 †75,18

BEHAR, Theodore Adam. 397 WALLACE RD, STE C-101 37211 #035-45-1987 L1994 **PS HS** *020 †65

BEHRENS, Nancy Virginia. 2100 PIERCE AVE, DEPT OF SLEEP MEDICINE 37212 #041-15-2001 L2005 **N** *100 †75

BELCHER, Richard, Jr. 1301 22ND AVE N 37232 #047-06-1989 L1992 **EM** *020 †16

BELDEN, Richard A. 4220 HARDING PIKE 37205 #012-05-1973 L1978 **DR** *020 †80

BELL, Ayrika Logan. ■ 37207 #047-07-2008 *012

BELL, Deanna Smith. 1161 21ST AVE S 37232 #047-20-2000 L2003 **PD** *020 †55

BELL, Kimberly Burns. 2400 PATTERSON ST STE 311, CENTER 37203 #005-02-1996 L2007 **P** *020

BELL, Robert Le Roy. 210 25TH AVE N, STE 602 37203 #016-02-1955 L1973 **NM UM** *071 †50,28

BELLARDO, Lewis Joseph. 2011 MURPHY AVE, STE 200 37203 #020-12-1991 L1996 **OBG** *020 †30

BELLETTI, John Joseph. ■ 37212 #047-05-2006 *012

BELL-WILLIS, Andrea R. 397 WALLACE RD, C-411 37211 #047-07-1995 L1998 **FM** *020 †18

BELOUS, Andrey Evgenievic. ■ 37212 #913-06-1986 **GS** *012

BELSCHES, Sara Jane. 8161 DOT", 2200 CHILDREN'S WAY 37232 #001-06-2006 **PD** *012

BENDER, Harvey Wm, Jr. 1161 21ST AVE S 37212 #048-04-1959 L1971 **TS** *071 †85,90

BENGELSDORF, Steven. ■ 37221 #024-05-1991 L2003 **GS AS** *020 †85 ‡

BENITEZ, Jorge Na, Jr. ■ 37209 #047-07-2008 *012

BENNETT, Joellen. ■ 37221 #047-05-2008 *012

BENNETT, Kelly Angela. VANDERBITL UNIV MED CTR, VUMC - DEPT OBGYN 37232 #063-01-1992 L1998 **FM** *020 †30

BENSON, Clayne. ■ 37209 #010-02-2004 L2007 **AN** *012

BENSON, George N. 1818 ALBION ST 37208 #005-12-1953 L1955 **DR NM** *071 †28,80

BERCH, Barry Robert. ■ 37215 #027-01-2001 L2004 **GS** *100 †85

BERG, Marion Challen. 1301 22ND AVE N 37232 #001-06-1989 L2005 **EM** *020 †16

BERGERON, Paul Marshall. 4220 HARDING PIKE 37205 #027-01-1988 L1993 **EM** *020 †16

BERGMAN, Mica Yael. ■ 37212 #047-05-2008 *012

BERI, Monica. ■ 37211 #495-45-2000 **IM** *012

BERKLACICH, Frank Martin. 2011 MURPHY AVE STE 309 37203 #016-43-1982 L1990 **ORS** *020 †40

BERKLEY, Nathan Ralph. ■ 37212 #016-11-2003 L2004 **DR** *012

BERKOMPAS, Robert Jay. 4230 HARDING PIKE, STE 400 37205 #048-12-1986 L1987 **IM** *020 †20

BERLIN, Jordan David. 1301 22ND AVE N 37232 #016-11-1989 L1999 **ON** *020 †20

BERMAN, M Lawrence. 21ST AVE SOUTH, DEPT OF ANESTH 37203 #036-01-1964 L1974 **AN PA** *072 †05

BERNARD, Aline Marguerite. ■ 37205 #047-05-2008 L2008 *012

BERNARD, Gordon Raphael. VANDERBILT UNIV, T-1208 MCN, 37232 #021-05-1976 L1979 **PUD CCM** *050 †20

BERNARD, Harold Oswald. 1005 DR DB TODD JR BLVD 37208 #047-07-1964 L1971 **OBG** *020 †30

BERNARD, Louis J. ■ 37218 #047-07-1950 L1951 **GS** *071 †85

BERNARD, Michael Labranch. 1310 24TH AVE S, TVHS 37212 #045-01-2005 L2006 **IM** *012

BERNET, William. 1601 23RD AVE S, STE 3050 37212 #024-01-1967 L1968 **PFP CHP** *020 †75

BERRIE, Warren Richard. 310 25TH AVE N STE 105 37203 #010-01-1969 L1977 **OPH GP** *071 †35

BERRY, Geoffrey. ■ 37215 #352-05-1954 L1966 **AN LM** *071 †05

BERRY, James Michael. 1301 22ND AVE N 37232 #048-14-1984 L2003 **AN UM** *040 †05

BERTHAUD, Vladimir. 1005 DR DB TODD JR BLVD 37208 #440-01-1980 L2001 **IM ID** *020 †20

BERUTTI, Tyler William. 5121 DOCTORS OFFICE TOWER, 2200 CHILDREN'S WAY 37232 #038-40-2001 L2004 **PD** *100 †55

BETTS, Jon Eric. 7640 HIGHWAY 70 S, STE 202 37221 #001-02-2000 L2003 **PD** *020 †55

BEUTER, Matthew Jon. 2400 PATTERSON ST, STE 101 37203 #017-20-1993 L1994 **IM** *020 †20

BEVERIDGE, John H. 1211 22ND AVE N 37232 #051-01-1944 L1952 **R RO** *071 †80

BEVERIDGE, Nancy Allen. 2000 RICHARD JONES RD, STE 270 37215 #036-05-1988 L1991 **PD** *020 †55

BEVERLEY, Heidi Ann. ■ 37211 #046-01-1999 L2005 **CCP** *020 †55 ‡

BEYDERMAN, Liya. ■ 37212 #047-05-2005 L2007 **N** *012

BEYER, Bruce Robt. 1211 21ST AVE S 37212 #047-05-1981 L1982 **OBG** *020 †30

BEYER, Deborah Dean. 4230 HARDING PIKE, STE 400 37205 #047-05-1991 L1994 **IM PD** *020 †55,20

BHATIA, Indumeet. 3443 DICKERSON PIKE # 440 37207 #496-17-1990 L2003 **IM** *020 †20

BHAVE, Gautam Bhaskar. ■ 37209 #048-04-2004 **NEP** *012 †20

BI, Jia. 4230 HARDING RD, STE 707E 37205 #243-16-1988 L2002 **HEM** *020 †20

BIAGGIONI DAVILA, Italo O. 1500 21ST AVE S STE 3500 37212 #737-06-1980 L1987 *020

BIALOSTOZKY, Adriana. AA-0232 MEDICAL CENTER NOR 37232 #649-01-1994 L2004 **PD** *020 †55

BIANCHI, Josette Marie. ■ 37221 #035-06-2006 **PD** *012

BIBER, Rachel Anne. 2200 CHILDRENS WAY 8161D, CHILDREN'S HOSPITAL 37232 #028-03-2006 **PD** *012

BICHELL, David P V. 1301 22ND AVE N 37232 #035-01-1987 L2005 **TS** *020 †85,90

BIENVENU, Gary L, Jr. 391 WALLACE RD 37211 #021-05-1982 L1982 **DR VIR** *020 †80

BIESMAN, Brian Stuart. 345 23RD AVE N, STE 416 37203 #025-01-1988 L1998 **OPH** *020 †35

BIHL, Patricia Marie. 3443 DICKERSON PIKE, STE 760 37207 #047-06-1974 L1974 **ON HEM** *071 †20

BILHARTZ, David Lee. 2801 CHARLOTTE AVE 37209 #048-16-1986 L1992 **U** *020 †95

BILIYAR, Vedavyasa Bhat. 2313 21ST AVE S 37212 #495-72-1978 L1990 **P CHP** *020 †75

BILLER, Daniel Harold. ■ 37205 #047-06-1999 L2007 **OBG** *020

BILLINGS, Frederic T, Jr. MEDICAL CENTER EAST, FLR 7 37232 #023-07-1938 L1946 IM *020 †20

BILODEAU, Matthew Lee. 383 PRB, 2220 PIERCE AVENU, VUMC 37232 #017-20-2003 L2005 CD *012 †20

BILYEU, Bridget Anne. ■ 37221 #016-45-2007 PD *012

BINFORD, Julia S. 275 CUMBERLAND BND, MENTAL HEALTH COOPERATIVE 37228 #048-12-1992 L2001 P *071 †75

BINFORD, Robert S. 2400 PATTERSON ST, STE 223 37203 #048-12-1992 L2001 TS *020 †85,90

BIRCHMORE, Danl Alexander. 1310 24TH AVE S # 11A, US VETERANS HOSP 37212 #012-01-1976 L1981 RHU IM *020 †20

BIRDSONG, Tekuila Renee. ■ 37218 #047-07-2005 L2008 AN *100

BIRDWELL, Kelly Ann. ■ 37215 #012-05-2001 L2006 NEP *012 †16

BISHOP, Jeffrey P. ■ 37204 #048-14-1993 L2007 IM *020 †20

BISHOP, Robert Grady. 397 WALLACE RD, BLDG C 37211 #001-02-1987 L1989 FM *020 †18

BISTOWISH, Joseph M, Jr. ■ 37215 #021-01-1943 L1964 PHP GPM *071 †70

BISWAS, Saptarshi. 1161 21ST AVE S 37232 #495-32-1995 GS *100

BITTLES, Mark Anthony. ■ 37205 #047-06-2001 L2007 VIR *100 †80

BLACKWELL, Lola Youmans. ■ 37212 #047-05-2005 NS *012

BLACKWELL, Timothy Scott. 1301 22ND AVE N 37232 #001-02-1988 L1992 PCC IM *020 †20

BLAKE, Joseph John. - RADI, VANDERBILT UNIV MED CTR 37232 #038-40-2005 L2008 DR *012

BLAKE, Mary Ann. 2201 MURPHY AVE, ANNE BLAKE MD 37203 #001-02-1982 L1986 OBG *020 †30

BLANTON, Donald Mc Lain. 1211 22ND AVE N, D7235 N 37232 #047-06-1984 L1986 EM *020 †20,16

BLAZES, Marian Stoney. ■ 37205 #023-07-1995 *100

BLEECKER, Elizabeth Bullo. ■ 37205 #047-05-2008 *012

BLEIBEL, Hani Ahmad. 1005 DR DB TODD JR BLVD, MEHARRY MED COLLEGE 37208 #913-35-2004 IM *012

BLOCH, Karen Charlotte. 1301 22ND AVE N 37232 #051-01-1990 L1997 ID *020 †20

BLOCK, John Jacob. 1301 22ND AVE N 37232 #039-01-1995 L1998 DR *020 †80

BLOCKER, Cynthia Lynn. 28 WHITE BRIDGE RD STE 111, ADVANCED DIAGNOSTIC IMAGIN 37205 #001-02-1995 L1998 DR *020 †80

BLUTH, Raymond F, Jr. 2010 CHURCH ST, STE 615 37203 #047-05-1988 L1989 PTH PCP *020 †50

BOATRIGHT, Donald J. 1005 DR DB TODD JR BLVD, MEHARRY MEDICAL COLLEGE 37208 #047-07-1982 L1985 IM *020 †20

BOCI, Mirian. ■ 37205 #039-01-2008 *012

BOEHM, Frank Henry. 1301 22ND AVE N 37232 #047-05-1965 L1965 OBG MFM *020 †30

BOGER, Eve Mc Donald. 2201 MURPHY AVE, STE 201 37203 #004-01-1998 L2002 MPD *020 †55

BOGER, Michael Sean. ■ 37212 #036-05-2003 L2006 ID *012 †20

BOGER, William Garland. 393 WALLACE RD STE 400, MIDDLE TENNESSEE 37211 #004-01-1998 L2001 IM *020 †20

BOHL, Jaime Lynne. ■ 37212 #051-01-2003 GS *012

BOLDS, John Michael. 300 20TH AVE N 37203 #047-05-1979 L1982 PUD *020 †20

BOLIAN, George Clement. 1301 22ND AVE N 37232 #021-01-1957 L1986 P CHP *030 †75

BOLINA, Parminder Singh. 300 20TH AVE N 37203 #016-11-1996 L2000 IM *020 †20

BOMBOY, James Dickson, Jr. 2011 CHURCH ST, STE 203 37203 #047-05-1968 L1973 END IM *020 †20

BONAU, Roger Anthony. 4230 HARDING RD, STE 525 37205 #021-01-1981 L1989 GS VS *020 †50

BOND, John B, III. 2201 MURPHY AVE, STE 210 37203 #047-05-1984 L1989 OPH *020 †35

BOND, John Benj. 2201 MURPHY AVE, STE 210 37203 #047-05-1955 L1955 OPH *020 †35

BONVISSUTO, Linda Smith. 4230 HARDING RD, STE 601E 37205 #016-11-1989 L2003 IM *020 †20

BOOKER, Tamela Powell. 222 22ND AVE N, STE 100 37203 #047-20-1993 L2002 FM *020 †18

BOOKMAN, James Andrew. 3443 DICKERSON PIKE, STE 100 37207 #021-01-1972 L1975 OPH *020 †35 ‡

BOOMERSHINE, Chad Stephen. 1161 21ST AVE S, T3219 MCN 37232 #038-40-2002 L2004 RHU *012 †20

BOONE, Paul Dale. T-4224 MCN, DEPT OF NEUROLOGICAL SURGE 37232 #030-05-1993 L1999 NS *020 †25

BOORD, Jeffrey Barton. 1301 22ND AVE N 37232 #036-05-1996 L1999 END *020 †20

BOOTH, Glenn Harwell, Jr. 2011 CHURCH ST 401 37203 #047-05-1971 L1977 IM *020 †20

BOOTHBY, Mark Robin. T-3217 MEDICAL CENTER NORT, DIV OF RHEUMATOLOGY, VUMC 37232 #028-02-1983 L1992 RHU IM *050 †20

BORKON, Matthew Jacob. ■ 37221 #019-02-2005 GS *012

BORN, Mark Leonard. 23 WASHINGTON PARK 37205 #005-11-1972 L1978 DR NM *020 †28,80

BOROWY, Barbara Jean. ■ 37212 #026-08-1996 L2006 PS *012 †85

BOSE, Jolly. 1005 D B TODD BLVD, MEHARRY MED COL 37208 #160-03-1994 GPM *012

BOSKIND, John Andrew. 3441 DICKERSON PIKE 37207 #005-12-1997 L2002 GS *020 †85

BOTTA, Eswara. 21 AVENUE SOUTH, 501 OXFORD HOUSE 37232 #495-11-1978 L1994 AN *020 †05

BOTTA, Lakshmis. 1310 24TH AVE S, TENN VALLEY HLT CARE SYS 37212 #495-58-1978 L2007 P *020 †75

BOTTOMY, Michael Bruce. 2010 CHURCH ST, STE 615 37203 #012-05-1974 L1977 PTH *020 †50

BOUDOULAS, Konstantinos D. ■ 37205 #038-40-2001 L2005 CD *012

BOUDREAUX, Kelly James. A-1302 MED CTR NORTH, 21ST AVE S AND GARLAND AVE 37232 #021-06-2005 U *012

BOULOS, Fouad Ismat. ■ 37212 #605-01-2001 L2006 *100 †50

BOUNDS, George Wm, III. 300 20TH AVE N, FL 9 37203 #047-06-1981 L1984 IM *020 †20

BOUNDS, Inez Boyd. 1919 CHARLOTTE AVE, STE 220 37203 #047-06-1986 L1987 OPH *020 †35

BOURNE, Phillip. 1035 14TH AVE N 37208 #047-07-1975 L1980 OBG *020 †30

BOUYER, Gregory D. ■ 37221 #047-07-2008 *012

BOWEN, Michael Edward. 1211 MEDICAL CENTER DR, VANDERBILT UNIVERSITY MEDI 37232 #047-05-2005 L2008 MPD *012

BOWENS, Clifford, Jr. 1301 22ND AVE N 37232 #036-07-1993 L1997 AN *100 †05

BOWLES, Harvey W. 2201 MURPHY AVE, STE 212 37203 #047-07-1985 L1988 IM *020 †20

BOWLES, Joan. 4220 HARDING RD 37205 #047-05-1998 L1999 IM *020 †20

BOWLES, Travis C. STE II, 7TH FLOOR, MEDICAL CENTER 37232 #048-14-2001 L2004 MPD *020 †55,20

BOYAPATI, Neeraja. 6100 MEDICAL CENTER EAST, VANDERBILT UNIVERSITY MED 37232 #047-05-1997 L2002 IM *020 †20

BOYCE, Robert Hunter. 2400 PATTERSON ST, STE 300 37203 #047-05-1996 L2002 ORS *020 †40

BOYD, Alan S. 1301 22ND AVE N 37232 #048-14-1986 L1993 D DMP *020 †15

BOYD, Jenny Melissa. ■ 37221 #047-06-2003 L2007 CCP *012 †55

BOYD, William Bradley. 313 SLOAN RD 37209 #047-06-1999 L2001 MPD *100

BOYLE, Daniel Patrick. ■ 37205 #028-34-2007 IM *012

BOYLE, Jill Kay. ■ 37204 #045-01-1980 L1998 AN *075 †05

BRABON, Christel Grace. ■ 37211 #020-02-2006 OBG *012

BRACIKOWSKI, Andrea C. 1301 22ND AVE N 37232 #035-06-1981 L1993 PD *050 †55

BRACIKOWSKI, James Paul. STE 1, 7TH FLOOR, MED. CENTER EAS 37232 #035-06-1979 L1988 IMG OPH *012

BRACKIN, Henry B, Jr. 310 25TH AVE N STE 309 37203 #047-05-1947 L1947 P *072 †75

BRADBURY, Thomas Aaron. 1 VANTAGE WAY STE B240, PHYSICIANS 37228 #051-01-2001 L2006 EM *020 †16

BRADHAM, William Glenn. 2400 PATTERSON ST, STE 220 37203 #045-01-1987 L1990 GS VS *020 †85

BRADHAM, William Simons. ■ 37221 #045-01-2003 CD *012

BRADNAN, Paula W Scizak. ■ 37209 #038-40-1968 L1968 GP *071

BRADY, Linda Diane. 5819 OLD HARDING RD, STE 201 37205 #047-05-1992 L1996 PD *020 †55

BRAKEFIELD, James Marion. 2000 CHURCH ST 37236 #021-01-1955 L1960 GYN *071 †30

BRANDES, Jan Lewis. 300 20TH AVE N STE 603 37203 #047-05-1989 L1991 N SME *020 †75

BRANDT, Stephen Jeffrey. 1301 22ND AVE N 37232 #012-05-1981 L1990 HEM IM *072 †20

BRANNON, Charles Travis. 2011 MURPHY AVE, FL 5 37203 #047-06-1986 L1990 AN PME *020 †05

BRANTLEY, Barrett Duane. 2010 CHURCH ST # 515 37203 #004-01-1984 L1986 PTH *072 †50

BRANYON, Edgar W, Jr. ■ 37205 #035-01-1947 L1955 R *071 †80

BRAREN, Herbert Victor. 329 21ST AVE N STE 2 37203 #021-01-1968 L1973 U *020 †95

BRASSETTI, Jorge Rojas. 2000 CHURCH ST DEPT PED 37236 #649-01-1973 L1978 NPM PD *020 †55

BREAM, Peter Reynolds, Jr. 1301 22ND AVE N 37232 #036-01-1996 L2001 VIR *020 †60

BREAUX, George Anthony. ■ 37218 #047-07-1965 L1978 PTH OS *040

BREAUX, Lori Antoinette. 3443 DICKERSON PIKE, TRICS, P.C. SUITE 370 37207 #047-07-1996 L1999 PD *020 †55

BREDENBERG, Helen Keipp. 7TH FLOOR MEDICAL CTR EAST, VANDERBILT UNIV MEDICAL CE 37232 #012-01-1999 L2002 ID *100 †20

BREGMAN, Daniel Koffler. 342 22ND AVE N, VISION AMERICA 37203 #041-02-1985 L1993 OPH *020 †35

BREINIG, John B. 4230 HARDING RD STE 900 37205 #047-05-1966 L1968 CD *071 †20

BREKKEN, Alissa Brooke. 2200 CHILDRENS WAY, 8161 DOT 37232 #047-05-2007 PD *012

BRENNAN, Kimberly Collis. 1301 22ND AVE N 37232 #020-12-1998 L2002 PDR *020 †80

BRESSMAN, Phillip L. 2011 MURPHY AVE, STE 200 37203 #047-05-1979 L1980 OBG *020 †30

BREWER, James Paul. ■ 37206 #038-45-2007 EM *012

BREY, David Matthew. ■ 37221 #020-02-2003 L2004 RHU *012 †20

BREY, Nicole Vessels. 4230 HARDING PIKE, STE 601E 37205 #020-02-2003 L2007 D *020 †15

BRIDGES, David Lee. ■ 37221 #016-11-1979 L1987 EM *020

BRIEN, Patrick Livingston. 2000 CHURCH ST 37236 #047-20-1995 L1999 DR *020 †80

BRIGGS, Nathaniel C. 1005 DR DB TODD JR BLVD, DIV OF PREVENTIVE MED 37208 #056-05-1991 L2003 EP GPM *050 †70

BRILEY, Susan. 2011 CHURCH ST, STE 703 37203 #055-01-1984 L1993 CRS *020 †85,10

BRITTAIN, Evan Luke. ■ 37204 #035-20-2007 IM *012

BRITTIN, Geoffrey Mellor. 1800 CHURCH ST, STE 300 37203 #035-01-1959 L1992 PTH CLP *020 †20

BRITTINGHAM, Thomas Evans. 300 20TH AVE N 37203 #047-05-1999 L2001 IM *020 †20

BROCK, John Wm, III. 2200 CHILDRENS WAY, 4102 DOCTORS' OFFICE TOWER 37232 #012-01-1978 L1979 UP *020 †95

BROOKS, Michelle Elise. ■ 37208 #011-04-2004 L2007 P *012

BROOKS, Philip Arnoldnich. ■ 37208 #047-07-2008 *012

BROOKS-SHUTES, Sonya F. 3443 DICKERSON PIKE, STE 520 37207 #047-20-1997 L2002 N *020 †75

BROOME, James Thomas. ■ 37204 #025-01-2003 L2008 GS *012

BROOME, Rochelle Annette. 40 BURTON HILLS BLVD # 200 37215 #038-44-1983 L2004 FM *030 †18

BROTHERS, Donald T, Jr. 300 20TH AVE N STE 100 37203 #047-06-1989 L1993 AI *020 †55,03

BROTHERS, John Cunningham. 2400 PATTERSON ST STE 300 37203 #047-05-1965 L1965 ORS *071 †40

BROTHERS, Kyle Bertram. 2200 CHILDRENS WAY, 8161 DOCTOR'S OFFICE TOWER 37232 #020-02-2004 L2007 PD *012

BROTHERTON, Wm De Roy, III. 4220 HARDING RD 37205 #012-05-1973 L1981 DR *020 †80

BROUGHTON, Gregory John. ■ 37211 #047-05-2007 GS *012

BROWN, Alice B. 1021 HAMMACK CT 37214 #047-07-1983 L1984 IM *100

BROWN, Alvin Montero. 1811 STATE ST 37203 #047-07-1960 L1983 PM *072 †60

BROWN, Amy Hart. ■ 37221 #047-20-2005 L2007 OBG *012

BROWN, Charles S. ■ 37215 #040-02-1950 L1952 IM *071

BROWN, Douglas Harrison. 222 22ND AVE N, STE 100 37203 #001-02-1976 L1977 OBG *020 †30

BROWN, Karyn Leigh. ■ 37221 #021-05-2006 P *012

BROWN, Kermit Rupert. 2201 MURPHY AVE, STE 220 37203 #047-07-1959 L1971 CD IM *071 †20

BROWN, Michael Clay, Jr. ■ 37208 #047-07-2008 *012

BROWN, Nancy Joan. 1301 22ND AVE N 37232 #024-01-1986 L1989 IM *050 †20

BROWN, Phillip Pendleton. 518 PARK CENTER AVE 37205 #039-01-1969 L1976 TS *020 †85,90

BROWN, Thomas Larry, Jr. 3106 ACKLEN AVE 37212 #011-03-1999 L2001 EM *020 †16

BROWN, Walter U, Jr. 1080 LYNNWOOD BLVD 37215 #027-01-1964 L1979 AN *020 †05

BROWNE, Edward W. ■ 37215 #047-07-1953 L1964 GS ON *071 †85

BROWNING, Alyssa Camille. CTR N, D-3100 VANDERBILT MED 37232 #028-02-2004 L2007 IM *020

BROWNING, Robert Elee, IV. ■ 37209 #047-05-2008 *012

BROWNING, Whitney Lee. ■ 37215 #020-12-2005 PD *012

BRUCE, Donald. 1005 DR DB TODD JR BLVD 37208 #047-07-1974 L1978 OBG *020

BRUCE, Michelle Townsend. 1421 ELM HILL PIKE 37210 #047-07-1994 L1997 GPM *020

BRUNNER, Alexander J. 7TH FLOOR, MCE, SUITE II, VUMC ADULT PRIMARY CARE CE 37232 #038-06-2001 L2005 MPD *100 †55,20

BRUNNER, Laura Ann. 2200 CHILDRENS WAY 8161D, CHILDREN'S HOSPITAL 37232 #047-05-2004 L2007 PD *100 †55

BRUNO, John III. 2000 CHURCH ST 37236 #047-05-1974 L1976 ORS OSM *020 †40

BRUNSTING, Louis Albert. 2400 PATTERSON ST, STE 223 37203 #005-18-1983 L1994 TS *020 †85,90

BRUST, Matthew Lorenz. 397 WALLACE RD BLDG C-100, FAM PRACTICE ASSOC OF S HL 37211 #017-20-1990 L1994 **FM** *020 †18

BRYANT, Andrew Justin. ■ 37209 #036-05-2007 **IM** *012

BRYANT, Deborah Mobley. 222 22ND AVE N 37232 #047-05-1980 L1982 **PD PHP** *020 †55

BRYANT, James David. 222 22ND AVE N, STE 100 37203 #047-05-1979 L1984 **FM** *020 †18

BRYANT, Kristina Michelle. ■ 37221 #011-02-2005 **P** *012

BRYANT, Susan Halperin. 610 GALLATIN RD 37206 #047-05-1979 L1984 **P** *020 †75 ‡

BRYANT, Tatanisha Patrice. ■ 37221 #047-07-2005 L2008 **PD** *012

BUCHANAN, Robt Norman, Jr. 504 ELMINGTON AVE # 417 37205 #047-05-1934 L1936 **D** *071 †15

BUCHHOLZ, Kristina Marie. ■ 37203 #046-01-2006 **IM** *012

BUCHHOLZ, Michael Claus. 1005 DR DB TODD JR BLVD, MEHARRY MEDICAL COLLEGE 37208 #064-01-1980 L2006 **IM GE** *020

BUCKLES, Tamara Lynn. ■ 37216 #047-05-2005 **PD** *012

BUCKSPAN, Glenn Scott. 2204 CRESTMOOR RD 37215 #048-02-1974 L1976 **PS** *020 †85,65 ‡

BUDGE, Philip Jensen. ■ 37205 #047-05-2007 **IM** *012

BULLOCK, Deann Marie. 1818 ALBION ST, MNGH EMERG DEPT 37208 #047-07-2003 L2007 **EM** *020 †16

BULUS, Nada Mitri. 1161 21ST AVE S SURG 37212 #605-01-1986 **GS** *100

BUNTIN, Charles Scott. 3108 MEDICAL CENTER EAST, MEDICAL CENTER 37232 #016-45-1986 L2004 **AN GS** *020 †05

BUNWORASATE, Udomsak. ■ 37221 #891-01-1993 L1995 **HO** *020 †20

BURBANK, Sally Willard. 2021 CHURCH ST STE 608, MEDIAL PLAZA II 37203 #050-02-1986 L1987 **IM** *020 †20

BURGOS, Elizabeth Boggio. 1301 22ND AVE N 37232 #001-06-1990 L1993 **FM** *020 †18

BURK, Raymond Franklin. 1301 22ND AVE N 37232 #047-05-1968 L1986 **IM HEP** *050 †20

BURKE, Renee Michelle. ■ 37212 #025-07-2002 L2008 **PS** *012

BURKEY, Brian Bernard. 7209 MED CTR E-SOUTH TOWER, 1215 21ST AVE S 37232 #051-01-1986 L1991 **HNS OTO** *020 †45

BURKHALTER, Michael Terry. 1800 STATE ST 37203 #047-06-1971 L1971 **OPH** *020 †35

BURKS, Heather Renee. ■ 37209 #047-05-2008 L2008 *012

BURLEY, Howard L. 2120 CRESTMOOR RD 37215 #047-07-1985 L1988 **P** *020 †75

BURNETT, Lonnie S. 1100B VANDERBILT MED CT 37232 #048-02-1953 L1976 **OBG GYN** *030 †30

BURNETT, Patrick Eugene. 1301 22ND AVE N 37232 #023-07-2000 L2004 **D** *020 †15

BURNETTE, Robert Eugene. 1818 ALBION ST, HOSPITAL DEPT OF PATHOLOGY 37208 #047-07-1972 L2000 **PTH GP** *020 †50

BURNETTE, William Bryan. ■ 37211 #047-05-2001 L2007 **NMN** *100 †75

BURNEY, Johnmarcel James. 1005 D B TODD BLVD, DEPT OF OB/GYN 37208 #047-07-2006 **OBG** *012

BURNS, James Jeremy. ■ 37204 #047-06-2005 L2006 **IM** *012

BURNS, Roberta Frances. 7575 COCKRILL BEND BLVD, RD. 37209 #041-07-1977 L2006 **IM OS** *020 †20 ‡

BURR, Ian Meadows. 3319 W END AVE, RM 218 37203 #143-02-1959 L1973 **PD END** *030 †55

BURRIER, Candice Marie. ■ 37205 #038-40-2007 **AN** *012

BURRIS, Howard A, III. 250 25TH AVE N, STE 200 37203 #001-06-1985 L1997 **HEM ON** *020 †20

BURRUS, Daniel Swan. 3443 DICKERSON PIKE, STE 480 37207 #027-01-1986 L1991 **ORS** *020 †40

BURWELL, Bronwen. 3441 DICKERSON PIKE 37207 #047-06-1975 L1975 **GP EM** *020 †16

BUSBEE, Brandon Greer. 2011 MURPHY AVE, BAPTIST NORTH STE 603 37203 #036-05-1998 L2004 **OPH** *020 †35

BUSBEE, Greer Albert, III. ■ 37205 #047-05-1969 L1970 **ORS** *020 †40

BUSKIRK, Elizabeth Jane. ■ 37221 #036-08-2006 **PD** *012

BUSS, Jason Charles. 3529 CRESTRIDGE DR 37204 #041-12-2002 L2005 **EM** *020 †16

BUTKA, Brenda Jo. 1211 22ND AVE N 37232 #012-05-1979 L1980 **PUD IM** *020 †20

BUTLER, Javed. MEDICAL CTR, VANDERBILT UNIV 37232 #704-25-1990 L1999 **CD** *020 †20

BUTLER, Matthew Allen. ■ 37203 #011-03-2006 **ORS** *012

BUTLER, Suzanne D. 2313 21ST AVE S 37212 #047-05-1979 L1981 **P** *020

BUZZELL, Jonathan Edward. ■ 37221 #030-06-2003 L2006 **ORS** *012

BYINGTON, Ashton Bart. ■ 37221 #056-05-2006 **PTH** *012

BYRAM, Ian Robert. ■ 37204 #036-01-2006 **ORS** *012

BYRAM, Mark Tyree. ■ 37215 #047-05-1996 L1996 **FM** *020 †18

BYRD, Benj Franklin, III. 1215 21ST AVE S, STE 5209 37232 #047-05-1977 L1980 **CD OS** *020 †20

BYRD, J W Thos. 2011 CHURCH ST STE 100, NASHVILLE SPORTS MEDICINE 37203 #047-05-1982 L1987 **ORS GS** *020 †40

BYRD, James Brian. 2200 PIERCE AVE, 560 ROBINSON RESEARCH BLDG 37232 #045-01-2002 L2006 **IM** *020 †20

BYRD, Miles Eugene. 1005 DR DB TODD JR BLVD, # 1822 37208 #047-07-2008 *012

BYRD, Teresa Tynese. ■ 37221 #047-07-2003 L2007 **OBG** *100

BYRD, Victor Morris. 222 22ND AVE N, STE 100 37203 #020-12-1991 L1994 **RHU** *020 †20

BYRD, William Bellew. ■ 37209 #020-02-2004 L2006 **AN** *012

BYRNE, John Gerald. 1215 21ST AVE S, RM 5025 37232 #024-05-1987 L2004 **TS CD** *020 †85,90

CABALLERO, Hector. 2410 PATTERSON ST, STE 400 37203 #275-04-1991 L2004 **CD** *012 †20

CABELL, Thomas Hargrave. CTR N, D-3100 VANDERBILT MED 37232 #027-01-2002 L2004 **CD** *012 †20

CADAVID, Adriana Margarit. 1161 21ST AVE S 37232 #264-02-1993 **APM** *100

CAGE, John Bright. 222 22ND AVE N, STE 100 37203 #048-15-1987 L1988 **CD** *020 †20

CAI, Anmei. 1005 DR DB TODD JR BLVD, MEHARRY MED COLL DEPT OF P 37208 #243-65-1983 **P** *012

CAI, Steven. ■ 37212 #035-06-2006 **GS** *012

CAIN, Terry Wayne. 2300 PATTERSON ST 37203 #048-14-2000 L2003 **EM** *020 †16

CAIN-SWOPE, Christina Lee. 4230 HARDING RD, STE 603 37205 #010-02-1995 L1999 **OBG** *020 †30

CALDERWOOD, Susan Adams. 1301 22ND AVE N 37232 #036-07-1976 L1999 **AN IM** *020 †20,05

CALDWELL, A De La Cruz. ■ 37205 #748-10-1962 L1972 **AN** *020

CALDWELL, Thomas B, III. ■ 37205 #008-01-1965 L1972 **AN** *075 †05

CALLAHAN, Alfred S, III. 3825 BEDFORD AVE, STE 201 37215 #047-05-1975 L1976 **N IM** *020 †20

CALLAHAN, Stephen Todd. 2200 CHILDRENS WAY, RM 2510 37232 #004-01-1994 L2002 **ADL PD** *020 †55

CALLAHAN-LIGHTFORD, C. 905 MAIN ST, FAMILY HEALTHCARE GRP 37206 #047-07-1987 L1988 **FM** *020

CALLAWAY, James J. 222 22ND AVE N 37203 #047-05-1947 L1947 **IM** *071 †20

CALLAWAY, Michael Denney. 222 22ND AVE N, STE 100 37203 #047-05-1983 L1985 **IM** *020 †20

CALLAWAY, Thomas Haile. 222 22ND AVE N, STE 100 37203 #047-06-1984 L1987 **IM** *020 †20

CALMET DEL CASTILLO, Erick. 1005 D B TODD BLVD 37208 #737-06-2000 **FP** *012

CALVERT, Jennifer Lynn. ■ 37209 #048-02-2005 L2008 **PD** *012

CAMARATA, Andrew S. ■ 37205 #047-05-2006 L2007 *012

CAMERON, Anthony Donald. ■ 37205 #143-05-1962 L1977 **R** *100 †80

CAMOENS, Reena Mary. 2021 21ST AVE S, STE B107 37212 #047-07-1993 L1995 **P** *020 †75

CAMPBELL, Brett Anthony. ■ 37211 #035-45-2008 *012

CAMPBELL, Earl V, Jr. 2410 PATTERSON ST, STE 402 37203 #566-01-1984 L1993 **PUD** *020 †20

CAMPBELL, Gretchen Lowell. 1301 22ND AVE N 37232 #047-07-1999 L2003 **N** *020 †75

CAMPBELL, Michael Jay. 2200 CHILDRENS WAY, STE 5230 37232 #045-04-2001 L2007 **PDC** *020 †55

CAMPBELL, Orville C. 2410 PATTERSON ST, STE 402 37203 #012-01-1990 L1996 **NEP** *020 †20

CAMPBELL, Susan Beverin. 2300 PATTERSON ST, MID TENNESSEE NEONATOLOGY 37203 #041-02-1973 L1986 **NPM PD** *020 †55

CAMPBELL, Thomas Way. 113 30TH AVE N 37203 #047-05-1968 L1977 **P PYA** *020 †75

CAMPBELL, W Barton. 1215 21ST AVE S, 5TH FL 37232 #035-45-1963 L1970 **CD IM** *040 †20

CANALE, Daniel Doyle, Jr. 2010 CHURCH ST, STE 615 37203 #047-05-1971 L1979 **PTH HEM** *020 †50

CANDIDO, Kimberly Ann. D-3100 MCN 37232 #025-01-2003 L2006 **NEP** *012 †20

CANLAS, Christopher Lored. ■ 37215 #021-05-2004 L2006 **AN** *012

CANNON, Charles Grady, Jr. 110 29TH AVE N, STE 201 37203 #045-01-1962 L1974 **PD OS** *071 †55

CANNON, Jennifer Leigh. 2200 CHILDRENS WAY, 8161 DOT 37232 #047-05-2005 **PD** *012

CANONICO, Angelo Edward. 4230 HARDING PIKE, STE 400 37205 #047-06-1984 L1989 **PCC** *020 †20

CANTER, Jeffrey Alan. 7TH FLOOR, STE IV, VANDERBILT MED CENTER EAST 37232 #038-41-1981 L1986 **IM** *020 †20

CAPECI, Nicholas Ernest. ■ 37205 #035-01-1947 L1963 **IM CD** *075 †20

CAPIZZI, Stephen Andrew. 2010 CHURCH ST, STE 710 37203 #051-07-1996 L2002 **PCC** *020 †20

CAPLAN, Stuart Harlan. 2000 CHURCH ST 37236 #012-01-1985 L1992 **R DR** *020 †80

CAPLE, Phillip M, Sr. 2000 CHURCH ST 37236 #047-07-1976 L1978 **OBG** *020

CARBONE, David Paul. 1301 22ND AVE N 37232 #023-07-1985 L1996 **IM** *020 †20

CAREW, Kehinde Abiola. 391 WALLACE RD, HOSPITAL GROUP 37211 #690-01-1998 L2006 **IM** *100 †20

CAREY, Christopher Don. D-4314 MCN 37232 #039-01-2004 L2007 **GS** *012

CAREY, Edmund L, Jr. 401 BOWLING AVE, UNIT 6 37205 #024-01-1970 L1980 **IM CD** *020 †20

CAREY, James Lee. SOUTH TOWER, STE 3200, MEDICAL CENTER EAST 37232 #041-01-2001 L2006 **OSM** *100

CARLSON, Brian Richard. 2201 CHARLOTTE AVE 37203 #047-05-1974 L1975 **PTH** *020 †50

CARLSON, Michael Glenn. 2400 PATTERSON ST, STE 101 37203 #047-05-1985 L1989 **END IM** *020 †20

CARLSSON, Charlotte E. VANDERBILT UNI A0126 MCN 37232 #858-05-1990 **NPM** *100

CARNES, Matthew Lehn. ■ 37205 #001-06-2000 L2007 **GE** *020 †20

CARNEY, Regina Maria. 1601 23RD AVE S, VANDERBILT PSYCHIATRIC HOS 37212 #035-48-2003 **P** *012

CARPENTER, Chace T. 2010 CHURCH ST STE 710 37203 #047-05-1992 L1994 **PCC** *020 †20

CARPENTER, Cody Garrett. 2200 CHILDRENS WAY 8161D, CHILDREN'S HOSPITAL 37232 #045-04-2004 L2007 **PD** *100 †55

CARPENTER, Geo Kenyon, Jr. 301 21ST AVE N 37203 #047-06-1955 L1955 **ORS** *020 †40

CARPENTER, George Kenyon. 4220 HARDING PIKE 37205 #047-06-1992 L2006 **EM** *020 †16

CARPENTER, Robert Owens. ■ 37211 #048-04-1999 L2004 **GS** *012

CARR, Mark Barham. 2000 CHURCH ST 37236 #020-12-1985 L1991 **ID IM** *020 †20

CARR, Ruth Michelle. 1301 22ND AVE N 37232 #047-06-1991 L1994 **FM** *020 †18

CARRAU, Jose L. ■ 37217 #649-14-2000 L2002 **CN** *012

CARRERO, Gilberto. 1215 21ST AVE S 37232 #042-01-1986 L1990 **AN** *040 †05

CARRILLO, Ysela Marie. 1211 21ST AVE S, STE 404 37212 #034-01-1994 L2000 **CCS** *020 †85

CARROLL, Clinton Michael. ■ 37212 #047-05-2008 *012

CARROLL, Elizabeth Louise. 2200 CHILDRENS WAY, 8161 DOT 37232 #017-20-2007 **PD** *012

CARROLL, Frank Edward, Jr. 1211 22ND AVE N 37232 #041-09-1967 L1983 **DR NM** *050 †80

CARROLL, Kecia Nicole. 2200 CHILDRENS WAY, RM 2510 37232 #047-05-1996 L2001 **PD** *020 †55

CARSON, Robert Paul. ■ 37206 #047-05-2005 **CHN** *012

CARTER, Brian Scott. -A-0126 MCN, PEDS / NEONATOLOGY 37232 #047-06-1983 L1985 **PD NPM** *020 †55

CARTER, Christopher Sean. ■ 37207 #047-07-2008 *012

CARTER, Jeffrey Bradbury. 324 22ND AVE N 37203 #047-05-1978 L1979 **OS EM** *020

CARTER, Kenneth. 2201 MURPHY AVE, STE 411 37203 #047-05-1986 L1986 **OBG** *020 †30

CARTER, Kimberly Nichole. CTR N, D-3100 VANDERBILT MED 37232 #012-01-2005 L2007 **IM** *012

CARTER, Richard Allan. 1818 ALBION ST 37208 #005-02-1964 L1974 **PHP** *040 †70

CARTER, Susan Leontyne. 1005 DR DB TODD JR BLVD, # 1926 37208 #047-07-2008 *012

CASEY, Sean Patrick. 1211 22ND AVE N, VANDERBILT UNIV MED CENTER 37232 #004-01-2004 L2006 **IM** *020 †20

CASH, Michael Paul. D-4314 MCN,, 1121 21ST AVENUE SOUTH 37232 #012-05-2005 L2008 **GS** *012

CASSIDY, Eileen Mary. 2201 MURPHY AVE STE 110, NASHVILLE 37203 #008-02-1997 L2006 **OBG** *020 †30

CASSIDY, Karen Vloedman. 1718 PATTERSON ST, VANDERBILT MEDICAL CENTER 37203 #011-03-1994 L1998 **IM PD** *020 †20

CASTALDO, Eric Thomas. D-4314 MCN 37232 #011-03-2002 L2005 **GS** *012

CATE, Ronald Cooke. 2410 PATTERSON ST 37203 #047-06-1973 L1974 **OTO** *020 †45

CATES, Justin Merrill M. 1301 22ND AVE N 37232 #024-07-1997 L2005 **PTH** *020 †50

CATINDIG-SALCEDO, Z A. ■ 37207 #748-10-1964 L1974 **PD OS** *020

CATO, Elizabeth Leigh. 222 22ND AVE N STE 100 37203 #047-05-1992 L1995 **IM** *020 †20

CATO, James Robert. 222 22ND AVE N 37203 #047-05-1979 L1983 **IM** *020 †20

CAUBLE, Stephanie Marie. 1210 22ND AVE N, VANDERBILT UNIVERSITY MEDI 37232 #021-05-2005 L2006 **IM** *012

CAUCCI, Michael Francis. 1601 23RD AVE S 37212 #010-02-2004 L2006 **P** *012

CAVANAUGH, Kerri Lyn. S-3223 MCN, DIVISION OF NEPHROLOGY 37232 #008-01-1999 L2006 **NEP** *020 †20

CAVAZOS, Edmund, III. ■ 37215 #048-14-1988 L1996 **P** *020

CAZORT, Ralph Jerry. ■ 37207 #047-07-1947 L1949 **PA** *071

CESAR, Fred Max. PO BOX 330788 37203 #047-07-2007 L2007 **MPD** *012

CESPEDES, Ana Eugenia. 2200 CHILDRENS WAY, CHILDREN'S HOSPITAL 37232 #047-07-2007 **PD** *012

CHA, Yong II. ■ 37212 #047-05-2008 *012

CHAKKAVARTHY, Anuradha. 1301 22ND AVE N, PRB-B1003 THE VANDERBILT C 37232 #010-01-1983 L1998 **RO ON** *020 †20,80

CHAKRABARTY, Sangita. 1005 DR DB TODD JR BLVD 37208 #495-13-1990 L2002 **GPM** *040 †70

CHAKRAVARTHY, Ashish K. 1818 ALBION ST 37208 #495-57-1977 L1998 **IM PTH** *020 †50,20

CHALFANT, Robert L. 3310 W END AVE 37203 #047-06-1945 L1945 **GYN** *071 †30

CHAMBERS, Eugene P, Jr. 1301 22ND AVE N 37232 #027-01-1990 L1995 **TS** *020 †85

CHAMBERS, Jill Fishback. 2201 MURPHY AVE STE 407 37203 #001-02-1974 L1975 **GYN** *020 †30

CHAMPION, Elizabeth Anne. ■ 37221 #036-01-2006 **PD** *012

CHAN, Emily. 1301 22ND AVE N 37232 #035-20-1998 L2005 **HO** *020 †20

CHANCE, Amanda Victoria. ■ 37208 #047-07-2008 *012

CHANDLER, Gina Gail. 2400 PATTERSON ST, STE 215 37203 #035-06-1994 L2001 **CD** *020 †20

CHANDRASHEKAR, Meera. 1301 22ND AVE N 37232 #495-33-1979 L1997 **AN** *020 †05

CHANG, Bernard Hyunki. 2400 PATTERSON ST, STE 201 37203 #047-05-1994 L2004 **OPH** *020 †35

CHANG, Chia-Yong. ■ 37220 #385-01-1963 L1973 **TS** *071

CHANG, Joel Mason. ■ 37212 #041-13-2007 **AN** *012

CHANG, Pong Moon. 110 29TH AVE N, STE 202 37203 #583-01-1959 L1971 **AN** *020 †05

CHANG, Sam Sungsoo. 1301 22ND AVE N 37232 #047-05-1992 L2000 **U** *072 †95

CHANNELL, John Calvin. 1809 CROMWELL DR 37215 #047-05-1989 L1996 **OBG** *020 †30

CHAPPELL, Clay H. CTR N, 3100 VANDERBILT MED 37232 #012-05-2004 L2007 **CD** *012 †20

CHAPPELL, James David. 1301 22ND AVE N 37232 #047-05-2001 L2003 **PTH** *100 †50

CHARI, Ravi Samavedam. 1301 22ND AVE N 37232 #068-01-1989 L2001 **GS** *020 †85

CHARLES, Michael Aaron. ■ 37215 #025-01-2007 **GS** *012

CHARLES, Philip David. 2311 PIERCE AVE, RM 2228 37232 #047-05-1990 L1992 **N CN** *050 †75

CHATTERJEE, Subhasis. ■ 37205 #056-05-1997 L2008 **TS** *020 †85,90

CHAUDHARY, Ripan. 8000 MEDICAL CTR EAST, VUMC 37232 #065-06-1998 L2003 *020

CHAUDHRY, Ahsen Raza. 1005 DR DB TODD JR BLVD 37208 #704-21-1992 L2006 **OBG** *020

CHAZEN, Eric Martin. 1301 22ND AVE N 37232 #047-06-1955 L1960 **PD** *020 †55

CHEEK, Daniel Woods. ■ 37205 #035-03-2003 L2003 **EM** *100

CHEIJ, Abraham Pacha. 4306 HARDING RD STE 304 37205 #308-01-1950 L1960 **OPH** *020 †35

CHEIJ, George Moon. 4306 HARDING RD STE 304 37205 #047-20-1988 L1995 **OPH** *020 †35

CHEN, Viola. 397 WALLACE RD, STE 314 37211 #035-46-1995 L1997 **FM** *020 †18 ‡

CHEN, Yuejin. 1921 RANSOM PL 37207 #243-85-1982 L2002 **P** *020 †75

CHENG, Joseph Shun-Che. 1301 22ND AVE N 37232 #056-06-1994 L2002 **NS SCI** *020 †25

CHENGER, Joseph D. 2400 PATTERSON ST, STE 300 37203 #060-02-1977 L1989 **ORS** *020 †40

CHERN, Andrew Lawson. 2201 MURPHY AVE, STE 103 37203 #056-05-1984 L1988 **OBG** *020 †30

CHERNEY, Edward Francis. 1301 22ND AVE N 37232 #005-14-1973 L1995 **OPH** *020 †35

CHESCHEIR, Nancy Custer. 1301 22ND AVE N 37232 #036-01-1982 L1999 **OBG MFM** *020 †30

CHESTER, Caroline Hudson. 2201 MURPHY AVE, STE 403 37203 #047-06-1983 L1992 **PS HS** *020 †85,65

CHESTER, Michael W. ■ 37209 #048-14-2003 L2005 **AN** *100

CHIDSEY, Geoffrey. 4230 HARDING RD STE 530 37205 #017-20-1994 L1997 **CD** *020 †20

CHIDSEY, Kelliann. 1900 BELMONT BLVD 37212 #045-01-1995 L2001 **IM** *020 †20

CHINRATANALAB, Sallaya. 1301 MEDICAL CENTER DR 37232 #891-02-1991 L1998 **RHU** *020 †20

CHINRATANALAB, Wichai. 1301 22ND AVE N 37232 #891-06-1990 L2002 **HO** *020 †20

CHISOLM, Joe Moffatt. 2010 CHURCH ST, 705 MID-STATE MEDICAL CENT 37203 #047-05-1972 L1972 **OPH IM** *020 †20,35

CHIU, Kou-Wei. ■ 37221 #047-05-2003 L2006 **FM** *100 †18

CH'NG, John Lai Chong. 4230 HARDING RD # 527E 37205 #825-01-1977 L1989 **END** *050 †20

CHOATE, Charles Philip. 3901 GRANNY WHITE PIKE, BOX 4180 37204 #047-06-1972 L1973 **IM** *020

CHOI, Chang Hyun. 320 PLUS PARK BLVD, DOCTORS HOSPITAL OF STARK 37217 #583-10-1980 L2006 **PTH PCP** *020

CHOMA, David Peter. ■ 37209 #035-03-2006 L2007 **IM** *012

CHOMA, Neesha Naik. 1310 24TH AVE S, DEPT OF VETERANS AFFAIRS 37232 #035-03-2002 L2006 **IM** *100 †20

CHOMSKY, Don B. 4230 HARDING PIKE, HEART GROUP PLLC 37205 #041-07-1991 L1997 **CD** *020 †20

CHONG, Paul Yungwei. ■ 37212 #047-05-2005 **ORS** *012

CHONGKOLWATANA, Viroje. VANDERBILT MED CTR 37232 #891-02-1981 **PTH** *020

CHOPRA, Nagesh. ■ 37221 #495-23-1996 L2007 **IM** *012

CHOUDHURY, Shahana A. 1005 DR DB TODD JR BLVD 37208 #160-02-1982 L1999 **PD PDI** *020 †55

CHRISTENBERRY, Robert H. 222 22ND AVE N, STE 100 37203 #001-02-1979 L1986 **CD IM** *020 †20

CHRISTIAN, Karla J Godwin. 1301 22ND AVE N 37232 #054-04-1985 L1994 **TS PS** *020 †85,90

CHRISTIE, Michael John. 4230 HARDING PIKE, STE 900 37205 #016-43-1978 L1984 **ORS** *020 †40

CHRISTMAN, Brian Wallace. PULMONARY MEDICINE, T-1219 MCN, VANDERBILT UNI 37232 #039-01-1981 L1985 **PUD CCM** *020 †20

CHRISTOFERSEN, Mark Rau. 3443 DICKERSON PIKE, STE 480 37207 #016-45-1978 L1981 **OP OFA** *020 †40

CHUKWUNYERE, Emmanuel Ama. 1005 DR DB TODD JR BLVD, MEHARRY MED COLLEGE 37208 #610-01-1989 **IM** *012

CHUNCHARUNEE, Suporn. 1161 21ST ST S 37212 #891-02-1981 **HEM** *020

CHUNG, Arleen. 316 22ND AVE N 37203 #001-02-1992 L1996 **PD** *020 †55

CHUNG, Christine Hwayong. 1301 22ND AVE N 37232 #051-07-1998 L2003 **HO** *020 †20

CHUNG, Ok Yung. 1301 22ND AVE N 37232 #016-06-1983 L1994 **AN** *020 †05

CHUNG, Sung Jang. ■ 37215 #583-02-1947 L1970 **CLP PTH** *071 †50

CHURCHWELL, Andre Lemont. 1215 21ST AVE S, STE 5209 37232 #024-01-1979 L1991 **IM CD** *020 †20

CHURCHWELL, Keith Burnell. 1301 22ND AVE N 37232 #028-02-1987 L1994 **CD** *020 †20

CHURCHWELL, Kevin Bernard. 2200 CHILDRENS WAY, RM 2510 37232 #047-05-1987 L1995 **CCP** *020 †55

CIAMPA, Philip John. VANDERBILT UNIV MED CTR, 6016 MED CTR EAST 37232 #047-05-2004 L2006 **MPD** *012

CICO, Stephen John. 703 OXFORD HOUSE, VANDERBILT UNIV-EMERG MED 37232 #038-41-1997 L2004 **PEM MPD** *020 †55,20 ‡

CLAIR, Walter Kevin. 1301 22ND AVE N 37232 #024-01-1981 L1993 **ICE CD** *020 †20

CLAMP, Chrystal Grupka. 2400 PATTERSON ST STE 4, THE FRIST CLINIC 37203 #047-06-2002 L2005 **IM** *020 †20

CLARK, Craig Anthony. 30 BURTON HILLS BLVD, STE 375 37215 #055-02-1988 L1989 **CHP** *020 †75

CLARK, Nathaniel Kim. 3060 PHV, DEPT OF PSYCHIATRY 37232 #024-05-2001 L2007 **P** *020 †75

CLARK, Peter Earl. A-1302 MEDICAL CENTER NORT, VUMC 37232 #024-01-1994 L2006 **U** *020 †95

CLARK, William Jos, Jr. ■ 37204 #050-02-1946 L1950 **IM** *071 †20

CLARK, William Mc Lean. 2300 PATTERSON ST 37203 #047-05-1955 L1955 **N** *072

CLARKSON, Kevin. ■ 37212 #539-04-1985 L1994 **CCA** *020 †05

CLAVENNA, Michael William. ■ 37215 #036-05-1997 *100

CLAY, C Stafford. ■ 37215 #036-07-1941 L1943 **FM** *072

CLAYTON, Anna Martine. 3973 THE VANDERBILT CLINIC, DIVISION OF DERMATOLOGY 37232 #023-12-1990 L2007 **D** *020 †15

CLAYTON, Ellen Wright. 1301 22ND AVE N 37232 #024-01-1985 L1988 **PD** *050 †55

CLEATOR, John Henry. 2311 PIERCE AVE, INSTITUTE 37232 #045-01-1999 L2002 **IC** *100 †20

CLEWNER, Lisa Michele. ■ 37221 #048-13-2005 **PD** *012

CLIFFORD, Concepcion G. 4536 NOLENSVILLE PIKE, STE F 37211 #048-13-1991 L2003 **FM** *020 †18

CLINTON, Mary E. 2400 PATTERSON ST, STE 307 37203 #005-06-1976 L1977 **N** *020 †75

CLOUDEN, Garrick Curt. ■ 37217 #047-07-2008 *012

CLUGSTON, Patricia Anne. 2021 CHURCH ST STE 806, NASHVILLE PLASTIC SURGERY, 37203 #061-01-1986 L1993 **PS** *020 †65

CLUNE, Jennifer Quinter. CTR N, D-3100 VANDERBILT MED 37232 #038-40-2005 L2006 **IM** *012

CMELAK, Anthony Jos. 1301 22ND AVE N, B-1003 TVC 37232 #016-05-1992 L1996 **RO** *020 †80

CO, Jerry Padpad. 275 CUMBERLAND BND, MENTAL HEALTH COOPERATIVE, 37228 #748-01-1988 L2005 **ADP** *020 †75

COBB, Cully A, Jr. 4230 HARDING RD, STE 303 37205 #024-01-1942 L1949 **NS** *071 †25

COBURN, Lori Ann. CTR N, D-3100 VANDERBILT MED 37232 #024-01-2004 **GE** *012 †20

COCHRAN, Bradley Mark. 28 WHITE BRIDGE RD, STE 209 37205 #001-02-1996 L2000 **DR** *020 †20

COCHRAN, Michelle R Macht. 2125 BELCOURT AVE, VILLAGE 37212 #020-02-1992 L1993 **P** *020 †75

COCHRAN, Robert Taylor. 2201 MURPHY AVE STE 301 37203 #047-05-1959 L1960 **N IM** *020

COFER, Shelagh Ann. 1301 22ND AVE N 37232 #016-11-1997 L2003 **OTO** *020 †45

COFFEY, Robert J, Jr. 465 21ST AVE S 4140, MRB III 37232 #010-02-1976 L1986 **GE IM** *050 †20

COHEN, Alan Gary. 1601 23RD AVE S 37212 #023-07-1971 L1974 **ON HEM** *020 †20

COHEN, Jonathan Adam. 4230 HARDING PIKE, STE 302 37205 #035-19-1994 L1999 **GS** *020 †85

COHEN, Renee Lynn. 4230 HARDING RD, STE 400 37205 #035-19-1994 L1999 **IM** *075 †20

COHN, Marvin Harris. 3443 DICKERSON PIKE, STE 310 37207 #047-05-1961 L1975 **IM RHU** *020 †20

COKER, Wesley Louis. 2400 PATTERSON ST, STE 300 37203 #051-01-1969 L1974 **ORS** *020 †40

COLBURN, Christopher A. 3443 DICKERSON PIKE # G30 37207 #020-02-1998 L2001 **IM** *020 †20

COLBURN, Jeffrey David. ■ 37211 #005-12-2005 L2005 **OPH** *012

COLEMAN, James Jackson. 2001 CHARLOTTE AVE, STE 101 37203 #001-02-1979 L1992 **PUD IM** *020 †20

COLEMAN, Nathaniel James. ■ 37221 #021-01-2005 **IM** *012

COLEMAN, Paul Houston. 1450 ELM HILL PIKE, ASSOCIATED PATHOLOGISTS 37210 #048-15-1984 L1991 **PTH IM** *020 †50 ‡

COLES, John H, III. 1401 BURTON VALLEY RD 37215 #047-05-1951 L1951 **GP GS** *071

COLLEN, Kevin B. 275 CUMBERLAND BND, MENTAL HEALTH COOPERATIVE, 37228 #048-13-1999 L2003 **P** *020 †75

COLLIER, Anderson Burton. 397 PRB, 22220 PIERCE AVE., RM 37232 #047-05-1998 L2005 **PHO** *020 †55

COLLIER, David Loyd. 310 GREAT CIRCLE RD, 4TH FL 37243 #004-01-1984 L1995 **FM** *020 †18

COLLIER, Jennifer Marie. 1586 MCGAVOCK PIKE 37216 #047-06-2003 L2006 **PD** *020 †55

COLLINS, Carletta Maria. 1211 22ND AVE N 37203 #001-02-2004 L2006 **HO** *012 †20

COLLINS, Cynthia E. 4126 NOLENSVILLE RD 37211 #038-41-1995 L2001 **FM** *020 †18

COLLINS, Harold B, II. B1100 MEDICAL CENTER NORTH, VANDERBILT UNIVERSITY/OBGY 37232 #047-06-1989 L2004 **OBG** *020 †30

COLLINS, Leslie Susan. 7177 COCKRILL BEND BLVD 37209 #047-06-1995 L1998 **IM** *020 †20

COLLINS, Millard Darnell. ■ 37211 #047-07-2001 L2003 **FM** *020 †18

COLON, Jose Enrique. ■ 37214 #011-04-2003 L2006 **CHN** *012

COLTHARP, William Hubert. 4230 HARDING PIKE, STE 450 37205 #027-01-1981 L1988 **TS** *020 †85,90

CONCEPCION, Raoul Sioco. 2801 CHARLOTTE AVE, STE 303 37209 #038-43-1984 L1986 **U** *020 †95

CONE, Cecil Wayne, II. 1005 DR DB TODD JR BLVD 37208 #010-03-1986 L1994 **PTH** *020 †50

CONEY, Ponjola. 1005 DR DB TODD JR BLVD, OFFICE OF THE DEAN 37208 #027-01-1978 L2002 **END OBG** *030 †30

CONLEY, Christopher N. 3443 DICKERSON PIKE, STE 430 37207 #012-01-1997 L2004 **CD** *100 †20

CONNER, Barrett Dow. 3443 DICKERSON PIKE, STE 680 37207 #016-42-1994 L1996 **PCC** *020 †20

CONNORS, Robert Dedick. ■ 37212 #047-05-2008 *012

CONOYER, Benjamin Michael. ■ 37205 #028-34-2007 **GS** *012

CONOYER, John Matthew. 7204 MEDICAL CENTER EAST, VANDERBILT U. MEDICAL CENT 37232 #047-05-2003 L2005 **OTO** *020

CONRAD, James Francis. 4306 HARDING PIKE, STE 300 37205 #025-01-1980 L1984 **OPH** *020 †35

CONSTANTINE, Arthur E. 4230 HARDING RD STE 330 37205 #001-02-1987 L1993 **CD IM** *020 †20

CONWAY, Michael Geo. ■ 37215 #649-14-1979 L1985 **OS** *020

COOGAN, Alice Clark. ■ 37215 #047-05-1988 L1997 **PTH** *020 †50

COOGAN, Philip Gerlach. 301 21ST AVE N 37203 #047-05-1988 L1997 **ORS HS** *020 †40,65

COOK, Stephen Lewis. ■ 37212 #047-05-2008 *012

COOKE, George Edward. 2300 PATTERSON ST 37203 #047-06-1958 L1958 **IM** *071

COOKSON, Michael Shawn. A1302 MCN 37232 #039-01-1988 L1998 **U** *020 †95

COONS, Benjamin John. A-1302 MED CTR NORTH, 21ST AVE S AND GARLAND AVE 37232 #017-20-2004 L2006 **U** *012
COOPER, Mark Elbert. 356 24TH AVE N, STE 400 37203 #001-02-1988 L1994 **CCS GS** *020 †85
COOPER, Michael Kane. 1301 22ND AVE N 37232 #001-02-1992 L2002 **N** *020 †75
COOPER, William Owen. 1161 21ST AVE S, AA-0216 MEDICAL CTR N 37232 #047-05-1991 L1993 **PD** *020 †55
COOPWOOD, Reginald W. 1301 22ND AVE N 37232 #047-07-1985 L1990 **GS** *020 †85
CORNELIUS, Lala A. 3443 DICKERSON PIKE # 300 37207 #913-92-1990 L2001 **HO** *020 †20
CORNEY, Robert Tyler. 4220 HARDING RD 37205 #051-01-1961 L1972 **P** *071 †75
CORRAL, Cathryn Jean. ■ 37209 #047-06-1968 L1970 **GP** *020
CORRALES REYES, Enme Gabr. 1161 21ST AVE S, DEPT OF NEUROLOGY 37232 #275-03-1993 **CHN** *012
CORREA, Pelayo. VANDERBILT MEDICAL CTR, DIV OF GASTROENTEROGY 37232 #264-03-1952 L2006 **ATP OS** *071 †50
CORREA-GRACIAN, Hernan. 2200 CHILDRENS WAY, 11219 DOCTOR'S OFFICE TOWE 37232 #264-05-1983 L2006 **PTH** *020 †50
CORRY, Patricia Ann. 221 STEWARTS FERRY PIKE 37214 #047-07-1970 L1974 **P** *020
COSTELLO, William Timothy. ■ 37221 #047-06-2006 **AN** *012
COTHREN, Jackson Danl. 1900 CHURCH ST, STE 100 37203 #047-06-1968 L1969 **GYN** *071 †30
COTTON, Bryan Alan. 1301 22ND AVE N 37232 #305-01-1997 L2004 **CCS** *020 †85
COTTON, Robert B, Jr. 1301 22ND AVE N 37232 #051-01-1965 L1976 **NPM PD** *020 †55
COUCH, Orrie A, Jr. 2120 HAYES ST 37203 #047-05-1940 L1948 **IM** *071 †20
COUCH, Robert Steven. 1301 22ND AVE N 37232 #048-04-1982 L1993 **OS** *020 †55
COULAM, Craig Merrill. ■ 37215 #036-07-1972 L1976 **DR** *071 †80 ‡
COURSEY, Stephanie B. 311 23RD AVE N, METROPOLITAN HEALTH DEPT. 37203 #047-07-1976 L1978 **IM** *020
COVARRUBIAS, Minerva B. 1161 21ST AVE S 37232 #033-06-2000 L2007 **PCC** *100
COVER, Timothy Lee. A3310 MEDICAL CTR N, DIVISION OF INFECT DIS 37232 #036-07-1984 L1990 **ID** *050 †20
COWAN, Hanson Buford. 2010 CHURCH ST STE 710 37203 #047-06-1983 L1987 **PUD CCM** *020 †20
COWAN, Ronald Lynn. 1500 21ST AVE S, STE 2200 37212 #035-20-1994 L2000 **P** *050 †75
COWDEN, Frederic Eugene. ■ 37205 #047-05-1942 L1943 **IM** *071 †20
COX, Charles Leonard, III. MEDICAL CENTER EAST, SOUTH 37232 #047-06-2002 L2007 **OSM** *012
COX, Jennifer Elaine. 330 WALLACE RD STE 109, CLINIC 37211 #047-06-2004 L2007 **PD** *020 †55
COX, Katie Lane. ■ 37205 #047-05-2007 **EM** *012
COX, Kevin Lee. 28 WHITE BRIDGE RD, STE 300 37205 #001-06-1996 L2002 **NEP IM** *020 †20
COXE, David Robertson. 1301 22ND AVE N 37232 #047-05-1989 L1992 **IM** *020 †20
CRAFT, Lisa Thompson. 1301 22ND AVE N 37232 #048-12-1979 L1982 **PD** *020 †55
CRAFTON, George B. 2000 CHURCH ST 37236 #020-02-1946 L1954 **OBG** *072 †30
CRAFTON, George West. 3443 DICKERSON PIKE, STE 430 37207 #020-02-1982 L1990 **CD IM** *020 †20
CRAIG, Allen Scott. TENNESSEE DEPARTMENT OF HE, 425TH AVE N, CEDS, 1ST FLO 37243 #035-46-1982 L1996 **FM PHP** *030 †18
CRAIG, Jim C, Jr. 6458 CURRYWOOD DR 37205 #047-06-1995 L1996 **FM** *020 †18
CRANFIELD, Robert Lewis. 2553 MURFREESBORO PIKE, ASSOCIATES 37217 #001-02-1980 L1990 **GP** *020
CRASE, Edward Cody. ■ 37205 #020-12-2001 L2004 **RNR** *020 †80
CRASE, Teresa Perry. 2200 CHILDRENS WAY, RM 2510 37232 #020-12-2002 L2004 **PD** *020 †55
CRAWFORD, James Clay. 4220 HARDING PIKE 37205 #016-11-2000 L2005 **EM** *100 †16
CREASY, Jeffrey Lee. 1161 21ST AVE S, CCC 1118 MCN 37232 #036-01-1980 L1988 **DR** *020 †80
CREECH, Clarence Buddy. 1301 22ND AVE N 37232 #047-06-1999 L2002 **PDI** *020 †55
CREIGHTON, Sarah Elizabet. ■ 37201 #047-05-2008 *012
CRENSHAW, Marshall House. 1215 21ST AVE S, MCE 5TH FLOOR S TOWER 37232 #021-01-1982 L1988 **IC CD** *020 †20
CRIGLER, Lakisha Antoinet. ■ 37209 #047-07-2005 **OBG** *012
CRISPENS, Marta Ann. 1301 22ND AVE N 37232 #001-02-1991 L2002 **GO OBG** *020 †30
CROFFORD, Oscar Bledsoe. 1161 21ST AVE S 37212 #047-05-1955 L1955 **DIA** *030
CROMWELL, Brian David. 4230 HARDING RD, STE 601E 37205 #020-12-2002 L2003 **IM** *020 †20
CROOK, Angus M G. 300 20TH AVE N STE 102 37203 #051-01-1953 L1953 **GYN** *020 †30
CROOK, Jerrall P, Jr. 2001 HAYES ST 37203 #047-06-1984 L1985 **OTO** *020 †45
CROOK, Jerrall Paul, Sr. 2001 HAYES ST 37203 #047-06-1958 L1959 **OTO** *020 †45
CROSS, David Lynn. 2001 HAYES ST 37203 #047-05-1982 L1991 **OTO** *020 †45
CROSSLEY, George Hinton. 222 22ND AVE N STE 400, MID-STATE CARDIOLOGY ASSOC 37203 #012-01-1984 L1999 **ICE CD** *020 †20
CROSSNO, Peter F. ■ 37221 #048-13-2002 L2005 **PCC** *012 †20
CROWDER, Robert A, Jr. 222 22ND AVE N, STE 100 37203 #047-06-1990 L1992 **IM** *020 †20
CROWE, Donna Jane. 300 20TH AVE N STE 302 37203 #047-05-1993 L1996 **OBG** *072 †30
CROWE, Elizabeth Harlan. 326 21ST AVE N, VANDERBILT UNIV STUDENT 37203 #036-01-1987 L1995 **FM** *020 †18
CROWE, James Earl, Jr. 1301 22ND AVE N 37232 #036-01-1987 L1995 **PD PDI** *050 †55
CROZIER, Ian. ■ 37215 #047-05-1997 L2002 **ID** *020 †20
CRUMP, William Drake. 1721 PATTERSON ST 37203 #047-06-1974 L1975 **HEM PTH** *071 †50
CSIKI, Ildiko. ■ 37211 #047-05-2007 **IM** *012
CUEVAS, Leslie A. 2410 PATTERSON ST, STE 106 37203 #018-03-1999 L2001 **RHU** *020 †20
CUEVAS, Ramon Fontanilla. 1301 22ND AVE N 37232 #018-03-1999 L2002 **PD** *020 †75 ‡
CULCLASURE, John Weeks. 4230 HARDING RD STE 901, NEUROSURGICAL CENTER 37205 #045-01-1983 L1997 **PME AN** *020 †05
CUMMINGS, Clinton Lee. 1005 18TH AVE S, MEHARRY MEDICAL COLLEGE 37212 #047-07-1972 L1978 **PUD IM** *040 †20
CURCIO, Natalie Marie. 1211 22ND AVE N 37232 #047-05-2004 **D** *012
CURTSINGER, Joseph C, Jr. 393 WALLACE RD, STE A-303 37211 #020-02-1980 L1997 **GS VS** *020 †85
CUSHMAN, Arthur Robt. 2021 CHURCH ST, STE 800 37203 #005-12-1969 L1975 **NS** *071 †25
DA FONSECA, Ricardo B. 1161 21ST AVE S, DEPT OF RADIOLOGY 37232 #187-12-1993 L2003 **DR** *020 †80,28
DAGEFORDE, Leigh Anne. ■ 37212 #047-05-2008 *012
DAILY, Donna K C. 1301 22ND AVE N 37232 #019-02-1972 L2002 **PD** *050 †55
D'ALMEIDA, Traciann Philo. ■ 37215 #473-02-1999 **P** *100
DAMP, Julie Alicia. 1215 21ST AVE S, MCE 5TH FL 37232 #047-05-2001 L2004 **CD** *100
DAMP, Peter Helge. 4220 HARDING PIKE 37205 #012-01-1998 L2000 **EM** *020 †16
DANG, Helen Huyen. 1005 D B TODD BLVD, DEPT OF INTERNAL MEDICINE 37208 #905-02-2004 L2008 **IM** *012
DANG, Thao Phuong. 1301 22ND AVE N 37232 #041-07-1993 L2000 **HO** *020 †20
DANIEL, Juliet Marie. 310 25TH AVE N, STE 204 37203 #016-06-1995 L2006 **PD** *020 †55
DANIELL, James F, Jr. 2011 MURPHY AVE, STE 305 37203 #047-06-1967 L1976 **GYN** *020 †30
DANIELS, Charles Wellman. 4230 HARDING PIKE, STE 400 37205 #035-01-1974 L1980 **IM** *020 †20
DANIELS, Titus L. A2200 MCN, 1161 21 AVE S 37232 #019-02-2001 L2007 **ID** *100
DANTZLER, Kamisha Adwoa. 1161 21ST AVE S, DEPT OF PSYCHIATRY 37232 #047-07-2004 **P** *012
D'AQUILA, Richard Thomas. U. SC, A2200 MED CENTER NORTH, VA 37232 #035-46-1979 L2001 **ID IM** *050 †20
DARBAR, Dawood. 1301 22ND AVE N 37232 #919-02-1989 L2002 **CD** *020 †20
DASTGHEIB, Sayyed M H. 311 GLENGARRY DR # 6 37217 #517-05-1976 L1985 *100
DATTA, Sukdeb. 1310 24TH AVE S, DEPARTMENT OF VETERANS AFF 37212 #495-32-1991 L2005 **APM AN** *020 †05
DATTILO, Jeffery B. 1301 22ND AVE N 37232 #036-08-1993 L2002 **VS** *020 †85
DAUME, Jason Thomas. ■ 37221 #038-40-2002 L2007 **PAN** *020 †05
DAVE, Utpal Pramod. ■ 37205 #016-06-1994 L2005 **IM** *100 †20
DAVIDSON, C Wade, II. 2021 CHURCH ST 37203 #047-06-1981 L1981 **OBG** *020 †30
DAVIDSON, William Raymond. 2201 MURPHY AVE, STE 201 37203 #047-06-1989 L1992 **PD** *020 †55
DAVIS, Beverley C. 300 20TH AVE N, FL 9 37203 #051-01-1990 L1996 **END** *020 †20
DAVIS, Bruce Allan. 1916 PATTERSON ST STE 700 37203 #021-05-1971 L1978 **IM OM** *020 †20
DAVIS, Carla Miller. 4220 HARDING PIKE 37205 #047-05-1974 L1974 **PTH** *020 †50
DAVIS, George Wm. 2300 PATTERSON ST 37203 #012-05-1957 L1962 **ORS OSS** *020 †40
DAVIS, Ivan Rizzie. 2817 W END AVE, STE 126-291 37203 #047-07-1974 L1974 **GS EM** *020
DAVIS, Jennifer Lise. 2200 CHILDRENS WAY, VANDERBILT CHILDREN'S HOSP 37232 #012-01-2003 L2006 **PE** *100 †55
DAVIS, John Lucian. 2400 PATTERSON ST STE 104 37203 #047-05-1971 L1977 **GS TS** *020 †85
DAVIS, Larry Taylor. ■ 37209 #047-05-2008 *012
DAVIS, Michael David. ■ 37220 #407-02-1949 L1961 **PTH PCP** *071 †50
DAVIS, Richard Andrew. 1301 22ND AVE N 37232 #010-02-1998 L2004 **ORS** *020 †40
DAVIS, Richard John. 2010 CHURCH ST, STE 503 37203 #047-05-1973 L1973 **GYN** *071 †30
DAVIS, Rodney. ■ 37232 #021-01-1982 L2007 **U** *020 †95
DAVIS, Stacy Faith. 222 22ND AVE N, STE 400 37203 #026-04-1988 L1995 **CD** *020 †20
DAVIS, Stephen Michael. 2400 PATTERSON ST STE 516 37203 #047-07-1981 L1995 **PS GS** *020 †65
DAVIS, Stephen N. 2213 GARLAND AVE, 7465 MRB IV 37232 #917-30-1979 L1993 *020
DAVIS, Thomas J. 300 20TH AVE N 37203 #041-01-1963 L1970 **CD** *071 †20
DAVIS, Thomas Lee. A0118 MCN, 1161 21ST AVE SOUTH 37232 #027-01-1985 L1991 **N IM** *050 †75
DAVIS, William Gray. 2201 MURPHY AVE, STE 220 37203 #047-06-1964 L1965 **OTO** *071 †45
DAY, Matthew Alan. - RADI, VANDERBILT UNIV MED CTR 37232 #047-05-2005 L2005 **DR** *012
DAY, Thomas Wayne. 24 WHITE BRIDGE RD 37205 #027-01-1981 L1990 **D** *020 †15
DEAL, Karen Marie. ■ 37221 #047-05-1995 L1998 **PTH** *020 †50
DEASON, Deborah Ruth. 610 GALLATIN RD 37206 #047-06-1977 L1977 **PUD IM** *020 †20
DEATON, Dana Marie. ■ 37215 #047-05-2004 L2008 **CHP** *012
DEATON, Mark Arey. 2410 PATTERSON ST STE 210 37203 #051-01-1986 L1991 **OTO GS** *020 †45
DE BOER, David Kent. 4230 HARDING PIKE, STE 900 37205 #047-05-1990 L1995 **ORS** *020 †40
DEBONA, Jill. 4301 HILLSBORO PIKE, STE 220 37215 #047-05-1990 L1991 **P** *020 †75
DEEGAN, Robert James. 1211 22ND AVE N SO2301, VANDERBILT UNIV MEDICAL CT 37232 #539-04-1986 L1996 **AN** *020 †05
DEERING, Thomas Anthony. 850 RS GASS BLVD 37216 #018-03-1988 L1996 **PTH FOP** *020 †50
DEES, Mary Ellen. 2200 CHILDRENS WAY, RM 2510 37232 #038-06-1991 L1998 **PDC** *050 †55
DEGRYSE, Amber Lee. CTR N, D-3100 VANDERBILT MED 37232 #011-04-2004 L2007 **PCC** *012 †20
DEHART, Roy Lynch. 3319 W END AVE, STE 950 37203 #047-06-1960 L1961 **OM AM** *030 †18,70
DEIS, Jamie Nichole. 1301 22ND AVE N 37232 #036-01-2003 L2006 **PE** *012 †55
DE JESUS, Policarpo S C. 1414 COUNTY HOSPITAL RD, METROPOLITAN BORDEAUX HOSP 37218 #748-01-1953 L1974 **IMG FM** *071 †18
DELBEKE, Dominique. 1301 22ND AVE N 37232 #165-01-1978 L1989 **NM PTH** *020 †28,50
DELBOY, Nancy Jane. 4230 HARDING PIKE, ANESTHESIOLOGISTS 37205 #048-04-1991 L1998 **CCA AN** *020 †05
DE LEON, Alejandro S. 1161 21ST AVE S DEPT OPH 37212 #748-02-1963 **OPH** *050
DELLAI, Alessandro. 1161 21ST AVE S 37232 #561-35-2004 **EM** *012
DELONEY, Curtis Ramon. ■ 37221 #036-05-2006 **N** *012
DELOZIER, Jan Stallings. CENTER EAST, STE 6000 MEDICAL 37232 #047-06-1982 L1984 **IM** *020 †20
DELOZIER, Joseph Benj. 209 23RD AVE N 37203 #047-06-1982 L1985 **PS GS** *020 †65
DELTORO, Christina Elena. ■ 37208 #047-07-2008 *012
DELVAUX, Thomas C, Jr. ■ 37205 #047-05-1952 L1952 **PTH** *071 †50
DEMPSEY, Jennifer Rebecca. ■ 37209 #020-02-2001 L2006 **D** *020 †15
DENDY, Nanette Eldridge. 1301 22ND AVE N 37232 #047-06-2001 L2004 **IM** *020
DENISON, Mark Randall. 2200 CHILDRENS WAY, RM 2510 37232 #019-02-1980 L1991 **ID PD** *050 †55
DENNEY, William David. 2400 PATTERSON ST, STE 400 37203 #047-05-1987 L1990 **CD IM** *020 †20
DENNY, Joshua Charles. ■ 37211 #047-05-2003 L2005 **IM** *100
DENT, Lemsuel Leon. 1005 DR DB TODD JR BLVD 37208 #012-21-1985 L2007 **CCS** *020 †85
DE PRIEST, Charles Vernon. 1161 21ST AVE S, DEPARTMENT OF RADIOLOGY 37232 #024-01-1982 L1998 **DR EM** *020 †80
DERLETH, Christina Louise. ■ 37212 #054-04-2004 L2007 **HO** *012 †20
DERMODY, Terence Shawn. 1301 22ND AVE N 37232 #035-01-1982 L1990 **ID IM** *050 †20
DESAI, Neerav Avinash. 1301 22ND AVE N 37232 #047-06-2002 L2006 **MPD** *020 †20,55
DESAI, Nikhil Kishor. ■ 37221 #047-05-2005 L2008 *100
DESHPANDE, Jayant K. 1301 22ND AVE N 37232 #047-06-1976 L1977 **PD AN** *040 †05,55
DESHPANDE, Seema Prafulla. 1211 22ND AVE N SO3255, DEPT OF ANESTH & CARDIOTHO 37232 #495-98-1992 L2005 **AN** *020 †05
DES PREZ, Roger Moister. 1301 22ND AVE N 37232 #035-01-1954 L1967 **IM PUD** *020 †20
DESRUISSEAU, Andrew James. 1005 DR DB TODD JR BLVD 37208 #019-02-2000 L2004 **ID** *012

DETTBARN, Wolf Dietrich. 2100 PIERCE AVE 37212 #407-07-1953 **OS N** *071

DETTORRE, Kristen B. ■ 37232 #038-44-2006 **EM** *012

DEUS, Amalia Alejandra. ■ 37209 #308-03-1986 **FM** *100

DEVASIA, Rose A. ■ 37204 #020-02-1999 L2001 **ID** *012 †20,55

DE VITO, Victoria Jeanne. 2200 CHILDRENS WAY, RM 2510 37232 #038-43-1979 L1998 **NPM PD** *020 †55

DEWEY, Charlene Maria. 1215 21ST AVE S - 6016, MEDICAL CE 37232 #012-21-1990 L2007 **IM** *020 †20

DE WITT, Joan Frances. ZERFOSS, STATION 17, VANDERBILT UNIVERSITY 37232 #026-04-1988 L2001 **IM** *020 †20

DIAZ, Jose J. 1211 21ST AVE S, 404 MAB 37212 #048-14-1992 L1998 **TRS CCS** *040 †85

DIAZ, Roberto. 1301 22ND AVE N, B-902 TVC 37232 #035-19-2004 **RO** *012

DIBBLE, Timothy David. 4230 HARDING PIKE, STE 400 37205 #004-01-1998 L2004 **IM** *020 †20

DICKSON, Natalie R. 4230 HARDING RD STE 707 37205 #566-01-1991 L1998 **HO** *020 †20

DIDIER, Aaron Juel. 1161 21ST AVE S, OF O 37232 #048-15-2005 **OBG** *012

DIGGS, Joseph. CCC-1106, VANDERBILT-MEDICAL CTR NOR 37232 #869-04-1967 L1982 **DR** *020

DIGNAN, Rebecca Joy. 1301 22ND AVE S, 2986 THE VANDERBILT CLINIC 37232 #051-04-1987 L1999 **TS** *020 †85,90

DILLER, Raegan Annemarie. 4611 NEVADA AVE 37209 #048-12-2001 L2005 **OBG** *100

DIMITRI, Elia Chas. ■ 37221 #047-06-1960 L1961 **PD PHP** *071 †55

DINA, Thomas Stewart. 1161 21ST AVE S CCC-1121, VANDERBILT UNIV MED CTR 37232 #016-06-1965 L1993 **DR** *040 †80

DIPAOLA, Frank Walter. ■ 37211 #036-01-2006 **PD** *012

DI SALVO, Thomas Gerard. 1301 22ND AVE N 37232 #038-41-1987 L2004 **IM CD** *020 †20

DISHER, Anthony C. 1005 DR DB TODD JR BLVD, DEPT OF RADIOLOGY 37208 #047-07-1984 L1985 **DR IM** *020 †80

DITTUS, Janet Lee. 2201 MURPHY AVE, STE 215 37203 #020-02-1979 L1980 **OBG** *020 †30

DITTUS, Robert Steven. 1301 22ND AVE N 37232 #017-20-1978 L1997 **IM** *050 †20

DIXON, Bryce Wm. 300 20TH AVE N, FL 9 37203 #048-04-1983 L1985 **IM IMG** *020 †20

DIXON, Gardner Luke. 707 YOUNGS LN 37207 #005-12-1958 L1960 **GP OS** *020

DIXON, John Holland. 1215 21ST AVE S, RM 5209 37232 #047-05-1973 L1974 **CD** *020 †20

DMOCHOWSKI, Roger Roman. 1301 22ND AVE N 37232 #048-02-1983 L1994 **U** *020 †95

DODD, Debra Ann. 2200 CHILDRENS WAY, PED CARDIOLOGY, SUITE 5230 37232 #023-07-1984 L1984 **PDC** *020 †55

DODD, Kenton Antoine. 2531 ELM HILL PIKE, CONCENTRA MEDICAL CENTER 37214 #047-07-2001 L2004 **OM** *100

DODGE, Debora B. 1920 CHURCH ST 37203 #017-20-1982 L1986 **EM** *020 †16

DOERING, Tracey Ellen. 2000 CHURCH ST 37236 #023-07-1985 L1985 **IM IMG** *020 †20

DOLHUN, Rachel Marin. ■ 37207 #036-05-2005 **N** *012

DOMM, Jennifer Ann. 1301 22ND AVE N 37232 #047-05-2000 L2004 **PD** *020 †55

DONAHUE, Brian Seamus. MEDICAL CENTER, VANDERBILT UNIV 37232 #012-05-1992 L1996 **AN** *020 †05

DONAHUE, Sean Parnell. 1301 22ND AVE N 37232 #012-05-1989 L1995 **OPH PO** *020 †35

DONG, Caiping. 4220 HARDING RD, SAINT THOMAS HOSPITAL, POB 37205 #243-65-1985 L2002 **IM** *020 †20

DONG, Chang-Hong. 1005 DR DB TODD JR BLVD, DEPT OF NEUROLOGY 37208 #243-52-1993 L2001 **N** *020 †70,75

DONLEVY, Elizabeth. T1218 MEDICAL CENTER NORTH, VANDERBILT UNIV. MEDICAL C 37232 #036-05-2000 L2002 **PCC** *100 †20

DONNELLY, Edwin Francis. - RADIOLOGY, 21ST AND GARLAND 37232 #038-41-1996 L1998 **DR** *020 †80

DONNELLY, Jennifer Marie. 4901 NOLENSVILLE RD 37211 #038-41-1996 L1998 **PD** *020 †55

DONOFRIO, Peter Danl. 2311 PIERCE AVE, VANDERBILT UNIVERSITY MED 37232 #038-40-1975 L2006 **N IM** *020 †20,75

DONOVAN, Jill Erin. 437 CUMBERLAND PL 37215 #035-20-1997 L2000 **PAN** *020

DOPP, Alan Christian. 2400 PATTERSON ST, STE 101 37232 #025-01-1970 L1977 **GE IM** *020 †20

DORRIS, Stacy Lynn. ■ 37205 #047-05-2007 **PD** *012

DOSSETT, Lesly Ann. ■ 37206 #047-05-2003 L2006 **GS** *012

DOSTER, Robert Thos. ■ 37205 #047-06-1954 L1954 **IM** *071 †20

DOUGHERTY, William R. 1211 21ST AVE S, 404 MAB 37212 #005-06-1985 L2004 **GS** *020 †65,85

DOUGLAS, Keith Cooper. ■ 37205 #047-05-2006 **ORS** *012

DOUGLAS, Leslie Diane. 300 20TH AVE N 37203 #041-12-1988 L1994 **IM** *020 †20

DOUGLAS, Susan Sharp. 2201 MURPHY AVE STE 310 37203 #047-20-1998 L2003 **P** *020 †75 ‡

DOUGLASS, Larry Earle. 1252 SAXON DR 37215 #047-05-1960 L1960 **PTH** *020 †20

DOVAN, Thomas Tuan. 2021 CHURCH ST, STE 200 37203 #012-05-1997 L2007 **HS** *020 †40

DOVE, Christine Kane. 1161 21ST AVE S, DEPT OF RADIOLOGY 37232 #047-05-2002 L2006 **DR** *100 †20

DOVE, Dwayne Everett. ■ 37212 #047-05-2007 **PD** *012

DOW, William Watlington. 1161 21ST AVE S DEPT PED 37212 #047-05-1971 **PD** *100

DOWELL, Shana Ruth. ■ 37212 #035-45-2003 L2007 **OBG** *020

DOWNING, John Watson. 1211 MEDICAL CENTER DR, 4202 VANDERBILT UNIV MEDIC 37232 #836-01-1961 L1991 **AN** *020 †05

DOWNS, Nevin Howard. 1144 GATEWAY LN 37220 #005-12-1968 L1974 **AN** *020 †05

DOYLE, Amy Robinson. A-2200 MCN, 1161 21ST AVE SOUTH 37232 #001-02-2001 L2003 **ID** *020

DOYLE, Thomas Philip. 1301 22ND AVE N 37232 #003-01-1987 L1994 **PDC IC** *020 †55

DOZIER, Carey Cameron. ■ 37204 #036-07-2007 **IM** *012

DRAUD, Jon Winston. 222 22ND AVE N, STE 100 37203 #020-12-1990 L1992 **P SME** *020 †75

DREGER, Marydiana Domurat. 801 DOMINICAN DR 37228 #047-05-2001 L2004 **IM** *020

DRINKWATER, Davis Clapp. 2400 PATTERSON ST, STE 400 37203 #050-02-1976 L1997 **CD TS** *020 †85,90

DRIVER, L Rowe, Jr. 2010 CHURCH ST STE 608 37203 #012-05-1944 L1950 **OPH** *071 †35

DRIVER, N Lynn. 2201 MURPHY AVE, STE 110 37203 #047-06-1986 L1989 **OBG** *020 †30

D'SOUZA, Sudhir Jude A. ■ 37215 #067-01-1991 **PD** *100 †55

DUBUISSON, Nancy Louise. ■ 37212 #021-05-2006 **AN** *012

DUEKER, Nathaniel David. ■ 37205 #047-05-2002 L2005 **DR** *100 †80

DUFF, Henry. 1161 21ST AVE S PHARM 37212 #067-01-1975 L1979 **PA** *050

DUFFY, John William. A-1302 MED CTR NORTH, 21ST AVE S AND GARLAND AVE 37232 #047-06-2004 U *012

DUKE, Elizabeth Anne. 2000 CHURCH ST, BAPTIST HOSPITAL 37236 #047-05-1979 L1981 **NPM** *020 †55

DUKE, Harold Wesley. 2020 21ST AVE S, STE 201 37212 #028-46-1990 L1995 **EM** *020 †16

DUKE, Naomi Nichele. 436 MEDICAL CENTER SOUTH, VANDERBILT UNIVERSITY MEDI 37232 #024-01-1996 L2005 **ADL** *020 †20,55

DULL, Christopher John. ■ 37215 #047-05-2001 L2005 **P** *020

DUMITRU, Jon Kenneth. ■ 37203 #045-01-2007 **GS** *012

DUMMER, John Stephen. 1301 22ND AVE N 37232 #041-12-1977 L1990 **ID IM** *020 †20

DUNBAR, Laura Lu. 300 20TH AVE N, STE 401 37203 #016-45-1979 L1981 **GS** *020 †85

DUNCAN, Gary Wm. 1301 22ND AVE N 3962, VANDERBILT CLC 37232 #047-05-1966 L1968 **N** *020 †75

DUNCAN, Michael Anthony. ■ 37218 #047-07-1988 L1992 **IM** *020

DUNCAVAGE, James Anthony. 1301 22ND AVE N 37232 #056-06-1975 L1986 **OTO** *020 †45

DUNKERLEY, Robert C, Jr. 222 22ND AVE N, STE 100 37203 #047-05-1968 L1970 **GE** *071 †20

DUNN, B Rentz, Jr. 2021 CHURCH ST, STE 305 37203 #001-06-1979 L1991 **NEP** *020 †20

DUNN, George Dewey. 1310 24TH AVE S 37212 #047-05-1960 L1971 **GE** *020 †20

DUNN, Julie Renee. 3443 DICKERSON PIKE, STE G30 37207 #047-06-1998 L1999 **IM** *020

DUNN, Melanie Ayres. 2300 PATTERSON ST 37203 #048-16-1987 L1994 **OBG** *020 †30

DUNN, Warren Reid. 1301 22ND AVE N 37232 #011-04-1997 L2004 **OSM** *020 †40

DUONG, Joy Louise. 222 22ND AVE N, STE 100 37203 #047-05-2002 L2007 **OBG** *100

DUTTON, William Jeff. 4300 SIDCO DR, CONCENTRA MEDICAL CENTERS 37204 #001-06-1993 L1997 **IM OM** *020

DUYGU, Remzi Aydemir. ■ 37217 #902-03-1949 L1976 **IM GP** *071

DWAMENA, Natasha Abena. ■ 37221 #033-05-2005 **OBG** *012

DWORSKI, Ryszard Tadeusz. 1301 22ND AVE N 37232 #759-01-1980 L2003 **IM** *020 †20,03

DYER, Calvin Robinson. 3443 DICKERSON PIKE, STE 480 37207 #047-05-1988 L1993 **ORS OSM** *020 †40

DYER, David Neil. 2200 MURPHY AVE, STE B 37203 #047-06-1979 L1980 **GS** *020 †85

DYKSTRA, Elizabeth Ponder. 310 25TH AVE N STE 203 37203 #012-01-1998 L2001 **PD** *020 †55

EACHUS, Patricia L. 425 5TH AVE N 1ST FL, CORDELL HULL BLDG 37247 #047-06-1976 L1976 **FM FSM** *030 †18

EADDY, Allison Grier. ■ 37209 #001-06-2005 **PD** *012

EAGLE, Susan Sodofsky. 1211 22ND AVE N, STE 3255VUH 37232 #012-01-1999 L2003 **AN** *020 †05

EARL, Truman Markley. VANDERBILT UNIV MEDICAL CE, 801 OXFORD HOUSE 37232 #048-13-2002 L2005 **IM** *020 †05

EARTHMAN, Webb Johnston. 2000 CHURCH ST 37236 #047-05-1982 L1987 **DR VIR** *020 †80 ‡

EASDOWN, Jane Letitia. 1301 22ND AVE N 37232 #067-01-1980 L1996 **AN** *020

EASSA, Eassa-Helmy M. 5211 LINBAR DR, STE 516 37211 #915-04-1949 L1973 **RO** *071

EBRHIM, Atef Eshak. 1005 DR DB TODD JR BLVD, DEPT OF FAMILY & COMM MED 37208 #915-03-1997 **FP** *012

EBY, Kathryn Grace. ■ 37212 #047-05-2008 **GS** *012

ECKHAUSER, Aaron Wesley. D-4311 MEDICAL CENTER NORT 37232 #012-12-2002 L2005 **GS** *012

ECKRICH, Michael J. 2220 PIERCE AVE, VANDERBILT MED CTR 37232 #035-15-2003 **PHO** *012

ECKSTEIN, Charles Wm. 2801 CHARLOTTE AVE, UROLOGY ASSOCIATES P.C. 37209 #047-05-1976 L1981 **U** *020 †95

EDBERG, Karl-Erik. 1161 21ST ST S 37212 #858-04-1972 **NPM** *020

EDGEWORTH, Michael Ladd. 2211 PIERCE AVE, SGOB 2236 37232 #027-01-2000 L2004 **N** *050 †75

EDMONDS, Ryane Alexandra. ■ 37208 #047-07-2007 *012

EDOSOMWAN, Emmanuel. 1005 DR DB TODD JR BLVD, MEHARRY MED COLLEGE 37208 #104-01-2004 **IM** *012

EDWARDS, Christina Marie. ■ 37214 #021-06-2005 **GS** *012

EDWARDS, David Linwood. 2400 PATTERSON ST, STE 500 37203 #036-01-1983 L1984 **IM** *020 †20

EDWARDS, Joe Michael. 2201 MURPHY AVE, STE 201 37203 #004-01-1966 L1972 **OBG** *020 †30

EDWARDS, Kathryn M C. 1301 22ND AVE N 37232 #018-03-1973 L1980 **ID PD** *050 †55

EDWARDS, Robert Harvey. 2801 CHARLOTTE AVE, UROLOGY ASSOCIATES P.C. 37209 #047-05-1960 L1960 **U** *020 †95

EDWARDS, William H. 4230 HARDING RD, STE 525 37205 #047-05-1953 L1953 **VS GS** *071 †85,90

EDWARDS, William H, Jr. 4230 HARDING RD, STE 525 37205 #047-05-1981 L1987 **VS GS** *020 †85

EFOBI, Deka Achufusi. 393 WALLACE RD, STE 100 37211 #759-10-1992 L2005 **N** *020

EGBUNIWE, Azuka Cassandra. PO BOX 291503 37229 #047-07-1999 L2007 **IM** *020 †20

EHST, Kristin Joy. 229B ORLANDO AVE, 229 B ORLANDO AVE 37209 #047-05-2003 L2006 **MPD** *100 †20

EHTESHAM, Moneeb Mohammad. ■ 37221 #704-25-1999 **NS** *100

EICHHOLZ, Kurt Michael. T-4224 MEDICAL CENTER NORT, VANDERBILT NEUROSURGERY 37232 #028-34-1999 L2006 **NS** *100

EISENBERG, Esther. R-1217 MCN, DEPT. OF OB/GYN, 37232 #035-46-1976 L1992 **REN GYN** *020 †30

EISERT, Donald Raymon. 1301 22ND AVE S, VANDERBILT CTR RADIATION 37232 #049-01-1964 L1987 **RO** *020 †80

EKBOM, Dale Christopher. ■ 37215 #026-04-2002 L2007 **OTO** *100

ELAM, Lloyd Chas. 1005 D B TODD BLVD 37208 #054-04-1957 L1962 **P** *075

ELAM, Morris Greg. 1425 ELM HILL PIKE 37210 #047-06-1981 L1986 **OBG** *020 †30

ELAM, Roy Oscar, III. 1301 22ND AVE N 37232 #047-06-1971 L1972 **IM PLM** *020 †20

ELASY, Tom Anass. 1301 22ND AVE N 37232 #023-01-1991 L1998 **IM** *020 †20

ELBASHIR, Mohammed Hassab. 1005 D B TODD BLVD 37208 #848-07-2002 **IM** *012

ELLIOTT, James H. 1301 21ST AVE S 37232 #039-01-1952 L1966 **OPH** *071 †35

ELLIS, Christopher R. APARTMENT #10, 1700 18TH AVENUE SOUTH 37232 #035-45-2000 L2001 **CD** *012

ELLIS, Darrel Lynn. 1301 22ND AVE S, 3900 THE VANDERBILT CLINIC 37232 #019-02-1976 L1984 **D IM** *020 †20,15

ELLIS, James W. ■ 37215 #047-05-1943 L1944 **OBG** *071 †30

ELLIS, Sharon Calef. ■ 37220 #011-03-1978 L1980 **NM DR** *072

ELLIS, Shelley E. 1301 22ND AVE N 37232 #048-12-1996 L1998 **IM** *020 †20

ELLIS, Truitt Clayton. 110 29TH AVE N, STE 301 37203 #047-05-2000 L2008 **AN** *020 †05

ELLISTON, Lewis Danl, Jr. ■ 37211 #048-04-1969 L1971 **PUD IM** *030 †20

ELROD, Burton Folk. 2021 CHURCH ST, STE 200 37203 #047-06-1975 L1976 **ORS** *020 †40

ELROD, James Patrick. 4220 HARDING PIKE 37205 #019-02-1978 L1990 **PTH** *020 †50

EL-SOURADY, Maie Hamdy. ■ 37209 #036-01-2006 **MPD** *012

ELUHU, Marcel Yemba. 317 18TH AVE N STE 101 37203 #654-01-1981 L1986 **CD** *020 †20

ELY, Eugene Wesley, Jr. 1301 22ND AVE N 37232 #021-01-1989 L1998 **PUD** *020 †20

ELY, Kim. 1301 22ND AVE N 37232 #021-01-1989 L1998 **PTH** *020 †50
EMBRY, Steven Allen. 4220 HARDING RD, DEPT OF INTERNAL MEDICINE 37205 #038-41-1984 L1997 **IM** *020 †20
EMERSON, Chas Whitley, Jr. 394 HARDING PL, STE 200 37211 #047-06-1959 L1960 **HS ORS** *020 †40
EMERSON, Edwin Boyette. 2410 PATTERSON ST STE 210 37203 #047-06-1981 L1982 **OTO** *020 †45
EMFINGER, C Wesley. 7640 HIGHWAY 70 S STE 110 37221 #027-01-1983 L1986 **FM** *020 †18
ENGEL, Christie Lee. 4230 HARDING RD, STE 603 37205 #011-03-1998 L2002 **OBG** *020 †30
ENGEL, Jeannine Zoe. MEDICAL CENTER, EAST, VUMC - 7TH FLOOR 37232 #005-18-1992 L1995 **IM** *020 †20
ENGEL, Michael Eugene. 2200 CHILDRENS WAY, MEDICAL STAFF OFFICE, VCH 37232 #047-05-2001 L2006 **PD** *020
ENGELHARDT, Barbara. VANDERBILT CHILDRENS HOSP, 11111 DR'S OFFICE TOWER NE 37232 #409-10-1978 L1985 **NPM PD** *020 †55
ENGELHARDT, Brian George. 2220 PIERCE AVE, VANDERBILT UNIVERSITY MEDI 37232 #038-06-2000 L2006 **HO** *100 †20 ‡
ENGLISH, Christopher Scot. ■ 37211 #047-07-2007 **IM** *012
ENKER, Mark Harold. ■ 37212 #035-08-2004 **AN** *012
ENTMAN, Stephen Saul. DEPT OF OB/GYN RM B-1100, VANDERBILT UNIVERSITY MEDI 37232 #036-07-1968 L1980 **GYN GP** *071 †30
EPPS, William Miguel. ■ 37217 #036-08-2002 L2007 **PS** *012
ERYASA, Yilmaz. 714 SUMMERLY DR 37209 #902-01-1952 L1971 **AN** *071 †05
ESCOBAR, Alfonso. 110 29TH AVE N, STE 301 37203 #264-05-1966 L1974 **AN** *020
ESEME, Wilson Lobe. 1005 DR DB TODD JR BLVD 37208 #217-01-2001 **GPM** *012
ESIN, Esiri. 1005 DR DB TODD JR BLVD, OF PSYCH 37208 #690-01-1984 **P** *012
ESKIND, Jeffrey Bein. 4230 HARDING PIKE, STE 400 37205 #021-01-1980 L1980 **GE IM** *020 †20
ESKIND, Steven Jos. 4230 HARDING RD, STE 603 37205 #021-01-1977 L1977 **VS GS** *020 †85
ESPINEL, Leonardo Ramon. 397 WALLACE RD, STE 302 37211 #021-01-1991 L2001 **GS VS** *020 †85
ESS, Jennifer K. ■ 37204 #007-02-1999 L2005 **PD** *020 †55
ESS, Kevin Christopher. 1301 22ND AVE N 37232 #038-41-1998 L2006 **CHN** *020 †75
ESTES, Robert Lewis. 1211 21ST AVE S, 104 MEDICAL ARTS BLDG. 37212 #005-14-1976 L1977 **PO** *020 †35 ‡
ESTOPINAL, Marcel Rene. 397 WALLACE RD STE 310, NASHVILLE EYE ASSOCIATES 37211 #021-05-1986 L1992 **OPH** *020 †35
ESTRADA, Cristina M. 1301 22ND AVE N 37232 #011-03-2001 L2004 **PE** *100 †55
ESURUOSO, Olumuyiwa Abola. ■ 37208 #690-05-1997 L2007 **IM** *100 †20
ETTIEN, James Thos. 397 WALLACE RD, BLDG C 37211 #012-01-1971 L2006 **GS** *020 †85
EVEN, Jesse Lee. ■ 37209 #048-14-2006 **ORS** *012
EVERS, Elizabeth Ann. 7640 HIGHWAY 70 S, STE 201 37221 #047-20-1989 L1993 **D** *020
EWERS, Ernest Wm. ■ 37205 #047-05-1948 L1948 **IM CD** *071 †20
EWING, Gideon Patelford. ■ 37205 #027-01-2004 L2007 **HO** *012 †20
EXIL, Vernat. 2200 CHILDRENS WAY, RM 2510 37232 #715-01-1985 L2001 **PDC** *020 †55
EXTON, John H. 1161 21ST AVE S MED 37212 #671-01-1958 **OS** *050
EYLER, Peter William Kenn. ■ 37205 #047-05-2006 **DR** *012
EZELL, Gilbert D. 2801 CHARLOTTE AVE 37209 #047-06-1983 L1985 **U GS** *020 †95
FABER, Robert Branch. 2801 CHARLOTTE AVE, UROLOGY ASSOCIATES, P.C. 37209 #047-05-1970 L1970 **U** *020 †95
FAHRENHOLZ, John Michael. 4230 HARDING RD, STE 307 37205 #038-40-1997 L2002 **AI** *020 †20,03
FAHRIG, Stephen Andrew. 4230 HARDING PIKE, HEART GROUP PLLC 37205 #038-40-1987 L1991 **CD ICE** *020 †20
FAIRHURST, Mark Victor. 3443 DICKERSON PIKE, STE 290 37207 #005-14-1988 L2002 **D** *020 †15
FAKHRUDDIN, Abu Saeed. 2400 PATTERSON ST, STE 101 37203 #047-06-1991 L1994 **GE** *020 †20
FALCONE, Michael Thomas. ■ 37211 #011-03-2004 L2005 **OTO** *012
FALK, Randall M. 267 CANA CIR 37205 #047-06-1981 L1983 **AM U** *030 †70
FALLIS, Robert John. 4230 HARDING PIKE, STE 501 37205 #020-12-1979 L2001 **N IG** *020 †75
FANG, John Yiwei. 1310 24TH AVE S 37212 #041-02-1991 L1998 **N** *050 †75
FANT, Andrea Tanyel. ■ 37232 #047-06-2007 **PD** *012
FARMER, Brenna Michelle. 109 FOX TRL 37221 #036-08-2004 L2006 **ETX** *012
FAROOQUE, Rokeya Sultana. 221 STEWARTS FERRY PIKE, HEALTH INSTITUTE 37214 #160-02-1975 L1985 **P** *020 †75
FARRAR, William Taylor. 1633 CHURCH ST 37203 #047-06-1955 L1963 **R** *071 †80
FARRIS, David Barkley. ■ 37202 #036-07-1991 **PTH** *100
FASIG, John Henry. ■ 37209 #018-03-2003 L2008 **PTH** *100
FASSLER, Cheryl Ann. 2000 CHURCH ST 37236 #038-40-1982 L1987 **END IM** *040 †20
FAULK, Jim Bob. 4230 HARDING RD STE 525 37205 #021-05-1998 L2001 **VS GS** *020 †85
FAULK, Wallace Hunter. ■ 37221 #047-05-1954 L1955 **OPH** *071 †35
FAULKNER, Charles Taylor. 1301 22ND AVE N 37232 #051-01-1970 L1974 **DR** *062 †80
FAULKNER, Marquetta L. 935 21ST AVE N, C/O DIALYSIS CLINIC, INC. 37208 #047-07-1981 L1981 **IM NEP** *020 †20
FAZILI, Mohammad F. 1301 22ND AVE N 37232 #704-04-1984 L2003 **PDP** *020 †55
FAZILI, Shazia. 1414 COUNTY HOSPITAL RD 37218 #495-51-1994 L2004 **FPG** *020 †18
FAZIO, Sergio. 383 PRB 2220 PIERCE AVE, VANDERBILT UNIV MED CTR 37232 #561-17-1983 **END** *050
FEILNER, Andrea C. 1310 24TH AVE S, VA HOSP DEPT-ANESTHINLGY 37212 #869-07-1997 L2005 **AN** *020 †05
FEINTUCH, Margot Gina. ■ 37221 #047-20-1993 L2007 **P CHP** *020 †75
FELDMAN, Marina. 1161 21ST AVE S, VANDERBILT UNIV MED CTR 37232 #550-02-2003 **GS** *100
FELDMAN, Richard Warren. 205 29TH AVE N 37203 #047-07-1975 L1976 **FM GS** *020
FELKEL, Thomas O. ■ 37205 #409-16-1996 **IM** *100 †20
FENICHEL, Gerald Mervin. 1301 22ND AVE N 37232 #008-01-1959 L1969 **CHN N** *020 †75
FENLASON, Lindy Christine. ■ 37215 #017-20-2005 L2008 **PD** *012
FENTRISS, Lee A. 222 22ND AVE N STE 100 37203 #047-05-1992 L1993 **IM** *020 †20
FERGUSON, Andrea Birch. 2000 CHURCH ST 37236 #047-07-1985 L1989 **DR** *020 †80
FERGUSON, Harold Austin. 610 GALLATIN AVE 37206 #047-05-1961 L1961 **PM ORS** *071 †40
FERLUGA, Elizabeth Dianne. ■ 37221 #018-03-2007 **IM** *012
FERNANDO, Chitra. ■ 37212 #220-02-2000 L2007 **IMG** *012 †20
FIECHTL, James Francis. 703 OXFORD HOUSE, DEPARTMENT OF EMERGENCY ME 37232 #047-06-2001 L2005 **EM** *100 †16
FIELDS, James Perry. 4301 HILLSBORO RD STE 200 37215 #048-02-1958 L1978 **D DMP** *020 †15,03
FIELDS, John Pershing. 2000 RICHARD JONES RD, STE 270 37215 #047-05-1957 L1957 **PD** *020 †55
FIFE, Karen Delane. ■ 37205 #047-06-2007 **IM** *012
FIGARO, Mary Kathleen. 1301 22ND AVE N 37232 #008-01-1996 L2001 **IMG** *012 †20
FIKE, Candice Denise. 1301 22ND AVE N 37232 #007-02-1979 L2005 **PD NPM** *050 †55
FINCH, William Tyree. 2000 CHURCH ST 37236 #021-01-1965 L1974 **VS TS** *020 †85,90
FINE, Jo David. 1900 PATTERSON ST, STE 100 37203 #020-12-1976 L2004 **D IG** *050 †20,15
FINKE, Frederick Leroy. 2021 CHURCH ST, STE 704 37203 #038-40-1970 L1974 **OBG GP** *020 †30
FINLAYSON, Alistair James. 1601 23RD AVE S, VANDERBILT PSYCH HOSPITAL 37212 #065-06-1969 L2001 **P ADM** *020
FINNEY, Sabrina Tanis. 1035 14TH AVE N 37208 #047-07-1996 L1999 **FM** *020 †18
FISCHER, Jean Teresa. 1301 22ND AVE N 37232 #048-02-1981 L1985 **AN** *020 †05
FISCHER, Kevin Michael. ■ 37221 #036-01-2006 **IM** *012
FISH, Frank Allan. 1161 21ST AVE S, VANDERBILT PED CARD D2220 37232 #017-20-1983 L1990 **PDC** *020 †55
FISH, Wendy H. 1121 22ND AVE S 37232 #017-20-1981 L1987 **NPM** *020 †55
FISHBEIN, Jonathan Marc. 1161 21ST AVE S DEPT SURG 37212 #023-07-1987 L1989 **GS** *020
FISHER, Alexander Newman. 1211 21ST AVE S, STE 324MAB 37212 #016-42-1999 L2003 **AN CCA** *020 †05
FISHER, Benjamin. 100 HARDINGWOODS PL 37205 #047-05-1957 L1967 **GS OS** *071 †85
FISHER, Cecelia Grace. 4230 HARDING PIKE, STE 400 37205 #047-20-1989 L1991 **IM** *020 †20
FISHER, Jack. 310 23RD AVE N, STE 101 37203 #012-05-1973 L1986 **PS** *020 †85,65
FISKE, William Haley. VANDERBILT UNIV MED CTR, 1030-C MRB-IV 37232 #047-05-2003 **GE** *012 †20
FITCH, Robert Warne. 1211 22ND AVE N, VANDERBILT EMERGENCY MEDIC 37232 #036-05-2001 L2004 **PSM** *020 †16
FITZGERALD, Desmond Jos. ■ 37205 #539-04-1977 L1984 *100
FITZPATRICK, Jeri Eileen. 4535 HARDING PIKE, STE 102 37205 #047-20-1986 L1988 **P CHP** *020 †75
FLANAGAN, John F K. 1215 21ST AVE S 37232 #047-07-1982 L1983 **AN** *020 †05
FLEET, William Floyd, III. 222 22ND AVE N, STE 400 37203 #036-01-1986 L1988 **IM** *020 †20
FLEISCHER, Arthur Carroll. 1301 22ND AVE N 37232 #012-01-1976 L1978 **DR R** *020 †80
FLEMING, Amy Elizabeth. 2200 CHILDRENS WAY, ROO, # 2510 37232 #051-01-1997 L2007 **PD** *020 †55
FLEMING, Geoffrey Michael. 2200 CHILDRENS WAY, 5121 DOCTORS OFFICE TOWER 37232 #051-01-1997 L2007 **PD** *020 †55
FLEMING, Gregory Allan. ■ 37221 #045-04-2003 **PDC** *012 †55
FLEMING, James Howard. ■ 37220 #047-05-1958 L1958 **PS ADM** *071 †85,65
FLEMING, Mary Elizabeth. ■ 37204 #047-05-2006 **OBG** *012
FLEMING, Ross, Jr. 100 WOODLAND ST, JUSTICE CTR 100 WOODLAND ST 37213 #047-07-1962 L1964 **PHP PD** *030
FLESER, Paul Steven. 1161 22ND AVE SOUTH, D-5237 MCN 37232 #025-07-1999 L2007 **VS** *020 †85
FLETCHER, Christopher W. 311 23RD AVE N RM 301, METRO PUBLIC HEALTH DEPT 37203 #035-01-1983 L1987 **IM OM** *020 †20
FLETCHER, Nicholas David. ■ 37204 #047-05-2004 L2007 **ORS** *012
FLISBERG, Anders Henrik. 1161 21ST ST S 37212 #858-01-1987 **NPM** *100
FLORA, Mark Dudley. 2801 CHARLOTTE AVE, UROLOGY SURGERY CENTER 37209 #017-20-1985 L1987 **U** *020 †95
FLOYD, Michael Dwight. 1005 DR DB TODD JR BLVD 37208 #045-01-1976 L1996 **IM** *020 †20
FLYNN, John C. ■ 37205 #047-06-1976 L1976 **EM OM** *071 †16
FOGO, Agnes Borge. 1301 22ND AVE N 37232 #047-05-1981 L1985 **PTH** *050 †50
FOHN, Laurel Elayne. ■ 37212 #048-14-2005 **PTH** *012
FOLEY, David Paul. 1313 21ST AVE S, OXFORD HOUSE, STE 912 37232 #024-05-1994 L2006 **TTS** *020 †85
FONG, Pete Pitaya. 383 PRESTON RESEARCH BLDG, DIV OF CARDIOLOGY 37232 #047-05-1998 L2003 **IC** *020 †20
FORBES, Digna Saunders. 1818 ALBION ST 37208 #035-06-1987 L1997 **PTH** *074 †50
FORBES, Jonathan Andrew. ■ 37208 #041-12-2006 **NS** *012
FORBES, Joseph Davidson. 2931 BERRY HILL DR 37204 #047-06-1990 L1993 **IM** *020 †20
FORBES, Rachel Christine. ■ 37205 #047-05-2005 **GS** *012
FORD, Nina Sheree. ■ 37209 #047-07-2008 *012
FORDICE, James Owens. 4230 HARDING PIKE 37205 #048-04-1991 L1998 **OTO** *020 †45
FORDICE, Sarina Williams. 4220 HARDING PIKE 37205 #048-04-1993 L1999 **NM** *020 †80,28
FORSKIN-BENNERMAN, Monique. 1818 ALBION ST, INTERNAL MEDICINE DEPT. 37208 #047-07-2001 L2004 **IM** *020 †20
FORSYTHE, Loy Allen. 210 25TH AVE N, STE 602 37203 #023-01-1999 L2003 **DR** *020 †80
FORTGANG, Ilana Sharon. VANDERBILT MRB IV, RM, DIVISION OF PEDS GI/PDTRC 37232 #023-07-1996 L1997 **PG** *100
FORTI, Robert Louis. 300 20TH AVE N 37203 #047-05-1985 L1989 **IM** *020 †20
FOSTER, Henry Wendell. 1005 DR DB TODD JR BLVD 37208 #004-01-1958 L1973 **OBG** *072 †30
FOSTER, John Randolph, III. ■ 37204 #045-01-2003 L2007 **AN** *020
FOSTER, Lagina Chelette. ■ 37217 #047-07-2002 L2007 **END** *100 †20
FOSTER, Nelson Ray. 3401 W END AVE, STE 380 37203 #047-06-1968 L1969 **AN OS** *072
FOTTRELL, Anne Austin. 1201 VILLA PL, STE 207 37212 #047-06-1988 L1989 **P CHP** *020 †75
FOURNIER, Karl. 2400 PATTERSON ST STE 300 37203 #067-02-1993 L2000 **ORS** *020
FOWINKLE, Eugene Wesley. D-3300 MCN, VANDERBILT UNIV 37232 #047-06-1958 L1959 **PHP** *071 †70
FOWLER, Michael James. 1301 22ND AVE N 37232 #047-20-1998 L1999 **END** *020 †20
FOX, George Albert. 397 WALLACE RD, STE 309 37211 #021-05-1990 L1994 **OBG** *020 †30
FOX, Randy Mark. 341 WALLACE RD, STE C 37211 #038-40-1983 L1996 **OBG** *020 †30
FOX, Richard Allen. 2010 CHURCH ST, STE 710 37203 #047-05-1973 L1988 **IM** *020 †20
FRANCIS, Irene S Pierre. ■ 37207 #047-07-1942 L1942 **GP** *072
FRANCIS, John J. 1450 ELM HILL PIKE 37210 #047-05-1940 L1940 **P PYA** *071 †75
FRANCIS, Robert Allen. 330 WALLACE RD, STE 200 37211 #018-03-1980 L2003 **DR** *020 †80
FRANCIS, Robert Stanley. 4350 CHICKERING LN 37215 #047-05-1969 L1969 **DR NM** *020 †80
FRANCIS, Rudolph N. 6978 SONYA DR, P O BOX 330967 37209 #019-02-1977 L1987 **AN** *020 †05
FRANGOUL, Hayder Adib. 1301 22ND AVE N 37232 #605-01-1990 L1999 **PHO** *020 †55
FRANKLIN, Dayanand Andrew. ■ 37212 #012-01-2005 L2007 **AN** *012
FRANKLIN, Leslie Huddlest. 2325 CRESTMOOR RD, HERITAGE MED ASSOC 37215 #047-07-2003 L2005 **IM** *020 †20

■ = Address Information Privacy Protected

FRANKS, John Julian. 1215 21ST AVE S 37232 #007-02-1954 L1986 **AN IM** *071 †05
FRANZESE, John N. 20 BURTON HILLS BLVD 37215 #422-01-1988 L1991 **GE** *020 †20
FRASE, Priscilla Anne. ■ 37221 #047-06-2000 L2005 **RHU** *100
FREDERICK, Candice L. VANDERBILT UNIV MED CTR, DIV OF RENAL PATHOLOGY/ELE 37232 #010-02-2001 **SP** *012
FREDERICK, Jonathan Willi. ■ 37220 #047-05-2006 L2007 **GS** *012
FREDERICKS, Charles Edwin. 1 VANTAGE WAY, STE B240 37228 #043-01-1980 L1996 **EM** *020 †16,18
FREDERIKSEN, Rand Terrell. 1301 22ND AVE N 37232 #028-02-1967 L1974 **CD IM** *020 †20
FREDI, Joseph Lawrence. 4230 HARDING RD, STE 530 37205 #047-06-1983 L1987 **CD IM** *040 †20
FREEDENBERG, Debra Lynne. DD2205 MCN, VANDERBILT UNIV MED 37232 #035-06-1982 L2005 **MG CMG** *020 †55,19
FREEMAN, Mark Pearce. 2000 CHURCH ST 37236 #047-06-1982 L1986 **DR OS** *020 †80 ‡
FREEMAN, Rufus Jack. 31 LINDSLEY AVE 37210 #047-05-1961 L1961 **PTH** *071 †50
FREEMON, Frank Reed. ■ 37215 #011-03-1965 L1972 **N** *071 †75
FRENCH, Lesley Christine. 1412 COUNTY HOSPITAL RD, KINDRED HOSPITAL NASHVILLE 37218 #047-05-2005 L2007 **OTO** *012
FREXES-STEED, Maria. 2011 CHURCH ST, STE 703 37203 #047-05-1982 L1985 **GS** *020 †85
FREY, Walter Willis. 4306 HARDING RD, STE 300 37205 #024-01-1960 L1968 **OPH** *020 †35 ‡
FRIDDELL, Colleen Desch. 2601 ELM HILL PIKE, STE M 37214 #047-06-1994 L1998 **P** *020
FRIEDMAN, Daniel Lester. 345 24TH AVE N STE 208 37203 #038-06-1965 L1989 **P** *020 †75
FRIEDMAN, Fred M. ■ 37205 #047-06-1950 L1950 **OM IM** *030
FRIESINGER, Gottlieb C. 1313 21ST AVE S, THE OXFORD HOUSE RM 210 37232 #023-07-1955 L1971 **CD** *020 †20
FRIESINGER, Gottlieb C. 1301 22ND AVE N 37232 #047-06-1984 L1990 **CD IM** *020 †20
FRISSE, Mark Edwin. 3401 W END AVE, STE 290 37203 #028-02-1978 L1980 **IM ON** *050 †20
FRIST, John Chester. 2000 CHURCH ST 37236 #028-02-1966 L1975 **PS** *020 †65
FRIST, Robert Armistead. 2400 PATTERSON ST, JOHN C FRIST JR MD PC 37203 #051-01-1968 L1970 **GS** *020 †85,90
FRIST, Thomas Fearn, Jr. 3100 W END AVE, STE 500 37203 #028-02-1965 L1966 **IM GS** *020
FRIST, William Harrison. 2908 POSTON AVE 37203 #024-01-1978 L1986 **TS GS** *020 †85
FRUIN, Alan Hartman. 1310 24TH AVE S 37212 #047-05-1967 L2000 **NS** *071 †25
FRY, James Alan. 2400 PATTERSON ST, STE 216 37203 #048-15-1985 L1992 **CHN** *020
FUCHS, Dickey Catherine. 1601 23RD AVE S, THE PSY. HOSP. VANDERBIL 37212 #047-05-1982 L1983 **CHP** *040 †75
FUCHS, Howard Adam. DIV OF RHEUMATOLOGY, T-3219 MCN VANDERBILT 37232 #047-05-1981 L1984 **RHU IM** *040 †20
FULLER, Melissa Emily. 2200 CHILDRENS WAY 8161D, CHILDREN'S HOSPITAL 37232 #048-13-2006 **PD** *012
FULLERTON, Randall Curtis. 2021 CHURCH ST STE 504 37203 #039-01-1984 L1986 **IM** *020 †20
FURMAN, Ben Thomas. 300 20TH AVE N, STE 401 37203 #036-01-1993 L2005 **GS** *020 †85
FUTRELL, Danny Wayne. 1818 ALBION ST 37208 #020-12-1983 L1987 **PD** *030 †55
GABBE, Steven Glenn. D-3300 MCN, 1161 21ST AVE S 37232 #035-20-1969 L2001 **OBG MFM** *030 †30
GADDIPATI, Radhika. 1005 DR DB TODD JR BLVD, MEHARRY MEDICAL COLLEGE 37208 #495-50-1987 L2008 **IM** *020 †20
GAFFNEY, Francis Andrew. 610 OXFORD HOUSE, VUMC 37232 #034-01-1972 L1992 **CD** *062 †20
GAFFNEY, Megan Elizabeth. ■ 37220 #010-02-2001 L2004 **IM** *020
GAGNER, Shauna Lynn. ■ 37221 #048-16-2005 **PD** *012
GAILANI, David. 777 PRB / 2220 PIERCE AVE, HEMATOLOGY/ONCOLOGY DIV. / 37232 #016-11-1984 L1995 **HMP HEM** *050 †20
GAINER, James V, III. RESEARCH BUILDING, 560 ROBINSON 37232 #055-01-1990 L1996 **IM** *020 †20
GALLAGHER, Martin Joseph. 1301 22ND AVE N, STE 3930TVC 37232 #028-02-1997 L2002 **N CN** *050 †75
GALLER, Kori Anne. 1215 21ST AVE S 8TH FL, VANDERBILT MC 37232 #021-01-2004 L2008 **OPH** *012
GANDHI, Amy Dinesh. VANDERBILT UNIV MED CTR, 6016 MED CTR EAST 37232 #001-02-2005 L2008 **MPD** *012
GARCIA, Kimberly Anne. ■ 37221 #011-02-2005 L2005 **DR** *012
GARDNER, Carl C, Jr. ■ 37215 #024-01-1941 L1952 **IM CD** *071 †20
GARDNER, Faithlore Patric. ■ 37221 #011-04-2007 **IM** *012
GARDNER, Kim F. ■ 37205 #036-07-2003 **PD** *100 †55
GARMAN, Richard Wm, Jr. 300 20TH AVE N FL 9 37203 #020-02-1980 L1981 **IM** *020 †20
GARNER, Juli Ann. 2400 PATTERSON ST, STE 101 37203 #036-07-1990 L1992 **ID** *020 †20
GARRARD, Clifford Louis. 356 24TH AVE N, STE 400 37203 #047-05-1990 L1993 **GS** *020 †85
GARRETT, Catherine Gaelyn. 1301 22ND AVE N 37232 #036-01-1988 L1994 **OTO** *020 †45
GARRISS, George Waldon, III. APCC, SUITE II 37232 #036-01-1993 L1996 **MPD** *020 †20,55
GARSIDE, William B, Jr. 3443 DICKERSON PIKE, STE 480 37207 #036-01-1990 L1995 **ORS** *020 †40
GARSIDE, William Blake. 301 21ST AVE N, TENNESSEE ORTHOPAEDIC ALLI 37203 #028-34-1964 L1973 **PS** *020 †85,65
GARTY, Itzhak. 1161 21ST AVE S 37212 #550-01-1973 **NM** *100
GASKIN, Angela Jean. 5552 FRANKLIN PIKE, STE 100 37220 #047-07-1982 L1991 **FM** *020 †18
GASKIN, Hubert S, III. 1035 14TH AVE N 37208 #047-07-1977 L1979 **IM EM** *020
GAUME, James Alan. 4230 HARDING PIKE, ENDOCRINOLOGY DIABETES 37205 #005-06-1976 L1990 **IM END** *020 †20
GAVIGAN, William Mitchel. 301 21ST AVE N 37203 #028-34-1970 L1977 **ORS** *020 †40
GAW, David Wisdom. 391 WALLACE RD 37211 #047-06-1964 L1964 **ORS** *071 †40
GAW, Julia Ann. 650 WEDGEWOOD AVE 37203 #047-05-1995 L1997 **P** *020
GAW, William Richard. ■ 37220 #047-06-1964 L1964 **EM FM** *075 †16,18
GAY, James Chalmers. 2200 CHILDRENS WAY, RM 2510 37232 #012-05-1978 L1980 **PHO PD** *040 †55
GEDDIE, Daniel Clark. 222 22ND AVE N, STE 100 37203 #047-05-1963 L1965 **DR NM** *071 †80
GEER, Richard John. 4230 HARDING PIKE, STE 603 37205 #001-02-1983 L1986 **SO GS** *020 †85
GEEVARGHESE, Liby John. 1310 24TH AVENUE SOUTH, TENNESSEE VALLEY HEALTHCAR 37232 #495-37-1996 L2007 **P** *100
GEEVARGHESE, Sunil Koshy. 1301 22ND AVE N 37232 #047-05-1994 L1997 **GS** *020 †85
GEISBERG, Carrie Anna. 2027 STOKES LN 37215 #045-01-2003 L2006 **CD** *012 †20
GEKAS, James Constantine. 2400 PATTERSON ST, STE 218 37203 #020-12-1970 L1975 **IM** *020 †20
GELLIN, Bruce Gary. VANDERBILT U SCH OF MED, A1124MCN PREVENTIVE MED 37232 #035-20-1983 L1989 **PHP ID** *030 †20
GENTILE, Joseph Michael. ■ 37212 #047-05-2008 *012
GENTUSO, Paul Jos. 222 22ND AVE N, STE 100 37203 #024-16-1984 L1985 **IM PD** *020 †20,55
GEORGE, Alfred Lewis, Jr. 1301 22ND AVE N 37232 #035-45-1982 L1985 **NEP IM** *020 †20
GEORGE, Diane Carol. 2201 MURPHY AVE, STE 110 37203 #048-13-1986 L1994 **OBG CLP** *020 †30
GERALD, Sekeyta Lashonda. ■ 37209 #047-07-2008 *012
GERBER, John Ellsworth. 850 RS GASS BLVD, FORENSIC MEDICAL 37216 #024-07-1974 L1997 **PTH** *020 †50
GEWIN, Leslie Stuart. ■ 37215 #001-02-2002 **NEP** *012 †20
GHAVAMI, Parham K. 1005 DR DB TODD JR BLVD, FAMILY MEDICINE DEPT 37208 #422-01-1998 L2002 **FM** *100 †55
GHIASSI, Mayshan. ■ 37211 #047-05-2007 **GS** *012
GIBBONS, Michael David. ■ 37209 #020-12-2007 **IM** *012
GIBSON, John Ragan. 300 20TH AVE N 37203 #028-02-1979 L1982 **IM** *020 †20
GIGANTE, Joseph. 2200 CHILDRENS WAY, RM 2510 37232 #035-48-1988 L1992 **PD** *020 †55
GIGLIA, Jennifer Lynne. ■ 37221 #011-04-2002 L2006 **HO** *012 †20
GILADI, Aviram Moshe. ■ 37212 #047-05-2008 *012
GILBERT, Abigail Lewis. ■ 37212 #047-05-2008 *012
GILBERT, Jill. ■ 37215 #001-02-1994 L2006 **ON** *020 †20
GILL, Charles Mc Clelland. 222 22ND AVE N, STE 504 37203 #047-06-1955 L1960 **GYN** *071
GILL, Gabrielle Marie. ■ 37203 #047-07-1986 L1993 **DR IM** *020
GILL, Riaz Q. 397 WALLACE RD, STE 103 37211 #704-02-1988 L1995 **GE** *020 †20
GILL, Yogeshwar Singh. 1005 DR DB TODD JR BLVD, DEPT OF INTERNAL MEDICINE 37208 #496-31-2001 **FP** *012
GILLES, Michael. CTR N, D-3100 VANDERBILT MED 37232 #031-01-2005 L2007 **IM** *012
GILLIG, Taressa Anne. 1215 21ST AVE S, DEPT OPH 37232 #030-06-2003 L2007 **OPH** *100
GILLIS, Lynette Ann. 1301 22ND AVE N 37232 #041-14-1996 L2004 **PG CBG** *020 †55
GILMER, Ronald Keith. 310 25TH AVE N, STE 204 37203 #047-06-1973 L1975 **PS** *020 †85,65
GILTNANE, Jennifer Margar. ■ 37209 #008-01-2008 *012
GIMPLE, Stephen Kyle. 493 WHISPERING HILLS DR 37211 #047-05-2003 L2005 **CD** *012 †20
GINGRASS, Mary Katherine. 1915 STATE ST 37203 #056-06-1989 L1993 **PS GS** *020 †65
GINN, H Earl. 28 WHITE BRIDGE RD, STE 300 37205 #012-05-1957 L1966 **NEP IM** *071
GIRARD, Timothy Daniel. MEDICAL CENTER, VANDERBILT UNIV 37232 #048-12-2000 L2003 **PCC** *100 †20 ‡
GIULLIAN, Jeffrey Allen. S-3223 MCN, 1161 21ST AVE 37232 #047-05-2001 L2006 **NEP** *012
GIVENS, Dingess Monroe. 100 CNA DR 37214 #036-07-1957 L1989 **OS** *030
GIVENS, Timothy Gerard. 1301 22ND AVE N 37232 #047-05-1987 L2001 **PD PEM** *020 †55
GLANTON, Shannon Nichele. ■ 37209 #047-07-2008 *012
GLASCOCK, Frank B. 2018 MURPHY AVE, STE 200 37203 #047-06-1967 L1975 **R DR** *020 †80
GLASSFORD, David M, Jr. 4230 HARDING PIKE, STE 450 37205 #048-02-1970 L1977 **TS** *020 †85,90
GLATTES, Rudolph C. 2021 CHURCH ST, CENTER, PLC SUITE 200 37203 #019-02-1997 L2001 **OSS** *020 †40
GLAZER, Mark Dennis. 1301 22ND AVE N 37232 #020-02-1979 L1986 **TS IM** *020 †20
GLENN, Ronald Edward, Jr. 4230 HARDING RD, STE 1000 37205 #047-05-1999 L2005 **OSM** *020 †40
GLUCK, Francis Wilcox. 2000 CHURCH ST, BAPTIST DEPT OF MEDICINE 37236 #023-07-1965 L1971 **IM** *040 †20 ‡
GOBBEL, Walter G, Jr. ■ 37205 #036-07-1944 L1967 **GS** *071 †85,90
GODFREY, James Clement. 2002 RICHARD JONES RD, STE A102 37215 #047-06-2001 L2004 **PD** *020 †55
GODWIN, Kristalynne Tina. ■ 37221 #035-45-2006 L2008 **AN** *012
GOERTZ, Steven Richard. VANDERBILT CLINIC, B-902 THE 37232 #051-04-1985 L2001 **RO** *020 †80 ‡
GOINS, William Post, II. ■ 37211 #021-05-2002 L2007 **ID** *012 †20
GOKHALE, Hemalatha Sanjiv. 4220 HARDING PIKE 37205 #035-19-1991 L2001 **VIR** *020 †80
GOLD, Michael Howard. 2000 RICHARD JONES RD #220 37215 #016-42-1985 L1989 **D DS** *020 †15
GOLDENRING, James Richard. ■ 37211 #008-01-1986 L1988 **GS** *020
GOLDNER, Fred, Jr. ■ 37205 #047-05-1948 L1948 **NEP IMG** *030 †20
GOLPER, Thomas Alan. S3303 MCN, VANDERBILT 1116 21ST AVE S 37232 #017-20-1973 L2000 **NEP** *020 †20
GOMEZ, Albert Jos. 393 WALLACE RD, BLDG A 37211 #649-14-1980 L1990 *020
GOMEZ, Pablo Fernando. ■ 37204 #264-16-1994 L2004 *020
GOMEZ, Paul Chas. ■ 37204 #917-21-1963 L1974 **PD** *071 †55
GONZALEZ, Adriana Leonor. 1301 22ND AVE N 37232 #021-06-1994 L1999 **PTH** *020 †50
GONZALEZ-BERNAL, Alberto. 3443 DICKERSON PIKE 37207 #649-38-1991 L2002 **PCC MPD** *020 †20
GOODMAN, Stacey Ann. 1301 22ND AVE N 37232 #035-19-1987 L1993 **HEM** *020 †20
GOODMAN, William M. 3443 DICKERSON PIKE # 240 37207 #047-06-1982 L1983 **OPH** *020 †35
GOODWIN, Maje Denise. 3443 DICKERSON PIKE, STE 370 37207 #047-07-2003 L2006 **PD** *020 †55
GOOLSBY, Mary Elizabeth. ■ 37221 #056-06-1997 L2003 **FOP** *020
GORDEN, David Lee. 1301 22ND AVE N 37232 #047-05-1990 L2001 **GS** *020 †85
GOREE, Robert Edward. ■ 37214 #047-07-2008 *012
GORING, Joann Stacey. 2601 VANDERBILT CLINIC, GME OFFICE 37232 #047-05-2003 L2005 **CD** *012 †20
GOTTERER, Gerald Saul. 320 LIGHT HALL, VANDERBILT SCH MED 37232 #016-02-1958 L1973 **OS** *040
GOUDY, Steven Lawrence. 1301 22ND AVE N 37232 #020-02-1998 L2005 **OTO** *020 †45
GOVINDASWAMY, Geetha. 397 WALLACE RD, STE 216 37211 #496-33-1997 L2002 **IM** *020 †20
GOWDA, H R Mallappa. 5600 OBRIEN AVE 37209 #495-35-1959 L1971 **GS OS** *071 †85
GRABER, Alan Lee. 1301 MEDICAL CENTER DR 37232 #028-02-1961 L1968 **DIA END** *020 †20
GRABER, Stanley Edwin. 3319 W END AVE STE 940 37203 #047-05-1964 L1964 **HEM IM** *030 †20
GRADY, William Mallory. C2104 MCN, 1161 21ST AVE SOUTH 37232 #025-01-1990 L1999 **GE** *050 †20
GRAHAM, Doyle Gene. C-3322 MCN, DEPARTMENT OF PATHOLOGY 37232 #036-07-1966 L1995 **PTH NP** *030 †50
GRAHAM, Emily Denise. 1161 21ST AVE S 37232 #047-06-2000 L2003 **CD** *100 †20
GRAHAM, Kendall Scott. 2000 CHURCH ST BOX 110, SERVICES 37236 #047-20-1997 L2002 **NPM** *020 †55
GRAHAM, Robert Parker, Jr. 300 20TH AVE N, STE 500 37203 #047-06-1981 L1981 **IM OS** *020 †20
GRAHAM, Steven Donald. 2410 PATTERSON ST 37203 #001-02-1987 L1988 **N** *020 †75

GRAHAM, Thomas Pegram, Jr. 1301 22ND AVE N 37232 #036-07-1963 L1971 PDC OS *071 †55

GRAN, Kimberly Allison. 2200 CHILDRENS WAY 8161D, CHILDREN'S HOSPITAL 37232 #012-01-2005 PD *012

GRANDA, Antonio Medardo. 4230 HARDING RD, ST THOMAS MEDICAL BLDG 37205 #041-02-1974 L1976 IM GE *020 †20

GRANT, Burton Paine. 4220 HARDING RD 37205 #047-06-1954 L1955 RO R *071 †80

GRANT, Neville. ■ 37212 #035-01-1954 L1957 IM END *071 †20

GRANT, Pearline Barbara. 1005 DR DB TODD JR BLVD, DEPT OF FAM & COMM MED 37208 #436-02-2004 FP *012

GRAU, Ana Magdalena. 1301 22ND AVE N 37232 #231-03-1990 L2001 GS *020 †85

GRAVES, Cornelia Rose. VANDERBILT UNIV, B-1100 MEDICAL CTR NORTH 37232 #004-01-1987 L1991 OBG MFM *020 †30

GRAVES, Herschel A, Jr. ■ 37205 #047-05-1948 L1948 GS *071 †85

GRAY, George Fleming, Jr. 1211 22ND AVE N 37232 #048-04-1961 L1981 ATP CLP *071 †50

GRAYSON, Britney Lynne. ■ 37212 #047-05-2008 *012

GRECO, Joseph Angelo, III. 1161 21ST AVE S, D-4314 MEDICAL CENTER NORT 37232 #012-01-2002 L2005 GS *012

GREELISH, James Patrick. 1215 21ST AVE S, MCE - 5TH FLOOR - STE 5209 37232 #036-05-1992 L2002 GS *020 †80

GREEN, James D. 1161 21ST AVE S, VANDERBILT MEDICAL CENTER 37232 #016-11-1977 L1982 DR *020 †80

GREEN, Jennifer Kiser. 4500 POST RD, E-50 37205 #036-01-2003 L2006 MPD *100 †55

GREEN, Neil Edward. 2200 CHILDRENS WAY # 4202 37232 #035-03-1968 L1976 ORS *020 †40

GREEN, Paul A, Jr. ■ 37205 #047-05-1953 L1953 OBG *071

GREEN, Synthia Elizabeth. ■ 37211 #005-12-1985 *074

GREENBAUM, Brad Andrew. 316 22ND AVE N 37203 #047-06-1995 L1998 PD *020 †55

GREENBAUM, Ralph Martin. 316 22ND AVE N 37203 #047-06-1962 L1962 PD *020 †55

GREENE, John Wayne. 1301 22ND AVE N 37232 #012-01-1970 L1977 ADL GYN *030 †55

GREENING, Allison Moss. ■ 37209 #034-01-2008 *012

GREER, John Pettry. 1301 MEDICAL CENTER DR, STE 2665 37232 #047-05-1976 L1981 HEM PHO *020 †20,55

GREGG, William Michael. 1301 22ND AVE N 37232 #011-02-1997 L2000 IM *020 †20

GREGORY, Andrew John M. STE 3200, MEDICAL CENTER EAST, SOUTH 37232 #001-02-1997 L2001 PD PSM *020 †55

GREGORY, David Wilson. 1301 22ND AVE N 37232 #047-05-1967 L1971 IM ID *071 †20

GREGORY, James P, II. 37205 #020-12-1966 L1969 IM *071

GREGORY, Marvin Geer, Jr. 20 BOSLEY OAKS 37205 #047-05-1966 L1971 GYN *020 †30

GREMILLION, Daniel E, Jr. 133 BRIGHTON CLOSE 37205 #021-05-1971 L1979 GE IM *071 †20

GRIFFIN, Donald Williams. 250 25TH AVE N, STE 316 37203 #047-05-1988 L1991 PS *020 †85,65

GRIFFIN, John Jos. 250 25TH AVE N, STE 315 37203 #028-34-1969 L1976 P *020 †75

GRIFFIN, Marie R. 1301 22ND AVE N 37232 #010-02-1976 L1986 IMG *050 †20,70

GRIFFITH, Andrew Lamonte. ■ 37214 #047-07-2004 L2008 FP *012

GRIFFITH, Mack Wilson. 110 29TH AVE N, STE 201 37203 #047-06-1995 L1999 AN *020 †05

GRIFFITH, Michelle Leslie. ■ 37209 #047-05-2005 L2008 IM *012

GRIFFITH, Patrick A M. 1005 DR DB TODD JR BLVD, DEPT OF NEURO FL 5 37208 #010-03-1971 L2005 N CHN *020 †75

GRIMES, Ephraim Thomas. ■ 37209 #047-07-2008 *012

GRINDE, Stephen Ernest. 3443 DICKERSON PIKE, STE 200 37207 #034-01-1976 L1983 OPH *020 †35

GRINDSTAFF, Ryan Jerrod. ■ 37221 #028-03-2004 L2007 AN *012

GRINER, Winston Henry. 316 CHARLOTTE AVE 37207 #047-07-1978 L1979 FM PM *020 †18

GRIPPO, Daniel Aaron. - RADI, VANDERBILT UNIV MED CTR 37232 #047-05-2003 L2004 DR *012

GRIPPO, Ryan Joseph. 1161 21ST AVE S, - RADI 37232 #047-05-2006 L2006 DR *012

GROGAARD, Jens Bernhard. 1161 21ST AVE S DEPT PED 37212 #858-02-1967 L1983 NPM *040

GROGAN, Eric Lee. 2971 THE VANDERBILT CLINIC, 1301 MEDICAL CENTER DRIVE 37232 #047-05-1999 L2002 TS *012 †85

GROOMES, Thomas Edward. 1215 22ND AVE S 37232 #047-06-1987 L1993 PM *020 †60

GROOS, Erich Bryan. 2000 CHURCH ST 37236 #047-05-1964 L1964 OBG *020

GROOS, Erich Bryan, Jr. 2400 PATTERSON ST, STE 201 37203 #047-05-1987 L1992 OPH *020 †35

GROVE, Robert Barry. 2300 PATTERSON ST 37203 #045-01-1968 L1977 NM OS *020 †20,28

GROWDON, James Harold, Jr. 2011 MURPHY AVE, STE 200 37203 #047-05-1969 L1969 OBG *020 †30

GRUBB, Peter Hayes. 1301 22ND AVE N 37232 #023-12-1992 L2005 NPM PD *020 †55

GRUBER, William Carl. T-3320 MCN SEC INFEC DIS, VANDERBILT UNIV-PEDIATRIC 37232 #048-04-1979 L1986 ID PD *050 †55

GRZESZCZAK, Ewa F. 1211 22ND AVE N, VANDERBILT UNIVERSITY MED 37232 #759-10-1984 L1999 DR *020 †80

GRZESZCZAK, Marek Janusz. 1301 22ND AVE N 37232 #759-10-1984 L1999 PD CCP *020 †55

GUENST, John Martin. 4230 HARDING PIKE, STE 400 37205 #047-05-1989 L1992 AN IM *020 †20

GUERRAH, Abdelmadjid. 1005 DR DB TODD JR BLVD 37208 #125-03-1988 L2007 GPM *100

GUILLAMONDEGUI, Oscar D. 1301 22ND AVE N 37232 #048-02-1993 L2003 CCS *020 †85

GULBENK, Celia Mariam. ■ 37215 #047-05-1983 L1985 PD *030 †55

GUNN, Daniel C. ■ 37203 #048-14-2005 AN *012

GUNN, Michael Conrad. 300 20TH AVE N, STE 607 37203 #047-07-1979 L1980 OBG *020

GUNN, Veronica S. 1301 22ND AVE N 37232 #047-05-1997 L2002 PD *071 †55

GUPTA, Rahul. 1005 D B TODD BLVD, MEHARRY MEDICAL COLL 37208 #496-09-1994 L2006 IM GPM *020

GUPTA, Rajnish Kumar. 3108 MCE, 1215 21ST AVE SOUTH 37232 #047-05-2002 L2005 AN *100 †05

GURLEY, Larry Dean. 300 20TH AVE N, STE 102 37203 #047-06-1977 L1979 GYN *020 †30

GURSES, Burak Kamil. ■ 37204 #902-19-1992 L2002 PCC *020 †20

GUTHRIE, Scott Osborn. 1301 22ND AVE N 37232 #047-20-1999 L2002 PD *020 †55

GUTOW, Gary Saml. 2011 MURPHY AVE, STE 603 37203 #025-01-1967 L1975 OPH *020 †35

GUY, Jeffrey Scott. 1211 21ST AVE S, 404 MEDICAL ARTS BUILDING 37212 #038-44-1991 L1999 CCS *020 †85

GUYER, Dana Levy. ■ 37206 #047-05-2008 *012

GUZMAN, Raul J, III. 1301 22ND AVE N 37232 #023-07-1986 L1997 VS *020 †85

GWIRTSMAN, Harry Edward. 1301 22ND AVE N 37232 #035-01-1976 L1995 P PYG *040 †75

HAAS, David Wm. 345 24TH AVE N STE 10 37203 #047-05-1983 L1985 ID *020 †20

HAAS, Kevin Frederick. 465 21ST AVE S, 6140 MEDICAL RESEARCH BLDG 37232 #025-01-1999 L2004 N *020 †75

HAASE, David Henry. 1301 22ND AVE N 37232 #047-05-1996 L2002 FM GPM *020 †18 ‡

HABERMANN, Ralf C. CENTER, EAST, 7TH FLOOR - MED. 37232 #409-33-1989 L1996 IMG *020

HABIBIAN, Mohammad Reza. VET ADMIN HOSP 37212 #517-01-1960 L1985 NM *020 †28

HADI, Sattar A. 514 MEDICAL ARTS BLDG, 1211 21ST AVENUE SOUTH 37232 #422-01-1996 L2003 IM *020 †20

HAFSTROM, Ola Mikael. VANDERBILT UNIV MED CTR, DEPT-PED 37232 #858-01-1987 PD *100

HAGAMAN, David Danl. 2611 W END AVE, STE 210 37203 #038-40-1987 L1993 IM AI *020 †20,03

HAGAMAN, Martha Himes. 2911 POLO CLUB RD 37221 #038-40-1987 L1993 PUD FM *020 †20

HAGAN, Keith W. 2801 CHARLOTTE AVE 37209 #047-05-1969 L1972 U *020 †95

HAGAN, Kevin Francis. RM 230MCN, DEPT OF PLASTIC SURGERY, 37232 #023-07-1974 L1982 PS *020 †85,65

HAGENAU, Curtis James. 222 22ND AVE N, STE 100 37203 #047-05-1982 L1983 N *020 †75

HAGERMAN, Heather Elise. ■ 37221 #028-34-2003 L2005 AN *100

HAGSTROM, Ruth C Murray. BUREAU HEALTH SERVICES, C1-100 CORDELL HILL BLDG 37247 #047-05-1956 L1956 PHP OM *030 †70

HAIN, Paul Douglas. 1301 22ND AVE N 37232 #047-05-1998 L2000 PD *020 †55

HAIRR, John Wyman. ■ 37221 #012-01-2001 L2006 AN *100

HAITAS, Byron. 2400 PATTERSON ST, STE 400 37203 #836-01-1977 L1988 CD *020 †20

HAKIM, Raymond M. 1500 21ST AVE S, STE 3600A 37212 #067-01-1976 L1987 NEP IM *020 †20

HALASA, Natasha Bassam. 2200 CHILDRENS WAY, RM 2510 37232 #038-43-1998 L2002 PDI *100 †55

HALEY, Connie L. ■ 37215 #047-05-1995 L2001 ID *020 †20

HALL, David Petrie. 4230 HARDING RD, STE 530 37205 #020-02-1977 L1984 CD *020 †20

HALL, Nathan James. 4230 HARDING PIKE, STE 400 37205 #047-06-2003 L2005 IM *020 †20

HALL, Randon Trenere. ■ 37212 #047-05-2008 *012

HALL, Wallace Howard, Jr. 2400 PATTERSON ST 37203 #047-05-1955 L1955 IM *020 †20

HALLAHAN, Dennis Eugene. 1301 22ND AVE N 37232 #016-01-1984 L1998 RO IM *020 †80

HALLIDAY, William Ross. ■ 37205 #010-01-1948 L1984 OS PM *071

HALPERIN, Linda Ruth. 1310 24TH AVE S, # 117 37212 #047-06-1981 L1999 PM *020 †60 ‡

HALPERN, Jennifer Lynne. 1215 21ST AVE S, ORTHOPAEDIC INSTITU 37232 #047-05-1999 L2002 ORS *100

HALTER, Susan Ann. VANDERBILT UNIVERSITY, MEDICAL CENTER N DEPT PTH 37232 #065-05-1973 L1977 ATP *020 †50

HALTIWANGER, Katherine A. 733 BENTON AVE 37204 #045-04-1998 L2008 EM *020 †55,16

HAMBERG, Marcelle Robt. 1916 PATTERSON ST STE 603 37203 #047-07-1957 L1969 U *071 †95

HAMBURGER, Norman Jerry. 397 WALLACE RD, STE 309 37211 #020-02-1980 L1985 OBG *020 †30

HAMDAN, Ashraf Hosni M. 1301 22ND AVE N 37232 #915-03-1984 L2002 NPM *020 †55

HAMEED, Kashif. 509 HOLT VALLEY RD 37221 #704-16-1991 *100

HAMID, Rizwan. 2200 CHILDRENS WAY, RM 2510 37232 #704-21-1985 L2003 PD CG *050 †19,55 ‡

HAMILTON, Eddie Dewayne. 310 25TH AVE N, STE 201 37203 #047-05-1985 L1988 PD *020 †55

HAMILTON, James Richard. 3900 VANDERBILT 37232 #047-05-1946 L1946 D *071 †15

HAMILTON, Katherine S. 4220 HARDING PIKE 37205 #047-05-1996 L2000 PTH *020 †50

HAMILTON, Tanisha Jamarri. ■ 37221 #007-02-2006 IM *012

HAMILTON, William M. ■ 37215 #047-06-1947 L1948 R *071 †80

HAMPF, Carl Richard. 2011 MURPHY AVE, STE 301 37203 #047-05-1982 L1987 NS *020 †25

HAMRANG, Gina Elizabeth. 397 WALLACE RD, STE 309 37211 #035-47-1994 L1999 OBG *020 †30

HAN, Jin Ho. 703 OXFORD HOUSE, VANDERBILT UNIVERSITY 37232 #035-08-1999 L2005 EM *020 †16

HANDE, Kenneth Robt. 1310 24TH AVE S, NASHVILLE VA MEDICAL CENTE 37212 #023-07-1972 L1978 IM *020 †20

HANDFIELD, Kent Stuart. ■ 37203 #047-05-2005 L2006 GS *020

HANES, Thomas Eugene. 3441 DICKERSON PIKE, SKYLINE MEDICAL CENTER, PA 37207 #047-05-1972 L1974 PTH *020 †50 ‡

HANEY, Katherine Clarke. 2201 MURPHY AVE, KATHERINE C HANEY MD 37203 #047-05-1997 L2001 OBG *020

HANLON, Allison Maureen. ■ 37209 #041-13-2005 D *012

HANNAH, Gene Allen. 1301 22ND AVE N 37232 #001-02-1988 L1990 FM *020 †18

HANSEN, Axel Carl. ■ 37218 #047-07-1944 L1946 OPH *071 †35

HANSEN, David Elwood. 1215 21ST AVE S 5TH FL, VANDERBILT HEART INST 37232 #035-20-1980 L1987 IM CD *020 †20

HANSEN, Erik Nels. ■ 37220 #048-04-2001 L2004 GS *012

HANSON, Alison Jean. ■ 37212 #047-05-2008 *012

HANSON, Katherine Louise. ST THOMAS MEDICAL PLAZA 37205 #047-05-1990 L1994 IM *020 †20

HAO, Jingming. 1005 D.B. TODD BLVD, DEPT OF PEDIATRICS 37208 #243-46-1982 L1998 PD *020 †55

HARA, Saburo. ■ 37206 #572-35-1953 L1965 PD FM *071 †55

HARAF, Frank Joseph, Jr. 2000 RICHARD JONES RD, STE 270 37215 #047-20-1997 L1999 PD *020 †55

HARB, William Joseph. 2011 CHURCH ST, STE 703 37203 #047-06-1999 L2006 CRS *020 †85,10

HARBISON, Elizabeth H. ■ 37215 #056-06-1999 L2005 EM *012

HARDIN, Bradley Allen. 7TH FLOOR MEDICAL CENTER E 37232 #017-20-2003 L2006 CD *012 †20

HARDIN, John Matthew. 703 OXFORD HOUSE, 1313 21ST AVE S 37232 #023-12-1998 L2001 D *012 †16

HARDIN, Robert Allen. 2000 CHURCH ST, CHIEF MEDICAL OFFICER 37236 #047-05-1956 L1956 TS VS *030 †85,90

HARGREAVES, Ray Martin. 4230 HARDING PIKE, STE 302 37205 #047-05-1985 L1990 GS *020 †85

HARLAN, Charles Warren. 620 DAVIDSON ST STE B 37213 #047-06-1972 L1972 FOP PTH *020

HARLEY, Erin Kristine. 2201 MURPHY AVE, STE 110 37203 #041-14-1999 L2003 OBG *020 †30

HARNISCH, Helmut Kurt. 5548 FRANKLIN PIKE, STE 203 37220 #049-14-1976 L1983 FM *020

HARPER, Marion Caldwell. ■ 37205 #012-01-1967 L1985 ORS *020 †40

HARRELL, Henry Lytle, III. 222 22ND AVE N, STE 100 37203 #047-05-1994 L1997 IM *020 †20

HARRIS, Barney A. PO BOX 629, MEHARRY MED COL 37208 #047-07-1980 P *100

HARRIS, Gamal. 2010 CHURCH ST, STE 314 37203 #915-02-1981 L1993 **IM** *020 †20
HARRIS, Heather Lynn. 1301 22ND AVE N 37232 #005-12-1999 L2001 **CHP** *020 †75
HARRIS, Jackson. ■ 37215 #008-01-1949 L1957 **TS** *071 †85,90
HARRIS, Leonard Jefferson. VANDERBILT UNIV MED CTR, 6016 MED CTR EAST 37232 #012-01-2005 L2007 **MPD** *012
HARRIS, Rachel Amanda. ■ 37212 #047-05-2008 *012
HARRIS, Ramon Stanton. ■ 37218 #047-07-1963 L1968 **AN** *071 †05
HARRIS, Raymond C, Jr. 1301 22ND AVE N 37232 #012-05-1978 L1987 **NEP IM** *020 †20
HARRIS, Thomas Raymond. RM-5824A STEVENSON CENTER, VANDERBILT UNIV 37235 #047-05-1974 L1974 **CD** *050
HARRISON, Nikki Patrice. ■ 37209 #021-05-2006 **IM** *012
HARRISON, Steven Marshall. ■ 37215 #012-01-2004 L2006 **AN** *012
HARROM, David Lou. 3443 DICKERSON PIKE, STE 380 37207 #005-12-1973 L1992 **IM** *020 †20
HART, Andrew James. ■ 37209 #017-20-2004 L2006 **IM** *100 †20
HART, James Robt. 310 25TH AVE N STE 309 37203 #047-05-1983 L1984 **P** *020 †75
HARTERT, Tina Vivienne. 1301 22ND AVE N 37232 #047-06-1990 L1995 **PCC EP** *050 †20
HARTMAN, Ryan Lee. ■ 37221 #007-02-2004 L2007 **ORS** *012
HARTMANN, Katherine E. SUITE 6000 MED. CTR. NORTH, VANDERBILT UNIV. MEDICAL C 37232 #023-07-1992 L2007 **OBG** *020 †30
HARTNESS, William Owen. 222 22ND AVE N, STE 100 37203 #027-01-1980 L1986 **CD IM** *020 †20
HARVEY, Sally Catharine. ■ 37215 #027-01-2007 **PD** *012
HARWELL, Wm Beasley, Jr. 1900 PATTERSON ST STE 205 37203 #047-06-1971 L1972 **D** *020 †15
HASLAM, Jason Kent. 2400 PATTERSON ST STE 300, MEDICINE, PLC 37203 #005-12-2000 L2005 **HS** *020
HASSELL, Sarah Emily. 2300 PATTERSON ST, MID TENNESSEE NEONATOLOGY 37203 #045-01-1988 L1992 **NPM** *020 †55
HASTY, Michael Langford. 1 VANTAGE WAY, STE B240 37228 #047-05-2001 L2004 **EM** *020 †16
HASTY, Norman Donald. 1 VANTAGE WAY, STE B240 37228 #047-05-1969 L1969 **IM OS** *071 †16
HATCHER, Stephanie Alison. 2000 CHURCH ST 37236 #047-07-1997 L1998 **IM** *020 †20
HATHAWAY, Jacob Walter. ■ 37206 #047-05-2005 L2007 **IM** *012
HATMAKER, Allison Romayne. ■ 37215 #020-02-2002 L2005 **GS** *012
HATOUM, Chehada. ■ 37215 #875-01-1992 L2007 **IM** *020
HAWIGER, Jacek Jan. ■ 37215 #759-01-1962 L1973 **HEM IM** *050
HAWK, Stephany Michelle. ■ 37205 #004-01-2005 **PD** *012
HAWKINS, Paul Edison. ■ 37221 #012-01-1960 L1964 **GS** *072 †85
HAWKINS, Ralph George. 4230 HARDING RD, STE 400 37205 #068-01-1981 L2000 **NEP** *020 †20
HAWKINS, Rowland Speck. 2010 CHURCH ST STE 608 37203 #047-06-1967 L1967 **OPH** *020 †35
HAWS, Melinda Jo. 1915 STATE ST 37203 #016-45-1991 L1997 **PS** *020 †65
HAYES, Andrea Lynn. 501 28TH AVE N 37209 #001-02-1991 L1994 **END IM** *020 †20
HAYES, Benjamin Bailey. 1301 22ND AVE N, TVC, SUITE 3903 37232 #024-05-2003 L2006 **D** *020 †15
HAYES, Marc Anthony. ■ 37221 #035-06-2006 **AN** *012
HAYNES, David Scott. 1301 22ND AVE N 37232 #047-06-1987 L1993 **OTO** *020 †45
HAYNES, James Brevard. 300 20TH AVE N, STE G8 37203 #047-05-1972 L1973 **PUD** *020 †20
HAYNES, James Hugh. 4230 HARDING PIKE, # 807E 37205 #036-07-1972 L1974 **PUD IM** *071 †20
HAYNES, Mary Jane. 2000 CHURCH ST BOX 110, NEONATOLOGISTS PROF SVC 37236 #055-02-1997 L2000 **NPM** *020 †55 ‡
HAYS, Stephen R. 2200 CHILDRENS WAY # 3115 37232 #023-07-1991 L1999 **PAN CCP** *020 †05,55 ‡
HAZINSKI, Thomas A. VANDERBILT UNIV, DEPT OF PEDIATRICS 37232 #028-34-1975 L1984 **NPM PUD** *050 †15
HEAD, Bronwyn Lillian. 3441 DICKERSON PIKE 37207 #539-06-2000 L2006 **EM** *020
HEAD, David Richmond. 1301 22ND AVE N 37232 #048-02-1968 L1989 **PTH HEM** *020 †50
HEAD, James Ross. 394 HARDING PL, STE 102 37211 #020-02-1971 L1980 **FM** *020 †18
HEAVNER, Steven Brett. ■ 37232 #036-01-2001 L2006 **OTO** *100 †45
HEAVRIN, Benjamin Sloan. 703 OXFORD HOUSE, VANDERBILT UNIV. MED. CENT 37232 #047-05-2004 L2006 **EM** *012
HECKERS, Stephan H W. 1601 23RD AVE S, PSYCHIATRIC HOSPITAL AT VA 37212 #409-22-1988 L2005 **P** *050 †75
HEDERA, Peter. 1301 22ND AVE N 37232 #286-03-1987 L2002 **N MG** *020 †75,19
HEERMAN, William John. ■ 37215 #047-05-2008 *012
HEFFERNAN, Alison R. ■ 37215 #021-05-2003 L2008 **PD** *020 †55
HEFFERNAN, Thomas Edward. ■ 37215 #021-05-2003 L2008 **DR** *012
HEFLIN, Asa Clyde. 4230 HARDING PIKE, STE 400 37205 #047-05-1973 L1978 **PUD IM** *020 †20
HEIL, Paul Jacob. 5819 OLD HARDING RD 37205 #047-05-1988 L1991 **PD** *020 †55
HEILPRIN, Kimberly Bell. ■ 37215 #056-05-1991 L1994 **IM** *020 †20
HEIMBERG, Steven Andrew. ■ 37234 #028-03-1979 L1988 **LM** *020
HEITZ, Julian Christopher. 2000 CHURCH ST 37236 #018-03-1984 L1988 **RO** *020 †80 ‡
HELDERMAN, Joel Harold. S-3305, VANDERBILT UNIVERSITY MED 37232 #035-08-1971 L1989 **IG NEP** *050 †20
HELLER, Richard Moss. 1301 22ND AVE N 37232 #016-06-1963 L1976 **PDR** *020 †80
HELOU, Bassam Nabil. 3443 DICKERSON PIKE, STE 600 37207 #047-05-1998 L2003 **GS** *020 †85
HEMACHANDRA, Loren Alan. ■ 37220 #048-04-2007 **AN** *012
HEMMINGWAY, Andrea Celest. ■ 37215 #047-05-2006 **OBG** *012
HEMPHILL, Robin Renee. 703 OXFORD HOUSE, DEPT OF EMERGENCY MEDICINE 37232 #010-01-1991 L1998 **EM** *012
HENDERSON, James P. 820 GALE LN, SILOAM FAMILY HEALTH CLINI 37204 #048-16-1982 L1986 **PD** *020 †55
HENDERSON, Melinda Shaw. 1718 PATTERSON ST 37203 #012-05-2001 L2004 **IM PLM** *020
HENDERSON, Robert R. 1800 STATE ST 37203 #047-06-1962 L1962 **OPH** *020 †35
HENDERSON, Thomas Wayne. 326 21ST AVE N 37203 #047-06-1972 L1972 **FM** *020 †18
HENDRIX, James P. ■ 37206 #047-06-1943 L1945 **PS** *071 †65
HENNING, Joan Margaret. 1301 22ND AVE N 37232 #047-05-1997 L2001 **EM** *020 †16
HENNINGSEN, Joy A. 210 25TH AVE N, STE 602 37203 #001-02-2002 L2008 **DR** *100 †80
HENRY, Arnold Fauntleroy, Jr. ■ 37207 #056-05-2006 **PD** *012
HENRY, Douglas Chas. 1801 W END AVE, CIGNA PPO-NASHVILLE 37203 #035-01-1972 L1977 **PD** *074 †55
HENSHAW, Nta Ekeng. ■ 37205 #012-01-1993 **IM** *100

HENSKE, Joseph Anthony. 1211 MEDICAL CENTER DR 37232 #048-13-2004 L2007 **END** *012 †20
HENSON, Christopher Patri. 1161 21ST AVE S, VANDERBILT UNIV MED CTR 37232 #039-79-2006, ▲ L2008 **AN** *012
HENSON, Michele Renee. ■ 37221 #036-07-2006 **MPD** *012
HERDA, George. 2553 MURFREESBORO PIKE, ASSOCIATES 37217 #016-11-1982 L1983 **GP** *020
HERHOLDT, Jan Andries. ■ 37209 #836-04-1985 L1996 **AN** *100 †20
HERLINE, Alan Joseph. D5248 MEDICAL CENTER NORTH, VUMC 37232 #012-01-1994 L1997 **CRS** *020 †85,10
HERMAN, Cheryl Roxanna. 1301 22ND AVE N 37232 #047-07-1990 L1997 **NM** *020 †80
HERMANN, Lisa Dawn. ■ 37221 #051-01-2006 **N** *012
HERMO, Casilda Ileana. 1919 CHARLOTTE AVE, STE 230 37203 #308-01-1980 L1995 **PDC** *020 †55
HERNANZ-SCHULMAN, Marta. 2200 CHILDRENS WAY, VANDERBILT CHILD HOSP 37232 #035-19-1977 L1988 **PDR** *020 †55,80
HERRELL, S Duke, III. CENTER NORTH, A 1302 MEDICAL 37232 #051-01-1990 L2001 **U** *020 †95
HERRING, Jeffrey Lance. 301 21ST AVE N, TENNESSEE ORTHOPAEDIC ALLI 37203 #039-01-1986 L1987 **ORS** *020 †40
HERSEY, Shannon Lee. 1717 PATTERSON ST, DEPARTMENT OF ANESTHESIOLO 37203 #023-01-1985 L1992 **AN** *020 †05
HERSH, Carol Beth. 2409 21ST AVE S STE 104 37212 #041-02-1969 L1992 **CHP P** *020 †55,75
HERZFELD, John G. ■ 37215 #561-01-1935 L1958 **BBK PUD** *071
HESHMATI, Nariman. ■ 37205 #011-05-2005 **OBG** *012
HESTER, Ray Willis. 345 23RD AVE N, STE 420 37203 #047-05-1963 L1964 **NS** *071 †25
HEUSINKVELD, David C. 4230 HARDING RD STE 530, WEST END MEDICAL GROUP 37205 #047-05-1991 L1993 **IM** *020 †20
HEWLETT, William Albion. 1601 23RD AVE S, STE 1030 37212 #005-11-1983 L1991 **P CHP** *020
HEYMAN, Stephen Joel. 300 20TH AVE N 37203 #035-45-1984 L1986 **PUD IM** *020 †20
HICAR, Mark Daniel. 2200 CHILDRENS WAY, MEDICAL STAFF OFFICE, RM 2 37232 #038-40-2002 L2005 **PDI** *012
HICKMAN, Anna Marie. 1313 21ST AVE S, 703 OXFORD HOUSE 37232 #047-20-1986 L1989 **EM** *020 †16
HICKS, Cynthia D. ■ 37215 #062-01-1993 **IM** *100 †20,03
HICKS, Kenneth. 1100 KERMIT DR, STE 106 37217 #047-07-1978 L1978 **IM** *020
HICKSON, Gerald Bennett. 1301 22ND AVE N 37232 #021-01-1978 L1982 **PD** *020 †55
HIGGINS, Michael Sean. 1211 22ND AVE N, 2301 VUH 37232 #047-05-1989 L1994 **IM** *020 †05
HIGHTOWER, Daniel Russell. 218 20TH AVE N 37203 #047-05-1964 L1964 **OTO** *020 †45
HILL, Benjamin Hiawatha. 4230 HARDING PIKE, STE 400 37205 #047-07-1995 L1998 **IM** *020 †20
HILL, Christopher C. 2801 CHARLOTTE AVE, UROLOGY ASSOCIATES P.C. 37209 #047-05-1988 L1994 **U** *020 †95
HILL, Danielle. ■ 37209 #047-07-2008 *012
HILL, Eric Michael. D-3100 MEDICAL CENTER NORT 37232 #039-01-2004 L2004 **IM** *020 †20
HILL, George Alan. 345 23RD AVE N, STE 401 37203 #047-06-1980 L1980 **REN OS** *020 †30
HILL, Jahana T. ■ 37208 #047-07-2007 **IM** *012
HILL, Kevin Dennis. ■ 37232 #036-05-2002 L2004 **PDC** *012 †55
HILL, Michael Duane. 2021 CHURCH ST STE 800, THE EVELYN FRYE CTR 37203 #047-06-1989 L1990 **P CHP** *020
HILLS, Edward Rudolph. ■ 37209 #047-07-1966 L1971 **OBG** *020 †30
HILMES, Melissa Anne. 1106 MCN, 1161 21ST AVE SOUTH, CCC 37232 #047-05-2000 L2007 **PDR** *020 †80
HIMES, Daniel Paul. 1301 22ND AVE N 37232 #036-05-1993 L1996 **EM** *020 †16
HIMMELFARB, Eric Andrew. ■ 37212 #047-05-2005 **PTH** *012
HINDS, William Lyle, III. ■ 37205 #001-02-1996 L1997 **CHP** *012
HINES, Bruce Edward. 1 VANTAGE WAY, STE B240 37228 #055-02-1995 L1998 **EM** *020 †16
HINES, Katherine Houston. ■ 37215 #047-20-2003 **AN** *012
HINGLE, Allyson Joy. ■ 37212 #021-06-2005 **OBG** *012
HINTON, Alice Angela. 1301 22ND AVE N 37232 #047-05-1982 L1983 **R NM** *020 †80
HINTON, Timothy John. 1301 22ND AVE N 37232 #023-01-2002 L2004 **IM** *020 †20
HIRSCH, Martin Bruce. 2021 CHURCH ST STE 704 37203 #001-02-1980 L1981 **OBG** *020 †30
HIRSHBERG, Charles Snyder. ■ 37205 #047-06-1957 L1958 **PD** *071 †55
HIWA, Snowden S. ■ 37208 #047-07-1986 *100
HIXSON, Melissa Eaton. 5552 FRANKLIN PIKE STE 100 37220 #047-06-2001 L2004 **IM** *020 †20
HO, Richard Hsinshin. 1301 22ND AVE N 37232 #047-05-1997 L2004 **PHO PA** *050 †55
HOBBS, Ralph S. 1811 STATE ST 37203 #047-07-1977 L1978 **FM EM** *020
HOBDY, Charlie Joe. ■ 37215 #047-05-1955 L1955 **OBG** *071 †12
HOCK, Richard Lloyd. 7TH FLOOR MC EAST, VUMC - ADULT PRIMARY CARE 37232 #047-05-1987 L1995 **IM** *030 †20
HODGE, Roger Alan. 4230 HARDING PIKE, STE 400 37205 #036-01-1984 L1986 **IM OS** *020 †20
HOENE, Kelly Ann. VANDERBILT UNIV MED CTR, DEPT OF PATHOLOGY MCN CC33 37232 #035-01-2006 **PTH** *012
HOFELDT, Timothy Sean. ■ 37203 #035-03-2004 **P** *012
HOFF, Steven Jeffrey. 1215 21ST AVE S, MCE - 5TH FLOOR, SUITE 520 37232 #023-07-1986 L1998 **TS** *020 †85,90
HOFFMAN, Scott. 1301 22ND AVE N 37232 #047-07-1990 L1992 **AN** *020 †05
HOLBERT, Kenneth Leo. 391 WALLACE RD 37211 #005-19-1982 L1991 **EM GS** *020 †16
HOLBROOK, James Trent. 2000 CHURCH ST 37236 #055-02-1987 L1991 **RNR VIR** *020 †80
HOLCOMB, George W, Jr. ■ 37205 #047-05-1946 L1949 **PDS** *071 †85
HOLCOMB, Robert Ray. 1301 22ND AVE N 37232 #047-05-1972 L1989 **CHN EM** *020
HOLLAND, Jessica Lynn. ■ 37209 #056-05-2006 **PD** *012
HOLLAND, Nancy Darden. 1301 22ND AVE N 37232 #051-04-1977 L2002 **DR** *075 †80
HOLLAND, Ralph Duane. 1301 22ND AVE N 37232 #051-04-1975 L2002 **DR NM** *020 †20,28,80
HOLLENBECK, Ryan Donald. ■ 37221 #018-03-2007 **IM** *012
HOLLIDAY, Hugh Douglas. 4230 HARDING PIKE, STE 530 37205 #047-05-1976 L1977 **IM** *020 †20
HOLLIE, Oba Hashim. ■ 37218 #047-07-2006 **IM** *012
HOLLIE, Shawnda Evans. ■ 37218 #047-07-2005 **IM** *012
HOLLINGER, Bruce. 300 20TH AVE N 37203 #027-01-1978 L1983 **IM** *020 †20
HOLLOWAY, Christopher D. 397 WALLACE RD BLDG C, SOUTHERN HILLS 37211 #051-01-1999 L2002 **FM PD** *020 †18
HOLLOWELL, Minal Delwadia. 110 29TH AVE N STE 301, ANESTHESIA MEDICAL GROUP, 37203 #001-02-2003 L2007 **AN** *020
HOLMES, George Landis, III. 397 WALLACE RD, STE 100 37211 #047-06-1972 L1972 **FM** *020 †18

HOLP, Debra Leigh. 3441 DICKERSON PIKE, NASHVILLE MEMORIAL HOSPITA 37207 #047-20-1987 L1988 **EM** *020 †16

HOLROYD, Kenneth James. 701 MEDICAL ARTS BUILDING, DEPARTMENT OF ANESTHESIOLO 37232 #023-07-1984 L2005 **AN PCC** *020 †20,05

HOLSEY, Charles Maceo Jr. ■ 37208 #047-07-1998 *100

HOLT, Ginger Emily. 1301 22ND AVE N 37232 #001-02-1996 L2002 **ORS OMO** *020 †40

HOLZEN, Thomas Werner. 393 WALLACE RD STE 403, SOUTHERN HILLS MEDICAL CEN 37211 #024-07-1970 L1979 **FPS OTO** *020 †45

HOLZMAN, Michael David. 1301 22ND AVE N 37232 #036-05-1988 L1991 **GS AS** *020 †85

HOMLAR, Kelly Elizabeth. ■ 37221 #012-01-2006 **ORS** *012

HON, Emily Louise. ■ 37205 #047-05-2008 *012

HONG, Charles Chansik. 2220 PIERCE AVE, MEDICINE 37232 #008-01-1998 L2006 **IM CD** *050 †20

HONG, Jung Ja. VET ADMIN HOSP, DEPT RAD 37212 #583-08-1966 L1974 **R** *020 †80

HONG, Myung Ho. 1005 DR DB TODD JR BLVD 37208 #583-03-1964 L1977 **FM EM** *020 †18

HONG, Shihkuang Sam. VANDERBILT UNIV MED CTR, 1030-C MRB-IV 37232 #047-05-2003 **GE** *012 †20

HONGO, Igen. ■ 37209 #572-10-1996 **ID** *100

HOOD, Rob Reid. 1215 21ST AVE S, STE 5209 37232 #021-01-1980 L1986 **CD** *020 †20

HOOD, Thomas Ruffin, Jr. 330 WALLACE RD, STE 200 37211 #036-01-1967 L1984 **DR TRS** *020 †85,80

HOOKER, Robert Liles. ■ 37212 #045-01-2004 L2004 **DR** *012

HOOPER, Michael Hee. DEPART. OF MEDICINE;D-3100, VANDERBILT U. MEDICAL CENT 37232 #047-05-2004 L2006 **IM** *020 †20

HOOS, Richard Tipton. 300 20TH AVE N 37203 #047-05-1973 L1978 **N** *020 †75

HOOVER, Elizabeth Brinton. 1321 MURFREESBORO PIKE, STE 800 37217 #001-06-1990 L1991 **P** *020 †75

HOOVER, Robert Donald, Jr. 415 ELLENDALE AVE, HOOVER CONSULTING, LLC 37205 #001-06-1990 L1991 **IM MDM** *030 †20

HOPP, Stanley Gilbert. 301 21ST AVE N 37203 #018-03-1982 L1988 **OSS** *020 †40

HORN, Alan Wade. 2000 CHURCH ST 37236 #048-14-1999 L2003 **MSR** *020 †80

HORN, Erin Roxanne. ■ 37205 #047-05-2008 *012

HORN, Janet. ■ 37203 #010-01-1978 L1979 **IM CLP** *020 †20

HORN, Jeffrey David. 2011 CHURCH ST, STE 801 37203 #035-15-1989 L1997 **OPH** *020 †35 ‡

HORN, Robert Gordon. 1916 PATTERSON ST, STE 501 37203 #047-05-1958 L1958 **PTH NEP** *020 †50

HOROWITZ, David Harvey. 1900 PATTERSON ST STE 205 37203 #047-07-1970 L1974 **D** *020 †15

HORRALL, Shawn Daniel. ■ 37232 #017-20-2006 L2007 **EM** *012

HORTON, Frederick T, Jr. 4535 HARDING RD STE 102 37205 #051-04-1970 L1975 **CHP P** *020 †75 ‡

HORVITZ, Sara Michelle. ■ 37204 #047-05-2008 *012

HOSSAIN, Mohammad A. 617 WHEATFIELD CT 37209 #160-02-1975 L1998 **IM EM** *020 †20

HOUSER, Frank Millard. 2515 PARK PLZ, BLDG 2 4 W 37203 #012-05-1966 L1997 **PHP PD** *030 †55

HOUSER, Joshua Russell. ■ 37209 #038-40-2003 L2006 **DR** *012

HOUSTON, Hugh Leavell, III. 2200 MURPHY AVE 37203 #020-02-1996 L2001 **GS** *020 †85

HOUSTON, Mark Clarence. 4230 HARDING PIKE, STE 400 37205 #047-05-1974 L1977 **IM** *020 †20

HOWARD, Gwendolyn Anita. 1301 22ND AVE N 37232 #041-13-1990 L1998 **IM** *020 †20

HOWARD, Jane Ellen. 1301 22ND AVE N 37232 #011-03-1982 L1991 **N** *020 †75

HOWARD, Leigh Meredith. ■ 37215 #048-12-2006 **PD** *012

HOWELL, Everette Irl, Jr. 2011 MURPHY AVE, STE 301 37203 #047-05-1969 L1969 **NS** *020 †25

HOWELL, Irvin Wendell. ■ 37210 #047-07-1975 **FM** *100

HOWERTON, Henry Clayton. 2000 CHURCH ST 37236 #038-41-1970 L1973 **R IM** *062 †80

HOWERTON, Richard Allen. 2400 PATTERSON ST, STE 201 37203 #012-01-1981 L1992 **CRS GS** *020 †85,10

HOWSON, Sheena Marie. ■ 37209 #048-04-2006 **AN** *012

HOYT, Tamarya Lea. 1161 21ST AVE S, VANDERBILT MED CTR-RADIOLO 37232 #017-20-2002 L2007 **DR** *020 †80

HSUEH, Yerng-Terng. 2623 GALLATIN PIKE 37216 #385-02-1962 L1973 **GS** *020 †85

HU, Joshua Ki. 1215 21ST AVE S 8TH FL, VANDERBILT MC 37232 #011-03-2004 L2007 **OPH** *012

HU, Judy Yungli. 2000 RICHARD JONES RD, GOLD SKIN CARE CENTER STE 37215 #047-20-2001 L2006 **D** *020 †15

HUANG, Lloyd Kumloy. 330 22ND AVE N 37203 #047-06-1985 L1986 **IM** *020 †20

HUANG, Paio-Fu. 5604 LENOX AVE 37209 #244-05-1978 L1986 **PTH EM** *020 †20

HUANG, Robert Long. 114 SLOAN RD, VANDERBILT UNIVERSITY 37209 #038-06-2002 L2004 **CD** *012 †20

HUBBARD, Jason R. 2011 MURPHY AVE, STE 301 37203 #047-06-1996 L2002 **NS** *020 †25

HUDGINS, Larry Burton. ■ 37205 #047-06-1971 L1971 **NEP IMG** *020 †20 ‡

HUDSON, Julie Kay. 1301 22ND AVE N 37232 #019-02-1990 L2002 **AN** *020 †05

HUENEKE, Michael Lothar. 328 22ND AVE N 37203 #017-20-1992 L1998 **PS** *020 †20

HUFF-IGNATIN, Kasey A. 3443 DICKERSON PIKE 37207 #305-01-1997 L2001 **PD** *020

HUFFMAN, Russell A, Jr. ■ 37215 #026-04-1965 L2001 **P** *020 †75

HUGHES, Alexander Kendall. 1211 22ND AVE N STE 3255, DEPT OF ANESTHESIOLOGY 37232 #050-02-1997 L2002 **AN** *020 †05

HUGHES, Mark David. 310 25TH AVE N, STE 201 37203 #047-06-2001 L2006 **AN** *100 †55

HUGHES, Sean Gillette. 4230 HARDING RD STE 330, THE HEART GROUP 37205 #011-03-1998 L2004 **CD** *020 †30

HUGHES, William Henry. 1916 PATTERSON ST, STE 604 37203 #047-07-1975 L1993 **U EM** *020 †95 ‡

HULGAN, Todd Michael. 1301 22ND AVE N 37232 #001-02-1996 L2000 **ID** *020 †20

HULLER, Martha Elizabeth. - RADI, VANDERBILT UNIV MED CTR 37232 #041-13-2002 L2006 **DR** *100 †80

HUMBLE, Stephen Crenshaw. 2011 CHURCH ST STE 501 37203 #047-06-1987 L1987 **P** *020 †75

HUMMELL, Donna Sedlak. 1301 22ND AVE N 37232 #023-07-1980 L1985 **PD RHU** *020 †55,03

HUMPHREY, Steven Scott. 395 WALLACE RD, STE B-300 37211 #012-22-2000 L2006 **CD** *100 †20

HUMPHREYS, Jonathan Ryan. ■ 37212 #001-02-2007 *012

HUNG, Rebecca R. 1301 22ND AVE N 37232 #024-01-1994 L2005 **CD** *020 †20

HUNLEY, Tracy Earl. 2200 CHILDRENS WAY, 11205 DOCTORS OFFICE TWR 37232 #047-06-1991 L1997 **PN PD** *020 †55

HUNT, Robert Don. 2129 BELCOURT AVE 37212 #005-02-1970 L1986 **CHP P** *050 †75

HUNTER, Rosemary. 4901 NOLENSVILLE RD 37211 #036-07-1994 L2000 **PD** *020 †55

HUNTER, Stephanie Holmes. 1301 22ND AVE N 37232 #012-05-1996 L2000 **PD** *020 †55

HUNTER, Thomas Andrew. 4220 HARDING RD, ONCOLOGY DEPARTMENT 37205 #047-06-1982 L1983 **RO** *020 †80

HUSTON, Joseph Wilson, III. 2410 PATTERSON ST, STE 106 37203 #047-05-1971 L1976 **RHU IM** *020 †20

HUTCHERSON, Helen W. ■ 37221 #047-20-2001 **P** *100

HUTCHISON, Kimberly Ann. 1301 22ND AVE N 37232 #019-02-2000 L2005 **N** *100

HUTCHISON, Ryan Bennett. 617 S 8TH ST 37206 #019-02-2000 L2004 **FM** *020 †18

HUTUL, Olivia Alana. ■ 37212 #047-05-2008 *012

HWANG, Carey Kanglun. 1301 22ND AVENUE SOUTH, THE VANDERBILT CLINIC-RM 2 37232 #055-01-2003 L2004 **ID** *012 †20

HYMAN, Steve Alan. 3108 MCE. N TOWER, 1215 21ST AVENUE SOUTH 37232 #017-20-1979 L1979 **AN** *020 †05

HYMES, Jeffrey L. 28 WHITE BRIDGE RD, STE 300 37205 #035-46-1977 L1986 **NEP IM** *020 †20

ICHIKAWA, Iekuni. 21ST & GARLAND AVE, MED CTR NORTH C-4204 37232 #572-20-1972 L1986 **PN** *050

IDOUX, John W. 37217 #048-15-2004 L2007 **IM** *020 †20

IDOWU, Rachel Tolulopeola. ■ 37203 #005-02-2004 L2007 **GS** *020 †20

IJIYODE, Ademola Joseph. 1005 D B TODD BLVD 37208 #690-05-1987 **IM** *100

IKARD, Robert Winston. 308 SUNNYSIDE DR 37205 #047-05-1963 L1963 **GS TS** *020 †85,90

IKIZLER, Talat Alp. 1161 21ST AVE S, S-3223 37232 #902-10-1987 L1996 **NEP** *020 †20

IKPEAZU, Chukwuemeka V. 1005 D B TODD BLVD 37208 #047-07-1992 L1995 **HO** *040 †20

IKPEAZU, Olunwa Chisara. 1818 ALBION ST, METROPOLITIAN NASHVILLE GN 37208 #690-04-1990 L1998 **PD** *020 †55

IM, Soo Jung. ■ 37212 #050-02-2003 L2006 **HO** *012 †20

IMRAN, Yasmeen Quddoos. 393 WALLACE RD, STE 303 37211 #704-16-1992 L2006 **FPG** *020 †20

INDUKURI, Raju Venkata S. 2011 ASHWOOD AVE 37212 #495-58-1980 L1996 **CHP** *020 †75 ‡

IRANI, Waleed Nabil. 1301 22ND AVE N 37232 #036-01-1990 L1996 **CD** *020 †20

IRWIN, Chance Loomis. 37215 #048-02-2002 L2005 **VS** *012 †85

ISBELL, James Michael. ■ 37205 #048-12-2003 L2006 **GS** *012

ISBELL, Rebecca Lynn. 310 25TH AVE N, STE 201 37203 #048-12-2003 L2006 **PD** *020 †55

ISENHOUR, Albert P, Jr. 345 24TH AVE N 37203 #036-07-1948 L1955 **U** *071 †95

ISLAM, Mohammed Shahidul. 2014 CHARLOTTE AVE 37203 #704-03-1969 L1978 **P** *020 †75 ‡

ISLAM, Shahidul. 2014 CHARLOTTE AVE 37203 #160-03-1992 L1999 **PTH** *020 †50 ‡

ISMAIL, Muhammad Sami. 2300 PATTERSON ST, MID TENNESSEE NEONATOLOGY 37203 #875-02-1977 L1988 **NPM PD** *012 †20

ISMAIL, Nuhad Mohamed. 1301 22ND AVE N 37232 #605-01-1978 L1987 **IM** *020 †20

ITANI, Doha Mohamad. ■ 37212 #605-01-2005 **PTH** *012

ITURREGUI, Juan Miguel. ■ 37221 #042-01-1999 L2005 **PTH** *100 †50 ‡

JABEEN, Shagufta. 1818 ALBION ST, METRO GENERAL HOSPITAL 37208 #704-06-1985 L2002 **P** *020 †75

JABS, Kathy Lee. 1301 22ND AVE N 37232 #035-01-1982 L2000 **PN PD** *020 †55

JACK, Meg Elizabeth. 1313 21ST AVE S, 703 OXFORD HOUSE 37232 #039-01-2004 L2006 **EM** *100

JACK, Robert Allen. 2300 PATTERSON ST 37203 #040-02-1979 L1981 **P** *020 †75

JACKSON, Autumn Lindsey. CTR N, D-3100 VANDERBILT MED 37232 #048-14-2005 L2007 **IM** *012

JACKSON, C Gary. 1301 22ND AVE N 37232 #041-13-1973 L1977 **OTO** *071 †45

JACKSON, Charity Lynn. ■ 37204 #003-01-2008 *012

JACKSON, John Albers. 1301 22ND AVE N 37232 #047-06-1999 L2002 **CHP** *020 †75

JACKSON, Richard Varney. GARLAND AND 21ST AVE S 37232 #143-08-1972 L1982 **END** *050

JACKSON, Roger Theodore. 2300 PATTERSON ST 37203 #047-06-1971 L1972 **IM ID** *071 †20

JACKSON, S Ann. 4230 HARDING RD STE 330 37205 #051-04-1985 L1991 **CD IM** *020 †20 ‡

JACKSON, Tamara Christine. - RADI, VANDERBILT UNIV MED CTR 37232 #047-05-2005 L2005 **DR** *012

JACKSON, Tonia Lynnette. 3101 WATERFORD CIR 37221 #035-09-1998 L2003 **AN** *020

JACKSON, Tracy Powell. ■ 37212 #036-01-2000 L2007 **AN** *020 †05

JACOBS, Joseph Kenneth. ■ 37205 #016-06-1954 L1954 **GS** *071 †85

JACOBSON, Ellen Russell. ■ 37205 #047-06-1986 L1989 **D IM** *020 †15

JACOBSON, Gregory H. 1301 22ND AVE N 37232 #048-04-2001 L2003 **EM** *020 †16

JACOBSON, Harry R. MEDICAL CENTER NORTH, ROOM D-3300 37232 #016-11-1972 L1985 **NEP IM** *050 †20

JACOKES, Mark Warner. 1210 STEVENSON CENTER LN, HEALTH SERVICE 37232 #036-01-1983 L1988 **IM** *020 †20

JAGASIA, Madan H. 1301 22ND AVE SOUTH, 2665 THE VANDERBILT CLINIC 37232 #496-38-1992 L1997 **HO** *020 †20

JAGGARD, Sally Ann. 222 22ND AVE N, STE 600 37203 #001-02-1982 L1988 **IM** *020 †20

JALEEL, Vijaya Lakshmi. 1005 DR DB TODD JR BLVD, OF PSYCH 37208 #495-21-1986 L2003 **P** *012

JAMES, Dorsha Nicole. 703 OXFORD HOUSE, VANDERBILT UNIV MED CTR, D 37232 #047-20-2005 L2008 **EM** *012

JAMES, Kaitlin Campbell. ■ 37205 #047-05-2006 **PD** *012

JAMES, Robert Franklin, IV. ■ 37232 #021-01-2001 L2007 **NS** *100

JAMIESON, Robert Cameron. 3441 DICKERSON PIKE 37207 #056-05-1976 L1977 **P** *020 †75

JANCO, Robert Lewis. 2220 PIERCE AVE, 397 PRB 37232 #008-01-1970 L1981 **PD GP** *050 †55

JANES, Cynthia Ann. 250 25TH AVE N, STE 304 37203 #020-02-1989 L1990 **P** *020 †75

JANZ, David Rutledge. ■ 37221 #021-05-2007 **IM** *012

JARNAGIN, Barry Kent. DEPT OF OB/GYN, R-1217 MCN, VANDERBILT UNIVERSITY MED 37232 #047-06-1984 L1985 **OBG** *020 †20

JARQUIN-VALDIVIA, Adrian. DEPT OF NEUROLOGY, VUMC-MCN A-0118 37232 #451-01-1993 L2002 **N IM** *020 †20,75

JARVIS, David Alan. 2400 PATTERSON ST, STE 101 37203 #020-02-1973 L1975 **PUD IM** *020 †20

JAVIER, Daniel Salvosa. 2021 RICHARD JONES RD 37215 #748-08-1983 L1994 **P PYG** *020 †75

JAYARAMAN, Adhi. 2553 MURFREESBORO PIKE, ASSOCIATES 37217 #495-59-1976 L1988 **IM** *020 †20

JEANTY, Philippe. 1900 CHURCH ST, STE 100 37203 #165-01-1978 L1987 **DR** *020 †80

JELSMA, Peter Franklin. 4220 HARDING PIKE 37205 #016-06-1991 L2000 **PTH** *020 †50

JENKINS, William Joseph. ■ 37221 #001-02-2006 **DR** *012

JENNINGS, Henry Smith, III. 1215 21ST AVE S, STE 5209 37232 #047-05-1977 L1978 **IC CD** *020 †20 ‡

JENSEN, Eric Robert. 2200 CHILDRENS WAY, STE 4150 37232 #016-06-1995 L2006 **PDS** *020 †20

JERKINS, Terri Wood. 2400 PATTERSON ST, STE 309 37203 #047-06-1981 L1982 **END IM** *020 †20 ‡

JEYAKUMAR, Alwin Seshaga. ■ 37215 #690-01-1992 **HO** *100 †20

JHINGADE, Varalakshmi. 1005 D B TODD BLVD 37208 #496-35-1993 **FP** *012

JIANG, Shazi. ■ 37221 #047-05-2007 *012

JIRJIS, Jim Najib. 1215 21ST AVE S, STE 4 37232 #016-02-1993 L1994 **ID** *020 †20

JOBIN, Tracy Lynn. ■ 37203 #012-22-2006 **AN** *012

JOE, Y Charles. 7182 WHITES CREEK PKE 37207 #583-01-1961 L1975 **FM OTO** *020 †18

JOGGERST, Steven James. ■ 37211 #035-01-2006 **IM** *012

JOHN, Bijoy Easso. 2010 CHURCH ST, STE 710 37203 #495-59-1993 L1998 **PCC** *020 †20

JOHNS, James Ashmore. 2200 CHILDRENS WAY, RM 2510 37232 #047-05-1980 L1984
PDC PD *050 †55

JOHNS, Karla J. 1919 CHARLOTTE AVE, STE 220 37203 #047-05-1980 L1984 **OPH** *020 †35

JOHNSON, Benj Wilbur, Jr. 2011 MURPHY AVE, STE 301 37203 #016-11-1980 L1991
PME AN *040 †05

JOHNSON, Bradley T. ■ 37204 #048-13-2007 **GS** *012

JOHNSON, Corbin Ross. 1301 22ND AVE N, TVC B-1003 37232 #028-02-1985 L2006
RO *020 †80

JOHNSON, David Horton. 777 PRESTON RESEARCH BLDG, 2220 PIERCE AVE, 37232
#012-01-1976 L1981 **IM** *020 †20

JOHNSON, Ernest Kaye. 1705 WINDOVER DR 37218 #047-07-1975 L1977 **GP GS** *020

JOHNSON, Harry Keith. 1633 CHURCH ST, STE 160 37203 #024-07-1963 L1971 **NEP** *020 †20

JOHNSON, Ira T, Jr. ■ 37215 #047-05-1948 L1948 **IM** *071 †20

JOHNSON, James Earl. 9 MUSIC SQ S, # 154 37203 #047-07-1987 L1988 **GP GPM** *075

JOHNSON, James Norris. 356 24TH AVE N, NASHVILLE ORTHOPAEDICS 37203
#047-05-1993 L2002 **FSM** *020 †18 ‡

JOHNSON, James Wm. 1620 CHURCH ST, PLASMA ALLIANCE 37203 #047-05-1958 L1958
OBG *071

JOHNSON, Jeffery C. 21ST AND GARLAND AVENUE, D-4314 MCN 37232 #048-14-2001 L2003
GS *012

JOHNSON, Jennifer Ann. 4220 HARDING RD, ST. THOMAS HOSPITAL 37205
#048-12-2003 L2007 **PCC** *012 †20

JOHNSON, John Settle. 1211 22ND AVE N 37232 #047-05-1961 L1961 **RHU IM** *071 †20

JOHNSON, Joyce Evelyn. 1301 22ND AVE N 37232 #047-05-1986 L1988 **ATP PCP** *020 †50

JOHNSON, Kevin Anthony. ■ 37208 #047-07-2008 *012

JOHNSON, Kevin Brian. 2209 GARLAND AVE RM 428, ESKIND BIOMEDICAL 37232
#023-07-1987 L2002 **PD OS** *050 †55

JOHNSON, Louis Collins. 2400 PATTERSON ST, STE 101 37203 #047-05-1990 L1992
IM *020 †20

JOHNSON, Paulette Marie. 1301 22ND AVE N 37232 #011-04-1994 L2003 **CCP** *020 †55

JOHNSON, Robert Marshall. 2410 PATTERSON ST, STE 106 37203 #047-05-1961 L1961
IM OS *071 †20

JOHNSON, Samuel Terry, Jr. ■ 37221 #047-07-2008 *012

JOHNSON, Steven P. 397 WALLACE RD STE 100, FAMILY PRACTICE ASSOCIATES 37211
#047-06-1994 L1997 **FM** *020 †18 ‡

JOHNSON, William Lee. 1005 DR DB TODD JR BLVD, MEHARRY MED COLL DEPT OF P 37208
#306-01-2000 L2008 **P** *012

JOHNSTON, Benjamin Joseph. ■ 37221 #020-02-2007 **OTO** *012

JOHNSTON, Michael Nolen. 703 OXFORD HOUSE, DEPARTMENT OF EMERGENCY ME 37232
#001-02-1994 L2004 **EM** *100 †55

JOHNSTON, Palmer Green. 2200 CHILDRENS WAY 8161D, CHILDREN'S HOSPITAL 37232
#021-05-2006 **PD** *012

JOHNSTON, Robert K. 4230 HARDING RD, STE 1000 37205 #047-05-1966 L1973 **ORS** *020 †40

JOHNSTON, Thomas Stevan. 2400 PATTERSON ST, STE 502 37203 #047-05-1988 L1990
CD *020 †20

JOHNSTON, William David. 2011 CHURCH ST STE 309 37203 #047-05-1967 L1980
GS *074 †85

JOHNSTONE, Scott Anthony. ■ 37211 #038-41-2006 L2008 **AN** *012

JONES, Ayanna N. ■ 37205 #048-04-2005 **IM** *012

JONES, Christopher M. 801 OXFORD HOUSE, 1313 21ST AVENUE SOUTH 37232
#010-02-2001 L2006 **GS** *012

JONES, David Scott. 301 21ST AVE N 37232 #047-06-1968 L1969 **ORS HS** *020 †40

JONES, Edmund Palmer. ■ 37205 #047-05-1943 L1944 **AN** *071 †05

JONES, Emma Marie. 1301 22ND AVE N 37232 #021-05-2002 L2005 **PHO** *012

JONES, Frank Emerson. 724 SUMMERLY DR 37209 #047-06-1958 L1958 **ORS HS** *071 †40

JONES, Howard Wilbur, III. DEPT OF OB/GYN, R-1217 MCN, VANDERBILT UNIV MEDICAL
CT 37232 #036-07-1968 L1980 **GO GYN** *020 †30

JONES, Ian David. 1301 22ND AVE N 37232 #047-06-1993 L1996 **EM** *020 †16

JONES, James Donald. 222 22ND AVE N STE 100 37203 #001-02-1986 L1987 **IM** *020 †20

JONES, Jeremy Dwayne. 2611 W END AVE STE 210, ALLERGY PROGRAM 37203
#020-02-2002 L2006 **AI** *012 †20

JONES, Jill Lunde. CENTER E STE 2, 7TH FLOOR MEDICAL 37232 #005-11-1991 L1997
IM *020 †20

JONES, Mark Clayton. 300 20TH AVE N, FL 7 37203 #028-34-1975 L2008 **N CN** *020 †75

JONES, Patrick Marsh. ■ 37209 #048-04-2003 L2006 **PD** *012

JONES, Robert C. 2400 PATTERSON ST, STE 502 37203 #047-05-1998 L2005 **ICE** *020 †20

JONES, Sonya Nicole. 1301 22ND AVE N 37232 #047-06-1999 L2005 **CHP** *020 †75

JONES, Timothy Frederick. 425 5TH AVE N, TN DEPT HEALTH CEDS 37247 #005-11-1990 L1998
FM EP *062 †18

JONES-MEADORS, Bernadette. 2011 CHURCH ST, STE 601 37203 #010-03-1997 L1998
OBG *020

JONGEWARD, Kathryn Lynn. ■ 37205 #047-05-2008 *012

JOOS, Karen Margaret. 1215 21ST AVE S S8017, VANDERBILT UNIVERSITY MED 37232
#018-03-1987 L1994 **OPH** *020 †35

JORDAN, Darryl Lambert. 1005 DR DB TODD JR BLVD 37208 #047-07-1989 L1991
PUD *020 †20

JORDAN, Harold Willoughby. MEHARRY MED COLL 37208 #047-07-1962 L1966 **P** *030 †75

JORDAN, Jeanne James. 310 GREAT CIRCLE RD 4TH FL 37243 #001-02-1990 L2007
PD *030 †50

JORDAN, Michael Wayne. 1708 21ST AVE S, STE 317 37212 #041-13-1992 L1993 **P** *020 †75

JORDANOV, Martin Ivanov. ■ 37205 #047-06-2001 L2006 **DR** *100 †80

JOSEPH, Preeti Mary. ■ 37209 #039-01-2003 L2004 **CN** *012

JOSLIN, Katherine Gillela. ■ 37209 #047-05-2005 **PD** *012

JUNARD, Frederick G. 393 WALLACE RD, STE 201 37211 #690-02-1986 L1999 **IM** *020 †20

JUNIOR, Keith Elliott. 617 S 8TH ST, CAYCE FAMILY HEALTH CENTER 37206
#047-07-1989 L1991 **P** *020 †20

JUSTICE, Nathaniel Allen. ■ 37205 #017-20-2007 **PD** *012

JUSTICE, Paul Andrew, Jr. 2553 MURFREESBORO PIKE, ASSOCIATES 37217
#047-05-1980 L1983 **IM** *020 †20

KACKI, Marek. 28 WHITE BRIDGE RD, STE 300 37205 #759-12-1980 L1993 **IM CD** *020 †20

KADLEC, Adam. ■ 37212 #056-05-2008 *012

KAHN, Kevin Michael. STE 4200, MEDICAL CENTER EAST, SOUTH 37232 #012-05-1997 L2007
ORS *020 †40

KAINER, Marion Angelika. 425 5TH AVE N, CEDS CORDELL HULL BLDG 37247
#143-02-1989 L2002 **ID EP** *020

KAISER, Allen Bernard. 1301 22ND AVE N 37232 #047-05-1967 L1972 **IM ID** *030 †20

KAISER, Clayton Allen. ■ 37212 #047-05-2008 *012

KAISER, Daniel Walter. ■ 37212 #047-05-2008 *012

KAISER, Rachel. 4220 HARDING PIKE 37205 #024-07-1989 L1994 **EM** *020 †16

KALAMS, Spyros Andrew. 1161 21ST AVE S, INFESTIOUS DISEASE UNIT/ME 37232
#042-07-1987 L2002 **ID** *020 †20

KALISZ, Ann Margaret. ■ 37215 #016-11-1988 L1991 **IM** *020 †20

KALLIANPUR, Asha Rosalind. 1310 24TH AVE S, TVHS VA MEDICAL CENTER 37212
#036-01-1988 L1994 **HEM** *020 †20

KALNAS, J Jonas. 3319 W END AVE STE 930, OCCUPTNL & ENVRMNTL MED 37203
#065-06-1976 L2002 **OM PTX** *062 †70 ‡

KAMAL, Abul Bashar Mohamm. 1161 21ST AVE S 37232 #160-03-1984 **GS** *012

KAMDAR, Biren Bharat. ■ 37212 #047-05-2006 **IM** *012

KAMINSKI, Michael James. 4230 HARDING RD, STE 501W 37205 #016-11-1976 L1982
N IM *020 †20,75

KAMMER, Jeffrey Aaron. 1215 21ST AVE S STE 8000, 8000 MED CTR E, NORTH TOWE 37232
#038-06-1996 L2002 **OPH** *020

KAN, J Herman. 1161 21ST AVE S, VANDERBILT UNIVERSITY MEDI 37232 #035-03-1998 L2005
PDR *020 †80

KANDULA, Manju. 300 20TH AVE N 37203 #038-44-1989 L1992 **N CN** *020 †75

KANG, Audrey H. 300 20TH AVE N STE 702, TN. MATERNAL FETAL MEDICIN 37203
#043-01-1992 L1995 **OBG** *020 †20

KANNANKERIL, Prince J. 2200 CHILDRENS WAY, RM 2510 37232 #041-02-1994 L2002
PDC *050 †20,55

KANTOR, Jeff Lawrence. GASTRO NUTRITION, DEPT OF PED 37232 #041-02-2001 L2001
PG *012

KANTROW, Sara Marshall. ■ 37212 #047-05-2002 L2007 **DMP** *100

KAPLAN, Herman Jacob. 1301 22ND AVE N 37232 #047-05-1954 L1954 **GE IM** *020 †20

KAPLAN, Hillary. 2002 RICHARD JONES RD, STE B300 37215 #038-06-1993 L1998
RHU *020 †20

KAPLAN, Mark Randall. 28 WHITE BRIDGE RD, STE 300 37205 #047-05-1988 L1991
NEP *020 †20

KARAVAS, Alexandros. 1301 MEDICAL CENTER DR, VANDERBILT UNIV MED CTR 37232
#408-30-1997 L2007 **TS** *012 †85

KARL, Edward Matthew. 2011 ASHWOOD AVE 37212 #001-02-1983 L1985 **P** *020 †50

KARMO, Hadeer Noori. 2300 PATTERSON ST, MID TENNESSEE NEONATOLOGY 37203
#306-01-1985 L1990 **NPM** *020 †55

KARNETT, Bernice. 1310 24TH AVE S, DEPT OF AMBULATORY CARE 11 37212
#012-05-1983 L1996 **IM** *020 †20

KARY, Jonathan Alex. 397 WALLACE RD BLDG C, SOUTHERN HILLS SUITE 100 37211
#016-11-1990 L1992 **FM** *020 †18

KARZON, David Theodore. 1049 OVERTON LEA RD 37220 #023-07-1944 L1969 **PD ID** *050 †55

KASSELBERG, Alfred Guy. ■ 37215 #023-07-1971 L1975 **PTH PD** *050,55

KASSIM, Adetola. 1301 MEDICAL CENTER DR, 2665 THE VANDERBILT CLINIC 37232
#690-02-1988 L2001 **IM HO** *050 †20

KATTIH, Osama M. 1211 21ST AVE S, # 714 MED ARTS BLDG 37212 #875-02-1990 L2000
CCP *100 †55 ‡

KAUFFMAN, Ryan Matthew. ■ 37203 #047-05-2004 L2007 **OTO** *012

KAUFMAN, Melissa Rae. ■ 37215 #004-01-2002 L2007 **U** *020

KAVANAUGH-MC HUGH, Ann L. 2200 CHILDRENS WAY, STE 5230 37232 #023-07-1984 L1992
PDC PD *020 †55

KAYE, Jeremy Jon. 1161 MED CTR DR MCN CCC112 37232 #035-20-1965 L1977 **DR** *030 †80

KAYLIE, David Marcus. 300 20TH AVE N, STE 502 37203 #051-04-1997 L2002 **OTO** *020

KAYSER, Sam Jos, III. 4230 HARDING PIKE, STE 400 37205 #021-01-1975 L1979
IM HEM *020 †20

KAZA, Sunil Choudary. 3441 DICKERSON PIKE 37207 #495-21-1990 L2001 **CD P** *020 †20

KEANE, William Sherman. 210 25TH AVE N, STE 602 37203 #017-20-1968 L1970
DR GP *020 †80

KEEDY, Vicki Leigh. ■ 37205 #038-41-2002 L2008 **HO** *012 †20

KEEFER, Christopher Jay. ■ 37209 #047-05-2001 L2007 **PDI** *012 †55

KELLETT, William J. ■ 37205 #011-75-2006, ▲ L2006 **OBG** *012

KELLEY, Mark Carlton. 597 PRB, 2220 PIERCE AVE STE 2 37232 #011-03-1989 L1997
SO GS *020 †85

KELLY, Burnett Stephens. ■ 37205 #010-03-1995 L2005 **GS** *020 †85

KELLY, Kevin Jos. 1611 21ST AVE S D-4207MCN 37232 #035-08-1982 L1989 **PS GS** *020 †65 ‡

KENDALL, Peggy L. GARLAND AT 21ST, T3219 MCN 37232 #048-12-1996 L1998
PCC *100 †20,55,03

KENNEDY, Barbara Gail. 1005 DR DB TODD JR BLVD 37208 #047-07-1972 L1978 **PD** *012

KENNER, William Davis, III. 113 30TH AVE N 37203 #047-06-1969 L1970 **PYA CHP** *020

KENNON, Julie Cox. 4220 HARDING PIKE 37205 #047-05-1991 L1995 **DR** *020 †80

KEOWN, Mary Elizabeth. 2201 MURPHY AVE, STE 201 37203 #001-02-1983 L1986 **PD** *020 †55

KERINS, David M. 2311 PIERCE AVE, PRB RM 383 37232 #539-02-1984 L1989 **CD** *020 †20

KERNODLE, Douglas Stuart. VANDERBILT UNIV MED CENTER, A-2200 MCN 37232
#036-01-1981 L1985 **ID IM** *050 †20

KERR, Mary Milam. 2010 CHURCH ST STE 608 37203 #051-01-1992 L1996 **OPH** *020 †35

KESSLER, Robert Michael. 1251 MRB 2222 PIERCE AVE, PET FACILITY 37232
#008-01-1971 L1984 **PDA NS** *020 †80

KETCH, Terry Robert. CTR N, D-3100 VANDERBILT MED 37232 #047-05-1997 L2006
CD *012 †20

KEY, Richard Garrett. ■ 37212 #047-05-2006 **P** *012

KEYSER, John Edward. 356 24TH AVE N, STE 400 37203 #016-11-1980 L1982 **VS** *020 †85

KHABELE, Dineo. ■ 37209 #035-01-1994 L2004 **OBG** *020 †30

KHALAF, Waleed Fahed. ■ 37209 #017-20-2007 **IM** *012

KHAN, Sophia Seher. ■ 37221 #704-26-2001 L2006 *100

KHAZAI, Bahram. ■ 37221 #517-04-2004 **IM** *012

KHAZAI, Laila. ■ 37221 #517-04-2002 L2003 **PTH** *012

KHOKHAR, Ubaid Aslam. ■ 37209 #308-11-1994 L2006 **PYM** *100

KIEFER, Alaina Marie. ■ 37205 #047-05-2008 *012

KIHLBERG, Courtney Johnso. ■ 37221 #020-12-2005 **GPM** *012

KIKKAWA, Rita Marie. 1310 24TH AVE S, VAMC NASHVILLE-RADIOLOGY 37212
#016-06-1991 L1998 **VIR** *020 †80

KILIMANJARO, Heidi A. ■ 37221 #047-07-1988 L1996 **P** *100
KILLIAN, Thomas Jos. 2400 PATTERSON ST, STE 400 37203 #001-02-1984 L1988 **CD IM** *020 †20
KILROY, Anthony Waldo. 2200 CHILDRENS WAY # 11244, DOCTORS OFFICE TOWER 37232 #917-20-1960 L1975 **CHN N** *040 †75
KIM, Brian D. 1211 21ST AVE S, 404 MED ARTS BLDG 37212 #019-02-2001 L2006 **GS** *020
KIM, Richard Brian. CLINICAL PHARMACOLOGY, DIV OF 37232 #068-01-1987 L1996 **IM** *020 †20
KIM, Sanford Jong. 4220 HARDING PIKE 37205 #047-05-1999 L2001 **IM** *020 †20
KIMBALL, James R. ■ 37203 #039-01-1976 L2005 **FM** *020 †18
KIMBRELL, Angela Frances. ■ 37203 #036-01-2007 **PD** *012
KIMBRELL, Fred Taylor, Jr. 1121 22ND AVE S 37232 #027-01-1967 L1975 **GS UM** *020 †85
KIMBROUGH, John Thomas, III. ■ 37212 #035-45-2000 L2007 **CD IM** *100 †20
KING, James Centre, III. 28 WHITE BRIDGE RD, STE 104 37205 #047-05-1987 L1988 **RNR** *020 †80
KING, Kelli Rae. ■ 37211 #011-04-2006 **IM** *012
KING, Kelly Fair Suzanne. ■ 37215 #012-22-2004 L2007 **PG** *012 †55
KING, Lloyd Elijah, Jr. 1900 PATTERSON ST, STE 104 37203 #047-06-1967 L1968 **D DMP** *020 †15
KING, Lloyd Gordon. 1301 22ND AVE N 37232 #035-19-1985 L1999 **GE IM** *020 †20
KING, Matthew Sidney. 21ST AVENUE SOUTH AND GARL, VUMC - GME OFFICE 37232 #017-20-2004 L2005 **PCC** *012 †20
KIOSCHOS, John Michael. 356 24TH AVE N, STE 200 37203 #055-01-1994 L2000 **ORS** *020 †40
KIPPENBROCK, Sarah Ann. ■ 37209 #030-05-2006 **MPD** *012
KIRBY, Kelly Ann. ■ 37221 #026-08-2004 L2006 **AN** *012
KIRCHNER, Frederick K, Jr. 1301 22ND AVE N 37232 #035-20-1967 L1970 **U** *030 †95
KIRK, Brianna Leigh. 2200 CHILDRENS WAY 8161D, CHILDREN'S HOSPITAL 37232 #048-15-2006 **PD** *012
KIRSHNER, Howard Stephen. A-0118 VANDERBILT MEDICAL, DEPT OF NEUROLOGY STROKE C 37232 #024-01-1972 L1978 **N VN** *020 †15 ‡
KISTLER, Henry B, Jr. 214 25TH AVE N 37203 #010-01-1988 L1994 **OPH** *020 †35
KLEIN, William Jeffery. 4220 HARDING PIKE 37205 #021-05-1998 L2006 **DR** *020 †80
KLINSKY, Lawrence Aaron. 222 22ND AVE N STE 100 37203 #047-05-1992 L1995 **PD** *020 †55
KLIPPENSTEIN, Kimberly A. 250 25TH AVE N, STE 216 37203 #047-05-1990 L1994 **OPH** *020 †35 ‡
KLOCHAN, Christen Marie. ■ 37203 #016-01-2007 **IM** *012
KLOTZ, Carrie Rose. 1313 21ST AVE S S703, DEPT OF EMERGENCY MED 37232 #023-07-2007 **EM** *012
KNAPP, David Solomon. 2410 PATTERSON ST, STE 106 37203 #011-02-1973 L1978 **RHU PMM** *020 †20
KNIGHT, Glenfield Saml. 1818 ALBION ST, DEPT. RADIOLOGY 37208 #010-03-1967 L2005 **DR** *020 †80
KNOEPP, Leise R. ■ 37212 #021-06-2004 L2008 **OBG** *012
KNOLL, L Dean. 345 23RD AVE N, STE 212 37203 #016-42-1982 L1987 **U** *020 †95
KNOLLMANN, Bjoern C. VANDERBILT UNIV. MED. CTR, 532 RRB, 23RD AND PIERCE A 37232 #038-41-1993 L2005 **IM PA** *050 †20
KNOTT, Latonya Denise. 800 GARRISON DR 37207 #047-06-2000 L2003 **IM** *020 †20
KNOWLES, Robert Bryan. 222 22ND AVE N STE 100 37203 #001-02-1995 L1996 **IM** *020 †20
KOCH, Jack L, Jr. 2125 BELCOURT AVE 37212 #001-06-1994 L1995 **CHP** *020 †75
KOCHTITZKY, Otto M. ■ 37205 #047-05-1950 L1950 **IM** *071
KOENIG, Mark. 4230 HARDING RD STE 330 37205 #051-07-1989 L1999 **CD IM** *020 †20
KOETHE, John Robert. ■ 37206 #008-01-2004 ID *012 †20
KOLAY, Indranil. ■ 37212 #495-02-1991 **AN** *020
KOLEYNI, Camellia Renee. ■ 37204 #047-06-2000 L2006 **FM** *020 †18
KOLLAR, Andras. 2984 TVC, 1301 22ND AVE SOUTH 37232 #473-01-1984 L1999 **TS** *020
KOLLER, Felicitas Lan-Fen. ■ 37206 #048-02-2006 **GS** *012
KOLMER, Harriet Lynn. 1301 22ND AVE N 37232 #051-04-1990 L2006 **IM** *020 †20
KOLNICK, Leanne. ■ 37211 #047-05-2008 *012
KON, Valentina. 1301 22ND AVE N 37232 #035-46-1977 L1986 **NEP PD** *020
KONDIS, Deborah Jean. CLINCH ST STE 403 37203 #035-07-1982 L1986 **GYN** *020 †30
KONRAD, Peter Erich. 1301 22ND AVE N 37232 #017-20-1991 L1997 **NS** *020 †25
KOONS, Donald Christopher. ■ 37203 #051-07-2006 L2007 **EM** *012
KOPECKY, Frances Barbara. 1301 22ND AVE N 37232 #030-05-1993 L1997 **N** *020 †75
KORPMAN, Ralph Andrew. 102 WOODMONT BLVD, STE 200 37205 #005-12-1974 L1997 **CLP HEM** *050 †50
KORZYNIOWSKI, Andrew Dono. ■ 37214 #047-06-2007 **AN** *012
KOSKI, Michelle Elaine. A-1302 MED CTR NORTH, 21ST AVE S AND GARLAND AVE 37232 #005-14-2005 **U** *012
KOSS, Theodore W. 1310 24TH AVE S 37212 #035-06-1941 L1986 **GP** *071
KOSTAMAA, Heikki Juhani. 342 22ND AVE N 37203 #005-15-1999 L2005 **OPH** *020 †35
KOUMTCHEV, Alexandre Atan. 1161 21ST AVE N 37203 #198-01-1990 L2006 **P** *100
KOURY, Mark Jay. 2220 PIERCE AVE, VANDERBILT UNIVERSITY 37232 #051-01-1973 L1977 **HEM IM** *050 †20
KRAFT, Bryan David. ■ 37221 #047-06-2007 **IM** *012
KRANTZ, Sanford Burton. 2220 PIERCE AVE, PRB 777 37232 #016-01-1959 L1970 **HEM** *020 ‡
KRAUSE, Jens Christian. ■ 37214 #409-10-2003 L2004 **PDI** *012
KRAVITZ, Jared Noah. ■ 37221 #035-47-2005 **IM** *012
KREGOR, Philip James. 1301 22ND AVE N 37232 #047-05-1988 L2002 **ORS** *050 †40
KRESSIN, Megan Kielt. ■ 37220 #048-13-2005 L2007 **PTH** *012
KRIPALANI, Sapna Parikh. 6005 MCE N TOWER, DIVISION OF INTERNAL MEDIC 37232 #012-05-1999 L2007 **IM** *020 †20
KRIPALANI, Sunil Bhagwan. 6005 MCE, N TOWER, DIVISION OF GENERAL INTERN 37232 #048-04-1997 L2007 **IM** *020 †20
KROLL, Mark Andrew. 7640 HIGHWAY 70 S, STE 100 37221 #005-12-2002 L2006 **OPH** *100
KRONENBERG, Marvin Wm. 1215 21ST AVE S, MED. CTR. EAST, SUITE 5209 37232 #038-40-1969 L1975 **CD NC** *020 †20
KROOP, Susan Faye. 1301 MEDICAL CENTER DR 37232 #035-20-1982 L2001 **RHU** *040 †20
KROPSKI, Jonathan Andrew. ■ 37212 #047-05-2008 *012
KUCHTEY, Rachel Wang. 8000 MEDICAL CTR E N TOWER, DEPT OF OPHTALOMOLOGY VISU 37232 #243-70-1991 L2005 **OPH** *020 †35
KUHN, John Edward. 3000 MCE SOUTH TOWER 37232 #025-01-1988 L2003 **ORS** *020 †40
KUHN, Karl Philip. VANDERBILT MEDICINE, CTR FOR LUNG RESEARCH 37232 #004-01-1996 L1999 **PCC** *020 †20
KULKARNI, Meenal Girish. ■ 37203 #038-44-2005 **AN** *012
KUMAH, Yaa Aboagyewa. ■ 37210 #047-05-2008 *012

KUNKLER, Kevin Jos. 1301 22ND AVE S STE 3667, THE VANDERBILT CLINIC 37232 #017-20-1992 **GS** *100
KUO, Philip Shih. ■ 37215 #048-12-2000 L2004 **IM** *020
KUOFIE, Ivy S. ■ 37221 #025-01-2006 **IM** *012
KUTNY, Diane Yaros. ■ 37206 #047-05-2005 **PD** *012
KUTNY, Matthew Adam. ■ 37206 #047-05-2005 **PD** *012
KUTTAB, Maurice Custandi. 4004 HILLSBORO PIKE, STE 125 37215 #605-01-1976 L1981 **PMM PTH** *020
KUTTESCH, John F, Jr. 1301 22ND AVE N 37232 #048-14-1985 L1988 **PHO PD** *020 †55
KUYKENDALL, Nathaniel, Jr. ■ 37215 #047-06-1939 L1939 **GP GS** *071
KUZNIAK, Christopher R. ■ 37205 #012-01-2003 L2006 **GS** *012
KYGER, Kent. 2011 ASHWOOD AVE 37212 #047-05-1958 L1960 **CHP P** *020 †75
KYLE-VEGA, Annette E. ■ 37212 #047-07-1964 L1980 **OS** *020
KYNE, Peter John. ■ 37215 #010-01-1959 L1964 **ORS** *071 †40
KYRIAKIDIS, Kyriakos E. 4220 HARDING RD, ST THOMAS HOSPITAL 37205 #005-02-1993 L2001 **IM** *012
KYSER, James Gregory. 2011 CHURCH ST, STE 501 37203 #004-01-1987 L1988 **P** *020 †75
KYZER, Annette Anderson. 300 20TH AVE N STE 302 37203 #021-01-1995 L1999 **OBG** *020 †30
LA, Hau Trung. ■ 37211 #047-07-2000 L2007 **IM** *100
LABADIE, Robert Frederick. 1301 22ND AVE N 37232 #041-12-1996 L2001 **OTO** *020 †45
LABORDE, Carrie Elizabeth. 2200 CHILDRENS WAY 8161D, VANDERBILT CHILDREN'S HOSP 37232 #021-05-2006 **PD** *012
LACHIVER, Richard Mark. SUITE 640, 1211 21ST AVENUE SOUTH 37232 #035-09-1984 L2004 **OM MDM** *020 †70
LA CROSS, Tiffany Michele. ■ 37209 #011-03-2007 **PD** *012
LADD, Michael David. 2002 RICHARD JONES RD 37215 #047-05-1992 L1995 **PD** *020 †55
LADSON, Gwinnett Mc Ghee. 1005 DR DB TODD JR BLVD 37208 #047-07-1984 L1984 **OBG** *020 †30
LA FLORE, John E, III. 1005 D B TODD BLVD 37208 #016-01-1981 L1982 **OM** *100
LAGRANGE, Andre Hollis. 2220 PIERCE AVE, DEPARTMENT OF NEUROLOGY/39 37232 #040-02-1997 L2002 **N CN** *050 †75
LAGRONE, Robert Paul. 2001 CHARLOTTE AVE, STE 102 37203 #047-05-1987 L1990 **AI** *020 †03,20
LAHIJANI, Soheil. ■ 37212 #305-01-1998 **PS** *100
LAKHANI, Carmel C. ■ 37209 #047-05-2001 L2006 **P** *020 †75
LAKHANI, Vipul Tulsi. 1301 22ND AVE N 37232 #047-05-2001 L2006 **END** *020
LALANNE, Mireille L. 3507 CHARLOTTE AVE 37209 #440-01-1977 L1982 **AN** *020
LALEZARY, Maziar. ■ 37203 #005-18-2006 *100
LAM, Humphrey Vo. ■ 37211 #012-05-2007 **AN** *012
LAMB, John Wm. 2010 CHURCH ST, STE 520 37203 #016-02-1964 L1970 **ORS** *020 †40 ‡
LAMBALLE, Adrian Kedward. 31 BANCROFT PL 37215 #917-07-1976 L1983 **RNR** *020 †80
LAMBERT, Frank Hayden. ■ 37205 #047-06-1961 L1962 **GS PDS** *075
LAMBRIGHT, Eric Shawnk. 1301 22ND AVE S, 2986 THE VANDERBILT CLINIC 37232 #041-01-1995 L2004 **TS** *020 †85,90
LAMORTE, Annette Isabelle. 2146 BELCOURT AVE 37212 #012-05-1986 L1996 **OBG** *020 †30
LAMPKIN, S L, IV. 901 12TH AVE S 37203 #047-07-1980 L1982 **FM PD** *020
LAMS, Peter Michael. 1301 22ND AVE N 37232 #917-24-1967 L1977 **R** *020 †80
LANCASTER, James Alan. 4230 HARDING PIKE, STE 400 37205 #027-01-1993 L1996 **IM** *020 †20
LANCASTER, Leland J, Jr. 1215 21ST AVE S, STE 711 DEPT OF ANES 37232 #001-02-1996 L2002 **AN EM** *020
LANCASTER, Lifford Lee. 3443 DICKERSON PIKE, STE 400 37207 #048-13-1982 L1989 **CD TS** *020 †85,90 ‡
LANCASTER, Lisa Hood. 1301 22ND AVE N 37232 #012-01-1993 L1996 **PCC** *020 †20
LANDIS, Benjamin John. ■ 37212 #047-05-2008 *012
LANDMAN, Jeffrey A. 4525 HARDING RD, STE 102 37205 #025-12-1979 L1985 **RNR R** *020 †80
LANDMAN, Matthew Paul. ■ 37204 #047-05-2006 **GS** *012
LANDON, Erwin Jacob. VANDERBILT U SCH MED 37237 #016-02-1948 L1948 *050
LANDSMAN, Ira Seth. 3000 MCE 37206 #035-06-1979 L2001 **AN PD** *020 †55,05
LANE, Jason Scott. ■ 37216 #021-01-2004 L2007 **AN** *012
LANE, Samuel David. 73 WHITE BRIDGE RD, STE 103 37205 #047-06-1968 L1968 **DR** *071 †80
LA NEVE, Ralph James. 1301 22ND AVE N 37232 #041-02-1985 L1994 **GS** *020 †85
LANFORD, Gregory Bryan. 2011 MURPHY AVE, STE 301 37203 #047-06-1984 L1991 **NS** *020 †25
LANGLEY, Melissa. 250 25TH AVE N, STE 307 37203 #012-05-1986 L1991 **D** *020 †20,15
LANGLEY-BROWN, Kimberlyn. 4220 HARDING RD 37205 #038-06-1996 L2002 **IM** *020 †20
LANGONE, Anthony James. 21ST & GARLAND, S-3223 MCN, VANDERBILT DIV OF NEPHROLO 37232 #035-06-1996 L2000 **NEP** *020
LANHAM, Philip. 1161 21ST AVE S 37232 #023-12-1993 L1995 **DR** *020 †80
LANIER, Deidre E. 404 DR DB TODD JR BLVD, STE 100 37203 #047-07-1982 L1985 **PD N** *020
LANPHER, Brendan Coe. 2200 CHILDRENS WAY, MEDICAL STAFF OFFICE, ROOM 37232 #051-01-2001 L2007 **MG** *100 †55,19
LAPRE, Robin E. 1211 21ST AVE S, MED ARTS BUILDING 514 37212 #032-01-1996 L2001 **IM** *020 †20
LARSON, Roy Gunnar. ■ 37221 #005-06-1958 L1959 **EM** *020
LASSITER, Winifred C. 1421 ELM HILL PIKE, THE LASSITER CLINIC 37210 #047-07-1989 L1991 *020
LATEV, Maria Dimitrova. ■ 37215 #047-05-2005 **OTO** *012
LATHAM, Robert Harry. 4220 HARDING RD 37205 #047-05-1977 L1978 **ID IM** *020 †20
LATTIMORE, Jamal Stephon. ■ 37217 #047-07-2008 *012
LAUTEN, Wright Benjamin. ■ 37212 #001-06-2005 **OPH** *012
LAVELY, Horace T, Jr. 2000 CHURCH ST 37236 #041-01-1943 L1946 **GYN** *071
LAVIE, Thomas John. 3000 VILLAGE 37232 #021-05-1988 L2006 **P** *100 †75
LAVIN, Patrick James. 1301 22ND AVE N 37232 #539-04-1970 L1983 **N** *020 †75
LA VOI, Samuel Jos. ■ 37215 #047-06-1963 L1963 **IM GP** *071
LAW, Janice Chungsee. ■ 37212 #038-45-2003 L2007 **OPH** *020
LAW, Melvin Douglas, Jr. 2400 PATTERSON ST, STE 300 37203 #051-04-1986 L1987 **OSS ORS** *020 †40
LAWRENCE, David Clement. 20 BURTON HILLS BLVD 37215 #024-07-1967 L1975 **CRS** *071 †10,85
LAWRENCE, Granville A, Jr. ■ 37215 #041-13-1942 L1948 **OPH** *072 †35
LAWRENCE, Jeffrey Pettus. 2400 PATTERSON ST STE 300 37203 #047-06-1983 L1984 **ORS OSM** *020 †40
LAWRENCE, Laurie M. 703 OXFORD HOUSE, 1313 21ST AVE SOUTH 37232 #047-05-1983 L1987 **PE** *020 †20,55

LAWS, Kenneth Howard. 2010 CHURCH ST, STE 626 37203 #023-07-1977 L1980 TS VS *020 †90,85

LAWSON, Albert Robt. ■ 37205 #047-05-1948 L1948 P *071

LAWSON, George Asbury. ■ 37209 #045-01-2005 GS *012

LAWSON, Mark Alan. 1215 21ST AVE S, MCE 5TH FLOOR 37232 #047-06-1988 L2002 CD *020 †20

LAWSON, William Edward. ■ 37215 #047-06-1996 L1999 PCC *100 †20

LAWTON, Alexander R, III. 1301 22ND AVE N 37232 #047-05-1964 L1964 PPR IG *020 †55

LAWTON, Jill Emmons. 1313 21ST AVE S, 703 OXFORD HOUSE 37232 #011-02-2006 EM *012

LE, Truc Minh. 5121 DOCTORS OFFICE TOWER, 2200 CHILDREN'S WAY 37232 #047-05-2002 L2004 CCP *012

LEA, Clark Dowell. 2010 CHURCH ST, STE 526 37203 #047-06-1974 L1974 GS *020 †85

LEA, John Willis, IV. 4230 HARDING PIKE, STE 450 37205 #047-05-1977 L1982 TS *020 †85,90

LEA, William Bradford. ■ 37204 #047-05-2008 *012

LEADFORD, Alicia Elizabet. 2200 CHILDRENS WAY 8161D, CHILDREN'S HOSPITAL 37232 #003-01-2006 PD *012

LEDFORD, Robert Levoy, Jr. 222 22ND AVE N, STE 100 37203 #047-05-1991 L1993 IM *020 †20

LEE, Arthur Nebert. ■ 37208 #047-07-1976 L1981 FM *020

LEE, Carla Tucker. 1301 22ND AVE N 37232 #047-05-2001 L2006 D *020 †15

LEE, Christopher David. A0118 MCN, 1611 21ST AVE S 37232 #036-05-2004 2008 N *012

LEE, Donald Han. 1301 22ND AVE N 37232 #055-01-1982 L2005 ORS HS *020 †40

LEE, Elisabeth Ranew. 1211 21ST AVE S STE 711, VANDERBILT UNIV MED CTR 37212 #011-03-2006 L2007 AN *012

LEE, George Rozier, III. ■ 37212 #012-01-1999 L2002 N *020

LEE, Jennifer Pauline. 4230 HARDING RD, STE 400 37205 #020-02-1995 L1997 IM *020 †20

LEE, John Theod. 1215 21ST AVE S, MCE 5TH FLOOR 37232 #005-02-1978 L1985 CD IM *020 †20

LEE, Joshua Ether, Jr. ■ 37221 #010-03-2002 L2006 GS *012

LEE, Marcy Janice. 2801 CHARLOTTE AVE 37209 #039-01-1999 L2004 U *020 †95

LEE, Myung Ae. 1601 23RD AVE S, STE 306 PSY HOSP/VANDEBILT 37212 #583-08-1976 L1996 P *020 †75

LEE, Stanley Michael. 242 ORLANDO AVE 37209 #539-03-1970 L1988 NEP IM *020 †20

LEEPER, Howard Brian. 2000 CHURCH ST 37236 #047-06-1983 L1985 PD *020 †55

LEFKOWITZ, Lewis B. 211 OXFORD HOUSE, VANDERBILT MED CTR 37232 #048-12-1956 L1966 GPM IM *071 †20

LEFTWICH, Russell Bryant. 317 WHITWORTH WAY 37205 #047-05-1978 L1983 AI PDA *020 †20,03

LEHMAN, Trang Diem. 1211 21ST AVE S STE 711, VANDERBILT UNIV MED CTR 37212 #005-11-2005 AN *012

LEINBACH, Conwell Barry. ■ 37206 #041-13-1977 L1979 FM *020

LEKSE, Jaclyn Mary. ■ 37215 #047-05-2002 OPH *100

LELAND, Kristina Jo. ■ 37221 #016-11-2003 L2007 PTH *100

LEMEH, Carol Ann. ■ 37205 #047-07-1994 L1998 OM FM *020

LEMELLE, Christopher M. 1211 21ST AVE S, STE 701 37212 #005-02-2000 L2006 AN *020

LEMLY, Diana Catharine. ■ 37203 #047-05-2008 *012

LENNENAN, Andrew J. D-3100 MEDICAL CENTER NORT, VANDERBILT UNIVERSITY HOSP 37232 #025-07-2004 L2006 IM *020 †20

LENTZ, Joseph Francis. 2002 RICHARD JONES RD, STE A102 37215 #047-05-1963 L1963 PD *020 †55

LEONARD, John Martin. 1301 22ND AVE N 37232 #047-05-1967 L1973 IM ID *020 †20

LEONARD, Martha Price. 4230 HARDING RD, STE 400 37205 #047-06-1999 L2002 IM *020 †20

LESSLY, Jean R. 1718 PATTERSON ST 37203 #048-02-1998 L2001 IMG PLM *012 †20

LEVERETT, Reagan R. 5543 EDMONDSON PIKE, # 25 37211 #020-02-2003 L2004 DR *012

LEVINE, Jon Howard. 2222 STATE ST STE C 37203 #065-01-1965 L1989 END IM *020

LEVITAN, Phillip I. ■ 37221 #047-05-1951 L1951 GS TS *071 †85

LEVY, Bruce Philip. 850 RS GASS BLVD 37216 #035-09-1988 L1997 FOP *020 †50

LEWIS, Adele. 850 RS GASS BLVD 37216 #001-02-1997 L2000 FOP *020

LEWIS, Julia Breyer. 1301 22ND AVE N 37232 #016-11-1980 L1986 NEP IM *020 †20

LEWIS, Lester Leroy, Jr. 7575 COCKRILL BEND BLVD, FACILITY 37209 #010-03-1978 L2001 PUD IM *020

LEWIS, Malcolm R. ■ 37215 #028-02-1952 L1959 GS CD *071 †85

LEWIS, Rani. ■ 37232 #010-03-1989 L1993 OBG MFM *020 †30

LEWIS, Rodney Preston. ■ 37205 #051-01-2000 IM *012

LEWIS, Thomas Cary. 1215 21ST AVE S 37232 #051-01-1973 L1986 AN IM *040 †20,05

LEWIS, Thomas Jackson, Jr. 2400 PATTERSON ST, STE 101 37203 #012-01-1989 L1990 IM *020 †20

LI, Feng. 850 RS GASS BLVD 37216 #243-43-1983 L2000 FOP PTH *020 †50

LIEBERMAN, Scott Howard. 393 WALLACE RD, STE 104 37232 #025-07-1990 L1993 IM *020 †20

LIGHT, Richard Wayne. 1301 22ND AVE N 37232 #023-07-1968 L1997 PUD IM *050 †20

LIGHTFORD, Melvin W. 131 FRENCH LANDING DR 37228 #047-07-1983 L1984 IM FM *020 †20

LILLARD, Robert H, Jr. 2000 RICHARD JONES RD, STE 270 37215 #001-02-1993 L1999 PD *020 †55

LIMBIRD, Thomas James. 1301 22ND AVE N 37232 #036-07-1973 L1979 ORS *020 †40

LIN, David Tzuping. 210 25TH AVE N, STE 602 37203 #005-11-1996 L2001 DR *020 †80

LIN, Kuang-Tzu Davis. 275 STEWARTS FERRY PIKE 37214 #385-02-1966 L1986 PD CG *020 †19

LIND, Christopher D. 1301 22ND AVE SOUTH, VANDERBILT UNIV MED CTR 37232 #047-05-1981 L1986 GE IM *020 †20

LINDSEY, Elizabeth Hearon. 1161 21ST AVE S, VANDERBILT UNIV 37232 #045-01-2000 L2006 GE *100

LINDSEY, Jason Isaac. 4220 HARDING PIKE 37205 #048-04-1998 L2006 DR *020 †80

LINDSEY, Jennifer Luiz. 4304 LILLYWOOD RD 37205 #048-04-1998 L2006 OPH *020 †35 ‡

LINDSTROM, Eric John. 809 HARPETH BEND DR 37221 #012-01-2000 L2003 DR *100 †80

LINK, John Louis, II. 2215 JACKSON DOWNS BLVD 37214 #047-06-1980 L1981 OBG *020 †30

LINN, Catherine Russell. 21ST AVENUE NORTH, VANDERBILT UNIVERSITY MED 37232 #047-05-2002 L2005 IM *100 †20

LINN, Joanne L. 28 WHITE BRIDGE RD, BAPTIST CONVENIENT CARE 37205 #047-05-1950 L1955 AN *071

LINTON, Mac Rae Fort. MEDICAL CENTER, VANDERBILT UNIV 37232 #047-06-1985 L1988 END IM *050 †20

LIPSCOMB, Amy Louise. 356 24TH AVE N, STE 400 37203 #055-01-1999 L2005 VS *020 †85

LIPSITZ, Nancy B. 1211 21ST AVE S 37212 #035-45-1993 L1998 OBG *020 †30

LISBOA, Rejane Costa. 393 WALLACE RD, STE 400 37211 #187-25-1990 L2002 N *020 †75

LISELLA, Richard Scott. 337 22ND AVE N 37203 #041-13-1968 L1975 N *071 †75

LISKE, Michael Robt. 1301 22ND AVE N 37232 #025-01-1989 L1999 PDC *020 †55

LITTLE, Joseph Alexander. ■ 37205 #047-05-1943 L1948 PD PDC *071 †55

LLOYD, Kenneth M. 2000 CHURCH ST 37236 #030-05-1981 L1985 RO *020 †80 ‡

LO, Andy Leeping. VANDERBILT UNIV MED CTR, DEPT OF PATHOLOGY MCN CC33 37232 #016-42-2005 PTH *012

LOCKERT-DANIELS, Cheryl L. ■ 37217 #047-07-1982 P *100

LOCKHART, Albert Craig. 1301 22ND AVE N 37232 #048-12-1993 L2001 HO *020 †20

LOGAN, Jimmi Holliman. 117 28TH AVE N 37232 #047-07-1964 L1968 OPH LM *071 †35

LOGAN, Quinisha Kayon. 1005 DR DB TODD JR BLVD, DEPT OBG 37208 #047-06-2007 OBG *012

LOGAN, Regan Ann. 4200 STAMMER PL, BELMONT MEDICAL GROUP 37215 #047-05-1991 L1998 PD *020 †55

LOHRASBI, Faryab. 345 23RD AVE N, STE 212 37203 #047-06-1993 L1998 U *020 †95

LOHREY, Charlotte Jean. ■ 37203 #005-15-1999 L2005 IM *020 †20

LOHSE, James Joseph. 310 25TH AVE N 37203 #305-01-2002 L2007 FM FSM *020 †18

LOMIS, Kimberly. 1301 22ND AVE N 37232 #048-12-1992 L1996 GS *020 †85

LOMIS, Michael Tsolomitis. 2010 CHURCH ST, STE 615 37203 #654-01-1992 L1995 PTH *020 †50

LONG, Chandler Alexander. ■ 37209 #038-06-2007 GS *012

LONG, John Royston. 5819 OLD HARDING RD, STE 201 37205 #047-05-2002 L2005 PD *020 †55

LONG, Ruth B. 2000 CHURCH ST 37236 #047-05-1982 L1985 PD *020 †55

LONG, Wendy Jo. 425 5TH AVE N, TN DEPT OF HEALTH-HSA-4TH 37247 #038-40-1985 L1988 GPM PHP *030

LONG, William Royston. 7640 HIGHWAY 70 S, STE 202 37221 #020-12-1973 L1976 PD *020 †55

LOOSEN, Peter Thos. 1310 24TH AVE S 37212 #409-16-1974 L1986 P END *050 †75

LORENZ, Robert Roman. S-2100 MEDICAL CENTER NORT, VUMC DEPT OF OTOLARYNGOLOG 37232 #035-45-1996 L2001 OTO *020

LORINC, Amanda Nicole. ■ 37221 #012-01-2007 AN *012

LOTSHAW, Richard R. 1211 21ST AVE S, STE 220 37212 #055-01-1988 L2007 OBG *030 †30

LOUGHRIDGE, Mary Elizabet. 2200 CHILDRENS WAY 8161, CHILDREN'S HOSPITAL 37232 #012-22-2007 PD *012

LOUIS, Catherine Elizabet. ■ 37212 #005-12-2007 P *012

LOVEJOY, Steven Arnett. 1301 22ND AVE N 37232 #055-01-1980 L2005 ORS *020 †40

LOVELADY, Cari Laine. 1161 21ST AVE S - NEUR 37232 #047-06-2002 L2007 RNR *012

LOVEN, Keith H. 3441 DICKERSON PIKE 37207 #047-05-1983 L1987 D *020 †15

LOVLY, Christine Marie. ■ 37215 #028-02-2006 IM *012

LOVVORN, Harold N, Jr. 2021 CHURCH ST 37203 #047-05-1963 L1967 GYN *020 †30

LOVVORN, Harold Newton. 1301 22ND AVE N 37232 #047-06-1993 L2002 PDS *020 †85

LOWE, Jere Whitson, Jr. 2801 CHARLOTTE AVE 37209 #047-05-1986 L1991 U GS *020 †95

LOWE, Robert Witherspoon. 2011 MURPHY AVE STE 309, TN SPINE & JOINT CENTER 37203 #047-05-1998 L2005 OSS *020

LOWE, Sandra Vogt. 1301 22ND AVE N 37232 #007-02-1987 L1991 AN PD *020 †05

LOWRANCE, William Thomas. ■ 37215 #045-01-2003 L2008 U *012

LOYD, James Emory. 1301 22ND AVE N 37232 #055-01-1973 L1977 PUD *050 †20

LU, Bo. 1301 22ND AVE N, B-902 TVC 37232 #243-16-1987 L2002 RO *020 †80

LU, Marina Yuqing. 391 WALLACE RD 37211 #004-01-1998 L2001 EM *020 †16

LUBELL, Karen L. 310 25TH AVE N 37203 #048-13-2001 L2004 PD *020 †55

LUKENS, John Nevius, Jr. VANDERBILT MEDICAL CENTER, 209 OXFORD HOUSE 37232 #024-01-1958 L1975 PD PHO *040 †55

LUMMUS, William Edward. 1301 22ND AVE N 37232 #001-02-1994 L1996 EM *020 †16

LUNDIN, Linda S. 2409 21ST AVE S STE 104 37212 #047-05-1977 L1978 P CHP *020 †75

LUSCHEN, Michelle Gere. 2000 CHURCH ST 37236 #047-05-1992 L1996 VIR *020 †80

LUSSNIG, Erich. 210 25TH AVE N, STE 602 37203 #016-43-1998 L2002 DR *020 †80

LUSTIG, Daniel Gardner. 1161 21ST AVE S 37232 #046-01-2002 L2004 PG *012

LUTHER, James Matthew. 5205 ANCHORAGE DR 37220 #047-05-2001 L2003 NEP *012 †20

LYLE, Cari Elizabeth. ■ 37215 #018-03-2002 L2006 OPH *100

LYN, Safiya Kim. ■ 37209 #047-07-2008 *012

LYNCH, Alan James. ■ 37221 #004-01-1992 L1993 P *020 †75

LYNCH, Amy L. 2200 CHILDRENS WAY, DOT5121 37232 #020-02-1990 L1994 PD *020 †55

LYNCH, George Brandon. 356 24TH AVE N, STE 400 37203 #047-05-1992 L2002 GS *020 †85

LYNCH, John Brown. 2100 PIERCE AVE RM 230 37232 #047-06-1952 L1953 PS *071 †85,65

LYSHCHIK, Andrej. 1161 21ST AVE S, - RADI 37232 #913-32-1996 DR *012

MAC DONALD, James Richard. 1301 22ND AVE N 37232 #064-01-1995 L1997 FM *020 †18

MAC DONALD, Robert Louden. 1301 22ND AVE N 37232 #051-01-1973 L2001 N *050 †75

MAC DONELL, Robert C, Jr. 6313 PERCY DR, MIDDLE TENNESSEE MENTAL HE 37205 #012-05-1963 L1978 PN IM *020 †55

MACE, Rachel Lenox. 1301 22ND AVE N 37232 #047-05-1986 L1989 PD *020 †55

MACEY, John Witherspoon. 2021 CHURCH ST 37203 #047-05-1986 L1990 OBG *020 †30 ‡

MACK, Harry Russell, Jr. 5802 NOLENSVILLE RD, STE 103 37211 #001-02-1988 L1988 OS *020

MACKEY, Susan Eades. 2201 MURPHY AVE, STE 110 37203 #047-05-1989 L1995 OBG *020 †30

MACMILLAN, Robert Duncan. 110 29TH AVE N, STE 201 37203 #038-40-1957 L1962 AN PME *012

MACMURDO, Christina Lynn. 1301 22ND AVE N 37232 #047-05-1997 L2001 ID *020 †20

MAC NEW, Heather Garnett. 1161 21ST AVE S, DEPT CCM 37232 #012-22-2002 L2007 CCS *012 †85

MACRAE, Robert M. 1301 22ND AVE N # B902, VUMC DEPT OF RADIATION 37232 #060-02-1995 L2000 DR *020 †80

MADDEN, James Jos, Jr. 1211 22ND AVE N 37232 #010-02-1966 L1976 PS HS *020 †85,65

MADDOX, Robert Emory. ■ 37221 #047-06-1953 L1953 R NM *071 †80

MAGEE, Michael Jos. 300 20TH AVE N, STE 506 37203 #047-06-1977 L1977 HEM ON *020 †20

MAGNUSON, Mark Alan. 2215 GARLAND AVE, 802 LIGHT HALL 37232 #018-03-1979 L1985 END *020 †20

MAGNUSON, Natasha Janelle. ■ 37212 #047-05-2005 L2008 IM *012

MAGNUSSEN, Robert Andrew. 1215 21ST AVE S, ORTHOPAEDIC INSTITU 37232 #036-07-2004 L2007 ORS *012

MAGPANTAY, Edmundo D. 339 WHITE BRIDGE PIKE, TENN URGENT CARE ASSOC 37209 #748-01-1965 L1972 GP GS *020

MAHLER, D Mark. 310 25TH AVE N, STE 201 37203 #038-40-1976 L1990 OS PD *030 †55

MAIKIS, Roseann. 2011 MURPHY AVE, STE 305 37203 #035-48-1996 L2000 OBG *020 †30

MAKARI, John Howard. 1302-A MEDICAL CENTER N, VANDERBILT UNIV MED CTR 37232 #038-40-2000 L2001 UP *012

MAKRANDI, Vijay Rani. 1310 24TH AVE S, VAMC 37212 #495-45-1965 L1981 AN *020 †05

MALCOLM, Arnold Wm. 902 TVC, 1301 22ND AVE SOUTH, B 37232 #047-07-1973 L1974 RO *020 †80

MALIK, Furrukh Sayyer. 2400 PATTERSON ST, STE 215 37203 #704-01-1987 L2003 **CD** *020 †20
MALKERNEKER, Dee. ■ 37215 #047-05-2003 L2006 **DR** *012
MALLARD, Lindsay Jenna. 2325 CRESTMOOR RD 37215 #047-05-2002 **PD** *020
MALLARD, Robert Elwood. 2325 CRESTMOOR RD 37215 #047-05-1974 L1977 **PD** *020 †55
MALLIK, Nasreen Azhar. 1310 24TH AVE S, VA TENNESSEE VALLEYHEALTHC 37212 #495-77-1989 L2000 **P CHP** *020 †75
MALOW, Beth Ann. 1301 22ND AVE N 37232 #016-06-1986 L2003 **N IM** *020
MANGIALARDI, Robert J. 2400 PATTERSON ST, STE 101 37203 #047-05-1991 L1995 **PCC IM** *020 †20
MANGIALARDI, Wendy. 345 24TH AVE N, STE 103 37203 #048-02-1993 L1996 **ID** *020 †20
MANGRUM, Timothy Carlton. 4230 HARDING PIKE, STE 400 37205 #047-06-1994 L1995 **MPD** *020 †20,55
MANN, George Vernon. 1211 22ND AVE N 37232 #023-07-1945 L1958 **NTR CD** *050
MANN, Steven Lee. 3443 DICKERSON PIKE, STE G30 37207 #005-12-1979 L1983 **IM DIA** †20
MANSOUR, Alfred Ameen. ■ 37206 #021-05-2005 L2008 **ORS** *012
MANTLE, Christopher Andre. ■ 37215 #001-02-2006 **OTO** *012
MANTLE, Sarah Marshall. 2200 CHILDRENS WAY 8161D, CHILDREN'S HOSPITAL 37232 #001-02-2006 **PD** *012
MANUEL, Lapulapu V. 1414 COUNTY HOSPITAL RD 37218 #748-01-1952 L1979 **IMG** *071
MAPARA, Khubaib Yusuf. ■ 37212 #704-25-2004 **GS** *012
MARKHAM, Melinda Houston. 2200 CHILDRENS WAY, RM 2510 37232 #004-01-1996 L2007 **NPM** *100 †55
MARLAR, Clinton Andrew. ■ 37211 #047-05-2004 **GS** *012
MARNEY, Annis Morison. ■ 37211 #047-05-2003 L2005 **END** *012
MARNEY, Samuel Rowe, Jr. 1500 21ST AVE S, STE 3500 37212 #051-01-1960 L1960 **AI** *030 †20,03
MARON, David Joel. 1215 21ST AVE S, FLOOR SOUT 37232 #005-06-1981 L1993 **CD IM** *020
MAROTTOLI, Vincenzo. 1161 21ST AVE S PATH 37212 #561-10-1979 **PTH** *100
MARSDEN, Mark Edward. 4220 HARDING PIKE 37205 #021-06-1990 L1994 **EM** *020 †16
MARSHALL, Andre Paul. ■ 37212 #039-01-2008 *012
MARSHALL, Gary Thomas. 1211 21ST AVE S S404 37212 #048-15-2000 L2005 **CCS GS** *100 †85
MARTEL, Benjamin Paul. VANDERBILT UNIV MED CTR, 6016 MED CTR EAST 37232 #003-01-2004 L2008 **MPD** *012
MARTIN, Jason Brantley. 3215 W END CIR 37203 #001-06-2002 L2004 **PCC** *012 †20
MARTIN, Karen Elizabeth. 300 20TH AVE N, FL 9 37203 #047-05-2003 L2006 **IM** *020 †20
MARTIN, Kenisha Rochelle. CTR N, D-3100 VANDERBILT MED 37232 #001-02-2005 L2008 **IM** *012
MARTIN, Peter Robt. 1601 23RD AVE S STE 3068, DEPT OF PSYCHIATRY 37232 #067-01-1975 L1986 **P ADP** *050 †75
MARTIN, Raymond S, III. 4230 HARDING RD STE 525 37205 #023-07-1976 L1987 **GS VS** *020 †85
MARTIN, Richard Blair. 2400 PATTERSON ST, STE 101 37203 #047-05-1991 L1993 **IM** *020 †20
MARTIN, Sara Frances. ■ 37209 #036-01-2006 **IM** *012
MARTIN, William Henry. 1301 22ND AVE N 37232 #045-01-1975 L1983 **NM END** *020 †20,28
MARTINEZ, Jose Andres. 1301 22ND AVE N 37232 #001-06-1999 L2004 **PG** *020 †55
MARTINEZ, Rogelio D. 391 WALLACE RD 37211 #748-10-1966 L1971 **IM CD** *020
MARTUS, Jeffrey Edward. ■ 37215 #025-01-2001 L2007 **OP** *100
MASON, William Jeffrey. D-3100 MEDICAL CENTER NORT, VANDERBILT UNIVERSITY MEDI 37232 #004-01-2003 L2006 **ID** *012 †20
MASSIE, James Danl. 1301 22ND AVE N 37232 #027-01-1964 L1969 **R NR** *020 †80
MASSIE, Ralph W. 2400 PATTERSON ST STE 500 37203 #047-05-1953 L1953 **CD IM** *071 †20
MASSION, Pierre Pascal. 1161 21ST AVE S, VANDERBILT UNIVERSITY MEDI 37232 #165-07-1987 L2000 **IM PCC** *020 †20
MATHEW, Puthenpurackal M. 1301 22ND AVE N 37232 #495-37-1970 L1997 **PDE** *072 †55
MATHEWS, Douglas Chas. 345 23RD AVE 37203 #047-05-1991 L1997 **NS** *020 †25
MATHEWS, Gregory C. 1301 22ND AVE N 37232 #028-02-1996 L2003 **N** *020 †75
MATHEWS, Letha. 1301 22ND AVE N 37232 #495-78-1982 L1994 **AN** *020 †05
MAU, I-Fan Theodore. 1212 MEDICAL CENTER DRIVE, 7302 MEDICAL CENTER EAST, 37232 #024-01-2002 L2007 **OTO** *020
MAURICIO, Lilia D. 1916 PATTERSON ST STE 50 37203 #748-01-1965 L1972 **PTH** *020 †50
MAUSKOPF, Alice Elizabeth. 2200 CHILDRENS WAY, RM 2510 37232 #036-07-1997 L2002 **PD** *020 †20
MAWN, Louise Ann. 2202 S GARGE OFC BLDG, 2311 PIERCE AVE. 37232 #036-05-1990 L1998 **OPH** *020 †35
MAXWELL, George Patrick. 2021 CHURCH ST, STE 310 37203 #047-05-1972 L1981 **PS** *020 †65
MAY, Addison Kemp. 1301 22ND AVE N 37232 #045-01-1988 L2001 **CCS** *020 †85
MAY, James Marion. 1301 MEDICAL CENTER DR 37232 #047-05-1973 L1986 **END** *050 †20
MAY, Michael Eagan. 1301 22ND AVE N 37232 #047-01-1978 L1986 **DIA END** *020 †20
MAY, Stephen Duane. 300 20TH AVE N 37203 #047-07-1994 L1995 **IM** *020 †20
MAYER, Ingrid Alina. 1301 22ND AVE N 37232 #187-12-1993 L2003 **HO** *020 †20
MAYFIELD, William Cato. 394 HARDING PL STE 200, PREM ORTHO & SPORTS MED PL 37211 #027-01-1998 L2004 **ORS** *100 †40
MAYNARD, O Jerry. ■ 37214 #005-12-1967 L1968 **FM OS** *071
MAYNARD, William Henry. 1301 22ND AVE N 37232 #047-06-1992 L1996 **IM** *020 †20
MAYO, Jackiel Robert. 1301 22ND AVE N 37232 #836-02-1968 L1996 **NM** *020 †80
MAYORQUIN, Francisco J. 2300 PATTERSON 37203 #011-04-1989 L1993 **IM** *020 †20
MAYS, William Randolph. 53 CENTURY BLVD, STE 200 37214 #047-07-1991 L1993 **P** *020 †75
MAZER, Murray James. UNIVERSITY HOSPITAL, VANDERBILT 37232 #062-01-1969 L1983 **DR** *020 †80
MAZUR, Alexander. ■ 37212 #913-39-1983 L2007 **ICE** *100
MAZZONI, Paul Andrew. 4230 HARDING PIKE, STE 435 37205 #021-01-1980 L1984 **AN** *020 †05
MC ABEE, Stephanie Ann. 1161 21ST AVE S, VANDERBILT UNIV 37232 #047-05-2001 L2007 **GE** *012
MC ADAM, Brendan Francis. 2311 PIERCE AVE, VUMC 37232 #539-03-1987 L1999 **CD** *020
MC ALISTER, Aileen Hood. 4535 HARDING RD STE 309C 37205 #001-02-1980 L1981 **P PYA** *020 †75
MCARDLE, Erin Julia. ■ 37203 #047-05-2003 *012
MC CAIN, Robt Williamson. 397 WALLACE RD, STE 415 37211 #047-05-1987 L1990 **PUD** *020 †20
MCCLINTOCK-TREEP, Sara An. ■ 37221 #056-06-2003 L2007 **PTH** *100 †50
MCCLURE, Ian Thomas. 703 OXFORD HOUSE, 1313 21 ST AVENUE S. 37232 #035-01-2005 L2007 **EM** *012

MC COIN, Nicole Streiff. 703 OXFORD HOUSE, 1313 21ST AVENUE SOUTH 37232 #047-05-2003 L2005 **EM** *100 †16
MC COMBS, Paul Raymond. 2011 MURPHY AVE STE 301 37203 #011-02-1977 L1982 **NS** *020 †25
MC CONNELL, Thomas G. DEPT OF PATHOLOGY/C3319, 21ST AVE GARLAND/MED CTR 37232 #048-04-1990 L2003 **PTH** *100 †50,30
MCCORD, David Hughes. 1718 CHARLOTTE AVE 37203 #035-20-1984 L1991 **OSS ORS** *020 †40
MC COY, David Michael. 397 WALLACE RD, STE 314 37211 #047-05-1984 L1990 **FM** *020 †18
MC CRACKEN, Robert Lazear. 504 ELMINGTON AVE 37205 #047-05-1939 L1939 **TS** *071
MC CRAY, Robert Daryl. CTR N, D-3100 VANDERBILT MED 37232 #047-07-2003 L2006 **IM** *100
MC CRYSTAL, Kathryn A. 1301 22ND AVE N 37232 #051-07-1999 L2004 **END** *100 †20
MC CURLEY, Thos Leon, III. 1301 22ND AVE N 37232 #047-05-1974 L1977 **PTH IM** *020 †50
MC DERMOTT, Diane Simone. 1035 14TH AVE N 37208 #047-07-1992 L1994 **FM** *020 †18
MC DERMOTT, Ronald Ian. 3951 WALLACE LN, BLDG B 37215 #047-07-1994 L1996 **FM** *018
MC DONALD, Edward Clayton. 4220 HARDING PIKE 37205 #047-06-1974 L1974 **PTH** *020 †50 ‡
MC DONALD, Gary Raymond. 4230 HARDING PIKE, STE 400 37205 #047-05-1988 L1989 **IM** *020 †20
MC DONALD, Michel Alice. STE 3900, 1301 22ND AVENUE SOUTH 37232 #020-02-1993 L1997 **D** *020 †15
MCDONOUGH, Elizabeth Mari. 2200 CHILDRENS WAY 8161D, CHILDREN'S HOSPITAL 37232 #021-05-2006 **PD** *012
MC DOW, Ronald A. 4220 HARDING RD 37205 #047-06-1981 L1982 **FM D** *020
MC DOWELL, James G. 356 24TH AVE N, STE 400 37203 #048-13-1998 L2002 **GS** *020 †85
MC ELANEY, Mary Agnes. 397 WALLACE RD STE 415, SUITE 415 37211 #021-01-1983 L1988 **PUD CCM** *020 †20
MC ELMURRAY, James H, III. ■ 37209 #045-01-2003 L2006 **DR** *012
MCELROY, Julie Anne. ■ 37211 #012-22-2006 **PD** *012
MC ELROY, Steven James. 1301 22ND AVE N 37232 #041-15-1999 L2003 **PD NPM** *050 †55
MC FARLAND, Chiatne Tahan. ■ 37208 #047-07-2008 *012
MC FARLAND, Ronald Eric. 2021 CHURCH ST STE 606 37203 #047-07-1980 L1987 **OPH** *020 †35
MC FERRIN, James Reed. 1211 22ND AVE N 37232 #047-06-1974 L1975 **P** *020 †75 ‡
MCGARY, Cheryl Ann. ■ 37209 #047-05-2005 **P** *012
MC GINNIS, Charles W. 1005 D B TODD BLVD, HUBBARD HOSP 37208 #047-07-1951 L1955 **IM** *071 †20
MC GOWAN, Catherine Carey. DEPT OF MEDICINE, VANDERBILT UNIVERSITY 37232 #019-02-1987 L1991 **ID** *020 †20
MCGRANE, Stuart. ■ 37212 #919-05-1998 **AN** *012
MC GREW, Susan G. 2100 PIERCE AVE 426 MCS, CHILD DEVELOPMENT CENTER 37232 #016-06-1981 L1988 **PDC PD** *020 †55
MC GREW, Wallace R, Jr. 2400 PATTERSON ST, STE 101 37203 #050-02-1978 L1981 **GE IM** *020 †20
MC GRIFF, James E, Jr. 2010 CHURCH ST, STE 514 37203 #047-07-1969 L1972 **GP GS** *020 †85
MC GRIFF, Shontaye P. MEDICAL CTR N, # B-0107 37232 #024-01-2000 L2000 **N** *100
MC GRUDER, Charles E. 1005 18TH AVE S 37212 #047-07-1952 L1956 **OBG** *030 †30
MCGUINN, Shaun Cristin. 1161 21ST AVE S, OF O 37232 #012-22-2005 **OBG** *012
MC HUGH, Daniel Jos. 394 HARDING PL, STE 200 37211 #020-02-1991 L1995 **PM PME** *020 †60
MC HUGH, Michael John. 1310 24TH AVE S, DEPARTMENT OF VETERANS AFF 37212 #023-07-1984 L1992 **ORS** *020 †40
MC INNIS, John Cameron. 215 2ND AVE N 37201 #060-01-1970 L1977 **ORS** *020 †40
MC KECHNIE, Kevin Stuart. 2400 PATTERSON ST, STE 101 37203 #012-01-1998 L1999 **IM** *020 †20
MC KEE, David Earl. 3443 DICKERSON PIKE, STE 740 37207 #020-12-1975 L1981 **PS** *020 †85,65
MC KEE, Guat-Siew. 1501 HERMAN ST 37208 #825-01-1956 L1977 **IM** *020 †28
MCKEE, Heather Christine. ■ 37203 #008-01-2006 **N** *012
MC KEE, L Clifford. ■ 37215 #047-05-1957 L1957 **IM HEM** *071 †20
MCKENNA, Samuel Jay. 1623 THE VANDERBILT CLNC 37232 #047-05-1983 L1984 **OS** *020
MC KENNA, Terence Jos. 1161 21ST AVE S 37212 #539-03-1966 L1976 **END IM** *050
MC KINNEY, Jared John. 1313 21ST AVE S, 703 OXFORD HOUSE 37232 #047-05-2003 L2005 **EM** *100 †16
MC KINZIE, Jeffry Paul. MEDICAL CENTER, VANDERBILT UNIV 37232 #051-04-1986 L1991 **EM PEM** *020 †16
MC LAUGHLIN, Steven G. 3443 DICKERSON PIKE, STE 190 37207 #055-01-1986 L1991 **ORS** *020 †40
MC LEAN, Michael John. 2201 CHILDRENS WAY 1222J, VANDERBILT/STALLWORTH REHA 37212 #051-01-1978 L1985 **N** *040 †75
MC LEOD, Alexander C. 2400 PATTERSON ST, STE 400 37203 #036-07-1960 L1964 **IM CD** *071 †20
MC MANUS, Kevin T. 1301 22ND AVE N 37232 #041-09-1982 L1999 **NM DR** *020 †80
MC MASTER, Amy Ralston. 5117 MILLBROOK DR 37221 #047-07-1996 L1999 **FOP** *020 †50
MC MILLEN, David Hart. 222 22ND AVE N, STE 100 37203 #048-14-1999 L2001 **GE** *020 †20
MC MORROW, Sheila P. 1301 22ND AVE N 37232 #012-01-2000 L2003 **PE** *020 †55
MC NABB, Paul Carter. 2000 CHURCH ST 37236 #047-06-1974 L1975 **ID IM** *040 †20
MCNAUGHTON, Candace Dorot. ■ 37204 #028-02-2006 **EM** *012
MC NEIL, Larry Wayne. 7575 COCKRILL BEND BLVD 37209 #047-07-1973 L1977 **END IM** *040 †20
MC NEILL, Susannah Kay. ■ 37206 #038-41-2002 L2007 **PD** *020 †55
MC PHERSON, Ewing Wm. ■ 37215 #051-04-1948 L1949 **OM** *020
MCPHERSON, Jeffrey Louis. ■ 37205 #007-02-2005 **DR** *012
MC PHERSON, John Addison. 1215 21ST AVE S, SOUTH, MCE, $5209 37232 #005-14-1993 L2000 **CD IC** *020 †20
MC RAE, Andrew T, III. 2400 PATTERSON ST, PHYSICIAN PARK, STE 502 37203 #012-22-1996 L2003 **CD** *020 †20
MC RAE, John Radford. 4230 HARDING PIKE, ENDOCRINOLOGY DIABETES 37205 #036-07-1972 L1981 **DIA END** *020 †20
MCTIGUE, Michael Paul. ■ 37212 #047-05-2008 *012
MC VIE, Andrew Kyle. 4220 HARDING PIKE 37205 #021-05-1998 L2001 **EM** *020 †16
MCVIE, Angela Rae. 310 25TH AVE N, STE 201 37203 #047-05-2001 L2004 **PD** *020 †55
MEACHAM, Patrick Wallace. 2011 CHURCH ST, SUITE 404 PLAZA I 37203 #047-05-1976 L1978 **VS** *020 †85

MEADOR, Clifton K. 1919 CHARLOTTE AVE, STE 300 37203 #047-05-1955 L1955 IM END *030 †20

MEADORS, Marvin Porter. 2410 PATTERSON ST, STE 106 37203 #027-01-1984 L1988 RHU IM *020 †20

MEADORS, Michael Hudson. 4220 HARDING RD, STE 500 37205 #010-03-1997 L1998 IM *020 †20

MEADORS, Michael Hudson. 2011 CHURCH ST, STE 601 37203 #047-07-1975 L1979 OBG EM *020

MEADOWS, James Richard. 1718 PATTERSON ST 37203 #005-12-2002 L2005 FM *020 †18

MEANS, Julie Ann. RESEARCH BUILDING, 777 PRESTON 37232 #036-08-1997 L2002 HO *020 †20

MEDEIROS, Milton De Olive, Jr. ■ 37205 #051-04-2006 IM *012

MEEKER, William Kelly. ■ 37205 #047-06-1984 L1987 EM FM *020 †18

MEIER, Karen Sue. 1313 21ST AVE S, 703 OXFORD HOUSE 37232 #047-05-2006 EM *012

MEINTS, Laura. ■ 37209 #047-05-2008 *012

MELEKHIN, Vlada Vicki. 1161 21ST AVE S, MCN A 2200 37232 #001-02-2002 L2005 ID *012 †20

MELLANDER, Mats Olof. 1161 21ST AVE S 37232 #041-02-1992 NPM *050

MELTZER, Herbert Yale. 1601 23RD AVE S STE 306 37212 #008-01-1963 L1996 P *050 †75

MELVIN, Kelly Edward. 1601 23RD AVE S 37212 #055-02-2005 L2006 CHP †012

MELVIN, Willie Valentenia. D5203 MEDICAL CENTER NORTH, VUMC 37232 #047-07-1989 L1995 GS VS *020 †85

MEMON, Faiza Baqui. 1005 DR DB TODD JR BLVD, MEHARRY MEDICAL COLLEGE DE 37208 #704-08-1994 L2004 *020 †75 ‡

MENCIO, Gregory Anthony. 1301 22ND AVE N 37232 #036-07-1980 L1991 OP OSS *020 †40

MENDES, Lisa Ann. 1215 21ST AVE S, 1124 RADNOR GLEN DR 37232 #008-02-1987 L2002 CD IM *020 †20

MENSAH, Darlington N, II. 905 MAIN ST 37206 #047-07-1999 L2002 IM *020 †20

MERANZE, Steven Greene. 1301 22ND AVE N 37232 #042-01-1979 L1992 VIR DR *020 †80

MERCHANT, Nipun Bharat. 2220 PIERCE AVE, RM 597PRB 37232 #035-08-1990 L2001 GS *020 †85

MEREDITH, Mark Logan. 1301 22ND AVE N 37232 #027-01-2002 L2005 PE *012 †55

MEREDITH, Timothy John. 501 OXFORD HOUSE 37232 #917-23-1975 L1995 *020

MERICLE, Robert Alan. 1301 22ND AVE N 37232 #047-05-1993 L2004 NS *020 †85

MERRITT, Cullen R, II. 2000 CHURCH ST 37236 #047-05-1960 L1960 IM DIA *071

MERTZ, Howard Randall. 4230 HARDING PIKE, STE 309 37205 #048-04-1986 L1994 GE IM *050 †20

MESZOELY, Ingrid Marie. 1211 22ND AVE N 37232 #024-05-1993 L1999 SO *020 †85

METCALF, Sally Beth. ■ 37209 #036-01-2006 IM *012

MEYER, Richard Warfield. 4230 HARDING RD, STE 601E 37205 #016-02-1995 L2007 IM IMG *020 †20

MGBEMERE, Celestine C.. ■ 37207 #308-12-1987 L1998 GPM *100

MIAH, John Kaku. ■ 37211 #412-01-1990 L1994 IM *020 †20

MICHAUD, Marilynn. 2400 PATTERSON ST, STE 101 37203 #047-05-1991 L1994 HEM *020 †20

MICHEL, Andrew Alan. ■ 37205 #047-05-2003 L2007 P *100

MICKIEWICZ, Marc Anthony. 1301 22ND AVE N 37232 #016-11-1999 L2003 EM *020 †16

MIHYU, Salim Suhayl. 2400 PATTERSON ST STE 400 37203 #605-01-1989 L2001 PUD CCM *012 ‡

MILAM, Carol Proops. 250 25TH AVE N STE 304 37203 #055-01-1987 L1991 P *020 †75

MILAM, Douglas F. A1302, DEPARTMENT OF UROLOGY 37232 #055-01-1986 L1991 U GS *020 †95

MILEHAM, Kathryn Finch. 2220 PIERCE AVE, 777 PRESTON BUILDING 37232 #045-01-2003 L2006 HO *012 †20

MILEK, Michael Andrew. 301 21ST AVE N 37203 #021-05-1965 L1970 HS *020 †40

MILERAD, Josef. ■ 37205 #858-02-1973 NPM *020

MILES, Kenya Chantel. PO BOX 330141 37203 #047-07-2008 *012

MILEY, La Verne Dale. ■ 37217 #047-06-1958 L1979 GP *071

MILLER, Alison Nemeth. 1161 21ST AVE S 37232 #036-01-2001 L2007 PCC *100 †20

MILLER, Andrew Caleb. ■ 37221 #047-05-2004 L2006 AN *012

MILLER, Andrew Herron. ■ 37215 #047-06-1947 L1947 ORS *071 †40

MILLER, Andrew John. ■ 37209 #047-05-2008 *012

MILLER, Bonnie Mersky. 203 LIGHT HALL, VANDERBILT UNIVERSITY 37232 #039-01-1980 L1982 GS *020 †85

MILLER, Eva K. 2200 CHILDRENS WAY, MEDICAL STAFF OFFICE 37232 #048-16-2002 L2007 PD *100 †55

MILLER, Geraldine Pearl G. 1301 22ND AVE N 37232 #005-18-1973 L1991 ID IM *020 †20

MILLER, Jami Lyn. 1301 22ND AVE N 37232 #051-01-1988 L1994 D IM *020 †20,15

MILLER, Joe M. ■ 37214 #047-06-1951 L1952 GS *071 †85

MILLER, John Maurice. 602 GALLATIN RD 37206 #047-05-1956 L1956 ORS *071 †40

MILLER, Mark Allen. 300 20TH AVE N, FL 9 37203 #041-13-1991 L2007 GE *020 †20

MILLER, Matthew S. SUITE II, 7TH FLOOR, MEDICAL CENTER 37232 #048-16-2002 L2005 MPD *100 †20,55

MILLER, Nicole Lara. CENTER NORTH, A-1302 MEDICAL 37232 #041-12-2000 L2007 U *100

MILLER, Richard Steven. 1301 22ND AVE N 37232 #308-07-1983 L1990 GS TRS *020 †85

MILLER, Robert Frank. 6134 MEDICAL CENTER EAST, CENTER 37232 #047-05-1982 L1986 PUD IM *020 †20

MILLIS, James Brown. ■ 37204 #047-06-1955 L1959 GYN *020 †30

MILLS, Kathryn. 710 HART LANE 37243 #048-13-1999 L2003 OBG *020

MILLS, Theresa Ann. 2220 PIERCE AVE, 383 PRB 37232 #016-06-1994 L2007 CD *100 †20,16

MILNER, Donald Eugene. ■ 37215 #001-02-1967 L2006 PHP *020

MILSTONE, Aaron Paul. 1301 22ND AVE N 37232 #025-07-1994 L1995 PCC *020 †20

MINCH, Michael Francis. ■ 37205 #038-40-1973 L1977 MDM DIA *030 †85

MINICH, Peter John. 2400 PARMAN PL, STE 8 37203 #065-05-1987 L1994 U *020 †95

MINTON, Lee Roy. 107 GILMAN AVE FL 3 37203 #047-06-1958 L1959 OPH †35

MIOTON, Guy Britton, Jr. 4230 HARDING RD, STE 330 37205 #021-01-1978 L2007 CD IM *020 ‡

MIRE, Ryan Damien. 4230 HARDING PIKE, STE 601E 37205 #047-06-1998 L2001 IM *020 †20

MIRKOVIC, Radmila R. MEHARRY MED COLL, DEPT PED 37208 #957-02-1952 MM *050

MIRZANEJAD, Yazdan. A-3310 MEDICAL CTR N, VANDERBILT UNIV M C/ID 37232 #517-11-1985 L1995 IM ID *020 †20

MISHRA, Gita. 205 DONELSON PIKE 37214 #495-13-1968 L1974 FM *020 †18 ‡

MISHU, Ban. VANDERBILT UNIVERSITY, A2200 MEDICAL CENTER NORTH 37232 #047-06-1985 L1990 ID IM *020 †20

MISRA, Amaresh. 1916 PATTERSON ST, STE 201 37203 #495-79-1979 L1994 FM *020 †18

MISRA, Reeta. 3443 DICKERSON PIKE, STE 370 37207 #495-41-1973 L1983 PDE *020 †55

MISRA, Sumathi K. 1301 22ND AVE N 37232 #495-16-1992 L2001 IM *020 †20

MITCHELL, Carl Edward. 2201 MURPHY AVE, STE 207 37203 #028-02-1961 L1966 IM PUD *020

MITCHELL, Douglas Park. 222 22ND AVE N, STE 100 37203 #047-05-1969 L1969 GE HEP *020 †20

MITCHELL, Erika J. 1301 22ND AVE N 37232 #043-01-1999 L2005 ORS *020

MITCHELL, Lacey Nicolle. ■ 37205 #001-02-2004 L2008 D *012

MITCHELL, Robert Edward. ■ 37211 #035-01-2006 U *012

MITCHELL, Stephen A. 4230 HARDING RD, STE 803 37205 #025-01-1973 L1992 OTO OS *020 †45

MITCHELL, William Marvin. 1301 22ND AVE N 37232 #047-05-1960 L1962 CLP ID *071 †50

MITTAL, Richa N. ■ 37203 #048-13-2004 L2007 IM *100 †20

MIXON, James Christopher. 2000 CHURCH ST, DEPT OF PATHOLOGY 37236 #001-06-1987 L1991 PTH CCG *020 †50

MKOMA, Amosy Ephreim. 900 SHERBROOKE CV 37211 #913-04-1984 *100

MOCK, Berthrone Lacalvin. 1161 21ST AVE S 37232 #047-07-2000 L2000 CD *100 †20

MOECKEL, Gilbert Wolfram. 1301 22ND AVE N 37232 #409-16-1989 L2000 PTH *020

MOFFAT, Kenneth Pryce. 300 20TH AVE N, STE 601 37203 #065-06-1977 L1990 OPH *020 †35

MOFFAT, Scott Kenneth. ■ 37215 #035-01-2008 *012

MOGAN, Thomas Francis. 3441 DICKERSON PIKE 37207 #047-06-1954 L1956 IM *020

MOHAMMAD, Saeed. 1161 21ST AVE S 37232 #704-25-2003 PD *012

MOHMED, Tahir Ibrahim. ■ 37209 #848-01-2000 L2007 CD *012 †20

MOHSIN, Saif-Uddin Masood. 1005 DR DB TODD JR BLVD, OF PSYCH 37208 #286-05-2001 L2004 P *012

MOHYUDDIN, A T M. ■ 37221 #160-02-1953 L1977 CLP PTH *075 †50

MOHYUDDIN, Naved. ■ 37221 #047-06-1997 L2000 IM *020 †20

MOHYUDDIN, Shuaib. 510 RECOVERY RD, STE 201 37211 #047-06-1993 L1996 IM *020 †20

MOLETTE, Sekou F. 1506 CHURCH ST, STE 210 37203 #047-07-1995 L1999 PM PMM *020 †60

MONAHAN, Kenneth Joseph. 2220 PIERCE AVE, DIVISION OF CARDIOVASCULAR 37232 #051-01-2001 L2004 CD *012

MONTAGUE-BROWN, Karla. 901 12TH AVE S, SOUTH STREET FAMILY MED 37203 #047-07-1987 L1987 FM *020 †18

MONTELLA, Diane L. 1310 24TH AVE S, GRECC/HSR 4TH FL 37212 #010-01-1988 L1991 IM MDM *030 †20

MONTGOMERY, Marcia Ann. 2400 PATTERSON ST, STE 204 37203 #047-06-1975 L1976 GYN *020 †30

MONTGOMERY, Stephen A. 1301 22ND AVE N 37232 #047-06-1994 L2001 PFP *020 †75

MONTIJO, Michael Francis. ■ 37215 #005-14-1977 L1978 IM *030 †20

MOODY, Brent Robert. 1900 PATTERSON ST, STE 201 37232 #012-05-1996 L2003 DS D *020 †20,15

MOORE, Daniel Jensen. VANDERBILT CHILDREN'S WAY, 8161 DOT 37232 #041-01-2004 L2007 PDE *012

MOORE, David Ryan. 2021 CHURCH ST, STE 200 37203 #047-05-1998 L2004 OSM *020 †40

MOORE, Ilene N. 405 OXFORD HOUSE, CTR FOR PT & PROF'L ADVOCA 37232 #035-19-1977 L2005 FM LM *040 †18

MOORE, James Donald, Jr. 1301 22ND AVE N 37232 #020-12-1991 L2000 PDC *020 †55

MOORE, James N. 200 ATHENS WAY 5TH FL 37228 #038-41-1951 L1980 FM *030 †18

MOORE, Jeffrey Karl. 514 FISK ST 37203 #047-07-1987 L1991 FM *020 †18

MOORE, Kelly Lynn. 425 5TH AVE N, 4TH FL CORDELL HULL BLDG 37247 #047-05-2000 L2002 GPM *020 †70

MOORE, Paul Edward. 2200 CHILDRENS WAY, DOT 11215 37232 #024-01-1992 L2001 PDP *020 †55

MOORE, Sean R. ■ 37212 #023-07-2003 PG *012 †55

MOORE, Walton Louis. 500 DEADERICK ST, ANDREW JACKSON BLDG 15TH 37242 #027-01-1978 L1988 GPM PTH *030 †50

MOORE, Wayne Earl. 1818 ALBION ST, EMERGENCY DEPARTMENT 37208 #047-07-1985 L1995 EM *020 †16

MOORE, Wesley Boyd. 425 5TH AVE N, TN DEPT OF HEALTH CORDELL 37247 #047-06-1978 L1979 OM FM *020 †70,18

MOORE, Willard Anson, III. ■ 37215 #047-05-2008 *012

MOORE, William Alfred. ■ 37203 #048-12-2007 GS *012

MOORE, William L, Jr. 425 5TH AVE N, CORDELL HALL BLDG 4TH FL 37247 #012-01-1959 L1994 IM MD *040 †20

MOOTS, Paul Lawrence. 2311 PIERCE AVE STE 2234, VANDERBILT UNIVERSITY MED 37232 #038-40-1980 L1991 N ON *020 †75

MORAN, Grace Quiz. 2000 CHURCH ST 37236 #748-02-1983 L2000 DR *020 †80

MORAN, Ryan A. 2200 CHILDRENS WAY, VANDERBILT CHILDREN'S HOSP 37232 #036-01-2004 L2004 CCP *012 †55

MORAN, Sam H. 329 21ST AVE N 37203 #047-07-1981 L1986 OBG *020 †30

MOREAU, Gordon Alfred, Jr. 1919 CHARLOTTE AVE, STE 230 37203 #035-15-1976 L1984 PDC *020 †55

MOREDOCK, Gerald Michael. 333 MURFREESBORO RD 37210 #017-20-1974 L1986 FM *040 †18

MORELLI, Vincent. 1005 DR DB TODD JR BLVD 37208 #005-06-1983 L2007 FM *020 †18

MORGAN, Carrie Ingram. ■ 37209 #020-12-2005 L2008 PD *012

MORGAN, David Scott. 1301 22ND AVE N 37232 #047-05-1990 L1997 ON *020 †20

MORGAN, H Brooks. ■ 37215 #047-05-1966 L1968 ORS *071 †40

MORGAN, Kita Laini. ■ 37209 #047-07-2008 *012

MORGAN, Lisa Brooks. 2201 MURPHY AVE, LISA MORGAN MD 37203 #020-12-1993 L1997 OBG *020 †20

MORGAN, Walter Mc Nairy. 2200 CHILDRENS WAY, STE 4150 37232 #047-05-1982 L1990 PDS *020 †20

MORI, John Kenneth. ■ 37211 #047-05-2003 L2007 SME *012

MORIARTY, Cynthia Jean. 1005 DR DB TODD JR BLVD 37208 #004-01-1992 L1996 AN *030 †70

MORINO, Taira. ■ 37221 #572-13-1965 L1975 IM *050

MORRIS, Eric Van. 391 WALLACE RD 37211 #047-07-1988 L1992 EM *020 †16

MORRIS, John Albert, Jr. 1301 22ND AVE N 37232 #020-12-1977 L1984 TRS GS *020 †85

MORRISON, David George. 1301 22ND AVE N 37232 #020-12-1999 L2003 OPH *020 †35 ‡

MORRISON, Jefferson Craig. 4230 HARDING RD, STE 900 37205 #048-04-1996 L2002 ORS *020 †40

MORROW, Jason Drew. 1301 22ND AVE N 37232 #028-02-1983 L1987 IM *020 †20

MORROW, Stephen Eric. 1301 22ND AVE N 37232 #023-12-1985 L2005 PDS *020 †85

MORTON, Charles Ernest. 2201 CHURCH ST STE 104, P O BOX 331457 37203 #047-06-1974 L1974 GS *020 †85

MORY, Stephen Carl. 275 CUMBERLAND BND 37228 #041-02-1975 L2007 P *020 †18,75

MOSES, Harold, Jr. 2201 CHILDRENS WAY RM 1222, VANDERBILT STALLWORTH REHA 37212 #036-01-1993 L1997 N *020 †75

MOSES, Harold Lloyd. ■ 37232 #047-05-1962 L1963 **PTH** *050 †50

MOSQUEDA-GARCIA, Rogelio. 1211 22ND AVE N 37232 #649-01-1981 L1995 **PA CD** *050

MOSS, Jessica Jane. ■ 37215 #020-02-2005 **IM** *012

MOSS, Jonathan Randall. CTR EAST-S, 7209 VANDERBILT MED 37232 #036-01-2004 L2007 **OTO** *012

MOSSE, Claudio Alberto. 1301 22ND AVE N 37232 #051-01-2001 L2005 **HMP** *100

MOULTON, Dedrick Earl. 2200 CHILDRENS WAY, RM 2510 37232 #045-04-1995 L2002 **PD** *020 †55

MOULTON, Patrick Howard. 4220 HARDING PIKE 37205 #047-06-1968 L1969 **DR IM** *020 †80

MOUTON, Stephanie Marie. 1301 22ND AVE N 37232 #021-01-1981 L1984 **AN** *020 †05

MOUTSIOS, Sandra A. 1215 21ST AVE S, STE#6000 MCE 37232 #011-03-1993 L1995 **MPD** *020 †55,60

MOWERY, Nathan Teague. 1211 21ST AVE S, 404 MAB 37212 #055-01-2000 L2006 **GS** *100 †85

MOYERS, James Richard. 4220 HARDING PIKE 37205 #047-06-1958 L1958 **NM R** *071 †80,28

MOYERS, John Philip. 4220 HARDING PIKE 37205 #047-05-1991 L1993 **NM** *020 †80,28

MUDDANA, Srikant. ■ 37205 #024-16-2003 L2003 **GE** *012 †20

MUKHERJI, Bhaskar Aditya. SUITE 4200, MEDICAL CENTER EAST, SOUTH 37232 #024-07-1998 L2001 **PM** *020 †60

MUKUNDAN, Chetan Ravindra. 2325 CRESTMOOR RD 37215 #047-05-1994 L1997 **PD** *020 †55

MULDOON, Roberta Lee. D5248 MEDICAL CENTER NORTH, DEPT OF GENERAL SURGERY 37232 #016-43-1989 L2004 **CRS** *020 †10,85

MULDOWNEY, James A, III. VANDERBILT UNIVERSITY MED., 383 PRESTON RESEARCH BUILD 37232 #047-05-1999 L2006 **CD** *100 †20

MULHERIN, Joseph Louis, Jr. 4230 HARDING RD, STE 525 37205 #012-01-1971 L1973 **TS GS** *020 †85

MULLINS, William Michael. 1301 22ND AVE N 37232 #047-06-1971 L1971 **OTO HNS** *020 †45

MULLOY, Matthew Ryan. 2984 TVC, 1161 21ST AVENUE SOUTH 37232 #017-20-2000 L2003 **GS** *100 †85

MUNDY, Gregory Robt. 1235 MRB 4, BIOLOGY 37232 #143-02-1966 L2006 **END IM** *050 †20

MUNSON, Gregory. ■ 37204 #016-02-2003 L2005 **IM** *100 †20

MURFF, Harvey Johnson. 1301 22ND AVE N 37232 #047-06-1996 L2002 **IM** *020 †20

MURFF, Lynda Suzanne. 1310 24TH AVE S, NASHVILLE VETERAN'S HOSPIT 37212 #047-06-1997 L2002 **IM** *020 †20

MURPHY, Andrew Jackson. ■ 37201 #012-05-2007 **GS** *012

MURPHY, Barbara Ann. 1301 22ND AVE N 37232 #036-05-1987 L1993 **ON** *020 †20

MURRAY, John Jos. 1919 CHARLOTTE AVE, STE 100 37203 #047-05-1979 L1988 **PA IM** *020 †20,03

MURRAY, Katherine Thompson. 1301 22ND AVE N 37232 #036-07-1980 L1984 **PA** *020 †20

MURRAY, Mark Magruder. ■ 37217 #047-07-2007 **IM** *012

MURRAY, Robert Edward. 8283 RIVER ROAD PIKE, CUMBERLAND HEIGHTS 37209 #047-07-1979 L1979 **P ADP** *020 †75

MUSCATO, Nicole Elizabeth. ■ 37205 #047-05-2002 L2006 **PTH** *100 †50

MUSIEK, Amy Christine Mor. ■ 37205 #047-05-2004 L2008 **D** *012

MUTTER, Robert Wesley. ■ 37212 #047-05-2007 **IM** *012

MWENYA, Christopher. 1005 D B TODD BLVD 37208 #965-01-1989 **IM** *100

MYERS, Kevin James. 2410 PATTERSON ST, STE 106 37203 #047-05-1983 L1987 **RHU** *020 †20

MYERS, Paul Robt. 2400 PATTERSON ST, STE 502 37203 #041-01-1983 L1995 **CD IM** *020 †20

MYERS, Timothy Preston. 4220 HARDING PIKE 37205 #028-03-2000 L2002 **EM** *020

NADEAU, John Hugh Jos. 1301 22ND AVE N 37232 #065-09-1973 L1975 **CD PA** *020

NADING, Mary Alice. ■ 37205 #047-05-2008 *012

NAFTILAN, Allen Joel. 1215 21ST AVE S, STE 5209 37232 #001-02-1982 L1992 **CD IM** *020 †20

NAHRWOLD, Daniel Alan. ■ 37203 #017-20-2005 L2007 **AN** *012

NAIDU, Rama T. 1005 DR DB TODD JR BLVD 37208 #495-04-1962 L1977 **PD** *050 †55

NAJAFIAN, Behzad. ■ 37205 #517-01-1996 L2003 **PTH** *100

NAJJAR, Jennifer Lee. 2200 CHILDRENS WAY, RM 2510 37232 #024-07-1977 L1982 **PDE DIA** *020 †55

NAJJAR, Victor Assad. 21ST AVENUS S AT GARLAND, DEPT PD BOX 300 T0107 37232 #605-01-1935 L1959 **PD** *071

NANCE, Elmer Paul, Jr. 1301 22ND AVE N 37232 #036-01-1976 L1978 **DR** *020 †80

NANDI, Siddharta Prasad. ■ 37205 #001-02-2007 **GS** *012

NASH, James Frank. ■ 37205 #047-06-1974 L1975 **FM EM** *020

NASLUND, Thomas Chas. 1161 21ST AVE S, # D5237 MED CTR N DEPT VS 37232 #047-05-1984 L1989 **VS CD** *020 †85

NATHAN, Jayashree Rani. 1005 D B TODD BLVD, DEPT OF FAMILY MEDICINE 37208 #495-59-1995 **FP** *012

NAVARRE, Jrichard, II. ■ 37205 #036-01-2001 L2007 **CHP** *100 †75

NAZNEEN, Salma. 1005 DR DB TODD JR BLVD 37208 #160-06-1990 **P** *012

NEADERTHAL, Robert Lee. 300 20TH AVE N, STE 602 37203 #010-02-1973 L1973 **IM** *020 †20

NEAL, Gregory Eugene. 3443 DICKERSON PIKE, STE 600 37207 #012-01-1991 L1996 **GS** *020 †85

NEBLETT, Wallace Ware, III. 4150 DOT, 2200 CHILDREN'S WAY 37232 #047-05-1971 L1973 **PDS GS** *020 †85

NECK, Andrew Charles. ■ 37209 #047-07-2002 L2004 **EM** *012 †55

NEELY, Emily Peoples. ■ 37221 #027-01-2006 **IM** *012

NEFF, Betty Katherine. 2010 CHURCH ST, MID STATE MED CTR 37203 #040-02-1977 L1979 **GYN OBS** *020 †30

NEILSON, Eric Grant. 1301 22ND AVE N 37232 #001-02-1975 L1998 **NEP IG** *050 †20

NEIN, Alexander Garry. 2011 MURPHY AVE STE 608 37203 #001-02-1987 L1993 **PS** *020 †85,65

NELSON, Amanda Jane. - RADI, VANDERBILT UNIV MED CTR 37232 #020-12-2004 **DR** *012

NELSON, Bryce Allen. ■ 37221 #047-05-2003 L2006 **PDE** *012

NELSON, George Edward. 1161 21ST AVE S, DEPT MED 37232 #038-06-2006 **IM** *012

NELSON, I Armistead. ■ 37215 #035-01-1953 L1955 **GS TS** *071 †85

NELSON, Jeremy Sebastian. ■ 37208 #047-07-2008 **IM** *012

NESBITT, Jonathan Carl. 4230 HARDING RD, STE 525 37205 #010-02-1981 L1984 **TS** *020 †90,85

NESBITT, Kimberly K. 110 29TH AVE N, STE 202 37203 #005-12-1989 L1998 **AN** *020 †05

NESBITT, Tom Edward. ■ 37205 #048-12-1948 L1957 **U** *071 †95

NESBITT, Tom Edward, Jr. 345 23RD AVE N, STE 212 37203 #010-02-1978 L1985 **U** *020 †95

NESS, Reid Michael. 1301 MEDICAL CENTER DR, 1660 THE VANDERBILT CLINIC 37232 #017-20-1990 L2000 **IM GE** *050 †20

NETTERVILLE, James Lee. 7209 MEDICAL CENTER EAST, VANDERBILT UNIV MED CTR 37232 #047-06-1980 L1981 **OTO SO** *020 †45

NETTERVILLE, Joseph David. 4230 HARDING PIKE, ANESTHESIOLOGISTS 37205 #047-06-1985 L1986 **AN CCA** *020 †05

NEW, Melinda Stacey. 1301 22ND AVE N 37232 #041-01-1993 L2005 **OBG** *020 †30

NEWBORN, Odie Vernon. 2214 KIRK AVE 37218 #047-07-1973 L1978 **FM** *020

NEWCOMER, Julianne. ■ 37211 #041-02-2007 **PTH** *012

NEWMAN, John Hughes. 1301 22ND AVE N 37232 #035-01-1971 L1979 **PUD IM** *050 †20

NEWSOME, Henry C, III. STE 310, 2010 CHURCH STREET 37236 #036-01-1973 L1974 **OBG** *020 †30

NGIANGIA, Fabiyaere J. PO BOX 787, MEHARRY MED COLL 37208 #047-07-1982 L1983 **FM** *100

NGO, Tue Hoc. ■ 37205 #036-08-2001 L2006 **ID** *012

NGUYEN, Tuan Quoc. 3443 DICKERSON PIKE, STE 680 37207 #047-07-1997 L2001 **IM** *020 †20

NICHOLAS, Philip Arnold. ■ 37208 #047-07-1954 L1960 **OBG** *071 †20

NICHOLS, Daryl Lewis. 2021 CHURCH ST, STE 506 37203 #047-06-1978 L1979 **IM** *020 †20

NICHOLS, John Keith. 2021 CHURCH ST, STE 200 37203 #012-01-1992 L1997 **PM** *020 †60

NICKOLS, Hilary Highfield. ■ 37204 #047-05-2006 **PTH** *012

NIEDERHAUSER, Blake D. ■ 37212 #047-05-2008 *012

NIEDERMEYER, Michael E. 2010 CHURCH ST STE 710 37203 #010-02-1978 L1981 **PUD CCM** *020 †20

NIERMANN, Kenneth John. ■ 37205 #047-05-2002 **RO** *012

NINAN, Mathew. 2971 THE VANDERBILT CLINIC, 1301 22ND AVE. SOUTH 37232 #495-98-1988 L2001 **TS** *020

NISWENDER, Kevin Dean. 7465 MRB IV, DIVISION OF ENDOCRONOLOGY 37232 #047-05-1998 L2004 **END** *020 †20

NOBIS, William Paul. ■ 37212 #047-05-2008 *012

NOLTE, Christopher M. 1161 21ST AVE S, VANDERBILT UNIVERSITY 37232 #047-05-2003 L2007 **SME** *012

NOMANY, Choudhury Shiblee. ■ 37217 #160-03-2002 **IM** *012

NORFLEET, Ursula Denise. 1818 ALBION ST, METROPOLITAN NASHVILLE GEN 37208 #047-07-1998 L2001 **EM** *020 †16

NORMAN, Andy Murray. CENTER NORTH, B-1100 MEDICAL 37232 #012-01-1976 L1994 **OBG** *020 †30

NORMAN, Sharon Alicia. R-1217 MEDICAL CENTER NORT, VANDERBILT UNIVERSITY MEDI 37232 #012-05-2001 L2005 **OBG** *020 †30

NORRIS, John Langdon. MEHARRY MED COLL 37208 #035-20-1943 **OS** *040

NORRIS, Margaret Swann. 300 25TH AVE N STE B6 37203 #035-20-1949 L1958 **P** *071 †75

NORVELL, Sara Melissa. ■ 37204 #056-05-2004 **AN** *012

NUMNUM, Thomas Michael. ■ 37215 #001-02-2001 L2008 **OBG** *100

NUNN, Craig Robt. 37221 #033-06-1990 L1995 **CCS** *075 †85

NUNN, Paula S. 4535 HARDING PIKE STE 210 37205 #047-05-1981 L1982 **CHP** *100 †75

NUR, Sareda Abdulkadir. 391 WALLACE RD, 4TH FL 37211 #704-06-1999 L2006 **IM** *020 †20

NWABUZOR, Emeka Benedict. 1005 DR DB TODD JR BLVD 37208 #690-04-2001 **P** *012

NYLANDER, Barbara Hartkop. 345 23RD AVE N STE 209 37203 #047-05-1981 L1984 **OBG OS** *020 †30

NYLANDER, William Arthur. 1301 22ND AVE N 37232 #041-12-1977 L1984 **GS TTS** *020 †85

OAKES, Gary Randall. 2 VANTAGE WAY 37228 #047-06-1985 L1991 **FM OS** *062 †18

OAKLEY, Jennifer Lynne. 2201 MURPHY AVE STE 202 37203 #047-06-1981 L1982 **GYN** *020 †30

OAKS, Danny Eugene. ■ 37209 #001-02-1986 L1987 **AN** *020 †05

OATES, John Alexander. 1301 22ND AVE N 37232 #036-05-1956 L1964 **IM PA** *020 †20

OBERST, Mary Leslie. 4230 HARDING RD, STE 330 37205 #020-12-1994 L2007 **CD** *020 †20

OBREMSKEY, Jill Suzanne C. 1301 22ND AVE N 37232 #036-01-1990 L2002 **PD** *020 †55

OBREMSKEY, William. STE 4200, MCE, SOUTH TOWER 37232 #036-07-1988 L2002 **ORS** *020 †40

O'BRIEN, Lee A. 330 WALLACE RD, STE 109 37211 #047-05-1991 L1994 **PD** *020 †55

O'BRIEN, Thomas Jefferson. 397 WALLACE RD, STE 410 37211 #030-05-1985 L1996 **ORS** *020 †40

O'BYRNE, William Thomas. 3108 MEDICAL CENTER EAST, 1215 21ST AVENUE, SOUTH 37232 #001-06-1997 L2006 **AN** *020 †20

OCHIENG', Milton Oludhe. ■ 37203 #047-05-2008 L2008 *012

O'CONNOR, Susan J M. ■ 37214 #011-03-1970 L1973 **P** *020 †55,75

O'DAY, Denis Michael. 1301 22ND AVE N 37232 #143-02-1960 L1974 **OPH** *050 †35

ODIBO, Michael Chukwuma. 1005 DR DB TODD JR BLVD, DEPT MED 37208 #690-16-1997 L2008 **IM** *012

ODOM, Harrell, II. 222 22ND AVE N STE 400, MID STATE CARDLGY CONSLTS 37203 #004-01-1982 L1987 **CD** *020 †20

O'DONNELL, Frederick T. ■ 37212 #048-14-2007 **AN** *012

ODU, Chinyere Iheoma. 1005 DR DB TODD JR BLVD, DEPT MED 37208 #690-02-2000 **IM** *012

O'DUFFY, Anne Elizabeth. 2311 PIERCE SGOB 2307, DEPT. OF NURO 37232 #539-04-1989 L2001 **N** *020 †75

OGLE, Marissa Joy. 397 WALLACE RD STE 309 37211 #011-02-1997 L2001 **OBG** *020 †30

OGLESBY, John Wills. 301 21ST AVE N 37203 #047-06-1978 L1983 **ORS** *020 †40

OGUNTOLU, Olusola. 5543 EDMONDSON PIKE # 44 37211 #690-02-1987 L2002 **IM PCC** *020 †20

O'HARA, Heather Marie. 1005 D B TODD BLVD, MEHARRY MED COLL 37208 #047-07-2006 **GPM** *012

OKAFOR, Henry Ewelike. 383 PRB 2220 PIERCE AVENUE, VANDERBILT UNIVERSITY MED 37232 #690-04-1986 L2002 **ICE** *100 †20

OKAFOR, Ndubuisi Chiamaka. 1005 DR DB TODD JR BLVD, DEPT MED 37208 #690-15-2004 **IM** *012

OKEN, Andrew Chas. 1211 22ND AVE N, STE 2301VUH 37232 #040-02-1988 L2004 **AN** *020 †05

OKPAKU, Samuel Osifo. 1233 17TH AVE S 37212 #919-03-1968 L1987 **P** *020 †75

OKWUEZE, Martina Ifeoma. 7805 DAN KESTNER CT 37221 #021-01-1999 L2004 **CCA** *012

OLALEKAN, David Babalola. 1005 D B TODD BLVD, DEPT OF INTERNAL MEDICINE 37208 #690-02-1992 **IM** *012

OLDFIELD, Elizabeth Lynn. 2011 MURPHY AVE 37203 #047-06-1983 L1984 **OBG** *020 †30

OLDHAM, William Michael. ■ 37215 #047-05-2008 *012

O'LEARY, Mandy Ann. ■ 37211 #021-05-2006 **PTH** *012

OLIVE, Michael G. 222 22ND AVE N STE 100 37203 #047-06-1994 L1995 **IM** *020 †20

OLSEN, Douglas Ole. 2200 MURPHY AVE, STE B 37203 #016-01-1978 L1986 **GS AS** *020 †85

OLSEN, Nancy Josephine. 1301 MEDICAL CENTER DR 37232 #016-02-1977 L1985 **RHU IM** *020 †20

OLSON, Barbara Jean. 2400 PATTERSON ST, STE 216 37203 #056-05-1976 L1982 **CHN PD** *020 †55,75

O'MALLEY, Lee Martha. 2200 CHILDRENS WAY 8161, CHILDERN'S HOSPITAL 37232 #048-12-2007 **PD** *012

O'MALLEY, Matthew Robert. VANDERBILT UNIV SCH OF MED, DEPT OF OTOLARYNGOLOGY 290 37232 #011-03-2001 L2006 **OTO** *020 †45

ONADEKO, Olayinka O. 1005 DR DB TODD JR BLVD 37208 #308-10-1984 L1989 **PD U** *020 †55

O'NEAL, Lindsey Ellen. 1161 21ST AVE S, DEPT IM 37232 #048-04-2007 IM *012

O'NEILL, James A, Jr. 1301 22ND AVE N 37232 #008-01-1959 L1971 **PDS GS** *020 †85,90

O'NEILL, Kevin Raymond. ■ 37209 #017-20-2007 *012

ONG, Cheri. VANDERBILT UNIV HOSP, DEPT OF PLASTIC SURGERY 37232 #041-02-2000 L2006 **PS** *012 †85 ‡

ONG, Desiree Swanlie. ■ 37221 #021-05-2005 L2005 **OPH** *012

ONOCHIE, Nnenna Nkiru. 1005 DR DB TODD JR BLVD, MEHARRY MED COLLEGE 37208 #690-10-2004 **IM** *012

ONYESO-NWACHUKU, Ugochuku. 2201 MURPHY AVE 37203 #198-01-1990 L1996 **IM EM** *020 †20

OOTHOUT, Kevin Bradbury. 3441 DICKERSON PIKE 37207 #019-02-1991 L1993 **EM** *020 †16

OPPENHEIMER, Jonathan R. 1450 ELM HILL PIKE 37210 #025-01-1986 L1998 **PTH U** *020 †50

ORCUTT, Thomas Wm. 310 23RD AVE N 37203 #047-05-1968 L1968 **PS GS** *020 †85,65

OREBAUGH, John Edwin. ■ 37205 #025-01-1944 L1945 **GS CD** *071 †85

ORFANAKIS, Andrea. ■ 37215 #007-02-2005 L2007 **AN** *012

ORLAND, Richard Alan. 1023 NOELTON LN 37204 #036-07-1979 L1980 **IM** *030 †20

ORTH, David Nelson. 1211 22ND AVE N, D7235 N 37232 #047-05-1962 L1964 **END ON** *071 †20

ORTIZ, Lisa Katryn. 391 WALLACE RD 37211 #041-02-1994 L1997 **EM** *020 †16

ORY, Bridget Anne. CTR N, D-3100 VANDERBILT MED 37232 #021-05-2005 L2007 **IM** *012

OSBORNE, Tracy Jean. 510 RECOVERY RD, STE 201 37211 #016-45-1991 L1997 **ID IM** *020

OSGOOD, Michael James. ■ 37205 #012-05-2007 **GS** *012

OSLIN, Bryan Dewey. 4230 HARDING RD, STE 101 37205 #047-05-1988 L1996 **PS GS** *020 †85,65

OSO, Ayodeji A. 1005 DR DB TODD JR BLVD 37208 #690-01-1987 L1997 **IM** *020 †20

OSSOFF, Robert H. 7302 MCE SOUTH, VANDERBILT UNIVERSITY MEDI 37232 #024-07-1975 L1986 **HNS OTO** *020 †45

O'TOOLE, Molly Patricia. ■ 37205 #038-06-1987 L1988 **P** *020 †75

OVERFIELD, Ronald Edwin. 222 22ND AVE N, STE 100 37232 #047-05-1963 L1969 **R NM** *071 †80,28 ‡

OWENS, Julie Lynne. 300 20TH AVE N, FL 7 37203 #020-12-1984 L1988 **IM** *020 †20

OWNBEY, Richard Phillip. ■ 37215 #047-06-1954 L1954 **R** *071 †80

OZDEN, Nuri. ■ 37212 #902-19-1993 L2004 **GE** *020 †20

PACK, Jason Ricklin. 1161 21ST AVE S, DEPT OF RADIOLOGY 37232 #039-01-2002 L2004 **DR** *100 †80

PADGUG, Andrew J. 1310 24TH AVE S, TENNESSEE VALLEY HLTH CARE 37212 #056-06-1978 L1982 **DR** *020 †80

PAGE, David Lee. C-3309 MCN, VANDERBILT U., 1161 21ST AVE S. 37232 #023-07-1966 L1972 **ATP DMP** *050 †50

PAGE, Harry Lee. 1215 21ST AVE S, SO-ROOM 5209 37232 #047-05-1959 L1959 **CD** *020 †20

PAGE, Kathleen Elizabeth. ■ 37203 #045-01-2007 **OBG** *012

PAGNANI, Michael Jos. 2011 CHURCH ST STE 5, SUITE 505 37203 #047-05-1987 L1993 **ORS GS** *020 †40

PAI, Ramachander K. 1301 22ND AVE N 37232 #495-57-1978 L1996 **GS AN** *020 †05

PAKKALA, Sailesh. 1005 D B TODD BLVD, DEPT OF INTERNAL MEDICINE 37208 #305-01-2004 **IM** *012

PALKA, Kevin T. 2220 PIERCE AVE, 777 PRB 37232 #048-12-2001 L2001 **HO** *012

PALLOW, Robert James, Jr. 1818 ALBION ST, NASHVILLE METROPLOTAN GEN 37208 #047-07-1990 L1997 **VIR** *020 †80

PALM, Kenneth Hugo. 1301 22ND AVE N 37232 #005-12-1988 L2003 **EM** *020 †16,18

PALMER, Eric S. 2300 PATTERSON ST, MID TENNESSEE NEONATOLOGY 37203 #041-13-1991 L1995 **NPM PD** *020 †55

PANDHARIPANDE, Pratik P. 1211 21ST AVE S, STE 526 37212 #495-85-1995 L2001 **CCA** *050 †05

PANDULA, Rekha Narendra. 222 22ND AVE N, STE 100 37203 #495-85-1991 L2006 **IM** *020

PANZEGRAU, Beata. 210 25TH AVE N, STE 602 37203 #759-01-1991 L2008 **DR** *100 †80,28

PAOLICCHI, Juliann Marie. 1161 21ST AVE S, A-0118 MEDICAL CENTER NORT 37232 #023-07-1988 L2007 **PD** *020 †75

PAPP, Marta. 2000 CHURCH ST BOX 110, NEONATOLOGISTS PROFESSIONA 37236 #473-04-1985 L2002 **NPM** *020 †55

PAPSON, Kendra. ■ 37205 #041-12-2005 L2008 **EM** *012

PARANJAPE, Shubhada V. 1301 22ND AVE N 37232 #496-38-1990 L1999 **END** *020 †20

PARBHU, Keshini Chunilal. ■ 37203 #047-05-2004 L2008 **OPH** *012

PARDUE, Chris C. 24 WHITE BRIDGE RD 37205 #047-07-1981 L1981 **D** *020 †15

PARIJA, Gopal Chandra. 1818 ALBION ST 37208 #495-13-1967 L1989 **PTH** *050 †50

PARIKH, Alexander A. 1301 22ND AVE N 37232 #041-01-1993 L2005 **GS** *020 †85

PARISH, Samuel Keith. 3443 DICKERSON PIKE, STE 670 37207 #020-12-1988 L2007 **FM** *020 †18

PARK, Charles R. 1161 21ST AVE S OXFORD HSE, VANDERBILT SCH MED STE 209 37212 #023-07-1941 L1951 **OS** *030

PARK, Don J. 2220 PIERCE AVE, 777 PRB 37232 #583-06-1985 L1998 **HO** *020 †20

PARKER, Joseph Patrick. 222 22ND AVE N, STE 100 37203 #038-43-1994 L2001 **GE** *020 †20

PARKER, Morgan Grey. 4306 HARDING RD, STE 300 37205 #047-05-2002 L2006 **OPH** *020

PARKER, Roy W. ■ 37203 #047-05-1944 L1944 **GYN** *071 †30

PARKER, Scott Robinson. 1301 22ND AVE N 37232 #001-06-1991 L1994 **FM** *020 †18

PARKER, Stephen Q. 1100 KERMIT DR, STE 210 37217 #045-01-1993 L2003 **PM** *020 †60

PARKS, Leon Lucien, III. 1215 21ST AVE S, CENTER EAST, SOUTH TOWER, 37232 #027-01-1991 L1994 **END** *020 †20

PARKS, Mitchell Hunter. 1005 DR DB TODD JR BLVD 37208 #056-05-1992 **P** *020

PARL, Fritz Focke. 1301 22ND AVE N 37232 #407-07-1968 L1980 **PTH** *020 †50

PARMAR, Purav Mahendrabha. 1005 DR DB TODD JR BLVD 37208 #495-76-2001 **IM** *012

PARMLEY, Clifford Lee. 1211 2ND AVE S STE 324, VUMC DIVISION OF CRITICAL 37210 #005-12-1976 L2004 **CCA LM** *040 †05

PARRA, David Andres. 1301 22ND AVE N 37232 #319-01-1993 L2004 **PDC** *020 †55

PARRISH, Carolyn Amelia. 1919 CHARLOTTE AVE, STE 220 37203 #039-01-1980 L1986 **OPH** *020 †35 ‡

PARSH, Brahm S. 1005 DR DB TODD JR BLVD 37208 #495-09-1965 L1974 **NPM PD** *040 †55 ‡

PARTAIN, Clarence Leon. RR1223, VANDERBILT UNIV MED CNTR 37232 #028-02-1975 L1977 **DR NM** *020 †28,80

PARTRIDGE, Megan E. ■ 37212 #051-07-2002 L2007 **AI** *020 †55,03

PARTRIDGE, Rebecca Lynn. 1301 22ND AVE N 37232 #049-01-2002 L2005 **PE** *012 †55

PARVEZ, Babar. 1005 D B TODD BLVD 37208 #704-21-2004 IM *012

PASCHAL, Rita Daniell. ■ 37221 #011-04-2005 L2008 **IM** *012

PASCHALL, Naomi S. 1035 14TH AVE N 37208 #047-07-1997 L2000 **OBG** *020

PASCHALL, Ray Lamar, Jr. 4202 VUH 7580, 1211 MEDICAL CENTER DR 37232 #004-01-1990 L1994 **AN** *020 †05

PASIPANODYA, Alphonse T. 1005 DR DB TODD JR BLVD 37208 #047-07-1974 L1976 **GS** *020 †85

PASS, Bernard J. 1211 22ND AVE N 37232 #016-11-1935 L1952 **D** *071 †15

PASS, Lawrence James. 2400 PATTERSON ST, STE 523 37203 #016-06-1977 L1988 **TS** *020 †85,90

PASSMORE, Roger Neil. 2400 PATTERSON ST, SPORTS MEDICINE, SUITE 300 37203 #045-01-1995 L1999 **ORS** *020 †40

PASTO-CROSBY, Douglas J. 4220 HARDING PIKE 37205 #035-15-1980 L1988 **FM** *020 †16,18

PATE, J Kirby. 310 25TH AVE N STE 309 37203 #047-06-1978 L1980 **SME P** *020 †75

PATEL, Ashish Shashikant. ■ 37221 #047-05-2004 *100

PATEL, Harshila R. ■ 37211 #495-16-1984 L1992 **PD** *020 †55

PATEL, Ilaben Pramodkumar. 1005 DR DB TODD JR BLVD, C/O DR ROGER ZOOROB 37208 #025-07-2002 L2005 **FM** *020 †18

PATEL, Jayesh Ambubhai. 3443 DICKERSON PIKE, STE G30 37207 #690-01-1984 L1993 **ID IM** *020 †20

PATEL, Manish Rajni. ■ 37209 #011-02-2005 **IM** *012

PATEL, Sachin. ■ 37221 #056-06-2006 **P** *012

PATEL, Sanjay Govind. ■ 37212 #047-05-2008 *012

PATIKAS, Louise Green. ■ 37215 #047-05-1965 L1968 **PD** *030

PATIKAS, Takis. 328 22ND AVE N 37203 #047-05-1965 L1972 **PS HS** *020 ‡

PATTEN, Allegra. 300 20TH AVE N, FL 7 37203 #047-05-1992 L1996 **N** *020 †75

PATTEN, William Thomas. 222 22ND AVE N, STE 100 37203 #047-05-1981 L1983 **FM** *020 †18

PATTERSON, Arthur Knox. 210 25TH AVE N, STE 611 37203 #004-01-1968 L1977 **DR** *020 †80

PATTERSON, Barron Lee. 1301 22ND AVE N 37232 #047-05-2000 L2004 **PD** *020 †55 ‡

PATTERSON, Warren R. 2000 CHURCH 71 ST 37236 #047-06-1964 L1965 **PS HNS** *020 †45,65

PATTON, Christopher M. 5819 OLD HARDING RD, STE 201 37205 #047-06-1994 L1997 **PD** *020 †20

PATTON, Jennifer Diane. 2200 CHILDRENS WAY 8161D, CHILDREN'S HOSPITAL 37232 #038-43-2004 L2007 **AI** *012 †55

PATTON, Leah Cordovez. 1911 STATE ST, UT MEDICAL CLINIC 37203 #715-01-2000 L2007 **IM** *012 †20

PATTON, Thomas Herbert. ■ 37211 #001-02-2005 **N** *012

PATZER, David Karl. ■ 37203 #016-06-1989 L2005 **CHP** *075 †75

PAUL, William Steven. ■ 37212 #016-11-1986 L2007 **ID PHP** *030 †20

PAVLOTSKY, Michael. ■ 37213 #913-50-1953 *100

PAYNE, Rose Anne. 2325 CRESTMOOR RD 37215 #051-01-1996 L1998 **IM** *020 †20

PAYNE, William Barrett. ■ 37212 #047-05-2008 *012

PAYNE, William Faxon. 21ST AND GARLAND, VANDERBILT UNIVERSITY 37232 #047-05-1948 L1948 **R** *071 †80

PEACH, John Paul. 2002 RICHARD JONES RD, STE B300 37215 #020-02-1994 L1996 **IM** *020 †20

PEACOCK, Mark Darrin. 2010 CHURCH ST, STE 710 37203 #028-03-1986 L1995 **CCM IM** *020 †20

PEARSON, Adrian Scott. 2220 PIERCE AVE, 597 PRESTON BLDG L CENTER 37232 #047-06-1991 L1999 **GS** *020 †85

PEARSON, Delinda L. 2300 PATTERSON ST, MID TENNESSEE NEONATOLOGY 37203 #023-07-1995 L2001 **NPM** *020 †55

PEARSON, Matthew Marshall. 2200 CHILDRENS WAY, 9226 DOT 37232 #023-07-1995 L2003 **NS** *012

PEARSON, Sam Smiseth. 2553 MURFREESBORO PIKE, ASSOCIATES 37217 #047-06-1985 L1986 **EM** *020

PEDIGO, Jeanne N. 230F CUMBERLAND BND, MEDICINE AT WORK 37228 #023-07-1984 L1985 **IM OM** *020 †20

PEDIGO, Thurman Lee, Sr. 230F CUMBERLAND BND 37228 #047-06-1965 L1965 **FM FPG** *030 †18

PEEBLES, Jacqueline Joyce. 703 OXFORD HOUSE, MEDICAL UNIVERSITY OF SC 37232 #045-04-2004 L2007 **PE** *012 †55

PEEBLES, Ray Stokes, Jr. 1301 22ND AVE N 37232 #047-05-1986 L1988 **PCC AI** *050 †20,03

PEEBLES, Roosevelt, Jr. 1916 PATTERSON ST STE 205 37203 #033-06-1985 L1993 **PS GS** *020 †85,65

PEEK, Julie Thomas. 316 22ND AVE N 37203 #036-01-1988 L1992 **PD** *020 †55

PEEK, Richard Maurice, Jr. VANDERBILT UNIVERSITY, 1030 MEDICAL RESEARCH BUIL 37232 #036-01-1988 L1992 **GE IM** *020 †20

PEERMAN, Charles G, Jr. 4220 HARDING RD 37205 #047-05-1949 L1949 **GYN** *071 †30

PEI, Zhiheng. 1301 22ND AVE N S4605, PATHOLOGY 37232 #243-99-1982 L2000 **PTH** *020

PELLEGRINO, Alicia Maria. 2002 RICHARD JONES RD, STE A102 37215 #027-01-2004 L2007 **PD** *020 †55

PELMORE, Janet. ■ 37211 #047-07-1990 L1992 **PUD** *020

PELTIER, Amanda C. 1301 22ND AVE N 37232 #038-40-1998 L2005 **N** *050 †75

PENNINGTON, Brent Edward. 2525 21ST AVE S 1ST FL, NASHVILLE SKIN & CANCER 37212 #047-05-2000 L2005 **D** *100 †15

PENNINGTON, Jefferson, Jr. ■ 37221 #047-05-1951 L1951 **GS** *071

PENNINGTON, Thomas S. ■ 37215 #047-05-1951 L1951 **A IM** *071 †20,03

PEPPER, Colleen. ■ 37212 #047-05-2008 *012

PERALES, Maria Isabel. 397 WALLACE RD BLDG C, SUITE 204 37211 #649-14-1975 L1982 **OBG** *020 †30

PERALES, Pedro Juan. 110 29TH AVE N, STE 301 37203 #649-14-1964 L1970 **AN** *020

PEREIRA, Jason Kyle. 1301 22ND AVE N 37232 #047-06-2001 L2003 **IM** *020

PERKINS, Jennifer Marie. 2213 GARLAND AVE, VANDERBILT UNIVERSITY 7474 37232 #032-01-2003 L2005 **END** *012 †20

PERKINS, Meghan Jane. 2200 CHILDRENS WAY 8161D, CHILDREN'S HOSPITAL 37232 #026-08-2004 L2007 **AI** *012 †55

PERLIN, Donna J. 11101 DOCTOR OFFICE TOWER, HOSPITAL DEPT OF PEDIATRI 37232 #051-04-1989 L2006 **PEM** *100 †55

PERLMAN, Stewart Neal. 1211 22ND AVE N SO2301, DEPT OF ANESTHES./MSA DIV 37232 #001-02-1981 L1984 **AN** *020 †05

PERRI, Aimee Priolo. 7069 HIGHWAY 70 S, CENTENNIAL PEDIATRICS, P.C 37221 #048-13-1999 L2006 **PD** *020 †55

PERRI, Roman Edward. 1301 22ND AVE N, 1501 TVC 37232 #056-05-1999 L2006 **GE** *100 †20

PERRY, James Murray, Jr. 3443 DICKERSON PIKE, STE 430 37207 #047-05-1963 L1963 **CD** *071 †20

PERRY, Ludwald O P. ■ 37207 #047-07-1946 L1959 **GE IM** *071

PERRY, Stephanie Annette. 425 5TH AVE N, 3RD FL CORDELL HULL BLDG 37247 #047-07-1980 L1982 **PD** *020

PETERS, Mark Thos. 4230 HARDING PIKE, STE 400 37205 #038-40-1987 L1991 PDP PD *020 †55,20

PETERSON, Josh Favrot. 1301 22ND AVE N 37232 #047-05-1997 L2002 IM *020 †20

PETHKAR, Rashmi. ■ 37215 #495-34-1991 L2003 N *020 †75

PETRACEK, Michael Ray. 1215 21ST AVE S 37232 #023-07-1971 L1981 TS *020 †85,90

PETRIE, William Marshall. 310 25TH AVE N, STE 309 37203 #047-05-1972 L1977 P PYG *020 †75

PETRONI, Kenneth Chas. 4230 HARDING PIKE, ANESTHESIOLOGISTS 37205 #047-05-1991 L2002 CCA *020 †05

PETRONI, Molly Boyce. ■ 37215 #047-05-1991 L1992 IM *020 †20

PETTIT, April Christine. 1215 21ST AVE S, MCE 7TH FLOOR, STE 4 37232 #025-07-2004 L2006 ID *012 †20

PETTIT, William Albert. 610 GALLATIN RD 37206 #047-05-1958 L1960 IM *020 †20

PETTUS, William Harold. 2021 CHURCH ST STE 305 37203 #047-06-1980 L1981 NEP IM *020 †20

PETWAY, Zandra Renee. 390 HARDING PL, STE 102 37211 #047-07-1994 L1996 OM *020

PFISTER, Kathleen Marie. ■ 37205 #026-04-2007 PD *012

PHARES, Joel Michael. 4230 HARDING RD, STE 330 37205 #033-06-1997 L2005 CD *020 †20

PHAY, John Edward. 1301 22ND AVE N 37232 #005-02-1993 L2002 GS *020 †85

PHEA, Theodora Yvette. 1211 22ND AVE N, D7235 N 37232 #048-12-1986 L1993 PD OS *020

PHELPS-WEAVER, Paula. PO BOX 158545 37215 #020-12-1982 L1985 IM *020 †20

PHILLIPS, Daniel Lee. 301 21ST AVE N 37203 #047-05-1983 L1988 ORS *020 †40

PHILLIPS, Erin Lea. ■ 37211 #048-13-2003 L2006 CN *012

PHILLIPS, John Atlas. 1301 22ND AVE N 37232 #036-05-1969 L1984 CG PD *050 †55,19

PHILLIPS, Scott Ashley. ■ 37205 #045-01-2002 L2004 CD *012 †20

PIANA, Robert Noel. 2311 PIERCE AVE, CAMPBELL HEART INST 37232 #041-01-1987 L2000 CD *020 †20

PIERCE, Donald Fay, Jr. 5604 KENDALL DRIVE, VANDERBILT MEDICAL CENTER 37232 #001-02-1986 L1988 AN *020

PIERRE, Ketsia Bersy. ■ 37215 #011-04-2003 L2006 GS *012

PIETSCH, John Brooke. CHILDRENS HOSP, 4150 VANDERBILT 37232 #025-01-1972 L1986 PDS *020 †85

PILKINTON, Robert D, Jr. 300 20TH AVE N STE 504 37203 #047-06-1990 L1995 OPH *020 †35

PILKINTON, Robert Dale. 3443 DICKERSON PIKE #S-350 37207 #047-06-1963 L1964 OS GP *020

PILLA, Michael Anthony. 1211 22ND AVE N, STE 2301 VUH (7115) 37232 #041-01-1994 L2003 AN *020 †05

PINA GARZA, Jesus Eric. 1301 22ND AVE N 37232 #649-02-1985 L1996 CHN *020 †55,75

PINCUS, Theodore Paul. 1301 MEDICAL CENTER DR 37232 #024-01-1966 L1980 RHU IG *071 †20

PINI, Tunghi May. ■ 37203 #047-05-2003 L2006 IM *100 †20

PINKLEY, Bram Ian. 316 22ND AVE N 37203 #047-20-2001 L2005 PDC *020 †55

PINSON, Charles Wright. 1301 22ND AVE N 37232 #047-05-1980 L1990 GS CD *020 †85

PINSON, Richard Duncan. 1301 22ND AVE N 37232 #047-05-1976 L1978 IM EM *062 †20,16 ‡

PIPER, Sharon Mehlman. 300 20TH AVE N, STE 302 37203 #051-07-1987 L1990 OBG *020 †30

PIRKLE, James Lester, Jr. 21ST AVENUE SOUTH AND GARL 37232 #001-02-2003 L2007 NEP *012 †20

PIRKLE, Stephanie Spauldi. ■ 37212 #001-02-2003 L2007 PD *020 †55

PIROLO, John Stephen. 4230 HARDING RD, INFORMATICS OFFICE 37205 #023-07-1986 L1994 TS *020 †85,90

PITCHFORD, Clovis Warren. ■ 37232 #047-05-2004 L2006 PTH *012

PITIYANUVATH, Nataria. ■ 37209 #028-34-2003 L2007 CN *012

PITTARD, Andrew Gordon. 2200 CHILDRENS WAY 8161D, CHILDREN'S HOSPITAL 37232 #045-01-2006 PD *012

PIYARATNA, Rohith Udaya. ■ 37212 #047-05-2008 *012

PLEMMONS, Gregory Scott. 2200 CHILDRENS WAY, VCH 8232 DOT 37232 #045-01-1992 L1998 PD OS *020 †55

PLOSA, Erin Thompson. ■ 37215 #036-05-2005 PD *012

PLOURDE, Kimberly Renee. 1210 22ND AVE N 37232 #048-14-2004 L2006 EM *100

PLUIM, Thomas Arthur, II. ■ 37209 #023-12-2003 L2003 CCP *012 †55

PLUMMER, Linda C. 6485 HOLT RD, P O BOX 110811 37211 #047-06-1982 L1984 EM *020

POE, Cupid Reese. 1811 STATE ST 37203 #047-07-1964 L1976 P *020

POGUE, James Herman. 5552 FRANKLIN PIKE, STE 100 37220 #047-05-1994 L1998 FM *020 †18 ‡

POH, Melissa Moonnan. ■ 37212 #010-02-2000 L2007 PS *012

POHLMANN, Paula Raffin. DIV OF HEMATOLOGY/ONCOLOGY, VANDERBILT UNIV SCH OF MED 37232 #187-02-1992 HO *012

POLK, David Brent. 1301 22ND AVE N 37232 #004-01-1984 L1990 PD GE *050 †55

POLK, William Howard, Jr. 356 24TH AVE N, STE 400 37203 #047-05-1985 L1988 GS ON *020 †85

POLKOWSKI, Gregory Gerald. ■ 37221 #004-01-2004 L2007 ORS *012

PONT, Molly M. ■ 37214 #048-12-2002 L2005 NPM *012 †55

PONT, Stephen J. 1301 22ND AVE N 37232 #048-12-2002 L2005 PD *100 †55

POORE, Brian Jeffrey. 4230 HARDING RD, STE 435 37205 #011-02-1992 L1993 CCA *020 †05

POPE, Jason Edward. GARLAND AVENUE, GME OFFICE VUMC 37232 #017-20-2004 L2006 AN *012

POPE, John Crittenden, IV. 2200 CHILDRENS WAY, 4102 DOT 37232 #047-06-1989 L1991 U *020 †95

PORASHKA, Tanya Dimitrova. 1161 21ST AVE S 37232 #198-01-1996 P *012

PORAYKO, Michael K. 1313 21ST AVE S 801, OXFORD HOUS 37232 #016-11-1981 L2002 IM HEP *020 †20

PORCH, Phillip P, III. 395 WALLACE RD, STE 206B 37211 #047-06-1981 L1981 U *020 †95

PORTER, Lester Lee. 4230 HARDING RD, STE 707 E PLAZA 37205 #012-01-1976 L1978 IM ON *020 †20

PORTER, Matthew William. 703 OXFORD HOUSE, 1313 21ST AVE. S. 37232 #039-01-2006 L2007 EM *012

POST, Robert Lickely. 1161 21ST AVE S 37212 #024-01-1945 OS *050

POTASH, David Lewis. ■ 37208 #050-02-1976 L1977 OS EM *030 †20

POTEET, Stephen Julian. ■ 37205 #001-02-2006 GS *012

POTTER, Amy E. 2200 CHILDRENS WAY, RM 4303 37232 #048-13-1997 L2000 END *020 †20,55

POTTER, Eric Colson. 4230 HARDING RD, STE 400 37205 #047-05-1999 L2002 MPD *020 †20,55

POTTER, Susan Michelle. 383 PRB 2220 PIERCE AVE 37232 #917-24-1998 CD *012 †20

POTTS, Thomas Edward. ■ 37221 #047-06-1957 L1959 GS *071

POULOS, Steve George. ■ 37211 #047-07-2008 *012

POULOSE, Benjamin K. 1161 21ST AVE S, D-5203 MEDICAL CENTER NORT 37232 #023-07-1999 L2002 GS *020 †85

POWELL, Neil G. 2010 CHURCH ST, STE 514 37203 #011-02-1984 L2001 NS *020 †25

POWELL-TYSON, Dorris E. 1301 22ND AVE N 37232 #056-05-1994 L2003 EM *020 †16

POWERS, Alvin Carter. 1301 22ND AVE N 37232 #047-06-1979 L1988 END *050 †20

POWERS, James Stephen. EAST, 7155 VANDERBILT MEDICAL CE 37232 #035-45-1977 L1980 IM IMG *020 †20 ‡

POWERS, Thomas Allen. 1301 22ND AVE N 37232 #047-05-1973 L1975 R NM *020 †28,20,80

P'POOL, David Bruce, Jr. 1301 22ND AVE N 37232 #047-06-1963 L1964 D *020

PRABHAKAR, Bangalore N. ■ 37221 #495-09-1976 FM *020

PRAKASH, Rudra. 221 STEWARTS FERRY PIKE, MIDDLE TN MENTAL HLTH INST 37214 #495-41-1972 L1983 P *020 †75

PRASAD, Subir. 4230 HARDING PIKE, STE 501 37205 #047-06-1995 L1996 N *020 †75

PRASS, Richard Lee. 4230 HARDING RD, STE 803 37205 #038-06-1981 L2004 OTO OS *020 †45

PRESENTATION, Philomina. 6723 COLD STREAM DR 37221 #496-21-1989 L2000 P ADP *020 †75

PRESLEY, Richard Eldon. 2011 MURPHY AVE, STE 202 37203 #047-06-1974 L1975 OBG *020

PRETORIUS, Mias. 1301 22ND AVE N 37232 #836-03-1993 L2000 AN *020 †05

PRICE, Ann Hutcheson. 21 ST GARLAND D-8212(MCN), ALUMNIAFFAIRS 37232 #047-05-1978 L1979 IM *020 †20

PRICE, James Sterling. 316 22ND AVE N 37203 #047-05-1968 L1968 PD *020 †55

PRICE, Jan Ellen. 1301 22ND AVE N 37232 #023-07-1997 L1998 IM *020 †20

PRICE, Jere Kenwood, Jr. ■ 37215 #021-05-1981 L1987 AN *020 †05

PRICE, Neil Morgan. 300 20TH AVE N 37203 #048-13-1981 L1987 GE *020 †20

PRIKHOJAN, Alexander. 1005 DR DB TODD JR BLVD, DEPT OF PSYCH 37208 #913-99-1982 L2005 P *020 †75

PRIYADARSHI, Snigdha Shri. 1412 COUNTY HOSPITAL RD 37218 #495-67-1998 L2006 IM *100

PROCTOR, George Thos. ■ 37221 #047-06-1947 L1947 R *071 †80

PROCTOR, John Hannon. 104 PARK GLN, STE 303 37204 #027-01-1986 L1990 EM PE *020 †16

PROPPER, Michael Wales. 1310 24TH AVE S, DEPT PSYCH MC 116A 37212 #021-01-1979 L1995 P OM *020 †20

PRUDHOMME, Julie B. 1161 21ST AVE S, STE T1217 37232 #047-05-1999 L2002 PCC *100 †20

PRUITT, Ronald Edward. 4230 HARDING PIKE, STE 309 37205 #036-01-1984 L1989 GE IM *020 †20

PRYOR, Joseph Albert. ■ 37215 #047-06-1962 L1963 OBG *071 †30

PURCELL, Gretchen P. 2200 CHILDRENS WAY, STE 4150 37232 #005-11-1997 L2006 PDS *020 †85

PUTINSKI, Cynthia Lee. 2011 MURPHY AVE, STE 301 37203 #038-40-1984 L1988 OBG *020 †30

PUTNAM, Karen Lowry. 1301 22ND AVE N 37232 #047-06-1983 L1984 PD *071 †55

PUTZI, Mathew John. 1450 ELM HILL PIKE 37210 #047-07-1994 L2002 PTH SP *020

PUZANOV, Igor. 1301 22ND AVE N 37232 #286-11-1991 L2002 HO *020 †20

QUADRINI, Michael Jeremy. 1161 21ST AVE S, DIVISION OF NEPHROLOGY - V 37232 #016-06-2012 L2005 NEP *020 †20

QUASEM, Susanna Leigh. 1601 23RD AVE S 37212 #047-06-2003 L2008 CHP *012

QUINN, Robert Sean. 2400 PATTERSON ST, STE 500 37203 #047-05-1975 L1977 IM *020 †20

QUISLING, Richard Warren. 593 STEWARTS FERRY PIKE 37214 #056-05-1972 L1977 OTO *020 †45 ‡

RAFFANTI, Stephen P. 1301 22ND AVE N 37232 #561-07-1985 L1990 IM *020 †20

RAGAN, Paul Wilhelm. 1301 22ND AVE N 37232 #003-01-1981 L1997 P ADP *020 †75

RAGSDALE, Jennifer M. 7640 HIGHWAY 70 S, STE 202 37221 #047-06-1997 L1999 PD *020 †55

RAHEJA, Ravi Kanwal. 310 25TH AVE N, STE 201 37203 #033-06-1997 L2001 PD *020 †55

RAHMAN, Sofie Fatima. ■ 37205 #047-05-2008 *012

RAIFORD, David Shepherd. 1660 THE VANDERBILT CLINIC, VANDERBILT HEPATOLOGY 37232 #023-07-1985 L1991 IM *020 †20

RAJ, Satish R. 1301 22ND AVE N 37232 #065-05-1993 L2002 *020 †20

RAJPURA, Bhupendra M. 2002 RICHARD JONES RD, STE C206 37215 #495-22-1987 L1995 P PYG *020 †75

R AL-KAYLANI, Muhammad M. 1301 22ND AVE N 37232 #528-05-1989 L2002 CN *020

RALPH, Wm Bennett, Jr. 330 22ND AVE N 37203 #047-05-1967 L1972 A IM *020

RAMAKRISHNAIAH, Bijavara. 8300 SAWYER BROWN RD # 303 37221 #495-37-1964 GP *020

RAMANNA, Nagendra. 3443 DICKERSON PIKE, STE 430 37207 #495-73-1981 L2001 CD IM *020 †20

RAMIREZ, Mario Luis. ■ 37203 #024-01-2007 EM *012

RAMMAGE, Jennifer Leigh. 2200 CHILDRENS WAY 8161, CHILDREN'S HOSPITAL 37232 #048-12-2007 PD *012

RAMO, Brandon Aaron. ■ 37221 #028-02-2005 L2008 ORS *012

RAMOS, Luis F, Jr. 1161 21ST AVE S, VANDERBILT UNIVERSITY MEDI 37232 #048-04-2000 L2005 NEP *100 †20

RAMSDEN, Danielle N. ■ 37208 #047-07-2008 *012

RAMSEY, James Albert. 1301 22ND AVE N 37232 #047-05-1973 L1977 AN LM *020 †05

RAMSEY, Lloyd H. ■ 37205 #028-02-1950 L1956 IM CD *071 †20

RAND, Heidi Katherine. 222 22ND AVE N, STE 100 37203 #016-45-1997 L2000 D *020 †15

RAND, Nahshon. ■ 37221 #550-01-1987 *100

RANDOLPH, Judson G. ■ 37205 #047-05-1953 L1954 GS TS *020 †85,90

RANKIN, Debra Sue. 1301 22ND AVE N 37232 #041-13-1992 L1996 IM *020 †20

RANKIN, James Scott. 2400 PATTERSON ST, STE 103 37203 #047-06-1969 L1971 TS *020 †85,90

RANKIN, Kevin Mark. 222 22ND AVE N STE 400, MID-STATE CARDIOLOGY ASSOC 37203 #016-11-1991 L1993 CD *020 †20

RANPARIA, Dipak Jaysukh. 4220 HARDING PIKE 37205 #036-01-1992 L2001 VIR DR *020 †80 ‡

RAO, Babu V. 2400 PATTERSON ST, STE 101 37203 #063-01-1985 L1991 GE IM *020 †20

RAO, Bapnad V N. 1005 D B TODD BLVD 37208 #495-33-1977 P *100

RAO, Gautam Gorantla. 250 25TH AVE N, STE 310 37203 #011-02-1997 L2005 OBG GO *020 †20

RAO, Vidya Narayana. 1310 24TH AVE S BA128, VA MEDICAL CENTRE NASHVILLE 37212 #495-96-1988 L2000 AN *020 †05

RAPELYEA, Melvin Seth. 210 25TH AVE N, STE 602 37203 #035-45-1976 L2001 DR *020 †80

RASCHE, Richard Albert. 99 WESTOVER DR 37205 #008-02-1973 L1977 IM *020 †20

RATCHFORD, Amber Vining. 1161 21ST AVE S, DEPT OF PSYCHIATRY 37232 #045-01-2006 P *012

RAULSTON, Gilbert Warner. 250 25TH AVE N, STE 304 37203 #027-01-1984 L1985 CHP *020 †75

RAUTH, Thomas Patrick. D4314 MEDICAL CENTER NORTH, VUMC 37232 #047-05-2002 L2005 GS *012

RAWLS, Adrianne Robertson. ■ 37212 #027-01-2006 PTH *100
RAWLS, Mark Elkin. ■ 37212 #027-01-2006 PD *012
RAY, Neelanjan. ■ 37203 #047-05-2007 IM *012
RAY, Wesley Clark. 222 22ND AVE N, STE 100 37203 #047-06-1988 L1989 IM *020 †20
RAYBURN, Joseph Lee. 1800 CHURCH ST, STE 200 37203 #020-02-1976 L1977 PTH *020 †50
REAGAN, Brendan Wesley. ■ 37211 #021-05-2005 L2007 IM *012
RECTOR, Cynthia Kay. 446 METROPLEX DR 37211 #028-03-1992 L1993 CHP P *020
REDDICK, Eddie Joe. 397 WALLACE RD STE 314 37211 #004-01-1975 L1975 GS VS *071 †85
REDDY, Adhikari Varaprasa. VANDERBILT UNIV MED CTR, DEPT OF NEUROLOGICAL
    SURGE 37232 #047-05-2004 NS *012
REDDY, Bhaskar C A. 1005 DR DB TODD JR BLVD 37208 #495-99-1983 L1989 AN *020 †05
REDDY, Churku Mohan. 1916 PATTERSON ST, STE 600 37203 #495-57-1966 L1975
    PD PDE *020 †55
REDDY, Tanuja. 310 25TH AVE N, STE 309 37203 #495-33-1986 L1989 P *020 †75
REDDY, Venkata Kandada. 1804 STATE ST 37203 #495-65-1976 L1998 FM *020 †18 ‡
REED, Michael Christopher. 30 BURTON HILLS BLVD, STE 375 37215 #047-20-1985 L1986
    P *020 †75
REESE, John Jeffrey. 2200 CHILDRENS WAY, RM 2510 37232 #019-02-1987 L1990
    NPM *020 †55
REGAN, Judith G Jefferson. 309 RIVERSTONE BLVD 37214 #020-02-1979 L1982
    CHP P *030 †75
REGAN, William Mark. 1161 21ST AVE S, S-1205 37232 #020-02-1982 L1983 P PFP *020 †75
REGEN, Eugene M, Jr. ■ 37215 #047-05-1955 L1959 ORS *071 †40
REHM, Christopher Richard. 4230 HARDING RD, STE 1000 37205 #016-06-1998 L2002
    PM *020
REHM, Kris. 1301 22ND AVE N 37232 #016-06-1998 L2002 PD *020 †55
REHMAN, Faiza. MEHARRY MED COLL SCH OF ME 37208 #704-05-1988 L2004 IM *020 †20
REHMAN, Luft Ur. 2400 PATTERSON ST, STE 115 37203 #704-01-1985 L1998 GS *020
REHME, Suzanne Lowe. 3441 DICKERSON PIKE 37207 #048-12-1998 L2001 EM *020 †16
REIG, Adam. ■ 37209 #011-03-2005 NS *012
REILLY, Thomas Bradley. 1161 21ST AVE S, MED CTR-NUCLEA 37232 #130-02-2006 NM *012
REISMAN, Stephen Lee. 2325 CRESTMOOR RD, STE P-150 37215 #024-05-1981 L1983
    OPH IM *020
REMBERT, Francis Marion. 2000 CHURCH ST 37236 #028-02-1962 L1969 IM HEM *071 †20
RENFRO, Roy J, Jr. 394 HARDING PL, STE 200 37211 #047-06-1984 L1989 ORS OSM *020 †40
RETIEF, Carla Rumley. 4301 HILLSBORO RD, STE 200 37215 #047-06-1994 L2000
    D DS *020 †15
REXER, Brent Neil. ■ 37209 #047-05-2003 L2005 HO *012 †20
REYES, David Phillips. 391 WALLACE RD, HILLS, LLC 37211 #047-05-1996 L2000 IM *020 †20
REYES, Loida Cruz. 1005 DR DB TODD JR BLVD, ELAM MENTAL HLTH CTR RM 20 37208
    #748-01-1986 P *012
REYNOLDS, Melissa Gay. 2011 MURPHY AVE, STE 305 37203 #017-20-1992 L1996
    OBG *020 †30
REYNOLDS, Paul Quayle. ■ 37209 #047-05-2008 *012
RHEA, Karen H. 1101 6TH AVE N 3RD FL, HEALTH CENTERS, INC. 37208 #036-01-1973 L1976
    P CHP *020 †55,75
RHODES, Melissa Mc Naull. 1301 22ND AVE N 37232 #051-07-1999 L2005 PD *020 †55
RHODES, Troy Edward. 2220 PIERCE AVE, DIVISION OF CARDIOVASCULAR 37232
    #051-07-2002 L2006 CD *012 †20
RIBEIRO, Lenor De Sa. 1414 COUNTY HOSPITAL RD 37218 #187-13-1947 L1963 OS PTH *071
RICE, Elizabeth Ann. FL MCE, 1161 21ST AVENU S. 7TH 37232 #017-20-1997 L1998
    IM *020 †20
RICE, Jack Overton. 62 REVERE PARK 37203 #047-05-1955 L1955 P *020
RICE, Melody Robin. ■ 37212 #051-04-2002 L2006 OBG *020
RICE, Robin Lee. ■ 37215 #047-06-1981 L1981 OPH *071
RICE, Todd William. 1301 22ND AVE N 37232 #017-20-1997 L2001 PCC *020 †20
RICE, Valerie Montgomery. 1005 DR DB TODD JR BLVD, DEANS OFF SCHL OF MED 37208
    #024-01-1987 L2003 OBG REN *020 †30
RICHARD, Floyd Anthony. 2201 MURPHY AVE, STE 411 37203 #047-07-1981 L1981
    OBG *020 †30
RICHARD-DAVIS, Gloria A. 1005 DR DB TODD JR BLVD 37208 #021-05-1982 L2007
    OBG REN *020 †30
RICHARDS, Bruce Earle. 300 20TH AVE N 37203 #047-05-1982 L1985 IM *020 †20
RICHARDS, James Paul. ■ 37221 #047-06-1961 L1962 OM EM *071
RICHARDS, Sarah E. 4220 HARDING RD, SAINT THOMAS HOSPITAL MEDI 37205
    #035-15-2001 L2006 IM *020
RICHARDS, Sherrie A. 2201 MURPHY AVE, SHERRIE RICHARDS MD 37203 #001-02-1982 L1983
    OBG *020 †30
RICHARDS, William Owen. 1301 22ND AVE N 37232 #023-01-1979 L1987 GS *020 †85
RICHARDSON, Michael G. 3108 MED CENTER EAST, 1215 21ST AVENUE SOUTH 37232
    #016-02-1989 L2002 AN *020 †05
RICHARDSON, Thomas Ramsey. 1215 21ST AVE S, MCE, #5209 37232 #051-01-1995 L2001
    IC *012
RICHIE, Robert Eugene. 912 OXFORD HOUSE 37232 #047-05-1959 L1959 TTS GS *020 †85,90
RICHMOND, Bradley Winston. ■ 37215 #020-02-2007 IM *012
RICHTER, Holly Denise. ■ 37221 #017-20-2003 L2006 AN *100
RICK, John J. ■ 37205 #025-01-1952 L1953 OS NTR *072
RICKETSON, Robert A G. ■ 37205 #036-07-1942 L1953 PS *071 †85,65
RIDDELL, Douglas H. ■ 37205 #047-05-1944 L1944 GS TS *071 †85,90
RIDDICK, John Alston. 2400 PATTERSON ST, STE 502 37203 #047-05-2001 L2003 CD *020
RIEBAU, Derek Aron. VUMC DEPT OF NEUROLOGY, A-01118 MCN 37232 #056-05-2001 L2005
    N *020 †75
RIECK, Richard William. 391 WALLACE RD, SOUTHERN HILLS MEDICAL CEN 37211
    #021-05-1993 L1995 RNR *020 †80
RIECK, Susan Overby. 1321 MURFREESBORO PIKE, STE 800 37217 #021-01-1987 L1993
    *020 †75
RIEDEL, Brian Dale. 2200 CHILDRENS WAY, RM 2510 37232 #047-05-1984 L1988 PG *020 †55
RIEGER, Dean Paul. 3343 PERIMETER HILL DR, STE 300 37211 #023-07-1974 L2005
    PHP GP *030 †70
RIES, William Russell. DEPT OF OTOLARYNGOLOGY, 7209 MCE SOUTH TOWER 37232
    #047-06-1978 L1980 FPS OTO *020 †45
RIGTRUP, Kevin Mark. 2400 PATTERSON ST, STE 101 37203 #047-05-1994 L1996 IM *020 †20
RILEY, Harris De Witt, Jr. 5028 MEDICAL CENTER E, VANDERBILT CHILDRENS HOSP 37232
    #047-05-1948 L1948 PD ID *020 †55
RILEY-BURT, Janice R. PO BOX 331268, 3109 JOHN A MERRITT BLVD 37203
    #047-07-1997 L2006 FM *020 †18

RINGSDORF, Lillian Macon. ■ 37215 #001-02-2006 TY *012
RIORDAN, William Patrick, Jr. 1211 21ST AVE S, DIV OF TRAUMA 37212 #020-12-1999 L2004
    TRS CCS *020 †85
RIPLEY, Robert Craig. 397 WALLACE RD, STE 216 37211 #010-01-1973 L1975 CD IM *020 †20
RIPPEN, Helga Edith. 1 PARK PLZ, HCA BLDG II-4W 37203 #011-03-1993 L1994 PHP *062 †70
RITCHIE, Steve Edward. 2410 CHARLOTTE AVE 37203 #036-01-1979 L1981 FM *020 †18
RITT, Wayne Alan. 1125 CHICKERING PARK DR 37215 #047-06-1970 L1971 AN *020 †05
RIVA, Suzanne Patricia. 2001 CHARLOTTE AVE, STE 201 37203 #047-05-1991 L1994
    IM *020 †20
RIVAS, Homero, II. ■ 37204 #048-02-2001 L2007 SCI *100 †60
RIVERA TYLER, Tanya G. ■ 37209 #051-07-2005 EM *012
ROBACK, Ellen Weiser. 2021 CHURCH ST, # 608 37203 #047-06-1984 L1988
    IM PD *020 †20,55,19
ROBB, Christopher William. 1301 22ND AVE N, STE 3900TVC 37232 #048-15-2003 L2006
    D *020 †15
ROBBINS, Ivan Michael. 1161 21ST AVE S, RM T 1218 37232 #038-06-1991 L1994
    PCC *020 †20
ROBBINS, Jason Booth. 4220 HARDING PIKE 37205 #047-05-1999 L2005 D *020 †15
ROBBINS, Lansdon B, II. ■ 37215 #047-05-1962 L1963 GS TS *072 †85
ROBBINS, Mark Anthony. 1215 21ST AVE S, MCE # 5209 37232 #027-01-1993 L1994
    CD IC *020 †20
ROBERSON, Clifford F. 611 WOODLAND ST 37206 #047-07-1982 L1982 P *020 †75
ROBERTS, Deanne Marie. ■ 37215 #047-05-2008 *012
ROBERTS, John Robt. 356 24TH AVE N STE 400 37203 #008-01-1985 L1997 TS SO *020 †85,90
ROBERTS, Lyman Jackson. VANDERBILT UNIVERSITY, DEPARTMENT OF
    PHARMACOLOGY 37232 #018-03-1969 L1978 PA IM *020 †20
ROBERTS, Matthew Adam. 2200 CHILDRENS WAY # 3115 37232 #048-02-1999 L2002
    PAN *020 †05
ROBERTS, Ryan Macdonald. 222 22ND AVE N, STE 100 37203 #021-05-1987 L1990
    IM GE *020 †20
ROBERTSON, David. 1161 21ST AVE S, RM AA-3228 37232 #047-05-1973 L1975
    PA IM *050 †20
ROBERTSON, Kesha Shunte. ■ 37218 #047-06-2005 OBG *012
ROBERTSON, Randolph H. 391 WALLACE RD 37211 #016-11-1983 L1987 DR *020 †80
ROBERTSON, Rose Marie. VANDERBILT UNIV MED CTR, 383 PRB DIV OF CARDIOLOGY 37232
    #024-01-1970 L1975 CD IM *050 †20
ROBIN, Deborah W. VANDERBILT UNIV MED CTR, DEPT IM # S1120 MCN 37232
    #035-15-1980 L1988 IM IMG *020 †20
ROBINETTE, Charles L, Jr. 210 25TH AVE N, STE 602 37203 #028-02-1978 L1979 DR *071 †80
ROBINSON, Nathaniel David. 100 CNA DR, CNA 37214 #561-01-1971 L1982 OS *030
ROBINSON, Robert Willard. 1 VANTAGE WAY, STE B240 37228 #047-06-1983 L1984 EM *020
ROBINSON, Roscoe Vause. 4230 HARDING PIKE, ANESTHESIOLOGISTS 37205
    #036-08-1987 L1995 AN *020 †20
ROBINSON, Tracy Merrill. ■ 37204 #036-07-2007 IM *012
ROCCO, Vito K. 28 WHITE BRIDGE RD, STE 300 37205 #005-06-1981 L1988
    NEP CCM *020 †20 ‡
RODE, Danielle Leigh. 2200 CHILDRENS WAY 8161D, CHILDREN'S HOSPITAL 37232
    #047-05-2005 L2008 PD *012
RODEN, Dan Mark. BUILDING IV, 1285 MEDICAL RESEARCH 37232 #067-01-1974 L1978
    CD PA *050 †20
RODGERS, Scott Mc Laurin. 1301 22ND AVE N 37232 #047-05-1994 L2000 CHP *020 †75
RODIER, Jacqueline Lee. 2201 MURPHY AVE, STE 302 37203 #047-05-1980 L1983
    OBG *020 †20
RODNEY, William M. 1005 DR DB TODD JR BLVD 37208 #035-20-1976 L1989
    FM EM *020 †16,18
RODRIGUEZ, Adrian. ■ 37209 #016-11-2003 L2006 D *020
RODRIGUEZ, Gibrham. ■ 37215 #047-07-2008 *012
RODRIGUEZ, Orlando Simeon. 3443 DICKERSON PIKE, ASSOC., PLLCSUITE 680 37207
    #748-01-1990 L2001 PUD CCM *020 †20 ‡
RODRIGUEZ MOLINA, Gerardo. 1005 DR DB TODD JR BLVD, DEPT OF FAM & COMM
    MED 37208 #275-04-1997 FP *012
ROGERS, Andrew Joseph, III. ■ 37205 #024-05-2006 GS *100
ROGERS, Judson Edward. 2400 PATTERSON ST STE 500 37203 #047-05-1976 L1986
    IM *020 †20
ROGERS, Karl Malone. 2011 CHURCH ST, STE 701 37203 #016-01-1987 L1988 ON IM *020 †20
ROGERS, William Dennis. 2011 MURPHY AVE, STE 400 37203 #012-01-1983 L1984
    AN *020 †20
ROGOWSKI KENT, Barbara A. 341 21ST AVE N 37203 #016-11-1992 L1993 IM *020 †20
ROHDE, John P. 1301 22ND AVE N 37232 #048-13-1999 L2002 EM *020 †16
ROHDE, Sarah Louise. ■ 37215 #051-01-2004 OTO *012
ROJAS, Mario Augusto. 1301 22ND AVE N 37232 #264-11-1980 L2003 NPM *020 †55
ROMANO, Mary Elizabeth. ■ 37215 #422-01-2001 L2007 ADL *020 †55
ROMFH, Richard Forrest. 37221 #041-09-1965 L1969 GS OS *071 †85
RORIE, Michelle Yvonne. 617 S 8TH ST, CAYCE MEDICAL CENTER 37206 #047-07-1996 L2002
    FM *020 †18
ROSE, Melissa Dawnelle. 3441 DICKERSON PIKE, SKYLINE MEDICAL CENTER 37207
    #005-12-1997 L2001 AN *020 †05
ROSEMAN, Hal Michael. 2400 PATTERSON ST, STE 215 37203 #047-06-1979 L1982
    CD NM *020 †20
ROSEN, Barrett Frank. 301 21ST AVE N 37203 #012-01-1968 L1975 ORS GP *020 †40
ROSEN, Howard E. 2400 PATTERSON ST STE 515 37203 #047-05-1963 L1969 GE IM *071
ROSEN, Jessica Lynn. ■ 37209 #051-01-2008 *012
ROSENBLOOM, Samuel Trent. BIOMEDICAL LIBRARY, 442 ESKIND 37232 #047-05-1996 L1997
    MPD *020 †20,55
ROSENBLUM, Howard Hillel. 4306 HARDING RD STE 204 37205 #035-45-1980 L1984
    OPH *020 †35
ROSENBLUM, Marvin Jonas. 1211 22ND AVE N 37232 #047-06-1947 L1948 IM *071 †20
ROSENTHAL, Philip K. 2201 MURPHY AVE STE 401, ASSOCIATES, P.C. 37203
    #035-20-1983 L1994 NS *020 †25
ROSS, Amy Simon. ■ 37205 #041-15-2003 L2003 D *100 †15
ROSS, Charles Brien. 1301 22ND AVE N 37232 #020-12-1984 L1985 VS *020 †85
ROSS, John Danforth. 1301 22ND AVE N 37232 #047-06-1999 L2004 DR *020 †80
ROSS, Joseph Comer. ■ 37215 #047-05-1954 L1954 PUD IM *071 †20
ROSS, Julie Rebecca. ■ 37215 #047-06-2006 PD *012
ROSS, Stephen Jon. 397 WALLACE RD, STE 309 37211 #047-20-1986 L1990 OBG *020 †30
ROSS, Warren Edward. ■ 37205 #011-03-1973 L1974 ON IM *030 †20

ROTH, Bruce Jos. 1301 22ND AVE N 37232 #028-34-1980 L1999 **ON IM** *020 †20

ROTH, James Edwards. ■ 37215 #047-06-1985 L1986 **AN** *020 †05

ROTHENBERG, Mace L. 1301 22ND AVE N 37232 #035-19-1982 L1998 **ON** *030 †20

ROTHMAN, Russell Lawrence. 1301 22ND AVE N 37232 #036-07-1996 L2002 **MPD** *050 †20,55

ROTKER, Jonathan David. 397 WALLACE RD, BLCG C, SUITE 103 37211 #035-03-1988 L2000 **GE IM** *020 †20 ‡

ROTTMAN, Jeffrey Nathan. 1301 22ND AVE N 37232 #035-01-1982 L1996 **IM CD** *020 †20

ROUMIE, Christianne L. 1301 22ND AVE N 37232 #033-05-1998 L2000 **MPD** *050 †20,55

ROWAN, Ben Hardin. 1301 22ND AVE N 37232 #047-06-2001 L2003 **IM** *020 †20

ROWAN, Shane Benton. 186 KENNER AVE, DEPT CD 37205 #047-05-2002 L2007 **CD** *012 †20

ROWATT, Ashley Jo. ■ 37204 #047-05-2007 **MPD** *012

ROWBATHAM, Gregory Paul. 28 WHITE BRIDGE RD, STE 300 37205 #021-05-1995 L2000 **NEP IM** *020 †20

ROWE, David Michael. 4220 HARDING PIKE 37205 #020-02-1981 L1986 **DR** *020 †80

ROWE, Heather D. 393 WALLACE RD BLDG A, SUITE 400 37211 #047-06-1994 L2000 **IM** *020 †20

ROY, Robert M. 2300 PATTERSON ST 37203 #047-05-1952 L1952 **ON HEM** *071 †20

RUBIN, Don H. 1301 22ND AVE N 37232 #047-06-1992 L1992 **ID IM** *050 †20

RUDER, Scott Edwin. 345 24TH AVE N, STE 208 37203 #047-05-1990 L1994 **P PFP** *020 †75

RUDINSKY, Michelle Joann. ■ 37208 #047-07-2008 *012

RUDZINSKI, Erin Renee. ■ 37215 #012-01-2003 L2006 **PTH** *100 †50

RUFF, Timothy Mark. 395 WALLACE RD, STE 301 37211 #041-09-1998 L2003 **GS** *062 †85

RUFFNER, Katherine Lyle. 2665 TVC, 1301 22ND AVE S 37232 #047-06-1995 L2001 **IM** *020 †20

RUMOHR, Jon Andrew. ■ 37215 #025-01-2003 L2005 **U** *012

RUSH, Charles Bennett. 1301 22ND AVE N 37232 #038-41-1984 L1987 **OBG** *040 †30

RUSH, Margaret Goettle. 2200 CHILDRENS WAY, RM 2510 37232 #038-41-1984 L1988 **PD NPM** *050 †55

RUSS, Stephan Edward. VUMC, DEPT OF EMERGENCY ME, 703 OXFORD HOUSE 37232 #047-06-2003 L2005 **EM** *100 †16

RUSSELL, Paul T, III. 7209 MEDICAL CENTER E, SOUTH TOWER DEPT OTO 37232 #048-15-1997 L2006 **OTO GS** *100 †45

RUSSELL, Robert Thomason. 1161 21ST AVE S, D-4314 MEDICAL CENTER NORT 37232 #045-01-2003 L2006 **GS** *012

RUSSELL, Robert Vance. 301 21ST AVE N 37203 #047-05-1962 L1962 **ORS HS** *071 †40

RUSSELL, William Evans. VANDERBILT UNIVERSITY MED, T-0107 MEDICAL CENTER NORT 37232 #024-01-1976 L1991 **PDE PD** *050 †55

RUTLAND, Craig Douglas. 300 20TH AVE N 37203 #001-02-1990 L1992 **IM** *020 †20

RUTLEDGE, Samuel Benton. 210 25TH AVE N STE 611 37203 #047-06-1963 L1964 **R OS** *062 †62

RYAN, Patrick Cyril. 356 24TH AVE N, STE 400 37203 #045-01-1996 L2003 **VS** *020 †85

RYAN, Sean Patrick. 4230 HARDING PIKE, STE 601E 37205 #012-05-1994 L1996 **IM** *020 †20

SAAVEDRA, Pablo Jose. 2311 PIERCE AVE, VANDERBILT UNIVERSITY MED 37232 #038-06-1996 L2005 **ICE** *100 †20

SACKS, Glynis Ann. 1301 22ND AVE N 37232 #836-01-1978 L1982 **OS R** *020 †28,80

SADEK, Robert N. ■ 37215 #047-06-1976 L1977 **IM** *020

SADLER, Robert Neil. ■ 37215 #047-05-1947 L1947 **IM** *071 †85,90

SAGER, Andrew Roberts. 300 20TH AVE N 37203 #051-01-1988 L1995 **CD** *020 †20

SAHA, Nihar R. 221 STEWARTS FERRY PIKE, MIDDLE TN MENTAL HEALTH IN 37214 #495-01-1974 L1994 **P** *020

SAHLGREN, Bo. 1161 21ST AVE S 37212 #858-02-1976 **PDC** *020

SALDIVAR-SALAZAR, Sergio. 511 UNION ST STE 1800 37219 #649-31-1982 **IM NEP** *050

SALLOUM, Joseph George. 1301 22ND AVE N 37232 #605-01-1996 L2004 **CD** *020 †20

SALMON, William D, Jr. ■ 37209 #047-05-1949 L1949 **IM END** *071 †20

SALOMON, Ronald Murray. 1500 21ST AVE S STE 2200 37212 #165-03-1983 L1995 **P PYG** *020 †20

SALYER, Howard Lee. 1900 PATTERSON ST STE 202 37203 #047-06-1961 L1961 **D** *020 †15

SALYERS, Steve Gary. 3443 DICKERSON PIKE, STE 190 37207 #047-05-1983 L1989 **ORS EM** *020 †40

SAMOYA, Steven William. 1211 21ST AVE S, MEDICAL ARTS BLDG RM 701 37212 #038-43-2002 L2007 **PAN** *100

SAMPSON, Uchechukwu K. ■ 37219 #690-01-1994 L2004 **CD** *012 †20

SAMUDRALA, Varalaxmi. 2011 MURPHY AVE, STE 201 37203 #025-07-1995 L2003 **DR** *020 †80

SANCHEZ, Gabriela Beatriz. ■ 37205 #048-04-2003 L2005 **OTO** *012

SANDALL, Justin Christoph. ■ 37211 #028-78-2007, ▲ **AN** *020

SANDERS, Dan Sumner, Jr. 2000 CHURCH ST 37236 #047-05-1941 L1941 **PD OS** *071 †55

SANDERS, Dan Sumner, III. 300 20TH AVE N STE 100 37203 #047-05-1978 L1979 **A PDA** *020 †55,03

SANDERS, David Lawrence. 502 RICHMAR DR 37211 #047-05-2000 L2004 **IM** *020 †20

SANDERS, Melinda Ellen. 1301 22ND AVE N 37232 #047-01-1995 L2001 **PTH** *062 †50

SANDERS, Mitchell Keith. 2000 CHURCH ST 37236 #047-07-1974 L1976 **OBG** *020

SANDIDGE, Paula Conaway. ■ 37215 #012-01-1960 L1966 **AN** *071

SANDIDGE, Robin Elizabeth. 2201 MURPHY AVE, STE 104 37203 #001-02-1987 L1991 **GYN** *020 †30

SANDLER, Alan Bart. 1301 22ND AVE N 37232 #016-01-1987 L2000 **ON IM** *020 †20

SANDLER, Martin Phainel. 1301 22ND AVE N 37232 #836-02-1972 L1980 **NM** *020 †28

SANDS-HESTER, Aladraine E. 395 WALLACE RD, STE B100 37211 #025-12-1989 L1998 **IM** *020 †20

SANGHANI, Neil Sanat. CTR N, D-3100 VANDERBILT MED 37232 #021-01-2005 **IM** *012

SANTEN, Sally Ann. 703 OXFORD HOUSE, DEPARTMENT OF EMERGENCY ME 37232 #010-01-1991 L1995 **EM OBG** *020 †20

SANTI, Michael Thos. 2400 PATTERSON ST, STE 201 37203 #047-06-1979 L1979 **CRS** *020 †85,10

SANTORO, Samuel Andrew. VANDERBILT UNIV SCH OF MED, DEPT PATH C-3322 MCN 37232 #047-05-1979 L2003 **CLP** *050

SARPONG, Yaw. ■ 37203 #047-05-2008 *012

SARRATT, C Madison H. 211 22ND AVE N 37203 #047-05-1947 L1947 **GYN** *071 †30

SASTRE, Elizabeth Ann. STE 6000 MCE (NORTH TOWER), VANDERBILT DEPT OF INTERNA 37232 #011-03-2001 L2005 **IM** *020

SATHYAMOORTHY, Mohan. ■ 37206 #035-48-2001 L2003 **CD** *100 †20

SATOR, Daisy P. METROPOLITAN BORDEAUX HOSP 37218 #748-08-1966 L1975 **PD** *020

SATPATHY, Panchanan. 2801 CHARLOTTE AVE 37209 #495-79-1965 L1978 **U** *020 †20

SAUNDERS, Kevin Joseph. 1301 22ND AVE N 37232 #654-01-1998 L2004 **PAN** *020 †05

SAUNDERS, Rene Christine. 2300 PATTERSON ST, COLUMBIA CENTENNIAL MED CN 37203 #005-15-1996 L1999 **EM** *020 †16

SAWYERS, John L. VANDERBILT MEDICAL CENTER 37232 #023-07-1949 L1957 **GS VS** *071 †90,85

SAWYERS, Julia Edwards. ■ 37205 #047-05-1960 L1960 **AN** *071 †05

SCALES, Thomas Risdon, Jr. 2000 CHURCH 37236 #047-06-1997 L2002 **IM P** *020 †20,75

SCARPERO, Harriette M. 1301 22ND AVE N 37232 #021-05-1995 L2002 **U** *020 †95

SCARPERO, Stephen C. 3443 DICKERSON PIKE, STE G30 37207 #021-05-1995 L2002 **IM** *020 †20

SCHADT, Courtney Reynolds. ■ 37212 #047-05-2007 **IM** *012

SCHAEFER, Heidi Maree. S3223 MCN, 1161 21ST AVE SOUTH 37232 #038-41-1998 L2004 **NEP** *020 †20

SCHAFFNER, William, II. 1500 21ST AVE S, VANDERBILT PREVENTIVE MED 37212 #035-20-1962 L1969 **ID IM** *040 †20,70

SCHAFII, Christine. ■ 37212 #409-12-1992 **IM** *100

SCHAPIRA, Marc Manuel. MCN VANDERBILT UN, MEDICAL CTR C3217 37232 #869-04-1971 L1988 *020

SCHEER-WILLIAMS, Mary C. ■ 37215 #030-05-1975 L1990 **DR** *020 †80

SCHEVING, Lawrence Allen. ■ 37205 #004-01-1984 L1984 **GE PTH** *100

SCHIERLING, Kevin Dale. 7440 LAKEVIEW DR 37209 #019-02-1998 L2005 **FM** *020 †18

SCHIERLING, Michelle Webe. ■ 37209 #019-02-2004 L2007 **EM** *012

SCHINDLER, Amy Elizabeth. ■ 37205 #048-12-2006 **IM** *012

SCHLECHTER, Nicole L. 300 20TH AVE N STE 302 37203 #047-05-1990 L1992 **OBG** *020 †30

SCHLESINGER, Joseph John, II. ■ 37204 #048-14-2008 *012

SCHMALBACH, Cecelia E. CENTER NORTH, S-2100 MEDICAL 37232 #041-02-1998 L2004 **OTO HNS** *020 †45

SCHMIDT, Adriana Natalia. ■ 37203 #047-05-2006 **D** *012

SCHMIDT, David Mark. 4230 HARDING RD STE 1000, LIPSCOMB CLINIC 37205 #020-12-1983 L1993 **ORS** *020 †40

SCHMITZ, Christine Marie. 5505 EDMONSON PIKE, STE 102 37211 #028-03-1999 L2003 **MPD** *020 †20,55

SCHNEIDER, Christopher Mi. ■ 37211 #017-20-2007 **EM** *012

SCHNEIDER, Jonathan A. CTR N, D-3100 VANDERBILT MED 37232 #048-14-2005 L2007 **IM** *012

SCHNEIDER, Richard Paul. 1301 22ND AVE S, 1660 THE VANDERBILT CLINIC 37232 #035-01-1967 L1973 **GE IM** *020 †20

SCHNEPPER, Gregory Dougla. ■ 37212 #005-12-2007 **GS** *012

SCHOENECKER, Jonathan G. CENTER NORTH, T-4319 MEDICAL 37232 #036-07-2003 L2008 **ORS** *012

SCHOETTLE, Timothy Porter. 2011 MURPHY AVE, STE 301 37203 #047-05-1978 L1982 **NS** *020 †25

SCHOFIELD, Hal Cortney. 1410 17TH AVE S 37212 #048-13-1994 L1995 **P** *020 †75

SCHOLER, Seth Jerome. MEDICAL STAFF OFFICE, VANDERBILT CHILDREN'S HOSP 37232 #017-20-1989 L1995 **PD** *020 †55

SCHRAG, Sherwin Phan. 1211 21ST AVE S, 404 MED ARTS BLDG 37212 #654-01-2001 L2007 **CCS** *012 †85

SCHUBERTH, Jennifer L. 4230 HARDING PIKE, STE 400 37205 #023-01-2001 L2004 **IM** *020

SCHUENING, Friedrich G. 2665 THE VANDERBILT CLINIC, 1301 22ND AVE SOUTH 37232 #409-21-1975 L1999 **HEM ON** *050

SCHULL, David Marshall. 2011 MURPHY AVE, STE 307 37203 #047-06-1985 L1997 **U** *020 †95 ‡

SCHULL, Katharine N. 2000 RICHARD JONES RD, STE 270 37215 #001-02-1985 L1997 **PD** *020 †55

SCHULMAN, Gerald. 1301 22ND AVE N 37232 #035-19-1977 L1988 **NEP IM** *020 †20

SCHULMAN, Herbert J. 4230 HARDING RD, STE 525 37205 #047-05-1950 L1950 **IM** *071 †20

SCHULTENOVER, Stephen J. 1301 22ND AVE N 37232 #026-04-1972 L1984 **PTH AM** *020 †50

SCHULTZ, Grace Lavera. ■ 37211 #047-06-1996 L1999 **IM** *020 †20

SCHUMACHER, Paul Michael. D-5237 MCN, 1611 22ND AVENUE SOUTH 37232 #021-01-2001 L2006 **VS** *012

SCHUMAN, Theodore Asher. ■ 37221 #035-20-2006 **OTO** *012

SCHWABER, Mitchell Keith. 4230 HARDING RD, STE 803 37205 #048-04-1975 L1981 **NO OS** *020 †45

SCHWARTZ, David Allen. STE 514, 1211 21ST AVENUE 37232 #047-07-1995 L2002 **GE** *020 †20

SCHWARTZ, Gary Robt. 1301 22ND AVE N 37232 #012-21-1985 L1991 **MPD PD** *020 †20,55,16

SCHWARTZ, Herbert Steven. 1301 22ND AVE N 37232 #016-02-1981 L1987 **ORS OS** *020 †40

SCHWARTZ, Jonathan Martin. 110 29TH AVE N, STE 201 37203 #047-06-1968 L1969 **AN** *071 †05

SCHWARTZ, Marvin N. ■ 37215 #041-02-1959 L2003 **OBG** *020 †30

SCHWEIKERT, Nancie R. ■ 37205 #047-05-1964 L1965 **PD** *071

SCLABAS, Guido Michael. ■ 37221 #869-02-1988 L2005 **GS** *012

SCOBEY, Joseph Wilburn. 3443 DICKERSON PIKE # 100, CUMBERLAND EYE CLC 37207 #047-06-1960 L1961 **OPH** *020

SCOGGINS, Robert Myles. 2400 PATTERSON ST, STE 101 37203 #051-01-2002 L2004 **PCC** *012 †20

SCOTT, Jimmy Lewis. 275 STEWARTS FERRY PIKE, CLOVER BOTTOM DEV CTR 37214 #047-06-1987 L1988 **FM** *020 †18

SCOTT, May Elizabeth. ■ 37209 #021-06-2007 **OBG** *012

SCOTT, Patricia Lee. 1161 21ST AVE S, HOSPITAL DEPT 37232 #047-06-2003 L2007 **OBG** *100

SCOTT, Shali Ricker. 300 20TH AVE N STE 302 37203 #047-06-1993 L1996 **OBG** *020 †30

SCUDDER, Donna Dugger. 222 22ND AVE N, STE 100 37203 #047-20-1989 L1991 **IM** *020 †20

SEAMENS, Chas Mc Intosh. 1313 21ST AVE S 37232 #010-02-1985 L1992 **EM** *020 †16

SEBALDT, Rolf-Jochem. 1161 21ST AVE S 37212 #067-01-1979 L1987 **PA** *020 †20

SEDDON, Margaret Rhea. 3601 TVC VANDERBILT MED CT 37232 #047-06-1973 L1974 **EM AM** *075

SEE, Raphael. 383 PRB, 2220 PIERCE AVENUE 37232 #048-12-2003 L2008 **CD** *012 †20

SEE, Sarah Hayter. ■ 37232 #048-12-2006 L2008 **IM** *012

SEEM, Rohit. 397 WALLACE RD, BLDG C 37211 #495-47-1994 L2006 **FM** *020 †18

SEETHALER, Neil Edward. 310 25TH AVE N, STE 210 37203 #047-05-1996 L2002 **PD** *020 †55

SEGER, Donna Louise. 501 OXFPRD HOUSE, UVMC 37232 #037-01-1977 L1988 **EM** *040 †16

SEIDNER, Douglas L. 1211 21ST AVE SOUTH, STE 514 MAB 37232 #035-15-1983 L2007 **GE NTR** *020 †20

SELBY, John Horace, Jr. ■ 37215 #048-12-1969 L1998 **CCS** *071 †85,90

SELL, Sarah Hamilton Wood. ■ 37215 #047-05-1948 L1954 **PHP** *071 †55

SEMDER, Christopher Allen. ■ 37205 #055-02-2007 **IM** *012

SEMENYA, Joyce G. 1035 14TH AVE N 37208 #412-01-1976 L1996 **FM** *020 †20

SENAPATI, Indu. 221 STEWARTS FERRY PIKE, MTMHI 37214 #495-11-1975 L1999 **P** *020

SENGSAYADETH, Salyka. ■ 37221 #047-20-2006 L2008 **IM** *012

SERAFIN, William Edward. 2002 RICHARD JONES RD, STE B300 37215 #047-05-1979 L1982 **RHU IM** *020 †20,03

SERGENT, John Stanley. 1301 22ND AVE N 37232 #047-05-1966 L1971 **RHU IM** *040 †20

SERRO, Robert John. 3443 DICKERSON PIKE, STE 520 37207 #033-06-1988 L2003 **PM** *020 †60

SETTLE, Charles Sidney. 2000 CHURCH ST 37236 #047-05-1967 L1987 **OBG** *020 †30

SEVIN, Carla Marin. ■ 37205 #011-04-2004 L2008 **PCC** *012 †20

SEWELL, Robert Alvin. 2801 CHARLOTTE AVE, UROLOGY ASSOCIATES P.C. 37209 #047-05-1968 L1968 **U** *020 †95

SEXTON, Kevin Wayne. ■ 37221 #020-12-2007 **GS** *012

SEYMOUR, Robert Lee. VUMC, 21ST AVENUE SOUTH 37232 #012-01-2004 **PTH** *012

SHACK, Robert Bruce. D-4207, MCN, DEPT OF PLASTIC SURGERY 37232 #048-02-1973 L1976 **PS CS** *020 †85,65

SHACKLEFORD, E Conrad, Jr. 1601 23RD AVE S 37212 #047-06-1959 L1959 **PD PHP** *071 †55

SHADINGER, Libby Lovett. ■ 37205 #001-02-2003 L2007 **DR** *012

SHAFF, Max Israel. 1161 21ST AVE S, VANDERBILT SCHOOL OF 37232 #836-01-1961 L1980 **R** *020 †85

SHAFFER, David. 912 OXFORD HOUSE, VANDERVILT UNIV MED CTR 37232 #035-01-1982 L2001 **OS GS** *020 †85

SHAH, Bhavish J. ■ 37215 #047-06-2001 L2004 **PCC** *020

SHAH, Chirayu Yatinkumar. ■ 37214 #047-07-2004 L2004 **NM** *100

SHAH, Rohan Jayraj. ■ 37212 #047-05-2008 **N** *012

SHAH, Umang Arun. 1005 DR DB TODD BLVD, MEHARRY MED COLL DEPT OF P 37208 #496-25-2003 **P** *012

SHAKIBI, Jami Guilani. 812 COBBLE CV 37211 #517-01-1964 L1985 **PDC** *050 †55

SHAKIL, Fouzia A.. ■ 37205 #160-03-1984 L2000 **HMP** *100

SHANKLE, Nelson Edward. 110 29TH AVE N, STE 301 37203 #047-06-1964 L1965 **AN** *020 †05

SHARBER, Trimble. ■ 37215 #024-01-1933 L1935 **ORS GP** *100

SHARIFI, Haydeh Ghanei. 317 18TH AVE N, STE 202 37203 #517-04-1975 L1996 **FM** *020 †18

SHARMA, Surendra Kumar. 1005 DR DB TODD JR BLVD 37208 #496-04-1984 **P** *012

SHARP, Kenneth Warren. RM D5203 MCN, VANDERBIT UNIVERSITY MED C 37232 #023-07-1977 L1984 **GS** *020 †70

SHARP, Stephan Chas. 2222 STATE ST STE C 37203 #047-06-1987 L1988 **END** *020 †85

SHARPE, Deron Vincil. 1301 22ND AVE N 37232 #028-03-1998 L2003 **CHN** *020 †75

SHARPE, Joseph Mc Connico. 222 22ND AVE N, STE 100 37203 #047-06-1999 L2003 **P** *020 †75

SHARPE, Kerry A. ■ 37205 #047-06-2008 *012

SHAVER, Aaron Corydon. ■ 37205 #016-02-2007 **PTH** *012

SHAVER, Ciara Geraldine. ■ 37205 #016-06-2007 **IM** *012

SHAW, John Thos. 2400 PATTERSON ST, STE 500 37203 #047-06-1990 L1994 **IM** *020 †20

SHAY, Scott Raymond. CENTER NORTH, CCC-1106 MEDICAL 37232 #028-34-1989 L2000 **DR** *020 †80

SHEALEY, Wesley R. ■ 37205 #001-02-2000 L2002 **PDI** *012 †20,55

SHELLER, James Robt. 1301 22ND AVE N 37232 #047-05-1973 L1981 **PUD IM** *050 †20

SHELTON, Julia Suzannahbr. ■ 37212 #012-01-2006 **GS** *012

SHELTON, Mark Wayne. 397 WALLACE RD, STE 302 37211 #048-14-1985 L1993 **VS GS** *020 †85

SHELTON, Richard Chas. 1301 22ND AVE N 37232 #020-02-1979 L1985 **P** *050 †75

SHENAI, Jayant Pandurang. 2200 CHILDRENS WAY, RM 2510 37232 #496-38-1968 L1978 **NPM PD** *040 †55

SHEPHERD, Bradley David. 3614 MAYFLOWER PL 37204 #012-01-2004 L2006 **GE** *012 †20

SHEPHERD, Cynthia Lester. 21ST AVENUE SOUTH AND GARL, VANDERBILT UNIVERSITY MEDI 37232 #012-01-2004 L2006 **IM** *012

SHERMAN, Deborah Dale. 4306 HARDING RD, STE 106 37205 #047-20-1986 L1987 **OPH** *020 †35

SHERMAN, Michael Henry. 1301 22ND AVE N 37232 #007-02-1976 L1990 **CHP P** *020 †75

SHETH, Lalit Ratilal. 221 STEWARTS FERRY PIKE 37214 #495-48-1962 L1980 **GP** *071

SHETH, Neela Lalit. 1501 MURFREESBORO PIKE 37217 #496-38-1962 *100

SHETH, Sonali Lalit. 1601 23RD AVE S 37212 #047-06-2002 L2007 **CHP** *020 †75

SHETTY, Shashirekha Kokka. 310 25TH AVE N, STE 201 37203 #495-09-1996 L2006 **PD** *020 †55,19

SHIAO, Wen Tsai. 4571 TROUSDALE DR 37204 #244-04-1968 L1980 **FM OTO** *020 †18

SHIBAO, Cyndya Adriana. 1161 21ST AVE S 37232 #737-06-2001 **IM** *012

SHIELDS, John Alfred. 20 BRIDGESTONE PARK, NATIONAL MEPS 37214 #047-06-1957 L1958 **GS TRS** *071 †85

SHIMER, Kimberly Suzanne. 2200 CHILDRENS WAY RM 2510, VCH MEDICAL STAFF OFFICE 37232 #055-02-2000 L2003 **PD** *020 †55

SHIN, Peter E. ■ 37212 #016-11-2002 L2007 **EM** *020 †16

SHINAR, Andrew Alan. 1215 21ST AVE S, STE 4200 37232 #035-01-1988 L2001 **ORS OAR** *020 †40

SHIPMAN, Jason Lee. CCC-1121 MCN 37232 #039-01-2001 L2004 **DR** *012

SHIVITZ, Ira Alan. 2011 MURPHY AVE STE 602 37203 #047-05-1978 L1984 **OPH** *020 †35

SHMERLING, Abram Carl. 394 HARDING PL, CORNERSTONE MEDICAL GROUP 37211 #047-05-1952 L1952 **IM** *071

SHOFNER, Robert Stewart. 2021 CHURCH ST STE 300 37203 #051-01-1983 L1990 **OPH** *020 †35

SHUKLA, Monica Erin. ■ 37212 #035-06-2008 *012

SHUKRALLAH, Bassam Nabih. ■ 37212 #104-01-2005 **GS** *012

SHULER, Franklin David. STE 4200, MEDICAL CENTER EAST, SOUTH 37232 #055-01-1996 L2003 **ORS OTR** *020 †40

SHULL, Harrison J, Jr. 222 22ND AVE N, STE 100 37203 #047-06-1970 L1970 **GE IM** *020 †20

SHULTZ, Edward K, Jr. 3401 W END AVE, STE 700 37203 #008-01-1979 L1998 **CLP** *030 †50

SHULTZ, Thomas Francis. 1301 22ND AVE N 37232 #028-34-1977 L1990 **AN** *020 †05

SHUMAN, Christina Michell. ■ 37211 #047-05-2007 **P** *012

SHUMAN, Todd Alan. 4230 HARDING PIKE, STE 450 37205 #047-05-1983 L1989 **TS** *020 †85,90

SHUPE, Jennifer Marsh. ■ 37211 #048-15-2006 **N** *012

SHU TANGYIE, Gerard Y. 1804 STATE ST, SASH HEALTHCARE, PLC 37203 #217-01-1975 L1994 **ID** *020 †20

SI, Xiaohong. 1161 21ST AVE S, VANDERBILT UNIV MED CTR 37232 #243-69-1990 L2003 **CN** *012

SIAMI, Ghodrat A. 1310 24TH AVE S, STE 111A 37212 #517-01-1955 L1982 **NEP IM** *020

SIDBERRY, Charles Ray. 7640 HIGHWAY 70 S STE 101, MYET MEDICAL CENTER 37221 #047-07-1985 L1986 **FM** *020 †18 ‡

SIEVEKING, Nicholas Erik. 310 25TH AVE N 37203 #047-06-1995 L2000 **PS** *020 †65

SIEW, Edward D. 53223 MEDICAL CENTER NORTH, DIVISION OF NEPHROLOGY 37232 #016-02-1999 L2005 **NEP** *012 †20

SIKES, James Gregory. 2400 PATTERSON ST STE 400 37203 #047-05-1976 L1979 **CD IM** *020 †20

SILBERT, Burton. 210 25TH AVE N # N 1212 37203 #047-05-1958 L1958 **DR** *071 †80

SIMA, Bogdan. 1005 DR DB TODD JR BLVD, DEPT OF INTERNAL MEDICINE 37208 #781-10-2003 L2007 **IM** *012

SIMAS, Gilbert Manuel. 1161 21ST AVE S, DEPT OF PSYCHIATRY 37232 #104-01-2004 **P** *012

SIMMONS, Amy Jean. 1301 22ND AVE N 37232 #041-07-1990 L1994 **OPH** *020 †35

SIMMONS, Jill Hickman. 2200 CHILDRENS WAY, 11136 DOCTORS' OFFICE TOWE 37232 #047-06-2000 L2006 **PDE PD** *050 †55

SIMON, Scott Douglas. NEUROLOGICAL SURGERY, DEPT OF 37232 #016-02-2003 **NS** *012

SIMPSON, Jean Fair. 1301 22ND AVE N 37232 #012-01-1983 L1990 **PTH** *020 †45

SIMPSON, Lucien Caldwell. 393 WALLACE RD, SOUTHERN HILLS MED OFF BLD 37211 #028-02-1973 L1977 **D** *071 †15

SIMS, Norman Le Master. 3443 DICKERSON PIKE, STE 190 37207 #047-06-1957 L1970 **ORS OS** *030 †40

SINARD, Robert Jos. 1313 21ST AVE S RM 602, VUMC-DEPT OF OTOLARYNGOLOG 37232 #025-01-1989 L1993 **OTO SO** *020 †45

SINATRA, Robbin Beth. 7640 HIGHWAY 70 S, STE 11 37221 #047-05-1988 L1992 **OPH PO** *020 †35

SINGER, Pamela. 2000 CHURCH ST 37236 #028-78-1985, ▲ L1999 **FM** *020 †18 ‡

SINGER, Robert James. 2410 PATTERSON ST, STE 500 37203 #030-05-1992 L1999 **NS** *020 †25

SINGH, Harshjit. 1005 D B TODD BLVD 37208 #495-29-1998 **FP** *012

SINGH, Narendra K. 2553 MURFREESBORO PIKE, ASSOCIATES 37217 #068-01-1983 L1986 **FM** *020 †70

SINGH, Pradumna Pratap. 1301 22ND AVE N 37232 #495-30-1987 L2002 **CN** *020 †75

SINGH, Prem. ■ 37221 #495-67-1971 L1983 *100

SINGH, Sudha Pradumna. 2200 CHILDRENS WAY, STE 1421 37232 #495-30-1986 L2002 **DR** *020 †80

SINGH, Vikas Prakash. ■ 37221 #047-07-2004 **OTO** *012

SINGLETON, Chasipy Dionne. 1301 22ND AVE N 37232 #047-05-1999 L2003 **OPH** *020 †35

SISLER, India Gail. ■ 37205 #051-01-2003 **PHO** *012 †55

SISON-ILARDE, Jeannette. 1301 22ND AVE N 37232 #748-02-1986 L1995 **ID** *020 †20

SITARICH, Silvio. 1301 22ND AVE N 37232 #957-01-1987 L2001 **AN** *020 †05

SITTON, Barbara Cameron. 1900 PATTERSON ST STE 20, STE 202 37203 #045-01-1988 L1996 **D** *020 †15

SIZEMORE, Christopher Mic. ■ 37221 #011-75-2005, ▲ **OBG** *012

SKELO, Anna Sadika. 4306 HARDING RD, STE 304 37205 #957-08-1981 L2004 **OPH** *020 †35

SKINNER, William. ■ 37214 #045-01-1948 L1950 **FM PD** *071 †18

SLATON, Paul Ernest. 1211 22ND AVE N 37232 #047-05-1957 L1957 **IM END** *071 †20

SLIGH, James Edwin, Jr. 1301 22ND AVE N 37232 #048-04-1995 L2000 **D** *020 †15

SLOSKY, David Alan. 1301 22ND AVE N 37232 #007-02-1976 L2005 **CD IM** *020 †20

SLOVIS, Bonnie Smith. 1301 22ND AVE N 37232 #012-05-1990 L1992 **PCC** *020 †20

SLOVIS, Corey Mitchell. 1301 22ND AVE N 37232 #033-05-1975 L1992 **EM** *020 †20,16

SMALL, Hamilton Arthur. 2011 ASHWOOD AVE 37212 #051-04-1996 L2002 **P** *020 ‡

SMALLEY, Walter E, Jr. 1301 22ND AVE N 37232 #036-07-1985 L1991 **GE** *020 †20

SMALLWOOD, Geoffrey Holt. 2011 MURPHY AVE, STE 200 37203 #021-01-1985 L1987 **OBS GYN** *020 †30

SMELTZER, Christopher P. 7640 HIGHWAY 70 S 37221 #047-05-1993 L1997 **PD** *020 †55

SMITH, Andrew Harold. ■ 37212 #023-01-2001 L2007 **CCP** *012 †55

SMITH, Anne Hope. ■ 37209 #051-01-2004 L2004 **HO** *012 †20

SMITH, Barton Eugene. ■ 37216 #047-05-1992 L2001 **FM** *020 †18

SMITH, Bradley Edgerton. 1301 22ND AVE N 37232 #039-01-1957 L1969 **AN** *072 †05

SMITH, Brian Scott. CENTER NORTH, D-3100 MEDICAL 37232 #017-20-1989 L2000 **HS ORS** *020 †40

SMITH, Catherine Joyce. A2200 MCN, 1161 21ST AVE SO. 37232 #021-05-2003 L2004 **ID** *012 †20

SMITH, Charles Ray. 2821 LEBANON PIKE STE 103 37214 #047-06-1965 L1965 **OPH** *020

SMITH, Clarence Edwin. - RADI, VANDERBILT UNIV MED CTR 37232 #047-05-2004 L2007 **DR** *012

SMITH, Clay Barton. 1301 22ND AVE N 37232 #047-06-1999 L2002 **EM** *020 †20,55,16

SMITH, Farin W. ■ 37209 #048-02-2001 L2007 **GS TRS** *020

SMITH, Gary Joe. 7640 HIGHWAY 70 S, STE 201 37221 #048-02-1984 L1988 **FM** *020 †18

SMITH, Grover R, Jr. 210 25TH AVE N, RADIOLOGY CONSULTANTS INC 37203 #047-06-1963 L1963 **DR** *071 †80

SMITH, Harold P. 300 20TH AVE N, STE 103 37203 #047-05-1975 L1982 **NS** *020 †25

SMITH, James Peter. 1161 21ST AVE S, S-3223 MCN 37232 #025-01-2000 L2006 **NEP** *100 †20

SMITH, Jeffrey Roser. 2215 GARLAND AVE, CENTER,529 LIGHT HALL 37232 #048-12-1992 L1999 **IM** *020 †20

SMITH, Jesse Joshua. D-4316 MEDICAL CENTER NORT, DEPT OF SURGICAL SCIENCES 37232 #048-14-2004 L2006 **GS** *012

SMITH, Joseph Aloysius. 1301 22ND AVE N 37232 #047-06-1974 L1974 **U ON** *020 †95

SMITH, Keegan Marcus. 2200 CHILDRENS WAY, STE 251 37232 #047-06-2002 L2004 **AI** *012 †55

SMITH, Kristin Paige. 1301 22ND AVE N 37232 #047-06-2002 L2005 **PD** *100

SMITH, Marion L. ■ 37205 #047-05-1949 L1950 **AN** *071 †55

SMITH, Martha Jane. 1215 21ST AVE S, DEPT OF ANES 3108 MEC 37232 #047-06-2002 L2006 **AN** *100 †05

SMITH, Mary Suzanne. ■ 37221 #023-01-2006 **EM** *012

SMITH, Michael Kevin. 4230 HARDING RD, STE 801 37205 #047-05-1993 L1996 **IM** *020 †20

SMITH, Michael Lee. 2200 CHILDRENS WAY, DOCTORS OFC TWR 8TH FL 37232 #036-08-1983 L1994 **D PD** *020 †55,15

SMITH, Raphael Ford. 1310 24TH AVE S, VA MED CTR 37212 #024-01-1960 L1969 **CD IM** *040 †20

SMITH, Richard Patrick. 310 25TH AVE N, STE 201 37203 #012-22-2004 L2007 **PD** *020 †55

SMITH, Richard Steven. 3443 DICKERSON PIKE, STE 460 37207 #016-06-1985 L1994 **IM** *020 †20

SMITH, Russell Raymond. 3441 DICKERSON PIKE 37207 #017-20-1973 L1974 **GE IM** *020 †20

SMITH, Scott Alan. ■ 37211 #020-02-2006 **IM** *012

SMITH, Stuart Eldridge. 301 21ST AVE N, TENNESSEE ORTHOPAEDIC ASSO 37203 #047-05-1990 L1996 **ORS** *020 †40

SMITH, William Barney. 300 20TH AVE N, STE 100 37203 #047-06-1985 L1985 **AI IM** *020 †20,03

SMITH, William Radford. 300 20TH AVE N, STE 100 37203 #047-06-1953 L1954 **IM** *071 †20

SMITHSON, Joshua Bradley. 2325 CRESTMOOR RD 37215 #047-07-2003 L2005 **IM** *030 †20

SNAPPER, James Robt. 1211 22ND AVE N, D7235 N 37232 #024-01-1974 L1979 **PUD IM** *050 †20

SNELL, Barbara L Burns. 2201 MURPHY AVE, MEDICAL PLAZA STE 204 37203 #047-05-1974 L1977 **IM** *074 †20

SNELL, James Danl. 1500 21ST AVE S STE 3100, VILLAGE OF VANDERBILT 37212 #047-05-1958 L1958 **PUD IM** *030 †20

SNOOK, Barbara Marie. 1310 24TH AVE S, NASHVILLE VAMC 37212 #017-20-1997 L2002 **IM** *020 †20

SNOW, Stanley Steve. 4535 HARDING PIKE STE 102 37205 #004-01-1977 L1977 **CHP** *020 †75 ‡

SNOWDEN, Mary Ann Regina. 2000 CHURCH ST 37236 #035-20-1980 L1981 **OBG** *071 †30

SNYDER, Howard Marc. 255 OLD HICKORY BLVD, # 135 37221 #025-01-1980 L1991 **IM** *020 †20

SNYDER, James G. 4220 HARDING RD, ST THOMAS HOSPITAL 37205 #048-12-1997 L2000 **IM** *020 †20

SNYDER, Rebecca Anne. ■ 37212 #047-05-2008 *012

SNYDER, Robert Bruce. 4230 HARDING RD STE 1000 37205 #025-07-1972 L1974 **ORS** *020 †40 ‡

SNYDER, Shannon Bishop. 1301 22ND AVE N 37232 #047-05-2000 L2002 **EM** *020 †16

SNYDER, Stanley Owen, Jr. 4535 HARDING RD, STE 100 37205 #020-02-1972 L1995 **VS GS** *020 †85

SNYDER, Suzanne Ross. 1211 22ND AVE N 37232 #048-14-1987 L1999 **IM PD** *030 †20,55

SODEIFI, Alireza. 21ST AVE S AT GARLAND AVE, VANDERBILT UNIV SCH OF MED 37232 #047-05-2000 **GS** *100

SOFRANKO, Joseph Edward. 3443 DICKERSON PIKE STE 1 37207 #041-12-1968 L1977 **OPH** *020 †35

SOLTANI, Reza. MEHARRY MED COLL, DEPT MED 37208 #517-01-1956 L1987 **PTH** *020 †50

SOMAYAJI, Buntwal N. 2010 CHURCH ST, STE 508 37203 #495-04-1958 L1971 **GE IM** *071 †20

SONG, Qilin. 1005 DR DB TODD JR BLVD 37208 #243-44-1989 **GPM** *012

SONI, Ashish. 28 WHITE BRIDGE RD, STE 300 37205 #422-01-1999 L2006 **NEP** *020 †20

SONKIN, Peter Laurence. 2011 MURPHY AVE, STE 603 37203 #036-07-1992 L1998 **OPH** *020 †35

SOPATA, Carrie. ■ 37221 #048-12-2007 **OBG** *012

SOPER, Brent Aleshire. 5895 FREDERICKSBURG DR 37215 #047-06-1965 L1966 **DR** *020 †80

SOPER, Richard Graves. 602 W IRIS DR, CTR INTEGRATED HLTH CARE 37204 #047-06-1977 L1981 **ADP ADM** *020 †50 ‡

SOPKO, Kelly Lee. 6000 MEDICAL CENTER EAST, DIVISION OF GENERAL INTERN 37232 #020-12-2001 L2007 **IM** *020

SORESCU, George Paul. ■ 37211 #781-01-1995 L2007 **IM** *012

SOSA, Iberia Romina. ■ 37205 #026-04-2007 **IM** *012

SOSLOW, Jonathan Harvey. ■ 37209 #021-05-2003 L2004 **PDC** *012 †55

SOSMAN, Jeffrey Alan. 1301 22ND AVE N 37232 #035-46-1981 L2001 **ON PTH** *020 †50,20

SOURIS, Patrick Alan. 3709 CENTRAL AVE 37205 #012-01-1989 L1993 **AN** *020 †05

SPALDING, Michael Jon. 345 23RD AVE N, STE 212 37203 #051-01-1966 L1972 **U** *020

SPANIER, Jonathan Michael. 330 WALLACE RD, STE 109 37211 #047-05-2003 L2006 **PD** *020 †55

SPARKS-BUSHNELL, Amanda. 2201 MURPHY AVE, STE 116 37203 #027-01-1995 L1999 **P** *020 †75

SPAULDING, Eman Gebral. 1005 DR DB TODD JR BLVD, SCH OF MED 37208 #047-07-2007 L2007 **PTH** *012

SPAW, Albert T. 2021 CHURCH ST, STE 104 37203 #047-05-1981 L1986 **GS** *020 †85

SPENGLER, Dan Michael. MEDICAL CENTAER E S TO, STE 4200 37232 #025-01-1966 L1983 **OSS** *020 †40

SPETALNICK, Bennett M. 1211 21ST AVE S, MEDICAL ARTS #220 37212 #047-05-1991 L1993 **OBG** *020 †30

SPEYER, Matthew Tiernan. 3443 DICKERSON PIKE, STE 320 SKYLINE MED CTR 37207 #001-02-1991 L1999 **OTO FPS** *020 †45

SPICKARD, W Anderson, Jr. 1107 OXFORD, RM 1107 OXFORD HOUSE 37232 #047-05-1957 L1957 **IM** *050 †20

SPICKARD, Wm Anderson, III. 7TH FLOOR - STE 1, MEDICAL CENTER, EAST 37232 #047-05-1989 L1995 **IM** *020 †20

SPIELVOGEL, Debra Elise. 37205 #010-02-1996 L1997 **DR** *100

SPINDLER, Kurt Paul. S TOWER, MEDICAL CENTER EAST, 37232 #041-01-1985 L1991 **OSM** *020 †40

SPOTTSWOOD, Stephanie E. 2200 CHILDRENS WAY # 1421, VANDERBILT CHILDRENS HOSP 37232 #036-01-1987 L1989 **DR PDR** *062 †80

SPRADLIN, Natalie Montgom. 1211 22ND AVE N, MCN D-3100 37232 #047-05-2005 L2007 **IM** *012

SPRING, Michele Donna. 1211 22ND AVE N 37232 #047-05-1999 L2004 **PDI** *050 †55

SRICHAI, Manakan Betsy. 21ST AND GARLAND AVE, S-3223 MEDICAL CENTER NORT 37232 #055-01-1998 L2003 **NEP** *100 †20

SRIPADA, Ramprasad. STE 2031 VUH, 1211 21ST AVENUE SOUTH 37232 #495-49-1981 L2006 **AN** *020 †20

SRIPRACHITTICHAI, Pin. 1211 21ST AVE S # 324MAB, VNDERBLT PAIN CNTRL CTR 37212 #891-01-1992 **APM** *100

SRIRAM, Subramaniam. 1301 22ND AVE N 37232 #495-04-1973 L1993 **N** *050 †20,75

STACK, Lawrence Benedict. 703 OXFORD HOUSE, 1313 21ST AVE. SOUTH 37232 #039-05-1987 L1995 **EM** *020 †16

STAELIN, Stephen Tyler. 4230 HARDING RD, STE 1000 37205 #047-05-1996 L2006 **HS** *020 †85

STAFFORD, John Michael. VANDERBILT MEDICAL CENTER, D-3100 MCN 37232 #047-05-2003 L2005 **END** *012 †20

STAHLMAN, Gray Clark. 301 21ST AVE N 37203 #047-05-1990 L1996 **ORS** *072 †40

STAHLMAN, Mildred T. 1211 22ND AVE N, D7235 N 37232 #047-05-1946 L1946 **PD NPM** *050 †55

STALLWORTH, Catherine R. 2300 PATTERSON ST 37203 #048-04-1990 L1994 **PM** *020 †60

STALLWORTH, Robert J. 2000 CHURCH ST 37236 #021-01-1987 L1994 **DR** *020 †80

STAMLER, Jeffrey David. ■ 37215 #047-05-2004 L2006 **AN** *012

STANBERRY, Carl Wm. 1301 22ND AVE N 37232 #054-04-1982 L1984 **AN** *020 †05

STANCOMBE, Bradley Blaine. 2200 CHILDRENS WAY, RM 2510 37232 #048-04-1984 L1984 **NPM PD** *020 †20

STANDARD, Scott Crawford. 2011 MURPHY AVE, STE 301 37203 #001-02-1989 L1996 **NS** *020 †25

STANKEWICZ, Mark Anthony. 4230 HARDING PIKE, HEART GROUP PLLC 37205 #008-02-1999 L2000 **CD** *020 †20

STANLEY, Eran Myranda. ■ 37205 #047-05-2006 **P** †012

STARR, Frederick Scott. 1601 23RD AVE S 37212 #033-05-1999 L2004 **CHP** *020

STARR, Sarah Aldrich. ■ 37204 #025-12-1998 L2003 **PME** *100 †05

STASKO, Thomas. 1301 22ND AVE N, 3900 TVC DEPT DERM 37232 #048-13-1977 L1992 **D DS** *020 †15

STEAD, William Wallace. 3401 W END AVE, MED CENTE 37203 #036-07-1973 L1991 **NEP IM** *030 †20

STEC, Andrew Alexander. A-1302 MED CTR NORTH, 21ST AVE S AND GARLAND AVE 37232 #012-05-2004 **U** *012

STEELMAN, Joel W. 1301 22ND AVE N 37232 #048-16-1991 L2001 **PD** *020 †55

STEIGELFEST, Jill. 2200 CHILDRENS WAY, RM 2510 37232 #035-46-1995 L2001 **PD** *020 †55

STEIN, Charles Michael. 1301 22ND AVE N 37232 #836-02-1978 L1994 *020

STEIN, Ira Edward. 2400 PATTERSON ST, STE 101 37203 #047-06-1990 L1992 **GE IM** *020 †20

STEIN, Richard S. 1301 22ND AVE N, 2617 TVC VANDERBILT HOSPIT 37232 #024-01-1970 L1977 **HEM ON** *020 †20

STEIN, Robert Elliot. 301 21ST AVE N 37203 #035-08-1967 L1976 **ORS** *020 †40

STEIN, Sharon Malkah. 1301 22ND AVE N 37232 #836-02-1974 L1986 **DR NM** *020 †80

STENNER, Shane Paul. 1215 21ST AVE S, 7TH FLOOR N TOWER 37232 #023-07-2005 L2007 **IM** *012

STEPHANIDES, Michael. 310 23RD AVE N 37203 #005-11-1992 L2000 **PS** *020 †20

STEPHENS, Merielle Marie. 1161 21ST AVE S, OF O 37232 #035-48-2004 L2008 **OBG** *012

STERANKA, Joe. 1211 22ND AVE N 37232 #047-05-1960 L1960 **PD** *071 †55

STERLING, Timothy Robt. 1301 22ND AVE N 37232 #035-01-1989 L2003 **ID** *020 †20

STERNBERG, Erez Gabriel. ■ 37203 #012-01-2002 L2007 **PS** *012

STERNBERG, Paul, Jr. 2311 PIERCE AVE 37232 #016-02-1979 L2003 **OPH** *040 †35

STEWART, Charles V, Jr. ■ 37215 #055-01-1964 L1971 **TS CD** *071

STEWART, James Oliver. ■ 37218 #047-07-1959 L1962 **OBG** *071 †30

STEWART, Lee Wm. ■ 37205 #047-06-1946 L1954 **AN** *071 †20

STEWART, Richard B. 4220 HARDING PIKE 37205 #012-05-1977 L1982 **DR NR** *020 †80

STILES, Eric Francis. 330 WALLACE RD, STE 109 37211 #035-20-1995 L2001 **CCP** *020 †55

STINSON-REYNOLDS, Julie C. 510 RECOVERY RD, STE 201 37211 #047-06-2000 L2003 **IM** *020 †20

ST JACQUES, Paul Jos. 1215 21ST AVE S, 3108 MEDICAL CENTER EAST 37232 #023-07-1992 L1996 **AN** *020 †05

ST JULIEN, Jamii Baraka. ■ 37203 #023-07-2007 **GS** *012

STOBER, Catherine Vanessa. 2002 RICHARD JONES RD, STE B300 37215 #023-07-1999 L2001 **IM** *020 †20

STOKES, Leann Simmons. 1161 21ST AVE S, VANDERBILT UNIV MC RAD DEP 37232 #020-12-1997 L2000 **VIR** *020 †80

STOLZ, Margaret Mary. 300 20TH AVE N 37203 #047-05-1981 L1984 **IM** *020 †20

STONE, Gertrude Oehmig. 393 WALLACE RD, STE 302 37211 #047-06-1987 L1990 **IM** *020 †20

STONE, William John. VA HOSP 37212 #023-07-1962 L1972 **NEP** *020 †20

STONEHOUSE, Stephen E. 326 21ST AVE N 37203 #036-05-1991 L2001 **FM** *020 †18

STONEY, William Shannon. 4230 HARDING PIKE, STE 450 37205 #047-05-1954 L1954 **TS** *071 †85,90

STORCK, Kristina Lynn. 1301 22ND AVE N 37232 #047-05-2001 L2003 **OBG** *020 †30

STORY, Julie Lynn. ■ 37209 #023-07-2007 **EM** *012

STOVALL, Marlynn Giles. 2601 ELM HILL PIKE, STE C 37214 #012-21-1990 L1991 **GP EM** *020

STOVER, Daniel Garvin. ■ 37212 #047-05-2008 *012

STOVER, Stephanie Andrea. 2021 CHURCH ST, BMP II STE 310 37203 #011-03-1996 L2005 **PS** *020 †85,65

STOWELL, Nicholas Gregory. ■ 37211 #051-01-2007 **OTO** *012

STRATTON, Charles Wm. 21ST ANDE EDGEHILL RD, VANDERBILT UNIVERSITY CLIN 37232 #050-02-1971 L1979 **ID IM** *020 †20

STRAUSS, Arnold Wilbur. VANDERBILT UNIV MED CTR, AA-0216 MEDICAL CTR N 37232 #028-02-1970 L2000 **PDC** *050 †55

STRAYHORN, Wm David, III. 2611 W END AVE 37203 #047-05-1959 L1959 **IM** *071 †20

STRICKLAND, Stephen A, Jr. RESEARCH BUILDING, 777 PRESTON 37232 #021-05-2002 L2005 **HO** *012 †20

STRICKLAND, William G. 300 20TH AVE N, STE 600 37203 #047-05-1984 L1986 **N CN** *020 †75

STRICKLIN, George Putnam. 1301 22ND AVE N 37232 #028-02-1977 L1984 **D** *050 †15

STRNAD, Sarah Allison. 4230 HARDING RD, STE 603 37205 #047-06-2000 L2004 **OBG** *020 †30

STRODE, Wilborn D. 2010 CHURCH ST 37203 #047-06-1958 L1959 **GYN** *071

STROHLER, Bradly. 5121 DOCTOR OFFICE TOWER, 2200 CHILDRENS WAY 37232 #033-06-2000 L2006 **CCP** *020 ‡

STROM, Sebastian Sune. 1161 21ST AVE S 37232 #297-01-2001 L2006 **IM** *100 †20

STROMBERG, Paul Ernst. ■ 37203 #047-05-2008 *012

STROTHER, Megan Kay. 1301 22ND AVE N 37232 #004-01-1998 L2004 **RNR** *020 †80

STUBLEFIELD, Mark Thomas. 7640 HIGHWAY 70 S, STE 110 37221 #047-06-1983 L1984 **IM EM** *020 †20

STUCKEY, Jordan William. ■ 37209 #010-02-2005 **AN** *012

STUMB, Paul Rust. 1211 21ST AVE S, STE 514 37212 #047-05-1960 L1960 **IM CD** *071 †20

STUTZ, Christopher Michae. 21 VAUGHNS GAP RD, APT 116 37205 #048-14-2005 **ORS** *012

SUGGS, Tammy Lynn. 1601 23RD AVE S, SUITE301 37212 #012-22-2002 L2008 **CHP** *012

SUKPANICHNANT, Sanya. ■ 37212 #891-02-1986 **PTH** *020

SULLIVAN, Andre Jawann. 221 STEWARTS FERRY PIKE 37214 #047-07-1999 L2007 **P** *012

SULLIVAN, James Nelson. 1005 DR DB TODD JR BLVD, DEPT OF INTERNAL MEDICINE 37208 #047-05-1974 L1976 **IM END** *020 †20 ‡

SULSER, Fridolin. TENN NEURO PSYCH INST 37217 #869-01-1955 **P PA** *050

SUMMAR, Marshall Lynn. 2200 CHILDRENS WAY, RM 2510 37232 #047-06-1985 L1990 **MG PD** *050 †19,55

SUMNER, Eric Larry. 1660 TVC, VANDERBILT UNIVERSITY 37232 #012-01-2001 L2004 **GE** *012

SUN, J George. ■ 37211 #045-01-2004 L2006 **IM** *020 †20

SUNDBERG, Jennifer Marie. CHILDREN'S HOSPITAL, VANDERBILT 37232 #012-01-2004 L2007 **PE** *012 †55

SUNDELL, Hakan Wilhelm. B1220 MCN, VANDERBILT UNIV HOSP 37232 #858-02-1963 L1973 **NPM** *050 †55

SUSSKIND, Cynthia Gaye. 2300 PATTERSON ST 37203 #055-01-1981 L1987 **N** *020 †75

SUSSMAN, Craig Richard. 1301 22ND AVE N 37232 #041-13-1973 L1977 **IM END** *020 †20

SUTTON, Hyatt Dibrell. 2400 PATTERSON ST, STE 101 37203 #001-02-1994 L1996 **IM** *072 †20

SWAN, Chad Russell. 3443 DICKERSON PIKE, STE 400 37207 #021-05-1997 L2005 **VS** *020 †85

SWAN, Michael Chas. 2010 CHURCH ST, STE 503 37203 #056-06-1990 L1997 **OBG** *020 †30

SWAN, Rebecca Ruth. 1301 22ND AVE N 37232 #051-04-1990 L1997 **PD** *020 †55

SWANSON, Erik Roger. ■ 37221 #036-08-2006 **OTO** *012

SWANSON, Gary Dennis. 610 GALLATIN RD 37206 #047-05-1975 L1978 **EM FM** *020 †16

SWEET, Stephanie Dianne. 1919 CHARLOTTE AVE 37203 #047-07-1991 L1995 **OBG** *020 †30

SWENSON, Brian Robt. 204 CARGILE LN 37205 #041-12-1979 L1980 **P** *062 †75

SWIFT, Melanie Dawn. 1301 22ND AVE N 37232 #047-06-1992 L1995 **IM** *020 †20

SWITTER, David John. 2010 CHURCH ST, STE 615 37203 #047-05-1974 L1976 **PTH CLP** *020 †50

SWOGGER, Marcy Marie. 5819 OLD HARDING RD, STE 201 37205 #028-03-2003 L2006 **PD** *020 †55
TABER, David S. 1301 22ND AVE N 37232 #017-20-1977 L1982 **DR** *020 †80
TABRIZI, Maryam Bita. ■ 37221 #047-06-2008 *012
TACOGUE, Loyda C. 4230 HARDING RD, STE 202 37205 #748-01-1964 L1971 **CD IM** *020
TACOGUE, Tranquilino, Jr. 1161 21ST AVE S DEPT ANES 37212 #748-07-1963 **AN** *100
TADKOD, Altaf Husain. ■ 37217 #012-01-2007 **IM** *012
TAFFEL, Myles Todd. ■ 37204 #012-01-2004 L2008 **DR** *012
TAI, Steven Hanley. 222 22ND AVE N, STE 100 37203 #021-06-1994 L2001 **IM** *020 †20
TAKACS, Istvan. T4224 MCN, VANDERBILT MEDICAL CENTER 37232 #858-01-1986 L2004 **GS** *020
TALBOT, Michael David. 4535 HARDING PIKE, STE 302 37205 #035-20-1970 L1993 **IM** *020 †20
TALBOT, Thomas Robert, III. 1161 21ST AVE S, A 2200 MEDICAL CENTER NORT 37232 #047-05-1996 L2002 **ID** *030 †20
TALLEY, Paul Alexis. 1005 DR DB TODD JR BLVD 37208 #047-07-1970 L1976 **PUD IM** *020
TAMMAREDDI, Kumar Navin. 1005 DR DB TODD JR BLVD, MEHARRY MED COLLEGE 37208 #422-01-2006 **IM** *012
TANAKA, Stacy Tricia. ■ 37205 #005-19-2001 L2003 **UP** *012
TANEDO, Joel Santos. 4230 HARDING RD, STE 330 37205 #748-01-1991 L2001 **IC** *020 †20
TANG, Tianlai. 1601 23RD AVE S, PSYCHIATRIC HOSP VANDERB 37212 #243-58-1985 L2001 **P** *020 †75
TANNER, S Bobo. 2611 W END AVE, STE 210 37203 #036-05-1983 L1985 **RHU AI** *020 †20,03
TAO, Yanli. 1161 21ST AVE S, DEPT OF NEUROLOGY 37232 #243-69-1990 L2007 **CHN** *012
TARANTOLA, Ryan Michael. ■ 37212 #028-34-2005 **OPH** *012
TARDY, Joshua Caleb. ■ 37209 #048-15-2007 **PD** *012
TARLETON, Gadson J, Jr. ■ 37218 #047-07-1944 L1944 **R** *071 †80
TARPLEY, Horton E. 4751 TROUSDALE DR 37220 #047-05-1950 L1950 **GP EM** *020
TARPLEY, John Leeman. ■ 37215 #047-05-1970 L1970 **GS ORS** *020 †85
TARQUINE, Steven Scott. 4220 HARDING RD, STE 500 37205 #001-02-1995 L1998 **EM** *020 †20
TARRANT, Tiffany E. ■ 37205 #048-04-2004 **OBG** *012
TARVIN, Emily M. ■ 37212 #047-05-2007 **IM** *012
TATINI, Ramasubba Rao. 1005 DR DB TODD JR BLVD, OF PSYCH 37208 #495-58-1978 **P** *012
TATSAS, Alon. 2200 CHILDRENS WAY, STE 3115 37232 #021-01-2001 L2005 **PAN** *020
TATSAS, Armanda Dawson. ■ 37215 #021-05-2005 **PTH** *012
TAULIEN, Christina Ann. 1161 21ST AVE S, A2200 MEDICAL CENTER NORTH 37232 #016-43-2003 **ID** *012 †20
TAYLOR, Henry Michael. 275 STEWARTS FERRY PIKE, COLVER BOTTOM DEVELOPMENTA 37214 #016-11-1977 L2001 **PD EM** *030 †55
TAYLOR, Joseph Eugene. ■ 37205 #047-07-1972 L2008 **OTO HNS** *071 †45
TAYLOR, Mary Barraza. 5121 DOCTORS OFFICE TOWER, 2200 CHILDRENS WAY 37232 #027-01-1991 L1997 **CCA PDC** *020 †55
TAYLOR, Robert Kevin. 28 WHITE BRIDGE RD STE 300 37205 #007-02-1989 L1997 **NEP IM** *020 †20
TAYLOR, Thomas Brelin, Jr. 3443 DICKERSON PIKE, STE 270 37207 #020-12-1990 L1997 **GS** *020 †85
TCHERNIKOVA-RAMEY, T. 2300 ELLISTON PL # 729 37203 #913-53-1978 **P** *100
TEDDER, Mark. 4230 HARDING RD STE 450, CARDIOVASCULAR SRGRY ASSOC 37205 #036-07-1988 L1997 **TS** *020 †85,90
TEMPLE, M Patricia C. 2200 CHILDRENS WAY, VANDERBILT CHILDS HOS 37232 #040-02-1969 L2001 **PD PHP** *030 †55
TENENHOLZ, Todd Carl. 1301 22ND AVE N B-902, RADIATION ONCOLOGY, VANDER 37232 #023-01-1999 L2004 **RO** *020 †80
TERHUNE, Kyla Phyllis. ■ 37211 #041-01-2004 L2007 **GS** *012
TERRY, Richard Bruce. 2011 CHURCH ST STE 703 37203 #047-06-1970 L1970 **GS CRS** *020 †85
TESAURO, Thomas Anthony. 4230 HARDING PIKE, STE 805 37205 #047-05-1994 L1995 **IM** *020 †20
TESCHAN, Paul Erhard. ■ 37215 #026-04-1948 L1971 **NEP IM** *071 †20
THACKER, Stephen Andrew. ■ 37216 #036-01-2007 **PD** *012
THAM, Kyi Toe. 1301 22ND AVE N 37232 #209-01-1961 L1985 **ATP MM** *020 †50
THARP, Kyle Marion. ■ 37221 #020-02-2001 L2004 **DR** *012 †28
THATI, Yoganandam. 1916 PATTERSON ST STE 600, DOCTORS PAVILION 37203 #495-21-1977 L1999 **IM** *020 †20
THEILADE, Karen Christian. ■ 37203 #297-01-2002 **CD** *012 †20
THOMAS, Anne Taggart. 1301 22ND AVE N, DIV OF HEMATOLOGY 2665 TV 37232 #028-03-1985 L1988 **HEM IM** *020 †20
THOMAS, Bradley Phillip. 1161 21ST AVE S, VUMC - DEPARTMENT OF RADIO 37232 #001-02-2002 L2005 **RNR** *012 †80
THOMAS, Christopher Bryan. ■ 37203 #038-40-2002 L2005 **PCC** *012 †20
THOMAS, Clarence S, Jr. ■ 37205 #047-05-1960 L1961 **TS** *071 †85,90
THOMAS, E Dewey. 2000 CHURCH ST 37236 #047-05-1959 L1959 **ORS LM** *071 †40
THOMAS, Frank Evans, Jr. 2510 MURFREESBORO PIKE, STE 2 37217 #047-07-1971 L1971 **ID IM** *020
THOMAS, James Ward. 1301 MEDICAL CENTER DR 37232 #047-06-1973 L1974 **RHU AI** *050 †20,03
THOMAS, John Christopher. 2200 CHILDRENS WAY, VANDERBILT CHILDREN'S HOSP 37232 #038-41-1998 L2006 **UP** *020 †95
THOMAS, Kenneth Tyson. 4230 HARDING RD, STE 525 37205 #047-05-2000 L2003 **GS** *020 †85
THOMAS, Tamara O. 2200 CHILDRENS WAY 8161, CHILDREN'S HOSPITAL 37232 #048-16-2007 **PD** *012
THOMASCH, James Richard. ■ 37212 #036-01-2006 **U** *012
THOMASON, Elizabeth Lynn. - RADI, VANDERBILT UNIV MED CTR 37232 #040-02-2005 **DR** *012
THOMASSON, Thomas Jackson. ■ 37203 #047-05-2004 L2004 **ORS** *012
THOMBS, David Dawson. 5819 OLD HARDING RD, STE 201 37205 #047-05-1963 L1963 **PD** *071 †55
THOMPSON, Annemarie. 1301 22ND AVE N 37232 #036-07-1995 L2002 **AN** *020 †20,05
THOMPSON, Brian Marshall. 4230 HARDING RD, STE 301 37205 #001-02-1978 L1992 **N** *020 †75
THOMPSON, Erin. ■ 37205 #005-76-2007, ▲ *012
THOMPSON, Harold Delane. 1161 21ST AVE S, VANDERBILT UNIV MED SCHOO 37232 #010-03-1972 L1979 **DR** *030 †80
THOMPSON, Ian M. ■ 37209 #048-13-2007 **GS** *012
THOMPSON, Ira Dell, Jr. 1005 18TH AVE S 37212 #047-07-1962 L1973 **VS TS** *030 †85,90
THOMPSON, Jeffrey Charles. ■ 37209 #047-07-2008 *012
THOMPSON, John Gill, Jr. 222 22ND AVE N, STE 100 37203 #012-05-1973 L1977 **IM** *020 †20
THOMPSON, Reid Carleton. T-4224 MEDICAL CENTER NORT 37232 #023-07-1989 L2002 **NS** *020 †25
THOMPSON, William Clark. 2010 CHURCH ST, MID STATE MEDICAL CENTER 37203 #027-01-1979 L1981 **PUD CCM** *030 †20
THOMPSON, William David. 4230 HARDING RD STE 33, HEART GROUP PLLC 37205 #047-05-1995 L1997 **ICE** *020 †20
THOMSEN, Isaac Peter. ■ 37211 #004-01-2004 L2006 **MPD** *012
THOMSON, Andrew Brian. 1301 22ND AVE N 37232 #020-12-2000 L2004 **ORS** *020
THORNBURG, Catherine M. 2021 CHURCH ST 37203 #047-06-1988 L1990 **OBG** *020 †30
THORNE, Charles B. 1500 22ND AVE S, KIM DAYANI CTR 37232 #047-05-1949 L1956 **IM** *071 †20
THORNTON, Spencer P. ■ 37220 #036-05-1954 L1958 **OPH** *071 †35
THRUSH, Thomas E. 1900 CHURCH ST, STE 511 37203 #055-01-1984 L1987 **EM GS** *020
THURMAN, Grafton H. 3443 DICKERSON PIKE, STE 512 37207 #020-02-1968 L1973 **IM RHU** *071 †20
THURMAN, Robert Jason. 1301 22ND AVE N 37232 #001-02-1998 L2002 **EM** *020 †16
TICARIC, Stephen Theodore. 3441 DICKERSON PIKE 37207 #048-12-1974 L1976 **CD** *020 †20
TIERNEY, Brian Patrick. 2011 CHURCH ST, STE 805 37203 #038-44-1993 L2003 **PS** *020 †65
TIKHONENKOV, Sergei N. A-1302 MED CTR NORTH, 21ST AVE S AND GARLAND AVE 37232 #036-01-2003 L2006 **U** *012
TILLEY, Kenneth Shannon. 200 ATHENS WAY 37228 #047-05-1964 L1964 **OPH OM** *071
TIPPENS, Robert Lane. 7200 CENTENNIAL BLVD, VISTEON NASHVILLE GLASS PL 37209 #047-05-1980 L1983 **OM EM** *020 †70,16
TISHLER, Steven David. 2000 CHURCH ST 37236 #001-02-1989 L1994 **R MSR** *020 †80 ‡
TODD, Kirkland W, Jr. 328 22ND AVE N 37203 #041-12-1946 L1948 **PS** *071 †65
TODD, Robert David. ■ 37206 #048-12-2006 **AN** *012
TODOROV, Katerina Bojikov. 1005 DR DB TODD JR BLVD, MEHARRY MED COLLEGE 37208 #198-01-1994 **IM** *012
TOLBERT, Todd Gregory. 300 20TH AVE N 37203 #047-06-1995 L1996 **CD** *020 †20
TOMICHEK, Richard Chas. 4230 HARDING PIKE, ANESTHESIOLOGISTS 37205 #041-02-1974 L1982 **AN CCA** *020 †05
TOMLINSON, Anne Kristin. ■ 37212 #010-02-2005 **OBG** *012
TOMLINSON, Ryan Christoph. ■ 37204 #047-05-2008 **AN** *012
TOMPKINS, Thomas Eugene. 2300 PATTERSON ST 37203 #047-05-1979 L1980 **ORS** *020 †40
TOMYCZ, Luke Daniel. ■ 37212 #025-01-2006 **NS** *012
TOOMEY, Thomas Philip. 110 29TH AVE N, STE201 37203 #035-20-1982 L1987 **AN** *020 †05
TORIBIO, Fe Bolanos. ■ 37221 #748-01-1954 L1975 **P GP** *071
TORQUATI, Alfonso. D-5203 MCN, VANDERBILT MEDICAL CENTER 37232 #561-32-1988 L2001 **GS** *020 †85
TORRENTE, Jessica. - RADI, VANDERBILT UNIV MED CTR 37232 #011-02-2003 L2007 **DR** *012
TORRENTE, Sandra Lissette. 1035 14TH AVE N 37208 #019-02-2000 L2004 **OBG** *020
TORRES, Carmen. 1005 DR DB TODD JR BLVD, DEPT OF FAM & COMM MED 37208 #275-03-1993 **FP** *012
TORRES, Jenny. ■ 37209 #047-07-2004 L2006 **IM** *100
TOSH, Robert H. 211 22ND AVE N 37203 #047-06-1953 L1953 **GYN** *071
TOURE, Sekou. ■ 37201 #047-07-1994 *100
TOUSSAINT, Rudiane. 304 WESSEX CT 37211 #047-07-2001 L2005 **OBG** *100
TOWNES, Alexander S. VANDERBILT UNIV MED CTR, 212 OXFORD HOUSE 37232 #047-05-1953 L1953 **IM RHU** *071 †20
TOWNS, Myron Bumstead, Jr. 971 16TH AVE N 37208 #047-07-1978 L1979 **GPM PTH** *030
TRABUE, Anthony Edward D. 2201 MURPHY AVE STE 308 37203 #047-05-1975 L1976 **OBG** *020 †30 ‡
TRABUE, Christopher H. ■ 37221 #047-20-2002 L2003 **ID** *012 †20
TRAN, Uyen Lam. 8009 MCE NORTH TOWER 37232 #051-04-1997 L2001 **OPH** *020 †35
TRAPPEY, Bernard Edgar. ■ 37212 #047-05-2008 *012
TRAUGHBER, Leslie E, Jr. ■ 37215 #047-06-1951 L1951 **AN** *071 †05
TRAVIS, Lawrence W, Jr. 2410 PATTERSON ST, STE 212 37203 #025-01-1969 L1987 **OTO** *020 †45
TRAWICK, Eric Powell. ■ 37220 #021-06-2007 **IM** *012
TREADWAY, Charles Richard. 1516 16TH AVE S 37212 #047-05-1964 L1970 **P** *030 †75
TREITSCHKE MILLAND, Thor. 1161 21ST AVE S 37232 #297-01-2001 **AN** *012
TRICHE, Rachel Gaines. 1215 21ST AVE S, ORTHOPAEDIC INSTITU 37232 #005-06-2005 **ORS** *012
TRIGGS, Elizabeth Grimes. 2002 RICHARD JONES RD, STE A102 37215 #027-01-1981 L1985 **PD** *020 †55
TROCHTENBERG, David Scott. 1005 DR DB TODD JR BLVD, DEPT OF INTERNAL MEDICINE 37208 #047-05-1986 L1989 **IM** *020 †20
TROPEZ-SIMS, Susanne. 1005 DR DB TODD JR BLVD 37208 #036-01-1975 L1997 **PD GPM** *030 †55
TRZPUC, Shelley Renee. VANDERBILT STALLWORTH, 2201 CAPERS AVE 37212 #037-01-2000 L2004 **PM** *100
TSAO, Leland Yehfong. 110 29TH AVE N, STE 201 37203 #051-04-1991 L1993 **DR** *020 †80
TSIATIS, Athanasios Chris. ■ 37212 #047-05-2004 L2007 **PTH** *012
TUCKER, Aubrey Lee, Jr. 300 20TH AVE N, FL 9 37203 #047-05-1975 L1976 **IM** *020 †20
TUCKER, Cortez Arthur. 1412 COUNTY HOSPITAL RD 37218 #047-07-1985 L2007 **IM** *020
TUCKER, Lindsey Conniece. ■ 37207 #045-01-2007 **AN** *012
TUCKER, Meredith A. 2300 PATTERSON ST, EMERGENCY DEPT 37203 #035-45-1989 L1997 **EM** *020 †16
TUCKER, Vernita Ann Tate. 1035 14TH AVE N 37208 #017-20-1985 L1993 **OBG** *020 †30
TUDOR, John M, Jr. 2801 CHARLOTTE AVE 37209 #018-03-1945 L1951 **U** *071 †95
TUDORICA, Mihaela. 2000 CHURCH ST, MARTIN MEDICAL CENTER, PC 37236 #781-01-1998 L2003 **IM** *020 †20
TULIPAN, Noel Bristow. 2200 CHILDRENS WAY, 9226 DOT 37232 #023-07-1981 L1985 **NS** *020 †25
TUMEN, Jon Jay. 4230 HARDING PIKE, STE 400 37205 #036-07-1980 L1982 **IM** *020 †20
TUNKS, Robert D. ■ 37221 #048-13-2007 **PD** *012
TUREK, Raymond Emil. 2506 FRANKLIN PIKE 37204 #030-05-1967 L1968 **GP R** *030
TURNER, Anthony Lanier. 1911 STATE ST 37203 #012-21-2005 L2007 **IM** *012
TURNER, Ernest Alvin. 388 HARDING PL, STE B 37211 #019-02-1976 L1987 **PD HEM** *020 †55
TURNER, Korie L. ■ 37211 #048-13-2008 *012
TURNER, Staci A. 850 RS GASS BLVD, FORENSIC MEDICAL 37216 #020-12-1996 L2004 **FOP** *020 †50
TURNER, Steven Terry. 391 WALLACE RD 37211 #047-05-2000 L2004 **EM** *020 †16
TURNER-GRAHAM, Cynthia A. 2414 BARTON AVE 37212 #019-02-1979 L1981 **P OS** *030 †75
TURNER-WINBUSH, Beverly. 4230 HARDING RD STE 5, INSTITUTE BUILDING 37205 #005-12-2000 L2002 **IM** *020

TYE, Georgia Kaye. 3441 DICKERSON PIKE, SARA CANNON CANCER CTR 37207 #020-02-1979 L1992 **FM EM** *020 †16

TYSON, Richard. 2720 N HIGHLANDS DR 37221 #047-05-1998 L2000 **PCC** *012 †20

TZANETOS, Douglas Bazil. 2611 W END AVE, UKCMC-GME 37203 #020-12-2002 L2007 **AI** *012 †20,55

UCHEYA, Blessing Chinonye. 1005 DR DB TODD JR BLVD, MEHARRY MED COLLEGE 37208 #690-16-2002 **IM** *012

UDDIN, Naeem. 710 HART LANE, MID-CUMBERLAND REGION 37247 #704-02-1973 L2002 **GPM** *020 †18

UETRECHT, Jack Paul. ■ 37205 #038-40-1975 L1978 **OS** *050 †20

UHEROVA, Patricia. ■ 37204 #286-11-1988 L2003 **HMP** *020 †50

UMEOZULU, Vivian Chinyere. ■ 37211 #690-04-1995 L2007 **IM** *100 †20

UPPAL, Dushant Singh. 1161 21ST AVE S 37232 #539-04-2007 **IM** *012

UQDAH, Jameel Amir. 37214 #047-07-2006 **IM** *012

URA, Jay Michael. 391 WALLACE RD DEPT ANES 37211 #047-06-1981 L1981 **AN** *020 †05

USKAVITCH, David Robert. A-0118 MEDICAL CENTER N, DEPT OF NEUROLOGY 37232 #051-01-1987 L1991 **N** *020 †75

VAEZI, Michael Fredrick. 1301 22ND AVE N 37232 #001-02-1992 L2005 **GE** *020 †20

VAGLIO, Joseph Charles. VANDERBILT UNIV SCH OF MED, CARDIOVASCULAR MED 37232 #019-02-2004 L2007 **CD** *012 †20

VAIKUNTH, Kunda Sudhir. 221 STEWARTS FERRY PIKE, M.T.M.H.I. 37214 #495-28-1965 L1979 **FM P** *020 †18

VALDEZ, Lawrence Joseph. 2300 PATTERSON ST, CENTENNIAL MED CTR-ED 37203 #047-06-2000 L2002 **EM IM** *020

VALENTINE, John David. 3443 DICKERSON PIKE, STE 270 37207 #027-01-2001 L2007 **GS** *020 †85

VALET, Robert Scott. ■ 37215 #047-05-2005 L2007 **IM** *012

VAN DER HEIJDEN, Yuri Fre. 4220 HARDING RD 37205 #047-05-2005 L2007 **IM** *012

VANDERPOOL, Charles Phill. ■ 37211 #017-20-2005 **PD** *012

VAN DERVOORT, Robt L, Jr. VANDERBILT CHILDREN'S HOSP, 11209 DOT 37232 #016-06-1966 L1979 **PD DBP** *020 †55

VAN DEVENDER, Frank Karl. 2400 PATTERSON ST, STE 101 37203 #027-01-1979 L1982 **IM** *020 †20

VAN DRIEST, Sara Lynn. ■ 37221 #026-08-2006 **PD** *012

VAN EYS, Jan. ■ 37215 #054-04-1966 L1967 **PHO PD** *071 †55

VANGALDER, Jon Russell. 37203 #047-05-2003 *100

VANHIMBERGEN, Daniel John. ■ 37211 #020-02-2003 L2005 **OTO** *012

VAN HOOYDONK, John Edward. 2011 MURPHY AVE STE 200 37203 #038-40-1974 L1975 **OBG** *020 †30

VANN, Harold Francis. 1601 23RD AVE S 37212 #047-06-1954 L1954 **PD** *071 †55

VAN ORDEN, Lucas Schuyler. 310 25TH AVE N 37203 #016-06-1956 L1997 **P ADM** *071 †75

VANSICKLE, Bradley James. ■ 37221 #038-43-2004 L2008 **PD** *100

VAN ZEELAND, Nathan L. ■ 37221 #056-05-2003 L2006 **ORS** *012

VAN ZYL, Heinro. ■ 37206 #047-06-2002 L2004 **EM** *012

VARGAS, Kenneth Eugene. 2400 PATTERSON ST, STE 500 37203 #047-06-1994 L1996 **IM** *020 †20

VARGAS, Pilar. ■ 37219 #035-46-1977 L2006 **CHP P** *074 †75

VASQUEZ, Jaime M. 2410 PATTERSON ST, STE 401 37203 #231-03-1974 L1991 **REN OBG** *020 †30

VASSALL, Alford Nathaniel. 1005 DR DB TODD JR BLVD 37208 #047-07-1959 L1977 **GP** *071

VEENSTRA-VANDERWEELE, J. 465 21ST AVE S, 7150 MRB III, VUMC 37232 #016-02-2001 L2006 **CHP P** *050 †75

VEMIREDDY, Roopa. ■ 37215 #047-05-2007 **TY** *012

VENKAT, Sonnepal. 1818 ALBION ST, NASHVILLE METROGENERAL HOS 37208 #495-33-1981 L1996 **EM** *020 †20,16

VERA, Kimberly Burke. ■ 37221 #047-06-2001 L2006 **PDC** *012 †55

VERMUND, Sten Halvor. 319 LIGHT HALL, 2215 GARLAND AVE 37232 #035-46-1977 L2006 **PHP PD** *050 †55,70

VERNON, John Thomas. ■ 37209 #051-04-2005 **P** *012

VICKERS, David Hunter. 360 WALLACE RD, SURGERY CENTER 37211 #020-12-1983 L1994 **AN FM** *018,05

VIGNES, Nicole Elizabeth. ■ 37209 #021-06-2006 L2008 **IM** *012

VILLAROSA, Imelda. 3443 DICKERSON PIKE 37207 #748-02-1991 L2001 **END IM** *074 †20 ‡

VILVARAJAH, Visualingam. 121 21ST AVE N, STE 206 37203 #220-02-1970 L1975 **AN** *020 †05

VINCENT, James Lawrence. 110 29TH AVE N, STE 201 37203 #001-02-1972 L1978 **AN** *071 †05

VINCENT, Kimberly Dawn. 24 WHITE BRIDGE RD 37205 #047-05-1994 L1997 **D** *020 †15

VINER, Daniel Dimitry. 2001 HAYES ST 37203 #047-05-1997 L2002 **OTO** *020 †45

VINSON, Jim Holder. 2000 CHURCH ST 37236 #047-20-1982 L1986 **PTH** *020 †50

VISSERS, Christian F, Jr. 356 24TH AVE N, STE 200 37203 #048-04-1999 L2005 **OSM** *020

VOGT, Jeanne Corliss. ■ 37212 #047-05-2004 L2008 **P** *012

VOLLMER, Donald Evans, II. 4200 STAMMER PL, OLYMPIC CONSULTING 37215 #005-12-1996 L1999 **FM** *071 †18

VOLNEY, Shane Joffre. ■ 37205 #011-03-2007 **AN** *020

VONCHA, Saritha Reddy. 1005 D B TODD BLVD, DEPT OF FAMILY & COMM MED 37208 #913-38-1999 **FP** *012

VORA, Pravinchandra Z. 1800 CHURCH ST, STE 304 37203 #495-39-1959 L1972 **GS** *020 †85

VORBUSCH, Elisabeth Maria. ■ 37209 #409-02-1944 L1975 **P** *072

VOSBERG, Diane Marie. 2000 CHURCH ST 37236 #047-06-1985 L1989 **PD** *020 †55

VOSKRESENSKY, Igor Vladim. ■ 37203 #047-05-2008 *012

VRANIC, Andrew Robert. ■ 37209 #011-03-2006 **IM** *012

VU, Hung Thanh. 2201 W END AVE, VANDERBILT UNIVERSITY MEDI 37235 #050-02-2005 L2006 **EM** *012

VUKSANAJ, Dila. 1301 22ND AVE N 37232 #035-48-1982 L1996 **AN PD** *020 †55,05

WAGNER, Martin Henry. 3441 DICKERSON PIKE 37207 #048-04-1978 L1984 **N P** *020 †75

WAGSTROM, Lois. 250 25TH AVE N, STE 301 37203 #016-43-1981 L1991 **PS** *020 †85,65

WALDMAN, Jeffrey Michael. ■ 37204 #036-01-2003 L2006 **AN** *100

WALDO, Douglas Anthony. 3443 DICKERSON PIKE, STE 430 37207 #035-06-1979 L1989 **CD IM** *020 †20

WALIA, Ann. 1310 24TH AVE S BA-128, TVHS/CHIEF OF ANESTHESIOLO 37212 #495-69-1984 L1999 **AN IM** *020 †05

WALKER, Andy, III. 111 VOSSLAND DR 37205 #047-06-1985 L1990 **EM PE** *020 †16

WALKER, Charles Julian. 4220 HARDING RD 37205 #047-07-1943 L1953 **GP** *072

WALKER, Charlotte Rose. 1501 HERMAN ST 37208 #047-06-1964 L1965 **GS SO** *020

WALKER, Garry Verette. 1301 22ND AVE N 37232 #026-04-1988 L1991 **AN** *020 †05

WALL, Jarrod Clarke Hende. 1161 21ST AVE S, VANDERBILT UNIV MED CTR 37232 #539-03-2002 L2002 **CCS** *012 †85

WALL, Michelle G. 300 20TH AVE N, NASHVILLE MEDICAL GROUP 37203 #012-05-1994 L2006 **IM** *020 †20

WALLACE, Rodger Terry. 341 WALLACE RD 37211 #047-06-1969 L1970 **FM GS** *020 †18

WALLSTEDT, Bruce Alan. 397 WALLACE RD, BUILDING C - SUITE 100 37211 #047-06-1993 L1994 **FM** *020 †18

WALSH, Dena Strube. A-1302 MED CTR NORTH, 21ST AVE S AND GARLAND AVE 37232 #021-01-2005 L2007 **U** *012

WALSH, Glynis Lee. 4220 HARDING PIKE 37205 #010-02-1998 L2000 **EM** *020 †16

WALSH, Ramona Nondine. 2201 MURPHY AVE STE 308 37203 #047-05-1978 L1979 **GYN** *074

WALSH, William Francis. 2200 CHILDRENS WAY, RM 2510 37232 #048-13-1976 L1992 **NPM PD** *020 †55

WALTERS, Travis Thomas. 2002 RICHARD JONES RD, STE A102 37215 #047-05-1999 L2002 **PD** *020 †55

WALTON, Amanda Rhea. ■ 37203 #048-04-2003 L2005 **NEP** *012 †20

WALTON, Kenneth Brian. 2400 PATTERSON ST, STE 223 37203 #048-15-1998 L2005 **TS** *020 †85

WALTON, Shana Marie. ■ 37203 #017-20-2005 L2007 **AN** *012

WANG, Jiakun. 1005 DR DB TODD JR BLVD, DEPT OF INTERNAL MEDICINE 37208 #243-95-1994 **IM** *012

WANG, Ming Xu. 1801 W END AVE, STE 1150 37203 #024-01-1991 L1997 **OPH OS** *020 †35

WANG, Xu. 1005 DR DB TODD JR BLVD 37208 #243-70-1982 L2005 **GPM** *020 †70

WANG, Yihan. VANDERBILT UNIV MED CTR, RENAL PATH C2317 MCN 37232 #243-85-1983 L2007 **PTH** *020

WARD, Russell Dorris. ■ 37216 #047-05-1944 L1944 **IM** *071

WARE, Lorraine Bell. 1301 22ND AVE N 37232 #023-07-1992 L2002 **IM** *020 †20

WARKENTIN, Jon Victor. 311 23RD AVE N, METROPOLITAN HEALTH DEPT 37203 #017-20-1988 L2004 **GPM** *020 †18

WARNER, John Jeffrey. 4230 HARDING RD, STE 521 37205 #016-06-1976 L1977 **U** *020 †95 ‡

WARNER, John Sloan. 4230 HARDING PIKE, STE 521 37205 #047-05-1956 L1956 **N** *071 †75

WARREN, Micahel Dale. ■ 37209 #036-08-2003 L2005 **PD** *100 †55

WASHINGTON, Chad Wayne. ■ 37209 #027-01-2007 L2007 **GS** *012

WASHINGTON, Mary Kay. 1301 22ND AVE N 37232 #036-01-1986 L1996 **PTH** *020 †20

WASUDEO, Geeta Pramod. 1310 24TH AVE S, VA HOSPITAL 37212 #495-17-1963 L1974 **AN** *020 †05

WASUDEV, P B. 3441 DICKERSON PIKE 37207 #495-17-1962 L1973 **GS TS** *020 †85

WATHEN, Mark Stephen. 1215 21ST AVE S, STE 5209 37232 #020-02-1984 L1992 **CD IM** *020 †20

WATKINS, Scott C. ■ 37206 #012-01-2003 L2005 **AN** *100

WATSON, Horace Eugene. 1301 22ND AVE N 37232 #001-02-1957 L1986 **OFA** *072 †40

WATSON, Jeffry Todd. 1215 21ST AVE S, MCE S. TOWER RM 3200 37232 #048-12-1994 L2001 **HS ORS** *040

WATSON, Paula Lou. RM T-1217 MCN, VANDERBILT UNIVERSITY 37232 #004-01-1990 L1993 **PCC** *020

WATSON, Sally Elizabeth. 2200 CHILDRENS WAY, RM 2510 37232 #047-05-1994 L1998 **CCP** *020 †55

WATSON, Stephen Mark. 7833 OLD HARDING RD 37221 #047-05-1994 L1996 **IM** *020 †20

WATTACHERIL, Julia Jacob. ■ 37215 #048-04-2004 L2007 **GE** *012 †20

WATTERSON, Michael K. 2410 PATTERSON ST, STE 106 37203 #036-08-1995 L1996 **RHU** *020 †20

WATTS, Bobby. ■ 37218 #047-07-1972 L1973 **R** *075

WATTS, Colin Wade. ■ 37218 #047-07-2008 *012

WATTS, Eli Marzette. 2001 CHARLOTTE AVE, STE 101 37203 #047-07-1999 L2003 *020 †20

WAWA, Fritz. 1005 DR DB TODD JR BLVD 37208 #440-01-1979 L1996 **FM** *020 †18

WAYBURN, Gates Jordan, Jr. 4306 HARDING PIKE STE 300 37205 #048-04-1970 L1976 **OPH** *020 †35 ‡

WAYMAN, Laura. 1301 22ND AVE N 37232 #026-08-1998 L2005 **OPH** *020 †55

WEAR, Vanessa Van Duyn. ■ 37215 #028-34-2004 L2007 **DR** *012

WEASTLER, Virginia P. ■ 37211 #264-01-1973 L1982 **PD** *020

WEAVER, Alissa Margaret. ■ 37212 #051-01-1998 L2004 **PTH** *100

WEAVER, Gregory Rynn. 2000 CHURCH ST 37236 #020-12-1981 L1985 **DR NR** *020 †80 ‡

WEAVER, Kyle Derek. 1301 22ND AVE N 37232 #036-01-1996 L2003 **NS** *020 †25

WEAVER, Lance Delaney. 1005 DR DB TODD JR BLVD 37208 #010-03-1976 L1994 **ORS GP** *020 †40

WEAVER, Patricia A. 1035 14TH AVE N 37208 #047-07-1988 L1989 **PHP FM** *030 †70,18

WEAVIND, Liza Monique. 1211 21ST AVE S STE 526 37212 #836-01-1990 L2006 **CCA** *030 †05

WEBB, Charles Nathan. ■ 37212 #012-01-2008 *012

WEBB, Roseanna Aileen. 2010 CHURCH ST STE 409 37203 #047-05-1983 L1986 **OPH** *020 †35

WEBB, Roslynn Elizabeth. 1301 22ND AVE N 37232 #010-03-1995 L2003 **AN** *020

WEBBER, Angus John. 4220 HARDING RD STE 500, P O BOX 380 37205 #047-06-1994 L2007 **IM** *020 †20

WEBBER, Heather L. ■ 37215 #047-06-1994 **OBG** *012

WEBBER, Jeffrey Craig. 2400 PATTERSON ST STE 400 37203 #035-20-1989 L1990 **CD IM** *020 †20

WEBSTER, Benjamin William. ■ 37211 #041-12-2008 **EM** *012

WEBSTER-CLAIR, Deborah C. 1301 22ND AVE N 37232 #024-07-1981 L1993 **OBG** *040 †30

WEEKS, Amy Gregory. 1301 22ND AVE N 37232 #047-06-1985 L1987 **OBG** *020 †30

WEIKERT, Douglas Ray. 1215 21ST AVE S, MCE, S.TOWER, STE 3200 37232 #047-05-1987 L1993 **HS** *020 †40

WEIKERT, Laura Forester. 391 WALLACE RD 37211 #047-05-1991 L1998 **PCC** *020 †20

WEINBERG, Jane Ruth. 602 W IRIS DR 37204 #041-01-1973 L1975 **P PPN** *020 †75

WEINBERG, Stuart T. 452 ESKIND BIOMEDICAL LIB, 2209 GARLAND AVE 37232 #038-41-1985 L1986 **PD OS** *020 †55

WEINER, Justin Benedict. ■ 37201 #025-01-2004 L2007 **CD** *012 †20

WEINGER, Matthew Bret. 1211 21ST AVE S, MAB 732, DEPT OF ANESTHESIOLOGY 37232 #005-18-1982 L2005 **AN** *050 †05

WEINSTEIN, David Danl. 1601 23RD AVE SOUTH, VANDERBILT SUITE 3068 37232 #016-43-1982 L1991 **P IM** *020 †20,15,75

WEISS, Manuel Robt. 4230 HARDING RD, STE 205 37205 #035-08-1980 L1984 **NS GS** *020 †25

WEITKAMP, Joern-Hendrik K. 11111 DOCTOR'S OFFICE TOWE, MONROE CARELL JR. CHILDREN 37232 #009-41-1994 L2004 **NPM** *100 †55

WEITZMAN, Glenn Allen. 345 23RD AVE N STE 401 37203 #023-07-1982 L1995 **REN OBG** *020 †30

WELCH, Jonathan Chase. ■ 37203 #048-04-2004 L2008 **OPH** *012

WELCH, Shenika Danielle. 1005 DR DB TODD JR BLVD, DEPT OBG 37208 #047-07-2007 **OBG** *012

WELLS, Charles E. 310 25TH AVE N 37203 #012-05-1953 L1961 **P N** *071 †75

WELLS, Christopher A. ■ 37221 #045-01-2004 **CD** *012

WENDEL, James Jason. D-4207 MEDICAL CTR NORTH 37232 #017-20-1996 L2002 **PS** *020 †65

WENDELL, James Isaac, Jr. ■ 37215 #041-01-1943 L1944 **PD OS** *071 †55

WENTZ, Dennis Keith. 1161 21ST AVE S, C/O DIV OF CME MEDICAL CEN 37232 #016-02-1961 L1977 **MDM GE** *071 ‡

WERKHAVEN, Jay Allen. 1301 22ND AVE N 37232 #036-05-1982 L1989 **PDO OTO** *020 †45

WERTHER, John Robt. 2011 MURPHY AVE, STE 604 37203 #047-05-1988 L1990 **FPS** *020

WESLEY, Ralph Edwards. 250 25TH AVE N, SUITE 216 THE ATRIUM 37203 #047-05-1972 L1979 **OPH PS** *020 †35 ‡

WEST, Jule Johnson. 4220 HARDING RD, STE 500 37205 #047-05-1997 L1998 **IM** *020 †20

WEST, Natalie Elliott. ■ 37209 #011-04-2004 L2006 **IM** *012 †20

WEST, Robert Rawlings. ■ 37215 #047-06-1967 L1969 **PTH IM** *020 †50

WEST, William Scott. 30 BURTON HILLS BLVD STE 3 37215 #047-06-1982 L1982 **P** *020 †75

WHATLEY, Valerie Ann. DEPT OF EMERGENCY MEDICINE, 703 OXFORD HOUSE 37232 #001-06-1997 L2007 **PEM** *020 †55

WHEATLEY, Robert Michael. 2400 PATTERSON ST, STE 502 37203 #020-02-1985 L1993 **CD IM** *020 †20

WHEELER, Arthur Preston. 1301 22ND AVE N 37232 #023-01-1982 L1984 **PUD IM** *020 †20

WHEELER, Arville Vance. 5819 OLD HARDING RD 37205 #047-05-1960 L1960 **PD** *020 †55

WHEELER, Jacqueline. ■ 37217 #047-07-1990 L1993 **GPM** *020

WHEELER, Paul Warren. 2410 PATTERSON ST, STE 106 37203 #001-02-1977 L1983 **ID RHU** *020 †20

WHEELOCK, Johnny Brian. 2021 CHURCH ST, STE 402 37203 #021-01-1978 L1990 **OBG GO** *020 †30

WHETSELL, Wm Otto, Jr. 4219 HILLSBORO RD, STE 211 37215 #045-01-1966 L1979 **NP N** *071 ‡

WHIGHAM, Amy Shibley. ■ 37209 #012-05-2004 **OTO** *012

WHITE, Bobby Joe. 1301 22ND AVE N 37232 #047-06-1985 L1986 **IM** *020 †20

WHITE, Edward Allan. 3443 DICKERSON PIKE, STE 750 37207 #041-02-2001 L2003 **GE** *020

WHITE, Jackson B. 221 STEWARTS FERRY PIKE 37214 #047-05-1969 L1982 **P NTR** *020

WHITE, Laura Louise. 300 20TH AVE N, STE 401 37203 #047-05-1998 L2003 **GS** *020 †85

WHITE, Lisa Marie. ■ 37205 #047-05-2006 **GS** *012

WHITE, Steven John. 703 OXFORD HOUSE, VANDERBILT UNIV MEDICAL CE 37232 #041-12-1983 L1992 **EM PE** *020 †16

WHITED, Brent William. 1215 21ST AVE S, ORTHOPAEDIC INSTITU 37232 #018-03-2004 L2007 **ORS** *012

WHITEMAN, Jules Alan. 4220 HARDING RD 37205 #047-06-1975 L1976 **EM GP** *020 †16

WHITFIELD, Jeff D. 395 WALLACE RD, STE 206B 37211 #047-06-1981 L1981 **U** *020 †95

WHITFIELD, Katherine. 1301 22ND AVE N 37232 #046-01-1991 L2005 **OPH** *071 †35

WHITMAN, Jonna H. VANDERBILT UNIV, STATION 17 ZERFOSS BLDG 37232 #051-01-1995 L1998 **FM** *020 †18

WHITNEY, Donna K. 1301 22ND AVE N 37232 #024-01-1979 L1994 **N** *020

WHITNEY, Gina Marie. 2200 CHILDRENS WAY, RM 2510 37232 #021-01-1998 L2005 **PD** *020 †55

WHITTAM, Benjamin Michael. ■ 37212 #032-01-2006 **U** *012

WHITTY, Janice Elizabeth. 1005 DR DB TODD JR BLVD, MEHARRY MED COLLEGE 37208 #035-08-1985 L2005 **OBG MFM** *020 †30

WHITWORTH, Christine M. 345 23RD AVE N, STE 401 37203 #047-06-1983 L1991 **REN GYN** *020

WHITWORTH, Pat W, Jr. 300 20TH AVE N, STE 401 37203 #047-06-1983 L1991 **SO GS** *020 †85

WHITWORTH, Thomas Clayton. 2000 CHURCH ST 37236 #047-05-1970 L1970 **NPM** *020 †55

WIATRAK, Mitchell Lee. 345 23RD AVE N, STE 212 37203 #025-01-1986 L2006 **U** *020 †95

WIDUCH, Maria B. ■ 37219 #759-05-1934 L1960 **PD GP** *072

WIECK, Joseph A. 394 HARDING PL STE 200 37211 #047-06-1985 L1987 **ORS** *020 †40

WIERUM, Craig. 222 22ND AVE N, STE 100 37203 #036-01-1990 L1992 **END IM** *020 †20

WIGFALL, Joy Lynette. ■ 37207 #047-07-1966 L1973 **P** *075

WIGGER, Mark Allen. 1313 21ST AVE S, 908 OXFORD HOUSE 37232 #047-20-1984 L1984 **NEP IM** *020 †20

WILBECK, James Christophe. ■ 37215 #001-06-2004 L2006 **IM** *100 †20

WILCOX, Allen Brian, Jr. 2010 CHURCH ST STE 303 37203 #047-06-1986 L1987 **TS VS** *020 †85,90

WILEY, Ronald Gordon. 1310 24TH AVE S 37212 #016-06-1975 L1983 **N IM** *050 †20,75

WILFORD, Casey Elizabeth. ■ 37212 #047-05-2006 L2006 **D** *012

WILKINS, John Jasper, III. 2200 CHILDRENS WAY 8161, CHILDREN'S HOSPITAL 37232 #036-07-2007 **PD** *012

WILLERS, Jeffrey Donald. 2021 CHURCH ST STE 200, ELITE SPORTS MED 37203 #012-01-1999 L2005 **ORS** *020 †40

WILLEY, Christopher Dougl. 1301 22ND AVE N, B-902 TVC 37232 #045-01-2003 L2003 **RO** *012

WILLIAMS, Bradley Verne. STUDENT HEALTH CENTER, VANDERBILT UNIVERSITY 37232 #027-01-1981 L1981 **PHO** *075 †73

WILLIAMS, Byron Douglas. 73 WHITE BRIDGE RD, STE 103-217 37205 #011-03-1989 L1993 **AN** *020 †05

WILLIAMS, Christopher S. 7409 KREITNER DR 37221 #047-05-2002 L2003 **GE** *020

WILLIAMS, Darrell James. 397 WALLACE RD # C-310 37211 #047-06-1990 L1991 **OPH** *020 †35

WILLIAMS, David Brandon. ■ 37205 #047-06-2000 L2007 **GS** *100

WILLIAMS, Dyane B. ■ 37204 #047-07-2004 *100

WILLIAMS, Ida Michele. 1035 14TH AVE N 37208 #047-05-1993 L1996 **PD** *020 †55

WILLIAMS, Jennifer Leslie. CCC-1106 MCN, DEPARTMENT OF RADIOLOGY 37232 #048-13-2001 L2007 **DR** *100 †80

WILLIAMS, John Albert. 460 SAGE CIRCLE RD 37228 #047-06-1990 L1992 **IM** *020 †20

WILLIAMS, John Vance. 1301 22ND AVE N 37232 #051-04-1994 L2000 **PDI** *020 †55

WILLIAMS, Kathleen Crews. 2021 CHURCH ST, PLAZA 2 STE 506 37203 #047-05-1993 L1995 **GS** *020 †55

WILLIAMS, Kent. S-4322 MCN, 21ST AND GARLAND AVE 37232 #016-11-1998 L2004 **PG** *020

WILLIAMS, Laura Ann. 2220 PIERCE AVE, 777PRB 37232 #048-13-2001 L2004 **HO** *100

WILLIAMS, Laura Lynn. 2021 CHURCH ST, STE 402 37203 #036-05-1984 L1990 **GO** *020 †30

WILLIAMS, Makeda A. ■ 37208 #047-07-2008 *012

WILLIAMS, Mark Anthony. 393 WALLACE RD, STE A202 37211 #038-41-2002 L2007 **OTO** *020

WILLIAMS, Pamela Canice. 1005 DR DB TODD JR BLVD 37208 #047-07-1981 L1983 **IM EM** *020

WILLIAMS, Sadhna Vijay. 5819 OLD HARDING RD, OLD HARDING PEDIATRICS 37205 #047-06-1989 L1992 **PD** *020 †55

WILLIAMS, Saralyn R. 1161 21ST AVE S, 501 OXFORD HOUSE 37232 #036-07-1990 L2005 **EM ETX** *020 †16

WILLIAMS, Shindana Laryce. ■ 37208 #047-07-2001 L2005 **IM** *020

WILLIAMS, Stacey Marie. 4901 NOLENSVILLE RD 37211 #041-12-1997 L2000 **PD** *020 †55

WILLIAMS, Trilby Elliston. 2400 PATTERSON ST STE 500, STERLING PRIMARY CARE, PLC 37203 #047-06-1994 L1997 **IM** *020 †20

WILLIAMS, Van Ralph. ■ 37205 #047-06-1960 L1961 **OPH** *020 †35

WILLIAMS, W Carter, Jr. ■ 37215 #047-05-1956 L1956 **IM END** *071

WILLIAMSON, Randy Conway. ■ 37221 #166-01-2002 L2002 **CN** *012

WILLIS, Adam Paul. ■ 37211 #047-06-2005 L2007 **AN** *012

WILLIS, Angela Lee. 341 WALLACE RD, STE A 37211 #047-20-2003 L2005 **FM** *100

WILLIS, Carl Rogaston. 2011 CHURCH ST, STE 701 37203 #001-02-1993 L2003 **IM** *020 †20

WILLS, Marcia Lynn. 2200 CHILDRENS WAY, 11223 DOCTOR'S OFF TOWER 37232 #032-01-1992 L2004 **PP** *020 †50

WILLS, Morgan Jackson. 820 GALE LN, SILOAM FAMILY HEALTH CENTE 37204 #047-05-1996 L2000 **IM** *020 †20

WILSON, Amanda Grace. ■ 37209 #001-02-2002 L2007 **P** *100 †75

WILSON, Cynthia Nicole. 1161 21ST AVE S, DEPT OF PSYCHIATRY 37232 #047-05-2006 **P** *012

WILSON, Gregory Jonathan. 2200 CHILDRENS WAY, RM 2510 37232 #023-07-1987 L1990 **PD** *050 †55

WILSON, Henry Benjamin. 2201 MURPHY AVE, STE 409 37203 #047-05-1996 L2004 **PS** *020 †85

WILSON, James Phillip. 1301 22ND AVE N 37232 #023-07-1966 L1972 **IM** *020 †20

WILSON, John Randolph. 315 MRB II, VANDERBILT UNIV MEDICAL CE 37232 #024-01-1974 L1993 **CD IM** *050 †20

WILSON, Keith Tucker. 2215 GARLAND AVE, 1030-C MRB-IV 37232 #024-01-1986 L2005 **GE** *050 †20

WILSON, Marshelya Denise. ■ 37208 #047-07-2004 L2007 **FM** *020

WILSON, Mary Ann. ■ 37217 #005-02-1975 L2004 **PD** *020 †18,30

WILSON, Raeshell Sharawn. 1246 DALEMERE DR 37207 #035-19-2008 *012

WILSON, Wendy Drew. ■ 37208 #047-05-2006 **DR** *012

WILTERS, John Howard. 2201 MURPHY AVE, STE 303 37203 #001-02-1984 L1996 **OBG** *020 †30

WILWAYCO, Stephanie Dawn. 5201 CHARLOTTE PIKE 37209 #020-02-1985 L1997 **FM** *020 †18

WINCE, William Benjamin. ■ 37217 #047-20-2002 L2004 **CD NM** *012 †20,28

WINDLAND, John Michael. 2400 PATTERSON ST, STE 311 37203 #047-06-1998 L2006 **IM** *020 †20

WINES, Phillip A. 3443 DICKERSON PIKE, STE 430 37207 #048-12-1989 L1995 **CD** *020 †20

WINGO, Carl Eugene. 2011 MURPHY AVE, STE 302 37203 #011-02-1986 L1987 **OBG** *020 †20

WINSTON, Nathaniel T, Jr. ■ 37215 #047-05-1953 L1953 **P** *030

WISE, Anne Courter. 300 20TH AVE N, STE 302 37203 #023-07-1996 L2000 **OBG** *020 †30

WISE, Paul Edward. 1161 21ST AVE S, VUMC, D5248 MCN 37232 #023-07-1996 L1999 **CRS** *040 †85,10

WISEMAN, William S, II. 3443 DICKERSON PIKE, STE 720 37207 #012-01-1995 L2000 **PD** *020 †20

WITHERSPOON, John Draper. 2001 HAYES ST 37203 #047-06-1968 L1970 **OTO** *050 †45

WITTKOPF, Justin Edward. ■ 37215 #018-03-2002 L2004 **OTO** *100

WODICKA, Susan Marie. 1310 24TH AVE S, SYSTEM-VA MEDICAL CENTER 37212 #047-05-1975 L1977 **IM** *020 †20

WOLF, Christine Terese. 1313 21ST AVE S, 703 OXFORD HOUSE 37232 #038-06-2006 **EM** *012

WOLFE, Lawrence Kenneth. 1301 22ND AVE N 37232 #047-05-1960 L1960 **END IM** *020 †20 ‡

WOLFF, Steven Neil. 1005 DR DB TODD JR BLVD 37208 #016-11-1974 L1976 **IM** *020 †20

WOLTER, Christopher E. A-1302 MEDICAL CENTER NORT, DEPARTMENT OF UROLOGY 37232 #016-11-2001 L2006 **U** *012

WOMACK, Benjamin Douglas. MEDICAL CENTER, VANDERBILT UNIVERSITY 37232 #028-02-2005 L2008 **IM** *012

WOMACK, Clara Ruth. 28 WHITE BRIDGE RD, STE 300 37205 #047-06-1984 L1985 **NEP IM** *020 †20

WON, Justin Ging Shing. 1161 21ST AVE S 37212 #244-04-1977 **END** *100

WONGPRAPARUT, Nattawut. ■ 37221 #891-01-1995 L2004 **IC** *100 †20

WOOD, Alastair James J. 1301 MEDICAL CENTER DR 37232 #919-02-1970 L1977 **IM PA** *020

WOOD, George Wallace. 2002 RICHARD JONES RD, STE A102 37215 #047-05-1966 L1971 **PD** *020 †55

WOOD, William Gardner. 22 CENTURY BLVD, STE 310 37214 #048-04-1974 L1983 **P** *062 †75

WOODALL, Gilbert Earl, Jr. 201 THOMPSON LN STE 102, PREMIER OHS 37211 #047-06-1977 L1978 **OM MDM** *020 †70

WOODARD, Craig S. 222 22ND AVE N 37203 #048-13-1987 L2003 **N CN** *020 †75

WOODHALL, Dana Marie. ■ 37212 #041-15-2007 **EM** *012

WOODS, Aubaine Michelle. ■ 37221 #020-02-2004 L2007 **PD** *020 †55

WOODS, Grayson Noel. 4230 HARDING RD, STE 603 37205 #047-20-1998 L2002 **OBG** *020 †30

WOODS-SWAFFORD, Wendy Lei. 2220 PIERCE AVE, VANCERBILT MEDICAL CENTER 37232 #028-46-2002 L2007 **PHO** *012

WOODWARD, Stephen Cotter. ■ 37215 #012-05-1959 L1985 **PTH NM** *071 †50,28

WORD, Jerry Lee. 1120 DICKERSON PIKE 37207 #047-07-1973 L1974 **GS GP** *075

WORKMAN, Barry Eugene. ■ 37211 #305-01-2000 L2006 **FM** *020 †18

WORKMAN, Claude Henry. 2801 CHARLOTTE AVE, UROLOGY ASSOCIATES PC 37209 #047-05-1973 L1976 **U** *020 †95

WORKMAN, Robert Jay. 1500 22ND AVE N, THE VANDERBILT DAYANI CTR 37232 #024-01-1969 L1973 **IM END** *020 †20

WORLEY, Kimberly Ann. MCN DD-2205, DIVISION OF GENETICS 37232 #047-20-1996 L1999 **PD** *100

WORRELL, John Anthony. 1161 21ST AVE S, DEPT OF RADIOLOGY 37232 #047-05-1971 L1972 **R** *020 †80

WORTHINGTON, William Brad. 2011 MURPHY AVE, STE 400 37203 #020-02-1982 L1986 **AN** *020 †05

WRAY, Charles Jackson. 2400 PATTERSON ST, STE 101 37203 #047-05-2000 L2003 **PCC** *020 †20

WRAY, Taylor Malone. 222 22ND AVE N, STE 400 37203 #023-07-1966 L1970 **CD IM** *020 †20

WRENN, Keith Dale. 1301 22ND AVE N 37232 #012-05-1976 L1992 **IM** *040 †20,16

WRIGHT, Charles Taylor. ■ 37205 #047-06-2006 **OTO** *012

WRIGHT, Doris Jacquelyn. 275 STEWARTS FERRY PIKE 37214 #047-07-1962 L1967 **PD HEM** *020

WRIGHT, Ellen Payne. 2010 CHURCH ST, STE 615 37203 #047-05-1981 L1985 **PTH PCP** *062 †20

WRIGHT, George Dewey. 222 22ND AVE N, STE 100 37203 #047-05-1981 L1983 **GE IM** *020 †20

WRIGHT, Jeffrey Glen. 4230 HARDING PIKE, STE 400 37205 #047-05-1997 L2000 **PCC** *020 †20

WRIGHT, John Edward. 4220 HARDING PIKE 37205 #048-04-1976 L1985 **PTH DMP** *020 †50

WRIGHT, John Kelly. MED CENT, VANDERBILT UNIVERSITY 37232 #047-06-1959 L1959 GS SO *040 †85

WRIGHT, John Kelly, Jr. 1301 22ND AVE N 37232 #023-07-1981 L1990 GS *020 †85

WRIGHT, Julie Anne. ■ 37209 #025-07-2004 L2007 NEP *012

WRIGHT, Margaret Bushnell. 4220 HARDING PIKE 37205 #047-05-1993 L1996 DR *020 †80

WRIGHT, Patty Walchak. 1301 22ND AVE N 37232 #001-02-1997 L2002 ID *020 †20

WRIGHT, Peter Farnum. 1301 22ND AVE N 37232 #024-01-1967 L1974 ID PD *050 †55

WRIGHT, Seth Warren. 1301 22ND AVE N 37232 #025-01-1985 L1989 EM *020 †16

WRIGHT, Whitney Alexandre. 1005 DR DB TODD JR BLVD, OF PSYCH 37208 #305-01-2002 L2002 P *012

WRIGHT, Wycliffe L. 2410 PATTERSON ST, STE 402 37203 #566-01-1985 L1998 ID *020 †20

WU, Eveline Yawei. CHILDREN'S HOSPITAL, VANDERBILT 37232 #012-22-2005 PD *012

WU, Ming. 1161 21ST AVE S 37232 #243-76-1983 L2007 SP *012

WU, Wayne Wei. 1215 21ST AVE S, 8000 MEDICAL CTR EAST N 37232 #025-01-2002 L2006 OPH *020

WUDEL, Leonard James, Jr. 4230 HARDING RD, STE 525 37205 #047-20-1994 L2000 TS *020

WUPPERMAN, Richard M. CENTER NORTH, T-4319 MEDICAL 37232 #048-12-2002 L2005 ORS *020

WUSHENSKY, Curtis Alan. 1301 22ND AVE N 37232 #041-12-1979 L1999 R IM *040 †80

WYCHE, Kimberlee Denise. 311 23RD AVE N, METRO PUBLIC HEALTH DEPT 37203 #024-16-1993 L2001 PD *030

WYCKOFF, David Aaron. 2201 MURPHY AVE, STE 201 37203 #047-06-2000 L2003 PD *020 †55

WYMAN, Kenneth Wayne. 1301 22ND AVE N 37232 #020-02-1990 L1992 IM ON *020 †20

WYTHOFF, Yulia Vladimirov. ■ 37211 #913-97-1997 P *012

XIA, Fen. 1301 22ND AVE N, TVC BUILDING, RM B-902 37232 #243-78-1983 L2006 RO *100

XIE, Wen. 1005 D B TODD BLVD 37208 #243-52-1992 GPM *012

YAN, Xuexian. ■ 37221 #243-63-1985 NM *012

YANG, Chun-Ai. ■ 37215 #244-03-1962 L1978 R *020

YANG, Edmund Yibin. 1301 22ND AVE N 37232 #047-05-1993 L2003 PDS *020 †85

YANG, Elizabeth W. 2200 CHILDRENS WAY, RM 2510 37232 #005-11-1987 L1997 PHO *020 †55

YANG, Shihhsin Eddy. ■ 37209 #011-02-2005 RO *012

YAO, Tom Lou. ■ 37212 #047-05-2002 NS *012

YARBRO, George Lawson, Jr. 3443 DICKERSON PIKE 37207 #047-06-1972 L1974 PS *020 †65

YARBROUGH, Barry Eugene. 2001 GLEN ECHO RD 37215 #010-02-1976 L1986 EM IM *020 †20,16

YARBROUGH, Mary Idyle. 1301 22ND AVE N 37232 #047-05-1981 L1984 PHP EM *030 †20,70

YARBROUGH, Wendell Gray. 7209 MEDICAL CENTER EAST, VANDERBILT UNIV MED CTR 37232 #036-01-1989 L2003 OTO *020 †45

YARID, Aida Ibrahim. 1301 22ND AVE N 37232 #605-01-1980 L1986 PN *020 †55

YEN, Leslianne Elizabeth. MCE SOUTH TWR, STE 3200, VANDERBILT SPORTS MEDICINE 37232 #032-01-2003 L2006 PSM *100 †20

YESKA, Melissa Lynn. ■ 37207 #030-05-2006 IM *012

YNARES, Christina. 1633 CHURCH ST, STE 160 37203 #748-02-1972 L1979 NEP *050 †20

YOANIDIS, Nancy Rumson. 275 CUMBERLAND BND, MENTAL HEALTH COOPERATIVE 37228 #041-14-1994 L2003 P CHP *020 †75

YOHANNES, Yordanos. 1301 22ND AVE N 37232 #017-20-2000 L2005 AN *020

YOON, Michelle Jaeim. 3443 DICKERSON PIKE, STE 320 37207 #019-02-2002 L2007 GS *100

YOUNG, Jadrien. ■ 37211 #027-01-2007 OTO *012

YOUNG, Jessica Lauren. ■ 37206 #047-05-2007 OBG *012

YOUNG, Kristie Lynn. CHILDREN'S HOSPITAL, VANDERBILT 37232 #020-02-2005 PD *012

YOUNG, Larry Creston. 345 23RD AVE N, STE 412 37203 #047-06-1978 L1979 FPS OTO *020 †45

YOUNG, Lorien Miranda. ■ 37215 #047-06-2005 D *012

YOUNG, Robert Steven. 1161 21ST AVE S, - RADI 37232 #051-04-2006 DR *012

YOUNG, Ruth T. 1301 22ND AVE N 37232 #047-06-1977 L1983 ON HEM *020 †20

YOUNG-WARDELL, Cheryl D. 94 ERIN LN 37221 #047-07-1997 L1999 CHP *020

YOUREE, Cynthia Catlett. 4544 HARDING PIKE, STE 215 37205 #021-01-1981 L1984 DR *020 †80 ‡

YOWELL, Georgia Elizabeth. ■ 37205 #051-04-2008 *012

YU, David Sung-Wen. ■ 37204 #048-12-2005 L2005 RO *012

YU, Guan-Hick. 1310 24TH AVE S 37212 #244-02-1972 L1977 PM IM *020 †60

YU, Hong. ■ 37211 #047-05-2002 NS *012

YU, James Robert. 301 21ST AVE N 37203 #041-14-1999 L2005 ORS *100 †40 ‡

YU, Mi. 113 30TH AVE N, DEPT. OF PSYCHIATRY AND BE 37203 #243-16-1987 L2005 PYG *020 †75

ZAFAR, Adnan. 1005 DR DB TODD JR BLVD, OF PSYCH 37208 #308-13-1999 L2007 P *012

ZAK, Beverly Marie. ■ 37204 #005-18-2006 D *012

ZANOLLI, Michael Dominic. 4230 HARDING RD, DERMATOLOGY CONSULTANTS 37205 #047-06-1981 L1982 D *020 †15

ZAYDFUDIM, Victor. ■ 37221 #043-01-2004 L2007 GS *012

ZELLEM, Ronald Theodore. 3441 DICKERSON PIKE 37207 #012-05-1980 L1990 NS *020 †25

ZENT, Roy. 1301 22ND AVE N 37232 #836-01-1985 L2001 *020

ZERFOSS, Thos Bowman, Jr. ■ 37215 #047-05-1946 L1946 PD ADL *071

ZHAN, Frank Qian. ■ 37215 #047-05-2002 L2008 D *012

ZHANG, Alex Xun. 850 RS GASS BLVD 37216 #243-03-1986 L2001 PTH *020 †50

ZHAO, Xiao-Ming. 1215 21ST AVE S, STE 5209 37232 #243-16-1985 L2001 CD *020 †20

ZIC, John Alan. 1301 22ND AVE N, 3900 TVC 37232 #047-05-1991 L1995 D *020 †15

ZIMMERMAN, Carl Wayne. 1301 22ND AVE N 37232 #047-06-1972 L1973 GYN *040 †30 ‡

ZIMMERMAN, David Lynne. ■ 37214 #028-34-2007 PTH *012

ZIMMERMAN, Thomas F. 3443 DICKERSON PIKE, G30 37207 #047-06-1976 L1977 IM IMG *020 †20

ZINKEL, Sandra Sue. 1301 22ND AVE N 37232 #016-02-1995 L2005 HO *020 †20

ZOOROB, Roger J. 1005 DR DB TODD JR BLVD, PROFESSOR AND CHAIR 37208 #605-01-1985 L2003 FM *030 †18

ZOUFAN, Ebrahim. ■ 37217 #517-06-1965 IM GP *100

ZUBAIR, Salman. 2100 WATERFORD CIR, # 3407 37221 #704-01-2001 L2006 CN *012

ZUTTER, Mary Mc Gehee. 1301 22ND AVE N 37232 #021-01-1981 L2003 PTH PD *020 †50

NEW JOHNSONVILLE – HUMPHREYS

MATHAI, George Thottakara. 224 LONG ST, HEALTH CENTER 37134 #047-07-1999 L2003 FM *020

NEW MARKET – JEFFERSON

WICKER, Kenneth David. ■ 37820 #047-06-1986 L1988 MPD PD *020 †20,55

NEW TAZEWELL – CLAIBORNE

BADARA, Mircea Ovidiu. 309 N BROAD ST 37825 #781-01-1997 L2003 PCC *020 †20

DEBUSK, Charles Hubert. 309 N BROAD ST 37825 #649-14-1983 L1992 IM *020

LAMBERT, Melody Camille. 1596 HIGHWAY 33 S 37825 #047-06-2002 L2004 FM *020 †18

PANNOCCHIA, Luis Carlos. 309 N BROAD ST 37825 #308-11-1984 L1987 FM *020 †18 ‡

QUIGLEY, Kimberly Anne. 1596 HIGHWAY 33 S 37825 #047-06-2001 L2006 P *100

SMITH, William N. 309 N BROAD ST, P O 1409 37825 #047-06-1951 L1951 GP *020 †18

NEWPORT – COCKE

BRAWLEY, Bolling W. 1829 CROWE LN 37821 #045-04-1989 L1991 PD *020 †55

CAPPARELLI, Edward Wm. 435 2ND ST 37821 #035-47-1979 L1993 FM *020 †18

CARPENTER, Joel Philip. 207 MURRAY DR 37821 #016-43-1989 L1995 FM *020 †18

CONWAY, Thomas Wm. 434 4TH ST, STE 310 37821 #023-01-1982 L1985 FM OBS *020 †18

DANIEL, Tony C. 235 MURRAY DR 37821 #060-02-1989 L1994 IM *020

DINGELS-SUTTON, C. ■ 37821 #051-04-1993 L1996 PD *020 †55

GRAY, Mc Donald, Jr. 434 4TH ST STE 309 37821 #020-12-1978 L1987 GS *020 †85

HARRIS, Christopher Dale. 434 4TH ST 37821 #025-01-1985 L1990 U *020 †95

HILL, Kenneth L. 222 HERITAGE BLVD, SMOKEY MOUNTAIN HOME HEALT 37821 #020-02-1982 L1985 FM *020 †18 ‡

JOHNSON, H Kenneth, II. 235 MURRAY DR 37821 #047-06-1982 L1983 IM *020

KARWAN, Sukhender K. 215 HEDRICK DR 37821 #495-65-1981 L1996 P *020

LARSON, Richard Duane. 434 4TH ST STE 310, PRIMARY CARE CENTER OF NEW 37821 #056-05-1970 L1996 FM *072 †18

MATHERS, Lawrence John. 207 MURRAY DR 37821 #041-12-2000 L2003 FM *020 †18

PUCKETT, Samuel Mack. 1829 CROWE LN 37821 #012-01-1982 L1985 PD *020 †55

SCHINDLER, James Brian. 215 HEDRICK DR 37821 #048-04-1983 L2001 FM PHP *040 †18

SHEPHERD, Terry Preston. 434 4TH ST 37821 #047-06-1982 L1982 U GS *020 †95

TOHME, Fady Elias. 434 4TH ST, STE 310 37821 #913-96-1996 L2004 FM *020 †18

VALENTINE, Fred M, Jr. ■ 37821 #047-06-1950 L1950 GP *071

WILLIAMS, James Robt. 434 4TH ST, STE 301 37821 #051-04-1981 L1983 FM *020 †18

NIOTA – MCMINN

TRENTHAM, Nathan Craig. ■ 37826 #047-06-1995 L1997 IM *020 †20

NOLENSVILLE – WILLIAMSON

JABOIN, Jerry Jeff. ■ 37135 #010-03-2004 RO *012

NGUYEN, Quoc Viet. ■ 37135 #048-14-1995 L2006 EM *020 †16

OFFODILE, Regina Stokes. ■ 37135 #005-14-1994 L2006 GS *020

REDDY, Nishitha Mandadi. ■ 37135 #496-20-1999 L2007 HEM *100 †20

RITCH, Patricia Sizemore. ■ 37135 #001-02-2004 CHN *012

SCHRAMM, Heather Elizabet. ■ 37135 #005-19-2006 PD *012

THOMPSON, John Richard. 940 OLDHAM DR 37135 #001-02-1988 L1990 FM AM *020 †18

NORRIS – ANDERSON

POPP, Rick Antone. 28 W NORRIS ROAD, NORRIS MED WALK-IN CLINIC 37828 #047-06-1991 L1992 AN *020

NUNNELLY – HICKMAN

GATLIN, Deborah Faye. 168 THREE SPRINGS RD, THERAPEUTIC PROGRAM 37137 #011-03-1990 L1991 P *020 †75

OAK RIDGE – ANDERSON

ALEXANDER, Alex Martin. 801 OAK RIDGE TPKE, OAK RIDGE 37830 #020-12-1983 L1993 FM *020 †18

ALLEN, Janet De Busk. 129 E DIVISION RD 37830 #047-06-1982 L1983 PTH *020 †50

BABAN, Nawras K. 990 OAK RIDGE TPKE, METHODIST MEDICAL CENTER 37830 #528-01-1980 L1996 IM *020 †20

BAKER, Craig Price. 990 OAK RIDGE TPKE 37830 #047-06-1987 L1990 FM *020 †18

BALTHROP, John E, Jr. 360 LABORATORY RD 37830 #047-06-1951 L1973 GP *071

BARONGAN, Paul Gregory. 145 E VANCE RD 37830 #051-04-1998 L2001 PD *020 †55

BARRON, David Michael. 990 OAK RIDGE TPKE 37830 #047-06-1985 L1985 DR *020 †80

BELL, William Reid, III. 100 VERMONT AVE 37830 #047-06-1981 L1984 FM OM *020 †18

BHATEJA, Renu. ■ 37830 #495-43-1971 L1993 P CHP *020 †75

BISHOP, Kathryn Ann. 145 E VANCE RD, STE 320 37830 #048-13-1989 L1992 PD *020 †55

BLOCK, Clem Henry, Jr. 988 OAK RIDGE TPKE 37830 #047-05-1974 L1975 GE IM *020 †20

BLOUNT, Howard P. 801 OAK RIDGE TPKE, OAK RIDGE 37830 #023-12-1987 L1997 FM *020 †18

BOEHM, Robert James. 990 OAK RIDGE TPKE 37830 #047-06-2000 L2004 IM *020

BONDRANKO, Jos Walter, Jr. 990 OAK RIDGE TPKE 37830 #047-20-1988 L1992 AN *020 †05

BRANTLEY, Richard Green. 800 OAK RIDGE TPKE, STE A101 37830 #001-02-1965 L1973 U *020 †95

BRIDGEMAN, Pamela A. 801 OAK RIDGE TPKE, OAK RIDGE 37830 #036-01-1986 L1989 FM *020 †18

BROWN, Geron, Jr. 116 AMANDA PL 37830 #047-06-1965 L1966 ORS *062 †40

BRUTON, Charles Wilson. 800 OAK RIDGE TPKE, STE C200 37830 #036-05-1974 L1981 PUD *020 †20

BULLOCK, Pamela Houston. 129 E DIVISION RD 37830 #047-06-1981 L1984 PTH PCP *020 †50

■ = Address Information Privacy Protected

BUNICK, Christopher Gerar. ■ 37830 #047-05-2008 *012

BUNICK, Elaine M. 200 NEW YORK AVE 37830 #041-07-1973 L1978 **END IM** *020 †20

BURRELL, John S. 990 OAK RIDGE TPKE 37830 #047-06-1960 L1961 **FM** *020 †18 ‡

BURRESS, Roger Dale. 150 E DIVISION RD STE 4 37830 #047-06-1985 L1985 **P CHP** *020 †75

BURRIS, Glenn William. 944 OAK RIDGE TPKE, METHODIST SLEEP DIAGNOSTIC 37830 #045-01-1997 L2006 **PCC** *100 †20

BURSTEN, Benjamin. 240 W TYRONE RD 37830 #008-01-1958 L1977 **P LM** *030 †75

CALDWELL, M Gene. ■ 37830 #047-06-1960 L1961 **PD** *071 †55

CAMPBELL, Bill M. ■ 37830 #047-06-1986 L1990 **FM** *020 †18

CAMPBELL, Charles Lynn. 221 W TYRONE RD 37830 #047-06-1967 L1970 **PD** *020 †55

CARDER, Lee J. 102 VERMONT AVE, DEPT OF RAD/ONC 37830 #011-03-1991 L1998 **RO** *020 †80

CARTER, Ann Marie. 988 OAK RIDGE TPKE, STE 245 37830 #047-06-1977 L1984 **FM** *020 †18

CARTER, Joseph Bradford. 200 NEW YORK AVE STE 150 37830 #004-01-1979 L1991 **OBG** *020 †30 ‡

CASEY, Robert R. 801 OAK RIDGE TPKE, OAK RIDGE 37830 #047-06-1976 L1978 **FM FPG** *020 †55

CHARITAT, Maurice Roland. 990 OAK RIDGE TPKE 37830 #021-05-1984 L1991 **AN IM** *020 †20,05

CHASAN, Stuart Alan. 800 OAK RIDGE TPKE, STE A101 37830 #001-02-1981 L1992 **U** *020 †95

CHEN, Ihung. ■ 37830 #047-07-2005 **P** *012

CHENEY, Jason Troy. 221 W TYRONE RD, CHILDREN'S CLINIC 37830 #047-05-1999 L2001 **PD** *020 †55

CLARY, Thomas Lafayette. 145 E VANCE RD, STE 320 37830 #047-20-1982 L1984 **PD** *020 †55

COMPTON, David Ross. 100 VERMONT AVE 37830 #047-06-1981 L1981 **FM** *020 †18

CONGDON, Charles C. ■ 37830 #025-01-1944 L1955 **ATP** *072 †50

CONRAD, Daniel Edward. 990 OAK RIDGE TPKE 37830 #016-11-1960 L1986 **OM IM** *071 †20,70

CONWAY, Shere E. 100 VERMONT AVE 37830 #054-04-1993 L2001 **FM** *020 †18

CRATER, Glenn D, Jr. 200 NEW YORK AVE, WESTMALL MEDICAL PARK, STE 37830 #047-06-1993 L1994 **PCC IM** *020 †20 ‡

CROOK, James Edward. 969 OAK RIDGE TPKE 37830 #023-01-1974 L1976 **PA CD** *050 †20

CROSS, Frances Lynn. 988 OAK RIDGE TPKE, OAK RIDGE SURGEONS PC 37830 #041-01-1983 L1991 **GS VS** *020 †85

DALLAS, William Stuart. 988 OAK RIDGE TPKE, OAK RIDGE SURGEONS PC 37830 #047-06-1988 L1990 **GS VS** *072 †85

DARLING, Chas Ellett, Jr. 200 NEW YORK AVE STE 150, WOMENS HLTH ASSOC 37830 #025-01-1968 L1973 **OBG** *020 †30 ‡

DE LISA, Angelica Maria. 990 OAK RIDGE TPKE, HOSPITALIST POSITION 37830 #264-12-1999 L2007 **IM** *020 †20

DOTSON, Robert Scott. 200 NEW YORK AVE, STE 130 37830 #047-06-1974 L1975 **OPH GP** *020 †35

DRY, Laurence Revelle. 140 E DIVISION RD, STE C3 37830 #016-06-1966 L1973 **GS LM** *020 †85

DUDANI, Babulal B. 240 W TYRONE RD, RIDGEVIEW PSYCH HOSP & CTR 37830 #495-23-1968 L1980 **P** *020

DUNLAP, Robert Weyer. ■ 37830 #038-06-1945 L1971 **GS PS** *071 †85

DYE, Charles Grant. 800 OAK RIDGE TPKE, STE A401 37830 #020-12-1978 L1988 **PS HS** *020 †65

DYKES, Michael Dean. 140 E DIVISION RD, P O BOX 4547 37830 #047-20-1991 L1995 **AN** *020 †05

EATHERLY, Joseph Bruce. 129 E DIVISION RD 37830 #047-06-1978 L1982 **PTH** *020 †50

ENYENIHI, Okon Atte. 240 W TYRONE RD, RIDGEVIEW PSYCHIATRY HOSPI 37830 #690-10-1985 L2003 **P** *020

EPPLER, Jason Wade. 990 OAK RIDGE TPKE, EMERGENCY DEPARTMENT 37830 #019-02-2003 L2006 **FM** *100 †18

EVERSOLE, Earl, Jr. 990 OAK RIDGE TPKE 37830 #047-06-1951 L1954 **GS** *071 †85

FABRICIUS, Diane Louise. 653 BRIARCLIFF AVE, FAMILY DOCTORS OF OAKRIDGE 37830 #016-42-1982 L1998 **FM** *020 †18

FINLEY, Brenda Brooks. 240 W TYRONE RD, RIDGEVIEW PSYCHIATRIC HOSP 37830 #047-20-1985 L1986 **P IM** *020 †12

FORTNEY, T Guy. ■ 37830 #020-02-1951 L1952 **OM OS** *071

FOUST, John Thornton. 102 VERMONT AVE, STE 200 37830 #047-06-1985 L1986 **HEM ON** *020 †20

FOUST, Rebecca Lide. 129 E DIVISION RD 37830 #047-06-1985 L1990 **PTH** *020 †50

FRENCH, Ronald James, Jr. 988 OAK RIDGE TPKE, STE 100 37830 #021-01-1988 L2001 **HS ORS** *020 †40

FRY, Shirley Ann. PO BOX 117 37831 #539-03-1957 *071

FULLER, Robert Paul, Jr. 800 OAK RIDGE TPKE, STE A300 37830 #027-01-1976 L1988 **D OS** *020 †15

GARTON, Anthony W. 990 OAK RIDGE TPKE 37830 #047-06-1976 L1977 **IM** *020 †20

GENELLA, Frank Henry. 990 OAK RIDGE TPKE 37830 #047-06-1958 L1958 **FM** *020 †18

GHOLSON, Charles Forbis. 988 OAK RIDGE TPKE 37830 #047-06-1978 L1979 **GE IM** *020 †20

GILES, James Wm. 801 OAK RIDGE TPKE, OAK RIDGE 37830 #018-03-1969 L1978 **IM IMG** *020 †20

GILLESPIE, James Trigg. 150 E DIVISION RD 37830 #051-01-1957 L1965 **GP** *071

GOSWITZ, Francis Andrew. 170 W TENNESSEE AVE, OAK RIDGE MED CLINIC 37830 #056-06-1956 L1965 **ON HEM** *075 †28

GOSWITZ, Helen A Vodopick. 170 W TENNESSEE AVE 37830 #056-06-1956 L1965 **ON IM** *020 †20 ‡

GOWDER, Timothy Dennis. 988 OAK RIDGE TPKE 37830 #047-06-1972 L1973 **OBG** *020 †30

GRABENSTEIN, Jeffrey John. 653 BRIARCLIFF AVE, FAMILY DOCTORS OF OAK RIDG 37830 #016-06-1980 L1998 **FM** *020 †18

GRACE, Sean Patrick. 988 OAK RIDGE TPKE, STE 100 37830 #021-05-2001 L2007 **OSM** *020

GURECKI, Paul James. 80 VERMONT AVE 37830 #007-02-1983 L1992 **SME N** *020 †75

GURLEY, Bradley Maxwell. 108 PARK MEADE DR 37830 #047-06-1990 L1991 **FM** *020 †18

GURNEY, Charles Bryson. 990 OAK RIDGE TPKE 37830 #023-07-1956 L1957 **GP** *071

HALL, William Charles. 988 OAK RIDGE TPKE, STE 380 37830 #012-01-1982 L1989 **TS** *020 †85,90

HALPERIN, Rebecca Louise. 665 EMORY VALLEY RD, STE B 37830 #016-02-1984 L1991 **P PYA** *020 †75

HAMWI, Safwan. 200 NEW YORK AVE, STE 310 37830 #875-02-1984 L1996 **END** *020 †20

HARDY, Constance Alexis. ■ 37830 #041-01-1999 L2005 **IM** *020 †20

HARRISON, Stephen Hopkins. 200 NEW YORK AVE STE 320 37830 #021-01-1974 L1981 **PTH** *020 †50

HARTMAN, Donald Lee. 990 OAK RIDGE TPKE 37830 #041-13-1961 L1969 **D** *071 †15

HEALD, David Grant. 100 VERMONT AVE 37830 #001-02-1974 L1976 **FM** *020 †18

HELTON, Michael Harold. 988 OAK RIDGE TPKE, STE L50 37830 #654-01-1988 L1992 **IM** *020 †20

HENDERSON, Michael Allen. 801 OAK RIDGE TPKE, OAK RIDGE 37830 #047-20-2003 L2005 **IM** *020 †20

HENRY, James Earl, Jr. 990 OAK RIDGE TPKE, METHODIST MED CTR EMGY DPT 37830 #047-06-1971 L1972 **EM** *020 †16

HILTON, James Isaiah. 944 OAK RIDGE TPKE 37830 #047-06-1966 L1967 **DR** *020 †80

HUGHES, R Hal. 800 OAK RIDGE TPKE, STE C200 37830 #004-01-1991 L1997 **PCC IM** *020 †20

ISANG, Mercy Emmanuel. 140 E DIVISION RD 37830 #690-10-1987 L2002 **P** *020

JAMES, Clifford D, III. 575 OAK RIDGE TPKE 37830 #048-15-1997 L2000 **PD** *020 †55

JOHNSON, Andrew Kelly. ■ 37830 #035-01-2008 *012

JONES, Jerry Wayne, Jr. 990 OAK RIDGE TPKE, METHODIST MEDICAL CENTER 37830 #047-06-1998 L2002 **AN** *020 †05

JUSTICE, Anthony Glen. 990 OAK RIDGE TPKE 37830 #047-06-1987 L1988 **AN** *020 †05

KHEMSARA, Vickas. 90 VERMONT AVE 37830 #048-13-1997 L2003 **OPH** *020 †35

KING, Joanna B. 988 OAK RIDGE TPKE, STE 245 37830 #047-06-1996 L1999 **IM** *020 †20

KNISELEY, Ralph Marion. 160A W TENNESSEE AVE 37830 #041-13-1943 L1951 **GP** *071 †50,28

KRISHNAN, Lalita. 988 OAK RIDGE TPKE, PHYSICIAN'S PLAZASTE140 OB 37830 #495-16-1972 L1979 **GYN** *020 †30

LANDS, Ronald Herman. 102 VERMONT AVE STE 200 37830 #047-06-1977 L1978 **ON HEM** *071 †20

LANE, David C. ■ 37830 #047-06-1951 L1952 **N NS** *075 †25

LEE, Larry Hugh. 102 VERMONT AVE 37830 #048-04-1983 L1984 **RO** *071 †80

LE NOIR, Daniel Richard. 100 VERMONT AVE 37830 #021-01-1984 L1993 **FM** *020 †18

LEW, Ira Eugene. 240 W TYRONE RD, HOSPITAL AND CENTER 37830 #047-05-1972 L1972 **P** *071

LINDSEY, Julianna. 990 OAK RIDGE TPKE, MMG OFFICE 37830 #020-12-1996 L2002 **IM EM** *020 †20

LONG, David Dale. 988 OAK RIDGE TPKE, STE 350 37830 #038-40-1980 L1987 **VS GS** *020 †85

LOY, William Allen. 129 E DIVISION RD 37830 #047-06-1972 L1973 **PTH** *020 †50 ‡

LUCKMANN, Kenneth F. 988 OAK RIDGE TPKE 37830 #047-05-1972 L1974 **GE IM** *020 †20

LUTTRELL, Bradley Johnson. 90 VERMONT AVE 37830 #047-06-2000 L2004 **OPH** *020 †35

MC CLINTON, Mark Edward. 800 OAK RIDGE TPKE, STE C100 37830 #021-01-1994 L2007 **OTO** *020 †45

MC KELLAR, Duncan L, Jr. 988 OAK RIDGE TPKE, STE 100 37830 #048-14-1983 L1990 **ORS** *020 †40

MEHTA, Saroj. 145 E VANCE RD, STE 320 37830 #496-07-1972 L1983 **PD** *020 †55

MESMER, John Philip. 990 OAK RIDGE TPKE 37830 #047-06-1988 L1989 **IM PD** *020 †20,55

METCALF, Joseph, IV. 988 OAK RIDGE TPKE, OAK RIDGE SURGEONS PC 37830 #012-05-1986 L1991 **GS** *020 †85

METCALF, Thomas Harlan. 988 OAK RIDGE TPKE, STE 140 37830 #047-06-1977 L1978 **OBG EM** *020 †30

MILLER, Kenneth T, Jr. 112 DANA DR 37830 #048-02-1969 L1977 **GS** *071 †85

MITCHELL, Charles S. 988 OAK RIDGE TPKE, SUITE 245 PHYSICIANS PLAZA 37830 #047-06-1976 L1977 **GS** *020 †85

MONTALVO, Ruth Datmare. 988 OAK RIDGE TPKE, STE 200 37830 #042-01-1992 L2007 **GE** *020 †20

MOUHAYAR, Elie Nassif. 80 VERMONT AVE 37830 #605-03-1996 L2003 **CD** *020 †20

MYNATT, Robert George. ■ 37830 #047-06-2003 L2003 **OTO** *012

NELSON, John Raymond. 140 E DIVISION RD, PEER OCC MED STE A-1 37830 #036-05-1955 L1962 **IM** *071 †20

NOONAN, Thomas Robt. 360 LABORATORY RD 37830 #035-06-1939 **OS** *071

O'BRIEN, Michael Patrick. 90 VERMONT AVE STE 300, OAK RIDGE 37830 #028-34-1994 L2003 **ORS** *020 †40

OESCH, Timothy Ralph. 115B S ILLINOIS AVE, PARK MED URGENT CARE CENTE 37830 #048-02-1980 L1987 **OM** *020

PALMER, Etna Little. ■ 37831 #036-05-1948 L1956 **IM** *071

PARET, Robert Walter. 100 UNION VALLEY RD, STE 120 37830 #035-09-1959 L1988 **OM** *020

PATTNI, Toral B. 100 VERMONT AVE 37830 #495-98-1986 L1996 **FM** *020 †18

PEARSON, Randall Eugene. 800 OAK RIDGE TPKE, STE A101 37830 #047-06-1982 L1982 **U** *020 †95

PERKERSON, Robert Joel. ■ 37830 #047-06-1974 L1975 **FM** *020 †18

PETERS, Scott Wesley. 988 OAK RIDGE TPKE, STE 140 37830 #039-01-1984 L1989 **OBG** *020 †30

PHILLIPS, James Edward. 990 OAK RIDGE TPKE 37830 #036-01-1974 L1982 **OM** *030 †70 ‡

PIETRASZ, Lech K. 80 VERMONT AVE, PARKWAY CARDIOLOGY ASSOC. 37830 #759-07-1981 L1993 **CD** *020 †20

PISANO, Frances Prentiss. 145 E VANCE RD, STE 320 37830 #041-07-1991 L1995 **PD** *020 †55

POWERS, Timothy Paul. 90 VERMONT AVE 37830 #047-20-1988 L1988 **OPH** *020 †35

PRATER, William Kyle. 990 OAK RIDGE TPKE 37830 #047-06-1974 L1975 **DR** *020 †80

PRINCE, Mark Dwane. 988 OAK RIDGE TPKE 37830 #020-12-1996 L2001 **GE** *020 †20

RAEF, Hussein. ■ 37830 #875-02-1983 L1993 **END** *020 †20

REID, Francis Randolph. 90 VERMONT AVE 37830 #047-06-1975 L1975 **OPH** *020 †35

RICCHE, David Allen. 100 VERMONT AVE, FAMILY CLINIC OF OAK RIDGE 37830 #055-01-1993 L1995 **FM** *020 †18

RICE, William Mark. 100 VERMONT AVE 37830 #020-12-1977 L1984 **FM** *020 †18

RICKS, Phillip Morgan. 988 OAK RIDGE TPKE 37830 #027-01-1973 L1974 **GE NTR** *020 †20

RIDINGS-HESSER, Sandra L. 944 OAK RIDGE TPKE 37830 #048-13-1986 L2004 **DR** *020 †80

ROBBINS, Randall Raymond. 961 OAK RIDGE TPKE 37830 #021-06-1989 L1994 **ORS** *020 †40

ROBERTS, William Jos. 990 OAK RIDGE TPKE 37830 #047-06-1983 L1983 **GP** *020

ROUSE, James Mitchell. 990 OAK RIDGE TPKE, DBA MM GROUP 37830 #047-06-1961 L1963 **R GS** *071 †80

SANCES, Andywlynn C. 988 OAK RIDGE TPKE, STE 140 37830 #047-20-1994 L1998 **OBG** *020 †30

SANJINES, Jorge Ariel. 113 VILLANOVA RD 37830 #654-01-1982 L1984 **EM** *020

SEAY, David Worrell. 100 VERMONT AVE 37830 #019-02-1969 L1972 **IM** *020 †18

SHARMA, Tanaz Mukesh. ■ 37830 #495-08-1976 L1993 **PTH** *071 †50

SHARP, Donald Alan. 800 OAK RIDGE TPKE, STE A300 37830 #047-06-1974 L1975 **D** *020 †15

SMALLEY, Lee Alan. 90 VERMONT AVE 37830 #047-06-1972 L1977 **OPH** *020 †35

SMITH, George Edward. 800 OAK RIDGE TPKE, STE A200 37830 #047-05-1968 L1988 **PS GS** *020 †85,65

SNODGRASS, Gregory Wayne. 944 OAK RIDGE TPKE, STE 200 37830 #047-06-1986 L1990 **AN** *020 †05

SPRAY, Paul Ellsworth. ■ 37830 #010-01-1944 L1950 **ORS** *071 †40

STANLEY, David Granville. 988 OAK RIDGE TPKE, PHYSICIANS PLAZA STE 350 37830 #047-06-1962 L1963 **UM VS** *020 †85

■ = Address Information Privacy Protected

STEVENS, Geo Miller, III. 988 OAK RIDGE TPKE STE 100 37830 #047-06-1959 L1959 ORS HS *071 †40

STRIKE, William Kenneth. 102 VERMONT AVE 37830 #036-05-1990 L1994 RO *020 †80

TAYLOR, Susan Joanne. 801 OAK RIDGE TPKE, OAK RIDGE 37830 #005-15-1984 L1994 FM *020 †18

THOMPSON, Michael Roger. 102 VERMONT AVE, STE 200 37830 #041-09-1989 L1995 ON *020 †20

VARGAS, Tanya Huerta. 221 W TYRONE RD 37830 #649-40-1982 L1991 PD *020 †55

VON DER LAGE, Frederick C. ■ 37830 #047-06-1973 L1975 AN *071

VORA, Amit Chandrakant. 990 OAK RIDGE TPKE 37830 #495-89-1995 L2001 END IM *020 †20

WALKER, Robert Earl. 90 VERMONT AVE 37830 #047-06-1974 L1975 OPH *020 †35

WALLACE, Thomas Everett. 990 OAK RIDGE TPKE, METHODIST MEDICAL CENTER 37830 #016-11-1976 L1992 CCM PUD *020 †20

WALTERS, William Gary. 665 EMORY VALLEY RD STE B 37830 #021-05-1964 L1970 P *020 †75

WEIGHT, Glen Richard. 988 OAK RIDGE TPKE, STE 245 37830 #048-04-1977 L1980 GS *071 †85

WELCH, John William, Jr. 221 W TYRONE RD 37830 #047-05-1974 L1977 PD AM *020 †55

WEST, Burton Carey. 990 OAK RIDGE TPKE 37830 #035-20-1967 L1972 IM ID *020 †20

WHITLEY, John Matthew. 200 NEW YORK AVE, STE 330 37830 #036-05-1990 L2004 NS *020 †25

WILEY, Albert Lee. 150 E VANCE RD, CENTER/ORAL 37830 #035-45-1963 L2002 RO NM *071 †80,28

WILKINSON, Indy Mcfall. ■ 37830 #008-01-2008 *012

WILLIAMS, Gordon Frank. ■ 37830 #047-20-2001 L2005 MPD *020 †20,55

WILSON, Timothy Paul. 115B S ILLINOIS AVE 37830 #047-06-1989 L1995 FM *020

WRAY, Ronald Keith. 988 OAK RIDGE TPKE 37830 #047-06-1987 L1992 IM *020 †20

ZANOLLI, Gino. 110 BALSAM RD 37830 #035-08-1954 L1955 OM P *071 †70

OAKLAND — FAYETTE

ELSEA, De Anna Marie. 7243 US HIGHWAY 64 38060 #047-06-1996 L1999 IM *020 †20

FAROOQ, Farha. 7070 HIGHWAY 64 38060 #704-21-1996 L2003 FM *020 †18

LYONS, Darrin Cortez. 7070 HIGHWAY 64, THE OAKLAND CLINIC 38060 #047-07-1988 L1998 FM *020 †18

TURNER, Kevin. 65 OAKCOURT CV 38060 #016-45-1981 L1989 P *020 †75

OLD HICKORY — DAVIDSON

ARRADONDO, John E. 128 DEKEWOOD DR 37138 #024-01-1968 L1974 FM GPM *020 †18

BECK, Larson Dale. ■ 37138 #047-06-1962 L1962 OTO *071 †45

CALDERON, Virginia N. 109 CHERRY BRANCH LN 37138 #748-08-1963 L1977 P *020

CHAN, Herbert Hoi To. ■ 37138 #462-01-1979 L1986 AN PD *020 †55

CHURCH, Celia Vivian. 4962 LEBANON PIKE 37138 #001-02-1988 L1994 EM IM *020 †20

COUDEN, Vincent Robt. 216 HIDDEN CT 37138 #017-20-1969 L1976 ORS *071 †40

CRANE, Joseph Michael. 1002 INDUSTRIAL DR 37138 #021-01-1967 L1968 GS *020 †85

EVANS, Janet Ernst. 725 GENERAL KERSHAW DR 37138 #024-07-1979 L1988 DR *020 †80

EVANS, Rose M Doucette. ■ 37138 #047-07-1977 L1978 PD *020

GENTRY, Harold Leffel. 609 BEDFORD FOREST CT 37138 #004-01-1963 L1970 R NM *020 †80

HUNT, Russell Wayne. 1415 ROBINSON RD 37138 #031-01-1992 L1995 FM PMM *020 †18

KENDALL, Robert Leon. ■ 37138 #005-12-1967 L1969 PTH *020

MANALAC, Abelardo Z. ■ 37138 #748-01-1966 L1972 FM GS *071

PHIBBS, Fenna Tanner. 508 GRANWOOD BLVD 37138 #007-02-2002 L2006 N *100

ROBERTSON, Amy C. 4317 BRACKENWOOD DR 37138 #056-05-2002 L2004 AN *100 †05

SANDERS, Richard James. ■ 37138 #045-01-1970 L1973 DR *071 †80

SATTERFIELD, Robert Guy. ■ 37138 #020-02-1970 L1973 OBG *071

SEELEY, James Edmund, III. 1903 HADLEY AVE 37138 #005-12-1976 L1979 FM *020 †18

TAYLOR, Robin Ray. 1456 STATION FOUR LN 37138 #005-12-1996 L2000 AN *020

TOPACIO-PECACHE, Conchita. ■ 37138 #748-01-1954 L1972 AN *071

OLIVER SPRINGS — ROANE

BINGHAM, William Barry. 103 BENNETT RD 37840 #047-20-1987 L1990 FM *020 †18

DAVIS, Scott Eric. PO BOX 611 37840 #047-20-1992 L1993 FM *020 †18

MEECE, Terrence L. 103 BENNETT RD 37840 #016-11-1976 L1993 FM *030 †18

ONEIDA — SCOTT

COFFEY, David B. 281 UNDERPASS DR 37841 #047-06-1976 L1976 FM *020 ‡

CROSS, Trent Wade. 2611 SMITH CREEK RD 37841 #047-06-2003 L2004 IM *020

DODD, Robert Tinnon. 369 MEADOW CREEK DR 37841 #047-06-1974 L1974 OBG *020

GONZALES, Eduardo Raoul. 615 N MAIN ST 37841 #036-05-1986 L2007 GS VS *020 †85

HALL, Thomas Kent. 19295 ALBERTA ST, P O BOX 4745 37841 #047-06-1974 L1975 DR *020

HARDY, William Laurence. 18797 ALBERTA ST 37841 #011-02-1973 L1996 ORS OSM *020

HUFF, Maxwell Ernest. 220 S CROSS ST 37841 #047-06-1959 L1959 FM *020 †18

LUI, Anita Y. 20445 ALBERTA ST, SCOTT CTY HOSP 37841 #748-01-1986 L2002 IM ID *020 †20

MARTIN, John Paul. 18859 ALBERTA ST, FAMILY CARE P.O. BOX 4908 37841 #051-04-1981 L1996 FM OBS *030 †18

MOHYUDDIN, Zahoor. 18797 ALBERTA ST 37841 #704-01-1965 L1997 EM *020

PERKINS, Michael David. PO BOX 4847 37841 #020-02-1976 L1977 GP *020

PERRY, Larry E. 20473 ALBERTA ST 37841 #654-01-1987 L1991 PD GP *020

PHILLIPS, Gary Robin. 460 INDUSTRIAL LN 37841 #024-07-1982 L1986 IM *020

ROBBINS, Jan Greg. 18797 ALBERTA ST 37841 #048-15-1992 L1994 EM *020

SILVER, Evelyn Y. 19067 ALBERTA ST, SCOTT CNTY PEDIATRIC CARE 37841 #748-08-1991 L2001 PD *020 †55

WARD, Charles Stanton. 21354 ALBERTA ST 37841 #047-06-1992 L1995 FM *020 †18

YBANEZ, Frances Mae Saile. 133 W 2ND AVE 37841 #748-10-1992 L2001 OS *100

ONLY — HICKMAN

SATOR, Inocentes A. RR 1, C/O TURNEY CTR IND PRISON 37140 #748-09-1966 L1973 GS GP *020

OOLTEWAH — HAMILTON

ALLEN, Billy Jason. 5623 MAIN ST 37363 #047-06-1963 L1963 PFP *020 †18

BOYD, Diana Reed. ■ 37363 #047-20-1983 L1984 IM *020

BRANSON, Kayce Diane. ■ 37363 #048-02-2008 *012

CASON, Garrick Wayne. ■ 37363 #027-01-2004 ORS *012

CONTARINO, Joseph Richard. ■ 37363 #011-02-1982 L1988 GP *020 †18

DREXLER, James Edward. ■ 37363 #005-12-1958 L1959 AN GPM *071

DUNLAP, Allan Bernard. ■ 37363 #012-21-1996 L2004 GS *100

HAMILTON, Fitzhugh L. 7229 GOLDENROD CT, SKY RIDGE MEDICAL CENTER 37363 #047-06-1994 L1995 IM *020 †20

HIGH, Lawrence W, Jr. ■ 37363 #047-07-1982 L1985 IM *075

KLINNER, Thomas Robt, Jr. 9203 LEE HWY STE 9 37363 #306-01-1984 L1988 IM *020 †20

LANE, Edmund S. 9236 INGLEBROOK DR, 7900 RHEA CO. HWY DAYTON T 37363 #047-07-1978 L1978 FM *030

LARGE, Bradley Patton. 9815 FROST CREEK DR 37363 #047-06-1998 L2000 IM *020 †20

LAYNE, J T. ■ 37363 #047-06-1952 L1964 GP OM *071

LECHLER, Donald Reid. ■ 37363 #005-12-1977 L1984 AN *020 †05

LOUNSBERRY, David Vernon. 5121 OOLTEWAH RINGGOLD RD, BROOKSIDE MEDICAL CENTER 37363 #005-12-1968 L2005 FM *020 †18

LYNCH, Bruce Andrew. ■ 37363 #041-02-2003 L2005 GS *012

MADIWALE, Taj Munir. ■ 37363 #010-01-2001 L2007 PEM PD *020 †55

MASHCHAK, Clarissa Ann. 9413 APISON PIKE, STE 124 37363 #005-12-1974 L1987 GYN REN *020 †30

MERRITT, Brandy Elizabeth. ■ 37363 #001-06-2007 PD *012

MILHOLM, Richard Le Roy. ■ 37363 #005-12-1963 L1966 FM *071 †18

OST, Walter Martin. ■ 37363 #005-12-1948 L1979 GP *071

SANFORD, Joy. ■ 37363 #047-07-1980 L1980 GS *075

SHERRER, James Scott. 9309 APISON PIKE 37363 #012-01-1991 L2000 FM *020 †18

THACKER, Jeremy Wayne. ■ 37363 #020-12-2005 GS *012

TURNER, David Herschel. ■ 37363 #047-06-1952 L1953 OPH *071 †35

PALMYRA — MONTGOMERY

MITCHUM, Patricia Anne. ■ 37142 #035-19-1985 L1991 GP NTR *020

PARIS — HENRY

ADAMS, Robert D. 301 TYSON AVE 38242 #047-06-1967 L1968 FM *020

BOYD, Amy Jill. 235 TYSON AVE, KENTUCKY LAKE SURGERY CENT 38242 #047-05-1995 L1998 AN *020 †05

BOYD, Russell Wayne. 235 TYSON AVE 38242 #047-05-1994 L1999 GS *020 †85

CAMPBELL, William Russell. 1323 E WOOD ST, EAST WOOD CLINIC P.C 38242 #047-06-1967 L1968 IM FM *071

CHANDLER, Gerald Blake. 1004 CORNERSTONE DR STE A 38242 #047-20-1995 L2000 ORS *020 †40

COLEMAN, Andrew Clark. 305 TYSON AVE 38242 #004-01-1993 L1996 IM *020 †20

COMPTON, Raymond Powell. 1323 E WOOD ST, JACKSON CLINIC 38242 #047-06-1991 L1993 GS CCS *020

DUNAGAN, Stephanie C. 430 S LAKE ST, GRIFFEY CLINIC 38242 #047-20-1998 L2001 FM *020 †18 ‡

EVANS, Pamela Ruth. 300 HOSPITAL CIR, STE 102 38242 #001-02-1995 L1999 OBG *020 †30

GARRETT, Glenn Sanders. 300 HOSPITAL CIR 38242 #047-06-1973 L1973 DR *020 †80

GINN, David Carroll. 1290 KELLEY DR 38242 #048-12-1984 L1989 ON HEM *020 †20

GLADWELL, Heather Anne. 1015 KELLEY DR, STE 200 38242 #041-01-1997 L2002 ORS *020 †20

GO, Virginia Rosales. 1323 E WOOD ST, THE JACKSON CLINIC 38242 #748-11-1971 L1980 IM GE *020 †20

GOLD, Donald Davis, Jr. 706 E WOOD ST 38242 #012-05-1974 L1976 P *020 †75

GRIFFEY, Walter P, Jr. 430 S LAKE ST 38242 #047-05-1958 L1958 IM GP *071

GRIFFEY, Walter Plummer. 430 S LAKE ST 38242 #047-20-1993 L1996 IM *020 †20

GULISH, Eugene Frank. 1015 KELLEY DR, STE 200 38242 #038-40-1964 L1994 ORS *020 †40

HARPER, Jason Louis. ■ 38242 #047-06-2001 L2006 GS *100

HARRISON, Terry Olean. 305 TYSON AVE 38242 #047-06-1974 L1975 GP EM *020

HERRON, Charles Burkhead. 305 TYSON AVE 38242 #036-07-1966 L1971 D IM *020 †20,15

HUDSON, James Hervey. 305 TYSON AVE 38242 #047-06-1981 L1983 IM *020

JACKSON, John Owens, Jr. 243 JIM ADAMS DR, PARIS PEDIATRICS P.C. 38242 #047-06-1980 L1982 PD *020 †55

JURIC, Mira J. 300 HOSPITAL CIR, STE 204 38242 #957-01-1969 L1999 PD ADL *020 †55

KIMBERLIN, Gibson Dan. 300 HOSPITAL CIR, STE 103 38242 #021-05-1974 L1989 OBG *020 †30

LUNDBERG, Andrew Hayward. 235 TYSON AVE 38242 #036-05-1995 L1997 VS GS *020 †85

MC CAIN, James R. ■ 38242 #047-06-1951 L1951 PD *071 †55

MC CREARY, Wm Herbert. ■ 38242 #047-05-1957 L1957 PYA P *071

MC GEE, James Wayne. 1323 E WOOD ST, JACKSON CLINIC OF PARIS 38242 #047-06-1986 L1987 IM *020

MC INTOSH, Barry Park. ■ 38242 #047-06-1953 L1966 DR R *071 †80

MINOR, Christy Farmer. 1323 E WOOD ST 38242 #047-06-1995 L1998 PD *020 †55

MINOR, Thomas Mc Swain. 300 HOSPITAL CIR 38242 #047-05-1957 L1957 GS TS *071 †85,90

MITCHELL, Stephen Robb. 301 TYSON AVE, HENRY CO MEDICAL CENTER 38242 #047-06-1986 L1989 DR *020 †80

MOBLEY, Emmett P, Jr. ■ 38242 #047-06-1949 L1950 FM *071 †18

MOBLEY, Joe D. 1005 E WOOD ST, KENTUCKY LK UROLOGY 38242 #047-06-1949 L1950 GS *071 †85

MOBLEY, Joe Dick, Jr. 1002 CORNERSTONE DR 38242 #047-06-1977 L1978 U EM *020 †95

MONETTE, Jean Gerard. 1009 E WOOD ST 38242 #067-06-1971 L1992 PYG *020

NANNEY, Philip Warren. 1323 E WOOD ST 38242 #047-06-1998 L1999 FM *020 †18

NELSON, Michael Wm. 1323 E WOOD ST 38242 #047-06-1990 L1991 EM FM *020 †18

NORMAN, Dwight Michael. 1323 E WOOD ST 38242 #047-06-1964 L1964 FM *071 †18

PERMENTER, William Dale. 1290 KELLEY DR 38242 #047-06-1964 L1973 OBG *071

RICHARDSON, Robt Lee, Jr. 1323 E WOOD ST 38242 #047-06-1960 L1961 TS *071 †85,90

ROBERTSON, James Buford. 1323 E WOOD ST 38242 #047-06-1972 L1972 IM *020 †20

SELBY, Debra Hinzman. 301 TYSON AVE 38242 #055-01-1987 L1992 PD *020 †55

■ = Address Information Privacy Protected

SENTER, John Maxwell, Jr. ■ 38242 #047-06-1966 L1966 **GS** *071 †85
SLEADD, Frank Bland. ■ 38242 #020-02-1955 L1969 **PTH** *071 †50
SUMMERS, Douglas Scott. 1323 E WOOD ST 38242 #047-06-1991 L1992 **FM** *020 †18
TUSA, Vince Chas. 305 TYSON AVE 38242 #047-06-1975 L1977 **IM** *020
VAN DYCK, John Thos. 1024 KELLEY DR, DBA VAN DYCK AMBULATORY SU 38242 #047-06-1973 L1974 **OPH** *020 †35
WALKER, Charles Allen. 707 E WOOD ST 38242 #047-06-1985 L1986 **EM** *020
WILLIAMS, Joseph Walter. 1103 KING ST 38242 #033-06-1982 L1986 **P GP** *020 †75
WOOD, Thomas Chas. 803 JOY ST 38242 #047-06-1958 L1958 **FM** *020 †18

PARROTTSVILLE — COCKE

MANOCK, Stephen Robt. 111 MOCKINGBIRD AVE 37843 #016-11-1988 L2007 **FM** *020 †18

PARSONS — DECATUR

ALDERSON, Charles Malcolm. 969 TENNESSEE AVE S 38363 #047-06-1962 L1963 **GS TS** *020 †85
CRIDER, John Paul. ■ 38363 #027-01-1983 L1983 **FM** *020
HOUCHIN, Michael Blaine. 103 PRICE ST 38363 #047-20-1995 L1996 **FM** *020 †18
JENNINGS, William Gordon. 969 TENNESSEE AVE S 38363 #047-06-1964 L1964 **GP N** *020
MASTERSON, John P. 969 TENNESSEE AVE S 38363 #048-12-1990 L1999 **ORS** *020 †40
MONTGOMERY, Joseph Harold. 103 PRICE ST, DECATUR COUNTY FAMILY PRAC 38363 #047-06-1989 L1992 **FM** *020 †18
MURPHREE, Vikki Louise. 79 PRICE ST 38363 #047-20-1998 L1999 **FM** *020 †18
PHILLIPS, John Barry. 50 SKYLINE LN 38363 #047-06-1977 L1977 **FM** *020 †18

PHILADELPHIA — LOUDON

BROOKS, Margaret H. 150 REED SPRINGS RD, MARGARET H BROOKS MD 37846 #047-06-1965 L1969 **AN GP** *071

PICKWICK DAM — HARDIN

TYLER, Louis Edward. ■ 38365 #047-06-1965 L1965 **FM** *020 †18

PIGEON FORGE — SEVIER

GARMANY, Tracie Silliman. 1022 DOLLYWOOD LN 37863 #047-20-1997 L1998 **FM** *020 †18
MANSY, Joseph M. ■ 37868 #051-01-1978 L1979 **EM FM** *020 †16,18
SMITH, Nelson Bryan. 3342 PARKWAY 37863 #047-06-1990 L1991 **FM** *020

PIKEVILLE — BLEDSOE

ALVAREZ, Jennifer Suzanne. ■ 37367 #041-13-2004 L2007 **PD** *020 †55
BOWNDS, Charles P. HWY 30 W 37367 #649-14-1976 L1981 **GP** *072
QUITO, Arturo Limcaco. HWY 30 W 37367 #748-01-1969 L1981 **GP** *020
SAPP, Robert David. 136 WHEELERTOWN AVE 37367 #047-06-2001 L2004 **MPD** *100 †20,55
SIMMONS, Everett Casey. 37367 #047-06-1971 L1972 **P** *040
TEZCAN, Ulker Persen. ■ 37367 #902-01-1957 L1968 **IM GP** *020

PINEY FLATS — SULLIVAN

CLAYTON, Buddy Joe. 5493 HIGHWAY 11 E, PINEY BLUFF MEDICAL CENTER 37686 #047-20-1994 L1995 **FM** *020 †18
CLAYTON, Steven Brian. 5493 HIGHWAY 11 E, PINEY BLUFF MEDICAL CENTER 37686 #047-20-2001 L2002 **FM** *020 †18 ‡
KESSLER, William A. 452 SUNNY LANE 37686 #038-41-1952 L1952 **GS TS** *071 †85
LAWSON, Robert Wesley. ■ 37686 #047-06-1975 L1975 **EM** *020 †18
MOHLER, Anastasia Clare. 6070 HIGHWAY 11 E 37686 #051-01-2005 L2007 **FP** *012
ONEDERA, Helen Louise R. ■ 37686 #047-20-1994 L2001 **AN** *020 †05
RABETOY, Gary Michael. ■ 37686 #065-05-1971 L2008 **NEP MPD** *020 †20
RAVAL, Abhijit Ajitkumar. ■ 37686 #495-22-2003 L2008 **IM** *012
RENTZ, Michael Wayne. ■ 37686 #045-04-2004 L2008 **PTH** *012
WESTBROOK, Scott Lee. 6070 HIGHWAY 11 E, CLINIC 37686 #016-06-1990 L1991 **CCM** *020 †20
WINKLER, Erin Carrick. ■ 37686 #055-01-2006 L2008 **PD** *012

PIONEER — SCOTT

KNAPP, Robert Hugh. ■ 37847 #035-15-1972 L1977 **P** *020

PLEASANT HILL — CUMBERLAND

BRAUN, Richard Chas. 146 LAKE ROAD 38578 #028-02-1955 L1971 **FM OS** *072
OLDMAN, Martha Jeane. ■ 38578 #041-77-1949, ▲ *071
SIMPSON, Robert L. ■ 38578 #047-06-1951 L1952 **GS OBS** *071
UPDEGRAFF, Richard B. ■ 38578 #041-01-1954 L2001 **FM** *071 †18
UPDEGRAFF, Virginia A. ■ 38578 #041-07-1954 L2001 **FM PHP** *071

PLEASANT VIEW — CHEATHAM

CHANG, Philemon Dawei. 1012 INDUSTRIAL DR, HOPE MEDICAL CLINIC 37146 #039-05-1985 L1987 **IM** *020
KAUFFMANN, Rondi Marie. ■ 37146 #026-04-2005 **GS** *012
MANNING, John Richard. 2536 HIGHWAY 49 E, SUITE 110 37146 #654-01-1993 L2005 **FM** *020

NORDQUIST, Fred Armand. 2536 HIGHWAY 49 E, STE 110 37146 #047-07-2002 L2003 **IM** *020 †20
ORLOWSKI, Elizabeth Ann. ■ 37146 #025-01-2006 **PTH** *012
RAY, Lori Annette. 254 REN MAR DR, STE 100 37146 #047-20-1999 L2001 **IM** *020 †20

PORTLAND — SUMNER

BAIN, Verna. 105 E MARKET ST 37148 #422-01-1993 L1999 **IM PD** *020 †20,55
DAY, Bruce Edward. 105 REDBUD DR 37148 #001-02-1972 L1977 **EM IM** *020 †20,16
DITTES, Albert G. ■ 37148 #005-12-1941 L1946 **GP** *071
FORSYTHE, Phillip David. 105 REDBUD DR 37148 #047-06-1984 L1986 **FM** *020 †16
GIBSON, William Donald. 105 REDBUD DR 37148 #001-06-1997 L2001 **EM** *020 †16
GREAVU, Cornell, Jr. ■ 37148 #005-12-1953 L1987 **GP** *071
GREEN, Mark Edward. 105 REDBUD DR 37148 #038-45-1999 L2002 **EM** *020 †16
KRISHNAMURTHY, Manickam. 105 REDBUD DR 37148 #035-01-2002 L2004 **EM** *020 †16
LUDI, Guillermo S. 103 REDBUD DR STE E, GROUP 37148 #132-02-1985 L2002 **IM** *020 †20
MC FARLAND, Marion Allen. 105 REDBUD DR 37148 #654-01-1985 L2002 **EM IM** *020 †20
MIN, Marcus Myungki. 105 REDBUD DR 37148 #005-12-1990 L1994 **GP** *020 †20
MOSKOWITZ, Robert Myles. 105 REDBUD DR 37148 #035-45-2001 L2004 **EM** *020 †16
PONCE, Lou. 102 W KNIGHT ST 37148 #748-08-1961 L1971 **GP OM** *020
PORTER, Paul Randall. 121 VILLAGE DR, STE 101 37148 #047-20-1982 L1983 **IM** *020 †20
SALCEDO, Pepito Yapit. 103 REDBUD DR, STE E 37148 #748-10-1965 L1972 **GS GP** *020
TAYLOR, John Allen. 307 S BROADWAY 37148 #005-12-1980 L1984 **FM** *020 †18
VANCE, Stacey Drott. 120 MAIN ST 37148 #027-01-1998 L2000 **FM** *012

POWELL — KNOX

BARTON, Ronald Patterson. 201 E EMORY RD 37849 #047-06-1986 L1987 **FM** *020 †18
BLACKMON, Gregory Dewayne. 7714 CONNER RD, STE 101 37849 #047-20-1995 L1996 **PD** *020 †55
BOGARTZ, Leon Jacob. 7540 DANNAHER WAY, # 300 37849 #016-42-1964 L1970 **SME PUD** *071 †20
CHISM, Kathy Nora Lee. 201 E EMORY RD, D.B.A. EMORY FAMILY PRACTI 37849 #036-01-1997 L1998 **FM** *020 †18 ‡
DEAN, Rhea Wesley, Jr. 201 E EMORY RD 37849 #047-06-1986 L1987 **FM** *020 †18
EISENSTADT, Michael L. 7540 DANNAHER WAY, STE 300 37849 #035-19-1974 L1980 **N** *020 †75
FARRIS, Richard Kent. 629 DELOZIER WAY 37849 #047-05-1966 L1973 **GE IM** *020 †20
FEHR, Robert Richard. 2125 W EMORY RD, ROBERT R FEHR MD 37849 #041-13-1981 L1984 **FM** *020 †18
FENG, Yi. 7551 DANNAHER WAY 37849 #243-20-1982 L2004 **HO** *020 †20
FLAMING, Brad Alan. 201 E EMORY RD 37849 #020-02-1990 L1992 **FM** *020 †18
GARBER, Brian Howard. 7557 DANNAHER WAY STE 11 37849 #036-05-1981 L1988 **GS VS** *020 †85
GENTRY, David Wayne. ■ 37849 #047-06-2003 L2005 **NM** *100
GIBBS, Cassandra Faye. 7557 DANNAHER WAY, ASSOCIATES AT EMORY ROAD 37849 #021-05-2001 L2006 **IM** *020
HARRELL, David J. 7557 DANNAHER WAY, STE 110 37849 #048-04-1991 L1997 **GS** *020 †85
HAYDEK, John Michael. 629 DELOZIER WAY 37849 #016-43-1988 L1996 **GE IM** *020 †20
HAYES, Wesley Lamar. 306 ASHWORTH TRL 37849 #047-06-2002 L2005 **IM** *020 †20
HOBART, Richard Loren, Jr. ■ 37849 #023-01-1948 L1954 **IM** *071
JOHNSON, Mark Wade. 2125 W EMORY RD, W JOHNSON MD 37849 #305-01-1994 L1997 **FM** *020 †18
JONES, Anna Lisa. ■ 37849 #048-15-2005 **OBG** *012
KELLY, Michael Edward. 7557 DANNAHER WAY, STE 110 37849 #047-06-1997 L2000 **GS** *020 †85
MARTIN, Mitchell Dane. 7551 DANNAHER WAY, CONSULTANTS, PLLC 37849 #011-03-1995 L1999 **HO** *020 †20
MILLER, Stanley Lee. 629 DELOZIER WAY 37849 #027-01-1984 L1998 **GE IM** *020 †20
MORRIS, Carl Timothy. 2157 W EMORY RD, CHILD AND TEEN CLINIC 37849 #047-20-1994 L1996 **PD** *020
NARAYANI, Raj Indru. 629 DELOZIER WAY 37849 #047-05-1995 L2004 **GE** *020 †20
NEWMAN, Maria Bonet. 629 DELOZIER WAY 37849 #042-01-1994 L1999 **GE** *020 †20
OCHOA, Peter Joseph. 7557 DANNAHER WAY, STE 140 37849 #041-14-1998 L2002 **GS** *020
PEEBLES, Fred Neal. 7557 DANNAHER WAY, STE 110 37849 #047-06-1969 L1970 **GS** *020 †85
PLIAGAS, George A. 7557 DANNAHER WAY, STE 110 37849 #418-03-1983 L1990 **GS** *020 †85
THARP, Daryl Ray, Jr. ■ 37849 #020-02-2007 **PTH** *012
THORNTON, Nick Perkins, IV. 201 E EMORY RD 37849 #047-20-2001 L2002 **FM** *020 †18
VON CLEF, Julius S, III. 2125 W EMORY RD, JULIUS S VON CLEF MD 37849 #041-02-1982 L1990 **FM** *020 †18 ‡
WALTERS, Elizabeth A. 7714 CONNER RD, STE 101 37849 #045-01-1996 L1998 **PD** *020 †55

PULASKI — GILES

AGEE, Robert B. 1265 E COLLEGE ST 38478 #047-06-1950 L1952 **FM GP** *071
ANTIC, Goran Djordje. 104 IVY LN 38478 #957-02-1990 L2000 **IM** *020 †20
BALATICO, Ferdinand A. 1109 E COLLEGE ST 38478 #748-01-1972 L1982 **IM** *020
BAYLES, Donald Earl. 1265 E COLLEGE ST 38478 #001-02-1963 L1990 **EM PS** *020
BEALL, James Harvey, III. 215 S CEDAR LN, PHYSICIANS & SURGEONS INC 38478 #012-01-1982 L1993 **FM** *020 †18
BEASLEY, Jerry Stephen. 1119 E COLLEGE ST, STE 3 38478 #001-02-1982 L1995 **FM** *020 †18
BENNETT, Rick Lee. 215 N CEDAR LN, THE HEART GROUP PLLC 38478 #011-03-1987 L1993 **CD** *020 †20
BOYD, Joseph J, Jr. 215 N CEDAR LN, THE HEART GROUP PLLC 38478 #012-01-1985 L1991 **CD IM** *020 †20
BURGER, Charles W. 215 S CEDAR LN, PHYSICIANS & SURGEONS INC 38478 #047-06-1975 L1976 **FM** *020 †18
CABATU, Eresvita Espejo. PO BOX 735 38478 #748-01-1972 L1982 **PD NPM** *020 †55
COLLINS, Robert Stewart. 1275 E COLLEGE ST, STE 1 38478 #025-12-1979 L1985 **ORS HS** *020 †40
COX, Malcolm Adelphus. 1275 E COLLEGE ST 38478 #036-01-1958 L1986 **PD** *020 †55
DAVIS, Buford Preston, Jr. 215 S CEDAR LN, PHYSICIANS & SURGEONS INC 38478 #047-06-1967 L1970 **GP** *071 †18

DUNLAP, James Earl. 215 S CEDAR LN, PHYSICIANS & SURGEONS INC 38478 #031-01-1990 L2006 **FM FSM** *020 †18

FAOUR, Muhamed Salah. 1275 E COLLEGE ST, GILES FAMILY HEALTH CENTER 38478 #875-01-1998 L2003 **IM** *100 †20

FORONDA, Armando Cabot. 1150 E COLLEGE ST 38478 #748-01-1964 L1971 **GS GP** *071

FRANCO-CHEN, Mildred. 1125 E COLLEGE ST, PULASKI PEDIATRICS 38478 #748-10-1991 L2003 **PD** *020 †55

GREGORY, Rodrick Richard. 170 LOCKER RD 38478 #026-04-1977 L1999 **P** *020 †75

HAGGAG, Akram Ibrahiem. 1275 E COLLEGE ST, STE 7 38478 #915-02-1991 L1999 **IM** *020 †20

HANEY, Charles Douglas. 215 S CEDAR LN, PHYSICIANS & SURGEONS INC 38478 #047-06-1979 L1981 **FM** *020 †18

LABBAN, George. 1255 E COLLEGE ST, STE 300 38478 #875-01-1990 L1998 **HO** *012 †20

LEGREID, Russel J, II. 1255 E COLLEGE ST, STE 200 38478 #018-03-1984 L2004 **OTO** *020 †45

LUCAS, Todd Jefferson. 1255 E COLLEGE ST 38478 #047-06-1996 L2005 **GS** *020 †85

MURREY, William Harwell. 215 S CEDAR LN 38478 #047-06-1960 L1961 **FM** *020 †18

RAHN, Norman Hill, III. 1265 E COLLEGE ST 38478 #001-02-1979 L1986 **R** *020 †80 ‡

ROHALEY, Kimberly Martin. 202 HILLSIDE DR 38478 #055-02-1994 L2007 **PD** *020

STEWART, William Robt, Jr. 1275 E COLLEGE ST 38478 #047-06-1979 L1981 **OTO AI** *020

SULLIVAN, Ryan Richard. ■ 38478 #047-06-2002 L2004 **AI** *020 †20,03

TEODOROVIC, Sima. ■ 38478 #957-02-1958 L1972 **OBG** *075 †30

TURMAN, Alfred Eugene. 1275 E COLLEGE ST 38478 #047-05-1957 L1957 **U GP** *071 †95

WILBURN, Charles D. 215 S CEDAR LN 38478 #047-06-1976 L1976 **ORS GP** *020 †40

ZIAUDDIN, Mohamed. 1275 E COLLEGE ST 38478 #495-42-1969 L1990 **IM** *020 †20

RAMER – MCNAIRY

CHASE, Barton Austin, III. 3856 HIGHWAY 57 W 38367 #010-03-1982 L1988 **FM EM** *020 †18 ‡

RED BANK – HAMILTON

DODDS, Joseph James. 628 MORRISON SPRINGS RD, STE 201 37415 #041-12-1955 L1963 **GS GP** *072 †85

RED BOILING SPRINGS – MACON

FESSENDEN, Stephen F. ■ 37150 #011-03-1971 L1972 **AN PME** *071 †05

RELIANCE – POLK

DE GROSS, Joseph Michael. 101B TOWEE PIKE, TOWEE MOPUNTAIN 37369 #033-05-1967 L1999 **NEP IM** *072 ‡

RICEVILLE – MCMINN

LYTLE-MC LEOD, Laura. ■ 37370 #047-06-1991 L1997 **DR** *020 †80

RIDGELY – LAKE

PANGILINAN, Lorimer A H. 111 N MAIN ST 38080 #748-01-1964 L1981 **FM PTH** *075

SIMBAQUEBA, Cesar Augusto. 130 N MAIN ST 38080 #264-04-1997 L2004 **IM IMG** *020 †20

RIDGETOP – ROBERTSON

BOTTSFORD, Elmer E. PO BOX 500 37152 #005-12-1943 L1956 **GP FM** *071

RIPLEY – LAUDERDALE

DUGGIRALA, Prasad S. 282 S WASHINGTON ST, STE 1 38063 #495-62-1971 L1980 **GS** *020 †85

FARRIS, Larry Mc Neal. 326 ASBURY AVE 38063 #047-06-1974 L1975 **R** *071

HUNT, Joe Wade. 202 TUCKER AVE 38063 #047-06-1981 L1981 **FM** *020 †18

MURRAY, Wayne Darrell. 326 ASBURY AVE 38063 #043-01-1987 L1988 **IM PD** *020

REAVES, John Andrew. 326 ASBURY AVE 38063 #047-06-1959 L1960 **R** *071 †80

ZAIDI, Syed A. 326 ASBURY AVE, STE 101 38063 #704-02-1989 L1997 **IM** *020 †20

ROAN MOUNTAIN – CARTER

DICKSON, Albert P, III. 152 HIGHWAY 143 37687 #051-04-1952 L1990 **FM PHP** *071

EARWOOD, Alfred Douglas. 146 BUCK CREEK RD, ROAN HIGHLANDS NURSING HOM 37687 #036-08-1988 L1990 **FM** *020 †18

HANSON, Wesley Robt. 152 HIGHWAY 143, BOX 250 37687 #056-06-1981 L1982 **FM** *020 †18

KIMMEL, David Paul. 146 BUCK CREEK RD, ROAN HIGHLANDS NURSING HOM 37687 #051-01-1981 L1994 **IM** *020 †20

ROCKFORD – BLOUNT

DAVIS, Bradley Jason. ■ 37853 #047-06-2008 *012

HOERSTEN, Linda Rose. ■ 37853 #038-43-1976 L1979 **PD** *020 †55

SONODA, Takuo. ■ 37853 #572-12-1967 L1974 **ON HEM** *071 †20

ROCKWOOD – ROANE

BLUMENTHAL, Mark Gary. 1362 N GATEWAY AVE, ROANE COUNTY HLTH DEPT 37854 #033-06-1987 L1997 **FM OM** *030 †70,18

COREA, Charles Jos. ■ 37854 #047-06-1961 L1961 **R** *071

FOSTER, James Moore. ■ 37854 #047-05-1969 L1969 **AN GP** *075 †05

HICKS, Robert Sloan. 208 S CHAMBERLAIN AVE 37854 #047-06-1942 L1942 **OPH** *072

HIGGS, Ronald D. 158 COFFEY CIR, P O BOX 68 37854 #306-01-1984 L1990 **FM** *020

MEADOWS, Angela Evans. 450 S CHAMBERLAIN AVE 37854 #047-06-1998 L2001 **IM** *020 †20

SAYANI, Dinar. 450 S CHAMBERLAIN AVE, STE 100 37854 #704-02-1987 L1998 **HO IM** *020 †20

SNODGRASS, John Vass. ■ 37854 #047-06-1959 L1959 **GP** *020 †18

ROGERSVILLE – HAWKINS

AKOURY, Dalal Anis. 851 LOCUST ST 37857 #915-03-1978 L1989 **EM PD** *020 †55

ALDER, Joseph Cullen, Jr. 851 LOCUST ST 37857 #047-06-1979 L1979 **FM EM** *020

ALHAYANI, Irfan. ■ 37857 #875-02-1997 L2006 **IM** *020 †20

BAIRD, Renfro B, Jr. 851 LOCUST ST 37857 #047-05-1946 L1953 **PHP GP** *030

CALENDINE, Chris Lawrence. 851 LOCUST ST 37857 #047-20-1997 L2000 **PD** *020 †55

DALLE-AVE, Mark Jos. 900 W MAIN ST 37857 #270-02-1990 L1994 **FM** *020 †18

FLOWER, Elizabeth. 5750 HIGHWAY 66 N 37857 #495-02-1997 L2005 **FM** *020 †18

FOSTER, Anita Moore. 405 SCENIC DR, MEDICAL ASSOCIATES OF ROGE 37857 #047-20-1998 L1999 **FM** *020 †18 ‡

GASCON, Pauline Marie. RR 1 BOX 915 37857 #065-09-1961 L1980 **GP** *071

GIBBONS, William E. 851 LOCUST ST 37857 #047-06-1948 L1949 **GP** *020

GOFORTH, Walter L. 900 W MAIN ST 37857 #047-06-1951 L1952 **GP OS** *020

GOYEAU, Francis Raymond. ■ 37857 #065-09-1961 L1980 **IM** *071

HAYNES, Amy Lizbeth. 405 SCENIC DR 37857 #047-20-1996 L1998 **FM** *020 †18

JONES, M Blaine, III. 405 SCENIC DR 37857 #047-20-1992 L1993 **FM** *020 †18

MARCELO, Josefina Quintos. 4966 HIGHWAY 11W, HAWKINS MED CTR 37857 #748-01-1956 L1987 **FM** *071 †18

PATEL, Kaushal Narayanbha. 851 LOCUST ST, INTERNAL MEDICINE 37857 #495-22-2000 L2006 **IM** *020 †20

PRATT, Keith Edward. 318 FAR SIDE DR, STE B 37857 #047-20-1986 L1990 **IM** *020

SHAH, Lata Snehrashmikant. 851 LOCUST ST, HAWKINS COUNTY MEMORIAL HO 37857 #495-23-1997 L2006 **PCC** *020

SMITH, Happy Earl, Jr. ■ 37857 #308-06-1981 L1985 **FM** *020

TRENTHAM, Shirley Devon. 405 S ARMSTRONG ST —, STE 5 37857 #047-20-1997 L1999 **P** *020

TUMKUR, Anil Venugopalara. 405 SCENIC DR 37857 #496-01-1994 L2001 **IM** *020 †20

VELASCO, Jose P. 900 W MAIN ST, ETSU PHYSICIANS & ASSOCS 37857 #748-01-1985 L1994 **FM** *020 †18

VERZOSA, Manuel S. 851 LOCUST ST, DEPT R 37857 #748-01-1963 L1971 **DR PD** *020 †55,80

WILSON, Stephen Kirby. 405 SCENIC DR, MED ASSOC ROGERSVILLE 37857 #016-11-1966 L1976 **GS TRS** *020 †85

RUTLEDGE – GRAINGER

BRYAN, Leander C. 104 W MAIN ST 37861 #047-05-1927 L1927 **GP** *071

DUCK, Dennis Howard. 8731 RUTLEDGE PIKE 37861 #047-06-1987 L1989 **IM EM** *020 †20 ‡

HILL, Tenny Jacob. PO BOX 187 37861 #047-06-1953 L1954 **GP AN** *071

HUSNAIN, Syed Shaukat. 8732 RUTLEDGE PIKE STE B, RUTLEDGE PRIMARY CARE CLIN 37861 #704-02-1993 L2000 **ID** *100 †20

KOTTMEIER, Peter Klaus. ■ 37861 #407-16-1950 L1960 **PDS** *071 †85

STEVENSON, Wm Frederick. ■ 37861 #038-40-1945 L1945 **FM EM** *072

STURDIVANT, Tara Lewynn. 8655 RUTLEDGE PIKE 37861 #027-01-1990 L1993 **FM** *020 †18

TEAGUE, Dale Alexander. ■ 37861 #047-06-1954 L1955 **OPH** *071

ZIMERMAN, Joseph. ■ 37861 #869-07-1951 L1953 **FM IM** *071 †18

SAVANNAH – HARDIN

ARMETTA, Nancy A. 765 FLORENCE RD, STE A 38372 #047-07-1984 L1985 **FM GPM** *020 †18

CONWAY, William Francis. 150 E END DR 38372 #038-40-1974 L2001 **EM OS** *020 †20

DAVIS, Gigi Wood. 115 PATTERSON RD 38372 #028-79-1988, ▲ L1990 **FM** *020 †18 ‡

DE SANDRE, Frank Arthur. 1900 WAYNE RD 38372 #016-11-1945 L A1 38372 **OBG** *020 †30

GREENE, Richard Stephen. 910 WAYNE RD 38372 #047-06-1978 L1979 **GS** *020 †85

HUFANA, Donna M. 765 FLORENCE RD, STE A 38372 #748-02-1987 L1996 **IM** *020 †20

KIRSCH, Scott Wood. 150 GUINN ST 38372 #047-20-2004 L2006 **FM** *020 †18

KLEIN, Timothy Robt. ■ 38372 #001-02-1984 L1987 **IM** *020

LARD, Janet K. 2020B WAYNE RD 38372 #047-06-1982 L1983 **IM** *020

LAY, John Danl. 855 WAYNE RD 38372 #047-06-1961 L1962 **FM** *020

LULL, Charles Roberts. ■ 38372 #047-06-1972 L1972 **DR VS** *020 †80

MITCHELL, Gregory Charles. 105 DAVIS ST 38372 #047-06-1996 L1998 **FM** *020 †18

NEWHOUSE, Patricia Ann. 150 E END DR 38372 #017-20-1981 L2006 **PD** *020 †55

ROE, Thomas Vance. 114 WILLIAMS ST 38372 #047-20-1956 L1957 **FM GPM** *071 †18

SMITH, Chadwick Parrish. 765 FLORENCE RD, STE A 38372 #047-06-2001 L2005 **GS** *020

SMITH, Michael Lewis. 1212 WAYNE RD 38372 #047-06-1973 L1973 **GP GS** *020

THAYER, Gilbert M. 105 DAVIS ST 38372 #047-06-1993 L1994 **OBG FM** *020 †30

THOMAS, Howard W. 150 GUINN ST 38372 #047-06-1954 L1955 **FM** *020

THOMAS, James Howard. 145 PICKWICK ST 38372 #047-06-1974 L1974 **GP** *020

SELMER – MCNAIRY

ARISTORENAS, Juan Tan, Jr. 705 E POPLAR AVE 38375 #748-01-1968 L1974 **GP GS** *020

BAKEER, Mohammed Said A. 714 FEDERAL DR 38375 #915-04-1973 L1984 **GS** *020

BARTZ, William R. ■ 38375 #028-78-2004, ▲ L2005 **FM** *020 †18

COFIE, Daniel Q. 705 E POPLAR AVE, ATTN: MEDICAL STAFF OFFICE 38375 #412-01-1981 L1999 **END** *020 †20

DICKSON, Kenneth L. 705 E POPLAR AVE 38375 #047-06-1975 L1977 **IM GS** *020

FEENEY, Sandra Nichole. 699 E POPLAR AVE 38375 #047-06-2000 L2005 **MPD** *020 ‡

FODERINGHAM, Nia Malene. 705 E POPLAR AVE, MCNAIRY REGIONAL HOSPITAL 38375 #041-12-2005 L2007 **EM** *100

GALIWANGO, Charles K. 705 E POPLAR AVE, MEDICAL STAFF OFFICE 38375 #905-01-1979 L1993 **AN** *020

GANAPATHY, Lakshmanan. 211 E COURT AVE 38375 #495-42-1972 L1986 **OBG** *020 †30

LINDER, Timothy Francis. 1 PRIME CARE DR, PRIME CARE MEDICAL CENTER, 38375 #047-06-1982 L1982 **FM** *020 †18

PEELER, Harry Lee. 203 PHARR AVE 38375 #047-06-1957 L1957 **FM GS** *020 †18
REDDY, Aparna Dubbaka. ■ 38375 #047-07-2004 *100
REDDY, Dubbaka Devender. 705 E POPLAR AVE 38375 #495-21-1969 L1979 **PD** *020
RODRIGUEZ, James Jay. ■ 38375 #048-13-1974 L1983 **IM PUD** *075
SMITH, James Hagy. 132 HOUSTON AVE, SMITHS CLINIC 38375 #047-06-1955 L1955 **GP** *020
STRASBERG, Gary D. 705 E POPLAR AVE 38375 #047-06-1976 L1976 **IM** *020 †20
WILLIAMS, Arthur Lee, II. 705 E POPLAR AVE, MCNAIRY REGIONAL HOSPITAL 38375 #047-07-1997 L2000 **FM** *020 †18

SEVIERVILLE – SEVIER

ANDERSON, Jennifer Lynn. ■ 37862 #047-06-2004 **OBG** *012
BOZEMAN, Chas Howard, II. 641 MIDDLE CREEK RD, CHARLES H BOZEMAN II MD 37862 #047-06-1975 L1976 **FM** *020 †18 ‡
BRADLEY, Jerry Wayne. 709 MIDDLE CREEK RD 37862 #047-06-1982 L1982 **EM** *020 †16
BURKE, Curtis Lewis. 675 MIDDLE CREEK RD, PRACTICE 37862 #047-06-1999 L2002 **FM** *020 †18
BUTT, Javed Aslam. ■ 37876 #704-09-1972 L1978 **GE IM** *020 †20
CARTER, Rodney G. 1017 MIDDLE CREEK RD 37862 #654-01-1990 L1998 **FM** *020 †18
DRONEN, Steven C. 1319 LICKLOG HOLLOW RD 37876 #016-11-1977 L2001 **EM** *020 †16
DURAND, Julie R. 816 MIDDLE CREEK RD, MIDDLE CREEK EYE CLINIC 37862 #045-01-1985 L1991 **OPH** *071 †35
FRY, William Justice. 1124 FOX MEADOWS BLVD, C WHEATLEY MD 37862 #047-20-1999 L2000 **FM** *020 †18
GREESON, Gordon Spencer. 124 N HENDERSON AVE, CENTER 37862 #047-06-1974 L1975 **CHP P** *020 †18
GRIBBLE, Gary Wayne. 2190 WINFIELD DUNN PKWY 37876 #047-06-1987 L1988 **FM** *020 †18
GUERRA, Julio Cesar. 1102 FOXWOOD DR STE 1 37862 #005-12-1987 L1991 **OBG** *020 †30
GULYASH, Joseph J F. ■ 37862 #016-11-1944 L1953 **OPH** *071 †35
GYURIK, Catherine E. 124 N HENDERSON AVE, CENTER 37862 #065-09-1966 L1973 **P** *020 †75
HANGGI, Matthew C. 1108 FOX MEADOWS BLVD, STE 2 37862 #047-20-2000 L2004 **D** *020 †15
HARRIS, Linda K Wahl. 208 PRINCE ST, (ALL CARE FAMILY PRACTICE) 37862 #048-13-1991 L1996 **FM** *020 †18
HAYS, Jack Mizell. ■ 37862 #047-06-1946 L1947 **P** *071
HIGGINS, Laura Elizabeth. 1124 FOX MEADOWS BLVD 37862 #001-02-1980 L1981 **GS VS** *020
HOLLINGSWORTH, James E. 1115 BLANTON DR 37862 #027-06-1975 L1998 **PD** *020 †55
HORTON, Deborah Elaine. 227 CEDAR ST 37862 #020-02-1996 L1999 **FM** *020 †18
HURST, Robin Allison. 631 MIDDLE CREEK RD 37862 #047-06-2003 L2006 **FM** *020 †18
JACOBS, John Clifton, Jr. ■ 37862 #047-06-1965 L1965 **R** *020
JORDAN, James Daryl. 958 DOLLY PARTON PKWY 37862 #011-04-1986 L1996 **ORS U** *020
JUSTICE, Kenneth Lee. ■ 37862 #654-01-1993 L1998 **FM** *020 †18
KHANNA, Manju. 124 N HENDERSON AVE, CENTER 37862 #496-07-1978 L1995 **P** *100 †75
KIDD, Charles Edward. 679 MIDDLE CREEK RD 37862 #047-06-1968 L1969 **GS** *020
KING, Jeffrey Scott. ■ 37876 #020-12-1997 L2001 **GS** *020 †85
KNOPP, Frank. ■ 37862 #048-02-1956 L1990 **GYN** *020
KOCHERT, Charles Joseph. 709 MIDDLE CREEK RD 37862 #017-20-1994 L1999 **EM FM** *020 †18
KOERTEN, James Michael. 1102 FOXWOOD DR, STE 1 37862 #056-06-1981 L1985 **OBG** *020 †30
LA MOTTE, Billie. ■ 37862 #012-01-1952 **DR R** *071
LIDDELL, Norman Eugene. 1240 FOX MEADOWS BLVD, STE 1 37862 #306-01-1983 L1996 **CD OPH** *020
LIEBERMAN-TELLEZ, Laraine. 124 N HENDERSON AVE, CENTER 37862 #847-08-1984 L1991 **P** *020
LINN, Frank. ■ 37876 #025-01-1955 L1956 **P IM** *071 †75
LITTLETON, Eric James. 631 MIDDLE CREEK RD, SUITE 5 & 6 37862 #047-06-1994 L2000 **FM** *020 †18
LOVE, Richard L, Jr. 715 MIDDLE CREEK RD 37862 #047-20-1993 L1997 **OBG** *020 †30
MC GAHA, Samuel W. 1235 DOLLY PARTON PKWY 37862 #047-06-1976 L1976 **FM** *020 †18
PARNELL, Donald H, Jr. 679 MIDDLE CREEK RD 37862 #047-06-1994 L1999 **GS** *020
PATEL, Anand Natvarlal. 709 MIDDLE CREEK RD 37862 #048-16-1999 L2003 **MPD** *020 †20,55
PATTERSON, William David. 1108 FOX MEADOWS BLVD, STE 1 37862 #047-05-1974 L1976 **CD IM** *020 †20
PETERSON, Glenn R. 124 N HENDERSON AVE, CENTER 37862 #010-02-1975 L1986 **P** *020 †75
RAZZAK, Ammar. 1124 FOX MEADOWS BLVD, AMMAR RAZZAK MD 37862 #012-01-1993 L1994 **IM** *020 †20
RIEDEL, Roger Aaron. 629 MIDDLE CREEK RD, CONSULTANTS PC 37862 #030-06-1997 L2002 **IC** *020 †20
SARASTI, Ana M. 124 N HENDERSON AVE, CENTER 37862 #264-10-1985 L1995 **P** *020
SHENKMAN, Michael. 707 DOLLY PARTON PKWY 37862 #561-17-1984 L2001 **IM** *020 †20
SMITH, Steven Mc Clay. 1110 VILLAGE DR 37862 #026-04-1978 L1984 **ORS** *020 †40
SONNER, John Louis, II. 675 MIDDLE CREEK RD 37862 #047-06-1962 L1962 **FM EM** *071 †18
SPURLOCK, Steven Randall. 1104 FOXWOOD DR, STE 1 37862 #047-06-1993 L1994 **FM** *020 †18
TOLLEY, Vincent Blane. 675 MIDDLE CREEK RD, PRACTICE 37862 #047-06-1973 L1973 **FM EM** *020 †18
TRAYNELIS, Christian L. 629 MIDDLE CREEK RD, EAST TN UROLGY 37862 #055-01-1990 L2000 **U GS** *072 †95
VAN ARSDALL, James R. 816 MIDDLE CREEK RD 37862 #047-06-1952 L1952 **OPH** *071 †35
WEAR, Edward Robt. 811 MIDDLE CREEK RD 37862 #047-06-1977 L1979 **IM** *020 †20
WECKESSER, Donald N. 1105 OAK CLUSTER DR 37862 #654-01-1993 L1996 **FM** *020 †18
WENINGER, Marvin G. 124 N HENDERSON AVE, CENTER 37862 #019-02-1971 L1974 **P** *020 ‡
WHEATLEY, Hubert Carl. 1124 FOX MEADOWS BLVD, C WHEATLEY MD 37862 #047-06-1978 L1979 **IM NEP** *020 †20
WHITON, Alan Louis. 1110 VILLAGE DR 37862 #026-04-1979 L1985 **ORS** *020 †40
WORDEN, Betty J Beauge. ■ 37862 #041-07-1952 L1976 **AN** *075

SEWANEE – FRANKLIN

CARUTHERS, Laird David. PO BOX 3333, 266 RATTLESNAKE SPRING LN 37375 #004-01-1983 L2003 **EM FM** *020 †18

CROOM, Frederick Hailey. SPO BOX 1248 37375 #035-01-1993 **PTH** *100
EVANS, Amy Hurst. 1310 UNIVERSITY AVE 37375 #036-01-1989 L1994 **PD** *020 †55
HILL, Elizabeth Wolfe. PO BOX 861 37375 #047-05-1972 L1975 **P CHP** *020 †75
JACKSON, Harold P. ■ 37375 #047-05-1945 L1945 **PD** *072 †55
KOELLA, Louis Edmund. 1314 UNIVERSITY AVE 37375 #047-20-1999 L2001 **FM** *020 †18
OSTROM, Anna Delores. 735 UNIVERSITY AVE, SPO 37383 #001-02-2006 **PD** *012
OWSIANY, Leonard Jos. 1260 UNIVERSITY AVE 37375 #046-01-1987 L1993 **FM** *020
PETRILLA, Diane Louise. 1314 UNIVERSITY AVE 37375 #010-02-1982 L1986 **FM** *020 †18 ‡
PETTES, Christy Lynn. ■ 37375 #047-06-2006 **FP** *012

SEYMOUR – SEVIER

BEAM, Robert Kenneth. 10622 CHAPMAN HWY 37865 #047-06-2000 L2001 **FM** *020 †18
BRADY, Paul Christopher. 11546 CHAPMAN HWY 37865 #036-05-1999 L2005 **ORS** *020 †40
CASTLE, Christopher Ellis. 10341 CHAPMAN HWY 37865 #047-20-1986 L1987 **FM** *020 †18
GOYNE, Kathleen Anne. 1016 IC KING RD, BROOKHAVEN RETREAT 37865 #005-12-1988 L1993 **P** *020 †75
HALL, Steven Fredrick. 10622 CHAPMAN HWY 37865 #047-06-1991 L1992 **FM** *020 †18 ‡
HARSH, Anil. 11616 CHAPMAN HWY 37865 #495-30-1991 L1996 **PD** *020 †55
HODGE, Frederick Wm. 11616 CHAPMAN HWY 37865 #047-06-1963 L1964 **PD** *020 †55
JACKSON, Robert Cecil. 11546 CHAPMAN HWY 37865 #047-06-1973 L1973 **ORS** *020 †40
LAKATOSH, Donald Andrew. 11560 CHAPMAN HWY, STE 1 37865 #051-07-1984 L1998 **PM PMM** *020 †60
LEGNER, Stanley Gayle. ■ 37865 #028-34-1947 L1948 **GP** *020
LETHCO, Gary Wayne. 126 PEACOCK CT, STE 2 37865 #047-06-1981 L1981 **FM PLI** *020 †18
MAYS, William Kendall. 10731 CHAPMAN HWY 37865 #047-20-1996 L1997 **FM** *020 †18
MC DOWELL, Jill Annette. 212 PHOENIX CT, STE 1 37865 #047-06-1994 L1997 **PD** *020 †55
MENDEZ, David Enrique. 212 PHOENIX CT STE 1 37865 #045-04-1998 L2001 **PD** *020 †55
MEYER, Melissa Witte. 11616 CHAPMAN HWY 37865 #047-06-1997 L1999 **PD** *020 †55
MOORE, Robert Saylor, Jr. 11657 CHAPMAN HWY 37865 #047-06-1991 L1992 **FM** *020 †18
NAYLOR, Paul Thos. 11546 CHAPMAN HWY 37865 #047-06-1985 L1990 **ORS** *020 †40
PARSONS, Rick. 11546 CHAPMAN HWY 37865 #036-08-1989 L1994 **ORS** *020
PAYNE, Wesley Kevin. 11657 CHAPMAN HWY 37865 #047-06-1985 L1987 **FM** *020 †18
PESUT, Jean Anne. 11546 CHAPMAN HWY 37865 #047-06-1999 L2005 **OFA** *020
REAT, Jean-Francois P. 11546 CHAPMAN HWY 37865 #048-04-1992 L1997 **ORS** *020 †40
RENFREE, Timothy John. 11546 CHAPMAN HWY 37865 #048-14-1999 L2005 **HS** *020 †40
RUTH, Alex. 11616 CHAPMAN HWY 37865 #047-06-1966 L1967 **PD** *020 †55
SCHIRO, Richelle. 10731 CHAPMAN HWY 37865 #011-04-1996 L1997 **FM** *020 †18
STALCUP, Clay Eugene. 10731 CHAPMAN HWY 37865 #047-06-2002 L2003 **FM** *020 †18
STALCUP, Staci K. 10731 CHAPMAN HWY 37865 #055-02-2002 L2004 **FM** *020 †18

SHARPS CHAPEL – UNION

SWISHER, Robert Wayne. ■ 37866 #051-04-1971 L1972 **GE** *020 †20

SHELBYVILLE – BEDFORD

ADAMS, Lynette Michelle. 1612 N MAIN ST, STE B 37160 #063-01-1995 L1997 **FM** *020 †18
AMONETTE, Robert Stanton. 845 UNION ST, BEDFORD RADIOLOGY LLC 37160 #047-20-2001 L2004 **DR** *020 †80
ATALLA, Nabil. 841 UNION ST STE 204, MEDICAL ARTS BUILDING #2 37160 #561-01-1980 L1993 **N** *020
BAGAI, Jayant. 1701 N MAIN ST, STE E 37160 #495-45-1995 L2002 **CD** *020 †20
BAGGA, Sudhir. 841 UNION ST, STE 106 37160 #495-45-1976 L2004 **FPG IMG** *020 †18 ‡
BARBEE, John Saml. ■ 37160 #016-11-1983 L2002 **EM FM** *020 †18
BARNES, Donald D. 841 UNION ST, STE F 37160 #047-06-1953 L1953 **OBG** *071 †30
BAYLOR, Debra M. 841 UNION ST, STE C 37160 #649-14-1987 L2007 **IM** *020 †18
BEAVERS, Lana Sharon. 885 UNION ST 37160 #047-06-1973 L1974 **FM OBG** *020 †18
BLANTON, Terrell Davis. ■ 37160 #027-01-1962 L1996 **OTO** *071 †45
CANONICO, Domenic Michael. 310 COLLOREDO BLVD, STE B 37160 #047-05-1987 L1988 **OTO PDO** *020 †45
CLARK, A Kent. 841 UNION ST STE A 37160 #064-01-1979 L1996 *020
CREAN, Jan L. 841 UNION ST STE K, OB & GYN MED ARTS BLDG 37160 #041-07-1990 L2002 **OBG OBS** *020 †30
GALVEZ, Pedro De Leon. 845 UNION ST, BEDFORD CNTRY MED CTR 37160 #748-01-1968 L1975 **GS PS** *020
GARRARD, Clifford L, Jr. 841 UNION ST, STE 201 37160 #047-05-1962 L1977 **CD** *020 †20
GEORGE, Wilburn Edwin, Jr. 1701 N MAIN ST, STE E 37160 #047-06-1976 L1977 **CD IM** *020 †20
GUPTA, Dinesh K. 1701 N MAIN ST, STE E 37160 #495-69-1982 L1993 **CD** *020 †20
ILARDE, Aldo Arrastia. 841 UNION ST STE 200 37160 #748-02-1984 L1995 **END** *020 †20
JAYAKODY, Frank Lorenz. 1701 N MAIN ST, STE C 37160 #220-01-1968 L1976 **FM EM** *020 †16,18
JOHNSON, Sue Welch. 841 UNION ST 37160 #047-06-1953 L1955 **FM** *071 †18
JOVANOVICH, Daniel Bruce. 1701 N MAIN ST, STE E 37160 #041-09-1982 L2003 **CD IM** *020 †20
KACZMARSKA, Barbara F. 880 COLLOREDO BLVD 37160 #759-10-1973 L1996 **PD** *020 †55
LUDWIG, Ann Marie. 310 COLLOREDO BLVD 37160 #026-04-1982 L1983 **FM** *020 †18
MAGNUSON, Carol L. 1701 N MAIN ST, STE D 37160 #047-06-1976 L1984 **PD** *020 †55
MAINWARING, Mark Geoffrey. 1610 N MAIN ST, STE B 37160 #025-07-1992 L2001 **HO IM** *020 †20
MELSON, Danny Lee. 1701 N MAIN ST STE B 37160 #047-06-1978 L1979 **PD GP** *020
MILLER, Stephen H. 841 UNION ST, STE 110 37160 #064-01-1991 L1996 *020
MONAJJEM, Navid. 841 UNION ST, STE 207 37160 #038-40-1991 L2006 **GS** *020 †85
MOYD, Linda. 841 UNION ST, STE E 37160 #038-41-1999 L2007 **PD** *020
NEWTON, Dale C. 845 UNION ST 37160 #047-07-1981 L1981 **DR RNR** *020 †80
PARAWAN, W Christina S. 841 UNION ST, STE 108 37160 #748-11-1982 L2002 **FM** *020 †18
PARTYKA, Scott Robt. 845 UNION ST 37160 #016-43-1990 L2002 **DR** *020 †80
RICHARDS, Aubrey Thos. 845 UNION ST 37160 #047-05-1958 L1959 **GP** *071 †18
RUPARD, Joseph Howard. 883 UNION ST 37160 #047-05-1990 L1993 **FM** *020
SALIBA, Norman Rudolph. 845 UNION ST 37160 #012-01-1958 L1973 **GP FM** *020
SCHERFF, Albert Hermann. 845 UNION ST RM 234, SLEEP DISORDERS & RESEARCH 37160 #001-06-1987 L1997 **PUD SME** *020 †20

SCHULL, Lawrence G, Jr. 841 UNION ST, STE 106 37160 #047-05-1978 L2004 IM *020 †20
SELLS, Samuel P, Jr. 1701 N MAIN ST STE A 37160 #047-06-1976 L1977 FM OM *020
SELLS, Samuel Riley, III. 1701 N MAIN ST, STE A 37160 #047-20-1986 L1987 P PYG *020 †75
SRIHARAN, Sivapragasam. 841 UNION ST, STE 205 37160 #220-02-1973 L1997 PUD CCM *020 †20
STIMPSON, Charles Lee. 1701 N MAIN ST, STE D 37160 #047-06-1978 L1984 FM *020 †18
STOCKING, Sharon Lea. 310 COLLOREDO BLVD 37160 #025-07-1984 L1994 R *020 †80
STOUT, Julianne. 260 WOMACK RD, COOL SPRINGS INTERNAL MEDI 37160 #017-20-1995 L1997 MPD *020 †20,55
STUBBLEFIELD, Carl Thos. MEDICAL ARTS BUILDING 37160 #047-06-1956 L1956 R *071 †80
TAMULA, Alma Macatangay. 841 UNION ST, STE G 37160 #748-10-1986 L1998 FM *020 †18
WADE, Jeffrey Trent. 845 UNION ST 37160 #017-20-1988 L2000 R *020 †80
WEBER-HANSON, Christiane. 310 COLLOREDO BLVD 37160 #409-23-1984 L1998 OBG *020
WIECK, Dennis Jos. 841 UNION ST, STE 202 37160 #047-06-1986 L1989 OBG *020 †30

SIGNAL MOUNTAIN – HAMILTON

ANDREESCU, Dorin. ■ 37377 #781-01-1994 L2005 IM *020 †20
ANDREESCU, Oana Ligia. ■ 37377 #781-01-1995 L2005 IM *020 †20
BAKER, Robert Keith. 4 BIG ROCK RD 37377 #032-01-1999 L2006 OPH *020 †35
BLACKWELL, Jamie Len. ■ 37377 #047-06-1988 L2005 PD PEM *020 †55
BRANTLY, Edmund Brook. ■ 37377 #047-06-1957 L1962 R NM *071 †80
BROWN, Kimberley Louise. ■ 37377 #048-02-1981 L1997 PTH *040 †50
BROWN, Peter J I. 24 MOUNTAIN ORCHARD PATH 37377 #065-06-1975 L1995 P *020
CARLTON, Kimberly. ■ 37377 #012-01-1984 L1991 FP *012
CRANWELL, John Dakin. 2600 TAFT HWY 37377 #047-06-1975 L1975 IM *020
CULLER, Elizabeth Edwards. ■ 37377 #045-01-2001 L2006 PTH *020 †50
DARKE, James Paul. 1303 TAFT HWY 37377 #047-06-2001 L2003 PD *020 †55
DAVIDOFF, Alan Brett. 320 CREEKSHIRE DR, MEDICAL PRACTICE MANAGEMEN 37377 #035-15-1980 L1990 R *020 †80
DE BOER, Andries. ■ 37377 #660-04-1953 L1959 OM GP *071 †70
ELLIS, John Clyde. ■ 37377 #047-06-1952 L1953 GP *020 †18
FRANCIS, Henry M, Jr. ■ 37377 #010-03-1982 L1986 OBG *020 †30
GINSBERG, Joel Fine. ■ 37377 #012-01-1975 L1980 PUD IM *071 †20
GOODIN, James William. ■ 37377 #047-06-2007 GS *012
HAMATY, Daniel. ■ 37377 #041-09-1953 L2007 PMM HOS *072 †20
HATCH, Elaine Watson. 1303 TAFT HWY 37377 #047-20-1988 L1989 PD *020 †55
HENNESSEN, John A, Jr. ■ 37377 #035-09-1948 L1965 OS ORS *071 †40
HILL, Russell Frank. ■ 37377 #012-01-1950 L1980 AN *020 †05
IRELAND, Charles R. ■ 37377 #012-01-1950 L1980 IM *071
JIA, Hongchen. ■ 37377 #243-29-1987 L2008 HMP *062 †50
KINGTON, John Michael. PO BOX 397 37377 #047-06-1969 L1969 P OS *020
MILBURN, Joseph Leslie. 802 SIGNAL MOUNTAIN BLVD 37377 #047-06-1958 L1958 GS *071 †85
MILLER, Beville Janelle. ■ 37377 #047-06-1977 L1978 PHP *030
MORGAN, Rufus S. ■ 37377 #047-06-1950 L1951 EM *071
NELSON, Merrill Frederick. ■ 37377 #016-02-1947 L1954 IM CD *071 †20
NOLAN, Paul Vernon. ■ 37377 #023-01-1948 L1960 PHP OM *071
OGLESBY, Jane Millard. 1303 TAFT HWY 37377 #047-06-1985 L1987 PD *020 †55
OSMUNDSEN, Robert N. ■ 37377 #035-45-1942 L1962 OM AS *072
PIEZ, Charles Wm. 1435 E BROW RD 37377 #038-06-1979 L1984 DR *020 †80 ‡
PLAYFAIR, John Andrew. ■ 37377 #065-05-1953 L1982 *030
POLLARD, Theresa Ann. 100 JAMES BLVD STE 401, (AT ALEXIAN VILLAGE) 37377 #045-04-1997 L2002 IM *020 †20
RIGSBY, Lonard C, III. 501 HATHAWAY DR 37377 #001-02-1977 L2000 IM *020 †20
RUSSELL, Don Jere. ■ 37377 #047-06-1954 L1954 PS *071 †85,65
SOTTONG, Philipp Curtis. ■ 37377 #035-45-1945 L1954 P PM *071 †75
STALLINGS, Susan Ashley. ■ 37377 #020-02-1996 L2002 PD *074 †55
SWANN, Nat Henderson. ■ 37377 #036-01-1954 L1958 IM *071
TALBERT, Malissa Gobbell. ■ 37377 #047-06-1988 L1989 RHU IM *100 †20
TEDESCO, Jason Michael. ■ 37377 #036-01-2007 PTH *012

SMITHVILLE – DEKALB

BLEVINS, Melvin Lee. 520 W MAIN ST 37166 #047-06-1972 L1973 FM *020 ‡
DINGLE, Denise R. 518 W MAIN ST STE A 37166 #017-20-1983 L1991 OBG *020
JONES, Richard Loren. ■ 37166 #004-01-1959 L1959 GP *071
PETTY, Ralph David. ■ 37166 #016-11-1961 L1995 FM OBG *071 †18
RHODY, Jack Randell. 302 N CONGRESS BLVD, FAMILY MEDICAL CENTER 37166 #047-06-1985 L1986 FM *020 †18
RHODY, Kevin Ryan. 302 N CONGRESS BLVD, FAMILY MEDICAL CENTER 37166 #047-06-1998 L2001 FM *020 †18
SCHENK, William Darryl. 518 W MAIN ST, STE A 37166 #030-05-1981 L1985 OPH *020 †35
TWILLA, John Kenneth. 302 N CONGRESS BLVD 37166 #047-06-1955 L1956 GP OS *071
WALL, James Clinton, Jr. 518 W MAIN ST STE C 37166 #047-06-1981 L1981 GP *020

SMYRNA – RUTHERFORD

ADAMS, Austin Anthony. 741 PRESIDENT PL, STE 110 37167 #047-07-1993 L1994 GP *020
ADEDOKUN, Muyiwa. 513 ENON SPRINGS RD E 37167 #047-07-1983 L1998 GS *020 †85
AHMAD, Saleh. 131 MAYFIELD DR 37167 #160-01-1977 L2001 P *020
ALIYU, Muktar Hassan. ■ 37167 #690-03-1994 L2008 GPM *012
BEATTY, Douglas Craig. 693 PRESIDENT PL, STE 103 37167 #005-14-1981 L1994 EM *020
BROWDER, Carey Foree. 515 STONECREST PKWY, STE 230 37167 #654-01-1983 L1996 FM *020 †18
BROWDY, Carole Kay. ■ 37167 #048-02-1977 L1999 OM *071 †20
BYRNES, John Mitchell. 115 ENON SPRINGS RD E, JETWAY AVIATION 37167 #748-10-1981 L1985 IM CCM *020 ‡
CALLAHAN, Barry Scott. 300 STONECREST BLVD, STE 230 37167 #047-06-1990 L2000 HS ORS *020 †40
CAMPBELL, Maura Lynne. 300 STONECREST BLVD, STE 155 37167 #036-01-1988 L1994 RO PLM *020 †80

CARDEN, Kelly Anna. 300 STONECREST BLVD, STE 370 37167 #047-06-1996 L2007 PCC CCM *020 †20
CARPENTER, Kenneth Jos. 1332 HAZELWOOD DR 37167 #047-05-1992 L1994 GE *020 †20
CLENDENIN, Robert Eli, III. 300 STONECREST BLVD, STE 300 37167 #047-06-1987 L1988 PM OM *020 †60
COBB, Peter Frederick. 300 STONECREST BLVD, PHYSICIANS 37167 #035-06-1998 L2001 FM *020 †18
CONATSER, Chad Alan. ■ 37167 #047-07-2007 IM *012
CONVERSE, George Marquis, IV. 300 STONECREST BLVD, MIDDLE TENNESSEE EAR NOSE 37167 #051-01-1996 L2002 OTO *020 †45
CORBAN, John Chas. ■ 37167 #047-06-1963 L1963 PHP GP *071
DHAR, Anitha S. 537 STONECREST PKWY, DHAR FAMILY MED STE 100 37167 #495-99-1990 L1999 FM *020 †18
DICKINSON, Mark Thomas. 300 STONECREST BLVD, STE 320 37167 #005-12-1997 L2003 U *020 †95
DRAKE, Debra Leann. 713A PRESIDENT PL 37167 #047-07-1998 L2002 FM *020 †18
FLETCHER, Suzanne M R. 460 9TH AVE, TENN REHAB CTR 37167 #566-01-1979 L1982 IM PM *020
GARVIN, Richard Paul. 351 QUECREEK CIR 37167 #308-07-1982 L1986 EM OS *020 †20
GILBERT, Felisa Lashun. 741 PRESIDENT PL, STE 200 37167 #047-06-1997 L2005 MPD *020 †55,20
GOCO, Paulino Edwardo. 300 STONECREST BLVD, MIDDLE TENNESSEE EAR NOSE 37167 #010-02-1992 L2002 FPS OTO *020 †45
GONZALEZ, Debra Ann. 301 WOLVERINE TRL, STE 100 37167 #035-20-1987 L1995 OTO *020 †45
HEATH, Jack Kevin. 983 NISSAN DR 37167 #021-01-1993 L1996 FM *020 †18
HERRING, Robert William, Jr. 429 NISSAN DR, STE 103 37167 #047-06-1980 L1986 GE IM *030 †20
HILGENHURST, Charles Graf. 1177 ROCK SPRINGS RD, PRECISION PAIN CARE 37167 #016-01-1983 L2004 AN *020 †05
HIXSON, Joshua Michael. 300 STONECREST BLVD, PHYSICIANS 37167 #012-01-1999 L2005 FM *020 †18
HUDDLESTON, Richard C. 300 STONECREST BLVD, STE 490 37167 #048-04-1976 L1995 OBG *020 †30
HUGGINS, Teresa G. 211 COMMERCE DR 37167 #047-06-1981 L1981 FM *020 †18
IKEJIANI, Afam Chukwuchem. 301 WOLVERINE TRL, STE 200 37167 #690-04-1984 L1994 OBG *020 †10
IKEJIANI, Olisaeloka O. 437 NISSAN DR STE 50 37167 #017-20-1995 L2000 OBG *020
JASKO, John Joseph. 300 STONECREST BLVD, STE 300 37167 #041-12-1997 L2003 ORS *020 †20
JONES, Cindi Elise. 300 STONECREST BLVD, STE 110 37167 #047-06-2000 L2003 IM *020 †20 ‡
JOYNER, Kyle Steven. 300 STONECREST BLVD, STE 300 37167 #048-15-2000 L2006 HS *020
KATKURI, Jithander Reedy. 713 PRESIDENT PL 37167 #495-57-1977 L1999 FM *020 †18
KAUFMAN, Alan Joel. 200 STONECREST BLVD 37167 #165-03-1979 L1983 R *020 †40
KLINE, Mary Frank. 515 STONECREST PKWY, STE 150 37167 #048-26-2001 L2003 PD *020 †55
KOZINSKI, Bryan Joseph. 300 STONECREST BLVD, PHYSICIANS 37167 #038-44-1999 L2001 FM *020 †20
KUBINA, Anne. 983 NISSAN DR, NISSAN NORTH AMERICA, INC. 37167 #041-07-1987 L2006 FM *020 †18,70
LANGONE, Susan Elizabeth. 741 PRESIDENT PL 37167 #035-06-1996 L1999 PD *020 †55
LARSEN, Jeffrey Arthur. 300 STONECREST BLVD # 360 37167 #027-01-1995 L1998 GS *020 †85
LIMBAUGH, Susan Robbins. 300 STONECREST BLVD, STE 110 37167 #048-02-2000 L2003 IM *020 †20
LOLEH, Samer. 515 STONECREST PKWY, STE 150 37167 #875-01-1996 L2003 PD *020 †55
LOWERY, Edwin Ray, Jr. 300 STONECREST BLVD, STE 300 37167 #047-06-1973 L1974 ORS *020 †40
LYNCH, Lori Ann. 200 STONECREST BLVD 37167 #047-06-2000 L2003 EM *020 †16
MANGIONE, Nelson J. 300 STONECREST BLVD, STE 410 37167 #011-04-1989 L1990 CD *020 †20
MC COLLUM, Joshua Mark. 741 PRESIDENT PL STE 200 37167 #047-06-1998 L1999 MPD *020 †20,55
MILLIGAN, Corbi Dianell. 300 STONECREST BLVD, STE 290 37167 #047-06-2000 L2004 MPD *020 †20 ‡
MOLETTE, Annalouise O. 739 PRESIDENT PL 37167 #047-07-1996 L2000 PM *020 †60
MONTEMURO, Anthony. 300 STONECREST BLVD, STE 455 37167 #041-02-1989 L2003 GE *020 †20
MORGAN, Susan L. 741 PRESIDENT PL 37167 #036-08-1987 L1990 PD *020 †55
MYERS, Willie J, Jr. 400 ENON SPRINGS RD 37167 #047-07-1985 L1988 FM *020
NICHOLS, Robert Hiram, Jr. ■ 37167 #047-06-2006 L2007 IM *012
NWANKWO, Ukpong E. 121 MAYFIELD DR 37167 #690-01-1987 L1999 IM *020 †20
PAFFRATH, Jeffrey A. 200 STONECREST BLVD, STE 375 37167 #041-02-1989 L1997 OTO *020 †45
PATTERSON, Donald Parker. 300 STONECREST BLVD, STE 110 37167 #001-02-2000 L2002 IM *020 †20
PERKINS, Matthew Lane. 741 PRESIDENT PL, STE 200 37167 #020-02-1994 L1998 IM PD *020 †20,55
PHILLIPS, Heather Nicole. 741 PRESIDENT PL, STE 200 37167 #001-02-2003 L2007 MPD *020 †20,55
PINTO-CISNEROS, Socrates. PO BOX 215 37167 #275-01-1954 L1966 GS GP *020
PULLIAS, Mitchell Andrew. 741 PRESIDENT PL, STE 200 37167 #047-06-1999 L2001 MPD *020 †20,55
RICAFORT, Rachel M. 515 STONECREST PKWY, STE 150 37167 #422-01-1997 L2000 PD *020 †55 ‡
RILEY, Louis Thos. 300 STONECREST BLVD, STE 490 37167 #020-12-1980 L1994 OBG FM *020 †18,30
ROGERS, Richard Alan. 300 STONECREST BLVD, STE 300 37167 #047-06-1978 L1979 ORS *020 †40
ROTH, Jason Kyle. ■ 37167 #047-06-2006 L2007 DR *012
RUDD, John Danl. 301 WOLVERINE TRL, STE 100 37167 #047-06-1980 L1980 IM *020 †20
RUNGEE, James Lundin, Jr. 300 STONECREST BLVD, STE 300 37167 #047-06-1985 L1990 ORS OSM *020 †40
SCHWARTZ, Gary Allen. 115 ENON SPRINGS RD 37167 #025-01-1979 L1983 IM EM *020 †20
SEE, Tahnya Kathy Dunn. 739 PRESIDENT PL, STE 140 37167 #038-06-1982 L1988 FM *020
SHELTON, Ben Allen. 211 COMMERCE DR 37167 #047-06-1954 L1954 GS GP *071

SHIBAYAMA, Juris Juris. 300 STONECREST BLVD, STE 300 37167 #016-11-2000 L2006 OSS *020

SIPE, Catherine Anne. 741 PRESIDENT PL 37167 #036-05-2002 L2005 PD *020 †55

THOMPSON, Christopher O. 300 STONECREST BLVD, PHYSICIANS 37167 #047-06-1994 L1996 FM *020 †18

UDOM, David Isonguyo. 611 POTOMAC PL, STE 105 37167 #690-12-1990 L1999 IM *020 †20

VAUGHAN, Roderick Andrew. 300 STONECREST BLVD, STE 300 37167 #047-06-1991 L1992 ORS *020 †40

WARD, Tija Letice. 301 WOLVERINE TRL, STE 200A 37167 #047-07-2000 L2002 FM *100 †18

WESLEY, Cynthia Marie. 300 STONECREST BLVD, STE 310 37167 #055-01-2000 L2004 OBG *020 ‡

ZYGLEWSKA, Teresa. 300 STONECREST BLVD, STE 260 37167 #759-11-1986 L2003 N CN *020 †75

SNEEDVILLE – HANCOCK

GALE, Donald Henry. ■ 37869 #047-06-1981 L1981 PTH PCP *020 †50 ‡

MUNARI, Renate G. 1861 MAIN ST, SNEEDVILLE MEDICAL CENTER 37869 #154-07-1974 L2008 IM *020 †20

PIERCE, Truett H. PO BOX 37 37869 #047-06-1953 L1953 FM GP *071

REED, Paul Emory. ■ 37869 #047-06-1971 L1972 GP *071

SHORT, John Anthony. PO BOX 125 37869 #047-06-1993 L1996 FM *020 †18

SODDY DAISY – HAMILTON

BONNER, John Douglas. 9453 DAYTON PIKE 37379 #001-06-1995 L1997 OPH *020 †35

CALHOUN, Frank Bivins, II. 9448 DAYTON PIKE 37379 #012-01-1974 L1977 EM *020 †16

CANSLER, Casandra Lou. 8804 DAYTON PIKE 37379 #012-01-1993 L1996 MPD PD *020 †20,55

GOULD, Frederick T. 210 WALNUT DR, STE 100 37379 #062-01-1972 L1996 FPG *020

KAUKAB, Shahla Amjad. 8804 DAYTON PIKE, STE F 37379 #704-01-1990 L2003 PD *020 †55

MC LAUGHLIN, Robert Haley. ■ 37379 #041-12-1992 L2007 GS *020 †85

MORRIS, Brent Sterling. W RIDGE TRAIL RD, CHATTANOOGA-HAMILTON COUNT 37379 #047-05-1977 L1980 PD *020 †55

RIKER, Walter F, Jr. ■ 37379 #035-20-1943 OS PA *071

SOLOMON, Harvey. ■ 37379 #067-01-1974 L2001 *020

SPAULDING, James H. 9527 W RIDGE TRAIL RD 37379 #047-06-1953 L1953 PD *020 †55

SOMERVILLE – FAYETTE

BISHOP, John Myron. 201 LAKEVIEW RD, STE A 38068 #047-06-1955 L1955 FM EM *020 †16,18

BURCH, William Eugene. 201 LAKEVIEW RD, STE A 38068 #047-06-1998 L1999 FM *020 †18

EVANS, Leslie Logan. ■ 38068 #047-06-2005 OBG *012

HAWKINS, Raymond, Jr. 214 LAKEVIEW RD 38068 #047-06-1966 L1974 GS *020 †85

MARTINEZ-LOPEZ, Antonio M. 214 LAKEVIEW RD, METHODIST FAYETTE HOSP 38068 #737-09-1993 L2003 EM *020 †18

MC KNIGHT, Frank S. 201 LAKEVIEW RD, STE A 38068 #047-06-1950 L1950 FM GP *020 †18

RHEA, Karl Byington. 17310 HIGHWAY 64 38068 #047-06-1954 L1954 FM *020 †18

RHEA, Karl Byington, Jr. 17310 US HIGHWAY 64 38068 #047-06-1986 L1987 FM *020 †18

SCATES, Paul E. 12995 HIGHWAY 64 38068 #047-06-1983 L1985 FM *020 †18

SEATON, David L. 213 LAKEVIEW RD, CLINIC 38068 #047-06-1994 L1995 FM *020 †18

SUBAYTI, Yahya Abdali. 214 LAKEVIEW RD 38068 #605-01-1979 L1986 PD *020 †55

SOUTH FULTON – OBION

BERG, Susan Ann. 1203 INDUSTRIAL PARK RD, SOUTH FULTON FAMILY CLINIC 38257 #422-01-1997 L2004 FM *020 †18

BOWLER, William Blake. ■ 38257 #065-06-1982 L1997 *020

NELSON, Andrew Pryor. PO BOX 5288 38257 #047-06-1960 L1961 GP *071

YATES, Virgil Dale. 1101 CHICKASAW DR 38257 #047-06-1980 L1983 PD *040 †55

SOUTH PITTSBURG – MARION

ADCOCK, Charles Russell. 520 E 12TH ST 37380 #047-06-1978 L1979 FM FPG *020

FOX, John Robert. 325 S CEDAR AVE, STE 1 37380 #047-06-1996 L1999 PD *020 †55

HACKWORTH, John Bible, Jr. 210 W 12TH STREET 37380 #047-06-1965 L1968 FM *071 †18

RYAN, Eugene Montford. TRI CITY CLINIC 37380 #047-06-1943 L1943 FM AN *071 †18

ZIEGLER, Martha Earlene. 520 E 12TH ST 37380 #047-20-2003 L2006 FM *020 †18

SPARTA – WHITE

ANBARI, Maan. 439 SEWELL DR 38583 #875-01-1988 L2001 GE *020 ‡

BAKER, Robert F. 207 E BOCKMAN WAY STE B 38583 #047-06-1950 L1950 FM GS *071 †18

BAKER, Robert Francis, Jr. 207 E BOCKMAN WAY 38583 #649-14-1981 L1989 FM *020 †18

BRADLEY, Donald H, Sr. ■ 38583 #047-06-1952 L1952 IM FM *072

DATA, Joann Lucille. 777 PIN HOOK RD 38583 #028-02-1970 L1973 PA IM *030

DODSON, Mollie June. 411 SEWELL DR 38583 #047-20-2000 L2003 MPD *020 †20 ‡

DRAKE, Alan Ross. 133 CHURCHILL DR 38583 #025-07-1982 L1985 FM OBS *020 †18

FLINT, Bryan A, Jr. 165 SHELTON ST 38583 #047-20-1995 L1996 FM *020 †18

JOHNSON, Joel Franklin. ■ 38583 #021-05-1967 L1973 GS GYN *020 †85

JONES, David Nando. 401 SEWELL DR 38583 #047-06-1969 L1970 EM GP *071 †16

KAKOULLIS, Stylianos. 705 HOWELL ST, STE B 38583 #473-03-1995 L2004 PCC *020 †20

KEMKAR, Abhaykumar G. 441 SEWELL DR 38583 #306-01-1988 L1999 IM IMG *020

LE MAIRE, Tara Spain. 341 N SPRING ST, TRADITIONS FAMILY MEDICINE 38583 #047-20-1997 L1998 FM OBS *020 †18

MC CAULEY, John Roger. 401 SEWELL DR 38583 #056-06-1972 L2000 GYN *020 †30

MITCHELL, Charles A. ■ 38583 #047-06-1949 L1949 GP *071

PATE, Donald Wayne. 431 SEWELL DR 38583 #012-22-1991 L1996 GS *020 †85

RASHID, Ahmad Mujtaba. 401 SEWELL DR, WHITE COUNTY COMMUNITYHOSP 38583 #704-01-1996 L2005 PUD *020 †20

RAYNE, Frederick Stanford. 207 E BOCKMAN WAY 38583 #048-04-1984 L1988 OTO FPS *020 †45

SMITH, Leighton H, Jr. 120 W COLLEGE ST 38583 #047-05-1948 L1948 GP *071 †18

THOMPSON, John Ralph. 435 SEWELL DR, STE A 38583 #041-13-1963 L1996 ORS *020 †40

WALL, George Theodore. ■ 38583 #030-05-1965 L1983 R *075

WEBB, Ty Townsend. 457 VISTA DR 38583 #047-06-1995 L1996 FM OBS *020 †18

SPEEDWELL – CLAIBORNE

THOMAS, Robert Lee, IV. 269 OLD HIGHWAY 63 37870 #047-06-1980 L1980 GS *020 †85

VAN BEBBER, India Love. 1528 OLD HIGHWAY 63 37870 #654-01-1985 L1988 FM *020 †18

SPENCER – VAN BUREN

JARRETT, Chas Leslie, Jr. ■ 38585 #047-06-1973 L1974 IM *071

RHINEHART, Margret Wrenn. COURTHOUSE SQUARE 38585 #005-12-1951 L1953 GP *071

SWENSEN, Kirk Walker. PO BOX 806 38585 #003-01-1991 L2000 FM *020 †18

SPRING CITY – RHEA

BOWMAN, Eric Christopher. ■ 37381 #047-07-2005 IM *012

SOLOMON, Alexandre. ■ 37381 #047-05-1959 L1978 NS *071 †25

WILSON, Robert Earl. 126 LAVENDER ST, SPRING CITY FAMILY MEDICAL 37381 #047-06-1963 L1964 GP *020

SPRING HILL – MAURY

ARENDALL, Elbert H, II. 5000 SPEDALE CT 37174 #047-05-1977 L1978 NS *020 †25

BANGURA, Lamin Shebora. ■ 37174 #275-03-1989 *100

BERKMAN, Richard Alan. 5000 SPEDALE CT 37174 #035-19-1987 L1993 NS *020 †25

BUTLER, Melvin Lynn. ■ 37174 #001-02-1964 L2002 OS IM *040 †20

CARNAHAN, David Neal. 100 SATURN PKWY, GM SPRING HILL MFT PB 1500 37174 #047-05-1978 L1979 IM EM *020 †20

COX, Jamie Roderick. PO BOX 1503, MD: 372-995-K09 37174 #064-01-1988 L2002 OM GP *030

DAVIDSON, Randall L, Jr. 5421 MAIN ST 37174 #047-06-1985 L1986 ORS OSM *020 †40

HARRELSON, Elizabeth U. ■ 37174 #012-01-2003 L2007 PD *100 †55

HARRELSON, Philip Ray. 3098 CAMPBELL STATION PKWY 37174 #012-01-1999 L2005 FM *020 †18

HAYES, James Rand, II. 5421 MAIN ST 37174 #001-02-1993 L1996 FM *020 †18

HUMPHREY, Andria Janet. ■ 37174 #047-07-2008 *012

JOHNSON, Eugene Emanuel. ■ 37174 #047-07-1987 *100

LAFFERTY, Nathanael L. 5421 MAIN ST, FAMILY HEALTH GROUP, INC. 37174 #047-06-2000 L2003 FM *020 †18

MALOOF, John A, III. 4847 MAIN ST 37174 #001-02-1983 L1989 CD *020 †20

MYERS, Gregory Jay. 2206 SPEDALE CT, ALTON MULTISPECIALISTS 37174 #035-08-1977 L1995 PD *020 †55

NEVELS, Harold V. 5073 MAIN ST, STE 100 37174 #047-07-1977 L1978 FM *040 †18

PETERSON, Christopher C. 5421 MAIN ST, FAMILY HEALTH GROUP 37174 #048-14-2002 L2005 FM *020 †18

RAY, Jennifer Lynn. 5073 MAIN ST, STE 150 37174 #020-02-1994 L2005 PD *020 †55

REZK, Hany Nimr. ■ 37174 #027-01-2002 L2007 NEP *020 †20

SCHLOSSER, Michael James. 5000 SPEDALE CT 37174 #008-01-1999 L2006 NS *020

SCHOOLEY, William Roy. 5000 SPEDALE CT 37174 #001-02-1986 L1994 NS *020 †25

SCHWARZ, Jacob Patrick. 5000 SPEDALE CT 37174 #023-07-1991 L2006 NS *020 †18

SIMPKINS, Carl N, Jr. PO BOX 246 37174 #012-01-1950 L1968 OM GS *020 †85,90

STEWART, Sharon M. 100 SATURN PKWY, SPRINGHILL MANUFACTURING 37174 #047-07-1976 L2003 OM GP *020

TALPOS-REED, Diana. ■ 37174 #005-15-1988 L1994 N *071 †75

WHITE, Teresa Stuart. 2206 SPEDALE CT, TENNESSEE PEDIATRICS 37174 #051-07-2001 L2004 PD *020 †55

SPRINGFIELD – ROBERTSON

ANIFOWOSHE, Olumide Ibrah. 100 NORTHCREST DR, NORTHCREST MED CTR 37172 #690-02-1991 L2003 IM *020 †20 ‡

BASSEL, John Burr, Jr. 430 NORTHCREST DR 37172 #047-05-1969 L1969 IM *020 †20

BAZALDUA, Gilbert. 100 NORTHCREST DR 37172 #649-14-1977 L1980 FM *020 ‡

BINKLEY, William Jos, Jr. 2104A PARK PLAZA DR 37172 #047-06-1966 L1967 U *020 †95

BRANNICK, William Jeffrey. 100 NORTHCREST DR 37172 #016-01-1991 L2001 DR *020 †80

BROWNING, Matthew Forrest. 471 NORTHCREST DR 37172 #047-06-1998 L1999 FM OBS *020 †18

CANTRELL, Carol Roberts. 2304 MEMORIAL BLVD 37172 #047-06-1986 L1987 FM *020 †18

CARDENO, Corazon Nevalga. 203 8TH AVE E 37172 #748-08-1992 L2000 MPD *020 †20,55

CARMODY, Daniel William. 224 NORTHCREST DR 37172 #047-20-2001 L2002 IM HOS *020

CHADALAVADA, Ramesh. 100 NORTHCREST DR 37172 #495-50-1980 L2001 PUD SME *020 †20

CHIU, Pauline P. 801 HILL ST 37172 #065-01-1993 L1998 FM *020 †20

CRAWFORD, Erika Lachelle. 426 22ND AVE E, ERIKA L. CRAWFORD, M.D. 37172 #047-07-2004 L2007 PD *020 †55

CRUNK, Tommy H. 224 NORTHCREST DR 37172 #047-06-1976 L1979 FM *020 †18

CUTRIGHT, Mark Theodore. 417 NORTHCREST DR, NORTHCREST ORTHOPAEDICS 37172 #038-40-1995 L2002 ORS *020 †40

DAHIR, George Anthony. 417 NORTHCREST DR 37172 #051-20-1990 L1999 OSM *020

DAVIS, Daniel Lee. 322 NORTHCREST DR, SPRINGFIELD SURGERY PC 37172 #019-02-1998 L2003 GS *020 †85

ESPELETA, Ferdinand Sunga. 801 HILL ST, MILLBROOK MEDICAL CENTER 37172 #748-01-1991 L2000 PD *020 †55

FERLAND, Robert Guy. 2102A PARK PLAZA DR 37172 #060-01-1977 L1993 FM *020 †18

FOSNES, Jeffrey Carl. 220 NORTHCREST DR 37172 #047-05-1980 L1983 **FM** *020 †18
GOLDBERG, Keith L. 320 NORTHCREST DR 37172 #021-01-1993 L1998 **GS** *020 †85
GRAY, James Travis. 100 NORTHCREST DR, NORTHCREST MEDICAL CENTER 37172 #020-02-1978 L1982 **DR** *020
GRAY, William Ryburn, Sr. ■ 37172 #020-02-1946 L1947 **CD** *071 †20
HAVENS, David Ward. 105 5TH AVE W, STE 103 37172 #024-01-1964 L1992 **P** *020
HAYES, Warren G. ■ 37172 #047-06-1958 L1958 **PHP** *071
JACK, Randall Ellis. 310 NORTHCREST DR 37172 #031-01-2000 L2004 **OBG** *020
JACKSON, Ronnie Lee. 496 NORTHCREST DR 37172 #047-07-1988 L1990 **IM PUD** *020
KELLEY, Karl David. ■ 37172 #045-04-1987 L2004 **EM** *020 †18
KROSER, Jonathan Mark. 320 NORTHCREST DR 37172 #041-07-1995 L2001 **GS VS** *020 †85 ‡
KRUEGER, Thomas C. 100 NORTHCREST DR 37172 #038-41-1979 L1982 **GS CRS** *020 †85
KUMAR, Sarbjeet Singh. 322 NORTHCREST DR 37172 #495-03-1970 L1977 **GS VS** *020 †85
LOONEY, Carroll Medley. ■ 37172 #047-06-1953 L1953 **GS GP** *071
MADELL, Spencer J. 100 NORTHCREST DR, ATTN IMAGING DEPT 37172 #035-46-1982 L1999 **R DR** *020 †80
MC ALLISTER, Shellon A. 426 22ND AVE E 37172 #011-04-2001 L2004 **PD** *020
O'DONNELL, John Wm, III. 225 NORTHCREST DR 37172 #047-05-1975 L1977 **OBG IM** *020
PEAVYHOUSE, Joel Queenor. 417 NORTHCREST DR 37172 #047-06-1968 L1969 **ORS** *071 †40
PENNINGTON, John Mark. 471 NORTHCREST DR 37172 #012-01-1990 L2000 **FM** *020
RHODES, Michael Allen. 801 HILL ST, MILLBROOK MEDICAL CENTER 37172 #047-07-1997 L2003 **FM** *020
RONE, Christopher Cordell. 224 NORTHCREST DR 37172 #047-06-1997 L2000 **FM** *020 †18
SADARANGANI, Nari T. ■ 37172 #495-97-1969 L1975 **TS** *075 †85,90
SELF, Nicholas Barrett. 426 22ND AVE E 37172 #021-01-1973 L1976 **PD** *071 †55
SELF, Zachary Barrett. ■ 37172 #047-06-2008 *012
SHABAYEK, Nazek. 100 NORTHCREST DR 37172 #915-02-1975 L1987 **AN** *020 †05
SHEARER, Robert Allen. 403 NORTHCREST DR 37172 #047-06-1976 L1977 **OBG** *020
SINGLETON, Jennifer D. 426 22ND AVE E 37172 #001-02-1997 L2000 **PD** *020 †55
TALMADGE, Todd Michael. 426 22ND AVE E 37172 #008-02-1989 L2002 **DR** *020 †80
TURNER, John Bunyan. 205 5TH AVENUE 37172 #047-06-1955 L1955 **FM IM** *072 †18
VALOSIK, Robert Andrew. 308 NORTHCREST DR 37172 #001-02-1975 L1978 **IM** *020 †20
WALTERS, Avis Diane. 805 MEMORIAL BLVD 37172 #030-05-1995 L1999 **FM** *020 †18
WILLIAMS, Teresa Marie. 221 NORTHCREST DR 37172 #020-02-2001 L2004 **IM** *020

SWEETWATER — MONROE

AMEEN, John Robt. 304 CHURCH ST 37874 #045-01-1982 L1995 **OBG** *020 †30
AMER, Syed Mohammad. 304 CHURCH ST 37874 #704-02-1990 L1995 **PD** *020 †55
CREUTZINGER, David John. 304 WRIGHT ST, SWEETWATER HOSP ASSOC 37874 #020-12-1973 L1978 **OBG** *020 †30
DITTENBER, Jaclyn E. 205 SUMMIT ST, SWEETWATER FAMILY MEDICINE 37874 #038-40-2003 L2006 **FM** *020 †18
EVANS, Thomas Saml. 304 CHURCH ST, SWEETWATER HOSPITAL 37874 #047-05-1976 L1979 **IM IMG** *020 †20
HARVEY, William Leon. 602 S MAIN ST 37874 #047-06-1976 L1977 **FM** *020 †18
HAYS, Robert Danl. 304 WRIGHT ST, POB II 37874 #047-06-1958 L1960 **R NM** *071
HUFF, Mary Lyle. 402 MAY ST, MARY M HUFF MD PLLC 37874 #047-06-1991 L1992 **FM** *020 †18
HYMAN, Orren W, Jr. RR 1 37874 #047-06-1951 L1951 **R** *071 †80
JOHNSON, Sigrid R. 205 SUMMIT ST, SWEETWATER FAM MED 37874 #011-04-1993 L1994 **FM** *020 †18 ‡
KHADKA, Deepali. ■ 37874 #496-30-1997 L2004 **IM** *020
KHAIROLLAHI, Vali. 304 CHURCH ST, SWEETWATER HOSPITAL 37874 #517-01-1958 L1970 **TS** *020 †85,90
KOZAWA, Kenya. 304 CHURCH ST 37874 #038-44-1988 L1994 **GE IM** *020 †20
O'MALLEY, Michael. 304 WRIGHT ST 37874 #033-06-1989 L1994 **DR** *020 †80
POSTON, Eric. 304 WRIGHT ST, SWEETWATER HOSPITAL ASSOC. 37874 #422-01-1997 L2000 **IM** *020 †20
ROBBINS, Wendy Nannette. 304 CHURCH ST, SWEETWATER MEDICAL CLINIC 37874 #047-20-1994 L1997 **PD** *020
VILLANUEVA, Ramon. 604 S MAIN ST 37874 #012-01-1975 L1976 **GS** *020 †85

TAFT — LINCOLN

ACUFF, Rachel Elizabeth. ■ 38488 #047-06-2006 **OBG** *012
BENNETT, Barbara Fiebig. 181 COLDWATER CREEK RD, N/A 38488 #047-20-1988 L1991 **FM** *020 †18

TALBOTT — HAMBLEN

KARWAN, Sobha Rani. 6350 W ANDREW JOHNSON HWY 37877 #495-70-1981 L1996 **PD** *020 †55
KRAUS, Laura Waters. 204 SHAVER DR 37877 #047-06-2001 L2006 **PD** *020 †55
KRAUS, Mathew Tyson. 204 SHAVER DR, PHILLIPS MEDICAL GROUP 37877 #047-06-2001 L2006 **IM PD** *020 †20,55
LEONARD, Charles Edwin. 1171 HIGHWAY 11 E, STE 101 37877 #047-06-1978 L1979 **FM** *020 †18
LUNSFORD, Aleshia Lynnann. 6350 W ANDREW JOHNSON HWY 37877 #047-20-1997 L1999 **PD** *020 †55
MAYS, Elizabeth. 6350 W ANDREW JOHNSON HWY 37877 #047-20-1996 L1997 **FM** *020 †18
PAGE, Catherine Marie. ■ 37877 #047-20-1982 L1984 **P IM** *075
PHILLIPS, Floyd E, Jr. 204 SHAVER DR, PHILLIPS MEDICAL GRP PC 37877 #047-06-1991 L1993 **MPD** *020 †55,20
PHILLIPS, Regina N. 204 SHAVER DR 37877 #001-02-1994 L1997 **PD** *020 †55
WARDEN, Angela. 6350 W ANDREW JOHNSON HWY 37877 #012-05-1996 L2001 **PD** *020 †55

TAZEWELL — CLAIBORNE

CASTILLO, Mariel Santos. 411 BLUE TOP RD 37879 #748-01-1999 L2006 **PD** *100
CLARK, Richard Dale. 1601 TAZEWELL RD, BOX 9 37879 #047-06-1969 L1970 **FM** *020 †18
GREEN, Edmon Lee. 1850 OLD KNOXVILLE RD 37879 #027-01-1966 L1970 **P** *071 †75

GUANZON, Ryan Rommel Sori. 411 BLUE TOP RD 37879 #748-02-2001 L2006 **IM** *020 †20
GUPTA, Ruchi. 1850 OLD KNOXVILLE RD 37879 #495-21-1988 L1996 **IM** *020 †20
MAPPALA, Francisco Dela C. 1850 OLD KNOXVILLE RD 37879 #748-07-1970 L1979 **EM** *020 †16
NEAL, Brent Sheldon. 411 BLUE TOP RD, STE 2 37879 #047-20-2001 L2004 **IM** *020
PAPADOPOL, Raluca. 411 BLUE TOP RD SE-2 37879 #781-02-1995 L2005 **PD** *020 †55
PATEL, Jaykrishna S. 209 IRISH CEMETERY RD 37879 #495-22-1971 L1981 **IM** *020 †20
PICKETT, James Clarke. 1850 OLD KNOXVILLE RD 37879 #047-06-1970 L1971 **EM IM** *020 †50,20,16
REDDY, Illuri. 1850 OLD KNOXVILLE RD 37879 #495-21-1987 L1994 **IM** *020 †20
REED, Fred W. 1850 OLD KNOXVILLE RD 37879 #047-06-1952 L1952 **GP PD** *071
SIVLEY, Rhonda S. 1850 OLD KNOXVILLE RD 37879 #001-02-1999 L2008 **IM** *020 †20
STEWART, Barry Arthur. 1850 OLD KNOXVILLE RD 37879 #047-06-1987 L1988 **FM** *020 †20
VONGKASEMSIRI, Sunan. 1850 OLD KNOXVILLE RD, CLAIBORNE CO HOSPITAL 37879 #891-01-1967 L1983 **R NM** *020 †80
WILMOTH, Robert Jeremy. 1836 MAIN ST 37879 #047-06-2001 L2005 **GS** *020 ‡

TELFORD — WASHINGTON

AIKEN, Todd William. ■ 37690 #047-20-2004 L2007 **PD** *100 †55

TELLICO PLAINS — MONROE

NESS, James Wilbur. ■ 37385 #038-40-1970 L1978 **FM** *020 †18
SPARKS, Vernon Corbett. ■ 37385 #005-12-1962 L1976 **GP GS** *071

TEN MILE — ROANE

PADGETT, John Craig. ■ 37880 #025-01-1966 L1967 **ORS** *071 †40

THOMPSONS STATION — WILLIAMSON

GERAUGHTY, James K. ■ 37179 #028-46-1982 L1989 **FM** *020 †18

THREE WAY — GIBSON

BREWER, Ashley Scott. ■ 38343 #047-06-2006 **FP** *012

TIPTONVILLE — LAKE

ALGEE, Wyatt Robt, Jr. 215 S COURT ST 38079 #047-06-1970 L1970 **IM** *020 †20
BRUCE, Daniel Wm. 1402 CHURCH ST 38079 #047-06-1957 L1958 **PTH** *020
DUBRULE, Rosaire Michel. 229 S COURT ST 38079 #051-01-1976 L1981 **FM** *020 †45
GUESS, Carol Winfred. 215 S COURT ST 38079 #020-02-1979 L1986 **TS** *020 †85

TOWNSEND — BLOUNT

GILREATH, Catherine Ann. 7765 RIVER RD 37882 #047-06-1962 L1963 **OBG** *020
MC ELLIGOTT, John. 1151 LAUREL RD 37882 #306-01-1986 L1989 **IM** *020 †20

TRACY CITY — MARION

SHOULDERS, Harrison H, Jr. HWY 150 S, TRACY CLINIC 37387 #047-05-1946 L1947 **FM CRS** *071 †85,10

TRENTON — GIBSON

ANTIQUE, Caroline T. 500 HOSPITAL DR, PRIMARY CARE CENTER 38382 #748-01-1988 L2001 **FM** *020 †18
DE SOUZA, Wm Celestino. 120 DAVY CROCKETT MALL 38382 #539-02-1965 L1974 **IM PUD** *020 †20
HALL, James Wilson. RR 3 38382 #047-06-1945 L1945 **FM** *071
HALL, Steven Edgar. 700 HOSPITAL DR 38382 #047-07-1995 L1996 **FM** *020 †18
HAMILTON, Thomas Milton. 700 HOSPITAL DR 38382 #047-06-1980 L1981 **GP** *020
NELSON, Thomas Harlan. 200 HOSPITAL DR, GIBSON GENERAL HOSPITAL 38382 #038-41-1979 L1997 **EM FM** *020 †70,18
OLUSANYA, Ayodele Adeleke. 120 DAVY CROCKETT MALL, TRENTON MEDICAL CLINIC 38382 #690-05-1991 L2003 **IM** *020 †20
PATEL, Hasmukh Dahyabhai. 400 HOSPITAL DR STE 401 38382 #495-23-1970 L1975 **GS CRS** *020
WILLIAMS, James Larry, II. 500 HOSPITAL DR 38382 #047-06-1987 L1987 **FM** *020 †18
WILLIAMS, Thomas Roderick. ■ 38382 #047-06-1944 L1944 **OS** *075

TROY — OBION

GOOCH, Allen C. 316 E HARPER ST, BOX 188 38260 #047-06-1976 L1976 **GS** *020 †85
GOOCH, Cynthia Hill. PO BOX 188 38260 #047-06-1976 L1977 **PTH** *020 †50
HILL, Chesley Hester. PO BOX 188, 316 HARPER ST 38260 #021-01-1947 L1953 **GS GP** *071
HILL, Robert P. 316 E HARPER ST, C.H. HILL CLINIC 38260 #047-06-1976 L1976 **IM** *020 †20

TULLAHOMA — COFFEE

AGNIHOTRI, Dinesh. 1805 N JACKSON ST, STE 100 37388 #495-45-1994 L2004 **IM** *020 †20
ANDERSON, John Alexander. 106 WESTSIDE DR 37388 #047-06-1982 L1984 **FM** *020 †18
BARD, Ralph Michael. 1805 N JACKSON ST, STE 8 37388 #047-06-1980 L1981 **GS** *071 †85

BARD, Shirley Ann. 710 KINGS LN 37388 #047-06-1980 L1981 **PD** *020 †55
BARTEE, Harry Albert, Jr. 1801 N JACKSON ST, MEDICAL STAFF OFFICE 37388 #047-07-1994 L1998 **MPD** *020
BILLS, Stephen Hunter. 1805 N JACKSON ST, STE 100 37388 #047-05-1979 L1982 **IM** *020 †20
BLACK, Randall Lester. 1805 N JACKSON ST STE 4 37388 #005-12-1972 L1994 **P** *020 †75
BRADFORD, William Butler. 2114 N JACKSON ST 37388 #020-02-1990 L1994 **RO** *020 †80
BRICKELL, Ralph L, Jr. ■ 37388 #047-06-1952 L1952 **FM** *020 †18
BUNN, Karen Fleenor. 1805 N JACKSON ST, BLDG B 37388 #047-20-1987 L1991 **OBG** *020 †30
BURR, Peter Merritt. 101 W BLACKWELL ST 37388 #020-12-1980 L2002 **PS DS** *020 †85,65
CANON, Robert Maurice. 600 E CARROLL ST 37388 #047-06-1971 L1971 **ORS OS** *020
CAPPS, Raymond Lee. 1330 CEDAR LN, STE 700 37388 #028-46-1978 L1998 **N IMG** *020 †75
CLARK, Patrick Wade. ■ 37388 #047-06-2007 **TY** *012
COLE, Richard Clinton. 2106 N JACKSON ST 37388 #001-06-1983 L1991 **FM A** *020 †18
COLLIER, Robert Craig. 1100 N JACKSON ST 37388 #047-06-1990 L1991 **OPH OS** *020 †35
COLLIER, Suzanne Chamblee. 150 JACK FARRAR LN 37388 #047-06-1990 L1991 **GE** *020 †20
CORRIE, Doug. 1801 N JACKSON ST 37388 #039-01-1992 L2003 **U** *020 †95
COTTRELL, Ben Edgar. ■ 37388 #020-02-1997 L2001 **FM EM** *020 †18
COWAN, Richard Howard. 710 KINGS LN 37388 #047-06-1971 L1977 **PD PN** *020 †55
CRABTREE, John Dennie, Jr. 1750 CEDAR LN STE 100 37388 #047-20-1991 L1992 **GS** *020 †85 ‡
CRAIG, Allen Robbins. 1801 N JACKSON ST 37388 #047-05-1982 L1983 **P** *020 †75
DEMBLA, Preeti Nanak. 1801 N JACKSON ST, HARTON REGIONAL MEDICAL CE 37388 #496-38-1994 L2004 **IM** *020 †20
DRUMMOND, Charles Stitt, II. ■ 37388 #051-04-1993 L2005 **CD** *100 †85,90
EMADIAN, Seyed Mohammad. 730 KINGS LN, SPINE CENTER 37388 #011-03-1991 L2002 **NS** *020 †25
ESPINOZA-MORATAYA, Rocio. 715 KINGS LN 37388 #649-14-1991 L1999 **PD** *020 †55
FERRELL, Brett Layne. ■ 37388 #047-06-2008 *012
FIALA, Martin Jason. 1905 N JACKSON ST 37388 #065-09-1989 L1995 **ORS HS** *020 †40
FIGAROLA, Tulio Antonio. 100 HUNTERS LN 37388 #001-02-1992 L2006 **ORS** *020 †40
FINKE, Garry Erskine. ■ 37388 #047-06-2004 L2007 **PD** *100 †55
FISHBEIN, Richard Eugene. 1801 N WASHINGTON ST, STE 200 37388 #035-09-1965 L1981 **OS** *020 †40
FRALEY, Marvin Clifford. ■ 37388 #047-06-1956 L1956 **R** *072 †80
FREEMAN, William James. 301 N JACKSON ST 37388 #023-07-1967 L1977 **HNS OTO** *020 †45
GALBRAITH, Bruce E. 1801 N JACKSON ST 37388 #047-06-1949 L1950 **GP** *072 †18
GEORGE, James Walton. 725 KINGS LN 37388 #021-05-1981 L1985 **CD AN** *020 †05
GOOD, Michael Clay. 1330 CEDAR LN, STE 500 37388 #036-08-1988 L1989 **OBG** *020 †30
GRAHAM, D Bruce. 1801 N JACKSON ST 37388 #047-06-1974 L1995 **GP** *020
GUPTA, Rimda. 1330 CEDAR LN, STE 100 37388 #495-30-1987 L1996 **IM** *020 †20
HARVEY, Charles Ben. ■ 37388 #047-06-1954 L1954 **FM** *071 †18
KEMP, Olan Baxter. 100 WILLIAM NORTHERN BLVD 37388 #047-06-1989 L1992 **FM** *020 †18
KENNEDY, Jerry Ledford. 106 WESTSIDE DR 37388 #047-06-1966 L1967 **GS GP** *020 †85
KIM, Ho Kyun. 1330 CEDAR LN, BLDG B 37388 #583-02-1962 L1972 **PD** *020 †55
KLARA, Peter Michael. 1940 N JACKSON ST, STE 150 37388 #021-01-1979 L1992 **NS** *020 †25
KRICK, Joseph Gerard. 1805 N JACKSON ST, STE 7 37388 #012-05-1982 L1987 **GS TS** *020 †85
KRISHNA, Gulla Bala. 705 NW ATLANTIC ST 37388 #209-01-1959 L1977 **U** *020 †85,95
LEE, Marcus William. 100 HUNTERS LN, STE 100 37388 #047-06-2000 L2001 **FM** *020 †18
LLOYD, Allen James. 1805 N JACKSON ST, STE 100 37388 #047-06-2000 L2004 **IM** *020 ‡
LOCKE, Charles Michael. 105 LEDFORD MILL RD, STE A 37388 #047-05-1996 L1999 **GS** *020
LOVEJOY, Morris Lester. 108 W BLACKWELL ST 37388 #005-12-1981 L1985 **P OS** *020 †75
LOVELADY, Gary Keith. 1801 N WASHINGTON ST, STE 300 37388 #047-06-1988 L1994 **PCC** *020 †20
MACEACHERN, Ronald T. 2106 N JACKSON ST 37388 #063-01-1996 L1998 **FM** *020 †18,80
MAHAN, Ben Bob. 926 N JACKSON ST 37388 #039-01-1979 L1988 **OPH** *020 †35
MARVEL, Jeffrey B. 1821 N WASHINGTON ST 37388 #048-14-1986 L1997 **OTO PS** *020 †45
MARVEL, Patty M. 1821 N WASHINGTON ST 37388 #048-14-1986 L1997 **P** *020 †75
MILAM, William M. 1970 N JACKSON ST 37388 #047-06-1976 L1976 **FM FPG** *020 †18
MURPHY, Robert Bryan. 100 HUNTERS LN, STE 100 37388 #047-06-2003 L2007 **OBG** *020
NORRIS, Hunter Willingham. 1100 N JACKSON ST 37388 #047-06-1987 L1991 **OPH** *020 †35
OMITOWOJU, Oladapo O. 1805 N JACKSON ST, STE 200 37388 #690-02-1984 L1996 **NEP** *020 †20
PATSIMAS, John. 100 WILLIAM NORTHERN BLVD, DOCTORS REGIONAL MEDICAL G 37388 #649-14-1985 L1993 **FM** *020 †18
PATTERSON, Teresita M. 209 WILSON AVE 37388 #748-02-1969 L1976 **PD** *020 †55
PHELPS, Thomas F. ■ 37388 #047-07-1983 L1987 **FM FPG** *020 †18
POU, Celio Francisco. 1805 N JACKSON ST, STE 300 37388 #649-14-1978 L1998 **OBG** *020 †30
RAMPRASAD, Mittur N. 509 NW ATLANTIC ST 37388 #495-33-1970 L1981 **ORS** *020
RIDLEY, Robert Wendell. 926 N JACKSON ST 37388 #016-02-1962 L1976 **OPH** *020 †35
ROBISON, Byron Keith. 1801 N JACKSON ST 37388 #001-02-1985 L1986 **IM** *020 †20
RUSSELL, Mark Roddy. 1801 N JACKSON ST, DEPT OF RADIOLOGY 37388 #047-06-1985 L1986 **DR** *020 †80
RUTLEDGE, Robb Geoffrey. 1801 N JACKSON ST 37388 #026-04-1979 L1984 **ORS** *020 †40
SANDERS, Wm Josiah, IV. 1805 N JACKSON ST, STE 100 37388 #047-05-1976 L1982 **IM ID** *020 †20
SEYLER, Clifford Alan. 1330 CEDAR LN, BLDG B 37388 #027-01-1971 L1990 **PD** *020 †55
SHUKLA, Sandip Rasiklal. 107 E GRUNDY ST 37388 #495-22-1971 L1977 **P** *020 †75
TAKEGAMI, Ken Takeshi. 100 WILLIAM NORTHERN BLVD, STE C 37388 #038-40-1989 L1990 **D** *020 †15
TAYLOR, Ian Stewart. 10054 OLD TULLAHOMA RD, NORTH LAKE MEDICAL CLNC 37388 #065-01-1968 L1995 **FM** *020
TEPEDINO, Michael J, Jr. 1801 N WASHINGTON ST, STE 400 37388 #561-01-1974 L1980 **U** *020 †95
THOMASSON, Joseph R. 100 HUNTERS LN, STE 100 37388 #047-06-1978 L1978 **GP** *020 †18
TUCKER, Donald. 100 WILLIAM NORTHERN BLVD, DOCTORS REGIONAL MEDICAL GROUP 37388 #654-01-1989 L1993 **IM** *020
UPENDER, Raghuveeren P. 707 KINGS LN, STE 7 37388 #008-02-1995 L2004 **N** *020 †75
VALLEJO, Francisco C. 1801 N JACKSON ST 37388 #748-11-1966 L1973 **IM EM** *020
VALLEJO, Luz A. 711 N ATLANTIC ST 37388 #748-01-1964 L1973 **GYN** *020
VAUGHN, Richard M. 710 KINGS LN 37388 #047-06-1997 L2000 **PD** *020 †55
WEBB, Charles Harris. ■ 37388 #047-06-1942 L1943 **FM** *071
WEBB, Charles Harry. 1801 N JACKSON ST 37388 #047-06-1952 L1952 **FM** *075
WEBB, John Ray. ■ 37388 #047-06-1968 L1969 **FM EM** *071 †16
WEIS, Richard Chas. 1940 N JACKSON ST, STE 220 37388 #041-12-1965 L1991 **OTO FPS** *020 †45
WOODFIN, Mose Clarke, Jr. 926 N JACKSON ST 37388 #047-05-1961 L1962 **OPH** *071 †35
WORONOWICZ, Andrew W. 317 S JACKSON ST 37388 #759-03-1977 L1989 **AN** *020 †05

TURTLETOWN – POLK

JONES, Jay Jerry. ■ 37391 #047-20-1996 L2007 **FM** *020 †18

UNICOI – UNICOI

CLARK, Bendik Larson. 3614 UNICOI DR 37692 #047-20-2000 L2002 **FM** *020 †18
ROVIRA, Brian Arthur. PO BOX 459 37692 #021-05-1964 L2008 **DR** *075 †80
SMITH, Richard S. ■ 37692 #047-06-1980 L1980 **AN EM** *071 †05

UNION CITY – OBION

ARMSTRONG, Mark Anthony. 1722 E REELFOOT AVE 38261 #005-19-1994 L1996 **AN** *020 †05
BATES, John Byron. ■ 38261 #001-02-2004 L2007 **PD** *020 †55
BATEY, James Thos. 1020 E REELFOOT AVE 38261 #047-06-1990 L1991 **FM** *020 †18
BLANTON, Marvin A, III. 1720 E REELFOOT AVE, STE 104 38261 #047-06-1966 L1967 **ORS** *020 †40
BRADBERRY, Samuel Wade. 1020 E REELFOOT AVE 38261 #047-06-1981 L1982 **FM** *020 †18
BROWN, Bruce Barton. 1020 E REELFOOT AVE 38261 #047-06-1974 L1975 **FM** *020 †18
BUTLER, Harold Dee. 2205 SOUTHLANE CIR, P O BOX 929 38261 #047-06-1958 L1968 **GP A** *071
CAMERON, Robert Lynn. 1312 BISHOP ST, WOMENS CLINIC PA 38261 #004-01-1967 L1972 **OBG** *020 †30
CAMPBELL, Joe. 1101 BISHOP ST 38261 #047-06-1954 L1955 **GS TS** *071 †85
CLENDENIN, John Brantley. 1020 E REELFOOT AVE 38261 #047-20-1993 L1994 **FM** *020 †18
CLENDENIN, Robert E, Jr. 1229 RUSSELL ST 38261 #047-06-1960 L1968 **FM** *071 †18
CONKRIGHT, William Aubrey. 1109 E REELFOOT AVE, STE G 38261 #935-01-1986 L2002 **IM ON** *020 †20
CUMMINGS, John M. 1208 EDWARDS ST 38261 #047-06-1977 L1978 **IM** *020 †20
DODD, Halbert B. 1117 S MILES AVE, STE 4 38261 #047-06-1973 L1973 **CD IM** *020
EASON, William Craig. 1720 E REELFOOT AVE 38261 #047-05-1979 L1984 **GS** *020 †85
ESCARCEGA, Rogelio. 1722 E REELFOOT AVE STE 1, UNION CITY SURGERY CENTER 38261 #649-01-1964 L1976 **GS PS** *020
FATTAH, Emad A. 1109 E REELFOOT AVE, STE D 38261 #915-04-1977 L2001 **PD** *020 †55 ‡
FOWLER, Mark Walton. 1020 REELFOOT AVE 38261 #047-06-1999 L2000 **FM** *020 †18
GORE, Margaret. 1012 S MILES AVE 38261 #036-07-1986 L1992 **HEM ON** *020 †20
GRAVENOR, Donald S. 1720 E REELFOOT AVE, STE 200 38261 #067-01-1981 L1998 **ON** *020 †20
GREGORY, Belinda Ann. 1720 E REELFOOT AVE # 201 38261 #016-11-1986 L1990 **PM** *020
HALE, John Wesley, Jr. 1020 REELFOOT AVE, DOCTORS' CLINIC/UNION CITY 38261 #047-20-1988 L1989 **FM OM** *020 †18
HALL, James Coker. 1720 E REELFOOT AVE, STE 200 38261 #047-06-1985 L1986 **CD** *020 †20
JAMES, William Alex. 1201 BISHOP ST 38261 #047-06-1985 L1986 **IM** *020
JERNIGAN, Thomas Wright. 1109 E REELFOOT AVE, STE I 38261 #047-06-1998 L2001 **VS** *020 †85
JOHNSON, Susan. 1720 E REELFOOT AVE, STE 205 38261 #047-06-1971 L1972 **OBG** *020
LAWRENCE, Roy Finch. 1312 BISHOP ST 38261 #047-06-1970 L1971 **OBG** *071 †30
LEWIS, Rodger Patrick. 1209 BISHOP ST 38261 #004-01-1962 L1972 **PTH** *020 †50
MALIK, Harbans Lal. BMH VC 38261 #495-45-1975 L1984 **AN** *020
MARSIDI, Paul. 1720 E REELFOOT AVE # 203 38261 #165-04-1975 L1981 **U** *020 †95
MOORE, Michael Neil. 1109 E REELFOOT AVE, STE C 38261 #001-02-1981 L1991 **AN** *020
MORGAN, Dennis Paul. 1720 E REELFOOT AVE, STE 200 38261 #027-01-1987 L2001 **ON** *020 †20
NEDUMTHOTTATHIL, Thomas J. ■ 38261 #495-63-1996 L2007 *100 †20
NUAKO, Kofi W. 1109 E REELFOOT AVE, STE C 38261 #412-01-1985 L1999 **GE IM** *020 †20
ORT, Michael E. 1201 BISHOP ST 38261 #004-01-1992 L1995 **FM** *020 †18
RAGSDALE, James Howard. ■ 38261 #047-06-1958 L1959 **FM EM** *071 †18
RESSER, John Randall. 1722 E REELFOOT AVE 38261 #038-41-1994 L2000 **OTO** *020 †45
SANNER, Robert F, Jr. ■ 38261 #041-01-1956 L1978 **GS** *020 †85
SCHLEIFER, Grover F, III. 702 SHERRILL ST, STE B 38261 #047-06-1970 L1971 **FM** *020 †18
SOUTH, Christy Dawn. ■ 38261 #047-20-2003 L2007 **OBG** *020
ST CLAIR, David Smith. 1101 BISHOP ST 38261 #020-02-1976 L1982 **ORS** *020 †40
STONE, William Kirk. 1020 E REELFOOT AVE 38261 #027-01-1993 L1994 **FM** *020 †18 ‡
SULLIVAN, David Wayne. 1720 E REELFOOT AVE, STE 200 38261 #027-01-1987 L1990 **HO** *020 †20
TRIPLETT, Jeffrey Thos. ■ 38261 #047-20-1989 L1990 **RO** *020
VIEN, Nguyen Luu. PO BOX 870 38281 #941-01-1952 L1979 **PTH** *072
WALSH, William Knight. 1720 E REELFOOT AVE, STE 200 38261 #047-06-1983 L1984 **HEM ON** *020 †20
WILSON, Paschal P, Jr. 1720 E REELFOOT AVE, STE 200 38261 #027-01-1996 L2005 **HO** *020 †20
WONG, Leandro L. 1201 BISHOP ST 38261 #319-03-1968 **GS OS** *020
YOUNG, Robert Roger, Jr. 1312 BISHOP ST, THE WOMAN'S CLINIC 38261 #047-06-1961 L1961 **OBG** *020 †30
ZELLER, Orville A, Jr. RR 1 BOX 75 38261 #020-02-1951 L1957 **AN** *071

VONORE – MONROE

BEAN, Michael William. 125 MOUNTAIN VIEW DR, STE 300 37885 #047-06-1973 L1974 **PD** *020 †55
COX, Thomas Ringo, III. 1206 HIGHWAY 411 37885 #047-06-1975 L1975 **EM GP** *020
GETTINGER, Joshua Selig. 1206 HIGHWAY 411 37885 #005-02-1976 L1979 **FM** *071 †18
LEVIN, Barbara Ann. 1206 HIGHWAY 411 37885 #005-02-1976 L1979 **FM** *020 †70,18
MILLER, Lawrence Howard. 1206 HIGHWAY 411 37885 #010-01-1967 L1993 **FM ADL** *020 †18
O'BRIEN, Kent Patrick. 261 WILLIAMS SHORE RD, KENT O'BRIEN 37885 #017-20-1994 L2004 **EM** *020 †16
WIGHT, Heather Stevens. 125 MOUNTAIN VIEW DR, STE 300 37885 #011-04-1998 L2004 **PD** *020 †55

■ = Address Information Privacy Protected

WALLAND – BLOUNT

HARWELL, Valton Carden. ■ 37886 #047-05-1954 L1954 **OBG** *071 †30

WARTBURG – MORGAN

ALLEN, Thomas G. 950 MAIN ST STE A 37887 #047-06-1982 L1983 **FM FSM** *020 †18
DABBS, C Harwell. 224 OLD MILL RD, STE 408 37887 #028-02-1945 L1952 **GP GS** *020 †85
HUDGENS, James F, Jr. 224 OLD MILL RD, STE 408 37887 #047-06-1966 L1967 **DR** *020 †80
KELLEY, Houston Adolpha. 224 OLD MILL RD, STE 408 37887 #010-03-1960 L1975 **GP OS** *020
LITTELL, Delvin Edmar. 224 OLD MILL RD 37887 #005-12-1959 L1978 **FM EM** *020 †70
THAKUR, Sanjay Prakash. 1236 KNOXVILLE HWY, WARTBURG P.O. BOX 368 37887 #496-16-1990 L2000 **FM** *020 †18
VORA, Bhavana. 1236 KNOXVILLE HWY, AMBULATORY CARE CENTER 37887 #496-25-1997 L2003 **FM** *020 †18 ‡

WATAUGA – CARTER

SHAW, Vance Cleveland. ■ 37694 #047-20-1989 L1990 **FM** *020 †18

WAVERLY – HUMPHREYS

ALI, Maysoon Shocair. 806 E MAIN ST 37185 #875-01-1971 L1976 **IM GE** *020 ‡
ALI, Subhi Dawud Suboh. 806 E MAIN ST 37185 #010-03-1968 L1976 **GS** *020 †85 ‡
JACKSON, Lawrence R, Jr. 102 HILLWOOD DR 37185 #422-01-1986 L1989 **FM** *020 †18
KARPOS, Philip Anthony. 451 HIGHWAY 13 S 37185 #048-12-1989 L1995 **ORS** *020 †40
KLEIER, Ernest Bobby, Jr. 209 W MAIN ST 37185 #047-06-1974 L1975 **GS OM** *020 †85
MC CLURE, Wallace Joe. 451 HIGHWAY 13 S 37185 #047-06-1961 L1961 **OS** *071
OJEDA, Nestor A. 300 S CLYDETON RD 37185 #308-03-1984 L1990 **PD** *020
SKELTON, Angela Mary. 110 HILLWOOD DR 37185 #028-34-1970 L1974 **PD OS** *020 †55
WALKER, Arthur Winfrey. 806 E MAIN ST 37185 #047-06-1952 L1953 **FM** *020
WASSYNGER, William W. 451 HIGHWAY 13 S 37185 #035-01-1989 L2003 **CD** *020 †20

WAYNESBORO – WAYNE

COBLE, Robert Vaughn. 103 JV MANGUBAT DR, C/O WAYNE MEDICAL CENTER 38485 #028-02-1972 L1976 **GS CD** *020 †85
GRAVES, James M. 418 S MAIN ST 38485 #047-06-1976 L1977 **P FM** *020 †18
HALL, Joe Irvin. 103 JV MANGUBAT DR, STE A 38485 #047-20-1993 L1994 **FM EM** *020 †18
HERRERA, Esmeraldo Diaz. 905 ANDREW JACKSON DR, STE A, P.O. BOX 1059 38485 #748-10-1979 L1994 **IM** *020
LANGLEY, Hubert Ernest. 103 JV MANGUBAT DR 38485 #047-06-1975 L1976 **DR** *020
MANGUBAT, Jaime Virata. 103 JV MANGUBAT DR 38485 #748-01-1952 L1967 **GP GS** *020
OCAMPO, Osler Paul Mirand. ■ 38485 #748-01-1994 L2003 **IM** *020 †20

WESTMORELAND – SUMNER

GAILMARD, William Robert. 1124 NEW HIGHWAY 52 E # 1 37186 #047-06-1997 L1998 **FM** *020 †18

WHITE BLUFF – DICKSON

FERGUSON, Teresa Irene. ■ 37187 #047-07-2002 L2005 **FM** *100
HENDERSON-SLAYDEN, Rita. ■ 37187 #047-07-1981 L1982 **OBS GYN** *020 †30
JACKSON, Thomas Mendel. ■ 37187 #047-06-1955 L1955 **GS TS** *020 †85

WHITE HOUSE – ROBERTSON

ALSTON, Charles Pernele. ■ 37188 #047-07-1997 L2002 **IM** *020 †20
JENKINS, Hal Jefferson. PO BOX 1669 37188 #027-01-2001 L2002 **FM** *020 †18
JORDAN, Jeffrey Scott. 491 SAGE RD N, STE 200 37188 #047-06-2000 L2002 **FM** *020 †18
JUDKINS, Jeremiah Wade. ■ 37188 #047-06-2006 **IM** *012
KASTNER, Jason Lynn. 131 EDENWAY DR 37188 #019-02-1998 L2001 **PD** *020 †55
MILLER, Ronald Veazey. 131 EDENWAY DR 37188 #047-01-1976 L1980 **PD** *020 †55
MURRAY, Samuel Judson, II. 131 EDENWAY DR 37188 #051-04-1996 L2004 **PD** *020 †55
WALKER, Allen Roy, Jr. 538 RAYMOND HIRSCH PKWY 37188 #001-02-1991 L1993 **FM** *020
WILSON, Justin Wesley. ■ 37188 #041-14-2006 **AN** *012
YIM, Paul Sungwon. 128 RAYMOND HIRSCH PKWY 37188 #051-04-1993 L1996 **FM** *020 †18

WHITE PINE – JEFFERSON

ALLEN, Erman Dale. ■ 37890 #012-05-1946 L1949 **OBG GP** *071
BROMBACH, Joseph Arthur. 3543 MOUNTAIN VIEW LN, DANDRIDGE FAMILY PRACTICE 37890 #035-09-1997 L2001 **OS** *020 †18,20

WHITES CREEK – DAVIDSON

BELL, Owen Carl. ■ 37189 #005-12-1966 L1973 **OS GYN** *071

WHITWELL – MARION

COOPER, Christian F. ■ 37397 #045-01-1996 L1997 **IM** *020 †20
HOOPER, Micah Linette. ■ 37397 #047-20-2005 L2006 **P** *012
MC CARTNEY, Lester D. ■ 37397 #048-13-1985 L1995 **FM EM** *020 †18
PARK, Jung Tae. 13851 HIGHWAY 28 37397 #583-04-1966 L1976 **GP** *020 ‡

WILLIAMSPORT – MAURY

DYSINGER, Paul Wm. 38487 #005-12-1955 L1964 **GPM PHP** *071 †70

WINCHESTER – FRANKLIN

AHMED, Mainuddin. 1894 COWAN HWY, STE 100 37398 #160-01-1979 L1995 **HEM** *020
BAGBY, Richard Albert, Jr. 183 HOSPITAL RD STE G 37398 #012-05-1974 L1979 **ORS** *020 †40
BHULLAR-BAL, Ramneet. 183 HOSPITAL RD, STE C 37398 #021-01-1994 L2002 **N** *020
BROWN, Esme Herholdt. 144 HOSPITAL RD 37398 #047-06-1986 L1992 **AN PME** *020
BROWN, Lloyd Keith. 144 HOSPITAL RD 37398 #047-06-1985 L1992 **ORS GS** *020 †40
BYSTRITSKII, Albert V. ■ 37398 #517-05-1996 L2003 **FM EM** *020 †18
COSTA, Lawrence Wm, Jr. 185 HOSPITAL RD 37398 #649-35-1983 L1987 **IM** *020 †20
COX, Tony Mitchell. 186 HOSPITAL RD, STE 500 37398 #654-01-1999 L2003 **IM** *020
DHILLON, Gursheel S. 183 HOSPITAL RD, STE K 37398 #047-07-1993 L1999 **IM** *020
DOCKRILL, Lionel G C. R185 HOSPITAL RD 37398 #064-01-1954 L1981 **FM** *071
EKO-ISENALUMHE, Arnold I. 185 HOSPITAL RD 37398 #690-06-1993 L2003 **IM** *020 †20
ELLIS, Paul David. 185 HOSPITAL RD, DEPARTMENT OF RADIOLOGY 37398 #020-12-2000 L2003 **DR** *020 †80 ‡
FORT, Dudley Clark, Jr. 185 HOSPITAL RD 37398 #047-05-1964 L1970 **EM GS** *071
FUJIYOSHI, Carol Aiko. 55 SUNRISE PARK 37398 #023-12-1984 L1995 **OBG** *020 †30
GAME, Robert Clifford. 185 HOSPITAL RD 37398 #001-06-1977 L1991 **DR** *020 †80 ‡
GAMMADA, Ephraim B. 1509 OLD COWAN RD 37398 #366-01-1985 L1995 **IM** *020 †20
GREER, Patrick Roddy. 155 HOSPITAL RD, STE D 37398 #047-07-1978 L1979 **GS** *020 †20,85
HARCY, Peter. 185 HOSPITAL RD 37398 #047-05-1974 L1975 **DR** *071 †80
HIXSON, Troy A. 83 MEMORIAL DR, GENERAL SURGEON 37398 #033-06-2002 L2007 **GS** *020
HOLDER, Terry Scott. 185 HOSPITAL RD 37398 #047-06-1987 L1988 **FM OBS** *020 †18
JOHNSON, David Arthur. 495 TRI CITIES FARM RD 37398 #025-07-1960 L1991 **P** *020
JOHNSON, Gerald Eugene. 1ST AV NE 37398 #004-01-1946 L1955 **OS GS** *071
KOHLER, Robert James. 185 HOSPITAL RD 37398 #051-04-1967 L1989 **U** *071 †95
LANYON, Kenneth Marr. ■ 37398 #012-22-1993 L1997 **AN** *020 †05
MANGRU, Nevindranath. 155 HOSPITAL RD STE E 37398 #566-01-1986 L1995 **PDC PD** *020 †55
MOHYUDDIN, Adil Ibrahim. 185 HOSPITAL RD 37398 #047-06-1987 L1988 **HO** *020 †20
MYERS, Bryan Christopher. 81 MEMORIAL DR 37398 #047-06-2001 L2005 **OBG** *100
OMOHUNDRO, William A, II. 242 SHADOWBROOK RD 37398 #051-07-1989 L1994 **AN** *020 †05
PETROCHKO, Nicholas, Jr. 186 HOSPITAL RD, STE 100 37398 #047-06-1976 L1976 **GS** *020 †85
PHILPOTT, Donald M. 155 HOSPITAL RD STE B 37398 #065-01-1968 L1996 **GP** *020
RIVERO, Jose Luis, Jr. 161 SHIRLEY DR 37398 #047-07-1993 L2000 **OBG** *020 †30
RUDOLPH, Councill C, II. 155 HOSPITAL RD, STE D 37398 #051-01-1983 L1994 **GS** *020 †85
SMITH, Thomas Anderson. 186 HOSPITAL RD, 300 MED-DENT CTR 37398 #047-06-1978 L1978 **FM FPG** *020 †18
STENSBY, James Derek. ■ 37398 #012-05-2008 *012
STENSBY, James Gilbert. 186 HOSPITAL RD, STE 500 37398 #001-02-1975 L1979 **IM IMG** *020 †20
STEPP, Dara J. 134 HOSPITAL RD 37398 #020-75-2003, ▲ L2007 **FM** *020 †18
STOCKTON, David L. 185 HOSPITAL RD 37398 #047-06-1976 L1976 **OBG** *020 †30
SZCZARKOWSKA, Jolanta. 155 HOSPITAL RD STE E, WINCHESTER PEDIATRICS 37398 #759-01-1982 L1998 **PD** *020 †55
SZEWCZYK, Damian T. 83 MEMORIAL DR 37398 #759-01-1987 L2001 **GS** *020 †85
VILLAR, Rodolfo. R185 HOSPITAL RD 37398 #275-01-1947 L1973 **GP PD** *020
WERT, Mark Edward. 185 HOSPITAL RD, EMERGENCY DEPT 37398 #038-40-1991 L1995 **UCM EM** *020 ‡

WOODBURY – CANNON

GREEN, Richard E. ■ 37190 #047-05-1949 L1949 **PM GS** *071 †85
MARFATIA, Neha Sudhir. 324 DOOLITTLE RD, STONES RIVER HOSPITAL 37190 #496-25-1998 L2003 **IM** *020
MARFATIA, Sudhir R. 324 DOOLITTLE RD, STONES RIVER HOSPITAL 37190 #495-28-1966 L1997 **GS PDS** *020
MYERS, Russell E. ■ 37190 #005-12-1947 L1947 **OS GP** *071
REUHLAND, Leon Lovon. PO BOX 170 37190 #005-12-1970 L1971 **FM EM** *072 ‡
SEBER, James David. 370 DOOLITTLE RD 37190 #047-20-1992 L1995 **FM** *020 ‡
SPURLOCK, James R, III. 370 DOOLITTLE RD, STE 1 37190 #055-75-2001, ▲ L2002 **FM EM** *020 †18
SURBER, Jerry Lee. 324 DOOLITTLE RD 37190 #005-06-1975 L1989 **UCM** *020 ‡
TODD, Jeffrey Lee. 205 S MCCRARY ST 37190 #047-06-2002 L2004 **FM** *020 †18
WOLF, Herbert Richard. 324 DOOLITTLE RD 37190 #005-12-1970 L1971 **FM** *071
YOUNG, Keith David. 205 S MCCRARY ST, WOODBURY MED CTR 37190 #047-06-1988 L2000 **FM** *020 †18

ABILENE – TAYLOR

ABERNATHY, Stephen W. 1665 ANTILLEY RD, STE 1 79606 #048-15-1996 L1997 **GS** *020 †85
ADAMS, Jami Alicia. 4542 S 14TH ST 79605 #048-02-1996 L2000 **PD** *020 †55
AGUILAR, Lydia. ■ 79602 #048-04-1999 L2002 **IM** *020 †20
AKIN, William Orlan. 702 HICKORY ST 79601 #048-02-1959 L1960 **OTO HNS** *020 †45
AKS, Carolyn S. 1957 ANTILLEY RD 79606 #422-01-1989 L2002 **HEM ON** *020 †20
ALBUQUERQUE, Anil. ■ 79605 #495-73-1985 L2004 **AN** *020 †05
ALEXANDER, Joe Bob. 1025 CYPRESS ST 79601 #048-02-1973 L1973 **OS** *020 †55
ALLEN, Edmund Lewis. S. MAPLE STREET, ABILENE STATE SCHOOL 79604 #004-01-1973 L1975 **FM** *071 †18
AL-SAYYAD, Mohammad M. 1150 N 18TH ST, STE 203 79601 #875-01-1988 L1998 **NEP IM** *020 †20
AMILINENI, Venkata K R. 401 CYPRESS ST, STE 110 79601 #495-21-1987 L2002 **DR** *020 †80
ANDERSON, Charles Glenn. 1680 ANTILLEY RD STE 350 79606 #048-04-1982 L1983 **OBG** *020 †30
ANDERSON, Rexford K, Jr. 1900 PINE ST 79601 #048-02-1968 L1968 **N** *020
APPLETON, Joel Timothy. 2110 N WILLIS ST 79603 #048-12-1961 L1961 **A PHP** *071 †03
ARRIGHI, David Anthony. ■ 79602 #019-02-1978 L2002 **GS CCM** *020 †85
ARTHUR, Angele Jeanette. ■ 79606 #012-05-2005 L2006 *020
ARTHUR, John Steven. 1665 ANTILLEY RD, STE 200 79606 #048-04-1975 L1975 **IM IMG** *071 †20
AU, Kin-Wing. 1957 ANTILLEY RD 79606 #244-04-1984 L2001 **RO** *020 †80
BACCHUS, Joanne N. 1150 N 18TH ST STE 206 79601 #065-01-1986 L1995 **N** *071 †20
BADER, Sara K. ■ 79605 #048-15-2002 L2004 **FM** *020
BARBER, Laura. 1933 PINE ST STE 1A 79601 #048-13-1982 L1983 **FM** *020 †18
BARGAINER, Jack Delano. 1100 N 19TH ST 79601 #023-07-1961 L1970 **CD IM** *020 †20
BASS, James G. 1850 HICKORY ST STE 200 79601 #048-13-1987 L1989 **OBG** *020 †30
BAUMAN, Tony Jon. 4543 HARTFORD ST 79605 #046-01-1984 L1987 **AN** *020 †05
BAYOUTH, Lanoard M, II. 1680 ANTILLEY RD, STE 270 79606 #048-02-1987 L1989 **IC CD** *020 †20
BEJARANO, Angel G. ■ 79606 #726-01-1995 **FM** *100
BENNETT, Laura Lorraine. 1665 ANTILLEY RD, STE 285 79606 #005-18-2001 L2003 **GS** *020
BERRY, Don Wayne. 1100 N 19TH ST STE 4B 79601 #048-12-1967 L1968 **TS VS** *020 †85,90
BLACKWOOD, David Randall. 1201 N 18TH ST 79601 #048-15-1985 L1986 **CD** *020 †20
BLIZNAK, Johnny. 750 N 18TH ST 79601 #028-02-1967 L1967 **R** *020 †80 ‡
BORGFELD, Paul Allen. ■ 79605 #048-12-1985 L1986 **IM** *020 †20
BOYD, Virginia Hawkins. ■ 79605 #021-05-1938 L1939 **OPH OTO** *071
BRANDECKER, Edward John. 1888 ANTILLEY RD 79606 #010-02-1984 L1992 **PM** *020 †60
BRAY, Willis J, Jr. 1749 PINE ST 79601 #048-12-1950 L1950 **ORS** *071 †40
BREITKREUTZ, Lawrence R. 1150 N 18TH ST, STE 401 79601 #021-01-1987 L1995 **TS** *020 †85,90
BRITTEN, Jeremy B. 1749 PINE ST 79601 #048-14-2001 L2004 **ORS** *020
BROCK, James Price, Jr. 1701 PINE ST 79601 #048-04-1966 L1966 **ORS** *020 †40
BUTZ, Mark Allan. ■ 79606 #010-02-1983 L1993 **EM** *020
CANNON, Joe Ronald. 802 ORANGE ST 79601 #048-13-1974 L1974 **D DMP** *020 †15
CAPRA, Jay D. 6300 REGIONAL PLZ 79606 #048-13-1995 L1997 **PD** *020 †55
CARLSON, David Edmund. 1680 ANTILLEY RD, STE 260 79606 #017-20-1978 L1985 **TS** *020 †85,90
CARTER, Troy L. 1750 PINE ST 79601 #048-13-1992 L1993 **OPH** *020 †35
CASEY, James Gordon. ■ 79605 #039-01-1954 L1957 **GS OS** *071
CASS, Roger Leroy. 1665 ANTILLEY RD, STE 1 79606 #060-02-1976 L1978 **GP** *020 †30
CAVUOTI, Clinton Peter. 1150 N 18TH ST, STE 300 79601 #048-12-1979 L1979 **IM** *020 †20
CHANT, George Noel. 1201 N 18TH ST 79601 #065-06-1959 L1994 **CD** *020 †20
CHARPENTIER, Leonard A. ■ 79606 #024-05-1952 L1956 **OBG** *040 †30
CLAUSE, Holly Jean. 1900 PINE ST 79601 #048-14-1991 L1992 **AN** *020 †05
COMPTON, Johnathan Mark. ■ 79606 #028-03-2002 L2007 **FM** *020 †18
COOKE, John Cary, III. 1900 PINE ST 79601 #024-01-1965 L1966 **P** *071 †75
COOKE, Shannon E. 1749 PINE ST 79601 #048-02-1989 L1990 **ORS** *020 †40
COOPER, Merril Morris. 4149 FORREST HILL RD, STE C-1 79606 #021-01-1954 L1954 **D** *071 †15
COPE, Matthew Warren. ■ 79602 #048-04-2008 *012
COTNEY, Thomas Wade. 1665 ANTILLEY RD, STE 1 79606 #048-02-1979 L1979 **OTO** *020 †45
COX, Conald Wayne. 1150 N 18TH ST, STE 203 79601 #048-12-1976 L1976 **NEP IM** *020 †20
CROCKER, Scott Harrison. 1665 ANTILLEY RD STE 260 79606 #007-02-1977 L1987 **TS** *020 †85,90
CRUMBLISS, Joseph Howe. 1665 ANTILLEY RD, STE 1 79606 #047-06-1971 L1979 **FM** *020 †18
DAGGUBATI, Nageswari. 1900 PINE ST 79601 #495-57-1973 L1982 **CD** *020 †20
DAGGUBATI, Sam. 1309 HICKORY ST 79601 #495-58-1969 L1982 **IM PM** *020
DANIELL, Randy Carroll. 1210 N 18TH ST 79601 #048-02-1980 L1980 **OBG** *020 †30
DAVIS, William Dillard. 1149 AMBLER AVE, CENTER 79601 #048-04-1961 L1961 **U** *071 †95
DAWSON, George Albert. ■ 79606 #048-12-1956 L1956 **FM** *071 †18
DEPRANG, Clifford L. 2074 ANTILLEY RD 79606 #048-14-1997 L1998 **ORS** *020 †40
DE PRIEST, Jerry C. 1818 PINE ST STE 123 79601 #048-02-1983 L1983 **PTH** *020 †50
DICKERSON, Russell S. 1100 N 19TH ST, STE 3C 79601 #048-12-1989 L1992 **N** *020 ‡
DICKEY, Robert L, Jr. 1701 PINE ST 79601 #048-04-1982 L1983 **ORS** *020 †40
DIXON, Joseph Andrew. 6300 REGIONAL PLZ 79606 #048-15-1986 L1987 **FM** *020 †18
DOZIER, Norman Jay. 2401 N TREADAWAY BLVD 79601 #048-02-1982 L1983 **PMM AN** *020 †05
DUFF, James Ira. 1150 N 18TH ST, STE 102 79601 #048-13-1972 L1972 **PTH** *020 †50
DUMAS, Michel Denis Jos. 401 CYPRESS ST, STE 110 79601 #065-09-1990 L1996 **DR** *020 †80
DWYER, William Jos. 5349 WILLOW RIDGE RD 79606 #008-01-1992 L1995 **NPM** *100 †55
DYER, Theodore C. 1850 HICKORY ST, STE 200D 79601 #048-12-1982 L1983 **OTO HNS** *020 †45
ESTES, Bobby Jack. 1150 N 18TH ST, STE 300 79601 #048-04-1956 L1956 **FM** *020 †18
EZZELL, Chad D. 1850 HICKORY ST, STE 105 79601 #048-12-2001 L2002 **FSM** *020 †18
FAEHNLE, Stephen Thos. 1850 HICKORY ST STE 102, FOR PEDIATRICS 79601 #038-40-1973 L1978 **PD PDP** *020 †55
FAKHOURY, Ibrahim Sami. 1150 N 18TH ST STE 203 79601 #026-04-1995 L1998 **NEP** *020 †20
FERGUSON, John D, III. ■ 79605 #048-14-2001 L2005 **AN** *020 †05
FERGUSON, Joseph Martin. 1150 N 18TH ST, STE 300 79601 #038-40-1973 L1975 **IM** *020 †20
FERNANDO, Victoria. 1857 PINE ST STE 10, TEXAS TECH PHYSICIANS OF A 79601 #748-01-1985 L1999 **FM OBS** *020 †18 ‡
FIERRO-CARRION, Gustavo. ■ 79605 #319-01-1986 L1993 **IM** *020 †20
FRANCE, Ratchnee. ■ 79608 #665-01-2002 L2002 **FM** *020 †18
FRAZEE, Richard C. 1665 ANTILLEY RD, STE 1 79606 #048-16-1983 L1983 **GS CRS** *020 †85
FREEMAN, Robert G. ■ 79606 #048-04-1949 L1949 **DMP D** *072 †50,15
FULLER, Charles Wilson. 1933 PINE ST, STE B 79601 #048-12-1979 L1979 **FM EM** *020 †18 ‡
FUNK, Dale A. 2074 ANTILLEY RD 79606 #048-12-1992 L1993 **ORS** *020 †40
GANESH, Brian Rabindranau. 6200 REGIONAL PLZ, STE 1450 79606 #030-06-1998 L2000 **IM** *020 †20
GARCIA, Elvira. 6250 REGIONAL PLZ, STE 1030 79606 #048-13-1986 L1987 **PD** *020 †55
GARCIA, Philip E. PO BOX 3536 79604 #048-14-1995 L2002 **AN** *020
GARRETT, Donald Clinton. ■ 79605 #048-12-1957 L1957 **AN** *071 †05
GARRETT, Richard Earl. ■ 79605 #048-12-1957 L1957 **AN** *071 †05
GARZA, Pedro Y. 1 VILLAGE DR, STE 250 79606 #048-12-1982 L1983 **AN GS** *020 †05
GEESLIN, Bertram Beal, Jr. 1150 N 18TH ST 79601 #048-04-1977 L1978 **PTH** *020 †50
GOLLIHAR, William Paige. ■ 79602 #048-12-1954 L1955 **OPH** *071 †35
GOODNIGHT, Ashley Marie. ■ 79605 #048-15-2008 *012
GRAY, William Ryburn, Jr. ■ 79606 #020-02-1973 L1976 **DR NM** *071 †28,80
GREWAL, Reena. 2616 S CLACK ST, BETTY HARDWICK CENTER 79606 #495-73-1987 L2004 **P** *020 †75
GRIFFIN, Somsri. 2616 S CLACK ST, BETTY HARDWICK CENTER 79606 #891-01-1955 L1977 **CHP** *020 †75
GUERRA, Jose J. 560 N JUDGE ELY BLVD 79601 #649-02-1952 L1960 **FM** *071
GULLETT, John H, II. 1150 N 18TH ST, STE 402 79601 #869-04-1973 L1998 **ID IM** *020 †20
HAGLUND, Rodger B. 1290 S WILLIS ST, STE 200 79605 #041-13-1962 L1978 **A D** *020 †50
HALBERT, David Stafford. 1665 ANTILLEY RD, DAVID S HALBERT MD 79606 #048-02-1959 L1959 **GS** *071
HALL, Joe David. 4403 S 20TH ST 79605 #047-06-1964 L1967 **PTH** *020 †50
HAMILTON, Hinton H. ■ 79606 #048-12-1944 L1945 **P GP** *071
HAMILTON, Rae Ann. 950 N 19TH ST STE 100 79601 #048-14-1984 L1985 **FM** *020 †18
HARDWICKE, Lawrence Gail. 1900 PINE ST 79601 #048-02-1961 L1961 **IM** *071 †20
HARPER, Johnny Mac. 401 CYPRESS ST, STE 110 79601 #048-02-1967 L1967 **DR** *071 †18,80
HARPER, Robert David. 1665 ANTILLEY RD, STE 1 79606 #048-02-1970 L1970 **FM** *020 †18
HARRIS, Paul C. 1100 N 19TH ST, STE 4B 79601 #048-12-1984 L1985 **N** *020
HARRISON, Berney Randolph. 6200 REGIONAL PLZ, STE 1600 79606 #021-01-1967 L1968 **OBG OS** *020 †30
HAYNES, William Comer. 1249 AMBLER AVE STE 200 79601 #048-02-1980 L1980 **GE IM** *020 †20
HEADSTREAM, Thomas Lee. 1665 ANTILLEY RD STE 200, ABILENE DIAGNOSTIC CLINIC 79606 #048-12-1979 L1982 **IM CCM** *020 †20
HEATH, Gary Lynn. 6399 DIRECTORS PKWY, SUITE 200 79606 #048-02-1978 L1978 **AN** *020 †05
HEAVEN, Ralph F, Jr. 1957 ANTILLEY RD, TEXAS CANCER CENTER - ABIL 79606 #016-11-1983 L1996 **ON HEM** *020 †20
HENDRIX, Henry Harold, Jr. 1665 ANTILLEY RD, STE 1 79606 #019-02-1986 L1988 **ORS** *020 †40
HIGGINS, Henry Lewis. 1900 PINE ST, HENDRICK TRAUMA CENTER 79601 #055-01-1996 L2003 **IM** *020
HILLER, Frederick E. 6200 REGIONAL PLZ, STE 1200 79606 #048-13-1978 L1978 **NEP** *020 †20,16
HIRSCH, Victor John. 2000 PINE ST, HENDRICK CANCER CENTER 79601 #048-12-1976 L1978 **ON HEM** *020 †20
HOLLAND, Gary Max. 1150 N 18TH ST, STE 300 79601 #048-02-1981 L1981 **FM** *020 †18
HOYNIAK-BECKER, Ann L. ■ 79606 #041-14-1992 L1993 **AM PHP** *020 †70
HUDMAN, Eugene Victor. 6200 REGIONAL PLZ STE 1 79606 #048-15-1996 L1997 **IM** *020 †20
IZBRAND, David James. 1750 PINE ST 79601 #048-14-1986 L1987 **OPH FM** *020 †35
JACKSON, Stephen Jeffery. 4009 RIDGEMONT DR 79606 #048-02-1979 L1979 **IM EM** *020 †20
JAMES, Janeen Halifax. PO BOX 7268 79608 #048-13-1982 L1983 **GS** *020 †85
JENKS, Michael Jeffrey. 560 N JUDGE ELY BLVD 79601 #005-18-1994 L2000 **FM** *020 †18
JOHNSON, Michele Pitts. 1149 AMBLER AVE 79601 #048-04-1975 L1975 **GYN** *020 †30
JOHNSON, Steven Kenneth. 1249 AMBLER AVE, STE 200 79601 #048-12-1990 L1991 **GE** *020 †20
JOHNSON, Terry Clay. 1149 AMBLER AVE 79601 #048-04-1975 L1975 **U** *020 †95
JONES, Billy Don. 1680 ANTILLEY RD, STE 100 79606 #048-12-1976 L1976 **CD** *020 †20
JONES, Kendall Maurice. 1231 CHARIOT CIR, ATTN CREDENTIAL OFFICE 79602 #010-01-1985 L1992 **DR** *020 †80
JORDAN, Larry K. 401 CYPRESS ST, STE 110 79601 #048-15-1997 L2002 **DR** *020 †80
JUDD, John Howard. 6250 REGIONAL PLZ, STE 1016 79606 #047-05-1973 L1977 **AM EM** *020 †40
KALLA, Hari Krishna. 1957 ANTILLEY RD 79606 #495-62-1990 L2003 **HO** *020 †20
KAPU, Ameeta. 1850 HICKORY ST 79601 #048-02-1994 L1996 **OBG** *020 †30
KASHYAP, Vikram. 1111 INDUSTRIAL BLVD, BLDG 2 79602 #495-43-1997 L2005 **CHP P** *020
KENDRICK, Brad Thos. 950 N 19TH ST STE 202 79601 #048-15-1989 L1990 **CRS** *020 †85,10
KING, Austin Irvin. 2217 S DANVILLE DR 79605 #048-04-1973 L1974 **OTO HNS** *020 †45
KROEGER, Gregory P. 1210 N 18TH ST 79601 #048-15-1999 L2001 **OBG** *020 †30
KUMAR, Krishna Prasanna. 6200 REGIONAL PLZ STE 1200 79606 #495-33-1969 L1991 **IM** *020 †20 ‡
LAWLER, Gerry N. 1317 N 8TH ST, STE 200 79601 #048-15-1975 L1975 **AN PME** *020
LAWSON, Robert Lee. 1900 PINE ST 79601 #048-12-1984 L1985 **FM** *020 †18
LEE, Seong Young. 5441 HEALTH CENTER DR 79606 #048-12-1998 L1999 **OPH** *020 †35
LENHERT, Kenneth Martin. 1900 PINE ST 79601 #048-12-1976 L1996 **EM** *020 †16
LEVERTON, Robert S, II. 6200 REGIONAL PLZ STE 1250 79606 #003-01-1976 L1979 **CD IM** *020 †20
LIEN, Jung Chin. 149 GRAPE ST 79601 #244-01-1975 L1980 **FM** *020 †18
LILLICK, Timothy Wm. 401 CYPRESS ST, STE 110 79601 #048-12-1981 L1981 **DR** *020 †80
LIN, Larry Wen. 1201 N 18TH ST 79601 #056-06-1992 L2000 **CD** *020 †20
LOCKHART, Robert West. 1680 ANTILLEY RD, STE 100 79606 #048-04-1958 L1958 **CD IM** *071 †20
LORENZO, Amelia. 4225 WOODS PL 79602 #308-11-1990 L2001 **IM** *020
LOTHIAN, Amy Catherine. 1850 HICKORY ST, STE 102 79601 #033-05-2001 L2004 **MPD** *020 †20,55 ‡
LOWRY, Henry Neal. 1900 PINE ST 79601 #048-13-1973 L1973 **AN FM** *020 †05
LOWRY, Stephen Ray. ■ 79606 #048-12-2000 L2004 **AN** *020 †05
LUND, Howard W. 1900 PINE ST, TRAUMA CENTER HENDRICK MED 79601 #048-13-1985 L1986 **EM FM** *020 †18
MABERRY, Mark C. 1850 HICKORY ST, 2ND FL 79601 #048-12-1983 L1983 **MFM OBG** *020 †30,19

■ = Address Information Privacy Protected

MAILAPUR, Yamini Veerayya. 1850 HICKORY ST STE 203, ABILENE INFECTIOUS DISEASE 79601 #496-01-1995 L2000 **ID** *020 †20
MALOWNEY, Scott Michael. 1900 PINE ST, HENDRICK EMERGENCY DEPARTM 79601 #039-01-1981 L1982 **EM GP** *020 †16
MARTIN, Timothy S. 950 N 19TH ST 79601 #048-12-1996 L1997 **FM** *020 †18
MARTINEZ, Robert Raul. ■ 79601 #048-02-1961 L1962 **U** *020
MASCORRO, Whitney L. ■ 79602 #048-14-2001 L2005 **OBG** *020 †30
MASLANKA, Paul Jos. 2150 CEDAR ST 79601 #016-11-1976 L1978 **PD** *020 †55
MAXWELL, Mark S. 1525 HICKORY ST 79601 #028-78-1987, ▲ L1996 **NS GS** *020
MC CAIN, David Brian. 6200 REGIONAL PLZ, STE 1400 79606 #004-01-1987 L1995 **CD** *020 †20
MC CAIN, Stefanie Bertie. 1680 ANTILLEY RD, STE 370 79606 #047-06-1989 L1996 **OBG** *020 †30
MC CLESKEY, Ralph M, Jr. 1100 N 19TH ST, STE 2 79601 #048-12-1969 L1969 **CD IM** *071 †20
MC DONOUGH, Paul W. 1701 PINE ST 79601 #005-14-1995 L2001 **ORS** *020 †40
MCHUGH, Colleen M. ■ 79606 #539-02-1991 L1995 **HEM** *071 †20
MC KNIGHT, Maxey Dell. 1933 PINE ST STE B, ABILENE FAMILY HEALTH CARE 79601 #048-02-1980 L1980 **FM** *040 †18
MEHTA, Sudha R. 4225 WOODS PL 79602 #495-48-1971 L1992 **IM** *020 †20
MEHTA, Zarna Mooljibhai. ■ 79602 #495-48-1979 L2001 **OBG** *020 †30
MELNYK, Anton Marcus. 1100 N 19TH ST, STE 1A 79601 #060-01-1988 L1995 **ON HEM** *020 †20
MERIWETHER, Paul Wright. 950 N 19TH ST STE 201 79601 #048-15-1980 L1980 **ORS** *020 †40
MERRICK, James Estes. ■ 79601 #005-12-1947 L1947 **GP GS** *020
MIKESKA, Joe Edward. 3101 S 27TH ST 79605 #048-12-1957 L1957 **GP IM** *020
MILLER, Duane C. 1111 INDUSTRIAL BLVD # 2 79602 #039-01-1960 L1969 **P ADL** *020
MILLER, Thomas Harrop, Jr. 6250 REGIONAL PLZ STE 1000 79606 #025-07-1971 L1977 **U** *020 †95
MOAK, Barry Lynn. 1150 N 18TH ST, STE 204 79601 #048-13-1983 L1984 **FM** *020 †18
MONTGOMERY, Michael Davis. 401 CYPRESS ST STE 110 79601 #048-02-1974 L1974 **DR** *020 †80 ‡
MOORE, Eddie Paul. 1900 PINE ST, TRAUMA CENTER 79601 #048-14-1975 L1975 **EM** *020
MORGAN, Clyde N. 1166 MERCHANT ST 79603 #048-02-1953 L1953 **D FM** *020
MORRISON, James E. 2233 WOODRIDGE DR 79605 #048-14-1988 L1989 **EM** *020 †18
MUNTON, Daniel L. 4545 HARTFORD ST 79605 #048-12-1995 L1996 **PM** *020 †60
NAFRAWI, Adel G. 1311 HICKORY ST 79601 #915-02-1949 L1971 **TS** *020 †85
NAIDOO, Randy Mel. ■ 79602 #048-14-2003 L2005 **PD** *020 †55
NGUYEN, Ta Van. 35 WINDMILL CIR 79606 #941-01-1965 L1978 **N** *020
NIEBELSKI, Andrzej L. 1680 ANTILLEY RD, STE 360 79606 #759-10-1978 L1997 **PD** *020
NITKE, Steven John. 401 CYPRESS ST, STE 110 79601 #026-04-1993 L1998 **NM** *020 †80,28
NORTON, Kathryn Susanne. 1100 N 19TH ST STE 4 79601 #048-15-1998 L1999 **GS** *020 †85
NORTON, Peter K. 1850 HICKORY ST, STE 200 79601 #048-04-1970 L1970 **OBG GYN** *020 †30
OGDEE, Robert Geo. 1680 ANTILLEY RD STE 20 79606 #048-16-1988 L1989 **OBG** *020 †30
O'NEAL, Kenneth Wilkey. 3900 N 1ST ST, STE 10 79603 #048-12-1969 L1969 **GP OS** *020
ONGER, Frederick R. 1857 PINE ST, STE 100 79601 #048-12-1995 L1998 **FM** *020 †18
PADON, Derek T. 1749 PINE ST 79601 #048-14-2003 L2008 **ORS** *012
PATE, Preston Leigh. 1850 HICKORY ST, STE 103 79601 #048-14-1989 L1990 **PUD IM** *020 †20
PATE, Tamren Brown. 1900 PINE ST 79601 #048-14-1989 L1990 **PUD IM** *020 †20
PATEL, Ashish Chandrakant. 401 CYPRESS ST, STE 110 79601 #025-07-1993 L2000 **RNR** *020 †80
PATEL, Laurie M. 1818 PINE ST STE 119 79601 #048-12-1992 L1997 **FM** *020 †18
PATEL, Nikunjkumar I. 1680 ANTILLEY RD, STE 100 79606 #917-02-1978 L2003 **CD** *020 †20
PATEL, Sunilkumar S. 5441 HEALTH CENTER DR 79606 #048-12-1991 L1997 **OPH** *020 †35
PATEL, Yogeshkumar T. 6200 REGIONAL PLZ, STE 1675 79606 #495-89-1983 L2001 **GE MPD** *020 †20,55
PATHMANATHAN, S. ■ 79606 #913-92-1971 L1986 **GE IM** *020 †20
PATTERSON, Sheila S. ■ 79606 #048-12-1982 L1983 **FM** *020 †18
PELFREY, Robert James. 1665 ANTILLEY RD 79606 #001-02-1976 L2006 **U** *020 †95
PHELAN, Mark Jos. 2120 ANTILLEY RD 79606 #025-01-1990 L1994 **OPH** *020 †35
PHILLIPP, Kathleen Ann. 1857 PINE ST STE 100 79601 #048-02-1981 L1982 **P** *020
PICKARD, J Lance. 1100 N 19TH ST, STE 3B 79601 #048-13-1988 L1994 **U** *020 †95
POLLOCK, Mark Allen. 1818 PINE ST STE 123, CLINICAL PATHOLOGY ASSOCIA 79601 #048-02-1978 L1978 **PTH** *020 †50
POPE, John Mckinley. ■ 79606 #665-01-2002 L2004 **FM** *020 †18
PORTERFIELD, D G. 1900 PINE ST 79601 #048-12-1955 L1955 **FM** *071 †18
PRICE, Michael Dewayne. 4400 BUFFALO GAP RD, STE 2250 79606 #039-01-1990 L1993 **APM** *020 †05
PRIESTNER, Vincent. 2120 ANTILLEY RD, ABILLENE EYE INST 79606 #065-09-1967 L1978 **FM** *020 ‡
RAINEY, William Cecil. ■ 79606 #004-01-1980 L1991 **PS** *020 †85
RAMSEY, Jack David. 401 CYPRESS ST, STE 110 79601 #048-02-1956 L1956 **R** *071 †80
RANDEL, Joseph Clay. ■ 79605 #048-12-1957 L1957 **AN** *071
RANDELL, David Joseph. 35 WINDMILL CIR 79606 #048-78-1988, ▲ L1989 **FM** *020 †18
REEDY, Mark Brendan. 2000 PINE ST, ABILENE HEMATOLOGY/ONCOLOG 79601 #048-15-1989 L1990 **OBG** *020 †30
REGAN, Kevin Wm. 13055 FM 3522, TEXAS TECH UNIV HSC MIDDLE 79601 #048-14-1986 L1988 **GP** *020
REINMUND, Richard Edward. 602 HICKORY ST, STE A 79601 #048-12-1982 L1983 **GYN** *020 †30
RICHERT, Harvey Miller. 1750 PINE ST 79601 #039-01-1974 L1978 **OPH** *020 †35
ROARK, Gary Dean. 1249 AMBLER AVE, STE 200 79601 #048-02-1975 L1975 **GE IM** *020 †20
ROBERTS, Justin K. 1100 N 19TH ST STE 4A 79601 #048-15-2002 L2004 **GS** *020
ROBINSON, Lynn Marie. 1666 ANTILLEY RD, STE 200 79606 #020-12-1998 L2005 **IM** *020 †20
ROBINSON, Noel K, Jr. ■ 79601 #048-14-1991 L1992 **IM** *020 †20
RODE, R Lee Henry. 1900 PINE ST 79601 #048-04-1946 L1946 **GYN OS** *071 †30
ROTHWELL, Richard O'Neil. 1680 ANTILLEY RD STE 320 79606 #048-13-1972 L1972 **OBG** *020 †30
ROWE, Ralph Wayne. ■ 79601 #048-02-1957 L1957 **FM** *071 †18
SANTMAN, Mark. 1701 PINE ST 79601 #041-13-1995 L2003 **ORS** *020 †40 ‡
SCHACKMUTH, Eric Michael. 401 CYPRESS ST, STE 110 79601 #056-05-1990 L1996 **DR** *020 †80
SCHAFFER, Herman E. 150 ORANGE ST 79601 #035-09-1959 L1965 **PD** *020 †55
SCHULTZ, Dean A, Jr. 1850 HICKORY ST, STE 103A 79601 #048-04-1991 L1992 **FM** *020 †18
SELBY, Stanly Theodore. 1115 INDUSTRIAL BLVD 79602 #048-15-1984 L1985 **FM** *020 †18
SHAH, Tushar Mafatlal. 2150 CEDAR ST, ABILENE CHILDRENS MED 79601 #495-48-1987 L1998 **PD** *020 †55
SHARP, Joseph Edward. ■ 79606 #048-02-1948 L1948 *071
SHOULTZ, Vardeman H. 401 CYPRESS ST, RADIOLOGY ASSOCIATES PA 79601 #048-02-1944 L1944 **R** *071 †80
SHRINGERI, Akkamahadevi C. 2100 ANTILLEY RD 79606 #495-72-1976 L1984 **AI PD** *020 †55,03
SHUDDE, William F. 950 N 19TH ST, STE 100 79601 #048-13-1991 L1992 **FM** *020 †18
SIBLEY, William R, Jr. 1900 PINE ST 79601 #048-04-1950 L1950 **GS GP** *071
SIMPAO, Vidal Ocampo, Jr. 3101 S 27TH ST 79605 #748-10-1973 L1980 **GP** *020
SINCLAIR, Jerry Wayne. 1680 ANTILLEY RD, STE 380 79606 #048-15-1982 L1983 **OBG** *020 †30
SINGH, Jessie Bhatia. 1111 INDUSTRIAL BLVD, BLDG 2 79602 #495-03-1972 L1980 **P GP** *020 †75
SINGH, Surinder Jasbir. 401 CYPRESS ST, STE 110 79601 #495-03-1972 L1980 **RO** *020 †80
SKAGGS, Lee Aylott. ■ 79605 #030-05-1961 L1961 **PTH** *020 †50
SPIER, Roger Douglas. ■ 79606 #035-01-1967 L1968 **GS** *071 †85
STANLEY, David P. 1150 N 18TH ST, STE 102 79601 #048-02-1988 L1993 **PTH** *020 †50
STANLEY, Richard Dean. 1680 ANTILLEY RD, STE 310 79606 #048-12-1972 L1972 **OBG** *020 †30
STARK, David Michael. 1749 PINE ST 79601 #048-04-1983 L1983 **ORS** *020 †40
STEADMAN, Brent M. 6300 REGIONAL PLZ STE 650 79606 #048-15-1993 L1998 **MPD PD** *020
STENDER, Evelyn Louise. ■ 79605 #025-12-2001 L2001 **P** *020
STEWARD, Mary Booth. 1459 TANGLEWOOD RD, BOX 5135 79605 #048-12-1949 L1949 **AN** *071
STOCKSTILL, Randall Dean. 4400 BUFFALO GAP RD, ABILENE DIAGNOSTIC CLINIC 79606 #048-14-1975 L1975 **AN** *020
STOEBNER, Andrew Alan. 1701 PINE ST 79601 #048-14-1989 L1990 **ORS** *020 †40
STOEBNER, Darrold Andrew. 302 MEDICAL DR 79601 #016-06-1960 L1984 **FM** *020
STOJANOVIC, Tamara. 1100 N 19TH ST, STE 3A 79601 #957-01-1991 L1999 **PCC** *020 †20
STRIEGLER, Robert L. 1801 HICKORY ST, # 1 79601 #048-15-1983 L1983 **IM** *020
STROBEL, Roddy M. 1111 INDUSTRIAL BLVD 79602 #048-13-1987 L1988 **CHP P** *020 †75
STRONG, Jimmy Lee. 1850 HICKORY ST STE 102, FOR PEDIATRICS 79601 #048-04-1981 L1981 **PD** *020 †55
SWARNA, Udaya Shankar. 1201 N 18TH ST 79601 #495-99-1984 L1993 **CD ICE** *020 †20
TADVICK, Joseph L. 1210 N 18TH ST 79601 #048-16-1997 L1998 **OBG** *020 †30
TALIAFERRO, Leigh. 1100 N 19TH ST STE 3G 79601 #048-15-1981 L1981 **GS** *020 †85
TAYLOR, Floyd Dean. ■ 79601 #048-04-1938 L1938 **GS** *071
TEAGUE, Brettly J. 1750 PINE ST 79601 #048-15-1990 L1991 **OPH** *020 †35
THAMES, Paul Burnett. 2120 ANTILLEY RD 79606 #048-12-1979 L1979 **OPH** *020 †35
THOMPSON, Charles D. 6250 REGIONAL PLZ, STE 1000 79606 #048-12-1988 L1989 **OBG** *020 †30
THORP, Gorman Murph. 1201 N 18TH ST 79601 #048-02-1978 L1978 **CD IM** *020 †20
TOBIN, Howard Allen. 6300 REGIONAL PLZ STE 475 79606 #048-04-1964 L1964 **FPS PS** *020 †45
TORO VASCO, Maria Teresa. ■ 79601 #264-03-2000 L2008 **FP** *012
TORRES, Quirico Umali. 1101 N 19TH ST, STE 103 79601 #748-10-1974 L1985 **NS** *020
TRAMMELL, James Talmadge. 1850 HICKORY ST STE 101 79601 #048-15-2001 L2007 **NS** *020
TRATNIK, Lek. 2626 S CLACK ST, ABILENE REGIONAL MHMR CENT 79606 #891-02-1956 L1980 **P FM** *020 †75
TRAUTH, Christopher Jos. 2000 PINE ST, ABILENE HEMATOLOGY/ONCOLOG 79601 #021-05-1974 L1978 **ON IM** *020
TRAVIS, Zane Roland. 2141 S 19TH ST 79605 #048-04-1958 L1958 **RHU IM** *030 †20 ‡
TREANOR, Willys L Curtis. ■ 79605 #033-05-1967 L1970 **AN** *020
TRIFILO, Richard David. 1888 ANTILLEY RD, SPINE ABILENE 79606 #028-34-1980 L2006 **AM FM** *030 †70,18
TROTTER, Billy Bob. 1900 PINE ST 79601 #048-02-1954 L1954 **PTH ON** *071 †50
TROTTER, Maureen E. 1150 N 18TH ST, STE 102 79601 #048-12-1976 L1978 **PTH BBK** *020 †50
TRUSLER, Carl Otis. 1665 ANTILLEY RD, STE 200 79606 #048-04-1972 L1973 **FM AM** *020
TUEGEL, Arthur Gregory. 1850 HICKORY ST STE 102, FOR PEDIATRICS 79601 #028-34-1980 L1982 **PD** *020 †55
TULL, Raymond H, Jr. 1900 PINE ST 79601 #048-02-1951 L1951 **GP FM** *020
TURNBULL, Marshall D. ■ 79605 #048-04-1950 L1950 **GS GP** *072
URBAN, Craig Devon. 3190 ANTILLEY RD 79606 #017-20-1976 L1978 **D OS** *020 †15
VADNEY, Victor Jonathan. 2501 MAPLE ST 79602 #048-04-1975 L1975 **FM** *020 †18
VAN ANDEL, Rodney Kent. 1100 N 19TH ST, STE 4C 79601 #056-06-1999 L2003 **FSM** *020 †18
VAUGHAN, Daniel J M. 1101 N 19TH ST, STE 102 79601 #064-01-1987 L1995 **N** *020
VEDATI, Durga Prasad. ■ 79606 #495-11-1999 L2004 **FP** *012
VIDAL, Jose Francisco. 1111 INDUSTRIAL BLVD, BLDG 2 79602 #264-05-1987 L2002 **PYG** *020 †75
VOELTER, William Wayne. 3190 ANTILLEY RD, AURORA HEALTH CENTER 79606 #048-12-1967 L1967 **D** *020 †15
VU, Boi Xuan. 2810 DARRELL DR, 2810 DARRELL ,ABILENE,TX 7 79606 #941-01-1972 L1978 **FM GP** *020
WALKE, John Skipper. 702 HICKORY ST 79601 #048-02-1973 L1973 **PUD CCM** *020 †20
WALKE, Martha Anne. 702 HICKORY ST 79601 #048-02-1973 L1973 **FM** *020 †18
WALKER, Gary David. 1100 N 19TH ST STE 4D 79601 #048-12-1979 L1979 **GS** *020 †85
WALKER, James Thos. 1100 N 19TH ST 79601 #048-02-1963 L1963 **OPH** *071
WARD, Stephen Craig. 1665 ANTILLEY RD, STE 1 79606 #048-04-1978 L1978 **OBG** *020 †30
WEBSTER, James Douglas. ■ 79606 #048-02-1964 L1964 **NEP IM** *071 †20
WEBSTER, John Adams, III. ■ 79606 #001-06-2001 L2007 **PCP** *100
WEHMEYER, Donald Lee. 1100 N 19TH ST STE 4E 79601 #028-03-1971 L1981 **PS HS** *020 †85,65 ‡
WHITE, Frederick Andreas. 2125 PINE ST 79601 #048-02-1969 L1969 **DIA END** *020 †20
WHITE, Roddy S. ■ 79602 #048-15-1994 L1995 **FM** *020 †18
WHITT, Amy Catherine. ■ 79602 #055-02-2003 **PD** *100 †55
WHITT, Theresa A. 12071 FM 3522, ROBERTSON UNIT 79601 #048-15-1990 L1991 **OBG** *020
WILEY, Robert D. 1850 HICKORY ST STE 102, FOR PEDIATRICS 79601 #048-13-1991 L1995 **PD** *020 †55
WILLIAMS, George Toby. 1100 N 19TH ST STE B 79601 #048-14-1977 L1977 **IM** *020 †20
WILLIAMS, Keith De Armond. 3101 S 27TH ST 79605 #038-41-1979 L1983 **EM FM** *030
WILLIAMS, Vernon Mark. 1100 N 19TH ST, STE 4D 79601 #020-12-1988 L2001 **GS** *072 †85
WILLIAMSON, Lee. ■ 79604 #048-02-1938 L1938 **PD** *071 †55
WOLF, Roland Orville. 1900 PINE ST, HYPERBARIC & WOUND CARE CE 79601 #048-02-1964 L1964 **PS GS** *020 †85,65
WOODWARD, George Alexande. 302 MEDICAL DR 79601 #048-13-1975 L1975 **GS** *020 †85

■ = Address Information Privacy Protected

WOODWARD, Thomas A. 1100 N 19TH ST, STE 1D 79601 #026-04-1976 L1989 IM AM *020 †20,70
YAZDANI, Imran A. 4225 WOODS PL 79602 #704-16-1983 L1994 IM *020
YEH, Amelia Yeepih. 3210 ANTILLEY RD, CHEST & SLEEP MEDICINE, PA 79606 #016-06-1991 L2001 PCC *020 †20
YEH, William L. ■ 79606 #917-30-1966 L1973 DR *071
ZHANG, Ren. 1680 ANTILLEY RD, STE 100 79606 #243-03-1996 L2006 CD *020 †20
ZHANG, Xiang Ling. ■ 79606 #243-69-1985 L2000 FM *020 †18

ADDISON – DALLAS

ALHILALI, Lea Marcie. ■ 75001 #024-01-2004 DR *012
BATALIS, Nicholas Ike. ■ 75001 #017-20-2003 L2004 FOP *012 †50
BEARER, Elizabeth Ann. 14131 MIDWAY RD STE 6 75001 #011-02-1990 L2005 IM ID *020 †20
BOLAJI, Olubukola D. 14131 MIDWAY RD STE 620 75001 #690-07-1984 L2006 IM *020 †20
BROWN, Zachary Edward. ■ 75001 #011-03-2004 L2006 DR *012
DAVIS, Larry Donnell. 5015 ADDISON CIR, # 532 75001 #048-02-1979 L1981 PD *020
DIMAFELIX, Crisanto Garci. 15810 MIDWAY RD, CONCENTRA URGENT CARE 75001 #748-08-1997 L2005 FM *020 †18
DUTTA, Ellen Joy. 16901 DALLAS PKWY # 206, STE 206 75001 #048-13-1997 L2001 AI IM *020 †20,03
FOGARTY, Gerald Jos. 15303 DALLAS PKWY STE 170 75001 #018-03-1968 L1985 FM OS *020 †18
FOGARTY, William Thos. 5080 SPECTRUM DR, STE 400W 75001 #048-15-1980 L1980 OM FM *020 †18
FOJTASEK, Marvin Franklyn. 15800 DOOLEY RD STE 1 75001 #048-02-1981 L1981 ID *020 †20
HATLEY, Warren G, Jr. 15810 MIDWAY RD 75001 #048-13-1985 L1986 FM *020 †18
HUGHES, Michael S. 14131 MIDWAY RD STE 6 75001 #048-16-1994 L1995 IM *020 †20
HUSAIN, Huned Muzaffer. 14131 MIDWAY RD STE 6 75001 #495-21-1988 L2003 FM *020 †18
KENG, Ephraim Timothy. 14131 MIDWAY RD STE 6 75001 #016-43-1996 L1999 IM *020 †20
KETHI REDDY, Prathyusha. 14131 MIDWAY RD STE 6 75001 #495-11-1997 L2004 IM *020 †20
KIM, Leroy Kyoungmann. 14131 MIDWAY RD STE 620, IPC THE HOSPITALIST COMP 75001 #056-05-1989 L1995 PD IM *020 †55,20
KURUP, Savita R. 14131 MIDWAY RD STE 620, IPC THE HOSPITAL COMPANY 75001 #495-35-1988 L2001 FM *020 †18
LA GRONE, Dawn Sheree. 16775 ADDISON RD, STE 350 75001 #048-02-1986 L1987 P *020 †75
LEVY, Brian Shawn. 14131 MIDWAY RD STE 6 75001 #012-01-2001 L2004 IM HOS *020
LOTAN, Sandra Yvonne. 14833 MIDWAY RD, STE 210 75001 #048-04-1998 L1999 CHP P *020 †75
NALEY, Lilly Ramphal. 5080 SPECTRUM DR, CONCENTRA HEADQUARTERS 75001 #033-03-1978 L1997 OM GPM *020
NIEBRUEGGE, Byron Alvin. 15800 MIDWAY RD 75001 #039-01-1966 L1980 OM *020 †70
OGBUE, Lauretta Ufuoma. 14131 MIDWAY RD, STE 620 75001 #690-06-1991 L2005 *020 †20
OLATUNJI, Adebola Sulaima. 14131 MIDWAY RD STE 6 75001 #690-14-1997 L2004 IM *020
PARKER, Brent Alan. ■ 75001 #026-04-2002 L2005 AN *020
PIA, Harold Ines. ■ 75001 #748-11-1965 ON *050
PIDGEON, Leslie Dawn. 15455 DALLAS PKWY, STE 600 75001 #048-78-2005, ▲ L2007 FP *012
REUBEN, Allen Geoffrey. 15800 DOOLEY RD, STE 100 75001 #048-12-1978 L1980 ID IM *020 †20
RYAN, William John. 4151 BELT LINE RD, STE 124 75001 #539-05-1971 L1978 GPM *020 †20,70
SMALL, James Wm. 15800 MIDWAY RD, CONCENTRA DFW-SW ADMIN 75001 #030-05-1982 L1998 OM GPM *030 †70
SMITH, Katharine Hutton. 5080 SPECTRUM DR, STE 1200W 75001 #048-02-1978 L1978 OM *016
SPILLERS, Christopher. ■ 75001 #048-13-2000 L2002 AN *020 †05
THATI, Vaishali. 14131 MIDWAY RD STE 6 75001 #495-21-1995 L2002 IM *020 †20
TRAN, Alexander Hung. 14131 MIDWAY RD STE 6 75001 #654-01-1999 L2004 IM *020 †20 ‡
UDDIN, Mohammad N. 14131 MIDWAY RD STE 6 75001 #704-02-1990 L2007 FM *020 †18 ‡
VERMA, Amit. ■ 75001 #030-05-2003 L2004 PDC *012 †55
WUEBKER, Margherita G. 14632 WINDSOR CT 75001 #561-11-1963 L1975 IM CD *020 †20

ADKINS – BEXAR

MELENYZER, Charles Louis. 6525 PITTMAN RD 78101 #010-01-1947 L1948 GP GS *020

ALAMO – HIDALGO

ALANIZ, Raul. 1001 FRONTAGE RD, STE R 78516 #025-01-1994 L1997 PD *020 †55
ALANIZ, Rolando. ■ 78516 #025-01-1994 L1997 FM *020 †18
GUTIERREZ, Marco A. 401 S ALAMO RD 78516 #048-15-1992 L1993 FM *020 †18 ‡
MARTINEZ, Rosalinda. ■ 78516 #048-04-2001 *100
VELA, Rene. 401 S ALAMO RD 78516 #048-13-1992 L1993 FM *020 †18

ALAMO HEIGHTS – BEXAR

BRAY, David Wayne. ■ 78209 #042-02-2001 L2002 D *020
GUNN, Shelly R. ■ 78209 #048-13-2002 L2006 PTH *100
LEVOYER, Thomas Eugene. ■ 78209 #047-05-1988 L1989 GS *020 †85
NGUYEN, Hang Thi. ■ 78209 #010-02-1999 L2001 RHU IM *020 †20
ORMAN, David Trent. ■ 78209 #023-12-1982 L1990 P *030 †75

ALBA – WOOD

SPILKER, William Lindsey. ■ 75410 #048-04-1978 L1978 OBG *071 †30

ALBANY – SHACKELFORD

FORD, Ryan Dean. 450 KENSHALO ST 76430 #048-15-2001 L2002 FM *020 †18
KEY, Luther Stone. 240 S 3RD ST 76430 #048-02-1947 L1947 FM *071

ALEDO – PARKER

HANSON, Margarete E. ■ 76008 #154-07-1937 L1955 OBG *020
OAKES, Rolland Fredrick. ■ 76008 #020-02-1953 L1960 R *071 †80
STOUFFER, James Glynn. ■ 76008 #056-05-1946 L1952 GYN *071 †30
WALSH, Deryk Lee. ■ 76008 #048-14-2003 L2007 PAN *012
ZAMBRANO, Hans Armand. ■ 76008 #048-02-1990 L1991 EM *020 †18

ALICE – JIM WELLS

ALANIZ, Andres, III. 201 MARIPOSA, SOUTH TEXAS FAMILY MED CEN 78332 #048-02-2003 L2006 FM *020 †18
ANSARI, Mukhtar Ahemad. N300 E 3RD ST 78332 #495-01-1971 L1985 PTH *075 †50
BANDEIRA TEIXEIRA, F M. 312 E 2ND ST 78332 #187-10-1964 L1967 GS OTR *020 †85
CESAR, Carlos R. 2520 E MAIN ST STE 200 78332 #649-14-1975 L2001 OTO *020 †45
CRISP, Euell Wm. 501 N REYNOLDS ST 78332 #005-12-1956 L1957 GP *020
CUKRAN, David. 1708 E MAIN ST 78332 #902-07-1990 L1998 NEP *020 †20
DIAZ, Roberto F. 2510 E MAIN ST STE 102 78332 #176-01-1990 L1995 IM *020 †20
ESTEVES, Daniel. 2510 E MAIN ST, STE 106 78332 #042-01-1999 L2003 OBG *020 †30
GARCIA, Clarisa Y. ■ 78332 #048-02-2008 *012
KAMAT, Suraj Govind. 1224 E MAIN ST 78332 #496-15-1985 L1993 CD IM *020 †20
KAMAT, Vandana Suraj. ■ 78332 #496-15-1988 L2002 FM *020 †18
LOPEZ, Alejandro. 201 MARIPOSA 78332 #048-02-1982 L1983 FM OBG *020 †18 ‡
MULDER, Donald L L. 700 AIRPORT RD STE 2 78332 #061-01-1967 L1994 GP *020
NEEDLEMAN, Louis Jos. 2500 E MAIN ST 78332 #048-02-1991 L1992 FM *020 †18
NISIMBLAT, Erik. 305 E 3RD ST 78332 #048-16-1996 L1998 PD *020 †55
NISIMBLAT, William. 305 E 3RD ST, ALICE PEDIATRIC CLINIC 78332 #264-05-1963 L1971 PD PHP *075
PATEL, Nirupama Pinakin. 415 E 4TH ST 78332 #495-76-1976 L1983 PD *020
PEPITO, Dante Maglasang. 700 FLOURNOY RD 78332 #748-11-1978 L1992 IM EM *020 †20
QURESHI, Usman. 1224 E MAIN ST 78332 #704-01-1984 L1995 CD IM *020 †20
REYNOLDS, Oscar, Jr. 317 E 1ST ST, 1328 JOSEPHINE DRIVE#7 78332 #048-13-1994 L1996 FM *020 †18
RODRIGUEZ, Diego M. 916 S REYNOLDS ST 78332 #649-02-1972 L1986 P N *020 †75
SAAVEDRA, Humberto. 2510 E MAIN ST STE 102 78332 #495-01-1977 L2006 IM *020 †20
SUBNANI, Rajkumar H. 211 E 4TH ST 78332 #496-38-1974 L1990 GS *020 †85
TORRES, Carlos Ramone. 1321 WASHINGTON DR 78332 #726-01-1968 L1978 AN *020
TORRES, Dennis. ■ 78332 #048-14-1998 FM *100
TURNER, Warren Duke. 700 FLOURNOY RD 78332 #005-15-1977 L1997 FM EM *020 †16,18
ZAMORA, Jose. 2510 E MAIN ST STE 104 78332 #649-27-1976 L1984 TS VS *020 †85,90

ALIEF – HARRIS

GUO, George S. PO BOX 847 77411 #048-12-1987 L1988 GS OS *075
ROZYCKI, Tadeusz. ■ 77411 #550-01-1962 L1976 PD *072 †55

ALLEN – COLLIN

ABERNETHY, Brett D. ■ 75013 #048-14-2001 L2006 P *012
ADAMS, Michael David. 1105 CENTRAL EXPY N, STE 120 75013 #048-15-1985 L1986 ORS *020 †40
AKBAR, Saleem. 1105 CENTRAL EXPY N, STE 230 75013 #704-02-1989 L2000 CD *020 †20
ALLEN, David D. 515 W MAIN ST, STE 102 75013 #048-14-1988 L1989 RM *020 †18
ALLU, Madhavi. ■ 75013 #495-50-1999 L2005 IM *020 †20
AMARA, Ramesh. 1314 W MCDERMOTT DR, STE 106 PMB 808 75013 #495-21-1991 L2008 IM *020 †20
ANDERSON, Pamela Lynn. 1717 ANGEL PKWY, # 107 75002 #021-05-1982 L1986 OBG END *071 †30 ‡
ARNOLDO, Brett Douglas. ■ 75013 #035-06-1995 L2000 CCS *020 †85
AZIZ, Syed. 1105 CENTRAL EXPY N 75013 #704-02-1989 L2004 IM *020 †20
BAHRANI, Ali Akbar. ■ 75013 #048-02-2006 L2008 IM *012
BARKER, Charles Oliver. 75002 #012-05-1971 L1973 AM FM *020 †18,70
BARKSDALE, Kimberly Ann. 1220 N ALMA DR 75013 #025-12-1984 L2000 PD *020 †55
BARROWS, Matthew D. 400 N ALLEN DR STE 301 75013 #048-15-1991 L1993 D *020 †15
BAYYA, Swathi Rao. 1314 W MCDERMOTT DR, STE 106 PMB 808 75013 #495-59-1999 L2004 IM *100
BEITSCH, Peter Donald. 1105 CENTRAL EXPY N 75013 #048-12-1986 L1987 SO GS *020 †85
BHAT, Shanker Khandige. ■ 75013 #495-04-1957 L1978 RO *071 †80
BHATIA, Monika Anil. 1505 W MCDERMOTT DR, STE 110 75013 #902-10-1992 L2004 PD *020 †55
BURCHARD, Jeffrey L. 1105 CENTRAL EXPY N, FAMILY HEALTH CARE 75013 #048-13-1995 L1996 FM *020 †18
CANTU, Leticia Lavita. ■ 75013 #048-12-2008 *012
CARDENAS, Paul Antonio. 75002 #737-10-1993 L2001 MG *012
CARRUTHERS, Jeffrey Todd. 1220 N ALMA DR 75013 #018-03-1995 L1998 FM *020 †18
CHAMBERS, Craig Anthony. 1105 CENTRAL EXPY N, STE 120 75013 #021-06-1996 L1999 PM *020 †60
CHAMPION, Gretchen Ann. 1105 CENTRAL EXPY N, STE 210 75013 #028-02-2000 L2005 OTO *020 †45
CHAUDHRY, Bushra Ijaz. ■ 75013 #704-06-1987 L2001 IM *020 †20
CHEN, Catherine Maiyu. 400 N ALLEN DR STE 108, N DALLAS PEDIATRIC OPTHALM 75013 #035-19-1995 L2007 OPH *020 †35
CHRISTIAN, Anne Louise. 1111 RAINTREE CIR STE 240 75013 #039-01-1993 L1997 PD *020 †20
COKE, Christine Jeanette. 107 SUNCREEK DR, STE 200 75013 #048-15-1999 L2001 GS *020
CONNOLLY, John R. 410 N ALLEN DR 75013 #048-13-1989 L1992 FM *020 †18
COOK, Yuri East. 1111 RAINTREE CIR, STE 290 75013 #048-04-1995 L1998 PD *020 †55
DANDONA, Neal Rajat. 1105 CENTRAL EXPY N, STE 375 75013 #048-04-2003 L2007 AN *020
DESALOMS, John Michael. 1105 CENTRAL EXPY N, STE 380 75013 #048-04-1992 L1994 NS *020 †25
DOERNER, Mark F. 1111 RAINTREE CIR, STE 240 75013 #048-12-2001 L2004 IM *020

DONACHIE, Robert James. 2023 W MCDERMOTT DR 75013 #048-14-1981 L1981 GE IM *020 †20

EDLING, Jason E. 2023 W MCDERMOTT DR 75013 #048-02-1985 L1986 GE IM *020 †20

EDWARDS, David C. 1105 CENTRAL EXPY N, STE 250 75013 #048-04-1987 L1988 FM *020 †18

ENGLUND, De Witt W. ■ 75002 #048-02-1941 L1944 RHU IM *071

ENNIS, Gregory Alan. 1101 RAINTREE CIR, STE 200 75013 #048-13-1997 L1998 FM *020 †18

FLAQUER, Maria Amelia. 820 S ALMA DR STE 130, CRESCENT FAMILY MEDICINE 75013 #935-07-1998 L2005 FM *020 †18

GOSWAMI, Anilkumar P. ■ 75013 #495-23-1966 L1976 R *075

GOTWAY, Garrett Kenneth. ■ 75002 #048-12-2007 PD *012

HANCOCK, Todd W. ■ 75002 #048-13-1999 L2003 AN *020

HAYEE, Muneeza. ■ 75002 #704-01-1990 L2005 P *020

HOLUBEC, Deborah Marie. 1111 RAINTREE CIR, STE 170 75013 #048-02-1980 L1980 PME *020 †05

HOPLEY, Richard Thornton. ■ 75002 #011-04-2007 PTH *012

HOWARD, Ben Keith. ■ 75013 #048-12-1947 L1947 OBG *071 †30

HUBER, Philip Jos. 1105 CENTRAL EXPY N 75013 #035-01-1972 L1974 CRS GS *020 †10,85

HUDDLESTON, Barton West. ■ 75013 #047-06-1990 L2007 PM *020 †60

HUSSAIN, Hasina. 600 W MCDERMOTT DR, STE B 75013 #704-16-1983 L1994 PD *020 †55

IMTIAZ, Saira. ■ 75002 #613-02-1997 L2007 FM *100 †18

ISLAM, Nurul. 1105 CENTRAL EXPY N, STE 2230 75013 #495-02-1982 L2002 PD *020 †55

JACKSON, Richard H. 1105 CENTRAL EXPY N, STE 380 75013 #039-01-1976 L1982 NS *020 †25

JACOB, Aris Nicholas. 1105 CENTRAL EXPY N, STE 2360 75013 #048-02-1998 L2001 END *020 †20

JAGANI, Azra Rayaz. 600 W MCDERMOTT DR, STE B 75013 #704-16-1980 L1998 PD *020 †55

JOE, Brian L. 515 W MAIN ST, STE 101 75013 #048-12-2000 L2004 N *020

JONES, Martin Byron. 1218 W MCDERMOTT DR 75013 #040-02-1991 L1994 FM *020 †18

JOYNER, Kevin T. 1105 CENTRAL EXPY N, FAMILY HEALTH CARE 75013 #048-13-1998 L2003 FM *020 †18

KAKISH, Humam Bassam. 1105 CENTRAL EXPY N, STE 2310 75013 #575-01-1986 L1996 GS VS *020 †85

KAMALI, Babak. ■ 75013 #422-01-2001 L2005 IM *020

KELLUM, Michael W. 1105 CENTRAL EXPY N, FAMILY HEALTH CARE 75013 #048-12-1984 L1985 FM *020 †18

KIM, John Young. ■ 75013 #024-05-1998 L2006 DR *100 †80

KODURI, Padmavathi. ■ 75013 #495-50-1997 L2002 IM *020 †20

KUMAR, Rajeshwar. 400 N ALLEN DR, STE 201 75013 #495-03-1982 L1998 IM *020 †20

KUO, David C. 541 W MCDERMOTT DR, STE A 75013 #016-11-1988 L1991 GP *020

KWON, Jeannie Kyungsun. ■ 75002 #033-06-2000 L2007 PDR *100 †80

LANDAU, Jeffrey H. 1105 CENTRAL EXPY N, STE 350 75013 #035-09-1978 L1998 U *020 †95

LEJEUNE, Derek James. 1314 W MCDERMOTT DR, PMB 808 75013 #021-05-2003 L2006 IM *020 †20

LELE, Eknath Vinayak. ■ 75013 #495-34-1961 L1974 GS GP *020

LUNA, Erin A. ■ 75013 #011-75-2005, ▲ FP *012

MERRITT, Wesley Joseph. 1111 RAINTREE CIR, PAIN CARE OF NORTH TEXAS 75013 #039-01-2000 L2004 AN *020 †05

MERRITT, William Robt, II. 315 S JUPITER RD, STE 210 75002 #048-02-1969 L1969 GP *020

MONTEIRO, Cheryl Ann. ■ 75013 #495-01-1996 L2006 ID *020 †20

MOORE, Eric Denning. ■ 75013 #021-01-2002 *100

MORGAN, Steven B. 1105 CENTRAL EXPY N, STE 120 75013 #048-02-1994 L2002 ORS *020 †40

MOULTON, Daniel Jay. 1105 CENTRAL EXPY N, STE 320 75013 #012-01-1995 L2000 PD *020 †55

NANCE, Jeff E, III. 1121 WINDMERE WAY 75013 #048-13-2001 L2003 AN *020 †05

NAPHADE, Snehal Ramesh. ■ 75013 #495-56-2000 L2006 *100 †20

NGUYEN, Baotram Xuan. ■ 75013 #024-05-1998 L2006 RNR *100 †80

NGUYEN, Benjamin N. 1001 RAINTREE CIR 75013 #048-14-1996 L1998 PM *020 †60

OBAITAN, Adebowale Anselm. ■ 75013 #690-06-1990 L2007 IM EM *020 †20

OCHOA, Marco Antonio. ■ 75013 #649-04-1961 L1970 ORS *020 †40

OLFSON, Theresa Marie. 1503 CORINTH CT 75013 #016-42-1995 L1998 EM *020 †16

PARKER, Linda I. 311 N ALLEN DR 75013 #048-14-1985 L1986 FM *020 †18

PEAKE, Reginald Thos. ■ 75013 #048-15-1974 L1974 EM R *020 †80,16

PERALES, Bobby Jess. 954 PANTHER LN 75013 #048-14-2002 L2006 AN *020 †05

PIERCE, Lawrence Scott. 1105 CENTRAL EXPY N, STE 380 75013 #048-12-1977 L1977 OBG *020 †30

POLLOCK, Todd Alan. 1105 CENTRAL EXPY N 75013 #016-42-1990 L1991 PS *020 †85,65

PONDER, Susan D. ■ 75013 #048-02-1994 L2007 FM *020 †18

PUTCHA, Suma. ■ 75013 #039-01-1995 L1996 PD *020 †55

RAJALA, Bruce W. 1105 CENTRAL EXPY N 75013 #016-76-1982, ▲ L1989 OBG *020 †30 ‡

RAMBALLY, Siayareh. ■ 75013 #048-12-2007 IM *012

REID, Shauna Sexton. ■ 75013 #048-02-2005 L2007 P *012

RINEHART, Tracy Doreen. ■ 75013 #023-01-1993 L1995 PD *020 †55

RODGERS, Harold L, Jr. 1105 CENTRAL EXPY N, STE 120 75013 #021-05-1982 L1983 ORS *020 †40

ROGERS, Sandra Dawn. 1105 CENTRAL EXPY N, FAMILY HEALTH CARE 75013 #005-12-2000 L2004 OS *020 ‡

SHAFIQ, Rashid. 1105 CENTRAL EXPY N, STE 230 75013 #704-02-1989 L1995 PCC SME *020 †20

SHAH, Nehal P. 1111 RAINTREE CIR # 24 75013 #048-15-2003 L2006 PD *020 †55

SHAH, Syed Zahid Hussain. 600 W MCDERMOTT DR, STE B 75013 #704-08-1982 L1999 IM *020 †20

SHARMA, Neeraj Raman. 1314 W MCDERMOTT DR SU, PMB 808 75013 #048-13-1996 L1997 IM *020 †20

SLACK, Charles T. 1105 CENTRAL EXPY N, STE 370 75013 #048-12-1990 L1991 PS *020 †85,65

SLAUGHTER, Laura L. ■ 75002 #048-14-1994 L1997 P *071 †75

SMITH, Adam Robert. 915 W EXCHANGE PKWY, STE 160 75013 #039-01-2002 L2005 FM *020 †18

SMITH, Kimberly Lynn. 1111 RAINTREE CIR, STE 290 75013 #039-01-2002 L2005 PD *020 †55

STACY, Charles Colin. 1105 CENTRAL EXPY N, STE 340 75013 #048-12-1985 L1986 OBG *020

TALUKDER, Nazneen Mohua. 600 W MCDERMOTT DR, STE B 75013 #160-06-1985 L1996 PD *020 †20

TAN, Mary Giok-Kim O. ■ 75002 #506-01-1959 L1978 PM GP *020 †60

TAYLOR, Walton A. 1105 CENTRAL EXPY N 75013 #048-02-1995 L2000 GS *020 †85

TOOLEY, William Roy. PO BOX 1207 75013 #048-12-1968 L1974 P *020

TSAI, Charles. ■ 75013 #035-19-1992 L2006 NR *020 †80

VANESKO, Grace Chen. 2023 W MCDERMOTT DR 75013 #048-12-1991 L1992 GE IM *020 †20

WATSON, Robert R. 515 W MAIN ST, STE 111 75013 #048-15-1987 L1991 IM *020 †20

WEISE, William J. 400 N ALLEN DR, STE 106 75013 #048-12-1985 L1986 OBG *020 †30

WHITE, John Spencer. 1105 CENTRAL EXPY N, STE 130 75013 #048-02-1977 L1977 GS *071 †85

WYRICK, James Stacey. 1008 STANSTED MANOR DR 75002 #048-13-1993 L1994 EM *020 †16

ALPINE – BREWSTER

ALSOP, George Y. ■ 79831 #048-02-2007 *100

ALSOP, George Yerby. 2600 N HIGHWAY 118 79830 #048-02-1976 L1977 GS *020 †85

BENNACK, Gene Edmund. 708 E BROWN ST # 1260 79830 #048-04-1955 L1955 ORS GS *071

BILLINGS, Adrian Nelson. 708 E BROWN ST 79830 #048-02-2003 L2004 FM *100 †18

HUANG, Hsiengchun. ■ 79830 #048-13-1998 L2000 FM *020 †18

HUDDLESTON, Harvey T. 2600 N HIGHWAY 118 STE 1 79830 #027-01-1962 L1966 GYN OS *020 †30

LE VINE, David S. ■ 79830 #004-01-1951 L1951 AN *071 †05

LUECKE, James Davis. 801 E BROWN ST 79830 #048-12-1984 L1988 FM *020 †18 ‡

MAINZ, David Lawrence. ■ 79830 #028-34-1965 L1976 IM IMG *020 †20

MILAM, Robert. ■ 79830 #035-01-1953 L1954 FM *071 †40

MOELLER, Gerhard. ■ 79830 #023-12-1981 L1999 DR *020 †80

PARSONS, Darrell Scott. 2600 N HIGHWAY 118 79830 #019-02-1997 L2000 IM *020 †20

SANCHEZ, David W. 202 N 2ND ST 79830 #048-02-1990 L1992 FM *020 †18

SFORZA, Anthony. 301 MILE HIGH RD 79830 #054-04-1974 L1993 FM EM *020 †18

STIEF, William C, IV. 2600 N HIGHWAY 118, C/O MEDICAL STAFF 79830 #038-40-1992 L2003 EM IM *020

VOGT, Fred Bitterman. ■ 79830 #048-04-1961 L1961 A OS *071

YOUNG, John Marcus. ■ 79831 #048-02-1965 L1965 R NM *062 †80

ALTAIR – COLORADO

GRIFFIN, Harold Lamar. ■ 77412 #048-12-1960 L1960 OTO PS *071 †45

ALTO – CHEROKEE

TODD, William David. ■ 75925 #034-01-1972 L1974 P GP *020 †75

ALTON – HIDALGO

ZAYED, Fuad. 3012 E MAIN AVE 78573 #649-31-1991 L2004 FM *020 †18

ALVARADO – JOHNSON

HARRIS, Oscar Terrell. PO BOX 306 76009 #048-12-1954 L1955 AN *071

NELSON, Stuart Lemuel. 208 E PURDOM AVE 76009 #005-12-1956 L1977 FM EM *020

TREVINO, Naomi Regina. 76009 #048-14-1996 L1998 OBG *020

ALVIN – BRAZORIA

ABOUMRAD, Michel H. ■ 77511 #396-31-1957 L1967 PTH *020 †50

AGENT, Cornelia L. 215 W BLACKSTONE LN 77511 #048-04-1981 L1981 IM FM *020 †20

ALAM, A S. ■ 77511 #160-02-1957 L1979 OPH *071

BERMAN, Robert Phillip. 304 MEDIC LN 77511 #061-01-1978 L1980 FM *020

BLOODWORTH, Donna Schramm. 385 COUNTY ROAD 133 77511 #051-04-1988 L1993 PM *020 †60

DE WITT, Joseph Cornell. ■ 77511 #048-02-1962 L1962 FM ADM *020 †18

DEWITT, Robert D. 304 MEDIC LN STE B 77511 #048-04-1986 L1987 IM *020 †20 ‡

DRESSEL, Karla L. RR 6 77511 #048-02-1984 L1985 GS *020

GO, Sheryllene Ereso. ■ 77511 #005-19-2008 *012

KAZMI, Syed K. 218 E HOUSE ST 77511 #308-11-1986 L1994 PD *020 †55

MAC DONALD, Donald Grant. 208 W COOMBS ST 77511 #917-06-1965 L1972 FM GS *020

MAJMUDAR, Saloni. 218 E HOUSE ST 77511 #496-38-1992 L1997 PD *020 †55

MC CARROLL, Kerry Donley. 1100 SMITH DR 77511 #048-14-1981 L1981 FM *020 †18

MC CUISTION, Loni L. ■ 77511 #048-14-2007 PD *012

MENDOZA, Samuel. ■ 77512 #048-02-1953 L1953 GP *071

MESSER, Dale Leonard. 711 W SIDNOR ST 77511 #048-02-1965 L1965 FM *020 †18

MILLER, Nina Lynn. 400 MEDIC LN STE A 77511 #048-02-1981 L1981 FM *020 †18

NGUYEN, Maria Phuong. 218 E HOUSE ST 77511 #028-34-1998 L2001 PD *020 †55

SCHAUDER, Keith Stewart. 1 MEDIC LN 77511 #048-04-1985 L1986 ORS *020 †40

SHEFFIELD, Katherine J. 304 MEDIC LN, STE B 77511 #048-15-1997 L1999 FM *020 †18

SMITH, James Reilly. 511 S GORDON ST 77511 #021-01-1971 L1971 FM *020 ‡

SMITH, Larry Don. 1100 SMITH DR 77511 #048-04-1963 L1963 GP GS *071

AMARILLO – POTTER

ABDALLA, Ismaile Sherine. 1901 PORT LN, AMARILLO HEART GROUP 79106 #915-03-1975 L1998 CD ICE *020 †20

AHMAD, Sobia. ■ 79124 #704-02-1996 IM *012

AHMED, Nafisa. ■ 79106 #048-15-2008 *012

AHMED, Osama Iqbal. ■ 79106 #048-15-2008 *012

AJALA, Moyosade Adeyinka. 1400 S COULTER ST, STE 4100 79106 #690-02-1995 FP *012

AKANGIRE, Gangaram Ganpat. 1400 WALLACE BLVD 79106 #496-51-2002 PD *012

ALAPATI, Srilatha. 1400 WALLACE BLVD 79106 #496-35-2001 PD *012

ALBRACHT, Brendan C. 1901 MEDI PARK DR, STE 103 79106 #048-78-1994, ▲ L1999 ORS *020

ALEXANDER, Jamison C. 1400 WALLACE BLVD, TX TECH UNIV 79106 #018-75-2004, ▲ OBG *012

ALI, Kashif Rahat. 1400 S COULTER ST, DEPARTMENT OF PEDIATRICS 79106 #704-02-1990 L2001 **PD** *020 †55
ALLISON, Walter M, III. 1400 S COULTER ST, TX TECH SCHOOL OF MEDICINE 79106 #047-06-1965 L1969 **CD** *020
ALPAR, John Jos. 5311 W 9TH AVE 79106 #473-01-1949 L1960 **OPH** *071 †35
AL ZEERAH, Masoud A. 1215 S COULTER ST, STE 101 79106 #517-01-1979 L1993 **TS** *020
AL-ZUBEIDI, Duha Naser Sa. 1400 WALLACE BLVD 79106 #575-01-2005 L2008 **PD** *012
ANTHONY, William Allen. ■ 79106 #048-04-1963 L1963 **U** *071 †95
APPEL, Carin A. 1301 S COULTER ST STE 3 79106 #048-16-1999 L2003 **OBG** *020 †30
APPEL, Jimmie R, Jr. 11 MEDICAL DR 79106 #048-15-1996 L1998 **IM** *020 †20
ARAGON, Antonio V, II. 7310 FLEMING AVE 79106 #023-07-1995 L2005 **OPH** *020 †35
ARAGON, Gary Lee. ■ 79124 #034-01-1991 L1999 **DR** *020 †80
ARCHER, Estelle. 1900 S COULTER ST STE C 79106 #048-12-1990 L1991 **GYN** *020 †30
ARCHER, Evelyn. 1915 S COULTER ST, FL 4 79106 #048-12-1985 L1986 **D** *020 †15
ARCHER, Grace Emily. 1215 S COULTER ST, STE 400 79106 #048-12-1982 L1983 **OBG** *020 †30
ARCHER, Mary Elizabeth. 1915 S COULTER ST, FL 4 79106 #048-02-1981 L1981 **D** *020 †15
ARCHER, Richard K. 1900 S COULTER ST 79106 #048-12-1956 L1956 **IM OS** *071 †20
ARCHER, Richard K. 1901 MEDI PARK DR STE 2050 79106 #048-12-1998 L1999 **VIR** *020 †80
ARIAS, Cesar J. 1215 S COULTER ST, STE 204 79106 #308-01-1981 L2002 **IM** *020 †20
ARIAS, Jose Pedro. 6010 W AMARILLO BLVD, AMARILO VA. HLTH CARE SYST 79106 #132-01-1968 L1978 **GS OS** *020 †85
ARREDONDO, Mark Anthony. 1400 S COULTER ST 79106 #048-12-1983 L1983 **SO GS** *020 †85
ARTHO, Brent L. 1600 WALLACE BLVD, AMARILLO ANESTHESIA CONSUL 79106 #048-15-2004 L2007 **AN** *012
ARTHUR, Jack Clinton. ■ 79102 #048-12-1966 L1966 **AN** *071 †05
ASHBY, Wendell Bob. 1901 MEDI PARK DR, STE 25 79106 #048-02-1974 L1974 **OBG** *020 †30
AWAD, Fadi. 1400 WALLACE BLVD 79106 #875-01-1991 **IM** *012
BAAY, Peter Lynn. 6 MEDICAL DR 79106 #048-12-1990 L1991 **GS** *020 †90,85
BAGGETT, Dhana R. 6209 CEDAR HOLLOW DR 79124 #048-15-1996 L1997 **FM** *020 †18
BAKER, Teresa E. 1400 S COULTER ST, FL 3 79106 #048-12-2000 L2003 **OBG** *020 †30
BAKER, Thomas Bruce. 6700 W 9TH AVE, AMARILLO DIAGNOSTIC CLINIC 79106 #048-02-1981 L1981 **PUD IM** *020 †20
BALLARD, Karen Suzanne. 1400 S COULTER ST 79106 #039-79-2004, ▲ L2008 **OBG** *012
BALLESTAS, Carmen Sofia. 1400 WALLACE BLVD 79106 #264-12-1999 L2006 **PHO** *012 †55
BALMES, Marichu M. 1400 WALLACE BLVD, TEXAS DEPT OF FAMILY MEDIC 79106 #748-20-1987 L1997 **FM** *020 †18
BANERJEE, Rumki. 1400 WALLACE BLVD, TX TECH UNIV HLTH SCI CTR 79106 #496-12-1995 L2006 **FM** *020 †18
BANISTER, William M. 320 S POLK ST, STE 400 79101 #048-15-1991 L1992 **NS** *072 †25
BANWAIT, Kuldip. 6833 PLUM CREEK DR, AMARILLO ENDOSCOPY CENTER 79124 #495-02-1988 L2006 **GE** *100 †20
BARCLAY, David Louis. 1400 S COULTER ST, FL 3 79106 #054-04-1955 L2002 **GYN GO** *071 †30
BARKLEY, Brian F. 1501 S COULTER ST 79106 #048-13-1997 L2000 **EM** *020 †16
BARNETT, George Thomas. ■ 79124 #048-15-2004 L2008 **OBG** *012
BARNHILL, Bill Scott. 7000 W 9TH AVE 79106 #048-12-1980 L1980 **ORS OSM** *020 †40
BASHIR, Mamoun Elsir. 1301 S COULTER ST 79106 #848-01-1998 L2008 **IM** *012
BASS, Cary S. 7201 I-40 W, PO 1110 79106 #048-02-1993 L1994 **AN** *020 †05
BASSETT, Perry Eugene. 1600 WALLACE BLVD, BSA HOSPITAL 79106 #048-13-1995 L1996 **FM** *020 †18
BASYE, Tommy R. 1600 WALLACE BLVD, EMERGENCY DEPARTMENT 79106 #048-13-1995 L1998 **EM** *020 †16
BATSON, Carey Joe. 1000 S COULTER ST 79106 #048-12-1961 L1967 **N** *071
BEGGS, Daniel Andrew. 6700 SW 9TH AVE 79106 #019-02-1992 L1998 **GE** *020 †20
BEGGS, David Francis. 1000 S COULTER ST, STE 100 79106 #019-02-1964 L2002 **ON HO** *020 †20
BELL, Todd Edward. ■ 79106 #004-01-2001 L2005 **MPD** *100 †20,55
BENITEZ, Jesus Rene, Jr. 6010 W AMARILLO BLVD 79106 #048-12-1986 L1988 **IM** *020 †20
BENJAMIN, Bonna Georjean. 1600 S COULTER ST, TEXAS TECH UNIV HLTH SCI 79106 #041-12-1973 L1995 **PDS GS** *020 †85
BENTON, Timothy J. 1400 WALLACE BLVD, DEPARTMENT OF FAMILY MEDIC 79106 #048-15-1994 L1995 **FM** *020 †18
BERG, Howard Lysle. 13 MEDICAL DR 79106 #023-07-1974 L1980 **ORS OAR** *020 †40
BHASKER, Chand. 800 QUAIL CREEK DR STE 102 79124 #019-02-1973 L1977 **FM** *020 †18 ‡
BICKERS, Gayle H. 1501 S COULTER ST, DEPT RAD 79106 #036-07-1968 L1969 **PDR PD** *020 †55,80
BICKERS, Peter Warren. 1901 MEDI PARK DR 79106 #036-07-1968 L1984 **PD** *075 †55
BIDWELL, Robert Marroquin. 850 MARTIN RD 79107 #048-15-1987 L1988 **FM** *020 †18
BIGGS, William Curtis. 1915 S COULTER ST, FL 4 79106 #048-12-1982 L1983 **END IM** *020 †20
BISKINIS, Evanthia K. 1400 S COULTER ST 79106 #418-01-1961 L1996 **PD NPM** *020 †55
BOGER, James Allen. 1400 S COULTER ST 79106 #048-02-1966 L1966 **PD** *020 †55
BORDELON, William Howard. 1600 S COULTER ST, STE 100 79106 #021-01-1978 L1983 **U** *020 †95
BORDERS, Charles W. ■ 79106 #048-14-2007 **IM** *012
BORER, Mary Margaret. ■ 79106 #012-01-2007 **IM** *012
BRADBURRY, Christopher M. 1501 S COULTER ST, EMERGENCY DEPARTMENT 79106 #048-15-2001 L2004 **EM** *020 †16
BRADFORD, Ako Dia. 1400 S COULTER ST, DEPARTMENT OF INTERNAL MED 79106 #051-04-2002 L2005 **IM** *020 †20
BRADSHAW, Chas Marshall. 6103 W AMARILLO BLVD 79106 #048-02-1965 L1965 **P SME** *071 †75
BRAM, Melvin Lewis. 5211 W 9TH AVE STE 101 79106 #035-03-1970 L1976 **GE IM** *020 †20
BRANTLEY, Kenny M. 1215 S COULTER ST, STE 400 79106 #048-15-1994 L1995 **END** *020 †20
BRAVO, Victor Leon. 1215 S COULTER ST STE 100 79106 #003-01-1985 L1987 **FM** *020 †18
BRIDGES, Walter Jos. 1600 S COULTER ST STE F600 79106 #048-15-1988 L1989 **IM PD** *020 †20,55
BRISTER, David Ernest. 1215 S COULTER ST, STE 100 79106 #027-01-1981 L1982 **FM** *020 †18
BRITTEN, Bartholomew Aloy. 1215 S COULTER ST, STE 100 79106 #048-14-2004 L2006 **FM** *020 †18
BROWN, Gary Lynn. 1900 MEDI PARK DR, AMARILLO UROLOGY 79106 #036-05-1976 L1976 **U** *020 †95
BROWN, Thomas Gordon. 12 MEDICAL DR 79106 #016-76-1951, ▲ L1957 **PTH LM** *071
BRULE, Gulnur Harisovna. 1400 WALLACE BLVD 79106 #913-82-1994 **PD** *012
BRUTON, Henry D, II. 6700 SW 9TH AVE 79106 #036-01-1985 L1994 **PUD IM** *020 †20
BRYAN, Garnett Cartmell. 1400 WALLACE BLVD, DEPARTMENT OF FAMILY MEDIC 79106 #048-12-1958 L1958 **FM** *071 †18
BRYAN, Gary Wm. 1600 WALLACE BLVD 79106 #048-12-1970 L1970 **OTO** *071 †45
BRYAN, James D. 1215 S COULTER ST, STE 100 79106 #048-16-2000 L2002 **FM** *020 †18
BUFORD, Robert Lee. 4 MEDICAL DR STE B 79106 #039-01-1968 L1976 **U NEP** *020 †95
BURGESS, Valerie Kaye. ■ 79106 #048-15-2008 *012
BURNS, Russell Frederick. 6700 SW 9TH AVE 79106 #048-02-1978 L1981 **CD** *020 †20
BUSH, Jon Damon. 6700 SW 9TH AVE 79106 #028-03-1989 L2003 **IM** *020 †20
BYRD, Bill Frank. 6700 SW 9TH AVE 79106 #048-12-1977 L1977 **NM IM** *020 †20,28
BYRD, Bruce Alan. ■ 79159 #048-12-1988 L1989 **GS** *020
CABRERO, Jose Eduardo. 1600 WALLACE BLVD, EMERGENCY DEPARTMENT 79106 #011-04-2000 L2006 **EM** *020 †16
CALDWELL, Jon Leslie. 1215 S COULTER ST, STE 100 79106 #048-14-1982 L1983 **FM** *020 †18
CALDWELL, Turner M, III. 4302 WOLFLIN AVE 79106 #048-12-1975 L1982 **D DMP** *020 †15
CARLISLE, Joseph T, Jr. 6700 SW 9TH AVE 79106 #048-04-1982 L1983 **ID IM** *071 †20
CARRASCO, Londa Leigh. 1600 S COULTER ST STE 205 79106 #048-02-1992 L1994 **OBG** *020
CARRASCO, Robert Bejarano. 1600 S COULTER ST, STE 205 79106 #048-02-1991 L1992 **OBG** *020 †30
CARRILLO, Arturo. 1911 PORT LN 79106 #649-27-1973 L1978 **OBG** *020 †30
CARRIZO, Debora E. 6010 W AMARILLO BLVD, MEDICAL CENTER 79106 #715-01-1984 L1993 **END** *020 †20
CARRIZO, Ricardo Jose. PO BOX 1110, WYATT HLTH CTR 79105 #264-04-1984 L1995 **IM** *020
CARROLL, William Allen, Jr. 1501 S COULTER ST 79106 #001-06-1999 L2004 **PTH** *020 †50
CARRUTH, David Gerald. 1215 S COULTER ST, STE 100 79106 #048-12-1972 L1977 **FM** *020 †18
CASTILLO, Rhodesia A. 1301 S COULTER ST, STE 300 79106 #048-12-1986 L1988 **OBG** *020 †30
CAZZOLA, Harry Jos. 1920 MEDI PARK DR STE 4 79106 #021-01-1971 L1981 **OBG FM** *020 †18,30
CHANDLER, Pamela Ann. 1301 S COULTER ST, STE 300 79106 #048-13-1983 L1983 **OBG** *020 †30
CHANDRA, Rahul. 1400 S COULTER ST, DEPT OF INTERNAL MEDICINE 79106 #496-09-2001 L2007 **IM** *020 †20
CHASTAIN, David Lyman. 1301 S COULTER ST, STE 300 79106 #048-02-1974 L1974 **OBG** *020 †30
CHEN, Ming. 1400 WALLACE BLVD 79106 #243-10-1984 **IM** *012
CHEN, Qiaofang. 1400 WALLACE BLVD 79106 #243-43-1992 **IM** *012
CHILLAKURU, Lakshmi Isana. 1400 WALLACE BLVD 79106 #495-99-1999 L2008 **FP** *012
CHU, Alfredo Enrique. 1901 PORT LN 79106 #715-01-1981 **OPH N** *100
CHU, Benjamin Fu-Han. ■ 79124 #048-15-2007 L2007 *012
CHUACHINGCO, Joyce C. 1400 S COULTER ST, DEPT PEDS TX TECH UNIV 79106 #748-11-1971 L1981 **NPM PD** *040 †55
CLARK, Beverley Alfretta. 6040 BELPREE RD, # F371 79106 #065-01-1954 L1979 **VS OPH** *071
CLARK, Crandon F, Jr. 1901 MEDI PARK DR STE 2050, HIGH PLAINS RAD ASSN 79106 #038-41-1978 L2000 **DR IM** *020 †80
CLARKE, Richard Bennett. 6 MEDICAL DR 79106 #019-02-1972 L1976 **GS OS** *020 †85
COHEN, Martin Irvin. 6700 W 9TH AVE 79106 #010-01-1969 L1977 **GE HEP** *020 †20 ‡
CONDE, Alfredo E. 1901 MEDI PARK DR STE 101A 79106 #308-02-1987 L1996 **CCM IM** *020 †20
CONE, Jeffrey Donald. 6822 PLUM CREEK DR 79124 #048-02-1975 L1975 **NS** *020 †25
COSCIA, John Louis, Jr. 1500 WALLACE BLVD, HARRINGTON CANCER CENTER 79106 #047-06-1973 L1975 **DR** *020 †80
COTTON, Robert Everett. 2300 W 7TH AVE 79106 #048-02-1960 L1960 **GP** *020
COX, Eric C. 1600 S COULTER ST 79106 #048-15-1996 L1997 **FM** *020 †18
COX, R H, Jr. 1901 MEDI PARK DR STE 2050 79106 #048-12-1969 L1969 **R NM** *020 †80,28
COX, Sammy Lane. 6700 W 9TH AVE 79106 #422-01-1997 L2001 **CD** *020 †20
COX, Samuel Foster. 6700 SW 9TH AVE 79106 #047-05-1961 L1962 **GS** *020
CRAIG, Peter Baker. 1501 S COULTER ST, EMERGENCY DEPARTMENT 79106 #003-01-1998 L2003 **EM** *020
CROSSNOE, Reagan L. 1901 MEDI PARK DR STE 10 79106 #048-15-1998 L2000 **ORS** *020 †40
CRUM, Ralph Lyle. 1400 S COULTER ST 79106 #030-06-1983 L1985 **GS** *020 †85
CUNNINGHAM, Samuel James. 6826 PLUM CREEK DR 79124 #048-02-2000 L2006 **OTO** *020
CURRIE, Hugh Bob. 15 MEDICAL DR 79106 #048-04-1963 L1963 **OPH** *020 †35
CURRIE, Tully Jenks. 1901 MEDI PARK DR STE 2050 79106 #048-14-2003 L2008 **DR** *012
CUTTS, Karen Joyce. 1400 S COULTER ST, TTUHSC 79106 #007-02-1986 L1989 **IMG** *020 †20
DAI, Lijun. 1400 WALLACE BLVD 79106 #243-21-1988 **IM** *012
DANESHFAR, Bejan Joe. 24 CARE CIR 79124 #028-03-1983 L1990 **AN GS** *020 †05
DAUD AGUERO, Benjamin Y. 1400 WALLACE BLVD 79106 #275-04-1994 **IM** *012
DAVID, John L. 1501 S COULTER ST 79106 #048-16-1982 L1983 **OBG** *020 †30
DAVIS, Lon Miles. 1600 S COULTER ST, STE D403 79106 #048-12-1979 L1979 **OBG** *020 †30
DESAI, Prakashkumar K. 1901 PORT LN, AMARILLO HEART GROUP 79106 #495-22-1984 L1994 **CD IM** *020 †20
DIAZ, Pablo Rafael. 1600 S COULTER ST STE E703 79106 #048-12-1975 L1979 **OBG** *020 †30
DILLEE, Ronald Dennis. 1000 S COULTER ST, TEXAS DIAGNOSTIC IMAGING 79106 #048-04-1972 L1972 **DR NM** *020 †80
DILLMAN, Richard D, Jr. 2 CARE CIR 79124 #048-02-1982 L1983 **GS VIR** *020 †85
DO, Nam H. 1215 S COULTER ST, STE 400 79106 #048-16-1995 L1996 **IM** *020 †20
DOBLER-DIXON, Amber Anne. 7310 FLEMING AVE 79106 #026-04-1986 L1993 **OPH** *020 †20,35
DODSON, Leonard Edwin, Jr. 1215 S COULTER ST, STE 400 79106 #019-02-1972 L1982 **END IM** *020 †20
DORMAN, John Wesley. 9601 SPUR 591 79107 #047-05-1967 L1968 **OBG** *020 †30
DOVE, Dennis Bryan. 1400 S COULTER ST, DEPT OF SURG 79106 #038-41-1972 L2002 **GS TRS** *030 †85
DREW, Mark C. 6900 I-40 W STE 150, ODYSSEY HOSPICE INPATIENT 79106 #023-12-1986 L1994 **EM** *020 †16
DUNN, James Wilmoth. ■ 79106 #048-12-1960 L1960 **OTO AI** *071 †45
DURRETT, Carole. PO BOX 3291 79116 #048-15-1989 L1991 **FM** *075
DYER, Keith. 7200 W 9TH AVE, BOX 51199 79106 #048-02-1990 L1998 **IM** *020 †60
EADES, Brian Jeffrey. 1301 S COULTER ST, STE 300 79106 #048-15-1985 L1986 **OBG** *020 †30
EAST, William Robt. 5211 W 9TH AVE 79106 #039-01-1961 L1965 **D** *020 †15
EKPEBEGH, Chukwuma O. 1400 WALLACE BLVD, TX TECH UNIV HLTH SCI CTR 79106 #690-01-1988 **IM** *100
EL- HAYEK, Jihad Michel. 1400 WALLACE BLVD 79106 #605-03-2001 **IM** *012
ELLINGTON, Richard Todd. 6700 SW 9TH AVE 79106 #048-13-1992 L1993 **GE** *020 †20

■ = Address Information Privacy Protected

ELLINGTON, S Elizabeth. 1400 S COULTER ST 79106 #048-13-1992 L1994 **PD** *020 †55
ELLIS, John Robt. 1600 WALLACE BLVD 79106 #048-04-1982 L1983 **N IG** *020 †75
ENGLISH, George Wm. 6333 SUNLAKE DR 79124 #759-01-1984 L1994 **PTH PCP** *020 †50
ERRINGTON, Bret D. 1900 S COULTER ST, STE A 79106 #048-13-1995 L1997 **NS** *020 †25
ESLER, William Vance. 1000 S COULTER ST, STE 100 79106 #048-12-1978 L1978 **HO NTR** *020 †20
ESTEVEZ, Roberto. 6010 W AMARILLO BLVD 79106 #924-01-1970 L1979 **CD** *062 †20
FAGALA, Gwen E. 6010 W AMARILLO BLVD, THOMAS E CREEK MED CENTER 79106 #048-02-1989 L1990 **P** *020 †75
FAKOURI, Mohammadhossein. 1400 S COULTER ST, STE 56 79106 #517-01-1993 **IM** *012
FENG, Ning. 1400 WALLACE BLVD 79106 #243-52-1994 **IM** *012
FILLMORE, Anthony Jay. 6 MEDICAL DR 79106 #048-12-1997 L1998 **GS** *020 †85
FLETCHER, Rex Albert. 17 CARE CIR 79124 #054-04-1989 L1997 **PD** *020 †55
FORD, Ronald W. 1900 MEDI PARK DR, AMARILLO UROLOGY 79106 #048-12-1994 L1996 **U** *020 †95
FORERO, Leonardo. 1000 S COULTER ST STE 1 79106 #264-10-1992 L2004 **HO** *020 †20
FORTNER, Bennie Ronald. 1901 PORT LN 79106 #048-02-1966 L1966 **CD IM** *020
FRANK, Donald Albert. 1000 CRAIG DR 79106 #047-06-1959 L1960 **FM ADM** *071 †18
FRANKLIN, Richard Harold. 1400 S COULTER ST, DEPT OF SURGERY 79106 #048-12-1971 L1971 **GS CCS** *020 †85
FRAZIER, Dustin Clyde. 8 MEDICAL DR 79106 #048-15-1986 L1987 **ORS** *020 †40
FRIEND, Lee Jos. 1600 WALLACE BLVD 79106 #030-05-1975 L1995 **OBG EM** *020 †18
FRIESEN, Wm Glenn Peter. 1215 S COULTER ST, STE 302 79106 #061-01-1961 L1988 **CD IM** *020 †20
FU, Hubert. 1901 MEDI PARK DR STE 105 79106 #039-01-2000 L2004 **AN** *020 †05 ‡
FULTON, Nona Dale Snyder. 1901 MEDI PARK DR STE 2050, HIGH PLAINS RAD-PO BX 3780 79106 #028-02-1964 L1979 **DR** *071 †80
GAJJELA, Hemlata Reddy. 1400 WALLACE BLVD, TX TECH UNIV HLTH SCI CTR 79106 #495-21-2002 **PD** *012
GENTRY, Jonathon Brett. 11 MEDICAL DR, SOUTHWEST NEUROSCIENCE & 79106 #048-14-1996 L2002 **NS** *020 †25
GEORGE, Bajie. 1901 MEDI PARK DR, STE 1059 79106 #495-27-1983 L1999 **AN** *020 †05
GEORGE, Mariada. 1500 S COULTER ST, STE 1 79106 #040-02-1998 L2001 **PD** *020 †55
GERALD, Robert Evans. 7308 FLEMING AVE 79106 #048-12-1974 L1977 **OPH** *020 †35
GIPSON, Jason Logan. ■ 79106 #048-15-2008 *012
GIRON, Milton A. 1215 S COULTER ST, STE 400 79106 #429-01-1981 L1994 **NEP IM** *020 †20
GLASS, Tracy Lee. 1400 WALLACE BLVD 79106 #048-78-2005, ▲ **OBG** *012
GOETZ, Susan Brim. 1400 WALLACE BLVD, DEPARTMENT OF FAMILY MEDIC 79106 #048-15-1995 L1998 **FM** *020 †18
GOLDSTEIN, Nathan. 1501 S COULTER ST 79106 #016-02-1970 L1978 **PD** *020 †55
GONZALEZ, Antonio Carmelo. ■ 79124 #036-07-1962 L1973 **DR NM** *020 †80,28
GOOCH, Jason L. 1400 S COULTER ST, DEPT OF OBSTETRICS & GYNEC 79106 #048-15-2001 L2005 **OBG** *100 †30
GOPALACHAR, Anuradha S. 6010 W AMARILLO BLVD, VA MEDICAL CENTER 79106 #495-33-1993 L1998 **IM** *020 †20
GRIFFITH, Larry Gene. 400 W 14TH AVE 79101 #048-02-1969 L1969 **GP** *020
GUERRA, Cesar Horacio. ■ 79107 #649-02-1959 L1975 **PS GS** *071
GUEST, James Alexander. 1901 MEDI PARK DR, STE 2050 79106 #048-13-1973 L1973 **DR** *020 †80
GUJJA, Pradeep Reddy. 1400 WALLACE BLVD 79106 #496-21-2004 **IM** *012
GULDE, Robert Emmett. 1 CARE CIR 79124 #028-34-1960 L1963 **CD IM** *071
GUTIERREZ, Elma Rosario. 1400 WALLACE BLVD, DEPT OF OB/GYN 79106 #034-01-2004 L2008 **OBG** *012
GUYNES, Wm Allison, Jr. 6 MEDICAL DR 79106 #021-01-1964 L1969 **CD TS** *071 †85,90
GWOZDZ, John Thomas. 1000 S COULTER ST STE 100 79106 #056-06-1992 L1997 **RO** *020 †80
HA, Linh Thi My. 1400 WALLACE BLVD 79106 #942-01-2002 **PD** *012
HAAS, Stephan O. 1901 MEDI PARK DR, STE 2050 79106 #039-01-1993 L1994 **RNR DR** *020 †80
HABERSANG, Rolf W. 1600 S COULTER ST STE F600 79106 #869-01-1969 L1979 **PD CCP** *020 †55
HABIBA, Nusrath Mohideen. 1400 WALLACE BLVD, TX TECH UNIV HLTH SCI CTR 79106 #495-16-1982 L2008 **PD** *012
HADDAD, Jon Luigi. 1901 PORT LN 79106 #305-01-1987 L1995 **CD** *020 †20
HAIDER, Agha Zia. 1600 WALLACE BLVD, NEONATOLOGY 79106 #704-16-1983 L1998 **PD NPM** *020 †55
HALE, James D. 1215 S COULTER ST, STE 100 79106 #048-13-1985 L1986 **FM** *020 †18
HALE, William Price. 1400 S COULTER ST 79106 #020-02-1958 L1960 **OTO** *040 †45
HAMMO BARAZI, Mahmoud. 1400 WALLACE BLVD 79106 #875-02-2002 **IM** *012
HAMOUS, James Edward. 1501 S COULTER ST 79106 #030-05-1979 L1984 **PTH** *020 †50
HAMPSTEN, Ellen Elizabeth. ■ 79106 #048-15-2008 *012
HANCOCK, Paul R. 1500 WALLACE BLVD, HARRINGTON PHYSICIANS INC 79106 #048-12-1987 L1988 **ON HEM** *020 †20
HANDS, Hollis Homer. 2418 SW 8TH AVE 79106 #019-02-1955 L1960 **OBG** *020
HANDS, Martin Andrew. 2418 SW 8TH AVE 79106 #048-15-1985 L1987 **OBG** *020 †30
HANDS, Victor Vern. 2418 SW 8TH AVE 79106 #048-04-1986 L1987 **GS VS** *020 †85 ‡
HARRAL, Ann Elaine. 1301 S COULTER ST, STE 300 79106 #048-13-1984 L1985 **OBG** *020
HASHAM-UL-HAQ, Muhammad. 1400 WALLACE BLVD 79106 #704-22-2000 L2008 **MPD** *012
HASHMI, Arouj A. 1901 MEDI PARK DR STE 2050 79106 #019-02-1998 L2006 **DR** *020 †80
HAYHURST, James Cole. 6 MEDICAL DR 79106 #048-12-1991 L1997 **GS** *020 †85
HAYS, Robert James. 6 MEDICAL DR 79106 #016-06-1963 L1971 **GS CD** *071 †85
HEFNER, James Richard. 1600 WALLACE BLVD, ST ANTHONYS HEALTH SYSTEM 79106 #039-01-1963 L1966 **AN** *020 †05
HENDRICK, Daniel Jay. ■ 79124 #048-12-2002 L2007 **NEP** *012 †20
HENSON, Harry Marc. 1900 S COULTER ST, STE H 79106 #048-15-1998 L2003 **FM** *100 †18 ‡
HERNANDEZ-LATTUF, Pedro R. 1901 MEDI PARK DR, STE 138 79106 #935-01-1967 L1976 **CD** *020
HERRICK, Shannon Laissle. 1400 S COULTER ST 79106 #048-12-2001 L2003 **PD** *020 †55
HIGGINS, Robert Wm. 1901 MEDI PARK DR, STE 2051 79106 #051-04-1980 L1990 **OSM OS** *020 †40
HIGH, Richard Melvin. 7120 W 9TH AVE 79106 #048-12-1981 L1981 **PS GS** *020 †85,65
HILTON, Gary John. 1500 S COULTER ST STE 6 79106 #048-02-1974 L1974 **FM** *020
HODGES, Ronald Howard. 1400 S COULTER ST, FL 3 79106 #028-03-1975 L1996 **OBG** *040 †30
HOLMES, Heather J. 1400 S COULTER ST, TEXAS TECH UNIVERSITY HSC 79106 #048-02-1998 L2002 **OBG** *020 †30
HOOT, Andrew Carl. 1501 S COULTER ST 79106 #023-01-1987 L2004 **PTH** *020 †20,50
HOVING, Debbie P. 1301 S COULTER ST 79106 #048-13-1996 L1998 **PD** *020 †55
HOWELL, John Franklin, Jr. 1501 S COULTER ST 79106 #021-01-1958 L1964 **OPH** *020 †35
HROMAS, Frank Denny. 1400 WALLACE BLVD 79106 #048-15-1997 L1998 **FM** *020 †18
HUDSON, Arlene Mc Nair. P.O. BOX 1110, 1411 AMARILLO BLVD EAST 79174 #005-12-1986 L1990 **FM** *020 †18
HUDSON, Curtis Randall. 1501 S COULTER ST, EMERGENCY DEPARTMENT 79106 #005-06-1986 L1991 **EM** *020 †16
HUEBNER, Melburn Kenton. 1901 MEDI PARK DR STE 10 79106 #048-12-1985 L1986 **ORS** *020 †40
HULSEY, Mark A. 1600 WALLACE BLVD 79106 #048-12-1989 L2001 **RHU** *020 †20
HURLEY, James Michael. 1901 MEDI PARK DR, STE 211 79106 #004-01-1977 L1981 **CD** *020 †20
HURLY, James M. 1501 S COULTER ST 79106 #037-01-1990 L1995 **PTH** *020 †50
HUSSAIN, Mohammad Farhad. 1400 WALLACE BLVD 79106 #160-03-1997 **IM** *012
HUSSAIN, Mustafa. 6900 W INTERSTATE 40 STE 2 79106 #704-02-1982 L1992 **P PYG** *020 †75
HUTCHESON, Zenas W, Jr. ■ 79106 #048-04-1943 L1943 **FM OM** *071 †18
HYDE, Gregory Edmund. 1901 MEDI PARK DR, STE 2001 79106 #054-04-1986 L2004 **OTO A** *020 †45
ICE, Dennis Alan. 11 MEDICAL DR, SOUTHWEST NEUROSCIENCE & 79106 #023-12-1985 L1996 **PM** *020 †60
ISKRENKO, Alexander Vladi. 1400 WALLACE BLVD 79106 #913-06-1983 **IM** *012
ISRAEL, Kim Eugene. 6010 W AMARILLO BLVD, THOMAS E CREEK MEDICAL CEN 79106 #048-15-1976 L1976 **IM EM** *020
JABER, Mouin Mahmoud. ■ 79124 #913-15-1986 L1997 **IM** *020 †20
JACKSON, Robert Earl, III. 1901 PORT LN 79106 #048-02-1975 L1975 **IM** *020 †20,28
JAFFAR, Ali. 1600 S COULTER ST 79106 #495-59-1987 L1997 **CD** *020 †20
JAMBULA, Prakruti Reddy. ■ 79124 #496-21-2004 L2007 **PD** *012
JARROUS, Ammar R. 6842 PLUM CREEK DR 79124 #875-02-1990 L2001 **TS** *020 †85,90
JAVED, Shahid. 1400 WALLACE BLVD 79106 #704-02-2001 **FP** *012
JENKINS, Daniel Gordon. 600 N TYLER ST 79107 #039-01-1982 L1983 **IM** *020 †20
JENKINS, Marjorie Runyon. 1400 S COULTER ST, FL 3 79106 #047-20-1995 L2003 **IM** *020 †20
JENKINS, Michael Dewayne. 1500 S TAYLOR ST 79101 #048-15-1986 L1987 **P PYG** *020 †75 ‡
JENNINGS, Richard Lee. 1920 MEDI PARK DR 79106 #034-01-1977 L1978 **EM FM** *020 †16
JEW, Paul. 1801 HALSTEAD ST STE A 79106 #048-15-1983 L1983 **FM EM** *020 †18
JOHNSON, Abiodun O K. 1400 S COULTER ST, DEPT PEDS 79106 #690-01-1965 L2000 **PD GE** *040 †55
JOHNSON, Gregory Royce. 1301 S COULTER ST, STE 405 79106 #048-14-1999 L2003 **HOS FM** *020 †18,20 ‡
JOHNSON, Thomas Lee. 6700 SW 9TH AVE 79106 #048-02-1977 L1977 **GE IM** *020 †20
JOHNSTON, Kenneth Henry. 1600 WALLACE BLVD, BAPTIST ST ANTHONYS HOSP 79106 #048-12-1959 L1959 **ORS** *030 †40
JONES, Billy R. 6010 W AMARILLO BLVD 79106 #035-01-1950 L1953 **IM CD** *071 †20
JONES, John Edgar. 814 MARTIN RD 79107 #048-04-1957 L1957 **PD PDC** *071 †55
JONES, W Mitchell. ■ 79106 #048-02-1955 L1955 **P** *071 †75
JORDAN, Richard Morris. 6010 W AMARILLO BLVD 79106 #017-20-1971 L1971 **END IM** *020 †20
JOU TINDO, Adeline Jacque. 1400 WALLACE BLVD 79106 #165-01-1999 L2008 **IM** *012
JUBANG, Geoffrey. 3603 NE 24TH AVE 79107 #065-09-1967 L1976 **FM OBG** *020
KADAKIA, Bhadresh Kantila. 1400 WALLACE BLVD 79106 #496-38-1979 **IM** *012
KALUSOVA-LISKOVA, Jindra. VET ADMIN HOSP 79106 #286-02-1960 L1974 **DR** *020
KANASE, Padmaneel B. 1200 WALLACE BLVD, AMERICAN LASER CTRS 79106 #495-01-1995 L2001 **FM** *020 †18 ‡
KARTCHNER, Keith Dale. 1901 MEDI PARK DR STE 2050 79106 #007-02-1964 L1974 **R NR** *020 †80
KASTNER, David Alan. 6010 W AMARILLO BLVD, VA MEDICAL CENTER 79106 #305-01-1997 L1997 **FM** *020 †18
KAUFFMAN, Robert Porter. 1400 S COULTER ST, FL 3 79106 #048-14-1979 L1979 **OBG OS** *075 †30
KEISTER, Alan W. 1215 S COULTER ST, STE 400 79106 #048-12-1996 L2000 **IM** *020 †20
KELLEHER, John Chas. 1810 S COULTER ST 79106 #016-06-1970 L1972 **PS HS** *020 †85,65
KELLEY, James Myles. 1619 S KENTUCKY ST 79102 #019-02-1961 L1972 **IM** *020
KENNEDY, Kyle Lee. 5211 W 9TH AVE 79106 #048-02-1994 L1996 **OTO** *020 †45
KHANDHERIA, Bharat. 1400 S COULTER ST, HSC/INT MEDICINE 79106 #496-08-1987 L1993 **IM** *020 †20
KHANDHERIA, Daksha B. 1411 E AMARILLO BLVD, J.O. WYATT CLINIC 79107 #495-76-1990 L1996 **IM** *020 †20
KHAZNADAR, Mohamedaouf A. 1901 MEDI PARK DR STE 124 79106 #875-02-1980 L1996 **IM** *020 †20
KHERDEKAR, Anjali S. ■ 79124 #028-46-1994 L2007 **IM** *020 †20
KHU, Richard Corvera. 1901 MEDI PARK DR STE 2050, HIGH PLAINS RADIOLOGY ASSO 79106 #008-02-1993 L2004 **DR** *020 †80
KIBBEY, Richard Glenn, III. 1900 MEDI PARK DR, AMARILLO UROLOGY 79106 #001-02-1969 L1970 **U** *020 †95
KIESLING, Carol A. 10200 KUKIHALO RD 79124 #048-02-1992 L1993 **OBG** *020
KING, Constancio Yuzon. 6010 W AMARILLO BLVD 79106 #748-01-1959 L1973 **GS AS** *071
KIRKLAND, Jerry Lynn. 1400 WALLACE BLVD 79106 #048-15-1986 L1987 **FM** *020 †18
KLEIN, John W. 13 CARE CIR 79124 #048-15-1993 L1994 **OPH** *020 †35
KRACKE, William Irvin. 1705 S POLK ST 79102 #048-04-1966 L1966 **P** *020
KUBALA, Stephen Francis. 1411 E AMARILLO BLVD, P O BOX 5884 79107 #038-43-1985 L1987 **IM** *020 †20
KULKARNI, Archana Govind. 1400 WALLACE BLVD 79106 #496-51-2002 **PD** *012
LACKAN, Dianne Sharon. 1301 S COULTER ST 79106 #048-13-1999 L2002 **PD** *020 †55
LACY, Ronald Rene. 7118 W I-40, BLDG D 79106 #048-02-1967 L1967 **FM** *062 †18
LAGRONE, Michael Odell. 13 MEDICAL DR 79106 #048-12-1978 L1980 **ORS OSS** *020 †40
LANGLEY, David C. 6 MEDICAL DR, BSA AMARILLO SURGICAL GROU 79106 #048-04-1998 L2000 **VS** *020 †85
LARY, Michael Alan. 6 MEDICAL DR 79106 #021-05-1978 L1979 **GS** *020 †85
LAUR, William Edward. ■ 79102 #025-01-1943 L1949 **D** *071 †15
LEEAH, Benjamin J. 1900 S COULTER ST, STE H 79106 #048-15-2000 L2002 **FM** *020 †18 ‡
LEEPER, Stephanie C. 1400 S COULTER ST 79106 #047-20-1987 L2006 **IM IMG** *040 †20
LENNARD, Jake C, Jr. 6700 SW 9TH AVE 79106 #027-01-1977 L1982 **GE IM** *020 †20
LEONG, Fahsean. 3300 S COULTER ST # 3-115 79106 #005-14-1991 L2002 **DR** *020 †80
LEVY, Eric N. 1301 S COULTER ST, STE 101 79106 #048-12-1984 L1985 **PD CCM** *020 †55
LI, Li. 1400 WALLACE BLVD 79106 #243-47-1994 **PD** *012

■ = Address Information Privacy Protected

LIE, Sien Hwie. 711 N TAYLOR ST 79107 #506-02-1963 L1977 **OBG** *020 †30
LIM, Seah Hooi. 1000 S COULTER ST, STE 100 79106 #919-01-1984 L2005 **HO** *020
LIU, Hongtao. 1400 WALLACE BLVD 79106 #243-47-1993 **IM** *012
LOFTON, Roger Owen. 850 MARTIN RD, REGENCE HEALTH NETWORK 79107 #048-02-1978 L1978 **FM** *020 †18 ‡
LOGSDON, John Robt. 6700 SW 9TH AVE 79106 #048-12-1971 L1977 **CD IM** *020 †20
LOTT, Bradley J. 1901 MEDI PARK DR, SUTIE 1059 79106 #048-15-1987 L1988 **AN** *020 †05
LUCKSTEAD, Eugene Freddie. 1400 S COULTER ST 79106 #018-03-1963 L1988 **PDC PD** *020 †55
LUND, Jon D. 1400 S COULTER ST, FL 3 79106 #048-12-1988 L1989 **OBG** *020 †30
LUSBY, James E. 6700 SW 9TH AVE 79106 #048-15-2000 L2002 **GE** *020 †20
LUSBY, Stacia Wolfe. 1501 S COULTER ST, NORTHWEST TEXAS HOSPITAL 79106 #048-15-2000 L2003 **P** *100 †75
LYONS, Lewis Clinton. 5211 W 9TH AVE, STE 201 79106 #004-01-1980 L1992 **FM** *040 †18
MAHDI, Khalida Malallah. 1400 WALLACE BLVD 79106 #528-01-1993 **FP** *012
MALIHA, George Mekhael. 1215 S COULTER ST, STE 400 79106 #012-21-1986 L1988 **NEP IM** *020 †20
MALKUCH, Gerald W. 1901 MEDI PARK DR STE 1059, AMARILLO ANESTHESIA CONSUL 79106 #048-15-1999 L2003 **AN** *020 †05
MANDERSON, Michael Scott. 13 MEDICAL DR 79106 #048-15-1997 L1998 **ORS OSS** *020
MANLAPAZ, Omar T. ■ 79106 #048-15-2008 *012
MARCK, George Jeffrey. 1215 S COULTER ST, STE 400 79106 #007-02-1980 L1985 **IM** *020 †20
MARTIN, Reg C. 1800 S WASHINGTON ST, ADVANCED PAIN CARE 79102 #048-15-1998 L2002 **AN** *020 †05
MARTIN, Todd H. 1800 S WASHINGTON ST, STE 315 79102 #048-16-1993 L1995 **AN** *020 †05
MARTINDALE, James Brett. 6700 SW 9TH AVE 79106 #048-15-1985 L1986 **IM** *020 †20
MARTINEZ, Robin Elaine. 1400 WALLACE BLVD 79106 #048-02-1986 L1987 **PD** *020 †55
MARTINEZ-ARRARAS, Joaquin. 1901 PORT LN 79106 #847-11-1982 L1991 **CD IM** *020 †20
MARUPUDI, Sambasiva Rao. 800 QUAIL CREEK DR, STE 103 79124 #495-50-1975 L1983 **CRS GS** *020 †10,85
MASON, James Wm. 814 MARTIN RD 79107 #065-09-1955 L1999 **PD FM** *020 †55
MAWLA, Nazre. 1215 S COULTER ST, STE 201 79106 #160-02-1972 L1981 **GS ON** *020 †85
MBA, Farley Esigfei. 1400 WALLACE BLVD 79106 #690-04-1998 **FP** *012
MC CALEB, Morgan Hoy. 1600 WALLACE BLVD 79106 #048-12-1956 L1956 **FM** *020
MC CARTHY, Edward M. 1915 S COULTER ST, FL 4 79106 #048-02-1999 L2003 **D** *020 †15
MCCARTHY, Rebecca Archer. 1915 S COULTER ST, FL 4 79106 #048-02-1997 L1999 **D** *020 †15
MC CARTY, Christopher A. 7310 FLEMING AVE 79106 #048-15-2000 L2004 **OPH** *020 †35 ‡
MC COLLUM, Deborah Burge. 7305 WALLACE BLVD STE B 79106 #039-01-1988 L1995 **TS** *020 †85,90
MC CORKLE, Allan J. 3 MEDICAL DR 79106 #048-15-1990 L1991 **P** *020
MC CORMACK, George Gordon. 1500 WALLACE BLVD 79106 #561-17-1969 L1990 **RO** *071 †80
MC COWN, James S. 1600 WALLACE BLVD, ST ANTHONYS HEALTH SYSTEM 79106 #048-15-1994 L1996 **AN** *020 †05
MC CURDY, Fredrick Arthur. 1400 S COULTER ST, DEPT PEDS 79106 #030-05-1976 L1983 **PD PN** *030 †55
MC DONALD, David Neal. 1600 WALLACE BLVD, ST ANTHONYS HEALTH SYSTEM 79106 #048-12-1966 L1966 **AN** *020 †05
MCKAY, Richard Ferris. 8 MEDICAL DR 79106 #048-02-1968 L1968 **ORS** *020 †40
MC KINLEY, John Perry. 6 MEDICAL DR 79106 #048-15-1980 L1980 **GS VS** *020 †85
MC NEIR, David G. 2 CARE CIR 79124 #048-15-1991 L1993 **GS** *020 †85
MEDFORD, Shari Orlicek. 17 CARE CIR 79124 #004-01-1989 L2000 **PD ID** *020 †55
MEEKS, Clyde A. 1301 S COULTER ST, STE 300 79106 #048-13-1988 L1989 **OBG** *020 †30
MEEKS, Robert G. ■ 79124 #048-15-1990 L1991 **AN** *020 †05
MEHTA, Rahul. ■ 79124 #495-17-1983 L1995 **DR NM** *020 †80,28
MENDOZA, Ruben Vinas. 22 CARE CIR 79124 #748-01-1986 L2001 **CHP P** *020
MENNEMEYER, Ralph Paul. 1901 MEDI PARK DR, STE 211 79106 #028-03-1969 L1979 **PTH** *071 †50
MEREDITH, Duane Wm. ■ 79159 #048-04-1943 L1943 **FM** *071
MERKI, Daniel J. 1000 CRAIG DR 79106 #048-13-1988 L1989 **FM PD** *020 †18
MERRIMAN, Robt Frederick. 1901 MEDI PARK DR, STE 1059 79106 #016-11-1957 L1971 **AN** *071 †05
MERRIMAN, Thomas E. 7201 I-40 W STE 210, LONE STAR ANESTHESIA 79106 #048-14-1988 L1989 **APM** *020 †05
MILLIGAN, Sean Michael. 6700 SW 9TH AVE 79106 #038-41-2000 L2004 **N** *020 †75
MILTON, John Leslie. 1000 S JEFFERSON ST, ODYSSEY HEALTHCARE 79101 #048-02-1960 L1960 **IM PLM** *020
MILTON, John S. 6700 SW 9TH AVE 79106 #048-14-1989 L1991 **ID** *020 †20
MITCHELL, Dawn Nicole. 1400 WALLACE BLVD, DEPARTMENT OF FAMILY MEDIC 79106 #047-06-2002 L2005 **FM** *020 †18
MITCHELL, Holly. 6700 SW 9TH AVE 79106 #048-13-1992 L1993 **IM** *020 †20
MOHANA SUNDARAM, Shamala. 1400 S COULTER ST, STE 4100 79106 #495-99-1999 **FP** *012
MOIR, Robin Noel. 3300 S COULTER ST, STE 3-317 79106 #671-01-1966 L1993 **CHP** *020
MOLINA-YELA, Luz M. 1215 S COULTER ST, STE 400 79106 #429-02-1986 L1993 **NEP IM** *020 †20
MOORE, Carroll Truett. 1600 WALLACE BLVD 79106 #048-12-1967 L1967 **ORS** *071 †40
MOORING, Timothy S. 1600 WALLACE BLVD 79106 #048-15-2000 L2005 **PCC** *020 †20
MOREAU, Marc Jos. 1901 MEDI PARK DR, B RONALD FORTNER MD 79106 #060-01-1973 **ORS PD** *050 †40
MOREAU, Marc Marie F. 1901 PORT LN 79106 #165-01-1985 L1994 **CD** *020
MORGAN, Darrell Ivan. 1501 S COULTER ST, EMERGENCY DEPARTMENT 79106 #048-02-1984 L1985 **EM** *020 †16
MORGAN, Ronald Thane. 7000 W 9TH AVE 79106 #048-13-1995 L1996 **ORS** *020 †40
MORTON, Dan Chas. 1501 S COULTER ST, EMERGENCY ROOM 79106 #048-15-1974 L1977 **FM** *020
MUNIZ, Sergio. 26 MEDICAL DR STE B 79106 #429-01-1980 L1992 **PUD IM** *020 †20
MURRAY, Richard Gerard. 1301 S COULTER ST, STE 403 79106 #539-02-1989 L2002 *020 †80
MURRELL, Walter John. 7411 WALLACE BLVD 79106 #024-07-1981 L1982 **OPH OS** *020 †35
MURTHY, Chaturvedula P. 800 QUAIL CREEK DR, STE 103 79124 #495-46-1964 L1980 **GS** *071 †85
NADESAN, Suhasini Basu R. 1000 S COULTER ST STE 100 79106 #495-04-1969 L2007 **IM ON** *020 †50,20
NAN, Bicheng. 1400 WALLACE BLVD 79106 #243-39-1990 **IM** *012
NAQVI, Mubariz. 1400 WALLACE BLVD 79106 #704-02-1969 L1978 **PD NPM** *020 †55
NASRALLAH, Basil Khaled. ■ 79106 #575-02-1999 **PD** *100
NATIVIDAD, Alejandro V. 1731 HAGY BLVD 79106 #748-01-1983 L1994 **P** *020 †75
NAWAZ, Sardar Karim. 5211 W 9TH AVE, STE 205 79106 #704-04-1966 L1973 **ON IM** *020 †20
NEEDLEMAN, Samuel W. 1500 WALLACE BLVD 79106 #041-01-1975 L2003 **HEM IM** *030 †20
NEELAGARU, Suresh. 6111 W AMARILLO BLVD 79106 #028-46-1994 L2002 **CD ICE** *020 †20
NEESE, Susan L. 1215 S COULTER ST, STE 400 79106 #048-15-1996 L1997 **IM** *020 †20
NEESE, Thomas Clinton. ■ 79106 #039-01-1965 L1968 **CD IM** *071
NEILSON, John Wm. 6 MEDICAL DR 79106 #048-12-1980 L1980 **GS VS** *020 †85
NEUMANN, Stephen Ralph. 1501 S COULTER ST, EMERGENCY DEPARTMENT 79106 #048-02-1996 L1999 **EM** *020 †16
NG, Erina Meemei. ■ 79124 #048-15-2008 *012
NGUYEN, Lam Ha Hoang. ■ 79124 #048-15-2008 *012
NGUYEN, Que Vu. 6010 W AMARILLO BLVD, VAMC IN AMARILLO 79106 #941-01-1971 L1991 **P PD** *020
NGUYEN, Son Vi. 1015 W 8TH AVE STE 1 79101 #941-01-1971 L1987 **P** *020
NICHOLS, Carl Thos. 205 E 10TH AVE, MED DIR AIG 79101 #017-20-1961 L1967 **IM END** *030 †20
NICKLAUS, Ted Maurice. 400 SW 14TH AVE 79101 #035-01-1960 L1965 **IM IMG** *030 †20
NIKAM, Navin Srinivas. ■ 79159 #048-15-2008 *012
NIRGIOTIS, Jason Geo. 1400 S COULTER ST, PEDIATRICS STE 600 79106 #016-02-1986 L1988 **PDS GS** *020 †85
NOLAN, Paul Keith. 1400 S COULTER ST, DEPT PEDS 79106 #048-15-1986 L1987 **PDP PD** *020 †55
NORRIS, Stephen Allen. 1215 S COULTER ST, STE 400 79106 #048-12-1975 L1975 **GS** *020 †85
NORRIS, Steven K. 1215 S COULTER ST, STE 301 79106 #048-15-2001 L2004 **IM** *020
NUNN, Howard Stubbs, Jr. 1901 MEDI PARK DR STE 2050, HIGH PLAINS RADIOLOGICAL A 79106 #017-20-1973 L1974 **DR NR** *020 †80
OKOGBO, Michael Ebhota. 1600 S COULTER ST, STE 500G 79106 #690-02-1974 L1998 **PD** *020 †55
OKUMBOR, David Osagie. ■ 79106 #690-06-1995 L2007 **FP** *012
OKUNGBOWA, Osaretin Danie. 1400 WALLACE BLVD 79106 #690-06-1992 **FP** *012
ORR, Richard Melvin. 9601 SPUR 591, TDCJ-CLEMENTS UNIT 79107 #048-02-1965 L1965 **P OS** *020
PAETZOLD, S Carl. 1501 S COULTER ST, EMERGENCY DEPARTMENT 79106 #048-02-1994 L1997 **EM** *020 †16
PAIGE, Robert Warren. 7100 W 9TH AVE 79106 #048-04-1970 L1970 **AN** *020 †05
PAN, Paul Paolung. 1901 MEDI PARK DR STE 205 79106 #005-14-1976 L1981 **DR** *020 †80
PARIKH, Rajendra C. 1501 S COULTER ST 79106 #495-23-1974 L1982 **PD** *020 †55
PARKER, Lynda Michele. 1616 S KENTUCKY ST, STE C200 79102 #035-20-1974 L2001 **P CHP** *020 †75
PATANKAR, Sandip Dilip. ■ 79106 #496-26-2003 **FP** *012
PATE, Virgil Albert, III. 1900 MEDI PARK DR, AMARILLO UROLOGY 79106 #048-12-1970 L1970 **U GP** *020 †95
PATEL, Milan. 6611 W AMARILLO BLVD 79106 #495-48-1987 L1994 **HO** *020 †20
PATEL, Suryakant Jashbhai. 6010 W AMARILLO BLVD, V.A.M.C. 79106 #495-01-1952 L1980 **ORS EM** *071 †40
PATEL, Vinod S. 1901 MEDI PARK DR, STE 2049 79106 #495-99-1977 L1983 **IM GP** *020
PATHAPATI, Srinivas. 6833 PLUM CREEK DR 79124 #495-11-1990 L2000 **GE** *020 †20
PAULLUS, Wayne Settle, Jr. 11 MEDICAL DR, SOUTHWEST NEUROSCIENCE & 79106 #047-06-1970 L1979 **NS** *020 †25
PEARSON, Harve Danl. 1600 WALLACE BLVD 79106 #048-02-1966 L1966 **AN** *020 †05
PEREZ-BARRIO, Jose Maria. 6010 W AMARILLO BLVD 79106 #847-03-1956 L1965 **PD OS** *075
PERIMAN, Phillip O'Keefe. 1000 S COULTER ST, STE 100 79106 #028-02-1965 L1975 **HEM ON** *020 †20
PHILIP, Rachel Moncy. 6010 W AMARILLO BLVD, VAMC MEDICAL SERVICE 79106 #880-01-1981 L1992 **N** *020
PICKETT, Carolyn M. ■ 79102 #048-78-2006, ▲ **OBG** *012
PIERCE, John Rush, Jr. 1400 S COULTER ST, DEPT IM 79106 #005-02-1977 L1981 **IM PHP** *040 †20,70 ‡
PILLAI, Narayana G. 6611 W AMARILLO BLVD 79106 #495-31-1974 L1981 **ON IM** *020 †20
PINKSTON, Robert L, Jr. 1901 MEDI PARK DR STE 2050, HPRA 79106 #048-15-1984 L1986 **R** *020 †80
PISKUN, Mary Ann. 1000 S COULTER ST 79106 #048-15-1974 L1996 **PS** *075 †85,65
PISTOCCO, Timothy Bruce. 1501 S COULTER ST 79106 #039-01-1987 L1988 **AN** *020 †05
PLATA-BERNAL, Carlos A. 1215 S COULTER ST, STE 400 79106 #264-10-1982 L1990 **RHU IM** *020 †20
PLUMMER, Dennis Patrick. 2400 LINE AVE 79106 #034-01-1977 L1979 **FM FPG** *020 †18
PODOLSKY, Howard Scott. ■ 79124 #035-06-1991 L1992 **LM IM** *062 †20
POLK, Gary Robt. 6700 SW 9TH AVE 79106 #048-12-1979 L1979 **PUD IM** *020 †20
POSEY, Randal Earl. 4302 WOLFLIN AVE 79106 #048-02-1963 L1968 **D** *020 †15
PRATT, Donald Geo. 1600 S COULTER ST STE 402 79106 #048-02-1974 L1974 **RO** *071 †18,80
PRICE, Wm Thomson, Jr. 1000 S COULTER ST, SPINE CENTER 79106 #047-05-1947 L1955 **NS OS** *071 †25
PROFFER, Liana H. 1301 S COULTER ST, STE 104 79106 #048-13-1996 L1998 **D** *020 †15
PROFFER, Patrick Jonathan. 1301 S COULTER ST STE 104 79106 #048-13-1999 L2005 **PS** *100 †65
PROFFER, Paul L. 1301 S COULTER ST STE 104 79106 #048-15-1995 L1997 **OPH** *020 †35
PRUITT, Brian Thos. 1500 WALLACE BLVD 79106 #048-02-1972 L1981 **ON** *020 †20
QIAN, Baoping. 1400 WALLACE BLVD, TX TECH UNIV HLTH SCI CTR 79106 #243-16-1988 **PD** *012
RABURN, Loralu. ■ 79106 #039-01-1979 L1980 **N** *071 †75
RAFIQUE, Mohammad Omer. ■ 79124 #704-21-1987 L2002 **APM** *020
RAGHURAM, Nandkishore. 1600 WALLACE BLVD 79106 #495-23-1987 L1998 **PD CCP** *020 †55
RAMAKRISHNAN, Mythili. 6010 W AMARILLO BLVD 79106 #495-16-1963 L1972 **IM** *020 †20
RANIN, Maria Teresa Jacob. 1400 WALLACE BLVD, FAMILY MEDICINE-GERIATRICS 79106 #748-10-2000 L2007 **IM IMG** *020 †20
RANKIN, Ron K. 400 SW 14TH AVE 79101 #048-15-1997 L1998 **FM PLM** *020 †18
RAY, Arunava D. 1901 PORT LN 79106 #496-38-1992 L1999 **CD IM** *020 †20
REED, Holley Wm. 1501 S COULTER ST 79106 #041-09-1946 L1950 **PD** *071 †55
REGUEIRA, Osvaldo. 1600 S COULTER ST STE F-6, UNIV PEDIATRIC GROUP FOUND 79106 #308-03-1981 L1989 **PD PHO** *020 †50,55
REIN, Tracy. 7310 FLEMING AVE 79106 #028-46-1998 L2003 **OPH** *020
RENTAS, Julio Joaquin. 1400 WALLACE BLVD, INT MED TX TEC UNIV SCI CT 79106 #042-01-2002 L2003 **N** *012
RICHARDSON, Mark W. 2 CARE CIR 79124 #048-16-1989 L1990 **AN** *020 †05

■ = Address Information Privacy Protected

RICHEY, Harvey M, III. 1400 S COULTER ST, DEPARTMENT OF MEDICINE 79106 #048-78-1977, ▲ L1977 **PUD IM** *020 †20
RICKWARTZ, Kevin J. 1501 S COULTER ST, EMERGENCY DEPARTMENT 79106 #048-14-1997 L2000 **EM** *020 †16
RIGGINS, Nina Yakovlevna. 1400 WALLACE BLVD 79106 #913-84-1997 **IM** *012
RIKER, Joan Eleanor. 400 SW 14TH AVE 79101 #048-15-1983 L1983 **IM IMG** *020 †20
RIMMER, Chas Winford, Jr. ■ 79159 #048-04-1966 L1966 **NS** *071 †25
RIOS, Cynthia Izeth. 1400 WALLACE BLVD, DEPT OF OB/GYN 79106 #048-14-2006 **OBG** *012
RIOS, Miguel A. 5920 W AMARILLO BLVD 79106 #429-01-1969 L1974 **NEP IM** *020 ‡
RIVERA, Ernesto. 1901 PORT LN, AMARILLO HEART GROUP, LLP 79106 #341-01-1980 L1989 **CD IM** *020
ROBBERSON, Joe F. 200 NW 7TH AVE 79107 #021-01-1953 L1953 **ORS** *072 †40
ROBERTS, Larry Clarke. 4302 WOLFLIN AVE 79106 #048-02-1977 L1977 **D** *020 †15
ROBINSON, Pamela Kay. 1000 CRAIG DR 79106 #027-01-1990 L1999 **FM** *020 †18
ROBINSON, William R. 1500 WALLACE BLVD 79106 #047-06-1985 L1999 **OBG** *020 †30
RODRIGUEZ, Manuel Iznaola. 1400 S COULTER ST, TEXAS TECH MED CTR 79106 #847-04-1977 L2003 **TS GS** *020 †85
RODRIGUEZ, Pablo S. 1215 S COULTER ST, STE 400 79106 #308-04-1983 L1992 **IM ID** *020 †20
ROLLINS, John H, Jr. ■ 79106 #048-15-1982 L1983 **IM** *020 †20
RUSH, James Avery. 7310 FLEMING AVE 79106 #048-04-1976 L1976 **OPH** *020 †35
RYAN, Michael Geo. 1411 E AMARILLO BLVD, WYATT CLINIC 79107 #016-11-1970 L1976 **N** *071 †75
SAADEH, Constantine K. 6842 PLUM CREEK DR 79124 #605-01-1982 L1989 **AI RHU** *020 †20,03
SAHAD, Jesus N. 1215 S COULTER ST, STE 400 79106 #308-04-1982 L1995 **PUD** *020 †20
SAMES, Thomas August. 400 SW 14TH AVE 79101 #048-16-1989 L1990 **EM** *020 †16
SAMIUDDIN, Mohammed. 1400 WALLACE BLVD, TX TECH UNIV HEALTH SCIENC 79106 #496-27-1998 L2007 **FPG** *100 †18
SANCHEZ GARCIA, Alice Ang. ■ 79106 #308-04-1998 L2007 **PYG** *100 †75
SANTILLAN, Carlos H. 6010 W AMARILLO BLVD, THOMAS E CREEK VA MEDICAL 79106 #737-06-1972 L1975 **NEP IM** *020 †20
SARALAYA, Raghavendra N. 1215 S COULTER ST, STE 400 79106 #495-17-1988 L2000 **IM** *020 †20
SARALAYA, Shilpa R. 1215 S COULTER ST, STE 400 79106 #496-38-1994 L2000 **IM** *020 †20
SARAVANAKUMAR, Paluchamy. 6010 W AMARILLO BLVD 79106 #495-42-1990 L1999 **IM** *020 †20
SAULOG-NATIVIDAD, Ruby. 1501 S COULTER ST 79106 #748-01-1984 L1994 **N** *020 †75
SCALAPINO, Matthew C. 1901 MEDI PARK DR, STE 2050 79106 #048-15-1985 L1987 **DR** *020 †80
SCHAEFFER, Lawrence A. 1915 S COULTER ST, FL 4 79106 #649-13-1983 L1988 **N** *020 †20,75
SCHNEIDER, Daniel Lewis. 1501 S COULTER ST 79106 #004-01-2000 L2006 **HMP** *100 †50
SCHWARTZENBERG, Janet K. 6700 SW 9TH AVE 79106 #048-12-1991 L1992 **RHU** *020 †20
SCOTT, Rebecca J. 17 CARE CIR 79124 #048-04-2002 L2005 **PD** *020 †55
SELVAN, Vani. ■ 79124 #495-66-1994 L2007 **FP** *012
SENNETT, Michael Dean. 1501 S COULTER ST 79106 #012-22-1993 L2006 **HMP** *020 †50
SEWARD, Charles Wendell. 2221 SE 27TH AVE 79103 #039-01-1967 L1972 **RHU IM** *020
SHAFI, Md Nahid. 1400 WALLACE BLVD 79106 #160-03-1997 **IM** *012
SHAH, Rakesh R. 1901 MEDI PARK DR STE 2058 79106 #048-12-1991 L1992 **RNR DR** *020 †80
SHAMSI, Tariq Samad. 6010 W AMARILLO BLVD, V.A. MEDICAL CENTER 79106 #495-75-1979 L1999 **IM** *020 †20
SHARP, Stewart Allen. 1500 WALLACE BLVD 79106 #018-03-1981 L2007 **ON IM** *020 †20
SHAW, Russell Franklin. 2300 TEE ANCHOR BLVD 79104 #035-03-1959 L1995 **OM PD** *071 †55,70
SHEEHAN, Marita Angleton. 1400 S COULTER ST, STE 4107 79106 #005-02-1968 L1972 **PD** *020 †55
SHELTON, Douglas R. 1901 MEDI PARK DR, STE 6 79106 #048-15-1991 L1992 **OBG** *020
SHERWOOD, Brent W. 5310 ANDREWS AVE, BRENT W. SHERWOOD, MD, PA 79106 #048-15-1999 L2004 **FM** *020 †18
SHUM, Shu. 1801 HALSTEAD ST STE B 79106 #462-01-1971 L1980 **PD PDT** *020 †55
SIDERIS, Eleftherios. 1600 S COULTER ST STE 200 79106 #418-01-1975 L1983 **PDC PD** *020 †55
SIDHU, Malwinder S. 1901 MEDI PARK DR, STE 1030 79106 #495-29-1976 L1995 **GE** *020 †20
SIDHU, Parvinder K. 1901 MEDI PARK DR, STE 1030 79106 #495-47-1978 L1995 **IM** *020
SIMJEE, Saeeda. 6010 W AMARILLO BLVD, PRIMARY/SPECIALITY CARE CL 79106 #704-02-1985 L1992 **IM** *020 †20
SMIRNOVA, Olga V. 6700 SW 9TH AVE 79106 #913-61-1984 L2004 **IM** *020
SMITH, Aubrey Lyndol. 13 MEDICAL DR 79106 #048-15-1984 L1985 **ORS OSM** *020 †40
SMITH, Earl Clifton, Jr. 320 S POLK ST STE 300 79101 #048-12-1970 L1970 **ORS** *020 †40
SMITH, Gregory William. 7000 W 9TH AVE 79106 #038-40-1997 L1998 **ORS** *020 †40
SMITH, H Wayne. 600 S TYLER ST, BOX 12019 79101 #048-12-1961 L1961 **IM** *062
SMITH, Paula E. 1400 S COULTER ST, DEPT OF OB 79106 #011-75-2007, ▲ **OBG** *012
SNYDER, Rush A, Jr. 6700 SW 9TH AVE 79106 #028-02-1970 L1977 **N** *020 †75
SOMMERFELDT, Lorraine A. 6103 W AMARILLO BLVD, STE A 79106 #016-01-1981 L1990 **P** *020
SORAJJA, Kent. 1900 S COULTER ST STE D 79106 #891-02-1970 L1976 **AI PD** *020 †55,03
SOYA, D Gary. 1901 PORT LN, AMARILLO HEART GROUP 79106 #033-05-1990 L1996 **CD** *020 †20
SPURLOCK, James Stephen. 1215 S COULTER ST STE 100 79106 #048-12-1970 L1970 **FM** *020 †18
SREENIVASAN, Chiyyarath V. 800 QUAIL CREEK DR 79124 #495-44-1972 L1984 **NEP IM** *020 †20
SRINIVASAN, Sarat Chander. 1400 WALLACE BLVD, TX TECH UNIV HLTH SCI CTR 79106 #495-73-1993 *100
STAFFORD, James Harry. 1600 S COULTER ST STE 402 79106 #038-40-1981 L1992 **RO** *020 †80
STENHOUSE, Andrew Carlyle. 1600 WALLACE BLVD, BSA HOSPITAL 79106 #671-01-1968 L1973 **IM ID** *020
STEVENS, Mark Elton. 1215 S COULTER ST, STE 100 79106 #048-14-1975 L1975 **FM** *020 †18
STEWART, Clay Lynn. 7000 W 9TH AVE, BARNHILL SPORTS MED CLINIC 79106 #012-01-1987 L2000 **FM FSM** *020 †18
STEWART, Randy Lee. 600 N TYLER ST 79107 #048-15-1984 L1985 **IM** *020 †20
STOUT, William W. 2300 W 7TH AVE 79106 #048-02-1952 L1952 **OS GP** *020
STRINGFELLOW, Grace Lea. 1901 MEDI PARK DR STE 1048 79106 #048-14-1987 L1988 **PM** *020 †60
STROUD, Robert Houston. 6826 PLUM CREEK DR 79124 #048-02-1996 L1997 **OTO** *020 †45
SUDHAKAR, Sivaram. 1901 MEDI PARK DR STE 1062 79106 #495-31-1974 L1990 **N** *020 †75
SUN, Dongxu. 1400 WALLACE BLVD 79106 #243-36-1986 **IM** *012
SUNDARAMURTHY, Chithraleka. 1400 WALLACE BLVD 79106 #495-04-1995 **IM** *012
SWAN, Janet Kay. 1600 WALLACE BLVD, ST ANTHONYS HEALTH SYSTEM 79106 #048-12-1981 L1981 **AN** *020 †55,05
TABACZEWSKI, Piotr Henryk. ■ 79106 #759-04-1985 **IM** *012
TAFEL, John Andrews, Jr. 1620 S POLK ST 79102 #051-01-1987 L1991 **PM** *020 †60
TAN, Cristiane Campos. 1400 WALLACE BLVD 79106 #187-15-2001 **FP** *012
TARIQUE, Zeeshan. 1400 WALLACE BLVD 79106 #704-02-1995 L2008 **PD** *012
TAYLOR, Coleman. 15 MEDICAL DR 79106 #012-05-1954 L1963 **OPH** *071 †35
TAYLOR, Robert L. 6 MEDICAL DR 79106 #048-04-1982 L1983 **TS** *020 †85,90
TAYLOR, Robert Lynn. 6 MEDICAL DR, AMARILLO SURGICAL GROUP 79106 #048-04-1966 L1966 **P OS** *030
TEDJARATI, Shaheen Sean. 1500 WALLACE BLVD 79106 #306-01-1993 L1996 **OBG** *020 †18,30
TEEPLE, Charles Sloan. 1900 MEDI PARK DR, AMARILLO UROLOGY ASSOCIATE 79106 #048-02-2000 L2004 **U** *020 †95
TEKESTE, Hagos. 1901 MEDI PARK DR STE 50 79106 #041-01-1978 L1984 **GE IM** *020 †20
THANNOUN, Abdul S. 1400 WALLACE BLVD, TTUHSC DEPT INT MED 79106 #048-14-1990 L1991 **GE HEP** *020 †20
THOMAS, Aabu Alex. 1400 WALLACE BLVD 79106 #495-08-1995 **IM** *012
THOMPSON, Evaline Jane. 6010 W AMARILLO BLVD 79106 #027-01-1981 L1987 **PTH** *020 †50
THOMPSON, Victoria Jean. 1901 MEDI PARK DR, SUTIE 1059 79106 #065-01-1970 L1977 **AN** *020 †05
THURMOND-ANDERLE, M. 6701 WOODWARD ST 79106 #048-14-1984 L1985 **RHU IM** *020 †20
TIMM, David M. ■ 79124 #048-15-1996 L1997 **OBG REN** *020
TODD, Robert M. 1501 S COULTER ST 79106 #048-14-1985 L1986 **PTH** *020 †50
TORRES, Sara M. 1500 WALLACE BLVD 79106 #319-04-1987 L1995 **ON** *020 †20
TOWNSEND, Mary Jane. 7500 WALLACE BLVD 79124 #048-12-1985 L1987 **PTH** *020 †50
TREHAN, Amit K. 6833 PLUM CREEK DR 79124 #495-29-1989 L1996 **GE** *020 †20
TREHAN, Salil K. 12 CARE CIR 79124 #495-29-1988 L1998 **IM** *020 †20
TREHUN, Anish Hardeep. 1400 WALLACE BLVD 79106 #496-47-2003 **PD** *012
TUCKER, Bobby Falcon. 3 MEDICAL DR 79106 #048-13-1976 L1977 **OBG** *020 †30
TUCKER, Keelie Renee. ■ 79103 #048-15-2007 **OBG** *012
TULLAR, Paul Edgar. 1400 S COULTER ST, TEXAS TECH UNIVERSITY HEAL 79106 #048-13-1977 L1977 **OBG** *040 †30
TURNER, Cleveland. ■ 79106 #021-01-1956 L1971 **GP EM** *072
TURNER, Curtis Wade. 1400 S COULTER ST, TEXAS TECH MED CENTER 79106 #045-01-1986 L2005 **PD PHO** *020 †55
TURNER, Dustin A. 1400 WALLACE BLVD, DEPT OF FAMILY MEDICINE 79106 #048-14-2006 L2008 **FP** *012
TYSON, David L. 1215 S COULTER ST STE 100 79106 #048-13-1995 L1996 **FM** *020 †18
URBAN, Robert Stephen. 1400 S COULTER ST 79106 #048-04-1978 L1978 **IM** *040 †20
USALA, Stephen John. 1215 S COULTER ST, STE 400 79106 #016-02-1982 L1996 **END IM** *020 †20
USZYNSKI, Martin. 1901 MEDI PARK DR STE 2050 79106 #759-04-1998 L2004 **DR** *020 †80 ‡
UTHAISANGSOOK, Suwannee. ■ 79106 #891-02-1987 **PD** *100 †55,03
UY, Julito P. 9601 SPUR 591, TTUHSC-RMCHC BILL CLEMENTS 79107 #748-12-1988 L1996 **IM** *020 †20
VASIREDDY, Padmaja. 1400 WALLACE BLVD 79106 #913-89-1993 **IM** *012
VASUDEV, Rejeesh Vijaya. ■ 79106 #495-31-2004 **IM** *012
VEERAMACHANENI, Murali. 22 CARE CIR 79124 #495-72-1992 L1998 **CHP** *020 †75
VEGGEBERG, Lisa Edelmon. 1600 WALLACE BLVD 79106 #048-04-1984 L1988 **PD** *020 †55
VIRANI, Zulfikarali R. 6010 W AMARILLO BLVD, VA HOSPITAL 79106 #539-03-1979 L1983 **IM** *020 †20
WALKER, James Whittenburg. 400 SW 14TH AVE 79101 #048-12-1990 L1991 **IM** *020 †20
WALKER, Shelly L. ■ 79124 #048-14-1993 L1994 **P** *020
WALLER, Jack Douglas. 4302 WOLFLIN AVE 79106 #048-02-1968 L1968 **D IM** *020 †15
WALSH, Margaret Anne. 716 N POLK ST 79107 #007-02-1990 L1992 **PD** *020 †55
WAN, Bang. 6010 W AMARILLO BLVD, DEPT VA 79106 #243-45-1982 L2002 **IM** *020 †20
WARREN, Max Elton. 1901 PORT LN, AMARILLO HEART GROUP, LLP 79106 #005-15-1970 L2005 **CD IM** *020
WAUGH, Kimberly Ann. 1301 S COULTER ST, STE 403 79106 #048-02-1984 L1986 **DR IM** *020 †80
WEINBERGER, Bruce London. 7310 FLEMING AVE 79106 #021-01-1968 L1968 **OPH** *020 †35
WEIS, Brian Charles. 1400 S COULTER ST, TEXAS TECH UNIVERSITY HSC 79106 #048-12-1997 L2000 **IM** *020 †20
WELCH, Cody J. 1501 S COULTER ST 79106 #048-15-2001 L2004 **EM** *020 †16
WERNER, Carmen Marie. 1301 S COULTER ST 79106 #016-06-1993 L1996 **PD** *020 †55
WERNER, Harold Vincent. 1400 WALLACE BLVD, TEXAS TECH SCHOOL OF MEDIC 79106 #016-06-1966 L1993 **END IM** *020 †20
WERNER, Jan Reinert. 2307 W 7TH AVE 79106 #048-15-1976 L1977 **U** *020 †95
WESTMORELAND, Michael Jay. ■ 79116 #039-01-1979 L1980 **SME** *071 †18
WHELCHEL, Jeffery T. 1215 S COULTER ST, STE 100 79106 #048-16-1994 L1995 **FM** *020 †18 ‡
WHITE, Lahroy Alward. 1920 MEDI PARK DR STE 1 79106 #048-12-1973 L1973 **FM** *020
WIKE, Charles Champion. ■ 79124 #012-01-1965 L1973 **GS** *071 †85
WILHELM, David Michael. 1900 MEDI PARK DR, AMARILLO UROLOGY 79106 #016-43-1998 L2001 **U** *020 †95
WILKERSON, Michael Dee. 1501 S COULTER ST 79106 #030-05-1979 L1981 **U** *020 †95
WILKINSON, William Joel. 1400 S COULTER ST, TEXAS TECH UNIVERSITY HEAL 79106 #048-13-1994 L1995 **IM** *050
WILLIAMS, Clyde Marion. 1501 S COULTER ST 79106 #048-13-1974 L1974 **GYN** *020
WILLIAMS, John Newton, IV. 1901 MEDI PARK DR STE 2050 79106 #048-14-1979 L1979 **DR** *020 †80
WILLIAMS, Michael Duane. 6009 BELPREE RD 79106 #048-12-1974 L1974 **OBG** *020 †30
WILLIAMS, Sheri L. 1500 S COULTER ST STE 1 79106 #048-15-1989 L1990 **PD** *020 †55
WILLIAMS, Sheryl Louise. 1215 S COULTER ST, STE 400 79106 #048-02-1988 L1989 **IM** *020 †20
WILLIAMSON, John Beau. 1901 MEDI PARK DR STE 2002, AMARILLO PAIN ASSOC 79106 #048-02-1991 L1992 **AN PMM** *020 †05
WILSON, Golder North. 1400 S COULTER ST, TTUHSC AT AMARILLO DEPT OF 79106 #016-02-1972 L1988 **PD CG** *020 †55,19
WINGO, Susan Tanner. 6700 SW 9TH AVE 79106 #023-12-1988 L2003 **END** *020 †20
WRIGHT, Charles Verdo, Jr. 1400 S COULTER ST, STE 2700 79106 #027-01-1975 L1976 **FM FPG** *030 †18

■ = Address Information Privacy Protected

WRIGHT, Stephen Edgar. 6010 W AMARILLO BLVD 79106 #004-01-1967 L1967 OS ON *020 †20 ‡

YALAMANCHILI, Chandana. 1400 WALLACE BLVD 79106 #495-37-1999 IM *012

YALAMANCHILI, Kishore. 1400 S COULTER ST, DEPT OF INTERNAL MEDICINE 79106 #048-13-1999 L2005 PCC *100 †20

YEARY, James Keith. 6010 W AMARILLO BLVD 79106 #048-15-1982 L1983 D IM *020 †20,15

YOUNG, John Martin. 1500 S COULTER ST, STE 1 79106 #048-12-1990 L1991 PD *020 †55

YOUNG, Rodney S. 1400 WALLACE BLVD, TEXAS TECH UNIV. HLTH SCI 79106 #048-15-1997 L1998 FM *040 †18

YSASAGA, Jason E. 7310 FLEMING AVE 79106 #048-13-1996 L2002 OPH OS *020

ZAID KAYLANI, Samer Hayda. 1400 WALLACE BLVD 79106 #575-02-2006 PD *012

ZAMANI NOOR, Shahryar. 1400 WALLACE BLVD 79106 #473-02-1995 IM *012

ZHANG, Qing. 1400 WALLACE BLVD 79106 #243-76-1982 IM *012

ZOLLER, Dennis Paul. 1400 S COULTER ST, STE 2700 79106 #016-06-1976 L2003 PG *020 †18

ZUSMAN, Jaime. 1600 S COULTER ST, STE 402 79106 #023-07-1969 L2005 PD *020 †80,55

AMARILLO – RANDALL

AHMED, Syed Haseen. ■ 79119 #704-02-1984 L2007 GS *020 †85

ALLISON, Charles Raymond. ■ 79121 #048-12-1981 L1982 GS *020 †16

ANDERSON, Jerry Meitzen, Jr. ■ 79109 #048-15-1999 L2002 OBG *100

ANDREW, John Lee. 8201 W 83RD AVE 79119 #048-02-1981 L1981 DR *020 †80

ANDREW, Leora Pate. ■ 79121 #048-02-1950 L1953 PD *071 †55

ARCHER, Branch. ■ 79109 #048-12-1991 L1992 DR *020 †80

ASSADOURIAN, Assadour. 3501 S SONCY RD STE 154 79119 #575-01-1991 L2002 CD *020 †20

AYLOR, Arden Leroy. ■ 79114 #305-01-2003 FPG *012

BAKER, Kimberly H. ■ 79109 #047-06-1984 L1993 IM *100

BALL, Robert Merrill. 3512 VAN WINKLE DR 79121 #038-40-1973 L1980 DR *020 †80

BENSON, Leslie W. ■ 79109 #048-12-1986 L1987 EM FM *020

BENZ, Nicolle. ■ 79118 #048-78-2001, ▲ L2002 IM *020 †20

BJORK, Keith D. 3501 S SONCY RD STE 129 79119 #048-15-1989 L1990 ORS *020 †40

BROOKER, Andrew F, Jr. 4514 CORNELL ST, STE B 79109 #023-07-1966 L1994 ORS *020 †40

BUI, Bao Quoc. ■ 79121 #942-01-1998 IM †012

BURGESS, Steven Eugene. ■ 79121 #048-15-2008 *012

BURGESSER, Mary Frances. 3501 S SONCY RD STE 162 79119 #028-34-1993 L1997 PM *020 †60

CHAFFIN, Ronald Lowell. 3501 S SONCY RD, STE 154 79119 #048-02-1972 L1972 CD IM *020 †20

CHAVEZ, Ben. 3501 S SONCY RD, STE 134 79119 #034-01-1989 L1994 FM *020 †18

COOK, Elaine Remmers. 2609 WOLFLIN VLG 79109 #039-01-1980 L1994 D PD *020 †55,15

CORNELIUS, Dena Lynn. 2201 CIVIC CIR, STE 503 79109 #048-14-2000 L2004 AN *020 †05

COTTER, Heath Earl. ■ 79109 #048-15-2007 FP *012

CURA, Alberto Cailles. 3611 S SONCY RD STE 5B 79119 #748-11-1972 L1979 AN GP *020

DE LA CRUZ, Rosa J. ■ 79121 #308-04-1982 L1996 FP *100

DIAZ DE LEON, Sandra. 2915 W INTERSTATE 40 79109 #034-01-2006 FP *012

DICKINSON, Walter Esmond. ■ 79121 #028-02-1965 L1966 GS *071 †85

DIXON, Thomas Michael. 3501 S SONCY RD STE 1001 79119 #048-15-1998 L1999 PS HS *020

DOW, Harold Dwight. ■ 79119 #048-02-1940 L1940 GP GS *071

DUKE, Chuck Alan. 7600 BAUGHMAN DR 79121 #039-01-1989 L1993 AN *020 †05

EASLEY, Thomas Danl. 3611 S SONCY RD STE 5B 79119 #048-12-1967 L1967 AN *020 †05

ESPOSITO, Salvatore. 4510 BELL ST, BSA URGENT CARE CENTER 79109 #561-12-1984 L1994 FM *020 †18

FAIRCLOTH, Johnnie Wayne. ■ 79109 #048-15-2008 *012

FELDER, Randall Lynn. ■ 79121 #048-15-1985 L1986 AN *020 †05

FLORES, Michael D. 7717 CERVIN DR 79121 #048-15-1999 L2001 FM *020 †18

FONG, Don Leon. ■ 79109 #048-12-1962 L1962 ORS *071 †40

FREEMAN, Dudley Earl, III. 3501 S SONCY RD, STE 140 79119 #021-01-1997 L1998 OBG *020 †30

GUTTENPLAN, Michael David. 3501 S SONCY RD STE 106, PANHANDLE EAR NOSE THROAT 79119 #041-01-1985 L1990 OTO *020 †45

HAMMOND, Debra Lyn. 4510 BELL ST, BSA URGENT CARE 79109 #048-15-1994 L1995 FM *020 †18

HENDRICK, Charles Kerr. ■ 79109 #048-02-1961 L1961 R *071 †80

HICKMAN, Thomas Jefferson. 3501 S SONCY RD STE 1001 79119 #021-05-1971 L1989 OBG AN *020 †30,05

HIERHOLZER, John D. 4510 BELL ST 79109 #048-14-2001 L2004 FM *020 †18

HINES, Thomas R. 3501 S SONCY RD STE 1002 79119 #048-15-1997 L1998 FM *020 †18 ‡

HOLMAN, Gerald Hall. ■ 79109 #062-01-1953 L1980 PLM PD *072 †55,19

HOLMAN, Karen Gayle. ■ 79118 #048-02-1973 L1973 FM *040 †18

HOPKINS, Richard C. 3501 S SONCY RD STE 140 79119 #048-15-2002 L2006 OBG *020 †30

HUANG, Qin. ■ 79109 #243-71-1984 IM *012

HUDSON, Thomas Leo. ■ 79121 #021-01-1954 L1974 GS CD *071 †85

HUQ, Nisarul Mikail. 3501 S SONCY RD, STE 154 79119 #065-06-1991 L2005 IC *020 †20

KACZMAREK, John Frederic. 3501 EDGEWOOD DR 79109 #025-01-1965 L1976 AN *020 †05

KHAN, Naeem Ullah. 7415 WOODMONT DR, BSA URGENT CARE 79119 #704-02-1989 L2003 FM *020 †18

KORDESTANI, Rouzbeh K. 3501 S SONCY RD STE 137 79119 #021-01-1994 L2004 PS *100

LAMPKIN, Angela B. ■ 79119 #048-13-1997 L1999 DR *100 †80

LASHER, John Chester. 7705 BENT TREE DR 79121 #012-05-1972 L1982 NM GP *020 †28

LEAKE, Abby S. ■ 79109 #048-14-2007 P *012

LEE, Billie Hughes. ■ 79118 #048-02-1956 L1956 GP GS *072 †18

LEVY, Maurice N, Jr. 4103 W 34TH AVE 79109 #024-01-1949 L1964 GS *071 †85

LUCE, James K. ■ 79109 #008-01-1952 L1966 ON IM *071

MAAYTAH, Taghreed Nayef. 3501 S SONCY RD STE 102 79119 #575-01-1988 L1995 PD *020 †55

MAC FARLANE, Bonny A M. 4510 BELL ST 79109 #067-01-1972 L1978 FM *020 †18

MAY, Gregory Allen. 3501 S SONCY RD STE 140 79119 #048-16-1999 L2003 OBG *020 †30

MC CUE, William Wheeler. ■ 79109 #048-02-1957 L1957 PD *071

MILLER, Kimball Austin. ■ 79119 #025-01-1975 L1977 GP *020 †55

MITCHELL, Roby Dean. 3501 S SONCY RD STE 110 79119 #048-15-1987 L1988 EM *020

MORGAN, Stacie R. 3501 S SONCY RD STE 106 79119 #048-13-1996 L2000 OTO *020 †45

MUNDEN, Paul M. 3501 S SONCY RD STE 100 79119 #048-15-1986 L1987 OPH AN *020 †35

MURDOCK, Amanda Dawn. ■ 79109 #039-01-2006 OBG *012

NEWMAN, James Jennings. 7411 WOODMONT DR 79119 #048-13-1989 L1990 DR *020 †80

NICKENS, Wesley Scott. ■ 79109 #048-15-2006 FP *012

NOVAK, Daniel Mc Cormick. ■ 79109 #048-15-1980 L1980 IM *040 †20

ORTIZ, Shayom J. ■ 79118 #048-12-2005 AN *012

OSBORN, Joel Craig. 3501 S SONCY RD, STE 154 79119 #048-02-1976 L1976 CD *020 †20

PARKER, James Robert. 3501 S SONCY RD STE 129 79119 #048-14-1996 L1999 ORS *020 †40

PATEL, Mahendra J. 7240 VERSAILLES DR 79121 #496-38-1968 L1974 AN GS *020

PATEL, Seema Vinubhai. ■ 79109 #048-15-2008 *012

PAUL, David Wayne. ■ 79118 #048-02-1976 L1976 OM *030 †70

PILCO-JABER, Ruth. 3501 S SONCY RD, STE 131 79119 #319-02-1981 L1997 IM NEP *020 †20

PISKUN, Walter Stanley. 3501 S SONCY RD STE 126 79119 #048-15-1974 L1974 NS *020 †25

PROFFER, Amy D. ■ 79119 #048-13-1999 L2005 AN *020 †05 ‡

RAMIREZ, Rigoberto. 2201 CIVIC CIR STE 5 79109 #024-05-1992 L1997 AN PAN *020 †05

RAUSCH, Tracy Kathryn. ■ 79109 #054-04-1996 L2000 IM PLM *012

REDUS, Lonnie C. ■ 79109 #048-12-1950 L1950 GP GS *071

REESE, Leslie Evan. 6606 PALACIO DR 79109 #038-40-1970 L1976 GE IM *071 †20

RITTER, Robert Houston. ■ 79109 #048-02-2001 L2007 U *020

ROBINSON, Joan Anita. ■ 79109 #047-07-1988 L1990 FM *020 †18

ROGERS, James Franklin. ■ 79109 #048-04-1977 L1977 ORS ISM *071 †40

SAMBERSON, Randall Ray. 3501 S SONCY RD STE 109 79119 #048-15-1976 L1976 GS CRS *020 †85

SCHNEIDER, Martin Lynwood. 3501 S SONCY RD STE 106 79119 #048-12-1971 L1973 NO *020 †45

SETHI, Usha. ■ 79119 #495-12-1967 L1974 OBG *020 †30

SETHI, Vinod Kumar. ■ 79119 #495-05-1963 L1972 PD *020 †55

SIMS, John B. 3501 S SONCY RD STE 129 79119 #048-15-1989 L1990 OP ORS *020 †40

SLATON, Byron T. ■ 79109 #048-14-2006 *012

SLATTON, Monte. 3501 S SONCY RD, STE 154 79119 #048-12-1989 L1990 CD *020 †20

SMITH, Frederic Warren. 3501 S SONCY RD STE 126 79119 #040-02-2000 L2000 GS *020

STREET, Tyler Clayton. ■ 79121 #048-15-2008 *012

SWICEGOOD, Erica Lynn. ■ 79109 #048-15-2007 OBG *012

TOLSCIK, Magdalena. ■ 79121 #759-01-1963 L1970 PD *071 †55

TOLSCIK, Olga Maria. ■ 79121 #759-04-1998 L2004 P *020 †75

TRAHERN, Lance Layne. 2201 CIVIC CIR, STE 503 79109 #019-02-2001 L2005 AN *020 †05

TRAN, Phieu Nguon. ■ 79114 #396-01-1956 L1978 FM OBG *012

TREHAN, Manishika Sharma. 4500 ABERDEEN DR 79119 #495-03-1995 L2003 IM *020

VEGGEBERG, Neil Roger. 5111 CANYON DR 79110 #048-04-1984 L1985 PM *020 †60

VELKY, Aniceta Veloso. ■ 79109 #748-01-1963 L1973 AN *020

WARD, John Edward, Jr. 4510 BELL ST, BSA-URGENT CARE CENTER 79109 #048-12-1997 L2002 FM *020 †18

WHINNERY, James Elliott. 3520 SLEEPY HOLLOW BLVD 79121 #048-02-1975 L1975 AM MDM *050

WIGGINS, Cynthia Nicole. ■ 79118 #048-15-2005 OBG *012

WINSTON, Thomas S. ■ 79119 #048-15-1996 L1997 FM *020 †18

WRIGHT, Geoffrey Lee. 3501 S SONCY RD STE 106 79119 #048-02-1981 L1981 OTO *020 †45

WYATT, Douglas Bryant. 3501 S SONCY RD STE 109 79119 #048-15-1984 L1985 GS VS *020 †85

ANDREWS – ANDREWS

BROWNE, James W. 714 HOSPITAL DR 79714 #048-02-1988 L1989 OBG *020 †30

GARCIA, Robert Wm. 208 NW 2ND ST 79714 #048-13-1987 L1988 FM *020 †18

GORDON, Brian Eugene. 714 HOSPITAL DR 79714 #007-02-1958 L1963 GS *072 †85 ‡

GUERRA, Jimmy J. 708 HOSPITAL DR 79714 #649-30-1985 L1992 IM ID *020 †20

JARIWALA, Natverlal T. 714 HOSPITAL DR 79714 #495-22-1962 L1974 GS HS *020

MUNCY, Bonnie Eugenia. 700 HOSPITAL DR 79714 #034-01-1999 L2002 FM *020 †18

NAYAK, Satish. 706 HOSPITAL DR 79714 #495-37-1990 L2002 FM OBG *020 †18

OLIVE, George Gilbert. 700 HOSPITAL DR 79714 #048-02-1976 L1976 FM *020 †18

PARKEY, Wendell W. 714 HOSPITAL DR 79714 #048-15-1993 L1994 OBG *020

REDMOND, Doytt Denton. 714 HOSPITAL DR 79714 #047-06-1974 L2004 GS *020 †85

SMITH, Darvin Wallace. 720 HOSPITAL DR 79714 #048-04-1962 L1962 ADM EM *062

WADDINGHAM, Rand Edward. 700 HOSPITAL DR 79714 #056-06-1987 L1989 FM OBS *020 †18

WILTZ, Armand De Leon. 1411 N MAIN ST 79714 #748-10-1972 L1980 OBG *020

ANGLETON – BRAZORIA

AHMED, Ashfaq. ■ 77515 #704-02-1958 L1977 PM *020

ALLEN, Thomas Earl. 1108 E MULBERRY ST 77515 #048-02-1963 L1963 PD *020 †55

ATTAR, Mohammed. 146 E HOSPITAL DR, STE 101 77515 #605-01-1973 L1976 CD IM *020 †20

AUSTIN-TOLLIVER, Felicia. 146 E HOSPITAL DR, STE 204 77515 #011-02-1997 L1999 IM *020 †20

BONNEN, Mark D. ■ 77515 #048-14-1999 L2004 RO *020 †80

CARPENTER, Suzan. 1113 E CEDAR ST 77515 #048-04-1984 L1985 FM *020 †18 ‡

COOKE, Gregory Carrington. 2315 E MULBERRY ST 35 77515 #005-06-1992 L1996 OBG *020 †30

DABAGHI, Salim Farid. 146 E HOSPITAL DR, STE 201 77515 #605-01-1988 L1992 CD IM *020 †20

DANIEL, Daryl Keith. 135 E HOSPITAL DR 77515 #048-16-1993 L1994 IM *020

DECKER, William Louis. 146 E HOSPITAL DR, TEXAS EYE INSTITUTE 77515 #048-02-1978 L1978 OPH *020 †35

DESAI, Rajendrakumar M. 2323 E HIGHWAY 35 77515 #495-23-1976 L1983 R *020 †80

EGGLESTON, Steven D. 146 E HOSPITAL DR, STE 106 77515 #048-02-1998 L2003 ORS *020 †40

HUANG, Mau-Ping. ■ 77516 #244-05-1968 L1980 OBG *071

JOHNSON, Charles A. 146 E HOSPITAL DR, TEXAS EYE INSTITUTE 77515 #048-14-1987 L1988 OPH *020 †35

KASHYAP, Kapil Kumar. 146 E HOSPITAL DR, STE 209 77515 #028-34-1992 L1996 AN *020 †05

KHAZANCHI, Kamlametharam. 1805 E HIGHWAY 35 77515 #495-05-1957 L1975 GP *071

KOOP, Michael Richard. 146 E HOSPITAL DR, TEXAS EYE INSTITUTE 77515 #048-13-1996 L2000 OPH *020 †35

LU, Hou-Teh. 146 E HOSPITAL DR STE 105 77515 #244-01-1976 L1986 PD PN *020 †55

MAGUIRE, James Patrick. 3015 E MULBERRY ST 77515 #539-06-1981 L1992 GS *020

MC DONALD, Craig L. 146 E HOSPITAL DR, STE 106 77515 #048-14-1987 L1988 **ORS** *020 †40
MIKKILINENI, Rajyalakshmi. 2030 E MULBERRY ST 77515 #495-11-1975 L1981
  IM GP *020 †20
O'GORMAN, Leo Dennis. 432 E MULBERRY ST 77515 #048-02-1961 L1961
  PHP R *030 †80,28,70
PARKER, Larry Keith. 2315 E MULBERRY ST 77515 #048-13-1985 L1986 **OBG** *020 †30
RANDHAWA, Manjit Singh. 132 E HOSPITAL DR 77515 #018-75-1992, ▲ L1993
  AN PME *020 †05
ROGERS, Anthony Scott. 136 E HOSPITAL DR 77515 #048-04-1982 L1983 **FM** *020 †18
SHARMA, Mukesh Kumar. 146 E HOSPITAL DR, STE 101 77515 #496-11-1981 L1998
  IM *020 †20
TSCHEN, Luis Fernando. 135 E HOSPITAL DR 77515 #429-02-1988 L1999 **FM** *020 †18
WEINER, Benjamin B. 135 E HOSPITAL DR 77515 #869-07-1956 L1960 **IM** *020
ZACCA, Nadim Michel. 146 E HOSPITAL DR, STE 101 77515 #605-01-1975 L1979
  CD IM *020 †20

ANNA – COLLIN

KURESHI, Ikram U. ■ 75409 #048-15-2001 L2007 **GS** *100

ANSON – JONES

CHAPANOS, Petros K. 215 N AVENUE J, VALLEY DAY & NIGHT CLINIC 79501
  #231-03-1992 L1996 **FM** *020 †18
KAPU, Gopichand. 215 N AVENUE J 79501 #495-50-1967 L1979 **GS GP** *020

ARANSAS PASS – SAN PATRICIO

EDWARDSON, Delbert Lloyd. 1731 W WHEELER AVE 78336 #019-02-1972 L1974 **FM** *020 †18
HALL, Pamela A. 1711 W WHEELER AVE 78336 #048-16-1986 L1987 **EM FM** *020 †18
MATTHEW, Earl Bertram. 1711 W WHEELER AVE 78336 #048-12-1967 L1968 **IM ID** *020 †20
MORRIS, Edward Hoy. ■ 78336 #038-06-1959 L1962 **FM GP** *071
YANG, Chau Rong. 1731 W WHEELER AVE 78336 #407-20-1958 L1973 **FM** *020

ARGYLE – DENTON

CALLEGAN, Cherye Celeste. 914 COUNTRY CLUB RD 76226 #021-06-1984 L1985
  P CHP *020 †75
CALVERT, Charles W. ■ 76226 #048-78-2005, ▲ L2007 **FP** *012
CATINO, Michael Augustine. ■ 76226 #041-12-1994 L2008 **ORS OSS** *020 †40
CONTRERAS, Yolanda. ■ 76226 #048-13-1988 L1989 **PD** *020
DONAHUE, Brian Kevin. ■ 76226 #048-14-1999 L2003 **DR** *020 †80
LESTER, Stephen Paul. 76226 #048-02-2003 L2006 **GS** *012
MARSDEN, John Michael. 415 HIGHWAY 377 S, STE 102 76226 #048-02-1982 L1983
  GS VS *020 †85
NORGAARD, Richard Paul. ■ 76226 #048-12-1964 L1964 **MDM GE** *030 †20
SNYDER, Lowell Emrick. ■ 76226 #019-02-1958 L1966 **IM** *071 †20
TOLEDO VILLANUEVA, J R. ■ 76226 #649-03-1965 L1973 **P PD** *020 †55

ARLINGTON – TARRANT

ACOSTA, Carlos, Jr. 811 INTERSTATE 20 W, STE 132 76017 #264-03-1961 L1968 **NS** *020 †25
ACUNA, Patrick. ■ 76017 #048-02-2007 *100
ADMASSU, Kifle. 909 MEDICAL CENTRE DR # A, TEXAS PREMIER INTERNAL MED 76012
  #025-01-2002 L2005 **IM** *100 †20
AGNEW, Hall Wayne. 723 N FIELDER RD 76012 #048-02-1958 L1958 **GYN** *071 †30
AHMED, Shakila. 10 HOME PLACE CT 76016 #495-21-1968 L1978 **R** *020 †80
AHSAN, Jiaul. 2596 E ARKANSAS LN # 1 76014 #160-02-1984 L2000 **IM** *020 †20
AKBANI, Sohail. 906 W RANDOL MILL RD 76012 #704-02-1987 L1994 **HO** *020 †20
AL-ASSI, Mohammad T. 1001 N WALDROP DR, STE 509 76012 #875-01-1986 L1993
  GE *020 †20
ALEGRE, Ticiano. ■ 76002 #042-03-1991 **CHP** *100
ALEXANDER, Garish K. 1741 E BARDIN RD 76018 #048-14-2002 L2007 **GS** *020
ALFORD, Mark Allan. 707 N FIELDER RD STE B 76012 #048-12-1991 L1992 **OPH PS** *020 †35
ALLEN, Bohn Dixon. 800 W RANDOL MILL RD 76012 #048-02-1961 L1961 **GS VS** *030 †85
ALLEN, Dale Ray. 800 ORTHOPEDIC WAY, ARLINGTON ORTHOPEDIC ASSOC 76015
  #005-12-1963 L1967 **ORS GP** *071 †40
ALLEN, Scott Eugene. 801 W RANDOL MILL RD, ARLINGTON SURGICAL 76012
  #048-02-1978 L1978 **GS VS** *020 †85
ALLOTEY, Emmanuel F. 800 W RANDOL MILL RD, MARSHFIELD CLINIC 76012
  #412-01-1991 L2007 **IM** *020 †20
AMIN, Anjani Narendra. ■ 76014 #654-01-1998 L2005 **FM** *020
AMOS, Aaron Michael. 1001 N WALDROP DR 76012 #025-01-1992 L2002 **U** *020 †95
ANAGNOSTIS, George. 1300 S FIELDER RD, FAMILY HEALTH CARE 76013 #048-15-1976 L1976
  FM *020 †18
ANAGNOSTIS, Jim. 1300 S FIELDER RD, FAMILY HEALTH CARE 76013 #048-02-1974 L1974
  FM EM *020 †18
ANDERSON, Teresa Loree. 3120 MATLOCK RD # 201 76015 #048-14-1994 L1996 **PD** *020 †55
ANKELE, Richard Dan. ■ 76002 #048-02-1960 L1960 **AN** *071 †05
ANTOHI, Octavian. ■ 76017 #035-46-2002 L2006 **AN** *100
APALISKI, Stephen James. 5421 MATLOCK RD 76018 #041-09-1981 L1993 **A** *020 †55,03
ARAGON, Michael A. 3030 MATLOCK RD, STE 205 76015 #048-14-2000 L2002 **NEP** *020 †20
ASSAR, Manish Dilip. 900 W RANDOL MILL RD, STE 206 76012 #005-02-1992 L1995
  ICE *020 †20
ATKINS, Baron Charles. 809 W RANDOL MILL RD 76012 #048-12-1998 L2000 **OBG** *020 †30
AUGUSTINE, Muddamalle. 912 WRIGHT ST STE E 76012 #495-21-1971 L1984 **IM CD** *020 †20
AUSTIN, Joseph, Jr. 911 MEDICAL CENTRE DR # C 76012 #033-06-1981 L1992
  IM PUD *020
AWASTHI, Sangeeta. 3901 W GREEN OAKS BLVD, STE B 76016 #004-01-1988 L1990 **P** *020
AWASTHI, Sanjay. 515 W MAYFIELD RD, STE 101 76014 #048-12-1986 L1990 **HEM ON** *020 †20
BAILEY, Arla Sue. ■ 76015 #649-14-1974 L1981 **IM FM** *020

BAKER, Donna Gay. 1300 S FIELDER RD, FAMILY HEALTH CARE 76013 #048-12-1975 L1975
  FM *020
BALLAYAN, Mona Deddah. 1741 E BARDIN RD, STE 291 76018 #011-04-2004 L2007
  FM *020 †18
BANE, Jerry Wm. 801 W RANDOL MILL RD, ARLINGTON SURGICAL 76012 #048-12-1968 L1968
  GS VS *071 †85
BARKE, Ronald Martin. 910 N DAVIS DR STE 100, SOUTHWEST OPTHALMOLOGY ASS 76012
  #005-06-1987 L1991 **OPH** *020 †35
BARKER, Thomas E. 811 INTERSTATE 20 W, STE 120 76017 #028-02-1996 L1997 **IM** *020 †20
BARNHART, James Alan. 4305 S BOWEN RD, STE 131 76016 #005-12-1979 L1980
  AN *020 †18,05
BASS, Robert Laverne. ■ 76016 #030-05-1956 L1956 **FM** *071 †18
BATTULA, Padmaja P. 801 INTERSTATE 20 W, MEDICAL STAFF SERVICES 76017
  #495-70-1994 L2003 **FM** *020 †18
BEATY, Andrew Dodson. 5421 MATLOCK RD, UTMB 76018 #048-02-2001 L2004 **AI** *020 †20,03
BECKER, Naum I. 6201 MATLOCK RD STE 139, VILLAGE MEDICAL CENTER 76002
  #913-97-1969 L1982 **OS PD** *020 †55
BENDEL, Henry Ward, Jr. ■ 76012 #047-06-1947 L1947 **ORS** *071 †40
BENEDICT, Thomas Bradley. 901 MEDICAL CENTRE DR # C 76012 #048-13-1973 L1973
  ORS *020 †40
BERGSTROM, Joan Louise. 1001 N WALDROP DR, STE 505 76012 #030-05-1982 L1985
  GYN OBS *020 †30
BERLIN, Scott A. 800 W ARBROOK BLVD STE 12 76015 #035-09-1989 L1995 **AN** *020 †05
BERRY, Shellie J. ■ 76001 #048-13-1987 L1989 **FM** *075 †18
BISHOP, Frederick L. 950 N DAVIS DR, STE 2 76012 #048-15-1983 L1983 **IM** *020 †20
BISHOP, Kristen Allison. ■ 76012 #048-12-2004 L2006 **DR** *012
BISHOP, Lydia A. 601 OMEGA DR STE 203, ARLINGTON PHYSICIANS GROUP 76014
  #048-14-1992 L1993 **PD** *020 †20
BLUM, Stephen Leon. 3939 W GREEN OKS BLVD #103 76016 #046-01-1982 L1985 **D** *020 †15
BLUMBERG, Elliott Jay. ■ 76012 #048-02-1955 L1955 **OPH** *075 †35
BLUMENSCHEIN, George M. 906 W RANDOL MILL RD, ARLINGTON CANCER CENTER 76012
  #035-20-1963 L1973 **ON HEM** *020
BLUMENSCHEIN, Sarah D. 800 W RANDOL MILL RD 76012 #035-20-1964 L1975 **PDC PD** *020
BOLE, Prafull V. 2903 VERONA CT 76012 #495-19-1965 L1977 **GS** *020 †85
BONTLEY, Paul T. 76013 #038-40-1951 L1952 **GP** *071
BOOTHE, Michael Curtis. ■ 76013 #048-13-1988 L1989 *020
BOWERS, Benjamin L. 801 W RANDOL MILL RD, ARLINGTON SURGICAL 76012
  #048-12-1987 L1988 **VS GS** *020 †85
BOWERS, William Thatcher. 801 W RANDOL MILL RD, ARLINGTON SURGICAL 76012
  #048-12-1962 L1962 **GS** *020 †85
BRACY, Waldo Parden, Jr. 1001 N WALDROP DR, STE 509 76012 #028-02-1986 L1990
  GE *040 †20
BRADFORD, Darien Wayne. 3150 MATLOCK RD, STE 411 76015 #025-07-1991 L2000
  TS *020 †85,90
BRANCH, Robin S. 3301 MATLOCK RD 76015 #048-02-1993 L2000 **PTH** *020 †50
BREEHL, Marc Dennis. 5203 VICKSBURG DR 76017 #020-12-1973 L1981 **AN** *020 †05
BRENTLINGER, Anthony B. 800 ORTHOPEDIC WAY, ARLINGTON ORTHOPEDIC ASSOC 76015
  #048-13-1981 L1981 **HS ORS** *020 †40
BRIGGS, William Henry, III. 800 W RANDOL MILL RD 76012 #048-12-1974 L1974 **OTO** *020 †45
BROCK, Steven David. 811 INTERSTATE 20 W, STE 120 76017 #048-02-1978 L1978 **IM** *020 †20
BRODY, Gordon Stewart. 1001 N WALDROP DR STE 708 76012 #649-14-1971 L1977 **U** *020
BROOKS, Jack Glen. ■ 76013 #004-01-1965 L1965 **R** *071 †80
BROWN, Phillip M. 3300 MATLOCK RD 76015 #048-12-1986 L1987 **OTO GS** *020 †45
BROWN, Raymond C, Jr. 800 W RANDOL MILL RD 76012 #048-13-1988 L1991 **TS** *020 †85,90
BROWN, Travis G. ■ 76010 #048-12-2006 **FP** *012
BROWNLEE, Ernest N, Jr. 1011 N COOPER ST 76011 #048-02-1978 L1978 **P ADP** *020 †75
BRUCE, Katherine Suzanne. 950 N DAVIS DR STE 4 76012 #048-04-1976 L1976 **PD** *020 †55
BUI, Tony Truong. 1032 W PIONEER PKWY # 400 76013 #035-06-1995 L1997 **PM** *020
BURNETT, James Warren. 800 ORTHOPEDIC WAY 76015 #021-01-1996 L1997 **ORS** *020 †40
BURNEY, Hamid. 3600 MATLOCK RD, STE 102 76015 #704-02-1984 L2000 **IM** *020 †20
BURNS, Wendell Mallory. ■ 76002 #020-02-1954 L1955 **R** *071 †80
BURZYNSKI, Michele A. 950 N DAVIS DR, STE 2 76012 #048-04-1998 L2001 **IM** *020 †20
BUSCH, Lyndon John. 907 MEDICAL CENTRE DR # B 76012 #021-06-1975 L1978 **AN** *020 †05
BUSCHOW, Robert Alexander. 800 W RANDOL MILL RD 76012 #048-12-1979 L1979
  IM *020 †20
CAHILL, Allen Jos. 600 SIX FLAGS DR, STE 632 76011 #016-43-1960 L1965 **P CHP** *020 †75
CALDWELL, Judith E. 835 E LAMAR BLVD, # 337 76011 #047-07-1985 L1991 **FM** *075
CANALES, Miguel Angel. 912 WRIGHT ST, STE A 76012 #341-01-1976 L1986 **IM** *020 †20
CANCEMI, Richard John. 1521 N COOPER ST 76011 #035-08-1966 L1972 **P CHP** *071
CANE, Michael Thos. 121 E RANDOL MILL RD, FAMILY HEALTH CARE 76011
  #016-11-1984 L1998 **OBG** *020 †20
CAPLAN, Brian Jeffrey. 3612 MATLOCK RD STE 1, ARLINGTON MEDICAL CLINIC 76015
  #836-01-1958 L1978 **FM EM** *020
CARLIN, Mary Esther. 801 E BORDER ST STE L 76010 #011-02-1970 L1992 **MG OS** *020 †19
CARLSON, Kenneth Philip. 3125 MATLOCK RD STE 108 76015 #035-09-1973 L1977
  PD PHO *020 †55
CARRINGTON, Dean Michael. 1001 N WALDROP DR, STE 605 76012 #048-12-1981 L1981
  IM AI *020 †20,03
CARTER, Jeffrey David. 800 ORTHOPEDIC WAY 76015 #049-01-1983 L1984 **ORS** *020 †40
CASTLEBERRY, Christina El. ■ 76002 #048-04-2004 L2007 **PD** *020 †55
CHAN, Paul Chian. 811 INTERSTATE 20 W, USMD MEDICAL CENTER 76017 #041-01-1993 L1999
  U *020 †95
CHAN, Ray. 1329 E PIONEER PKWY 76013 #048-12-1995 L1996 **OPH** *020
CHANDUPATLA, Samatha. 203 W RANDOL MILL RD 76011 #495-57-1996 L2005 **NEP** *020 †20
CHANG, Yong Dae. 2623 MATLOCK RD, STE 105 76015 #036-01-1991 L1994 **IM** *020 †20
CHEONG, Adrian Stanley. 800 W RANDOL MILL RD 76012 #065-09-1974 L1977
  EM FM *020 †16
CHERRY, Richard Kent. 912 WRIGHT ST, STE D 76012 #048-12-1959 L1959 **GP** *020
CHIARELLO, Richard A. 717 N FIELDER RD 76012 #010-02-1971 L1973 **PD** *020 †55
CHIEN, Lawrence Weiwen. 3301 MATLOCK RD, MEDICAL CENTER OF ARLINGTO 76015
  #048-12-1996 L1999 **EM** *020 †16
CHINEME, Thos Ekenechukwu. ■ 76017 #005-02-1969 L1975 **EM GS** *020 †16
CHINTALA, Vijaya Shree. 800 W RANDOL MILL RD, ARLINGTON MEMORIAL HOSPITA 76012
  #495-65-1997 L2008 **IM** *020 †20
CHUONG, Tony Tuan. 4860 MATLOCK RD, STE 140 76018 #021-05-1993 L1997 **IM PD** *020 †20
CLARK, David Roger. 910 N DAVIS DR STE 100 76012 #004-01-1969 L1974 **OPH** *071 †35

CLARK, Kennard. 900 W RANDOL MILL RD, STE 109 76012 #048-12-1968 L1968 **GS** *020 †85

CLUCK, Robert Nance, Jr. 809 W RANDOL MILL RD 76012 #048-12-1964 L1964 **OBG** *020 †30

CO, Tran Ba. ■ 76016 #941-01-1972 L1977 **GP** *071

COLBY, Fred Vail. 800 W RANDOL MILL RD 76012 #016-11-1963 L1977 **FM OS** *020

CONLEY, Richard Albert. ■ 76013 #039-01-1959 L1959 **GP GS** *071 †18

CONNER, Kevin Eugene. 501 RITA LN STE 105 76014 #040-02-1986 L1990 **N** *020 †75

CONNER, Margaret Eileen. ■ 76017 #048-13-1988 L1989 **FM** *018

CONNOLLY, Claire M. ■ 76016 #048-14-2008 *012

CORIA, Jean F. ■ 76006 #025-12-1979 L1984 **GP OM** *020

CORNWELL, Janis Rebecca. 515 W MAYFIELD RD, STE 305 76014 #021-05-1982 L1986 **OBG** *020 †30

COTTINGHAM, Andrew J, III. 800 W ARBROOK BLVD, STE 120 76015 #021-05-1992 L1996 **AN PMM** *020 †05

CREE GREEN, Melanie. ■ 76002 #048-02-2007 L2008 *012

CRIM, David Whitten. 918 N DAVIS DR, ARLINGTON DAY SURGERY 76012 #048-02-1971 L1971 **AN** *020 †05

CROUCH, Theresa Vogel. 2114 BAY COVE CT, TRSOLUTIONS, P.A. 76013 #041-01-1979 L1999 **DR** *020 †80

CRUIT, Tara Tolleson. ■ 76012 #048-14-2004 L2006 **CHP** *012

DANG, Hung Thien. 3020 MATLOCK RD STE 200 76015 #048-02-1997 L1998 **FM** *020 †18 ‡

DANIELS, Michael T. 800 ORTHOPEDIC WAY 76015 #048-14-1998 L1999 **PM PRS** *020 †60

DAO, Timothy Phi. 501 RITA LN, STE 109 76014 #048-02-1995 L1997 **IM** *020 †20

DAVE, Pramesh Chandrakant. 620 MATLOCK CENTRE CIR 76015 #495-48-1991 L1996 **IM** *020 †20

DAVIDSON, Randal David. 811 INTERSTATE 20 W, STE 30G 76017 #048-14-1985 L1986 **AI PD** *020 †55

DAVIS, Bradford Leroy. 707 N FIELDER RD, STE 3 76012 #048-04-1962 L1962 **OPH** *071 †35

DAVIS, Donald Jay. 1550 JONES DR 76013 #048-13-1984 L1985 **OBG** *020 †30

DAVIS, Patrick Leon. 1300 S FIELDER RD, FAMILY HEALTH CARE 76013 #004-01-1971 L1972 **FM** *020 †18

DEFESCHE, Charles L. ■ 76012 #165-04-1973 **PA VS** *050

DENNIS, Wesley D. 811 INTERSTATE 20 W, STE 212 76017 #048-14-1994 L1995 **N** *020 †75

DEUR, Charles Jay. 3301 MATLOCK RD 76015 #017-20-1975 L1979 **ON HEM** *020 †20

DIAS, Keryn Marie. 809 W RANDOL MILL RD 76012 #024-05-1991 L1995 **OBG** *020 †30

DIAZ, Rebecca Ann. ■ 76011 #048-04-2003 L2006 **IM** *100

DIAZ DE LEON, Victor, Jr. 205 BILLINGS ST STE 450, WEE TOTS PEDIATRICS 76010 #649-19-1983 L1988 **PD** *020 †55

DICKE, Karel Adriaan. 906 W RANDOL MILL RD, ARLINGTON CANCER CENTER 76012 #660-03-1964 L1977 **ON HEM** *020

DICKEY, Russell Allison. 811 INTERSTATE 20 W, STE 218 76017 #048-12-1986 L1987 **OBG** *020 †30

DILLEY, E Duane. 601 OMEGA DR, STE 206 76014 #048-12-1982 L1983 **PUD IM** *020 †20

DINGWERTH, Frank Sherrod. ■ 76016 #048-02-1954 L1954 **FM** *071

DINH, Dana Huyen My. 1115 E PIONEER PKWY, STE 135 76010 #942-01-1990 L2006 **FM** *020 †18

DISHON, Neil Homer. BOX 19329, UNIV OF TEXAS AT ARLINGTON 76019 #038-40-1956 L1959 **P OS** *020

DI STEFANO, Alfred. 906 W RANDOL MILL RD STE 2 76014 #035-08-1973 L1977 **ON HEM** *020 †20

DITTO, Michael Mayo. ■ 76013 #048-12-1963 L1963 **IM** *071 †20

DONOVITZ, Gary Steven. 811 INTERSTATE 20 W, STE 130 76017 #048-13-1980 L1980 **OBG** *020 †30

DOSHI, Gopal Harikrishna. 3295 S COOPER ST STE 1, STE131 76015 #495-22-1993 L2000 **NEP IM** *020 †20

DOYLE, James Edward. 900 W RANDOL MILL RD STE 1 76012 #016-43-1960 L1969 **PS GS** *020 †85,65

DUPPSTADT, Edwin R. 3223 OMEGA DR 76014 #048-15-1997 L1999 **FM** *020 †18

DURAND, Jaime P. 1150 W PIONEER PKWY 76013 #737-06-1981 L1987 **RHU IM** *020 †20

EARL, Harry Seymour, Jr. 5421 MATLOCK RD 76018 #048-02-1981 L1981 **AI IM** *020 †20,03

EASLEY, Gilbert Carlos. 900 W RANDOL MILL RD, STE 111 76012 #048-02-1966 L1966 **OTO** *020 †45

EISNER, Eric Abraham. ■ 76006 #005-19-2005 **ORS** *012

ELBAOR, James Edward. 3225 OMEGA DR # 760148, AMERICAN INSTITUTE OF ORTH 76014 #016-43-1969 L1976 **ORS RHU** *020 †40

ELLIS, David S. 1001 N WALDROP DR STE 708 76012 #048-14-1982 L1983 **U** *020 †95

ENGER, Michael Glenn. 1300 S FIELDER RD, FAMILY HEALTH CARE 76013 #048-02-1982 L1983 **FM** *020 †18

ENGLISH, Paul Eugene. ■ 76014 #049-01-1986 L1988 **D** *020 †15

ENGLISH, William Danl, II. 729 N FIELDER RD, STE 4 76012 #004-01-1966 L1975 **CD IM** *020 †18

ESCAMILLA, David F. 811 INTERSTATE 20 W, STE 22G 76017 #048-02-1995 L1998 **FM** *020 †18

EVANGELISTA, Anthony W. 3025 MATLOCK RD, ARLINGTON OPHTHAL 76015 #026-04-1992 L1996 **OPH** *020 †35

FERGUSON, Lorna T Lim. 3148 MATLOCK RD STE 501 76015 #748-11-1991 L2003 **IM GP** *020 †20

FERRY, Michael Terence. 900 W RANDOL MILL RD, STE 209 76012 #021-05-1986 L1987 **CD** *020 †20

FIELDER, Martin William. 809 W RANDOL MILL RD 76012 #039-01-1995 L2004 **OBG** *020 †30

FIKKERT, Chimene Willis. 811 INTERSTATE 20 W, STE 214 76017 #048-78-1998, ▲ L2002 **PD** *020 †55

FINKE, Mary A. 811 INTERSTATE 20 W, STE 218 76017 #048-12-1989 L1990 **OBG** *020 †30

FISHER, Maria Jackson. 1144 W PIONEER PKWY, STE E 76013 #030-05-1991 L1995 **PD** *020 †55

FLORES, Victor H. 901 MEDICAL CENTRE DR, STE A 76012 #308-07-1982 L1988 **PM** *020 †60

FOGLEMAN, James Douglas. ■ 76017 #048-12-1952 L1952 **FM PHP** *071 †18

FORD, Douglas Todd. 707 N FIELDER RD STE B 76012 #021-05-1994 L1996 **OPH** *020 †35

FORDJOUR, Kusi. 909 MEDICAL CENTRE DR # A, TEXAS PREMIER INTERNAL MED 76012 #056-05-1997 L2000 **IM** *020 †20

FRANK, David F. 701 HIGHLANDER BLVD, STE 105 76015 #017-20-1964 L1976 **R** *020 †80,28

FRANK, Rosalind Claire. 1011 N COOPER ST 76011 #048-12-1973 L1974 **P ADP** *020 †18

FRAZER, Jacqueline Ann. ■ 76016 #030-05-1996 L2006 **EM** *020 †18,16

FRENZEL, Hoyt W. 800 W RANDOL MILL RD 76012 #048-13-1998 L2001 **EM** *020 †16

FRISINA, Carl I. 811 INTERSTATE 20 W, STE 114 76017 #016-43-1960 L1976 **U** *020 †95

FROEHNER, Robert Nolan. 3301 MATLOCK RD 76015 #048-12-1977 L1977 **DR FM** *020 †18,80

FROESCHKE, Harry Peter. 515 W MAYFIELD RD, STE 305 76014 #025-07-1982 L1985 **OBG** *020 †30 ‡

GANDHI, Neelu. 906 W RANDOL MILL RD, ARLINGTON CANCER CENTER 76012 #495-22-1972 L1981 **R NM** *020 †80

GANDHI, Rajendra Pratap. 912 WRIGHT ST STE B 76012 #496-04-1971 L1980 **N P** *020 †75

GANO, Stephen Erik. 1100 ORCHARD DR STE B 76012 #021-05-1971 L1977 **D** *020 †15

GARCIA, Chris L. 121 E RANDOL MILL RD, FAMILY HEALTH CARE 76011 #048-14-1992 L1993 **FM** *020 †18

GATMAITAN, Bienvenido G. 621 MATLOCK CENTRE CIR 76015 #748-02-1965 L1977 **ID IM** *020

GAYDOS, Maria Ann. 121 E RANDOL MILL RD, FAMILY HEALTH CARE 76011 #041-13-1993 L1995 **FM** *020 †18

GEIGER, Joseph Russell. 907 MEDICAL CENTRE DR # B 76012 #048-13-1980 L1980 **AN** *020 †20

GENTRY, Kim Roland. 1001 N WALDROP DR STE 509 76012 #048-13-1984 L1990 **GE IM** *020 †20

GEPPERT, Daniel Jos. 950 N DAVIS DR 76012 #048-12-1980 L1980 **PD** *020 †55

GERA, Surendra Nath. 2304 COPPER RIDGE RD 76006 #495-36-1962 L1980 **P OS** *020

GESLANI, Alexis Same. 800 W RANDOL MILL RD 76012 #748-10-1973 L1980 **EM** *020 †16

GIBBS, Dana Bernice. 800 W RANDOL MILL RD 76012 #048-13-1994 L1999 **OTO** *020 †45

GILBERT, Julius Morris. 3301 MATLOCK RD 76015 #048-12-1966 L1966 **PTH** *020 †50

GILBEY, Jack Goetz, Jr. 1000 N COOPER ST 76011 #017-20-1995 L2003 **PCC** *020 †20

GILLIGAN, George Ryan. 1615 JEFFERSON CLIFFS WAY 76006 #048-13-2002 L2005 **PCC** *012 †20

GOLD, Stephanie Paige. 2624 MATLOCK RD, KIDS' DOC 76015 #008-02-1998 L2005 **PD** *020 †55

GOLDABER, Kenneth Gordon. 515 W MAYFIELD RD, STE 304 PROF BLDG A 76014 #011-02-1986 L1988 **MFM OBG** *020 †30

GONZALEZ, Eduardo Arturo. 121 E RANDOL MILL RD, FAMILY HEALTH CARE 76011 #048-02-1984 L1985 **FM** *020 †18

GORDON, Sherry. ■ 76006 #048-02-2000 L2005 **U** *020 †95

GORSKI, Timothy Noel. 1001 N WALDROP DR, STE 815 76012 #056-05-1982 L1987 **OBG REN** *020 †30

GOSSLEE, Jeffrey Michael. 1001 N WALDROP DR, STE 512 76012 #021-06-2002 L2006 **IM** *100

GOWDAGERE, Shivaram K. 614 MATLOCK CENTRE CIR 76015 #495-09-1982 L2003 **N** *020 †75

GRACEFFO, Michael Andrew. 515 W MAYFIELD RD, STE 201 76014 #005-18-1985 L1986 **CD IC** *020 †20

GRAHAM, John H Melton. 4305 S BOWEN RD, STE 131 76016 #048-13-1972 L1972 **AN** *020 †05

GRAHAM, Maudie Marie. 800 W RANDOL MILL RD 76012 #048-12-1965 L1965 **AN OS** *020

GRAY, Jack Allan. ■ 76013 #048-12-1956 L1956 **AN** *071 †05

GRECO, Jeffrey Robert. 800 W RANDOL MILL RD, ARLINGTON MEMORIAL HOSPITA 76012 #028-34-2003 L2005 **IM** *100 †20

GREEN, Andrea Lynette. 5 TWIN SPRINGS DR 76016 #018-03-1979 L1986 **EM** *020 †16

GREEN, Justin Matthew. ■ 76002 #048-02-2001 L2004 **U** *100

GREER, Electra Brown. 601 W SANFORD ST, JPS HEALTH CENTER 76011 #010-03-1972 L1978 **PD** *020 †55

GUERRA, Luis Fernando. 911 MEDICAL CENTRE DR, TEXAS PULMONARY CONSULTANT 76012 #048-04-1982 L1983 **IM** *020 †20

HALE, Nathan Darwin. 912 WRIGHT ST, STE D 76012 #048-02-1965 L1965 **FM** *020

HALL, Michelle C. 3301 MATLOCK RD 76015 #048-12-1995 L1998 **FM** *020 †18

HAMEL, Charles Rene. 4412 MATLOCK RD STE 300 76018 #025-01-1965 L1975 **OTO A** *020 †45

HAMPTON, Earl Stuart. 811 INTERSTATE 20 W, STE 30G 76017 #048-04-1979 L1980 **PD** *020 †55

HANSEN, Minah Molly. 3301 MATLOCK RD 76015 #048-12-1961 L1961 **PD** *071 †55

HAQ, Faisal Ehsan. 1000 N DAVIS DR 76012 #024-05-1998 L2005 **OPH** *020 †35

HARMON, Keith Hanna. 950 N DAVIS DR, STE 4 76012 #048-12-1978 L1978 **PD** *020 †55

HARPER, Donald Ray. 4275 LITTLE RD STE 202 76016 #027-01-1966 L1972 **FM** *020 †18

HARRINGTON, James W, Jr. 3300 MATLOCK RD 76015 #048-12-1964 L1964 **OTO** *071 †45

HARRIS, Desiree A. 848 W MITCHELL ST 76013 #048-15-1998 L2000 **PD** *020 †55

HARRIS, Thomas Wm. ■ 76013 #048-12-1956 L1956 **AN OM** *071 †05

HARRISON, Jason Michael. 515 W MAYFIELD RD, STE 402 76014 #034-01-1999 L2004 **GS** *020 †85

HARTMAN, Israel A. 501 RITA LN, STE 113 76014 #270-02-1989 L1994 **IM END** *020 †20

HASELOFF, Brian J. ■ 76002 #048-15-2002 L2004 **FSM** *012 †18

HASHIM, Shahzad. 3030 MATLOCK RD STE 2, UTHSC-HOUSTON, INTERNAL ME 76015 #704-25-1999 L2004 **NEP IM** *020 †20

HATCH, Garth Spilsbury. 900 W RANDOL MILL RD # 106 76012 #048-12-1954 L1955 **OBG** *071

HATCH, Mark Edward. ■ 76012 #048-13-1984 L1985 **IM** *020

HEATH, Dara Varga. ■ 76017 #048-02-1988 L1990 **NPM** *020 †55

HEBERT, Christopher Alan. 3030 MATLOCK RD STE 205 76015 #048-14-1999 L2002 **NEP** *020

HEESE, Theresa A. ■ 76017 #068-01-1992 L1995 **FM** *020

HEFLIN, Charles Robert. 800 W RANDOL MILL RD, ARLINGTON MEMORIAL HOSPITA 76012 #048-14-2001 L2004 **EM** *020 †16

HEISEL, Kaitlin Wells. ■ 76012 #056-06-2007 **GS** *012

HEITKAMP, Jeffrey Wade. 1001 N WALDROP DR STE 801, LB 55 76012 #048-04-1979 L1979 **NS** *020 †25

HELGESON, James Eugene. 801 INTERSTATE 20 W, PATHOLOGY DEPARTMENT 76017 #048-12-1971 L1971 **PTH** *020 †50

HENDERSON, Elizabeth A. 3120 MATLOCK RD, STE 201 76015 #038-41-1994 L2007 **PD** *020 †55

HENDERSON, Robert B. 723 N FIELDER RD STE E 76012 #048-12-1993 L1994 **GS** *020

HENRY, Bruce A. 811 INTERSTATE 20 W, STE 22G 76017 #048-13-1986 L1987 **FM** *020 †18

HENRY, Craig Bradford. 811 INTERSTATE 20 W, STE 22G 76017 #048-02-1984 L1987 **IM** *020 †20

HENSLEY, David Randall. 811 INTERSTATE 20 W, STE G40 76017 #048-15-1995 L1997 **D** *020 †15

HERNANDEZ, Antonio C. 5200 CORNVALLEY DR 76017 #048-16-2001 L2002 **OBG** *020

HERNANDEZ, Thelma M. ■ 76006 #748-02-1965 L1977 **AN** *072

HERRERA, Moses. 1741 E BARDIN RD, STE 106 76018 #048-14-1977 L1978 **FM P** *020 †18

HESKETT, Delbert Leon. ■ 76017 #039-01-1968 L2004 **AN** *071 †05 ‡

HEZMALL, Howard Patterson. 811 INTERSTATE 20 W, STE 114 76017 #048-13-1978 L1978 **U** *020 †95

HILLIARD, Robert James. 800 ORTHOPEDIC WAY 76015 #048-02-1979 L1979 **ORS** *020 †40

HINKLEY, Bruce Stanton. 701 HIGHLANDER BLVD # 400 76015 #048-04-1972 L1972 **ORS** *075 †40

HOFFMAN, Eric Joseph. 1300 S FIELDER RD, FAMILY HEALTH CARE 76013 #048-12-1993 L1994 **FM** *020 †18

HOLMBERG, John Milton. 10 HEMINGFORD CT, JOHN M. HOLMBERG, M.D. 76016 #048-04-1965 L1965 **DR AM** *020 †80

HONG, Chian Huey. 1000 N DAVIS DR, STE H 76012 #048-12-1998 L2003 **OPH** *020 †35
HOWARD, Thomas Edward, Jr. 515 W MAYFIELD RD, STE 403A 76014 #001-02-1968 L1981 **MFM OBG** *020 †30
HSU, Alice Lynn. 3030 MATLOCK RD STE 2 76015 #028-02-2001 L2004 **NEP** *020
HUCK, Minor Lewis. 4275 LITTLE RD STE 20 76016 #021-01-1959 L1962 **AN** *020 †05
HUGHES, Donald Duane. 1105 N COOPER ST 76011 #048-02-1977 L1977 **CHP P** *020 †75
HUMPHREY, Alfred L, Jr. 910 N DAVIS DR STE 400 76012 #048-02-1968 L1968 **OPH** *020 †35
HUNTER, David Scott. 811 INTERSTATE 20 W, STE 120 76017 #048-02-1977 L1977 **IM** *020 †20
HUYNH, Christine H. 3301 MATLOCK RD 76015 #048-14-1994 L1995 **PM** *020 †60
HYBARGER, Steven E. 907 MEDICAL CENTRE DR # B 76012 #048-13-2000 L2002 **AN** *020 †05
IHDE, Glenn Michael, II. 515 W MAYFIELD RD, STE 402 76014 #019-02-1993 L1998 **GS** *020 †85
INGLE, Donald Curtis. 1926 SW GREEN OAKS BLVD, FAMILY HEALTH CARE 76017 #004-01-1984 L1986 **FM EM** *020 †18
JACKSON, Richard Oscar. 3301 MATLOCK RD 76015 #048-02-1973 L1973 **EM** *020
JAGMIN, Chris L. 4300 CENTREWAY PL 76018 #048-04-1982 L1984 **FM** *030 †18
JAMES, Marie Diane. 2505 E ARKANSAS LN, STE 119 76010 #035-47-1991 L1999 **OBG** *020
JAMESON, Michael David. 1132 S BOWEN RD 76013 #048-14-1985 L1986 **NEP IM** *020 †20
JAMPOLIS, Samuel Lewis. 906 W RANDOL MILL RD, ARLINGTON CANCER TREATMENT 76012 #016-43-1969 L1983 **RO TS** *071 †80
JARADAT, Majd I. 3030 MATLOCK RD STE 2 76015 #575-01-1991 L2006 **NEP** *020 †20
JEFFERS, John Richard. 809 W RANDOL MILL RD 76012 #001-02-1968 L1969 **OBG** *020 †30
JENKINS, Brian Knox. 7008 ESCONDIDO DR 76016 #048-02-2003 L2005 **FM** *020 †18
JENKINS, Frederick R, Jr. ■ 76016 #048-04-1961 L1961 **DR** *071 †80
JEYARAJ, David Vijay. 800 W RANDOL MILL RD 76012 #495-27-1987 L2001 **IM** *020 †20
JOHN, Berchmans. 515 W MAYFIELD RD, STE 101 76014 #495-63-1973 L1980 **RO** *020 †80
JOHNSON, Vanessa Lynn. 3301 MATLOCK RD, EMERGENCY DEPARTMENT 76015 #025-07-1996 L1999 **EM** *020 †16
JOHNSTON, David Jay. 300 W ARBROOK BLVD STE C 76014 #049-01-1999 L2006 **DR** *020 †80
JOHNSTON, Robin L. 809 W RANDOL MILL RD, ASSOCIATES 76012 #048-12-1993 L1995 **OBG** *020 †30
JOKI, Melvin T. 3132 MATLOCK RD STE 3 76015 #048-13-1987 L1988 **PD** *020 †55
JONES, Dudley Davenport. 908 WRIGHT ST, ARLINGTON PATHOLOGY ASSOC 76012 #048-12-1965 L1965 **DMP PTH** *020 †50
JONES, Kory. 1001 N WALDROP DR, STE 802 76012 #048-15-2002 L2006 **GS** *020 †85
JONES, Wendell Emmett. 2301 E LAMAR BLVD, STE 650 76006 #012-21-1985 L1999 **IM** *020 †20
JOSHI, Mandar Vishwas. 906 W RANDOL MILL RD, ARLINGTON CANCER CENTER 76012 #495-28-1995 L2005 **AR** *020 †80 ‡
KALLAM, George Byron. 809 W RANDOL MILL RD 76012 #055-01-1968 L1970 **GYN GP** *020 †30
KAMRAN, Hamid. 515 W MAYFIELD RD, STE 403 76014 #704-21-1986 L2002 **GE** *020 †20
KAPSOS, Joseph Ernest. 800 W RANDOL MILL RD 76012 #065-01-1967 L1976 **OBG** *071
KATCHER, Aaron Honori. 3008 SPRING OAK PL 76017 #041-01-1956 L1956 **P** *030
KAY, Joseph Hiram, Jr. 3301 MATLOCK RD 76015 #305-01-1991 L1995 **PM PRS** *020 †60
KELLER, Ben Robt, Jr. 109 W RANDOL MILL RD, STE 101 76011 #048-12-1961 L1961 **GYN** *071 †30
KENG, Beng-Suan Tan. UNIV OF TX AT ARLINGTON UT, STUDENT HEALTH SERVICES 76019 #748-01-1958 L1979 **GP PD** *071
KENNARD, Charles David. 811 INTERSTATE 20 W, # G14 76017 #016-11-1986 L1996 **DS D** *020 †15
KHADEMOL-REZA, Linda Gail. 2408 GARDEN PARK CT STE B 76013 #019-02-1981 L2001 **GYN** *020 †30
KHAN, Muhammad A. 2303 MEGAN WAY 76016 #704-02-1989 L1995 **NEP** *020 †20
KHAN, Sarah. 906 W RANDOL MILL RD 76012 #016-01-1994 L2000 **DR** *020 †80
KHURSHID, Anwar. 906 W RANDOL MILL RD 76012 #704-02-1989 L1997 **HEM** *020 †20
KIPP, Mark B. 800 W RANDOL MILL RD, ARLINGTON MEMORIAL HOSPITA 76012 #048-15-1998 L2001 **EM** *020 †16
KIRBY, Vernon Victor. 1722 SPRING LAKE DR 76012 #048-12-1957 L1957 **R** *071 †80
KLEIMAN, David Alan. 3025 MATLOCK RD 76015 #048-02-1979 L1979 **OPH** *020 †35
KLINE, Ronald Steven. 515 W MAYFIELD RD STE 416 76014 #048-02-1973 L1973 **CRS** *020 †10
KNIPSTEIN, Robert Chas. 731 N FIELDER RD 76012 #048-12-1971 L1973 **P** *020 †75
KOAY, Jeannine Lehim. ■ 76015 #048-04-2002 L2005 **D** *020 †15
KOBETT, Patrick Thos. 1926 SW GREEN OAKS BLVD, FAMILY HEALTH CARE 76017 #048-14-1991 L1992 **FM** *020 †18
KOCUREK, Daniel L. 800 W RANDOL MILL RD, ARLINGTON MEMORIAL HOSPITA 76012 #048-13-1992 L1997 **EM** *020 †16
KORD, John Phillip. 809 W RANDOL MILL RD STE B 76012 #017-20-1964 L1973 **PS** *020 †85,65
KRISHNAN, Rohini. 3301 MATLOCK RD 76015 #495-35-1978 L1985 **PTH** *020 †50
KROMBACH, Robert Stephen. 809 W RANDOL MILL RD 76012 #045-01-2003 L2005 **OBG** *020
KUPPINGER, Mitchell Clark. 911 MEDICAL CENTRE DR, STE C 76012 #019-02-1970 L1978 **PUD IM** *020 †20
KWAN, Christine. ■ 76012 #048-02-2008 *012
LAL, Vinit Rashbihari. 900 W RANDOL MILL RD, STE 209 76012 #495-22-1989 L2002 **IC** *020 †20
LAM, Jonathan Q. 1926 SW GREEN OAKS BLVD, FAMILY HEALTH CARE ASSOC 76017 #048-13-1992 L1993 **FM** *020 †18
LANKFORD, Frances Pierce. ■ 76001 #048-02-1950 L1950 **PD** *071
LAUB, Donald Rudolf. ■ 76010 #056-06-1960 L1972 **PS GS** *071 †85,65
LAVAKE, Thomas Edward. 2623 MATLOCK RD STE 101 76015 #048-02-1966 L1966 **FM** *020 †18
LAYLAND, David H. 1200 E COPELAND RD, STE 200 76011 #048-15-1975 L1975 **OTO** *030 †45
LE, Thang Doan. 1115 E PIONEER PKWY, STE 147 76010 #048-12-1989 L1994 **IM** *020 †20
LEACH, Charles Raymond. 1001 N WALDROP DR, STE 615 76012 #021-05-1977 L1979 **IM** *020 †20
LEDESMA, Gilbert. 707 N FIELDER RD 76012 #048-12-1985 L1986 **FM** *020 †18
LEE, Charles Poyang. 906 W RANDOL MILL RD, ARLINGTON CANCER CENTER 76012 #021-01-1996 L2001 **RO** *020 †80
LEE, Justin Tabor. 811 INTERSTATE 20 W, STE 114 76017 #048-13-1996 L2002 **U** *020 †95
LEE, Moonhee. 3939 W GREEN OKS BLVD #210 76016 #583-01-1979 L1988 **A** *020 †20,03
LEE, Thomas Leroy. 950 N DAVIS DR, STE 2 76012 #048-02-1974 L1974 **IM GP** *020 †20
LEFFINGWELL, James Fred. 1001 N WALDROP DR STE 807 76012 #038-41-1981 L1982 **OTO HNS** *020 †45
LEFFINGWELL, Thos Forrest. 1001 N WALDROP DR, STE 605 76012 #038-41-1981 L1984 **IM** *020 †20
LEGGETT, Kenneth R. 905 MEDICAL CENTRE DR # B 76012 #048-04-1955 L1955 **OBG** *071 †30
LENHOFF, Stephen John. 900 W RANDOL MILL RD, STE 206 76012 #836-02-1977 L1992 **CD** *020 †20
LEON, Walter. 3120 MATLOCK RD, # 201 76015 #048-02-1987 L1990 **PD** *020
LETTIERI, Michael Frank. PO BOX 150167 76015 #048-12-1956 L1956 **D OS** *075 †15
LIM, Helen Ju. 3600 S COOPER ST 76015 #035-09-1994 L1999 **IM** *020 †20
LOGAN, David Malcom. ■ 76011 #048-02-1965 L1965 **OM IM** *020 †20
LOUDERMILK, John W. 409 CENTRAL PARK DR 76014 #048-15-1975 L1975 **OTO** *020 †45
LOUIS, Thomas H. ■ 76013 #048-12-2008 *012
LOWERY, Jamel Edward. ■ 76011 #048-12-2007 **OTO** *012
LUSK, Clu Flu. ■ 76013 #021-01-1950 L1954 **FM** *071 †18
LYMAN, Bradley D. 907 MEDICAL CENTRE DR # B 76012 #048-12-1989 L1990 **AN** *020 †05
MAHAPATRA, Rajat Kanti. ■ 76016 #495-79-1967 L1982 **CD IM** *020 †20
MAILEG, Concepcion Alejo. 619 MATLOCK CENTRE CIR 76015 #748-02-1965 L1978 **PD** *020 †55
MALINOWSKI, Danuta J. 800 W RANDOL MILL RD 76012 #065-01-1973 L1981 **FM** *020
MANNING, Allen Bryant. 1300 S FIELDER RD, FAMILY HEALTH CARE 76013 #048-02-1962 L1962 **FM EM** *071 †18
MARROQUIN, Robbin Bubb. ■ 76006 #048-02-2005 L2007 **FP** *012
MARTIN, David R. 3030 MATLOCK RD STE 205 76015 #048-14-1999 L2002 **NEP** *020 †20
MARTIN, John Russell. 811 INTERSTATE 20 W, STE 120 76017 #048-12-1977 L1979 **IM NEP** *020 †20
MAYFIELD, Corey Justin. ■ 76006 #048-02-2006 L2008 **EM** *012
MCALHANEY, Maureen Sia. ■ 76012 #016-42-2004 **GS** *012
MC ANALLEY, E R. 4275 LITTLE RD STE 20 76016 #048-12-1981 L1981 **AN** *020 †05
MC CLARAN, Joseph Dwight. 3150 MATLOCK RD STE 407 76015 #047-06-1999 L2006 **IM** *020 †20
MC CONNELL, Robert Warren. ■ 76012 #038-41-1946 L1967 **DR NR** *071 †80,28
MC CRARY, Michael W. 800 W RANDOL MILL RD 76012 #048-13-1992 L1993 **DR** *020 †80
MC DONALD, John Edward. 3301 MATLOCK RD 76015 #048-14-1982 L1983 **PTH PCP** *020 †50
MC ELVAIN, Ricky Lynn. 800 W ARBROOK BLVD STE 110 76015 #048-14-1986 L1987 **IM** *020 †20
MC GOWEN, Bernard Alvin. 811 INTERSTATE 20 W, STE 22 76017 #048-02-1974 L1974 **IM** *020 †20
MC INNIS, Michael G. 950 N DAVIS DR, STE 2 76012 #048-14-2000 L2003 **IM** *020 †20 ‡
MC KAIG, Calvin Newton. ■ 76013 #048-04-1964 L1964 **OPH** *071 †35
MEADOWS, Charles David. 900 WRIGHT ST 76012 #047-06-1966 L1969 **A PD** *020 †55,03
MEHTA, Bhasker Rai. 3295 S COOPER ST STE 137 76015 #917-24-1975 L1981 **NEP IM** *020 †20
MEISTER, Keith. 515 W MAYFIELD RD, STE 116 76014 #024-05-1986 L2004 **ORS OSM** *020 †40
MELTZER, Victor Neal. 1132 S BOWEN RD 76013 #016-06-1975 L1984 **NEP IM** *020 †20
MENDELSON, Michael. 1001 N WALDROP DR, STE 509 76012 #010-01-1971 L1977 **GE IM** *020 †20
MEYER, Matthew Galien. 811 INTERSTATE 20 W, STE 214 76017 #007-02-2001 L2004 **PD** *020 †55
MILHOAN, Rusty Allen. 3150 MATLOCK RD STE 401 76015 #048-13-1985 L1987 **CCS OBG** *020 †85,30
MILLER, Harry Shawn. 121 E RANDOL MILL RD 76011 #048-15-1996 L1997 **FM** *020 †18
MILLER, Thomas J. 3602 MATLOCK RD STE 200 76015 #017-20-1978 L1983 **FM** *020 †18
MILLIGAN, Donald Gray. 1125 W ABRAM ST STE 104 76013 #019-02-1971 L1979 **CHP P** *020 †75
MIMS, Robert Lewis. 900 W MITCHELL ST 76013 #048-12-1981 L1981 **P ADM** *020 †75
MITCHELL, Donald Hugh. 2000 E LAMAR BLVD STE 400 76006 #048-13-2000 L2002 **AN** *020
MITCHELL, Rodger D. 605 S W ST, UTA HEALTH SERVICES 76019 #048-15-1992 L1993 **FM** *020 †18
MOAYYAD, Edward Ehsan. 2624 MATLOCK RD 76015 #649-02-1984 L1988 **PD** *020 †55
MOHAN, Ponnaiah Chandra. 203 W RANDOL MILL RD 76011 #495-04-1991 L2005 **NEP** *020 †20
MOORE, Todd Oland. 711 E LAMAR BLVD STE 200 76011 #048-02-1998 L2003 **CRS** *020 †85,10
MORALES, Carlos Juan. 800 W RANDOL MILL RD, EMERGENCY DEPT 76012 #042-01-1997 L2006 **EM** *020 †16
MORGAN, Mark A. 4275 LITTLE RD STE 20 76016 #048-13-1984 L1985 **AN** *020
MORING, Sylvia Arlene. 1035 ENFILAR LN 76017 #004-01-1978 L1991 **P** *020
MORRIS, Richard Earl. ■ 76012 #039-01-1963 L1964 **AN** *071 †05
MOSELEY, Karan Ruth. 1001 N WALDROP DR STE 402 76012 #048-02-1982 L1983 **OBG** *020 †30
MULLANAX, Milton Gayle. 811 INTERSTATE 20 W, STE G40 76017 #048-02-1964 L1964 **D** *020 †15
MURPHY, Daniel John, Jr. ■ 76016 #034-01-1984 L1993 **RO** *071 †80
MURUGAN, Tsr. 203 W RANDOL MILL RD 76011 #495-04-1989 L2001 **NEP IM** *020 †20
MYCOSKIE, Bernard J. ■ 76013 #038-40-1951 L1952 **PHP FSM** *071
MYCOSKIE, Michael Lee. 800 ORTHOPEDIC WAY 76015 #021-01-1976 L1976 **ORS** *020 †40
MYCOSKIE, Philip John. 800 ORTHOPEDIC WAY, ARLINGTON ORTHOPEDIC ASSOC 76015 #048-15-1976 L1976 **ORS** *020 †40
NABERHAUS, Daniel R. 2594 E ARKANSAS LN # 190 76014 #048-13-1987 L1988 **FM** *020 †18
NAKAMURA, Yukihiro A. 3030 S COOPER ST 76015 #048-02-1981 L1981 **PS CS** *020 †65
NALAJALA, Vasu. 800 W RANDOL MILL RD 76012 #495-21-1995 L2006 **IM** *020 †20
NANCE, Brenna Jacinth. ■ 76016 #028-46-1990 L1995 **EM PE** *020 †16
NAUS, Peter Jon. 1001 N WALDROP DR, STE 702 76012 #056-05-1969 L1974 **IM** *020 †20
NEILL, Chris L. 1107 W RANDOL MILL RD 76012 #048-15-1988 L1989 **OBG** *020 †30
NELSON, Leslie Wilmot. 800 W RANDOL MILL RD, ARLINGTON INPATIENT PHYSIC 76012 #025-07-2001 L2004 **IM** *020
NEWBY, Hi Eastland. ■ 76011 #048-04-1957 L1957 **FM OM** *020 †18 ‡
NEWLAND, Earl Frederick. 1000 N DAVIS DR STE H 76012 #025-07-1971 L1976 **OPH AM** *071 †35
NGUYEN, Duc Y. ■ 76012 #941-01-1964 L1979 **FM P** *071
NGUYEN, Dung C. 1102 ORCHARD DR 76012 #048-15-1991 L1996 **N** *020 †75
NGUYEN, Dung Chi. ■ 76013 #048-13-1998 L2005 **N** *020
NGUYEN, Kimloan Phi. ■ 76017 #305-01-2007 **FP** *012
NGUYEN, Linh Mythi. P.O. BOX 190964 76019 #048-13-2006 **IM** *012
NGUYEN, Luat Quang. 3132 MATLOCK RD STE 307 76015 #396-03-1969 L1973 **D GP** *020 †15
NGUYEN, Luat Tien. 3150 MATLOCK RD, STE 407 76015 #004-01-1987 L1992 **GE** *020 †20
NGUYEN, Phan Ton. 601 OMEGA DR, STE 206 76014 #018-03-1994 L2000 **PCC** *020 †20
NGUYEN, Son Xuan. ■ 76014 #048-02-2003 L2007 **GS** *012
NGUYEN, Thomas Manh. 5405 S COOPER ST 76017 #028-34-2002 L2006 **FM** *100 †18
NGUYEN, Tri Minh. 811 INTERSTATE 20 W, STE G40 76017 #021-05-2001 L2005 **D** *020 †15

■ = Address Information Privacy Protected

NGUYEN, Yen V. 1321 E PIONEER PKWY 76010 #048-12-1993 L1994 **GP AN** *020
NIEMIROWSKI, George John. 2100 E RANDOL MILL RD 76011 #048-02-1985 L1986 **OM** *020
NIETO, Roberto M. 811 INTERSTATE 20 W, STE 212 76017 #048-14-1989 L1993 **N** *020 †75
NORCROSS, James Frederic. 900 W RANDOL MILL RD, STE 206 76012 #035-06-1977 L1978 **TS** *020 †85,90
NUE-SESSAREGO, Hugo M. 905 MEDICAL CENTRE DR 76012 #737-01-1962 L1971 **OPH** *020 †35
NUGENT, Barbara Ann. 3301 MATLOCK RD 76015 #048-13-1984 L1985 **OPH** *020 †35
NUNEZ, Ignacio Trujillo. 121 E RANDOL MILL RD, FAMILY HEALTH CARE 76011 #048-12-1979 L1979 **OBG** *020 †30
NUSSBAUM, Sherry. 1408 W ABRAM ST SU 76013 #048-02-1998 L2003 *020
OCAMPO, Fabio. ■ 76017 #264-01-1956 L1972 **GP** *071
OWEN, Charles Callis, Jr. 1001 N WALDROP DR, STE 509 76012 #024-01-1998 L2004 **GE** *020 †20
OWENS, Joe Allen. 950 N DAVIS DR STE 2 76012 #048-12-1989 L1990 **IM** *020 †20
PADMANABHAN, Rajesh S. ■ 76015 #028-46-1995 L2004 **GS** *020 †85
PANG, Shing Y. ■ 76006 #048-13-1990 L1992 **GP** *020
PAREKH, Hiren Rameshchand. 2623 MATLOCK RD STE 1 76015 #056-06-1998 L2002 **OPH** *020 †35
PAREKH, Navinchandra T. 601 OMEGA DR, STE 201 76014 #495-01-1970 L1974 **GE IM** *020
PARKER, Paul Mark. 3200 MATLOCK RD 76015 #048-12-1979 L1979 **PM** *020 †60
PARRILL, Ellen M. 811 INTERSTATE 20 W, STE 218 76017 #048-02-1990 L1991 **OBG** *020 †30
PATEL, Anant Nanubhai. 501 W SANFORD ST 76011 #048-15-2002 L2005 **P** *100
PATEL, Chandrakant H. 501 W SANFORD ST STE 11 76011 #495-89-1980 L1989 **P** *020
PECANA, Manuel C. 907 MEDICAL CENTRE DR # B 76012 #748-01-1969 L1984 **AN** *020
PEDDICORD, Orene Whitcomb. ■ 76006 #048-12-1949 L1949 **FM** *050 †18
PENCA, Stephen John. 4305 S BOWEN RD, STE 131 76016 #048-02-1977 L1977 **AN** *020 †05
PEPPLER, Dawnette Kay. 1001 N WALDROP DR, STE 505 76012 #030-05-1996 L2000 **OBG** *020 †30
PERRYMAN, Joe L, III. 2623 MATLOCK RD, STE 105 76015 #048-13-1997 L1998 **IM** *020 †20
PETTWAY, John Byron. 121 E RANDOL MILL RD, FAMILY HEALTH CARE 76011 #048-13-1992 L1993 **FM** *020 †18
PEVEY, Ryan Rogers. ■ 76006 #048-02-2005 **GS** *012
PHAM, Chat Van. 1327 E PIONEER PKWY 76010 #942-01-1970 L1980 **P GP** *020
PHI-DAO, Michael Vu. 501 RITA LN, STE 109 76014 #048-13-1993 L1995 **FM** *020 †18
PHILLIPS, Charles A. 3301 MATLOCK RD, QUESTCARE 76015 #048-15-1992 L1993 **EM** *020 †16
PHILLIPS, Paul, III. 800 ORTHOPEDIC WAY 76015 #048-13-1986 L1987 **HS ORS** *020
PIERCE, John Rush. 950 N DAVIS DR STE 2 76012 #048-12-1952 L1952 **IM CD** *071 †20
PILGRIM-KING, Karen A. 817 BENGE DR 76013 #035-01-1995 L2005 **PD** *020 †55
PLEMONS, Ralph Peter. 907 MEDICAL CENTRE DR # B 76012 #048-15-1984 L1985 **AN EM** *020 †05
PLUMP, David Harry. 911 MEDICAL CENTRE DR, STE C 76012 #038-41-1976 L1983 **PUD CCM** *020 †20
POINDEXTER, Craig. 801 W RANDOL MILL RD 76012 #048-02-1960 L1960 **ORS OS** *071 †40
POMBO, J F. 729 N FIELDER RD STE A 76012 #264-02-1963 L1971 **CD IM** *020 †20
POND, Jay D. 800 ORTHOPEDIC WAY 76015 #048-12-1990 L1991 **ORS** *020 †40
POQUIZ, Dennis Edward. 2309 W GREEN OAKS BLVD 76016 #048-14-1996 L1998 **FM** *020 †18 ‡
PORTMAN, Robt Kennedy, Jr. ■ 76012 #048-12-1963 L1963 **PD** *071 †55
PORTO, Lito. 800 W RANDOL MILL RD 76012 #264-02-1958 L1964 **NS** *020 †25
POTTER, Brittany Rochelle. ■ 76016 #048-02-2007 **FP** *012
PREVOST, Robert Ward, Jr. 800 W RANDOL MILL RD 76012 #047-06-1952 L1973 **PM** *071 †60
PRICE, Vernon Gary. 811 INTERSTATE 20 W STE 11 76017 #048-12-1973 L1977 **U** *020 †95
PULLIAM, Scott Robt. 1926 SW GREEN OAKS BLVD, FAMILY HEALTH CARE 76017 #048-14-1985 L1987 **FM** *020 †18 ‡
PURGASON, Thomas Jos. 3600 MATLOCK RD STE 100 76015 #048-02-1979 L1979 **IM** *020 †20
RAE, Mary Louise. 800 W RANDOL MILL RD, EMERGENCY DEPARTMENT 76012 #039-01-1981 L1988 **EM** *071 †16
RAILEY, Bruce J. 3301 MATLOCK RD 76015 #048-02-1982 L1983 **DR** *020 †80
RAINE, Wilfred Leroy. 848 W MITCHELL ST 76013 #036-07-1979 L1982 **PD** *020 †55
RAJAGOPALAN, Sashi Kala. ■ 76006 #495-84-1990 *020
RAJORA, Nilum. 1132 S BOWEN RD, ARLINGTON 76013 #048-12-2000 L2003 **NEP** *030 †20
RAMIREZ, Jesus. 3814 HASTINGS CT 76013 #048-15-1984 L1985 **EM FM** *020 †18
RANDALL, Elizabeth Marie. ■ 76016 #038-41-1988 L1990 **OBG** *020
RASMUSSEN, David Louis. 1017 W RANDOL MILL RD 76012 #017-20-1973 L1978 **PS OS** *020 †65
RASMUSSEN, Kent Robert. 950 N DAVIS DR 76012 #028-02-1976 L1979 **IM** *020 †20
RASMUSSEN, Virginia Diane. 950 N DAVIS DR STE 4 76012 #028-02-1976 L1979 **PD** *020 †55
RAVKIND, Brett R. 3612 MATLOCK RD STE 103 76015 #048-13-1988 L1990 **IM** *020 †20
REDDY, Praba Narayana. 707 N FIELDER RD SU, FORD EYE CENTER 76012 #004-01-1996 L2004 **OPH** *071 †35
REDDY, Tarakumar Battula. 1011 N COOPER ST 76011 #495-58-1977 L1991 **CHP P** *020 †75
REDWOOD-KIDDOE, Alva Mae. ■ 76012 #566-01-1975 *100
REICHELT, Edward Geral. 5732 INTERSTATE 20 W 76017 #039-01-1964 L1965 **FM** *020
REZAI, Kourosh. 907 MEDICAL CENTRE DR # B 76012 #048-12-1998 L2001 **AN** *020 †05
RHEA, Dalton Lee. 515 W MAYFIELD RD STE 200 76014 #048-02-1973 L1973 **FM** *020
RICHARDS, Barna Allen. 800 W RANDOL MILL RD 76012 #048-02-1963 L1963 **GP** *020 †16
RICHARDSON, James A. 1001 N WALDROP DR, STE 602 76012 #010-01-1955 L1978 **IM** *071 †20
RICHARDSON, James Allan. 1001 N WALDROP DR, STE 602 76012 #048-02-1974 L1974 **CD IM** *020 †20
RIOJAS, Dalila V. 4201 INTERWAY PL 76018 #649-45-1984 L1995 **PD** *020 †55
RISING, Ernest Eugene. 800 W RANDOL MILL RD 76012 #048-02-1955 L1955 **ORS** *020 †40
RIZKALLA, Sherif M. ■ 76002 #048-78-2006, ▲ **IM** *012
RIZZO, Laura Anne. 3301 MATLOCK RD 76015 #048-14-1993 L1994 **FM** *020 †18
ROBERTS, Thomas Wayne. 3301 MATLOCK RD 76015 #004-01-1978 L1979 **PTH** *020 †50
ROBINSON, Chili. 1000 N DAVIS DR, STE B 76012 #048-13-1975 L1975 **PS** *020 †65
RODGERS, Mark Alan. 707 N FIELDER RD 76012 #048-12-1985 L1986 **IM** *020 †20
RODRIGUEZ, Francisco J. 800 ORTHOPEDIC WAY, ARLINGTON ORTHOPEDIC ASSOC 76015 #048-13-1988 L1990 **ORS OSM** *020 †40
RODRIGUEZ, Roberto. 1114 E PIONEER PKWY, STE 15 76010 #025-12-1976 L1979 **FM** *020
ROSEN, Neil. 3223 OMEGA DR 76014 #067-01-1970 L1977 **FM** *020 †18
ROSENBLOOM, Shelley Breen. 800 W ARBROOK BLVD STE 300, DIAGNOSTIC NEUROIMAGING 76015 #041-12-1976 L1984 **DR RNR** *020 †80
ROSENSTEIN, Jacob. 800 W ARBROOK BLVD STE 150 76015 #023-07-1979 L1980 **NS** *020 †25
RUSH, Avril Brickley. ■ 76016 #048-12-1984 L1985 **FM** *020 †18
SACHER, Edward C. 509 SUNLIGHT DR 76006 #048-02-1953 L1953 **U** *071 †95
SAHL, Christiana. ■ 76012 #048-12-2008 *012
SAINI, Rakesh K. 3600 S COOPER ST, STE 100 76015 #495-36-1987 L1994 **IM ON** *020 †20
SAKOWSKI, Michael Jos. 907 MEDICAL CENTRE DR, STE B 76012 #048-12-1970 L1970 **AN** *020 †05
SALEEMI, Anees-Ur-Rahman. 2726 MATLOCK RD STE C 76015 #704-01-1971 L1979 **CD** *020 †20
SAMPSON, Marcia Joy. 212 W SOUTH ST, ATTN: EMERGENCY DEPT 76010 #039-01-1982 L1985 **PD** *020 †55
SAMS, Joseph Terence. 900 WRIGHT ST 76012 #035-20-1961 L1966 **A IM** *020 †20,03
SARAN, Nirmal. 2726 MATLOCK RD STE A 76015 #495-19-1959 L1975 **OPH** *020 †35
SARDAR, Winfred Amer. 3200 MATLOCK RD 76015 #005-18-2001 L2003 **AN PME** *020
SARMINI, Omar. 515 W MAYFIELD RD STE 305 76014 #875-01-1977 L1983 **OBG** *020 †30
SAUNDERS, Bradley Michael. ■ 76017 #048-14-2006 **ORS** *012
SAUNDERS, Charles Glenn. 1100 ORCHARD DR, STE A 76012 #047-06-1973 L1985 **OBG GP** *020 †30
SAZY, John Anthony. 431 OMEGA DR, STE 104 76014 #025-07-1986 L1989 **ORS OSS** *020
SCHARF, Paul L. 1115 W RANDOL MILL RD 76012 #035-06-1977 L1978 **NS GS** *020 †25
SCHMIDT, Rebecca Smith. 3200 MATLOCK RD 76015 #048-14-1995 L1997 **PM** *020 †60
SEDRAK, Faten Mikhael. ■ 76016 #915-04-1977 L1984 *100
SEDRAK, Peter, Sr. ■ 76016 #048-14-2006 **DR** *012
SEGAL, Andrew. 801 ROAD TO SIX FLAGS W, STE 123 76012 #495-20-1976 L1984 **CD** *050 †20
SERRALTA, Victoria Watt. 501 W MAIN ST, JOHN PETER SMITH PHYSICIAN 76010 #011-02-2001 L2005 **D DS** *020 †15
SERRANO, Antonio P. 100 W PIONEER PKWY, STE 111 76010 #748-10-1973 L1978 **GP UCM** *020
SEWELL, Charles Thos, Jr. 907 MEDICAL CENTRE DR # B 76012 #048-12-1978 L1978 **AN** *020 †05
SHAH, Mita Rajendra. ■ 76006 #495-17-1978 *074
SHAH, Sahibzada Mohsin. 1001 N WALDROP DR, STE 509 76012 #704-01-1970 L1977 **GE IM** *020 †20
SHAH, Syed Irfan. 2726 MATLOCK RD 76015 #704-02-1982 L1996 **N IM** *020 †20
SHAH, Syed-Rizwan. 2726 MATLOCK RD STE B 76015 #704-02-1984 L1995 **N** *020 †75
SHELLENBERGER, David Luke. 1001 N WALDROP DR STE 807 76012 #048-04-2001 L2006 **OTO** *020 †45
SHELTON, Annette Marie. 690 E LAMAR BLVD, THE PHYSICIAN & TUTOR, P.A 76011 #007-02-1980 L1983 **P** *020
SHENG, Samuel. 1525 S COOPER ST, COOK CHILDREN'S NEIGHBORHO 76010 #422-01-1987 L1992 **PD** *020 †55
SHERE, Khalda. ■ 76006 #495-54-1977 L2004 **FM** *020 †18
SHETLER, Robert Weldon. 2805 OAK TRAIL CT # 5987 76016 #005-12-1966 L1967 **P LM** *071
SHIFLETT, Roland M, Jr. ■ 76016 #048-04-1945 L1945 **FM GS** *071 †18
SIEGLER, Roland Eugene. 3215 OMEGA DR 76014 #065-05-1971 L1977 **FM GP** *020
SIEGLER, Steve A. 3215 OMEGA DR 76014 #305-01-1984 L2003 **FM** *020 †18
SILVESTER, Michael Peter. ■ 76011 #132-01-1960 L1971 **OBG** *071 †30
SIMMONS, Cynthia A. 3301 MATLOCK RD, EMERGENCY DEPARTMENT 76015 #048-12-1994 L1998 **EM** *020 †16
SKAGGS, Murray Collins. 1107 N COOPER ST 76011 #048-12-1965 L1965 **P OS** *071 †75 ‡
SMITH, Ellawese Yvonne. 3909 TRISHA VAL CT, JPS HEALTH NETWORK 76016 #010-03-1986 L1992 **AN PAN** *020
SMITH, James John. 908 WRIGHT ST 76012 #039-01-1995 L2001 **PTH PCP** *020 †50
SMITH, Theodore Cecil. ■ 76016 #017-20-1956 L1957 **AN** *071
SOBTI, Ajay. 901 MEDICAL CENTRE DR 76012 #495-69-1976 L1987 **IM** *020 †20
SOHAIL, Atif. 2621 MATLOCK RD, STE 102 76015 #704-01-1985 L2003 **CD IM** *020 †20
SPIKES, Christopher S. 907 MEDICAL CENTRE DR # B 76012 #048-04-1994 L1998 **AN** *020 †05
STEGALL, William C. 907 MEDICAL CENTRE DR # B 76012 #048-12-1991 L1993 **AN** *020 †05
STEIDL, Erin Tews. ■ 76012 #048-78-2004, ▲ L2008 **OBG** *012
STEIN, Howard Allen. 1001 N WALDROP DR STE 811 76012 #067-01-1973 L1981 **GE** *075 †20
STEPHENS, Joseph Wm, III. 1000 N DAVIS DR STE B 76012 #024-01-1969 L1976 **PS** *020 †65
STIEFEL, Harry Paul. 801 W RANDOL MILL RD, ARLINGTON SURGICAL 76012 #048-12-1978 L1978 **GS VS** *020 †85
STONEDALE, Roderick D J. 6016 ENGLISHOAK DR 76016 #048-02-1976 L1977 **EM** *020 †16
STRAFACE, Angela L. 3301 MATLOCK RD 76015 #048-14-1994 L1999 **EM** *020 †16
STRAUSS, Murray R. 808 N CENTER ST 76011 #020-02-1967 L1978 **PS HS** *020 †65 ‡
STROO, Hans Herman. 101 E RANDOL MILL RD, STE 100 76011 #660-03-1949 L1976 **P** *071 †75
STUBBS, Theodore B. ■ 76017 #048-02-1977 L1977 **CD IM** *071 †20
STUMPF, Michael William. ■ 76006 #021-05-2008 *012
SU, Allen D. 800 W RANDOL MILL RD 76012 #005-12-1990 L1996 **IM** *020 †20
SU, Tony Hunhwon. 911 MEDICAL CENTRE DR, STE C 76012 #048-04-1988 L1994 **PUD CCM** *020 †20
SUDHAKAR, Rumalla. 625 MATLOCK CENTRE CIR 76015 #495-57-1968 L1976 **IM HEM** *020
SUNDGREN, Nathan Cole. ■ 76016 #040-02-2005 L2007 **NPM** *012
SUSS, Richard Alan. 800 W ARBROOK BLVD, STE 300 76015 #035-47-1976 L1983 **DR RNR** *020 †80
SYNGHAL, Anil. ■ 76017 #495-45-1983 L2007 **IM** *020 †20
TABER, Cynthia M E. 4400 NEW YORK AVE 76018 #048-14-1997 L1998 **AN PME** *020 †05
TABOR, Bannie Lee. 515 W MAYFIELD RD, STE 403A 76014 #048-13-1982 L1983 **NPM** *020 †30
TALKINGTON, Kenneth Max. ■ 76013 #048-12-1965 L1965 **GYN** *071 †30
TATE, Darren Randall. 515 W MAYFIELD RD, STE 305 76014 #048-15-1999 L2002 **OBG** *020 †30
TAVAKOLI, Babak. ■ 76011 #048-02-2002 L2007 **AN** *020
TAYLOR, Alan Mack, II. 1001 N WALDROP DR, STE 602 76012 #016-43-1986 L1998 **CD IM** *020 †20
TAYLOR, Denise Johnson. ■ 76006 #003-01-1981 L1982 **DR** *020 †80
TEAL, Kevin Renard. 624 MATLOCK CENTRE CIR, IMMANUEL BRAIN, SPINE AND 76015 #048-12-1991 L1992 **NS** *020 †25
TENG, Mark Pailuen. 900 W RANDOL MILL RD, STE 209 76012 #024-05-1995 L2003 **CD** *020 †20
TESFA, Ganana. 811 INTERSTATE 20 W, STE 212 76017 #041-12-1987 L1990 **N** *020 †75
THOMAS, Edward F. ■ 76017 #004-01-1942 L1947 **ORS PM** *072 †40
THOMAS, Lawrence Eugene. 3300 MATLOCK RD 76015 #048-12-1958 L1958 **OTO** *071 †45
THOMAS, Stuart N. 409 CENTRAL PARK DR 76014 #048-12-1989 L1994 **OTO HNS** *020 †45
THOMPSON, Gerald Griffith. 1300 S FIELDER RD, FAMILY HEALTH CARE 76013 #048-12-1965 L1965 **FM EM** *020

■ = Address Information Privacy Protected

TINGLEY, F Warren. ■ 76016 #012-05-1959 L1964 **IM CD** *071 †20
TIPS, Thomas Conrad. 1001 W RANDOL MILL RD 76012 #048-02-1957 L1957 **P** *071
TISDELL, Scott C. 800 W RANDOL MILL RD 76012 #048-02-1982 L1983 **NPM** *020 †55
TIU, John L. 601 OMEGA DR STE 206 76014 #748-02-1992 L1999 **PCC** *020 †20
TODD, Frederick Douglas. 800 W ARBROOK BLVD, STE 250 76015 #048-12-1979 L1979 **NS** *020 †25
TORGERSON, Jane. 800 W RANDOL MILL RD, EMERGENCY DEPT 76012 #049-01-1983 L1990 **EM** *020 †16
TOUCHSTONE, David Blake. 800 W RANDOL MILL RD 76012 #021-05-2001 L2003 **EM** *020 †16
TRAN, Anthony Thanh Ba. 515 W MAYFIELD RD, STE 302 76014 #048-02-1983 L1983 **PS GS** *020 †65
TRAN, Bao Ngoc. 1000 N COOPER ST 76011 #017-20-1999 L2001 **FM** *020 †18
TRAN, Dennis Dinh. 2535 E ARKANSAS LN STE 321 76010 #048-13-1989 L1993 **IM** *020 †20
TRAN, Hillary Hien Thi. ■ 76002 #942-01-1990 L2006 **NEP** *100 †20
TRAN, Huy Minh. 101 W RANDOL MILL RD, STE 142-0-1995 L1997 **OPH** *020 †35
TRUE, Robert Le Roy. 1001 N WALDROP DR STE 405 76012 #031-01-1980 L1986 **OBG** *020 †30
TRUONG, Charles Thuan. ■ 76006 #048-14-1988 L1989 **AN** *020
TYE, Timothy Talbot. 2000 E LAMAR BLVD 76006 #048-78-2004, ▲ L2008 **AN** *012
UDELL, Kimberly. 3602 MATLOCK RD, STE 206 76015 #028-78-1992, ▲ L2000 **OBG** *020
UMANA, Cesar Robt. 912 WRIGHT ST 76012 #429-01-1959 L1973 **FM** *071 †18
UNELL, Alan Marshall. ■ 76012 #048-15-1980 L1980 **OBG** *020 †30
UPTON, Gary Lee. ■ 76012 #048-12-1965 L1965 **D** *071 †15 ‡
URE, Robert David. 4738 LITTLE RD 76017 #065-06-1977 L1978 **GP** *020
USELTON, Michael T. 1926 SW GREEN OAKS BLVD, FAMILY HEALTH CARE 76017 #048-02-1992 L1993 **FM** *020 †18
VAN ZANDT, Roscoe L. 801 STADIUM DR, STE 111 76011 #021-05-1961 L1962 **OBG OS** *020 †30
VARGA, George Theodore. 3921 W GREEN OAKS BLVD, STE D 76016 #041-01-1954 L1980 **GP OBG** *020 †18
VAVRIN, Charles Richard. 800 ORTHOPEDIC WAY 76015 #056-05-1962 L1964 **ORS** *071 †40
VERGES, Lisa Blount. ■ 76012 #021-01-1981 L1982 **P** *020 †75
VERKRUYSE, Linda A. 515 W MAYFIELD RD 76014 #048-12-1999 L2005 **HO** *020 †20
VESTAL, James Clifton. 1001 N WALDROP DR STE 708 76012 #048-16-1986 L1987 **U** *020 †95
VONO, Mary Beth. 3301 MATLOCK RD 76015 #001-02-1996 L2002 **PTH NP** *020 †50
VORA, Hujefa Yusufali. 3150 MATLOCK RD STE 403, BHARMAL INT. MED. ASSOC, P 76015 #048-12-1999 L2002 **IM** *020 †20
WAECHTER, Walter Leslie, Jr. 811 INTERSTATE 20 W, STE 224 76017 #048-12-1976 L1976 **GS VS** *020 †85
WAHBY, Samir Cecil. 905 MEDICAL CENTRE DR 76012 #330-02-1960 L1975 **P CHP** *020 †75
WALKER, John Jefferson. ■ 76011 #048-02-1956 L1956 **IM** *071 †20
WALLEY, Andrew F. ■ 76010 #048-15-2000 **PD** *100
WALLING, Peter Thorburn. 2000 E LAMAR BLVD, STE 400 76006 #917-25-1967 L1978 **AN** *020
WANG, Jason. ■ 76006 #048-12-2008 †012
WARD, James Wm. 811 INTERSTATE 20 W, UNITG10 76017 #048-02-1979 L1979 **PS HS** *020 †65
WARREN, Kimberly K. 1000 N DAVIS DR 76012 #048-15-1995 L1998 **OPH** *020 †35
WATTS, Bruns Arnold, Jr. 907 MEDICAL CENTRE DR # B 76012 #048-02-1960 L1960 **AN** *071 †05
WAY, Matthew Shoemaker. 800 W RANDOL MILL RD 76012 #048-12-1997 L1998 **EM** *020 †16
WELCH, Harold Mark, Jr. 3019 MEDLIN DR STE 100 76015 #048-02-1966 L1966 **PD OS** *020 †05
WESTBROOK, Raymond R. 2623 MATLOCK RD, STE 105 76015 #048-78-1999, ▲ L2000 **IM** *020
WESTERHEIDE, Christopher. 907 MEDICAL CENTRE DR, STE C 76012 #028-46-1989 L1990 **AN** *020 †05
WESTRICK, Mary A. 1002 CROWLEY RD, MEDICAL DIMENSIONS ASSOC 76012 #016-11-1975 L1986 **ON HEM** *020 †20
WHITTEN, David Nelson. 3301 MATLOCK RD 76015 #005-02-1974 L1998 **EM** *020 †16
WIESER, Eric Scott. 800 ORTHOPEDIC WAY, ARLINGTON ORTHOPEDIC ASSOC 76015 #048-04-1998 L2004 **ORS** *020 †40
WILDEMANN, Mark Frederick. 900 W RANDOL MILL RD STE 2 76012 #010-01-1960 L1978 **FM AM** *071 †18
WILKERSON, Keith Wade. 3150 MATLOCK RD STE 409 76015 #048-12-1985 L1986 **FM EM** *020 †18
WILKINSON, Terry Lee. 800 W RANDOL MILL RD 76012 #048-15-1984 L1985 **FSM FM** *020 †18
WILLIAMS, Patrick D. 1001 N WALDROP DR STE 512 76012 #048-15-2001 L2005 **OPH** *020 †35
WILLIAMS, Timothy Everett. 1926 SW GREEN OAKS BLVD, FAMILY HEALTH CARE 76017 #048-12-1983 L1983 **FM EM** *020 †18
WILSON, Paul Hudson. ■ 76014 #004-01-1966 L1983 **OPH** *071 †35
WIMMER, Michael E. 901 MEDICAL CENTRE DR, STE A 76012 #048-14-1987 L1988 **PM** *020 †60
WOLDESENBET, Elleni. 3132 MATLOCK RD, STE 309 76015 #366-01-1991 L2000 **ID** *020 †20
WOLFF, Nelly E. ■ 76001 #042-04-1980 L1986 **GP** *020
WONG, Christopher Matthew. 609 MATLOCK CENTRE CIR, FAMILY ORTHO REHAB 76015 #005-14-1993 L1997 **ORS** *020 †40
WOOD, John Paul, Jr. 811 INTERSTATE 20 W, STE 218 76017 #048-12-1969 L1969 **OBG** *020 †30
WOOLF, Mark Watson. 800 ORTHOPEDIC WAY, ARLINGTON ORTHOPEDIC ASSOC 76015 #048-02-1980 L1980 **ORS** *020 †40
WORRELL, John Trace. 801 INTERSTATE 20 W, PATHOLOGY DEPARTMENT 76017 #048-12-1988 L1989 **DMP** *020 †50
WRAY, Richard A. 515 W MAYFIELD RD, STE 201 76014 #048-02-1985 L1986 **CD IM** *020 †30
WU, Edward Earlkang. 907 MEDICAL CENTRE DR # B 76012 #033-05-2000 L2006 **AN** *100 †05
YOO, Stephen. 801 ROAD TO SIX FLAGS W, STE 139 76012 #005-14-2003 L2006 **D** *020 †15
ZAIDI, Mustafa Husnain. ■ 76018 #704-16-2001 **P** *012
ZAIDI, Uzma. ■ 76017 #704-16-1994 L2007 **P** *100
ZIEGLSCHMID ADAMS, Mary E. 801 ROAD TO SIX FLAGS W, STE 139 76012 #048-12-1988 L1989 **D** *020 †20,15
ZINNANTE, Marian. 723 N FIELDER RD STE C 76012 #048-14-1994 L1998 **OBG** *020 †30

ARP — SMITH

SHORT, William Joseph. ■ 75750 #048-12-2002 L2004 **PTH** *020 †50

ARTHUR CITY – LAMAR

YEAKLEY, Robert Arlen. 1329 COUNTY ROAD 35860 75411 #039-01-1960 L1981 **GYN OBS** *062 †30

ATASCOCITA – HARRIS

GAJIC, Nikola. 8067 FM 1960 RD E 77346 #957-02-1986 L1996 **FM EM** *020

ATHENS – HENDERSON

ABADIE, Marcus Geo. 117 MEDICAL CIR, LAKELAND MEDICAL ASSOCIATE 75751 #048-04-1982 L1983 **FM** *020 †18
ANDERSON, Gregory M. 2000 S PALESTINE ST 75751 #048-12-1993 L1994 **AN** *020 †05
ANDERSON, Mitchell Dixon. 1801 S PALESTINE ST 75751 #048-12-1980 L1980 **RO** *020 †80
ASHIGBI, Michael P. 115 MEDICAL CIR, ATHENS HEMATOLOGY 75751 #412-01-1981 L1995 **HO** *020 †20
BARRETT, David B. 1336 S PALESTINE ST, ATHENS CTR FOR WOMENS 75751 #048-15-1984 L1985 **OBG** *020
BASS, James Wm. III. 1505 STATE HIGHWAY 19 S 75751 #048-02-1986 L1997 **FM** *020 †18 ‡
BAUMGARTNER, Teri Lynne. ■ 75752 #048-14-1995 L1999 **OBG** *020 †30
BERNARD, Jack L. 115 MEDICAL CIR 75751 #035-03-1993 L1995 **IM** *020 †20
BLANEY, John Charles. 115 MEDICAL CIR, STE 107 75751 #030-06-2000 L2005 **GS** *020 †85
BOWLES, David Lance. 600 S PALESTINE ST 75751 #048-12-1977 L1977 **ORS** *020 †40
BRADY, Ernest Lacey. 2000 S PALESTINE ST 75751 #048-12-1973 L1973 **AN** *020 †05
BROWN, William James. 2000 S PALESTINE ST 75751 #038-41-1969 L1973 **AN** *071 †05
BRYCE, Ronald W. 2000 S PALESTINE ST 75751 #039-05-1986 L1988 **FM EM** *020 †05
BYWATERS, Daniel W. ■ 75752 #048-16-1989 L1992 **FM EM** *020 †18
CALDWELL, Christian. 2000 S PALESTINE ST 75751 #048-15-1993 L1994 **AN** *020 †05
CARNEY, Donald Andrew. 117 MEDICAL CIR 75751 #048-02-1992 L1993 **FM** *020 †18
CATES, Ronald Dwayne. 704 S PALESTINE ST 75751 #048-14-1982 L1983 **EM FM** *020 †18
COPELAND, John A. 510 E CLINTON AVE 75751 #048-13-1999 L2003 **AN** *020 †05
CREATH, Deborah Linn. 2000 S PALESTINE ST 75751 #048-14-1989 L1990 **AN** *020 †05
CURRAN, Douglas Warren. ■ 75751 #004-01-1974 L1977 **FM** *020 †18 ‡
DAVID, Richard Thos. 117 MEDICAL CIR, LAKELAND MEDICAL ASSOCIATE 75751 #048-04-1981 L1982 **FM** *020 †18 ‡
DRODER, Robert Michael. 115 MEDICAL CIR, ATHENS HEMATOLOGY 75751 #041-09-1985 L1996 **HEM IM** *020 †20
ECKERT, Robert Mason. 2000 S PALESTINE ST 75751 #048-02-1960 L1960 **GP FPG** *071
ECKERT, Terri L. 117 PENNY LN 75751 #048-02-1987 L1988 **FPG** *020 †18 ‡
EDWARDS, Jonathan D. 115 MEDICAL CIR, STE 100B 75751 #048-16-1990 L1991 **FM** *020 †18
ELDORE, Mark Lawrence. 824 SOUTHPARK CIR 75752 #030-06-1995 L1996 **OBG** *020 †30
ELKINS, Tina Peikert. 1701 S PALESTINE ST, STE B 75751 #048-14-2000 L2005 **OTO** *020 †45
FAIN, Kevin L. 600 S PALESTINE ST 75751 #048-13-1987 L1988 **ORS** *020 †40
FIGUEROA, Sergio V, Jr. 2000 S PALESTINE ST 75751 #048-02-1987 L1989 **FM EM** *020 †05
FLANDERS, Douglas R. 2000 S PALESTINE ST 75751 #048-12-1992 L1993 **AN** *020 †05
FURLONG, Timothy James. (ANDREWS CENTER), HWY 19 S & FM 1615 75751 #048-14-1987 L1988 **P** *020 †75
GARCIA, Ruben Luis. 1701 S PALESTINE ST 75751 #048-12-1981 L1981 **U** *020 †95
GEDDIE, Nolen D, Jr. ■ 75751 #016-06-1950 L1950 **GP OS** *071
GONZALES, Joseph Manuel. 2000 S PALESTINE ST 75751 #048-16-1989 L1991 **AN** *020 †05
GREY, Curtis Eric. 115 MEDICAL CIR, STE 100F 75751 #019-02-1996 L2003 **FM** *020 †18
GRIFFIN, Oscar R. ■ 75752 #021-05-1952 L1957 **PTH** *071 †50
HARDIN, Thad David. 1260 S PALESTINE ST, HEATON EYE ASSOCIATES 75751 #019-02-1993 L2000 **OPH** *020 †35
HEINE, Ronald Wayne. 117 MEDICAL CIR, LAKELAND MEDICAL CENTER 75751 #039-01-1982 L1983 **FM** *020 †18
HELF, Steven J. 1505 STATE HIGHWAY 19 S 75751 #048-13-1987 L1988 **IM** *020 †20
ISKANDER, Sherif Saad. 1212 S PALESTINE ST 75751 #915-03-1989 L1999 **CD** *020 †20
JENNINGS, Norman L. 117 MEDICAL CIR, LAKELAND MEDICAL ASSOCIATE 75751 #048-16-1988 L1989 **FM** *020 †18
JONES, Christopher R. 2000 S PALESTINE ST 75751 #048-16-1998 L1999 **AN** *020
KIBLINGER, Gregory D. 608 S PALESTINE ST 75751 #048-12-2000 L2003 **OPH** *020 †35
KOERTH, Steven Michael. 117 MEDICAL CIR, LAKELAND MEDICAL ASSOCIATE 75751 #048-14-1999 L2000 **FM** *020 †18
LIEBERMAN, Scott Michael. 1212 S PALESTINE ST 75751 #035-09-1987 L1994 **CD IM** *020 †20
LOCKHART, Asa Carroll. 2000 S PALESTINE ST 75751 #048-14-1973 L1974 **AN MDM** *030 †05
MARTINS, Joseph Todd. 115 MEDICAL CIR, ATHENS HEMATOLOGY 75751 #048-12-1995 L1997 **HO IM** *020 †20
MC CARTHY, Daniel A. 2000 S PALESTINE ST 75751 #048-14-1992 L1994 **AN** *020 †05
METTETAL, Charles Ted. ■ 75751 #004-01-1975 L1979 **FM A** *071 †18
MICHIELS, Paul Jos. 5313 FM 2494 75751 #065-06-1974 L1976 **FM** *020 †18
MITCHELL, Derek Turner. 2000 S PALESTINE ST 75751 #028-34-1997 L1999 **AN** *020 †05
MONDINI, Gregory Francis. 607 E CLINTON AVE 75751 #035-47-1978 L1994 **OBG PHP** *020
MONGARE, Job Bogonko. 115 MEDICAL CIR, STE 102 75751 #048-14-1998 L1999 **CN** *020
NETTUNE, Gregory Robert. ■ 75752 #048-12-2007 **IM** *012
NICODEMUS, Wm Lawrence. ■ 75752 #048-12-1976 L1976 **EM** *020 †16
NOBLE, Robert Wm. ■ 75751 #048-12-1960 L1960 **FM A** *071 †18
OO, Maung Maung. 115 MEDICAL CIR, STE 106 75751 #209-01-1973 L2000 **HO** *020 †20
OPESANMI, Obafemi Oluseun. 2000 S PALESTINE ST 75751 #690-02-1982 L1998 **EM** *020 †16
PERKINS, Stanley R. 2000 S PALESTINE ST 75751 #048-13-1990 L1991 **AN** *020 †05
PRITCHARD, Rex C. 2000 S PALESTINE ST 75751 #048-02-1989 L1991 **AN** *020 †20
PUGH, Danny Paul. 115 MEDICAL CIR STE 107 75751 #048-12-1981 L1981 **GS VS** *020 †85
QUIROZ, Andrew. 2000 S PALESTINE ST 75751 #048-12-1975 L1975 **AN** *020 †05
RADIGHIERI, Alessandro C. 2000 S PALESTINE ST 75751 #048-12-1974 L1974 **AN** *020 †05
RISKO, Robert John. 115 MEDICAL CIR, STE 100 75751 #045-01-1972 L1973 **FM** *020 †18
RUDAK, Ronald. 2000 S PALESTINE ST 75751 #065-09-1972 L1977 **AN** *020
SALEM, Nagaratina. 1336 S PALESTINE ST 75751 #495-59-1993 L1997 **PD** *020 †55
SHAW, Elaine F. 1505 STATE HIGHWAY 19 S, FAMILY PRACTICE 75751 #035-01-1957 L1985 **PDC PD** *074
SHAW, Joan Elaine. 1505 S PALESTINE ST 75751 #048-13-1982 L1983 **PD** *020 †55
SMITH, Joe Ed. 1004 E TYLER ST 75751 #048-12-1960 L1960 **GS** *020
STEELE, Eldon Roy. 2000 S PALESTINE ST 75751 #048-13-1982 L1983 **AN** *020 †05

■ = Address Information Privacy Protected

TAKATA, Jay Anthony. 901 S PALESTINE ST 75751 #016-11-1989 L1999 **GE** *020 †20
THOMAS, Ronald Lee. 2000 S PALESTINE ST 75751 #048-12-1976 L1976 **EM** *020
THOMAS, Shawn A. 2000 S PALESTINE ST 75751 #048-13-1999 L2003 **AN** *020 †05
TOBES, Michael C. 1212 S PALESTINE ST 75751 #011-02-1990 L1997 **CD** *020 †20
TWADDELL, Timothy J. 2000 S PALESTINE ST 75751 #048-12-1999 L2003 **AN** *020 †05
WATSON, Robert Bruce. 2000 S PALESTINE ST 75751 #048-02-1979 L1979 **FM EM** *020 †18
WILCOX, John R. 810 LUCAS DR 75751 #048-12-1973 L1978 **R NR** *020 †80
WILLIAMS, Phillip E, Jr. 115 MEDICAL CIR, STE 108 75751 #021-01-1963 L1965 **NS** *020 †25
WITTEN, Bobby D. 115 MEDICAL CIR STE 100E, MEDICAL ARTS CLINIC 75751
#048-14-1997 L2000 **FM** *020 †18

ATLANTA – CASS

BALACHANDRAN, Subramaniam. 1007 S WILLIAM ST 75551 #220-02-1967 L1981
GS CCS *020 †85
FRUGE, Lloyd Mason. 1011 S WILLIAM ST, ELLINGTON MEMORIAL CLINIC 75551
#048-12-1983 L1983 **FM** *020 †18
HENDERSON, Kristi D. 1011 S WILLIAM ST 75551 #048-15-1996 L1997 **FM** *020 †18
HOGAN, Matthew E. 1011 S WILLIAM ST 75551 #048-12-1988 L1989 **FM** *020 †18
HOZDIC, Richard L, II. 1011 S WILLIAM ST, ELLINGTON MEM CLINIC 75551 #048-12-1994 L1995
FM *020 †18 ‡
LAW, Linda M. 410 E MAIN ST, # 69 75551 #048-14-1989 L1991 **EM** *050 †16
MC MILLAN, Donald Eugene. 1007 S WILLIAM ST 75551 #004-01-1966 L1972 **R** *020 †80
MORRIS, David Bruce. 1011 S WILLIAM ST, ELINGTON MEMORIAL CLINIC L 75551
#048-12-1974 L1974 **FM** *020 †18
MORRIS, James W. 506 W MAIN ST, P O BOX 1228 75551 #020-02-1968 L1978 **FM** *020 †18
NICHOLS, Joe Danl, Jr. 1011 S WILLIAM ST 75551 #047-06-1966 L1967 **FM** *020 †20
O'KELLEY, Edward Timothy. 1011 S WILLIAM ST, ELLINGTON MEMORIAL CLINICL 75551
#048-13-1982 L1983 **FM** *020 †18

AUBREY – DENTON

WYSS, Albert Michael. ■ 76227 #028-03-1968 L1974 **GPM** *020 †70

AUSTIN – HAYS

BAKER, James Keith. 7900 FM 1826, HILL COUNTRY SPORTS 78737 #021-01-1988 L2006
ORS *020 †40
BRENT, Byron D. 7900 FM 1826, STE 100 78737 #048-13-1986 L1987 **OPH** *020 †35
COX, Geoffrey H. 7900 FM 1826, STE 240 78737 #048-14-1991 L1996 **FM** *020 †18
EDUARDO, Ana Maria. 7900 FM 1826, STE 280 78737 #048-02-1991 L1992 **OBG** *020 †30
FRITZ, Andrea A. 8901 MCMEANS TRL 78737 #048-02-1995 L2001 **FM** *020 †18
FRITZ, Jeffery M. 8901 MCMEANS TRL 78737 #048-02-1995 L2000 **AN** *020 †05
GREEN, James Wm. ■ 78737 #021-01-1965 L1966 **D** *020 †15
GUPTA, Madhurima. 7900 FM 1826, STE 220 78737 #495-72-2001 L2005 **PD** *020 †55
HARDAGE, Joseph P. 10105 SILVER MOUNTAIN DR 78737 #048-13-1989 L1990 **AN** *020 †05
HART, Chris Cravey. 7900 FM 1826, STE 280 78737 #048-02-2003 L2007 **OBG** *020
HATTON, Craig Thos. 7900 FM 1826, HILL COUNTRY SPORTS 78737 #023-12-1982 L1993
ORS GS *018 †
HEYDEN, Lisa Diane. ■ 78737 #008-02-2005 **AN** *012
JOLET, Kelly Noelle. 7900 FM 1826, STE 220 78737 #048-14-1993 L2000 **PD** *020 †55
JONES, Allen Maulsby. ■ 78737 #048-04-1965 L1965 **IM** *020 †20
KARNES, Julie C. ■ 78737 #048-14-2005 L2006 **GS** *012
LANDWERMEYER, Margaret R. 7900 FM 1826, STE 280 78737 #048-14-1993 L1994
OBG *020 †30
LICHTENHAN, John Bradford. 7900 FM 1826 STE 240 78737 #019-02-1987 L1996 **FM** *020 †18
MC CLUSKEY, Marilyn Meade. 7900 FM 1826, STE 100 78737 #027-01-1985 L1989
OPH *020 †35
MURRAY, John David. ■ 78737 #021-05-1988 L1988 **IM** *020
PARIKH, Sangita Dilip. 7900 FM 1826, STE 240 78737 #011-02-1998 L2001 **FM** *020 †18
PATIL, Vaishalee Sanjay. 7900 FM 1826 STE 220 78737 #495-01-1992 L2001 **PD** *020 †55
PENNINGTON, Gerard M. 7900 FM 1826, HILL COUNTRY SPORTS 78737 #027-01-1983 L1992
ORS *020 †40
PIERCE, Karl Randolph. 7900 FM 1826, STE 100 78737 #048-16-1989 L1990 **OPH** *020 †35
RICHARDSON, Patrice K. ■ 78737 #031-01-1981 L1983 **DR NR** *071 †80
RIMER, Haydee Coromoto. 7900 FM 1826, BLDG 2 78737 #935-02-1986 L2001 **PD** *020 †55
SCHNEIDER, Lisa Beth. 7900 FM 1826, STE 280 78737 #048-13-1994 L1997 **OBG** *020 †30
SCHRAM, Richard Arnold. 7900 FM 1826, STE 170 78737 #048-04-1981 L1981 **ORS** *020 †40
SEWELL, Julian Jay. ■ 78737 #048-12-1965 L1965 **OPH** *071 †35
SIMMONS, Donovan Mitchell. 7900 FM 1826, SETON SOUTHWEST EMERG. DEP 78737
#036-01-1999 L2003 **FM** *020 †18
SMITH, Howard Lamoyne. ■ 78737 #039-01-1985 L1991 **NS** *071 †25
STEWART, Kerby James. 14419 FRIENDSWOOD LN 78737 #049-01-1981 L1993 **GP CD** *020
STIEGLER, Ashley. 7900 FM 1826, STE 240 78737 #048-12-1998 L2001 **FM** *020 †18
WILSON, Frederic Jeanfran. ■ 78737 #025-12-2007 **P** *012

AUSTIN – TRAVIS

ABELL, Joseph Miles, Jr. 3100 RED RIVER ST 78705 #048-04-1957 L1957 **ORS** *071 †40
ABIKHALED, John A. 3901 MEDICAL PKWY, STE 301 78756 #048-04-1992 L1993 **GS** *020 †85
ABIKHALED, Shannon M. 1301 W 38TH ST, DRS DESROSIERS & WERNECKE 78705
#048-14-1992 L1993 **OBG** *020 †30
ABOUMATAR, Sami M. 2200 PARK BEND DR, BLDG2-201 78758 #605-01-1992 L2003
N *020 †75
ABRAHAM, Ann. 3508 FAR WEST BLVD, FL 2 78731 #043-01-1994 L2002 **FM** *020 †18
ABRAHAM, Ronny. ■ 78745 #305-01-2001 **PM** *100
ABRAMOWITZ, Joshua G. 6101 W COURTYARD DR, AUSTIN RADIOLOGICAL ASSOCI 78730
#048-13-1985 L1986 **DR RNR** *020 †80
ABRAMS, David Saul. 3801 N LAMAR BLVD, STE 300 78756 #011-02-1977 L1978 **CD** *020 †20
ABREU-MACOMBER, Martha B. 2113 WELLS BRANCH PKWY, STE 1200 78728
#048-13-1992 L1994 **PD** *020 †55

ACKRELL, Mark Kuhio. 901 W BEN WHITE BLVD 78704 #041-12-1992 L1997 **EM** *020 †16
ADAIR, Maureen Lenore. 1801 N LAMAR BLVD 78704 #048-04-1980 L1980 **CHP P** *020 †75
ADENI, Sikander. 601 E 15TH ST, 2ND FL 78701 #495-58-1980 L2001 **NPM PD** *020 †55
ADKINS, Alan Jeffrey. ■ 78704 #048-02-1974 L1974 **P** *030 †75
ADKINS, Samuel Brenton. 1313 RED RIVER ST, STE 100 78701 #041-12-1983 L2003
FM *020 †18
ADLER, Susan Karen. 3705 MEDICAL PKWY STE 350 78705 #048-13-1974 L1974
HS GS *020 †75
AESCHBACH, Heinz. 2824 S CONGRESS AVE 78704 #869-07-1972 L1973 **P ADP** *020 †75
AFROOZ, Iman. 601 E 15TH ST, AUSTIN MED EDUC PROG-SETON 78701 #517-01-2004 L2007
IM *012
AGUEROS, Horacio M. 2609 E 7TH ST 78702 #048-02-1995 L1998 **FM** *020 †18
AHMED, Ammar Moin. ■ 78749 #048-04-2007 **IM** *012
AHMED, Rehana Parveen. 3005 S LAMAR BLVD, D-109-393 78704 #496-07-1994 L2000
IM *020 †20
AIELLO, Leslie Franklin. 1500 W 38TH ST, STE 20 78731 #038-40-1972 L1974 **PD** *020 †55
AITCHESON, Gary Edward. 3571 FAR WEST BLVD # 252 78731 #671-01-1970 L1982
PFP P *062 †75
AKIN, Mark Donnell. 1301 W 38TH ST STE 109 78705 #048-12-1979 L1979 **OBG EM** *020 †30
AKKINEPALLY, Sudha. 601 E 15TH ST 78701 #496-24-2003 **IM** *012
ALAM, Imtiaz. 12201 RENFERT WAY 78758 #919-02-1988 L1997 **GE** *020 †20
ALAMIA, Rodolfo Rogelio. 1221 W BEN WHITE BLVD, STE 200 78704 #025-12-1979 L1979
FM *020 †18
ALBERDA, Kelly Joe. 1313 RED RIVER ST, STE 100 78701 #007-02-2000 L2004
FM OBS *040 †18
ALBERT, Kimberly Vail. 3508 FAR WEST BLVD, FL 2 78731 #005-02-1994 L1995 **PD** *020 †55
ALBRECHT, Michael M. 3003 BEE CAVE RD 78746 #048-13-1994 L1999 **ORS** *020 †40
ALCOCER, Angel Eduardo. 1111 W 34TH ST, STE 200 78705 #649-14-1988 L1992 **GE** *020 †20
ALCORN, Amy Michell. 8204 BRODIE LN # 101 78745 #048-12-1997 L2000 **PD** *020 †55 ‡
ALDREDGE, Horatio Ransome. 313 E 12TH ST, STE 101 78701 #024-01-1964 L1971 **N** *020 †75
ALEMAN, Micaela. 2911 MEDICAL ARTS ST, STE 15A 78705 #048-04-1990 L1996 **U** *020 †95
ALEXANDER, Anne Lynn. 2911 MEDICAL ARTS ST, STE 18 78705 #048-12-1990 L1991
IM *020 †20
ALEXANDER, Archibald, III. ■ 78734 #048-02-1981 L1981 **R PD** *020 †80
ALEXANDER, Charles Dale. 1201 W 38TH ST 78705 #048-12-1968 L1968 **FM** *020 †18
ALEXANDER, Lee R. ■ 78736 #012-05-1978 L1981 **AN** *020 †05
ALEXANDER, Maureen M. 4207 JAMES CASEY ST # 303 78745 #048-12-1978 L1978
OPH *020 †35
ALEXANDER, Richard James. ■ 78703 #048-02-1955 L1955 **P OS** *020 †75
ALEXANDER, William A. 8501 N MOPAC EXPY, STE 200 78759 #048-15-1987 L1988
AN CCA *020 †05
ALFARO, Priscilla J. ■ 78759 #048-14-1989 L1990 **PD** *020 †55
ALI, Aaron Ashoka. 3705 MEDICAL PKWY, STE 570 78705 #048-13-2000 L2004 **AN** *020 †05
ALI, Genevieve Shepherd. 3705 MEDICAL PKWY, STE 570 78705 #048-13-2000 L2004
AN *020 †05
ALI, Salima Arif. ■ 78735 #704-25-1995 L2004 **IM** *020 †20
ALLEN, Erick Seth. 12221 N MO PAC EXPY 78758 #048-02-1991 L1992 **AN** *020 †05
ALLEN, Francis A. ■ 78734 #048-12-1953 L1953 **PD** *071
ALLEN, Gregory Garth. 6611 E HIGHWAY 290 78723 #048-14-1983 L1983 **FM** *020 †18
ALLEN, Ryan Thomas. 901 W BEN WHITE BLVD 78704 #048-12-2003 L2006 **EM** *020 †16
ALSUP, Ace Hill, III. 3407 GLENVIEW AVE 78703 #048-02-1972 L1972 **IM** *020 †20
ALVAREZ, Melissa Marie. ■ 78749 #035-47-2005 **GS** *012
ALVAREZ, Sonia. 4500 STEINER RANCH BLVD, ROAD #402 78732 #048-02-2001 L2005
IM *020 †20
ALWARD, Ian Steven. 2555 WESTERN TRAILS BLVD 78745 #017-20-1999 L2006 **FM** *020 †18
AMBLER, Mark S. 6835 AUSTIN CENTER BLVD 78731 #048-14-1998 L1999 **FM** *020 †18
AMJADI, Nima. 4316 JAMES CASEY ST, STE A 78745 #422-01-1997 L2000 **CD IC** *020 †20 ‡
ANDERSON, Cynthia Lee. 1313 RED RIVER ST 78701 #041-15-2000 L2007 **OBG** *012 †18
ANDERSON, George R. ■ 78727 #008-01-1949 L1970 **AM OM** *071 †70
ANDERSON, Jack Loyd. ■ 78744 #048-12-1959 L1959 **P** *071 †75
ANDERSON, Mary Iva. 4101 PARKSTONE HEIGHTS DR, STE 370 78746 #048-12-1990 L1991
P *020 †75
ANDERSON, Milton H. 601 E 15TH ST, BRACKENRIDGE HOSP-ED 78701 #047-05-1973 L1978
EM PD *020 †55,16
ANDERSON, Rhonda L. 4110 GUADALUPE ST 78751 #048-13-1997 L2004 **CHP** *020
ANDREO, Michael A. 1301 W 38TH ST, STE 102 78705 #048-14-1991 L1992 **ORS** *020 †40
ANDREWS, Giles Jones. ■ 78735 #048-04-1956 L1956 **R** *071 †80
ANGLIN, David Lee. 4900 MUELLER BLVD, C/O DELL CHILDREN'S MEDICA 78723
#047-06-1978 L1994 **CCP** *050 †55
ANNAMALAI, Valliammai R. 1400 N I H 35, CHILDREN'S HOSPITAL OF AUS 78701
#048-16-1998 L2005 **PD** *020 †55
ANNAPUREDDY, Karunakar. ■ 78733 #495-50-1989 L1997 **IM** *020 †20
ANNE, Vijay. 601 E 15TH ST 78701 #496-23-2004 **IM** *100
ANUPINDI, Renu Murthy. 3508 N 2ND ST 78702 #495-65-1990 L2006 **CHP** *020 †75
APPEL, Louis P. 2909 N INTERSTATE 35 78722 #024-01-1996 L1999 **PD** *020 †55
AQUL, Amal Ahmad. 601 E 15TH ST 78701 #915-02-1998 **PD** *012
ARBITMAN, Michael. ■ 78704 #020-02-1967 L1968 **DR** *071 †80
ARCHIBALD, Mark Henry. 12221 N MO PAC EXPY 78758 #048-16-2002 L2006 **AN** *020
ARGUN, H Murat. 2901 MONTOPOLIS DR 78741 #048-14-1991 L1992 **IM** *020 †20
ARGUN, Turan. ■ 78738 #902-10-1958 L1976 **PD** *071
ARHELGER, Erik J. 1313 RED RIVER ST STE 100 78701 #048-13-2005 L2008 **FP** *012
ARIZEMENDEZ, Mariaelena. 1215 RED RIVER ST # 427, HEALTH SOUTH REHAB HOSP 78701
#018-03-2000 L2004 **PM** *020 †60
ARIZPE, Suzan D. 4100 DUVAL RD BLDG 1 # 103 78759 #048-13-1992 L1995 **FM** *020 †18
ARNECILLA, Jennifer A. 7600 BURNET RD, STE 270 78757 #016-11-1995 L1997 **FM** *020 †18
ARNOLD, Homer S. 1010 W 40TH ST 78756 #016-06-1949 L1965 **TS CD** *071 †90,85
ARNOLD, Lloyd Elvin, Jr. 4534 W GATE BLVD STE 106 78745 #048-02-1962 L1962 **GP** *020
ARONIN, Patricia Anne. 1106 CLAYTON LN STE 200 78723 #036-01-1975 L1997 **NS** *020 †25
ARRANT, Amy Jo. ■ 78738 #048-12-1996 L1997 **IM** *020 †20
ARSHAD SAEED, Mohammad. 13831 N HIGHWAY 183 78750 #704-04-1966 L1977 **EM OS** *020
ASHLEY, Pamela K. 919 E 32ND ST 78705 #040-02-1997 L1998 **EM** *020 †16
ASHWORTH, Rodney Brian. 1015 E 32ND ST 78705 #048-12-1989 L1992 **GS** *020 †85
ASKARI, Sasan. 4007 JAMES CASEY ST, STE A100 78745 #048-12-1990 L1991 **OBG** *020 †30
ASKEW, Robert E, Jr. 3901 MEDICAL PKWY, STE 200 78756 #048-02-1986 L1987 **GS** *020 †85

ASKEW, Robert Edward. 3901 MEDICAL PKWY, STE 200 78756 #048-02-1959 L1959 GS *020 †85

ASKEW, William G. 3705 MEDICAL PKWY, STE 200 78705 #048-02-2001 L2004 AN *020 †05

ASLAM, Sohail I. 919 E 32ND ST 78705 #048-13-2001 L2004 EM *020 †16

ATKINSON, Bryan R. 4201 MARATHON BLVD, STE 304 78756 #048-14-1992 L2001 N *020 †75

ATWAL, Nasib Kaur. 5750 BALCONES DR STE 107 78731 #495-43-1971 L1975 P *020

AUNG, Soe Myint. 711-F W 38TH ST, AUSTIN NEUROLOGICAL CLINIC 78705 #209-03-1995 L2005 CN *100 †75

AUSTIN, John Riley. 3705 MEDICAL PKWY, STE 310 78705 #049-01-1986 L1992 HNS FPS *020 †45

AUSTIN, Sara G. 711 W 38TH ST F 78705 #048-02-1985 L1991 N IM *020 †75

AVASHIA, Swati Bipin. 3706 S 1ST ST, SETON KOZMETSKY CLINIC 78704 #055-01-1998 L2004 MPD *020 †55,20

AVENTA, Anthony R. 1301 W 38TH ST, STE 60 78705 #048-13-1996 L2002 IM *020 †20

AVERY, Sarah Stansbury. 6101 W COURTYARD DR, BLDG 5 78730 #012-01-1993 L1999 DR *020 †80

AZADI, Roya Abbasian. ■ 78746 #048-13-1998 L2007 IM *020 †20

BABCOCK, Chad Francis. 11614 BEE CAVES RD, STE 130 78738 #048-12-2001 L2004 FM *020 †18

BACH, Russell W. 1631 E 2ND ST STE D 78702 #048-02-1988 L1990 P *020 †75

BACHUS, Lois Ann. 1221 W BEN WHITE BLVD, STE B-250 78704 #016-45-1983 L1984 GYN *020 †30

BACON, Kenneth Terry. 4315 JAMES CASEY ST 78745 #048-12-1969 L1969 R *020 †80

BAER, Susan C. 9200 WALL ST 78754 #041-02-1987 L1993 DMP ATP *020 †50

BAGGETT, Durward Augustus. ■ 78731 #048-02-1959 L1959 FM GS *020 †18

BAGGETT, Seldon Osborn. 919 E 32ND ST 78705 #048-02-1938 L1938 GP *071

BAGWELL, John Todd. 1301 W 38TH ST, STE 403 78705 #048-02-1980 L1980 ID IM *020 †20

BAILES, Dallas Elliot. 900 WEST AVE, CAPITOL EMERGENCY ASSOCIAT 78701 #005-12-2002 L2007 EM *100

BAILES, Joseph Switz. 2205 SUNNY SLOPE DR 78703 #048-12-1981 L1981 ON *020 †20

BAILEY, Charles William, Jr. 8500 SHOAL CREEK BLVD, BLDG 3 78757 #048-02-1967 L1967 PS *020 †65

BAILEY, Ralph Vincent. 6818 AUSTIN CENTER BLVD 78731 #048-12-1971 L1976 CRS *071 †10,85

BAILEY, Shane Michael. ■ 78735 #005-12-1998 L2007 ICE *020 †20

BAIN, Ruth Marie. ■ 78703 #048-02-1942 L1943 FM *071

BAKER, Brett W. 3100 RED RIVER ST 78705 #048-14-2001 L2006 U *020 †95

BAKER, John Lindsey. 1007 E 41ST ST 78751 #048-02-1967 L1967 OBG *071 †30

BALDACCHINO, Thomas Chas. 4207 JAMES CASEY ST STE 21 78745 #561-17-1985 L1991 CD IM *020 †20

BALDWIN, Amy Benay. 901 W BEN WHITE BLVD 78704 #048-12-2003 L2006 EM *020 †16

BALITE-NUNEZ, Susan O. 1301 BARBARA JORDAN BLVD, CHILDREN'S NATIONAL MED CT 78723 #748-08-1981 L2008 PDE PD *020 †55

BALLARD, Richard Lewis. ■ 78734 #649-02-1963 PTH *071 †50

BALUCH, Abdul Rashid. 111 CONGRESS AVE, STE 1400 78701 #704-04-1971 L1980 IM *020

BANDFIELD, Lori M. 10401 ANDERSON MILL RD, STE 110B 78750 #048-12-2000 L2002 FM *020 †18

BANGSTON, John F, Jr. 11671 JOLLYVILLE RD # 203 78759 #045-04-1994 L1999 FM *020 †18

BANKS, Cheryl Sebesta. ■ 78730 #048-02-1986 L1987 PD *020 †55

BANKS, William J. 1400 IH 35 N 78702 #048-12-1994 PDR DR *020 †80

BANNISTER, John H, II. 1301 S CPTL TX HWY A 240 78745 #048-02-1970 L1970 PYA P *020 †75

BAPTISTE, Reginald Carl. 1015 E 32ND ST STE 404 78705 #048-04-1990 L1991 TS *020 †85,90

BARBOUR, William Alan. 12221 N MO PAC EXPY, STE 243 78758 #048-12-1980 L1980 OBG *020 †30

BARNES, William Earl. ■ 78746 #048-04-1957 L1957 PS *071 †65

BARNES, William Pinckney. 3705 MEDICAL PKWY STE 5 78705 #048-12-1979 L1979 AN EM *020 †05

BARNETT, Stephen Embree. 15 WALLER ST, RBJ BLDG 5TH FL 78702 #048-12-1966 L1966 PD GPM *050 †55

BARR, Lori Lee. 6101 W COURTYARD DR, BLDG 5 78730 #021-06-1984 L1986 PDR DR *020 †80

BARRE, Barrow H. ■ 78703 #021-05-1992 L1993 PTH *020 †50

BARRE, Gregg Maurice. ■ 78703 #021-05-1991 L2006 SP *020 †50

BARRETT, Shawn Adrian. 12221 N MO PAC EXPY 78758 #048-04-1992 L1994 AN *020 †05

BARSTOW, Douglas Grey, Jr. 3410 FAR WEST BLVD STE 146 78731 #048-02-2001 L2008 IM *020,03

BARTA, Adam Paul. 1313 RED RIVER ST, STE 100 78701 #045-01-1995 L1998 FM *020 †18

BARTEK, William Matthew. 4007 JAMES CASEY ST 78745 #048-12-1996 L1997 PCC *020 †20

BARTLETT, Elizabeth A. 6618 SITIO DEL RIO BLVD, STE 101 78730 #048-14-1993 L1994 PD *020 †55

BARTOS, Sara J. 2911 MEDICAL ARTS ST 7 78705 #048-14-1984 L1986 IM EM *020 †20

BARTRA, Homar Javier. 7201 MANCHACA RD, STE B 78745 #737-05-1990 L1995 IM *020 †20 ‡

BARTZ, Mary Liptak. 900 E 30TH ST STE 300 78705 #048-14-1990 L1991 FM *020 †18

BARUA, Alak. ■ 78720 #160-02-1989 *100

BASHAR, Farhana. ■ 78732 #654-01-2000 L2007 IM *020 †20 ‡

BATEMAN, John Robt. 1111 W 6TH ST APT 250 78703 #048-02-1957 L1957 P N *071

BATES, Benjamin Clary. 1201 W 38TH ST 78705 #048-02-1945 L1945 U *071 †45

BATTIEST, Melissa. 1301 W 38TH ST, STE 205 78705 #048-12-2003 L2006 IM *020 †20

BAUGH, Gerald Anthony. 1010 W 40TH ST 78756 #048-03-07-1963 L1965 TS *071 †85,90

BAUSERMAN, Steven C. 601 E 15TH ST, DEPT PATHOLOGY 78701 #018-03-1963 L1987 PTH NP *020 †50

BAXTER, Corby Daniel. ■ 78753 #422-01-2003 L2006 GS *100

BAYARDO, Roberto J. 1213 SABINE ST 78701 #649-03-1959 L1969 FOP *071 †50

BAYER, Michael. 711 W 38TH ST STE C2 78705 #048-02-1977 L1977 PD *020 †55

BAYLISS, James Milward. 4110 GUADALUPE ST, DEPT OF MHMR 78751 #048-02-1976 L1976 P GP *020

BEACH, Gary Jay. 825 E RUNDBERG LN 78753 #048-12-1981 L1981 FM *020 †18

BEASLEY, Haley Kent. 1301 W 38TH ST, STE 60 78705 #021-01-1962 L1962 CD IM *020 †20

BEATHARD, Gerald Avon. 919 E 32ND ST 78705 #048-02-1964 L1964 NEP PTH *071 †20,03,50

BEATHARD, Steven D. 1015 E 32ND ST, STE 414 78705 #048-14-1992 L1993 NEP *020 †20

BECKER, Emilie Attwell. 2414 EXPOSITION BLVD, STE 280 78703 #048-04-1986 L1987 CHP P *020 †75

BECKER, Scott David. 4310 JAMES CASEY ST, STE 4A 78745 #024-05-1983 L1990 GE IM *020 †20

BECKHAM, Patrick Hubert. 630 W 34TH ST, STE 201 78705 #048-04-1961 L1971 PS HS *020 †65

BEDILLION, Theodore M. 12221 N MO PAC EXPY 78758 #048-02-1982 L1983 AN *020 †05

BEDOLLA, John Philip. 720 W 34TH ST STE 1 78705 #048-12-1992 L1997 EM *020 †16

BEERBOWER, John David. ■ 78734 #048-14-1981 L1981 DR PME *020 †80

BEGUM, Mahmuda. 601 E 15TH ST 78701 #160-04-2000 IM *012

BEHARA, Shailaja Savitri. 12221 N MO PAC EXPY, THE AUSTIN DIAGNOSTIC CLIN 78758 #495-11-1994 L2001 GE *020 †20

BEISEL, Lisa J. 4029 S CAPITAL OF TEXS HWY, STE 200 78704 #048-02-1990 L1992 P *020 †75

BELL, Charles Emerson. 4900 N LAMAR BLVD, STE 7140 78751 #048-12-1983 L1983 PHP *030

BELL, Gregory Kittredge. 8038 MESA DR 78731 #055-02-1991 L1996 DR VIR *020 †80

BELL, Ira, III. 2911 MEDICAL ARTS ST, STE 12 78705 #048-02-1974 L1974 FM *030

BELL, James. 3705 MEDICAL PKWY, STE 570 78705 #048-02-1990 L1991 AN *020 †05

BELT, Melanie Marie. 4101 JAMES CASEY ST # 300, AUSTIN REG CLC SOUTH OB 78745 #048-14-2001 L2007 OBG *020

BEN-AVI, Hillel Ari. 10900 STONELAKE BLVD, STE 250 78759 #048-13-1984 L1985 DR *020 †80

BENEVICH, Matthew Alan. ■ 78748 #017-20-2002 L2005 IM *100

BENGTSON, Hans E. ■ 78723 #048-13-1998 L2000 AN *020 †05

BENNETT, Bari Lynn. 3705 MEDICAL PKWY, STE 570 78705 #048-15-1986 L1987 AN *040 †05

BENNETT, Edward John. 3705 MEDICAL PKWY STE 570 78705 #143-03-1950 L1967 AN *071 †05

BENOLD, Terrell Barnes. 1201 W 38TH ST 78705 #048-16-1983 L1983 FM *040 †18

BENSCHOTER, Maureen M. ■ 78739 #048-15-1990 L1991 IM *020 †20

BENTON, Cynthia Lynn. 56 EAST AVE 78701 #048-04-1998 L2006 P *020

BERENT, Craig Tobias. 715 W 34TH ST 78705 #011-04-1975 L1997 IM *020 †20

BERGER, Brian Bernard. 3705 MEDICAL PKWY, STE 410 78705 #016-02-1975 L1981 OPH OS *020 †35

BERGER, Michelle A. 4100 DUVAL RD, BLDG 4 78759 #056-06-1981 L1982 OPH *020 †35

BERGIN-NADER, Barbara Lee. 4700 SETON CENTER PKWY, STE 200 78759 #048-15-1981 L1981 ORS *020 †40

BERHANE, Rahel. 1301 BARBARA JORDAN BLVD, STE 200 78723 #366-01-1984 L1996 PD *020 †55

BERKOWITZ, Steven Michael. 1632 RESACA BLVD 78738 #028-03-1979 L1993 IM *030 †20

BERRY, David Lee. 911 W 38TH ST 78705 #048-02-1991 L1992 OBG MFM *020 †30

BERRY, Luisa Edith. ■ 78735 #021-01-2007 EM *012

BERRY, Phillip Lee. 1301 BARBARA JORDAN BLVD, STE 200 78723 #048-04-1974 L1974 PN *020

BERTELSON, John A. 313 E 12TH ST, STE 101 78701 #048-14-1998 L2003 N NUP *020 †75

BERUMEN, Joe F. ■ 78759 #649-01-1946 L1953 ORS *071 †40

BERUMEN, Thelma Chouest. ■ 78759 #021-05-1948 L1952 AN *020

BESSERMAN, Abraham M. ■ 78731 #187-03-1960 L1971 PDS GS *071 †85

BETHEL, Whitney R. 1015 E 32ND ST STE 405, PEDIATRIX MEDICAL GROUP 78705 #048-16-2002 L2005 PD *020 †55

BETTS, Judith Ann. 408 W 45TH ST, CENTRAL TEXAS KIDNEY ASSOC 78751 #048-12-1985 L1986 IM NEP *020 †20

BETZ, Thomas Geo. 1100 W 49TH ST, TX DEPT OF HEALTH 78756 #025-01-1969 L1981 PHP ID *062 †70

BEYER, Allison Anne. 1313 RED RIVER ST STE 303B, UNIV OF TEXAS 78701 #038-44-2007 OBG *012

BEZERRA, Hermino. 2529 S 1ST ST 78704 #187-10-1983 L1998 IM IMG *020 †20

BHATIA, Sonia. 1301 W 38TH ST, STE 109 78705 #495-30-1992 L2006 IM *020 †20

BHATNAGAR, Juanita K. 1015 E 32ND ST, STE 405 78705 #038-45-1998 L2001 PD *020 †55

BHATT, Kunjan Ashvin. 1301 W 38TH ST, STE 500 78705 #035-08-2001 L2007 CD *020

BHATT, Satish S. 4110 GUADALUPE ST 78751 #495-76-1981 L1988 CHP *075

BIBUS, Frederick Chas. 2203 W 35TH ST 78703 #048-12-1981 L1981 GP FM *020

BIEBAS, Carolyn Grace. 12221 N MO PAC EXPY 78758 #048-12-1981 L1981 AN *020 †05

BIEBERDORF, Fredrick A. 8501 N MOPAC EXPY, STE 200 78759 #048-12-1964 L1965 GE IM *050

BINFORD, Nancy E. 1301 W 38TH ST, STE 109 78705 #048-12-1994 L1996 OBG *020 †30

BIREWAR, Sonali Prabhakar. 12221 N MO PAC EXPY 78758 #495-19-1997 L2006 NEP *100 †20

BIRING, Ravneet. ■ 78759 #048-02-2002 L2006 AN *020 †05

BIRING, Timinder S. 12221 N MO PAC EXPY 78758 #048-13-1999 L2006 IC *020 †20

BISSETT, Jack Daulton. 1301 W 38TH ST, STE 403 78705 #048-02-1981 L1981 ID IM *020

BITTAR, Antonious Rafic. 4101 JAMES CASEY ST # 310 78745 #875-01-1974 L1985 OTO HNS *020 †45

BLACK, James Arthur. 4007 JAMES CASEY ST, C-110 78745 #048-12-1971 L1972 P *071 †75

BLACKLOCK, Bonnie Jean. 6101 E OLTORF ST, TEXAS REHAB COMM 78741 #048-02-1963 L1963 AN *062

BLACKMAN, Patricia A B. ■ 78723 #028-02-1950 L1977 PD ADL *071 †55

BLACKSTOCK, Mathis W. 1313 RED RIVER ST 78701 #048-02-1948 L1948 FM *071 †18

BLAIR, Kenneth Jos. 801 W 34TH ST, STE 102 78705 #023-07-1980 L1980 FM *020 †18

BLAIR, Shannon K. ■ 78746 #048-02-1994 *100

BLAIS, Robert Edward. 4534 W GATE BLVD, STE 110 78745 #011-03-1990 L1994 ORS *020 †40

BLANCARTE, Gilbert. 1701 W BEN WHITE BLVD, STE 140 78704 #048-04-1976 L1976 IM *020 †20

BLANKENSHIP, Jennifer E. 9200 WALL ST 78754 #048-13-2001 L2006 ATP HMP *020 †50

BLAYDON, Sean Matthew. 3705 MEDICAL PKWY, STE 120 78705 #021-01-1989 L1998 OPH FPS *020 †35

BLEDSOE, Maya Badachhape. 11111 RESEARCH BLVD, STE 334 78759 #048-16-1987 L1988 END OS *020 †20

BLEVINS, Thomas Craig. 6500 BALCONES DR, STE 3-200 78731 #048-04-1981 L1981 END IM *020 †20

BLEWETT, John Henry. ■ 78750 #035-03-1971 L1977 EM *020 †85,16

BLINDERMAN, Joseph. 1403 W 12TH ST 78703 #021-01-1972 L1974 P NTR *071

BLISSARD, Paul K. 1109 E 6TH ST B 78702 #048-12-1980 L1980 FM *020 †18

BLOIS, Marsden S. 3801 N LAMAR BLVD, STE 300 78756 #048-04-1993 L1995 CD *020 †20

BLUDWORTH, Whitney G. 919 E 32ND ST 78705 #048-02-1999 L2002 EM *020 †16

BLUMHAGEN, Guy Van. 11111 RESEARCH BLVD, STE 334 78759 #048-02-1986 L1987 OBG *020 †30

BOCCHICCHIO, Jeffrey F. 10401 ANDERSON MILL RD, STE 110B 78750 #051-07-1998 L2004 PD *020 †55

BOCKMON, Kimball Wayne. 825 E RUNDBERG LN STE B1, AUSTIN REGIONAL CLINIC 78753 #048-12-1980 L1980 FM *020 †18

BOEHM, Teresa E. 5900 BALCONES DR STE 160 78731 #048-12-1995 L1997 EM *020 †16

BOES, Sheila Frank. 1500 W 38TH ST, STE 20 78731 #027-01-1995 L1996 PD *020 †55

BOKHARI, Syed Khuzaima Ar. 601 E 15TH ST 78701 #704-20-2003 **FP** *012
BOLTON, Kim Patrick. 6835 AUSTIN CENTER BLVD 78731 #023-07-1975 L1996 **FM GS** *020 †18
BONGU-CHADHA, Anurekha. 11111 RESEARCH BLVD, STE 334 78759 #028-46-1996 L2006 **RHU** *020 †20
BOOKER, Brooks William, IV. 10401 ANDERSON MILL RD, STE 110B 78750 #048-13-1999 L2002 **PD** *020 †55
BOORTZ, Hillary Elizabeth. ■ 78704 #048-02-2008 *012
BOOTH, Patrick Kenneth. 3205 HATLEY DR 78746 #027-01-1987 L1998 **EM** *020 †20
BOOTH, Stephanie Ann. 1301 W 38TH ST, STE 110 78705 #048-02-2000 L2005 **RHU** *020 †20
BOOTON, Steve Kirkwood. 900 E 30TH ST STE 100 78705 #048-14-1983 L1983 **IM** *020 †20
BORDELON, Jerry Phillip. ■ 78703 #021-01-1961 1972 **OTO PS** *071 †45
BORER, Drake Stuart. 1313 RED RIVER ST STE 200, AUSTIN SKELETAL TRAUMA SPE 78701 #048-12-1993 L1995 **ORS** *020 †40
BORICH, Damon Vincent. 2508 ASHLEY WORTH BLVD, STE 200 78738 #048-04-1999 L2001 *020
BOULOS, Abdelmesih E M. ■ 78739 #915-02-1966 L1981 **P** *020
BOWMAN, May Lynn. 4107 SPICEWOOD SPRINGS RD, STE 100 78759 #048-12-1990 L1991 **PTH** *020 †50
BOWYER, Denis Edward. 3705 MED PARKWAY STE 570 78705 #048-12-1967 L1967 **AN** *071 †05
BOYD, Jack Raymond. 6101 W COURTYARD DR, BLDG 5 78730 #048-04-1961 L1961 **R** *071 †80
BOYSEN, James Lee. 4007 JAMES CASEY ST, STE A220 78745 #018-03-1981 L1984 **PUD** *020 †20
BOZYAN, Frank Bedros. ■ 78759 #048-15-2006 **IM** *012
BRADY, Bridget M. 11111 RESEARCH BLVD, STE 350 78759 #048-14-1999 L2002 **GS** *020 †85
BRAGG, Thomas Guy, III. 711 W 38TH ST, STE D4 78705 #048-01-1962 L1969 **NS** *071 †25
BRAND, James Rutland. ■ 78704 #048-13-1976 L1976 **EM GP** *062
BRAND, Jeffrey D. 3705 MEDICAL PKWY, STE 570 78705 #048-04-1991 L1992 **AN** *020 †05
BRANDT, Otto, Jr. 1301 W 38TH ST 78705 #048-02-1942 L1943 **GP** *071
BRANHAM, Andrew Michael. ■ 78754 #048-14-2006 L2007 *012
BRASHEAR, James Donald. ■ 78739 #039-01-1965 L1965 **OPH** *071 †35
BRASHER-GILES, Sharyl R. 11111 RESEARCH BLVD, STE 334 78759 #048-15-1995 L1996 **OBG** *020 †30
BRATTENG, Eliz M Holliday. 78751 #048-02-1945 L1945 **P CHP** *072
BRAUN, Roberta Melena. 900 E 30TH ST, STE 213 78705 #048-02-1976 L1976 **GYN** *020 †30
BRAUNSTEIN, Maryjane E. 11113 RESEARCH BLVD 78759 #048-15-1993 L1994 **OBG** *020 †30
BRAVO, Jose Luis. ■ 78759 #649-01-1952 L1983 **GS TRS** *071 †85
BREAZEALE, Jimmy Levan. 1712 E RIVERSIDE DR, # 202 78741 #048-12-1958 L1959 **GP** *071
BREAZEALE, Nathan. 900 W 38TH ST, AUSTIN SPORTS MEDICINE 78705 #048-12-1991 L1992 **OSM** *020 †40
BREED, David R. 1015 E 32ND ST, STE 405 78705 #048-13-1989 L1990 **NPM** *020 †55
BREEN, Michael Timothy. 313 E 12TH ST, STE 104 78701 #048-02-1981 L1981 **OBG** *020 †18,30
BRENNER, Bradley A. 10900 STONELAKE BLVD, STE 250 78759 #048-12-1996 L2001 **DR** *020 †80
BRENNER, Max. 12444 RESEARCH BLVD, BRENNER EYE CENTER 78759 #561-17-1964 L1978 **OPH** *071
BRENNIG, Christopher W. 3112 WINDSOR RD, STE A-122 78703 #048-14-1999 L2003 **VS** *020 †85
BRIBIESCA, Gerardo Sergio. 1201 W 38TH ST 78705 #649-14-1977 L1983 **FM** *020 †18
BRIDGES, Robert Ashe. 1010 W 40TH ST 78756 #048-12-1974 L1974 **VS** *020 †85
BRIEGER, Benjamin C. 601 E 15TH ST, BRACKENRIDGE HOSPITAL 78701 #036-01-1997 L2000 **EM** *020 †16
BRIENO, Elsa G. 800 W 34TH ST, STE 208 78705 #048-14-1988 L1989 **PD** *020
BRIGGS, Deborah Elaine. 11507 ANTIGUA DR, NORTH AUSTIN NEUROLOGICAL 78759 #048-14-2000 L2006 **N** *020 †75
BRIGGS, Richard Biddle. 1201 W 38TH ST 78705 #048-15-1983 L1983 **OPH EM** *020 †35
BRIGGS, Richard Hoppe. ■ 78716 #051-01-1967 L1967 **PD** *020 †55
BRINKLEY, Robert Harold. 3005 S LAMAR BLVD, STE D109-416 78704 #047-06-1979 L1983 **AN** *020
BRINKMAN, Diane Loise. 1301 W 38TH ST, STE 109 78705 #038-40-1978 L1983 **OBG** *020 †30
BRINKMAN, Donna Serene. 313 E 12TH ST, CAPITAL OBSTETRICS & 78701 #046-01-2000 L2004 **OBG** *020
BRINSON, Cynthia Curll. 4614 N IH 35 78751 #048-15-1990 L1991 **FM** *020 †18
BRISH, Eldor Lass. ■ 78746 #023-07-2005 **AN** *012
BRISKEY, Enzie Natasha. 12201 RENFERT WAY, STE 230 78758 #038-06-2000 L2004 **OBG** *020
BRISTOL, Paul Ellis. 2013 WELLS BRANCH PKWY, STE 113 78728 #010-03-1984 L1986 **FM** *020 †18
BRITT, Kendall A. 6101 BALCONES DR, STE 300 78731 #048-13-1998 L2002 **IM** *020 †20
BROBERG, Peter Harlan. 4207 JAMES CASEY ST, STE 305 78745 #048-04-1978 L1979 **OPH** *020 †35
BROBERG, Scott Alan. 3816 S 1ST ST 78704 #048-13-1981 L1981 **PD** *020 †55
BROCKUNIER, Craig K. 1600 W 38TH ST, STE 321 78731 #422-01-1984 L1994 **P** *020 †75
BROD, Delbert Ray. 6101 BALCONES DR STE 300, HOSPITAL INTERNISTS OF AUS 78731 #048-15-2003 L2005 **IM** *020 †20
BRODE, Donald Robert. 4614 N IH 35 78751 #038-06-1997 L1998 **FM** *020 †20
BROLINE, Shelly Kristin. 3107 STARDUST DR 78757 #048-02-2001 L2004 **NM** *020 †28
BROOKE, Dawn Sabrina. 10401 ANDERSON MILL RD, STE 110B 78750 #048-04-1986 L1989 **PD** *020 †55
BROOKE, William F. 3508 FAR WEST BLVD, FL 2 78731 #048-04-1986 L1987 **FM** *020 †18
BROOKS, Karen M. 8140 N MOPAC EXPY, BLDG 1 78759 #048-15-1998 L2000 **CHP** *020 †75
BROOKS, Magdalena Lorrain. ■ 78741 #308-03-1999 L2008 **FM** *100
BROTZMAN, S Brent. 12201 RENFERT WAY STE 355, NORTH AUSTIN SPORTS MEDICI 78758 #048-04-1988 L1989 **ORS OSM** *020 †40
BROWN, Ari Zamutt. 4100 DUVAL RD, BLDG 4 78759 #048-04-1992 L1993 **PD** *020 †55
BROWN, Carlos V. 601 E 15TH ST, BRACKENRIDGE HOSPITAL-TRAU 78701 #048-02-1993 L2006 **CCS** *020 †85
BROWN, Charles Edward Lee. 1313 RED RIVER ST, STE 303 78701 #021-01-1980 L1983 **OBG MFM** *040 †30
BROWN, David Warren. 8334 CROSS PARK DR 78754 #048-14-1986 L1987 **P** *020 †75
BROWN, Dor W, Jr. ■ 78731 #048-02-1943 L1960 **A OTO** *071
BROWN, George Rhamy. 2600 E MARTN LTHR KNG JR 78702 #048-02-1962 L1962 **RO** *020 †80
BROWN, Gilmore W, Jr. 1101 W 40TH ST 78756 #048-02-1951 L1951 **OPH** *071 †35
BROWN, James R. 7715 CHEVY CHASE DR, BLDG N STE 225 78752 #048-14-1982 L1983 **FM MDM** *030 †18

BROWN, Katherine Blodgett. 4614 N IH 35, DAVID POWELL CLINIC 78751 #040-02-1997 L2004 **IM** *020 †20
BROWN, Kenton Allan. 1600 W 38TH ST, STE 404 78731 #021-01-1970 L1976 **P PHP** *020 †75
BROWN, Kirk Washington Ge. ■ 78727 #011-03-2004 L2007 **EM** *020
BROWN, Lauren L. 10900 STONELAKE BLVD, STE 250 78759 #048-02-1986 L1987 **DR OS** *020 †20
BROWN, Lynus, Jr. 4534 W GATE BLVD, STE 114 78745 #048-13-1987 L1989 **FM** *020 †18
BROWN, Mark Thos. 11762 JOLLYVILLE RD 78759 #048-04-1989 L1999 **OTO** *020 †45
BROWN, Michael David. ■ 78703 #021-05-1995 L2006 **PTH** *020 †50
BROWN, Stephen Longmoor. 11111 RESEARCH BLVD, AUSTIN CANCER CENTER NORTH 78759 #048-02-1992 L1993 **RO** *020 †80
BROWN, Thomas Chas. 7600 N CAPITAL OF TEXS HWY, STE A 78731 #021-05-1991 L2007 **GS** *020 †85
BROWN, Ward Everett. 7508 DOWNRIDGE DR 78731 #056-06-1946 L1976 **FM** *071 †18
BROWNING, Norman. ■ 78759 #038-40-1955 L1955 **GS** *071 †85
BROWNING, Robt Locke, Jr. 2100 S IH 35, STE 202 78704 #036-01-1962 L1965 **FM** *030 †18
BROWNING, Stewart R. 3708 JEFFERSON ST, STE 103 78731 #048-15-1998 L2000 **FM** *020 †18
BRUCE, Jinnie A. 8701 SHOAL CREEK BLVD, STE 201 78757 #021-01-1999 L2007 **GS** *020 †85
BRUMLEY, Harold Wayne. 1301 W 38TH ST, STE 109 78705 #048-02-1958 L1958 **OBG** *020 †30
BRYANT, Deborah Williams. 10710 RESEARCH BLVD, STE 120 78759 #021-06-1989 L1993 **PD** *020 †55
BUCHANAN, William Lee. 7551 METRO CENTER DR, STE 200 78744 #030-05-1975 L1979 **OS** *020
BUCHHOLZ, Elizabeth L. 12221 N MO PAC EXPY 78758 #048-13-1993 L1999 **AN** *020 †05
BUCHHOLZ, William Andrew. 12221 N MO PAC EXPY 78758 #048-13-1994 L1999 **AN** *020 †05
BUCKINGHAM, Dawn Carlisle. 13376 RESEARCH BLVD, STE 104 78750 #048-02-1997 L1998 **OPH** *020 †35
BUCKMAN, Jimmie David, Jr. 1301 W 38TH ST, STE 300 78705 #048-02-1967 L1967 **OBG** *071 †30
BUCKNALL, William Eric. ■ 78703 #024-01-1967 L1974 **PD** *071 †55
BUEHLER, Eric Andre. 3705 MEDICAL PKWY, STE 570 78705 #038-44-1988 L1993 **AN** *020 †05
BUELL, Howard Arthur. 6101 W COURTYARD DR, BLDG 5 78730 #040-02-1962 L1971 **R** *071 †80
BUI, David Richard. 12221 N MO PAC EXPY 78758 #016-42-1989 L1996 **IM** *020 †20
BUI, Thieu. 8738 N LAMAR BLVD 78753 #941-01-1961 L1982 **FM** *020 †18
BUNCH, Kenneth, II. 4700 SETON CENTER PKWY, STE 200 78759 #038-06-2002 L2007 **PM** *020 †60
BUNCH, Laura Christopher. 901 W 38TH ST, STE 200 78705 #001-06-1997 L2005 **HO** *020 †20
BUNDRANT, Lu Ann. 6101 BALCONES DR, STE 300 78731 #048-12-1996 L1997 **IM** *020 †20
BUNKER, Noah Stephen. 12221 N MO PAC EXPY 78758 #048-13-2002 L2007 **PAN** *020 †05
BURGER, David G. 4316 JAMES CASEY ST, STE A 78745 #048-04-1996 L1998 **IC** *020 †20
BURGER, Natalie Zlatica. ■ 78731 #012-01-2000 L2007 **OBG REN** *020 †30
BURGESS, Christine R. ■ 78704 #048-13-2002 L2007 **HMP** *020 †50
BURNS, George Paul. 3705 MED PARKWAY STE 320 78705 #048-04-1963 L1963 **OTO** *071 †45
BURNS, Thomas Patrick. 3001 BEE CAVE RD, STE 220 78746 #048-12-1985 L1986 **ORS OSM** *020 †40
BURRIS, Michael W. 12201 RENFERT WAY, STE 355 78758 #048-14-2001 L2004 **OSM** *100
BURROWS, Maureen Sarah. 1600 W 38TH ST, STE 404 78731 #021-01-2001 L2006 **P PFP** *020 †75
BURUGU, Sukanya. 1301 W 38TH ST, STE 109 78705 #495-65-1996 L2003 **IM** *020 †20
BURZYNSKI, Gregory Stanis. 601 E 15TH ST 78701 #759-01-2007 **IM** *012
BUSHART, Paul Scott. 1301 W 38TH ST, STE 109 78705 #048-14-1982 L1983 **OBG** *020 †30
BUSHORE, David Alan. 8240 N MOPAC EXPY, STE 350 78759 #047-06-1999 L2003 **D** *020 †15
BUSH-VEITH, Stacie. ■ 78759 #048-16-1989 L1990 **IM** *020 †20
BUSSE, Franklin K, Jr. 4700 SETON CENTER PKWY, STE 150 78759 #048-04-1988 L1989 **OPH PO** *020 †35
BUSTER, Edwin Roane, III. 711 W 38TH ST, STE D4 78705 #048-04-1962 L1962 **NS ORS** *020 †25
BUTEN, Jonathan Bernard. 11111 RESEARCH BLVD, STE 220 78759 #836-01-1975 L1979 **OBG** *020 †30
BUTLER, Cheryl. 4010 N LAMAR BLVD 78756 #048-02-1995 L1999 **OBG** *020
BUTLER, David. 11940 JOLLYVILLE RD, STE 115 78759 #048-13-1986 L1998 **FM** *020 †18
BUTLER, Ernest Charles. ■ 78703 #048-04-1962 L1962 **OTO** *071 †45
BUTLER, Robert E. 4207 JAMES CASEY ST, AUSTIN EAR NOSE & THROAT 78745 #048-02-1992 L1998 **OTO** *020 †45
BUTSCHEK, Chris Matthew. 6101 W COURTYARD DR, BLDG 5 78730 #048-12-1978 L1978 **DR** *020 †80
BUTTERMANN, Karl Michael. 1313 RED RIVER ST STE 206 78701 #028-34-1988 L1993 **OBG** *020 †30
BUTTREY, Sarah. 2811 E 2ND ST 78702 #034-01-1999 L2002 **FM** *020 †18
BUXBAUM, Lauren Renee. 12710 RESEARCH BLVD, STE 360 78759 #035-46-1989 L1993 **PD** *020 †55
BUZAD, Francis Anthony. 7600 N CAPITAL OF TEXS HWY, STE A 78731 #041-12-1994 L1999 **HS** *020 †85
BYERS, David Jos. 3705 MEDICAL PKWY, STE 570 78705 #048-13-1984 L1985 **AN** *020 †05
BYNUM, Grover La Fayette. 1301 W 38TH ST, STE 60 78705 #021-01-1953 L1960 **IM** *071
BYRD, Charles Ronald, Jr. 2712 BEE CAVE RD, STE 122 78746 #021-06-1992 L1994 **FM** *020 †18
CABRERA, Elizabeth. ■ 78730 #048-02-2002 L2006 **D** *020 †15
CAIN, Harold Dean. 12201 RENFERT WAY STE 260 78758 #048-12-1971 L1971 **PUD CCM** *020 †20
CAIN, Robert Michael. 900 W 38TH ST, STE 350 78705 #038-40-1966 L1973 **N R** *020 †75
CALDERON, Antonio F. ■ 78701 #649-17-1975 *100
CALDWELL, William David. 1305 W 34TH ST, STE 210 78705 #021-01-1973 L1977 **PD** *020 †55
CALLAWAY, Susan. 3828 S 1ST ST 78704 #048-02-1976 L1976 **OBG** *020
CAMP, Darryl S. 8024 MESA DR, NO. 189 78731 #048-13-1994 L1997 **N** *020 †75
CAMP, Thomas Felton, Jr. ■ 78747 #048-02-1955 L1955 **GS FM** *072 †85,18
CAMPBELL, Scott Eugene. 4316 JAMES CASEY ST, STE 110 78745 #036-01-1987 L1998 **RNR** *020 †80
CANBY, Robert Clay. 1301 W 38TH ST, STE 705 78705 #048-12-1988 L1989 **CD ICE** *020 †20
CANON, Honor Lee. ■ 78750 #047-06-2000 L2007 **PD** *100 †55
CANON, Stephen J. ■ 78750 #048-02-1999 L2007 **UP** *100
CANTU, Julius F, Jr. 1221 W BEN WHITE BLVD, STE 212B 78704 #048-16-1981 L1981 **DR GS** *020
CANTU, Robert E. 1015 E 32ND ST STE 501 78705 #048-02-1987 L1988 **P** *020 †75

CAPELLE, Jonathan H. ■ 78736 #048-14-2008 *012

CARAMELLI, Keith Wm. 5806 MESA DR, STE 350 78731 #048-04-1988 L1992 **CHP** *020 †75

CARDENAS, Francisco, Jr. ■ 78701 #649-01-1974 L1979 **NEP IM** *071 †20

CARDWELL, David Williams. 800 W 34TH ST STE 210 78705 #048-02-1974 L1974 **P N** *020 †75

CARDWELL, Jennifer Mills. 2499 S CAPITAL OF TEXS HWY, B-100 78746 #055-01-1998 L2001 **PD** *020 †55

CAREY, Holly Christine. 3508 FAR WEST BLVD, FL 2 78731 #048-13-2003 L2007 **PD** *020 †55

CAREY, Kira. 3501 MILLS AVE 78731 #143-01-1966 L1977 **CHP P** *075 †75

CARLSON, Kevin Robert. 919 E 32ND ST 78705 #048-02-1976 L1976 **FM** *020 †18

CARLSON, Thomas Allen. 1301 W 38TH ST, STE 500 78705 #026-04-1988 L1993 **CD** *020 †20

CARMICHAEL, Douglas A. 12701 FM 620 78750 #034-01-1984 L1987 **EM** *020

CARMODY, Karen. 11004 SPICEWOOD CLUB DR 78750 #016-11-1980 L1988 **EM** *020 †16

CARRASCO, Ruy. 1301 BARBARA JORDAN BLVD, STE 200 78723 #034-01-1999 L2005 **PPR** *020 †55

CARRELL, Paul Timothy. 12221 N MO PAC EXPY 78758 #048-14-2001 L2006 **AN** *020 †05

CARSNER, Jack Chas. 8140 N MOPAC EXPY, BLDG 3 78759 #048-02-1991 L1992 **AN** *020 †05

CARTER, David Courtney. 313 E ANDERSON LN, COVANCE CRU, INC. 78752 #010-03-1988 L1990 **FM** *020 †18

CARTER, Jennifer Y. 12365 RIATA TRACE PKWY 78727 #048-04-1984 L1985 **PD** *030 †55

CARTER, Kimberly. 9601 RAINLILLY LN 78759 #048-04-1998 L2003 **OBG** *020 †30

CARTER, Shelby Henry, III. 1301 W 38TH ST, STE 102 78705 #035-19-1980 L1991 **ORS GS** *020 †40

CARTER, Teresa Lutz. ■ 78746 #032-01-1988 L1991 **PD** *020 †55

CASAUBON, Luis. ■ 78731 #048-02-2000 L2005 **END** *020 †20

CASE, Ann M. 802 CRYSTAL CREEK DR 78746 #048-14-1992 L1994 **PD** *020 †55

CASMEDES, Harry Paul. 7551 METRO CENTER DR, STE 200 78744 #048-13-1993 L1995 **AN** *020

CASNER, Stanley Wayne. ■ 78731 #048-02-1958 L1958 **FM** *071

CASTRO, Raymond Fabri. 1015 E 32ND ST, STE 405 78705 #018-03-1996 L2003 **NPM** *100 †55

CAUVIN, Paul. 10401 ANDERSON MILL RD, STE 110B 78750 #048-12-1991 L1992 **FM** *020 †18

CAVEN, Walter Thos, Jr. 601 E 15TH ST, BRECKENRIDGE HOSPITAL 78701 #048-13-1980 L1980 **FM** *020 †18

CEARLEY, Holly Alissa. 3508 FAR WEST BLVD, FL 2 78731 #047-06-1999 L2003 **PD** *020 †55

CEBALLOS, Nelson J. 3705 MEDICAL PKWY STE 360 78705 #264-05-1961 L1971 **CHP P** *020 †75

CEPEDA, Eduardo Javier, II. 4315 JAMES CASEY ST 78745 #042-03-2000 L2004 **RHU** *020 †20

CERVANTES, Cecilia Marina. 1215 RED RIVER ST, STE 427 78701 #035-48-1986 L1992 **IM** *020

CHADHA, Punit. 2911 MEDICAL ARTS ST, STE 13 78705 #016-06-1999 L2006 **HO** *020 †20

CHADHA, Tina. 11111 RESEARCH BLVD, STE 395 78759 #016-06-2000 L2005 **AI** *020 †20

CHAFIZADEH, Edward Robt. 1015 E 32ND ST, STE 508 78705 #048-04-1989 L1990 **CD** *020 †20

CHALASANI, Renu. 11111 RESEARCH BLVD, STE 334 78759 #021-06-1994 L1998 **OBG** *020 †30

CHALKIAS, Fotini Maria. 11111 RESEARCH BLVD, STE 360 78759 #035-48-1997 L2006 **CD** *020 †20

CHAN, Annie Yenyi. ■ 78746 #048-13-2008 *012

CHANDA-KIM, Mousumi. 4303 VICTORY DR 78704 #048-02-1996 L1999 **IM** *020 †20

CHANDLER, Thomas Yoder. 7600 N CAPITAL OF TEXS HWY, STE A 78731 #048-14-1981 L1981 **OPH** *020 †20,35

CHANG, Kevin Carlo. 601 E 15TH ST 78701 #028-46-2004 **IM** *100

CHANG, Peter. 6402 DRY CLIFF CV, DRY CLIFF RADIOLOGY, PA 78731 #048-13-1979 L1980 **R OS** *020 †55,80

CHANG, Tingchuan. ■ 78741 #048-15-2003 L2006 **PD** *100 †55

CHANG, Yufang J. ■ 78704 #048-02-2006 L2008 **P** *012

CHAPIN, James Carlson. 12221 N MO PAC EXPY 78758 #025-01-1974 L1982 **AN** *020 †05

CHASSAY, C Mark. 3200 RED RIVER ST, STE 201 78705 #048-14-1992 L1993 **FM FSM** *020 †18

CHAUDHURI, Mitali. 2901 MONTOPOLIS DR, DEPT OF PSYCHIATRY 78741 #048-13-1996 L1998 **P** *020 †75

CHAUDHURY, Saswati. ■ 78759 #495-78-1997 L2008 **FM** *100

CHEN, Andre Shaw. 3508 FAR WEST BLVD, FL 2 78731 #023-01-1992 L1993 **FM MDM** *020 †18

CHEN, Dean. 4310 JAMES CASEY ST, STE 3C 78745 #048-04-1994 L1999 **ORS** *020 †40

CHEN, Dillon. 8038 MESA DR 78731 #005-02-1995 L2001 **DR** *020 †80

CHEN, Eric. 3705 MEDICAL PKWY, STE 410 78705 #048-04-2001 L2007 **OPH OS** *020 †35

CHEN, Eunice Shin. 11902 BROAD LEAF CV, WEST LAKE FAMILY PRACTICE 78750 #048-02-1994 L2001 **FM** *020 †18

CHEN, Franklin Mingjui. 3708 SPICEWOOD SPRINGS RD, STE 220 78759 #035-45-1992 L1996 **IM** *020 †20

CHENAULT, Christopher S. ■ 78727 #048-04-1964 L1964 **ORS HS** *071 †40

CHENVEN, Norman Herbert. 6937 N IH 35, STE 500 78752 #035-08-1970 L1973 **FM** *030 †18

CHERICO, Felix Wm, Jr. 1015 E 32ND ST, STE 30 78705 #048-12-1972 L1977 **GS CD** *020 †85

CHERRY, Tara Douglas. 4101 JAMES CASEY ST, STE 300 78745 #048-16-2000 L2004 **OBG** *020 †30

CHERUKU, Sunil Reddy. 1301 W 38TH ST, STE 109 78705 #495-57-1992 L1997 **IM** *020 †20

CHHIKARA, Subir. 6500 N MO PAC EXPY, BLDG 2 78731 #048-04-1993 L1994 **U UP** *020 †95

CHIAPETTA, Vanessa Lea. 3508 FAR WEST BLVD, FL 2 78731 #048-12-1981 L1981 **PD** *020 †55

CHILDS, Allen. ■ 78732 #048-12-1966 L1966 **P** *030 †75

CHILDS, Nancy. 1407 W STASSNEY LN 78745 #027-01-1977 L1982 **N** *020 †75

CHILES, Ross Pershing. ■ 78731 #025-01-1964 L1971 **END IM** *071 †20

CHILTON, Raymond L, III. 3801 N LAMAR BLVD, HEART HOSPITAL OF AUSTIN 78756 #048-04-1990 L1995 **EM** *020 †16

CHINDALORE, Aruna P K. ■ 78749 #496-22-1999 *100

CHING, Peter Vincent. 1015 E 32ND ST 78705 #048-12-1997 L2005 **GS** *020 †85

CHIPMAN, Zachary A. 313 E 12TH ST, CAPITAL OBSTETRICS & 78701 #048-14-1990 L1994 **OBG** *020 †30

CHO, Frank Shengshyan. 1015 E 32ND ST, STE 405 78705 #048-02-1986 L1987 **NPM PD** *020 †55

CHO, Ronald Yongsang. ■ 78739 #048-15-1998 L2000 **IM** *020 †20

CHOPP, Richard Thomas. 11410 JOLLYVILLE RD, BLDG 1 78759 #026-04-1971 L1982 **U** *020 †95

CHOUTEAU, Ruth Michelle. 2911 MEDICAL ARTS ST, STE 19A 78705 #048-04-1985 L1987 **OBG** *020 †30

CHOW, Frank Michael. 1301 W 38TH ST, STE 109 78705 #019-02-1994 L2002 **IM** *020

CHRIST, Michael John. 601 E 15TH ST, PEDIATRIX MEDICAL GROUP OF 78701 #041-14-1992 L2004 **NPM** *020 †55

CHU, Laurence. 1015 E 32ND ST, STE 316 78705 #024-05-1988 L2004 **OTO** *020 †45

CHUDLEIGH, James P, Jr. 8627 N MOPAC EXPY, STE 110 78759 #004-01-1978 L1978 **GP** *020

CHURCH, Phillip John. 1010 W 40TH ST 78756 #048-12-1975 L1975 **VS** *020 †85

CIPLEU, Cristian Dumitru. 1015 E 32ND ST, STE 414 78705 #781-03-1994 L2005 **NEP** *100 †20

CISHEK, Marybeth. 42 EAST AVE, CONSULTANT 78701 #028-34-1988 L1997 **CD** *020 †20

CISNEROS, Alfredo David. 4301 W WILLIAM CANNON DR, BLDG B STE 150 101 78749 #048-04-1996 L1998 **FM** *020 †18

CLAPPER, Patrick Wm. 4110 GUADALUPE ST, ADULT SERVICES 78751 #048-02-1989 L1990 **P** *020 †75

CLARDY, Catherina Jo. 2911 MEDICAL ARTS ST # 16 78705 #047-07-1975 L1979 **OBG** *020 †30

CLARK, Cheryl Monet. 9400 MAGNA CARTA LOOP 78754 #048-02-1998 L2003 **FM** *020 †18

CLARK, Margaret Kreisle. 1201 W 38TH ST 78705 #048-13-1980 L1980 **IM** *020 †20

CLARK, Mark Colin. 1305 W 34TH ST 78705 #048-13-1976 L1978 **PUD CCM** *020 †20

CLARK, Stephen Sidney. 3705 MEDICAL PKWY, STE 250 78705 #048-12-1968 L1968 **GS** *020 †85

CLARKE, Chas Edward Peter. ■ 78750 #917-19-1959 L1980 **EM GP** *071

CLELAND, William Oliver. ■ 78759 #041-02-1955 L1978 **IM HEM** *071

CLEMENT, Robert Lynn. 3003 BEE CAVE RD, STE 203 78746 #048-02-1967 L1967 **PS** *020 †65

CLEMONS, Lisa Keely. 1313 RED RIVER ST, STE 100 78701 #048-02-1996 L1997 **FM** *020 †18

CLINE, Robert W. 4106 MEDICAL PKWY 78756 #048-12-1988 L1990 **CRS GS** *020 †85,10

CLINKSCALES, Anna Beth. ■ 78735 #027-01-2004 L2007 **PD** *020 †55

CLITHEROE, Scott W. 11211 TAYLOR DRAPR LN #202 78759 #048-14-1992 L1993 **IM** *020 †20

CLYBOURN, Clyde Corwin. ■ 78701 #041-02-2002 L2007 **IM** *020 †20

COATS, Teresa Lejeune. 1015 E 32ND ST STE 309 78705 #048-15-1985 L1988 **IM** *020 †20

COFFEEN, Paul Raymond. 3801 N LAMAR BLVD STE 3, LAWSON PARKER 78756 #023-07-1988 L1997 **CD IM** *020 †20

COFFEY, Aida R. 7004 BEE CAVE RD STE 105, BLDG 2 78746 #051-01-1991 L1998 **P** *020 †75

COFFMAN, Amy M. 3705 MEDICAL PKWY, STE 570 78705 #048-13-1994 L1997 **AN** *020

COGHE, David Wm. ■ 78747 #055-01-1967 L1986 **CHP P** *071 †75

COLDWATER, Cheryl Lynn. 6835 AUSTIN CENTER BLVD 78731 #048-13-1983 L1984 **PD** *020 †55

COLE, Donald D, III. 3828 S 1ST ST 78704 #048-12-1997 L1998 **FM** *020 †18

COLLEBRUSCO, Alan D. 3705 MEDICAL PKWY, STE 570 78705 #048-02-1989 L1990 **AN** *020 †05

COLLIER, Cory Brooks. ■ 78732 #048-15-2008 *012

COLLINS, Jason N. 720 W 34TH ST, PARKLAND HOSPITAL 78705 #048-13-2003 L2005 **EM** *100 †16

COLLINS, Melanie A. 12201 RENFERT WAY, STE 205 78758 #048-14-1991 L1992 **OBG** *020 †30

COLLINS, Phillip Clyde. 601 E 15TH ST 78701 #048-12-1977 L1977 **PTH** *020 †50

COMBS, Aaron Lee. 4701 WEST GATE BLVD STE B- 78745 #038-40-1981 L1986 **ORS** *020 †40

COMPTON, Paul Martin. 4131 SPICEWOOD SPRINGS RD 78759 #048-13-1986 L1990 **P PYA** *020 †75

CONCEPCION, Constancio V. 7112 ED BLUESTEIN BLVD Z 78723 #748-02-1991 L2006 **PD** *020 †55

CONNELL, Donald Mitchel. 919 E 32ND ST 78705 #048-12-1974 L1974 **EM** *071 †16

CONNOLLY, Jule Tom. 6835 COUGAR RUN 78731 #048-04-1958 L1958 **GP** *020

CONNOLLY, Patrick Kevin. 3705 MEDICAL PKWY, AUSTIN ENT PEDIATRICS 78705 #048-04-1985 L1986 **OTO PDO** *020 †45

CONNOR, Gregory Francis. 10900 STONELAKE BLVD, STE 250 78759 #045-01-1999 L2005 **DR** *020 †80

CONNOR, Robert Emmet. 9200 WALL ST 78754 #028-02-1979 L1985 **PTH** *020 †50

CONOLY, Scott O. 10305 WOMMACK RD 78748 #048-14-2001 L2005 **IM** *020

CONRAD, Lawrence Kirkland. 10900 STONELAKE BLVD, STE 250 78759 #011-04-1996 L2006 **RNR** *020 †80

CONTALDI, Robert Gaetano. ■ 78745 #008-02-1980 L1982 **P IM** *020

COOK, Henry Morgan. ■ 78746 #030-05-1945 L1971 **PUD IM** *071 †20

COOK, Jeanne Wynn. 100F W DEAN KEETON ST, UNIV OF TX STUDENT HEALTH 78712 #048-12-1986 L1987 **FM** *020 †18

COOK, Margaret Eileen. 2220 HANCOCK DR 78756 #039-01-1980 L1998 **NEP IM** *020 †20

COOK, Robert David. 4150 N LAMAR BLVD 78756 #048-12-1977 L1977 **AI IM** *020 †20,03

COONS, Richard Edmunds. 1600 W 38TH ST, STE 404 78731 #048-02-1968 L1968 **P GP** *020 †75

COOPER, Anne Elizabeth. 8204 BRODIE LN STE 101 78745 #005-19-1991 L1995 **FM** *020 †18

COOPER, Timothy Robt. 1015 E 32ND ST STE 405, PEDIATRIX MEDICAL GROUP OF 78705 #048-04-1979 L1984 **NPM PD** *062 †55

COOPWOOD, Thomas B, Jr. 601 E 15TH ST, SURGERY EDUCATION CTMF 78701 #048-14-1990 L1995 **GS** *020 †85

COOPWOOD, Thomas Benton. 2911 MEDICAL ARTS ST STE 2 78705 #048-04-1963 L1963 **GS TRS** *071 †85 ‡

CORAK, Jadranko. 601 E 15TH ST 78701 #957-08-1981 L2000 **IM** *020 †20

CORAK, Ksenija. 11901 HOBBY HORSE CT # 1 78758 #957-08-1981 L2001 **IM** *020 †20

CORDOBA, J Bernard. 3301 NORTHLAND DR STE 409 78731 #649-33-1977 L1987 **P** *020

CORTES, Leslie Ludwig. PO BOX 149030, 701 W 51ST ST 78714 #048-04-1979 L1979 **IMG IM** *030 †20

CORTEZ, Jose Carlos. 1301 BARBARA JORDAN BLVD, STE 302 78723 #048-04-1985 L1986 **UP U** *020 †95

CORTEZ, Monique. 3828 S 1ST ST 78704 #048-14-1999 L2001 **FM** *020 †18

COSENTINO, Robert Jos. 1301 W 38TH ST STE 201 78705 #048-12-1978 L1978 **OBG** *020 †30

COSTANZI, John Julio. 11044 RESEARCH BLVD, STE D400 78759 #010-02-1961 L1972 **ON HEM** *020 †20

COTTEY, Jessica A. 10813 GALSWORTHY LN 78739 #048-12-1998 L2002 **EM** *020

COTTEY, John H, II. 10813 GALSWORTHY LN 78739 #048-12-1998 L2001 **EM** *020 †16

COUGHLIN, James P. ■ 78704 #048-02-1988 L1989 **EM IM** *020 †20

COUGHLIN, Sean J. ■ 78732 #048-14-1992 L1995 **IM** *020 †20

COUNTS, Donald Ray. 2905 SAN GABRIEL ST, STE 306 78705 #048-02-1972 L1972 **FM** *020 ‡

COUNTS, Harold Kermit, Jr. 3705 MEDICAL PKWY, STE 570 78705 #025-01-1968 L1972 **AN** *020 †05

COURTNEY, James Tucker. 601 E 15TH ST, STE L-502 78701 #048-04-1976 L1981 **NPM PD** *020 †55

COVERMAN, Michael Howard. 11623 ANGUS RD STE 25 78759 #011-02-1971 L1978 **D IM** *020 †20,15

COVERT, Frank M, III. ■ 78731 #021-01-1945 L1947 **GS** *071

COWAN, Robert Kyle, Jr. 1301 W 38TH ST, STE 109 78705 #048-02-1991 L1992 **OBG** *020 †30

COWPER, Pamela Ann. 1301 W 38TH ST, STE 109 78705 #012-01-1995 L1996 **IM** *020 †20

COX, Alinda Roberta. 1301 W 38TH ST, STE 109 78705 #016-06-1984 L1988 **OBG** *020 †30

COX, Johnston Stewart. ■ 78748 #048-02-1980 L1980 **FM** *075

■ = Address Information Privacy Protected

COX, Shannon Douglass. 2600 E MARTN LTHR KNG JR 78702 #048-02-1982 L1983 RO *020 †80

CRADDOCK, Patrick Allen. 720 W 34TH ST, STE 101 78705 #048-02-2002 L2005 EM *020 †16

CRAIG, David Leo. 3705 MEDICAL PKWY, STE 570 78705 #048-15-1990 L1991 AN *020 †05

CRAIG, John Almon. ■ 78731 #048-02-1968 L1968 OS OPH *071

CRAVEN, Cameron Ryon. 6836 BEE CAVE RD, STE 111 78746 #048-02-2001 L2007 PS *020

CRAVEN, Clinton Earl. 3508 FAR WEST BLVD, FL 2 78731 #048-02-1962 L1962 PD *020 †55

CRAVEN, John C. 3705 MEDICAL PKWY 78705 #048-02-1990 L1992 AN *020 †05

CREEL, George Barnett. 8402 CROSS PARK DR 78754 #048-02-1990 L1991 N *020 †75

CRESSMAN, Marvin Richard. 1301 W 38TH ST STE 709, 709 MED PARK TOWERS 78705 #041-09-1959 L1970 NS *020 †25

CRESWELL, James Senter. 1201 W 38TH ST 78705 #048-13-1975 L1982 NPM *020 †55

CROOK, Gretchen L. 6835 AUSTIN CENTER BLVD, AUSTIN REGIONAL CLINIC 78731 #011-03-1997 L2001 FM *020 †18

CROOKES, Paul Wesley. ■ 78738 #062-01-1954 L1961 AN *071 †05

CROSBY, Bernard Lester. 800 W 34TH ST, STE 201 78705 #048-12-1980 L1980 AI PD *020 †55,03

CROSS, David Jonathan. 12221 N MO PAC EXPY 78758 #025-07-1988 L1993 AN *020 †20

CROUT, James Everett. 12221 N MO PAC EXPY 78758 #048-04-1970 L1970 RHU IM *020 †20

CROW, Steven Curtis. 2909 N INTERSTATE 35 78722 #048-13-1991 L1992 FM *020 †18

CROWLEY, William James. 12221 N MO PAC EXPY 78758 #028-03-1990 L1994 AN *020 †05

CROZIER, Mark Allen. 6204 BALCONES DR, TEXAS ONCOLOGY CANCER CENT 78731 #048-02-1981 L1981 GO *020 †30

CRUMB, Robert Stephen. 313 E 12TH ST, STE 104 78701 #016-02-1996 L2003 OBG *030 †30

CRUMP, Todd E. 1313 RED RIVER ST STE 100 78701 #048-13-1999 L2000 FM *020 †18

CUELLAR, David C. 12180 N MO PAC EXPY, STE A 78758 #048-12-1996 L2003 U *020 †95

CULLINGTON, James Richard. 1010 W 9TH ST 78703 #048-02-1972 L1972 PS *020 †85,65

CULPEPPER, Walter Shelley. ■ 78703 #021-05-1972 PDC *071 †55

CUNNINGHAM, F Kelly. 900 W 38TH ST, AUSTIN SPORTS MEDICINE 78705 #048-12-1983 L1983 ORS OSM *020 †40

CUNYUS, James Anderson. ■ 78746 #021-01-1958 L1964 R NM *071 †80,28

CURRAN, Tim A. ■ 78704 #048-13-1989 L1990 EM FM *020 †18

CURRY, Margaret A. 8240 N MO PAC EXPY, STE 350 78759 #048-13-1989 L1990 D *020 †15

CURRY, Nick Ullman. 1100 W 49TH ST 78756 #048-04-1977 L1982 PHP PTH *030 †70

CURTIS, B Will. 12221 N MO PAC EXPY 78758 #048-40-1996 L2000 AN *020 †05

CURTIS, Vard. 919 E 32ND ST 78705 #020-12-1998 L2005 EM *020 †16

CUSTER, Gilbert Jos, Jr. 1101 S CPTL OF TX HWY A200 78746 #048-13-1977 L1977 CHP P *020 †75

CUTLER, Wendy. 12221 N MO PAC EXPY 78758 #007-02-1999 L2001 OBG *020 †30

CWAZKA, Walter F. 1301 W 38TH ST, SUITE 601, 605 & 609 78705 #010-02-1967 L1982 RHU *020 †20

DABAGHI, Rashad Eugene. 1111 W 34TH ST, STE 200 78705 #048-12-1975 L1975 GE IM *020 †20,16

DAGHESTANI, Anas. 3828 S 1ST ST 78704 #875-01-1994 L2005 IM *020 †20 ‡

DAI, Stephen. ■ 78727 #041-15-2006 P *012

DAILY, Teresa Wooten. 3705 MEDICAL PKWY 78705 #008-01-1992 L1995 PD *020 †55

DALTON, Leslie W, III. 601 E 15TH ST DEPT PATH 78701 #034-01-1983 L1988 PTH *020 †50

DALTON, Mark Ray. 901 W 38TH ST, STE 301 78705 #048-14-1997 L1998 ORS *020

DAMORE, Stuart. 8038 MESA DR 78731 #028-34-1974 L1983 CD *020 †20

DANG, Hoa T. 8745 N LAMAR BLVD 78753 #942-01-1973 L1995 IM *020

DANG, Ngoc-Yen Thi. 5717 BALCONES DR 78731 #048-14-1999 L2003 OPH *020 †35

DANG, Tony. 8557 RESEARCH BLVD, STE 128 78758 #654-01-1997 L2006 FM *020 †18

DANIEL, Thomas Morris. 7610 W HIGHWAY 71, STE F, PLAZA 71 78735 #048-02-1969 L1969 IM P *020

DANKS, Clyde Richard. ■ 78731 #020-02-1955 L1962 R NR *071 †80

DANO, Jaculeen Ann. 1600 W 38TH ST, STE 315 78731 #021-01-1990 L1993 D IM *020 †20,15

DANSEY, Kenisha Laronda. 1313 RED RIVER ST STE 303B, UNIV OF TEXAS 78701 #038-06-2007 OBG *012

DAPPER, Jessica. 78731 #048-16-1996 L1997 EM *020 †16

DARBY, Byron Galloway. 12201 RENFERT WAY, STE 350 78758 #048-12-1977 L1977 OBG MFM *020 †30

DATE, Swati Dinesh. 4515 SETON CENTER PKWY, STE 220 78759 #048-02-1991 L1992 IM *020 †20

DAUGHERTY, Clarence G. ■ 78759 #048-12-1968 L1968 OM UM *020 †70,18

DAVIDSON, Antonia Marie. ■ 78746 #048-12-2002 L2005 CD *100 †20

DAVIDSON, Joel Todd. 3705 MEDICAL PKWY, STE 570 78705 #048-04-1999 L2003 AN *020 †05

DAVIDSON, Todd Lee. ■ 78746 #054-04-2008 *012

DAVIS, Brent Lee. 810 W BRAKER LN 78758 #043-01-1975 L1977 OM IM *020

DAVIS, David Garland. 11623 ANGUS RD STE 15 78759 #048-13-1973 L1973 ORS *020 †40

DAVIS, Donald Robert. 12411 HYMEADOW DR, STE 3B 78750 #048-13-1972 L1974 ORS *020 †40

DAVIS, Harold Clayton, Jr. ■ 78701 #048-13-1991 LM PHP *030

DAVIS, Jacqueline Alpheus. 2901 MONTOPOLIS DR 78741 #065-01-1975 L1986 GP *020 ‡

DAVIS, Jay Alan. 202 ASHWORTH DR 78746 #021-05-1982 L1985 CHP P *020 †75

DAVIS, L L Tad. 1902 S I H 35 78704 #048-13-1970 L1971 OBG *020 †30

DAVIS, Tinku. ■ 78748 #495-63-2001 L2007 PD *100 †55

DAVIS, William Mc Loughry. 3705 MEDICAL PKWY, STE 510 78705 #048-02-1969 L1969 PS GS *020 †85,65

DAWSON, Mark Clifton. 5716B W HIGHWAY 290 # 111 78735 #048-02-1982 L1983 FM *020 †18

DAWSON, Thomas Britton. 1111 W 34TH ST, STE 102 78705 #048-02-1983 L1983 PD *020 †55

DAY, Avis Meeks. 3816 S 1ST ST, SOUTH AUSTIN MEDICAL ASSOC 78704 #056-06-1982 L1988 PD *020 †55

DAY, John W. 100 W DEAN KEATON ST, UT AUSTIN UNIVERSITY HEALT 78712 #048-14-1986 L1987 FM *020 †18

DEAN, Robert Mann. 78730 #020-02-1953 L1954 OS GS *030 †85

DEATON, John G. ■ 78731 #048-02-1963 L1963 OS *040 †20

DEATON, William Joel. 1305 W 34TH ST, STE 400 78705 #048-04-1969 L1969 PUD CCM *020 †20

DE BEHNKE, Richard Davis. 4315 JAMES CASEY ST, AUSTIN DIAGNOSTIC CLINIC 78745 #048-04-1978 L1978 IM *020 †20

DECHERD, Jonathan Frank. 12221 N MO PAC EXPY 78758 #048-02-1964 L1964 NEP IM *071 †20

DE GINDER, William L. ■ 78731 #048-02-1947 L1947 DR *071 †80

DEHAN, Christopher Paul. 3705 MEDICAL PKWY, AUSTIN EAR NOSE & THROAT 78705 #039-01-1984 L1985 OTO *020 †45

DEHIPITIYA, Chandima S. 1301 W 38TH ST, STE 60 78705 #048-02-1996 L1999 IM *020 †20

DEHNE, Robert. 1301 BARBARA JORDAN BLVD, BLVD, STE 723 78723 #048-14-1983 L1983 OP ORS *020 †40

DE HOYOS, Juan Antonio. 1612 E CESAR CHAVEZ ST, MENTAL HLTH MENTAL RETARD 78702 #034-01-1988 L1994 P *020

DEKOWSKI, Steven Anthony. 1015 E 32ND ST, STE 405 78705 #016-02-1987 L1998 NPM PD *020 †55

DE LA MORENA, Alfonso L. ■ 78745 #847-04-1961 L1988 DR EM *071 †80

DEL ANGEL, Alma Patricia. 4900 MUELLER BLVD, DELL CHILDREN'S MEDICAL CE 78723 #649-19-1982 L2008 PD OS *020 †55

DE LA PAZ, Monica Ann. ■ 78741 #005-11-1987 L1988 OPH *071 †35

DELCAMBRE, Pamela Sue. 1519 W KOENIG LN 78756 #048-15-1977 L1977 GP PTH *020 †50

DELEON, Hector E. ■ 78703 #048-13-2005 PD *012

DELGADO, Abraham. 2901 MONTOPOLIS DR, BARTON OAKS PLAZA TWO 78741 #048-04-1974 L1975 IM EM *020 †20

DELK, Gerald Tyree. 720 W 34TH ST STE 1, MEDICAL CITY OF DALLAS 78705 #048-15-1998 L2000 EM *020 †16

DELL, Steven Jonathan. 5717 BALCONES DR 78731 #048-04-1988 L1989 OPH *020 †35

DEL MUNDO, Rufo G, Jr. 4110 GUADALUPE ST 78751 #748-01-1972 P *100

DE MAIO, Samuel J, Jr. 4207 JAMES CASEY ST, STE 215 78745 #033-05-1983 L1984 CD IM *020 †20

DEMING, Daniel Wayne. 3705 MEDICAL PKWY 78705 #005-14-2003 L2007 AN *020

DEMPSEY, Anne Elizabeth. 6101 BALCONES DR, STE 300 78731 #048-12-2002 L2005 IM *020 †20

DENG, Yue. 601 E 15TH ST, AUSTIN MED EDUC PROG-SETON 78701 #243-76-1994 L2007 IM *100 †20

DENHAM, Charles Ray. 3011 N IH 35 78722 #060-01-1979 L1983 RO *020

DENNISON, Robert A, Jr. 900 E 30TH ST, STE 100 78705 #048-12-1953 L1953 ORS *071 †40

DENSON, Melody Ann. 11410 JOLLYVILLE RD, BLDG 1 78759 #030-05-1996 L2005 U *030 †95

DEREBERY, Virginia Jane. 8868 RESEARCH BLVD, STE 601 78758 #039-01-1978 L1986 FM *020 †70

DESAI, Arpan Narendra. 900 W 38TH ST, STE 400 78705 #048-78-2000, ▲ L2005 AN PME *020 †05

DESAI, Parul Mahendra. 3801 N LAMAR BLVD, STE 300 78756 #024-07-1992 L1998 CD *020 †20

DESAI, Ulka. 601 E 15TH ST 78701 #495-17-2006 IM *012

DE SANTO, Gina T. 601 E 15TH ST 78701 #048-13-1995 L1997 IM *020 †20

DESHPANDE, Mrudula Abhay. 13740 N HWY 183, STE V1 78750 #495-19-1976 L1985 PD *020

DES ROSIERS, Joseph Louis. 1301 W 38TH ST, DRS DESROSIERS & WERNECKE 78705 #268-34-1957 L1962 OBG *020 †30

DEVINENI, Rao J. 4110 GUADALUPE ST, AUSTIN STATE HOSPITAL 78751 #495-58-1970 L1978 P EM *020

DE WAAL, Craig Thomas. 720 W 34TH ST, STE 101 78705 #048-12-2002 L2007 EM *100

DEWAN, Brian D. 8140 N MO PAC EXPY 78759 #048-14-1999 L2003 AN *020 †05

DE WETTE, Julia Regina. 8204 BRODIE LN, STE 101 78745 #048-13-1980 L1980 PD *062 †55

DHAWAN, Nikhil. ■ 78735 #048-04-2008 *012

DHRUVA, Achal Rahul. ■ 78732 #033-05-2001 L2006 OTO *020 †45

DICKEY, Mark Rayner. 4405 GUADALUPE ST, HOLISTIC FAMILY PRACTICE 78751 #048-13-1999 L2006 FM *020 †18

DIECK, John A, Jr. 4316 JAMES CASEY ST STE B 78745 #048-04-1984 L1985 CD IM *020 †20

DIETERICHS, Chad Paul. 3705 MEDICAL PKWY STE 570 78705 #048-02-2000 L2005 AN *020 †05

DILL, Lawrence Clyde. 3705 MEDICAL PKWY, STE 570 78705 #045-01-1977 L1991 AN *020 †05

DILLAWN, Patrick C. 4007 JAMES CASEY ST, STE B140 78745 #048-14-1993 L1996 GS *020 †85

DILLING, Emery Walter. 1010 W 40TH ST 78756 #039-01-1973 L1980 TS *020 †85,90

DILLON, Brian T. 11113 RESEARCH BLVD, EMG DEPT SETON NW HOSP 78759 #048-02-1985 L1988 EM *020 †16

DING, Evelyn. 3403 GLENVIEW AVE 78703 #048-04-1994 L1996 IM *020 †20

DINH, Mai Le. 1313 RED RIVER ST, STE 100 78701 #305-01-2007 FP *012

DIVEN, Steven Cory. 12109 CAPELLA TRL, PEDIATRIX 78732 #048-02-1986 L1987 NPM *020 †55

DIXON, Frederick Earl. 11149 RESEARCH BLVD, STE 125 78759 #051-01-1979 L2003 CD IM *020 †20

DLABAL, Paul W. 901 W 38TH ST 78705 #023-07-1975 L1978 CD IM *020 †20

DO, Khoa Dang. 8140 N MOPAC EXPY # 3-210 78759 #054-04-2002 L2006 AN *020

DOBBERFUHL, Steven B. 7201 MANCHACA RD, STE B 78745 #048-14-1997 L2000 IM *020 †20

DOBYNS, Robert Floyd. 4810 SPICEWOOD SPGS STE B 78759 #048-12-1971 L1971 CHP P *020

DODD, Bob Marlin. 6101 E OLTORF ST 78741 #048-02-1975 L1975 IM *020 †20

DODD, Julie E. 720 W 34TH ST 78705 #048-02-1999 L2002 EM *020 †16

DOGGETT, Lisa. 2909 N IH 35 78722 #048-04-1999 L2002 FM *020 †18

DOLINAK, David. ■ 78746 #038-44-1993 L1999 FOP *020 †50

DOLLAR, Debra Lee. 4515 SETON CENTER PKWY, STE 220 78759 #024-07-1999 L2003 EM *020 †16

DOMUCZICZ, Kenneth W, Jr. 720 W 34TH ST, STE 101 78705 #024-07-1999 L2003 EM *020 †16

DONER, Kevin Turhan. 12201 RENFERT WAY, STE 245 78758 #017-20-1999 L2001 HO *020 †20

DONNELLY, Joseph L, III. 12221 N MO PAC EXPY, EMERGENCY DEPT 78758 #048-13-1994 L1996 EM *020 †16

DOO, Elizabeth. ■ 78757 #060-01-1982 L1991 IM EM *020 †28

DOOLEY, Linda Williams. 15 WALLER ST 78702 #048-15-1980 L1980 IM IMG *020 †20 ‡

DOONER, James W. 801 W 38TH ST, AUSTIN RETINA ASSOCS 78705 #539-06-1991 L1998 OPH OS *020 †35

DOPATHI, Saraswathi. 601 E 15TH ST 78701 #496-59-2001 IM *012

DORMAN, Kenneth R. ■ 78705 #048-02-1968 L1968 P CHP *020 †75

DORNAK, Allen David. 8140 N MOPAC EXPY, BLDG 3 78759 #048-02-1983 L1984 AN *020 †05

DOSS, Noble Webster. 4201 MARATHON BLVD STE 301 78756 #048-12-1973 L1975 OBG *020 †30

DOTY, John Donald. 711 W 38TH ST 78705 #048-02-1977 L1977 ON IM *020 †20

DOUGLAS, Michal Aaron. 711 W 38TH ST, BLDG F 78705 #048-12-1973 L1982 N CN *020 †75

DOUGLASS, Elizabeth T. 601 E 15TH ST, MEDICINE DEPARTMENT 78701 #048-14-1991 L1992 ID *020 †20

DOYLE, Emily Jane. 3501 MILLS AVE, DEPARTMENT OF PSYCHIATRY 78731 #048-13-2000 L2005 PFP *100 †75

DOYLE, Marilyn. 4900 MUELLER BLVD, UTMB-AUSTIN PEDIATRICS 78723 #048-02-1979 L1979 PD *020 †55

DOZIER, Susan Elizabeth. 8240 N MOPAC EXPY STE 355 78759 #048-02-1989 L1990 **D DS** *020 †15
DRISCOLL, James Andrew. 1305 W 34TH ST, STE 400 78705 #048-12-2000 L2007 **PCC** *012 †20
DRISCOLL, Peter Vail. 5910 COURTYARD DR, STE 300 78731 #033-06-1993 L2004 **OTO CS** *020 †45
DROSU, Daniela Camelia. 1301 W 38TH ST, STE 109 78705 #781-01-1994 L2002 **IM** *020 †20
DRYER, Randall Frederick. 6818 AUSTIN CENTER BLVD, STE 200 78731 #018-03-1977 L1983 **OSS ORS** *020 †40
DUBEY, Sanjeev. 1201 W 38TH ST, SETON EMERGERY DEPARTMENT 78705 #048-02-1996 L2000 **EM** *020 †16
DU BOIS, Craig Robt. 7307 CREEKBLUFF DR, NEURAL LOGICS PA 78750 #018-03-1978 L1983 **N** *020 †75
DU BOIS, Dwight B. 1301 W 38TH ST, AUSTIN INFECTIOUS DISEASE 78705 #048-13-1987 L1994 **ID** *020 †20
DUBOIS, Janet C. 11671 JOLLYVILLE RD, # A-104 78759 #048-13-1987 L1995 **D** *020 †15
DUBOIS, Susan K. 2200 PARK BEND DR, BLDG 3 78758 #048-14-1988 L1989 **END IM** *040 †20
DUBOSE, Charles D. 4900 MUELLER BLVD, DELL CHILDREN'S MEDICAL CE 78723 #048-15-1991 L1992 **FM** *020 †18,55
DUDLEY, Courtney Relyea. 12174 N MO PAC EXPY, STE A 78758 #048-13-2003 L2006 **PD** *020 †55
DUNHAM, Jean Anderson. ■ 78748 #048-13-2005 **PD** *100
DUNKERLEY, George Garner. ■ 78736 #048-02-1962 L1962 **IM** *072 †20
DUONG, Mai Xuan. 8204 BRODIE LN, STE 101 78745 #048-13-1994 L1996 **PD** *062 †55
DUPONT, Cedric. ■ 78746 #048-14-2001 L2002 **AN** *100 †05
DUPUY, Fred Garrison. ■ 78703 #048-12-1963 L1963 **GYN** *071
DURAISWAMY, Sangeethapriya. 601 E 15TH ST 78701 #495-94-2002 **IM** *012
DUREN, Murray, Jr. 2100 W WILLIAM CANNON DR, STE C 78745 #048-02-1987 L1988 **FM** *020 †18
DURFOR, John Howard. ■ 78703 #048-14-1975 L1976 **GP** *020
DUSKA, Alois Albin. 720 W 34TH ST, EMERGENCY SERVICE PARTNERS 78705 #061-01-1973 L1994 **EM GP** *020 †16
DUTTON, Newell E. 10900 STONELAKE BLVD, STE 250 78759 #048-13-1983 L1983 **DR CD** *020 †80
DWINELL, Mark Edward. ■ 78704 #041-02-1991 L1999 **IM** *020 †20
DYER, Philip Dennis. 3303 NORTHLAND DR, STE 301 78731 #019-02-1981 L1991 **AI IM** *020 †20,03
DZIUK, Timothy W. 805 W 37TH ST 78705 #048-02-1989 L1990 **RO** *020 †80
EATON, Jeffrey Karl. ■ 78724 #048-02-2005 **IM** *012
EBERT, Andrew M. ■ 78735 #048-02-2001 L2007 **ORS** *100
EBERT, Elizabeth A. 2200 PARK BEND DR, BLDG 2 78758 #048-15-2000 L2006 **CD** *020 †20
ECKERT, Edward Randolph. 601 E 15TH ST 78701 #048-16-1984 L1985 **PTH** *020 †50
ECKERT, Mary Kathleen. 1301 W 38TH ST, STE 109 78705 #041-01-1997 L2001 **IM** *020 †20
ECKERT, Stanley Robt. 12221 N MO PAC EXPY 78758 #017-20-1979 L1982 **AN** *020 †05
ECKLEY, Robert. ■ 78741 #041-02-1942 L1955 **OPH** *071 †35
EDEN, David E. ■ 78746 #028-03-1967 L1974 **AN GP** *071 †05
EDGERTON, Screven T. 1301 W 38TH ST, STE 109 78705 #021-06-2001 L2005 **OBG** *020 †30
EDMOND, Betty Jean. 1400 IH 35 N, CHILDRENS ADMINISTRATION 78701 #048-02-1975 L1975 **PD ID** *020 †55
EDMOND, Michael Toole. 901 W 9TH ST, APT 304 78703 #048-02-1976 L1976 **N IM** *020 †20,75
EDOKA, Emmanuel C. 805 E 32ND ST, STE 103 78705 #690-01-1980 L1993 **IM IMG** *020 †20
EDOKA, Joanne Wise. 800 W 34TH ST, STE 208 78705 #047-07-1988 L1993 **PD** *020 †55
EDWARDS, George Ambrose. 601 E 15TH ST 78701 #048-04-1972 L1972 **PD NEP** *040 †55
EDWARDS, Jaime Marguerite. ■ 78731 #021-06-2007 **OBG** *012
EDWARDS, John C. 7793 BURNET RD 78757 #048-15-1999 L2006 **DR** *020 †80
EDWARDS, Kimberly Cruzita. 6835 AUSTIN CENTER BLVD 78731 #024-01-1999 L2002 **PD** *020 †55
EDWARDS, William Mills. 3616 FAR WEST BLVD, # 117-184 78731 #016-06-1977 L1997 **EM MDM** *030 †16 ‡
EGERTON, John Ronald. ■ 78730 #917-18-1965 L1976 **FM IM** *071
EGERTON, Judith Margaret. ■ 78730 #917-18-1967 L1980 **PD FM** *071
EICHLER, Elwood James. 1015 E 32ND ST, STE 101 78705 #048-02-1956 L1956 **ORS** *071 †40
EKERY, Deborah L. 3801 N LAMAR BLVD, STE 300 78756 #048-12-1993 L1995 **CD** *020 †20
ELA, Dennis De Vries. ■ 78731 #056-05-1973 L1975 **OM FM** *020 †18
EL-ASFOURI, Souhail Ali. 4316 JAMES CASEY ST STE F, STE 200 78745 #048-02-1989 L1991 **OBG** *020 †30
EL-DOMEIRI, Ali Abd E. 4010 BALCONES DR 78731 #330-02-1958 L1976 **SO GS** *020 †85
ELENZ, Douglas Reed. 900 W 38TH ST, AUSTIN SPORTS MEDICINE 78705 #048-14-1990 L1991 **OSM** *020 †40
ELIZONDO, Eduardo Raul. 3001 BEE CAVE RD, STE 200 78746 #048-13-1989 L1994 **PM** *020 †60
ELLINGTON, Kent T. 711-F W 38TH ST 78705 #048-04-1991 L1993 **N** *020 †75
ELLIS, Leighton Elizabeth. 12201 RENFERT WAY, STE 110 78758 #011-04-1988 L1997 **PD** *040 †55
ELLIS, Lisa C. 1301 W 38TH ST, STE 403 78705 #048-04-1989 L1991 **ID** *020 †20
ELLISON, Dale Alicia. ■ 78731 #051-07-1988 L1994 **PTH** *020 †50
EMERSON, Robert Keith. 12221 N MO PAC EXPY, STE 29 78758 #016-06-1966 L1971 **PUD IM** *020 †20
ENGLES, Leslie Ann. ■ 78703 #007-02-2002 L2004 **IM** *100
ENRIQUEZ, Humberto. 11645 ANGUS RD 78759 #649-01-1973 L1974 **FM** *020 †18
EPSTEIN, Anne. 4007 JAMES CASEY ST, STE B210 78745 #048-02-1987 L1989 **D IM** *020 †20,15
EPSTEIN, Susan Zane. ■ 78746 #048-13-1993 L1994 **GP** *071
ERKO, Amsalu. ■ 78754 #366-02-1998 L2006 **NEP** *012 †20
ERLINGER, Thomas P. 1601 RIO GRANDE ST, STE 340 78701 #048-13-1993 L2006 **IM** *020 †20
ERSEK, Robert Allen. 630 W 34TH ST STE 201 78705 #041-09-1966 L1977 **PS HS** *020 †65
ERWIN, Geoffrey Taylor. 11111 RESEARCH BLVD, STE 345 78759 #048-14-1979 L1979 **OBG** *020 †30
ESCHE, Mark A. 3636 EXECUTIVE CENTER DR, STE 158 78731 #048-15-1997 L2002 **P** *020
ESCOBEDO, Michael S. 3801 S LAMAR BLVD 78704 #048-15-1995 L1996 **GP** *020
ESKEW, James Robt. 4207 JAMES CASEY ST, AUSTIN EAR NOSE & THROAT 78745 #048-13-1977 L1977 **OTO HNS** *020 †45
ESMAIL, Aliya. ■ 78703 #016-11-2001 L2007 **PD** *020 †55
ESPARZA, Ray Joseph. 3801 S LAMAR BLVD, PROMED MEDICAL CARE CENTER 78704 #048-13-1979 L1979 **GP** *020
ESPARZA, Robert Albert. 8204 BRODIE LN, STE 101 78745 #048-04-1979 L1979 **PD** *020 †55
ESPINOSA, Valerie Diane. 900 W 38TH ST 78705 #048-13-1993 L1998 **IM** *020 †20
ESQUIVEL, Alejandro. 4101 JAMES CASEY ST STE 34 78745 #048-15-1994 L2001 **GS** *020 †85
ESWAY, Jan-Eric. 1015 E 32ND ST, STE 101 78705 #041-12-2000 L2006 **ORS** *100
EUBANKS, Virginia M T. ■ 78703 #048-02-1972 L1972 **PYA P** *020 †75
EVANS, Colby Craig. 9701 BRODIE LN, STE A106 78748 #048-12-2000 L2003 **D** *020 †15
EVANS, James Stewart. 1301 W 38TH ST, STE 108 78705 #054-04-1990 L1999 **ID** *020 †20
EVANS, Mitchell Dean. 3705 MEDICAL PKWY, STE 570 78705 #048-14-1986 L1987 **AN** *020 †05
EVANS, William Mason. 3508 FAR WEST BLVD, FL 2 78731 #019-02-1971 L1988 **FM AM** *020 †18
EZEKIEL, Bennett John. ■ 78747 #048-15-2005 **PM** *012
FAGERBERG, Marcia Diane. 6835 AUSTIN CENTER BLVD 78731 #041-14-1995 L2001 **IM** *020 †20
FAGET, Carol Jean. 6835 AUSTIN CENTER BLVD 78731 #048-02-1976 L1976 **PD** *020 †55
FAGIN, Randy Scott. 11410 JOLLYVILLE RD, BLDG 1 78759 #035-06-1997 L2002 **U** *020 †95
FAIN, Becky Keller. ■ 78746 #048-02-1988 L1989 **PM** *020 †60
FALVEY, Thos Seymour, III. 5205 VALBURN CIR, THOMAS S FALVEY III 78731 #308-11-1983 L1989 **IM** *020
FALVO, Heather Marie. 3706 S 1ST ST 78704 #048-13-1998 L2001 **IM** *020 †20
FANNIN, Oliver W, III. 601 E 15TH ST, EMERG DEPT 78701 #048-02-1993 L1995 **EM** *020 †16
FARADY, Katherine K. 8240 N MO PAC EXPY, STE 350 78759 #048-02-1984 L1986 **D** *020 †15
FARHOOD, Anwar. ■ 78730 #875-02-1980 L1989 **PTH** *020 †50
FARKAS, Lia-Ana. 601 E 15TH ST 78701 #781-03-1998 **IM** *012
FARMER, Kelley. 4601 SPICEWOOD SPRINGS RD, BLDG 4 78759 #048-02-1991 L1993 **P** *020
FASCI, Siv Huy. ■ 78748 #048-02-1998 L2003 **PD** *020 †55
FASON, Sam D. 8140 N MOPAC EXPY, BLG 3 STE 210 78759 #048-13-1995 L1997 **AN** *020 †05
FASS, Steven M. 3705 MEDICAL PKWY STE 250 78705 #048-12-1994 L2000 **GS** *020 †85
FAULKENBERRY, Tim Larry. 919 E 32ND ST 78705 #048-02-1974 L1974 **GS** *020 †85
FEARHEILEY, Corey Ray. ■ 78727 #016-11-2004 L2007 **EM** *020
FEASEL, Adrienne Marie. 11671 JOLLYVILLE RD, STE 104 78759 #048-14-2000 L2001 **D** *020 †15
FEHRENKAMP, Steven Harry. 3005 S LAMAR BLVD, STE 109D 78704 #048-12-1977 L1977 **END** *020 †20
FEIN, Bernard T. ■ 78745 #020-02-1938 L1946 **AI IM** *071
FELDMAN, David Jay. 10900 STONELAKE BLVD, STE 250 78759 #048-04-1986 L1987 **DR** *020 †80
FELGER, Charles Edward. 12221 MOPAC EXP N 78756 #021-01-1961 L1964 **GE IM** *071 †20
FELKINS, Barbara Joyce. ■ 78701 #048-14-1977 L1977 **CHP P** *062 †75
FELTER, Daniel F. ■ 78751 #048-13-2002 L2005 **DR** *100 †80
FERNANDEZ, Jim B. 900 W 38TH ST, AUSTIN SPORTS MEDICINE 78705 #048-15-1997 L2001 **PM** *020 †60
FERNANDEZ, Marisol. 1301 BARBARA JORDAN BLVD, STE 200 78723 #935-01-1991 L2003 **PD** *020 †55
FIELDER, W Drew. 313 E 12TH ST STE 100 78701 #048-14-1991 L1992 **GS TRS** *020 †85
FILARDI, Jon P. 3705 MEDICAL PKWY, STE 570 78705 #048-02-1984 L1985 **AN PAN** *020 †05
FINK, Lou Anna. ■ 78759 #048-02-1973 L1973 **P** *071 †75
FINNIGAN, James P. 4314 MEDICAL PKWY, STE 200 78756 #048-02-1986 L1989 **PDC PD** *020 †55
FISCHER, Charles Henry. 4110 GUADALUPE ST 78751 #048-13-1978 L1984 **CHP P** *020 †75
FISHER, Monica M. 6101 E OLTORF ST 78741 #021-01-1988 L1996 **PD** *020 †55
FITZPATRICK, Timothy Sean. 1301 W 38TH ST, STE 102 78705 #041-02-2000 L2004 **EM** *020 †16
FITZWATER, John Bradley. 1015 E 32ND ST, STE 306 78705 #026-08-1997 L2000 **OBG** *020 †30
FLEEGER, David Clark. 4208 MEDICAL PKWY, AUSTIN COLON & RECTAL CLNC 78756 #048-16-1985 L1991 **CRS** *020 †85,10 ‡
FLEMING, Richard D. 1015 E 32ND ST 78705 #048-02-1988 L1990 **GS** *020 †85
FLETCHER, Thomas Boudol. 10900 STONELAKE BLVD, STE 250 78759 #048-12-1983 L1983 **DR GS** *020 †80
FLOCA, Frank Stewart. 1009 E 40TH ST STE 305 78751 #048-02-1976 L1976 **P** *020 †75
FLORES, Nicole Susanne. 720 W 34TH ST, STE 101 78705 #048-04-1999 L2003 **EM** *020 †16
FLOYD, Michael. 6818 AUSTIN CENTER BLVD, STE 201 78731 #048-13-1989 L1990 **U** *020 †95
FLOYD, Roland Matthews. ■ 78739 #048-04-1969 L1969 **DR** *071 †80
FLUME, David Lawrence. 300 BEARDSLEY LN, BLDG C 78746 #048-12-1985 L1989 **P** *020 †75
FLUME, Shiree C. 106 E 6TH ST, STE 900 78701 #048-12-1985 L1989 **P** *020 †75
FLUSCHE, Gary Allen. 3705 MEDICAL PKWY, STE 570 78705 #048-12-1982 L1983 **AN** *020 †05
FLYNN, Kevin J. 12201 RENFERT WAY, STE 305 78758 #026-08-1976 L1978 **D DMP** *020 †50,15
FOGELMAN, Jay. 711 W 38TH ST # 14 78705 #048-02-1974 L1974 **P CHP** *020 †75
FOLKERS, David. 4007 JAMES CASEY ST, STE B130 78745 #019-02-1990 L1995 **GS AS** *020 †85
FORAGE, Jean-Pierre. 4101 JAMES CASEY ST # 340 78745 #048-14-1983 L1983 **GS** *020 †85
FORBES, Marion Mc Laurin. 601 E 15TH ST 78701 #048-12-1988 L1989 **PD** *020 †55
FORE, Bennie Frank, III. 720 W 34TH ST, STE 101 78705 #048-12-1980 L1981 **EM** *020 †16
FOREMAN, Wesley Darrell. 1215 RED RIVER ST 78701 #048-14-1998 L2003 **PME PM** *020 †60
FORGASON, Judy. 710 WEST AVE 78701 #048-14-1982 L1983 **P** *020 †75
FORK, Heather Elizabeth. 1600 W 38TH ST, STE 308 78731 #048-02-1991 L1995 **D** *071 †15
FOSS, John Dudley. 7201 MANCHACA RD, STE B 78745 #001-02-1998 L2007 **IM** *020 †20
FOSTER, Gary Lee. 4316 JAMES CASEY ST, STE C 78745 #048-12-1988 L1990 **CD** *020 †20
FOSTER, Nancy Elizabeth. 1301 W 38TH ST, STE 402 78705 #048-02-1983 L1983 **IM** *020 †20
FOUGHT, Jason R. ■ 78731 #048-15-2001 L2007 **NEP IM** *100 †20
FOX, James Wilson. 3901 MEDICAL PKWY STE 300 78756 #048-02-1968 L1968 **PS** *020 †65
FOX, Kenneth Alan. 1010 W 40TH ST 78756 #016-11-1991 L2001 **PCS** *020 †90,85
FOX, Kermit W. 1015 E 32ND ST STE 101 78705 #048-02-1936 L1936 **ORS OS** *071 †40
FOX, Matthew Charles. ■ 78731 #048-14-2007 **IM** *012
FOX, R John. 3807 SPICEWOOD SPRINGS RD, AUSTIN DERMCARE 78759 #038-06-1970 L1976 **D DMP** *020 †15
FOX, Teresa Benjamin. 3301 NORTHLAND DR, STE 216 78731 #048-14-1987 L1988 **IM** *074
FRACHTMAN, Robert Lee. 1111 W 34TH ST, STE 200 78705 #048-12-1978 L1978 **GE** *040 †20
FRANK, Allan Lawrance. 4100 DUVAL RD, BLDG 4 78759 #048-13-1973 L1973 **PD** *020 †55
FRANK, Brannon R. 2501 W WILLIAM CANNON DR, STE 401 78745 #048-02-1999 L2004 **APM AN** *020 †05
FRANKLIN, William Gordon. 4303 VICTORY DR 78704 #048-02-1983 L1984 **FM** *020 †18
FRASER, Linda J. ■ 78750 #067-01-1978 L1999 **IM** *020 †18
FRAZIER, Viviana Carolina. 8913 COLLINFIELD DR 78758 #264-21-1999 L2006 **FM** *100 †18
FREDERICK, John Kurt. 4534 W GATE BLVD, STE 108 78745 #048-12-1986 L1987 **FM** *020 †18
FREDERICK, Sarah Renee. ■ 78751 #048-02-2007 **PD** *012

FREDHOLM, Leigh Anne. 4107 SPICEWOOD SPRINGS RD, STE 100 78759 #028-46-1992 L1993 **FM PLM** *020 †18

FREEMAN, Donald Mac. 3701 EXECUTIVE CENTER DR, STE 105 78731 #048-02-1963 L1964 **FM** *020 †18

FREER, Rebecca Lynn. 3708 JEFFERSON ST, STE 102 78731 #038-40-1990 L2001 **GS** *020 †85

FRIEDMAN, Alice Diane. 7600 N CAPITAL OF TEXS HWY, STE A 78731 #048-16-1981 L1981 **GE IM** *020 †20

FRIEDMAN, Robert Alan. 7800 SHOAL CREEK BLVD, STE 130W 78757 #005-06-1980 L2007 **FM PLM** *020 †18

FRIERSON-STROUD, Leonor B. 3301 NORTHLAND DR, STE 216 78731 #048-13-1985 L1987 **IM** *020 †20

FRISCHHERTZ, Eric James. 4207 JAMES CASEY ST STE 21 78745 #021-01-2000 L2006 **CD** *020 †20

FRY, Liam Mc Coy. 320 W 13TH ST, STE 1A 78701 #048-12-2002 L2006 **IMG** *020 †20

FRYE-HARPER, Ruth Ann. 3410 FAR WEST BLVD, STE 305 78731 #039-05-1986 L1995 **NTR** *020 †20

FUDMAN, Edward Joel. 1301 W 38TH ST, STE 702 78705 #036-07-1981 L1986 **RHU IM** *020 †20

FUENMAYOR, Mariela Josefi. 4110 GUADALUPE ST 78751 #935-09-1988 L2008 **P** *020 †100

FULLER, Rob A. 3705 MEDICAL PKWY, STE 250 78705 #048-12-1994 L1996 **GS** *020 †85

FULLERTON, Bradley. 2714 BEE CAVE RD, STE 106 78746 #048-12-1990 L1997 **PM PMM** *020 †60

FULLMER, Jason J. 3305 NORTHLAND DR 78731 #048-14-1998 L2000 **PDP PD** *020 †55

FUNICELLA, Toni. 13740 RESEARCH BLVD STE P4 78750 #048-02-1972 L1972 **D** *020 †20,15

FURST, Edward Dunton. 3705 MEDICAL PKWY STE 570 78705 #048-15-1986 L1987 **AN PD** *020 †05,55

FUSELIER, James Clay. 2501 W WILLIAM CANNON DR, BLDG 6 78745 #048-12-1996 L1997 **GS** *020 †20

FYFE, Steven Trey. 6818 AUSTIN CENTER BLVD, STE 202 78731 #048-04-1984 L1986 **OTO HNS** *020 †45

GABRIEL, David J. 11651 JOLLYVILLE RD, STE 110 78759 #048-13-1986 L1987 **FM** *020 †18

GABRYSCH, Jeremy Charles. ■ 78736 #048-12-2002 L2004 **EM** *100 †16

GADARIA, Umeshchandra G. 1015 E 32ND ST STE 208 78705 #495-17-1970 L1984 **PS HS** *020 †85,65

GADI, Ramprasad. 1301 W 38TH ST, STE 202 78705 #495-59-1995 L2005 **IM** *020 †20

GAGE, Joel T. 2200 PARK BEND DR, STE 300 78758 #048-14-1997 L1998 **CD** *020 †20 ‡

GAGLANI, Binaca. 2312 WESTERN TRAILS BLVD, STE 101 78745 #495-32-1988 L1994 **AI** *020 †55,03

GAGNEJA, Harish Kumar. 4310 JAMES CASEY ST, STE 4A 78745 #495-03-1991 L2000 **GE HEP** *020 †20

GALIAN, Antonio Cordero. 10001 SCULL CREEK DR 78730 #748-07-1955 L1971 **GP EM** *071 †16

GALIAN, Emerita Angeles. 10001 SCULL CREEK DR 78730 #748-01-1963 L1977 **PM** *020

GALLINGHOUSE, Gerald, Jr. 1301 W 38TH ST, TEXAS CARDIOVASCULAR CONSU 78705 #021-05-1988 L1992 **CD IM** *020 †20

GALLOWAY, Christopher D. ■ 78704 #048-02-1997 L2000 **EM** *020 †16

GAMBARIN, Kimberly. 1301 W 38TH ST, STE 403 78705 #035-48-1998 L2001 **ID** *020 †20

GAMBARIN, Semyon. 3708 JEFFERSON ST, STE 102 78731 #035-48-1998 L2003 **GS** *020 †85

GAMBLE, David Earl. 4615 LAUREL CANYON DR 78749 #048-12-1968 L1968 **PD** *071 †54

GAMEL, William Glenn. ■ 78703 #048-02-1963 L1963 **IM GE** *050 †20

GAMMON, Roger S. 3801 N LAMAR BLVD # 300 78756 #028-46-1984 L1985 **CD IM** *020 †20

GANESHAN, Sumati. ■ 78746 #048-04-1996 L2001 **MPD** *020 †

GANEY, Cathy. 720 W 34TH ST, STE 101 78705 #036-05-1996 L2004 **PD** *020 †55

GANTA, Sashidhar Venkata. 11851 JOLLYVILLE RD, STE 104 78759 #495-58-1991 L2005 **GS** *020 †85

GAO, Chuanyun. 601 E 15TH ST, AUSTIN MED EDUC PROG-SETON 78701 #243-47-1995 L2007 **END** *012 †20

GARCIA, Derrick John. 6835 AUSTIN CENTER BLVD, AUSTIN REGIONAL CLINIC 78731 #021-05-1998 L2001 **FM** *020 †18

GARCIA, Donald C. ■ 78732 #748-01-1963 L1971 **R** *020 †80

GARCIA, Donald J, Jr. 4200 MARATHON BLVD, STE 200 78756 #048-02-1990 L1991 **P** *020 †75

GARCIA, Eduardo Ignacio. 3851 AIRPORT BLVD, STE 101 78722 #048-04-1979 L1979 **PME** *020

GARCIA, Jose Reymundo. ■ 78749 #048-04-1976 L1976 **GP** *020

GARCIA, Joseph E. 3708 JEFFERSON ST, # 102 78731 #048-12-1985 L1986 **GS** *020 †85

GARCIA, Pamela. 1101 W 40TH ST, JEFFERSON STREET FAMILY PR 78756 #048-12-1985 L1986 **FM** *020 †18

GARCIA, Patrick R. 1313 RED RIVER ST STE 303 78701 #048-02-1996 L1999 **IM** *020 †20

GARCIA, Pete. 805 E 32ND ST STE 103, 9103 SCOTTISH PASTURES COV 78705 #048-04-1977 L1980 **IM** *020

GARCIA, Sandy L. 4900 MUELLER BLVD 78723 #048-12-1991 L1998 **PD** *020 †55

GARMON, Gregg Wesley. 3724 JEFFERSON ST STE 114 78731 #048-04-1978 L1978 **P** *071

GARRETT, James Stanley. 901 W BEN WHITE BLVD 78704 #048-14-1981 L1981 **FM** *020 †18

GARZA, Aldo Azael. ■ 78748 #649-02-1992 **GE** *100 †20

GARZA, David Alberto. 900 E 30TH ST STE 315 78705 #005-18-1974 L1976 **CD** *020 †20

GARZA, Devin Martin. 11111 RESEARCH BLVD, STE 450 78759 #048-13-1989 L1993 **OBG** *020 †30

GARZA, Diane Sue. 3508 FAR WEST BLVD, FL 2 78731 #048-02-1991 L1992 **PD** *020 †55

GASAL, Mary E. 2909 N INTERSTATE 35 78722 #039-01-1984 L1988 **OBG** *020 †30

GASIC, Slavisa. ■ 78701 #957-02-1991 L2006 **HO** *100

GATES, Rodney Elliott. 8140 N MOPAC EXPY, BLDG 3 78759 #025-01-1991 L1995 **AN** *020 †05

GAUDIN, Paul Brooks, II. 9200 WALL ST 78754 #025-01-1990 L2000 **ATP** *020 †50

GAUR, Sunita Parasher. 3828 S 1ST ST 78704 #495-05-1989 L1998 **IM** *020 †20

GAVANDE, Shaila Sampat. ■ 78731 #495-01-1967 L1975 **GP PD** *020 †55

GECK, Matthew Joseph. 3001 BEE CAVE RD, STE 200 78746 #056-05-1996 L2002 **OSS** *020 †40

GEIGER-DOW, Joan E. 11111 RESEARCH BLVD 78759 #048-12-1988 L1990 **IM** *020 †20

GENUNG, John Allen. 12411 HYMEADOW DR, STE 3B 78750 #048-12-1967 L1967 **ORS** *020 †40

GEORGE, Constance Elaine. 1600 W 38TH ST, STE 321 78731 #056-06-2002 L2008 **P** *020

GEORGE, Jaya K. ■ 78723 #048-13-2006 **PD** *012

GEORGE, Timothy Merrill. 1301 BARBARA JORDAN BLVD, STE 307 78723 #035-19-1986 L2006 **NS PD** *020 †25

GESSLER, Donald Jos. 8303 N MO PAC EXPY, STE 450 78759 #019-02-1967 L1983 **FM** *071 †18

GETMAN, William Francis. 6835 AUSTIN CENTER BLVD 78731 #047-05-1994 L1999 **CCP** *020 †55

GETTO, Christopher Alan. 3705 MEDICAL PKWY, STE 570 78705 #041-07-1998 L2002 **AN** *020 †05

GEYER, Darren E. 4534 W GATE BLVD, STE 108 78745 #048-14-1989 L1990 **FM ESM** *020 †18

GHAURI, Arshad. 1201 W 38TH ST 78705 #704-21-1985 L2001 **IM** *020 †20

GHIDONI, John Jos. 8229 SHOAL CREEK BLVD #101 78757 #048-15-1983 L1983 **D** *020 †15

GHODSI, Ezam. 1301 BARBARA JORDAN BLVD, STE 200 78723 #517-01-1979 L1990 **CHN PD** *020 †55,75

GIGLIOTTI, Osvaldo Steven. 4207 JAMES CASEY ST, STE 215 78745 #041-12-1995 L2006 **IC** *020 †20

GILBERT, Michele H. 12201 RENFERT WAY, STE 215 78758 #048-02-1996 L2000 **OBG** *020 †30

GILBEY, Laura Kathryn. 12201 RENFERT WAY STE 260 78758 #048-04-1995 L1996 **PCC** *020 †20

GILBEY, Sean Craig. 4007 JAMES CASEY ST, B-200 78745 #017-20-1995 L1998 **PCC** *020 †20

GILL, Ellis Charles. 1500 W 38TH ST STE 20 78731 #048-12-1970 L1970 **PD** *020 †55

GILLAR, Patricia Jo. 3210 LAFAYETTE AVE 78722 #048-13-1991 L1992 **END** *020 †20

GILLILAND, Robt Mc Murtry. 4110 GUADALUPE ST 78751 #048-02-1978 L1978 **P** *020 †75

GLASS, Gary. 4601 SPICEWOOD SPRINGS RD, BODG 4 STE 200 78759 #035-45-1973 L1979 **P** *020 †75

GLASS, Paul F, Jr. ■ 78735 #048-04-1946 L1946 **CHP PD** *071

GLASSCOCK, Michael E. ■ 78723 #047-06-1958 L1961 **OTO** *071 †45

GLAWE, Jane Marie. 3828 S 1ST ST, AUSTIN REGIONAL CLINIC 78704 #018-03-1998 L1999 **FM** *020 †18

GLAZE, Sylvia S. 4515 SETON CENTER PKWY, STE 220 78759 #048-12-1984 L1985 **FM** *020 †18

GLAZENER, Stanton W. ■ 78703 #048-02-1955 L1955 **IM** *071

GLAZENER, Wesley S. 1305 W 34TH ST, STE 206 78705 #048-14-1988 L1990 **PD** *020 †55

GLEN, Mildred. 1600 W 38TH ST STE 321 78731 #048-02-1952 L1957 **P** *071

GLENN, Lisa Biry. 2802 WEBBERVILLE RD 78702 #048-12-1987 L1988 **FM** *030 †18

GLOMB, William Brendle. 3305 NORTHLAND DR 78731 #048-02-1986 L1987 **PDP SME** *020 †20

GMITTER, Richard C. 720 W 34TH ST, STE 101 78705 #048-13-1994 L1995 **EM** *020 †16

GODELL, Chris M. 8217 SHOAL CREEK BLVD 78757 #048-02-1999 L2005 **GE** *020 †20

GODSY, Jennings Tyson. ■ 78754 #048-13-2005 **P** *012

GOEHRS, Homer R. 919 E 32ND ST 78705 #048-04-1950 L1950 **RHU IM** *071 †20

GOLDBERG, Edwyn Irving. 900 W 38TH ST, STE 100 78705 #048-12-1970 L1970 **DR** *020 †80

GOLDBERG, Tyler D. 4700 SETON CENTER PKWY, STE 200 78759 #048-12-1998 L2004 **ORS** *020 †40

GOLDBLATT, David. 11011 RESEARCH BLVD 78759 #038-41-1980 L1988 **R DR** *020 †80

GOLDEN, J Stephen. ■ 78746 #048-12-1972 L1972 **GE IM** *020 †20

GOLDSTEIN, Gary Edward. 1215 RED RIVER ST # 427 78701 #048-13-1998 L2001 **PM** *020 †60

GONZALES, Mary Anastasia. 1215 RED RIVER ST # 427 78701 #048-13-1998 L2001 **PM** *020 †60

GONZALEZ, Juan Carlos. 4200 MARATHON BLVD STE 200, FUTURE SEARCH TRIALS 78756 #048-04-1990 L1991 **P** *020 †75

GONZALEZ, Oscar. 7112 ED BLUESTEIN BLVD, STE 155 78723 #264-01-1954 L1971 **FM** *020 †18

GONZALEZ, Peter W. 2600 VIA FORTUNA STE 410 78746 #048-02-1988 L1990 **CHP** *020 †75

GOOCH, Michelle Cabray. 1301 W 38TH ST, STE 205 78705 #048-15-2002 L2006 **OBG** *020

GOOLSBY, James Philip, Jr. 3801 N LAMAR BLVD, STE 300 78756 #047-05-1969 L1978 **CD** *071 †20

GORCHS, Andrew C. 2901 MONTOPOLIS DR 78741 #048-13-1993 L2000 **IM** *020 †20

GORDON, Anne. ■ 78735 #048-13-1996 L1999 **FM** *100

GORDON, Ashley Elizabeth. 901 W 38TH ST, STE 400 78705 #021-05-1998 L2006 **PS** *020 †40

GORDON, Francois Antoine. 720 W 34TH ST 78705 #048-04-1995 L1997 **EM** *020 †16

GORDON, Henri. ■ 78763 #035-19-1963 L1969 **IM GPM** *020 †20

GORE, Arthur James. 2909 N INTERSTATE 35 78722 #007-02-1980 L1985 **OBG** *020 †30

GORMAN, Mary Gwen. ■ 78731 #048-13-1986 L1988 **EM** *020 †18

GORMAN, William H. 3003 BEE CAVE RD, STE 203 78746 #048-15-1975 L1975 **PS HS** *020 †65

GOSWAMI, Vivek J. 11149 RESEARCH BLVD, BLDG 1 78759 #305-01-2000 L2007 **CD** *020

GOWDA, Suma Sanjay. 12328 CENTRAL PARK, STE 205 78732 #496-35-1994 L2006 **IM** *020 †20

GRAD, Michael Scott. 2200 PARK BEND DR, STE 300 78758 #011-02-1998 L2002 **IC** *020 †20

GRAHAM, Robert Duane, II. 12201 RENFERT WAY, STE 355 78758 #036-07-1997 L2003 **ORS** *020 †40

GRANT, Earl Lee. ■ 78703 #048-02-1958 L1958 **AN** *071

GRANT, James Adrian. 14415 OWEN TECH BLVD, AUSTIN BIO MED LAB 78728 #016-11-1954 L1955 **BBK OM** *071

GRANT-JENNINGS, Grace A. 12221 N MO PAC EXPY 78758 #048-02-1994 L1996 **IM HOS** *020 †20

GRAS, Troy W. 12221 N MO PAC EXPY 78758 #026-08-2000 L2004 **AN** *020 †05

GRAVES, Ernest D, III. 4208 MEDICAL PKWY 78756 #021-05-1982 L1988 **CRS GS** *062 †85,10

GRAVES, Glenn Richard. 2555 WESTERN TRAILS BLVD, STE 101 78745 #048-12-1968 L1968 **FM** *020 †18

GRAY, Barbara Lynne. 12233 RANCH ROAD 620 N, STE 202 78750 #048-02-1984 L1985 **FM** *020 †18

GRAY, Carlos E. 2900 S I H 35 78704 #737-01-1971 L1980 **IM** *020 †20

GRAY, Mark Badollet. 10900 STONELAKE BLVD, STE 250 78759 #017-20-1975 L1984 **R** *020 †80

GRAYSON, David D, Jr. 720 W 34TH ST 78705 #048-14-1981 L1981 **EM FM** *020

GREENWAY, Larry Don. 1015 E 32ND ST, STE 101 78705 #048-12-1961 L1961 **ORS** *020 †40

GREGORY, Charles Hardy. ■ 78746 #035-01-1957 L1957 **IM EM** *072

GREMMEL, Gregory S. 919 E 32ND ST 78705 #048-13-1997 L2001 **EM** *020 †16

GRETZINGER, Thomas. 12211 ANDERSON MILL RD 78726 #048-02-1964 L1964 **D DMP** *020 †15

GRIER, Mark. 10710 RESEARCH BLVD 78759 #016-11-1998 L2006 **PD** *020 †55

GRIFFIN, Charles Berlin. 2901 MONTOPOLIS DR, OUTPATIENT CLINIC 78741 #011-02-1984 L1997 **IM** *020 †20

GRIFFIN, Moya M. 3705 MEDICAL PKWY, STE 250 78705 #048-14-1996 L2001 **GS** *020 †85

GRIFFIN, Robert A. 3708 JEFFERSON ST, STE 102 78731 #048-14-1976 L1976 **IM** *030 †20

GRIFFITHS, Frederick E A. ■ 78739 #065-01-1954 L1978 **FM AI** *071

GRIGGS, Mary Richardson. 1313 RED RIVER ST STE 100, AUSTIN MED EDUC PROGRAMS 78701 #036-08-2001 L2005 **FSM** *020 †18

GRIGGS, Stephen Randal. 1500 W 38TH ST, STE 20 78731 #048-12-1967 L1967 **PD** *020 †55

GRIMES, Andrew Edward. 3705 MEDICAL PKWY, STE 570 78705 #048-14-1988 L1989 **AN** *020 †05

GRIMES, Julie A. 4101 JAMES CASEY ST, STE 330 78745 #048-16-2002 L2006 OBG *020
GRIMES, Wilford A. 7600 CHEVY CHASE DR, STE 500 78752 #039-01-1950 L1957 U *071 †95
GRIMSHAW, Beverly. 6937 N IH 35 STE 400 78752 #048-14-1987 L1988 FM *020 †18
GROGHAN, Meghan Jennifer. ■ 78748 #007-02-2006 PD *012
GROGONO, Sally Margaret. 1301 W 38TH ST, DRS DESROSIERS & WERNECKE 78705 #021-01-1995 L1999 OBG *020 †30
GROS, Albert Thad. 4007 JAMES CASEY ST, STE A250 78745 #048-04-1976 L1976 OBG *020 †30
GROSS, Cathy Lowder. 3705 MEDICAL PKWY STE 5 78705 #048-13-1981 L1982 AN *020 †05
GROVES, Robert Lester. 1301 W 38TH ST, STE 60 78705 #048-02-1973 L1973 IM *020 †20
GRUNDY, David Lynn. 1305 W 34TH ST, STE 206 78705 #048-15-1984 L1986 PD P *020 †55
GUCKIAN, James Collins. 1601 RIO GRANDE ST, STE 340 78701 #048-02-1962 L1962 IM ID *071 †20
GUDE, Warren Wm. 2604 SAINT ANTHONY ST 78703 #048-12-1992 L1996 FSM EM *020 †16
GUDEWICH, Rhonda Marie. ■ 78703 #024-07-1987 L1990 IM *020 †20
GUEDEA, Tom R. ■ 78759 #649-14-1978 *100
GUERAMY, Timothy Cyrus. 1301 W 38TH ST, STE 102 78705 #025-07-1996 L2004 ORS *020 †40
GUERRERO, Juan Manuel. 3508 FAR WEST BLVD, FL 2 78731 #048-12-1981 L1981 PD *020 †55
GUERRERO, Laura J. 3300 W ANDERSON LN, CENTER, SUITE 308 78757 #048-13-1977 L1977 IM *020 †20
GUINN, Rebecca Lynn. ■ 78728 #048-15-2005 OBG *012
GUNLOCK, Michael G. 10900 STONELAKE BLVD, STE 250 78759 #048-04-1994 L1997 DR *020 †80
GUNN, Holly C. 3705 MEDICAL PKWY, STE 570 78705 #041-01-1990 L1998 AN *020 †05
GUNN, Mark L. 3705 MEDICAL PKWY, STE 570 78705 #048-14-1984 L1998 AN GS *020 †05
GUNTER, Patricia A. 900 E 30TH ST STE 303 78705 #048-04-1983 L1986 GYN *020 †30
GUPTA, Ajay Kumar. 1101 W 40TH ST, JEFFERSON STREET FAMILY PR 78756 #048-13-1994 L1995 FM *020 †18
GUTIERREZ, Emilio, Jr. 4400 RED RIVER ST 78751 #048-14-1986 L1988 FM PD *020 †18
GUTIERREZ, Jaime A. #1 MUIRFIELD GREENS LAND 78738 #275-01-1960 L1965 AN PUD *020
GUTIERREZ, Maria G. 800 W 34TH ST STE 201 78705 #048-02-1992 L1993 AI IM *020 †20,03
GUTIERREZ, Michael L. 1009 E 40TH ST 78751 #048-02-1989 L1990 FM *020 †18
GUTIERREZ-SCHIEFFER, Y M. 12221 N MO PAC EXPY 78758 #048-12-1989 L1990 OBG *020 †30
HAAS, Jacqueline Joan. 9200 WALL ST 78754 #033-05-1993 L2000 PTH *072 †50
HAAS, Michael Rudolph. 720 W 34TH ST STE 101, EMERGENCY SERVICE PARTNERS 78705 #048-12-1982 L1983 EM *020 †16
HAAS, Michelle Saenz. 1015 E 32ND ST, STE 405 78705 #048-14-1997 L1998 PD *020 †55
HABENICHT, David Wm. 901 W BEN WHITE BLVD 78704 #048-15-1984 L1989 EM *020 †16
HADDEN, Gregory M. 720 W 34TH ST, STE 101 78705 #048-04-2002 L2005 EM *020 †16
HAEST, John Marion. 3800 S CONGRESS AVE STE A 78704 #048-12-1981 L1981 FM *020 †18
HAFKIN, Barry. ■ 78755 #048-13-1973 L1973 ID IM *050
HAFKIN, Jeffrey Samuel. PO BOX 29750 78755 #048-04-2001 L2004 IM *020 †20
HAGEMAN, James Moffett. 3724 JEFFERSON ST STE 111 78731 #048-02-1984 L1985 P CHP *020 †75
HAHN, James Sancho. 631 W 38TH ST, STE 2 78705 #048-13-1990 L1991 FM *020 †18
HAJI, Amina Karim. 500 E 7TH ST 78701 #048-16-2001 L2004 FM *020 †18
HALDEN, William Jos. 1301 W 38TH ST STE 309 78705 #048-02-1952 L1952 PD *020 †55
HALFANT, Kerri Ann. ■ 78759 #048-12-1994 L2002 P *074 †75
HALL, Truly Peterson. 1301 W 38TH ST, STE 109 78705 #048-14-2003 L2005 IM *020 †20
HAMERSLEY, Shannon Philip. 2712 WHITIS AVE, APT C 78705 #061-01-1999 L2005 *100
HAMILL, Deborah L. 12221 N MO PAC EXPY 78758 #048-14-1996 L1998 AN *020
HAMILTON, Renee Christine. ■ 78730 #048-13-2008 *012
HAMLIN, Thomas Allen. 504 LAVACA ST, STE 850 78701 #048-12-1976 L1978 P CHP *030 †75
HAMMER, Jo Bess. 2911 MEDICAL ARTS ST, STE 19A 78705 #048-04-1976 L1976 OBG *020 †30
HAMMER, Richard D. 9200 WALL ST 78754 #045-01-1988 L1996 PTH *020 †50
HAMMER, Roy David. ■ 78731 #048-04-1977 L1977 P *020
HANFT, Valerie Nicole. 6836 BEE CAVE RD, STE 111 78746 #036-07-1998 L2005 D *020 †15
HANNA, Constance Irene. 6104 S 1ST ST, STE 102 78745 #048-02-1972 L1972 FM PTH *020 †18
HANNA, Nancy Dafashy. 3501 MILLS AVE, DEPT OF PSYC 78731 #915-07-1983 L2005 P *100 †75
HANSARD, Lisa J. 6500 N MO PAC EXPY, STE 1-1200 78731 #048-16-1989 L1990 REN *020 †30
HANSCHEN, Stephen Richard. 3708 JEFFERSON ST, STE 102 78731 #048-13-1978 L1983 GS *020 †85
HANSEN, Fred Wild. PO BOX 49368 78765 #048-02-1958 L1958 GYN *071 †30
HANSEN, James Edward. 3724 EXECUTIVE CENTER DR, STE G10 78731 #025-12-1981 L1987 NS *020 †25
HANSER, Naomi. 2909 N INTERSTATE 35 78722 #035-47-1994 L2000 IM *020 †20
HANSON, Robert Emile. 8401 N IH 35, STE 200 78753 #047-07-1967 L1973 OBG *020 †30
HANZELKA, Keeli Ann. 601 E 15TH ST, BRACKENRIDGE HOSPITAL EMER 78701 #048-02-2004 L2007 EM *020
HARAWAY, Erin Ashley. 919 E 32ND ST 78705 #048-12-2002 L2004 EM *100 †16
HARDEMAN, Stephen Walter. 11410 JOLLYVILLE RD, BLDG 1 78759 #048-12-1980 L1980 U *020 †95
HARDEN, Roger Arthur. 11623 ANGUS RD STE 11 78759 #023-07-1978 L1982 AI IM *020 †20,03
HARDWICK, Wayne Randol. 3100 RED RIVER ST 78705 #048-12-1972 L1972 ORS *071 †40
HARDY, Dan H. 9200 WALL ST 78754 #048-04-1986 L1991 PTH *020 †50
HARDY, Linda Kerr. ■ 78746 #048-04-1983 L1983 *020
HARFORD, Paul Henry. 1305 W 34TH ST 78705 #048-14-1983 L1983 CCM PUD *020 †20
HARGRAVE, Kenneth L. 1500 W 38TH ST, STE 20 78731 #048-04-1998 L2001 PD *020 †55
HARKINS, John Gehring. 313 E 12TH ST, CAPITAL OBSTETRICS & 78701 #055-01-1993 L1995 OBG *020 †30
HARO, Julian Lowell. 900 W 38TH ST STE 400 78705 #021-05-1974 L1977 PME AN *020 †05
HARPER, Clio A, III. 801 W 38TH ST 78705 #039-01-1988 L1995 OPH *020 †35
HARPER, Clio Armitage, Jr. 801 W 38TH ST, AUSTIN RETINA ASSOC 78705 #047-05-1963 L1967 OBG *071 †30
HARPER, Michael T. 4316 JAMES CASEY ST, STE 110 78745 #048-13-1990 L1991 DR *020 †80
HARRINGTON, C Bennett, Jr. 601 E 15TH ST 78701 #048-12-1980 L1981 EM IM *020 †16
HARRIS, Cynthia Ellis. ■ 78739 #047-07-1985 L1991 OPH *020
HARRIS, David K. 3001 BEE CAVE RD, STE 200 78746 #048-12-1988 L1992 PM *020 †60
HARRIS, David Kent. 3705 MEDICAL PKWY, STE 570 78705 #048-13-1983 L1984 AN EM *020 †05
HARRIS, Rubin Wayne. 10308 VAN WINKLE CT 78739 #047-07-1983 L1989 IM *020
HARRISON, Christine. 8140 N MO PAC EXPY 78759 #051-01-1988 L1995 AN PAN *020 †05,55
HARRISON, Robert Harvel. ■ 78758 #004-01-1945 L1945 P *071 †75
HARSHAW, David Hare. 601 E 15TH ST 78701 #041-01-1957 L1969 HNS GS *020 †85
HART, Margaret K. 3807 SPICEWOOD SPRINGS RD, AUSTIN DERMCARE 78759 #048-13-1999 L2003 D *020 †15
HART, Steven Broyles. 825 E RUNDBERG LN, STE B1 78753 #021-06-1996 L1999 FM *020 †18
HARTLEY, Taylor Lowe. 7610 W HIGHWAY 71 STE F, HOUSE CALL MED MGMT INC 78735 #048-15-2001 L2004 IM *020
HARWOOD, Consuelo Emma. ■ 78733 #649-02-1984 FM *020
HASLUND, Karen. 1305 W 34TH ST, STE 210 78705 #048-02-1982 L1983 PD *020 †55
HASSON, Newton Earl. 4310 JAMES CASEY ST STE 3C 78745 #036-07-1977 L1982 ORS *020 †40
HATFIELD, Jason Thatcher. 900 WEST AVE, CAPITOL EMERGENCY ASSOCIAT 78701 #019-02-2000 L2004 EM *020
HATHAWAY, Alecia Anne. 1100 W 49TH ST 78756 #023-12-1982 L1985 PHP GPM *062 †70
HATHAWAY, Deborah K. 3112 WINDSOR RD, STE A # 239 78703 #048-13-2000 L2003 FM *020 †18
HATRIDGE, Eleanor Travis. 12221 N MO PAC EXPY 78758 #048-13-1997 L2004 AN *020 †05
HATRIDGE, John Irvin. 12221 N MO PAC EXPY 78758 #048-02-1980 L1980 AN *020 †20,05 ‡
HAUGER, Sarmistha Bhaduri. 1301 BARBARA JORDAN BLVD, STE 200 78723 #016-43-1976 L1996 PD ID *020 †55
HAUSER, Lawrence Allan. 1600 W 38TH ST, STE 404 78731 #048-13-1981 L1982 P *020 †75
HAUSER, Michele A. 3724 JEFFERSON ST STE 207, FRANKLIN SQ BLDG 78731 #048-14-1986 L1987 P CHP *020 †75
HAUSER, Ronald Joseph. 1433 FAIRFIELD DR 78758 #048-02-1962 L1962 P N *072 †75
HAUSMAN-COHEN, Sharon R. 11149 RESEARCH BLVD, STE 210 78759 #024-01-1993 L1996 FM *020 †18
HAWKINS, Michael Murphy. 1250 CAPITOL BLVD BLDG 1, STE 400 78746 #048-12-1975 L1997 OBG *030 †30
HAYAT, Jabeen. ■ 78705 #704-16-1983 L2007 CHP *100
HAYDON, Hans Peter. 6835 AUSTIN CENTER BLVD 78731 #048-02-1980 L1980 IM *020 †20
HAYDON, M Scott. 3003 BEE CAVE RD STE 203 78746 #048-02-1994 L2002 PS *020 †65
HAYES, David Wayne. 900 E 30TH ST, STE 315 78705 #019-02-1984 L1992 CD IM *020 †20
HAYES, Royce Daniel. 3705 MEDICAL PKWY, STE 570 78705 #048-12-2000 L2005 PAN *020 †05
HAYHURST, Russell Alan. 901 W 38TH ST, STE 303 78705 #048-14-1988 L1991 OPH *020 †35
HAZLEWOOD, Robert Emmett. ■ 78701 #048-02-1965 L1965 P OS *072
HEAD, Jerald L. 2171 WOODWARD ST # B 78744 #048-13-1988 L1990 AN *020
HEDRICK, David Spicer. ■ 78746 #049-01-1961 L1967 R *020 †80
HEFNER, James Friedrich. ■ 78746 #048-14-1982 L1983 EM *020 †16
HEGDE, Amita S. ■ 78759 #048-13-1993 L2001 IM *020 †20
HEGDE, Sanjay Sudhakara. 3705 MEDICAL PKWY, STE 570 78705 #036-07-1993 L2000 AN *020 †05
HEILMAN, Stephen Robt. 4110 GUADALUPE ST, TX DEPT OF MHMR 78751 #048-04-1973 L1973 GP P *020
HEINRICH, Eric M. 1015 E 32ND ST, STE 200 78705 #048-15-1998 L1999 ORS *020 †40
HEINZE, Everett G, Jr. 12221 N MO PAC EXPY, STE 24 78758 #035-20-1963 L1972 N IM *020 †20,75
HEISER, Albert Leo. ■ 78745 #038-06-1952 L1966 P *071
HEISLER, Gerald P. 1918 E RIVERSIDE DR 78741 #048-14-1987 L1988 FM *020 †18
HELD, Theodore N. 313 E 12TH ST, CAPITAL OBSTETRICS & 78701 #048-02-1992 L1993 OBG *020 †30
HELDT, Sara Lynn. ■ 78705 #048-04-2006 D *012
HELLERSTEDT, Beth A. 6204 BALCONES DR 78731 #041-12-1997 L2003 HO *020 †20
HELLERSTEDT, John W. 4900 MUELLER BLVD 78723 #041-12-1978 L1980 PD *020 †55
HELMER, Richard Earle, III. 11111 RESEARCH BLVD, STE 400 78759 #048-02-1971 L1971 HEM ON *020 †20
HELMS, Thomas Parker. ■ 78731 #048-12-1981 L1981 LM AN *062 †05
HEMKUMAR, Sasikala. 4101 JAMES CASEY ST, STE 350 78745 #495-59-1993 L2003 OBG *020 †30
HEMLOCK, Camille. 701 W 51ST ST 78751 #035-06-1986 L1993 IM P *020 †75,20
HEMPHILL, Ross Seymour. 6101 BALCONES DR, STE 300 78731 #048-12-1975 L1977 IM *020 †20
HENDEE, Robert Wm, Jr. ■ 78739 #007-02-1961 L1962 PD NS *071 †25
HENDERSON, Jeffrey L. 720 W 34TH ST STE 101, EMERGENCY SERVICE PARTNERS 78705 #048-14-2003 L2006 EM *020 †16
HENDERSON, Thomas Thoman. 3410 FAR WEST BLVD STE 140 78731 #048-12-1973 L1979 OPH *020 †35
HENDRIX, Jay Anthony. 801 W 34TH ST, STE 101 78705 #048-12-1986 L1991 D IM *020 †20,15
HENGES, David Faulkner. 11603 JOLLYVILLE RD # 101 78759 #048-02-1965 L1966 HS ORS *071 †40
HENNIGAN, Henry W, Jr. 10900 STONELAKE BLVD STE 2, AUSTIN RADIOLOGICAL ASSOCI 78759 #021-05-1966 L1972 R *020 †80
HERBERT, Jeffrey Raymond. 9200 WALL ST 78754 #048-14-1997 L2002 PTH *020 †50
HERLIN, George Louis. 901 W BEN WHITE BLVD 78704 #048-02-1975 L1975 AN *020 †05
HERMAN, Roberta Marie. 11651 JOLLYVILLE RD # 150 78759 #025-07-1984 L1987 IM FM *020 †20
HERNANDEZ, Brandan. 12221 N MO PAC EXPY 78758 #048-02-1992 L1993 AN *020 †05
HERNANDEZ, Mary Josephine. 6101 E OLTORF ST, DARSIDDS SAMC 78741 #048-13-1977 L1978 OPH *030 †35
HERNE, Kathleen B. 6836 BEE CAVE RD, STE 111 78746 #048-14-1993 L1994 D DS *020 †15
HERRMAN, Kristy K. ■ 78738 #048-12-2001 L2004 NPM *020 †55
HERRON, Jannifer G. 3215 STECK AVE, STE 100 78757 #048-13-1999 L2004 CHP *020 †75
HERZOG, Ld Radcliff. 12221 N MO PAC EXPY 78758 #003-01-1990 L1994 AN *020 †05
HESTER, Stasha S. ■ 78731 #048-04-2004 L2007 PD *100 †55
HEWITT, Kimberly M. 1015 E 32ND ST, STE 205 78705 #048-13-2001 L2007 OTO *100
HEWITT, Steven Spencer. 12221 N MO PAC EXPY 78758 #049-01-2003 L2007 AN *020
HEYTENS, Jill Barstow. 900 W 38TH ST, STE 350 78705 #024-05-1989 L1995 N OM *020 †75
HICKS, Anthony M. 4100 DUVAL RD, STE 4-202 78759 #039-01-1987 L1993 OM PTX *020
HICKS, James Mackey. 7600 N CAPITAL OF TEXS HWY, STE A 78731 #048-02-1974 L1974 OTO FPS *020 †45
HIGGS, Paul C. ■ 78734 #048-02-1949 L1950 P PHP *072 †75
HILL, Alex Stephens. 1206 NUECES ST 78701 #004-01-1961 L1975 PYA P *020

■ = Address Information Privacy Protected

HILL, Larry Wayne. 6101 W COURTYARD DR 78730 #039-01-1964 L1972 **R OS** *020 †80
HILL, Malone Vincent, Jr. 1301 W 38TH ST, STE 102 78705 #048-02-1971 L1971 **ORS** *020 †40
HILL, Meagan R. 601 E 15TH ST, DEPT OF FAMILY MEDICINE 78701 #048-14-2005 L2007 **FP** *012
HILL, Thomas Andrew. 1015 E 32ND ST STE 406 78705 #048-02-1972 L1972 **N** *020 †75
HILLMAN, Farrell Arlen. ■ 78758 #048-02-1956 L1956 **P N** *020
HIMES, Richard Singer. 12221 N MO PAC EXPY 78758 #051-01-1973 L1979 **AN** *020 †05
HINE, Louis Kennedy. 3828 S 1ST ST 78704 #048-13-1983 L1983 **IM PHP** *020 †20
HINE, Peter Wm. 4007 JAMES CASEY ST # D140 78745 #048-03-1990 L1991 **PD** *020 †55
HINES, Lorissa Lyn. 1111 W 34TH ST 78705 #048-16-2002 L2005 **PD** *020 †55
HINES, Peter Bryson. ■ 78732 #048-16-2002 L2007 **NEP** *100 †20
HINES, Timothy Reed. 408 W 45TH ST, CENTRAL TEXAS KIDNEY ASSOC 78751 #048-04-1986 L1988 **IM** *020 †20
HINMAN, Charles Rhodes. 8868 RESEARCH BLVD STE 601 78758 #027-01-1979 L2000 **IM** *020 †20
HIRSCH, Glenn David. 4111 MARATHON BLVD STE A 78756 #047-05-1974 L1977 **P** *020 †75
HITT, Curtis Lee. 11410 JOLLYVILLE RD, BLDG 1 78759 #048-12-1967 L1967 **U** *020 †95
HOANG, Thi D. ■ 78751 #048-04-1992 L1993 **IM** *020
HODDE, Lefayne Anell. 11113 RESEARCH BLVD 78759 #048-04-1985 L1986 **EM** *020 †16
HODES, Kristyn Tiffany. ■ 78746 #041-14-1994 L2002 **FM** *020 †18
HOELSCHER, David D. 7551 METRO CENTER DR, STE 200 78744 #048-12-1989 L1990 **IM** *050 †20
HOELSCHER, Ronald L. 10900 STONELAKE BLVD, STE 250 78759 #048-02-1987 L1988 **DR** *020 †80
HOFMANN, Robert Francis. 601 E 15TH ST 78701 #016-06-1974 L1982 **OPH GPM** *020 †35
HOGG, John. 10900 STONELAKE BLVD, STE 250 78759 #048-04-1989 L1990 **FM** *020 †80
HOLDEMAN, Michael Louis. ■ 78759 #048-12-1988 L1997 **PAN** *020 †20,55,05
HOLLEY, Ariel Eden. ■ 78731 #051-04-2006 **OBG** *012
HOLME, Josef Edward. 1221 W BEN WHITE BLVD, STE 100B 78704 #048-04-1995 L1997 **FM** *020 †18
HOLT, Dudley Byron. 900 E 30TH ST STE 311, PEDIATRIC CARDIOLOGY OF AU 78705 #048-13-2000 L2007 **PDC** *020 †55
HOLT, Richard Mc Gregor. 601 E 15TH ST, BRACKENRIDGE/SPECIALTY CAR 78701 #048-02-1970 L1970 **PD** *020 †55
HOLZMAN, Grace Austin. 1301 W 38TH ST, STE 514 78705 #004-01-1993 L1997 **PD** *020 †55
HOLZMAN, Steven. 6818 AUSTIN CENTER BLVD, STE 206 78731 #048-14-1988 L1989 **PS** *020 †65
HOOD, Jerry L. 901 W BEN WHITE BLVD 78704 #019-02-1976 L1982 **IM PD** *020 †55,20
HOOD, Megan Grimmet. 919 E 32ND ST 78705 #047-06-2003 L2006 **EM** *020 †16
HOOD, Stefan Patrick. 919 E 32ND ST 78705 #047-06-2003 L2006 **EM** *020 †16
HOODA, Madhu. 10401 ANDERSON MILL RD, STE 110B 78750 #495-69-1995 L2005 **FM** *020 †18
HOOI, Emily Elizabeth. 4101 JAMES CASEY ST, STE 300 78745 #038-40-2000 L2004 **OBG** *020 †30
HOOPER, Patrick Andrew. 3705 MEDICAL PKWY STE 57, CAPITOL ANESTHESIOLOGY ASS 78705 #048-02-1998 L2000 **AN** *020
HOOTKINS, Robert. 12221 N MO PAC EXPY 78758 #048-12-1985 L1986 **NEP IM** *020 †20
HOPKINS, David Gordon, Jr. 3705 MEDICAL PKWY STE 570 78705 #025-01-1965 L1972 **AN** *020 †05
HOPKINS, Gary Alan. 601 E 15TH ST 78701 #005-12-1996 L1999 **EM** *020 †16
HORAN, John Jos. 3100 RED RIVER ST 78705 #050-02-1985 L1992 **U** *020 †95
HORN, Albert B, III. 711 W 38TH ST # F 78705 #048-02-1976 L1976 **N** *020 †75
HOROWITZ, Barry Louis. ■ 78746 #034-01-1972 L1977 **DR IM** *020 †80
HOROWITZ, Barry Scot. 10900 STONELAKE BLVD, STE 250 78759 #035-46-1987 L1988 **IM END** *020 †20
HORTON, Diana Millman. 4207 JAMES CASEY ST, STE 302 78745 #048-12-1990 L1991 **IM** *020 †20
HORTON, Jack. 8204 BRODIE LN, STE 101 78745 #048-12-1991 L1992 **PD** *020 †55
HORTON, Rodney Paul. 1301 W 38TH ST, STE 705 78705 #048-12-1988 L1989 **CD ICE** *020 †20
HORVIT, Padma Krothapalli. 12501 HYMEADOW DR STE 1C 78750 #048-04-1992 L1993 **END** *020 †20
HORWITZ, Jeffrey Ronald. 1410 N I H 35 STE 100 78701 #048-02-1987 L1988 **PDS** *020 †85
HOUGH, Travers Eugene. 78755 #048-12-1956 L1957 **FM AN** *071 †18
HOUSER, Elizabeth E. 11410 JOLLYVILLE RD, BLDG 1 78759 #048-13-1987 L1988 **U** *020 †95
HOUSTON, Everett B, Jr. 8140 N MO PAC EXPY 78759 #048-12-1984 L1985 **AN** *020 †05
HOUSTON, Stephen Douglas. 4419 FRONTIER TRL, STE 110 78745 #048-13-1973 L1973 **D** *020 †15
HOVERMAN, Claire Elizabet. ■ 78703 #048-13-2008 #012
HOVERMAN, Isabel Vreeland. 3407 GLENVIEW AVE 78703 #036-07-1972 L1978 **IM** *020 †20
HOVERMAN, John Russell. 6204 BALCONES DR, TEXAS ONCOLOGY CANCER CENT 78731 #036-07-1971 L1977 **ON HEM** *030 †20
HOWARD, Donald Lester. 12221 N MO PAC EXPY 78758 #048-02-1969 L1969 **R** *071 †80
HOWARD, Earl Winfield. ■ 78701 #048-02-1969 L1969 **GS** *075 †85
HOWELL, Sean S. 1301 W 38TH ST, STE 700 78705 #048-01-2004 L2008 **P** *012
HOWERTON, Ernest E, Jr. 2610 S I H 35 78741 #048-02-1973 L1973 **OPH** *020
HOWLAND, George R, Jr. 4110 GUADALUPE ST, AUSTIN STATE HOSPITAL 78751 #048-14-1992 L1993 **CHP** *020
HOWLAND, William Charles, III. 10801 N MO PAC EXPY, STE 150 78759 #048-02-1981 L1981 **AI IM** *020 †20,03
HSIEH, Dale P. 3501 MILLS AVE 78731 #048-15-2004 L2006 **P** *012
HSU, Chia W. 4310 JAMES CASEY ST STE 4A, AUSTIN GASTROENTEROLOGY 78745 #132-01-1991 L1999 **GE** *020 †20
HSU, Connie Ichih. 10900 STONELAKE BLVD, STE 250 78759 #048-12-1997 L1999 **VIR** *020 †80
HU, Xiaoyi. 601 E 15TH ST 78701 #242-75-1998 **IM** *012
HUANG, Patti Chiasue. 7600 N CAPITAL OF TEXS HWY, STE A 78731 #036-07-1994 L1999 **OTO** *020 †45
HUANG, Philip P. 1100 W 49TH ST, TEXAS DEPT OF STATE HEALTH 78756 #048-12-1986 L1987 **PHP FM** *030 †18
HUANG, Wei-Li. 9200 WALL ST 78754 #048-13-1984 L1994 **ATP CLP** *020 †50
HUDSON, Jerome James. 2499 S CAPITAL OF TEXS HWY, STE B100 78746 #048-02-1974 L1974 **PD** *020 †55
HUDSON, John Douglas. 4200 MARATHON BLVD, STE 310 78756 #048-02-1963 L1963 **N SME** *020 †75 ‡
HUG, Henry Robert. PO BOX 9249 78766 #132-04-1956 L1968 **TS VS** *071 †85,90
HUGHES, Francis Howard. 100 W DEAN KEATON ST, UNIVERSITY OF TEXAS HEALTH 78712 #048-12-1966 L1966 **FM** *020 †18

HUGHES, Robert Scott. 11111 RESEARCH BLVD, STE 475 78759 #048-13-1979 L1979 **OBG** *020 †30
HUGHES, Thomas Edward, Jr. 1100 W 39TH 1/2 ST, CAPITAL PEDIATRIC GROUP 78756 #041-12-1967 L1973 **PD MG** *020 †55
HULL, Felix. 2911 MEDICAL ARTS ST, STE 16 78705 #048-04-1976 L1976 **OBG** *020
HULL, James Miller. 6835 AUSTIN CENTER BLVD 78731 #048-14-1981 L1981 **IM** *020 †20
HUME, Andrew Tucker. 1010 W 40TH 78756 #027-01-1989 L1992 **TS** *020 †85,90
HUMMELL, Matthew Kimberly. 400 W 15TH ST, STE 800 78701 #048-13-1986 L1988 **NS** *020 †25
HUMMER, Michael Gorman. 711 W 38TH ST, BLDG F 78705 #039-01-1973 L1985 **N** *020 †75
HUNT, Thomas Lynn. 7551 METRO CENTER DR, STE 200 78744 #048-13-1983 L1983 **IM** *020
HURD, Stephen Chas. ■ 78735 #048-04-1979 L1979 **IM** *030 †20
HURLEY, Donna Schroeder. 12201 RENFERT WAY, STE 225 78758 #048-02-1979 L1980 **OBG** *020 †30
HURT, Bruce Alan. ■ 78746 #048-12-1973 L1973 **PTH** *071 †50
HURT, Joel Harborth. 4700 SETON CENTER PKWY, STE 200 78759 #048-12-1999 L2004 **OSM** *020 †40
HUTCHENS, Mark H. 3200 RED RIVER ST, STE 201 78705 #048-12-1984 L1985 **FSM FM** *020 †18
HUTH, Robert Gordon. 601 E 15TH ST 78701 #010-01-1986 L1988 **ID IM** *040 †20
HYDARI, Irfan H. 720 W 34TH ST, STE 101 78705 #048-15-2001 L2004 **EM** *020 †16
HYDE, Carolyn Morrow. 4700 SETON CENTER PKWY, STE 200 78759 #048-15-1986 L1988 **ORS** *020 †40
HYDE, William Harold. 601 E 15TH ST, RM L502 78701 #030-05-1975 L1984 **NPM PD** *020 †55
HYDER, Rishad. 3801 N LAMAR BLVD 78756 #047-07-2001 L2006 **EM** *020
IBACH, Harold F. ■ 78759 #056-05-1951 L1952 **R NM** *071 †20
IBANEZ, Kent Ernest. 10900 STONELAKE BLVD, STE 250 78759 #030-06-2000 L2006 **DR** *100 †80
IFESINACHUKWU, Francisca. 4131 SPICEWOOD SPGS, STE L2 78759 #690-06-1990 L2001 **P CHP** *020
IMM, Mitchell Dongjun. 10647 BRAMBLECREST DR, THE WOMEN'S HOSP OF GREENS 78726 #001-02-1996 L2007 **NPM** *020 †55
IMMKEN, Ladonna Lynn. 1301 BARBARA JORDAN BLVD, STE 200 78723 #028-03-1977 L1983 **PD CG** *020 †55,19
IN, Kwang-Il. 1313 RED RIVER ST STE 303 78701 #048-13-2003 L2006 **FM** *100 †18
INGRAM, Wayne Wadell. 711 W 38TH ST STE G4 78705 #025-07-1974 L1977 **GYN REN** *020 †30 ‡
INMAN, William Buford. 1301 W 38TH ST, STE 60 78705 #048-16-1984 L1985 **IM** *020 †20
ISLAM, Nazmul. ■ 78750 #160-02-1988 **END** *100 †20
ISLAM, Nazrul. 1600 W 38TH ST, STE 415 78731 #160-01-1988 L2002 **P** *020
ISLAM, Tanzina A. ■ 78750 #048-14-1999 L2007 **FM** *020 †18
ITAYA, Sharon S. 2529 S 1ST ST 78704 #005-18-1975 L1980 **IM** *075 †20
IZOR, Robert M. 12201 RENFERT WAY, STE 360 78758 #048-14-1999 L2003 **N** *020 †75
IZUNDU, Christine Ifeyinw. ■ 78741 #048-04-2007 **PD** *012
JABEEN, Sarwat. 601 E 15TH ST 78701 #704-16-1999 **FP** *012
JACKNOW, Gerald. 9200 WALL ST, CLINICAL PATHOLOGY LAB 78754 #025-01-1978 L1984 **PTH** *020 †50
JACKSON, James M. ■ 78703 #048-12-1987 L1988 **EM** *020 †16
JACKSON, Oscar B, Jr. 3509 LAWTON AVE 78731 #048-02-1971 L1971 **PO OPH** *020 †35
JACKSON, Philip Clay, Jr. 1301 W 38TH ST, STE 109 78705 #048-01-1995 L2003 **IM** *020 †20
JACKSON, Robert Michael. 8240 N MO PAC EXPY, STE 350 78759 #048-14-1983 L1983 **D** *020 †15
JACKSON, Thomas I. 601 E 15TH ST, BRACKENRIDGE HOSP 78701 #048-02-1998 L2005 **EM** *020 †16
JACOBSON, Karen Ann. 10611 MACMORA RD 78758 #048-14-1981 L1981 **EM GP** *020
JAEHNE, Robert Jennings. ■ 78752 #048-04-1935 **OS** *075
JAHANGIRI, Farnaz. ■ 78727 #048-12-2003 L2007 **OBG** *100
JAKKULA, Partha Saradhi. ■ 78753 #495-21-1963 L1974 **FM PD** *020 †55
JAMES, Jeffree Augusta. 3232 E MARTN LTHR KNG JR 78721 #005-18-1976 L1981 **IM** *020 †20
JAMES, Larry Wayne. 11770 JOLLYVILLE RD 78759 #021-05-1971 L1976 **A** *020 †55
JAMES, Sherri Yvette. 12129 RANCH ROAD 620 N, STE 600E 78750 #011-02-1992 L1994 **FM** *020 †18
JANG, Zeeyoung Theresa. 12221 N MO PAC EXPY 78758 #011-02-1998 L2004 **AN** *020
JANISH, Kelly Michelle. ■ 78749 #048-15-2008 #012
JANKOWSKI, Renee Ann. 601 E 15TH ST BOX 44 78701 #011-02-1989 L1999 **CCP PD** *020 †55
JANNAPUREDDY, Sai Kavitha. 601 E 15TH ST, AUSTIN MED EDUC PROG-SETON 78701 #495-57-2002 **N** *012
JANSA, Frances J Hanrahan. ■ 78730 #048-02-1950 L1950 **FM LM** *071 †05
JAQUA, Jamie L. ■ 78759 #046-01-2007 **PD** *012
JARRATT, Michael Taylor. 8140 N MO PAC EXPY, STE 3-130 78759 #048-12-1966 L1966 **D** *020 †15
JAYAWANT, Amar Mark A. 6500 N MO PAC EXPY, STE II-2207 78731 #036-07-1993 L2007 **TS** *020 †85,90
JEBSEN, Robert Harry. ■ 78759 #035-08-1956 L1957 **PM** *071 †60
JEFFERY, Jacqueline Anne. 1201 W 38TH ST 78705 #035-08-1971 L1976 **EM** *020 †16
JEKOT, Jeffrey M. 12221 N MO PAC EXPY 78758 #048-02-1983 L1983 **AN** *020 †05
JENG, Dana. 12505 HIGH MEADOW DR 78750 #048-15-1999 L2002 **D** *020 †15 ‡
JENNINGS, F Lamont, Jr. ■ 78705 #017-20-1947 L1961 **PTH** *071 †50
JEPSON, Bryan Layne. 3001 BEE CAVE RD, STE 120 78746 #049-01-1995 L2006 **EM** *020 †16
JEWELL, Janet N. 6835 AUSTIN CENTER BLVD 78731 #021-05-1988 L1992 **FM** *020 †18
JHAVERI, Ravi Jay. 10900 STONELAKE BLVD, STE 100 78759 #048-04-1995 L1996 **VIR** *020 †80
JHAVERI, Ravi Ramesh. 10900 STONELAKE BLVD, STE 250 78759 #035-47-1996 L1996 **PDI** *020 †55
JINDAL, Priti Vijay. 1301 W 38TH ST, STE 109 78705 #422-01-2001 L2006 **IM** *100
JOBE, Jeffrey Scott. 1010 W 40TH 78756 #048-15-1979 L1979 **VS GS** *020 †85
JOE, Emily May. 2501 W WILLIAM CANNON DR, STE 401 78745 #048-04-2002 L2007 **PME AN** *020 †05
JOGI, Vikas. ■ 78756 #496-17-1996 L2008 **IMG** *100 †20
JOHANNSEN, Lee Cal. 901 W BEN WHITE BLVD 78704 #018-03-1993 L1998 **EM** *020 †16
JOHN, George L. ■ 78746 #048-12-1950 L1950 **GP OS** *071
JOHN, Paul W. 11671 JOLLYVILLE RD, STE 202 78759 #048-13-1989 L1992 **FM** *020 †18
JOHNSON, Charles Ernest. 10900 STONELAKE BLVD, STE 250 78759 #018-03-1991 L1996 **P** *020 †75
JOHNSON, Don Emery. 3705 MEDICAL PKWY, STE 530 78705 #038-41-1964 L1981 **HS ORS** *020 †40

JOHNSON, Gregory Leigh. 4314 MEDICAL PKWY STE 200, CHILDRENS CARDIOLOGY ASSOC 78756 #030-06-1989 L1996 **PDC** *020 †20,55
JOHNSON, Martha Elizabeth. 7107 SPURLOCK DR 78731 #016-02-2008 *012
JOHNSON, Mary Marvin. 4700 SETON CENTER PKWY, STE 125 78759 #036-05-1977 L1982 **PD PHO** *020 †55
JOHNSON, Neal D. 11651 JOLLYVILLE RD, STE 100 78759 #048-04-1982 L1983 **FM** *020 †18
JOHNSON, Tamina E. 4316 JAMES CASEY ST, STE 110 78745 #048-02-1993 L1994 **DR** *020 †80
JONES, Alison Rhea. 2901 MONTOPOLIS DR 78741 #048-13-1993 L1994 **ADP P** *020 †75
JONES, Corey Robert. 919 E 32ND ST 78705 #036-01-1999 L2002 **EM** *020 †16
JONES, David Garfield. 6406 N I H 35, STE 1805 78752 #047-07-1967 L1968 **FM PHP** *020 †18
JONES, Donna Pulido. ■ 78750 #016-43-1989 L1989 **PD** *020
JONES, Harry Lamar, Jr. 3901 MEDICAL PKWY, STE 200 78756 #048-02-1972 L1972 **GS** *020 †85
JONES, Jacob A. 900 WEST AVE, CAPITAL EMERGENCY ASSOCIAT 78701 #048-12-2003 L2006 **EM** *020 †16
JONES, John K. 6012 W WILLIAM CANNON DR, STE B101 78749 #048-13-1989 L1990 **OS PS** *020
JONES, Kenneth James. 3705 MEDICAL PKWY STE 5 78705 #048-02-1980 L1980 **AN** *020 †05
JONES, Kent Paul. 1301 W 38TH ST, STE 109 78705 #016-06-1989 L1998 **OTO** *020 †45
JONES, Lisa Day. ■ 78759 #048-13-1986 L1987 **P** *020 †75
JONES, Patsy. 2113 E MARTN LTHR KNG JR, STE 106 78702 #048-12-1979 L1979 **FM** *020 †18
JONES, Sarah L. 2499 S CAPITAL OF TEXS HWY, STE B100 78746 #048-14-2000 L2003 **PD** *020 †55
JONES, Stacy L. 3705 MEDICAL PKWY, STE 570 78705 #048-13-1989 L1992 **AN** *020 †05
JONES, William Edward. 3301 NORTHLAND DR STE 211 78731 #048-02-1970 L1970 **FM** *020 †18
JORDAN, Dowdell Wylie. 3600 GREAT HILLS 150W 78759 #048-02-1964 L1964 **P** *020
JOSEPH, David G. 3508 FAR WEST BLVD, FL 2 78731 #048-13-1987 L1988 **FM** *020 †18
JOSEPHS, Michael David. 1301 BARBARA JORDAN BLVD, STE 400 78723 #010-02-1994 L2002 **PDS** *020 †85
JOSEPHS, Shana Lea. ■ 78756 #048-04-2006 **P** *012
JOSEY, Robert Anthony. 1015 E 32ND ST, STE 505 78705 #048-04-1998 L1999 **ORS** *020 †40
JOSHI, Anand. 1221 W BEN WHITE BLVD, STE 208A 78704 #021-06-1992 L1995 **PM PMM** *020 †60
JOURNEAY, Glen Eugene. ■ 78731 #048-02-1960 L1960 **FM OS** *071 †18
JOYNSON-ADOLPH, Anthony R. 4304 RIMDALE DR 78731 #539-02-1969 L1990 **EM** *020 †16,05
JUDICE, Stephanie Megna. ■ 78733 #048-04-1987 L1988 **P CHP** *020 †75
JUKES, Lisa M. 5508 W HIGHWAY 290, STE 207 78735 #048-12-1996 L1998 **GYN** *020 †30
JULIAN, Jerry Don. 1201 W 38TH ST 78705 #048-02-1960 L1960 **ORS OSM** *071 †40
JUREN, Joe Henry. 4005 SPICEWOOD SPGS, A-300 78759 #048-12-1973 L1980 **N IM** *020 †20,75
KADIR, Lamia. 6835 AUSTIN CENTER BLVD 78731 #305-01-2001 L2006 **FM** *020 †18
KAHAN, Jerald Anton. 7551 METRO CENTER DR, STE 300 78744 #035-09-1993 L2007 **HO** *020 †20
KAHN, Anthony. 1301 BARBARA JORDAN BLVD, BLVD, STE 723 #836-01-1983 L1997 **OP** *020 †40
KAHN, Jeffrey Benjamin. 11623 ANGUS RD, AUSTIN EAR NOSE & THROAT 78759 #005-02-1995 L2001 **OTO** *020 †45
KAISER, John F. 8240 N MO PAC EXPY, STE 350 78759 #048-02-1985 L1986 **D AM** *020 †15
KALIDAS, Mamta. 12221 N MO PAC EXPY 78758 #048-14-1995 L2001 **HO** *020 †20
KALPAXIS, James Geo. ■ 78759 #051-01-1974 L1976 **OPH FM** *020 †18,35
KAMPE, Carsten E. 6204 BALCONES DR 78731 #035-45-1988 L1994 **HO HEM** *020 †20 ‡
KANE, Jeffrey S. 1301 BARBARA JORDAN BLVD, STE 200 78723 #048-12-1995 L2001 **CHN** *020 †75
KANG, Roy Chi-Kwang. ■ 78731 #242-17-1944 L1961 **AN** *071
KANGOS, Peter Alexis. 12411 HYMEADOW DR STE 3F 78750 #035-09-1979 L1983 **PD** *020 †55
KANNAN, Vidhya Lakshmi. 601 E 15TH ST 78701 #496-32-2005 **IM** *012
KANSAS, Bryan Todd. 11410 JOLLYVILLE RD, BLDG 1 78759 #021-06-2000 L2006 **U** *020 †95
KAPADIA, Deepti Govind. 8204 BRODIE LN, STE 101 78745 #023-01-1984 L1987 **FM** *020 †18
KAPLAN, Eldrid. 3705 MEDICAL PKWY, STE 550 78705 #836-02-1967 L1978 **OBG** *020 †30
KARAKOURTIS, Mark Harold. 12201 RENFERT WAY, STE 345 78758 #036-01-1992 L2002 **HNS FPS** *020
KARNAZE, Gregory Conrad. 10900 STONELAKE BLVD, STE 250 78759 #019-02-1976 L1983 **VIR DR** *020 †80
KARNIK, Anita Dilip. ■ 78746 #048-16-2006 **P** *012
KARNIK, Dilip Jagannath. 1301 BARBARA JORDAN BLVD 78723 #495-01-1973 L1982 **CHN PD** *020 †55,75
KARNIK, Shubha Dilip. ■ 78746 #495-01-1979 L1983 **CHP AN** *020 †75
KARTHIKEYANI, Kathiresan. 601 E 15TH ST 78701 #495-94-1994 L2008 **N** *012 †20
KASPER, Michael Lawrence. 6204 BALCONES DR 78731 #023-07-1979 L1979 **ON HEM** *020 †20
KAVOUSSI, Keikhosrow M. 4303 JAMES CASEY ST 78745 #517-05-1969 L1982 **GYN REN** *020 †30
KAVOUSSI, Shahryar K. 4303 JAMES CASEY ST STE A 78745 #048-02-2000 L2006 **OBG** *020 †30
KAYE, Miriam Molitch. 4919 WESTVIEW DR 78731 #041-01-1957 L1974 **P** *020 †75
KAYSER, Jackee Dawn. 1301 BARBAR JRDN BLVD #200 78723 #048-13-2000 L2003 **AI** *020 †55,03
KEAHEY, Eric H. ■ 78754 #048-13-2000 L2008 **FM** *100
KECK, Kristopher Aaron. 3705 MEDICAL PKWY, STE 570 78705 #034-01-1992 L2000 **AN** *020 †05
KEE, Robert Chas. ■ 78753 #047-06-1960 L1969 **GS** *071
KEELAND, Kimberly Ruth. 1700 S MO PAC EXPY 78746 #048-14-1982 L1983 **OPH** *020 †35
KEENAN, Patrick Aloysius. ■ 78749 #019-02-1995 L1997 **P** *020
KEINARTH, Paul D. 5222 BURNET RD, STE 200 78756 #048-13-1987 L1988 **FM** *020 †18 ‡
KEITH, Dona Athey. 608 W 31ST 1/2 ST 78705 #034-01-1995 L2003 **P IM** *020
KELINSKE, Marilyn Albers. 11623 ANGUS RD STE 12 78759 #048-02-1977 L1977 **OPH** *020 †35
KELLER, Whitney B. ■ 78751 #048-02-2001 L2005 **OBG** *100 †30
KELLEY, Donald Kyle. 1201 W 38TH ST, PEDIATRIX MEDICAL GROUP OF 78705 #001-02-1987 L1993 **NPM PD** *020 †55
KELLEY, Patrick K. 1010 W 9TH ST 78703 #048-04-1998 L2005 **PS** *020 †65
KELLEY, Richard Dwain. 2416 S LAMAR BLVD STE B, PHYSICIAN'S WAY 78704 #033-06-1993 L2003 **FM** *020 †18
KELLY, Jacqueline Sue. 300 E 8TH ST STE G159, FEDERAL BLDG 78701 #048-02-1978 L1980 **GP** *020
KELSO, Kalin Don. 12221 N MO PAC EXPY, STE 327 78758 #048-16-1992 L1993 **ORS** *020 †40
KEMPER, Craig Martin. 400 W 15TH ST, STE 800 78701 #048-02-1988 L1996 **NS** *020 †25
KEMPER, James V, Jr. 5750 BALCONES DR, STE 200 78731 #048-14-1990 L1992 **OTO** *020 †45
KENDRICK, Allison M. ■ 78705 #043-01-2004 L2007 **IM** *100
KENT, Susan M. 1015 E 32ND ST, STE 405 78705 #048-12-1990 L1992 **PD** *020 †55
KERN, Jonathan W. 4316 JAMES CASEY ST, STE 110 78745 #048-12-1987 L1988 **DR** *020 †80
KERR, David Milton. 715 E 8TH ST 78701 #048-02-1966 L1967 **FM FSM** *071
KERR, Jacqueline Marie. 2811 E 2ND ST 78702 #048-13-1986 L1988 **FM** *020 †18
KERR, Jeffrey Stuart. 1301 BARBARA JORDAN BLVD, STE 200 78723 #048-16-1984 L1985 **CHN** *020 †75,55
KERR, Keith Allen. 601 E 15TH ST, BOX 44 78701 #045-04-1988 L1995 **CCP** *020 †55
KERR, Robert O. 11111 RESEARCH BLVD, STE 400 78759 #041-12-1968 L1974 **ON HEM** *020 †20
KESSLER, David Joshua. 1301 W 38TH ST, STE 500 78705 #041-02-1989 L1990 **CD** *020 †20
KEY, Samuel Newton, III. 900 W 38TH ST STE 340 78705 #041-01-1971 L1975 **OPH GP** *020 †35
KHAMBATI, Munira Abizar. 4007 JAMES CASEY ST, STE D240 78745 #495-17-1996 L2002 **FM** *020 †18
KHAN, Farah Yaqoob. 601 E 15TH ST 78701 #704-16-1997 **FP** *012
KHAN, Ghulam Mustafa. 1631 E 2ND ST STE D, ATCMHMR 78702 #704-16-1991 L2003 **P** *020
KHAN, Sanober. 1301 W 38TH ST, STE 109 78705 #496-39-1994 L2004 **IM** *020 †20
KIBEL, Liane Baidelman. 1313 RED RIVER ST, STE 100 78701 #187-09-1992 L2007 **FM** *020 †18
KIBLER, Elise Louisa Sue. 4100 DUVAL RD, BLDG 4 78759 #048-04-2002 L2005 **PD** *020
KIDD, Jack Clayton. 621 RADAM LN, STE 104 78745 #048-12-1961 L1963 **PD** *071
KIDD, Jennifer R. ■ 78731 #048-15-1992 L1994 **GPM P** *020 †70
KIDD, Rodney Desmond. ■ 78731 #048-15-1994 L2003 **DR** *020 †80
KILBRIDE, Earl John, Jr. 3001 BEE CAVE RD, STE 220 78746 #021-05-1996 L1998 **OSM** *020 †40
KILLIAN, Maie Armstrong. 1301 W 38TH ST STE 514 78705 #048-04-1988 L1989 **PD** *020 †55
KILLIAN, Michael E. 900 E 30TH ST, STE 300 78705 #048-04-1988 L1989 **FM** *020 †18
KIM, Bernard Clement. 3724 JEFFERSON ST STE 212 78731 #048-02-1998 L2004 **P** *020 †75
KIM, John S. 4303 VICTORY DR, VICTORY MEDICAL & FAMILY C 78704 #048-02-1994 L1997 **FM** *020 †18
KIM, Rebecca. ■ 78753 #048-15-2005 **PD** *012
KIM, Ronald Sulhy. 919 E 32ND ST 78705 #023-01-2002 L2005 **EM** *020 †16
KIM, Stanley Hyochon. 12180 N MOPAC STE B 78758 #025-07-1990 L2003 **NS** *020 †25
KIMBROUGH, Amanda N. 601 E 15TH ST, STE 410 78701 #048-13-2004 L2007 **IM** *100
KIMBROUGH, Anthony Curtis. 211 COMAL ST, E AUSTIN HEALTH CTR 78702 #048-02-1972 L1972 **PD** *040 †55
KIMBROUGH, Birch Duke. 901 W BEN WHITE BLVD 78704 #048-13-1974 L1974 **EM GS** *020 †16,85
KINCHELOE, Robert Weldon. 4307 JAMES CASEY ST 78745 #048-12-1981 L1981 **AN** *020 †05
KING, David L. ■ 78750 #064-01-1964 L1979 **FM** *020
KING, Lewis G. 1015 E 32ND ST STE 404 78705 #048-02-1984 L1985 **TS** *020 †85,90
KING, Susan Coroline. 11645 ANGUS RD, STE 3 78759 #063-01-1997 L2001 **FM** *020 †18
KING, Thomas A. ■ 78757 #048-12-1996 L1999 **FM** *020 †18
KIRKHAM, Richard Dean. 201 W STASSNEY LN, PMB 306 78745 #010-02-1980 L1989 **FM** *020 †18
KIRKLAND, Hunter Q. 1314 WESTOVER RD 78703 #048-13-1998 L2004 **TS** *020 †85
KIRKSEY, Thomas David. 2711 BOWMAN AVE 78703 #048-02-1959 L1959 **TS GS** *020 †85,90
KISH, John William. 901 W 38TH ST, STE 100 78705 #041-13-1999 L2005 **DR** *020 †80
KISH, Karen M. 1301 W 38TH ST, MEDICAL PARK TOWER #300 78705 #041-13-1999 L2005 **OBG** *020 †30
KITLOWSKI, Andrew David. 1512 SIRUS CV 78732 #007-02-1999 L2003 **EM** *020
KITZMILLER, George Edward. ■ 78731 #048-04-1962 L1962 **GE** *030 †20
KLEIN, Jefferey Patrick. 3705 MEDICAL PKWY, STE 570 78705 #048-14-1998 L2002 **AN** *020
KLEPPER, Mark Stuart. 1305 W 34TH ST 78705 #028-46-1986 L1987 **PUD CCM** *020 †20
KLOCEK, Jonathan R. 1301 W 38TH ST, STE 601 78705 #048-13-1995 L1996 **IM** *020 †20
KLUGMAN, Yale Lee. ■ 78731 #023-01-1955 L1955 **P CHP** *020
KNAPP, Elizabeth Cheney. 6835 AUSTIN CENTER BLVD 78731 #021-06-1998 L2001 **PD** *020 †55
KNAUTH, Kurt J. 3705 MEDICAL PKWY, STE 570 78705 #048-14-1997 L2002 **AN** *020 †05
KNIGHT, Peter. 4110 GUADALUPE ST, AUSTIN STATE HOSP 78751 #917-19-1957 L1984 **FM FPG** *071 †18
KNOWLES, Lynne Marie. 2911 MEDICAL ARTS ST, STE 13 78705 #030-05-1999 L2003 **OBG** *100 †30
KOCAY, Dean Alphonse. 4007 JAMES CASEY ST, STE B130 78745 #048-02-1979 L1979 **GS AS** *020 †85
KOCEN, Byron Phillip. 12710 RESEARCH BLVD, STE 360 78759 #051-04-1958 L1963 **DBP** *020 †55
KOCKS, Joe D, Jr. 12221 N MO PAC EXPY 78758 #048-12-1988 L1992 **AN** *020 †05
KOCKS, Joe Darryl. 12221 N MO PAC EXPY 78758 #048-02-1959 L1959 **AN** *020 †05
KOCUREK, Jeffrey Neal. 3100 RED RIVER ST 78705 #048-02-1991 L1993 **U** *020 †95
KODACK, Stephanie L. 900 E 30TH ST 78705 #036-01-1974 L1976 **GYN** *020 †30
KOEN, Lyle Dorsey. 601 E 15TH ST 78701 #028-02-1975 L1977 **OPH GP** *020 †35
KOHLI, Nandini. 12201 RENFERT WAY, STE 315 78758 #495-36-1980 L2001 **IM** *020 †20
KOLDA, Timothy Frank. 9200 WALL ST 78754 #048-04-1991 L1992 **SP** *020 †50
KOLTE, Bharati P. 1301 W 38TH ST, STE 109 78705 #495-83-1993 L2000 **IM** *020 †20
KONDUR, Bharathi Prathap. 7112 ED BLUESTEIN BLVD, STE 155 78723 #495-35-1997 L2002 **IM** *020 †20
KONYECSNI, William M. 9701 BRODIE LN, STE 203 78748 #048-13-1995 L1997 **P** *020
KOO, Hyunmo L. 3508 FAR WEST BLVD, FL 2 78731 #048-16-1998 L2001 **FM** *020 †18
KOOPS, Beverly Louise. 1100 W 49TH ST, TEXAS DEPT OF HEALTH 78756 #005-11-1969 L1983 **PD NPM** *030 †55
KOSETICKY, Jirina. ■ 78731 #286-02-1950 L1973 **GP** *071
KRATZER, Shannon Stuart. 9200 WALL ST 78754 #017-20-1992 L1998 **PCP** *020 †50
KRAUSE, Richard Duane. 2901 MONTOPOLIS DR 78741 #030-05-1970 L1990 **IM END** *020 †20
KRAVITZ, Larry Chas. 11111 RESEARCH BLVD, STE 485 78759 #010-01-1979 L1988 **FM** *020 †18
KREISLE, James Edwin, Jr. 1600 W 38TH ST, ASSOCIATES OF AUSTIN 78731 #012-05-1975 L1982 **P** *020 †75
KRENEK, Caryn D. 1015 E 32ND ST STE 203, PLAZA ST. DAVID 78705 #048-02-1992 L1994 **PD** *020 †55
KRIENKE, Russell Brannum. 3828 S 1ST ST, AUSTIN REGIONAL CLINIC PA 78704 #048-04-1978 L1978 **FM** *020 †18

KRIESEL, Kevin John. 1301 W 38TH ST, STE 109 78705 #048-12-1997 L2002 **OTO** *020 †45

KROLL, Glenda Whitaker. ■ 78746 #048-14-1985 L1986 **CHP** *020 †75

KROLL, Kenneth C. 1301 W 38TH ST, STE 60 78705 #048-14-1985 L1986 **IM** *020 †20

KRONBERG, Gregory Mark. 3705 MEDICAL PKWY STE 5 78705 #005-02-1973 L1978 **AN IM** *020 †20,05

KRSTIC, Biljana. 601 E 15TH ST, AUSTIN MED EDUC PROG-SETON 78701 #957-02-1997 L2008 **PCC** *100 †20

KUENAST, Edda Ingeborg. 6101 E OLTORF ST, TX REHAB DISABILITY MED SV 78741 #407-25-1946 L1960 **N P** *071

KUGLEN, Craig Charles. 1201 W 38TH ST 78705 #001-02-1962 L1963 **OPH** *071 †35

KUHLMANN, Terrence Albert. 1007 E 41ST ST 78751 #048-02-1973 L1973 **OBG** *020 †30

KUMAR, Pratima Vijay. 2802 WEBBERVILLE RD, ROSEWOOD ZARAGOSA HEALTH C 78702 #495-05-1995 L1999 **END** *012 †20

KURKTCHIJSKI, Raytcho Gen. ■ 78732 #198-01-1995 **FM** *100 †18

KUTCHER, Mark. 100A WEST 26TH STREET, UNIVERSITY OF TEXAS 78712 #035-08-1981 L1993 **P** *020 †75

KUUSISTO, Karla A. 1430 COLLIER ST 78704 #048-02-1982 L2007 **P** *020 †75

KWUN, Eun K. ■ 78746 #048-13-1991 L1993 **FM** *020 †18

LABARDINI, Mario M. ■ 78726 #649-01-1960 L1977 **U** *020 †95 ‡

LAIBOVITZ, Robert Alan. ■ 78731 #028-02-1971 L1975 **OPH** *071 †35

LAIN, Edward Lewis. 4300 N QUINLAN PARK RD, STE 225 78732 #048-04-2002 L2005 **D** *020 †15

LALL, Asha P. 3708 JEFFERSON ST, STE 102 78731 #048-15-1998 L2001 **FM** *020 †18

LA LONDE, Albert Aeneas. 601 E 15TH ST 78701 #048-02-1942 L1942 **NS** *072 †25

LAM, Leanne Trinh Thu. 1301 W 38TH ST, STE 109 78705 #422-01-2002 L2006 **IM** *020 †20

LAM, Shiva Kumar. 1600 W 38TH ST, STE 422 78731 #495-65-1990 L1998 **CHP** *020

LAMBETH, James E. 900 E 30TH ST, STE 300 78705 #048-14-1989 L1990 **FM** *020

LAMY, Keith Harvey. 1106 CLAYTON LN, STE 102W 78723 #035-47-1985 L2000 **FM** *020 †18

LANDERS, Susan. 1015 E 32ND ST, STE 405 78705 #045-01-1977 L1983 **NPM PD** *020 †55

LANEY, Cleatis Edward. 2000 W ANDERSON LN 78757 #023-01-1960 L1961 **EM** *071

LANEY, Shawn M. ■ 78732 #048-13-1999 L2001 **IM** *020 †20

LANGSTON, William T, Jr. ■ 78746 #012-01-1997 L2004 **PEM** *020

LAUBE, Richard Leonard. 12221 N MO PAC EXPY 78758 #017-20-1980 L1983 **AN CCM** *020 †05

LAURENT, Aziz Lawoyin. ■ 78747 #008-01-1981 L1987 **IM CD** *050 †20

LAVA, Jeffrey Stuart. 10900 STONELAKE BLVD, STE 250 78759 #026-04-1968 L1973 **DR** *020 †80

LAVALLEY, J William Gerar. ■ 78759 #048-04-1986 L1988 **GPM** *020

LAVERTY, David Charles. 1313 RED RIVER ST STE 200, AUSTIN SKELETAL TRAUMA SPE 78701 #018-03-1998 L2004 **ORS** *100 †40

LAVIE, Isaac. 1313 RED RIVER ST, STE 303B 78701 #048-04-2001 L2005 **OBG** *020 †30

LAWRENCE, Silvana Molossi. 4314 MEDICAL PKWY, STE 200 78756 #187-42-1985 L2004 **PD** *020

LAWSON, Janet Denise. 1100 W 49TH ST, TEXAS DEPT. OF STATE HEALT 78756 #048-04-1980 L1980 **OBG** *030 †30

LAY, Jack Francis. ■ 78746 #045-01-1996 L1997 **AN** *020 †05

LEAHY, John Raymond. 10900 STONELAKE BLVD, STE 250 78759 #023-07-1991 L1999 **NM** *020 †20,80,28

LEAKE, David Ray. 6101 W COURTYARD DR, BLDG 5 78730 #048-02-1978 L1978 **RNR DR** *020 †80

LEARY, Joseph M C. 1301 W 38TH ST, STE 109 78705 #048-13-1988 L1993 **OTO** *020 †45

LE BLANC, Hobson E, Jr. 11113 RESEARCH BLVD, SETON NORTHWEST HOSPITAL 78759 #036-05-1983 L2007 **FM** *020 †18

LE BOURGEOIS, Paul A. 901 W BEN WHITE BLVD, DEPT PATHOLOGY 78704 #021-05-1975 L1976 **PTH GP** *020 †50

LEDET, Suzanne Robin. 9200 WALL ST 78754 #021-05-1992 L1997 **PTH** *020 †50

LEE, Ava M. 1631 E 2ND ST, STE B 78702 #048-14-1991 L1992 **P** *020 †75

LEE, Cynthia Jeanne. 4622 BURNET RD 78756 #048-02-1980 L1980 **FM EM** *020 †18

LEE, Edward Young. 901 W BEN WHITE BLVD, DEPT OF EMERGENCY MEDICINE 78704 #035-45-1997 L2002 **EM** *020 †18

LEE, Jonathan Jeong. 12221 N MO PAC EXPY 78758 #033-05-1998 L2003 **AN** *020 †05

LEE, Karen Ling. 100 W DEAN KEATON ST, UNIV HEALTH SERV 78712 #005-19-1977 L1980 **IM GP** *020 †20

LEE, Michelle Tinyen. ■ 78751 #048-14-1999 L2004 **FM** *020 †18

LEEMAN, Daniel James. 1015 E 32ND ST, STE 205 78705 #033-05-1992 L2000 **OTO FPS** *020 †45

LEGETT, Carey, Jr. 2904 SWISHER ST 78705 #048-02-1941 L1941 **OPH** *071 †35

LEGETT, Georgia R Felter. 2904 SWISHER ST 78705 #048-02-1942 L1942 **GYN** *071 †30

LEGETT, Sarah Martin. 1301 BARBARA JORDAN BLVD, STE 200 78723 #028-34-1983 L2005 **PD** *020 †55

LEIBOVICH, Lewis. 901 W BEN WHITE BLVD 78704 #007-02-1977 L1993 **EM FM** *020 †16,18

LEIBOWITZ, Mark Todd. 8501 N MOPAC EXPY, STE 200 78759 #035-46-1982 L1984 **IM** *020 †20

LEIGHTY, Scott James. 12221 N MO PAC EXPY 78758 #011-03-1989 L1996 **AN** *020 †05

LEMASTERS, Paige A Humes. 3508 FAR WEST BLVD, STE 200 78731 #048-02-1988 L1995 **PD** *020 †55

LEON, Stacy Lee. ■ 78703 #048-02-1992 L1993 **CHP** *020 †75

LEONARD, Philip Jos. 711 W 38TH ST STE C6 78705 #048-02-1977 L1977 **N CHN** *075 †75

LEONARD, Thomas Plin. 3307 NORTHLAND DR STE 250 78731 #010-01-1958 L1964 **GS GP** *020 †85

LEONG, Kian V. 1301 W 38TH ST, STE 109 78705 #048-13-1993 L1995 **IM** *020 †20

LEONG, Sharon C. 10710 RESEARCH BLVD, STE 120 78759 #048-13-1994 L1995 **PD** *020 †55

LEROM, Jennifer Anne. ■ 78750 #048-04-1996 FP *012

LESLIE, C Doyle. 1020 W 34TH ST 78705 #048-12-1964 L1964 **OPH** *071 †35

LESSER, Robert David. ■ 78758 #048-17-1978 L1978 **IM PHP** *020 †20

LEUNG, Toan. ■ 78731 #025-01-2000 L2004 **EM** *020

LEVERICH, Walter R. 2555 WESTERN TRAILS BLVD, STE 101 78745 #048-13-1986 L1987 **FM** *020 †18

LEVESQUE, Andre Y. ■ 78728 #048-02-2006 **PS** *012

LEVITAN, Mark. 801 W 38TH ST 78705 #035-08-1985 L1993 **OPH** *020 †35

LEVY, Bruce Allen. 8015 SHOAL CREEK BLVD, STE 118 78757 #041-09-1971 L1980 **LM** *030 †05

LEVY, David Raphael. 500 E 7TH ST 78701 #836-01-1963 L1989 **PD OS** *030 †55

LEVY, Mark J. 2555 WESTERN TRAILS BLVD, STE 101 78745 #048-14-1988 L1990 **FM** *020 †18

LEVY, Moise Leopold. 1301 BARBARA JORDAN BLVD, STE 200 78723 #048-14-1979 L1979 **D PD** *020 †55,15

LEWIS, Douglas Edward. 1020 W 34TH ST 78705 #048-14-1988 L1989 **OPH** *020 †35

LEWIS, Edward Sibley. 11623 ANGUS RD STE 15 78759 #028-02-1971 L1979 **ORS** *020 †40

LEWIS, George Orin. ■ 78747 #016-06-1954 L1977 **OM AM** *071 †70

LEWIS, Richard Michael. 12221 N MO PAC EXPY, EXPRESSWAY NORTH 78758 #050-02-1976 L1987 **NEP IM** *020 †20,95

LIEBERMAN, Allen Keith. 10801 N MO PAC EXPY, STE 150 78759 #035-08-1986 L1994 **AI PD** *020 †55,03

LIEBERMANN, Thomas Robt. 7600 N CAPITAL OF TEXS HWY, STE A 78731 #649-01-1966 L1972 **GE IM** *020 †20

LIGHT, Stacy Sanderson. 3215 STECK AVE, STE 200 78757 #048-12-1999 L2004 **PYG** *020

LIMA, Suzanne Nassar. 12221 N MO PAC EXPY 78758 #048-13-1998 L2000 **AN** *020

LIN, Mona Chiai. 1111 W 34TH ST, STE 200 78705 #024-01-1997 L2005 **GE** *020 †20

LINDSEY, Chas Alfred, Jr. 3200 RED RIVER ST STE 210 78705 #048-12-1966 L1966 **FM IM** *020

LINDSEY, James Otis, II. 1201 W 38TH ST 78705 #028-02-1969 L1970 **IM** *020 †20

LINDSEY, Janet Andrene. 3300 W ANDERSON LN, STE 308 78757 #048-04-1979 L1980 **OPH** *020 †35

LINDSEY, Mark Raymond. 3901 MEDICAL PKWY, STE 200 78756 #048-13-2000 L2005 **GS** *020 †85

LINDSEY, William H. ■ 78738 #004-01-1951 L1952 **IM** *072

LINDSEY, William H. 720 W 34TH ST 78705 #048-15-1995 L1998 **EM** *020 †20

LINES, Marcus L. 10900 STONELAKE BLVD, STE 250 78759 #048-13-1984 L1985 **DR** *020 †80

LINGLE, Susan Josephine. 6835 AUSTIN CENTER BLVD 78731 #005-06-1978 L1981 **PD** *020 †55

LIPELAEZ, Joanne Raquel. ■ 78731 #048-78-1998, ▲ L1999 **PD** *100 †55

LI-PELAEZ, Victor Justo. 711 W 38TH ST STE E3 78705 #056-06-1956 L1971 **PS** *020

LIPPMAN, Glenn. ■ 78733 #003-01-1979 L1981 **P OS** *030 †75

LIPSCHER, Randolph Bruce. ■ 78730 #048-13-1994 L1996 **EM** *020 †16

LISTROM, Margaret Barron. 9200 WALL ST 78754 #051-01-1980 L1991 **PTH** *020 †50

LITTLE, Cathy Leigh. 3508 FAR WEST BLVD, FL 2 78731 #048-02-1982 L1985 **PD** *020 †55

LITTLE, James Hart. 2901 MONTOPOLIS DR, AUSTIN OUTPATIENT CLINIC 78741 #048-02-1982 L1983 **FM** *020 †75

LITTLES, Joel Tyrone. 3705 MEDICAL PKWY, STE 570 78705 #045-01-1999 L2003 **AN** *020 †05

LITZINGER, Jill A. 631 W 38TH ST 78705 #048-04-1991 L1992 **FM** *020 †18

LITZINGER, Linda Jane. 12201 RENFERT WAY, STE 200 78758 #048-13-1985 L1986 **OBG** *020 †30

LIU, Yu-Mei. 10705 BAY LAUREL TRL 78750 #048-14-1990 L1992 **FM** *020 †18

LIVINGSTON, Chas Duncan. 3901 MEDICAL PKWY, STE 200 78756 #048-04-1976 L1976 **GS** *020 †85

LOCKEY, Renee G. 11111 RESEARCH BLVD, STE 334 78759 #048-02-1998 L2002 **OBG** *020 †30

LOCKHART, Lonn Bradley. 1912 W 35TH ST, CHILDREN'S EYE CENTER 78703 #048-02-1980 L1980 **PO OPH** *020 †35

LOCKHART, Sharon K. 1301 BARBARA JORDAN BLVD, STE 401 78723 #048-14-1982 L1983 **PD HEM** *020 †55

LOCUS, Paul Andrew. 4007 JAMES CASEY ST # A240 78745 #048-02-1985 L1986 **OBG GP** *020 †30

LODWICK, Gwilym Savage. 1631 E CESAR CHAVEZ ST 78702 #028-03-1989 L1994 **P** *020

LOEB, Michael Delee. 12411 HYMEADOW DR, STE 3B 78750 #021-05-2000 L2006 **ORS** *100

LOFTUS, Thomas S. 2200 PARK BEND DR, BLDG 2-202 78758 #048-12-1997 L2002 **NS** *020 †25

LOGUE, Henry Elby. ■ 78732 #649-14-1972 L1973 **FM** *020 †18

LOMBAS, Antonio. ■ 78723 #275-01-1946 L1967 **GP** *020

LONERGAN, Gael Joan. 1400 IH 35 N 78701 #023-12-1985 L1992 **DR PDR** *020 †80

LONG, Sharon M. 601 E 15TH ST, BRACKERRIDGE HOSPITAL 78701 #048-16-1992 L1993 **EM** *020 †16

LONGORIA, Mario A. 8701 SHOAL CREEK BLVD, STE 201 78757 #048-02-1999 L2005 **GS** *100 †85

LOOMIS, Richard Mark. ■ 78702 #025-01-2007 **TY** *012

LOOSE, Isaac A. 5717 BALCONES DR 78731 #048-12-1987 L1988 **OPH** *020 †35

LOPEZ, Monica Esperanza. ■ 78749 #048-01-2002 L2007 **PDS** *012 †85

LOPEZ, Ramona Griffith. 4007 JAMES CASEY ST # D140 78745 #048-04-1987 L1988 **PD** *020 †55

LOPEZ-CONCEPCION, Laura L. ■ 78738 #748-02-1992 L2006 **IM** *074 †20

LORE, John. 919 E 32ND ST, HYPERBARIC MEDICINE 78705 #143-01-1957 L1967 **AN OS** *020 †05

LOUIS, Jack Allan. 711 W 38TH ST STE C2 78705 #048-13-1977 L1977 **PD** *020 †55

LOUKAS, Demetrius F, Jr. 11111 RESEARCH BLVD, STE 400 78759 #048-02-1971 L1971 **ON HEM** *020 †20

LOVE, Ian Leslie. 8038 MESA DR 78731 #016-42-1973 L1995 **DR** *020 †80

LOVE, Mikeal R. 900 E 30TH ST STE 107 78705 #048-13-1988 L1990 **OBG** *020 †30

LOVERING, Donald E. ■ 78731 #048-02-1982 L1983 **FM EM** *020 †18 ‡

LOVING, William Monning. 1106 W DITTMAR RD 78745 #048-02-1974 L1974 **P ADM** *020 †75

LOWE, George Walter. 10805 BEACHMONT LN, AUSTIN HEART 78739 #048-02-1966 L1966 **CD** *020 †20

LOWELL, George Gardiner. 2610 S IH 35 78704 #026-04-1966 L1984 **OPH** *020 †35

LOWENSTEIN, Jason Ernest. 3001 BEE CAVE RD, STE 200 78746 #041-12-2000 L2006 **ORS** *100

LOWERY, Brian Douglas. 1821 WESTLAKE DR 78746 #048-04-1965 L1965 **GS TS** *071 †85,90

LOWERY, George Singleton. ■ 78752 #649-12-1957 L1958 **P** *071

LOWREY, Robert Warren. 6835 AUSTIN CENTER BLVD 78731 #021-05-1981 L1984 **PD** *020 †55

LOWRY, Thomas Irvin. 3001 BEE CAVE RD, STE 200 78746 #048-04-1958 L1958 **OSS** *071 †40

LOYD, John D. 1201 W 38TH ST, SETON NEONATAL CENTER 78705 #048-13-1997 L2003 **NPM** *020 †55

LOZANO, Anna Marie. 919 E 32ND ST 78705 #048-13-1981 L1981 **GYN** *020 †30

LUBIN, Craig Howard. 1111 W 34TH ST, STE 200 78705 #039-01-1977 L1983 **GE IM** *020 †20

LUCID, Emily Jean S. 3801 N LAMAR BLVD, AUSTIN HEART HOSPITAL 78756 #048-02-1970 L1970 **EM** *030 †16

LUCKSINGER, Gregg Hudson. 900 E 30TH ST, STE 300 78705 #048-13-1989 L1990 **FM** *020 †18

LUK, John C. 1400 N I H 35, CHILDREN'S HOSPITAL OF AUS 78701 #041-09-1996 L2001 **PD** *020 †55

LUKER, John Alonzo. 4029 S CAPITAL OF TEXS HWY, STE 115 78704 #048-02-1974 L1974 **GP ADM** *020

LUM, James. ■ 78738 #008-01-1955 L1957 **R** *071 †80

LYNN, Cynthia Jene. 1015 E 32ND ST, STE 405 78705 #038-43-1986 L1987 **NPM PD** *020 †55

LYSON, Krzysztof Jerzy. 1015 E 32ND ST, STE 414 78705 #759-09-1980 L1999 **NEP IM** *020 †20

LYSON, Teresa Krystyna. ■ 78730 #759-09-1980 L1999 **IM** *020 †20

LYTTLE, James Arthur. 3705 MEDICAL PKWY, STE 570 78705 #048-13-1994 L1998 **AN** *020 †05

MA, Helen. 4100 DUVAL RD, BLDG 4 78759 #018-75-1994, ▲ L1998 **PD** *020 †55

MAAMAR-TAYEB, Mokhtar. ■ 78752 #048-02-2004 **PTH** *012

MABEN, Sam Edward. ■ 78757 #004-01-1965 L1965 **IM** *071

MABEN, Sue Ann. 10710 RESEARCH BLVD, STE 120 78759 #019-02-1997 L1998 **PD** *020 †55

MAC CONNELL, Terence P. 13831 N HIGHWAY 183 78750 #048-02-1975 L1975 **FM EM** *020

MAGGI, S Pasquale. 3410 FAR WEST BLVD, STE 110 78731 #048-02-1991 L1992 **PS HS** *020 †65

MAGILL, Alfred Morton. 711 W 38TH ST STE B5W 78705 #016-42-1958 L1979 **IM CD** *071 †20

MAGNUSON, Larry Wayne. 3801 S LAMAR BLVD 78704 #039-01-1965 L1981 **GPM OM** *020 †70,18

MAHAN, Anne W. ■ 78704 #048-14-2005 **PD** *012

MAHENDRU, Vivek. 4100 DUVAL RD, BLDG III 78759 #495-43-1989 L1995 **AN PME** *020 †05

MAIDMENT, Helen J. 10000 METRIC BLVD, STE 100 78758 #048-13-1989 L1990 **IM NEP** *020 †20

MAILMAN, Gary Martin. 919 E 32ND ST, HYPERBARIC MEDICAL SERVICE 78705 #038-41-1978 L1995 **UM EM** *020 †16

MAKKENA, Rama. 9617 GREAT HILLS TRL # 431 78759 #495-50-1980 L1993 **IM RHU** *020 †20

MAKSYMOWICZ, Gregory John. 708 W 10TH ST 78701 #035-03-1972 L1973 **P** *020 †18,75

MALCOLM, Douglas Barry. 919 E 32ND ST 78705 #049-01-1986 L1990 **EM** *020 †16

MALDONADO, Humberto Jr. 1301 W 38TH ST, STE 60 78705 #048-12-1995 L1996 **IM** *020 †20

MALIK, Durdana A. 4007 JAMES CASEY ST, STE A150 78745 #704-16-1983 L1997 **PD** *020 †55

MALLESKE, Joseph James. 2555 WESTERN TRAILS BLVD, STE 101 & 102 78745 #038-40-1976 L1977 **FM** *020 †18

MALLETT, Chas Baker, III. 4007 JAMES CASEY ST, STE A200 78745 #048-14-1978 L1978 **FM** *020 †18

MALONE, Charles Bruce, III. 1201 W 38TH ST 78705 #036-07-1969 L1977 **ORS OSM** *020 †40 ‡

MALONE, Mark Thos. 6818 AUSTIN CENTER BLVD, STE 205 78731 #048-12-1982 L1983 **PME AN** *020 †05

MANDALAPU, Bhuvana Prasad. 11111 RESEARCH BLVD, STE 330 78759 #496-24-1990 L2000 **N** *100 †20

MANGIONE, John Stewart. 4106 MEDICAL PKWY 78756 #048-13-1981 L1981 **CRS GS** *020 †10,85

MANI, Jayashree. 1201 W 38TH ST 78705 #495-04-1977 L1988 **PD** *020 †55

MANKOVSKY, Jerald Alan. 3705 MEDICAL PKWY, STE 220 78705 #048-15-1976 L1976 **OBG** *020 †30

MANN, Trudi-Brooke. ■ 78739 #048-13-1995 *100

MANNERBERG, Frederick D. ■ 78701 #039-01-1959 L1975 **NTR GPM** *020

MANNING, John Edward, Jr. 10900 STONELAKE BLVD, STE 250 78759 #035-01-1993 L2001 **VIR** *020 †80

MANROE, Barbara Lee. ■ 78731 #005-11-1971 L1975 **LM NPM** *071 †55

MANSOURI, Azad. ■ 78759 #028-02-2006 L2006 **OPH** *012

MANUEL, Anthony J. 3705 MEDICAL PKWY, STE 570 78705 #048-14-1997 L2002 **AN** *020 †05

MANZANERO, Ronald Michael. 911 W 38TH ST, STE 200 78705 #048-02-1984 L1985 **FM** *020 †18

MANZOOR, Syed Zia. 3501 MILLS AVE, SETON SHOAL CREEK HOSP 78731 #704-16-1992 L2008 **CHP** *012

MARADANI, Sarita. 4007 JAMES CASEY ST, STE D250 78745 #495-21-1984 L2002 **OBG** *020 †30

MARCHAND, Gregory. 4534 W GATE BLVD, STE 108 78745 #034-01-1979 L1985 **FM** *030 †18

MARCUS, Howard Richard. 6835 AUSTIN CENTER BLVD 78731 #024-07-1971 L1982 **IM CD** *020 †20

MAREINISS, Darren Peter. ■ 78750 #035-19-1999 L2000 **GS** *071

MARGOLIN, Steven Philip. 5222 BURNET RD, STE 200 78756 #038-40-1976 L1976 **FM** *020 ‡

MARIETTA, John Robt. 1201 W 38TH ST 78705 #048-04-1977 L1977 **IM** *020 †20

MARKING, George Henry, II. 3828 S 1ST ST 78704 #026-04-1971 L1982 **FM** *020 †18

MARKLEY, Michelle Le. 3708 JEFFERSON ST, STE 103 78731 #048-02-1997 L1999 **FM** *020 †18

MARKOWITZ, Sheldon L. 1301 W 38TH ST, STE 60 78705 #023-01-1967 L1973 **IM** *020 †20

MARKUS, Robert M, Jr. 4007 JAMES CASEY ST # A220 78745 #048-12-1990 L1991 **GS** *020 †85

MARQUEZ, David Michael. 78703 #048-15-1985 L1988 **IM** *020 †20

MARQUEZ, Nancy. 8701 SHOAL CREEK BLVD, STE 201 78757 #048-04-1986 L1987 **GS** *020 †85

MARQUIS, Robert Edward. 5717 BALCONES DR 78731 #048-12-1999 L2003 **OPH** *020 †35

MARROQUIN, Jaclyn Teresa. ■ 78751 #016-43-2006 **PD** *012

MARSHALL, Gordon Patrick. 4310 JAMES CASEY ST, STE 3C 78745 #021-01-1987 L1999 **ORS** *020 †40

MARTIN, David L. 12411 HYMEADOW DR, STE 3A 78750 #048-13-1988 L1989 **FM** *020

MARTIN, Fred R. 12233 RANCH ROAD 620 N, STE 110 78750 #048-14-1984 L1985 **FM** *020 †18

MARTIN, Irma Antoinette. 12233 RANCH ROAD 620 N 78750 #048-04-1983 L1985 **FM** *020 †18

MARTIN, Manuel J. 2555 WESTERN TRAILS BLVD, STE 102 78745 #048-12-1988 L1989 **EM FM** *020 †18

MARTIN, Mary K. 78733 #016-06-1981 L1982 **OBG** *020 †30

MARTIN, Michael Beckett. 6101 W COURTYARD DR, BLDG 5 78730 #004-01-1975 L1981 **DR** *020 †80

MARTIN, Michael Dean. 2901 MONTOPOLIS DR 78741 #048-04-1978 L1979 **IM** *020 †20

MARTIN, Richard B. ■ 78746 #048-12-1982 L1983 **AN** *020 †05

MARTINEZ, Aldrich Aronson. 11645 ANGUS RD, STE 9 78759 #847-06-1959 L1979 *071

MARTINEZ, Cecilia Isabel. 4201 MONTEREY OAKS BLVD, SOUTHERN REGIONAL AHEC 78749 #048-14-2004 L2007 **FM** *020 †18

MARTINEZ, Enrique Antonio. 809 LYDIA ST 78702 #748-08-1974 L1978 **PD** *020

MARTINEZ, George David. 13729 RESEARCH BLVD # 890 78750 #048-13-1980 L1980 **EM FM** *020 †18

MARTINEZ, Jose A. 801 W 38TH ST, STE 200 78705 #048-12-1988 L1989 **OPH OS** *020 †35

MARTINEZ, Jose Alejandro. ■ 78703 #019-02-1991 L1996 **AI** *020

MARTINEZ, Kelly. 6818 AUSTIN CENTER BLVD, STE 105 78731 #048-13-1985 L1995 **GS** *020 †85

MARTZ, Rosalind E. 6603 ROBBIE CREEK CV 78750 #048-04-1995 L1997 **IM** *020 †20

MASARYK, Anthony Michael. 10900 STONELAKE BLVD, STE 250 78759 #038-40-1988 L2000 **DR** *020 †80

MASI, Christopher A. 3215 STECK AVE STE 100 78757 #048-02-1992 L1993 **CHP** *020 †75

MASON, Amy Rominger. 3708 JEFFERSON ST, STE 103 78731 #048-13-2000 L2003 **D** *020 †20,15

MASOOD, Mujahid. 901 W BEN WHITE BLVD 78704 #704-02-1982 L2000 **IM HOS** *020 †20

MASSA, Joseph Anthony. 510 W 29TH ST 78705 #048-02-1954 L1954 **IM PUD** *071

MASSMAN, Andrew Evan. 919 E 32ND ST 78705 #048-12-1974 L1974 **OBG** *020 †30

MASTERS, Matthew E, Jr. ■ 78746 #048-14-1987 L1988 **IM** *020 †20

MATHEW, Betzi Sarah. 7112 ED BLUESTEIN BLVD, STE 100 78723 #048-04-1999 L2002 **PD** *020 †55

MATTA, Shaili Suresh. 1400 IH 35 N, PEDIATRIC RESIDENCY PRG 78701 #048-02-2002 L2005 **PD** *020 †55

MATTINGLY, Arthur Thos. 12221 N MO PAC EXPY 78758 #048-02-1972 L1972 **AN** *020 †05

MAURER, Laura K. 2100 W WILLIAM CANNON DR, STE C 78745 #048-04-1991 L1993 **FM** *020 †18

MAXSON, Robert T. 4900 MUELLER BLVD, DELL CHILDREN'S MEDICAL CE 78723 #048-02-1990 L1998 **PDS** *020 †85

MAXWELL, Aaron C. 601 E 15TH ST, DEPT. OF INTERNAL MEDICINE 78701 #048-04-2000 L2004 **IM** *020

MAXWELL, John Mc Kay. 4207 JAMES CASEY ST, STE 301 78745 #036-05-1979 L1984 **OBG** *020 †30

MAXWELL, Mary Spies. 601 E 15TH ST 78701 #048-15-1985 L1986 **IM** *020 †20

MAY, Robin Renee. 9901 BRODIE LN STE 160 78748 #024-01-1999 L2001 **P** *020 †75

MAYABB, Virgil M, Jr. 3508 FAR WEST BLVD, FL 2 78731 #048-02-1977 L1977 **IM** *020 †20

MAYER, William Danl. 1015 E 32ND ST #041-02-1987 L2000 **GS** *020 †85

MAYFIELD, Jodi Rachelle. ■ 78754 #034-01-2008 *012

MAYNARD, James J. 418 GRACE LN 78746 #048-14-1983 L1983 **P CHP** *020 †75

MAYORGA, Napoleon Ramon. 2901 MONTOPOLIS DR, VA OUT-PATIENT CLINIC 78741 #048-04-1978 L1978 **IM** *020 †20

MAYS, Everett Truman, Jr. 3301 NORTHLAND DR, STE 216 78731 #020-02-1986 L1988 **GP GS** *020

MAZURSKY, Jon Eric. 1015 E 32ND ST, STE 405 78705 #012-05-1989 L1997 **NPM PD** *020 †55

MAZZA, Frank. 1201 W 38TH ST, SETON MEDICAL CENTER 78705 #041-12-1978 L1983 **CCM PUD** *030 †20

MAZZETTI, Robert F. 11615 ANGUS RD STE 104 78759 #005-02-1955 L1956 **ORS** *071 †40

MC CAFFREY, Amy J. 11673 JOLLYVILLE RD, STE 205 78759 #048-02-1983 L1983 **OBG** *020 †30

MC CALEB, William Todd. 11901 JOLLYVILLE RD 78759 #039-01-1991 L1996 **AN** *020 †05

MC CALEB, Wm Edward, III. 12221 N MO PAC EXPY, STE 123 78758 #048-12-1966 L1966 **OPH** *020 †35

MC CARRON, David Lee. 3100 RED RIVER ST, STE 1 78705 #048-02-1962 L1962 **U** *071 †95

MC CARRON, Wm Edwards, Jr. 3801 N LAMAR BLVD STE 300 78756 #048-02-1967 L1967 **CD IM** *071 †20

MC CARTY, Matthew F. 2501 W WILLIAM CANNON DR, STE 401 78745 #039-01-1985 L1986 **APM** *020 †05

MC CARTY, Robyn Ellison. 3200 RED RIVER ST STE 201 78705 #028-02-1991 L1998 **FM FSM** *020 †18

MC CARY, Leigh Susan. 6836 BEE CAVE RD 78746 #048-02-1995 L1998 **FM** *020 †18

MCCLELLAND, Michael L, Jr. 3100 RED RIVER ST 78705 #048-02-1997 L2002 **U** *020 †95

MC CLISH, John C. 2200 PARK BEND DR BLDG 2, STE 300 78758 #048-02-1998 L2004 **IC** *020 †20

MC CLURG, Curtis Alfred. 1600 W 38TH ST, STE 100 78731 #048-12-1968 L1968 **DR** *020 †80

MC COLL, Richard Lones. 3215 STECK AVE # 200, STE 200 78757 #051-01-1997 L2001 **P** *020 †75

MC CORMICK, Annette Saenz. 1015 E 32ND ST, STE 405 78705 #048-13-1990 L1991 **NPM** *020 †55

MC COY, Georgia Anne T. ■ 78704 #041-09-1964 L1977 **P** *071

MC CRANIE, Dolph Barnes. ■ 78739 #005-06-1961 L1962 **GS VS** *071 †85

MC DERMOTT, Michele T. 12221 N MO PAC EXPY 78758 #051-07-1980 L1982 **IM END** *020 †20

MC DONALD, Bruce Bradford. 1201 W 38TH ST 78705 #036-05-1972 L1973 **GS** *020 †85

MC DONALD, George Michael. ■ 78738 #017-20-1968 L1969 **GS** *020 †85

MC DONALD, Newton F, Jr. ■ 78759 #048-02-1948 L1948 **U** *071 †95

MC ELVEEN, Michael S. 901 W BEN WHITE BLVD 78704 #048-04-1978 L1978 **EM** *020 †16

MC FARLAND, David Chas. 3708 JEFFERSON ST STE 102 78731 #048-12-1978 L1978 **GS** *020 †85

MC FARLANE, John Russell. 3705 MEDICAL PKWY, AUSTIN EAR NOSE & THROAT 78705 #048-04-1969 L1969 **OTO A** *020 †45

MC GAHREN, Thomas Jos. ■ 78731 #051-01-1985 L1987 **DR** *020

MC GEE, Amy Padgett. 12221 N MO PAC EXPY 78758 #048-14-1990 L1991 **DR** *020 †80

MC GLATHERY, William T, IV. 4207 JAMES CASEY ST, STE 305 78745 #027-01-2000 L2006 **OPH** *020 †35

MC GRAW, Katherine E. 2802 WEBBERVILLE RD, PEDIATRICS UNIT 3 78702 #048-14-2001 L2004 **PD** *020 †55

MC HORSE, Thomas Steven. 1301 W 38TH ST, STE 402 78705 #048-04-1967 L1967 **GE IM** *020 †20

MC INTYRE, Douglas K. 4201 MARATHON BLVD STE 201 78756 #048-12-1975 L1976 **OBG** *020 †30 ‡

MC INTYRE, Francis E. 2301 W NORTH LOOP BLVD 78756 #048-12-1957 L1958 **FM** *071 †18

MC INTYRE, Kathryn Irene. 2901 BEE CAVE RD, BOX N 78746 #048-02-1980 L1980 **P** *020 †75

MC INTYRE, Randall Wade. 3160 BEE CAVE RD, STE 201 78746 #048-14-1985 L1986 **CHP FM** *020 †75

MC KOWN, Rebecca Jean. 3801 S LAMAR BLVD 78704 #048-02-1981 L1981 **GP P** *020

MC LELLAND, Mark L. 10900 STONELAKE BLVD, STE 250 78759 #048-14-1979 L1979 **DR** *020 †80

MCLOUGHLIN, Ian Daragh. 10900 STONELAKE BLVD, STE 250 78759 #038-41-2001 L2007 **DR** *020 †80

MC MAINS, Merrick J. 13740 N HIGHWAY 183, STE V1 78750 #048-15-2000 L2004 **PD** *020 †55

MC MICHAEL, James Patrick. 3705 MEDICAL PKWY STE 5 78705 #048-13-1970 L1970 **AN** *020 †05

MC MICHAEL, Melinda Cook. 100F W DEAN KEETON ST, UNIV OF TX HSC 78712 #019-02-1978 L1979 **IM** *020 †20

MC MILLAN, Berit Holen. ■ 78704 #048-12-1981 L1981 **CHP** *075 †75

MC MINN, Thomas Robt, Jr. 3801 N LAMAR BLVD, STE 300 78756 #028-02-1990 L1993 **CD IM** *020 †20

MC MULLEN, Douglas Nelson. 5303 MARYANNA DR 78746 #048-14-1978 L1978 **IM IMG** *020 †20

MC NABB, James David. 5011 BURNET RD 78756 #048-02-1969 L1969 **OPH** *020 †35

MC NEESE, Marsha Diane. ■ 78731 #021-05-1974 L1978 **RO** *071 †80

MC NELIS, Stephanie A. 12221 N MO PAC EXPY 78758 #048-04-1998 L2002 **OBG** *020 †30

MC REYNOLDS, Tad Donnice. 720 W 34TH ST, STE 101 78705 #003-01-2000 L2003 **EM** *020

MC WILLIAMS, Bennie C, Jr. 3305 NORTHLAND DR, STE 512 78731 #048-02-1978 L1978 **PDP PD** *020 †55

TEXAS
AUSTIN

MEBANE, William Anthony. 919 E 32ND ST 78705 #021-05-1972 L1975 **OBG** *020 †30
MEDFORD, Rex Eugene. 919 E 32ND ST 78705 #048-16-1988 L1989 **EM** *020 †16
MEDLEY, Ronald L. ■ 78728 #048-15-1994 **CHP** *100
MEDLOCK, Matthew Morris. ■ 78749 #048-12-1994 L2006 **IM** *020 †20
MEDRANO, William. 825 E RUNDBERG LN STE B1, RUNDBERG SQUARE 78753 #005-11-1981 L1984 **FM** *020 †18
MEHARRY, Roger Alvin. 8508 LORALINDA DR 78753 #649-14-1970 L1975 **FM GP** *071
MEHLISCH, Donald Robt. 1025 E 32ND ST 78705 #026-04-1975 L1976 **PA** *050
MEHTA, Nilima N. 1407 W STASSNEY LN 78745 #495-76-1981 L1987 **P CHP** *020 †75
MEIGS, Matthew Montgomery. ■ 78746 #048-02-2001 L2007 **OTO** *020 †45
MEISENBACH, Albert E. 100 W DEAN KEATON ST, UNIVERSITY HEALTH SERVICES 78712 #048-04-1974 L1974 **GP** *020
MEJIA, Jose Wilis. 8038 MESA DR 78731 #308-05-1985 L2006 **CD** *020 †20
MELROSE, Evan Scott. 221 W 6TH ST, STE 700 78701 #017-20-1996 L2004 **FM** *020 †18
MENDELSON, Neil A. 901 W BEN WHITE BLVD 78704 #048-12-1994 L1998 **EM** *020 †16
MENDELSON, Roger Hugh. 4010 N LAMAR BLVD 78756 #048-12-1976 L1976 **OBG** *020 †30
MERCHANT, Malik M. 4515 SETON CENTER PKWY, STE 215 78759 #704-25-1992 L2006 **IM** *020 †20
MERITT, Laura Ann. 12201 RENFERT WAY, STE 205 78758 #004-01-1988 L1992 **OBG** *020 †30
MESSER, Ann Hanes. 7 LAKE TRL 78746 #016-01-1989 L1995 **FM** *020 †18
METCALF, Steven. 3705 MEDICAL PKWY, STE 570 78705 #007-02-1987 L1993 **AN PD** *020 †05,55
MEWHINNEY, Hugh Stephens. 2529 S 1ST ST 78704 #048-13-1983 L1984 **IM** *020
MEYER, Margaret Stirling. ■ 78763 #048-04-1988 L1989 **P** *062 †75
MEYER, Scott David. 1301 W 38TH ST 78705 #048-13-1985 L1987 **IM** *020 †20
MEYER, Tory A. 1301 BARBARA JORDAN BLVD, STE 400 78723 #035-01-1991 L2000 **PDS** *020 †85
MEYERSON, Robert Yale. 3708 JEFFERSON ST, STE 103 78731 #048-02-1980 L1986 **FM** *020 †18
MEYNIG, Jeffrey T. 3901 MEDICAL PKWY, STE 200 78756 #048-14-1989 L1990 **GS** *020 †85
MEZARAUPS, Gunar Gundis. 10900 STONELAKE BLVD, STE 250 78759 #035-01-1973 L1980 **R** *020 †80
MIAN, Tahir Shabbir. 601 E 15TH ST, AUSTIN MED EDUC PROG-SETON 78701 #704-04-2000 L2006 **IM** *100 †20
MICHEL, Jeffrey Bryan. 2200 PARK BEND DR, BLDG 2 78758 #048-12-1990 L1991 **CD** *020 †20
MICHELS, Sheryl Diane. 9200 WALL ST, ATTN WENDY LANG 78754 #012-05-1980 L1990 **PTH HMP** *020 †50
MIHM, Gary James. 12221 N MO PAC EXPY 78758 #056-06-1977 L1984 **AN** *020 †05
MILES, Stacia Christine. 4315 JAMES CASEY ST 78745 #028-03-2002 L2006 **D** *020 †15
MILISCI, Richard E. ■ 78747 #561-17-1966 L1973 **IM** *071
MILLER, Harold Lee. ■ 78703 #048-12-1978 L1978 **IM** *020
MILLER, Hillary Gwen. 3708 JEFFERSON ST, STE 102 78731 #024-01-1982 L1983 **FM OS** *020 †18
MILLER, Lysbeth Wheelus. 601 E 15TH ST, DEPT OF INTERNAL MEDICINE 78701 #048-13-1979 L1979 **IM** *040 †20
MILLER, Neil Elden. ■ 78731 #021-01-1963 L1971 **OTO A** *071 †45
MILLER, Peter Leonid. 1015 E 32ND ST STE 414 78705 #035-47-1982 L1995 **IM NEP** *020 †20
MILLER, Steven E. 12221 N MO PAC EXPY 78758 #048-14-1998 L1999 **AN** *020 †05
MILLER, Tesa Taryn. ■ 78722 #038-44-2005 **OBG** *012
MILLER, Thomas Huff. 12221 N MO PAC EXPY 78758 #048-02-1981 L1981 **AN** *020 †05
MILLIKEN, Martin Curtis. 12221 N MO PAC EXPY 78758 #048-12-1988 L1992 **AN** *020 †05
MILLING, Truman J, Jr. ■ 78731 #048-04-2002 L2005 **EM** *020 †16
MILLS, Joseph E. 1313 RED RIVER ST STE 220, AUSTIN ACADEMIC MEDICINE A 78701 #048-04-1987 L1988 **IM** *020 †20
MILLS, Robert Douglas. 12221 N MO PAC EXPY 78758 #048-15-1983 L1983 **EM IM** *020 †20
MILLS, Tara A. 12201 RENFERT WAY STE 340, RENAISSANCE WOMEN'S GROUP, 78758 #048-14-2000 L2004 **OBG** *020
MILNER, William N. 901 W BEN WHITE BLVD 78704 #048-02-1989 L1990 **EM** *020 †16
MINARD, Evan Enloe. 720 W 34TH ST 78705 #048-02-2000 L2003 **EM** *020 †16 ‡
MINER, George Rufus, IV. ■ 78751 #048-15-2007 **PD** *012
MINGEA, Cynthia Jones. 900 E 30TH ST, STE 303 78705 #048-04-1983 L1983 **OBG** *020 †30
MINGEA, Robert M, III. 900 E 30TH ST, STE 209 78705 #001-02-1981 L1986 **CD IM** *020 †20
MINTEK, Victor Jos. ■ 78748 #016-02-1946 L1947 **P** *071 †75
MINTZ, Uri M. 11044 RESEARCH BLVD, D400 78759 #550-01-1968 L1998 **HO HEM** *020 †20
MIRANDA, David Anthony. 720 W 34TH ST, STE 101 78705 #035-20-1998 L2006 **EM** *020 †16
MIRANDA, Roberto. 110 CHALMERS AVE, STE B 78702 #187-11-1969 L1974 **GS** *020 †85
MIREUR, John Robert. 4316 JAMES CASEY ST, STE 110 78745 #048-12-1994 L1995 **RNR** *020 †80
MIRROP, Samuel A. 1500 W 38TH ST STE 20, OF AUSTIN, P.A. 78731 #048-12-1989 L1991 **PD** *020 †55
MITCHELL, Gary Ralph. 901 W BEN WHITE BLVD 78704 #048-02-1972 L1972 **EM** *020 †16
MITCHELL, Janet Fuscaldo. 10710 RESEARCH BLVD # 120 78759 #048-14-1985 L1986 **PD** *020 †55
MITCHELL, Kenneth White. 12221 N MO PAC EXPY, NORTH AUSTIN MED CTR 78758 #048-14-1985 L1986 **IM HOS** *020 †20
MITCHON, August James. 901 W BEN WHITE BLVD 78704 #048-12-1984 L1985 **EM** *020 †16 ‡
MITTAL, Deepa. 1201 W 38TH ST 78705 #496-04-1995 L2001 **IM** *020 †20
MOELLER, Jan Christen. 4007 JAMES CASEY ST, STE B130 78745 #025-01-1954 L1974 **ORS** *071 †40
MOELLER-RUIZ, Erica M. 3508 FAR WEST BLVD, FL 2 78731 #048-13-1994 L1995 **FM** *020 †18
MOLNAR, Albert Csaba. 1015 E 32ND ST, STE 411 78705 #038-40-1969 L1975 **PM PRS** *020 †60
MOMIN, Inayat Ali. 1301 W 38TH ST, STE 205 78705 #704-25-1999 L2007 **IM** *100 †20
MOMIN, Zahir A. 1301 W 38TH ST, STE 205 78705 #704-08-1989 L2005 **NEP** *020 †20
MONCRIEF, Jack Wesly. 800 W 34TH ST, STE 101 78705 #048-02-1962 L1962 **IM NEP** *020 †20
MONHEIT, Blythe Elizabeth. 901 W 38TH ST, STE 303 78705 #001-02-2000 L2006 **OPH** *020 †35
MONKS, Brian Eugene. 2909 N INTERSTATE 35 78722 #048-14-1987 L1988 **OBG** *040 †30
MONTERO, Karin Elena A. 5114 BALCONES WOODS DR, STE 307-391 78759 #132-02-1980 L1987 **PS** *020 †65
MONTOYA, Juan M. ■ 78745 #264-03-1964 L1974 **AN** *071
MONTS, Jane Lee. 3705 MEDICAL PKWY STE 570 78705 #048-02-1979 L1979 **AN** *071 †05
MOORE, Alan Townes. ■ 78703 #048-12-1976 L1976 **PTH** *020 †50
MOORE, Amanda Jean. 5900 BALCONES DR, STE 160 78731 #038-06-1998 L2001 **EM** *020 †16
MOORE, Charles Thos. 1305 W 34TH ST, STE 408 78705 #048-02-1975 L1975 **IM** *020 †20
MOORE, Joseph Wm. 3724 JEFFERSON ST STE 301 78731 #048-13-1981 L1981 **CHP P** *075
MOORE, Paul Benard. 4315 JAMES CASEY ST 78745 #048-02-1975 L1975 **END IM** *020 †20
MOORE, Sharon. 1301 W 38TH ST, STE 109 78705 #048-12-1975 L1979 **IM** *020 †20
MOORE, Walter Scott. 1015 E 32ND ST STE 414 78705 #048-12-1974 L1979 **IM** *020 †20
MOOREHEAD, Elizabeth Ann. 10900 STONELAKE BLVD, STE 250 78759 #017-20-1995 L1996 **DR** *020 †80
MOOSANI, Aquilla Bashir. 919 E 32ND ST 78705 #704-16-1990 L1995 **PD** *020 †55
MORALES, Hector Elias. 1015 E 32ND ST, STE 212 78705 #649-04-1960 L1971 **GS VS** *071 †85
MORAN, William James. 4201 MARATHON BLVD, STE 204 78756 #048-13-1975 L1975 **GS** *020
MOREHEAD, Charles David. 5914 INTER COUNCIL CV 78731 #048-12-1962 L1962 **PD ID** *071 †55
MOREHEAD, Daniel B. 708 W 10TH ST 78701 #048-16-1994 L2001 **P** *020 †75
MORENO, Alejandro. 601 E 15TH ST, MEDICINE DEPARTMENT 78701 #264-16-1992 L2001 **IM** *020 †20
MORENO, Rosa Alicia. 1301 W 38TH ST, STE 109 78705 #048-12-1983 L1985 **OBG** *020 †30
MORGAN, Arthur Boyd. 3705 MEDICAL PKWY, STE 205 78705 #048-04-1975 L1976 **HNS** *020 †45
MORGAN, Edward Allen. 1910 W 35TH ST 78703 #048-16-1982 L1983 **OBG** *020 †30
MORGEN, Robert O. 805 E 32ND ST, STE 101 78705 #038-06-1949 L1963 **NEP IM** *071 †20
MORITZ, Charles Edwin. 2800 S IH 35, STE 120 78704 #048-14-1984 L1985 **NEP IM** *020 †20
MORLEDGE, David Walker. 711 W 38TH ST F, AUSTIN NEUROLOGICAL CLINIC 78705 #048-15-1986 L1987 **N** *040 †75
MOROZ, Lee E. 3001 BEE CAVE RD 78746 #048-14-2001 L2005 **PM** *020 †60
MORRIS, David Lyonel. 1301 W 38TH ST, STE 500 78705 #048-02-1974 L1974 **CD IM** *020 †20
MORRIS, Francis A, Jr. 3100 RED RIVER ST 78705 #036-07-1952 L1960 **PS PN** *071 †65
MORRISON, Patricia Jeanne. 11111 RESEARCH BLVD, STE 380 78759 #048-13-1977 L1977 **GS** *020 †85
MORRISON, Robert John. 1305 W 34TH ST 78705 #048-12-1988 L1990 **PUD CCM** *020 †20
MORROW, John Michael. 10401 ANDERSON MILL RD, STE 110B 78750 #048-02-1982 L1983 **FM** *020 †18
MORTON, Gary Dale. 1 UNIVERSITY STA # A3500, UNIV OF TX 78712 #048-15-1985 L1986 **P** *020 †75
MOSCOE, Newton Dee. 3705 MEDICAL PKWY STE 460 78705 #028-02-1972 L1979 **PS** *020 †65
MOSIER, Nina F. ■ 78731 #041-09-1988 L1994 **IM** *020 †20
MOSKOVITZ, Wm Sanford. 2911 MEDICAL ARTS ST, STE 20 78705 #041-12-1955 L1964 **GS GP** *020 †85
MOSKOW, John Bruce. 720 W 34TH ST 78705 #048-02-1979 L1979 **EM LM** *020 †16
MOSLEY, Kim Allyson. 3508 FAR WEST BLVD, FL 2 78731 #048-13-1988 L1990 **PD** *020 †55
MOSS, Jennifer M. ■ 78759 #048-02-1995 L1999 **OBG** *020
MOTAL, Lisa Allison. ■ 78704 #048-04-2002 *100
MOTT, Charles Louis. 3508 FAR WEST BLVD, FL 2 78731 #048-02-1968 L1968 **DR** *020 †80
MOUSER, Rebecca E. 8204 BRODIE LN, STE 101 78745 #048-16-1984 L1985 **PD** *020 †55
MOUW, Michael Wayne. 601 E 15TH ST 78701 #048-14-1983 L1983 **EM** *020 †16
MOY, Clifford K. 4507 CAT MOUNTAIN DR 78731 #048-14-1985 L1986 **P MDM** *030 †75
MOY, Julie Graves. 8127 MESA DR, # B206-54 78759 #048-12-1983 L1983 **FM EM** *020 †18
MOYLE, James Wm. 10900 STONELAKE BLVD, STE 250 78759 #025-07-1976 L1986 **DR** *020 †80
MUELLER, Susan Dee. 11728 RED OAK VALLEY LN 78732 #048-14-1986 L1987 **IM** *020 †20
MULCIHY, Casey Thos. 4007 JAMES CASEY ST, STE D200 78745 #048-13-1982 L1983 **PD GP** *020
MULLINS, Charles Brown. ■ 78731 #048-12-1958 L1958 **CD IM** *071 †20
MUMFREY, Paul Douglas, II. 4316 JAMES CASEY ST, STE B101 78745 #021-06-2001 L2005 **OBG** *020
MUNDEN, Herbert Claude. 2100 KRAMER LN, STE 200 78758 #048-02-1977 L1977 **GP** *020
MUNIR, Muhammad. 12414 ALDERBROOK DR, STE 100 78758 #704-05-1984 L2003 **CN** *020 †75
MUNOZ, Abilio. 2115 NORTHLAND DR, MUNOZ FAMILY HEALTH CLINIC 78756 #007-02-1996 L1999 **FM** *020 †18
MUNYON, William Harrison. 4111 MEDICAL PKWY, STE 201 78756 #025-01-1959 L1978 **P NTR** *020 †75
MUQUIM, Ayesha. 4110 GUADALUPE ST 78751 #704-02-1987 L1994 **CHP** *020 †75
MURRAY, John Sinclair. 2911 MEDICAL ARTS ST, STE 18 78705 #048-12-1979 L1979 **IM** *020 †20
MURRAY, Robert V, Jr. 18 MED ARTS SQUARE 78705 #048-02-1945 L1945 **IM OS** *071
MURRY, Scott R. ■ 78759 #048-13-1995 L1997 **P** *020 †75
MUSE, Nina Jo. PO BOX 162563 78716 #048-02-1981 L1981 **P CHP** *062 †75
MUSEMECHE, Catherine Anne. ■ 78751 #048-14-1982 L1983 **PDS GS** *020 †85
MUSHTALER, Jennifer Lynn. 11111 RESEARCH BLVD, STE 450 78759 #048-12-1998 L2000 **OBG** *020 †30
MUZAFFAR, Syema. 8913 COLLINFIELD DR, SETON TOPFER CHC 78758 #704-02-1987 L2001 **PD** *020 †55
MYERS, Joseph Wm. 4101 JAMES CASEY ST, STE 100 78745 #017-20-1973 L1980 **ON HEM** *020 †20
NADER, Paul Chas. 1015 E 32ND ST STE 414 78705 #048-15-1981 L1981 **NEP IM** *020 †20
NAGARAJ, Pankaj. ■ 78746 #496-22-2004 **PD** *012
NAGAVARAPU, Shanti Sony P. 601 E 15TH ST, AUSTIN MED EDUC PROG-SETON 78701 #496-24-1998 L2007 **IM** *100 †20
NAGHAVIANI, Norma Linda. 100 W DEAN KEATON ST POB73, UNIVERSITY OF TX AT AUSTIN 78712 #048-02-1984 L1985 **FM** *020 †18
NAIK, Manish M. 4515 SETON CENTER PKWY, STE 220 78759 #028-46-1992 L1996 **IM** *020 †20
NAIL, Steven Gerald. 4316 JAMES CASEY ST STE B1, HEALING CENTER 78745 #048-13-1983 L1983 **FM** *020 †18
NAIR, Prasanna Kumaran. 7600 N CAPITAL OF TEXS HWY, STE A 78731 #495-36-1970 L1979 **GE** *020 †20
NAKONECHNA, Olena. 3706 S 1ST ST, SETON SOUTH COMMUNITY CTR 78704 #913-10-1993 L2005 **PD** *020
NARAHARI, Shantha Lakshmi. ■ 78728 #495-33-1985 **AN** *100
NARAYANAN, Deepa. ■ 78735 #495-44-1997 L2007 **FM** *100 †18
NAREPALEM, Vakula. 8204 BRODIE LN STE 101 78745 #018-03-1996 L2000 **FM** *020 †18
NARSETE, Thomas Anthony. 630 W 34TH ST 78705 #016-43-1974 L2002 **PS HS** *020 †65
NARULA, Jinny. 601 E 15TH ST 78701 #495-29-2000 **FP** *012
NASH, Felicia B. 1305 W 34TH ST STE 308, WOMEN PARTNERS IN HLTH 78705 #048-14-2001 L2005 **OBG** *020 †30
NASH, Todd Allen. 6402 MESA DR 78731 #048-14-2001 L2005 **EM** *020 †16
NASRI, Hamzeh. ■ 78767 #875-01-1981 L1988 **PDE PD** *075 †55
NATALE, Andrea. 1015 E 32ND ST 78705 #561-06-1985 L2008 **CD** *020 †20

■ = Address Information Privacy Protected

NATARAJA, Sara. 601 E 15TH ST, DEPT OF FAMILY MEDICINE 78701 #036-01-2006 **FP** *012
NAU, Larry Melvin. ■ 78703 #039-01-1968 L1973 **ORS HS** *071 †40
NAUERT, Beth Webb. 3508 FAR WEST BLVD, FL 2 78731 #048-16-1981 L1981 **PD** *020 †55
NAVARRO, Maritza. 12414 ALDERBROOK DR, STE 201 78758 #033-06-1988 L1996 **AI** *020 †03,55
NEAVEL, Celia Beth. 2909 N INTERSTATE 35 78722 #048-04-1985 L1986 **FM ADL** *020 †18
NEEDHAM, David C. 2811 E 2ND ST 78702 #048-02-1982 L1983 **PD** *020 †55
NEELY, Byron Davis. 4314 MEDICAL PKWY 78756 #048-02-1972 L1972 **NS** *020 †25
NEFF, Philip Edward. 1301 BARBARA JORDAN BLVD, STE 401 78723 #028-03-1996 L2006 **PD PHO** *020 †55
NELSON, David Austin. 11111 RESEARCH BLVD, STE LL3 78759 #048-13-1989 L1990 **AN** *020 †05
NELSON, Forrest Murphy. ■ 78723 #048-02-1945 L1945 **AS CRS** *071 †85
NELSON, Jane Carolyn. 6500 N MO PAC EXPY, STE 2-2205 78731 #014-01-1984 L1995 **GS** *020 †85
NELSON, Jefferson Edward. 1600 W 38TH ST, ASSOCIATES OF AUSTIN 78731 #048-04-1973 L1973 **P** *020 †75
NELSON, Paul Brian. 12221 N MO PAC EXPY 78758 #048-04-1991 L1992 **AN** *020 †05
NEMAWARKAR, Anjali Shasha. 12221 N MO PAC EXPY 78758 #496-38-1994 L2003 **IM** *020 †20
NEMETH, William Chas. 7551 METRO CENTER DR, STE 100 78744 #003-01-1973 L1979 **ORS** *020 †40
NEPUSTIL, Ivan Robt. 211 COMAL ST 78702 #038-43-1989 L2007 **IM** *020 †20
NEUHAUS, Russell Wayne. 3705 MEDICAL PKWY, STE 120 78705 #048-04-1976 L1977 **OPH** *020 †35
NEYMAN, Sherry Lamar. 12201 RENFERT WAY, STE 215 78758 #048-12-1992 L1993 **OBG** *020 †30
NGUYEN, Cam Ha Thi. 10401 ANDERSON MILL RD, STE 110B 78750 #048-04-1992 L1993 **PD** *020 †55
NGUYEN, Joe Thanh. 4515 SETON CENTER PKWY, STE 220 78759 #038-40-1994 L1997 **FM** *020 †18
NGUYEN, Michael H. ■ 78753 #048-16-1998 L1999 **EM** *020 †16
NGUYEN, Thanh Tam. 8557 RESEARCH BLVD, STE 128 78758 #941-01-1964 L1980 **GP** *071
NGUYEN, Truong-Chinh Quoc. 601 E 15TH ST, DEPT OBGYN 78701 #048-14-1999 L2002 **OBG** *040
NGUYEN, Tuan Dinh. 1015 E 32ND ST, STE 508 78705 #025-07-2000 L2004 **CD IM** *020
NGUYEN, Vu Dinh. 1015 E 32ND ST, STE 508 78705 #025-07-1998 L2005 **CD** *020 †20
NICHOLS, David Haskell. 10900 STONELAKE BLVD, STE 250 78759 #048-15-1977 L1977 **DR** *020 †80
NICHOLS, Jill Elizabeth. 3508 FAR WEST BLVD, FL 2 78731 #048-12-1991 L1993 **PD** *020 †55
NICOL, Patricia Bailey. ■ 78746 #021-06-1986 L1989 **PD** *020 †55
NICOLAU, John Nicholas. 2610 S IH 35, C/O HOWERTON EYE CENTER 78704 #048-15-2003 L2007 **OPH** *020
NIELSEN, Joy. 7600 N CAPITAL OF TEXS HWY, STE A 78731 #007-02-1995 L2008 **U** *020 †95
NIEMAN, Richard Ernest. 11901 JOLLYVILLE RD 78759 #011-02-1965 L1968 **OPH** *020 †35
NIKITINA, Nina. ■ 78748 #913-04-1941 L1961 **PEM** *071
NIKOLAIDIS, Gregory A. 6836 BEE CAVE RD, STE 111 78746 #048-04-1995 L2002 **D** *020 †15
NITZSCHE, Jeffrey Joel. 12221 N MO PAC EXPY 78758 #030-05-1996 L2000 **AN** *020 †05
NIX, Michael L. 1313 RED RIVER ST STE 303B 78701 #048-12-1998 L2001 **OBG** *040 †30
NOLAN, Patrick C. 12221 N MO PAC EXPY 78758 #016-11-1999 L2004 **CN** *020 †75
NORA, Araceli E. 1015 E 32ND ST, STE 405 78705 #048-02-2003 L2007 **NPM** *100
NORRIS, Robert W. 6705 W HIGHWAY 290, STE 601 78735 #048-02-1982 L1983 **FM** *020 †18
NORTHWAY, Robert Orcutt, III. 6818 AUSTIN CENTER BLVD, STE 201 78731 #012-05-1996 L2002 **U** *020 †95
NORTON, Lydia W. 2499 S CAPITAL OF TEXS HWY, BLDG B 78746 #021-05-1997 L2006 **PD** *020 †55
NORTON, Wallace Berry. 6400 E MARTN LTHR KNG JR # 78724 #048-02-1968 L1968 **P PYA** *020
NORWOOD, Cynthia Ford. ■ 78738 #048-12-1982 L1983 **D** *020 †15
NORWOOD, Stephen Mark. 3003 BEE CAVE RD, STE 201 78746 #048-12-1982 L1983 **ORS OSM** *020 †40
NOSTER, Richard Mc Kinley. ■ 78746 #048-12-1978 L1979 **AN** *020 †05
NOWICKI, Stephen Paul. 6937 N IH 35, STE 120 78752 #048-14-1994 L1995 **FM** *020 †18
NOWLIN, John Howard. 3705 MEDICAL PKWY, AUSTIN ENT PEDIATRICS 78705 #048-02-1981 L1981 **OTO PDO** *020 †45
NOWLIN, Scott W. 720 W 34TH ST STE 10 78705 #048-14-1986 L1988 **EM** *020 †20,16
NUESCH, Carl E. 6204 BALCONES DR 78731 #039-05-1985 L1987 **RO IM** *020 †80
NUGENT, Mark Andrew. 3828 S 1ST ST 78704 #036-01-1997 L2000 **FM** *020 †18
NUNNELLY, Patrick Dale. 1301 W 38TH ST, DRS DESROSIERS & WERNECKE 78705 #048-02-1977 L1977 **OBG** *020 †30
NUNO, Olga Maria. ■ 78749 #016-11-1985 L1994 **PHP P** *071
NURI, Asma. 211 COMAL ST, EAST AUSTIN CHC 78702 #496-20-1995 L1999 **IM** *020 †20
NUTSON, Peter Alan. 1301 W 38TH ST, STE 402 78705 #005-19-1994 L2001 **IM** *020 †20
NUZHATH, Vikhar. 4110 GUADALUPE ST 78751 #495-65-1975 L2002 **P** *020
NYE, Diana Del Castillo. 12221 N MO PAC EXPY 78758 #048-02-1985 L1986 **IM** *020 †20
OBERMILLER, John Peter. 1005 E 32ND ST 78705 #048-15-1983 L1983 **PM** *020 †60
O'BRIEN, Michael Terrence. 9200 WALL ST 78754 #005-06-1961 L1969 **PTH PHP** *071 †50
OCKERSHAUSEN, Thomas G. ■ 78759 #048-13-1999 L2002 **IM** *020 †20
O'CONNELL, Deborah Mary. 3508 FAR WEST BLVD, FL 2 78731 #539-03-1979 L1985 **R** *020 †80
O'CONNOR, David E. 1407 W STASSNEY LN 78745 #048-14-1990 L1999 **CHP P** *020 †75
OEHRING, Patricia Elaine. 601 E 15TH ST, BOX 44 78701 #030-05-1994 L2000 **CCP** *020 †55
O'FARRELL, Kevin Patrick. 3708 JEFFERSON ST, STE 102 78731 #030-05-1993 L1999 **GS** *020 †85
OGAH, Ediom. ■ 78726 #047-07-1996 L1998 **IM** *020 †20
OGLETREE, Jan Newton. 3705 MEDICAL PKWY 78705 #048-02-1966 L1966 **U** *071 †95
O'GRADY, Brian James. 4319 JAMES CASEY ST, STE 100 78745 #034-01-1987 L1994 **NS** *020 †25
OKAYLI, Ghadeer A. 720 W 34TH ST STE 1 78705 #797-03-1988 L2003 **P** *020 †75
OLEJNIKOVA, Silvia. ■ 78705 #048-13-2003 L2007 **AN** *020
OLINGER, Sheff D. ■ 78735 #051-01-1953 L1959 **N** *071 †75
OLIVER, Donell Baird. 1305 W 34TH ST STE 300 78705 #048-12-1997 L1998 **OBG** *020 †30
OLIVER, Paula S. 11111 RESEARCH BLVD, STE 350 78759 #021-05-1987 L1992 **GS** *020 †85
OLIVERAS, Edith Jenissa. 7112 ED BLUESTEIN BLVD 78723 #042-02-1999 L2002 **PD** *020 †55
OLMOS, Santos Absalon. 1301 W 38TH ST STE 601 78705 #132-02-1955 L1973 **PD** *071
ONAN, Okay Atilla. 6818 AUSTIN CENTER BLVD, STE 200 78731 #048-04-1995 L1997 **ORS** *020 †40 ‡
ONDASH, Robert Joseph. 2901 MONTOPOLIS DR, AUSTINVA OUTPATIENT CLINIC 78741 #038-43-1994 L1994 **IM** *020 †20
O'NEILL, Timothy James. ■ 78731 #048-02-1955 L1955 **R** *071 †80
ONG, Jinfon. ■ 78703 #016-01-2007 **PD** *012
ONG, Stacy Eileen. 601 E 15TH ST, C/O DEPT. OF MEDICAL AFFAI 78701 #048-12-1993 L1995 **U** *020 †95
ONWUDIEGWU MUOLOKWU, Enyio. ■ 78741 #048-04-2006 **OBG** *012
ORTALIZ, Ramon L. ■ 78732 #748-10-1967 L1976 **PD** *020
ORTH, Oliver Edward. 12221 N MO PAC EXPY 78758 #028-03-1990 L1991 **AN** *020 †05
ORTIQUE, Carla F. 12221 N MO PAC EXPY 78758 #016-11-1986 L1995 **OBG** *020 †18,30
ORTIZ, Edward H. 4200 MARATHON BLVD, STE 310 78756 #048-12-1998 L2006 **PCC** *020 †20
ORTIZ, Vanessa C. 3267 BEE CAVE RD, STE 107-98 78746 #042-01-1994 L1995 **DR** *020 †80
ORY, Joel Henry. ■ 78727 #021-05-1969 L1969 **GS** *020 †05
OSKOUI, Gassem Zebarjadi. ■ 78732 #517-01-1966 L1971 **AN** *071 †05
OTERO, Javier. 1015 E 32ND ST, STE 508 78705 #847-02-1990 L1998 **IC** *020 †20
OTTEN, Robert Bernard. 720 W 34TH ST STE 100 78705 #836-01-1960 L1981 **P** *020 †75
OTTEN, Stacie M. 720 W 34TH ST, STE 101 78705 #048-02-1995 L1998 **EM** *020 †16
OVERTON, Philip Marvin. 900 W 38TH ST, STE 460 78705 #048-02-1955 L1955 **ORS** *071 †40
OWENS, Juliette L Howes. 1500 W 38TH ST, STE 20 78731 #021-05-2000 L2004 **PD** *020 †55
OXFORD, Sharon Ann. 12221 N MO PAC EXPY 78758 #048-12-1975 L1975 **AN** *020 †05
OZDIL, Erol Huseyin. 4316 JAMES CASEY ST, STE A 78745 #047-20-1989 L1993 **CD** *020 †20
PACINDA, Susan. 9200 WALL ST 78754 #048-14-1992 L1993 **PTH** *020 †50
PAEZ, Blanca F. ■ 78748 #275-01-1959 L1974 **P** *072
PAGE, Bruce Paul. 3508 FAR WEST BLVD, FL 2 78731 #005-12-1986 L1993 **FM** *020 †18
PAGLEY, Paul Richman, Jr. 3801 N LAMAR BLVD, STE 300 78756 #041-13-1990 L2003 **CD IM** *020 †20
PAINTER, Theophilus S, Jr. 800 W 34TH ST STE 201 78705 #048-02-1947 L1947 **A IM** *020 †20,03
PAKIER, Philip. ■ 78759 #407-15-1949 L1953 **GP** *071
PAMPE, Eugene David. 6012 W WILLIAM CANNON DR, STE D101 78749 #048-14-1981 L1981 **FM** *020 †18
PAMPLIN, Gary Neil. 3571 FAR WEST BLVD # 258 78731 #048-02-1962 L1962 **GS** *020 †40
PANA, Andrea Louise. 2012 ROBERT DEDMAN DR, MNC 1.218 78712 #010-01-1991 L2005 **FSM** *020 †18
PANDIAN, Balakumar. 2802 WEBBERVILLE RD 78702 #026-04-1998 L2002 **MPD** *020 †55,20
PANNELL, Jennifer Carol. 8204 BRODIE LN, STE 101 78745 #038-45-2000 L2003 **PD** *020 †55 ‡
PAPE, Robert Wm. 900 E 30TH ST, STE 300 78705 #048-02-1956 L1956 **FM EM** *020
PAREKH, Sheila. 12201 RENFERT WAY, STE 230 78758 #048-16-2000 L2004 **OBG** *020
PARICIO, Todd Steven. ■ 78731 #048-14-1990 L1992 **AN** *020 †05
PARIKH, Aashish Ramesh. ■ 78753 #048-13-2004 L2008 **CHP** *012
PARISH, Michael Sidney. 3705 MEDICAL PKWY, STE 578 78705 #048-13-1974 L1974 **AN** *020 †05
PARK, Augustine Sewon. 3705 MEDICAL PKWY, STE 570 78705 #056-05-1999 L2004 **PAN** *020 †05
PARKER, Carlos Dale. 800 W 34TH ST, STE 201 78705 #048-02-1960 L1960 **AI** *071 †03
PARKER, Eugene Richard. 4220 BULL CREEK RD 78731 #048-02-1969 L1969 **PS** *020 †65
PARKER, Paul Thos. 1201 W 38TH ST 78705 #048-12-1984 L1985 **AN** *020 †05
PARKER, Thomas Michael. 4500 STEINER RANCH BLVD 78732 #021-01-1967 L1971 **TS** *071 †85,90
PARKER, Thomas Sterling. 1130 CAMINO LA COSTA, APT 307 78752 #048-14-1978 L1978 **CD IM** *020 †20
PARKER, William B. 1301 W 38TH ST STE 102 78705 #048-12-1986 L1987 **ORS** *020 †40
PARKS, Walter Saml, Jr. 630 W 34TH ST STE 201 78705 #048-02-1942 L1944 **GYN GP** *020 †30
PARR, Angelica Kuenast. 2499 S CAPITAL OF TEXS HWY, STE B100 78746 #048-12-1985 L1987 **PD** *020 †55
PARRA, Cheryl Belknap. 9200 WALL ST 78754 #055-01-1991 L1994 **PTH** *020 †50
PARRISH, Jerry Allan. ■ 78704 #048-02-1968 L1968 **OPH** *071 †35
PARRISH, Paul Christian. 517 S PLEASANT VALLEY RD 78741 #048-02-1995 L2006 **GPM** *020 †70
PARRISH, Shelly L. ■ 78739 #048-02-1994 L1997 **FM** *020 †18
PASAPULETI, Soumya Vijayk. ■ 78759 #496-34-1992 L2006 **FM** *100 †18
PAST, Ivan Hans. ■ 78759 #407-16-1948 L1981 **OTO A** *071
PATEL, Anant Ishverlal. 12180 N MOPAC STE B 78758 #036-05-1989 L1998 **NS** *020 †25
PATEL, Dimpal R. 12221 N MO PAC EXPY 78758 #048-13-1999 L2003 **AN** *020 †05
PATEL, Jigish Navin. 3705 MEDICAL PKWY, STE 570 78705 #048-04-1999 L2003 **AN** *020 †05
PATEL, Manish Vitthalbhai. 3003 BEE CAVE RD, STE 201 78746 #048-04-1995 L2000 **ORS** *020 †40
PATEL, Samir Rashmikant. 6001 LONDON DR 78745 #038-43-1995 L2000 **RHU IM** *020 †20
PATEL, Shephali Kantilal. 211 COMAL ST, DEPT OF CHC 78702 #422-01-2003 L2006 **FM** *020 †18
PATEL, Vinodkumar C. 4110 GUADALUPE ST 78751 #495-76-1973 L1981 **P** *020
PATRICK, Donald Wood. 711 W 38TH ST, STE D4 78705 #048-04-1962 L1962 **NS** *030 †25
PATT, Hanoch Avraham. 4314 MEDICAL PKWY, STE 200 78756 #048-04-1999 L2005 **PDC** *100 †55
PATTERSON, Bruce Wayne. 2000 W ANDERSON LN 78757 #019-02-1973 L1977 *020
PATTERSON, Robert Milton. 4201 MARATHON BLVD 78756 #048-04-1977 L1977 **OBG DR** *071 †30
PATTON, Robert Clyde. 720 W 34TH ST, STE 101 78705 #004-01-1973 L1986 **EM FM** *020 †16,18
PAUL, Gregory Michael. ■ 78749 #036-01-1999 L2005 **PFP** *100 †75
PAUL, Love Dev. 12201 RENFERT WAY, STE 315 78758 #495-69-1976 L1980 **FM** *020 †18
PAUTLER, Denise Lea. ■ 78727 #048-16-2006 **PD** *012
PAXTON, Raymond Charles. 4315 JAMES CASEY ST 78745 #040-02-1997 L2000 **IM** *020 †20
PAZZAGLIA, Peggy Jo. 8334 CROSS PARK DR 78754 #048-14-1984 L1985 **P** *020 †75
PEACOCK, Elizabeth A. PO BOX 1748, TRAVIS COUNTY MED EXAMINER 78767 #048-15-1987 L1988 **PTH** *020 †50
PEARCE, John Chas. 3003 BEE CAVE RD 78746 #021-01-1982 L1984 **ORS OSM** *020 †40
PEARCE, Marcellus Malcolm. ■ 78754 #021-05-2003 L2008 **OBG** *100
PEARCE, Stephen Moe. 1015 E 32ND ST, STE 101 78705 #048-12-1979 L1979 **ORS** *020 †40
PEARLSON, Yale Stuart. 13831 N HIGHWAY 183 78750 #035-46-1986 L1993 **IM** *020
PEAVEY, Richard Ross. 2909 N INTERSTATE 35 78722 #048-12-1976 L1980 **EM** *020
PECINA, Jennifer Lynn. 3508 FAR WEST BLVD, FL 2 78731 #018-03-1996 L1997 **FM** *020 †18
PEDERSON, Robert Warren. 3801 N LAMAR BLVD, STE 300 78756 #048-14-1973 L1974 **CD IM** *020 †20
PEEL, Deborah C. 2905 SAN GABRIEL ST STE 20 78705 #048-02-1974 L1974 **PYA P** *020 †75

■ = Address Information Privacy Protected

PEGUERO SANCHEZ NAVARRO, J. 601 E 15TH ST 78701 #649-14-2004 IM *012
PELLEGRINI, Michael F. 3705 MEDICAL PKWY, STE 230 78705 #048-14-1993 L1994
  IM *020 †20
PELOGITIS, Peter Joseph. 1631 E 2ND ST STE A 78702 #041-07-1994 L1996 IM *100
PELPHREY, Charles Frank. ■ 78756 #048-12-1944 L1944 PTH *050
PENA, Annie Carter. 3705 MEDICAL PKWY, STE 570 78705 #048-12-1992 L1993 AN *020 †05
PENA, Jose O, Jr. 720 W 34TH ST, THIRD COAST EMER PHYSICIAN 78705 #048-12-1992 L1994
  EM *020 †16
PENA, Roberto M. 900 E 30TH ST STE 210 78705 #048-13-1982 L1983 FM *020 †18
PENFIELD, Susan Carol. 1100 W 49TH ST, TX DEPT STATE HLTH SERV 78756
  #048-04-1979 L1980 PD *062 †55
PENNINGTON, Debra Jo. 10900 STONELAKE BLVD, STE 250 78759 #041-01-1988 L1999
  PDR R *020 †80
PEREZ-DEL-RIO-CEBALLOS, Ro. 601 E 15TH ST, DEPT OF FAMILY MEDICINE 78701
  #048-13-2006 L2008 FP *012
PERRET, Kenneth A, II. 1305 W 34TH ST 78705 #048-01-1990 L1998 PCC *020 †20
PERRY, Jeremie Jesse. 500 CANYON RIDGE DR 78753 #047-05-2001 L2002 AN *020
PERSCHAU, Richard Alan. 12221 N MO PAC EXPY 78758 #026-04-1969 L1977 AN AM *020 †05
PETERMAN, Kristen Hansen. 1301 W 38TH ST, STE 109 78705 #048-02-1992 L1993
  OBG *020 †30
PETERS, Edward John. 800 W 34TH ST, STE 201 78705 #048-02-1980 L1980 AI IM *020 †20,03
PETERSON, Craig Jon. 9200 WALL ST 78754 #026-04-1990 L1996 PTH *020 †50
PETERSON, Daniel Lee. 400 W 15TH ST, STE 800 78701 #007-02-1988 L1994 NS *020 †25
PETERSON, H Duane. ■ 78746 #016-06-1962 L1965 PS GS *020 †85,65
PETROFF, George Alexander. 900 W 38TH ST, STE 350 78705 #048-02-1986 L2006 N *020 †75
PETROPOULOS, Mary Chris. 11673 JOLLYVILLE RD # 104 78759 #048-04-1994 L1997
  PD *020 †55
PETRUS, Edward Jos. 3807 SPICEWOOD SPRINGS RD, NO 250 78759 #033-05-1966 L1969
  OPH PHM *050 †35
PETTIT, George H. ■ 78703 #048-12-1986 *100
PETTY, Preston Donald. ■ 78747 #048-12-1947 L1947 P GP *071
PEVOTO, Carl Alton. 3801 N LAMAR BLVD 78756 #048-02-1963 L1963 EM PD *020 †16
PEVOTO, Patrick S. 11111 RESEARCH BLVD, STE 450 78759 #048-02-1983 L1983
  OBG OS *020 †30
PFEIFER, Fredric Michael. 10900 STONELAKE BLVD, STE 250 78759 #019-02-1993 L1994
  DR *020 †80
PHALEN, Letitia E. ■ 78703 #048-12-1993 L1996 IM *020 †20
PHAM, Dang H. 12221 N MO PAC EXPY 78758 #048-02-1993 L1997 DR *020 †80
PHAM, Theresa Huong. 12201 RENFERT WAY, STE 360 78758 #048-04-1993 L1995 IM *020 †20
PHILLIPS, David L. 6818 AUSTIN CENTER BLVD, STE 201 78731 #048-13-1988 L1990
  U *020 †95
PHILLIPS, Larry Ewing. 3100 RED RIVER ST # 1, UROLOGY SPECIALISTS 78705
  #048-02-1969 L1969 U *071 †95
PHILLIPS, Lyman George. 4110 GUADALUPE ST, AUSTIN STATE HOSPITAL 78751
  #649-02-1962 L1967 P *020
PHILLIPS, Michael F. 1301 W 38TH ST STE 109, AUSTIN AREA OB/GYN 78705
  #048-14-1988 L1989 OBG *020 †30
PICKETT, Steven H. 12180 N MO PAC EXPY, STE A 78758 #048-13-1987 L1992 U *020
PIEFER, Gary Wayne. 11113 RESEARCH BLVD 78759 #048-14-1984 L1985 FM *020 †18
PIERCE, Jack Wm. 3300 W ANDERSON LN STE 308 78757 #048-13-1981 L1981 OPH *020 †35
PIERCE, Paul Michael. ■ 78705 #048-14-2007 *012
PILLAI, Deepak. ■ 78731 #048-12-1998 L1998 OS *062
PILLAI, Sangeetha Ramesh. 601 E 15TH ST 78701 #913-80-2002 IM *012
PILLOW, Michael B. 12221 N MO PAC EXPY 78758 #048-14-1989 L2003 AN *020 †05
PLAYFAIR, Cynthia Blaise. 4101 PARKSTONE HEIGHTS DR, STE 370 78746 #047-20-1991 L1998
  P *020 †75
PLUNKETT, Mark Alan. 13376 RESEARCH BLVD, STE 104 78750 #048-12-1991 L1992
  OPH *020 †35
POAG, Mark Gordon. 15401 BAT HAWK CIR, ADVANCED DIAGNOSTIC IMAGIN 78738
  #048-13-1983 L1983 DR *020 †80
POHL, David Frederick. 1600 W 38TH ST STE 312 78731 #048-14-1979 L1979 PUD IM *020 †20
POHL, Donald E. ■ 78731 #018-03-1944 L1951 IM CD *071 †20
POLITZ, John Kenneth. 1010 W 40TH ST, CARDIOTHORA & VASCULAR SUR 78756
  #021-05-1990 L1993 VS GS *020 †85
POLON, Clive. 900 E 30TH ST STE 107 78705 #836-01-1978 L1996 OBG *020 †30
POLSON, Wilbert Arvid. 10900 STONELAKE BLVD, STE 250 78759 #048-04-1967 L1967
  DR *020 †80
PONDER, Stewart Michael. ■ 78759 #048-04-1942 L1942 GP P *071
PONTERIO, Albert Edward. 11703B KINGS VIEW CT 78750 #048-14-1998 L1997 IM OM *030
POOLE, Edward Kern. ■ 78731 #041-02-1959 L1967 R NM *071 †80,28
POOLE, Rex Darrel, Jr. 1927 LOHMANS CROSSING RD, STE 200 78734 #027-01-1995 L1996
  FM *020 †18 ‡
POONAWALA, Robina Nadir. 4007 JAMES CASEY ST, STE D240 78745 #495-01-1978 L1984
  FM *020 †18 ‡
POREDDY, Vijayrama Reddy. 12201 RENFERT WAY # 365, NORTH AUSTIN
  GASTROENTEROL 78758 #495-21-1994 L2004 GE *100 †20
PORRAS, Rebecca. 3705 MEDICAL PKWY, STE 570 78705 #048-13-1993 L1995 AN *020
PORTER, Barbara Jean. 8204 BRODIE LN 78745 #007-02-1977 L1994 FM *020 †18
PORTER, Robert Wayne. 3705 MEDICAL PKWY STE 5 78705 #048-02-1967 L1967 AN *020 †05
POTHALA, Padmavathamma. 919 E 32ND ST 78705 #495-70-1994 L2000 IM *020 †20
POUTOU, Jose Antonio. ■ 78745 #275-01-1960 L1976 GP *075
POWELL, Harry Chester, Jr. 78757 #001-02-1947 L1949 PD *020
POWELL, Joe Thos. 3705 MEDICAL PKWY, STE 440 78705 #048-02-1967 L1967 PM N *020 †60
POWERS, Michael Scott. 3705 MEDICAL PKWY, STE 570 78705 #048-02-1991 L1993
  AN *020 †05
PRABHU, Anuradha. 3801 N LAMAR BLVD 78756 #496-01-1990 L2001 EM *020 †16 ‡
PRABHU, Vishwanath G. 1400 N I H 35 78701 #495-37-1982 L2001 NPM PD *020 †55
PRAKASH, Rajeev. 12221 N MO PAC EXPY 78758 #021-05-1998 L2006 IM EM *020 †20,16
PRASHNER, Heather Rytting. ■ 78703 #048-14-1992 L1994 PTH *020 †50
PRENTICE, James Archer. ■ 78703 #048-12-1962 L1962 AN *071 †05
PRENTICE, Linda Gilbert. ■ 78703 #010-02-1970 L1978 PD END *071 †55
PRETE, Michael James. 6835 AUSTIN CENTER BLVD 78731 #048-14-1986 L1987 IM *020 †20
PREUSS, Jennie. 4029 S CAPITAL OF TEXS HWY, STE 200 78704 #048-13-1982 L1983
  CHP P *020 †75
PREWITT-BUCHANAN, Laura K. 2501 W WILLIAM CANNON DR, STE 401 78745
  #048-14-1989 L1991 PM *020 †60

PRICE, Bradley Bryan. 2911 MEDICAL ARTS ST STE 6 78705 #048-12-1973 L1975
  OBG *020 †30
PRICE, Brian S. 3402 DAY STAR CV 78746 #048-02-1995 L1998 EM *020 †16
PRICE, P Clift. ■ 78731 #048-02-1947 L1947 PD *071 †55
PRINCE, Michelle Marie. 1301 BARBARA JORDAN BLVD, STE 300 78723 #016-43-1996 L2003
  ORS *020 †40
PRIVITERA, William John. 2600 VIA FORTUNA, STE 410 78746 #048-14-1984 L1992 P *020 †75
PROCHNOW, Ross Fred. 10710 RESEARCH BLVD, STE 120 78759 #048-12-1980 L1984
  PD *020 †55
PRONSKE, Erik Harald. 3705 MEDICAL PKWY, STE 570 78705 #048-02-1983 L1983
  GS *020 †30
PROSISE, Emily Liga. 3807 SPICEWOOD SPGS 78759 #036-07-1997 L2008 D *020 †15
PRUETT, Moira Teresa. ■ 78748 #016-11-1984 L1990 OM IM *030 †20
PRZYBYLA, Rachael Anne. 1301 W 38TH ST, STE 201/205 78705 #035-01-1995 L1999
  OBG *030 †30
PUGH, Theresa Jones. 1101 W 40TH ST, JEFFERSON STREET FAMILY PR 78756
  #051-04-2001 L2004 FM *020 †18
PULIM, Leela Reddy. 4110 GUADALUPE ST, AUSTIN STATE HOSPITAL 78751
  #495-11-1971 L1991 P CHP *020 †75
PUNJABI, Narendra S. 11615 ANGUS RD STE 106 78759 #495-23-1977 L1985 IM A *020
PURGASON, John R. ■ 78723 #048-02-1953 L1953 GP P *071
PUSCH, Tobias. ■ 78759 #409-35-2003 L2007 IM *020 †20
PUTMAN, H Paul, III. 1114 LOST CREEK BLVD STE 2 78746 #048-02-1982 L1983 P *020 †75
PUTNAM, Russell Drew. 2501 W WILLIAM CANNON DR, BLDG 5 78745 #048-14-1995 L1996
  RNR *020 †80
PUTNUM, Christine C. 10900 STONELAKE BLVD, STE 250 78759 #048-14-1996 L1997
  CHP *020 †75
PYRON, Martha I. PO BOX 7339, UNIVERSITY HLTH SERVICES 78713 #048-13-1996 L2000
  FM FSM *020 †18
QUANDER, Jos Pearson, Jr. ■ 78727 #010-03-1961 L1965 OBG *071 †30
QUARONI, Andrea L. 711 W 38TH ST 78705 #048-13-1994 L1996 OS *020
QUEEN, Charles Richard. ■ 78703 #048-12-1956 L1956 FM *071 †18
QUENG, John A. 6835 AUSTIN CENTER BLVD 78731 #048-14-1998 L2001 FM *020 †18
QUERALT, Mark V. 4029 S CAPITAL OF TEXS HWY, STE 111 78704 #048-12-1992 L1993
  PM PMM *020 †60
QUERALT, Yvonne Marie. 10900 STONELAKE BLVD, STE 250 78759 #048-02-1997 L1999
  DR *020 †80
QUINONES, Carlos A. ■ 78703 #042-01-1984 L1987 IM *020 †20
RACE, George Wm Daryl. 2465 WESTLAKE DR 78746 #048-02-1976 L1976
  MDM PYG *030 †75 ‡
RACE, Jonathan Clark. 4534 W GATE BLVD, STE 110 78745 #048-02-1977 L1977
  ORS OFA *020 †40
RACHT, Edward Macleod. 517 S PLEASANT VALLEY RD 78741 #012-05-1984 L1996
  EM IM *020 †20
RAGSDALE, Anne Barrett. ■ 78735 #012-05-1994 L2004 FM *020 †18
RAGULA, Vitaut N. 12221 N MO PAC EXPY 78758 #065-10-1976 L1979 EM *020 †16
RAHMAN, Aminur. 3501 MILLS AVE, SHOAL CREEK HOSP 78731 #160-08-1989 L2008
  CHP P *012
RAHMAN, Sofia. ■ 78730 #704-15-1990 L2005 FM *100
RAINEY, Annis M. 1912 W 35TH ST, CHILDREN'S EYE CENTER 78703 #048-04-1992 L1994
  OPH *020 †35
RALEY, Robert Cecil. 2301 W NORTH LOOP BLVD 78756 #048-12-1972 L1972 FM AM *020 †18
RAMACHANDRAN, Jagadheeswar. 601 E 15TH ST, AUSTIN MED EDUC PROG-SETON 78701
  #495-04-1997 L2008 IM *100 †20
RAMACHANDRAN, Rajeev. 601 E 15TH ST, AUSTIN MED EDUC PROG-SETON 78701
  #495-44-1996 L2007 PD *100 †55
RAMAMIRTHAM, Pradeep. 3508 FAR WEST BLVD, FL 2 78731 #048-12-1991 L1992
  GE *020 †20
RAMIREZ, David Arthur. 601 E 15TH ST, AUSTIN REGIONAL CLINIC 78701 #024-01-2000 L2003
  IM *020 †20
RAMIREZ, Jaime Eduardo. 1111 W 34TH ST, STE 102 78705 #048-02-1983 L1983 PD *020 †55
RAMSEY, Daniel Ewart. 901 W BEN WHITE BLVD 78704 #048-14-1983 L1983 FM EM *020 †18
RAMSEY, Ryan P. 919 E 32ND ST 78705 #048-16-2001 L2003 EM *020 †16
RANA, Pauravi Jayant. 1 UNIVERSITY STA, STOP A3500 78712 #048-02-1988 L1990
  P CHP *020 †75
RANDAL, H Brook. ■ 78751 #048-13-1982 L1983 EM *020 †16
RANE, Nishigandha Y. 4700 SETON CENTER PKWY, STE 125 78759 #495-17-1996 L2007
  PD *020 †55
RANEY, R Beverly, Jr. ■ 78757 #041-01-1965 L1991 PHO PD *020 †55
RANKIN, Douglas Hall. 4029 S CAPITAL OF TEXS HWY, STE 103 78704 #021-05-1978 L1978
  FM ADM *020 †18
RAO, Jalaja Krishna. PO BOX 202633 78720 #496-34-1995 L2005 MPD *020
RAO, Sekhar Suryadevara. ■ 78750 #048-13-1998 L2001 VIR *020
RAPP, Robert Paul. ■ 78757 #048-02-1956 L1956 GP *020
RARDIN, Rebekah E. 12201 RENFERT WAY, STE 110 78758 #048-13-2004 L2007 PD *020 †55
RASMUSSEN, Steven E. 1717 W 6TH ST, STE 120R 78703 #023-12-1995 L2006 D *020 †15
RATCLIFF, Daniel Jonathon. 3705 MEDICAL PKWY, STE 310 78705 #048-12-1996 L1997
  OTO *020 †45
RAVULA, Vijay K. 12221 N MO PAC EXPY 78758 #048-12-1999 L2003 AN *020 †05
RAWAL, Vandana Mahajan. 3508 FAR WEST BLVD, FL 2 78731 #496-07-1994 L1999
  PD *020 †55
RAWLINSON, William K. 711 W 38TH ST, STE C1 78705 #049-01-1981 L2003
  PUD CCM *020 †20
READING, Patience H. 12221 N MO PAC EXPY 78758 #048-12-1998 L2003 N *020 †75
REAM, Roy Scott. 3407 GLENVIEW AVE 78703 #038-40-1973 L1976 IM *020 †20
REARDON, Michael Shane. 1301 BARBARA JORDAN BLVD, STE 200 78723
  #007-02-1997 L2003 PD *020 †75
REDDY, Ashvini Kattegummu. ■ 78705 #048-04-2007 *012
REDDY, Geeta. ■ 78727 #495-21-1971 L1980 IM GP *020
REDDY, Leelavathy C. 7708 SHOAL CREEK BLVD 78757 #495-72-1989 L1995 P *020 †75
REDDY, Naveen K. 900 W 38TH ST, STE 420 78705 #048-02-1993 L1995 OBG *020 †30
REDDY, Patolla Venkat R. ■ 78727 #495-65-1963 L1976 EM GS *071 †18,16
REDDY, Ramasahayam Ashok. 7112 ED BLUESTEIN BLVD, NORTHEAST AUSTIN HLTH
  CTR 78723 #495-57-1968 L1981 PD *020 †55
REDDY, Sridhar Patlolla. 2911 MEDICAL ARTS ST, STE 9B 78705 #495-65-1986 L1995
  GE IM *020 †20

REDFERN, Richard Wilder. 3705 MEDICAL PKWY STE 5 78705 #048-14-1982 L1983
AN *020 †05

REED, Rhett A. 601 E 15TH ST, BRACKENRIDGE HOSPITAL 78701 #048-02-1989 L1990
EM *020 †16

REEVES, James Franklin. 3100 RED RIVER ST 78705 #048-04-1960 L1960 U UP *020 †95

REGAN, Michael Paul. 11111 RESEARCH BLVD, STE 334 78759 #035-06-1979 L1990
GS *020 †85

REHMAN, Shabnam A. ■ 78759 #495-17-1992 L1999 IM *020 †20

REICH, Stephanie J. 1305 W 34TH ST STE 308 78705 #048-02-1988 L1990 OBG *020 †30

REICHENBERG, Jason. 313 E 12TH ST, STE 103 78701 #024-05-2002 L2006 D *020 †15

REID, Dustin L. 901 W 38TH ST STE 401, RESTORA AUSTIN PLASTIC SUR 78705
#048-15-1997 L2005 PS *020 †85,65

REIDY, Elizabeth Terando. 2499 S CAPITAL OF TEXS HWY, STE B100 78746
#016-06-1985 L1998 PD *020 †55

REIFSLAGER, Walter E, Jr. 720 W 34TH ST 78705 #048-02-1952 L1952 P *071

REIFSNYDER, Andrew C. 10900 STONELAKE BLVD, STE 250 78759 #048-12-1987 L1988
DR *020 †80

REINARZ, James Allen. 601 E 15TH ST, DEPARTMENT OF MEDICINE 78701 #048-02-1959 L1959
ID IM *071 †20

REITMEYER, William Jos. 601 E 15TH ST, PATHOLOGY 78701 #025-12-1975 L1978
PTH PP *020 †50

REMKUS, James Edward. 4316 JAMES CASEY ST, STE 110 78745 #028-03-1972 L1995
DR CD *020 †20,80

RENEAU, Joe Rex. 3900 HOWARD LN 78728 #048-02-1965 L1965 FM OM *020

RENTEA, Gheorghe. ■ 78746 #781-03-1952 L1972 P GP *071

REQUEIJO, Paula Veronica. 6101 BALCONES DR, STE 300 78731 #132-01-2000 L2004 IM *020

REUE, David William. 1301 W 38TH ST, DRS DESROSIERS & WERNECKE 78705
#048-13-1986 L1987 OBG *020 †30

REYES, Randy Craig. 919 E 32ND ST 78705 #048-12-1993 L1994 EM *020 †16

REYNOLDS, Brian Joe. 4110 GUADALUPE ST, AUSTIN STATE HOSPITAL 78751
#048-02-1968 L1968 P CHP *020 †75

REYNOLDS, James C. 6818 AUSTIN CENTER BLVD, STE 200 78731 #035-01-1963 L1972
OFA *071 †40

RHOAD, Deirdre M. 11111 RESEARCH BLVD # 310 78759 #048-02-1987 L1988 PS *020 †65

RHODES, Jeffrey Paul. 9503 ASHTON RDG, CEA 78750 #048-13-2000 L2003 EM *020 †16

RHODES, Kerry Don. 631 W 38TH ST, STE 2 78705 #048-13-1990 L1991 FM *020 †18

RHODES, Lisa Marie. 6836 BEE CAVE RD, STE 300 78746 #048-13-2000 L2004 D *020 †15

RHODES, Roxana A. 631 W 38TH ST 78705 #048-02-1991 L1993 IM *020

RICE, Dan Craddock. 4310 JAMES CASEY ST, STE 4A 78745 #048-14-1981 L1981
GE IM *020 †20

RICE, William Hamilton. 78 PASCAL LN 78746 #048-13-1983 L1984 PHP OM *030

RICHARDS, Christopher R. 10900 STONELAKE BLVD, STE 250 78759 #048-12-1984 L1985
DR *020 †80

RICHARDS, Karen C. 1301 BARBARA JORDAN BLVD, STE 200 78723 #023-07-1993 L1996
CN *020 †75,55

RICHARDS, Kristin Lane. ■ 78702 #048-14-2008 *012

RICHARDSON, Dan N. 10900 STONELAKE BLVD, STE 250 78759 #048-13-1983 L1983
RNR DR *020 †80

RICHBURG, Paul Lewis. ■ 78759 #048-12-1947 L1947 IM PUD *071 †20

RICOT, Georges Lionel. ■ 78704 #440-01-1992 L2000 DR *020

RIDOUT, Robert Gladstone. ■ 78703 #048-13-1973 L1973 R *020 †80

RIE, Michael. 1313 RED RIVER ST, STE 100 78701 #048-43-2005 L2007 FP *012

RIES, David Christopher. ■ 78733 #005-18-2008 *012

RILEY, Shelly Lynn. 3660 STONERIDGE RD, STE F101 78746 #048-13-1999 L2004
CHP P *020 †75

RIMEL, Warden Miller. ■ 78759 #018-03-1955 L1981 CHP P *072 †75

RINARD, Jeremy Ronald. ■ 78702 #048-15-2003 GS *100

RIOPEL, Maureen Ann. 9200 WALL ST 78754 #045-04-1991 L1998 PTH *020 †50

RISINGER, Christy Taylor. 8913 COLLINFIELD DR, SETON COMMUNITY CLINIC 78758
#010-02-2002 L2005 IM *020 †20

RISINGER, James Edsel. 6101 W COURTYARD DR, BLDG 5 78730 #048-13-1973 L1973
DR *071 †80

RISINGER, Norman S, Jr. 2559 WESTERN TRAILS BLVD, STE 100 78745 #048-02-1991 L2005
CD IM *020 †20

RIVERA, Audelio. 1015 E 32ND ST, STE 405 78705 #048-02-1983 L1985 NPM NTR *020 †55

RIVERA, Douglas Jason. 2600 E MARTN LTHR KNG JR 78702 #031-01-2000 L2005 RO *020 †80

RIZOV, Vladimir Z. 111 CONGRESS AVE STE 1400, C/O ACE PICKENS BROWN MCCA 78701
#913-01-1963 L1983 GP *020

ROACH, Paul Jeffrey. 1015 E 32ND ST, STE 508 78705 #016-06-1984 L1992 CD IM *020 †20

ROARK, Glenn E. 3724 JEFFERSON ST STE 308 78731 #048-02-1953 L1953 P *071

ROARK, Tom R. 3807 SPICEWOOD SPRINGS RD, AUSTIN DERMCARE 78759
#048-12-1998 L2000 D *020 †15

ROBERTS, Cathey Jean. 4131 SPICEWOOD SPRINGS RD 78759 #048-13-1976 L1979
P CHP *020 †75

ROBERTSON, Amy Neuhoff. 1700 S MO PAC EXPY 78746 #007-02-1993 L1997 OPH *020 †35

ROBERTSON, Steven C. 3705 MEDICAL PKWY STE 570 78705 #048-14-1993 L1994
AN *020 †05

ROBERTSON, William Geo. 4106 MEDICAL PKWY 78756 #048-02-1972 L1972
CRS GS *020 †10,85

ROBIN, Sidney Thos. 631 W 38TH ST STE 1 78705 #048-02-1974 L1974 FM *020

ROBINSON, Frank E. 3407 GLENVIEW AVE 78703 #048-04-1980 L1980 IM *020 †20

ROBINSON, Glenn Crane. PO BOX 10597 78766 #055-01-1987 L2001 GE IM *020 †20

ROBINSON, Wm Archie, Jr. 1301 W 38TH ST, STE 500 78705 #048-04-1965 L1965
CD IM *020 †20

ROBISON, George Randolph. 1000 PAYTON GIN RD, STE S 78758 #036-07-1972 L1976
IMG IM *020 †20

ROBISON, James Thos. 8101 FM 969, TRAVIS STATE JAIL 78724 #048-02-1958 L1958
GP OTO *020

ROBUCK, Katie V. ■ 78749 #048-14-2001 L2004 PD *020 †55

ROCK, Robert Lee. 13376 RESEARCH BLVD, STE 104 78750 #039-01-1968 L1962
OPH *020 †35

ROCKWELL, Jeffrey John. 12221 N MO PAC EXPY 78758 #003-01-1992 L1996 AN *020 †05

ROCKWOOD, Sheldon E. 1403 W 30TH ST 78703 #048-02-2003 L2005 EM *100 †16

RODEN, Sean K. 720 W 34TH ST, STE 101 78705 #048-02-1994 L1995 EM AM *020 †16

RODEN, William Clarence. 4316 JAMES CASEY ST # F100 78745 #036-07-1976 L1986
ORS *020 †40

RODGERS, George Piper. 3300 DUVAL RD, STE 150 78759 #048-12-1983 L1983
CD IM *020 †20

RODGERS, Sarah Ann. ■ 78705 #039-01-2007 IM *012

RODRIGUEZ, Abe Garcia. 900 E 30TH ST 78705 #048-02-1959 L1959 OBG *071 †30

RODRIGUEZ, Jesse Steven. 720 W 34TH ST, STE 101 78705 #016-43-1996 L1999 EM *020 †16

RODRIGUEZ, Juan L. 3828 S 1ST ST, AUSTIN REG CLINIC SOUTH 78704 #042-01-1983 L2005
AI *020 †20,03

RODRIGUEZ, Raul Marcelo. 13831 N HIGHWAY 183 78750 #024-01-1981 L1984
OM FM *071 †70

RODRIGUEZ, Roberto Luis. 4900 MUELLER BLVD, DELL CHILDREN'S MEDICAL CE 78723
#005-02-2001 L2006 PD *020 †55

RODRIGUEZ, William, Jr. ■ 78746 #048-13-2000 L2006 IM *020 †80

RODRIGUEZ, William A. 408 W 45TH ST, CENTRAL TEXAS KIDNEY ASSOC 78751
#048-14-1998 L2000 NEP *020 †20

ROEBUCK, Gil Patrick. 3508 FAR WEST BLVD STE 150 78731 #048-15-1975 L1975 IM *020

ROGERS, James Allen. 701 W 51ST ST E654, TX DEPT OF FAM & PROT SERV 78751
#048-13-1973 L1973 CHP P *030 †75

ROGERS, Matthew T. 1301 W 38TH ST, STE 705 78705 #048-14-1988 L1989 CD IC *020 †20

ROGERS, Samuel H. 78750 #048-13-1982 L1983 EM *020

ROLOSON, Gary James. 1201 W 38TH ST 78705 #036-07-1980 L1993 PTH *020 †50

ROSE, Verna M. ■ 78727 #048-16-1988 L1989 MG PD *020 †19,55 ‡

ROSECAN, Marvin. ■ 78747 #028-02-1949 L1973 IM DIA *071 †20

ROSEN, Patricia Beth. 3303 NORTHLAND DR, STE 310 78731 #038-43-1977 L1992
EM IM *020 †20,16

ROSENBAUM, Amy Ann. ■ 78748 #048-02-2008 *012

ROSENBERG, Elise Diane. ■ 78730 #035-09-2000 L2008 OBG *020

ROSENBLATT, Howard Max. 1301 BARBARA JORDAN BLVD, STE 200 78723
#005-19-1975 L1982 AI PD *020 †55,03

ROSENSTOCK, Robin Jill. PO BOX 7339 78713 #048-02-1981 L1981 ADL PD *020 †55

ROSS, Andrew William. 3300 W ANDERSON LN, STE 308 78757 #048-04-2000 L2004 OPH *071

ROSS, Charlie Price, III. 601 E 15TH ST, SURGERY EDUCATION 78701 #048-02-1967 L1967
GS TS *020 †85,90

ROSS, Michael Delbert. 12221 N MO PAC EXPY 78758 #048-16-1984 L1985 GS *020 †85

ROSS, Warran Allan. 4004 MARATHON BLVD 78756 #048-05-1955 L1957 ORS *020

ROSSETOS, Ourania S. 2200 PARK BEND DR, BLDG 2 78758 #033-06-1993 L1997
OBG *020 †30

ROSSON, Barry Allen. ■ 78759 #048-12-1971 L1971 P N *020 †75

ROTMAN, Michael. ■ 78746 #048-02-1966 L1966 CD IM *071 †20

ROTTS, Michael Brian. ■ 78722 #021-05-2003 L2006 EM *020

ROWE, Stuart Allen. 4314 MEDICAL PKWY, STE 200 78756 #023-07-1981 L1994
PDC PD *020 †55

ROWLANDS, Kim L. ■ 78759 #048-13-1993 L1995 IM *020 †20

ROWLEY, Patricia Staudt. 5222 BURNET RD, ST DAVIDS SENIOR HLTH CTR 78756
#048-15-1985 L1986 NEP IM *040 †20

RUBIN, Heino. ■ 78731 #407-04-1962 GPM *071

RUBIN-DE-CELIS, Carlos. 2911 MEDICAL ARTS ST, STE 13 78705 #649-04-1990 L2002
ON *020 †20

RUFF, Peter A. 12180 N MO PAC EXPY, STE A 78758 #048-13-1997 L2006 U *020 †95

RUFF, Tibor. 78701 #065-09-1968 L1977 OTO *071 †45

RUIZ, David. 2499 S CAPITAL OF TEXS HWY, STE B100 78746 #847-04-1965 L1977
PD PDI *020 †55

RUIZ, Elena. 2499 S CAPITAL OF TEXS HWY, STE B100 78746 #048-14-2001 L2005 PD *020 †55

RUIZ CUEVAS, Claudia Ceno. 601 E 15TH ST, AUSTIN MED EDUC PROG-SETON 78701
#270-02-1997 L2008 FM *100

RUIZ CUEVAS, Grethel Vero. 601 E 15TH ST, AUSTIN MED EDUC PROG-SETON 78701
#270-02-2002 FP *012

RUNDE, Marina Victorovna. ■ 78703 #913-36-1993 FM *100

RUNGE, Gretchen Herrmann. ■ 78763 #048-02-1947 L1947 PD N *020 †55

RUNKLE, William M. ■ 78704 #051-01-1962 L1981 GP AM *071 †70

RUSH, William Nevins. 3705 MEDICAL PKWY STE 57 78705 #050-02-1970 L1974 AN *020 †05

RUSK, Natalie Wakeman. 10710 RESEARCH BLVD, STE 120 78759 #041-01-2001 L2006
PD *020 †55

RUSSELL, Peggy Martin. 603 W 13TH ST STE 1A # 320 78701 #048-78-1979, ▲ L1979
IM IMG *020 †20

RUSSELL, Terri A. 811 E 32ND ST 78705 #048-13-1987 L1988 PD *020 †55

RUTLEDGE, John Neal. 1301 W 38TH ST STE 118, AUSTIN RADIOLGICAL ASSOC 78705
#039-01-1980 L1987 RNR *020 †80

RUTMAN, Steven M. 3705 MEDICAL PKWY STE 570 78705 #048-12-1993 L1994 AN *020 †05

RUTTER, Kimberly. 313 E 12TH ST, CAPITAL OBSTETRICS & 78701 #048-14-1999 L2003
OBG *020 †30

RYAN, Jeanne Wham. 2901 MONTOPOLIS DR, AUSTIN VA OUTPATIENT CLINI 78741
#048-02-1981 L1981 IM *020 †20

RYAN, Lisa Ann. ■ 78756 #021-01-1997 L2003 IM HOS *020 †20

RYAN, Stephen Edward. ■ 78756 #021-01-1996 L2003 IM *020 †20

RYLANDER, Gary Ray. 3300 W ANDERSON LN, STE 308 78757 #048-02-1977 L1974
OPH *020 †35

RYLANDER, Henry Grady, III. 3300 W ANDERSON LN, STE 308 78757 #048-13-1974 L1974
OPH IM *020 †35

RYTTING, James Edward. ■ 78703 #049-01-1964 L1972 PDR DR *071 †80

SAARIKOSKI, Heikki Herman. 4804 GROVER AVE 78756 #409-20-1976 L1984 OBG *020 †30

SABRA, John P. 601 E 15TH ST 78701 #043-01-1995 L2003 GS *020 †85

SACK, Marshall Rich. 12221 N MO PAC EXPY, RADIANT RESEARCH-AUSTIN 78758
#020-02-1964 L1971 RHU IM *050 †20

SAEED, Sohail A. 13831 N HIGHWAY 183 78750 #048-78-2004, ▲ L2007 FM *020 †18

SAGE, William Matthew. 727 E DEAN KEETON ST, UNIV OF TX 78705 #005-11-1988 L1989
LM AN *071

SAIF, Maryam. 601 E 15TH ST, AUSTIN MED EDUC PROG-SETON 78701 #704-09-1996 L2005
IM *100 †20

SALAS, John Cobos. 10020 US HIGHWAY 183 S 78747 #048-14-2003 L2005 IM *020 †20

SALAZAR, Dora L. 2911 MEDICAL ARTS ST, STE 15B 78705 #048-02-1984 L1985 FM *020 †18

SALAZAR, Patricia. ■ 78757 #048-13-2006 PD *012

SALIB, Sherine Eskander. 601 E 15TH ST, ANNEX E- DEPT. OF INTERNA 78701
#917-02-1993 L2003 IM *020 †20 ‡

SALMON, Douglas Russell. 4007 JAMES CASEY ST, STE C220 78745 #003-01-1979 L1980
CD EM *020 †20

SAMAAN, Michael J. 911 W 38TH ST 202T 78705 #048-14-2002 L2004 FM *020 †18

SAMARATUNGA, Kelvin A. ■ 78748 #220-01-1962 L1982 **N NS** *062 ‡

SANCHEZ, Eduardo Jose. 1100 W 49TH ST M-751, TEXAS DEPT OF HEALTH 78756 #048-12-1988 L1989 **FM** *020 †18

SANCHEZ, Guillermo G. ■ 78727 #048-02-2000 **FM** *100

SANCHEZ, Javier Enrique. 2200 PARK BEND DR, BLDG 2 78758 #042-01-1994 L1995 **ICE** *020 †20

SANCHEZ, Julie Isabel. 1410 N I H 35, STE 310 78701 #048-12-1993 L2001 **PDS** *020 †85

SANCHEZ FUENTES, E. 3706 S 1ST ST, SETON KOZMETSKY 78704 #048-04-1999 L2006 **FM** *020 †18

SANCHEZ GUTIERREZ, Roberto. 601 E 15TH ST 78701 #270-03-2002 L2007 **FP** *012

SANDBACH, Emily J. 1501 CONCORDIA AVE 78722 #048-14-2000 L2005 **IM** *020

SANDBACH, John Franklin. 6204 BALCONES DR, TEXAS ONCOLOGY CANCER CENT 78731 #020-12-1971 L1977 **HO HEM** *020 †20

SANDER, Hans Michael. 11410 JOLLYVILLE RD, STE 2101 78759 #048-16-1983 L1983 **D** *020,15

SANDERS, J Nelson. 919 E 32ND ST 78705 #047-06-1949 L1954 **U** *071 †95

SANDERS, Kathleen Denning. 1301 BARBARA JORDAN BLVD 78723 #005-14-1976 L1999 **PD** *020 †55

SANDS, Arthur Thos. ■ 78746 #048-04-1992 *100

SANKAR, Aravind B. 1015 E 32ND ST STE 308, SURGICAL ASSOCIATES OF AUS 78705 #048-02-1995 L2008 **GS** *020 †85

SANTHANAM, Sripriya. ■ 78705 #496-07-1998 L2008 **HO** *100 †20

SANTIAGO, Jose F. 2624 W WILLIAM CANNON DR 78745 #042-04-1984 L1993 **FM** *020 †18 ‡

SANTIAGO, Joseph A. ■ 78731 #035-46-1961 L1962 **PM U** *020 †95

SARAI, Paul Singh. 3704 LAGOOD DR, AUSTIN RADIOLOGICAL ASSOCI 78730 #030-06-2001 L2003 **DR** *020 †80

SARDANI, Yahya. 601 E 15TH ST, AUSTIN MED EDUC PROG-SETON 78701 #875-02-1995 L2005 **PD** *020 †55

SARGENT, Julia Beth. 5717 BALCONES DR 78731 #048-04-1983 L1983 **OPH** *020 †35

SARGENT, Kristin Anne. 5717 BALCONES DR 78731 #048-12-1995 L1996 **OPH** *020 †35

SATTAR, Naeem Abdul. 601 E 15TH ST, AUSTIN MED EDUC PROG-SETON 78701 #704-02-1997 L2005 **IM** *100 †20

SAUNDERS, Gary K. 601 E 15TH ST, DEPT OF PSYCHIATRY 78701 #048-13-2001 **P AN** *012

SAVAGE, David Clyde. 4534 W GATE BLVD, STE 110 78745 #048-04-1983 L1985 **ORS** *020 †40

SAVAGE, Hilbert Bryant. ■ 78747 #047-06-1958 L1997 **FM AM** *071 †70,18

SAVAGE, Lisa Lapinta. 900 E 30TH ST, STE 205 78705 #048-04-1988 L1993 **OBG** *020 †30

SAVAGE, Michael Francis. 2171B WOODWARD ST 78744 #010-01-1989 L1996 **IM** *020 †20

SAWYER, Drew Grant. 3705 MEDICAL PKWY, AUSTIN ENT PEDIATRICS 78705 #048-02-1972 L1972 **OTO PDO** *020 †45

SAYERS, Brian Sam. 1301 W 38TH ST STE 110 78705 #048-12-1981 L1981 **RHU IM** *020 †20 ‡

SAYERS, Leonard J. ■ 78731 #016-06-1953 L1957 **IM** *071

SCALES, Garrett W, Jr. 3705 MEDICAL PKWY, STE 570 78705 #048-13-1996 L2000 **AN** *020 †05

SCALO, Jordan Victor. 3305 NORTHLAND DR 78731 #035-47-1996 L2002 **PDP** *020 †55

SCHAEFER, Dale Glenn. 3807 SPICEWOOD SPRINGS RD, AUSTIN DERMCARE 78759 #048-04-1983 L1983 **D** *020 †15

SCHANEN, Dean E. 720 W 34TH ST 78705 #048-02-1995 L1997 **EM** *020 †20,16

SCHARNBERG, John Todd, II. 11113 RESEARCH BLVD 78759 #048-04-1975 L1975 **NPM PD** *020 †55

SCHEDLER, Paul Wagner. 3002 BRIDLE PATH 78703 #048-02-1954 L1954 **GP** *071

SCHINDEL, Jeffrey. 12221 N MO PAC EXPY 78758 #048-04-1983 L1985 **PUD IM** *020 †20

SCHLAB, Jeffrey S. 720 W 34TH ST STE 101 78705 #048-04-1995 L1999 **EM** *020 †16

SCHLECHTER, Robert David. 1301 BARBARA JORDAN BLVD, STE 400 78723 #016-42-1977 L1984 **PDS GS** *020 †85

SCHLEUSE, William. ■ 78759 #048-02-1957 L1957 **PYA P** *071 †75

SCHLITT, John Tyler. 3705 MEDICAL PKWY, STE 570 78705 #048-12-2001 L2005 **AN** *020 †05

SCHMEIL, Christopher Jon. 2501 TOWER DR, CAPITOL EMERGENCY ASSOCIAT 78703 #051-04-1997 L2000 **EM** *020 †16

SCHMIDT, Baruch Samson. ■ 78783 #028-02-1962 L1975 **GS** *071

SCHMIDT, Ingrid Elisabeth. 5750 BALCONES DR, STE 109 78731 #409-23-1972 L1976 **P CHP** *020

SCHMIDT, Rodney Duane. 10900 STONELAKE BLVD, STE 250 78759 #048-04-1976 L1976 **RNR LM** *020 †80 ‡

SCHMITZ, Martha E. 4007 JAMES CASEY ST, STE A240 78745 #048-02-1989 L1994 **OBG** *020 †30

SCHNEIDER, Adam J. 1301 W 38TH ST, STE 60 78705 #048-12-1993 L1994 **IM** *020 †20

SCHNEIDER, Douglas A. 1718 BARTON SPRINGS RD, TRLRG 78704 #048-13-1982 L1983 **EM** *020 †16

SCHNEIDER, John Phillip. ■ 78735 #021-01-1952 L1956 **U** *071 †95

SCHNEIER, Rose L. 1301 BARBARA JORDAN BLVD 78723 #041-12-1975 L2003 **PD END** *020 †55

SCHOCH, Eugene Paul, Jr. 3A MEDICAL ARTS SQUARE 78705 #048-02-1946 L1946 **D** *071 †15

SCHOCH, Eugene Paul, III. 3001 BEE CAVE RD, STE 220 78746 #048-02-1974 L1974 **ORS** *020 †40

SCHOEN, Robert W, Jr. 630 W 34TH ST STE 30 78705 #048-14-1982 L1983 **ORS** *020 †40

SCHOLL, Catherine Lee. 12221 N MO PAC EXPY 78758 #048-02-1981 L1983 **AN PD** *020 †05

SCHOLL, Peter Dennis. 3705 MEDICAL PKWY STE 310 78705 #048-14-1981 L1981 **HNS** *020 †45

SCHOTT, Liesl Christine. 1918 E RIVERSIDE DR, SOUTH AUSTIN MEDICAL & HEA 78741 #048-02-2003 L2005 **GP** *020

SCHROEDER, Lorraine K. 2013 WELLS BRANCH PKWY, STE 113 78728 #048-13-1985 L1986 **FM** *020 †18

SCHUHMACHER, Richard H. ■ 78727 #039-01-1972 L1979 **AN** *020 †05

SCHULTZ, Kenneth A. 6001 W PARMER LN, STE 370 NMR 189 78727 #048-15-1999 L2003 **FM** *020 †18

SCHULTZ, Thomas Leonard. 4007 JAMES CASEY ST 78745 #038-06-1955 L1955 **ORS** *071 †40

SCHULTZ, William Randall. 12411 HYMEADOW DR, STE 3B 78750 #048-04-1998 L2003 **OSM** *020 †40

SCHULZE, T W. 801 W 34TH ST 78705 #048-12-1966 L1966 **D** *020 †15

SCHWAB, Paige Clark. 3508 FAR WEST BLVD, FL 2 78731 #048-15-1989 L1990 **PD** *020 †55

SCHWAB, Thomas. 10215 HOLME LACEY LN 78750 #957-01-1965 L1977 **FM GP** *020

SCOTT, Nakia Gray. 1407 W STASSNEY LN, MAGNOLIA ACHIEVEMENT PROGR 78745 #048-12-2002 L2004 **CHP** *100 †75

SCOTT, Serena Edna. 1201 W 38TH ST, SETON MEDICAL CENTER 78705 #061-01-1998 L2004 **NPM** *020 †55

SCUMPIA, Simona M. 2200 PARK BEND DR, BLDG 3 #300 AUSTIN THYROID 78758 #781-01-1980 L1988 **END OS** *020 †20

SEADE, Louis Edward. 1015 E 32ND ST STE 500 78705 #048-12-1993 L1995 **ORS** *020 †40

SEAQUIST, Jack Linden. 1301 W 38TH ST STE 102, 102 MEDICAL PARK TOWER 78705 #048-04-1972 L1972 **ORS** *020 †40

SEBESTYEN, Christina E. 12201 RENFERT WAY, STE 230 78758 #041-01-1999 L2005 **OBG** *020 †30 ‡

SEEKER, Christopher Glenn. 1301 W 38TH ST, STE 109 78705 #048-13-1984 L1985 **OBG REN** *020 †30

SEELIYUR DURAISWAMY, Sathi. 5604 SW PARKWAY 78735 #496-71-2003 **IM** *012

SEIDEL, Scott Andrew. 1010 W 40TH ST, CARDIOTHORACIC AND VASCULA 78756 #048-12-1994 L2000 **VS** *020 †85

SEIDENBERG, Philip David. ■ 78703 #005-11-2000 L2003 **EM** *100 †16

SEILER, Robert K. 1301 W 38TH ST, STE 109 78705 #048-12-1993 L1995 **IM** *020 †20

SELMON, Matthew Rowland. 3801 N LAMAR BLVD, STE 300 78756 #048-12-1979 L1979 **CD IM** *020 †20

SENTER, Jerald R. 1106 CLAYTON LN 78723 #039-01-1952 L1953 **GP** *071

SEREMETIS, George Michael. 1301 BARBARA JORDAN BLVD, STE 302 78723 #010-02-1986 L1995 **UP U** *020 †95

SEREMETIS, L. 603 W 18TH ST 78701 #035-15-1989 L1995 **P** *020 †75

SETHUPATHI, Anandhi. 3501 MILLS AVE, SETON SHOAL CREEK HOSP 78731 #495-04-1998 L2008 **CHP** *012

SETHURAMAN, Girish. 720 W 34TH ST, STE 101 78705 #025-07-2003 L2007 **EM** *020

SETTLE, Halsey Marvin. 4207 JAMES CASEY ST # 305 78745 #048-02-1971 L1971 **OPH** *020 †35

SETTLE, Stephen Michael. 1010 W 40TH ST 78756 #048-12-1986 L1987 **VS** *020 †85

SEWELL, Bennett N, III. 919 E 32ND ST 78705 #021-01-1957 L1969 **PTH** *020 †50

SEXTON, Richard Allen. ■ 78731 #004-01-1997 L2003 **EM** *020 †16

SFEIR, Mouna G. 1600 W 38TH ST, STE 321 78731 #605-01-1992 L2005 **P** *020 †75 ‡

SHAFFER, Kenneth Mark. 4314 MEDICAL PKWY, STE 200 78756 #023-07-1990 L1993 **PDC** *020 †55

SHAFFER, Linda Govea. 1301 BARBARA JORDAN BLVD, STE 401 78723 #023-07-1990 L1993 **PHO** *020 †55

SHAH, Deepa Mayank. 720 W 34TH ST, STE 101 78705 #495-76-1994 L2000 **PD** *020 †55

SHAH, Gaurang N. 900 WEST AVE, DEPT OF EMERGENCY MEDICINE 78701 #048-16-2000 L2003 **EM** *020

SHAH, Prati Kadakia. ■ 78754 #495-65-1978 L2003 **PYG** *020 †75

SHAH, Purvi Harkishan. 919 E 32ND ST 78705 #048-12-2003 L2005 **EM** *100 †16

SHAH, Rajeev Kisan. 10900 STONELAKE BLVD, STE 250 78759 #048-02-2000 L2004 **RNR** *020 †80

SHAH, Rakhi Sameer. 601 E 15TH ST 78701 #495-83-2000 **IM** *012

SHAH, Rita R. 6835 AUSTIN CENTER BLVD 78731 #056-06-1994 L1997 **IM** *020 †20

SHAH, Sandeep Anil. 10900 STONELAKE BLVD, STE 250 78759 #048-02-2001 L2007 **DR** *100 †80

SHAH, Sangeeta J. 6835 AUSTIN CENTER BLVD 78731 #048-02-2001 L2005 **PD** *020 †55

SHAH, Toral Darshan. 7409 BLUE BEACH CV 78759 #495-23-1994 L1999 **PD** *020 †55

SHAKIL, Rubina. 3501 MILLS AVE, OF PSYCHIATRY 78731 #704-02-1994 L2003 **PYG** *012

SHANE, J Howard, III. 6101 BALCONES DR, STE 300 78731 #048-02-1992 L2002 **IM** *020 †20

SHANE, James Austin, Jr. ■ 78759 #030-05-1962 L1962 **FM** *071 †20

SHANGHVI, Roopal Rajendra. ■ 78730 #035-08-2001 L2007 **D** *020

SHAPIRO, Ira. 1201 W 38TH ST 78705 #048-02-1978 L1979 **OBG** *020 †30

SHAPIRO, Jay. 1301 BARBARA JORDAN BLVD 78723 #048-02-1984 L1985 **OP OS** *020 †40

SHAPIRO, Michael. 1305 W 34TH ST 78705 #048-02-1978 L1978 **PUD CCM** *020 †20

SHAPIRO, Ronald Bruce. 900 E 30TH ST, STE 311 78705 #036-01-1987 L1999 **PDC PD** *020 †55

SHARIFIAN, Mehdi. 7003 WINTERBERRY DR 78750 #517-01-1965 L1976 **CHP P** *020

SHARMA, Sanjay Kumar. 4220 BULL CREEK RD 78731 #048-04-1996 L1998 **PS HS** *020 †65

SHARMAN, Ralph S, Jr. 4614 N I H 35 78751 #048-13-1996 L1998 **FM** *020 †18

SHARP, Erica Catterall. 12201 RENFERT WAY, STE 110 78758 #041-01-1997 L2000 **PD** *020 †55

SHARP, James Calvin, Jr. 1301 BARBARA JORDAN BLVD, STE 401 78723 #048-02-1963 L1963 **PHO PD** *020 †55

SHAW, David Jon. 10900 STONELAKE BLVD, STE 250 78759 #041-09-1997 L2004 **RNR** *012 †80

SHAW, Koushik Kumar. 7600 N CAPITAL OF TEXS HWY, STE A 78731 #024-05-1998 L2004 **U** *020 †95

SHEEHAN, Timothy Daniel, III. 3501 MILLS AVE, AMEP DEPT OF PSYCHIATRY 78731 #048-02-2007 **P** *012

SHEER, Todd Alex. 7600 N CAPITAL OF TEXS HWY, STE A 78731 #010-02-1997 L2007 *020 †20

SHEFF, Gregory Scott. 8204 BRODIE LN, STE 101 78745 #034-01-1999 L2002 **FM** *020 †18

SHEIKH, Farzana. 601 E 15TH ST 78701 #704-16-1996 **FP** *012

SHEINBERG, Jonathan I. 1301 W 38TH ST STE 705, TEXAS CARDIOVASCULAR 78705 #010-02-1994 L2004 **CD** *020 †20

SHEKARCHI, Azim G. 3828 S 1ST ST 78704 #048-02-1996 L1998 **IM** *020 †20

SHELTON, Deborah. 4615 SPICEWOOD SPRINGS RD 78759 #031-01-1993 L1999 **CHP** *020 †75

SHEN, Mark Wayne. 4900 MUELLER BLVD, UTMB AUSTIN PEDIATRICS 78723 #048-12-1999 L2000 **PD** *020 †55

SHEN, Yue. ■ 78733 #048-16-1999 L2004 **CN** *020 †75

SHENEMAN, Jeffrey Scott. 10900 STONELAKE BLVD, STE 250 78759 #048-04-2001 L2002 **VIR** *100 †80

SHEPLER, Maria Cristina. 12221 N MO PAC EXPY 78758 #039-01-1998 L1999 **OPH** *020 †35

SHEPLER, Todd Robert. 3705 MEDICAL PKWY, STE 120 78705 #039-01-1998 L1999 **OPH** *020 †35

SHEPPARD, Joy Celeste. 4100 DUVAL RD, BLDG 2 78759 #048-12-1989 L1990 **OBG MFM** *020 †30

SHERMAN, Howard H. 8709 ESCABOSA DR 78748 #035-08-1960 L1961 **IM AM** *062

SHERO, Charlene Margot. 1430 COLLIER ST, HEALTH 78704 #018-03-1990 L1996 **P PYG** *020 †35

SHERROD, Mark Robert. 3705 MEDICAL PKWY, STE 250 78705 #048-02-1976 L1976 **GS** *020 †85

SHETH, Mehul Vikram. ■ 78723 #021-05-1999 L2002 **IM** *020 †20

SHETTIGAR, Raghu Dev. 313 E 12TH ST, CAPITAL OBSTETRICS & 78701 #035-09-1999 L2003 **OBG** *020 †30

SHIH, Angela H. 12201 RENFERT WAY, STE 300 78758 #048-04-1999 L2002 **IM** *020 †20

SHIH, Daniel S. ■ 78735 #048-02-2001 L2004 **IM** *020

SHIN, Edward Jaywon. 301 CONGRESS AVE, FL 9 78701 #041-01-1997 **IM** *050 †20

SHIN, Hyonho. 4101 JAMES CASEY ST, STE 340 78745 #048-14-1993 L1994 **GS VS** *020 †85

SHIPPEN, Judy Renae. ■ 78701 #049-01-1996 L1997 **IM** *020 †20

SHIPPY, Ann Marie. 3267 BEE CAVE RD, STE 107-261 78746 #048-14-1999 L2002 **IM** *020 †20

SHOBERG, Richard Saml, Jr. 3705 MEDICAL PKWY, STE 570 78705 #034-01-1968 L1974 **AN** *071 †05

SHON, Steven Paul. 909 W 45TH ST, TX DEPT. OF STATE HEALTH S 78751 #005-02-1972 L1993 P *020

SHORE, John Wm. 3705 MEDICAL PKWY, STE 120 78705 #028-02-1977 L1978 OPH *020 †35

SHRIKHANDE, Shubhada S. 12221 N MO PAC EXPY 78758 #495-83-1992 L2003 ON HEM *020 †20

SHUFORD, Jennifer Ann. ■ 78735 #048-12-1999 L2002 ID *100 †20

SHULMAN, Edie E. 12201 RENFERT WAY, STE 300 78758 #048-14-1991 L1992 IM *020 †16

SHULTZ, James Michael. 1413 W 6TH ST 78703 #048-12-1968 L1968 PYA P *020 †75

SHUNG, Sheila X. 12201 RENFERT WAY, STE 320 78758 #048-13-1999 L2001 IM *020

SIAREZI, Sherry. ■ 78756 #035-08-2001 L2004 OBG *012

SIDDIQUI, Asif Muhammad. 3636 EXECUTIVE CENTER DR, STE 216 78731 #704-16-1990 L2000 CHP P *020

SILBERMAN, Mark A. 9200 WALL ST 78754 #023-07-1991 L1999 PTH HMP *020 †50

SILVA, Peter. 3101 BEE CAVE RD, STE 310 78746 #048-14-1994 L1995 P *020 †75

SILVERBERG, Kaylen Mark. 6500 N MO PAC EXPY, STE 1-1200 78731 #048-04-1984 L1986 REN OBG *030

SILVERTHORN, Andrew Chas. 1420 W 51ST ST 78756 #045-01-1977 L1979 FM *020 †18

SIMMANG, Dana Lee. 1015 E 32ND ST, STE 405 78705 #048-16-1995 L1996 PD *020 †20

SIMMONS, Edith Marie. 1015 E 32ND ST, STE 414 78705 #027-01-1997 L2004 NEP *020 †20

SIMON, Craig Alan. 421 W 3RD ST, STE 1501 78701 #019-02-1988 L1996 ORS *020 †40

SIMON, David Henry. 1301 BARBARA JORDAN BLVD #011-02-2000 L2006 PN *020 †55

SIMON, Katherine Ellen. 601 E 15TH ST, STE L502 78701 #048-02-2000 L2006 NPM *020 †55

SIMONSEN, Rodney Jesse. 1015 E 32ND ST, STE 411 78705 #023-07-1967 L1971 PM PME *020 †60

SIMPAO, Marc Philip. 1301 W 38TH ST, STE 205 78705 #048-13-2005 L2007 IM *012

SIMPSON, John Scott. 8303 N MO PAC EXPY STE 450 78759 #048-02-1979 L1979 OBG *030 †30

SIMPSON, Karon. 1015 E 32ND ST STE 414 78705 #048-02-1979 L1979 NEP IM *020 †20

SINGER, Don Bernard. 601 E 15TH ST 78701 #048-04-1959 L1960 PTH PP *040 †50

SINGH, Herb. 3100 RED RIVER ST 78705 #041-01-1999 L2005 U *020 †95

SINGH, Suneet Kumar. 720 W 34TH ST STE 101, EMERGENCY SERVICE PARTNERS 78705 #051-04-2002 L2005 EM *020 †16

SINGIREDDY, Sudha. ■ 78738 #495-57-1991 L2000 IM *020 †20

SINGLETON, Rasheed Amir. ■ 78732 #041-15-2000 L2005 APM *100

SIVAM, Senthil Kumar. 601 E 15TH ST 78701 #496-23-2004 IM *012

SIVARAMAKRISHNAN, Lakshmy. 601 E 15TH ST, STE L502 78701 #495-44-1992 L2000 PD *020 †55

SJOBERG, Walter Eugene. 600 CONGRESS AVE, 1380 ONE AMERICAN CENTER 78701 #048-02-1956 L1956 GE IM *020

SKAGGS, Harold, Jr. 4615 LENNOX DR 78745 #048-02-1967 L1967 N OS *071 †75

SKJONSBY, Robert Allen. 919 E 32ND ST, ST. DAVIDS MEDICAL CTR 78705 #026-04-1980 L1985 EM *020 †16

SKOGLUND, Daniel Neil. 3305 NORTHLAND DR STE 401 78731 #016-45-1993 L1997 P *020

SLATER, Patrick W, II. 12201 RENFERT WAY, STE 100 78758 #036-08-1990 L1998 OTO *020 †45

SLAUGHTER, Daniel P. 12201 RENFERT WAY STE 105 78758 #048-04-1990 L1991 OTO *020 †45

SLAWSKY, Richard Chas. ■ 78746 #010-01-1980 L2007 P *020 †75

SMART, Virgil Clay. ■ 78703 #048-02-1956 L1956 A *071 †18 ‡

SMILEY, Sarah I. 919 E 32ND ST 78705 #048-78-1991, ▲ L1992 IM OS *020 †20

SMITH, Amy Burton. 901 W BEN WHITE BLVD 78704 #048-14-1996 L2000 EM *020 †16

SMITH, Archie Dan, Jr. 1215 RED RIVER ST 78701 #048-04-1977 L1977 IM IMG *020 †20

SMITH, Arthur Mitchell. 3801 N LAMAR BLVD, STE 300 78756 #067-01-1981 L1993 CD IM *020 †20

SMITH, Bobby Joe. 1106 CLAYTON LN STE 102 78723 #048-02-1958 L1958 FM GS *020

SMITH, Charlotte Hoehne. 605 E 15TH ST, BRACKENRIDGE REHABILITATIO 78701 #048-04-1986 L1987 PM SCI *060

SMITH, Christopher Todd. 6835 AUSTIN CENTER BLVD 78731 #004-01-1993 L1996 FM *020 †18

SMITH, Deborah K. 6406 N IH 35, STE 1805 78752 #048-13-1997 L1998 P *020

SMITH, Donovan Davidson. 2555 WESTERN TRAILS BLVD, STE 101 78745 #048-15-2002 L2005 FM *020 †18

SMITH, Ellen Blair. 901 W 38TH ST STE 200 78705 #036-01-1977 L1978 GO OBG *020 †30

SMITH, F Ames, Jr. 1015 E 32ND ST 78705 #048-02-1984 L1985 GS *020 †85

SMITH, Ferril Chris. 4207 JAMES CASEY ST, STE 304 78745 #048-13-1981 L1981 IM *020 †20

SMITH, Gary Wayne. 12221 N MO PAC EXPY 78758 #048-12-1984 L1986 AN *020 †05

SMITH, Gerald James. ■ 78731 #035-01-2000 PD *100

SMITH, Grayson K. 4315 JAMES CASEY ST 78745 #048-14-1986 L1987 IM *020 †20

SMITH, James L, Jr. 6818 AUSTIN CENTER BLVD, STE 200 78731 #048-02-1983 L1983 OSS *020 †40

SMITH, Laurette Nasrat. 12201 RENFERT WAY STE 215, RENAISSANCE WOMENS GRP 78758 #011-02-1995 L1999 OBG *020 †30

SMITH, Mark B. 1410 IH 35 N 78701 #048-02-1985 L1986 PDS *020 †85

SMITH, Marshall Leroy, Jr. 78759 #048-02-1975 L1975 OBG *020 †30

SMITH, Melissa Coolidge. 2811 E 2ND ST 78702 #054-04-1988 L1996 FM *020 †18

SMITH, Michael A. ■ 78748 #048-12-1999 DR *100

SMITH, Quintin James. 4012 N LAMAR BLVD 78756 #048-02-1965 L1965 OPH GP *020 †35

SMITH, Randolph T. 3300 W ANDERSON LN, STE 308 78757 #048-02-2001 L2005 *020

SMITH, Thomas Henry. 919 E 32ND ST 78705 #051-01-1975 L1984 FM RM *020 †18

SMOLIK, Erwin John, Jr. 3801 S LAMAR BLVD 78704 #048-02-1975 L1975 EM FM *020

SMUTS, Erin Michelle. 6101 BALCONES DR STE 300 78731 #048-02-1997 L2002 IM *020 †20

SNEED, Dennis R. 7301 RANCH ROAD 620 N, STE 155 78726 #048-02-1977 L1977 IM OS *020 †20

SNIDER, Robert N. 4212 MEDICAL PKWY 78756 #048-02-1950 L1950 R NM *071 †80

SNYDER, Kimberly. 12221 N MO PAC EXPY, DEPT EMERGENCY MED 78758 #033-05-1988 L1995 EM *020 †16

SNYDER, Ned, IV. 901 W 38TH ST, STE 410 78705 #048-02-2000 L2005 PS *020 †65 ‡

SNYDER, Renee Remi. 901 W 38TH ST, STE 410 78705 #048-02-2001 L2004 D *012 †15

SOFINOWSKI, Richard E. 56 EAST AVE 78701 #048-04-1991 L1992 P *020 †75

SOLIS, Ricardo L. 4007 JAMES CASEY ST STE D150 78745 #048-12-1994 L2001 CRS *020 †85,10

SOLOMON, Steven Kirk. 11111 RESEARCH BLVD, STE 334 78759 #048-13-1984 L1985 OBG *020 †30

SONNENBERG, Stephen M. 1600 W 38TH ST STE 403 78731 #035-46-1965 L1994 PYA P *020 †75

SONSTEIN, Allen. 7201 MANCHACA RD, STE B 78745 #041-02-1972 L1974 IM FPG *020 †20,18

SOO, Ann C. 12201 RENFERT WAY STE 300 78758 #048-12-1994 L1995 IM *020 †20

SOO, Peter C. 6836 BEE CAVE RD, STE 205 78746 #048-02-1995 L1996 P *020 †75

SOOD, Lily. 3816 S 1ST ST 78704 #495-39-1976 L1981 PD *020 †55

SOUBRA, Said Hassane. 720 W 34TH ST STE 101, EMERGENCY SERVICE PARTNERS 78705 #605-01-1996 L2003 PCC *020 †20

SOUSARES, Teddy Malcolm. 3501 MILLS AVE 78731 #048-02-1956 L1956 P *071

SPAHT, Katherine Lindley. 4900 MUELLER BLVD, DELL CHILDREN'S MEDICAL CE 78723 #021-05-2003 L2007 PD *100 †55

SPALDING, Theresa Rose. 100 W DEAN KEATON ST, SSB 2.212 78712 #048-02-1984 L1985 FM *030 †18

SPANN, Joseph Logan. 2901 MONTOPOLIS DR 78741 #048-12-1980 L1980 IM *020 †20

SPANN, June M D. 2901 MONTOPOLIS DR, VETERAN'S ADMINISTRATION C 78741 #048-12-1979 L1979 IM *020 †20

SPARKMAN, Ryan L. ■ 78750 #048-14-2008 *012

SPEARS, Teddie Dwayne. 9737 GREAT HILLS TRL, STE 240 78759 #048-02-1980 L1980 ORS *020 †40

SPENCER, Donald Carson. 2911 MEDICAL ARTS ST, STE 19A 78705 #048-02-1959 L1959 GS *071 †85

SPENCER, John N, Jr. 12741 RESEARCH BLVD, STE 303 78759 #048-13-1993 L1994 P *020 †75

SPENCER, Kevin Patrick. 4534 W GATE BLVD, STE 108 78745 #048-14-1994 L2004 FM *020 †18

SPERLING, Richard Michael. 1111 W 34TH ST, STE 200 78705 #048-04-1988 L1995 GE IM *020 †20

SPIDLE, James Lloyd. 601 E 15TH ST 78701 #048-02-1955 L1955 PTH *071 †50

SPILLAR, Edna Myrl Hughes. ■ 78746 #048-04-1954 L1954 AN *071 †05

SPINDEL, Enrique. 1015 E 32ND ST, STE 211 78705 #649-01-1978 L1984 GE IM *020 †20

SPINDLER, Melanie Marino. 12221 N MO PAC EXPY 78758 #048-02-2002 L2007 END *100 †20

SPOOR, Scott D. 12221 N MO PAC EXPY 78758 #048-02-1984 L1985 N IM *020 †20,75

SPRUTE, Dana. 1313 RED RIVER ST STE 100, BLACKSTONE FAMILY HEALTH C 78701 #048-13-1993 L1994 FM *020 †18

SRIRAM, Padman M. 4614 N IH 35 78751 #048-14-1997 L2001 ID IM *020

STAATS, Marsha Ann. 1201 W 38TH ST 78705 #028-46-1981 L1984 IM *020

STAHL, Marion Leonard. 919 E 32ND ST 78705 #047-06-1948 L1948 OBG *071 †30

STAHLMAN, Matthew B. 1301 W 38TH ST, STE 705 78705 #048-14-1997 L2000 CD *020 †20

STALEY, Jennings Ryan. ■ 78701 #016-45-2001 L2001 IM *020 †20

STANCIU, Thomas Jeffrey. 3705 MEDICAL PKWY, STE 570 78705 #017-20-1993 L1998 AN *005

STANLEY, Sharilyn K. 1100 W 49TH ST, TEXAS DEPT. OF HEALTH 78756 #048-04-1983 L1983 AI IM *050 †20,03

STANSBERRY, Paul Kevin. 12221 N MO PAC EXPY 78758 #048-04-1977 L1977 ON IM *020 †20

STARCHE, Paula Noelke. 12221 N MO PAC EXPY, AUSTIN DIAGNOSTIC CLINIC 78758 #048-14-1975 L1976 IM IMG *020 †20

STAVINOHA, William D. 11671 JOLLYVILLE RD, STE 102 78759 #048-02-1982 L1983 FM *020 †18 ‡

STECHER, Michael David. 11614 BEE CAVES RD, STE 130 78738 #019-02-2002 L2004 FM *020 †18

STEFANI, Anne Milia. 2100 W WILLIAM CANNON DR, STE C 78745 #027-01-1989 L1998 FM *020 †18

STEFFENSEN, Stephan Lewis, II. ■ 78747 #039-01-2001 L2003 *020 †75

STENZEL, Loretta Sutphin. 8656A W HIGHWAY 71, STE C 78735 #036-07-1986 L2008 FM *020 †18

STENZEL, Timothy Todd. 2150 WOODWARD ST, STE 100 78744 #036-07-1992 L1996 PTH *062 †50,19

STEPHENS, Christopher T. ■ 78701 #048-02-2002 L2007 AN *100

STEPHENS, Elena Valerie. 100 W DEAN KEATON ST, UNIVERSITY HEALTH SERVICES 78712 #913-11-1991 L2003 FM *020 †18

STEPHENS, Harold Dean. ■ 78732 #048-12-1961 L1961 GP *071

STEPHENS, Kevin. 4100 DUVAL RD, STE 2-202 78759 #003-01-1993 L1996 FM *020 †18

STEVENS, Jack O. 3705 MEDICAL PKWY, STE 570 78705 #048-12-1987 L1988 AN *020 †05

STEWART, Kendal L. 6836 BEE CAVE RD STE 180 78746 #048-14-1988 L1989 OTO *020 †45

STEWART, Lynn Nicole. 1010 LAVACA ST, STE 221 78701 #021-01-2003 L2006 FM *020 †18

STEWART, Mark Thos. 1010 W 40TH ST 78756 #048-12-1977 L1977 VS GS *020 †85

STEWART, Sidney Carl. 8613 CROSS PARK DR 78754 #048-12-1960 L1960 CLP PTH *071 †50

STOKES, John Klotz. 400 W 15TH ST, STE 800 78701 #048-13-1995 L2002 NS *020 †25

STONE, James Byron. 5750 BALCONES DR STE 101A 78731 #048-14-1981 L1981 CHP P *020 †75

STONECIPHER, Robert F. 4107 SPICEWOOD SPRINGS RD, HOSPICE AUSTIN 78759 #048-04-1989 L1991 FM *020 †18

STONEDALE, Felicia Ann. ■ 78734 #048-02-1978 L1980 EM OS *020 †16

STOUFFLET, Paul E. 715 W 34TH ST 78705 #048-16-1989 L1990 IM *020 †20

STOVALL, Richard Bernard. 2200 PARK BEND DR, BLDG 2-201 78758 #048-12-1997 L1998 NS *020

STRACENSKY, Sean A. ■ 78735 #023-12-1998 AN *100

STRANDHAGEN, Tracy D. 12221 N MO PAC EXPY 78758 #048-04-1993 L1995 AN *020 †05

STREUSAND, William Chas. 3215 STECK AVE, STE 100 78757 #048-04-1980 L1980 CHP P *020 †75

STROGATZ, Melissa Lynne. 3816 S 1ST ST 78704 #041-01-2001 L2007 PD *020 †55

STRONG, James Arthur. 11111 RESEARCH BLVD, STE 150 78759 #048-12-1970 L1970 PD *030 †55

STROUD, Robert Lee. 4007 JAMES CASEY ST, STE C120 78745 #048-02-1974 L1974 IM *020 †20 ‡

STUART, Julie Elise. 1313 RED RIVER ST, STE 100 78701 #017-20-1986 L1994 FP *012 †50

STULTZ, Daniel Rex. 11600 BOULDER LN 78726 #048-14-1975 L1975 IM *020 †20

STURGEON, Ryan C. 12221 N MO PAC EXPY 78758 #038-41-2002 L2006 AN *020 †05

SU, Eric Chienchih. 919 E 32ND ST, 750 WASHINGTON ST 78705 #035-09-2000 L2007 NPM *020 †55

SUAREZ, Luis Maria. ■ 78731 #132-02-1959 L1977 P N *020 †75

SUBRAHMANYAM, Narra. 12411 HYMEADOW DR, BLDG 3 STE E 78750 #495-98-1975 L1984 CD IM *020 †20

SULLIVAN, Brian Loren. 3003 BEE CAVE RD, STE 201 78746 #048-04-1973 L1974 ORS *020 †40

SUPNET, Benjamin Depante. 4101 JAMES CASEY ST, STE 330 78745 #016-42-1997 L2001 OBG *020 †30

SURRATT, John Kilpatrick. ■ 78705 #048-14-2004 L2007 DR *012

SUTTON, Beverly E Jewell. 3501 MILLS AVE 78731 #025-01-1957 L1962 CHP PD *072 †55,75

SUTTON, Terry John. ■ 78746 #019-02-1966 L1990 **GP** *071
SVENKERUD, Erik Knut. 1100 W 49TH ST # T811 78756 #048-02-1974 L1974 **PM** *062 †70
SWAMY, Sunita. 900 E 30TH ST, STE 200 78705 #048-15-2000 L2002 **FM** *100 †18
SWANSON, Beth A. 3705 MEDICAL PKWY, STE 570 78705 #048-14-1995 L2000 **AN PAN** *020 †05
SWANSON, Christopher E. 10900 STONELAKE BLVD, STE 250 78759 #048-04-1995 L1999 **DR** *020 †80
SWEARINGEN, Robert Lee. ■ 78703 #048-04-1959 L1960 **ORS OS** *062 †40
SWEENEY, Lyda Shelley. 1301 W 38TH ST, DRS DESROSIERS & WERNECKE 78705 #048-12-1985 L1986 **OBG** *020 †30
SWENSON, Karen Grace. 1305 W 34TH ST STE 308, WOMEN PARTNERS IN HLTH 78705 #048-04-1981 L1981 **OBG** *020 †30
SYMONS, Samantha Clare. 1600 W 38TH ST, STE 404 78731 #048-12-2000 L2004 **P** *020 †75
TACHE, Mara Suzanne. 4315 JAMES CASEY ST 78745 #021-01-1997 L2000 **PD** *020 †55
TACQUARD, Stephanie L. ■ 78759 #048-14-2007 **PD** *012
TAI, James Wen-Huang. 100 W DEAN KEATON ST 78712 #025-01-1980 L1983 **IM** *020 †20
TALBOT, Milton Wm, Jr. ■ 78731 #021-01-1946 L1951 **PD** *071 †55
TALBOTT, L Brent. 9200 WALL ST 78754 #019-02-1974 L1995 **PTH DMP** *020 †50
TALLMAN, Richard Dean. 12221 N MO PAC EXPY, STE 58 78758 #026-08-1977 L1984 **N MDM** *020 †20,75
TALUKDAR, Feroza Begum. 4110 GUADALUPE ST, D UNIT 78751 #160-02-1975 L1992 **CHP** *020 †75
TAMIMI, Raed Radi. 2901 MONTOPOLIS DR 78741 #915-02-1979 L1994 **P** *020 †75
TAN, Alice Hyun-Kyung. ■ 78735 #583-27-2000 L2003 **IM** *100 †20
TAN, Thomas C. 4110 GUADALUPE ST 78751 #506-02-1965 L1973 **CHP P** *020 †75
TANG, Mingsheng. 5208 CRYSTAL WATER DR 78735 #048-02-1999 L2002 **FM** *020
TANNER-INMAN, Lynne. 4110 GUADALUPE ST, AUSTIN STATE HOSPITAL 78751 #048-16-1984 L1985 **CHP P** *020 †75
TANNOUS, Rawah. 1301 W 38TH ST, STE 202 78705 #875-01-1995 L2005 *020 †20
TAPIA, Socorro. ■ 78735 #649-27-1965 L1983 **PD** *071
TARRANT, Natalie Blanche. 6507 JESTER BLVD, STE 301 78750 #048-04-2000 L2003 **PD** *020 †55
TATE, Robert Atchison. 601 E 15TH ST 78701 #048-02-1962 L1962 **TS VS** *071 †85,90
TATINENI, Latha. ■ 78759 #495-94-2000 L2008 **IM** *020 †20
TAYLOR, Cesar Jacobo. 8310 N CAPITAL OF TEXS HWY, STE 350 78731 #048-12-1998 L2000 **AN** *020 †05
TAYLOR, Eulon Ross. 4110 GUADALUPE ST, AUSTIN STATE HOSPITAL 78751 #048-13-1978 L1980 **P** *020 †75
TAYLOR, William Josiah. 3724 EXECUTIVE CENTER DR, STE G10 78731 #048-04-1978 L1979 **FM EM** *020 †18
TAYLOR, William Peyton. 6818 AUSTIN CNTR BLVD #100 78731 #048-12-1968 L1968 **OSS** *020 †40
TCHENG, Jason Wing. ■ 78758 #048-15-2007 **GS** *012
TEAGUE, Robert Burdette. ■ 78746 #038-41-1975 L1976 **PUD OM** *062 †20
TEEL, Karen L Williams. 1305 W 34TH ST, STE 410 78705 #048-04-1963 L1963 **PD** *071 †55
TEMPEST, Gregory Richard. 901 W BEN WHITE BLVD 78704 #025-07-2000 L2005 **N** *020 †75
TERMINELLA, Luigi. 1305 W 34TH ST, STE 400 78705 #561-04-1986 L2004 **PCC** *020 †20
TERRESON, David Whitten. 1301 W 38TH ST, STE 705 78705 #027-01-1986 L1987 **CD** *020 †20
TERRILL, Mildred Kemper. U OF T STUDENT HLTH 78712 #016-06-1943 L1946 **OS GP** *071
TERRY, Douglas W. 5609 COURTYARD CV 78731 #048-02-1949 L1950 **IM HEM** *071 †20
TERWELP, Daniel Rome. 3410 FAR WEST BLVD 78731 #048-14-1975 L1975 **PD** *020 †55
THADANI, Anita H. 4515 SETON CENTER PKWY, STE 220 78759 #495-99-1979 L1986 **IM** *020 †20
THAKRAR, Yaksha Dhiraj. ■ 78715 #496-38-1970 L1979 **AN** *020
THAMARUS, Warren Edward. 1701 E 7TH ST, VISTA MEDICAL CENTER 78702 #025-01-1954 L1981 **FM EM** *020 †55
THAMPOE, Karen Xuan. 6101 BALCONES DR STE 300, HOSPITAL INTERNISTS OF AUS 78731 #422-01-2001 L2004 **IM** *071
THANT, Le-Wai. 2529 S 1ST ST 78704 #209-01-1985 L1996 **PD** *020 †55
THERIAULT, Gabrielle R. 10900 STONELAKE BLVD, STE 250 78759 #048-12-1991 L1998 **DR** *020 †80
THIRUNARAYANAN, Supriya. 601 E 15TH ST 78701 #496-34-2002 **N** *012
THOMPSON, Christopher P. 12201 RENFERT WAY, STE 105 78758 #048-12-1992 L1993 **OTO** *020 †45
THOMPSON, Daniel Otha, III. ■ 78746 #048-13-1976 L1977 **PD GP** *020
THOMPSON, Jesse Luke. ■ 78759 #048-12-1976 L1976 **FM** *071 †18
THOMPSON, John Michael. 3705 MEDICAL PKWY, STE 570 78705 #048-04-1993 L1994 **AN** *020 †05
THOMPSON, Kara A. 1301 W 38TH ST, STE 705 78705 #048-04-1993 L1994 **CD** *020 †20
THOMPSON, Margaret M. 12201 RENFERT WAY, STE 220 78758 #036-07-1978 L1982 **OBG** *020 †30
THOMPSON, Susan S. 4411 MEDICAL PKWY 78756 #048-12-1984 L1985 **CHP P** *020 †75
THOMPSON, William Saml. 2911 MEDICAL ARTS ST STE 3 78705 #048-02-1964 L1964 **D** *071 †15
THORNE, Geo Clifford, Jr. 1201 W 38TH ST 78705 #048-13-1976 L1976 **OPH** *020 †35
THORNE, Lansing S. ■ 78731 #048-12-1944 L1945 **PD** *071 †55
THORSTAD, Kelly Gayle. 12174 NORTH MOPAC, STE A 78758 #048-04-1998 L2000 **PD** *020 †55
THORSTAD, Willis Myron. 7701 VALLEY DALE DR 78731 #026-04-1962 L1971 **P** *072
THU, Christopher Steven. ■ 78746 #048-04-2003 L2007 **AN** *020
TIBLIER, Eric Stuart. 901 W 38TH ST, STE 400 78705 #048-13-1993 L1994 **CD** *020 †20
TIEMAN, Elizabeth K. 919 E 32ND ST 78705 #048-13-1992 L1997 **DR** *020 †80
TINDALL, John William. ■ 78728 #048-13-2007 **GS** *012
TINDEL, Jerry Ray. 12221 N MO PAC EXPY 78758 #048-02-1969 L1969 **N** *020 †75
TIPTON, George Washington. 1301 W 38TH ST STE 102 78705 #048-02-1938 L1938 **GS** *071 †85
TJELMELAND, Kelly Eugene. 4220 BULL CREEK RD 78731 #048-04-1993 L1995 **PS** *020 †65
TOBEY, David Neilson. 11623 ANGUS RD, AUSTIN EAR NOSE & THROAT 78759 #048-02-1971 L1971 **OTO HNS** *020 †45
TOKITA, Hanae Kristina. ■ 78704 #024-07-2007 **TY** *012
TOKUR SRIDHAR, Charitha R. 601 E 15TH ST 78701 #496-39-2002 L2007 **IM** *100 †20
TONG, Eugene. 10900 STONELAKE BLVD, STE 250 78759 #028-02-1996 L2001 **DR** *020
TONG, Weigang. PO BOX 2029 78768 #243-70-1997 *100
TORRES, Emilio Mario. 3205 N IH 35 78722 #048-04-1980 L1980 **OBG** *020 †30
TORRES, Manuel Aristo. 1110 W WILLIAM CANNON DR, STE 502 78745 #737-01-1977 L1988 **PD** *020 †55
TOUMA, Marlin. ■ 78749 #875-01-1992 L2008 **PD** *012
TOUPIN, Leo Roland, Jr. 12335 HYMEADOW DR, STE 150 78750 #017-20-1990 L2001 **IM** *020 †20
TOVAR, Reuben Wencis. ■ 78732 #048-04-1994 L1996 **IM** *020 †20
TOWELL, Brenda Lee. 4101 JAMES CASEY ST, STE 250 78745 #048-14-1979 L1979 **HO HEM** *020 †20
TOWNSEND, Bryan L. 8044 SHOAL CREEK BLVD 78757 #048-14-1992 L1993 **D** *072 †15
TRACEY, Thomas N. 4316 JAMES CASEY ST, STE A 78745 #048-14-1982 L1983 **CD IM** *020 †20
TRAMMELL, Linda Ann. 3801 N CAPITAL OF TEXS HWY, E240-114 78746 #005-06-1986 L1992 **PDR R** *020 †80
TRAN, Chuong Nguyen. 1101 PORTERFIELD DR 78753 #048-12-2000 L2002 **EM** *020 †16
TRAN, Kimthu. 11651 JOLLYVILLE RD, STE 150 78759 #048-15-1995 L1998 **FM** *020 †18
TRAN, Viet N. 4029 S CAPITAL OF TEXS HWY, STE 111 78704 #048-02-1996 L2001 **ORS OSS** *020 †40
TRAN, Xuan Kim. 8656 W HIGHWAY 71, STE C 78735 #048-02-2001 L2004 **FM** *020 †18
TRAWEEK, Stephen Thos. ■ 78733 #048-12-1980 L1980 **PTH** *050 †50
TRAYLOR, Rebecca J. 2901 MONTOPOLIS DR, CTVHCS-AUSTIN 78741 #048-14-1992 L1993 **PCC IM** *020 †20
TRENTIN, Ann Marie. 1301 W 38TH ST, STE 109 78705 #048-02-1979 L1979 **FM** *020 †18
TRESTER, Elliot J. 801 W 34TH ST, STE 102 78705 #038-43-1978 L1979 **FM** *020 †18
TRETJAK, Ziga. 901 W BEN WHITE BLVD 78704 #957-03-1973 L1996 **GE IM** *020 †20
TREVINO, Anthony K. 10900 STONELAKE BLVD, STE 250 78759 #048-04-1989 L1990 **DR** *020 †80
TREYBIG, Sandra K. 1100 W 39TH 1/2 ST, CAPITAL PEDIATRICS 78756 #048-14-1992 L1994 **PD** *020 †55
TRIPATHY, Rita. 11673 JOLLYVILLE RD, STE 104 78759 #039-01-1996 L2007 **PD** *020 †55
TRIZNA, Zoltan. 8500 BLUFFSTONE CV, STE A101 78759 #473-01-1983 L1999 **D** *020 †15
TROTTER, Michael David. 1111 W 34TH ST, STE 210 78705 #048-02-2000 L2004 **U** *020 †95
TROUTNER, John Leroy. 1631 E 2ND ST, STE D 78702 #024-07-1986 L1995 **P** *020 †20,75
TRUBEK, Simon. 10900 STONELAKE BLVD, STE 250 78759 #048-04-1998 L2000 **DR** *020 †28,80
TRUONG, Binh Cu. 1301 BARBARA JORDAN BLVD, STE 104 78723 #021-06-1993 L1998 **PDR** *020 †80
TRUONG, Kimphuong Pham. 825 E RUNDBERG LN STE B1 78753 #051-04-1994 L1998 **FM** *020 †18
TSAI, David Byeshin. 6836 BEE CAVE RD STE 112, BEE CAVES MEDICAL 78746 #041-13-1996 L2000 **FM** *020 †18 ‡
TSAI, Joanne E. ■ 78703 #048-12-1998 L2000 **CD** *020 †20
TSCHOPP, David Rene, Jr. 1301 W 38TH ST, STE 500 78705 #056-05-1997 L2006 **ICE** *100 †20
TSE, Jeffrey. 919 E 32ND ST 78705 #035-46-2002 L2004 **EM** *100 †16
TSOURMAS, Jessica Erin. ■ 78746 #010-01-2006 **P** *012
TSOURMAS, Mary V. 6835 AUSTIN CENTER BLVD 78731 #010-02-1978 L1985 **PTH** *020 †50
TSOURMAS, Nicholas F. 3003 BEE CAVE RD, STE 201 78746 #010-02-1978 L1984 **ORS** *020 †40
TUCKER, Paul A, II. 4316 JAMES CASEY ST, STE A 78745 #048-04-1987 L1988 **CD IM** *020 †20
TUCKER, Thomas Boynton. 711 W 38TH ST 78705 #048-12-1984 L1985 **HO HEM** *020 †20
TULLIS, William Hershey. 1600 W 38TH ST, STE 321 78731 #048-13-1978 L1980 **P GP** *020 †75
TUMU, Hari. 400 W 15TH ST 78701 #027-01-1996 L2002 **NS** *020
TUNG, Ihua. 2607 S I H 35 78741 #048-12-2004 **PD** *100
TURBIN, Richard Martin. ■ 78704 #011-02-1973 L1974 **FM** *030 †18
TURNER, Bruce Mc Laughlin. 711 W 38TH ST STE B1 78705 #048-04-1982 L1983 **RO** *020 †80
TURNER, David Michael. 711 W 38TH ST STE C8 78705 #048-15-1980 L1980 **PS GS** *020 †65
TURNER, Michaeltren T. ■ 78705 #048-13-1996 L1997 **FM** *020 †18
TURNER, Nancy Alice. 1221 W BEN WHITE BLVD, STE B250 78704 #048-02-1981 L1981 **GYN** *020 †30
TURNER, Samara Paulette. 100F W DEAN KEETON ST, AUSTIN UNIV STATION BOX 73 78712 #048-12-1982 L1983 **PD GP** *020 †55
TURNER, Tiffany Johnnie. ■ 78759 #047-07-2006 **PD** *012
TURNIPSEED, Robert Brent. 3501 MILLS AVE 78731 #048-14-2006 L2008 **P** *012
TUTT, Jennifer Marie. 3508 FAR WEST BLVD, FL 2 78731 #041-15-2000 L2006 **FM** *020 †18 ‡
TYNES, Steven Shelby. 1215 RED RIVER ST, STE 442 78701 #649-30-1980 L1985 **PM FSM** *020 †60
TYSON, Edward Page. 4200 MARATHON BLVD, STE 340 78756 #048-14-1982 L1983 **ADL FM** *020 †18
TYSON, Kenneth R T. ■ 78757 #048-02-1960 L1960 **PDS GS** *071 †85,90
UECKER, John M. 313 E 12TH ST STE 103, AMEP 78701 #048-02-1993 L1997 **GS** *020
UNDERHILL, Carla Sue. 3200 RED RIVER ST STE 210 78705 #048-14-1981 L1981 **FM** *020 †18
UNTALAN, Peter Bradford. 1015 E 32ND ST, STE 405 78705 #014-01-1996 L1999 **NPM** *012 †55
UPSHAW, Leon Reuben. ■ 78731 #048-02-1946 L1946 **OBG** *071
UPTON, Ralph Eric. 313 E 12TH ST, STE 100 78701 #048-04-1977 L1977 **OBG** *071 †30
URIBE, Marco Arturo. 1201 W 38TH ST 78705 #048-04-1983 L1983 **OBG** *020 †30
URRATE, David Christian. 3636 EXECUTIVE CENTER DR, STE 158 78731 #048-02-1997 L1998 **P** *020
UTTS, Stephen James. 4310 JAMES CASEY ST, STE 4A 78745 #023-01-1977 L1987 **GE IM** *020 †20
VACHE, Marilyn Jean. 3724 JEFFERSON ST 78731 #003-01-1976 L1979 **P ADM** *020 †75
VAGNER, Gregg Alan. 1015 E 32ND ST, STE 505 78705 #048-04-1997 L2001 **ORS** *020 †40
VALADEZ, Adolfo M. 15 WALLER ST, STE 410 78702 #048-02-1993 L2003 **IM** *030 †20
VALENTIN-BENACHEZ, L. 3801 S LAMAR BLVD 78704 #935-01-1991 L1998 **IM** *020 †20
VALLS, Mary T. ■ 78731 #048-04-1989 L1990 **CHP** *020 †75
VAN BAVEL, Julius Henry. 3410 FAR WEST BLVD STE 146 78731 #048-02-1981 L1981 **PD AI** *020 †55,03
VAN DE GRAAF, Wm Conkling. 3705 MEDICAL PKWY, STE 570 78705 #025-07-1983 L1988 **AN CD** *020 †05
VANDEL, Jerry Dean. 900 E 30TH ST STE 100 78705 #024-07-1973 L1978 **IM** *020 †20
VANDER STRATEN, David. 211 COMAL ST, E AUSTIN CHC 78702 #048-16-1993 L2000 **FM** *020 †18
VANDER STRATEN, Melody R. 6836 BEE CAVE RD, STE 111 78746 #048-16-1994 L2005 **D** *020 †15
VAN HOOK, Steven Maurice. ■ 78703 #011-04-2000 L2006 **ID** *020 †20
VAN NORMAN, James Russell. 1430 COLLIER ST 78704 #048-14-1987 L1988 **P** *030 †75
VARELA, Alexandra. ■ 78745 #048-13-2007 *012
VARENBRINK, Johan. ■ 78759 #660-01-1958 L1962 **GP** *020
VARGAS, Linda. 1109A E 6TH ST, PROVISTA EYE CLINIC 78702 #030-05-1987 L2002 **OPH** *020 †35

■ = Address Information Privacy Protected

VARGHESE, Zacharia Poycat. ■ 78727 #048-14-2005 P *012

VARGO, Christopher Joseph. ■ 78758 #012-01-2000 L2007 VIR *020 †80

VAUGHAN, Thurman Ray. 3303 NORTHLAND DR, STE 301 78731 #004-01-1980 L1992 AI *020 †20,03

VAUGHN, Shelby L. 12221 N MO PAC EXPY 78758 #048-13-2003 L2007 AN *020

VAUGHN, Thomas Claude. 6500 N MO PAC EXPY, STE 1-1200 78731 #048-02-1974 L1974 REN GYN *030 †30

VELASQUEZ, Nelly D. 900 E 30TH ST, STE 200 78705 #264-08-1985 L2004 FM *020 †18

VELUR, Prasuna Latha. 601 E 15TH ST 78701 #495-11-2003 IM *012

VENDRELL, Amelia. PO BOX 164106 78716 #048-12-1987 L1988 PTH *020 †50

VENEGONI, Paolo Vincenzo. 2200 PARK BEND DR, STE 300 78758 #561-03-1987 L1993 CD *020 †20

VENKATESH, Sujatha. 408 W 45TH ST 78751 #021-01-1993 L2000 NEP *020 †20

VEZZETTI, Robert M. 720 W 34TH ST STE 101, EMERGENCY SERVICE PARTNERS 78705 #048-13-1999 L2007 PEM *020 †55

VICKERS, Albert F. 601 E 15TH ST 78701 #035-19-1949 L1952 OM FM *071

VICTOR, Brant Edward. 3901 MEDICAL PKWY, STE 200 78756 #048-14-1984 L1985 GS *020 †85

VIERNES, Jay L. 3701 W 38TH ST, STE 401 78705 #023-12-1989 L2006 D *020 †15

VIETZ, Hugo. ■ 78750 #016-11-1952 L1953 GP *020

VIGO, Paul Gerard D. 800 W 34TH ST, STE 201 78705 #748-02-1993 L1998 AI IM *020 †20,03

VIJAYAN, Soumia. 601 E 15TH ST 78701 #496-64-2003 IM *012

VIK, Michael Paul. 3801 S LAMAR BLVD 78704 #048-14-1991 L1996 FM UCM *020 †18

VILLARREAL-LEVY, C. ■ 78703 #048-04-1991 L1992 PD *020 †55

VILLARREAL-LEVY, Gerardo. 4316 JAMES CASEY ST, STE A 78745 #649-52-1985 L1990 IC *020 †20

VINEYARD, John Pendleton. 1301 W 38TH ST, 402 MEDICAL PARK TOWER 78705 #048-12-1955 L1955 IM PUD *071

VO, Chi Buu. 12221 N MO PAC EXPY 78758 #011-03-1999 L2003 AN *020 †05

VO, Nghi Van. ■ 78731 #941-01-1969 L1986 *020

VO, Phu Thai. 822 FAIRFIELD DR 78758 #942-01-1975 L1997 IM *020 †20

VOLPE, Joseph Andrew. 7600 N CAPITAL OF TEXAS HWY, STE A 78731 #048-02-1994 L2000 PM *020 †60

VOLPE, Joseph Anthony. ■ 78703 #030-06-1962 L1971 NM *020 †28,20

VONRUEDEN, Kurt Wm. 3001 BEE CAVE RD, STE 200 78746 #026-04-1982 L1996 OSS *020 †40

WAGES, John William. 2501 W WILLIAM CANNON DR, STE 401 78745 #012-01-2002 L2007 APM *020 †05

WAGNER, Nicholas Joseph. ■ 78757 #012-01-2008 *012

WAGNER, Tara Tilicek. ■ 78757 #048-02-2007 P *012

WAGNER, Theresa Ebanks. 1201 W 38TH ST 78705 #048-02-1988 L1993 OPH *020 †35

WAHLBERG, Christopher S. ■ 78738 #048-13-1983 L1983 GP *020

WAI, Tin Tin. 2901 MONTOPOLIS DR 78741 #209-01-1982 L1995 IM *020 †20

WAJIMA, Yutaka. ■ 78731 #048-02-1993 L1995 AN *020 †05

WAKEFIELD, Jos Sefton, Jr. 4131 SPICEWOOD SPRINGS RD, STE D7 78759 #005-11-1968 L1980 PYA P *020 †75

WALIA, Arvinder Pal Singh. 8140 N MOPAC EXPY, BLDG 4 78759 #495-43-1995 L2003 P *020

WALKER, Andrea S. 10900 STONELAKE BLVD, STE 250 78759 #048-12-1989 L1990 DR *020 †20

WALKER, John Danl. ■ 78703 #048-04-1982 L1983 EM *020 †16

WALKER, Kirt. 3701 EXECUTIVE CENTER DR, STE 105 78731 #048-14-1978 L1978 EM OS *020 †16

WALKER, Lesa Janine. ■ 78703 #048-04-1980 L1980 PHP *030 †70

WALKER, William Alfred. 900 W 38TH ST, STE 100 78705 #048-02-1959 L1959 R RO *020 †80

WALLIS, Gonzalo Alberto. 601 E 15TH ST, AUSTIN MED EDUC PROG-SETON 78701 #935-01-2001 PDC *012 †55

WALLIS, Ted Wm. 4007 JAMES CASEY ST, STE B200 78745 #048-12-1976 L1976 PUD IM *020 †20

WALTERS, Robert Merrill. 3705 MEDICAL PKWY STE 5 78705 #016-01-1974 L1983 HS ORS *020

WALTERS, Thomas R. 1020 W 34TH ST 78705 #048-12-1982 L1983 OPH *020 †35

WALTON, Amy Elise. ■ 78746 #048-14-2002 L2007 P *020 †75

WALTON, David J. 12221 N MO PAC EXPY 78758 #048-14-2002 L2007 AN *020

WALTRIP, Laura S. 720 W 34TH ST 78705 #048-14-1988 L1989 EM *020 †16

WANG, Diana Yun-Guan. ■ 78746 #048-02-2005 OBG *012

WANG, Liang. 12221 N MO PAC EXPY 78758 #048-13-2002 L2004 IM *020 †20

WANG, Stanley Suchy. 2559 WESTERN TRAILS BLVD, STE 100 78745 #048-12-2001 L2007 CD *012 †20

WARD, Brant Russell. ■ 78749 #048-12-2008 *012

WARD, Donald Patrick. 4007 JAMES CASEY ST, STE B220 78745 #048-04-1980 L1980 GYN *020 †30

WARD, Michael Mc Lean. 3816 S 1ST ST 78704 #048-13-1994 L1998 PD *020 †55

WARD, Tina Elaine. 11651 JOLLYVILLE RD # 150 78759 #016-11-1995 L1998 FM *020 †18

WARE, Lewis L, Jr. 8038 MESA DR 78731 #048-04-1973 L1973 PD DR *020 †55,80

WARHOE, Kirsten Anne. 11111 RESEARCH BLVD, LL2 78759 #007-02-1987 L1992 RO IM *020 †20,80

WARMANN, Christine Louise. 11673 JOLLYVILLE RD, STE 204 78759 #048-14-1986 L1987 P IM *020 †75

WARR, Winston Roger. 7301 BURNET RD STE 102 78757 #048-02-1962 L1962 PHP *030 †20

WASSERBURGER, Lori Beth. 7600 BURNET RD, STE 515 78757 #048-13-1986 L1987 PM *020 †60

WASSERMAN, David P. 1927 LOHMANS CROSSING RD, STE 200 78734 #048-78-1995, ▲ L1999 FM *020

WASSMUTH, Shawn R. 601 E 15TH ST, DEPT ER 78701 #048-13-1988 L1992 EM *020 †16

WASSMUTH, Zachary D. 12201 RENFERT WAY, STE 105 78758 #048-02-1994 L2002 OTO *020 †45

WATKINS, Michael Geo. 1301 W 38TH ST, STE 705 78705 #048-14-1981 L1981 IM CD *020 †20

WATTS, Dennis Raymond. 4310 MEDICAL PKWY, STE 101 78756 #004-01-1980 L1986 FM *020 †18

WEAVER, Charlotte A. 7004 BEE CAVE RD, BLDG 1 78746 #048-15-1975 L1975 PD *020 †55

WEBB, Charles Robt, Jr. ■ 78759 #038-06-1957 L1975 PHP *071 †70

WEEKS, David Dee. 6835 AUSTIN CENTER BLVD 78731 #030-05-1999 L2002 IM *020 †20

WEIDMANN, Eric Windsor. 2555 WESTERN TRAILS BLVD, STE 101 78745 #048-12-1985 L1986 FM *020 †20

WEIHS, Diana Gay. 1305 W 34TH ST STE 308 78705 #048-04-1981 L1981 OBG *020 †30 ‡

WEINER, Michael Saml. 4607 AGARITA CV # 1 78734 #024-01-1966 L1972 CHP *020 †75

WEINER, Scott Jeffrey. 4900 MUELLER BLVD, UTMB AUSTIN-PEDIATRICS 78723 #028-02-1993 L2002 PD *020 †55

WEINER, Sherry Lynn. 3005 S LAMAR BLVD STE 109D 78704 #048-02-1988 L1990 PTH *071

WEINGARTEN, Jordan S. 1305 W 34TH ST 78705 #048-04-1980 L1981 CCM PUD *020 †20

WEINSTEIN, Bernard A. 6304 SHADOW MTN DR, BAILEY SQUARE UROLOGY CLIN 78731 #067-01-1968 L1974 OS *020 †95

WEIR, Edward Gerard. ■ 78731 #041-12-1995 L2006 HMP PTH *020 †50

WEIR, Tracey Elizabeth. 720 W 34TH ST, STE 101 78705 #048-02-1992 L1993 EM *020 †16

WELCH, Byron Russell. 1015 E 32ND ST 78705 #048-12-1985 L1986 NEP IM *020 †20

WELCH, Dennis Evan. 3508 FAR WEST BLVD 78731 #048-02-1962 L1962 IM ON *020 †20

WELLBORN, John Wm. PO BOX 161058 78716 #034-01-1983 L1987 PM *020 †60

WELLS, Donald Thos. 1301 BARBARA JORDAN BLVD, STE401 78723 #048-02-1989 L1995 PHO *020 †55

WELLS, Douglas Graeme. ■ 78731 #143-02-1976 L1985 AN *020 †05

WELLS, Joe K, III. 1010 W 40TH ST 78756 #048-12-1994 L1996 VS *020 †85

WELLS, Leslie L. 6507 JESTER BLVD STE 301 78750 #048-13-1997 L2000 PD *020 †55

WELLS, Margaret Rose. 8868 RESEARCH BLVD, STE 601 78758 #048-14-1974 L1982 OM *020

WELLS, Max Michael. 919 E 32ND ST 78705 #019-02-1976 L1981 PTH DMP *062 †50

WENZEL, Marc Evan. 4007 JAMES CASEY ST, STE C220 78745 #033-05-1982 L1992 END IM *020 †20

WERMER, David Earl. 1201 W 38TH ST 78705 #051-01-1976 L1981 NPM PD *020 †55

WERNECKE, Robert Herman. 1301 W 38TH ST STE 300 78705 #048-02-1964 L1964 OBG *071 †30

WERNER, Gerhard. ■ 78731 #154-07-1945 PYA PA *050

WERNER, Peter Wm. 8408A MESA DR 78759 #016-02-1963 L1969 N *020 †05

WERNTZ, Gary Leon. 900 E 30TH ST, STE 300 78705 #021-06-1982 L1986 FM PTH *020 †18

WESTGATE, Sara. 5900 SW PARKWAY, BLDG 4 78735 #048-14-1994 L1998 N *020 †75

WESTMORELAND, Gregory L. 4534 W GATE BLVD STE 110, SO AUSTIN ORTHOPAEDIC CLIN 78745 #048-12-1995 L2000 OSM *020 †40

WESTON, Gregory H. 919 E 32ND ST 78705 #048-02-1994 L1997 EM *020 †16

WESTON, Koren Dingeman. ■ 78750 #048-02-1998 L2002 MPD *020 †20,55

WESTON, Robert A. ■ 78751 #048-12-2004 L2007 EM *020

WHALLEY, Peggy Joyce. ■ 78704 #048-12-1956 L1956 OBS *071 †30

WHEELER, Amy Burrier. ■ 78704 #036-01-2006 FP *012

WHEELOCK, Valerie G. 7004 BEE CAVE RD STE 21 78746 #048-12-2003 L2006 PD *020 †55

WHISENANT, Norman M. 1106 W DITTMAR RD 78745 #048-78-1995, ▲ L1997 PM *020

WHITAKER, Timothy L. ■ 78726 #048-13-2000 L2000 PD *020 †55

WHITE, Amy Lee. 4700 SETON CENTER PKWY, STE 125 78759 #056-05-2000 L2005 PD *020 †55 ‡

WHITE, Ben Henson. ■ 78703 #048-12-1952 L1952 OS GE *030 †55

WHITE, Eric James. 3705 MEDICAL PKWY, STE 570 78705 #056-05-2000 L2004 AN *020 †05

WHITE, Gordon Leroy. 4200 MARATHON BLVD STE 340 78756 #041-14-1979 L1982 NS *020 †85

WHITE, Wilbur Owen. 1201 W 38TH ST 78705 #048-02-1955 L1955 GP GS *071 †18

WHITEHILL, Jeffrey N. 3801 N LAMAR BLVD STE 300, ATTN: DEBORAH LAWSON 78756 #048-04-1996 L1997 ICE *020 †20

WHITELOCK, Paul Richard. 3501 MILLS AVE 78731 #048-02-1970 L1970 P *020 †75

WHITESIDE, Stephen B. 9705 RESEARCH BLVD 78759 #048-04-1991 L1994 OPH *020 †35

WHITNEY, Debra Ann. 6204 BALCONES DR 78731 #048-04-1999 L2003 ON *020 †20

WHITTEMORE, Archie Kent. 630 W 34TH ST, STE 302 78705 #048-13-1970 L1972 ORS *020 †40

WIEDOWER, Ronnie Chas. 8038 MESA DR 78731 #004-01-1978 L1983 DR *020 †80

WIER, John Rex, III. 3724 JEFFERSON ST, STE 111 78731 #649-01-1979 L1982 P *020 ‡

WIGGINS, Terry Stone. 2712 BEE CAVE RD, STE 102 78746 #048-02-1974 L1974 FM *020 †16

WIGODA, Carlos. 1313 RED RIVER ST, STE 314 78701 #649-01-1966 L1973 OBG *020 †30

WILBANKS, John Harrison. 2600 E MARTN LTHR KNG JR, AUSTIN CANCER CENTER/MLK 78702 #048-04-1973 L1973 RO *020 †80

WILDE, Waldemar Tito. ■ 78759 #132-01-1952 L1964 IM CD *072

WILDER, Alfred Christian. 3003 BEE CAVE RD, STE 203 78746 #048-04-1977 L1978 PS EM *020 †85,65

WILK, Joel David. 7600 CHEVY CHASE DR # 400 78752 #048-04-1973 L1974 GS GP *020 †85

WILKERSON, James A, IV. ■ 78767 #001-02-1986 L2006 FOP PTH *020 †50

WILLCOX, James Greer. 4507 EDGEMONT DR 78731 #012-01-1974 L1985 FM *062 †18

WILLEFORD, George, Jr. 3933 STECK AVE 78759 #048-02-1946 L1946 CHP PD *071 †55

WILLEFORD, George, III. 1111 W 34TH ST, STE 200 78705 #048-12-1975 L1975 GE IM *020 †20

WILLIAMS, David Russell. 3705 MEDICAL PKWY, STE 570 78705 #048-04-1996 L2000 AN *020 †05

WILLIAMS, Donald Michael. 4900 MUELLER BLVD 78723 #048-04-1998 L2002 MPD *020 †20,55

WILLIAMS, Gary Richard. 12320 ALAMEDA TRACE CIR #8 78727 #048-02-1978 L1978 P *020 †40

WILLIAMS, James Browning. 4207 JAMES CASEY ST # 215 78745 #021-05-1976 L1982 CD IM *020 †20

WILLIAMS, John G. 10900 STONELAKE BLVD, STE 250 78759 #048-15-2001 L2007 R AR *020 †80

WILLIAMS, John J. 1301 BARBARA JORDAN BLVD 78723 #043-01-1985 L1992 PD ORS *020 †40

WILLIAMS, Michael K. 313 E 12TH ST, STE 101 78701 #048-02-1976 L1982 IM *020 †20

WILLIAMS, Shawn Patrick. ■ 78704 #048-02-2005 IM *012

WILLIAMSON, Gary Wayne. ■ 78731 #004-01-1963 L1967 DR NR *071 †80

WILLIAMSON, John Chas. 4007 JAMES CASEY ST # C150 78745 #048-13-1976 L1976 U *020 †95

WILLIS, Andrew Kenneth. 720 W 34TH ST STE 101, THIRD COAST EMERGENCY PHYS 78705 #048-13-1998 L2001 EM *020 †16

WILLMAN, Joseph Howard. 9200 WALL ST 78754 #017-20-1997 L2003 DMP PTH *020 †50

WILLOUGHBY, Vickie L. ■ 78731 #048-78-2003, ▲ L2006 PTH *100 †50

WILLS, Robert P. 2501 W WILLIAM CANNON DR, STE 401 78745 #048-12-1989 L1990 PME AN *020 †05

WILSON, Alexandra Kim. 601 E 15TH ST BOX 4 78701 #005-11-1993 L2004 CCP *020 †55

WILSON, Barbara Ann. ■ 78704 #048-14-1989 L1990 N *020 †75

WILSON, Christopher John. 1007 E 41ST ST 78751 #048-04-1973 L1974 OBG *020 †30

WILSON, Ronald Jesse. 400 W 15TH ST, STE 800 78701 #048-14-1976 L1976 NSP NS *020 †25

WILSON, Stephen Eugene. 3705 MEDICAL PKWY, STE 570 78705 #048-12-1980 L1980 AN *020 †05

WINDLER, Edwin Carey. 900 W 38TH ST, AUSTIN SPORTS MEDICINE 78705 #048-04-1973 L1973 ORS OSM *020 †40

WINEGAR, Bradford Chas. 3705 MEDICAL PKWY, STE 320 78705 #048-12-1980 L1980 OTO *020 †45

WINN, Melissa Guzman. 2911 MEDICAL ARTS ST, STE 3 78705 #048-13-1998 L1999 OBG *020 †30

WINSETT, Mary Zelsman. 10900 STONELAKE BLVD, STE 250 78759 #048-02-1980 L1980 DR *020 †80

WINSETT, Owen Ewing. 2905 SAN GABRIEL ST, STE 310 78705 #048-02-1979 L1979 OS *020 †85

WINSTON, Jaron Lerner. 3215 STECK AVE STE 200 78757 #048-14-1981 L1981 P PYG *020 †75

WISEMAN, Lisa. 4700 SETON CENTER PKWY, STE 125 78759 #048-13-1983 L1983 PD *020 †55

WISEMAN, Richard John. 11615 ANGUS RD STE 107 78759 #064-01-1969 L1977 FM *020

WISHNEW, David Stanley. 1015 E 32ND ST, STE 216 78705 #165-01-1979 L1984 PS HS *100 †65

WITWER, Gordon Allen. 4405 MICHAELS CV 78746 #054-04-1980 L1993 DR *020 †80

WOLF, Kari Marguerite. 3501 MILLS AVE 78731 #018-03-1997 L2006 P *020 †75

WOLF, Lydia Lee. 4515 SETON CENTER PKWY, STE 220 78759 #654-01-2000 L2004 IM *020 †20

WOLF, Paul Mitchell. 1301 W 38TH ST, STE 109 78705 #654-01-2000 L2004 PCC *100

WOLLAN, Megan Hahn. 3705 MEDICAL PKWY, STE 570 78705 #048-14-2001 L2005 AN *020 †05

WOLLAN, Peter T. 5011 BURNET RD, EYE PHYSICIANS OF AUSTIN 78756 #048-14-2000 L2005 OPH *020 †35

WOMBLE, Joe Dean. ■ 78735 #048-02-1952 L1952 OM FM *071 †18

WON, Mai Vu. 12221 N MO PAC EXPY 78758 #055-01-2001 L2006 N *020 †75

WONG, Albert J. 10401 ANDERSON MILL RD, STE 110B 78750 #048-13-1996 L1997 FM *020 †18

WONG, Alicia Ann. 1313 RED RIVER ST 78701 #715-01-1989 FM *100

WONG, Frank. 900 E 30TH ST, STE 311 78705 #048-13-1998 L1999 PDC *100 †55

WONG, Lawrence Shawn Tsao. 4019 SPICEWOOD SPRINGS RD, STE 100 78759 #048-04-1989 L1991 OPH *020 †35

WONG, Mitchel. 1009 E 40TH ST STE 200, AUSTIN MED BLDG SUITE 200 78751 #048-04-1964 L1964 OPH *020 †35

WONG, Shannon M. 11901 JOLLYVILLE RD 78759 #048-04-1993 L1994 OPH *020 †35

WONGSATHUAYTHONG, Rosanee. PO BOX 13163 78711 #891-04-1988 IM *100

WOOD, Glenn Gordon. 3660 STONERIDGE RD # C102 78746 #048-12-1979 L1979 PD *020 †55

WOOD, Gregg L. 4207 JAMES CASEY ST # 203 78745 #048-02-1993 L2002 AN *020 †05

WOOD, Robert Wm. ■ 78703 #048-11-1955 L1956 PS *071 †65

WOODRUFF, Rebecca L. ■ 78705 #048-13-1991 *100

WOODS, Sara S. 4315 JAMES CASEY ST 3RD FL, AUSTIN DIAG CLC 78745 #048-14-1999 L2001 PD *020 †55

WOODWARD, Wm Robinson. 1301 W 38TH ST, STE 601 78705 #048-14-1981 L1981 IM *020 †20

WORCHEL, Harvey Barton. 4007 JAMES CASEY ST, STE A210 78745 #048-13-1974 L1976 GS *020 †85

WORREL, John Richard. 4315 JAMES CASEY ST 78745 #048-12-1979 L1979 PD ADL *020 †55

WOZNIAK, Robert John. 2200 PARK BEND DR BLDG 2, STE 300 78758 #010-02-1986 L1996 CD IM *020 †20

WRAY, Mary Jane. 3303 NORTHLAND DR, STE 308 78731 #048-02-1974 L1983 PD PDE *020 †55

WRIGHT, David Philip. 1313 RED RIVER ST STE 100 78701 #048-02-1980 L1980 FM PHP *020 †18

WRIGHT, Karen L. 4314 MEDICAL PKWY STE 200 78756 #016-06-1986 L1999 PDC *020 †55

WROE, Wm Augustus, Jr. 3705 MEDICAL PKWY, STE 570 78705 #048-02-1980 L1980 AN *020 †05

WU, Andy C. ■ 78759 #048-02-2001 L2004 IM *020

WURTSBAUGH, Ronald B. 8000 CENTRE PARK DR, STE 340 78754 #649-19-1981 L1982 P *100

YADAV, Ajay S. 919 E 32ND ST 78705 #048-16-2001 L2004 EM *020 †16

YALAMANCHILI, Vijay L. 12411 HYMEADOW DR STE 3E 78750 #495-21-1978 L1985 IM *020 †20

YAMAMOTO, Krissy M. 78727 #048-14-2007 OBG *012

YANDOW, Suzanne Marie. 1301 BARBARA JORDAN BLVD, STE 300 78723 #011-04-1984 L2007 OP OMO *020 †40

YANG, Jae Hong. ■ 78759 #583-10-1969 L1974 GP *020

YATSU, John Shigeru. 919 E 32ND ST 78705 #048-16-1984 L1985 GS CCS *030 †85

YBARRA, Bruno. 811 E 32ND ST 78705 #048-02-1963 L1963 GYN *071 †30

YEE, Tung. ■ 78705 #048-12-2006 IM *012

YEH, Grace S. 3624 N HILLS DR, STE B102 78731 #244-04-1978 L1994 FM *020 †18

YERGER, David Hack. ■ 78748 #051-04-1965 L1965 GS *020 †85

YIP, Virginia Y. 8038 MESA DR 78731 #016-11-1993 L2007 DR *020 †80

YIUM, Michael Joe. 4207 JAMES CASEY ST, AUSTIN EAR NOSE & THROAT 78745 #048-04-1997 L1999 OTO *020 †45

YIUM, Vanessa Leigh. 1305 W 34TH ST STE 308 78705 #048-04-1997 L1998 OBG *020 †30

YOOSFANI, Khalid A. ■ 78759 #704-08-1964 L1985 N PD *020 †55

YOOSUFANI, Fatima Khalid. ■ 78759 #048-04-1964 L1968 NM PTH *020

YORK, Jennifer A. 5750 BALCONES DR STE 110 78731 #048-04-1993 L1994 N CN *020 †75

YOUNG, Stanford R. 3705 MEDICAL PKWY STE 570 78705 #048-15-1993 L1994 AN PAN *020 †05

YOUNG, Stephen Wiley. 6101 W COURTYARD DR, BUILDING 78730 #036-01-1968 L1979 DR *071 †80

YOUNGKIN, Jeffrey Thos. 805 E 32ND ST STE 201 78705 #048-04-1978 L1978 OBG REN *020 †30

YURCO, Stephen. 9200 WALL ST 78754 #016-06-1978 L1979 PTH *020 †50

ZABANEH, Evelyn E. 11851 JOLLYVILLE RD, STE 204 78759 #048-13-1996 L1999 PD *020 †55

ZACHARY, James Allen. 4614 N IH 35, DAVID POWELL CLINIC 78751 #021-05-1983 L2006 ID IM *020 †20

ZAGRODZKY, Jason D. 1301 W 38TH ST, STE 705 78705 #048-12-1992 L1993 ICE *020 †20

ZAKIULLAH, Nida. 601 E 15TH ST 78701 #704-25-2004 FP *012

ZAMORA, Belda. 2100 E 6TH ST, # B 78702 #048-02-1995 L1997 FM *020 †18

ZAMORA, Guadalupe. 2100 E 6TH ST, STE A 78702 #048-02-1985 L1986 FM *020 †18

ZANGER, Blossom. 1010 LAVACA ST 78701 #035-08-1963 L1968 IM HO *020 †20

ZAPALAC, Jeffrey Scott, Jr. 1400 IH 35 N 78701 #048-12-1996 L1997 OTO HNS *020 †45

ZAPALAC, Robert Lawrence. ■ 78703 #048-02-1966 L1966 P *071 †75

ZAVALETA, Thomas Peter. 6835 AUSTIN CENTER BLVD 78731 #048-13-1974 L1974 FM *020 †55,18 ‡

ZBYLOT, Phillip L. 601 E 15TH ST 78701 #048-02-1974 L1974 *075

ZEB, Taimur. 4900 MUELLER BLVD RM4B062, BRACKENRIDGE HOSPITAL 78723 #704-09-1991 L1993 NPM *020 †55

ZEGARRA, Carmen L. 1631 E 2ND ST, 56 EAST AV. 78702 #737-09-1980 L2007 P *020 †75

ZEINEDDIN, Mohamad. 4316 JAMES CASEY ST, STE A 78745 #875-01-1982 L1988 CD *020 †20

ZELAZNY, Gary Allen. 3705 MEDICAL PKWY, STE 455 78705 #048-12-1967 L1967 D *020 †15

ZELLNER, Marvin Ted. ■ 78730 #047-06-1965 L1966 OBG *071 †30

ZIARI, Shaida A. 1015 E 32ND ST 78705 #048-13-2000 L2003 PD *100 †55

ZIDAR, Francis Joseph. 3801 N LAMAR BLVD, STE 300 78756 #025-01-1997 L2005 IC CD *020 †20

ZIEBELL, Christopher M. 720 W 34TH ST, STE 101 78705 #026-04-1990 L1998 EM OS *020 †16

ZIEBERT, Carol Lynn. 1305 W 34TH ST 78705 #048-15-1990 L1994 IM *020 †20

ZIEDONIS, Jennifer Elaine. 1301 W 38TH ST, STE 205 78705 #033-06-1993 L1996 IM *020 †20

ZIENTEK, David Michael. 3801 N LAMAR BLVD, STE 300 78756 #023-07-1985 L1992 CD IM *020 †20

ZIMMET, Steven Eric. 1500 W 34TH ST 78703 #010-02-1978 L1981 PHL DS *020 †18

ZINGERY, Lewis Worth. 2525 WALLINGWOOD DR, STE 1B 78746 #048-13-1979 L1979 OBG *020 †30

ZINN, Steven Edward. 3705 MEDICAL PKWY, STE 570 78705 #048-12-1974 L1977 AN *020 †05

ZWIENER, Robert Jeffrey. 1301 BARBARA JORDAN BLVD 78723 #048-13-1983 L1983 PG GE *020 †55

AUSTIN – WILLIAMSON

ADETUTU, Taiwo E. ■ 78729 #690-02-1986 L1994 PD *020 †55

BEIL, Kenneth Allen. ■ 78729 #001-02-1973 L1997 DR RNR *062 †80

BOWEN, Kanika Alake. ■ 78717 #048-02-2005 GS *012

BULATHSINGHALA, Rathu Gam. ■ 78729 #220-01-2002 *100

CHERNG, Eric Lee-An. ■ 78729 #048-15-2007 PD *012

CHUNG, Yu-Chen. ■ 78729 #048-15-2007 PD *012

DASGUPTA, Nilanjana Sen. ■ 78729 #495-85-1997 L2004 IM *020 †20 ‡

DUBLE, Shannon Leigh. ■ 78717 #048-13-2002 L2004 PD *020 †55

FERNANDEZ-LOPEZ, Esteban. ■ 78729 #048-04-2007 *012

GOLDSMITH, Bonnie Gayle. ■ 78717 #048-02-2007 PD *012

GREEN, Keith Wayne. 7403 RANKIN TRL 78729 #019-02-1991 L1991 AN *020 †05

HASAN AKHTAR, Syed. 12460 LOS INDIOS TRL, AL MAHDI GET WELL CHARITY 78729 #495-21-1965 L2004 CD IM *020 †20

IBAD, Samina. ■ 78717 #704-02-1995 L2006 P *100 †75

JOHNSON, Scott Conrad. ■ 78717 #038-06-1982 L1989 IM *020

LAWLIS, Marjorie Grover. 12151 HUNTERS CHASE DR 78729 #048-12-1950 L1950 CHP PD *071 †55,75

LONG, Theresa M. ■ 78717 #048-14-2008 *012

MARTIN, Hodges. ■ 78717 #048-12-1964 L1964 P GPM *071 †18,70

MC TRUSTY, Robert Lloyd. ■ 78729 #016-02-1960 L1990 OBG OS *071 †30

OZA, Saleem Mohammed. ■ 78717 #704-02-1986 L2006 IM *020 †20

PARVEZ, Najma. ■ 78729 #704-06-1992 L2006 ID *012 †20

PENDERGRASS, Robert K. ■ 78729 #025-01-1949 L1950 GP IM *071

PERKINS, Michael Steven. ■ 78729 #048-13-1984 L1985 FM OM *020 †70

POER, Leslie Gail. ■ 78729 #048-04-2000 L2006 GS *020

RYLANDER, Nathaniel R. ■ 78729 #048-02-2006 P *012

SALAS, Mingshing Nancy. ■ 78729 #048-12-2007 AN *012

STOKES, Jason Richard. 10625 W PARMER LN # 10400, URGENT & FAMILY CARE 78717 #041-15-1999 L2001 FM UCM *020 †18

VAELLO, Bettina A. 8459 LYNDON LN 78729 #024-01-1987 L1989 PD *020 †55

VALMIKI, Himabindu Anand. ■ 78717 #495-21-1994 L2006 PD *100

WALENTA, Amy Lynn. ■ 78729 #048-02-2008 *012

WARFIELD, Kimberly L. 6301 W PARMER LN, STE 102 78729 #048-02-1995 L1999 IM *020 †20,18

WONG, Tai Keong. ■ 78729 #244-03-1977 L1982 FM *020

ZAD, Omid Haghshenas. ■ 78729 #517-12-2001 *075

AXTELL – MCLENNAN

COX, Ethel E. ■ 76624 #048-15-1998 IM *100

AZLE – TARRANT

BRADY, Bernard Francis. ■ 76020 #649-30-1980 L1995 EM *071

BROOKS, Kathleen Lawlor. 108 DENVER TRL 76020 #048-04-1993 L1994 FM *020 †18

COWAN, Todd Kreig. 108 DENVER TRL 76020 #048-15-1985 L1986 FM *020 †18

DEEM, Adrianne Marie. 909 SE PARKWAY ST, STE 102 76020 #028-03-1998 L2002 OBG *020 †30

GAY, Arthur Mitchell. 108 DENVER TRL 76020 #048-12-1960 L1960 R *071 †80

GONZALEZ, Pedro D. 141 INDUSTRIAL AVE, HEALTHFIRST MEDICAL GROUP 76020 #048-12-1998 L1999 FM *020 †18

HAMILTON, Kenneth W. 108 DENVER TRL 76020 #048-16-1992 L1993 IM *020 †20

HUDMAN, Jennifer M. 909 SOUTHEAST PKWY STE 101 76020 #048-12-2002 L2005 PD *020 †55

JACK, Bernard Roy. 108 DENVER TRL 76020 #036-01-1965 L1978 GS *071 †90,85

LOBLEY, Brenda J. 108 DENVER TRL 76020 #048-13-1988 L1989 FM *020 †18

LONERGAN, Francis Raymond. 108 DENVER TRL 76020 #024-01-1977 L1984 FM *020 †18

MOBLEY, Jack Clement. ■ 76020 #048-02-1958 L1958 GYN GP *071

MORRISON, Marshall C. 108 DENVER TRL 76020 #048-13-1983 L1983 IM *020 †20

MYERS, Kriss E. 108 DENVER TRL 76020 #048-14-1987 L1988 FM *020 †18

PACE, Clinton J. 336 FOSSIL ROCK DR 76020 #048-14-1985 L1992 GS VS *020 †55

QUIJANO-VEGA, Omayra M. ■ 76020 #042-01-1998 L2005 END *050 †20

RODRIGUEZ, Luis Angel. ■ 76020 #308-03-1982 L1985 FM *020

SAVAGE, James Munroe. 112 DENVER TRL 76020 #048-12-1954 L1954 GP *020

SEGER, William Michael. 108 DENVER TRL 76020 #048-15-1985 L1986 FM *020 †18

SHAH, Kavita Sanjiv. 108 DENVER TRL 76020 #495-76-1986 L2006 IM *020 †20

TERRELL, Mary Frances E. 401 STRIBLING DR 76020 #051-01-1980 L1983 IM EM *020 †20

TURNER, Russell L, Jr. ■ 76020 #048-12-1952 L1952 GP *071

VELASCO SEGARRA, Luis A. 401 STRIBLING DR, NORTHWEST COMMUNITY HEALTH 76020 #308-03-1980 L1988 FM *020 †18

■ = Address Information Privacy Protected

TEXAS
BACLIFF — BAYTOWN

BACLIFF – GALVESTON

CHACKO, Pulparampil. 1125 GRAND AVE 77518 #409-05-1964 L1974 **GP** *071
PENA, Manuel G. 1032B GRAND AVE 77518 #275-01-1949 L1966 **FM GP** *020 †18
PRESTON, Brian Allan. ■ 77518 #048-02-1963 L1963 **GP** *071 †18
STOGRE, Rosemary A. 1136 GRAND AVE 77518 #065-09-1971 L1978 **FM PHP** *020

BAGWELL – RED RIVER

GONZALES, Carmen Marie. ■ 75412 #048-14-2006 **EM** *012

BAIRD – CALLAHAN

CALVO, Raul Niduaza, Jr. 140 W 5TH ST, RURAL CLINIC 79504 #748-10-1970 L1976 **FM** *020

BALCH SPRINGS – DALLAS

MAHMOOD, Asiya. ■ 75180 #704-21-1997 L2007 **IM** *020 †20
NORMAN, Charles Randall. ■ 75180 #039-01-1985 L1991 **OPH** *020 †35

BALLINGER – RUNNELS

GREEN, John Edward, Jr. ■ 76821 #048-02-1948 L1948 **FM** *071 †18
MC KINNON, Mark S. 302 N 3RD ST 76821 #048-15-1994 L2008 **FM** *020 †18

BANDERA – BANDERA

ELLINGER, Heather Leanne. ■ 78003 #048-04-2004 **AN** *012
HOWARD, Byron Laburt. PO BOX 2732 78003 #048-12-1967 L1968 **P** *020 †75
MEADOR, George D. ■ 78003 #048-02-1950 L1950 *071
PATEL, Muhammad Junaid. PO BOX 565, 1300 CEDAR ST 78003 #704-02-1994 L2001 **IM** *020 †20
SORATHIA, Ayesha Latif. PO BOX 565, 1300 CEDAR ST 78003 #704-16-1995 L2001 **IM** *020 †20
STONE, Lawrence Anderson. ■ 78003 #048-12-1958 L1958 **CHP P** *020
VIEYRA, George Ray. ■ 78003 #005-19-1975 L1985 **OTO AM** *020 †45
WOMACK, James Chanslor. PO BOX 2870 78003 #048-13-1984 L1985 **FM FPG** *020 †18

BARTONVILLE – DENTON

ROWE, William Scott. 538 DOVE CREEK RD 76226 #649-14-1980 L1986 **PM** *020

BASTROP – BASTROP

AKKANTI, Venkat R. 47 LOOP 150 W 78602 #495-57-1975 L1995 **PD** *020 †55
BATLLE, Augustin Roger. 195 S HASLER BLVD, STE B-1 78602 #026-04-1992 L1994 **IM GP** *020 †20
BOUCHER, Jean Denis. 441 HIGHWAY 71 W, STE E 78602 #067-02-1978 L1999 **D** *020 †15
CARROLL, Lance Dee. 441 W HIGHWAY 71 STE B 78602 #016-43-1997 L1998 **FM** *020 †18 ‡
CHAVEZ PEYRONE, Pompeyo C. 3101 HWY 71 E, STE 101 78602 #737-10-2001 L2007 **FM** *020 †18
CORTES, Virginia Ruiz De. ■ 78602 #847-02-1973 L1976 **GP** *071
COSTELLO, John Jos. 81 LOOP 150 W 78602 #048-02-1971 L1975 **OBG** *020
DOUGHERTY, Robert James. 441 HIGHWAY 71 W, STE B1 78602 #048-13-1999 L2001 **FM** *020 †18
EDMONDSON, Larry Dean. 605 LAUREL ST 78602 #422-01-1999 L2002 **FM** *020 †18
GOSS, Adrian. 441 HIGHWAY 71 W, STE C 78602 #048-02-1995 L1998 **FM OBS** *020 †18
GOSS, Harry F, Jr. 423 OLD AUSTIN HWY 78602 #048-12-1990 L1991 **NEP** *020 †20
GUPTA, Rajeev. 475 HIGHWAY 71 W 78602 #495-45-1987 L1996 **IM** *020 †20
HAGEN, Jeffrey E. 301 HIGHWAY 71 W STE 111 78602 #048-12-1982 L1983 **OBG** *020 †30
LAWLIS, Virgil B. ■ 78602 #048-02-1950 L1950 **GE IM** *071 †20
MC LAUGHLIN, Darlene W. 150 SETTLEMENT DR STE E 78602 #048-12-1980 L1980 **P** *020 †75
MOLINA-BATLLE, Claudia M. 105 BUSH CV 78602 #026-04-1992 L1994 **FM** *020 †18
NORWOOD, Patricia Ann. 111 N HASLER BLVD 78602 #021-06-1983 L1986 **AN GS** *020 †05
PALADUGU, Kanaka Durga. 108 LEI CT 78602 #496-34-1998 L2007 **FM** *020 †20
PORTER, Brent Alan. ■ 78602 #028-02-1995 L2001 **IM** *020 †20
PRESCOTT, Deana Jung. 150 SETTLEMENT DR, STE E 78602 #048-13-1984 L1985 **P** *020 †75
PRIVITERA, Vincent John. ■ 78602 #048-02-1966 L1966 **P** *071
REYES, Raquel. ■ 78602 #024-01-2008 *012
SARGENT, Charles Alden. 85 LOOP 150 W 78602 #025-01-1954 L1957 **OPH** *071 †35
SHIMKUS, Brian Jay. 301 HIGHWAY 71 W, STE 204 78602 #012-01-1998 L2003 **ON** *020 †20
VILLARICO, Remigio C. ■ 78602 #748-07-1955 L1974 **AN OS** *071
VOCAL, Laurier Alain. 3101 HWY 71 E STE 101 78602 #065-09-1973 L1978 **FM FSM** *020 ‡
WALKES, Desmar. 441 HIGHWAY 71 W STE F 78602 #048-02-1986 L1987 **FM** *020

BATESVILLE – ZAVALA

FOLCK, Michael Paige. ■ 78829 #048-13-2003 **GS** *020
WELLS, Stephen C. ■ 78829 #048-13-2005 **IM** *012

BAY CITY – MATAGORDA

AGGARWAL, Ajay. 1115 AVENUE G, MATAGORDA COUNTY HOSPITAL 77414 #495-43-1984 L1995 **AN PME** *020 †05
CADORE, Judith Martin. 1221 AVENUE F 77414 #048-02-1990 L1994 **FM** *020
CANNON, Joseph N, Jr. 111 AVENUE F, SOUTH TEXAS MEDICAL CLINIC 77414 #048-04-1953 L1953 **FM** *020

COWART, James E. 111 AVENUE F 77414 #048-04-1953 L1953 **GP OS** *020
DADA, Mohammed Atiq. 1115 AVENUE G, CAPITAL AREA HEALTH CONSOR 77414 #422-01-2001 L2008 **NEP** *012
DANIEL, Tillman Moody. 1120 AVENUE G 77414 #048-04-1955 L1955 **GP** *020
DE YOUNG, Stephen. 720 AVENUE F N 77414 #048-14-1976 L1976 **ORS** *020 †40
DIMMICK, Gregg Jeffry. 111 AVENUE F N 77414 #030-05-1977 L1978 **PD** *020 †55
D'LIMA, Shanta Lorna G. 1115 AVENUE F 77414 #496-15-1983 L1999 **FM** *020 †18
DOWLING, Kevin Price. 1115 AVENUE G 77414 #016-06-1987 L1994 **ORS** *020 †40
DUMAS, Natascha Tove. 1115 AVENUE G 77414 #027-01-1998 L2002 **FSM** *020 †18
ESSES, Stephen Ivor. 720 AVENUE F N 77414 #065-01-1978 L1992 **ORS** *020 †40
FERNANDEZ, Jose M. 1115 AVENUE G 77414 #048-15-1992 L1993 **P** *020 †75
GABEL, Gerard T. 720 AVENUE F N 77414 #048-04-1983 L1984 **HS ORS** *020 †40
GRIFFITH, W Barton. 1120 AVENUE G 77414 #048-02-1960 L1960 **FM** *071 †18
HESTER, Fletcher. 1115 AVENUE G 77414 #048-12-1954 L1954 **AN OM** *075
HUEBNER, Jennifer Dunn. ■ 77414 #048-14-2005 **OBG** *012
HUG, George Edward. 2009 MARGUERITE ST 77414 #132-04-1960 L1972 **OBG** *020 †30 ‡
HUYNH, Linhtrang Thi. 1713 MERLIN ST 77414 #048-04-1994 L1996 **OPH** *020 †35
ILAHI, Omer Aslam. 720 AVENUE F N 77414 #048-04-1989 L1990 **OSM** *020 †40
JOHNSTON, Richard Reed. 1302 MARLIN CT 77414 #038-40-1961 L1972 **PTH** *020 †50
KALDIS, Michael Gregory. 720 AVENUE F N 77414 #048-02-1984 L1985 **ORS** *020 †40
KEFFER, Amy Lynn. 1700 GOLDEN AVE, STE 1002 77414 #030-06-1986 L1988 **IM** *020 †20
LAMBUJON, Jesus Rodriguez. MATA GORDO GEN HOSP 77414 #748-01-1972 L1980 **NEP IM** *050
LIBERONI, Barry Joseph. 720 AVENUE F N 77414 #654-01-1996 L1999 **IM** *020 †20
LIONBERGER, David R. 720 AVENUE F N 77414 #028-03-1977 L1978 **ORS EM** *020 †40
MATTHES, Fred Taylor. 1809 MERLIN ST 77414 #048-04-1955 L1955 **PD** *071 †55
MAXCEY, Bob Reams. 1115 AVENUE G 77414 #048-02-1972 L1974 **DR** *020
MAXWELL, Patricia E. 2417 AVENUE I 77414 #048-14-1975 L1975 **PD** *020 †55
METCALF, Priscilla J. 111 AVENUE F 77414 #056-06-1978 L1982 **OPH** *020 †35
NERET, Michael George. 1809 MERLIN ST 77414 #935-01-1994 L2002 **FM** *020 †18
NIETO, Sandra Leah. PO BOX 1710, BAY CITY FAMILY MEDICAL CE 77404 #048-13-1994 L1997 **FM** *020 †18
ORTH, Scott Thos. 720 AVENUE F N 77414 #048-16-1981 L1981 **ORS** *020 †40
PAPPAS, Gregory Alex. 1701 GOLDEN AVE 77414 #048-13-1989 L1990 **OBG** *020 †30
PEGGS, Michael Alphonso. 1713 MERLIN ST 77414 #041-13-1985 L2007 **OPH** *020 †35
PESEK, Edward Frank. 1701 GOLDEN AVE 77414 #048-04-1955 L1955 **GP OS** *071
PREM SWARUP, Immaraju J. 1115 AVENUE G, MATAGORDA COUNTY HOSPITAL 77414 #495-62-1979 L2002 **IM** *020 †20
RAJU, Roman Palivela. ■ 77414 #035-01-2007 *012
ROGERS, Ronald Lee. 1115 AVENUE G 77414 #048-02-1974 L1974 **P PYA** *020 †75
RORIG, James Christopher. 1120 AVENUE G 77414 #016-11-1978 L2004 **IM** *020 †20
RUTLEDGE, Ladonna Patrice. 1701 GOLDEN AVE 77414 #010-02-2002 L2006 **OBG** *020
SACCO, Cheryl Forbes. 1115 AVENUE G 77414 #048-15-1995 L2002 **FM** *020 †18
SEBASTIAN, Kunjamma. 1410 AVENUE F 77414 #561-11-1971 L1982 **PD** *020 †55
SERGIE, Assad. 1115 AVENUE G 77414 #396-06-1955 L1975 **FM GS** *020
SHER, Andrew Michael. 1120 AVENUE G 77414 #048-04-1979 L1979 **GS VS** *020 †85
SIMONS, Dane D. 1120 AVENUE G 77414 #048-15-1991 L1992 **FM** *020 †18 ‡
UGORJI, Clement C. 1115 AVENUE G, MATAGORDA GENERAL HOSPITAL 77414 #023-01-1970 L1981 **TS** *050
VALLOPPILLIL, Ammini J. 1407 AVENUE H 77414 #495-31-1967 L1976 **PD** *020 †55
VALLOPPILLIL, Joseph A. 1407 AVENUE H 77414 #154-07-1969 L1976 **IM** *020
WHITT, John Wayne. 1115 AVENUE G 77414 #048-02-1971 L1971 **U** *020 †95
YOUNG, Jerry Don. 1700 MERLIN ST, STE 1 77414 #048-78-1992, ▲ L1993 **GS** *020

BAYOU VISTA – GALVESTON

CHU, Bobby S. 1014 REDFISH ST 77563 #048-02-1993 L1995 **IM** *020 †20

BAYTOWN – HARRIS

AARONS, Scott. 2707 W BAKER RD 77521 #030-06-1977 L1985 **U** *020 †95
ABBASI, Noma. ■ 77521 #704-02-1995 **FP** *012
ABDELSAYED, Magdy. 4201 GARTH RD STE 203 77521 #915-02-1970 L1977 **U** *020 †95
AHMED, Mohamed Safwat. 4201 GARTH RD, STE 208 77521 #915-02-1992 L2002 **P CHP** *020 †75
AHMED, Mohammad. ■ 77521 #704-01-1999 **FP** *012
AKINYEYE, Adetokunbo A. 4401 GARTH RD 77521 #690-01-1983 L1995 **FM** *020 †18
ALAM, Nimat. 1101 DECKER DR 77520 #160-09-1999 **FM** *100
ALI, Shahid Dawood. 1700 JAMES BOWIE DR 77520 #704-16-2000 **FM** *100
ALI, Shahina Q. 2802 GARTH RD, STE 111 77521 #690-03-1984 L1997 **FM** *020 †18
ALLEN, Monte Lee. 1610 JAMES BOWIE DR # A1 77520 #019-02-1961 L1989 **OTO** *020
ALMY-HOWARD, Cynthia C. 4401 GARTH RD 77521 #048-02-1990 L1992 **IM** *020 †20
ANDREWS, John Huey. 2802 GARTH RD, STE 109 77521 #021-05-1954 L1959 **OPH** *071 †35
ANSARI, Kashif Hussain. 4401 GARTH RD, STE 102 77521 #704-02-1992 L2002 **ON** *020 †20
ANTHONY, Kent E. 4301 GARTH RD STE 400, FAMILY PRACTICE RESIDENCY 77521 #035-01-1980 L1983 **FM EM** *040 †18
ARISCO, Martin Jos. 4301 GARTH RD 77521 #048-02-1965 L1965 **OPH** *020 †35
ATA, Mohammad. 1610 JAMES BOWIE DR, STE A110 77520 #704-01-1956 L1974 **IM** *040 †20
AZHAR, Rukshan. 2802 GARTH RD, STE 105 77521 #495-56-1983 L1995 **CHP** *020 †75
AZHAR, Syed S. 1 PRICE RD, BAY AREA PSYCHIATRIC ASSN 77520 #495-21-1978 L1993 **FM OPH** *020 †18
BAHMANPOUR, Kaveh. ■ 77521 #517-12-1998 **FP** *012
BALDWIN, Susan L. 4201 GARTH RD STE 207 77521 #048-02-1992 L1993 **OBG** *020 †30
BARBANDI, Farouk. 4301 GARTH RD STE 300 77521 #875-01-1972 L1977 **PUD IM** *020 †20
BARG, Vadim A. 4401 GARTH RD 77521 #913-66-1986 L2001 **AN** *020
BARNES, Marcia A Jack. 4401 GARTH RD 77521 #041-01-1990 L1998 **PTH** *020 †50
BARRETT, Kevin Francis. 4401 GARTH RD 77521 #048-02-1977 L1977 **EM** *020 †16
BEDI, H S. 4401 GARTH RD 77521 #495-08-1984 L1990 **NPM PD** *020 †55
BERNICK, James Jay. 2717 W BAKER RD STE 2 77521 #048-12-1977 L1977 **FM** *020 †18
BISCAMP, Jason Gregory. 4301 GARTH RD, STE 400 77521 #048-02-2004 L2008 **FM** *100
BONTHALA, Savitri. 4401 GARTH RD 77521 #495-62-1978 L1994 **NPM** *020 †55
BROWN, Jean Bombach. 4401 GARTH RD 77521 #048-14-1995 L1997 **FM** *020 †18
BROWN, William C. 4301 GARTH RD, STE 400 77521 #048-12-1987 L1988 **FM GS** *020

8544

■ = Address Information Privacy Protected

BUREAU, Cynthia Lim. 4301 GARTH RD, STE 202 77521 #748-11-1981 L1997 **PD** *020 †55
BURIANEK, Julius Jos. ■ 77520 #048-02-1955 L1955 **PD NEP** *020 †55
BURKI, Abida. 1610 JAMES BOWIE DR # B101 77520 #704-06-1959 L1974 **FM** *020 ‡
BURNS, Carrie K. 4401 GARTH RD 77521 #048-14-1982 L1983 **FM** *020 †18
BURTON, Shawn Darnese. 4301 GARTH RD STE 400 77521 #048-16-2001 L2003 **FM** *020 †18
CHALLA, Lyla Sarma. 4201 GARTH RD STE 305 77521 #495-50-1972 L1983 **PD** *020 †55
CHALLA, Sarma Subrahmanya. 4201 GARTH RD, STE 307 77521 #495-50-1972 L1983 **CD IM** *020 †20
CHHIBBER, Suparna. 4301 GARTH RD, STE 400 77521 #495-32-1994 L2005 **FM** *020 †18
CHUA, Albert Joseph. 4301 GARTH RD STE 400 77521 #748-10-2003 **FP** *012
CUMMINGS, David Howard. ■ 77520 #021-05-1965 L1971 **OBG** *071 †30
DACCAK, Rukan. 2800 GARTH RD, DEPT OF GASTROENTEROLOGY 77521 #875-01-1984 L1995 **GE** *020 †20
DANCEL, Federico L, Jr. 1610 JAMES BOWIE DR, STE B108 77520 #748-01-1978 L1982 **IM** *020 †20
DANCEL, Marietta. 2919 FOREST GATE DR, UNIVERSITY OF TEXAS HEALTH 77521 #748-01-1978 L1981 **FM** *020 †18
DAVIS, Anthony Alexander. 4201 GARTH RD 77521 #048-13-1986 L1987 **FM** *075 †18
DELL'ARIO, Alfred Valare. 4401 GARTH RD 77521 #012-01-1969 L1975 **CHP P** *020
DEMMLER, Richard Wayne. 6707 INDEPENDENCE BLVD 77521 #048-15-1977 L1977 **FM IMG** *020 †18
DIGILOVA, Irina Yefimovna. 2610 N ALEXANDER DR, STE 200 77520 #913-22-1984 L2002 **P** *020 †75
DITTMAN, Ralph Ernest. 207 BURNETT DR 77520 #048-04-1973 L1973 **OBG** *020
DIZON, Efren Mejia. 4401 GARTH RD 77521 #748-01-1963 L1978 **PD** *020 †55
DIZON, John Edward. 4401 GARTH RD 77521 #048-12-1992 L1993 **AN** *020
DOGAN, John Ibrahim. 2802 GARTH RD, STE 301 77521 #902-07-1996 L2008 **OBG** *020
DUKE, Herbert Hampton, Jr. 4201 GARTH RD, STE 205 77521 #048-04-1960 L1960 **U OS** *020 †95
DZIADEK, Ted. 4401 GARTH RD 77521 #759-03-1968 L1984 **AN** *020 †05
EADES, James Francis. 2001 CEDAR BAYOU RD 77520 #048-02-1958 L1958 **P** *020
EICHELBERGER, Philip T. 1610 JAMES BOWIE DR, STE A103 77520 #048-02-1957 L1957 **GP A** *020
ERIKSON, Christian L. ■ 77521 #001-06-2001 **CCP** *012 †55
ESPINO-DIZON, Perla A. 4301 GARTH RD STE 302 77521 #748-01-1963 L1978 **PD** *020 †55
FAGARASON, Lawrence Allan. 2802 GARTH RD, STE 315 77521 #016-43-1959 L1984 **GS TS** *071 †85,90
FAN, Susan Willig. 2800 GARTH RD, DEPT OF RADIOLOGY 77521 #021-01-1985 L1990 **DR** *020 †80 ‡
FRANKLIN, Mark Edens. 4201 GARTH RD, STE 107 77521 #048-14-1982 L1983 **ORS** *020 †40
FREDRICKS, Michelle S. 2800 GARTH RD 77521 #048-13-1995 L1996 **FM OM** *020 †18
FREY, Patricia Ann. 4201 GARTH RD STE 290 77521 #048-14-1995 L1997 **OBG** *020 †30
FUENTES, Juan Carlos. ■ 77521 #451-01-1996 L2007 **FP** *012
GARCIA, Luis Carlos. 1101 DECKER DR 77520 #264-12-1985 **FM** *100
GARRISON, Richard Lewis. 4301 GARTH RD, STE 400 77521 #055-01-1979 L1994 **FM** *020 †18
GAUR, Puja. ■ 77521 #048-12-2004 L2008 **GS** *012
GAYLE, Rosalyn Ann. 1010 W BAKER RD STE 104 77521 #048-02-1988 L1989 **OBG FM** *020 †18,30
GEORGE, Shefaa Shahaat. 4301 GARTH RD, STE 400 77521 #915-05-1987 **FP** *012
GERNALE, Virgilio Cabioc. ■ 77521 #748-01-1972 L1995 **FM** *020 †18
GIACONA, Jewel A. 2802 GARTH RD STE 211 77521 #048-14-1989 L1990 **FM** *020 †18
GLADU, Rebecca. 4301 GARTH RD STE 400 77521 #048-12-1988 L1989 **FM** *020 †18
GOKHALE, Ashok Vidyadhar. 4001 GARTH RD, STE 105 77521 #028-02-1991 L1999 **EM IM** *020 †20
GOMBERAWALLA, Mustafa H. 3711 GARTH RD, HEALTHSOUTH DIAGNOSTIC BAY 77521 #495-17-1975 L1992 **DR** *020 †80
GOMEZ, Mario Augusto. 1700 JAMES BOWIE DR 77520 #176-03-1965 L1974 **PTH** *071
GONZALEZ, Kimberlie J. 2802 GARTH RD STE 301 77521 #048-14-1989 L1993 **FM** *020 †18
GONZALEZ-FRAGA, Luis E. 1600 JAMES BOWIE DR, STE D107 77520 #048-14-1982 L1983 **IM** *020
GOSWITZ, Mary Sue. 4021 GARTH RD STE 105 77521 #021-01-1986 L1994 **RO** *020 †80
GRAVE, Diana Romo. 4301 GARTH RD STE 303 77521 #048-14-1989 L1990 **PD** *020 †55
GROSE, William. 4021 GARTH RD, STE 103 77521 #065-01-1970 L1976 **ON IM** *020 †20
GUIDRY, Kory Renard. 1010 W BAKER RD STE 105 77521 #048-14-1996 L1997 **FM** *020 †18
GUPTA, Ganesh P. 1610 JAMES BOWIE DR STE A 77520 #495-75-1982 L1993 **FM** *020 †18
HADIDI, Fayez Hussin J. 4301 GARTH RD STE 212 77521 #875-01-1976 L1990 **CD IM** *020 †20
HAMEED, Mohammed Abdul. 2802 GARTH RD STE 107 77521 #495-21-1985 L1996 **IM** *020 †20
HAMID, Bassam Ahmad. 2802 GARTH RD 77521 #875-01-1985 L1995 **IM** *020 †20
HANNA, Fikry Melek. 1700 JAMES BOWIE DR 77520 #330-02-1941 L1971 **PD NTR** *071 †55,03
HANNA, Lourdes Alej. 1610 JAMES BOWIE DR 77520 #748-01-1953 L1975 **CHP PD** *071 †55
HARRINGTON, Michael L. 4001 GARTH RD, STE 105 77521 #048-14-2000 L2003 **EM** *020
HARRIS, Vincent O. 1010 W BAKER RD, STE 101 77521 #043-01-1986 L1992 **DR** *020 †80
HASAN, Aziza Quadri. 1602 GARTH RD 77520 #704-23-1984 L1998 **FM** *020 †18
HASAN, Shamsa. 2802 GARTH RD STE 107, PRIMARY MED TOWER 77521 #704-06-1958 L1974 **FM IM** *020
HAWKINS, Clare Arnot. 4301 GARTH RD STE 400 77521 #062-01-1984 L1998 **FM** *020 †18 ‡
HAYS, Christopher D. 1310 MASSEY TOMPKINS RD 77521 #048-14-1985 L1986 **IM** *020 †20
HERNANDEZ-BUCK, Ludie. 4201 GARTH RD STE 119 77521 #010-02-1976 L1980 **GE IM** *020 †20
HEWITT, Mary F. 4401 GARTH RD 77521 #048-16-1997 L1998 **FM** *020 †18
HINES, Dennis Thos, Jr. 2610 N ALEXANDER DR, STE 201 77520 #026-04-1978 L1998 **FM** *020 †18
HOASJOE, Denis K. 4301 GARTH RD, STE 216 77521 #065-01-1984 L1997 **OTO FPS** *020 †45
HODGES, Lynn Powell. 4301 GARTH RD, STE 200 77521 #048-02-1957 L1957 **GP OBS** *020
HOFMANN, James Carl. 2610 N ALEXANDER DR # 208 77520 #035-15-1964 L1972 **OBG** *020 †30
HOLDER, William Robt. 2610 N ALEXANDER DR # 205 77520 #048-02-1966 L1966 **D** *020 †15
HOLSOMBACK, Thomas N. 1700 JAMES BOWIE DR 77520 #047-06-1968 L1969 **GS OM** *020 †85
HORN, James K. 2635 W BAKER RD 77521 #048-02-1989 L1991 **ORS** *020 †40
HUANG, Eddie Hsu. ■ 77521 #048-04-2007 **ORS** *012
HUDGINS, Philip Townsend. 4021 GARTH RD, STE 105 77521 #048-04-1954 L1954 **R RO** *071 †80
HUGHES, Louis B. 4301 GARTH RD STE 400 77521 #021-01-1949 L1953 **GP OBG** *020
HUNTER, Oliver Clifford. 4401 GARTH RD 77521 #048-13-1987 L1988 **DR** *020 †80
ILAHI, Arifa A. 4201 GARTH RD, STE 111 77521 #704-06-1966 L1973 **AN GP** *020 †05
ILAHI, Mohammad Arif. 4201 GARTH RD, STE 111 77521 #704-01-1956 L1972 **CD IM** *020
ILAHI, Mohammad Aslam. 4201 GARTH RD STE 111 77521 #704-01-1957 L1973 **GS GP** *020
IRANMANESH, Hamidreza. ■ 77521 #517-12-1995 **FP** *012
JAFARNIA, Mohamed Reza. 4301 GARTH RD, STE 209 77521 #517-01-1958 L1980 **OBG** *020 †30
JANKOWSKI, Yulan Y. 1001 W BAKER RD 77521 #048-15-1992 L1996 **IM** *020 †20
JOHNSTON, Caroline S. 2800 GARTH RD 77521 #048-16-1988 L1989 **FM** *020 †18
KAHKESHANI, Saeed. 4201 GARTH RD STE 211 77521 #517-01-1979 L1988 **N IM** *020 †75
KAHLA, Boutros. 4201 GARTH RD, STE 315 77521 #875-01-1980 L2007 **GS** *020 †85
KALANGI, Sathya Sundari. 2802 GARTH RD, STE 201 77521 #308-10-1983 L1992 **GE IM** *020 †20
KANG, Eugene. 4401 GARTH RD 77521 #048-13-1992 L1993 **FM** *020 †18
KAVIEFF, Robert Douglas. 1600 JAMES BOWIE DR # D105 77520 #025-07-1980 L1986 **OPH** *020 †35
KENNEDY, Bruce Clark. 4301 GARTH RD STE 303 77521 #048-14-1984 L1988 **PD IM** *020 †20,55
KHOSHNEJAD, Feridoon. 4201 GARTH RD STE 303 77521 #517-01-1970 L1996 **OBG** *020 †30 ‡
KHOSHNEJAD, Mani. ■ 77521 #654-01-2006 *012
KHOSHNEVIS-ASL, Mohammad. 4201 GARTH RD STE 111 77521 #517-08-1994 L2001 **PCC** *020 †20
KLUPPEL, Shannon Keith. 1000 E JAMES ST 77520 #048-16-1984 L1985 **PD** *020 †55
KRELL, Ted Wm. 1700 JAMES BOWIE DR 77520 #048-02-1968 L1968 **P** *020 †75
LAMUG, Marietta B. 1610 JAMES BOWIE DR, STE B103 77520 #748-02-1989 L1996 **PD** *020 †55
LEAHEY, Edward Wm. 4201 GARTH RD, STE 100 77521 #064-01-1976 L1977 **IC CD** *020 †20
LUCIUS, Alfred Danl, Jr. 4301 GARTH RD STE 311 77521 #021-05-1961 L1965 **OBG** *020 †30
MALDONADO, Joyce Elaine. 4401 GARTH RD, SAN JACINTO METHODIST HOSP 77521 #039-01-1983 L1986 **PTH PCP** *020 †50
MALIK, Geeta Kumari. 4301 GARTH RD STE 400 77521 #030-06-1993 L1998 **FM** *020 †18
MARROQUIN, Monica. 4301 GARTH RD, STE 303 77521 #048-04-2003 L2006 **PD** *020 †55
MARSHALL, Thomas E. 4301 GARTH RD 77521 #048-13-1985 L1986 **OPH** *020 †35
MATIAS, Daisy Ann Soriano. 4301 GARTH RD, STE 400 77521 #748-21-1995 **FP** *012
MC GEE, Scott B. 4401 GARTH RD 77521 #048-04-1997 L2005 **AN** *100
MC KINNON, James Graham. 2800 GARTH RD STE A 77521 #065-01-1958 L1968 **OPH** *020
MEDELLIN, Pamela Louisa. 4021 GARTH RD, STE 101 77521 #048-02-1977 L1977 **ON HEM** *020 †20
MEGLEY, Svetlana Zakcharo. 2800 GARTH RD 77521 #913-86-1995 L2007 **FM** *020
MELCHER, Steven Mclain. 2610 N ALEXANDER DR 77520 #021-06-2001 L2004 **FM** *020 †18
MENDOZA, Alfonso Gonzalez. ■ 77521 #649-02-1960 L1962 **GP OS** *075
MOORE, Bufford D. 4301 GARTH RD STE 101 77521 #048-13-1985 L1986 **HS PS** *020 †18,65
MUAYAD, Mohamad Salem. 4201 GARTH RD, STE 313 77521 #875-01-1986 L1993 **GE** *020 †20
MUSFY, Nofal. 2800 GARTH RD 77521 #875-01-1968 L1976 **FM** *020 †18
NAZARI-ADLI, Fariborz. 4308C GARTH RD 77521 #654-01-1987 L1994 **FM OM** *020 †18
NESSELRODE, John E. 4401 GARTH RD 77521 #048-04-1952 L1952 **FM** *075
NGUYEN, Chinh Quoc. 1010 W BAKER RD, STE 102 77521 #048-15-1997 L1999 **FM** *020 †18
NGUYEN, Daniel Nha. 4401 GARTH RD 77521 #048-02-2002 L2005 **IM** *020 †20
NORTHCUTT, Brian S. ■ 77521 #048-12-2005 L2006 **FP** *012
NURRE, Christopher Allen. 1602 GARTH RD 77520 #018-03-1987 L1991 **FM** *020 †18
PANCHBHAYA, Shoyab A. 4401 GARTH RD 77521 #048-13-2000 L2004 **AN** *020 †05
PANDEY, Hemant Kumar. 2800 GARTH RD, DEPT OF NEUROLOGY 77521 #495-15-1996 L2004 **CN** *100 †75
PANNU, Anupam Kay. 4301 GARTH RD, STE 400 77521 #104-01-2005 **FP** *012
PANZARELLA, Robert Louis. 4401 GARTH RD 77521 #048-15-1980 L1980 **EM FM** *020 †16,18
PAPROSKI, Alvin C J. 1700 JAMES BOWIE DR 77520 #068-01-1968 L1977 **FM** *071
PARDO, Rafael Raymundo. 2800 GARTH RD 77521 #847-06-1976 L1980 **FM** *020 †18
PARDO, Ricardo Rafael. 2800 GARTH RD STE A 77521 #048-14-1981 L1981 **N** *020 †75
PATEL, Madhura V. 1700 JAMES BOWIE DR 77520 #495-28-1978 L1988 **PM N** *020 †60
PINA, Edward M. 4201 GARTH RD STE 301 77521 #048-14-1989 L1991 **GS** *020 †85
PONCE, Frank Joseph, III. 4301 GARTH RD, STE 400 77521 #305-01-2006 **FP** *012
PRATT, Francis Eugene. ■ 77520 #048-04-1960 L1960 **OTO** *071 †45
PRIHODA, Alton Roy. 4201 GARTH RD STE 318 77521 #048-14-1981 L1981 **PD** *020 †55
PUNAR, Metin. ■ 77520 #902-05-1991 L2007 **SP** *012 †50
PUPPALA, Lakshmi Swarna. 4301 GARTH RD STE 400 77521 #495-50-1999 L2007 **FP** *012
PYLE, James Geo. 4201 GARTH RD, STE 107 77521 #056-06-1978 L1979 **ORS OSM** *020 †40
QUADRI, Syed F. 4401 GARTH RD 77521 #496-01-1983 L1997 **PTH** *020 †50
QUANSAH, Araba Buabema. ■ 77521 #041-01-1989 L1994 **AN** *020 †05
QUENZER, Fred August, Jr. 4401 GARTH RD 77521 #048-04-1965 L1965 **R NM** *020 †80
QURESHI, Parvez Anjum. 4401 GARTH RD 77521 #704-02-1990 L1998 **FM FPG** *020 †18 ‡
RADFORD, Tres T. 1700 JAMES BOWIE DR 77520 #048-13-1997 **FM** *100
RAMOS, Tryna Marie. 4301 GARTH RD STE 400, SAN JACINTO FAMILY MEDICIN 77521 #005-14-2000 L2001 **FM** *020 †18
RAUF, Shariq J. 4401 GARTH RD 77521 #704-20-1987 L1997 **ID IM** *020 †20
RAVI, Shivarajpur K. 2802 GARTH RD, STE 207 77521 #495-99-1981 L1993 **PME N** *072 †75
RISER, Clarence Alfred. 4308 GARTH RD 77521 #039-01-1967 L1972 **OM FM** *071 †70
ROMAN, Rocio Lolita. 1602 GARTH RD, BAYTOWN HEALTH CENTER 77520 #319-03-1985 L1997 **FM** *020 †18
ROTHENBERG, Eric Scott. 4201 GARTH RD, STE 111 77521 #035-09-1985 L1992 **PS** *020 †65
ROUNTREE, Paul Pollard. 5000 BAYWAY DR 77520 #048-02-1969 L1969 **OM FM** *020 †18,70
SACHDEV, Atul Kumar. 4301 GARTH RD, STE 200 77521 #048-13-1995 L1996 **FM** *020 †18
SANJAR, Mansour R. 2802 GARTH RD STE 215, ADVANCE PSY CTR 77521 #517-01-1959 L1983 **P CHP** *020
SARTI, Figueroa Fernando. 4301 GARTH RD # 30 77521 #429-01-1966 L1975 **IM GE** *020
SASHITAL, Deepa. 4021 GARTH RD, STE 101 77521 #496-38-1993 L2007 **HO** *020 †20
SCHLAGENHAUF, Geo K, Jr. 2001 CEDAR BAYOU RD, BAYSHORE MEDNTAL HEALTH CL 77520 #048-02-1961 L1961 **P CHP** *020 †75
SCHULTZ, Alan Keith. 1 PRICE ST STE 200B, AMERICA 77520 #026-04-1963 L1984 **FPG IMG** *020 †18
SCHWARTZ, Stephanie Myra. 2800 GARTH RD 77521 #409-16-1981 L1988 **N SME** *020
SHAH, Atul T. 2800 GARTH RD, DEPT OF GASTROENTEROLOGY 77521 #495-23-1980 L1992 **GE IM** *020 †20
SHAWISH, Hisham Mustafa. 1101 DECKER DR 77520 #575-01-1993 **FP** *012
SHETTY, Shubha Premnath. 4301 GARTH RD STE 400 77521 #496-31-2003 **FP** *012

■ = Address Information Privacy Protected

TEXAS
BAYTOWN — BEAUMONT

SHULKE, Kirk Bradley. 1700 JAMES BOWIE DR, PROFESSIONAL 77520 #048-14-1984 L1985 OPH EM *020

SIDDIQI, Rashid M. 4201 GARTH RD, STE 201 77521 #704-16-1989 L2005 CCM *020 †20

SIEGELMAN, Richard Edward. 4401 GARTH RD, 6711 SJOLANDER RD 77521 #048-02-1980 L1980 AN *020 †05

SISMAN, Julide. ■ 77520 #902-10-1993 L2007 PD *100 †55

SMITH, Thomas Elmo. 6019 THOMPSON RD 77521 #016-42-1943 L1959 GP OM *071

SOLIS, Itzel S. 7 SWALM CENTER DR 77520 #715-01-1973 L1975 PM PD *020 †60

SOTO, Efrain Eduardo, Jr. ■ 77521 #308-03-2004 L2008 FP *012

STRANGMEIER, James Melvyn. ■ 77521 #021-01-1964 L1965 GS *071 †85

STUMM, Philip Wolcott. ■ 77521 #007-02-1943 L1962 PD AM *071

TERRY, Gregory Morrell. 4301 GARTH RD STE 200 77521 #048-16-1985 L1986 FM *020 †18

THOMSON, Richard Jos. ■ 77521 #048-02-1959 1959 OPH *071 †35

TOMSIC, Kevin Lee. ■ 77521 #305-01-2007 FP *012

TRIFILIO, Aristides A. 2610 N ALEXANDER DR # 200 77520 #308-01-1948 L1963 U *071 †95

VALYASEVI, Mickey. 2802 GARTH RD, STE 309 77521 #041-09-1986 L2001 AI *020 †20,03

VILLAR, Joseph R. 1610 JAMES BOWIE DR # B103 77520 #748-02-1987 L1996 PD *020 †55

WALKER, Beverly A Thir. 4301 GARTH RD, STE 309 77521 #048-15-1993 L1994 FM *020 †18

WALKER, Lawrence R. 4301 GARTH RD, STE 309 77521 #048-15-1994 L1995 FM *020 †18

WALLS, George S, III. 5000 BAYWAY DR, EXXONMOBIL CORPORATION 77520 #048-02-1998 L2001 GPM *020 †70

WALMSLEY, George Lee. ■ 77520 #048-02-1954 L1954 FM *071 †18

WALMSLEY, George Storn. 3711 GARTH RD, STE 306 77521 #654-01-1983 L1987 FM *020 †18

WAMBLE, John Lee, Jr. 1600 JAMES BOWIE DR, STE D103 77520 #027-01-1970 L1989 P PYG *020 †75

WHITACRE, Hannah Eunice. ■ 77520 #005-16-1993 GP OS *071

WHITMAN, Donald Lee. 4301 GARTH RD, PLZ II STE 214 77521 #048-14-1979 L1979 GS *020 †85

WILLIAMS, Drew Davis. ■ 77520 #048-02-1960 L1960 GS *072 †85 ‡

WILLISTON, Hubert N. 4301 GARTH RD, STE 400 77521 #061-01-1971 L1976 FM OBS *020 †18

WITSON, Anne Shumate. 4401 GARTH RD 77521 #048-14-1995 L1996 PCP *020 †50

WOLFE, Jean Guy. 4401 GARTH RD 77521 #067-02-1962 L1977 FM *020

WONG, Danny. 4201 GARTH RD STE 321 77521 #048-02-1985 L1986 OTO *020 †45

YAO, Hsitai. 4401 GARTH RD 77521 #048-13-1989 L1990 AN *020 †05

YATES, Ernest Keith. 4301 GARTH RD STE 101 77521 #064-01-1967 L1978 PS *071

YOUNG, Paul C. 1700 JAMES BOWIE DR 77520 #020-02-1994 L1999 P *020 †75

YOUSUF, Adnan. 4301 GARTH RD, STE 400 77521 #495-46-1991 L2006 FM *100 †18

YUSUF, Qaiser. 2306 N ALEXANDER DR 77520 #690-01-1986 L1992 N IM *020

ZACHAREK, Anthony Mehdi. 4301 GARTH RD, STE 101 77521 #025-07-1999 L2004 PS *020 †65

ZAMIRPOUR, Payman. 4301 GARTH RD, STE 400 77521 #517-07-1991 L2007 FM *100 †18

BEACH CITY – HARRIS

MAYHEW, Carle Crane, III. ■ 77520 #048-02-1965 L1965 GP *071

BEAUMONT – JEFFERSON

ABBAS, Asad. 3570 COLLEGE ST, STE 200 77701 #704-25-1989 L2002 OPH *020 †35

ABRAHAM, Aleyamma Ivy. 3560 DELAWARE ST, STE 601A 77706 #690-07-1987 L2002 FM *020 †18

ACHILLES, Jackson Todd. 810 HOSPITAL DR STE 320 77701 #048-02-1977 L1977 P *020 †75

ADKINS, Charles F. 3260 FANNIN ST 77701 #048-02-1944 L1944 P N *071 †75

AGOMUO, Peter Ndubisi. 25 N 11TH ST, BEAUMONT RADIOLOGY GROUP, 77702 #033-06-1991 L2000 DR *020 †80

AHMED, Jehanara. 3570 COLLEGE ST, STE 200 77701 #704-06-1994 L2005 END *020 †20

AHMED, Safeer. ■ 77706 #704-02-1987 L2000 PD *100 †55

AHMED, Shariq. 3070 COLLEGE ST STE 300 77701 #704-02-1991 L2005 NEP *020 †20

AHMED, Talat. 4365 BROWNSTONE DR 77706 #495-15-1979 L1998 PD NPM *020 †55

AKHTAR, Syed Usama. 690 N 14TH ST 77702 #704-01-1987 L2001 ON *020 †20

ALASWAD, Bashar A. 740 HOSPITAL DR STE 120 77701 #875-01-1976 L1996 PG PD *020 †55

ALDRICH, Andrew J. 3030 NORTH ST STE 510 77702 #048-14-1984 L1985 PUD IM *020 †20

ALEXANDER, David. 3560 DELAWARE ST, STE 601A 77706 #045-01-1989 L2003 EM *020 †20

ALFORD, Nathaniel J, Jr. 3030 NORTH ST, STE 510 77702 #048-02-1978 L1978 PUD CCM *020 †20

ALLEN, Joshua A. 755 N 11TH ST, STE P3600 77702 #048-14-2000 L2004 AN *020

AMSDEN, Michael Nancy. 2830 CALDER ST 77702 #012-05-1972 L1975 EM PLM *020 †16

ANDERSON, Corey Haynes. 3560 DELAWARE ST, STE 601A 77706 #048-15-1994 L1995 FM *020 †18

ANDREWS, Jocelyn Anne. ■ 77703 #025-07-1997 L2001 P *020

ANGEL, Ian F. 2965 HARRISON ST, GOLDEN TRIANGLE NEUROCARE 77702 #048-14-1991 L1992 NS *020 †25

ANWAR, Syed Imtiaz. 3570 COLLEGE ST 77701 #704-02-1993 L1997 IM *020 †20

ARFEEN, Qamar Ul. 3070 COLLEGE ST STE 300 77701 #704-02-1988 L1995 PCC *020 †20

ARMSTRONG, George G, Jr. ■ 77708 #016-11-1956 L1971 AM *071

ATAYA, Raja Hani. 3070 COLLEGE ST, STE 302 77701 #915-02-1970 L1984 PD HEM *020

ATKINSON, Jane Clare. 755 N 11TH ST, STE P4200 77702 #021-05-1993 L1997 OBG *020 †30

AVERY, Graham Douglas. 740 HOSPITAL DR, STE 200 77701 #048-02-1979 L1979 OPH *020 †35

AWAR, Omar Ghaleb. ■ 77706 #048-04-2007 *012

AYDELOTT, George Alan. ■ 77706 #016-11-1978 L1991 DR *020 †80

AZIZ, Muhammad T. 2929 CALDER ST STE 100 77702 #704-16-1987 L1996 IM *020 †20

BAERTL, Juan Manuel. ■ 77713 #737-01-1953 L1978 IM GP *071

BAGRI, Kashi S. 2194 EASTEX FWY STE A 77703 #495-55-1972 L1979 P PYG *020 †75

BAKER, Frank John. 3030 NORTH ST STE 460 77702 #039-01-1973 L1984 ID IM *020 †20

BALUYOT, Griselda Everga. 3480 FANNIN ST, STE 0 77701 #748-01-1965 L1977 AN *020

BALUYOT, Restituto E. 3480 FANNIN ST 77701 #748-01-1965 L1976 DR NM *020 †80,28

BANATWALA, Marissa. ■ 77706 #048-15-2004 L2007 FM *100

BARCLAY, Geo Willis, Jr. 3576 COLLEGE ST 77701 #048-12-1961 L1961 CD IM *071 †20

BARENBERG, Andrew Henry. 950 N 14TH ST, STE 100 77702 #048-02-1986 L1987 GE IM *020 †20

BARNES, John Edward. ■ 77706 #047-06-1963 L1970 OM GS *071

BARRY, Gene Norman. 2900 NORTH ST STE 310 77702 #048-12-1990 L1991 OBG *020 †30 ‡

BEAN, Lonnie James. 3030 NORTH ST, STE-320 77702 #048-04-1979 L1979 IM *020 †20

BEAUDRY, Dominique Josee. ■ 77706 #048-14-2001 L2008 IC *012

BEAVER, Byron Kevin. 755 N 11TH ST, ST ELIZABETH WOUND CARE 77702 #048-12-1999 L2003 EM UME *020

BECKERT, Benjamin Wallace. 755 N 11TH ST STE P3500 77702 #028-03-1998 L2004 PS *020 †65

BENCOWITZ, Harold Zalmon. 3030 NORTH ST STE 510 77702 #048-04-1973 1974 PUD IM *020 †20

BERNDT, Robert Barry. 755 N 11TH ST, STE P3600 77702 #048-12-1979 L1979 AN *020 †05

BESSELL, Alfred. 2830 CALDER ST 77702 #048-02-1959 L1959 ORS *071 †40

BHARATHI, Aiyanadar. 2830 CALDER ST, NEONATAL INTENSIVE CARE UN 77702 #495-53-1965 L1978 PD NPM *020 †55

BHAT, Krishna Devaru. 2627 LAUREL ST, PULM CLINIC 77702 #495-35-1972 L1977 A PDA *020 †55,03

BIRDWELL, Robert Rankin. 3070 COLLEGE ST, STE 301 77701 #048-12-1974 L1976 ON HEM *020 †20

BLACK, Jack Dennis. 2929 CALDER ST, STE 201 77702 #048-02-1973 L1973 OBG *020

BLAHEY, Maria S. 755 N 11TH ST, BEAUMONT INTERNAL 77702 #060-01-1978 L1982 FM PLM *020 †18

BOMMER, Kathryn Keen. 2830 CALDER ST 77702 #012-01-1990 L1995 SP *020 †50

BONILLA, Pedro Osmin B. ■ 77706 #649-14-1972 *100

BORRELL, Rogelio Menendez. 2830 CALDER ST 77702 #275-01-1953 L1968 PM *071 †60

BOSCH, George Alexander. 2900 NORTH ST STE 401 77702 #275-01-1952 L1961 OBG *071

BOST, Brent Wayne. 755 N 11TH ST, STE P4200 77702 #048-04-1981 L1981 OBG MDM *020 †30

BOURQUE, J Gardiner. 2955 HARRISON ST, STE 104 77702 #021-05-1961 L1964 R RO *071 †80

BOWLING, James Robt. 2929 CALDER ST STE 212 77702 #028-78-1982, ▲ L1983 AN *020 †05

BRADY, Alfred Bernard, Jr. 2955 HARRISON ST, STE 200 77702 #021-01-1966 L1966 CD IM *020 †20

BRANNAN, Wade Melbry. 2830 CALDER ST 77702 #036-01-1956 L1963 PTH *071 †50

BRAUER, Bodo. 6510 FOLSOM DR 77706 #048-02-1986 L1988 FM *020 †18

BRISCOE, Michael. ■ 77705 #048-02-2005 OTO *012

BROOKS, Holly Ann. ■ 77706 #048-12-1977 L1977 IM *020 †20

BROWN, Bertron Travis. 3030 NORTH ST, STE 420 77702 #048-12-1981 L1981 IM *020 †20

BROWN-NEMBHARD, Tonya R. 3127 COLLEGE ST, STE 410 77701 #010-03-1990 L1993 PD *020 †55

BUKHARI, Talat Hassan. 4365 BROWNSTONE DR 77706 #704-01-1964 L1975 P *020

BURGER, Nanette Louise. ■ 77706 #048-15-1984 L1985 IM *020 †20

BURKE, Carroll A. 3560 DELAWARE ST, STE 601A 77706 #048-15-1987 L1988 FM *020 †18

BURKES, William Sidney. 3150 MEDICAL CENTER DR, STE 1 77701 #048-12-1980 L1980 SME IM *020 †20

CALLAS, Gerald R. 3576 COLLEGE ST 77701 #048-02-2000 L2004 AN *020 †05 ‡

CANLAS, Aida M. 3155 STAGG DR 77701 #748-01-1967 L1979 AN *074 †05

CASELLI, Marco. 3570 COLLEGE ST, STE 200 77701 #561-06-1971 L1992 GS *020 †85

CASKEY, Charles Jos. 3070 COLLEGE ST, STE 207 77701 #048-02-1955 L1957 FM *071 †18

CHARLESTON, Craig Anthony. 755 N 11TH ST, STE P5600 77702 #048-02-2000 L2004 APM *020

CHAVIS, Tamerla D. 2900 NORTH ST, STE 408 77702 #048-13-1987 L1988 NS VIR *020 †25

CHENNUPATI, Raja Sekhar. 950 N 14TH ST, STE 100 77702 #495-58-1993 L2000 GE *020 †20

CHEREWATY, Stephen N. 25 N 11TH ST 77702 #051-04-1977 L1989 DR *020

CHOI, Mehee. ■ 77706 #048-13-2008 *012

CHOW, Danny Ching-Fai. 3555 STAGG DR 77701 #005-11-1988 L1993 RO *020 †80

CLARK, Charles B, III. 2955 HARRISON ST 77702 #048-02-1972 L1972 NS *020

CLARKE, Burnet Todd. 3650 LAUREL ST 77707 #048-12-1990 L1991 ORS *020 †40

CLARKE, Henri De Saussure. ■ 77706 #012-01-1958 L1964 GYN OS *071 †30

CLAYTON, Gary R. 3395 PLAZA 10 DR, STE C 77707 #048-16-1987 L1989 FM *020 †18

COLBERT, Bobbie Henry. 3570 COLLEGE ST, STE 200 77701 #048-13-1976 L1978 PD *020 †55

COLBERT, Christle Denise. ■ 77706 #047-07-2008 *012

COLGAN, Timothy Kelly. 755 N 11TH ST, STE P2200 77702 #056-05-1976 L1982 CD IM *020 †20

COLLINS, Weldon Edward. 2929 CALDER ST STE 312 77702 #048-04-1981 L1981 D *020 †15

CONNER, Douglass C. 3560 DELAWARE ST STE 209 77706 #012-01-1995 L2001 R *020 †80

COOK, William Kearney. 3560 DELAWARE ST, STE 209 77706 #027-01-1984 L1989 DR *020 †80

COOPER, Darrella L. 3080 COLLEGE ST 77701 #047-07-1998 L2005 EM *020 †16

CRAIG-MINALDI, Susan Kay. 740 HOSPITAL DR, STE 110 77701 #048-02-1996 L1997 FM *020 †18

CREED, James Bennett, Jr. 3560 DELAWARE ST STE 1204 77706 #048-02-1971 L1971 P CD *020

CRIM, Charles Brian. 2965 HARRISON ST STE 217 77702 #048-02-1969 L1969 D *020 †15

CROSSLEY, Michael. 3560 DELAWARE ST, STE 601A 77706 #048-02-1990 L1991 EM *020

CRUMPLER, Paul Hulen. 755 N 11TH ST STE P5600 77702 #048-15-1982 L1983 FM *062 †18

DAILEY, Karen B. ■ 77706 #048-15-2001 L2005 FM *020 †18

DAVILA, Juan Elias. 3650 LAUREL ST 77707 #649-02-1979 L1988 PM *020 †60

DAVIS, James L. 4471 CALDER AVE 77706 #048-02-1996 L1997 FM OM *020 †18

DAVIS, John Ivy. ■ 77706 #028-02-1955 L1975 GE IM *071 †20

DEAN, Kevin L. 2900 NORTH ST STE 200 77702 #048-13-1991 L1992 GS *020 †85

DEIPARINE, Caesar F. 6510 FOLSOM DR 77706 #748-11-1988 L1998 IM *020 †18

DE PAIVA, S P Correa. 3650 LAUREL ST 77707 #187-02-1957 L1975 ORS *020 †35

DERDERIAN, Raymond. 3965 PHELAN BLVD STE 200, GOLDEN TRIANGLE DIALYSIS 77707 #781-01-1980 L1986 NEP IM *020 †20

DERRICK, Joseph Parker. 3480 FANNIN ST 77701 #016-06-1954 L1957 PD *020

DESAI, Rajen Bhulabhai. 3560 DELAWARE ST STE 905 77706 #495-23-1982 L1992 P *020 †75

DE SILVA, Sriyawathie T M. 85 INTERSTATE 10 N, STE 201 77707 #220-01-1962 L1979 P *020 †75

DEUTMEYER, David Jos. 755 N 11TH ST, STE P3600 77702 #018-03-1990 L1994 AN *020 †05

DIAZ, Gregory Christopher. 3560 DELAWARE ST, STE 209 77706 #025-07-1995 L2000 DR *020 †80

DIAZ-SALDANA, Alberto. 3129 COLLEGE ST 77701 #042-01-1979 L1987 OPH *020 †35

DINEEN, Eric Jordan. 2900 NORTH ST, STE 414 77702 #048-13-1981 L1997 CD IM *030 †20

DOIRON, Michael Jack. 890 19TH ST 77706 #048-02-1974 L1974 DR *020 †80

DOMINGUES, Chas Chester. 3650 LAUREL ST 77707 #021-05-1970 L1973 ORS *020 †40

DOSHI, Sharda Jitendra. 2929 CALDER ST STE 300 77702 #495-22-1971 L1981 PD EM *020 †55

DOSHI, Taral Jitendra. 4890 ELMWOOD LN 77706 #016-02-2008 *012

8546

■ = Address Information Privacy Protected

DOUGLAS, Jake S. ■ 77701 #047-07-1939 L1940 **FM GP** *075
DOWDY, Christopher P. 3070 COLLEGE ST, STE 207 77701 #048-04-1992 L1994 **OBG** *020 †30
DUKE, Andy Brian. 3333 NORTH ST 77706 #048-12-1997 **GS** *100
DUNDAS, Robert B. 810 HOSPITAL DR, STE 301 77701 #060-02-1974 L1995 **PD** *020 †55
EDE, Ezea Daniel. 740 HOSPITAL DR, STE 230 77701 #038-41-1986 L1991 **IM** *020 †20
EGER, Ronald K. 740 HOSPITAL DR 77701 #062-01-1969 L1978 **FM** *071
ELAHI, Lubna. 2929 CALDER ST, STE 100 77702 #704-16-1987 L1996 **FM** *020 †18 ‡
ERHARD, Peter Sims. ■ 77706 #048-02-1945 L1945 **AN** *071 †05
ERNST, Jo Ann. 2355 INTERSTATE 10 E 77702 #048-13-1983 **PD** *075
ESTRADA-GORDILLO, Rolando. 550 INTERSTATE 10 S, STE 201 77707 #429-01-1965 L1972 **PTH DMP** *071 †50
EVANS, Charles Alexander. 2830 CALDER ST 77702 #060-02-1984 L1993 **GP END** *020
EZIKE, Elias Nnamdi. 3127 COLLEGE ST 77701 #561-17-1990 L2006 **PD PDI** *020 †55
FAM, Dean. 755 N 11TH ST, STE P3600 77702 #001-02-1995 L2000 **AN** *020 †05
FAMA, J R. ■ 77706 #021-05-1943 L1948 **CD IM** *071
FATO, Jeffrey Warren. 3560 DELAWARE ST, STE 601A 77706 #048-12-1981 L1981 **EM FM** *020 †18,16
FAWCETT, William Arthur. 2965 HARRISON ST, STE 315 77702 #036-05-1973 L1978 **AI PD** *020 †55,03
FERRILL, Shelley C. 3560 DELAWARE ST, STE 601A 77706 #048-12-1998 L2001 **FM** *020 †18
FIELD, John B. 755 N 11TH ST, STE P3600 77702 #048-02-1992 L1996 **AN** *020 †05
FIGARI, Shawn M. 3650 LAUREL ST 77707 #048-14-1991 L1994 **ORS** *020 †40
FINLEY, Joseph Marion. 490 IH 10 N # 200 77702 #048-12-1968 L1969 **FM** *020 †18 ‡
FINNEY, James Wm. ■ 77706 #028-34-1943 L1944 **GP GS** *071
FONTENOT, Ray, Jr. 740 HOSPITAL DR, STE 300 77701 #021-05-1984 L1986 **OTO A** *020 †45
FOWLER, John Terry. 755 N 11TH ST, BEAUMONT INTERNAL 77702 #048-02-1998 L2001 **IM** *020 †20
FREESE, Sarah Elizabeth. 3576 COLLEGE ST 77701 #048-15-1985 L1986 **PD** *020 †55
GALLOWAY, Carolyn Sue. 3560 DELAWARE ST, STE 601A 77706 #048-14-1978 L1978 **EM** *020 †16
GARCIA-MALDONADO, M. 3420 VETERANS CIR, CMO BEAUMONT VA CLNC 77707 #649-14-1976 L1987 **MDM IM** *030 ‡
GERHARDT, Herman. 2830 CALDER ST 77702 #030-05-1970 L1971 **GS EM** *020 †85,16
GIANNONE, Nick Frank. 3560 DELAWARE ST, STE 601A 77706 #649-14-1980 L1987 **FM EM** *020 †18
GIGLIO, Frank Anthony. 3560 DELAWARE ST 77706 #048-02-1955 L1955 **GYN OBS** *071 †30
GILMORE, John Frank. 3110 FANNIN ST 77701 #048-02-1945 L1945 **D** *071
GILMORE, Wm Allen, II. 3110 FANNIN ST 77701 #048-02-1979 L1979 **D** *020 †15
GISH, James Robt. ■ 77726 #017-20-1947 L1956 **RO DR** *071 †80
GLASS, Cecil R. 2525 CALDER ST 77702 #048-02-1949 L1950 **AN** *071 †05
GOMEZ, Jonathon. 755 N 11TH ST, STE P3600 77702 #048-12-1984 L1987 **AN** *020 †05
GONZALES, Gaylon Albert. 2900 NORTH ST, STE 203 77702 #048-02-1978 L1978 **GS VS** *020
GONZALEZ, Juan M. 4229 TOLIVAR CANAL RD 77713 #048-13-1982 L1983 **AN** *020
GONZALEZ, Rosa C. 3560 DELAWARE ST, STE 109 77706 #048-14-1990 L1992 **CHP** *020 †75
GRABER, William James, III. ■ 77706 #021-01-1957 L1957 **U** *071 †95
GRANGER, John K. 2830 CALDER ST 77702 #021-06-1988 L1994 **PTH** *020 †50
GREENER, Donald Jos. 755 N 11TH ST, STE P3600 77702 #028-02-1969 L1972 **AN GP** *020 †05
GRIPON, Edward Brown. 3560 DELAWARE ST STE 502 77706 #048-02-1968 L1968 **P PFP** *020 †75
GROVES, George Edward, Jr. 740 HOSPITAL DR, STE 220 77701 #048-14-1986 L1989 **P** *020 †75
GUILLET, Glen Gordon. 5875 N MAJOR DR 77713 #048-02-1965 L1965 **GP CD** *020 †18
GURGUN, Mehmet. 3560 DELAWARE ST, STE 209 77706 #048-04-1988 L1990 **DR** *020 †80
HAAK, Lee W. 5875 N MAJOR DR, STE 134 77713 #048-16-2000 L2001 **FM** *020 †18
HAISTEN, Maurice Wyatt. ■ 77706 #001-02-1947 L1960 **OPH** *071 †35
HALASWAMY, Ravi H. 2666 CALDER ST 77702 #495-99-1988 L1992 **AN** *020 †05
HALBERT, Dean T. 2010 DOWLEN RD, SETMA WEST END MEDICAL PLA 77706 #048-13-1989 L1991 **FM** *020 †18
HALBERT, John Thos. 6255 WILCHESTER LN 77706 #048-02-1960 L1960 **P PYG** *071 †75
HALIM, Jamil Saeed. 3420 VETERANS CIR, VA - OPC 77707 #495-37-1960 L1979 **IM** *020
HARDIN, Barry Todd. 755 N 11TH ST, STE P3600 77702 #048-78-1994, ▲ L1998 **AN** *020 †05
HARMON, Daniel J. 3030 NORTH ST, STE 420 77702 #030-06-1977 L1981 **IM OS** *020 †20
HARMON, Mark Kevin. 3345 PLAZA 10 DR 77707 #039-01-1988 L1990 **OPH** *020 †35
HARRIS, Daniel L. 755 N 11TH ST STE P5600, UT SOUTHWESTERN MEDICAL CE 77702 #048-14-2002 L2005 **APM** *020 †05
HARRIS, Joseph Denton, IV. 755 N 11TH ST STE P3200 77702 #048-12-1974 L1975 **U** *020 †95
HARTMAN, Sam Feiss. ■ 77706 #021-05-1941 L1947 **GP** *071
HAWKINS, William Noel. 3560 DELAWARE ST, STE 1001 77706 #047-07-1989 L1993 **OBG** *020 †30
HAYES, Erica Jean. 5925 PHELAN BLVD, # 130 77706 #048-02-1997 L2001 **P** *020
HAYES, Marshall Wade. 3650 LAUREL ST 77707 #048-13-1973 L1973 **ORS** *020 †40
HEARTFIELD, Edward Linn. 3070 COLLEGE ST, STE 300 77701 #021-01-1964 L1967 **OTO PS** *020 †45
HENDERSON, John Abe, III. ■ 77706 #048-04-1953 L1953 **GYN** *071
HENDERSON, John Abe, IV. 755 N 11TH ST STE P3200 77702 #048-02-1981 L1981 **U** *020 †95
HENNINGTON, Herbert M. ■ 77706 #004-01-1947 L1947 **FM** *071 †18
HENSEL, Jo Ann. 3345 PLAZA 10 DR 77707 #048-15-1979 L1979 **OPH** *020 †35
HERNANDEZ, Jorge Anibal. 755 N 11TH ST 77702 #649-04-1992 L1998 **CD** *020 †20
HICKS, Leon Milton. 2955 HARRISON ST STE 201 77702 #027-01-1971 L1972 **PDS GS** *020 †85
HIGH, William Lank. 2910 FANNIN ST STE B 77701 #036-07-1973 L1978 **N** *020 †20,75
HILL, Keith Jay. 3650 LAUREL ST, EAST HOSPITAL ROAD 77707 #028-03-1995 L2007 **ORS OFA** *020 †40
HILL, Teresa Tram N. 3030 NORTH ST, STE 300 77702 #048-15-1999 L2003 **OBG** *020 †30
HINKLE, Thomas Varian. 3480 FANNIN ST, STE O 77701 #048-02-1958 L1958 **R** *020 †80
HITT, Rankin V, Jr. 2830 CALDER ST 77702 #048-02-1956 L1956 **FM PD** *071 †18
HO, Victor Shenpou. ■ 77713 #039-01-1994 L1997 **EM** *020 †16
HODGES, Timothy M. ■ 77707 #048-13-2000 L2006 **CCS** *020
HOFFMAN, George Saml. 2900 NORTH ST, STE 401 77702 #041-13-1977 L1979 **U** *020 †95
HOLDER, Joanne. 810 HOSPITAL DR, STE 300 77701 #041-01-1998 L2002 **OBG** *020
HOLLAND, Joseph Wm, Jr. 950 N 11TH ST, STE 100 77702 #048-15-1981 L1981 **GE** *020 †20
HOLLOWAY, Ruby L. 3070 COLLEGE ST STE 405 77701 #038-06-1983 L1983 **OBG** *020 †30
HOLLY, James Larry. 3570 COLLEGE ST, STE 200 77701 #048-13-1973 L1973 **FM** *020
HOLMES, Michael Wesley. 6622 PHELAN BLVD 77706 #027-01-1975 L1976 **EM** *020 †16
HOOD, Robert Cameron. 3030 NORTH ST, STE 560 77702 #065-01-1981 L1987 **END** *020 †20
HORTON, Douglas Leslie. ■ 77706 #048-02-1967 L1967 **GS** *071 †85
HUANG, Xisong. 3420 FANNIN ST, STE 190 77701 #243-21-1984 L2003 **AN** *020 †05
HUBBELL, Carl Jos. 3127 COLLEGE ST, STE 410 77701 #048-14-1984 L1985 **PD** *020 †55
HUGHES, James J. 810 HOSPITAL DR, STE 170 77701 #048-13-1998 L2001 **FM** *020 †18
HUMBLE, John Timothy. 810 HOSPITAL DR STE 340 77701 #048-12-1978 L1981 **GS VS** *020
IN, Young Gul. 3432 FANNIN ST 77701 #583-02-1972 L1976 **FM PM** *020
INDUPALLI, Suresh Babu. 4180 DELAWARE ST, STE 102 77706 #495-50-1980 L2000 **FM** *020 †18
ISAAC, Peter Chas. 3080 MILAM ST 77701 #025-01-1968 L1975 **PTH** *020 †50
ISERN, Raul D. 3438 FANNIN ST, # B-3 77701 #275-01-1944 L1969 **GP** *071
ISERN, Raul Dario, Jr. 3438 FANNIN ST, # B-3 77701 #429-01-1983 L1988 **P CHP** *020
ISERN, Reuben A. 2625 LAUREL ST 77702 #847-06-1976 L1977 **RHU** *020 †20
JACOBS, Robert. ■ 77707 #041-01-1955 L1976 **R** *071 †80
JAFRI, Adnan Zia. 755 N 11TH ST, STE P5200 77702 #704-02-1993 L1999 **IM** *020 †20
JANJUA, Aamer Wali. 5875 N MAJOR DR 77713 #704-20-1991 L2004 **IM** *020 †20
JAVAID, Muhammad. 3560 DELAWARE ST, STE 601A 77706 #704-21-1988 L2002 **PD** *020 †55
JEAN-LOUIS, Hubert. ■ 77707 #649-01-1973 L1980 **GP** *020
JEFFERO, Algianon Moses. 2929 CALDER ST, STE 312 77702 #047-07-1986 L1987 **FM** *020 †18
JENNINGS, Rex B. 3560 DELAWARE ST, STE 209 77706 #028-78-2000, ▲ L2006 **RNR** *020
JESSEN, Robert H, Jr. 3530 FANNIN ST, DIAGNOSTIC PATHOLOGY 77701 #049-01-1982 L2001 **PTH PCH** *020 †50
JOHNSON, Earl Francis, Jr. 3560 DELAWARE ST STE 601A 77706 #039-01-1970 L1974 **EM** *020 †16
JOHNSON, Jerry. 145 E CIRCUIT DR 77706 #048-02-1948 L1948 **OPH** *071 †35
JOHNSTON, Jack Clark. 3650 LAUREL ST 77707 #024-05-1992 L1998 **OSM** *020 †40
JONES, Troy A. 3560 DELAWARE ST, STE 209 77706 #048-15-1994 L2000 **VIR** *020 †80
JORDAN, Carl Carey, Jr. 740 HOSPITAL DR, SOUTHEAST TEXAS EAR NOSE 77701 #021-05-1980 L1982 **OTO** *020 †45
KACY, Stuart Scott. 2900 NORTH ST, STE 200 77702 #048-02-1978 L1978 **GS** *020 †85
KALBAUGH, Elmore P, Jr. ■ 77706 #051-04-1946 L1953 **P** *071
KANDASWAMY, Jayaraj. 3080 COLLEGE ST 77701 #495-16-1992 L2003 **IMG** *020 †20
KANE, Larry Earl. 3530 FANNIN ST, DIAGNOSTIC PATHOLOGY 77701 #048-04-1976 L1976 **PTH** *020 †50
KANNEGANTI, Ravikumar. 3250 MEDICAL CENTER DR 77701 #495-50-1980 L1989 **CHP** *020
KANOJIA, Mahesh Durgadas. 3455 STAGG DR, STE 101 77701 #496-38-1973 L1981 **ON HO** *020
KANOJIA, Uma Mahesh. 3455 STAGG DR STE 101 77701 #496-38-1973 L1981 **PD ADL** *020 †55
KANSARA, Girish B. 755 N 11TH ST, BEAUMONT INTERNAL 77702 #495-22-1978 L1991 **IM PTH** *020 †20
KARNICKI, Daniel Casimir. 25 N 11TH ST 77702 #016-11-1970 L1977 **DR** *020 †80
KAVOUSPOUR, Darioush. 2900 NORTH ST, STE 312 77702 #012-05-1990 L1998 **TRS** *020 †85
KAYANI, Khalid. 3560 DELAWARE ST STE 1202 77706 #704-01-1969 L1982 **OBG** *020 †30
KAYANI, Nargis. 3560 DELAWARE ST STE 1202 77706 #704-01-1974 L1982 **PD** *020 †55
KAZA, Raja. ■ 77706 #495-58-1978 **FM** *020
KAZA, Sudheer. 3560 DELAWARE ST, STE 905 77706 #495-62-1976 L1991 **P** *020
KESSLER, Michael Lee. 3530 FANNIN ST, DIAGNOSTIC PATHOLOGY 77701 #021-05-1972 L1976 **ATP CLP** *020 †20,50
KHAN, Saira. 2010 DOWLEN RD 77706 #704-25-1992 L2004 **MG** *020 †55
KING, James Dawson. 3220 MEDICAL CENTER DR 77701 #047-06-1972 L1976 **R** *020 †80
KING, Steven Wade. 3560 DELAWARE ST, STE 601A 77706 #041-12-2001 L2004 **EM** *020 †16
KIRBY, James Frederic. 755 N 11TH ST, STE P4200 77702 #048-02-1981 L1981 **OBG** *020 †30
KIRCHMER, John Thos, Jr. 2955 HARRISON ST STE 204 77702 #048-02-1970 L1970 **TS** *020 †85,90
KIRCHMER, Nancy Ann. 3420 FANNIN ST, STE 170 77701 #048-02-1973 L1974 **PDR R** *020 †80
KLEM, Jeffrey Alan. 3160 FANNIN ST, STE 105 77701 #039-01-1995 L2001 **CD** *020 †20
KONG, Joseph Sek-Man. 3555 STAGG DR 77701 #038-43-1979 L1981 **RO** *020 †80
KRAMER, Robert Chas. 3650 LAUREL ST 77707 #007-02-1991 L1996 **HS** *020 †40
KRISHNAN, Vijay Kumar. 3420 FANNIN ST, STE 190 77701 #495-45-1979 L1990 **AN** *020 †05
KUBALA, Mark Jerome. 2965 HARRISON ST, GOLDEN TRIANGLE NEUROCARE 77702 #048-02-1958 L1958 **NS N** *020 †25
KUMAR, Vijay. 3070 COLLEGE ST, STE 300 77701 #495-15-1985 L2003 **RHU** *020 †20
KUMARI, Neelu. 3560 DELAWARE ST, STE 601A 77706 #496-14-1994 L2004 **IM** *020 †20
KUSNOOR, Rita Vijay. 3420 VETERANS CIR 77707 #496-38-1971 L1979 **GP** *020
LA FLEUR, Christopher W. 755 N 11TH ST, STE P3600 77702 #021-05-1994 L1999 **GS** *020 †05
LAKSHMANAN, Karuppana G. 2830 CALDER ST 77702 #495-04-1972 L1977 **AN** *020 †05
LAKSHMANAN, Ramaswamy. 3560 DELAWARE ST STE 1103 77706 #495-21-1979 L1990 **P ADM** *020 †75
LAL, Radha J. 3120 NORTH ST 77702 #495-42-1969 L1978 **GYN** *020 †30
LAMBERT-PITT, Shawna Ceci. 3560 DELAWARE ST, STE 601A 77706 #035-08-2001 L2004 **EM** *020
LA MENDOLA, Stephen L. 2955 HARRISON ST 77702 #016-42-1982 L1990 **TS** *020 †85,90
LANGE, Gerald Thos. ■ 77706 #048-02-1970 L1970 **P FM** *100
LARKINS, Alvin Wayne. 755 N 11TH ST, STE P2300 77702 #047-07-1970 L1972 **ORS OS** *020 †40
LARSON, Curtis D. 3070 COLLEGE ST, STE 202 SUTIE 202 77701 #048-14-1993 L1995 **PS** *100 †85,05
LARSON, Mark D. ■ 77702 #048-14-1989 L1990 **PS** *020 †85,65
LAVALAIS, Gwendolyn L. 3555 STAGG DR 77701 #048-02-1999 L2005 **ON** *020 †20
LEE, Jack Bennett. ■ 77706 #048-02-1938 L1938 **LM OPH** *071 †35
LEE, Shung-Man Kurt. 2965 HARRISON ST STE 116 77702 #065-01-1976 L1982 **IM NEP** *020 †20
LEHMANN, Jerry Spruce. 3129 COLLEGE ST 77701 #048-12-1967 L1967 **OPH** *020 †35 ‡
LEHMILLER, David John. 3530 FANNIN ST, DIAGNOSTIC PATHOLOGY 77701 #048-13-1972 L1972 **PTH** *071 †50
LEIFESTE, Alan Elliot. 5875 N MAJOR DR 77713 #048-16-1999 L2005 **FM** *020 †18 ‡
LEVACY, Richard Anton. 3345 PLAZA 10 DR, STE B 77707 #048-02-1972 L1972 **OPH** *020 †35
LEVINE, Msonthi B. 3560 DELAWARE ST, STE 1104 77706 #048-13-1997 L1999 **IM** *020 †20
LO, Erwin S. 2965 HARRISON ST, STE 111 77702 #016-01-1996 L2001 **NS** *020
LOMBARDO, Carlos Roy. 2955 HARRISON ST STE 204 77702 #001-02-1956 L1967 **TS** *071 †85,90
LOMBARDO, Thomas A. 2830 CALDER ST 77702 #048-12-1951 L1954 **CD** *020 †20
LOMBARDO, Thomas Randolph. 755 N 11TH ST, STE P2200 77702 #048-12-1981 L1981 **IM CD** *020 †20
LOZANO, Jose. 2955 HARRISON ST, STE 100 77702 #341-01-1965 L1974 **NEP IM** *020 †20 ‡

■ = Address Information Privacy Protected

LUGO, Gustavo Adolfo. 2929 CALDER ST STE 206 77702 #264-01-1954 L1979 **NPM PD** *020 †55
LUVIANO, Damien M. 3570 COLLEGE ST, STE 100 77701 #048-12-2003 L2005 **OPH** *020
MAC DOUGALL, David John. 3576 COLLEGE ST 77701 #016-76-1984, ▲ L1986 **NS OS** *020
MACKAN, Emmett R. 2900 NORTH ST, STE 200 77702 #048-16-1986 L1987 **GS** *020 †85
MAHESHWARI, Yugal Kishore. 2194 EASTEX FWY STE B 77703 #495-98-1971 L1978 **END IM** *020 †20
MAINWARING, Brent Lee. 3220 MEDICAL CENTER DR 77701 #045-01-1985 L1990 **DR** *020 †80
MANN, James Cooper. ■ 77706 #048-12-1957 L1957 **GP** *071
MANNE, Sailaja P. 3570 COLLEGE ST 77701 #495-50-1997 L2007 **RHU** *020 †20
MANUEL, Mary. 710 S 8TH ST 77701 #495-66-1969 L1978 **PD NPM** *020 †55
MARCHAND, Sharon Heartfie. 3030 NORTH ST, STE 430 77702 #021-05-1999 L2004 **D** *020 †15 ‡
MARCHAND, Sidney Albert. 3030 NORTH ST, STE 430 77702 #021-06-1999 L2004 **FM** *020 †18 ‡
MARGOLIS, Wayne Scott. 740 HOSPITAL DR, STE 260 77701 #016-01-1980 L1981 **CD CCM** *020 †20
MARIA-SOOSAI, Manuel. 710 S 8TH ST STE A 77701 #495-42-1968 L1978 **U** *020 †95 ‡
MARKS, Eric Adam. 740 HOSPITAL DR, STE 280 77701 #016-42-1989 L1997 **IM** *020 †20
MARRERO, Roy Rodger, Jr. 3070 COLLEGE ST STE 205 77701 #047-07-1986 L1996 **FM** *020 †18
MARTIN-DEL-CAMPO, Enrique. 85 INTERSTATE 10 N, STE 101 77707 #649-01-1974 L1986 **CHP P** *020 †75
MASON, Charles Allen. 755 N 11TH ST, STE P3600 77702 #016-11-1997 L2001 **AN** *020 †05
MATHERNE, Jason E. 3530 FANNIN ST, DIAGNOSTIC PATHOLOGY 77701 #048-14-1997 L2002 **PTH** *062
MATSUDA, Ronaldo S. 3560 DELAWARE ST, STE 601A 77706 #748-08-1970 L1978 **EM** *020
MATTHEWS, Ralph L. 755 N 11TH ST, STE P3600 77702 #064-01-1979 L1996 **AN A** *020 †05,18
MAY, Norman Chalmers. 810 HOSPITAL DR STE 270 77701 #065-06-1971 L1993 **D** *020 †15
MAYO, John Mooring. ■ 77707 #027-01-1967 L1981 **GP** *020 †16
MC CONNELL, Robt Gaylord. 3560 DELAWARE ST, STE 209 77706 #047-06-1977 L1981 **DR** *020 †80
MCCORD, Michael D. 2830 CALDER ST 77702 #017-20-1989 L1993 **AN** *020 †05
MC CORMICK, Paul Wayne. 2830 CALDER ST 77702 #021-05-1975 L1981 **ORS NM** *020 †80
MC CREDIE, Michael James. 755 N 11TH ST, STE 93600 77702 #048-15-1984 L1985 **AN** *020 †05
MC KENNEY, Scott Alan. 3070 COLLEGE ST, STE 301 77701 #048-04-1980 L1980 **ON IM** *020 †20
MC MEANS, Patrick M. 324 N 23RD ST, # 201 77707 #048-02-1984 L1985 **AN** *020
MC NEILL, Jack Gober. 3650 LAUREL ST 77707 #048-02-1959 L1959 **ORS** *020 †40
MENDOZA, Rogelio Dungo. 15321 HIGHWAY 124 77705 #748-02-1965 L1978 **PD HEM** *020 †55
MERKET, Robin Michele. 3570 COLLEGE ST, STE 200 77701 #048-02-1996 L2001 **FSM** *020 †18
MEYERS, Clyde Chandler, Jr. ■ 77707 #048-02-1975 L1975 **N** *071 †75
MILLER, John K. 3560 DELAWARE ST, STE 209 77706 #048-04-1990 L1992 **VIR** *020 †80
MITCHELL, Lylieth P. 3560 DELAWARE ST, STE 601A 77706 #038-41-2001 L2004 **EM** *020 †16
MOORE, Darwin David. ■ 77706 #035-06-1948 L1950 **IM** *071
MOORE, Samara Renee. 3560 DELAWARE ST, STE 601A 77706 #016-42-2001 L2004 **EM** *020 †16
MOWERS, Doreen Lynn. 2965 HARRISON ST, STE 320 77702 #018-03-1978 L1982 **GPM** *020 †30
MUNROE, Martin J. ■ 77707 #048-15-2002 L2007 **FM** *020
MURPHY, Janice Bryant. ■ 77706 #048-13-1989 L1991 **FM** *020 †18
MURPHY, Vincent Prague. 2929 CALDER ST STE 100, SOUTHEAST TX MEDICAL AS 77702 #048-13-1989 L1990 **FM** *020 †18 ‡
MUSA, Mustafa I. 755 N 11TH ST, BEAUMONT INTERNAL 77702 #781-06-1985 L1999 **IM** *020 †20
NANAN, Dave Nigel. 755 N 11TH ST, STE P3600 77702 #566-01-1984 L2001 **AN** *020 †05
NELSON, Randolph Alvin. 3560 DELAWARE ST, STE 601A 77706 #025-07-1998 L2001 **EM** *020 †16
NOVELLI, William Jos, Jr. 24 BELLCHASE GARDENS DR, INTEGRATIVE MED CLINIC OF 77706 #048-13-1981 L1981 **EM IM** *020 †20,16
NUNEZ, Janna K. 2929 CALDER ST, STE 312 77702 #048-14-1999 L2003 **D** *020 †15 ‡
NUNN, Darla Sue. 3560 DELAWARE ST, STE 601A 77706 #048-02-1975 L1975 **EM** *020 †16
NUNNALLY, Cleon Sims. 3560 DELAWARE ST STE 601A 77706 #048-02-1957 L1957 **GP** *020
NWAUKWA, Chima Christian. 3070 COLLEGE ST, STE 202 77701 #690-04-1992 L2006 **IC** *020 †20
O'BRYAN, Robert Keene. 2830 CALDER ST 77702 #048-04-1972 L1972 **AN GP** *020 †05
OJIAKU, Uchenna Kennedy. 3560 DELAWARE ST STE 601A 77706 #010-03-2000 L2004 **EM** *020 †16
OLSEN, Mary Louise. 3030 NORTH ST, STE 450 77702 #028-02-1982 L1983 **IM RHU** *020 †20
O'MARA, William Ellis, Jr. 740 HOSPITAL DR, STE 300 77701 #027-01-1997 L2003 **OTO FPS** *020
OMOKEHINDE, Timi Rotimi. 2955 HARRISON ST, STE 100 77702 #010-03-2000 L2005 **NEP** *020 †20
O'NEIL, Stephen Blair. 3150 MEDICAL CENTER DR, STE 1 77701 #048-02-1988 L1993 **PM PMM** *020 †60
ONG, Albert Michael. 10 BAYOU BEND PL 77706 #005-14-1999 L2006 **U** *020 †95
ONG, Bryan Allan. ■ 77706 #048-12-2007 **IM** *012
ONG, Michael. 740 HOSPITAL DR, STE 100 77701 #506-02-1962 L1978 **GE IM** *020 †20
ORAZULIKE, Uchenna O. ■ 77713 #690-02-1991 L2007 **IM** *020 †20
OROCOFSKY, Vasantha C. 2750 S 8TH ST 77701 #495-56-1969 L1980 **P** *020 †75
ORRICK, Robert J, Jr. ■ 77707 #048-02-1952 L1952 **GS** *071 †85
ORTIZ, Carlos Bernabe. 2929 CALDER ST STE 212 77702 #048-12-1977 L1977 **AN** *020 †05
ORTIZ, Jose Maria. 2830 CALDER ST 77702 #847-06-1982 L1993 **IM DIA** *020 †20
OSBORNE, John Alden. 2929 CALDER ST STE 212 77702 #047-06-1953 L1956 **AN** *071 †05
OSMAN, Ali Mohamed. 3080 COLLEGE ST, MEMORIAL HERMAN BAPTIST EM 77701 #047-07-1998 L2003 **EM** *020 †16
OSZCZAKIEWICZ, Michael T. 2955 HARRISON ST STE 204 77702 #048-14-1983 L1983 **CD GS** *020 †85,90
OWEN, Charles Basil. 3560 DELAWARE ST, STE 601A 77706 #048-02-1980 L1980 **EM** *020 †16
PALANG, Ronald Perez. 3030 NORTH ST, STE 420 77702 #748-15-1985 L1998 **IM** *020 †20
PARKS, Harold S, Jr. 740 HOSPITAL DR, SOUTHEAST TEXAS EAR NOSE 77701 #021-05-1972 L1975 **OTO A** *020 †45
PARKUS, David Edward. 2900 NORTH ST, STE 312 77702 #012-05-1990 L1998 **CCS TRS** *020 †85
PARMA, David Allan. 755 N 11TH ST, STE P3600 77702 #048-12-1993 L1994 **AN** *020 †05
PATEL, Minesh M. 3091 COLLEGE ST 77701 #495-48-1995 L2002 **FM** *020 †18
PATHAPATI, Rajasekhar. 3420 VETERANS CIR 77707 #495-11-1991 L2007 **IM** *020 †20
PATIBANDLA, Sumalatha. 3070 COLLEGE ST, STE 301 77701 #495-50-1996 L2003 **HO** *020 †20
PATIL, Jairaj Mhala. 2830 CALDER ST 77702 #495-34-1979 L1983 **IM** *020
PATTERSON, Patricia Ethel. 3260 FANNIN ST 77701 #010-03-1971 L1980 **PD** *020
PENIUK, Heather Joy. 2830 CALDER ST 77702 #062-01-1993 L1995 **EM** *020 †18 ‡
PEPPER, Robert T. ■ 77706 #048-16-1986 L1987 **FM** *075 †18
PERRY, Thomas C. 3560 DELAWARE ST, STE 601A 77706 #041-09-1976 L1998 **EM FM** *020 †16
PIETERNELLE, J Coffy. 3030 NORTH ST STE 310 77702 #047-07-1984 L1989 **OBG** *020 †30
PONNURU, Hari Babu. 755 N 11TH ST, STE P3600 77702 #495-50-1980 L1984 **AN** *020 †05
POWELL, David Carey. 755 N 11TH ST, STE P3600 77702 #021-06-1976 L1976 **AN** *020 †05
PRAUSE, Alvin H. 2965 HARRISON ST, STE 220 77702 #048-04-1975 L1975 **PD** *020 †55
PROCTOR, Jay Clifford, III. 6450 FOLSOM DR 77706 #048-02-1978 L1978 **FM** *020 †18
PUNAY, Nestor Cagol. 755 N 11TH ST, STE P3900 77702 #748-27-1989 L2004 **CN** *020
QUINTIN, Arden C. 2830 CALDER ST 77702 #748-01-1976 L1989 **NPM PD** *020 †55
QURAISHI, Shama P. 1050 S 11TH ST 77701 #496-01-1984 L1996 **FM** *020 †18
RAFIQ, Shahid. 490 IH 10 N, STE 100 77702 #704-08-1987 L2003 **CHN** *020 †55
RAIZADA, Vivek. 3345 PLAZA 10 DR 77707 #035-48-2001 L2005 **OPH** *020 †35
RAJA, Vijay N. ■ 77707 #021-01-2008 *012
RAMACHANDRAN, Parthiban. ■ 77707 #048-13-2003 L2007 **DR** *012
RAMACHANDRAN, Subbiah T. 755 N 11TH ST, BEAUMONT INTERNAL 77702 #220-02-1970 L1993 **IM ON** *020 †20
RANDOLPH, Steven H. 148 S DOWLEN RD # 604 77707 #048-02-1986 L1987 **FM** *020 †18
RAO, Mootha Venkata R. 3576 COLLEGE ST 77701 #495-50-1960 L1975 **GS** *020 †85
RAY, Linda J. 3030 NORTH ST, STE 420 77702 #048-02-1982 L1983 **IM FM** *020 †20
REDDY, Keshava C. 3030 NORTH ST STE 460 77702 #495-21-1983 L1993 **ID IM** *020 †20
REDKO, Vladimir. 3650 LAUREL ST 77707 #913-99-1979 L1992 **AN** *020 †05
REMIREZ, Antonio. 4222 COLLEGE ST 77707 #048-04-1989 L1991 **IM** *020 †20
REMIREZ, Juan P. 4222 COLLEGE ST 77707 #048-04-1987 L1988 **IM** *020 †20
REMIREZ, Mario Jose. 4222 COLLEGE ST 77707 #275-01-1951 L1965 **GP IM** *071
REN, Min. 3129 COLLEGE ST 77701 #018-03-2003 L2007 **OPH** *020
RICE, Tiffany Eliese. ■ 77713 #001-02-2002 L2008 **MPD** *100
RICHARD, John Wesley, III. ■ 77705 #048-02-2005 **IM** *012
RIENSTRA, Richard Byron. 857 E VIRGINIA ST, LAMAR UNIVERSITY HEALTH CE 77705 #048-02-1963 L1963 **GP** *020
RISING, Kelly W. 755 N 11TH ST, STE P4200 77702 #048-02-1990 L1992 **OBG** *020 †30
RIZK, Wagdy S. 3650 LAUREL ST, BEAUMONT BONE & JOINT INST 77707 #915-04-1984 L2006 **ORS** *020
ROBERT, Wm Pierre, Jr. 2965 HARRISON ST # 11 77702 #048-04-1959 L1959 **PD** *071 †55
ROBERTSON, Dawn E. 755 N 11TH ST, STE P3600 77702 #021-06-1993 L1997 **AN** *020 †05
ROBINSON, Robert Obie. 3129 COLLEGE ST, STE 300 77701 #048-02-1968 L1968 **P** *020 †35,75
RODMAN, Charles John. 740 HOSPITAL DR STE 1 77701 #020-12-1973 L1974 **VS TS** *020 †85,90
ROEBUCK, Jeremy C. 740 HOSPITAL DR, STE 300 77701 #048-14-2001 L2006 **OTO** *020 †45
ROESLER, Nathan R. 3127 COLLEGE ST 77701 #048-13-2001 L2004 **PD** *020 †55
ROMANKO, Michael John. 3560 DELAWARE ST, STE 601A 77706 #048-02-1980 L1980 **EM FM** *020 †16
ROPER, John Wesley. 2750 S 8TH ST 77701 #017-20-1954 L1962 **P** *071
ROTENBERG, Michel. 3345 PLAZA 10 DR, STE H 77707 #396-06-1976 L1991 **CD** *020 †20
ROUBEIN, Daniel Richard. 3560 DELAWARE ST, STE 209 77706 #021-06-1987 L1990 **DR RNR** *020 †80
ROY, Achyutananda. 2929 CALDER ST, STE 304 77702 #495-02-1961 L1977 **GS** *071 †85
SACKS, Steven Michael. 3480 FANNIN ST STE I 77701 #041-09-1986 L1991 **PMP** *020
SAMUELS, Marie. ■ 77713 #041-15-2008 *012
SANTIAGO, Fredric A. 3030 NORTH ST, STE 500 77702 #051-04-1980 L1995 **IM** *020 †20
SARRAFIAN, Edgar Karnig. 3405 COLLEGE ST 77701 #605-01-1960 L1964 **OBG** *071 †30
SATTERWHITE, Kelli B. ■ 77706 #024-01-1999 L2008 **FM** *100
SAYYED, Tawfeeq Amjadali. 3560 DELAWARE ST, STE 209 77706 #495-28-1991 L2004 **DR** *020 †80,28
SCHACHNER, Jay Reggie. 3070 COLLEGE ST, STE 301 77701 #033-05-1981 L1986 **ON HEM** *020 †20
SCHAENING, Orlando. 3030 NORTH ST STE 460, INFECTIOUS DISEASE ASSOC 77702 #042-03-1990 L1998 **ID IM** *020 †20
SCHANGE, Stephen J. 755 N 11TH ST, STE P3600 77702 #048-13-1988 L1992 **AN** *020 †05
SCHRAPPS, Jerome Francis. 2900 NORTH ST, STE 200 77702 #038-43-1991 L1993 **GS SO** *020 †85
SCOTT, George C. 3560 DELAWARE ST, STE 209 77706 #048-02-1989 L1991 **R NM** *020 †80,28
SENTHILKUMAR, Kandasami. 2929 CALDER ST, STE 204 77702 #495-04-1992 L2001 **N** *020 †75
SHAW, Paul Bernard. 2830 CALDER ST 77702 #021-01-1957 L1961 **IM PUD** *030 †20
SHERMAN, Deborah C. 755 N 11TH ST STE P4200 77702 #048-04-1996 L2000 **OBG** *020 †30
SHERRON, Charles Richard. 490 IH 10 N 77702 #048-02-1966 L1966 **OS** *030 †18
SHERRON, Scott R. 2830 CALDER ST 77702 #048-13-1988 L1989 **CD** *020 †20
SHRONTZ, Carl Edward. 740 HOSPITAL DR, STE 210 77701 #045-01-1978 L1985 **NS** *020 †25
SHUFFIELD, James W, Jr. ■ 77706 #004-01-1948 L1957 **ORS** *071 †40
SILVA, Marco Tulio. 2965 HARRISON ST, GOLDEN TRIANGLE NEUROCARE 77702 #005-18-1997 L2003 **NS** *020
SIMMONS, Karen B. 3560 DELAWARE ST, STE 209 77706 #048-04-1984 L1985 **DR VIR** *020 †80
SIMMS, John Harris, II. ■ 77705 #048-02-1960 L1960 **P N** *071
SINGH, Harrypersad. 3576 COLLEGE ST 77701 #566-01-1978 L1982 **IM** *020 †20
SINGH, Ranjit Rajendra. 3150 MEDICAL CENTER DR 77701 #495-09-1971 L1980 **AI PDA** *020 †55,03
SINGZON, Victorico F. 3420 VETERANS CIR 77707 #748-08-1964 L1979 **IM GP** *020 †18
SIY, Frankie Tiong Lu. 2186 EASTEX FWY 77703 #748-01-1974 L1978 **PM** *020
SLACK, Tobin Alexander. 755 N 11TH ST, STE P3600 77702 #021-06-1996 L1998 **AN** *020 †05
SLATER, Mark Wiley. 3620 AUGUSTA DR 77707 #048-02-1998 L2001 **IM** *020
SMITH, David Barton. 755 N 11TH ST, STE P4200 77702 #048-04-1993 L1995 **OBG** *020 †30
SMITH, Jack Line. ■ 77706 #048-02-1948 L1948 **PTH** *071 †50
SMITH, John T. 2830 CALDER ST 77702 #048-04-1951 L1951 **A FM** *071 †03
SMITH, Linda C. 3150 MEDICAL CENTER DR, STE 1 77701 #048-02-1985 L1994 **PM** *020 †60
SMITH, Lulu Lafait. ■ 77708 #048-02-1959 L1959 **GP PHP** *071
SMITH, Roger Allen. 3030 NORTH ST, STE 300 77702 #017-20-1985 L1987 **OBG** *020 †30
SOBERON, Santos Marcelo. 755 N 11TH ST, BEAUMONT INTERNAL 77702 #649-01-1980 L1986 **NTR IM** *020 †20

■ = Address Information Privacy Protected

SOCHER, Steven Adam. 755 N 11TH ST STE P3200 77702 #024-01-1991 L1997 **U** *020 †95

SOCKLER, David Lee. 2900 NORTH ST STE 308 77702 #039-01-1956 L1961 **OTO** *071 †45

SOOUDI, Matthew M. 2830 CALDER ST 77702 #517-01-1962 L1971 **CRS GS** *071 †85,10

SOOUDI, Steven K. 2830 CALDER ST 77702 #016-06-1995 L1997 **CD** *020 †20

SPANGLER, William W. 3560 DELAWARE ST, STE 601A 77706 #041-14-1984 L1991 **EM** *020 †16

SPERLING, Howard. 755 N 11TH ST, STE P3600 77702 #048-14-1991 L2000 **AN** *020 †05

SPROTT, Maxie C, II. 3440 FANNIN ST, BEAUMONT, INC. 77701 #047-07-1980 L1982 **OBG** *020

SRINANTHAKUMAR, S. 740 HOSPITAL DR STE 180 77701 #220-01-1978 L1987 **IM** *020 †20

STAFFORD, Michael Todd B. 3560 DELAWARE ST STE 601A 77706 #048-12-1980 L1980 **EM** *020 †16

STAGG, Daniel Philip, III. 950 N 14TH ST, STE 100 77702 #021-06-1991 L1994 **GE** *020 †20

ST AMAND, Pamela. 2965 HARRISON ST STE 320 77702 #048-02-1980 L1980 **OBG** *020 †30

STOUT, Keith Bernard. 2010 DOWLEN RD 77706 #039-01-1969 L1977 **EM** *020 †35,16

STOVALL, Felix Russell. 3150 MEDICAL CENTER DR, STE 2 77701 #048-15-1976 L1976 **IM** *020

STOVALL, Francis H. 3420 VETERANS CIR 77707 #048-15-1974 L1974 **GP** *020

SUEOKA, Ben Lorrin. 25 N 11TH ST, BEAUMONT RADIOLOGY GROUP, 77702 #050-02-1980 L2004 **VIR R** *020 †80

SULTANA, Munnaver. 2965 HARRISON ST STE 301 77702 #495-21-1969 L1977 **OBG** *020 †30

SURAPANENI, Prasad L N. 3060 FM 3514, STILES FACILITY 77705 #495-50-1978 L1983 **FM** *020 †18

SURI, Muhammad Fareed Kha. ■ 77706 #704-22-1992 L2001 **N** *100 †75

SWEET, Robert Leldon. 3345 PLAZA 10 DR 77707 #039-01-1969 L1974 **CD IM** *020 †20

TAJONG, Nelson Atembe. 950 N 14TH ST, STE 100 77702 #041-13-2000 L2006 **GE** *020 †20

TALBERT, Ronald Eugene. 3650 LAUREL ST, BEAUMONT BONE & JOINT INST 77707 #048-02-1983 L1983 **ORS** *020 †40

TAMMAREDDI, Vijayalakshmi. 2965 HARRISON ST, STE 316 77702 #495-37-1973 L1979 **AN** *020

TANNER, Charles Richard. 755 N 11TH ST, STE P3600 77702 #004-01-1959 L1962 **AN** *020 †05

TAYLOR, John T. 3650 LAUREL ST 77707 #048-14-1976 L1976 **ORS HS** *020 †40

TAYLOR, Luis Glenn. 740 HOSPITAL DR, STE 160 77701 #649-14-1980 L1995 **PD** *020 †55

TEUSCHER, David Dean. 3650 LAUREL ST 77707 #048-13-1984 L1985 **ORS OSM** *020 †40

THOMAS, George Ellis. 755 N 11TH ST, BEAUMONT INTERNAL 77702 #048-02-1971 L1972 **IM** *020 †20

THOMAS, Michael Paul. 1010 PEYTON DR 77706 #409-39-1985 L1999 **IM** *020 †20

THOMPSON, Daniel Michael. 3650 LAUREL ST 77707 #048-02-1996 L2000 **ORS** *020

THOMPSON, Lauree L. 2830 CALDER ST, NEONATAL INTENSIVE CARE UN 77702 #048-02-1996 L2000 **NPM** *020 †55

THORN, Kendra Lynn. 2929 CALDER ST STE 205 77702 #048-04-1999 L2003 **OBG** *020 †30

THORNHILL, Earle Stephen. 3576 COLLEGE ST 77701 #048-02-2001 L2005 **IM** *100

THORPE, Curtis Doyle. 3650 LAUREL ST # 200 77707 #048-04-1983 L1985 **ORS** *020 †40

TIEFERT, Jerome Werner. 3560 DELAWARE ST, STE 601A 77706 #038-43-1976 L2005 **GPM** *020 †18,16,70

TOUPS, Dwight Mark. 3030 NORTH ST, STE 420 77702 #048-12-1977 L1977 **IM** *020 †20

TOUPS, Robert Michael. 2929 CALDER ST STE 212BO 77702 #021-05-1966 L1971 **AN** *020 †05

TRINH, John Arthur. 810 HOSPITAL DR, STE 105 77701 #396-32-1975 L2006 **IM** *020 †20

TRUJILLO, Jorge Danl. 3560 DELAWARE ST, STE 601A 77706 #048-14-1985 L1987 **EM** *020 †16

TUCKLER, Edgar. 4471 CALDER AVE, BEAUMONT WEST MEDICAL 77706 #682-01-1967 L1977 **OM FM** *020

TYLER, Richard Lynn. ■ 77702 #021-06-1985 L1991 **FM** *020 †18

UR-REHMAN, Syed Shafiq. ■ 77706 #704-22-1987 L2003 **NEP** *020

VALDERRAMA-BAZAN, F. 3070 COLLEGE ST, STE 100 77701 #649-01-1969 L1974 **FM** *020 †18 ‡

VARDIMAN, John Sanders. 2010 DOWLEN RD 77706 #048-12-1963 L1963 **GP** *020 †18

VAUGHN, Gary Edward. 810 HOSPITAL DR, STE 240 77701 #021-05-1972 L1973 **D** *020 †50,15

VERTIL, Cyprien. 3030 NORTH ST STE 340 77702 #440-01-1983 L1995 **NEP** *020 †20

VICTORES, Ruben D. 755 N 11TH ST, STE 4200 77702 #035-15-1985 L1991 **OBG** *020 †30 ‡

VILLASAN, Antonio J. 1001 PEARL ST 77701 #748-08-1986 L1996 **FM** *020 †18

WADDELL, Kevin Ray. 740 HOSPITAL DR, STE 250 77701 #048-15-1998 L2006 **OBG** *020 †30

WALKER, Charles Ray. 3480 FANNIN ST STE G 77701 #048-02-1951 L1951 **DR** *072 †80

WALKER, Daniel Gordon. 3195 DOWLEN RD 101-312 77706 #048-04-1960 L1960 **P CHP** *071

WALLACE, Loring S. ■ 77706 #021-05-1945 L1953 **ORS OS** *071 †40

WASHBURN, Wesley W, Jr. ■ 77708 #035-08-1948 L1958 **PS** *071 †65

WATLEY, Vernon T. 1292 LIBERTY ST 77701 #008-01-1949 L1954 **FM** *075

WEATHERALL, Richard H. ■ 77706 #048-04-1955 L1955 **OPH** *071 †35

WEATHERFORD, Renee S. ■ 77706 #048-14-1982 L1983 **PTH** *075

WEBB, Donald Ray. 2830 CALDER ST 77702 #048-02-1970 L1970 **FM OM** *020 †18

WEIR, Sylvia Mae. ■ 77701 #056-05-1977 L1985 **FM** *030 †70,18

WELDON, Victoria M. 3576 COLLEGE ST 77701 #028-46-1985 L1989 **OM IM** *030 †20

WESSON, Mae Edwardna. 3576 COLLEGE ST 77701 #048-04-1978 L1978 **OPH** *020 †35

WILCOX, Howard Douglas. 5875 N MAJOR DR, PREVENTIVE MEDICINE OF SE 77713 #048-14-1982 L1983 **FM GS** *020 †70,18

WILGERS, Kenneth D. 3070 COLLEGE ST, STE 300 77701 #048-02-1998 L1999 **FM EM** *020 †18

WILLIAMS, Debra Nell. ■ 77708 #048-13-1978 L1978 **IM** *020

WILLIAMS, Henry Oldham. 690 N 14TH ST, FL 3 77702 #048-04-1970 L1970 **RO** *020 †80

WILSON, Mark Alan. 3859 STAGG DR 77701 #048-02-1980 L1981 **FM** *020

WOMBLE, John Carl. ■ 77713 #048-04-1981 L1982 **FM** *020

WORLEY, Kyle E. 3127 COLLEGE ST, STE 410 77701 #048-04-1993 L1994 **PD** *020 †55

WU, George G. 2965 HARRISON ST, STE 116 77702 #065-01-1978 L1995 **NEP** *020 †20

YU, Sue Jin. 2965 HARRISON ST, GOLDEN TRIANGLE NEUROCARE 77702 #016-01-1994 L1997 **N** *020 †75

ZAPPIA, Rosario Robt. ■ 77726 #010-01-1966 L1977 **IM ID** *071 †20

ZUZUKIN, George Vladimir. 2929 CALDER ST STE 308 77702 #913-06-1971 L1985 **IM** *020

BEDFORD – TARRANT

ALDAY, Miguel Remo. 1600 HOSPITAL PKWY, CONSULTANTS IN RADIOLOGY 76022 #748-10-1969 L1983 **DR VIR** *020 †80

ALI, Iman H. 2036 BEDFORD RD 76021 #875-01-1986 L2000 **RHU** *020 †20

ALKHERSAM, Husam Hashim. 1604 HOSPITAL PKWY, STE 200 76022 #528-04-1989 L2002 **CN N** *020 †75

ALLDREDGE, Barry Jon. 1604 HOSPITAL PKWY, STE 100 76022 #048-15-1975 L1975 **IM** *020 †20

ALLEN, Kevin Michael. 1600 HOSPITAL PKWY 76022 #048-02-1986 L1988 **EM** *020 †16

ANDING, Brian Sheldon. 1604 HOSPITAL PKWY STE 104 76022 #048-12-1986 L1988 **OPH** *020 †35

BAKER, George C. 1615 HOSPITAL PKWY STE 306 76022 #048-12-1987 L1990 **D** *020 †15

BALCH, Emmet H, III. 1600 HOSPITAL PKWY, CONSULTANTS IN RADIOLOGY 76022 #048-02-1981 L1981 **DR** *020 †80

BARRY, James M, Jr. 1305 AIRPORT FWY, STE 205 76021 #048-04-1979 L1980 **N** *020 †75

BEESON, Michelle C. 1600 HOSPITAL PKWY, EMERGENCY DEPARTMENT 76022 #005-12-1995 L1997 **EM** *020 †16

BERNSTEIN, Melvyn L. PO BOX 826, BEDFORD CENTRAL STATION 76095 #035-08-1975 L2002 **OPH LM** *100

BHAKTHAVATHSALAN, Amrutha. ■ 76095 #495-09-1956 L1990 **MFM** *075 †30

BINDNER, Stephen Robert. 1615 HOSPITAL PKWY, STE 103 76022 #018-03-1994 L2000 **FSM** *020 †18

BLESSING, William Scott. 1600 HOSPITAL PKWY 76022 #048-12-1973 L1973 **AN CCA** *020 †05

BOYD, James Talmadge. 2700 TIBBETS DR, STE 100 76022 #004-01-1965 L1967 **GYN** *071 †30

BRAUER, Kirk Innes. 1600 HOSPITAL PKWY 76022 #409-36-1996 L2003 **AN** *100 †05

BREDENBERG, Amy. 1615 HOSPITAL PKWY, STE 103 76022 #035-06-1999 L2001 **FM** *020 †18

BRIAN, Mary Belva. 1615 HOSPITAL PKWY STE 109 76022 #003-01-1978 L1982 **GS** *020 †85

BUSH, Martha Griffin. 1600 HOSPITAL PKWY, HARRIS METHODIST 76022 #004-01-1980 L1988 **EM PD** *020 †55,16

CAPELLO, Juan Jose. 2636 TIBBETS DR 76022 #048-02-1967 L1967 **ORS OSS** *020 †40

CARSON, Stephanie Renee. 1615 HOSPITAL PKWY, STE 204 76022 #048-04-1999 L2002 **OBG** *100 †30

CARTER, David James. 1615 HOSPITAL PKWY, STE 211 76022 #048-12-1979 L1979 **TS** *020 †85,90

CHANG, Wesley E. 1600 HOSPITAL PKWY, CONSULTANTS IN RADIOLOGY 76022 #048-12-1996 L1997 **RNR R** *020 †80

CHUNG, Charles R. 1850 CENTRAL DR, STE B 76021 #583-02-1961 L1971 **OTO A** *020 †45 ‡

CIPRIANO, Gilda. 1615 HOSPITAL PKWY, STE 100 76022 #033-05-1994 L1998 **OBG** *020 †30

COFFMAN, Donna S. 1600 HOSPITAL PKWY, EMERGENCY DEPT 76022 #048-02-1984 L1985 **EM** *020 †16

COOK, Stanley Duane. 1600 HOSPITAL PKWY 76022 #039-01-1980 L1985 **DR** *020 †80

DERDEYN, Leslie John. 1600 HOSPITAL PKWY, CONSULTANTS IN RADIOLOGY 76022 #048-02-1979 L1979 **DR NR** *020 †80

DHINGRA, Davinder Harish. 807 FOREST RIDGE DR # 100, TARRANT COUNTY MHMR 76022 #495-45-1963 L1973 **P** *020 †75

DICKINSON, John Arvil. 1600 HOSPITAL PKWY 76022 #048-12-1963 L1963 **D** *071 †15

DO, Ha Chieu. 1600 HOSPITAL PKWY, BOX 62 76022 #048-14-2002 L2005 **IM** *020 †20

DOODY, Kathleen Marie. 1701 PARK PLACE AVE 76022 #048-14-1984 L1985 **REN OBG** *020 †30

DOODY, Kevin J. 1701 PARK PLACE AVE 76022 #048-04-1982 L1983 **REN GYN** *020 †30

DUBEY, Ajay Kumar. 1612 HOSPITAL PKWY 76022 #024-01-1993 L1998 **RO** *020 †80

DURAN, Michael John. 1924 FOREST RIDGE DR 76021 #035-09-1978 L1987 **CD EM** *020 †20

EATON, Jerome P. 1604 HOSPITAL PKWY, STE 505 76022 #048-04-1993 L1994 **GS** *020 †85

EMMET, Emily Ryan. 1615 HOSPITAL PKWY, STE 310 76022 #048-02-2001 L2003 **OBG** *020

ESTES, Boyce L, Jr. 1600 CENTRAL DR, STE 310 76022 #001-02-1983 L1984 **GE IM** *020 †20

FARHAT, Georges Antoun. 1305 AIRPORT FWY STE 202 76021 #605-02-1989 L1994 **APM AN** *020 †05

FARMER, Stephen James. 3001 AIRPORT FWY STE A 76021 #048-02-1984 L1985 **OBG** *020 †30

FERGUSON, Matthew Paul. ■ 76022 #048-14-2007 **ORS** *012

FERNEY, David Michael. 1600 CENTRAL DR, STE 155 76022 #049-01-1981 L1984 **GE IM** *020 †20

FERNEY, Stephen James. 1600 CENTRAL DR, STE 310 76022 #049-01-1977 L1978 **GE IM** *020 †20

FIELDS, Steven L. 1600 HOSPITAL PKWY 76022 #048-12-1992 L1993 **DR** *020 †80

FISHER, Martin Benson. 1604 HOSPITAL PKWY, STE 302 76022 #048-14-1983 L1983 **P** *020 †75

FORTE, Thalia Bratton. 1615 HOSPITAL PKWY 76022 #036-01-1991 L1994 **DR** *020 †80

FOSTER, Tabitha. 1600 HOSPITAL PKWY 76022 #048-12-1992 L1993 **AN** *020 †05

FRAGA, Lisa. 1604 HOSPITAL PKWY STE 101 76022 #048-15-1994 L1995 **GS** *020 †85

FRAGA, Mark Jos. 1600 HOSPITAL PKWY 76022 #048-12-1989 L1990 **AN** *020 †05

FRANK, Carol Sue. 1305 AIRPORT FWY, STE 424 76021 #025-07-1977 L1996 **IM** *020 †20

GEORGELAS, Timothy John. 1615 HOSPITAL PKWY, STE 108 76022 #023-12-1980 L1982 **DR AM** *020 †70,80

GODFREY, Karen Konrad. 1604 HOSPITAL PKWY, STE 100 76022 #048-14-1988 L1989 **FM** *020 †18

GOJER, Bernard. 1924 FOREST RIDGE DR 76021 #048-12-1986 L1988 **CD** *020 †20

GOLDEN, Leverett L. 1615 HOSP PKWY 76022 #048-12-1963 L1963 **FM** *071 †18

GONZALES, James David. 1615 HOSPITAL PKWY, STE 210 76022 #048-12-1984 L1985 **OTO FPS** *020 †45

GORDON, Jack Chas. 1604 HOSPITAL PKWY STE 207 76022 #004-01-1976 L1977 **ORS** *020 †40

GRANT, Cathal Patrick. 1604 HOSPITAL PKWY STE 507 76022 #918-01-1981 L1990 **P PFP** *020 †75

GREENBERG, Scott Lawrence. 1924 FOREST RIDGE DR 76021 #048-04-1999 L2006 **CD** *020 †20

GULDEN, Richard Heath. 1600 HOSPITAL PKWY 76022 #048-12-1992 L1993 **AN PME** *020 †05

HABBU, Shrinivas S. 2520 HARWOOD RD STE 400 76021 #495-35-1971 L1990 **IM DIA** *020

HALL, David Awyn. 1600 CENTRAL DR, STE 310 76022 #017-20-1999 L2001 **GE** *020 †20

HALL, Scott. 1305 AIRPORT FWY, STE 205 76021 #048-02-1980 L1980 **N** *020 †75

HANNA, Sherif Yacoub. 1604 HOSPITAL PKWY, STE 100 76022 #021-05-1992 L1997 **IM** *020 †20

HAQUE, Atif. ■ 76021 #027-01-2003 **NS** *012

HARRISON, Emmanuel Elmo. 1600 HOSPITAL PKWY 76022 #021-01-1988 L2001 **AN** *020 †05

HELDRIDGE, Tod C. 3024 HIGHWAY 121, MID-CITIES FAMILY CARE 76021 #048-12-1984 L1985 **FM EM** *020 †18

HILLIARD, Duane Ashley. 1600 HOSPITAL PKWY 76022 #005-12-1998 L2003 **AN** *020 †05

HINZMANN, Michael Scott. 1600 HOSPITAL PKWY, CONSULTANTS IN RADIOLOGY 76022 #056-06-1973 L1978 **R EM** *020 †80

HLAING, Monica Hwie. 1600 HOSPITAL PKWY 76022 #209-01-1974 L1984 **AN** *020 †05

HOLDEN, Scott Carr. 1600 HOSPITAL PKWY 76022 #048-12-1993 L1994 **AN** *020 †05

HUFF, Joshua Andrew. ■ 76022 #048-12-2001 L2003 **DR** *100 †80

HURLBUT, Stephen C. 1604 HOSPITAL PKWY, STE 200 76022 #048-02-1990 L1995 **N** *020

IOSSO, Colin Thomson. 1305 AIRPORT FWY, STE 205 76021 #033-05-1988 L2007 **N** *020 †75

ISHAM, A Chapman. ■ 76022 #038-41-1941 L1955 **P** *071 †75

■ = Address Information Privacy Protected

JACKSON, Sharon. 2716 TIBBETS DR 76022 #010-03-1993 L1997 **PD** *020 †55
JANICKI, Peter Thomas. 1615 HOSPITAL PKWY, STE 210 76022 #048-04-1986 L1987 **OTO** *020 †45
JOHN, Elizabeth Mani. 2700 TIBBETS DR STE 408 76022 #495-63-1973 L1983 **P** *020 †75
JONES, Gary Lewis. 1604 HOSPITAL PKWY, STE 403 76022 #048-04-1977 L1977 **PUD CCM** *020 †20
JONES, Michael B. 1600 HOSPITAL PKWY, CONSULTANTS IN RADIOLOGY 76022 #048-04-1999 L2005 **DR** *020 †80
JUTRAS, Michael A. 3024 HIGHWAY 121, MID-CITIES FAMILY CARE 76021 #048-12-1984 L1985 **FM EM** *020 †18
KADOKO, Robert Gonza. 2008 L DON DODSON DR, STE 100 76021 #008-01-2000 L2005 **ORS** *100
KANE, Jerome Marc. 1305 AIRPORT FWY STE 205 76021 #021-01-1980 L1984 **N** *020 †75
KARPER, Robert Earl. 1600 HOSPITAL PKWY, DEPT OF PATHOLOGY 76022 #048-12-1970 L1970 **PTH HMP** *020 †50
KHAN, Atique Alam. 2600 TIBBETS DR STE B 76022 #704-02-1983 L1990 **P** *020 †75
KIETA, Derek Ray. 1600 HOSPITAL PKWY 76022 #048-13-1998 L2003 **AN** *020 †05
KING, Gary Michael. 1600 HOSPITAL PKWY 76022 #048-04-1980 L1980 **IM** *020
KLAVON, Aziz Albert. 1305 AIRPORT FWY, STE 424 76021 #010-01-1987 L1993 **IM** *020 †20
KOSMOSKI, David E. 1604 HOSPITAL PKWY 76022 #048-14-1987 L1988 **NS GS** *020 †25
KREIDER, Lorraine Fae. 1604 HOSPITAL PKWY, STE 100 76022 #039-01-1985 L1988 **IM ADM** *020 †20
KREKOW, Lea. 1615 HOSPITAL PKWY, STE 109 76022 #048-13-1990 L1991 **ON** *020 †20
KWONG, Peter C. 1600 CENTRAL DR 76022 #035-03-1989 L1995 **ORS** *020 †40
LEITKO, Jeffrey K. 1600 HOSPITAL PKWY, CONSULTANTS IN RADIOLOGY 76022 #048-12-2001 L2007 **DR** *100 †80
LEPAK, Keith Austin. 1600 HOSPITAL PKWY, EMERGENCY DEPARTMENT 76022 #021-01-1989 L1991 **EM** *020 †16
LESLEY, Amber Marie. ■ 76022 #048-12-2005 L2008 **IM** *012
LESLEY, Nathan Edwin. ■ 76021 #048-15-2005 **ORS** *012
LEWIS, Billy Wayne. 1600 HOSPITAL PKWY 76022 #048-02-1970 L1970 **OBG** *020
LIGHT, Jerry Thos, Jr. 1604 HOSPITAL PKWY, STE 309 76021 #021-01-1985 L1997 **VS** *020 †85
LIVINGSTONE, David K. 1305 AIRPORT FWY, STE 220 76021 #048-12-1972 L1972 **FM** *020 †18
LONG, Nikki I. 1600 HOSPITAL PKWY 76022 #005-18-2000 L2002 **EM** *020
LOONEY, James K, III. 1701 FOREST RIDGE DR, BEDFORD FAMILY MEDICINE 76022 #048-13-1996 L1998 **FM** *020 †18
LOWRY, Wade L. 1600 HOSPITAL PKWY, STE 201 76022 #036-01-1978 L1983 **U** *020 †95
LUK, Gordon D. 1600 CENTRAL DR, STE 310 76022 #024-01-1975 L1996 **GE IM** *050 †20
LUM, Daniel Cone. 837 BROWN TRL, NORTHEAST CLC JPS 76022 #004-01-1991 L1994 **FM** *020 †18
LUTZ, Robert F, III. 1600 HOSPITAL PKWY 76022 #048-14-1992 L1993 **EM** *020 †16
MAKAR, James, Jr. 1600 HOSPITAL PKWY 76022 #038-41-1970 L1981 **PTH** *020 †50
MANSEN, Joseph Robt. 3024 HIGHWAY 121 76021 #038-41-1988 L1999 **FM** *020 †18 ‡
MARLING, Carl Kelley. 1850 CENTRAL DR, STE C 76021 #008-01-1967 L1972 **OPH** *020 †35
MELTZER, Robert G. 1604 HOSPITAL PKWY, STE 208 76022 #041-09-1970 L1976 **GS** *020 †85
MEYER, Barry Dale. 1600 HOSPITAL PKWY 76022 #048-12-1986 L1987 **AN** *020 †05
MILLER, Andrea Elizabeth. 1604 HOSPITAL PKWY, STE 301 76022 #048-12-1983 L1983 **OBG** *020 †30
MILLER, John David. 1615 HOSPITAL PKWY, STE 306 76022 #048-02-1970 L1970 **D** *020 †15
MILLER, Laurie Crowe. 1604 HOSPITAL PKWY, HARRIS METHODIST HEB 76022 #027-01-1982 L1992 **IM** *020 †20
MINA, Eva S. 1305 AIRPORT FWY, STE 220 76021 #915-02-1988 L1999 **IM** *020 †20
MITCHELL, Laura C. 2341 LEAFY GLEN CT 76022 #048-12-2001 L2004 **CD** *012
MOORE, William Christen. 1600 HOSPITAL PKWY 76022 #048-03-2001 L2005 **APM** *100 †05
MYERS, Lyndakay Greenway. 2205 HIGHWAY 121, CARTER BLOOD CARE 76021 #001-02-1997 L2003 **PTH** *020
MYLES, Robert Tytan. 2008 L DON DODSON DR, STE 100 76021 #005-15-1991 L1996 **ORS** *020 †40
NACKLEY, Anna Chan. 1701 PARK PLACE AVE 76022 #035-03-1994 L2001 **OBG** *020 †30
NACKLEY, James J. 1600 CENTRAL DR, STE 155 76022 #035-03-1994 L2001 **GE** *020 †20
NAIR, Radha P. 1117 BEDFORD RD STE B 76022 #495-77-1969 L1982 **AN** *020
NEAL, William Walker. 837 BROWN TRL, UNIVERSITY MEDICAL ASSOCIA 76022 #048-12-1967 L1967 **IM** *020 †20
NGUYEN, Gary D. 1600 HOSPITAL PKWY, BOX 62 76022 #048-14-2004 L2007 **IM** *020
NOELL, Courtney A. 1615 HOSPITAL PKWY, STE 210 76022 #048-12-1995 L1996 **OTO** *020 †45
NUSSBAUMER, Samuel Andre. 1924 FOREST RIDGE DR 76021 #048-12-1983 L1983 **CD** *020 †20
OBREGON, Troy M. 1600 HOSPITAL PKWY, DEPT OF EMERGENCY MED 76022 #048-12-1995 L1999 **EM** *020 †16
OLIVO, Julie Ann Lomonaco. 1615 HOSPITAL PKWY, STE 103 76022 #048-04-2000 L2004 **MPD** *020
OLTERSDORF, Timothy Paul. 1600 HOSPITAL PKWY, CONSULTANTS IN RADIOLOGY 76022 #003-01-1973 L1981 **DR** *020 †80
PACE, Christopher Michael. 1604 HOSPITAL PKWY, STE 202 76022 #035-06-1996 L1998 **U** *020 †95
PARANANDI, Srinivas N. 1924 FOREST RIDGE DR 76021 #495-62-1983 L1999 **CD IM** *020 †20
PARMER, David E. 2121 CENTRAL DR 76021 #048-13-1997 L1998 **OS** *020
PATEL, Mrugesh P. 1615 HOSPITAL PKWY, STE 300 76022 #048-12-1995 L2000 **HO** *020 †20
PATEL, Neena Mrugesh. 2700 TIBBETS DR STE 502, H.E.B. BEHAVIORAL MEDICINE 76022 #496-38-1997 L2004 **P** *020 †75
PATEL, Rajeev J. 1600 HOSPITAL PKWY, EMERGENCY DEPT 76022 #048-16-1993 L1994 **EM** *020 †16
PAVEY, Scott Arnold. 1615 HOSPITAL PKWY, STE 103 76022 #048-12-1980 L1980 **FM** *020 †18
PEEBLES, Jeffrey S. 1600 HOSPITAL PKWY, HARRIS METHODIST HEB HOSPI 76022 #048-14-1991 L1995 **EM** *020 †16
PERSONS, Charles Martin. 1604 HOSPITAL PKWY, STE 402 76022 #048-14-1979 L1979 **ORS OSS** *020 †40
POETTCKER, James Douglas. 1604 HOSPITAL PKWY, STE 505 76022 #048-02-1977 L1977 **GS GP** *020 †85
POLLARD, Robert Stephen. 1604 HOSPITAL PKWY, STE 505 76022 #048-13-1981 L1981 **VS GS** *020 †85
POSNOCK, Eugene Robbins. 2305 CENTRAL PARK BLVD 76022 #035-08-1973 L1986 **A PDA** *020 †55,03
POWELL, Ted Blake. 1600 HOSPITAL PKWY 76022 #048-12-1984 L1985 **PTH** *020 †50
PRENTICE, Linda Anderson. 1615 HOSPITAL PKWY STE 204 76021 #021-06-1991 L1996 **OBG** *020 †30

PRESTON, Ted L. 1615 HOSPITAL PKWY, STE 100 76022 #011-02-1976 L1985 **OBG** *020 †30
PRICKETT, Josh Lv. 1600 HOSPITAL PKWY, EMERGENCY DEPARTMENT 76022 #039-01-1986 L1999 **EM FM** *020 †18
QUADRI, Syed Maqdoom M.. 1604 HOSPITAL PKWY, STE 305 76022 #496-40-1997 L2006 **P** *020 †75
RADIMECKY, Valen James. 2716 TIBBETS DR 76022 #048-13-1984 L1985 **PD** *020 †55
RAILSBACK, Charles Hickma. 1615 HOSPITAL PKWY, STE 210 76022 #048-02-1969 L1969 **OTO A** *020 †45
REDALEN, Rick Ray. 2301 L DON DODSON DR 76021 #030-05-1968 L1968 **FM** *075
REDDY, Geetha Devi. 807 FOREST RIDGE DR, CLINIC 76022 #495-50-1980 L1991 **P** *075 †75
REDDY, Nalini Patel. 1600 HOSPITAL PKWY, CONSULTANTS IN RADIOLOGY 76022 #048-12-1995 L2002 **DR** *020 †80
REDDY, Raghuram Mulamalla. 1600 HOSPITAL PKWY, CONSULTANTS IN RADIOLOGY 76022 #422-01-1996 L2006 **VIR** *020 †80
REES, David Warren. 2029 PARK PLACE BLVD # 18 76021 #027-01-1983 L1986 **EM** *020 †18
ROUSCH, Bernard L. 111 BEDFORD RD STE B 76022 #035-19-1962 L1965 **P** *020 †75
ROUSCH, Daniel E. 111 BEDFORD RD STE B, MID CITIES PSYCH CTR 76022 #018-75-1992, ▲ L1993 **P** *020 †75
ROWLAND, Robert B, Jr. 1600 HOSPITAL PKWY, DEPT OF EMERGENCY MEDICINE 76022 #041-02-1985 L1988 **EM** *020 †16
SALEEM, Shahnaz. 500 GOLD HAWK LN 76022 #495-65-1979 L1986 **P** *020
SANTESTEBAN, Alfredo O. 1600 HOSPITAL PKWY 76022 #132-04-1964 L1979 **PD** *071 †55
SAUNDERS, Ralph Craig. 1305 AIRPORT FWY, STE 121 76021 #038-44-1984 L1992 **ORS HS** *020 †40
SAYERS, Merlyn Herbert. 2205 HIGHWAY 121 76021 #836-01-1968 L1979 **BBK IM** *020
SCROGGINS, Mark Edward. 2612 HARWOOD RD STE A 76021 #048-02-1977 L1977 **OBG** *020 †30
SHAW, Albert Lovell. 1305 AIRPORT FWY STE 202 76021 #021-05-1969 L1971 **AN OS** *030 †05
SHEA, Andrew Chaoyu. 1600 CENTRAL DR 76022 #048-12-1999 L2002 **GE** *020 †20
SHETTY, Manisha Sharad. 1615 HOSPITAL PKWY, STE 100 76022 #012-01-2002 L2005 **OBG** *100
SIMINSKI, James Thos. 1604 HOSPITAL PKWY, STE 403 76022 #017-20-1985 L1992 **PUD CCM** *020 †20
SINGH, Davinder S. 1600 HOSPITAL PKWY 76022 #048-15-2002 L2003 **NEP** *020 †20
SIRAM, Sunitha. 1604 HOSPITAL PKWY, STE 100 76022 #308-13-1998 L2003 **IM** *020 †20
SMITH, Blake T. 1600 HOSPITAL PKWY 76022 #048-14-1991 L2003 **EM** *020 †16
SPRINGER, Terry W. 301 CAROLYN DR 76021 #048-14-1984 L1985 **GP** *020
SPURDON, Chantal H J. 1615 HOSPITAL PKWY STE 100 76022 #035-06-1982 L1990 **OBG** *020 †30
STANLEY, Susan Mary. ■ 76021 #048-02-2005 L2008 **AN** *012
STAPP, Melissa Anne. 2816 CENTRAL DR 76021 #028-03-1991 L1992 **FM EM** *020 †18
STURGEON, John Millard, III. 1305 AIRPORT FWY, STE 424 76021 #021-05-1996 L2000 **MPD** *020 †20,55
SUTOR, Laurie Jayne. 2205 HIGHWAY 121, CARTER BLOOD CARE 76021 #012-05-1985 L1988 **PTH BBK** *020 †50
SWE, Nini. 1901 CENTRAL DR STE 20 76021 #209-01-1975 L1987 **P** *020
TAJANI, Hadi R. 1604 HOSPITAL PKWY, STE 507 76022 #704-16-1980 L1986 **P** *020 †75
TANDY, Charles C. 1600 HOSPITAL PKWY 76022 #048-12-1953 L1953 **AN** *071 †05
TAREEN, Naeem Khan. 2700 TIBBETS DR, STE 102 76022 #704-04-1972 L1981 **CD** *020 †20
TAYLOR, Stephanie Reed. 1615 HOSPITAL PKWY 76022 #021-05-2002 L2006 **OBG** *020
TAYYABA, Talat. 1604 HOSPITAL PKWY, MERCY HOSPITAL 76022 #496-27-1996 L2007 **P** *020 †75
TERRY, James Richard. 3024 HIGHWAY 121 76021 #048-12-1984 L1985 **FM** *020 †18
THANIGARAJ, Srihari. 1924 FOREST RIDGE DR 76021 #495-16-1993 L2006 **CD** *040 †20
TICHENOR, Gregory Andrew. 1600 HOSPITAL PKWY, EMERGENCY DEPT 76022 #031-01-1989 L1991 **EM** *020 †16 ‡
VAN HAL, Marvin Eugene. 1305 AIRPORT FWY STE 121 76021 #018-03-1978 L1991 **ORS EM** *020 †40
VEERAPPAN, Balaji A. 1924 FOREST RIDGE DR 76021 #496-32-1997 L2004 **CD** *100 †20
VU, Thuan Quang. 1260 HARWOOD RD 76021 #007-02-1986 L1995 **IM RHU** *020 †20
WALIA, Usha. 2905 BROWN TRL, STE E 76021 #495-77-1976 L1991 **N CHP** *020 ‡
WALKER, Joel Wayne. 1615 HOSPITAL PKWY, STE 103 76022 #048-12-1995 L2002 **MPD** *020 †20,55 ‡
WARD, Richard P, Jr. 1600 HOSPITAL PKWY, THE HOSPITALISTS AT HEB 76022 #048-15-1999 L2002 **IM** *020
WASHINGTON, Donald L, Jr. 1604 HOSPITAL PKWY STE 403 76022 #056-06-1976 L1990 **IM PUD** *030 †20
WEBB, Sarah. 1600 HOSPITAL PKWY, PATHOLOGY DEPT 76022 #021-01-1985 L1991 **DR** *020 †50
WEBSTER, Barbara W. 1615 HOSPITAL PKWY, STE 204 76022 #048-78-1999, ▲ L2003 **OBG** *020 †30 ‡
WELCH, Robert Morrow, III. 1600 HOSPITAL PKWY 76022 #048-14-1983 L1983 **FM** *020 †18
WHEELER, James Chas. 2716 TIBBETS DR 76022 #047-05-1991 L1994 **PD** *020 †55
WILBERT, Lloyd G, III. 1600 HOSPITAL PKWY, CONSULTANTS IN RADIOLOGY 76022 #048-12-1995 L1996 **DR** *020 †80
WILKINS, Nikki Renae. 1600 HOSPITAL PKWY, DEPT OF EMERGENCY MEDICINE 76022 #048-02-1984 L1985 **EM** *020 †16
WILSON, Kendal Phillip. 1600 HOSPITAL PKWY 76022 #031-01-1985 L1990 **PM** *020 †60
WINGO, Richard Jay. 1600 HOSPITAL PKWY 76022 #048-12-1982 L1983 **AN CCA** *020 †05
WOOD, Beverly Gail. 1615 HOSPITAL PKWY, STE 310 76022 #048-02-1989 L1990 **OBG** *020 †30
WOODS, Curt E. 1604 HOSPITAL PKWY STE 308 76022 #048-12-1983 L1983 **AN** *020 †05
WU, Horace Chia-Shun. 1600 HOSPITAL PKWY, PATHOLOGY LAB 76022 #024-05-1992 L2004 **PTH** *020 †50
YAMADA, Roy Kenji. 1600 HOSPITAL PKWY 76022 #014-01-1980 L1982 **EM** *020 †16
YI, Min W. 1600 HOSPITAL PKWY 76022 #048-78-2001, ▲ L2004 **IM** *020
YIANTSOU, Chris G. 2600 TIBBETS DR 76022 #048-15-1975 L1975 **GE IM** *020 †20
YUEH, Hwai C. 1600 HOSPITAL PKWY, EMERGENCY DEPARTMENT OFFIC 76022 #048-13-1992 L1995 **EM** *020 †16

BEE CAVE – TRAVIS

STANFORD, Thomas Enos, Jr. 12400 W HWY 71 350-189 78738 #027-01-1981 L2000 **IM EM** *020 †20

BEEVILLE – BEE

AVET, Patrick Philip. 1406 E HOUSTON ST 78102 #021-06-1994 L1998 OPH *020 †35

BALL, Robert Morris. 1406 E HOUSTON ST, STE 2 78102 #036-07-1975 L1985 CD IM *020 †20

BEATO, Milton Alexandro. 1406 E HOUSTON ST, STE 2 78102 #308-01-1988 L2000 CD *020 †20

CALICA, Francisco J. 711 E HOUSTON ST, P O BOX 400 78102 #048-13-1995 L1997 FM *020 †18

CHANDLER, James M, Jr. 1500 E HOUSTON ST 78102 #048-04-1979 L1979 FM *020 †18

CHIN, Arthur Kelvin. 1602 E HOUSTON ST, STE C 78102 #064-01-1973 L1977 FM *072

COMISO, Emma Cacas. 2709 QUARTER HORSE DR 78102 #748-08-1961 L1977 GP *074

COUTIN, Rafael Francisco. 1406 E HOUSTON ST, STE 2 78102 #036-01-1977 L1979 CD *020 †20

DEHNISCH, Frank R, Jr. 1602 E HOUSTON ST, STE C 78102 #048-12-1971 L1971 FM *020 †18

HERRERA, Maximiliano J. 2435 OAK BEND RD 78102 #649-02-1966 L1973 FM *020

HOGUE, Grady Claude, Jr. 302 S HILLSIDE DR 78102 #048-13-1984 L1985 FM *020 †18

JACK, William David, II. 1406 E HOUSTON ST, STE 2 78102 #023-07-1967 L1974 CD *020 †20

KHAN, Behram Ali. 1602 E HOUSTON ST, STE C 78102 #704-25-1998 L2005 NEP *020 †20

LAMBORN-BEASLEY, Karole. 1602 E HOUSTON ST, STE C 78102 #005-14-1977 L1980 FM *020 †18

LARAKERS, Joseph Anthony. 302 S HILLSIDE DR 78102 #016-11-1994 L1995 FM *020 †18

LIFLAND, Paul Dennis. 301 S HILLSIDE DR STE 10 78102 #748-08-1977 L1990 ORS *020

MADRY, Robert Wilson, Jr. 1406 E HOUSTON ST, STE 2 78102 #036-01-1967 L1975 IM *020 †20

MARTINEZ, Carlos Eduardo. 1406 E HOUSTON ST, STE 2 78102 #042-01-1977 L1982 CD IM *020 †20

NEWBERRY, William Clark. 1406 E HOUSTON ST 78102 #021-05-1977 L1981 OPH *020 †35

OKPALO, Christian N. 301 S HILLSIDE DR, SUITE 8 & 9 78102 #690-02-1988 L2002 MPD *020 †20,55

ORMAND, Jackson E, Jr. 1406 E HOUSTON ST, STE 2 78102 #048-02-1970 L1970 CD IM *020 †20

RASHID, Mohammad Hammad. 1211 E HOUSTON ST, SOUTH TEXAS INST OF CANCER 78102 #704-01-1995 L2004 HO *020 †20

ROELL, Joseph Carl. 711 E HOUSTON ST, ABELIA MEDICAL ASSOCIATES 78102 #048-13-1983 L1986 FM EM *071

ROZO, Juan Carlos. 1406 E HOUSTON ST, STE 2 78102 #264-18-1991 L2003 CD *020 †20,55 ‡

SALAZAR, Mario Rey. 301 S HILLSIDE DR 78102 #048-14-2001 L2007 GS *020 †85

SANCHEZ, Vicente. 1600 E HOUSTON ST, STE A 78102 #042-01-1993 L2000 OBG *020

SCHIAVONE, Juan Pablo. 1602 E HOUSTON ST, STE C 78102 #132-06-1999 L2008 FM *020

SCHORLEMMER, Rodney N. 1406 E HOUSTON ST 78102 #048-15-1981 L1981 GS *020 †85

SIERRA HOFFMAN, Miguel A. ■ 78102 #451-01-1991 L2005 PUD *020

STARK, Thomas Lytton. 1500 E HOUSTON ST 78102 #048-02-1956 L1956 GP *071

TOTH, Zoltan Karoly. 1406 E HOUSTON ST, STE 2 78102 #473-01-1992 L2005 ICE CD *020 †20

UPMANYU, Sant Kumar. 1406 E HOUSTON ST, STE 2 78102 #495-36-1962 L1971 CD IM *020 †20

BELLAIRE – HARRIS

AKANBI, Bolarinwa Ganiyu. 6800 WEST LOOP S, STE 520 77401 #690-01-1988 L1997 FM *020 †18

ALADE, Oladapo Abimbola. ■ 77401 #011-03-2002 L2006 ORS *020

ALAGAPPAN, Alagappan. 5116 BISSONNET ST 77401 #495-66-1984 L1995 NPM PD *020 †55

AMANCHARLA, Maneesh Ram. ■ 77401 #048-04-2005 L2007 AN *012

ANDERSON, Andrew English. 5304 BRAEBURN DR 77401 #048-02-1974 L1974 AN *020 †05

ANDREWS, Joann. 4417 VIVIAN ST 77401 #048-04-1979 L1979 PD *020 †55

ANSELL, Lee Vanderpool. 5420 WEST LOOP S 77401 #048-12-1978 L1978 NS *020 †25

ANTHONY, James Wm. 5350 BELLAIRE BLVD, P O BOX 603 77401 #010-03-1966 L1971 U *071 †95

AQUILINA, John Paul. 6565 WEST LOOP S, STE 600 77401 #627-01-1971 L1978 AN *020

ATHANASSAKI, Ioanna Dimit. ■ 77401 #418-04-1996 L2006 PD *100 †55

AXELRAD, A David. 4545 BISSONNET ST, STE 131 77401 #048-02-1970 L1970 P PMM *020 †75

BARRASH, Jay Martin. 5959 WEST LOOP S STE 470 77401 #023-01-1966 L1968 NS *020 †25

BARROWS, Linda Christine. 6800 WEST LOOP S, STE 525 77401 #048-04-1988 L1989 D *020 †15

BENNETT, Tanya Jaylan. 6750 WEST LOOP S STE 970 77401 #048-02-1999 L2005 CHP *020 †75

BERKMAN, Eric F. 5420 WEST LOOP S, STE 4100 77401 #048-13-1989 L1990 ORS *020 †40

BHARWANI, Salim K. 5959 WEST LOOP S, STE 260 77401 #495-01-1989 L2006 PHO *020 †55

BHOSALE, Priyadarsranjit. ■ 77401 #496-36-1995 L2006 DR *020 †80

BLANCO, Angel Ignacio. ■ 77401 #048-04-1999 L2005 RO *100 †80

BLUM, Henry Jacob. 5420 WEST LOOP S, STE 4100 77401 #048-14-1983 L1983 ORS *020 †40

BONEFAS, Elizabeth Terese. 6800 WEST LOOPS, STE 520 77401 #048-13-1984 L1986 GS *020 †85

BRENER, Seth Adam. ■ 77401 #048-02-2007 IM *012

BRITTON, Marcus Louis. ■ 77401 #027-01-2004 L2007 NEP *012 †20

CABLER, Christopher James. 5555 W LOOPS, STE 150 77401 #048-02-1973 L1973 OPH *020

CAJAHUARINGA, Kelly. 4606 EVERGREEN ST 77401 #048-02-1998 L2001 FM *020 †18

CAMPBELL, Catherine J M. ■ 77401 #065-10-1983 L1991 FM *071 †18

CARUSO, Charles James. 5111 BELLAIRE BLVD # 200 77401 #021-01-1955 L1958 PD *071 †55

CASTELLANO, Dominic M. ■ 77401 #011-04-2002 L2007 PS *012

CHAFTARI, Patrick Samir. ■ 77401 #605-02-1992 L2006 IM EM *020 †20

CHAN, Carolyn Melynn. ■ 77401 #028-34-1991 L1997 PD *020 †55

CHANDRASEKHAR, Aruna Amba. ■ 77401 #048-13-2008 *012

CHAVEZ, Manuel Isidoro. ■ 77401 #649-01-1947 PD OS *071

CHEN, Teris Minsue. ■ 77401 #048-04-2002 L2007 D *100 †15

CHENG, Danny Da-Yeh. 6565 WEST LOOP S, STE 300 77401 #048-14-1995 L1998 IM *020 †20

CHILUKURI, Suneel. 6565 WEST LOOP S STE 800, PRECISION DERMATOLOGY 77401 #048-04-1999 L2004 D *020 †15

COHAN, Caryn M. 4710 BELLAIRE BLVD, STE 130 77401 #048-04-1988 L1990 PD *020 †55

COLLINS, Riva Linda. 6750 WEST LOOP S, STE 420 77401 #035-08-1992 L1997 D *020 †15

CORDELL, Linda J. 4545 BISSONNET ST STE 297 77401 #048-13-1991 L1990 CHP *020

COYNE, Terrance Chas. 6700 WEST LOOP S STE 400 77401 #056-05-1972 L1973 OS *030

DACSO, Mara Melanie. ■ 77401 #048-02-2008 *012

DACSO, Matthew Michael. ■ 77401 #048-02-2006 L2006 IM *012

DARA, Bina Elizabeth. ■ 77401 #495-65-1983 L2001 AN *020 †05

DARVEAUX, Rene Eugene. 6565 WEST LOOP S, STE 300 77401 #047-07-1978 L1980 FM *020 †18 ‡

DEGNER, Eugene Allen. 6565 WEST LOOP S, STE 525 77401 #048-04-1961 L1961 ADM FM *020 †18

DEMONTE, Franco. ■ 77401 #065-06-1985 L1993 NS *020 †25

DHOLAKIA, Sonal D. 4617 HOLT ST 77401 #065-01-1993 L1998 *020 †18

DUAN, Xiuzhen. ■ 77401 #243-44-1982 L2005 PTH *020 †50

EASON, Elizabeth Ball. 5959 WEST LOOP S, UTHSC AT HOUSTON 77401 #021-06-2000 L2004 NPM *020 †55

EICHENWALD, Eric C. ■ 77401 #024-01-1984 L2006 PD *020 †55

ESCOBAR, Marco R. 5420 BELLAIRE BLVD, STE A 77401 #319-01-1966 L1976 OTO *020 †45

EZELLE, James Shumate, Jr. 4545 BISSONNET ST STE 297 77401 #045-01-1978 L1985 P PYA *020 †75

FAILLACE, Louis Anthony. 4747 BELLAIRE BLVD STE 300 77401 #056-06-1957 L1971 P *071 †75

FANG, Ting. 6565 WEST LOOP S, STE 650 77401 #187-04-1982 L2000 OPH *020 †35

FELTOVICH, Michael John. 5420 WEST LOOP S, STE 3200 77401 #041-01-1969 L1973 IM *030 †20

FRANCIS, Richard Randolph. 5420 WEST LOOP S, STE 2500 77401 #566-01-1988 L2002 OSS *020

FRANKEL, Scott. ■ 77401 #048-12-1991 L1993 GS *020

FREEMAN, Maynard Lloyd. 4425 VIVIAN ST, SOUTHWEST DOCTORS, PA 77401 #016-01-1975 L1991 NM VS *020 †28

FRIEDMAN, Bernard S. 5420 WEST LOOP S, STE 4200 77401 #869-02-1956 L1960 OPH *071 †35

FRIEDMAN, James Alan. ■ 77401 #017-20-1956 L1957 OBG *071 †30

FRITZHAND, Kevin Stuart. 4747 BELLAIRE BLVD, STE 580 77401 #048-14-1995 L1997 AN *020

GARCIA, Rodolfo Luis. ■ 77401 #048-12-2002 L2004 RNR *012 †80

GERBER, Bernard Michael. 5959 WEST LOOP S, STE 600 77401 #048-12-1973 L1978 P PMM *020 †75

GERBER, Howard B. 6565 WEST LOOP S, STE 800 77401 #048-14-1987 L1988 D DMP *020 †15

GLANTON, Christopher L. 5959 WEST LOOP S, HAUSER CLINIC & ASSOCIATES 77401 #048-14-1989 L1990 P *075 †75

GO, Charito Chua. 5116 BISSONNET ST, PMB 347 77401 #748-07-1989 L1998 PM *020 †60

GOLDBERG, Ivan. PO BOX 1139 77402 #143-03-1971 L1978 *100

GORME, Neil L. ■ 77401 #035-08-1996 GS *100

GOURISHANKAR, Anandapadman. ■ 77401 #495-61-1996 L2005 PD *100 †55

GOVINDAN, Kalyani. 4618 BEECH ST 77401 #495-59-1988 L2005 PAN *020 †05

GUPTA, Nandita. ■ 77401 #496-22-2003 L2008 FM *100

GUY, Esther. 6800 WEST LOOP S, STE 580 77401 #048-14-1997 L1998 IM *020 †20

HAJJAR, Anne-Marie Pierre. ■ 77401 #605-02-1992 L2006 IM IMG *020 †20

HAKEMACK, Brenda Svrcek. 4511 PINE ST, 77401 #048-14-1989 L1990 PD *020 †55

HAN, Xin. ■ 77401 #243-75-1987 L2005 HMP *100

HANCHER, Shannon Brooke. ■ 77401 #048-02-2005 AN *012

HANEY, Peter Michael. 5116 BISSONNET ST 77401 #038-06-1986 L1998 NPM PD *071 †55

HAUSER, Donald E. 5959 WEST LOOP S STE 600, STE 600 77401 #048-14-1983 L1983 P PYG *020 †75

HAYWOOD, Theodore J. 4710 BELLAIRE BLVD STE 200 77401 #047-05-1952 L1959 A PDA *020 †55,03

HENDIN, Benjamin Nathan. ■ 77401 #035-20-1993 L2000 U *020 †95

HICKEY, Weston Chearis. ■ 77401 #048-14-2008 *012

HISSE, Emilio Bahill. 5555 WEST LOOP S, STE 435 77401 #132-01-1984 L1994 TS VS *020

HOLLADAY, Jack Taylor. ■ 77401 #048-14-1974 L1974 OPH *020 †35

HORWITZ, Paul Brian. 4811 PINE ST, PAUL B. HORWITZ, M.D., P.A 77401 #048-04-1996 L1997 P *020 †80

HUO, Lei. ■ 77401 #243-47-1994 L2007 SP *100

IERO, Phillip Thomas. 6800 WEST LOOP S, STE 350 77401 #048-12-1997 L2000 GS *020

IZUMI, Akihiro. 4747 BELLAIRE BLVD, STE 580 77401 #048-16-1991 L1992 AN *020 †05

JOGI, Medhavi. 4564 BELLAIRE BLVD 77401 #048-04-2002 L2005 END *012 †20

JOHNSON, Lawrence W. ■ 77401 #019-02-1946 L1948 FM *071 †18

KAGAN, Anna. ■ 77401 #035-46-2004 L2007 NEP *012 †20

KANG, Sonia Songhee. ■ 77401 #024-07-1999 L2001 GS *100

KAVANAGH, Robt James, Jr. 4747 BELLAIRE BLVD, STE 580 77401 #048-14-1977 L1977 AN *020 †05

KENNEDY, Alana Adele. ■ 77401 #048-13-2001 L2007 PHO *100 †55

KHAN, Fareed Mahmood. 17 AZALEA TRAIL LN 77401 #704-02-1987 L1999 FM *020 †18

KIM, Edward Daewuk. ■ 77401 #016-06-2000 EM *100

KLEIN, Adam Edward. 5420 WEST LOOP S, STE 4100 77401 #041-02-1992 L1998 ORS *020 †40

KOPEL, Andrew Charles. 6750 WEST LOOP S, STE 1060 77401 #048-14-2001 L2006 OPH *020

KRISHNAN, Bhuvaneswari. ■ 77401 #495-65-1984 L1990 BBK *020 †50

KUSHWAHA, Vivek Pratap. 5420 WEST LOOP S STE 2300 77401 #048-13-1991 L1997 OSS *020 †40

LARKIN, Kelly Jean. 4553 BELLAIRE BLVD, MEDICAL CTR EMERG. PHYSICI 77401 #035-03-1994 L1998 EM *020 †16

LEE, Chung C. ■ 77401 #048-02-1989 L1990 AN *020 †05

LEE, Kelvin M. 5116 BISSONNET ST, STE 438 77401 #048-04-1992 L1993 IM *020 †20

LEE, Lyna Kit. 4710 BELLAIRE BLVD, STE 200 77401 #048-04-1976 L1976 AI PD *020 †55

LEUGERS, Camille. 5300 PATRICK HENRY ST, HEALTHCARE FOR THE HOMELES 77401 #035-45-1988 L1994 FM *020 †18

LEVENTON, George Steven. 4747 BELLAIRE BLVD STE 350 77401 #048-02-1987 L1988 CHP P *020

LEVINE, Andrew Stephen. 5959 WEST LOOP S, STE 375 77401 #016-42-1969 L1976 ORS *020 †40

LEWINBUK, Dan David. 6565 WEST LOOP S, STE 600 77401 #016-42-1994 L2006 CHP *020 †75

LEWIS, Stanley T, Jr. 6800 WEST LOOP S STE 560 77401 #048-14-1994 L1997 IM *020

LEWY, Robert Ira. 4606 LAUREL ST 77401 #041-01-1971 L1979 ON HEM *020 †20

LI, Wei. ■ 77401 #243-44-1983 L2004 FM *020

LI, Wei. ■ 77401 #243-61-1983 L2003 PTH *020 †50

LI, Yining. 4610 WILLOW ST 77401 #243-76-1985 L2002 AN *020

LOFTUS, Brian D. 6565 WEST LOOP S, STE 401 77401 #048-04-1990 L1991 N *020 †75 ‡

LOPEZ, Gabriel. ■ 77402 #016-06-2004 HPM IM *100

LOPEZ-BERESTEIN, Gabriel. ■ 77402 #847-11-1976 L1980 IM ON *050

LORD, Edward A R, Jr. 6800 WEST LOOP S STE 225 77401 #047-07-1963 L1968 OBG *020 †30 ‡

MAAT, Owen S. 4710 BELLAIRE BLVD, STE 325 77401 #048-02-1992 L1994 **GE** *020 †20

MACHINSKI, Gerald Thos. 4710 BELLAIRE BLVD STE 200 77401 #035-06-1958 L1976 **A PDA** *020 †55,03

MADDOCK, Mary L Purnell. 4747 BELLAIRE BLVD, STE 580 77401 #048-02-1968 L1968 **AN** *020 †05 ‡

MALONE, Clinton Michael. ■ 77401 #048-04-2001 L2005 **IC** *012 †20

MANIHA, Robert Wm. 6800 WEST LOOP S STE 500 77401 #048-02-1963 L1963 **OBG** *071 †30

MARCO, Rex Alexander. 6700 WEST LOOP S, STE 110 77401 #005-14-1992 L2001 **ORS** *020 †40

MARTINEZ, Waldo Miguel. 4710 BELLAIRE BLVD, STE 200 77401 #275-01-1954 L1963 **AI PDA** *071 †55,03 ‡

MASHARANI, Anish Harshad. 4710 BELLAIRE BLVD, STE 130 77401 #048-04-1998 L1999 **PD** *020 †55

MAYO, Mark Lewis. 6565 WEST LOOP S, STE 650 77401 #048-12-1990 L1991 **OPH** *020 †35

MC QUEEN, Katherine Ayer. 6565 WEST LOOP S, STE 525 77401 #048-04-1997 L2000 **IM** *020 †20

MEDRANO, Karla. ■ 77401 #048-02-2007 **AN** *012

MENON, Venugopal K. 4710 BELLAIRE BLVD, STE 200 77401 #495-31-1962 L1973 **A PD** *020 †55,03 ‡

METZGER, Charles L. 5420 WEST LOOP S, STE 4100 77401 #048-02-1992 L1997 **ORS** *020 †40

MINIFEE, Paul K. ■ 77401 #048-02-1982 L1983 **PDS PD** *020 †55,85

MOELLER, Mark S. 6300 WEST LOOP S STE 680 77401 #048-04-1988 L1989 **P** *020 †75

MONTALVO, Cristina. ■ 77401 #048-12-2002 L2006 **HMP** *100 †50

MULLINAX, Kimberly Ann. 6565 WEST LOOP S, STE 800 77401 #048-16-2003 L2007 **D** *020 †15

MUSSER, James M. ■ 77401 #035-45-1988 L1991 **PTH** *020

NAJJAR, Amjad Farid. ■ 77401 #605-01-1983 L1986 **IM IMG** *071

NELMS, Barry Allen. 5420 W LOOPS STE 2400 77401 #048-04-1978 L1978 **ORS OSS** *020 †40

NELSON, Page Walker. 6750 WEST LOOP S 77401 #048-04-1960 L1960 **ORS** *071 †40

NGUYEN, Dominique Hung. 4747 BELLAIRE BLVD, STE 580 77401 #021-05-1993 L1997 **AN** *020 †05

NGUYEN, Mai Anh K. 6750 WEST LOOP S STE 375 77401 #048-14-1996 L2003 **CHP P** *020 †75

NGUYEN, Thanh Tien. 411 N 1ST ST, CHRISTUS ST. JOSEPH HOSPIT 77401 #049-01-1983 L1993 **AN** *020 †18,05

NGUYEN, Vinh. 5116 BISSONNET ST # 438 77401 #048-14-1998 L2000 **IM** *020 †20

OLIVAS, Benjamin. ■ 77401 #649-14-1981 *074

O'MALLEY, Adrian Eoin. 6750 WEST LOOP S, STE 1060 77401 #048-14-1996 L2002 **OPH** *020 †35

O'MALLEY, Ronan Eugene. 6750 WEST LOOP S, STE 1060 77401 #539-05-1968 L1979 **OPH OS** *020 †35

ORENGO, Claudia A. 6300 WEST LOOP S # 420, BAYLOR COLLEGE OF MEDICINE 77401 #048-14-1991 L1992 **P** *020 †75

OTT, Michael Thos. 4603 WILLOW ST, 4603 WILLOW 77401 #020-12-1979 L1991 **EM GS** *020 †85,10

PARKER, Marcus K. ■ 77401 #048-14-2005 **AN** *012

PARRIS, Ronald Neal. 4503 MAPLE ST 77401 #041-09-1991 L2002 **AN** *020 †05

PARSONS, Jessica L. 6750 WEST LOOP S, STE 420 77401 #005-06-1990 L2001 **D** *075 †15

PATEL, Dipsu Dilip. ■ 77401 #048-02-2001 L2005 **CD** *012

PATT, Nurit Hale. 6750 WEST LOOP S 77401 #550-01-1970 L1977 **CHP P** *071 †75

PENOUCOS, Hector Enrique. 4747 BELLAIRE BLVD, STE 580 77401 #132-01-1967 L1971 **AN OS** *020

PIAO, Yingchao. ■ 77401 #243-10-1985 L2007 **PCP** *100 †50 ‡

PILOT, Mitchell Chas. ■ 77401 #036-07-1973 L1988 **PTH** *020 †50

POKORNY, Alex D. ■ 77401 #048-02-1942 L1943 **P** *071 †75

PROCTOR, Peter H. 5555 WEST LOOP S, STE 225 77401 #048-02-1982 L1983 **PA D** *020

QUENG, Theresa Chan. 4710 BELLAIRE BLVD, STE 200 77401 #748-01-1963 L1970 **A PDA** *020

RADULESCU, Adriana E. 77401 #781-01-1983 L1996 **CCA** *020 †05

RAMESH, Rekha C. 4747 BELLAIRE BLVD, STE 580 77401 #495-99-1986 L1991 **AN** *020 †05

RAMSEY, Ashley Ford. ■ 77401 #036-05-2002 L2008 **NM** *012

RASEKH, Lili. ■ 77401 #396-36-1992 L1996 **PTH** *100

RASHTI, Denise Jaye. 5909 WEST LOOP S, STE 610 77401 #048-04-1996 L1997 **P** *020 †75

RAUCH, Gaiane Margishvili. ■ 77401 #913-23-1988 L2008 **DR** *012

REBELLO, Elizabeth. ■ 77401 #048-13-2002 L2004 **AN** *100 †05

REINER, Eric B, II. 6565 WEST LOOP S, STE 300 77401 #019-02-1962 L1965 **IM GE** *020 ‡

RIOS, Arturo. 5959 WEST LOOP S, STE 600 77401 #048-13-1976 L1976 **P** *020 †75

ROOSTH, Thomas Steven. ■ 77401 #048-13-1974 L1974 **PTH** *020 †50

ROSE, Gregory Hugh. 5116 BISSONNET ST # 433 77401 #048-02-1993 L1995 **DR** *020 †80

ROSENSTOCK, Harvey Allan. 4747 BELLAIRE BLVD STE 550 77401 #040-02-1966 L1969 **P CHP** *071 †75

ROUTBORT, Mark Jules. ■ 77401 #036-07-1999 L2004 **HMP** *020

ROXAS, Cathleen Park. 5111 LOCUST ST 77401 #048-14-1999 L2002 **FM** *020

RUBIO, Nunilo. ■ 77401 #016-11-1998 L2006 **END** *100 †55,20

RUIZ-PUYANA, Ines. 5116 BISSONNET ST 77401 #847-01-1976 L1997 **NPM PD** *020

SALLER, Christy Lois. 4710 BELLAIRE BLVD STE 210 77401 #028-03-1966 L1971 **NEP** *020

SANCHEZ, Miguel Angel. ■ 77401 #042-03-1990 **AI** *100

SARMAN, Gulnihal. ■ 77401 #902-07-1987 L1992 **NPM PD** *020 †55

SARMAN, Kemal Mehmet. ■ 77401 #902-07-1988 L1993 **BBK** *020

SATCHER, Robert Lee, Jr. ■ 77401 #424-01-1994 L2005 **ORS** *020 †40

SAVITZ, Sean Isaac. ■ 77401 #035-46-2000 L2007 **N VN** *020 †75

SEGGER, Franz Josef. ■ 77401 #048-02-1958 L1971 **AN P** *071

SEIFERT, Heidi J. 6565 WEST LOOP S, STE 500 77401 #048-14-1991 L1992 **APM AN** *020 †05

SEVY, Alexander Barrygale. ■ 77401 #048-04-2007 **OTO** *012

SHAH, Mahnaz N. 5116 BISSONNET ST, # 165 77401 #048-04-1996 L1998 **OPH** *100 †35

SHARMA, Padmanee. ■ 77401 #041-14-1998 L2004 **HO** *012

SHEPARD, Maria Karras. 4747 BELLAIRE BLVD # 580 77401 #048-14-1997 L1998 **AN** *020 †05

SIMCHOWITZ, David I. 5959 WEST LOOP S, STE 260 77401 #836-01-1980 L1993 **NPM** *020 †55

SINGH, Sapandeep K. ■ 77401 #028-46-2002 L2007 **RHU** *012 †20

SISTRUNK, Shari Glynn. 6750 WEST LOOP S STE 375 77401 #021-06-1996 L2001 **OS** *020 †55,75

SMALL, Henry N. 5420 WEST LOOP S, STE 3300 77401 #048-04-1987 L1988 **ORS OSM** *020 †40

SMITH, Jack Willard, Jr. ■ 77401 #055-01-1977 L1981 **OS** *050 †20

SOLOMON, James Wolfe. ■ 77401 #011-02-1959 L1969 **OTO AM** *040 †45

SPARKMAN, Susan Kay. 6300 WEST LOOP S # 420 77401 #048-02-1975 L1975 **CHP P** *020 †55,75

STAVINOHA, John Lamar, Jr. 807 MULBERRY LN 77401 #048-13-1983 L1984 **PTH PCP** *020 †50

STENGEM, Jodi Lynn. ■ 77401 #048-04-2000 L2005 **D** *100 †15

STOCKWELL, Douglas J. 5959 WEST LOOP S STE 600 77401 #048-14-1983 L1983 **PYG P** *020 †75

STOERR, Komal Frances. 6800 WEST LOOP S, STE 500 77401 #028-46-1995 L1996 **D** *020 †15

SULE, Norbert. ■ 77401 #473-03-1994 L2003 **PTH** *020 †50

SUTTON, Sarah Louise. ■ 77401 #056-06-1990 L1992 **AN** *020

SYKES, Daniel Melvin, Jr. 4747 BELLAIRE BLVD, STE 580 77401 #010-03-1994 L1998 **AN** *020 †05

TANAULI, Nasir Ahmed. 4747 BELLAIRE BLVD, STE 580 77401 #704-24-1993 L2002 **AN CCA** *020 †05

TAYAR, Jean Hanna. 5119 CHESTNUT ST 77401 #605-02-1997 L2008 **IM RHU** *020 †20

TELLER, Craig F. 6565 WEST LOOP S, STE 800 77401 #048-14-1991 L1992 **D PHL** *020 †15

THOMAS, Abraham G. 5420 WEST LOOP S STE 4300 77401 #048-14-1991 L1992 **PMM** *020 †05

THORNE, Lawrence Geo. 4710 BELLAIRE BLVD, STE 200 77401 #036-07-1958 L1972 **A PDA** *020 †55,03

TIONGSON, Benjamin B. 4710 BELLAIRE BLVD, STE 189 77401 #748-08-1986 L1996 **PME** *020

TOM, Robert John. 4747 BELLAIRE BLVD, STE 580 77401 #028-34-1991 L1995 **AN** *020 †05

TSCHEN, Jaime Antonio. 4747 BELLAIRE BLVD, STE 575 77401 #429-01-1975 L1977 **DMP D** *020 †50,15

VINH, Huy B. 5116 BISSONNET ST, # 438 77401 #048-12-1998 L1999 **IM** *020 †20

VO, Thomas Thien. ■ 77401 #048-02-2000 **EM** *020 †16

VU, Trien Ba. ■ 77401 #019-02-1993 L1996 **IM EM** *020 †20

WADE, Edward Charles. 6565 WEST LOOP S, STE 650 77401 #048-04-1984 L1986 **OPH** *020 †50

WALDREP, Harold Cayce. ■ 77401 #047-06-1971 L1975 **OBG** *020

WANG, Huamin. ■ 77401 #243-52-1987 L2005 **SP** *100 †50

WANGSA, Fuju. ■ 77402 #016-42-1993 L1993 **PTH** *100

WASSERSTRUM, Nathan. 142 PAMELLIA DR, BAYLOR COLLEGE OF MEDICINE 77401 #005-11-1976 L1986 **OBG IM** *040 †20,30

WEINSTEIN, John Newman. ■ 77401 #024-01-1971 L1973 **ON PA** *050

WHITMAN, Gene Alan. 4800 FOURNACE PL, BALIKPAPAN POUCH 77401 #024-16-1977 L1978 **FM** *020 †18

WOODFORK-RICHARDSON, C. 5116 BISSONNET ST, 181 77401 #047-07-1984 L1987 **PD** *020 †55 ‡

WYATT, Angela J. 6565 WEST LOOP S, STE 800 77401 #003-01-2001 L2006 **D DMP** *020 †15

YAO, Alice Shufeng. ■ 77401 #023-07-2008 *012

YEH, Peter Jinnbin. 6565 WEST LOOP S, STE 450 77401 #016-06-1994 L1998 **NS** *020 †25

YEN, Aihua Edward. ■ 77401 #048-04-2006 **IM** *012

ZANDER, Erik Henry. 5313 HOLLY ST 77401 #011-03-1986 L2002 **AN IM** *020 †05

ZHAI, Qi-Hui. ■ 77401 #243-46-1987 L2004 **SP** *020 †50

ZHANG, Fangyi. ■ 77401 #243-69-1986 L2007 **NS** *100

ZHANG, Hong. ■ 77401 #243-44-1990 L2003 **SP** *020 ‡

BELLEVUE – CLAY

SANDERS, Ivan T. ■ 76228 #048-12-1947 L1947 **GP GS** *071

BELLMEAD – MCLENNAN

HARDIN, Donald Mike, Jr. 556 N LOOP 340 76705 #048-14-1992 L1993 **FM** *020 †18

PALTJON, Jason M. 556 N LOOP 340 76705 #048-15-2002 L2004 **FM** *020 †18

PARTIN, Patrick B. 556 N LOOP 340 76705 #048-13-1997 L1998 **FM** *020 †18

BELLVILLE – AUSTIN

BORNE, Charles Albert. ■ 77418 #021-05-1958 L1965 **NS** *071

BOSSE, Don R. 235 W PALM ST STE 105 77418 #048-13-1982 L1983 **IM CCM** *020 †20

CHAMBERLAIN, Charles, Jr. 44 N CUMMINGS ST 77418 #048-02-1954 L1958 **GS VS** *071 †85

CUNNINGHAM, Richard R. ■ 77418 #020-02-1967 L1981 **OBG** *020 †30

DOAN, Dao Van. 44 N CUMMINGS ST 77418 #941-01-1969 L1977 **IM FM** *020

DORNON, Robert Frederick. ■ 77418 #018-03-1971 L1977 **P** *071

GAY, Charles Christophe. 235 W PALM ST STE 102 77418 #048-02-1981 L1981 **FM** *020 †18

HILL, Welton Ellis. 235 W PALM ST, STE 104 77418 #048-02-1980 L1980 **FM** *020 †18

KRUEGER, David Wayne. PO BOX 827 77418 #021-05-1973 L1976 **P PYA** *075 †75

LEIGH, Richard E, Jr. 44 N CUMMINGS ST 77418 #048-02-1942 L1943 **OPH** *071 †35

NEELY, Robert Allen. ■ 77418 #048-02-1944 L1944 **OPH** *071 †20

NEELY, Winston B. ■ 77418 #048-02-1949 L1949 **IM** *071 †20

NOBLES, Wiley Edward. 235 W PALM ST, STE 106 77418 #048-13-1985 L1986 **OBG** *020 †30

WOOD, James Kenneth, Jr. 620 W MAIN ST, FARM BUREAU INS 77418 #048-04-1946 L1946 **OTO** *071 †45

BELMONT – GONZALES

WOLFE, David Clay. ■ 78604 #047-06-1957 L1968 **ORS** *071 †40

BELTON – BELL

ADAMS, Crystal Teal. ■ 76513 #048-16-2008 *012

ADKISON, Jonathan Scott. ■ 76513 #001-06-2007 **DR** *012

BARTELS, Walton Geo. 1505 N MAIN ST, SCOTT & WHITE BELTON CLINI 76513 #048-13-1980 L1980 **FM FSM** *020 †18

BRENNAN, Michael L. ■ 76513 #048-14-2002 L2007 **ORS** *100

BURGAR, Charles G. ■ 76513 #048-13-1984 L1985 **PM OS** *030 †60

CARMONA, Juan Jose. ■ 76513 #649-14-1978 L1991 **ADP ADM** *020 †75

CHUNG, Amy A. ■ 76513 #048-02-2001 L2005 **PTH** *020 †50

CODY, James Reginald. ■ 76513 #047-06-1953 L1956 **AN OS** *071 †05

CRAIG, William Frederick. ■ 76513 #065-09-1958 L1978 **ADM PMM** *050

CRIDER, J Paul. 1703 ATRIUM CIR 76513 #048-12-1973 L1973 OBG PHL *020 †30
CROLEY, Janis. ■ 76513 #023-12-1993 L2005 OPH *020 †35
DEKAY, Kenneth Bryon. ■ 76513 #023-12-2005 L2006 EM *012
DE LEON, Fernando A. ■ 76513 #649-02-1953 L1966 IM *071
DULA, Jon Alan. 2980 HELLUMS RD LOT 201 76513 #038-40-1970 L1975 FM *020 †18
EDWARDS, Thomas P. ■ 76513 #048-02-1950 L1950 GP IM *072
FASOLINO, Edward. 1505 N MAIN ST 76513 #033-05-1985 L1990 FM *020 †18
FORD, Joseph Chas. ■ 76513 #047-06-1957 L1958 PS *071 †85,65
FOURNET-GLASSBERG, Jocylen. ■ 76513 #048-16-2003 OBG *012
FRENTZ, Gary David. ■ 76513 #021-01-1968 L1974 U TTS *040 †95
GRAHAM, Loyce J. 1300 E 6TH AVE 76513 #048-13-1990 L1992 FM GYN *020 †18
GUTIERREZ, Marciano. ■ 76513 #748-02-1936 L1966 RUP GP *071
HAGEN, Michael Peter. 1505 N MAIN ST 76513 #048-14-1981 L1981 FM *020 †18
HOLLAND-BARKIS, Penelope. 1505 N MAIN ST 76513 #048-12-1996 L1997 FM *020 †18
JONES, Arthur Lloyd. ■ 76513 #047-06-1964 L1969 IM END *071
KAGEL, Andrew. ■ 76513 #023-12-2004 L2007 EM *012
KEHLER, Gabriella E. ■ 76513 #409-21-1985 L1991 IM ID *020 †20
KHAN, Ahmed Sultan. ■ 76513 #704-25-1995 L2008 GE *020 †20
LEWIS, Shane D. ■ 76513 #010-01-2006 L2008 GS *012
LIGON, William F, Jr. 1505 N MAIN ST 76513 #048-04-1990 L1991 FM *020 †18
LIPTON, Merrill I. ■ 76513 #035-45-1991 L1966 P *071 †75
LONG, William B. ■ 76513 #048-04-1951 L1951 GP *071
MAHANEY, Billy Wade. ■ 76513 #023-12-2001 L2008 *020 †80
MANN, Jason K. ■ 76513 #048-02-2008 *012
MC ALLISTER, Daniel G. ■ 76513 #048-02-2001 L2006 PD *020 †55
MC ANINCH, Scott Allen. 2004 RIVER RUN RD, MEMORIAL HERMANN HOSPITAL 76513 #048-16-2003 L2005 EM *012
MCDONALD, Darin Kent. 1505 N MAIN ST 76513 #034-01-2004 L2006 FM *020 †18
MINJA, Emmanuel. ■ 76513 #048-16-2008 *012
MOCK, Jonathan D. ■ 76513 #048-15-2004 L2006 IM *100 †20
MONTANY, Paul Francis. 147 MONTARA CIR 76513 #010-02-1984 L1990 GS *020 †85
MOORE, Deborah Lea. ■ 76513 #048-16-2006 FP *012
PARKER, Elton D, Jr. 1505 N MAIN ST 76513 #048-04-1994 L2000 FM *020 †18
PSOLKA, Maximilian. ■ 76513 #023-12-1995 L1997 OPH *020
RAHM, Adolf Eugen, Jr. ■ 76513 #048-04-1977 GE ID *071 †70,20
RUNYAN, Thomas Earl. 6558 ARMSTRONG RD 76513 #036-07-1963 L1979 OPH *071 †35
SEWELL, Stephen Jay. 1505 N MAIN ST, SCOTT AND WHITE CLINIC 76513 #048-13-1994 L1995 FM *020 †18
SHADLEY, Lorine Lagatta. ■ 76513 #038-06-1999 L2006 PTH *020
SKAGGS, Tiffany Ann. 255 SPARTA RD, HILLCREST FAMILY HEALTH CE 76513 #048-16-1999 L2001 FM *020 †18
SUNDIN, Paul Wm. ■ 76513 #005-12-1955 L1978 OS GP *030 †18
TALLEY, William Murphy. 1300 E 6TH AVE 76513 #048-13-1981 L1981 FM *020 †18
THYEN, Andrew Bernard. ■ 76513 #048-15-1998 L1999 AN *012 †18
TONKINSON, Brien Windus. ■ 76513 #023-12-1995 L1997 OTO *020 †45
VILLANUEVA, Melanie A. ■ 76513 #048-78-2007, ▲ PD *012
VILLANUEVA, Omar. ■ 76513 #048-78-2007, ▲ FP *012
VISINTINE, Robert Edward. ■ 76513 #038-40-1957 L1991 EM IM *071 †16
WALKER, Bryan K. ■ 76513 #048-13-1996 L1999 PM *100
WARD, Russell Alan. ■ 76513 #048-16-2003 L2007 ORS *012
WARTHAN, Everett Lynn. 3500 S IH 35, CEDAR CREST HOSPITAL 76513 #048-14-1973 L1974 FM P *020
WOODS, Barbara Jean. ■ 76513 #048-15-2007 PD *012

BEN WHEELER — VAN ZANDT

WILSON, Roy D. RR 1 BOX 344 75754 #048-04-1955 L1955 AN *071 †05

BENBROOK — TARRANT

BERNSTEIN, Basil. 5521 BELLAIRE DR S STE 110 76109 #836-02-1973 L1979 *020
CORRAL, David F. 6410 SOUTHWEST BLVD # 220 76109 #039-01-1983 L1990 IM *020 †20
DAVIS, Sandra. 6410 SOUTHWEST BLVD, STE 225 76109 #048-15-1996 L2000 P *020 †75
DICKEY, Robert Ralph. ■ 76116 #048-12-1968 L1968 IM *071 †20
HANSON, Natalia Castro. ■ 76132 #048-15-1998 L1998 PD *020 †55
HARMON, John Bertrand. ■ 76132 #048-13-1982 L1983 PD *020
HEATH, Jennifer Claire. ■ 76109 #048-14-1990 L1994 P *020 †75
KIMBROUGH, John Louis. ■ 76126 #040-02-1972 L1991 GS *071 †85
KOWALSKI, Debra Atkisson. 6410 SOUTHWEST BLVD, STE 205 76109 #048-15-1986 L1987 CHP P *020 †75
LANIER, Bobby Quentin. 6407 SOUTHWEST BLVD 76132 #048-02-1970 L1970 FM AI *020 †55,03 ‡
LEHMANN, Deborah Kay. 6420 SOUTHWEST BLVD, STE 128 76109 #035-45-1978 L1990 OBG *020 †30
MYERS, Terry Lewis. ■ 76126 #051-01-1973 L1989 CG *071 †19
PERDUE, Stephanie Wilks. 998 WINSCOTT RD 76126 #024-05-1990 L1996 PD *020 †55
ROBERTS, Robin A. 6100 SOUTHWEST BLVD, STE 100 76109 #048-12-1982 L1987 D *020 †15
SABATER, Gilberto Masallo. ■ 76132 #748-01-1959 L1975 OPH *020 †18
SNYDER, Roy Edwin. 4798 HIGHWAY 377 76116 #025-01-1943 L1945 GP GS *071 †85
THOMAS, Danny Ray. 6100 SOUTHWEST BLVD, STE 100 76109 #048-02-1979 L1979 D *020 †15
TONYMON, Daniel. ■ 76126 #047-06-1959 L1977 GP *071
VIA, E Rick. 1004 WINSCOTT RD, STE A 76126 #048-13-1993 L1994 FM *020 †18

BERGHEIM — KENDALL

HURSH-CASTRO, Hester. ■ 78004 #016-11-1964 L1965 HS OM *071 ‡

BERTRAM — BURNET

HAYES, Sigman Wilson. PO BOX 409, RR 1174 NORTH 78605 #048-02-1948 L1948 GP *071

LEATHERMAN, Louis Levy. 618 CR 324 78605 #021-05-1962 L1968 CD IM *071 †20

BIG LAKE – REAGAN

SUDOLCAN, Joseph E. 800 N MAIN AVE, STE 3 76932 #048-13-1985 L1986 FM *020 †18
WRIGHT, John L, Jr. 805 N MAIN AVE 76932 #021-01-1941 L1946 GP GS *071

BIG SPRING – HOWARD

ABEL, Alan Edwin. 1501 W 11TH PL 79720 #048-02-1980 L1980 GS *020 †85
ADKINS, Larissa Gail. 1611 OSAGE RD 79720 #048-15-2008 *012
AHMED, Saeed. 1700 W FM 700 79720 #704-16-1987 L1996 PD *020 †55 ‡
AMOAKO, Isaac Kwesi. 300 W VETERANS BLVD 79720 #913-32-1991 L2004 IM *100 †20
BANGO, Kim Lisa. 1608 W FM 700, STE D 79720 #308-03-1998 L2006 FM *020 †18
BAZZELL, William Earl. 1901 N HIGHWAY 87, BIG SPRINGS STATE HOSP 79720 #039-01-1975 L1980 P IM *020
BROADRICK, Broadway. ■ 79720 #039-01-1945 L1948 IM *071
BUTLER, Gregory A. 1901 N HIGHWAY 87 79720 #048-15-1995 L1996 P *020
BYERLY, Lee E. 1501 W 11TH PL STE 204 79720 #048-14-1997 L2001 OBG *020 †30
CARRASCO, Manuel R. 1501 W 11TH PL, STE 302 79720 #308-01-1979 L1994 IM *020 †20
CASTILLO, Mario J. ■ 79720 #011-02-1989 L1999 DR *020 †80
CHAVEZ, Joseph Edward. 1501 W 11TH PL STE 205 79720 #034-01-1995 L1999 PD *020 †55
CHU, Patricia Shihann. 1601 W 11TH PL 79720 #047-05-2000 L2003 EM *020 †16
CIVELLO, Ellis John, Jr. 4409 CHAPARRAL RD 79720 #048-13-1981 L1984 P *071 †75
COLE, Charles Patrick. ■ 79720 #048-02-1998 L2003 IM *020
COLLIER, Wm Eddins, Jr. ■ 79720 #021-06-1974 L1975 FM *020 †18
COX, Bruce Edward. 710 S GREGG ST STE 100 79720 #048-02-1975 L1975 FM OS *020
COX, William Henry. ■ 79720 #024-01-1957 L1960 IM *071
DEL MORAL, Jose F. 300 W VETERANS BLVD 79720 #649-03-1973 L1999 P *020
DURAND-HOLLIS, Gabriel. 1901 N HIGHWAY 87 79720 #649-01-1956 L1974 P *072
FARQUHAR, John S. 1601 W 11TH PL 79720 #017-20-1959 L1981 FM EM *020 †16,18
FINN, Nomie L. ■ 79720 #748-01-1974 L1983 HEM IM *020
FISH, John H. 207 E 7TH ST, FISH OPHTHALMOLOGY CLINIC 79720 #048-02-1942 L1942 OPH OTO *071 †35
FISH, John Ronald. 207 E 7TH ST 79720 #048-02-1970 L1970 OPH *020 †35
FISH, Larry A. 207 E 7TH ST 79720 #048-15-1999 L2003 OPH *020 †35
GILLALA, Meghana Reddy. 1501 W 11TH PL 79720 #027-01-2003 L2007 AN *020
GUNDLAPALLI, Sai Prakash. 1501 W 11TH PL, STE 304 79720 #496-39-1999 L2006 APM *020 †05
HADDAD, R I. 1501 W 11TH PL 79720 #915-03-1973 L1980 U *020 †95
HAN, Ba Lim Htyan Hoe. 1901 N HIGHWAY 87 79720 #209-01-1973 L1999 P *020 †75
HARRIS, Heather N. 1801 BAYLOR BLVD 79720 #048-02-2008 *020
HAYES, Robert Patrick. 1501 W 11TH PL STE 102 79720 #038-41-1967 L1983 ORS *020 †40
HEICHMAN, Walter James. ■ 79720 #062-01-1957 L1978 GS *071 †85
JOHANSEN, Betty K. ■ 79720 #048-15-1975 L1975 FM *020
JUAN, Melencio Francisco. 2301 S GREGG ST, FAMILY MEDICAL CENTER 79720 #748-01-1984 L1999 FM *020 †18
KLEIN, Donald Roger. 300 W VETERANS BLVD 79720 #016-76-1963, ▲ L1963 R NM *071 †28
KUPRIANOWICZ, Cezary. 1605 W 11TH PL 79720 #759-03-1989 L1997 PUD IM *020 †20
LEDFORD, Keith J. 2301 S GREGG ST 79720 #025-07-1978 L2003 OBG *020 †30
LONG, David Dean. 910 S MAIN ST 79720 #048-15-1985 L1986 FM *020 †18
LOPEZ, Elias Oswaldo. 1901 N HIGHWAY 87, BIG SPRING STATE HOSPITAL 79720 #737-01-1957 L1979 P *020
LWIN, Aung Naing. 5 GLENWICK CV 79720 #209-01-1985 L2001 IM *020 †20
MARKS, Shirley Faye. 300 W VETERANS BLVD 79720 #024-01-1973 L1976 P *020 †75
MATHEWS, James Evert. ■ 79720 #021-01-1964 L1964 GS *071 †85
MC DANIEL, Clark Richard. 1608 W FM 700 79720 #016-11-1964 L1974 FM *020 †18
MERCER, Jimmy Randall. 1901 N HIGHWAY 87, BIG SPRING STATE HOPITAL 79720 #048-02-1977 L1977 P *075 †75
MYINT, Tin Than. PSYCHIATRY SERVICE VAMC 79720 #209-02-1967 L1986 P PHP *020
NAQVI, All-E Raza. 300 W VETERANS BLVD, VA MED CTR 79720 #308-11-1991 L1999 IM *020 †20
NYUNT, Tin. 1901 N HIGHWAY 87, BIG SPRING STATE HOSP 79720 #209-01-1977 L1997 P *020
OLSON, Kurt Collin. 300 W VETERANS BLVD, DEPT OF MED /URGENT CARE 79720 #561-01-1969 L1971 FM NTR *020 †18
PARTIDA, Jorge L. 1900 SIMLER AVE, US DEPT OF JUSTICE 79720 #649-02-1988 L2001 FM EM *020 †18
PATEL, Nandlal Mangaldas. 1510 SCURRY ST, STE D 79720 #495-89-1982 L1992 IM *020 †20
PETERS, Mary Hanna. 1901 N HIGHWAY 87 79720 #915-04-1998 L1998 FM PD *020 †18
PHILLIPS, William P. 1901 N HIGHWAY 87, BIG SPRING STATE HOSPITAL 79720 #048-02-1996 L1998 IM *020 †20
POLEPALLE, Silpi. 207 E 7TH ST 79720 #028-46-1999 L2003 OPH *020 †35
PORTER, Melvin A. MALONE & HOGAN CLINIC, M H SHROFF MD 79720 #010-01-1949 L1953 OBG *071 †30
POWELL, Darryl Homer. ■ 79720 #048-12-1960 L1960 GS *030 †85
PURGASON, Dorothy G. ■ 79721 #039-01-1970 L1971 GP *020
QUINN, William Lawrence. 300 W VETERANS BLVD 79720 #422-01-1982 L1985 IMG IM *020 †20
REDDY, Gaddum J M. 300 W VETERANS BLVD, SURGICAL SERVICE 79720 #495-21-1965 L1972 AS TS *020 †85,90
REHMAN, Faiz U. 300 W VETERANS BLVD, PRIMARY CARE CLINIC 79720 #704-01-1987 L2000 CD IM *020 †20
RODRIGUEZ, Wilfredo. 300 W VETERANS BLVD, BIG SPRING VAMC 79720 #042-02-1985 L1989 P *020 †75
SAENZ, Kimberly J. 2301 S GREGG ST 79720 #048-12-2002 L2005 PD *020 †55
SHROFF, Manish Kumar H. MALONE & HOGAN CLINIC, M H SHROFF MD 79720 #495-20-1979 L1988 CD IM *020 †20
SRIRAMAMURTHY, Subbaraman. 1700 W FM 700 79720 #495-04-1971 L1984 GS *020 †85
STANLEY, Kenneth Emerson. 2400 S GREGG ST, SURGERY 112 VAMC 79720 #019-02-1956 L1956 U *071 †95
SULATAN, Oseas R. VET ADMIN HOSP, DEPT MED 79720 #748-07-1968 L1971 IM *020
THEIN, Aung Myint. 710 CRAIGMONT DR 79720 #005-12-1996 L1998 DR *020 †80
THURMAN, Harold C, Jr. 319 RUNNELS ST 79720 #048-13-1988 L1989 P *020 †75

TIPTON, James Warren. ■ 79720 #047-06-1956 L1961 **OTO** *071 †45
VAN, Huong Thi. ■ 79720 #942-01-1980 L2002 **IM** *020 †20
VASANAWALA, Kokila S. ■ 79721 #495-22-1970 L1977 **PTH IM** *020 †50
VASANWALA, Shreenivas K. 300 W VETERANS BLVD 79720 #495-23-1970 L1976 **GS** *020 †85

BISHOP – NUECES

GINTHER, Clarke E. 106 E MAIN ST 78343 #016-11-1943 L1960 **FM** *071

BLACKWELL – NOLAN

KLETTER, Guno George. ■ 79506 #850-01-1973 L1980 **IM** *071

BLANCO – BLANCO

BLACK, Ann Patrice. 825 4TH ST 78606 #048-14-1984 L1986 **FM** *020 †18
BLANCHARD, Janna. ■ 78606 #048-13-1983 L1983 **AN** *020 †05
CLINE, Barnett Louis. PO BOX 1477 78606 #048-04-1962 L1962 **OS PHP** *050 †70
DIERINGER, Norbert John. ■ 78606 #048-13-1985 L1986 **AN** *020 †05
VAUSE, David Dwight. PO BOX 1108 78606 #036-07-1961 L1974 **FM GPM** *071

BLUFF DALE – ERATH

CLARK, Cary Byron. 10901 BAKERS CROSSING RD 76433 #048-02-1982 L1983 **FM EM** *020 †18

BLUFFTON – LLANO

WILKERSON, William Geo. ■ 78607 #048-02-1963 L1972 **FM N** *020 †18

BOERNE – BEXAR

ADAMS, Sylvia Proctor. ■ 78015 #048-02-1985 L1986 **FM** *062 †18
HOLLAND, Francis Thos. ■ 78015 #010-02-1992 L1994 **FM PM** *020 †18
PALMA-VARGAS, Juan Manuel. ■ 78015 #649-14-1991 L2007 **GS** *100 †85
PERSYN, Lisa D. ■ 78015 #048-13-2000 L2002 **PM** *020
REHRER, Matthew William. ■ 78015 #048-04-2008 *012
SMALLIGAN, Lowell Dean. ■ 78015 #048-04-1960 L1960 **AN** *071 †05
TARRY, Kirby Bruce. ■ 78015 #017-20-1966 L1982 **U** *071 †95
THORNTON, William Edgar. ■ 78015 #036-01-1963 L1975 **AM** *062
WOOD, Sheralyn Mott. ■ 78015 #048-02-1995 L1996 **PD** *020 †55

BOERNE – KENDALL

ADRIAN, Erle Keys, Jr. PO BOX 254 78006 #024-01-1963 L1964 **OS** *071
AFFLECK, John Hannay. 25 CORLEY RD 78006 #012-01-1956 L1966 **OM GP** *071
ANDERSON, John Richard. ■ 78006 #048-12-1969 L1969 **ORS** *071 †40
ARANDES, Michelle Marie. 34910 IH 10 W STE 5 78006 #048-13-1998 L2000 **PD** *020 †55
ATKINS, James Hugh, Jr. 34910 IH 10 W 78006 #048-04-1985 L1986 **OTO** *020 †45
BANNISTER, Gary Lee. ■ 78006 #030-05-1959 L1981 **OBG EM** *020 †30
BARNETT, Lawrence M. ■ 78006 #048-13-1943 L1943 **GP GS** *020
BASS, Isabel Sue. ■ 78006 #024-07-1981 L2006 **DR** *020 †80
BATES, Brian A. 216 GREYSTONE CIR 78006 #048-13-1987 L1988 **PD PEM** *020 †55
BEAUCHAMP, Kristine Lynne. 134 MENGER SPGS, STE 1100 78006 #048-02-2001 L2003 **FM** *020 †18
BLACKBURN, David L. 305 WOLLSCHLAEGER DR 78006 #048-14-1989 L1990 **EM** *020
BUNDRANT, Bradly. 407 DEER CREEK DR 78006 #048-15-1987 L1990 **FM SME** *020 †18
CAVAZOS, Filiberto. ■ 78006 #649-02-1958 L2004 **PTH CLP** *020 †50
CHAVES, Ignacio A. 114 TRADE AVE 78006 #748-01-1959 L1998 **FM OS** *071
COLEMAN, Vincent N. 34910 IH 10 W STE 507 78006 #048-13-1998 L1999 **PPD** *020 †55
DAY, Harold C. 117 S SAUNDERS ST 78006 #017-20-1950 L1951 **FM** *072
DICE, Y Gia. 124 E BANDERA RD, STE 301 78006 #041-09-1994 L2003 **HO** *020 †20
DUNN, Bryan. 1201 S MAIN ST 78006 #048-14-1991 L1995 **EM** *020 †16
EICHLER, Allen Charles. ■ 78006 #048-02-1962 L1962 **GS** *071 †85
FEIGEN, Michael. 171 LAKE FRONT DR 78006 #041-12-1963 L1990 **R NR** *020 †80
FUENTES, David. 109 FALLS CT, STE 100 78006 #048-13-1991 L1993 **AI** *020 †03,55
GARZA, Ricardo A. 128 W BANDERA RD 78006 #048-12-1984 L1985 **CD IM** *020 †20
GATES, George Arthur. ■ 78006 #025-01-1959 L1971 **OTO** *071 †45
GREENLEES, David L. ■ 78006 #021-01-1943 L1946 **FM** *071
HARRISON, Cathleen Dye. 119 ROEDER ST 78006 #021-06-2000 L2002 **P** *020 †75
HOONJAN, Malvinder Singh. ■ 78006 #033-06-2003 L2007 **OPH** *012
HUBBARD, Kathryn R. 113 FALLS CT, STE 100 78006 #028-46-1983 L1994 **OPH** *020 †35
HULL, Jaime Jaime. ■ 78006 #048-13-1982 L1983 **OBG** *020 †30
JOHNSON, Jennifer S. 497 RIO COLORADO 78006 #048-16-1994 L1999 **CHP** *020 †75
KAUFFMANN, Adolph F, III. ■ 78006 #048-02-1943 L1943 **GS** *071 †85
KIEFER, Richard Francis. 208 WOLLSCHLAEGER DR 78006 #033-05-1963 L1980 **NM GS** *075 †28
KIPHART, Ridlon Jos. ■ 78006 #016-06-1957 L1968 **TS** *071 †85,90
KOTTI, George Harold, III. ■ 78006 #023-12-2003 L2005 **PCC** *012 †20
KOUDOURIS, Spyridon. ■ 78006 #418-01-1952 L1968 **IM CLP** *020
LEE, Emmanuel John. 114 TRADE AVE 78006 #010-03-2003 L2006 **FM** *020 †18
LIVINGSTON, Shannon Sarto. 1201 S MAIN ST, STE 114 78006 #048-12-2001 L2005 **FM** *020 †18
LOBAR, Bruce Ian. ■ 78006 #654-01-1982 L2007 **N** *071 †75
LOGAN, Anne Doering. 124 E BANDERA RD STE 304 78006 #041-12-1988 L1995 **PD** *020 †55
LOPEZ, Fernando. 128 W BANDERA RD 78006 #005-11-1992 L1998 **CD IM** *020 †20
MARTINEZ, Richard E. 114 TRADE AVE 78006 #048-13-1982 L1983 **FM** *020 †18
MC COY, Jimmy Eugene. 120 MEDICAL DR 78006 #048-13-1972 L1972 **FM** *020 †18

MC RAE, Elizabeth Thea. 117 S SAUNDERS ST 78006 #039-01-1985 L1988 **IM** *020 †20
MUEHLBERGER, Gerald Lee. ■ 78006 #010-02-1977 L2005 **FM AM** *030 †70,18
MURPHY, C William. 1201 S MAIN ST, STE 119 78006 #048-12-1980 L1980 **AN** *020 †05
OZAN, Aydin Mazlum. 1028 N MAIN ST 78006 #048-13-1993 L2000 **IM** *020 †20
PETERSON, Joseph Roger. 1414 E BLANCO RD, STE 9 78006 #048-13-1999 L2002 **D** *020 †15
PRIETO, Robert. 124 E BANDERA RD, STE 301 78006 #023-12-1993 L2006 **HO** *020 †20
RADDIN, James Hallow, Jr. ■ 78006 #034-01-1975 L1977 **AM** *030 †70
ROUSE, Veronica Lee. 134 MENGER SPGS, STE 2110 78006 #001-02-1974 L1980 **R** *020 †80
SALINAS, Carl. 26904 AUTUMN GLN 78006 #048-02-1992 L1993 **FM** *020 †18
SANT'AMBROGIO, Giorgio. 234 W BANDERA RD # 110 78006 #048-02-1988 L1989 **CHP** *020 †75
SCHUHMACHER, Lawrence, III. 179 TWIN CANYON DR, ANESTHESIA DEPT 78006 #048-02-1961 L1961 **AN** *075 †05
SCHWARZ, R Marc. ■ 78006 #407-04-1966 L1977 **GP A** *071
SIMS, Ronald Esteene. 1421 S MAIN ST STE 107 78006 #048-02-1981 L1981 **IM** *020 †20
SMITH, Michael James. 124 E BANDERA RD, STE 204 78006 #021-05-1987 L2001 **OBG** *020 †30
SPURGAT, Thomas Steven. 234 W BANDERA RD, STE 157 78006 #025-01-1981 L1984 **PEM PD** *020 †55
SRP, Tracey Signe. ■ 78006 #048-13-2005 **P** *012
STAHL, Benjamin Adam. ■ 78006 #048-13-2006 **FP** *012
STYSKAL, Kendall Wm. 134 MENGER SPGS, METHODIST BOERNE MEDICAL C 78006 #007-02-1991 L1995 **IM** *020 †20
TOLBERT, Cynthia Rae. 518 N MAIN ST, COTTONWOOD SPRINGS FAMILY 78006 #041-07-1986 L1997 **FM** *020 †18
TURAY, Lynette Diane. ■ 78006 #038-41-2003 L2005 **P** *020
VELA, Victor Danl. 1201 S MAIN ST STE 114 78006 #018-03-1982 L1985 **FM** *020 †18
VIGIL, Justin Joaquin. 1201 S MAIN ST, STE 119 78006 #034-01-1998 L2003 **APM** *020 †05
WALLACE, Teddy Paul. ■ 78006 #048-02-1960 L1960 **P N** *071
WILLIG, Donald. ■ 78006 #048-13-1991 L1992 **RNR** *020 †80
WILSON, Frank Carroll. ■ 78006 #048-04-1960 L1960 **R** *071 †80
WITTMER, James Frederick. ■ 78006 #028-02-1957 L1979 **OM PHP** *072 †70 ‡

BOGATA – RED RIVER

BROOKS, Earl E. ■ 75417 #048-02-1951 L1951 **FM IM** *071 †18

BONHAM – FANNIN

ALLISON, Richard Gerard. 504 LIPSCOMB ST 75418 #062-01-1965 L1976 **R NM** *020 †80,28
ANANDARAMAN, Ramanathan. 1201 E 9TH ST 75418 #495-53-1956 L1971 **IM GP** *071
BAIN, Robert Cleve. ■ 75418 #566-01-1973 L1990 **OS** *020
DUNCAN, Jeff Davis. 504 LIPSCOMB ST 75418 #048-12-1971 L1971 **FM** *020
GEORGE, Muttavancheril J. 1209 E 9TH ST, SAM RAYBURN VETERANS MED C 75418 #495-44-1981 L1997 **IM** *020 †20
GUDUGUNTLA, Venkatesham. 1201 E 9TH ST, VA MEDICAL CENTER 75418 #495-57-1974 L1993 **IM** *020 †20
HUGHES, Tracy. 1201 E 9TH ST, NE. TX. MENTAL HEALTH CTR 75418 #048-02-1978 L1978 **P** *020 †75
JAMES, Doris Schatte. SAM RAYBURN MEM VET CTR 75418 #048-02-1960 L1960 **PTH** *020 †50
JAN, Muhammad A. 1201 E 9TH ST, VETERANS AFFAIRS NORTH TEX 75418 #704-02-1988 L1996 **IM** *020 †20
LE, Toi Van. 1201 E 9TH ST 75418 #941-01-1972 L1984 **IM IMG** *020 †20
LE, Xuan-Dao T. 1201 E 9TH ST, BONHAM VA MEDICAL CENTER 75418 #942-01-1978 L1997 **IM** *020 †20
MA, Trang To. 1201 E 9TH ST, SAM RAYBURN MEM VET CTR 75418 #941-01-1972 L1985 **P** *020 †75
NANDIMANDALAM, Vijayalaksh. 1211 E 6TH ST STE 100 75418 #495-70-1995 L2007 **IM** *020
SCHONFELD, Alan Douglas. 1201 S MAIN ST, 11-C 75418 #048-15-1986 L1987 **END** *020 †20
SCHREIBER, Lee R. 2201 N STATE HIGHWAY 121, TEXOMACARE BONHAM 75418 #048-13-1989 L1991 **FM** *020 †18
SIDOTI, V James. 75418 #038-06-1945 L1958 **GP GS** *072
SISK, Dana Lee. 2201 N STATE HIGHWAY 121, TEXOMACARE BONHAM 75418 #048-02-1976 L1976 **FM** *020 †18
SISK, Walter Lee. 2201 N HIGHWAY 121 75418 #048-12-1956 L1956 **OS GP** *020
SURAPANANI, Mallikharjuna. 9TH & LIPSCOMB STS 75418 #495-37-1968 L1977 **IM** *020
THOYAKULATHU, Sam Geo. 1211 E 6TH ST, STE 300 75418 #495-53-1976 L1994 **IM** *020 †20
WHITE, Dena E. 75418 #048-14-2006 L2008 **OBG** *012
ZAKI, Nasir. 1201 E 9TH ST 116A, VA NORTH TEXAS HEALTH CARE 75418 #704-16-1985 L2000 **PYG** *020

BORGER – HUTCHINSON

BARNS, Debra Kay. 200 S MCGEE ST 79007 #039-01-1979 L1989 **PTH** *062 †50
HUDSON, Carl Stephen. 115 S MCGEE ST, BOX 662 79007 #048-13-1973 L1973 **GP** *020
MADSEN, Henrik. PO BOX 1709 79008 #297-01-1960 L1981 **PM OS** *071
MANN, Wallace Harper, Jr. 200 S MCGEE ST 79007 #048-13-1997 L1998 **FM** *020 †18
MAZA, Vicente F M. 200 S MCGEE ST 79007 #748-02-1962 L1976 **DR OS** *020 †80
MOZA, Joseph. 200 S MCGEE ST, STE 101 79007 #915-05-1978 L2007 **GS** *020 †85
NELSON, Luther Sullivan. 200 S MCGEE ST 79007 #036-01-1958 L1968 **R** *071 †80
PERALES, Jesse Itaas. 202 S MCGEE ST 79007 #748-10-1965 L1974 **IM CD** *020
PURL, Carmen Rae. 200 S MCGEE ST 79007 #048-13-1985 L1986 **FM EM** *020 †18
QUIROS, Corazon. 600 W 3RD ST 79007 #748-01-1970 L1978 **OBG** *020
QUIROS, Edward Espinosa. 200 S MCGEE ST 79007 #748-01-1970 L1977 **GS HS** *020 †85
RHOTON, Joel S. 503 W 1ST ST, STE C 79007 #048-12-2001 L2005 **OBG** *020
ROGERS, Bard Layne. 104 N BRYAN ST, BORGER MEDICAL CLINIC 79007 #422-01-1997 L2000 **FM** *020 †18
SAMPAT, Kala G. 503 W 1ST ST STE B 79007 #495-76-1970 L1978 **PD** *020 †55
SHETLAR, Christina R. 79007 #048-12-2005 **PTH** *012
SHOOP, Stephen Allen. 200 S MCGEE ST 79007 #021-01-1979 L1999 **GS** *020 †85
SIFUENTES, Jorge Antonio. 713 DEAHL ST 79007 #048-15-2002 L2005 **FM** *020 †18

TRIVINO, Cesar David. 200 S MCGEE ST 79007 #264-11-1986 L2002 AN PME *020 †05
VIOLA, Juan Fidel. 200 S MCGEE ST, GOLDEN PLAINS FAMILY PRACT 79007 #748-08-1971 L1977 GP *020
WEBER, Ammon David. 202 S MCGEE ST, MEDICAL PLAZA BUILDING 79007 #654-01-2001 L2006 FM *020 †18
WHEELER, Jim E. 115 S MCGEE ST 79007 #048-02-1953 L1953 GP *072
WRIGHT, John Chas. 200 S MCGEE ST, STE 100 79007 #048-13-1974 L1974 ORS *020 †40

BOWIE — MONTAGUE

AUJLA, Surinder Singh. 1010 N MILL ST, UNITED CLINICS OF NORTH 76230 #917-10-1970 L1980 GS FM *020
BROWDER, Maurice Mac. 705 E GREENWOOD AVE 76230 #048-12-1958 L1958 FM *071
CHANDLER, Eddie Ray. 500 E LONDON ST 76230 #048-02-1967 L1967 GS *071 †85
DINGLER, Chance W. 702 E GREENWOOD AVE 76230 #048-02-1995 L1996 FM *072 †18
DINGLER, Leonard T. 702 E GREENWOOD AVE 76230 #048-14-1987 L1988 FM OBG *020 †18
DUNN, James Floyd. 1004 N MILL ST, UNITED CLINICS OF NORTH 76230 #048-12-1975 L1975 IM END *050 †20
EVANS, Gary Thos. 1010 N MILL ST, UNITED CLINICS OF NORTH 76230 #048-13-1977 L1977 IM EM *020 †20
EVANS, H Lorain. 500 E LONDON ST, MEDICAL SURGICAL CLINIC OF 76230 #048-12-1958 L1958 FM *071
HODDE, James Douglas. 1010 N MILL ST, UNITED CLINICS OF NORTH 76230 #048-15-1991 L1992 FM *020 †18
JENKINS, James Mark. 1010 N MILL ST, UNITED CLINICS OF NORTH 76230 #012-01-1982 L2004 GS PDS *020 †85
LATHAM, Max Gordon. ■ 76230 #048-12-1963 L1963 FM *071 †18
NEAL, Robert Thos. 1010 N MILL ST 76230 #048-02-1979 L1979 DR *020 †80
TURK, Albert J, Jr. 1010 N MILL ST, UNITED CLINICS OF NORTH 76230 #048-15-1993 L1994 FM *020 †18
WEST, George Russell. 702 E GREENWOOD AVE 76230 #048-15-1985 L1986 FM *020 †18

BOYD — WISE

CLARK, James Richard, Jr. 305 PR 3367 76023 #048-12-1967 L1967 OBG *020 †30

BRADY — MCCULLOCH

ALLEN, James H, Jr. 2010 NINE RD 76825 #048-15-1984 L1985 FM *020 †18
BURST, Donald O. ■ 76825 #028-34-1945 L1945 ORS *071 †40
DIETRICH, Alfred G. NINE RD 76825 #019-02-1940 L1962 GS *071 †85
GRAVES, Nathan A. 2010 NINE RD 76825 #048-12-2001 L2005 FM *020 †18
MAYS, Jeffry P. 2026 S BRIDGE ST 76825 #048-13-1993 L1995 IM *020 †20
MC ANELLY, Stanley Merlin. 2008 NINE RD 76825 #048-02-1962 L1962 GP GS *020
VICKERS, Lonnie Lee. 2010 NINE RD 76825 #048-15-1982 L1983 FM *020 †18

BRAZORIA — BRAZORIA

HINKLE, Marcus Eric. 104 E SH 332, STE G 77422 #308-11-1987 L1996 FM *020 †18

BRECKENRIDGE — STEPHENS

FORD, Thomas C. 4176 FM 1800, WALKER SAYLES UNIT 76424 #041-01-1950 L1952 GP PHP *062
JEFFERY, Penny Elizabeth. 2802 W WALKER ST 76424 #018-03-1995 L2000 FM *020 †18
LAWRENCE, Jim Tom. 1000 E WILLIAMS ST 76424 #048-12-1947 L1947 GP *020
NICHOLS, Dwight James. 101 S HARTFORD ST, # D 76424 #048-02-1963 L1963 FM *020
PRATER, William E, Jr. 101 S HARTFORD ST STE C, W E PRATER MD 76424 #048-02-1984 L1985 FM *020 †18 ‡
PROCTOR, Matthew Todd. 101 S HARTFORD ST 76424 #048-15-2000 L2002 FM *020 †18 ‡
WORICK-DABELIC, Rachael K. 101 S HARTFORD ST STE A 76424 #048-14-2002 L2005 FM *020 †18

BRENHAM — WASHINGTON

ALI, Mohammad Mahmud. 600 N PARK ST 77833 #160-02-1968 L1976 AN *020
AMARAL, Peter Gregory. 635 MEDICAL PKWY 77833 #048-02-1975 L2000 FM OPH *020 †35
APPELT, Gary Leslie. 633 MEDICAL PKWY 77833 #048-12-1974 L1974 U *020 †95
BAKER, Kenneth Clyde. 600 N PARK ST 77833 #048-02-1979 L1979 PD *020 †55
BEIM, Steve Alexander. 1205 S AUSTIN ST 77833 #005-15-1990 L1995 OPH *020 †35
BODE, Jon Frederick. 605 MEDICAL CT, STE 203 77833 #048-12-1993 L1994 FM OBS *020 †18 ‡
BOEHM, Henry Julius, Jr. 516 HIGHWAY 290 W, P O BOX 787 77833 #048-02-1962 L1962 FM OBG *071 †18
BROYLES, Geo Dilley, Jr. ■ 77833 #048-02-1940 L1940 GS *072 †85
BRYANT, Cassandra M. 700 MEDICAL PKWY 77833 #048-02-1965 L1998 PD *020 †55
CHERUKU, Rajanarender R. 605 MEDICAL CT, STE 202 77833 #495-57-1983 L1991 HO IM *020 †20
CONDREN, Howard Byrd. 600 N PARK ST 77833 #048-02-1965 L1965 ORS *075
DELGADO, Emilio H. ■ 77833 #737-01-1956 L1970 GS FM *062
DOMINIC, Anthony J. ■ 77833 #010-02-1982 L1984 VIR DR *074
DRAEHN, Donald Kenneth. 600 N PARK ST 77833 #048-02-1974 L1974 PD *020 †55
FLYNN, Chester John, Jr. 604 W MASONIC DR 77833 #024-05-1963 L1969 IM A *020 †05
GREGORY, Eugene Bryan. ■ 77833 #048-04-1956 L1956 OPH *071 †35
HASSKARL, Walter F, Jr. BRENHAM CLINIC 77833 #048-02-1942 L1943 GP GS *071
HAYDON, Robert Lynn. 539 MEDICAL PKWY 77833 #048-02-1973 L1973 FM *020 †18
HOOD, John Bret. 4001 HIGHWAY 36 S, BRENHAM STATE SCHOOL HEALT 77833 #048-14-1996 L1997 FM *020 †18
HORTON, Cheryl J. 1102 HIGHWAY 290 W 77833 #046-01-1978 L1995 OPH *020 †35
JANTZI, Paul D. 6522 FM 50 77833 #048-14-1998 L2002 AI *020 †55,20,03

LANDGRAF, Kenneth. 600 N PARK ST 77833 #048-12-1977 L1977 IM *020 †20
LEAL, Francisco A, Jr. 600 N PARK ST, BRENHAM CLINIC ASSOCIATION 77833 #048-04-1983 L1983 FM OBG *020 †18
LOCHIEL, Malcolm C. 605 MEDICAL CT, STE 201 77833 #048-14-1995 L2001 FM *020 †18 ‡
MALINAK, Lewis Russell. ■ 77833 #021-01-1960 L1964 GYN OS *071 †30
MANFRE, Anthony Saml. ■ 77833 #048-02-1959 L1959 FM P *071 †18
MAREK, Bobby Wayne. 600 N PARK ST 77833 #048-02-1979 L1979 IM *040 †20
MAY, Richard Herman. ■ 77833 #021-01-1971 L1978 IM EM *071 †16,20
MC INTIRE, John Randall. 600 N PARK ST 77833 #048-12-1977 L1977 DR *020 †80
MILLER, Sue D. 539 MEDICAL PKWY 77833 #047-20-1995 L1997 FM *020 †18
MILLER, Susan Carol. 539 MEDICAL PKWY 77833 #048-02-1993 L1995 FM *020 †18
PALTER, Geoffrey M. 905 MAE WAY ST 77833 #048-04-1992 L1995 FM *020 †18
PENA, Leonidas. 600 N PARK ST, BRENHAN CLINIC ASSOCIATION 77833 #649-01-1972 L1992 GS *020
SCHUCK, Michael Robert. 605 MEDICAL CT STE 103 77833 #048-02-1997 L2001 ORS *020 †40
SCHUCK, Michelle. ■ 77833 #048-02-1997 L2001 AN *020
SPAW, Jeffrey N. 600 N PARK ST, BRENHAM CLINIC ASSOC. 77833 #048-16-1993 L1994 ORS *020 †40
STOLTENBERG, Jeffrey R. 600 N PARK ST, BRENHAM CLINIC ASSOCIATION 77833 #048-02-1983 L1983 GS EM *020 †85
WILLIAMS, Scott M. 605 MEDICAL CT STE 103 77833 #011-04-1980 L1982 ORS OSM *020 †40
WORKMAN, Gregg A. 605 MEDICAL CT, STE 203 77833 #048-14-1997 L2002 FM *020 †18
YOFFE, Stuart James. 6522 FM 50, BRENHAM INDEPENDENCE 77833 #020-12-1968 L1972 PD AI *020 †55

BRIARCLIFF — TRAVIS

ZIMMERMAN, Erika Irene. 21909 MOFFAT DR 78669 #048-12-1993 L1994 FM *020 †18

BRIDGE CITY — ORANGE

MOVVA, Anand Babu. 2515 TEXAS AVE 77611 #495-50-1994 L2000 IM *020

BRIDGEPORT — WISE

BURCH, Joseph Shelton, Jr. 4000 N 10TH ST, WACKENHUT CORRECTIONS CORP 76426 #048-12-1968 L1968 FM *071 †18
GARRISON, Cynthia A. ■ 76426 #048-15-1991 L1993 OBG *071 †30
HUDDLESTON, William E. 1306 13TH ST 76426 #004-01-1953 L1956 FM *071 †18

BROADDUS — SAN AUGUSTINE

JONES, Gordon Wm. ■ 75929 #048-02-1956 L1957 R OS *072

BROCK — PARKER

BLACKBURN, Gilden Blair. ■ 76087 #017-20-1974 L2003 OBG *030 †30

BRONTE — COKE

HEROLD, Joseph J. ■ 76933 #035-08-1971 L1976 EM *020 †16

BROOKELAND — JASPER

HEARE, Charles R. ■ 75931 #048-02-1952 L1952 OTO *071 †45

BROOKESMITH — BROWN

LOCKER, S Braswell. ■ 76827 #048-02-1940 L1940 OPH OTO *071

BROOKS CITY-BASE — BEXAR

BONNEMA, Albert H, Jr. 2509 KENNEDY CIR 78235 #045-01-1993 L1994 FM GPM *030 †18,70 ‡
BROOKS, Mark John. 2507 KENNEDY CIR 78235 #054-04-1999 L1999 FM *020 †18
BURNETT, Daniel Garrison. ■ 78235 #031-01-1989 L1992 GPM *050 †18,70
DELGADO, Antonio Jose. 2507 KENNEDY CIR BLDG 110, OFF 286 78235 #264-01-1989 L1993 IM OM *020 †20
DOPPELT, Fredric F. ■ 78235 #035-15-1956 AM IM *030 †70,20
DOWNES, Andrew. 2601 LOUIS BAUER DR 78235 #062-01-1992 AM *100 †70
FAJARDO, Kevin Anthony. 8050 LINDBERGH LNDG, 311 MDS 78235 #023-12-2004 L2005 *100 †70
FEIG, Jill Catalano. 2513 KENNEDY CIR # 180, AFIOH/RSRH 78235 #023-12-1994 L2006 PHP *062 †70
FOX, Karen Ann. 2507 KENNEDY CIR 78235 #048-04-1984 L1985 AM OM *030 †70
GOLDHAGEN, Marc Vincent. 8005 LINDBERGH LNDG, ATTN:CREDENTIAL OFFICE 78235 #016-42-1988 L1990 GPM *020 †70
GOULD, Philip Laird. 8005 LINDBERGH LNDG, BROOKS AFB 78235 #021-01-1993 L1996 FM *020 †20
GREEN, Layne Bedford. 2507 KENNEDY CIR, BROOKS CITY BASE 78235 #049-01-2006 L2007 IM *020
HETRICK, Steven Matthew. 8005 LINDBERGH LNDG, BROOKS AFB 78235 #023-12-1988 L1990 AM OM *020 †70
HURSH, Timothy Alan. 8050 LINDBERGH LNDG, 311 MDS/SGOQ 78235 #039-01-1988 L1989 AM *020 †70
IVAN, Douglas Jos. 2507 KENNEDY CIR, USAFSAM FECO 78235 #035-03-1973 L1980 OPH AM *020 †35

KRUYER, William Bernard. 2507 KENNEDY CIR, 37TH MDG-LACKLAND AFB 78235 #005-14-1975 L1984 **CD IM** *050 †20

KURZ, Christopher John. 8050 LINDBERGH LNDG, ATTN: CREDENTIAL OFFICE 78235 #005-18-2002 L2003 **OPH** *012

LINN, Cheryl Ann. 8005 LINDBERGH LNDG, ATTN:CREDENTIAL OFFICE 78235 #001-02-1992 L1995 **GPM** *020 †8,70

LITTLE, James Ronald. 8050 LINDBERGH LNDG, ATTN: CREDENTIAL OFFICE 78235 #422-01-1981 L1983 **FM AM** *020 †8,70

MARSH, Royden Woodward. 2507 KENNEDY CIR, SAM/AFCN 78235 #007-02-1973 L1983 **P AM** *030 †75

MICHAELSON, Robert S. 8050 LINDBERGH LNDG, 37TH MDG 78235 #018-75-1984, ▲ L1985 **AM** *020

MOONEY, Richard L. 2601 LOUIS BAUER DR, USAF SAM/GE RAM2008 78235 #051-04-1995 L1995 **GPM** *012 †8,70

NEVILLE, James Salisbury. 2513 KENNEDY CIR, AFIOH/CC 78235 #023-12-1984 L1986 **GPM** *030 †8,70

PICKARD, Jeb Stuart. 8005 LINDBERGH LNDG, 311 MDS/SGOQ(USAFSAM) 78235 #020-02-1978 L1981 **PUD IM** *020 †20

REYNOLDS, Rolland C, Jr. 2601 LOUIS BAUER DR, USAF SAM/GE 78235 #048-13-1986 L1987 **FM AM** *040 †8,70

RUBIN, Richard Mark. 2507 KENNEDY CIR, BLDG 100 78235 #023-01-1985 L2000 **OPH AM** *020 †35

SKY, Joseph Cameron. 8050 LINDBERGH LNDG, 311 MEDICAL SQUADRON/SGOQ 78235 #005-12-1999 L2000 **IM** *020 †20

STRADER, James Russell, Jr. 2507 KENNEDY CIR BLDG 1 78235 #012-05-1999 L2001 **CD AM** *020 †20

TONG, Andrew Bunwai. 7980 LINDBERGH LNDG, 311 HSW/YA BLDG 578 78235 #016-01-1984 L1984 **AM UM** *050 †70

TREDICI, Thomas Jos. 2507 KENNEDY CIR, USAF SAM 78235 #041-12-1952 L1971 **OPH AM** *040 †35

WALDROUP, Anthony Wayne. 2601 LOUIS BAUER DR SU, USAFSAM/GE 78235 #039-01-1996 L1997 **FM** *020 †18

WINDHORST, Dana John. 2601 LOUIS BAUER DR, USAFSAM/GE 78235 #019-02-1981 L1982 **AM** *070

YAMANE, Grover Kunihiro. 8050 LINDBERGH LNDG, 311 MDS/SGOQ 78235 #035-09-1985 L1988 **GPM** *020 †0,18

ZARR, Shawn Patrick. 2507 KENNEDY CIR, BROOKS AFB 78235 #048-13-1996 L1997 **AN** *012 †20

BROWNFIELD – TERRY

CHEBIB, Paul Farid. 703 E FELT ST, BRMC CLINIC 79316 #605-02-1993 L1996 **IM** *020 †20

HOPE, Sherman Allen. 705 E FELT ST 79316 #039-01-1957 L1961 **FM A** *071 †18

HORD, Michael S. 706 E FELT ST 79316 #048-13-2000 L2002 **FM** *020 †8 ‡

KNOX, Morris Salem. 919 E MAIN ST 79316 #048-02-1959 L1959 **FM PHP** *071 †18

MOORE, Sharman A. 705 E FELT ST 79316 #048-15-1997 L1998 **FM** *020 †18

SMITH, Carl Raymond. 1212 US HIGHWAY 82 79316 #048-12-1964 L1964 **FM EM** *020 †20

SMYRL, Ronnie G. 79316 #048-04-1971 L1971 **P** *050 †75

STONE, Noah Wilson. ■ 79316 #048-02-1957 L1957 **FM** *071 †18

TEDFORD, Dennis Duane. 705 E FELT ST 79316 #019-02-1986 L1993 **FM EM** *020 †18

BROWNSBORO – HENDERSON

ODOM, Sharon H. ■ 75756 #048-12-2001 **GPM** *012

BROWNSVILLE – CAMERON

ABAYA-DUAZO, Florina S. 645 VILLA MARIA BLVD 78520 #748-02-1987 L1995 **END** *020 †20

ABRAHAM, Ricardo Abdon. 3302 BOCA CHICA BLVD, STE 109 78521 #132-02-1978 L2006 **IM** *100 †20

ACHLEITNER, Oliver. 535 PAREDES LINE RD 78521 #065-01-1990 L1996 **ORS** *020 †40

ADAMES, Ricardo A. 4970 N EXPRESSWAY, STE D 78526 #308-04-1985 L1995 **IM ID** *020 †20

ADOBBATI, Ricardo N. 134 E PRICE RD 78521 #132-01-1966 L1975 **ORS** *020 †40

AGUIRRE, Consuelo. ■ 78521 #649-01-1946 L1967 **CHP** *020

AKRAM, Novera. 3025 BOCA CHICA BLVD, BROWNSVILLE CHILDREN'S CLI 78521 #690-02-1986 L2004 **PD** *020 †55

ALFAYOUMI, Fadi Moh'D. 213 HEART DR 78520 #575-02-1997 L2006 **IC** *020 †20

AL HROOB, Assad Ismail. 864 CENTRAL BLVD, STE 1100 78520 #575-01-1985 L1999 **PDC PD** *020 †55

ALMEIDA, Alberto Edmundo. 1096A E LOS EBANOS BLVD 78520 #308-03-1987 L2000 **FSM FM** *020 †18

ALVARADO, Pastor. 880 RIDGEWOOD ST, STE 2 78520 #715-01-1975 L1982 **CRS GS** *020

ANANDASIVAM, Loganayaki. 1900 N EXPRESSWAY, STE 78521 #220-04-1995 L2002 **IM** *020 †20

ANANDASIVAM, Subramaniam. 1900 N EXPRESSWAY, STE D&E 78521 #220-04-1985 L1996 **IM NEP** *020 †20

ANDERSON, Carroll L, Jr. 1755 W PRICE RD 78520 #048-14-1980 L1980 **GP** *020

APOLINARIO, Jumar Balaos. 425 E ALTON GLOOR 78526 #748-14-1990 L2005 **PM APM** *020 †60

ARREDONDO, Rafael R. 1084 E LOS EBANOS BLVD 78520 #649-01-1974 L1976 **OTO HNS** *020 †45

ASASE, Danilo K. 844 CENTRAL BLVD, STE 430 78520 #610-01-1985 L1996 **U UP** *020 †95

AZHAR, Aafia. 1780 BRIARWYCK DR 78520 #704-25-1992 L1999 **IM** *020 †20

BADUEL, Winnifer Lourdes. 645 VILLA MARIA BLVD, STE B 78520 #748-02-1980 L1996 **IM** *020 †20

BANGASH, Shahid Ali. 844 CENTRAL BLVD, STE 420 78520 #704-09-1989 L1997 **AI** *020 †55,03

BANGASH, Shaukat Ali. ■ 78526 #704-09-1984 L1992 **ID** *100 †20

BARRON, Eric Ramiro. 1040 W JEFFERSON ST 78520 #264-01-1955 L1970 **OPH** *020 †35

BENAVIDES, Marco Antonio. 1040 W JEFFERSON ST 78520 #264-01-1955 L1970 **PTH** *020 †50

BERNAL, Carlos V. 835 N EXPRESSWAY STE A 78520 #048-02-1986 L1987 **FM** *020 †18

BLANTON, David Edward R. 3125 INTERNATIONAL BLVD 78521 #004-01-1966 L1972 **FM** *020 †18

BONUEL-SILVERIO, Maria T. 145 UPTOWN AVE 78520 #748-08-1991 L1997 **PD** *020 †55

BOSSOLO, Jose Antonio. 864 CENTRAL BLVD STE 2900 78520 #042-01-1994 L1999 **HS** *020 †40

BROMILEY, Adele C Ward. 100 E ALTON GLOOR BLVD # A 78526 #047-06-1957 L1973 **PD** *071

BROOKS, Karen J. 800 W JEFFERSON ST 78520 #048-14-1988 L1989 **GS** *020 †85

BUETTGEN, Johann Wilhelm. ■ 78521 #407-19-1953 L1975 **OBG** *072 †30

CAMACHO, Homero. 943 N EXPRESSWAY STE 15, PMB 21 78520 #264-01-1966 L1971 **OBG FM** *071

CAQUIAS, Jesus Antonio. 625 E PRICE RD 78521 #047-07-1979 L1980 **FM** *020

CARRERA-LEAL, Benito. 100 E ALTN GLR #B #150, SOUTH TEXAS WOMEN'S CONSUL 78526 #649-04-1990 L1998 **OBG** *020

CASTANEDA, Jose Luis. 1092 E LOS EBANOS BLVD 78520 #649-01-1974 L1979 **PD** *020 ‡

CASTILLO, Virgilio R. 230 RESACA POINT RD 78526 #451-01-1968 L1982 **AN** *020

CHAVEZ, Carlos Manuel. 425 E LOS EBANOS BLVD 78520 #737-01-1958 L1979 **TS** *020 †85,90

CHUGHTAI, Saleem Zia. 100 E ALTON GLOOR BLVD, DEPT. RADIOLOGY, UNIT A 78526 #704-01-1985 L2003 **VIR** *100 †80

CHUMACERA, Belen Barit. ■ 78526 #748-10-1989 L1996 **PD** *020 †55

CISNEROS, David Louis. ■ 78521 #649-01-1964 L1969 **GS GP** *071 †85

CISNEROS, Jose Santos. 1001 CALLE MILAGROS 78526 #048-15-1995 L1998 **OBG** *020 †30

COOVER, Richard Burton. 3147 BOCA CHICA BLVD, STE A 78521 #051-04-1966 L1976 **OPH** *020 †35

CUA, Mark C. 213 HEART DR 78520 #748-02-1986 L1998 **CD** *020 †20

CUBAS-COLMENARES, Ignacio. 4801 E 14TH ST 78521 #649-01-1957 L1975 **GP** *020

DAGHESTANI, Ghanem. 302 LORENALY DR, STE G 78526 #875-02-1984 L2006 **HO** *020 †20

DE LA CRUZ, Rafael Marcos. 44 W JEFFERSON ST 78520 #275-01-1948 L1967 **PD** *020

DE LA VEGA, Humberto H. 2137 E 22ND ST 78521 #264-12-1991 L1998 **FM** *020 †18

DEL CASTILLO, Francisco J. 4970 N EXPRESSWAY # 77-83, STE B 78526 #649-04-1976 L1982 **OBG** *020 †30

DE LUNA, Jose Antonio. 1040 W JEFFERSON ST 78520 #649-02-1978 L1989 **PD** *020 †55

DIAZ, Roberto. 844 CENTRAL BLVD, STE 140 78520 #042-01-1985 L1993 **OBG** *020 †30

DIAZ, Rolando, Jr. ■ 78526 #048-12-2003 L2006 **EM** *100

DIAZ DE LEON, Alberto. 235 RUBEN M TORRES BLVD 78520 #649-01-1953 L1967 **GS** *071 †85

DRIGGS, Shane Cash. 3150 INTERNATIONAL BLVD, STE 100 78521 #048-15-1997 L2001 **OBG** *020

ECHEVARRIA, John. 535 STOVAL RD 78520 #040-02-1964 L1984 **OTO PS** *071 †45

ELKINS, William Jerry. 100 E ALTON GLOOR BLVD # A 78526 #047-06-1961 L1963 **GS** *020

ERWIN, Carol Miriam. 844 CENTRAL BLVD, STE 260 78520 #026-04-1972 L1990 **GS VS** *020 †85,18

FACTORIZA, Ronaldo D. 680 PAREDES LINE RD 78521 #748-08-1990 L1998 **IM** *020 †20

FIGUEROA, Antonio. 1740 BOCA CHICA BLVD, STE 100 78520 #341-01-1977 L1995 **PD** *020 †55

FLORES, Magdalena. 844 CENTRAL BLVD, STE 140 78520 #042-01-1994 L1999 **OBG** *020 †30

FLORES-GALLARDO, Jorge L. 1885 E PRICE RD, STE A 78521 #737-06-1990 L1997 **PD** *020 †55

FRYER, Ronald Ernest. ■ 78526 #352-11-1952 L1959 **GYN** *072

GAITAN, Luis E. 4770 N EXPRESSWAY STE 100 78526 #319-03-1984 L1996 **N CN** *020 †75

GARCIA, Claudia Patricia. 844 CENTRAL BLVD, STE 470 78520 #048-02-2001 L2005 **OBG** *020 †30

GARCIA, Luis Manuel Z. ■ 78526 #649-02-1981 L1988 **PTH** *020 †50

GOEL, Jai Narain. 1 TED HUNT BLVD 78521 #495-05-1952 L1979 **OPH** *020 †35

GOMEZ, Jaime Salvador. 213 HEART DR 78520 #048-14-1999 L2002 **IC** *020 †20

GOMEZ, Ruben. 15 W MADISON ST 78520 #649-01-1954 L1970 **GS OBG** *071

GONZALEZ, Eloisa Thelma. 825 LAKESIDE BLVD 78520 #649-19-1984 L1988 **PD** *020

GONZALEZ-ANGULO, Carlos E. 2150 N EXPRESSWAY, STE 83 78521 #264-02-1982 L1999 **RO** *020 †20,80

GONZALEZ-CEPEDA, Juan H. 5460 PAREDES LINE RD, STE 209 78526 #649-02-1988 L1996 **FM** *020 †18

GOWEN, Rose M Zavaletta. 34 S CORIA ST 78520 #048-12-1984 L1985 **OBG** *020 †30

GRIFFIN, Marsha Rae. 213 HEART DR 78521 #048-13-2003 L2006 **PD** *100 †55

GROSS, Rickey Lynn. 1424 W PRICE RD, # 525 78520 #654-01-1981 L1986 **EM IM** *020

GUAJARDO, Juan G. 300 LORENALY DR 78526 #048-02-2002 L2004 **OBG** *020

GUAJARDO, Manuel Garza. 300 LORENALY DR 78526 #048-14-1983 L1983 **OBG** *020 †30

GUEVARA, Jorge R. 425 E LOS EBANOS BLVD, STE 100 78520 #737-06-1988 L1995 **IM** *020 †20

GUMBEL, Francis Minnes. 26 S CORIA ST, STE B 78520 #028-46-1978 L1982 **IM** *020

GUTIERREZ, Ana Constanza. ■ 78521 #264-04-1970 L1990 **PTH** *020 †50

GUTIERREZ, Carlos Augusto. 1040 W JEFFERSON ST 78520 #649-02-1974 L1981 **GS VS** *020

HABET, Kalim Jesus. 213 HEART DR 78520 #270-02-1988 L1997 **CD CCM** *020 †20

HENAO, Mario J. 848 RIDGEWOOD ST 78520 #264-01-1959 L1975 **D DMP** *020

HERNANDEZ, Edgar I. ■ 78526 #048-14-2006 L2007 **GS** *012

HESTERBERG, Raymond C, Jr. 1100 HM 802, STE 103 78521 #048-12-1979 L1979 **OPH** *020 †35

HUSSAIN, Khadim. 100 E ALTON GLOOR BLVD # A, VALLEY REG MED CTR-EMG DEP 78526 #704-21-1986 L1999 **IM** *020 †20

HUSSAIN, Nisar. 2137 E 22ND ST 78521 #704-21-1990 L2003 **IM** *020 †20

HUSSAIN, Waqar. 394 MILITARY HWY 78520 #704-20-1994 L2004 **IM** *100 †20

IMPERIAL, Henry L. 2137 E 22ND ST 78521 #748-08-1988 L1994 **IM MDM** *020 †20 ‡

JALIL, Tania Qamar. 2137 E 22ND ST, CENTER 78521 #704-02-1989 L1997 **PD** *020 †55

JONES, Lee D. ■ 78526 #048-02-1953 L1953 **FM GP** *071 †18

JONES, Makeda Naomi. 861 OLD ALICE RD, DEPARTMENT OF PSYCHIATRY 78520 #041-14-2004 L2008 **P** *012

JOVER, Javier A. 5235 SOUTHMOST RD STE A, SUITE A 78521 #726-01-1985 L2002 **PCC** *020

KARKOUTLY, Ahmad. 864 CENTRAL BLVD STE 400 78520 #875-01-1988 L1998 **CCM** *020 †20

KHETARPAL, Umang. 844 CENTRAL BLVD, STE 280 78520 #495-73-1985 L2000 **OTO** *020 †45

KOFMAN, Eduardo. ■ 78520 #132-01-1986 L1997 **GE** *020 †20

KURI, Jose. 98 E PRICE RD 78521 #341-01-1948 L1975 **NS** *020 †25

LAKSHMIKANTH, Bangalore N. 315 JOSE MARTI BLVD 78526 #495-09-1968 L1983 **ORS** *020 †40

LANGAN, Terence. 409 BOCA CHICA BLVD 78520 #352-06-1961 L1976 **FM OBG** *020

LECUSAY, David. 44 W JEFFERSON ST 78520 #275-01-1983 L2004 **PD** *020 †55

LEIJA, Graciela M. 3302 BOCA CHICA BLVD, STE 109 78521 #649-02-1987 L2003 **IM** *020

LEMUS, Ricardo Alberto. 1076 E LOS EBANOS BLVD, CLINICA SANTA MARIA 78520 #341-01-1984 L2003 *020

LOAISIGA, Raul Ernesto. 4920 N EXPRESSWAY, ALTON GLOOR PLAZA#101 78526 #198-01-1975 L2000 **PD** *020

LOOTENS, Robert Jeffrey. 213 HEART DR 78520 #025-01-1971 L1998 **CD CCM** *020 †20,16
LOZANO, Robert Anderson. 864 CENTRAL BLVD, STE 3100 78520 #025-12-1984 L1985 **N** *020
MADI, Jamil M. 864 CENTRAL BLVD STE 400 78520 #605-01-1997 L2004 **CCM** *020 †20
MALASKO, Daniel Wm. 1040 W JEFFERSON ST 78520 #056-06-1975 L1980 **NEP IM** *020 †20
MALDONADO, Yasmin S. 120 UPTOWN AVE 78520 #429-01-1990 L1999 **IM** *020 †20
MANCILLAS, Juan Jose. 844 CENTRAL BLVD, STE 470 78520 #048-13-1984 L1989 **OBG EM** *071 †30
MARTINEZ, D. 3855 SOUTHMOST RD 78521 #231-01-1970 L1979 **OBG** *020 †30
MARTINEZ, Jorge A Sanchez. 831 RIDGEWOOD ST 78520 #649-01-1970 L1987 **PTH OS** *020 †50
MARTINEZ, Juan Manuel. 1 TED HUNT BLVD 78521 #048-04-1981 L1982 **IM** *020 †20
MARTINEZ, Martha M. 95 E PRICE RD BLDG 8 78521 #048-02-1984 L1985 **OBG** *020 †30
MARTINEZ, Yanira Marisol. 100B E ALTON GLOOR BLVD, STE 200 78526 #035-48-1999 L2003 **IM** *020
MARTINEZ OHARA, Joseph J. 2150 N EXPRESSWAY, STE 83 78521 #649-30-1976 L1980 **IM GP** *075
MAYMI, Jose Luis. 844 CENTRAL BLVD, STE 430 78520 #042-01-1998 L2006 **GS** *020 †95
MAZZINI PEREZ-REYES, J C. 765 PAREDES LINE RD STE A 78521 #737-06-1983 L1994 **PD PDI** *020 †55
MC GLYNN, E. PO BOX 4355 78523 #539-04-1969 L1974 **CD IM** *074
MCKINNEY, Margaret Edging. PO BOX 4195 78523 #043-01-2008 *012
MC KINNEY, William James. 1040 W JEFFERSON ST 78520 #039-01-1966 L1971 **R** *020 †80
MEDINA-DE GARCIA, Gloria. 900 E ALTON GLOOR BLVD, STE 7 78526 #649-01-1961 L1977 **PD NPM** *020 †55
MENDIOLA, Horacio. 500 PAREDES LINE RD, STE 1 78521 #649-02-1958 L1962 **PD OS** *071
MENDOZA, Dora. ■ 78520 #847-04-1959 L1977 **OBG FM** *020
MENDOZA, Elsa Santos. ■ 78521 #748-08-1991 L1998 **PD** *020 †55
MENDOZA, Manuel. 1040 W JEFFERSON ST 78520 #649-19-1980 L1985 **NPM** *020 †55
MERCADO, Jairo. 3354 INTERNATIONAL BLVD 78521 #264-12-1992 L2000 **PD** *020 †55
MERCADO MORALES, Luis S. ■ 78520 #649-01-1965 L1979 **OBG** *071
METCALF, Nicholas A K. ■ 78526 #030-05-1979 L1981 **EM** *020 †16
MICO, Mario Ramon. 3150 INTERNATIONAL BLVD, BROWNSVILLE ADOLESCENT PED 78521 #726-01-1988 L1997 **PD** *020 †55
MIMBELA, Rafael A. 425 E LOS EBANOS BLVD, STE 104 78520 #649-30-1990 L1997 **CHN** *020
MININA, Irina Anatoliyevn. ■ 78526 #913-12-1997 **IM** *012
MIRAFZALI, Vahid. 5850 FM 802, ST C 6-7 78526 #305-01-1984 L1998 **PD** *020 †55
MOHAN, Aparna. 2934 INTERNATIONAL BLVD 78521 #495-05-1992 L2004 **FM IM** *020 †20
MOLINAS, Miguel A. 5235 SOUTHMOST RD STE A 78521 #726-01-1987 L1996 **IM** *020 †20
MONARREZ, Carlos Norberto. 864 CENTRAL BLVD, STE 1100 78520 #649-27-1972 L1976 **PDC** *020 †55
MONCADA, Edgar Enrique. 100B E ALTON GLOOR BLVD, STE 240 78526 #935-03-1993 L2003 **VS** *020
MORALES, Francisco. ■ 78521 #661-01-1988 **OBG** *100
MORALES, Luis Francisco. 5235 SOUTHMOST RD STE B 78521 #737-06-1988 L1997 **MPD** *020 †20,55
MORALES, Robert. ■ 78520 #048-02-2004 L2006 **FM** *020
MOWERS, Jenny L. 865 CENTRAL BLVD 78520 #048-13-1995 L1996 **PD** *020
MULLANE, Geraldine F. 100 E ALTON GLOOR BLVD A 78526 #007-02-1993 L2002 **EM** *020 †16
MUNOZ, Ramiro, Jr. 844 CENTRAL BLVD, STE 380 78520 #048-04-1977 L1977 **OBG** *020 †30
NAGARAJA, Vaddarse N H. 3302 BOCA CHICA BLVD # 206, ABC PEDIATRICS 78521 #495-09-1993 L2004 **NPM** *020 †55
NAVARRETE, Antonio R. 1035 E SAINT FRANCIS ST 78520 #649-01-1958 L1970 **ATP** *020
NGUYEN, Chi Dang. 4770 N EXPRESSWAY, STE 106 78526 #030-05-1988 L1996 **OTO** *020 †45
NIEVERA, Everett Antonio. 2501 PAREDES LINE RD, A-10 78526 #748-01-1994 L2000 **PD** *020 †55
NIEVERA, Haydee Te. 2501 PAREDES LINE RD, STE A10 78526 #748-01-1993 L2000 **PD** *020 †55
NIEVES, Jose R. 1 TED HUNT BLVD 78521 #042-01-1990 L1995 **OBG** *020 †30
NORDYKE, Bradley Wm. 3914 PAREDES LINE RD STE B 78526 #046-01-1989 L1994 **GP PD** *020
NUNEZ-AVELAR, Jesus. 100 E ALTON GLOOR BLVD A 78526 #649-03-1976 L1993 **EM** *020 †16
O'HAGAN, Thomas Vincent. 101 SAINT JOSEPH DR 78520 #035-09-2007 *012
OKEREKE, Okezika U John. 110 UPTOWN AVE STE A 78520 #690-04-1975 L1996 **TS** *020
OLMEDO QUEVEDO, Pablo De. 4000 FM 511 STE A 78526 #649-38-2002 L2007 **FM** *020
OLSON, Christopher Evan. 1134 E LOS EBANOS BLVD 78520 #026-04-1978 L2001 **ORS** *020 †40
OLVERA, Raul. ■ 78526 #649-01-1967 **AN** *020
ORTIZ, Maria De Jesus. ■ 78523 #649-19-1964 L1970 **PCP** *020 †50
PADGINTON, Clay. 100 E ALTON GLOOR BLVD, UNIT A 78526 #035-75-1999, ▲ L2005 **R VIR** *020 †80
PATEL, Yesroon Yaseen. 3025 BOCA CHICA BLVD 78521 #704-25-1991 L1997 **PD** *074 †55
PATINO, Jorge A. 5460 PAREDES LINE RD, STE 198 78526 #264-01-1988 L1998 **PD** *020 †55
PAULET, Fedora Esther. 844 CENTRAL BLVD STE 420 78520 #737-01-1996 L2004 **IM** *100 †20
PELLY, Lorenzo Ricardo. 864 CENTRAL BLVD STE 250 78520 #649-28-1975 L1982 **IM** *020 †20
PETROZZI, Miguel Angel. 425 E LOS EBANOS BLVD # 1 78520 #737-01-1986 L2005 **CHN** *100
PETTORINO, Roselle C. 425 E LOS EBANOS BLVD #109 78520 #035-06-1990 L1999 **GS** *020 †85
PISHARODI, Madhava A P. 3475 W ALTON GLOOR BLVD 78520 #495-44-1970 L1981 **NS** *020 †25
PLOTKIN, Jacob Saul. 1040 W JEFFERSON ST 78520 #011-02-1979 L1980 **OPH** *020 †35
PLOTKIN, Ruth Ann. 847 RIDGEWOOD ST 78520 #011-02-1979 L1982 **PD PDE** *020 †55
PONCE, Roberto. 5700 N EXPRESSWAY, STE 303 78526 #847-10-1969 L1979 **GE IM** *020 †20
PRATT, Peyton Thos. ■ 78520 #030-05-1944 L1948 **HEM** *071
RAGUTHU, Manjula. 425 E ALTON GLOOR BLVD 78526 #495-50-1990 L2005 **FM** *020 †18
RAGUTHU, Surya Prakash R. 425 E ALTON GLOOR BLVD 78526 #495-21-1993 L2004 **PM** *020
REDDY, Madhavi Gajjala. 2969 SOUTHMOST RD, STE A 78521 #495-65-1986 L1997 **OPH** *020 †35
REDDY, Sundeep Gajjala. 864 CENTRAL BLVD STE 250 78520 #495-65-1986 L1997 **IM** *020 †20
REIS, Marcos A M. 864 CENTRAL BLVD STE 700 78520 #187-03-1971 L1981 **IM** *020
ROBERTS, Howard Harrison. 1072 E LOS EBANOS BLVD 78520 #048-02-1956 L1956 **AN** *020 †05
ROBLES, Luis Humberto. 130 UPTOWN AVE 78520 #649-03-1980 L1999 **FM** *020 †18 ‡
ROCCO, Carmen Delacruz. 95 E PRICE RD, BLDG E, STE A 78521 #048-02-1982 L1983 **PD** *020 †55
RODRIGUEZ, J Raul. 1040 W JEFFERSON ST 78520 #649-02-1966 L1973 **GS** *020
RODRIGUEZ, Jairo. 844 CENTRAL BLVD, STE 420 78520 #264-01-1987 L1999 **PUD IM** *020 †20
RODRIGUEZ ALCALA, J F. 4970 N EXPRESSWAY, STE A 78526 #649-02-1967 L1971 **GS VS** *020 †85
ROGANS, John Albert. 2300 CENTRAL BLVD, MINOR EMERGICENTER CENTRAL 78520 #061-01-1970 L1977 **GP** *071
ROSAS, Alfredo Carlos. 5850 FM 802, STE C2 78526 #649-01-1974 L1977 **GP** *020
RURANGIRWA, Charles. 1119 CENTRAL BLVD 78520 #649-38-1987 L1997 **OBG** *020 †30
RUSSELL, John Francis. ■ 78520 #035-09-1960 L1962 **P** *072
SALHADAR, Amer. 864 CENTRAL BLVD, STE 1100 78520 #875-02-1985 L1998 **PD** *020 †55
SALINAS, Manuel A. 4000 FM 511, SU CLINICA FAMILIAR 78526 #025-12-1979 L1985 **FM** *020 †18
SANCHEZ, Erwin Danilo. 44 W JEFFERSON ST 78520 #429-02-1998 L2003 **PD** *020 †55
SANCHEZ, Gerardo Javier. ■ 78520 #042-03-1993 L1997 **PM** *020
SAUCEDA, David. 1474 W PRICE RD, # 540 78520 #048-15-2004 L2006 **PD** *020 †55
SEMLER, Jeffrey Howard. 5460 PAREDES LINE RD, STE 206 78526 #048-15-1983 L1983 **AN** *020 †05
SHAMIM, Muhammad. 2137 E 22ND ST 78521 #704-02-1987 L2004 **IM RHU** *020 †20
SHARMA, Balesh. 2150 N EXPRESSWAY, STE 83 78521 #495-45-1990 L1995 **HO** *020 †20
SILVA, Jaime Luis. 864 CENTRAL BLVD, STE 2400 78520 #649-19-1978 L1993 **CD IM** *020 †20
SIMMONS, Ray Lyle. ■ 78520 #048-02-1956 L1988 **ORS** *072 †40
SLOBODKIN, David. 1 TED HUNT BLVD 78521 #550-02-1985 L1991 **EM** *020 †16
SOLIS, Santiago Flores. ■ 78522 #649-02-1955 **IM GP** *100
STERN, Gustavo Fernando. 864 CENTRAL BLVD STE 300 78520 #132-01-1969 L1976 **GS** *020 †85
STERN, Milton Harrold. 1754 OLD CREEK CT 78521 #048-02-1963 L1963 **P N** *071
SUDARSHAN, Alexander P. 1058 E LOS EBANOS BLVD 78520 #048-14-1983 L1983 **OPH** *020 †35
SUDARSHAN, Yvonne A. 1058 E LOS EBANOS BLVD 78520 #040-02-1983 L1993 **PD** *020 †55
SURI, Seema. 3675 BOCA CHICA BLVD, STE E 78521 #495-45-1989 L1996 **PD** *020 †55
SY, Stanley Peter S. 844 CENTRAL BLVD STE 420 78520 #748-01-1996 L2005 **CCM** *020 †20
SZUMILEWICZ, Marek Jan. 100 E ALTON GLOOR BLVD A, EMERGENCY DEPT 78526 #759-03-1973 L1993 **EM FM** *020 †18,16
TEO ONG, Willie Chua. 844 CENTRAL BLVD, STE 370 78520 #748-10-1989 L1996 **END** *020 †20
THURBER, Timothy P. 18 PASEO PLZ 78521 #451-01-1983 L1990 **PD** *020 †55
TORO DE ZAREI, Bricia O. 100B E ALTON GLOOR BLVD, STE 203 78526 #649-13-1994 L2002 **RHU** *020 †20
TRAKRU, Yogesh. 3675 BOCA CHICA BLVD, STE E 78521 #495-45-1990 L1996 **PD** *020 †55
UGALINO, Joey Andrew T. 95 E PRICE RD, BLDG F 78521 #748-02-1994 L2003 **IMG** *020 †20
UKOLI, Preston M. 2945 CENTRAL BLVD STE B, UKOLI CARE CLINIC 78520 #690-01-1978 L1995 **NEP IM** *020 †20
URIBE, Maria Cielo. 2137 E 22ND ST, BCHC 78521 #264-20-1988 L1998 **IM** *020 †20
UTTURKAR, Arant Krishnaji. 260 RESACA POINT RD 78526 #495-28-1972 L1982 **R** *062
UTTURKAR, Pratima Joshi. 147 E PRICE RD 78521 #495-28-1974 L1982 **OPH** *020 †35
VANDE MAELE, Dominique. 864 CENTRAL BLVD STE 300 78520 #165-07-1987 L1997 **CRS** *020 †10,85
VASQUEZ, Pedro Luis. 1040 W JEFFERSON ST 78520 #737-06-1992 L2003 **NPM PD** *020 †55
VIADA, Jorge Verdes. 1040 W JEFFERSON ST 78520 #275-01-1951 L1963 **NS** *075
VIADA, Raul Manuel. ■ 78520 #847-04-1963 L1973 **P** *071
VILLALOBOS, Jose Luis. 864 CENTRAL BLVD STE 50 78520 #649-02-1967 L1973 **U** *020 †95
VILLARREAL, Daniel F. 1 TED HUNT BLVD 78521 #649-30-1991 L1997 **P** *020 †75
VILLARREAL, Jaime F. 100 E ALTON GLOOR BLVD # B, # 240 78526 #649-30-1982 L1986 **GS** *020 †85,90
WALSS-RODRIGUEZ, Rodolfo. 4770 N EXPRESSWAY STE 205 78526 #649-23-1970 L1992 **OBG** *020 †30 ‡
WATKINS, Mary L. ■ 78521 #047-07-1979 L1982 **GP** *020
WATSON, Andrea Lynn. 2137 E 22ND ST, BROWNSVILLE COMM HLTH CTR 78521 #038-41-1990 L1993 **PD** *020 †55
WELLS, John Arthur. 425 E LOS EBANOS BLVD, STE 105 78520 #048-15-1979 L1980 **UCM PME** *020
WONG, She Ling. 844 CENTRAL BLVD 78520 #187-04-1972 L1994 **GS VS** *020 †85
WRIGHT, James T. 4770 N EXPRESSWAY, VALLEY EAR NOSE & THROAT 78526 #048-12-1990 L1991 **OTO** *020 †45
WRIGHT, Steven Turner. 4770 N EXPRESSWAY, VALLEY EAR NOSE & THROAT 78526 #048-02-2001 L2004 **OTO** *020 †45
ZAMIR, Asim. 4430 E 14TH ST, STE A 78521 #704-17-1987 L1996 **PD** *020 †55
ZAVALA, Charles W. 840 W PRICE RD 78520 #726-01-1969 L1977 **IM PCC** *020 †20
ZAVALETTA, Joseph Albert. 605 E SAINT CHARLES ST 78520 #048-02-1963 L1963 **OBG GP** *071

BROWNWOOD - BROWN

ALLEN, Gwendolyn J. 1604 14TH ST 76801 #048-02-1983 L1983 **FM** *020 †18
ALLEN, Homer B, Jr. ■ 76801 #048-02-1950 L1950 **OPH** *071 †35
ALLMAN, James M. 850 COUNTY ROAD 553 76801 #048-15-1999 L2003 **AN** *020 †05
ALTSTATT, Daniel Mark. 100 MILLER DR 76801 #051-07-2001 L2006 **U** *020 †95
BELLI, Deanna Dudzik. 1501 BURNET RD, BROWNWOOD HOSP LAB 76801 #025-07-1985 L1995 **ATP CLP** *020 †50
BELLI, Martin Francis. 1501 BURNET RD, LAB DEPARTMENT 76801 #035-47-1985 L1995 **PTH FOP** *020 †50
BIKLE, Jeffrey Millard. 105 STRECKERT DR 76801 #041-02-1982 L1986 **DR** *020 †80
BOREN, Carol Bickelman. 109 S PARK DR 76801 #034-01-1995 L1997 **OPH** *020 †35
BOREN, Rance A. 125 S PARK DR, STE H 76801 #048-13-1992 L1993 **N** *020 †75
BROWN, William Keller. 2222 HIGHWAY 377 S, STE 1 76801 #021-05-1957 L1969 **DR** *071 †80
BUTKA, Gary Neal. 2502 CROCKETT DR 76801 #649-05-1978 L1984 **IM ID** *020 †20
BYRD, Tom D. 109 S PARK DR 76801 #048-13-1992 L1993 **IM** *020 †20
CASS, Allan Wayne. 1501 BURNET RD, WALKER CANCER CENTER 76801 #048-12-1972 L1981 **RO** *020 †80
CHANDLER, Sarah Ryman. 101 S PARK DR STE B 76801 #048-15-1985 L1986 **FM** *020 †18
COX, Tamara. 2502 CROCKETT DR 76801 #048-14-2000 L2002 **FM** *020 †18
CUTBIRTH, Seale Tippen. ■ 76801 #048-04-1955 L1955 **GP AS** *071
DHAVALE, Anant Kashinath. 1501 BURNET RD 76801 #495-35-1980 L2007 **HEM** *020 †20
DUNN, John Dale. 1501 BURNET RD 76801 #030-06-1971 L1984 **EM** *020 †18,16
FRAGUA, Paul Louis. 2410 CROCKETT DR 76801 #048-02-1972 L1972 **OBG** *020
GREEN, Edwin Alfred, Jr. 2400 CROCKETT DR, # 200 76801 #047-07-1986 L1997 **N** *020

■ = Address Information Privacy Protected

GWIN, John Franklin. 1501 BURNET RD 76801 #056-05-1971 L1984 **EM PEM** *020 †55,16
HAYS, James Blair. 120 S PARK DR, STE F 76801 #048-12-1967 L1967 **GP OS** *020
HAYS, John W. ■ 76801 #048-15-1999 L2001 **DR** *100 †80 ‡
HEINRICH, Michael Seth. ■ 76801 #654-01-1999 L2006 **AN** *020
HOGUE, Robert Lane. 101 S PARK DR STE A 76801 #048-15-1976 L1976 **FM OBG** *020 †18 ‡
HORTON, Sammy Joe. 120 S PARK DR, STE D 76801 #048-12-1996 L2000 **GE** *020 †20
HULL, Truett A. 2500 CROCKETT DR 76801 #048-02-1987 L1989 **PD** *020 †55
HUMPHREY, John Lynn. ■ 76801 #048-02-1962 L1962 **FM** *071 †18
HURD, Cheryl Lynn. 125 S PARK DR STE H 76801 #048-16-1998 L2003 **OS** *020 †75,20
JOLLIFFE, Mike Prinkey. 1501 BURNET RD 76801 #010-01-1994 L2002 **AN IM** *020
KELLY, Stephen Powell. 100 S PARK DR 76801 #048-12-1976 L1976 **OPH** *020 †35
LE, Hieu Hue. 1501 BURNET RD 76801 #941-01-1969 L1976 **AN** *020 †05 ‡
LEIPZIG, Bruce. 2410 CROCKETT DR 76801 #035-15-1973 L1978 **OTO** *020 †45
LOCKER, Dan Lewis. 2502 CROCKETT DR 76801 #048-13-1973 L1973 **GS** *020 †85
LOCKLEAR, Travis Ward. 1617 BROADMOOR DR 76801 #048-12-1966 L1966 **GS** *020 †85
MARTIN, Ray Mark. 2506 CROCKETT DR 76801 #048-02-1979 L1979 **GP** *020
MC GONAGLE, Martin Eugene. 107 S PARK DR STE B 76801 #918-01-1974 L1984 **OTO** *020 †45
MC GOWEN, Henry Wilcox. ■ 76801 #021-05-1965 L1970 **R NM** *020 †80
MENENDEZ, Isabel C. 105 STRECKERT DR 76801 #042-01-1981 L1984 **DR** *020 †80
MOORE, Richard Howard. 1000 COUNTY ROAD 553 76801 #007-02-1969 L1974 **ORS** *020 †40
MOORE, Timothy R. 2510 CROCKETT DR STE B 76801 #048-15-1999 L2004 **CD** *020 †20
MORALES, David G. 1501 BURNET RD 76801 #048-13-1992 L1993 **IM** *020 †20
MORRIS, Scot R. 2500 CROCKETT DR 76801 #048-13-1998 L2000 **PD** *020 †55
NEEL, Michael F. 106 S PARK DR 76801 #048-15-1995 L1999 **OBG** *020 †30
NICHOLS, Stephen R. 4573 PARK ROAD 15 76801 #036-07-1985 L1995 **EM IM** *020 †20
NIGALYE, Narendra L. 2502 CROCKETT DR 76801 #495-34-1987 L1997 **IM** *020 †20
NIGALYE, Ranjana Narendra. 2502 CROCKETT DR 76801 #495-34-1987 L2001 **FM** *020 †18
O'CONNOR, Brendan Dominic. 105 STRECKERT DR 76801 #566-01-1971 L1993 **DR** *020 †80
OINES, Stephen P. 109 S PARK DR 76801 #048-13-1992 L1993 **IM** *020 †20
PHILBRICK, Darey Allen. 2510 CROCKETT DR 76801 #048-14-1993 L1994 **ORS** *020 †40
POPE, Donald Delmer. 1501 BURNET RD 76801 #048-12-1979 L1979 **FM** *020 †18
PURSLEY, Terry Vincent. 2504 CROCKETT DR 76801 #048-02-1976 L1976 **D** *020 †15
ROSE, Terrance Lynn. 500 FM 45 E, TR HAVINS STATE JAIL 76801 #048-04-1981 L1981 **GP** *020
SCHULTZ, Fred Michael. 2410 CROCKETT DR 76801 #048-12-1971 L1972 **OBG EM** *020 ‡
SCHWEGEL, Douglas Kevin. 1501 BURNET RD, BROWNWOOD REGIONAL MEDICAL 76801 #048-04-1983 L1983 **DR** *020 †80
SCOGGIN, Stephen Donald. 118 S PARK DR STE D 76801 #048-14-1987 L1988 **GS** *020 †85
SCOTT, Harold Dean. 1501 BURNET RD 76801 #048-02-1969 L1969 **P** *020 †75
SKINNER, Russell B. 103 S PARK DR 76801 #048-12-1997 L1998 **FM** *020 †18 ‡
SMITH, David Alan. 901 N FISK AVE PMB 224 76801 #030-05-1974 L1996 **FPG** *030 †18
STANLEY, Malcolm M. ■ 76801 #020-02-1941 L1941 **IM GE** *071 †20
STEPHENS, Christopher G. 101 S PARK DR 76801 #048-12-1976 L1981 **RHU IM** *020 †20
STEVENSON, John Alfred. 118 S PARK DR STE A 76801 #005-06-1976 L2002 **NEP IM** *020 †20
STEWART, Daniel Jason. 120 S PARK DR STE C 76801 #048-14-2003 L2007 **OBG** *020
STREFLING, Marlen Stanley. 125 S PARK DR, STE B 76801 #025-01-1969 L1994 **ORS** *020 †40
TESSMER, Jon F. 102 S PARK DR 76801 #048-02-1983 L1983 **IM** *075 †20
THOMAS, Harry Negus. 1501 BURNET RD 76801 #048-02-1957 L1957 **GP** *020
TINDOL, Amy Brough. 109 S PARK DR 76801 #048-12-1998 L1999 **IM** *020 †20
TIPTON, George Bledsoe. 408 MULBERRY ST 76801 #048-04-1961 L1961 **P** *030 †75
VINUESA, Eduardo. ■ 76801 #847-04-1969 L1980 **GP** *020
WHEELIS, Paul Matthews. ■ 76801 #004-01-1943 L1944 **GP U** *071
WILEY, D Eric. 118 S PARK DR STE D 76801 #048-13-1997 L2001 **GS VS** *020 †85
WOODWARD, Halbert O. 2500 CROCKETT DR 76801 #048-13-1973 L1973 **PD** *020 †55
WORTHINGTON, Lathon D. 118 S PARK DR 76801 #048-15-1995 L1998 **FM** *020 †18
WRIGHT, David Stanton. 1501 BURNET RD 76801 #048-12-1970 L1970 **DR** *020 †80

BRYAN – BRAZOS

ACKER, Betty Gingold. 2700 E 29TH ST STE 330 77802 #010-02-1986 L1996 **OBG** *020 †30
ADAMS, Rae. ■ 77802 #048-16-2008 *012
ADAMS, Sjoerd Hendrik. 1737 BRIARCREST DR, STE 14 77802 #048-02-1982 L1983 **AN** *020 †05
AKINS, Charles Wesley, Jr. 3608 E 29TH ST, STE 108 77802 #027-01-1967 L1972 **OPH** *020 †35
ALFORD, Richard Dee. 2700 E 29TH ST 77802 #048-02-1984 L1985 **GS VS** *020 †85
ALLEN, Lisa L. ■ 77802 #048-16-2007 **FP** *012
AMIN, Anup Gordhanbhai. 2700 E 29TH ST, STE 260 77802 #495-37-1975 L1981 **PUD IM** *020 †20
ANAND, Veena. 3370 S TEXAS AVE # 2, B CS COMMUNITY HEALTH CLIN 77802 #495-37-1983 L1994 **PD** *020 †55
ANDERSON, Frank Gist. ■ 77802 #048-02-1954 L1954 **OPH** *071 †35
ANDERSON, Fred Graydon. 2801 FRANCISCAN DR 77802 #048-02-1962 L1962 **U** *071 †95
ANDRADE GRIMALDO, Rosa Me. ■ 77801 #737-06-2001 L2007 **IM** *012
AVILA, Fausto. 2010 E VILLA MARIA RD, STE A 77802 #264-04-1974 L1997 **FM** *020 †18
BACAK, Russell B. 2715 OSLER BLVD 77802 #048-04-1997 L1998 **FM** *020 †18
BAKER, James Robt. 2801 FRANCISCAN DR, COGENT HEALTHCARE OF TEXAS 77802 #039-01-1982 L1983 **IM** *020 †20
BARINA, Samuel John. 3201 UNIVERSITY DR E # 345 77802 #048-02-1992 L1993 **IM** *020 †20
BASS, Bill. 2801 FRANCISCAN DR 77802 #048-02-1969 L1969 **EM** *020 †16
BENSON, Royal Henry, III. 3740 COPPERFIELD DR # 105 77802 #048-15-1985 L1986 **OBG** *020 †30
BERIGAN, Elizabeth C. 2310 DE LEE ST, THE INTERNAL MED CTR 77802 #030-05-1989 L1993 **IM** *020 †20
BERTSCH, Nancy M. 2801 FRANCISCAN DR 77802 #048-14-1993 L1994 **OBG** *020 †30
BLACK, Leslie Suzanne. 2714 OSLER BLVD 77802 #048-13-1986 L1987 **FM OBS** *020 †18
BLANTON, Herman Mack. 2670 E 29TH ST, COGENT HEALTHCARE 77802 #048-02-1980 L1980 **PUD IM** *020 †20
BLINKOV, Andrew. 1301 MEMORIAL DR, STE 200 77802 #048-15-1994 L1996 **FM** *075
BONDS, James V, Jr. 3201 UNIVERSITY DR E, STE 360 77802 #048-16-1988 L1989 **IM** *020 †20
BRADEN, Stephen Anthony. 2210 E 29TH ST, BRAZOS PHYSICIANS GROUP 77802 #048-12-1979 L1979 **FM** *020 †18
BRAMHALL, Joe Paul. 3201 UNIVERSITY DR E STE 1 77802 #048-16-1985 L1986 **ORS** *020 †40
BRANDON, Timothy Michael. 2801 FRANCISCAN DR, EMERGENCY SERVICES DEPT 77802 #048-13-1994 L1995 **EM** *020 †16
BRAUER, Mark Horton. 1737 BRIARCREST DR, STE 14 77802 #048-02-1988 L1990 **AN** *020 †05
BRINER, Rudy Phillip. 3201 UNIVERSITY DR E 77802 #048-02-1982 L1983 **NS** *020 †25
BROSSART, Fred J F. 2700 E 29TH ST STE 105 77802 #028-03-1965 L1997 **GS AS** *071 †85
BROWN, Hartwell Phillip. 1100 URSULINE AVE, FEDERAL PRISON CAMP BRYAN 77803 #409-16-1973 L1977 **GP** *020
BUENGER, Kimberly M. 3370 S TEXAS AVE # B 77802 #048-14-1997 L1999 **PD** *020 †55
BULHOF, Justinus. 2206 E VILLA MARIA RD 77802 #048-02-1987 L1988 **AN** *020 †05
BURAS, David Patrick. 3201 UNIVERSITY DR E, STE 345 77802 #010-02-1994 L1996 **IM** *020 †20
BURROUGH, Cory Brenson. 1737 BRIARCREST DR, STE 14 77802 #048-14-2003 L2007 **AN** *020
CAPISTRANO, C Mark. 3201 UNIVERSITY DR E, STE 250 77802 #748-10-1983 L1995 **ON HEM** *020 †20
CASTILLO, Juanita. ■ 77807 #048-16-2008 *012
CHANG, Phyllis Clara. 2206 E VILLA MARIA RD 77802 #048-16-1990 L1991 **GE** *020 †20
CHERIAN, Frances. 401 S TEXAS AVE 77803 #495-31-1971 L1981 *020
CHERIAN, Rany Antony. 401 S TEXAS AVE 77803 #495-31-1972 L1984 **FM ADM** *020
CHOW, Shirley Ann. 3131 UNIVERSITY DR E 77802 #019-02-1985 L1991 **R** *020 †80
CLEGG, Patrick D. 1737 BRIARCREST DR, STE 14 77802 #048-02-1987 L1988 **AN** *020 †05
COHEN, Michael K. 2801 FRANCISCAN DR, ST. JOSEPH REGIONAL HEALTH 77802 #048-16-1990 L1991 **PTH** *020 †50 ‡
COLEMAN, Lawrence Wofford. 2700 CAMELOT DR 77802 #048-02-1962 L1962 **ORS** *020 †40
COOPER, James F. 2010 E VILLA MARIA RD 77802 #047-06-1952 L1955 **GP AM** *020
COOPER, John Ross. 2722 OSLER BLVD BOX 5306 77802 #018-03-1967 L1978 **DR GP** *020 †80
COWLEY, Doris Marie Moss. ■ 77802 #063-01-1979 L1982 **GP PHP** *062
CRUMPLER, Charles D, Jr. 2308 E VILLA MARIA RD, STE 100 77802 #048-15-2000 L2004 **END** *020 †20
DAFTARIAN, Arezu. 2710 OSLER BLVD, OLSER BLVD. FAMILY PRACTIC 77802 #048-16-1997 L1998 **FM** *020 †18
DAMIAN, Anna Paru. 2210 E 29TH ST, BRAZOS PHYSICIANS GROUP 77802 #048-14-1989 L1990 **FM** *020 †18
DAMIAN, David R, Jr. 2210 E 29TH ST, BRAZOS PHYSICIANS GROUP 77802 #048-14-1988 L1989 **FM** *020 †18
DAVE, Mahesh R I. 1201 BRIARCREST DR 77802 #495-23-1972 L1980 **P CHP** *020 †75
DAVE, Nalini Maheshkumar. 1201 BRIARCREST DR 77802 #495-45-1974 L1981 **IM** *020 †20
DAWSON, Daniel Duncan. 2700 E 29TH ST, STE 330 77802 #048-04-1993 L1994 **OBG** *020 †30
DERBES, Christopher J. 2206 E VILLA MARIA RD 77802 #048-02-1993 L1995 **GE** *020 †20
DE VAUL, Richard Allan. 1301 MEMORIAL DR STE 200, FAMILY MEDICINE CENTER 77802 #035-45-1966 L1974 **P** *040 †75
DHADUK, Shailesh D. 2709 OSLER BLVD 77802 #495-76-1996 L2001 **FM** *020 †18
DOSS, David Randall. 2700 E 29TH ST, STE 330 77802 #048-02-1978 L1978 **OBG** *020 †30
ELMENDORF, Ernest Arnold. 2722 OSLER BLVD 77802 #048-12-1955 L1955 **R** *071 †80
EMMICK, Robert Harold, Jr. 2801 FRANCISCAN DR, ST. JOSEPH REG. HEALTH CNT 77802 #048-15-1991 L1992 **EM** *040 †16
FEASTER, Robert S. 1301 MEMORIAL DR, STE 200 77802 #048-16-2006 L2007 **FP** *012
FLEENER, Erin Elyse. 2215 E VILLA MARIA RD, STE 110 77802 #048-13-2001 L2006 **HO** *020
FLORIAN, Mark Julius. 3201 UNIVERSITY DR E, STE 345 77802 #048-02-1995 L1997 **IM** *020 †20
FOCKE, John Herman, III. 1920 W VILLA MARIA RD #201, MED EXP URGENT CARE 77807 #048-14-1975 L1975 **FM EM** *020 †18 ‡
FRIEDMAN, Jennifer Diane. 2700 E 29TH ST, STE 330 77802 #005-02-1997 L2005 **OBG** *020 †30
FRIEDMAN, Jonathan A. 3201 UNIVERSITY DR E, STE 410 77802 #005-02-1997 L2005 **NS** *020 †25
GALLEGOS GARCIA, Fernando. 1301 MEMORIAL DR STE 200, RES PROGRAM 77802 #649-27-1979 **FP** *012
GARZA, Pablo A. 1301 MEMORIAL DR STE 200, BRAZOS VAL 77802 #048-12-2003 **FM** *100
GEORGE, Robert David. 2670 E 29TH ST, COGENT HEALTHCARE 77802 #048-02-1987 L1990 **IM** *020 †20
GHALICHI, Mohammad Seyed. ■ 77801 #048-13-2006 **IM** *012
GIBSON, John Owen. 1301 MEMORIAL DR, STE 200 77802 #048-12-1980 L1980 **FM EM** *020 †18
GILES, James Board. 2700 E 29TH ST STE 100 77802 #048-04-1978 L1978 **ORS** *020 †40
GILL, Kory Lee. 1301 MEMORIAL DR STE 200 77802 #028-78-2005, ▲ L2008 **FP** *012
GILLETT, David Paul. 5946 STEEP HOLLOW CIR 77808 #034-01-2000 L2002 **FM UCM** *100 †18
GINN, Thomas Alan. 3201 UNIVERSITY DR E # 345 77802 #048-02-1979 L1979 **IM** *020 †20
GLENN, John Barry, Jr. 2901 E 29TH ST STE 101 77802 #027-01-1968 L1969 **OPH** *020 †35
GLIDDEN, Angella M. 1301 MEMORIAL DR STE 200 77802 #011-02-1995 L1998 **FM** *020 †18
GOBLE, Scott Douglas. 2215 E VILLA MARIA RD, STE 130 77802 #020-02-1992 L1996 **RO** *020 †80
GOSWICK, Claude Benj. ■ 77802 #036-07-1955 L1973 **GP** *020
GRAY, Brent Morgan. 2206 E VILLA MARIA RD 77802 #048-02-1985 L1986 **GE IM** *020 †20
GREER, Deena L. 1737 BRIARCREST DR, STE 14 77802 #020-02-1986 L1989 **AN** *020 †05
GUNDANNA, Mukund Iyengar. 3201 UNIVERSITY DR E, STE 255 77802 #033-06-1998 L2004 **OSS ORS** *020 †40
HAJI, Asha Mitrasen. 2801 FRANCISCAN DR 77802 #496-38-1966 L1974 **FM** *020
HAJI, Karim Ismail Ali. 2010 E VILLA MARIA RD # A 77802 #495-01-1967 L1974 **GS** *030 †85
HALL, John Jos. 1301 MEMORIAL DR, STE 200 77802 #026-04-1955 L1960 **FM** *071 †18
HANNA, Emad Fayek. 2206 E VILLA MARIA RD 77802 #915-03-1988 L1999 **AN** *020 †05
HARRIS, Nena A. ■ 77801 #021-05-1948 L1951 **PD** *071
HARRISON, Samuel H. 3201 UNIVERSITY DR E, STE 370 77802 #048-04-1989 L1990 **U** *071 †95
HART, Umbert, Jr. 1737 BRIARCREST DR, STE 14 77802 #048-02-1984 L1985 **AN** *020 †05
HAYNES, Chanseya A. 2010 E VILLA MARIA RD, STE A 77802 #048-13-2003 L2005 **FM** *020
HEBERT, Jesse D. 2305 BERGER DR 77802 #048-14-1998 L2004 **AN** *020 †05
HILLNER, Kenneth D. 2210 E 29TH ST, BRAZOS PHYSICIANS GROUP 77802 #048-13-1988 L1990 **FM** *020 †18
HOWARD, Charles H, Jr. ■ 77807 #048-12-1951 L1951 **GS** *020
HOYT, Thomas Alan. ■ 77802 #025-07-1975 L1984 **AN** *071 †20,05
HUDSON, Angela Price. PO BOX 7161 77805 #048-12-2005 **IM** *012
IERO, Joseph John. 2700 E 29TH ST, STE 100 77802 #048-14-1996 L1997 **OSM** *020 †40
IGUH, Bernadette Uche. 1301 MEMORIAL DR STE 200, BRAZOS VAL 77802 #305-01-2005 **FP** *012
JANSKY, Cynthia A. 2700 E 29TH ST, STE 330 77802 #048-04-1993 L1994 **OBG** *020 †30
JENKINS, Terry R. 2215 E VILLA MARIA RD #110 77802 #010-02-1975 L1980 **HEM ON** *020 †20

■ = Address Information Privacy Protected

JONES, Michael Edward. 1121 BRIARCREST DR, STE 303 77802 #048-13-1985 L1987 FM GP *020 †18

JONES, Terry Miller. 1707 BROADMOOR DR 77802 #048-04-1974 L1974 D *020 †15

KAKWAN, Ume Haney. 3370 S TEXAS AVE, STE B 77802 #704-06-1987 L2001 FM *020 †18

KEELE, Marjorie Sue H. ■ 77807 #048-12-1949 L1949 PD CHN *071

KIRBY, James Michael. 2700 E 29TH ST 77802 #048-02-1977 L1977 TS VS *020 †85,90

KIRK, Isaac Raymond, III. 2801 FRANCISCAN DR 77802 #028-46-1986 L1988 RNR VIR *020 †80

KRAFT, Joseph W. 1211 E 31ST ST 77802 #048-15-1991 L1992 IM PD *020 †55,20

KRAUS, Trevor Tegan. 1737 BRIARCREST DR, STE 14 77802 #048-13-2002 L2005 AN *020 †05

KROHN, Nancy Jane. ■ 77802 #047-07-1976 L1981 FOP ATP *020 †50

KRUEGER, Janet A. 2801 FRANCISCAN DR, EXPRESS CARE 77802 #048-16-1995 L1996 FM *020

KUHL, Derek Peter. 2806 E 29TH ST 77802 #048-04-1995 L2001 OPH *020 †35

KUNJAPPY, Alexander. 401 S TEXAS AVE 77803 #495-01-1983 L1996 HO *020 †20

LAWYER, James Todd. 3131 UNIVERSITY DR E 77802 #034-01-1986 L2004 AN *020 †05

LAZCANO, Oscar. 2801 FRANCISCAN DR, ST JOSEPH REG HLTH CTR 77802 #649-02-1981 L1993 PTH *020 †50

LEBLEU, Gregory E. 1600 JOSEPH DR STE 2 77802 #048-15-1991 L1992 PM *020 †60

LEMOS, Ricardo Souza. 2801 E 29TH ST STE 1 77802 #187-02-1981 L1994 ID IM *020 †20

LICHORAD, Anna. 2801 FRANCISCAN DR 77802 #048-14-1994 L2002 FM *020 †18

LIGHT, Randall Ray. 2700 E 29TH ST, STE 305 77802 #048-02-1977 L1977 N *020 †75 ‡

LIM, Julie W. 2801 E 29TH ST, STE 117 77802 #748-01-1984 L1999 IM *020 †20

LINDSAY, James Irwin. 511 SULPHUR SPRINGS RD 77801 #048-02-1954 L1954 FM *071 †18

LINDSAY, Mark Boughton. 2725 E 29TH ST 77802 #048-12-1967 L1967 OPH *020 †35

LOBB, Kelly Wendell. 1600 JOSEPH DR STE 2 77802 #048-02-1997 L1999 PM *020 †60

LYTTON, Lynn E. ■ 77802 #048-15-2002 IM *100

MARR, William Harris. 2801 E 29TH ST, STE 101 77802 #048-13-1980 L1980 OPH *040 †35

MARTIN, Jay Wilfred, Jr. ■ 77802 #048-02-1945 L1945 IM *071

MASON, John Albert, Jr. 3201 UNIVERSITY DR E, STE 320 77802 #048-12-1986 L1987 GS *020 †85

MAYS, Gloria Jean. 2700 E 29TH ST STE 220 77802 #654-01-1989 L1997 CD *020 †20

MC CLELLAN, David Arthur. 1301 MEMORIAL DR, STE 200 77802 #048-14-1975 L1975 FM *020 †18

MC NEW, John Thomas Lamar. 1301 MEMORIAL DR, STE 200 77802 #048-12-1962 L1962 FM *020 †18

MC QUAIDE, Henry C, Jr. ■ 77805 #048-04-1944 L1944 GS *071 †85

MILLS, Council C, III. 2220 E BRIARGATE DR 77802 #048-02-1976 L1976 IM *020 †20

MITCHELL, Gordon Geo. 2700 E 29TH ST, STE 220 77802 #048-14-1981 L1981 CD IM *020 †20

MONTGOMERY, Gary Mark. 2700 E 29TH ST STE 330 77802 #048-12-1978 L1978 OBG *071 †30

MONTROSS, Eileen Tewes. 2801 FRANCISCAN DR, ST JOSEPH REGIONAL HEALTH 77802 #264-05-1970 L1980 EM IM *020 †16 ‡

MOORE, Charles Henry. 2206 E VILLA MARIA RD 77802 #004-01-2000 L2006 GE *020 †20

MOQUIST, Dale Clifford. 1301 MEMORIAL DR, STE 200 77802 #048-12-1973 L1998 FM FPG *040 †18 ‡

MORENO, John Alvin. 1737 BRIARCREST DR STE 14 77802 #005-11-1985 L1989 AN *020 †05

MORGAN, Richard Greenlee. 2801 FRANCISCAN DR 77802 #020-27-1972 L1976 NEP IM *020 †20

NAPOLI, Peter Jos. 2700 E 29TH ST 77802 #010-02-1985 L1996 TS *020 †85,90

NEELA, Rekha S.. 1301 MEMORIAL DR STE 200, BRAZOS VAL 77802 #496-33-1994 FP *012

NEFF, Timothy L. PO BOX 6155 77805 #048-15-1995 L1996 EM *020 †16

NGUYEN, John Quyet Tu. 2801 FRANCISCAN DR 77802 #028-34-1993 L1997 IM *020 †20

NICOLWALA, Zenia A. 1301 MEMORIAL DR STE 200 77802 #048-02-1985 L2003 FM *020

OWENS, Brian K. 3131 UNIVERSITY DR E 77802 #048-14-2000 L2004 AN *020 †05

PALMER, Landon L. ■ 77802 #038-40-1953 L1953 P *071

PARRENT, Bryan D. 2700 E 29TH ST 77802 #048-16-2000 L2004 GS *020 †85

PATEL, Damyanti Sudhir. 1201B BRIARCREST DR 77802 #495-23-1971 L1979 PD *020 †55

PATEL, Sudhir Dahyabhai. 1201 BRIARCREST DR 77802 #495-01-1971 L1974 OBG *020 †30

PAULL, Barry Richard. 2801 FRANCISCAN DR 77802 #011-02-1973 L1978 A PD *020 †55,03

PEIRCE, Charles Kevin. 3201 UNIVERSITY DR E, STE 370 77802 #048-04-1988 L1994 U *020 †95

PERKINS, Terry Don. 3811 SAGEBRIAR DR 77802 #048-13-1994 L1995 OPH *020 †35

PHAM, L Henry. 2206 E VILLA MARIA RD 77802 #048-14-1990 L1992 GE *020 †20

POCURULL, Ricardo Luis. 3201 UNIVERSITY DR E, STE 475 77802 #011-04-1995 L1997 RHU *020 †20

POTTS, Robert Chas. 804 S TEXAS AVE, MR OF BRAZO VALLEY 77803 #048-02-1965 L1965 P *020 †75

PRICE, Linda Scipper. 3201 UNIVERSITY DR E, STE 210 77802 #005-06-1976 L1976 IM *020 †20

PRICE, William Franklin. 2700 E 29TH ST, STE 300 77802 #048-02-1975 L1975 OBG *020 †30

QUARTEMONT, Stuart R. 1301 MEMORIAL DR, STE 200 77802 #021-05-1985 L1987 FM *020 †18

QUIGLEY, Daniel Donald. 3370 S TEXAS AVE 77802 #048-14-1995 L1997 PD *020

RAGUPATHI, Rohini. 3400 S TEXAS AVE, # A 77802 #495-16-1979 L1987 IM *072

RAMIREZ, Steve. ■ 77801 #048-16-2007 *012

RAPHAEL, Leonard S. 2206 E VILLA MARIA RD 77802 #048-02-1986 L1987 AN *020 †05

RASBERRY, Leon Wm Burnett. ■ 77802 #048-04-1964 L1964 OBG *020 †30

RAVICHANDRAN, Latha Mahes. 1301 MEMORIAL DR, STE 200 77802 #495-66-1996 L2006 FM *100 †18

RICHARDSON, George Adams. 3201 UNIVERSITY DR E, STE 255 77802 #048-14-1978 L1978 ORS *020 †40

RILEY, Mark Bennett. 2700 E 29TH ST STE 100 77802 #020-02-1978 L1979 ORS *020 †40

ROBERMAN, Susan. 1301 MEMORIAL DR, STE 200 77802 #048-14-1990 L1991 FM *020 †18

ROBINSON, Claudius Emet. 2801 FRANCISCAN DR, ST JOSEPH REG HEALTH CTR L 77802 #039-01-1999 L2002 PTH *020

ROBINSON, Richard D. 1301 MEMORIAL DR, STE 200 77802 #048-13-2000 L2002 EM *020 †16

ROMAN, William Buchanan. ■ 77805 #048-02-1954 L1954 GYN *071 †30

ROQUET, Warren Paul. 3201 UNIVERSITY DR E, STE 135 77802 #048-02-1981 L1981 FM *020 †18

RUDE, Malcolm J. 2304 DE LEE ST 77802 #048-15-1998 L2000 PS *020 †65

RYAN, Patrick B. 1737 BRIARCREST DR, STE 14 77802 #048-16-1982 L1983 AN *020 †05

SCHEINOST, Nancy Ann. 3201 UNIVERSITY DR E, STE 205 77802 #030-05-1988 L1994 RHU *020

SCHWARTZ, Marc Stephen. 2700 E 29TH ST STE 220 77802 #036-07-1989 L1997 CD *020 †20

SEABOLT, Brian R. 3201 UNIVERSITY DR E # 115, CT TX SPORTS MED 77802 #048-16-1996 L2001 ORS OSM *020 †40

SEGREST, David Rivers. 2801 FRANCISCAN DR 77802 #048-04-1969 L1969 FM *020 †18

SHIPMAN, Nolan Danl. 3201 UNIVERSITY DR E, STE 425 77802 #038-40-1966 L1974 OTO *020 †18

SHIRK, Carl D. 2801 FRANCISCAN DR 77802 #005-02-1961 L1992 EM *020 †16

SICILIO, Mark Stephen. 1301 MEMORIAL DR, STE 200 77802 #048-16-1981 L1981 PD *020 †55

SIMMONS, John Franklin. ■ 77802 #001-02-2006 FP *012

SMART, Danny Ray. 3201 UNIVERSITY DR E, STE 345 77802 #048-02-1983 L1983 IM *020 †20

SMITH, Charles H. 2700 E 29TH ST 77802 #048-16-1993 L1995 TS *020 †90,85

SMITH, Richard Alan. 3201 UNIVERSITY DR E, STE 430 77802 #048-14-1983 L1983 FM *020 †18

SOKUNBI, Abimbola Olayink. ■ 77801 #048-16-2008 *012

SOLCHER, Barry W. 3201 UNIVERSITY DR E, STE 255 77802 #048-12-1988 L1989 ORS OSM *020 †40

SORIANO, Anthony Tabora. 1301 MEMORIAL DR STE 200, RES PROGRAM 77802 #748-20-1996 FP *012

SPENCER, Scott E. 2700 E 29TH ST, STE 260 77802 #048-13-1995 L2001 PUD CCM *020 †20

SREERAM, Suha. 2801 FRANCISCAN DR, ST. JOSEPH CENTER FOR WOUN 77802 #012-05-1989 L2000 FM *020 †20

STAUCH, Douglas Martin. 2700 E 29TH ST, STE 100 77802 #048-04-1970 L1970 ORS *020 †40

STEBBINS, Nancy K Griffin. 601 MARY LAKE DR 77801 #048-14-1987 L1988 P *020 †75

STEINES, Michael W. 2700 E 29TH ST 77802 #048-04-1991 L1996 GS VS *020 †85

STEPHENSON, Stephen V. ■ 77802 #039-01-1968 L1976 AN OS *020

STONECIPHER, James V. 3201 UNIVERSITY DR E, STE 405 77802 #048-14-1990 L1991 AN *020 †20

STRAWN, Alan A. ■ 77802 #048-16-2007 GS *012

SUKKAWALA, Jothi A. 1737 BRIARCREST DR, STE 14 77802 #048-13-2000 L2006 AN *020 †05 ‡

SULEMAN, Mohamed R. ■ 77805 #905-01-1972 L1982 DR *020 †80

TAN, Frederick San Jose. 1705 E 29TH ST 77802 #048-10-1982 L1999 IM NEP *020 †20

TIFFAULT, Rock Gerard. 2670 E 29TH ST STE A, ST. JOSEPH REGIONAL HEALTH 77802 #035-19-1996 L2000 FM *040 †18

TOMLINSON, John Anthony. 2801 FRANCISCAN DR, LABORATORY/ST JOSEPH HOSP 77802 #056-05-1976 L1984 PTH *020 †50

TOUSSAINT, Leonide Gerard. 3201 UNIVERSITY DR E 77802 #036-01-2000 L2007 NS *020

TRIMBLE, Shea E. 2801 FRANCISCAN DR, ST JOESPH REG HLTH EMERG 77802 #048-13-2002 L2005 EM *020

TRIPATHY, Kumud Shankar. 2215 E VILLA MARIA RD # 11 77802 #495-15-1971 L1981 ON *020 †20

TSENG, Stephen Shipin. 3201 UNIVERSITY DR E, STE 345 77802 #048-12-1982 L1983 IM *020 †20

VANAMERONGEN, Alexander W. 2801 FRANCISCAN DR 77802 #046-01-1993 L2002 PCP *020 †50

VEAZEY, Barry L. 2700 E 29TH ST 77802 #048-12-1987 L1988 ORS *020 †40

VILLANUEVA, Imelda Chan. 1301 MEMORIAL DR STE 200, BRAZOS VAL 77802 #748-08-1994 L2008 FP *012

WEBER, Thomas M. 2700 E 29TH ST STE 260, INTERNAL MEDICINE 77802 #048-02-1985 L1986 PUD IM *020 †20

WHITE, Herman Alexander. ■ 77801 #065-01-1955 L1978 FM *071

WHITE, Jeremy Christopher. ■ 77802 #048-12-1995 L1999 EM *020 †16

WHITMIRE, Andrew Gayle. 2722 OSLER BLVD 77802 #048-14-1977 L1977 DR EM *020 †80,18

WIGLEY, Kennon Donald. 2700 E 29TH ST, STE 220 77802 #048-14-1983 L1983 CD IM *020 †20

WILLIAMS, Charles B. 2801 FRANCISCAN DR 77802 #048-02-1993 L1997 EM *020 †16

WUTHRICH, Paul. 3811 SAGEBRIAR DR 77802 #048-16-1989 L1990 OPH *020 †35

YOUNG, Alan Keith. 1404 BRISTOL ST 77802 #048-12-1974 L1979 U *020 †95

YOUNG, Ralph Raymond, Jr. 1404 BRISTOL ST 77802 #048-12-1970 L1970 U *020 †95

ZOBAL, Kimberly A. 1301 MEMORIAL DR, STE 120 77802 #048-02-1992 L1993 FM *020 †18

BUDA – HAYS

AHMED, Mumtaz. ■ 78610 #649-33-1981 L1983 IM ID *050

CARNEY, Linda. ■ 78610 #005-12-1986 L2005 GP EM *020 †16

COLLINS, Karyn W. 211 RAILROAD ST 78610 #048-15-2002 L2005 PD *020

EEDS, Edna Louise. ■ 78610 #048-12-1962 L1962 IMG ADL *020

ELEQUIN, Cleto T, Jr. ■ 78610 #748-08-1957 L1971 FM P *071

FERGUSON, Susan Elainehul. ■ 78610 #048-13-2007 L2007 IM *012

GILCREASE, Gary Lawrence. 155 CIMARRON PARK LOOP 78610 #048-02-1994 L1999 FM *020 †18

KRAMER, Julius Fred, Jr. 304 COMMERCIAL DR 78610 #048-12-1961 L1961 FM *072

LINCOLN, Anna Patrick Mcm. 211 RAILROAD ST 78610 #048-04-2001 L2005 PD *020

MC CORMICK, Thaddeus C. N LOOP 4 AT SEQUOYAH ST 78610 #048-02-1942 L1942 P N *072 †75

SHAKTMAN, Diane. 331 CREEKSIDE DR 78610 #048-13-1976 L1976 P *020 †75

SHERMAN, Terry James. 112 CIMARRON PARK LOOP 78610 #048-02-1972 L1972 FM GP *020 †18 ‡

VISCARDI, Margie E. 112A CIMARRON PARK LOOP 78610 #048-14-1991 L1992 FM *020 †18

BUFFALO – LEON

AGUIRRE, Irma L. 1686 W US HIGHWAY 79 75831 #048-14-1993 L1994 FM *020 †18

COLE, Ronald L. ■ 75831 #028-03-1977 L1981 OBG *020

KNIGHT, Harmon Madison. ■ 75831 #048-02-1966 L1966 OBG OS *071

TORNO, Curtis J. 1487 FM 1618, RT 1 BOX 141F 75831 #048-02-1949 L1949 FM PHP *071

BUFFALO GAP – TAYLOR

FAGAN, Linda D. 170 COUNTY ROAD 695 79508 #048-15-1991 L1992 IM *020 †20

BULLARD – SMITH

BONE, Robert Donnell. ■ 75757 #048-12-1946 L1946 IM *071 †20

COTTLE, Kenneth Edward. ■ 75757 #048-12-1956 L1956 EM AM *072 †70

LANGSJOEN, Jens O. ■ 75757 #048-02-2008 *012
ROPER, Marjorie C Ferrell. PO BOX 195 75757 #048-02-1943 L1943 **GP** *020
VERZOSA, Eduardo Sievert. ■ 75757 #748-08-1963 L1972 **TS** *071 †85,90

BULVERDE — COMAL

ALTIERI, Lizette M. ■ 78163 #042-01-1990 L1993 **IM** *020
BAKER, John Adelbert. ■ 78163 #051-04-1972 L1987 **ADL PD** *020 †55
FEINSTEIN, Glen Ira. 32665 US HIGHWAY 281 N, STE 210 78163 #011-03-1995 L1996
   OBG *020 †30
GIBBONS, Donna Rae. ■ 78163 #004-01-1985 L1992 **HNS** *020 †45
LANG, Thomas Chris. 32665 US HWY 281 N 78163 #048-04-1981 L1981 **FM** *020 †18
MANN, Michael W. 32665 US HIGHWAY 281 N 78163 #048-13-1993 L1994 **FM** *020 †18
NEUMANN, William L. ■ 78163 #048-13-2006 **PTH** *012
PERKINS, Kristi E. ■ 78163 #048-13-1986 L1987 **PD** *020 †55
STORK, Leslie Fair. 32665 US HIGHWAY 281 N, STE 202 78163 #004-01-1980 L2007
   FM *020 †18

BUNA — JASPER

CUMMINGS, Robert Dale. PO BOX 160 77612 #048-02-1964 L1964 **GP** *020 †18
WYNN, Bob K. PO BOX 1270 77612 #244-03-1971 L1978 **GP PTH** *020

BURKBURNETT — WICHITA

ADAMS, Jerome Mark. 501 E 3RD ST 76354 #039-01-1953 L1956 **FM IM** *020 †18
EWELL, Mark G. ■ 76354 #048-15-1983 L1983 **AN** *020 †05
TILLES, David A. ■ 76354 #048-78-1994, ▲ L1995 **EM** *020
TORRES, Rosa Angeles. 600 S RED RIVER EXPY 76354 #682-01-1981 L1993 **FM** *020 †18 ‡
WILLIAMS, Jonathan W. 312 S AVENUE D 76354 #048-12-1996 L1999 **FM** *020 †18

BURKEVILLE — NEWTON

BIBBY, Douglas Earl. ■ 75932 #048-02-1946 L1946 **R** *071 †80
CADE, Charlie Bruton. ■ 75932 #048-12-1960 L1960 **GP** *071
FORREST, Peter E C. 181 BEECH GROVE DR, THE NAMASTE CENTER 75932
   #049-01-1970 L1980 **FM EM** *020 †18

BURLESON — JOHNSON

ADAMS, Elvin Eugene. 714 SW WILSHIRE BLVD 76028 #005-12-1967 L1978 **IM GPM** *071 †20
ANEES, Mukhtar. 701 E RENDON CROWLEY RD, SW GASTROENTEROLOGY CLINIC 76028
   #704-01-1970 L1979 **GE IM** *020 †20
BAINE, Ralph F. ■ 76028 #048-12-2007 **EM** *012
BASS, Barry Jack. ■ 76028 #028-03-1977 L2003 **GS VS** *020 †85
BATES, Edward E. 663 NE ALSBURY BLVD 76028 #048-15-1996 L1997 **IM** *020 †20
BAZIR, Khalid. 714 SW WILSHIRE BLVD 76028 #655-01-1995 L2004 **IM** *020 †20 ‡
BECERRA, Oscar David. 663 NE ALSBURY BLVD 76028 #264-09-1981 L1994 **FM** *020 †18
BIRDSONG, Karl Kieffer. ■ 76028 #004-01-1945 L1948 **AN** *071 †05
BISMAR, Hisham. 11807 SOUTH FWY, STE 362 76028 #875-01-1983 L1988 **PUD CCM** *020 †20
BISMAR, Mike Mouhanad. 12001 SOUTH FWY STE 305, GASTRO CTR 76028
   #048-14-1998 L2000 **GE IM** *020 †20
BODEA-BAROTHI, Paul S. 11797 SOUTH FWY, DOCTORS BUILDING, SUITE 33 76028
   #781-03-1980 L2006 **P ADP** *020 †75
BOWYER, Darrell Lynn. 11797 SOUTH FWY, STE 250 76028 #005-12-1989 L1993 **OBG** *020 †30
BRADSHAW, Barbara Sue. 1016 RED CEDAR WAY 76028 #048-02-1991 L1992 **IM** *020 †20
CHADWICK, Daniel Howard. 11797 SOUTH FWY, STE 358 76028 #005-12-1997 L2003 **FM** *020
CHAKER, Mohammed Basem. 12001 SOUTH FWY, STE 205 76028 #875-01-1981 L1991
   D DMP *020
CHIANG, Robert. 1161 SW WILSHIRE BLVD, STE 108 76028 #016-01-1990 L1997 **OPH** *020 †35
CHICHANE, Hanane. 714 SW WILSHIRE BLVD 76028 #655-03-1995 L2005 **ADP** *100 †75 ‡
CHOLLETI, Rajanarender. 1161 SW WILSHIRE BLVD, STE 115 76028 #495-21-1983 L2000
   CD *020 †20
COOK, Deborah T. 108 NW RENFRO ST 76028 #027-01-1985 L1996 **PD** *020 †55
COULTER, Tuere Saran. ■ 76028 #047-06-2007 **FP** *012
CRESWELL, Wiltie A, Jr. ■ 76028 #048-04-1957 L1957 **OPH** *071 †35
CRISTOL, David A. 11807 SOUTH FWY, STE 365 76028 #048-12-1953 L1953 **CD IM** *071 †20
CRISTOL, Louis Saml. 11807 SOUTH FWY, STE 365 76028 #048-12-1987 L1991 **IM** *020 †20
CUNNINGHAM, Henry Smith. 11797 SOUTH FWY STE 222, TX PULM & CRTCL CARE
   CNST 76028 #047-05-1983 L1984 **PCC CCM** *020 †20
DSOUZA, Denzil G. 11807 SOUTH FWY, STE 365 76028 #048-14-1990 L1991 **CD** *020 †20
DUNN, David Todd. 11797 SOUTH FWY 76028 #005-12-1996 L2005 **FM** *020 †20
DURAN, Donna Marie. 11803 SOUTH FWY STE 218 76028 #048-15-1993 L1994 **OBG** *020 †30
EKADI, Kofoworola. 11803 SOUTH FWY 76028 #690-02-1991 L2000 **IM** *020 †20
EVANS, Von Landon, Jr. 11797 SOUTH FWY, STE 346 76028 #048-02-1987 L1988 **ORS** *020 †40
FARAH, Roula. ■ 76028 #605-02-1992 L1995 **PHO** *100 †55
FRANZ, Jennie Rose Heim. ■ 76028 #020-12-1972 L1982 **OS** *071 †55
HASLAM, Dennis Raymond, Jr. 11801 SOUTH FWY, HUGULEY MEMORIAL MEDICAL C 76028
   #055-02-2002 L2005 **EM** *020 †16
HEIN, Robert Mathew. ■ 76028 #048-14-2002 L2007 **FSM** *020 †18
JAGADISH, Lalitha. 11797 SOUTH FWY, STE 362 76028 #495-99-1983 L2001 **IM** *020 †20
JIRCIK, Frank Paul. 11803 SOUTH FWY STE 1 76028 #048-02-1981 L1981 **IM** *020 †20
JONES, Timothy Charles. 11797 SOUTH FWY STE 140 76028 #048-78-2000, ▲ L2004
   OBG *020 ‡
LAUE, Edward Arthur. 1600 COUNTY ROAD 1021 76028 #005-12-1984 L1999 **OBG** *030 †30
LILLY, Theodore Jos. 434 SW WILSHIRE BLVD 76028 #018-03-1982 L1985 **IM** *020 †20
LOONEY, Warren Hunter. ■ 76028 #012-01-2005 L2005 *100
LOWRY, Oliver I. ■ 76028 #005-12-1953 L1963 **GP** *071
MAAS, Charles Jos. ■ 76028 #041-12-1963 L1977 **AN** *071 †05
MALONIS, John Adam. 11797 SOUTH FWY STE 34 76028 #048-12-1990 L1991 **OSS** *020 †40

MANITO, Mirla G. 11797 SOUTH FWY, STE 246 76028 #748-01-1970 L1984 **NPM** *020 †55
MEMON, Muhammad A. 701 E RENDON CROWLEY RD 76028 #704-02-1989 L2005
   GE IM *020 †20
MODLINSKI, Ryan Edward. ■ 76028 #051-04-2003 L2007 **FSM** *020 †18
MUKKA, Mallikarjuna Reddy. 11803 SOUTH FWY 76028 #495-65-1997 L2004 **IM** *020
OCHOA, Pedro Martinez. ■ 76097 #649-01-1960 L1971 **EM** *020 †85
ONDRIZEK, Richard Roy. 11797 SOUTH FWY, STE 242 76028 #005-12-1995 L1999
   OBG *020 †30
PATEL, Rajnikant T. 11807 SOUTH FWY, ARIZONA MEDICAL CLINIC LTD 76028
   #495-23-1995 L1999 **IC** *020 †20
RHODES, Michael Allen. 1161 SW WILSHIRE BLVD, STE 105 76028 #005-12-1990 L1997
   FM *020 †18
RIOS, Alvaro Saul. 11807 SOUTH FWY, STE 365 76028 #429-02-1989 L2002 **CD** *020 †20
SATYANARAYANA, Bhavani M. 220 SW WILSHIRE BLVD 76028 #495-09-1970 L1981 **P** *075
SAYAD, Alain. ■ 76028 #605-02-1992 L1995 **PG** *100 †55
SHAMBURGER, Wallace H, Jr. ■ 76028 #048-04-1944 L1944 **FM** *071
SHAW, Robert Harris. 220 SW WILSHIRE BLVD 76028 #021-01-1971 L1971 **FM** *020
SHEA, John Patrick. 11797 SOUTH FWY, STE 132 76028 #048-02-1974 L1974 **OTO A** *020 †45
SIDDIQUI, Ashfaq Hussain. 701 E RENDON CROWLEY RD 76028 #704-02-1969 L2002
   OS TS *020 †85
TRIVEDI, Bhargav R. 11797 SOUTH FWY, STE 140 76028 #495-48-1991 L1999 **PD** *020 †55
WILLIAMS, Ella M. 11797 SOUTH FWY, STE 226 76028 #004-01-1995 L1997 **P** *020 †75
YUNUS, Tariq Mahmood. 12001 SOUTH FWY STE 201, ALLERGY ENT ASSOCIATES OF 76028
   #011-03-2001 L2006 **OTO** *020 †45
ZGOURIDES, George Dean. ■ 76028 #654-01-2006 **FP** *012

BURNET — BURNET

BROUGHTON, Alan. ■ 78611 #917-06-1958 L1974 **CLP PTH** *030 †50
DIRE, Daniel J. PO BOX 665 78611 #028-03-1984 L1990 **EM PEM** *020 †16
DOUGLAS, Deborah Denney. ■ 78611 #048-13-1978 L1978 **PTH** *071 †50
FOX, Lay Martin. ■ 78611 #023-07-1947 L1969 **CD NM** *071 †20
GARWACKI, Janusz John. 101 E JACKSON ST, BURNET FAMILY PRACTICE 78611
   #759-04-1951 L1971 **GP** *071 †75
JONES, Herbert W. ■ 78611 #048-04-1949 L1950 **AN** *071 †05
KINGSTON, Brian J. 101 E JACKSON ST, BURNET FAMILY PRACTICE 78611
   #048-15-1995 L1997 **FM** *020 †18
MORRIS, Susan Morrey. PO BOX 220 78611 #048-02-1978 L1978 **FM** *020 †18,16
OZIER, Billy Burton. ■ 78611 #048-02-1955 L1955 **FM** *071 †18
RICE, Lee Roy. 200 CR 340A 78611 #048-02-1973 L1973 **GYN** *020 †30
RIPPERDA, Candace M. ■ 78611 #048-14-2006 L2007 **OBG** *100
ROBINSON, Jere Lee. 2309 W HWY 29 78611 #048-12-1979 L1979 **IM EM** *020
SPAW, Raymond Gebhart. ■ 78611 #654-01-1980 L1987 **FM** *020 †18
VALADEZ, Charles David. 516 BUCHANAN DR, FAMILY MED SURGERY 78611
   #649-30-1982 L1990 **FM** *020

CALDWELL — BURLESON

FERGUSON, Charles E. 1101 WOODSON DR 77836 #048-16-1996 L1997 **FM EM** *020 †18
KHAN, Muhammad Idrees. 1101 WOODSON DR 77836 #704-04-1979 L1983 **PD EM** *020 †55
LEUBNER, Kristel Dawn. 1103 WOODSON DR 77836 #048-78-2005, ▲ L2006 **FP** *012
PARSI, Kia E. 1103 WOODSON DR, CLINIC 77836 #048-04-1995 L1998 **FM** *020 †18
SMITH, Joe C. ■ 77836 #048-04-1951 L1951 **FM OBG** *071 †18
STIGLER, Del Barker. 302 W HIGHWAY 21 77836 #007-02-1974 L1975 **FM** *020 †18
TINDALL, Leah B. 5900 COUNTY ROAD 229 77836 #048-16-1996 L1997 **IM** *020 †20

CAMERON — MILAM

HARPER, Brian Stanley. 502 N CROCKETT AVE 76520 #048-14-1977 L1977 **OPH DIA** *020 †35
MAHMOOD, Tariq. 806 N CROCKETT AVE 76520 #704-01-1973 L1978 **IM** *020
RICHARDSON, Sidney Holt. 908 N CROCKETT AVE 76520 #048-12-1954 L1954 **GP** *020
VALLABHANENI, Vani Shree. 806 N CROCKETT AVE, CENTRAL TEXAS HOSP 76520
   #496-07-1994 L2004 **IM** *020
YOUSUF, Almas. 908 N CROCKETT AVE 76520 #704-04-1983 L2004 **FM** *020 †18

CAMP WOOD — REAL

HART, Raymond Pate. ■ 78833 #048-04-1958 L1958 **AN** *071 †05

CAMPBELL — HUNT

PATTRANUPRAVAT, Prapan. ■ 75422 #891-01-1967 L1977 **GS GP** *020 †85

CANADIAN — HEMPHILL

ABRAHAM, Malouf, Jr. 720 ASH ST 79014 #048-12-1964 L1964 **A GP** *071
COOK, George Anthony. ■ 79014 #048-12-2002 L2003 **FM** *020 †18
ISAACS, William Calvin, Jr. 817 HILLSIDE AVE 79014 #048-12-1979 L1979 **FM** *020 †18
KENDRICK, Roy B. ■ 79014 #048-15-2002 L2003 **FM** *020 †18
VERBI, Valerie Heather. 817 HILLSIDE AVE, BOX 1389 79014 #034-01-1979 L1980 **FM** *020 †18

CANTON — VAN ZANDT

DAUGHERTY, Nora Crady. ■ 75103 #048-02-1982 L1983 **FM** *071 †18
HILLIARD, Dan Richardson. ■ 75103 #048-04-1957 L1957 **FM** *072
LUGOADAMS, Felix David. ■ 75103 #042-01-1999 L2005 **ICE** *020
NIXON, Kenneth Wayne. 18780 INTERSTATE 20 75103 #048-13-1988 L1989 **FM** *020
NIXON, Kevin A. 18780 INTERSTATE 20 75103 #048-13-1999 L2000 **EM FM** *020 †18
VAN CLEAVE, Charles E, Jr. ■ 75103 #048-12-1953 L1953 **GS** *071

CANUTILLO – EL PASO

RODRIGUEZ, Juan Angel. PO BOX 160, 6740 DONIPHAN 79835 #649-02-1952 L1957 GP GS *020
RUIZ, Julia Dolores. ■ 79835 #048-16-2007 PD *012
TYSON, Sam T. 6898 DONIPHAN DR 79835 #004-01-1984 L1987 EM IM *020 †20
VAQUERA, Manuel. ■ 79835 #649-33-2004 FP *012

CANYON – RANDALL

BURNER, Scott Howard. 23120 BROWN RD 79015 #045-01-1978 L1992 EM *030 †16
CANON, Dennis Lane. 2001 4TH AVE 79015 #010-01-1970 L1977 FM AM *020 †18
CARTER, Bonnie C. WTAMU BOX 61401, 2402 RUSSELL LONG BLVD 79016 #048-15-2001 L2003 FM *020 †18
CLARKE, David Bruce. 911 23RD ST, FAMILY MEDICINE OF CANYON 79015 #048-15-1992 L1993 FM *020 †18
GROSS, Robert Danl. 911 23RD ST, FAMILY MEDICINE OF CANYON 79015 #048-15-1981 L1981 GP *070
IRWIN, Marc David. 911 23RD ST, FAMILY MEDICINE OF CANYON 79015 #026-04-1988 L1997 FM *020 †18
MARABLE, Eric Ryan. ■ 79015 #048-12-2007 MPD *012
MC AFEE, Lawrence Rush. 911 23RD ST, FAMILY MEDICINE OF CANYON 79015 #048-15-1987 L1988 FM *020 †18
NELSON, Lance Eric. ■ 79015 #025-01-1969 L1970 OS *020
OGUEJIOFOR, Kenneth C. 2 HOSPITAL DR 79015 #690-01-1980 L1997 IM EM *020 †20
OLES, Charles P. ■ 79015 #048-12-1953 L1953 GS CD *071 †85
TURNER, Tom Roy. ■ 79015 #048-02-1960 L1961 PD OS *020
VESELKA, James E. 2 HOSPITAL DR 79015 #048-04-1983 L1983 FM OBS *020 †18

CANYON LAKE – COMAL

BUCCI, Robert J F. 78133 #048-04-1952 L1958 PTH *071 †50
DOUGHERTY, James Jos. 78133 #048-04-1975 L1975 AM EM *071 †70
HAUVER, Robert Carlson. 78133 #038-40-1959 L1959 AM OS *030 †70
MOORE, Michael E. 1435 SATTLER RD UNIT C 78132 #048-13-1993 L1994 P *020 †75
ROBINSON, Peter Barry. 40970 FM 3159 78133 #917-23-1965 L1979 GP A *020

CARBON – EASTLAND

FAGAN, Walter John. ■ 76435 #010-01-1963 L1964 OM *020

CARRIZO SPRINGS – DIMMIT

DORIA, Abelardo S. 403 S 7TH ST 78834 #748-12-1989 L1996 PD *020 †55
LANKES, Richard Allen. 400 S 8TH ST 78834 #649-04-1975 L1976 GP *020
ROMERO, Fermin Arreola. ■ 78834 #649-19-1992 L2005 GS *020 †85
SANCHEZ, Claudio. 704 HOSPITAL DR 78834 #649-01-1966 L1974 EM IM *020 †16
SHINDLE, Richard Dale. 1115 N 9TH ST 78834 #041-01-1967 L1972 OPH *072 †35
VARSHNEY, Devandra K. 704 HOSPITAL DR 78834 #495-45-1967 L1981 FM GS *020
VARSHNEY, Maya. 300 S 5TH ST, BOX 100 78834 #495-12-1971 L1984 OBG FM *040

CARROLLTON – DALLAS

ABSALOM, Nicholas Michael. ■ 75006 #048-12-2007 IM *012
ANSARI, Anis A. PO BOX 118708 75011 #496-38-1983 L1994 IM *020 †20
DAY, Hemant Kumar. ■ 75011 #495-08-1997 L2003 CHP *012
ELLISTON, Bruce Kirby. 1345 VALWOOD PKWY STE 306, CONCENTRA MEDICAL CTR 75006 #048-02-1982 L1983 OM *020 †70,18
ESSA, Joanne L. ■ 75006 #048-13-2006 IM *100
FERRY, Maria Alice. 1025 TERRY WAY 75006 #011-03-2000 L2005 GS *020 †85,10
GEORGE, Joel Glenn. ■ 75006 #048-15-2003 L2006 OPH *100
GINTHER, Stephanie Ann. ■ 75006 #048-14-1999 L2002 PD *020 †55
HASSAN YOUSSEF, Mohamed H. 3330 EARHART DR, STE 206 75006 #915-04-1985 L2002 PM *020 ‡
HOOPMAN, Todd C. 1606 S I35 STE 101, NORTH DALLAS DRC 75006 #048-12-1999 L2002 PCC *100 †20
HUYNH, Thuan Phuong. 1218 N JOSEY LN, STE 108 75006 #021-05-1994 L1997 FM *020 †18
KASPER, Candace Sue. 2840 KELLER SPRINGS RD, STE 1104 75006 #048-12-1981 L1981 DMP ATP *020 †50
KEYES, D Christopher. 3220 KELLER SPRINGS RD, STE 106 75006 #005-14-1985 L1995 OM *020 †20,16,70
KING, William Harold. 3220 KELLER SPRNGS RD #106, CONCENTRA HLTH SERVICES 75006 #048-12-1959 L1961 AM OM *030 †70 ‡
KURICHETY, Kiran R. 2340 E TRINITY MILLS RD, STE 118 75006 #028-46-1997 L2004 CD *020 †20
LEE, Tae Young. ■ 75011 #048-12-2004 L2008 P *012
LEGGATT, Claire Campbell. ■ 75006 #048-13-1979 L1979 GP *020
MC EVOY, Susan Saville. 1205 N JOSEY LN, STE 200 75006 #048-12-1987 L1989 FM *020 †18
MEKKER, George Charles. 1913 WALNUT PLZ 75006 #038-40-1962 L1964 FM AM *071 †18
NEAVILLE, William Allen. ■ 75006 #004-01-1997 L2003 AI *020 †03,55
PETTIJOHN, Trent Leon. 2340 E TRINITY MILLS RD, STE 118 75006 #048-15-1992 L1993 CD *020 †20
POWERS, Amy Elizabeth. ■ 75006 #048-12-2005 AN *012
PUAR, Harjodh Singh. 2761 E TRINITY MILLS RD, STE 100 75006 #495-03-1976 L1987 IM PUD *020 †20
PUAR, Ravinder K. 2761 E TRINITY MILLS RD, STE 100 75006 #495-29-1976 L1987 FM *020 †18
PUNZI, Henry Anthony. 1932 WALNUT PLZ 75006 #132-01-1980 L1982 IM OS *020
RULE, William Gary. ■ 75006 #040-02-2006 IM *012
SANCHEZ, Christian F. 2537 FOUNTAIN CV 75006 #030-06-1999 L2003 MPD *020 †20,55
SEGOVIA, Felix. 1810 S JOSEY LN 75006 #649-02-1954 L1964 ORS *020

STINE, Christina Nicole. ■ 75006 #048-12-2008 *012
TENG, Li Ray. 1735 KELLER SPRINGS RD, STE 100 75006 #048-12-1975 L1975 IM *020 †20
THOR, Guat Ngoh. ■ 75006 #825-01-1976 1978 *020
TIJERINA, Bertha Edith. ■ 75006 #048-02-1980 *075
TRIGO, Luis C. 2135 DENTON DR 75006 #042-01-1982 L1992 IM *020
WELP, Mary Lucille. 1735 KELLER SPRINGS RD, STE 100 75006 #017-20-1975 L1984 FM EM *020 †16,18
WILSON, Lewis Jos, Jr. ■ 75011 #048-02-1964 L1964 GYN *071 †30
WUNNEBURGER, Richard Lee. ■ 75006 #048-02-1976 L1977 EM *074

CARROLLTON – DENTON

ALEMAN, Cesar Julio. 1809 GOLDEN TRAIL CT # 120 75010 #737-01-1972 L1976 IM *020
BAILEY, John Wesley. 4125 FAIRWAY DR, STE 190 75010 #012-01-1995 L2003 FM *020 †18
BAKER, Kristen Nicole. ■ 75007 #048-13-2008 *012
BANNISTER, Paul. 4343 N JOSEY LN 75010 #048-02-1996 L2001 PTH *020 †50
BAXTER, Shiu-Yueh. 1837 W FRANKFORD RD, STE 116 75007 #048-14-1990 L1991 FM *020 †18
BEAMER, Monica J. 4443 N JOSEY LN STE 150, KIDSDOCS 75010 #048-14-1993 L1994 PD *020 †55
BHOGARAJU, Anil K. 1809 GOLDEN TRAIL CT, STE 240 75010 #495-21-1992 L2003 HO *020 †20
BICKERT, Mark A. 4100 FAIRWAY DR STE 100 75010 #041-77-1997, ▲ L2006 OTO FPS *020
BLUMENAU, Joe. 3740 N JOSEY LN, STE 205 75007 #836-01-1954 1978 FM GP *020
BROWNLEE, Michael K. ■ 75007 #021-05-1989 L1997 IM *020
BURBANO, Jose Luis. 3020 E HEBRON PKWY, STE A100 75010 #048-13-1981 L1981 FM *020 †18
CARTER, Kyle K. 4125 FAIRWAY DR, STE 190 75010 #048-12-1988 L1989 FM *020 †18
CASSELLA, Robert Romeo. ■ 75007 #041-12-1960 L1979 FM GS *071 †85
CHAPMAN, John C. ■ 75007 #048-12-2005 PD *012
CHEN, Yijia. ■ 75010 #048-15-2007 GS *012
CHIHAL, David Michael. 4325 N JOSEY LN STE 101 75010 #021-05-1979 L1985 OTO HNS *020 †45
CHIHAL, Helen Jane. 4325 N JOSEY LN, STE 101 75010 #021-05-1976 L1985 REN GYN *071 †30
CHINIWALA, Rupal. 4333 N JOSEY LN, STE 202 75010 #041-02-1994 L2001 MPD *020 †20,55
CHODIMELLA, Vidyasagar. 4325 N JOSEY LN, STE 301 75010 #495-11-1979 L2000 CD *020 †20
CHOUSAND, Maxi Theodorine. ■ 75010 #035-08-1994 L1999 IM PD *020 †20,55
COCO, William Durham. 4443 N JOSEY LN, STE 160 75010 #021-01-1979 L1983 PD *020 †55
COULTER, Lynn V. 4443 N JOSEY LN, STE 160 75010 #012-01-1983 L1997 PD *020 †55
CRENSHAW, Allen, Jr. ■ 75007 #048-04-1942 L1942 GS OBG *071
CREUTZMANN, Fredrick H. 4323 N JOSEY LN STE 203 75010 #048-12-1983 L1983 OBG *020 †30
CUMMINS, Kathryn Elizabet. ■ 75010 #021-06-2008 PD *012
CURRY, Bryan P. 1706 IVY LN 75007 #048-14-2001 L2005 AN *020
DAR, Vaqar Ahmad. 4360 N JOSEY LN 75010 #495-51-1986 L1998 IM *020 †20
DASARI, Neeraja. 4352 N JOSEY LN 75010 #495-65-1994 L2002 RO *020 †80
DAYA, Nadirkhan N. 4323 N JOSEY LN, STE 100 75010 #704-16-1988 L2000 FM *020 †18
DAYA, Noor N. 4323 N JOSEY LN, STE 100 75010 #704-16-1988 L2000 PD *020 †55
DEVDAS, Geetha Malini. ■ 75010 #048-16-2004 L2007 PEM *012 †55
ENDELMAN, Irwin Robt. 4325 N JOSEY LN, PLZ 1 STE 100 75010 #048-13-1986 L1987 OBG *020 †30
FAGELMAN, Mitchell F. 4780 N JOSEY LN 75010 #048-14-2000 L2006 OAR *020
FAIRBANKS, John Lawrence. 4333 N JOSEY LN, STE 104 75010 #016-42-1986 L1995 U GS *020 †95
FEATHERSTON, Wm Edward. 2801 N I35, STE 130 75007 #051-07-1978 L1979 FM *020 †18
FRANKEN, Mary Ann. 4323 N JOSEY LN, STE 306 PLAZA 1 75010 #048-15-1995 L1997 OBG *020 †30
FRAZIER, Lewis, Jr. 4780 N JOSEY LN 75010 #048-13-1991 L1995 OS *020 †60
FULLER, Julie Marie. ■ 75008 #048-16-2006 PD *012
GIOMETTI, Ronald P, Jr. 4325 N JOSEY LN STE 105 75010 #047-06-1992 L2000 FM *020 †18
GLASSINGER, Michael C. 4343 N JOSEY LN 75010 #021-06-2002 L2007 EM *020
GOLDBERG, Kenneth Allen. 4333 N JOSEY LN, STE 104 75010 #038-06-1974 L1979 U *020 †95
GOODHART, Craig William. 4780 N JOSEY LN 75010 #038-40-1984 L1990 ORS *020 †40
GRAEHL, Phillip Madsen. 4780 N JOSEY LN 75010 #005-15-1981 L1986 ORS *020 †40
GRUBB, Thomas Edwin. 4443 N JOSEY LN, STE 160 75010 #021-06-1979 L1982 PD *020 †55
GUESS, James Allen. 4780 N JOSEY LN 75010 #025-01-1988 L1995 ORS *020 †40
HAMILTON, Joey L. 4333 N JOSEY LN 75010 #048-14-1989 L1990 FM *020 †18
HARPER, David Crockett. 4343 N JOSEY LN 75010 #048-14-1983 L1983 FM *030 †18
HECHT, Phillip J. 4325 N JOSEY LN, STE 301 75010 #048-02-1987 L1988 CD IM *020 †20
HEDLUND, Mark Louis. 4333 N JOSEY LN, STE 302 75010 #026-04-1980 L1997 FM *020 †18
HEIER, Keith Alan. 4780 N JOSEY LN 75010 #011-03-1993 L1995 ORS GS *020 †40
HISCHKE, Jeffrey R. 4333 N JOSEY LN 75010 #048-15-1995 L1996 FM *020 †18
HONAKER, Richard Albert. 4333 N JOSEY LN 75010 #051-01-1977 L1978 FM EM *020 †18 ‡
HONG, Chi-Tzong. ■ 75007 #244-04-1978 L1988 N *020
HOWARD, Wilbur F, Jr. 4325 N JOSEY LN 75010 #048-12-1970 L1970 REN GYN *020 †30
HUGGINS, Ginger Laurine. 4343 N JOSEY LN 75010 #048-15-1982 L1983 GS *020 †85
HULL, Gene I. ■ 75007 #024-07-1949 L1950 IM GP *071
IJAZ, Asifa. 1445 MAC ARTHUR DR, STE 122 75010 #704-06-1986 L2001 FM *020 †18
IM, Benjamin H. ■ 75007 #048-12-2001 L2008 AN *100
JACOBS, Barry Reuben. 4323 N JOSEY LN, STE 201 75010 #048-02-1970 L1970 GYN END *020 †30
JAFRY, Raza Ahmed. ■ 75006 #048-12-2006 IM *012
JAMES, Thomas M. 4343 N JOSEY LN 75010 #039-01-1977 L1982 PTH *020 †50
JENNINGS, Leslie Desmond. 4323 N JOSEY LN STE 307 75010 #048-14-1981 L1981 ORS *020 †18
JOSEPH, John Maliakkal. 2008 E HEBRON PKWY, STE 100 75007 #495-52-1976 L1982 IM *020 †20
KALIDINDI, Vishnu V. 2008 E HEBRON PKWY, STE 114 75007 #495-58-1981 L1997 CD IM *020 †20

KAPUSTA, Ronald. 3012 E HEBRON PKWY 75010 #067-01-1960 L1977 **GYN** *020

KASPER, Ira Joel. ■ 75010 #165-04-1973 L1983 **GS** *020 †85

KASSUBE, James Michael. 2316 HEATHERWOODS WAY 75007 #040-02-2002 L2005 **PM** *020

KIM, Bonnie E. ■ 75007 #048-13-2004 L2007 **PPR** *012 †55

LAGRONE, Howard Alan. ■ 75010 #048-02-1982 L1983 **P** *075 †75

LAL, Anjana. 75007 #048-12-2008 *012

LAM, Van. 4333 N JOSEY LN, STE 202 75010 #021-01-1996 L2000 **PD IM** *020,55

LAWSON, John William Rand. 4325 N JOSEY LN, STE 301 75010 #051-01-1978 L1982 **CD IM** *020 †20

LAXMINARAYAN, Amarnath. ■ 75010 #495-35-1993 L2000 **IM** *020 †20

LE, Lam D. ■ 75007 #048-16-2007 **GS** *012

LEE, Albert Eugene. ■ 75007 #422-01-2003 L2005 **NS** *012

LEE, Hun Kyu. 3044 OLD DENTON RD STE 317 75007 #583-01-1971 L1978 **PD** *020

LEE, Jong H. 4325 N JOSEY LN, STE 305 75010 #048-12-1999 L2001 **OPH** *020 †35

LEE, Seung S. 1809 GOLDEN TRAIL CT, STE 220 75010 #048-13-1995 L1998 **IM** *020 †20

LEFKOF, Gary David. 4100 INTERNATIONAL PKWY, STE 1010 75007 #048-12-1980 L1982 **P CHP** *062 †75

LESTER, Ronald Alexander. ■ 75010 #047-07-1998 L2001 **IM** *020 †20

LO, Laurence Fabian. 4325 N JOSEY LN STE 211 75010 #016-06-1981 L1989 **GS** *020 †85

LYDE, Paul Danl. 4343 N JOSEY LN 75010 #048-12-1985 L1986 **IM** *020 †20

MADHAV, Venkatesh V. 4323 N JOSEY LN 75010 #048-12-2001 L2001 **IM IMG** *020 †20

MAHON, Kirk Davis. 1016 E HEBRON PKWY 75010 #048-04-1996 L1997 **EM** *020 †16

MATHUR, Shelly. ■ 75010 #048-13-2007 **IM** *012

MC KENAS, David Karl. 3110 ANDREW LN 75007 #035-15-1981 L1992 **OM AM** *030 †70

MEGGS, Paul Douglas. 4323 N JOSEY LN, STE 301 75010 #048-12-1980 L1980 **OBG REN** *020 †30

MILLER, Margarita Maria. 2801 N I35 STE 110 75007 #649-14-1993 L1999 **PD** *020 †55

MILNOR, William Henry, Jr. 4100 INTERNATIONAL PKWY, STE 1 75007 #048-04-1971 L1971 **ORS HS** *030 †40

MIRABAL, Christine Anne. ■ 75007 #011-03-2004 **OTO** *012

MIRZA, Muhammad A. 4300 N JOSEY LN 110 75010 #704-02-1982 L1991 **PD** *020 †55 ‡

MOCEK, Frank Wm. 4325 N JOSEY LN, PLAZA III SUITE 202 75010 #028-34-1988 L1995 **GS** *020 †85

MONTANARO, Louis. 4300 N JOSEY LN, STE 106 75010 #048-14-1984 L1991 **OBG** *020 †30

MORRIS, Tricia Judith. ■ 75007 #048-04-2006 *012

MURPHY, Amy C. 4125 FAIRWAY DR, STE 190 75010 #048-13-1996 L1997 **FM** *020 †18

MYERS, David P. 2300 PLACID DR 75007 #048-12-2002 L2005 **PCC** *020

NADIR, Adnan. 4323 N JOSEY LN STE 302, PROFESSIONAL PLAZA I 75010 #704-02-1988 L2000 **GE** *020 †20

NAIL, George Alan. 1813 GOLDEN TRAIL CT, # 100 75010 #048-12-1993 L1994 **OS** *020

NAZ, Roobila. 4360 N JOSEY LN 75010 #704-16-1990 L2005 **IM** *020 †20

NEAGLE, Charles Edward. 4780 N JOSEY LN 75010 #023-01-1986 L1992 **HS** *020 †40

NGUYEN, Julie Caotrieu. ■ 75007 #048-02-2006 **IM** *012

OBIALO, E Elizabeth. 2008 E HEBRON PKWY, STE 120 75007 #690-04-1991 L1999 **END IM** *020 †20

OQAIL, Syed Mohammad. 4323 N JOSEY LN, STE 204 PLAZA I 75010 #704-02-1985 L1994 **GE** *020 †20

OVERSTREET, Susan L. ■ 75007 #048-12-2007 *012

PADAKANDLA, Udaya Bhaskar. 1505 SUNDANCE CIR 75007 #495-62-1988 L1998 **AN CCA** *020 †05

PANJWANI, Mahmood B. 3740 N JOSEY LN STE 2 75007 #704-16-1988 L1994 **NEP IM** *020 †20

PAPAILA, Elizabeth Marie. ■ 75007 #048-12-2007 **GS** *012

PARK, Michael Hyungwook. 1809 GOLDEN TRAIL CT, STE 240 75010 #048-12-1994 L1995 **ON** *020 †20

PARKER, Cinda. 4343 N JOSEY LN 75010 #049-01-1997 L1999 **PTH** *020 †50

PARKER, David R, Jr. 4323 N JOSEY LN STE 304 75010 #048-13-1983 L1987 **FM** *020 †18

PATHAK, Ajay Jayendrabhai. 2117 E ROSEMEADE PKWY 75007 #495-48-1982 L1994 **IMG** *020 †20

PENMETCHA, Mohan. 2008 E HEBRON PKWY, STE 100 75007 #495-58-1977 L1996 **RHU** *020 †20

PEREZ VALENTIN, Enrique A. 4352 N JOSEY LN, CENTER 75010 #042-01-1987 L1994 **ON HEM** *020 †20

PHAM, Van. ■ 75010 #396-01-1956 L1979 **GP** *020

POSCH, Ralph John. 4333 N JOSEY LN, STE 205 75010 #005-18-1982 L1987 **U** *020 †95

PRANULIS, Joseph Anthony. 4343 N JOSEY LN 75010 #048-02-1986 L1987 **IM EM** *020

PRUETT, Jon Davis. 4340 N JOSEY LN, STE 100 75010 #021-05-2002 L2006 **D** *020 †15

QUINTON, Reade Alan. ■ 75007 #021-05-1999 L2003 **FOP** *012

RAY, Mark K. 4340 N JOSEY LN STE 100, TRINITY DERMATOLOGY 75010 #048-02-1986 L1987 **D** *020 †15

REDDY, Shirisha Ravi. ■ 75007 #048-12-2001 L2004 **HO** *012

REZNICK, Lisa Renee. 4100 FAIRWAY DR STE 12 75010 #025-01-1989 L1996 **ORS HS** *020 †40

RIVERA, Richard Arthur. 4443 N JOSEY LN, STE 150 75010 #048-12-1979 L1979 **PD PSM** *020 †55

ROBERTS, Tami R. 4325 N JOSEY LN, STE 105 75010 #048-13-1999 L2002 **FM** *020 †18

SABATINI, Peter Raymond. ■ 75007 #001-06-2004 L2006 **OTO** *012

SAQUIB, Rehana. ■ 75007 #160-05-1992 L2004 **NEP** *012

SATODIYA, Mukesh Bhutabha. ■ 75007 #495-22-1999 L2007 **IM** *020 †20

SEO, Myungseok Rick. ■ 75007 #048-12-2008 *012

SETHI, Shikha. 4780 N JOSEY LN, METROCREST ORTHOPEDICS 75010 #035-08-1998 L2007 **PM** *100 †60

SHAH, Kirankumar P. 4217 MARSH RIDGE RD 75010 #495-48-1989 L1996 **N** *020 †75

SHAH, Neil Dilip. ■ 75007 #048-16-2005 **ORS** *012

SHANNON, John Daniel. 4343 N JOSEY LN 75010 #021-06-1990 L1995 **PTH** *020 †50

SIDDIQUI, Zafreen Arfeen. ■ 75007 #704-02-1992 L2005 **FM** *020 †18

SIGMAN, Gerald. 3012 E HEBRON PKWY, STE 104 75007 #067-01-1962 L1977 **GYN** *020

SINGH, Satnam K. 4100 WOODLAND TRL 75007 #495-41-1969 L1979 **EM** *020 †16

SIRI, Vicha. 4333 N JOSEY LN, STE 200 75104 #891-04-1972 L1983 **OBG** *020 †30

STEPHENS, Stephanie Renee. 4325 N JOSEY LN, PLAZA III, STE 103 75010 #010-03-1991 L2004 **ORS OSM** *020 †40

STEWART, Jeffrey G. 4333 N JOSEY LN 75010 #048-12-1988 L1989 **FM** *020 †18

STEWART, Robert Louis. 4343 N JOSEY LN 75010 #048-04-1978 L1978 **EM FM** *020 †18

STIMAGE, Rachenetta V. 4325 N JOSEY LN STE 300, PROFESSIONAL PLAZA 3 75010 #048-02-2003 L2008 **OBG** *020

STORRIE, Martha C. 4333 N JOSEY LN, STE 104 75010 #048-13-1985 L1987 **U** *074 †95

SUBRAMANIAN, Joysree. 4333 N JOSEY LN STE 204 75010 #495-38-1986 L2004 **AN** *020 †05

SULLINGER, Jana Cyrisse. 3118 GLENMERE CT 75007 #019-02-1983 L1991 **PTH PCP** *020 †50

SUSTER, Gerschon. 3730 N JOSEY LN, STE 111 75007 #264-03-1962 L1971 **PD GE** *020 †20

TALATALA, Rufino Gerona. 3730 N JOSEY LN STE 104 75007 #748-10-1991 L1999 **IM** *020 †20

TENG, Jay. 4323 N JOSEY LN, PLAZA I, STE 200 75010 #048-12-1975 L1978 **IM** *020 †20

THOMAS, Julie A. 4323 N JOSEY LN, PLAZA 1 STE 306 75010 #048-14-1992 L1993 **OBG** *020 †30

TOWNDEND-PARCHMAN, Janis. ■ 75007 #048-13-1985 L1987 **PTH GS** *020 †50

TRINH, Anh L. 3044 OLD DENTON RD, STE 138 75007 #048-16-2002 L2005 **PD** *020 †55

TUCKER, Lucy C. ■ 75007 #036-07-1976 L1986 **CHP P** *071

TUCKER, Michelle Scott. 1821 GOLDEN TRAIL CT, STE 200 75010 #048-12-2000 L2003 **PD** *020 †55 ‡

TULLBERG, Ian Roy. ■ 75010 #305-01-2006 **FP** *020

TURNER, Carrie A. 4333 N JOSEY LN 75010 #048-14-2002 L2005 **FM** *020 †18

VENINGA, Francis David. 4333 N JOSEY LN, STE 207 75010 #048-12-1981 L1983 **GS OS** *020 †20

VORA, Manik U. 4333 N JOSEY LN STE 301 75010 #495-20-1974 L1983 **OBG** *020 †30

WALDEN, Nikki Amina. 4325 N JOSEY LN, STE 300 75010 #051-04-2000 L2004 **OBG** *020

WARDELL, Deborah Frankia. 4443 N JOSEY LN, STE 160 75010 #048-02-1982 L1983 **PD** *020 †55

WATSON, Melvin E. 4100 INTERNATIONAL PKWY, STE 1010 75007 #041-09-1973 L1999 **PD** *020 †55

WEST, Diane C. 4343 N JOSEY LN 75010 #048-02-1995 L1998 **U** *020 †95

WHEELESS, Glenn Stephen. 4780 N JOSEY LN 75010 #048-12-1981 L1981 **ORS** *020 †40

WILSON, Terrence James. 4100 INTERNATIONAL PKWY, STE 1010 75007 #041-02-1980 L1990 **PM OM** *030 †60

ZHANG, Wei. 4333 N JOSEY LN 75010 #243-95-1991 L2005 **OBG** *100 †30

CARTHAGE – PANOLA

AKPASSA, Gerald Joseph. 409 COTTAGE RD 75633 #690-02-1994 L2005 **IM** *020

CALLAHAN, Robert Gipson. 307 COTTAGE RD 75633 #028-34-1915 L1949 **GS GP** *020 †85

FARHAT, Niaz. 409 COTTAGE RD, EAST TX MEDICAL CENTER 75633 #704-21-1996 L2007 **IM** *020 †20

HILL, Louie Royce. 409 COTTAGE RD 75633 #048-13-1975 L1975 **FM** *020 †18

KEELING, James Keith. 409 COTTAGE RD 75633 #048-12-1977 L1977 **FM** *020 †18

KORTIKERE, Saritha Arun. 704 DAVIS ST, EAST TEXAS MEDICAL CENTER 75633 #495-37-1995 L2005 **IM** *020 †18

MALVIYA, Prakash. 409 COTTAGE RD 75633 #495-49-1978 L2007 **PD** *020 †55

NIELSEN, John Francis. 702 DAVIS ST, STE 4 75633 #654-01-1988 L1995 **FM** *020 †18

PERKINS, Christopher J. 4188 NW LOOP 436 75633 #048-78-1997, ▲ L1998 **PHP UCM** *020

PHILLIPS, Jim Jason. 1410 W PANOLA ST 75633 #048-15-1997 L1998 **FM** *020 †18 ‡

REDDY, Gurram Vidyasagar. 409 COTTAGE RD, EMERGENCY DEPARTMENT 75633 #495-57-1987 L2004 **PD** *020 †55

ROSHAN, Iraj. 704 DAVIS ST STE 702 75633 #048-14-1994 L1995 **CD** *020 †20

ROSHAN, Sohaila Y. 704 DAVIS ST, STE 500 75633 #048-14-1994 L1995 **END** *020 †20

RUBIN, Gary David. 704 DAVIS ST 75633 #016-45-1982 L2006 **ORS GS** *020 †40

SMITH, William Cecil. ■ 75633 #048-02-1944 L1944 **FM** *071

STURDIVANT, Arlen Young. 409 COTTAGE RD 75633 #048-02-1968 L1968 **FM** *071 †18

WESSMAN, Robert Clinton. 702 DAVIS ST, STE 2 75633 #048-15-1998 L2002 **FM** *020 †18

CASTLE HILLS – BEXAR

LOWRY, George Mc Clellan. 2161 NW MILITARY HWY # 101 78213 #028-02-1966 L1972 **OPH** *020 †35

REED, Amanda Beth. ■ 78213 #021-01-2004 L2006 **U** *012

CASTROVILLE – MEDINA

CRESPO, Rodrigo. 1051 US HIGHWAY 90 E 78009 #429-02-1994 L2006 **IM** *020

HYMER, Joe Donald. 109 US HIGHWAY 90 W 78009 #048-02-1964 L1964 **GP OS** *071

JAAFAR, Saleh N. 1051 US HIGHWAY 90 E 78009 #654-01-1991 L1996 **IM** *020

KURI, Kalife. 1051 US HIGHWAY 90 E 78009 #649-44-1988 L1994 **IM CD** *020 †20

NASRALLAH, Ammar Fathi. 1051 US HIGHWAY 90 E, MEDCARE ASSOCIATES 78009 #575-01-1999 L2006 **ID** *020

PFEIFFER, John P, Jr. ■ 78009 #028-34-1951 L1952 **GYN** *071 †30

VAN WINKLE, Lloyd Pierce. 409 MADRID ST 78009 #048-14-1982 L1983 **FM** *020 †18 ‡

CAT SPRING – COLORADO

SAMAAN, Jean Moffatt. ■ 78933 #917-02-1957 L1973 **FM IMG** *071

CATARINA – DIMMIT

BROWN, Dorothy Mainland. PO BOX 53 78836 #017-20-1943 L1946 **PHP GP** *072

CEDAR CREEK – BASTROP

NAIRN, Michael Andrew. ■ 78612 #039-01-1977 L1983 **EM GP** *071 †16

CEDAR HILL – DALLAS

BAILEY, Cecil Cedric. 128 W BELT LINE RD STE 1 75104 #010-03-1997 L2000 **IM** *020 †20

BAKER, Karen Kay. 326B COOPER ST 75104 #048-14-1996 L1997 **FM** *020 †18

BATEMAN, Cathleen Pekor. 130 W BELT LINE RD, STE 2 75104 #048-02-1978 L1978 **D** *020 †15 ‡

BROWN, Benton Lee. ■ 75104 #048-12-2008 *012

BUBLEWICZ, Michael Bogumi. ■ 75104 #048-15-2008 *012

CHAVEZ, Estrella Ganaban. ■ 75104 #748-01-1965 L1974 **P OS** *071

COLEMAN, Kathleen Adele. ■ 75104 #048-12-2008 *012

CRAWFORD, Franklin L. 501 JEFFERSON ST 75104 #048-12-1949 L1949 **FM** *071 †18
DICKINSON, Jeri Elizabeth. ■ 75104 #019-02-2005 **GS** *012
JACKSON, Albert Jerome, Jr. ■ 75104 #017-20-2004 L2007 **AN** *012
JONES, Brian D. 326 COOPER ST B 75104 #048-15-1997 L1998 **FM** *020 †18
KRUEGER, Henry Geo. ■ 75104 #041-13-1944 L1945 **GYN** *071 †30
MARSHALL, Michael S. 326 COOPER ST 75104 #048-12-1985 L1986 **MPD PD** *020 †20,55
MCANALLEY, Shayne Anthony. ■ 75104 #048-02-2007 *012
MC COLLUM, David N. ■ 75104 #048-02-2007 *012
MC CONNELL, John Willard. ■ 75104 #048-13-1978 L1978 **AN** *020
MENES, Stephanie Ifeoma. ■ 75104 #690-02-2001 **IM** *074
OZANNE, Stephen. 128 W BELT LINE RD STE 1 75104 #023-01-1981 L1985 **OSS** *020 †40
PATEL, Ashok Gordhanbhai. 500 N HIGHWAY 67 75104 #495-23-1970 L1980 **FM** *020 †18 ‡
PERKINS-EDWARDS, Beverley. ■ 75104 #017-20-1975 L2006 **IM PMM** *072
PHILLIPS, Donald Hardy. 105 S MAIN ST 75104 #048-12-1986 L1987 **IM** *020 †20
PRASAD, Jyotsna S. 445 E FM 1382, STE 3354 75104 #496-35-1998 L2002 **FM** *020 †18
RASHID, Mousumy Khan. ■ 75104 #305-01-2003 **FP** *012
RODRIGUE, Linda Ann. 950 E BELT LINE RD SU 75104 #021-05-1985 L2007 **OBG** *020 †30
SERRANO, Bethzaida. ■ 75104 #649-14-1990 L1992 **IM** *072
SHANNON, Donna Arlene. 326 COOPER ST 75104 #048-12-1999 L2001 **FM** *020 †18
SHARP, Collin Frasier. ■ 75104 #007-02-2004 **GS** *012
SMITH, Lori Patrice. ■ 75104 #048-02-2005 L2008 **PD** *012
STERN, Mary Jane. ■ 75104 #016-11-1945 L1948 **PD PHP** *071 †70
VANGALA, Karuna Reddy. 350 W BELT LINE RD 75104 #495-21-1977 L1983 **IM** *020 †20
VAUGHAN, Jeremy Brandon. ■ 75104 #048-12-2007 **OBG** *012
VITACCA, Rocco John. 642 N HIGHWAY 67 75104 #065-09-1960 L1982 **FM** *071 †18
VITTIMBERGA, Frank John. ■ 75104 #024-16-1994 L2005 **GS** *020 †85
WASHINGTON, Evelyn T. ■ 75104 #048-13-1981 L1981 **FM** *020 †18
WHITE, Steven Robt. ■ 75104 #917-03-1978 L1989 **NS** *020
WIXTROM, Keith A. 445 E FM 1382, STE 3 75104 #048-12-1984 L1985 **FM** *040 †18
WOOD, Prescilla B. ■ 75104 #048-12-2006 **PTH** *012
YOUSUF, Uzma. ■ 75104 #704-02-1991 **PTH** *100

CEDAR PARK — WILLIAMSON

ABANDO, Alan Richard. 1401 MEDICAL PKWY, STE 101 78613 #016-01-2000 L2007 **GS** *020 †85
ANGELOCCI, Tracy L. 500 W WHITESTONE BLVD, STE 100 78613 #048-14-1992 L1996 **MPD** *020 †20,55
AUNG, Thomas Lee. 801 E WHITESTONE BLVD 78613 #048-12-1995 L1996 **HO** *020 †20
BASA, Nicole Reyes. 1401 MEDICAL PKWY, STE 101 78613 #016-01-2000 L2007 **GS** *020 †85
BIBA, Frank Jos. ■ 78613 #048-04-1967 L1967 **AN** *071 †05
BLADUELL-RAMOS, Wallace. ■ 78613 #847-10-1956 L1983 **OS OBG** *030
BLUMBERG, Joel Saul. 1401 MEDICAL PKWY, STE 100 78613 #048-02-1989 L1990 **PD** *020 †55
BOGDANOVICH, Michael B. 500 W WHITESTONE BLVD, STE 100 78613 #054-04-1981 L1989 **FM** *020 †18
BUTLER, Harrel D, Jr. 801 E WHITESTONE BLVD, STE B 78613 #048-14-1994 L1995 **FM** *020 †18
CARDWELL, Brent Steven. 345 CYPRESS CREEK RD, STE 104 78613 #019-02-1998 L2001 **PD** *020 †55
CHENG, Arthur Chihhao. 715 DISCOVERY BLVD, STE 117 78613 #016-42-1997 L2006 **PD** *020 †55
COHEN, Joseph Ira. 200 BUTTERCUP CREEK BLVD 78613 #056-06-1986 L1988 **FOP** *020 †50
COHEN, Joseph Isaac. 200 BUTTERCUP CREEK BLVD, STE 100 78613 #654-01-1999 L2003 **PD** *020 †55
FOSTER, Steven K. 190 BUTTERCUP CREEK BLVD 78613 #048-14-1987 L1988 **IM PD** *020 †20,55
GOGULSKI, David H. 900 QUEST PKWY 78613 #048-16-1995 L1996 **FM PD** *020 †18
HALL, Christopher S. 500 W WHITESTONE BLVD, STE 100 78613 #048-12-2004 L2007 **FM** *020 †18
HARTMANN, Aubrey C. 1401 MEDICAL PKWY, BLDG B # 300 78613 #048-12-1998 L2001 **D** *020 †15
JAYAWANT, Gina Cottle. 12171 W PARMER LN, STE 201 78613 #051-04-1996 L2007 **OPH** *020 †35
JOHARI, Soma B. 900 QUEST PKWY 78613 #048-16-1998 L2000 **FM** *020 †18
KARABINAS, Steven P. ■ 78613 #418-02-1954 L1975 **PHP ORS** *030
KILLGOAR, Christina Moore. 345 CYPRESS CREEK RD, STE 104 78613 #047-06-2000 L2006 **PD** *020 †55
KING, Cameron Todd. 345 CYPRESS CREEK RD, STE 104 78613 #019-02-1998 L2001 **FM** *020 †18
LANKFORD, Wendy Suzanne. 801 E WHITESTONE BLVD, STE B 78613 #048-14-1997 L2004 **FM** *020 †18
LENGEL, Brian W. 701 E WHITESTONE BLVD, CLINIC 78613 #048-14-1983 L1983 **IM** *030 †20
LEPGOLD, Edith Lee. 1401 MEDICAL PKWY, STE 220 78613 #056-06-1984 L2007 **IM** *020 †20
MEADOWS, Jennifer Lynn. 1401 MEDICAL PKWY, STE 410 78613 #048-15-2003 L2007 **OBG** *020
MELVILLE, Sharon Kay. ■ 78613 #048-14-1985 L1986 **GPM** *050
MEROLA, Wendy Mara. 901 CYPRESS CREEK RD, BLDG 1 78613 #048-13-1986 L1991 **FM GS** *020 †18
MODAK, Ajit Kumar. ■ 78630 #495-39-1958 L1976 **AN** *071 †05
MONDAL, Sabiha Akhtar. 701 E WHITESTONE BLVD, DEPARTMENT OF VETERANS AFF 78613 #048-04-1995 L2000 **IM** *020 †20
NASH, William Dewayne. 801 E WHITESTONE BLVD, STE B 78613 #004-01-1982 L1989 **FM** *020 †18
NAVARRO, Carlos Fernando. 801 E WHITESTONE BLVD, STE B 78613 #270-02-1998 L2005 **FM** *020 †18
ORGERON, Joseph E. 345 CYPRESS CREEK RD, STE 104 78613 #021-06-2004 L2007 **FM** *020 †18
PHIPPS, Henry Kirk. 100 E WHITESTONE BLVD 78613 #016-45-1976 L1991 **EM** *071 †16
RAO, Ajanta Bellamkonda. ■ 78613 #495-21-1992 L2004 **FM** *100
RESTIVO, Vincent Anthony. 12171 W PARMER LN 78613 #048-14-1997 L1999 **OPH** *020 †35
RICHARDS, Daniel Gary. ■ 78613 #041-15-2000 L2007 **PD** *100 †55
ROTH, Stephanie D. 500 W WHITESTONE BLVD, STE 100 78613 #048-14-1994 L1999 **FM** *020 †18
SANDHU, Anita Raminder. 1401 MEDICAL PKWY, BLDG B 78613 #048-15-2003 L2007 **OBG** *020

SHAMI, Nejla S. 190 BUTTERCUP CREEK BLVD, FAMILY MED CTR BOX 189 78613 #048-13-2000 L2002 **FM** *020 †18
SMITH, Benjamin L. 900 QUEST PKWY 78613 #048-16-1997 L1998 **FM** *020 †18
SPENCER, Christopher C. 715 DISCOVERY BLVD, STE 117 78613 #021-06-1989 L1994 **PD** *020 †55
STEWART, Christopher A. 900 QUEST PKWY 78613 #048-02-1996 L1997 **FM** *020 †18
STOECKEL, Mark D. 701 E WHITESTONE BLVD, BLDG II 78613 #048-14-1997 L2002 **FM FSM** *020 †18
SU, John Renn. ■ 78613 #048-14-2000 L2001 **GPM** *100 †50
SURAPANENI, Veena. 801 E WHITESTONE BLVD 78613 #495-50-1993 L1998 **IM** *020 †20
TABBAA, Rashed. 500 W WHITESTONE BLVD, STE 250 78613 #915-03-1972 L1981 **CD IM** *020 †20
TROSKY, Kathryn C. 2501 CYPRESS CREEK RD 78613 #041-02-1977 L1984 **P** *020 †75
URREA, Melissa Jeanine. 201 S BELL BLVD STE 104 78613 #048-02-1999 L2000 **FM** *020 †18
VAN WISSE, Celia Ruiz. 201 S BELL BLVD, STE 104 78613 #649-03-1970 L1976 **GS** *020 †85
VELASCO, Jeanne Michelle. ■ 78613 #048-02-2008 *012
WARREN, Pamela Ann. 1909 CYPRESS CREEK RD 78613 #048-13-1983 L1983 **FM** *020 †18
WILSON, Joy Denise. 900 QUEST PKWY 78613 #038-40-2004 L2006 **FM** *020 †18
WINN, David Lawrence. 500 W WHITESTONE BLVD #200 78613 #048-04-1981 L1982 **FM** *020 †18
YANIV, Esther. 715 DISCOVERY BLVD, STE 117 78613 #550-02-2000 L2005 **PM** *020 †60
YEE, Bing G. 200 S BELL BLVD STE B4 78613 #048-02-1989 L1992 **FM** *020 †18
ZIARI, Alison D. 715 DISCOVERY BLVD STE 1 78613 #048-13-1995 L1998 **PD** *020 †55

CELINA — COLLIN

ASSELSTINE, Robert C. PO BOX 839, 241 W PECAN 75009 #065-09-1968 L1993 **FM FPG** *020
HAYNES, William M. ■ 75009 #048-12-1952 L1952 **R** *071 †80
PIRANIO, Joe C. RR1 BOX 135A 75009 #021-01-1942 L1943 **PD** *071

CENTER — SHELBY

ALINDADA, Juliana B. 602 HURST ST, # 1686 75935 #748-07-1974 L1985 **OBG** *020
CHANDRAMOHAN, Ajitha. 1743 SOUTHVIEW CIR 75935 #495-53-1989 L1999 **IM** *020 †20
HOOKER, Joe Ben. 602 HURST ST 75935 #047-06-1963 L1964 **GP GYN** *020
MALLORY, Conway H, Jr. 602 HURST ST 75935 #047-06-1960 L1961 **GP DR** *071
MC MULLEN, Craig Marlin. 233 HURST ST 75935 #048-13-2000 L2003 **FM OBG** *020 ‡
MILLER, Keith Edward. 620 TENAHA ST 75935 #004-01-1985 L1987 **FM** *020 †18
OATES, L Stephen, Jr. 205 CORA ST, BOX 1717 75935 #048-02-1957 L1957 **FM** *020
REED, Vera M. 602 HURST ST 75935 #048-15-1988 L1989 **EM** *020
SINGSON, Florencio. 602 HURST ST, MEMORIAL PLAZA 75935 #748-08-1977 L1983 **IM** *020
TODD, Jane Dilling. 304 LOGANSPORT ST, CRC 75935 #036-05-1973 L1981 **GP GS** *020 †85

CENTER POINT — KERR

CECALA, Philip J. ■ 78010 #016-43-1940 L1946 **GP** *071
PATTEN, Charles Grey. ■ 78010 #065-05-1945 L1957 **GP** *075

CHANDLER — HENDERSON

CHERRY, Thomas I, Jr. ■ 75758 #048-15-1995 L1998 **FM** *020 †18 ‡
GRIFFITHS, John Paul. ■ 75758 #041-13-1980 L1982 **IM** *020 †20

CHANNELVIEW — HARRIS

ARROYO, Carlos. 1003 SHELDON RD, UNIT B 77530 #035-19-1979 L1981 **IM** *020
BERBERIAN, Esteban N. 15035 EAST FWY 77530 #429-01-1993 L1999 **IM** *020 †20
BURMAN, Gary Robt. 15035 EAST FWY 77530 #649-14-1983 L1992 **IM** *020 †20
HEARN, Donald Rena. 15055 EAST FWY, STE A30 77530 #048-16-1987 L1988 **FM EM** *020 †18
KILLAM, Ronald W. 15055 EAST FWY, STE A20 77530 #048-14-1987 L1989 **IM OM** *020 †20
MULLOY, Wayne Gale. 15035 EAST FWY, STE A 77530 #048-02-1959 L1959 **GP LM** *020
NGUYEN, Anh Bao. 16007 EAST FWY 77530 #941-01-1971 L1982 **PM** *020
NINO, Donald R. 15055 EAST FWY, STE A10 77530 #048-14-1983 L1983 **FM** *020 †18 ‡
PEREZ, Angel. 15055 EAST FWY STE B60 77530 #048-14-1998 L2001 **IM** *020 †20
SHAH, Afaf Zahra. 15101 EAST FWY, TRIUMPH EAST 77530 #704-01-1975 L1981 **ATP CLP** *020 †50
SMITH, Howard James. 15055 EAST FWY, STE B30 77530 #018-03-1969 L1970 **GP** *020
WASSERSTEIN, Jerome C. 15055 EAST FWY, STE B10 77530 #016-76-1974, ▲ L1975 **GP FPG** *020
WILLITS, Verne Leroy. 15035 EAST FWY 77530 #039-01-1969 L1972 **IM HEM** *020 †20
WONG, Carmen. 15055 EAST FWY, STE B50 77530 #048-14-1991 L1993 **FM** *020 †18

CHAPPELL HILL — WASHINGTON

KLINE, Charles Danl. ■ 77426 #017-20-1955 L1964 **AN OS** *071 †05

CHILDRESS — CHILDRESS

CALDWELL, Richard D. 1001 US HIGHWAY 83 N 79201 #048-14-1993 L1994 **FM** *020 †18
CARTER, Tom Stephen. 7059 US HIGHWAY 287, JACKSON COUNTY MEMORIAL HO 79201 #308-11-1987 L1994 **FM** *020 †18
DARTER, Thomas C. 1001 US HIGHWAY 83 N 79201 #048-15-1988 L1989 **FM** *020 †18
GREEN, Weldon Dee. 2020 COUNTRY CLUB DR 79201 #048-12-1976 L1976 **FM** *020 †18
HENDERSON, James Michael. 2020 COUNTRY CLUB DR 79201 #048-14-1975 L1975 **FM** *020 †18
HORTON, Kenneth C. 200 COMMERCE ST, THE CLINIC FOR FAMILY MEDI 79201 #048-15-1998 L1999 **FM** *020 †18
OLAY, Honorato Prado, Jr. HWY 83 NORTH, FOX RURAL HEALTH CLINIC 79201 #748-01-1963 L1975 **GS GP** *020

■ = Address Information Privacy Protected

WESTENBURG, Jacobus J. 300 N MAIN ST 79201 #660-01-1948 L1953 **GP IM** *072 †18

CHILLICOTHE – HARDEMAN

AHMED, Naseer. ■ 79225 #704-05-1982 L1998 **IM** *020 †20

CHILTON – FALLS

ROOT, Deborah. ■ 76632 #048-15-1987 L1988 **P PYG** *020 †75

CIBOLO – GUADALUPE

ABARICIA, Sophia Tee. ■ 78108 #028-03-2005 L2008 **PD** *012
BATEMAN, Terry Alan. ■ 78108 #049-01-2005 L2007 **AN** *012
CLIVE, Kevin Scott. ■ 78108 #038-41-2007 **GS** *012
JENKINS, Christopher. ■ 78108 #048-13-2000 L2004 **GS** *100
NGUYEN-MINH, Nhat Canh. ■ 78108 #026-04-1995 L1995 **GS** *020 †85
OLSON, Kasi Meredith. ■ 78108 #038-44-2003 L2003 **ADL** *012 †55
PRAKASH, Vidhya. ■ 78108 #038-41-2004 L2006 **ID** *012 †20
ROBINSON, Mark Allan. ■ 78108 #023-12-2001 L2003 **ORS** *020
SETO, Jiffy Chung. ■ 78108 #010-02-2001 L2003 *020 †18
SMITH, Thomas Wm. ■ 78108 #016-11-1974 L1977 **FM** *020 †18 ‡
STERNER, James Boyd. ■ 78108 #028-03-2005 L2007 **IM** *012
THIELE, Arthur J, Jr. ■ 78108 #041-13-1949 **AM OTO** *071 †45
WARD, Allan Edmund. ■ 78108 #024-16-1996 L1997 **GPM** *012 †20,70
WILKIE, Brandi Sha. ■ 78108 #048-13-2006 L2007 **OBG** *012

CLARENDON – DONLEY

HOWARD, John Cooper. 205 ORPE ST, DONLEY CNTY RURAL HLTH CLN 79226 #021-01-1982 L1984 **FM AM** *020 †70

CLARKSVILLE – RED RIVER

EDWARDS, Rex Lee. ■ 75426 #048-02-1955 L1955 **GP GS** *071 †18
GANGULY, Devabrata. HWY 82 WEST 75426 #495-79-1989 L1999 **IM IMG** *020 †20
MILLIKAN, Robert Randolph. HWY 82 WEST 75426 #048-02-1976 L1976 **FM** *020 †18
MUTHAPPA, Bachranianda C. 120 FM 2825, BOX 1429 75426 #495-09-1966 L1978 **GS FM** *020
SREERAMA, Ravi Kumar. 103 N COLLEGE ST 75426 #495-50-1975 L1989 **IM** *020
TSENG, Angela. 3000 W MAIN ST 75426 #429-01-1979 L1982 **CD IM** *020

CLEAR LAKE SHORES – GALVESTON

KONDEJEWSKI, Richard J. 828 FM 2094 RD STE A 77565 #065-09-1971 L1978 **FM OM** *020

CLEBURNE – JOHNSON

ABOUKHAIR, Nabil K. 825 N NOLAN RIVER RD 76033 #048-16-1990 L1991 **GYN** *020 †30
ANYADIEGWU, Andrew E. 203 WALLS DR STE 208 76033 #690-04-1991 L2007 **CCM** *100 †20
ARANETA, Maria Mercedes M. 2100 HARVEST HILL RD 76033 #748-02-1979 L1993 **PTH BBK** *020 †50
BALDWIN-PRICE, H K. ■ 76033 #917-06-1958 L1962 **GS** *071 †85
BENKE, Theodore Thos. 203 WALLS DR STE 101, CLINIC, P.A. 76033 #048-02-1989 L1990 **OTO** *020 †45
BORKOWSKI, Joanna Lucja. 201 WALLS DR, WALLS REGIONAL HOSPITAL 76033 #759-09-1979 L2001 **PTH** *020 †50
BOSWORTH, William Chas. 808 N NOLAN RIVER RD 76033 #039-01-1960 L1975 **IM CD** *071
BOYETT, George Thos, Jr. 505 N RIDGEWAY DR 76033 #048-12-1967 L1967 **OBG** *020 †30
BROZYNSKI, Krzysztof K. 505 N RIDGEWAY DR, STE 282 76033 #759-09-1982 L2001 **IM** *020 †20
CINCO, Narciso M, Jr. 1650 W HENDERSON ST 76033 #748-02-1953 L1976 **OPH OTO** *071
COHEN, Elliott Lee. 201 WALLS DR 76033 #016-06-1972 L2003 **EM IM** *020 †20,16
COOMANSINGH, Belden J. ■ 76031 #047-07-1973 L1980 **OBG** *071
DALLEY, Albert S. 141 HYDE PARK BLVD 76033 #048-12-2000 L2002 **IM** *100 †20
DANG, Danhjohn T. 220 N RIDGEWAY DR, FAMILY MEDICINE ASSOCIATES 76033 #048-16-1992 L1993 **FM** *020 †18
DANG, John Duong. 220 N RIDGEWAY DR, STE A 76033 #048-04-1986 L1987 **IM** *020 †20
DANIELS, Herbert B, Jr. ■ 76033 #004-01-1952 L1953 **GS TS** *071 †85
DANIELS, Herbert B, III. 201 WALLS DR 76033 #048-02-1981 L1981 **FM** *020 †18
DAVIDSON-COX, Karla K. 203 WALLS DR STE 206 76033 #048-16-2000 L2003 **FM** *020 †18 ‡
FARLESS, Blaine Lee. 2010 W KATHERINE P RANS RD, STE 300 76033 #048-13-1987 L1992 **ORS OSM** *020 †40
FARZAM, Steven Amir. 201 WALLS DR, STE 502 76033 #048-02-1994 L1995 **OBG** *020 †30
FORD, William Ray. 201 WALLS DR STE 501 76033 #021-06-1999 L2003 **OBG** *020
FURMAN, Erik Jon. 505 N RIDGEWAY DR, STE 160 76033 #037-01-1997 L1998 **FM** *020 †18
GUROVA, Yelena Vyacheslav. 624 N MAIN ST 76033 #913-06-1993 L2003 **IM** *020 †20
HARMAN, Bradley D. 2010 W KATHERINE P RANS RD, STE 300 76033 #048-14-1998 L2000 **ORS** *020 †40
HUGHES, Kent Chas. 203 WALLS DR 76033 #056-05-1990 L1992 **PS** *020 †85,65
JENSEN, Jay Bert. ■ 76033 #023-07-1965 L1971 **CD IM** *071 †20
JOHNSON, James Allen. 808 N NOLAN RIVER RD 76033 #048-02-1962 L1962 **IM** *062 †20
JOHNSON, Joe Stanley. 220 N RIDGEWAY DR, STE A 76033 #048-14-1975 L1975 **FM A** *020 †18
JOHNSON, Stephen Gail. 220 N RIDGEWAY DR, STE A 76033 #048-02-1967 L1967 **FM** *020 †18
KIEL, Gerald Lewis. 220 N RIDGEWAY DR 76033 #048-14-1981 L1981 **FM** *020 †18
LUCUS, Dale Ray. 201 WALLS DR 76033 #048-02-1976 L1976 **FM OBS** *020 †18 ‡
MADDOX, Barney Thos. 829 N NOLAN RIVER RD 76033 #048-12-1979 L1979 **U** *020 †95
MARTELL, John R, Jr. 201 WALLS DR STE 500 76033 #041-02-1981 L2001 **ORS MDM** *020 †40 ‡

MC KENZIE, Heather Lynn. 220 N RIDGEWAY DR 76033 #048-13-2003 L2005 **FM** *020 †18
MERTZ, Bruce Leighton. 203 WALLS DR STE 204 76033 #048-13-1979 L1979 **FM OBS** *020 †18
MORTON, Stephanie Johnson. 220 N RIDGEWAY DR, STE A 76033 #048-14-1997 L1998 **FM** *020 †18 ‡
ORINA, Adolf Doria. ■ 76033 #748-02-1962 L1973 **IM** *071 †50
PARRISH, David Lewis, Jr. 203 WALLS DR, STE 203 76033 #019-02-1992 L1993 **CD** *020 †20
PHILLIPS, Michael S. 2010 W KATHERINE P RANS RD, STE 200 76033 #048-15-1995 L1997 **AN PMM** *020 †05
RAINES, Arthur Lee. 201 WALLS DR 76033 #048-02-1967 L1967 **PTH OS** *020 †50
REDDY, Srinivas. 1601 N ANGLIN ST, PECAN VALLEY MHMR 76031 #495-57-1979 L1990 **P** *020
REED, Yvonne Slater. 505 N RIDGEWAY DR, STE 283 76033 #048-12-1997 L1998 **IM** *020 †20
ROE, Robert David. 201 WALLS DR 76033 #035-09-1959 L1976 **GS** *020 †85
SAMLOWSKI, Eberhard Roy. 220 N RIDGEWAY DR 76033 #038-40-1985 L1992 **GS** *020 †85
SELLMAN, Jack Claude. 2100 CR1224 76033 #049-01-1958 L1964 **IM NEP** *075 †20
SHARMA, Ranbir Kumar. 203 WALLS DR STE 103 76033 #048-02-1991 L1992 **PD** *020 †55
SMITH, Wade Hamrick. 812 N NOLAN RIVER RD 76033 #048-02-1972 L1972 **D** *020 †15
SURRATT, Steve Glenn. 203 WALLS DR STE 209 76033 #048-14-1984 L1985 **OPH** *020 †35
THOMAS, Scot Ethan. ■ 76033 #005-18-2003 **IM** *100
VANZANT, Greg A. 201 WALLS DR, WALLS REGINAL HOSPITAL 76033 #048-13-1984 L1985 **AN** *020 †05
WALLACE, Brent Holmes. 141 HYDE PARK BLVD 76033 #048-02-1978 L1978 **IM** *020
WHITE, Joe Michael. 220 N RIDGEWAY DR 76033 #048-12-1975 L1980 **FM** *020 †18
WILSON, Gregory Stephan. 203 WALLS DR, STE 205 76033 #048-02-1981 L1981 **FM OBS** *020 †18
ZAMBRANO, Sergio Sanchez. 811 N MAIN ST 76033 #649-01-1968 L1976 **CD IM** *020 ‡

CLEVELAND – LIBERTY

AHMAD, Nabil Mahmood. 200 E BOOTHE ST, STE 220 77327 #704-01-1995 L2000 **CD** *020 †20
AISENBERG, Gabriel Marcel. 705 E HOUSTON ST 77327 #132-01-1990 L2006 **IM** *020 †20
ASLAM, Ambreen. 108 S WILLIAM BARNETT AVE 77327 #704-16-1987 L1994 **PD** *020 †55 ‡
BAKER, Merrimon W. 1000 S WASHINGTON AVE 77327 #048-04-1983 L1983 **ORS** *020 †40
BASI, Anand. 213 S COLLEGE AVE, CLEVELAND PRIMARY HLTH CTR 77327 #495-33-1991 L2002 **IM** *020 †20
BOZTEPE, Sureyya. 705 E HOUSTON ST 77327 #902-10-1956 L1974 **GP GS** *071
BUSSELBERG, Lorin Fred. 203 N COLLEGE AVE STE 1001, FAMILY HEALTH CLINIC 77327 #056-05-1970 L2003 **PS** *020 †85,65
CHERLO, Sreenivasulu. 213 S COLLEGE AVE 77327 #495-62-1991 L1996 **IM** *020 †20
EL-ZAIM, Diana Ruiz. 203 N COLLEGE AVE, STE 3001 77327 #048-02-2002 L2006 **PD** *100
FOUTZ, Charles Douglas. 300 E CROCKETT ST 77327 #048-12-1973 L1973 **EM** *020
GOIN, Joseph. 108 S WILLIAM BARNETT AVE 77327 #690-10-1984 L1998 **PD** *020 †55
GOTTIPATI, Anita Rani. 401 E CROCKETT ST, STE B 77327 #495-58-1992 L2005 **CN** *020
HOWIE, David I. 901 E HOUSTON ST, STE C 77327 #048-12-1986 L1987 **OP ORS** *020 †40
HUSAINI, Innad Hasan. 203 N COLLEGE AVE, E.C.R. CLINIC PA 77327 #875-01-1978 L1998 **OPH** *020
JAIKARAN, Jacques S. 203 N COLLEGE AVE 77327 #917-05-1968 L1978 **PS FPS** *020
KIM, Myung Jin. 307 E CROCKETT ST 77327 #583-01-1965 L1979 **IM PUD** *071 †20
KREIT, Camil Ibrahim. 403 E DALLAS ST 77327 #875-02-1978 L1994 **FM** *020 †18
KREIT, Mark Maher. 203 N COLLEGE AVE, STE 1001 77327 #875-01-1978 L1995 **FM** *020 †18
KREIT, Samir Ibrahim. 203 N COLLEGE AVE, STE 2001 77327 #875-01-1976 L1995 **GS** *040 †85
LANDRY, Robert Kieth. 108 S WILLIAM BARNETT AVE 77327 #027-01-1998 L2004 **FM** *020 †18
LE, Duc Minh. 300 E CROCKETT ST 77327 #305-01-2002 L2007 **FM** *100
MC TIGUE, Timothy Fallon. 300 E CROCKETT ST 77327 #045-01-1998 L2007 **MPD** *020 †20,55
MIR, Ahmed-Ullah. 300 E CROCKETT ST 77327 #704-02-1962 L1977 **GS GP** *020
OUAIS, Samir Geo. 203 N COLLEGE AVE 77327 #875-01-1965 L1988 **END IM** *020 †20
PIPKIN, Tracy Snell. 403 E DALLAS ST 77327 #035-20-1998 L2002 **OBG** *020
PRASAD, G V. 110 E CROCKETT ST 77327 #495-50-1974 L1983 **CD** *020 †20
REDDY, Akhila Cheruku. 108 S WILLIAM BARNETT AVE 77327 #496-37-2000 L2004 **FM GP** *020
ROBBINS, Leonard Roy. PO BOX 838 77328 #048-04-1948 L1950 **IM DIA** *071 †20
SAMPSON, Lorenzo Keith. 216 N COLLEGE AVE, 403 E. DALLAS ST. 77327 #045-01-1992 L1999 **GS** *020 †85
SCHAEFFER, Luis G. 113 S COLLEGE AVE 77327 #737-03-1976 L1996 **IM GP** *020 †20
SMITIH, Jeanne Jian. 300 E CROCKETT ST, DEPT. OBGYN 77327 #005-14-1996 **OBG** *020
SPOONER, Keith Ian. 117A S WILLIAM BARNETT AVE 77327 #048-04-1980 L1982 **OBG** *020 †30
SULAIMAN, Jasmine. ■ 77327 #495-44-1990 L2005 **FM** *020 †18 ‡
TAYLOR, Trina Louise. 210 E HOUSTON ST 77327 #041-15-2000 L2004 **PD** *020
TEMPLE, John Rogers, Jr. 300 E CROCKETT ST 77327 #496-15-1987 L1988 **EM PS** *020 †85
VAUGHN, Traci Lydricka. 107 S BONHAM AVE 77327 #024-01-1996 L2006 **OTO** *100 †45
WILLIAMS, Balmore W. 309 E CROCKETT ST, STE A 77327 #048-02-1998 L2001 **FM** *020 †18

CLIFTON – BOSQUE

BARNARD, James A, III. PO BOX 495 76634 #048-12-1962 L1962 **OBG** *071 †30
BLANTON, Kevin J. 201 S AVENUE T 76634 #048-78-2002, ▲ L2003 **FM** *020 †18
BROCK, James Lynch. 201 S AVENUE T 76634 #048-02-1970 L1970 **FM** *072
CLAY, Nancy Jill. 201 S AVENUE T 76634 #048-16-1992 L2000 **FM** *020 †18
COTTEN, Leon Brady, Jr. 201 S AVENUE T 76634 #048-02-1970 L1970 **GS GP** *020 †85
DELUE, Sean D. 201 S AVENUE T 76634 #048-14-2002 L2003 **FM** *020 †18
GLOFF, Donald Arthur. 201 S AVENUE T, CLIFTON MED & SURGICAL CLI 76634 #048-02-1961 L1961 **FM GS** *071 †18
HOLDER, Wiseman T. 201 S AVENUE T 76634 #048-04-1947 L1947 **GP OBG** *071
HOOVER, George M. ■ 76634 #004-01-1952 L1957 **ORS** *071 †40
KEY, William F, Jr. ■ 76634 #048-02-1953 L1953 **GP** *071
O'REILLY, Martha Lee. 201 S AVENUE T, CLIFTON MEDICAL CLINIC 76634 #048-15-2002 L2006 **IM** *020 †20
SCAFF, Bruce Edward. 101 S AVENUE T 76634 #048-12-1981 L1981 **FM** *020 †18
TROTTER, William Payne. RR 1 76634 #047-06-1958 L1960 **R** *071 †80
TURNER, Richard Thos. 201 S AVENUE T 76634 #048-12-1982 L1985 **AN** *020 †05
WEBB, Phil Abernethy. 201 S AVENUE T, CLIFTON MEDICAL CLINIC 76634 #048-02-1956 L1956 **ORS** *071 †40

CLUTE – BRAZORIA

MARKETTE, James Rickard. ■ 77531 #048-02-1956 L1956 **P** *075

COLDSPRING – SAN JACINTO

MC MURREY, Samuel Patrick. ■ 77331 #048-04-1948 L1948 **GP** *071
TENGG, Nicholas Edwin. ■ 77331 #048-04-1956 L1956 **PD** *071 †55
WISIACKAS, Philip Robert. 110 HILL AVE 77331 #024-05-1977 L1979 **FM** *020 †18

COLEMAN – COLEMAN

ATWOOD, Darron Todd. 310 S PECOS ST, 2ND FLOOR CLNIC 76834 #422-01-2002 L2005
    FM *020 †18
MATHUR, Sandip V. 310 S PECOS ST, 2ND FL 76834 #495-73-1985 L1994 **IM** *020 †20
MURCHISON, Robert Julien. ■ 76834 #048-02-1970 L1970 **U** *020 †95
ORAL, Orhan Cemil. 115 WEST ST 76834 #902-01-1956 L1973 **IM GP** *072
REYNOLDS, Jarrell Paul. 310 S PECOS ST, 2ND FL 76834 #048-15-1985 L1986 **FM** *020 †18
SCHAEFFER, Fenella. ■ 76834 #048-02-1967 L1967 **GP** *071

COLLEGE STATION – BRAZOS

ACKERMAN, Lani K. 1600 UNIVERSITY DR E 77840 #048-16-1985 L1986 **FM** *020 †18
AHMED, Syed Nadeem. 1602 ROCK PRAIRIE RD, STE 2200 77845 #704-16-1980 L2000
    IM NEP *020 †20
ALEXANDER, Philip Ross. 1602 ROCK PRAIRIE RD, STE 4880 77845 #048-04-1971 L1971
    IM *020 †20
ALIKHAN, Amina Naqi. 1604 ROCK PRAIRIE RD 77845 #048-16-1992 L1999 **IM** *020 †20
AMOROSO, Anthony D. ■ 77845 #048-12-2000 L2003 **EM** *020 †16
ANDERSON, Charles Raymond. 1602 ROCK PRAIRIE RD, STE 430 77845 #030-05-1974 L1974
    OBG *020 †30
APPLETON, Margaret Page. 1600 UNIVERSITY DR E, SCOTT & WHITE CLINIC 77840
    #048-16-1988 L1989 **OBG** *020 †30
BAILEY, Margaret Mary. 1600 UNIVERSITY DR E 77840 #025-76-1988, ▲ L1991 **FM** *020 †18
BAINS, Yadvendra S. 1602 ROCK PRAIRIE RD, STE 130A 77845 #048-13-1995 L1996
    RO *020 †80
BEKKER, Jessica Belinda. ■ 77840 #048-16-2008 *012
BERGERON, Jon Anthony. 1600 UNIVERSITY DR E 77840 #048-12-2001 *100
BERZON, David Michael. 1602 ROCK PRAIRIE RD, STE 2100 77845 #038-40-1977 L2005
    PUD IM *020 †20
BILES, Russel K. 1600 UNIVERSITY DR E 77840 #048-14-1989 L1990 **FM** *020 †18
BIX, Gregory Jaye. ■ 77842 #048-04-2000 **CHN** *100
BLASINGAME, Jennifer J. 1602 ROCK PRAIRIE RD, ROAD #3000 77845 #035-01-1997 L2002
    OBG *020 †30
BLOUNT, Alice B. ■ 77845 #048-13-2004 L2007 **FM** *020 †18
BOHNE, Henry Elo. 1602 ROCK PRAIRIE RD, STE 3500 77845 #048-02-1976 L1976 **GS** *020 †85
BOSSE, David Aaron. 1600 UNIVERSITY DR E, DEPT OF RADIOLOGY 77840 #048-12-1978 L1983
    R PD *020 †55,80
BOYSEN, Dirk Le Van. 1600 UNIVERSITY DR E 77840 #026-04-1980 L1987 **GS TRS** *020 †85
BRAMSON, Rachel. 1600 UNIVERSITY DR E 77840 #054-04-1991 L1994 **FM** *020 †18 ‡
BRIEGER, Duane A. 1600 UNIVERSITY DR E 77840 #048-13-1995 L1996 **FM** *020 †18
BRIEN, James Howard. 1600 UNIVERSITY DR E 77840 #048-78-1977, ▲ L1986 **ID PD** *020 †55
BROWN, Angeletta Luree. 1602 ROCK PRAIRIE RD 77845 #020-02-1978 L1979 **PS** *020
BROWN, Michael Lamar. 1600 UNIVERSITY DR E 77840 #048-14-1989 L1990 **P PME** *020 †75
BRYANT, William P. 1600 UNIVERSITY DR E 77840 #039-01-1989 L2002 **PDE** *020 †55
CABANISS, James Wm. 77840 #021-05-1972 L1980 **FM EM** *020 †16,18
CAPPEL, Jolie Caroline. ■ 77840 #048-16-2008 *012
CARLTON, Paul Kendall. 301 TARROW ST 7TH FL, JOHN CONNALLY BUILDING 77840
    #007-02-1973 L1977 **GS** *040 †85
CARMAN, James Welch G. A P BEUTEL HEALTH CTR, TX A&M UNIVERSITY 77843
    #041-12-1956 L1966 **FM PTH** *071 †50
CASE, David J. ■ 77845 #048-02-2008 L2008 *012
CASTIGLIONI, Aldo J. 1604 ROCK PRAIRIE RD 77845 #048-16-1987 L1988 **P** *020 †75
CASTILLO, Paulina. ■ 77840 #048-16-2008 *012
CAYLOR, Arthur B, Jr. 1600 UNIVERSITY DR E 77840 #048-13-1981 L1981 **071 †18
CERMIN, Ayres Robt. 1500 LAURA LN 77840 #048-02-1967 L1967 **FM** *020 †18
CHILDS, James Neumann. 1605 ROCK PRAIRIE RD, STE 312 77845 #048-15-1986 L1987
    D PD *020 †15
CHILDS, Maria V. 1605 ROCK PRAIRIE RD, STE 312 77845 #020-02-1990 L1994 **D** *020 †15
CLARK, Russell Jay. 1600 UNIVERSITY DR E 77840 #048-15-2002 L2004 **ORS** *020
COCHRAN, John Lee. 1602 ROCK PRAIRIE RD, STE 270 77845 #039-01-1978 L1994 **U** *020 †95
COCHRAN, Robert Glenn, Jr. 1604 ROCK PRAIRIE RD 77845 #048-04-1971 L1971 **FM** *020 †18
COHEN, Rachel Michelle. ■ 77840 #048-14-2008 *012
COLE, Christopher John. 1602 ROCK PRAIRIE RD 77845 #038-40-1991 L1993 **FM** *072 †18
COLENDA, Christopher C, III. 147 JOE H REYNOLDS MED BLD, TEXAS A & M UNIVERSITY
    HEA 77843 #051-04-1977 L2003 **P PYG** *040 †75
COLUNGA, Frank L. ■ 77845 #048-12-1983 L1983 **EM OBG** *020 †16
CONKLIN, Andrea Jan. 1602 ROCK PRAIRIE RD, RR 220 77845 #048-14-1973 L1974
    FM CLP *020 †50
CRISCIONE, John Carl. ■ 77845 #023-07-1999 *100
CRUMBAKER, Deborah H. 1604 ROCK PRAIRIE RD, COLUMBIA MEDICAL CTR 77845
    #048-14-1984 L1986 **PTH** *020 †50
DANNENBAUM, Martha C. TAMU MAILSTOP 1264 77843 #048-13-1987 L1988 **OBG** *020 †30 ‡
DAVIS, George Edward. ■ 77843 #005-18-1986 L1993 **ATP** *020 †50
DAVIS, Joyce S. ■ 77840 #048-04-1947 L1947 **PTH** *071 †50
DAVIS, Philip S. 1604 ROCK PRAIRIE RD 77845 #048-16-1985 L1986 **IM** *020 †20
DAVIS, Thomas W, Jr. 1600 UNIVERSITY DR E 77840 #048-15-1991 L1992 **OBG** *020 †30
DAVIS, W Rex. ■ 77842 #048-02-1954 L1955 **OM FM** *071 †70,18
DE JONG, Andrew L. 1602 ROCK PRAIRIE RD, STE 230 77845 #048-04-1990 L1992
    OTO *020 †45
DE SOUZA, Antonio A. ■ 77845 #187-01-1945 L1959 **OTO** *071
DICKEY, Nancy Wilson. 301 TARROW ST 7TH FL 77840 #048-14-1976 L1976 **FM** *040 †18 ‡
DILLARD, Ruth Abrams. ■ 77840 #041-01-1951 L1971 **PD** *071 †55
DIRKS, Kenneth Ray. TEXAS A-M UNIVERSITY 77843 #048-02-1947 L1979 **PTH** *071 †50
DOTT, J B, Jr. 1604 ROCK PRAIRIE RD 77845 #048-12-1980 L1980 **AN** *020
DRAKE, Terrance Stephen. ■ 77845 #025-07-1972 L1974 **END OBG** *100 †30

DUSOLD, Richard J. 1600 UNIVERSITY DR E, DEPARTMENT OF GASTROENTERO 77840
    #048-02-1987 L1988 **GE** *020 †20
EAKIN-WEGENER, Kimberly. 1600 UNIVERSITY DR E 77840 #048-16-1994 L1996 **IM** *020 †20
EDMISTON, Frank Gerald. ■ 77845 #048-04-1956 L1961 **EM** *071
ELLIOTT, Byron Dean. 1602 ROCK PRAIRIE RD, STE 220 77845 #021-01-1985 L1989
    MFM OBG *020 †30
ELNIHUM, Ibrahim Muftah. 1602 ROCK PRAIRIE RD #4400 77845 #613-01-1977 L1989
    NS NSP *020 †25
ENGLISH, Mark W. 1600 UNIVERSITY DR E 77840 #048-14-1988 L1989 **FM** *020 †18 ‡
FARNAM, Kevin Saman. PO BOX 1633 77841 #048-04-2008 *012
FARROW, Wade Phil. 1605 ROCK PRAIRIE RD 77845 #012-05-1998 L2000 **OS UM** *020
FAUSTINO, Benigno D. ■ 77845 #737-01-1957 L1967 **PTH FOP** *020 †50
FEDORCHIK, Jos John, Jr. 1604 ROCK PRAIRIE RD 77845 #025-01-1977 L1979
    TS CD *020 †20
FINK, Tami Neal Glenn. 1600 UNIVERSITY DR E 77840 #048-04-1998 L1999 **DR** *020 †80
FINO, Remon A. 1602 ROCK PRAIRIE RD, STE 4600 77845 #048-02-1993 L1995 **PM** *020 †60
FLANAGAN, Lourdes M. ■ 77842 #048-02-1992 L1993 **N** *020
FOSTER, Dayne M. 1600 UNIVERSITY DR E 77840 #048-16-1983 L1983 **PD** *020 †55
FOSTER, Mikaela Dayne. ■ 77845 #048-16-2005 **OBG** *012
GAINES, William G, Jr. 8405 WHITEROSE CT 77845 #048-15-1982 L1983 **OM EM** *030 †20,70
GARZA, Robert Maldonado. 1604 ROCK PRAIRIE RD 77845 #005-18-1979 L1982 **IM** *020 †20
GASTEL, Barbara Jean. TEXAS ATM UNIV, INTEGRATIVE BIOSCIENCES 77843 #023-07-1978
    OS *062
GAYLE, Lelve Justin. 1602 ROCK PRAIRIE RD, STE 430 77845 #048-15-1993 L1994
    OBG *020 †30
GEHRING, Donald Raymond. 1600 UNIVERSITY DR E 77840 #048-78-1989, ▲ L1990
    FM *020 †18
GHATTAS, Noshi Boushra. 1605 ROCK PRAIRIE RD, STE 220 77845 #915-02-1973 L1982
    OBG *020 †30
GIBBS, James Edward. MAIL STOP 1264, STUDENT HEALTH CENTER 77843
    #048-13-1983 L1983 **FM EM** *020 †18
GLAMANN, David Brent. 1600 UNIVERSITY DR E 77840 #048-04-1985 L1986 **CD** *020 †20
GLASS, Dale S. 1600 UNIVERSITY DR E, DEPT. OF RADIOLOGY 77840 #048-14-1988 L1989
    DR *020 †80
GOEN, Tracy H. 2911 TEXAS AVE S, STE 103 77845 #048-16-1995 L1997 **FM** *020 †18
GOGULSKI, Scott Casimer. 1600 UNIVERSITY DR E 77840 #016-76-2000, ▲ L2007 *100
GORDON, Julius Arthur. 208 REYNOLDS MEDICAL BLDG 77843 #028-02-1955 L1955 **PTH** *050
GORE, Garry L. ■ 77845 #048-16-1996 L1997 **EM** *020 †16
GRAY, Ryan Lane Alexan. ■ 77840 #048-02-2007 **IM** *012
GRILLO, Kelly Holley. 1600 UNIVERSITY DR E, SCOTT & WHITE COLLEGE STAT 77840
    #048-13-1986 L1991 **IM** *020 †20
GULLETT, Christopher J. 1721 BIRMINGHAM DR, STE 202 77845 #048-02-1998 L2008
    GS *100 †85
GUO, Jadie Y. 1600 UNIVERSITY DR E 77840 #048-02-1999 L2002 **IM** *020 †20
HACHEM, Charles Youssef. 1605 ROCK PRAIRIE RD # 212, CENTRAL TX VET HLTH CARE 77845
    #306-01-1999 L2000 **FM** *020
HACKNEY, Kenneth U, Jr. UNIVERSITY MS1264, TEXAS A&M 77843 #048-02-1974 L1974
    EM *020 †16
HAN, George Shin. ■ 77845 #048-04-2004 L2007 **PD** *100 †55
HANSEN, Henry Andrew, II. 1721 BIRMINGHAM DR, STE 202 77845 #048-15-1975 L1975
    TS VS *020 †85,90
HARRELL, Amy L. 1600 UNIVERSITY DR E 77840 #048-16-1998 L1999 **OBG** *020 †30
HARSTAD, Timothy Walter. 1602 ROCK PRAIRIE RD, STE 220 77845 #056-05-1979 L1989
    OBG *020 †30
HAWKINS, Henry A, Jr. ■ 77840 #004-01-1949 L1952 **FM** *071
HAWRYLUK, Myron Taras. ■ 77845 #065-01-1968 L1978 **GYN** *020
HENDERSON, Kyle D. 1602 ROCK PRAIRIE RD, STE 340 77845 #048-14-1989 L1990
    PD *020 †55
HENRY, Lorene H. 1721 BIRMINGHAM DR, STE 208 77845 #048-13-1983 L1983 **P** *020 †75
HENRY, Tanya Larone. ■ 77845 #021-05-2006 **PD** *012
HERRON, Richard Edward. 1602 ROCK PRAIRIE RD, STE 1100 77845 #048-16-1983 L1983
    FM *020 †18
HIGGINBOTHAM, Steven W. 1600 UNIVERSITY DR E 77840 #048-12-2001 L2003 **FM** *020
HIGGINS, Mark S. 1600 UNIVERSITY DR E 77840 #048-14-1989 L1990 **FM** *020 †18
HOAK, Bruce Allyn. 1605 ROCK PRAIRIE RD, STE 100 77845 #048-12-1983 L1983
    GS VS *020 †85
HOGANSON, Neal Edward. 1600 UNIVERSITY DR E 77840 #035-45-1987 L1995 **HS** *020 †85,65
HOOD, Davelyn K. STUDENT HEALTH SERVICES, MAIL STOP 1254 77843 #048-14-1997 L1999
    FM *020 †18
HOWARD, Robert Alexander. 4401 STATE HIGHWAY 6 S 77845 #021-05-1978 L1979
    FM *020 †18
HUBBLE, Levi. ■ 77845 #048-16-2008 *012
HUNTER, John M. 1600 UNIVERSITY DR E 77840 #048-12-2000 L2007 **GS** *020
HUSSAIN, Feroze Abid. ■ 77845 #704-25-2001 L2008 **IM** *020 †20
JEJURIKAR, Sameer Subhash. 1600 UNIVERSITY DR E 77840 #025-01-1997 L2006 **PS** *100 †65
JOHNSON, Noreen Zenita. 1604 ROCK PRAIRIE RD 77845 #010-03-1977 L1981 **OBG** *020 †30
JONES, Joseph B. 1604 ROCK PRAIRIE RD 77845 #048-02-1983 L1983 **IM** *020 †20
KENNEY, John S. 1600 UNIVERSITY DR E 77840 #048-16-1994 L1995 **AN PME** *020 †05
KUPPERSMITH, Ronald Barry. 1602 ROCK PRAIRIE RD, STE 230 77845 #025-01-1993 L2003
    OTO *020 †45
LAMBERT, Gary Newton. 1602 ROCK PRAIRIE RD, STE 1100 77845 #048-02-1980 L1980
    FM *020 †18
LAMMOGLIA, Mario Angel. 1721 BIRMINGHAM DR 77845 #019-02-1989 L1997 **CD IM** *020 †20
LARKIN, Elicia Dawn. ■ 77845 #048-13-2003 **PD** *100
LARSEN, Daniel James. 1600 UNIVERSITY DR E 77840 #056-06-1995 L2002 **CD** *020 †20
LAWHORN, Nancy B. ■ 77845 #048-14-1994 L2004 **MPD** *072 †20,55
LAWRENCE, Glenn Lee. 1600 UNIVERSITY DR E 77840 #048-16-1993 L1995 **PD** *020 †55
LECHIN, Marcel E. 1721 BIRMINGHAM DR 77845 #935-01-1987 L1993 **CD IM** *020 †20
LEE, Ruby. 77841 #048-16-2007 **P** *012
LENEHAN, Eric Andrew. ■ 77840 #048-16-2008 *012
LEVINTHAL, Robert. 1602 ROCK PRAIRIE RD, STE 4400 77845 #048-13-1970 L1970
    NS *020 †25
LEWIS, Annisa Lee. ■ 77840 #048-02-2007 **PTH** *012
LINDNER, Luther Edward. TX A&M UNIV PATH LAB MED 77843 #038-06-1967 L1983
    PTH *050 †50
LISTER, Thomas Wm. ■ 77845 #048-02-1968 L1968 **GP** *071

LOCKE, Catherine Susan. ■ 77845 #048-16-2006 FP *012
LOO, Rodolfo Villaflores. TX A&M UNIV AP BEUTEL CTR 77840 #748-02-1959 L1976 IM *071
LYON, Kent Jackson. 1602 ROCK PRAIRIE RD, STE 2600 77845 #005-14-1978 L1989
  IM END *020
MAEDO, Kelly Marie. 2911 TEXAS AVE S, STE 103 77845 #048-16-1999 L2002 FM *020 †18
MAJUMDAR, Sudeep. 310B 2ND ST 77840 #495-53-1988 *100
MARAIST, Todd A. 1105 UNIVERSITY DR E, STE 100 77840 #048-13-1988 L1989
  N PME *020 †75
MARQUARDT, Michael P. 1600 UNIVERSITY DR E 77840 #048-16-1985 L1986 PD *020 †55
MARSH, John E, Jr. 1604 ROCK PRAIRIE RD 77845 #048-02-1950 L1950 FM PD *071
MARTIN, Joseph Paul. 1600 UNIVERSITY DR E 77840 #028-78-1999, ▲ L2003 P *020
MASON, James Michael. 1602 ROCK PRAIRIE RD, STE 2400 77845 #048-12-1971 L1972
  IM *020 †20
MASSOUD, Adel Amin. 1602 ROCK PRAIRIE RD, STE 1100 77845 #915-02-1979 L2001
  FM *020 †18
MATTHEWS, Kenneth Earl. 1602 ROCK PRAIRIE RD, STE 340 77845 #048-02-1969 L1969
  PD *020 †55
MC CORD, Gary C. TAMU MAILSTOP 1114, TEXAS A&M COLLEGE OF MEDIC 77843
  #048-02-1983 L1983 DR *020 †80
MC ILHANEY, George Robt. 1512 HOLLEMAN DR, BRAZOS PHYSICIANS GROUP 77840
  #048-04-1970 L1970 FM *020 †18
MC MAHON, Michael Francis. 1602 ROCK PRAIRIE RD, STE 230 77845 #030-06-1975 L1986
  OTO *020 †45
MEADE, Linda P. 1600 UNIVERSITY DR E 77840 #048-14-1993 L1997 IM *020 †20
MEADE, Thomas H. 1600 UNIVERSITY DR E, SCOTT & WHITE CLINIC 77840
  #048-14-1993 L2000 ICE *020 †20
MEDUNA, David. 1602 ROCK PRAIRIE RD, STE 3100 77845 #048-13-2003 L2006 OBG *020
MEYER, Arlene Summers. 1600 UNIVERSITY DR E, 1600 UNIVERSITY DRIVE EAST 77840
  #048-16-1986 L1987 PD *020 †55
MILLER, Michael J. 1600 UNIVERSITY DR E 77840 #048-13-1982 L1983 OTO *020 †45
MITTER, Ajay. 1602 ROCK PRAIRIE RD, STE 2660 77845 #495-45-1986 L1995 HO IM *020 †20
MOO-MING, Paporn. ■ 77840 #891-02-1994 PD *020 †55
MOORE, Audrey V. ■ 77845 #048-14-2006 P *012
MOORE, John Steven. 4912 AUGUSTA CIR 77845 #048-12-1978 L1995 OM *050 †70
MOORE, Rachel Lewis. 1600 UNIVERSITY DR E 77840 #048-16-2002 L2006 D *020 †15
MORAN, Kate Rose. 1604 ROCK PRAIRIE RD 77845 #048-14-2003 L2005 IM *020 †20
MORGAN, Garth R. 1602 ROCK PRAIRIE RD, STE 400 77845 #048-16-1996 L1998 FM *020 †18
MORROW, Maryhelen K. 1712 SERVAL LN, MOBILE DOCS, PLLC 77840 #008-02-1991 L1997
  FM *020 †18
NEAL, Gabriel Alexander. 1512 HOLLEMAN DR, BRAZOS PHYSICIANS GROUP 77840
  #039-01-2001 L2005 FM *020
NGO, Van T. 1600 UNIVERSITY DR E 77840 #048-14-1993 L1994 FM *020 †18
NICOLWALA, Adil Noshir. 1602 ROCK PRAIRIE RD, STE 1100 77845 #704-02-1984 L2000
  FM *020 †18
NUNLEY, Amanda W. ■ 77845 #048-13-2007 FP *012
OGUNLEYE, Olubunmi Temito. ■ 77840 #048-04-2006 GS *012
OPERSTENY, Steve Chas. 1602 ROCK PRAIRIE RD # 370 77845 #048-02-1986 L1987
  PM GP *020 †60
O'SHEA, Thomas Patrick. 1600 UNIVERSITY DR E 77840 #021-01-1985 L1994 ORS *020 †40
PALM, Michael Lee. 1602 ROCK PRAIRIE RD, STE 150 77845 #048-02-1997 L1999 N *020 †75
PARR, Jesse Wm. 1604 ROCK PRAIRIE RD 77845 #021-05-1973 L1975 PD *020 †55
PATTON, Samuel H. 1600 UNIVERSITY DR E 77840 #048-02-1995 L1996 AN *020 †05
PAULL, Keith Jeremy. 3306 LONGMIRE DR 77845 #048-16-1998 L2004 AI *100 †55,03
PEIRCE, Diana Marie. ■ 77845 #048-04-1988 L1989 GS *075
PELTIER, Suzanne Alisia. ■ 77845 #048-12-2007 AN *012
PINKSTAFF, John Edmond. ■ 77845 #048-02-2004 L2007 EM *020
POLING, Matthew C. 1600 UNIVERSITY DR E 77840 #048-12-1995 L1996 FM *020 †18
QUIRK, Lauren Elizabeth. ■ 77845 #048-16-2008 *012
RAGUPATHI, Kuppusamy. 1602 ROCK PRAIRIE RD, STE 200 77845 #495-94-1975 L1987
  GE IM *020 †20
RANSOM, Daniel G. 1600 UNIVERSITY DR E, SCOTT & WHITE CLINIC 77840
  #048-02-1985 L1986 PD *020 †55
RAYBURN, William Lowell. 1600 UNIVERSITY DR E, SCOTT & WHITE CLINIC 77840
  #048-16-1983 L1983 OBG *020 †30
REED, Ann Marie. A P BEUTEL HLTH CARE, TEXAS A & M UNIV 77843 #048-02-1975 L1975
  FM *020 †18
RICHARDS, Robert M. 1600 UNIVERSITY DR E, SCOTT AND WHITE CLINIC 77840
  #048-02-1988 L1989 IM GE *020 †20
RICHARDSON, Wade A. 1600 UNIVERSITY DR E, SCOTT AND WHITE CLINIC 77840
  #048-16-1993 L1994 FM *020 †18
RIDGEWAY, Jeffrey Joseph. 1602 ROCK PRAIRIE RD, STE 220 77845 #012-01-1997 L2005
  OBG *020 †30
RIGGS, William L. 1600 UNIVERSITY DR E 77840 #048-16-2002 L2006 OPH *020
RIORDAN, Tiffany Dawn. 1604 ROCK PRAIRIE RD 77845 #048-16-2002 L2008 EM *020 †16
ROA, Mario Rizalino Basco, Jr. 147 J H REYNOLDS MED 77843 #748-19-1991 FP *012
ROBINSON, Haywood James. 1602 ROCK PRAIRIE RD, RD. #3000 77845 #005-15-1978 L1981
  FM *020 †18
RODRIGUEZ, David Andrew. 1600 UNIVERSITY DR E 77840 #047-06-1991 L1995 IM *020 †20
ROLLO, Robert Olide. 5114 CONGRESSIONAL DR, ROLLO FAMILY PRACTICE CLIN 77845
  #048-04-1995 L1997 FM *020 †18
ROMAN, Joseph Jason. ■ 77845 #048-15-2003 L2007 IM *020 †20
ROSEN, David Henry. ■ 77840 #028-03-1970 L1987 P PYA *040 †75
ROUFEH, Ramin. ■ 77845 #048-16-2008 *012
SAENZ, Christopher W. 1602 ROCK PRAIRIE RD, STE 340 77845 #048-16-2000 L2002
  PD *020 †55 ‡
SAMMARELLI, Patricia. 1602 ROCK PRAIRIE RD SU, MED PLAZA EAST 77845
  #561-17-1991 L2005 FM *020 †18 ‡
SCHAMS, Scott Thos. 1602 ROCK PRAIRIE RD, #340 WEST 77845 #048-04-1987 L1988
  PD MDM *020 †55
SCHEMIDT, Randy Alfred. 1602 ROCK PRAIRIE RD, STE 2880 77845 #025-07-1999 L2002
  EM *020 †16
SCHOENVOGEL, Clarence W. ■ 77840 #048-04-1944 L1944 AI *071 †03
SCOTT, David Lawrence. 1600 UNIVERSITY DR E 77840 #048-02-1997 L2003 U *020 †95
SCOTT, Robert Emmett. ■ 77840 #048-02-1958 L1958 FM *071
SHANMUGAM, Aiyanadar. 1602 ROCK PRAIRIE RD, STE 210 77845 #495-42-1976 L1981
  END IM *020 †20

SHELTON, Margaret M Kirk. ■ 77840 #021-01-1947 L1962 IM ADL *020
SILAS, Megan E. ■ 77845 #035-15-2000 L2000 PD *100
SIMON, Troy D. 1600 UNIVERSITY DR E 77840 #048-13-1993 L1994 OTO *020
SMITH, Bruce Walter. 1264 TAMU, A.P. BEUTEL STUDENT HEALTH 77843 #048-13-1990 L2000
  FM *020 †18
SMITH, Kerry Hamilton. ■ 77845 #048-16-1993 L1995 IM *020 †20
SMITH, Randy Wallace. 1602 ROCK PRAIRIE RD, STE 430 77845 #048-14-1982 L1983
  OBG *020 †30
SPEEGLE, Stanley Roger. 1427 ANDOVER CT 77845 #048-12-1983 L1984 EM *020 †18
STAUFFER, Curtis C. 1604 ROCK PRAIRIE RD 77845 #048-02-1987 L1988 CD IM *020 †20
STERLING, James Anthony. 1600 UNIVERSITY DR E 77840 #048-78-1989, ▲ L1990
  FM *020 †18
SUAREZ, Elizabeth. 1602 ROCK PRAIRIE RD, STE 3000 77845 #033-06-2000 L2004
  FM *020 †18
SUMAYA, Ciro Valent. PUBLIC HEALT, SCHOOL OF RU RAL 77843 #048-02-1966 L1966
  PD PDI *062 †55
SVENDSEN, Betty Ann E. 1600 UNIVERSITY DR E 77840 #048-15-1995 L1996 PD *020 †55
TELLER, David Crockett. ■ 77845 #048-02-1986 L1987 OTO FPS *020 †45
THAKRAR, Mahendrakumar O. 1602 ROCK PRAIRIE RD, STE 3100 77845 #495-01-1970 L1976
  OBG *020 †30
TOMLIN, Terri L. 1602 ROCK PRAIRIE RD, STE 340 77845 #048-04-1990 L1991
  PDC PD *020 †55
TRONO, Ruben. 1721 BIRMINGHAM DR 77845 #048-14-1982 L1983 CD IM *020 †20
TYLER, Barbara Ann. TEXAS A & M UNIV, AP BEUTEL HLTH CTR 77843 #048-16-1984 L1985
  FM *020
VENKATRAJ, Usha. 1602 ROCK PRAIRIE RD #130B 77845 #495-59-1983 L1998
  ON HEM *020 †20
WAGNER, Jackson Wayne. COLLEGE OF MED TX A&M UNIV, DEPT OF ANATOMY MED
  SCIENC 77843 #048-04-1973 L1974 *030
WAGNER, Thomas J. 1600 UNIVERSITY DR E 77840 #048-14-1990 L1991 FM *020 †18
WAGUESPACK, Jeffrey W. 1600 UNIVERSITY DR E 77840 #048-16-1996 L1999 FM *020 †18
WATTS, Fenwick Leigh. ■ 77845 #048-04-1951 L1951 D *071 †15
WEAVER, Jason Michael. ■ 77845 #048-02-2003 L2006 D *020 †15
WEGENER, Allen Clayton. 1600 UNIVERSITY DR E, SCOTT & WHITE CLINIC 77840
  #027-01-1991 L1992 U *020 †95
WEIDENBACH, Carl Price. ■ 77845 #048-02-1964 L1964 FM *071 †18
WELCH, Thomas K. 1600 UNIVERSITY DR E 77840 #048-14-1990 L1991 FM *020 †18
WELDON, David Randolph. 1600 UNIVERSITY DR E 77840 #048-15-1984 L1985
  AI IM *020 †20,03
WELLS, Gregg Bennett. 208 JOE H REYNOLDS, MED BLDG DEPT PATH & LAB M 77843
  #016-02-1989 L2000 NP ATP *050 †50
WENGER, Scott Andrew. 1602 ROCK PRAIRIE RD, STE 460 77845 #048-12-1998 L2003
  OSM ORS *020 †40
WHITELEY, William D. 1602 ROCK PRAIRIE RD, STE 460 77845 #017-20-1969 L2002
  ORS *020 †40
WILDE, Jennifer D. ■ 77840 #048-16-2008 *012
WILKE, Eric K. 1602 ROCK PRAIRIE RD, STE 2880 77845 #048-16-1995 L2000 EM *020 †16
WILLIAMS, Josie Ruth. 301 TARROW ST, # 733 77840 #048-13-1975 L1975 IM GE *050 †20
WILLIAMS, Laura Lynette. 1651 ROCK PRAIRIE RD, STE 102 77845 #020-02-2001 L2004
  PD *020
WIPRUD, Robt Menzies, Jr. 1700 UNIVERSITY DR E 77840 #030-06-1980 L1988 FM *020 †18 ‡
WRIGHT, Paul Albert. 1600 UNIVERSITY DR E 77840 #019-02-1968 L1976 ORS *020 †40
XUAN, Bo. TEXAS A&M UNIV, AP BUETEL HEALTH CTR 77843 #243-24-1984 L2007 FM *020 †18
YANEZ, Veronica Lagunas. 147 J H REYNOLDS MED 77843 #649-01-1990 FP *012
YOUNG, Lon Kendall. 1604 ROCK PRAIRIE RD, TRADITIONS EMERGENCY MEDIC 77845
  #048-04-2001 L2004 EM *020 †16
ZIVNEY, Ben S. 1602 ROCK PRAIRIE RD, STE 430 77845 #048-14-1988 L1989 OBG *020 †30
ZOGHI, Behyar. ■ 77840 #048-16-2007 IM *012

COLLEYVILLE – TARRANT

ADAMS, Quentin Mark. 1207 HALL JOHNSON RD 76034 #048-13-1985 L1986 N *020 †75
ALDERETE, Wesley Allan. 4301 BROWN TRL, FAMILY HEALTH CARE 76034 #048-12-1982 L1983
  FM *020 †18 ‡
BARLOCO, Severn Gerome. ■ 76034 #048-12-2001 L2005 GS *020 †85
BULLARD, Jeffrey Morris. 3930 GLADE RD, STE 105 76034 #030-06-1993 L1996 FM *020 †18
DAVIS, Mayli Louisa. 6407 COLLEYVILLE BLVD, STE B 76034 #019-02-1990 L1994
  OPH *020 †35
DEFILIPPIS, Nicholas Jame. ■ 76034 #048-14-2005 AN *012
FAWCETT, Barry Keyes. 3 COUNTRY WAY 76034 #048-12-1963 L1963 FM *020 †18
FAWCETT, Maria Aquino. 4301 BROWN TRL, FAMILY HEALTHCARE ASSOCIAT 76034
  #064-01-1980 L1983 FM *020
FOX, Lawrence Steven. ■ 76034 #011-03-1974 L1992 TS *020 †85,90
FRANK, Bryan Lee. 2108 STONEHAVEN DR 76034 #048-16-1981 L1981 AN PME *062
GILL, Gurpreet K. 117 MILL XING E 76034 #495-29-1976 L2000 IM *020 †20
GULIZIA, Julie Anne. ■ 76034 #030-05-1994 L2006 PTH *020 †50
HAHN, Jane Meehae. ■ 76034 #038-44-1988 L2004 P *020 †75
HAHN, Young Soo. ■ 76034 #583-02-1958 L1975 AN *071
HAYES, Lorrie Powell. 5408 COLLEYVILLE BLVD 76034 #039-01-1988 L2001 IM *074 †20
HERRERA, Eduardo R, Jr. ■ 76034 #048-14-1989 L1990 AN *020 †05
HILLEBRAND, John Alvin. 7804 TILLMAN HILL CT 76034 #003-01-1982 L1985 AN *020 †05
HUSAIN, Nisreen Siraj. ■ 76034 #048-13-2007 IM *012
HUSAIN, Siraj. ■ 76034 #495-21-1952 L1972 GS EM *071
JATOI, Alcina Francis. ■ 76034 #495-01-1950 L1972 PTH *075 †50
JATOI, Alimadad M. ■ 76034 #495-01-1950 L1972 GS GP *020
JOHNSON, Melissa Ann. ■ 76034 #030-05-2000 L2006 EM *100
JUSTICE, Marilyn Kay. 5408 COLLEYVILLE BLVD, COLLEYVILLE FAM MED 76034
  #048-12-1996 L1997 FM *020 †18
KOLLIPARA, Vani. ■ 76034 #495-99-2000 L2007 IM *020 †20
KOPER, Dennis Paul. ■ 76034 #002-02-1988 L1988 EM *020
KRISHNAMURTHY, Radha. ■ 76034 #495-04-1969 L1976 FM EM *020
LALANI, Iqbal Ibrahim. ■ 76034 #495-22-1962 L1974 AN *071 †05
LAND, Susann Faye. 4703 MILL BROOK DR 76034 #048-04-1979 L1979 IM *030 †20
LAWSON, David Scott. 4301 BROWN TRL, FAMILY HEALTH CARE 76034 #048-16-1981 L1981
  FM *020 †18

LECROY, Kenneth D. 6630 COLLEYVILLE BLVD 76034 #048-13-1996 L1997 **FM** *020 †18 ‡
LECROY, Tara Fulbright. 6630 COLLEYVILLE BLVD, LECROY FAMILY MEDICINE 76034 #048-13-1996 L1998 **FM** *020 †18
LEE, Song Y. 6220 COLLEYVILLE BLVD # B 76034 #048-14-1994 L1998 **FM** *020 †18
LEITENBERGER, Justin John. ■ 76034 #048-14-2008 *012
MANGROLA, Prabhatsinh P. 612 BRIDLEWOOD N 76034 #495-23-1971 L1979 **AN** *071
MANN, Christopher Michael. ■ 76034 #048-12-1989 L1991 **AN** *020 †05
MCNAIR, David Paul. 7167 COLLEYVILLE BLVD 76034 #048-16-1984 L1985 **FM** *020 †18
MOORHEAD, John Alexander. 5207 HERITAGE AVE 76034 #012-21-1986 L1996 **FM** *020 †18
MUDROVICH, Steven Anthony. 1424 PLANTATION DR N 76034 #056-05-1975 L1977 **PTH** *020 †50
NAIR, Lakshmi Prabhakaran. ■ 76034 #048-16-2005 L2007 **AN** *012
O'DEA, Patrick Thos. 4301 BROWN TRL, FAMILY HEALTH CARE 76034 #034-01-1979 L1983 **FM** *020 †18
PECKENPAUGH, Danl Eugene. 4107 WOOD CREEK CT 76034 #048-02-1980 L1980 **EM** *020 †18,16
PHELAN, Alvin J. ■ 76034 #025-07-1949 L1950 **GP EM** *071 †16
PILLOW, David James. 312 TIMBERLINE DR S 76034 #010-01-1953 L1954 **FM** *020 †18
PROTZMAN, Robert Reavis. 8300 PRECINCT LINE RD, STE 108 76034 #019-02-1968 L1983 **ORS** *020 †40
REDDY, Gautham T N. ■ 76034 #495-62-1973 L1978 **P** *020
REDDY, Sruthi N. 6609 CARRIAGE DR 76034 #035-19-2008 *012
RICHARD, Jonathan Patrick. 6220 COLLEYVILLE BLVD # B 76034 #048-13-1982 L1983 **IM** *020 †20
SCHLAGER, Seymour I. ■ 76034 #011-02-1985 L1985 **LM IM** *075
STARR, Brian Michael. ■ 76034 #048-02-2005 **AN** *012
STROMAN, David Lynn. 75 MAIN ST, STE 150 76034 #048-12-1996 L1998 **VS** *020 †85
SUTERWALA, Smita Mustafa. ■ 76034 #495-01-1989 L2004 **PTH** *020 †50
TAYLOR, Mark W. 4301 BROWN TRL, FAMILY HEALTH CARE 76034 #048-02-1982 L1983 **FM** *020 †18
TEBBETTS, Maria Elena. 1106 PLANTATION DR N 76034 #004-01-1979 L1984 **AN** *020 †05
TENNANT, Jerald Lee. ■ 76034 #048-12-1964 L1964 **OPH** *071 †35
THOMAS, George. ■ 76034 #048-02-2005 **IM** *012
TYE, Christopher Lee. 6904 COLLEYVILLE BLVD, STE 100 76034 #001-02-1991 L1992 **FPS** *020
WEINBERG, Steven Michael. ■ 76034 #018-03-1967 L1970 **GS** *030 †85
WINERITER, Nicole Teresa. ■ 76034 #048-12-2007 **PD** *012
YARLAGADDA, Uma. ■ 76034 #495-09-1995 L2006 **P** *100 †75 ‡
ZAKHARY, Adel Alphonse. 4109 BROWN TRL STE 101 76034 #915-02-1988 L1998 **IM** *020 †20

COLORADO CITY – MITCHELL

GROSS, Gustavo Adolfo. 997 W INTERSTATE 20 79512 #308-03-1985 L1994 **IM** *020 †18
MERRITT, Sherman H. 505 CHESTNUT ST 79512 #048-04-1951 L1951 **R** *071 †80
ROACH, Dee Alan. 997 W INTERSTATE 20 79512 #048-16-1983 L1983 **FM** *020 †18
SCOTT, Joseph Danl. 997 W INTERSTATE 20 79512 #048-14-1978 L1978 **FM** *020

COLUMBUS – COLORADO

ANDERSON, Kirk L. 109 SHULT DR STE 102 78934 #064-01-1974 L1979 **FM** *020
AREBALO, Julio. 1860 HIGHWAY 71 S 78934 #176-03-1983 L1998 **GS GE** *020 †85
BARFIELD, Frank Todd. 148 BURFORD ST 78934 #048-04-1957 L1957 **OPH** *071
BURROWS, Donna Sue. PO BOX 134, DONNA CAMPBELL MD PA 78934 #048-15-1989 L1990 **FM EM** *020 †35
CAPLAN, William. ■ 78934 #352-06-1955 L1981 **OBG** *071
GOBERT, Charles Robert. 109 SHULT DR, STE 207 78934 #048-02-1995 L1999 **D EM** *020 †18 ‡
HANCHER, Thomas Beattie. 109 SHULT DR STE 100 78934 #048-02-1972 L1972 **IM IMG** *020 †20
HRACHOVY, James Jos. 110 SHULT DR 78934 #048-02-1965 L1965 **FM FSM** *071 †18
LOWE, Robert James. 1214 FM 806, 1214 FM 806 78934 #021-01-1968 L1969 **OPH** *071 †35
MARBURGER, Robert Cecil. 1220 BOWIE ST 78934 #048-02-1959 L1960 **FM** *071
MILLICAN, Troy Alfred. 2122 HIGHWAY 71 S, STE 101 78934 #048-13-1994 L1999 **FM AM** *020 †18
MUELLER, Thomas Edwin. 2122 HIGHWAY 71 S STE 101 78934 #048-14-1977 L1977 **FM OBS** *020 †18
NEISNER, David R. 110 SHULT DR 78934 #048-16-1992 L1993 **FM** *020 †18
QUENNEVILLE, Kenneth B. 110 SHULT DR 78934 #048-02-1985 L1987 **EM GP** *020
RAO, Madhu Buddah. 1460 WALNUT ST 78934 #495-04-1975 L1990 **P** *020 †75

COMANCHE – COMANCHE

BYRD, Richard Wayne. 201 VALLEY FORGE ST 76442 #048-15-1983 L1983 **FM** *020 †18 ‡
CHIANG, Michael Chihao. ■ 76442 #017-20-1994 L1997 **IM** *020 †20
EISENRICH, Forrest Aubrey. 10201 HIGHWAY 16 76442 #048-02-1961 L1961 **FM** *020 †18
GIUSTINO, Vincenzo. ■ 76442 #561-21-1967 L1980 **FM IM** *071
HOWELL, Robert Gene. ■ 76442 #048-12-1960 L1960 **GP** *071
HUBBARD, Joe Carl, Jr. 10201 HIGHWAY 16, DOCTORS MED CTR CLNC 76442 #039-01-1984 L1985 **IM** *020 †20
MC CRORY, Beau L. 105B VALLEY FORGE ST 76442 #048-14-1998 L1999 **PME** *020 †18
MILLER, Dwayne Carol. 10201 HIGHWAY 16, DOCTORS MED CLNC 76442 #048-15-1985 L1986 **FM** *020 †18

COMFORT – KENDALL

CROW, Sue Ella. 602 N CREEK RD 78013 #048-12-1986 L1987 **IM IMG** *020 †20

COMMERCE – HUNT

KING, Charles Franklin. 1705 LIVE OAK ST 75428 #021-05-1967 L1998 **GP** *020
PERON, Ronald James. 1705 LIVE OAK ST, LIVE OAK PROFESSIONAL CENT 75428 #048-12-1984 L1985 **EM** *020 †18

SELVAGGI, Richard Rossi. 1705 LIVE OAK ST 75428 #048-02-1980 L1980 **FM IMG** *020 †18
SELVAGGI, Thomas Carl. 1705 LIVE OAK ST 75428 #048-02-1985 L1986 **FM** *020 †18
STINNETT, James T, III. ■ 75428 #048-12-1966 L1966 **CHP P** *072

CONROE – MONTGOMERY

ABDULLAH, Arif Bin. 500 MEDICAL CENTER BLVD, STE 218 77304 #704-22-1990 L2006 **IC** *020 †20
AHERON, Jessica. 100 MEDICAL CENTER BLVD, STE 206 77304 #048-14-1996 L1997 **MPD** *020 †55
ALAM, Tawfiq. 508 MEDICAL CENTER BLVD 77304 #048-02-1995 L2004 **GE** *020 †20
AL-AZZEH, Haytham Asad. 508 MEDICAL CENTER BLVD 77304 #575-01-1994 L2003 **CD** *020 †20
ALI, Fozia Akhtar. 31703 CATTAIL PARK CT 77385 #704-21-2002 *100
ALLAMON, Patricia A. 704 OLD MONTGOMERY RD 77301 #048-16-2004 L2005 **FM** *020 †18
ALLEN, Stiles Wesley. ■ 77304 #020-02-1956 L1957 **PD** *071
AMBROSE, Sugumar. 504 MEDICAL CENTER BLVD 77304 #495-66-1975 L2001 **AN** *020 †05
ANGELOS, Erin Leigh. ■ 77301 #048-15-2007 **FP** *012
ARCURI, Raynold A. ■ 77385 #035-19-1941 **AN** *071 †05
AVERY, Maple Leroy. 400 S LOOP 336 W 77304 #048-02-1965 L1965 **OPH** *020 †35
AWAN, Aamir Yaqoob. 508 MEDICAL CENTER BLVD 77304 #704-20-1994 L2006 **PCC** *012 †20
AWASUM, Sergealain Babila. 508 MEDICAL CENTER BLVD 77304 #047-20-1996 L2005 **GE** *020 †20
BABB, Susan Karla. 508 MEDICAL CENTER BLVD, SADLER CLINIC 77304 #048-02-1991 L1992 **IM** *020 †20
BAKER, James Elwood. 508 MEDICAL CENTER BLVD 77304 #048-12-1979 L1982 **FM** *020 †18
BEGUM, Afroza. 17191 ST LUKES WAY 77384 #160-02-1985 L2002 **PD** *020 †55
BELLUR, Shashikumar S. 500 MEDICAL CENTER BLVD, MONTGOMERY CNTY CRDVSCLR 77304 #495-98-1981 L1993 **CD** *072 †20
BERWICK, Alfred Glen. 508 MEDICAL CENTER BLVD 77304 #048-02-1976 L1976 **IM CD** *020 †20
BOCK, John Edward. 800 RIVERWOOD CT STE 104 77304 #035-01-1977 L1983 **N** *020
BOGAN, Robert Eugene. 1020 RIVERWOOD CT 77304 #048-02-1996 L2002 **CHP** *020 †20
BOULWARE, Ronald Arch. ■ 77304 #048-02-1968 L1968 **ORS** *071 †40
BOYLE, George Steven. 508 MEDICAL CENTER BLVD 77304 #019-02-1975 L1978 **CD IM** *020 †20
BROWN, Taylor D. 17350 ST LUKES WAY, STE 370 77384 #048-04-2000 L2006 **ORS** *020
BROWN, William R. 704 OLD MONTGOMERY RD 77301 #048-04-1994 L1997 **FM** *020 †18
BULLOCK, Gerald L. 500 MEDICAL CENTER BLVD, STE 200 77304 #048-02-1969 L1969 **OBG LM** *030 †30
CALDWELL, Jody Ann. 508 MEDICAL CENTER BLVD, SADLER CLINIC 77304 #048-14-1982 L1983 **FM** *020 †18
CALVIN, Richard Thos. 404 RIVER POINTE DR, STE 100 77304 #021-01-1973 L1975 **PD GE** *020 †55
CAMPBELL, Robert Wm. ■ 77304 #048-13-1973 L1973 **OBG** *071 †30
CAPERTON, Martin Vestal. 508 MEDICAL CENTER BLVD 77304 #048-12-1976 L1976 **FM** *020 †18
CASPERSON, Thomas Lee. 504 MEDICAL CENTER BLVD 77304 #024-07-1975 L1980 **AN** *020 †05 ‡
CECIL, Linda Marie. 500 MEDICAL CENTER BLVD 77304 #048-02-1971 L1971 **OBG OBS** *071 †30
CHANG, Jay. 100 MEDICAL CENTER BLVD, STE 102 77304 #244-05-1972 L1997 **IM PD** *020 †20
CHAPMAN, James Henry. 508 MEDICAL CENTER BLVD 77304 #048-12-1970 L1970 **FM** *020 †18
CHENG, Yaiyun J. 1501 RIVER POINTE DR, STE 140 77304 #048-13-1992 L1993 **OBG** *020 †30
CHOBY, Beth Ann. 704 OLD MONTGOMERY RD 77301 #055-01-1995 L2004 **FM** *020 †18
COGLIANESE, Carol Lynn. 100 MEDICAL CENTER BLVD, STE 212 77304 #016-11-1991 L1999 **PDI ID** *020
COLLIER, Richard E, Jr. 1501 RIVER POINTE DR, STE 150 77304 #047-06-1972 L1982 **GS** *020
COLLINS, James Kenneth. 11054 S HIDDEN OAKS 77384 #048-12-1990 L1992 **AN** *020 †05
COX, Kenneth Melvin. 800 RIVERWOOD CT, STE 101 77304 #048-02-1964 L1964 **R NM** *071 †80
CROCKETT, Howard Lawhon. 508 MEDICAL CENTER BLVD 77304 #048-02-1975 L1975 **ORS** *020 †40
CURBOW, Amie Rachelle. 704 OLD MONTGOMERY RD, FAMILY PRACTICE CTR 77301 #048-02-2006 **FP** *012
CURLING, Patrick Ernest. 504 MEDICAL CENTER BLVD 77304 #061-01-1972 L1983 **AN** *020 †05
DANG, Linh Thi. 100 MEDICAL CENTER BLVD, STE 220 77304 #048-13-1994 L1995 **N** *020 †75
DAVIS, Edward K. ■ 77304 #048-04-1957 L1957 **NM R** *071 †80
DAVIS, Francis O'Bryan. ■ 77304 #016-11-1963 L1968 **AN** *071 †05 ‡
DAVIS, Kenneth Gayle. 508 MEDICAL CENTER BLVD 77304 #048-02-1973 L1973 **FM** *020 †18
DECKER, Paul Wayne. 508 MEDICAL CENTER BLVD 77304 #039-01-1995 L1996 **FM** *020 †18
DEJEAN, Baptiste J, III. 400 S LOOP 336 W, AVERY EYE CLINIC 77304 #048-12-1992 L1993 **OPH** *020 †35
DENDY, Charlie F. 500 MEDICAL CENTER BLVD, STE 340 77304 #048-78-2002, ▲ L2003 **GS** *020
DENYER, Garth Chas. 9420 COLLEGE PARK DR, STE 130 77384 #836-02-1973 L1981 *020
DE WITZ, Scott David. 508 MEDICAL CENTER BLVD 77304 #048-15-1983 L1983 **FM** *020 †18
DIAZ ROHENA, Roberto. 100 MEDICAL CENTER BLVD, STE 218 77304 #024-01-1988 L1993 **OPH AI** *020 †35
DOUCET, Timothy Wayne. 508 MEDICAL CENTER BLVD 77304 #048-13-1973 L1973 **OPH PS** *020 †35
DOUGLIS, Franklin M. 3000 W DAVIS ST 77304 #023-01-1978 L1982 **OTO A** *020 †45
DYKE, Marshall James. ■ 77304 #048-02-1964 L1964 **OTO A** *075
ELAHEE, Trecia L. 3115 COLLEGE PARK DR, STE 104 77384 #048-13-1997 L1998 **PD** *020 †55
EL ZUFARI, Mohammad H. 3074 COLLEGE PARK DR 77384 #875-01-1993 L2003 **FM** *020 †18
FACKLER, John M. 1501 RIVER POINTE DR # 100 77304 #048-15-1996 L1997 **ORS** *020 †40
FARBER, Steven Howard. 600 RIVER POINTE DR, STE 200 77304 #041-09-1977 L1981 **CD IM** *020 †20
FERNANDES, Laura S. 508 MEDICAL CENTER BLVD 77304 #187-21-1985 L1999 **IC** *020 †20
FERSHTMAN, Murray Bruce. 3115 COLLEGE PARK DR, STE 104 77384 #048-02-1991 L1992 **PD** *020 †55
FIESINGER, Troy T. 704 OLD MONTGOMERY RD 77301 #048-04-1996 L1999 **FM** *020 †18

■ = Address Information Privacy Protected

FITE, Kevin D. ■ 77304 #048-13-2007 **FP** *012

FLORES, Edward M. 110 COMMERCIAL CIR 77304 #048-02-1983 L1983 **PUD** *020 †20

FOLTERMANN, Miles O. ■ 77306 #048-14-2006 **TY** *012

FROELICH, Kara E. 404 RIVER POINTE DR, STE 100 77304 #048-12-1995 L1996 **PD** *020 †55

FURGATCH, Alysia N. 17191 ST LUKES WAY 77384 #048-13-2003 L2005 **FM** *020 †18

GARCIA, Elena. 100 MEDICAL CENTER BLVD, STE 206 77304 #048-14-1998 L2000 **FM** *020 †18

GARCIA-DEL PINO, Leticia. 100 MEDICAL CENTER BLVD, STE 206 77304 #048-02-1995 L1997 **FM** *020 †18

GEORGE, John K. ■ 77302 #759-18-2004 L2008 *100

GEROW, Frank T. 17350 ST LUKES WAY, STE 370 77384 #048-04-1990 L1991 **ORS** *020 †40

GHANEM, Fadi Geo. 27854 I H 45 N 77385 #605-01-1986 L1990 **FM** *020 †18

GILL, Shazia Akhtar. 100 MEDICAL CENTER BLVD, STE 200 77304 #025-07-1999 L2006 **ID** *100 †20

GLASER, Matthew J. 504 MEDICAL CENTER BLVD, CONROE REG MED CENTER 77304 #048-02-1992 L1993 **DR** *020 †80

GORDON, Robert Louis. ■ 77304 #048-02-1959 L1959 **FM** *071

GORDON, Yvette F. 704 OLD MONTGOMERY RD 77301 #016-45-1995 L2002 **OBG** *020 †30

GRANBERRY, William M. 17350 ST LUKES WAY, STE 370 77384 #048-04-1986 L1987 **ORS OFA** *020 †40

GREIDER, Thomas David. 17350 ST LUKES WAY, STE 370 77384 #048-13-1975 L1976 **ORS OSM** *020 †40

GRIEME, Martin Dietrich. 500 MEDICAL CENTER BLVD, STE 110 77304 #016-11-1989 L1991 **FM** *020 †18

GRIFFIN, John Russell. 110 COMMERCIAL CIR 77304 #048-02-1985 L1986 **PUD IM** *020 †20

GUERRERO, Teresa Trumble. 9420 COLLEGE PARK DR, STE 130 77384 #048-14-1989 L1990 **IM PD** *020 †55,20

HARMON, Charles Wilton. 504 MEDICAL CENTER BLVD 77304 #048-02-1969 L1969 **DR** *020 †80

HARRELL, Angelica L. 1020 RIVERWOOD CT 77304 #048-04-1998 L2001 **P** *020 †75

HART, Nora Catherine. 508 MEDICAL CENTER BLVD 77304 #050-02-1998 L2006 **FM** *020 †18

HATHAWAY, Robert G. 333 N RIVERSHIRE DR, STE 140 77304 #056-06-1951 L1953 **AN** *071 †05

HERRIN, James Robt. 333 N RIVERSHIRE DR, STE 190 77304 #048-02-1976 L1976 **PD** *020 †55

HINDS CAMPA, Samantha L. 3205 W DAVIS ST, STE B150 77304 #048-15-1999 L2002 **FM** *020 †18

HIRD, Travis W. 1501 RIVER POINTE DR, STE 100 77304 #048-14-1999 L2003 **PM** *020 †60

HOLMES, Robert Ryan. 500 MEDICAL CENTER BLVD, STE 240 77304 #048-02-2002 L2006 **IM** *020 †20

HOLMES, Sonia Nadine. 500 MEDICAL CENTER BLVD, STE 240 77304 #048-02-2002 L2006 **IM** *020 †20

HORTON, Sheryl Lee. 704 OLD MONTGOMERY RD 77301 #021-05-2005 L2008 **FP** *012

HOUGH, Bradley H. 701 E DAVIS ST, DEPT FM 77301 #048-13-2007 **FP** *012

HUIE, William S. 504 MEDICAL CENTER BLVD 77304 #048-12-1988 L1989 **AN** *020 †05

HURST, William Robt. ■ 77304 #048-02-1954 L1954 **EM** *071 †18

HYDE, Linda C. 333 N RIVERSHIRE DR, STE 285 77304 #048-04-1990 L1991 **FM** *020 †18

INNIS, Ray Anthony. 504 MEDICAL CENTER BLVD, CRMC ANESTHESIA DEPARTMENT 77304 #025-01-1997 L2001 **AN** *020 †05

IYER, Mallika V. 100 MEDICAL CENTER BLVD, STE 120 77304 #495-96-1982 L1996 **AI** *020 †55,03

JABLECKI, Nathaniel Thoma. 704 OLD MONTGOMERY RD 77301 #048-13-2004 L2007 **FSM** *012 †18

JAFRI, Abbas Haider. 100 MEDICAL CENTER BLVD, STE 110 77304 #704-25-1997 L2002 *020 †20

JENNINGS, Ryan Errol. 704 OLD MONTGOMERY RD, FAMILY PRACTICE CTR 77301 #048-15-2006 **FP** *012

JOHNSON, Mark Alan. 100 MEDICAL CTR BLVD # 100 77304 #048-16-1990 L1995 **GS** *020 †85

JOHNSON, Raymond, Jr. 508 MEDICAL CENTER BLVD, THE SADLER CLINIC 77304 #048-04-1976 L1976 **FM** *020 †18

JONES, Charles Alvin. 504 MEDICAL CENTER BLVD 77304 #048-02-1965 L1965 **FM OS** *071 †18

JORDAN, Blair Phillip. 508 MEDICAL CENTER BLVD 77304 #038-41-1980 L1981 **GS VS** *020 †85

JOSHI, Lata. 704 OLD MONTGOMERY RD 77301 #495-41-1989 L2000 **FM** *020 †18

KAREH, Victor. 500 MEDICAL CENTER BLVD, STE 355 77304 #042-01-1980 L1991 **NS** *020 †25

KEESEE, Daniel Cleve. ■ 77305 #020-02-1965 L1989 **FM P** *020 †18

KELLY, Cecily Nicole. 704 OLD MONTGOMERY RD, FAMILY PRACTICE CTR 77301 #048-14-2007 **FP** *012

KELLY, Stephen Michael. 1501 RIVER POINTE DR, STE 240 77304 #048-02-1981 L1981 **GE** *020 †20

KENWORTHY, Paul Richard. 1501 RIVER POINTE DR, STE 160 77304 #038-40-1990 L1996 **U** *020 †95

KERN, Kara Lea. 800 RIVERWOOD CT STE 105 77304 #011-02-1999 L2002 **FM** *020 †18

KERSEY, Susan Elizabeth. 333 N RIVERSHIRE DR, STE 160 77304 #035-20-2001 L2005 *100 †35

KHAWLY, Joseph Anthony. 100 MEDICAL CENTER BLVD, STE 218 77304 #036-07-1991 L1997 **OPH** *020 †35

KLEIN, Alexander Benj, Jr. 508 MEDICAL CENTER BLVD 77304 #048-04-1965 L1971 **GYN** *020 †30

KRENEK, Gregory. 333 N RIVERSHIRE DR, STE 100 77304 #048-16-1993 L1994 **D IMG** *020 †15

KUGLEN, Craig Charles, Jr. 400 S LOOP 336 W 77304 #048-14-1990 L1991 **OPH** *020 †35

KWATRA, Ajay. 506 MEDICAL CENTER BLVD, SADLER CLINIC 77304 #048-04-1993 L1994 **U** *020 †95

LABBE, Marc Robert. 17350 ST LUKES WAY, STE 370 77384 #048-04-1997 L2003 **ORS OSM** *020 †40

LAMBERT, Harry Michael. 100 MEDICAL CENTER BLVD, STE 218 77304 #048-04-1977 L1977 **OPH** *020 †35

LANCASTER, Kevin Lee. 183 GOLDEN AUTUMN PL 77384 #048-15-1993 L1994 **AN** *020 †05

LANINGHAM, Robert Jeremy. 506 MEDICAL CENTER BLVD 77304 #048-14-1996 L1997 **FM** *020 †18

LAYTON, Billy James. 504 MEDICAL CENTER BLVD 77304 #004-01-2000 L2002 **AN** *020 †05

LEDE, Raul Ignacio. ■ 77305 #132-01-1960 L1967 **PTH** *071 †50

LEEVES, Edward Jerry. 2105 N THOMPSON ST 77301 #048-02-1960 L1960 **GS GP** *071

LEGHARI, Rahmat U. ■ 77305 #704-04-1971 L1978 **IM CD** *020 †20

MANISCALCO, Stephen P. 500 MEDICAL CENTER BLVD, STE 340 77304 #048-12-1995 L2001 **TS** *020 †85,90

MARCHAND, Kristina. ■ 77384 #048-16-2004 L2007 **FM** *100 †18

MARTEL, Armand Harvey. 504 MEDICAL CENTER BLVD, DEPT OF PATHOLOGY 77304 #649-07-1981 L1984 **PTH** *020 †50

MARTIN, Randall Val. 508 MEDICAL CENTER BLVD 77304 #048-13-1976 L1976 **FM** *020 †18

MC AFEE, Wayne. 17198 ST LUKES WAY 77384 #048-12-1962 L1962 **OBG** *020 †30

MC CORMACK, Callie Elaine. 704 OLD MONTGOMERY RD, FAMILY PRACTICE CTR 77301 #048-14-2004 L2006 **FM** *020 †18

MC GOWAN, Jack David. 504 MEDICAL CENTER BLVD, MONTGOMERY COUNTY MEDICAL 77304 #017-20-1976 L1986 **NPM PD** *020 †55

MCKAY, Eileen. ■ 77384 #035-45-2000 L2000 **PP** *020 †50

MC PHERSON, Charles Keith. 404 RIVER POINTE DR, STE 100 77304 #048-12-1986 L1987 **PD** *020 †55

MEMON, Ilyas Muhammad. 100 MEDICAL CENTER BLVD, STE 130 77304 #704-02-1991 L2005 **GE IM** *020 †20

MILLER, Helen Jean Vine. ■ 77301 #048-02-1954 L1954 **OPH** *071 †35

MOBLEY, Robert Alan. 600 RIVER POINTE DR, STE 100 77304 #020-02-1975 L1980 **CD IM** *020 †20

MOHAMED-ALY, Mohamed S. 508 MEDICAL CENTER BLVD 77304 #915-02-1988 L2005 **PUD** *020 †20

MOLINA, Alyssa Beth. ■ 77385 #048-02-2007 **FP** *012

MORAN, Kevin M. 1501 RIVER POINTE DR, STE 100 77304 #048-14-1990 L1992 **ORS** *020 †40

MORRISON, Francis Jos. 2912 W DAVIS ST, STE 400 77304 #048-02-1978 L1978 **FM** *071 †18

NEELAND, Barry Norman. 200 RIVER POINTE DR # 120 77304 #035-46-1976 L1978 **NEP IM** *020 †20

NEWMAN, Ronald Kent. 1501 RIVER POINTE DR STE 1 77304 #048-13-1978 L1978 **OTO** *020 †45

NGUYEN, Co Hai. 100 MEDICAL CENTER BLVD, STE 214 77304 #048-02-1990 L1991 **FM** *020 †18

NISHIMURA, Akio. 508 MEDICAL CENTER BLVD, SADLER CLINIC 77304 #572-29-1961 **CD** *020

NISHIMURA-KOMURO, Akira. 508 MEDICAL CENTER BLVD 77304 #649-01-1965 L1972 **CD IM** *020 †20

NJUKI, Frederick Ivan. 206A S LOOP 336 W 77304 #905-01-1987 L2003 **IM** *020 †20

NORRIS, Kim Sheree. 704 OLD MONTGOMERY RD, LONESTAR FPC 77301 #048-14-2005 L2008 **FP** *012

O'BRIEN, Timothy Jos. 504 MEDICAL CENTER BLVD, COLUMBIA CONROE REGIONAL M 77304 #048-14-1991 L1998 **EM** *020 †16

O'GORMAN, Thomas M, Jr. ■ 77304 #048-02-1966 L1966 **U** *071 †95

PARKER, Robert Bruce. ■ 77384 #048-02-1965 L1966 **FM** *071 †18

PATEL, Nimesh Mafat. 508 MEDICAL CENTER BLVD 77304 #305-01-2002 L2006 **IM** *020 †20

PEET, John Vernon. 508 MEDICAL CENTER BLVD 77304 #048-12-1970 L1970 **FM** *020

PERCHES, Richard Anthony. 508 MEDICAL CTR BLVD 77304 #048-12-1986 L1987 **DR** *020 †80

PERRY, John Edward, III. 3500 W DAVIS ST, STE 220 77304 #010-03-1993 L2001 **CD** *020

PICKETT, James Dwayne. 508 MEDICAL CENTER BLVD 77304 #048-04-1980 L1980 **CD IM** *020 †20

PIERRE, James Darian. 206A S LOOP 336 W STE 157, PIERRE PHYSICIAN GROUP 77304 #048-02-1997 L2004 **IM** *020

POHL, Donald Richard. 448 CUMBERLAND TRL 77302 #048-12-1963 L1963 **U** *020 †95

POINDEXTER, Hugh Reeves. 17350 ST LUKES WAY, STE 150 77384 #048-14-1974 L1974 **FM** *020 †18

PONTANI, Bradley Alan. 500 MEDICAL CENTER BLVD, STE 110 77304 #048-13-1983 L1983 **FM** *020 †18

POPE, George Danl. 11815 WHITE OAK TRL, THE PROFESSIONAL ASSOCIATI 77385 #048-04-1970 L1970 **PD** *071 †55

PRICE, Charles Downey. 333 N RIVERSHIRE DR # 160 77304 #023-01-1966 L1971 **OPH** *020 †35

PUNSALAN, Tricia L. 953 FIFE DR 77301 #048-13-2006 **FP** *012

PUTMAN, James Tyler. 800 RIVERWOOD CT, STE 100 77304 #018-03-1989 L2008 **FM** *020 †18

QUARLES, Marjorie Ann. 404 RIVER POINTE DR, STE 100 77304 #048-16-1999 L2002 **PD** *020 †55

REDDY, Karunakar P. 2101 S LOOP 336 W 77304 #495-49-1982 L1992 **IM CD** *020 †20

REDDY, Shanti Baireddy. 504 MEDICAL CENTER BLVD, NICU 77304 #495-21-1982 L1991 **NPM PD** *020 †55

REDDY, Sunil Kamatam. 1501 RIVER POINTE DR, STE 220 77304 #495-21-1985 L1993 **GE IM** *075

REYES, Lucio. 701 E DAVIS ST STE C, MONTGOMERY CO MED ED 77301 #048-13-1990 L1992 **FM** *075

RIVAS, Teresa D. ■ 77384 #048-14-1998 L2001 **PD** *020

ROBBINS, Judy Cleo. ■ 77384 #039-01-1967 L1967 **GP OS** *030

ROBERTS, Richard Royston. 333 N RIVERSHIRE DR, STE 270 77304 #048-04-1973 L1973 **OBG** *020 †30

ROWE, Caroline Webster. ■ 77384 #048-02-1944 L1944 **R** *071 †80

SASSARD, Walter Randall. 17350 ST LUKES WAY, STE 370 77384 #045-01-1967 L1974 **OSS ORS** *020 †40

SCARBOROUGH, Kyle L. 508 MEDICAL CENTER BLVD, SADLER CLINIC 77304 #048-14-1989 L1990 **FM** *020 †18

SCHOPPE, Kurt Alton. ■ 77304 #048-04-2007 **IM** *012

SCHOPPE, Leslie Errol. 508 MEDICAL CENTER BLVD, THE SADLER CLINIC 77304 #048-02-1975 L1975 **GE** *020 †20

SHAH, Daksha Shantilal. 504 MEDICAL CENTER BLVD, CONROE REGIONAL MEDICAL CE 77304 #495-98-1989 L2002 **AN** *020 †05

SHAH, Parul Yogendra. 17191 ST LUKES WAY 77384 #028-46-1997 L2007 **D** *020 †15 ‡

SHARPLESS, Gary N. 508 MEDICAL CENTER BLVD, SADLER CLINIC 77304 #048-14-1989 L1991 **IM** *020 †20

SHEIH, Samson S. 3205 W DAVIS ST, STE B150 77304 #048-13-1998 L2001 **FM** *020 †18

SHORT, Patricia D. 6 HARTWICK CT 77304 #028-02-1998 L2001 **EM** *020 †16

SIFF, Sherwin Jay. 17350 ST LUKES WAY, STE 370 77384 #041-12-1964 L1970 **ORS** *020 †40

SIFF, Todd Elliott. 17350 ST LUKES WAY, STE 370 77384 #048-04-1994 L1995 **ORS HS** *020 †40

SIMS, Charles Ray. 10 MEDICAL CENTER BLVD, STE 212 77304 #048-14-1996 L2006 **ID** *020 †20

SLONE, Dennis. INTERSTATE 45 S, SADLER CLINIC SOUTHWOO 77385 #836-01-1955 L1964 **PHP IM** *050 †55

SMITH, Roy Bascom. 17350 ST LUKES WAY 77384 #048-12-1974 L1974 **ORS** *020 †40

SPARKS, John C. 1501 RIVER POINTE DR, STE 100 77304 #048-13-1986 L1990 **ORS** *020 †40

SPINKS, Shaun Robert. 704 OLD MONTGOMERY RD, FAMILY PRACTICE CTR 77301 #021-05-2006 **FP** *012

SPLENSER, Pablo Ernesto. ■ 77301 #048-02-2006 L2008 **FP** *012

STARTZ, John Alan. 100 MEDICAL CENTER BLVD, STE 104 77304 #048-14-1986 L1987 **IM** *020 †20

STOREY, Gayle Scott. 508 MEDICAL CENTER BLVD 77304 #048-02-1988 L1989 **RNR** *071 †80

STOWE, Krenie Kimberly. 27854 I H 45 N 77385 #035-46-1985 L1994 **PD** *020

SUBRAMANIAN, Vidhya. 506 MEDICAL CENTER BLVD 77304 #495-96-1993 L2006 END *020 †20

SULLIVAN, Peter Vincent. ■ 77304 #047-06-1975 L1996 FM OM *050 †18

THOMAS, Annie. 506 MEDICAL CENTER BLVD 77304 #495-33-1989 L2002 END *020 †20

THOMASON, Edgar Maurice. ■ 77304 #048-04-1946 L1946 GP *071

TOLAT, Darshan Vipin. 200 RIVER POINTE DR # 120 77304 #048-04-1988 L1989 NEP IM *020 †20

TORRES, Daniel Augusto. 333 N RIVERSHIRE DR, STE 240 77304 #847-02-1958 L1973 AN *020

TRAHAN, Leonard. 504 MEDICAL CENTER BLVD 77304 #048-02-1990 L1994 AN *020 †05

TURLEY, Brian Raynior. 100 MEDICAL CENTER BLVD, STE 118 77304 #019-02-1992 L1997 VIR R *075 †80

VALENCIA, Sharee Anne. 101 PINE MANOR DR 77385 #030-05-1995 L2006 OBG *020 †30

WALKER, Daniel Richard. 100 MEDICAL CENTER BLVD, STE 212 77304 #048-14-1981 L1981 ID *020 †20

WALLER, Stephen Frank. 333 N RIVERSHIRE DR, STE 265 77304 #048-12-1973 L1980 N IM *020 †20,75

WALLS, Michael J. 200 RIVER POINTE DR # 12 77304 #048-14-1993 L1994 NEP *020 †20

WATSON, Irving M, Jr. 508 MEDICAL CENTER BLVD 77304 #048-02-1953 L1953 GP *075

WATTERS, William Charles, II. 17350 ST LUKES WAY, STE 370 77384 #024-01-1974 L1982 OSS OS *020 †40

WESTERHEIDE, Wm Scott. 504 MEDICAL CENTER BLVD 77304 #048-02-1991 L1995 AN *020 †05

WESTMORELAND, James B. 1501 RIVER POINTE DR, SUITE100 77304 #048-02-1999 L2004 ORS *020 †40

WHITE, James Wheeler. ■ 77304 #047-06-1961 L1969 GP *071 †85

WHITMAN, Daniel Emmanuel. 1501 RIVER POINTE DR, STE 240 77304 #048-04-1978 L1979 IM *020 †20

WILKENFELD, Richard S. 800 RIVERWOOD CT STE 102 77304 #165-04-1977 L1983 GS VS *020

WILKERSON, Walter D, Jr. 3205 W DAVIS ST, SADLER CLINIC 77304 #048-12-1955 L1955 FM *071 †18

WILLIAMS, Kellie Jo. 404 RIVER POINTE DR, STE 100 77304 #005-12-1997 L1999 PD *020 †55

WILLIS, Arthur Wm, Jr. 100 MEDICAL CENTER BLVD, STE 218 77304 #017-20-1966 L1973 OPH *020 †35

WONG, Christopher B H. 100 MEDICAL CENTER BLVD, STE 213 77304 #462-01-1986 L1996 CD *020 †20

WOOD, Herman Clifford. ■ 77301 #016-11-1951 L1960 FM *071 †18

WUEST, Wilmer Leo. 333 N RIVERSHIRE DR STE 24 77304 #007-02-1972 L1978 PS *020 †65

YABAR, Cesar F. 610 S FRAZIER ST STE A 77301 #737-01-1983 L1996 FM *020 †18 ‡

YEE, Hilton Wong. 508 MEDICAL CENTER BLVD 77304 #021-05-1976 L1983 PS HS *020 †65

YOUNG, Milicent Eva. ■ 77384 #016-42-1999 L2002 IM *020

YOUNGBLOOD, Katie Beth H. 327 W ROLLING HILLS DR 77304 #048-02-1969 L1969 FM *071 †18

ZAHEER, Syed Javeed. ■ 77301 #704-21-1984 L2001 PD *020 †55

ZHANG, Donghong. 508 MEDICAL CENTER BLVD 77304 #243-47-1987 L2005 PCC *020 †20

CONVERSE – BEXAR

FALCON, Maria G. ■ 78109 #048-13-2007 PD *012

HIGEY, Jason Allen. ■ 78109 #051-01-2005 L2007 IM *012

HSUE, Gunther. ■ 78109 #005-12-1992 L1995 ID *020 †20

WILLIAMS, Megan Rose-Lee. ■ 78109 #048-13-2007 FP *012

WILSON, Eugene Wiley, IV. ■ 78109 #041-78-2004, ▲ L2005 *020

COOKVILLE – TITUS

DANIEL, Clifton Ray. ■ 75558 #048-12-1968 L1968 PTH *071 †50

COOPER – DELTA

MONDAY, Suzanne Elizabeth. 91 W SIDE SQ 75432 #048-02-1997 L2000 FM *020 †18

COPPELL – DALLAS

ALLEN, Clarence R, Jr. ■ 75019 #048-04-1971 L1971 LM PHP *062 †70 ‡

ANDERSON, Antony Don. 601 CANYON DR STE 10 75019 #048-12-1992 L1993 FM OBS *020 †18

ANDUSS, Marc Leighton. 601 CANYON DR STE 10 75019 #048-13-1986 L1987 IM GP *020 †20

ARTHUR, John M. 580 S DENTON TAP RD, STE 123 75019 #048-13-1985 L1986 FM *020 †18

BAHRASSA, Feraydoon. ■ 75019 #517-01-1970 L1988 RO R *020 †80

BAILEY, Aaron S. 171 COVE DR 75019 #048-12-1999 L2001 DR *020 †80

BALCK, Sarah Phoebe. ■ 75019 #025-01-2005 L2008 PD *012

BAUER, Paul Wade. 370 S STATE HWY 121 N #100, ENT FOR CHILDREN 75019 #030-05-1995 L2002 PDO OTO *020 †45

BOSWELL, John Scott. ■ 75019 #021-01-2005 L2007 D *012

CAHAN, Nina Gale. 848 S DENTON TAP RD, STE 100 75019 #032-01-1980 L1984 FM OBS *020 †18

CHANG, Alice Yoonju. ■ 75019 #008-01-1995 L2004 END *100 †20

CHARLES, Brandon C. 413 W BETHEL RD, STE 300 75019 #048-15-1988 L1989 OBG *020 †30

COLDWELL, Cory D. 1199 S BELT LINE RD 75019 #048-04-1989 L1995 CHP *020 †75

COLON, Gregory Lawrence. 580 S DENTON TAP RD # 123 75019 #048-15-1991 L1994 FM *020 †18

COX, Ralph F, Jr. 546 E SANDY LAKE RD, STE 210 75019 #048-14-1982 L1983 FM *020 †18

COXSEY, Diana Ferguson. 580 S DENTON TAP RD, STE 123 75019 #048-14-1991 L1992 FM *020 †18

DESHPANDE, Devyani Vilas. ■ 75019 #496-49-1999 ID *012

DIBONA, Daniel J. ■ 75019 #048-12-1985 L1986 IM EM *020 †20

ERFE, Dolores Torre. ■ 75019 #748-01-1972 L1980 GP PD *020 †55

FREEMAN, Patrick Scott. 546 E SANDY LAKE RD, STE 210 75019 #003-01-1989 L1998 FM *020 †18

GELLMAN, Steven Perry. 580 S DENTON TAP RD, STE 123 75019 #048-14-1979 L1979 FM *020 †18

GEORGULAS, Anne M. 150 S DENTON TAP RD # 116 75019 #048-13-1991 L1992 PD *020 †55

GHOSE, Subroto. ■ 75019 #495-45-1991 L2005 P *020 †75

GILLEAN, Myra Gail. 627 STRATFORD LN 75019 #004-01-1977 L1986 FM *020 †18

GUEVARA, Esequiel Carreon. 308 WOODHURST PL 75019 #048-12-1979 L1979 EM PD *020 †55,16

GUMBO, Tawanda. ■ 75019 #775-01-1991 L1997 ID *020 †20

HALL, John Culley. 820 S MACARTHUR BLVD # 100, TOWN CENTER ER 75019 #048-12-1995 L2001 EM *020 †20

HAVEMANN, Leslie K. ■ 75019 #048-12-2000 L2005 OBG *020

HERNANDEZ, Martin M. ■ 75019 #649-52-1985 L1992 PCC IM *020 †20

HODGES, Jennifer Kristen. ■ 75019 #048-12-2004 L2006 OBG *012

INGRAM, Jonathan David. 747 PLAZA BLVD 75019 #047-20-1998 L1999 DR *020

JAMES, John. ■ 75019 #046-01-2005 L2007 DR *012

KALU, Victor C. ■ 75019 #690-02-1985 L1994 NEP *020 †20

KAZI, Farhana. 708 WAVERLY LN 75019 #704-25-1991 L2001 CD *020 †20

KIMMONS, John Henry. ■ 75019 #001-02-1957 L1968 IM PD *020 †20

KINCAID, Darletta Joan. 546 E SANDY LAKE RD, STE 130 75019 #048-12-1982 L1983 PD *020 †55

KING, Jeffrey Brian. 601 CANYON DR STE 100, CARE NOW 75019 #041-13-1999 L2004 FM *020 †18

KLIMA, Eva. 722 S DENTON TAP RD, STE 240 75019 #048-14-1989 L1991 FM *020 †18

KUTZ, Joe Walter, Jr. ■ 75019 #048-04-2000 L2007 OTO *020 †45

LINKIEWICZ, Ania Justyna. ■ 75019 #030-06-2006 AN *012

LIU, Benny. ■ 75019 #048-02-2001 L2006 GE *012

MACKEY, Jesse James. ■ 75019 #005-11-1980 L1991 EM IM *020 †16

MARTIN, Sharhonda L. 601 CANYON DR, STE 100 75019 #038-40-1995 L1999 FM *020 †18

MARTINEZ, Tanya Milagros. ■ 75019 #042-01-1997 L2006 PDP *020 †55

MASCARENHAS, Francis Kevi. ■ 75019 #495-52-1983 L2006 FM *020 †18

MATHAI, Samuel. ■ 75019 #495-27-1987 L2002 PYG *020 †75

MC ANELLY, George, II. 652 E SANDY LAKE RD 75019 #047-20-1989 L1994 AI PDA *020 †55

MC DANALD, Conway L. 1199 S BELT LINE RD, STE 100 75019 #048-02-1978 L1978 P *030 †75 ‡

MIKE, Margaret E. 232 BEECHWOOD LN 75019 #041-02-1986 L1992 N SME *020 †75

MURRAY, Alan Douglas. 370 S STATE HWY 121 N #100, ENT FOR CHILDREN, P.A. 75019 #048-02-1990 L1996 OTO PDO *020 †45

NALEY, Rolf Keith. 546 E SANDY LAKE RD, STE 210 75019 #026-04-1973 L1997 FM *020 †18

NASEEM, Rao Haris. 708 WAVERLY LN 75019 #704-25-1991 L2002 ICE *100 †20

NELSON, Wayne Kent. ■ 75019 #026-08-2006 GS *012

NGUYEN, Tu Huu. ■ 75019 #941-01-1969 L1979 PTH *020 †50

OHEARN, Charles John. 651 N DENTON TAP RD 75019 #035-09-1987 L1989 EM *020

OKPON, Catherine S. ■ 75019 #690-07-1986 L1997 FM *020 †18

OSUJI, Azunwanne I. ■ 75019 #690-07-1985 L1998 IM *020 †20

PANESAR, Atinder Pal S. 624 NATCHES TRCE 75019 #495-29-1991 L2002 NEP *020 †20

PARKEY, Joe Ed. 747 PLAZA BLVD 75019 #048-02-1998 L2003 RNR *020 †80

PARTAP, Anu Nita. ■ 75019 #028-46-1995 L1998 PD *020 †55

PINCKARD, James Keith. ■ 75019 #028-02-1998 L2003 FOP *020 †50

PRESTON, Wm Howard Bailey. ■ 75019 #065-01-1951 L1980 *071

QUINONES, Henry. ■ 75019 #042-01-1995 L2002 NEP *020 †20

RAJA, Kalyani. 1705 E BELT LINE RD, COPPELL PEDIATRIC ASSOCIAT 75019 #048-12-1995 L1996 PD *020 †55

RAM, Sunil Kumar. 747 PLAZA BLVD 75019 #473-01-1998 L2004 DR *100 †80

REDDICK, Mark Anthony. ■ 75019 #021-01-2005 DR *012

ROCHE, Melissa Mae. ■ 75019 #025-07-2007 FP *012

ROLAND, Christina Lynn. ■ 75019 #011-02-2004 GS *012

SALMON, Watt Thos. ■ 75019 #047-06-1954 L1955 P *020 †75

SCHLICHTEMEIER, Tammi L. 1705 E BELT LINE RD 75019 #048-12-1990 L1991 PD *020 †55

SHAH, Nosheen Rizvi. ■ 75019 #704-05-1997 L2007 FM *100 †18

SHARMA, Bina. 722 S DENTON TAP RD, STE 190 75019 #495-49-1988 L2000 IM *020 †20

SIMMANG, Clifford Liles. 608 CANEMOUNT LN 75019 #048-02-1982 L1983 CRS CBG *020 †85,10

SINGH, Maulshree. 601 CANYON DR STE 100 75019 #495-24-2003 L2008 FM *100 †18

SLATER, David A. 546 E SANDY LAKE RD, STE 210 75019 #048-12-1995 L2000 FM *020 †18

SMITH, Stephen T. ■ 75019 #048-12-2001 L2003 VS *100 †85

SO, Ashley Unwoo. 546 E SANDY LAKE RD, STE 210 75019 #048-02-1998 L2002 FM *020 †18

SPERRY, Jane Elizabeth. ■ 75019 #048-13-2005 L2008 IM *012

STEELE, James Darrell. ■ 75019 #048-46-1995 L1997 GS *020

STORY, Jay Courtlin. 580 S DENTON TAP RD, STE 123 75019 #026-04-1981 L1985 FM *071 †18

SUGUMARAN, Radha. ■ 75019 #496-23-2003 FP *012

SWALDI, Steven A. 413 W BETHEL RD 75019 #048-12-1991 L1992 FM *020 †18

TAYLOR, Julie A. 652 E SANDY LAKE RD 75019 #048-12-1988 L1992 PD *020 †55

THOMAS, Mini. 601 CANYON DR, STE 100 75019 #048-02-1996 L1999 FM *020 †18

UFRET-VINCENTY, Rafael L. ■ 75019 #042-01-2000 L2006 OPH *100 †35

ULANOSKI, James Robert. 150 S DENTON TAP RD, STE 116 75019 #041-14-1994 L1997 PD *020 †18

ULANOSKI, Pamela Alberts. 150 S DENTON TAP RD, STE 116 75019 #041-14-1993 L1996 PD *020 †18

VAN DE MAE, Michele. ■ 75019 #041-14-1999 L2004 IM *020 †20

VAQUERA, Key Ansley. ■ 75019 #048-12-2008 *012

WULLER, Eugene Geo. ■ 75019 #010-02-1966 L1972 AN GP *071 †05

YOUN, Paul Y. ■ 75019 #025-01-1993 L1997 AN *020 †05

ZRNIC, Uros. ■ 75019 #957-02-1988 L2003 CHP *020 †75

COPPERAS COVE – CORYELL

BAKA, Jennifer Ann. ■ 76522 #035-15-2005 L2006 FP *012

DICKERSON, James Albert. ■ 76522 #023-12-1998 L2008 GS *020 †85

HARRISON, Karen Powell. 806 E AVENUE D, STE E 76522 #048-13-1996 L1999 IM *020 †20

HARRISON, Raymond Josef. 806 E AVENUE D, STE E 76522 #036-01-1996 L1999 IM *020 †20

KHOSHNEVIS-YAZDI, H. 76522 #517-01-1961 L1987 DR *020 †80

KIETZMAN, Laurel I. 76522 #016-43-1986 L1987 RO *020 †16

OWENS, Brenda Diane. 819 E HIGHWAY 190, DACH FAMILY CARE CLINIC 76522 #048-15-1987 L1988 FM *020 †18

PRESCOTT, Paul Robt. 819 E HIGHWAY 190 76522 #041-12-1974 L1981 PD *020 †55

CORINTH – DENTON

CAMPBELL, Odette Louise. 4851 S I-35 E, STE 101 76210 #051-07-1984 L1991 **RO IM** *020 †80
ELTERMAN, Joel B. ■ 76210 #048-12-2005 L2006 **GS** *012
GLASS, William James, Jr. 3440 CORINTH PKWY 76208 #041-02-1940 L1941 **GP** *071
IGNACIO, Bienvenido M. ■ 76210 #748-01-1959 L1982 **PD** *071
IGNACIO, Madonna M. ■ 76210 #748-01-1960 L1982 **PD** *020
JARSTFER, Bruce Stacy. ■ 76210 #025-01-1962 L1982 **TS GS** *071 †85
LEWIS, Jeffrey Earl. 4851 S I-35 E, STE 101 76210 #005-06-1974 L1980 **OPH** *020
MC DOWELL, Adam Wayne. 3901 FM 2181, STE 300 76210 #039-01-2001 L2004 **FM** *020 †18
MCDOWELL, Ronda Christine. 3901 FM 2181 STE 300 76210 #039-01-2000 L2004 **PD** *020
MUBARAK, Jamal. 2233 KNOB HILL DR 76210 #704-25-1988 L1998 **PUD CCM** *020 †20
REED, Don R. ■ 76210 #030-05-1951 L1951 **FM** *071 †18
SULIMAN, Ahmed Ali Ahmed. ■ 76210 #848-01-1995 **IM** *100 †20
SULIMAN, Yasir Ali Ahmed. ■ 76210 #539-06-1991 L2006 **VS** *020 †85
WALDEN, Jacci Gayle. 4845 S INTERSTATE 35 E, STE 101 76210 #048-02-1999 L2002 **FM** *020 †18
WOODS, Brian P. ■ 76210 #048-13-1999 L2000 **PD** *020

CORPUS CHRISTI – NUECES

ABREU, Pedro Julian. 613 ELIZABETH ST, STE 702 78404 #847-10-1975 L1981 **IM** *020
ACEBO, Francisco A. 515 CLIFFORD ST 78404 #048-02-1988 L1989 **FM** *020 †18
ACEBO, Raymond B. 2601 HOSPITAL BLVD STE 201 78405 #048-14-1990 L1991 **IM** *020
ACEVEDO-BERNAL, Jessica I. 5920 SARATOGA BLVD, STE 470 78414 #042-03-2001 L2004 **PD** *100 †55
ACOSTA, Daniel. 1301 OCEAN DR, ABDOMINAL SPECIALISTS OF 78404 #048-12-1983 L1983 **GE IM** *020 †20
AGARWAL, Sanjay. 3301 S ALAMEDA ST, STE 307 78411 #055-01-1989 L1997 **OPH** *020 †35
AHMED, Aisha Jamil. 3533 S ALAMEDA ST 78411 #704-02-1999 L2007 **PD** *020 †55
AITKEN, Alexander T. 7101 WILLIAMS DR, WILLIAMS IMAGING CENTER 78412 #048-16-1991 L1992 **DR** *020 †80
AKHTAR, Noorullah. 3533 S ALAMEDA ST, ANESTHESIOLOGY ASSOCS 78411 #704-16-1985 L1996 **CCP** *020 †55
ALANMANOU, Euleche Arsene. 3533 S ALAMEDA ST FL 2, ANESTHESIOLOGY ASSOCIATES #170-01-1993 L2000 **APM** *020
ALBARRACIN, Cesar A. 702 MORGAN AVE 78404 #264-10-1980 L1997 **IM** *020 †20
ALBRIGHT, James Edward. 2481 MORGAN AVE # 5608 78405 #048-12-1955 L1955 **DR** *071 †80
ALEMAN, Ann. 613 ELIZABETH ST, STE 812 78404 #042-03-1987 L1992 **IM** *020 †20
ALEXANDER, Mathew. 3643 S STAPLES ST 78411 #035-03-1995 L2004 **NS** *020
ALEXANDER, Thomas. 613 ELIZABETH ST, STE 502 78404 #495-37-1986 L1991 **CD IC** *020 †20
ALI HASSAN, Ali Mohamed S. 3533 S ALAMEDA ST 78411 #915-06-1996 **PD** *012
AL-KHALIL, Ihsan. 3533 S ALAMEDA ST 78411 #875-01-1972 L1991 **PD PHO** *020 †55
ALLEN, Marsha Monhollon. 13738 CAYO GORDA CT 78418 #051-04-1988 L2002 **FM** *020 †18
ALLEN, Shawn Michael. ■ 78418 #048-02-2007 *012
ALMANZA, Ruben J. 6200 SARATOGA BLVD, BLD 5 STE A 78414 #048-02-1998 L1999 **FM** *020 †18
ALMOUIE, Muhamad Nazm. 14041 NORTHWEST BLVD, STE 1 78410 #875-03-1990 L1997 **PD** *020 †55
ALONSO, Javier. 613 ELIZABETH ST, STE 703 78404 #847-11-1982 L2001 **GS** *020 †85,90
ALTER, Nejemie. 3240 FORT WORTH ST, STE 101 78411 #649-01-1985 L1997 **PHO** *020 †55
ALVARADO, Rudolph. 7101 WILLIAMS DR, WILLIAMS IMAGING CENTER 78412 #005-02-1977 L1987 **R** *020 †80
ALVAREZ, Alejandro A. 10651 E ST, ATTN: CREDENTIAL OFFICE 78419 #016-42-2001 L2003 **FP** *012
AMAYA DE HELLMAN, Diana. 3533 S ALAMEDA ST 78411 #264-11-1994 **PD** *012
ANDERSON, William Elsthon. 3315 S ALAMEDA ST 78411 #020-02-1947 L1955 **PUD IM** *071 †20
ANDRADE, Antonio Carlos C. 3533 S ALAMEDA ST 78411 #187-18-1972 L1981 **OTO A** *020
ANNABLE, Charles Roy. 3533 S ALAMEDA ST 78411 #025-01-1961 L1986 **PTH TS** *071 †85,90,50
ANTONI, Jose Ernesto. 2606 HOSPITAL BLVD 78405 #308-01-1949 L1961 **FM** *071 †18
ANUNOBI, Endaline Amaka. 3533 S ALAMEDA ST 78411 #690-15-2002 L2008 **PD** *012
ANYAEGBU, Elizabeth Ijeom. 3533 S ALAMEDA ST 78411 #690-04-2003 **PD** *012
AQUINO, Eduardo Luis M. 1901 MORGAN AVE 78404 #726-01-1970 L1977 **OBG** *020
ARCHER, Leslie S. ■ 78412 #539-03-1947 L1970 **OBG** *071 †30
ARCHER, Marjorie J Barry. ■ 78412 #539-04-1952 L1971 **FM** *020 †18
ARIRIGUZO, Jude A. 2421 MORGAN AVE 78405 #690-07-1987 L1997 **IM** *020 †20
ARMSTRONG, Edward Allan. 6625 PHARAOH DR, ASSOC 78412 #060-02-1975 L1981 **R** *020 †80
ARMSTRONG, Luis Angel, III. 8114 DECK ST, 1701 THIRD ST 78412 #042-02-2000 L2006 **GE** *020 †20
ARNOLD, Allister Derwin. 3533 S ALAMEDA ST 78411 #010-03-1997 L2005 **RNR** *020 †80
ARNOLD, Harrell R. 3226 REID DR 78404 #048-04-1952 L1952 **DR** *071 †80
ARNOLD, James Anthony. 613 ELIZABETH ST, STE 605 78404 #048-02-1980 L1980 **AN** *020 †05
ARREAZA GRATEROL, Maria M. 3533 S ALAMEDA ST 78411 #935-01-2000 **PD** *012
ARRINGDALE, Wallace John. 1521 S STAPLES ST STE 604 78404 #030-05-1965 L1969 **CD** *020
ASHMORE, Alexander J. 1521 S STAPLES ST STE 803 78404 #048-04-1960 L1960 **U** *020 †95
ASISTIDO, Anthony F. 613 ELIZABETH ST, STE 702 78404 #748-17-1989 L1998 **IM** *020
AVALOS, Sergio Antonio. 2444 MORGAN AVE 78405 #649-02-1956 L1959 **FM** *020 †18
AYAR, Divyang Chhagan. 7101 WILLIAMS DR, WILLIAMS IMAGING CENTER 78412 #001-02-1995 L2000 **VIR** *020 †80
AYARS, Paul Kenneth, Jr. 1521 S STAPLES ST, STE 204 78404 #036-07-1970 L1975 **OPH** *020 †35
AYERS, James Alton. 3130 S ALAMEDA ST 78404 #021-01-1973 L1974 **A** *020
AYESTARAN CASSANI, Alejand. ■ 78414 #935-01-2000 **PD** *012
AYLIFFE, Howard Edward. ■ 78414 #065-10-1977 L1978 **FM** *020 †18
AYOUB, Samy Y. 10651 E ST, ATTN: CREDENTIAL OFFICE 78419 #915-02-1957 L1976 **DR** *020 †80
BABER, Elena Diana. 3533 S ALAMEDA ST 78411 #649-30-1996 L2002 **PD** *012
BACALING, Jose Hector. 13725 NORTHWEST BLVD 78410 #748-02-1972 L1978 **AN** *020 †05
BADDOUR, George A. ■ 78413 #330-02-1959 L1989 **GS GYN** *071 †85

BADDOUR, Ruby Tchekidjian. ■ 78413 #330-04-1963 L1994 **PTH ATP** *074 †50
BADEA-MIC, Daniela. 817 AYERS ST 78404 #781-06-1982 L1994 **P** *020 †75
BADRUDDIN, Shamim B. 613 ELIZABETH ST, STE 402 78404 #704-25-1988 L1994 **CD IM** *020 †20
BAHAMON, Juan Ernesto. 3301 S ALAMEDA ST, STE 501 78411 #264-09-1981 L1988 **N** *020 †75
BAILEY, James Edward. ■ 78412 #048-02-1959 L1959 **AN** *071
BAILEY, Michael. 3853 S ALAMEDA ST 78411 #048-12-1989 L1990 **PTH** *020 †50
BALLAS, Maurice. 15002 DASMARINAS DR 78418 #048-12-1962 L1962 **PTH OS** *030 †50
BARKER, Kirby Gordon. 1625 RODD FIELD RD 78412 #048-02-1963 L1963 **ON HEM** *071 †20
BARRY, Richard Ed. 2606 HOSPITAL BLVD, CORPUS CHRISTI FAMILY PRAC 78405 #065-05-1963 L1984 **FM PHP** *030 †18
BARTH, Stephen H. 3301 S ALAMEDA ST # NO-204 78411 #048-02-1977 L1977 **FM** *020 †18
BASTARDO CAMPANINI, Emir. ■ 78414 #935-01-2000 **PD** *012
BATLLE, Ivan Ricardo. 5540 SARATOGA BLVD, STE 200 78413 #021-01-1985 L1987 **OPH OS** *020 †35
BEAUCHAMP, Robert. 7101 WILLIAMS DR, WILLIAMS IMAGING CENTER 78412 #048-02-1990 L1991 **DR** *020 †80
BELALCAZAR ARDILA, Rodrigo. 3533 S ALAMEDA ST, DRISCOLL CHILDREN'S HOSP 78411 #264-04-1986 **PD** *012
BENAVIDEZ, George. 7121 S PADRE ISLAND DR 78412 #034-01-1978 L1979 **FM** *020 †16,18
BENSON, Lanie James. ■ 78404 #048-02-1972 1972 **PHP** *074
BERASTAIN, Miguel A. 7121 S PADRE ISLAND DR, BAY AREA PROF PLZ STE 106 78412 #847-06-1976 L1982 **ORS** *020
BERASTAIN, Miguel Arturo. ■ 78414 #038-06-2000 **ORS** *020
BERIOS, Ioannis. 2606 HOSPITAL BLVD, DEPT EM 78405 #022-75-2006, ▲ **EM** *012
BERNWANGER, Damon C. ■ 78404 #048-12-1950 L1950 **FM** *071
BERRY, Richard Wm. 2606 HOSPITAL BLVD, STE 5 78405 #048-02-1973 L1973 **FM** *020 †18 ‡
BHATIA, Gurdip Singh. ■ 78413 #305-01-2001 L2001 **AN** *020
BIELEFELD, Mark Richard. 3533 S ALAMEDA ST, DIRSCOLL CHLDRN HOSP 78411 #056-06-1988 L2001 **TS** *020 †85,90
BIERY, Diane June. 613 ELIZABETH ST, STE 605 78404 #048-12-1982 L1983 **AN IM** *020 †20,05
BILOLIKAR, Suresh G. 5283 OLD BROWNSVILLE RD 78405 #495-56-1967 L1978 **P** *020 †75
BISHOP, John Edward. 4707 EVERHART RD STE 108 78411 #048-13-1980 L1980 **OPH PO** *020 †35
BIVONA, Charles Lee. 613 ELIZABETH ST, STE 605 78404 #048-15-1986 L1986 **AN** *020 †05
BLACKBURN, Archie Barnard. ■ 78410 #048-04-1965 L1965 **P** *071 †75
BLAINE, Mose H. 3314 S ALAMEDA ST 78411 #048-12-1946 L1946 **GS GE** *071 †85
BLANKENSHIP, Billy Jim. 13810 SUNTAN AVE, BILLY J BLANKENSHIP DDS MD 78418 #048-02-1963 L1963 **OM UM** *071 †18
BLOW, Osbert. 2606 HOSPITAL BLVD, C.S.H.S.—MEMORIAL 78405 #036-07-1987 L2001 **CCS** *020 †85
BOETTGER, Hans F. ■ 78411 #048-04-1942 L1942 **OS** *071
BOND, Richard M. ■ 78411 #048-13-1985 L1986 **OPH** *020 †35
BONELLI, Andres. 1521 S STAPLES ST, STE 403 78404 #042-03-1980 L1986 **IMG IM** *020 †20
BONIKOWSKI, Frank Peter. 1521 S STAPLES ST, NEUROLOGY PA 78404 #041-09-1970 L1987 **N IM** *020 †75
BORCHARD, Eddie Lee. 5833 SPOHN DR 78414 #649-19-1988 L1998 **PD** *020 †55
BORIACK, Leroy Adolph. 5866 S STAPLES ST STE 202 78413 #048-02-1958 L1958 **FM** *071 †18 ‡
BORKOWSKI, John Michael. 3702 S ALAMEDA ST 78411 #060-02-1995 L2001 **ORS** *020
BOSQUEZ, Roberto. 2020 GOLLIHAR RD, STE B 78416 #048-02-1958 L1958 **GP** *071
BOURNE, Cecil Martindale. 3301 S ALAMEDA ST STE 306 78411 #048-04-1971 L1971 **IM** *020 †20
BOWN, Nicholas M. 2606 HOSPITAL BLVD 5W, HOSPITAL MEMORI 78405 #055-02-2002 L2004 **EM** *012 †18
BOYNTON, Gerard Wayne. 3301 S ALAMEDA ST, STE 201 78411 #048-04-1979 L1979 **FM EM** *030 †18
BRACKETT, Fred Brandon. 613 ELIZABETH ST STE 612 78404 #045-01-1969 L1977 **CRS** *020 †85,10
BRAGLIA, Roberto L. 714 BOOTY ST 78404 #132-02-1971 L1979 **CRS** *020 †10,85
BRECKENRIDGE, Charles Wm. 3702 S ALAMEDA ST 78411 #016-42-1989 L1995 **ORS** *020 †40
BREELING, Charles Lee. 3301 S ALAMEDA ST, STE 201 78411 #030-06-1979 L1981 **FM** *020 †18
BREHM, N Christopher. 1521 S STAPLES ST STE 803, CORPUS CHRISTI UROLOGY GRO 78404 #048-04-1987 L1988 **U** *020 †95
BRENNER, Lawrence David. 613 ELIZABETH ST, STE 502 78404 #041-02-1983 L1999 **CD IM** *020 †20
BRITO-SUAREZ, Jane. 5262 S STAPLES ST, STE 310 78411 #042-03-1986 L1992 **AN PME** *020
BRITT, Michael W. 3702 S ALAMEDA ST 78411 #048-02-1990 L1991 **ORS** *020 †40
BROSS, Michael Hartwell. 2606 HOSPITAL BLVD 78405 #039-01-1979 L2005 **FM FPG** *040 †18
BROWN, Eugene Lee, Jr. 3825 S PADRE ISLAND DR 78415 #051-04-1966 L1969 **FM ADM** *020 †18
BROWN, Norma Raney. 902 AIRPORT RD, CORPUS CHRISTI STATE SCHOO 78405 #051-04-1966 L1969 **GP** *020
BRUNDRETT, Josephine A. 3533 S ALAMEDA ST 78411 #048-15-2004 L2007 **PD** *012
BRUSCO, Osvaldo A. 613 ELIZABETH ST, STE 301 78404 #132-01-1986 L1997 **END** *020 †20
BUCHANAN, Bryan D. 2606 HOSPITAL BLVD, DEPT EM 78405 #048-13-2007 L2007 **EM** *012
BUCK, Ernest Dale. 3533 S ALAMEDA ST # 303 78411 #016-01-1977 L1979 **PD EM** *020 †55
BUCK, Loren Leander, Jr. ■ 78463 #048-04-1970 L1970 **IM** *071 †20
BUGAY, Glenn La Mar. 601 TEXAN TRL, SOUTH TEXAS ADULT 78411 #038-06-1976 L1978 **IM** *020 †20
BUI, Christina P. ■ 78404 #048-13-2001 L2007 **OPH** *100
BULLEN, Michael Glen. 1521 S STAPLES ST STE 605 78404 #039-01-1974 L1981 **ID IM** *020 †20
BURGIN, Wm Walter, Jr. 2601 HOSPITAL BLVD STE 117 78405 #030-05-1961 L1974 **PUD IM** *020 †20
BURKE, Michael James. 3643 S STAPLES ST, NEUROSURGERY INSTITUTE OF 78411 #007-02-1987 L1993 **NSP** *025
BUSSIERES, Catherine. 601 TEXAN TRL, SOUTH TEXAS ADULT 78411 #067-01-1998 L2001 **FM** *020 †18
CACERES MORGAN, Juan F. 5920 SARATOGA BLVD STE 160 78414 #737-03-1971 L1981 **OBG** *020 †30
CADENA-GARZA, Aracely. ■ 78413 #048-13-2006 **FP** *012
CAIRE, William James. 2606 HOSPITAL BLVD, STE 5 78405 #039-01-1997 L1998 **FM** *020 †18
CALLEGARI-PUENTE, Bruna. 3435 S ALAMEDA ST 78411 #649-30-1978 L1985 **PD** *020 †55

■ = Address Information Privacy Protected

CAMPBELL, Charles Harvey. 5540 SARATOGA BLVD 78413 #021-01-1967 L1968 OPH OS *020 †35

CAMPBELL, Morgan Skiles. 3301 S ALAMEDA ST, STE 501 78411 #048-04-1992 L1993 N *020 †75

CAMPOS, Crystal. 4617 GREENWOOD DR, CORPUS CHRISTI MEMORIAL HO 78416 #048-02-2002 L2004 FM *020 †18

CANALES, Carlos Orlando. 1006 TEXAS AVE 78404 #048-02-1964 L1964 NEP IM *071

CANALES, Lynae Striker. 3533 S ALAMEDA ST, ABC PEDIATRICS 78411 #048-04-1999 L2002 PD *020 †55

CANDAS, Ali Fatih. 3533 S ALAMEDA ST 78411 #902-03-1984 L1994 PD *020 †55

CANO, Patricia. 2606 HOSPITAL BLVD, CHRISTUS SPOHN MEM HOSP 78405 #048-14-2006 FP *012

CANTERBURY, Christine L. 7121 S PADRE ISLAND DR, STE 302 78412 #048-12-1993 L1997 OBG *020 †30

CANTU, Patricia Ann. 7101 S STAPLES ST, STE 105 78413 #048-02-1996 L2000 FM *020 †18

CAPITAINE, Raul Ricardo. 6629 WOOLDRIDGE RD 78414 #132-01-1967 L1988 P *020

CAPLIN, James Alan. 2502 MORGAN AVE 78405 #017-02-1974 L1978 AI D *020

CAPPS, Julian Huntley. 230 ABERDEEN AVE 78411 #038-06-1959 L1966 DR *071

CARDENAS, Charles Donald. 14317 NORTHWEST BLVD 78410 #048-13-1978 L1978 ORS OSM *020 †40

CARDENAS, Glenn D. ■ 78413 #649-02-1947 L1968 GS GP *071

CARDONA, Barbara Yvonne. 3533 S ALAMEDA ST 78411 #166-01-2005 L2007 PD *012

CARLSON, Daniel Mark. 613 ELIZABETH ST, STE 605 78404 #048-02-1988 L1992 AN *020 †05

CARMICHAEL, John Alan. 3533 S ALAMEDA ST 78411 #048-02-1973 L1973 FM *020 †18

CARO, Robert Edward. 2606 HOSPITAL BLVD, STE 5 78405 #048-16-1998 L1999 FM *040 †18

CARR, Jean-Jacques. 13701 NORTHWEST BLVD, STE B1 78410 #048-02-1996 L1997 FM *020 †18 ‡

CARR, Lana B. 13701 NORTHWEST BLVD, STE B1 78410 #048-02-1999 L2002 IM *020 †20

CARRENO, Fernando. 5141 CAPE ROMAIN DR 78412 #649-30-1991 L1997 FM OBS *020 †18

CARRENO-CACERES, Antonio. 1201 OCEAN DR 78404 #847-04-1955 L1964 OBG *071

CARROLL, Herman Grey, Jr. ■ 78418 #047-06-1965 L1978 N *071 †75

CARTER, Timothy Andrew. 2606 HOSPITAL BLVD 5, DEPT OF FAMILY PRACTICE 78405 #654-01-2006 FP *012

CARVAJAL, Monica Lisa. 8 W BAR LE DOC DR, 8 W BAR LE DOC 78414 #048-02-2003 L2005 EM *020 †16

CASAS, Carmen Cecilia. 5756 S STAPLES ST STE J1 78413 #264-04-1969 L1979 D *020 †15

CASTRO, Juan F. 6300 OCEAN DR, NRC 3500 78412 #048-16-1988 L1989 FSM FM *020 †18

CASTRO, Steven. 10651 E ST, NAVAL HOSPITAL 78419 #025-12-1996 L1998 FM *100 †18

CAVEDA, Eduardo Otto. 3022 MCKINZIE RD 78410 #024-05-1991 L1997 FM *020 †18

CAYCE, Rachael Lynn. ■ 78412 #048-12-2008 *012

CERNA, Sebastian. 10651 E ST, ATTN: CREDENTIAL OFFICE 78419 #048-13-1990 L1992 EM FM *020

CERVANTES, Miguel I, III. 3315 S ALAMEDA ST, DEPT OF ANESTHESIOLOGY 78411 #048-14-1998 L2004 AN *020 †05

CHAO, David Michael. 2606 HOSPITAL BLVD, DEPT OF FAMILY MEDICINE 78405 #048-78-2003, ▲ L2004 FP *012

CHAPA, Luis. ■ 78412 #048-16-2007 EM *012

CHATMAN-POLLARD, Ester. 712 BOOTY ST 78404 #048-02-1976 L1976 ON HEM *020 †20

CHEKURI, Kasi V Raju. 613 ELIZABETH ST STE 502 78404 #495-21-1998 L2005 CD *020 †20

CHEN, Alice Pinting. 1625 RODD FIELD RD, SOUTH TEXAS, PA 78412 #047-06-1986 L1988 ON IM *050 †20

CHEN, Defeng. 600 ELIZABETH ST 78404 #243-41-1983 L2003 IM *020 †20 ‡

CHEN, Jackson Chiasheng. 5920 SARATOGA BLVD, STE 320A 78414 #048-13-1994 L1998 FM *020 †18

CHEPEY, Julius Jos. 2481 MORGAN AVE 78405 #016-43-1959 L1964 R *071 †80

CHILDERS, Cecil A, Jr. 6625 WOOLDRIDGE RD, STE 101 78414 #047-06-1959 L1961 P N *020 †75

CHINNERY, Martha Steele. 3533 S ALAMEDA ST 78411 #039-01-1976 L1978 DR PD *020

CHITRIT, Isaac. 3262 S ALAMEDA ST 78404 #649-44-1979 L1994 IM *020 †20

CHIU, Kevin. ■ 78412 #048-15-2005 L2008 EM *012

CHO, Parina Gupta. 7101 WILLIAMS DR, WILLIAMS IMAGING CENTER 78412 #495-29-1995 L2002 DR *020 †80

CHOU, Richard Shihshien. 10651 E ST, NAVAL HOSPITAL 78419 #023-12-2004 L2006 GS *020

CINTRON, C A. 3315 S ALAMEDA ST, OPERATING ROOM 78411 #056-05-1991 L2005 AN *020 †05

CLARK, Charles Stuart. 3315 S ALAMEDA ST 78411 #048-02-1946 L1946 FM MDM *071 †18

CLARK, Charles Stuart, Jr. 6118 PARKWAY 78414 #048-02-1972 L1972 ORS *020 †40

CLEAVES, Wilbur Ratliff. 3301 S ALAMEDA ST, STE 201 78411 #048-12-1966 L1966 FM *020 †18

COHN, Jacqueline Ellen. 1521 S STAPLES STE 801 78404 #011-02-1974 L1977 END IM *020

COLE-PEREZ, Mary Cathleen. 5920 SARATOGA BLVD STE 400 78414 #048-02-1986 L1987 D *020 †15

COMAY, Matthew Aaron. 7101 WILLIAMS DR, WILLIAMS IMAGING CENTER 78412 #035-08-1996 L2002 DR *020 †80

COMER, Susan Sherard. ■ 78418 #019-02-1977 L1978 RHU *071 †20

COMSTOCK, Christopher P. 3533 S ALAMEDA ST, DEPT OF ORTHOPAEDICS 78411 #025-01-1988 L1996 OP *020 †40

CONARD, Rey Dean. 10651 E ST, NAVAL HOSPITAL 78419 #028-03-1973 L1983 EM *020

CONCKLIN, Charles Lewis. 2606 HOSPITAL BLVD 78405 #026-04-1936 L1937 PD *071

CONE, John Robt. 3560 S ALAMEDA ST, STE C 78411 #012-05-1972 L1974 FM *020 †18

CONLEE, Jack Lynn. 221 OCEAN VIEW PL 78411 #048-02-1967 L1967 PS *020 †65

CORNELIUS, Angela Michell. ■ 78414 #048-02-2003 L2007 EM *012 †18

CORRADA, Romulo Gaspar. 7121 S PADRE ISLAND DR, COASTAL BEND WOMENS 78412 #042-01-1995 L1995 OBG *020 †30

CORTES, Edgar Lozano. 3533 S ALAMEDA ST 78411 #048-02-1969 L1969 PD PEM *020 †55

CORTES, Edgar Richard. 3533 S ALAMEDA ST 78411 #048-02-1994 L1996 PD *020 †55

CORTESE, Jack L. 1521 S STAPLES ST STE 603 78404 #047-06-1976 L1978 NEP IM *020 †20

COTTINGHAM, James W. ■ 78411 #048-12-1962 L1962 AN *071 †05

COUTINHO, Rohan Paul. 2606 HOSPITAL BLVD 78405 #305-01-2005 FP *012

COVARRUBIAS, Baldemar, Jr. 5718 SPOHN DR 78414 #048-02-1987 L1988 FM *020 †18 ‡

COX, Ann Kathleen. ■ 78401 #048-12-1985 L1987 DR *020 †80

COX, William Andrew. ■ 78401 #012-05-1954 L1967 TS *071 †85,90

CRAIG, Charles Rea. 4115 UP RIVER RD 78408 #048-02-1958 L1958 FM *072 †18

CRAM, John Fitzhugh. 1521 S STAPLES ST, STE 803 78404 #021-01-1958 L1964 U *020 †95

CRAWFORD, Jerry A. 613 ELIZABETH ST, STE 605 78404 #048-12-1988 L1989 AN *020 †05

CROSLEY, Debby. ■ 78413 #305-01-2000 L2007 FM *100

CROZIER, Wallace Allen. 1415 3RD ST, STE 400 78404 #007-02-1955 L1960 A D *071 †55,03

CULLEN, Billy Bradford. 1521 S STAPLES ST, STE 102 78404 #048-01-1956 L1956 GP *075

CURTIS, William G. 13725 NORTHWEST BLVD, MEDICAL PLAZA A & B 78410 #048-13-1999 L2000 FM *020 †18

CURVIN, Thomas Jos. 3825 S PADRE ISLAND DR 78415 #039-01-1983 L1990 EM *020 †16

CUTBIRTH, Mance A. 5756 S STAPLES ST, STE F 78413 #048-13-1994 L1996 GS *020

CUYA, Francisco O. 2601 HOSPITAL BLVD STE 2, PHYSICIAN PLAZA WEST 78405 #132-03-1987 L1997 FM *020 †18

CYPHER SPRINGER, Shelley. 3533 S ALAMEDA ST, NICU 78411 #038-43-1994 L2004 NPM PD *020 †55

DAMARAJU, Srikanth. 613 ELIZABETH ST, STE 402 78404 #495-53-1992 L1997 CD IM *020 †20

DARRIGAN, David R. ■ 78412 #048-78-2007, ▲ *012

DAVE, Navnitray Kantilal. 3533 S ALAMEDA ST 78411 #495-48-1972 L1979 NPM *020 †55

DAVIS, Howard F, Jr. ■ 78418 #021-05-1970 L1979 ORS *071 †40

DAVIS, Jennifer L. 3533 S ALAMEDA ST 78411 #048-13-1992 L1993 PD *020 †55

DAVIS, Jonathan L. 601 TEXAN TRL, STE 100 78411 #048-15-1998 L2001 IM *020 †20

DAVIS, Richard Carver. 1702 SANTA FE ST, CHRISTUS SPOHN HLTH SYSTEM 78404 #048-02-1975 L1975 MDM FM *030 †18

DE CARVALHO, Guaracy F. ■ 78414 #649-14-1973 L1975 FM *071

DEFRAWI, Tarek Ghaleb. 2606 HOSPITAL BLVD, DEPT EM 78405 #048-15-2006 EM *012

DE LA GUARDIA, Alberto E. 2601 HOSPITAL BLVD STE 216 78405 #021-01-1962 L1969 OBG *020 †30

DELAROSA, Kristina Marie. ■ 78414 #023-12-2005 GP *020

DE LA ROSA, Ralph Anthony. 1406 MARTIN LUTHER KING DR, CHRISTUS SPOHN NEIGHBOR CA 78401 #048-13-1980 L1980 FM EM *020 †18

DELCORE, Romano. 1546 S BROWNLEE 78404 #649-01-1954 L1987 P *030

DELEON, Jose C. 3315 S ALAMEDA ST, DEPT. OF ANESTHESIA 78411 #748-01-1973 L1978 AN *020 †05

DELEON-SALINAS, Miguel A. 4525 GOLLIHAR RD STE 100 78411 #649-30-1983 L1988 NPM PD *020 †55

DEL GALLO, Walter Allen. 14317 NW BLVD STE A, CALALLEN ORTHOPEDICS 78410 #024-16-1991 L1996 ORS *020 †40

DE LINE, Carol Compton. 5950 SARATOGA BLVD 78414 #021-05-1976 L1998 CHN PD *020 †55,75

DE LOS SANTOS, Maria D. 4444 CORONA DR, STE 232 78411 #048-13-1978 L1978 AN *020

DEL ROSARIO, Lourdes B. ■ 78414 #748-02-1957 IM FM *020

DENNIS, Bill Matthew. 600 ELIZABETH ST 78404 #048-46-1978 L1980 FM GE *020 †18

DEPOLITI TOWER, Susan. ■ 78427 #041-07-1991 L2003 PM *020 ‡

DE VERA, Erlinda F. 902 AIRPORT RD 78405 #748-10-1968 L1980 PD *020

DHAR, Pradip Kumar. 3533 S ALAMEDA ST 78411 #495-36-1981 L2001 PDC PD *020 †55

DHAR, Renu. 5920 SARATOGA BLVD STE 300 78414 #496-04-1978 L2001 IM *020 †20

DIAZ, Kristan Tara. 2606 HOSPITAL BLVD, DEPT FM 78405 #043-01-2007 FP *012

DIAZ, Pedro. 5920 SARATOGA BLVD STE 480 78414 #737-03-1972 L1977 OBG *020 †30

DIAZ, Peter Ernest. 5920 SARATOGA BLVD STE 480 78414 #048-15-1999 L2004 OBG *020 †30

DIAZ-CALDERON, Wilder Edu. 613 ELIZABETH ST, STE 702 78404 #737-01-1998 L2006 IM *020 †20

DIAZ-CAMPOS, Salvador. 2606 HOSPITAL BLVD, DEPT SURG 78405 #649-02-1972 L1977 GS *100

DIAZ HERNANDEZ, Elsi Mari. 2606 HOSPITAL BLVD 78405 #649-38-2004 FP *012

DICKSON, Efrain O. 2601 HOSPITAL BLVD, STE 219 78405 #264-01-1956 L1984 FM GP *020 ‡

DIEGUEZ, Enrique Benjamin. 3533 S ALAMEDA ST 78411 #308-03-2000 PD *020

DIETERICH, Susan C. 3533 S ALAMEDA ST 78411 #038-41-1989 L2006 PM PD *020 †55,60

DIETZE, Thomas Russell. 13725 NORTHWEST BLVD, STE C 78410 #030-05-1982 L1987 OPH OS *020 †35

DIMAZANA, Epifanio Viril. 3825 S PEDRO ISALND DR, WELLCARE MED CLINIC 78415 #748-08-1966 L1974 GP PTH *020 †50

DINKLER, Fred. ■ 78418 #039-01-1947 L1949 GP OS *071

DINN, James Rankin. 6118 PARKWAY 78414 #048-02-1973 L1973 ORS OSM *020 †40

DIRKSEN, William Harry. 3533 S ALAMEDA ST 78411 #016-45-1975 L1978 PD PEM *040 †55

DISCHEL, Jennifer Jo. ■ 78411 #041-02-1997 L2003 *020

DODSON, Mark Anton. 3310 S ALAMEDA ST # 201 78411 #048-15-1985 L1986 FM *020 †18

DOLCH, Stanley F N, Jr. 13725 NORTHWEST BLVD 78410 #048-02-1947 L1947 EM GP *020

DONALD, David Melville. 7121 S PADRE ISLAND DR, STE 118 78412 #060-01-1970 L1993 U *020 †95

DORRELL, Thos Wendell, Jr. 14433 S PADRE ISLAND DR 78418 #048-02-1992 L1993 FM *020 †18

DOUCET, Daniel Wayne. 600 ELIZABETH ST 78404 #048-13-1990 L1992 FM EM *020 †18

DOUCET, Roxanna V. 7121 S PADRE ISLAND DR, COASTAL BEND WOMENS 78412 #048-13-1997 L1999 OBG *020 †30

D'SOUZA, Sandra. ■ 78403 #495-28-1987 L2007 FM *020

DUBBERLY, Danny Lee. 3301 S ALAMEDA ST STE 100 78411 #048-13-1977 L1977 FM *020 †18 ‡

DUGAN, John Thos. 1333 3RD ST STE 100 78404 #030-06-1971 L1973 OPH OS *020 †35

DUKE, John Morgan. 5920 SARATOGA BLVD STE 200 78414 #048-04-1975 L1975 OBG *020 †30

DULAK, Catherine E. 5920 SARATOGA BLVD STE 440 78414 #048-14-1986 L1988 GYN *020 †30

DULANEY, Robert Michael. ■ 78413 #038-40-1962 L1967 PD *020 †55

DUMAS, Susan. 3301 S ALAMEDA ST, STE 403 78411 #048-13-1979 L1979 OPH *071 †35

DUMIC, John F. ■ 78412 #047-06-1976 L1977 DR NM *071 †80

DUNDAS, Chris Robert. ■ 78412 #649-45-1986 PD *100

DURAN, Jose Miguel. 2222 MORGAN AVE STE 111 78405 #847-04-1970 L1980 GE IM *020 ‡

DWYER, J Michael. 4444 CORONA DR 78411 #048-14-1989 L1990 AN *020 †05

DYE, James. 5920 SARATOGA BLVD, SURGICAL ASSOCIATES 78414 #048-15-2000 L2005 GS *020 †85

EARLY, Linda Lee. 613 ELIZABETH ST, STE 605 78404 #048-02-1979 L1979 AN *020

ECHEVERRY RAMIREZ, A. 1415 3RD ST 78404 #264-01-1966 L1977 NS *020

ECKMAN, Laurie Nelson. 600 ELIZABETH ST 78404 #036-07-1972 L1978 HEM FM *071 †40

EDWARDS, Ricky Dale. 2606 HOSPITAL BLVD, STE 5 78405 #048-14-1977 L1977 FM *040 †18

EDWARDS, Thomas Wm. 4918 HOLLY RD, STE B 78411 #012-05-1974 L1982 AN *020 †05

EFTIMESCU, Dina Floriana. 5920 SARATOGA BLVD, STE 570 78414 #781-01-1979 L1997 OBG *075

ELIZONDO, Mayra Belem. ■ 78411 #048-04-2006 FP *012

EL-MILADY, Nabil Abd El K. 2601 HOSPITAL BLVD, STE 205 78405 #330-03-1965 L1975 OBG *020 †30

ELOVITZ, Stuart. 5525 S STAPLES ST, STE A3 78411 #020-02-1968 L1975 **OPH** *020
EMRAN, Mohammad A. 3533 S ALAMEDA ST 78411 #048-12-1997 L2006 **GS** *020 †85
ENRIQUEZ, Jose Luis. 3533 S ALAMEDA ST, EMERGENCY DEPARTMENT 78411 #649-33-1981 L1989 **PD** *020 †55
ERTZNER, Thomas Wayne. 7101 WILLIAMS DR, WILLIAMS IMAGING CENTER 78412 #030-05-1981 L1987 **R NM** *020 †80,28
ESCOBAR, Hugo. 3533 S ALAMEDA ST, DRISCOLL CHILDREN'S HOSPIT 78411 #264-21-1999 **PD** *100 †55
ESPADA, Roberto A. 5920 SARATOGA BLVD, STE 475 78414 #176-02-1983 L1998 **OBG** *020 †30
ESPADA, Yvonne Bonnet. 613 ELIZABETH ST, STE 502 78404 #264-11-1983 L1998 **CD** *020 †20
ESPINA, Eisen Jover. 5525 S STAPLES ST STE E2 78411 #748-02-1972 L1977 **FM EM** *020 †18 ‡
ESTMENT, Barbara A. 2606 HOSPITAL BLVD, STE 5 78405 #048-15-1998 L2002 **FM** *020 †18
ESTRADA, Carlos. 6625 WOOLDRIDGE RD, STE 201 78414 #429-01-1963 L1985 **P PYA** *020 †75
ESTRADA, Jose L. 3533 S ALAMEDA ST 78411 #649-07-1975 **PD** *100
ETHERIDGE, John M. ■ 78401 #048-12-1953 L1953 **OS GS** *071
ETUKNWA, Uduak Tennyson. 3533 S ALAMEDA ST, DRISCOLL CHILDREN'S HOSPIT 78411 #690-04-1981 L1997 **PD** *020 †55
EUBANK, Charles Dale. 5920 SARATOGA BLVD, STE 101 78414 #048-12-1979 L1979 **GYN** *020 †30
EVANS, Richard Rowland. 1301 OCEAN DR, ABDOMINAL SPECIALISTS OF 78404 #048-04-1974 L1974 **GE** *020 †20
EVE, Frank Rodney. 807 CRAIG ST 78404 #919-02-1966 L1976 **OPH PO** *071
EVERETT, Carlos Barrera. 917 S PORT AVE 78405 #048-13-1982 L1983 **FM** *020 †18
EVERETT, Orel M. 6458 SARATOGA BLVD 78414 #048-02-1995 L1996 **FM** *020 †18
EWING, Dwight Sherwood. 2606 HOSPITAL BLVD 4TH FL 78405 #048-12-1956 L1956 **FM** *071 †18
EWING, Nicole Fawn. ■ 78418 #030-06-2000 L2005 **MPD EM** *020 †55,20
FADER, William Arthur. 7101 S STAPLES ST, STE 101 78413 #649-14-1982 L1987 **PD** *020 †55
FAGAN, Wayne A. 1300 3RD ST 78404 #048-13-1992 L1993 **D** *020 †15
FALCAO, Germano Correia L. 3533 S ALAMEDA ST 78411 #187-10-2001 L2007 **PD** *100
FANT, William Milton. ■ 78413 #027-01-1958 L1963 **DR NM** *071 †80
FAREK, Paul Eugene. 613 ELIZABETH ST STE 811 78404 #048-13-1982 L1983 **GS** *020 †85
FAWEYA, Ayotunde Gregory. 3533 S ALAMEDA ST 78411 #690-01-1981 **PD** *012
FERGIE, Jaime E. 3455 S ALAMEDA ST 78411 #935-01-1984 L1994 **PDI** *020 †55
FERNANDEZ, Christopher L. 613 ELIZABETH ST, STE 605 78404 #748-01-1991 L2001 **AN OS** *020 †05 ‡
FERNANDEZ, Imelyn Mirador. 2606 HOSPITAL BLVD 78405 #305-01-2006 **FP** *012
FERNANDEZ, Ray. 2610 HOSPITAL BLVD, OFFICE OF MEDICAL EXAMINER 78405 #048-13-1989 L1991 **FOP** *020 †50
FERNANDEZ, Roberto A. 613 ELIZABETH ST, STE 601 78404 #048-13-1989 L1991 **PS** *020 †85,65
FERNANDEZ-MARTORELL, P. 3533 S ALAMEDA ST 78411 #649-31-1983 L2007 **PD** *012 †55
FICENEC, Matthew James. 2606 HOSPITAL BLVD 78405 #030-05-1996 L2001 **GS** *020 †85
FIELDS, Michael D. 613 ELIZABETH ST, STE 702 78404 #030-06-1992 L2004 **FM** *020 †18
FISHER, George Homer, Jr. 13701 FM 624, STE D4 78410 #001-02-1970 L1974 **OTO** *020 †45
FLOOD, George Wm. 3533 S ALAMEDA ST 78411 #056-06-1954 L1959 **PD** *020 †55
FLORES, William Caesar. 2634 GOLLIHAR RD, STE C 78415 #048-13-1975 L1975 **FM** *020 †18
FORDTRAN, Robert Lee. 1001 LOUISIANA AVE, STE 201 78404 #048-02-1956 L1956 **CD IM** *020 †20
FOSTER, David Peyton. 14202 S SPID DR 78418 #048-13-1994 L1996 **FM** *020 †18
FRAME, James Earl. 600 ELIZABETH ST 78404 #016-01-1987 L2007 **EM** *020 †16
FRATILA, Antonio Bogdan. ■ 78412 #048-14-2003 L2005 **AN** *020
FREE, Marcus K. ■ 78414 #048-04-1994 L2000 **GS** *020
FREYSDOTTIR, Drifa. ■ 78414 #484-01-1993 L2006 **NPM PD** *020 †55
FUENTES, Antonio. 1101 S 19TH ST 78405 #649-02-1962 L1965 **GP** *020
FUENTES, Dorothy Doris E. 2502 MORGAN AVE 78405 #748-01-1982 L1999 **PD** *020 †55
FUENTES, Jose Eliud. 2222 MORGAN AVE 78405 #649-02-1969 L1971 **OPH** *071
FUENTES, Michael Gerard. 5656 S STAPLES ST, STE 252 78411 #649-02-1991 L1997 **PM** *020
FUENTES, Randy Anthony. 1101 S 19TH ST 78405 #048-04-1980 L1980 **IM** *020 †20
FUQUA, Burcham Cooper. 600 ELIZABETH ST 78404 #048-12-1981 L1981 **IM** *020 †20
GALARZA, Jusan. 3533 S ALAMEDA ST 78411 #737-06-1999 **PD** *012
GALATZAN, Stephen James. 3315 S ALAMEDA ST 78411 #048-02-1977 L1977 **PTH CLP** *020 †50
GALLAGHER, Patricia H. 7101 WILLIAMS DR, WILLIAMS IMAGING CENTER 78412 #048-12-1981 L1981 **DR** *020 †80
GAMBLE, Robert Dale. ■ 78413 #017-20-1948 L1975 **OM GP** *071
GARCIA, Anselmo. ■ 78414 #048-02-2001 L2007 **PCC** *020
GARCIA, Dalia Penez. ■ 78404 #649-01-1973 *020
GARCIA, Humberto. 1521 S STAPLES ST STE 601 78404 #048-02-1964 L1964 **NEP IM** *020 †20
GARCIA, Jesse Gabino. 3829 SARATOGA BLVD 78415 #048-14-2002 L2004 **FM** *020 †18
GARCIA, Jessica A. 2613 NOGALES ST 78416 #048-02-2008 *012
GARCIA, Kathleen May. 5920 SARATOGA BLVD STE 200 78414 #048-14-2000 L2004 **OBG** *020 †30
GARCIA, Octavio. 822 KINNEY ST 78401 #649-02-1971 L1978 **GS** *020 †85
GARCIA, Rafael F. ■ 78414 #048-12-1992 L1993 **EM** *020 †16
GARCIA, Toribio R. 3302 S ALAMEDA ST 78411 #649-30-1981 L1985 **PD** *020
GARCIA, Vilma. 2601 HOSPITAL BLVD 78405 #048-02-1982 L1983 **CD IM** *020
GARCIA-ALONSO, Patricia. 3533 S ALAMEDA ST BOX 6530 78411 #649-34-1980 **PD** *100
GARCIA CIPOLLETTI, Carla. 3533 S ALAMEDA ST, DRISCOLL CHILDREN'S HOSPIT 78411 #935-01-2000 **PDI** *012 †55
GARCIA-OLIVARES, Leonilo. ■ 78412 #649-02-1970 L1976 **PD** *071
GARDNER-CORTES, Brenda S. 5283 OLD BROWNSVILLE RD, CORPUS CHRISTI VA OUTPATIE 78405 #048-02-1997 L2001 **FM** *020 †18
GARZA, Dahlia. ■ 78416 #048-13-1982 L1989 **IM** *020 †20
GARZA, H Ross. ■ 78404 #048-02-1953 L1953 **OBG** *071 †30
GASCOT RIOS, Luz M. 2606 HOSPITAL BLVD 78405 #048-14-1994 L1996 **FM** *020 †18
GENTILE, Herve Felice S. 1102 OCEAN DR 78404 #561-11-1976 L1982 **PS FPS** *020 †45,65
GENTILE, Patrizia E. 7121 S PADRE ISLAND DR, STE 302 78412 #561-11-1975 L1980 **OBG** *020 †30
GEST, Albert L. 2606 HOSPITAL BLVD, ED CHRISTUS SPOHN MEM 78405 #028-78-1990, ▲ L1998 **EM** *020 †16
GHRAOWI, Mahomad Ayman. 1205 S 19TH ST, P O BOX 5407 78405 #875-01-1979 L1994 **ON HEM** *020 †20
GIBSON, Bruce Anthony. 1301 OCEAN DR, ABDOMINAL SPECIALISTS OF 78404 #017-20-1976 L1981 **GE IM** *020 †20
GIEGER, Michael. 3643 S STAPLES ST, NEUROSURGERY INSTITUTE OF 78411 #035-46-1989 L1996 **NS** *020 †25
GILLELAND, Charles Wayne. 2606 HOSPITAL BLVD 78405 #048-04-1975 L1975 **EM FM** *020 †18,16
GLAZENER, Leighanne. 7121 S PADRE ISLAND DR, STE 302 78412 #048-13-1987 L1995 **OBG** *020 †30
GOLDEN, Ali Akbar. ■ 78418 #517-01-1961 L1990 **DR** *020
GO-MALIWANAG, Celia A. 10651 E ST, ATTN: CREDENTIAL OFFICE 78419 #748-08-1986 L2000 **PD** *020 †55
GONSOULIN, Whitney Jos. 7121 S PADRE ISLAND DR, STE 303 78412 #021-05-1979 L1988 **OBG** *020 †30
GONZALEZ, Alejandro A. 3533 S ALAMEDA ST 78411 #649-30-1992 L1999 **PD** *020 †55
GONZALEZ, Belinda. 5525 S STAPLES ST, STE E1 78411 #048-14-1993 L1994 **FM** *020 †18
GONZALEZ, Jaime. 101 N SHORELINE BLVD, STE 303 78401 #264-05-1960 L1965 **NM RO** *071 †80
GONZALEZ, Rufino H. 2601 HOSPITAL BLVD, STE 212 78405 #649-02-1962 L1966 **ORS** *020 †40
GONZALEZ RANGEL, Ismael E. 3533 S ALAMEDA ST 78411 #264-09-2002 **PD** *012
GOODING, Elizabeth Hope. 5262 S STAPLES ST, STE 310 78411 #016-45-1992 L1996 **AN** *020 †05
GOODMAN, Paul Hill. 1415 3RD ST 78404 #047-06-1941 L1952 **R** *071 †80
GORCHYNSKI, Julie Ann. 2606 HOSPITAL BLVD 5W 78405 #030-06-1991 L2006 **EM** *020 †16
GOUVERNE, Max Leopold. 5642 ESPLANADE DR 78414 #028-03-1985 L1991 **PS** *020 †65
GRABHORN, Larry Lee. 308 CRECY ST, CORPUS CHRISTI ARMY DEPOT 78419 #017-20-1967 L1993 **OM FM** *020 †70
GRAF, Raymond Henry, Jr. 613 ELIZABETH ST STE 402 78404 #048-15-1976 L1976 **CD** *020 †20
GRAHAM, Camille Sandra. 3533 S ALAMEDA ST, DRISCOLL CHILDREN'S HOSPIT 78411 #048-13-1997 L2002 **AN** *020 †05
GRAHAM, Lydia Martinez. 2552 MORGAN AVE 78405 #048-04-1979 L1979 **FM** *020 †18
GRAY, Blanca Gonzalez. 14646 COMPASS ST STE 8 78418 #048-13-1992 L1993 **IM** *020 †20
GRAY, David C. 3301 S ALAMEDA ST STE 10 78411 #048-13-1992 L1993 **IM** *020 †20
GRAY, David Julius. 1818 GREEN JAYS CT 78418 #016-01-1977 L1978 **EM OS** *020 †16
GREENLEE, Mark E. 321 BAYSHORE DR 78412 #016-45-1995 L1997 **FM** *020 †18
GRIMES, William John. 3533 S ALAMEDA ST 78411 #048-04-1977 L1977 **PAN PD** *020 †55,05
GROFF, Terry Robt. 5920 SARATOGA BLVD, STE 280 78414 #055-01-1972 L1987 **OBG REN** *020 †30
GRONER, Edwin Ben. 601 TEXAN TRL, SOUTH TEXAS ADULT 78411 #021-01-1943 L1950 **IM** *020 †20
GROSSER, Dawn Marie. 3702 S ALAMEDA ST 78411 #008-01-2000 L2006 **ORS** *100
GROSSMAN, Maurice S. 1001 LOUISIANA AVE STE 307 78404 #048-12-1952 L1952 **GE IM** *020 †20
GUAJARDO, Richard Joseph. 2606 HOSPITAL BLVD 5W 78405 #056-05-2003 L2005 **OBG** *100 †18
GUERRERO, Victor C. ■ 78415 #048-13-1996 L1997 **FM** *020 †18
GUIDO, Ernesto Hugo. 5920 SARATOGA BLVD, STE 500 78414 #341-01-1969 L1976 **N** *020 †75
GUIDO, Hugo Ernesto. 2606 HOSPITAL BLVD, CHRISTUS SPOHN MEM HOSP 78405 #270-02-2002 L2008 **FM** *020
GUINN, Albert Lee, Jr. 3301 S ALAMEDA ST, STE 100 78411 #048-13-1977 L1977 **IM** *020 †20
GUPTA, Ruchi. 3533 S ALAMEDA ST 78411 #495-45-1994 **PD** *012
GUPTA, Sunil Kumar. 7633 OUTREAU DR 78414 #495-14-1983 L2004 **HOS IM** *020 †20
GUTHRIE, Gregory Morris. 3533 S ALAMEDA ST # 303, JOSEPH M SLOAN MED. BLDG. 78411 #048-13-1975 L1975 **PD** *020 †55
GUTIERREZ, Armando I. ■ 78414 #048-14-2006 **FP** *012
GUTIERREZ, Louis Robert. 2606 HOSPITAL BLVD, CORPUS CHRISTI FAMILY PRAC 78405 #048-13-2006 L2007 **FP** *012
GUTIERREZ CANO, Martha D. ■ 78412 #048-02-2005 **FP** *012
GUTIERREZ-QUEHL, Carlos R. 7101 WILLIAMS DR, WILLIAMS IMAGING CENTER 78412 #341-01-1978 L1988 **OS DR** *020 †80 ‡
GUZMAN, Antonio. 7121 S SPID DR STE 104A 78412 #048-13-1993 L1995 **IM** *020 †20
HAAS, Michael Edward. ■ 78414 #048-02-2004 **PD** *012
HAGEMEISTER, Brent Bruce. 613 ELIZABETH ST, STE 605 78404 #024-07-1989 L1996 **AN** *020 †05
HAHN, Tara Lynn. 613 ELIZABETH ST STE 612 78404 #017-20-1995 L2005 **CRS** *020 †85,10
HAMMERICK, John M, Jr. 5833 SPOHN DR, STE 701 78414 #048-12-1970 L1970 **OTO HNS** *020 †45
HANISCH, Martin Edward. 1521 S STAPLES ST, STE 803 78404 #048-04-1973 L1973 **U** *020 †95
HARPER, Nancy Sanders. 3533 S ALAMEDA ST 78411 #032-01-1995 L2007 **PD** *020 †55
HART, Alicia Dawn. 613 ELIZABETH ST, STE 702 78404 #048-16-2003 L2004 **EM** *012 †18
HARTMAN, Samuel Christian. 13725 NORTHWEST BLVD, STE 230 78410 #048-14-1995 L1996 **FM** *020 †18
HARTMAN, Walter F, Jr. 13725 NORTHWEST BLVD, STE 230 78410 #048-02-1965 L1965 **GP** *020 †18
HARVEY, Thomas De Witt. 2606 HOSPITAL BLVD, 5 WEST 78405 #048-02-1955 L1955 **FM** *040 †18
HAU, Horacio Guillermo. 2606 HOSPITAL BLVD 5W, HOSPITAL MEMORI 78405 #048-13-2004 L2007 **FM** *020
HEATH, Paul W. 613 ELIZABETH ST, STE 502 78404 #039-01-1976 L1982 **CD IM** *020 †20
HECKRODT, Stanly B. 4646 CORONA DR STE 280, IMC CORPUS CHRISTI 78411 #039-01-1976 L1977 **FM OM** *020 †18 ‡
HEIN, Anthony Nicholas. 3226 REID DR 78404 #005-14-1995 L2001 **DR VIR** *020 †80
HELD, Beverly Louise. 5756 S STAPLES ST, STE J2 78413 #048-02-1967 L1967 **D** *020 †15
HENDERSON, Bruce Moreton. 3533 S ALAMEDA ST, STE 302 78411 #803-03-1958 L1974 **PDS UP** *020 †85
HENRY, J Wm. 2601 HOSPITAL BLVD, STE 207 78405 #012-01-1959 L1970 **ORS** *020
HENRY, Marion Jack. 3226 S ALAMEDA ST 78404 #004-01-1957 L1966 **R** *071 †55,80
HERNANDEZ, Michael A. 5022 HOLLY RD STE 104 78411 #017-20-2001 L2003 **P** *020 †75
HERRERA, Yvonne. 2606 HOSPITAL BLVD, STE 5 78405 #018-03-1995 L2006 **FM** *020 †18
HESLEP, J Haynes. 1415 3RD ST STE 101 78404 #027-01-1958 L1969 **R** *071 †80
HESSERT, David Dawes. 10651 E ST, NAVAL HOSPITAL 78419 #056-05-2002 L2003 **GP** *020
HINES, James Cornell. 7121 S PADRE ISLAND DR, STE 300 78412 #048-02-1974 L1974 **IM** *071 †20
HINOJOSA, Jose R, Jr. 2606 HOSPITAL BLVD, STE 5 78405 #018-03-1994 L2005 **FM** *020 †18
HINOJOSA, Lizze Anel. 13310 LEOPARD ST, STE 27 78410 #048-13-1990 L1993 **PD** *020

■ = Address Information Privacy Protected

HISEY, Julie Cristine. ■ 78412 #048-13-2007 PD *012
HOLLAND, Scott Woodrow. 3435 S ALAMEDA ST 78411 #048-02-2001 L2005 PD *020
HOLZMAN, Madelyn. 7121 S PADRE ISLAND DR, STE 303 78412 #048-04-1985 L1986 U *074 †95
HONRUBIA, Dynio. PO BOX 6160 78466 #005-14-1996 L2005 NPM *020 †55
HORNE, Jo-Allene. 5656 S STAPLES ST, STE 350 78411 #036-05-1962 L1971 PLM *020 †55,05
HORNUNG, John Robt. ■ 78411 #019-02-1969 L1978 GS *020 †85
HOWELL, Scott Wayne. 7121 S PADRE ISLAND DR 78412 #048-02-1983 L1992 IM GE *020 †20
HSIANG, Jim Yang. 1205 S 19TH ST, STE A 78405 #005-19-1999 L2004 RO *020 †80
HUDSON, George C. ■ 78412 #048-04-1966 L1971 GP *020
HUMMELL, Paul R. 1415 3RD ST 78404 #038-41-1950 L1961 AN *071 †05
HUNSAKER, Jerry Dean. 4707 EVERHART RD STE 106 78411 #048-04-1983 L1983 OPH *020 †35
HYDE, Mary Joy S. 5920 SARATOGA BLVD, STE 200 78414 #048-78-1999, ▲ L2004 OBG *020
IBANEZ, Marc A. 5920 SARATOGA BLVD, STE 475 78414 #048-12-2004 L2006 IM *020 †20
IBANEZ, Michele Bergeron. 5920 SARATOGA BLVD, STE 475 78414 #048-13-1997 L2000 IM *020 †20
IDEN, Donald Lee. 4521 S STAPLES ST STE 100 78411 #016-43-1973 L1976 D ID *020 †15 ‡
IMAM, Quazi Muhammad H. 820 ELIZABETH ST 78404 #913-12-1979 L1993 PYG CHP *020 †75 ‡
IMAM, Selina Hasan. 820 ELIZABETH ST 78404 #160-02-1984 L1995 IM *020 †20
ISENSEE, Christopher Hugo. 601 TEXAN TRL STE 300 78411 #048-04-1958 L1958 ORS *071 †40
ISIDRO, Erlinda Q. 3533 S ALAMEDA ST 78411 #748-08-1970 PD *100
ISLAM, Shah Faizul. 1521 S STAPLES ST, STE 601 78404 #495-77-1982 L1999 NEP *020 †20
JACKSON, Joseph Hoyt, Jr. 3533 S ALAMEDA ST, DRISCOLL FOUNDATION CHILDR 78411 #036-07-1956 L1965 PDR *071 †80
JACKSON, Kurt Thomas. 5540 SARATOGA BLVD, STE 200 78413 #035-46-2003 L2007 OPH *100
JACKSON, Phillip Fletcher. 4609 SCHWERIN LAKE DR 78413 #028-03-1988 L1993 AM GP *020
JAKUBOWSKI, Robert Gerard. 613 ELIZABETH ST, STE 509 78404 #056-06-1981 L1986 IM *020 †20
JAKUBOWSKI, Wesley Joseph. 5920 SARATOGA BLVD, STE 340 78414 #759-08-1975 L1996 PD *020 †55
JANAKI, Lalitha Madhav. 1625 RODD FIELD RD, CORPUS CHRISTI CANCER CTR 78412 #495-21-1969 L1980 RO *020 †80 ‡
JARAMILLO, Alejandro Adol. 3533 S ALAMEDA ST, DRISCOLL CHILDREN'S HOSPIT 78411 #264-07-1984 L2006 PD *020
JEVRIC, Nicholas. 613 ELIZABETH ST, STE 605 78404 #026-04-1976 L1981 AN *020 †05
JEYARAJ, Jenitha. 3533 S ALAMEDA ST 78411 #495-42-2000 PD *012
JIFI-BAHLOOL, Haitham. 5920 SARATOGA BLVD, STE 420 78414 #875-03-1981 L1996 IM *020 †20
JIFI-BAHLOOL, Samer I. 1125 3RD ST 78404 #875-03-1992 L2000 IM *020 †20
JIMENEZ, Alejandro. 13725 NORTHWEST BLVD, STE 10 78410 #016-45-2002 L2004 FM *100 †18
JIMENEZ, Joseph Raymond. 613 ELIZABETH ST, STE 605 78404 #005-02-1976 L1977 AN *020 †05
JIMENEZ, Michelle Ann Iba. 3533 S ALAMEDA ST 78411 #748-01-1999 PD *012
JOHNSON, David Lawrence. 2606 HOSPITAL BLVD 78405 #048-04-1970 L1974 GS *020 †85
JOHNSON, Larry Dee. 3315 S ALAMEDA ST 78411 #019-02-1977 L1979 EM FM *020 †18,16
JOHNSON, Maria Cristina. 3533 S ALAMEDA ST 78411 #048-02-1997 L2008 PD HO *020 †55
JOHNSON, R Martin. ■ 78410 #040-02-1957 L1960 FM OS *071
JOHNSON, Tone, Jr. 3138 S ALAMEDA ST STE A, COMPLETE MEDICAL CARE 78404 #035-06-1975 L1984 FM EM *020 †18 ‡
JONES, Timothy Robert. 2606 HOSPITAL BLVD, DEPT FM 78405 #041-09-1997 L1999 EM *012
JUAN, Vicente Mario. 1425 SANTA FE ST 78404 #048-12-1978 L2006 GS VS *020 †85
JUSTICE, Deanna Lynn. 3853 S ALAMEDA ST 78411 #005-06-1987 L1993 PTH *020 †50
KARAGAS, Michael D. 7121 S PADRE ISLAND DR, COASTAL BEND WOMENS 78412 #048-12-1982 L1983 OBG *030
KATRAGADDA, Chandra S. 3226 S ALAMEDA ST, RADIOLOGY & IMAGING OF TX 78404 #495-11-1972 L1976 VIR DR *020 †80
KENNEDY, Charles Wm. 601 TEXAN TRL STE 701 78411 #021-05-1965 L1974 ORS *020 †40
KENYON, Paul D. 600 ELIZABETH ST, EMERGENCY DEPARTMENT 78404 #048-04-1989 L1990 FM *020 †18
KEPP, Lowell Jennings. 3435 S ALAMEDA ST, THE CHILDREN'S CLINIC 78411 #012-01-1957 L1961 PD OS *072 †55
KHAN, Alamgir Ahmad. 613 ELIZABETH ST, STE 813 78404 #704-09-1992 L2006 CCM *100 †20
KHAN, Muhammad Sher. 3533 S ALAMEDA ST 78411 #704-02-1991 L2001 PDC *020 †55
KHIMANI, Sultana Alamin. 5920 SARATOGA BLVD, STE 570 78414 #704-02-1985 L2005 OBG *100
KIM, Jae Doo. 7121 S PADRE ISLAND DR, STE 205B 78412 #041-12-1998 L2004 GE *020 †20
KIRKHAM, Charles Ray. 7121 S PADRE ISLAND DR, STE 302 78412 #048-12-1980 L1980 OBG *020 †30
KIRKLAND, Kathryn Lee. 600 ELIZABETH ST 78404 #048-14-1984 L1985 EM *020
KLOTZ, Joseph Geo. ■ 78411 #017-20-1945 L1950 NS N *071 †25
KOHLHAAS, Bernice Ann K. ■ 78411 #018-03-1947 L1954 AN *071
KOHLHAAS, John K. 600 ELIZABETH ST 78404 #018-03-1950 L1954 AN *071 †05
KOOMOS, George Louis, Jr. 5950 SARATOGA BLVD 78414 #027-01-1964 L1974 AN *020 †05
KOSKA, Adolph J, III. 3533 S ALAMEDA ST 78411 #048-14-1985 L1986 AN PD *020 †05,55
KOVARIC, John J. 2601 HOSPITAL BLVD 78405 #035-03-1950 L1970 GS *072 †85
KRISHNAN, Ravinderan. 5729 ESPLANADE DR 78414 #048-16-1992 L1997 OPH *020 †35
KRYNSKI, Gregory Andrzej. 2601 HOSPITAL BLVD STE 106 78405 #759-03-1978 L1992 IM *020 †20
KUDLUR CHANDRAPPA, Vani. 3533 S ALAMEDA ST 78411 #495-99-2004 PD *012
KUFFEL, Ronald R, Jr. 5656 S STAPLES ST, STE 280 78411 #016-06-1991 L1996 OPH *020 †35
KUTNICK, Joel. 1630 S BROWNLEE BLVD 78404 #011-02-1966 L1973 P *020 †75 ‡
KYLSTRA, Johannes A. ■ 78411 #660-03-1952 L1966 PUD AI *071
LANDRY, Anayda Graciela. 3533 S ALAMEDA ST 78411 #935-07-1985 PD *012
LANE, Patricia Ann. 14202 S PADRE ISLAND DR D 78418 #048-13-1984 L1985 FM *040 †18
LANSER, Michael Jon. 3301 S ALAMEDA ST, STE 506 78411 #048-14-1982 L1983 OTO *020 †45
LARKIN, Allyson Chavez. 600 ELIZABETH ST, 2ND FL 78404 #048-16-1997 L1998 FM *020 †18
LE, Khoa Dang. ■ 78414 #026-04-1999 L2005 GS *020 †85
LEE, Dennis James. 5742 SPOHN DR 78414 #048-15-1979 L1980 DR *071 †80
LEE, Kang Sun. 2606 HOSPITAL BLVD, 8TH FL 78405 #025-07-1983 L1998 PM IM *020 †60

LEIBFARTH, James Helmut. 7121 S PADRE ISLAND DR 78412 #050-02-1972 L1976 RHU IM *020 †20
LEMONS, Mark Franklin. 2606 HOSPITAL BLVD, STE 310 78405 #039-01-1985 L1993 AN *020 †20
LEONG, Thomas Allan. 502 MORGAN AVE 78404 #010-02-1992 L2006 ORS *020 †40
LERMA, Ruben Florez. ■ 78410 #048-04-1980 L1980 EM *020
LESHIN, H Len. 5945 SARATOGA BLVD, STE C 78414 #048-14-1984 L1985 PD *020 †55
LEWANDOWSKI, Raymond C. 3533 S ALAMEDA ST 78411 #016-11-1970 L1976 CG PD *020 †19
LEWIS, Joe Alton. 600 ELIZABETH ST 78404 #048-04-1955 L1955 PTH *020 †50
LEWIS, Robert Quarles. 6118 PARKWAY 78414 #048-04-1978 L1978 ORS *020 †40
LEYTON-GONZALEZ, Luis Edu. 3825 S SPID DR 78415 #264-11-1986 L2001 IM *020 †20
LEYVA, Edward S. ■ 78414 #048-14-2006 FP *012
LIM, Alexander R. 1521 S STAPLES ST, NEUROLOGY PA 78404 #748-01-1964 L1971 N IM *020
LINGENFELDER, John. ■ 78413 #005-02-1943 L1952 GYN *071 †30
LINVILLE, William Kenneth. 3853 S ALAMEDA ST 78411 #004-01-1985 L1995 PTH *020 †50
LIRA, Ernesto. 2606 HOSPITAL BLVD 78405 #649-02-1985 L2000 PD OS *020 †55
LIRA, Luisa Maria. 5950 SARATOGA BLVD 78414 #649-02-1983 L1996 PD *020 †55
LIRA, Noe. 4525 S STAPLES ST 78411 #649-02-1986 L1997 OBG *020
LLERAS SANTANA, Idelisa. 2425 WINDHOLLOW DR 78414 #042-01-1973 L2002 PDR R *020
LOEFFLER, Paul Wm. 3318 S ALAMEDA ST 78411 #048-16-1987 L1993 OTO FPS *020 †45
LONGWELL, Paxton J. 3301 S ALAMEDA ST, STE 501 78411 #048-14-1990 L1991 N SME *020 †75
LOPEZ, Barbara. ■ 78404 #048-13-2004 L2007 FP *012
LOPEZ, Gabriel. 5315 EVERHART RD, STE 4 78411 #048-14-2000 L2004 APM PMM *020 †05
LOPEZ, Jose. ■ 78414 #048-13-2005 L2008 FP *012
LOPEZ-GUERRA, Alicia. 1315 SANTA FE ST STE 204 78404 #649-25-1960 L1972 PD *072
LOPEZ-GUERRA, Raul, Jr. 1315 SANTA FE ST 78404 #649-02-1960 L1966 GS *071 †85
LOPEZ-LIRA, Thelma. 4525 S STAPLES ST 78411 #649-02-1983 L1996 P CHP *020 †75
LORICA, Cherish De Villa. 3533 S ALAMEDA ST 78411 #748-02-2005 PD *012
LOVOI, Michael S. 13725 NW BLVD STE 260 78410 #048-14-1987 L1988 IM *020
LOYAL, Sabine. 3533 S ALAMEDA ST, DRISCOLL CHILDREN'S HOSPIT 78411 #409-38-1992 L2002 PAN *100
LUCCI, Christopher. 3301 S ALAMEDA ST, STE 100 78411 #048-14-1991 L1992 OS *020
LUCKAY, Frank Arthur. 601 TEXAN TRL, STE 300 78404 #038-40-1959 L1962 ORS *020 †40
LYON, Jane. 3533 S ALAMEDA ST 78411 #041-15-2000 L2008 DR *100 †80
MACKRIZZ, Luis Antonio. 5710 ESPLANADE DR 78411 #737-09-1980 L1999 IM *020 †20
MAC LACHLAN, Andrew A. 613 ELIZABETH ST, STE 605 78404 #048-12-1997 L1999 AN *020 †05
MADALIN, Herbert E. ■ 78413 #025-01-1952 L1960 TS *071 †85,90
MADIGAN, Coleen Maureen. 613 ELIZABETH ST STE 704A 78404 #048-13-1980 L1980 IM *020 †20
MAHER, John. 3533 S ALAMEDA ST 78411 #010-01-1989 L1999 CCP *020 †55
MAHESHWARI, Mukul Pintoo. 7101 WILLIAMS DR, WILLIAMS IMAGING CENTER 78412 #055-02-1989 L1998 RNR *020 †80
MAHMOOD, Aftab. 1625 RODD FIELD RD 78412 #704-26-1997 L2005 HO *020 †20
MALDONADO, Gilberto G. 2606 HOSPITAL BLVD 78405 #649-02-1958 L1965 P *020 ‡
MAMIDI, Murali K. 3533 S ALAMEDA ST, DRISCOLL CHILDREN'S HOSPIT 78411 #048-13-2001 L2006 PAN *100 †05
MANALO, Yvonne S. 1415 SANTA FE ST, STE C 78404 #748-11-1987 L2002 HO *020 †20
MANGIPUDI, Murthy V S. 4234 WEBER RD, SOUTH TEXAS PSYCHIATRIC 78411 #495-11-1972 L1995 P *020 †75 ‡
MANGLA, Narain Dass. 2601 HOSPITAL BLVD STE 103 78405 #495-45-1974 L1982 CD IM *020 †20
MANJARRIS, Jon Francis. 14317 NORTHWEST BLVD, STE A 78410 #048-13-1978 L1978 ORS *020 †40
MANKODI, Foram Ashwin. 3533 S ALAMEDA ST 78411 #495-17-2002 PD *012
MANUEL, Gudelio Najarro. US NAVAL HOSP BOX 634 78403 #748-11-1980 *100
MARTIN, Frank Stemple. 613 ELIZABETH ST, COASTAL BEND NEUROSURGEONS 78404 #012-01-1957 L1961 NS *020 †20
MARTIN, Jonathan E. 3301 S ALAMEDA ST # 205 78411 #048-02-1982 L1983 FM *020 †18
MARTIN, Lorenzo Felix. 1521 S STAPLES ST, STE 401 78404 #048-12-1971 L1971 PUD IM *020 †20
MARTINEZ, Frank Eloy. 5920 SARATOGA BLVD, STE 320 78414 #048-15-1997 L1999 FM *020 †18
MARTINEZ, Mario Arturo. 5833 SPOHN DR STE 805 78414 #048-02-2003 L2006 IM *020 †20
MARUVADA, Sreekar. 3533 S ALAMEDA ST, DRISCOLL CHILDREN'S HOSPIT 78411 #496-01-2003 PD *012
MARUVADA, Umamaheswara R. 4234 WEBER RD, SOUTH TEXAS PSYCHIATRIC 78411 #495-11-1971 L1988 P *020 †75
MASCIALE, John Philip. 3702 S ALAMEDA ST 78411 #035-08-1985 L1988 OSS ORS *020 †40
MASON, Robert William. 5540 SARATOGA BLVD, STE 200 78413 #035-01-1996 L1997 OPH *020 †35
MASTIN, Robert Eldon. 7121 S PADRE ISLAND DR, STE 302 78412 #048-04-1966 L1966 OBG *020 †30
MATHIS, Toya Jenniffer. 2606 HOSPITAL BLVD, DEPT EM 78405 #422-01-2005 L2007 EM *012
MAURER, Frederick S. 2606 HOSPITAL BLVD 78405 #649-01-1972 L1975 AN FM *020
MAY, James Meredith. 6625 WOOLDRIDGE RD STE 402 78414 #054-04-1965 L1970 P *020 †75 ‡
MAY, Robert A, Jr. 5920 SARATOGA BLVD, STE 630 78414 #048-02-1994 L1999 U *020 †95
MAY, Robert Arthur. 5920 SARATOGA BLVD, SURGICAL ASSOCIATES 78414 #048-04-1975 L1975 GS VS *020 †85
MC CASKEY, Mary Matthews. ■ 78412 #048-04-1950 L1950 PD *071
MC CLUNG, Robert Edward. 4646 CORONA DR STE 255 78411 #011-02-1986 L1988 P *020 †75
MC CUTCHON, Michael. 600 ELIZABETH ST 78404 #048-02-1990 L1992 AN *020 †05
MC CUTCHON, Sandra Ewing. ■ 78411 #048-02-1990 L1990 AN *020 †05
MC DOUGALL, Virginia H. 5833 SPOHN DR STE 203 78414 #021-05-1994 L2006 GS *020 †85
MCEWAN, Gavin Carter. 10651 E ST, NAVAL HOSPITAL 78419 #035-09-2005 L2006 *020
MC FARLAND, Bruce Robin. 600 ELIZABETH ST 78404 #038-40-1986 L1988 PM *020 †15
MC FARLING, David Allan. 1521 S STAPLES ST, NEUROLOGY PA 78404 #021-01-1972 L1982 N *020 †75
MCGARRY, Jonathon Howard. 2606 HOSPITAL BLVD, DEPT EM 78405 #017-20-2005 L2008 EM *012
MC KEEVER, John Duncan. 2601 HOSPITAL BLVD, STE 212 78405 #041-02-1965 L1972 ORS TRS *020 †40

MC LELLAND, Claude Allen. 3301 S ALAMEDA ST STE 506 78411 #048-12-1960 L1973 NO OTO *020 †45

MCLEMORE, Kerrie R. ■ 78418 #048-13-2006 L2008 FP *012

MC NEIL, Elbert Danl. ■ 78413 #007-02-1948 L1948 PD *071 †55

MC NEIL, Tom Scott. 3533 S ALAMEDA ST 78411 #019-02-1982 L1986 PD *020 †55

MC NITZKY, Adam Alexander. 600 ELIZABETH ST, SPOHN HOSPITAL 78404 #048-02-1955 L1955 OBG AM *071 †30

MC REYNOLDS, Enoch C, Jr. ■ 78418 #047-06-1943 L1963 AN *071

MEANEY, William Martin. 6621 WOOLDRIDGE RD 78414 #048-13-1978 L1978 P *075 †75

MEDINA, Maria Lucia C. 3533 S ALAMEDA ST, STE 303 78411 #748-11-1981 L1996 PD *020 †55

MEDLIN, Vernon Leon. 3226 REID DR 78404 #047-06-1955 L1961 RO R *071 †80 ‡

MEISENHEIMER, Ben Alan. 4444 CORONA DR, STE 232 78411 #020-02-1988 L1989 AN *020 †05

MEISTRELL, Michael L. ■ 78404 #021-01-1970 L1971 GS CD *030 †85,90

MEJIA, Roberto. 246 CAPE HATTERAS DR, 246 CAPE HATTERAS 78412 #264-03-1957 L1965 PD PUD *071 †55

MELENDEZ CRUZ, Edwin. 601 TEXAN TRL, STE 300 78411 #042-01-1970 L1988 HS ORS *020 †40

MELGOZA, Victor. 5424 HOLLY RD 78411 #649-02-1985 L1996 FM *020 †18 ‡

MENDIRATTA, Meenal S. ■ 78413 #495-96-1984 L2008 FM *012

MENDIZABAL, Jorge E. 3301 S ALAMEDA ST, STE 501 78411 #429-02-1991 L2003 N *020 †75

MERCADO, Leah Albano. 3533 S ALAMEDA ST 78411 #748-10-2003 PD *012

MERCHANT, Frederick John. 2606 HOSPITAL BLVD 78405 #016-11-1968 L1977 GS *071 †85

MICHEL, Yenni Lillia. 2606 HOSPITAL BLVD, CHRISTUS SPOHN MEM HOSP 78405 #048-78-2006, ▲ FP *012

MILANO, Emil Luciano. 5913 PATTON ST 78414 #649-30-1987 L1993 NPM *020 †55

MILCU, Ion Andrei. ■ 78413 #781-01-1971 L1986 PM PME *020 †60

MILLER, David Arthur. 1521 S STAPLES ST # 503 78404 #025-01-1972 L1977 PUD IM *020 †20

MILLIGAN, Thomas Wm. 3533 S ALAMEDA ST 78411 #048-13-1983 L1983 PTH MM *020 †50

MINTZ, Michael Lewis. 3318 S ALAMEDA ST, EAR NOSE & THROAT ASSOCIAT 78411 #025-07-1969 L1976 OTO *020 †45

MIRANDA, Egbert. 5866 S STAPLES ST, STE 403 78413 #042-02-1984 L1990 END IM *020 †20

MISKOVSKY, Christopher. 6118 PARKWAY, OTHOPEDIC SURGERY & SPORTS 78414 #010-02-1992 L1998 ORS HS *020 †40

MITCHELL, Robert Scott. 7121 S PADRE ISLAND DR, STE 205B 78412 #024-07-1990 L1996 IM *020 †20

MIWA, Edward Alejandro. 1802 ENNIS JOSLIN RD, APT 1032 78412 #649-02-2001 FP *012

MODAK, Arvind Gopal. 1315 SANTA FE ST, STE 102 78404 #495-96-1995 L2001 IM *020 †20

MOLLEDA CASTRO, Imgard Ca. 3533 S ALAMEDA ST 78411 #935-01-2003 PD *012

MOLONEY, Thomas Martin. 7406 UP RIVER RD DEPT OM 78409 #539-05-1975 L1984 OM EM *020 †18

MONAGAS RIVAS, Javier Jos. 3533 S ALAMEDA ST 78411 #935-07-2002 PD *012

MOORE, Charles Henry, III. 613 ELIZABETH ST, STE 511 78404 #048-02-1964 L1964 TTS CD *020 †85,90

MOORE, Pruett, Jr. 7121 S PADRE ISLAND DR, STE 300 78412 #048-02-1963 L1963 IM *072

MORALES, John Mark. 3533 S ALAMEDA ST, # 209 78411 #649-14-1985 L1994 PCS TS *020 †85,90

MORAN, J Patrick. 613 ELIZABETH ST 78404 #026-04-1951 L1951 OTO A *072 †45

MORENO, Martha Alejandra. 3533 S ALAMEDA ST, DRISCOLL CHILDREN'S HOSPIT 78411 #264-19-1995 PD *012

MORGAN, Frank Louis. 601 TEXAN TRL, THOMAS SPANN CLINIC 78411 #025-01-1977 L1982 RHU IM *020 †20

MORGAN, Michael Alwyn. 5515 SARATOGA BLVD 78413 #566-01-1981 IM *100

MORRIS, Thomas Eugene. 3435 S ALAMEDA ST 78411 #048-02-1975 L1975 PD *020 †55

MOTES, James Merrill, Jr. 13701 FM 624, STE D4 78410 #001-02-1969 L1976 OTO A *020 †45

MOYA, Medgar Marcial. 10651 E ST, ATTN: CREDENTIAL OFFICE 78419 #025-12-1994 L1997 FM *020 †18 ‡

MULLINS, James Dale. 3853 S ALAMEDA ST 78411 #048-02-1968 L1968 PTH *020 †50

MULLINS, Judith K Hebert. 3315 S ALAMEDA ST 78411 #048-13-1971 L1971 PHO *020 †55

MUMMADY, Pradyumna C. 5833 SPOHN DR, STE 201A 78414 #495-21-1985 L1998 PUD *020 †20

MUNIR, Lubna. ■ 78412 #704-22-1986 L2003 FM *020

MUNIZ, Margarita Amalia. 5209 INVERNESS DR 78413 #308-03-1980 L1985 IM *020 †20

MUNSON, Ronald Gerald. 4838 HOLLY RD, STE 209 78411 #048-13-1979 L1979 FM FPG *020 †18

MURO, Daniel, Jr. 613 ELIZABETH ST, STE 702 78404 #030-06-1982 L1986 IM *020

MURPHY, Ira J. 5920 SARATOGA BLVD, STE 110 78414 #495-97-1987 L1999 OBG *020 †30

MURPHY, Samuel Geo. ■ 78411 #038-04-1973 L1976 ON *071

MUSTAFA, Syed Ghulam. ■ 78418 #704-03-1969 L1977 IM ON *020 †20

MUTHALI, Dave Ganesha. 5283 OLD BROWNSVILLE RD, OUT PATIENT CLINIC 78405 #220-01-1974 L1981 PUD CCM *020 †20

MUTHALI, Lilani. 902 AIRPORT RD 78405 #220-01-1975 L1988 PD *020 †55

MYSTER, Stuart Howard. ■ 78413 #041-01-1967 L1990 PTH *020 †50

NARANG, Rajeev. 2601 HOSPITAL BLVD STE 220, PHYSICIANS PLAZA WEST 78405 #496-09-1987 L1995 PUD CCM *020 †20

NAST, Maurice Danl. 613 ELIZABETH ST, STE 701 78404 #048-04-1947 L1947 IM *071 †20

NAVAR, John Joe. 613 ELIZABETH ST, STE 605 78404 #649-01-1973 L1977 AM *020

NEFF, James Michael. 7121 S SPID DR, STE 300 78412 #048-12-1979 L1982 IM *020 †20

NELSON, Darrick Patton. 2606 HOSPITAL BLVD, STE 5 78405 #048-13-2000 L2002 FM *040 †18

NGUYEN, Bao N. 3533 S ALAMEDA ST, ANESTHESIOLOGY ASSOCIATES 78411 #048-02-1998 L2002 AN *100

NGUYEN, Minh V. 7121 S PADRE ISLAND DR 78412 #048-13-1988 L1989 IM *020 †20

NGUYEN, Nhung H. ■ 78404 #048-02-1994 L1996 AN *020 †05

NGUYEN, Tay Hoang. 2606 HOSPITAL BLVD 78405 #422-01-2006 EM *012

NGUYEN, Thomas Tuan. 1802 ENNIS JOSLIN RD 78412 #010-02-1992 L1997 AM *020

NISBET, R Michael. 3301 S ALAMEDA ST STE 307 78411 #048-02-1969 L1969 OPH *020 †35

NISIMBLAT, Andres. 601 TEXAN TRL, SOUTH TEXAS ADULT 78411 #048-02-2000 L2002 FM *020 †18 ‡

NOLLIE, Devereaux L. ■ 78404 #048-02-1999 L2006 CHP *020

NOORUDDIN, Karim N. 2733 SWANTNER ST 78404 #704-02-1981 L1992 NEP IM *020 †20

NOORUDDIN, Nadia K. ■ 78414 #704-02-1986 L1993 IM *020 †20

NORIEGA, Sandra I. 7121 S PADRE ISLAND DR, COASTAL BEND WOMENS 78412 #048-14-1989 L1990 OBG *020 †30

NORRIS, Walter Beale. ■ 78412 #048-02-1973 L1973 FM *071

NOWITZKY, Theressa James. 7121 S PADRE ISLAND DR, STE 302 78412 #010-02-1987 L2007 OBG *020 †30 ‡

NWOSU, Hilary Chukwudinma. 2606 HOSPITAL BLVD, DEPT EM 78405 #690-04-1992 L2003 EM *012

OBREGON, Joseph. 2222 MORGAN AVE STE 115 78405 #649-03-1950 L1963 GS FM *071

O'DANIELL, Estela Maria. 3533 S ALAMEDA ST, DRISCOLL CHILDREN'S HOSPIT 78411 #048-15-2001 L2004 PD *100

O'LAVIN, Blake Bernard. 1521 S STAPLES ST, NEUROLOGY PA 78404 #056-05-1968 L1974 N *020 †75

OLCESE, Victor Hector. ■ 78411 #132-01-1962 L1969 IM END *071 †20

OLOFSSON, Shatha M. 6000 S STAPLES ST, STE 406 78413 #528-01-1980 L1992 P NM *020

OLOYO, Samuel Duro. 2472 MORGAN AVE 78405 #690-01-1984 L1999 IM *020 †20

OLSON, Lyle C. ■ 78414 #028-78-1955, ▲ L1966 AN *071

ORTIZ, Fernando. 5283 OLD BROWNSVILLE RD 78405 #737-06-1969 L1983 IM *020

ORTIZ, Lilia Maria. 5283 OLD BROWNSVILLE RD, CCOP VETS CLINIC 78405 #275-01-1962 L1978 P *020

ORTIZ, Rosa Margarita. ■ 78414 #048-12-1977 L1977 NPM *020 †55

ORTIZ, Victor Bracamontes. 5920 SARATOGA BLVD, SURGICAL ASSOCIATES 78414 #048-04-1992 L1993 GS *020 †85

ORTIZ-GARCIA, Roberto. 2727 MORGAN AVE, STE 200 78405 #649-50-1987 L2006 FM *020 †18

O'SHEA, Zofia M Johannsen. 2606 HOSPITAL BLVD 78405 #759-03-1960 L1971 AN *071 †05

OSHMAN, Joseph. 3533 S ALAMEDA ST 78411 #048-02-1946 L1946 PD *071 †55

OSHMAN, Robert Duncan. 13701 FM 624, STE D4 78410 #048-13-1979 L1979 OTO *020 †45

OSHMAN, Steven Irving. 3533 S ALAMEDA ST 78411 #048-15-1980 L1980 OTO *020

OWSLEY, Jimie Dianne. 2606 HOSPITAL BLVD, TRAUMA SERVICES 78405 #016-42-1997 L2006 *020 †85

OYAFEMI, Oluyemis M. 3533 S ALAMEDA ST, PEDIATRIX MEDICAL GROUP 78411 #690-07-1994 L2003 NPM *100 †55

PA, Shun. 2606 HOSPITAL BLVD, DEPT EM 78405 #016-11-2005 L2006 EM *012

PADMANABHAN, Sivakumar. 5920 SARATOGA BLVD, STE 635 78414 #495-66-1990 L2000 PCC *020 †20

PAGAN, Jose Enrique. 5934 S STAPLES ST, STE 230 78413 #042-03-1992 L1996 P *020 †75

PALMERO, Leonel Rodo. 4444 CORONA DR, STE 232 78411 #924-01-1980 L1984 AN FM *020 †05

PALUMBO, Ralph Richard. 13725 NORTHWEST BLVD, STE 9 78410 #024-05-1958 L1982 IM UM *020 ‡

PAPINENI, Sudhakar. 3315 S ALAMEDA ST, DOCTORS REGIONAL HOSPITAL 78411 #495-21-1997 L2005 IM *020 †20

PAPPAS, John D. 1521 S STAPLES ST, STE 700 78404 #048-15-1987 L1988 CD IC *020 †20

PARK, Myung Kun. 3533 S ALAMEDA ST, MCIVER-FURMAN BLDG #202 78411 #583-02-1960 L1976 PDC PD *020 †55

PARKER, David Norfleet. ■ 78404 #036-05-1964 L1976 HS ORS *071 †40

PARKS, Francis Marion. 2606 HOSPITAL BLVD 78405 #048-02-1964 L1969 PTH BBK *020 †50

PARUTHI, Naresh Kumar. 5283 OLD BROWNSVILLE RD 78405 #495-69-1974 L1982 FM EM *020 †18

PATEL, Ashvinkumar A. 3435 S ALAMEDA ST 78411 #495-01-1976 L1995 PD *020 †55

PATEL, Girish Ambalal. 3435 S ALAMEDA ST, SUIE D 78411 #495-23-1976 L1979 PD *020 †55

PATHIKONDA, Meena G. 5920 SARATOGA BLVD, STE 570 78414 #495-22-1974 L1985 OBG *020 †30

PATTERSON, Brian L. 6118 PARKWAY, THE ORTHOPAEDIC CENTER OF 78414 #048-14-1999 L2002 ORS *020 †40

PAUL, Jonathan Daniel. 10651 E ST, ATTN: CREDENTIAL OFFICE 78419 #024-05-2004 L2005 *020

PEARCE, David Earl. 5920 SARATOGA BLVD, STE 350 78414 #011-03-1978 L1986 GS VS *020 †85

PELTIER, Bradley Geo. 613 ELIZABETH ST, STE 605 78404 #048-02-1983 L1983 AN *020 †05

PENA, Jaime. 7121 S PADRE ISLAND DR 78412 #048-13-1982 L1983 OBG *020 †30

PENDLETON, Michael J. 4210 WEBER RD, STE 2 78411 #010-03-1998 L2002 IM *020

PEREZ, Abimael. 600 ELIZABETH ST 78404 #781-04-1968 L1986 TS *071

PEREZ, Manuel Mireles. 7101 S PADRE ISLAND DR 78412 #023-07-1974 L1980 GE IM *020 †20

PEREZ, Rene Eloy, II. ■ 78413 #048-02-1986 L1987 FM *071 †18

PEREZ, Tessa V. 3533 S ALAMEDA ST, STE 303 78411 #048-02-1999 L2002 PD *020 †55

PEREZ MONTES, Maria D. 7121 S PADRE ISLAND DR, STE 302 78412 #042-02-1991 L1993 OBG *020 †30

PERO, Thomas. ■ 78418 #422-01-2005 L2007 EM *012

PERRON, Bernard. 4025 S PADRE ISLAND DR 78411 #065-09-1961 L1977 ORS *020

PETERS, Bonnie A. 3533 S ALAMEDA ST 78411 #048-12-1987 L1988 PD *020 †55

PETERS-DO, Glenda J. 4626 WEBER RD, STE 6 78411 #048-13-1994 L1995 FM *020 †18

PETERSON, Mary Dahlen. 3533 S ALAMEDA ST 78411 #048-02-1981 L1981 AN MDM *030 †05

PETRILA, Petru A. 600 ELIZABETH ST 78404 #781-04-1968 L1986 TS *071

PETROS, David Paul. 7121 S PADRE ISLAND DR 78412 #041-12-1982 L1991 RHU IM *020 †20

PETTIGROVE, John Robt. 7121 S PADRE ISLAND DR 78412 #039-01-1967 L1972 PUD IM *020 †20

PHAM, David Hong. ■ 78414 #048-02-2005 L2006 IM *020

PHAM, Duyen Thien. ■ 78412 #056-06-2003 L2005 PD *020 †55

PHILIPS, Thos Frederick B. ■ 78411 #067-01-1953 L1983 DR *071

PINKEL, Donald P. 3533 S ALAMEDA ST 78411 #035-06-1951 L1986 PHO PD *071 †55

PIZARRO, Fe Eviota. ■ 78418 #748-10-1968 L1984 PD NPM *020 †55

PIZARRO, Maria Delosange. 7121 S PADRE ISLAND DR, COASTAL BEND WOMENS 78412 #042-03-1987 L1995 OBG *020 †30

POLUKOFF, Gerald I. 613 ELIZABETH ST, STE 502 78404 #654-01-1985 L1989 CD IM *020 †20

POND, Matthew Darren. 10651 E ST, NAVAL HOSPITAL 78419 #010-01-2004 L2005 *020

POP, Adriana M. 613 ELIZABETH ST STE 704 78404 #781-04-1970 L2000 IM RHU *020 †20

PORTER, John Richard. 309 CAPE ARON DR, STE 78412 #048-04-1969 L1969 IM *071 †20

POTTER, Ryan N. 5734 SPOHN DR 78414 #048-02-1995 L1996 APM AN *020 †05

PRADERIO, Nestor Hugo. 817 AYERS ST 78404 #132-03-1973 L1994 P PYG *020 †75

PRADO, Alfonso M. 5913 PATTON ST 78414 #737-03-1966 L1975 NPM PD *020 †20

PUENTES, Jairo Antonio. 5262 S STAPLES ST STE 200, SARATOGA MED CTR 78411 #264-01-1967 L1974 PM PME *020 †60

PUJOL, Jose Manuel. 613 ELIZABETH ST, STE 702 78404 #308-03-1985 L1993 IM *020 †20

PURCELL, Debra Lee. 3533 S ALAMEDA ST 78411 #048-02-1991 L1994 PD *020 †55

PURNELL, Christina P. 3533 S ALAMEDA ST # 303, JM SLOAN MED BLDG 78411 #048-16-1999 L2001 PD *020 †55

QUEZADA, Gerardo. 3533 S ALAMEDA ST, DRISCOLL CHILDRENS HOSP 78411 #048-14-2000 L2007 PHO *100

QUINTANILLA, Mario A. 5350 S STAPLES ST, STE 203 78411 #649-02-1971 L1978
   CHP P *020 †75
QUISENBERRY, Delia Marie. 601 TEXAN TRL, SOUTH TEXAS ADULT 78411 #020-02-1996 L2004
   MPD *020 †20,55
RABINDRAN, Padmanabhan N. ■ 78415 #495-16-1945 L1978 GP *020
RACETTE, Guy Julien. 4025 S PADRE ISLAND DR 78411 #067-02-1982 L1988 FM OM *020 †18
RADUNSKY, Daniel. 2606 HOSPITAL BLVD 5W, HOSP MEMORIAL 78405 #132-01-1989 L2008
   FP *012
RAFAEL, Marita L. 3435 S ALAMEDA ST 78411 #748-01-1984 L1999 PD PEM *020 †55
RALEIGH, Edward N, Jr. 3853 S ALAMEDA ST 78411 #010-02-1967 L1986 PTH *020 †50
RAMAKRISHNA, Mulukutla. 3845 S PADRE ISLAND DR 78415 #495-11-1972 L1975 PD *020 †55
RAMCHANDANI, Sanjay Mohan. 5920 SARATOGA BLVD STE 110 78414 #033-05-1998 L2002
   OBG *020 †30
RAMIREZ, Guillermo Salas. ■ 78413 #649-01-1982 L2004 FM *020 †18
RAMIREZ, Manuel L, Jr. 3315 S ALAMEDA ST 78411 #649-02-1966 L1968 FM *071
RAMIREZ, Roque Joel. 13701 NW BLVD, SUIE B 2 78410 #305-01-1993 L1997 GS *020
RAMIREZ-MENDEZ, Alicia. 5283 OLD BROWNSVILLE RD, VA MEDICAL OUTPATIENT CLIN 78405
   #042-01-1954 L1962 IM *020 †20
RAMON, Roger Gilberto. 10635 LEOPARD ST 78410 #048-13-1980 L1980 FM EM *020 †18
RAMOS, Alvaro Jesus. 3554 S ALAMEDA ST 78411 #264-02-1969 L1977 R *020 †80
RAMSAY, Patricia Lynn. 3533 S ALAMEDA ST, NEONATOLOGY DEPARTMENT 78411
   #048-04-1995 L1997 NPM *020 †55
RANA, Jamal. 3533 S ALAMEDA ST, EMERGENCY DEPARTMENT 78411 #704-01-1986 L2003
   PD PEM *020 †55
RASHID, Lubna. ■ 78412 #704-09-1999 L2008 NEP *012 †20
RASMUSSEN, Kathleen Ruth. 5920 SARATOGA BLVD, STE 200 78414 #049-01-1995 L2002
   OBG *020 †30
RASMUSSON, Mark Douglas. 13725 NORTHWEST BLVD # 12 78410 #030-05-1981 L1986
   IM *020 †20
RAYASAM, Krishnaiah. 4234 WEBER RD, SOUTH TEXAS PSYCHIATRIC 78411
   #495-11-1973 L1991 P GP *020 †75
RAYMOND, Thomas Martin. 1301 SANTA FE ST, # A 78404 #025-07-1981 L1992 PM *020 †60
REDDY, Geeta P. 5920 SARATOGA BLVD STE 510 78414 #495-21-1997 L2004 NEP *100 †20
REDDY, Veena Kommera. 5920 SARATOGA BLVD, STE 395 78414 #495-37-2000 L2005 IM *020
REED, William Jerome. 3533 S ALAMEDA ST, DRISCOLL CHILDRENS HOSP 78411
   #048-02-1968 L1968 PD ADL *040 †55
REEMSNYDER, Curtis C. 2481 MORGAN AVE 78405 #026-04-1957 L1964 DR *071 †80,28
REEVES, Gerald Andrew. 1533 S BROWNLEE BLVD 78404 #028-02-1945 L1955 IM *071
REGAN, Tyce L. 613 ELIZABETH ST, STE 605 78404 #048-13-1992 L1993 AN *020 †05
REVERT FONT, Maria Luisa. 3533 S ALAMEDA ST 78411 #847-01-1986 PD *012
REYES, Yvette. 5283 OLD BROWNSVILLE RD 78405 #042-03-1988 L1996 END IM *020 †20
REYES-ACUNA, Celia D. 4444 S STAPLES ST 78411 #748-01-1962 L1968 PD *020 †55
RICCA, Maria Fabiana. 3533 S ALAMEDA ST, DRISCOLL CHILDREN'S HOSPITAL 78411
   #132-07-1994 PD *100 †55
RICE, James Philip. 10651 E ST, ATTN: CREDENTIAL OFFICE 78419 #028-34-1983 L1989
   GS *020 †85
RIGONAN, Alma Samatra. 10651 E ST, NAVAL BASE HOSPITAL CORPUS 78419
   #748-20-1991 L1997 PD *020 †55
RINCON RIVERO, Rosa Isabe. 3533 S ALAMEDA ST 78411 #264-24-2004 PD *012
RIOS, Billy. 3502 S ALAMEDA ST 78411 #649-30-1975 L1982 PDC PD *020
RIVERA, Christine R. 9702 S PADRE ISLAND DR, PEDIATRIC CLINIC OF SOUTH 78418
   #748-01-1987 L1997 PD *020 †55
RIVERA, Julio Manuel. 2601 HOSPITAL BLVD, STE 218 78405 #737-03-1970 L1979 PS *020
RIVERA, Ramon J. 3533 S ALAMEDA ST, ANESTHESIOLOGY ASSOC 78411 #308-05-1989 L2006
   CCP *020 †55
ROBERTS, Daniel M. 45 W BAR LE DOC DR, MCLENNAN COUNTY EMERGENCY 78414
   #048-02-1993 L1997 EM *020 †16
ROBERTS, Richard Martin. 5920 SARATOGA BLVD, STE 340 78414 #016-45-1975 L1982
   MG CG *020 †19,55
RODGER, Malcolm R, III. 613 ELIZABETH ST, STE 601 78404 #028-34-1965 L1971
   GS VS *071 †85
RODRIGUES, Edison D. 1301 OCEAN DR, ABDOMINAL SPECIALISTS OF 78404
   #495-28-1985 L1994 GE *020 †20
RODRIGUEZ, Angel. 613 ELIZABETH ST, STE 402 78404 #042-01-1990 L2007 CD *020 †20
RODRIGUEZ, Jorge Salvador. 3845 S PADRE ISLAND DR 78415 #649-14-1979 L1984 PD *020
RODRIGUEZ, Leo. 2481 MORGAN AVE, COASTAL BEND WOMENS 78405 #048-12-1991 L1993
   OBG *020 †30
RODRIGUEZ, Marco Antonio. 2606 HOSPITAL BLVD 78405 #649-30-2004 *100
RODRIGUEZ, Mike Edward. 1521 S STAPLES ST, STE 700 78404 #016-42-1987 L1994
   CD *020 †20
RODRIGUEZ, Rene M. 5846 WOOLDRIDGE RD 78414 #429-01-1971 L1979 IM EM *020 †20
ROGOFF, Eric Todd. 4444 CORONA DR STE 215 78411 #035-46-1997 L2004 IM *020 †20
ROLONG CANAS, Alvaro E. 2606 HOSPITAL BLVD 78405 #264-02-1973 L1984 GS *020 †85
ROMERO, Elena. 3533 S ALAMEDA ST, CLDRN PHY SVC HOSP 78411 #042-01-1979 L2003
   DR *020 †80
ROMERO, Ricardo N. 7121 S PADRE ISLAND DR, STE 312 78412 #649-01-1953 L1969
   IM *071 †20
ROMRIELL, Eric Kent. 5540 SARATOGA BLVD, STE 200 78413 #028-78-2001, ▲ L2005 *020
ROOSTH, Hyman P. 2606 HOSPITAL BLVD 78405 #048-02-1948 L1948 ORS *071 †40
ROPER, Mary L. 4444 CORONA DR, STE 215 78411 #048-14-1993 L1994 AN *020 †05
ROSE, James K. 11559 LEOPARD ST 78410 #048-02-1992 L1993 GP FM *020
ROTHSCHILD, Bernhardt F. 5950 SARATOGA BLVD, COASTAL BEND WOMENS 78414
   #048-02-1973 L1973 OBG *020 †30
ROTTA, Alexandre. 3533 S ALAMEDA ST, ANESTHESIOLOGY DEPARTMENT 78411
   #187-02-1989 L2004 CCP *020 †55
RUPP, Joseph Chas. ■ 78411 #038-06-1961 L1970 FOP PTH *071 †50
RUSNAK, James Loren. 6625 WOOLDRIDGE RD, STE 301 78414 #030-06-1994 L1996
   CHP *020 †20
RUTHERFORD, Clyde Escall. 600 ELIZABETH ST 78404 #048-02-1975 L1975 NEP IM *020 †20
RUTHERFORD, Robert B. 14337 DORSAL ST 78418 #023-07-1956 L1956 VS GS *071 †90,85
RYAN, David Ian. 3533 S ALAMEDA ST, DEPT. OF ANESTHESIA 78411 #051-04-1995 L2003
   CCP *020 †55
SAENZ, Angel, Jr. 13725 NORTHWEST BLVD, STE C 78410 #649-04-1973 L1977 OPH FM *020
SAENZ, Octavio. 2440 MORGAN AVE 78405 #682-01-1953 L1964 U *071
SAHADI, Jack Alex. 900 MORGAN AVE 78404 #048-13-1971 L1971 OPH EM *020 †35
SAIEH, Teodoro A. 1521 S STAPLES ST STE 404 78404 #264-05-1972 L1982 PS *020 †65

SALAMAT, Mehrdad. 3533 S ALAMEDA ST, P O BOX 6636 78411 #409-05-1987 L2001
   PDC *020 †55
SALES, Teofilo Espiritu. 3533 S ALAMEDA ST 78411 #748-08-1973 L1992 PD *020
SALLOUM, Cynthia Genuino. 614 FURMAN AVE 78404 #748-20-1983 L1998 IM *020 †20
SALLOUM, Emile Chawki. 1415 SANTA FE ST, STE C 78404 #605-02-1985 L1997
   ON HEM *020 †20
SAMUELS, Martel George. 3533 S ALAMEDA ST 78411 #566-01-1992 PD *012
SANCHEZ, Eduardo Arturo. ■ 78413 #308-01-1956 L1969 AN OS *071
SANCHEZ, Jesus V. ■ 78413 #048-14-2002 L2004 AN *020
SANCHEZ, Julian A. 613 ELIZABETH ST, STE 502 78404 #264-03-1984 L1998 CD *020
SANDERS, Chas Cornelius. 7121 S PADRE ISLAND DR 78412 #048-02-1973 L1973 FM *020
SANDOVAL, Jaime David. 1301 SANTA FE ST, # B 78404 #737-01-1983 L1997 IM *020 †20
SANTIAGO, Walter. 3533 S ALAMEDA ST 78411 #042-02-1982 L1994 PD *020 †55
SANTOS, Juan Felipe. 2601 HOSPITAL BLVD, STE 206 78405 #048-04-1986 L1987 N *020 †75
SANUSI, Lukuman Adesola. 2606 HOSPITAL BLVD, CHRISTUS SPOHN MEM HOSP 78405
   #690-02-1983 L2007 PD *020 †18
SAVELL, Van Henry, Jr. 3533 S ALAMEDA ST 78411 #025-01-1991 L2001 PP *020 †50
SCHECHTER, Charles Jacob. 613 ELIZABETH ST STE 402 78404 #042-03-1980 L1983
   CD *020 †20
SCHERER, James Murray. 2606 HOSPITAL BLVD 78405 #048-12-1965 L1969 PTH *020 †50
SCHLIMMER, Jeffrey Ronald. 6118 PARKWAY, THE ORTHOPAEDIC CENTER OF 78414
   #048-13-1996 L1997 OSM ORS *020 †40
SCHOFIELD, Norman D. ■ 78418 #025-07-1942 L1943 PTH P *071 †50
SCHROEDER, Jennifer Ann. 2606 HOSPITAL BLVD, STE 5 78405 #038-45-1997 L1998
   FM *020 †18
SCHUBERT, Joanna Michelle. 3753 CASTLE VIEW CIR 78410 #048-13-2003 L2004 FM *020 †18
SCHUENEMAN, Aaron Joel. 10651 E ST, NAVAL HOSPITAL 78419 #047-05-2005 L2006 *020
SCHULZE, John Paul. 3234 S ALAMEDA 78404 #048-12-1955 L1955 FM GS *020 †18
SCHULZE, Susan A. 3533 S ALAMEDA ST # 303 JM, JM SLOAN MED. BLDG #303 78411
   #035-06-1987 L1988 PD *020 †55
SCHWARTZ, Daniel Stephen. ■ 78412 #550-02-2003 L2008 EM *012
SCHWIRTLICH, Lonnie Ray. 4200 OCEAN DR 78411 #048-04-1979 L1980 EM *020 †16
SEGER, Bernard Manuel. 601 TEXAN TRL, STE 300 78411 #048-02-1979 L1979 ORS *020 †40
SEIDNER, Roberto E. ■ 78418 #429-01-1974 L1983 PD *012
SEIF, Rahmat. 10651 E ST, ATTN: CREDENTIAL OFFICE 78419 #517-01-1962 L1969
   GS ON *020 †85
SERRAO, Karl Leon. PO BOX 6530, 3533 S ALAMEDA 78466 #566-01-1991 L1999
   CCP *020 †55
SHAFFER, William Lee. 1521 S STAPLES ST, STE 601 78404 #048-02-1981 L1981
   IM NEP *020 †20
SHELTON, Laura L. 5920 SARATOGA BLVD, STE 200 78414 #048-16-1995 L1999 OBG *020 †30
SHIELDS, Marty Win. ■ 78414 #048-02-1985 L1986 VS *020 †85
SHINDEL, Liomira N. 3533 S ALAMEDA ST 78411 #913-85-1960 PD *100
SIFUENTES, Roger Michael. 13701 NORTHWEST BLVD, STE A 78410 #048-02-1996 L1997
   FM *020 †18
SILVA, Estrella. ■ 78413 #649-33-1981 L1990 IM *020
SILVA, Michael. ■ 78413 #649-33-1981 PD *100
SILVERMAN, Gregg Lee. 613 ELIZABETH ST STE 402 78404 #048-15-1990 L1991
   CD IM *020 †20
SILVERMAN, Jerome. PO BOX 3758 78463 #028-02-1958 L1967 ATP CLP *020 †50
SIMON, Colette. 2601 HOSPITAL BLVD, STE 117 78405 #440-01-1980 L2005 IM ID *020 †20
SIMONSEN, Randall Lee. 1403 3RD ST, PATH ASSOCS CORPUS CHRISTI 78404
   #041-12-1979 L1990 PTH *020 †50
SINGH, Raghujit. 1301 OCEAN DR, ABDOMINAL SPECIALISTS OF 78404 #028-02-1989 L1994
   GE IM *020 †20
SISLEY, Nina M. 1702 HORNE RD, OF PUBLIC HEALTH 78416 #048-02-1950 L1950
   PHP PUD *071 †70
SISON, Rosemarie Gomez. 3533 S ALAMEDA ST, DRISCOLL CHILDREN'S HOSPITAL 78411
   #748-08-1990 L2008 PD *012
SLOAN, Morris Gayle. ■ 78404 #018-03-1954 L1955 R *071 †80
SMITH, Charles Thos. 1001 LOUISIANA AVE, STE 200 78404 #048-12-1969 L1978
   CD IM *020 †20
SMITH, Gary Lynn. 3533 S ALAMEDA ST 78411 #004-01-1975 L1987 AI PD *020 †55,03
SMITH, Jack G. ■ 78413 #048-02-1953 L1953 ADM IM *071
SMITH, Pamela Kay. 601 TEXAN TRL, SOUTH TEXAS ADULT 78411 #036-01-1982 L1983
   IM *020 †20
SMITH, Robert D. 2606 HOSPITAL BLVD, # 5W 78405 #048-13-2003 FP *012
SMITH, Stephen Thomas. 3765 S ALAMEDA ST, STE 427 78411 #308-07-1981 L1987
   EM FM *020 †18
SMITH, Teresa Kay. ■ 78414 #048-14-2006 FP *012
SOCH, Kathleen Ruth. 2606 HOSPITAL BLVD, STE 5 78405 #048-02-1981 L1981 FM *020 †18
SOE, Han. 5283 OLD BROWNSVILLE RD 78405 #665-01-2003 L2003 P *020
SOHOCKI, John Bernard, II. 2222 MORGAN AVE, STE 101 78405 #025-07-1966 L1967
   OPH GP *020 †35
SOIN, Jagmeet Singh. 3301 S ALAMEDA ST STE 100 78411 #495-36-1966 L1973
   NM IM *020 †20,28
SOLANO, Iliana. 3533 S ALAMEDA ST 78411 #270-02-2000 PD *012
SOLOMON, Tabitha Eunice. 3533 S ALAMEDA ST, DRISCOLL CHILDREN'S HOSPITAL 78411
   #496-32-2001 L2007 PD *012
SOLORZANO, Sergio Martin. 4637 S PADRE ISLAND DR 78411 #048-14-2003 L2005
   FM *020 †18
SORENSON, Robert Bruce. 10651 E ST, NAVAL HOSPITAL 78419 #037-01-1985 L1986
   FM OBG *020 †18
SORIANO, Ma. Cristina Ma. 3533 S ALAMEDA ST, DRISCOLL CHILDREN'S HOSPITAL 78411
   #748-10-1994 L2007 PD *020 †55
SOUCHICK, Annmarie. 3853 S ALAMEDA ST 78411 #056-06-1990 L1997 BBK *020 †50
SOZA, Noe. 3765 S ALAMEDA ST STE 427, CHEP CORPUS CHRISTI 78411 #048-12-1976 L1976
   EM FM *020 †18
SPECK, Pat Kelly. ■ 78403 #048-15-1976 L1976 PD FM *020
STAFFORD, Jane Oliver. 5920 SARATOGA BLVD STE 200 78414 #048-02-1978 L1978
   OBG GP *020 †18
STAFFORD, Wesley Warren. 1718 BRAESWOOD DR 78412 #048-02-1978 L1978
   AI PD *020 †55,03
STANCIELL, Earbin C. 5656 S STAPLES ST STE 250 78411 #048-02-1991 L1994 P *020 †75
STEARNS, Clark Hayden. ■ 78413 #048-12-1976 L1976 EM FM *020 †18
STEELE, Steven Juedeman. 3301 S ALAMEDA ST STE 304 78411 #048-02-1973 L1973
   VS GS *020 †85

STEIN, Karl Vaughn. 7121 S PADRE ISLAND DR 78412 #048-02-1975 L1975 **GP** *020

STOCKS, Alton Leroy. 10651 E ST, NAVAL HOSPITAL 78419 #010-02-1986 L1988 **PN PD** *030 †55

STRAIN, Bonnie Boenig. 4444 CORONA DR STE 232 78411 #048-14-1991 L1992 **AN** *020 †05

STRAIN, Shawn M. 7121 S PADRE ISLAND DR, COASTAL BEND WOMENS 78412 #048-14-1988 L1991 **OBG** *020 †30

STRAUSS, Mark Gladwin. 601 TEXAN TRL, STE 100 78411 #016-11-1972 L1975 **IM** *020 †20

STRUVE, Clemens Aram. 3301 S ALAMEDA ST STE 403 78411 #048-02-1954 L1954 **OPH** *071 †35

SUPNET, Ben-Brigido. 5262 S STAPLES ST 78411 #748-01-1962 L1983 **AN GP** *020

SUPNET, Leonora Defante. 3301 S ALAMEDA ST 78411 #748-01-1962 L1973 **GP** *020 †18

SURANI, Salim R. 613 ELIZABETH ST STE 813, PHYSICIANS TOWERS 78404 #704-02-1988 L1994 **PCC SME** *020 †20

SUSSMAN, Marian Beth. 3315 S ALAMEDA ST, MEDICAL STAFF OFFICE 78411 #035-09-1983 L2006 **AN** *020 †05

SUTTER, David Franklin. 3301 S ALAMEDA ST STE 201 78411 #016-45-1993 L1995 **FM** *020 †18

SWAN, William Everett, Jr. 1521 S STAPLES ST STE 303 78404 #005-12-1967 L1973 **ORS** *020 †40

SYGAL, Juan Jose. 13725 FM 624, STE 9 78410 #649-01-1981 L1998 **IM** *020

TABOADA, Libardo Jose. 4444 CORONA DR STE 232, SUITE 232 78411 #264-05-1972 L1976 **AN** *020 †05

TARUC-LIBED, Cheryle Phoe. 3533 S ALAMEDA ST, DRISCOLL CHILDREN'S HOSPIT 78411 #748-02-1996 **PD** *012

TAVARES, Sergio. 601 TEXAN TRL, STE 205 78411 #187-03-1974 L1983 **TS** *020 †85,90

TAYLOR, Bruce D. ■ 78411 #048-15-1975 L1975 **AN PD** *020 †55,05

TEENIER, Thomas James. 4210 WEBER RD STE 1 78411 #021-06-1996 L2000 **OMF** *020

TEJEDA, Heriberto Alfredo. 4609 S PADRE ISLAND DR 78411 #308-01-1986 L1999 **IM PHP** *020 †20

TELLO, Vincent Osmund, Jr. ■ 78414 #048-12-2006 **GS** *100

TEMPESTA, James Elias. ■ 78411 #649-01-1956 L1958 **OPH OS** *071

THACKERAY, Bridget Yvonne. 2606 HOSPITAL BLVD, CHRISTUS SPOHN MEM HOSP 78405 #048-78-2005, ▲ **FP** *012

THERIOT, Eugene Chas. 613 ELIZABETH ST, STE 605 78404 #021-05-1988 L1992 **AN** *020 †05

THOELECKE, Heather Ann. ■ 78413 #005-06-2004 L2006 **EM** *012

THOMAS, Fred Purnell, Jr. 613 ELIZABETH ST STE 302 78404 #048-12-1969 L1969 **TS GS** *020 †85,90

TILLEY, Melissa Mae. 3533 S ALAMEDA ST, DRISCOLL CHILDREN'S HOSPIT 78411 #649-45-2005 L2007 **PD** *012

TIMMERMAN, John Wm. 3240 FORT WORTH ST, STE 100 78411 #030-05-1973 L1974 **GYN** *071 †30

TIMPERLAKE, Roger Wm. 3533 S ALAMEDA ST 78411 #021-01-1983 L1993 **OP** *020 †40

TINOCO, Amalia. 5950 SARATOGA BLVD 78414 #049-01-1977 L1979 **EM FM** *020 †16,18 ‡

TOBIAS-MERRILL, Evelyn A. 2606 HOSPITAL BLVD 78405 #048-12-1993 L1994 **FM** *020 †18

TOLENTINO, Hugo R. 613 ELIZABETH ST, STE 605 78404 #048-16-1993 L1995 **AN** *020

TOM, Timothy Danl. ■ 78410 #023-01-1991 L1999 **AN** *050 †05

TOMPKINS, Kent E. 13725 NORTHWEST BLVD, STE 15 78410 #048-13-1990 L1991 **FM** *020 †18

TORELL, Jacqueline Ann. ■ 78411 #030-05-1979 L1980 **PTH** *020 †50

TORRES, Laura Patricia. ■ 78413 #649-30-1980 **IM** *020

TORRES, Pedro P. 3301 S ALAMEDA ST, STE 305 78411 #935-01-1974 L1983 **CRS** *020 †10,85

TORRES-GARCIA, Josefina. 6110 PARKWAY 78414 #649-02-1979 L1983 **PD** *020

TOWNSEND, Dwight Anthony. 7101 WILLIAMS DR, WILLIAMS IMAGING CENTER 78412 #036-05-1996 L1998 **DR** *020 †80

TOWNSEND, Thomas Michael. 5920 SARATOGA BLVD, SURGICAL ASSOCIATES 78414 #048-13-1986 L1987 **VS GS** *020 †85

TOZER, James Michael. ■ 78418 #007-02-1968 L1991 **FM** *071 †18

TRAVLAND, Clayton Arno. 600 ELIZABETH ST 78404 #047-06-1962 L1963 **IM** *020

TREVINO, Jose De Jesus. 613 ELIZABETH ST, STE 805 78404 #025-12-1976 L1978 **PME PMM** *020 †18 ‡

TRILLOS, Gonzalo Eduardo. 3435 S ALAMEDA ST 78411 #264-04-1976 L1982 **PD** *020 †55

TRYGGESTAD, Maryann Cecel. ■ 78414 #048-13-2005 L2008 **FP** *012

TSCHAUNER, Rob M. 5934 S STAPLES ST, STE 224 78413 #048-14-1987 L1988 **FM** *020 †18

TSCHICKARDT, Michael E. 1001 3RD ST, STE 9 78404 #011-04-1998 L2003 **PME AN** *020 †05

TSIAOUSSIS, Constantinos. 4310 OCEAN DR 78411 #418-01-1965 L1979 **IM** *074

TURNER, Jennifer Elisabet. 7101 WILLIAMS DR, WILLIAMS IMAGING CENTER 78412 #048-13-1996 L2002 **DR** *020 †80

TURNER, Stephen A. 613 ELIZABETH ST, STE 402 78404 #048-14-1986 L1992 **CD** *020 †20

TURNER, Thomas M, Jr. 3853 S ALAMEDA ST 78411 #048-13-1997 L2002 **PTH** *020 †50

TYMINSKI, Beatrice. ■ 78404 #048-13-1988 L1990 **PTH** *020

TYREE, James Brooks. 1521 S STAPLES ST 8 78404 #048-04-1980 L1981 **U** *020 †95

UD-DIN, Sabeeh. 614 FURMAN AVE 78404 #704-01-1990 L2004 **NEP** *020 †20

UGWUIBE, Maurice N. PO BOX 5069 78465 #690-04-1982 L1995 **IM** *020 †20

ULATE DUARTE, Kalia Patri. 3533 S ALAMEDA ST 78411 #270-02-2001 L2007 **PD** *020 †55

UPMANYU, Marilyn Jean L. ■ 78412 #047-06-1965 L1971 **END DIA** *071

VANEXAN, Kenneth Stewart. 3226 REID DR 78404 #027-01-1984 L2001 **RNR DR** *020 †80

VANFRANK, Timothy Dean. 7121 S PADRE ISLAND DR, STE 205B 78412 #047-06-1991 L1997 **GE** *020 †20

VARIN, Carmen Richard. 613 ELIZABETH ST STE 612 78404 #050-02-1984 L1986 **CRS GS** *020 †85,10

VAZQUEZ, Jorge Luis. ■ 78414 #649-14-2002 L2005 **NEP** *020 †20

VELA, Jose Julio. 2606 HOSPITAL BLVD 78405 #048-12-1979 L1979 **GE IM** *020 †20

VELA, Robert. 2201 CLEO ST # A 78405 #048-12-1977 L1977 **IM** *020 †20

VELA, Steven Andrew. 5920 SARATOGA BLVD, SURGICAL ASSOCIATES 78414 #025-01-2001 L2006 **GS** *020 †85

VELAZQUEZ, Wilson Luis. ■ 78414 #042-01-1988 L2004 **AN** *020

VENECIA, David, Jr. 613 ELIZABETH ST, STE 605 78404 #054-04-1985 L1986 **AN** *020

VIELMA, Luis Humberto. 3533 S ALAMEDA ST 78411 #649-54-1998 **PD** *100

VIJJESWARAPU, Daniel V. 601 TEXAN TRL, STE 301 78411 #495-58-1983 L1999 **PD** *020 †55

VILLA, Florencio Castillo. ■ 78411 #748-01-1955 L1968 **GP GS** *071

VILLAFLOR, Antonio Gonong. 10651 E ST, ATTN: CREDENTIAL OFFICE 78419 #748-08-1969 L1980 **GS** *020

VILLARREAL, Arnoldo Raul. 1521 S STAPLES ST STE 204 78404 #005-15-1975 L1979 **OPH IM** *020 †35

VILLARREAL, Juan Antonio. 13725 NORTHWEST BLVD # 110 78410 #048-02-1984 L1988 **OBG** *020

VOLK, Charles Thomas. 5920 SARATOGA BLVD, SURGICAL ASSOCIATES 78414 #048-02-1980 L1980 **VS** *020 †85

VOORHEES, Gerard Joseph. 1625 RODD FIELD RD, CORPUS CHRISTI CANCER CENT 78412 #030-06-1987 L1997 **RO** *020

WAGNER, Daniel Jason. ■ 78418 #048-02-2002 L2004 **EM** *100 †16

WAKEFIELD, Peggy Lea. 3435 S ALAMEDA ST, STE C 78411 #048-02-1975 L1975 **PD ADL** *071 †55

WALKER, James Carroll. 6000 S STAPLES ST, STE 400 78413 #048-02-1962 L1962 **P OS** *071

WALLACE, Grant Charles. 10651 E ST, ATTN CREDENTIAL OFFICE 78419 #023-12-1993 L2008 **DR** *020 †80

WANG, Robert Ming-Cheug. 2601 HOSPITAL BLVD STE 105 78405 #244-01-1969 L1977 **PUD IM** *020 †20

WARD, Harold Wm Cowper. ■ 78404 #917-07-1953 L1977 **RO ON** *071 †80

WARE, Stephen H, Jr. 4628 WEBER RD 78411 #021-01-1946 L1947 **FM EM** *071

WEAVER, Kaycee Leigh. 2606 HOSPITAL BLVD 5, CORPUS CHRISTI FAM PRCTCE 78405 #305-01-2006 **FP** *012

WEAVER, Shaun H. 2606 HOSPITAL BLVD 5W, HOSP MEMORIAL 78405 #048-13-2005 L2008 **FP** *012

WEBSTER, Robert Andrew. 3301 S ALAMEDA ST, STE 402 78411 #048-15-1997 L1998 **FM** *020 †20

WEISMAN, Perry Russell. 3315 S ALAMEDA ST, MED ASSOCS OF NORTHERN VA, 78411 #422-01-1999 L2005 **IM** *020 †20

WELCH, Gordon Robert, Jr. 1521 S STAPLES ST STE 803 78404 #048-12-1972 L1972 **U** *020 †95

WELCH, William Mauk. ■ 78414 #041-12-1959 L1964 **D** *071 †15

WEST, B Kendrick. 10651 E ST 78419 #048-12-1961 L1965 **GS** *020 †85

WIEMERS, Marcy Renee. 2606 HOSPITAL BLVD, CCFPRP 78405 #048-16-2003 L2004 **FM** *040 †18

WILDER, Thomas Lowell. 7121 S SPID DR, STE 302 78412 #048-13-1974 L1981 **OBG** *020 †30

WILK, Lawrence Harvey. 1001 LOUISIANA AVE 78404 #025-01-1958 L1965 **ORS** *071 †40

WILLIAMS, David K. 4444 CORONA DR STE 200, CASPER MEDICAL IMAGING 78411 #048-15-1997 L2000 **DR** *020 †80

WILLIAMS, Robert S. 5920 SARATOGA BLVD # 600A 78414 #048-13-1990 L1996 **OSS ORS** *020 †40

WILLIAMSON, David Carlton. 613 ELIZABETH ST STE 605, GULF SHORE ANESTHESIA ASSO 78404 #021-06-1986 L1990 **AN** *020 †05

WILLIS, Dennis E. ■ 78413 #048-13-1998 L1999 **EM** *012 †18

WILMAN, Joel B.. 2606 HOSPITAL BLVD 5W 78405 #649-02-1995 **FM** *100

WILSON, David Coles. ■ 78418 #018-03-1973 L1999 **GS** *020 †55

WILSON, James David. 2606 HOSPITAL BLVD 5W, HOSP MEMORIAL 78405 #748-10-2006 **FP** *012

WILSON, Mark Sean. 4444 CORONA DR, STE 215 78411 #056-06-1998 L2002 **AN** *020 †05

WILSON, Melissa Ann. 144 ROPES ST 78411 #048-12-1985 L1986 **END IM** *030 †20

WINNIE, Michael G. 5920 SARATOGA BLVD STE 610 78414 #048-16-1996 L1997 **FM** *020 †18

WIRASZKA, Adam. 5920 SARATOGA BLVD STE 460 78414 #759-10-1982 L2001 **PD** *020 †55

WOOD, Robert C. 724 MORGAN AVE 78404 #048-02-1953 L1953 **FM GP** *020

WOODSON, Ronald Cole. 5920 SARATOGA BLVD, STE 170 78414 #048-02-1980 L1980 **GYN** *020

WOOLVIN, Samuel Carmon. 600 ELIZABETH ST 78404 #028-02-1954 L1967 **PTH** *020 †50

WRIGHT, Arthur G. 600 ELIZABETH ST 78404 #048-02-1953 L1953 **EM** *020

WRIGHT, Edward N. ■ 78414 #048-13-2007 **EM** *012

WRIGHT, Joseph House. ■ 78413 #021-01-1955 L1962 **ORS** *071 †40

XIONG, Dingding. 3533 S ALAMEDA ST 78411 #243-62-1987 **PD** *012

YANEZ, Carlos Manuel. 3315 S ALAMEDA ST 78411 #275-01-1946 L1963 **ORS** *071

YANG, Chien I. 3226 REID DR 78404 #048-13-1998 L2002 **RNR** *020 †80

YARRABOLU, Tharakanatha R. 3533 S ALAMEDA ST 78411 #495-21-1999 **PD** *012

YAYLALI, Yalin Tolga. ■ 78413 #902-05-1992 L1998 **IM** *020 †20

YE, Qilin. 3533 S ALAMEDA ST 78411 #243-63-1985 L2005 **PD** *020

YONG, Yongqi. 613 ELIZABETH ST, STE 502 78404 #243-21-1989 L1999 **CD** *020 †20

YULO, Katherine Jean Valm. 3533 S ALAMEDA ST 78411 #748-01-2004 **PD** *012

ZAMORA MUNOZ, Salvador. 2222 MORGAN AVE, STE 112 78405 #132-02-1967 L1979 **U** *020 †95

ZANE, Randall Scott. 3318 S ALAMEDA ST 78411 #048-12-1986 L1987 **OTO NO** *020 †45

ZANETTI, Paul Henry. ■ 78413 #025-01-1965 L1972 **NS** *071 †25

ZARINETCHI, Fariba. 1521 S STAPLES ST, STE 601 78404 #024-07-1989 L1996 **NEP IM** *020 †20

ZEBAIDA, Yeheskel. 3533 S ALAMEDA ST 78411 #550-01-1963 L1967 **PD** *020 †55

ZIA-ULLAH, Mohammad. 3533 S ALAMEDA ST, DRISCOLL CHILDREN'S HOSPIT 78411 #704-01-1990 L2003 **NPM** *020 †55

ZIMMERMANN, Claudia. 1621 S BROWNLEE BLVD # 100 78404 #737-01-1988 L1997 **N** *020 †75

ZUNIGA ACOSTA, Fabricio J. ■ 78413 #270-02-2001 L2007 **FM** *020 †18

CORSICANA – NAVARRO

AGARWAL, Ashwani Kumar. 301 HOSPITAL DR 75110 #495-73-1983 L1997 **HO** *020 †20

BANCROFT, Charles E. ■ 75151 #048-04-1946 L1948 **OBG** *071 †30

BEEBE, Walter Edward. 301 HOSPITAL DR, CORNEA ASSOCIATES OF 75110 #017-20-1981 L1982 **OPH** *020 †35

BILTZ, Charles Irving. 3201 W HIGHWAY 22 75110 #038-41-1960 L1967 **GE IM** *020 †20

BILTZ, John M. 401 HOSPITAL DR, TX DERMATALOGY ASSOC 75110 #048-12-1993 L1994 **D** *020 †15

BINFORD, Oswald S. 3124 W HIGHWAY 22 75110 #048-12-1997 L2001 **OPH** *020 †35

BRANCH, Matthew P. 301 HOSPITAL DR 75110 #048-14-2000 L2005 **OTO** *020 †45

BROPHEY, Mike D. 301 HOSPITAL DR 75110 #048-14-1986 L1987 **IM** *020 †28

BROWN, Charles Henry, Jr. ■ 75110 #048-12-1944 L1944 **GP GS** *071

BURKHART, Kelly Paul. 3201 W HIGHWAY 22 75110 #048-12-1956 L1956 **OBG** *071 †30

CAMPBELL, Calvin David. 219 W 6TH AVE 75110 #048-04-1954 L1954 **FM AM** *020 †18

CAMPBELL, Dale Keith. 3124 W STATE HIGHWAY 22 75110 #048-02-1979 L1979 **FM** *020 †18

CAMPBELL, Robert L. 3201 W HIGHWAY 22 75110 #048-04-1952 L1952 **GP FM** *071

CAMPBELL, Robert Millet. 3201 W HIGHWAY 22 75110 #021-01-1975 L1980 **EM P** *020 †75

CHAPA, Homero Javier. 75109 #048-02-1964 L1964 **R** *020 †50

COLE, Robert Dale. 401 HOSPITAL DR 75110 #048-02-1988 L1992 **OPH** *020 †35

CONFER, Michelle A. 1115 W 2ND AVE 75110 #048-13-1989 L2006 **OBG** *020 †30

CROUCH, Eron Demone. 301 HOSPITAL DR 75110 #048-16-2000 L2002 **CD** *020 †20 ‡
DOTSON, James Alfa. ■ 75110 #048-04-1967 L1967 **ORS** *071 †40
DOUGLASS, Alexander B. 3201 W HIGHWAY 22 75110 #041-09-1973 L1978 **U** *020 †95
EVANS, Kimberly L. 400 HOSPITAL DR 75110 #041-15-2002 L2006 **OBG** *020
FATIREGUN, Agboola O. ■ 75110 #041-09-1998 L2007 **PD** *020 †55
GIBSON, Joseph V, Jr. ■ 75110 #041-02-1951 L1952 **GP** *100
GIBSON, Louis Ervin. 301 HOSPITAL DR, MEDICAL ARTS CLINIC 75110 #048-02-1946 L1946 **GS CD** *072 †85
GLICKSMAN, Joseph Morris. 301 HOSPITAL DR, TRINITY CLNC 75110 #048-02-1963 L1963 **D** *020 †15
GREEN, Richard Neal. 301 HOSPITAL DR, BOX 841 75110 #048-02-1971 L1971 **OBG GP** *020 †30
HALL, Shelley Anne. 301 HOSPITAL DR 75110 #048-12-1991 L1992 **CD** *020 †20
HAMILTON, Kyle Lloyd. 3201 W HIGHWAY 22 STE 200 75110 #048-12-1979 L1979 **FM** *020 †18
HART, Gary Ray. 3201 W HIGHWAY 22 75110 #048-12-1975 L1975 **IM** *020 †20
HO, Linh Hong. 301 HOSPITAL DR 75110 #048-02-2002 L2005 **PD** *020
JAHNKE, Karen Ann. 400 HOSPITAL DR STE 2, MEDICAL ARTS CLINIC ASSOC. 75110 #005-12-1981 L1996 **PD** *020 †55
JOHNSON, Kenneth Barry. 301 HOSPITAL DR 75110 #034-01-1994 L1995 **CD** *020 †20
KENNEDY, Leslie Ann. 1737 W 2ND AVE 75110 #016-06-1974 L1979 **DR PDR** *020 †80
KINGMAN, Robert G. 301 HOSPITAL DR, MEDICAL SURG ASSOC 75110 #048-12-1982 L1983 **GS VS** *020 †85
LEE, Bill Ray. 301 HOSPITAL DR 75110 #048-12-1972 L1972 **FM** *020 †18 ‡
LE MAY, Sonley Robt. 75110 #048-12-1957 L1957 **OTO HNS** *071 †45
MC COY, Danny Ken. 301 HOSPITAL DR 75110 #048-12-1993 L1994 **D** *020 †15
MC GARY, Lester E, Jr. ■ 75110 #056-05-1952 L1956 **U** *071 †50
MC HENRY, William Lionel. 3124 W HIGHWAY 22 75110 #039-01-1979 L1980 **FM** *020 †18
MC NALLY, Joseph F, Jr. 301 HOSPITAL DR, MEDICAL AND SURGICAL ASSOC 75110 #048-02-1974 L1974 **AI PDA** *020 †55,03
MERRILL, Ronald Wm. 3124 W HIGHWAY 22 75110 #048-12-1975 L1975 **FM** *020 †18
MIDDLETON, Elliott Scott. 301 HOSPITAL DR 75110 #048-04-1962 L1962 **GS** *071 †85
NELSON, John Darrell. 301 HOSPITAL DR, MEDICAL ARTS CLINIC 75110 #048-12-1965 L1965 **IM** *071 †20
NORRIS, James Ted. ■ 75110 #048-02-1976 L1977 **GP NTR** *020
PATEL, Deepak C. 400 HOSPITAL DR, STE 101 75110 #495-37-1985 L1998 **IM** *020 †20
RODRIGUEZ, Ronald. 3201 W HIGHWAY 22 75110 #003-75-2000, ▲ L2004 **IM** *020 †20
SCHUSSLER, Jeffrey M. 301 HOSPITAL DR 75110 #048-02-1985 L1986 **CD** *020 †20
SHAFIK, Shawkat N. 400 HOSPITAL DR, STE 106 75110 #915-02-1982 L1996 **NEP** *020 †20
SHAW, Grady Carlton. 301 HOSPITAL DR, TRINITY CLINIC 75110 #048-04-1976 L1980 **FM** *020 †16
SHWARTS, Kalman Jay. 1430 W 7TH AVE, CENTER 75110 #021-01-1974 L1976 **EM** *030 †16
SMITH, Jerry Dee. ■ 75110 #017-20-1968 L1974 **D** *020 †15
STEVENER, Larry Ray. 3201 W HIGHWAY 22, NAVARRO REGIONAL HOSPITAL 75110 #048-12-1974 L1974 **AN** *020 †05
WILLIAMS, J R, II. 301 HOSPITAL DR 75110 #048-12-1977 L1977 **OTO** *020 †45
WOMACK, Grover Kenneth. 301 HOSPITAL DR, MEDICAL ARTS CLINIC ASSOCI 75110 #048-04-1955 L1955 **PD PTH** *071 †55

COTTONWOOD SHORES – LLANO

HOWARD, Paxton H, Jr. 100 PECAN CREEK DR 78657 #048-04-1962 L1962 **IM ID** *071 †20
ROCHE, Warren Province, Jr. 100 PECAN CREEK DR 78657 #048-15-1994 L1995 **IM** *020
TURNER, Terry Lee. 100 PECAN LN 78657 #028-34-1971 L1982 **EM IM** *020

COTULLA – LA SALLE

HOOD, Richard H, Jr. 207 TILDEN 78014 #020-02-1949 L1964 **FM** *020 †85,90
KHAN, Muhammad Bashir. 304 N MAIN ST, KHAN MEDICAL CLINIC 78014 #704-09-1989 L2001 **IM** *020 †20

CRANDALL – KAUFMAN

BYINGTON, Meredith A. 1317 E US HIGHWAY 175 #800, KALEIDOSCOPE KIDS 75114 #048-12-2002 L2005 **PD** *020

CRANE – CRANE

HERNANDEZ, Ernesto. 79731 #048-02-2008 *012
MAYNARD, Billy Joe. 79731 #004-01-1947 L1948 **GP** *071
SOTELO, Sixta C. 103 S GASTON ST 79731 #748-16-1986 L1997 **IM** *020 †20

CRAWFORD – MCLENNAN

SCHMIDT, Terri Davis. ■ 76638 #048-16-1990 L1991 **PTH** *020 †50

CRESSON – HOOD

ANAYA, Samuel, Jr. ■ 76035 #048-12-2003 L2006 **OBG** *100
NILES, Ileana R. ■ 76035 #011-02-1996 L1998 **DR** *071 †80

CROCKETT – HOUSTON

ALIKHAN, Mir Zulfiquar. 1100 E LOOP 304 75835 #495-21-1990 L1999 **DR NM** *020 †28,80
BURNETT, John Allan. 1100 E LOOP 304, EAST TEXAS MEDICAL CENTER 75835 #065-05-1975 L1977 **EM GP** *020
CAMPBELL, James M. 1100 E LOOP 304 75835 #048-13-1983 L1983 **DR** *020 †80
CLOSE, Kenneth R. 1100 E LOOP 304 75835 #048-02-1999 L2002 **VIR** *020 †80
COCHRAN, James Michael. 1050 E LOOP 304, STE 200 75835 #021-06-1987 L1988 **FM** *020 †18

CURRAN, Kevin Alan. 951 E LOOP 304 STE 100 75835 #048-12-1985 L1986 **NEP IM** *020 †20
EIKENHORST, Ronald Ray. 1100 E LOOP 304 75835 #048-04-1976 L1977 **DR** *020 †80
HAECKLER, Christopher R. 1122 E LOOP 304, CROCKETT CLINIC 75835 #030-06-1978 L1980 **FM IMG** *020 †18
KASH, Frederick Farzad. 1100 E LOOP 304 75835 #028-03-1990 L1996 **RNR** *020 †80
KELLY, Daniel Patrick. ■ 75835 #048-14-2008 *012
KELLY, Richard Joseph. 1122 E LOOP 304, CROCKETT CLINIC 75835 #048-14-1979 L1979 **FM FPG** *020 †18
MURRAY, Carl Otis, Jr. 1018 E LOOP 304, EASTGATE SHOPPING CENTER 75835 #021-01-1948 L1949 **FM FPG** *071 †18
NAM, Jerry II. 1100 E LOOP 304 75835 #048-04-1993 L1994 **RNR R** *020 †80
PATEL, Pulin Piyush. 1100 E LOOP 304 75835 #038-43-1999 L2006 **IM** *020 †80
RAMSEY, Everett Perry, III. 1050 E LOOP 304, STE 200 75835 #048-12-1975 L1975 **FM FPG** *020 †18
RUST, Ronald Melvin. 1100 E LOOP 304 75835 #048-02-1976 L1976 **DR NR** *020 †80
SMITH, Frank Albert, III. 1122 E LOOP 304, CROCKETT CLINIC 75835 #012-05-1969 L1971 **FM** *020 †18
THOMASON, Charles Benton. 1100 E LOOP 304 75835 #039-01-1972 L1986 **DR FM** *020 †80,18
TINDALL, B Shane. 1100 E LOOP 304 75835 #048-16-1996 L1997 **DR VIR** *020 †80
WALKER, John Patrick. 1050 E LOOP 304, STE 110 75835 #048-02-1981 L1981 **GS** *020 †85

CROSBY – HARRIS

DAUGHERTY, Brian Russell. 20959 FLAMING ARROW TRL 77532 #048-15-1995 L1997 **FM** *020
HENDERSON, Judson S, III. 14700 FM 2100 RD, # A 77532 #048-02-1970 L1973 **FM** *020 †18 ‡
MC CASLIN, Charles Wm. ■ 77532 #038-40-1962 L1970 **IM** *071

CROSBYTON – CROSBY

AGUAS, Enrico G. 710 W MAIN ST 79322 #748-08-1988 L1992 **IM** *020 †20
ALLEY, Steve Bryan. 710 W MAIN ST 79322 #048-12-1979 L1979 **FM** *020 †18

CROSS PLAINS – CALLAHAN

HOSKINS, Godfrey Curtis. ■ 76443 #048-12-1960 L1960 **PTH** *062 †50
WILLIAMS, J O. ■ 76443 #048-12-1955 L1955 **GYN END** *071 †30

CROSSROADS – DENTON

AUVENSHINE, Michael Scott. 3201 US HIGHWAY 380, STE 101 76227 #048-12-2002 L2004 **FM** *020 †18
BAKER, Jeremy Scott. 3201 US HIGHWAY 380, STE 101 76227 #011-03-2002 L2007 **PD** *100

CROWLEY – TARRANT

ACOSTA, Melchor Jesus B. ■ 76036 #748-01-1984 L2003 **IMG** *020
SAADE, Walid Habib. ■ 76036 #048-02-2003 L2006 **FM** *020 †18
SUESS, James Francis. ■ 76036 #016-06-1952 L1953 **P** *071 †75

CRYSTAL BEACH – GALVESTON

NICOTRA, Mary B K. PO BOX 2467 77650 #011-03-1968 L1973 **PUD IM** *020 †20
WEAVER, Patricia Ruth. ■ 77650 #048-02-1971 L1971 **PTH** *071 †50

CRYSTAL CITY – ZAVALA

ENRIQUEZ, Gerardo Pugal. 523 W ZAVALA ST, THE CHILDRENS CLINIC OF DI 78839 #748-01-1992 L2004 **PD** *020 †55
GONZALEZ, Salvador. 308 S CESAR CHAVEZ AVE 78839 #005-15-1963 L1976 **FM** *020
MARTIN, Gregorio Manuel. 308 S CESAR CHAVEZ AVE, VIDAY SALUD HLTH SYS INC 78839 #275-01-1953 L1977 **FM AN** *071
MORENO P, Eduardo. ■ 78839 #451-01-1967 L1975 **IM** *020
RIVERA, Antonio H. 308 S 3RD AVE 78839 #048-13-1981 L1981 **GP** *020

CUERO – DE WITT

DAVIS, John Crispen. 2550 N ESPLANADE ST 77954 #048-02-1954 L1954 **GP** *071
HEARD, Mark Alan. 2500 N ESPLANADE ST # 102 77954 #048-15-1982 L1983 **FM FPG** *020 †18
HERBST, Walter Egon. 2550 N ESPLANADE ST 77954 #048-02-1963 L1963 **R** *071 †80
HIGH, Harold Rutledge. 2500 N ESPLANADE ST, CUERO MEDICAL CLINIC-R H C 77954 #048-02-1954 L1954 **FM** *072 †18
KING, David Leroy. 1109 E BROADWAY ST 77954 #039-01-1996 L2002 **FM** *020 †18
MC LEOD, Michael R. 1109 E BROADWAY ST 77954 #048-12-1996 L1999 **FM OBS** *020 †18 ‡
REESE, Raymond Randolph. 2500 N ESPLANADE ST, STE 101 77954 #048-02-1961 L1961 **FM** *020
RENGER, Harvey, Jr. 2500 N ESPLANADE ST, STE 101 77954 #048-02-1972 L1972 **FM** *071 †18 ‡

CYPRESS – HARRIS

ABBAS, Rashida S. 17330 SPRING CYPRESS RD, STE 150 77429 #704-02-1979 L2005 **PD** *020 †55
AHMAD, Aftab Syed. ■ 77433 #704-16-1984 L2007 **FM** *020
ARTHUR, Allison Marie. 13203 FRY RD, STE 600 77433 #048-02-2002 L2005 **PD** *020 †55

BALAY, Kimberly Sierra. ■ 77429 #048-04-2004 **NPM** *012

BEHAR, Robert Alexander. 21216 NORTHWEST FWY, STE 640 77429 #016-02-1987 L1994 **RO IM** *020 †80

BROWN, David Mark. 21216 NORTHWEST FWY, STE 630 77429 #048-04-1987 L1989 **OPH** *020 †35

BUAL, Nirmal S. 21216 NORTHWEST FWY, STE 650 77429 #495-29-1970 L1983 **CD IM** *020

CHANDRAKAR, Veena. 21216 NORTHWEST FWY, NORTHWEST CANCER CENTER 77429 #422-01-1998 L2003 **ON** *020 †20

CROW, Mary Kurtz. 21216 NORTHWEST FWY, NORTHWEST CANCER CENTER 77429 #048-04-1989 L1990 **ON HEM** *020 †20

DANG, Joseph Minhvuhuy. 21216 NORTHWEST FWY, NORTHWEST CANCER CENTER 77429 #048-04-2000 L2002 **ON** *100 †20

DINH, Trung Dinh. 15201 MASON RD STE 1200 77433 #025-12-1998 L2001 **FM** *020 †18

ENGLUND, Kelly Marie. ■ 77433 #047-06-2001 L2007 **IM** *020 ‡

ESANTSI, Michael. 15114 WINDSDOWNE LN 77429 #412-01-1987 L1996 **IM** *020 †20

FISH, Richard Harris. 21216 NORTHWEST FWY, STE 630 77429 #048-04-1985 L1986 **OPH** *020 †35

FLEETWOOD, Wallace W. ■ 77429 #012-01-1953 L1955 **P** *071 †75

FOSTER, Ami C. 8190 BARKER CYPRESS RD, STE 1500 77433 #048-14-2000 L2002 **FM** *020 †18

GRESSOT, Laurent. 21216 NORTHWEST FWY, NORTHWEST CANCER CENTER 77429 #869-04-1985 L1989 **HO** *020 †20

HENDERSON, Kasey Joanne. ■ 77429 #048-14-2006 L2006 **PD** *012

HIMEL, Bernard. 21216 NORTHWEST FWY # 260 77429 #065-01-1970 L1979 **FM GP** *020

HOEFER, Heidi Fullerton. ■ 77433 #048-02-1999 L2002 **AN** *100 †05

JIMENEZ-BELINOSKI, Anita. 13215 GRANT RD, STE 100 77429 #048-04-1993 L1994 **PD** *020 †55

KELLER, Kim Dorian. 21216 NORTHWEST FWY, STE 210 77429 #004-01-1983 L1989 **GS** *020 †85

KHAN, Tahseen. 21216 NORTHWEST FWY, STE 430 77429 #704-16-1985 L1994 **PD** *020 †55

KIM, Rosa Yoomee. 21216 NORTHWEST FWY, STE 630 77429 #005-11-1993 L2000 **OPH** *020 †35

KIRKMAN, Kerry Anne. 21216 NORTHWEST FWY, STE 520 77429 #048-02-1999 L2003 **OBG** *020 †30

KLEINBAUM, Eric Paul. 21216 NORTHWEST FWY, NORTHWEST CANCER CENTER 77429 #041-02-2000 L2003 **IM** *020 †20

KNAPICK, Michael Frank. 21216 NORTHWEST FWY, STE 430 77429 #048-02-1979 L1979 **PD** *020 †55

KUMAR, Arun. 12101 GRANT RD, STE G 77429 #495-24-1993 L2006 **FM** *020 †18

KWAK, Jennifer Soohyun. 15040 FAIRFIELD VLG SQR DR, STE 150 77433 #048-13-2000 L2002 **FM** *020 †18

LEE, Jimmy W C. 21216 NORTHWEST FWY, STE 310 77429 #048-13-1978 L1978 **OTO** *020 †45

LIU, Lin-Lin. 21216 NORTHWEST FWY, NORTHWEST CANCER CENTER 77429 #048-04-1987 L1989 **IM** *020 †20

MAYER, Marilyn Barbara. 21216 NORTHWEST FWY, STE 560 77429 #048-14-1990 L1992 **IM** *020 †20

MAZHAR, Mobeen. 21216 NORTHWEST FWY, STE 550 77429 #025-07-1993 L2000 **IC CD** *020 †20

MC CARTNEY, Gene W. ■ 77429 #012-05-1950 L1955 **IM** *071

MC CLINTOCK, Michael Ray. 21216 NORTHWEST FWY, STE 430 77429 #034-01-1989 L2000 **PD** *020 †55

MERBACK, Wayne Joseph. ■ 77429 #049-01-2005 L2007 **PD** *012

MITRA, Mitali C. 14707 DAUBERN CT 77429 #690-04-1987 L1998 **PD IM** *020 †55

MONIR, Ziauddin. ■ 77433 #704-16-1987 **PM** *100

MORGAN, Warren Edward. 21216 NORTHWEST FWY # 310 77429 #012-01-1988 L1989 **OTO PDO** *020 †45

MUZUMDAR, Kamini S. 21216 NORTHWEST FWY, STE 430 77429 #495-23-1989 L1995 **PD ADL** *020 †55

NGO, Hoan Ngoc. 13203 FRY RD, STE 800 77433 #654-01-2000 L2005 **IM** *020

OGUNRO, Christopher O. 25801 HIGHWAY 290, EXCEL IMMEDIATED MED CARE 77429 #690-01-1991 L2000 **IM UCM** *020

PATEL, Sunjeev Madhu. 13215 GRANT RD, STE 100 77429 #028-34-1999 L2002 **PD** *020 †55

QUINN, John Milton. ■ 77429 #035-01-1993 L1995 **IM** *020 †20

RAMIREZ, Karina. 25801 HIGHWAY 290 77429 #024-05-2003 L2007 **MPD** *020

RAMSEY, Karla Swenson. 21216 NORTHWEST FWY, STE 570 77429 #048-14-1984 L1985 **PD** *020 †55

ROFF, John H, III. 21216 NORTHWEST FWY, STE 530 77429 #048-04-1984 L1985 **PS** *020 †65

ROSENBALM, Thomas Joe. ■ 77429 #048-04-1955 L1955 **GP** *071

SHESHADRI, Bhaguan. ■ 77433 #495-15-1961 L1972 **U EM** *071 †95

SHESHADRI, Rashmi M. ■ 77433 #016-42-2002 L2007 **FM** *100 †18

SINGH, Rupinder. ■ 77429 #038-06-1997 L2007 **IM** *020 †20

SONTAG, Kurt Warren. ■ 77429 #036-07-1971 L1972 **PTH** *020 †50

SPRINGER, Paula Lynn. 17333 SPRING CYPRESS RD #F 77429 #048-02-1982 L1983 **FM** *020

STATON, Jonathan Bond. 13611 SKINNER RD, STE 240 77429 #010-02-1997 L2002 **OTO** *020 †45

TAWA, Cyril B. 21216 NORTHWEST FWY, STE 420 77429 #605-01-1987 L1991 **IM CD** *020 †20

TAYLOR, Charnette Page. 13215 GRANT RD, STE 100 77429 #048-14-2000 L2003 **PD** *020 †55

TAYLOR, Ronald Jos. 21216 NORTHWEST FWY, STE 560 77429 #048-14-1985 L1986 **IM** *020 †20

THOMPSON, Latricia M. ■ 77429 #048-14-2005 **OBG** *012

TOSCANO CASIMIR, Mirtha G. 21216 NORTHWEST FWY, NORTHWEST CANCER CENTER 77429 #132-02-1973 L1979 **ON OS** *020 †20

TROTTER, Jennifer R. 21216 NORTHWEST FWY, STE 430 77429 #048-15-1998 L2001 **PD** *020 †55

VO, Tommy C. 9740 BARKER CYPRESS, STE 116 77433 #048-16-1998 L1999 **FM** *020

VU, Duc P. ■ 77429 #048-14-2003 L2006 **FM** *020

WAGGONER, Bradley S. 21216 NORTHWEST FWY, STE 540 77429 #048-15-1999 L2004 **GS** *020

WELLS, Paul H. ■ 77429 #048-02-1985 L2007 **IM** *020 †20 ‡

WILKINSON, David Carroll. ■ 77429 #048-12-1976 L1976 **IM EM** *020 †20

WINER, Audrey May. 21216 NORTHWEST FWY, STE 430 77429 #011-03-1983 L1989 **PD ADL** *020 †55

WORRALL, Thomas Patrick. 13215 GRANT RD, STE 100 77429 #007-02-2003 L2006 **PD** *020 †55

YEN, Charles L. 21216 NORTHWEST FWY, NORTHWEST CANCER CENTER 77429 #048-02-1992 L1994 **HO** *020 †20

DAINGERFIELD — MORRIS

MITCHELL, Roderick Lee. 303 WEBB ST 75638 #048-15-1981 L1981 **IM EM** *020 †20

DALHART — DALLAM

BASSE, David R. 11950 FM 998, DALHART UNIT 79022 #048-02-1995 L1999 **IM** *020

ESPINEL, Jose Enrique. 320 E TEXAS BLVD 79022 #319-04-1997 L2005 **GS** *020 †85

HERRING, Randy Dwayne. 204 E 16TH ST STE B 79022 #048-13-1994 L1995 **FM** *020 †18 ‡

TURNER, Mathew S. 204 E 16TH ST, 204 E 16TH SUITE A 79022 #048-02-1990 L1993 **FM** *020 †18

VERMEDAHL, Nathan Arthur. 206 E 16TH ST 79022 #048-13-2003 L2006 **FM** *020 †18

DALLAS — COLLIN

AFSHAR, Sam. ■ 75287 #048-13-2006 **IM** *012

ALAIDROOS, Hania. 17610 PRESTON RD 75252 #704-02-1990 L2004 **FM** *020 †18 ‡

BABIAK, Michael John. ■ 75287 #060-02-1979 L2004 **AN IM** *020 †05

BASKIND, Roy Douglas. ■ 75252 #048-12-2001 *100

BASSICHIS, Benjamin A. ■ 75287 #048-14-1996 L1997 **FPS** *020 ‡

BEAUCHAMP, Cynthia Lais. ■ 75252 #016-06-2002 L2005 **OPH** *100

BERGMAN, Karin Kay. 4222 TRINITY MILLS RD, STE 110 75287 #018-03-1999 L2002 **FM** *020 †18

BISHOP, Robert Ten Eyck. ■ 75287 #035-01-1955 L1959 **OS FM** *071

BLACK, William Howard. 5216 SCARBOROUGH LN 75287 #028-02-1982 L1988 **ICE CD** *071 †20

BOWMAN, Erin M. ■ 75287 #048-12-2005 **DR** *012

BRENNER, Adam Marshall. ■ 75252 #024-01-1990 L2006 **P** *020 †75

BRYAN, John Manly. ■ 75252 #048-02-1954 L1954 **OS FM** *071 †18

BUCKLEAIR, Linda W. ■ 75252 #048-04-1998 L2000 **PTH** *020 †50

BURGOS, Denise M. ■ 75287 #048-04-1997 L1998 **EM** *020 †16

BUTLER, Gordon Marion, III. ■ 75287 #016-06-2007 **DR** *012

BUTLER, Lewell C, Jr. ■ 75287 #021-05-1946 L1949 **PS OS** *071 †65

CALENOFF, Emanuel. ■ 75252 #038-40-1974 L1974 **A OTO** *050 †45

CAUDILL, William H. ■ 75287 #048-12-1993 L1995 **EM** *020 †16

CHAN, Stephen M. ■ 75287 #048-12-2005 *100

CHU, Tzong-Shinn. ■ 75287 #244-02-1982 **NEP** *100

COLE, Andrew Travis. ■ 75287 #067-01-1966 L1986 **OM** *020 †95,70

COOLEY, Steven Wayne. 17950 PRESTON RD, STE 200 75252 #021-05-1977 L1988 **EM** *030 †16

CUDJOE, Stephanie Dove. ■ 75287 #048-12-2005 **FP** *012

DOAN, Ellis Ducdat. ■ 75287 #048-02-2008 *012

DROEMER, Lee Reinhold. ■ 75287 #048-02-2006 **PD** *012

EVANS, Rachael C. ■ 75252 #018-75-2007, ▲ **FP** *012

GANNAVARAPU, Bhargava Nar. ■ 75287 #016-42-2008 *012

GOACHER, Paula J. ■ 75252 #917-10-1987 L1997 **IM** *020 †20

GRIMM, Clark Alden. ■ 75252 #028-02-1957 L1957 **R NM** *020 †80

GROSSLING, Sergio F. ■ 75287 #231-01-1954 L1975 **GS FM** *072 ‡

HATE, Meghana Nitin. ■ 75287 #011-02-2003 L2005 **PG** *012

HORNSBY-LEWIS, Lynn. ■ 75252 #001-02-1983 L1984 **GE IM** *050 †20

HUEY YOU, Geraldine S. 17430 CAMPBELL RD 75252 #048-14-1989 L1990 **P** *020 †75

ISAACSON, Brandon. ■ 75287 #012-01-1999 L2004 **OTO** *020 †45

JACOBSON, Harold Neil. 17440 DALLAS PKWY, STE 208 75287 #064-01-1976 L1984 **CHP** *020 †75

JAMES, Leighton Rolston. ■ 75287 #065-01-1994 L2006 **NEP** *020 †20

JAMES-WILLOBY, Jerry E. 18715 GREENSIDE DR 75252 #039-01-1990 L1991 **EM** *020

KARUNANAYAKE, Mala Ranjan. ■ 75252 #220-02-1992 L2007 **PTH** *012

KHATRI, Sameer Dawood. ■ 75252 #023-12-2002 **FM** *020 †18

KOVARIC, Kelly Lynn. ■ 75287 #048-12-2007 **PD** *012

KRAMEN, Martin Alan. 4222 TRINITY MILLS RD #110 75287 #048-13-1983 L1983 **FM EM** *020 †18

LAW-YONE, Byron. 18170 DALLAS PKWY, STE 502 75287 #209-01-1966 L1989 **P ADP** *020 †75

LE, Toan Huu. ■ 75252 #048-12-2004 L2007 **FM** *020

LI, Jingbo. ■ 75252 #243-47-1984 L2000 **AN** *020

LO, Joseph Juchieh. 17430 CAMPBELL RD 75252 #056-05-1984 L1990 **AN IM** *020 †05

MANGA, Pravin. ■ 75252 #836-01-1974 L1985 **CD IM** *020

MANZOURI, Souren. ■ 75252 #654-01-2000 L2001 **FM** *100

MARTINEZ, Benjamin Seth. ■ 75287 #048-12-2007 **AN** *012

MC CANN, Stefanie J. 18800 PRESTON RD STE 314, SUITE 314 75252 #048-12-1989 L1990 **FM** *020

MC LENDON, Kristi Ruth. 18419 TETTENHALL DR 75252 #039-01-1992 L1998 **EM** *020 †16

MIER, Carmen Enid. ■ 75287 #847-06-1980 L1992 **P CHP** *020

MITCHELL, Thos Alexander. 18352 DALLAS PKWY, STE 136558 75287 #028-03-1980 L1982 **N** *020 †75

MOTGI, Shashi Raj. ■ 75287 #495-35-1983 L1992 **CHP** *020 †75

MUKKAMALA, Aparna. 5119 AMBERGATE LN 75287 #048-37-1998 L2004 **MM** *020

NANDA, Anil. ■ 75252 #047-07-1999 L2004 **AI** *020 †20,03

NEWBY, Patricia Dean. ■ 75252 #054-04-2003 L2008 **OBG** *012

NORMAN, Mary Anepohl. 8000 FRANKFORD RD, DALLAS DIAGNOSTIC ASSOCIAT 75252 #005-02-1997 L2002 **IMG** *020 †20

PAREKH, Julie Sharad. ■ 75287 #048-13-2004 L2007 **IM** *100 †20

PATIL, Rajashri Iswaragow. ■ 75287 #495-37-1998 L2005 **IM** *100

PENG, Yan. ■ 75287 #243-47-1986 L2005 **PCP** *100 †50

POWELL, Christina Janine. ■ 75252 #048-15-2008 *012

PRYOR, Susan Lee. 5515 INVERRARY CT 75287 #056-06-1982 L1986 **CD** *020 †20

PULIVARTHI, Venkata R. ■ 75287 #495-50-1982 L1993 **IM** *020

RAFF, Susan A. ■ 75252 #048-02-2004 L2007 **PD** *100

RAMAKRISHNA, Sudha. ■ 75287 #495-33-1962 L1977 **FM** *020 †50

RAY, Eric Isaac. ■ 75287 #048-15-2006 L2008 **FM** *012

RAZZUK, Aziz Maruf. ■ 75287 #048-02-1992 L1993 **GS** *020

REGAN, Christopher Martin. 3355 TRINITY MILLS RD 75287 #048-02-1976 L1976 **FM** *020 †18

REIHSEN, Julie Lynn. 4222 TRINITY MILLS RD, STE 108 75287 #028-03-1989 L1994 **FM** *020 †18

RUBIN-REMER, Dana. 17300 PRESTON RD STE 160 75252 #025-07-1990 L1993 PD OS *040 †55

RUSSUM, William John. ■ 75287 #030-05-1953 L1953 PTH *071 †50

SADEH, Christopher. 18048 FIRECREST CT, ER PHYSICIAN 75252 #012-05-2001 L2004 FM *020

SCHOEN, Matthew Steven. 4222 TRINITY MILLS RD, STE 285 75287 #035-15-1983 L1996 OBG *020 †30

SCOTT, Wilbert Ewing. ■ 75252 #016-06-1941 L1946 IM *071 †20

SHALET, Malcolm Fredric. ■ 75287 #019-02-1959 L1959 IM HEM *071 †20

SHANKS, Mitra H. ■ 75287 #048-13-2003 L2006 IM *100

SIMPSON, Corey Brooke. ■ 75287 #048-12-2003 L2005 PD *020 †55

SONG, Lei. ■ 75252 #243-47-1984 P *100

STALKUP, Jennifer R. ■ 75252 #048-04-2002 L2005 D *020 †15

STEIN, Jaryd C. ■ 75287 #048-13-2006 L2008 DR *012

SUGERMAN, Susan Tucker. 17300 PRESTON RD STE 16 75252 #048-04-1989 L1991 PD PHP *020 †55

SUMER, Baran Devrim. ■ 75287 #038-06-2001 L2008 OTO HNS *020 †45

THOMAS, John Mauldin, Jr. 18352 DALLAS PKWY, STE 136-309 75287 #048-02-1975 L1975 ORS GS *020 †40

TODD, Christopher Scott. ■ 75287 #051-01-2000 L2007 CCP *012 †55

TRAN, Quoc-Hung. 17736 PRESTON RD STE 100 75252 #048-02-1991 L1995 CHP *020 †75

TRINH, Vu Thanh. ■ 75287 #305-01-2007 FP *012

TURBEVILLE, Ann R Cook. 2323 SILVERTHORNE DR, 5436 COLLINWOOD 75287 #048-02-1961 L1961 P IM *062 †75

VANJANI, Jaya. ■ 75252 #495-05-1986 L1997 IM *071 †20

VIDAL, Pedro. ■ 75287 #308-01-1955 L1968 AN *071

VRUSHAB, Basanti R. ■ 75287 #495-98-1997 L2007 IM *020 †20

WANG, Jim Jiemin. ■ 75287 #243-16-1984 *100

WEI, Peter Chih-Peng. 17300 PRESTON RD, STE 555 75252 #048-02-1989 L1990 IM EM *020

WHITE, Lillian R. 18800 PRESTON RD, STE 314 75252 #048-04-1995 L1997 IM *020 †20

WILLS, John Steven. 3355 TRINITY MILLS RD, STE 211 75287 #012-01-1979 L1984 IM *020 †20

YAO, Min. ■ 75287 #243-21-1984 L2008 RO *020 †80

YOGANANDAN, Prameela. 17305 PRESTON RD, STE 555 75252 #496-23-1993 L2005 FM *020 †18

DALLAS – DALLAS

AALUND, Gordon R. 2909 MCKINNEY AVE STE B, CITYDOC 75204 #048-13-1999 L2001 EM *020 †16

AARON, Houston Michael. ■ 75204 #021-06-2005 L2007 DR *012

ABATE, Nicola Iginio. 6011 HARRY HINES BLVD., U.T. SOUTHWESTERN MEDICAL 75390 #561-09-1985 L1998 IM *020 †20

ABATSO, George Wisdom. 14651 DALLAS PKWY, STE 700 75254 #016-42-1968 L1986 EM AS *020

ABBAS, Dennis Rahim. 6300 SAMUELL BLVD STE 154 75228 #065-06-1973 L1985 OBG *020 †30

ABBASOGLU, Ozlem. 3500 GASTON AVE 75246 #902-05-1990 OPH *100

ABBASSIGHANAVATI, Mina. 5323 HARRY HINES BLVD, SOUTHWESTERN MED 75390 #048-02-2003 L2004 OBG *100

ABBOTT, John Keith, III. 75228 #039-01-2006 GS *012

ABDELFATTAH, Kareem Reda. ■ 75219 #011-04-2007 GS *012

ABDULLA, Zainab. 8820 SOUTHWESTERN BLVD 75206 #496-35-2002 *100

ABDULLAH, Shuaib M. ■ 75204 #048-12-2001 L2005 CD *012

ABDURRAHIM, Shehetaj G. 3650 W WHEATLAND RD, STE C 75277 #495-66-1991 L2002 IM *020 †20 ‡

ABEL, Christopher D. 12200 PRESTON RD, COOPER CLINIC 75230 #048-13-1995 L1997 IM *020 †20

ABEL, Christopher Scott. 8350 N CENTRAL EXPY, STE M1025 75206 #048-12-1995 L1997 PD ADL *020 †55

ABEL, Philip Carol. 2921 FAIRMOUNT ST 75201 #048-02-1970 L1970 EM *020 †16

ABELE, Travis Austin. ■ 75219 #048-12-2007 DR *012

ABERNATHY, Stacy D. 5001 SPRING VALLEY RD, STE 400 75244 #048-13-2002 L2006 AN *020

ABO KAYASS, Ahmad. 5323 HARRY HINES BLVD, SOUTHWESTERN MED 75390 #875-01-1994 SME *012

ABOUBAKER, Kaiss. 75230 #042-03-2004 IM *020 †20

ABOUSSIE, Mitchell A, Jr. 40 DOWNS LAKE CIR 75230 #048-02-1965 L1965 R *020 †80

ABRAHAM, Ayodele Adebola. 5323 HARRY HINES BLVD, SOUTHWESTERN MED 75390 #690-01-1987 CHP *012

ABRAMOVITS, William. 5310 HARVEST HILL RD, STE 160 75230 #935-01-1972 L1989 D IM *020 †15 ‡

ABRAMS, Raymond Henry. 7 MEDICAL PKWY 75234 #016-11-1941 L1948 GYN *071 †30

ABRAMSON, Aubry. 8220 WALNUT HILL LN # 416 75231 #836-02-1963 L1978 OPH *020

ABRAMSON, David Charles. 8200 WALNUT HILL LN 75231 #836-02-1983 L1996 AN *020 †05

ABRAMSON, Edra Simone. 8220 WALNUT HILL LN, STE 416 75231 #048-04-1992 L1993 OPH *020 †35

ABU ZAROUR, Randa H. 1935 MOTOR ST 75235 #575-01-1983 *020

ACHARYA, Veena Kalmanje. 75214 #001-02-2006 IM *012

ACKERMAN, David Stephen. 13601 PRESTON RD, # 900-WEST 75240 #048-02-1981 L1981 AN *020 †05

ACKERMAN, Gary Edwin. 5909 HARRY HINES BLVD 75235 #035-08-1972 L1978 END OBG *020 †30

ADAMS, Cedric Cordell. 3600 GASTON AVE STE 858 75246 #048-04-1986 L1987 OPH IM *020 †35

ADAMS, Richard Caldwell. 2222 WELBORN ST, PEDIATRICS/DEV DISABILITIE 75219 #021-06-1977 L1992 PD *020 †18

ADAMS, Richard Martin, Jr. 3700 ROSS AVE 75204 #021-05-1966 L1969 PD *071 †55

ADAMS, Thomas, Jr. 5001 SPRING VALLEY RD, NCAC ANESTHIA CONSULTANTS 75244 #048-02-1983 L1983 AN EM *020 †05

ADAMS, Tracey Rae. 5303 VICKERY BLVD 75206 #010-02-1991 L1995 PM *020 †60

ADAMS, William Peter, Jr. 5323 HARRY HINES BLVD, DEPARTMENT OF PLASTIC SURG 75390 #047-05-1991 L1994 PS *020 †65

ADCOCK, William Robert. 13605 PRESTON RD, STE 900W 75240 #039-01-1999 L2003 AN *020 †05

ADDISON, James Henry. 8400 DOUGLAS AVE 75225 #649-33-1974 GS *071

ADDO, Tayo A. 5323 HARRY HINES BLVD 75390 #048-12-1997 L1998 IC CD *020 †20

ADESANYA, Adebola O. 5223 HARRY HINES BLVD 75390 #690-02-1988 L1996 CCA *020 †05,20

ADHIKARI, Soumya. SOUTHWESTERN MED, UNIV OF TEXAS 75390 #011-02-2001 L2004 PDE *100 †55

ADINOFF, Bryon Harlen. 4500 S LANCASTER RD, VA MEDICAL CENTER 75216 #025-12-1979 L1996 P *030 †75

ADKINS, Carl Eugene. 5323 HARRY HINES BLVD, STOP 9031 75390 #021-06-1986 L1990 AN *020 †05

ADLER, Max Frank. 8226 DOUGLAS AVE, STE 540 75225 #048-13-1976 L1976 D PD *020 †55,15

ADMIRE, Jane Farrar. 7777 FOREST LN, STE C100 75230 #048-12-1979 L1979 OTO *020 †45

ADORABLE, Benedicto C. 14616 BROOKWOOD LN 75230 #748-01-1960 L1978 AN *071

AFFOLTER, Jeremy Todd. ■ 75219 #019-02-2002 L2007 CCP *012 †20,55

AFOLABI, Folashade D. ■ 75235 #048-12-2008 *012

AFRIDI, Imran. 221 W COLORADO BLVD STE 8, NORTH TEXAS CARDIOVASCULAR 75208 #704-02-1988 L1992 IM CD *020 †20

AFTAB, Lala F. 5323 HARRY HINES BLVD, SOUTHWESTERN MED 75390 #704-01-1975 L1992 HMP *012 †50

AFTERGUT, Kent Stuart. 3450 W WHEATLAND RD, STE 225 75237 #048-12-1999 L2001 D *020 †15

AGADI, Satish. SOUTHWESTERN MED, UNIV OF TEXAS 75390 #495-35-1997 CHN *012

AGANA, Benjamin T, Jr. 8210 WALNUT HILL LN # 805 75231 #016-01-1991 L1993 PM *020 †60

AGATSTON, Stephen Andrew. 3206 SAINT JOHNS DR 75205 #048-13-1985 L1986 DR *020 †80

AGGARWAL, Paul Anil. 3600 GASTON AVE, WADLEY TOWER, STE 851 75246 #063-01-1996 L2005 CD *020 †20

AGGARWAL, Raymon Kumar. 3434 SWISS AVE, STE 320 75204 #048-12-1996 L1997 IM *020 †20

AGIM, Nnenna Gebechi. ■ 75230 #048-12-2005 L2008 D *012

AGOSTINI, Mark Andrew. 5323 HARRY HINES BLVD 75390 #024-01-1989 L1998 N IM *020 †75

AGRAWAL, Anuradha. 3310 LIVE OAK ST STE 201 75204 #913-13-1998 L2003 PD *020 †55

AGRAWAL, Manju Lata. 5201 HARRY HINES BLVD, PARKLAND HEALTH & HOSP SYS 75235 #495-47-1970 L1974 PD *020 †55

AGUILAR, Silvestre F. 1 MEDICAL PKWY STE 209 75234 #847-01-1969 L1974 PD *020 †55

AGUILAR KITSU, Maria A. ■ 75219 #649-01-1990 PN *040

AGURA, Edward Dimiter. 7777 FOREST LN, STE D220 75230 #035-19-1982 L1994 ON IM *020 †20

AGYARKO, Afua Serwaa. ■ 75201 #048-12-2005 IM *012

AHAD, Grace. 1935 MOTOR ST, GRADUATE MEDICAL EDUCATION 75235 #048-14-2003 L2005 PD *020

AHLUWALIA, Jasbir Singh. 6546 LBJ FWY, STE 200 75240 #495-23-1967 L1979 OBG GP *020

AHMAD, Abrar. 3600 GASTON AVE STE 550, TEXAS PRIMARY CARE 75246 #496-04-1994 L2004 IM *020 †20

AHMAD, Jamil. 5323 HARRY HINES BLVD, UNIV OF TX SOUTHWESTERN ME 75390 #539-06-2005 PS *012

AHMAD, Junaid. 3920 WORTH ST 75246 #039-01-2001 L2005 AN *020 †05

AHMAD, Omar Nazir. ■ 75219 #016-45-2002 L2007 RNR *012 †80

AHMAD, Rizwan Saeed. ■ 75206 #919-05-1998 L2007 CRS *012 †85

AHMAD, Zahid Salman. 5323 HARRY HINES BLVD, SOUTHWESTERN MED 75390 #021-01-2004 L2007 END *012

AHMED, Syed. 4500 S LANCASTER RD, DALLAS VA MED CTR APMS112A 75216 #704-02-1991 L1998 AN CCA *020 †05

AHN, Chai Ho. ■ 75225 #583-01-1947 L1964 PUD CD *020

AHN, Sam Seunghae. 221 W COLORADO BLVD, PAVILION 2, STE 625 75208 #048-12-1978 L1978 VS GS *020 †85

AILLON-PEREZ, Gonzalo A. 400 S ZANG BLVD, STE 802 75208 #264-02-1965 L1971 P *020 †75 ‡

AKBAR, Muhammad. 9202 ELAM RD, STE 350 75217 #704-01-1987 L2005 IM *020 †20

AKPAN, Jean Penrose. 7920 ELMBROOK DR STE 120, HOSPITAL SYSTEM 75247 #016-02-1977 L1984 IM *020 †20

ALAMGIR, Nusrat. 9202 ELAM RD STE 120, SEDHC 75217 #704-02-1983 L1993 PD *020 †55

ALATOOM, Adnan Abdulkarim. ■ 75235 #575-02-2000 PTH *012

ALBERT, Antoine Robt. 8702 SPRING VALLEY RD # B 75240 #067-03-1971 L1981 FM OBG *020

AL-BOZOM, Issam Adel. 75243 #575-01-1989 L1996 PTH *100 †50

ALBRACHT, David E, Jr. 6901 SNIDER PLZ STE 1 75205 #048-12-1991 L1993 IM *020 †20

ALBRITTON, Ford D, IV. 8440 WALNUT HILL LN, TEXAS MEDICAL & SURGICAL 75231 #048-16-1996 L2001 OTO HNS *020 †45

AL-CHALABI, Mustafa Tarik. 12221 MERIT DR STE 1 75251 #422-01-2001 L2005 EM *100 †16

ALDER, Adam Craig. SOUTHWESTERN MED, UNIV OF TEXAS 75390 #021-01-2002 L2005 GS *012

ALDERS, Richard Warren. 1441 N BECKLEY AVE 75203 #048-12-1961 L1961 GS *071 †85

ALDHAM, Abdallah N. 3946 S BUCKNER BLVD # 100 75227 #915-02-1971 L1978 IM *020

ALEXANDER, Cora Leisa. 2959 S BUCKNER BLVD, STE 700 75227 #048-12-1985 L1986 GP OS *020

ALEXANDER, Drew Wilson. 12800 HILLCREST RD STE 216 75230 #038-43-1973 L1977 ADL PD *020

ALEXANDER, Gail Susan. 1935 MOTOR ST 75235 #035-19-1966 L1992 P CHP *020 †75

ALEXANDER, James M, Jr. 5323 HARRY HINES BLVD, STOP 9031 75390 #048-14-1991 L1995 OBG *020 †30

ALEXANDER, John C. ■ 75235 #048-12-2005 L2007 AN *012

ALEXANDER, John H. 8 MEDICAL PKWY, STE 310 75234 #118-02-1977 L1982 GS ON *020 †85

ALEXANDER, Stuart Kalman. 2815 S HAMPTON RD 75224 #035-46-1970 L1985 GP EM *020

ALEXANDROVA, Daria I. 3701 W NORTHWEST HWY, PHYSICIANS FOR CHILDREN 75220 #198-01-1982 L1998 PD *020 †55

ALFORD, Lorien K. ■ 75209 #048-12-2003 PPR *012 †55

ALHAJERI, Abdulnasser Ahm. ■ 75235 #155-01-1999 RNR *012

ALI, Ashraf. 2600 LONE STAR DR, UTMB MEDICAL 75212 #160-05-1974 L1998 P CHP *020 †75

ALI, Beshir Osman Ahmed. 9229 LBJ FWY, MEDICALEDGE HEALTHCARE GRO 75243 #848-01-1991 L2007 IM *020 †20

ALI, Deeba Nohi. ■ 75219 #048-12-2006 IM *012

ALI, Zahra Karam. ■ 75390 #048-12-2008 *012

ALIBHAI, Hussamuddin H. 3450 W WHEATLAND RD, STE 110 75237 #905-01-1971 L1982 OBG *020 †30

ALI HOSSEINI, Hassan. 12221 MERIT DR, STE 460 75251 #409-38-1992 L1998 IM *020 †20

ALISHARAN, Robert Myboo. 1935 MOTOR ST, CHILDRENS MEDICAL CENTER 75235 #010-03-1999 L2006 CCP *100 †55

ALIVIZATOS, Peter A. 3600 GASTON AVE STE 404 75246 #418-01-1962 L1985 GS TS *020 †85,90

ALIZADEH NADERI, Amir Sai. 5323 HARRY HINES BLVD, DEPT OF INT MED 75390 #409-21-2001 **IM** *012

ALKALAY, Avishai Albert. 5323 HARRY HINES BLVD, SOUTHWESTERN MED 75390 #550-02-2003 L2007 **OBG** *100

ALKALAY, Michele J. 5323 HARRY HINES BLVD, SOUTHWESTERN MED 75390 #550-02-2003 **PG** *012 †55

ALKAWADRI, Mhd Rafeed. ■ 75235 #875-01-2005 **N** *012

ALKEK, David Saml. 7150 GREENVILLE AVE, STE 100 75231 #048-12-1965 L1965 **D** *020 †15

ALLADA, Naveena. 5323 HARRY HINES BLVD, SOUTHWESTERN MED 75390 #495-11-2001 L2006 **HO** *012 †20

ALLAM, Anand Mohan. ■ 75235 #048-12-2008 *012

ALLDAY, Robert Louie. 7806 HANOVER ST 75225 #021-01-1962 L1968 **IM** *071 †20

ALLEGRA, Piergiorgio. 7777 FOREST LN STE C724 75230 #561-06-1983 L1994 **PS** *020 †85,65

ALLEN, David Michael. 7777 FOREST LN, STE B412 75230 #048-12-1983 L1983 **ID IM** *020 †20

ALLEN, Elaine Espey. 13601 PRESTON RD, STE 900 75240 #048-12-1989 L1990 **AN** *020 †05

ALLEN, Jason W. ■ 75205 #048-12-2004 **GS** *012

ALLEN, Kyle Pierce. ■ 75209 #021-01-2006 **OTO** *012

ALLEN, Lauren Aleta. 2222 WELBORN ST 75219 #068-01-2002 **OP** *012

ALLEN, Marcus Lamkin. ■ 75225 #048-12-2000 L2004 **OPH** *020 †35

ALLEN, Melvin A. ■ 75231 #016-11-1942 L1981 **GYN** *071 †30

ALLEN, Meredith Brooke. 5323 HARRY HINES BLVD, SOUTHWESTERN MED 75390 #048-15-2006 L2008 **OPH** *012

ALLEN, Michael Harry. 6023 WOODLAND DR 75225 #028-03-1972 L1977 **GE** *071 †20

ALLEN, Rhufus Ethan. 7777 FOREST LN, STE B434 75230 #048-12-1968 L1972 **OTO NO** *072 ‡

ALLEN, Ruth Isadora. 3448 ROSEDALE AVE, # 1 75205 #048-02-1941 L1941 **ADL** *071

ALLEN, Terry Devereux. 6300 HARRY HINES BLVD, STE 1401 75235 #048-04-1955 L1955 **U** *071 †95

ALLEN, Virginia Lou. 5323 HARRY HINES BLVD, UT SOUTHWESTERN MED SCH 75390 #048-02-2005 L2008 **P** *012

ALLETAG, Michelle A. ■ 75208 #048-12-2005 L2008 **PD** *012

ALLISON, Michael Gregory. 4131 N CENTRAL EXPY, METRO ANESTHESIA 75204 #038-40-1982 L1984 **AN** *020 †20

ALLISON, Robert Bryan. 4015 WORTH ST 75246 #048-12-1957 L1957 **IM CD** *071 †20

ALLISON, Robert Bryan, Jr. 3434 SWISS AVE, STE 430 75204 #048-15-2001 L2003 **IM** *020 †20

ALLISON, Scott Anthony. ■ 75204 #039-01-2001 L2007 **VIR** *100 †80

ALLRED, Anna Marie. ■ 75235 #048-13-2007 **GS** *012

AL-MAR'ASHI, Abdul-Husein. 9205 SKILLMAN ST STE 130, SKILLMAN MEDICAL CENTER 75243 #495-01-1960 L1976 **GS PS** *071

ALONSO, Emilio. ■ 75248 #847-08-1953 L1961 **GP** *071

ALRIFAI, Muhammad Talal. 1935 MOTOR ST, NEUROLOGY DEPARTMENT 75235 #875-01-1989 L1998 **CHN** *020 †75,55

AL-SAMMAK, Mohammed Saeed. ■ 75390 #155-01-1996 L2003 **BBK** *100 †50

ALTENAU, Mark M. 7777 FOREST LN STE B434 75230 #038-41-1966 L1972 **OTO NO** *020 †45

ALTMAN, William Alfred. ■ 75208 #024-01-1939 L1939 **OS GS** *071 †85

ALTRABULSI, Basel. 7777 FOREST LN, BLDG C 75230 #875-01-1996 L2004 **SP** *100 †50

ALTSHULER, Kenneth Z. 5323 HARRY HINES BLVD 75390 #035-06-1952 L1977 **P OS** *040 †75 ‡

ALVARES, Michael L. 5323 HARRY HINES BLVD, DEPT MED 75390 #048-14-2005 **IM** *012

ALVAREZ, Sergio Arturo. ■ 75219 #048-12-2005 *012

AMANZADEH, Jamshid. ■ 75201 #517-01-1991 L2003 **NEP** *020 †20

AMARASINGHAM, Ruben. 5123 HARRY HINES BLVD, SUPPORT BLDG B, ROOM G106 75235 #048-12-1999 L2001 **IM** *050 †20

AMARASINGHAM, Sarah N. 1935 MOTOR ST 75235 #048-12-2003 L2007 **PD** *020 †55

AMARE, Mammo. 1441 N BECKLEY AVE, STE 101 75203 #605-01-1961 L1993 **HEM IM** *020 †20

AMATRUDA, James Francis. 5323 HARRY HINES BLVD MC, UT SOUTHWESTERN MEDICAL CE 75390 #028-02-1993 L2005 **HO** *020 †20

AMEND, Amy Ann. 6808 MERRILEE LN 75214 #032-01-2003 L2006 **GS** *100

AMES, Mary Kathryn. 13601 PRESTON RD STE 1000 75240 #021-05-1982 L1985 **AN** *020 †05

AMIN, Neesha Parashar. ■ 75219 #011-03-2005 L2007 **P** *012

AMIRKHAN, John Nelson. 75209 #048-12-1977 L1977 **PTH** *020 †50

AMIRKHAN, Robin H. ■ 75209 #048-12-1991 L1992 **PTH** *020 †50

AMJAD, Mehreen. 3310 LIVE OAK ST, 3RD FL 75204 #704-01-2000 L2006 **FM** *020 †18

AMOS, Joseph Darryl. 221 W COLORADO BLVD, PAVILION 1, STE 318 75208 #012-21-1991 L2004 **OS** *020 †85

AMPIL, James Robert. 8200 WALNUT HILL LN 75231 #048-12-1995 L1996 **IM** *020 †20

AMSBAUGH, Sean Thomas. ■ 75206 #056-06-2001 L2005 **DMP D** *020 †15

AMUSAN, Adeola Anthony. 9202 ELAM RD 75217 #690-01-1989 L2001 **IM** *020 †20

AN, Jae-Koo. 6032 STEFANI DR 75225 #048-12-1996 L2003 **PD** *020 †55

ANAND, Rangasamy Krishnan. 1935 MOTOR ST, OF D 75235 #495-04-1997 L2008 **CCP** *012 †55

ANAND, Vivek. 1441 N BECKLEY AVE, SPECIAL CARE NURSERY 75203 #495-45-1991 L2006 **PD** *020 †55

ANANDAM, Joselin Leelavat. ■ 75219 #048-12-2004 **GS** *012

ANDERSEN, Anne E Kolb. 16800 DALLAS PKWY STE 150 75248 #041-01-1970 L1975 **P IM** *020 †75

ANDERSEN, John Milton. 1935 MOTOR ST 75235 #041-01-1970 L1975 **GE PD** *040 †55

ANDERSON, Allan Lynn. 7777 FOREST LN, STER A-341 75230 #048-04-1976 L1976 **CD IM** *020 †20

ANDERSON, Amy Stevens. 3434 SWISS AVE STE 320 75204 #048-02-1992 L1994 **IM** *020 †20

ANDERSON, Angela. 3500 GASTON AVE, 3RD FLOOR TRUETT 75246 #048-12-1998 L2000 **GE** *020 †20

ANDERSON, Howard Eugene, Jr. 221 W COLORADO BLVD, STE 640 PAVILLION II 75208 #048-14-1996 L1997 **IM** *020 †20

ANDERSON, John Flake. 621 N HALL ST, STE 520 75226 #048-04-1973 L1974 **TS GS** *020 †85

ANDERSON, John Frederick. ■ 75229 #048-12-1994 **GE** *020

ANDERSON, Martha Ann. 25 HIGHLAND PARK VLG # 100 75205 #048-12-1970 L1970 **AN** *020 †05

ANDERSON, Matthew A. 5201 HARRY HINES BLVD, PARKLAND HOSPITAL S 75235 #048-13-2004 L2007 **PCC** *012

ANDERSON, Matthew Eric. 5427 EMERSON AVE 75209 #048-12-1999 L2000 **VIR** *100 †80

ANDERSON, Paul Kenneth. 7777 FOREST LN, STE C340 75230 #021-01-1976 L1979 **GE** *020 †20

ANDERSON, Richard Scott. 8230 WALNUT HILL LN, STE 408 75231 #048-14-1982 L1983 **GS VS** *020 †85

ANDERSON, Robert D. ■ 75214 #048-02-2001 L2003 **GE** *020

ANDERSON, Ron Joe. 5201 HARRY HINES BLVD #039-01-1973 L1975 **IM PHM** *030 †20

ANDRADE, Nicholas Stephen. ■ 75205 #048-12-2008 *012

ANDRADE BANUELOS, Andrea. 5323 HARRY HINES BLVD 75390 #649-13-1998 **CHN** *012

ANDRESEN, Jeffry John. ■ 75223 #041-01-1964 L1991 **PYA P** *040 †75

ANDREWS, J Valerie. 5323 HARRY HINES BLVD 75390 #047-05-1986 L1996 **SO OS** *020 †85

ANDREWS, Thomas Chas. 3500 GASTON AVE 75246 #047-05-1986 L1996 **CD IM** *020 †20

ANDUJO, Oscar R. 4323 HARRY HINES BOULEVARD, SOUTHWESTERN MEDICAL CENTE 75390 #649-05-1970 L1981 **OBG NPM** *020

ANGARITA, Luis. ■ 75206 #935-07-1992 L2000 **CRS** *020 †85,10

ANGEL, Angela Marie. 8160 WALNUT HILL LN, STE 200 75231 #005-14-1994 L1996 **OBG** *020 †30

ANGLAS, Pablo H. 221 W COLORADO BLVD, PAY I, SUITE 212 75208 #737-01-1983 L2002 **PD** *020 †55

ANGUS, Ronald Granville. 8200 WALNUT HILL LN, DEPT. OF MEDICINE 75231 #021-06-1989 L1992 **IM** *020 †20

ANIGIAN, Gregg M. 8220 WALNUT HILL LN # 108 75231 #048-12-1984 L1990 **PS GS** *020 †85,65 ‡

ANIGIAN, Michael Jos. 8220 WALNUT HILL LN # 412 75231 #028-34-1958 L1964 **IM** *072

ANNASWAMY, Thiru Mandyam. 4500 S LANCASTER RD, DEPT OF PHYSICAL MED & REH 75216 #495-09-1993 L1999 **PM PMM** *020 †60

ANTHONY, Paul Brooks. 4500 S LANCASTER RD, ICU WING B 75216 #007-02-1978 L1980 **IM IMG** *020 †20

ANTHONY, Robert Ray. 8160 WALNUT HILL LN, STE 106 75231 #048-12-1978 L1978 **OBG EM** *020 †30

ANTHONY, Thomas. 5323 HARRY HINES BLVD, UT SOUTHWESTERN MED CTR 75390 #019-02-1988 L1995 **GS** *020 †85

ANTONETTI, Alfredo G. 1135 N BISHOP AVE 75208 #275-01-1943 L1965 **GS GP** *020

ANTONETTI, Alfredo R. 221 W COLORADO BLVD # 400 75208 #039-01-1971 L1973 **PS HS** *020 †85,65

ANTONETTI, John William. 7777 FOREST LN, BLDG C 75230 #048-02-2002 L2007 **PS** *100

ANTONETTI, Robert Stanley. 221 W COLORADO BLVD 75208 #048-02-2000 L2006 **GS** *100 †85

ANWAR, Azam. 621 N HALL ST, STE 500 75226 #028-46-1983 L1984 **CD IM** *020 †20

ANWAR, Nauman. 142 WEBBS ROYAL PLZ, WEBB ROYAL MEDICAL GROUP 75229 #704-08-1982 L1997 **IM** *020 †20

ANWAR, Temoor Sajjad. 3500 GASTON AVE, RADIOLOGY DEPT 75246 #048-02-2002 L2004 **VIR** *012 †80

APPLEWHITE, Andrew J. 5481 BLAIR RD, WOUND CARE CONSULTANTS 75231 #048-14-1996 L2002 **UM OS** *020 †18

AQUI, Ernest A. 5909 HARRY HINES BLVD 75235 #649-38-1989 L1994 **AN** *020 †05

AQUINO, Deborah Ballard. 5201 HARRY HINES BLVD 75235 #035-15-1989 L1997 **PTH** *020 †50

AQUINO, Victor M. 5323 HARRY HINES BLVD, UT SOUTHWESTERN MED CENTER 75390 #035-15-1989 L1996 **PHO PD** *020 †55

ARAGON, Patricia Lynn. ■ 75214 #422-01-1994 L2000 *020

ARAJ, Faris George. 5323 HARRY HINES BLVD, DEPT OF INT MED 75390 #605-01-2004 **IM** *012

ARANDA, Jennifer. 4111 COLE AVE # 311 75204 #012-05-1999 L2003 **D** *020 †15

ARAUZ-PACHECO, Carlos. 9323 GARLAND RD STE 112 75218 #270-01-1983 L1992 **END IM** *020 †20

ARAZOZA, Antonio Carlos. 810 N ZANG BLVD 75208 #048-14-1979 L1979 **ORS** *020 †40

ARBINI, Arnaldo Augusto. ■ 75219 #264-04-1984 L2006 **PTH** *020 †50

ARCHAVACHOTIKUL, Kwanchai. 3500 GASTON AVE, DEPARTMENT OF NEONATOLOGY 75246 #891-01-1991 L2002 **NPM** *020 †55

ARENAS, Juan D. ■ 75229 #264-18-1987 L2007 **GS** *020 †85

AREY, Mark Lindsey. 5323 HARRY HINES BLVD, UT SOUTHWESTERN MEDICAL CE 75390 #036-05-2002 L2006 **OPH** *100

ARGAO, Eric Arthur S. 7777 FOREST LN, STE B304 75230 #748-02-1983 L1999 **PD** *020 †55

ARIAS, Juan Wilfrido. 1330 N BECKLEY AVE, STE 103 75203 #649-01-1973 L1978 **OBG MFM** *020 †30

ARMBRUSTER, Steven C. 5323 HARRY HINES BLVD, U.T. SOUTHWESTERN MEDICAL 75390 #048-02-1993 L1994 **AN** *020 †05

ARMSTRONG, Henry R. 302 W 9TH ST STE C 75208 #048-12-1983 L1983 **IM** *020

ARMSTRONG, James Anthony. 4606 CEDAR SPRINGS RD 75219 #008-01-1990 L1994 **N** *020 †75

ARMSTRONG, Nancy Eileen S. ■ 75229 #048-12-1974 L1977 **IM** *071 †20

ARMSTRONG, William Mark. 3434 SWISS AVE STE 420 75204 #001-02-1972 L1974 **IM** *020 †20

ARNAUD, Angelique Marie. 3310 LIVE OAK ST, COPC RESOURCE TEAM PHHS 75204 #005-18-1987 L1995 **IM** *020 †20

ARNDT, Jerome Harrison. 3500 GASTON AVE, BAYLOR UNIV MED CTR 75246 #039-01-1958 L1960 **DR** *071 †80

ARNOLD, Cody Claude. 3500 GASTON AVE, NEONATOLOGY 3 HOBLITZELLE 75246 #039-01-1980 L1988 **NPM** *020 †55

ARNOLD, David Thomas. 3808 SWISS AVE 75204 #004-01-1996 L1998 **GS** *020 †85

ARNOLD, John C. 13601 PRESTON RD STE 1000 75240 #048-12-1991 L1992 **AN** *020 †05

ARNOLD, Larrie J Willis. ■ 75225 #048-12-1966 L1966 **PYA P** *020 †75

ARONOFF, Billie L. ■ 75209 #048-04-1938 L1938 **GS SO** *071 †85

ARONOFF, Ronald Jos. 7777 FOREST LN STE B111 75230 #048-12-1977 L1977 **GS OS** *020 †85

ARONOFF, Stephen Louis. 10260 N CENTRAL EXPY, STE 100N 75231 #048-12-1972 L1972 **END IM** *020 †20

ARONOWICZ GALLEGO, Joel D. 5323 HARRY HINES BLVD, SOUTHWESTERN MED 75390 #935-01-2000 L2006 **OPH** *012

ARONOWITZ, Ray F. 810 N ZANG BLVD 75208 #048-13-1993 L1998 **ORS** *020 †40

ARRAUT, Alfredo Luis, Jr. 75204 #011-03-2001 L2004 **DR** *020 †80

ARRIAGA, Yull E. 2201 INGWOOD ROAD, UT SW MEDICAL CENTER 75390 #737-06-1991 L2006 **HO** *020 †20

ARSLANLAR, Sami Naci. 4008 BUENA VISTA ST 75204 #048-12-1999 L2000 **GE** *020 †20

ARUMUGHAM, Akilan. 12700 PARK CENTRAL DR, STE 430 75251 #048-13-1996 L2003 **VIR R** *020 †80

ARVIND, Vijayasree. 8230 WALNUT HILL LN # 320 75231 #495-59-1992 L2000 **AN PMM** *020 †05

ARZAC-RIQUELME, Jorge A. 221 W COLORADO BLVD, PAVILION I, SUITE 330 75208 #649-28-1981 L1996 **OBG** *020 †30

ASAMOA, Nancy N Y. 1441 N BECKLEY AVE 75203 #412-01-1993 L2002 **IM** *020 †20

ASHBY, Richard Harlan. 8918 VISTA VIEW DR 75243 #048-02-1958 L1959 **NS** *071 †25

ASHFAQ, Raheela. 5323 HARRY HINES BLVD, STOP 9031 75390 #704-06-1982 L1990 **PTH** *020 †50

ASHKINAZ, Barry Craig. 2777 N STEMMONS FWY, STE 300 75207 #016-11-1970 L1994 **FM FPG** *030 †18

ASHRAF, Asma Mohamed. 12221 MERIT DR, STE 1610 75251 #704-20-1994 L2006 **IM** *020 †20

ASOLATI, Massimo. 4500 S LANCASTER RD, VA MEDICAL CENTER, MC 112 75216 #561-11-1983 L2004 **GS** *020 †85

ASSADI, Mohammed Ashfak H. 13601 PRESTON RD, STE 900W 75240 #495-09-1978 L1991 **AN** *020 †05

ASTON, James Wm, Jr. ■ 75205 #048-02-1963 L1963 **ORS HS** *071 †40

ASUNDI, Ashoka Rama. 5201 HARRY HINES BLVD, PHHS 75235 #042-01-2006 L2008 **EM** *012

ATEF-ZAFARMAND, Alireza. ■ 75205 #517-01-1991 L2007 **NEP** *100

ATEN, Laurie Anne. 5481 BLAIR RD, WOUND CARE CONSULTANTS 75231 #030-05-1980 L1991 **AM FM** *020 †70,18

ATHRE, Raghu Sudarshan. 5060 WATEKA DR 75209 #048-12-2002 L2006 **OTO** *020

ATIYEH, Stephanie Lauren. 7777 FOREST LN, PEDIATRICS 6D 75230 #005-18-2001 L2004 **PD** *020 †55

ATKINS, James Michael. 5323 HARRY HINES BLVD, UNIV OF TX SW MED SCH 75390 #048-12-1967 L1967 **CD EM** *040 †20

ATKINS, Ronald West. 4500 S LANCASTER RD 75216 #047-06-1964 L1967 **PS** *030 †65

ATKINSON, Frederick C. 9528 WEBB CHAPEL RD 75220 #021-01-1958 L1964 **FM** *020 †18

AUCHUS, Mary Louise. UTSWMC MC 8852, DEPT OF HEMATOLOGY/ONCOLOG 75390 #028-02-1988 L2000 **HO** *020 †20

AUCHUS, Richard Jos. 5323 HARRY HINES BLVD, BOX 8857 75390 #028-02-1988 L2000 **END IM** *050 †20

AUERBACH, David M. 5323 HARRY HINES BLVD, UT SOUTHWESTERN MEDICAL CE 75390 #035-15-1978 L2001 **IM** *020 †20

AUMAN, Sherrill Leonard. 5362 WENONAH DR 75209 #036-01-1985 L1992 **AN GS** *020 †05

AUNG, Fleur Min. ■ 75220 #209-01-1973 L1977 **PTH PCP** *071 †50

AUSTIN, Ned Alvin. ■ 75214 #021-01-2005 **PTH** *012

AUTREY, Ezell Stallworth. 7777 FOREST LN, STE C512 75230 #051-04-1980 L1982 **OBG REN** *020 †30

AVILES, Arturo Emilio. 221 W COLORADO BLVD, STE 440 75208 #341-01-1965 L1975 **PUD CCM** *020 †20

AVILES, Sandra. 7777 FOREST LN STE B-, PEDIATRIC CRITICAL CARE AS 75230 #451-01-1983 L2000 **PD CCP** *020 †55

AWAD, Amer Moh'D Saddin. ■ 75235 #575-01-2002 **N** *012

AWODIPE, Abimbola Yetunde. 4811 HARRY HINES BLVD, SUPPORT BLDG C/SR HOUSE 75235 #690-14-1992 L2004 **IMG** *020 †20

AWWAD, Shady Tanus. 5323 HARRY HINES BLVD 75235 #605-01-1998 **OPH** *100

AXELSON, Michael David. 5323 HARRY HINES BLVD 75390 #025-01-2003 L2006 **HO** *012 †20

AXMANN, David G. 13601 PRESTON RD, STE 900 75240 #048-12-1986 L1988 **AN** *020 †05

AYAD, Ramy F. 3500 GASTON AVE, MEDICAL EDUCATION DEPT 75246 #048-12-2001 L2008 **IM** *020

AYBAR, Raphael Richard. 4131 N CENTRAL EXPY, METRO ANESTHESIA 75204 #047-07-1988 L1994 **AN** *020 †05

AYDIN, Faruk. 4350 ALPHA RD 75244 #902-10-1982 L1999 **PTH** *020 †50

AYMOND, Allen H, Jr. 6757 ARAPAHO RD, PMB 335 75248 #048-12-1978 L1978 **AN** *020 †20

AZAD, Nelofer Hashim. 12201 MERIT DR STE 440 75251 #704-16-1983 L1991 **IM** *020 †20

AZIZ, Syed H. 4500 S LANCASTER RD 75216 #704-02-1987 L1999 **IM** *020 †20

AZOUZ, David. PO BOX 801209 75380 #067-01-1978 L1985 **PS HS** *020 †65 ‡

BACA, Frances M. 5323 HARRY HINES BLVD, UT SOUTHWESTERN MEDICAL CE 75390 #048-12-2004 L2006 **OBG** *012

BACHIR, Natalie Myrna. ■ 75235 #539-04-2003 **IM** *100 †20

BACKMAN, Lars Anders. ■ 75218 #858-02-1987 L1994 *020

BADHEY, Neeraj Surender. ■ 75204 #495-73-2003 L2008 **CD** *012 †20

BAE, Jae-O. ■ 75201 #033-06-2000 L2007 **PDS** *012 †85

BAEK, Peter Sungjae. 13601 PRESTON RD, STE 900W 75240 #036-07-1998 L2005 **AN** *020

BAETIONG, Ma Arlina M. 3500 GASTON AVE 75246 #748-02-1994 L2008 **NPM** *020 †55

BAEZ, Suzette. 809 SINGLETON BLVD 75212 #042-02-2001 L2004 **PD** *020 †55

BAGHERI, Ali. 3600 GASTON AVE 75246 #048-12-1989 L1990 **IM** *020 †20

BAGRI, Amola S. 13154 COIT RD, STE 100 75240 #048-12-1999 L2003 **NEP** *020 †20

BAHADORANI, John Nader. ■ 75219 #048-02-2007 **IM** *012

BAHL, Dinesh. 5323 HARRY HINES BLVD 75390 #035-08-2002 L2006 **OPH** *100

BAHRA, Pauldeep. ■ 75226 #025-01-2007 **GS** *012

BAILES, James Oscar. 10641 STEPPINGTON DR # 101 75230 #308-07-1982 L1982 **PM** *075

BAILEY, April Alexander. SOUTHWESTERN MED, UNIV OF TEXAS 75390 #021-01-2007 **DR** *012

BAILEY, Paul Reed. 5201 HARRY HINES BLVD 75235 #048-14-1985 L1986 **EM TRS** *020

BAIRD, Robert Wade. 3500 GASTON AVE 75246 #027-01-1976 L1977 **PUD CCM** *020 †20

BAIRD, William Leroy. ■ 75205 #048-04-1929 L1929 **GP** *071

BAKER, Bryant Orland, Jr. ■ 75232 #048-12-1955 L1955 **IM CD** *071

BAKER, James Guy. 4600 SAMUELL BLVD 75228 #039-01-1982 L1983 **MDM CHP** *030 †75 ‡

BAKER, John Adair. 9301 N CENTRAL EXPY, STE 400 75231 #028-03-1980 L1981 **ORS** *020 †40

BAKER, Linda Alford. 2350 N STEMMNS FWY #F-4300, DEPT PEDIATRIC UROLOGY 75207 #020-02-1989 L1999 **UP** *095

BAKER, Mark Douglas. ■ 75230 #041-13-1978 L2007 **PD EM** *020 †55

BAKER, Noel Susan. 1935 MOTOR ST, DEPARTMENT OF NEUROLOGY 75235 #028-34-1986 L1998 **CN** *100 †55,75

BAKOS, Sharon Mae. 1311 N WASHINGTON AVE 75204 #048-04-1982 L1983 **OBG** *020 †30

BAKSHI, Rajbir Singh. 5201 HARRY HINES BLVD, UT SOUTHWESTERN MEDICAL CE 75235 #496-20-1993 L2002 **P** *020

BAKTHAVACHALAM, S. ■ 75204 #024-05-2003 L2007 **OTO** *012

BALDERAS, Valeska. 5201 HARRY HINES BLVD, UT SOUTHWESTERN/PARKLAND H 75235 #048-02-2004 L2007 **IM** *100 †20

BALDWIN, Brian Jay. 5909 HARRY HINES BLVD 75235 #023-01-1965 L1972 **CD IM** *020 †20

BALDWIN, Hilary Joy. 8210 WALNUT HILL LN # 718 75231 #041-12-1998 L2002 **PD SME** *020 †55

BALDWIN, William David. ■ 75229 #048-13-1988 L1989 **ID PTH** *071

BALFOUR, Margaret Ellen. 5323 HARRY HINES BLVD, UNIV TX SOUTHWESTERN 75390 #038-41-2006 L2008 **P** *012

BALIS, David Scott. 5303 HARRY HINES BLVD 75390 #048-12-1992 L1993 **IM** *020 †20

BALLARD, David Jos. 8080 N CENTRAL EXPY, STE 500 75206 #036-01-1983 L1984 **OS** *050 †20

BALLDIN, Bjorn Christian. 75208 #048-14-2006 **ORS** *012

BALLEZA, Phillip B. ■ 75219 #048-08-2008 *012

BALLINGER, Richard H, III. 5124 WESTGROVE DR 75248 #048-12-1980 L1980 **DR** *020 †80

BALLIVIAN, Roberto Alejan. 75235 #048-12-2008 *012

BAN, Kathryn Elizabeth. ■ 75219 #048-14-2007 **PD** *012

BANACH, Theodore Martin. 12222 MERIT DR, STE 365 75251 #062-01-1973 L1978 **GP** *020 †16

BANARER, Miriam. ■ 75230 #048-12-2001 L2005 **PD** *020 †55

BANARER, Salomon. 7777 FOREST LN, STE 618 75230 #737-06-1995 L2005 **END** *020 †20

BANERJEE, Pooja. 8440 WALNUT HILL LN, STE 340 75231 #913-32-1992 L2005 **RHU** *020 †20

BANERJEE, Subhash. 4500 S LANCASTER RD, DALLAS VA MEDICAL CENTER 75216 #913-32-1992 L2005 **CD** *100 †20

BANKHEAD, Mary Gill. ■ 75225 #048-12-1970 L1970 **PTH** *020 †50

BANKS, Kathleen S. 12880 HILLCREST RD STE 104 75230 #048-12-1988 L1989 **CHP P** *020 †75

BANKS, Matthew W. 3920 WORTH ST 75246 #048-14-1993 L1994 **AN** *020 †05

BANNON, Lori Demlow. ■ 75225 #024-01-1986 L1990 **AN** *020 †05

BANNON, Michael Gridley. 10830 N CENTRAL EXPY # 330 75231 #043-01-1986 L1998 **AN** *020 †05

BANSAL, Bharati B. 1935 MOTOR ST, CHILDREN MEDICAL CENTER 75235 #014-01-1994 L1997 **PD** *020 †55

BANSAL, Nidhi. ■ 75230 #495-23-1998 L2008 **IM** *100 †20

BANTA, Charles Jack, II. 8220 WALNUT HILL LN, STE 608 75231 #021-05-1985 L1991 **ORS OSS** *020 †40

BARBER, Chad A. 5323 HARRY HINES BLVD 75390 #048-02-2001 L2006 **NPM** *020 †55

BARBOSA, Leyka M. 7777 FOREST LN, STE C610 75230 #042-02-1989 L1994 **RHU IM** *020 †20

BARBOSA, Vera Lucia. 1935 MOTOR ST, ANESTHESIOLOGISTS FOR CHIL 75235 #187-10-1980 L2005 **AN** *050 †05

BARCELO, Carlos Raul. 7777 FOREST LN STE C717 75230 #649-03-1980 L2005 **PS CFS** *020

BARDAN, Antoanella. 2330 BUTLER ST, STE 115 75235 #005-18-2002 L2007 **DMP** *012 †15

BARDEN, Catherine Brooks. ■ 75201 #021-01-1999 L2006 **GS** *100 †05

BARKER, Adam David. ■ 75204 #030-06-2008 *012

BARKER, Bradford T. ■ 75230 #048-12-2001 L2005 **PTH** *100 †50

BARKER, Jerry Lee. 8200 WALNUT HILL LN, RADIATION ONCOLOGY CENTER 75231 #048-12-1970 L1970 **RO** *071 †80 ‡

BARKER, Wade Neal. 1151 N BUCKNER BLVD, STE 308A 75218 #048-15-1991 L1992 **GS** *020 †85

BARKOCY, Gary A. 3450 W WHEATLAND RD, STE 240 75237 #041-77-1994, ▲ L2001 **CD IM** *020

BARKSDALE, Stephen Webb. 10405 E NORTHWEST HWY, STE 100 75238 #048-02-1979 L1980 **P** *020

BARNARD, Jeffrey Jos. 5230 MEDICAL CENTER DR, SWESTERN INST FORENSIC SCI 75235 #048-16-1981 L1981 **PTH FOP** *020 †50

BARNER, Robert Jos. ■ 75243 #048-02-1969 L1969 **R** *071 †80

BARNES, Aliessa Renee. 8005 NIMROD TRL 75238 #048-12-2001 L2003 **PDC** *100 †55

BARNES, Gregory Scott. 3409 WORTH ST 75246 #048-04-1999 L2004 **GS** *020 †85

BARNETT, Carlton C, Jr. ■ 75205 #007-02-1992 L1999 **GS** *020 †85

BARNETT, Charles Robt. 8080 N CENTRAL EXPY, STE 1700 LB 83 75206 #048-02-1976 L1976 **OS N** *071

BARNETT, David Wesley. 3600 GASTON AVE, STE 907 75246 #048-12-1989 L1995 **NS GS** *020 †25

BARNETT, Duane A. 5201 HARRY HINES BLVD 75235 #039-01-1952 L1978 **GS** *040 †85

BARNETT, Gary S. 13601 PRESTON RD STE 10 75240 #048-15-1991 L1992 **AN** *020 †05

BARNETT, Jack Alvis. 1441 N BECKLEY AVE, METHODIST MEDICAL CENTER 75203 #048-12-1956 L1956 **IM GPM** *040 †20

BARNETT, John Bryan, Jr. 5489 BLAIR RD STE 500 75231 #048-12-1969 L1969 **PS GP** *020

BARNETT, Michael Andrew. ■ 75390 #048-13-1999 L2007 **IM** *100 †20

BARNETT, Samuel Lee. UT SOUTHWESTERN MEDICAL CE 75390 #038-41-1999 L2007 **NS** *020

BARNETT, William D. 1004 N WASHINGTON AVE 75204 #048-02-1952 L1952 **CRS GS** *071 †85,10

BARRERA, Pete Flores. ■ 75218 #048-13-1982 L1983 **EM** *020

BARRERA, Richard David. 5323 HARRY HINES BLVD, UT SOUTHWESTERN MEDICAL CE 75390 #048-13-2003 L2006 **ETX** *012 †20

BARRETT, Terry Lee. 8267 ELMBROOK DR, STE 100 75247 #055-01-1978 L2004 **D** *020 †50,15

BARRIS, William Henri. 2709 HOOD ST 75219 #048-12-1946 L1946 **IM** *020

BARROGA, Deno Baltazar. 7502 GREENVILLE AVE STE 4 75231 #021-01-2001 L2005 **PM** *020 †60

BARRON, Janice Elizabeth. 8210 WALNUT HILL LN # 120 75231 #036-01-1978 L1981 **OPH** *030 †35

BARROWS, Thomas Henry. 5323 HARRY HINES BLVD, EMERGENCY MEDICINE RESIDEN 75390 #048-04-1997 L2008 **EM** *020 †16

BARTELS, Moritz Christian. 5720 FOREST PARK RD # 3 75235 #409-38-2000 L2005 **OBG** *020

BARTH, Bradley Alan. 1935 MOTOR ST, GASTROENTEROLOGY CLINIC 75235 #048-13-1998 L2004 **PG** *020

BARTLEY, Scott R. ■ 75248 #048-12-2001 L2004 **CHP** *020

BARTON, Fritz Engel. 411 N WASHINGTON AVE, STE 6000 75246 #048-12-1967 L1967 **PS GS** *020 †85,65

BARTON, Paul Edwin. 9426 OVERWOOD RD 75238 #048-12-1998 L2000 **AN** *020 †05

BARTON, Theresa. 1935 MOTOR ST, DEPARTMENT OF PEDIATRICS 75235 #048-12-1997 L1999 **PD PDI** *020 †55 ‡

BARVE, Minal Atul. 8200 WALNUT HILL LN, STE 700 75231 #496-30-1993 L2000 **ON** *020 †20

BARZUNE, Lawrence Stephen. 7777 FOREST LN STE A339 75230 #048-12-1969 L1969 **GS** *020

BASH, Robert Owen, Jr. 1935 MOTOR ST 75235 #017-20-1986 L1994 **PHO** *020 †55

BASILICO, Leopoldo M. 7522 CAMPBELL RD, STE 100 75248 #132-01-1972 L1998 **FM** *020 †18

BASKARAN, Gautam. ■ 75235 #048-12-2008 *012

BASKIND, Denise Lalla. 9440 POPPY DR 75218 #048-15-1985 L1986 **EM** *012

BASS, Robert King. 5323 HARRY HINES BLVD, STOP 9031 75390 #021-01-1954 L1954 **IM CD** *071

BASSEL, Katrina Smith. 7777 FOREST LN, STE C340 75230 #048-12-1991 L1992 **GE** *020 †20

BASSETT, Wallace H. ■ 75243 #048-04-1938 L1938 **PUD IM** *071

BASSHAM, Brian S. ■ 75204 #048-14-2007 **PD** *012

BASSICHIS, Michelle Mante. 8267 ELMBROOK DR STE 100 75247 #025-01-1995 L2003 **PTH** *020 †50

BATES, Angela Joy. ■ 75219 #048-13-2003 L2007 **N** *100

BATES, Evan Scott. 8230 WALNUT HILL LN # 420, SOUTHWEST ENT ASSOCIATES 75231 #036-01-1986 L1992 **OTO HNS** *020 †45

BATES, James Douglas. 3001 KNOX ST, STE 301 75205 #048-15-1985 L1986 **OMF** *020

BATLLE, Francisco Jesus. 8215 WESTCHESTER DR, STE 320 75225 #016-11-1987 L1994 **NS** *020

BATZ, Richard C, Jr. ■ 75230 #048-15-1999 L2006 **DR** *100 †80

BAUER, Brent J. ■ 75235 #048-13-2003 **ORS** *012

BAUGH, Jimmy Dee, II. ■ 75204 #305-01-2007 **FP** *012

BAUM, Howard Bruce. 7777 FOREST LN, STE C618 75230 #023-07-1987 L1995 **END** *020 †20

BAUM, Michel Gerard. 5323 HARRY HINES BLVD 75235 #005-14-1978 L1985 **PN PD** *020 †55

BAUM, Sue Ellen. 8230 WALNUT HILL LN, STE 414 75231 #010-02-1996 L2001 **ID IM** *020 †20

BAXTER, Barbara Stark. 6114 SHERRY LN 75225 #035-01-1979 L1980 **AI IM** *020 †20,03

BAYER, Zeynep. 4500 S LANCASTER RD, DEPT OF ANESTHESIOLOGY & P 75216 #902-09-1991 L2002 **APM** *020 †05

BAYOUD, George S. ■ 75201 #605-01-1948 L1957 **GS** *071 †85

BAYS, Leonard Jerald. 13601 PRESTON RD, STE 900 75240 #039-01-1988 L1989 **AN** *020 †05

BEALE, Evan W. 5323 HARRY HINES BLVD, UNIV TX SW MED SCH 75390 #048-13-2006 **GS** *012

BEAN, Lawrence Albert. 5201 HARRY HINES BLVD 75235 #048-12-2003 L2005 **EM** *020 †16

BEARD, Laura. 5445 LA SIERRA DR STE 250 75231 #048-15-1998 L2000 **P** *020 †75

BEARD, Robert H. 3500 GASTON AVE 75246 #048-15-1997 L2000 **MPD** *020 †55,20

BEAUCHAMP, George Robt. 8222 DOUGLAS AVE, STE 400 75225 #016-06-1968 L1976 **OPH** *020 †35

BEAUDOING, Denis Lee. 8226 DOUGLAS AVE STE 540 75225 #065-09-1971 L1977 **D FM** *071 †18,15

BEAUDOING, Roger Jos. 6161 HARRY HINES BLVD, STE 105 75235 #065-09-1957 L1977 **FM** *020 †18

BEAUDRY, Brigitte. 6301 GASTON AVE, EAST TOWER, SUITE 400 75214 #067-04-1987 L2002 **AN** *020

BEAVERS, Bret Dewayne. ■ 75235 #048-12-2008 *012

BEAVERS, Bruce Robt. 8220 WALNUT HILL LN, STE 300 75231 #048-12-1982 L1983 **ORS** *020 †40

BEAVERS, William R. 7738 FOREST LN STE 261, 3613 CEDAR SPRINGS ROAD 75230 #048-12-1953 L1953 **P** *020 †75

BECERRA, Carlos H. 3535 WORTH ST, STE 250 75246 #264-05-1989 L1995 **HO** *020 †20

BECK, Jay Mortimer. 3600 GASTON AVE, BARNETT TOWER #601 75246 #048-12-1956 L1956 **GYN** *071 †30

BECK, Perry M. 13601 PRESTON RD, STE 900 75240 #048-12-1989 L1990 **AN** *020 †05

BECKER, Amy Michelle. 5323 HARRY HINES BLVD, UT SOUTHWESTERN MEDICAL CE 75390 #048-12-2000 L2004 **PN** *100 †55

BECKER, Christine A. 8335 WALNUT HILL LN, STE 105 75231 #048-02-1984 L1985 **IM** *020 †20

BECKER, Christopher T. 9101 N CENTRAL EXPY, STE 420 75231 #038-40-1996 L2001 **PD** *020 †55

BECKER, Philip Michael. 5477 GLEN LAKES DR, STE 100-125 75231 #056-06-1978 L1987 **SME P** *020 †55

BECKER, Stephen B. ■ 75205 #048-12-2001 L2001 **PS** *012

BECKHAM, Grant Patrick. 9101 N CENTRAL EXPY, STE 350 75231 #048-04-1991 L1992 **IM** *020 †20

BECKHAM, Joseph M. ■ 75219 #048-12-2004 L2008 **AN** *012

BECKSTROM, Harriett Mae P. 3946 S BUCKNER BLVD 75227 #028-78-1948, ▲ L1948 *071

BEDIMO, Roger Jean. 4500 S LANCASTER RD, ROAD, 111-D 75216 #217-01-1989 L2001 **ID** *020 †20

BEDNAR, Marian Jeanne. 8160 WALNUT HILL LN 75231 #048-14-1999 L2001 **EM** *020 †16

BEDOLLA, Edgar. ■ 75211 #048-12-2008 *012

BEDROSSIAN, Varujan B. 4323 S HAMPTON RD 75232 #198-02-1970 L1977 **GP** *020

BEECHERL, Ernest Edward. 8230 WALNUT HILL LN, STE 408 75231 #021-01-1991 L1993 **GS** *020 †85

BEER, Alison Marguerite. ■ 75219 #048-12-2007 L2007 **IM** *012

BEERAVOLU, Lakshmi Reddy. 8200 WALNUT HILL LN 75231 #495-21-2004 **N** *012

BEERS, Sara Lynn. 1935 MOTOR ST, EMERGENCY MEDICINE 75235 #034-01-2001 L2003 **PEM** *100 †55

BEHAN, Joseph P. 8140 WALNUT HILL LN, TEXAS MEDICAL & SURGICAL 75231 #048-15-1993 L1995 **OBG** *020 †30

BEHNAM, Soroush. 9229 LBJ FWY STE 250, METROPLEX GERIATRIC ASSOCI 75243 #409-23-1994 L2003 **IMG** *020 †20

BEHR, Leonard Michael. 8230 WALNUT HILL LN, STE 600 75231 #836-01-1967 L1977 **FM** *020 ‡

BEISCHER, Andrew. 411 N WASHINGTON AVE, STE 7000 75246 #143-02-1986 *100

BEISER, Ned Elmer. 1935 MOTOR ST 75235 #028-78-1963, ▲ L1963 **FM AM** *020

BEKKER, Alex. 6500 E MOCKINGBIRD #115 75214 #048-13-1996 L1997 **GP** *012

BELIRGEN, Muhittin. 1935 MOTOR ST 75235 #902-19-1999 *100

BELITERE-BLESSING, Lorie. PO BOX 655999 75265 #104-01-2005 **FP** *012

BELL, Ayned Mitchell. ■ 75248 #028-03-1960 L1960 **A OM** *071 †55,03

BELL, Christopher L. 7777 FOREST LN, STE 645 75230 #048-15-2000 L2003 **GS** *020 †85

BELL, Clinton Stephen. 3503 W WHEATLAND RD 75237 #048-02-1998 L2004 **ORS** *020 †40

BELL, Margaret E. 4350 ALPHA RD 75244 #048-14-1987 L1989 **PTH** *020 †50

BELL, Miller Stephens. 3600 GASTON AVE, WADELY TOWER SUITE 753 75246 #012-01-1963 L1970 **GS** *071 †85,90

BELL, Patricia E. 7 MEDICAL PKWY 75234 #065-01-1972 L1979 **OBG** *020 †30

BELLOS, Nicholaos C. 2909 LEMMON AVE 75204 #048-04-1981 L1982 **ID IM** *020 †20

BELMORE, Danielle Jean. 13601 PRESTON RD, STE 900 75240 #048-14-1992 L1994 **AN** *020 †05

BENAVIDES, Raul. ■ 75228 #048-12-2005 **PTH** *012

BENAVIDES, Richard Alex. 7920 BELT LINE RD STE 310, SUITE 100 75254 #048-12-1981 L1981 **GS** *020 †85

BENDAPUDI, Pavan Kasi. ■ 75234 #005-11-2008 *012

BENITEZ, Fernando Luis. 5323 HARRY HINES BLVD, U.T. SOUWESTERN MEDICAL CT 75390 #042-01-1996 L1999 **EM** *020 †16

BENNETT, Benjamin James. 12880 HILLCREST RD STE 104 75230 #048-12-1989 L1990 **PYA CHP** *020 †75

BENNETT, John D. 2600 N STEMMONS FWY 75207 #048-12-1990 L1991 **P** *020 †75

BENNETT, Katherine M. 5323 HARRY HINES BLVD, SOUTHWESTERN MED 75390 #048-12-2004 L2004 **NPM** *012 †50

BENNETT, Lee Wall. 5909 HARRY HINES BLVD, DEPARTMENT OF RADIOLOGY 75390 #048-12-1962 L1963 **DR** *020 †80

BENNETT, Marty Neal. 10000 N CENTRAL EXPWY, STE 1420 75390 #036-01-1998 L2000 **P** *020 †75

BENNETT, Michael. 5323 HARRY HINES BLVD 75235 #048-04-1961 L1961 **ATP** *050 †50

BENNETT, Robert David. 6330 LBJ FWY STE 150 75240 #048-04-1980 L1980 **P** *020 †75

BENNETT, William James. 1835 TIMBERGROVE CIR 75208 #048-12-1958 L1958 **GS** *020 †85

BENNION, Alka B. ■ 75204 #030-06-2002 L2007 **OBG** *020

BENNION, Phil Washburn. ■ 75204 #030-06-2002 L2007 **ORS** *100

BENSON, Paul Alan. 3600 GASTON AVE STE 261, PBM LABOTATORIES 75246 #039-01-1983 L1985 **PTH** *020 †50

BENTLEY, James Arthur, Jr. 4633 N CENTRAL EXPY # 305 75205 #047-05-1969 L1976 **OPH** *020 †35

BENTON, Susan Daniel. 13601 PRESTON RD, STE 900 75240 #048-02-1989 L1990 **AN** *020 †05

BERBARIE, Rafic F. 2801 LIVE OAK ST # 520 75204 #048-02-2001 L2006 **CD** *020

BERGEN, Patricia Celine. 5201 HARRY HINES BLVD 75235 #012-05-1983 L1984 **GS CCS** *040 †85

BERGER, Brian David. 3500 GASTON AVE, STE HOB1 75246 #048-12-1996 L2001 **RO** *020 †80

BERGER, Israel R. 75230 #012-01-1943 L1943 **R** *071 †80

BERGER, Joseph Rossi. ■ 75234 #048-12-2004 **IM** *100 †20

BERGER, Richard Eric. 7777 FOREST LN STE B430 75230 #041-07-1976 L1981 **END IM** *020 †20

BERGMAN, Barry Eric. 7777 FOREST LN # 224 75230 #056-06-1980 L1982 **PD** *020 †55

BERGMAN, Joseph Henry. ■ 75220 #048-12-2008 *012

BERGSTRESSER, Paul R. 5323 HARRY HINES BLVD, # F4 206A 75390 #005-11-1968 L1976 **D** *030 †15

BERHE, Mezgebe. 3409 WORTH ST, NORTH TEXAS INFECTIOUS 75246 #366-01-1993 L2005 **ID** *020 †20

BERK, Alan Michael. 9 MEDICAL PKWY STE 103 75234 #048-12-1989 L1990 **AN** *020 †05

BERNIER, Elise Carole. 8226 DOUGLAS AVE STE 609 75225 #067-06-1978 L1988 **OS FM** *020 †20

BERNSTEIN, Steven Glenn. 8160 WALNUT HILL LN, STE 316 75231 #051-01-1975 L1981 **GO** *020 †30

BERNSTIEN, Mark Steven. 7777 FOREST LN, STE 550 75230 #030-05-1975 L1976 **OBG** *020 †30

BERRY, Deaina M. 9202 ELAM RD, STE 140 75217 #048-12-1993 L1995 **PD** *020 †55

BERRY, Emily Carolineru. ■ 75214 #039-01-2007 **PTH** *012

BERRY, Jeff Matthew. SOUTHWESTERN MED, UNIV OF TEXAS 75390 #045-01-2002 L2006 **CD** *012 †20

BERRY, Leonard A, Jr. 6507 ROBIN RD 75209 #047-07-1986 L1988 **GE IM** *020 †20

BERRY, Phil Hunter, Jr. 810 N ZANG BLVD 75208 #027-01-1966 L1967 **ORS** *020 †40

BERRY, Priscilla M Burch. 8222 DOUGLAS AVE, STE 400 75225 #048-12-1967 L1967 **PO** *020 †35

BERRY, William Larkin. 3600 GASTON AVE STE 609 75246 #048-12-1967 L1967 **OPH** *020 †35

BERRYMAN, Robert Brian. 7777 FOREST LN, STE D220 75230 #048-12-1994 L1995 **HO** *020 †20

BERTRAND, John David. 8305 WALNUT HILL LN, WALNUT HILL OBSTETRICS & 75231 #048-12-1975 L1975 **OBG** *020 †30

BESANT-MATTHEWS, P E. ■ 75230 #352-07-1962 L1970 **FOP PTH** *062 †50

BESCOS, Jess F. ■ 75225 #847-04-1959 L1971 **AN** *071

BESCOS, Pilar Marie. 7777 FOREST LN, STE C420 75230 #847-21-1987 L1993 **FM** *020 †18

BEST, Susan E. 4500 S LANCASTER RD, DALLAS VA MEDICAL CENTER 1 75216 #048-16-1990 L1991 **IM ADM** *020 †20

BESWICK, Tracy. 4424 VANDELIA ST 75219 #048-12-2008 *012

BETANCOURT, Arlene. 9323 GARLAND RD STE 3, EASTLAKE PRIMARY CARE 75218 #042-01-1995 L1996 **IM** *020 †20

BEUTLER, Bruce Alan. 5201 HARRY HINES BLVD 75235 #016-02-1981 L1988 **IG** *050

BEVAN-THOMAS, Richard H. 7777 FOREST LN STE C-61 75230 #028-34-1996 L1998 **U** *020 †95

BEVERIDGE, Thomas P. 7777 FOREST LN, STER A-341 75230 #062-01-1986 L1996 **CD** *072 †20

BEYER, Chester W, Jr. 4144 N CENTRAL EXPY # 700 75204 #048-12-1970 L1970 **AN FM** *020 †05

BEYER, Lawrence Aloysius. 4918 FOREST LN 75244 #048-12-1957 L1957 **GS** *071 †85

BHAGAT, Ramesh Kumar. ■ 75209 #048-12-2008 *012

BHAGAVATH, Balasubramania. 5323 HARRY HINES BLVD, UT SOUTHWESTERN MEDICAL CE 75390 #495-04-1990 L2003 **OBG** *100 †30

BHALODIA, Dhiren Meghji. 13601 PRESTON RD, STE 900 75240 #038-40-1999 L1999 **AN** *020 †05

BHAMIDIPATI, Prabhakar Ve. 4500 S LANCASTER RD, DEP RADIOLOGY-DALLAS VA HS 75216 #495-62-1979 L2002 **RNR** *020

BHATTATHIRY, Manu Madhava. 4500 S LANCASTER RD, DEPARTMENT OF RADIOLOGY 75216 #690-04-1984 L2005 **DR** *020 †28,80

BHELLA, Paul S. ■ 75214 #045-01-2002 L2005 **CD** *012 †20

BHUSHAN, Vikas. 3535 WORTH ST, STE 500 75246 #005-02-1991 L2002 **DR** *062 †80

BHUSHAN, Vikas. 7777 FOREST LN, STE D220 75230 #495-27-1985 L2002 **ON** *020 †20

BHUTANI, Sumit. 3600 GASTON AVE STE 500, TEXAS PRIMARY CARE 75246 #048-02-2002 L2005 **AI** *012 †20

BIAVATI, Michael J. 8325 WALNUT HILL LN # 100 75231 #039-05-1987 L1993 **OTO PDO** *020 †45

BICK, Rodger Lee. 10455 N CENTRAL EXPY, STE 109 PMB 320 75231 #005-15-1970 L1993 **HO VM** *040

BIDIC, Sean Michael. ■ 75205 #035-01-1996 L2005 **HS** *020 †65

BIERNER, Samuel M. 1801 INWOOD ROAD, 7TH FLOOR 75390 #048-13-1983 L1983 **PM PMM** *020 †60 ‡

BIGHAM, Gene O. 221 W COLORADO BLVD, STE 640 75208 #048-13-1993 L1994 **IM** *020 †20

BILLINGHURST, John Craig. 9107 CHURCH RD 75231 #065-01-1971 L1978 **IM GE** *062 †20

BILLMAN, David Karl. 3600 GASTON AVE 75246 #048-12-1988 L1993 **AN** *020 †05

BIRBARI, John L. 3500 GASTON AVE, 1ST FLR ROBERTS - SURGERY 75246 #048-13-2004 L2007 **GS** *012

BIRBARI, Lori E. ■ 75238 #048-13-2004 *100

BIRCH, John G. 2222 WELBORN ST 75219 #065-06-1975 L1984 **OP** *020 †40

BIRDSELL, Frank N. 13601 PRESTON RD 75240 #048-12-1984 L1985 **AN** *020 †05

BIREDDY, Suman Kumar. 5939 HARRY HINES BLVD, STE 500 75390 #495-65-1997 L2006 **NEP** *020 †20

BIRK, Diane Fagelman. 12880 HILLCREST RD STE 104 75230 #025-07-1966 L1969 **P PYA** *071 †75

BIVENS, Trina Lee. 7515 GREENVILLE AVE, STE 503 75231 #048-14-1996 L1997 **P** *020 †75

BLACHLEY, Jon David. 7777 FOREST LN 75230 #048-12-1976 L1976 **IM CCM** *020 †20

BLACK, James Wm, Jr. 12854 SPURLING RD 75230 #048-12-1967 L1967 **P** *071 †75

BLACK, Jeffrey Lynn. 2222 WELBORN ST 75219 #038-40-1975 L1990 **PD VS** *020 †55

BLACK, Melissa Gruber. ■ 75214 #048-12-1990 L1991 **FM** *020 †18

BLACK, Michael Edward. 3500 GASTON AVE, DEPT PTH 75246 #039-01-1994 L1997 **PTH** *020 †50

BLACK, Robert Dan. 3600 GASTON AVE, STE 806 75246 #048-12-1980 L1980 **PUD CCM** *020 †20

BLACK, Roland Eugene. 7777 FOREST LN, STE B238 75230 #048-02-1965 L1965 **GYN** *020 †30

BLACK, Stephen Thayer. 13601 PRESTON RD, STE 900 75240 #034-01-1988 L1992 **AN** *020 †05

BLACK, Stuart Barry. 7515 GREENVILLE AVE, STE 500 75231 #017-20-1966 L1972 **N CHN** *020 †75

BLACKBURN, Larry Wayne. 3107 W CAMP WISDOM RD #115 75237 #048-13-1984 L1985 **FM** *020 †18

BLACKBURN, Raymond C. 5959 HARRY HINES BLVD, STE 320 75235 #005-12-1974 L1978 **D** *020

BLAIR, Amanda Bock. ■ 75225 #048-13-2004 L2004 **PHO** *012 †55

BLAIR, D Shelton. ■ 75225 #048-04-1939 L1939 **D** *071 †15

BLAIR, Donald L. 221 W COLORADO BLVD, STE 431 75208 #048-16-1987 L1988 **OBG** *020 †30

BLAIR, Ronald M, Jr. 7777 FOREST LN STE 445, BLDG B 75230 #048-13-1985 L1991 **PD** *020 †55

BLAIR, William Shelton. ■ 75225 #539-06-1975 L1979 **AN** *020

BLAKELEY, Katherine Ryan. 7777 FOREST LN, STE A310 75230 #048-12-1988 L1990 **AN EM** *020 †05

BLAKENEY, Catherine Mary. 4131 N CENTRAL EXPY, METRO ANESTHESIA 75204 #917-22-1967 L1977 **AN** ‡

BLALOCK, Shannon E. ■ 75219 #048-16-2002 L2005 **PDC** *012 †55

BLANCO, Gabriela Maria. SOUTHWESTERN MED, UNIV OF TEXAS 75390 #048-12-2008 *012

BLAND, James Ellsworth. 7777 FOREST LN, STE A109 75230 #048-12-1963 L1963 **NS CD** *071 †25

BLANTON, Don Edward. ■ 75229 #048-02-1962 L1962 **IM** *071 ‡

BLEAKNEY, Dana Allison. 3600 GASTON AVE STE 454 75246 #048-12-1999 L2000 **FM** *020 †18

BLEIBERG, Alan Howard. 1935 MOTOR ST RM J112, CHILDREN'S MEDICAL CENTER 75235 #035-46-1993 L2003 **PD PE** *020 †55

BLEICH, April T. 5201 HARRY HINES BLVD, UTSW MEDICAL CENTER 75235 #048-14-2004 L2006 **OBG** *012

BLEND, Sheldon Louis. 5323 HARRY HINES BLVD, DEPT OF RADIOLOGY 75390 #048-12-1975 L1975 **DR** *020 †20

BLEWETT, Christopher Glen. 5323 HARRY HINES BLVD, DEPT OF INTERNAL MEDICINE 75390 #048-12-2000 L2002 **PCC** *100 †20

BLEWETT, Emerson Kenney. ■ 75205 #048-02-1938 L1938 **OBG** *071 †30

BLEWETT, Kavitha Sunku. 8160 WALNUT HILL LN, MARGOT PEROT BLD #200 75231 #035-03-2000 L2004 **OBG** *020 †30

BLOCKER, Laura Gambini. 8160 WALNUT HILL LN # 304 75231 #048-02-1977 L1977 **OBG** *020 †30

BLOEMENDAL, Lee S. 5907 VELASCO AVE 75206 #048-02-1999 L2004 **GS** *020 †85

BLOGG, Colin Edward. 3600 GASTON AVE STE 860 75246 #917-25-1966 L1978 **AN** *020

BLOIS, Erik Mendell. 5323 HARRY HINES BLVD, SOUTHWESTERN MED 75390 #048-04-2001 L2005 **P** *100 †75

BLOME, Bruce Richard. 5323 HARRY HINES BLVD, DEPT RAD 75390 #048-12-1964 L1964 **R RO** *062 †80

BLOMQUIST, C Gunnar. CARDIOLOGY H-9 -122, SOUTHWESTERN MEDICAL SCHOO 75390 #858-01-1960 L1968 **CD** *071

BLOMQUIST, Preston H. 5323 HARRY HINES BLVD, UNIV TX SOUTHWESTERN MC 75390 #048-12-1986 L1987 **OPH** *020 †30

BLOOM, Bernard Howard. 7777 FOREST LN STE C520 75230 #030-05-1966 L1971 **PS GS** *020 †85,65 ‡

BLOOM, Christopher Atkins. 1151 N BUCKNER BLVD, C.A. BLOOM, M.D., PLLC 75218 #047-07-1983 L2006 **IM** *020 †20

BLOOM, Steven Louis. 5323 HARRY HINES BLVD, DEPT OF OB/GYN 75390 #048-12-1990 L1991 **OBG MFM** *040 †30

BLOTCKY, Mark Joel. 8226 DOUGLAS AVE STE 805 75225 #048-12-1971 L1971 **CHP P** *020 †75 ‡

BLUM, Jerald Leonard. ■ 75225 #048-04-1957 L1957 **ORS** *071 †40

BLUM, Joanne Lorraine. 3535 WORTH ST, STE 110 75246 #023-01-1979 L1988 **ON HEM** *020 †20

BLUM, Ronald Hyman. 8210 WALNUT HILL LN, STE 130 75231 #048-02-1962 L1962 **ORS** *020 †20

BLUNTZER, Mary Ellen. 12810 HILLCREST RD, STE B127 75230 #048-12-1983 L1983 **IM** *020 †20

BOARD, John P. ■ 75208 #048-02-1936 L1936 **PUD** *075

BOBB, David Samuel, Jr. 5323 HARRY HINES BLVD, SOUTHWESTERN MED 75390 #048-14-2007 **P** *012

BOCKMAN, Thomas M. ■ 75211 #048-12-2004 L2008 **IM** *100

BOECK, Marjorie Ann. 7515 GREENVILLE AVE, STE 504 75231 #036-07-1976 L1997 **ADL NTR** *020 †55

BOEHNING, Harold C. ■ 75225 #048-12-1953 L1953 **AN** *071 †05

BOEHRER, James Danl. 5939 HARRY HINES BLVD, STE 630 75235 #016-02-1987 L1989 **CD** *020 †20

BOEHRER, Robyn Horsager. 5323 HARRY HINES BLVD, UT SOUTHWESTERN OB-GYN DEP 75390 #016-11-1987 L1989 **MFM** *020 †30

BOGAN, Tiffany Nicole. 5323 HARRY HINES BLVD 75390 #004-01-2006 **OBG** *012

BOGUSZ, Agata Monika. 5323 HARRY HINES BLVD 75390 #409-39-1999 **PTH** *012

BOKER, Andres. ■ 75204 #649-31-1998 L2005 **D** *012

BOLAND, C Richard. 3500 GASTON AVE, BAYLOR UNIV MED CTR H-250 75246 #008-01-1973 L2003 **GE IM** *050 †20

BOLDEN, Ruby Gladys. 809 SINGLETON BLVD, LOS BARRIOS UNIDOS COMM CL 75212 #010-03-1974 L1981 **PD** *020

BOLESTA, Michael Jos. 1801 INWOOD RD, UTSW ORTHOPAEDIC SURGERY 75390 #028-03-1981 L1994 **OSS ORS** *040 †40

BOLEY, Candice Lee. ■ 75205 #025-01-2007 **P** *012

BOLTON, Christopher John. 1717 MAIN ST STE 5200 75201 #038-41-1984 L1986 **EM** *020

BOLTON, Craig Alan. 10670 N CENTRAL EXPY, STE 170 75231 #048-12-1974 L1975 **OPH** *020 †35

BOMELA, Hlwelekazi Noludw. 5323 HARRY HINES BLVD, UNIV TX SOUTHWESTERN MED S 75390 #836-05-1991 **NPM** *100

BOND, Kathryn Marie. 3500 GASTON AVE 75246 #021-05-1988 L1989 **DR** *020 †80

BONE, George Edward. 7777 FOREST LN STE A-2 75230 #048-12-1968 L1968 **GS VS** *071 †85

BONHAM, Robert Ellis. 10 MEDICAL PKWY STE 203 75234 #048-02-1966 L1966 **OTO** *020 †45

BONSELL, Shawn Curtis. 411 N WASHINGTON AVE #7000, ORTHOPEDIC ASSOC OF DALLAS 75246 #040-02-1993 L1999 **ORS** *020 †40

BONTE, Frederick James. 5323 HARRY HINES BLVD, NUCLEAR MEDICINE CENTER 75390 #038-06-1945 L1956 **NM R** *050 †80,28

BOOKOUT, David Michael. 8160 WALNUT HILL LN LL006 75231 #048-12-1964 L1964 **GYN REN** *020 †30

BOONE, David Wolf. 3503 W WHEATLAND RD # 100 75237 #020-02-1979 L1984 **ORS** *020 †40

BOONE, Janet Elizabeth. 6303 HARRY HINES BLVD, STE 101 75235 #047-07-1975 L1984 **PD** *020

BOONE, Nuntavan. 1935 MOTOR ST, REFERRAL CARE CTR 75235 #047-06-1997 L2002 **PD** *020 †55

BOONE, Thetford Bolton. ■ 75214 #048-02-1954 L1954 **U** *071 †95

BOONE, Wei Wei L. 1935 MOTOR ST, 75235 #243-69-1984 L2003 **AN** *020

BOOS, Stephanie Catherine. 5323 HARRY HINES BLVD, U TX OUTHWESTERN MED 75390 #021-05-2006 **PD** *012

BOOTH, Timothy Nicholas. 1935 MOTOR ST, DEPT OF RADIOLOGY 75235 #021-05-1990 L1997 **PDR** *020 †80

BORDLEE, Annie Marie. ■ 75204 #021-05-1974 L1982 **DR** *020 †80

BOREHAM, Muriel Lee. 3600 GASTON AVE, WADLEY TOWER, STE 558 75246 #039-01-1995 L1998 **OBG** *020 †30

BORMANN, Brian Eric. 13601 PRESTON RD, STE 900W 75240 #048-13-1977 L1977 **AN** *020 †05

BORNSTEIN, Sue Levey. 3801 GASTON AVE 75246 #048-15-1992 L1993 **IM** *020 †20

BORRELLI, Joseph, Jr. 1801 INWOOD RD, # WA4-312 75235 #011-04-1988 L2007 **ORS** *020 †40

BOSE, Rahul. 3500 GASTON AVE, MEDICAL CENT 75246 #048-16-2004 L2008 **IM** *100 †20

BOSSARD, Robert Franklin. 13601 PRESTON RD, STE 900 75240 #016-02-1977 L1985 **AN EM** *020 †05

BOSWELL, George M, Jr. 3600 GASTON AVE STE 556, WADLEY TOWER 75246 #048-12-1950 L1950 **ORS** *071 †40

BOSWORTH, Carly Jeanne. ■ 75204 #048-14-2007 **PD** *012

BOTONE, Zachary Querino. ■ 75219 #012-05-2006 **FP** *012

BOTTS, John T. 6757 ARAPAHO RD, STE 711 75248 #048-13-1995 L1999 **AN** *020 †05

BOTTY SAMAYOA, Carlos F. ■ 75248 #429-01-1963 L1974 **AN** *071 †05

BOUDREAUX, John Kelly. 13601 PRESTON RD STE 10 75240 #021-05-1986 L1991 **AN** *020 †05

BOUFFARD, John-Paul. 3600 GASTON AVE, WADLEY TOWER, SUITE 261 75246 #023-12-1990 L2004 **ATP NP** *020 †50

BOULAS, H Jay. 8220 WALNUT HILL LN, STE 514 75231 #048-12-1984 L1985 **ORS HS** *020 †40

BOULAS, Stanley H. 8230 WALNUT HILL LN 75231 #041-01-1958 1964 **GYN** *071 †30

BOURLAND, Christina Castr. 5323 HARRY HINES BLVD, UT SOUTHWESTERN MEDICAL CE 75390 #001-02-2003 L2006 **PD** *020 †55

BOURLAND, John Bookhout. 3500 W WHEATLAND RD 75237 #023-07-1967 L1967 **ORS** *020 †40

BOURLAND, Walter Lee, Jr. 8160 WALNUT HILL LN, STE 113 75231 #027-01-1975 L1976 **GS** *020 †85

BOUTROS, Hoda Ishak. 221 W COLORADO BLVD, STE 420 75208 #915-05-1972 L1982 **OPH** *020 †35

BOWDEN, Ben Wanslee. 9440 POPPY DR 75218 #048-12-1948 L1948 **GP** *071

BOWEN, Paul A, II. ■ 75224 #012-05-1978 L1981 **NEP OS** *020 †20

BOWER, Jeffrey Harding. 7777 FOREST LN STE B2 75230 #048-04-1976 L1980 **PUD IM** *020 †20

BOWER, Matthew Richard. ■ 75208 #048-12-2003 L2008 **GS** *012

BOWERMAN, Minerva. 14020 COIT RD 75240 #649-10-1974 L1988 **RO** *020

BOWERS, Bruce Stroehman. 7777 FOREST LN STE A202 75230 #422-01-1998 L2006 **IC** *020 †20

BOWERS, Daniel C. 1935 MOTOR ST 75235 #048-12-1993 L1994 **PHO** *020 †55

BOWERS, Steven Paul. 111 COMMERCE ST 75201 #048-12-1973 L1973 **IM** *020 †20

BOWMAN, Patricia Ann. ■ 75229 #028-03-1979 *100

BOWMAN, Robert Wayne, Jr. 5323 HARRY HINES BLVD, UT SW DEPT OF OPHTHAL 75390 #028-03-1976 L1982 **OPH** *020 †35

BOYD, John W. 13601 PRESTON RD, STE 900 75240 #048-12-1982 L1983 **AN** *020 †05

BOYD, Katherine K. 2301 S HAMPTON RD, STE 200 75224 #039-79-1992, ▲ L1994 **OBG** *020

BOYDEN, Margaret Ann. ■ 75235 #048-12-2007 **PD** *012

BOYER, Craig Allan. 4131 N CENTRAL EXPY, METRO ANESTHESIA 75204 #045-04-1997 L2007 **AN** *020 †05

BOZEMAN, George P. 1717 MAIN ST STE 5200 75201 #011-04-1977 L1978 **EM OM** *020 †16

BRADLEY, Frank Joseph. 7525 SCYENE RD 75227 #028-78-1959, ▲ L1959 **R** *072

BRADLEY, Vincent Henry. 7777 FOREST LN, STE C704 75230 #918-01-1968 L1974 **AN** *020 †05

BRADSHAW, Karen Dorothy. 5323 HARRY HINES BLVD, DEPT OBGYN 75235 #048-12-1981 L1988 **REN OBG** *030 †30

BRADY, Wesley Anne. 9101 N CENTRAL EXPY, STE 550 75231 #048-12-1998 L1999 **GYN** *020

BRAJTBORD, Dan. 6301 GASTON AVE, EAST TOWER, SUITE 400 75214 #038-43-1985 L1986 **AN** *020 †05

BRAKENRIDGE, Scott Charle. ■ 75204 #016-01-2004 **GS** *012

BRANCACCIO, Anne Marie. 5151 HARRY HINES BLVD 75235 #038-41-1995 L2004 **IM** *020 †20

BRANCACCIO, Frank A. 3600 GASTON AVE, STE 806 75246 #048-12-1994 L1995 **PCC** *020 †20

BRANCH, George Robt, Jr. 8200 WALNUT HILL LN 75231 #048-02-1941 L1941 **PD** *071 †55

BRANCH, Rudolph Elroy. 15150 PRESTON RD, STE 300 75248 #027-01-1968 L1969 **OTO** *020 †45

BRANCH, William Milton. 8210 WALNUT HILL LN, STE 212 75231 #048-12-1944 L1945 **ORS** *071 †40

BRANCHEAU, Michael R. 9330 POPPY DR, MEDICINE 75218 #048-14-1993 L1997 **IM** *020 †20

BRANDL, Amy Lynn. 8355 WALNUT HILL LN 75231 #048-14-2003 L2005 **PD** *020 †55

BRANDON, David Charlton. ■ 75229 #048-04-2004 L2007 **NM** *100 †28

BRANNING, George B. 3600 GASTON AVE 75246 #048-12-1989 L1990 **OBG** *020 †30

BRANNON, Robert L. 7834 CARUTH CT 75225 #048-12-1962 L1962 **OBG** *020 †30

BRANNON, Timothy S. 3500 GASTON AVE, 3 HOB PEDIATRICS BUMC 75246 #048-12-1988 L1989 **NPM PD** *020 †55

BRAR, Avathar. 3500 GASTON AVE 75246 #495-43-1951 L1970 **OBG** *020

BRAR, Jangsher Singh. 5909 HARRY HINES BLVD 75235 #495-43-1960 L1970 **IM** *071

BRAS, Paul Johannes. 1935 MOTOR ST 75235 #917-25-1980 L1994 **AN** *020 †05

BRASIER, Cynthia Louise. 12801 MIDWAY RD STE 212, # 109 75244 #048-12-1999 L2003 **P** *020 †75 ‡

BRATTELI, Christopher W. ■ 75201 #026-04-2000 L2007 **RNR** *020 †80

BRAUN, Lea. 3626 N HALL ST STE 900 75219 #048-13-1971 L1971 **OBG** *020

BRAVENEC, Brian J. 7777 FOREST LN STE B 75230 #048-14-2002 L2006 **AN** *100 †05

BRAWLEY, Wm Lowell, Jr. ■ 75230 #048-12-1960 L1960 **AM** *071

BRAY, Steven Richard. 3600 GASTON AVE, BARNETT TOWER, SUITE 206 75246 #048-12-1999 L2002 **IM** *020 †20

BRAZDA, Amy Claire. ■ 75204 #021-05-2006 **GS** *012

BREHM, David W. 6190 LBJ FWY, STE 800 75240 #048-12-1997 L2000 **FM** *020 †18

BREKKEN, Alvin Lee. 2915 VINE ST 75204 #056-05-1958 L1971 **OBG** *030 †30

BRENNAN, J Michael. 3600 GASTON AVE, 1155 WADLEY TOWER 75246 #048-12-1989 L1993 **P PYG** *020

BRENSKI, Amy C. 5323 HARRY HINES BLVD, U.T. SOUTHWESTERN MEDICAL 75390 #016-01-1993 L2000 **PDO** *020 †45

BRESLAU, Neil Art. 910 N CENTRAL EXPY 75204 #047-05-1972 L1978 **END IM** *020 †20

BRESSLER, Peter Edward. 9301 N CENTRAL EXPY, TOWER II, STE 570 75231 #003-01-1987 L1990 **END** *020 †20

BRESSLER, Robert Kloeb. ■ 75204 #048-12-2003 L2007 **DR** *012

BRET, Mary E. 5323 HARRY HINES BLVD #048-14-1998 L2003 **PYG** *020 †75

BREWER, Bryan Daniel. ■ 75204 #048-14-2006 **GS** *012

BREWER, Jacquelyn Michell. ■ 75204 #021-01-2006 **OTO** *012

BRICKNER, Mary Elizabeth. 5909 HARRY HINS BLVD HA913, UTSW MEDICAL CENTER 75235 #038-40-1985 L1989 **CD IM** *020 †20

BRIDGES, Debbie Ann. 3409 WORTH ST STE 710, NORTH TX INFECTIOUS DISEAS 75246 #017-20-2001 L2003 **ID** *020 †20

BRIGGS, Douglas Garrett. 9528 WEBB CHAPEL RD 75220 #036-01-1987 L1988 **FM** *020 †18

BRILAKIS, Emmanouil S. 4500 S LANCASTER RD, # 111A 75216 #418-01-1995 L2004 **IC CD** *020 †20

BRIN, Barbara Jeanne. ■ 75225 #008-01-1977 L1993 **PS GS** *020 †85

BRINER, Susan Rebekah. 2875 MERRELL RD 75229 #048-02-1978 L1978 **PD** *020 †55

BRINKER, Stephanie K. ■ 75248 #048-14-2008 *012

BRINKMAN, Uta Kathrin. ■ 75205 #051-04-1996 L1997 **PD** *075 †55

BRINKMAN, William Tumpane. 7777 FOREST LN, STE A323 75230 #012-05-1996 L2007 **TS** *100 †85,90

BRION, Luc P. 5323 HARRY HINES BLVD, STOP 9063-PEDS DEPT 75390 #165-01-1976 L2007 **PD NPM** *030 †55

BRISTOW, Ronald Griffith. 1110 N BUCKNER BLVD # 103 75218 #047-06-1971 L1974 **GYN** *020 †30

BROCHU, Francis Louis. ■ 75208 #067-01-1947 L1957 **GS** *030 †85

BROCK, Michelle Jean. ■ 75235 #048-12-2008 *012

BROCKIE, Robert Edwin. 9330 POPPY DR STE 405 75218 #048-12-1982 L1983 **CD IM** *020 †20

BRODERS, Albert C, III. 8160 WALNUT HILL LN, STE 007 75231 #036-07-1974 L1975 **EM IM** *020 †20,16

BRODSKY, Alan Lawrence. 7777 FOREST LN 75230 #028-02-1967 L1972 **RHU IM** *020 †20

BRODSKY, Charles Stuart. 3600 GASTON AVE, STE 300 75246 #035-08-1992 L1996 **OBG** *020 †30

BRODSKY, James White. 7777 FOREST LN, STE C106 75230 #038-06-1979 L1979 **ORS OS** *020 †40

BROKER, Harshal S. 4400 W UNIVERSTY BLVD #510 75209 #048-12-2002 L2006 **VS** *012 †85

BROOKING, Donald G W. 3600 GASTON AVE, 912 BARNETT TOWER 75246 #026-04-1949 L1955 **D** *020 †15

BROOKS, Alison Jeanne. 5323 HARRY HINES BLVD, SOUTHWESTERN MED 75390 #035-48-2003 L2007 **OBG** *100

BROOKS, Barry Don. 7777 FOREST LN, STE D400 75230 #048-12-1976 L1976 **ON HEM** *020 †20

BROOKS, Durado Dante. 4916 GULFSTREAM DR 75244 #038-45-1982 L1990 **IM** *020 †20

BROOKS, James Gordon, Jr. 9330 POPPY DR, STE 300 75218 #001-02-1973 L1975 **ORS OAR** *020 †40

BROOKS, James Lee. 6211 W NORTHWEST HWY 75225 #048-12-1973 L1973 **AN CD** *020 †05

BROOKS, John Craven. 3434 SWISS AVE, STE 310 75204 #048-02-1980 L1980 **IM** *020 †20

BROOKS, Lynn. 4500 S LANCASTER RD, SOUTH SHORE MEDICAL CENTER 75216 #048-02-1988 L1989 **OBG** *020 †30

BROOKS, Sally B. 8220 WALNUT HILL LN, STE 214 LB 101 75231 #048-12-1995 L1996 **GE** *020 †20

BROOKS, William Cecil. 5201 HARRY HINES BLVD 75235 #048-12-1958 L1958 **SO OM** *040 †85

BROTANEK, Jane Marie. 5323 HARRY HINES BLVD 75390 #035-19-1998 L2008 **PD** *020 †55

BROTHERMAN, Donald Peter. 10 MEDICAL PKWY, NO 102 75234 #048-02-1964 L1964 **OPH** *035 †35

BROTHERS, Sandra Zoe. 411 N WASHINGTON AVE, STE 2700 75246 #048-12-1994 L1995 **OBG** *020 †30

BROUGH, Jonathan R. 8160 WALNUT HILL LN, STE 200 75231 #048-02-1989 L1990 **OBG** *020 †30

BROWDER, Frederick H. 13601 PRESTON RD, STE 900W 75240 #048-13-1982 L1983 **AN** *020 †05

BROWN, Bertrand James, Jr. ■ 75230 #025-07-2000 L2006 **AN** *100

BROWN, Byron Lindsay. 3600 GASTON AVE 75246 #048-12-1962 L1962 **PS** *020 †65

BROWN, Christine Dunham. 3801 GASTON AVE, STE 302 75246 #011-04-1987 L1988 **D DS** *020 †15 ‡

BROWN, Donald S. 9543 LOSA DR, AT CASA LINDA 75218 #048-12-1946 L1953 **IM CD** *071 †20

BROWN, Douglas Kirk. 3500 W WHEATLAND RD 75237 #048-12-1976 L1976 **AN** *020

BROWN, Edson S, Jr. 5323 HARRY HINES BLVD 75390 #048-14-1993 L1995 **P** *050 †75

BROWN, Forrest Carroll. 7777 FOREST LN STE C528 75230 #048-12-1966 L1966 **DS D** *020 †15

BROWN, Geri R. 5323 HARRY HINES BLVD 75235 #048-12-1988 L1989 **GE** *020 †20

BROWN, Herbert C. 8200 WALNUT HILL LN 75231 #048-12-2000 L2003 **AN** *020 †05

BROWN, Irwin Hubert, Jr. 4500 S LANCASTER RD, ANESTHESIOLOGY (112A) 75216 #039-01-1987 L2008 **AN** *020 †05

BROWN, John Hallum. 9616B WEBB CHAPEL RD 75220 #048-12-1965 L1965 **FM** *020 †18

BROWN, Jroyston. 4500 S LANCASTER RD # 11C1 75216 #004-01-1954 L1958 **OS AN** *030 †05 ‡

BROWN, Kathryn Angela. 1441 N BECKLEY AVE, STE 4116 75203 #048-12-1998 L2001 **IM** *020 †20

BROWN, Kendall O. 7777 FOREST LN, ST B304 75230 #048-12-1984 L1987 **PG PD** *020 †55

BROWN, Kevin Thomas. ■ 75372 #048-12-2004 L2006 **P** *012

BROWN, Marc Robt. 4131 N CENTRAL EXPY, METRO ANESTHESIA 75204 #025-01-1985 L1986 **AN** *020 †05

BROWN, Michael Edwin. 8345 WALNUT HILL LN, BLDG D 75231 #047-05-1978 L1979 **PD** *020 †55

BROWN, Michael Stuart. 5323 HARRY HINES BLVD 75390 #041-01-1966 L1973 **CD IM** *050 †20

BROWN, Orval Eric. 5303 HARRY HINES BLVD, FL 7 # 104 75390 #048-12-1977 L1977 **OTO** *040 †45

BROWN, Philip Michael. 3600 GASTON AVE STE 360, BAYLOR PAIN MGMT CTR 75246 #917-05-1971 L2003 **PME** *020

BROWN, Ray H. ■ 75248 #048-12-1987 L1988 **FM** *020 †18

BROWN, Stuart M. 5310 HARVEST HILL RD 75230 #023-01-1954 L1960 **D** *020 †15

BROWNE, Michael Gerard. ■ 75225 #035-09-1988 L1990 **OSM** *020 †40

BROWN-ELLIOTT, Carol Lace. 8160 WALNUT HILL LN, STE 114 75231 #005-02-1990 L1996 **OBG** *020 †20

BROWNING, Adrianne Cones. ■ 75218 #048-12-2006 **OBG** *012

BROWNING, Jeffrey D. 5323 HARRY HINES BLVD, UT SOUTHWESTERN MEDICAL CE 75390 #048-12-1998 L2001 **GE** *100 †20

BROXHAM, Eric Jeffrey. ■ 75235 #048-12-2008 *012

BROYLES, Rebecca S. 5201 HARRY HINES BLVD 75235 #048-02-1982 L1983 **NPM PD** *050 †55

BRUCE, Gordon. 1935 MOTOR ST 75235 #048-12-1992 L1993 **PD** *020 †55

BRUCE, Laura Marie. 3409 WORTH ST, STEMMONS TOWER, STE 640 75246 #027-01-1995 L2001 **GS** *020 †85

BRUCE, Robert Lance. 909 N WASHINGTON AVE 75246 #649-14-1972 L1978 **PM** *020 †60

BRUCK, William Albert. 9301 N CENTRAL EXPY, STE 400 75231 #048-12-1976 L1976 **ORS OSS** *020 †40

BRUCKS, Anton Bernhard. 4224 SWISS AVE 75204 #048-12-1960 L1960 **GYN** *030 †30

BRUEL, Brian Mendoza. ■ 75390 #748-10-2001 L2007 **APM** *020 †60

BRUGAROLAS, James Brufau. 5323 HARRY HINES BLVD, DEPT HEMATOL-ONCOL 75323 #847-11-1993 L2006 **ON IM** *020 †20

BRUGGMAN, Amanda Renee. ■ 75201 #048-02-2005 L2007 **EM** *012

BRUNKEN, Robert B. 3767 FOREST LN STE 11 75244 #048-12-1953 L1953 **OBG** *020 †30

BRUNS, Brandon Robert. SOUTHWESTERN MED, UNIV OF TEXAS 75390 #048-14-2003 L2008 **GS** *012

BRYAN, Bertell Collis. 8210 WALNUT HILL LN, STE 100 75231 #047-05-1961 L1967 **OPH** *071 †35

BRYAN, Vance W, Jr. 8200 WALNUT HILL LN, DEPT OF PATHOLOGY 75231 #048-02-1974 L1974 **PTH** *020 †50

BRYANT, David E. 13601 PRESTON RD STE 900W, CONSULTANTS, P.A. 75240 #048-04-1986 L1987 **AN** *020 †05

BRYANT, Morris R. 1441 N BECKLEY AVE, METHODIST DALLAS MEDICAL C 75203 #048-12-1990 L1991 **OBG** *020 †30

BRYANT, Sullivan Ross. 3534 N HAMPTON RD 75212 #028-79-1973, ▲ L1974 *020

BRYLOWSKI, Andrew. 12300 FORD RD, STE 150 75234 #048-14-1987 L1988 **P** *020 †75

BUCA, Stefan Cosmin. 75219 #048-12-2008 *012

BUCH, Richard Geo. 7777 FOREST LN STE C737 75230 #016-11-1982 L1989 **ORS** *020 †40

BUCHANAN, George. 5323 HARRY HINES BLVD 75390 #016-02-1970 L1977 **PD HEM** *050 †20

BUCHANAN, Jennifer Sue. 12655 N CENTRAL EXPY, STE 300 75243 #048-04-1983 L1983 **PD** *020 †55

BUCHOLZ, Robert Wm. 5323 HARRY HINES BLVD 75390 #008-01-1973 L1977 **ORS TRS** *020 †40

BUDDRUS, David James. ■ 75231 #030-06-1947 L1948 **PA PD** *071 †55

BUDHWAR, Nitin. ■ 75390 #065-09-1997 L2007 **FPG** *020 †18

BUFORD, Don Alex, Jr. 1015 N CARROLL AVE, STE 2000 75204 #005-14-1993 L1995 **ORS OSM** *020 †20

BUHNER, David Morrow. 7777 FOREST LN STE B214 75230 #048-04-1979 L1979 **RHU IM** *020 †20,03

BUI, David Truong. 5600 W LOVERS LN, # 116-113 75209 #035-45-1987 L1996 **AN** *020 †05

BUKHARI, Hassan Imam. 9330 POPPY DR, STE 500 75218 #704-01-1962 L1973 **VS GS** *020 †85

BUKHARI, Rizwan Hassan. 621 N HALL ST, STE 520 75226 #048-12-1991 L1992 **VS VIR** *030 †85

BULL, Shawna Lyn. 5323 HARRY HINES BLVD, RM J7.124 75390 #011-02-2000 L2004 **OBG** *020

BULLEN, Ricardo. 5323 HARRY HINES BLVD 75235 #715-01-1979 L1990 **D GS** *020 †15

BULLOCH, Gerald Franklin. 221 W COLORADO BLVD, PAVILION II STE 545 75208 #025-01-1977 L1982 **CD** *020 †20

BULLOCK, Emily C. 2854 DUVAL DR 75211 #048-15-2002 L2006 **OBG** *020

BUNDRICK, Lindsay Taylor. ■ 75204 #048-14-2007 **IM** *012

BUNTING, Liza Danielle. ■ 75204 #048-16-2004 L2007 **EM** *020

BURCH, Robert R. ■ 75201 #021-01-1951 L1951 **IM OB** *071 †20

BURDICK, James Steven. 3600 GASTON AVE, STE 556 75246 #039-01-1985 L1996 **GE** *020 †20

BURESH, Cary Jocelyn. 8267 ELMBROOK DR, STE 100 75247 #030-05-1994 L2002 **SP** *020 †50

BURGARDT, John David. 606 N WASHINGTON AVE 75246 #027-01-1990 L1993 **DR** *020 †80

BURGHER, Stephen Woods. 3500 GASTON AVE, BAYLOR UNIV MED CTR-EMERG 75246 #048-14-1990 L1991 **EM** *020 †16

BURK, Linda L. 8230 WALNUT HILL LN, STE 308 LB 25 75231 #025-01-1980 L1987 **OPH** *035

BURKE, Andrew Barrand. 1717 N GARRETT AVE 75206 #028-78-1980, ▲ L1981 **FM PD** *020

BURKE, Anna S. 9101 N CENTRAL EXPY, STE 300 75231 #048-02-2001 L2004 **IM** *020

BURKE, Robert J. 3535 TRAVIS ST STE 210 75204 #048-12-1982 L1983 **AN** *020 †05

BURKE, Sara Lee Stewart. 13601 PRESTON RD, STE 900W 75240 #048-12-1982 L1983 **AN** *020 †05

BURKHART, Zachary. ■ 75204 #048-12-2008 *012

BURKHEAD, W Zealous, Jr. 9301 N CENTRAL EXPY, STE 400 75231 #048-02-1978 L1978 **ORS** *020 †40

BURKLE, Frederick M, Jr. ■ 75248 #050-02-1965 L1978 **EM PD** *040 †55,16

BURLESON, Dale D, Jr. 7777 FOREST LN STE A321, TEXAS COLON & RECTAL SURGE 75230 #048-16-1990 L1991 **CRS GS** *020 †85,10

BURMAN, Malika. 8440 WALNUT HILL LN, STE 510 75231 #035-01-2003 L2004 **P** *100

BURMAN, Sudeep. 8440 WALNUT HILL LN, STE 510 75231 #495-36-1975 L1981 **RNR R** *020 †80

BURNER, James D. ■ 75219 #037-01-1994 L2004 **BBK** *020 †50

BURNETT, Karen Lynn. ■ 75209 #048-12-2005 **GS** *012

BURNETT, William David. 9323 GARLAND RD STE 104 75218 #048-12-1975 L1975 **GP** *020

BURNS, Alton Jay. 411 N WASHINGTON AVE, SUITE 5300,LB 13 75246 #048-12-1981 L1981 **PS GS** *040 †85,65

BURNS, Carol Jane. 10830 N CENTRAL EXPY 75231 #048-12-1979 L1979 **AN** *020 †05

BURNS, Debra Lou. 8315 WALNUT HILL LN, STE 140 75231 #036-05-1983 L1984 **PD** *020 †55

BURNS, Dennis Kendall. 5323 HARRY HINES BLVD 75235 #048-12-1978 L1978 **NP PTH** *020 †50

BURNS, John L. 411 N WASHINGTON AVE, DALLAS PLASTIC SURGERY INS 75246 #048-02-1998 L2003 **PS** *020 †65

BURNS, Robert Richard. ■ 75208 #048-12-1955 L1955 **R OS** *071 †80

BURNS, Robert White. 9440 POPPY DR 75218 #048-12-1973 L1973 **ON HO** *020 †20

BURNSIDE, John Wayne. 5201 HARRY HINES BLVD 75235 #016-11-1966 L1988 **IM RHU** *020 †20

BURRIS, Scott Bradley. 13601 PRESTON RD, STE 900 75240 #048-02-1984 L1986 **AN** *020 †05

BURRIS, William J. 13601 PRESTON RD STE 10 75240 #048-12-1985 L1986 **AN** *020 †05

BURTON, Elizabeth C. 3500 GASTON AVE, BUMC 75246 #021-05-1994 L2001 **PTH FOP** *020 †50

BURTON, Valerie Lynn. 12655 N CENTRAL EXPY # 300, DEV PEDIATRIC SERVICES 75243 #039-01-1988 L2008 **NDP OS** *020 †55

BURY, Dixie L. 13601 PRESTON RD 75240 #048-14-1988 L1989 **AN** *020 †05

BUSCH, Robert J. ■ 75204 #048-12-2007 *012

BUSH, Matthew D. 7777 FOREST LN, MEDICAL CITY EMERGENCY SER 75230 #048-12-1996 L1999 **EM** *020 †16

BUSSEY, Linda Susan. 3500 GASTON AVE 75246 #048-12-1980 L1980 **AN** *020 †05

BUSTAMANTE, Julia A. 13601 PRESTON RD, STE 900 75240 #028-03-1985 L1993 **AN** *020 †05

BUSTELO, Carlos Girod. 5323 HARRY HINES BLVD, U.T. SOUTHWESTERN MED CTR 75390 #042-01-1988 L1989 **PUD IM** *020 †20

BUTLER, Kira Linell. 7777 FOREST LN 75230 #025-07-1996 L2000 **OBG** *020 †30

BUTTERFIELD, Jeffery Todd. 8160 WALNUT HILL LN # 007, EMERGENCY MEDICINE 75231 #012-01-1995 L1999 **EM** *020 †16

BUXIE, Caraleigh N. ■ 75204 #048-14-2008 *012

BYERLY, Matthew John. 6363 FOREST PARK RD, STE 651 75235 #003-01-1990 L1998 **P** *020 †75

BYERLY, Stephanie Ilene. 5323 HARRY HINES BLVD, DEPT OF ANESTHESIOLOGY 75390 #011-03-1992 L1999 **AN** *020 †05

BYERS, Jerome L. ■ 75205 #048-02-1952 L1952 **OPH** *071 †35

BYRD, David William. 13601 PRESTON RD, STE 900 75240 #051-04-1993 L1997 **AN** *020 †05

BYRD, Henry Stephenson. 411 N WASHINGTON AVE STE 5, # 6000 75246 #048-02-1972 L1972 **PS GS** *020 †85,65

BYWATERS, Theodore W, Jr. 3500 GASTON AVE 75246 #048-12-1957 L1957 **ORS** *071 †40

CADE, Samuel Houston, Jr. 3701 JUNIUS ST # CS11-012 75246 #021-05-1966 L1969 **DR R** *020 †80

CADEDDU, Jeffrey Anthony. 5323 HARRY HINES BLVD, UT SW MED CENTER 75390 #023-07-1993 L1999 **U** *020 †95

CADERAO, Jess B. 1863 W MOCKINGBIRD LN, APT 221 75235 #748-02-1957 L1973 **RO** *020 †80 ‡

CAERO, Joseph German. 13601 PRESTON RD, STE 900W 75240 #176-03-1985 L1990 **AN IM** *020 †05

CAI, Wenhui. 16800 DALLAS PKWY, STE 150 75248 #243-16-1991 L2003 **P** *020 †75

CAIN, Charles Reasor. 4006 LIVE OAK ST 75204 #048-12-1957 L1957 **OM FM** *071 †18

CAIN, John W. 5323 HARRY HINES BLVD 75390 #048-14-1982 L1983 **P** *040 †75

CALDERA, Javier Rafael. ■ 75390 #042-01-2001 L2004 **ETX** *020 †16

CALDWELL, Joe B. ■ 75238 #048-12-1952 L1952 **DR** *020 †80

CALLEJAS, Heriberto Jose. 129 W 9TH ST 75208 #649-14-1992 L1996 **IM** *020 †20

CALLEWART, Craig Carter. 3900 JUNIUS ST, STE 705 75246 #048-12-1986 L1987 **OSS** *020 †40

CALLEWART, Robert A. ■ 75229 #048-12-1986 **ORS** *071 †40

CALOSS, Ron, Jr. ■ 75390 #048-13-1999 L2002 **GS** *020

CALVO, Ricardo Ernesto. 1935 MOTOR ST 75235 #048-15-1986 L1990 **CHN PD** *020 †55,75

CAMAK, James Newton, Jr. 221 W COLORADO BLVD, STE 440 PAV II 75208 #048-12-1968 L1968 **DR** *071 †80

CAMARGO, Carlos E. 9440 POPPY DR 75218 #264-01-1958 L1975 **AN** *071 †05

CAMERON, Jennifer Gail. 4121 THROCKMORTON ST 75219 #030-06-1996 L1998 **DR** *020 †80

CAMERON, John Scott. 5323 HARRY HINES BLVD, DEPARTMENT OF PEDIATRICS 75390 #024-01-1992 L2001 **PD** *020 †55

CAMP, Julie E. ■ 75243 #048-15-2004 **DR** *012

CAMPBELL, Allen Dryer, Jr. 1310 STEMMONS AVE 75208 #048-12-1947 L1947 **OPH** *071 †35

CAMPBELL, Andrew Foil. 400 S ZANG BLVD, STE 1005 75208 #012-05-1980 L1982 **P** *020

CAMPBELL, Donovan. 3600 GASTON AVE STE 860 75246 #048-12-1954 L1954 **AN** *071 †05

CAMPBELL, Tamara. 5323 HARRY HINES BLVD, STOP 9031 75390 #048-12-1995 L1997 **DR** *020 †80

CANADAS-ZIZZIAS, Rafael. 12200 PARK CENTRAL DR, STE 200 75251 #132-06-1990 L1996 **IM IMG** *020

CANCEMI, Eric T. 3701 JUNIUS ST, CS11 C001 75246 #422-01-1993 L1998 **AN** *020 †05

CANCEMI, Mark R. 6301 GASTON AVE, EAST TOWER, SUITE 400 75214 #048-02-1988 L1989 **AN** *020 †05

CANDY, Errol J. 8440 WALNUT HILL LN, STE 510 75231 #775-01-1978 L1988 **RNR** *071 †80

CANNADA, Lisa Kaye. 5323 HARRY HINES BLVD MC, UTSW 75390 #023-01-1996 L2005 **ORS** *020 †40

CANNADAY, John Jarred. 12200 PRESTON RD, CT NORTH 75230 #039-01-1984 L1991 **DR R** *020 †80

CANNON, Stephen Caldwell. ■ 75205 #023-07-1986 L2004 **N** *020 †75

CANNON, Walter, Jr. 3500 GASTON AVE, AMERICAN RADIOLOGY 75246 #025-01-1995 L2005 **MSR** *020

CAO, Dianjun. SOUTHWESTERN MED, UNIV OF TEXAS 75390 #243-69-1987 L2004 **CD** *012 †20

CAO, Uyen-Thi T. ■ 75219 #048-13-2000 L2003 **IM** *020

CAPATI, Remigio. 1400 N WESTMORELAND ST, STE 402 75211 #748-01-1990 L1994 **PD** *020 †55

CAPEHART, John Edward. 3600 GASTON AVE STE 404 75246 #039-01-1974 L1985 **TS** *020 †85,90

CAPEHART, Raeann G. 1151 N BUCKNER BLVD, STE 105 75218 #039-01-1977 L1986 **GS VS** *020

CAPPS, Erin Frankie. ■ 75208 #048-12-2006 **DR** *012

CARAMELA, Calvin Michael. 7704 WILLOW WIND CT, # 20-101 75230 #010-02-1948 L1965 **U** *071 †95

CARDER, Henry Maurice. 8315 WALNUT HILL LN, STE 135 75231 #048-12-1963 L1963 **OTO** *020 †45

CARDER, Kerry Robin. 9900 N CENTRAL EXPY, STE 225 75231 #048-14-1992 L1993 **D** *020 †15,55

CARINO, Enrique. 3601 SWISS AVE 75204 #042-01-1993 L1998 **NEP** *020 †20

CARLEY, Michael Edward. 3600 GASTON AVE, WADLEY TOWER, STE 558 75246 #035-03-1995 L1997 **OBG** *020 †30

CARLILE, Mary Culver. 909 N WASHINGTON AVE 75246 #039-01-1988 L1989 **PM** *020 †60

CARLO, John Thomas. 2377 N STEMMONS FWY, # 515 75207 #048-12-2000 L2004 **GS** *030 ‡

CARLOS, Joseph J. 7777 FOREST LN, STE 560 75230 #025-12-1977 L1981 **OBG** *020 †30

CARLSON, Karen Sue. 7777 FOREST LN 75230 #056-06-1992 L1996 **OBG** *020 †30

CARLSON, Theodore J. 8210 WALNUT HILL LN, STE 912 75231 #048-02-1983 L1983 **PDC PD** *020 †55

CARMAN, Alisa K. ■ 75218 #048-12-2002 L2004 **PPR** *012 †55

CARMAN, George H. 3500 GASTON AVE 75246 #035-20-1951 L1960 **CD IM** *071 †20

CARNEGIE, Alfred Lind D. ■ 75237 #803-03-1936 **OS** *050

CARNES, Christina Louise. 8350 N CENTRAL EXPY, CAMPBELL CENTRE I, SUITE M 75206 #021-01-1999 L2002 **PD** *020 †55

CARNES, Kevin S. 13601 PRESTON RD, STE 900 75240 #048-12-1993 L1994 **AN** *020 †05

CARNEY, David Spencer. ■ 75206 #012-05-2001 L2007 **GE** *012

CARNEY, Leonard Robin. ■ 75219 #803-03-1958 L1965 **N** *071 †75

CARPENTER, Marsha B. 2222 WELBORN ST 75219 #019-02-1976 L1981 **PD GP** *020 †55

CARPENTER, William M. 3409 WORTH ST STE 630 75246 #048-15-1986 L1988 **PS** *020 †65

CARR, Bruce Richard. 5323 HARRY HINES BLVD, STOP J6114 75390 #025-01-1971 L1973 **OBG REN** *020 †30

CARRASCO, Michael John. 7777 FOREST LN 75230 #048-12-1999 L2001 **EM** *020 †16

CARRICK, Kelley Suzanne. 5323 HARRY HINES BLVD 75390 #011-04-1995 L1998 **PTH** *020 †50

CARRINGTON, Tatyana F. 5909 HARRY HINES BLVD 75235 #935-01-1970 L1975 **IM** *071

CARROLL, James M. 8200 WALNUT HILL LN 75231 #048-12-1999 L2002 **IM** *020 †20

CARROLL, James Patrick. 3409 WORTH ST STE 640, URGENT SURGERY ASSOCIATES 75246 #021-01-1998 L2003 **GS** *020 †85

CARROLL, Michael Lindsey. 9208 ELAM RD STE 220 75217 #048-15-1979 L1979 **IM IMG** *020

CARROLL, Timothy Glenn. 1935 MOTOR ST, ATTN: MEDICAL EDUCATION DE 75235 #019-02-2002 L2003 **CCP** *012 †55

CARRUTH, Dolores M Hutto. 1935 MOTOR ST 75235 #048-12-1963 L1963 **NPM PD** *030 †55

CARTER, Bill R. 5310 BELT LINE RD 75254 #048-12-1964 L1964 **FM GP** *071 †18

CARTER, Carrie L. 8210 WALNUT HILL LN # 50 75231 #048-12-2001 L2004 **IM** *100 †20

CARTER, Gregory Sterling. 4500 S LANCASTER RD 75216 #055-01-1975 L1984 **N SME** *020 †75

CARTER, Harvey L, III. 7502 GREENVILLE AVE # 700 75231 #021-05-1982 **OPH** *020 †35

CARTER, Harvey Lee. 7502 GREENVILLE AVE # 700 75231 #021-05-1953 L1987 **PD** *071 †55

CARTER, Julian Gayden. 1311 N WASHINGTON AVE 75204 #048-02-1978 L1978 **OBG** *020 †30

CARTER, Khalil Jamal. 5323 HARRY HINES BLVD, SOUTHWESTERN MED 75390 #036-07-2004 **OBG** *012

CARTER, Peter R. 2222 WELBORN ST, ORTHOPAEDIC DEPT 75219 #034-01-1968 L1970 **HS** *040 †40

CARUANA, Albert Gasper, Jr. ■ 75204 #048-12-2003 L2007 **OPH** *020

CARY, Paul Raymond. 8210 WALNUT HILL LN, STE 230 75231 #005-02-1977 L1980 **IM IMG** *020 †20

CASAD, Connie. 7777 FOREST LN STE C202 75230 #048-13-1982 L1983 **GYN** *020 †30

CASANOVA, Mark A. 3434 SWISS AVE STE 2 75204 #048-02-2000 L2003 **IM** *020 †20

CASAS-GANEM, Jorge. 8230 WALNUT HILL LN, STE 514 75231 #048-01-1998 L2001 **ORS** *100

CASENAVE, Kristen L. 5959 HARRY HINES BLVD, STE 812 75235 #048-12-1998 L2000 **IM** *020 †20

CASEY, Brian. 5323 HARRY HINES BLVD, U.T. SOUTHWESTERN MEDICAL 75390 #041-13-1991 L1995 **OBG** *020 †30

CASEY, Donna Lynn. 8210 WALNUT HILL LN, STE 218 75231 #048-12-2000 L2003 **IM** *020 †20

CASEY, Franklin Le Roy. 8210 WALNUT HILL LN # 218 75231 #048-12-1964 L1964 **IM HEM** *020 †20

CASEY, John Geo. 3434 SWISS AVE STE 310 75204 #048-02-1973 L1973 **IM** *020 †20 ‡

CASEY, Patrick C. 9 MEDICAL PKWY, STE 107 75234 #048-12-1990 L1994 **AN** *020 †05

CASEY, Sara Beth. 5323 HARRY HINES BLVD, U.T. SOUTHWESTERN MED CTR. 75390 #028-03-1997 L1998 **P** *020 †75

CASIPIT, Calvin M. ■ 75367 #748-08-1971 L1980 **HEM IM** *020

CASIPIT, Concepcion. ■ 75367 #748-01-1972 **PD** *100

CASSIDY, Sharon Sue M. ■ 75218 #048-12-1971 L1973 **PUD IM** *020 †20

CASTANEDA, Rogelio. 1717 MAIN ST STE 5200 75201 #649-14-1990 L2001 **IM** *020 †20

CASTILLO, Jose Antonio. 1150 N BISHOP AVE 75208 #042-01-1988 L1993 **NEP** *020 †20

CASTILLO, Leticia. 75235 #024-01-2007 **IM** *012

CASTILLO, Luis Orlando. 1881 SYLVAN AVE STE 115 75208 #341-01-1968 L1982 **OBG** *020

CASTILLO, Michael P. ■ 75204 #048-12-2003 L2007 **OTO** *020

CASTILLON, Frank, III. 7515 GREENVILLE AVE, STE 1030 75231 #048-14-1999 L2005 **NS** *020

CASTORENA, Robert, Jr. 1935 MOTOR ST, CHILDREN'S MEDICAL CENTER 75235 #048-12-1998 L2003 **AN** *020 †05

CASTRILLON, Diego Hernan. 5323 HARRY HINES BLVD, PATHOLOGY DPT 75390 #048-12-1996 L2004 **PTH SP** *020 †50

CASTRO, Manuel Eduardo. 221 W COLORADO BLVD, PAVILION II, STE. 740 75208 #649-27-1983 L1994 **GS CCS** *020 †20

CASTRO-ANDRES, Grace. 1400 N WESTMORELAND RD, PARKLAND COPC - PROGRAM 75211 #748-01-1981 L1995 **IM** *020

CATHER, Jennifer Ann. 9101 N CENTRAL EXPY # 150 75231 #048-12-1994 L1996 **D** *020 †15

CATHER, John C. 5323 HARRY HINES BLVD, UT SOUTHWESTERN MED SCH 75390 #048-12-1994 L1996 **ADP** *012 †35

CAUDY, Debra Louise. 2201 INWOOD RD 75235 #011-02-1982 L1984 **ON** *020 †20

CAVANAGH, Harrison Dwight. 5323 HARRY HINES BLVD 75390 #023-07-1965 L1992 **OPH** *030 †35

CAVENEE, Michael Robt. 8160 WALNUT HILL LN, STE 1 75231 #048-12-1985 L1987 **OBG MFM** *071 †30

CAYTON, Evangeline T. 411 N WASHINGTON AVE, STE 4000 75246 #748-08-1972 L1978 **PM** *020 †60

CEARLEY, Carrie J. 5323 HARRY HINES BLVD 75390 #048-13-2007 **EM** *012

CEJUDO, Raul Fernando. 11457 LAMPLIGHTER LN 75229 #649-03-1973 L1988 **AN** *020 †05

CHA, Choon H. 4244 UNIVERSITY BLVD 75205 #048-04-1989 L1990 **N** *020 †75

CHA, Gloria Hyeyoung. 12221 MERIT DR STE 4 75251 #048-12-1996 L1999 **IM** *020 †20

CHA, Joseph Keun. 75219 #005-12-2007 **IM** *012

CHADHA, Mandeep Singh. ■ 75201 #048-02-1998 L2006 **CCP** *020 †55

CHADHA, Ruby Kaur. 75201 #012-05-1997 L2006 **DR** *020 †80

CHAGOYA, Marisa Luz. ■ 75206 #048-12-2008 *012

CHAKMAKJIAN, Zaven Hagop. 910 N CENTRAL EXPY 75204 #605-01-1963 L1969 **END DIA** *020 †20

CHAKRABORTY, Sayantani. 8230 WALNUT HILL LN, STE 410 75231 #012-01-2001 **IM** *020

CHALLAGUNDLA, Suneetha. 5323 HARRY HINES BLVD, SOUTHWESTERN MED 75390 #496-35-2000 **HO** *012 †20

CHAMNANVANAKIJ, Sangkae. 5323 HARRY HINES BLVD, UT SOUTHWESTERN MED CNTR 75390 #891-01-1986 **NPM** *100

CHAMPINE, Julie Gibson. 5323 HARRY HINES BLVD, DEPT RAD 75390 #048-13-1988 L1990 **DR** *040 †80

CHAN, Calvin C. 4131 N CENTRAL EXPY, METRO ANESTHESIA 75204 #048-16-2002 L2006 **AN** *020 †05

CHAN, Daniel Steven. ■ 75209 #048-13-2004 L2006 **ORS** *012

CHAN, Joanna Laihwa. ■ 75219 #005-11-2006 **D** *012

CHAN, Joseph. 2997 LBJ FWY, STE 215 75234 #028-02-1994 L1995 **VIR** *020 †80

CHAN, Samuel C. 5787 S HAMPTON RD STE 300 75232 #048-78-1990, ▲ L1991 **IM** *020 †20

CHAN, Vincent. ■ 75201 #048-12-2003 L2006 **GE** *012 †20

CHANDALIA, Manisha S. 6011 HARRY HINES BLVD, STE V5.100 75390 #495-17-1988 L1997 **IM** *020 †20

CHANDLER, Donald Stanley. 424 S CORINTH STREET RD 75203 #047-07-1969 L1981 **PD GP** *020 †55

CHANDLER, Matthew T. 16800 DALLAS PKWY, STE 150 75248 #048-12-1993 L1994 **P** *020 †75
CHANDRA, Krishna. 7777 FOREST LN STE B238 75230 #495-41-1964 L1978 **AN** *020 †05
CHANDRAKANTAN, Arun. 3500 GASTON AVE 75246 #033-05-1996 L2006 **NEP** *020 †20
CHANDRAN, Ramesh. 4500 S LANCASTER RD, 11C 75216 #496-28-1991 L2006 **SME IM** *012 †20
CHANDRASEKHARA, Ravi. 3450 W WHEATLAND RD # 240, RAVI CHANDRASEKHARA MD 75237 #011-03-1994 L2000 **CD** *020 †20
CHANEZ, James. 8230 WALNUT HILL LN, DRS COX FRATER & CHANEZ 75231 #048-13-2000 L2002 **IM** *020 †20 ‡
CHANG, Alin. 4131 N CENTRAL EXPY STE 4, METROPOLITAN ANESTHESIA 75204 #035-08-2003 L2007 **AN** *020
CHANG, Jitsen. 75203 #048-12-2008 *012
CHANG, Michael Lee. 1935 MOTOR ST, GRADUATE MEDICAL EDUCATION 75235 #048-12-2003 L2006 **PDI** *012 †55
CHANG, Shelly Ann. 1441 N BECKLEY AVE, MEDICAL EDUCATION DEPARTME 75203 #048-13-1997 L1998 **IM** *020 †20
CHANG, Suzie Heejeong. 75204 #010-02-2006 **PS** *012
CHANG, Thomas. 221 W COLORADO BLVD SU, ANESTHESIA CONSULTANTS OF 75208 #056-06-1994 L1998 **AN** *020 †20
CHANNABASAPPA, Nandini. 5323 HARRY HINES BLVD 75390 #894-01-2000 L2007 **PG** *012
CHANTILIS, Samuel J. 8160 WALNUT HILL LN, STE 328 75231 #048-12-1987 L1988 **REN OBG** *020 †30
CHAO, John Chiasu. ■ 75229 #048-12-2007 **ORS** *012
CHAPA, Hector O. 1135 N BISHOP AVE 75208 #048-12-1996 L1998 **OBG** *020 †30
CHAPMAN, Don Robt. 1015 N CARROLL AVE, STE 2000 75204 #048-14-1975 L1975 **ORS** *020 †40
CHAPMAN, Gregory Alan. 8160 WALNUT HILL LN # 224 75231 #048-15-1984 L1985 **OBG** *020 †20
CHAPMAN, Huntly Gordon. 3900 JUNIUS ST, STE 705 75246 #061-01-1971 L1977 **ORS OSS** *020 †40
CHAPMAN, Julie Ann. ■ 75248 #048-02-1979 L1979 **D** *020 †15
CHAPMAN, Michael Crenshaw. 12200 PRESTON RD 75230 #048-02-1999 L2002 **FM** *020 †18
CHARLESTON, Warren H. 13140 COIT RD, STE 518 75240 #048-16-1997 L1998 **P CHP** *020
CHARNSANGAVEJ, Nalinda. ■ 75219 #048-12-2006 **PD** *012
CHASMAWALA, Jayshri. 1911 ABRAMS PKWY STE A 75214 #048-78-2002, ▲ L2003 **FM** *020 †18
CHASON, David Paul. 5323 HARRY HINES BLVD 75390 #025-07-1981 L1991 **RNR DR** *020 †80
CHASON, Jacob Leon. ■ 75225 #051-01-1940 L1941 **NP ATP** *071 †50
CHATURVEDI, Ram Priya. ■ 75206 #045-04-1985 L1992 **DR** *020 †80
CHAU, Brandon. ■ 75201 #048-02-2003 L2006 **DR** *012
CHAUDHRY, Sameer. 4500 S LANCASTER RD, DALLAS VA MED SVC III 75216 #577-01-1990 L1995 **IM** *020 †20
CHAUVEAUX, Bert Lawson. ■ 75214 #048-13-1975 L1975 **EM** *012
CHAVEZ, Antonio Feliciano. 7557 RAMBLER RD STE 7 75231 #008-01-1995 L1999 **AN** *020 †05
CHEATHAM, David Alan. 8335 WALNUT HILL LN, STE 105 75231 #048-02-1975 L1975 **IM** *020 †20
CHEATUM, Don Elwood. 8440 WALNUT HILL LN, TEXAS MEDICAL & SURGICAL 75231 #028-02-1964 L1964 **RHU IM** *020 †20
CHEE-AWAI, Randall. 3650 W WHEATLAND RD, STE B 75237 #011-02-1986 L1996 **OBG** *020 †30
CHEEK, Brennen S. 3535 WORTH ST, FL 1 75246 #048-15-1994 L1995 **RO** *020 †20,80
CHEEK, J Harold. 3500 GASTON AVE 75246 #048-12-1944 L1945 **GS** *071 †85
CHEEK, John Paul, Jr. 8210 WALNUT HILL LN STE 51 75231 #004-01-1960 L1966 **D** *020 †15
CHEEK, Joseph Norman. 2777 N STEMMONS FWY 75207 #048-02-1978 L1978 **GS** *030
CHEIRIF, Jorge. 8440 WALNUT HILL LN # 700, NORTH TEXAS HEART CTR 75231 #649-01-1981 L1982 **CD** *020 †20
CHEMELLI, Richard Mark. 7777 FOREST LN STE D569, PEDIATRIC ACUTE CARE ASSOC 75230 #035-06-1993 L1999 **CCP** *020 †55
CHEN, Carolyn. ■ 75201 #048-04-2006 **OPH** *012
CHEN, Clifford Newton. 5323 HARRY HINES BLVD, MAILING CODE 9063 75390 #048-12-2003 L2006 **PD** *012
CHEN, Connie Lynn. 7515 GREENVILLE AVE, STE 400 75231 #023-07-1998 L2004 **N** *020 †75
CHEN, David. 221 W COLORADO BLVD, STE 208 75208 #041-12-1987 L1991 **N** *030 †75
CHEN, Dreeny. ■ 75219 #012-05-2001 L2003 **PD** *020 †55
CHEN, Edward Chiahsing. ■ 75225 #019-02-1994 L1999 **DR** *020 †80
CHEN, Jun. 3600 GASTON AVE 75246 #243-47-1992 L2005 **NEP** *012 †20
CHEN, Kenneth Sungman. 5323 HARRY HINES BLVD, SOUTHWESTERN MED 75390 #048-12-2006 **PD** *012
CHENG, Edaire. ■ 75219 #048-12-2005 L2006 **PD** *012
CHENG, Jonathan Juinjen. ■ 75214 #048-04-2000 L2007 **HS** *100
CHENG, Michael Mingkwang. 9015 GARLAND RD 75218 #039-01-2002 L2005 **FM** *020 †18
CHENG, Stephen Shouheng. 1411 N BECKLEY AVE, STE 268A 75203 #056-06-1986 L2003 **TTS GS** *020 †85
CHERUKURI, Sunanda. 12221 MERIT DR STE 1, STE 220 75251 #495-58-1994 L2001 **IM** *020 †20
CHESLEY, Rachel Margaret. ■ 75201 #012-01-2007 **PD** *012
CHESSHIR, Kimberly A. 9 MEDICAL PKWY, PLAZA A STE 308 75234 #048-13-1996 L1998 **OBG** *020 †30
CHEUNG, Alexander Tzeyau. ■ 75219 #048-04-2001 **IM** *012
CHEUNG, Conrad Honglik. 13601 PRESTON RD, STE 900W 75240 #016-06-2000 L2006 **AN** *020 †05
CHEUNG, Edson Hoi Kam. 3409 WORTH ST, SAMMONS TOWER - STE 720 75246 #048-14-1981 L1981 **TS** *020 †85,90
CHHUTANI, Sheila. 8160 WALNUT HILL LN, STE 100 75231 #028-34-1999 L2004 **OBG** *020
CHI, Cynthia Yvonne. 12221 MERIT DR STE 161, UNIVERSITY OF MICHIGAN 75251 #048-02-2002 L2005 **PD** *100 †55
CHI, Jung II. 221 W COLORADO BLVD, STE 315 75208 #583-01-1969 L1978 **IM** *020 †20
CHIANG, Jingtzyh. ■ 75204 #048-12-2007 **IM** *012
CHIAO, Hsi. 5323 HARRY HINES BLVD, UT SOUTHWESTERN/PARKLAND 75390 #243-69-1986 L2004 **AN** *020 †05
CHILDS, Amy. 3500 GASTON AVE 75246 #039-01-1996 L2002 **DR** *020 †80
CHILDS, Harold K. 6901 SNIDER PLZ, STE 105 75205 #048-02-2000 L2002 **IM** *020 †20
CHIN, Kelly Marie. 5939 HARRY HINES BLVD, STE 711 75235 #048-12-1996 L2000 **PCC** *020 †20
CHINNAKOTLA, Srinath. 3500 GASTON AVE 4, BAYLOR UNIVERSITY MEDICAL 75246 #495-53-1988 L2001 **TTS** *020

CHITALE, Aniruddha A. 7929 BROOKRIVER DR, STE 300 75247 #048-13-1992 L1998 **GE** *020
CHITKARA, Pranav. ■ 75235 #048-12-2008 *012
CHITNIS, Shilpa Padmakar. 5323 HARRY HINES BLVD SU 75390 #495-01-1989 L2007 **N** *020 †75
CHIU, Hsienchang Thomas. 5201 HARRY HINES BLVD, PULMONARY & CRITICAL CARE 75235 #048-12-2001 L2002 **PCC** *100
CHO, Gina Juhwei. 5323 HARRY HINES BLVD, STOP 9031 75390 #048-13-1994 L1999 **DR** *020 †80
CHOE, Paul C. 5909 HARRY HINES BLVD, DEPT IM 75235 #048-13-1994 **IM** *100
CHOE, Zachia. 8200 WALNUT HILL LN 75231 #011-02-2004 L2007 **IM** *100 †20
CHOI, Bryan Yoonsok. ■ 75235 #048-12-2008 *012
CHOI, Duke J. 221 W COLORADO BLVD # 160 75208 #583-03-1963 L1972 **GYN GO** *020 †30
CHOI, Hoo-Kun Lee. ■ 75229 #583-03-1964 L1972 **PTH** *071 †50
CHOI, James W. 621 N HALL ST STE 400, CARDIOLOGY CONSULTANTS 75226 #016-06-1997 L2004 **IC CD** *020 †20
CHOI, Tak-Shun. 4500 S LANCASTER RD, ROUTE 113 75216 #035-08-1993 L1999 **BBK CLP** *020 †20
CHOICE, Tanishia Desha. ■ 75249 #048-12-2008 *012
CHOKSHI, Neema Yogesh. ■ 75235 #048-12-2008 *012
CHONG, David Kuoh-Hou. 7777 FOREST LN STE C717, WORLD CRANIOFACIAL INST 75230 #143-06-1993 **CFS** *020
CHOUCAIR, Ramsey Joe. 9301 N CENTRAL EXPY 75231 #048-12-1983 L1983 **PS GS** *020 †85,65
CHOULAKIAN, Armen. ■ 75219 #028-46-2003 **NS** *012
CHOWDHURY, Renuka. 5323 HARRY HINES BLVD, DEPT OF INTERNAL MEDICINE 75390 #495-51-1993 L2002 **NEP** *012 †20
CHOY, Hak. 5801 FOREST PARK ROAD, DEPT OF RADIATION ONCOLOGY 75390 #048-02-1987 L1989 **RO IM** *020 †80
CHOY, Judy. ■ 75204 #048-12-2008 *012
CHRISSIAN, Ara Ararat. 4606 CEDAR SPRINGS RD 75219 #005-18-2003 L2006 **PCC** *012 †20
CHRISTENSEN, Katherine. ■ 75206 #041-02-2005 L2008 **EM** *012
CHRISTENSEN, Margaret H. 6750 ABRAMS RD # 103-129 75231 #048-04-1986 L1991 **OBG** *020 †30
CHRISTENSEN, William T. 3801 GASTON AVE STE 201 75246 #048-02-1989 L1990 **IM** *020 †20
CHRISTIAN, John E, Jr. 7777 FOREST LN 75230 #048-12-1980 L1980 **AN** *020 †05
CHRISTINA, Melanie Ann. 8210 WALNUT HILL LN, STE 408 75231 #021-01-1990 L1993 **IM** *020 †20
CHRISTY, Rosemary Garza. ■ 75209 #048-13-1980 L1980 **PAN** *020 †05 ‡
CHU, Tuanhong Ba. ■ 75206 #048-12-1999 L2007 **VS** *020 †85
CHUANG, Weber Weichung. 802 N OAK CLIFF BLVD 75208 #048-04-1996 L2004 **U** *020 †95
CHUANG, Wendy T. ■ 75204 #048-15-2002 L2006 **DR** *100 †80
CHUBICK, Andrew, Jr. 712 N WASHINGTON AVE 75246 #038-06-1970 L1978 **RHU IM** *020 †20
CHUKA, Yuri. 6122 NORTHWOOD RD, P O BOX 671013 75225 #913-01-1988 L2001 **AN** *020 †05
CHUMLEY, Christopher Ray. 4310 BUENA VISTA ST, APT 18 75205 #048-02-2004 **IM** *012
CHUNG, Andrew Dongwook. 3600 GASTON AVE STE 1001, BARNETT TOWERS 75246 #024-07-1992 L1997 **IM** *020 †20
CHUNG, Mary Sue. ■ 75225 #048-04-2001 L2006 **PDR** *020 †80
CHUNG, Paul Chul. 3434 SWISS AVE STE 330 75204 #048-04-1986 L1987 **IM** *020 †20
CHUNG, Wendy. 3523 MCKINNEY AVE 75204 #048-13-1997 L1998 **PDI** *020 †55
CHUOKE, Barbara Dawn. ■ 75205 #048-01-1979 L1982 **IM** *071 †20
CIAROCHI, Joel Frederick. 4131 N CENTRAL EXPY, METRO ANESTHESIA 75204 #048-14-1996 L1997 **AN** *020 †05
CIGARROA, Joaquin E. 5201 HARRY HINES BLVD, CARDIAC LABS - BASEMENT 75235 #035-20-1989 L1996 **IM** *020 †20
CLAGETT, George Patrick. 5909 HARRY HINES BLVD, UT SOUTHWESTERN MED CTR 75390 #051-01-1969 L1983 **VS GS** *020 †85
CLAMAN, Lawrence. 8911 HARRY HINES BLVD, CHILD & FAMILY GUIDANCE CT 75235 #041-01-1953 L1962 **CHP** *071 †75
CLAPP, Sandra K. 8210 WALNUT HILL LN, STE 912 75231 #038-40-1974 L1975 **PDC PD** *020 †55
CLARIDAY, John M. 9528 WEBB CHAPEL RD 75220 #047-05-1951 L1958 **GP GS** *071
CLARK, Camille Ann. 7777 FOREST LN 75230 #048-13-1983 L1983 **OBG** *020 †30
CLARK, Cordell. PO BOX 4058, 1114 N BISHOP AVE 75208 #047-07-1970 L1981 **OPH GP** *075
CLARK, Daniel Cole. 3500 GASTON AVE, AMERICAN RADIOLOGY 75246 #004-01-1998 L2004 **DR** *100 †80
CLARK, Fannie Machles. 5959 HARRY HINES BLVD, STE 1122 75235 #048-02-1942 L1942 **FM** *071 †18
CLARK, Gordon Michael. ■ 75205 #021-01-1979 L1989 **IM OM** *020 †20
CLARK, James H, III. 5323 HARRY HINES BLVD, UTSW MED CTR DEPT OF PATH 75390 #048-14-1985 L1991 **PTH MDM** *020 †50
CLARK, Jason P. ■ 75229 #048-12-2001 L2003 **PCC** *012 †20
CLARK, Lisa Harper. 8220 WALNUT HILL LN # 110 75231 #027-01-1982 L1983 **IM IMG** *020 †20
CLARK, Steven Anthony. ■ 75229 #048-12-2005 **GS** *012
CLARK, Steven Michael. 12200 PRESTON RD 75230 #048-13-1984 L1985 **IM** *020 †20
CLARK, William Kemp. 5323 HARRY HINES BLVD 75235 #048-02-1948 L1948 **NS** *071 †25
CLARKE, John Charles. 5323 HARRY HINES BLVD, UNIV OF TX SOUTHWESTERN 75390 #048-12-2003 L2004 **DR** *012
CLARKE, Tamlamae Carmen. ■ 75231 #048-12-2000 **P** *100
CLAUS, James Gerard. 3530 FOREST LN STE 35 75234 #048-12-1964 L1964 **GP** *020
CLAVENNA, Andrew Lee. 9301 N CENTRAL EXPY, STE 400 75231 #021-06-2000 L2003 **ORS** *020 ‡
CLEGG, Cynthia O. 9301 N CENTRAL EXPY, STE 180 75231 #048-12-1997 L1998 **D IM** *020 †15
CLER, Kristin Michelle. ■ 75249 #048-12-2006 **PTH** *012
CLER, Leslie Ryan. ■ 75249 #048-12-2006 **IM** *012
CLICK, Robert Reed, Jr. 5323 HARRY HINES BLVD, U.T. SOUTHWESTERN MEDICAL 75390 #048-12-1975 L1978 **IM** *020 †20
CLIFFORD, Jenny Tu. 9101 N CENTRAL EXPY, STE 420 75231 #048-14-1990 L1991 **PD** *020 †55
CLIFFORD, Lori Bevis. 13601 PRESTON RD, STE 900 75240 #045-01-1991 L1995 **AN** *020 †05
CLIFFORD, Susan Green. 9 MEDICAL PKWY, STE 302 75234 #048-12-1982 L1983 **PD** *020 †55
CLOUD, Robert Royce. 12200 PARK CENTRAL DR, STE 100 75251 #021-01-1980 L1981 **CRS** *020 †10,85
CO, Mark Allen. 9323 GARLAND RD, STE 103 75218 #748-11-1983 L1989 **PUD CCM** *020 †20
COATES, Geoffrey Stephen. 1717 MAIN ST 75201 #018-03-1973 L1977 **EM** *020 †16
COBASKO, David Frank. 6301 GASTON AVE, #400 WEST TOWER 75214 #005-18-1991 L2004 **N** *020

■ = Address Information Privacy Protected

COCHRAN, Christopher S. 8144 WALNUT HILL LN, STE 170 75231 #048-13-2001 L2002 CS OTO *020 †45

COCHRAN, Donald Ray. 8200 WALNUT HILL LN 75231 #048-12-1978 L1978 AN *020 †05

COCHRAN, James Sheridan. 8230 WALNUT HILL LN, UROLOGY CLINICS OF NORTH 75231 #048-12-1970 L1970 U *020 †95

COCJIN, Juan Tirol. 12606 GREENVILLE AVE, COOK CHILDREN'S 75243 #748-08-1983 L1995 PD *020 †55

COCKERELL, Clay Jefferies. 2330 BUTLER ST, STE 115 75235 #048-04-1981 L1981 D DMP *020 †15

COCKRELL, Rex Daniel. ■ 75218 #048-15-2001 L2008 GS *100

CODY, Cecelia. 5323 HARRY HINES BLVD, ASTON RADIOLOGY 75390 #030-05-1991 L1993 DR *020

CODY, Vaydor Frank. 5956 SHERRY LN STE 1819 75225 #048-02-1967 L1967 P PYA *020

COFFEY, Amy R. 5303 HARRY HINES BLVD, FL 7 # 104 75390 #048-02-1985 L1986 PDO *020 †45

COGGINS, James Tyler. 3450 W WHEATLAND RD, STE 122 75237 #048-12-1964 L1964 U *020 †95

COHEN, Brian Michael. 7777 FOREST LN, MED CITY HOSP STE C625 75230 #836-02-1966 L1983 REN GYN *020 †30

COHEN, Donald Mortimer. 3500 GASTON AVE, 4TH FL 75246 #041-01-1956 L1963 PTH PCP *020 †50

COHEN, Ethan Oren. 5201 HARRY HINES BLVD 75235 #048-12-2005 L2006 DR *012

COHEN, Howard Mark. 5701 MAPLE AVE, STE 100 75235 #020-02-1985 L1986 PMM P *020 †75

COHEN, Martin Bennett. 5461 LA SIERRA DR 75231 #048-12-1965 L1965 IM *020 †20

COHEN, Robert Alan. 5615 LOBELLO DR 75229 #056-06-1977 L1979 OBG *020 †30

COHEN, Stanley Bruce. 5939 HARRY HINES BLVD, STE 400 75235 #001-02-1975 L1978 RHU IM *020 †20

COHN, Peter D. 8210 WALNUT HILL LN, STE 907 75231 #024-05-1974 L1977 IM *020 †20

COLE, Charles Max. 8210 WALNUT HILL LN # 609, STE 609LB51 75231 #018-03-1942 L1943 GS *071 †85

COLE, Kenneth M, Jr. 4500 S LANCASTER RD 75216 #023-07-1951 L1952 PM OS *071 †60

COLE, Suzanne Marie. 8200 WALNUT HILL LN 75231 #048-12-2003 L2006 HO *012 †20

COLEMAN, Charles Wm. 3434 SWISS AVE 75204 #048-13-1975 L1975 GS *020 †85

COLEMAN, Jayne Elizabeth. 5323 HARRY HINES BLVD, UTSWMC 75390 #039-01-1993 L1997 AN *020 †05

COLLAZO, Roberto L. 1150 N BISHOP AVE 75208 #042-01-1993 L1998 NEP *020 †20

COLLIER, John Clayton. 3904 GASPAR DR 75220 #021-05-1994 L1996 GS *020 †85

COLLIER, Richard Earl. 5420 LYNDON B JOHNSON FWY 75240 #048-12-1948 L1948 RO R *071 †80

COLLIER, Robert T. ■ 75214 #048-12-1996 L1997 EM *020 †16

COLLINS, Janet A. 8226 DOUGLAS AVE, STE 805 75225 #048-02-1987 L1988 CHP *020 †75

COLLINS, Kimberly Michell. ■ 75231 #028-34-2004 L2007 P *012

COLLINS, Laura Jean. 4500 S LANCASTER RD, DALLAS VAMC CARDIOLOGY #11 75216 #023-07-1987 L1996 CD *020 †20

COLLINS, Robert H. 5323 HARRY HINES BLVD, UPSWMC 75390 #028-46-1984 L1986 ON IM *020 †20

COLLOP, Robert N. 5004 COLUMBIA AVE 75214 #028-79-1949, ▲ L1949 GP *071

COLN, C Dale. 3600 GASTON AVE, BARNETT 406 75246 #048-04-1961 L1961 PDS TRS *020 †85

COLOMBO, Stacy Marie. ■ 75206 #048-14-2005 OBG *012

COLUMBUS, Cristie. 3409 WORTH ST, NORTH TEXAS INFECTIOUS 75246 #048-12-1988 L1989 ID *030 †20

COMBES, Burton. 5323 HARRY HINES BLVD 75235 #035-01-1951 L1958 OS IM *050 †20

COMBES, Mollie H A. ■ 75225 #035-01-1952 L1958 PD FM *071 †55

COMESS, Leonard J. 1130 BEACHVIEW ST STE 100 75218 #016-06-1965 L1969 IM *020 †20

COMMODORE, Marius Marcel. ■ 75209 #012-05-2002 L2007 OS *100 †20

COMMONS, Bradford Stager. ■ 75225 #005-18-2007 EM *012

COMPTON, Lindsay Michelle. ■ 75225 #048-12-2006 DR *012

COMPTON, Paul A. 7902 AMHERST AVE 75225 #048-12-2005 L2006 IM *012

CONANAN, Margarita Lopez. 14902 PRESTON RD 75254 #748-08-1965 L1971 PM *020 †60

CONARD, Scott Edward. 9229 LBJ FWY 75243 #011-04-1986 L1987 FM *020 †18

CONDRY, Leesa Blake. ■ 75205 #048-12-1977 L1977 OBG *071 †30

CONNALLY, Jack Dennis. 10500 STEPPINGTON DR, STE 100A 75230 #039-01-1968 L1973 DR *020 †80

CONNELL, Stuart M. ■ 75254 #048-12-2008 *012

CONNER, Blair. 3434 SWISS AVE STE 206, DIGESTIVE HEALTH ASSOCIATE 75204 #028-02-1993 L1994 GE *020

CONNER, Paul Kay, Jr. 8315 WALNUT HILL LN 75231 #048-04-1956 L1956 IM CD *071 †20

CONNER, William C. 3500 GASTON AVE 75246 #048-12-2000 L2002 AN *020 †05

CONNOR, Robert Lanham. 3310 FAIRMOUNT ST, D2A 75201 #048-12-1970 L1972 PTH *020 †50

CONNORS, Thomas Mitchell. 5949 SHERRY LN STE 1150, STERLING PLAZA 75225 #030-05-1977 L1979 SO GS *020 †85

CONRAD, Jason Albert. ■ 75249 #048-02-2003 L2005 DR *012

CONSTANT, Richard Riley. 12200 PRESTON RD 75230 #048-12-1963 L1963 CD IM *020

CONSTANTINE, Fadi Christo. 4686 MEADOWOOD RD 75220 #048-02-2008 *012

CONTRACTOR, Manijeh. 5323 HARRY HINES BLVD, TEXAS SOUTHWESTE 75390 #517-08-1973 L2008 OPH *020

CONTRERAS, Robert. 5610 LEMMON AVE STE B 75209 #024-07-2000 L2003 FM *020 †18

CONVERY, Paul Bernard. 3600 GASTON AVE, STE 150 75246 #016-11-1974 L1975 IM MDM *030 †20

COOK, Alan Dell. SOUTHWESTERN MED, UNIV OF TEXAS 75390 #050-02-2001 L2007 CCS *012

COOK, Charles Everett. 8440 WALNUT HILL LN, STE 110 75231 #021-05-1983 L1986 ORS *020 †40

COOK, Daniel Curtis. 6510 ABRAMS RD, STE 645 75231 #028-34-1990 L1991 FM *020 †20

COOK, Daphne Denise. 1717 MAIN ST STE 52, EMCARE 75201 #038-06-2000 L2004 IM *020 †16

COOK, Hubert David. 5939 HARRY HINES BLVD, STE 411 75235 #048-12-1975 L1975 GYN *020 †30

COOK, James D. ■ 75229 #048-12-1984 L1985 OPH *020

COOK, Lucius Pinckney, III. 7777 FOREST LN, STE B218 75230 #047-06-1970 L1974 D *020 †20

COOK, Patricia Anne. 5323 HARRY HINES DEPT IM 75235 #024-01-1977 L1981 IM *071 †20

COOMBS, Caroline Hellin. ■ 75214 #048-02-2005 GS *012

COOPER, Ashley Marie. ■ 75209 #048-12-2007 PD *012

COOPER, Barry. 3535 WORTH ST, STE 110 75246 #023-07-1971 L1979 HEM ON *020 †20

COOPER, Esther Nicholas. 8111 PRESTON RD STE 811 75225 #010-02-1991 L1998 P *020

COOPER, Jack Crawford. ■ 75205 #048-12-1954 L1954 OPH *071 †35 ‡

COOPER, Kenneth Hardy. 12200 PRESTON RD 75230 #039-01-1956 L1970 GPM AM *050 †70

COOPER, Lauren Beth. ■ 75204 #035-08-2008 *012

COOPER, R Kathryn. 5445 LA SIERRA DR 75231 #039-01-1988 L1989 P *020

COOPER, Tiffany Sims. ■ 75217 #048-13-2002 L2007 OBG *020

COPENHAVER, Steven Craig. 8210 WALNUT HILL LN, STE 718 75231 #048-16-1989 L1997 PDP *020 †55

COPLEY, Lawson Ashley. 1935 MOTOR ST, CHILDREN'S MEDICAL CENTER 75235 #019-02-1991 L1996 OP *020 †40

CORCORAN, Scott Allen. 12221 MERIT DR STE 1610 75251 #019-02-2002 L2005 EM *020 †16

CORDRAY, Scot Alan. 411 N WASHINGTON AVE, STE 7000 75246 #020-02-1995 L2006 OSM *020

CORDRAY, Yvonne M. PO BOX 25474 75225 #012-01-1953 L1960 PM OM *071

CORNETTE, Marvin Clifford. 4205 BUENA VISTA ST, STE 200 75205 #048-12-1981 L1981 P PFP *075

CORONA JOUANEN, Jorge. ■ 75248 #649-31-1995 L2006 OPH OS *020 †35

CORPIER, Cindy Lou. 13154 COIT RD, STE 100 75240 #021-06-1984 L1989 NEP *020 †20

CORRIGAN, Nicole Julia. ■ 75244 #048-14-2008 *012

CORRIGAN, Suzanne Le Bel. 1935 MOTOR ST 75235 #048-12-1976 L1976 PD *020 †55

CORTON, Marlene Mercedes. 5323 HARRY HINES BLVD, DEPARTMENT OF OB/GYN 75390 #033-06-1994 L1998 OBG *020 †30

COST, Nicholas Glenn. ■ 75230 #012-05-2005 U *012

COSTNER, Melissa Irene. 9301 N CENTRAL EXPY, STE 180 75231 #048-14-1993 L1994 DMP *020 †15

COTTEL, Willis Irving. 8230 WALNUT HILL LN # 808 75231 #040-02-1961 L1976 D ON *071 †15

COTTEY, John Higbee. 8210 WALNUT HILL LN # 609 75231 #028-03-1960 L1980 GS ORS *020 †85

COTTON, Katrina Voe. 7777 FOREST LN STE B238 75230 #048-12-2002 L2006 AN *100

COUCH, Jason L. 13601 PRESTON RD 75240 #048-12-1999 L2003 AN *020 †05 ‡

COULSON, Colby James. ■ 75206 #048-12-2006 DR *012

COWDEN, Daniel Joseph. ■ 75240 #025-07-1998 L2005 PTH *020 †50

COWLING, Cari L. ■ 75220 #048-12-2005 OBG *012

COX, John V. 1441 N BECKLEY AVE, STE 101 75203 #048-78-1978, ▲ L1978 HEM ON *020 †20

COX, Matthew John. 1935 MOTOR ST, DIVISION OF GENERAL PEDIAT 75235 #048-14-1998 L2004 PD *020 †55

COX, Nancy Aylett. 8200 WALNUT HILL LN 75231 #422-01-1987 L1991 IM *020 †20

COX, Rody P. 5323 HARRY HINES BLVD, MC 8889 75235 #041-01-1952 L1989 IM CBG *040 †20

COX, Susan Marie. 5323 HARRY HINES BLVD 75390 #048-04-1982 L1983 OBG MFM *040 †30

COX, William F. 8230 WALNUT HILL LN, DRS COX FRATER & CHANEZ 75231 #048-14-1993 L1995 IM *020 †20

COYLE, Yvonne M. 5323 HARRY HINES BLVD, UT SOUTHWESTERN 75390 #054-04-1979 L1990 IM HEM *050 †20

CRABTREE, Robert N. 3535 TRAVIS ST, STE 210 75204 #048-15-1987 L1988 AN GS *020 †05

CRAIG, Dwight Chas. ■ 75209 #048-12-1966 L1966 R *071

CRAIG, John Renwick. 712 N WASHINGTON AVE, STE 509 75246 #025-07-1995 L2001 VS *020 †85

CRAIG, Kelli E. ■ 75201 #048-13-2006 L2007 AN *100

CRAIG, Marcia Reiners. ■ 75209 #048-12-1966 L1966 PD *071 †55

CRAIG, Margaret Gill. 5323 HARRY HINES BLVD, MC 9068 75390 #024-05-2001 L2003 AN *100 †05

CRAIGMILES, Laura A. ■ 75204 #028-78-2006, ▲ EM *012

CRAMER, Charles Raymond. 7777 FOREST LN 75230 #048-12-1972 L1973 PTH *020 †50

CRAMER, Charles Wm, Jr. 411 N WASHINGTON AVE #2200 75246 #048-04-1974 L1974 CD IM *020 †20

CRAMER, Dwight Evers. ■ 75230 #023-01-1970 L1974 OTO *020 †45

CRAMPTON, William M. 13601 PRESTON RD STE 1000, PINNACLE PARTNERS IN MEDIC 75240 #004-01-1968 L1969 AN *020 †05

CRANE, Charles Robt. 10850 SWITZER AVE, STE 113 75238 #048-12-1964 L1964 PM PME *020 †60

CRANE, John Michael. 1935 MOTOR ST, CHILDRENS MEDICAL CENTER E 75235 #048-02-1982 L1983 PD *020 †55

CRANK, Michelle Christine. 75235 #048-12-2006 IM *012

CRAVEN, Michelle Marie. ■ 75205 #048-13-2007 AN *012

CRAWFORD, Ana Maria. ■ 75202 #001-02-2004 AN *012

CRAWFORD, Chris Wayne. 5924 ROYAL LN STE 104 75230 #039-01-1991 L1995 D *020 †15

CRAWFORD, Kimberly T. 12221 MERIT DR STE 4 75251 #028-03-1994 L1997 IM *020 †20

CRAWFORD, Natalie Minns. ■ 75214 #048-02-2008 *012

CREAGAN, Susan M. 8210 WALNUT HILL LN, STE-600 75231 #036-07-1975 L1978 IM *020 †20

CREECH, Kristin Nicole. ■ 75204 #048-02-2007 IM *012

CREED, Karen Camille. 5323 HARRY HINES BLVD, MED CT 75390 #036-08-2007 OBG *012

CRESS, Marshall Chandler. ■ 75204 #004-01-2007 GS *012

CRIPE, Patrick J. 5323 HARRY HINES BLVD, U OF TX SOUTHWESTERN MED 75390 #048-02-2006 PD *012

CRISAN, Luminita Sanda. 1441 N BECKLEY AVE 75203 #781-04-2001 L2008 OBG *012

CRITES, Frances B. 8160 WALNUT HILL LN # 308 75231 #048-04-1987 L1988 OBG *020 †30

CROCHET, Melissa Kay. 411 N WASHINGTON AVE, STE 2700 75246 #021-05-1990 L1998 OBG *020 †20

CROCKETT, Barbara C. 8160 WALNUT HILL LN, STE 306 75231 #048-12-1984 L1986 OBG *020 †30

CROFFORD, William Luther. 8267 ELMBROOK DR, STE 100 75247 #048-02-1957 L1957 PTH *071 †50

CROFT, Carol Lynn. 5323 HARRY HINES BLVD 75390 #041-01-1991 L1993 IM *020 †20

CROLL, Gary A. 9330 POPPY DR STE 403 75218 #048-01-1977 L1983 IM OS *020 †20

CROMWELL, Keith T. 13601 PRESTON RD, STE 900 75240 #048-12-1991 L1992 AN *020 †05

CRONHOLM, Michael Wayne. 8611 RICHARDSON BRANCH TRL 75243 #048-12-1978 L1978 EM IM *020 †20,16

CRONIN, Donald F, Jr. 13154 COIT RD STE 100 75240 #030-05-1994 L1999 NEP *020 †20

CRONIN, Robert Emmet. 4500 S LANCASTER RD 111, VA NORTH TX HLTH CARE SYS 75216 #016-43-1968 L1971 IM NEP *020 †20

CROSBY, Uel Doyle, Jr. 5323 HARRY HINES BLVD #OBG 75390 #048-12-1962 L1962 OBG *020 †20

CROTTY, Karen Lynne. 4500 S LANCASTER RD, DALLAS VETERANS MEDICAL CE 75216 #005-18-1988 L1990 U *020 †95

CROW, W A, III. ■ 75219 #048-04-1977 L1978 IM *020 †20

CROWDER, Jaye Douglas. 13140 COIT RD STE 518 75240 #048-12-1980 L1980 P PFP *020 †75

CROWLEY, Leo Michael. ■ 75230 #352-08-1966 L1984 GPM IM *020 ‡

CROWLEY, Samuel R. ■ 75214 #048-13-2001 L2004 EM *020 †16

CRUDUP, Travis W. 3500 GASTON AVE 75246 #048-15-2002 L2007 GS *020 †85

CRUMLEY, Frank Edward. 12860 HILLCREST RD 75230 #048-02-1963 L1963 CHP P *020 †75

CRUMPACKER, David William. 3600 GASTON AVE 75246 #035-20-1993 L1995 PYG *020 †75

CRUTCHER, William Monroe. 4548 SHADY HILL DR 75229 #048-12-1961 L1961 OS OTO *030 †45

CRUZ, Erwin Amilcar. 12800 PRESTON RD, STE 101 75230 #429-01-1980 L1989 N PME *020 †75

CRUZ, Hernan. 5323 HARRY HINES BLVD MC, UT SOUTHWESTERN MEDICAL CE 75390 #264-05-1974 L2006 PD *020 †55

CRUZ, Pedro Antonio. 737 N BISHOP AVE 75208 #341-01-1968 L1976 IM ON *020 †20

CRUZ, Ponciano D, Jr. 5323 HARRY HINES BLVD, MEDICAL CENTER 75390 #748-02-1979 L1985 D IM *020 †20,15

CRYER, Byron Leon. 4500 S LANCASTER RD, RD (111B1) 75216 #048-04-1986 L1987 GE IM *020 †20

CUBILLAS MANRIQUE, Raul E. ■ 75204 #737-06-2000 L2006 GE *012

CUBILLOS, Luis E. 13601 PRESTON RD, WEST TOWER, STE 600 75240 #264-01-1955 L1980 OPH *020 †35

CUDD, Jere Leonard. 2003 PARK AVE 75215 #048-13-1992 FM *100

CUETO, Jorge. 7777 FOREST LN 75230 #649-05-1962 L1984 GS *020 †85

CULBERTSON, Marvin C, Jr. 5303 HARRY HINES BLVD 75390 #048-02-1950 L1950 PDO NO *071 †45

CULPEPPER, Donnie D. 4131 N CENTRAL EXPY, METRO ANESTHESIA 75204 #048-15-1975 L1975 AN *020 †05

CULPEPPER, Kelli Lynn. 7777 FOREST LN STE D550 75230 #048-13-1996 L2000 OBG *020 †30

CUMBIE, Todd Allen. ■ 75205 #048-04-2005 GS *012

CUMMINGS, Karen A. 6405 HILLCREST AVE 75205 #048-12-1999 L2002 ORS *012

CUNNINGHAM, Charles Casey. 3535 WORTH ST, STE 110 75246 #048-12-1982 L1983 IM *020 †20

CUNNINGHAM, Francis G. 5323 HARRY HINES BLVD 75390 #021-05-1968 L1973 OBS MFM *040 †30

CUNNINGHAM, Robert Lewis, III. 5323 HARRY HINES BLVD, DIV OF EMERGENCY MED 75390 #039-01-2006 L2007 EM *012

CUNNINGHAM, Russell Drew. ■ 75219 #048-15-2005 L2008 GS *100

CUNNYNGHAM, Christopher B. 1935 MOTOR ST, OF D 75235 #039-01-2002 L2003 CCP *012 †55

CURLEY, Eric James. ■ 75235 #048-12-2007 *012

CURRARINO, Guido. 5323 HARRY HINES BLVD 75235 #561-07-1945 L1965 PDR PD *072

CURRY, Anna Maria. 13321 FORESTWAY DR 75240 #048-12-1972 L1972 AN *020 †05

CURRY, Claude Daryl. 221 W COLORADO BLVD # 206 75208 #020-02-1983 L1984 PD *020 †55

CURRY, Eugene Emil. 9301 N CENTRAL EXPY, STE 400 75231 #048-04-1990 L1991 ORS OFA *020 †40

CURRY, George Clyde. 5323 HARRY HINES BLVD 75235 #048-12-1962 L1962 DR *030 †80

CURRY, Robert Bittle. 3330 S LANCASTER RD 75216 #048-02-1957 L1958 IM P *071

CURRY, Thomas Sherrod, III. 5303 HARRY HINES BLVD 75390 #048-12-1960 L1960 DR *071 †80

CURTIS, Claire S. 8325 WALNUT HILL LN, STE 225 75231 #048-12-1998 L1999 PD *020 †55

CURTIS, Richard Stephen. 9301 N CENTRAL EXPY, STE 400 75231 #048-12-1969 L1969 ORS *020 †40

CUSH, John Jos. 9900 N CENTRAL EXPY, STE 550 75231 #422-01-1981 L1989 RHU IM *050 †20

CUSICK, Matthew Garrett. ■ 75233 #048-12-2004 GS *012

CUTHBERT, Jennifer Anne. 5323 HARRY HINES BLVD, UT SW MED SCH DEPT IM 75390 #143-03-1973 L1981 IM *020 †20

CUTLER, Todd D. ■ 75230 #048-12-2005 L2007 OBG *012

CUTRELL, James Bradford. ■ 75218 #048-12-2007 IM *012

CZERWINSKI, Marcin. 7777 FOREST LN 75230 #067-01-2003 *100

DACEY, Mark Stefan. 5323 HARRY HINES BLVD, TEXAS SOUTHWESTE 75390 #025-01-2005 OPH *012

DADFARMAY, Faranak. 13601 PRESTON RD 75240 #130-01-2006 *012

DADSON, Jesse J. 1935 MOTOR ST, CHILDREN'S MED. CTR. OF DA 75235 #412-02-1985 L1999 AN *020 †05

DAGAN HABAZA, Amit. SOUTHWESTERN MED, UNIV OF TEXAS 75390 #550-04-1999 PN *012

DAI, Eric. ■ 75219 #048-04-2003 L2007 OPH *100

DALEHITE, Jesse J, III. 2812 PURDUE AVE 75225 #048-12-1982 L1983 DR *020 †80

DALEY, Gilroy L. 11729 CORAL HILLS DR 75229 #020-02-1967 L1971 DR *071 †30,80

DALEY, Jennifer. 13737 NOEL RD, TENET HLTHCARE 75240 #024-07-1976 L1978 IM *030 †20

DAL NOGARE, Anthony Roy. UNIV TX SW MED CTR 75235 #041-02-1978 L1984 IM PUD *020 †20

DALTON, Gordon Dennis. 5949 SHERRY LN, STE 1210 75225 #048-04-1966 L1966 P *020

DALTON, Thomas Oran. ■ 75229 #048-12-2008 *012

DALY, Ella Joanne. ■ 75214 #539-04-1990 L2007 *100

DALY, Patrick Wm. 3629 FAIRMOUNT ST 75219 #048-15-1983 L1983 IM *020 †20

DAMERON, Zechariah C, III. 8 MEDICAL PKWY STE 208 75234 #048-12-1970 L1970 OM FM *020 †18

DAMMERT, William. 7128 HELSEM BND, PEDIATRIC SURGICAL ASSOCIA 75230 #407-21-1964 L1975 PDS *020 †85

DAND, Hemant Pratap. ■ 75214 #048-12-2003 L2006 PCC *012 †20

DANEY, William Chester. 1717 MAIN ST, STE 5200 75201 #007-02-1960 L1991 EM FM *020 †18,16

DANIEL, Britt Talley. 7777 FOREST LN, STE B220 75230 #048-02-1970 L1970 N *020 †75

DANIEL, Eric Joseph. ■ 75214 #021-06-2002 L2004 EM *020 †16

DANIEL, Kris D. 5151 HARRY HINES BLVD 75235 #048-15-1994 L1995 IM *020 †20

DANIELS, James Deets. ■ 75229 #048-12-2001 L2005 CD *012

DANSBY, Daniel Milton. 7777 FOREST LN, STE A103 75230 #048-12-1969 L1971 OTO FM *020 †45

DAO, Kathryn H. 9301 N CENTRAL EXPY, STE 675 75231 #048-12-1999 L2002 RHU IM *020 †20

DAO, Lori Michele. 5323 HARRY HINES BLVD, DIV OF EMERGENCY MED 75390 #048-12-2006 OPH *012

DAO, Tuoc Ngoc. ■ 75219 #048-16-2003 GS *012

DARNELL, Cindy Maria. 1935 MOTOR ST, PEDIATRIC CRITICAL CARE 75235 #020-02-1998 L2004 PD *020 †55

DAROS, Vanessa Irene. 8160 WALNUT HILL LN, STE 214 75231 #187-26-1996 L2006 OBG *020

DARROW, Robert Scott. 8140 WALNUT HILL LN # 80 75231 #048-12-1976 L1976 OBG U *020 †30

DAS, Sandeep Ram. SOUTHWESTERN MED, UNIV OF TEXAS 75390 #041-09-1998 L2008 CD *010 †20

DAS, Shounak. 8200 WALNUT HILL LN 75231 #061-01-1990 L2008 IM *012 †20

DASA, Sridhar. ■ 75230 #496-01-1993 L1996 IM *020

DASGUPTA, Debasis. 2901 CITYPLACE WEST BLVD 75204 #021-06-2001 L2004 IM *020

DASHE, Jodi Sue. 5323 HARRY HINES BLVD, DEPT OF OB/GYN-MC9032 75390 #008-01-1992 L1996 MFM OBS *040 †30

DASHEIFF, Richard M. 4500 S LANCASTER RD, NEUROLOGY SECTION /111H 75216 #023-01-1976 L1995 N CN *020 †75

DAUGHETY, Michael Jewel. 13601 PRESTON RD, STE 900 75240 #048-02-1966 L1966 AN *020 †55

DAULAT, Seema Janak. ■ 75243 #048-12-2008 *012

DAULAT, Sonak Bhalchandra. 10216 GARLAND RD 75218 #024-05-1997 L1998 AI *020 †20,03

DAULAT, Veena Bhalchandra. 10216 GARLAND RD 75218 #496-38-1971 L1973 DR NM *071 †80

DAVE, Nilesh Bhupendra. MC 8842, 5939 HARRY HINES BLVD 75390 #041-15-1999 L2006 SME PCC *020 †20

DAVENPORT, Jill Frey. 8200 WALNUT HILL LN, DEPT OF INTERNAL MEDICINE 75231 #048-13-2003 L2006 DR *100

DAVENPORT, Owen R. ■ 75201 #048-13-2004 AN *012

DAVIDOFF, Steven Leigh. ■ 75219 #021-01-2002 L2006 PCC *012 †20

DAVIDSON, Ingemar Josef. 5909 HARRY HINES BLVD, SOUTHWESTERN MED SCH 75390 #858-05-1970 L1982 GS OS *020

DAVIDSON, Jaime Abraham. 7777 FOREST LN STE C-2 75230 #649-01-1968 L1975 DIA END *020

DAVIDSON, James Alan. 8210 WALNUT HILL LN, STE 513 LOCK BOX 43 75231 #056-06-1971 L1981 GS VS *020 †85

DAVIDSON, Joseph W, Jr. 7920 ELMBROOK DR, STE 120 75247 #048-12-1953 L1953 IM *071 †20

DAVIDSON, Laura K. 1935 MOTOR ST, DEPARTMENT OF GENERAL PEDI 75235 #048-12-2002 L2005 PD *020 †55

DAVIDSON, Malcolm David. 7777 FOREST LN STE B224 75230 #035-15-1966 L1971 PD *020 †20

DAVILA, Raquel Eunice. 4500 S LANCASTER RD MC, PHYSICIANS PAVILION 75216 #041-01-1996 L1998 GE *020 †20

DAVIS, Brad R. 13601 PRESTON RD STE 90 75240 #048-13-2000 L2003 AN *020 †05

DAVIS, Carl Lewis. ■ 75230 #047-06-1954 L1954 PYA P *071 †75

DAVIS, David S. 13601 PRESTON RD, STE 900 75240 #048-12-1989 L1990 AN *020 †05

DAVIS, Gary Lee. 3500 GASTON AVE, BAYLOR UNIVERSITY MEDICAL 75246 #026-04-1976 L2002 GE IM *050 †20

DAVIS, Jerry F. 221 W COLORADO BLVD, STE 730 75208 #048-04-1989 L1990 IM *020 †20

DAVIS, Lance Edwin. ■ 75225 #048-12-2008 *012

DAVIS, Matthew Frederick. 6901 SNIDER PLZ, STE 130 75205 #019-02-1994 L1999 FSM *020 †20

DAVIS, Nicholas John. ■ 75204 #056-06-2007 GS *012

DAVIS, Sarah Blom. 6901 SNIDER PLZ, STE 130 75205 #019-02-1995 L1998 FM *020 †18

DAVIS, Stanley Lynn. 1935 MOTOR ST, PICU CHILDRENS MEDICAL CTR 75235 #048-12-1983 L1983 AN PD *020 †55,05

DAVIS, William Gordon. 7557 RAMBLER RD STE 706 75231 #012-05-1984 L1991 AN *020 †85

DAWER, Marshall Jay. 8350 N CENTRAL EXPY, STE M1000 75206 #035-08-1980 L1995 IM EM *020 †20,16

DAWSON, Lanita Monae. 12712 PARK CENTRAL DR, STE B150 75251 #038-40-1994 L2000 R RNR *020 †80

DAY, Donald Wayne. 7777 FOREST LN, STE C706 75230 #016-11-1968 L1984 MG PD *030 †55,19

DAY, Gustavo H. 7777 FOREST LN STE 416, BLDG B 75230 #132-06-1990 L1996 IM *020 †20

DAY, Micah Anthony. 14114 DALLAS PKWY STE 411, EMERGENCY STAFFING SOLUTIO 75254 #021-06-2002 L2005 GS *100

DAYIAN, Ara Robert. 4801 S BUCKNER BLVD, STE 200 75227 #062-01-1993 L1997 FM *020 †18

DE, Sayan. ■ 75208 #012-05-2006 ORS *012

DEAR, Wayne Englehardt. 4500 S LANCASTER RD 75216 #048-04-1962 L1962 CD IM *020 †20

DEBERARDINIS, Ralph John. ■ 75208 #041-01-2000 L2001 OS *020 †55,19

DEBUS, John R. 5477 GLEN LAKES DR, STE 100-125 75231 #048-12-1984 L1985 P *020 †75 ‡

DECAMP, Byron S. ■ 75204 #048-04-2003 GS *012

DECKER, Daniel Benjamin. 5323 HARRY HINES BLVD, UTSW UROLOGY DEPT 75390 #036-05-2006 U *012

DEEGAN, Michael John. ■ 75223 #023-01-1968 L1969 CLP PTH *020 †50

DEEN, John Richard. 3535 TRAVIS ST STE 210 75204 #020-02-1960 L1963 AN *020 †05

DEES, Tom Moore. 3434 SWISS AVE, STE 420 75204 #048-12-1956 L1956 IM *071

DE FEX, Armando Jose. 800 N BISHOP AVE, STE 2 75208 #264-15-1982 L1998 FM ADM *020 †18 ‡

DE FORD, Horace Andrew. 2639 WALNUT HILL LN # 14 75209 #048-02-1956 L1956 P FM *062

DE GRAVELLES, Charles E. ■ 75231 #021-05-2002 L2006 P *100

DEISCH, Jeremy Keith. 5323 HARRY HINES BLVD, DEPT OF PATHOLOGY 75390 #005-12-2006 PTH *012

DEKAT, Laurette Kathryn. 6263 HARRY HINES BLVD 75235 #048-14-1983 L1983 PD *020 †55

DE LA CRUZ, Roberto C. 3600 GASTON AVE, STE 550 75246 #042-01-1993 L1994 IM *020 †20

DE LA MORENA, Maria T. 5323 HARRY HINES BLVD, SOUTHWESTERN MED CTR AT DA 75390 #847-04-1983 L2005 AI *020 †55,03

DELANEY, Kathleen Ann. 5323 HARRY HINES BLVD, SOUTHWESTERN MEDICAL SCHOO 75390 #035-01-1980 L1990 EM IM *020 †20,16

DE LA PENA, Rosinda C. 4500 S LANCASTER RD, RT # 115 75216 #649-31-1984 L1999 NM *020 †28

DE LARIOS, Arthur T. ■ 75225 #048-12-1952 L1952 GP *071 †18

DELASHAW, Mini R. 12221 MERIT DR, STE 1610 75251 #048-14-2003 L2006 EM *020 †16

DE LEMOS, James Andrew. 5323 HARRY HINES BLVD, 7.147 75390 #024-01-1992 L1993 CD *020 †20

DE LEON, Guillermo. 9101 N CENTRAL EXPY, BAYLOR SAMMONS BREAST 75231 #041-13-1994 L2000 DR *020 †80

DE LEON, Jean Marie. 3504 SWISS AVE, BAYLOR SPECIALTY HOSPITAL 75204 #039-01-1992 L1993 PM *020 †60

DE LEON, Joe Alex. ■ 75243 #048-12-1961 L1961 CD PUD *071

DE LEON, Jose F. 5939 HARRY HINES BLVD, ST PAUL PROFESSIONAL BLDG 75235 #048-12-1995 L1997 OBG *020 †30

DELGADO-AYALA, Mauricio. 2222 WELBORN ST 75219 #649-30-1980 L1985 **N CHN** *020 †75

DELLARIA, Marco Frank. 5323 HARRY HINES BLVD, DEPARTMENT OF RADIOLOGY 75390 #041-14-1989 L2002 **VIR** *020 †20,80

DELLARIA, Suzanne M. 5161 HARRY HINES BLVD CS2-1, DEPT OF ANESTHESIOLOGY 75390 #041-14-1992 L2002 **AN** *020 †05

DE LOS SANTOS, Jose Luis. 6401 MAPLE AVE, APT 10305 75235 #308-01-1986 L2002 **PCP** *012

DEL ROSARIO, Gracia Chua. 6161 HARRY HINES BLVD SU 75235 #748-02-1987 L1999 **PM** *020 †60

DELVISCO, Stephen Michael. DEPT RADIOLOGY, UNIV TX SW MED CTR 75390 #021-05-2006 **DR** *012

DE MARCO, Brendan Michael. ■ 75209 #048-14-2003 L2005 **ID** *012 †20

DE MARCO, Daniel C. 712 N WASHINGTON AVE, DIGESTIVE HEALTH ASSOC OF 75246 #048-12-1981 L1981 **GE IM** *020 †20

DEMOPULOS, John Anthony. 7777 FOREST LN STE B- 75230 #021-06-1989 L1990 **IM** *020

DE MOYA VEGA, Laura Catal. ■ 75206 #308-02-2001 L2006 **IM** *020 †20

DEMPSEY, Molly Elizabeth. 2222 WELBORN ST 75219 #012-05-1991 L1998 **PDR** *020 †80

DENISON, Early B, II. 8345 WALNUT HILL LN, BLDG D 75231 #048-12-2001 L2003 **PD** *020 †55

DENMAN, John L. ■ 75205 #028-02-1952 L1955 **U** *071 †95

DENTON, Ira Claude, Jr. ■ 75219 #047-06-1963 L1974 **NS** *071 †25

DENTON, Wayne Holt. 5323 HARRY HINES BLVD, U OF TX SWSTRN MED CTR 75390 #016-02-1982 L2005 **P** *020 †75

DEON, Laura Louise. 5201 HARRY HINES BLVD, PARKLAND HOSPITAL 75235 #047-06-2005 L2007 **PM** *012

DE PASSE, John Andrus. 7557 RAMBLER RD STE 7 75231 #048-12-1978 L1978 **AN** *020 †05

DE PRISCO, Gregory. ■ 75204 #048-12-2002 L2008 **DR** *100 †80

DERBES, Charles Wayne, Jr. 1441 N BECKLEY AVE, METHODIST HOSPITAL OF DALL 75203 #021-05-1974 L1984 **IM** *020 †20

DERRICK, Howard C, III. 3600 GASTON AVE 75246 #012-01-1972 L1974 **GS SO** *020 †85

DESAI, Dev Mahendra. 1935 MOTOR ST, DETP OF PED TRANSPLANT 75235 #005-02-1995 L2008 **GS TTS** *020 †85

DESAI, Madhukar Chimanlal. 11888 MARSH LN, STE 104 75234 #495-23-1960 L1981 **UCM** *020

DESAI, Manish Dilip. 7777 FOREST LN, STE A222 75230 #065-09-1994 L1997 **FM** *020

DESKIN, Ronald Wilson. 5303 HARRY HINES BLVD, FL 7 # 104 75390 #048-02-1969 L1969 **OTO PDO** *020 †45

D'ETIENNE, James P. 6051 ROYAL CREST DR 75230 #048-12-1996 L1998 **EM** *020 †16

DEUBER, Christina G. 5470 W LOVERS LN 75209 #035-45-1992 L1996 **PD** *020 †55

DEUBER, Mark Andrew. 2801 LEMMON AVE, STE 300 75204 #035-45-1996 L1999 **PS** *020 †65

DEV, Devasmita. 4500 S LANCASTER RD, MAIL CODE 111G1 75216 #051-07-1985 L1998 **NEP IM** *020 †20

DEVILLIER, Britton M. 5323 HARRY HINES BLVD, PEDIATRICS DEPT 75390 #021-01-1989 L1991 **PEM PD** *020 †55

DEVORA, Gene A. ■ 75209 #048-12-2005 L2007 **IM** *012

DE VRIES, Robert A C. 11661 PRESTON RD STE 12, PRESTON-FOREST FAMILY CLIN 75230 #660-01-1969 L1975 **GP END** *020

DEWAN, Tina Sheetal. 3500 GASTON AVE, MEDICAL CENT 75246 #028-34-2005 **IM** *012

DEWEES, Jason Douglas. 3600 GASTON AVE 75246 #021-06-1996 L1998 **IM** *020 †20

DEWEY, Richard B, Jr. 5323 HARRY HINES BLVD 75390 #048-04-1989 L1990 **N** *040 †75

DEWEY, Todd M. 7777 FOREST LN, STE A202 75230 #048-15-1990 L1991 **GS** *020 †85,90

DHARANI, Murad. 4201 BROOK SPRING DR, DBA: OAKWEST HEALTH CENTE 75224 #704-25-1990 L1994 **PD** *020 †20

DHARIA, Ami Desai. 1935 MOTOR ST 75235 #048-12-2003 L2005 **PD** *020 †55

DHARMA, Kalamani Rachel. 900 JACKSON ST, STE 180 75202 #048-15-1982 L1983 **OBG** *020 †05,30

DHARMAGUNARATNE, C. 5959 HARRY HINES BLVD, STE 200 75235 #048-13-1996 L1997 **FM** *020 †18

DHARMAPAL, Nirmala. ■ 75234 #495-27-1964 **N P** *020

DHAWAN, Sumeesh. 12221 MERIT DR STE 450 75251 #495-69-1994 L2005 **IM** *020 †20

DIANA, Lawrence Gardner. 4131 N CENTRAL EXPY # 435 75204 #048-13-1984 L1986 **AN** *020 †05

DIAS, Sharmila. ■ 75204 #016-01-2001 L2004 **IM** *020

DIAZ, Elena Susana. 5323 HARRY HINES BLVD 75390 #026-04-2006 **OBG** *012

DIAZ, Monica M. 7777 FOREST LN, STE 560 75230 #048-13-2002 L2005 **OBG** *020

DIAZ, Ricardo. 5959 HARRY HINES BLVD 75235 #048-15-1990 L1991 **IM** *020

DIAZ-ARRASTIA, Ramon R. 5323 HARRY HINES BLVD, UNIV TX SW MED SCH NEURO 75235 #048-04-1988 L1989 **N** *050 †75

DIAZ-ESQUIVEL, Maribel. 8345 WALNUT HILL LN, BLDG D 75231 #048-02-1986 L1987 **PD** *020 †55

DI BELLA, Arnold Vincent. 3600 GASTON AVE, STE 450 75246 #836-02-1974 L1983 **HS ORS** *020 †40

DIBS, Susan Darlyne. ■ 75230 #038-06-1991 L2007 **PEM** *020 †55

DICK, Randall Merle. 7777 FOREST LN 75230 #010-02-1983 L1984 **AN** *020 †05

DICKENHORST, Richard W. ■ 75205 #004-01-1946 L1946 **R** *071 †80

DICKERMAN, Richard M. 221 W COLORADO BLVD, SURGICAL ASSOCIATES 75208 #035-03-1971 L1976 **GS** *020 †85

DICKSON, Beverly Ann. 8200 WALNUT HILL LN, DEPT OF PATHOLOGY 75231 #048-13-1984 L1986 **PTH** *020 †50

DICKSON, Bryan A. 5323 HARRY HINES BLVD, UT SW MED CTR 75390 #048-13-1984 L1985 **PDE PD** *020 †55

DIEHL, Jan Torsten. 4500 S LANCASTER RD # RAD, VA HOSPITAL 75216 #858-02-1961 L1977 **RNR R** *040

DIEROLF, Leon Wm, Jr. ■ 75232 #041-13-1943 L1948 **IM OM** *071

DIETSCHY, John Maurice. 5201 HARRY HINES BLVD 75235 #028-02-1958 L1965 **IM GE** *050

DIETZ, Geral Wayland. 5323 HARRY HINES BLVD 75235 #048-12-1963 L1963 **DR** *040

DIGGS, Roderick Peter, Jr. 5323 HARRY HINES BLVD, STOP 9032 75390 #047-06-1971 L1985 **OBG** *040 †30

DIGIOVANNI, David Andrew. 13601 PRESTON RD STE 900W, PINNACLE ANESTHESIA CONSUL 75240 #003-01-1988 L2000 **AN EM** *020 †05

DIGNAN, Ricky D. 3600 GASTON AVE, STE 1209 75246 #048-02-1969 L1969 **CRS GS** *020 †10,85

DILGER, Joseph Thos, Jr. 15190 PRESTONWOD BLVD #728 75248 #039-01-1981 L1984 **GS** *020 †85

DILIBERTI, Thomas C. 9301 N CENTRAL EXPY, STE 340 75231 #048-04-1991 L1992 **ORS** *020 †40

DILLENBECK, Jeanne Roe. 1935 MOTOR ST 75235 #048-14-1993 L1998 **DR** *071 †80

DIMAIO, John Michael. 5323 HARRY HINES BLVD, DEPT THRC & CRDVSLR SURG 75390 #011-02-1987 L1999 **TS** *020 †85,90

DIMAS, Billy Chris. ■ 75230 #039-01-2002 L2005 **CD** *012

DIMAS, Vasiliki Vivian. ■ 75230 #039-01-1999 L2003 **PDC** *100 †55

DIMIJIAN, Gregory Gordon. A7777 FOREST LN 75230 #035-20-1961 L1968 **OS P** *071

DIM-JAMORA, Krisinda Clar. 5323 HARRY HINES BLVD, UNIV OF TEXAS SOUTHWEST ME 75390 #748-02-2000 **PRD** *100

DIMMETTE, James E. 3600 GASTON AVE, BARNETT TOWER SUITE 805 75246 #036-07-1951 L1953 **GYN GO** *020 †30

DIMMITT, Dean C. 3801 GASTON AVE STE 201 75246 #048-02-1982 L1983 **IM CD** *020 †20

DINEEN, Sean Patrick. SOUTHWESTERN MED, UNIV OF TEXAS 75390 #020-02-2003 L2007 **GS** *012

DING, Jiantao. 5323 HARRY HINES BLVD 75235 #243-03-1996 L2007 **HO** *012 †20

DING, Michael Pham. ■ 75228 #048-15-2007 **GS** *012

DINGWERTH, Douglas John. 8222 DOUGLAS AVE 75225 #048-15-1998 L1999 **GS** *020

DINH, Marie Thi. 7777 FOREST LN, STE B412 75230 #048-02-2002 L2007 **IM ID** *020 †20

DINH, Quynh Chi Thi. 7777 FOREST LN 75230 #048-12-1999 L2003 **OBG** *020 †30

DIPPREY, Trisha L. ■ 75208 #048-02-1995 L1997 **CCM** *020

DIRTING, James Leland. 4131 N CENTRAL EXPY, STE 435 75204 #048-13-1984 L1985 **AN GS** *020 †05

DITTRICK, George William. 3500 GASTON AVE, DEPARTMENT OF SURGERY 75246 #030-05-2003 L2005 **GS** *012

DO, Kim. 7777 FOREST LN, STE C350 75230 #048-04-1995 L1996 **PTH** *062 †50

DOBBIE, Alison Elizabeth. 6263 HARRY HINES BLVD, MC 9067 75390 #919-05-1982 L2001 **FM** *020 †18

DOBBS, Kenneth Patrick. ■ 75208 #048-02-1954 L1954 **P EM** *071

DOBBS-WIGGINS, Paula C. 8140 WALNUT HILL LN, STE 603-LB62 75231 #024-01-1983 L1983 **P** *020 †75

DOBROSOTSKAYA, Irina Yuri. 8650 SOUTHWESTERN BLVD #41 75206 #913-02-2000 L2007 **IM** *012

DOBSON, Robin Wynn Sage. ■ 75202 #028-03-2005 **PTH** *012

DOCKERY, William Dee, III. 3500 GASTON AVE, DPT OF RADIOLOGY 75246 #008-01-1993 L1999 **DR CD** *020 †80

DOCKSTADER, Steven F. 13601 PRESTON RD, STE 900 75240 #048-02-1989 L1990 **AN** *020 †18

DODGE, William D. 7125 MARVIN D LOVE FWY, STE 107 75237 #048-13-1995 L1998 **FM** *020 †18

DODSON, Marvin H. 8200 WALNUT HILL LN, PRES HOSP OF DALLAS PSY 75231 #011-03-1969 L1973 **P** *020 †75

DOLAN, Elizabeth Tierney. 9330 POPPY DR STE 503 75218 #048-12-1983 L1983 **D** *020 †20,15

DOLENZ, Bernard Jos. ■ 75214 #039-01-1957 L1959 **LM P** *071 †75

DOLMATCH, Bart Lewis. 5323 HARRY HINES BLVD, UT SOUTHWESTERN MED CTR 75390 #036-07-1982 L2002 **VIR** *020 †80

DOMINGUEZ, Aniceto P. ■ 75219 #847-02-1956 L1975 **OS GS** *020

DONACHIE, Nancy Davis. 16800 DALLAS PKWY STE 150 75248 #048-14-1979 L1979 **P** *020 †75

DONAHUE, Stephen Manus. 1935 MOTOR ST 75235 #025-01-1991 L1998 **AN** *020 †05

DONNELL, David Norman. 4848 LEMMON AVE, STE 100LB508 75219 #039-01-1989 L1990 **FM ID** *020

DONSKY, Michael Stephen. 621 N HALL ST, STE 500 75226 #048-02-1969 L1969 **CD** *020

DOORES, Steven Allen. 3521 OAK LAWN AVE, # 135 75219 #048-12-1980 L1980 **PS HS** *020 †85,65 ‡

DORFMAN, Saml Yandell, Jr. ■ 75254 #048-12-1967 L1971 **IM** *072

DOSSETT, Andrew Bienvenu. 9301 N CENTRAL EXPY, STE 400 75231 #048-12-1988 L1990 **ORS** *020 †40

DOSSETT, Lucy Maryanna. 1909 HI LINE DR 75207 #048-12-1987 L1989 **DR PME** *020 †80

DOTSON, Ronald L. 75230 #039-01-1990 L1992 **OBG** *020 †30

DOTT, Raymond Neil. 75359 #016-76-1953, ▲ L1959 **DR** *071

DOUGHTY, Kyle Edward. 3600 GASTON AVE, WADLEY STE 1158 75246 #039-01-1999 L2005 **NS** *020 †05

DOUGLASS, Hal C, Jr. ■ 75230 #021-01-1957 L1964 **IM A** *020

DOUGLASS, Jennifer S. ■ 75211 #048-12-2004 L2006 **OBG** *012

DOUNING-OLIVO, Linda K. 5323 HARRY HINES BLVD, STOP 9031 75390 #048-12-1988 L1990 **AN** *020 †05

DOWDEY, Albert Ben Clark. ■ 75244 #048-02-1957 L1957 **PCH PTH** *071 †50

DOWELL, Jonathan Edwards. 5323 HARRY HINES BLVD, UNIV OF TX SOUTHWESTERN 75390 #016-02-1993 L1994 **HO** *020 †20

DOWLING, Michael Morgan. 1935 MOTOR ST, CHILDREN'S MEDICAL CENTER 75235 #035-01-1995 L2000 **CHN** *020 †75

DOWNING, David Maxwell. 7557 RAMBLER RD STE 7 75231 #005-11-1974 L1979 **AN** *020 †05

DOWNING, Michael J. 5445 LA SIERRA DR STE 101 75231 #048-14-1990 L1992 **P** *020 †75

DOWNS, John Marcus. 8315 WALNUT HILL LN # 220 75231 #028-03-1983 L1993 **CRS** *020 †85,10

DOWNS, William Allen. 7777 FOREST LN STE B131 75230 #025-01-1969 L1977 **IM** *020 †20

DOYLE, Michael Vernon. 8220 WALNUT HILL LN # 606 75231 #047-06-1970 L1978 **HS** *020 †40

DOYNE, Mark Alan. ■ 75229 #047-06-1967 L1992 **ORS** *030 †40

DRAGOMAN, Monica Virginia. 5323 HARRY HINES BLVD, SOUTHWESTERN MED 75390 #038-43-2002 L2006 **OBG** *100

DRAKE, Casey Ellen. 3523 MCKINNEY AVE, STE 263 75204 #030-05-1994 L1996 **PD** *020 †55

DRAKE, Richard David. 5323 HARRY HINES BLVD J7, UT SOUTHWESTERN MEDICAL CE 75390 #025-07-1998 L2002 **OBG** *020

DRAPER, Brenda Mc Cain. 5468 LA SIERRA DR STE 100 75231 #036-05-1987 L1998 **GS** *020 †65

DRAPER, Thomas K. ■ 75205 #048-15-2006 **GS** *012

DRAZNER, Bryan Scott. 10300 N CENTRAL EXPY, STE 350 75231 #035-15-1986 L1992 **PM PME** *020

DRAZNER, Mark Howard. 5323 HARRY HINES BLVD, UT SOUTHWESTERN MED CTR 75390 #028-02-1989 L1990 **CD** *020 †20

DRECHSLER, Henning Johann. 4500 S LANCASTER RD 111-D, VA MEDICAL CENTER 75216 #869-01-1990 L2006 **IM ID** *020 †20

DREDAR, Serag. 5323 HARRY HINES BLVD, STOP IM 75390 #539-06-2005 **IM** *012

DREES, Donna. ■ 75230 #018-03-1965 L1992 **GP** *071 †18

DREES, Jeffrey Joseph. ■ 75248 #036-05-2000 L2007 **AN** *012

DREILING, Christopher K. 8345 WALNUT HILL LN, BLDG D 75231 #048-12-1997 L1999 **PD** *020 †55

DRENNON, Donald L. 7777 FOREST LN 75230 #048-14-1984 L1985 **AN** *020 †05

DRESEL, Alexandra. 8210 WALNUT HILL LN, STE 609 75231 #056-05-1998 L2003 **GS** *020 †85

DRIGGS, Guy K. 1441 N BECKLEY AVE 75203 #023-01-1946 L1949 **ORS** *071 †40

DRIGGS, Guy Kenneth, Jr. 5920 FOREST PARK RD, STE 530 75235 #048-02-1975 L1975 **HS ORS** *020 †40

DRUMMOND, Waymon. 5959 HARRY HINES BLVD 75235 #010-03-1973 L1974 **IM** *020

DUAN, Jessica Joyce. ■ 75205 #028-02-2008 *012

DUARTE, Jose Adolfo. 1151 N BUCKNER BLVD # 201, THE PAIN MEDICINE CENTER 75218 #048-15-1986 L1987 **AN** *020 †05

DUBIN, Ruth Farnham. ■ 75211 #005-02-2005 **IM** *012

DUBROW, Donald Neil. 1151 N BUCKNER BLVD 75218 #041-02-1958 L1960 **IMG IM** *071 †20

DUBY, Allan David. 12201 MERIT DR STE 610 75251 #067-01-1979 L1987 **RHU IM** *020 †20

DU CHAMP, Philip James. 5323 HARRY HINES BLVD MC, UTSW MEDICAL CENTER 75390 #048-12-1980 L1980 **AN EM** *020 †70,05

DUCHICELA, Sacha Isabel. ■ 75229 #048-12-2008 *012

DUCHOUQUETTE, Robt Gordon. ■ 75244 #048-12-1965 L1965 **OM FM** *071 †18

DUDNEY, Blonie Wayne. ■ 75235 #047-06-2004 L2008 **OPH** *012

DUFFY, Frederick Jos. 7777 FOREST LN, STE C504 75230 #033-06-1987 L1997 **PS** *020 †85,65

DUGI, Daniel D, III. 75220 #048-04-2003 L2008 **U** *012

DULLYE, Tara Ann. 8160 WALNUT HILL LN, STE 219 75231 #048-13-1996 L1998 **OBG** *020 †30

DUMONT, Natalie Lorraine. ■ 75204 #048-13-2008 *012

DUNAGIN, Rachel L. 9301 N CENTRAL EXPY, STE 670 75231 #048-13-2004 L2007 **IM** *020 †20

DUNCAN, Andrea Freeman. 1935 MOTOR ST 75235 #048-12-2002 L2005 **NPM** *012 †55

DUNCAN, Jay Matthew. 7777 FOREST LN STE D569 75230 #028-46-2000 L2006 **CCP** *020 †55

DUNLAP, Melinda Sue. 5201 HARRY HINES BLVD, PARKLAND HOSPITAL 75235 #004-01-2004 L2007 **IM** *100 †20

DUNN, Ernest Lewis. 1441 N BECKLEY AVE, MEDICAL EDUCATION DEPT 75203 #025-01-1971 L1981 **GS** *020 †85

DUNN, Fred Harry. 5959 HARRY HINES BLVD #101 75235 #048-02-1955 L1955 **R** *071 †80

DUNN, Fredrick Laurence. ■ 75205 #016-11-1974 L1976 **END IM** *020 †20

DUNN, Mitchell Harold. 5952 ROYAL LN STE 268 75303 #048-12-1990 L1991 **P PFP** *020 †75

DUNTON, Edgar F. 75218 #048-02-1953 L1953 **PS GS** *071 †65

DUPLANTIS, Kathryn. 6750 HILLCREST PLAZA DR, STE 223 75230 #051-04-1979 L1993 **PS OS** *020 †15

DURET, Jenny Jeanjulien. 5323 HARRY HINES BLVD 75390 #011-02-2006 **OBG** *012

DURSO, Barbara Louise. 8335 WALNUT HILL LN, STE 220 75231 #048-12-1995 L1997 **PD** *020 †55

DUTTON, Wm Allan Webb. 202 W 10TH ST 75208 #352-02-1950 L1965 **GYN** *020 †30 ‡

DYER, Adrian Albertini. ■ 75229 #048-02-2007 **PD** *012

DYER, John Mc Cord. 1200 MAIN ST 75202 #047-06-1961 L1961 **PHP OS** *030 †55

DYER, Tracy Jane. 5230 MEDICAL CENTER DR, OF FORENSIC 75235 #040-02-2003 L2007 **FOP** *020 †50

DYKE, Allen S. 3500 GASTON AVE 75246 #048-14-2004 L2007 **DR** *012

DYLL, James Wellington. 3801 GASTON AVE 75246 #025-01-1956 L1963 **NS** *020

DYRVED, Niels-Jorgen. 75209 #048-12-2002 L2007 **PTH** *100 †50

DYSERT, Peter Allen, II. 3500 GASTON AVE 75246 #039-01-1979 L1981 **PTH** *020 †50

EAPEN, Reenu Sara. 1935 MOTOR ST, CHILDRENS MED CTR 75235 #038-40-1994 L2000 **PDC** *020 †55

EARLY, John Stockton. 8210 WALNUT HILL LN, STE 130, LB 11 75231 #048-12-1987 L1988 **ORS OFA** *020 †40

EAST, Cara Anne. 3500 GASTON AVE 75246 #048-12-1981 L1981 **CD IM** *020 †20

EASTMAN, Alexander L. 5323 HARRY HINES BLVD, UT SOUTHWESTERN MEDICAL CE 75390 #010-01-2001 L2004 **GS** *012

EBAUGH, Irvin Atwood, Jr. PO BOX 802304 75380 #048-02-1959 L1960 **P CHP** *020 †75

ECHOLS, Bruce Alan. 3500 W WHEATLAND RD 75237 #048-14-1979 L1980 **FM** *020 †18

EDIONWE, Mercy Oghosa. ■ 75219 #048-02-2007 **IM** *012

EDLIN, John Chas. 12800 HILLCREST RD STE 216 75230 #047-06-1968 L1973 **ADL** *020 †55

EDMAN, Clare Danl. 1441 N BECKLEY AVE, MEHTODIST HOSPS OF DALLAS 75203 #055-01-1965 L1974 **OBG REN** *071 †30

EDMISTON, Laurie K. 5201 HARRY HINES BLVD 75235 #048-12-1983 L1983 **AN** *020 †05

EDMONDSON, Heidi Danielle. ■ 75209 #048-15-2007 **PD** *012

EDMONSON, Robt Elkin, Jr. 221 W COLORADO BLVD, STE 831 75208 #048-12-1963 L1963 **CD IM** *020 †20

EDMUNDSON, Lida Lacy. 12700 HILLCREST RD STE 260 75230 #048-02-1966 L1966 **P** *020 †75

EDWARDS, Charlotte Margar. ■ 75219 #027-01-2005 **IM** *100

EDWARDS, James J. 9314 W JEFFRSN BLVD #49-17, VOUGHT AIRCRAFT IND INC 75211 #004-01-1970 L1993 **OM** *030 †70

EDWARDS, Jennifer L. 3434 SWISS AVE STE 4, MEDPROVIDER 75204 #048-14-1993 L1995 **IM** *020 †20

EDWARDS, Maurice Owen. 5959 HARRY HINES BLVD # 81 75235 #065-01-1966 L1977 **OTO** *020 †45

EDWARDS, W L Jack. ■ 75205 #048-12-1948 L1948 **IM CD** *071 †20

EFUNE, Guy E. 75204 #048-12-2008 *012

EGAN, Robert J. 13601 PRESTON RD, STE 900 75240 #048-13-1983 L1984 **AN** *020 †05

EGELSTON, James Russell. 10246 MIDWAY RD 75229 #039-01-1955 L1959 **GS GP** *071 †85

EHEMANN, Larry Joe. 9202 ELAM RD, SOUTH EAST DALLAS CLINIC 75217 #004-01-1965 L1987 **FM OM** *071 †18

EHMER, Dale Robt. 712 N WASHINGTON AVE, STE 250 75246 #048-12-1990 L1991 **OBG** *020 †30

EHRETT, Stuart William. 7777 FOREST LN STE C737 75230 #028-46-1986 L1993 **PD ID** *020 †55

EHRHARDT, John Allen. 3515 HOWELL ST 75204 #048-12-1956 L1956 **OPH** *071 †35

EICHENWALD, Heinz F. 5323 HARRY HINES BLVD, U.T. SOUTHWESTERN MEDICAL 75390 #035-20-1950 L1964 **PD PDI** *040

EICHENWALD, Theresa F. 7777 FOREST LN STE C300, DALLAS MEDICAL SPECIALISTS 75230 #041-07-1988 L2001 **IM** *020 †20

EICHHORN, Phillip James. 1851 PRAIRIE VIEW DR, STE E 75235 #048-12-1972 L1972 **D** *020 †15

EID, Jouhaina. 8553 SOUTHWESTERN BLVD #22 75206 #067-01-1991 L1992 **NEP** *100 †20

EINSPRUCH, Burton C. 8330 MEADOW RD STE 117 75231 #048-12-1960 L1960 **P** *020 †75

EISENLOHR, John Edward. ■ 75205 #048-12-1954 L1954 **OPH** *071 †35

EISENSTEIN, Abram Morton. 12220 PRESTON RD, COOPER CLINIC 75230 #048-12-1967 L1967 **GE NTR** *020 †20

EL AGHA, Mohamed-Sameh H. 5323 HARRY HINES BLVD, DEPT OF OPHTHALMOLOGY 75390 #915-02-1989 L2002 **OPH** *100

ELDER, Laura Jane. 5445 LA SIERRA DR STE 250 75231 #038-41-1979 L1988 **P** *020 †75

ELETE, Uma Reddy. 6901 SNIDER PLZ 75205 #495-57-1995 L2004 **IM** *020 †20

EL-FEKY, Waleed Hamed. 6301 GASTON AVE, STE 400W 75214 #915-04-1990 L1997 **N CN** *075

ELHALABI, Lana Ghandi. ■ 75204 #605-01-2003 **P** *012

EL-HAWARY, Rany. 5323 HARRY HINES BLVD 75390 #064-01-1998 *100

EL KHASHAB, Mostafa Aly F. ■ 75206 #915-02-1982 L2007 *100

ELKINS, David Geoffrey. 13601 PRESTON RD, STE 900 75240 #023-12-1989 L2000 **AN** *020 †05

ELKINS, Linda Carol. 5323 HARRY HINES BLVD, SOUTHWESTERN MED 75390 #012-05-2004 L2008 **OBG** *012

ELKINS, Wm Nelson, Jr. 221 W COLORADO BLVD STE 73 75208 #048-12-1968 L1968 **IM** *020 †20

ELLERMEYER, William Patri. 13601 PRESTON RD STE 900W 75240 #030-06-1981 L1982 **AN** *020 †05

ELLIOTT, Frank E, III. 7777 FOREST LN, STE B211 75230 #048-12-1968 L1968 **IM** *020

ELLIOTT, Gary Bruce. 2708 FAIRMOUNT ST, STE 202 75201 #048-12-1979 L1979 **AN EM** *075 †05

ELLIOTT, Jeffrey Leigh. 5323 HINES BLVD, UNIV OF TEXAS 75235 #028-02-1988 L1997 **N** *020 †75

ELLIOTT, Stephen Carroll. ■ 75208 #048-12-2007 **P** *012

ELLIOTT, Teresa Marie. 7979 INWOOD RD STE 21 75209 #020-12-1972 L1979 **PS GS** *020 †85,65

ELLIS, Benton Ramsey. 13601 PRESTON RD, STE 900 75240 #048-12-1989 L1990 **AN** *020 †05

ELLIS, Elaine Marie. 11615 FOREST CENTRAL DR, STE 300 75243 #021-01-1978 L1988 **OS PD** *020 †55

ELLIS, Henry Bone. ■ 75214 #048-13-2005 **ORS** *012

ELLIS, Paul R, III. 3600 GASTON AVE, STE 450 75246 #048-12-1982 L1983 **HS ORS** *020 †40

ELLIS, Stephen R. 4131 N CENTRAL EXPY, METRO ANESTHESIA 75204 #048-15-2001 L2005 **AN** *100 †05

ELLISTON, Walter Ray. 7777 FOREST LN, STE C833 75230 #016-45-1997 L2004 **P** *020 †75

ELLMAN, Brian A. 11551 FOREST CENTRAL DR, STE 108 75243 #836-02-1957 L1978 **DR** *062

ELLZEY, Allison Rene. ■ 75235 #048-12-2008 *012

ELMORE, Jeffrey Carl. 7557 RAMBLER RD STE 7 75231 #048-02-1984 L1985 **AN** *020 †05

ELMQUIST, Alison Mc Kay. 7777 FOREST LN, VERNON & WALDREP OB GYN 75230 #048-12-1989 L1991 **OBG** *020 †30

ELOVITZ, Reuben Jeremiah. 3434 SWISS AVE, STE 320 75204 #048-04-1998 L2001 **IM** *020 †20

ELTERMAN, Roy Dana. 1935 MOTOR ST 75235 #011-02-1974 L1977 **CHN N** *020 †75

ELTON, Lindsay E. ■ 75229 #048-15-2002 L2005 **CHN** *012

ELWAZIR, Esmail Mohamed. 3409 WORTH ST, STE 700 75246 #035-01-1992 L1997 **GE** *020 †20

EMERSON, Nathan Luther. 3500 GASTON AVE, SURGERY DEPARTMENT 75246 #017-20-2003 L2008 **GS** *012

EMMERT, John A. ■ 75225 #048-04-1947 L1947 **IM** *071

EMMETT, Daniel Seth. ■ 75218 #048-02-2001 L2003 **GE** *012

EMMETT, Michael. 3500 GASTON AVE 75246 #041-13-1971 L1976 **IM NEP** *040 †20

EMMONS, Jacqueline. ■ 75205 #048-13-2004 L2008 **PTH** *012

EMSLIE, Graham John. 5323 HARRY HINES BLVD 75235 #919-01-1974 L1981 **CHP P** *020 †75

END, Douglas Arthur. 7557 RAMBLER RD STE 7, NORTH TEXAS ANESTHESIA 75231 #048-14-2004 L2008 **AN** *012

ENGELS, Jennifer Earle. 5323 HARRY HINES BLVD MC, UT SOUTHWESTERN MEDICAL CE 75390 #048-02-1997 L1998 **DR** *020 †80

ENGELS, Matthew James. 13601 PRESTON RD, STE 900 75240 #048-02-1997 L1998 **AN** *020 †05

ENGLE, William Douglas. 5201 HARRY HINES BLVD 75235 #024-07-1974 L1981 **NPM PD** *020 †55

ENGLEMAN, David Andrew. 8117 PRESTON RD, STE 470 75225 #038-44-1990 L1995 **CD** *020 †20

ENGLISH, James Martin. 6901 SNIDER PLZ, STE 140 75205 #011-02-1981 L1983 **PS** *020 †85,65

ENRIGHT, Julie Anne. ■ 75219 #005-06-2006 **OPH** *012

EPSTEIN, Henry Aron. 9440 POPPY DR 75218 #396-06-1940 L1960 **GS** *071

EPSTEIN, Maurice Wm. 3600 GASTON AVE # 864 75246 #021-01-1956 L1957 **AN** *071 †05

EPSTEIN, Robert Henry. 5201 HARRY HINES BLVD 75235 #011-02-1972 L1983 **DR** *050 †80

ERDMAN, George Brown, Jr. 13601 PRESTON RD, STE 900W 75240 #048-12-1972 L1975 **AN** *020 †05

ERDMAN, Kathleen B Barry. 5477 GLEN LAKES DR, STE 210 75231 #048-12-1972 L1976 **P** *020 †75

ERDMAN, William A. 5323 HARRY HINES BLVD, GROUND FL 75390 #035-08-1971 L1986 **DR NM** *020 †80,28

ERFE, Felix Estayo, Jr. 809 SINGLETON BLVD 75212 #748-01-1972 L1981 **PD** *020

ERICKSON, Christof P. ■ 75235 #003-01-2003 L2007 **DMP** *012 †50

ERICKSON, Judith Gail. 9528 WEBB CHAPEL RD, DALLAS 75220 #048-13-1998 L2001 **FM** *020 †18

ERICSON, Ruth A. 3026 MOCKINGBIRD LN # 101 75205 #048-02-1951 L1955 **P** *072

ERWIN, Karl D. 7502 GREENVILLE AVE, STE 600 75231 #048-13-1983 L1983 **IM EM** *020 †20

ESBER, Webb Jonathan. 7777 FOREST LN, BLDG A 75230 #041-01-1971 L1972 **PTH** *062 †50

ESCALANTE, Mirna X. 5323 HARRY HINES BLVD, UT SOUTHWESTERN MED SCH 75390 #048-12-2005 L2008 **PD** *012

ESCOBAR, Angela Jill. ■ 75205 #048-12-2008 *012

ESCOBAR-VAZQUEZ, Edwin. 2909 S HAMPTON RD, STE F-122 LB #29 75224 #042-01-1990 L1992 **IM** *020

ESEDEBE, Michael Emeka. 9661 AUDELIA RD STE 1 75238 #690-01-1980 L2000 **OBG** *020 †18

ESHAGHI, Nahid. 4500 S LANCASTER RD, RADIOLOGY DEPARTMENT 75216 #517-01-1974 L1990 **DR** *020 †80

ESKINS, Barry Scott. 8585 N STEMMONS FWY, STE 700 75247 #055-01-1991 L2003 **IM PLM** *020 †20

ESMAIL, Nadeem S. ■ 75235 #048-12-2007 *012

ESPEY, Richard A. 1341 W MOCKINGBIRD LN, STE 710E 75247 #048-14-1981 L1989 **PM** *020 †60

ESPINOZA-ERVIN, Christophe. ■ 75204 #007-02-2007 **ORS** *012

ESPLIN, Edward David. 5201 HARRY HINES BLVD 75235 #048-12-2005 L2007 **IM** *012

ESSARY, Lydia H. 2330 BUTLER ST STE 115, COCKERELL DERMATOPATHOLGY 75235 #737-06-1986 L1999 **DMP** *012 †50

ESTEPHAN, Bachir Johnny. ■ 75206 #605-01-2002 **N** *012

ESTESS, Berthold H, Jr. ■ 75220 #048-02-1964 L1964 **GYN** *071 †30

ESTEVEZ, Ryan Felipe. 8650 SOUTHWESTERN BLVD 75206 #422-01-2002 L2005 **P** *100 †75

■ = Address Information Privacy Protected

ESTRADA-ARZENO, Roberto E. 3330 DOUGLAS AVE 75219 #308-04-1988 L2002 **PD** *020 †55

ESTRERA, Aaron Solante. 5909 HARRY HINES BLVD, BLVD, HA0913 75390 #748-11-1966 L1977 **TS TRS** *020 †85,90

ESTROFF, Jordan Mitchell. ■ 75204 #012-01-2007 **GS** *012

ETEZADI-AMOLI, Neda. ■ 75251 #031-01-2002 L2006 **OBG** *100

ETUFUGH, Chukwuemeka Nwan. ■ 75236 #035-19-2003 L2004 **PTH** *012

EUBANK, Kathryn Jean. ■ 75219 #048-14-1997 L2000 **IMG** *020 †20

EUHUS, David Michael. 5323 HARRY HINES BLVD E6, U.T. SOUTHWESTERN MEDICAL 75390 #028-34-1984 L1996 **GS** *020 †85

EUN, Jay Ho. ■ 75206 #005-15-2004 **PM** *012

EUWER, Rebecca Lee. 9 MEDICAL PKWY, STE 101 75234 #007-02-1986 L1987 **D** *020 †15

EVANS, James Baker. 75229 #048-12-1968 L1968 **DR** *020 †80

EVANS, James David. 4131 N CENTRAL EXPY, STE 435 75204 #048-02-1999 L2003 **AN** *020 †05

EVANS, James Patrick. 411 N WASHINGTON AVE #1000, SPORTS MEDICINE CLINIC 75246 #048-12-1959 L1959 **OSM** *072 †40

EVANS, Neil Anson. ■ 75223 #048-15-2004 **PEM** *012 †55

EVANS, Patricia. 5323 HARRY HINES BLVD, UTSOUTHWESTERN DEPT PEDIAT 75390 #048-15-1983 L1983 **CHN** *020 †55,75

EVANS, Rebecca Harrell. 5201 HARRY HINES BLVD, DEPT OF RADIO PARKLAND MEM 75235 #027-01-1969 L1980 **DR** *020 †80

EVANS, Steven Dennis. 12606 GREENVILLE AVE 75243 #005-14-1989 L1998 **AN** *020 †05

EVANS, W Phil. 5323 HARRY HINES BLVD, UT SW CTR FOR BREAST CARE 75390 #048-12-1972 L1972 **DR** *020 †80

EVANS, Walter Francis, II. 8160 WALNUT HILL LN, STE 214 LOCK BOX 40 75231 #035-01-1979 L1980 **OBG** *020 †30

EWING, Gene Edward. 8267 ELMBROOK DR, STE 100 75247 #016-11-1977 L1983 **PTH BBK** *020 †50

EWING, Joseph E. 13601 PRESTON RD, STE 900 75240 #048-12-1993 L1995 **AN** *020 †05

EWING, Philip Hughston. 5323 HARRY HINES BLVD, SOUTHWESTERN MED 75390 #051-04-2002 **PEM** *012 †55

EWTON, Maynard Franklin. 8440 WALNUT HILL LN, STE 830 75231 #048-04-1961 L1961 **IM GE** *030

EZAKI, Marybeth. 2222 WELBORN ST, TEXAS SCOTTISH RITE HOSP 75219 #008-01-1977 L1978 **ORS HS** *020 †40

FA, Kosunarty. 1150 N BISHOP AVE, STE 100 75208 #409-21-1990 L2005 **NEP** *020 †20

FABI, Cipriano Ochon, Jr. 1000 EMERALD ISLE DR, STE 107 75218 #748-08-1959 L1979 **FM** *071

FACTOR, Dennis John. 5939 HARRY HINES BLVD, STE 411 75235 #056-06-1961 L1962 **GYN** *020 †30

FADAHUNSI, Patrick Kola. 4650 S HAMPTON RD STE 123 75232 #047-07-1978 L1987 **GS GP** *020 †85

FAGADAU, Warren Robt. 6131 LUTHER LN STE 216 75225 #048-12-1978 L1978 **OPH** *020 †35

FAGNER, Joseph S. 1717 MAIN ST, STE 5200 75201 #048-12-1995 L1996 **EM** *020 †16

FAIR, Rogers Pressley, Jr. 221 W COLORADO BLVD, STE 730 75208 #047-07-1975 L1990 **IM** *020 †20

FALCON, James Antonio. ■ 75235 #048-12-2008 *012

FALKE, Clarence G. 221 W COLORADO BLVD, STE 625 PAVILLION II 75208 #048-12-1950 L1950 **GS VS** *072 †85

FALLENA, Margarita. 5323 HARRY HINES BLVD, UNIV TX SOUTHWESTERN MED S 75390 #649-13-2003 L2008 **RHU** *012 †20

FALOLA, Elizabeth O. 7920 ELMBROOK DR, STE 120 75247 #690-06-1980 L1996 **FM** *020 †18

FAM, Fathi Gohar. 7616 LYNDON B JOHNSON FWY, THE VASCULAR CLINIC 75251 #915-02-1955 L1977 **GE IM** *072

FAN, Ellen. 7001 PRESTON RD, SUITE 410 LB 17 75205 #048-13-1998 L1999 **P** *020 †75

FAN, Yijun. 8440 WALNUT HILL LN, TEXAS MEDICAL & SURGICAL 75231 #243-47-1987 L2001 **RHU** *020 †20

FANCHER, James Richard. 6111 HARRY HINES BLVD 75235 #047-06-1965 L1969 **OTO** *020 †45

FANONI, Roy Henry. ■ 75229 #035-01-1955 L1959 **P GS** *072 †85,75

FARAH, Nabeel William. 8220 WALNUT HILL LN, STE 101 75231 #048-12-2002 L2006 **IM** *020 †20

FARKAS, Babette Frances. 17103 PRESTON RD, STE 100 75248 #048-15-1985 L1986 **P** *020 †75

FARKAS, Robert Allen. 7777 FOREST LN, C-206 75230 #035-06-1978 L1980 **NEP IM** *020 †20

FARLEY, Leroy Bradley. ■ 75214 #048-02-1955 L1955 **PD** *071

FARNER, Robert Ernst, Jr. 3500 GASTON AVE, DEPARTMENT OF SURGERY 75246 #056-05-1994 L1996 **CRS** *020

FARNUM, Laura Marjorie. 2922 MARTIN LTHR KNG JR 75215 #041-13-1982 L1989 **IM** *020 †20

FARRIS, James Randolph. 5909 HARRY HINES BLVD 75235 #010-03-1976 L1980 **OS IM** *020

FARROW-GILLESPIE, Alan C. 1935 MOTOR ST D03-309, CHILDREN'S MEDICAL CTR DAL 75235 #048-14-1978 L1978 **APM** *100 †05

FARUKHI, Irfan Mohammed. SOUTHWESTERN MED, UNIV OF TEXAS 75390 #048-15-2002 L2005 **NM** *020 †28

FATTER-BLACK, C Sean. 6721 LAKEWOOD BLVD 75214 #048-14-1993 L1995 **EM** *020 †16

FAVOUR, Susan E. 5323 HARRY HINES BLVD, DIV GEN INTERNAL MED 75390 #048-12-1993 L1994 **IM** *020 †20

FAWCETT, Michael L. 8160 WALNUT HILL LN # 007 75231 #048-02-1990 L1991 **EM FM** *020 †18

FAY, Joseph Wayne. 3535 WORTH ST, STE 200 75246 #038-40-1972 L1982 **HEM ON** *050 †20

FAZAL, Samina. 3601 SWISS AVE 75204 #704-06-1988 L2002 **NEP** *020 †20

FAZEL, Poorya. ■ 75201 #039-01-2006 **IM** *012

FEAGINS, Brian A. 7424 GREENVILLE AVE, STE 211 75231 #048-12-1987 L1989 **U** *020 †95

FEAGINS, Linda Anne. 7110 CASA LOMA AVE 75214 #048-04-2001 L2003 **GE** *020

FEAGINS, Pamela Lindsay. 9101 LBJ FWY STE 710 75243 #048-12-1985 L1986 **IM** *020 †20

FEARON, Jeffrey Archer. 7777 FOREST LN # 700 75230 #038-41-1981 L1990 **CFS PS** *020 †85,65

FEDYK, Adam Ross. ■ 75204 #028-03-2004 L2007 **OPH** *012

FEHR, Bettina S. 1966 INWOOD RD 75235 #869-07-1982 L1997 **P** *020 †75

FEIN, David C. 8230 WALNUT HILL LN # 304 75231 #048-12-1982 L1983 **OBG** *020 †30

FEINER, Joel S. 4500 S LANCASTER RD, DALLAS VETERANS AFFAIRS ME 75216 #035-46-1964 L1993 **P CHP** *020 †75

FEINSTEIN, David M. 7777 FOREST LN STE C604 75230 #065-01-1973 L1978 **END** *020

FEKETE, Lorand. 75115 GREENVILLE AVE, STE 400 75231 #781-05-1956 L1971 **N** *072 †75

FELDHENDLER, Moshe. 9 MEDICAL PKWY STE 107 75234 #056-06-2003 L2007 **AN** *020

FELDMAN, Mark. 8200 WALNUT HILL LN, DEPARTMENT OF INTERNAL MED 75231 #041-13-1972 L1976 **IM GE** *020 †20

FELDMAN, Mary Melinda. ■ 75219 #028-03-1998 L2005 **DMP** *020 †15

FELICIANO, Mario C. 5350 AMESBURY DR 75206 #748-01-1961 L1975 **GS** *071

FELICIANO, N M. 5323 HARRY HINES BLVD, STOP 9031 75390 #048-14-1994 L1997 **PTH** *020 †50

FELLMAN, Ronald Leigh. 7150 GREENVILLE AVE, STE 300 75231 #021-01-1978 L1982 **OPH** *020 †35

FENG, Singyi. 1935 MOTOR ST, CHILDRENS MED CTR DALLAS 75235 #041-02-1998 L2002 **ETX** *100 †55

FENTON, Barry J. 3710 RAWLINS ST STE 1370 75219 #035-15-1975 L1981 **P FM** *020 †75

FENVES, Andrew Zoltan. 3601 SWISS AVE 75204 #048-12-1979 L1979 **NEP IM** *020 †20

FENYVES, Steven. 129 W 9TH ST 75208 #065-01-1972 L1978 **GPM** *062

FERANCHAK, Andrew Philip. ■ 75204 #041-12-1992 L2005 **PG** *020 †55

FERNANDES, Devin G. 1935 MOTOR ST 75235 #048-12-2004 L2007 **PD** *020 †55

FERNANDEZ, Ernesto M. 8355 WALNUT HILL LN, STE 105 75231 #048-12-1988 L1989 **PD** *020 †55

FERNANDEZ-SUEIRO, Jose L. 6646 SHADY BROOK LN 75206 #847-05-1987 **RHU** *100

FERRARI, Christine E. 2777 N STEMMONS FWY, STE 300 75207 #054-04-1994 L1996 **PD** *020 †55

FERRIS, Mark Chas. 9330 POPPY DR 75218 #039-01-1985 L1994 **PCC IM** *020 †20

FERRY, Kathryn Irene. 712 N WASHINGTON AVE, AMERICAN RADIOLOGY 75246 #048-04-2003 L2007 **MPD** *020

FESMIRE, Susan I. 5461 LA SIERRA DR 75231 #048-12-1997 L2000 **CD** *020 †20

FETNER, Christopher D. 7777 FOREST LN, DALLAS UROLOGY ASSOCIATES 75230 #028-34-1972 L1972 **U** *020 †95

FETNER, Erik Glenn. 3500 GASTON AVE, DEPARTMENT OF SURGERY 75246 #048-12-1995 L1997 **CRS** *020 †85,10

FIELDER, Jon Frederic. 5323 HARRY HINES BLVD MC91, UT SOUTHWESTERN MEDICAL CE 75390 #048-04-1999 L2007 **IM** *020 †20

FIERKE, Shelby Ryan. ■ 75204 #048-12-2006 **DR** *012

FIGUEROA, Stephen Andrew. ■ 75219 #028-34-2007 **N** *012

FILLER, Robert Dean. 75219 #048-13-1980 L1980 **FM OM** *020 †18

FINCH, Michael L. 3450 W WHEATLAND RD # 325 75237 #048-13-1994 L1997 **IM** *020 †20

FINE, Bruce A. 7777 FOREST LN, TEXAS ONCOLOGY D400 75230 #048-02-1988 L1989 **GO OBG** *020 †30

FINE, Joshua K. 3600 GASTON AVE STE 1002, BARNETT TOWER 75246 #048-15-1988 L1989 **U** *020 †95

FINE, Kenneth D. 3500 GASTON AVE, MEDICAL EDUCATION 75246 #028-46-1986 L1987 **GE** *020 †20

FINE, Myron G. 3600 GASTON AVE, BARNETT TWR STE 1002 75246 #047-06-1951 L1958 **U** *020 †95

FINE, Robert Lee. 3434 SWISS AVE, STE 330 75204 #048-12-1978 L1978 **IM OS** *020 †20 ‡

FINK, Karen Lynn. 3600 GASTON AVE, BARNETT TOWER, STE 605 75246 #026-08-1990 L1992 **N** *050 †75

FINN, Maxwell D. 4015 WORTH ST 75246 #048-15-1995 L1996 **OMF** *020

FINN, Shlomo. 3600 GASTON AVE, STE 856 75246 #396-21-1979 L1986 **NS** *020 †25

FINNEGAN, Maureen Anne. 5323 HARRY HINES BLVD, STOP 9031 75390 #061-01-1974 L1989 **GS ORS** *020 †40

FIRAT, Ahmet Kemal. 5323 HARRY HINES BLV 75235 #902-05-1996 **RNR** *100

FISCHBACH, Bernard Victor. 3601 SWISS AVE 75204 #030-06-1996 L2003 **NEP** *020 †20

FISCHER, John P. 3500 GASTON AVE 75246 #021-01-1944 L1950 **OM IM** *072 †20

FISCHER, Robert Paul. 8230 WALNUT HILL LN 75231 #047-06-1984 L1991 **IM** *020 †20

FISHER, John W. 3500 GASTON AVE 75246 #021-05-1948 L1954 **IM GE** *071

FISHER, Michielle Nichole. 303 E OVERTON RD, BLUITT-FLOWERS HEALTH CENT 75216 #047-07-1997 L2002 **IM IMG** *020 †20

FISHER, Neal Leon. 13601 PRESTON RD, PINNACLE ANESTHESIA CONSUL 75240 #039-01-1986 L1987 **AN** *020 †05

FISHER, Thomas Boone. 1717 MAIN ST 75201 #048-12-1976 L1976 *020

FISHKIN, Semyon Maxovitch. 1935 MOTOR ST D03-309, ANESTHESIOLOGISTS FOR CHIL 75235 #913-15-1985 L2006 **AN** *020 †20,05

FISK, John Douglas. 9090 SKILLMAN ST, STE 182-371 75243 #054-04-1975 L1991 **DR R** *020 †80

FITZ, John Gregory. 5323 HARRY HINES BLVD, INTERNAL MEDICINE MC-9030 75390 #036-07-1979 L2005 **GE IM** *030 †20

FITZGERALD, Andrew Scott. 8200 WALNUT HILL LN, DEPT MED 75231 #048-12-1990 L1991 **IM** *020 †20

FITZGERALD, Bruce E. 12201 MERIT DR, STE 420 75251 #048-14-1989 L1990 **PAN** *020 †05

FITZGERALD, John Edward. 5323 HARRY HINES BLVD, UT SOUTHWESTERN MEDICAL CE 75390 #048-02-1989 L1990 **PUD** *020 †20

FITZHARRIS, Thomas Jos. 1130 BEACHVIEW ST 75218 #017-20-1984 L1986 **IM** *020 †20

FITZPATRICK, Michael C. 1341 W MOCKINGBIRD LN 75247 #012-01-1973 L1980 **P PMM** *020 †75

FITZWATER, Joseph Leon. ■ 75218 #048-12-2008 *012

FIXLER, David Ellsworth. 1935 MOTOR ST, CARDIOLOGY CHILDRENS MED 75235 #016-02-1964 L1971 **PDC** *020 †55

FLANAGAN, Brian Kevin. 9301 N CENTRAL EXPY, STE 585 75231 #021-01-1995 L1996 **APM** *020 †20

FLANGIN, Kathryn M Haley. 111 COMMERCE ST 3RD FL, INFIRMARY 75207 #048-12-1974 L1974 **IM** *020

FLATT, Adrian Ede. 3500 GASTON AVE, # 6TH 75246 #352-03-1946 L1982 **HS** *071 †40

FLEISCHLI, Mary. 3600 GASTON AVE STE 1051 75246 #024-01-1993 L1997 **D** *020 †15

FLEISCHMAN-BRUCE, Cheryl. 4500 S LANCASTER RD 75216 #028-34-1989 L1993 **PM** *020 †60

FLEISCHMANN, Ronald S. 8411 PRESTON RD, STE 712 75225 #035-09-1969 L1985 **P** *020 †75

FLEISCHMANN, Roy Mitchell. 5939 HARRY HINES BLVD #400 75235 #035-08-1969 L1975 **RHU IM** *020 †20

FLEISHMAN, Justin Nathani. ■ 75204 #048-02-2006 L2008 **EM** *012

FLEMING, Sean Duane. 8160 WALNUT HILL LN, STE 007 75231 #019-02-2001 L2003 **EM** *020 †16

FLESCHLER, Mark Joe. 8210 WALNUT HILL LN, STE 604 75231 #048-12-1984 L1985 **IM IMG** *020 †20 ‡

FLETCHER, Matthew Benjami. ■ 75235 #021-05-2008 *012

FLEWELLEN, Eugene H, III. 13601 PRESTON RD, STE 900 75240 #048-02-1969 L1969 **AN** *020 †05

FLORES, Glenn. 5323 HARRY HINES BLVD, UNIVERSITY OF TX SW MED CT 75390 #005-02-1989 L2008 **PD** *050 †55

FLOYD, Bonnie Lee. 7777 FOREST LN, STE B215 75230 #037-01-1980 L1985 **CD** *020 †20

FOGEL, Elaine Renee. 7777 FOREST LN, C-STE 210 75230 #041-12-1980 L1984 **OBG** *020 †30

FOGELMAN, Morris Jos. ■ 75230 #016-11-1944 **GS** *071 †85

FOGLIA, Robert Peter. 1935 MOTOR ST RM D03-, CHILDREN'S MEDICAL CENTER 75235 #010-02-1974 L2006 **PDS GS** *020 †85

FOGWELL, Theodore Ernest. 8160 WALNUT HILL LN # 220 75231 #048-12-1973 L1973 **OBG** *020 †30

FONG, Benton Dodwah. 5201 HARRY HINES BLVD, PARKLAND HOSPITAL 75235 #040-02-2003 L2006 **AN** *100

FONTAINE, Catherine S. 12700 HILLCREST RD, STE 260 75230 #011-03-1991 L1995 **P PYG** *020

FORBES, Caryn M. 3450 W WHEATLAND RD, STE 440 75237 #048-12-2000 L2002 **PD** *020 †55 ‡

FORBESS, Joseph Matthew. 1935 MOTOR ST E03-320, DIV OF PED CARDIOTHORACIC 75235 #024-01-1990 L2000 **TS** *020 †85,90

FORBESS, Lisa. 5323 HARRY HINES BLVD, UT SOUTHWESTERN MED CTR 75390 #024-01-1991 L2004 **CD IM** *020 †20

FORDTRAN, John S. 3500 GASTON AVE DEPT MED 75246 #021-01-1956 L1957 **IM GE** *050

FOREE, Kenneth, III. 3600 GASTON AVE 75246 #048-12-1948 L1948 **OPH** *071 †35

FOREMAN, Michael Lynn. 3409 WORTH ST STE 640 75246 #048-13-1982 L1983 **TRS CCS** *020 †85

FORESTNER, John Edward. 5323 HARRY HINES BLVD, U.T. SOUTHWESTERN MEDICAL 75390 #016-06-1970 L1973 **AN** *020 †05

FORNITO, Anthony Peter. ■ 75228 #035-09-1986 L2000 **P** *020 †75

FORT, David Gibson. ■ 75227 #048-12-1979 L1979 **P** *020 †85

FORT, Wana A Gibson. ■ 75227 #048-04-1949 L1949 **PD FM** *071

FOSDICK, David Allan. 8230 WALNUT HILL LN, STE 208 75231 #025-01-1976 L1977 **TS** *020 †85,90

FOSMIRE, George Perry. ■ 75214 #019-02-1955 L1966 **GS** *020 †85

FOSTER, Christopher A. 3600 GASTON AVE, STE 303 75246 #021-01-1990 L1993 **IM** *020 †20

FOSTER, Coy Zenith. 4623 ARCADY AVE, DALLAS COUNTY HEALTH & HUM 75209 #048-02-1969 L1969 **PS GS** *020

FOSTER, Daniel Willett. 5323 HARRY HINES BLVD, UNIV OF TX SO WESTERN MED 75390 #048-12-1955 L1955 **END** *040

FOSTER, Fred Memnon. ■ 75214 #048-12-1955 L1955 **AN** *071 †05

FOSTER, John Robt. 8345 WALNUT HILL LN, BLDG D 75231 #048-12-1982 L1983 **PD** *020 †55

FOSTER, Steven Victor. 1441 N BECKLEY AVE 75203 #048-04-1990 L1991 **PTH** *020 †50

FOTEH, Kousta Issa. ■ 75204 #048-14-2003 L2008 **GS** *012

FOTEH, Mazin I. ■ 75204 #048-14-2005 **GS** *012

FOTIADIS, Christos. 5323 HARRY HINES BLVD 75235 #418-02-2000 L2005 **NP** *100 †50

FOWLER, Amy Catherine. ■ 75204 #048-14-2004 L2006 **PD** *100 †55

FOWLER, Donald Robt. 4500 S LANCASTER RD # 116A, VA HOSPITAL 75216 #048-12-1961 L1961 **P** *030 †75

FOWLER, Raymond Logan. 5323 HARRY HINES BLVD, UT SOUTHWESTERN MEDICAL CE 75390 #012-01-1976 L2002 **EM PHP** *020 †16

FOX, James G. ■ 75205 #048-14-2007 **IM** *012

FOX, John Birkhead. ■ 75230 #036-01-1964 L1964 **DR NR** *020 †80,28 ‡

FOX, Joshua Carrick. ■ 75208 #048-13-2006 **ORS** *012

FOX, L George. 13601 PRESTON RD, STE 900W 75240 #048-15-1989 L1990 **AN PME** *020 †05

FOX, Louis. 7777 FOREST LN, C-865 75230 #023-01-1975 L1980 **VS** *020 †85

FRANKE, Curtis A. 2731 LEMMON AVE E, STE 200 75204 #048-13-2003 L2006 **FM** *020 †18

FRANKEL, Heidi Lee. 5323 HARRY HINES BLVD, RM E5.514 75390 #023-01-1987 L2005 **GS TRS** *020 †85

FRANKFURT, Alan Irwin. 13601 PRESTON RD, STE 900W 75240 #048-12-1981 L1981 **AN EM** *020 †05

FRANKLIN, Zachary A. ■ 75232 #005-06-1994 L1998 **EM** *020

FRANKS, Danika N. ■ 75208 #048-12-2006 **EM** *012

FRATER, Dirk Anthony. 8230 WALNUT HILL LN 75231 #035-46-1984 L1986 **EM IM** *020 †20

FRAZIER, William James. 11941 FORESTWOOD DR 75244 #017-20-1968 L1969 **U EM** *020 †95

FREDERICK, Hugh Allen. 9301 N CENTRAL EXPY, STE 350 75231 #048-02-1985 L1986 **HS ORS** *020 †40

FREED-SIGURDSSON, Ana R. 12221 MERIT DR STE 460 75251 #048-12-1995 L1996 **PM** *020 †60

FREELAND, Charlotte D. 7 MEDICAL PKWY 75234 #048-12-1984 L1985 **IM** *020 †20

FREELAND, King Irving. 13601 PRESTON RD, STE 900 75240 #048-12-1984 L1985 **AN** *020 †05

FREELE, Robert B, Jr. 7777 FOREST LN BLDG C 75230 #048-02-2001 L2006 **P IM** *020 †20,75

FREEMAN, Andrew Branch. 7777 FOREST LN STE A310 75230 #048-12-1981 L1981 **AN** *020 †05

FREEMAN, Jennifer C. 8160 WALNUT HILL LN, STE 212 75231 #048-02-1983 L1983 **OBG** *020 †30

FREEMAN, Michael Brandon. ■ 75201 #030-05-2001 L2007 **PS** *100

FREEMAN, Scott Andrew. ■ 75390 #016-06-1994 L2007 **P** *020 †75

FREEMAN, Tandy R. 7115 GREENVILLE AVE, STE 310 75231 #048-12-1984 L1985 **ORS** *020 †40

FRENCH, David Manning. 1717 MAIN ST STE 5200, ALBANY MEDICAL CENTER 75201 #036-01-2002 L2007 **EM** *100 †16

FRENCH, Todd Hobart. 13601 PRESTON RD STE 1000 75240 #030-05-1980 L1986 **AN FM** *020 †18,05

FRENKEL, Eugene P. 5323 HARRY HINES BLVD 75235 #025-01-1953 L1962 **ON HEM** *020 †20

FRENKEL, Rhoda B Smilay. 5310 HARVEST HILL RD, LB 132 75230 #025-01-1961 L1962 **PYA CHP** *020 †75

FREUDIGMAN, Paul Thos. 3600 GASTON AVE, WADLEY TWR STE 755 75246 #010-02-1991 L1998 **ORS** *020 †40

FREY, Robert Dale. 4929 VICTOR ST 75214 #004-01-1983 L1990 **FM** *020 †18

FRIBLEY, Corinne Beth. 5323 HARRY HINES BLVD MC, UT SOUTHWESTERN MEDICAL CE 75390 #017-20-1999 L2000 **CHP** *020 †75

FRID-HONIGSBLUM, Leon. 6757 ARAPAHO RD, STE 711 75248 #649-01-1981 L1988 **AN PD** *020 †05

FRIED, Gabriel. 13740 MIDWAY RD, STE 610 75244 #748-10-1964 L1972 **FM AM** *020 †70

FRIEDBERG, Errol C. 5323 HARRY HINES BLVD 75390 #836-01-1961 L1992 **PTH** *030

FRIEDEN, Blake E. 7777 FOREST LN STE D- 75230 #048-13-2002 L2004 **OBG** *020

FRIESE, Randall Scott. 5323 HARRY HINES BLVD, DEPT SURG MAIL CODE 9158 75390 #023-01-1990 L2001 **CCS** *020 †85

FROEHLICH, Thomas Wm. 5323 HARRY HINES BLVD, UTSOUTHWEST MED CTR 75390 #048-12-1975 L1978 **ON HEM** *020 †20

FROHMAN, Elliott Mark. 5323 HARRY HINES BLVD, DEPARTMENT OF NEUROLOGY 75390 #005-15-1990 L1995 **N** *020 †75

FROST, Janet Dann. 1151 N BUCKNER BLVD, STE 206 75218 #048-15-1985 L1986 **OBG** *020 †30

FROST, Steve Marshall. 3600 GASTON AVE, UROLOGY CLINICS OF NORTH 75246 #048-12-1975 1975 **U** *020 †95

FROSTENSON, Phyllis Joan. 7777 FOREST LN 75230 #034-01-1978 L1984 **DR** *020 †80

FU, Chiawan. ■ 75209 #048-12-2002 L2006 **AN** *100 †05

FU, Selena Yue. ■ 75209 #023-07-2003 L2007 **IM** *100

FULCHIERO, Gregory John. ■ 75231 #041-13-2003 L2003 **PRD** *012 †15

FULGHAM, Pat Fox. 8230 WALNUT HILL LN, STE 700 75231 #048-12-1981 L1981 **U** *020 †95

FULLER, Ashley Elizabeth. 5323 HARRY HINES BLVD 75390 #026-04-2006 **OBG** *012

FULLER, Christopher G. ■ 75229 #048-15-2001 L2007 **OPH** *020

FULLER, Dale Eugene. 5420 LYNDON B JOHNSON FWY 75240 #018-03-1960 L1968 **RO R** *071 †80

FULLER, Dana Allen. 12700 PARK CENTRAL DR, STE 430 75251 #048-13-1977 L1977 **DR** *020 †80

FULLER, Deborah Anne. 8440 WALNUT HILL LN, TEXAS MEDICAL & SURGICAL 75231 #048-02-1984 L1985 **OBG** *020 †30

FULTON, Mark K. 4500 S LANCASTER RD 75216 #048-02-1986 L1995 **P** *020 †75

FUNG, Sanford Han Ming. 6310 LBJ FWY STE 208 75240 #048-14-1997 L2002 **FM** *020 †18

FURLAN, Scott Nicholas. 5323 HARRY HINES BLVD, SOUTHWESTERN MED 75390 #005-06-2006 **PD** *012

FURZE, Alexis Dorian. ■ 75204 #011-02-2005 L2008 **OTO** *012

FUSTER, Daniel Guido. 5323 HARRY HINES BLVD, UNIV OF TEXAS SOUTHWESTERN 75390 #869-02-1998 **NEP** *100

FYFE, Alistair Ian. 7777 FOREST LN, STE C655 75230 #143-10-1984 L1999 **CD** *020 †20

FYNES, Margaret Mary. 6166 PRESTON CREEK PL, MARGARET M. FYNES, MD 75240 #048-09-1992 L1999 **DR** *020 †80

GABRIEL, Vincent A. 5323 HARRY HINES BLVD 75390 #068-01-2000 L2005 *100

GADHIA, Monika Mohanbhai. 5323 HARRY HINES BLVD, U OF TX SOUTHWESTERN MED 75390 #048-12-2006 **PD** *012

GAGNON, Garry Francis. 5323 HARRY HINES BLVD, DIV OF EMERGENCY MED 75390 #028-34-2004 L2007 **EM** *100

GAHAGAN, Lawrence O. 8200 WALNUT HILL LN 75231 #021-05-1953 L1960 **OPH** *071 †35

GAIDARSKI, Alexander A. 1441 N BECKLEY AVE, PHYSICIAN EMERGENCY CARE A 75203 #198-01-1990 L1995 **IM** *020 †20

GAILIUNAS, Peter, Jr. 9115 FOREST LN 75243 #016-43-1972 L1978 **PM IM** *020 †20

GAINES, George Yeaman, III. 5323 HARRY HINES BLVD, STOP 9031 75390 #048-12-1968 L1968 **AN** *071 †05

GAIR, Ashley Brinton Ring. ■ 75214 #007-02-2007 **PD** *012

GAITONDE, Ashwin G. ■ 75238 #048-16-2007 **OBG** *012

GALA, Rajiv Babulal. ■ 75219 #001-02-2000 L2004 **OBG** *020 †30

GALBRAITH, James W. 5909 HARRY HINES BLVD 75235 #048-02-1974 L1974 **FM LM** *020

GALLAGHER, Michael P. 5323 HARRY HINES BLVD, SOUTHWESTERN MED 75390 #017-20-2003 **AN** *100

GALLIEN, Brandy Michelle. ■ 75204 #021-05-2006 L2008 **P** *012

GAMBLE, Bradford Allen. 8230 WALNUT HILL LN, STE 420 75231 #048-12-1993 L1997 **OTO** *020 †45

GAN, Vanthaya N. 1935 MOTOR ST, CMC 75235 #891-04-1973 L1978 **PD** *020 †55

GANARAJ, Archana. 8160 WALNUT HILL LN, STE 113 75231 #027-01-1996 L2001 **SO** *020 †85

GANARAJ, Swathi P. 5939 HARRY HINES BLVD, STE 500 75235 #027-01-1997 L2003 **NEP** *020 †20

GANDHI, Nainesh Kumudchan. ■ 75201 #048-12-2006 **IM** *012

GANDY, Woodrow Wayne. 4020 MCEWEN RD, STE 281 75244 #048-12-1980 L1980 **EM IM** *030 †20,16

GANESA, Prasanthi. 3500 GASTON AVE, MEDICAL CENT 75246 #048-16-2003 L2006 **ON** *012 †20

GANT, Norman Ferrell, Jr. 2915 VINE ST 75204 #048-12-1964 L1964 **OBG MFM** *030 †30

GARCIA, Alfredo. 3600 GASTON AVE STE 1001, BAYLOR MEDICAL PLAZA 75246 #024-07-1992 L1997 **IM** *020 †20

GARCIA, Annabelle Lozano. ■ 75204 #048-04-2007 **PD** *012

GARCIA, Catalina E. 3515 HOWELL ST 75204 #048-12-1969 L1969 **AN** *020 †05

GARCIA, Cecilia Alejandra. ■ 75219 #048-12-2003 **PS** *012

GARCIA, Christine K. 5323 HARRY HINES BLVD, U T SOUTHWESTERN MC 8591 75390 #048-12-1996 L2001 **IM PUD** *050 †20

GARCIA, Damian David. 3450 W WHEATLAND RD, STE 440 75237 #048-12-1984 L1985 **FM** *020 †18

GARCIA, Erica C. 5323 HARRY HINES BLVD, SOUTHWESTERN MED 75390 #048-13-2004 L2006 **P** *012

GARCIA, Ismael. ■ 75206 #048-12-2006 **EM** *012

GARCIA, Joseph A, Jr. CARDIOLOGY DIVISION 75390 #005-14-1993 L1996 **CD** *020 †20

GARCIA, Lilia Deguilmo. ■ 75208 #748-01-1961 L1987 **IMG** *012

GARCIA, Nilda M. 1935 MOTOR ST D310, DEPT OF PED SURG 75235 #048-12-1989 L1990 **PDS** *020 †85

GARDEA, Ann Marie. 8230 WALNUT HILL LN # 600 75231 #048-02-1985 L1986 **P** *020 †75

GARDNER, Jack David. 1441 N BECKLEY AVE, FL 5 75203 #048-12-1982 L1983 **N IM** *020 †75

GARDNER, Robert Lynn. 433 W 12TH ST 75208 #048-12-1970 L1970 **OBG OM** *020

GARG, Abhimanyu. 5323 HARRY HINES BLVD 75320 #495-36-1979 L1988 **DIA END** *020 †20

GARG, Sandeep A. 6161 HARRY HINES BLVD, STE 224 75235 #495-69-1982 L1995 **AN** *020 †05

GARG, Vidu. 1935 MOTOR ST, DIVISION OF CARDIOLOGY 75235 #041-02-1994 L1999 **PDC** *020 †55

GARNER, Leslie Bryan. 1935 MOTOR ST 75235 #048-12-1996 L1998 **CCP** *020 †55

GARNER, William Lance. 3500 GASTON AVE STE H102, DEPT OF INTERNAL MEDICINE 75246 #039-01-2002 L2004 **CD** *012 †20

GARRE, William C. ■ 75209 #048-12-1958 L1958 **PS** *062

GARRETT, Robert K. 3100 CARLISLE ST, STE 109 75204 #048-12-2000 L2002 **P PYG** *020 †75 ‡

GARRETT, Wilson Van. 621 N HALL ST, STE 100 75226 #048-12-1968 L1968 **VS** *020 †85

GARRETT-PRICE, Ahmad Rahm. ■ 75201 #048-12-2008 *012

GARRETT-PRICE, Ivory Cal. 4201 BROOK SPRING DR 75224 #048-04-1977 L1978 **IM** *020

GARRISON, Aubrey Garth. ■ 75204 #048-12-2008 *012

GARRISON, Daniel Lee. 1441 N BECKLEY AVE 75203 #001-02-1994 L1995 **IM** *020 †20

GARRISON, James Stanley. 8210 WALNUT HILL LN, STE 614 LB 54 75231 #048-12-1970 L1977 **PM** *020 †60

GARVEY, Ronald F. ■ 75230 #035-06-1953 L1953 **GS** *071 †85

GARWOOD, Dan Patrick. 5801 FOREST PARK BLVD. 75390 #048-12-1985 L1992 **RO IM** *020 †20,80

GARY, Joshua L. ■ 75209 #048-12-2005 L2007 **ORS** *012

GARZA, Ralph Zachary. ■ 75203 #649-14-2006 **GS** *012

GARZA, Roberto Reynaldo. ■ 75228 #649-19-1992 L2000 *020 †18

GARZA, Shanna Shahid. 8330 ABRAMS RD, STE 112 75243 #048-04-2004 L2006 FM *020 †18

GASPAR, Harold Eugene. 75230 #039-01-1955 L1962 AN *071 †05

GASPARI, Joseph Donald. 5956 SHERRY LN STE 540 75225 #048-04-1979 L1979 P ADP *020 †75

GASTON, Carolyn Jo. 4500 S LANCASTER RD, ROUTING#11A 75216 #048-12-1980 L1980 IM IMG *020 †20

GATES, Johnny Lee. 707 N ZANG BLVD, STE 2 75208 #048-30-06-1976 L1979 IM *020

GATES, Troy Steven. 221 W COLORADO BLVD, STE 943 75208 #038-40-1992 L1998 OTO HNS *020 †45

GAW, Lisa Wunkam. ■ 75235 #048-12-2008 *012

GAYNOR, Richard Brian. 5323 HARRY HINES BLVD, STOP 9031 75390 #048-12-1975 L1975 HEM *050 †20

GAZDAR, Adi Framroze. 5201 HARRY HINES BLVD 75235 #917-23-1961 L1994 ON PTH *050 †50

GAZMEN, Nina Marie. 4500 S LANCASTER RD, DALLAS VA MEDICAL CENTER 75216 #305-01-2000 L2006 NM *100 †28

GDALEVITCH, Perry. 5323 HARRY HINES BLVD, DEPT OF PLASTIC SURGERY 75390 #067-01-2004 PS *100

GEISER, John Francis. 4131 N CENTRAL EXPY, METRO ANESTHESIA 75204 #016-11-1990 L2003 AN *020 †05

GEISLER, Gerald Franklin. 5959 HARRY HINS BLVD #1122 75235 #028-34-1961 L1962 TS *071 †85,90

GEIST, Frederick Stewart. ■ 75214 #038-06-1947 L1955 IM *071 †20

GELENDER, Henry. 7150 GREENVILLE AVE, CORNEA ASSOCIATES OF 75231 #016-42-1973 L1984 OPH *020 †35

GELFAND, Andrew S. 8210 WALNUT HILL LN 75231 #048-04-1990 L1991 PDP *020 †55

GEMAS, Terry Keith. 9219 GARLAND RD STE 2107 75218 #045-04-1995 L2001 OSM *020 †40

GENECOV, David G. 7777 FOREST LN, STE C717 75230 #048-13-1990 L1997 CFS *020 †85,65

GENECOV, Lisa Ann. 7777 FOREST LN STE B312 75230 #048-13-1989 L1990 PD *020 †55

GENIO-HARDING, Celia. 12606 GREENVILLE AVE, BLDG #4, STE 100 75243 #748-02-1972 L1993 PD *020

GENTA, Marcia Santos. ■ 75230 #187-20-1986 L1993 RHU *020 †20

GENTA, Robert M. ■ 75230 #561-20-1971 L1990 PTH IM *050 †50 ‡

GENTILELLO, Larry Michael. 5323 HARRY HINES BLVD, DEPARTMENT OF SURGERY 75390 #035-46-1982 L1985 GS *020 †85

GEPPERT, Thomas David. 5939 HARRY HINES BLVD #400 75235 #056-05-1980 L1984 RHU *020 †20

GERARD, Marvin. 8160 WALNUT HILL LN, NO 228 75231 #035-08-1954 L1954 OBG *020 †30

GERARD, Quin A. 7777 FOREST LN, STE A310 75230 #048-12-1988 L1989 AN *020 †05

GERBER, David Eric. 5323 HARRY HINES BLVD, UT SOUTHWESTERN MED CTR 75390 #035-20-2000 L2002 ON *050 †20

GERHARDT, Steven Karl. 7515 GREENVILLE AVE, STE 400 75231 #030-05-1997 L2002 CN *020 †75

GERMANY, Jenelle E. 4131 N CENTRAL EXPY, METRO ANESTHESIA 75204 #048-14-2002 L2006 AN *020 †05

GERSHENFELD, Howard K. 5323 HARRY HINES BLVD, DEPT OF PSYCHIATRY 75390 #035-11-1987 L1995 P *050 †75

GETACHEW, Yonas. ■ 75206 #056-05-2000 L2003 GE *012 †20 ‡

GHALIB, Reem H. 1411 N BECKLEY AVE, STE 268A 75203 #584-01-1989 L1999 GE *020 †20

GHAYEE, Hans K. 5323 HARRY HINES BLVD, STE Y5-318 75390 #048-78-2002, ▲ END *012 †20

GHERMAY, Abbeselom. 7515 GREENVILLE AVE, STE 505 75231 #005-02-1992 L2002 APM *100 †05

GHIDONI, Lorraine Agnes. 3500 GASTON AVE 75246 #048-02-1984 L1985 PD *020 †55

GHOBADI, Armin. ■ 75206 #517-11-2003 IM *012

GHOLE, Vidisha Vasant. 4500 S LANCASTER RD 75216 #496-42-1995 L2000 AR *100 †80

GHONEIM, Nada. ■ 75235 #048-12-2008 *012

GHOSH, Kirat S. 13350 TI BLVD MS 327, BAYLOR CLINIC AT T.I. 75243 #048-02-1999 L2002 FM *020 †18

GHOSH, Pritam. 5323 HARRY HINES BLVD, DEPT OF INT MED 75390 #048-12-2006 IM *012

GHURANI, Rasha Marwan. 2909 LEMMON AVE 75204 #605-01-1999 L2005 ID *020 †20

GIBBONS, Larry Wayne. 12200 PRESTON RD 75230 #049-01-1970 L1974 PHP CD *020 †70

GIBBONS, Raymond Robt. 4500 S LANCASTER RD 75216 #048-12-1955 L1955 GS *020 †85

GIBBS, Wende Nocton. ■ 75248 #048-15-1997 DR *012

GIBBY, Diane Louise. 7777 FOREST LN STE C820 75230 #011-02-1980 L1987 PS *020 †85,65

GIBSON, Burney Wm. 13601 PRESTON RD, STE 900 75240 #048-15-1975 L1975 AN PD *020 †55,05

GIBSON, Michael Louis. 7633 SOUTHWESTERN BLVD, MICHAEL L. GIBSON MD 75225 #048-15-1976 L1977 AN *020 †05

GIBSON, Valentine Ayodeji. 4131 N CENTRAL EXPY, METROPOLITAN ANESTHESIA CO 75204 #055-01-2003 L2007 AN *020

GIDCOMB, Michael Lee. 9330 POPPY DR 75218 #004-01-1971 L1973 PUD CCM *020 †20

GIERHART, Mickey Ray. 13601 PRESTON RD, STE 900W 75240 #039-01-1989 L1993 AN *020 †05

GIESECKE, Adolph Hartung. U TEX SW MED SCH, DEPT ANES 75390 #048-12-1957 L1957 AN *071 †05

GIESER, Steven M. 3601 SWISS AVE, DALLAS NEPH ASSOC 75204 #048-15-2000 L2003 NEP IM *020 †20

GILBERT, Allan David. 10 MEDICAL PKWY STE 204 75234 #021-01-1964 L1969 A OTO *020 †45,03

GILBERT, Edward Howard. 12606 GREENVILLE AVE 75243 #041-13-1969 L1994 RO *020 †80

GILBERT, John Barry. ■ 75248 #065-01-1961 L1981 AN *071 †05

GILBERT, Nathan Frazier. 411 N WASHINGTON AVE 75246 #048-12-2001 L2005 OMO *100

GILBERT, Steven C. 712 N WASHINGTON AVE 75246 #048-13-1996 L2002 RNR *020 †80

GILBREATH, Roy Earl, III. 2901 CITY PLACE WEST BLVD 75204 #011-02-1979 L1993 IM *020 †20

GILCHRIST, Alienor Sylvai. 5323 HARRY HINES BLVD, UTSW UROLOGY DEPARTMENT 75390 #012-05-2005 U *012

GILES, Brian Paul. ■ 75214 #048-12-2000 L2003 DR *012

GILES, Robert B, Jr. 8200 WALNUT HILL LN 75231 #024-01-1949 L1957 IM RHU *071

GILL, James Edwin. 13601 PRESTON RD STE 900W 75240 #048-13-1982 L1983 AN EM *020 †05

GILL, Javed Iqbal. 3600 GASTON AVE, DEPT OF PATHOLOGY, SUITE 2 75246 #704-01-1977 L1991 PTH *020 †50

GILL, John Torbet. 8230 WALNUT HILL LN # 708 75231 #048-12-1982 L1983 ORS OSM *020 †40

GILL, Kevin. 1801 INWOOD RD 75390 #048-04-1980 L1980 ORS OSS *020 †40

GILL, Navneet Kaur. 3320 LIVE OAK ST, E DALLAS HEALTH CTR PARKLA 75204 #495-10-1994 L2003 IM *020 †20

GILL, Zaheer A. 5323 HARRY HINES BLVD, SOUTHWESTERN MED 75390 #704-21-1986 CCP *012 †55

GILLER, Cole A. 3600 GASTON AVE STE 115, BAYLOR NEUROSURGERY ASSOCI 75246 #005-14-1984 L1985 NS *020 †25

GILLESPIE, Alexandra Jean. 5327 N CENTRAL EXPY 75205 #005-19-1988 L1993 PTH CLP *020 †50

GILLETTE, Arve Ward. 1441 N BECKLEY AVE, STE 101 75203 #025-01-1976 L2005 OS *020 †20,80

GILLIE, Mark Hayward. 13601 PRESTON RD, STE 900 75240 #039-01-1986 L1991 AN OBS *020 †05

GILLIGAN, Robert. PO BOX 809050, OCCIDENTAL CHEM COR 75380 #016-43-1974 L1975 OM GPM *030

GILLILAND, Grant Donald. 9301 N CENTRAL EXPY, STE 595 75231 #048-12-1988 L1989 OPH *020 †35

GILMAN, Alfred Goodman. 5323 HARRY HINES BLVD, DIV PF PHARMACOLOGY 75390 #038-06-1969 OS *020

GILMORE, Jim E. 6750 HILLCREST PLAZA DR, CONCORDE ON THE CREEK 75230 #048-12-1962 L1962 CS PSH *020 †45

GILMORE, John Russell. 8230 WALNUT HILL LN, STE 308LB25 75231 #048-12-1981 L1981 OTO FPS *020 †45

GILSTRAP, Larry Cowan, III. 2915 VINE ST 75204 #011-02-1970 L1979 OBG MFM *020 †30

GIMPEL, Nora Esther. 6263 HARRY HINES BLVD 75390 #132-01-1992 FM *020

GINCHANSKY, Elliot Joel. 7777 FOREST LN STE C530 75230 #035-08-1971 L1975 A PDA *020 †55,03

GINSBURG, Charles Morris. 5323 HARRY HINES BLVD, U.T. SOUTHWESTERN MEDICAL 75390 #030-05-1970 L1972 PD *040 †55

GINSBURG, Michael I. 12700 PARK CENTRAL DR 75251 #836-03-1984 L1998 DR RNR *040 †80

GIRGIS, Magda Kamel. 2222 WELBORN ST 75219 #048-12-1991 L1992 AN *020 †05

GIRI, Bala K. 221 W COLORADO BLVD, PAVILLION I, SUITE 155 75208 #023-07-1993 L1995 NS GS *020 †25

GIROD, Roxanne Elizabeth. 75204 #021-05-2006 OBG *012

GIRSCHICK, Hermann Josef. UNIV TX SOUTHWESTERN M CTR, DEPT RHEUMATOLOGY 75235 #409-20-1991 RHU *100

GIST, Adolphus V. ■ 75218 #048-13-2001 L2003 IM *020

GIST, Stephen E. 5461 LA SIERRA DR 75231 #048-15-1995 L1996 IM *020 †20

GLASS, Jeffrey. 12810 HILLCREST RD STE 220 75230 #836-01-1975 L1983 P PYG *020 †75

GLASS, Jonathan Saul. ■ 75229 #035-20-2003 L2003 D *012

GLASS, Kenneth David. ■ 75205 #143-03-1951 L1973 HS ORS *071 †40

GLATZ, Robert E. 3100 MONTICELLO AVE, STE 890 75205 #048-15-1997 L2000 EM *020 †16

GLAZE, William Henry. 2922 MARTN LTHR KNG JR, STE B 75215 #018-03-1978 L1980 OBG *020

GLAZER, Craig Steven. 5323 HARRY HINES BLVD, UTSW DIV OF PULM & CRIT 75390 #011-02-1994 L1995 PCC OM *040 †20,70

GLICK, Gina P Moran. 5323 HARRY HINES BLVD, STOP 9031 75390 #016-43-1956 L1985 AN *071 †05

GLYNN, Corinne Marie. ■ 75206 #048-12-2008 IM *012

GO, Leonard Hamiltontan. ■ 75206 #016-11-2005 IM *012

GODAT, David Michael. 7777 FOREST LN, STE C216 75230 #048-12-1998 L2005 PS *020 †65

GODAT, Mark Jos. 7777 FOREST LN STE C828 75230 #048-15-1983 L1983 OBG EM *075 †30

GODFREY, David Gray. 7150 GREENVILLE AVE, STE 300 75231 #048-02-1994 L1999 OPH *020 †35

GODFREY, Wm Aubrey, Jr. 75231 #048-12-1955 L1955 IM *071 †20

GOEL, Anuj. ■ 75219 #024-08-2005 IM *012

GOETZ, Lance Leander. 4500 S LANCASTER RD, DALLAS VAMC SCI (128) 75216 #018-03-1992 L1998 PM SCI *020 †60

GOFF, Gary E. 5939 HARRY HINES BLVD, STE 310 75235 #048-12-1993 L1994 IM *020 †20

GOGEL, Brian Matthew. 7777 FOREST LN STE C585 75230 #035-03-1995 L1997 GS *020 †85

GOH, Ewe Ghee. 302 W 9TH ST, STE G 75208 #065-01-1964 L1979 PD *020

GOHIL, Jitendra Nandlal. 4500 S LANCASTER RD, VA MED CTR DALLS 75216 #407-33-1968 L1974 DR NM *020 †28,80

GOKASLAN, Sefik Tunc. 5323 HARRY HINES BLVD 75390 #902-10-1984 L1996 ATP PCP *020 †50

GOLARZ, Scott Raymond. ■ 75202 #016-06-2000 L2002 VS *012 †85

GOLDBERG, Robert Alan. 10611 GARLAND RD, WHITE ROCK ORTHOPEDIC ASSO 75218 #016-06-1965 L1973 ORS *072 †40

GOLDENBERG, Julio. ■ 75219 #132-01-1953 L1974 PA IM *050

GOLDFARB, Abraham. 1717 MAIN ST STE 5200 75201 #737-06-1971 L1981 EM *020

GOLDFARB, Jill Ann. 5323 HARRY HINES BLVD, SOUTHWESTERN MED 75390 #007-02-2002 L2004 PDE *012 †55

GOLDIE, Gainneos Roy. 1936 AMELIA CT, PARKLAND GERIATRIC CLINIC 75235 #495-37-1997 L2005 IMG IM *020

GOLDINGS, Audrey Stein. 9440 POPPY DR 75218 #041-12-1976 L1980 N *020 †75

GOLDMAN, Marc Stephen. 10611 GARLAND RD 75218 #023-01-1990 L1996 ORS *020 †40

GOLDMAN, Stanton Carl. 7777 FOREST LN, STE D400 75230 #024-05-1990 L1998 PHO *020 †55

GOLDSMITH, Gary Paul. 8230 WALNUT HILL LN # 714 75231 #048-04-1976 L1976 OTO *020 †45

GOLDSTEIN, Gordon I. 13601 PRESTON RD, STE 900 75240 #047-06-1960 L1961 AN *071 †05

GOLDSTEIN, Jerald Steven. 8230 WALNUT HILL LN, STE 300 75231 #048-12-1992 L1993 REN OBG *020 †30

GOLDSTEIN, Joseph Leonard. 5323 HARRY HINES BLVD, UNIV OF TX SW MED SCH 75390 #048-12-1966 L1966 IM OS *050 †20

GOLDSTEIN, Lon Michael. 3600 GASTON AVE, UROLOGY CLINICS OF NORTH 75246 #021-01-1967 L1998 U *020 †95

GOLDSTRICH, Josh H. ■ 75248 #048-13-2001 L2004 GS *100

GOLLA, Sailaja. SOUTHWESTERN MED, UNIV OF TEXAS 75390 #495-72-2000 CHN *012

GOLSORKHI, Amir Hossen. 13601 PRESTON RD, STE 1000W 75240 #048-02-2003 L2007 AN *100

GOMBERG, Herbert Leslie. 5924 ROYAL LN, STE 260 75230 #035-19-1965 L1979 PYA P *020 †75

GOMEZ, Jaime Hugh. 3600 GASTON AVE, STE 303 75246 #048-13-1990 L1991 IM *020 †20

GOMEZ, Martin. 9202 ELAM RD, STE 110 75217 #264-05-1990 L2000 PD *020 †55

GOMEZ, Michael Enrique. SOUTHWESTERN MED, UNIV OF TEXAS 75390 #021-01-2006 NS *012

GOMEZ, Victor Manuel. 7777 FOREST LN, STE B202 75230 #264-16-1992 L2006 **CCM** *020 †20

GONG, Wei. 3320 LIVE OAK ST 75204 #243-16-1989 L2002 **PD** *020 †55

GONZALES, Cynthia Robledo. 1935 MOTOR ST RM B3302, DEPT OF ANESTHESIOLOGY 75235 #748-10-1990 L2003 **AN** *020 †05

GONZALES, David James. 8200 WALNUT HILL LN, INTERNAL MEDICINE DEPT 75231 #034-01-2002 L2004 **IM** *020 †20

GONZALEZ, Anna B. ■ 75219 #048-12-2005 L2008 **OBG** *012

GONZALEZ, Mandy Marie. 3500 GASTON AVE, DEPT OF OB/GYN 75246 #041-15-2006 **OBG** *012

GONZALEZ, Maria V. ■ 75231 #048-16-2006 **GS** *012

GONZALEZ, Robert. ■ 75214 #048-12-2002 L2007 **P** *100

GONZALEZ, Victor. 7777 FOREST LN STE A- 75230 #018-03-1995 L2006 **GS** *020 †85

GOOD, Meadow. ■ 75205 #003-75-2007, ▲ **OBG** *012

GOODFRIED, Max Paul. ■ 75230 #035-19-1941 L1950 **ORS** *071 †40

GOODMAN, Edward Leo. 8230 WALNUT HILL LN, STE 414 75231 #035-20-1968 L1969 **ID IM** *020 †20

GOODMAN, Philip. ■ 75230 #010-01-1960 L1966 **IM CD** *071 †20

GOODWIN, Grady George. 3500 GASTON AVE, MEDPROVIDER INPATIENT CARE 75246 #048-15-2003 L2006 **IM** *020 †20

GOODWIN, Wendy Elizabeth. ■ 75208 #048-12-2000 L2006 **PM** *100

GOOMAR, Aneeta Anne. 3500 FAIRMOUNT ST 75219 #064-01-1997 L2007 *100 †18

GOOVA, Mouza T. 5323 HARRY HINES BLVD, UT SOUTHWESTERN MEDICAL CE 75390 #913-01-1983 L2006 **GS** *100

GORANTLA, Vikram. ■ 75235 #048-12-2008 *012

GORDON, Catherine Mary. ■ 75214 #048-14-2002 L2005 **IM** *020 †20

GORDON, Melissa Dawn. 8200 WALNUT HILL LN, DEPT OF PATHOLOGY 75231 #012-01-1990 L1998 **PTH** *020 †20

GORDON, Murray Jacob. 12700 PARK CENTRAL DR #430 75251 #048-12-1974 L1976 **DR VIR** *020 †80

GORE, Lauren K. 1935 MOTOR ST, DEPARTENT OF MEDICAL EDUCA 75235 #048-14-2004 L2006 **PD** *100 †55

GOSS, Jan Jensen. 7777 FOREST LN STE B443 75230 #054-04-1975 L1979 **GYN** *020 †30

GOSS, Jordan Matthew. SOUTHWESTERN MED, UNIV OF TEXAS 75390 #035-01-2007 **DR** *012

GOSSARD, Wayne H. 1441 N BECKLEY AVE 75203 #048-12-1949 L1949 **GS** *071 †85

GOTO, Collin Satoshi. 1935 MOTOR ST, EMERGENCY DEPARTMENT 75235 #014-01-1990 L1995 **PD** *020 †55

GOTTESMAN, Andrew Rodney. 7515 GREENVILLE AVE, STE 706 75231 #048-02-1986 L1992 **GE NTR** *020 †20

GOTTLICH, Charles Morton. 621 N HALL ST, STE 500 75226 #048-12-1970 L1970 **CD** *020 †20

GOTTSCHALK, Frank Albert. 5323 HARRY HINES BLV ORTHO 75390 #836-01-1970 L1984 **ORS** *020 †40

GOUDREAU, Jeffrey Bennitt. 5461 LA SIERRA DR 75231 #048-02-1986 L1987 **IM AMI** *020 †20

GOUGE, Diane M. ■ 75235 #048-12-2004 *100

GOUGH, John Lysius. ■ 75231 #048-12-1956 L1956 **GS** *071 †85

GOVINDA, Namitha C. 8200 WALNUT HILL LN 75231 #495-23-1991 L2006 **IM** *012 †55

GOWANI, Nausheen. 3500 W WHEATLAND RD, HOSPITALISTS GROUP EMCARE 75237 #704-02-2001 L2007 **IM** *020 †20

GOWLIKAR, Tulsiram. 7777 FOREST LN 75230 #495-65-1973 L1987 **AN** *020 †05

GOYAL, Manju Rani. 16800 DALLAS PKWY STE 150 75248 #495-29-1976 L1982 **P** *020 †75

GRABLE, Kristen H. 4645 SAMUELL BLVD, C/O ALTSHULER MHMR CENTER 75228 #048-14-1994 L1995 **P** *020 †20

GRACE, Robert Willoughby. 6331 PROSPECT AVE 75214 #048-12-1956 L1956 **GP** *071

GRACIA, Carlos. 13601 PRESTON RD, STE 900W 75240 #048-13-1991 L1995 **AN** *020 †05

GRAFTON, Edwin G, Jr. ■ 75205 #048-14-1981 L1982 **OPH** *071 †35

GRAHAM, Audrey Lynn. 3310 LIVE OAK ST, STE 400 75204 #010-02-1988 L1990 **OBG** *020 †30

GRAHAM, Charles Eugene. 9900 N CENTRAL EXPY, STE 215 75231 #048-12-1959 L1959 **ORS MDM** *071 †40

GRAHAM, David Bennet. ■ 75214 #035-03-2006 **GS** *012

GRAHAM, Marion Francis. 1000 EMERALD ISLE DR 75218 #048-12-1945 L1945 **PDA PD** *071 †03

GRAHAM, Mateel Azar. UNIV TX HLTH SCI CTR 75235 #067-01-1958 L1976 **HEM OS** *020 †20

GRAHAM, Stephen A. 9 MEDICAL PKWY, STE 103 75234 #048-14-1993 L1994 **APM** *020 †05

GRAIVIER, Leonard. ■ 75219 #016-42-1954 L1958 **OS PDS** *071 †85

GRAMMER, John C, Jr. 5959 HARRY HINES BLVD, STE 720 75235 #048-12-1947 L1947 **CD** *020 †20

GRAND, Harrell Anthony. 3801 GASTON AVE, STE 260 75246 #021-06-1982 L1983 **IM** *020 †18

GRANDJEAN, Richard Leon. 9323 GARLAND RD, STE 207 75218 #048-12-1978 L1978 **FM** *020 †20

GRANETO, Donald Anthony. ■ 75219 #038-40-2007 **FP** *012

GRANT, La Faine Marie. 3500 GASTON AVE, HEPATOLOGY DEPT 75246 #036-05-1997 L2007 **HEP** *100 †20

GRANT, Michael D. 3900 JUNIUS ST, STE 220 75246 #048-14-1987 L1988 **GS SO** *020 †85

GRAUPERA, Ruth Mode. 3701 W NORTHWEST HWY, STE 112 75220 #023-07-1998 L2002 **PD** *020 †55

GRAVES, Christopher Lane. 5323 HARRY HINES BLVD, SOUTHWESTERN MED 75390 #036-05-2006 **AN** *012

GRAVES, Gregory Keith. 1380 RIVER BEND DR 75247 #048-13-1992 L1993 **P** *020 †75

GRAVES, Julia C. 2731 LEMMON AVE E, STE 200 75204 #048-13-1998 L2001 **FM** *020 †18

GRAVES, Nichole Kay. 3500 GASTON AVE 75246 #048-15-2005 L2007 **IM** *012

GRAY, Carol L Coleman. 3600 GASTON AVE STE 760 75246 #048-13-1972 L1972 **PD** *020 †55

GRAY, Deshawndran Deshae. 3650 W WHEATLAND RD, STE B 75237 #048-13-2001 L2005 **OBG** *020 †30

GRAY, James Howard. 3600 GASTON AVE STE 760 75246 #048-13-1971 L1971 **OPH** *020 †35

GRAY, John H. 6220 CHESLEY LN 75214 #048-15-1998 L2004 **VIR** *100 †80

GRAY, Kevin Franklin. 4500 S LANCASTER RD, DALLAS VA MEDICAL CENTER 75216 #048-12-1976 L1977 **P OS** *020 †20

GRAY, Larry Emmitt. 8200 WALNUT HILL LN 75231 #038-40-1967 L1972 **PD** *020 †55

GRAY, Paul Edward, Jr. 3409 WORTH ST STE 640, URGENT SURGERY ASSOCIATES 75246 #020-02-2007 L2007 **GS** *020 †85

GRAY, Rebecca Ann. ■ 75204 #020-12-2007 **OBG** *012

GRAY, Richard Newton V. 3600 GASTON AVE, WADLEY TOWER, STE 1158 75246 #021-05-1978 L1995 **NS** *020 †25

GRAY, Theronica R. ■ 75227 #048-12-2002 L2007 **PM** *012

GRAY, Toby James. ■ 75219 #048-13-2002 L2002 **PTH** *100 †50

GRAYBEAL, Dion F. 3600 GASTON AVE, BARNETT TOWER STE 600 75246 #048-04-1994 L1998 **N** *020 †75

GREEN, Hubert Gordon. 5323 HARRY HINES BLVD, ALLIED HEALTH SCIENCES SCH 75390 #048-12-1968 L1968 **PD PHP** *040 †55

GREEN, Kenneth Wayne, Jr. ■ 75219 #048-02-1986 L1987 **OS IM** *075 †20

GREEN, Rufus, Jr. 9 MEDICAL PKWY, PLAZA 4 STE 307 75234 #005-06-1973 L1989 **U AM** *020 †95

GREENBERG, Jeffrey Evan. 5420 LYNDON B JOHNSON FWY 75240 #011-02-1981 L1989 **RO IM** *020 †20,80

GREENBERG, Paul Allen. 8220 WALNUT HILL LN # 410 75231 #028-03-1961 L1963 **IM** *020

GREENE, Robert Wolfe. 4500 S LANCASTER RD, VA MEDICAL CENTER - DALLAS 75216 #023-01-1983 L1992 **OS** *050

GREENE, Warren Mortimer. 1441 N BECKLEY AVE 75203 #035-45-1955 L1964 **U** *071 †95

GREENFIELD, C Fish. 6301 GASTON AVE, STE 400W 75214 #039-01-1990 L1991 **N** *020 †75

GREENWAY, Kathryn Audra. 3500 GASTON AVE 75246 #048-15-2000 L2006 **VIR** *020 †80 ‡

GREENWOOD, John M, III. 5201 HARRY HINES BLVD 75235 #048-12-1988 L1989 **PD** *020 †55

GREER, Laura Gay. 5201 HARRY HINES BLVD 75235 #048-12-2003 L2006 **OBG** *100

GREGG, Clark Red. 4500 S LANCASTER RD, MEDICAL SERVICE (111) 75216 #048-12-1972 L1973 **ID IM** *040 †20

GREGGS, Sharon Elaine. 9 MEDICAL PKWY, STE 303 75234 #048-04-1980 L1981 **OBG** *020 †30

GREGORCYK, Sharon G. 7777 FOREST LN, STE A321 75230 #048-12-1991 L1999 **CRS** *020 †10,85

GREIF, Jules. 303 E OVERTON RD 75216 #035-15-1983 L1990 **PD** *020 †55 ‡

GREILICH, Nancy Brown. 5323 HARRY HINES BLVD, U.T. SOUTHWESTERN MED CTR 75390 #048-02-1989 L1997 **AN** *020 †05

GREILICH, Philip Edmund. 5323 HARRY HINES BLVD, DEPT ANES/PAIN MGMT-UTSWMC 75390 #048-15-1987 L1988 **AN** *020 †05

GRIFFIN, Billy Nick. 5323 HARRY HINES BLVD, DEPT OB-GYN UT SW MED CTR 75390 #048-12-1970 L1972 **OBG** *040 †30

GRIFFIN, James Dale. 5323 HARRY HINES, DEPT ANESTHESIOLOGY 75235 #048-12-1986 L1987 **AN** *071 †05

GRIFFIN, James Emmett, III. 5323 HARRY HINES BLVD 75390 #019-02-1970 L1976 **END IM** *030 †20

GRIFFIN, John Edward. 16827 VILLAGE LN 75248 #048-12-1956 L1958 **R OS** *020 †80

GRIFFITH, Clark Wells. 8160 WALNUT HILL LN # 224 75231 #030-06-1974 L1978 **OBG** *020 †30

GRIFFITH, Rachel A. ■ 75240 #048-02-1977 L1977 **PD NPM** *020 †55

GRIFFITH, Russell F. 8200 WALNUT HILL LN 75231 #048-02-1966 L1966 **D** *020 †15

GRIFFITH, William F, III. 5323 HARRY HINES BLVD, DEPT OF OB & GYN 75390 #007-02-1982 L1983 **OBG** *020 †30

GRIMBERG, Salomon. 12700 PRESTON RD STE 260 75230 #649-01-1974 L1979 **P CHP** *040

GRIMES, Clarice L. 7777 FOREST LN 75230 #048-16-1989 L1990 **OBG** *020 †30

GRIMES, Tate Alexander. 2929 CARLISLE ST, STE 200 75204 #048-14-1997 L2000 **FM** *020 †18

GROMOV, Irina. 8222 DOUGLAS AVE STE 375, MATRIX ALLIANCE INC 75225 #913-50-1984 L2002 **ADP P** *020 †75

GROSS, Andrew Michael. 5489 BLAIR RD 75231 #035-46-1981 L1982 **GS** *020

GROSS, Gary Neil. 5499 GLEN LAKES DR 75231 #048-12-1969 L1970 **AI IM** *020 †20,03

GROSS, Perry Edward. 3600 GASTON AVE, STE 454 75246 #016-42-1952 L1953 **FM** *071 †18

GROSS, Robert David. 2731 LEMMON AVE E STE 302, CHILDREN'S EYE SPECIALISTS 75204 #048-12-1979 L1979 **PO OPH** *020 †20

GRUBER, Michael B. 7777 FOREST LN, STE C618 75230 #048-02-1977 L1979 **U** *020 †95

GRUCHALLA, Rebecca S. 5323 HARRY HINES BLVD, IM DEPT 75390 #048-12-1985 L1989 **AI IM** *050 †20,03

GRUNDY, Scott Montgomery. 5323 HARRY HINES BLVD, UT SW MED CTR #Y3-206 75390 #048-04-1960 L1961 **IM** *020

GRUNTMANIS, Ugis. 5323 HARRY HINES BLVD 75390 #913-16-1992 L2001 **END** *040 †20

GRUSCHKUS, Gerhard Fritz. 809 SINGLETON BLVD 75212 #048-12-1968 L1968 **IM** *020 †20

GRYSEN, Katie Lynn. ■ 75229 #048-12-2005 L2008 **IM** *012

GUBERT, Matt T. 9 MEDICAL PKWY, STE 107 75234 #048-14-2001 L2003 **AN** *020 †05

GUEDALIA, John C. 3515 HOWELL ST 75204 #035-06-1971 L1973 **AN** *020

GUERAMI, Ali R. 8160 WALNUT HILL LN # 208 75231 #517-01-1973 L1985 **REN GYN** *020 †30

GUERRA, Ricardo, Jr. 8440 WALNUT HILL LN, LANE-STE 700 75231 #005-02-1990 L2004 **CD IM** *020 †20

GUERRERO, Ramon. 13601 PRESTON RD, STE 900 75240 #005-19-1990 L1993 **AN** *020 †05

GUERRIERO, Charles P, III. 8315 WALNUT HILL LN, STE 105 75231 #021-05-1951 L1957 **GYN** *020 †30

GUESNER, Scott Channing. 5201 HARRY HINES BLVD, PARKLAND HOSPITAL 75235 #016-42-2004 L2007 **AN** *012

GUETERSLOH, Chad David. 7777 FOREST LN 75230 #048-12-1996 L1997 **PD** *020 †55

GUIDRY, David Wayne. ■ 75206 #021-05-2006 **IM** *012

GUILEYARDO, Joseph Manuel. 5230 MEDICAL CENTER DR 75235 #021-05-1976 L1990 **PTH** *020 †50

GUILLAMONDEGUI, Oscar M. ■ 75229 #132-01-1960 L1969 **HNS GS** *071 †85

GUL, Fatma. 7777 FOREST LN STE C648 75230 #902-10-1973 L1985 **PM** *020 †60

GULATI, Pankaj Peter K. 129 W 9TH ST, OAK CLIFF FAMILY HEALTHCAR 75208 #065-05-1991 L1997 **FM** *020

GULESERIAN, Kristine Jane. ■ 75204 #024-05-1994 L2005 **TS** *020 †85,90

GULICK, Jennifer Rose. ■ 75204 #005-12-2006 **OBG** *012

GUNBY, Robert Tau, Jr. 4224 SWISS AVE 75204 #012-01-1971 L1974 **OBG** *020 †30

GUNNING, Thomas C, III. 6301 GASTON AVE, EAST TOWER, SUITE 400 75214 #048-12-1986 L1987 **AN** *020 †05 ‡

GUNST, Mark A. ■ 75234 #048-15-2001 L2007 **CCS** *012

GUNTER, Jack Pershing. 8144 WALNUT HILL LN, STE 170 75231 #039-01-1963 L1969 **PS FPS** *020 †45,65 ‡

GUO, Linsheng. 3500 GASTON AVE, DEPARTMENT OF HEPATOLOGY 75246 #243-65-1983 L2005 **IM HEP** *020 †20

GUPTA, Amit. 5323 HARRY HINES BLVD, UNIV TX SOUTHWESTERN MED S 75390 #495-36-2002 **U** *012

GUPTA, Arti. 1150 N BISHOP AVE, STE 100 75208 #495-36-1993 L2000 **P** *020 †20

GUPTA, Gaurav. 621 N HALL ST STE H030, BAYLOR UNIVERSITY MEDICAL 75226 #495-36-1993 L2001 **CD** *012 †20

GUPTA, Manu. 3500 GASTON AVE, AMERICAN RADIOLOGY 75246 #028-46-1995 L2003 **RNR** *020 †80

GUPTA, Nakul. ■ 75235 #048-12-2008 *012

GUPTA, Nalini. ■ 75225 #035-03-2001 L2005 **OPH** *100 †35 ‡

GUPTA, Neelam. ■ 75206 #496-07-2001 L2007 **IM** *012

GUPTA, Nimisha. 5323 HARRY HINES BLVD, SOUTHWESTERN MED 75390 #495-77-2000 L2007 **NPM** *020 †55

GUPTA, Pramod K. 4500 S LANCASTER RD, DALLAS VA MED CTR 75216 #495-74-1992 L2007 **R NM** *020 †80,28

GUPTA, Puja. ■ 75204 #017-20-2003 L2007 **PHO** *012 †55
GUPTA, Sachin. 5909 HARRY HINES BLVD, UT SOUTHWESTERN MEDICAL CE 75390 #495-36-2002 L2006 **CD** *012 †20
GUPTA, Samir. 5323 HARRY HINES BLVD, UT SOUTHWESTERN MEDICAL CE 75390 #025-01-2000 L2006 **GE** *020 †20
GUPTA, Sandeep. 8220 WALNUT HILL LN # 101 75231 #005-06-1998 L2004 **AI** *020 †20,03
GUPTA, Shubham. ■ 75206 #495-20-2000 L2005 **IM** *020 †20
GUPTA, Shyam Kelly. 12700 PRESTON RD, STE 260 75230 #003-01-2001 L2005 **P** *100
GURGUIS, George N M. 4500 S LANCASTER RD, MENTAL HLTH 116A DALLAS VA 75216 #915-02-1977 L1991 **P OS** *020 †75 ‡
GUSTAFSON, Klemens Eldon. 5323 HARRY HINES BLVD, U.T. SOUTHWESTERN MEDICAL 75390 #030-05-1966 L1983 **FM GS** *020 †18
GUSTAFSON, William Clay. ■ 75219 #048-02-2005 **PD** *012
GUTEKUNST, Roscoe A. 9323 GARLAND RD 75218 #026-04-1946 L1955 **GP** *071 †18
GUTH, Eve Susanne. 5323 HARRY HINES BLVD 75390 #005-14-1988 L2004 **IM NTR** *020 †20
GUTIERREZ, Maureen Shevli. 75209 #048-04-2004 L2004 **IM** *012 †20
GUTIERREZ ESPINOSA, Natali. ■ 75240 #264-21-2001 L2008 **FP** *012
GUTTIGOLI, Amit Baburao. 221 W COLORADO BLVD, STE 831 75208 #495-98-1996 L2004 **ICE CD** *020 †20
GUZMAN, Guillermo. 8200 WALNUT HILL LN 75231 #649-01-1962 L1968 **RHU IM** *071
HA, Richard Youngmin. 411 N WASHINGTON AVE, STE 6000 75246 #017-20-1997 L2000 **PS** *020 †65
HAALAND, Elizabeth M. 500 W ILLINOIS AVE 75224 #026-04-1960 L1968 **D** *071 †15
HAAS, Christopher M. ■ 75204 #048-12-1997 L2007 **AN** *020
HAAS, Paul David. 4500 S LANCASTER RD, CARDIOLOGY DIVISION (111A) 75216 #028-34-2003 L2005 **CD** *012 †20
HABIB, Amyn Aziz. 5323 HARRY HINES BLVD, MC 8594 75390 #704-02-1986 L2004 **N** *020 †75
HABIB, Sabeen Yousuf. 5323 HARRY HINES BLVD, UTSOUTHWESTERN MED CTR 75390 #704-26-2001 L2004 **PN** *012 †55
HABTE, Sara Helen. ■ 75209 #041-13-2007 **AN** *012
HACKEL, Joseph G. 2330 BUTLER ST STE 1 75235 #012-22-1995 L2003 **PTH DMP** *020 †50
HACKERMAN, Clayton David. ■ 75219 #048-04-2004 **GS** *012
HACKNEY, Fred L. 8315 WALNUT HILL LN, STE 225 75231 #001-02-1990 L1995 **PS** *020 †65
HACKNEY, Gail L. 2222 WELBORN ST, TX SCOTTISH RITE HOSP CHIL 75219 #001-02-1990 L1994 **AN** *020 †05
HADDOCK, Leann Ermel. 3600 GASTON AVE, STE 601 75246 #048-12-1998 L2003 **OBG** *020 †30
HADDOX, Robert J. 1130 BEACHVIEW ST STE 100 75218 #048-12-1983 L1983 **IM** *020 †20
HADEN, William C. 3500 GASTON AVE 75246 #048-12-1996 L1997 **PCC** *020 †20
HAFERKAMP, Scott David. ■ 75219 #048-12-2004 *100
HAFFORD, Melanie Lynette. ■ 75209 #012-01-2007 **GS** *012
HAGEDORN, Max B. 3707 GASTON AVE 75246 #016-43-1949 L1959 **IM** *071
HAGGARD, Lloyd Clifford. 13601 PRESTON RD STE 90 75240 #048-13-1982 L1983 **AN** *020 †05
HAGIWARA, Eugene. 75219 #048-12-2004 **DR** *012
HAGOOD, Robert M. 8230 WALNUT HILL LN, STE 408 75231 #012-05-1997 L1999 **GS** *020 †85
HAIL, Stacey Lynn. 5323 HARRY HINES BLVD, DIV OF EMERGENCY MED 75390 #012-01-1999 L2001 **ETX** *100 †16
HAIRSTON, Lucy E. 5959 HARRY HINES BLVD, PRO BLDG 1 STE 708 75235 #048-12-1986 L1987 **OBG** *020 †30
HAITHCOCK, Jeffrey Allan. 3500 GASTON AVE, DEPARTMENT OF RADIOLOGY 75246 #038-40-2002 L2005 **DR** *012
HALDEMAN, Richard Charles. 4131 N CENTRAL EXPY, METRO ANESTHESIA 75204 #019-02-1991 L1996 **AN** *020 †05
HALE, Price Edward. 17110 DALLAS PKWY, MASCARENHAS ALIPIO 75248 #048-02-1986 L1989 **P** *075 †75
HALEBIAN, Paul Hratch. ■ 75214 #048-12-1979 L1979 **TRS GS** *020 †85
HALES, David Charles. 4500 S LANCASTER RD, 18 GERIATRICS AND EXTENDED 75216 #027-01-1987 L1996 **IM** *020 †20
HALEY, Arvel Edward. ■ 75214 #048-04-1942 L1942 **IM CD** *071 †20
HALEY, Barbara Jean. 2201 INWOOD RD, UTSW MEDICAL CENTER 75390 #048-12-1976 L1976 **HO ON** *020 †20
HALEY, Charles Edwin. 8330 LYNDON B JOHNSON FWY 75243 #048-12-1975 L1975 **PHP ID** *030 †20
HALEY, Clinton C. ■ 75230 #048-16-2000 L2003 **ID** *012 †20
HALEY, Robert Ware. 5323 HARRY HINES BLVD 75390 #048-12-1971 L1971 **PHP IM** *050 †70
HALEY, Steven Arvel. 221 W COLORADO BLVD, STE 831 75208 #048-12-1973 L1973 **CD IM** *020 †20
HALL, Barrett Craig. 13601 PRESTON RD, STE 900W 75240 #039-01-1984 L1989 **AN** *020 †05
HALL, Catherine Lela. 6114 SHERRY LN 75225 #048-12-1992 L1994 **IM** *020 †20
HALL, John A. ■ 75205 #004-01-1951 L1951 **GP** *071
HALLER, Amy Michelle. 1441 N BECKLEY AVE 75203 #028-46-2003 L2006 **IM** *100 †20
HALLER, Ronald Gerald. 7232 GREENVILLE AVE, STE 435 75231 #054-04-1969 L1977 **N IM** *050 †20,75
HALLOCK, Keith R. 5001 LBJ FWY, STE 600 75244 #005-12-1982 L1983 **P** *030 †75
HALSELL, Karen Ruth. 8325 WALNUT HILL LN, STE 225 75231 #048-02-1996 L1999 **PD** *020 †55
HALVORSON, Lisa Marie. 5323 HARRY HINES BLVD, BOX 9032 75390 #023-07-1987 L2003 **OBG** *020 †30
HAM, Melissa Rebecca. 5323 HARRY HINES BLVD, DEPT OF PEDS STE G2-236 75390 #045-04-1996 L1999 **PDE** *020 †55
HAMAS, Robert Steven. 8345 WALNUT HILL LN # 120 75231 #038-40-1971 L1979 **PS HS** *020 †65
HAMAWY, Adam Hisham. 1801 INWOOD RD, DEPT OF PLASTIC SURGERY 75390 #033-05-1996 L1997 **PS GS** *012 †85
HAMDARD, Iram. 5201 HARRY HINES BLVD, DEPARTMENT OF AMBULATORY C 75235 #704-25-1990 L1996 **IM** *012 †20
HAMID, Cherine Adel. 5323 HARRY HINES BLVD, UTSW MEDICAL CENTER 75390 #024-05-1998 L2006 **OBG** *020 †30
HAMID, Farrukh. 7 MEDICAL PKWY 75234 #704-02-1989 L1995 **PM PME** *020 †60
HAMID, Shazia. ■ 75219 #704-06-1997 L2007 **CHP** *012
HAMILL, Mark E. 5323 HARRY HINES BLVD, SOUTHWESTERN MED 75390 #035-15-2002 L2007 **CCS CCS** *012
HAMILTON, Heather Alyse. ■ 75248 #048-04-2007 **IM** *012
HAMILTON, John Kent. 3434 SWISS AVE, STE 206 75204 #039-01-1971 L1975 **GE IM** *020 †20
HAMILTON, Paul Mason. 16970 DALLAS PKWY, STE 800 75248 #048-02-1977 L1977 **P** *020 †75
HAMMACK, Mary Margaret. 8230 WALNUT HILL LN # 614 75231 #048-13-1988 L1989 **IM** *020 †20

HAMMAN, Baron Lloyd. 621 N HALL ST, STE 500 75226 #048-12-1988 L1997 **TS** *020 †85,90
HAMMAN, Susan Mosier. 12700 PARK CENTRAL DR #430 75251 #020-02-1992 L1998 **PDR** *020 †80
HAMMES, Stephen R. 5323 HARRY HINES BLVD, STOP 9031 75390 #036-07-1992 L2000 **END** *020 †20
HAMMONDS, John D. 13601 PRESTON RD STE 900W, PINNACLE ANESTHESIA CONSUL 75240 #048-15-1999 L2002 **AN** *020
HAMMOUD, Khaled. ■ 75204 #875-01-2003 L2005 **N** *012
HAMNER, Jane Simms. 8215 WESTCHESTER DR 75225 #012-05-1983 L1988 **PD** *020 †55
HAMPTON, Tom Lauren. 9101 N CENTRAL EXPY # 300 75231 #048-12-1971 L1971 **IM CCM** *020 †20
HAMRA, Sam T. 2731 LEMMON AVE E # 3 75204 #039-01-1963 L1973 **PS** *020 †85,65
HAN, Fu-Chi. ■ 75248 #638-01-1945 L1979 **PUD IM** *071
HAN, Jeong Seok. 5323 HARRY HINES BLVD 75235 #583-03-1999 **PTH** *012
HAN, Ping Allison. ■ 75235 #048-12-2007 **PD** *012
HANAHAN, Laura Jane. 12700 PARK CENTRAL DR, STE 430 75251 #005-11-1978 L1985 **R PDR** *020 †55,80
HANCZYC, Malgorzata. 5303 HARRY HINES BLVD, DEPT OF RHEUMATOLOGY, MC 9 75390 #759-10-1989 L1997 **RHU** *020 †20
HANI, Pedro Jose Paredes. 7777 FOREST LN, A-315 75230 #935-07-1981 L1993 **PCC IM** *020 †20
HANIG, Joseph Arthur. 8355 WALNUT HILL LN, STE 105 75231 #047-06-1980 L1982 **PD** *020 †55
HANKE, Dode Mae. 5323 HARRY HINES BLVD 75390 #048-12-1958 L1958 **P** *071
HANLEY, Stacey Corlett. 6301 GASTON AVE, STE 400 75214 #039-01-1995 L1996 **AN** *020 †05
HANNA, Sami Fahim Mossad. 510 W GREENBRIAR LN 75208 #915-02-1958 L1976 **CD PUD** *020
HANNAN, Uzma. ■ 75251 #704-01-1987 L2006 **IM** *100 †20
HANSEN, Brent J. ■ 75208 #048-12-2007 *012
HANSEN, Paul Adrian. ■ 75204 #048-12-2007 **IM** *012
HANSEN, Phillip Eugene. 7777 FOREST LN, STE C106 75230 #048-04-1978 L1978 **ORS** *040 †40
HANSON, Shelby Suzanne. 4131 N CENTRAL EXPY, STE 435 75204 #305-01-2000 L2005 **AN** *100 †05
HANZ, Kevin Robert. ■ 75214 #038-06-2002 **PS** *100
HAQ, Anwarul. 5323 S LANCASTER RD, DEPT NEU 75241 #704-02-1984 L1998 **N PMM** *020 †75
HAQUE, Asma. 1935 MOTOR ST 75235 #704-25-1991 L2001 **PD** *020 †55
HAQUE, Wasim Afzal. 5323 HARRY HINES BLVD, UT SOUTHWESTERN MED CTR 75390 #704-25-1991 L2001 **END** *020 †20
HARDEE, Martha Love. 8335 WALNUT HILL LN, STE 105 75231 #048-12-1977 L1977 **IM** *020 †20
HARDIN, Audra Renata. 12221 MERIT DR STE 1, ACUTE KIDS URGENT CARE/ QU 75251 #048-02-2004 L2007 **PD** *020
HARDIN, Mark Alan. 3434 SWISS AVE STE 204 75204 #048-04-1982 L1987 **OTO** *020 †45
HARDY, Robert Doug. 5323 HARRY HINES BLVD, UNIVER OF TEXAS SOUTHWESTE 75390 #048-12-1993 L1994 **PDI ID** *020 †20,55
HARFORD, Madeline W. 5477 GLEN LAKES DR STE 210 75231 #048-12-1971 L1971 **P CHP** *020 †75
HARFORD, William Vandiver. 4500 S LANCASTER RD # GAST, VA HOSPITAL 75216 #048-12-1973 L1973 **GE IM** *040 †20
HARGRAVE, Sylvia Lynn. 221 W COLORADO BLVD, PAVILION II, SUITE 728 75208 #024-05-1990 L1994 **OPH TTS** *020 †35
HARKER-MURRAY, Amy. 5323 HARRY HINES BLVD 75390 #026-08-1999 L2007 **HO** *020 †20
HARKER-MURRAY, Paul D. ■ 75218 #026-08-2001 L2008 **PHO** *020 †55
HARKLEY-ALLEN, Kimulique. 8440 WALNUT HILL LN, STE 580 75231 #027-01-1998 L2002 **IM** *020
HARLAN, Melissa Gabriella. ■ 75251 #048-14-2007 **PD** *012
HARMON, Robert Waldon. ■ 75246 #004-01-1958 L1963 **OM OS** *020
HARNESS, Cayce Lynn. ■ 75235 #048-12-2007 **IM** *012
HARON, Eliane Sadi. 8230 WALNUT HILL LN, STE 414 75231 #187-11-1979 L1990 **IM ID** *020 †20
HARPER, Clayton Scott. ■ 75204 #048-13-2004 *100
HARPER, David Spencer. 8440 WALNUT HILL LN, STE 700 75231 #048-12-2000 L2006 **CD** *020 †20
HARPER, James David. 13601 PRESTON RD, STE 900W 75240 #040-02-1971 L1976 **AN** *020 †05
HARPER, Jeffry C. 13601 PRESTON RD, STE 900W 75240 #048-12-1986 L1987 **AN** *020 †05
HARPER, John Frank. 8440 WALNUT HILL LN, STE 700 75231 #048-12-1972 L1972 **CD** *020 †20
HARPHAM, Wendy S. ■ 75248 #035-45-1980 L1981 **IM** *071 †20
HARRINGTON, Cynthia. ■ 75209 #005-11-2004 L2007 **D** *012
HARRINGTON, John Norris. 9301 N CENTRAL EXPY, STE 595 75231 #047-06-1966 L1967 **FPS** *020 †35
HARRIS, Ashby Thos. 7777 FOREST LN, STE A204 75230 #048-02-1966 L1966 **N IM** *071 †75
HARRIS, Mary F. 10830 N CENTRAL EXPY 75231 #048-12-1970 L1970 **AN** *020 †05
HARRIS, Melvin Eugene. 16135 PRESTON RD, STE 130 75248 #048-12-1969 L1969 **IM GP** *020 †20
HARRIS, Michael Spellman. 1906 PEABODY AVE 75215 #048-12-1966 L1966 **OPH** *020 †35
HARRIS, Robert Alan, Jr. 8210 WALNUT HILL LN, STE 604 75231 #048-12-1976 L1976 **IM** *020 †20
HARRIS, Steven Albert. 712 N WASHINGTON AVE, STE 250 75246 #048-12-1985 L1986 **OBG** *020 †30
HARRIS-HENDERSON, Kesha R. 1441 N BECKLEY AVE, STE 101 75203 #021-05-1995 L2000 **RO** *020 †95
HARRISON, Clanton Bedford. 6300 HARRY HINES BLVD, STE 1401 75235 #048-02-1982 L1983 **UP** *020 †95
HARRISON, Edwin Earl. 3500 GASTON AVE 75246 #048-12-1959 L1959 **OBG** *071 †30
HARRISON, Frank. ■ 75220 #048-12-1956 L1956 *071
HARRISON, Yaprak Egilmez. 8200 WALNUT HILL LN, FL 5 75231 #902-05-1987 L2000 **P** *020 †75
HARSHMAN, Leeanne K. 3500 GASTON AVE, DEPARTMENT OF RADIOLOGY 75246 #048-16-2004 L2006 **DR** *100
HARSORA, Parul. 6363 HARRY HINES BLVD, FAMILY PRAC & COMMUNITY ME 75390 #065-06-1992 L2002 **FM** *020 †18
HART, Judith K. ■ 75223 #041-07-1972 L1978 **DR** *071 †80

HARTH, Cheryl Anne. 1441 N BECKLEY AVE, STE 101 75203 #033-06-1980 L1982
IM ON *020 †20

HARTONO, John Robert. ■ 75206 #026-04-2004 NEP *012 †20

HARTZLER, Robert. ■ 75208 #048-12-2008 L2008 *012

HARVEY, Jay Harrison. 7777 FOREST LN, STE B122 75230 #048-78-1988, ▲ L1989
CN SME *020 †75

HARVEY, Shelly Mc Carron. 7777 FOREST LN STE B3 75230 #048-12-1997 L2002
AI *020 †55,03

HARVIN, John Andrew. ■ 75229 #048-12-2008 *012

HASAN, Mirza S. 8230 WALNUT HILL LN, STE 414 75231 #704-02-1989 L1994 ID *020 †20

HASTINGS, Jeffrey L. ■ 75208 #048-12-2003 CD *012

HATANPAA, Kimmo J. BLDG H 2130, MC 9073, 5323 HARRY HINES BLVD 75390
#374-05-1991 L2002 PTH *020 †50

HATCHETTE, Charles Vernon. 75219 #010-02-2007 GS *012

HATHAWAY, Clinton Russell. 8226 DOUGLAS AVE 75225 #048-12-1954 L1954 OBG *071 †30

HATLEY, Mark Edward. 5323 HARRY HINES BLVD, DEPT MOLECULAR BIOLOGY 75390
#048-12-2004 PHO PD *012 †55

HATTON, William Pinkney. ■ 75220 #048-12-1977 L1977 GS *071 †85

HAUCK, Nicole Maria-Phyll. 809 SINGLETON BLVD 75212 #048-02-2003 L2006 PD *100 †55

HAUSER, Natalie Susan. ■ 75220 #030-05-2003 L2005 PD *100 †55

HAVARD, Steven Paul. 14800 LANDMARK BLVD, STE 700 75254 #016-42-1998 L2004
CD *020 †20

HAWK, Thomas Parker. 6131 LUTHER LN STE 216 75225 #048-14-1975 L1975 OPH *020 †35

HAWKINS, Joe. ■ 75248 #048-12-1959 L1959 R *071 †80

HAWKINS, Josiah Z Seth. 5323 HARRY HINES BLVD, UT SOUTHWESTERN MEDICAL CE 75390
#067-01-2001 L2005 OBG *020

HAWKINS, Shalaun J. 7777 FOREST LN, STE C300 75230 #047-07-2001 L2005 *020 †20

HAYDAR, Ziad Rafic. 8080 N CENTRAL EXPY, STE 1050 LB 81 75206 #605-01-1987 L1996
FPG FM *030 †18

HAYES, Daniel Joseph. SOUTHWESTERN MED, UNIV OF TEXAS 75390 #021-01-2004 GS *012

HAYES, Horace T. ■ 75230 #012-01-1950 L1951 GS *071 †85

HAYES, Julie Ann. ■ 75230 #021-01-2004 L2007 PD *100 †55

HAYES, Kamakki Jannirenee. ■ 75209 #048-12-2005 IM *012

HAYES, Ryan Elizabeth. ■ 75214 #048-12-2007 EM *012

HAYES, William Brendan. 13601 PRESTON RD STE 1000 75240 #048-12-1994 L1995
AN PME *020 †05

HAYGOOD, Julie T. 8160 WALNUT HILL LN, WALNUT HILL OBSTETRICS & 75231
#048-13-2000 L2003 FM *020 †18

HAYMES, David Anderson. 12830 HILLCREST RD, D216 75230 #048-12-1966 L1966
IM GPM *020 †20

HAYNES, Shane P. 1935 MOTOR ST 75235 #048-02-1994 L1998 EM *020 †16

HAYS, Amaryllis M. 5201 HARRY HINES BLVD 75235 #048-12-2005 L2006 OBG *012

HAYS, Steven R. 3601 SWISS AVE 75204 #016-11-1979 L1982 NEP IM *050 †20

HAYS, Tracy D. 1311 N WASHINGTON AVE 75204 #048-16-1996 L1998 OBG *020 †30

HAZBUN, Munir E. 221 W COLORADO BLVD, STE 440 75208 #231-01-1985 L1993
IM PUD †20

HE, Chenyin. ■ 75204 #049-01-2006 IM *012

HE, Yu-Guang. 5323 HARRY HINES BLVD 75390 #243-52-1982 L2002 OPH *020 †35

HEABERLIN, James Ralph. 13601 PRESTON RD, STE 900 75240 #048-02-1986 L1987
AN *020 †05

HEARTSILL, Lucas Grant. ■ 75205 #048-13-2006 AN *012

HEASLEY, David Cressler. 8440 WALNUT HILL LN, STE 510 75231 #051-01-1999 L2005
DR *020 †80

HEATH, A Chris. 7515 GREENVILLE AVE STE 70 75231 #048-13-1993 L1996 P *020 †75

HEATON, David Alex. 13601 PRESTON RD, STE 900 75240 #048-04-1986 L1990 AN *020 †05

HEBELER, Robert F, Jr. 3409 WORTH ST STE 720 75246 #021-01-1977 L1984
TS CD *020 †85,90

HEBERT, Mark Hamilton. 4515 PRENTICE ST, STE 201 75206 #048-12-1977 L1977 AN *020 †05

HEBERT, Steven John. 4350 ALPHA RD 75244 #021-06-1992 L1999 PTH *020 †50

HECK, David Alan. 810 N ZANG BLVD 75208 #035-15-1977 L2005 ORS OAR *030 †40

HECKMAN, Glen Wayne. 712 N WASHINGTON AVE 75204 #048-13-1981 L1981 OBG *020 †30

HEDAYATI, Saghar Susan. 4500 S LANCASTER RD M, VA MEDICAL CENTER 75216
#010-01-1998 L2007 NEP *020 †20

HEDGES, Patsy Ann. 13601 PRESTON RD, STE 900 75240 #048-02-1982 L1983 AN *020 †05

HEFFERNAN, Thomas Patrick. 5323 HARRY HINES BLVD, UT SOUTHWESTERN MEDICAL
CE 75390 #011-02-2001 L2005 OBG *012

HEGDE, Jay Narayan. ■ 75219 #048-12-2008 *012

HEGE, Katherine Kae. 13601 PRESTON RD, STE 900 75240 #040-02-1992 L1996 AN *020 †05

HEIGHTEN, Clay Matthew. 9229 LBJ FWY STE 25 75243 #048-13-1982 L1983 EM IM *020 †20

HEIL, Barbara Lawson. ■ 75229 #048-02-2008 *012

HEIN, H A Tillmann. 4131 N CENTRAL EXPY, METRO ANESTHESIA 75204 #409-33-1976 L1985
AN *020 †05

HEINRICH, John Bradfield. 75225 #017-20-2003 L2006 ORS *012

HEINTGES, Michelle Lynn. 7777 FOREST LN, STE A331 75230 #048-12-1999 L2003
OBG *020 †30

HEINTZ, Dennis Dyer. ■ 75227 #048-14-2007 PD *012

HEINZERLING, John Henry. ■ 75218 #048-12-2007 L2007 TY *012

HEINZMAN, Kristopher M. 5201 HARRY HINES BLVD 75235 #048-12-2003 L2006 CD *012 †20

HEISE, Ryan Henry. 8200 WALNUT HILL LN, MD ON CALL 75231 #039-01-2001 L2004 IM *020

HEISTEIN, Lisa. 1935 MOTOR ST 75235 #038-40-1998 L2002 PDC *100 †55

HEITZMAN, Daragh. 6301 GASTON AVE, STE 400 75214 #048-15-1989 L1990 N CN *020 †75

HELFAND, Sarah Lynn. 221 W COLORADO BLVD, STE 216 75208 #048-13-1984 L1986
PD *020 †55

HELGESON, Norman G P. 3600 GASTON AVE, STE 261 75246 #056-05-1961 L1966
PTH *020 †50

HELLER, Howard J. 910 N CENTRAL EXPY, U.T. SOUTHWESTERN MEDICAL 75204
#048-12-1989 L1990 END *020 †20

HELLER, Justin Boyd. ■ 75201 #008-01-2006 PS *012

HELLMAN, Wayne Lamont. 1441 N BECKLEY AVE 75203 #056-06-1955 L1957 AN *020

HELLSTERN, Ronald Allan. ■ 75229 #008-03-1971 L1976 EM MDM *030 †16

HELM, Phala Aniece Womack. 5323 HARRY HINES BLVD, DEPT OF PHYS MED & REHAB 75390
#048-12-1966 L1966 PM *071 †60

HELMS, Ed Bumpass. ■ 75204 #021-01-1948 L1955 GP OM *020

HEMPEL, G Kennedy. 621 N HALL ST, STE 520 75226 #048-12-1959 L1959 GS VS *071 †85

HEMSELL, David Lindsey. 5323 HARRY HINES BLVD, U.T. SOUTHWESTERN MEDICAL 75390
#019-02-1964 L1978 OBG *020 †30

HENDERSON, Harold Clay. 9850 N CENTRAL EXPY, STE 230 75231 #048-12-1982 L1983
FM PMM *020 †18

HENDERSON, Hodgie C, Jr. 75201 #048-12-1944 L1945 GYN *071 †30

HENDERSON, Michael Dale. 13601 PRESTON RD STE 1000 75240 #048-13-1979 L1979
AN AM *020

HENDERSON, Robert James. 1261 RECORD CROSSING RD 75235 #030-05-1974 L1975
OSS GS *020 †85

HENDERSON, Robert Waldrup. 2929 CARLISLE ST, STE 260 75204 #004-01-1972 L1973
GP OM *020 ‡

HENDERSON, Samuel Alva. ■ 75230 #048-02-2008 *012

HENDLER, Albert F. 1000 EMERALD ISLE DR, HENDLER COMES HILLERT 75218
#024-01-1949 L1955 IM *020 †18

HENDLER, Robert S. 13737 NOEL RD, STE 100 75240 #048-02-1974 L1974 GE IM *020 †20

HENDRICKSE, William A. 5323 HARRY HINES BLVD, U.T. SOUTHWESTERN MED CTR 75390
#917-06-1974 L1991 P PD *020 †75

HENNESSY, Michael Ware. ■ 75205 #010-02-2005 L2008 ORS *012

HENRY, Albert Carl, III. 3409 WORTH ST, STE 720 75246 #048-14-1974 L1974 TS *020 †85,90

HENRY, Bruce B. 7777 FOREST LN # 222 75230 #065-01-1969 L1985 FM *020 †18

HENRY, Johnny Lee. 6161 HARRY HINES BLVD, STE 220 75235 #048-12-1973 L1973
OBG *020 †30

HENRY, Katherine S. 8345 WALNUT HILL LN, ENVIRONMENTAL HEALTH 75231
#012-05-1971 L1973 FM IM *020 †18 ‡

HENRY, Robert R, II. 9528 WEBB CHAPEL RD 75220 #054-04-1962 L1964 GP *020 †18

HENRY, Robert Stanley. 5939 HARRY HINES BLVD, STE 503 75235 #048-12-1973 L1973
GS VS *020 †85

HENRY, William Taylor, Jr. ■ 75204 #004-01-2002 L2004 DR *100 †80

HENSEL, Steven Douglas. 13601 PRESTON RD 75240 #048-02-1985 L1986 AN *020 †05

HERAZO, Luis Fernando. 4500 S LANCASTER RD 75216 #649-02-1982 L1996 AN *020

HERBERT, Robert John. ■ 75360 #035-01-1958 L1962 P *071 †75

HEREDIA, Franklin Oswaldo. 1400 N WESTMORELAND RD, DE HARO-SALDIVAR HEALTH
CT 75211 #319-01-1984 L1997 IM *020 †20

HERLIHY, William G. 3600 GASTON AVE, STE 261 75246 #039-01-1979 L1979
PTH CLP *062 †50

HERMAN, Solomon Michael. ■ 75248 #024-15-1945 L1947 IM OS *020

HERNANDEZ, Cathy. 12221 MERIT DR STE 460 75251 #048-12-1996 L1999 IM *020 †20

HERNANDEZ, Michael J. 5201 HARRY HINES BLVD, DEPARTMENT OF INTERNAL MED 75235
#011-02-2003 L2006 PCC *012

HERNANDEZ, Miguel Angel. 810 N ZANG BLVD 75208 #048-12-1992 L1993 ORS *020 †40

HERNANDEZ, Nicole Bialek. 7777 FOREST LN, EMERGENCY SERVICES, MC 946 75230
#048-13-1996 L1999 EM *020 †16

HERNANDEZ, Wilson Leon. ■ 75230 #264-05-1990 L1997 RO *020 †20,80

HERNANDEZ-REYES, V. 6235 PALO PINTO AVE 75214 #649-01-1960 L1980 EM *020 †90,85

HERNANDO-GREGORY, Leticia. ■ 75230 #748-01-1956 L1968 P *020

HERNDON, Emily Susanne. PO BOX 9249 75209 #048-12-1999 L2002 NP *012 †50

HERNDON, James Henry, Jr. 8230 WALNUT HILL LN # 500 75231 #048-12-1963 L1965
D IM *020 †15

HERNDON, John C, III. 6301 GASTON AVE, EAST TOWER, SUITE 400 75214
#048-12-1987 L1988 AN *020 †05

HERRERA, Juan M, Jr. 5959 HARRY HINES BLVD, STE 108 75235 #048-12-1983 L1983 IM *020

HERRING, John Anthony. 2222 WELBORN ST, TX SCOTTISH RITE HOSP 75219
#048-04-1967 L1968 OP GS *020 †40

HERRING, Maurice Earl. 8200 WALNUT HILL LN 75231 #048-02-1957 L1958 FM CD *030 †20

HERRSCHER, Richard F. 8440 WALNUT HILL LN, STE 350 75231 #048-12-1986 L1987
AI *020 †20,03

HERSHEY, David Wm. 4600 SAMUELL BLVD 75228 #025-01-1966 L1981 P PYA *020 †75

HERZOG, Steven Paul. 6301 GASTON AVE STE 400W 75214 #003-01-1985 L1988 N *020 †75

HESSELTINE, Bret Henry. 13601 PRESTON RD, STE 900 75240 #030-05-1986 L1990 AN *020

HESSION, Peter Michael. 5323 HARRY HINES BLVD, SOUTHWESTERN MED 75390
#030-06-2006 AN *012

HEYNE, Edward F, IV. 13601 PRESTON RD STE 1000 75240 #048-02-1995 L1997 AN *020 †05

HEYNE, Roy Jos, Jr. 5323 HARRY HINES BLVD, DEPARTMENT OF PEDIATRICS 75390
#007-02-1971 L1977 PD OS *020 †55

HICKL, Andrew G. 3434 SWISS AVE, STE 430 75204 #048-12-1995 L1996 IM *020 †20

HICKMAN, John Fredrick. 3626 N HALL ST STE 720 75219 #048-12-1958 L1958 P N *020

HICKS, Barry Alan. 1935 MOTOR ST, RM B3250 75235 #017-20-1984 L1993 PDS TRS *020 †85

HICKS, Michael Ray. 13601 PRESTON RD, STE 1000 75240 #055-01-1985 L1986
AN MDM *030 †05

HICKS, Patricia Joan. 1935 MOTOR ST, CHILDRENS MEDICAL CENTER 75235
#017-20-1984 L1994 PD *020 †55

HIDALGO, Hector Osvaldo. ■ 75381 #024-05-1947 L1948 PD *071 †55

HIEBER, James Patrick. 4305 GLENLEIGH DR 75220 #016-06-1971 L1976 PD ID *020 †55

HIGGINS, Edmund W. 5909 HARRY HINES BLVD, DEPARTMENT OF OB/GYN 75235
#048-14-1994 L1997 OBG *020 †30

HIGH, Shyla. 621 N HALL ST STE 4 75226 #048-15-1992 L1993 CD *020 †20

HIGHBAUGH, David Michael. 3434 SWISS AVE, STE 310 75204 #027-01-1971 L1972
IM *020 †20

HIGHGENBOTEN, Carl Lee. 7777 FOREST LN STE C106 75230 #018-03-1965 L1973
ORS OSM *071 †40

HILARIO, Rufina Lipana. 9000 HARRY HINES BLVD 75235 #748-01-1966 L1977 HEM ON *071

HILL, Brandon Robert. ■ 75248 #048-14-2005 GS *012

HILL, Gary Edward. 5323 HARRY HINES BLVD, U.T. SOUTHWESTERN MED CTR. 75390
#030-06-1970 L1974 AN *030 †05

HILL, Joseph Addison, Jr. 5323 HARRY HINES BLVD, UT SW MED CTR 75390
#036-07-1987 L2005 CD IM *050 †20

HILLER, Michael S. 13601 PRESTON RD, STE 900 75240 #048-12-1988 L1989 AN *020 †05

HILLERT, Melbert Carl. 1130 BEACHVIEW ST, STE 100 75218 #048-12-1971 L1971
CD IM *020 †20

HILTON, Deborah Sue. 8267 ELMBROOK DR, STE 100 75247 #048-15-1989 L1990
PTH *020 †50

HINDS, Stephanie S. 13140 COIT RD, STE 518 75240 #048-12-2002 L2004 P *020 †75

HINES, Benjamin Travis. ■ 75204 #048-12-2003 L2007 DR *012

HINES, Stephen Lee. 122 W COLORADO BLVD, GOLDEN CROSS CLINIC 75208
#047-05-1977 L2004 IM *040 †20

HINGORANI, Vinita B. 4119 LOMO ALTO DR 75219 #048-13-1992 L1993 AI *020 †55,03

HINKLE, John Christian. 3500 W WHEATLAND RD 75237 #048-02-1978 L1978 AN *020 †05

HINNANT, Jerry Herbert. 800 N BISHOP AVE, STE 4 75208 #048-12-1957 L1958
GS OS *020 †85

HINO, Peter Donnelly. 8230 WALNUT HILL LN # 500 75231 #034-01-1985 L1989 **D** *020 †15

HINOJOSA, Lauren Nicole. ■ 75229 #048-02-2008 *012

HINTON, Emily Arnold. 5909 HARRY HINES BLVD 75235 #004-01-1999 L2001 **OBG** *020 †30

HINTON, Richard Chas. 7515 GREENVILLE AVE, STE 400 75231 #048-04-1972 L1972 **N IM** *020 †20,75

HIRJEE, Laila Nooruddin. 5617 BELMONT AVE, STE 206 75206 #704-02-1991 L2002 **NEP** *020 †20

HIRSCH, Albert Linz, Jr. 1902 MARTN LTHR KNG JR 75215 #048-13-1978 L1979 **OM** *020

HIRSCH, Bradford R. ■ 75204 #048-12-2006 **IM** *012

HIRSCHBERG, Jeff Michael. 1441 N BECKLEY AVE, METHODIST DALLAS MEDICAL C 75203 #038-43-2005 L2008 **IM** *012

HITTSON, William J. 5801 FOREST PARK ROAD, MC, UT SOUTHWESTERN MEDICAL CE 75390 #048-02-1988 L1990 **RO** *020 †80

HLA MYINT, Sofie. ■ 75231 #495-01-1947 **P** *050

HO, An Dinh. 4500 S LANCASTER RD, AMBULATORY CARE (11C) 75216 #422-01-1997 L2004 **IM** *020 †20

HO, Angelena M W. 12200 PRESTON RD 75230 #825-01-1976 L1991 **R** *020 †80

HO, Christine Ann. 1935 MOTOR ST, CHILDRENS MED CTR-ORTHOPED 75235 #048-12-2000 L2006 **OP** *020

HO, John Sheda. 12200 PRESTON RD 75230 #048-02-1997 L1998 **CD** *020 †20

HO, Michelle May. 9101 N CENTRAL EXPY, STE 300 75231 #048-12-1994 L1995 **IM** *020 †20 ‡

HO, Tao Anh. 7777 FOREST LN, STE C300 75230 #048-13-1994 L1996 **IM** *020 †20

HO, Vu The. 5005 LBJ FWY STE 17, UNIVERSITY OF MICHIGAN 75244 #026-04-2001 L2007 **OTO** *100

HOANG, Khanh Lan. 7777 FOREST LN, STE D565 75230 #005-02-1992 L1999 **CD IM** *020 †20

HOANG, Stephen Quoc. 1935 MOTOR ST B3302, CHILDREN'S MEDICAL CENTER 75235 #048-13-2000 L2004 **PAN** *020 †05

HOANG, Thomas Van. 3500 GASTON AVE 75246 #048-12-1990 L1992 **TS VS** *020 †85,90

HOBAR, Paul Creighton. 411 N WASHINGTON AVE, STE 6000 75246 #011-02-1982 L1983 **PS OS** *020 †85,65

HOBBS, Helen Haskell. 5323 HARRY HINES BLVD, UT SOUTHWESTERN MED CTR 75390 #038-06-1979 L1982 **END** *040 †20

HOBBS, Jean Fellenser. ■ 75238 #035-46-1971 **NPM PD** *020 †55

HOBLIT, David Louis. 1000 EMERALD ISLE DR, STE 107 75218 #021-05-1970 L1972 **PTH GP** *020 †50

HOCKETT, Debra Jean. 7777 FOREST LN, BLDG C 75230 #048-12-1982 L1983 **P CHP** *020 †75

HODGES, Patrick Lynn. 8220 WALNUT HILL LN, STE 206 75231 #048-12-1975 L1975 **PS GS** *020 †65

HODGES, Ralph Gail. 2610 ALLEN ST, APT 1312 75204 #048-02-1957 L1957 **CHP P** *020

HODGES, Wm Gregory. 3409 WORTH ST, STE 700 75246 #048-12-1988 L1989 **GE** *020 †20

HOFFMAN, Barbara Lynn. 5323 HARRY HINES BLVD, UNIV OF TEXAS SOUTHWESTERN 75390 #017-20-1987 L1991 **OBG** *020 †30

HOFFMAN, David Matthew. ■ 75244 #048-14-2004 **MPD** *012

HOFFMAN, Glenden A. 5909 HARRY HINES BLVD 75235 #056-06-1952 L1953 **OBG** *071

HOFFMAN, Mary Sabo. 5909 HARRY HINES BLVD 75235 #056-06-1952 L1952 **PD GP** *020

HOFMANN, Laura Ann. 6303 HARRY HINES BLVD # 20, PARKLAND FAMILY MEDICAL CL 75235 #048-12-2003 L2006 **FM** *100 †18

HOFMANN, Sandra Lee. 5323 HARRY HINES BLVD, DEPT HEMATOLOGY-ONCOLOGY 75390 #028-02-1983 L1989 **IM HO** *020 †20

HOGAN, Reed Blanchard, III. ■ 75223 #027-01-2008 *012

HOGAN, Robert Nickey. 5303 HARRY HINES BLVD #010-01-1990 L1991 **OPH** *020 †35

HOGG, Wilma E. 75205 #040-02-1948 L1978 **FM** *071

HOGGE, Amy J. 1935 MOTOR ST 75235 #016-11-1980 L1987 **PD** *020 †55,05

HOHN, Joyce Tolles. 211 W COLORADO BLVD # 310 75208 #048-02-1990 L1992 **PCC** *020 †20

HOLCOMB, Robert Owen. 5956 SHERRY LN, STE 1601 75225 #039-01-1989 L1990 **P** *020 †75

HOLCOMBE, Kenneth Ezzard. 3351 LOCKMOOR LN 75220 #001-02-1984 L1999 **IM** *020 †20

HOLDEN, Alfred Mason, Jr. 9330 POPPY DR, DALLAS UROLOGY ASSOCIATES 75218 #021-06-1982 L1990 **U** *020 †95

HOLDEN, Bridget Katherine. 8210 WALNUT HILL LN, STE 609 75231 #048-02-2000 L2003 **GS** *020 †85

HOLDER, David Paul. 13601 PRESTON RD, STE 900 75240 #048-02-1982 L1983 **AN** *020 †05

HOLDER, Heather Michelle. ■ 75229 #048-12-2008 *012

HOLICK, Michelle D. ■ 75219 #048-02-2006 L2008 **PD** *012

HOLINER, Joel Alan. 7777 FOREST LN, STE C833 75230 #048-12-1979 L1979 **P ADP** *020 †75 ‡

HOLLAND, John Byrl, Jr. 13601 PRESTON RD, STE 900 75240 #021-05-1986 L1993 **AN** *020 †05

HOLLAND, Robert Charles. 8160 WALNUT HILL LN, STE 007 75231 #048-04-2003 L2004 **EM** *020 †16

HOLLAND, Robert Hughes. 75205 #041-02-1944 L1966 **TS** *071 †85,90

HOLLANDER, Priscilla A. 3600 GASTON AVE, WADLEY TOWER - SUITE 656 75246 #024-01-1974 L1977 **IM** *020 †20

HOLLENSHEAD, Andy Ray. 4131 N CENTRAL EXPY, STE 435 75204 #048-14-2003 L2007 **AN** *020

HOLLEY, Glen Edward. 13601 PRESTON RD, STE 900 75240 #048-02-1978 L1978 **AN** *020 †05

HOLLEY, Lisa Marie. 17194 PRESTON RD, STE 102-322 75248 #048-02-1987 L1988 **AN** *020 †18

HOLLIER, John Michael. 75235 #048-12-2008 *012

HOLLINGSWORTH, John L, Jr. 12830 HILLCREST RD, STE 216 75230 #048-04-1966 L1966 **IM** *020

HOLLIS, Marie E. ■ 75203 #048-16-2006 **OBG** *012

HOLMAN, James. 8220 WALNUT HILL LN, STE 101 75231 #048-12-1945 L1945 **AI** *020 †03

HOLMES, Eric. 6011 HARRY HINES BLVD 75235 #352-06-1954 L1966 **AN OS** *020 †05

HOLMES, Houston E, III. 3535 WORTH ST, STE 110 75246 #048-12-1990 L1991 **HO ON** *020 †20

HOLMES, Laila Wang. 12712 PARK CENTRAL DR, STE B150 75251 #048-12-2001 L2006 **DR** *100 †80

HOLMES, Michael Lewis. 13601 PRESTON RD, STE 900W 75240 #023-12-1984 L2005 **AN GP** *020 †05

HOLPER, Elizabeth Mary. ■ 75230 #016-02-1995 L2007 **CD** *020 †20

HOLT, Roxanne. ■ 75205 #048-12-2004 L2006 **OBG** *012

HOLT, Shelby Anne. 5323 HARRY HINES BLVD, UT SOUTHWESTERN MEDICAL CE 75390 #048-14-1995 L1996 **GS** *020 †85

HOLTZMAN, Steven Fredric. 6348 BLAIR RD 75231 #016-42-1971 L1990 **GS EM** *020 †85

HOLUB, Michael C. 13601 PRESTON RD, STE 1000W 75240 #048-12-1994 L1995 **AN** *020 †05

HOLZER, Michael Scott. 5323 HARRY HINES BLVD, U TX SOUTHWESTERN MED SCH 75390 #039-01-2007 **GS** *012

HOMINICK, David Paul. 9301 N CENTRAL EXPY, STE 670 75231 #048-12-1975 L1975 **IM** *020 †20

HONG, Kailin. ■ 75204 #048-13-2007 **PD** *012

HONG, Suzette C. 13601 PRESTON RD, STE 900 75240 #048-12-1989 L1991 **AN** *020 †05

HOOD, Teresa Maria. 8440 WALNUT HILL LN, STE 700 75231 #048-12-1984 L1985 **CD IM** *020 †20

HOOKER, Benjamin O. ■ 75211 #048-14-2007 **GS** *012

HOOVER, Jeffrey C. 7831 BRYN MAWR DR 75225 #048-15-1989 L1990 **AN PME** *020 †05

HOOVER-KIRBY, Judith Anne. 8230 WALNUT HILL LN, STE 512 75231 #041-09-1991 L1995 **OPH** *020 †35 ‡

HOPKINS, Andrew C. 7808 CLODUS FIELDS DR, GREEN OAKS HOSPITAL 75251 #037-01-1991 L1999 **P** *020 †75

HOPKINS, Jeffrey Donald. 3450 W WHEATLAND RD, STE 425 75237 #001-02-1993 L1995 **HS** *020 †65

HOPKINS, John. 13601 PRESTON RD 75240 #130-01-2006 *012

HOPKINS, Scott James. 13601 PRESTON RD, STE 900W 75240 #048-78-1980, ▲ L1980 **AN** *020 †05 ‡

HOPKINS, Shelton Geo. 411 N WASHINGTON AVE, STE 7000 75246 #048-12-1971 L1980 **ORS OSM** *020 †40

HOPKOVITZ, Aviva M. 8200 WALNUT HILL LN, DEPT OF PATHOLOGY 75231 #048-13-1987 L1988 **PTH PCP** *020 †50

HOPPENSTEIN, Jay Marshall. ■ 75229 #048-12-1964 L1964 **GS** *020 †85

HORN, Vernon Paul Henry. 5939 HARRY HINES BLVD, STE 630 75235 #016-02-1973 L1975 **CD** *020 †20

HORNA, Pedro. 5323 HARRY HINES BLVD, DEPT OF PATHOLOGY 75390 #737-06-2002 L2007 **PTH** *012

HORNE, Malcolm, Jr. 4500 S LANCASTER RD, VETERANS AFFAIRS MED CTR 75216 #047-06-1968 L1970 **IM HEM** *020 †20

HORSWELL, Jeffrey Lee. 7777 FOREST LN 75230 #048-02-1981 L1981 **AN** *020 †05

HORTON, Jay D. 5323 HARRY HINES BLVD, U.T. SOUTHWESTERN MEDICAL 75390 #018-03-1988 L1990 **GE** *020 †20

HORTON, Jeffrey Bauer. ■ 75212 #048-12-2006 **PS** *012

HORTON, Marilyn S. 75214 #048-15-2000 L2004 **IM** *020

HOSFORD, Joy S. ■ 75235 #048-12-2008 *012

HOSFORD, Richard Gordon. ■ 75205 #024-01-1957 L1963 **IM** *071 †20

HOSLER, Gregory Alan. 8267 ELMBROOK DR 75247 #048-12-2001 L2006 **DMP** *100 †50

HOTZ, Susan Elaine. 7777 FOREST LN, STE B116 75230 #019-02-1997 L2001 **N** *020 †75

HOUPT, Karen R. 5323 HARRY HINES BLVD, DEPT DERM 75390 #048-14-1982 L1983 **D IM** *020 †20,15 ‡

HOWARD, William Stubbs. 221 W COLORADO BLVD, PAVILION II #640 75208 #048-02-1985 L1986 **IM** *020 †20

HOWELL, Mary Lanette. 3617 EUCLID AVE 75205 #048-12-1981 L1981 **AN** *020 †05

HOWSDEN, Susan C Mayse. 9330 POPPY DR, STE 503 75218 #005-11-1967 L1971 **D DMP** *020 †15

HOXWORTH, Ronald Edward. ■ 75219 #041-02-2000 L2007 **PS** *100 †85

HROM, John Stewart, III. ■ 75248 #027-01-2003 L2007 **HO** *012 †20

HSIA, Connie C W. 5323 HARRY HINES BLVD, DEPT OF INTERNAL MEDICINE 75230 #065-01-1982 L1989 **IM** *020 †20

HSIAO, Chris L. 5323 HARRY HINES BLVD, UT SOUTHWESTERN MED SCH 75390 #048-12-2007 **AN** *012

HSIEH, Susan Yi-Hsian. 1935 MOTOR ST, PEDIATRIC PHYSICIANS 75235 #048-02-2004 L2007 **PD** *100

HU, Jian. ■ 75248 #243-94-1984 L2004 **PM** *012

HUANG, Chou-Long. 5323 HARRY HINES BLVD, H5-112 75390 #244-04-1981 L1997 **IM** *020

HUANG, Chung-En. 3450 W WHEATLAND RD # 300 75237 #244-04-1978 L1983 **OTO** *020 †45

HUANG, Craig James. 1935 MOTOR ST M-7, DIVISION OF EMERGENCY MED 75235 #048-02-1996 L2002 **PEM** *012 †20

HUANG, Theresa Tienho. 5323 HARRY HINES BLVD, UTSW-DEPT OF RADIOLOGY 75390 #048-02-2001 L2006 **DR AR** *020 †80

HUBBARD, Jacqueline C. 8210 WALNUT HILL LN, STE 230 75231 #917-05-1971 L1976 **IM** *020 †20

HUBBARD, Susan Jeanne. 8345 WALNUT HILL LN, BLDG D 75231 #048-14-1981 L1981 **PD** *020 †55

HUDAK, Anne Mary. 5323 HARRY HINES BLVD, DEPT OF PHYS MED & REHAB 75390 #035-08-1990 L2002 **PM** *020 †05,60

HUDGINS, William Robt. 7515 GREENVILLE AVE, STE 1030 75231 #027-01-1964 L1973 **NS** *020 †25

HUDSON, Ashton Henry. 12221 MERIT DR STE 161 75251 #021-06-2000 L2006 **EM** *020 †16

HUDSON, Karen A. 7500 W CAMP WISDOM RD, COUNSELING DEPT. 75236 #026-08-1983 L1990 **P** *020 †75

HUEBNER, Mitchell Lee. 9301 N CENTRAL EXPY, STE 670 75231 #048-12-1989 L1990 **IM** *020 †20

HUERTA, Sergio. 8303 HARRY HINES BLVD 75235 #005-14-1998 L2001 **GS** *100 †85

HUFF, John Frederick. 13601 PRESTON RD STE 100, TEJAS ANESTHESIA, P.A. 75240 #048-13-1980 L1982 **AN** *020

HUGHES, Ann Hanszen. ■ 75204 #048-12-1959 L1959 **CHP** *071 †75

HUGHES, Christopher Aaron. 3500 GASTON AVE, DEPARTMENT OF INTERNAL MED 75246 #048-15-2003 L2006 **IM** *020 †20

HUGHES, Delbert E. ■ 75205 #048-04-1951 L1951 **P** *071 †75

HUGHES, Erica Jo. 1441 N BECKLEY AVE 75203 #048-02-2002 L2003 **PCC** *012 †20

HUGHES, Jenevieve Holton. ■ 75204 #048-16-2002 L2008 **GS** *100 †85

HUGHES, Joseph M. 13601 PRESTON RD, STE 900 75240 #048-02-1983 L1999 **AN** *020 †05

HUGHES, Lannie Ray. 7777 FOREST LN, STE C300 75230 #048-12-1966 L1966 **GE IM** *020 †20

HUGHES, Len B. 7777 FOREST LN STE B238, BMW ANESTHESIOLOGISTS, P.A 75230 #048-12-1970 L1970 **AN** *020 †05

HUGHES, Linda R Loveless. ■ 75254 #048-12-1967 L1967 **P** *071 †75

HUGHES, Randall S. UT SOUTHWESTERN, 2201 INWOOD ROAD 75390 #048-02-1985 L1986 **ON** *020 †20

HUGHES, Stephen Mark, Jr. 2330 BUTLER ST, STE 115 75235 #004-01-2001 L2005 **DMP** *012 †50

HULL, Rhiannon Michelle. ■ 75204 #048-02-2007 **PD** *012

HUM, Lawrence. 8160 WALNUT HILL LN, STE 007 75231 #016-42-1994 L1997 **EM** *020 †16

HUMPHREY, Irving Leslie. 4230 LYNDON B JOHNSON FWY 75244 #041-01-1967 L1971 **PYA CHP** *020 †75

HUMPHREY, John A. 3920 WORTH ST 75246 #048-12-1985 L1986 **AN** *020 †05

HUMPHREY, Laurel Lee. ■ 75237 #048-02-2000 L2005 **GS** *020 †85

HUNG, Thomas Yuang-Lung. 7777 FOREST LN STE B107 75230 #024-16-1996 L2005 **OTO** *020 †45

HUNT, Corbin Q. 1441 N BECKLEY AVE 75203 #048-15-2000 L2006 **IM** *020 †20

HUNT, Eugene Pitts, III. 8160 WALNUT HILL LN # 230 75231 #021-06-1978 L1979 **OBS** *020 †30

HUNT, John Lee. 5323 HARRY HINES BLVD 75390 #038-41-1964 L1974 **GS** *020 †85

HUNT, Judson Mark. 7777 FOREST LN STE C750 75230 #056-05-1976 L1978 **NEP IM** *020 †20

HUNTER, Irby Barnett, Jr. ■ 75244 #048-13-1997 **IM** *100

HUNTER, Judith A. 3330 S LANCASTER RD, ANNEX BUILDING 75216 #048-14-1987 L1988 **P** *020 †75

HUNTER, Leigh Kouns. 1441 N BECKLEY AVE 75203 #021-06-1982 L1985 **IM HD** *040 †20

HUO, Michael Hao. 5323 HARRY HINES BLVD, DEPT OF ORTHOPAEDIC SURGER 75390 #010-01-1984 L1997 **ORS GS** *020 †20

HUQ, Nujhat Nadia. ■ 75206 #160-11-2003 *100

HURD, Eric Ray. 712 N WASHINGTON AVE # 300 75246 #039-01-1962 L1967 **RHU IM** *020

HURLEY, Mary Elizabeth. 9301 N CENTRAL EXPY, STE 180 75231 #021-01-1996 L1998 **D** *020 †15

HURST, George W. 13601 PRESTON RD, STE 900 75240 #048-02-1992 L1993 **AN** *020 †05

HURST, Martin Luther. 3500 GASTON AVE 75246 #048-12-1970 L1970 **IM** *020 †20

HURT, George Ellison. 3600 GASTON AVE STE 1205 75246 #048-12-1957 L1957 **U** *071 †95

HURWITZ, Jodie Linda. 8440 WALNUT HILL LN 75231 #035-46-1981 L1982 **IM CD** *020 †20

HUSAIN, Mustafa M. 5323 HARRY HINES BLVD 75390 #704-02-1981 L1991 **IMG** *020 †75

HUSBANDS, Milton Earl, Jr. 7777 FOREST LN 75230 #048-02-1965 L1965 **OBG** *071 †30

HUSBERG, Bo Stigson. 1411 N BECKLEY AVE, PAVILION III, STE 268 - A 75203 #858-01-1969 L1985 **GS TTS** *020

HUSSAIN, Aamir Bin I. 4500 S LANCASTER RD, DALLAS VA MEDICAL CENTER 75216 #704-02-1988 L2001 **IM** *020 †05

HUSSAIN, Asadullah. 13601 PRESTON RD, STE 900 75240 #495-04-1989 L2000 **AN PME** *020 †05

HUSSAIN, Mir Tajammul. 13601 PRESTON RD, STE 900W 75240 #495-21-1978 L2000 **AN** *020 †05

HUSSAINI, Raziuddin Syed. 13601 PRESTON RD, STE 900W 75240 #048-12-2002 L2006 **AN** *100 †05

HUSSEIN, Mohamed Abdel Wa. 5323 HARRY HINES BLVD, SOUTHWESTERN MED 75390 #915-02-1991 **OPH** *012

HUTCHISON, Michele R. 1935 MOTOR ST, OFFICE OF MEDICAL EDUCATIO 75235 #048-12-1999 L2001 **PDE PD** *050 †55

HUTH, James Frank. 5323 HARRY HINES BLVD, UTSW SURGERY DEPT - MC 915 75390 #035-45-1975 L1994 **GS ON** *050 †85

HUTSON, Thomas E. 3535 WORTH ST, SAMMONS CANCER CENTER BA 75246 #038-75-1997, ▲ L2003 **HO** *020 †20

HUTYRA, John Marcus. ■ 75204 #048-12-1983 L1983 **AN** *020 †05

HWANG, Chiufang Huang. 5521 GREENVILLE AVE, STE 104-734 75206 #048-13-1992 **P CHP** *100

HWANG, Frederic. 13601 PRESTON RD STE 900W 75240 #048-14-1990 L1994 **AN** *020 †05

HWANG, William James. 3450 W WHEATLAND RD, POB 1 75237 #048-13-1990 L1992 **N PM** *020 †60,75

HYATT, John Robt, Jr. 7777 FOREST LN, STE C340 75230 #024-07-1978 L1989 **GE IM** *020 †20

HYDE, Matthew Ryan. 8440 WALNUT HILL LN, STE 510 75231 #051-01-2000 L2007 **RNR** *020 †80

HYSLOP, Alvin T. 12200 PARK CENTRAL DR #403 75251 #048-12-1988 L1989 **OBG** *020 †30

IANNACCONE, Susan Theresa. 5323 HARRY HINES BLVD, DEPT OF CHILD NEURO 75390 #035-15-1969 L1990 **N P** *050 †55,75

IBRAHIM, Hisham Mohsen. ■ 75219 #605-01-1996 L1997 **PYG** *020 †75

IDRIS, Ahamed H. ■ 75225 #016-01-1979 L2004 **EM IM** *040 †20,16

IGARASHI, Peter. 5323 HARRY HINES BLVD, UT SOUTHWESTERN MEDICAL CE 75390 #605-14-1981 **NEP IM** *040 †20

IGHANI, Afsaneh. 7777 FOREST LN STE C30 75230 #048-02-1996 L1998 **IM** *020 †20

IKBAL, Natasya Ann. 411 N WASHINGTON AVE 75246 #048-12-2003 L2007 **OBG** *020

IKEGAMI, Toru. 9600 THACKERY ST 75225 #572-12-1994 *100

IKEMBA, Catherine Minor. 1935 MOTOR ST, DEPARTMENT OF CARDIOLOGY 75235 #005-06-1996 L2003 **PDC** *020 †55

IKEMBA, Chukwuma I. ■ 75218 #690-01-1988 L2004 **IM** *020 †20

ILIYA, Adil A. 5201 HARRY HINES BLVD 75235 #605-01-1948 L1953 **GS** *071 †85

ILIYA, Charles Alfred. 1151 N BUCKNER BLVD, STE 202 75218 #048-12-1983 L1983 **GS VS** *020 †85

ILIYA, Fawzi A. ■ 75238 #605-01-1959 L1979 **OBG** *071

INANOGLU, Didem. 7777 FOREST LN, STE C648 75230 #902-19-1993 L2003 **PM SCI** *020 †60

INYANG, Emmanuel E. 1400 N WESTMORELAND RD, DEHARO-SALDIVAR HEALTH CEN 75211 #690-10-1983 L1995 **FM** *020 †18

INZER, Robert Wayne. 3600 GASTON AVE, STE 300 75246 #048-04-1979 L1979 **OBG EM** *020 †30

IPPOLITO, Rosario Robert. 9 MEDICAL PKWY STE 102 75234 #561-12-1971 L1991 **PS HS** *020 †65

IRIZARRY, Benito Jumbo. 13601 PRESTON RD 75240 #048-02-2002 L2006 **AN** *100 †05

IRVIN, Amy Jo. 12221 MERIT DR STE 161 75251 #018-03-1999 L2007 **EM** *020 †75,16

IRVIN, Larry Wayne. 5201 HARRY HINES BLVD 75235 #048-02-1980 L1980 **IM** *020 †20

IRWIN, Charles F. 13601 PRESTON RD, STE 900 75240 #048-14-1982 L1983 **AN** *020 †05

IRWIN, Stephen Alexander. ■ 75214 #011-04-2003 L2007 **PMM** *012

ISAAC, Sanjai R. 13601 PRESTON RD, PINNACLE ANESTHESIA CONSUL 75240 #048-14-1993 L1994 **AN** *020 †05

ISAACSON, Tove Virginia. 5323 HARRY HINES BLVD, U TX SOUTHWESTERN MED CTR 75390 #034-01-2002 L2005 **PP** *012

ISARADISAIKUL, David. ■ 75251 #038-44-2001 L2006 **CN** *020

ISBELL, Gerald M, III. 7777 FOREST LN STE C675 75230 #036-05-1982 L1987 **GE** *020 †20

ISLAHI, Nazish S. 9409 GARLAND RD STE 1 75218 #048-12-1996 L1998 **FM** *020 †18

ISLAM, Arsalla. 5323 HARRY HINES BLVD, DEPT OF GEN SURG 75390 #704-01-1998 **GS** *012

ISOM-BATZ, Ginger. 75230 #048-15-2000 L2006 **U** *100

ISTRE, Gregory Roy. 7777 FOREST LN, STE B300 75230 #039-01-1974 L1991 **PDI EP** *020 †55 ‡

ITANI, Kamel M. 5323 HARRY HINES BLVD, DEPARTMENT OF OPHTHALMOLOG 75390 #605-01-1983 L1991 **OPH** *020 †35

IVANOVSKIS, George. 4500 S LANCASTER RD, DALLAS VA MEDICAL CENTER 75216 #048-14-1985 L1987 **IM** *020 †20

IVY, Roy, III. 4131 N CENTRAL EXPY, METRO ANESTHESIA 75204 #048-12-1995 L1997 **AN** *020 †05

JACKS, Samuel Porter. ■ 75204 #036-05-2004 **GS** *012

JACKSON, David E. 13601 PRESTON RD, STE 1000 75240 #048-12-1985 L1986 **AN** *020 †05

JACKSON, Elisabeth V. 2222 WELBORN ST, CHILD DEVELOPMENT DIV 75219 #036-08-1986 L1995 **PD** *040

JACKSON, Gregory Lawrence. 1935 MOTOR ST 75235 #048-04-1972 L1972 **PD NPM** *040 †55

JACKSON, John Willard. 3600 GASTON AVE, STE 1051 75246 #048-02-1958 L1995 **AN OS** *071

JACKSON, Joseph Jordan. 9440 POPPY DR 75218 #019-02-1980 L1981 **GP EM** *075

JACKSON, Robert Wayne. 411 N WASHINGTON AVE, STE 2100 75246 #048-14-1975 L1975 **OBG** *071 †30

JACKSON, William Kenneth. 9301 N CENTRAL EXPY # 400 75231 #048-12-1964 L1964 **ORS** *020 †20

JACOB, Julie. 7777 FOREST LN, STE B326 75230 #035-01-1999 L2007 **PD** *020 †55

JACOBE, Russell L, III. 13601 PRESTON RD, STE 900 75240 #048-14-1997 L1998 **AN** *020 †05

JACOBI, Joshua A. 14800 LANDMARK BLVD, CARDIOVASCULAR PROVIDER RE 75254 #048-13-2000 L2002 **CD** *100 †20

JACOBS, John William, Jr. ■ 75204 #011-02-2008 *012

JACOBSON, Coleman G. 3600 GASTON AVE STE 1051 75246 #018-03-1949 L1954 **D** *071 †15

JACOBSON, Robert Morris. 3409 WORTH ST, STE 500 75246 #041-13-1971 L1974 **CRS GS** *020 †10,85

JACOBY, M Dean. 5939 HARRY HINES BLVD #935 75235 #025-07-1956 L1962 **PD** *071 †55

JACOMIDES, Jenny R. 5323 HARRY HINES BLVD, DEPT OF PEDIATRICS UTSWMC 75390 #048-12-1998 L2000 **PD** *020 †55

JACQMIN, Kelley R. ■ 75238 #048-12-2002 L2005 **EM** *100 †16

JAECKLE, Richard Gilbert. 8220 WALNUT HILL LN STE 40 75231 #048-12-1961 L1961 **CHP A** *020 †75

JAFARI, Mitra. ■ 75219 #048-16-2008 *012

JAFFE, Mark Robt. 2801 LEMMON AVE, STE 310 75204 #028-46-1991 L1995 **OPH** *020 †35

JAFFEE, Jay Bennett. 13601 PRESTON RD, STE 900 75240 #016-42-1991 L1996 **AN** *020 †05

JAFRI, Hasan S. ■ 75390 #704-21-1990 L1999 **PD PDI** *040 †54

JAGANI, Naseem N. 5201 HARRY HINES BLVD 75235 #495-17-1969 L1993 **OBG MFM** *030 †30

JAIN, Mamta. ■ 75205 #048-04-1996 L1997 **ID** *020 †20

JAIN, Manish. ■ 75219 #048-12-2004 L2007 **IM** *100 †20

JAIN, Rajeev. 8230 WALNUT HILL LN 75231 #048-04-1993 L1994 **GE** *020 †20

JAIN, Raksha. 5201 HARRY HINES BLVD, DEPT OF INTERNAL MEDICINE 75235 #048-14-2001 L2003 **PCC** *012 †20

JAIN, Satyam. 4500 S LANCASTER RD, MENTAL HEALTH 75216 #495-32-1997 L2005 **P** *100

JAIN, Shailesh. SUITE 13.354, 6363 FOREST PARK RD 75390 #495-02-1995 L2003 **P CHP** *020 †75

JAIN, Sonal. 3701 W NORTHWEST HWY, PHYSICIANS FOR CHILDREN 75220 #496-38-1997 L2006 **PD** *100

JAIN, Tulika. 7150 GREENVILLE AVE, STE 500 75231 #048-12-1998 L2000 **CD** *020 †20

JAIN, Vinay Kumar. 3535 WORTH ST, STE 110 75246 #495-36-1981 L1993 **IM ON** *040 †20

JAKUBIETZ, Rafael Gregor. 5323 HARRY HINES BLVD, UNIV TX SOUTHWESTERN MED S 75390 #409-04-2003 **PS** *012

JALEEL, Mambarath Abdul. 5323 HARRY HINES BLVD 75390 #496-39-1995 L2006 **PD** *020 †55

JALIU, Bogdan Cristian. ■ 75254 #048-11-2004 **PM** *012

JAMAL, Karim Nasiruddin. ■ 75204 #048-12-2003 L2007 **OPH** *100

JAMIESON, Andrew O. 5477 GLEN LAKES DR, STE 100-125 75231 #037-01-1982 L1988 **SME** *020 †20

JAMISON, Harwin B. 221 W COLORADO BLVD, STE 350 PAVILLION I 75208 #048-02-1952 L1952 **GYN** *071 †30

JAMISON, John Paul. 3503 W WHEATLAND RD, STE 100 75237 #048-02-1981 L1981 **ORS OSM** *020 †40

JANAK, Donald Ray. ■ 75225 #048-02-1963 L1963 **R** *071 †80

JANIS, Jeffrey Edward. 1801 INWOOD RD, #WA4.240 75390 #038-06-1998 L2000 **PS** *020 †65

JANSSEN, Brian John. 6301 GASTON AVE, EAST TOWER, SUITE 400 75214 #056-06-1989 L1994 **AN** *020 †05

JARABA, Jaime Isaac, Jr. 8200 WALNUT HILL LN 75231 #048-13-2001 L2004 **FM** *020 †18

JAREM, Bohdan John. 5323 HARRY HINES BLVD, STOP 9031 75390 #038-40-1966 L1972 **AN PME** *020

JARRETT, Althea Kay. 7920 ELMBROOK DR STE 120, EMPLOYEE PHYSICIAN'S OFFIC 75247 #011-04-1995 L2000 **PD** *020 †55

JARRETT, Latasha Nicole. 1151 N BUCKNER BLVD, STE 301A 75218 #038-41-2001 L2005 **OBG** *020

JARVIS, Kathryn. ■ 75248 #010-01-2008 *012

JASO, Jesse. ■ 75226 #048-02-2006 **GS** *100

JAYASEELAN, Chitra L. 7557 RAMBLER RD STE 7 75231 #048-15-1988 L1990 **AN** *020 †05

JAYASEELAN, Nirmal S. 7777 FOREST LN, STE C670 75230 #048-15-1994 L1999 **GS VS** *020

JAZRAWI, Saad Fahmi Y. ■ 75235 #528-04-1996 L2008 **GE** *100

JEFFERSON, Henry C. 221 W COLORADO BLVD 75208 #048-16-1990 L1991 **GS** *020 †85

JEFFREY, Patricia. ■ 75229 #048-12-1985 *075

JENEVEIN, Edwin Patrick. 8267 ELMBROOK DR, STE 100 75247 #021-05-1958 L1961 **PTH CLP** *030 †50

JENEVEIN, Nolan Bruce. 6301 GASTON AVE, STE 400W 75214 #048-12-1986 L1987 **N** *020 †75

JENKINS, Celia. 5323 HARRY HINES BLVD 75390 #027-01-1992 L1996 **P** *020 †75

JENKINS, Elizabeth P. 7777 FOREST LN, STE C300 75230 #048-15-1986 L1989 **END** *020 †20

JENKINS, George Mark. 221 W COLORADO BLVD, STE 831 75208 #023-07-1988 L1998 **CD IM** *020 †20

JENKINS, Madden D, Jr. 7910 BELT LINE RD 75254 #048-02-1951 L1951 **PD** *020 †55

JENNINGS, Andrew Wayne. ■ 75204 #048-12-2008 *012

JENNINGS, Richard Allan. 14800 LANDMARK BLVD, STE 70 75254 #041-09-1985 L2004 **CD IM** *020 †20

JENSEN, Pamela Jean. 8200 WALNUT HILL LN, DEPT OF PATHOLOGY 75231 #018-03-1983 L1986 **PTH** *020 †50

JERNBERG, William Curtis. 1717 MAIN ST STE 5200 75201 #027-01-1972 L1973 **EM** *020

JEROME, Raymond Jeff. 5959 HARRY HINS BLVD #1116 75235 #048-12-1960 L1960 **AN** *071 †55

JESSEN, Michael Erik. 5323 HARRY HINES BLVD, UT SOUTHWESTERN MED CTR 75390 #062-01-1981 L1990 **TS TTS** *020 †90,85

JEWELL, Nathaniel Ryan. 3500 GASTON AVE, BAYLOR UNIVERSITY MEDICAL 75246 #019-02-2003 L2006 **DR** *012

JEYARAJAH, Dhiresh Rohan. 221 W COLORADO BLVD, SURGICAL ASSOCIATES 75208 #043-01-1989 L1997 **GS PS** *020 †85

JEZ, Joseph Michael. 13601 PRESTON RD, 960W 75240 #048-12-1976 L1976 **AN** *020 †05

JIMENEZ, Alfredo H. 8440 WALNUT HILL LN, STE 700 75231 #264-01-1986 L1999 **CD** *020 †20

JIMENEZ, Patricia T. ■ 75219 #048-12-2005 L2007 **OBG** *012

JIMENEZ-OLIVA, Juan M. 8160 WALNUT HILL LN, STE 216 75231 #429-01-1963 L1972 **MFM OBG** *020 †30

■ = Address Information Privacy Protected

JIMENEZ-PAZOS, Cesar O. 5909 HARRY HINES BLVD 75235 #649-01-1961 L1971 **IM** *020

JINDAL, Shefali. 5323 HARRY HINES BLVD, SOUTHWESTERN MED 75390 #495-38-1993 L2008 **CHP** *012

JOE, Thomas. 221 W COLORADO BLVD, STE 318 PAVILLION I 75208 #011-02-1986 L1987 **DR** *020 †80

JOGLAR, Jose Angel. 5323 HARRY HINES BLVD, STOP 9031 75390 #042-01-1991 L1993 **ICE** *020 †20

JOHN, George. 7920 ELMBROOK DR STE 170 75247 #495-37-1991 L1997 **IM** *020 †20 ‡

JOHNSON, Andrea Shavonne. 1572 DRURY PL 75232 #048-12-2008 *012

JOHNSON, Brett Andrew. 3500 W WHEATLAND RD 75237 #035-06-1988 L2002 **FM** *020 †18

JOHNSON, Dawn Denise. 1935 MOTOR ST, UT SOUTHWESTERN MEDICAL CE 75235 #036-01-2000 L2002 **PD** *020 †55

JOHNSON, Dennis D. 3535 TRAVIS ST, STE 210 75204 #005-15-1969 L1970 **AN** *020

JOHNSON, Douglas Wm. 3920 WORTH ST 75246 #021-01-1977 L1978 **AN** *020

JOHNSON, Edward Robt. 5323 HARRY HINES BLVD, DEPT ANESTHESIOLOGY 75390 #016-06-1964 L1969 **AN** *040 †05

JOHNSON, Jimmie Dale. 2301 S HAMPTON RD STE 900 75224 #028-78-1962, ▲ L1962 **GP** *071

JOHNSON, Kelly Annette. ■ 75243 #422-01-2000 L2003 **PD** *020 †55

JOHNSON, Larry Turner. 2301 S HAMPTON RD STE 800 75224 #047-07-1972 L1984 **ORS** *020 †40,85

JOHNSON, Mark Douglas. 5323 HARRY HINES BLVD, DEPT OF NEUR 75390 #042-03-1992 L1998 **N** *020 †75

JOHNSON, Neysa Leigh. 5323 HARRY HINES BLVD 75390 #048-02-2003 L2005 **P** *100

JOHNSON, Raymond Robt. 8440 WALNUT HILL LN, TEXAS MEDICAL & SURGICAL 75231 #056-05-1973 L1994 **PD** *020 †55 ‡

JOHNSON, Richard Bard. 13601 PRESTON RD, CARILLON TOWER EAST SUITE 75240 #039-01-1957 L1963 **A** *071 †55,03

JOHNSON, Robert L, Jr. 5323 HARRY HINES BLVD, U.T. SOUTHWESTERN MEDICAL 75390 #016-06-1950 L1954 **PUD CD** *050

JOHNSON, Romaine F. 5303 HARRY HINES BLVD, FL 7 # 104 75390 #041-15-1999 L2006 **PDO** *020 †45

JOHNSON, Shanan Leigh. ■ 75204 #056-06-2004 **PM** *012

JOHNSON, Shyamala. ■ 75248 #495-16-1969 L1988 **P** *071

JOHNSON, Van A. ■ 75208 #048-12-2006 **GS** *012

JOHNSON, Warren Calvin. 9440 POPPY DR 75218 #048-02-1960 L1960 **P N** *071

JOHNSON, William Bernard. 10405 E NORTHWEST HWY, STE 300 75238 #012-01-1948 L1950 **PD** *020

JOHNSON-WELCH, Sarah Fran. 1935 MOTOR ST, DEPT PATHOLOGY 75235 #035-46-1977 L2002 **PP PTH** *020 †50

JOHNSTON, Chas Eugene, II. 2222 WELBORN ST 75219 #035-01-1976 L1985 **ORS** *020 †40

JOHNSTON, Jeffrey L. 4131 N CENTRAL EXPY, STE 435 75204 #048-02-2003 L2007 **AN** *100

JOHNSTON, Mark Anthony. 7515 GREENVILLE AVE, STE 600 75231 #048-12-1984 L1987 **IM** *020 †20

JOHNSTON, Michael Thomas. 3434 SWISS AVE, STE 420 75204 #048-13-1995 L1996 **IM** *020 †20

JOLISSAINT, Stephen Lacy. 4350 ALPHA RD 75244 #021-05-1976 L2004 **PTH** *062 †50

JONAS, Federico R. 9090 SKILLMAN ST, STE 182A 75243 #132-09-1967 L1973 **OM** *020 †70

JONES, Alan L. 3600 GASTON AVE, BARNETT TOWER STE 1109 75246 #048-04-1987 L1989 **ORS GS** *020 †40

JONES, Christopher Eric. 4845 CEDAR SPRINGS RD 75219 #048-12-2007 L2007 **IM** *012

JONES, Evelyn M Robinson. ■ 75214 #004-01-1955 L1955 **IM FM** *020

JONES, Jay M. 8210 WALNUT HILL LN, HARVILL-TSCHUMY CLINIC 75231 #048-12-1985 L1986 **IM** *020 †20

JONES, Laurel R. 5445 LA SIERRA DR STE 2 75231 #048-12-1987 L1988 **P** *020 †75

JONES, Michelle Alexandri. ■ 75235 #048-12-2008 *012

JONES, Ramana S. 7777 FOREST LN, STE 560 75230 #048-14-1993 L1995 **OBG** *020 †30

JONES, Richard Edward, III. 5920 FOREST PARK RD STE 60 75235 #011-03-1966 L1968 **ORS** *020 †40

JONES, Robert Ellwood, III. 5323 HARRY HINES BLVD, UT SOUTHWESTERN MEDICAL CE 75390 #048-12-1966 L1966 **IM** *020 †20

JONES, Ronald Coy. 3500 GASTON AVE 75246 #047-06-1957 L1963 **GS SO** *040 †85

JONES, Sara Elizabeth. 8267 ELMBROOK DR, STE 100 75247 #010-01-1989 L1998 **PCP** *020 †50

JONES, Shalita Monique. 3600 GASTON AVE 75246 #047-06-2003 L2006 **IM** *020 †20

JONES, Stephen Ellis. 3535 WORTH ST, STE 110 75246 #048-06-1966 L1969 **ON IM** *020 †20

JONES, Sydney R. 8210 WALNUT HILL LN # 814 75231 #027-01-1967 L1968 **GS VS** *020 †85

JONES, Wendell Alton. ■ 75225 #048-12-1959 L1959 **PD** *020 †55

JONES, William Gerald, II. 221 W COLORADO BLVD, STE 825 75208 #004-01-1983 L1992 **TS GS** *020 †85,40

JORDAN, Jennifer Ann. 1130 BEACHVIEW ST, STE 240 75218 #017-20-1993 L1996 **OTO** *020 †45

JORDAN, L Darrel. 12200 PARK CENTRAL DR, STE 210 75251 #048-13-1994 L1995 **OBG** *020 †30

JOSEPH, Richard Joseph. 3600 GASTON AVE, STE 300 75246 #027-01-1970 L1971 **OBG** *020 †30

JOSEPHS, Shellie Craig. 5323 HARRY HINES BLVD, DEPARTMENT OF RADIOLOGY 75390 #048-12-1992 L1993 **VIR** *020 †80

JOSHI, Girish Premji. 5323 HARRY HINES BLVD, STOP 9031 75390 #495-28-1993 L1997 **AN APM** *020 †05

JOUBERT, Michelle Ann. 5323 HARRY HINES BLVD, UTSW MEDICAL CENTER 75390 #021-06-1995 L2003 **PDI** *020 †55

JOURNEYCAKE, Janna Marie. 1935 MOTOR ST, CHILDRENS MED CTR 75235 #039-01-1996 L2002 **PHO** *020 †55

JOYNER, Kristin Lee. 712 N WASHINGTON AVE 75246 #048-14-2001 L2004 **NR** *020 †80

JUDD, Kathryn M. 4600 SAMUELL BLVD 75228 #048-78-2000, ▲ L2007 **P** *020

JUDY, Emily Catherine. 75229 #012-05-2007 **PD** *012

JUNG, Anthony Chas. 9229 LBJ FWY, STE 250 75243 #048-12-1977 L1977 **FM** *020

JUNG, Ghap Joong. 3616 WORTH ST APT 211 75246 #583-09-1977 L2001 *020

JUTURI, Jaya Vanisri. 9525 GREENVILLE AVE 75243 #495-58-1993 L2001 **HO** *020 †20

JUVVADI, Sridevi. 5939 HARRY HINES BLVD, STE 800 75235 #495-21-1992 L2002 **HO** *020 †20

KABBANI, Wareef. ■ 75390 #875-02-1994 L2002 **PCP** *020 †50

KADANE, Sheffield A, III. 11884 GREENVILLE AVE, STE A102 75243 #048-12-1992 L1993 **AN** *020 †05

KADESKY, Melvin C. 8230 WALNUT HILL LN, STE 700 75231 #018-03-1953 L1958 **U** *071 †95

KAGEYAMA, Nobuyoshi. 5924 ROYAL LN, STE 104B 75230 #014-01-1996 L2002 **D DS** *020 †15

KAHN, Amy Laura. 1717 MAIN ST STE 5200 75201 #048-02-2004 L2006 **EM** *100

KAHN, Andrew Jacob. ■ 75244 #048-14-2003 L2007 **AN** *100

KAHN, Andy. 1717 MAIN ST STE 5200 75201 #048-02-2004 L2006 **EM** *100

KAINTH, Manvinder Kaur. 8330 ABRAMS RD STE 11 75243 #048-04-2003 L2007 **FM** *020 †18

KAISER, Fran Elizabeth. ■ 75205 #035-09-1974 L1999 **IMG END** *062 †20

KAIZER, Ellen Cippora. ■ 75204 #030-06-2000 L2003 **PDE** *100 †55

KAKASKA, George H. 8215 WESTCHESTER DR # 135 75225 #056-05-1953 L1955 **FM** *020 ‡

KALINOWSKI, Janusz M. 7777 FOREST LN 75230 #759-03-1967 L1978 **OBG** *020 †30

KALISER, Lyle Alan. 8210 WALNUT HILL LN, HARVILL-TSCHUMY CLINIC 75231 #012-01-1969 L1974 **IM** *020 †20

KALISKI, David N. ■ 75230 #836-01-1981 L1993 **RNR** *020 †80

KALOYANOVA, Polina Filipo. 7777 FOREST LN STE C206 75230 #198-03-1997 L2007 **END** *020

KAM, Jeffrey. 12700 PARK CENTRAL DR, STE 430 75251 #836-01-1970 L1980 **DR** *020 †80

KAMAL, Zeba. 3320 LIVE OAK ST, EAST DALLAS HEALTH CENTER 75204 #704-20-1988 L2001 **IM** *020 †20

KAMATH, Sandeep Arvind. ■ 75204 #048-12-2001 L2003 **CD** *012

KAMENS, Cathy Ann. 5323 HARRY HINES BLVD, FAMILY PRACTICE 75390 #008-02-1997 L2000 **FM** *020 †18

KAMPAS, Christopher Peter. 7777 FOREST LN, STE C420 75230 #048-04-1994 L1995 **FM** *020 †18

KANAAN, Hassan Zahi. 3225 TURTL CRK BLVD #11222 75219 #605-01-1998 L2003 **FM OS** *020 †18

KANCHARLA, Kiran Reddy. 8440 WALNUT HILL LN # 600 75231 #495-21-1992 L2001 **HO** *020 †20

KANDALA, Geeta. 4500 S LANCASTER RD # 117 75216 #016-01-1997 L1997 **PRS** *020 †60

KANE, Katherine Y. ■ 75204 #048-12-2004 **GS** *012

KANOFF, Justin Michael. ■ 75248 #048-12-2007 L2007 **IM** *012

KANTOR, William N. 221 W COLORADO BLVD, STE 625 75208 #016-42-1985 L2000 **GS CCS** *020 †85

KANWAR, Balraj Mohan Sing. 809 SINGLETON BLVD 75212 #495-29-1983 L2004 **FM** *020 †18

KAO, Jane Malan. 7777 FOREST LN, STE B320 75230 #047-20-1989 L1995 **PDC** *020 †55

KAPADIA, Pratik C. 3600 GASTON AVE, STE 1004 75246 #048-13-1996 L1998 **IM** *020 †20

KAPLAN, Edward Paul. 7777 FOREST LN, STE C618 75230 #041-01-1991 L1992 **U** *020 †95

KAPLAN, Norman Mayer. 5323 HARRY HINES BLVD 75235 #048-12-1954 L1954 **CD END** *040 †20

KAPUR, Payal. 5323 HARRY HINES BLVD 75235 #496-09-1997 L2006 **PTH** *100 †50

KARA, Amynah. 7900 CHURCHILL WAY # 10107 75251 #035-08-1999 L2004 **EM** *020 †16

KARAM, Albert Gerard. 12200 PARK CENTRAL DR, STE 405 75251 #021-06-1981 L1984 **PD** *020 †55

KARAM ABDALLAH, Jose Anto. 5323 HARRY HINES BLVD 75390 #605-01-2002 **U** *012

KARANDIKAR, Nitin Jayant. 5323 HARRY HINES BLVD, DEPT OF PATHOLOGY-UT SW MC 75390 #495-28-1990 L2000 **PTH HMP** *050 †50

KARIN, Daniel S. 7557 RAMBLER RD, STE 706 75231 #028-02-1973 L1976 **AN** *020 †05

KARJEKER, Shamema Begum. 5151 HARRY HINES BLVD 75235 #836-02-1978 L1981 **AN** *020 †20

KARNI, Catherine. 5323 HARRY HINES BLVD, UT SOUTHWESTERN MEDICAL CE 75390 #418-02-1988 L2002 **CHP** *020 †75

KAROL, Lori A. 2222 WELBORN ST 75219 #025-01-1985 L1994 **ORS** *020 †40

KARP, David Ross. 5151 HARRY HINES BLVD 75235 #028-02-1984 L1991 **IM RHU** *050 †20

KARUNAPUZHA, Cherian Abra. ■ 75244 #495-31-2004 **N** *012

KASHNER, Tetyana Kinal. ■ 75230 #913-18-1994 L2005 **OBG** *100

KASSA, Sentayehu K G. 8224 PARK LN STE 130, STE 130 75231 #366-01-1985 L1998 **FM** *020 †18

KASSANOFF, Arnold Howard. 7115 GREENVILLE AVE, STE 220 75231 #021-01-1956 L1962 **IM CD** *020 †20

KASSANOFF, Ruby Elizabeth. 3434 SWISS AVE, STE 410 75204 #048-12-1996 L1999 **IM** *020 †20

KASSIR, Martin. 8335 WALNUT HILL LN, STE 140 75231 #048-12-1991 L1994 **D** *020 †15,20

KASTNER, Aaron M. ■ 75248 #062-01-1950 L1976 **FM** *075

KATDARE, Ameeta Vidyadhar. ■ 75235 #048-12-2008 *012

KATNENI, Ratnaja. ■ 75204 #495-37-2001 L2006 **NEP** *012

KATZ, Andres Ungar. 8230 WALNUT HILL LN # 408 75231 #847-11-1972 L1975 **GS VS** *020 †85

KATZ, Michael Mordecai. 8220 WALNUT HILL LN # 615 75231 #048-12-1979 L1979 **ORS** *020 †40

KATZ, Solomon M. ■ 75225 #048-02-1935 L1935 **CD IM** *071

KATZ, Warren Jay. 6200 LYNDON B JOHNSON FWY, STE 110 75240 #016-42-1968 L1975 **FPS** *020 †45

KAUFMANN, Margaret C. 5646 MILTON ST STE 705 75206 #048-12-1979 L1979 **P** *020 †75

KAUFMANN-LYNCH, Isaac P. 5323 HARRY HINES BLVD, SOUTHWESTERN MED 75390 #048-12-2005 **AN** *075

KAUSAR, Rehana. 13601 PRESTON RD, STE 900W 75240 #704-09-1975 L1983 **AN** *020 †05

KAWALSKY, Darryl Lindsay. 7777 FOREST LN, STE D565 75230 #836-01-1980 L1992 **CD IM** *020 †20

KAWASAKI, Masashi. ■ 75214 #065-06-1957 L1968 **FPS** *071 †45

KAY, Dennis Bryan. 8345 WALNUT HILL LN, STE 140 75231 #038-41-1976 L1981 **OPH** *020 †35

KAYE, Alan G. 8440 WALNUT HILL LN, STE 410 75231 #048-02-1993 L1994 **IM** *020 †20

KAYE, Harold Louis. 8160 WALNUT HILL LN, STE 100 75231 #007-02-1964 L1971 **OBG** *020 †30 ‡

KAZEMI, Massuma. 7777 FOREST LN, STE C208 75230 #118-01-1964 L1984 **PD ID** *020 †55

KAZI, Sabiha. ■ 75229 #048-12-2008 *012

KAZI, Salahuddin. 9301 N CENTRAL EXPY, STE 675 75231 #704-02-1986 L1991 **RHU IM** *020 †20

KEDORA, John Christopher. 3500 GASTON AVE 75246 #028-34-2002 L2007 **VS** *012

KEISER, Philip Harry. 1936 AMELIA CT MC9173, PARKLAND HIV RESEARCH CLIN 75235 #023-01-1986 L1994 **ID** *020 †20

KELLEY, Urszula Barbara. 8200 WALNUT HILL LN, FL 5 75231 #759-01-1990 L1997 **P CHP** *020 †75

KELLY, Cindy Kay. 2222 WELBORN ST, TEXAS SCOTTISH RITE HOSP. 75219 #048-12-1987 L1988 **AN PAN** *020 †05

KELLY, Colleen E. ■ 75205 #048-13-2004 L2006 **AN** *012

KELLY, Derek Michael. 2222 WELBORN ST, RITE HOSP 75219 #004-01-2002 L2007 **OP** *012

KELLY, Leon Keith. 5230 MEDICAL CENTER DR, OF FORENSIC 75235 #017-20-2003 L2004 **FOP** *012 †50

KELLY, Nancy R. ■ 75214 #048-02-1987 L1989 **PD** *020 †55

KELSEY, Mark Charles. 3109 KNOX ST, # 521 75205 #028-34-1994 L1995 **AN** *100

KELTON, Philip L, Jr. 3600 GASTON AVE 1054 75246 #048-02-1970 L1970 **PS** *020 †85,65 ‡

KEMEYOU, Line. ■ 75209 #048-12-2008 *012

KEMPE, William Wendell. 7979 W VIRGINIA DR 75237 #048-12-1954 L1954 **GP** *071

KEMPKE, Camille E. 5201 HARRY HINES BLVD, JAIL HEALTH PARKLAND HHS 75235 #025-01-1978 L2005 **P PYG** *020 †75

KENG, Moses Joshua, Jr. 7 MEDICAL PKWY, REHAB UNIT 75234 #016-42-2001 L2005 **PM** *020

KENJARSKI, Brian Matthew. 1717 MAIN ST STE 52, ROCHESTER GENERAL HOSPITAL 75201 #035-06-2002 L2007 **EM** *100 †16

KENJARSKI, Thomas P, II. 7955 HARRY HINES BLVD 75235 #035-45-1998 L2003 **AN** *020

KENKEL, Jeffrey Miller. 1801 INWOOD RD 75390 #010-02-1989 L1996 **PS** *020 †65

KENNEDY, Colleen Irene. 3409 WORTH ST STE 4 75246 #041-02-1996 L2007 **GS** *100 †85

KENNEDY, James M, Jr. 6263 HARRY HINES BLVD 75235 #012-01-1989 L2002 **PD** *020 †55

KENNEDY, Joy D. ■ 75219 #048-12-2006 L2007 **P** *012

KENNEDY, Tammy L. 8215 WESTCHESTER DR, STE 111 75225 #034-01-1992 L2002 **PD** *020 †55

KENNERLY, Donald Alan. 8080 N CENTRAL EXPY, STE 500 LB 81 75206 #028-02-1980 L1984 **IM AI** *030 †20,03

KENT, Mary Ellen. 9 MEDICAL PKWY 75234 #048-12-1986 L1987 **OPH** *071 †35

KERBER, Irwin Jos. 5201 HARRY HINES BLVD 75235 #035-08-1961 L1970 **GYN REN** *040 †30

KERMANI, Asra. 9323 GARLAND RD STE 112 75218 #704-25-1992 L2006 **END** *020 †20

KERNER, Elizabeth. 9 MEDICAL PKWY 75234 #048-04-1981 L1981 **PS HS** *020 †65

KERNIE, Steven Gerard. 5323 HARRY HINES BLVD, DEPARTMENT OF PEDIATRICS 75390 #054-04-1992 L1995 **CCP PD** *020 †55

KERR, Trevor John. ■ 75235 #048-12-2008 *012

KESAVA, Prabhakar P. 12700 PARK CENTRAL DR, STE 430 75251 #021-06-1989 L1997 **RNR** *020 †80

KESTEL, John Lawrence, Jr. 1926 CHATTANOOGA PL 75235 #030-06-1958 L1962 **D** *072 †15

KETTLES, Michele Anne. 12200 PRESTON RD 75230 #041-01-1990 L1998 **GPM** *020 †70

KEY, Charles Bain. 2801 LEMMON AVE 75204 #048-02-1955 L1955 **OPH** *071 †35

KEY, James David. PO BOX 720608 75372 #047-06-1965 L1974 **ORS AM** *030 †40

KEYES, Elizabeth Rose. ■ 75249 #048-12-2006 **PD** *012

KHALID, Imrana. 8267 ELMBROOK DR, STE 100 75247 #704-20-1982 L1992 **PTH** *020 †50

KHALID, Mohammad. 5939 HARRY HINES BLVD #745 75235 #704-01-1975 L1979 **N P** *020 †75

KHALIFA, Ismail Ibrahim M. ■ 75248 #915-04-1975 *071 ‡

KHALIL, Alfy Amin. ■ 75244 #330-02-1957 L1974 **GE IM** *071

KHALILI, Hamed. 5323 HARRY HINES BLVD, DEPT OF INT MED 75390 #048-12-2006 L2008 **IM** *012

KHALILI, Houman. ■ 75206 #048-12-2008 *012

KHAMBATI, Shamin Khozema. 8210 WALNUT HILL LN STE 23 75231 #495-01-1991 L1999 **IM** *020 †20

KHAN, Arif Masood. 4500 S LANCASTER RD, MAIL CODE 116A 75216 #704-01-1990 L1999 **P** *020 †75

KHAN, Bilal. 4801 S BUCKNER BLVD, STE 600 75227 #704-02-1988 L2002 **IM** *020 †20

KHAN, David Ali. 5323 HARRY HINES BLVD, STOP 9031 75390 #016-11-1988 L1994 **AI IM** *020 †20,03

KHAN, Iffat Zamani. 4350 ALPHA RD, DALLAS 75244 #495-33-1970 L1978 **PTH** *062 †50

KHAN, Liaqat Hayat. 5323 HARRY HINES BLVD 75390 #704-25-2000 L2003 **NPM** *012

KHAN, Muna Qamar. ■ 75219 #704-25-1997 **PD** *100

KHAN, Saadat Ali. 6300 HARRY HINES BLVD, CHASE BANK BUILDING, 12TH 75235 #704-16-1994 L2006 **CHN** *100

KHAN, Zarrish Saeed. 5323 HARRY HINES BLVD 75390 #704-25-2005 **GS** *012

KHANANI, Nazeer Ahmed. 13601 PRESTON RD 75240 #048-12-2002 L2006 **AN** *020 †05

KHANNA, Nisha. ■ 75204 #048-12-2005 **IM** *012

KHANNA, Priti. 5323 HARRY HINES BLVD, UT SOUTHWESTERN MEDICAL CE 75390 #016-11-1994 L2001 **PM** *020 †60

KHATAMI, Manoochehr. 5939 HARRY HINES BLVD #823, PSYCHIATRY AND NEUROLOGY 75235 #517-05-1972 L1980 **P** *020 †75

KHATTAK, Asif Zia. 3500 GASTON AVE, DEPARTMENT OF NEONATOLOGY 75246 #704-25-1996 L2003 **NPM** *020 †55

KHATTI, Sanjay Ram. 6146 GOLIAD AVE, SANJAY KHATTI, M.D. 75214 #654-01-1997 L2003 **DR** *020 †80

KHERA, Amit. 5323 HARRY HINES BLVD, UT SOUTHWESTERN MEDICAL CE 75390 #048-04-1998 L2003 **CD** *020 †20

KHETAN, Rainer A. 3500 GASTON AVE 75246 #048-14-1994 L1997 **IM** *020 †20

KHETAN, Roger S. 3500 GASTON AVE 75246 #048-14-1994 L1997 **IM** *020 †20

KHO, Nathaniel Acebedo. 9 MEDICAL PKWY, STE 304 75234 #748-26-1989 L2000 **PD CHN** *020 †75,55

KHOSLA, Rohit Kumar. SOUTHWESTERN MED, UNIV OF TEXAS 75390 #008-02-2002 L2007 **PS** *100

KHOURI, Georges. 8200 WALNUT HILL LN 75231 #875-02-1995 L2002 **IM** *020 †20

KHOURI, Michel G. 5201 HARRY HINES BLVD, INTERNAL MEDICINE DEPARTME 75235 #035-01-2004 L2007 **IM** *012 †20

KHOURY, Ernest Lawrence. 7777 FOREST LN BLDG C, PMB106 75230 #048-02-1976 L1976 **AN EM** *020

KHOUW, Raymond Sinkie. 3650 W WHEATLAND RD, STE A 75237 #048-02-1982 L1983 **OBG REN** *020 †92

KHURANA, Kiran. 133 N INDUSTRIAL BLVD, 5TH FLOOR / RM A-14 75207 #495-29-1992 L2000 **IM** *020 †20

KIA, Kevin. ■ 75204 #025-01-2006 L2006 **D** *012

KIDD, Christi Ann. ■ 75204 #021-06-2005 **OBG** *012

KIDD, Paul Clinton. 13601 PRESTON RD, STE 900 75240 #047-06-1988 L1992 **AN** *020 †05 ‡

KIDWAI, Zarin. 8224 PARK LN STE 130 75231 #495-27-1984 L1998 **IM** *020 †20

KIELAR, Moriusz M. 5323 HARRY HINES BLVD, U T SOUTHWESTERN MED CTR 75390 #759-11-1989 L1997 **NEP** *020 †20

KILGORE, Bassett Blanton. ■ 75205 #048-12-1953 L1953 **RNR DR** *071 †80

KILGORE, David Paul. 8440 WALNUT HILL LN, STE 510 75231 #048-12-1980 L1980 **DR** *020 †80

KILLEN, Kenneth Carroll. 8411 PRESTON RD, STE 200 75225 #048-12-1969 L1969 **IM** *020 †20

KILMAN, William James. 5201 HARRY HINES BLVD 75235 #048-12-1955 L1955 **R** *040 †80

KIM, Andrea S. 6315 VICKERY BLVD 75214 #048-12-2003 L2005 **P** *100

KIM, Benjamin H. 4144 N CENTRAL EXPY, STE 700 75204 #048-13-1998 L2002 **AN** *020 †05

KIM, Billy J. ■ 75219 #048-13-2003 L2006 **GS** *012

KIM, Chong Won. 5201 HARRY HINES BLVD, PARKLAND HOSPITAL (ACC) 75235 #583-02-1966 L1970 **IM EM** *020 †20

KIM, Jonathan Taesung. ■ 75243 #048-12-2006 **OBG** *012

KIM, Jong Moon. ■ 75248 #305-01-2004 L2004 **EM** *020

KIM, Kevin Yang Ho. 12221 MERIT DR, STE 460 75251 #048-13-1995 L1997 **IM** *020 †20

KIM, Misoo. ■ 75219 #048-12-2008 *012

KIM, Ryomin. 5959 HARRY HINES BLVD #101 75235 #041-14-1991 L1998 **RNR** *020 †80

KIMBALL, Thomas Eugene. 12200 PRESTON RD 75230 #039-01-1973 L1994 **DR** *020 †80

KINDBERG, Shirley Jane. 3600 GASTON AVE, STE 406 75246 #048-04-1961 L1961 **NPM PD** *071 †55

KING, Carey G, Jr. ■ 75225 #048-02-1943 L1943 **IM** *071 †20

KING, David. 4350 ALPHA RD 75244 #048-13-1991 L1997 **PTH** *020 †50

KING, Jarrod Todd. 5201 HARRY HINES BLVD 75235 #048-13-2003 L2006 **ORS** *012

KING, Kimberly Michelle. ■ 75201 #045-01-2006 **EM** *012

KING, Lewis Ray. 8224 PARK LN, STE 130 75231 #004-01-1990 L1994 **PD** *020 †55

KING, Louise Perkins. ■ 75208 #048-12-2006 **OBG** *012

KING, Raymund C. 901 MAIN ST, STE 4000 75202 #048-14-1990 L1991 **LM OTO** *030

KINGSTON, Adean Audace. ■ 75204 #041-12-2004 **D** *012

KINKADE, Scott Edward. 6263 HARRY HINES BLVD, MC 9067 75390 #048-14-1995 L1998 **FM EM** *020 †18

KINNEY, Cheryl Cox. 7777 FOREST LN STE B443 75230 #017-20-1981 L1985 **GYN** *020 †30 ‡

KINSEY, Richard Shawn. 5323 HARRY HINES BLVD, DEPT OF PATHOLOGY 75390 #004-01-2004 L2008 **PTH** *012

KIPPELS, Kenneth Michael. 14180 DALLAS PKWY STE 520 75254 #021-05-1974 L1976 **OS** *020 †30

KIRBY, Juanita F H. ■ 75236 #048-12-1958 L1966 **P** *071 †75

KIRBY, Randall P. 8220 WALNUT HILL LN, STE 616 75231 #048-04-1988 L1989 **VS GS** *020 †85

KIRCHER, Stephen Wayne. 5323 HARRY HINES BLVD 75390 #048-02-1997 L2002 **DR** *020 †80

KIRK, Lynne Marcum. 5323 HARRY HINES BLVD, MC 9005 75390 #030-05-1977 L1980 **IM** *040 †20

KIRK, Steve Thomas. ■ 75238 #048-02-2005 **N** *012

KIRKHAM, Wayne Robt. 7777 FOREST LN STE C506 75230 #056-05-1972 L1977 **OTO** *020 †45

KIRKPATRICK, Haskell M, III. 8200 WALNUT HILL LN, STE 700 75231 #048-12-2000 L2002 **ON HEM** *020 †20

KIRKPATRICK, Susan W. 3636 DICKASON AVE STE 2 75219 #056-06-1990 L1995 **P PFP** *012

KIRLANGITIS, Jeffery J. 13601 PRESTON RD, STE 900 75240 #038-45-1984 L1993 **AN** *020 †05

KIRSCH, David Scott. 3500 GASTON AVE, RADIOLOGY DEPT 75246 #021-05-2000 L2002 **VIR** *012 †80

KITZIGER, Kurt John. 9301 N CENTRAL EXPY, STE 400 75231 #021-05-1985 L1986 **ORS** *020 †40

KLEIMAN, Laurie. 5001 SPRING VALLEY RD, STE 400E 75244 #048-13-1995 L1997 **P** *020 †75

KLEIN, Alan Michael. 1441 N BECKLEY AVE 75203 #035-09-1971 L1978 **NPM PD** *020 †55

KLEIN, Kevin Wayne. 5323 HARRY HINES BLVD 75390 #048-12-1981 L1981 **AN** *020 †05

KLEIN, Mordecai Noah. 9229 LBJ FWY STE 25 75243 #016-11-1983 L1988 **CD IM** *020 †20

KLEINSASSER, Le Roy J. 3500 GASTON AVE 75246 #030-05-1936 L1946 **GS VS** *071 †85,90

KLEINSCHMIDT, Kurt C. 5323 HARRY HINES BLVD, UNIVERSITY TEXAS SOUTHWEST 75390 #011-04-1986 L1992 **EM** *020 †16

KLEMOW, Steven Robert. 5323 HARRY HINES BLVD - MC, SOUTHWESTERN MED 75390 #048-12-1999 L2007 **ID** *020 †20

KLESSE, Laura Jean. ■ 75205 #048-12-2001 L2007 **PHO** *012 †55

KLINGER, Daniel Robert. ■ 75235 #048-12-2008 *012

KLYMIUK, Andrew Michael. 6750 HILLCREST PLAZA DR, STE 215 75230 #759-10-1990 L1999 **P PME** *020

KNAPE, Kelly Gordon. 13601 PRESTON RD, 4242 MEDICAL DRIVE 75240 #048-13-1983 L1983 **AN** *040 †05

KNAPTON, Susan. 5323 HARRY HINES BLVD 75390 #048-12-1997 L1998 **PM** *100 †60

KNEZEK, Barry K. 12810 HILLCREST RD, STE B120 75230 #048-13-1991 L1992 **P** *020 †75

KNIGHT, David R. 3500 W WHEATLAND RD, BOX 225357 75237 #049-01-1979 L1992 **DR EM** *020 †80

KNIGHT, Kristin Brooke. ■ 75201 #048-02-2008 *012

KNIGHT, Walter Miller. 8210 WALNUT HILL LN # 404 75231 #048-04-1976 L1977 **ORS GP** *020 †40

KNOCHEL, James Paul. 8200 WALNUT HILL LN 75231 #016-43-1956 L1970 **NEP IM** *071 †20

KNORPP, Heike Christiane. 5323 HARRY HINES BLVD, UNIV OF TEXAS SOUTHWESTERN 75390 #409-05-2002 **AN** *012

KNOTT, James Kirk. 8200 WALNUT HILL LN 75231 #048-12-1960 L1960 **GYN** *071 †30

KNOWLES, Martyn. 5323 HARRY HINES BLVD, U TX SOUTHWESTERN MED SCH 75390 #036-05-2007 **GS** *012

KNOX, Sally M. 3535 WORTH ST # 610 75246 #048-02-1980 L1980 **GS SO** *020 †85

KOBES, Rodger Dale. 3878 OAK LAWN AVE STE 616 75219 #011-02-1974 L1983 **P IM** *020 †75

KOCH, Joshua Daniel. 1935 MOTOR ST 75235 #019-02-2001 L2002 **CCP** *012 †55

KOCH, Justin Lee. 5323 HARRY HINES BLVD, DEPT OF ANES & PAIN MNGMT 75390 #048-02-2003 L2007 **AN** *100

KOCH, Yvonne Piedrahita. ■ 75219 #047-07-2001 **U** *012

KODALI, Jyothsna. 3450 W WHEATLAND RD, 4TH FLOOR, STE 430 75237 #495-50-1994 L2001 **NEP** *020 †20

KODALI, Sreedevi. 5323 HARRY HINES BLVD, SOUTHWESTERN MED 75390 #035-01-2004 L2007 **D** *012

KODAMA, Atsuko. ■ 75218 #572-30-1988 **D** *012

KOERBER, Ellen Benedicta. 8335 WALNUT HILL LN, STE 105 75231 #048-12-1975 L1978 **IM** *020 †20

KOGAN, Allan Jay. 8350 N CENTRAL EXPY 75206 #048-04-1974 L1974 **FM OM** *020 †18

KOGAN, Inna. 13101 PRESTON RD, STE 504 75240 #913-16-1964 L1991 **P** *020

KOGANTI, Anil Kumar. ■ 75230 #012-05-1999 L2005 **ORS** *020 †40

KOHANSKI, Michael Shane. 4131 N CENTRAL EXPY, STE 435 75204 #048-12-2002 L2006 **AN** *020 †05

KOHL, Susan. 3600 GASTON AVE, STE 550 75246 #048-12-1991 L1994 **IM** *020 †20

KOHLER, Lisa Michelle. ■ 75204 #048-13-2003 L2006 **EM** *012

KOKER, Ahmet. 4500 S LANCASTER RD 75212-A, VA MED CTR 75216 #902-10-1963 L1973 **AN** *062 †20

KOLLAR, Carolyn Ann. 3450 W WHEATLAND RD, STE 443 75237 #041-77-1999, ▲ L2004 *020

KOLLMEYER, Kenneth Robt. 221 W COLORADO BLVD STE 62 75208 #007-02-1977 L1977 **VS VIR** *020 †85

KOLNI, Harold Wolf. 1441 N BECKLEY AVE 75203 #047-06-1979 L1984 **NPM PD** *020 †55

KOLOSTROUBIS, Laura N A C. 1936 AMELIA CT 75235 #649-31-1988 L1998 **IM** *020 †20

KONDURI, Kartik. 3535 WORTH ST, SAMMONS CANCER CENTER BA 75246 #496-09-1994 L2002 **ON** *020 †20

KONEN, Andrew Albert. 9301 N CENTRAL EXPY, STE 585 75231 #048-16-1995 L1996 **APM** *020 †05

KONG, Jun H. 2731 LEMMON AVE E, STE 200 75204 #048-12-1998 L2000 **FM** *020 †18

KONIG, Laurence E. 13601 PRESTON RD, STE 900 75240 #048-14-1987 L1988 **AN** *020 †05

KONTAK, Andrew Carl. ■ 75219 #028-46-2005 **IM** *012

KOON, Erik C. 3535 WORTH ST, FL 2 75246 #048-12-1998 L2000 **OBG** *020

KOONER, Karanjit Singh. 5161 HARRY HINES BLVD 75390 #495-43-1974 L1989 **OPH OS** *020 †35

KOONSMAN, Martin L, Jr. 221 W COLORADO BLVD # 100 75208 #048-15-1988 L1989 **GS** *020 †85

KOPANATI, Shashikala. 5323 HARRY HINES BLVD, UNIV TX SOUTHWESTERN MED S 75390 #495-65-1988 **PN** *100

KOPMAN, Norman M. 2909 S HAMPTON RD STE C102 75224 #041-77-1968, ▲ L1975 **PUD IM** *020

KORAL, Kadriye Meltem. 5323 HARRY HINES BLVD, UNIV TX SW MED SCH 75390 #902-05-1992 L2008 **DR** *012

KORAL, Korgun. 1935 MOTOR ST, DEPT OF RADIOLOGY 75235 #902-05-1992 L2002 **RNR PDR** *020 †80

KORNELL, Bernard David. 1441 N BECKLEY AVE 75203 #025-07-1972 L1978 **D OTO** *020

KORNGUT, Irwin Steven. 8220 WALNUT HILL LN # 110 75231 #036-07-1976 L1977 **IM** *020 †20

KOSHY, Sunita Sara. ■ 75208 #011-02-2000 L2003 **ICE** *012 †20

KOSTER, Robert Louis. 3600 GASTON AVE, STE 1001 75246 #011-02-1971 L1973 **IM** *020 †20

KOTAS, Lisa Pace. 8160 WALNUT HILL LN, SUITE104 75231 #048-12-2000 L2003 **OBG** *020

KOTAS, Robert Vincent. 5201 HARRY HINES BLVD 75235 #035-06-1963 L1984 **PD PDP** *020 †15

KOTHARI, Pamela. ■ 75204 #011-03-2007 **OBG** *012

KOTTUR, Sunil Kumar. 5323 HARRY HINES BLVD 75390 #495-33-1990 L1998 **CHP** *020 †75

KOTWAL, Dhiraj Kumar. 1 MEDICAL PKWY STE 210, I.D. DOCOTRS, P.A. 75234 #496-17-1993 L2008 **IM** *020 †20

KOUATLI, Amjad. 1935 MOTOR ST, CHILDREN'S MEDICAL CENTER 75235 #875-01-1984 L1995 **PDC** *020 †55

KOVACS, William Jos. 5323 HARRY HINES BLVD MC, UT SOUTHWESTERN MEDICAL CE 75390 #016-02-1977 L1983 **END** *050 †20

KOVAL, Robert John. 8226 DOUGLAS AVE, STE 730 75225 #065-09-1965 L1982 **FM OS** *020

KOWAL, Janis Rosenfeld. 606 N WASHINGTON AVE 75246 #048-12-1990 L1991 **RNR DR** *020 †80

KOWAL, Robert Charles. 14800 LANDMARK BLVD, STE 700 75254 #048-12-1993 L1998 **ICE** *020 †20

KOWALSKE, Karen Jean. 6263 HARRY HINES BLVD, STE DF 3 75390 #011-03-1986 L1990 **PM** *020 †20

KOZIELEC, Gregory Frank. 3414 OAK GROVE AVE 75204 #048-14-1994 L2000 **OPH** *020 †35

KOZLOWSKI, Eufrozyna J. ■ 75233 #407-25-1949 L1961 **PTH** *071 †50

KRAMER, Michael Simon. 12200 FORD RD, STE 220 75234 #836-02-1969 L1979 **FM GPM** *020 †18 ‡

KRAMER, Robert Ivan. 1935 MOTOR ST 75235 #024-07-1958 L1960 **PD PUD** *072 †55

KRAMPITZ, Daniel Edward. 7515 GREENVILLE AVE 75231 #016-11-1990 L1994 **N** *020 †75

KRAVITZ, Brian Neil. 1935 MOTOR ST B3302, ANESTHESIOLOGISTS FOR CHIL 75235 #023-12-1991 L2007 **AN PAN** *020 †20

KRAVITZ, Michelle Boymann. 1935 MOTOR ST, DEPT OF PEDIATRICS 75235 #023-12-1992 L2007 **PD** *020 †55

KREBS, Matthew Brian. 5005 LBJ FWY STE 350, OCCIDENTAL CHEMICAL CORP 75244 #028-02-1989 L1996 **OM AM** *030 †70

KRECH, Ryan Nathaniel. ■ 75204 #048-12-2008 *012

KREMER, Michael Andreas. 7777 FOREST LN STE C717 75230 #409-40-1991 **CFS** *100

KRESH, Herbert. 8535 FERNDALE RD 75238 #020-02-1953 L1954 **FM** *072 †18

KRESIE, Lesley Ann. 3500 GASTON AVE, DEPT OF PATHOLOGY 75246 #035-15-1991 L2000 **CLP BBK** *030 †50

KRIDELBAUGH, Leann. 3320 LIVE OAK ST, 7547 GREENBRIER ST 75204 #048-12-1994 L1995 **PD** *020 †55

KRINSKY, Harlan Stuart. 1717 MAIN ST STE 5200 75201 #016-11-1982 L1982 **EM CCM** *020 †20

KRIPPNER, William John. 5323 HARRY HINES BLVD, SOUTHWESTERN MED CTR 75390 #048-12-1970 L1970 **AN IM** *020 †20,05

KRISHNAMOORTHY, Arun. ■ 75204 #012-05-2007 **IM** *012

KRISHNAN, Sumant G. 9301 N CENTRAL EXPY, STE 400 75231 #048-04-1995 L1996 **OSM** *020 †40

KROCK, Marc David. 14800 LANDMARK BLVD, STE 700 75254 #054-04-1998 L2005 **CD** *020 †20

KROFT, Steven H. 5323 HARRY HINES BLVD, STOP 9031 75390 #016-11-1991 L1997 **PCP** *020 †50

KROMELIS, Frank John. 12201 MERIT DR, STE 440 75251 #016-11-1973 L1983 **IM** *020 †20

KRONENBERGER, Michael B. 411 N WASHINGTON AVE 75246 #048-04-1991 L1999 **OTO** *020 †45

KROUSKOP, Norman W. 221 W COLORADO BLVD, STE 730 75208 #048-12-1973 L1973 **IM** *020 †20

KRUEGER, Jeffery K. 8220 WALNUT HILL LN # 206 75231 #048-12-1996 L1998 **PS** *020 †65

KRUEGER, Joellen R. 7777 FOREST LN, BLDG A 75230 #048-12-1996 L1999 **PTH** *020 †50

KRULICH, Ludmila. ■ 75225 #286-02-1957 L1974 **FM** *071

KRUSZ, John Claude. 5446 GLEN LAKES DR 75231 #035-06-1983 L1984 **N PA** *020 †75

KU, Andrea Zumen. 13601 PRESTON RD 75240 #017-20-1994 L1998 **AN** *020 †05

KUBLAOUI, Bassil M. 7777 FOREST LN 75230 #024-05-1997 L2002 **PDE** *100 †55,20

KUCHTA, Ann Marie. 5323 HARRY HINES BLVD 75235 #035-08-1970 L1972 **R** *020

KUHN, Joseph Allen. 3409 WORTH ST STE 420 75246 #048-02-1984 L1985 **GS SO** *020 †85

KUIPER, Johannes Jacob. 621 N HALL ST STE 500 75226 #035-19-1991 L1998 **CD** *020 †20

KUJAK, Jennifer Lynn. ■ 75214 #040-02-2003 L2003 **DR** *012

KULKARNI, Mona Shrikrishn. ■ 75219 #028-46-2006 **AN** *012

KUMAR, Grace Vivekini. 8220 WALNUT HILL LN, STE 616 75231 #496-37-1994 L2005 **GS** *020 †85

KUMAR, Mithilesh. 4500 S LANCASTER RD 75216 #495-77-1976 L2001 **DR** *020 †28,80

KUMAR, Sumit. 13154 COIT RD, STE 100 75240 #495-36-1991 L2001 **NEP** *020 †20

KUMAR, Suneel Samuel. 8220 WALNUT HILL LN 75231 #048-14-1997 L1998 **PCC IM** *020 †20

KUMMER, Elizabeth Anne. 9323 GARLAND RD STE 2 75218 #048-14-1983 L1983 **IM** *020 †20

KUNJU, Aysha. 3600 GASTON AVE STE 550, WADLEY TOWER 75246 #495-37-1996 L2006 **IM** *020 †20

KUNKEL, Monique P. 5323 HARRY HINES BLVD 75390 #065-09-1967 L1980 **P** *020

KUO, Wei H. 12225 GREENVILLE AVE #1000 75243 #048-02-1988 L1989 **OM P** *020 †70

KUREPA, Zoran. 5939 HARRY HINES BLVD, PROF. BLDG II, STE. 400 75235 #957-01-1988 L2006 **RHU** *020 †20

KURIAN, Benji T. 6363 FOREST PARK RD., STE 75390 #048-16-2002 L2006 **P** *100

KURTZ, Richard Anthony. 703 MCKINNEY AVE, STE 433 75202 #035-19-1969 L1975 **IM CD** *020 †20

KURUVILLA, Abraham. 3900 JUNIUS ST, STE 710 75246 #495-31-1988 L1999 **D** *020 †15

KURZON, Jeffrey David. ■ 75204 #011-02-2002 L2005 **VIR** *012 †80

KURZON, Rebecca Joan. ■ 75204 #035-01-2004 L2008 **OPH** *012

KUSHWAHA, Anita. 3500 GASTON AVE, #4 ROBERTS 75246 #048-14-1995 L1999 **PCC** *020 †20

KWAN, Yuenjong. 2519 LOVING AVE 75214 #024-07-1998 L2004 **IM** *020 †20

KWAW, Charles Amonle. 9229 LBJ FWY STE 25 75243 #913-48-1992 L1998 **MPD** *020 †20,55

KWONG, Wilson Takyu. ■ 75235 #048-12-2008 *012

LA BARBA, Julie. ■ 75205 #048-13-2002 L2006 **PD** *020

LABAT, Marc Joseph. 5201 HARRY HINES BLVD, DEPARTMENT OF EMERGENCY 75235 #035-19-2003 L2006 **ETX** *012 †16

LABICHE, Lise Amy. 6301 GASTON AVE, STE 400W 75214 #021-05-1998 L2000 **N** *020 †75

LACHAR, Gregory Samuel. 7167 KENDALLWOOD DR 75240 #048-02-2002 L2004 **EM** *100 †16

LACHAR, Whitney Anne. 75240 #048-02-2002 L2006 **PCP** *020 †50

LACHMAN, Barry Stephen. 2777 N STEMMONS FWY, STE 1750 75207 #041-13-1970 L2003 **PD PHP** *030 †70,55

LACOUR, Thomas Alcade, Jr. 5323 HARRY HINES BLVD, DEPT OF ANESTHESIA MC 9068 75390 #021-06-1987 L1991 **AN PME** *020 †05

LACY, Adrian Robert. ■ 75233 #048-12-2005 **CHN** *012

LACZKOWSKI, Andrzej W. ■ 75225 #759-07-1963 L1972 **DR NM** *071 †80

LAFERNEY, Jimmy Don. 13601 PRESTON RD, STE 900 75240 #048-12-1980 L1980 **AN** *020 †05

LAGOMARSINO, Elizabeth M. 1935 MOTOR ST, DEPARTMENT OF RADIOLOGY 75235 #048-13-2000 L2003 **PDR** *020 †80

LAHAM, Alexander J. ■ 75231 #019-02-1944 L1979 **IM PUD** *071

LAI, Peggy Sue. ■ 75238 #035-01-2004 L2006 **IM** *100 †20

LAIBL, Vanessa Renee. 5323 HARRY HINES BLVD, DEPARTMENT OF OB/GYN 75390 #011-02-1999 L2003 **OBG** *100 †30

LAIDLEY, Alison Lisa. 7777 FOREST LN, STE C614 75230 #060-01-1984 L1992 **GS SO** *020 †85

LAIDLEY, Daniel T. 6301 GASTON AVE, EAST TOWER STE 400 75214 #065-06-1982 L1992 **AN PME** *020

LAIRD, Tracy Harpel. 7777 FOREST LN, STE C855 75230 #021-01-1994 L2001 **PDC** *020 †55

LAIRD, W Pennock. 7777 FOREST LN STE C- 1963 75230 #041-01-1966 L1973 **PDC** *020 †55

LAIRD, W Pennock, II. 7777 FOREST LN, STE C855 75230 #048-12-1995 L1997 **PDC** *020 †55

LAJARA, Rosemarie. 3500 GASTON AVE 75246 #042-01-1983 L1993 **END IM** *020 †20 ‡

LAKHIA, Ronak Krishnakant. ■ 75233 #048-12-2008 *012

LAM, Russell Chanh. 8230 WALNUT HILL LN 75231 #048-13-2000 L2007 **VS** *020 †85

LAMANNA, Jack Edward. 2409 ALCO AVE 75211 #048-78-1992, ▲ L1993 **FM** *020

LAMAR, Rachel Marie. 3600 GASTON AVE, STE 300 75246 #048-16-2002 L2006 **OBG** *100

LAMARRE, Louise. 3917 W CAMP WISDOM RD, STE 108 75237 #067-03-1980 L1984 **EM** *020 †16

LAMBERT, Michael T. 4500 S LANCASTER RD # 116 75216 #048-13-1983 L1984 **P** *030 †75

LAME, Raheleh. 75244 #517-01-1999 L2007 **FM** *100 †18

LAMMERS, Bonnie Jean. ■ 75205 #048-05-1984 L1990 **RHU IM** *071 †20

LAMONT, Jeffrey Paul. 3409 WORTH ST, SAMMONS TOWER, SUITE 420 75246 #025-01-1996 L1998 **GS** *020 †85

LAMPE, Charles V. 8220 WALNUT HILL LN 75231 #048-12-1998 L2002 **ICE** *100 †20

LAMPE, Kristen Herring. 5959 HARRY HINES BLVD, PROFESSIONAL OFFICE BUILDI 75390 #048-12-1998 L2000 **IM** *020 †20

LANCASTER, James Mack. 411 N WASHINGTON AVE #7000, ORTHOPEDIC ASSOC OF DALLAS 75246 #048-12-1979 L1979 **ORS** *020 †40

LANCASTER, Karine Rokeby. 2377 N STEMMONS FWY 75207 #143-03-1971 L1978 **PD** *071 †55

LANCOURT, Jerold Ezra. 7777 FOREST LN, STE C500 75230 #036-01-1968 L1986 **ORS** *020 †40

LAND, Robert Newell. 10 MEDICAL PKWY, STE 202 75234 #048-12-1969 L1969 **A** *071 †55,03 ‡

LANDAY, Michael J. 5201 HARRY HINES BLVD 75235 #041-12-1968 L1976 **R** *040 †80

LANDER, Allison Richey. 3600 GASTON AVE STE 550, TEXAS PRIMARY CARE 75246 #048-15-2003 L2006 **IM** *020 †20

LANDERS, Dennis Frank. ■ 75214 #030-05-1969 L1995 **AN FM** *020 †18,05

LANDERS, Stephen Alan. 10 MEDICAL PKWY STE 205 75234 #036-05-1983 L1983 **OTO NO** *020 †45

LANDES, Bruce Wayne. 8150 N CENTRAL EXPY, STE 1250 75206 #028-03-1980 L1983 **IM OS** *030 †20

LANDESMAN, Dennis Jon. 2777 N STEMMONS FWY # 300 75207 #021-01-1961 L1963 **OTO** *071

LANDGARTEN, Michael Jay. 6200 LBJ FWY STE 100 75240 #039-01-1995 L2004 **NEP** *020 †20

LANE, B Ward. 7777 FOREST LN STE A214 75230 #048-12-1967 L1967 **GS VS** *020 †85

LANE, Frank Elmer. 9533 LOSA DR STE 3 75218 #048-02-1982 L1983 **P ADP** *020 †75

LANE, Randall Brent. 8350 MEADOW RD STE 266 75231 #048-02-1974 L1984 **P CHP** *020 †75

LANG, Cathleen Ann. ■ 75204 #028-34-2007 **PD** *012

LANG, Jennifer Lynn. ■ 75231 #048-12-2006 **GS** *012

LANGDON, Robert W. 6764 WINTERWOOD LN 75248 #062-01-1978 L1980 **EM** *020 †16

LANGE, Elisa Blum. 8440 WALNUT HILL LN # 350 75231 #048-12-1985 L1986 **PDA AI** *020 †55,03

LANGE, Kurt C. 9330 POPPY DR 75218 #048-12-1985 L1987 **GE IM** *020 †20

LANGER, Thomas Geo. 9101 N CENTRAL EXPY, BAYLOR SAMMONS BREAST 75231 #035-15-1974 L1995 **DR FM** *020 †80,18

LANGERT, Joshua Samuel. ■ 75235 #048-12-2008 L2008 *012

LANGLEY, James Willis. 1441 N BECKLEY AVE 75203 #034-01-1972 L1978 **BBK PTH** *020 †50

LANGLEY, John Mark. 1717 MAIN ST STE 52 75201 #038-06-1982 L1988 **EM** *020 †16

LANIER, Paul F. 13601 PRESTON RD, STE 900W 75240 #048-14-1986 L1987 **AN** *020 †05

LANIUS, John Walter. ■ 75244 #048-12-1967 L1967 **GS VS** *020 †85

LANKFORD, Craig Brandon. ■ 75229 #028-46-2001 L2006 **APM** *100 †60

LANKFORD, L Lee. 3600 GASTON AVE, WADLEY TOWER SUITE 450 75246 #048-02-1946 L1946 **HS** *071 †40

LANKFORD, Lawrence Eugene. 4131 N CENTRAL EXPY, METRO ANESTHESIA 75204 #012-01-1987 L1991 **AN** *020 †05

LAOS, Carlos Alberto. 301 W COLORADO BLVD 75208 #737-01-1971 L1980 **NPM ID** *020 †55

LA PORTE, Paul Andrew. 6263 H HARRY HINES BLVD 75231 #018-03-1954 L1969 **PD** *071 †55

LARA, Luis Fernando. 1801 INWOOD RD STE 6-102, UT SOUTHWESTERN DIV DIGEST 75390 #649-52-1994 L2004 **IM GE** *020 †20

LARKIN, Sharon Louise. 5959 HARRY HINES BLVD #408 75235 #048-12-1980 L1980 **IM** *020 †20

LARKIN, William Frederick. 5959 HARRY HINES BLVD #408 75235 #048-02-1959 L1959 **GS OS** *020 †85

LARSEN, Fiona. 5323 HARRY HINES BLVD 75390 #671-02-1999 **PRD** *012

■ = Address Information Privacy Protected

LARSON, Arlan Phil. 14902 PRESTON RD, STE 810 75254 #048-02-1952 L1952 ORS GP *071 †40

LARSON, G Donald. ■ 75204 #025-07-1958 L1965 OPH *071 †35

LA RUE, Patricia Ann. 221 W COLORADO BLVD, STE 933 75208 #048-12-1979 L1979 OBG EM *020 †30

LATHAM, Paige. 13601 PRESTON RD STE 10 75240 #048-16-1990 L1991 AN *020 †05

LATIMER, Mary J. 5323 HARRY HINES BLVD, STOP 9031 75390 #048-12-1988 L1989 PTH *050

LATSON, Terry Wm. 13601 PRESTON RD, STE 900 75240 #048-13-1979 L1986 AN *020 †05

LAU, Amanda Diane. 5323 HARRY HINES BLVD, SOUTHWESTERN MED 75390 #039-01-2007 AN *012

LAU, May Chi. 5323 HARRY HINES BLVD, UT SOUTHWESTERN 75390 #035-03-1998 L2003 PD ADL *020 †55

LAU, Steve K. 7777 FOREST LN, STE C300 75230 #048-12-1996 L1997 IM *020 †20

LAUFMAN, Alan Kerry. 3811 TURTLE CREEK BLVD, STE 1000 75219 #048-12-1979 L1979 LM *062

LAUGHLIN, Michael Wesley. 5323 HARRY HINES BLVD, STOP 9031 75390 #048-12-1972 L1972 DR *020 †80

LAUGHLIN, William Robt. 8200 WALNUT HILL LN, DEPT OF PATHOLOGY 75231 #048-12-1961 L1961 PTH HMP *071 †50

LAUNIUS, John Arthur. 14856 PRESTON RD, STE 100 75254 #021-05-1983 L1987 EM *020 †16

LAURIE, Louba. 9101 N CENTRAL EXPY, BAYLOR SAMMONS BREAST 75231 #048-13-1995 L1996 DR *020

LAURIE, Scot A. 9301 N CENTRAL EXPY, STE 465 75231 #048-13-1996 L1997 AI *020 †20,03

LAW, Robert Murray. 3312 STANFORD AVE 75225 #001-02-1999 L2005 DMP *100 †50

LAWANI, Phyllis Ebun. ■ 75209 #048-14-2005 L2007 OBG *012

LAWLEY, Wraymon Randle. 8702 SPRING VALLEY RD, STE B 75240 #048-12-1957 L1958 OBG FM *020

LAWRENCE, Andrew A. 1825 MARKET CENTER BLVD, STE 410 75207 #035-08-1995 L2004 EM *020 †16

LAWSON, Lee R. 2909 LEMMON AVE 75204 #048-04-1953 L1953 ORS *071 †40

LAWSON, Yolanda Renee. 3310 LIVE OAK ST, STE 400 75204 #004-01-1997 L2002 OBG *020 †20

LAYCOCK, Royce. 4397 BOCA BAY 75390 #048-12-1954 L1954 GS GP *071 †85

LAYDEN, James David. 13601 PRESTON RD, STE 900 75240 #048-02-1980 L1980 AN *020 †05

LAYTON, Kenneth Franklin. 712 N WASHINGTON AVE, AMERICAN RADIOLOGY 75246 #039-01-1999 L2002 RNR *100 †80 ‡

LAZAR, Martin Lewis. 7777 FOREST LN STE 2420 75230 #065-09-1966 L1973 NS *030 †25

LAZARTE HERAUD, Susana Ma. 5323 HARRY HINES BLVD, DEPT OF INT MED 75390 #737-06-2003 L2008 IM *012

LE, Brian D. 8200 WALNUT HILL LN 75231 #048-12-1998 L1999 ICE †20

LE, Lan Huu. 1935 MOTOR ST 75235 #941-01-1967 L1977 AN GP *020

LE, Lankristie T. 5323 HARRY HINES BLVD, SOUTHWESTERN MED 75390 #048-12-2006 PD *012

LE, Thu T. 5626 PRESTON OAKS RD # 3 75254 #048-12-2003 L2005 P *100

LE, Trang Doan. ■ 75212 #048-12-2003 L2006 IM *020 †20

LE, Tu. 221 W COLORADO BLVD, STE 831 75208 #005-14-1997 L2003 CD *100 †20

LEA, Jayanthi Sivasothy. 5323 HARRY HINES BLVD, UNIV.TEXAS SOUTHWESTERN 75390 #036-08-1996 L2000 OBG *020 †30

LEACH, Erin Elizabeth. ■ 75209 #048-12-2006 IM *012

LEACH, Joseph L. 5323 HARRY HINES BLVD, BLDG G7 75390 #048-14-1985 L1986 OTO GS *020 †45

LEACH, Steven Lamar. 5323 HARRY HINES BLVD 75390 #016-02-1993 L1994 IM *040 †20

LEAVENS, Thomas A. 221 W COLORADO BLVD, STE 205 75208 #048-14-1990 L1993 N *020

LEAVEY, Patrick J. 1935 MOTOR ST, CHILDREN'S MED CTR-DALLAS #539-06-1986 L1998 PD *020 †55

LE BLANC, Kirk E. 6757 ARAPAHO RD, PMB 335 75248 #048-02-1989 L1990 AN *020 †05

LEBRON VALDEZ, Ricardo Ar. ■ 75214 #308-02-2000 GS *012

LEDOUX, Mark A. ■ 75229 #048-13-2004 L2008 AN *100

LEE, Allen Philip. 5323 HARRY HINES BLVD, U TX SOUTHWESTERN MED SCH 75390 #024-07-2006 GS *012

LEE, Andrew Kihyuk. 5959 HARRY HINES BLVD #101 75235 #026-04-1996 L2002 RO *020 †80

LEE, Benjamin K. 1935 MOTOR ST, CHILDREN'S MEDICAL CENTER 75235 #041-13-2001 L2003 PD *020 †55

LEE, Dale Young. 5323 HARRY HINES BLVD, U OF TX SOUTHWESTERN MED 75390 #048-12-2006 PD *012

LEE, David H. 8200 WALNUT HILL LN 75231 #048-15-1994 L1997 FM *020

LEE, David M. 2929 CARLISLE ST STE 260 75204 #048-02-1999 L2000 IM *020 †20

LEE, Dwight Augustus. 1130 BEACHVIEW ST, STE 240 75218 #021-01-1973 L1981 OTO HNS *020 †45

LEE, Grace Lauren. 5323 HARRY HINES BLVD, DEPT OF INT MED 75390 #048-12-2007 IM *012

LEE, Howard Norman. 4500 S LANCASTER RD, VA MEDICAL CENTER 75216 #506-01-1962 L1980 RO *020 †80

LEE, Jane Joo. 411 N WASHINGTON AVE, STE 2400 75246 #005-14-1994 L2001 IM *020 †20,03

LEE, Jason Eunjae. ■ 75201 #035-19-2001 L2007 OPH *100

LEE, Ji Sun. 809 SINGLETON BLVD 75212 #583-03-2001 L2006 FM *100 †18

LEE, Ji Yeon. 8200 WALNUT HILL LN 75231 #583-08-2002 IM *012

LEE, Ji-Soo. UNIV OF TX SO WESTERN SCH, DEPT RHEUMATOLOGY 75235 #583-08-1998 *100

LEE, Jiwon Ester. 12221 MERIT DR, STE 1610 75251 #048-16-2002 L2006 EM *020 †20

LEE, John Chenhan. 8220 WALNUT HILL LN, STE 214 75231 #016-02-1993 L1999 GE IM *020 †20

LEE, Karen Lynn. 8160 WALNUT HILL LN # 328 75231 #024-01-1998 L2005 REN *020

LEE, Kevin Brian. ■ 75235 #048-12-2008 *012

LEE, Mark Chong. ■ 75201 #035-46-2001 L2007 OP *012

LEE, Michael Anthony. 5959 HARRY HINES BLVD #101 75235 #048-02-1993 L2000 DR *020 †80

LEE, Michael C. 1935 MOTOR ST, CHILDREN'S MEDICAL CENTER 75235 #048-12-1995 L1996 PD *020 †55

LEE, Michael J. SOUTHWESTERN MED, UNIV OF TEXAS 75390 #048-14-2006 GS *012

LEE, Olivia A. ■ 75219 #048-13-2004 L2008 OPH *012

LEE, Steven Weibun. 13601 PRESTON RD, STE 900W 75240 #005-15-1998 L2002 AN *020 †05

LEE, Warren Gamaliel, III. ■ 75244 #048-02-2007 P *012

LEE, William Martens. 5939 HARRY HINES BLVD, HP4 420E 75390 #035-01-1967 L1991 IM OS *020 †20

LEE, Yong Chan. ■ 75204 #048-04-2001 L2004 AN *020 †16

LEEDY, Carolyn Margaret. 12221 MERIT DR, STE 1610 75251 #016-06-1998 L2003 PD *020 †55

LEFFERT, Jonathan David. 9301 N CENTRAL EXPY, STE 570 75231 #026-04-1983 L1984 END IM *020 †20

LEFTIN, Howard Irwin. 4600 SAMUELL BLVD 75228 #048-04-1977 L1977 P *020 †75

LEHMAN, Irwin. ■ 75240 #048-12-1955 L1955 GS OS *071

LEHNER, Anthony Dee. 6906 WESTLAKE AVE 75214 #023-07-1975 L1980 AN *020 †05

LEIBNER, Efraim David. 411 N WASHINGTON AVE, STE 7000 75246 #550-01-1990 *100

LEIMAN, Herbert Irwin. 3600 GASTON AVE STE 705, BAYLOR MEDICAL PLAZA 75246 #048-02-1969 L1969 N *071 †75

LEITCH, Ann Marilyn. 5323 HARRY HINES BLVD, DEPT SURGERY 75390 #048-12-1978 L1978 OS GS *020 †20

LEITCH, Robert Bruce. 13601 PRESTON RD, STE 900W 75240 #048-12-1981 AN *020 †05

LEMACK, Gary Evan. 5323 HARRY HINES BLVD, U.T. SOUTHWESTERN MED CTR. 75390 #035-20-1991 L1997 U *020 †95

LEMBCKE, Bradley T. 3600 GASTON AVE STE 550, INTERNAL MEDICINE 75246 #048-14-1994 L1997 IM *020 †20

LEMLER, Matthew Stuart. ■ 75230 #048-02-1989 L1990 PDC *020 †55

LEMM, John Thomas. ■ 75235 #048-12-2008 *012

LEMMON, Mark Leonard. 1717 MAIN ST STE 5 75201 #048-02-1948 L1948 PS *071 †65

LEMONS, Holly Sara. ■ 75214 #048-12-1997 L1998 IM *071 †20

LEN, Julio E. 9 MEDICAL PKWY, # 206-4 75234 #715-01-1988 L1996 PD *020 †55

LENARSKY, Carl. 7777 FOREST LN STE D400, PEDIATRIC HEMATLOGY/ONCOLO 75230 #035-09-1977 L1996 PHO *020 †55

LENKOVSKY, Fima. 4500 S LANCASTER RD, DEPT OF ANES 75216 #913-66-1972 L2004 AN *020 †05

LENOIR, Donald Grey. 13601 PRESTON RD STE 1000 75240 #048-13-1980 L1980 AN *020 †05

LENSING, Forrester Dubus. ■ 75230 #048-12-2007 DR *012

LEONARD, Frank A. 8335 WALNUT HILL LN, STE 105 75231 #051-04-1977 L1984 IM *020 †20

LEONARD, John Sloan, Jr. 4350 ALPHA RD STE 101 75244 #048-12-1965 L1965 PTH *020 †50

LEONARD, Peter Dexter. 13601 PRESTON RD, STE 900W 75240 #048-12-1980 L1980 AN EM *075 †05

LEONARD, Steven Roy. 1935 MOTOR ST, STE E03-320Z 75235 #007-02-1980 L1982 PCS PDC *020 †90,85

LEPE-SUASTEGUI, Maria R. 3500 GASTON AVE, DEPARTMENT OF HEPATOLOGY 75246 #649-14-1996 L2004 GE *100 †20

LERMAN, Mark Jeffrey. 13154 COIT RD STE 100 75240 #048-02-1973 L1973 NEP IM *020 †20

LERMAN, Melvyn. 7777 FOREST LN STE 2145 75230 #048-02-1968 L1968 PS *020 †65

LEROY, Robert Frederick. 7777 FOREST LN, STE B122 75230 #041-14-1977 L1983 N *040 †21

LESCOUFLAIR, Emmeline. 5323 HARRY HINES BLVD, U OF TX SW MED CTR 75235 #649-43-1982 P *100

LESCZYNSKI, Patricia. 801 N PEAK ST 75246 #048-13-2002 L2004 FM *020 †20

LESHIN, Mark. 3600 GASTON AVE, SUITE 1160-WADLEY TOWER 75246 #028-02-1974 L1977 END IM *022 †20

LESSLY, Gregg Alan. 6757 ARAPAHO RD STE 711, PMB 335 75248 #035-15-1990 L2004 AN *020 †05

LESTER, Andrew Hugh. 3109 KNOX ST 75205 #048-14-2004 L2008 PD *100 †55

LESTER, Frederick Carroll. 3600 GASTON AVE STE 751 75246 #048-02-1979 L1979 PS GS *020 †85,65

LESTER, Randolph Carl. 1441 N BECKLEY AVE 75203 #048-13-1978 L1978 PTH *020 †50

LETT, Charles Reginald. 3938 S FRANKLIN ST 75233 #047-07-1961 L1966 P *071 †75

LEUNG, Christina Y. 14800 ENTERPRISE DR # 9 75234 #048-12-1995 L1997 PD *020 †55

LEUNG, Nora Yinyin. 1441 N BECKLEY AVE, METHODIST MED CTR 75203 #028-34-2005 OBG *012

LEVENE, Donald Lyon. 7777 FOREST LN STE C804 75230 #062-01-1962 L1984 CD NM *020 †20

LEVENO, Debra Marie. ■ 75248 #048-02-1995 L1997 DR *100 †80

LEVENO, Kenneth Jos. 5323 HARRY HINES BLVD, SOUTHWEST MED SCHOOL 75390 #030-06-1968 L1978 MFM OBG *020 †30

LEVENO, Matthew John. ■ 75220 #048-12-2002 L2007 EM *100 †16

LEVENSON, Brian Michael. ■ 75205 #048-12-2006 HMP *012

LEVIN, David Jackson. ■ 75229 #048-13-2007 *012

LEVIN, Robert Randall. ■ 75204 #028-46-1988 L1989 P CHP *020

LEVINE, Benjamin David. 5323 HARRY HINES BLVD, DIV OF CARDIOLOGY 75215 #024-01-1982 L1987 CD IM *020 †20

LEVINE, David. 221 W COLORADO BLVD, STE 831 75208 #028-02-1981 L1986 ICE CD *020 †20

LEVINSON, Barry Simpson. 5323 HARRY HINES BLVD, STOP 9031 75390 #035-19-1986 L1988 ON *020 †20

LEVY, Fiona Howard. ■ 75225 #035-09-1987 L2005 AN *020 †55

LEVY, Kathyn Hasson. 8200 WALNUT HILL LN 75231 #048-02-1990 L1992 PD *020 †55

LEW, David C. 13601 PRESTON RD STE 10 75240 #048-02-1989 L1990 AN *020 †05

LEWIN, Matthew. ■ 75240 #048-12-2002 L2008 PTH *020 †50

LEWIS, Carol Ann S. 4525 LEMMON AVE, STE 200 75219 #048-12-1971 L1971 *020 †75

LEWIS, David L. 315 SUNSET AVE 75208 #051-01-1957 L1975 ORS *071

LEWIS, Deri Michelle. 3500 GASTON AVE 75246 #048-34-2001 L2006 GS *020

LEWIS, Elbert H. ■ 75219 #048-12-1952 L1952 PS HS *071 †85,65

LEWIS, Harold Ray. 1 MEDICAL PKWY, PROF PLAZA I #139 75234 #048-12-1971 L1971 TS *020 †20

LEWIS, Jerry M. 2750 GROVE HILL RD 75227 #048-12-1951 L1951 P *020 †75

LEWIS, Jerry Mermod, III. 8226 DOUGLAS AVE, STE 805 75225 #048-12-1977 L1977 PYA P *020 †75

LEWIS, John David. 1717 MAIN ST STE 5200 75201 #054-04-2000 L2002 FM EM *020 †18 ‡

LEWIS, Robert B, Jr. 13601 PRESTON RD, STE 900 75240 #048-02-1985 L1986 AN *020 †05

LI, Ben Chung. 5323 HARRY HINES BLVD 75390 #005-02-2006 OBG *012

LI, Gang. 221 W COLORADO BLVD, STE 845 75208 #028-46-1992 L1993 AN *020 †20,05

LI, Hsiao Ching. 5323 HARRY HINES BLVD, UT SOUTHWESTERN MEDICAL CE 75390 #035-03-1999 L2006 HO *020 †20

LI, Lily Yi. ■ 75209 #048-12-2004 D *012

LI, Shujun. 5201 HARRY HINES BLVD 75235 #243-69-1965 L1997 GS TTS *020

LIACI, Julia Ann. 8210 WALNUT HILL LN, STE 700 75231 #021-01-1999 L2004 OBG *020 †30

LIANG, Lawrence Weisui. ■ 75219 #048-12-2002 L2006 AN *100

LIAO, Robert. 5939 HARRY HINES BLVD, STE 630 75235 #048-12-1993 L1996 CD *020 †20

LICHTENBERGER, Frank John. ■ 75219 #038-40-2006 IM *012

LICHTENWALTER, Christopher. ■ 75229 #048-12-2002 L2004 CD *012 †20

LICHTIGER, Marcie Dawn. 11617 N CENTRAL EXPY, STE 132 75243 #011-02-1992 L1993 DR *020 †80

LICHTMAN, Michael Keith. ■ 75204 #054-04-2005 L2007 D *012

LICKER, Heather Lindsey. 5323 HARRY HINES BLVD, SOUTHWESTERN MED 75390 #048-12-2004 L2006 OBG *012

LIDDELL, Allison. 8230 WALNUT HILL LN, STE 414 75231 #048-12-1994 L2002 **ID** *020 †20

LIDDELL, Jeffrey Earl. 3626 N HALL ST STE 702 75219 #048-13-1993 L1995 **FM OS** *020

LIE, Chiao Yung. 8210 WALNUT HILL LN, STE 230 75231 #038-06-1992 L1994 **IM** *020 †20

LIEBERMAN, Zelig H. 3600 GASTON AVE 75246 #021-01-1950 L1955 **GS SO** *020 †85

LIECHTY, Joseph Matthew. ■ 75204 #003-01-2007 **GS** *020

LIFSHITZ, Samuel. 8160 WALNUT HILL LN # 316 75231 #649-01-1968 L1981 **GO GYN** *020 †30

LIGHT, Natalie Chambliss. 8160 WALNUT HILL LN, STE 224 75231 #048-12-2000 L2003 **OBG** *020

LIGON, C Wayne. 8220 WALNUT HILL LN, STE 506 LOCK BOX 124 75231 #048-12-1957 L1964 **OTO** *020 †45

LILAND, David Lynn. 4509 LEMMON AVE 75219 #048-12-1983 L1983 **PS HS** *020 †65

LILLY, Steven Mark. 4500 S LANCASTER RD 111E, DALLAS VA MEDICAL CENTER 75216 #047-05-1998 L1999 **IM** *020 †20

LILLY, Travis K. 1441 N BECKLEY AVE, PECA 75203 #048-12-1997 L1999 **EM** *020 †16

LIM, Lloyd Andrew. 1717 MAIN ST 75201 #649-14-1979 L1994 **EM GP** *020

LIN, Chun M. 3900 JUNIUS ST, STE 705 75246 #016-06-2002 L2008 **PM** *100 †60

LIN, Fangming. 5323 HARRY HINES BLVD, MAIL STOP 9063 75390 #243-33-1984 L2001 **PN** *050 †55

LIN, Hwai-Jeng. ■ 75231 #244-04-1979 **GE** *020

LIN, Julie. ■ 75205 #048-04-2003 L2006 **PD** *100 †55

LIN, Scott F. 12700 PARK CENTRAL DR 75251 #048-55-1997 L2003 **RNR** *020 †80

LIND, Karen Rebecca. ■ 75219 #048-12-2008 *012

LIND, Leon Dwight. 1439 JUNIOR DR 75208 #048-02-1964 L1964 **OBG** *020 †30

LINDBERG, Guy Matthew. 5323 HARRY HINES BLVD, STOP 9031 75390 #048-02-1990 L1992 **PTH** *020 †50

LINDER, Jeffrey Don. 3450 W WHEATLAND RD, STE 215 75237 #048-14-1996 L1997 **GE** *020 †20

LINDER, Steven Le Roy. 7777 FOREST LN, STE A307 75230 #016-11-1971 L1972 **CHN EM** *020 †55,75

LINDERMAN, Julie Klesse. ■ 75225 #007-02-2004 L2008 **PD** *012

LINDSAY, Rodney D. 5481 BLAIR RD 75231 #048-12-1994 L1996 **FM** *020 †18

LINDSEY, Jason Benjamin. 2700 CANTON ST STE 217 75226 #047-06-2001 L2007 **CD** *012

LINDSEY, Sara Ashley. ■ 75206 #048-12-2008 *012

LINK, Jeffrey Joseph. 5201 HARRY HINES BLVD, INTERNAL MEDICINE 75235 #016-45-2005 L2007 **IM** *012

LIOU, Nelson Eddie. ■ 75235 #048-12-2008 *012

LIPPAS, John. 8144 WALNUT HILL LN # LB25 75231 #024-07-1946 L1953 **OPH** *071 †35

LIPPAS, Matthew Danl. 8144 WALNUT HILL LN # LB25 75231 #048-14-1983 L1984 **OPH** *020 †35

LIPSCHITZ, Avron Herschel. SOUTHWESTERN MED, UNIV OF TEXAS 75390 #836-02-1999 **GS** *012

LIPSCOMB, Kirk Morris. 1420 VICEROY DR 75235 #021-05-1966 L1981 **CD** *020 †20

LIPTON, Anne M. 7515 GREENVILLE AVE SU 75231 #016-06-1995 L1999 **N** *020 †20

LISTER, George, Jr. MEDICAL SCHOOL, SOUTHWESTERN 75390 #008-01-1973 L2004 **PDC PD** *020 †55

LISTI, Samuel Jerome. ■ 75244 #048-12-1981 L1981 **IM** *020 †20

LITLE, Marc S. 8411 PRESTON RD STE 820 75225 #048-12-1991 L1993 **P** *020 †75

LITTLE, Christie Jo. 75230 #048-12-1985 L1986 **OBG** *020 †20

LITTLE, Katherine Hardy. 712 N WASHINGTON AVE, STE 200 75246 #027-01-1981 L1985 **GE IM** *020 †20

LITTLES, Xercerla Adrenna. 5323 HARRY HINES BLVD MC, UT SOUTHWESTERN MEDICAL CE 75390 #021-01-1998 L2000 **OBG** *020 †30

LITTRELL, Christine Perez. 4224 SWISS AVE 75204 #048-02-2000 L2003 **OBG** *020

LIU, Joan Elizabeth. ■ 75220 #005-12-1990 L1995 **PD** *020 †20

LIU, Rebecca H. ■ 75248 #048-15-2007 **IM** *012

LIU, Xue-Hui. 5323 HARRY HINES BLVD, SOUTHWESTERN MED 75390 #243-33-1987 L2006 **NEP** *100 †20

LIU, Yinghui. 5323 HARRY HINES BLVD 75390 #243-72-1994 **IM** *012

LIVINGSTON, Edward Harry. 5323 HARRY HINES BLVD, DEPARTMENT OF SURGERY 75390 #005-14-1985 L2004 **GS** *020 †85

LIVINGSTON, Harriette L. ■ 75225 #028-02-1950 L1956 **AN** *071 †05

LIVINGSTON, Shields O. ■ 75225 #028-02-1950 L1955 **GS** *071 †85

LLARENA, Corazon Ledesma. 10611 GARLAND RD, STE 114 75218 #748-01-1973 L1985 **IM** *020 †20

LLOREN, Ellaine A. ■ 75251 #048-78-2005, ▲ L2008 **PD** *012

LLOYD, Aaron Thos. 13601 PRESTON RD, STE 900 75240 #041-14-1990 L1997 **AN** *020 †05

LLOYD, Kyle Lance. 3600 GASTON AVE STE 303, BAYLOR UNIV MED CENTER 75246 #048-12-1990 L1991 **IM** *020 †20

LLOYD, Michael D. ■ 75214 #048-14-2007 **DR** *012

LO, Ann. 5323 HARRY HINES BLVD, SOUTHWESTERN MED 75390 #005-06-2005 L2008 **OBG** *012

LO, Julie Yupu. 5323 HARRY HINES BLVD, STOP 9031 75390 #048-12-1995 L1997 **OBG** *020 †20

LO, Matthew Chungyin. ■ 75235 #048-12-2004 L2007 **IM** *100 †20

LOCKRIDGE, Joseph Brendan. ■ 75214 #048-14-2008 *012

LOCUS, Kathy Jo. 75234 #048-02-1985 **FM** *075

LODOWSKI, Charles Harry. ■ 75229 #048-12-1948 L1948 **OS IM** *071

LODOWSKI, Ruth Ellen. 4500 S LANCASTER RD, STE 116-A 75216 #048-13-1986 L1987 **P** *020 †75

LOEB, Peter M. 8230 WALNUT HILL LN 75231 #048-12-1965 L1965 **GE IM** *020 †20

LOEHR, Charles Richard. 1 MEDICAL PKWY, STE 105 75234 #048-02-1975 L1975 **FM OM** *020 †18

LOGAN, Donald James. ■ 75220 #016-06-1957 L1965 **U** *071 †95

LOGAN, William Miller. 8226 DOUGLAS AVE STE 711 75225 #048-14-1985 L1986 **P** *020 †75

LOHMANN, Thomas Philip. 3500 GASTON AVE, DEPT OF PATHLGY 75246 #021-06-1979 L2006 **PTH CLP** *030 †50

LOMBARDI, David Gary. 8160 WALNUT HILL LN, STE 100 75231 #048-12-2001 L2005 **OBG** *020 †30

LONE, Jamal Qamar. 8230 WALNUT HILL LN 75231 #297-01-2000 L2006 **IM** *020 †20

LONERGAN, John Jenkins. 4500 S LANCASTER RD, DALLAS VAMC 75216 #019-02-1977 L1980 *020

LONG, Daniel S. 4131 N CENTRAL EXPY, STE 435 75204 #048-12-1989 L1990 **AN** *020 †05

LONG, Nathan Paul. ■ 75208 #048-14-2002 L2006 **IM** *012

LONG, Robert Gordon. ■ 75205 #047-05-1955 L1964 **NS** *071 †25

LONGSHAW, Kevin Maurice. 9528 WEBB CHAPEL RD 75220 #038-45-1995 L1996 **FM** *020 †18

LONIAN, Robert Duke. 8 MEDICAL PKWY STE 1 75234 #024-01-1973 L2002 **IM OS** *020 †20

LOO, Christine K. 5323 HARRY HINES BLVD, UT SOUTHWESTERN MED CTR 75390 #016-42-1999 L2002 **PD** *020 †55

LOPEZ, Annabelle. 5323 HARRY HINES BLVD 75390 #048-12-2006 **OBG** *012

LOPEZ, Cynthia Anna. ■ 75220 #048-12-1977 L1977 **AN** *020

LOPEZ, Humberto. 10 MEDICAL PKWY, STE 208 75234 #649-07-1984 L1997 **FM** *020 †18

LOPEZ, Jorge Arturo. 4500 S LANCASTER RD, DEPT RADIOLOGY VAMC 75216 #005-02-1987 L1992 **VIR R** *020

LOPEZ, Jorge F. 7777 FOREST LN, STE C538 75230 #048-14-1993 L1994 **OBG** *020 †30

LOPEZ, Joseph Alexander. 1412 MAIN ST 75201 #048-12-1996 L1996 **FM** *020 †18

LOPEZ, Kim Landefeld. 1935 MOTOR ST, CHILDRENS MEDICAL CENTER O 75235 #048-13-1991 L1994 **AN** *020 †05,55

LORENTE, Maria Eugenia. ■ 75230 #649-01-1963 L1969 **IM** *071

LORENZ, Richard Francis. 1717 MAIN ST STE 5200 75201 #048-78-1989, ▲ L1990 **GP EM** *020

LORENZO, Manuel. ■ 75254 #042-01-1990 L2007 **GS** *020 †85

LOTAN, Yair. 5323 HARRY HINES BLVD, UT SW MED CTR DALLAS 75390 #048-04-1997 L1999 **U** *020 †95

LOTHES, Christian Summers. ■ 75204 #033-05-2002 **NS** *012

LOU, Leland. 5323 HARRY HINES BLVD 75390 #021-01-1992 L1996 **APM** *020 †05

LOUDERMILK, Jan Ernest. 8220 WALNUT HILL LN, STE 408 75231 #048-12-1967 L1967 **PUD IM** *020 †20

LOUIS, Peter. 5959 HARRY HINES BLVD #530 75235 #010-03-1964 L1970 **IM CD** *020 †20

LOUW, David Hariman Santo. 4131 N CENTRAL EXPY, METROPLITAN ANESTHESIA CON 75204 #035-09-2003 L2007 **AN** *020

LOVITT, Matthew Alan. 3409 WORTH ST, STE 640 75246 #047-05-1986 L1988 **GS** *020 †85

LOWE, Kevin. 13601 PRESTON RD 75240 #048-14-1990 L1991 **AN** *020 †05

LOWELL, James Russell. ■ 75229 #039-01-1953 L1975 **IM PUD** *071 †20

LOWRIMORE, Patricia A. 9900 N CENTRAL EXPY, STE 500 75231 #048-13-1992 L2002 **P NUP** *020 †75

LOWRY, James Sidney. 500 HILLSIDE VLG, NE CORNER MOCKINGBIRD & AB 75214 #048-02-1952 L1952 **IM** *071

LOWRY, Jeffrey Clinton. 5323 HARRY HINES BLVD, DIV OF EMERGENCY MED 75390 #048-02-2004 L2006 **EM** *100

LOZANO, Ivette Concepcion. 10425 GARLAND RD 75218 #048-15-1992 L1993 **FM GS** *020

LU, Christopher Yu-Hua. 5323 HARRY HINES BLVD, DIV OF NEPHROLOGY 75390 #024-01-1974 L1989 **IG NEP** *050 †20

LU, Jane Huei. ■ 75230 #048-12-2003 L2005 **OBG** *100

LU, Jimmy Kien-Teh. ■ 75237 #021-01-1965 L1967 **FM** *071 †18

LUBAHN, Jordon George. ■ 75205 #048-12-2008 *012

LUBER, Samuel David. 5323 HARRY HINES BLVD, EMERGENCY MEDICINE 75390 #021-01-2001 L2005 **EM** *100 †16

LUBY, James Phillip. 5323 HARRY HINES BLVD, UNIV OF TEXAS SW MED CTR 75390 #016-06-1961 L1966 **ID IM** *020 †20

LUBY, Maureen Theresa. 3920 WORTH ST 75246 #019-02-1990 L2002 **AN** *020 †05

LUCAS, Elena Anatolyevna. 5323 HARRY HINES BLVD 75390 #913-80-1989 **PTH** *012

LUCAS, Steven Mark. ■ 75219 #016-01-2004 **U** *012

LUCIANO, Awilda Michelle. 5201 HARRY HINES BLVD 75235 #042-01-2001 L2005 **RHU** *012 †20

LUCKETT, Peter Michael. 1935 MOTOR ST, CHILDREN'S MED CTR OF DALL 75235 #020-12-1978 L1993 **PD** *050 †55

LUEBBEHUSEN, Hillary Inez. ■ 75219 #048-15-2008 *012

LUECKE, Percy Edgar, Jr. 3500 GASTON AVE 75246 #048-02-1952 L1955 **PD** *020 †55

LUGO, Carlos E. 5909 HARRY HINES BLVD, NUCLEAR MED ASSOC 75235 #649-14-1966 L1973 **NM R** *020 †80,28

LUGO-OLIVIERI, Carlos H. 5959 HARRY HINES BLVD #101 75235 #042-02-1993 L1996 **DR** *020

LUHN, Nellie Ryan. ■ 75229 #024-07-1951 L1953 **AN** *071 †05

LUK, Alvin Diphing. 7777 FOREST LN 75230 #048-13-1986 L1987 **AN** *020 †05

LUKE, Lisa Frances. 3500 GASTON AVE, 4 ROBERTS 75246 #021-05-1996 L1999 **IM** *020 †20

LUKE, Steven J. 13601 PRESTON RD # 1000W, PINNACLE ANESTHESIA CONSUL 75240 #048-12-1989 L1990 **AN** *020 †05

LUMRY, William Raymond. 9900 N CENTRAL EXPY, STE 525 75231 #048-02-1977 L1977 **AI IM** *020 †20,03

LUNA, Michael. ■ 75235 #048-12-2005 **IM** *012

LUNDELL, John Carl. 3600 GASTON AVE STE 654 75246 #008-01-1994 L2000 **AN** *020 †05

LUNSFORD, Lee M. ■ 75206 #048-12-2005 **IM** *100

LUONG, Kristy Le. 5400 PRESTON OAKS RD # 4 75254 #007-02-2003 L2005 **PAN** *012

LURIE, Sol David. ■ 75240 #836-01-1956 L1978 **FM** *071 †18

LUSBY, Rachel Diane. 5201 HARRY HINES BLVD 75235 #048-12-2005 L2007 **OBG** *012

LUSZCZYNSKA, Kazia Maria. 5909 HARRY HINES BLVD 75235 #048-14-1989 L1991 **P** *020 †75

LUTERMAN, David Lynn. 3600 GASTON AVE, BARNETT TOWER, STE 806 75246 #048-12-1970 L1970 **PUD CCM** *020 †20

LUTICH, Ann E. 8160 WALNUT HILL LN, STE 306 75231 #003-01-1986 L1987 **OBG** *020 †30

LUTKEN, Emily Ray. 5337 LIVINGSTON AVE 75209 #048-12-1980 L1980 **FM** *020 †18

LUTZ, Linda Ann. 4505 CHAPEL HILL RD 75214 #048-13-1972 L1972 **AN** *020 ‡

LYLE, Diana Carol. 8226 DOUGLAS AVE STE 449 75225 #048-12-1969 L1969 **GP** *020

LYLES, Boyd Daryl, Jr. 9900 N CENTRAL EXPY, STE 215 75231 #048-02-1979 L1979 **IM EM** *020 †20

LYNN, John Roland. 7150 GREENVILLE AVE, STE 300 75243 #048-02-1955 L1955 **OPH** *071 †35

LYON, Robert Thomas. 3920 WORTH ST 75246 #039-01-2001 L2005 **AN** *062 †05

LYONS, Calvin Darnell, Jr. ■ 75241 #048-12-2008 *012

LYONS, Mark Anthony. 1441 N BECKLEY AVE 75203 #047-07-2004 L2007 **FM** *020 †20

MA, Patrick Tung Sang. 5201 HARRY HINES BLVD 75235 #539-03-1980 L1985 **CD IM** *020 †20

MA, Yanjun. 3500 GASTON AVE 75246 #048-12-1992 **IM** *012

MAA, April Yauguang. ■ 75229 #048-04-2004 L2008 **OPH** *012

MAALE, Gerhard Emil, III. 8230 WALNUT HILL LN, STE 514 75231 #011-03-1978 L1985 **ORS** *020 †20

MAALOUF, Naim Mounif. ■ 75231 #605-01-1998 L2004 **END** *100 †20

MABRY, Richard Lee. 5323 HARRY HINES BLVD, UNIV OF TEXAS SW MEDICAL C 75390 #048-12-1960 L1960 **OTO A** *071 †45

MACALUSO, Amy Denning. 5323 HARRY HINES BLVD, DEPT OF ANESTHESIOLOGY 75390 #048-12-1994 L1996 **AN** *020 †05

MACALUSO, Anthony, Jr. 7777 FOREST LN 75230 #048-12-1993 L1994 **CRS** *020 †85,10

MACHUPALLI, Surekha. ■ 75235 #495-21-1997 L2007 **OBG** *100

MACK, Michael Jos. 7777 FOREST LN, STE A202 75230 #028-34-1973 L1979 **TS** *020 †20,85,90

MACKO, Sharon Lynn. 8200 WALNUT HILL LN 75231 #065-06-1975 L1984 **RO** *020 †80

MACURAK, Randal Bruce. 3450 W WHEATLAND RD, STE 307 75237 #048-02-1976 L1976 **GE** *020 †20

MADDEN, Christopher J. 5323 HARRY HINES BLVD 75390 #048-13-1995 L2003 **NS** *020 †25
MADDEN, James Donald. 8160 WALNUT HILL LN STE 32 75231 #016-43-1965 L1973 **REN GYN** *020 †30
MADDREY, Willis Crocker. 5323 HARRY HINES BLVD 75390 #023-07-1964 L1991 **HEP IM** *030 †20
MADELEY, Paul Ewing. 3434 SWISS AVE, STE 430 75204 #048-12-1976 L1976 **IM** *020 †20
MADIGAN, Michael Jos. 5646 MILTON ST, STE 336 75206 #021-05-1979 L1981 **P** *020 †75
MADSON, Katherine L. 5323 HARRY HINES BLVD, DEPTARTMENT OF RHEUMATOLOG 75390 #036-08-1987 L2004 **PPR PD** *020 †55
MAFTOUN BANANKHAH, Sepideh. 5323 HARRY HINES BLVD, DEPT OF PATHOLOGY 75390 #517-05-2001 **PTH** *012
MAGEE, David Jude. 9330 POPPY DR STE 501, DIGESTIVE HEALTH ASSOCIATE 75218 #048-04-1989 L1992 **GE** *020 †20
MAGEE, Kevin P. 7777 FOREST LN 75230 #048-13-1988 L1989 **MFM OBG** *020 †30
MAGEE, Michael Douglas. 6757 ARAPAHO RD STE 711, PMB 335 75248 #041-14-1986 L1992 **AN** *074 †05
MAGEE, Robert Van Gordon. 2710 VALLEY VIEW LN 75234 #004-01-1948 L1950 **OS GP** *071
MAGETO, Yolanda Nyaboke. 5323 HARRY HINES BLVD, PULMONARY/CRITICAL CARE 75390 #028-02-1991 L1992 **PCC EP** *020 †20
MAHADY, Ivan Barry. 1717 MAIN ST, STE 5200 75201 #010-01-1967 L1978 **IM AM** *020 †20
MAHAJAN, Sajan Thapar. ■ 75238 #028-02-2005 **DR** *012
MAHER, Elizabeth Anne. 5323 HARRY HINES BLVD, DANA-FARBER CANCER INSTITU 75390 #067-01-1993 L2006 **HO IM** *020 †20
MAHER, Joseph Francis. ■ 75214 #048-12-1987 L1988 **IM** *020 †20,19
MAHER, Margaret Eileen. 5806 OVER DOWNS DR 75230 #048-02-1974 **FM** *020 †18 ‡
MAHONY, Lynn. 1935 MOTOR ST, CMC-CARDIOLOGYICAL CENTER 75235 #005-11-1975 L1985 **PDC** *020 †55
MAHOWALD, Ward Joseph. 1441 N BECKLEY AVE 75203 #056-06-1962 L1968 **OPH** *071 †35
MAI, Martin Louis. 3500 GASTON AVE, DEPARTMENT OF MEDICAL EDUC 75246 #048-12-1983 L1983 **NEP OS** *020 †20
MAIER POPA, Emilia. 9101 N CENTRAL EXPY, STE 350 75231 #781-01-1985 L2001 **IM** *020 †20
MAISEL, Christopher Marc. 3535 WORTH ST, STE 110 75246 #041-12-1999 L2005 **HO** *020 †20
MAJEED, Kazi Imran. 7777 FOREST LN STE A307 75230 #704-01-1990 L2005 **CHN** *020 †55,75
MAKAM, Anil N. ■ 75204 #041-15-2007 **IM** *012
MALET, Peter Francis. 5323 HARRY HINES BLVD, LIVER UNIT UTSW 75390 #035-08-1976 L1998 **HEP GE** *040 †20
MALIK, Amtul M.. UNIV TX SOUTHWESTERN MED S, UNIV TX SOUTHWESTERN MED S 75390 #704-01-2003 **FP** *012
MALIK, Perveen F. 133 N INDUSTRIAL BLVD, DALLAS COUTY JAIL 75207 #495-15-1970 L1992 **FM** *020 †18
MALIK, Rubina. 5323 HARRY HINES BLVD, STOP 9031 75390 #065-01-1991 L1996 **FM** *020
MALLAMS, John Thos. 3812 ELM ST DEPT R 75226 #041-13-1946 L1953 **RO** *071 †80
MALLAT, Damien Bassam. 3434 SWISS AVE STE 206 75204 #605-03-1992 L2000 **GE IM** *020 †20
MALLIPEDDI, Rajeev. 5323 HARRY HINES BLVD, UNIV OF TEXAS SOUTHWEST ME 75390 #917-29-1997 **PRD** *100
MALLOU, Fernando. PO BOX 743156 75374 #847-06-1953 L1964 **PME OM** *020
MALLOY, Craig Riggs. 5323 HARRY HINS BLVD #NE42, ADVANCED IMAGING RESEARCH 75390 #005-02-1977 L1984 **CD** *050 †20
MALONE, Elizabeth B. 5323 HARRY HINES BLVD, DEPT MED 75390 #048-14-2006 **IM** *012
MAMMEN, Pradeep Pa. 5323 HARRY HINES BLVD, DIV OF CARDLGY UT SW MED 75390 #056-05-1995 L1998 **CD** *020 †20
MANDERS, Dustin B. ■ 75206 #048-12-2006 L2007 **OBG** *012
MANDUJANO, Jose Fernando. 7777 FOREST LN, STE C565 75230 #451-01-1986 L1997 **PDP PD** *020 †55
MANG, John Edward, Jr. 5323 HARRY HINES BLVD, STOP 9031 75390 #035-19-1994 L1997 **DR** *020 †80
MANGRAM, Alicia Jeannine. 221 W COLORADO BLVD, STE 100 75208 #047-07-1994 L1995 **CCS** *020 †85
MANGWIRO, Audrey Natsai. 12887 MONTFORT DR 75230 #775-01-1991 L2006 **IM** *020 †20
MANHOFF, Charles Mordecae. ■ 75214 #048-02-1942 L1942 **IM CD** *071
MANI, Usha Shanthini. ■ 75229 #010-01-1999 L2004 **OSM** *100 †40
MANKIN, Lowell Steede. 13601 PRESTON RD, STE 900 75240 #048-02-1991 L1995 **EM AN** *020 †05
MANNING, David Taylor. ■ 75219 #039-01-1966 L1969 **FM** *071 †18
MANSFIELD, Erin Elizabeth. ■ 75220 #003-01-2005 **PD** *100
MANSOUR, John Clancy. ■ 75390 #038-06-1999 L2007 **GS** *100 †85
MANTADAKIS, Elpis. 1935 MOTOR ST, CHILDRENS HOSP DALLAS 75235 #418-05-1991 L1997 **PHO** *020 †55
MANTAS, Alexi Michael. ■ 75225 #048-12-2007 **IM** *012
MANTAS, Michail Alexander. 7203 JOHN W CARPENTER FWY 75247 #048-15-1979 L1979 **OM PM** *020
MANZORI, Arash. 14800 LANDMARK BLVD, STE 700 75254 #048-78-1994, ▲ L2001 **CD IM** *020
MAO, Qinwen. 5323 HARRY HINES BLVD, DEPT OF PATHOLOGY 75390 #243-95-1989 **NP** *012
MARCUS, Peter Brian. 1441 N BECKLEY AVE 75203 #836-04-1966 L1977 **ATP** *020 †50
MARDER, Ellen June. 7515 GREENVILLE AVE, STE 500 75231 #034-01-1979 L1997 **N** *020 †75
MAR DOCK, Julian King. 13601 PRESTON RD 75240 #048-12-1976 L1976 **AN** *020 †05
MARDOCK, Ruth Anne. 3415 WESTMINSTER AVE, STE 204 75205 #048-13-1981 L1981 **P** *020 †75
MARENGO-ROWE, Alain J. 3500 GASTON AVE 75246 #917-25-1961 L1971 **HEM BBK** *020 †50
MARGOLIS, Mark A. 4131 N CENTRAL EXPY, METRO ANESTHESIA 75204 #021-01-1990 L2006 **AN** *020 †05
MARGRAF, Linda Russell. 1935 MOTOR ST, CHILDRENS MED CTR PATH DEP 75235 #011-04-1985 L1992 **PTH PP** *020 †50
MARICHAL, Daniel Alan. 3500 GASTON AVE 75246 #011-04-2004 L2007 **GS** *100
MARIN, Vincent Patrick. 8200 WALNUT HILL LN 75231 #035-01-1999 L2005 **PS** *020 †65
MARINESCU, Rodica Catrine. ■ 75235 #781-01-1995 L2002 **NPM** *012 †55
MARINO, Benton Robert. 5323 HARRY HINES BLVD, SOUTHWESTERN MED 75390 #021-05-2006 **PD** *012
MARIS, Michael L. 10 MEDICAL PKWY, STE 304 75234 #048-15-1975 L1975 **D DS** *020 †15
MARKHAM, David Wayne. 5909 HARRY HINES BLVD, DIVISION OF CARDIOLOGY, HA 75235 #012-05-1995 L2005 **CD** *020 †20
MARKHAM, Jeffrey Collins. ■ 75249 #051-07-2005 L2006 **DR** *012
MARKLE, Rae Lynn. 3609 CEDAR SPRINGS RD 75219 #035-19-1960 L1976 **P** *020
MARKOWSKI, Andrew John. ■ 75206 #012-05-2004 L2007 **EM** *100
MARKS, James Frederic. 5323 HARRY HINES BLVD, UT SOUTHWESTERN MED CTR 75390 #024-01-1954 L1962 **PDE PD** *040 †55
MARKWARD, Charles Gale. ■ 75214 #021-01-1947 L1947 **P** *072 †75 ‡
MARLIN, Gerald Vincent. 8220 WALNUT HILL LN, STE 604 75231 #048-02-1979 L1979 **NS** *020 †25
MARLOW, George S. 13601 PRESTON RD STE 1000 75240 #048-12-1991 L1993 **AN** *020 †05
MARPLE, Bradley Franklin. 5323 HARRY HINES BLVD, DEPT OF OTELARNY 75390 #039-01-1988 L1992 **OTO HNS** *040 †45
MARQUEZ-KERGUELEN, Otto J. 10455 N CENTRL #109-327 75231 #048-12-1989 L1991 **IM** *020
MARSDEN, Chad Anthony. 7557 RAMBLER RD STE 706, NORTH TX ANESTHESIA ASSOCI 75231 #035-20-2003 L2007 **AN** *020
MARSH, Jeanne Marie. 1935 MOTOR ST, DEPARTMENT OF RADIOLOGY 75235 #048-12-1991 L1992 **PDR** *020 †80
MARSHALL, Cindy Deanne. 7515 GREENVILLE AVE, STE 503 75231 #001-02-1998 L1999 **PYG** *020
MARSHALL, Mark Damien. 3500 GASTON AVE 75246 #008-01-1957 L1964 **NS OS** *071 †25
MARTIN, Alan Wm. 6301 GASTON AVE, SUITE 100 WEST TOWER 75214 #048-16-1984 L1985 **N** *020 †75
MARTIN, Amy G. 1311 N WASHINGTON AVE 75204 #041-13-1998 L2000 **OBG** *020 †30
MARTIN, David Exline. 7777 FOREST LN 75230 #048-12-1983 L1983 **PS** *020 †65
MARTIN, George Wm. ■ 75244 #016-43-1943 L1965 **GS** *071 †85
MARTIN, Jack. 3636 DICKASON AVE 75219 #047-05-1953 L1958 **CHP P** *071 †75
MARTIN, John Edwin, Jr. 1906 PEABODY AVE, PEABODY HEALTH CENTER 75215 #048-13-1985 L1986 **IM** *020 †20 ‡
MARTIN, Mary Anne. ■ 75228 #048-12-1968 L1968 **D** *075
MARTIN, Richard Duane. 7 MEDICAL PKWY 75234 #048-04-1959 L1959 **OBG** *020 †30
MARTIN, Robert L, Jr. 7777 FOREST LN STE C4 75230 #047-06-1976 L1986 **OBG** *020 †30
MARTIN, Russell L, Jr. 3500 GASTON AVE 75246 #048-12-1960 L1960 **IM P** *071 †20
MARTIN, Thomas Wade. ■ 75219 #001-02-2003 L2007 **PMM** *012
MARTIN, Warren C. ■ 75238 #048-12-2003 L2008 **DR** *012
MARTINEZ, Dee L. 2301 S HAMPTON RD STE 100 75224 #048-13-1992 L1993 **DR PMM** *020 †80
MARTINEZ, Joseph N. 5201 HARRY HINES BLVD, MEDICAL/HOUSESTAFF SERVICE 75235 #048-12-1994 L1998 **EM** *020 †16
MARTINEZ, Marsha Ann. 3320 LIVE OAK ST, 7TH FL 75204 #048-02-1985 L1986 **PD** *020 †55
MARTINEZ, Nilda M. 4630 HEATHERBROOK DR, STE 100 75244 #048-12-1987 L1989 **PD** *020 †55
MARTINEZ, Oscar J. ■ 75205 #048-12-2005 **EM** *012
MARVIN, Andrea Stephanie. 5323 HARRY HINES BLVD, UTSW UROLOGY DEPT 75390 #024-16-2004 L2004 **U** *012
MARWAHA, Vaneeta. ■ 75205 #024-07-2005 L2005 **D** *012
MARYNICK, Samuel Philip. 3600 GASTON AVE, 506 BARNETT TOWER 75246 #048-12-1972 L1972 **END REN** *020 †20
MASCARENHAS, Alipio B. 16800 DALLAS PKWY, STE 150 75248 #496-15-1974 L1979 **P** *020 †75
MASCARENHAS, Winston L. 4131 N CENTRAL EXPY, METRO ANESTHESIA 75204 #048-13-1979 L1980 **AN GP** *020
MASICA, Andrew Lyness. 3500 GASTON AVE 75246 #017-20-1999 L2006 **IM** *020 †20
MASON, Roy Carrington. 221 W COLORADO BLVD, STE 414 75208 #048-78-1990, ▲ L1991 **U** *020 †95
MASSAND, Manoj Gopal. 712 N WASHINGTON AVE, AMERICAN RADIOLOGY 75246 #016-02-1998 L2000 **RNR** *020 †80
MASSARE, Jorge E. SOUTHWESTERN MED, UNIV OF TEXAS 75390 #726-01-1998 L2001 **CD** *012
MATEJA, Chester A, Jr. 7777 FOREST LN, STE D220 75230 #016-43-1966 L1972 **RO** *071 †80
MATEVOSYAN, Karen. 5323 HARRY HINES BLVD, DEPT OF PATHOLOGY 75390 #913-19-1981 **BBK** *012
MATHAI, Nirmala. 7920 ELMBROOK DR STE 120, EMPLOYEE PHYSICIAN OFFICE 75247 #495-52-1979 L1991 **IM** *020 †20
MATHEW, Sean Paul. 5323 HARRY HINES BLVD, SOUTHWESTERN MED 75390 #021-05-2003 L2006 **CHP** *012
MATHEWS, Dana. 5323 HARRY HINES BLVD, DEPT OF RADIOLOGY UTSWMC 75390 #048-12-1987 L1988 **NM** *020 †75,28
MATHEWS, Richard Harrison. 5959 HARRY HINS BLVD #1104 75235 #047-05-1966 L1970 **GS** *071 †85
MATHEWS, Robert Jace. 3600 GASTON AVE, STE 300 75246 #048-02-1977 L1977 **OBG** *020 †30
MATHIEU, Reese Alfred. 7777 FOREST LN 75230 #048-12-1978 L1978 **PD** *020 †55
MATHIS, John Proctor. 3600 GASTON AVE STE 804 75246 #048-04-1954 L1955 **AN OS** *071
MATSON, James Reese. 7777 FOREST LN, STE C737 75230 #030-06-1974 L1988 **CCP PD** *020 †55
MATSUNO, Wendy Chiemi. 5323 HARRY HINES BLVD, SOUTHWESTERN MED 75390 #030-06-2002 L2003 **PEM** *012
MATTER, Gregory John. 621 N HALL ST, STE 500 75226 #048-04-1985 L1986 **TS** *020 †85,90
MATTHEWS, Henry Bertel. ■ 75243 #010-03-1936 L1937 **IM GP** *071
MATTHEWS, Joseph Michael. ■ 75228 #021-01-2005 L2007 **EM** *012
MATTISON, Tanner L. 6060 N CENTRAL EXPY, STE 262 75206 #048-13-1998 L2001 **PTH** *020 †50
MATTSON, Harold Andrew. 4500 S LANCASTER RD 75216 #030-05-1943 L1950 **ORS** *071 †40
MATULEVICIUS, Susan A. ■ 75229 #041-01-2002 L2002 **CD** *012 †20
MATWIJECKY, Cornelius. 3426 MILTON AVE 75205 #065-09-1975 L1983 **NS N** *020 †25
MATYAS, Michael A. 11617 N CENTRAL EXPY, STE 132 75243 #048-04-1989 L1990 **DR NM** *020 †80,28
MAUCK, Ryan James. ■ 75204 #011-04-2007 **GS** *012
MAULDIN, Donald Maurice. 5920 FOREST PARK RD, STE 600 75235 #048-12-1974 L1974 **ORS OFA** *020 †40
MAY, Richard Thos. 9323 GARLAND RD STE 204 75218 #048-04-1976 L1976 **OPH** *020 †35
MAYDEW, Randall P. 6910 WILDGLEN DR 75230 #034-01-1981 L1991 **AN** *020 †05
MAYER, Eric Kanoalani. 5701 MAPLE AVE STE 100 75235 #010-02-2001 L2005 **PM** *020 †60
MAYER, Tom Gerald. 5701 MAPLE AVE STE 100 75235 #035-01-1968 L1981 **ORS PME** *020 †40
MAYFIELD, William Brooks. ■ 75201 #048-04-1945 L1945 **IM** *071
MAYNARD, Gary Don. 777 FOREST LN STE A240, COLUMBIA HOSP 75230 #025-01-1966 L1967 **AN OS** *030 †05
MAYNARD, Malea Pruszenski. 13350 TI BLVD, MS 327 75243 #048-04-1996 L1999 **FM** *020 †18
MAYNARD, Sheri Lee. ■ 75204 #048-02-2008 **OBG** *012
MAYO, Marlyn J. 5323 HARRY HINES BLVD, DIV OF DIGESTIVE & LIVER D 75390 #048-04-1990 L1992 **GE HEP** *050 †20

■ = Address Information Privacy Protected

MAYS, Edward Johnson, III. ■ 75201 #027-01-1999 L2006 **BBK** *100 †50

MAZOW, Mark L. 7150 GREENVILLE AVE # 305 75231 #048-14-1986 L1987 **OPH PS** *020 †35

MBURU, Albert Macharia. ■ 75206 #577-01-1997 L2006 **IM** *020 †20

MCADAMS, Rocky L. ■ 75209 #048-12-2008 *012

MC AFEE, Mildred Arlene. 8200 WALNUT HILL LN 75231 #048-12-1996 L1997 **IM** *020 †20

MC ALISTER, James R. ■ 75233 #048-12-1952 L1952 **IM** *020

MC ANALLEY, Lynley K. 5917 SHERRY LN 75225 #004-01-1989 L1990 **FM EM** *020 †18

MC ARDLE, Craig Bryant. 2997 LBJ FWY, STE 215 75234 #048-12-1980 L1980 **R** *020 †80

MC CANN, Samuel Mc Donald. 75214 #041-01-1948 L1973 **ON REN** *050

MC CANTS, Shannon Elizabe. 3500 GASTON AVE, DEPT OF OB/GYN 75246 #048-12-2005 **OBG** *012

MC CARTER, Leo D. 4144 N CENTRAL EXPY # 700 75204 #048-02-1986 L1987 **AN PME** *020 †05

MC CARTY, Todd Mason. 1920 ABRAMS PKWY, STE 431 75214 #048-12-1990 L1991 **GS** *020 †85

MC CASKILL, Bernie Louis. 8220 WALNUT HILL LN # 310 75231 #021-01-1975 L1977 **ORS** *020 †40

MC CAVIT, Timothy L. 1935 MOTOR ST, DEPARTMENT OF MEDICAL EDUC 75235 #048-12-2002 L2004 **PHO** *012 †55

MC CLAIN, Joni Lynn. 5230 MEDICAL CENTER DR 75235 #039-01-1983 L1992 **FOP** *020 †50

MCCLARD, Karen Barker. ■ 75229 #048-12-2005 L2008 **PD** *012

MC CLAY, John E. 5303 HARRY HINES BLVD, FL 7 # 104 75390 #048-04-1990 L1991 **OTO** *020 †45

MC CLELLAND, Robt Nelson. 5323 HARRY HINES BLVD, UT SOUTHWESTERN MEDICAL CE 75390 #048-02-1954 L1954 **GS GE** *040 †85

MC CLENDON, Laura Catheri. ■ 75229 #048-12-2005 **PD** *012

MC CLESKEY, Ottis Lynn. ■ 75229 #048-02-1954 L1954 **DR** *071 †80

MC CLINTOCK, Jean. 7777 FOREST LN, NORTHLAKE OB GYN P A 75230 #048-16-1993 L1994 **OBG** *020 †30

MC CLOSKEY, Karin A. 1935 MOTOR ST, CHILDREN'S MED CENTER - DA 75235 #047-05-1983 L1995 **EM PD** *020

MC CLUNG, Hugh Lawson. 5939 HARRY HINES BLVD, STE 719 75235 #048-02-1978 L1978 **IM** *020 †20

MC CLURE, Howard H, Jr. 1301 YOUNG ST STE 310 75202 #035-45-1958 L1962 **IM CD** *030

MC CLUSKEY, Jessica D. ■ 75204 #027-01-2000 L2006 **OPH** *020 †35

MC CLUSKEY, Paul Duncan. ■ 75204 #027-01-2000 L2000 **PS** *012

MC COIG, Cynthia Corinne. 5323 HARRY HINES BLVD, U.T. SOUTHWESTERN MEDICAL 75390 #048-13-1993 L1994 **PPR PDI** *020 †55

MC COLLUM, Amy Elizabeth. 1935 MOTOR ST, DEPARTMENT OF MEDICAL EDUC 75235 #027-01-2002 L2005 **PD** *100 †55

MC COLLUM, Andrew D. 3535 WORTH ST, STE 110 75246 #048-12-1995 L1996 **HO** *020 †20

MCCOLLUM, David Layne. 6337 LLANO AVE 75214 #027-01-2002 L2005 **IM** *020 †20

MC CONNELL, John Carroll. 7777 FOREST LN STE C425 75230 #048-12-1977 L1977 **ORS** *020 †40

MC CONNELL, John Dowling. 5323 HARRY HINES BLVD 75390 #016-43-1978 L1980 **U** *020 †95

MC CONNELL, Thomas H, III. ■ 75225 #048-12-1962 L1962 **PTH** *072 †50

MC CORD, Don L. 7777 FOREST LN, STE C608 75230 #048-12-1953 L1953 **GS GP** *020 †85

MC CORD, Eddie Houston. 5323 HARRY HINES BLVD, DEPARTMENT OF OB/GYN 75390 #048-12-1979 L1979 **OBG** *020 †30

MCCORD, Mary Warren. ■ 75201 #048-12-2007 **IM** *012

MC CORD, Steven A. 13601 PRESTON RD, # 900-WEST 75240 #048-04-1985 L1986 **AN** *020 †05

MC CORKLE, Jack Warren. 7777 FOREST LN 75230 #028-78-1953, ▲ 1953 **R** *071 †80

MC COY, Holly Anne. 14856 PRESTON RD 75254 #048-13-2001 L2004 **FM** *020 †18

MC COY, Medford Theodore. 9440 POPPY DR 75218 #048-02-1976 L1976 **PTH** *020 †50

MC COY, Rosemary C. 7777 FOREST LN 75230 #048-12-1978 L1978 **DR** *020 †30

MC CRACKEN, George H, Jr. 5323 HARRY HINES BLVD 75235 #035-20-1962 L1965 **PD OS** *040 †55

MC CRADY, Kathryn D. 13601 PRESTON RD 75240 #048-16-1985 L1986 **AN** *020 †20

MC CRAE, William Harland. 4516 LOVERS LN STE 134 75225 #065-01-1955 L1978 **U** *020

MC CREA, Robert Stanley. 5323 HARRY HINES BLVD, DEPT OF OB-GYN 75390 #048-02-1974 L1974 **OBG IM** *040 †30

MC CRORY, Thomas Milton. 2811 LEMMON AVE E, STE 3 75204 #048-12-1944 L1944 **OPH** *071 †35

MC CULLEY, James Parker. 5323 HARRY HINES BLVD, DEPT OF OPH 75390 #028-02-1968 L1981 **OPH** *030 †35 ‡

MCCULLOUGH, Jessica Welda. ■ 75204 #045-04-2007 L2007 **OBG** *012

MC CULLOUGH, Michael Lee. 8411 PRESTON RD STE 200 75225 #048-12-1963 L1963 **IM** *020

MCDANIEL, Jarred M. ■ 75235 #048-12-2008 *012

MC DONALD, Frank Edward. 3301 SWISS AVE 75204 #028-34-1969 L1973 **PD PM** *020 †55,60

MC DONALD, Helen Halliday. ■ 75214 #048-12-2005 L2007 **D** *012

MCDONALD, John Edward. ■ 75214 #048-12-2005 L2007 **ORS** *012

MC DONALD, Julia A. 5323 HARRY HINES BLVD, STOP 9031 75390 #048-13-1993 L1994 **PD PEM** *020 †55

MC DONALD, Lauren Anne. 8700 STEMMONS FWY, STE 133 75247 #041-13-1984 L1986 **NEP IM** *020

MC DONALD, Millicent L. ■ 75240 #048-12-1976 L1976 **AN** *074

MCELROY, Ryan D. 1935 MOTOR ST, CHILDREN'S MED CNTR OF DAL 75235 #048-12-2004 L2007 **PD** *100 †55

MCELYA, Martin G. 5917 BELT LINE RD 75254 #048-78-1995, ▲ 1996 **FM** *020

MC FARLAND, Julie. 8305 WALNUT HILL LN STE 10 75231 #048-14-1997 L1998 **OBG** *020

MCFARLAND, Regina Bell. 5110 TRACY ST 75205 #048-14-1998 L2001 **CHP** *020 †75 ‡

MC FARLAND, Warren Lynn. 5323 HARRY HINES BLVD 75390 #048-12-1965 L1965 **DR** *020 †80

MC FARLIN, Wendell L, Jr. 12200 PRESTON RD 75230 #048-14-1984 L1985 **FM** *020 †18

MC GARRY, Mary Theresa. 5151 HARRY HINES BLVD 75235 #048-12-1991 L1993 **IM** *020 †20

MC GAUGH, Ronald Clay, Jr. 1409 S LAMAR ST 75215 #004-01-1992 L2007 **FM** *020 †18 ‡

MC GILL, Ruth Gordon. 5950 SHERRY LN, STE 222 75225 #048-12-1974 L1974 **P** *062

MC GONNELL, Christopher M. 7777 FOREST LN, STE 445 75230 #041-07-1998 L2006 **PD** *020 †55

MCGOWAN, John Bradley. ■ 75204 #048-12-2004 L2004 **NS** *012

MC GRAW, Scott R. 13601 PRESTON RD, STE 900 75240 #048-02-1992 L1994 **AN** *020 †05

MC GREW, Jerry Conrad. 8200 WALNUT HILL LN, STE A 75231 #004-01-1957 L1962 **OPH P** *071 †35

MC GRORY, Patrick Simon. 1935 MOTOR ST, EMERGENCY ROOM 75235 #048-12-1996 L1999 **AN** *012 †55

MC GUIRE, Darren Keith. 5323 HARRY HINES BLVD 75390 #023-07-1993 L1994 **CD** *020 †20

MC GUIRE, Donald E, Jr. 75219 #025-01-1951 L1955 **OBG** *020 †30

MC HENRY, John Geiser. 5323 HARRY HINES BLVD MC, UT SOUTHWESTERN MEDICAL CE 75390 #041-13-1987 L2002 **OPH** *020 †35

MC HENRY, Michael Andrew. 810 N ZANG BLVD, P O BOX 781551 75208 #047-07-1993 L1995 **PM** *020 †60

MC INTOSH, Amy Lynn. 2222 WELBORN ST, HOSPITAL F 75219 #025-12-2001 L2006 **OP** *100

MCINTYRE, John Bradley. ■ 75209 #039-01-2007 *012

MC INTYRE, Kristi Jo. 8200 WALNUT HILL LN, STE 700 75231 #021-01-1982 L1991 **HEM IM** *020 †20

MCKAY, Lyndsey Allison. ■ 75219 #004-01-2007 **OBG** *012

MC KEE, John Cooper. 3500 GASTON AVE 75246 #048-02-1978 L1978 **OTO A** *020 †20

MCKENNA, Robert Wilson. 5323 HARRY HINES BLVD 75390 #026-04-1966 L1986 **HMP CLP** *020 †50

MC KENZIE, Richard Scott. 12606 GREENVILLE AVE, DEPT OF MEDICAL ONCOLOGY 75243 #030-05-1984 L1991 **HEM ON** *050 †20

MCKEY, Joanna Lynn. ■ 75381 #048-02-2008 *012

MC KINNEY, James M. ■ 75219 #048-02-1944 L1944 **PD** *071 †55

MC KINNEY, Susan E. 8210 WALNUT HILL LN, STE 230 75231 #048-12-1992 L1993 **IM** *020 †20

MC KOWN-PULLIAM, Rebecca. 221 W COLORADO BLVD, METHODIST PAVILION II 75208 #048-15-1983 L1983 **OBG** *020 †30

MC LAUCHLAN, Gail Levatin. 221 W COLORADO BLVD, STE 730 75208 #041-07-1995 L1996 **IM** *020 †20

MCMAHAN, Zsuzsanna Hortob. ■ 75219 #048-14-2006 **IM** *012

MC MENAMY, John Michael. ■ 75219 #048-14-2004 L2006 **DR** *012

MCMURTRY, Shaun A. ■ 75201 #048-13-2006 **FP** *012

MC NABB, Malcolm Wm. 1441 N BECKLEY AVE 75203 #065-06-1950 L1978 **OBG** *071 †30

MC NALLY, James A. 25 HIGHLAND PARK VLG, # 100-381 75205 #048-15-1975 L1976 **AN** *020 †20

MC NALLY, Lawrence B. 6029 BELT LINE RD 75254 #067-01-1963 L1982 **FM** *020 †18

MCNEIL, Candice Paula. 5323 HARRY HINES BLVD, DIV OF EMERGENCY MED 75390 #024-05-2006 **EM** *012

MCNULTY, Michael Jesse. ■ 75219 #048-12-2004 L2007 **ORS** *012

MC PHAIL, Gary L. 1935 MOTOR ST 75235 #048-12-2001 L2003 **PDP** *100 †55

MC PHAUL, Donald Martin. 8210 WALNUT HILL LN, STE 614 75231 #036-05-1972 L1973 **PM** *020 †60

MC PHAUL, John J, Jr. ■ 75229 #010-02-1956 L1976 **IM NEP** *071 †20

MC PHAUL, Michael John. ■ 75390 #048-12-1981 L1981 **IM** *050 †20

MC PHILLIPS, Andrea Miche. ■ 75231 #048-15-2008 *012

MC QUADE, Karen L. ■ 75214 #048-15-2003 **GS** *012

MC WHORTER, Gregory W. 13601 PRESTON RD # 1000W, PINNACLE ANESTHESIA CONSUL 75240 #020-02-1986 L1994 **AN** *020 †05

MEACHAM, Joseph Arden. 9330 POPPY DR STE 506 75218 #038-40-1975 L1993 **CD IM** *020 †20

MEADE, Ricardo Alberto. 411 N WASHINGTON AVE, STE 6000 75246 #649-52-1997 L2005 **PS** *020 †65

MEADOR, Robert Stewart. 3419 WESTMINSTER AVE, APT 318 75205 #048-12-1948 L1948 **PUD IM** *062 †20

MEARS, Brenda Jean. 1935 MOTOR ST, FIRST CARE CHILD MED CTR 75235 #048-12-1983 L1983 **PD** *020 †55 ‡

MEDINA, Carlos Alfredo. 7777 FOREST LN, STE C565 75230 #737-06-1996 L2004 **PD PDP** *020 †55

MEDINA, Francisco S. 528 CENTRE ST 75208 #016-76-1975, ▲ 1976 **FM OS** *020

MEDINA-RAMIREZ, Corazon. 6161 HARRY HINES BLVD, STE 121 75235 #748-01-1977 L1982 **AN** *020

MEDLOCK, Virgil B, III. 7777 FOREST LN, STE C106 75230 #048-12-1995 L1997 **ORS** *020 †40

MEDURI, Naga B. 9101 N CENTRAL EXPY, STE 150 75231 #035-03-2002 L2006 **D** *020 †15

MEEHAN, John Patrick. 4500 S LANCASTER RD 75216 #041-09-1975 L1990 **P** *030 †75

MEGGYESY, Christopher M. 3721 STANFORD AVE 75225 #048-12-1997 L1998 **AN** *020 †05

MEGISON, Stephen Mark. 1935 MOTOR ST RM H-310, DEPARTMENT OF SURGERY 75235 #021-06-1985 L1988 **PDS** *020 †85

MEGOWEN, Gretchen Lee. ■ 75214 #024-07-1980 L1981 **P OS** *020 †75

MEHDI, Muzaffer. 7910 BELT LINE RD 75254 #495-49-1970 L1977 **PD IM** *020 †55

MEHR, Elon Herschel. 13601 PRESTON RD, STE 900W 75240 #041-09-1987 L1999 **AN** *020 †05

MEHTA, Ankit Nikhil. 3600 GASTON AVE STE 550, WADLEY TOWER 75246 #495-01-2002 L2008 **IM** *012

MEHTA, Praveen S. 4500 S LANCASTER RD, HEALTH CARE SYSTEM 75216 #496-38-1989 L1991 **IM** *020 †20 ‡

MEHTA, Saumil A. 12606 GREENVILLE AVE, STE 120 75243 #495-76-1987 L1993 **IM** *020 †20

MEHTA, Sunil. ■ 75204 #048-04-2006 L2007 **P** *012

MEICHES, Mark Danl. 606 N WASHINGTON AVE 75246 #048-12-1988 L1989 **DR** *020 †80

MEIER, Joseph Howard. 8160 WALNUT HILL LN # 007 75231 #048-12-1988 L2001 **EM** *020 †16

MEISER, John Brennan. 7777 FOREST LN, STE B332 75230 #048-14-1995 L1996 **AI** *020 †20,55,03

MEJIA, Alejandro. 1411 N BECKLEY AVE, STE 268A 75203 #264-13-1995 L2003 **GS** *020 †85

MEJIAS, Maria Asuncion. 5323 HARRY HINES BLVD, DEPT OF PEDIATRICS 75390 #847-21-1995 L2008 **PDI** *100

MELAMED, Norma Bernice. 12810 HILLCREST RD STE 220 75230 #836-01-1978 L1983 **N** *020 †75

MELCHIODE, Gerald A. 8226 DOUGLAS AVE 75225 #049-01-1966 L1980 **PYA P** *020 †75

MELENDEZ, Elizabeth. 1441 N BECKLEY AVE, INFERTILITY/GYNECOLOGY/OBS 75203 #048-14-2001 L2005 **OBG** *020 †30

MELENDEZ, Maria Mercedes. ■ 75219 #038-43-2005 L2006 **PM** *012

MELLER, Stephen L. 13601 PRESTON RD STE 10 75240 #048-13-1998 L1999 **AN** *020 †05

MELMED, Edward Peter. 7777 FOREST LN # 210 75230 #836-01-1958 L1974 **PS** *020 †65

MELMED, Gavin M. ■ 75225 #048-12-2004 **ON** *012 †20

MELO JUNIOR, Silvio Wande. ■ 75219 #187-07-2001 **GE** *012 †20

MELTON, Larry Benton. 3601 SWISS AVE 75204 #048-13-1982 L1983 **NEP IM** *020 †20

MELTZER, David Wm. 8210 WALNUT HILL LN, STE 109 75231 #011-02-1975 L1983 **OPH** *020 †35

MELVIN, John Noble. ■ 75229 #048-12-1963 L1963 **OS AN** *020 †05

MENDELOFF, Eric Neil. 7777 FOREST LN, STE B115 75230 #005-14-1985 L2003 **TS** *020 †85,90

MENDELOW, Donald Arthur. 4500 S LANCASTER RD 75216 #016-42-1962 L1984 **OBG** *020 †30

MENDELSOHN, Dianne B. 5151 HARRY HINES BLVD 75235 #836-01-1974 L1977 **RNR** *040 †80

MENDEZ DE MACOSSAY, L. 9500 FOREST LN STE 11 75243 #649-01-1953 L1954 **PD OS** *071

MENDIOLA, Laura Leticia. ■ 75206 #048-12-2007 **IM** *012

MENDIZABAL, Susanna M. 4444 S HAMPTON RD, OAK WEST HEALTH CENTER 75232 #264-04-1981 L1986 **PD** *020 †55

MENDOZA, Charles C N. 5726 BELMONT AVE 75206 #649-14-1967 L1975 **FM PTH** *071

MENDOZA, Paul David. ■ 75218 #004-01-2007 **IM** *012

MENDRYGAL, Nikolas M. 5201 HARRY HINES BLVD, DEPT OF EMEGENCY MED 75235 #048-12-2003 L2006 **EM** *100 †16

MENENDEZ, Christopher A. 75214 #004-01-2002 **GS** *100

MENG, Jin. 5323 HARRY HINES BLVD 75390 #243-44-1983 L2002 **AN** *020

MENNEL, Robert Gary. 3535 WORTH ST, STE 110 75246 #041-01-1970 L1979 **ON IM** *020 †20

MENTER, Martin Alan. 3900 JUNIUS ST, STE 145 75246 #836-01-1966 L1976 **D** *020 †15 ‡

MENZEL, Carol Elaine. 7777 FOREST LN, BLDG C 75230 #034-01-1989 L1994 **IM** *020,28

MENZER, Leon. ■ 75229 #024-07-1964 L1975 **N** *071 †75

MERCAU DE GANDOLFO, Ana M. 5959 HARRY HINES BLVD, STE 314 75235 #132-02-1974 L1999 **IM** †20

MERCIER, David W. 5323 HARRY HINES BLVD 75390 #048-14-1990 L1991 **AN** *020 †05

MERIL, Scott S. 13601 PRESTON RD, STE 1000W 75240 #048-12-1989 L1991 **AN** *020 †05

MERRELL, Lewis Frederick. A7777 FOREST LN 75230 #021-01-1969 L1985 **ORS** *071 †40

MERRILL, Sonya L. 7777 FOREST LN STE B116 75230 #024-01-2000 L2003 **SME IM** *020 †20

MERRIMAN, Richard Charles. 712 N WASHINGTON AVE 75246 #025-01-1970 L1979 **RHU** *020 †20

MERRITT, James Hansel. 8230 WALNUT HILL LN, PB III, SUITE 508 75231 #048-14-1978 L1978 **OPH PS** *020 †35

MERWAT, Shehzad Nawaz. ■ 75204 #704-25-2001 L2007 **IM** *100 †20

MESARWI, Omar Abdulwahab. ■ 75206 #048-12-2007 **IM** *012

MESHACK, Valerie Vonne. 3803 BOULDER DR 75233 #039-01-1992 L1995 **CHP** *020 †75

MESSIER, Christopher Bria. ■ 75204 #021-05-2004 **DR** *012

METCALF, Boyd H. 381 CASA LINDA PLZ, RM 353 75218 #036-07-1953 L1963 **GS** *071 †85

METCALF, Charles Wm. ■ 75230 #016-11-1954 L1989 **MDM IM** *072 †20

METNI, Fouad N. 7777 FOREST LN STE A323 75230 #605-02-1964 L1972 **TS** *020 †85,90

METTMAN, Amy Katherine. ■ 75204 #038-41-2006 **OTO** *012

METZGER, Jeffery C. 5323 HARRY HINES BLVD 75390 #005-14-2002 L2005 **EM** *020 †16

MEWAR, Manas. 3600 GASTON AVE STE 550 75246 #048-12-2002 L2005 **IM** *100 †20

MEYAPPAN, Thiyagaraja R. 1935 MOTOR ST, CRITICAL CARE SERVICES 75235 #035-08-1999 L2006 **CCP** *100 †55

MEYER, Bruce Alan. 5323 HARRY HINES BLVD, UT SOUTHWESTERN MEDICAL 75390 #048-13-1984 L1988 **MFM OBG** *020 †30

MEYER, Dan Marshall. 5323 HARRY HINES BLVD, UNIV OF TEXAS SOUTWESTERN 75390 #005-14-1983 L1985 **TS GS** *020 †85,90

MEYER, Lisa. ■ 75209 #048-13-1992 L1993 **PTH PCP** *062 †50

MEYER, Morris Jacob. 13001 HILLCREST RD, # 216 75240 #836-01-1940 **NM DR** *071 †80,28

MEYER, Richard Lutz. 3600 GASTON AVE STE 261 75246 #048-04-1983 L1986 **PTH MM** *020 †50

MEYER, Steven L. 8440 WALNUT HILL LN, STE 700 75231 #836-03-1970 L1973 **CD IC** *020

MEYERHOFF, William Lee. 5323 HARRY HINES BLVD, SOUTHWESTERN MED SCHOOL 75390 #016-06-1966 L1975 **OTO NO** *071 †45 ‡

MEYERS, David Laurence. 1717 MAIN ST STE 5200, EM CARE INC 75201 #041-13-1975 L1976 **EM IM** *030 †20,16

MEYERS, Harry F. 7777 FOREST LN STE A109 75230 #038-40-1981 L1998 **GS EM** *020 †85

MEYERSON, Michael Allen. ■ 75230 #048-12-1993 L1994 **BBK** *100

MEYRAT, Richard B. ■ 75229 #048-02-2001 L2008 **NS** *100

MEZERA, Kimberly K. 5323 HARRY HINES BLVD, UT SOUTHWESTERN MEDICAL CE 75390 #048-12-1991 L1992 **HS** *020 †40

MIAO, Darryl. ■ 75243 #048-12-2002 L2005 **NPM** *012 †55

MICHAEL, Christopher B. 3600 GASTON AVE, STE 907 907 BARNETT TOWER 75246 #048-04-1995 L2001 **NS** *020 †25

MICHAEL, Ludwig A. 8440 WALNUT HILL LN, TEXAS MEDICAL & SURGICAL 75231 #035-19-1943 L1948 **OTO A** *020 †45

MICHAELIS, Christina L. 5201 HARRY HINES BLVD, PARKLAND HOSPITAL 75235 #048-12-2005 L2007 **IM** *012

MICHAELSON, Jerold Dennis. 8220 WALNUT HILL LN # 512 75231 #048-12-1967 L1967 **D GP** *020 †15

MICHAELSON, Paul Stanley. 5952 ROYAL LN, STE 253 75230 #048-12-1963 L1963 **N OS** *062 †75

MICKEY, Bruce Edward. 5323 HARRY HINES BLVD 75390 #048-12-1978 L1978 **NS** *020 †25

MIDDLEMAN, Benton Rider. 3600 GASTON AVE, STE 261 75246 #048-14-1993 L1994 **PTH** *020 †50

MIEARS, Barbara Ann. 6115 BERKSHIRE LN, STE 240 75225 #048-15-1984 L1985 **P** *074

MIERS, Jeb Stuart. 8210 WALNUT HILL LN, NORTH DALLAS INTERNAL MEDI 75231 #048-12-1977 L1977 **IM** *020 †20 ‡

MIERZWIAK, Donald S. ■ 75244 #028-34-1959 L1969 **CD IM** *071 †20

MIERZWIAK, Jesse Lee. SOUTHWESTERN MED, UNIV OF TEXAS 75390 #038-41-2007 **GS** *012

MIESCH, Margaret Louise. 8200 WALNUT HILL LN, FL 5 75231 #048-02-1986 L1987 **P** *020

MIHALIC, Angela. 1935 MOTOR ST, MEDICAL EDUCATION DEPARTME 75235 #048-12-1995 L1997 **PD** *020 †55

MIJARES, Daniel W. 8230 WALNUT HILL LN # 41 75231 #048-14-1999 L2002 **IM** *020 †20

MIKHAEL, Georges. 8 MEDICAL PKWY STE 106 75234 #605-02-1978 L1982 **CD** *020 †20

MIKLIUS, Audrey Bettina. 10260 N CENTRAL EXPY # 1 75231 #014-01-1988 L1997 **END IM** *020 †20

MILANI, John C. 1341 W MOCKINGBIRD LN, STE 710E 75247 #033-05-1977 L1978 **ORS SCI** *020

MILBURN, Joseph L, Jr. 3832 COLGATE AVE, OFC 75225 #048-12-1984 L1985 **IM** *020 †20

MILCHGRUB, Sara. 5323 HARRY HINES BLVD 75235 #935-01-1973 L1989 **PTH** *020 †50

MILES, Darryl Keith. 1935 MOTOR ST, DEPARTMENT OF CRITICAL CAR 75235 #005-02-1997 L2004 **PD** *020 †55

MILES, Jane Jasna. 6350 LBJ FWY, STE 252 75240 #957-08-1980 L2004 **CHP P** *020 †75 ‡

MILICI, Marjorie Rush. 9101 N CENTRAL EXPY, STE 420 75231 #048-14-1990 L1992 **PD** *020 †55

MILLARD, Mark Warren. 4004 WORTH ST, STE 300 75246 #048-12-1976 L1981 **PUD IM** *020 †20

MILLER, Barbra Sue. SOUTHWESTERN MED, UNIV OF TEXAS 75390 #038-41-2000 L2006 **GS** *100 †85

MILLER, Daniel Lawrence. 3604 LIVE OAK ST 75204 #048-04-1977 L1978 **R** *020 †80

MILLER, David Scott. 5323 HARRY HINES BLVD, J7-124 75390 #039-01-1977 L1991 **GO GYN** *020 †30

MILLER, Ed C. 8226 DOUGLAS AVE STE 533 75225 #048-04-1952 L1952 **D** *020

MILLER, Gary Wayne. 7777 FOREST LN, STE B238 75230 #048-12-1971 1971 **AN** *020 †05

MILLER, Gregory S. 13601 PRESTON RD, STE 900 75240 #048-12-1993 L1994 **AN** *020 †05

MILLER, Howard Brian. 4347 W NORTHWEST HWY, STE 120 PMB 342 75220 #025-01-1970 L1974 **P ADP** *020

MILLER, James Henry. ■ 75201 #039-01-2004 **FP** *012

MILLER, John Burr, III. 3600 GASTON AVE, BARNETT TOWER STE 703 75246 #048-12-1970 L1970 **OBG** *020 †30

MILLER, Linda Sue. ■ 75229 #048-02-1988 L1991 **IM** *020 †20

MILLER, Maisie O. 5909 HARRY HINES BLVD 75235 #048-02-1979 L1979 **PD** *020 †55

MILLER, Matthew J. 5323 HARRY HINES BLVD, STOP 9031 75390 #048-02-1993 L1994 **AN** *020 †05

MILLER, Nicole Michelle. 4500 S LANCASTER RD 75216 #004-01-1996 L1996 **FM** *020 †18

MILLER, Robin Louise. ■ 75233 #048-12-2003 L2006 **BBK** *012

MILLER, Rodney Thos. 8267 ELMBROOK DR, STE 100 75247 #025-01-1979 L1993 **PTH** *020

MILLER, Ronna Gail. ■ 75214 #048-04-1986 L1993 **PDS GS** *020 †85

MILLER, Rudolph H, III. 2997 LBJ FWY, STE 215 75234 #024-01-1979 L1985 **R** *020 †80

MILLER, Samuel Clifton. 3107 W CAMP WISDOM RD, STE 115 75237 #048-12-1971 1971 **FM CD** *020 †30

MILLER, Troy Lee, II. 10455 N CENTRAL EXPY, STE 109 75231 #003-01-1987 L1992 **EM** *020 †16

MILLER, Wayde Dirk. 13601 PRESTON RD STE 10 75240 #048-02-1992 L1994 **AN** *020 †05

MILLER, William Franklin. 5323 HARRY HINES BLVD, STOP 9031 75390 #038-06-1945 L1948 **PUD IM** *071 †20

MILLINGTON, Eidi Kaye. ■ 75222 #016-11-2001 L2008 **IM** *012

MILLS, Chadwick Michael. ■ 75219 #048-02-1997 L2001 **DR** *020 †80

MILLS, Jonathan Compton. ■ 75235 #048-12-2008 *012

MILLWEE, Marilyn Kay. 25 HIGHLAND PARK VLG, STE 100 PMB 309 75205 #422-01-1997 **PD** *100

MILNER, Michael Spencer. 3600 GASTON AVE, STE 609 75246 #021-06-1990 L1992 **OPH** *020 †35

MILSTEIN, Robert Ian. 7777 FOREST LN, STE 550 75230 #038-06-1975 L1976 **OBG** *020 †30

MIMS, Harold Maurice. 5909 HARRY HINES BLVD 75235 #012-01-1948 L1953 **GS** *071 †85

MIN, Douglas D. ■ 75238 #012-05-1999 L2001 **AI** *012 †55

MINEI, Joseph Paul. 5323 HARRY HINES BLVD 75235 #035-20-1984 L1991 **GS CCS** *020 †85

MING, Bristol. 303 E OVERTON RD, BLUITT FLOWERS CLINIC-COPC 75216 #836-01-1974 L1982 **IM** *020 †20

MINIGUTTI, Andrew P. 9528 WEBB CHAPEL RD 75220 #048-02-1994 L2002 **FM** *020 †18

MINNA, John Dorrance. 5323 HARRY HINES BLVD, HAMON CTR THER ONOLOGY RES 75390 #005-11-1967 L1992 **ON HEM** *050 †20

MINNIEFIELD, Nicole Elise. ■ 75248 #041-13-2003 L2003 **CD** *012 †20

MINODIN, Mike Odsinada. ■ 75231 #748-11-1982 L1998 **FM** *020 †18

MINTZ, Howard Martin. 8210 WALNUT HILL LN, STE 314 75231 #005-15-1977 L1983 **PUD CCM** *020 †20

MIRTSCHING, Barry Clinton. 7777 FOREST LN STE B242 75230 #048-14-1987 L1988 **ON HEM** *020 †20

MIRZA, Tariq. 12606 GREENVILLE AVE 75243 #704-16-1991 L2004 **PD** *020 †55

MIRZATUNY, Ardashes. 5963 LEWIS ST, ARTASHES MIRZATUNY MD 75206 #517-05-1979 L1981 **CHP P** *050

MITCHELL, Christopher Dru. ■ 75219 #039-01-2007 **GS** *012

MITCHELL, Damien H. 1935 MEDICAL DISTRICT DR, UT SOUTHWESTERN MEDICAL CE 75235 #048-04-2005 L2008 **PD** *012

MITCHELL, Ian Crichton. ■ 75219 #038-06-2003 **GS** *012

MITCHELL, Jere Holloway. 5323 HARRY HINES BLVD 75235 #048-12-1954 L1954 **CD** *050

MITCHELL, Teddy L. 12200 PRESTON RD 75230 #048-02-1987 L1988 **IM ISM** *020 †20

MITHANI, Aamir Haider. 3320 LIVE OAK ST 75204 #042-03-2000 L2003 **IM** *020 †20

MITHANI, Haider Ali. ■ 75243 #704-02-1958 L1983 **FM OPH** *020 †20

MITHILESH, Shubhada. ■ 75209 #496-07-1980 L2006 **IM** *020 †20

MITTAL, Alka. ■ 75204 #048-13-2004 **GE** *012 †20

MITTAL, Naveen Kumar. 1935 MOTOR ST, DIVISION OF PEDIATRIC GI 75235 #495-45-1985 L2004 **PD PG** *020 †55

MITTAL, Vivek. 4500 S LANCASTER RD, VA VA MEDICAL CENTER 75216 #495-36-2003 L2007 **IM** *100 †20

MITZ, Samuel R. 1441 N BECKLEY AVE 75203 #048-13-2001 L2002 **IM** *020 †20

MIZE, Charles Edward. 10716 PARK VILLAGE PL 75230 #023-07-1962 L1967 **MG PD** *040 †55

MIZE, Roby Dan. 8210 WALNUT HILL LN, LB 11 75231 #004-01-1968 L1973 **ORS** *020 †40

MOBLEY, Henry Brown. ■ 75223 #048-12-1954 L1954 **IM CD** *020 †20

MOCK, Presley M. 8440 WALNUT HILL LN, TEXAS MEDICAL & SURGICAL 75231 #048-13-1986 L1987 **OTO A** *020 †45

MODRALL, John Gregory. 5323 HARRY HINES BLVD, U OF TX/SOUTHWESTERN MC 75390 #007-02-1989 L1998 **VS** *020 †85

MOE, Orson Willy. 5323 HARRY HINES MED CTR 75390 #065-01-1982 L1989 **NEP** *020 †20

MOEIN, Mahshid. ■ 75248 #517-06-1998 L2007 **CHN** *100

MOGBO, Kirsten Ice. 1935 MOTOR ST, CHILD MED CTR OF DALLAS 75235 #025-01-1992 L1999 **DR** *020 †80

MOHAMED, Khadijah Abdul A. 8224 PARK LN STE 130, VICKERY HEALTH CENTER 75231 #704-16-1984 L1998 **FM** *020 †18

MOHAN, Alok. 5323 HARRY HINES BLVD MC, UT SOUTHWESTERN MEDICAL CE 75390 #496-17-1998 L2006 **IM** *100

MOHL, Paul Cecil. 5323 HARRY HINES BLVD 75235 #036-07-1971 L1976 **P** *040 †75

MOLBERG, Kyle Hayden. 5323 HARRY HINES BLVD 75390 #048-14-1985 L1986 **PTH** *020 †50

MOLDREM, Amy Waltrip. 5323 HARRY HINES BLVD 7TH, DEPARTMENT OF SURGERY 75390 #020-02-1999 L2003 **GS** *020 †85

MOLINA, Arthur. 3535 WORTH ST, STE 110 75246 #048-04-1994 L1995 **ON** *020 †20

MOLINA, Rodolfo. 7777 FOREST LN, STE C833 75230 #048-02-1990 L1993 **P** *020 †75

MOLL, Allan L. 10 MEDICAL PKWY, PLAZA 3 75234 #065-01-1993 L1995 **FM** *020

MOLLABASHY, Allaaddin. 411 N WASHINGTON AVE, STE 7000 75246 #017-20-1994 L2004 **ORS** †40

MOMIY, Janneth Paola. ■ 75223 #005-14-2006 **GS** *012

MOMPOINT, Alex. 9262 FOREST LN STE 101, METROPLEX ORTHOPEDICS, PA 75243 #035-06-1997 L2004 **PM** *020 †60

MONCRIEF, Christian Lee. 5939 HARRY HINES BLVD 75235 #045-01-1977 L1980 **TS** *020 †85,90

MONGA, Ashish Grover. 12700 PARK CENTRAL DR, STE 430 75251 #048-12-1997 L2003 **DR** *020 †80

MONGA, Narinder Kumar. 221 W COLORADO BLVD # 165 75208 #495-03-1969 L1980
CRS GS *020 †85,10

MONINGER, George A. 10 MEDICAL PKWY STE 102 75234 #048-14-1991 L1992
OPH *020 †35 ‡

MONK, Joe Edwin. 3600 GASTON AVE STE 654 75246 #048-02-1985 L1986 AN GS *020 †05

MONROE, George Alfred. 7777 FOREST LN STE C525, MED CITY HOSP-DALLAS 75230
#048-12-1965 L1965 PD OS *020 †55

MONTALVO, Jessica E. ■ 75235 #048-12-2004 L2008 OBG *012

MONTGOMERY, James Bertram. 5920 FOREST PARK RD, STE 600 75235 #048-12-1977 L1977
ORS OSM *020 †40

MONTGOMERY, James Chester. 7515 GREENVILLE AVE STE 70 75231 #021-05-1979 L1995
P ADM *020 †18,75

MONTGOMERY, Samuel James. 13601 PRESTON RD, STE 900 75240 #918-01-1964 L1973
AN *020

MONTI, Lauren B. 3600 GASTON AVE STE 560 75246 #048-15-1989 L1990 OBG *020 †20

MONTIGUE, Tre. 13601 PRESTON RD, STE 900 75240 #048-12-1995 L1999 AN *020 †05

MONTOYA, Elva Juanita. 10342 TRAILCLIFF DR 75238 #048-04-1979 L1982 PD *020

MOODY, James Aubrey. 221 W COLORADO BLVD # 155 75208 #048-02-1972 L1973
NS *020 †25

MOODY, Marilyn Kay. 2222 WELBORN ST, TEXAS SCOTTISH RITE HOSPIT 75219
#048-02-1978 L1978 PDR *040 †80

MOORE, Al Jos, Jr. 4131 N CENTRAL EXPY, METRO ANESTHESIA 75204 #021-05-1989 L1994
AN *020 †05

MOORE, Angela Yen. 3500 GASTON AVE 75246 #048-04-1992 L1993 D DMP *020 †15 ‡

MOORE, Carolyn Joy. 8440 WALNUT HILL LN, STE 510 75231 #048-12-1998 L2003 DR *020 †80

MOORE, Catherine Porter. ■ 75206 #051-04-2004 L2007 PEM *012 †55

MOORE, Daniel Shawn. 5303 HARRY HINES BLVD 75390 #024-07-1992 L2002 DR *020 †80

MOORE, Howard Austin. 3500 GASTON AVE 75246 #021-01-1973 L1975 ORS OSM *020 †40

MOORE, Hugh Leslie. ■ 75225 #048-12-1964 1964 PD *071 †55

MOORE, Michael Collins. 5939 HARRY HINES BLVD, STE 923 75235 #021-01-1967 L1968
HEM HO *020

MOORE, Robert Anthony. 3878 OAK LAWN STE 630 75219 #048-13-1973 L1973 P *020 †75

MOORE, Rodney Carl. 637 KESSLER LAKE DR 75208 #048-12-1960 L1960 GYN *020 †30

MOORE, S Halcuit, Jr. 3500 GASTON AVE 75246 #024-01-1935 L1938 PD *071 †55

MOORE, Sterling Emory. 12930 JASONCREST TRL 75243 #048-02-1957 L1957
RHU IM *020 †20

MOORE, Timothy Alan. 13601 PRESTON RD, STE 1000W 75240 #048-12-1985 L1986
AN *020 †05

MOORE, William H. 8350 N CENTRAL EXPY, STE M1025 75206 #048-14-1989 L1991
PD *020 †55

MOORE, Yondell Elvas. 3450 W WHEATLAND RD, STE 107 75237 #047-07-1965 L1970
U *020 †95

MOOTHA, Sudha Lakshmi. ■ 75205 #048-02-1991 L1992 PDE *020 †55

MOOTHA, Venkateswar. 5323 HARRY HINES BLVD, UT SOUTHWESTERN MED CTR 75390
#023-07-1993 L1998 OPH *020 †35

MOOTY, Robert Clark. ■ 75206 #048-15-2005 GS *012

MOOTZ, Ann Ratliff. ■ 75205 #048-12-1981 L1981 DR *020 †80

MOOTZ, Brady L. 5323 HARRY HINES BLVD 75235 #048-12-1984 L1985 AN *020 †05

MOPARTY, Bhavani. 3409 WORTH ST STE 700, TEXAS DIGESTIVE DISEASE CO 75246
#021-01-2000 L2007 GE *100 †20

MOPARTY, Deepa Adunuthula. ■ 75204 #021-01-2007 IM *012

MORALES, David. 3409 WORTH ST, STE 630 75246 #024-01-1994 L1997 HS *020 †65

MORALES, Marlene Elena. 3500 GASTON AVE 75246 #048-02-2006 OPH *012

MORA MORA, Pablo Felipe. 5323 HARRY HINES BLVD, UT SOUTHWESTERN MEDICAL
CE 75390 #270-01-1986 L1995 *020

MORAN, Brett A. 5323 HARRY HINES BLVD, DIV OF GENERAL INTERNAL ME 75390
#048-12-1994 L1995 IM *020 †20

MORCHOWER, Andrew Henry. ■ 75230 #021-01-2006 L2006 PM *012

MOREHEAD, John Mark. 12221 MERIT DR, STE 1060 75251 #048-12-1980 L1980
OTO FPS *020 †45

MOREY, Allen Frank. 5323 HARRY HINES BLVD, SOUTHWESTERN MED CTR 75390
#023-12-1987 L2000 U *020 †95

MORGAN, Christopher Alan. 13601 PRESTON RD, STE 900 75240 #039-01-1992 L1996
AN *020 †05

MORGAN, David Lee. 4350 ALPHA RD 75244 #048-12-1982 L1983 PTH HMP *020 †50

MORGAN, Howard William, Jr. 5323 HARRY HINES BLVD, DEPT NEUR SURG 75390
#047-06-1969 L1977 NS *020 †25

MORGAN, John R, Jr. 6331 PROSPECT AVE 75214 #048-02-1979 L1979 FM *020 †18

MORGAN, Samuel S. ■ 75238 #028-78-1950, ▲ L1950 PM *072

MORGAN, Thomas Lloyd. 4611 WALNUT HILL LN 75229 #048-14-2008 *012

MORI, Shailesh. 13601 PRESTON RD, STE 900 75240 #048-12-1992 L1993 AN *020 †05

MORRELL, Steven Gerard. 221 W COLORADO BLVD, PAVILION II SUITE 845 75208
#048-12-1982 L1983 AN *020 †05

MORRILL, Kevin Charles. 5323 HARRY HINES BLVD, UNIV TX SW DEPT NEURO SURG 75390
#048-12-1996 L1997 NS SCI *040

MORRIS, Brian Scott. 8210 WALNUT HILL LN, HARVILL-TSCHUMY CLINIC 75231
#023-07-1992 L2001 IM *020 †20

MORRIS, Charles Rudolph. 5909 HARRY HINES BLVD 75235 #056-05-1941 L1951
OS GS *071 †85

MORRIS, Eugene Ira. 7929 BROOKRIVER DR, STE 300 75247 #048-02-1974 L1974
GE IM *020 †20

MORRIS, Joseph J, Jr. 13601 PRESTON RD, STE 900 75240 #048-12-1990 L1991 AN *020 †05

MORRIS-HARRIS, Deborah G. 303 E OVERTON RD 75216 #024-01-1981 L2006 IM *020 †20

MORRISON, Blake Alan. 8230 WALNUT HILL LN STE 21 75231 #048-02-1998 L2003 HS *020

MORRISS, Frances Connally. 1935 MOTOR ST 75235 #048-12-1970 L1970 AN PD *020 †55,05

MORRISSEY, James Michael. 221 W COLORADO BLVD, PAVILION 2 STE 727 75208
#010-02-1994 L1996 PS *020 †65

MORRONE, Frank Chas. 8200 WALNUT HILL LN 75231 #010-01-1966 L1971 OBG *020 †30

MORROW, Paul R. 7557 RAMBLER RD STE 7 75231 #048-12-1992 L1993 AN *020 †05

MORROW, Philip Raymond. ■ 75238 #048-12-1954 L1954 GS *071 †85

MORSE, Brian Gregory. ■ 75205 #048-13-2004 L2008 DR *012

MORSE, Ladelle Lynne. ■ 75205 #048-13-2004 PM *012

MORSE, Lisa Steen. 5323 HARRY HINES BLVD 75235 #048-12-1987 L1988 AN *020 †05

MORTON, Katharine Ann. ■ 75205 #048-02-2006 PD *012

MOSCHOS, Elysia. 5323 HARRY HINES BLVD, DEPT OB/GYN UTSW 75390 #048-04-1997 L1999
OBG *020 †30

MOSELY, Erica Mallisye. 5201 HARRY HINES BLVD 75235 #010-03-2000 L2002 EM *020 †16

MOSKOWITZ, Mitchell Owen. 7777 FOREST LN STE A230, DALLS UROLOGY
ASSOCIATES 75230 #035-48-1987 L1993 U *020 †95

MOSTAFA ELSAWY, Bassem Mo. 3500 W WHEATLAND RD 75237 #915-02-1997 L2006
IMG *020 †18

MOTES, Jos Lafayette, Jr. ■ 75214 #001-02-1959 L1971 GS *071 †85

MOTGI, Gurubasappa V. 221 W COLORADO BLVD, STE 204 75208 #495-98-1981 L1992
N *020 †75

MOTOLA, Daniel Lewis. ■ 75219 #048-12-2008 *012

MOTTERSHAW, Ann Marie. 1717 MAIN ST STE 5200 75201 #021-06-1998 L2007 IM *020 †80

MUALLEM, Gaia. ■ 75229 #048-14-2008 *012

MUBARAK, Abdullah. 1411 N BECKLEY AVE 75203 #495-72-1993 L2006 IM *020 †20

MUELLER, James Bernhard. 7777 FOREST LN, STE B202 75230 #045-01-1983 L1992
AN PME *020 †05

MUELLER, John Geo. 7 MEDICAL PKWY 75234 #023-01-1965 L1977 AN OS *071

MUELLER, Stephen Edward. 3450 W WHEATLAND RD, STE 220 75237 #048-03-1978 L1986
PCC IM *020 †20

MUIR, John Robt. 7777 FOREST LN, STE B238 75230 #040-02-1968 L1975 AN GP *020 †05

MULEBA, Ndaya. 5303 HARRY HINES BLVD 75390 #041-14-1999 L2003 OBG *100

MULLICAN, Mary Ann A. 5323 HARRY HINES BLVD, UT SOUTHWESTERN MEDICAL CE 75390
#039-01-1966 L1967 R *020 †80

MUNCY, Paul A. 3434 SWISS AVE STE 420 75204 #047-06-1976 L1976 IM *020 †20

MUNFORD, Robert Sims. 5201 HARRY HINES BLVD 75235 #024-01-1970 L1978 ID IM *050 †20

MUNIZ, Jose Rafael. ■ 75235 #042-01-2007 IM *012

MUNOZ, Alan Kirt. 12200 PARK CENTRAL DR #410 75251 #021-05-1978 L1980
GYN GO *020 †30

MUNOZ, Louis Lee. 7777 FOREST LN, STE D110 75230 #030-05-1974 L1984
RO PHO *020 †55,80

MUNOZ, Raymond. 1411 N BECKLEY AVE 75203 #048-02-1996 L1999 IM *020 †20

MUNOZ, Shanan Brinson. 7777 FOREST LN STE B, THE NEUROLOGICAL CLINIC OF 75230
#039-01-1984 L1995 N OS *020 †20

MUNRO, Ian Ross. 7777 FOREST LN, THE CRANIOFACIAL CENTER 75230 #917-21-1963 L1986
PS *071 †65

MUNS, James A. ■ 75209 #048-15-2008 *012

MURALI, Sameer B. 5323 HARRY HINES BLVD, DEPT OF INTERNAL MED 75390 #048-12-2006
IM *012

MURALIRAJ, Vijay. SOUTHWESTERN MED, UNIV OF TEXAS 75390 #048-12-2007 GS *012

MURILLO, Ricardo Alonso. 3600 GASTON AVE, STE 708 75246 #715-01-1987 L1996
IM *020 †20

MURILLO, Sergio A. 6301 GASTON AVE, EAST TOWER, SUITE 400 75214 #018-03-2001 L2003
AN *020

MURILLO, Sergio L. 4343 MAPLE AVE STE 101 75219 #649-02-1952 L1958 FM OBG *020

MURPHY, Charles Michael. 12870 HILLCREST RD, STE 201 75230 #048-13-1981 L1985
IM *020 †20

MURPHY, Erin Heather. SOUTHWESTERN MED, UNIV OF TEXAS 75390 #010-02-2005 GS *012

MURPHY, Gerald D, Jr. 4144 N CENTRAL EXPY, STE 700 75204 #048-12-1989 L1990
AN *020 †05

MURPHY, James Mark. 5477 GLEN LAKES DR, AND DIAGNOSTIC CLINIC 75231
#039-01-1980 L1984 AN *020

MURPHY, Joseph S. 7777 FOREST LN, STE C300 75230 #048-13-1996 L1997 IM *020 †20

MURPHY, Joseph Thos. 5323 HARRY HINES BLVD, UTSWMC DEPT GS MC 9158 75235
#048-12-1989 L1990 PDS *100 †85

MURPHY, Mildred Laura. 1935 MOTOR ST, PICU DALLAS CHILDREN'S HOS 75235
#039-01-1998 L2005 CCP *012 †55

MURPHY, Susan Mary. 5323 HARRY HINES BLVD, UNIV OF TEXAS SWMC 75390
#539-02-1987 L1998 PM PHO *020 †20

MURRAY, Consuelo M. 2929 CARLISLE ST STE 200, SUITE 200 75204 #048-02-1976 L1979
ON HEM *020 †20

MURRAY, Du Bose White. 9262 FOREST LN, STE 101 75243 #012-05-1956 L1986 ORS *071 †40

MURRY, Maureen Anne. 1700 PACIFIC AVE STE 3300 75201 #048-12-1975 L1975 LM EM *062

MURUGEN, Claude S. ■ 75235 #048-12-2008 *012

MUSSELL, Joseph Robt. 3555 W WHEATLAND RD, DALLAS SOUTHWEST 75237
#041-13-1957 L1966 ON IM *020 †20

MUSSELMAN, David Roy. 8440 WALNUT HILL LN, STE 700 75231 #023-01-1986 L1992
CD IM *020 †20

MUSSLEWHITE, Lauren Ann. 3500 GASTON AVE, DEPT OF OB/GYN 75246 #048-14-2006
OBG *012

MYER, Brij Narain Singh. ■ 75244 #495-08-1958 L1973 IM CD *020 †20

MYER, Punam S K. ■ 75244 #495-03-1959 L1974 PHP CD *030

MYER, Shivani. 2700 N STEMMONS FWY 5TH FL, EAST TOWER 75207 #048-13-1993 L1998
P *020 †75

MYERS, Dan Allen. 3600 GASTON AVE, STE 1001 75246 #048-04-1962 L1962 CHP P *020 †75 ‡

MYERS, Larry L, Jr. 5323 HARRY HINES BLVD, UT SOUTHWESTERN MED CTR 75390
#016-02-1992 L2000 OTO HNS *020 †45

MYERS, Lynn Marie. 9229 LBJ FWY 75243 #039-01-1985 L1986 FM *030 †18

MYERS, Robert Ian. 3600 GASTON AVE, BARNETT TOWER STE 1001 75246
#917-09-1980 L1985 IM CD *020 †20

MYINT, Christina Mary. 8210 WALNUT HILL LN, STE 515 75231 #048-14-1995 L1997
IM *020 †20

MYINT, Hla. 8200 WALNUT HILL LN, COMM MENTAL HEALTH CENTER 75231
#495-01-1947 L1975 P *071 †75

NAARDEN, Allan Leslie. 7407 MALABAR LN 75230 #035-08-1964 L1969 N *020 †75

NABORS, Grover C. ■ 75225 #036-05-1946 L1952 OBG *071 †30

NACE, Edgar Paul. 12700 HILLCREST RD, STE 260 75230 #041-01-1965 L1981
P ADP *020 †75 ‡

NACPIL, Newell R. ■ 75220 #748-10-1981 L1985 *100

NADASY, Krisztina Anna. 3500 GASTON AVE 75246 #473-01-2003 L2007 IM *020 †20

NADLER, Eric Samuel. 3535 WORTH ST, STE 110 75246 #024-01-2000 L2005 HO *100 †20

NAFTALIS, Elizabeth Z. 5909 HARRY HINES BLVD 75235 #048-14-1986 L1987 GS *020 †85

NAFTALIS, Jerome Melvin. 5959 HARRY HINES BLVD, STE 500 75235 #033-05-1961 L1963
*020

NAFTALIS, Richard Craig. 5959 HARRY HINES BLVD, STE 500 75235 #048-14-1985 L1986
NS *020 †20

NAGARADDI, Venkatesh Nara. 7777 FOREST LN, STE B122 75230 #495-37-1998 L2007
CN *100 †75

NAGINENI, Lavanya Latha. ■ 75201 #495-11-1998 L2008 NMN *012

NAIFEH, Jerome Geo. 5949 SHERRY LN, STE 500 75225 #048-04-1972 L1973 TS GS *020 †90,85

NAIK, Nalini Mahendra. 2909 S HAMPTON RD, STE F228 75224 #905-01-1966 L1980 FM HEM *020

NAIK, Suraj A. ■ 75204 #048-12-2003 L2006 IM *100 †20

NAIR, Priya Kaimal. 712 N WASHINGTON AVE, STE 300 75246 #495-31-1994 L2001 RHU *020 †20

NAKAMURA, Alyson Kiyoko. 5151 HARRY HINES BLVD 75235 #003-01-2001 L2005 P *020 †75

NAKORNSRI, Saspin Tina. 303 E OVERTON RD 75216 #021-06-2000 L2003 IM *100 †20

NALE, Daniel Dean. 12200 PARK CENTRAL DR, STE 405A 75251 #048-14-1978 L1978 PD *020 †55

NALLY, Susan Ann. 221 W COLORADO BLVD, STE 318 PAVILLION I 75208 #041-01-1979 L1981 DR *071 †80

NAM, Young-Jae. ■ 75201 #583-02-1994 CD *012

NAMA, Vijay K. 3500 GASTON AVE, NEONATOLOGY DEPT #3 HOBLIT 75246 #495-45-1980 L2003 NPM *020 †55

NANDIPATI, Vidya. 12221 MERIT DR STE 460 75251 #665-01-1998 L2003 IM *020 †20

NAQVI, Fauzia Masood. 809 SINGLETON BLVD, DALLAS 75212 #704-02-1990 L1998 PD *020 †55

NAQVI, Syed Kamal M. 1935 MOTOR ST, SLEEP DISORDERS CENTER 75235 #704-02-1989 L2005 PDP *100 †55

NARAT, Roxana. ■ 75235 #048-02-2006 PD *012

NARDIZZI, Louis Robt. 8210 WALNUT HILL LN, STE 613 75231 #048-12-1975 L1975 IM OS *020

NASH, Gloria Hansel. ■ 75214 #041-01-1945 L1951 AN *071

NASIR, Dawood. 5323 HARRY HINES BLVD, UTSOUTHWESTERN MEDICAL CEN 75390 #704-15-1979 L1997 AN *020 †05

NASIR, Muhammad Anwer. 303 E OVERTON RD, BLUITT-FLOWERS HEALTH CTR 75216 #704-02-1989 L1998 IM *020 †20

NASSI, Shahryar Sean. 3500 W WHEATLAND RD, METHODIST CHARLTON MEDICAL 75237 #048-12-2004 L2008 IM *100

NASUHOGLU, Cem. 1935 MOTOR ST 75235 #902-19-1996 L2005 PDC *012 †55

NATIONS, Sharon Pond. 5323 HARRY HINES BLVD, STOP 9031 75390 #048-02-1981 L1981 N *074 †75

NAUFAL, Richard W. ■ 75254 #605-02-1968 L1978 DR *020 †80

NAVARRO, Erika. 4500 S LANCASTER RD, CSTP 116-A 75216 #649-31-1989 L2001 P *020 †75

NAYAK, Neeta Gopinath. 9229 LBJ FWY, BAYLOR GERIATRICS CENTER 75243 #495-09-1994 L1999 IM IMG *020 †20

NAYAK, Venkatesh Sujir. 12221 MERIT DR, STE 1610 75251 #495-37-1989 L2003 IM OPH *020 †20

NAYLOR, Rebekah Ann. 5323 HARRY HINES BLVD 75390 #047-05-1968 L1968 GS OBG *020 †85 ‡

NAZARIO, Hector Enrique. 5201 HARRY HINES BLVD, PARKLAND HOSPITAL- OFFICE 75235 #042-01-2002 L2005 IM *100 †20

NAZIR, Cid. ■ 75248 #005-12-2003 L2007 PM *100

NEAL, Troy Michael. ■ 75204 #039-01-2006 IM *012

NEBEN, Michael E. 13601 PRESTON RD, STE 900W 75240 #048-04-1990 L1991 AN *020 †05

NEEDHAM, Perry Q. 4500 S LANCASTER RD 75216 #048-02-1946 L1946 IM CD *072

NEEDLEMAN, Steven M. 13601 PRESTON RD, STE 900 75240 #016-42-1991 L1996 AN *020 †05

NEEL, Joseph Croskell. ■ 75225 #048-02-1943 L1943 GP *020 †60

NEELAKANTAN, Arvind. 7150 GREENVILLE AVE, GLAUCOMA ASSOCIATES OF TEX 75231 #495-17-1989 L2007 OPH *100 †35

NEELY, Joe B. 8325 WALNUT HILL LN, STE 225 75231 #048-12-1990 L1992 PD *020 †55 ‡

NEGRINE, John Peter. 411 N WASHINGTON AVE #7000 75246 #143-03-1985 *020

NEILAN, Ryan Eric. ■ 75204 #048-02-2008 *012

NEILL, James Norris. 9321 MOSS TRL, OF DAL 75231 #048-12-1970 L1970 DR *020 †80

NEIMAN, Richard Newton. 3988 HIGHGROVE DR 75220 #048-12-1957 L1957 P *020

NEIRA, Francisco X. 9429 EL CENTRO DR, STE 100 75214 #319-04-1986 L1998 FM *020 †18

NELSON, Arthur Glenn. ■ 75218 #048-12-1948 L1948 FM FPG *071

NELSON, Camron Eugene. 12200 PRESTON RD 75230 #048-14-1984 L1986 FM *020 †18

NELSON, Carey James. 13601 PRESTON RD STE 1000 75240 #048-14-1995 L1997 AN *020 †05

NELSON, David Bryan. 75219 #004-01-2007 OBG *012

NELSON, Joel Stephen. 8160 WALNUT HILL LN, STE 204 75231 #048-12-1983 L1983 OBG *075 †30

NELSON, John Douglas. 5323 HARRY HINES BLVD 75235 #026-04-1954 L1961 ID PD *040 †55

NELSON, Mark Stephen. 4500 S LANCASTER RD 75216 #048-12-1982 L1983 IM *020 †20

NELSON, Richard W. 5001 LBJ FWY STE 60 75244 #045-09-1968 L1981 FM *030 †18 ‡

NEMETH, Ira Robert. 2377 N STEMMONS FWY 75207 #010-01-2001 L2005 EM *100 †16

NEMUNAITIS, Jon Jos. 3535 WORTH ST, STE 110 75246 #038-06-1982 L1993 ON HEM *050

NEMUNAITIS, Michael C. 3535 WORTH ST, STE 110 75246 #038-43-2001 L2005 ON *012

NERENBERG, David J. 129 W 9TH ST 75208 #065-01-1972 L1978 GP *020

NESBITT, Julye Adele. 8210 WALNUT HILL LN, STE 310 75231 #001-02-1996 L1997 PCC *020

NESBITT, William Hampton. 5735 ANITA ST 75206 #048-14-1998 L1999 ICE *020 †20

NESSER, David Allen. 3604 LIVE OAK ST, STE 100 75204 #048-12-1975 L1978 IM NEP *020 †20

NESTLER, Eric Jonathan. 5323 HARRY HINES BLVD, DEPT PSYCHIATRY 75390 #008-01-1983 L2003 P *050 †75

NETTLES, Karl Matthew. DEPT RADIOLOGY, UNIV TX SW MED CTR 75390 #021-05-2005 L2008 DR *012

NEUBACH, Paul Arnold. 3434 SWISS AVE, STE 410 75204 #048-02-1975 L1975 IM *062 †20

NEUFELD, John Alonzo. ■ 75219 #005-12-1965 L1974 ORS *020 †40

NEUNERT, Cindy Elizabeth. ■ 75204 #051-07-2001 L2007 PHO *100 †55

NEUROHR, G Hunt. 6120 SHERRY LN 75225 #048-12-1981 L1981 PS *020 †85,65

NEVIN, Harlan Wells. 8440 WALNUT HILL LN, STE 440 75231 #012-01-1963 L1968 IM *040

NEWCOMER, Kelley L. ■ 75230 #048-12-1995 L1997 IM *020 †20

NEWCOMER, Mark Troy. 4163 PARK LN 75220 #048-12-1995 L1997 OTO *020 †45

NEWFELD, Edgar A. 10830 N CENTRAL EXPY, STE 100 75231 #016-06-1962 L1977 PDC PD *071 †55

NEWMAN, Gordon Harry. 5744 LYNDON B JOHNSON FWY, STE 150 75240 #035-09-1963 L1969 OPH *020 †35

NEWMAN, Martin Eric. ■ 75214 #154-07-2002 OBG *012

NEWMAN, Rita. ■ 75214 #154-07-2001 CHN *012

NEWMAN, Stephen Louis. ■ 75230 #047-06-1975 L1975 PD GE *020 †55

NEWSOM, Asa Armstrong, Jr. ■ 75230 #048-12-1947 L1947 OBG *071 †30

NEWSOM, Hamlet Tatum. 8220 WALNUT HILL LN, STE 314 75231 #001-02-1967 L1968 PS *020 †85,65

NEWSOME, Thos Willingham. 3600 GASTON AVE STE 904 75246 #023-07-1967 L1972 GS *020 †85 ‡

NEWTON, Patricia Ann. 8200 WALNUT HILL LN 75231 #038-40-1981 L1986 CHP *020 †75

NEWTON, William Garner. 8230 WALNUT HILL LN 75231 #027-01-1994 L2001 ORS *020 †40

NGO, Nghiem Q. 135 W 10TH ST 75208 #941-01-1971 L1982 GP PTH *020

NGUYEN, Buu. 5201 HARRY HINES BLVD 75235 #941-01-1963 L1978 PHP GP *020

NGUYEN, Colin. #011-04-2003 CHN *012

NGUYEN, Duy Tran. 5323 HARRY HINES BLVD, SOUTHWESTERN MED 75390 #018-03-2004 L2006 AN *012

NGUYEN, Dylan Vinh. 3920 WORTH ST 75246 #001-02-2003 L2007 AN *020

NGUYEN, Hoang D. 8220 WALNUT HILL LN, STE 505 75231 #048-14-1994 L1998 AN *020 †05

NGUYEN, Kenneth Cq. 14444 DALLAS PKWY, STE 101 75254 #005-02-2000 L2006 IM *020 †20

NGUYEN, Lam Nhu. ■ 75206 #048-12-2008 *012

NGUYEN, Langiao Thi. ■ 75219 #048-12-2008 *012

NGUYEN, Lynn. 5323 HARRY HINES BLVD, DEPT OF INTERNAL MED 75390 #048-12-2006 IM *012

NGUYEN, Mannhhai. ■ 75206 #048-16-2005 L2007 IM *100

NGUYEN, Ngo Khoi. 5323 HARRY HINES BLVD, DEPT OF ANESTH 75390 #046-01-2000 L2002 AN *020 †05

NGUYEN, Oanh Kieu. ■ 75204 #005-18-2007 IM *012

NGUYEN, Phuc Dinh. 5323 HARRY HINES BLVD 75390 #941-01-1975 L1983 RO *020 †80

NGUYEN, Phuong Thi. ■ 75206 #021-06-2006 PD *012

NGUYEN, Quan Bao. 3500 W WHEATLAND RD 75237 #021-05-2003 L2005 FM *020 †18

NGUYEN, Thai Quoc. 5323 HARRY HINES BLVD, SOUTHWESTERN MED 75390 #035-46-1999 L2005 NEP *100 †20

NGUYEN, Thanh-Nhan. 4500 S LANCASTER RD, ROAD (11C) 75216 #048-13-1991 L1992 IM *020 †20

NGUYEN, Tri T. 7777 FOREST LN, STE C300 75230 #048-12-1998 L2000 IM *020 †20

NGUYEN, Van M. 4500 S LANCASTER RD, VA MEDICAL CENTER 75216 #048-02-1998 L2000 IM *020 †20

NGUYEN-NGO, Hien Luong. 9 MEDICAL PKWY STE 305 75234 #048-04-1985 L1986 OPH *020 †35

NGWU, Samuel Chukwuka. 5959 HARRY HINES BLVD, STE 204 75235 #048-13-1994 L1997 IM *020 †20

NICHOLS, Hall Eugene. 7920 ELMBROOK DR STE 120 75247 #649-14-1981 L1983 FM *020 †18

NICHOLS, Jaime Diane. 1935 MOTOR ST 75235 #039-01-2004 L2007 PD *100 †55

NICHOLS, Michelle J. ■ 75204 #048-12-2002 L2007 P *020 †75

NICHOLS, Timothy Dale. 12606 GREENVILLE AVE, STE 160 75243 #023-01-1987 L1992 RO *020 †80 ‡

NICHOLS-HOSTETTER, Susan. 5201 HARRY HINES BLVD 75235 #048-14-1983 L1983 DR *020 †80

NICKEY, Sue Lester. 5515 GLEN LAKES DR 75231 #047-06-1952 L1972 P *020

NICOLAOU, George Theodore. 75225 #048-02-1945 L1945 P *072 †75

NIECE, Julia Allyson. 1935 MOTOR ST 75235 #028-46-2002 L2007 PHO *012 †55

NIKAIDOH, Hisashi. 1935 MOTOR ST 75235 #572-03-1959 L1977 PCS PDS *020 †85,90

NILASENA, David S. 75218 #048-13-1986 L1987 GPM *020 †70

NINALA, Ranil Ronald. 6612 HARRY HINES BLVD, CTR FOR MUSCULOSKELETAL ME 75235 #005-12-1992 L1996 PM *020 †60

NIROOMAND, Farhad. 2501 OAK LAWN AVE STE 450 75219 #012-01-1988 L1995 D *020 †15

NIXON-FULTON, Jackie Lee. 9330 AMBERTON PKWY 75243 #048-12-1979 L1979 D IG *020 †15

NIZAM, Ahmad. ■ 75206 #875-01-2005 L2007 *100

NOACK, John M. 8440 WALNUT HILL LN, STE 110 75231 #048-12-1998 L2003 ORS *020 †40

NOBLE, Marvin Jacob. 8350 MEADOW RD 75231 #048-12-1961 L1961 AN OS *071 †05

NOBOA, Fausto Enrique. 1441 N BECKLEY AVE 75203 #319-01-1972 L1976 PUD IM *020 †20

NOCHUMSON, Joshua A. ■ 75204 #048-12-2003 GS *012

NOCHUMSON, Monica Yawen. ■ 75235 #048-12-2006 IM *012

NOE, Carl Edward. 3600 GASTON AVE, STE 360 75246 #048-13-1984 L1985 AN *020 †05

NOKLEBERG, Jane Ellen. 8160 WALNUT HILL LN, WALNUT HILL OBSTETRICS & 75231 #016-42-1995 L1997 OBG *020 †30

NOMANBHOY, Fatema. 5323 HARRY HINES BLVD, SOUTHWESTERN MED 75390 #021-01-2006 L2008 P *012

NORCROSS, James D. 5323 HARRY HINES BLVD, UNIV OF TX SW MED CTR 75390 #048-15-1991 L1993 CHP P *020 †75

NORCROSS, William Harold. 10455 N CENTRAL EXPY, STE 109 75231 #048-13-1981 L1981 EM *020 †20,16

NORMAN, Natalie D. ■ 75206 #048-13-2007 IM *012

NORRINGTON, Eric Geo. ■ 75248 #035-09-1939 L1950 OBG *071 †30

NORTH, Carol S. 6363 FOREST PARK RD, STE 651 75390 #028-02-1983 L2007 P *050 †75

NORTH, Richard Ralph. 7777 FOREST LN STE B116 75230 #065-05-1959 L1967 N SME *071 †75

NORTH, Robert Lee. ■ 75254 #021-05-1955 L1972 IM CD *071 †20

NORTON, Dee Hart, Jr. 75225 #048-12-1959 L1959 OBG *071 †30

NORTON, Linda Ann Eck. 5430 LBJ FWY STE 1200, III LINCOLN CENTRE 75240 #036-07-1971 L1976 FOP *062 †50

NORWOOD, James Timothy. 3600 GASTON AVE, STE 300 75246 #048-12-1980 L1980 OBG *020 †30 ‡

NUANGCHAMNONG, Nina. ■ 75235 #048-12-2008 *012

NUGENT, Rod M. ■ 75230 #048-12-1967 L1967 PTH *071 †50

NUMAJIRI, Akira S. 4004 WORTH ST STE 100, BAYLOR GERIATRICS CENTER 75246 #048-02-1992 L1993 IM *020 †20

NUNEZ, Michael John. 8230 WALNUT HILL LN 75231 #036-07-1991 L1993 GE *020 †20

NURENBERG, Michael Edward. ■ 75225 #024-05-2001 L2004 NEP *100

NURENBERG, Pamela. 2222 WELBORN ST 75219 #048-12-1982 L1986 DR *020 †80

NUSBAUM, Jean Marie. 6757 ARAPAHO RD STE 711, BOX 335 75248 #026-04-1989 L2000 GP *020 †05

NUSS, Geoffrey Robert. ■ 75219 #036-05-2005 L2007 U *012

NUSSENZVEIG, Daniel Ronss. ■ 75204 #187-04-1980 L2005 HMP *100 †50

NWACHUKWU, Franklin Ginik. 4500 S LANCASTER RD 75216 #690-04-1992 L2005 IM *020

NWANGUMA, Charles. 4500 S LANCASTER RD, LOGAN REGIONAL CANCER CENT 75216 #690-04-1983 L1999 RO *020 †80

NWARIAKU, Ohwofiemu E. 5323 HARRY HINES BLVD, STOP 9031 75390 #690-01-1987 L1994 GS *020 †85

NYMAN, Randall Day. ■ 75206 #016-11-1944 L1949 PD *071 †55

OBEL, Owen Abraham. 4500 S LANCASTER RD, CARDIOLOGY-111A 75216 #836-01-1986 L2007 *020

■ = Address Information Privacy Protected

O'BRIEN, Erin Collen. ■ 75206 #012-05-2006 PD *100
O'BRIEN, John Chas, Jr. 3600 GASTON AVE, STE 958 75246 #028-34-1969 L1970 OTO SO *020 †85
OCHANI, Teekam Das. 4500 S LANCASTER RD, ANESTHESIA 112A 75216 #704-16-1990 L2005 AN *020 †05
OCHOA, Ernest Ronald. ■ 75218 #025-01-1992 L1992 U *020
O'CONNELL, Anthony James. 7777 FOREST LN BLDG C, SUITE 828 75230 #033-05-1993 L1998 OBG *020 †30
O'CONNELL, Ellen Jane. ■ 75204 #028-34-2002 L2004 ETX *100 †16
O'CONNOR, Andrew Mary. 17194 PRESTON RD, STE 128 75248 #539-02-1971 L1977 P *075
O'CONNOR, Angela Delese. 17194 PRESTON RD, STE 128 75248 #539-02-1972 L1977 FM *020
O'CONNOR, John Kevin. 3500 GASTON AVE, HOBLITIZELLE 1 75246 #021-01-1998 L2006 RO *020 †20
ODELL, Dale Sylvester. 8200 WALNUT HILL LN, DEPT PATH 75231 #026-04-1973 L1980 PTH *020 †50
O'DELL, David Melton. ■ 75382 #048-12-1973 L1973 LM OBG *062
ODEN, Jon D. 5323 HARRY HINES BLVD MC, UT SOUTHWESTERN MEDICAL CE 75390 #048-15-1997 L1998 PDE *020 †55
ODOM, Floyd Clark. 8220 WALNUT HILL LN, STE 205 75231 #048-13-1972 L1972 CRS *020 †85,10
ODSTRCIL, Elizabeth Anne. ■ 75204 #048-12-2003 GE *012 †20
ODVINA, Clarita Villaluz. 5323 HARRY HINES BLVD, CTR FOR MINERAL & METABLSM 75390 #748-10-1977 L1998 END IM *020 †20
OETMAN, Bradley James. 13601 PRESTON RD, STE 900W 75240 #005-12-2001 L2005 AN *020 †05
OFFENBACH, Howard A. 1110 N BUCKNER BLVD 75218 #048-13-1979 L1979 OBG EM *075 †30
OFOMATA, Ikechukwu Robert. 1350 N WESTMORELAND RD, WESTMORELAND ADULT O P CLI 75211 #690-07-1984 L2003 P PYG *020
OGBURN, James. 4350 ALPHA RD 75244 #048-14-1991 L1992 PTH *020 †50
OGUNJI, Oreoluwa Tolulope. 4400 W UNIVERSITY BLVD 75209 #048-12-2003 L2005 EM *100
OGUNNAIKE, Babatunde O. 5201 HARRY HINES BLVD, DEPARTMENT OF ANESTHESIOLO 75235 #690-08-1983 L1999 AN *020 †05
OGUNRO, Olayinka Ernest. 7989 W VIRGINIA DR, STE 105 75237 #803-05-1968 L1978 HS ORS †40
OKADA, Pamela Joy. 5323 HARRY HINES BLVD, UT SOUTHWESTERN MEDICAL CE 75390 #021-01-1990 L1996 PD PEM *012
OKECHUKU, Theodore Emeka. 6757 ARAPAHO RD, STE 711 PMB 335 75248 #690-02-1981 L2000 AN PD *020 †05,55
OKUYAMA SASAKI, Sonia. 5323 HARRY HINES BLVD, DEPT OF INT MED 75390 #737-06-2004 IM *012
OLAOLORUN, Akintayo David. 5201 HARRY HINES BLVD, PMH HOUSESTAFF MIRM 75235 #690-07-1982 GS *100
O'LEARY, Jacqueline G. 3500 GASTON AVE, BAYLOR UNIV. MED. CTR 75246 #005-02-1999 L2001 GE *020 ‡
OLIAI, Bahram. 8267 ELMBROOK DR, PROPATH LABORATORY 75247 #016-11-1998 L2006 PTH PCP *062
OLIVEIRA, Marcia Jill. 7777 FOREST LN STE C210 75230 #048-13-1997 L1998 OBG *020 †30
OLIVEIRA, Wanderley. 5959 HARRY HINES BLVD, STE 1030 75235 #649-14-1970 L1974 OBG *020 ‡
OLIVER, Frank Edmond. 7777 FOREST LN 75230 #048-12-1978 L1983 OBG *020 †30
OLIVER, George Reinhold. 3834 CONSTITUTION DR 75229 #048-12-2003 L2008 ON *012 †20
OLIVER, Patricia V. 12221 MERIT DR, STE 1610 75251 #048-13-2000 L2003 PD *020 †55
OLIVIERI, Julio Cesar. 7525 MILITARY PKWY 75227 #042-01-1992 L1997 IM *020
OLMSTED, William R. 8330 MEADOW RD STE 114 75231 #048-12-1990 L1992 CHP *072
OLSON, Craig Howard. DEPT OF GEN SURG, UNIV OF TX SW MED SCH 75390 #018-03-2003 L2008 GS *012
OLSON, Edwin Geo. 221 W COLORADO BLVD, STE 831 75208 #008-01-1975 L1992 CD IM *020 †20
OLSON, Micah Lynn. 5323 HARRY HINES BLVD, SOUTHWESTERN MED 75390 #003-01-2003 L2006 PDE *012 †55
OLTMANN, Sarah. ■ 75229 #048-15-2004 GS *012
OMAR, Anees Javed. 12221 MERIT DR STE 460 75251 #016-06-2001 L2006 IM *020 †20
OMAR, Hythem Adnan. 5323 HARRY HINES BLVD 75390 #021-06-2000 L2003 DR *020 †80
OMAR, Sadia. 8160 WALNUT HILL LN, LANE SUITE104 75231 #048-02-1996 L1997 OBG *020 †30
ONACA, Nicholas. 3500 GASTON AVE, 4 ROBERTS, TRANSPLANT SERV 75246 #781-01-1998 L2004 TTS SO *020
O'NEAL, Barry Lee. 4500 S LANCASTER RD, VETERANS AFFAIRS HOSPITAL 75216 #048-12-1971 L1971 IM *020 †20
O'NEILL, Thomas Joseph, Jr. ■ 75215 #021-05-2003 DR *012
ONG, Soon Chao Say. 3650 N BUCKNER BLVD # 108 75228 #748-02-1966 L1980 IM NEP *020 †20
ONTIVEROS, Jorge Anthony. 1151 N BUCKNER BLVD, STE 408 75218 #048-02-1996 L1999 IM *020 †20
ONUR, Kutsi. 3310 LIVE OAK ST STE 250, LB 15 75204 #902-05-1970 L1998 PD DIA *020 †55
ONUR, Nesrin. 8000 SOVEREIGN ROW 75247 #902-05-1971 L1978 PTH CLP *062 †50
OPPEDAL, Rebecca J. ■ 75235 #048-12-2008 *012
ORAL, Deniz. 5323 HARRY HINES BLV, UNIV TX 75235 #902-05-1996 OPH *020
ORENSTEIN, Harry Herman. 411 N WASHINGTON AVE, STE 5300 75246 #035-01-1979 L1986 ORS *020 †85,65
ORFALY, Hayan. 6901 SNIDER PLZ STE 130 75205 #875-01-1985 L2007 IM *020 †20
O'ROURKE, Brian Donovan. 3500 GASTON AVE, AMERICAN RADIOLOGY 75246 #016-43-1998 L2006 RNR *020 †80
OROZCO, Catalina. 9301 N CENTRAL EXPY, STE 675 75231 #264-16-2000 L2007 RHU *100 †20
ORR, Douglas Wayne. 3535 WORTH ST, STE 200 75246 #047-05-1978 L1990 ON HEM *020 †20
ORR, Nathan Terry. 75235 #048-12-2008 *012
ORR, William R, Jr. 4205 N HALL ST 75219 #004-01-1952 AN *071
ORSAK, Catherine B. 4500 S LANCASTER RD, DALLAS VA MC MENTAL HEALTH 75216 #048-04-1990 L2007 P *020 †15
ORTEGA, Maria Elena. 1935 MOTOR ST, DEPT OF ANES 75235 #048-12-1973 L1978 AN CCM *020 †05
ORTEN, Steven Stacy. 5005 LBJ FWY STE 17 75244 #039-01-1992 L2004 OTO *020 †45
ORTIZ, Kathryn A. 10405 E NORTHWEST HWY, STE 100 75238 #048-02-1986 L1987 CHP *020
ORTIZ, Vanessa. ■ 75218 #042-01-1996 L2005 ON *020
OSAKWE, Adaora Ifeyinwa. 5323 HARRY HINES BLVD, DIV OF EMERGENCY MED 75390 #012-05-2006 EM *012

OSBORNE, Cynthia R. 3535 WORTH ST, STE 110 75246 #048-02-1996 L1999 IMG *020 †20
OSBORNE, Donald. 12201 MERIT DR STE 420 75251 #048-13-1983 AN *020 †05
OSBORNE, Walter Geo. 4500 S LANCASTER RD, DALLAS VETERANS ADMINISTRA 75216 #048-02-1975 L1975 EM GP *020 †16
OSBORNE, William Mays. 5959 HARRY HINES BLVD, STE 804 75235 #048-04-1959 L1959 ORS *071 †40
OSBORNE, William Phillip. 1327 EMPIRE CENTRAL DR 75247 #048-02-1966 L1966 OM *020
O'SHAUGHNESSY, Joyce Ann. 3535 WORTH ST, STE 110 75246 #008-01-1982 L1997 ON IM *030 †20
OSIBAMOWO, Abiodun O. 11910 GREENVILLE AVE 75243 #690-06-1985 L1999 IM *020 †20 ‡
OSIER, Charles Joseph, Jr. ■ 75229 #012-05-2007 ORS *012
OSTAPOFF, Katherine Tatij. SOUTHWESTERN MED, UNIV OF TEXAS 75390 #036-05-2007 GS *012
OSTROW, David E. 221 W COLORADO BLVD, PAVILION I STE 155 75208 #041-02-1964 L1980 NS *020 †25
O'SUILLEABHAIN, Padraig. 5323 HARRY HINES BLVD 75390 #539-03-1991 L1998 N *020 †75
OSWALD, Catherine Carter. ■ 75219 #004-01-2007 PD *012
OTA, Floyd Shizuo. 1935 MOTOR ST, EMERGENCY DEPT 75235 #014-01-1999 L2002 PD *020 †55
OTTO, James Martin, Jr. 3600 GASTON AVE STE 1004 75246 #048-12-1990 L1991 IM *020 †20
OU, Jiafu. 5323 HARRY HINES BLVD, DEPT OF INT MED 75390 #243-21-1995 L2008 IM *012
OUTHOUSE, Karma Cookson. 5323 HARRY HINES BLVD, U TX SOUTHWESTERN SCH 75390 #048-14-2004 L2006 P *012
OWEN, David Bruce. 7777 FOREST LN, STE A307 75230 #048-13-1981 L1981 CHN PD *020 †55,75
OWEN, Heather Shipman. ■ 75243 #048-02-2005 L2007 EM *012
OWEN, Stuart Frederick. 3600 GASTON AVE, STE 1004 75246 #025-01-1977 L1980 IM *020 †20
OWENS, Fred Delano. 3600 GASTON AVE STE 1103 75246 #020-02-1959 L1972 OTO *020 †45
OWENS, Robert Malcolm. 3600 GASTON AVE 75246 #048-02-1992 L1999 OTO *020 †45
OXFORD, Lance Edward. 411 N WASHINGTON AVE, STE 2800 75246 #048-12-1999 L2003 OTO *100 †45
OYSTER, Christina Ann. ■ 75229 #048-12-2003 CHP *012
OYULA, Ignatius Pancrass. 4500 S LANCASTER RD 75216 #577-01-1997 L2004 IM *020 †20
OZ, Orhan Kemal. 5323 HARRY HINES BLVD, SW MED CTR DEPT RADIOLOGY 75235 #005-11-1991 L1993 NR *020 †80
OZA, Umesh D. 712 N WASHINGTON AVE, AMERICAN RADIOLOGY 75246 #048-14-1999 L2005 NM R *020 †80,28 ‡
OZUMBA, Donald Okey. 3523 MCKINNEY AVE 75204 #048-12-1999 L2005 OSM *100
PACHECO, Maria Fides M. ■ 75204 #748-02-1994 L2002 SCI *020 †60
PACHIGOLLA, Gowri. ■ 75209 #048-04-2004 OPH *012
PACINI, Eric Louis. 7232 GREENVILLE AVE, STE 435 75231 #041-13-2004 CD CD *012 †20
PACKARD, Dighton Carl. 3500 GASTON AVE 75246 #048-13-1974 L1974 EM *030 †16
PADALECKI, Jeffrey Ryan. ■ 75208 #048-14-2006 ORS *012
PADILLA, Constantino. 5909 HARRY HINES BLVD, DPT SURG 75235 #649-02-1971 L1976 GS *100
PADILLA, Marlon Daymond. 1201 MAIN ST, STE P350 75202 #005-15-1984 L1997 EM CCM *020
PADRON, Nick A. 7125 MARVIN D LOVE FWY, STE 107 75237 #048-13-1986 L1987 FM OM *020 †18
PAI, Sher-Lu. ■ 75218 #048-14-2006 GS *012
PAK, Charles Yong Chul. 5323 HARRY HINES BLVD, MC 8885 75235 #016-02-1961 L1972 IM *050
PAKAKASAMA, Samart. 3443 MAHANNA ST # 121 75209 #891-02-1992 PHO *100
PALACHERLA, Jithendranath. 5323 HARRY HINES BLVD, UTSW/GIM/ MC 8889 75390 #495-62-1997 L2005 IM *020
PALACIO, Natalia Angela. 8200 WALNUT HILL LN 75231 #132-10-2003 IM *012
PALACIOS, Elizabeth Anne. 9330 POPPY DR, MEDICINE 75218 #048-02-1988 L1990 IM *020 †20
PALACIOS, Luis Cardenas. 6333 E MOCKINGBIRD LN, STE 126 75214 #048-02-1985 L1986 FM FSM *040 †18
PALMER, Barron Markf. ■ 75201 #017-20-2001 L2004 CRS *012 †85
PALMER, Biff Franklin. 5323 HARRY HINES BLVD, U OF TX SW MED CTR 75390 #048-12-1981 L1981 NEP IM *040 †20
PALMER, David Odell. 3535 TRAVIS ST, STE 210 75204 #027-01-1974 L1976 AN *020 †05
PALMER, Lawrence Robt. 5323 HARRY HINES BLVD 75390 #143-01-1977 L1995 FM OS *020 †18
PANCORVO, Carlos Enrique. 3450 W WHEATLAND RD, STE 430 75237 #429-02-1993 L2000 IM *020 †20
PANDIAN, Geetha. 5323 HARRY HINES BLVD, DEPT OF P M R 75390 #495-95-1971 L1977 PM *020 †60
PANDIT, Rajiv. 221 W COLORADO BLVD, STE 943 PAVILLION II 75208 #016-01-1995 L2001 OTO *020 †45 ‡
PANDYA, Amit Girish. 5323 HARRY HINES BLVD 75390 #048-12-1985 L1986 D IM *020 †20,15
PANSICK, Bob Lee. 12200 PARK CENTRAL DR, STE 180 75251 #041-02-1978 L1983 OPH *020 †35
PAO, Julie. 12200 PARK CENTRAL DR, STE 403 75251 #048-13-1986 L1988 OBG *020 †20,30
PAPAVASILIOU, Pavlos. ■ 75204 #048-14-2005 GS *012
PAPLOMATA, Elisavet. 8200 WALNUT HILL LN, PRESBYTERIAN HOSP-MED 75231 #902-07-2001 *100
PAPO, Michele Cecile. 7777 FOREST LN, STE D569 75230 #654-01-1985 L1997 CCP PD *020 †55
PARANJAPE, Geeta S. 7777 FOREST LN 75230 #495-28-1986 L2003 CLP BBK *062
PARANJPE, Pooja D. ■ 75219 #048-12-2005 L2007 IM *012
PARAS, Dante Magistrado. 13601 PRESTON RD, STE 1000W 75240 #748-01-1977 L1984 AN *020 †05
PARDUE, Ayten S. ■ 75229 #902-03-1955 L1964 HEM ON *071
PAREKH, Monica Suryakant. ■ 75226 #048-04-2003 PD *020
PARIKH, Ashesh Shirish. 7515 GREENVILLE AVE, STE 710 75231 #016-06-2001 L2007 VIR *020 †80
PARIKH, Sachin Rajendra. ■ 75219 #028-46-2005 DR *012
PARIKH, Shailja Vrajesh. ■ 75219 #028-46-2004 L2007 CD *012 †20
PARITI, Sreevalli. 5323 HARRY HINES BLVD, SOUTHWESTERN MED 75390 #495-11-2001 NEP *012 †20
PARK, Andrew Eunkoo. 3900 JUNIUS ST, STE 705 75246 #016-06-1997 L2003 ORS *020 ‡
PARK, Betty Lee. 75225 #016-06-2001 L2004 D *020
PARK, James Byung R. 7150 GREENVILLE AVE, STE 500 75231 #005-15-1991 L1998 CD *020 †20

■ = Address Information Privacy Protected

PARK, Ken. 8200 WALNUT HILL LN 75231 #048-02-1998 L1999 **IM** *020 †20
PARKER, Clarence R. 3636 DICKASON AVE, SUITE 75219 #048-12-1949 L1949 **PYA P** *075
PARKER, Keith Langston. 5323 HARRY HINES BLVD J610, UT SOUTHWESTERN MEDICAL CT 75390 #028-02-1981 L1997 **END IM** *050
PARKER, Madge Ann. 5445 LA SIERRA DR 75231 #048-12-1965 L1965 **DR** *020 †80
PARKER, Patrice Stephens. 5909 HARRY HINES BLVD 75235 #048-12-1979 L1979 **PTH** *020 †50
PARKER, Susanna. 8230 WALNUT HILL LN, STE 508 75231 #048-14-1979 L1979 **P** *030 †75
PARKER, Thornwell Hay, III. 8230 WALNUT HILL LN, STE 808 75231 #048-04-2001 L2006 **DS PS** *020
PARKER, Thos Foreman, III. 1420 VICEROY DR 75235 #021-05-1966 L1973 **NEP IM** *030 †20
PARKER, William Lee. 909 N WASHINGTON AVE 75246 #039-01-1956 L1957 **PM** *071 †60
PARKEY, Robert Wayne. 5323 HARRY HINES BLVD # RA 75390 #048-12-1965 L1965 **NM R** *030 †80,28
PARKS, Donna Jean. 7230 CENTENARY AVE, DONNA PARKS MD 75225 #048-12-1964 L1964 **PD OS** *020 †55
PARKS, Gregory Martin. ■ 75218 #048-12-2008 *012
PARKS, Robert Irvin. 6301 GASTON AVE, EAST TOWER SUITE 400 75214 #048-12-1972 L1972 **AN** *020 †05
PARMAR, Dipak Navnitlal. 5323 HARRY HINES BLVD 75390 #917-21-1993 **OPH** *100
PARMAR, Rohit Jamnadas. 621 N HALL ST STE 500 75226 #917-02-1989 L1996 **CD** *020 †20
PARMAR, Simrit. 5323 HARRY HINES BLVD NC, UT SOUTHWESTERN MEDICAL CE 75390 #495-43-1998 L2005 **HO** *100 †20
PARNELL, Wendy Carmen. ■ 75219 #041-13-2007 **OBG** *012
PARNELL, Winfred. 7777 FOREST LN, STE 560 75230 #011-03-1977 L1979 **OBG** *020 †30
PARNESS, Howard Arthur. 8200 WALNUT HILL LN 75231 #035-08-1966 L1975 **IM** *020 †20
PARTRIDGE, Kara. 5323 HARRY HINES BLVD, DEPT OF PATH 75390 #048-12-1999 L2004 **PTH** *100 †50
PARUPIA, M F Haroon. 3500 GASTON AVE, NEONATOLOGY DPT/3 HOBLITZE 75246 #704-16-1986 L1998 **NPM** *020 †55
PARVATHANENI, Sunthosh Ve. ■ 75201 #056-06-2005 **IM** *012
PASCHAL, Scott Owen. 7115 GREENVILLE AVE STE 3 75231 #048-12-1982 L1983 **ORS** *020 †40
PASCOE, John David. 1110 N BUCKNER BLVD # 102 75218 #005-06-1988 L1993 **P** *020 †75
PASCUAL, Juan Manuel. ■ 75230 #847-03-1990 L2007 **CHN** *020 †75
PASCUAL, Maria Virginia. 3434 LIVE OAK ST, BAYLOR INSTITUTE FOR IMMUN 75204 #847-04-1981 L1997 **PD** *030 †55
PASSANANTE, Michael V. 1441 N BECKLEY AVE, PECA C/O METHODIST HOSPTIA 75203 #048-12-2001 L2004 **EM** *020 †16
PASUPULA, Selvi Mohan. 5323 HARRY HINES BLVD, U.T. SOUTHWESTERN MEDICAL 75390 #495-28-1990 L2001 **AN** *020 †05
PATAKI, John. 9323 GARLAND RD, STE 207 75218 #473-01-1955 L1977 **IM IMG** *071 †20
PATEL, Anilkumar Rameshch. 12221 MERIT DR STE 161, QUESTCARE PARTNERS 75251 #495-23-1998 L2005 **IM** *100 †20
PATEL, Ashish Sudhir. 1935 MOTOR ST, CHILDREN'S MEDICAL CENTER 75235 #048-16-2000 L2003 **PD** *020 ‡
PATEL, Bhairav N. SOUTHWESTERN MED, UNIV OF TEXAS 75390 #048-12-2002 L2008 **RNR** *012 †80
PATEL, Chirag H. 7955 HARRY HINES BLVD 75235 #495-76-1996 L2002 **IM** *020 †20
PATEL, Helen. 909 N WASHINGTON AVE, BAYLOR INSTITUTE FOR REHAB 75246 #048-14-1991 L1992 **PM** *020 †60
PATEL, Hetal J. ■ 75204 #048-12-2004 L2007 **PCC** *012 †20
PATEL, Jaynish B. 606 N WASHINGTON AVE 75246 #048-13-1997 L2001 **VIR** *020 †80
PATEL, Mehul Dilip. ■ 75204 #048-12-2008 *012
PATEL, Muhammad Ali. 4131 N CENTRAL EXPY, METRO ANESTHESIA 75204 #704-02-1985 L1998 **AN** *020 †05
PATEL, Nova Conner. 5942 VANDERBILT AVE 75206 #048-02-1998 L2001 **DR** *100 †80
PATEL, Parag Chatur. SOUTHWESTERN MED, UNIV OF TEXAS 75390 #016-06-2002 **CD** *012 †20
PATEL, Pratul. 10 MEDICAL PKWY, STE 106 75234 #048-13-1990 L1991 **NR** *020 †80
PATEL, Rupa R. 3225 TURTLE CREEK BLVD # 1 75219 #025-07-2004 L2006 **IM** *100 †20
PATEL, Satin Suryakant. ■ 75390 #005-14-2003 L2007 **OBG** *100
PATEL, Sneha Ishwar. 3500 GASTON AVE, BAYLOR UNIV MED CTR 75246 #048-15-2003 **IM** *100 †20
PATEL, Snehal Ishwar. ■ 75219 #048-12-2008 *012
PATEL, Sukeshi Rajnikant. ■ 75235 #048-12-2008 *012
PATEL, Viralkumar V. 3500 GASTON AVE, GI FELLOW 75246 #048-15-2002 L2004 **GE** *012 †20
PATEL, Vishal Vishnu. ■ 75235 #048-12-2008 *012
PATEL, Vishalkumar Dilipb. 5323 HARRY HINES BLVD, SOUTHWESTERN MED 75390 #496-41-2000 L2001 **NEP** *100
PATEL, Vivek Amrat. ■ 75209 #048-12-2007 **IM** *012
PATHAK, Pushpa Raj. 3320 LIVE OAK ST, EAST DALLAS HEALTH CENTER 75204 #243-16-1989 L2002 **IM** *020 †20
PATIL, Abhitabh. 5323 HARRY HINES BLVD, U TX SOUTHWESTERN MED SCH 75390 #011-03-2002 L2004 **GE** *012 †20
PATINO CADAVID, Willmar D. 5323 HARRY HINES BLVD, DEPT OF PATHOLOGY 75390 #264-03-2000 **PTH** *012
PATMAN, Ralph Donald. 621 N HALL ST STE 520 75226 #048-12-1958 L1958 **VS GS** *020 †85
PATRICK, Stephen Kyle. 1441 N BECKLEY AVE 75203 #048-16-1988 L1989 **OBG** *020 †30
PATTERSON, Brent A. 621 N HALL ST 75226 #048-12-2002 L2006 **IM** *020 †20
PATTERSON, Debra L. 8330 LYNDON B JOHNSON FWY, MS 8 1134 EXEC CTR III 75243 #048-15-1977 L1977 **IM** *030 †20
PATTON, David Ernest. 8160 WALNUT HILL LN, STE 114 75231 #026-04-1983 L1988 **MFM OBG** *020 †30
PATTON, Theresa M. 221 W COLORADO BLVD # 933 75208 #028-46-1999 L2000 **OBG** *020 †30
PATURU, Prasad V R. 9 MEDICAL PKWY, PLAZA 4 STE 207 75234 #495-50-1985 L2005 **CD** *020 †20
PAULK, Mary Elizabeth. 5323 HARRY HINES BLVD 75390 #012-05-1996 L1997 **IM** *020 †20
PAULSON, Andrew Scott. ■ 75220 #048-12-2008 *012
PAULSON, Roy Steven. 3535 WORTH ST, STE 110 75246 #048-12-1977 L1977 **ON HEM** *020 †20
PAVELKA, Cathy Sue. 6541 SHADY BROOK LN, APT 2211 75206 #048-02-1996 L1998 **IM** *020 †20
PAVULURI, Sridevi. 6901 SNIDER PLZ STE 130, INPATIENT PHYSICIAN ASSOCI 75205 #495-18-2000 L2005 **IM** *020 †20
PAWGAN, Arthur Sheldon. 9535 FOREST LN STE 100 75243 #035-09-1965 L1973 **R** *020 †80
PAYNE, Frank Corry, Jr. 8350 N CENTRAL EXPY, STE M1025 75206 #048-12-1954 L1954 **PD** *020
PAYNE, Frank Corry, III. 7115 GREENVILLE AVE, STE 310 75231 #048-12-1979 L1979 **ORS OSM** *020 †40
PAYNE, Paul Bradley. 4224 SWISS AVE 75204 #048-15-1980 L1980 **OBG** *020 †30
PAYSEUR, Garnett Stephon. 5959 HARRY HINES BLVD #312 75235 #010-03-1967 L1975 **OPH** *020 †35
PAYTE, James Thos. 1900 MARKET CENTER BLVD 75207 #039-01-1957 L1958 **ADM** *020
PAYVAR, Saeed. 5323 HARRY HINES BLVD, DEPT OF INT MED 75390 #517-01-1999 **IM** *012
PAZANDAK, Bradford Bruce. ■ 75229 #026-04-1978 L1987 **OPH** *075 †35
PEARLE, Margaret Sue. 5323 HARRY HINES BLVD, UT SWESTERN MED CTR J8106 75390 #016-02-1987 L1994 **U** *020 †95
PEARLMAN, Allen Kenneth. 8210 WALNUT HILL LN # 315 75231 #035-08-1969 L1972 **IM CD** *020 †20
PEARSE, Jack Hamer. ■ 75244 #007-02-1952 L1953 **FM** *071 †18
PEARSE, Lee Ann. 7777 FOREST LN STE B141 75230 #007-02-1983 L1998 **PDC** *020 †55
PEARSON, Daniel B, Jr. 302 W 9TH ST STE D 75208 #039-01-1941 L1946 **P N** *020 ‡
PEARSON, Danl Bester, III. 302 W 9TH ST STE D, OAK CLIFF MED CTR 75208 #048-13-1985 L1986 **P** *020 †75 ‡
PEARSON, Glen Thos, Jr. 3303 LEE PKWY STE 220 75219 #027-01-1969 L1971 **CHP** *020 †75
PECKHAM, Elizabeth L. ■ 75243 #048-78-2000, ▲ L2007 **IM** *100
PEDDADA, Arvind Venkata. 8200 WALNUT HILL LN, JACKSON BLDG 75231 #021-06-1990 L1995 **PM** *020 †60
PEDDADA, Darlene M. 3500 GASTON AVE 75246 #021-06-1990 L1993 **IM** *020 †20
PEIFFER, Nicholas James. ■ 75201 #038-40-2005 L2008 **OTO** *012
PEIKAR, Nader M.. UT SOUTHWESTERN MEDICAL, 6300 HARRY HINES BLVD 75390 #308-11-1985 L2003 **GP N** *020
PEIKARI, Cyrus. 8305 WALNUT HILL LN, STE 140 75231 #048-12-1995 L1996 **IM** *020 †20
PELOSOF, Henri V. 6410 CLUBHOUSE CIR 75240 #396-06-1961 L1970 **PM** *071 †60
PELOSOF, Lorraine Cheryl. ■ 75219 #028-02-2007 **IM** *012
PELOZA, John Henry. 7115 GREENVILLE AVE, STE 210 75231 #016-06-1983 L1984 **OSS ORS** *020 †40
PELPHREY, Andrew C. 5939 HARRY HINES BLVD, STE 500 75235 #048-12-2000 L2003 **NEP** *020
PELTZ, Matthias. ■ 75206 #048-12-1999 L2007 **TS** *012 †85
PEMBERTON, Wesley E. ■ 75240 #048-12-2008 *012
PENDOLA, Michael John. 3409 WORTH ST STE 5 75246 #030-06-1998 L2002 **CRS** *020 †85,10
PENFIELD, Jeffrey Guy. 4500 S LANCASTER RD 75216 #021-06-1988 L1992 **NEP** *020 †20
PENG, Noel. 7777 FOREST LN 75230 #048-02-1996 L1998 **REN GYN** *020 †30
PENKAR, Shirley. ■ 75235 #048-12-2008 *012
PENNANT, John Hugh. 5323 HARRY HINES BLVD, DEPT OF ANESTHESIOLOGY 75390 #917-19-1979 L1991 **AN** *020 †05
PENTA, Pradeep. ■ 75219 #048-12-2004 **GS** *100
PEOPLES, Lanikwa Catrice. ■ 75232 #048-12-2007 *012
PEPERMINWALA, Shamsuddin. 1340 RIVER BEND DR, DALLAS METROCARE 75247 #496-38-1992 L1998 **CHP** *020 †75
PERDUE, Lisa S. 5323 HARRY HINES BLVD, UNIV OF TX SOUTHWESTERN ME 75390 #021-05-1990 L1991 **P** *020 †75
PERELMUTER, Bezalel. 3500 GASTON AVE, DEPT OF PEDIATRICS 75246 #550-01-1972 L1993 **NPM** *020 †55
PERELMUTER, Peleg. ■ 75225 #048-12-2002 L2005 **GS** *100
PEREZ, Arminda. 238 W 10TH ST 75208 #032-01-1977 L1980 **FM** *020 †18
PEREZ, Carlos Luis. 5323 HARRY HINES BLVD, DEPARTMENT OF RADIOLOGY 75390 #048-12-1996 L1998 **RNR** *020 †80
PEREZ, Enrique. 1717 MAIN ST STE 5200 75201 #132-06-1968 L1977 **IM END** *020
PEREZ, Nicholas James. ■ 75249 #019-02-2007 **OBG** *012
PEREZ, Reynaldo P. 13601 PRESTON RD, # 900-WEST 75240 #748-08-1967 L1978 **AN** *020
PEREZ DELPUERTO, Gonzalo. ■ 75219 #035-20-2007 **PS** *012
PEREZ-FONTAN, J Julio. ■ 75225 #847-05-1977 L1986 **PD CCM** *050 †55
PERIJOC, Mihaela. 6901 SNIDER PLZ, STE 130 75205 #781-01-1989 L1998 **IM** *020 †20
PERIS, Luke P. 14800 QUORUM DR, STE 465 75254 #495-37-1984 L1994 **P ADM** *020 †75
PERIS, Maya C. 5477 GLEN LAKES DR, STE 210 75231 #495-37-1987 L1994 **P PYA** *020
PERKINS, Cheryl Leigh. ■ 75230 #027-01-1980 L1980 **PHP** *075
PERKINS, David Lewis. 13601 PRESTON RD, STE 900 75240 #048-02-1979 L1979 **AN** *020 †05
PERKINS, Steve. 5939 HARRY HINES BLVD, STE 800 75235 #836-01-1978 L1986 **HO ON** *020 †20
PERKINS, Tonya Yvette. 8600 THACKERY ST 75225 #012-21-1996 L2004 **OBG** *020
PERONE, Jennifer Beth. 5323 HARRY HINES BLVD MC, UT SOUTHWESTERN MEDICAL CE 75390 #035-19-1999 L2006 **PRD** *100 †15
PERRI, Anthony Jos. 4500 S LANCASTER RD, SURGICAL SERVICE #112 75216 #010-02-1972 L1982 **U** *020 †95
PERRILLO, Robert P. 3500 GASTON AVE 4, BAYLOR UNIVERSITY MEDICAL 75246 #010-02-1970 L2006 **GE IM** *020 †20
PERRIN, Robert W. 221 W COLORADO BLVD, STE 318 75208 #048-02-1953 L1953 **DR** *020 †80
PERRY, Malcolm Oliver. 5939 HARRY HINES BLVD 75235 #048-12-1955 L1955 **VS** *071 †85
PERRY, Paul Bryan. 12201 MERIT DR, STE 420 75251 #004-01-1984 L1986 **AN** *020 †05
PERRY, Radie Floyd. 8210 WALNUT HILL LN # 805 75231 #048-02-1983 L1984 **PM** *020 †60
PERSAUD, Donna Indira. 1935 MOTOR ST, CHILDREN'S MED CTR OF DALL 75235 #566-01-1984 L1991 **PD** *020 †55
PERSLEY, Kimberly M. 8230 WALNUT HILL LN 75231 #048-12-1993 L1994 **GE** *020 †20
PERUGINI, Francesca. 8160 WALNUT HILL LN, STE 212 75231 #017-20-1985 L1989 **OBG** *020 †30
PERUSEK, Carol Ann. 13601 PRESTON RD, STE 900 75240 #048-12-1977 L1977 **AN** *020 †05
PESHOCK, Ronald Michael. 5939 HARRY HINES BLVD 75390 #048-12-1976 L1976 **CD IM** *050 †20
PESSA, Joel E. 5323 HARRY HINES BLVD, DEPT PLASTIC SURG 75390 #024-16-1980 L2001 **PS GS** *020 †85,65
PETERMAN, Dana Corrinne. 8350 N CENTRAL EXPY, CAMPBELL CENTRE 1, SUITE M 75206 #048-12-2000 L2002 **PD** *020 †55
PETERMAN, Joseph P. 8222 DOUGLAS AVE, STE 500 75225 #048-12-1987 L1988 **PD ADL** *020 †55
PETERMAN, Mark A. 14800 LANDMARK BLVD, STE 700 75254 #048-12-2000 L2002 **CD** *100 †20
PETERS, Brian R. 7777 FOREST LN STE A103 75230 #048-02-1983 L1983 **OTO NO** *020 †45
PETERS, George Nick. 5323 HARRY HINES BLVD, UT SOUTHWESTERN MEDICAL CE 75390 #027-01-1974 L1977 **GS SO** *020 †85

■ = Address Information Privacy Protected

PETERS, John Michael. 5323 HARRY HINES BLVD, DEPT OF PATHOLOGY 75390 #048-12-2005 PTH *012

PETERS, Mark Thos. PO BOX 12328 75225 #048-02-1982 L1983 MFM OBG *020 †30

PETERS, Paul C. 9301 N CENTRAL EXPY, STE 400 75231 #048-12-1984 L1985 ORS *020 †40

PETERSEN, Erika Ann. ■ 75203 #036-01-2003 NS *012

PETERSEN, Katharine Jo. ■ 75248 #049-01-2001 L2004 PD *020 †55

PETERSON, Charles Allan. ■ 75225 #026-04-1957 L1957 TS CD *071 †85,90

PETERSON, Dolores M. 5323 HARRY HINES BLVD, SOUTHWESTERN MEDICAL SCHOO 75390 #048-13-1987 L1988 IM *020

PETERSON, Gail Elizabeth. 5909 HARRY HINES BLVD, HA9.133 75235 #025-01-1991 L1993 CD *020 †20

PETRONE, Dianne Lynn. 712 N WASHINGTON AVE 75246 #055-01-1978 L1987 RHU IM *020 †20

PETTETT, David N. 4131 N CENTRAL EXPY, METRO ANESTHESIA 75204 #048-02-1990 L1994 AN *020 †05

PETTIBON, Michael Danl. 13601 PRESTON RD, STE 900W 75240 #048-13-1985 L1986 AN OS *020 †05 ‡

PETTY, Kevin J. 5323 HARRY HINES BLVD, STOP 9031 75390 #048-12-1984 L1991 IM *020 †20

PFANNSTIEL, Joy Michele. ■ 75219 #048-13-2007 GS *012

PFISTER, James G. 10218 MIDWAY RD 75229 #048-14-1997 L1999 FM *020 †18

PHAM, Chi M. 5201 HARRY HINES BLVD, HEMATOLOGY/ONCOLOGY CLINIC 75235 #048-12-2001 L2004 HO *012

PHAM, Han N. 7808 CLODUS FIELDS DR, GREEN OAKS HOSPITAL 75251 #048-15-2002 L2004 ID *012

PHAM, Huy Dinh. ■ 75212 #048-12-2004 L2007 IM *100

PHAM, Trong Quang. 207 S HOUSTON ST 75202 #941-01-1972 L1979 GP *020

PHAN, Andrew K. 8210 WALNUT HILL LN, STE 230 75231 #048-12-1995 L1996 IM *020 †20

PHARO, Milam B. 8215 WESTCHESTER DR STE 11 75225 #021-01-1949 L1953 PD *020 †55

PHELAN, Amy Haynie. ■ 75219 #048-14-1997 L2004 PM PMM *020 †60

PHELPS, Carrie Elizabeth. 5323 HARRY HINES BLVD, SOUTHWESTERN MED 75390 #048-15-2005 L2004 OBG *020 †

PHELPS, James Richard. 75205 #048-15-2006 ORS *012

PHELPS, William Lee. 10611 GARLAND RD STE 217 75218 #016-11-1958 L1965 OPH *020 †35

PHILIP, Anne V. 5787 S HAMPTON RD, #1 75232 #880-01-1984 L1996 FM *020 †18

PHILIP, Christo Thomas. ■ 75212 #026-08-2008 *012

PHILIP, John. 5323 HARRY HINES BLVD, UT SOUTHWESTERN-ANESTHESIO 75390 #048-12-1991 L1997 AN *020 †05

PHILIP, Joseph V. 712 N WASHINGTON AVE, STE 101 75246 #048-13-1997 L2004 R RNR *020 †

PHILIPS, Robert Oliver. 7777 FOREST LN, STE C420 75230 #047-06-1965 L1967 GP *020 †18

PHILLEAUX, Ronald W. 10246 MIDWAY RD 75229 #048-02-1964 L1964 GP *020

PHILLIPS, Bruce A. 8201 PRESTON RD STE 560 75225 #048-13-1986 L1987 FM *020 †18

PHILLIPS, Diane Schlup. 8201 PRESTON RD STE 560 75225 #048-13-1986 L1987 IM *020 †20

PHILLIPS, Jan Elizabeth. 4210 MERRELL RD 75229 #305-01-2005 L2005 IM *012

PHILLIPS, Jeffrey Harris. 8210 WALNUT HILL LN, STE 604 75231 #041-13-1983 L1984 IM *020 †20

PHILLIPS, Joseph T, Jr. 6301 GASTON AVE, STE 400W 75214 #048-12-1981 L1981 N IG *020 †

PHILLIPS, William Ralph, III. 9101 N CENTRAL EXPY, STE 550 75231 #048-15-2000 L2003 AN *020

PHUNG, Neil N. 7115 GREENVILLE AVE, STE 220 75231 #048-14-2001 L2006 CD *020

PIANTINI, Rebeca Eileen. 1935 MOTOR ST, REACH PROGRAM 75235 #005-12-1989 L2000 PD *020 †55

PICKEL, Stephanie A. 5323 HARRY HINES BLVD, SOUTHWESTERN MED 75390 #048-14-2005 OBG *012

PICUS-FREEMAN, Marlene B. 6363 FOREST PARK RD # 800, WOMEN'S MENTAL HEALTH CENT 75235 #016-06-1994 L2007 P *020 †75

PIENIEK, Marc Steven. 7777 FOREST LN, STE A341 75230 #012-05-1990 L1996 CD *020 †20

PIERCE, Ava Edwana. 5323 HARRY HINES BLVD, UT SOUTH WESTERN MEDICAL C 75390 #021-06-1994 L1998 EM *020 †16

PIERCE, Damon Scott. ■ 75219 #048-13-2002 L2006 VS *012 †85

PIERCE, Graham L, Jr. 2710 VALLEY VIEW LN 75234 #048-12-1948 L1948 OBG *071 †30

PIERCE, Jessica Barnes. ■ 75219 #048-12-2005 FP *012

PIEROTTI, Christopher P. ■ 75214 #048-12-2005 L2007 EM *012

PILAND, James Edward. 13601 PRESTON RD STE 1000 75240 #048-02-1981 L1981 AN *020 †05

PILLAI, Chidambara Thanu. PARKLAND HOSP 75235 #495-53-1980 OPH *100

PILLAY, Prem Kumar. ■ 75206 #825-01-1980 NS *100

PILLOW, David James, Jr. 5909 HARRY HINES BLVD 75235 #048-12-1972 L1988 EM *020 †16

PILLSBURY, Edmund. 3521 OAK LAWN AVE 75219 #048-04-2005 L2008 DR *012

PIN, Paul Gordon. 3600 GASTON AVE STE 410 75246 #036-07-1981 L1988 PS HS *020 †65

PINA, Jorge Ignacio. 9991 MARSH LN 75220 #649-03-1969 L1978 GP FM *020

PINEIRO PEREZ, Luis A. 7777 FOREST LN, STE D220 75230 #024-07-1983 L1991 HEM ON *020 †20

PINKUSIEWICZ, Enrique. 6546 LBJ FWY STE 20 75240 #132-01-1968 L1979 GYN *020

PINO, Alfonso E. 11884 GREENVILLE AVE, STE A102 75243 #048-12-1992 L1993 AN *020 †05

PINTO, Anil Bosco Manuel. 3800 SAN JACINTO ST 75204 #048-16-1985 L2002 OBG *020 †30

PINTO, Karen Rose. 75230 #496-15-1988 L2002 PCP *020 †50

PIPER, Paul K. 3600 GASTON AVE, STE 550 WADLEY TOWER 75246 #048-13-2002 L2003 IM *020 †20

PIPPEN, John E, Jr. 3535 WORTH ST, STE 110 75246 #048-12-1982 L1983 ON *020 †20

PIPPIN, John J. 12200 PRESTON RD, COOPER CLINIC 75230 #024-16-1980 L1998 CD *020 †20

PISTENMAA, David Andrew. 5801 FOREST PARK ROAD, UNIV OF TEXAS SW MED CTR 75390 #005-11-1969 L1993 RO *040 †80

PITA, Alice. ■ 75243 #016-02-1968 L1972 PD PHP *071 †55

PITA, David S. 3500 GASTON AVE 75246 #891-03-1964 L1972 CRS *020

PITAFI, Ali Asim. ■ 75206 #704-01-1997 L2002 IM *100 †20

PITCHER, William Doug. 4500 S LANCASTER RD, DEPT PUD 111-F 75216 #048-04-1979 L1980 PUD CCM *020 †20

PITTMAN-HOBBS, Shawnta Re. 3600 GASTON AVE 75246 #048-14-2003 L2006 IM *020 †20

PITTS, Elizabeth Carroll. ■ 75235 #048-12-2005 GS *012

PIVNICK, Lawrence Neil. 10 MEDICAL PKWY # NO-206 75234 #065-01-1971 L1977 FM EM *020

PIZETTE, Murray. 1130 BEACHVIEW ST, STE 100 75218 #035-19-1955 L1959 IM *071 †20

PLAGENHOEF, Richard Lee. ■ 75225 #025-01-1965 L1989 FM *075 †18

PLANK, Mary Carol. 3600 GASTON AVE 75246 #030-05-1995 L1997 OBG *020 †30

PLATT, Julie Fay. ■ 75229 #048-12-1995 L1996 DR *020

PLATT, Melvin Ray. 8230 WALNUT HILL LN, STE 208 75231 #048-04-1965 L1965 TS *020 †85,90

PLEITEZ, Jose Alberto. ■ 75379 #429-01-1965 L1973 P *071 †75

PLOTKIN, Allen Stanley. 8200 WALNUT HILL LN 75231 #056-05-1965 L1967 U *020 †95

PLUM, George E. 3500 GASTON AVE 75246 #024-01-1951 L1963 DR *071 †80

PLUMMER, Ellen Stilz. ■ 75219 #020-12-2006 PD *012

PLUMMER, Mitchell Martin. ■ 75219 #048-12-2008 GS *012

POBEE, Marian Imelda. 1717 MAIN ST STE 5200, EMCARE INC 75201 #412-01-1988 L1999 PD *020 †55

PODESZWA, David Alexander. 1935 MEDICAL DISTRICT DR, STE E2300 75235 #025-07-1995 L2000 OP *020 †40

POISSON, Jessica Lynne. ■ 75235 #048-12-2008 *012

POKALA, Hanumantha Rao. SOUTHWESTERN MED, UNIV OF TEXAS 75390 #039-01-2004 PHO *012 †55

POLANCO, Elizabeth Marie. ■ 75214 #048-12-1981 L1981 IM *020 †20

POLASKY, Hartley. ■ 75230 #028-79-1956, ▲ L1957 FM *071

POLATIN, Peter Barth. 5701 MAPLE AVE STE 100 75235 #035-01-1968 L1985 P PM *020 †75

POLINER, Lawrence Richard. 7777 FOREST LN, STE C 75230 #035-20-1969 L1975 CD IM *020 †20

POLLARD, Casey W. 5323 HARRY HINES BLVD, U TX SW MED SCH 75390 #048-13-2007 DR *012

POLLARD, Rupert Maury. 4404 LORRAINE AVE 75205 #048-12-1963 L1968 AN LM *020 †05

POLLOCK, Harlan. 8305 WALNUT HILL LN 75231 #038-40-1962 L1964 PS *020 †85,65

POLLOCK, Madelyn P. ■ 75206 #048-14-1986 L1987 FM *020 †18

POLO CARBAYO, Juan Jose. 5323 HARRY HINES BLVD, UNIV TX SOUTHWESTERN MED S 75390 #847-01-1992 IM *100

POLTER, Daniel Earl. 3500 GASTON AVE, 2ND FL 75246 #048-12-1959 L1959 GE IM *020 †20

POMPEO, Matthew Q. 8198 WALNUT HILL LN, PRESBYTERIAN WOUND CLINIC 75231 #011-02-1988 L1990 GS OS *020 †90,85

PON, Tammy Lee. 6263 HARRY HINES BLVD 75235 #048-14-1990 L1991 FM *020 †18

PONDER, Timothy Hilton. ■ 75230 #056-06-1977 L1983 DR *020 †80

PONGDEE, Thanai. 13601 PRESTON RD, CARILLON TOWER EAST, # 310 75240 #020-12-1997 L2003 AI *020 †55,05,03

POOL, John M. 3500 GASTON AVE, DEPT OF GENERAL SURGERY 75246 #048-12-2004 L2007 GS *012

POOL, Kenneth Darrell, Jr. 221 W COLORADO BLVD, STE 140 75208 #048-13-1976 L1976 N *020 †75

POOLE, Julie Diane. 9550 FOREST LN, STE 606 75243 #018-03-1995 L2000 PD *020 †55

PORTER, Homa J, II. 8230 WALNUT HILL LN, BLDG 3 75231 #048-13-1999 L2004 U *020 †95

PORTER, Leslie D. 909 N WASHINGTON AVE 75246 #048-14-1983 L1983 PM *020 †60

PORTER, Scott Anthony. 7777 FOREST LN # NO-A310 75230 #048-12-1981 L1981 AN *020 †05

PORTERA, Louis Anthony. 3500 GASTON AVE, EMERGENCY DEPT 75246 #027-01-1973 L1974 EM IM *020 †20,16

PORTEUS, Matthew Hebden. ■ 75214 #005-11-1994 L2003 PHO *020 †55

PORTILLA, Maurice Michael. 9209 ELAM RD STE 104 75217 #048-78-1991, ▲ L1992 FM PD *020

PORTTEUS, Andrew Michael. 1935 MOTOR ST, CHILDREN'S MEDICAL CENTER 75235 #039-01-1997 L2003 P *020

POSNER, Martin Stanley. 8330 MEADOW RD STE 124 75231 #035-09-1963 L1968 P *020

POSTEN, William David. 12222 COIT RD, STE 102 75251 #008-01-2000 L2004 D *020 †15

POSTMA, Tom Wedekind. 12700 PARK CENTRAL DR, STE 430 75251 #011-03-1976 L1978 DR *020 †80

POTTER, Jason Kyle. 8220 WALNUT HILL LN 75231 #048-12-1999 L2007 GS *020 †65

POTTI, Aruna Koney. 1151 N BUCKNER BLVD, STE 103 75218 #495-70-1990 L1997 IM *020 †20

POTTS, Robert Jos. ■ 75228 #035-06-1946 L1958 IM GPM *071 †70

POTTS, Robyn M. 5323 HARRY HINES BLVD, SOUTHWESTERN MED 75390 #039-01-2002 L2007 HMP *020 †50

POULOS, Ernest. 5959 HARRY HINES BLVD 75235 #048-12-1950 L1950 VS *071 †85

POUNDERS, Steven M. 3500 OAK LAWN AVE, STE 600 75219 #048-02-1985 L1986 IM *020 †20

POWELL, Craig Motlow. 5323 HARRY HINES BLVD, STOP 9031 75390 #048-04-1997 L2001 N *020 †75

POWELL, Jerry Allen, Jr. 1935 MOTOR ST 75235 #048-12-1992 L2002 DR *020 †80

POWELL, Robert Owen. 7920 BELT LINE RD 75254 #024-01-1972 L1988 TS GS *020 †90,85

POWELL, Tiffany Michele. ■ 75219 #036-07-2004 L2004 CD *012 †20

POWELL, William Joe. ■ 75240 #048-12-1988 L1998 GS GP *071

POWNELL, Patrick H. 7150 GREENVILLE AVE, STE 310 75231 #048-12-1986 L1987 PS OTO *020 †45,65 ‡

PRADHAN, Amit Prakash. 5323 HARRY HINES BLVD, SOUTHWESTERN MED 75390 #495-73-2003 P *012

PRASAD, Ashoka. ■ 75225 #048-41-1977 *100

PREJEAN, Edward Jos. 5323 H HINES BLVD, DEPT ANES 75235 #048-13-1982 L1984 AN PD *020 †05

PRENGLER, Irving David. 3600 GASTON AVE STE 550, BAYLOR MEDICAL CENTER 75246 #048-12-1980 L1980 IM *020 †20

PRESKITT, John Thos. 3600 GASTON AVE 75246 #048-12-1975 L1975 HNS GS *020 †85

PRESTIDGE, Claude B. 8345 WALNUT HILL LN, BLDG D 75231 #048-12-1968 L1968 PD *020 †55

PRESTON, Charles M. 5757 W LOVERS LN, STE 300 75209 #132-01-1954 L1963 OM *071 †80

PRICE, Angela Vivian. 1935 MOTOR ST 75235 #060-02-1994 L2003 OS *020 †25

PRIDDY, Leah Paige. 13601 PRESTON RD, STE 900 75240 #048-12-1991 L1992 AN *020 †05

PRIDE, Glenn Lee. ■ 75248 #017-20-1967 L1986 OBG GO *071 †30 ‡

PRIDE, Glenn Lee, Jr. 5352 HARRY HINES BLVD, U T SOUTHWESTERN MEDICAL C 75390 #001-02-1989 L1991 RNR *020 †75,80

PRIETO SAAVEDRA, Juan Car. 5323 HARRY HINES BLVD, UNIV TX SOUTHWESTERN MED S 75390 #264-06-1996 UP *012

PRINCE, Robert Lee, Jr. ■ 75230 #047-07-1960 L1964 OBG *072 †30

PRITCHARD, Marcia Ann. 1935 MOTOR ST, DEPT. RADIOLOGY 75235 #048-02-1985 L1988 DR R *020 †80

PROBST, Lori Christine. 3600 GASTON AVE, STE 300 75246 #048-12-2001 L2004 OBG *020 †30

PROCTER, Jessica. 7777 FOREST LN, B-242 75230 #048-12-1988 L1989 RHU *020 †

PRODANOVIC, Maria Lubitza. 1935 MOTOR ST, CHILDREN'S MEDICAL CENTER 75235 #048-15-2004 L2006 PD *020

PROVOST, David Anders, Jr. 5323 HARRY HINES BLVD, U TX SW MED CTR DEPT SURG 75390 #048-15-2004 L2008 GS CCS *020 †85

PRUEITT, Rouhollah F. 5323 HARRY HINES BLVD, EMERGENCY MEDICINE/ TOXICO 75390 #042-01-2001 L2004 ETX *020 †16

PRUETTE, Autumn Lynn. ■ 75201 #048-12-2008 *012

PRUITT, Bryan H. 8315 WALNUT HILL LN, STE 125 75231 #048-02-1985 L1987 **PS P** *020 †85,65

PRUITT, Jeffrey Hamilton. 5323 HARRY HINES BLVD 75390 #048-12-1992 L1997 **DR AR** *020 †80

PRYZANT, Charles Zanwill. 5925 FOREST LN STE 41 75230 #048-04-1990 L2001 **CHP** *020 †75

PSYK, Andrew Michael. 5323 HARRY HINES BLVD, SURG DEPT/EMERGENCY MEDICI 75390 #024-05-1999 L2000 **EM** *100 †16

PUDUPAKKAM, Jayanth R. 12221 MERIT DR STE 460, HOSPITAL INTERNIST ASSOCIA 75251 #038-45-1993 L1997 **IM** *020 †20

PUGACH, Isaac Zinovy. 8989 FOREST LN, STE 146 75243 #048-02-2002 L2006 **IM** *020 †20

PUIG, A Winston. 3424 GILLESPIE ST 75219 #028-34-1967 L1968 **R NM** *030 †80,28

PUNARO, Marilynn G. 2222 WELBORN ST 75219 #021-01-1977 L1980 **RHU PD** *050 †55

PUNJWANI, Poonam Lachman. ■ 75248 #422-01-2004 L2007 **PDC** *012 †55

PUNNOOSE, Jennifer. 5323 HARRY HINES BLVD, DEPT OF INT MED 75390 #048-12-2007 **IM** *012 †20

PUPOLS, Anita Zenta. 7777 FOREST LN, STE C804 75230 #065-01-1977 L1984 **DR** *020 †80

PURCELL, Craig W. 4410 BLUFFVIEW BLVD 75209 #048-15-1998 L2000 **EM** *020 †16

PURDUE, Gary Frederick. 5323 HARRY HINES BLVD, UT SOUTHWESTERN MED CTR 75390 #041-02-1976 L1981 **GS** *020 †85

PURDY, Phillip Douglas. 5323 HARRY HINES BLVD, UT SOUTHWESTERN MEDICAL CE 75390 #028-03-1978 L1980 **R RNR** *020 †80

PURINTON, Scott C. 2222 MEDICAL DISTRICT DR 75235 #011-02-2003 L2008 **OBG GO** *100

PURNELL, Robert Q. 13601 PRESTON RD, STE 900 75240 #048-15-1989 L1991 **AN** *020 †05

PUTMAN, John Michael. 3600 GASTON AVE, STE 502 BARNETT TOWER 75246 #012-01-1973 L1974 **OBG REN** *020 †30

PUTNAM, Robert Savell. 5323 HARRY HINES BLVD UT S 75235 #048-12-1962 L1962 **CLP** *030 †50

PUZZIFERRI, Nancy. ■ 75235 #056-06-1995 L2005 **GS** *100 †85

PYEATT, John Edward. 13601 PRESTON RD, STE 900 75240 #048-15-1994 L1997 **AN** *020 †05

PYRON, James Thurman. 6301 GASTON AVE, EAST TOWER, SUITE 400 75214 #047-05-1971 L1976 **AN** *020

QAMIRANI, Erion. ■ 75238 #048-16-2007 *012

QASSAM, Mehboob S. 1717 MAIN ST, STE 5200 75201 #704-16-1983 L1993 **IM EM** *020 †20

QUADRI, Arshia Jabeen. 12221 MERIT DR STE 450, QUESTCARE HOSPITALISTS 75251 #495-65-1999 L2007 **IM** *020 †20

QUAN, Albert Haine. 5323 HARRY HINES BLVD, SOUTHWESTERN MED CTR 75390 #005-02-1986 L1993 **PN** *050 †55

QUAN, Carolyn. 3600 GASTON AVE STE 550 75246 #048-12-1993 L1994 **IM** *020 †20

QUARLES, Elizabeth A. 5201 HARRY HINES BLVD 75235 #048-12-2001 L2004 **PD** *020 †55

QUARLES, Stephanie Renee. 5323 HARRY HINES BLVD, DIV OF EMERGENCY MED 75390 #001-02-2006 **EM** *012

QUEENAN, Kip Edward. ■ 75390 #021-05-1999 L2002 **PYG** *020 †75

QUICENO, Guillermo Andres. 8200 WALNUT HILL LN, ARTHRITIS CONSULTATION CTR 75231 #264-16-1993 L2001 **RHU IM** *020 †20

QUICENO, Mary Ellen. 5323 HARRY HINES BLVD, MC 9129 75390 #011-02-1999 L2003 **N NUP** *020 †75

QUIGLEY, Raymond Phillip. 5323 HARRY HINES BLVD, UT SOUTHWESTERN MED CENTER 75390 #001-02-1985 L1991 **PN NPM** *020 †55

QUINBY, Jonathan Scott. 3600 GASTON AVE, BARNETT #1101 75246 #048-12-1999 L2005 **ORS OSM** *020 †40

QUINN, Charles T. 5323 HARRY HINES BLVD, UT SOUTHWESTERN MED CTR 75390 #048-12-1994 L1996 **PHO PD** *050 †55

QUINN, John Jos, III. 5323 HARRY HINES BLVD, U.T. SOUTHWESTERN MEDICAL 75390 #004-01-1991 L1995 **P** *020

QUINTANILLA, Norma Maria. ■ 75206 #737-06-1983 L2001 **PCP** *012 †50

QUIROZ, Juan Francisco. 2445 W NORTHWEST HWY, STE 105 75220 #649-02-1985 L1997 **FM** *020 †18

QURESHI, Atif Mahmood. 5323 HARRY HINES BLVD 75390 #704-02-1997 L2008 **FP** *012

RAB, Gregory Steven. 75248 #048-02-1982 L1983 **EM** *020 †16

RABELER, Brandon Chase. ■ 75204 #030-05-2007 **GS** *012

RACASA, Zenaida. 3111 SYLVAN AVE 75212 #748-08-1966 L1977 **PD GPM** *020

RACCASI, Mark A. 7557 RAMBLER RD, STE 706 75231 #048-14-1991 L1992 **AN** *020 †05

RACE, Elizabeth Rinker. 5323 HARRY HINES BLVD, UT SOUTHWESTERN DIV OF INF 75390 #048-02-1991 L1999 **ID** *020 †20

RACE, George Justice. 3701 JUNIUS ST, BOX H006 75246 #048-12-1947 L1947 **PTH FOP** *071 †50

RACE, James Edward. 2301 S HAMPTON RD, STE 900 75224 #047-07-1984 L1988 **IM** *020

RADAIDEH, Sofyan Morshed. 2222 MEDICAL DISTRICT DR, APT 4403 75235 #575-02-2003 **IM** *012

RADFORD, Lee Roy. 5909 HARRY HINES BLVD, ST PAUL UNIV HOSP 75235 #048-12-1956 L1956 **DR VIR** *020 †80

RADFORD, Nina Butwell. 12200 PRESTON RD, COOPER CLINIC 75230 #035-47-1986 L1987 **CD** *020 †20

RADFORD, Traci K. 4144 N CENTRAL EXPY # 450 75204 #048-12-1992 L1993 **IM** *020 †20

RAFEA, Veeda. ■ 75204 #517-03-1973 L1996 **FOP** *071

RAFF, Barry Wallace. 5323 HARRY HINES BLVD, STOP 9031 75390 #024-05-1979 L1995 **IM** *020 †16

RAFFERTY, Michael Patrick. 4500 S LANCASTER RD, VA NORTH TX HLTH CARE SYS 75216 #026-04-2002 L2002 **P** *100 †75

RAGHU, Aarti. 8200 WALNUT HILL LN, DEPT OF INTERNAL MEDICINE 75231 #496-39-2002 L2007 **IM** *012

RAGHUWANSHI, Anita P. ■ 75235 #035-46-2008 *012

RAGLE, Theron D. 8230 WALNUT HILL LN # 600 75231 #048-02-1984 L1985 **FM** *020 †18 ‡

RAHEJA, Suresh Kumar. 3450 W WHEATLAND RD, STE 216 75237 #495-20-1981 L1990 **IM** *020

RAHIMIZADEH, Hootan. 14800 LANDMARK BLVD, SUITER 700 75254 #024-07-1993 L2002 **CD** *020 †20

RAHL, Riva Louise. 12200 PRESTON RD, COOPER CLINIC 75230 #005-02-1999 L2000 **IM** *020 †20,16

RAHMAN, Pervaiz. 12800 HILLCREST RD, STE 123 75230 #704-02-1972 L1980 **GE IM** *020 †20

RAHMAN, Syed Mizanur. 4500 S LANCASTER RD, DALLAS VA MEDICAL CENTER 75216 #160-03-1985 L1993 **IM** *020 †20

RAHN, David D. ■ 75229 #048-12-2001 L2005 **OBG** *100

RAI, Hardeep S. 142 WEBBS ROYAL PLZ 75229 #495-03-1997 L2003 **IM** *020 †20

RAI, Shiwali. 2909 MCKINNEY AVE 75204 #021-05-2002 L2005 **FM** *100 †18

RAI, Vasdev Singh. 7777 FOREST LN # 612 75230 #495-29-1973 L1982 **PS GS** *020 †85,65 ‡

RAISANEN, Jack Michael. 5323 HARRY HINES BLVD MC 75390 #025-01-1986 L2000 **PCP PTH** *020

RAIZMAN, Emma Jane. 1935 MOTOR ST, CHILDRENS MED CTR 75235 #041-12-1998 L2004 **PD** *020 †55

RAJ, Guna. 4500 S LANCASTER RD, VA MEDICAL CENTER (111E) 75216 #495-33-1977 L1987 **IM HEM** *040 †20

RAJA, Harikrishna. 5323 HARRY HINES BLVD, STOP 9031 75390 #048-12-1995 L1996 **IM** *020 †20

RAJAGOPAL, Arthi. ■ 75225 #495-04-1996 L2007 **NEP** *100 †20

RAJAKRISHNAN, Deepalakshmi. 11910 GREENVILLE AVE, PRIMACARE MEDICAL CENTRES 75243 #495-04-1997 L2005 **FM** *100 †18

RAM, C Venkata S. 1420 VICEROY DR 75235 #495-21-1971 L1977 **CD** *020 †20

RAMACHANDRAN, Bala. 1935 MOTOR ST 75235 #495-50-1989 L1995 **CCP** *100 †55

RAMACIOTTI, Claudio. 1935 MOTOR ST, DIVISION OF CARDIOLOGY 75235 #187-03-1977 L1996 **PDC PD** *020 †55

RAMAKRISHNA, Kalpana. 12700 PARK CENTRAL DR, STE 430 75251 #048-12-1994 L1995 **DR** *020 †80

RAMAMANI, Prathivadi B. 4811A COLUMBIA AVE, CLINICA MEDICA DE DALLAS 75226 #495-09-1963 L1978 **OBG GYN** *020

RAMAMURTHY, Hariharan. 4500 S LANCASTER RD, DALLAS VA AMBULATORY MED 75216 #495-21-1978 L1988 **IM** *020 †20

RAMAN, Jay Dilip. ■ 75204 #035-20-2001 L2007 **U** *100

RAMANADHAM, Kilaru. 5812 ENCORE DR 75240 #495-50-1970 L1977 **DR NM** *020 †80,28

RAMARATHNAM, Vivek Shreed. ■ 75204 #048-04-2004 L2004 **IM** *012

RAMASWAMI, Anjali Sriniva. 5323 HARRY HINES BLVD, SOUTHWESTERN MED 75390 #496-51-1996 L2008 **HO** *012

RAMILO, Octavio. 5323 HARRY HINES BLVD, UT SW MED CTR DEPT PEDS 75235 #847-04-1982 L1994 **PD** *050 †55

RAMIREZ, Alfonso. 1121 W JEFFERSON BLVD 75208 #048-12-1978 L1978 **FM OM** *020 †18 ‡

RAMIREZ, Charina Marie. 1935 MOTOR ST M-700, MEDICAL EDUCATION DEPARTME 75235 #048-02-2003 L2005 **PG** *012 †55

RAMIREZ, Jaime. 1935 MOTOR ST #048-04-1982 L1985 **GP OM** *020

RAMIREZ, Javier Tade. 1441 N BECKLEY AVE 75203 #048-02-1962 L1962 **IM** *020 †20

RAMIREZ, Manuel Ramon T. 9080 HARRY HINES BLVD, STE 110 75235 #748-01-1974 L1982 **AN PME** *020 †05

RAMNATH, Devesh. 411 N WASHINGTON AVE, STE 7000 75246 #038-44-1996 L2001 **ORS** *020 †40

RAMON, Victor Josep. 712 N WASHINGTON AVE, STE 404 75246 #048-13-1976 L1981 **AN** *020 †18,05

RAMOS, Enrique A. 13601 PRESTON RD, # 900-WEST 75240 #048-15-1994 L1997 **AN** *020 †05

RAMOS, Faustino Gustavo. 1935 MOTOR ST, CARDIOLOGY DEPARTMENT 75235 #035-20-2000 L2005 **PDC** *012 †55

RAMSAY, Michael Anthony E. 3500 GASTON AVE, DEPT OF ANESTHESIOLOGY 75246 #917-25-1968 L1977 **AN** *020 †05 ‡

RANA, Humair. 5323 HARRY HINES BLVD 75390 #048-13-2006 **AN** *012

RANA, Setal Ramnik. 8202 ELAM RD 75217 #654-01-2004 L2007 **FM** *020 †18

RANALLO, Gregory Joseph. 700 N PEARL ST, STE N208 75201 #039-01-1997 L1999 **FM** *071 †18

RANDALL, Henry Bernard. 3500 GASTON AVE, 4TH FLOOR ROBERT'S BLDG 75246 #025-07-1990 L2002 **TTS** *020 †85

RANDALL, Steve Eric. ■ 75214 #661-02-2005 L2008 **FP** *012

RANDEL, Randy Chas. ■ 75205 #048-02-1979 L1979 **PD NPM** *020 †55

RANDLES, Ryan Timothy. 5323 HARRY HINES BLVD 75390 #836-03-2004 **EM** *012

RANDOLPH, Donald A. 1015 N CARROLL AVE # 2000 75204 #035-01-1995 L2005 **OSM ORS** *020 †40

RANGINWALA, Najeeb Ahmed. ■ 75219 #704-02-1990 **PYG** *020

RANNEY, David Francis. ■ 75234 #038-06-1969 L1980 **PTH GS** *071

RAO, Archana. 3500 GASTON AVE, MEDICAL CENT 75246 #496-39-2000 L2007 **NEP** *012

RAO, Krishna T. 13601 PRESTON RD, STE 900 75240 #048-12-1986 L1987 **AN** *020 †05

RAO, Namrata. 8411 PRESTON RD, STE 820 75225 #495-45-1993 L2001 **CHP** *020

RAO, Roshni. ■ 75390 #028-03-1999 L2004 **GS** *100 †85

RAO, Shobha S. 5550 HARVEST HILL RD, STE 100 75230 #495-70-1985 L1995 **FM FPG** *020 †18

RAO, Uma. 5323 HARRY HINES BLVD, UT SOUTHWESTERN MED CENTE 75390 #495-33-1982 L2003 **CHP P** *020 †75

RAPHAEL, Alan Arthur. 6301 GASTON AVE, EAST TOWER STE 400 75214 #048-02-1986 L1987 **AN** *020 †20

RARDIN, Kristin D. ■ 75201 #048-12-2008 *012

RASHEED, Shams. ■ 75220 #704-04-1962 L1985 **NPM** *071 †55

RASKIN, Philip. 5323 HARRY HINES BLVD, UT SOUTHWESTERN MED CTR 75390 #041-12-1966 L1970 **DIA IM** *050 †20

RASKO, Yvonne Marsha. ■ 75220 #010-01-2005 **GS** *012

RASTOGI, Padmashri. 4500 S LANCASTER RD, RAOD, 111E 75216 #496-10-1984 L2002 **IM** *020 †20

RATAKONDA, Ravindra. 4500 S LANCASTER RD, AMBULATORY CARE DEPT 75216 #495-58-1978 L1995 **IM** *020 †20

RATHJEN, Karl Eric. 2222 WELBORN ST 75219 #048-12-1990 L1991 **OP** *020 †40

RATHJEN, Kurt Walter. 411 N WASHINGTON AVE # 75 75246 #048-12-1983 L1983 **ORS** *020 †40

RATLIFF, Arleen F. 1935 MOTOR ST, CHILDREN'S MEDICAL CENTER 75235 #047-06-1990 L1997 **PHO PD** *020 †55

RATZLAFF, Roland Wesley. ■ 75244 #021-01-1958 L1964 **AN** *075

RAUER, James Michael. 5521 GREENVILLE AVE, 104-437 75206 #026-04-1975 L1979 **DR** *071 †20

RAVENELL, Joseph Errick. 5323 HARRY HINES BLVD, STE J4.130 75390 #016-02-2000 L2006 **IM** *020 †20

RAVULA, Radhika E. 8230 WALNUT HILL LN 75231 #495-59-1991 L1999 **AN** *020 †05

RAWLINGS, Marsden Keith. 1906 PEABODY AVE 75215 #023-01-1983 L1993 **IM** *020

RAWOT, Bonnie Westrope. 7777 FOREST LN, STE B412 75230 #035-06-1990 L1996 **ID** *020 †20

RAY, Peter Campbell. 8300 DOUGLAS AVE STE 731, BEHAVIORAL & DEVELOPMENTAL 75225 #048-12-1974 L1977 **PD** *020 †55

RAYANI, Afsar Ismail. ■ 75206 #495-65-1981 AN *100

RAYCHAUDHURI, Ratul. ■ 75235 #016-06-2006 **NS** *012

RAYMOND, Dennis M. 5495 BELT LINE RD STE 260 75254 #048-14-1984 L1985 **P** *020

RAYMOND-MARTIMBEAU, P. 5439 GLEN LAKES DR 75231 #067-02-1970 L1984 **D OS** *072

RAZI-SYED, Saba. 5323 HARRY HINES BLVD, MC 9070 75390 #048-16-1991 L2004 **P** *100 †75

REA, Roy Lynn. 8200 WALNUT HILL LN, DEPARTMENT OF EMERGENCY ME 75231 #048-12-1982 L1983 **EM IM** *020 †20,16

REA, William James. 8345 WALNUT HILL LN, ENVIRONMENTAL HEALTH 75231 #038-40-1962 L1965 **TS** *020 †85,90

READ, Don Robt. 7777 FOREST LN, STE 1-321 75230 #048-02-1968 L1968 **CRS GS** *020 †10,85

REAHARD, Amanda Leigh. ■ 75201 #017-20-2007 **P** *012

REARDON, William Condon. 8210 WALNUT HILL LN, HARVILL-TSCHUMY CLINIC 75231 #048-12-1974 L1974 **CD IM** *020 †20

REDDY, Jagan Mohan S. 1350 N WESTMORELAND RD, DALLAS METEROCARE 75211 #495-21-1971 L1982 **P CHP** *020 †75

REDDY, Rathidevi M. 16800 DALLAS PKWY, STE 150 75248 #495-21-1983 L1994 **P** *020 †75

REDDY, Sandeep Guduru. SOUTHWESTERN MED, UNIV OF TEXAS 75390 #048-04-2001 L2006 **AI** *012

REDDY, Suman. ■ 75204 #048-14-2001 L2006 **IM** *020 †20

REDDY, Virginia. ■ 75209 #048-04-2001 L2006 **RHU** *012

REDFIELD, Vance Allan. 3500 GASTON AVE, BAYLOR UNIV MED CTR 75246 #030-05-1985 L1991 **NPM PD** *020 †20

REDISH, Gregory Alan. 9330 POPPY DR STE 40 75218 #017-20-1978 L1982 **CD** *020 †20

REECE, Edward Martin. 5720 FOREST PARK RD STE 1 75235 #038-06-2003 L2008 **PS** *012

REED, Jason Thomas. 3600 GASTON AVE, STE 261 75246 #004-01-1996 L2001 **PTH** *020 †50

REED, Kenneth Lyle. 8220 WALNUT HILL LN, STE 202 LB#98 75231 #048-02-1980 L1980 **AN IM** *020 †20,05

REED, Melanie L. 3600 GASTON AVE, WADLEY TOWER SUITE 454 75246 #048-15-2001 L2004 **FM** *020

REED, Scott E. 13601 PRESTON RD, STE 900 75240 #048-02-1994 L1996 **AN** *020 †05

REED, William Gary. 5323 HARRY HINES BLVD, DEPT INTERNAL MEDICINE 75390 #048-12-1977 L1977 **IM EM** *020 †20

REEDER, Steven Frigaard. 7777 FOREST LN STE B248 75230 #040-02-1965 L1969 **GS VS** *020 †85

REESE, Daryl W. 12221 MERIT DR STE 1 75251 #010-03-2002 L2005 **EM** *020

REESE, Floyd Curtis. ■ 75248 #048-12-1963 L1966 **P** *020

REEVES, Bradford Frank. ■ 75206 #048-12-1962 L1962 **R** *071 †80

REFFINO PEREYRA, Maria R. 7522 CAMPBELL RD, STE 100 75248 #132-01-1975 L1998 **FM** *020 †18

REGE, Robert Vincent. 5323 HARRY HINES BLVD 75390 #041-14-1975 L1999 **GS** *040 †85

REGGIARDO, Diana Beatriz. 6303 HARRY HINES BLVD, STE 101 75235 #847-03-1982 L1991 **PD PDE** *020 †55

REHMAN, Zia-Ur. 303 E OVERTON RD 75216 #704-02-1989 L2001 **HO** *020 †20

REHMET, Robert Wallace. 3500 GASTON AVE 75246 #048-02-1966 L1966 **AN** *071 †05

REID, James Anthony. 1935 MOTOR ST, CENTER DALLA 75235 #039-01-2003 L2003 **CCP** *012 †55

REID, Stewart Ross. 10830 N CENTRAL EXPY, STE 330 75231 #065-01-1972 L1992 **AN** *020 †05

REILLY, Christopher W. 222 WELBORN ST 75219 #061-01-1988 **OP** *100

REILLY, Robert Franklin. 4500 S LANCASTER RD, DALLAS VA 111G1 75216 #010-02-1980 L2007 **NEP IM** *020 †20

REIMOLD, Andreas Michael. 5323 HARRY HINES BLVD, RHEUMATIC DISEASES DIVISIO 75390 #035-01-1984 L2000 **RHU IM** *050 †20

REIMOLD, Ekkehard Werner. 7777 FOREST LN 75230 #407-10-1953 L1968 **PD NEP** *020 †55

REIMOLD, Renate M. 7777 FOREST LN 75230 #407-33-1955 L1968 **FM IMG** *020 †18

REIMOLD, Sharon Coplen. 5323 HARRY HINES BLVD, HA9 - 133 75390 #028-02-1985 L2000 **CD IM** *020 †20

REINECK, John Robert. ■ 75206 #016-01-2002 L2007 **ORS** *020

REINERT, Carol Gladys. 4500 S LANCASTER RD 75216 #048-12-1969 L1969 **OPH OS** *020 †35

REINERT, Charles Marshall. 5323 HARRY HINES BLVD, UT SOUTHWESTERN MED CTR 75390 #048-12-1969 L1969 **ORS** *020 †18

REIS, Ololade Arajua. 3500 OAK LAWN STE 400, VISITING PHYSICIANS ASSOC. 75219 #010-03-1992 L1996 **IM** *020 †20

REITMANN, John Henry. 3636 DICKASON AVE 75219 #026-04-1945 L1962 **P** *071 †75

REKERDRES, Carolyn Marie. ■ 75244 #048-02-2006 **P** *012

REMBERT, Franklin Chester. 5323 HARRY HINES BLVD 75235 #021-05-1957 L1964 **AN** *071 †05

REMEDIOS, Lisa Gabrielle. 5323 HARRY HINES BLVD 75390 #026-04-2003 L2005 **OBG** *020

RENARD, Kyle Anders. ■ 75229 #048-12-1986 L1987 **PD** *075 †55

RENO, Sherine E. 7522 CAMPBELL RD STE 104, NATURAL CORRECTIONS, PA 75248 #048-04-1993 L1995 **PM** *020 †60

REPLOGLE, Robert Edward. 5323 HARRY HINES BLVD 75390 #016-02-1992 L2000 **NS** *020 †25

RESHEIDAT, Ashraf Musa. ■ 75201 #575-02-2002 L2008 **CCP** *012 †55

RESPESS, Benjamin Richard. 8730 KING GEORGE DR 75235 #048-14-1975 L1975 **EM** *020

REUSCHE, Mark David. 13601 PRESTON RD, STE 900W 75240 #036-05-1995 L2002 **AN** *020 †05

REYES, Hector M. 1420 VICEROY DR 75235 #048-12-1999 L2002 **NEP** *020 †20

REYES, Maria Teresa. 9101 N CENTRAL EXPY, STE 250 75231 #024-07-1999 L2003 **OBG** *020 †30

REYES, Nelson Ivan. 3500 W WHEATLAND RD, CHARLTON METHODIST HOSPITA 75237 #016-11-2003 L2007 **AN** *020

REYES, Oscar. 9330 AMBERTON PKWY 75243 #748-01-1975 L1985 **AN** *030 †05

REYNA, Michelle Renee. 221 W COLORADO BLVD, PAVILION I, STE 212 75208 #048-12-1998 L2003 **OBG** *020 †30

REYNOLDS, Ferman Ray, Jr. ■ 75204 #004-01-1987 L1990 **EM** *020

REYNOLDS, Jack. 5201 HARRY HINES BLVD, PARKLAND MEMORIAL HOSPITAL 75235 #035-01-1952 L1957 **DR** *071 †80

REYNOLDS, Michele Diane. 7515 GREENVILLE AVE, SUTIE 801 75231 #048-13-1982 L1983 **FM PLM** *020 †18

REZA, Julia Holly. ■ 75205 #048-12-2005 L2008 **PD** *012

REZAI, Maryam. 5323 HARRY HINES BLVD 75390 #048-02-1993 L1994 **P CHP** *020 †75

RHEE, Chanhaeng. 5323 HARRY HINES BLVD, SOUTHWESTERN MED 75390 #583-04-2000 L2007 **END** *100

RHEE, Kyoo Hwan. 7777 FOREST LN STE B 75230 #583-01-1972 L2002 **CCM PDC** *020 †55

RHODEN, Sandra Jean Allen. 8230 WALNUT HILL LN, STE 100 75231 #027-01-1973 L1997 **R** *020 †80

RHODES, Jennifer Lynn. ■ 75206 #041-01-2000 L2007 **PS** *100 †85

RICCIARDIELLO, Luigi. ■ 75201 #561-01-1994 **IM** *012

RICE, Elizabeth Eunhae. 5323 HARRY HINES BLVD, DEPT OF INT MED 75390 #012-05-2006 **IM** *012

RICE, Kim Melody. 3601 SWISS AVE 75204 #047-06-1993 L1996 **NEP** *020 †20

RICE, Michael T. 13601 PRESTON RD STE 1000 75240 #048-13-2002 L2004 **AN** *020 †05

RICE, Murray Chas. ■ 75254 #065-09-1959 L1978 **FM OM** *030

RICE, Norman S. 4131 N CENTRAL EXPY, METRO ANESTHESIA 75204 #010-03-1988 L1996 **AN** *020 †05

RICE-DORROUGH, Mollie F. 221 W COLORADO BLVD, STE 640 75208 #004-01-1990 L1992 **IM** *020

RICHARD, Gene Kevin. 1441 N BECKLEY AVE 75203 #038-40-1986 L1993 **PTH** *020 †50

RICHARDS, Ashleigh Anne. 1935 MOTOR ST 75235 #048-12-2003 L2005 **PDC** *012 †55

RICHARDS, Benjamin S, III. 2222 WELBORN ST 75219 #028-34-1981 L1988 **ORS OP** *020 †40

RICHARDS, James Kyle. 8160 WALNUT HILL LN, WALNUT HILL OBSTETRICS & 75231 #048-12-1975 L1975 **OBG** *020 †30

RICHARDSON, Amy Lynn. ■ 75254 #048-15-2005 L2008 **PD** *012

RICHARDSON, Chas Talmadge. 3409 WORTH ST STE 700 75246 #048-12-1966 L1966 **GE NTR** *020 †20

RICHARDSON, John Marshall. ■ 75205 #024-01-1970 L1979 **IM NEP** *020

RICHMOND, John Revere. 5303 ROSS AVE, HEALTHCARE 75206 #016-11-1976 L1977 **FM** *040 †18

RIDZ, Sherry Lynn. 5323 HARRY HINES BLVD, UT SOUTHWESTERN MED CTR 75390 #021-01-2000 L2004 **AI** *020 †20,03

RIETZ, Charles Wm. 3500 GASTON AVE 75246 #012-05-1971 L1974 **PTH** *020 †50

RIGGS, Leonard M, II. 8226 DOUGLAS AVE, STE 709 75225 #048-12-1968 L1968 **EM** *030

RIGSBY, Keith Douglas. 1441 N BECKLEY AVE, METHODIST HOSPITAL 75203 #047-06-2003 L2005 **IM** *020 †20

RILEY, Samuel Lee. 7777 FOREST LN, STE B238 75230 #020-02-1973 L1977 **AN** *030 †05

RINEHART, Brian Keith. 8160 WALNUT HILL LN # 114 75231 #023-01-1993 L2000 **OBG** *020 †30

RING, Gary. 6757 ARAPAHO RD, STE 711LB335 75248 #011-02-1972 L1978 **AN OS** *020 †05

RING, William Steves. 5323 HARRY HINES BLVD 75390 #024-01-1971 L1988 **TS PCS** *020 †85,90

RINKENBERGER, Robt Lowell. 5959 HARRY HINES BLVD, STE 202 75235 #019-02-1971 L1983 **CD** *020 †20

RINNERT, Kathy J. 5323 HARRY HNS BLVD MC8890, UNIN OF TEXAS SOUTHWESTERN 75390 #038-40-1991 L1997 **EM OS** *040

RIVAS, Homero. 5323 HARRY HINES BLVD, UTSW MED CTR SURGERY DPT 75390 #649-22-1993 L2005 **GS** *020 †85

RIVAS, Jose Rolando. 4633 N CENTRAL EXPY, STE 310 75205 #024-01-1986 L1988 **EM** *020

RIVERA, Antonio Francisco. 12221 MERIT DR STE 1 75251 #012-01-2002 L2006 **EM** *020 †16

RIVERA, Diana Belen. ■ 75248 #042-01-1980 **DR** *020

RIVERA, Rachel. ■ 75235 #048-13-2007 **IM** *012

RIVERA, Regina Paz. 12221 MERIT DR STE 1 75251 #016-42-2002 L2006 **EM** *020 †16

RIVERA, Wilfredo. 5323 HARRY HINES BLVD, UTSW EMERGENCY MEDICINE 75390 #042-01-1998 L2001 **EM ETX** *020 †16

RIVERA ALSINA, Manuel E. 1441 N BECKLEY AVE, DEPT OF MED EDUC 75203 #308-02-1974 L1981 **OBG NPM** *020 †30

RIVERA-ALVARADO, Jose M. 8440 WALNUT HILL LN, STE 700 75231 #041-01-1988 L1992 **IM CD** *020 †20

RIVERA TORRES MOIR, P. ■ 75209 #023-07-2002 L2008 **GE** *012 †20

RIVERO, Mary H. 5201 HARRY HINES BLVD, HOSPITAL SYSTEM 75235 #048-16-1990 L1993 **HO** *020 †20

RIZWAN, Syed Ali. 13154 COIT RD, STE 100 75240 #704-02-1982 L1998 **NEP** *020 †20

ROACH, Joe Garland, Jr. ■ 75243 #048-12-1945 L1945 **PD** *071

ROARK, Courtney. 9528 WEBB CHAPEL RD 75220 #048-12-1988 L1989 **FM** *020 †18

ROATEN, Shelley Poe, Jr. 6263 HARRY HINES BLVD, STE DF 3 75390 #048-13-1974 L1974 **FM** *040 †18

ROBBEN, John Whitmore. ■ 75219 #004-01-2007 **AN** *012

ROBBINS, Jacob Hyman. ■ 75251 #048-12-1948 L1949 **ADM** *071

ROBERTS, Albert Dee, Jr. 5323 HINES BLVD #8889, UT SOUTHWESTERN MED 75390 #048-12-1954 L1954 **IM NEP** *020 †20

ROBERTS, Bruce John. 7777 FOREST LN, NORTHLAKE OB GYN P A 75230 #035-08-1967 L1971 **OBG** *020 †30

ROBERTS, Catherin Ann. 6510 ABRAMS RD STE 210 75231 #048-04-1982 L1983 **CHP P** *020

ROBERTS, Cory Anthony. 8267 ELMBROOK DR, STE 100 75247 #030-05-1994 L2000 **PTH** *020 †50

ROBERTS, Joliekathe Culle. 5323 HARRY HINES BLVD, SOUTHWESTERN MED 75390 #048-14-2007 **P** *012

ROBERTS, L Clayton. 6301 GASTON AVE, EAST TOWER, SUITE 400 75214 #048-12-1987 L1988 **AN** *020 †05

ROBERTS, Lynne Jeanine. 7502 GREENVILLE AVE, STE 330 75231 #017-20-1978 L1980 **D PD** *020 †15,55

ROBERTS, Scott Wm. 5323 HARRY HINES BLVD, DEPARTMENT OF OB/GYN, MC90 75390 #019-02-1986 L1992 **OBG** *020 †30

ROBERTS, Tana Peterson. 5323 HARRY HINES BLVD, SOUTHWESTERN MED 75390 #048-14-2006 **PD** *012

ROBERTS, Tiffany Ann. 13601 PRESTON RD, STE 900 75240 #030-05-1994 L2000 **AN** *020 †05

ROBERTS, William Clifford. 3500 GASTON AVE, BAYLOR HEART/VASCULAR INST 75246 #012-05-1958 L1994 **ATP CD** *050 †20

ROBERTSON, Charles Arnold. ■ 75219 #016-06-1978 L1979 **FM OS** *075

ROBERTSON, Ellis Franklin. 12700 PARK CENTRAL DR, STE 430 75251 #019-02-1989 L1994 **RNR** *020 †80

ROBERTSON, Katheryn Joy. ■ 75248 #048-12-1962 L1962 **PUD CCM** *071 †20

ROBERTSON, Kiran Sehdev. 4144 N CENTRAL EXPY, STE 700 75204 #019-02-1994 L1997 **AN** *020 †20

ROBERTSON, Wm Douglas. 3500 GASTON AVE, DEPARTMENT OF RADIOLOGY 75246 #061-01-1969 L1997 **R** *071 †80

ROBINS, Keith I. 11912 JAMESTOWN RD 75230 #048-12-1952 L1952 **PD** *071 †55

ROBINSON, Albert Gordon. 1400 STEMMONS AVE 75208 #048-02-1963 L1963 **PD** *071 †55

ROBINSON, Amanda Nicole. SOUTHWESTERN MED, UNIV OF TEXAS 75390 #048-12-2006 **GS** *012

ROBINSON, Lamar Boynton. 1929 RECORD CROSSING RD 75235 #021-01-1979 L1985 **OBG** *020

ROBINSON, Maria C. 1400 N WESTMORELAND RD, DE HARO SALDIVAR HEALTH CE 75211 #025-07-1992 L1995 **IM** *020 †20

ROBINSON, Trayce L. 1400 N WESTMORELAND RD, DEHARO SALDIVAR HEALTH CEN 75211 #048-12-1996 L1998 **PD** *020 †55

ROCHA, Ricardo Armando. 3330 DOUGLAS AVE 75219 #176-01-1956 L1966 **GP GS** *020

ROCHE, Steve Andrew. 12201 MERIT DR STE 250 75251 #035-06-1982 L1984 **P** *020 †75

ROCHE, Vivyenne M. 5323 HARRY HINES BLVD, U.T. SOUTHWESTERN MEDICAL 75390 #539-06-1987 L1999 **IM IMG** *020 †20

ROCHELLE, Jethro Battle. 4500 S LANCASTER RD, 11C 75216 #048-02-1953 L1953 **IM** *020 †20

RODAN, Aylin Rachel. ■ 75229 #005-02-2004 L2008 **IM** *020 †20

RODEN, Shannon L. 1935 MOTOR ST, DEPARTMENT OF ANESTHESIOLO 75235 #048-14-2002 L2006 **PAN** *020 †05

RODRIGUE, Renaud Paul. 8230 WALNUT HILL LN, STE 320 75231 #021-05-1988 L1997 **APM** *020 †05

RODRIGUES, Stephen S. 5445 LA SIERRA DR, STE 102 75231 #010-03-1983 L1997 **FM PME** *020 †18

RODRIGUEZ, Erin S. ■ 75235 #048-12-2008 *012

RODRIGUEZ, Norberto. 1935 MOTOR ST STE D, CHILDREN'S MEDICAL CENTER 75235 #042-01-1994 L2001 **PD** *020 †55

RODRIGUEZ, Raul Castillo. 1400 N WESTMORELAND RD 75211 #048-04-1984 L1985 **PD** *020 †55

RODRIGUEZ, Raul Pedro. 7839 PARK LN, STE 120 75225 #048-12-1983 L1983 **GS PS** *020 †85

RODRIGUEZ, Rene. ■ 75390 #048-12-2002 L2006 **AN** *100 †05

RODRIGUEZ CERRATO, V. UNIV TX SOUTHWESTERN MED S 75235 #847-04-1990 **PDI** *100

RODRIGUEZ-LAGUER, Myriam. 4500 S LANCASTER RD, DALLAS VA HOSP 75216 #308-03-1980 L1985 **IM PHP** *020

RODRIGUEZ RUESGA, Roberto. 3409 WORTH ST STE 500, SAMMONS TOWER 75246 #649-02-1990 L2001 **CRS** *020 †85,10

ROE, Charles Rider. 3812 ELM ST 75226 #036-07-1964 L1997 **PD OS** *050

ROE, Kimberlea A. 8160 WALNUT HILL LN, STE 304 75231 #048-02-1993 L1997 **OBG** *020 †30

ROEHRBORN, Claus Georg. 5323 HARRY HINES BLVD #148, UT SOUTHWESTERN MED CTR 75390 #409-06-1980 L1990 **U** *020 †95

ROFFE, Jacob E. 6757 ARAPAHO RD, STE 711 PMB 335 75248 #649-14-1980 L1989 **AN** *020

ROFFMAN, Joel Alan. 411 N WASHINGTON AVE 75246 #024-05-1975 L1980 **CD** *020 †20

ROGERS, Beverly Barton. 1935 MOTOR ST, CHILDREN'S MEDICAL CENTER 75235 #048-02-1982 L1985 **PTH** *050 †50

ROGERS, Donza Jenai. ■ 75204 #025-12-2003 L2006 **PD** *020 †55

ROGERS, Hubert Paul. 2997 LBJ FWY, STE 215 75234 #048-12-1977 L1977 **DR** *020 †80

ROGERS, Kent Eugene. 5151 HARRY HINES BLVD 75235 #048-12-1971 L1975 **IM** *020 †20

ROGERS, Lon Edmond. ■ 75229 #048-12-1959 L1959 **D HEM** *071 †55,15

ROGERS, Tammie L. 3450 W WHEATLAND RD, STE 325 75237 #028-03-1994 L1995 **IM** *020 †20

ROGERS, Zora R. 5323 HARRY HINES BLVD, DEPT OF PEDIATRICS 75390 #005-18-1983 L1987 **PD PHO** *020 †55

ROGOFF, Thomas Michael. 7777 FOREST LN, STE C675 75230 #038-06-1972 L1977 **HS** *020 †20

ROHRICH, Rodney James. 411 N WASHINGTON AVE, STE 6000 75246 #048-04-1979 L1979 **PS HS** *020 †65

ROIG, Andres Ignacio. ■ 75219 #042-02-2001 L2006 **GE** *020

ROLAND, Cynthia R. ■ 75219 #048-12-2008 *012

ROLAND, Peter Sargent. 5323 HARRY HINES BLVD, UT SOUTHWESTERN MEDICAL CE 75390 #048-02-1976 L1985 **OTO NO** *020 †45

ROLLINS, Nancy Katherine. 1935 MOTOR ST DEPT RAD 75235 #048-02-1982 L1983 **PDR RNR** *020 †80

ROMAN, Antonio. 3600 GASTON AVE STE 1155 75246 #042-01-1993 L1995 **PYG** *020 †75

ROMANS, Bradford Lane. 8215 WESTCHESTER DR, STE 240 75225 #048-12-1984 L1985 **IM** *020 †20

ROMERO, Jorge Antonio. 3600 GASTON AVE STE 901 75246 #024-01-1972 L1997 **N** *020 †75

ROMERO-JOSEPH, Raul A. 1135 N BISHOP AVE, WOMEN'S SPECIALTY CENTER 75208 #042-02-2002 L2006 **OBG** *020

RON, Victor Hugo. 8 MEDICAL PKWY, STE 301PLAZA 75234 #319-04-1983 L2001 **IM** *020 †20

RONDEROS, Jaime R. 13601 PRESTON RD, STE 900W 75240 #001-02-1983 L1994 **AN PD** *020 †55,05

RONDON, Luisa. 1400 N WESTMORELAND RD 75211 #308-05-1988 L1995 **PD** *020 †55

ROPER, Suzanne Gwynne. ■ 75219 #020-02-2005 L2007 **PD** *012

ROPPOLO, Lynn Palacol. 5323 HARRY HINES BLVD, DIVISION OF EMERGENCY MEDI 75390 #005-18-1998 L2002 **EM** *020 †16

ROQUEMORE, Anna C. ■ 75204 #048-12-2003 L2007 *012

ROSE, Patrick F. 8215 WESTCHESTER DR, STE 111 75225 #048-12-1953 L1953 **PD CD** *071 †55

ROSE, Roy R. ■ 75229 #047-06-1949 L1966 **GP GS** *071

ROSEN, Robert Kenneth. 3434 SWISS AVE, STE 330 75204 #048-12-1977 L1977 **IM** *020 †20

ROSEN, Robin Susan. 5323 HARRY HINES BLVD, DEPARTMENT OF OB/GYN 75390 #005-19-1983 L2000 **OBG OS** *020 †19,30

ROSENBAUM, David Harrison. ■ 75201 #020-02-2001 L2004 **GS** *012

ROSENBERG, Max Yale. ■ 75225 #028-34-1954 L1958 **GYN** *020 †20

ROSENBERG, Roger Newman. 5323 HARRY HINES BLVD, UNIV TEXAS SW MED CTR 75390 #016-06-1964 L1974 **N** *050 †75

ROSENBLATT, Barbara G. 13601 PRESTON RD, STE 900 75240 #011-03-1990 L1994 **AN** *020 †05

ROSENBLATT, Randall Lee. 5323 HARRY HINES BLVD, STOP IM 75390 #017-20-1973 L1975 **PUD CCM** *040 †20

ROSENER, Gregory Lee. 5201 HARRY HINES BLVD 75235 #030-05-1981 L1983 **AN** *020 †05

ROSENFELD, Chas Richard. 5323 HARRY HINES BLVD, UT SOUTHWESTERN MED CTR 75390 #012-05-1966 L1973 **NPM PD** *040 †55

ROSENFELD, Craig Sterling. 5420 LYNDON B JOHNSON FWY 75240 #028-46-1979 L1994 **ON HO** *020 †20

ROSENFELDT, Wolfgang P. 6350 LBJ FWY STE 2, UT SOUTHWESTERN MEDICAL CE 75240 #048-02-2003 L2005 **P** *100

ROSENSTEIN, David Michael. 1441 N BECKLEY AVE, MEDICAL EDUCATION 75203 #048-15-2002 L2006 **MPD** *020 †20

ROSENSTOCK, David S. 3443 W WHEATLAND RD 75237 #270-01-1970 L1978 **RHU IM** *020 †20

ROSENSTOCK, Julio. 7777 FOREST LN, STE C618 75230 #270-01-1975 L1985 **END DIA** *050 †20

ROSENTHAL, Jonathan E. ■ 75220 #048-12-2000 L2003 **IM** *100 †20

ROSENTHAL, Leon D. 5477 GLEN LAKES DR, STE 100-125 75231 #649-01-1983 L1986 **SME P** *020 †75

ROSENTHAL, Michael Robt. 8210 WALNUT HILL LN, PROFESSIONAL BLDG 1 STE. 6 75231 #048-12-1971 L1971 **P** *020

ROSENTHAL, Robert Louis. 621 N HALL ST, STE 500 75226 #035-01-1978 L1981 **CD** *020 †20

ROSHANAEI-MOGHADDAM, Babak. ■ 75204 #517-12-2000 L2007 **P** *012

ROSHANRAVAN, Shayzreen M. 5323 HARRY HINES BLVD, UT SOUTHWESTERN MEDICAL CE 75390 #048-12-2002 L2006 **OBG** *100 †30

ROSKOS, S Richard. 4514 COLE AVE STE 1010 75205 #026-04-1968 L1981 **P OS** *020 †75

ROSNES, Jon Scott. 8160 WALNUT HILL LN, STE 210 75231 #005-12-1990 L2003 **OBG MFM** *020 †20

ROSS, Harding Dudley. 5925 FOREST LN, STE 218 75230 #048-13-1980 L1980 **OTO** *020 †45

ROSS, Samuel Lee. 7920 ELMBROOK DR, STE 120 75247 #048-13-1980 L1980 **FM** *020 †18

ROSSI, Edith Marta. 8200 WALNUT HILL LN 75231 #781-05-1956 L1971 **CHP P** *071

ROSSI, Renee Marie. 7777 FOREST LN STE C- 75230 #025-01-1986 L1997 **OTO** *020 †45

ROTHSTEIN, Joseph Martin. 3600 GASTON AVE, BARNETT TOWER STE 1004 75246 #048-12-1981 L1981 **IM** *020 †20

ROTHSTEIN, Roni L. ■ 75230 #048-12-1983 L1983 **PD PN** *071 †55

ROTTENBERG, Leon. ■ 75225 #025-07-1939 L1939 **GP GS** *020

ROUSH, Karen Sue. 1441 N BECKLEY AVE 75203 #004-01-1996 L2001 **BBK** *020 †50

ROUSSEAU, Wyatt E. 8220 WALNUT HILL LN, STE 408 75231 #047-05-1969 L1970 **PUD IM** *020 †20

ROUTH, L Keith. 411 N WASHINGTON AVE #2200 75246 #048-16-1986 L1987 **CD IM** *020 †20

ROWE, Kinsey Elizabeth. ■ 75204 #048-12-2008 *012

ROY, Dave Ashish. ■ 75201 #001-02-2005 L2008 **DR** *012

ROY, Rosemarie Anna. 3500 GASTON AVE, DEPT OF PATHOLOGY 75246 #037-01-2002 L2004 **PTH** *012

ROYAPPA, Sudha Meena. 5461 LA SIERRA DR 75231 #027-01-2001 L2004 **IM** *020 †20

ROYER, Christian Thomas. 7777 FOREST LN STE C106 75230 #041-02-1996 L2001 **ORS** *020 †40

ROZEMBERG, David. 8 MEDICAL PKWY, STE 303 75234 #264-01-1954 L1979 **GYN OBS** *071 †30

ROZEN, Shai M. ■ 75204 #550-02-1997 L2006 **CFS** *100

RUBENFIELD, Arnold David. 5323 HARRY HINES BLVD, DEPT OF OTOLARYNGOLOGY 75390 #041-12-1971 L1985 **OTO** *040 †45

RUBENSTEIN, Melissa Anne. ■ 75205 #048-04-2004 L2006 **D** *012

RUBEY, Charles Nathan. 8210 WALNUT HILL LN # 910 75231 #017-20-1968 L1969 **GS** *020 †85

RUBIN, Andrew Ryan. ■ 75219 #023-01-1999 L2001 **EM** *020 †16

RUBIN, Craig Douglas. 5323 HARRY HINES BLVD 75235 #033-05-1982 L1983 **IMG IM** *050 †20

RUBIN, Howard A. 12890 HILLCREST RD STE 203 75230 #048-04-1988 L1989 **D** *020 †15

RUBIN, Michael A. ■ 75202 #048-15-2004 L2008 **N** *012

RUBY, Charlie. 3500 W WHEATLAND RD 75237 #048-78-1999, ▲ L2000 **FM** *020 †18

RUCH, Raynal. ■ 75206 #048-12-2002 L2008 **DR** *100 †80

RUDMAN, Brian David. 7557 RAMBLER RD STE 7 75231 #028-03-1992 L1996 **AN** *020 †05

RUDOLPH, Carrye Anne. ■ 75230 #012-05-2005 L2008 **PD** *012

RUFF, James Edward. ■ 75219 #027-01-1962 L1962 **P** *072 †75

RUFF, Michael Edward. 5499 GLEN LAKES DR STE 100 75231 #048-02-1978 L1984 **AI PDA** *020 †55,03

RUGGIERO, Rosechelle Mary. 5201 HARRY HINES BLVD, HOUSE STAFF/GME OFFICE 75235 #010-02-2005 L2006 **IM** *012

RUIZ, Jose Javier. 809 SINGLETON BLVD, LOS BARRIOS UNIDOS COMM 75212 #042-02-2000 L2004 **FM** *020

RUIZ-DAVILA, Dennisse. 5323 HARRY HINES BLVD, SOUTHWESTERN MED 75390 #042-02-2003 L2007 **OBG** *020

RUIZ-VELASCO RIZO, Jesus. ■ 75219 #649-32-1976 L1994 **PD** *020

RUK, Michael T. 7777 FOREST LN, NORTHLAKE OB GYN P A 75230 #048-12-1996 L1999 **OBG** *020 †30

RUPP, Timothy Joseph. 5201 HARRY HINES BLVD, DIVISION OF EMERGENCY MEDI 75235 #041-13-1995 L1998 **EM** *020 †16

RUSH, Augustus John, Jr. 5323 HARRY HINES BLVD 75390 #035-01-1968 L1978 **P IM** *050 †75

RUSHING, Elisabeth Jane. 5323 HARRY HINES BLVD, STOP 9031 75390 #012-01-1980 L1994 **NP** *020 †75,50

RUSHING, Lige B, Jr. 8210 WALNUT HILL LN, STE 120 75231 #048-04-1951 L1951 **RHU IM** *020 †20

RUSSELL, Thomas J. 2801 LEMMON AVE, STE 310 75204 #048-12-1986 L1987 **OPH** *020 †35

RUSSELL, Thomas Kemp. 8200 WALNUT HILL LN 75231 #048-12-1975 L1975 **AN CD** *020 †05

RUSSO, Michael Anthony. 5323 HARRY HINS BLVD #9063, DEPT OF PEDIATRICS 75390 #001-06-1998 L2001 **PG** *020 †55

RUSSO, Rachel Andrea. ■ 75219 #048-12-2006 L2007 **P** *012

RUTHERFORD, Andrew Cright. ■ 75238 #048-12-2008 *012

RUTHERFORD, Chas Storey. 411 N WASHINGTON AVE, STE 7000 75246 #048-12-1980 L1980 **ORS OAR** *020 †40

RUTHERFORD, Cynthia Jean. 5323 HARRY HINES BLVD, STOP 9031 75390 #671-01-1969 L1996 **HEM** *050

RUTHERFORD, John D. 5323 HARRY HINES BLVD, MC 8831 75390 #671-01-1969 L1994 **CD** *020 †20

RYAN, Matthew W. ■ 75390 #048-02-1996 L2001 **OTO** *020 †45

RYBKIN, Igor Ivanovich. 5323 HARRY HINES BLVD 75390 #913-27-1993 **IM** *012

RYDER, Kristi Lane. 7777 FOREST LN, NORTHLAKE OB GYN P A 75230 #048-13-1999 L2003 **OBG** *020 †30

RYMELL, Thomas A. 13601 PRESTON RD, STE 900W 75240 #048-13-1991 L1992 **AN** *020 †05

RYTLEWSKI, Jason Alan. ■ 75214 #025-01-2005 **IM** *012

SAAD, Assad Joe. 1441 N BECKLEY AVE, DEPT OF PATHOLOGY 75203 #605-01-1985 L1991 **PTH PCP** *020 †50

SAADEH, Sherif Nabil. 3500 GASTON AVE, 4 ROBERTS 75246 #575-01-1993 L2003 **GE** *020 †20 ‡

SAADI, Paul. 9330 POPPY DR STE 300 75218 #041-02-1992 L1998 **ORS OSS** *020 †40

SAALFIELD, James Geo. 5500 DRANE DR, 291423596 75209 #021-01-1971 L1976 **U** *020 †95

SAAVEDRA, Jesus. UNIV TX SOUTHWESTERN MED S 75235 #847-13-1990 **PDI** *100

SABOORIAN, Mohammad H. 5323 HARRY HINES BLVD, STOP 9031 75390 #409-21-1984 L1992 **PTH** *020 †50

SACCO, David John. 1935 MOTOR ST 75235 #016-43-1995 L2002 **NS** *020 †25

SACKETT, James Reginald. 9301 N CENTRAL EXPY, STE 40 75231 #021-01-1983 L1989 **ORS OP** *020 †40

SACKLER, Jay P. ■ 75230 #035-09-1953 L1977 **R** *071 †80

SACKLER, Marian Eleanor. 712 N WASHINGTON AVE 75246 #048-12-1990 L1993 **RHU IM** *020 †20

SADEGHIAN, Hamid. ■ 75235 #517-08-1996 **N** *012

SADEK, Hesham Ali. ■ 75390 #915-04-1995 L2005 **CD** *020 †20

SADLER, John Zell. 5323 HARRY HINES BLVD 75235 #017-20-1980 L1984 **P** *062 †75

SAEED, Qaiser. 12221 MERIT DR STE 1 75251 #704-02-1997 L2006 **IM** *100 †20

SAEEDI, Osamah Jawaid. ■ 75235 #048-12-2007 *012

SAFARI, Nasrin. ■ 75205 #517-01-1991 L2007 **IM** *020 †20
SAFEEK, Abraham. 133 N INDUSTRIAL BLVD 5T 75207 #047-07-1998 L2005 **FM** *020 †18
SAFO, Yaw. 3500 W WHEATLAND RD, CHARLTON METHODIST HOSP 75237 #412-01-1976 L1983 **AN** *020 †05
SAGALOWSKY, Arthur Isaac. 5323 HARRY HINES BLVD, UT SOUTHWESTERN MED CTR 75390 #017-20-1973 L1978 **U** *020 †95
SAHA, Devjani. 5323 HARRY HINES BLVD, SOUTHWESTERN MED 75390 #035-09-2003 L2007 **AN** *100
SAHERWALA, Shabbir Ismail. 4645 SAMUELL BLVD 75228 #704-02-1988 L1996 **P** *020 †55
SAHIN, Bogachan. ■ 75235 #048-12-2008 *012
SAILORS, Joseph L. 5323 HARRY HINES BLVD, UT SOUTHESTERN-DEPT PATH 75390 #025-07-1991 L2001 **PCP ATP** *020 †50
SAINT-CYR, Michel. 5323 HARRY HINES BLVD, DEPT OF PLASTIC SURGERY 75390 #067-02-1997 L2004 **PS HS** *020
SAKAI, Tomoya. ■ 75219 #048-12-2005 **PM** *012
SAKHAEE, Khashayar. 5323 HARRY HINES BLVD 75235 #517-05-1974 L1983 **NEP** *040
SAKHAI, Hadi. 1935 MOTOR ST RM D03.309, ANESTHESIOLOGISTS FOR CHIL 75235 #038-40-1999 L2004 **PAN** *020 †05
SALAM, Ambareen. 7777 FOREST LN, STE C420 75230 #048-13-1994 L1995 **IM** *020 †20
SALAND, Karen Bassichis. 8210 WALNUT HILL LN, STE 812 75231 #048-12-1999 L2003 **OPH** *020 ‡
SALAS, Jeremy Rey. 8200 SOUTHWESTERN BLVD #10 75206 #048-12-2004 L2004 **N** *012
SALAZAR, Angel. ■ 75214 #048-14-2002 L2005 **FM** *020 †18
SALCIDO, Paul Anthony. 13601 PRESTON RD, STE 900 75240 #003-01-1992 L1996 **AN** *020 †05
SALDANA, Luis E. 8160 WALNUT HILL LN, STE 007 75231 #048-12-1984 L1987 **EM FM** *020
SALDANA, Luis E. 8160 WALNUT HILL LN, STE 007 75231 #847-02-1970 L1974 **EM** *020
SALDIVAR, Jorge Arturo. 1441 N BECKLEY AVE 75203 #026-04-1980 L1981 **OBG** *020 †30
SALEH, Walid Ali. 7777 FOREST LN, STE C638 75230 #605-01-1987 L2005 **REN** *020 †30
SALINAS, Heriberto. 2445 W NORTHWEST HWY, STE 105 75220 #649-02-1986 L1992 **FM OM** *020 †18
SALINAS, Marisa C. ■ 75208 #048-13-1996 L1999 **FM** *040 †18
SALO MEADOR, Karen E. 1935 MOTOR ST, CHILD MED CTR DALLAS ADMIN 75235 #048-14-1997 L1998 **PD** *030 †55
SALTZMANN, Robert Michael. 75204 #016-06-2005 **OPH** *012
SALVAGGIO, John Anthony. 5521 GREENVILLE AVE, STE 104-248 75206 #021-05-1989 L1992 **IM** *020 †20
SALVATORE, Christine M.. 5323 HARRY HINES BLVD, F3202 75390 #561-24-1993 L2007 **PDI** *100 †55
SALYER, Kenneth Everett. 7777 FOREST LN, STE C717 75230 #019-02-1962 L1964 **PS OS** *071 †85,65
SALZBERGER, Lynn A. 5230 MEDICAL CENTER DR 75235 #048-12-1993 L1994 **ATP FOP** *020 †50
SAM, Colleen. 5323 HARRY HINES BLVD, UT SOUTHWESTERN MED CTR 75390 #836-01-1990 L2006 **IM** *040 †20
SAMS, Shannan Renee. ■ 75204 #020-02-2004 L2004 **IM** *100 †20
SAMSON, Duke Staples. 5323 HARRY HINES BLVD 75235 #028-02-1969 L1971 **NS** *020 †25
SAMUELSON, Robert John. 4131 N CENTRAL EXPY, STE 435 75204 #048-12-1971 L1971 **AN** *020 †05
SANCHEZ, Pablo Jose. 5323 HARRY HINES BLVD, UT SOUTHWESTERN MEDICAL CE 75390 #041-12-1981 L1988 **PD NPM** *050 †55
SANCHEZ, Rey. 5952 ROYAL LN, STE 202 75230 #048-02-1974 L1974 **OTO A** *020 †45
SANCHEZ, Xochiti Blanca. 9440 POPPY DR 75218 #649-03-1974 L1977 **AN** *020 †05
SANCHEZ VELEZ, Catalina. ■ 75206 #264-16-2005 **IM** *012
SANDELL, Sharon R. ■ 75218 #048-02-1987 L1988 **PD** *020 †55
SANDERS, Clayton. ■ 75231 #048-14-2003 L2006 **DR** *012
SANDERS, John Paul. 7515 GREENVILLE AVE, STE 600 75231 #048-02-1973 L1973 **IM** *020 †20
SANDERS, John Walter. 1717 MAIN ST, STE 5200 75201 #048-02-1985 L1986 **EM** *020
SANDERS, Wilford M, Jr. ■ 75229 #048-12-1947 L1947 **U** *020 †95
SANDOVAL, Ruben Ernesto. 9330 POPPY DR STE 501, DIGESTIVE HEALTH ASSOC OF 75218 #030-06-1990 L1996 **GE IM** *020 †20
SANGA, Raghuram. 13601 PRESTON RD, STE 900 75240 #005-18-1990 L1994 **OS** *020 †05
SANGHANI, Vinaychandra V. 9440 POPPY DR 75218 #917-28-1976 L1982 **EM** *020
SANGHAVI, Sarah Fay. ■ 75235 #048-12-2008 *012
SANKARAN, Aarthi. 3500 GASTON AVE, RADIOLOGY 1ST FL ROBERTS 75246 #048-16-2001 L2004 **DR** *020 †80
SANKARY, Edward M. 13601 PRESTON RD, STE 900W 75240 #048-12-1962 L1962 **AN PME** *020 †05
SANTANGELO, William. 5323 HARRY HINES BLVD, DIV OF DIGESTIVE & LIVER 75390 #011-02-1980 L1985 **GE IM** *040 †20
SANTAROSA, Julianne Marie. SOUTHWESTERN MED, UNIV OF TEXAS 75390 #035-06-2007 **GS** *012
SANTIAGO-MUNOZ, Patricia. 5323 HARRY HINES BLVD, DEPT OF OB/GYN - MC 9032 75390 #042-01-1996 L2002 **OBG** *020 †30
SANTINI, Noel O. ■ 75201 #042-01-1993 L1994 **IM** *020 †20
SANTOS, Alejandro. 2909 S HAMPTON RD, STE C106 75224 #048-02-1985 L1987 **GS** *020
SANTOS, Roberto Parulan. ■ 75214 #748-01-1995 **PDI** *012 †55
SANTOS-RAMOS, Rigoberto. 5323 HARRY HINES BLVD, U.T. SOUTHWESTERN MEDICAL 75390 #429-01-1960 L1974 **OBG** *071 †30
SAPORITO, Frank Charles. 3900 JUNIUS ST, STE 710 75246 #048-12-2001 L2006 **DS D** *020 †15
SARAF, Manohar Krishna. 13601 PRESTON RD 75240 #495-01-1989 L1998 **AN** *020
SARETSKY, Neil Howard. 5468 LA SIERRA DR STE 100 75231 #025-01-1974 L1976 **PS** *020 †85,65
SARODE, Ravindra S. 5303 HARRY HINES BLVD, UTSWMC CS3114 75390 #495-75-1981 L2001 **BBK** *020 †50
SARODE, Venetia Rumnong. ■ 75205 #495-78-1984 L2001 **PTH** *020 †50
SARRIS, Arthur Lewis. 5959 HARRY HINES BLVD, STE 420 75235 #056-05-1955 L1957 **ORS** *020 †40
SATERIALE, Mark. 1909 HI LINE DR, INTERNATIONAL RADIOLOGY GR 75207 #024-16-1984 L1999 **DR IM** *020 †80
SATHY, Ashoke. ■ 75209 #048-12-2003 L2008 **ORS** *012
SATPATHY, Satyajit. 4500 S LANCASTER RD, MAIL CODE 116A 75216 #495-13-1991 L2004 **P** *020 †75
SATTAR, Muhammad Aijaz. 303 E OVERTON RD, DEPARTMENT OF ADULT MEDICI 75216 #704-02-1989 L2000 **IMG** *020 †20

SAUL, Noel Denise. 13601 PRESTON RD, STE 900 75240 #018-03-1990 L1991 **AN** *020 †05
SAUNDERS, Clark T. 4131 N CENTRAL EXPY, METRO ANESTHESIA 75204 #048-12-1988 L1989 **AN** *020 †05
SAUNDERS, David Henry. 7150 GREENVILLE AVE, STE-305 75231 #038-40-1970 L1977 **OPH** *020 †35
SAUNDERS, Justin Taylor. ■ 75201 #048-13-2005 L2008 **IM** *012
SAUNDERS, Leonard Anthony. ■ 75248 #035-08-1992 L1997 **FM** *072 †18
SAVAGE, Clare Michelle. ■ 75225 #048-02-2000 L2006 **VIR** *020 †80
SAVIN, Michael Alan. 7777 FOREST LN, STE D400 75230 #041-12-1969 L1987 **ON HEM** *020
SAVINO, Daniel Angel. 3500 GASTON AVE, DEPT 75246 #132-04-1972 L1982 **PTH** *020 †50
SAWAYA, Rasha Dorothy Tou. 5323 HARRY HINES BLVD 75390 #605-01-2004 **PD** *012
SAXEMA, Kirti. 5323 HARRY HINES BLVD, UT SOUTHWESTERN MEDICAL CE 75390 #473-02-1992 L2006 **P** *020 †75
SAXENA, Ramesh. 5323 HARRY HINES BLVD, DIV OF NEPHROLOGY 75390 #495-45-1979 L1999 **NEP** *020 †20
SAYE, Timothy David. 13601 PRESTON RD, STE 900 75240 #048-12-1986 L1993 **AN** *020 †05
SCAGLIONI, Pier Paolo. 5323 HARRY HINES BLVD, HEMATOLOGY/ONCOLOGY 75390 #561-09-1989 L2007 **ON IM** *020 †20
SCALFANO, Laura Hamaway. 1935 MOTOR ST 75235 #001-06-1993 L1996 **PD** *020 †55
SCANNELL, Stacy M. 4500 S LANCASTER RD, DEPT OF MENTAL HEALTH 75216 #048-12-1988 L1989 **P ADP** *020 †75
SCARDELLO, Elizabeth Rose. 5323 HARRY HINES BLVD, SOUTHWESTERN MED 75390 #048-12-2006 AN *012
SCHAFFER, Joseph Ira. 5323 HARRY HINES BLVD, U.T. SOUTHWESTERN MED CTR 75390 #038-41-1987 L1997 **OBG** *020 †30
SCHAFFER, Martin Harry. 9400 N CENTRAL EXPY, STE 1212 75231 #005-11-1975 L1988 **P** *020 †75
SCHATZ, Daniela M. 809 SINGLETON BLVD, LOS BARRIOS URIDOS COMM CL 75212 #286-07-1970 L1988 **PD** *020
SCHAUB, Timothy Allen. SOUTHWESTERN MED, UNIV OF TEXAS 75390 #016-11-2002 L2007 **PS** *012 †85
SCHECTER, Arnold Joel. 5323 HARRY HINES BLVD, V2 112E MPH PRG AT UTSW 75390 #010-03-1962 L1969 **OM PHP** *040 †70
SCHEIDEMAN, Erin Elizabet. ■ 75235 #048-13-2007 **PD** *012
SCHEINBERG, Robt Russell. 8210 WALNUT HILL LN # 130 75231 #047-06-1985 L1986 **ORS OSM** *020 †40
SCHERFFIUS, Stephen W. 5207 MCKINNEY AVE STE 26 75205 #048-12-1975 L1975 **PYA P** *020
SCHERMERHORN, James E. 1151 N BUCKNER BLVD # 206, STE 206 75218 #048-12-1980 L1980 **OBG** *020 †30
SCHILLER, Lawrence R. 3500 GASTON AVE 3, BAYLOR UNIV MED CTR 75246 #041-02-1972 L1978 **GE IM** *020 †20
SCHILSKY, Angela Marie. ■ 75214 #016-45-2002 L2005 **DR** *100 †80
SCHINDEL, David T. 1935 MOTOR ST RM D03-310Y, DEPT OF PEDIATRIC SURGERY 75235 #048-12-1992 L2000 **PDS** *020 †25
SCHLESSER, Michael A. 5939 HARRY HINES BLVD 75235 #018-03-1976 L1980 **P** *020 †75
SCHLOMER, Bruce Jeremy. 5323 HARRY HINES BLVD, UTSW UROLOGY DEPT 75390 #028-02-2006 **U** *012
SCHLUMBRECHT, Matthew Pet. 5201 HARRY HINES BLVD, DEPARTMENT OF OB/GYN 75235 #048-14-2004 L2006 **OBG** *012
SCHLUTER, Walter Wm. PO BOX 612325, CDC DFW QUARANTINE STATION 75261 #030-06-1990 L1991 **GPM FM** *062 †18,70
SCHMALSTIEG, Aurelia M. ■ 75204 #048-12-2006 **IM** *012
SCHMIDT, Kelly Suzanne. 5323 HARRY HINES BLVD, DEPT OF NEUROLOGY 75390 #010-01-2002 **NS** *012
SCHMIDT-NOWARA, Wolfgang. 4331 BROOKVIEW DR 75220 #038-06-1967 L1997 **SME PUD** *072 †20
SCHNEIDER, Allen Robt. 3450 W WHEATLAND RD, STE 314 75237 #018-75-1973, ▲ L1974 **IM** *020 †20
SCHNEIDER, Gerald Arthur. 8350 MEADOW RD STE 270 75231 #010-01-1960 L1969 **P OS** *020
SCHNEIDER, Jay Warren. 6000 HARRY HINES BLVD, NB1, UT SOUTHWESTERN MEDICAL CE 75390 #008-01-1989 L2004 **CD** *020 †20
SCHNEIDER, Joseph H. 1935 MOTOR ST, CHILDRENS MED CTR 75235 #012-05-1995 L1997 **PD MDM** *020 †55
SCHNEIDER, Reva Elaine. 3500 GASTON AVE, MEDICAL CENT 75246 #048-16-2006 **IM** *012
SCHNEIDLER, Cynthia. 3600 GASTON AVE STE 905 75246 #048-14-1977 L1977 **ID** *020 †20
SCHNELL, John Lane. 8160 WALNUT HILL LN 75231 #040-02-2004 L2007 **EM** *020
SCHNIEDERJAN, Matthew Ble. ■ 75204 #048-02-2004 **GS** *012
SCHNITZER, Ben. 3600 GASTON AVE STE 508 75246 #048-12-1957 L1957 **U** *020 †95
SCHNUTE, Karen Louise. 9323 GARLAND RD, STE 201 75218 #017-20-1981 L1984 **PD** *020 †55
SCHOEN-KIEWERT, Erich S. 6702 CAULFIELD DR 75248 #847-04-1977 L1995 **FM EM** *020 †18
SCHOENVOGEL, Robt Clifton. 3409 WORTH 540 SAMMONS TWR 75246 #048-12-1974 L1974 **U** *020 †95
SCHONFELD, Murry D. 5323 HARRY HINES BLVD, DEPT RAD 75235 #024-01-1951 L1955 **DR** *071 †80
SCHORGE, John Orland. 5323 HARRY HINES BLVD, DEPT OB-GYN 75390 #047-05-1993 L2000 **GO OBG** *020 †30
SCHORLEMER, Roger O'Lee. 8355 WALNUT HILL LN # 105 75231 #048-12-1964 L1965 **PD** *020 †55
SCHOTT, Lawrence H. 12700 PARK CENTRAL DR 75251 #011-03-1978 L1990 **RNR R** *071 †80
SCHRODER, Catherine A. 3500 GASTON AVE H102 75246 #048-16-2003 L2006 **IM** *020 †20
SCHROEDER, James G. 3500 GASTON AVE, BAYLOR UNIV MEDICAL CENTER 75246 #048-13-1992 L1993 **DR** *020 †80
SCHUBERT, Richard Darryl. 9301 N CENTRAL EXPY, STE 400 75231 #048-12-1979 L1979 **ORS** *020 †40
SCHULLER, Joris M, Jr. 3601 SWISS AVE 75204 #048-12-1995 L1997 **NEP** *020 †20
SCHULTZ, Barbara Ann. 5323 HARRY HINES BLVD, DEPT OTOLARYNGOLOGY 75390 #048-12-1980 L1980 **OTO** *020 †45
SCHULZ, Tommy Wade. 3920 WORTH ST 75246 #048-12-1978 L1978 **AN** *071 †05
SCHUMAN, Anastasia D. 5909 HARRY HINES BLVD 75235 #048-16-2001 L2003 **AN** *100 †05
SCHWADE, Jack Lester. 7537 BAXTERSHIRE DR 75230 #048-12-1966 L1966 **CD** *020 †20
SCHWARTZ, Armond Gluck, Jr. 221 W COLORADO BLVD # 630, METHODIST PAVILION II 75208 #048-12-1976 L1976 **GE** *020 †20 ‡
SCHWARTZ, Brian Gabriel. 3500 GASTON AVE, MEDICAL CENT 75246 #048-15-2005 L2007 **IM** *012

SCHWARTZ, John Chas. 3601 SWISS AVE, DALLAS NEPHROLOGY ASSOCIAT 75204 #056-05-1976 L1991 **IM NEP** *020 †20

SCHWARTZ, Robert Chas. 3878 OAK LAWN AVE STE 625 75219 #048-02-1974 L1974 **P** *020 †75

SCHWARZ, Barry Eugene. U TEX SW MED SCH, DEPT OBG 75390 #048-12-1968 L1968 **OBG** *040 †30

SCHWARZ, Donald Everett. 8200 WALNUT HILL LN, DEPT OF RAD ONCOLOGY 75231 #020-02-1972 L1981 **RO DR** *020 †80

SCHWARZ, Margaret Arlene. ■ 75230 #028-46-1987 L2008 **CCP** *020 †55

SCHWARZ, Roderich E. ■ 75230 #409-38-1984 L2007 **GS** *020 †85

SCHWEERS, John Jos. 13601 PRESTON RD, STE 900 75240 #048-04-1982 L1983 **AN** *020 †05

SCHWIMMER, Craig L. 6901 SNIDER PLZ, STE 225 75205 #012-05-1991 L2000 **OTO** *020 †45

SCHWIMMER, Shanon Smith. 7557 RAMBLER RD STE 7, STE 706 75231 #023-07-1994 L2000 **AN** *020 †05

SCORESBY, Tyler Wilson. 5201 HARRY HINES BLVD 75235 #048-12-2004 L2007 **OTO** *012

SCOTT, Bennie Bench. 3600 GASTON AVE, STE 605 75246 #039-01-1970 L1975 **NS** *020 †25 ‡

SCOTT, Byron Christopher. 1717 MAIN ST STE 5200 75201 #005-18-1990 L1995 **EM** *020 †16

SCOTT, Cynthia Lynn. ■ 75225 #051-04-1984 L1997 **IM** *020 †20

SCOTT, Daniel Emory. 8200 WALNUT HILL LN 75231 #048-12-1991 L1961 **OBG MFM** *071 †30

SCOTT, Daniel Joseph. 5323 HARRY HINES BLVD 75390 #021-05-1995 L1997 **GS** *020 †85

SCOTT, Larry Brian. 221 W COLORADO BLVD, STE 845 # 2 75208 #023-07-1988 L1995 **AN** *020 †05

SCOTT, Leigh A. 5909 HARRY HINES BLVD 75235 #048-02-1984 L1986 **OBG** *020 †30

SCOTT, Sarah Rodman. 5924 ROYAL LN, STE 104 75230 #048-12-1999 L2006 **D** *071 †15 ‡

SCOTT, Susan Marie. 1935 MOTOR ST 75230 #048-12-1982 L1985 **PD** *020 †55

SCOTT, Terilyn Rene. 7777 FOREST LN, STE C340 75230 #048-04-1998 L2002 **GE** *020 †20

SCOTT, Troy Wallace, III. 3600 GASTON AVE STE 906 75246 #017-20-1968 L1972 **U** *020 †95

SCOTT, William A. 1935 MOTOR ST 75235 #017-20-1982 L1990 **PDC PD** *020 †55

SCROGGINS, Virginia L. ■ 75219 #048-12-2001 L2006 **DR** *100 †80

SCRUGGS, Granger Ryan. 3535 WORTH ST, FL 1 75246 #048-02-2002 L2007 **RO** *100

SCRUGGS, R Pickett, III. 3535 WORTH ST, FL 1 75246 #047-06-1969 L1970 **RO** *020 †80

SEABROOK, Robert Todd. 5201 HARRY HINES BLVD 75235 #047-06-2005 L2007 **AN** *100

SEALE, Thomas M, IV. 75214 #048-12-2008 †012

SEALS, Michael Roy. 10 MEDICAL PKWY STE 201 75234 #027-01-1985 L1993 **N** *020 †75

SEARS, Laura Lea. 5924 ROYAL LN, STE 104-B 75230 #048-15-1984 L1988 **D** *020 †15

SEAY, Frank Oliver. ■ 75219 #048-04-1947 L1947 **IM** *071

SEBASTIAN, Lisa M. 3450 W WHEATLAND RD, STE 430 75237 #042-01-1992 L1997 **NEP** *020 †20

SEBASTIAN, Vinod Antony. ■ 75235 #495-63-2001 L2006 **TS** *012 †85

SECOR, John Wm. 8220 WALNUT HILL LN, STE 214 75231 #048-12-1979 L1979 **GE IM** *020 †20

SECREST, Leslie Harold. 8400 WALNUT HILL LN 75231 #048-12-1968 L1968 **P PYA** *020 †75

SEDDIGHZADEH, Marian M. 5323 HARRY HINES BLVD, DEPT OF OBG 75390 #048-15-2003 **OBG** *020

SEDIGHI, Hooman. 6161 HARRY HINES BLVD, STE 100 75235 #017-20-1988 L1992 **PM** *020 †60

SEE, Isaac. ■ 75220 #048-12-2008 *012

SEELEY, Christina E. ■ 75224 #048-12-2008 *012

SEGAL, Allen Tevis. ■ 75230 #048-12-1962 L1962 **A PDA** *071 †55,03

SEGAL, Mark Elliott. 6757 ARAPAHO RD, STE 711, LOCK BOX 335 75248 #032-01-1993 L1998 **AN** *020 †05

SEGOVIA, Arturo A. ■ 75244 #649-02-1961 L1970 **AN NTR** *020

SEHGAL, Supriya. 5323 HARRY HINES BLVD, DEPT OF INT MED 75390 #065-05-2003 **IM** *012

SEIBERT, Lori Shinell. 7777 FOREST LN 75230 #054-04-1998 L2001 **PD** *020 †55

SEIDEL, Clifford C. 148 SYNNEWOOD PROF BLDG 75224 #048-12-1949 L1949 **GP IM** *072

SEIDEL, Jack D. 1 MEDICAL PKWY STE 253 75234 #048-12-1987 L1988 **PD** *020 †55

SEIDENFELD, Steven M. 7777 FOREST LN STE B412 75230 #035-19-1977 L1980 **ID IM** *020 †20

SEIFER, Mark S. 4131 N CENTRAL EXPY, METRO ANESTHESIA 75204 #048-14-2000 L2004 **AN** *020 †05

SEIKALY, Mouin G. 5323 HARRY HINES BLVD, UT SOUTHWESTERN MED CTR 75390 #605-01-1981 L1987 **PN PD** *040 †55

SEKHAR, Deepa L. 1935 MOTOR ST, DEPT. OF GENERAL PEDIATRIC 75235 #043-01-2003 L2007 **PD** *100 †55

SELDIN, Donald W. 5323 HARRY HINES BLVD, MC 9030 75390 #008-01-1943 L1950 **IM NEP** *050

SELMAN, Forrest Benj. ■ 75243 #048-12-1957 L1957 **P** *071

SEMRANI, Pierre Nadim. 8440 WALNUT HILL LN, STE 550 75231 #605-01-1987 L1995 **FM** *020 †18

SEMRIN, Mhammad Gaith S. 1935 MOTOR ST, DEPT OF GASTROENTEROLOGY 75235 #575-01-1995 L2004 **PD** *020 †55

SENDELBACH, Dorothy M. 5323 HARRY HINES BLVD, UT SW MED SCHL DEPT PEDS 75390 #033-05-1982 L1983 **PD** *040 †55

SENITKO, Martin. ■ 75235 #286-06-2000 L2006 **NEP** *100

SENKTAS, Marzenna Janina. 5323 HARRY HINES BLVD, MED CTR DEPT OF PSYCHIATRY 75390 #759-03-1987 L1998 **P** *020

SENZER, Neil N. 3535 WORTH ST, FL 1 75246 #035-06-1971 L1985 **RO PHO** *020 †55,80

SEPULVEDA, Ricardo. 6757 ARAPAHO RD, STE 711 75248 #054-04-1993 L2004 **AN** *020 †05

SERKIN, Bryan S. 221 W COLORADO BLVD, PAVILION 2 SUITE 943 75208 #048-14-1997 L2002 **OTO** *020 †45

SEROTA, David Brett. 9440 POPPY DR 75218 #041-13-2000 L2006 **AN** *020 †05

SESSIONS, Chas Rutherford. 4131 N CENTRAL EXPY, METRO ANESTHESIA 75204 #048-12-1964 L1964 **AN** *020

SETIAWAN, Hartono. 5323 HARRY HINES BLVD, STOP 9031 75390 #506-02-1972 L1978 **DR** *020 †80

SETLIFF, Relda Jeanne. 5959 HARRY HINES BLVD, STE 1104 75235 #048-15-1983 L1983 **IM GS** *020 †20

SETLIFF, Stephanie Carol. 1935 MOTOR ST, CHILDREN'S MEDICAL CENTER 75235 #030-06-1994 L2000 **P** *020

SEVERS, Frederick Joseph. 5323 HARRY HINES BLVD, DEPT OF DIAG RADIOLOGY 75390 #048-15-2003 L2004 **DR** *012

SEWELL, Marjorie E. 1936 AMELIA CT 75235 #048-12-1950 L1950 **PHP** *030

SEYMOUR, Michael Edward, Jr. ■ 75206 #048-12-2008 *012

SHAD, Mujeeb U. 6363 HARRY HINES BLVD, FL6.628 75243 #704-16-1983 L2006 **P** *020 †75

SHADDOCK, Samuel H. ■ 75234 #048-02-1965 L1965 **NS** *071 †25

SHADE, Ronnie Dee. 1441 N BECKLEY AVE 75203 #019-02-1974 L1984 **ORS** *020 †40

SHADID, Larry Geo. 8226 DOUGLAS AVE, STE 805 75225 #039-01-1980 L1987 **CHP P** *020 †75

SHAFI, Shahid. 5323 HARRY HINES BLVD, MAIL STOP 9158 75390 #704-25-1988 L2003 **CCS** *020 †85

SHAFIQ, Moiz M. 5323 HARRY HINES BLVD J4, UT SOUTHWESTERN MEDICAL CE 75390 #048-12-2003 L2006 **IM** *100 †05

SHAH, Alpa Kiran. 5323 HARRY HINES BLVD, UNIV TX SOUTHWSTRN MED SCH 75390 #495-17-1997 L2005 **NMN** *020

SHAH, Amit Arvind. 5323 HARRY HINES BLVD, UTSW DIV OF GIM/GERIATRICS 75390 #048-04-2002 L2007 **IMG IM** *020 †20

SHAH, Anjali Naresh. ■ 75219 #051-04-2000 L2005 **PM** *100 †60

SHAH, Arjav Jayendra. 5001 SPRING VALLEY RD, STE 400 75244 #028-02-1994 L1999 **CCA** *020 †20

SHAH, Harivadan Vadilal. 12700 PARK CENTRAL DR, STE 430 75251 #495-76-1969 L1982 **DR** *020 †80

SHAH, Hasmukhlal Himatlal. 3600 GASTON AVE 75246 #495-17-1953 L1970 **TS** *071 †85,90

SHAH, Indira Hasmukhal. 3600 GASTON AVE STE 402 75246 #495-17-1952 L1971 **OBG** *020 †30

SHAH, Jessica Praful. 5201 HARRY HINES BLVD, PARKLAND HOSPITAL 75235 #020-12-2004 L2006 **IM** *020 †05

SHAH, Jheel Hasmukh. ■ 75204 #048-12-2005 L2007 **P** *012

SHAH, Malee Vinod. ■ 75230 #759-12-2003 **PEM** *012 †55

SHAH, Manisha Jay. 4500 S LANCASTER RD, DEPT OF CARDIOLOGY, 111A 75216 #048-12-1994 L1995 **CD** *020 †20

SHAH, Mary N. 5323 HARRY HINES BLVD 75390 #048-02-1996 L2001 **AN** *020 †05

SHAH, Monal Bipin. 3600 GASTON AVE STE 550 75246 #021-06-2002 L2005 **IM** *020 †20

SHAH, Mrugeshkuma K. 9262 FOREST LN STE 10 75243 #021-01-1999 L2003 **PM** *020 †60

SHAH, Nisarg Nitin. 8160 WALNUT HILL LN # 007 75231 #025-07-1999 L2000 **EM** *020 †16

SHAH, Punita. 1935 MOTOR ST, FIRST CARE 75235 #917-13-1994 L2003 **PD** *020 †55

SHAH, Shuchi. 5323 HARRY HINES BLVD, UT SOUTHWESTERN MEDICAL CE 75390 #036-05-2002 L2004 **PDE** *012 †55

SHAH, Sudhir H. 8440 WALNUT HILL LN, STE 510 75231 #048-38-1961 L1976 **DR** *020

SHAH, Tejas Krish. ■ 75235 #028-46-2001 L2008 **PDC** *012 †20,55

SHAH, Urmesh Subhash. 4201 BROOK SPRING DR 75224 #021-06-1992 L1996 **PD** *020 †55

SHAH, Zeeshan Ali. ■ 75219 #051-20-1996 L2007 **DR** *020 †60

SHAH, Zille Huma. 5323 HARRY HINES BLVD 75390 #704-21-1998 **FP** *012

SHAHAB, Imran. 8200 WALNUT HILL LN, DEPT OF PATHOLOGY 75231 #704-21-1986 L1992 **PTH HMP** *020 †50

SHAIKH, Zakir Hussain A. 1441 N BECKLEY AVE, INFECTION CONTROL 75203 #495-49-1992 L1999 **IM** *020 †20

SHAKIL, Amer. 6263 HARRY HINES BLVD, CLINICAL BUILDING 1 75235 #704-20-1990 L1998 **FM** *020 †18

SHAKOURIGARAKAN, Alireza. 5323 HARRY HINES BLVD, DEPT OF INT MED 75390 #048-12-2006 **IM** *012

SHALAN, Gregg Andrew. 1441 N BECKLEY AVE, FL 5 75203 #033-05-1990 L1995 **N OS** *020 †75

SHALEV, Daniel. 5744 LYNDON B JOHNSON FWY, STE 175 75240 #550-02-1973 L1985 **AN PME** *020 †05

SHAMIM, Sadat Anwar. 6301 GASTON AVE, STE 400, W TOWER 75214 #704-02-1998 L2007 **IM** *100

SHANMUGAM, Ganesh. ■ 75201 #048-08-2003 L2007 **AI** *012 †20

SHANNON, Arthur W, Jr. 3500 GASTON AVE 75246 #048-12-1945 L1945 **U** *020 †20

SHANNON, Donelson Neal. ■ 75225 #048-02-1978 L1978 **OTO** *071 †45

SHANNON, John J. ■ 75214 #016-01-1986 L1987 **PUD** *020 †20

SHAPIRO, Gabriel Avrum. 8440 WALNUT HILL LN, STE 600 75231 #039-01-1969 L1972 **ON HEM** *020 †20

SHAPIRO, Kenneth Neil. 1935 MOTOR ST 75235 #041-12-1970 L1987 **NS PD** *071 †25

SHAPIRO, Murray Halpert. ■ 75204 #048-12-2008 *012

SHAPPELL, Heidi W. 8200 WALNUT HILL LN, DEPARTMENT OF PATHOLOGY 75231 #048-04-1996 L2004 **PTH** *020 †50

SHAPPELL, Scott Barry. ■ 75214 #048-04-1991 L2005 **PTH** *020 †50

SHARAF, Mai F. 15190 PRESTONWOOD BLVD 75248 #004-01-1997 L2005 **IM** *020 †20

SHARDONOFSKY, Felix R. 75390 #132-01-1971 L1996 **PD PDP** *050 †55

SHARIAT, Shahrokh Francoi. 5323 HARRY HINES BLVD, UROLOGY DEPT. 75390 #154-07-1998 **U** *012

SHARIFI, Nima. ■ 75204 #041-12-2001 L2008 **ON** *100

SHARMA, Anita. PO BOX 824592 75382 #495-41-1989 L2001 **GS** *100

SHARMA, Kapil. 5323 HARRY HINES BLVD, DIV OF EMERGENCY MED 75390 #038-44-2005 **EM** *012

SHARMA, Manisha. ■ 75201 #001-02-2005 L2007 **OBG** *012

SHARMA, Pooja Bhawana. 3500 GASTON AVE, DEPT RAD 75246 #039-01-2006 L2006 **DR** *012

SHARMA, Poonam Surina. 3500 GASTON AVE, BAYLOR UNIV MED CTR 75246 #039-01-2007 **IM** *012

SHARMA, Sarita. 8200 WALNUT HILL LN 75231 #048-14-1997 L2001 **IM** *020 †20

SHARMA, Shiv Kumar. 5323 HARRY HINES BLVD, STOP 9031 75390 #495-49-1981 L1998 **AN** *020 †05

SHARMA, Vijay K. 7910 BELT LINE RD 75254 #495-03-1982 L1997 **IM** *020 †05

SHARP, Doyle Louis. 2927 MAPLE AVE # 616 75201 #048-12-1956 L1956 **GS EM** *071 †16

SHARP, Jason Wayne. ■ 75201 #047-06-2006 **DR** *012

SHARP, Lydia Jane. ■ 75235 #048-12-2008 *012

SHASTRY, Savitha. ■ 75206 #025-07-2004 L2004 **END** *012 †20

SHAUL, Philip Warren. U TX SW MED CTR, DEPT PED 75390 #038-41-1981 L1987 **NPM PD** *050 †55

SHAW, Joanna Etheltahsi. ■ 75219 #035-06-2003 L2007 **ID** *012 †20

SHEA, Heidi L. 10260 N CENTRAL EXPY, STE 100N 75231 #016-43-1996 L2000 **PDE END** *020 †20,55

SHEARER, Vance E. 5151 HARRY HINES BLVD 75235 #048-12-1985 L1986 **AN** *020 †05

SHEEHAN, Kathleen Sue. 4600 SAMUELL BLVD 75228 #048-16-1983 L1983 **P** *020 †75

SHEEHAN, Maeve. ■ 75390 #539-04-1993 L2002 **PD** *020 †55

SHEEHAN, Richard G. 4500 S LANCASTER RD, VETERAN ADM HOSPITAL 75216 #035-20-1961 L1967 **ON HEM** *040

SHEEHAN, Valerie Agatha. 5924 ROYAL LN STE 103 75230 #048-12-1956 L1956 **P DR** *071 †80

SHEENA, Douglas Abraham. 4925 GREENVILLE AVE, STE 200 75206 #048-12-1983 L1983 **EM IM** *020 †20

SHEERA, Mitul Mohan. 2403 N WASHINGTON AVE # 42 75204 #041-02-2001 L2004 **EM** *016

SHEFFEY, David Warren. 13601 PRESTON RD, STE 900 75240 #048-12-1984 L1985 **AN** *020 †05

SHEFFIELD, Eugene Guild. 1935 MOTOR ST, DEPT OF RADIOLOGY 75235 #027-01-1985 L1989 DR *020 †80

SHEFFIELD, Gerald A. ■ 75230 #047-06-1981 L1982 EM *020 †16

SHEFFIELD, Jeanne S. 5303 HARRY HINES BLVD 75390 #001-02-1993 L1997 OBG *020 †30

SHEFFIELD, Michael Allen. 1441 N BECKLEY AVE 75203 #001-02-1993 L1997 IM *020 †20

SHELBY, Sarah Marie. ■ 75235 #048-12-2008 *012

SHELMIRE, David Sutton. 8226 DOUGLAS AVE STE 549 75225 #028-02-1960 L1961 D *020 †15

SHELOKOV, Alexis Ioann. ■ 75219 #005-11-1948 GPM *071 †70

SHELTON, Heather Powell. 4500 S LANCASTER RD, GEN INT MED 111E 75216 #048-04-2000 L2003 IM *040 †20

SHELTON, James Houston. 3600 GASTON AVE, STE 851 75246 #024-01-1970 L1977 CD IM *020 †20

SHEN, Yumin Paul. 5323 HARRY HINES BLVD, MC 8852 75390 #005-18-1995 L1997 HO *020 †20

SHEPHERD, Laquita A. 6263 HARRY HINES BLVD 75235 #048-12-1987 L1988 FM *020 †18

SHER, Ellen Susan. 7777 FOREST LN STEB303 75230 #010-01-1990 L1998 PDE *020 †55

SHERBET, Daniel Paul. ■ 75235 #048-12-2006 IM *012

SHERMAN, Stephen Harris. 1909 HI LINE DR, INTERNATIONAL RADIOLOGY GR 75207 #016-11-1966 L1982 DR NM *020 †80,28

SHERMAN BROWNE, Pamela J. ■ 75225 #043-01-1992 L2008 ORS *020 †40

SHERREN, Edward Lee. 13601 PRESTON RD, STE 900 75240 #049-01-1988 L2000 AN IM *020 †05

SHERROD, Sue A Ormiston. PO BOX 35966 75235 #028-03-1967 L1969 P *020 †05

SHERWOOD-BERNER, Dorothy. 8200 WALNUT HILL LN, PRESBYTERIAN HOSP 75231 #038-41-1979 L1990 IM IMG *040 †20

SHETTY, Anupkumar. 3450 W WHEATLAND RD, STE 430 75237 #495-37-1986 L2002 IM *020 †20

SHEWCHUK, Dwight M. 10830 N CENTRAL EXPY, STE 120 75231 #062-01-1980 L1984 AN *020 †05,16

SHI, Beien. 1717 MAIN ST STE 5200 75201 #243-43-1984 L2001 IM *020 †20

SHI, Chen. 5323 HARRY HINES BLVD, STOP 9031 75390 #038-41-1991 L1997 AN *020 †05

SHIEKH, Michael A. 3625 N HALL ST STE 680 75219 #048-04-1999 L2001 P *020 †75

SHIFFLETTE, Vanessa Kiana. ■ 75230 #048-14-2007 GS *012

SHIN, Jiyeon. 3500 GASTON AVE, DEPT OF OB/GYN 75246 #048-12-2004 L2008 OBG *012

SHINGHAL, Anil Kumar. 8200 WALNUT HILL LN 75231 #035-19-1998 L1999 IM *020 †20

SHINN, Barbara Ann. 4350 ALPHA RD 75244 #048-02-1977 L1977 PTH *020 †50

SHINN, Bonner Lewis. 301 W COLORADO BLVD 75208 #004-01-1944 L1947 P IMG *071

SHINN, Carolyn V. 8355 WALNUT HILL LN, STE 105 75231 #048-14-1988 L1992 PD *020 †55

SHIPE, Gwendolyn Kay. ■ 75206 #020-02-2004 L2007 CHP *012

SHIPMAN, Kristin Elaine. ■ 75214 #028-46-2000 L2005 PDS *012 †85

SHIRES, George Thos, III. 8230 WALNUT HILL LN, STE 408 75231 #036-07-1978 L1991 GS TRS *020 †85

SHIU, Jimmie. ■ 75230 #048-12-1961 L1964 OTO *071 †45

SHIUE, Steve Chiahua. 13601 PRESTON RD, STE 900 75240 #023-12-1990 L2001 AN *020 †05

SHIVAKUMAR, Geetha N. 5323 HARRY HINES BLVD, BIPOLAR DISORDER RES CLINI 75390 #496-39-1996 L2005 P *100 †75 ‡

SHIVVERS, Stephan Allan. 5323 HARRY HINES BLVD, UT SOUTHWESTERN DEPT OF OB 75390 #024-07-1992 L1996 OBG *020 †30

SHIWACH, Rajinder Singh. ■ 75209 #495-73-1976 L1997 P *020 †75

SHOEMAKER, Craig Thos. 3500 GASTON AVE STE 3, DEPARTMENT OF NEONATOLOGY 75246 #026-04-1976 L2004 NPM PD *020 †55

SHOGREN, Dawn Leslie. 5495 BELT LINE RD STE 260 75254 #038-06-1982 L1984 P *020 †75

SHORE, Paul Michael. 1935 MOTOR ST, DEPARTMENT OF PEDIATRICS 75235 #041-09-1997 L2004 CCP *100 †55

SHOREY, James Wright, Jr. 4500 S LANCASTER RD # 111L, VA HOSPITAL 75216 #035-03-1963 L1970 OS *020 †20

SHOSID, Nancy Soll. 12880 HILLCREST RD STE 104 75230 #048-04-1988 L1989 CHP P *020 †75

SHOTWELL, Joyce Merle. 3600 GASTON AVE, STE 1052 75246 #048-02-1979 L1979 PUD IM *020 †20

SHRAGO, Evan Louis. 6757 ARAPAHO RD STE 711, BOX 335 75248 #016-01-1994 L1998 AN *020 †05

SHREEDHARA VASUDHA, Meera. 3500 GASTON AVE, BAYLOR UNIV MED CTR 75246 #496-39-2000 L2006 IM *100 †20

SHRIDHARAN, Lata. 3701 W NORTHWEST HWY, PHYSICIANS FOR CHILDREN 75220 #495-01-1996 L2001 PD *020 †55

SHROPULOS, George P. 8200 WALNUT HILL LN 75231 #048-12-1952 L1952 U *071 †95

SHUEY, Charles Bliss, Jr. 3600 GASTON AVE STE 210 75246 #048-12-1961 L1961 PUD CCM *020 †20

SHUFORD, Matthew Dawson. 3600 GASTON AVE, UROLOGY CLINICS OF NORTH 75246 #048-12-2000 L2005 U *020 †95

SHULKIN, Allan Neil. 7777 FOREST LN STE B202 75230 #048-13-1975 L1975 CCM PUD *020 †20

SHULKIN, Zev Andrew. ■ 75225 #048-12-2006 OPH *012

SHUTZE, William Patrick. 621 N HALL ST, STE 100 75226 #048-04-1984 L1985 VS GS *020 †85

SHYAM, Roopam. 142 WEBBS ROYAL PLZ, WEBB ROYAL MEDICAL PLAZA 75229 #495-34-1997 L2007 FM *020 †20

SIADATI, Abdolreza. 221 W COLORADO BLVD, STE 155 75208 #017-20-1998 L2004 NS *020 †25

SIBLEY, Alison H. 3434 SWISS AVE STE 330 75204 #019-02-1999 L2002 IM *020 †20

SIBLEY, George W. ■ 75201 #021-05-1950 L1951 ORS *071 †40

SIDAWI, Juanita E. 5323 HARRY HINES BLVD, DEPT OF ANESTHESIOLOGY 75390 #048-12-1987 L1988 AN *020 †05

SIDDIQI, M Rani. 1717 MAIN ST STE 5200, EMCARE, INC. 75201 #028-46-1998 L2001 PD *020 †55

SIDDIQUE, Aleem. 5323 HARRY HINES BLVD, DEPT OF GEN SURG 75390 #704-25-2000 GS *012

SIDDIQUI, Ali Ahmed. ■ 75219 #704-21-1997 L2001 GE *020 †20

SIDDONS, Ivan Doyle. ■ 75219 #039-01-1957 L1963 R *071 †80

SIDHARTHA, Tanuj. ■ 75235 #495-45-1999 L2007 P *012

SIEGEL, Jane D. SOUTHWESTERN MED SCH PD 75235 #024-05-1974 L1979 ID PD *040 †55

SIEGELMAN, Mark Howard. 5323 HARRY HINES BLVD, STOP 9031 75390 #048-12-1983 L1994 PTH *020

SIEMERS, Paul Timothy. 3500 GASTON AVE DEPT RAD 75246 #010-01-1973 L1978 RNR R *020 †80

SIENKO, Mark Edward. 6238 LAKEHURST AVE 75230 #016-11-1989 L1991 HO *020 †20

SIGURDSSON, Sigurdur Saml. 6301 GASTON AVE, EAST TOWER SUITE 400 75214 #484-01-1977 L1995 AN *020 †05

SIKORA, David. ■ 75219 #048-12-1957 L1957 GP *020 †18

SILBERMAN, Muriel K. ■ 75228 #048-12-1946 L1946 OS *040

SILVER, Charles. 2909 S HAMPTON RD STE C108 75224 #005-14-1968 L1970 GS *020 †85

SILVER, Richard Bruce. 7777 FOREST LN STE C565 75230 #021-01-1974 L1980 PD PDP *020 †55

SILVERMAN, Eric Scott. 13601 PRESTON RD STE 900W, PINNACLE ANESTHESIA CONSUL 75240 #003-01-1989 L2002 AN *020 †05

SILVERSTEIN, Russell Lee. 13154 COIT RD, STE 100 75240 #048-02-1972 L1972 NEP IM *020 †20

SIMHA, Vinaya A. ■ 75205 #495-37-1994 L2003 END *020 †20 ‡

SIMKIN, Nancy Jane. ■ 75219 #035-46-1981 L1984 IG RHU *050 †20

SIMMONDS, Charity T. 7441 MD LOVE FWY, STE 201 75237 #016-11-1977 L1983 OBG *020 †30

SIMMONS, Donald Chad. 7777 FOREST LN STE C630 75230 #021-01-2000 L2004 OBG *020 †30

SIMMONS, Kevin James. 5201 HARRY HINES BLVD 75235 #048-14-2004 L2006 CHP *012

SIMON, Roberta Stanley. 3600 GASTON AVE STE 705 75246 #035-19-1972 L1974 D *020 †15

SIMON, Roger C. ■ 75220 #654-01-1996 L1999 FM *100

SIMON, Stuart Ben. 6301 GASTON AVE STE 400 75214 #027-01-1986 L1987 AN *020 †05

SIMON, Theodore Ronald. 2929 S HAMPTON RD 75224 #008-01-1975 L1980 NM R *020 †28

SIMON, Walter. 3600 GASTON AVE, WADLEY #262 75246 #048-04-1995 L1997 PTH *020 †50

SIMONTON, Charles Thos. 8315 WALNUT HILL LN # 110 75231 #021-01-1967 L1975 CRS *071 †10,85

SIMPSON, Charles Wm. 8230 WALNUT HILL LN, STE 220 75231 #048-02-1952 L1952 NS *071 †25

SIMS, Deborah Jewel. 3534 N HAMPTON RD 75212 #047-07-1981 L1986 FM *020

SIMS, John Bryan. ■ 75214 #048-13-2001 L2004 CD *020

SIMS, Richard Dale. 221 W COLORADO BLVD, STE 845 75208 #001-02-1977 L1981 AN *020 †05 ‡

SIMS, Robert Douglas. 5801 FOREST PARK RD, ROGERS MAGNETIC RES CTR 75235 #048-12-1997 L1999 DR *020 †80

SINCLAIR, Gary Ian. ■ 75214 #038-06-1994 L2000 ID *020 †20

SINGEETHAM, Sarita D. ■ 75235 #048-12-2008 *012

SINGER, Alejandro R. 5959 HARRY HINES BLVD, PROF BLDG # ONE - STE 708 75235 #048-12-1988 L1989 OBG GYN *020 †30

SINGER, Allison Friss. 3600 GASTON AVE STE 350 75225 #048-14-1995 L1997 D *020 †15

SINGER, Mike Amirom. 5323 HARRY HINES BLVD, UNIVERSITY OF TEXAS SOUTHW 75390 #016-02-2000 L2005 N *020 †75

SINGER, Miriam. 7777 FOREST LN STE C755 75230 #016-02-2001 L2007 D *020 †15

SINGH, Sameer Kumar. 12319 CREEKSPAN DR 75243 #048-02-2008 *012

SINGH, Sundeep. ■ 75205 #025-01-2007 IM *012

SINHA, Ajay Kumar. ■ 75284 #495-57-1982 L1996 IM *020 †20

SINKRE, Prasanna Ajay. 2330 BUTLER ST, STE 115 75235 #496-38-1993 L2001 DMP *020 †50

SIRBASKU, Donna M. 4350 ALPHA RD, AMERIPATH NORTH TEXAS 75244 #016-11-1967 L2003 PTH *020 †50

SIVADASAN, Rekha. 3701 W NORTHWEST HWY, PHYSICIANS FOR CHILDREN 75220 #422-01-1997 L2005 PD *020 †55

SIVASANKAR, Lakshmi. 7777 FOREST LN STE C400 75230 #495-59-1989 L1998 IM *020 †20

SKAGGS, Lauren Claire. ■ 75214 #048-12-2008 *012

SKILES, Andrew Leonard. ■ 75214 #048-02-2005 L2008 EM *012

SKINNER, Michael Allen. 1935 MOTOR ST RM B03-3250, DEPT OF PEDIATRIC SURGERY 75235 #016-01-1984 L2007 PDS *020 †85

SKINNER, Walter Nathaniel. 5919 GREENVILLE AVE, # 374 75206 #048-12-1959 L1959 IM *020 †20

SKINNER, William T. 5939 HARRY HINES BLVD 75235 #048-12-1953 L1953 P OS *020

SKLAR, Frederick Herman. 7777 FOREST LN, STE B308 75230 #023-07-1971 L1976 NS NSP *020 †25

SKLAR, Jerald Louis. 5924 ROYAL LN, STE 104-B 75230 #048-02-1987 L1988 D *020 †15

SKLAVER, Neal Lawrence. 5461 LA SIERRA DR 75231 #041-01-1968 L1974 IM *020 †20 ‡

SKLUZACEK, Paul Anthony. 3450 W WHEATLAND RD, STE 430 75237 #030-06-1997 L2003 NEP IM *020 †20

SKRIVANEK, Gary Danl. 5323 HARRY HINES BLVD, U.T. SOUTHWESTERN MEDICAL 75390 #048-12-1986 L1987 AN *020 †05

SLADE, Reginald Harold. 4323 S HAMPTON RD 75232 #065-05-1964 L1978 FM EM *020 †20

SLAUGHTER, Stephen M. 13601 PRESTON RD, STE 900W 75240 #048-14-1993 L1994 AN *020 †05

SLAYBAUGH, Abbie Leigh. ■ 75218 #048-02-2008 *012

SLAYMAKER, Elizabeth Ann. 5323 HARRY HINES BLVD, DEPT OF ANESTHESIOLOGY 75390 #016-11-1991 L1992 AN *020 †05

SLOAN, Bradley. 1717 MAIN ST, ST.E. 5200 75201 #048-13-1990 L1991 FM EM *020 †18

SLOAN, Charles M. 1441 N BECKLEY AVE 75203 #048-12-1949 L1949 AN *071 †05

SLOAN, Emily Kay. 809 SINGLETON BLVD 75212 #048-14-2003 L2006 PD *020 †55

SLOAN, James Morrison. ■ 75225 #004-01-1955 L1955 GYN *071 †30

SLOAN, Louis Marshall. 3409 WORTH ST, NORTH TEXAS INFECTIOUS 75246 #048-13-1989 L1990 ID *020 †20

SLOBODIN, Gleb. 5323 HARRY HINES BLV 75235 #913-73-1988 RHU *100

SLUSHER, Norman. 3600 GASTON AVE, STE 964 75246 #028-03-1974 L1975 OPH *020 †35

SLYWKA, Shawn Wm. 13601 PRESTON RD, STE 900W 75240 #025-01-1992 L1996 AN *020 †05

SMALL, Gregg L. 9301 N CENTRAL EXPY, STE 389 75231 #048-12-1983 L1983 GYN EM *020

SMALL, Neal Chas. 75225 #048-12-1970 L1970 ORS GS *020 †40

SMARKUSKY, Loren Nicole. 75204 #011-02-2003 L2007 OBG *100

SMART, Don Merrill. PO BOX 180219 75218 #016-11-1954 L1954 OPH *071 †35

SMERUD, Michael John. 3500 GASTON AVE, AMERICAN RADIOLOGY 75246 #026-08-1980 L1981 DR *020 †80

SMITH, Alice Lorraine. UTSOUTHWESTERN, DEPT PATHOLOGY 75390 #048-12-1946 L1946 PTH PCP *050 †50

SMITH, Allison Leigh. 5323 HARRY HINES BLVD, SOUTHWESTERN MED 75390 #048-12-2004 OBG *012

SMITH, Allison Leigh. ■ 75214 #020-02-2005 IM *012

SMITH, Angelica. ■ 75228 #048-12-2005 IM *012

SMITH, Bertram Leon, III. 621 N HALL ST, STE 100 75226 #048-12-1974 L1974 VS GS *020 †85

SMITH, Bruce Allen. 3600 GASTON AVE, STE 710 75246 #048-12-1978 L1978 GS AS *020 †85

SMITH, Claire Gibbons. ■ 75205 #048-12-2007 IM *012

SMITH, Craig Douglas. 12222 MERIT DR, STE 1420 75251 #048-04-1976 L1976 OPH *020 †35

SMITH, Cynthia Lynn. 6247 WOODLAND DR 75225 #048-02-1989 L1997 **PM** *020 †60
SMITH, Demetria Michele. 801 N PEAK ST 75246 #038-41-2000 L2003 **FM** *100 †18
SMITH, Douglas Maclean. 3500 GASTON AVE, BUMC/TRANSPLANT IMMUNOLOGY 75246 #018-03-1976 L1999 **PTH** *071 †50
SMITH, Eric Bryan. 3600 GASTON AVE STE 1002 75246 #048-12-2000 L2006 **U** *020 †95
SMITH, Henry Roy. ■ 75234 #012-01-1956 L1961 **GP** *075
SMITH, Herbert J. 4500 S LANCASTER RD, DEPT RAD 75216 #016-11-1971 L1976 **DR** *071 †80
SMITH, Howard Brian. 6750 HILLCREST PLAZA DR, STE 306 75230 #048-02-1991 L1992 **P** *020 †75
SMITH, James Wm. 4500 S LANCASTER RD 75216 #020-02-1960 L1966 **ID** *040 †20
SMITH, Jason Landon. 5201 HARRY HINES BLVD, PARKLAND MEMORIAL HOSPITAL 75235 #036-07-2004 L2007 **IM** *012 †20
SMITH, Kamilia. 3600 GASTON AVE, STE 601 75246 #048-13-2003 L2007 **OBG** *020
SMITH, Liesl B. 8160 WALNUT HILL LN, STE 212 75231 #048-12-1996 L1997 **OBG** *020 †30
SMITH, Mary Wilcox. ■ 75219 #041-13-1971 L1972 **GP OBG** *075
SMITH, Micke Joe. 9323 GARLAND RD STE 301, EAST LAKE PRIMARY CARE 75218 #027-01-1985 L2003 **FM** *020 †18
SMITH, Mose. ■ 75219 #004-01-1956 L1956 **GYN** *071 †30
SMITH, Philip Orien. 3535 TRAVIS ST STE 210 75204 #048-12-1980 L1980 **AN** *020 †05
SMITH, Randlow, Jr. 3434 SWISS AVE STE 207 75204 #048-12-1975 L1975 **IM** *020 †20
SMITH, Richard Carroll. 3500 GASTON AVE 75246 #048-02-1956 L1956 **GYN** *071 †30
SMITH, Ryan R. 6711 WINTON ST, CHILDREN'S MEDICAL CENTER 75214 #048-13-2002 L2005 **PD** *020 †55
SMITH, Scott Emerson. 10830 N CENTRAL EXPY, STE 330 75231 #048-13-1983 L1983 **AN** *020 †05
SMITH, Susan Sharon. 11715 PINE FOREST DR 75230 #048-14-1982 L1983 **AN CCM** *020 †05
SMITH, Sydnie Gershon. 5200 KELLER SPRINGS RD 75248 #048-04-1942 L1942 **PS** *020 †65
SMITH, Taylor Andrew. 75206 #021-05-2004 **GS** *012
SMITH, Troy R. 5909 HARRY HINES BLVD, RADIOLOGY ST PAUL UNIV HOS 75235 #048-12-1971 L1971 **DR** *020 †20
SMITH, Weldon Lloyd, Jr. 3434 SWISS AVE STE 430 75204 #048-12-1976 L1976 **IM** *020 †20
SMITH, Wesley D. ■ 75228 #048-15-2000 L2004 **AN** *100
SMITH, Wright K. 2514 S BUCKNER BLVD 75227 #048-12-1952 L1952 **GP** *071
SMITH-BLAIR, Gayle L. 221 W COLORADO BLVD, STE 431 75208 #048-16-1987 L1988 **P** *020 †75
SMYTH, Edward Meiling. 13601 PRESTON RD, STE 900W 75240 #028-34-1989 L2002 **AN** *020 †05
SNG, Karen Wei-Ee. 7777 FOREST LN STE C717 75230 #917-13-1995 **CFS** *100
SNIPES, George J, Jr. ■ 75209 #047-05-1988 L2002 **PTH** *020 †50
SNODGRASS, Warren Thos. 6300 HARRY HINES BLVD, # 1401 75235 #048-02-1980 L1980 **UP** *020 †95
SNOOTS, Wynne Mc Callie. 3434 SWISS AVE, STE 104 75204 #048-12-1964 L1964 **ORS SO** *020 †40
SNOWBERGER, Noel Lavonne. 7777 FOREST LN, STE C675 75230 #048-02-2000 L2006 **GE** *020 †20
SNYDER, Elliott Harvey. ■ 75219 #035-46-1973 L1978 **P** *071 †75
SNYDER, Richard W, II. 7777 FOREST LN, STER A-341 75230 #048-12-1987 L1988 **CD** *020 †20
SNYDER, William Henry, III. UNIV TX MED SCH, DEPT GS 75235 #048-04-1962 L1962 **GS TS** *020 †85,90
SODEN, Kevin Jos. 1601 LBJ FWY, CELANESE, LTD 75234 #011-03-1974 L1998 **EM FM** *030 †18
SODHI, Preeti. 8915 HARRY HINES BLVD 75235 #051-01-1998 L2004 **CHP** *020 †05
SOHN, Mie Mie. 5323 HARRY HINES BLVD, SOUTHWESTERN MED 75390 #048-12-2004 L2006 **OBG** *012
SOKAL, Paul Jonathan. 9101 N CENTRAL EXPY, STE 300 75231 #023-07-1978 L1979 **IM** *020 †20
SOKOL, Saul. 5323 HARRY HINES BLVD 75390 #132-01-1952 L1964 **CRS** *020
SOKOLICH, Julio Cesar. 7414 E GRAND AVE 75214 #737-10-2000 **GS** *012
SOLANKI, Dilipsinh. 3555 W WHEATLAND RD 75237 #495-23-1966 L1993 **IM HEM** *020 †20
SOLE, Timothy John. 5323 HARRY HINES BLVD 75235 #836-02-1979 **RHU** *020
SOLLIE, David. 8230 WALNUT HILL LN # 800 75231 #132-04-1944 L1965 **AN** *020
SOLOMON, Murray D. 4350 ALPHA RD 75244 #048-16-1985 L1986 **PTH** *020 †50
SOLOMON, Ratna. 5939 HARRY HINES BLVD, POB 2 75235 #495-08-1969 L1975 **OBG** *020
SOLTES, Richard Stephen. 5625 RIDGEDALE DR 75206 #048-12-1986 L1987 **IM EM** *020 †20
SOMER, Joseph. ■ 75225 #048-12-1954 L1954 **IM** *071
SOMERS ARIETTI, Cynthia C. 5323 HARRY HINES BLVD, DEPT OF PEDIATRICS 75390 #726-01-1998 L2008 **PDI** *012 †55
SOMMER, Raymond Lee. 7 MEDICAL PKWY 75234 #048-02-1978 L1978 **EM IM** *020 †20,16
SOMMERFELT, Kathryn Ann. 5646 MILTON ST, STE 635 75206 #048-02-1981 L1981 **P** *020 †75
SONG, Wenru. 3535 WORTH ST, STE 520 75246 #243-06-1987 L2007 **ON** *020 †55
SONGONUGA, Olubunmi K. 1935 MOTOR ST, FIRST CARE 75235 #033-06-2001 L2004 **PD** *020
SONN, Thomas Michael. 5956 SHERRY LN, STE 540 75225 #023-01-1961 L1978 **P** *020 †75
SONNIER, Jos Albert, III. 4350 ALPHA RD STE 101 75244 #021-06-1979 L1981 **PTH** *020 †50
SORENSEN, Kent Wm. 17194 PRESTON RD, STE 102-112 75248 #025-07-1972 L1982 **DR NR** *020 †80
SOROKIN, Michelle Faye. ■ 75235 #041-09-1998 L2001 **PD** *100
SORSBY, Mitchell Ian. 10260 N CENTRAL EXPY, STE 100N 75231 #649-01-1988 L1994 **END IM** *020 †20
SORY, William Crysup. 12700 PARK CENTRAL DR, STE 430 75251 #048-13-1979 L1979 **DR** *020 †80
SOTILLO, Rodrigo W. ■ 75215 #715-01-1978 L1994 **IM IMG** *020 †20
SOUDA, Robert Mc Carrel. 8330 MEADOW RD STE 128 75231 #039-01-1960 L1964 **P** *075 †75
SOUERS, Rachel Marie. ■ 75204 #001-06-2007 **PD** *012
SOURYAL, Tarek Omar. 6901 SNIDER PLZ, STE 200 75205 #048-13-1982 L1983 **ORS OSM** *020 †40
SOUTHERN, Paul Morris. 5323 HARRY HINES BLVD 75390 #048-12-1959 L1959 **ID MM** *040 †20
SOWADA, Margaret Aileen. 1935 MOTOR ST 75235 #048-12-1981 L1981 **IM** *020 †20
SOWELL, David S, III. 3500 GASTON AVE 75246 #048-12-1966 L1966 **IM CD** *020 †20
SO-WILTZ, Leilani Arzaga. ■ 75225 #748-10-1972 L1980 **PD GP** *020
SPAETH, Stefanie Dawn. 9101 N CENTRAL EXPY, STE 420 75231 #051-01-1997 L1999 **PD** *020 †55
SPAIN, Thomas Lynn, Jr. 1935 MEDICAL DISTRICT DR 75235 #048-13-1999 L2001 **PAN** *012 †05
SPAK, Cedric Wojciech. 3409 WORTH ST, STE 710 75246 #048-12-1999 L2000 **ID** *020 †20

SPALDING, Susan. 5000 HARRY HINES BLVD, HOMELESS OUTREACH MED SERV 75235 #038-41-1986 L1993 **PD** *030 †55
SPANGLER, Ann Elizabeth. 5323 HARRY HINES BLVD 75390 #041-07-1985 L2002 **RO** *020 †80
SPANN, Michael Gregory. 10830 N CENTRAL EXPY 75231 #047-06-1990 L1991 **AN** *020 †05
SPARAGANA, Steven P. 2222 WELBORN ST, FOR CHILDREN 75219 #048-13-1989 L1994 **CHN** *020 †75
SPEARS, Michael D. 5323 HARRY HINES BLVD, DEPT OF PATHOLOGY 75390 #048-14-2005 **PTH** *012
SPECHLER, Stuart J. 4500 S LANCASTER RD, DALLAS VA MED CTR 75216 #024-05-1974 L1999 **GE IM** *020 †20
SPEEG, Sarah Woodward. 5323 HARRY HINES BLVD 75390 #048-13-2003 L2007 **PFP** *012
SPEEGLE, Robert E. 6350 E MOCKINGBIRD LN 75214 #048-02-1951 L1951 **UCM FM** *020
SPEIGHT, Craig William. ■ 75201 #011-02-2005 **EM** *012
SPEIGHT, Tracy Elizabeth. 8160 WALNUT HILL LN # 304 75231 #004-01-1996 L1998 **OBG** *020 †30
SPENCER, Roger Allen. 13601 PRESTON RD, STE 900W 75240 #047-06-1985 L1986 **AN** *020 †05
SPENCER, Todd Andrew. 7777 FOREST LN 75230 #048-02-1997 L2002 **VS** *020 †85
SPERRY, David Bartow. 7777 FOREST LN, STE A307 75230 #025-07-1972 L1977 **CHN** *020 †55,75
SPIEGEL, Mark Kenneth. 1 MEDICAL PKWY STE 102 75234 #047-06-1979 L1984 **GE IM** *020 †05
SPIEKER, John Brian. 4131 N CENTRAL EXPY, METRO ANESTHESIA 75204 #048-02-1986 L1995 **AN PME** *020 †05
SPIGEL, Joseph John. 3409 WORTH ST STE 320 75246 #041-13-1996 L2001 **DR** *020 †80
SPOTSWOOD, Sheila Donele. 5230 MEDICAL CENTER DR, DALLAS CO MED EXAMINER OFC 75235 #048-12-1983 L1983 **FOP** *020 †50
SPRUEIL, Ramano Alvarez. 5201 HARRY HINES BLVD 75235 #011-03-1998 L1999 **EM** *020 †16
SPURLOCK, William Marcus. 8345 WALNUT HILL LN, ENVIRONMENTAL HEALTH 75231 #021-06-1981 L1994 **FM OS** *020 †18
SREENARASIMHAIAH, J. ■ 75390 #028-46-1996 L2002 **GE** *020 †20,55
SRIDHAR, Pudu. 12700 PARK CENTRAL DR, STE 430 75251 #495-65-1995 L2003 **DR** *020 †80
SRINIVASAN, Karthik R. 5323 HARRY HINES BLVD, UNI OF TX. S. WESTERN 75390 #048-12-2003 L2006 **PD** *020 †55
SRINIVASAN, Rajashree. 3301 SWISS AVE 75204 #496-39-1991 L2001 **PM** *020 †55,60
SRIVASTAVA, Archana. 221 W COLORADO BLVD, STE 831 75208 #495-41-1990 L2001 **CD** *020 †20
SRIVASTAVA, Ashwani D. 3450 W WHEATLAND RD, STE 419 75237 #495-41-1990 L2002 **IM** *020 †20
SRIVATHANAKUL, S. 2630 N FITZHUGH AVE 75204 #891-02-1962 L1976 **PD** *020
SRIVATHANAKUL, Sunti S. 9202 ELAM RD # 225 75217 #048-12-1994 L1995 **FM** *020 †18
SRUNGARAM, Praveen Ranga. ■ 75204 #048-02-2003 L2006 **IM** *100 †20
STADLER, Montserrat G. 1 MEDICAL PKWY, STE 209 75234 #048-04-1997 L2000 **PD** *020 †55
STAGE, Key Hutchinson. 5323 HARRY HINES BLVD 75390 #040-02-1973 L1977 **U AM** *071 †95
STAGER, David Richard. 8222 DOUGLAS AVE, STE 400 75225 #038-40-1961 L1968 **PO OS** *020 †35
STAGGS, Deacon Wayne. 909 N WASHINGTON AVE 75246 #048-04-2003 L2008 **PM** *012
STAGNONE, Gregory John. 6190 LBJ FWY, STE 500 75240 #034-01-1983 L1984 **PS** *020 †65
STANDEFER, John A, Jr. 14902 PRESTON RD, STE 404 75254 #048-13-1978 L1978 **FPS OTO** *020 †45
STANFIELD, Eunice F. 501 MAIN ST STE 100, DALLAS COUNTY EMPLOTEE HEA 75202 #041-09-1973 L1978 **OPH** *071 †35
STANIUNAS, Raymond Jude. 12200 PARK CENTRAL DR, STE 189 75251 #051-07-1984 L2000 **GS** *020 †85,10
STANLEY, Gregory A. ■ 75204 #048-13-2007 **GS** *012
STANNARD, Michael Wenley. 1935 MOTOR ST, CHILDRENS MEDICAL CENTER 75235 #917-25-1966 L1984 **PDR OS** *071 †80
STARGHILL, Charlotte T. 7010 AMERICAN WAY STE D 75237 #047-07-1991 L1992 **FM** *020 †18 ‡
STARITA, Richard J. 7150 GREENVILLE AVE STE 3 75231 #033-05-1977 L1987 **OPH** *020 †35
STARR, Adam Jennings. 1801 INWOOD ROAD 75390 #048-12-1992 L1993 **ORS** *020 †40
STASTNY, Peter. 5323 HARRY HINES BLVD 75390 #737-01-1958 L1966 **IG RHU** *050
STATON, Robert Scott. 13140 COIT RD STE 518 75240 #035-20-2002 L2007 **PYG** *020
STATON, Walter L. 14275 WELCH RD 75244 #048-04-1981 L1981 **IM** *072
STAUB, A Jay. 8160 WALNUT HILL LN # 224 75231 #048-12-1979 L1979 **OBG** *020 †30 ‡
STAWORN, Dusit. 1935 MOTOR ST 75235 #891-02-1986 L1993 **CCP** *100 †55
STEADMAN, Sarah Kay. ■ 75206 #048-12-2008 *012
STECKLER, Robert Michael. 7777 FOREST LN, STE C585 75230 #035-09-1967 L1972 **SO HNS** *020 †85
STEELMAN, Rush Barrett. 8440 WALNUT HILL LN, STE 700 75231 #041-09-1963 L1978 **CD** *020 †20
STEEN, Eric Montague. 5323 HARRY HINES BLVD, DEPT OF INTERNAL MEDICINE 75390 #051-04-1983 L1985 **IM** *040 †20
STEEN, Jennifer Sheryl. 3500 GASTON AVE, DEPT OF OB/GYN 75246 #007-02-2004 L2008 **OBG** *012
STEEN, Rolly Robt. 8409 PICKWICK LN, PMB 102 75225 #048-13-1978 L1978 **AN** *020 †05
STEEN, Shawn Thomas. ■ 75201 #007-02-2004 **GS** *012
STEFFEK, Haden A. 4131 N CENTRAL EXPY, METRO ANESTHESIA 75204 #048-15-2001 L2005 **AN** *020 †05
STEFFEY-DUARTE, Coral Les. 5323 HARRY HINES BLVD, SOUTHWESTERN MED 75390 #048-13-2006 **PD** *012
STEGER, Katherine Anne. ■ 75206 #048-12-2005 *100
STEGNER, Martha Marie. ■ 75209 #048-12-2003 L2005 **PHO** *012 †55
STEHEL, Edward J. 5323 HARRY HINES BLVD, SOUTHWESTERN MED CTR RADIO 75390 #048-12-1996 L1998 **RNR** *100 †80 ‡
STEHEL, Elizabeth K Irwin. 5323 HARRY HINES BLVD, DEPARTMENT OF PEDIATRICS 75390 #048-12-1997 L1998 **PD** *020 †55
STEINBACH, Herbert L, Jr. 7030 TOKALON DR, BAYLOR UNIVERSITY MED CTR 75214 #048-02-1963 L1963 **DR NR** *020 †80
STEINBACH, Sandra C. 1920 ABRAMS PKWY APT 376 75214 #048-12-1962 L1962 **P** *020
STEINBERG, Joel Bernard. 1935 MOTOR ST 75235 #021-01-1959 L1960 **PD** *040 †55
STEINFINK, Dan Elliot. 16800 DALLAS PKWY, STE 150 75248 #048-12-1973 L1975 **CHP P** *020 †75
STEINMETZ, Samuel Edwin. 8210 WALNUT HILL LN, PRESBYTERIAN PRO STE 414 75231 #028-02-1981 L1982 **D** *020 †15
STEPENASKIE, Shelly A. 5323 HARRY HINES BLVD, DEPT OF PATHOLOGY 75390 #048-04-2002 L2007 **PTH** *100

STEPHAN, Maria. 1935 MOTOR ST, EMERGENCY RM J-112 75235 #038-41-1981 L2004 PEM PD †55

STEPHEN, George A. 4500 S LANCASTER RD # 11H, N TEXAS VAMC 75216 #028-03-1988 L1989 SME IM *020 †20

STEPHENS, Jason Scott. 2403 N WASHINGTON AVE 75204 #012-01-2002 L2005 DR *100 †80

STEPHENS, Leonora. 6350 LYNDON B JOHNSON FWY, STE 252 75240 #048-12-1978 L1983 P *020 †75

STEPHENS, Michael Knox. 13154 COIT RD, STE 100 75240 #021-01-1967 L1976 NEP IM *020 †20

STEPHENSON, Jill Stanley. 3600 GASTON AVE, STE 958 75246 #048-15-2001 L2006 GS *020

STEPTEAU, Torrence James. 13601 PRESTON RD STE 900W, PINNACLE ANESTHESIA CONSUL 75240 #047-07-1993 L1998 APM AN *020 †05

STERLING, James C. 7115 GREENVILLE AVE, STE 310 75231 #048-13-1982 L1983 PM *020 †70,60

STERN, Charles. 75204 #021-05-1952 L1952 OPH *071 †35

STERN, Jack. 13601 PRESTON RD, STE 900 75240 #048-02-1953 L1953 NS *071 †25

STERN, Joshua Michael. ■ 75205 #035-20-2003 L2004 U *012

STETLER, Lori Donohue. 8201 PRESTON RD STE 350 75225 #048-12-1989 L1990 D *020 †15

STEUBING, Johnathon B. 7557 RAMBLER RD, STE 706 75231 #048-12-1999 L2001 AN *100 †20,05

STEVENS, Meribeth H. 5201 HARRY HINES BLVD, PARKLAND HOSPITAL 75235 #048-12-1987 L1991 AN *020 †05

STEVENS, William E. 8230 WALNUT HILL LN 75231 #048-12-1987 L1991 GE IM *020 †20

STEVENSON, George Valedon. 2026 N HENDERSON AVE, P O BOX 407 75206 #042-01-1963 L1981 FM PD *020

STEVENSON, Lisa Christine. ■ 75220 #048-15-2008 *012

STEVENSON, Matthew Terren. ■ 75209 #048-12-2007 N *012

STEVENSON, Susan May. 8200 WALNUT HILL LN 75231 #041-02-1974 L1983 PD GP *020 †55

STEVENSON, Walter Danl. 9528 WEBB CHAPEL RD 75220 #041-02-1961 L1963 GS *020 †85

STEWART, Chris Colquitt. 5201 HARRY HINES BLVD 75235 #048-12-1985 L1986 AN *020 †05

STEWART, Michael Allen. 606 N WASHINGTON AVE 75246 #041-07-1985 L1986 RO *020 †80

STEWART, Rege P Szuts. 5959 HARRY HINES BLVD, UT SOUTHWESTERN MED CENT 75390 #016-06-1967 L1977 P *071 †75

STEWART, Robert David. ■ 75238 #048-15-2007 OBG *012

STEWART, Robert Malcolm. 7515 GREENVILLE AVE # 500 75231 #016-06-1967 L1977 N PA *020 †75

STEWART, Ryan A. 1935 MOTOR ST 75235 #048-12-2004 L2006 PDE *012 †55

STEWART-SMITH, Marilyn. 8204 ELMBROOK DR STE 360 75247 #021-05-1966 L1971 P IM *020

STICHWEH, Dorothee Sophie. 5323 HARRY HINES BLVD, UNIV TX SOUTHWESTERN MED S 75390 #715-01-1993 PPR *100

STIDD, David A. ■ 75215 #048-12-2007 GS *012

STIGALL, William L. 1935 MOTOR ST, DEPARTMENT OF PEDIATRICS 75235 #048-12-2002 L2003 CCP *012 †55

STILES, Cristina Marie. 8160 WALNUT HILL LN, STE 007 75231 #051-01-1982 L1983 EM IM *020 †20

ST JOHN, William Thos. ■ 75218 #035-03-1947 L1953 P GP *071

STOCK, Renee C. 7777 FOREST LN STE C300, DALLAS MEDICAL SPECIALISTS 75230 #048-78-1999, ▲ L2002 IM *020 †20

STOCK, Timothy Thomas. 4600 SAMUELL BLVD 75228 #048-12-1997 L1998 P *020 †75

STOCKTON, Kristopher Geor. ■ 75220 #048-14-2007 ORS *012

STOFF, Benjamin K. 3500 GASTON AVE, MEDICAL CENT 75246 #048-12-2006 D *012

STOLL, Matthew L. ■ 75206 #035-15-2001 L2007 PPR *100 †55

STONE, Dennis Keith. 5323 HARRY HINES BLVD, UT SOUTHWESTERN MED CTR 75390 #048-12-1977 L1983 NEP IM *050 †20

STONE, Jeffrey Wayne. 7557 RAMBLER RD, STE 706 75231 #001-02-1996 L2001 AN *020 †05

STONE, Marvin Jules. 3535 WORTH ST, STE 110 75246 #016-02-1963 L1970 ON HEM *020 †20

STONE, Ramsey Aaron. 5323 HARRY HINES BLVD 75390 #048-12-2005 GS *012

STONE, Robert Geo. 1936 AMELIA CT 75235 #048-02-1963 L1964 ORS GS *020 †40

STONE, Stuart Ronald. 5323 HARRY HINES BLVD 75390 #018-03-1961 L1964 OBG *040 †30

STOOL, Louis Allan. 5323 HARRY HINES BLVD 75390 #048-12-1979 L1979 AN *020 †05

STORY, Herbert B, III. 6728 CHEVY CHASE AVE 75225 #048-12-1999 L2002 AN *020 †05

STOUT, Bryce L. 10300 N CENTRAL EXPY, STE 205 75231 #062-01-1979 L1981 AN *020 †05

STOYANOVA, Antonia Plamen. ■ 75209 #048-12-2008 *012

STRAIN, Byron Earl. 9433 DIXIE LN 75228 #047-07-1993 L1995 PM *020 †60

STRAUGHN, Christopher J. 7777 FOREST LN, STE B445 75230 #048-04-1999 L2002 PD *020 †55

STRAUS, Brian Elliot. 6901 SNIDER PLZ, STE 200 75205 #048-12-2001 L2006 ORS OFA *020

STRAUSS, James Fredric. 8200 WALNUT HILL LN, STE 700 75231 #035-19-1972 L1974 ON HEM *020 †20

STRAYER, Reuben J. ■ 75209 #048-12-2002 L2007 *100

STREAM, Amanda Rae. ■ 75204 #007-02-2006 IM *012

STREBE, Sara Elisabeth. ■ 75214 #023-01-2004 L2007 ORS *012

STRECKMANN, David H. ■ 75243 #016-06-1950 L1955 IM *071 †20

STREITMATTER, David E. ■ 75243 #016-06-1950 L1955 IM *071 †20

STRICKLAND, Richard Mark. 550 E ANN ARBOR AVE, FAITH HOSPICE 75216 #048-12-1979 L1979 GO GYN *020 †30

STRINGER, Claude Allen, Jr. 3535 WORTH ST, FL 2 75246 #048-14-1976 L1976 GP EM *020 †20

STRINGER, Drennon Durwood. 9696 SKILLMAN ST, STE 285 75243 #028-34-1958 L1978 HS ORS *020 †40

STRIPLING, Wilton Dennis. 8230 WALNUT HILL LN # 212 75231 #048-02-1968 L1968 DR *012

STRITTMATTER, Heather Gal. ■ 75206 #021-05-2005 L2007 PDC CCP *020 †20

STROMBERG, Daniel. 1935 MOTOR ST, DIV OF CARDIOLOGY, CMCD 75235 #005-02-1990 L1998 GO GYN *020 †30

STROUD, Malcolm Herbert. ■ 75205 #352-03-1945 L1963 OTO *071 †45

STRUTHERS, William Burton. 13601 PRESTON RD, STE 900 75240 #003-01-1987 L1989 AN *020 †05 ‡

STUART, John Arthur, Jr. 8315 WALNUT HILL LN, STE 105 75247 #047-06-1945 L1953 OBG *071

STUART, Robert John. 5520 S WESTMORELND RD #200, CONCENTRA MEDICAL CENTERS 75237 #048-02-1977 L1980 OM *020

STUBBS, Garry Wayne. 5323 HARRY HINES BLVD 75390 #039-01-1989 L1990 AN *020 †05

STUCKA, Kristy Renee. 7777 FOREST LN, EMERGENCY SERVICES 75230 #016-01-1998 L2001 EM *020 †16 ‡

STUDLEY, Jill Louise. 4004 WORTH ST, STE 100 75246 #005-12-1998 L2002 IMG *012

STUEBNER, Megan Erin. ■ 75249 #021-05-2005 L2007 IM *012

STUKE, Lance Eugene. ■ 75227 #021-01-2002 L2007 GS *012

STUVE, Olaf. 5323 HARRY HINES BLVD, DEPT OF NEUROLOGY 75390 #409-33-1993 L2005 N *020 †75

STYRVOKY, Ann Elizabeth. ■ 75202 #048-15-2007 P *012

SU, David Keisho. ■ 75235 #048-12-2008 *012

SU, Mu. 5323 HARRY HINES BLVD, DEPT OF PATHOLOGY 75390 #243-92-1985 PTH *012

SU, Wei. 2330 BUTLER ST, STE 115 75235 #243-52-1992 L2006 DMP *012

SU, Xuehui. ■ 75254 #243-77-1993 L2003 PD *100 †10

SUBHAN, Alia. 5323 HARRY HINES BLVD 75390 #704-02-2002 FP *012

SUBRAMANIAN, Ramiah. 5323 HARRY HINES BLVD, UNIV OF TX SOUTHWESTERN 75390 #495-61-1972 L1979 PTH CD *050 †50

SUCATO, Daniel Jos. 2222 WELBORN ST, TEXAS SCOTTISH RITE HOSP 75219 #035-06-1991 L1997 OP OSS *020 †40

SUDDERTH, Michael Earle. 12200 PARK CENTRAL DR 75251 #048-12-1967 L1967 OTO *020 †45

SUGERMAN, Robert W. 7777 FOREST LN, STE B332 75230 #048-04-1990 L1991 AI *020 †55,03

SUGHAYER, Maher Abdel. ■ 75240 #575-01-1983 L1989 PTH *020 †50

SULE, Sandeep Dileep. 12221 MERIT DR, STE 1060 75251 #001-02-2000 L2006 OTO *100 †45

SULEMAN, Amer. 7777 FOREST LN, STE A236 75230 #704-01-1990 L1997 ICE *020 †20

SULLIVAN, Anna Burns. ■ 75219 #048-04-2006 EM *012

SULLIVAN, Brian R. 4500 S LANCASTER RD, # 112C 75216 #048-14-1989 L1990 OPH *020 †35

SULLIVAN, Tara Lynn. ■ 75220 #048-14-2005 L2008 PD *012

SULUR, Paulgun. ■ 75219 #047-05-2004 L2006 IM *100 †20

SUMAYLO, Aldous Dennis. ■ 75206 #041-01-2000 L2004 PD *020 †55

SUMPTER, Kathryn Maria. ■ 75220 #048-12-2003 L2005 PDE *012 †55

SUMPTER, Rhea M, Jr. ■ 75222 #048-12-2006 IM *012

SUN, Amie Mao. ■ 75204 #048-15-2005 IM *012

SUN, Sophie. 5323 HARRY HINES BLVD MC, UT SOUTHWESTERN MEDICAL CE 75390 #065-01-2000 L2006 *100

SUN, Tiffany Bo. ■ 75235 #048-12-2008 *012

SUNDERAJAN, Prabha. 6363 FOREST PARK RD 13-354, UTSW MED CTR DEPRES CLINIC 75235 #495-11-1969 L1994 P *020

SUNG, Jane. ■ 75230 #036-07-1992 L1995 PUD IM *020 †20

SURESH, Vikrum. 13601 PRESTON RD STE 1000 75240 #048-02-1993 L1994 AN *020 †05

SUSAT, George G. 5920 FOREST PARK RD # 600 75235 #016-06-1952 L1960 ORS *071 †40

SUTCLIFFE, David L. ■ 75235 #048-12-2008 *012

SUTER, Robert Neil. 3500 W WHEATLAND RD, FAMILY PRACTICE AND 75237 #048-78-2001, ▲ L2002 FSM *100

SUTERWALA, Mustafa Saleh. 3500 GASTON AVE, BAYLOR UNIVERSITY MEDICAL 75246 #495-01-1989 L2003 PD *020 †55

SUTHUN, Parisa Ann. 4500 S LANCASTER RD, RD 111 75216 #014-01-1996 L1998 IM *020 †20

SUTKER, Michael Jason. ■ 75201 #048-04-2005 ORS *012

SUTKER, William Levin. 3409 WORTH ST, NORTH TEXAS INFECTIOUS 75246 #016-42-1974 L1975 ID IM *071 †20

SUTLIFF, Elizabeth Whitne. ■ 75205 #048-12-2007 GS *012

SWAFFORD, Selma R. 5461 LA SIERRA DR 75231 #048-13-1993 L1994 IM *020 †20

SWANCUTT, Mark Alan. 5323 HARRY HINES BLVD, UT SOUTHWESTERN MEDICAL CE 75390 #048-12-1991 L1993 ID *020 †20

SWARTZ, Kevin Allen. 1936 AMELIA CT, AMELIA COURT CLINIC 75235 #017-20-2003 L2006 ID IM *012 †20

SWEATT, James Leonard, III. ■ 75237 #028-02-1962 L1964 TS CD *071 †85,90

SWIFT, Dale Matthew. 7777 FOREST LN, STE B308 75230 #038-06-1984 L1992 NS NSP *020 †25

SWIFT, Edward K. 3920 WORTH ST 75246 #048-02-1999 L2002 AN *020 †05

SWIFT, Timothy Joseph. 13601 PRESTON RD, STE 900 75240 #019-02-1993 L2001 AN *020 †05

SWYGERT, Lynn. 7777 FOREST LN, STE D570 75230 #048-12-1981 L1981 OBG *020 †30

SWYGERT, Thos Hodnett, Jr. 6301 GASTON AVE, EAST TOWER STE 400 75214 #048-12-1981 L1981 AN *020 †05

SYED, Asif. 7777 FOREST LN 75230 #495-35-1960 L1978 U *020 †95 ‡

SYED, Shahzad Muhammad. 9 MEDICAL PKWY, STE 107, PLAZA 4 75234 #704-02-1990 L2001 GE *020 †20

SYED ALI, Asghar. 13154 COIT RD STE 100 75240 #704-05-1992 L1998 NEP *020 †20

SYKES, John R, Jr. 1935 MOTOR ST 75235 #654-01-1984 L1991 AN PD *020 †20

SYNEK, Thomas Robert. SOUTHWESTERN MED, UNIV OF TEXAS 75390 #048-14-2002 PM *100

SYRQUIN, Maurice G. 3414 OAK GROVE AVE 75204 #024-07-1989 L1991 OPH *020 †35

SZE, Michael John. 9440 POPPY DR 75218 #056-05-1996 L2002 DR *020 †80

SZESZKO, Dennis R. ■ 75254 #649-28-1977 L1982 OM FM *071 †18

SZMUK, Eleonora. ■ 75204 #781-05-1981 L2004 P *020 †75

SZMUK, Peter. 1935 MOTOR ST D03.309, ANESTHESIOLOGISTS FOR CHIL 75235 #781-05-1981 L2002 AN *020

TABACZEWSKA, Ludmila. 5201 HARRY HINES BLVD 75235 #759-04-1985 L1998 AN *020 †05

TABOADA, Carlos Alberto. 1441 N BECKLEY AVE, STE 101 75203 #042-03-2000 L2003 HO *020 †20

TAGHIZADEH, Sascha Darius. ■ 75248 #019-02-2003 L2008 ORS *012

TAHA, Riyad Abdalla. 8 MEDICAL PKWY, STE 302 75234 #605-01-1959 L1969 CD IM *020 †20 ‡

TAKANO, Jeanne S. 5323 HARRY HINES BLVD, DEPT PEDS 9063 75235 #048-12-1991 L1998 CCP *040 †05

TALKINGTON, Clement M. 3500 GASTON AVE 75246 #048-12-1969 L1969 VS GS *020 †85

TALMADGE, John Mills. 4500 S LANCASTER RD, MH 116-A MENTAL HEALTH 75216 #036-07-1973 L1974 P N *020 †20

TAMMINGA, Carol Ann. ■ 75209 #047-05-1971 L2008 PA PA *050

TAN, Jessela D. 2901 CITYPLACE WEST BLVD 75204 #305-01-1998 L2006 AN *020 †18

TAN, John Lionghan. 8440 WALNUT HILL LN, STE 700 75231 #005-11-1992 L1999 CD IM *020 †20

TAN, Sioe Sien. 3330 S LANCASTER RD 75216 #506-01-1959 L1977 P *020

TANDON, Anumeha. ■ 75254 #496-59-2004 IM *012

TANEJA, Aanchal. ■ 75219 #495-29-2002 N *012

TANEJA, Rishi. 5323 HARRY HINES BLVD 75390 #048-12-2003 L2003 ACA *012

TANEJA, Vibha. 3500 GASTON AVE 75246 #048-15-2006 IM *012

TANELIAN, Darrell Lee. 5323 HARRY HINES BLVD STE C204 75320 #048-05-1984 L1993 AN *020 †05

TANG, Pheng M. 13601 PRESTON RD STE 1000 75240 #048-15-2002 L2006 AN *100 †05

TANGNARARATCHAKIT, K. ■ 75235 #891-04-1988 PN *100

TANGUILIG-ROBINSON, Cynthi. 12222 MERIT DR STE 3, DESTINATION LOCUM TENENS 75251 #055-01-2001 L2003 *020

TANKERSLEY, Stephen M. 3878 OAK LAWN AVE, STE 616 75219 #048-13-1981 L1981 P *020 †75

TANNEN, Richard. 6805A WOODMARK CT 75230 #018-03-1972 L1984 PUD CCM *020 †20

TANNIN, Grace Michele. 5323 HARRY HINES BLVD, STOP 9031 75390 #028-02-1985 L1998 PDE *050 †55

TANRIOVER, Bekir. 1150 N BISHOP AVE, STE 100 75208 #902-05-1993 L2003 NEP *020 †20

TANSEY, Keith E. 5323 HARRY HINES BLVD 75390 #048-12-1994 L2003 N *050 †75

TAO, Weike. 5323 HARRY HINES BLVD, UT SOUTHWESTERN MEDICAL CE 75390 #243-52-1983 L2002 AN *100 †05

TAQUET, Sybil Jane. 6263 HARRY HINES BLVD 75235 #396-41-2001 L2007 FM *020 †18

TARANGO, Cristina. ■ 75219 #005-11-2003 PHO *012 †55

TARNASKY, Paul Randall. 221 W COLORADO BLVD, PAVILION II, SUITE 630 75208 #054-04-1989 L1997 GE *020 †20 ‡

TARRANT, Nicole A. 1935 MOTOR ST 75235 #048-14-1998 L2002 PD *020 †55

TASIAN, Berge Ohanes. 5939 HARRY HINES BLVD, STE 935 75235 #048-12-1974 L1976 CD IM *020 †20

TATE, Chad Roland. 3600 GASTON AVE 75246 #048-12-2000 L2005 GS *020 †85

TATE, Michael Bradford. 7777 FOREST LN STE D5 75230 #048-14-2003 L2007 CCP *012 †55

TATE, Temeka Lott. SOUTHWESTERN MED, UNIV OF TEXAS 75390 #021-05-2006 PM *012

TAUB, Larry R. 5744 LBJ FWY STE 150 75240 #048-04-1989 L1990 OPH *020 †35

TAUROG, Joel David. 5323 HARRY HINES BLVD, UNIV TX SW MED CTR 75390 #048-12-1974 L1986 RHU IM *050 †20

TAYLOR, Bruce Carson. ■ 75225 #018-03-1964 L1965 OPH *071 †35

TAYLOR, David Patton. 3600 GASTON AVE, STE 548 75246 #021-01-1978 L1986 PS HS *020 †65,85

TAYLOR, Dennis Alva. 13601 PRESTON RD 75240 #005-12-1976 L1979 EM FM *075 †16,18

TAYLOR, Edward Eric. 3409 WORTH ST, STE 640 75246 #048-15-1999 L2007 CCS *100

TAYLOR, Ellen Lee. 9440 POPPY DR 75218 #048-12-1970 L1970 GS EM *020 †20

TAYLOR, James N. 13601 PRESTON RD, STE 900W 75240 #048-13-1985 L1986 AN FM *020

TAYLOR, Jennifer Anne. ■ 75204 #023-01-2003 L2006 CD *012 †20

TAYLOR, John. ■ 75230 #539-03-1972 L1977 PS GS *020 †85,65

TAYLOR, Moirae M. 13601 PRESTON RD, STE 900 75240 #048-13-1997 L1998 AN *020

TAYLOR, Monique M. 2718 FLOYD ST 75204 #048-12-2001 L2003 CCP *012 †55

TAYLOR, Nathan Samuel. ■ 75204 #010-02-2005 PS *012

TAYLOR, Paul B. 10677 E NORTHWEST HWY, STE 100 75238 #048-12-1984 L1986 FM *020 †18

TAYLOR, Richard Loren. ■ 75225 #028-02-1960 L1965 PD OS *030 †55

TAYLOR, Robert S, III. 5323 HARRY HINES BLVD, DEPT DERM 75390 #048-02-1985 L1986 DS HNS *020 †15

TAYLOR, Roosevelt, Jr. 9209 ELAM RD STE 100 75217 #010-03-1964 L1972 OBG *020 †30

TAYLOR, Wayne Edward. 7777 FOREST LN, BLDG A 75230 #048-12-1973 L1975 PTH *020 †50

TAYLOR, William B, III. ■ 75214 #048-02-2008 *012

TAYLOR, William Wilkinson. ■ 75229 #048-12-1957 L1964 CD TS *071 †85,90

TAYLOR-KENNEDY, Lisa C. 4500 S LANCASTER RD 75216 #048-16-1990 L1993 AN *020 †05

TEAGUE, Leslie Ann. ■ 75204 #047-20-2004 L2004 FM *100

TEAGUE, Linda Gail. 712 N WASHINGTON AVE, STE 300 75246 #051-04-1980 L1996 IM *020 †20

TEBBETTS, John Beryl. 2801 LEMMON AVE STE 300 75204 #048-02-1972 L1972 PS *020 †85,65

TECHASAENSIRI, Chonnamet. 5323 HARRY HINES BLVD, STE F3-202 75390 #891-04-1997 PDI *012

TEDDLIE, Merritt Bonar. 3010 LBJ FWY STE 40, OCCUSYSTEMS 75234 #048-12-1960 L1960 OM *071

TEHLIRIAN, Christopher V. 712 N WASHINGTON AVE 75246 #048-14-2002 L2007 RHU *020 †20

TEJAN, Joseph Moi. 3450 W WHEATLAND RD, STE 214 75237 #539-04-1983 L1999 ORS OTR *020 †40

TELFORD, Van Quincy. 4350 ALPHA RD RM 101 75244 #048-12-1965 L1965 PTH *071 †50

TELLEZ, Juan Matiella. 13601 PRESTON RD STE 900W 75240 #048-04-1985 L1987 AN *020 †05

TEMPLE, Bobby Louis. 8200 WALNUT HILL LN 75231 #048-02-1954 L1954 IM *071 †20

TEMPLE, James Terry. ■ 75209 #003-01-1972 L1983 AN *020 †05

TENERY, Robert Mayo, Jr. 7777 FOREST LN, B424 MEDICAL CITY DALLAS 75230 #048-02-1968 L1968 OPH ADL *020 †35

TENG, Hsi Ching. 8 MEDICAL PKWY, STE 301 75234 #242-09-1945 L1956 CD IM *072

TERADA, Lance Shizuo. 4500 S LANCASTER RD, DALLAS VAMC MC151 75216 #014-01-1983 L2001 PUD IM *020 †20

TERAUCHI, Stephanie Yuko. 3600 GASTON AVE STE 550, TX PRIMARY CARE ASSOCIATES 75246 #004-01-2005 L2008 IM *012

TERMULO, Cesar Santacruz. 3320 LIVE OAK ST, DEPARTMENT OF PEDIATRICS 75204 #048-12-1996 L1999 PD *020 †55

TERRILL, Bruce Steven. 5310 FOREST LN, STE 204 75244 #048-04-1947 L1947 GYN *071 †30

TERRY, Carolyn Marie. 12200 PRESTON RD 75230 #048-02-1997 L1998 IM *020 †20

TERRY, Stacy L. ■ 75230 #019-02-1996 L1998 PD *020 †55

TESSNOW, Alexander Herman. 5201 HARRY HINES BLVD 75235 #048-12-1996 L2007 END *012 †20

TEWICH-JACOBE, Heidi C. 6263 HARRY HINES BLVD, STE DF 3 75390 #048-04-1996 L1998 D *012 †15

THAKAR, Hemangini J. ■ 75220 #047-05-2003 PS *012

THAKKAR, Aminidhan D. 12221 MERIT DR STE 1610, QUESTCARE PARTNERS 75251 #035-46-1995 L1999 EM *020 †16

THAKUR, Sivarevathi. ■ 75235 #495-21-1999 FP *012

THAL, Erwin R. 5323 HARRY HINES BLVD, DEPT OF SURGERY 75390 #038-40-1962 L1966 GS *040 †85

THAMMASITHIBOON, Sandy. ■ 75204 #048-12-2006 AN *012

THANKAVEL, Bharath. ■ 75248 #422-01-2004 L2007 PD *020 †55

THAYER, Stone Rangarajan. ■ 75209 #048-12-2007 *012

THAYIL, Tom Thomas. 8200 WALNUT HILL LN, MD ON CALL 75231 #048-02-2000 L2003 IM *020 †20

THEISEN, James Eric. ■ 75223 #048-02-2002 L2008 GS *100

THEIVAGT, Charles Patrick. 3523 MCKINNEY AVE, # 358 75204 #016-45-2003 L2006 OTO *012

THIAGARAJAH, Mahesh C. ■ 75204 #045-04-2002 L2004 EM *100 †16

THIELE, Dwain Louis. U TX SOUTHWESTERN MED CTRT 75390 #048-04-1977 L1977 IM HEP *030 †20

THIELE, Johannes Peter. ■ 75244 #407-15-1959 L1974 TS *071 †85,90

THIELEN, Maura Lyn. 801 N PEAK ST 75246 #048-02-1997 L2000 FM *020 †18

THIEME-SKLAR, Robyn. 8222 DOUGLAS AVE STE 500 75225 #039-01-1990 L1993 PD *020 †55

THIGPEN, Darrell Edward. 1001 N BISHOP AVE 75208 #027-01-1982 L1984 IM *020

THOMAS, Cealee Antrea. 221 W COLORADO BLVD, STE 431 75208 #048-12-2000 L2004 OBG *020 †30

THOMAS, Charles Philip. ■ 75209 #048-15-2008 *012

THOMAS, Emilia V. 5323 HARRY HINES BLVD, DEPT OF INTERNAL MED 75390 #495-36-1991 L1998 IM *020 †20

THOMAS, Fay Elaine. 3434 SWISS AVE STE 41 75204 #048-14-2002 L2005 IM *020 †20

THOMAS, Fred C. 9353 ELAM RD 75217 #047-07-1978 L1982 IM *020

THOMAS, James Alanson. 5323 HARRY HINES BLVD 75235 #005-11-1989 L1992 CCP *020 †55

THOMAS, Katherine Anne. ■ 75225 #041-15-2007 AN *012

THOMAS, Kevin Francis. 13601 PRESTON RD 75240 #012-21-1992 L1997 AN *020 †55

THOMAS, Lia Andrea. 4500 S LANCASTER RD, UT SOUTHWESTERN MEDICAL CE 75216 #021-01-2003 L2005 P *100

THOMAS, Madhavi. 7515 GREENVILLE AVE, STE 500 75231 #495-11-1992 L2001 N *020 †75

THOMAS, Milton Dean. 909 N WASHINGTON AVE 75246 #049-01-1982 L1991 PM *020 †60

THOMAS, Robin L. 5201 HARRY HINES BLVD, PARKLAND HOSPITAL 75235 #048-13-2005 L2007 OBG *012

THOMAS, Teena Catherine. ■ 75219 #048-12-2007 PD *012

THOMAS, Timothy Harris. 1935 MOTOR ST, DIVISION OF CARDIOLOGY 75235 #012-05-2000 L2003 PDC *020 †55

THOMAS, William R. ■ 75205 #048-12-1953 L1953 GS *020

THOMPSON, Christopher Jay. 5201 HARRY HINES BLVD 75235 #016-42-2005 L2007 EM *012

THOMPSON, Jeffrey Reed. 5939 HARRY HINES BLVD, STE 500 75235 #016-11-1982 L1985 NEP IM *020 †20

THOMPSON, Jesse Eldon. 712 N WASHINGTON AVE, STE 509 75246 #024-01-1943 L1954 VS GS *071 †85

THOMPSON, Lloyd Gilbert. 5452 GLEN LAKES DR STE 101 75231 #048-02-1961 L1962 OS *071

THOMPSON, Mandy M. 3600 GASTON AVE, STE 206 75246 #048-14-1990 L1991 IM *020 †20

THOMPSON, Marita Toby. 1935 MOTOR ST, DEPT OF CRITICAL CARE 75235 #016-11-1989 L1995 CCP *020 †55

THOMPSON, Mayra Jimenez. 7777 FOREST LN, BUILING C, SUITE 210 75230 #016-11-1980 L1984 GYN *020 †30

THOMPSON, Robert Dee. 3434 SWISS AVE STE 310 75204 #021-01-1967 L1973 IM *020 †20

THOMPSON, Robert Leon, Jr. 13154 COIT RD, STE 100 75240 #041-12-1998 L2003 IM *020 †20

THOMPSON, Stephen Kelly. 4811A COLUMBIA AVE 75226 #051-01-1981 L1982 OS FM *020

THOMPSON, William M, Jr. 5323 HARRY HINES BLVD, STOP 9031 75390 #012-01-1982 L1986 GS *020 †85

THOMPSON-BELL, Gwendell. 13601 PRESTON RD, STE 900 75240 #048-16-1991 L1992 AN *020 †05

THOMPSON-FREEMAN, Chiarra. SOUTHWESTERN MED, UNIV OF TEXAS 75390 #038-40-2006 L2006 NM *012

THORNTON, James. 5323 HARRY HINES BLVD, DEPT OF PLASTIC SURGERY 75390 #048-12-1989 L1990 PS *020 †65

THORNTON, Katherine Boyle. ■ 75225 #048-12-1990 L1991 AN *062 †05

THORNTON, Steven Jackson. 7115 GREENVILLE AVE STE 3 75231 #027-01-1998 L2001 OSM *020 †40

THORNTON, William L. 5323 HARRY HINES BLVD, U TX DEPT PSYCH 75235 #048-12-1987 L1988 P *020 †75

THORP, Darin Russell. 13601 PRESTON RD, STE 900 75240 #048-02-1992 L1993 AN *020 †05

THRASH, Dustin Breck. 3500 GASTON AVE, MEDICAL CENT 75246 #039-01-2006 IM *012

THRIFT, Rollin Louis. 9 MEDICAL PKWY, PLAZA 4 STE 306 75234 #011-03-1980 L1981 GS EM *020 †85

THROPP, Richard Brian. 606 N WASHINGTON AVE 75246 #011-04-1995 L1998 DR *020 †80

THUDI, Amitha Reddy. 5309 HARRY HINES BLVD, UNIV OF TX SOUTHWESTERN ME 75390 #496-24-2002 L2006 IM *100 †20

THUDI, Narotham Reddy. 5939 HARRY HINES BLVD, STE 800 75235 #495-21-1995 L2004 HO *020 †20

THUNDER, Megan Ann. ■ 75229 #047-05-2004 ORS *012

THURSTON, Jeffrey M. 5323 WALNUT HILL LN, WALNUT HILL OBSTETRICS & 75231 #048-04-1981 L1982 OBG *020 †30

TIEGERMAN, Christopher. 9440 POPPY DR 75218 #243-69-1983 L2001 PTH *020 †50

TILL, Mark Andrew. 1906 PEABODY AVE 75215 #048-04-1983 L1983 IM EM *020 †20

TILLERY, Glenn Weldon. 3500 GASTON AVE 75246 #048-12-1959 L1959 PTH *071 †50

TILLMAN, Felicia Mae. 8160 WALNUT HILL LN # 224 75231 #005-19-1992 L1996 OBG *020 †30

TIMARAN, Carlos Hernando. 5323 HARRY HINES BLVD, MC 9157 75390 #264-07-1991 L2004 VS *020 †85

TIMKEN, Kenneth Roach. 3636 DICKASON AVE 75219 #048-12-1959 L1959 P *071 †75

TIMMERMAN, Robert Dale. 5801 FOREST PARK ROAD, DEPT OF RADIATION ONCOLOGY 75390 #046-01-1990 L2004 RO *020 †80

TIMMONS, Charles F, Jr. 1935 MOTOR ST, CHILDRENS MED CTR DEPT PTH 75235 #036-01-1977 L1989 PTH PP *020 †50

TINGLE, Eric Justin. 3500 GASTON AVE, DEPARTMENT OF RADIOLOGY 75246 #048-02-2004 L2007 DR *012

TINLEY, Sandra Eisele. 1935 MOTOR ST, DALLAS CHILDREN'S HOSPITAL 75235 #012-01-1977 L2006 PD EM *020 †55

TIRADO, Carlos Francisco. 5323 HARRY HINES BLVD, UNIVERSITY OF TEXAS SOUTHW 75390 #048-14-1999 L2001 P *020 †75

TITTLE, Ben Jackson. 5939 HARRY HINES BLVD, STE 739 75235 #048-12-1980 L1980 PS *020 †85,65

TOBLEMAN, Wm Taylor Jr. 8 MEDICAL PKWY STE 306 75234 #048-12-1977 L1977 N *020

TOBOLOWSKY, Dave. ■ 75205 #048-12-1944 L1945 GP GPM *071 †55

TODD, Charles Wayne. 5323 HARRY HINES BLVD, DIV OF EMERGENCY MED 75390 #056-06-2004 L2007 EM *100

TODD, Robert Mainord. 8160 WALNUT HILL LN # 200 75231 #047-06-1956 L1960 GYN *020 †30

TOKER, Anna-Maria Blake. 221 W COLORADO BLVD, PAVILLION 2 SUITE 441 75208 #021-06-1997 L1998 CRS GS *020 †85,10

TOLEDO, George A. 6110 SHERRY LN 75225 #048-12-1980 L1980 PS HNS *020 †45,65

TOLER, Gretchen Faye. 12200 PRESTON RD 75230 #048-12-1984 L1988 M *020 †20

TOLER, Kathy Adrienne. 10 MEDICAL PKWY STE 201 75234 #038-41-1984 L1988 N *020 †75

TOMPKINS, Frances Lora. 5959 HARRY HINES BLVD #217 75235 #048-12-1952 L1953 ORS *071

TONDAPU, Prasanthi. 5323 HARRY HINES BLVD 75235 #496-24-2000 L2006 END *012 †20

TONGIER, William K. 5323 HARRY HINES BLVD 75390 #048-14-1989 L1990 AN *020 †05

TONN, Melissa D. 8117 PRESTON RD, STE 530 75225 #048-13-1986 L1987 OM PME *030 †70

■ = Address Information Privacy Protected

TONREY, Frank Gerald. 4515 PRENTICE ST STE 201 75206 #010-02-1980 L2000 AN EM *020 †05,16

TON-THAT, Quynh Anh. 7777 FOREST LN, STE C300 75230 #019-02-1996 L1997 IM *020 †20

TOOFANIAN, Ali. 8160 WALNUT HILL LN, STE 211 75231 #517-01-1971 L1980 OBG GYN *020 †30

TOOMAY, Seth Michael. ■ 75201 #048-12-2002 L2004 VIR *012 †80

TORANTO, I Richard. ■ 75230 #016-06-1969 L1973 PS HS *075 †65

TORNELLI-MITCHELL, Janet. 5323 HARRY HINES BLVD 75230 #048-02-1988 L1989 IM *020 †20

TORRES, Cesar Omar. 2403 N WASHINGTON AVE 75204 #048-02-2002 L2004 FM *020 †18

TORRES, Fernando. ■ 75225 #035-20-1994 L1995 PCC *020 †20

TORRISI, John Russell. 2804 AMHERST AVE, UROLOGY CLINICS OF NORTH T 75225 #035-45-1980 L1994 RO *020 †80

TORTORIELLO, Tia A. ■ 75225 #048-12-1996 L1998 PDC *020 †55

TOTO, Robert Danl. 5323 HARRY HINES BLVD 75390 #016-11-1977 L1980 NEP IM *050 †20

TOUBIN, Jeffrey C. 3450 W WHEATLAND RD, STE 122 75237 #048-13-1993 L1995 U *020 †95

TOUCHY, James Quenton. 3500 GASTON AVE, DEPT OF EMERGENCY MEDICINE 75246 #021-05-1986 L1990 EM *020 †16

TOUHEY, John Edward. 5481 BLAIR RD, WOUND CARE CONSULTANTS 75231 #048-04-1964 L1964 GP AM *020 †70

TOUPS, Marisa Sarapalumbo. 5323 HARRY HINES BLVD, SOUTHWESTERN MED 75390 #021-01-2005 P *012

TOUSSAINT, Richard F, Jr. 3112 SAINT JOHNS DR 75205 #048-12-1983 L1983 AN *020 †05

TOVAR, Winfred Scilla. 5323 HARRY HINES BLVD, SOUTHWESTERN MED 75390 #023-07-2002 L2006 OBG *012

TOYE, Leon R. 3500 GASTON AVE, AMERICAN RADIOLOGY 75246 #048-13-1998 L2004 DR *020 †80

TRAGUS, Eugene Theodore. ■ 75235 #045-01-1961 L1963 EM *020

TRAN, Anhhong Huan. 5323 HARRY HINES BLVD, UROLOGY DEPT. 75390 #048-04-2003 L2005 GS *100

TRAN, Bach D. 3600 GASTON AVE STE 550 75246 #048-12-2001 L2004 IM *020 †20

TRAN, Christina Vy. ■ 75229 #048-12-2008 *012

TRAN, Duc. 7515 GREENVILLE AVE, STE 400 75231 #010-02-1995 L1998 N *020 †75

TRAN, Hai H. 9 MEDICAL PKWY, STE 107 75234 #048-16-2004 AN *012

TRAN, Hien Thienhai. ■ 75219 #048-12-2008 *130

TRAN, Kien Trung. ■ 75204 #041-12-2005 L2005 D *012

TRAN, Long D. 3601 SWISS AVE, DALLAS NEPHROLOGY ASSOC 75204 #048-04-1998 L2000 NEP *020 †20

TRAN, Minh Pho. ■ 75205 #019-02-2006 GS *012

TRAN, Nhunha. 4606 CEDAR SPRINGS RD, APT 322 75219 #035-06-2006 PD *012

TRAN, Quyen Hong. ■ 75248 #048-12-2004 L2007 EM *100

TRAN, Steve Hoang. 6757 ARAPAHO RD STE 711, PMB 335 75248 #019-02-2001 L2003 AN *100 †05

TRAN, Suong Mai. ■ 75204 #048-14-2004 RHU *012 †20

TRANCHINA, Sara Eileen. 8230 WALNUT HILL LN, STE 800 75231 #048-12-1990 L1991 FM OBS *020 †18

TRAPP, Erika Furst. 5323 HARRY HINES BLVD 75390 #023-07-1960 L1987 IM OS *020 †20

TRAPP, George Alexander. VET ADMIN HOSP, DEPT PSYCH 75240 #023-07-1959 L1987 P LM *020 †75

TRAVIS, Gabriel Harvey. 5323 HARRY HINES BLVD, UT SOUTHWESTERN MED CTR 75390 #005-14-1977 L1978 N *012

TRAVIS, James Eldrid. 13601 PRESTON RD, STE 900 75240 #048-12-1980 L1980 AN *020

TRAVIS, Jo Ann. ■ 75214 #028-03-1975 L1977 AN *020 †05

TREEN, Meridith. 7777 FOREST LN 75230 #038-40-1985 L1991 NPM PD *020 †55

TREICHLER, Don Brent. 5323 HARRY HINES BLVD 75390 #051-07-1998 L1999 EM *020 †16

TREVINO, Guillermo. 221 W COLORADO BLVD, STE 100 75208 #649-01-1959 L1983 OS GS *020 †85

TREVINO, Jessica Marie. 5201 HARRY HINES BLVD, DEPARTMENT OF INTERNAL MED 75235 #048-02-2004 L2006 GE *012 †20

TRIBBLE, Marc Alan. 2929 CARLISLE ST STE 260 75204 #048-02-1997 L1998 ID IM *020 †20

TRIEU, Loc Hoang. 12200 PARK CENTRAL DR, SUITE189 75251 #422-01-2000 L2004 MPD *020

TRIKHA, Anita. ■ 75204 #035-48-1997 L2007 IM *020 †20

TRIPATHY, Debasish. 3500 MAPLE AVE, STE 700 75219 #036-07-1985 L2002 ON IM *020 †20

TRIVEDI, Jaya Raghav. 5323 HARRY HINES BLVD, UT SOUTHWESTERN MED CTR 75390 #495-76-1992 L2000 N *020 †20,75

TRIVEDI, Madhukar H. STE 13354, 6363 FOREST PARK ROAD 75390 #495-23-1981 L1992 P *050 †75

TROENDLE, Sarah M. 5323 HARRY HINES BLVD, UT SOUTHWESTERN MED SCH 75390 #048-12-2007 PD *012

TROJAN, Timothy David. ■ 75204 #048-12-2008 *012

TRONE, Timothy Howard. 7777 FOREST LN, STE B107 75230 #048-12-1974 L1976 OTO PDO *020 †16

TROOP, Craig A. 13601 PRESTON RD, STE 900 75240 #062-01-1978 L1980 AN EM *020 †05,16

TROST, Margaret Julian. ■ 75204 #056-06-2007 PD *012

TROUSDALE, Devin Mitchell. ■ 75206 #048-02-2001 L2004 AN *100 †05

TROWBRIDGE, Ann Marie. 5323 HARRY HINES BLVD, DEPT OF ANESTHESIOLOGY 75390 #048-02-1970 L1970 AN *040

TRUELSON, John Morrow. 5323 HARRY HINES BLVD, MC 9035 75390 #048-12-1981 L1981 OTO HNS *020 †45

TRUITT, Michael S. 1441 N BECKLEY AVE 75203 #048-14-2002 L2007 GS *020 †85

TRUONG, Hieu Trong. 2437 VALWOOD PKWY 75234 #941-01-1961 L1977 GP P *020 ‡

TRUONG, Huong Thanh. ■ 75235 #048-12-2008 *012

TRUONG, Tam C. 5909 HARRY HINES BLVD 75235 #048-13-1987 L1988 OBG *020 †30

TRUONG, Tich Ngoc. 6465 E MOCKINGBIRD LN, STE 314 75214 #941-01-1967 L1982 PM *020 †60

TRUSSLER, Andrew Peter. ■ 75390 #005-06-1999 L2006 GS *100 †85

TSAI, Catherine Suefin. ■ 75230 #048-14-1984 L2004 FM *020

TSEGGAY, Gebre Kidan. 8230 WALNUT HILL LN, STE 414 75231 #473-01-1983 L1995 ID *020 †20

TSENG, Anna Siuling Tjeng. 7515 GREENVILLE AVE STE 40 75231 #048-04-1992 L1997 N OS *020 †75

TSOU, Joe Mengwei. 3500 W WHEATLAND RD 75237 #048-02-1981 L1981 EM *020 †16

TUBBS, Charles Gordon. ■ 75235 #048-02-1970 L1970 FM *071 †48

TUCKER, M Susan. ■ 75205 #048-13-1977 L1994 U *020 †95

TUCKER, Paul May. 6310 LBJ FWY, STE 218 75240 #748-07-1963 L1973 AN *020

TUCKER, Spencer Paul. ■ 75214 #021-06-2002 CRS *012

TUCKER, William F, Jr. 8210 WALNUT HILL LN, STE 404 75231 #048-12-1989 L1990 ORS *020 †40

TUEN, Charles C. 221 W COLORADO BLVD, STE 208 75208 #244-01-1979 L1983 N CN *020 †75

TULANON, Vanee. ■ 75243 #891-02-1972 L1985 P *020

TUMMALA, Chaitanya V. 1 MEDICAL PKWY, STE 210 75234 #496-24-1996 L2004 ID *020 †20

TUNELL, Gary Lee. 6301 GASTON AVE, STE 400W 75214 #028-03-1975 L1977 N *020 †75

TUNG, Christina Tao. ■ 75219 #048-12-2005 L2008 PD *012

TUNINK, Bryan Peter. 13601 PRESTON RD, STE 900 75240 #005-06-1990 L1996 AN PME *020 †05

TURGEON, Douglas Randolph. 6901 SNIDER PLZ, STE 200 75205 #021-05-1985 L1991 ORS *020 †40 ‡

TURNAGE, Richard Hampton. 5323 HARRY HINES BLVD, STOP 9031 75390 #021-06-1983 L1991 GS *020 †85

TURNER, David L. 7777 FOREST LN, STE C420 75230 #048-12-1982 L1983 FM UM *020

TURNER, Ellen Okeefe. 8222 DOUGLAS AVE, STE 950 75225 #048-15-2001 L2005 D *020

TURNER, Gary Robt. 10830 N CENTRAL EXPY 75231 #038-40-1978 L1981 AN CCP *020 †55,05

TURNER, Jack Calvin, III. 4131 N CENTRAL EXPY 75204 #048-15-2003 L2007 AN *020

TURNER, Kent Beauregard. 6757 ARAPAHO RD STE 71, BOX 335 75248 #021-01-1996 L1998 AN *020 †05

TURNER, Sylvia Joyce. ■ 75223 #035-06-1980 L1987 CHP OS *020 †75

TURNER, William Wood, Jr. 5323 HARRY HINES BLVD 75390 #021-01-1972 L1973 GS *020 †85

TURNEY, David Clark. 8200 SOUTHWESTERN BLVD # 2 75206 #048-12-2000 L2006 FM *020 †18

TUSTIN, James F, Jr. ■ 75367 #005-06-1970 L1972 R OS *071 †80 ‡

TUTHILL, Edward Wilmar. 11107 LAWNHAVEN RD, GUEST HOUSE-LEFT REAR 75230 #048-02-1967 L1967 P *020 †18

TWICKLER, Diane Mary. 5323 HARRY HINES BLVD, SOUTHWEST MEDICAL SCH 75390 #048-12-1984 L1985 DR *020 †20

TWOMBLEY, Katherine Eliza. 5323 HARRY HINES BLVD, UTSOUTHWESTERN MED CTR 75390 #045-01-2004 PN *012 †55

TYLER, David Lendon. 5323 HARRY HINES BLVD, DEPT OF PSYCH 75390 #048-13-1976 L1976 P *020 †75

TYLER, Debra Sue. ■ 75230 #048-15-1987 L1988 PAN *020 †05

TYSON WICKS, Joyclyn E. 9 MEDICAL PKWY, STE 107 75234 #048-02-1997 L1998 AN *020 †05

TYULUMAN, Samuel A. 8160 WALNUT HILL LN, STE 200 75231 #048-12-1986 L1987 OBG *020 †30

UAUY-DAGACH, Ricardo. 5201 HARRY HINES BLVD 75235 #231-01-1972 L1985 NPM NTR *020 †55

UBINAS-BRACHE, Emmanuel E. 411 N WASHINGTON AVE, STE 2000 75246 #847-04-1977 L1985 PS *020

UCEDA, Pablo Victor. 221 W COLORADO BLVD, SURGICAL ASSOCIATES 75208 #737-01-1983 L1993 TS *020 †85

UCHIYAMA DE LA PUENTE, Edu. 5323 HARRY HINES BLVD 75390 #737-10-2004 IM *012

UDDIN, Naseem. 5323 HARRY HINES BLVD, DEPT OF PATHOLOGY 75390 #704-27-1999 L2007 PP *012

UHR, Barry Wayne. 3600 GASTON AVE STE 609, LB 120 75246 #048-12-1965 L1965 OPH *020 †35

UHR, Jonathan W. 5323 HARRY HINES BLVD 75390 #035-19-1952 L1975 IG *050 †20

UHR, Sarita Betsy. 5495 BELT LINE RD 75254 #048-13-1982 L1983 P *020 †75

UHRBROCK, David H. ■ 75390 #048-02-1998 L1999 RNR *020 †20

UHRICH, M Melinda. 3310 LIVE OAK ST, 3RD FLOOR - COPC RESOURCES 75204 #030-06-1978 L1986 PD OS *030 †55

ULISSEY, Michael J. 4441 NORTHCREST RD 75229 #048-16-1991 L1992 DR *020 †80

ULUALP, Omer Seckin. ■ 75229 #902-07-1992 *100

UNGER, Douglas H. 13601 PRESTON RD STE 10 75240 #048-12-1986 L1987 AN *020 †05

UNGER, Roger Harold. 4500 S LANCASTER RD 75216 #035-01-1947 L1957 END IM *030 †20

UNSELL, Randal F. 3024 WESTMINSTER AVE 75205 #048-12-1989 L1990 ADP *020 †05,75

UNTERBERG, Mark Paul. 8330 MEADOW RD, STE 128 75231 #035-08-1970 L1976 P IM *020 †75

UNVERDI, Cemal. 4500 S LANCASTER RD, DVAMC MENTAL HEALTH 116A 75216 #902-03-1954 L1972 P ADP *020

URBAN, Jill Elise. ■ 75214 #019-02-1994 L1996 FOP *020 †50

URIBE, Mercedes Margarita. 5323 HARRY HINES BLVD, SOUTHWESTERN MED 75390 #649-38-1998 L2007 PEM *012

URREGO, Hernan Dario. ■ 75211 #048-12-2008 *012

URSCHEL, Harold C, Jr. 3600 GASTON AVE, STE 1201 75246 #024-01-1955 L1963 TS VS *071 †85,90

URSCHEL, Harold C, III. 8222 DOUGLAS AVE STE 375 75225 #048-12-1986 L1987 ADP *020 †75

USREY, David C. SMU HEALTH CENTER 75275 #048-12-1953 L1953 PD *071

UTSET, Ofelia Maria. 5939 HARRY HINES BLVD, STE 711 75235 #005-02-1986 L1989 PUD *020 †20

VADER, Justin Marinus. ■ 75214 #048-12-2006 IM *012

VAGEFI, Ali. 5323 HARRY HINES BLVD, DEPARTMENT OF OPTHALMOLOGY 75390 #517-05-1971 L1980 OPH *020 †35

VALACHOVIC, Michael S. 3434 SWISS AVE, STE 420 75204 #048-12-2005 L2007 IM *012

VALADEZ, Javier Arnoldo. 1922 W 10TH ST 75208 #048-02-1983 L1983 IM *020 †20

VALDEZ, Thomas Reid. ■ 75204 #012-01-2005 EM *012

VALEK, Timothy Ray. 6301 GASTON AVE, EAST TOWERM SUITE 400 75214 #048-13-1983 L1983 AN *020 †05

VALENTINE, Rawson James. 5323 HARRY HINES BLVD, UNIV TX SW MED CTR SURG 75390 #012-05-1980 L1981 VS GS *020 †85

VALLEJOS, Jose Trinidad. ■ 75216 #048-02-2007 AN *012

VALLERA, Raphaelle Della. 910 N CENTRAL EXPY 75204 #041-09-1990 L1996 END *020 †20

VANATTA, John C, III. 5323 HARRY HINES BLVD, U TX SW MED CTR MC 9139 75390 #017-20-1944 L1950 OS IM *040 †20

VANBUREN, Peter Noel. ■ 75201 #048-13-2005 IM *012

VANCE, Estil A, III. 7777 FOREST LN, STE D220 75230 #023-07-1990 L1998 ON *020 †20

VANCE, Greta Lee. 3434 SWISS AVE, STE 410 75204 #048-12-1991 L1993 IM *020 †20

VANDER BERGE, Kevin Marin. ■ 75225 #048-15-2006 ORS *012

VAN DERMARK, Jeffrey Todd. ■ 75225 #038-41-1989 L2005 EM *020 †16

VANDERMEER, Robert Derry. 9301 N CENTRAL EXPY, STE 400 75231 #048-12-1958 L1958 ORS *020 †40

VANDERPOOL, David. 1008 N WASHINGTON AVE 75204 #048-12-1956 L1956 GS *020 †85

VANDERPOOL, Donald Warne. ■ 75230 #048-04-1960 L1960 ORS *020 †40

VANDEVENTER, Jon Nelson. 5323 HARRY HINES BLVD, DEPT OF PHYS MED & REHAB 75390 #003-01-1984 L1985 PM *020 †60

VAN DE VYVER, Hubert L. ■ 75205 #165-04-1958 L1969 AN *071

VANDINTER, Thomas George. 3500 GASTON AVE 75246 #048-02-2004 L2006 **GE** *012

VANHORN, Allan C. 1441 N BECKLEY AVE 75203 #048-12-1987 L1988 **U** *020 †95

VAN NESS, Paul Cyril. 5323 HARRY HINES BLVD, DEPT NEURO 75390 #005-14-1981 L1995 **N CN** *020 †75

VARDAMAN, Celeste Jolly. 7777 FOREST LN, C-350 C/O LAB CORP 75230 #027-01-1984 L1989 **PTH PCP** *050

VARDI, Amir. ■ 75248 #550-02-1986 **CCP** *020

VARELA, Javier Esteban. 4500 S LANCASTER RD # 112, NORTH TEXAS VA HCS 75216 #264-01-1995 L2007 **GS** *100 †85

VARGAS-CORTES, Fernando. 8200 WALNUT HILL LN 75231 #264-04-1963 L1977 **PTH** *020 †50

VARGHESE, Thomas. ■ 75204 #048-12-1999 L2004 **RNR** *100 †80

VARSHNEY, Deepa. ■ 75219 #048-02-2008 *012

VAS, Collin John B. 4500 S LANCASTER RD 75216 #495-52-1994 L2006 **P** *020

VASAN, Vasantha. 12700 PARK CENTRAL DR, STE 430 75251 #496-35-1995 L2002 **DR** *020 †80

VASQUEZ, Javier, Jr. 9330 POPPY DR, STE 500 75218 #048-12-1997 L2004 **VS VIR** *020 †85

VAUGHAN, Elizabeth R. 4131 N CENTRAL EXPY, STE 725 75204 #048-12-1966 L1966 **OPH** *020 †35 ‡

VAUGHAN, Paul Allan. 5959 HARRY HINES BLVD 75235 #064-01-1976 L1989 **ORS** *020 †40

VAZQUEZ, Miguel A. 5323 HARRY HINES BLVD, DEPT OF INTERNAL MEDICINE 75390 #042-01-1985 L1986 **NEP IM** *020 †20

VELAPHI, Sithembiso C. 5323 HARRY HINES BLVD, UT SOUTHWESTERN MEDICAL C 75390 #836-05-1986 **NPM** *100

VELASCO, Carlos Ernesto. 3600 GASTON AVE, BAYLOR UNIV WADLEY 851 75246 #319-04-1979 L1993 **CD IM** *020 †20

VELASQUEZ, Auden C. ■ 75235 #048-12-2008 *012

VELASQUEZ, Otto R. 1935 MOTOR ST 75235 #429-02-1989 L1997 **PD HOS** *020 †55

VELAZQUEZ, Daniel Jesus. 5323 HARRY HINES BLVD, DIV OF EMERGENCY MED 75390 #042-03-2003 L2007 **EM** *100

VELAZQUEZ, Francisco R. ■ 75390 #042-03-1981 L1986 **PTH** *030 †50

VELEZ, Eduardo. 2301 S HAMPTON RD, STE 500 75224 #264-07-1993 L1996 **PD** *020 †55

VELEZ, Larissa I. 5323 HARRY HINES BLVD, U.T. SOUTHWESTERN MEDICAL 75390 #048-12-1996 L1999 **EM** *040 †16

VELEZ, Melinda J. 3450 W WHEATLAND RD, PROF BLDG 2 SUITE 443 75237 #048-78-1999, ▲ L2001 **OBG** *020

VELLANKI, Srilatha. 6901 SNIDER PLZ STE 1 75205 #495-65-1999 L2004 **IM** *020 †20

VELTKAMP, Daniel Lane. 1935 MOTOR ST, OF UT SOUTHWESTERN MEDICAL 75235 #020-12-1994 L1999 **RNR** *020 †80

VENEGAS, Carlos Luis. 8222 DOUGLAS AVE, STE 601 75225 #016-42-1991 L1996 **IM** *020 †20

VENEGAS, Gonzalo. 1135 N BISHOP AVE 75208 #649-01-1977 L1989 **OBG** *030

VENGROW, Michael Ian. 11884 GREENVILLE AVE, STE 110A 75243 #024-16-1977 L1996 **N** *020 †75 ‡

VENINCASA, Michael D. 221 W COLORADO BLVD, STE 831 75208 #048-12-1986 L1988 **CD** *020 †20

VENKATARAMAN, Aditya. ■ 75235 #048-12-2008 *012

VERGNE-MARINI, Pedro Juan. 740 WYNNEWOOD VILG SHP CTR 75224 #023-01-1968 L1973 **NEP CD** *071 †20

VERMA, Avesh Raja. ■ 75204 #021-06-2006 **N** *012

VERMA, Udit N. 5151 HARRY HINES BLVD 75235 #495-05-1983 L2003 **HO IM** *020 †20

VERMETTE, Heidi L. 4500 S LANCASTER RD, MENTAL HEALTH, 116A 75216 #048-15-1997 L2004 **P PFP** *020 †75

VERNINO, Steven Arthur. 5323 HARRY HINES BLVD, DEPT OF NEUROLOGY 75390 #048-04-1994 L2004 **N** *050 †75

VERNON, Kim Taylor. 7777 FOREST LN, VERNON & WALDREP OB GYN 75230 #048-13-1979 L1979 **OBG** *030

VERSTRINGHE, Louis E, III. ■ 75204 #028-46-2002 L2007 **OPH** *020

VEST, Zachary Daniel. ■ 75201 #048-12-2008 *012

VESY, Christopher John. 3600 GASTON AVE, BARNETT TOWER, SUITE 809 75246 #038-40-1993 L1997 **GE** *020 †20

VIA, Mickey Wayne. 3535 TRAVIS ST STE 210 75204 #048-12-1974 L1974 **AN** *020

VICENTE, Chris Michael. ■ 75204 #035-09-1994 L2006 **N** *020 †75

VICIOSO VARELAS, Belinda. 5201 HARRY HINES BLVD 75235 #308-05-1979 L1995 **IMG IM** *020 †20

VICTOR, Ronald Gary. 5323 HARRY HINES BLVD # H, CARDIOLOGY UTSMCD 75390 #021-01-1978 L1987 **CD IM** *040 †20

VICTORY, Raymond Adrian. 5201 HARRY HINES BLVD 75235 #539-03-1983 L1997 **AN PME** *020 †05

VIELMA, Valentina Marie. 3710 SWISS AVE, STE 205 75204 #048-13-1994 L1996 **PD** *020 †55

VIERE, Robert Gerard. 3900 JUNIUS ST, STE 705 75246 #026-04-1984 L1986 **OSS** *020 †40

VIGNALE, Steven J. 14800 LANDMARK BLVD, HEART PLACE 75254 #048-02-1987 L1990 **CD IC** *020 †20

VINES, Victor Lee. 12200 PARK CENTRAL DR, STE 403 75251 #048-12-1984 L1985 **OBG FM** *020 †30

VIRELLA, Cesar D. 13601 PRESTON RD STE 900W, PINNACLE ANESTHESIA CONSUL 75240 #042-01-1989 L1994 **AN GP** *020 †05

VIROSLAV, Joseph. 5939 HARRY HINES BLVD, SOUTHWEST PULMONARY ASSOCI 75235 #649-01-1962 L1969 **PUD IM** *020 †20

VIRTUCIO, Anna Liza C. ■ 75238 #748-01-1993 L1996 **PM** *100

VISWANATHAN, Sundeep. ■ 75235 #048-12-2008 *012

VO, Thinh Qui. 9330 POPPY DR 75218 #048-14-1995 L1997 **PCC** *020 †20

VOBACH, Stephen F. 3600 GASTON AVE, STE 1155 75246 #048-14-1989 L1990 **P PYG** *020 †75

VOET, Richard Leo. 8200 WALNUT HILL LN, DEPT OF PATHOLOGY 75231 #038-41-1975 L1981 **PTH GP** *020 †50

VOIGT, Jason M. 5201 HARRY HINES BLVD 75235 #048-13-2005 L2007 **AN** *012

VONGPATANASIN, Wanpen. 5323 HARRY HINES BLVD, DIV HYPERTENSION RM J4.134 75390 #891-01-1991 L1995 **CD** *050 †20

VORHIES, John Royal H. 8215 WESTCHESTER DR # 225 75225 #048-12-1972 L1972 **IM** *020 †20

VOTTELER, Theodore P. 12200 PARK CENTRAL DR, STE 400 75251 #021-01-1951 L1951 **PDS** *071 †85

VRUSHAB, Rajesh B. 14800 LANDMARK BLVD, STE 700 75254 #495-35-1993 L2006 **CD** *020 †20

VU, Giac Tien. 13601 PRESTON RD STE 900W, PINNACLE ANESTHESIA CONSUL 75240 #048-14-1998 L2002 **GS** *020 †05

VU, Hung James. 13601 PRESTON RD, STE 900W 75240 #021-06-1993 L1997 **AN** *020 †05

VU, Manhan K. 5323 HARRY HINES BLVD, SOUTHWESTERN MED 75390 #048-78-2004, ▲ L2006 **OBG** *012

VU, Phat. 13601 PRESTON RD, STE 900 75240 #048-12-1991 L1992 **AN** *020 †05

VURIMI, Siva Kumari. 12221 MERIT DR STE 45 75251 #496-24-1998 L2005 **IM** *100 †20

VUSIRIKALA, Madhuri. 2201 INWOOD ROAD, MC 8565, UT SOUTHWESTERN MEDICAL CE 75390 #496-07-1992 L2006 **HO ON** *020 †20

VUSTAR, Mirjana. 1935 MEDICAL DISTRICT DR, STE B3302 75235 #957-07-1991 L2007 **AN** *020 †05

WABER, Lewis Jos. 5323 HARRY HINES BLVD, UNIV TX DEPT PED 75235 #038-06-1977 L1989 **MG PD** *040 †55,19

WACHENDORFER, Ruth. ■ 75209 #048-15-1992 L1993 **GS** *020

WACHSMANN, Jason W. ■ 75204 #048-14-2007 **DR** *012

WADA, Suzanne Yuri. 5323 HARRY HINES BLVD, SOUTHWESTERN MEDICAL SCHOO 75390 #041-13-1989 L1997 **ID** *020 †20

WADA, Takaaki. 5323 HARRY HINES BLVD, SOUTHWESTERN MED 75390 #550-04-2003 L2007 **ID** *012 †20

WADDELL, Douglas Howard. 10473 EPPING LN, FAMILY PRACTICE INDUSTRIAL 75229 #047-06-1969 L1971 **FM OM** *020 †18

WADDLE, Jean Luby. 3920 WORTH ST 75246 #028-34-1991 L1998 **AN** *020 †05

WADE, Dean Edward. 13601 PRESTON RD, STE 900W 75240 #034-01-1977 L1980 **AN GP** *020 †05

WADE, Paul Douglas. 9301 N CENTRAL EXPY, STE 670 75231 #004-01-1976 L1979 **IM** *020 †20

WAGGONER, Jill. 2506 S LANCASTER RD, SOUTH TEXAS MEDICAL CENTER 75216 #039-01-1992 L1993 **FM** *020 †18

WAGMAN, Felicia Ann. 8230 WALNUT HILL LN, STE 406 75231 #041-13-1997 L2001 **OBG** *020 †30

WAGNER, James M. 5323 HARRY HINES BLVD, MC 9006 75390 #048-12-1986 L1987 **IM** *030 †20

WAGNER, K James. ■ 75240 #056-06-1964 L1972 **ORS** *071 †40

WAHEED, Salman. 12221 MERIT DR 75251 #704-16-1992 L2001 **CCM IM** *020 †20

WAI, Clifford Yipwing. 5323 HARRY HINES BLVD, RM G6.220 UNIF OF TX SWSTN 75390 #010-02-1996 L2001 **OBG** *020 †30

WAINSCOTT, Michael P. 5323 HARRY HINES BLVD, MC 8579 75235 #048-15-1981 L1981 **EM** *040 †20

WAIT, Juliette Louise. 7777 FOREST LN STE B2 75230 #019-02-1974 L1987 **CCM PUD** *040 †20

WAIT, Michael Alton. 5909 HARRY HINES BLVD 75235 #048-12-1983 L1983 **TS** *020 †85,90

WAITES, Lucius. 2222 WELBORN ST 75219 #047-06-1947 L1951 **CHN PD** *071 †55

WAKHLU, Sidarth. 4500 S LANCASTER RD, V A LAMP CLINIC 75216 #495-45-1991 L2004 **ADP** *020 †75

WALBERG, Mark Wm. 3535 WORTH ST, SAMMONS CANCER CENTER BA 75246 #005-11-1984 L1994 **ON IM** *020 †20

WALD, Tina Gay. 4500 S LANCASTER RD, GERIATRICS & EXTENDED CARE 75216 #005-14-1986 L2000 **IM ID** *040 †20

WALDREP, Kathryn K. 7777 FOREST LN, VERNON & WALDREP OB GYN 75230 #048-12-1978 L1979 **OBG** *020 †33 ‡

WALDROP, Charles Wesley. 3500 W WHEATLAND RD 75237 #020-02-1959 L1962 **FM** *020 †18

WALKER, Brandy Shawna. ■ 75229 #048-12-1980 L1980 **NM** *050 †28

WALKER, Danya Khalilah. 5323 HARRY HINES BLVD, SOUTHWESTERN MED 75390 #041-13-2006 **PD** *012

WALKER, Fabianne Latresha. 5323 HARRY HINES BLVD 75390 #028-03-2006 **OBG** *012

WALKER, Jamie Lin. ■ 75235 #048-12-2008 *012

WALKER, Jonathan Edward. 12870 HILLCREST RD, STE 201 75230 #048-04-1965 L1965 **N PA** *020 †75

WALKER, Ramona. ■ 75206 #016-01-1999 L2004 **PCC** *020

WALKER, Steven Craig. 13601 PRESTON RD, STE 900 75240 #048-13-1993 L1994 **AN UM** *020 †05

WALL, Bruce Raleigh. 13154 COIT RD, STE 100 75240 #021-01-1981 L1982 **NEP** *020 †20

WALL, James Bennett. 5323 HARRY HINES BLVD, U.T. SOUTHWESTERN MEDICAL 75390 #012-01-1987 L1992 **AN** *020 †05

WALL, Jean A. 2222 WELBORN ST, DEPARTMENT OF ANESTHESIOLO 75219 #048-13-1983 L1983 **AN** *020 †05

WALL, Vivekananda M. 1717 MAIN ST STE 5200 75201 #030-05-1976 L1987 **EM OS** *020 †16

WALLACE, Donald H. 5323 HARRY HINES BLVD 75235 #143-02-1957 L1983 **AN** *040

WALLACE, John David. 10830 N CENTRAL EXPY, STE 495 75231 #048-12-2002 L2007 **OMF** *100

WALLER, Barbara L Chasen. ■ 75254 #023-07-1970 L1980 **P** *030

WALLER, David Allan. 5323 HARRY HINES BLVD 75235 #023-07-1968 L1980 **CHP** *020 †55,75

WALSH, Raymond J. 6303 HARRY HINES, DEPT OF FAMILY MEDICINE 75390 #048-12-1999 L2006 **FM** *020

WALTERS, David Lee. 3500 W WHEATLAND RD 75237 #048-14-1985 L1986 **FM** *020 †18

WALTERS, Jack Allison, Jr. 8335 WALNUT HILL LN # 215 75231 #048-04-1974 L1975 **OBG** *020 †30

WALTERS, Kendall Marie. ■ 75201 #048-12-2008 *012

WALTERS, Leslie Lewis. 7777 FOREST LN, BLDG A 75230 #014-01-1980 L1988 **PTH** *020 †50

WALTERS, Nathan. 13601 PRESTON RD, STE 900W 75240 #048-12-1996 L1997 **AN** *020 †05

WALTERS, Nathan S. 8335 WALNUT HILL LN # 215 75231 #048-13-2002 L2003 **PM** *100 †60

WALTERS, Steven Mark. 8200 WALNUT HILL LN, PRESBYTERIAN HOSP OF DALLA 75231 #048-12-1999 L2002 **IM** *020 †20

WALTON, William James. 12200 PARK CENTRAL DR, STE 120 75251 #064-01-1973 L1978 **FM** *020

WALTRIP, Travis William. 3141 HOOD ST STE 610, LEE PARK CENTER 75219 #048-02-1971 L1971 **P** *020 †75

WAMBI-KIESSE, Christel Or. 5323 HARRY HINES BLVD, UROLOGY DEPT. 75390 #016-06-2003 **U** *100

WANAT, Alycia Meegan. ■ 75201 #048-12-2008 *012

WANG, Chiyu. 8220 WALNUT HILL LN, BLDG II 75231 #243-16-1990 L2004 **ON** *020 †20 ‡

WANG, Chun K. 5611 ELLSWORTH AVE 75206 #048-15-1993 L1995 **IMG** *100 †20

WANG, Huan-You. 5323 HARRY HINES BLVD, DEPT OF PATH 9073 75390 #243-13-1987 L2006 **HMP** *100 ‡

WANG, Jean Chi. 9101 N CENTRAL EXPY, BAYLOR SAMMONS BREAST 75231 #035-06-1996 L2002 **DR** *020 †80

WANG, Jessica Jenchu. 5201 HARRY HINES BLVD 75235 #041-01-2004 L2007 **IM** *100 †20

WANG, Jian. 3320 LIVE OAK ST 75204 #243-47-1984 L1998 **PD** *020 †55

WANG, Peter. 1935 MOTOR ST 75235 #047-05-1991 L1993 **AN** *020 †05

WANG, Richard Chihchien. ■ 75219 #035-20-2006 L2008 **D** *012

WANG, Serena Xiaohang. 5323 HARRY HINES BLVD, DEPT OF OPTHAMOLOGY 75390 #243-25-1985 L2004 **OPH PO** *020 †35

WANG, Xuecheng. 8 MEDICAL PKWY, PLZ 2 STE 204 75234 #243-72-1968 L1996 **IM** *020 †20

WANG, Yili. 8411 PRESTON RD, STE 200 75225 #048-04-1996 L1997 **IM** *020 †20

WANG, Yuchi Annie. ■ 75214 #004-01-1999 L2004 **PDE** *100 †55

WANSBROUGH, Scott Robt. 5323 HARRY HINES BLVD 75390 #048-04-1975 L1976 **AN** *040 †05

WARD, Michael Harold. 6616 LONGFELLOW DR 75230 #005-02-1975 L1994 **ON HEM** *020 †20

WARD, Paula Leonne. 5323 HARRY HINES BLVD, STOP 9031 75390 #035-06-1992 L1996 **EM** *020 †16

WARDEN, Susan Kay. 411 N WASHINGTON AVE, STE 4000 75246 #019-02-1988 L1990 **PM** *020 †60

WARE, Athol John. 5323 HARRY HINES BLVD 75235 #143-03-1964 L1977 **GE OS** *050

WARE, Elgin Willis, Jr. 3223 BASIL CT 75204 #048-12-1946 L1946 **U** *020 †95

WARE, John Roscoe. 3600 GASTON AVE, UROLOGY CLINICS OF NORTH 75246 #048-15-1981 L1981 **U** *020 †95

WARNACK, Worthy Ray, Jr. 7777 FOREST LN BLDG B, STE 115 75230 #048-12-1981 L1981 **N** *020 †75 ‡

WARNER, John Jay. 5323 HARRY HINES BLVD, DIVISION OF CARDIOLOGY 75390 #047-05-1992 L1993 **CD** *020 †20

WARREN, Kelly J. 1450 PRESTON FOREST SQ, STE 281 75230 #035-01-1995 L1999 **D** *020 †15

WARREN, Russell Scott. ■ 75214 #048-15-2005 L2008 **GS** *100

WASHINGTON, Paula Jo. 8267 ELMBROOK DR STE 100 75247 #021-01-1979 L1988 **PTH** *020 †50

WASHINGTON, Ronald J. 831 S R L THORNTON FWY, PROVIDENT MEDICAL CNTR 75203 #010-03-1973 L1973 **IM** *020 †20

WASSERMAN, Jeffrey L. 13601 PRESTON RD, STE 900 75240 #041-14-1990 L1995 **PMM AN** *020 †05

WASSERMAN, Richard L. 7777 FOREST LN, STE B332 75230 #048-12-1977 L1983 **AI PD** *020 †55,03

WATERS, Melissa Ann. ■ 75219 #048-14-2005 L2007 **PD** *012

WATERS, Samuel Wayne. 3500 GASTON AVE 75246 #048-02-1972 L1973 **IM** *020

WATKINS, Brennan Montgome. ■ 75204 #048-13-2004 L2006 **AN** *012

WATKINS, Cheletta L. 1151 N BUCKNER BLVD, STE 302 75218 #048-02-1997 L2002 **FM** *020 †18

WATKINS, David Louis. 3500 GASTON AVE 75246 #048-12-1978 L1983 **PTH** *020 †50

WATKINS, James Wilson. 8325 WALNUT HILL LN, STE 225 75231 #048-04-1976 L1976 **PD** *020 †55

WATKINS, Myron Hinton. 5939 HARRY HINES BLVD, STE 323 75235 #047-07-1957 L1963 **OBG** *020 †30

WATKINS, Richard Martin. 12740 HILLCREST RD, STE 274 75230 #012-05-1973 L1975 **AN CCM** *020 †05

WATSON, Mark Jay. 5323 HARRY HINES BLVD, UT SOUTHWESTERN MEDICAL CE 75390 #028-02-1988 L2001 **GS** *040 †85

WATSON, Mark Layton. ■ 75218 #036-07-1994 **PTH** *020

WATSON, Mary Nelson. 2777 N STEMMONS FWY, STE 300 75207 #034-01-1982 L1984 **IM** *030 †20 ‡

WATSON, Terry R. 3618 FAIRMOUNT ST 75219 #048-78-1978, ▲ L1979 **FM ID** *020

WATSON, Thos Douglas, III. 7777 FOREST LN, STE B238 75230 #048-12-1971 L1971 **AN** *020 †05

WATTANAKIT, Keattiyoat. SOUTHWESTERN MED, UNIV OF TEXAS 75390 #016-42-1998 L1998 **CD** *012 †20

WATTS, Jonathan Michael. ■ 75235 #048-12-2008 *012

WATTS, Maureen Wooten. 7515 GREENVILLE AVE, STE 500 75231 #003-01-1985 L1990 **N** *020 †75

WATTS, Nathaniel T, Jr. 3324 MALCOLM X BLVD 75215 #047-07-1960 L1965 **GS GP** *071 †85

WATTS, Stephen Edward. ■ 75224 #047-07-1957 L1963 **PD GP** *020

WATTS, Susan Ruth. 8160 WALNUT HILL LN, STE 306 75231 #048-14-1994 L2000 **OBG** *020 †20

WATUMULL, Lori Meril. 5909 HARRY HINES BLVD 75235 #048-12-1986 L1987 **DR** *020 †80

WAUGH, Jeffrey Lynn. ■ 75205 #048-12-2007 **PD** *012

WAW, Kristen Deann. ■ 75254 #048-02-2007 **PD** *012

WAY, Anthony Biden. ■ 75229 #041-01-1967 L1972 **GPM** *071 †70

WAY, Barbara H. ■ 75229 #041-01-1968 L1972 **D** *071 †15

WAY, Mary Catherine. 6211 BISHOP BLVD 75275 #048-12-1988 L1989 **P** *020 †75

WAY, Sarah Shoemaker. 3747 ALTA VISTA LN 75229 #016-06-2004 L2007 **EM** *020

WAYHS, Amelia Cassettari. 3500 W WHEATLAND RD 75237 #187-17-1992 L2003 **FM** *040 †18 ‡

WAYHS, Roberto. 3450 W WHEATLAND RD # 340 75237 #187-17-1992 L1996 **CD IC** *020 †20

WAYNE, Leslie G. 7557 RAMBLER RD 75231 #048-15-2002 L2006 **AN** *020 †05

WEAKLEY, David R, Jr. 3120 STANFORD AVE 75225 #048-02-1984 L1985 **OPH** *020 †35

WEAKLEY, Devri Lane. ■ 75225 #048-12-1996 L1997 **DR** *100 †80

WEATHERALL, Paul T. 2221 INWOOD RD 75390 #048-04-1982 L1983 **DR** *020 †80

WEATHERFORD, Wilson. 3504 SWISS AVE 75204 #048-12-1958 L1958 **IM IMG** *030 †20

WEATHERS, Seaborn Beck. 7777 FOREST LN, BLDG A 75230 #048-12-1972 L1973 **PTH** *020 †50

WEAVER, Kevin Len. 13601 PRESTON RD STE 100 75240 #048-13-1994 L1998 **AN** *020 †05

WEAVER, William Richard. 1845 WOODALL RODGERS FWY, STE 1275 75201 #048-12-1967 L1967 **FM GPM** *071 †18 ‡

WEBB, Arthur Lawson. ■ 75251 #010-02-2002 L2002 **GS** *100

WEBB, Carmen Thurston. 4100 MCEWEN RD STE 285 75244 #048-12-1987 L1989 **P** *020 †75

WEBB, Cynthia G. 8345 WALNUT HILL LN, BLDG D 75231 #048-12-1993 L1994 **PD** *020 †55

WEBB, David Robt, Jr. 3500 GASTON AVE 75246 #028-02-1959 L1967 **ORS** *071 †40

WEBB, Jerry Lee. 13601 PRESTON RD, STE 900 75240 #048-13-1987 L1989 **AN** *020 †05

WEBB, John Stafford. 5939 HARRY HINES BLVD, STE 903 75235 #048-12-1975 L1975 **IM** *020

WEBB, Joseph Felton. 13601 PRESTON RD, STE 900W 75240 #048-12-1983 L1983 **AN** *020 †05

WEBB, Linda Singer. 1935 MOTOR ST 75235 #048-12-1974 L1977 **OBG** *071 †30

WEBB, Stephen E. 9301 N CENTRAL EXPY, STE 460 TOWER 2 75231 #048-14-1974 L1974 **OPH** *020 †35

WEBER, Denise S. 3434 SWISS AVE STE 330 75204 #048-12-1995 L1997 **IM** *020 †20

WEBSTER, Winston Scott. 3600 GASTON AVE, BARNETT TOWER, STE 1205 75246 #048-12-2001 L2007 **U** *020

WEDGEWORTH, Richard James. 13601 PRESTON RD, STE 900 75240 #048-12-1979 L1979 **AN** *020 †05

WEIDER, Laurence Avram. 221 W COLORADO BLVD # 929 75208 #048-04-1992 L1993 **PS** *035,65

WEIDO, Joey Lachelle. 5323 HARRY HINES BLVD, SOUTHWESTERN MED 75390 #048-02-2003 L2007 **AN** *100

WEIER, Alan Victor. ■ 75219 #048-13-2005 L2007 **EM** *012

WEIGEL, Sofia Maristany. 6161 HARRY HINES BLVD, STE 123 75235 #021-05-1992 L1995 **PM** *020 †60

WEINBERG, Arthur Geo. 1935 MOTOR ST 75235 #038-06-1963 L1970 **PTH** *020 †50

WEINBERGER, Debra Gail. 5323 HARRY HINES BLVD 75390 #016-06-1990 2006 **OTO PDO** *020 †45

WEINER, Howard Jay. 8210 WALNUT HILL LN, SUITE 212 LB1`7 75231 #048-12-1977 L1977 **GE IM** *020 †20

WEINER, Myron Frederick. 5323 HARRY HINES BLVD 75390 #021-01-1957 L1958 **PYG** *050 †75

WEINER, Richard Lawrence. 8230 WALNUT HILL LN 75231 #056-06-1975 L1981 **NS N** *020 †25

WEINKAUFF, Regine. ■ 75230 #409-37-1981 L1995 **HMP** *100

WEINMEISTER, Kenney Don. 8220 WALNUT HILL LN, STE 408 75231 #039-01-1987 L1988 **PUD CCM** *020 †20

WEINSTEIN, Gary Lewis. 8220 WALNUT HILL LN, STE 408 75231 #019-02-1986 L1989 **PCC IM** *020 †20

WEINSTEIN, Jeffrey Scott. 1411 N BECKLEY AVE, STE 268 75203 #048-12-1988 L1990 **GE HEP** *072 †20

WEINSTEIN, Sheldon Alan. 8160 WALNUT HILL LN, STE 100 75231 #041-12-1963 L1969 **OBG** *020 †30

WEISS, Joshua L. 7777 FOREST LN, STE D569 75230 #048-12-1996 L1998 **OBG** *020 †30

WEISS, Shelley Ethan. 7777 FOREST LN, STE C550 75230 #016-01-1999 L2000 **PD** *020 †55

WEISS, Simma Gorchov. 6303 HARRY HINES BLVD, STE 200 75235 #016-01-1999 L2001 **FM** *020 †18

WEISSLER, Jonathan C. 3108 PURDUE AVE 75225 #035-19-1979 L1980 **PUD IM** *050 †20

WEISSMAN, George. ■ 75218 #035-19-1943 L1979 **IM OS** *072 †20

WEITZEL, Robert A. ■ 75209 #048-12-1986 L1987 **P** *075 †75

WEITZUL, Sarah Bartles. 5323 HARRY HINES BLVD, DEPT.OF DERMATOLOGY 75390 #048-12-1997 L1998 **D DS** *020 †15

WELCH, Brian J. 910 N CENTRAL EXPY 75204 #048-12-2000 L2004 **END** *020 †20

WELCH, Erin Marie. ■ 75204 #048-12-2000 L2006 **D** *020 †15

WELLS, Peter John. 3450 W WHEATLAND RD, STE 340 75237 #017-20-1982 L1986 **CD** *020 †20

WELLS, Robert R. ■ 75231 #048-13-1997 L1999 **OBG** *020

WELSH, Erica C. 6170 SHERRY LN STE 20 75205 #048-12-1995 L1997 **IM** *020 †20

WELTGE, Craig Wm. 13601 PRESTON RD, STE 900 75240 #038-43-1992 L1998 **AN** *020 †05

WENDEL, George Dorian, Jr. 5323 HARRY HINES BLVD, OBSTETRICS & GYNECOLGY DEP 75390 #028-34-1978 L1981 **OBG MFM** *040 †30

WENZEL, Jeffrey S. 7515 GREENVILLE AVE, STE 707 75231 #048-14-1997 L1998 **DR** *020 †80

WEPRIN, Bradley Edward. 7777 FOREST LN, STE B308 75230 #048-12-1992 L1993 **PDS** *020 †25

WEPRIN, Rebecca Burton. 8160 WALNUT HILL LN, STE 100 75231 #048-12-1992 L1993 **OBG** *020 †30

WERNER, Claudia Lynn. 5323 HARRY HINES BLVD, UNIV TX SW MED CTR 75390 #048-14-1981 L1981 **OBG** *040 †30

WERNLI, Ashley. 3551 ASBURY ST 75205 #048-12-2000 L2002 **P** *020

WESEVICH, Jay W. 13601 PRESTON RD STE 1000 75240 #048-12-1993 L1995 **AN** *020 †05

WEST, April L. ■ 75208 #048-13-2005 **AN** *012

WEST, Don Maurice. 4103 SWISS AVE 75204 #048-13-1983 L1983 **PM** *020 †60

WEST, William Watkins, Jr. 4321 N CENTRAL EXPY, ROUTH STREET WOMEN'S CLINI 75205 #048-12-1962 L1962 **FM P** *020

WESTERBERG, Robert John. 7777 FOREST LN, EMERGENCY DEPARTMENT 75230 #016-11-1995 L1998 **EM** *020 †16

WESTERGAARD, Deborah M. 6901 SNIDER PLZ STE 150 75205 #021-06-1985 L1988 **APM** *020 †05

WESTERGAARD, Henrik. 5323 HARRY HINES BLVD, UT SOUTHWESTERN INT MED 75390 #297-01-1964 L1981 **GE IM** *020 †20

WESTMORELAND, Matthew V. 3808 SWISS AVE 75204 #048-12-1984 L1985 **GS CCS** *020 †85

WESTON, Arthur Sherwin. 3600 GASTON AVE STE 1001 75246 #025-01-1954 L1960 **CD IM** *071 †20

WESTOVER, Arthur Naoki. 5323 HARRY HINES BLVD, MC-9070 75390 #048-04-2002 L2004 **P** *100 †75

WETZEL, Raegan Kay. 5323 HARRY HINES BLVD, U TX SOUTHWESTERN MED 75390 #021-05-2006 **PD** *012

WHARTON, George Wm. 1341 W MOCKINGBIRD LN, STE 710E 75247 #028-03-1966 L1980 **ORS SCI** *020 †40

WHARTON, Keith Allen, Jr. 5323 HARRY HINES BLVD, UTSW PATHOLOGY NB6440 75390 #005-14-1994 L2001 **PTH** *050 †50

WHEELAHAN, Patricia C. 9304 FOREST LN STE 150N 75243 #021-05-1981 L1984 **PD** *020 †55

WHEELAN, Kevin Robt. 621 N HALL ST, STE 500 75226 #028-02-1980 L1980 **CD IM** *020 †20

WHEELER, Craig L. 13601 PRESTON RD, STE 900 75240 #048-14-1993 L1994 **AN** *020 †05

WHEELER, Jennifer L. 8222 DOUGLAS AVE, STE 500 75225 #048-12-1999 L1999 **PD** *020 †55

WHELPLEY, Douglas Paul. 8 MEDICAL PKWY STE 10 75234 #016-11-1974 L1977 **IM** *020 †20

WHIDDON, Brent Booth. 5323 HARRY HINES BLVD, SOUTHWESTERN MED 75390 #001-02-2007 **OBG** *012

WHIDDON, Lonnie L, Jr. 7777 FOREST LN STE B248 75230 #001-02-1971 L1973 **TS** *020 †85,90

WHITAKER, John Fredric. PO BOX 802406 75380 #048-12-1962 L1962 **P** *071

WHITAKER, Phillip Ray. 13601 PRESTON RD, STE 900 75240 #048-12-1987 L1988 **AN** *020 †05

WHITE, Amanda Bona. ■ 75214 #048-12-2003 L2005 **OBG** *100

WHITE, Anna Marie. ■ 75219 #001-02-1999 L2004 **OBG** *020 †30

WHITE, Beverly E. 1441 N BECKLEY AVE, MEDICAL EDUCATION 75203 #048-04-2000 L2004 **IM** *012

WHITE, Bryan K. 5151 HARRY HINES BLVD 75235 #048-02-1992 L1993 **IM** *020 †20

WHITE, Catherine Louise. ■ 75219 #048-14-2001 **PG** *020 †55

WHITE, Chas Stanley, III. 7777 FOREST LN, STE D400 75230 #041-12-1969 L1976 **ON HEM** *020

WHITE, Jonathan Ari. 5323 HARRY HINES BLVD 75390 #034-01-1993 L1995 **NS** *020 †25

WHITE, Lenae. 8222 DOUGLAS AVE STE 390 75225 #048-14-1996 L1996 **ADP P** *020 †75

WHITE, Lisa Jean. 13601 PRESTON RD 75240 #048-02-1992 L1994 **AN** *020 †05

WHITE, Martin G. 3710 RAWLINS ST, STE 1100 75219 #016-06-1963 L1968 **NEP IM** *071 †20

WHITE, Michael Barclay. ■ 75209 #020-02-1988 L1989 **OTO** *020

WHITE, Nancy Ray. 8350 N CENTRAL EXPY, STE M1025 75206 #048-12-1963 L1963 **PD** *071 †55

WHITE, Paul Frederick. 5323 HARRY HINES BLVD, UNIV TX SOUTHWESTERN MED C 75390 #005-02-1977 L1993 **AN IM** *020 †20,05

WHITE, Perrin Chas. 6300 HARRY HINES BLVD, STE 1200 75235 #024-01-1976 L1995 **PDE** *050 †55

WHITE, Robert Brown. ■ 75225 #048-02-1944 L1944 **P PYA** *071 †75

WHITE, Robert Ellison. 3801 GASTON AVE, STE 308 75246 #047-06-1965 L1970 **OBG** *020 †30

WHITE, Roland Livesay. ■ 75238 #048-02-1944 L1944 **IM CD** *020

WHITE, Stephen Curtis. ■ 75244 #049-01-1996 L2001 **ORS** *020 †40

WHITE, Steven J. 8230 WALNUT HILL LN, STE 814 75231 #048-04-1988 L1989 **PS** *020 †45,65

WHITE, Wendy L. 5323 HARRY HINES BLVD, UT SOUTHWESTERN MEDICAL CE 75390 #048-13-1993 L2005 **GS** *020 †85

WHITEHEAD, Bruce Edward. 7777 FOREST LN, STE C420 75230 #028-34-1990 L1993 **OM AN** *020

WHITEHORN, John Frank. 5909 HARRY HINES BLVD 75235 #047-06-1967 L1968 **FM** *020 †18

WHITE-JACKSON, Sheila L. 1400 N WESTMORELAND RD, DE HARO SALDIVAR CLINIC 75211 #024-07-1980 L1989 **PD** *020 †55

WHITFIELD, Jonathan M. 3500 GASTON AVE, 3 HOB PEDS 75246 #919-05-1970 L1991 **NPM** *020 †55

WHITFILL, John Martin. 10611 GARLAND RD 75218 #048-12-1962 L1962 **IM HEM** *071

WHITING, David Ashby. 3600 GASTON AVE STE 1058 75246 #836-01-1953 L1978 **D DMP** *020 †15

WHITLEY, Agnes Vessey. 8200 WALNUT HILL LN 75231 #011-03-1962 L1966 **P** *071 †75

WHITLEY, John Truett. ■ 75230 #048-12-1956 L1956 **AN OS** *071

WHITLOW, Warren David. 8440 WALNUT HILL LN, STE 510 75231 #039-01-1982 L1984 **DR** *020 †80

WHITMAN, Jeffrey. 2801 LEMMON AVE, STE 400 75204 #048-12-1980 L1980 **OPH** *020 †35

WHITNEY, Annette E. 7777 FOREST LN, STE B304 75230 #048-14-1993 L1994 **PD PG** *020 †55

WHITNEY, Gordon Aaron. 7500 W CAMP WISDOM RD 75236 #054-04-1974 L1983 **FM** *020 †18

WHITSON, Jess Thos. 5323 HARRY HINES BLVD 75235 #023-07-1986 L1987 **OPH** *020 †35

WHITTAKER, Elaine P. 8200 WALNUT HILL LN, DEPT OF MEDICINE 75231 #048-12-1994 L1995 **IM** *020

WHITTEN, Charles Wesley. 5323 HARRY HINES BLVD, DEPT ANEST 75390 #048-12-1984 L1985 **AN CD** *030 †05

WHITWORTH, Daniel B. 5461 LA SIERRA DR 75231 #048-14-2002 L2005 **IM** *020 †20

WHITWORTH, Louis Anthony. 5323 HARRY HINES BLVD, MC 8855 75390 #021-01-1996 L2003 **NS** *020

WICKISER, Jonathan Eric. 5323 HARRY HINES BLVD, UT SOUTHWESTERN MEDICAL CE 75390 #048-15-1999 L2006 **PHO** *100 †55

WICKREMASINGHE, Itala Man. ■ 75243 #422-01-1998 L2006 **SCI** *020 †60

WIDING, Harry Francis. 1501 LYNDON B JOHNSON FWY, STE 650 75234 #048-12-1977 L1977 **IM** *020 †20

WIEBE, Robert Arthur. 1935 MOTOR ST, EMERGENCY CTR 75235 #021-01-1967 L1992 **PEM PD** *040 †56

WIEDERKEHR, Michael R. 3601 SWISS AVE 75204 #869-07-1988 L1994 **NEP IM** *020 †20

WIEGN, Phi. UT SOUTHWESTERN MED CTR, CARDIOLOGY DIV HA9133 75390 #035-09-1996 L2004 **ICE** *012 †20

WIGGANS, David Frank. 8335 WALNUT HILL LN, STE 105 75231 #048-12-1979 L1979 **IM** *020 †20

WIGGINTON, Jane Grayson. 5161 HARRY HINES CS2114-MC 75390 #048-12-1997 L1998 **EM** *020 †16

WILCOX, Barry N. 3535 WORTH ST, FL 1 75246 #048-13-1992 L1993 **RO** *020 †80 ‡

WILCOX, Duncan Thomas. 6300 HARRY HINES BLVD, DEPT OF UROLOGY 75235 #917-29-1987 *100

WILDENTHAL, Claud Kern. 5323 HARRY HINES BLVD, B12100 75390 #048-12-1964 L1964 **CD** *030

WILDER, Cynthia Kay. 3434 SWISS AVE, BAYLOR UNIVERSITY MEDICAL 75204 #048-12-2001 L2004 **IM** *020

WILFONG, Lalan S. 8200 WALNUT HILL LN, STE 700 75231 #048-12-1997 L1998 **HO** *020 †20

WILHELM, Kenneth Michael. ■ 75202 #037-01-2005 L2008 **AN** *012

WILKERSON, Jennifer Lynn. 3434 SWISS AVE, STE 320 75204 #048-12-1996 L1997 **IM** *020 †20

WILKES, David Craig. 2222 WELBORN ST, DEPARTMENT OF RADIOLOGY 75219 #036-07-1987 L1992 **PDR** *020 †80

WILKINSON, Paul Samuel. ■ 75214 #048-15-2007 **GS** *012

WILL, Kelly R. 8220 WALNUT HILL LN # 202 75231 #048-02-1984 L1985 **AN PME** *020 †05

WILLETT, Duwayne Lee. 5323 HARRY HINES BLVD, STOP 9031 75390 #056-06-1986 L1992 **CD** *020 †20

WILLIAMS, Charlotte Ann. 3500 GASTON AVE, DEPT OF GENERAL SURGERY 75246 #048-16-2006 **GS** *012

WILLIAMS, Derek Edwin. ■ 75235 #028-02-2007 **GS** *012

WILLIAMS, Elizabeth Coyle. ■ 75225 #048-02-1937 L1937 **OPH** *071

WILLIAMS, Geoffrey M. 9229 LBJ FWY STE 250, MEDICAL EDGE HEALTHCARE GR 75243 #048-12-1981 L1981 **IM** *020 †20

WILLIAMS, Owen Dale. 8200 WALNUT HILL LN 75231 #048-12-1957 L1957 **IM** *071 †20

WILLIAMS, Phillip Earle, III. 7515 GREENVILLE AVE, STE 1000 75231 #021-01-2001 L2004 **IM** *020

WILLIAMS, Royce Mahone. ■ 75230 #047-06-1957 L1957 **FM GYN** *071 †30,18

WILLIAMS, Scott Shields. 5323 HARRY HINES BLVD MC, UTSW - PEDIATRIC NEPHROLOG 75390 #048-02-1999 L2005 **PN** *100 †55

WILLIAMS, Sharenda Lana. ■ 75204 #004-01-2004 **PTH** *012

WILLIAMS, Stormee Renai. 2922B MARTN LTHR KNG JR 75215 #012-21-2002 L2006 **PD** *020 †20

WILLIAMS, Sue A. 3600 GASTON AVE STE 550 75246 #048-12-1993 L1994 **IM** *020 †20

WILLIAMS-KING, Elicia E. 9101 N CENTRAL EXPY, STE 300 75231 #048-02-2004 L2007 **IM** *020 †25

WILLINGHAM, Irene Rae. 3600 GASTON AVE STE 1158 75246 #048-04-1985 L1986 **NS** *020 †25

WILLIS, Charles. 5201 S WESTMORELAND RD 75237 #048-14-1990 L1991 **AN PME** *020 †05

WILLIS, Jason S. ■ 75219 #048-12-2006 **PTH** *012

WILLIS, Monte Shaw. 5323 HARRY HINES BLVD, DEPT PATHOLOGY 75390 #030-05-2001 L2006 **PTH** *100

WILLKOMM, Christopher Mic. ■ 75238 #011-04-2005 **GS** *012

WILSON, Amy J. 3500 GASTON AVE 75204 #048-14-1992 L1993 **PM** *020 †60

WILSON, Carmen Rios. 3320 LIVE OAK ST, EAST DALLAS HLTH CTR 75204 #649-14-1977 L1989 **PD** *020 †55

WILSON, Ellen Elizabeth. 5201 HARRY HINES BLVD 75235 #048-04-1984 L1986 **REN GYN** *020 †30

WILSON, James Wade. 5201 HARRY HINES BLVD, PARKLAND HOSPITAL 75235 #048-12-2005 L2007 **IM** *012

WILSON, Jean Donald. 5323 HARRY HINES BLVD 75390 #048-12-1955 L1955 **END IM** *050 †20

WILSON, Julia I Quinones. ■ 75229 #025-01-1944 **OS** *075

WILSON, Kathleen Sanders. 5323 HARRY HINES BLVD, CV1 110 75390 #048-12-1991 L1992 **CLP CCG** *020 †50,19

WILSON, Philip Lamar. 1935 MOTOR ST D03-370 75235 #048-12-1995 L1997 **ORS** *020 †40

WILSON, Randall Gene. 3450 W WHEATLAND RD, STE 340 75237 #012-01-1983 L1985 **CD IM** *020 †20

WILSON, Steven G. 2377 N STEMMONS FWY 75207 #048-02-1988 L1990 **PD** *020 †70

WIMBERLY, Kelly L. 17101 PRESTON RD, STE 100 75248 #048-12-1990 L1993 **FM** *020 †18

WINGO, Shana Nicolle. 75219 #048-12-2002 L2006 **OBG** *100 †30

WINICK, Naomi Joan. 5323 HARRY HINES BLVD 75235 #016-06-1978 L1984 **PHO** *050 †55

WINKELMAN, George Wm. 5323 HARRY HINES BLVD 75235 #039-01-1940 L1940 **IM P** *071 †20

WINKELMANN, Eugene Chas. ■ 75225 #048-04-1943 L1943 **P N** *020

WINKLER, Nurit. ■ 75229 #561-14-1995 L2003 **OBG** *100 †30

WINSLOW, Heather Hahn. ■ 75229 #048-12-2004 **OPH** *012

WINSLOW, Richard Lee. ■ 75229 #035-01-1967 L1975 **OPH GS** *072 †35

WINTER, Fred David, Jr. 3434 SWISS AVE STE 410 75204 #048-02-1975 L1975 **IM IMG** *020 †20

WINTER, John Wm, IV. 7777 FOREST LN, STE A214 75230 #021-01-1973 L1973 **GS VS** *020 †85

WINTERS, Karl N. 13601 PRESTON RD, STE 900 75240 #035-20-1988 L2002 **AN** *020 †05

WISCHMEYER, Jason Blair. 621 N HALL ST STE 500 75226 #048-02-1992 L1994 **CD IM** *020 †20

WISE, David Andrew. 5201 HARRY HINES BLVD, DEPT OF RADIOLOGY 75235 #048-04-2002 L2003 **DR** *100 †20

WISS, Geoffrey Alan. 1717 MAIN ST STE 52, SINAI-GRACE HOSPITAL 75201 #005-12-1999 L2007 **EM** *020 †16

WITHEILER, Daniel David. 221 W COLORADO BLVD, PAVILLION2 STE 945 75208 #048-12-1991 L1992 **D DS** *020 †15

WITTE, Zita M. 7151 GASTON AVE 75214 #048-14-1993 L1994 **DR** *020 †80

WOERZ, Cynthia Ann. 2222 WELBORN ST, DEPT ANES 75219 #019-02-1992 L2001 **AN PD** *020 †55,05

WOHLFELD, Bryan Jacob. ■ 75209 #017-20-2004 **NS** *012

WOLF, Jared A. 5201 HARRY HINES BLVD, PARKLAND HOSPITAL 75235 #048-12-2005 L2007 **EM** *012

WOLF, Matthias Tilmann Fl. ■ 75204 #409-16-1999 **PD** *012

WOLFE, Gil. 5323 HARRY HINES BLVD 75390 #048-12-1989 L1990 **N** *020 †75

WOLFF, Timothy K. 5323 HARRY HINES BLVD 75390 #048-12-1983 L1983 **P** *020 †75

WOLFFARTH, Mark W. ■ 75204 #048-02-2008 *012

WOLFRAM, Julius. 9 MEDICAL PKWY, PLAZA 4, SUITE 202 75234 #035-01-1936 L1946 **IM** *071 †20

WOMACK, Kyle B. 5323 HARRY HINES BLVD 75390 #048-12-1987 L1988 **N** *020 †75

WOMACK, R Lee. ■ 75214 #048-13-1982 L1984 **PM OS** *020

WOMACK, Ryan David. ■ 75228 #048-02-2005 L2007 *100

WONG, Alvin Puishui. 8220 WALNUT HILL LN, STE 505 75231 #021-01-1993 L1997 **AN** *020 †05

WONG, Grace Elsa. ■ 75204 #016-43-2003 **ORS** *012

WONG, Kevan Lee. 3920 WORTH ST 75246 #023-12-1988 L2000 **AN** *020 †05

WONG, Marshall Lee. 4131 N CENTRAL EXPY 75204 #023-12-1982 L1984 **AN** *020 †05

WONG, Melissa. ■ 75209 #048-12-2008 *012

WONG, Wendy Lynn. 712 N WASHINGTON AVE, AMERICAN RADIOLOGY 75246 #048-04-1999 L2004 **DR** *100 †80

WOO, Garry. 2377 N STEMMONS FWY 75207 #048-13-1984 L1987 **IM** *020

WOOD, Frances Oliver. ■ 75205 #051-07-2007 **IM** *012

WOOD, Helen Marie. 12900 PRESTON RD STE 1117 75230 #056-06-1984 L1995 **IM** *020 †20

WOOD, Judy Lee. 7557 RAMBLER RD, STE 706 75231 #048-15-1983 L1983 **AN** *020 †05

WOOD, Richard Eugene. 3600 GASTON AVE STE 404 75246 #056-06-1962 L1969 **TS** *020 †85,90

WOOD, Scott D. 5939 HARRY HINES BLVD, SOUTHWEST PULMONARY ASSOCI 75235 #048-13-1996 L2002 **IM PUD** *020 †20

WOODARD, William C. 5909 HARRY HINES BLVD 75235 #048-02-1953 L1953 **FM** *071 †18

WOODFIN, William Smiley. 7515 GREENVILLE AVE, STE 500 75231 #048-04-1968 L1968 **N CN** *020 †75

WOODRUFF, Heather Anne. ■ 75204 #017-20-2007 **GS** *012

WOODRUFF, Sharon Lynn. 11882 GREENVILLE AVE, STE 115 75243 #028-02-1965 L1988 **N P** *020

WOODRUFF, Stacey Lynne. ■ 75204 #017-20-2003 L2008 **GS** *012

WOODS, Channing. 8201 PRESTON RD, STE 200 75225 #048-12-1949 L1949 **IM** *071

WOODWARD, John Reagan. 7777 FOREST LN, STE A338 75230 #008-01-1961 L1968 **GYN OBS** *020 †30

WOOLEY, Randall M. 8210 WALNUT HILL LN, STE 230 75231 #048-12-1999 L2002 **IM** *020 †20

WOOLLEY, Stephanie May. 3600 GASTON AVE STE 550, TEXAS PRIMARY CARE 75246 #048-13-1997 L1998 **PCC** *020 †20

WOOMING, George Andrew. 12200 PARK CENTRAL DR, STE 220 75251 #011-02-1987 L1995 **D DS** *020 †15

WOOTAN, Richard Chas. 9335 GARLAND RD 75218 #048-12-1977 L1977 **GS VS** *020 †85

WOOTEN, Tyler Allen. 5323 HARRY HINES BLVD, DEPT OF PSYCHIATRY 75390 #004-01-1999 L2004 **CHP** *020

WORD, Larry Edwin. 5323 HARRY HINES BLVD, DEPARTMENT OF OB/GYN 75390 #048-14-1978 L1978 **OBG** *040 †20

WORD, Ruth Ann West. 5323 HARRY HINES BLVD, STOP 9031 75390 #048-14-1978 L1978 **OBG FM** *020 †30

WORLEY, Kevin C. ■ 75204 #048-12-2001 L2005 **OBG** *100 †30

WORREL, Daniel A. 9301 N CENTRAL EXPY, STE 400 75231 #048-12-1998 L2004 **ORS** *020 †40

WORSHAM, A Gordon. ■ 75205 #004-01-1950 L1956 **PD** *071 †55

WORSHAM, Robin Lee. 550 E ANN ARBOR RD 75216 #048-15-1986 L1988 **FM** *020 †18

WRIGHT, Beth Fromberg. 1441 N BECKLEY AVE 75203 #048-13-1995 L1996 **HMP** *020 †50

WRIGHT, Damaris Young. 10830 N CENTRAL EXPY 75231 #039-01-1971 L1972 **PDC PD** *020 †55

WRIGHT, Kenneth Lloyd, III. 6363 FOREST PARK RD, STE 810 75235 #048-02-1980 L1980 **IM** *020 †20

WRIGHT, Robert Lee. 4849 GREENVILLE AVE, STE 350 75206 #048-12-1990 L1991 **EM** *020 †16

WRIGHT, Woodring Erik. U T SOUTHWESTERN MED CTR 75235 #005-11-1975 *050

WU, Joanna Qiong. ■ 75204 #025-07-2005 L2007 **IM** *012

WU, Jonathan Shyangruey. ■ 75235 #048-12-2008 *012

WU, Richard Chaochung. 75206 #036-07-1994 L2006 **ICE** *020 †20

WYATT, Carrie Justine. 5323 HARRY HINES BLVD, U TX SOUTHWESTERN SCH 75390 #048-04-2000 L2008 **P** *012

WYCKOFF, Myra Helen. 5323 HARRY HINES BLVD, U.T. SOUTHWESTERN MEDICAL 75390 #048-12-1994 L1997 **NPM** *020 †55

WYMAN, Michael Louis. 3500 GASTON AVE, BAYLOR UNIVERSITY MED CENT 75246 #005-11-1972 L1994 **PD** *020 †55

XIAO, Hong. 6263 HARRY HINES BLVD, FAMILY PRACTICE DEPARTMENT 75390 #243-44-1983 L2001 **FM** *020 †18

YABRAIAN, Juan Carlos. 5920 FOREST PARK RD, STE 600 75235 #132-01-1963 L1970 **ORS** *020

YAEGER, Matthew Melville. 8325 WALNUT HILL LN # 225 75231 #048-14-1992 L1994 PD *020 †55

YAGER, Mariana. 12009 COIT RD, APT 3430M 75251 #187-89-2006 *012

YALAMANCHILI, Radha Devi. 3600 GASTON AVE STE 550 75246 #495-21-1999 L2005 IM *020

YAMADA, Joyce Masaye. 1526 ABRAMS RD 75214 #048-12-1979 L1979 DR *020 †80

YAMANOUCHI, Kimberly Jean. 5201 HARRY HINES BLVD 75235 #021-01-1983 L1989 AN *040

YANCEY, Kim Bruce. 5323 HARRY HINES BLVD 75390 #012-01-1978 L1979 D DDL *040 †15 ‡

YANCY, Clyde W, Jr. 3500 GASTON AVE, STE H-030 75246 #021-01-1982 L1984 CD *040 †20

YANG, Caroline. ■ 75204 #048-04-2005 L2005 DR *012

YANG, Weibin. 4500 S LANCASTER RD # 117, VA NORTH TEXAS HEALTHCARE 75216 #243-43-1988 L1999 PM *020 †60

YANOFSKI, Jason R. 5323 HARRY HINES BLVD, SOUTHWESTERN MED 75390 #041-15-2004 L2008 CHP *012

YARBROUGH, William C, Jr. 4500 S LANCASTER RD, PULMONARY 111F 75216 #027-01-1981 L1985 PUD IM *050 †20

YAUSSY, Catherine Mary. 3434 SWISS AVE, STE 206 75204 #010-01-1990 L1991 GE *020 †20

YEAGLEY, Susanne Carol. 2731 LEMMON AVE E, STE 200 75204 #048-12-1987 L1989 FM *020 †18

YEGANOV, Vladislav L. 3600 GASTON AVE, 1155 WADLEY TOWER 75246 #913-19-1987 L2004 P *020 ‡

YEH, Clement Carol. 5201 HARRY HINES BLVD, DALLAS COUNTY HOSPITAL DIS 75235 #048-15-2005 L2006 AN *012

YEH, Jason Samuel. ■ 75235 #048-12-2008 *012

YELDERMAN, Mark Lowell. ■ 75367 #048-04-1973 L1974 AN *071 †05

YEN, Kathleen Rudrung. ■ 75204 #048-12-2004 L2007 P *012

YETKIN, Zerrin Fatma. ■ 75235 #902-04-1976 L2008 *100

YEUNG, John Ngai Man. ■ 75204 #919-03-1988 *100

YEW, David T. 13601 PRESTON RD, STE 900 75240 #048-04-1991 L1992 AN *020 †05

YOLLICK, Bernard Lawrence. 1935 MOTOR ST 75235 #065-01-1945 L1954 OTO HNS *071 †85,45

YOO, Min Chong. ■ 75209 #048-12-2005 GS *020

YOON, Donghi Anthony. 621 N HALL ST STE 400 75226 #048-12-1999 L2000 CD *100 †20

YOON, Lillienne Ujee. ■ 75204 #048-02-2006 PD *012

YORIO, Jeffrey Thomas. ■ 75218 #048-12-2008 *012

YORK, Jackie Renee. 3500 GASTON AVE STE 3, DEPARTMENT OF NEONATOLOGY 75246 #047-20-1996 L2008 NPM *020 †55

YOUNG, Alisha Y. ■ 75219 #048-12-2008 *012

YOUNG, Carl. 6750 HILLCREST PLAZA DR, STE 306 75230 #048-12-1991 L1992 P *020 †75

YOUNG, Christopher F. 3920 WORTH ST 75246 #021-01-2002 L2006 AN *100 †05

YOUNG, Connie Lynn. 12221 MERIT DR, STE 1610 75251 #016-06-2001 L2007 IM *020

YOUNG, David Wm. 10246 MIDWAY RD 75229 #048-12-1955 L1963 GS *020 †85

YOUNG, Lance Trevor. ■ 75214 #054-04-2006 EM *012

YOUNG, Lindsay Erin. ■ 75204 #048-12-2007 OTO *012

YOUNG, Mark D. 2807 ALLEN ST 75204 #048-13-1988 L1991 ORS *020

YOUNG, Patrick Gerard. ■ 75208 #028-03-1981 L1982 CHP *020

YOUNG, Walter, Jr. 2909 S HAMPTON RD, STE E225 75224 #035-45-1975 L1982 IM *020 †20

YOUNG, William N. 13601 PRESTON RD 75240 #048-12-2002 L2006 AN *100 †05

YOUNGBLOOD, Kneeland C. 300 CRESCENT CT, STE 1380 75201 #048-12-1982 L1983 EM *020 †16

YOUNIS, Basil A. 9 MEDICAL PKWY, PLAZA 4 STE 204 75234 #748-09-1987 L2000 IM *020 †20

YOUNT, Mitchell Lee. 12700 PARK CENTRAL DR, STE 430 75251 #038-43-1996 L2001 DR *020 †80

YTEM, Jose B. 5909 HARRY HINES BLVD 75235 #748-01-1974 L1987 AN CD *020

YU, Beth Jeeyoung. 12200 PARK CENTRAL DR, STE 550 75251 #048-16-2000 L2003 IM *020 †20 ‡

YU, Jan Hanchu. 5151 HARRY HINES BLVD 75235 #035-09-1992 L2002 IM *020 †20

YU, Ling. 5323 HARRY HINES BLVD, DEPT OF INT MED 75390 #243-47-1995 IM *012

YU, Wengui. 5323 HARRY HINES BLVD, UT SOUTHWESTERN MEDICAL CE 75390 #243-62-1983 L2007 N *020 †75

YU, Yung Lei. 4511 CHEROKEE TRL, STE 170 75209 #016-06-1993 L2003 PS *020

YUAN, Ho-Ming. 4500 S LANCASTER RD, VA MEDICAL CENTER 75216 #243-16-1957 L1979 DR *020 †20

YUCEL, Selcuk. 5323 HARRY HINES BLVD, UNIV TX SOUTHWESTERN MED S 75390 #902-19-1995 UP *100 †20

YUEN, Honling. 1130 BEACHVIEW ST STE 100 75218 #048-12-1995 L1998 IM *020 †20

YUNYONGYING, Pete. 4500 S LANCASTER RD, ROAD (111E) 75216 #023-01-2002 L2007 IM *020 †20 ‡

YUSUFALI, Iddriss K. 13601 PRESTON RD, STE 900 75240 #048-02-1993 L1995 APM *020 †05

ZAATARI, Ghazi Saadedine. ■ 75230 #605-01-1976 L1986 PTH CLP *030 †20

ZADEH, Jaffar Abbas. 7777 FOREST LN STE C300 75230 #048-12-1996 L1998 IM *020 †20

ZAFAR, Saboohi. 3310 LIVE OAK ST, COPC- PHHS CLINICAL RESOUR 75204 #704-01-2000 L2006 FM *020 †18

ZAIMI, Zahra Farzaneh. 2222 WELBORN ST 75219 #917-23-1975 L1989 *020

ZAJICEK, Hubert Karl. ■ 75214 #154-07-1996 *100

ZAMANIAN, Maryam. 8200 WALNUT HILL LN, INTERNAL MEDICINE DEPT 75231 #048-12-2002 L2005 HOS *020 †20

ZAMORA, Berto Miguel. 5959 HARRY HINES BLVD #904 75235 #270-02-1989 L1995 IM *020 †20

ZAMORA, Juan-Luis. 6310 LBJ FWY, STE 218 75240 #429-01-1980 L1993 FOP *020

ZAMORANO, Jose Raul, Jr. 3600 GASTON AVE STE 709 75246 #275-01-1960 L1963 IM *020 †20

ZARETSKY, Michael Victor. 5323 HARRY HINES BLVD, U.T. SOUTHWESTERN MED CTR 75390 #038-44-1997 L1998 OBG *020 †30

ZASHIN, Scott Jeffrey. 8230 WALNUT HILL LN, STE 818LB11 75231 #032-01-1984 L1985 RHU *020 †20

ZASTEROVA, Ingrid Jana. ■ 75225 #286-02-1968 L1979 FM *020 †18

ZAVADIL, Velouette. 7777 FOREST LN, 6TH FLOOR N TOWER 75230 #051-01-1996 L1998 PD *020 †55

ZAVALA-CALDERON, Enrique. 1717 MAIN ST STE 5200 75201 #649-07-1969 L1975 EM GS *020

ZEBAIDA, Oren Yehuda. 7777 FOREST LN STE C300 75230 #048-12-1998 L2000 IM *020 †20

ZEBALLOS, Pablo Patricio. 75229 #048-78-2003, ▲ L2004 PMM *012

ZEDLITZ, William Halley. 8210 WALNUT HILL LN, STE 510 75231 #048-12-1960 L1960 GS *020 †85

ZEHR, David Juan. 3600 GASTON AVE STE 450, LANKFORD HAND ASSOCIATION 75246 #017-20-1975 L1981 HS ORS *020 †40

ZELLER, Kathleen Rae. 7777 FOREST LN, STE C340 75230 #035-45-1979 L1984 IM *020 †20

ZELLERS, Thomas M. 5323 HARRY HINES BLVD 75235 #048-12-1983 L1983 PDC PD *020 †55

ZELTSER, Ilana Joy. 1935 MOTOR ST, DEPARTMENT OF CARDIOLOGY 75235 #035-19-1997 L2004 PDC *020 †55

ZENT, Rachel Marie. 3600 GASTON AVE, BARNETT TOWER STE 1109 75246 #026-04-2000 L2005 SO GS *020 †85 ‡

ZEVALLOS, Alfred Gonzalo. 5959 HARRY HINES BLVD, STE 904 75235 #048-15-1992 L1993 IM *020 †20

ZEVALLOS, Alfredo. 5939 HARRY HINES BLVD, ST PAUL PROF BLDG #1 75235 #737-01-1962 L1970 OBG *020 †30

ZHANG, Ling. DEPT OF PHYS MED/REHAB, UNIV OF TEXAS SOUTHWESTERN 75390 #243-52-1982 PM *012

ZHANG, Min. 8200 WALNUT HILL LN 75231 #243-45-1985 L2004 NPM *020 †55

ZHANG, Yanzheng. 5323 HARRY HINES BLVD 75390 #243-71-1985 PTH *012

ZHAO, Guangquan. 5323 HARRY HINES BLVD 75390 #243-46-1984 IM *012

ZHAO, Ying. ■ 75205 #243-44-1982 L2005 RNR *020 †18

ZHONG, John Wei. 1935 MOTOR ST STE D03-309, AFC 75235 #243-24-1994 L2005 PAN *020 †05

ZHOU, Connie Qingyun. ■ 75209 #048-12-2006 OTO *012

ZHOU, Weiguo. 9 MEDICAL PKWY STE 106 75234 #243-76-1982 L1999 AN *020 †05

ZHOU, Xin Jin. 5323 HARRY HINES BLVD, STOP 9031 75390 #243-47-1986 L1998 PTH *020 †50

ZHU, Xia Ying. 9101 N CENTRAL EXPY, STE 300 75231 #012-05-1997 L1999 RHU *020 †20

ZHUK, Stanislav A. ■ 75219 #048-12-2005 OPH *012

ZIADA, Ali Mahmoud. 5323 HARRY HINES BLVD, UNIV TX SOUTHWESTERN MED S 75390 #915-02-1992 *100

ZIADIE, Mandolin Summer. ■ 75235 #011-02-2004 PTH *012

ZIARI, Mohammadbagher. 9105 LA STRADA CT 75220 #517-05-1995 L2007 IM *100 †20

ZIDAN, Amr Mohamed Z. 4500 S LANCASTER RD, ANESTHESIA AND PAIN MANAGE 75216 #915-04-1990 L2000 AN PME *020 †05

ZIDE, Jacob Rothschild. ■ 75205 #048-13-2007 ORS *012

ZIELINSKI, Tanya Ann. 5323 HARRY HINES BLVD, UNIV OF TEXAS SOUTHWESTERN 75390 #048-12-1997 L1998 CHP *020 †75

ZIESKE, Arthur William. 3500 GASTON AVE, DEPT OF PATHOLOGY 75246 #021-05-1993 L2004 HMP *020 †50

ZIK, Bruce Dani. 12700 PRESTON RD STE 260 75230 #035-08-1982 L1983 P *020 †75

ZIMMERN, Philippe E. 5323 HARRY HINES BLVD, UTSOUTHWESTERN MEDICAL CTR 75390 #396-12-1983 L1995 U *020 †95

ZINN, Andrew Robt. 5323 HARRY HINES BLVD, STOP 9031 75390 #048-12-1988 L1996 IM *050 †20

ZINSER, William Edward. 2350 N STEMMONS FWY I-35E, CHILDRENS MED CTR PAV 75207 #649-14-1979 L1996 CHN PD *020 †55,75

ZIPPER, John Vincent. 6757 ARAPAHO RD STE 7, PMB 335 75248 #016-42-1990 L2007 AN *020 †05

ZOGAKIS, Theresa Gertrude. 5323 HARRY HINES BLVD 75390 #028-02-1995 L2005 GS SO *050 †85

ZON, Jennifer T. ■ 75205 #048-12-2008 *012

ZOPOLSKY, Paul Raymond. 8220 WALNUT HILL LN, STE 214 75231 #016-42-1972 L1977 GE IM *020 †20

ZOYS, Timothy N. 7777 FOREST LN, STE C502 75230 #048-15-1990 L1992 AN *020

ZSOHAR, Julius. 5201 HARRY HINES BLVD, PARKLAND HOSPITAL 75235 #048-13-2005 L2007 AN *012

ZUZUKIN, Vladimir. ■ 75219 #048-12-1999 L2007 OTO *071

DAYTON – LIBERTY

BANGER-HILL, Shemeka Joyc. 205 N MAIN ST 77535 #048-04-2001 L2005 MPD *020

BEHRNS, Robert Louis. 902 FM 686, JUSTICE, INST. DIVISION 77535 #748-10-1980 L1987 FOP *020

MAC DONALD, John Wayne. 202 N CHURCH ST 77535 #064-01-1973 L1980 FM *020

PATEL, Satiskumar Purshot. 400 E HIGHWAY 90, THS MEDICAL CLNC 77535 #917-05-1994 L2006 FM *100 †18

REDMAN, John Loren. ■ 77535 #048-02-2004 L2007 FP *012

REDMAN, Paul Clark. 107 N WINFREE ST 77535 #048-02-1970 L1970 FM *071 †18 ‡

TALOSIG, Pedro Perez, Jr. 402 S WINFREE ST 77535 #748-07-1965 L1979 FM OBS *020

WILSON, Reginald. ■ 77535 #048-12-1944 L1944 FM *071

DE KALB – BOWIE

LITTLE, Bridger P, Jr. ■ 75559 #051-01-1949 L1973 EM FM *020

MC CRARY, Mark Wm. 307 N RUNNELS ST 75559 #048-02-1979 L1979 FM *020

SINGH, Raghbir. ■ 75559 #495-03-1954 L1969 FM PUD *074 †18

DE LEON – COMANCHE

FAGAN, Peter Gail. ■ 76444 #048-12-1972 L1974 OM FM *020 †18,70

PINO, Alfonso E. 224 N TEXAS ST 76444 #275-01-1957 L1969 ORS UME *071

STONE, Rowlinda A. ■ 76444 #048-12-1991 L1993 FM *020 †18 ‡

DECATUR – WISE

ALLING, Jeff B. 1001 W EAGLE DR 76234 #048-16-1987 L1988 FM *020 †18

AUGUST, Anissa G. 2014 BEN MERRITT DR, STE B 76234 #048-02-1996 L1999 PD *020 †55

AULDS, Meria G. 2014 BEN MERRITT DR 76234 #048-12-1987 L1988 IM *020 †20

BERDINE, Gilbert G. 2014 BEN MERRITT DR, STE A2 76234 #024-01-1978 L1984 PUD IM *020 †20

BERGER, Marc Steven. 2000 S FM 51 76234 #035-46-1971 L1977 DR OS *020 †80,28

CAIRE, Mary Louise. 2250 S FM 51, STE 600 76234 #021-05-1997 L2002 PM *020 †60

CAMPBELL, Michael Gregg. 1713 S FM 51 STE 201 76234 #048-15-1994 L2000 OBG *020

COOPER, Larry Joe. 1001 W EAGLE DR 76234 #048-12-1965 L1965 R *020 †80

GARRETT, Guy Gregory. 2010 BEN MERRITT DR, UNIT A 76234 #048-12-1974 L1974 RO *020 †80 ‡

GLASS, Melissa Marie. 2000 S FM 51 76234 #048-12-2004 L2007 PD *020 †55

GOSS, Mark G. 1710 S FM 51 # 150 76234 #048-13-1992 L1993 **GS** *020 †85

HELM, Christian B. 1713 S FM 51, STE 103 76234 #048-02-1997 L2007 **PM** *071

HOLLAND, Christine W. 800 MEDICAL CENTER DR, STE C-1 76234 #048-14-2002 L2005 **FM** *020 †18

HOLLIS, Leslie Michelle. 609 MEDICAL CENTR DR #2300 76234 #039-01-1996 L1997 **PD** *020 †55

KEY, Frederick Maurice. 2000 S FM 51 76234 #027-01-1958 L1964 **EM AM** *020 †16

KYLE, Douglas E, Jr. 1713 S FM 51 STE 201 76234 #048-02-1988 L1989 **OBG** *020 †30

LONG, Thomas Nielsen. 1001 W EAGLE DR 76234 #048-12-1973 L1978 **GS** *020 †85

LONGACRE, Steven E. 2000 S FM 51 76234 #048-13-1996 L1999 **EM** *020 †16

LOVETTE, Amanda. 2014 BEN MERRITT DR STE B 76234 #048-12-1996 L1997 **PD** *020 †55

MC GEE, Chris E. 1001 W EAGLE DR 76234 #048-12-2001 L2002 **FM** *020 †18

MCINTYRE, Timothy W. 1001 W EAGLE DR 76234 #048-13-1989 L1990 **FM** *020 †18

MC KENNA, Randall Wade. 1713 S FM 51, STE 103 76234 #039-79-1990, ▲ L1991 **ORS** *020

PARK, Robert Conrad. 1001 W EAGLE DR 76234 #048-12-1979 L1979 **CD** *020 †20

PHAM, Joanne. 2014 BEN MERRITT DR, STE C 76234 #048-16-1999 L2004 **OTO** *020 †45

RENSHAW, Charles Lucius. ■ 76234 #023-07-1961 L1961 **ORS** *071 †40

RIBEIRO, John Anthony. 1713 S FM 51 STE 103, N CENTRAL TX ORTHO & SPORT 76234 #054-04-1991 L1999 **ORS** *020 †40

RICHARDSON, John W, Jr. 2000 S FM 51 76234 #048-16-1998 L1999 **FPG** *020 †18

SCHUH, Jason Reese. 2000 S FM 51 76234 #005-12-1999 L2006 **AN** *020 †05

SENKOWSKY, Jon. 1001 W EAGLE DR 76234 #048-12-1983 L1983 **VS CCS** *020 †85

SHMERLIN, Inna. 2010 BEN MERRITT DR, UNIT A 76234 #048-02-2001 L2003 **ON** *020

SIDDIQUE, Haroon Wasil. 2000 S FM 51 76234 #704-02-1994 L2007 **PYG** *012 †75

SMITH, Renee Christine. 1713 S FM 51 STE 20 76234 #039-01-1999 L2003 **OBG** *020 †30

STEFFEN, Thomas Edward. 1001 W EAGLE DR 76234 #021-01-1973 L1974 **GP** *020 †18

SWAIN, Gary Dennis. 1821 S FM 51 76234 #031-01-1985 L2001 **FM** *020 ‡

TIBBELS, Charles Kelley. 1001 W EAGLE DR 76234 #048-14-1976 L1976 **FM EM** *020 †18

TIBBELS, Jason K. 2250 S FM 51 STE 400 76234 #048-12-2001 L2002 **FM** *020 †18

TUTTON, Craig Steven. 2000 S FM 51, WISE REGIONAL HEALTH SYSTE 76234 #016-43-1992 L2001 **P CHP** *020 †75 ‡

WALKER, Jon W. 1001 W EAGLE DR 76234 #048-02-1986 L1987 **FM** *020 †18

WALTER, Ryan K. 1713 S FM 51 STE 20 76234 #048-14-2002 L2006 **OBG** *020

WANG, Ck. 2010 BEN MERRITT DR, UNIT A 76234 #048-13-2000 L2000 **HO** *100

WHITE, Shawn Lee. 1001 W EAGLE DR 76234 #048-12-1994 L1995 **FM** *020 †18

ZUBERI, Aamir. 2000 S FM 51 76234 #704-02-1986 L1996 **NEP** *020 †20

DEER PARK — HARRIS

ALLEN, Charles Wesley. 2810 CENTER ST 77536 #048-02-1965 L1965 **GP OS** *020

BROWN, George Erwin, Jr. 321 W SAN AUGUSTINE ST 77536 #048-02-1998 L2004 *020

FULLER, John Burt. 77536 #051-04-1943 L1969 **PTH** *071 †50

MC CREA, Richard Dale. 2110 CENTER ST 77536 #025-01-1960 L1969 **PS** *020

MOERS, Robert Westergaard. 2106 CENTER ST 77536 #001-02-1974 L1975 **FM OM** *020

NGUYEN, Vu Anh. ■ 77536 #048-15-2008 *012

TSE, Paul. 1900 TIDAL RD 77536 #030-06-1988 L1995 **IM** *020 †20

WITTELS, Ellison Harold. HEALTH SERVICES, 6600 LAPORTE FREEWAY 77536 #039-01-1968 L1975 **P IM** *020 †20,70

DEL RIO — VAL VERDE

ABBOTT, Emile Glines, III. 501 W CANTU RD, STE 500 78840 #012-01-1966 L1990 **IM GPM** *020 ‡

BARENCHI, Ryan Anthony. ■ 78840 #005-12-2005 L2006 **GS** *020

BURNS, Jason David. 608 N BEDELL AVE, MEDICAL CENTER 78840 #028-03-1998 L2002 **OPH** *020 †35

CADENA, Antonio, Jr. 3809 VETERANS BLVD, P O BOX 420367 78840 #048-13-1993 L1994 **FM** *020 †18

CADENA, Veronica G. 801 N BEDELL AVE 78840 #048-13-1992 L1994 **FM** *020 †18

CHARTRAND, Daniel Jos. 2209 N BEDELL AVE 78840 #033-05-1988 L1998 **OBG** *020 †30

DI BLASI, Tina Pilumeli. 3809 VETERANS BLVD 78840 #561-06-1989 L2004 **END IM** *020 †20

DOCTOR, Shamoon Abbas. 1205 N BEDELL AVE 78840 #495-21-1960 L1978 **U GS** *020

FAZ, Cesar Hipolito. 109 W MARTIN ST, FRONTERA PEDIATRICS, PA 78840 #649-02-1983 L2004 **PD** *100

FRAUSTO, Manuel Jesus. 1117 W DE LA ROSA ST 78840 #649-04-1975 L1977 **GP** *020 ‡

GALINDO, Conrado Gus, III. 1300 N BEDELL AVE 78840 #005-18-1977 L1978 **FM OBG** *020

GUTIERREZ, Alfredo, Jr. 612 N BEDELL AVE STE D 78840 #048-02-1960 L1960 **GS** *020

GUTIERREZ, Beverly. 119 E ACADEMY ST, FAMILY CARE CLINIC 78840 #649-30-1980 L1985 **FM** *040 †18

GUTIERREZ, Jaime J. 913 S MAIN ST 78840 #048-02-1992 L1996 **FM** *020

HAVERLAH, Gene Vernon. 913 S MAIN ST 78840 #048-12-1958 L1958 **FM** *020

LINDSEY, Terry Michael. 1200 N BEDELL AVE # C 78840 #048-04-1970 L1970 **GS OBG** *020 †85

LUZ, Agustin Quiambao. 801 N BEDELL AVE, VALVERDE REGIONAL MED CTR 78840 #748-01-1950 L1968 **IM** *071

MAEDA, Jose Antonio. 517 N BEDELL AVE 78840 #649-02-1982 L1992 **GS** *020 †85

MARTINEZ, Manuel A, Jr. 1120 S MAIN ST 78840 #649-02-1966 L1967 **GP GS** *075

MARTINEZ HERNANDEZ, Angel. 712 N BEDELL AVE 78840 #649-02-1981 L1984 **GS** *020

MC DONALD, Kent Drexel. ■ 78840 #023-12-1993 L1996 **P** *020

MEISSNER, Frank Wm. 217 GANCHO, LA CALETTA ESTATES 78840 #023-12-1982 L1991 **CD CCM** *030 †24

MONTEMAYOR, Eduardo J. 106 FOSTER DR 78840 #649-02-1984 L1998 **IM** *020

MONTEMAYOR, Irma Elena. 106 FOSTER DR, NORTHSIDE HEALTH CLC 78840 #649-02-1983 L1997 **GP** *020

MUSQUIZ, Noe Moreno. 801 N BEDELL AVE 78840 #056-06-1982 L1984 **IM** *020

O'BRIEN, Lawrence Alan. 1801 N BEDELL AVE 78840 #048-13-1982 L1983 **PD EM** *020 †55

OVIEDO, Jose. 1801 N BEDELL AVE 78840 #649-30-1985 L1994 **PD** *020 †55

PADRO GUIOT, Fernando. ■ 78840 #275-01-1940 L1946 **PHP** *071

PARKER, Amy Louise. ■ 78840 #023-12-2000 L2001 **AI** *100 †55,03 ‡

PITT, Wendy Yvonne. 1117 W DE LA ROSA ST, SAN FELIPE HEALTH CENTER 78840 #039-01-2002 L2007 **PD** *020 †55

RIOS, Oscar. ■ 78840 #048-14-2002 L2007 **GS** *020

SALINAS, Luis Carlos. 1205 N BEDELL AVE 78840 #649-02-1958 L1964 **AS OBG** *020

SOLIS, Rafael. 104 FLETCHER DR STE A 78840 #847-10-1958 L1990 **P CHP** *020 †75

STOREY, Stephen Travisder. ■ 78840 #017-20-2005 L2005 **GS** *020

TAYLOR, Susan Jane. 1301 AVENUE G 78840 #048-12-1969 L1969 **HO** *020 †20

VAN, Tuong Ba. 1109 AVENUE K 78840 #048-13-1985 L1986 **CD** *020 †20

VASQUEZ, Hector H. 913 S MAIN ST 78840 #649-02-1971 L1977 **OBG** *020 †30

WEED, Olga. PO BOX 101A, HWY 90 E 78841 #048-12-1950 L1950 **GP OS** *075

DEL VALLE — TRAVIS

HART, Daniel Culver, II. 3614 BILL PRICE RD, TRAVIS COUNTY SHERIFFS DEP 78617 #048-02-1972 L1972 **EM** *020 †16

DENISON — GRAYSON

ALBRAND, Otmar Wolf. ■ 75020 #429-01-1962 L1975 **NS** *071 †25

ALLA, Srinivasa Reddy. 1014 MEMORIAL DR 75020 #495-50-1991 L2001 **CD** *020 †20

ANG, Peter Gwan Pa. 1302 N STATE HIGHWAY 91 75020 #011-02-1987 L1993 **DR** *020 †80

AYAD, Fouad Mohamed. PO BOX 65 75021 #330-02-1957 L1976 **OS AN** *071 †05

BALCH, Bill Mark. 1000 MEMORIAL DR 75020 #048-12-1981 L1981 **IM** *020 †20

BARNS, Joseph Edward, Jr. 102 MEMORIAL DR, TEXOMA PATHOLOGY 75020 #048-02-1976 L1976 **PTH IM** *020 †20,50

BREEZE, Jill Elise. 1014 MEMORIAL DR 75020 #048-14-2000 L2003 **PD** *020 ‡

BROWN, A Elaine. 100 MEMORIAL DR 75020 #035-09-1948 L1976 **AI PD** *071

BROWN, Charles H. ■ 75020 #048-12-1996 **DR** *100

BROWN, William Herbert. 4022 S TEXOMA 75020 #048-04-1953 L1953 **GP** *071

BRUMIT, Timothy Dwight. 1014 MEMORIAL DR, TEXOMACARE 75020 #048-02-1978 L1978 **PD ADL** *055

CARLSON, Gregory B. 1014 MEMORIAL DR 75020 #048-12-1990 L1996 **FM** *020 †18

CHAPPELL, Vicky L. 1201 MARTIN LUTHER KING ST, STE 100 75020 #048-02-1996 L2006 **TS VS** *020 †85

CHURCH, Robert Joe. 1014 MEMORIAL DR 75020 #654-01-2004 L2008 **FM** *020 †18

COLON-POLANCO, Javier. 2402 W MORTON ST, STE 4 # C 75020 #042-03-1986 L1994 **AN OS** *020 †05

DELANEY, Wayne Edward. ■ 75020 #048-12-1959 L1959 **GS VS** *071 †85

DENISON, Harry Lafayette. ■ 75020 #048-04-1957 L1957 **U OS** *071 †95

DICKSON, Mark E. 1014 MEMORIAL DR STE 208 75020 #048-15-1988 L1989 **GS** *020 †85

DUNCAN, Michael D. 1014 MEMORIAL DR 75020 #048-14-1992 L1993 **PCC** *020 †55,20 ‡

ELLIS, Katherine Lee. 1200 REBA MACENTIRE LN 75020 #039-01-1989 L1993 **PM** *020 †20,60

ELMORE, Nancy Jane. 3561 CARPENTERS BLUFF RD 75021 #048-02-1969 L1969 **R OS** *020 †80

FRIETSCH, Werner H. 1300 N STATE HIGHWAY 91 75020 #048-04-1953 L1953 **GP PD** *020

FRY, Wilburn S, Jr. ■ 75020 #048-12-1950 L1950 **GP** *071

GANGASANI, Aravind. 1014 MEMORIAL DR, TEXOMA HEART GROUP 75020 #495-65-1984 L1995 **CD** *020 †20

GARVIN, Clifford David. 1300 N STATE HIGHWAY 91 75020 #048-13-1981 L1981 **FM** *020 †18

GONZALEZ, Ignacio J. 1014 MEMORIAL DR 75020 #649-14-1983 L1996 **IM** *020 †20

HABAL, Nadia. ■ 75020 #048-13-2005 L2007 **IM** *012

HATT, Jeannine. 1014 MEMORIAL DR 75020 #048-02-1976 L1980 **PD** *020 †55

HAYES, Clint A. 102 MEMORIAL DR, STE 101 75020 #048-15-1994 L1999 **PHL** *020 †85

HAYES, David T. 1014 MEMORIAL DR 75020 #048-02-1985 L1987 **PD** *020 †55

HAYES, Shannon Williams. 1014 MEMORIAL DR, STE 212 75020 #039-01-1986 L1989 **PD ADL** *075 †55

HERMANN, Jeffrey M. 1014 MEMORIAL DR, STE 324 75020 #048-14-1996 L1997 **OBG** *020 †30

HICKS, Mary Dianne. 1014 MEMORIAL DR 75020 #039-01-1996 L2000 **OBG** *020 †30

JIMENEZ, Humberto R. 2401 BROOKHAVEN DR 75020 #264-03-1954 L1968 **OPH** *020

JOHNSON, Gerald Jerard. 1014 MEMORIAL DR 75020 #048-14-2003 L2006 **IM** *020 †20

JOHNSON, Steven Arnold. 1014 MEMORIAL DR, STE G18 75020 #021-06-1990 L1996 **U** *020 †95

JONDAHL, Irvin Errol. 1014 MEMORIAL DR, TEXOMACARE 75020 #654-01-1988 L1994 **FM** *020 †18

KNOBBE, Chris Alan. 1014 MEMORIAL DR, STE 312 75020 #007-02-1990 L1996 **OPH** *020 †35

LAL, Birendra Narayan. 1000 MEMORIAL DR, TEXOMA MEDICAL CENTER 75020 #495-24-1990 L2005 **IM** *020 †20

LANDRUM, Marilyn M. 1014 MEMORIAL DR 75020 #046-01-1994 L2000 **MPD PD** *020 †20,55

LATHAM, Angela C. 1000 MEMORIAL DR 75020 #048-16-1993 L1994 **FM** *020 †18

LAU, Fred Gene. 1302 N STATE HIGHWAY 91 75020 #010-01-1989 L1997 **DR** *020 †80

LEWIS, John E. 1000 MEMORIAL DR 75020 #039-01-1969 L1971 **PTH PCP** *020 †50

LIPSCOMB, Joseph Allen. 1014 MEMORIAL DR 75020 #048-14-2002 L2005 **PD** *020 †55

LOONEY, William Franklin. 1014 MEMORIAL DR, MORRISON BLDG STE 308 75020 #048-02-1968 L1968 **OTO** *020 †45

LOTAN, Ori M. 1014 MEMORIAL DR 75020 #048-13-1996 L1997 **IM** *020 †20

MAGGI, Darius Roderick. 3621 POTTSBORO RD # 150 75020 #039-01-1974 L1980 **OBG** *020 †30

MC CLAIN, Lanna Brooke. 1000 MEMORIAL DR 75020 #048-16-1993 L1994 **PD** *020 †55

MC DONALD, Ruth Key. 1014 MEMORIAL DR 75020 #004-01-1975 L1999 **ON** *020 †20

MC GOWAN, Peter Michael. 4141 S FM 131 75020 #048-02-1991 L1996 **DR** *020 †80

MC GRAEL, John Patrick. 1014 MEMORIAL DR STE 324 75020 #048-13-1982 L1983 **U** *020 †95

MC GUIRE, Philip R, Jr. ■ 75020 #016-06-1960 L1961 **P** *020 †75

MEINCKE REZA, Jeffrey W. 1014 MEMORIAL DR, STE 314 75020 #018-03-1993 L1998 **ORS** *020 †40

MIKSITS, David. 102 MEMORIAL DR, TEXOMA PATHOLOGY 75020 #033-05-1993 L1998 **PTH** *020 †50

MYERS, Douglas Paul. 102 MEMORIAL DR 75020 #019-02-1986 L1992 **NEP IM** *020 †20

NGUYEN, An Thien. 1000 MEMORIAL DR, BOX 890 75020 #021-01-1998 L2006 **EM** *020 †16

ORO, Rolando P. 1014 MEMORIAL DR 75020 #748-02-1967 L1980 **GS EM** *072

ORO-CASTILLO, Febe L P. 1105 MEMORIAL DR, STE 110 75020 #748-11-1973 L1983 **ON HEM** *075

PARKER, James Timothy. 1014 MEMORIAL DR 75020 #048-15-1986 L1987 **OBG** *020 †30

PEARLMAN, Eric B. 1000 MEMORIAL DR, U-MASS MEMORIAL HEALTH CAR 75020 #048-13-2004 L2007 **EM** *020

RICHMOND, Charles H. 1014 MEMORIAL DR 75020 #048-02-1985 L1992 **OTO** *020 †45

ROBINSON, Chester E. 1014 MEMORIAL DR 75020 #048-15-1991 L1991 **FM** *020 †18

ROBINSON, Jean Marie. 2402 W MORTON ST, STE 4 # C 75020 #048-14-1990 L1993 **AN** *020 †05

ROCKHILL, Teresa A. 3405 W FM 120 75020 #048-14-1984 L1985 **OBG** *020 †30

ROGERS, Charles Michael. 1014 MEMORIAL DR 75020 #039-01-1997 L2003 **IM** *020 †20

SALTZ, Richard Kenneth. 1014 MEMORIAL DR # 216 75020 #010-02-1978 L2006 **GE LM** *020 †20

SANDERS, Robert Carroll. 1014 MEMORIAL DR, TEXOMACARE 75020 #048-02-1975 L1975 **IM** *020 †20

SAUNDERS, John Chapman. 3126 W FM 120, TEXOMA HEALTHCARE SYSTEM 75020 #048-02-1954 L1954 **FM** *020

SELZ, Peter Alan. 1014 MEMORIAL DR 75020 #016-43-1990 L2004 **OTO** *020 †45

SHETH, Mukesh Ranchoddas. 1014 MEMORIAL DR, TEXOMA HEART GROUP 75020 #495-22-1980 L1988 **CD IM** *020 †20

SHIN, Michael John. 1302 N STATE HIGHWAY 91 75020 #028-34-1997 L2002 **DR** *020 †80

SHORT, Phillip Lloyd. 1001 W MAIN ST, STE 102 75020 #039-01-1975 L1999 **P** *020 †75

STOKES, Melmoth Young, III. 100 MEMORIAL DR, P O BOX 1098 75020 #048-12-1956 L1956 **FM P** *071 †18

SULISTIO, Thomas Budi. 1000 MEMORIAL DR, TEXOMA MEDICAL CENTER 75020 #506-01-1965 L1983 **R** *071 †80

THOMPSON, Kevin Lee. 1000 MEMORIAL DR, EMERGENCY DEPARTMENT 75020 #649-03-1980 L1993 **EM** *020 †16

TRAN, Tung Thomas. 1014 MEMORIAL DR STE 21, MORRISON MEDICAL OFFICE BU 75020 #048-04-2001 L2004 **GE** *020

TRULY, Ted F. 1014 MEMORIAL DR, TEXOMA CARE 75020 #048-02-1992 L1996 **IM** *020 †20

TYSON, John Paul. 1000 MEMORIAL DR 4TH FL 75020 #048-02-1963 L1963 **FM GP** *020 †18

VILLARREAL, Mark Charles. 2402 W MORTON ST, STE 4 # C 75020 #048-12-1991 L1993 **AN** *020 †05

WHITE, Michelle Alexandra. 1014 MEMORIAL DR, TEXOMA CARE 75020 #016-43-1996 L2003 **FM** *020 †18 ‡

WHITFIELD, Larry Alan. 1014 MEMORIAL DR 75020 #048-12-1976 L1989 **END DIA** *020 †20

WILCOTT, Robert James. 1201 MARTIN LUTHER KING ST, STE 100 75020 #048-14-1983 L1984 **TS GS** *071 †85,90

WOOD, Larry K. 1000 MEMORIAL DR 75020 #048-14-1989 L1990 **OPH** *020 †35

WYNN, Don Tuan. 1000 MEMORIAL DR, STE G12 75020 #012-01-2001 L2007 **PCC** *020

ZAKIN, Paavo Ralf. 1000 MEMORIAL DR 4TH FL 75020 #035-47-1982 L1988 **ORS** *020

DENTON – DENTON

ACUFF, Tea Edward, Jr. 209 N BONNIE BRAE ST # 303 76201 #047-06-1978 L1980 **TS** *020 †85,90

ADAMI, Gilbert Ernest. 1400 CRESCENT ST, STE 4 76201 #021-01-1945 L1948 **GP** *020

ADAMS, Amy Jo. 2609 SCRIPTURE ST 76201 #048-15-2001 L2004 **PD** *020 †55

ADMIRE, Robert Chas. 2509 SCRIPTURE ST STE 100 76201 #048-12-1979 L1979 **U** *020 †95

ADUGBA, Ikenna. 400 S CARROLL BLVD, STE 2000 76201 #690-07-1982 L1999 **IM EM** *020

AHMAD, Nasiha. 2515 SCRIPTURE ST, STE 201 76201 #160-02-1970 L1986 **OBG** *020

AILLON, Gonzalo Alberto. 3200 COLORADO BLVD 76210 #048-78-1998, ▲ L2001 **IM** *020

AKRAM, Javed M. 2515 SCRIPTURE ST, STE 104 76201 #704-20-1987 L1997 **ID** *020 †20

ALLO, Simon Ngotcho. 319 N BONNIE BRAE ST 76201 #001-06-1994 L1998 **CD** *020 †20

ALVAREZ, Victor Raul. 306 N LOOP 288 STE 183 76209 #737-01-1960 L1967 **PD** *020 †55

ANBARASU, Rani. 4206 N INTERSTATE 35 76207 #495-16-1989 L2000 **IM** *020 †20

BABCOCK, Terence Lee. 10113 SORIANO ST 76207 #010-01-1971 L1982 **TS VS** *020 †85,90

BADIE, Bediola. 207 N BONNIE BRAE ST 76201 #517-01-1967 L1975 **AI** *020 †03

BALSLEY, Gerard Earl. 207 N BONNIE BRAE ST 76201 #005-14-1978 L1980 **OBG** *071 †30

BARTON, Courtney K. 3323 COLORADO BLVD, STE B 76210 #048-15-2001 L2003 **FM** *020 †18

BELL, M E Johnson. ■ 76201 #019-02-1963 L1987 **P CHP** *071

BERGSTROM, Jon Fredrick. 1614 SCRIPTURE ST STE 2 76201 #018-03-1966 L1973 **R NR** *020 †80 ‡

BHANGOO, Jaspaul Singh. 3304 COLORADO BLVD STE 101 76210 #306-01-2001 L2006 **IM** *020 †20

BHANGOO, Parmbir Shalini. 3537 S I-35 E, STE 207 76210 #495-43-2000 L2007 **PD** *020 †55

BHATT, Jitendra Nandlal. 1108 DALLAS DR STE 337 76205 #495-23-1971 L1977 **IM** *020 †20

BLAIR, Major E, Jr. 1209 BENT OAKS CT 76210 #048-04-1981 L1982 **ORS** *020 †40

BLANKENAU, Andrew James. 2438 LILLIAN MILLER PKWY, STE 100 76205 #030-05-1990 L1993 **EM FM** *020 †18

BLUCKER, Thomas Otis. 2509 SCRIPTURE ST, NORTH TEXAS MEDICAL 76201 #004-01-1970 L1971 **FM** *020

BOATWRIGHT, Russell Bryan. 3537 S INTERSTATE 35 E, STE 206 76210 #048-04-1963 L1963 **GYN OBG** *020 †30

BOKOVOY, Alexis P. ■ 76207 #005-12-1945 L1976 **GS VS** *071 †85

BONNICK, Sydney Lou. 2921 COUNTRY CLUB RD, STE 101 76210 #048-12-1973 L1973 **IM** *050 †20

BOREN, Robert Jones. 1614 SCRIPTURE ST 76201 #004-01-1958 L1965 **D** *071 †15

BRADLEY, William D. 2817 S MAYHILL RD STE 100 76208 #048-15-1995 L2000 **OSS** *020 †40

BROWN, Scott Dennis. ■ 76210 #028-34-1990 L1998 **OBG** *020 †30

BURKHALTER, Ewell R. 3537 S I-35 E, STE 305 76210 #021-05-1951 L1960 **GS TS** *071 †85

CADENHEAD, Thomas Alan. 2210 SAN JACINTO BLVD # 2 76205 #021-06-1980 L1985 **OTO HNS** *020 †45

CAI, Tung. 3333 COLORADO BLVD 76210 #035-03-1992 L2002 **TS** *020 †85,90

CALDWELL, Daniel Wesley. 3319 COLORADO BLVD 76210 #016-45-1988 L1994 **CD** *020 †20

CASEY, David L. 2509 SCRIPTURE ST, STE 100 76201 #048-04-1991 L1993 **U** *020 †95

CASEY, Sharon K. 207 N BONNIE BRAE ST 76201 #048-12-1992 L1993 **PTH** *020 †50

CASEY, Terri J. 3000 N I-35 76201 #048-13-1993 L1994 **PTH** *020 †50

CAVEY, Matthew Lee. 3537 S I-35 E, STE 111 76210 #048-02-2001 L2003 **RO** *020 †80

CEJA, Jose Francisco. 209 N BONNIE BRAE ST # 200 76201 #649-20-1987 L1997 **FM** *020 †18

CHARNEY, Franklin Jeffrey. 3321 COLORADO BLVD 76210 #007-02-1972 L1977 **GS VS** *020 †85

CHOWDHURY, Mostaque Hossa. 505 S LOCUST ST, PEOPLE'S CLINIC OF DENTON 76201 #160-01-1997 L2006 **FM** *020 †18

CICHON, Jolanta Urszula. 3000 N I-35 76201 #759-10-1990 L1999 **ON** *020 †20

COBOS, Victor L. 1300 FULTON ST STE 203 76201 #048-02-1994 L1999 **GS VS** *020 †85

COFFEY, Jesse A, Jr. 3201 COLORADO BLVD 76210 #048-04-1984 L1986 **PS** *020 †85,65

CONNAUGHTON, Robert H. 3535 S INTERSTATE 35 E 76210 #048-13-1994 L1999 **GS VS** *020 †85

CORTEZ, Olga L. 2501 SCRIPTURE ST, STE 200 76201 #048-12-2002 L2005 **OBG** *020 †30

CRESON, Daniel Lennard. 914 N LOCUST ST, NORTH TEXAS PSYCHIATRY 76201 #048-02-1962 L1963 **P** *020 †75

CROISSANT, Robert Seavey. ■ 76205 #024-07-1958 L1964 **FM OS** *071 †18

CROWELL, John M. ■ 76201 #036-07-1946 L1952 **R** *071 †80

CRUZ, Carlos P. 3537 S INTERSTATE 35 E, STE 305 76210 #048-02-1994 L2004 **VS** *020 †85

CRUZ, Ramon Apostol. 2625 SCRIPTURE ST 76201 #748-10-1991 L1997 **FM** *020 †18

CUMMINGS, Frederick P. 209 N BONNIE BRAE ST, STE 304 76201 #010-03-1981 L1983 **OBG** *020

DAVE, Ajit. 3327 COLORADO BLVD STE 200 76210 #495-89-1974 L1985 **ON IM** *020 †20

DAVE, Beena Ajitkumar. 3327 COLORADO BLVD STE 200 76210 #495-89-1974 L1985 **IM** *020 †20

DAVE, Ketaki B. 3720 S INTERSTATE 35 E 76210 #495-22-1981 L1992 **ON HO** *020 †20

DAVIS, Timothy Jefferson. ■ 76207 #048-12-1964 L1965 **DR** *071 †80

DAY, Jeffrey L. 3201 TEASLEY LN STE 102 76210 #048-14-1998 L2001 **PD** *020 †55

DE FREITAS, Junior. 3537 S I-35 E STE 218 76210 #041-13-1984 L1996 **OTO GS** *020 †45

DELOS REYES, Jonathan C. 4308 MESA DR STE A 76207 #748-02-1990 L1999 **RHU** *020 †20

DONOVITZ, James A. ■ 76201 #048-02-1994 L1997 **FM** *020 †18

DOOLEY, Christina Ann. 2501 SCRIPTURE ST, STE 200 76201 #048-12-2001 L2003 **OBG** *020 †30

DULEMBA, John Frank. 3304 COLORADO BLVD 76210 #041-01-1982 L1987 **OBS OBG** *020 †30

DYER, Peggy J. 1121 DALLAS DR, STE 6 76205 #048-12-1960 L1961 **PS GP** *072 †65

ECKEL, Bruce Alan. 1160 N BONNIE BRAE ST 76201 #018-03-1980 L1983 **PD** *020 †55

EIFLER, Eric Alan. 2515 SCRIPTURE ST, STE 100 76201 #048-13-1995 L1996 **ORS OSM** *020 †40

ELSHAZLY, Shehab Mohamed. ■ 76210 #915-04-1996 L2004 *020 †28

ESTORQUE, Pedro E. 2625 SCRIPTURE ST, STE 103 76201 #748-14-1981 L1995 **FM** *020 †18

EVUARHERHE, Aghogho. ■ 76210 #690-06-1987 **APM** *100

FARHATAZIZ, Dr. 2321 GEORGETOWN DR, STRONG HEALTH 76201 #048-13-1988 L1989 **RO** *020 †80

FAZIO, Gary Paul. 3333 COLORADO BLVD 76210 #035-09-1986 L1996 **CD** *020 †20

FELDMAN, James Jehiel. 4405 N INTERSTATE 35 76207 #035-19-1965 L1972 **GS CD** *071 †85

FINGER, Laura Scheall. 2805 S MAYHILL RD 76208 #001-06-1998 L2002 **OBG** *020 †30

FLACHOFSKY, Elisabeth K. 3000 N I-35, PRESBYTERIAN HOSPITAL - D 76201 #048-16-2003 L2007 **AN** *020

FLETCHER, Joseph Duiane. 3527 S INTERSTATE 35 E # 2 76210 #047-06-1973 L1976 **GE IM** *020 †20

FORD, Kenneth Lecil, Jr. 1600 SCRIPTURE ST, STE U7 76201 #048-12-1962 L1962 **CLP PTH** *020 †50

FORD, Lesa Dawn. 1600 SCRIPTURE ST 76201 #048-13-1983 L1983 **PTH** *020 †50

FREEMAN, Mahlon V. 4401A N INTERSTATE 35 76207 #008-01-1955 L1979 **MG OBG** *071 †30,19

FREIMER, Gregory Leo. 3000 N I-35, PRESBYTERIAN HOSPITAL-DENT 76201 #041-02-2001 L2004 **EM** *020 †16

GARCIA, Carlos. 1108 DALLAS DR STE 31 76205 #056-06-1982 L1987 **AN** *020 †05

GARNER, Carolyn N. 3321 COLORADO BLVD, END & ONC SURGCL ASSOCS 76210 #048-13-2001 L2007 **GS SO** *020 †85

GENOVESE, Glenn. 3333 COLORADO BLVD 76210 #048-02-1988 L1990 **CCM PUD** *020 †20

GILL, Henry Alexander. ■ 76207 #048-15-1995 **AN** *100

GINNINGS, Mark Lee. 1121 DALLAS DR, STE 6 76205 #048-02-1986 L1987 **IM** *020 †20

GOFF, David Hubbard. 3201 TEASLEY LN, STE 102 76210 #036-05-1993 L1997 **PD** *020 †55 ‡

GOFF, Karen O. 3201 TEASLEY LN 76210 #048-04-1994 L1996 **PD** *020 †55 ‡

HAGEN, Douglas Beriah. 2509 SCRIPTURE ST, NORTH TEXAS MEDICAL 76201 #041-02-1970 L1981 **FM** *020 †18

HAGGARD, Scott. ■ 76209 #048-04-1951 L1951 **GP** *071

HALEY, James A. 2817 S MAYHILL RD, STE 120 76208 #048-13-1976 L1991 **GE IM** *020 †20

HANSON, Victor Eugene. 4405 N INTERSTATE 35 76207 #039-01-1959 L1961 **GP** *071

HARRIS, Glenna Beth. 1100 DALLAS DR, STE 108 76205 #048-12-1978 L1978 **PD** *020 †55

HARRIS, Timothy Laird. 2900 N INTERSTATE 35, STE 110 76201 #038-44-1993 L2004 **HO** *020 †20

HEATH, Timothy Raymond. 1204 BENT OAKS CT STE 2 76210 #048-14-1990 L1991 **IM** *020 †20

HEDAYATI, Mohrokh A. 2501 SCRIPTURE ST STE 303 76201 #187-71-1977 L1991 **PD** *020 †55

HELSTEN, Robert Allen. 2436 S INTERSTATE 35 E 76205 #004-01-1977 L1978 **EM** *020

HENRY, Clara Hutchinson. 2548 LILLIAN MILLER PKWY, STE 100 76210 #021-05-1976 L1980 **D** *020 †15

HOLLADAY, George Erwin. ■ 76205 #047-06-1958 L1960 **OPH** *071 †35

HOLT, Don Frederick. 1614 SCRIPTURE ST 76201 #048-13-1970 L1970 **FM** *020 †18

HOLZMAN, Jo Anne Frances. ■ 76210 #048-02-1962 L1962 **PTH** *071 †50

HOMER, Gregory Douglas. 1614 SCRIPTURE ST, STE 2 76201 #005-12-1994 L1995 **DR** *020 †80

HOPKINS, Charles Drennen. 700 W OAK ST 76201 #048-02-1971 L1971 **ORS** *020 †40

HOUSE, Michael A. 2515 SCRIPTURE ST, STE 100 76201 #048-15-1993 L1995 **ORS** *020 †40

HOWARD, Galen Evan. 3204 COLORADO BLVD 76210 #048-04-2002 L2007 **U** *020

HUSSAIN, Atif. 1901 WIND RIVER LN, STE 100 76210 #065-01-1992 L2003 **CD IC** *020 †20

HUTCHISON, Gary Clinton. 3537 S INTERSTATE 35 E, STE 220B 76210 #048-12-1959 L1959 **NS** *071 †25

IRION, Oren Coolidge. ■ 76207 #007-02-1948 L1980 **IM** *071 †20

JADERLUND, John W. 2817 S MAYHILL RD, STE 220 76208 #048-14-1983 L1983 **U UP** *020 †95

JAIN, Sharad Kumar. 2900 N INTERSTATE 35, STE 100 76201 #495-45-1981 L2001 **ON HEM** *020 †20

JANKE, Marilyn Rose. 1160 N BONNIE BRAE ST 76201 #048-02-1977 L1977 **PD** *020 †55

JANUS, Eugene Frank. ■ 76205 #759-09-1955 L1974 **IM END** *020

JASTI, Sushama. 2900 N I-35 STE 111, DENTON ONCOLOGY ASSOCIATES 76201 #495-09-1999 L2006 **HO** *020 †20

JOHNSON, George Wm, Jr. 3333 COLORADO BLVD 76210 #047-07-1976 L1977 **TS VS** *020 †85,90

JOHNSON, William Cone. ■ 76205 #048-02-1954 L1954 **PUD** *071 †20

JONES, Carrie Ann. 2609 SCRIPTURE ST 76201 #048-02-1998 L2004 **PD** *020 †55

JORDAN, William Mc Call. 3537 S I-35 E, STE 111 76210 #028-78-1973, ▲ L1973 **ON** *020

JOSEPH, Roy Maliakkal. 3537 S I-35 E, STE 203 76210 #495-52-1986 L1997 **GE IM** *020 †20

KAGAL, Dinesh Pandurang. 3537 S I-35 E, STE 203 76210 #495-37-1964 L1978 **PUD IM** *020

KAHN, Melanie Ford. 1600 SCRIPTURE ST 76201 #048-13-1987 L1988 **PTH** *020 †50

KAPLAN, Jeffrey David. 1901 WIND RIVER LN, STE 100 76210 #024-07-1986 L1999 **IM CD** *020 †20 ‡

KELLY, Roger Eugene. 3535 S INTERSTATE 35 E 76210 #021-01-1967 L1975 **NEP IM** *020 †20

KIM, Yoon Kyu. ■ 76205 #583-10-1972 L1979 **IM FM** *020

KINARD, Conrad L. ■ 76205 #012-05-1949 L1953 **IM CD** *071 †20
KING, Teresa Elisabeth. 2509 SCRIPTURE ST, STE 200 76201 #048-14-1996 L2004 **FM** *020 †18 ‡
KING, William Foxworth. ■ 76205 #016-06-1955 L1959 **R** *020 †80
KITCHENS, Wm Claude, Sr. ■ 76208 #012-01-1943 **IM** *071
KLEMOW, Dawn Leslie. 3720 S I-35 E, TEXAS CANCER CENTER - DENT 76210 #048-02-1981 L1981 **HEM ON** *020 †20
KRISTOFERSON, John S. 3320 COLORADO BLVD 76210 #048-12-1980 L1980 **ORS** *020 †40
KRUGER, Mitchel. 1901 WIND RIVER LN, STE 100 76210 #041-02-1985 L1995 **CD IM** *020 †20
KRUMERMAN, Jon Achsen. 3537 S INTERSTATE 35 E, STE 220B 76210 #011-03-1995 L1996 **NS** *020 †25
KURRUS, Frederick Dunham. 405 S ELM ST, STE 303 76201 #048-02-1961 L1961 **GS VS** *020 †85
LANASA, Peter Anthony. 3537 S I-35 E, STE 111 76210 #051-01-1989 L2004 **RO** *020 †80
LATIF, Umar. 2026 W UNIVERSITY DR, UNIVERSAL BEHAVIORAL HEALT 76201 #704-21-1997 L2005 **P PYG** *020 †75
LAWSON, Craig Rafe. I-35 STATE SCHOOL ROAD, DENTON STATE SCHOOL 76202 #048-02-1981 L1981 **FM** *071 †18
LEE, Robert Joe. 2509 SCRIPTURE ST, STE 200 76201 #048-12-1955 L1955 **GYN OBG** *071
LERTDILOK, Chantanaros. 1600 SCRIPTURE ST 76201 #891-02-1970 L1979 **PTH CLP** *020 †50
LOCKWOOD, Robert M, III. 1614 SCRIPTURE ST STE 2 76201 #041-01-1945 L1956 **R** *020 †80
LOWE, Mark S. 3537 S I-35 E, STE 302 76210 #048-12-1997 L1999 **APM** *020 †05
LOWRY, Joe Lee. 10904 SOUTHERLAND DR 76207 #039-01-1969 L1976 **PTH** *020 †50
MACARAEG, Leby Avanzado. 4141 BOXWOOD DR 76208 #748-07-1962 L1978 **P** *020
MACK, Suzanne Eileen. 3200 COLORADO BLVD, STE 202 76210 #064-01-1988 L1993 *020
MALIK, Salman Naseeruddin. 2900 N I-35, STE 400 76201 #704-01-1985 L2005 **CD IM** *020 †20
MALIK, Shezad A. 2324 SAN JACINTO BLVD, STE 211 76205 #917-12-1983 L2002 **CD IM** *020 †20
MANDELL, H Lance. 3537 S I-35 E, STE 111 76210 #048-04-1990 L1991 **HEM IM** *020 †20
MANSOOR, Shadan. 3537 S I-35 E, STE 111 76210 #704-02-1989 L2005 **HEM** *020 †20
MANTRI, Suhas Dattatray. 3304 COLORADO BLVD 76210 #495-01-1973 L1979 **OBG** *020
MARCHETTI, Jason M. 2817 S MAYHILL RD STE 100, TEXAS BACK INSTITUTE 76208 #048-12-2001 L2003 **PM** *020 †60
MASCIARELLI, Filippo. 3303 COLORADO BLVD 76210 #067-01-1986 L1996 **FM** *020 †18
MC ADAMS, Chas Armstrong. 2515 SCRIPTURE ST STE 100 76201 #067-01-1954 L1963 **ORS** *072 †40
MC BRIDE, Dan G. 3204 COLORADO BLVD 76210 #048-16-1986 L1987 **U GS** *020 †95
MC CLURE-DAVIS, Melissa. 207 N BONNIE BRAE ST, EMERGENCY DEPARTMENT 76201 #045-01-1992 L2000 **EM** *020 †16
MC DONALD, Daniel Paul. 323 N BONNIE BRAE ST, OB/GYN SPECIALISTS 76201 #001-06-1994 L1998 **OBG** *020 †30
MC GUIRE, Timothy C. 1614 SCRIPTURE ST, STE 12 76201 #048-04-1985 L1986 **FM** *020 †18
MC KINNEY, Kevin Moore. 2509 SCRIPTURE ST STE 104 76201 #048-02-1981 L1981 **FM** *020 †18 ‡
MC QUAID, Martha Morales. 3537 S INTERSTATE 35 E 76210 #048-12-1992 L1993 **DR** *020 †80
MENARD, Constance C. STUDENT HEALTH SERVICES 76204 #048-12-1991 L1992 **PD** *020 †55
MIDGETT, William Melvin. 3535 S INTERSTATE 35 E 76210 #048-12-1960 L1960 **GYN** *020 †30
MIZER, Glen Lavell. 3537 S INTERSTATE 35 E, STE 305 76210 #028-03-1971 L1979 **GS EM** *020 †85
MOORE, Terrence Lee. 2324 SAN JACINTO BLVD 76205 #048-13-1976 L1976 **FM** *020 †18
MORGAN, James A. 1512 TEASLEY LN 76205 #048-02-1995 L1996 **FM** *020 †18
MORRILL, Audrey Carr. 3323 COLORADO BLVD, STE B 76210 #048-02-1995 L1997 **FM** *020 †18
MORTON, Jeffery Douglas. 3720 S INTERSTATE 35 E 76210 #008-01-1985 L1992 **RO** *020 †80
MORYAN, Anwar I. 3537 S INTERSTATE 35 E # 3 76210 #915-02-1975 L1986 **END IM** *020 †20
MOSIER, Curtis Lee. 3535 S INTERSTATE 35 E 76210 #018-03-1978 L1985 **GS** *020 †85
MULLAN, Bertram Strancham. ■ 76207 #836-03-1955 L1978 **AN APM** *020
NAUGHER, Gregory R. 1614 SCRIPTURE ST STE 2, FAMILY RADIOLOGY 76201 #048-13-1989 L1990 **DR** *020 †80
NEEDLEMAN, Wanda L S. ■ 76209 #024-05-1971 L1972 **P PYA** *071
NGUYEN, Trang N. 209 N BONNIE BRAE ST, STE 305 76201 #048-04-1994 L1997 **IM** *020 †20
NOBLE, Decarlo. 209 N BONNIE BRAE ST, STE 205 76201 #040-02-1998 L2003 **OBG** *020
NORRIS, Jackie Roy. 625 DALLAS DR STE 375 76205 #030-06-1980 L1988 **IM** *020
NUBY, Marquis Jerue. 1306 TEASLEY LN 76205 #035-20-1991 L2003 **PD** *020 †55
NUNN, Roger David. 525 BRYAN ST STE A 76201 #038-40-1967 L1972 **OPH** *020 †35
OCHS, Ann Margaret. 3537 S I-35 E, STE 111 76210 #028-79-1998, ▲ L1999 **ON** *020 †20
OSTREA, Rhodora Urbano. 2625 SCRIPTURE ST 76201 #748-10-1991 L2002 **FM** *020 †18
OTTO, Russell Jon. 2900 N I-35 STE 416 76201 #028-03-1988 L1998 **OTO** *020 †45
PAGE, Ray D. 3537 S I-35 E, STE 111 76210 #048-78-1991, ▲ L1992 **ON** *020
PALCHURU, Sree Lakshmi. 2519 SCRIPTURE ST, DENTON COUNTY MHMR 76201 #495-70-1988 L2002 **P** *020
PARK, Randy Lynn. 3333 COLORADO BLVD 76210 #048-14-1981 L1981 **EM** *020 †18
PATEL, Bharatkumar N. 2519 SCRIPTURE ST, DENTON COUNTY MHMR 76201 #495-89-1980 L1988 **P** *020
PATEL, Narendrakumar A. 2509 SCRIPTURE ST STE 103A 76201 #495-76-1974 L1981 **ON IM** *020
PATEL, Rajeshkumar P. 2519 SCRIPTURE ST, DENTON COUNTY MHMR CENTER 76201 #495-89-1979 L1989 **CHP P** *020
PATEL, Sanjay B. 3000 N I-35 76201 #422-01-1997 L2001 **IM** *020 †20
PATEL, Vishal Ghanshyam. ■ 76205 #048-04-2007 **IM** *012
PERRY, Kerri Lynn. 2817 S MAYHILL RD, STE 270 76208 #048-12-1990 L1991 **GS** *020 †85
PILKINGTON, Steven G. 323 N BONNIE BRAE ST 76201 #048-16-2002 L2006 **OBG** *020
POPOV, Monica. 2805 S MAYHILL RD 76208 #001-02-1996 L2000 **OBG** *020 †30
PORTERFIELD, Rhonda Ruth. 207 N BONNIE BRAE ST 76201 #048-15-1982 L1983 **PTH** *020 †50
POTLURI, Vinaya. 3537 S I-35 E, STE 111 76210 #496-24-1998 L2004 **HO** *020 †20
POURZAN, Darius Peter. 207 N BONNIE BRAE ST 76201 #038-41-1983 L1987 **AN** *020
PRESCOTT, Kara H. 2900 N I-35, STE 110 76201 #048-15-2001 L2003 **RHU** *020
PRICE, David Wm. 2210 SAN JACINTO BLVD, STE 3 76205 #021-05-1977 L1982 **OTO A** *020 †45
QASIM, Mohammad. 3535 S INTERSTATE 35 E 76210 #704-01-1988 L1994 **HO** *020 †20
QUAN, Gang. 2900 N INTERSTATE 35, STE 101 76201 #243-46-1985 L2002 **IM** *020 †20
QURESHI, Tanveer Ahmad. 3304 COLORADO BLVD, STE 101 76210 #704-04-1968 L1976 **IM CD** *020
RAMASWAMY, Geetha. 1901 WIND RIVER LN 76210 #495-04-1996 L2006 **CD** *020 †20
RANA, Tahir. 2900 N I-35, STE 119 76201 #704-04-1985 L1997 **RO** *020 †80
RANKIN, Manly W. 3535 S INTERSTATE 35 E 76210 #048-04-1947 L1947 **FM GS** *071
REAVES, Caren Crane. 2805 S MAYHILL RD 76208 #048-12-1997 L1998 **OBG** *020 †30
REDDY, Indrani Nallu. 3537 S I-35 E STE 214, DENTON OB/GYN PA 76210 #496-01-1999 L2004 **OBG** *020 †30
REDMOND, Daniel Pierson. 3409 SUNDOWN BLVD 76210 #048-12-1968 L1970 **IM PA** *050 †20
REINHOLTZ, Richard R. 1614 SCRIPTURE ST STE 2, ASSOCIATED RADIOLOGISTS, L 76201 #048-02-1994 L2005 **DR** *020 †80
REMLEY, William A. ■ 76205 #038-41-1944 **IM** *020
ROMANUCCI, Eric. 3321 COLORADO BLVD 76210 #051-07-1992 L2006 **CRS GS** *020 †10,85 ‡
ROOBOL, Sara Elizabeth. 3000 N I-35, DEPT OF INTERNAL MEDICINE 76201 #025-07-1996 L2000 **IM** *020 †20
ROSS, Michael Barry. 3537 S I-35 E, STE 111 76210 #051-04-1971 L1979 **ON HO** *020 †20,18
RUIZ, Mario Alonso. 3537 S INTERSTATE 35 E, STE 317 76210 #005-18-1994 L1997 **NEP IM** *020 †20
SARAIYA, Mukesh C. 3200 COLORADO BLVD, STE 200 76210 #495-22-1982 L1990 **IM PUD** *020 †20
SAXON, Selby Ann. 4401A N INTERSTATE 35, STE 345 76207 #039-01-1988 L1992 **AN** *020 †05
SAYANI, Namrata Mukesh. 2501 SCRIPTURE ST STE 103 76201 #495-23-1995 L2003 **OPH** *020
SCHULMAN, Stephen Alan. 2515 SCRIPTURE ST STE 203 76201 #025-01-1978 L1985 **PD** *020 †55
SCOTT, Joseph M. 1512 TEASLEY LN 76205 #041-14-1972 L1980 **FM** *020 †18
SEARS, Joseph Warren. ■ 76208 #048-02-1956 L1956 **OS PD** *020 †55
SHAFRON, Lawrence Aaron. 2210 SAN JACINTO BLVD, ADVANCED EYE CARE CENTER 76205 #035-46-1985 L1992 **OPH** *020 †35
SHAH, Aitazaz A. 2900 N I-35 STE 118 76201 #704-04-1986 L2004 **IM** *020 †20
SHAH, Farah Aftab. 207 N BONNIE BRAE ST, PRESBYTERIAN HOSPITAL OF D 76201 #704-20-1989 L2006 **IM** *020 †20
SHELTON, John Scott. 1614 SCRIPTURE ST STE 1 76201 #048-12-1979 L1979 **FM** *020 †18
SHORT, Arvin Dale. 3000 N I-35, WOUND CLINIC 76201 #039-01-1969 L1971 **GS** *020 †85
SHORT, Bobby J. ■ 76209 #048-04-1943 L1943 **OS** *071
SIMMONS, William H. ■ 76210 #016-06-1950 L1950 **R** *020 †80
SIMMS, Scott A. 700 W OAK ST 76201 #048-12-1996 L2003 **FM** *020 †18
SMITH, Robert C. 2515 SCRIPTURE ST STE 202 76201 #048-12-1992 L1993 **D** *020 †15
SPILLER-HISEY, Jeannine F. 3537 S I-35 E STE 211 76210 #005-18-1992 L1998 **OBS OBG** *071 †30
SPIVEY, Michael Ray. 2900 N INTERSTATE 35, STE 100 76201 #048-04-1978 L1978 **ON IM** *020 †20
SQUIERS, Milton David. 1160 N BONNIE BRAE ST 76201 #010-03-1973 L1980 **PD ADL** *020 †55
STEWART, Daryl A. 3321 COLORADO BLVD 76210 #048-13-1987 L2002 **GS** *020 †85
STRITTMATTER, Marla Ann. 3323 COLORADO BLVD, STE B 76210 #048-16-1997 L1998 **FM** *020 †18
SUOMINEN, David C. 3000 N I-35, ATTN - RADIOLOGY 76201 #048-02-1993 L1994 **DR** *020 †80
SUTTON-WALSH, Heather G. 209 N BONNIE BRAE ST, STE 304 76201 #048-15-2002 L2004 **OBG** *100
TABOADA, Erwin Liewald. ■ 76205 #231-01-1951 L1966 **P** *071 †75
TALBOT, Scott Elliot. 2609 SCRIPTURE ST 76201 #048-02-1997 L2000 **FM** *020 †18
TAYLOR, Eugene Madison. 2509 SCRIPTURE ST, NORTH TEXAS MEDICAL 76201 #048-12-1963 L1963 **GP PD** *020
THOMAS, Thomas Jos. 3535 S INTERSTATE 35 E 76210 #017-20-1968 L1974 **U** *020 †95
THOMPSON, Travis L. 3537 S I-35 E, STE 111 76210 #048-02-1999 L2004 **RO** *020 †80
TORRIE, Susan C. 3201 TEASLEY LN STE 102 76210 #048-12-1991 L1994 **PD** *020 †55
TOWNSEND-PARCHMAN, W. 207 W HICKORY ST STE 110 76201 #048-02-1978 L1978 **P** *020 †75
TUCKER, David Maury. 215 W MULBERRY ST, STE A 76201 #021-01-1996 L2006 **CHP P** *020
VAKHARIA, Akshay S. 2515 SCRIPTURE ST, STE 200 76201 #495-22-1982 L1996 **APM IM** *020 †20,05
VALENTI, Joseph Samuel. 2805 S MAYHILL RD 76208 #035-06-1994 L1998 **OBG** *020 †30
VAN MAELE, Diane G. 1160 N BONNIE BRAE ST 76201 #048-78-2004, ▲ L2007 **PD** *020 †55
VELAYOS, Edward E. ■ 76205 #132-01-1959 L1973 **RHU IM** *072 ‡
VYAS, Meena B. 2519 SCRIPTURE ST, DCMHMR 76201 #495-76-1983 L1995 **P** *020 †75
WAHLERT, Charles Hancock. 521 BRYAN ST 76201 #048-02-1976 L1976 **IM** *020
WANG, Lynn. 2509 SCRIPTURE ST STE 103 76201 #243-47-1987 L1999 **N** *020 †75
WARD, Lyn D. 2535 W OAK ST 76201 #048-14-1996 L1998 **ORS OSM** *020 †40
WASSERMAN, Alan S. 1512 TEASLEY LN 76205 #028-46-1979 L1989 **GP OBG** *020 †30
WATTS, Gary Byron. 2925 COUNTRY CLUB RD, STE 102 76210 #048-12-1988 L1989 **P** *020 †75
WEI, David Hao. ■ 76205 #035-01-2008 *012
WEINBERG, Stephen Allen. 3300 COLORADO BLVD 76210 #038-41-1971 L1984 **ORS** *020 †40
WILLIAMS, Joseph Ralph. ■ 76207 #047-07-1945 L1946 **PHP** *072
WILSON, Carol Jane. 3800 W CHESTNUT, UNT STUDENT HEALTH 76203 #048-04-1967 L1967 **NEP PD** *020 †55
WILSON, Caroline M. 3303 COLORADO BLVD, STE A 76210 #048-12-1993 L1995 **FM** *020 †18
WILSON, Marc Aaron. 323 N BONNIE BRAE ST 76201 #039-01-1996 L2000 **OBG** *020 †30
WILSON, Ronald Thos. 3323 COLORADO BLVD, STE A 76210 #049-01-1974 L1979 **OBG** *020 †30
WISE, Scott Cannon. 2223 COLORADO BLVD 76205 #048-12-1993 L1994 **FM** *020 †18
WOLSKI, Edward Frank. 2436 S INTERSTATE 35 E 76205 #065-01-1978 L1980 **FM OM** *020
XIONG, Henry Qing Hua. 3537 S I-35 E, STE 111 76210 #243-16-1984 L1999 **ON IM** *020 †20
YEATTS, Linda Sue. 2701 W OAK ST, STE 101 76201 #051-01-1982 L1988 **FM** *020 †18
YOUNG, Melvin Carl, Jr. 3905 ANDREW AVE, M.C. YOUNG, M.D. 76210 #039-01-1980 L1984 **AN** *020 †05
YOUNG, Robyn R. 3537 S I-35 E, STE 111 76210 #048-14-1990 L1991 **HO** *020 †20
ZEITLIN, Mark Harold. ■ 76207 #041-02-1966 L1967 **AN** *071 †05
ZISMAN, Myron Richard. ■ 76207 #035-08-1958 L1976 **ORS** *071 †40 ‡

DENVER CITY - YOAKUM

CLARK, Kristie Michelle. 415 N AVENUE F 79323 #012-05-2000 L2003 **PD** *020 †55
CLARK, Robert Thomas, Jr. 415 N AVENUE F 79323 #048-12-2003 L2006 **FM** *020 †18
COTTON, Chris Douglas. 415 N AVENUE F 79323 #036-05-1991 L1995 **GP** *020
KAHN, Dan. 415 N AVENUE F 79323 #891-02-1972 L1980 **GP GS** *020 †85
RUIZ, Francisco R. 412 MUSTANG DR 79323 #042-03-1992 L1997 **GE** *020 †20
THEPCHATRI, Bodindr. 415 N AVENUE F 79323 #891-03-1972 L1977 **GP IM** *050 †20

■ = Address Information Privacy Protected

DEPORT – LAMAR

GLOVER, Thomas Hale. ■ 75435 #048-12-1958 L1958 **GP** *071

DESOTO – DALLAS

AHN, Richard Seung. 1001 ROBBIE MINCE WAY 75115 #048-02-1989 L1990 **P** *020 †75

ALVAREZ, Eliazar. 2727 BOLTON BOONE DR # 109 75115 #005-12-1988 L2000 **FM** *020 ‡18

ANDERSON, Carla Anne. 1750 N HAMPTON RD, RADIOLOGICAL CONSULTANTS A 75115 #035-46-1989 L1995 **DR** *020 †80

ARIYO, Abraham Adeniran. 2727 BOLTON BOONE DR 1 75115 #690-01-1988 L2002 **CD** *020 †20

ATTIAH, Augustine Kwadwo. 2707 BOLTON BOONE DR, STE 100 75115 #028-02-1979 L1984 **PUD IM** *020 †20

AZUBUIKE, Ebere Israel. 2727 BOLTON BOONE DR STE 1 75115 #048-02-2005 L2008 **FP** *012

BALTAZAR, Romeo Cruz. 951 YORK DR STE 102 75115 #748-10-1973 L1985 **AN** *020 †05

BARR, Vincent Peter. 2707 BOLTON BOONE DR, STE 101 75115 #056-05-1972 L1979 **CD IM** *020 †20

BEALL, James Leber. 1750 N HAMPTON RD, RADIOLOGICAL CONSULTANTS A 75115 #048-13-1979 L1980 **DR** *020 †80

BEISERT, Gene E. 1750 N HAMPTON RD, RADIOLOGICAL CONSULTANTS A 75115 #048-14-1993 L1994 **DR** *020 †80

BENNETT, Bridget Renee. ■ 75115 #048-04-2005 **PM** *012

BLACKBURN-BROWN, Andrea V. 526 E PLEASANT RUN RD 75115 #025-12-1983 L1997 **FM** *020 †18

BOYD, Albert Odili. 941 YORK DR STE 200 75115 #690-01-1978 L2003 **FM** *020 †18 ‡

BRYANT, Richard S. 2805 PRINCE GEORGE AVE 75115 #048-13-2001 L2004 **FM** *020 †18

BULLOCK, Lois Leach. ■ 75115 #041-02-1984 L1985 **OM AM** *062

BURKETT, Richard Jerry. 2801 BOLTON BOONE DR 75115 #027-01-1981 L1982 **PS HS** *020 †85

CARDENAS, Edgar Alejandro. ■ 75115 #048-02-2006 *012

CHANDER, Prem. ■ 75115 #495-29-1970 L1986 **AN** *020 †05

CHARNOCK, Edwin Howard. 1001 ROBBIE MINCE WAY 75115 #048-02-1983 L1983 **N SME** *020 †75

CHOE, Wonsick. ■ 75115 #583-02-1977 L1995 **NM** *020 †28

DEACON, Thomas W. 2828 DUKE OF GLOUCESTER ST, STE 106 75115 #048-13-1987 L1988 **PD** *020 †55

DEAN, Frank Thos. 2727 BOLTON BOONE DR, STE 105 75115 #048-13-1973 L1973 **OBG** *020

DINH, Neil Hong. 951 YORK DR, STE 102 75115 #018-03-1991 L1996 **AN** *020 †05

FAHMI, Saleemah Yasmeen. ■ 75115 #035-19-2001 L2008 **END** *020 †20

FARRELL, Robert S. 1750 N HAMPTON RD, RADIOLOGICAL CONSULTANTS A 75115 #048-12-1990 L1991 **DR** *020 †80

FUCHS, Ingbert Elmar. ■ 75115 #409-42-1975 **IM** *100

GORREPATI, Jayashree N. 632 BENT CREEK DR, SILVER CREEK CROSSING 75115 #495-58-1976 L1986 **AN** *020 †05

HAMILTON, Pamela Gerie. 1801 N HAMPTON RD, STE 315 75115 #039-01-1983 L1985 **P** *020 †75

HE, Yong. 1001 ROBBIE MINCE WAY 75115 #243-47-1986 L2005 **N** *020 †75

HILL, Richard B, Jr. 921 YORK DR 75115 #004-01-1971 L1972 **GS** *020

HOLMAN, Nicole D. 900 N POLK ST STE 120, JUST FOR YOU FAMILY CARE 75115 #047-07-1998 L2004 **FM** *020 †18

HORVATH, David Herman. ■ 75115 #048-12-1991 **P** *100

HUFF, Angela Lenora. 2719 BOLTON BOONE DR 75115 #048-13-1992 L1993 **N** *020

HUNKE, Louis Allen. 2828 DUKE OF GLOUCESTER ST, STE 106 75115 #048-13-1983 L1986 **PD** *020 †55

IDOWU, Olubayo Ayotunde. 2727 BOLTON BOONE DR 75115 #690-01-1976 L1998 **IM IMG** *020 †20

IQBAL, Husna. 2801 DUKE OF GLOUCESTER ST, STE 101 75115 #496-27-1991 L1997 **FM** *020 †18

JAIN, Siddharth G. 2705 PRINCE GEORGE AVE 75115 #495-16-1988 L2008 **U** *020 †95

KAKARLA, Mahendra Nath. 2801 BOLTON BOONE DR, STE 104 75115 #495-58-1969 L1981 **IM** *020 †60,20

KAKARLA, Rajyalakshmi. 2801 BOLTON BOONE DR, STE 103 75115 #495-50-1969 L1981 **OBG** *020 †30

KELT, Sidney A, Jr. 1801 N HAMPTON RD, STE 315 75115 #030-05-1983 L1987 **P** *020 †75

KHOUW, Harry Wie Goan. ■ 75115 #506-01-1956 L1970 **GYN** *071 †30

KING, Lisa Angela. 950 SCOTLAND DR 75115 #035-06-1991 L1995 **OBG REN** *020 †30

KONDA, Janardhan. 2727 BOLTON BOONE DR # 108 75115 #495-57-1972 L1981 **GE IM** *020 †20

LAMMATA, Viswanadham. 925 YORK DR 75115 #495-11-1974 L1982 **CD IM** *020 †20

LEIFER, David Marc. 1750 N HAMPTON RD, RADIOLOGICAL CONSULTANTS A 75115 #016-02-1993 L1996 **DR** *020 †80

LICKER, Kenneth Ira. 935 YORK DR 75115 #035-09-1972 L1980 **U** *020 †95

LONGSHAW, Jacquelynn G. 2828 DUKE OF GLOUCESTER ST, STE 106 75115 #038-45-1995 L1997 **PD** *020 †55

LUCAS, Thomas Wm. 1801 N HAMPTON RD, STE 315 75115 #039-01-1969 L1990 **NUP PYM** *020 †55

MAHAPATRA, Dipta. ■ 75115 #495-39-1973 **IM MM** *050

MATHIS, Chas Edward, III. 2000 OLD HICKORY TRL 75115 #048-15-1976 L1978 **PYG P** *020 †75

MC REE, Cecil Allen. ■ 75115 #048-12-1958 L1958 **GS** *071 †85

MEYER, Parker Henry. 900 N POLK ST, STE 124 75115 #021-01-1965 L1967 **FM** *071 †18

MIDDLETON, Robert Aaron. ■ 75115 #048-02-1956 L1956 **RO R** *020

MOATE, Michelle Elaine. 1750 N HAMPTON RD 75115 #027-01-1995 L1996 **DR** *020 †80

MORGAN, Jerry Meldon. 2727 BOLTON BOONE DR # 101 75115 #038-40-1973 L1976 **PD** *020 †55

MUES, Gabriele Irmingard. ■ 75115 #409-42-1975 L2004 **PTH** *020

NADALO, Lennard Albert. 1750 N HAMPTON RD 75115 #016-06-1913 L1976 **DR GP** *020 †80

NARAYANA, Jayaprakash. 917 N HAMPTON RD STE 247 75115 #495-16-1980 L1994 **FM** *020 †18

NEWMAN, Jose. 900 N POLK ST, STE 150 75115 #649-01-1961 L1969 **IM GP** *020

NIBLETT, Kevin W. 921 YORK DR 75115 #048-12-1990 L1993 **GS** *020 †85

NICHOLAS, Donald Gene, Jr. 2805 PRINCE GEORGE AVE 75115 #048-12-1985 L1987 **IM** *020 †20

NISBET, Robert J. 1750 N HAMPTON RD, RADIOLOGICAL CONSULTANTS A 75115 #048-14-1998 L2001 **RNR** *020 †80

OCHEI, Dennis O. 2727 BOLTON BOONE DR, STE 103 75115 #690-04-1986 L1999 **FM** *020 †18 ‡

OCHEI, Nnalu Felicia. 2727 BOLTON BOONE DR # 103 75115 #690-04-1988 L2004 **PD** *100 †55

OLUSOLA, Benedict Oladipo. 1670 N HAMPTON RD STE 115 75115 #690-02-1984 L1994 **FM** *020 †18

PAGE, Christine E. 1750 N HAMPTON RD, RADIOLOGICAL CONSULTANTS A 75115 #048-12-1986 L1987 **DR** *020 †80

PATEL, Santosh C. 2625 BOLTON BOONE DR 75115 #041-07-1996 L2006 **OPH** *020 †35 ‡

PFLANZER, Joseph. 2801 BOLTON BOONE DR, NO 101 75115 #165-07-1967 L1971 **A IG** *020 †03

RAMOS, Edid Gerardo. 315 E PLEASANT RUN RD 75115 #847-11-1990 L1995 **IMG** *020

RAMOS, Teofilo Moses, Jr. 1510 N HAMPTON RD STE 250 75115 #748-02-1981 L1987 **CHP P** *020 †75

REDDY, Nallu Ramappa. 2727 BOLTON BOONE DR, STE 111 75115 #495-57-1971 L1980 **IM ON** *020 †20

RICE, Gregg D. 1750 N HAMPTON RD 75115 #048-12-1992 L1993 **DR NR** *020 †80

RINGHAM, Jarrett. ■ 75115 #020-02-1946 L1946 **CHP P** *075

RODRIGUEZ, Joselita D. 941 YORK DR, STE 202 75115 #748-01-1971 L1979 **PD IM** *020 †55

ROGERS, Thomas Eugene. 824 NEWPORT WAY 75115 #048-02-1982 L1993 **IM** *020 †20,50

SELLARS, William A. 2801 BOLTON BOONE DR, STE 101 75115 #048-12-1953 L1953 **A PDA** *071 †55,03

SLONIM, Suzanne M. 1750 N HAMPTON RD, RADIOLOGICAL CONSULT ASSOC 75115 #010-01-1989 L2000 **VIR** *020 †80

SPRATT, Lorenzo. 1116 BLUFFVIEW DR 75115 #028-02-1979 L1981 **FM** *040

THOMPSON, Jimmie Lee. 1119 SHADOW WOOD TRL 75115 #028-02-1978 L1980 **AN PME** *020

THOMPSON, William E. 1750 N HAMPTON RD 75115 #048-16-1992 L2001 **VIR** *020 †80

TOWNS, Mark Douglas. 2828 DUKE OF GLOUCESTER ST 75115 #048-12-1983 L1983 **PD** *020 †55

TU, Misty Yi. ■ 75115 #048-15-2004 L2006 **P** *012

VALENZUELA, Diego G, Jr. ■ 75115 #748-02-1977 L1979 **FM PHP** *020 †18

VANDIVER, Carolyn Jill. 1750 N HAMPTON RD, RADIOLOGICAL CONSULTANTS A 75115 #025-12-1993 L1999 **DR** *020 †80

VAN METER, Travis Allen. 1750 N HAMPTON RD, RADIOLOGICAL CONSULTANTS A 75115 #048-14-1992 L1993 **DR VIR** *020 †80

VARGHESE, K Thomas. 1704 N HAMPTON RD STE 204 75115 #495-04-1952 **P** *020

VARGHESE, Kochuparampil T. 1704 N HAMPTON RD STE 204 75115 #495-63-1979 L1985 **P** *020

VELEZ, Ruben Luis. 900 N POLK ST STE 146, PLEASANT RUN DIALYSIS 75115 #042-01-1978 L1979 **NEP CCM** *020 †20

WALLNER, Richard Lee. 2715 BOLTON BOONE DR 75115 #048-02-1980 L1980 **OBG ID** *020 †30

WEIR, Lori Michelle. 1750 N HAMPTON RD, RADIOLOGICAL CONSULTANTS A 75115 #028-46-1999 L2005 **VIR DR** *020 †80

WILSON, John Douglas. 1750 N HAMPTON RD, RADIOLOGICAL CONSULTANTS A 75115 #036-01-1988 L1995 **DR RNR** *020 †80

ZERNER, James Joseph. 1750 N HAMPTON RD, RADIOLOGICAL CONSULTANTS A 75115 #024-05-1995 L2000 **DR** *020 †80

DETROIT – RED RIVER

DOTIN, Larry Nicholas. ■ 75436 #038-40-1962 L1969 **NEP IM** *030 †20

DEVINE – MEDINA

BEST, Max E, Jr. 211 W COLLEGE AVE 78016 #048-02-1979 L1979 **AM** *020

BRETT, Mary Anne G. 1250 STATE HWY 173 N, DEVINE FAMILY HEALTH CENTE 78016 #065-09-1988 L1993 **FM** *020 †18

DICKINSON – GALVESTON

ABRAHAM, Bincy Paulose. ■ 77539 #048-02-2002 L2008 **GE** *012 †20

ANDREW, Susan Louise. 914 FM 517 RD W 77539 #035-01-1982 L1988 **AI** *020 †20,03

BISONNI, Roberto Sergio. 1804 FM 646 RD W, STE J 77539 #132-01-1970 L1995 **FM** *020 †18

BOLAND, Howard Leland. 914 FM 517 RD W STE 201B 77539 #048-02-1982 L1983 **P ADP** *020 †75

BOLANO, Carlos Ramon. 3828 HUGHES CT STE 104 77539 #264-04-1959 L1975 **PD ID** *020

BOLANO, Carlos Ramon. 3828 HUGHES CT STE 204 77539 #048-78-2001, ▲ L2004 **PD** *020 †55

CAFFEY, Jennifer. 3828 HUGHES CT STE 204 77539 #048-78-2001, ▲ L2004 **PD** *020 †55

CHAVASON, Arthur Arrit. ■ 77539 #048-15-2004 L2007 **P** *012

COURY, Cameron Layne. ■ 77539 #048-14-2005 **PDM** *012

DAVIS, Justin Mark. ■ 77539 #039-01-2006 **AN** *012

DAWLETT, Marie Foty. ■ 77539 #048-02-2005 L2008 **PD** *012

EVANS, Paul Douglas. ■ 77539 #048-14-2008 *012

FOREMAN, Adolphus. 2503 MAIN ST STE B 77539 #048-02-1968 L1968 **OBG** *071 †30

FREY, Paul Wm. ■ 77539 #048-02-1976 L1976 **EM FM** *020 †18

FULCHER, Perry Larue. 3828 HUGHES CT, STE 207 77539 #048-02-1980 L1980 **OBG** *020 †30

GASKILL, Susan Curby. 2211 FM 646 RD W STE 100, VICTORY BREAST DIAGNOSTICS 77539 #048-14-1987 L1988 **DR** *020 †80

GRAY, Laurie Pepper. ■ 77539 #048-02-2005 L2008 **PD** *012

GREGONIS, Erica Greer. ■ 77539 #020-02-2005 L2008 **IM** *012

GRIFFIS, Kathleen Mueller. 3828 HUGHES CT, STE 207 77539 #011-03-1984 L1999 **OBG** *020 †30

GUILBEAU, Julie Claire. ■ 77539 #021-06-2003 L2007 **AN** *100

JONES CLINE, Marrietta. 3828 HUGHES CT, STE 106 77539 #048-12-1992 L1996 **PD** *020

KARGEL, Jennifer Schklair. ■ 77539 #048-02-2007 **PS** *012

KHAN, Mona Sameen. ■ 77539 #704-25-1999 L2008 **NPM** *012

KNIGHTON, Toure Ali. ■ 77539 #048-07-2006 **AN** *012

LACASSE, Albert L. ■ 77539 #048-13-2004 L2006 **AN** *012

LINN, Heather M. 914 FM 517 RD W 77539 #048-02-1988 L1989 **N** *020 †75

LOUIS, Edward Emile. 303 FM 517 RD E 77539 #048-02-1963 L1963 **IM GE** *020 †20

MELENDEZ, Rene. ■ 77539 #042-02-1996 L1998 **FP** *012

■ = Address Information Privacy Protected

MOLINA, Ana Maria. ■ 77539 #041-13-2004 L2008 **MPD** *012
NATIVIDAD, Toribio Tomas. ■ 77539 #048-02-2005 **ORS** *012
NGUYEN, Vince Thuan. ■ 77539 #001-02-2004 **CD** *012
PARK, John W. 316 MAMMOTH SPRINGS LN 77539 #048-13-2001 L2005 **AN** *020 †05
PATEL, Premal Gautam. ■ 77539 #048-02-2006 L2006 **IM** *012
PERRY, John Elliott. 914 FM 517 RD W 77539 #048-02-1957 L1957 **A IM** *072 †20,03
POFFENBARGER, Phillip L. 2902 FROSTWOOD CIR 77539 #017-20-1963 L1970 **IM DIA** *020 †20
RAMCHANDRA, Mahalakshmi. 2251 FM 646 RD W, BAY COLONY PEDS STE 155 77539 #495-21-1990 L2000 **PD** *020 †55
RAMEDEN, Theresa A. 3828 HUGHES CT, STE 106 77539 #048-02-1988 L1989 **GP** *020 †18
ROSENBLAD, Joanna Moser. ■ 77539 #048-04-1947 L1947 **PD PHP** *071
RUBIO, Ruby Navarro. ■ 77539 #048-02-2006 **AN** *012
RUIVIVAR, Felix Santos. ■ 77539 #748-02-1957 L1974 **GP EM** *072
SCHNAKE, Edward Geo. ■ 77539 #035-06-1956 L1957 **FM** *071
SCOTT, Cynthia Christina. ■ 77539 #048-02-2006 **IM** *012
SIERRA, Crystal Ann Aceve. ■ 77539 #048-02-2006 **PD** *012
SIKAND, Sulochana. ■ 77539 #495-33-1973 **P** *100
SIMMONS, Donna Lynn. ■ 77539 #048-02-2006 **FP** *012
SIMPSON-WHITE, Elcenia. 1804 FM 646 RD W, STE J 77539 #010-03-1979 L1981 **FM** *020 †18
SNIFF, Shannon Lynne. ■ 77539 #048-14-2006 **P** *012
YAMANI, Hussein Nooruddin. ■ 77539 #048-02-2004 **CD** *012 †20
YOUNG, Georgina. 2401 FM 646 RD W, STE C 77539 #020-02-1995 L2003 **P** *020 †75

DILLEY — FRIO

AHMED, Zahoor. 230 W MILLER ST 78017 #704-08-1973 L2006 **FM** *020 †18
CAMERO, Elva Oralia. 111 E MILLER ST, HOOD MEDICAL CLINIC 78017 #056-06-1985 L1994 **FM P** *020 †18

DIMMITT — CASTRO

BIZZELL, Skylar K. 300 W HALSELL ST 79027 #048-15-1998 L2001 **FM OBS** *020 †18
GRIFFIS, Daniel C. 300 W HALSELL ST 79027 #048-12-2003 L2004 **FM** *020 †18
HARDEE, Gary Randall. 300 W HALSELL ST 79027 #048-02-1978 L1981 **FM** *020 †18
MATOS, Gregorio. 300 W HALSELL ST 79027 #042-01-1958 L1974 **GS VS** *020 †85
PATEL, Dhiraj Somabhai. 310 W HALSELL ST 79027 #495-22-1970 L1984 **GS GP** *020 †85
PERCY, Marie Denise. 600 SW 10TH ST 79027 #025-07-1993 L2002 **FM** *020

DOBBIN — MONTGOMERY

FRAUSTADT FLEMMING, U. ■ 77333 #649-01-1971 L1976 **PD** *071 †55

DONNA — HIDALGO

ALQUIZA, Mark Tablizo. 301 S 17TH ST 78537 #748-11-1992 L2004 **FM** *020 †18
AVILA, Celestino Z. 308 N SALINAS BLVD 78537 #649-30-1974 L1978 **FM FSM** *020 †18
BUSTOS, Fernando. ■ 78537 #132-01-1947 L1969 **U GS** *071 †95
FLORES, Elida Leticia. 301 S 17TH ST 78537 #649-38-1981 L1997 **PD** *020 †55
FLORES, Michael Anthony. 111 N 17TH ST, STE B 78537 #025-12-2000 L2003 **IM** *020 ‡
JIMENEZ, David L. ■ 78537 #048-04-2005 L2008 **PD** *012
KHAN, Salman Muhammad. 307 N D SALINAS AVE, DONNA MEDICAL CLINIC 78537 #704-22-1992 L2004 **PD** *020 †55
RUIZ, Alberto. ■ 78537 #025-12-2003 **FP** *012

DOSS — GILLESPIE

HAHN, Robert Wm. PO BOX 2 78618 #048-12-1973 L1975 **GYN** *020 †30

DOUBLE OAK – DENTON

PETERSON, Michael Wayne. 301 VALLEY VIEW TRL 75077 #023-12-1985 L1996 **EM GP** *020 †16

DRIFTWOOD — HAYS

CHAVIS, Rebecca Aimee. ■ 78619 #048-14-1994 L1998 **FM** *020 †18
ESCALERA, Javier Ponce. ■ 78619 #048-16-2004 L2007 **CHP** *012
JOHNSON, Jeffrey W. 313 SHELF ROCK 78619 #048-14-1997 L1999 **GS** *020 †85
JOHNSON, Laura Anton. 313 SHELF ROCK 78619 #048-14-1997 L1999 **PD** *062 †55
ZIMMERMAN, Frank Wm, Jr. ■ 78619 #048-02-1959 L1959 **P** *072 †75

DRIPPING SPRINGS — HAYS

BOLBOCK, Bruce L. 1500 KIRBY SPRINGS DR 78620 #028-46-1982 L1988 **AN** *020 †05
BOYETT, Eleanor Sue. ■ 78620 #048-02-1955 L1955 **AN** *020 †05
BUCHANAN, Todd D. 104 W MERCER ST 78620 #048-13-1989 L1991 **FM** *020 †18
CARTALL, Louis M. ■ 78620 #048-02-1942 L1943 **GP** *071 †18
CREMONA, Frederick Jos. ■ 78620 #048-04-1957 L1957 **ORS** *071 †40
CROSBY, Jack Bradford. STAR RT 1B BOX 110A 78620 #017-20-1957 L1964 **OS GP** *030
HOLMES, Faith Louise. 1505 W HIGHWAY 290, STE A 78620 #039-05-1987 L1999 **FM** *020 †18
MARTIN, Dieter Robert. ■ 78620 #048-12-2001 L2003 **IM** *020
ROUNTREE, Joe Harold. ■ 78620 #048-02-1961 L1961 **P** *020
STINSON, Kathleen S. 331 SPORTSPLEX DR, STE C 78620 #048-13-2000 L2003 **PD** *020 †55

DUBLIN — ERATH

BRISTER, Marilyn K. 305 N PATRICK ST 76446 #048-16-1982 L1983 **FM FPG** *020 †18

DUMAS — MOORE

BAYKAN, Turhan I. 110 S BLISS AVE 79029 #902-05-1979 L1985 **OBG** *020
BUNCH, Christopher Lou. 202 S MEREDITH AVE 79029 #028-34-1987 L1990 **FM** *020 †18
COVINGTON, Benjamin W, IV. 201 S BLISS AVE, STE A 79029 #048-13-2001 L2003 **FM** *020 †18
GRAHAM, Gordon Keith. 212 S BLISS AVE 79029 #065-01-1977 *100
GRAHAM, Judith Elaine. 212 S BLISS AVE 79029 #060-02-1991 L2002 *020
LANGEVIN, James Maurice. 212 S BLISS AVE 79029 #048-02-1977 L1999 **CRS** *050
MIGUEL, Edilberto R. 224 E 2ND ST 79029 #748-01-1971 L1981 **IM** *020
MOHAPATRA, Pramoda Kumar. 419 E 1ST ST, STE S2 79029 #007-02-1999 L2003 **FM** *020 †18
OPARA, Ositadinma O. 201 S BLISS AVE 79029 #041-77-1999, ▲ L2003 **IM** *020
STEPHENSON, Robert Dudley. 109 BINKLEY AVE 79029 #048-02-1962 L1962 **DR GP** *020 †80
TAN, Stella Tinga. 224 E 2ND ST 79029 #748-01-1991 L2003 **GP AN** *020
WAGLE, Manisha Vithal. 224 E 2ND ST 79029 #495-01-1973 L1996 **CCA** *020 †05

DUNCANVILLE – DALLAS

ALI, Ashmead. ■ 75116 #566-01-1984 L1992 **NPM** *020 †55
ANYANWU, Isabel C. 315 S COCKRELL HILL RD, PAIN TREATMENT CLINICS, PA 75116 #690-04-1983 L2003 **APM AN** *020 †05
ARNOUVILLE, Jennifer Thom. ■ 75116 #048-78-2006, ▲ **FP** *012
BAKER, Byron Brent. 1110 REDMAN LN 75137 #048-14-1985 L1986 **FM AM** *020
BISHARA, Munir Fariz. 1214 GREEN LEAF LN 75137 #605-01-1963 L1972 **PD ID** *020 †55
BISHOP, Beverly Brown. 907 S MAIN ST, STE 203 75137 #001-02-1993 L1997 **OPH** *020 †35 ‡
BRAUN, F Gene. 777 E WHEATLAND RD 75116 #041-12-1958 L1964 **OPH** *020 †35
CALHOUN, Ronnie Edward. 1010 E WHEATLAND RD, STE B 75116 #048-12-1985 L1986 **GS AS** *020 †85
CHIU, Thomas Chiaho. 726 S COCKRELL HILL RD 75137 #048-12-2001 L2003 **FM** *020 †18
CIAROCHI, Fred F. 903 S MAIN ST STE 101 75137 #041-12-1969 L1976 **END IM** *020 †20
COLEMAN, Jamie Lynn. ■ 75137 #004-01-1999 L2000 **DR** *100
COOPER, Jack Medford. 907 S MAIN ST STE 203 75137 #026-04-1964 L1978 **OPH** *020 †35
DIXON, Calvin Lee. 1016 E WHEATLAND RD 75116 #048-12-1975 L1975 **PCC IM** *020 †20
ETESSAM, Houshang. 1119 COVENTRY LN 75137 #517-01-1957 L1967 **OBG GP** *020 †85
FADAHUNSI, Titilola Oluju. ■ 75137 #048-13-2007 **OBG** *012
FAIN, Rickey Maurice. 306 1/2 FOUTS AVE 75137 #048-04-1982 L1983 **FM** *020 †18
FEARS, William Burton. 1014 E WHEATLAND RD 75116 #039-01-1975 L1984 **IM END** *020 †20
FREEMAN, Michael Lee. 545 W WHEATLAND RD 75116 #048-12-1971 L1971 **FM GPM** *020 †18
GARTNER, Jay S. 626 W WHEATLAND RD, STE B 75116 #035-06-1981 L1984 **AI IM** *020 †20,03
GONZAGA, Fe Rosario Q Y M. 529 W WHEATLAND RD 75116 #748-01-1961 L1981 **IM** *020
HSU, Liang Rong. 315 S COCKRELL HILL RD #10 75116 #244-05-1968 L1978 **U** *020
HUBLER, Lloyd David. 1010 W WHEATLAND RD 75116 #048-02-1973 L1973 **ORS OSM** *020 †40
IQBAL, Imran. 903 S MAIN ST 75137 #704-16-1990 L2000 **RHU IM** *020 †20
JENKINS, Robert N. 903 S MAIN ST 75137 #048-04-1986 L1987 **RHU IM** *020 †20
LAM, Kyaw Win. ■ 75137 #209-01-1967 L1977 **R** *071 †80
LAWRENCE, David J. ■ 75137 #048-13-2001 *100
LE, Trang D. 907 S MAIN ST STE 203 75137 #048-04-1989 L1990 **OPH** *020 †35
LEE, Andy M. 614 W WHEATLAND BLVD 75116 #048-14-1993 L1994 **OPH** *020 †35 ‡
MARULL, Javier Horacio. 1010 E WHEATLAND RD, STE A 75116 #048-15-1992 L1993 **AN PME** *020 †05
MATEWERE, George Gerald. 726 S COCKRELL HILL RD 75137 #047-07-1988 L2005 **FM** *020 †20
MIDDLEMAN, Edward Louis. 310 E HIGHWAY 67 75137 #041-12-1965 L1969 **ON IM** *020 †20
MILLER, Elaine K. 111 W DANIELDALE RD 75137 #048-78-2002, ▲ L2003 **D** *020
MILLER, Verlyn Michael. PO BOX 381668 75138 #018-03-1951 L1952 **TS GP** *075 †90,85
MITCHELL, Joshua Delbert. ■ 75116 #048-12-2008 *012
PARKER, Michael P. 726 S COCKRELL HILL RD 75137 #048-02-1982 L1983 **FM** *020
REDDY, Maryada Srinivas. 310 E HIGHWAY 67 75116 #495-62-1986 L2002 **ON** *020 †20
ROBERTSON, Jeffrey Brent. 907 S MAIN ST STE 203, EYE CARE ASSOCIATES OF TEX 75137 #021-06-1997 L2001 **OPH** *020 †35
ROMO, Monica Victoriana. ■ 75116 #010-02-2004 L2006 **FM** *100 †18
SANDUSKY, George Walker. 623 MERCURY AVE 75137 #048-12-1967 L1967 **IM** *020
SANDUSKY, Jane A Baethe. 777 E WHEATLAND RD, STE 108 75116 #048-12-1967 L1967 **GP PD** *020
SMIRMAUL, Heinz Jos. 614 W WHEATLAND RD 75116 #065-10-1973 L1979 **OPH OS** *071 †35
SORIANO, Salvador Luis. ■ 75116 #649-02-1960 L1967 **GP GS** *020
TAYLOR, Vicky R. 714 WOOD LN 75116 #048-13-1997 L2001 **PD** *020
TURNG, Shu Ying. 315 S COCKRELL HIL RD #206 75116 #583-03-1971 L1979 **PD** *020 †55
URRUTIA, Ricardo Frank. 523 W WHEATLAND RD 75116 #341-01-1972 L1980 **PD NPM** *020 †55
WAGNON, Charles Lee. 777 E WHEATLAND RD STE 102 75116 #048-02-1967 L1967 **GYN IM** *020
WEBB, Thomas Pervy. 777 E WHEATLAND RD, STE 106 75116 #048-04-1954 L1962 **GS OS** *020 †85
WILLIS, Benjamin Lee. 614 W WHEATLAND RD 75116 #048-12-1980 L1980 **OPH** *071 †35
YOUNG, Angela Darlene. ■ 75116 #028-34-2003 **AN** *012
ZIMMER, Judith Ann. ■ 75137 #048-14-1985 L1986 **AN ORS** *020

DYESS AIR FORCE BASE – TAYLOR

BURTON, Bret D. ■ 79607 #048-13-1993 L1995 **PD** *020 †55
GELLER, Schuyler Keith. 697 HOSPITAL RD, 7TH MDG 79607 #017-20-1976 L1976 **GPM PD** *020 †20,55,70
KISER, Henry Jackson. 697 HOSPITAL RD, 7TH MDG 79607 #021-06-1995 L1996 **NEP** *020 †20
KLAZYNSKI, Philip Thos. 697 HOSPITAL RD 79607 #047-06-1979 L1987 **MDM GS** *030 †85

EAGLE LAKE – COLORADO

BORNSTEIN, Leonard Edward. 610 S AUSTIN RD, RICE MEDICAL ASSOCIATES 77434 #005-12-1962 L1996 **GP** *071 †18

EAGLE PASS – MAVERICK

ALEXANDER, Billy Don. 350 S ADAMS ST 78852 #048-02-1967 L1968 **ORS NS** *020 †40
BARBOZA-SOSA, Jorge A. 1951 N VETERANS BLVD 78852 #048-13-1994 L1995 **IM** *020
BATRES, Arturo Enrique. 393 S MONROE ST 78852 #048-12-1961 L1961 **FM IMG** *020 †18 ‡
BEAVAN, Reginald A, Jr. PO BOX 4020 78853 #048-02-1953 L1953 **IM CD** *071
DE LOS SANTOS, Ramiro. PO BOX 4430 78853 #649-02-1969 L1979 **OBG** *075
DE LOS SANTOS, Ricardo. 2198 E GARRISON ST, PEDIATRIC SPEC RURAL HLTH 78852 #649-02-1973 L1979 **PD** *020
DE LOS SANTOS-MARTINEZ, R. 1955 E MAIN ST 78852 #649-02-1976 L1989 **IM PUD** *020
DURAN, Roberto A. 229 N ADAMS ST 78852 #649-30-1990 L1995 **FM** *020 †18
FLORES, Heriberto J. 617 E RIO GRANDE ST 78852 #042-01-1954 L1973 **GS R** *071
FOWLER, James Hugh. ■ 78852 #004-01-1975 L1980 **OTO FPS** *020 †45
GARCIA, Eric Luis. 1975 N VETERANS BLVD, STE 6 78852 #042-01-1984 L1994 **GS** *020
GONZALES, Frank H, III. 290 JEFFERSON ST 78852 #048-13-1978 L1979 **GP** *020
HERNANDEZ, Carlos Enrique. 1975 N VETERANS BLVD STE 6 78852 #264-04-1988 L1997 **OBG** *020
HERNANDEZ, Erika. ■ 78852 #048-13-2006 **GS** *012
HERNANDEZ-ORTIZ, Eliezer. 1975 N VETERANS BLVD, STE 5 78852 #649-01-1972 L1994 **PD** *020
LAL, Prem. ■ 78852 #209-02-1966 L1999 **PD GP** *071 †55
LASTRACHE, Jacobo. 1975 N VETERANS BLVD 78852 #649-45-1988 L1993 **PD** *020 †55
MANI, Palani Subra. 2525 N VETERANS BLVD 78852 #495-04-1964 L1979 **GS** *020 †85
MANI, Ranga Subra. 2139 RICKS DR 78852 #495-16-1968 L1982 **PD NPM** *020
MARQUINEZ, Robert V. 2525 N VETERANS BLVD 78852 #048-10-1990 L2000 **IM** *020
MITTAL, Manjula. 2605 ZACATECAS DR 78852 #495-67-1966 L1978 **PTH** *020
MONTEMAYOR, Raul Martin. 670 E MAIN ST 78852 #021-01-1937 L1937 **OS** *020
NWANNA, Romanus Ochiabuto. 350 S ADAMS ST 78852 #035-19-1986 L2004 **OBG** *020 †30 ‡
PERRY, Luis Gutierrez. 2149 EL INDIO HWY 78852 #649-30-1980 L1985 **GS VS** *020 †85
RIOS, Luis Gonzalez. #649-01-1953 **ORS OS** *020
RODRIGUEZ, Carlos E. 708 S BIBB AVE 78852 #048-12-1980 L1980 **OPH** *020
SAIGAL, Navid. 3065 MEGAN ST 78852 #704-02-1990 L1998 **IM NEP** *020 †20
SALCEDO, Jorge. ■ 78852 #264-09-1991 L2002 **DR** *020
SETH, Suresh Chandra. 341 N CEYLON ST 78852 #495-45-1967 L1987 **IM END** *020 †20
SORIANO, Carlos Cruz. 2151 EL INDIO HWY 78852 #748-01-1964 L1978 **GS HS** *020
TREVINO-GUERRA, Hector R. 2176 E GARRISON ST, STE C 78852 #649-02-1988 L2000 **FM SME** *020 †18 ‡
URUETA, Guillermo. 1975 N VETERANS BLVD, STE 5 78852 #737-06-1988 L1998 **PD** *020 †55
USGAONKER, Rajanikant S. 330 NUECES ST 78852 #495-17-1959 L1981 **IM** *020
VALDES, Armando Valdes. ■ 78853 #649-02-1960 **GP** *020
VALDES-GARCIA, Victoriano. ■ 78853 #649-14-1979 L1991 **IM** *020

EAST BERNARD – WHARTON

FARRELL, Robert Michael. 1007 PHILLIPS CIR 77435 #048-02-1978 L1978 **FM** *020 †18
PENICK, Larry Hollis. 703 MORRIS ST 77435 #016-43-1983 L1984 **FM EM** *020 †18

EASTLAND – EASTLAND

ALEXANDER, Billy Bob. 400 W PLUMMER ST 76448 #048-02-1955 L1955 **GP GS** *071
COX, Jamie W. 400 W PLUMMER ST 76448 #048-15-2001 L2002 **FM** *020 †18
MATTHEWS, Robert C. 400 W PLUMMER ST 76448 #048-02-1983 L1983 **FM** *020 †18
MICKISH, Alan Bart. 400 W PLUMMER ST 76448 #048-13-1973 L1973 **EM** *020
TREADWELL, Mose A, Jr. 400 W PLUMMER ST 76448 #048-02-1946 L1946 **GP GS** *020

EDCOUCH – HIDALGO

RAMAMURTHY, Mangala M. 1200 SANTA ROSA AVE 78538 #495-59-1980 L1993 **IM** *020 †20

EDDY – MCLENNAN

CHUMAK, Bogdan Alberto. 1175 WESTGATE I RD 76524 #649-14-1980 L1986 **EM FM** *020 †18
TROMPLER, Vicky Ann. ■ 76524 #011-02-1979 L1982 **LM EM** *062 †18,16

EDINBURG – HIDALGO

AJERO, Corazon Glady. 316 CONQUEST STE 300, BEHAVIOR CENTER 78539 #748-01-1992 L2005 **PD** *020 †55
ALANBARI, Amer. 502 S CLOSNER BLVD 78539 #875-01-1982 L2004 **IM** *020 †20
ALBUSTAMY, Abdulrahman M. 502 S CLOSNER BLVD 78539 #875-01-1983 L1998 **END** *020 †20
ALEMAN, Miguel G. 1110 W 10TH AVE 78539 #649-02-1960 L1970 **GP** *020
AL-HAMMAMI, Ghassan. 5416 S JACKSON RD STE A 78539 #875-02-1979 L2000 **DR IM** *020,80
ALTER, Donald E. 5501 S MCCOLL RD 78539 #048-02-1984 L1985 **AN** *020 †05
ALVAREZ, Oscar A. 5525 DOCTORS DR 78539 #264-16-1983 L1994 **GE** *020 †20
AMARO, Rafael. 5525 DOCTORS DR STE A 78539 #737-06-1992 L2001 **GE HEP** *020 †20
AMEGIN, George P. 2005 W UNIVERSITY DR 78539 #028-78-1970, ▲ L1990 **OPH** *020
ARANGO, Dario. 5407 S MCCOLL RD 78539 #649-02-1986 L1997 **FM** *020
ARANGO, Maria Catalina. 5407 S MCCOLL RD 78539 #649-02-1987 L1998 **FM** *020 †18
ASISTORES, Marilyn Sayson. 1615 S CLOSNER BLVD, EDINBURG MEDIPLEX SUITE F 78539 #748-07-1979 L1992 **FM** *020 †20
BARREDA, Raul, Jr. 4302 S SUGAR RD, STE 201 78539 #048-02-2001 L2006 **GS** *020
BAUER, Andrew Wm. 5501 S MCCOLL RD 78539 #041-02-1990 L1994 **DR** *020 †80
BELANDRES, Rosie Cadiz. 3145 W ALBERTA RD 78539 #748-02-1984 L1998 **PD** *020
BROWN, Jetta Marie. 1019 TANGLEWOOD DR 78539 #048-02-1977 L1977 **FM** *020
CABEZA, Hector Manuel. ■ 78539 #048-02-1993 L2007 **PD** *100 †55
CABRERA, Ernest Edward. 1102 W TRENTON RD 78539 #649-14-1970 L1973 **EM** *020 †18
CALLAHAN, John W. ■ 78539 #056-06-1951 L1964 **FM** *071

CAPELLA, Jose J. 2302 CORNERSTONE BLVD, CONSULTANTS 78539 #042-02-1988 L1992 **AN** *020 †05
CARDENAS, Carlos J. 5525 DOCTORS DR 78539 #048-02-1985 L1986 **GE IM** *020 †20
CHACON, Ingrid Maria. 5525 DOCTORS DR 78539 #270-01-1995 L2005 **GE** *020 †20
CHET, Myo. ■ 78539 #209-02-1976 L2003 **PD** *020 †55
CHOWDHURY, Tajul I M S. 2637 CORNERSTONE BLVD 78539 #160-05-1975 L1984 **PME** *020
CORTES-HERNANDEZ, Oscar. 1615 S CLOSNER BLVD, STE A 78539 #649-02-1978 L1992 **FM OBS** *020 †18
CRUZ GONZALEZ, Edgar V. 4302 S SUGAR RD, STE 201 78539 #308-04-1985 L1997 **CCS** *020 †85
DE CANDIA, Michael Thos. 5325 S MCCOLL RD, SUITE A STONERIDGE PLZ 78539 #033-06-1991 L1997 **DR** *020 †80
DE JUANA, Carlos Publio. 2123 CORNERSTONE BLVD 78539 #649-01-1970 L1975 **U** *020 †95
DE LA CRUZ, Celedonio. 704 W SCHUNIOR ST 78541 #649-04-1973 L1980 **EM** *020
DOUGLAS, Argelia. 5323 S MCCOLL RD STE 102 78539 #649-01-1986 L1995 **PD** *020 †55
ESTRELLADO, Johnny F. 802 E UNIVERSITY DR, STE B 78539 #748-01-1991 L1997 **PD** *020 †55
FAROLAN, Lorenzo Madamba. 2616 CORNERSTONE BLVD 78539 #748-02-1967 L1979 **DR OS** *020 †80
FLORES, Luis Felipe. 4302 S SUGAR RD STE 210 78539 #429-01-1973 L2005 **GS** *020
GALINDO, Eugenio G. 2717 MICHAEL ANGELO 78539 #649-30-1984 L1992 **ON IM** *020 †20
GALLO, Albert Edward. ■ 78541 #048-12-1958 L1958 **P** *071 †75
GARCIA, Carlos. 4302 S SUGAR RD, STE 201 78539 #649-30-1984 L1996 **GS** *020 †85
GARCIA, Chris Tim. 2112 JOY ST 78539 #026-04-1980 L1996 **AN** *020 †05
GARCIA, Oscar Jimmy. 2717 MICHAEL ANGELO 78539 #649-02-1984 L1994 **RO** *040 †80
GARZA, Alison S Hensel. 2514 W FREDDY GONZALEZ DR 78539 #048-16-1989 L1990 **FM OBG** *020 †18
GARZA, Ben L. 1200 S 10TH AVE 78539 #048-02-1969 L1969 **FM** *020
GARZA, Gumaro. 502 S CLOSNER BLVD 78539 #005-18-1975 L1977 **IM** *020 †20
GARZA, Jaime Rene. 2821 MICHAEL ANGELO 78539 #048-02-1985 L1987 **OBG** *020 †30
GARZA, Marin. 1901 S 24TH AVE 78539 #005-18-1975 L1976 **P** *020
GARZA, Martin. 2506 W FREDDY GONZALEZ DR 78539 #018-03-1997 L2000 **PD** *020 †55
GARZA, Omar C. 304 S JACKSON RD 78539 #048-12-1965 L1965 **GP** *071
GARZA-MONTALVO, Ayda. 2821 MICHAEL ANGELO, STE 400 78539 #048-12-1991 L1992 **OBG** *020 †30
GELMAN, Lawrence R. 5501 S MCCOLL RD 78539 #056-06-1982 L1984 **AN CCA** *020 †05
GENOVESE, Robert J. 5215 S MCCOLL RD 78539 #561-01-1964 L1976 **GP** *020
GONZALEZ, Alberto P. 2717 CORNERSTONE BLVD 78539 #649-02-1983 L1992 **PTH** *020 †50
GUERRA, Rebecca M. 2821 MICHAEL ANGELO, STE 400 78539 #048-16-1996 L1997 **OBG** *020 †30
GUILLEN, Eduardo. 802 E UNIVERSITY DR STE B 78539 #737-06-1991 L1996 **PD** *020 †55
GUTIERREZ, Alberto H, Jr. 122 W CHAMPION ST, GUTIERREZ MEDICAL CTR 78539 #048-02-1966 L1966 **FM D** *020 †18
GUTIERREZ, Daniel. 1901 S 24TH AVE 78539 #649-38-1986 L1991 **CHP** *020 †75
HADDAD, Victor T. 4302 S SUGAR RD, STE 201 78539 #649-01-1974 L1981 **GS** *020 †85
HALL, Donald Lee. 5505 S MCCOLL RD 78539 #005-06-1961 L1992 **AN OM** *020
HIDALGO, Humberto Arturo. 303 CONQUEST 78539 #021-01-1981 L1984 **PDP PD** *020 †55
HUQ, Mahfuzul. 514 S CLOSNER BLVD 78539 #160-02-1979 L2004 **PD** *020 †55
IKONDU, Desmond Okey. 2502 W TRENTON ST 78539 #048-13-1997 L2001 **FM** *020 †18 ‡
IRIZARRY, Ricardo Enrique. 5115 S MCCOLL RD, TROPICAL TEXAS CENTER FOR 78539 #042-02-2001 L2005 **P** *020 †75
JEAN-MICHEL, Marie J. 922 S CLOSNER BLVD, AVE 78539 #649-14-1977 L2001 **PD** *020 †55
JELINEK, Michael Thos. 3108 CENTER POINT DR, INFECTIOUS DISEASE SPECIAL 78539 #308-07-1982 L1990 **ID IM** *020 †20
JIMENEZ, Jaime A. 615 E UNIVERSITY DR, UNIVERSITY PEDIATRICS 78539 #737-06-1991 L1996 **PD** *020 †55
JIMENEZ, Juan F. 4302 S SUGAR RD, STE 201 78539 #649-01-1970 L1975 **GS** *020 †85
JORDAN, Belinda V. 2621 W TRENTON RD 78539 #048-13-1999 L2001 **FM** *020 †18
KATO, Haruna. ■ 78541 #048-04-2008 *012
KIRKHAM, Peter F. 2302 CORNERSTONE BLVD, CONSULTANTS 78539 #048-14-1994 L2001 **AN** *020 †05
KUMAR, Sajal. 4717 S SUGAR RD STE H, ANDREW LEVINE, MD., PA 78539 #495-36-1997 L2007 **NEP IM** *020 †20
LASTRA, Manuel P. 2614 CORNERSTONE BLVD 78539 #748-08-1966 L1972 **NM R** *020
LEVINE, Andrew. 4717 S SUGAR RD STE H 78539 #649-38-1983 L1997 **IM** *020 †20
LIESER, Mark Jeffrey. 4302 S SUGAR RD, STE 201 78539 #033-45-1989 L1998 **GS** *020 †85
LINDEMANN, John Arthur. 333 W FREDDY GONZALEZ DR, BLDG E 78539 #016-42-1989 L1990 **FM** *020 †18
LOSADA, Yoalveth. ■ 78541 #264-01-1973 L2001 *020
MAC DOWELL, Frederick, Jr. ■ 78539 #035-09-1953 L1966 **PS** *071 †85,65
MACKIE, Eugene Scott. 2709 CORNERSTONE BLVD 78539 #030-05-1979 L1980 **OTO** *020 †45
MANRIQUE DE LARA, Carlos. 2518 W TRENTON RD 78539 #649-52-1988 L1997 **OPH** *020 †35
MARQUEZ, Raul A. 2402 CORNERSTONE BLVD 78539 #649-31-1980 L1992 **ORS OSM** *020
MARTINEZ, Agustin. 910 S CLOSNER BLVD, WOMENS CLINIC OF SOUTH TEX 78539 #011-02-1991 L1994 **OBG** *020 †30
MARTINEZ, Matthew B. ■ 78539 #048-04-2003 *100
MARTINEZ, Michael Joel. ■ 78539 #048-01-2008 *012
MARTINEZ, Milagros A. ■ 78539 #048-02-2008 *012
MARTINEZ, Raul Armando. 1120 S CLOSNER BLVD 78539 #649-01-1965 L1974 **IM CD** *020 †20
MARTINEZ, Ricardo D. 5513 DOCTORS DR, RIO GRANDE SURGICAL ASSOCI 78539 #048-13-1988 L1993 **GS** *020 †85
MATAR, Raymundo G. 5501 S MCCOLL RD 78539 #649-02-1986 L1991 **AN CCP** *020 †55,05
MC LEAN, Daniel Patrick. 4302 S SUGAR RD, STE 201 78539 #048-13-1993 L1999 **GS** *020 †85
MEDRANO, Carlos J. 304 S JACKSON RD 78539 #048-13-1998 L1999 **FM** *020 †18
MEEDE, John, Jr. 505 S CLOSNER BLVD 78539 #649-01-1971 L1972 **GP** *071
MEHKRI, Imtiaz A. 505 S CLOSNER BLVD 78539 #495-33-1985 L1990 **OPH** *072 †35
MEHKRI, Sumyra. 502 S CLOSNER BLVD 78539 #495-51-1989 L1999 **FM** *020 †18
MEJIA SILVERIO, Luis E. 5525 DOCTORS DR 78539 #308-04-1995 L2001 **GE** *020 †20
MERCADO, Allan M. 316 CONQUEST, STE 300 78539 #649-02-1991 L1996 **PD** *020 †55
MERCADO, Steven A. 1203 E EL CIBOLO RD, LOPEZ STATE JAIL 78541 #048-12-1993 L1995 **IM** *020
MEZA, Fausto Santiago. ■ 78539 #048-02-2000 L2007 **IMG** *020
MEZA, Michele Marie. ■ 78539 #048-02-2001 L2007 **NPM** *100 †55
MITCHELL, Lionel Stacy. 3115 CENTER POINT DR 78539 #047-07-1992 L1999 **ORS** *020 †40
MOHAMED, Naif Carlos. 2821 MICHAEL ANGELO, STE 400 78539 #649-02-1971 L1980 **OBG GO** *020 †30

MYERS, Frances Alethea. 300 N 86TH ST 78541 #010-03-1984 L1988 **FM** *020 †18
NAHAS, Osama B. 2505 W TRENTON 78539 #875-01-1980 L1995 **IM OM** *020 †70,20
OCHOA, Ricardo. 2703 W TRENTON RD 78539 #048-02-1999 L2003 **PD** *020 †55
OGUNLANA, Victor O A. 922 S CLOSNER BLVD, EDINBURG PEDIATRIC NETWORK 78539 #690-01-1987 L2000 **PD** *020 †55
ORFANOS, Gerardo A. 4302 S SUGAR RD STE 2 78539 #649-02-1984 L2001 **PD** *020 †55
ORTEGON, Jorge A. 2821 MICHAEL ANGELO, STE 300 78539 #649-02-1987 L1998 **RHU** *020 †20
OTERO, Fernando Javier. 910 S CLOSNER BLVD 78539 #035-46-1998 L2002 **OBG** *020 †30
PALACIOS, Melva. 505 S CLOSNER BLVD 78539 #048-13-2002 L2003 **FM** *020 †18
PALOMO, Guillermo Ernesto. ■ 78539 #341-01-1955 L1990 **P** *020
PEACOCK, Lester W. 2227 CORNERSTONE BLVD 78539 #048-14-1993 L1994 **OPH** *020 †35
PEREZ, Fred Laurel, Jr. 5009 S MCCOLL RD 78539 #649-30-1977 L1980 **ORS** *020
PEREZ, Guillermo Ramon. 4302 S SUGAR RD, STE 201 78539 #308-04-1991 L2003 **GS** *100 †85
QUARAISHI, Rafath H. 2616 CORNERSTONE BLVD 78539 #035-47-1987 L1999 **DR** *020
QURAISHI, Aadam Zaheer. 2616 CORNERSTONE BLVD 78539 #035-48-1987 L1996 **DR** *020 †80
RABOT, Leda Mae Tabamo. 316 CONQUEST, STE 300 78539 #748-02-2002 L2007 **PD** *020 †55
RAVINDRA, Veeramachaneni. 2117 CORNERSTONE BLVD 78539 #495-09-1995 L2004 **PTH** *020 †50
RIOS, Luis Manuel, Jr. 2101 CORNERSTONE BLVD 78539 #048-12-1990 L1991 **PS HS** *020 †65,85
RODRIGUEZ DELIMA, Maria E. 2302 CORNERSTONE BLVD 78539 #048-02-1998 L2002 **OBG** *020
ROJAS, Rogelio Eduardo. 2601 CORNERSTONE BLVD 78539 #649-02-1994 L2004 **RHU** *020 †20
ROMERO, Maria Luisa A. 3108 CENTER POINT DR 78539 #748-02-1993 L2000 **ID** *020 †20
RUEDA, Jaime Javier. ■ 78539 #048-04-2007 **MPD** *012
RUIZ, Roberto C, Jr. 815 S CLOSNER BLVD 78539 #035-19-1978 L1979 **FM** *020
RYAN, John Joseph. 1615 S CLOSNER BLVD, STE A 78539 #649-02-1990 L2005 **FM** *020 †18 ‡
SALINAS, Fulgencio P. 1102 W TRENTON RD 78539 #649-27-1979 L1984 **PTH** *020
SANCHEZ, Arlene T. 2123 S JACKSON RD 78539 #748-11-1987 L1998 **PD** *020 †55
SANCHEZ-GONZALEZ, Miguel. ■ 78539 #649-19-1978 L1997 **PTH** *020 †50
SIDHARTHAN, Arandapallam. 1102 W TRENTON ST 78539 #495-37-1968 L1985 **R** *020
SILBERMAN, Herschl B. 520 S CLOSNER BLVD, VALLEY CARDIOLOGY PA 78539 #737-06-1987 L1996 **CD IM** *020 †20
STEWART, Roy Ben. 4302 S SUGAR RD 78539 #048-12-1954 L1954 **GS** *071
SUBRAHMANYAM, Behara. 5525 DOCTORS DR 78539 #495-11-1971 L1982 **GE** *071 †20
TAMESIS-DIMAYUGA, Grace P. 2208 PARK PLACE DR 78539 #748-02-1990 L1996 **AI** *012 †55 ‡
TCHOKOEV, Vassil Vastanov. 4701 S SUGAR RD 78539 #198-01-1961 L1979 **N FM** *020
THOMPSON, Hilda Yvonne. 2117 CORNERSTONE BLVD 78539 #048-02-1987 L1989 **PTH** *020 †50
TIJERINA, Orlando S. 5501 S MCCOLL RD 78539 #649-02-1979 L2001 **AN** *020
TIONGSON, Corrinna T. 2606 CORNERSTONE BLVD 78539 #748-02-1990 L1996 **PD** *020 †55
TIU, Jimmy Liu. 802 E UNIVERSITY DR, STE B 78539 #748-01-1991 L1996 **PD** *020 †55
TURLAPATI, Krishna Mohan. 1102 W TRENTON RD 78539 #495-65-1982 L1995 **CCP** *020 †55
UCHOA, Denise Pacheco D M. 922 S CLOSNER BLVD STE C 78539 #187-72-1983 L2002 **PD** *020
UDOR, Inemesit Ephraim. 920 S CLOSNER BLVD 78539 #690-10-1984 L1998 **PD** *020 †55
VALDES, Jesus Hector. 4302 S SUGAR RD STE 201 78539 #649-04-1985 L1995 **GS ORS** *020 †85
VANN, Vincent R. 2128 MICHAEL ANGELO DR, RETINA SPEC OF RGV, PA 78539 #011-02-1994 L1998 **OPH** *020 †35
VILLARREAL, E Linda. 1501 S CLOSNER BLVD 78539 #649-35-1984 L1989 **IM** *020
VILLARREAL, Leonel C. 5517 DOCTORS DR 78539 #649-02-1984 L1998 **IM** *020 †20
VITKO, Roger James. 2123 CORNERSTONE BLVD 78539 #026-04-1967 L1973 **U NEP** *020 †95
WIERNIK, Paola Debora. 5323 S MCCOLL RD STE 102 78539 #132-01-1990 L1997 **PD** *020 †55
WILLIAMS, Kenneth Egbert. 5017 S MCCOLL RD STE D, SPECTRUM ANES & PAIN SVCS 78539 #041-13-1992 L1995 **AN** *020 †05
WINKFIELD, Letreise D. 4705 S SUGAR RD 78539 #048-13-1995 L1998 **FM** *020 †18
WONG, Antonio. 122 W CHAMPION ST 78539 #737-06-1992 L1996 **IM** *020 †20
YARRITU, Rolando. 1200 S 10TH AVE 78539 #048-04-1980 L1980 **FM** *020 †18
YAZJI, Monzer Hassan. 502 S CLOSNER BLVD 78539 #875-01-1989 L1996 **IM PUD** *020 †20
ZAMORA-QUEZADA, Jorge C. 2601 CORNERSTONE BLVD 78539 #649-03-1980 L1991 **RHU END** *020 †20
ZAVALA-SPINETTI, Livania. 4709 S JACKSON RD 78539 #935-01-1994 L2000 **PDI** *020 †55
ZORRILLA, Mirta Caridad. 4937 S JACKSON RD 78539 #737-01-1980 L1991 **P** *020

EDNA — JACKSON

AIMONE, Roy Jos. ■ 77957 #869-05-1957 L1958 **OBG** *020
HERNANDEZ, Eugenio. 1013A S WELLS ST 77957 #264-03-1962 L1972 **FM PTH** *020 †50
HERNANDEZ, Eugenio J. 1013A S WELLS ST 77957 #036-07-1992 L1993 **GE** *020 †20
JUDGE, Deepinder Kaur. 1013A S WELLS ST 77957 #495-03-1993 L1999 **PD** *020 †55
JUDGE, Satinder Pal Singh. 1013A S WELLS ST 77957 #495-45-1987 L1996 **AN** *020 †05
OU, Paul K. 1013 S WELLS ST 77957 #048-14-1994 L1995 **FM** *040 †18
SEHORN, Samuel Leroy. 1013 S WELLS ST 77957 #036-05-1972 L1999 **TS VS** *020 †85,90
SHAH, Naveed Hussain. 1013 S WELLS ST 77957 #704-02-1962 L1978 **EM GS** *020
WILLIAMS, Wilford S, Jr. 1013 S WELLS ST 77957 #016-06-1979 L1980 **FM** *020 †18

EL CAMPO — WHARTON

CASSIN, Stanley Bernard P. 305 SANDY CORNER RD 77437 #065-01-1963 L1978 **FM EM** *020 †18
COCHRAN, Ronald Jay. 303 SANDY CORNER RD 77437 #048-02-1978 L1978 **D** *020 †15
DUQUE, Carlos D. 305 SANDY CORNER RD 77437 #319-01-1974 L1994 **FM** *020 †18
ERWIN, Melissa A Kainer. ■ 77437 #048-14-2000 L2004 **D** *020 †15
GOERIG, Brian J. 305 SANDY CORNER RD, STE 120 77437 #048-15-2002 L2003 **FM FSM** *020 †20
HAND, William Arnold, Jr. 305 SANDY CORNER RD, STE 120 77437 #048-04-1976 L1976 **FM** *020 †18

JOHNSON, Patrick Earl. 305 SANDY CORNER RD 77437 #422-01-1983 L1986 **FM EM** *020 †18
MAYEN-SAPRISSA, Myriam E. ■ 77437 #341-01-1982 *075
MELBURN, Colleen M. ■ 77437 #028-03-1961 L1967 **AN LM** *020 †05
PHILIP, Suresh. 1602 N MECHANIC ST 77437 #023-01-1988 L1994 **CD** *020 †20
RAJU, Palivela P. 305 SANDY CORNER RD 77437 #495-58-1970 L1981 **OTO** *020 †45
SARKAR, Ankur. 305 SANDY CORNER RD 77437 #495-08-1986 L1997 **IM** *020 †20
SCOTT, Ted Chas. 305 SANDY CORNER RD, STE 230 77437 #048-12-1973 L1973 **GS EM** *020 †20
TORIO, Rulour C. 1602 N MECHANIC ST 77437 #748-20-1988 L1995 **IM** *020 †20
VU, Philip M. 1602 N MECHANIC ST 77437 #048-02-1995 L1996 **IM** *020 †20
WINCHELL, Susan Annette. 1602 N MECHANIC ST 77437 #048-04-1985 L1987 **PD** *020 †55
WISSINGER, John Frederick. 1602 N MECHANIC ST 77437 #048-02-1982 L1983 **IM** *020 †20
ZORRILLA, Carlos Danl. 1602 N MECHANIC ST 77437 #737-06-1971 L1979 **CD IM** *020 †20

EL INDIO — MAVERICK

BRAITHWAITE, John Ronald. PO BOX 145 78860 #005-15-1969 L1970 **PTH** *020 †50

EL LAGO — HARRIS

SPECTOR, Bernard. ■ 77586 #035-09-1949 L1975 **P** *071 †75

EL PASO — EL PASO

AALURI, Srinivasa Reddy. 10555 VISTA DEL SOL DR, STE 115 79925 #495-57-1991 L2004 **FM** *020
ABDULKARIM, Saba A. 4882 LOS REALES DR 79912 #528-04-1986 **P** *012
ABEDIN, Zainul. 1701 N LEE TREVINO DR 79936 #495-19-1968 L1979 **ICE CD** *020 †20
ABEL, Michael Philip. 5005 N PIEDRAS ST, ATTN:CREDENTIAL OFFICR 79920 #023-12-1997 L1998 **RHU** *020 †20
ABOUD, Ambrose. 1900 N OREGON ST, SUIE 500 79902 #539-04-1970 L1981 **ON IM** *020 †20
ABRESCH, Robert Jos. 2022 MURCHISON DR STE 104 79902 #048-02-1973 L1973 **RHU IM** *020 †20
ACEVEDO, Jose R. ■ 79925 #275-01-1953 L1976 *071
ACOSTA, Jorge. 10201 GATEWAY BLVD W, STE 110 79925 #048-02-1998 L2003 **GS** *020 †85
ACOSTA, Manuel L. 1700 N OREGON ST, STE 610 79902 #649-01-1969 L1973 **GS** *020
ACOSTA CORRALES, Luis D. 1201 N MESA ST, STE E 79902 #649-01-1971 L1993 **N OS** *020
ADAMS, Bruce Douglas. ■ 79912 #023-12-1990 L1992 **EM** *020 †20,16
AEMISEGGER, Kyle Dean. ■ 79934 #039-01-2007 **TY** *012
AESCHBACH, Walter. 4800 ALBERTA AVE, DEPT PSYCHIATRY 79905 #869-07-1972 L1973 **P** *020 †75
AFZAL, Khalid Imran. 4800 ALBERTA AVE, TX TECH U HLTH SCI CTR 79905 #704-22-1995 L2006 **P** *012
AGARWAL, Ajai. 3022 TRAWOOD DR, STE A 79936 #495-34-1983 L1996 **FM** *020 †18
AGUILAR, Oscar M. 101 RIM RD STE 300 79902 #649-52-1994 L1999 **CD IC** *020 †20
AGUIRRE-HAUCHBAUM, S. 4800 ALBERTA AVE, TX TECH UNIV HLTH SCIENCE 79905 #649-27-1971 L1979 **P** *020 †75
AGUNANNE, Enoch Echezona. 8030 N LOOP DR 79915 #690-04-1992 L2003 **IM** *020 †20
AHMAD, Samir Abed. 3022 TRAWOOD DR, STE A 79936 #198-02-1989 L2000 **IM IMG** *020 †20
AHMAD, Shakeel. ■ 79912 #704-02-1992 **IM** *100
AHMED, Gaafar Taha. 9200 VISCOUNT BLVD # 232 79925 #915-02-1980 **P** *100
AHMED, Zulfiqar. 2295 TRAWOOD DR STE B 79935 #704-02-1985 L2002 **IM IMG** *020 †20
AHMETI, Mentor. 4800 ALBERTA AVE, TX TECH UNIV HLTH SCI CTR 79905 #120-01-2003 **GS** *012
AIKINS, Noble L. 9155 DYER ST, # 125 79924 #005-06-1991 L2001 **AN** *020 †05
AKINJAIYEJU, Akintoluwa A. 10755 KENWORTHY ST 79924 #759-07-1994 L2004 **PD** *020 †55
ALARCON, Victor M R. ■ 79935 #649-33-1981 L1982 **EM FM** *071
ALCALA, Patricia H. 125 W HAGUE RD STE 260 79902 #048-13-1979 L1979 **OBG** *020
ALEKSANDER, Bernardo G. 5308 EL PASO DR 79905 #132-01-1959 L1978 **P** *072 †75
ALEXANDER, Warren Leeric. 5005 N PIEDRAS ST, WILLIAM BEAUMONT ARMY MED 79920 #051-01-1997 L1998 **HO** *020 †20
ALHAJ, Hayat Ahmad. 5005 N PIEDRAS ST 79920 #913-89-1989 **IM** *012
ALICEA, Jose Antonio. 3100 N LEE TREVINO DR 79936 #024-05-1987 L1994 **ORS** *020 †40
ALLEN, Mariano. 10301 GATEWAY BLVD W, PATHOLOGY DEPARTMENT 79925 #649-05-1964 L1977 **PTH** *020 †50 ‡
ALLEN-CLAPP, Luz Del Carm. ■ 79902 #649-33-1995 L2002 **PD** *020
ALMANZA, Emma. 1612 ARLINGTON ST 79915 #048-15-2000 L2003 **EM** *020
ALMQUIST, Sam Fehring. 5005 N PIEDRAS ST, ARMY MEDICAL 79920 #023-12-2007 **TY** *012
AL-NAJJAR, Mohammed R. 3233 N MESA ST STE 301 79902 #875-02-1994 L2000 **IM** *020 †20
ALONZO, Jesus N. 8061 ALAMEDA AVE 79915 #048-15-1992 L1994 **FM** *020 †18
ALOST, Thomas E, Jr. 10525 VISTA DEL SOL DR, STE 206 79925 #021-05-1984 L1989 **ORS** *020 †40
ALPARD, Allan Jos. 9398 VISCOUNT BLVD, STE 2 79925 #048-02-1968 L1968 **PD** *020 †55
ALPERN, Louis M. 4171 N MESA ST, STE 100 79902 #024-01-1974 L1974 **OPH** *020 †35
ALTENBERG, Leo Lawrence. ■ 79913 #048-15-1984 L1985 **FM EM** *020 †18
ALVA, Jose D. 2311 N MESA ST STE G 79902 #649-03-1962 L1968 **PD NPM** *020 †55
ALVAREZ, Dionicio Manuel. 125 W HAGUE RD, STE 570 79902 #649-33-1981 L1986 **NEP IM** *020
ALVAREZ, George Hill. 217 BLACKER AVE 79902 #048-14-2001 L2006 **AN** *100
ALVAREZ, Roman D. 1900 N OREGON ST, STE 312 79902 #847-05-1980 L1984 **PD NPM** *020 †55
ALVAREZ, Sergio Raul. 2311 N MESA ST STE E 79902 #649-01-1972 L1977 **CD CCM** *020
ALVILLAR, Ricardo Ernesto. ■ 79936 #048-04-1979 L1980 **RHU IM** *020 †20
ALY, Fatima Fidahusayn Mu. 4800 ALBERTA AVE, DEPARTMENT OF PEDIATRICS 79905 #917-08-1985 L2008 **PD** *012
AMBAT, Ma. Teresa Cosa. 4800 ALBERTA AVE, DEPARTMENT OF PEDIATRICS 79905 #748-01-1994 L2006 **PD** *100 †55
AMORO, Florence Bosibori. ■ 79938 #048-15-2007 **PD** *012
ANAYA, Alice Marie. 5005 N PIEDRAS ST, WILLIAM BEAUMONT AMC 79920 #048-13-1999 L2002 **NEP IM** *020 †20
ANCHONDO, Adolfo Noe. 1900 N OREGON ST, STE 610 79902 #649-27-1996 L2004 **PCC** *020 †20

ANDERSON, James Roy. 2001 N OREGON ST 79902 #048-02-1964 L1964 AN *071 †05

ANDERSON, James S. 5400 SUNCREST DR, STE B3 79912 #048-12-1989 L1990 AN CCA *020 †05

ANGLIN, Walter M. ■ 79904 #038-06-1949 L1949 P *071

ANISZEWSKI, Jaroslaw. 1201 E SCHUSTER AVE, BLDG 7 79902 #759-03-1991 L2006 END *020 †20

ANNABI, Hani M. 615 E SCHUSTER AVE, STE 7 79902 #847-01-1971 L1996 U *020 †95

ANNABI, Jeffrey Hani. 1625 MEDICAL CENTER ST 79902 #042-02-2000 L2004 AN *020

ANNABI, Michael Hani. 4930 OSBORNE DR 79922 #654-01-1987 L1998 IM *020 †20

ANTONIO, Melvin Quetulio. ■ 79912 #748-08-1965 L1975 AM GS *020 †70

ANTONY, Savarimuthusosai. ■ 79912 #220-01-1984 L1999 MPD *100

ANTONY, Suresh J. 1205 N OREGON ST 79902 #495-99-1983 L1996 ID IM *020 †20

ANTOWAN, Cenan Michael. 4800 ALBERTA AVE 79905 #528-01-1988 L2005 PD *020 †55

APPLEBAUM, Bruce Jeffrey. 1700 CURIE DR STE 1500, EL PASO SURGICAL ASSO 79902 #048-15-1991 L1993 GS *020 †85

APPLEBAUM, Richard Myron. 2001 N OREGON ST 79902 #028-34-1957 L1978 PD *020 †55

ARAGON, Lorenzo B. 9849 KENWORTHY ST, FAMILY PRACTICE 79924 #682-01-1984 L1996 FM *020 †18

ARANDA, Diego Aguilar. 1801 N OREGON ST 79902 #847-04-1955 L1969 PS *072

ARANDA, Manuel, Jr. 10301 GATEWAY BLVD W 79925 #005-02-1994 L1996 EM *020

ARANGO, Carmen Perez. 643 S MESA HILLS DR 79912 #042-01-1985 L1991 DR *020 †80

ARANGO, Jorge J. 7300 REMCON CIR, STE 300 79912 #042-01-1985 L1992 OTO HNS *020 †45

ARAT, Arsavir. ■ 79912 #902-01-1956 L1964 ORS *071

ARBONA, Jaime. 5915 SILVER SPRINGS DR, BLDG 3B 79912 #429-01-1972 L1993 CHP P *020 †75

ARBONA, Miriam Ivanova. 5915 SILVER SPRINGS DR, BLDG3B 79912 #429-01-1975 *074

ARDESHIRI, Farnaz. 4800 ALBERTA AVE 79905 #517-01-1996 L2005 PD *100

ARELLANO, Paul P. 1700 CURIE DR, STE 1500 79902 #048-15-1999 L2004 GS *020 †85

ARENAL, Luis Torres. ■ 79912 #649-01-1958 L1974 GP EM *071

ARGUEDAS VARGAS, Marcela. 4800 ALBERTA AVE 79905 #270-04-2002 FP *012

ARISTIZABAL ORTIZ, Andres. 4800 ALBERTA AVE 79905 #264-18-1996 PD *012

ARMENDARIZ, Eugenio M. 1900 N OREGON STE 610 79902 #649-27-1981 L1993 CCM IM *020 †20

ARREDONDO, Cecil Rene. 1221 N COTTON ST 79902 #048-02-1969 L1969 ORS *020 †40

ARROYAVE RAMIREZ, Ana Mar. 9849 KENWORTHY ST, TEXAS TECH UNIV-FAMILY PRA 79924 #264-05-1996 FM *100

ARZABALA, Alejandro, Jr. 4800 ALBERTA AVE 79905 #649-33-2004 IM *012

ASCHERL, Martin Vincent. 4800 ALBERTA AVE 79905 #048-12-1977 L1977 ON HEM *040 †20

ASGHARIAN, Robert B. ■ 79904 #048-15-1998 L2000 OBG *030

ASIAIN, Maria De Lourdes. 2905 N STANTON ST 79902 #649-33-2001 L2007 PD *020 †55

AUGUST, Brian James. 2022 MURCHISON DR, STE 104 79902 #048-15-1990 L1991 PM *020 †60

AUN, Jose. 125 W HAGUE RD, STE 220 79902 #048-14-1993 L1994 OBG *020 †30

AUNG, Mark Kyaw. 10510 MONTWOOD DR, STE A,B & C 79935 #209-01-1967 L1979 HEM ON *071 †20

AUTREY, Walter C, Jr. 41 79925 #048-12-1951 L1951 FM CD *071 †18

AVILA-HERNANDEZ, Jorge. 5959 GATEWAY BLVD W, STE 120 79925 #649-27-1973 L1982 AN GS *020 †05

AVILES CEVASCO, Fernando. 4800 ALBERTA AVE 79905 #682-03-2000 FP *012

AYALA MOLINA, Jose Ruben. 4800 ALBERTA AVE 79905 #341-01-1994 FP *012

AYO-ZAMBRANA, Luis A. 2001 N OREGON ST 79902 #176-01-1973 L1978 NPM PD *020 †55

AYUB, Pablo. 5301 ALAMEDA AVE 79905 #028-34-1948 L1950 GP *071

AZARCON-SAMONTE, Patricia. 11544 VISTA DEL SOL DR, BLDG A 79936 #748-02-1989 L1996 PD *020 †55

BACA, Antonio. ■ 79936 #048-15-2008 *012

BACA, Jose J, II. 5959 GATEWAY BLVD W, STE 120 79925 #048-14-1989 L1991 AN *020

BACKUS, Julia Antonia. ■ 79902 #407-32-1953 L1970 PTH *071 †50

BAGG, Michael Damien. 2201 N STANTON ST, PROVIDENCE MEDICAL PLAZA 79902 #048-15-1989 L1990 U *020 †95

BAGG, Raymond James. 4800 ALBERTA AVE 79905 #035-09-1958 L1976 ORS OP *020 †40

BAIDA, Nicolas. 4800 ALBERTA AVE 79905 #649-03-1979 L1993 P *020 †75

BAJAJ, Veeresh. 4800 ALBERTA AVE 79905 #495-34-2000 P *012

BAKER, Ronald F. 1418B GEORGE DIETER DR, PRIMARY HEALTHCARE PHYSICI 79936 #048-13-1998 L2002 FM *020 †18

BAKER, Thomas Patrick. 5005 N PIEDRAS ST, WBAMC PATHOLOGY DEPT 79920 #056-05-1988 L2004 PTH *020 †50

BAKIR, Ali Mohammed. 1131 MONTANA AVE 79902 #528-01-1969 L1978 IM END *020 †20

BAKR, Aboubakr Abdelaziz. 1400 N EL PASO ST, STE C 79902 #915-02-1966 L1982 N *020 †75

BALOCH, Nadeem Akbar. TX TECH U HLTH SCI CTR-PED 79905 #704-16-1990 PD *100

BANERJEE, Rahul Roy. 4800 ALBERTA AVE, TEXAS TECH HSC-DEPT OF ORT 79905 #016-02-1999 L2005 ORS ‡

BANTA, Bruce Edward. ■ 79932 #048-02-1962 L1962 PD *071 †55

BARAHONA, Jose A. 11355 MONTWOOD DR 79936 #649-14-1987 L1996 IM *020 †20

BARFIELD, Russell Lee. 5005 N PIEDRAS ST 79920 #023-12-2001 L2007 DR *100 †80

BARNEY, Pedro A. 4800 ALBERTA AVE, DEPT OF PEDIATRICS 79905 #016-11-2007 PD *012

BARRON, Elaine Mowinski. 5005 N PIEDRAS ST 79920 #649-33-1984 L1989 IM *020 †20

BARRON, Julio Ramirez. ■ 79912 #649-01-1951 L1959 OM *071

BARRON, Miguel Luis. 3030 GATEWAY BLVD E 79905 #649-01-1966 L1974 VS TS *020

BAUSAS, Wilma I. 700 S OCHOA ST 79907 #748-01-1982 L1996 PD *020 †55

BAZIL-MIESES, Osvaldo D. 6974 GATEWAY BLVD E, STE F 79915 #308-02-1978 L1997 IM *020

BEAN, James W. 1755 CURIE DR, STE B 79902 #048-02-1982 L1983 ORS *020 †40

BECKER, Marion A Schanz. 444 EXECUTIVE CENTER BLVD, STE 238 79902 #024-07-1967 L1975 DR *071 †80

BECKER, Philip Andrew. 6320 GATEWAY BLVD E 79905 #035-03-1955 L1974 OM GS *071 †85

BECKER, Philip Andrew, Jr. 5400 SUNCREST DR, STE B3 79912 #048-13-1979 L1979 AN *020 †05

BEERS, Jeffrey Robert. ■ 79912 #048-15-2008 *012

BELGRAVE, Genevieve M. 2311 N MESA ST, STE E 79902 #033-05-1981 L1984 IM *020 †20

BELK, Elbert Marion, III. ■ 79912 #001-06-1996 L2008 FM *020 †18

BELL, Robert Randolph. 3100 N LEE TREVINO DR 79936 #028-46-1989 L1995 ORS *020 †40 ‡

BELMONT, Philip James, Jr. ■ 79912 #048-06-1995 L1998 ORS *020 †40

BELOCURA, M L Jonnalyn R. 11345 MONTWOOD DR, STE A1 79936 #748-17-1989 L2001 FM *020 †18

BELTRAN, Armando. 2022 MURCHISON DR STE 100 79902 #649-27-1983 L1987 HEM ON *020

BELTRAN, Celina Renee. ■ 79922 #048-15-2008 *012

BENDER, Arianna. 125 W HAGUE RD, STE 310 79902 #473-01-1991 L1999 IM *020 †20

BENIQUEZ-NIEVES, Enrique. 5005 N PIEDRAS ST, WILLIAM BEAUMONT AMC 79920 #847-06-1981 L2002 GE *020 †20

BENITEZ, Adolfo Leon. 4800 ALBERTA AVE 79905 #264-05-1999 FP *012

BENJAMIN, Robert Emmanuel. ■ 79912 #041-12-1996 L1999 CCS *020 †85

BENSON, Peter Jon. 5005 N PIEDRAS ST STOP 3, WILLIAM BEAUMONT AMC 79920 #023-12-1993 L1995 EM *016

BENTLEY, Karl Coblenz. 4800 ALBERTA AVE, TEXAS TECH UNIVERSITY HSC 79905 #048-15-2007 TY *012

BERDEJA, Cesar E. 5400 SUNCREST DR, STE B3 79912 #649-03-1975 L1982 AN *020

BERDEJA, Cesar Ruben. ■ 79936 #042-02-2008 *012

BEREHANE, Yohannes Tesfay. ■ 79913 #166-01-2004 *100

BERRIOS, Gaston Alberto. 9849 KENWORTHY ST, TEXAS TECH UNIV-FAMILY PRA 79924 #682-01-1997 L2007 FP *012

BERRY, William Randolph. ■ 79912 #048-04-1965 L1965 DR *020 †80,28

BERUMEN, Kenneth A. 1625 MEDICAL CENTER ST 79902 #048-12-1998 L1999 EM *020

BHATIA, Nidhi. ■ 79924 #010-01-2003 L2005 IM *020 †20

BIEGANOWSKI, Arthur C, Jr. ■ 79924 #024-07-1969 L1978 N P *075 †75

BILBAO, Jorge Eduardo. 1300 MURCHISON DR 79902 #649-27-1982 L1986 PTH *020 †50

BIRO, George. 1100 N STANTON ST 707 79902 #649-14-1975 L1980 FM *020 †18

BLACK, Gordon L. ■ 79912 #048-02-1943 L1943 R NM *071 †80,28

BLACKBURN, Arthur Bertram. 1733 CURIE DR, STE 300 79902 #048-15-1983 L1983 OBG *020 †30

BLAKELY, Gail Elizabeth. 3800 N MESA ST, STE 331 79902 #007-02-1974 L1982 R *020 †80

BLANC, Oscar Herrera. 11615 PELLICANO DR 79936 #016-11-1990 L1994 PD *020

BLANCHETT, Leo Mose, III. ■ 79912 #048-13-1976 L1976 IM *100 †20

BLANDON, Pedro Antonio. 4800 ALBERTA AVE, TTUHSC-INTR MED/NEPHROLOGY 79905 #649-03-1995 L2002 IM NEP *020 †20

BLANK, Elizabeth Ann. 5005 N PIEDRAS ST, MED CTR 79920 #041-14-2006 ORS *012

BLESIUS, Cornelius Klaus. 2100 E YANDELL DR 79903 #407-05-1964 L1968 IM GPM *020

BLOCK, Harold Morris, Jr. 804 COREY CREEK DR 79912 #048-04-1963 L1963 PTH CLP *020 †50

BLUMENFELD, Daniel Gray. 2001 N OREGON ST 79902 #048-12-1991 L1992 OPH *020 †35

BLUMENFELD, Ronald Joel. 10470 VISTA DEL SOL DR, STE 110 79902 #016-11-1961 L1968 OTO HNS *020 †45

BLUMENFELD, Scott Alan. 1625 MEDICAL CENTER ST, SIERRA MED CTR 79902 #048-12-1989 L1990 DR *020 †80

BLUNK, Dan Isbell. 4800 ALBERTA AVE, DEPARTMENT OF NEUROPSYCHIA 79905 #048-02-1974 L1977 P *020 †75

BOBADILLA, Melissa S. 1527 BROWN ST STE C, # C 79902 #748-02-1989 L1995 END IM *020 †20

BOE, Nicholas Olav. ■ 79930 #025-12-2006 L2008 IM *012

BOGGIANO, Humberto F. 1200 BOGGIANO DR 79912 #737-01-1956 L1973 ORS *071 †40

BOMAN, Darius Ardeshir. 4815 ALAMEDA AVE 79905 #496-38-1972 L1979 PD *100 †50

BOONE, James Byron, Jr. 1720 MURCHISON DR, THE EL PASO ORTHOPAEDIC SU 79902 #048-13-1973 L1973 ORS *020 †40

BOONE, James Byron, III. 1296 MORGAN MARIE ST 79936 #048-15-2000 L2003 AN *020 †05

BOONE, Michael K. 1700 MURCHISON DR 79902 #048-13-1987 L1988 PM *020 †60

BORNSTEIN, Natalie T. 2260 TRAWOOD DR 79935 #048-13-1981 L1982 IM *020 †20

BORREGO, Alejandro. ■ 79904 #649-33-1997 FP *012

BORREGO, Ed Jose. 5750 N MESA ST 79912 #048-13-2000 L2005 P *020

BORREGO, Manuel. 9849 KENWORTHY ST, TEXAS TECH UNIV-FAMILY PRA 79924 #649-33-1998 L2006 FM *020

BOUSHKA, Wm Matthias, Jr. 6065 MONTANA AVE, DIAGNOSTIC OUTPATIENT IMAG 79925 #048-13-1990 L1992 DR *020 †80

BRANDL, Christine A. 125 W HAGUE RD STE 260, RIO GRANDE OB/GYN 79902 #048-15-1996 L1998 OBG *020 †30

BRANDON, Jeffrey Lee. 1100 N STANTON ST, STE 304 79902 #040-02-1970 L1978 ORS *020 †40

BRIGHT, Kevin Edward. 1600 MEDICAL CENTER ST, SOUTHWEST EAR NOSE & 79902 #016-43-1989 L1999 OTO *020 †45

BRIGHT, Tamis Marie. 4800 ALBERTA AVE, DEPT OF INTERNAL MEDICINE 79905 #016-43-1989 L1996 END *040 †20

BRILL, Elizabeth Lumsden. 5005 N PIEDRAS ST, STOP 36 79920 #016-02-1994 L1997 OBG *020 †30

BRIONES, David Francisco. 4800 ALBERTA AVE 79905 #048-02-1971 L1971 P SME *040 †75

BROOKER, O Ronnie. 1418 GEORGE DIETER DR, STE B-1 79936 #048-12-1973 L1975 IM *020 †20

BROWER, Mary Carrizal. 9398 VISCOUNT BLVD, STE 2 79925 #048-02-1985 L1986 PD *020 †55

BROWER, Richard David. 4800 ALBERTA AVE, TX. TECH HEALTH SCIENES CE 79905 #048-02-1985 L1986 N CN *020 †15

BROWN, Courtney G. 1201 E SCHUSTER AVE STE 3A 79902 #048-12-1998 L2003 GS *020 †85

BROWN, James M. 10710 GATEWAY BLVD N, STE B5 # 185 79924 #048-15-1994 L1995 EM *020 †16

BROWN, Joseph, III. 4800 ALBERTA AVE, TTU SCHOOL OF MEDICINE 79905 #012-05-1961 L1983 PD *071 †55

BRUNO, Felice. 1600 MEDICAL CENTER ST, EL PASO SOUTHWESTERN 79902 #561-20-1970 L1977 TS VS *020

BRYAN, E David. ■ 79902 #048-14-1991 L1992 EM *020 †16

BUCHANAN, Judith Renee. ■ 79912 #048-15-2008 L2008 *012

BUCHWALD KOLINSKI, David. 4171 N MESA ST, STE B100 79902 #649-14-1966 L1974 NEP IM *020

BUDIG, Ira Adolph, Jr. ■ 79912 #016-11-1946 L1950 PD CHN *071 †55

BULLOCH, Edgar M. 4800 ALBERTA AVE 79905 #048-14-2006 OBG *012

BURGUETE, Leopoldo H. ■ 79932 #649-01-1969 *012

BURNETTE, Solange Pitarel. 4800 ALBERTA AVE 79905 #187-11-1989 FP *012

BUSCEMI, Jon Howard. ■ 79912 #034-01-1968 L1993 N *040 †75

BUTLER, Jack M. 4800 ALBERTA AVE - GME, ATTN; ELIZABETH MAESE 79905 #048-15-1999 L2001 EM *020 †20

BUXTON, Brian Fowell. 1250 E CLIFF DR STE 4A 79902 #143-02-1962 L1976 TS *020

CABALLERO, Yuri. 2022 MURCHISON DR, STE 104 79902 #737-06-1987 L1995 IM *020 †20

CABALUNA, Marifi Urieta. 4800 ALBERTA AVE, DEPARTMENT OF PEDIATRICS 79905 #748-29-1991 L2008 PD *012

CABANISS, Tex P, Jr. ■ 79911 #048-14-1992 L1993 EM *012 †18

CABRERA, Marlyn Lucia. 4800 ALBERTA AVE, PEDIATRICS DEPARTMENT 79905 #649-31-1991 L1999 PD *020

CAJAS, Oswaldo Cabrera. 1721 N LEE TREVINO DR 79936 #319-03-1967 L1975 FM *020

CALDERONI, Henry H. 1721 N LEE TREVINO DR, EASTSIDE MEDICAL CARE 79936 #649-03-1976 L1980 **FM EM** *020 †18

CALDERON-QUINTANILLA, M. 1717 BROWN ST STE 3 79902 #649-19-1963 L1974 **OPH** *020 †35

CALERO, George. 10301 GATEWAY BLVD W, COLUMBIA E MED CTR 79925 #042-02-1983 L1985 **IM EM** *020 †20

CALIANGA, Cesar R. 7806 GATEWAY BLVD E 79915 #748-02-1984 L1995 **IM ID** *020 †20

CAMARENA GONZALEZ, Omar. 9001 CASHEW DR 79907 #649-33-1985 L1998 **IM** *020 †20

CAMPAGNA, Leopoldo Jose. 4800 ALBERTA AVE, TEXAS TECH UNIV HEALTH SCI 79905 #935-01-1995 **IM** *012

CAMPOS, Antonio. 125 W HAGUE RD, C/O SERGIO ALVAREZMD 79902 #649-27-1969 L1983 **GS** *050 †85

CANALES, Roberto. 1733 CURIE DR STE 103 79902 #649-01-1972 L1980 **PD HO** *020 †55

CANESSA, Juan F. 2001 N OREGON ST 79902 #924-01-1958 L1969 **AN** *071

CANTU, Adex Heberto. ■ 79903 #649-02-1957 L1969 **IMG P** *072

CAPELLA, Jorge Edwin. 5005 N PIEDRAS ST, DEPT MED/GME 79920 #042-02-2006 **IM** *012

CAPEN, David Alan. ■ 79902 #038-40-1966 L1971 **ORS AM** *020 †40

CARBALLO, Juan Eduardo. 4800 ALBERTA AVE, TX TECH U HLTH SCI CTR 79905 #275-01-1989 **PD** *100

CARCAMO, Benjamin. 125 W HAGUE RD, STE 500 79902 #429-01-1980 L1992 **PHO** *020 †55

CARDENAS, Maria Guadalupe. 1400 GEORGE DIETER DR, # 170 79936 #649-14-1981 L1993 **IM** *020 †20

CARDENTEY, Luis Alberto. 9849 KENWORTHY ST, TEXAS TECH UNIV-FAMILY PRA 79924 #275-01-1988 **FP** *012

CARIGMA, Cecilia Santiago. 4800 ALBERTA AVE, TX TECH U HLTH SCI CTR 79905 #748-29-1990 **PD** *012

CARNES, David M. 1221 N COTTON ST 79902 #048-02-1952 L1952 **GP** *072

CARR, Brian James. ■ 79912 #023-12-2004 L2006 **ORS** *012

CARRILLO, Raul. ■ 79932 #048-14-2004 L2006 **EM** *020

CARTY, Brian Matthew. 1221 E SAN ANTONIO AVE, STE 1 79901 #036-08-1984 L1998 **IM** *020 †20 ‡

CASAS, John Paul. 5005 N PIEDRAS ST, WM BEAUMONT ARMY MED CTR 79920 #042-02-2007 **GS** *012

CASAVANTES, Louis. 914 N STANTON ST 79902 #048-04-1951 L1951 **GS OBG** *075

CASILLAS, Arturo. 1400 N EL PASO ST STE E 79902 #649-23-1982 L1994 **PD** *020 †55

CASNER, Paul Ross. 4800 ALBERTA AVE 79905 #035-09-1980 L1984 **IM** *020 †20

CASTANEDA, Gino Antonio S. 4800 ALBERTA AVE 79905 #748-31-2005 **GS** *012

CASTANEDA, Robert Dillow. 10301 GATEWAY BLVD W, MEDICAL STAFF SERVICES 79925 #048-02-1985 L1986 **AN AM** *020 †05

CASTELLON, Danelia Salaza. 4800 ALBERTA AVE 79905 #913-22-1997 **FP** *012

CASTILLO, Gregorio Joel A. 10501 VISTA DEL SOL DR, STE 200 79925 #748-01-1990 L1995 **IM** *020 †20

CASTILLO, Mauricio Jose. 4800 ALBERTA AVE, TX TECH U HLTH SCI CTR 79905 #682-01-1991 L2007 **FM** *100 †18

CASTILLO-BOONE, Jose O. ■ 79922 #649-02-1961 L1973 **GS** *071 †85

CASTRO, Jesus Arturo. 10460 VISTA DEL SOL DR, STE 100 79925 #649-27-1974 L1983 **RO** *020

CASTRO GARCIA, Jose Anton. 4800 ALBERTA AVE, TX TECH U HLTH SCI CTR 79905 #649-04-2004 **GS** *012

CASTROLONDONO, Jairo De J. 5005 N PIEDRAS ST 79920 #665-03-2005 L2007 **IM** *012

CAVARETTA, Chas Patrick. ■ 79912 #035-09-1961 L1967 **PM RHU** *071 †20

CAZARES, Jose. 2311 N MESA ST, STE A 79902 #649-01-1962 L1971 **OBG GS** *020

CEPEDA, Eduardo. 1625 MEDICAL CENTER ST 79902 #649-01-1969 L1977 **IM PUD** *020 †20

CERVANTES, Sandra M. ■ 79936 #048-14-2007 **OBG** *012

CHALUPA, Orest A. 5001 N PIEDRAS ST, HEALTH CARE CENTER 79930 #649-33-1990 L1996 **FM** *020 †18

CHAMBERLIN, Brett Marar. ■ 79912 #048-16-2007 *012

CHAMBERLIN, Santha M. 4800 ALBERTA AVE, DEPT PD 79905 #825-01-1975 L1992 **PD** *020 †55

CHAMBERLIN, William Mann. 4800 ALBERTA AVE, INTERNAL MED 79905 #024-07-1975 L1992 **GE IM** *020 †20

CHAN, James Ying-Hong. ■ 79902 #385-02-1963 L1971 **U** *071 †95

CHANDLER, Nathan Chase. ■ 79912 #024-07-2002 L2008 **DR** *100 †80

CHANDRA, Phool. ■ 79932 #495-05-1954 L1980 **AN** *071 †05

CHASE, Danielle Heather. ■ 79912 #051-01-2007 **EM** *012

CHAUDHURI, Kallol. 4800 ALBERTA AVE, DEPT. OF ANESTHESIOLOGY 79905 #495-39-1981 L1994 **AN PD** *020 †05

CHAUDHURI, Swapna M. 4800 ALBERTA AVE, DEPT OF ANESTHESIOLOGY 79905 #495-32-1982 L1994 **AN** *020 †05

CHAUVET AGUILAR, Marcelo. 4800 ALBERTA AVE, TEXAS TECH UNIV HEALTH SCI 79905 #649-30-2003 **IM** *012

CHAVARRIA, Myrna. 1900 N OREGON ST, STE 312 79902 #649-48-1999 L2008 **NPM** *012 †55

CHAVEZ, Alfonso. 1225 E CLIFF DR 79902 #649-27-1970 L1977 **NEP IM** *020

CHAVEZ, Alfredo. 1620 N MESA ST 79902 #649-33-1991 L1998 **GE** *020 †20

CHAVEZ, Angelica. 401 ELAINE PL 79915 #048-13-1998 L2001 **CCP** *100 †55

CHAVEZ, Edna Melina. ■ 79938 #018-03-2007 **EM** *012

CHAVEZ, Eva P. 1517 N MESA ST 79902 #048-13-1999 L2005 **PS** *020 †85 ‡

CHAVEZ, Pedro Sergio H. 1517 N MESA ST 79902 #649-27-1970 L1976 **PS** *020 †85,65

CHAVEZ-RICE, Eugenio. ■ 79904 #649-01-1969 L1979 **P N** *020 †75

CHEA, John N N. ■ 79913 #306-01-1993 *100

CHEE, Benson. 6065 MONTANA AVE STE C9 79925 #048-13-2003 L2004 **GP** *020

CHEN, Yin-Ting. 5005 N PIEDRAS ST, ARMY MEDICAL 79920 #023-12-2007 **TY** *012

CHESBRO, Byron Harold. 1901 GRANDVIEW AVE, CENTER-WEST 79902 #035-15-1976 L1981 **ON IM** *020 †20

CHHEDA, Sadhana. 1900 N OREGON ST, STE 601 79902 #690-01-1987 L1993 **NPM PD** *020 †55

CHILDS, Megan Laura. ■ 79912 #023-12-2005 L2007 **IM** *012

CHITTI, Srinivas Reddy. 10555 VISTA DEL SOL DR, STE 115 79925 #495-57-1991 L2000 **NEP** *020 †20

CHIZEN, Robert Paul. 1742 N ZARAGOZA RD, STE A 79936 #065-06-1985 L1991 **EM FM** *020 †18

CHONG, Claude Yuk-Leung. ■ 79932 #462-01-1958 L1977 **RO** *071 †80

CHOUBKHA, Nora. 4800 ALBERTA AVE 79905 #125-01-1992 **P** *012

CHRISTENSON, Robert Allan. 4800 ALBERTA AVE, DEPT PEDS 79905 #005-12-1980 L1994 **PDE PD** *020 †55

CIBLEY, Leonard J. ■ 79912 #024-05-1952 L1953 **OBG** *071 †30

CIUBUC, Radu. 1626 MEDICAL CENTER DR, STE 503 79902 #781-01-1984 L1996 **IMG** *020 †20

CLAPP, Benjamin L. 1700 N OREGON ST STE 500 79902 #048-15-2000 L2005 **GS** *020 ‡

COBIELLA, Jose Antonio. 4800 ALBERTA AVE 79905 #275-10-1995 L2008 **IM** *012

COHEN, Arthur Allen. 5407 N MESA ST 79912 #048-04-1966 L1966 **PUD IM** *071 †20

COHEN, Richard. 1625 MEDICAL CENTER ST 79902 #048-12-1966 L1966 **R** *062 †80

COLATO ZAVALETA, Luis Ram. 4800 ALBERTA AVE, TEXAS TECH UNIV HEALTH SCI 79905 #341-03-2003 **IM** *012

COLEMAN, Scott K. 1733 CURIE DR, STE 210 79902 #048-15-1994 L1996 **PD** *020 †55 ‡

COLON, Rosa Ivelisse. ■ 79912 #042-03-1987 L1989 **FM** *020 †18

COLON-DORDAL, Ramon A. 10201 GATEWAY BLVD W # 200 79925 #042-02-1991 L1994 **PD GP** *020

COMBS, Jan Arvin. 5005 N PIEDRAS ST, ORTHOPEDIC SURG 79920 #023-12-1988 L1989 **ORS HS** *100 †40

COMPEAN, Jessica M. 1011 E ROBINSON AVE 79902 #048-15-2001 L2004 **AN** *100 †05

COMPTON, Michael Dennis. 2001 N OREGON ST, EMERGENCY DEPARTMENT 79902 #034-01-1973 L1977 **EM PD** *020 †55,16

CONTIN, Juan U. 11155 GATEWAY BLVD W, CENTER 79935 #308-01-1960 L1971 **PTH GP** *020 †50

CONTRERAS, Arturo. 1700 MURCHISON DR, STE 104 79902 #649-27-1973 L1977 **AN** *020 †05

CONTRERAS, Elizabeth. ■ 79915 #649-33-1982 L2005 **CCP PD** *020 †55

COOK, Kathy A. 6090 SURETY DR, STE 412 79905 #048-14-2002 L2004 **EM** *020 †16

CORDOVA-HOY, Annette M. 4815 ALAMEDA AVE 79905 #048-12-1988 L1990 **OBG** *020 †30

CORRAL, Carlos Humberto. 1700 N OREGON ST, STE 750 79902 #048-12-1981 L1982 **TS** *020 †85,90

CORRAL, Javier. 2200 N YARBROUGH DR, # B319 79925 #005-11-1984 L1986 **HO IM** *020 †20

CORTES, Erasto. 1207 N OREGON ST 79902 #649-33-1987 L1993 **PCC** *020 †20

CORTEZ, Pilarita G. 2001 N OREGON ST 79902 #748-02-1970 L1983 **PD GP** *020 †55

COSTA, Henry. 7806 GATEWAY BLVD E STE 1 79915 #748-02-1984 L1996 **ID IM** *020 †20

COTA, Francisco J. 1700 MURCHISON DR STE 201 79902 #649-30-1980 L1992 **P** *020 †75

COURTINES, Michel R. 5005 N PIEDRAS ST, WILLIAM BEAUMONT AMC 79920 #035-09-1998 L1999 **NM** *020 †20,28

COVARRUBIAS, Eduardo. 1570 LOMALAND DR, STE A 79935 #649-04-1980 L1991 **PD** *020

COWAN, Christopher Mccall. ■ 79934 #045-01-2006 L2008 **IM** *012

CRABB, Benjamin E. ■ 79904 #048-14-2005 L2007 **EM** *012

CRAIG, Christopher Hardin. 650 BELVIDERE ST 79912 #048-12-2002 L2005 **PD** *020 †55

CRAIG, Greer Wilson. ■ 79912 #048-13-1973 L1973 **OBG** *020 †30

CRAIGE, Branch, III. 1700 CURIE DR STE 5800 79902 #021-01-1976 L1980 **IM** *020 †20

CRESPO, Jose Raul. 4171 N MESA ST 79902 #016-45-1995 L1997 **EM** *020 †16

CROCKER, Patty Jane. 1755 CURIE DR, EL PASO SPECIALTY HOSPITAL 79902 #034-01-1991 L1993 **EM** *040 †16

CROMER, Barry Lee. 3100 N LEE TREVINO DR 79936 #005-18-1989 L2000 **ORS** *020 †40

CROSSEN, John Jacob. 10301 GATEWAY BLVD W, DEL SOL MC 79925 #016-43-1957 L1963 **R** *071 †80

CROUSE, Steven Keith. 1700 CURIE DR STE 4100 79902 #007-02-1967 L1973 **N** *020 †75 ‡

CRUZ, Cristina. 619 E CROSBY AVE 79902 #649-33-1985 L1996 **CHP** *020 †75

CRUZ, Kariktan Epifania G. 4800 ALBERTA AVE 79905 #748-02-2001 **PD** *012

CUADRAS, Conrado Eduardo. 10301 GATEWAY BLVD W 79925 #847-04-1964 L1973 **DR** *071

CUETTER, Albert C. 4800 ALBERTA AVE, SCIENCES CENTER 79905 #264-02-1964 L1972 **N OS** *020 †75 ‡

CUNNINGHAM, Thomas. 5959 GATEWAY BLVD W #120 79925 #649-14-1970 L1975 **AN** *020

CURBELO, Niurka. 4800 ALBERTA AVE 79905 #275-01-1989 **PD** *012

CUTHBERTSON, Jeremy R. 1625 MEDICAL CENTER ST 79902 #048-12-1999 L2003 **OPH** *020 †35

DAAB, Leo Joseph. ■ 79912 #011-03-2005 L2007 **GS** *012

DADOYAN, Talin A. ■ 79912 #605-01-1996 L2007 **P** *020 †75

DANDADE, Pritam Bajirao. 615 E SCHUSTER AVE STE 8 79902 #495-19-1962 L1973 **TS GS** *020 †85,90

DANDADE, Usha Pritam. 615 E SCHUSTER AVE STE 8 79902 #495-34-1965 L1980 **OBG** *020 †30

DANIELL, Walter Chas. 125 W HAGUE RD STE 260 79902 #007-02-1970 L1980 **OBG** *020 †30

DAVALOS, Antonio C. 10201 GATEWAY BLVD W, STE 410 79925 #649-27-1971 L1979 **GS** *020

DAVIS, Harry Earl, II. 4800 ALBERTA AVE, TEXAS TECH UNIV HSC 79905 #055-01-1966 L1996 **IM** *040 †20

DAVIS, Kurt Glenn. 5005 N PIEDRAS ST, ATTN: CREDENTIAL OFFICE 79920 #047-20-1997 L1998 **CRS** *020 †85

DAVIS, Patricia Marie. 9870 GATEWAY BLVD N, STE B7 79924 #048-02-1979 L1979 **OBG** *020 †30

DAVITT, Wm Francis, III. 8815 DYER ST STE 130 79904 #048-15-1979 L1996 **OPH OS** *020 †35

DE ANDA-ORTIZ, Jose Luis. ■ 79912 #649-23-1994 L2002 **PD** *020

DEAS, Bernard Winford, Jr. 5005 N PIEDRAS ST 79920 #045-01-1971 L1989 **IM ON** *040

DEBBA, Bachir. ■ 79912 #125-04-1990 L2007 **P** *100

DE JESUS, Eduardo Miguel. 7878 GATEWAY BLVD E, STE 102 79915 #308-02-1989 L1995 **IM** *020 †20

DE LA GARZA, Albert. 5005 N PIEDRAS ST, WBAMC 79920 #003-01-2000 L2006 **EM** *020 †16

DE LA ROSA, Antonio I. 4800 ALBERTA AVE 79905 #048-02-2000 L2002 **OBG** *020

DE LA ROSA, Jose Manuel. 4800 ALBERTA AVE, STE 101 79905 #048-15-1984 L1985 **PD** *040 †55

DELASCASAS, Luis E. ■ 79912 #737-06-1989 L2005 **PCP** *020 †50

DEL MORAL, Cecilia Ivonne. 5005 N PIEDRAS ST, MEDICINE CLINIC 79920 #649-14-1977 L1999 **IM** *020 †20

DE LUCA, Michael A. 910 E REDD RD STE K 79912 #561-01-1967 L1979 **ORS DR** *020

DELUCA, Michael J. 1700 CURIE DR, STE 3400 79902 #422-01-1992 L1999 **CD** *020 †20

DEMAREST, Harry Wm. ■ 79935 #016-06-1947 L1953 **OBG** *071 †30

DEMICK, Diane S. 1600 MEDICAL CENTER ST, STE 120 79902 #048-15-1995 L2001 **NEP** *020 †20

DENT, Tommy Edward. 1800 N MESA ST 79902 #048-02-1962 L1962 **AN** *071 †05

DE SANTOS, Christina. 125 W HAGUE RD, STE 260 79902 #048-14-2000 L2002 **OBG** *020

DESHIELDS, Denise Lavette. 3901 STATE JAIL RD 79938 #024-07-1986 L1989 **GP** *020

DE VARGAS, Cecilia C. 2701 E YANDELL DR 79903 #264-05-1966 L1978 **CHP P** *020 †75

DEZEE, Kent John. 5005 N PIEDRAS ST, ATTN: CREDENTIAL OFFICE 79920 #038-40-1997 L1997 **IM** *020 †20

DIAS, Cesar Augusto. ■ 79912 #048-15-2005 L2007 **EM** *012

DIAZ, Jose Arnaldo. 5959 GATEWAY BLVD W, STE 120 79925 #039-05-1985 L1986 **AN** *020 †05

DIAZ, Jose L. 10400 VISTA DEL SOL DR, STE 103 79925 #042-01-1990 L2003 **OAR** *020 †40

DIAZ, Marco. ■ 79902 #034-01-2006 **FP** *012

■ = Address Information Privacy Protected

DIAZ, Victor Alfredo, Jr. 1700 CURIE DR STE 1500 79902 #049-01-1978 L1980 **GS** *020 †85

DIAZ-BALL, Fernando L. ■ 79904 #042-01-1959 L1988 **U GS** *020 †95

DIAZ COPETE, Jaime A. 1301 E RIVER AVE, PATH PROFSNL SERV 79902 #264-04-1964 L1978 **PTH DMP** *020 †50

DIAZ DIAZ, Francisco Javi. 9849 KENWORTHY ST, TEXAS TECH UNIV-FAMILY PRA 79924 #270-01-1999 **FP** *012

DIAZ-LUNA, Hector Juan. 1601 N BROWN ST, EL PASO ACCESS CENTER 79902 #649-14-1979 L1992 **OS GS** *020 †85

DIAZ RODRIGUEZ, Gonzalo A. 1900 N OREGON ST STE 610 79902 #649-14-1977 L1983 **PUD IM** *020 †20

DIAZ RUEDA, Jesus Rafael. 4800 ALBERTA AVE 79905 #649-27-1997 **TY** *012

DIAZ VIDAL, Jose Maria E. 1700 N OREGON ST STE 750 79902 #132-01-1977 L1987 **TS** *020 †85,90

DIAZ-VOGT, Josefina A. 10525 VISTA DEL SOL DR, STE 200 79925 #715-01-1983 L1999 **P** *020 †75

DICKASON, John Marcus. 1700 MURCHISON DR, SURGERY GROUP 79902 #048-02-1976 L1976 **ORS** *020 †40

DICKEY, Billy Melvin. 1625 MEDICAL CENTER ST 79902 #048-02-1960 L1960 **U** *071 †95

DIDIA, Silvia Claudia. 4800 ALBERTA AVE, DEPT IM 79905 #132-01-1989 L2006 **IM** *020 †20

DI DONNA, Michael L. 1755 CURIE DR, STE B 79902 #048-12-1997 L1999 **HS** *020 †40

DI NARDO-EKERY, Dorothy M. 4815 ALAMEDA AVE 79905 #035-19-1963 L1965 **CD IM** *071 †20

DITTERT, Henry Marion, Jr. ■ 79936 #048-02-1962 L1964 **FM** *071 †18

DITTMER, Joshua Eugene. ■ 79912 #024-05-1999 L2000 **P** *020 †75

DO, Thong Huy. 4800 ALBERTA AVE, TEXAS TECH UNIV HEALTH SCI 79905 #942-01-1995 L2002 **IM** *012

DOAN, Janie T. ■ 79912 #048-15-2008 *012

DOBBINS, Tiffani. ■ 79912 #016-11-1999 **PD** *020

DOBRIN, David Jay. 1250 E CLIFF DR STE 2A 79902 #016-01-1981 L1987 **CD IM** *020 †20

DOKA, David Scott. 10460 VISTA DEL SL DR #300 79925 #048-04-1977 L1977 **OPH** *020 †35

DOKA, Julie Christine. 10201 GATEWAY BLVD W # 140 79925 #048-04-1977 L1977 **AN** *020 †05

DOLINER, Adir. 4800 ALBERTA AVE, DEPT EM 79905 #048-15-2006 **EM** *012

DON, Rita Louisa. ■ 79912 #048-12-1954 L1954 **AI** *071 †03

DONG, Ling. 4800 ALBERTA AVE, TEXAS TECH UNIV HEALTH SCI 79905 #243-65-1982 **IM** *100

DORSEY, David Allen. ■ 79912 #023-12-1995 L1996 **PCC** *100 †20

DORSEY, Deanna Lynn. 5400 SUNCREST DR, STE B3 79912 #036-05-1989 L2000 **AN** *020 †05

DOUGHERTY, Steve Hudson. 4800 ALBERTA AVE 79905 #005-02-1973 L1982 **GS ID** *020 †85

DROUTSAS, Louis John. 1900 N OREGON ST, STE 508 79902 #048-02-1958 L1958 **DR** *020 †80

DUARDO GUERRA, Yamirka. 4800 ALBERTA AVE 79905 #275-01-1999 **FP** *012

DUDREY, Ellen Frances. 10301 GATEWAY BLVD W 79925 #048-13-1982 L1983 **PTH PCP** *020 †50

DUONG, Huyen Vu. ■ 79912 #048-15-2008 *012

DUPICHE, Christine Anne. ■ 79912 #048-14-2004 L2007 **IM** *100 †20

DU PLESSIS, Leon Philip. 1700 CURIE DR STE 4800 79902 #067-01-1961 L1969 **GE IM** *071 †20

DURAN PEREZ, Jesus Robert. 4800 ALBERTA AVE, HEALTH SCIENCE 79905 #649-27-2001 L2007 **IMG** *100 †20

DURU, Valentine. ■ 79912 #166-01-1999 **IM** *100

DWYER, Edward Jos. ■ 79912 #048-02-1969 L1970 **OPH** *071

EAGER, Jeremy Morgan. 5005 N PIEDRAS ST 79920 #023-12-2002 L2008 **AN** *020 †05

EASTER, Thomas Glenn, II. 2126 MONTANA AVE 79903 #561-17-1980 L1985 **GS EM** *020 †20

EBERLEY, Leah Dougherty. 1201 E SCHUSTER AVE, STE 4A 79902 #026-04-1982 L1987 **IM IMG** *020 †20

EDWARDS, Roy D. ■ 79934 #055-75-2007, ▲ **GS** *012

EGBERT, O Edward. 1700 CURIE DR 79902 #048-02-1951 L1951 **A PUD** *071

EHRHARDT, Nicole Marie. ■ 79902 #023-12-2002 L2004 **IM** *100 †20

EISENBERG, Kenneth L. 1600 MEDICAL CENTER ST, EL PASO SOUTHWESTERN 79902 #048-04-1981 L1982 **TS VS** *020 †85,90

EISENHAUER, Michael David. 5005 N PIEDRAS ST STOP 3, WILLIAM BEAUMONT ARMY MED 79920 #010-02-1990 L2003 **CD IM** *020 †20

EISNER, David Geo. 4800 ALBERTA AVE 79905 #038-06-1937 L1972 **GS OS** *072 †85

EKERY, Fred Nicholas. 7848 GATEWAY BLVD E 79915 #048-12-1963 L1963 **ON IM** *071 †20

ELDER, James N. ■ 79934 #037-01-2006 L2008 **GS** *012

ELDER, William Larry. 1625 MEDICAL CENTER ST 79902 #048-02-1972 L1972 **EM** *020 †16

ELDER QUINTANA, William F. 4800 ALBERTA AVE 79905 #649-33-2000 L2005 **FM** *020 †18

ELEJE, Augustine O. 1700 N OREGON ST, STE 780 79902 #690-01-1981 L2001 **IM PD** *020 †55,20

ELKINS, Greg Chas. 1625 MEDICAL CENTER ST, SIERRA MED CTR DEPT PATH 79902 #039-01-1988 L1996 **PTH** *020 †50

ELLIS, Randy S. 1069 LOS JARDINES CIR 79912 #036-01-1977 L2006 **EM MDM** *020 †16

ELLMAN, Marc. 1400 COMMON DR 79936 #041-14-2000 L2004 **OPH** *020

ELM, Michael Keola. ■ 79902 #014-01-2007 **TY** *012

EL MARAGHY, Hala Raafat. 4800 ALBERTA AVE 79905 #915-04-1989 **PD** *012

ELOY, Maria C.. 9849 KENWORTHY ST, TEXAS TECH UNIV-FAMILY PRA 79924 #275-03-1994 L2007 **FP** *012

EL SHAFEI, Laila M. 4800 ALBERTA AVE 79905 #915-02-1964 **PD** *100

ENRIQUEZ, Andres S. 836 E REDD RD 79912 #048-15-1995 L1999 **FM** *020 †18

ENZ, Jason Charles. ■ 79912 #048-15-2003 L2006 **EM** *100

EPPLER, Maia Fiodor. 4800 ALBERTA AVE, DEPARTMENT OF PEDIATRICS 79905 #913-50-2000 **PD** *012

ERASO, Luis Hernan. 4800 ALBERTA AVE, TX TECH UNIV DEPT IM 79905 #264-10-1996 L2006 **IM** *020 †20

ESCANDON, Carmen G. 550 S MESA HILLS DR, STE C2 79912 #048-14-1999 L2002 **FM** *020 †18

ESCOBAR, Andres Felipe. 4800 ALBERTA AVE, TEXAS TECH UNIV HEALTH SCI 79905 #264-03-1999 L2008 **IM** *012

ESCOBAR, Herbert. ■ 79922 #264-01-1958 L1977 **TS VS** *020 †85,90

ESCOBAR, Juan M. 101 RIM RD STE 300, EL PASO HEART CENTER 79902 #048-12-1989 L1990 **CD** *020 †20

ESCOBEDO, Luis Gerardo. 401 E FRANKLIN AVE STE 210 79901 #005-11-1979 L1984 **PHP** *050 †70

ESCOBEDO, Miguel Angel. 401 E FRANKLIN AVE 79901 #005-11-1983 L1985 **PHP FM** *020 †18

ESCONTRIAS, Adrian M. 5959 GATEWAY BLVD W, STE 120 79925 #048-12-1997 L2000 **AN** *020 †05

ESPINOSA, Jose Ricardo. 300 S ZARAGOZA RD, THOMASON 79907 #649-01-1971 L1982 **IM** *020 †20

FAIRE, Andrew Curtis. 5005 N PIEDRAS ST STOP 3, WILLIAM BEAUMONT ARMY MED 79920 #024-05-1975 L1978 **IM EM** *020

FALLON, Michael Anthony. ■ 79912 #023-12-1994 L2007 **ORS** *020 †40

FARAZMAND, Seyedeh Maryam. 4800 ALBERTA AVE 79905 #517-12-1998 **FP** *012

FARLEY, Patrick Clare. 4800 ALBERTA AVE 79905 #016-11-1971 L1982 **ON HEM** *075 †20

FARNAM, Richard W. ■ 79912 #048-13-2001 L2006 **OBG** *100

FARRELL, Mitchell James. 1400 GEORGE DIETER DR, STE 100 79936 #048-15-1981 L1981 **EM FM** *020 †16,18

FASIHI, Najam Geerman. 5005 N PIEDRAS ST, MED CTR 79920 #047-07-2004 L2006 **ORS** *012

FASIHI, Tahira Geerman. ■ 79934 #047-07-2007 **TY** *012

FEBINGER, Dennis Loyal. 5005 N PIEDRAS ST, DEOT IF SURGERY 79920 #007-02-1985 L1986 **TS** *020 †85

FEINBERG, Walter D. ■ 79912 #048-12-1952 L1952 **IM** *071 †20

FELIBERTI, Manuel. 10400 VISTA DEL SOL DR 79925 #396-04-1957 L1958 **OS** *100

FELIBERTI-IRIZARRY, M C. 10301 GATEWAY BLVD W 79925 #396-01-1965 L1980 **PS HS** *030 †85,65

FIERRO-STEVENS, Rodolfo. 1400 N EL PASO ST, STE B 79902 #649-33-1989 L1993 **CHN** *020 †75,55

FIGUEROA-CASAS, Juan B. 4800 ALBERTA AVE RM 136 79905 #132-04-1991 L2004 **PCC** *020 †20

FITZ, Juan Francisco. 3737 N MESA ST, STE C 79902 #048-15-1986 L1987 **EM APM** *020 †16

FLEMING, Rhonda Violeta. 4800 ALBERTA AVE 79905 #935-01-1991 L2006 **ID IM** *020 †20

FLORES, Ernesto. ■ 79907 #649-33-1981 **P** *075

FOLEY, John D. 4800 ALBERTA AVE, TEXAS TECH HSC 79905 #035-06-1970 L1995 **ADL PD** *020 †55

FOOLADI, Mike Mehdi. ■ 79912 #649-33-1982 **FM GP** *071

FOOTE, Michael W. 1900 N OREGON ST STE 210 79902 #048-02-1998 L1999 **OPH** *020 †35

FOOTE, William Chas. 1700 N OREGON ST, STE 530 79902 #016-06-1967 L1977 **CD IM** *020 †20

FOREMAN, Bruce Phillip. 1727 N LEE TREVINO DR 79936 #005-11-1976 L1981 **DR RNR** *020 †80

FOWLER, Justin Thomas. ■ 79912 #016-01-2007 **ORS** *012

FOX, Melvin. 125 W HAGUE RD, STE 550 79902 #035-06-1966 L1972 **NEP IM** *071 †20

FRANCO, Carlos. 1700 N OREGON ST, STE 570 79902 #649-01-1962 L1972 **CD IM** *020

FRANCO, Hector Lastra. 10500 VISTA DEL SOL DR 79925 #005-15-1975 L1980 **D GP** *020 †15

FRANK, Thomas Wayne. ■ 79912 #021-01-1989 L1993 **AI IM** *020 †20,03

FRAUSTO, Marcella Anne. 12350 MONTWOOD DR, STE 300 79928 #025-12-1997 L2001 **PD** *020 †55

FREEMYER, Ryan Ross. 4800 ALBERTA AVE, TEXAS TECH UHSC 79905 #048-15-2001 L2006 **GS** *100

FREWAN, Naima Omar. 4800 ALBERTA AVE 79905 #613-02-1993 **PD** *012

FUNCHES, Levi. ■ 79912 #023-07-2002 L2002 **PD** *020 †55

FUNKHOUSER, Todd Allen. 5005 N PIEDRAS ST, DEPT OF ALLERGY IMMUN 79920 #034-01-1999 L2002 **AI IM** *100 †20,03

FURLONG, Joseph Brian. 5005 N PIEDRAS ST, STOP 36 79920 #030-06-1994 L2000 **DR** *020 †80

FUSHILLE, Michael. 1800 N MESA AT RIM STE B 79902 #869-05-1957 L1962 **OPH** *071

GABBERT, Michael Kirk. 1700 CURIE DR STE 5600 79902 #048-02-1973 L1973 **IM HEM** *020 †20

GADBERRY, Kate H. ■ 79936 #048-78-2006, ▲ **PD** *012

GAGOT, Julio. 5959 GATEWAY BLVD W, STE 120 79925 #042-02-1983 L1986 **AN** *020 †05

GAINES, Lelia Teressa. 1733 CURIE DR STE 205 79902 #010-03-1975 L1993 **AI IM** *020

GALLARDO, Mark Joseph. ■ 79925 #048-15-2001 L2005 **OPH** *020 †35

GALLEGO, Maria Rebecca. 560 LISBON ST 79905 #026-04-1985 L1988 **IM** *020 †20

GARCIA, Blanca Ivette. 4800 ALBERTA AVE 79905 #048-15-1998 L2001 **PD** *020 †55

GARCIA, Carlos Mariano. 1550 HAWKINS BLVD STE 16 79925 #649-14-1972 L1978 **EM GP** *020

GARCIA, Cecilia Beatrice. 8229 BURNHAM RD, EL PASO MHMR 79907 #048-15-1984 L1987 **P** *020 †75

GARCIA, Henry F. 1700 N OREGON ST, STE 530 79902 #048-15-1994 L1997 **OBG** *020 †30

GARCIA, Rafael Isidro. 5959 GATEWAY BLVD W, STE 160 79925 #042-01-1986 L2002 **GS** *020 †45

GARDNER, Danuta. 5001 N PIEDRAS ST, VETERANS AFFAIRS HCC 79930 #759-08-1978 L1998 **IM** *020 †20

GARDUNO, Abel. 125 W HAGUE RD, STE 400 79902 #649-01-1962 L1971 **U** *020 †95

GARNER, Jason Carl. 5005 N PIEDRAS ST 79920 #665-02-2007 **IM** *012

GARRASTEGUI-BIGAS, Luis M. 5005 N PIEDRAS ST STOP 36, WILLIAM BEAUMONT AMC 79920 #308-03-1977 L1979 **EM** *020 †16

GARZA, Delfino R. 4800 ALBERTA AVE, DEPT OF SURGERY 79905 #048-13-2005 **GS** *012

GARZA-ARREOLA, Luis. 1700 N OREGON ST, STE 660 79902 #649-02-1987 L1997 **CD** *020 †20

GARZA LOZANO, Gilberto. 4800 ALBERTA AVE, DEPT OF INTERNAL MED 79905 #649-30-2003 L2007 **IM** *020 †20

GASCON, Jose Alexei. ■ 79912 #275-01-1993 **IM** *012

GAUR, Sumit. ■ 79936 #496-02-1997 L2005 **HO** *020 †20

GAZAROV, Aleksandr G. ■ 79912 #913-19-1978 L1998 **P** *020

GHALEB, Melhem R. 4815 ALAMEDA AVE 79905 #048-02-1995 L2002 **VIR** *020 †80

GHANS, Wayne Oliver. ■ 79938 #025-01-1987 L1990 **FM** *020 †20

GHATALI, Mohammad Aghil. 4800 ALBERTA AVE 79905 #496-20-1998 **FP** *012

GHISELLI, Antonio Angelo. 3100 N LEE TREVINO DR 79936 #836-03-1970 L1979 **ORS** *020 †40

GHOTBI, Seyed Abdolali. 5001 N PIEDRAS ST 79930 #517-05-1960 L1974 **D IM** *020 †15

GIBSON, James Brown D. 1721 WESTON BRENT LN 79935 #065-09-1969 L1977 **GP FM** *020

GILARDONI, Paul Garner. ■ 79912 #005-06-2004 L2006 **EM** *020

GILBERT, Stanley Zane. ■ 79912 #016-11-1945 L1973 **FM** *071

GILDEA, Janet Carol. 8061 ALAMEDA AVE 79915 #017-20-1982 L1991 **FM** *020 †18

GILLESPIE, Christina M. ■ 79912 #035-09-1999 L2000 **OTO** *020 †45

GILSON, Violet M. 4800 ALBERTA AVE 79905 #038-43-1976 L1981 **IM** *020 †20

GIORDANO, Frank Lawrence. 4800 ALBERTA AVE 79905 #030-06-1967 L1986 **P** *020 †75

GIVENS, Melissa L. ■ 79925 #023-12-1997 L1999 **EM** *100

GIYANANI, Vishan Lilaram. 10420 VISTA DEL SOL DR, STE 100 79925 #495-96-1971 L1985 **OS DR** *020 †80

GLADSTONE, Larry A. ■ 79912 #048-12-1952 L1952 **IM** *071 †20

GLIDDEN, Aimee Jean. 4800 ALBERTA AVE 79905 #022-75-2004, ▲ **OBG** *012

GLUCK, Brion Alan. 1800 N MESA ST STE 200 79902 #048-12-1990 L1991 **OBG** *020 †30

GLUSMAN, Steven Philip. 10400 VISTA DEL SOL DR, STE 103 79925 #035-46-1988 L2001 **N** *020

GOLDFARB, Irvin J. 2001 N OREGON ST 79902 #048-12-1953 L1953 **PD** *071 †55

GOLDMAN, Edward Mark. 100 E SCHUSTER AVE 79902 #034-01-1976 L1977 **OTO FPS** *020 †45

GOLDSTEIN, Randy Jason. 2001 N OREGON ST 79902 #035-06-1995 L2000 **EM** *020 †16,55

GOMEZ, Edward Ramon. 1700 N OREGON ST, STE 550 79902 #034-01-1978 L1988 **GS** *020 †85

GOMEZ, Gilberto. ■ 79922 #048-13-2001 L2004 **PD** *100

GOMEZ, Jaime Rafael. 1225 E CLIFF DR, STE 2B 79902 #048-13-1990 L1991 **CRS GS** *020 †85,10

GOMEZ, Jesus Alberto. 1733 CURIE DR, STE 305 79902 #048-14-1986 L1987 **ON IM** *020 †20

GOMEZ, Melissa Marie. 4800 ALBERTA AVE, TEXAS TECH UNIV HSC 79905 #034-01-2007 **IM** *012

GOMEZ, Oscar Eduardo. ■ 79911 #270-02-2000 L2007 **EM** *020 †16

GOMEZ, Patrick J. 7300 REMCON CIR, STE 300 79912 #034-01-1983 L1992 **OTO FPS** *020 †45

GOMEZ, Rebeca M. 4815 ALAMEDA AVE 79905 #042-01-1983 L1986 **PD** *020 †55

GONZALEZ, Abraham. 101 RIM RD # 300 79902 #005-11-1983 L1984 **CD IM** *020 †20

GONZALEZ, Alberto Alexand. 4801 ALBERTA, STE B3200 79905 #270-02-2002 L2008 **EM** *012

GONZALEZ, Alfredo. 9849 KENWORTH ST, TEXAS TECH UNIV-FAMILY PRA 79924 #275-03-1990 L2007 **FP** *012

GONZALEZ, Alfredo E. 125 W HAGUE RD, STE 570 79902 #341-01-1987 L1996 **FM** *020 †20

GONZALEZ, Jose L. 4800 ALBERTA AVE 79905 #042-01-1986 L1997 **OBG** *020 †30

GONZALEZ, Jose M. ■ 79997 #275-01-1957 L1974 **FM** *071 †18

GONZALEZ, Luis Antonio. 10400 VISTA DEL SOL DR, STE 201 79925 #649-27-1981 L1998 **AI** *020 †55,03

GONZALEZ, Mariaelena. 125 W HAGUE RD, STE 110 79902 #935-01-1990 L1998 **MPD PD** *020 †20,55

GONZALEZ, Omar. 1015 N ZARAGOZA RD 79907 #056-06-1979 L1981 **FM** *020 †18

GONZALEZ, Patricio. ■ 79925 #048-15-2008 *012

GONZALEZ, Rogelio, Jr. 10555 VISTA DEL SOL, STE 200 79925 #048-13-1980 L1980 **FM** *020 †18

GONZALEZ, Saul. ■ 79912 #048-02-1958 L1958 **ORS** *075

GONZALEZ, Sylvia Valles. 4800 ALBERTA AVE, TX TECH REG ACAD CTR MED 79905 #048-04-1984 L1985 **NEP IM** *020 †20

GONZALEZ, Zorisadday. ■ 79912 #048-15-2008 *012

GONZALEZ-AYALA, Emilio. 1900 N OREGON ST STE 610 79902 #649-33-1990 L1995 **PCC IM** *020 †20

GONZALEZ-AYALA, Rafael. 4800 ALBERTA AVE, DEPT OF IM 79905 #649-33-1995 L2005 **IM** *020 †20

GONZALEZ-MORALES, Evelyn. 2400 TRAWOOD DR, STE 300 79936 #042-02-1991 L1994 **P** *020

GORBY, Earl Wilbert. ■ 79912 #005-11-1953 L1972 **PUD** *071 †20

GORDON, Ilyssa Avery. ■ 79912 #048-14-2006 L2006 **PTH** *012

GORE, Ney Mc Kinley, III. ■ 79904 #027-01-1977 L1977 **CCM IM** *040 †20

GOUGH, David Christopher. 4800 ALBERTA AVE, DEPT IM 79905 #019-02-1967 L1978 **CD IM** *020 †20

GRACIA, Edgar Ismael. ■ 79912 #649-45-1987 L2004 **P** *020 ‡

GRASS, Adrian Lamar. 2001 N OREGON ST 79902 #036-05-1954 L1960 **ORS** *071 †40

GREENBERG, Harvey. 1500 N MESA ST 79902 #035-06-1971 L1987 **GO OBG** *020 †30

GREENE, Scott P. 6090 SURETY DR, STE 412 79905 #048-15-1996 L1997 **EM** *020 †16

GREER, Veronica Latee. 6090 SURETY DR STE 412, DEPT OF EMERGENCY MEDICINE 79905 #048-14-1989 L1990 **EM** *020 †16,16

GREGORY-QUINONES, Gerardo. 1717 N BROWN ST, STE 2B 79902 #847-10-1966 L2002 **P CHP** *071 †75

GREWAL, Preetpal K. 4800 ALBERTA AVE 79905 #035-75-2004, ▲ **OBG** *012

GRIESHOP, Neil Anthony. 1600 MEDICAL CTR, STE 300 79902 #056-05-1989 L1995 **GS VS** *020 †85

GROENING-WANG, Mary Traci. 4800 ALBERTA AVE 79905 #005-77-2005, ▲ **OBG** *012

GROSS, Kirby Robt. 5005 N PIEDRAS ST, WILLIAM BEAUMONT ARMY MED 79920 #017-20-1980 L1980 **GS** *040 †85

GROST, John Jos, III. 1801 N OREGON ST 79902 #025-07-1970 L1974 **EM LM** *071 †16

GUERRA, Francisco Javier. 10965 BEN CRENSHAW DR # 1 79935 #649-19-1976 L1980 **FM EM** *020 †18 ‡

GUERRA DE LA FUENTE, Luis. 1900 N OREGON ST, STE 600 79902 #042-02-1986 L1988 **IM** *020 †20

GUERRERO, Martin. 4800 ALBERTA AVE, PSYCHIATRY DEPT 79905 #048-04-1983 L1983 **P** *040 †75

GUEVARA, Adrian M. 110 MESA PARK DR, STE 100 79912 #048-13-2001 L2006 **D** *100 †15

GUGGEDAHL, John Eric. 6955 N MESA ST STE 104 79912 #048-02-1979 L1979 **PD** *020 †55

GUM, Ronald Adelbert. 1740 CURIE DR 79902 #048-02-1963 L1963 **PS GS** *020 †85,65

GUPTA, Anuradha Jain. 1901 GRANDVIEW AVE, RADIATION ONCOLOGY ASSOCIA 79902 #496-02-1981 L1989 **RO** *020 †80

GUPTA, Manisha. ■ 79912 #048-12-2002 L2004 **EM** *020 †16

GUPTA, Tej Pratap. 1733 CURIE DR, STE 200 79902 #495-30-1977 L1989 **GE IM** *020 †20 ‡

GURNEY, Jennifer Margaret. ■ 79904 #024-05-1999 L2001 *020 †85

GUTIERREZ, Carlos. 10460 VISTA DEL SOL DR 79925 #026-04-1977 L1980 **PD** *020 †55

GUTIERREZ, Delia. 6600 MONTANA AVE STE P, BIENVIVIR SENIOR HELATH SE 79925 #048-15-2000 L2003 **IM** *020 †20

GUTIERREZ, Michael E. 1250 E CLIFF DR, STE 2A 79902 #048-13-1999 L2005 **CD** *020 †20

GUTIERREZ, Octavio E. 2030 GATEWAY BLVD N 79903 #649-02-1970 L1975 **P CHP** *020

GUTIERREZ MACIAS, Rodolfo. 9849 KENWORTHY ST, TEXAS TECH UNIV-FAMILY PRA 79924 #649-03-1998 L2004 **FM** *020 †18

GUTKNECHT, Michael G. 122 W CASTELLANO DR, DESERT IMAGING 79912 #047-05-1975 L1986 **DR** *020 †20

GUZMAN, Jorge G. 300 S ZARAGOZA RD 79907 #048-13-1996 L2000 **FM** *020 †18

HABIB, Shahnaz. ■ 79912 #160-06-1989 L2007 **FM** *100

HABICHT, Nina E.. 4800 ALBERTA AVE, TX TECH U HLTH SCI CTR 79905 #286-13-2005 **IM** *012

HACKER, Callenda Anne. ■ 79902 #048-15-2007 **TY** *012

HAJJ, Ahmad Mohammad. 1700 N OREGON ST, STE 540 79902 #605-01-1990 L1996 **PCC IM** *020 †20

HAKES, Joseph David. ■ 79912 #048-15-2008 *012

HAKIM, Mohammad Nawar. 4800 ALBERTA AVE, DEPT OF PATHOLOGY AND LABO 79905 #875-01-1987 L1994 **PTH** *020 †50

HALABY, Gerald Allan. 1600 MEDICAL CENTER DR, STE 218 79902 #847-10-1972 L1979 **ORS** *071

HALL, William Martin. ■ 79936 #047-07-1953 L1970 **OBG** *071 †30

HALLUM, Basil A, Jr. 1201 N MESA ST 79902 #048-04-1944 L1944 **OPH** *071 †35

HALSTED, Maria A. 10201 GATEWAY BLVD W, STE 420 79925 #048-14-1991 L1992 **GS** *020 †85

HAMAM, Hisham Dowood. 5005 N PIEDRAS ST 79920 #166-01-2004 L2007 **IM** *012

HAN, Nyun. 10460 VISTA DEL SOL DR, STE 100 79925 #005-06-1986 L2004 **RO** *020 †80

HANBALI, Fadi M Samir. 4800 ALBERTA AVE, DIV OF NEUROSURGERY 79905 #605-01-1992 L2005 **NS** *020

HAND, William Lee. 4800 ALBERTA AVE, DEPT RES DEVLPMNT 79905 #012-05-1962 L1967 **IM ID** *020 †20

HANDAL, Gilberto A. 4800 ALBERTA AVE, TEXAS TECH UNIVERSITY - HS 79905 #231-01-1967 L1976 **PDI CCP** *040 †55

HANSEN, Uel Dean. ■ 79912 #016-42-2004 L2005 **ORS** *012

HARDAWAY, Robert M, III. 4800 ALBERTA AVE 79905 #028-02-1939 L1977 **GS** *075 †85

HARLASS, Frederick Edward. 10201 GATEWAY BLVD W, STE 330 79925 #054-04-1980 L1991 **OBG MFM** *020 †30

HARPER, William D. 2626 N MESA ST # 437 79902 #048-15-1993 L1998 **EM** *020

HARRINGTON, George David. 4800 ALBERTA AVE, ORTHOPAEDIC SURGERY 79905 #034-01-1983 L1998 **ORS** *040 †40

HARRIS, Richard Jay. ■ 79912 #048-02-1955 L1955 **MDM GS** *071 †85

HARRIS, Stephen Richard. 7300 REMCON CIR, STE 200 79912 #048-14-1984 L1991 **AN** *020 †05

HARTENBACH, James Anthony. ■ 79912 #035-20-2000 L2005 **FM** *020

HASSAN, Humaira. 4800 ALBERTA AVE, HEALTH SCIENCE 79905 #704-02-1998 L2002 **IM** *012

HASSAN, Mohamad Charif. 4800 ALBERTA AVE 79905 #875-03-2000 L2008 **PD** *100

HATCHETT, John Garner. 6955 N MESA ST STE 112 79912 #039-01-1966 L1972 **OPH** *020 †35

HAYDAR, Zafer H. 6065 MONTANA AVE, STE A2 79925 #649-33-1978 L1984 **IM DIA** *020 †20

HAYNES, John Fletcher, Jr. 4800 ALBERTA AVE, EMER 79905 #048-13-1980 L1984 **EM ETX** *020 †16

HAZARIAN, Eduardo. 4646 N MESA ST 79912 #132-02-1963 L1972 **ORS** *030 †40

HEISE, Amber Sharp. ■ 79912 #048-02-2006 L2006 **PD** *020 †55

HEITZMAN, Martin. 1250 E CLIFF DR, STE 5C 79902 #539-02-1964 L1977 **N** *071 †75

HELLER, Solomon. 125 W HAGUE RD # 280 79902 #048-02-1952 L1952 **IM** *071 †20

HENDERSON, Brett Robert. 4800 ALBERTA AVE, DIVISION OF NEUROSURGERY 79905 #016-11-1994 L2001 **NS** *020 †25

HERMAN, Karen L. 2100 N MESA ST 79902 #051-04-1995 L1999 **FM** *020 †18

HERMAN, Peter Simon. 2100 N MESA ST 79902 #143-02-1962 L1974 **D** *020 †15 ‡

HERNANDEZ, Alvaro Ariel. 10525 VISTA DEL SOL DR, STE 206 79925 #048-13-1982 L1983 **ORS** *020 †40

HERNANDEZ, Arturo A. 4800 ALBERTA AVE 79905 #048-15-2000 L2004 **PD** *020

HERNANDEZ, Christine Kay. 1724 WESTON BRENT LN 79935 #026-04-1980 L1984 **FM** *020 †18

HERNANDEZ, Gabriel Arment. 4800 ALBERTA AVE 79905 #649-38-1988 L2003 **P** *020

HERNANDEZ, German Teran. 4800 ALBERTA AVE, TEXAS TECH HSC 79905 #024-01-1998 L2005 **NEP IM** *020 †20

HERNANDEZ, Jesus A. 125 W HAGUE RD STE 590 79902 #042-01-1983 L1992 **GE IM** *020 †20

HERNANDEZ, Jose L. 10201 GATEWAY BLVD W # 210 79925 #026-04-1980 L1985 **OBG** *020 †30

HERNANDEZ, Leticia Susana. 1700 N OREGON ST STE 640, SUITE 640 79902 #048-12-1992 L1993 **OBG** *020 †30

HERNANDEZ, Manuel. 2415 MONTANA AVE 79903 #048-02-1955 L1955 **P** *020 †75

HERNANDEZ, Ramiro. 2931 MONTANA AVE STE A 79903 #649-14-1972 L1976 **GP P** *071 ‡

HERNANDEZ RAMOS, Arturo. 4800 ALBERTA AVE 79905 #649-33-2002 **FP** *020

HERRADA, Juan. 1901 GRANDVIEW AVE 79902 #847-04-1986 L1992 **ON** *020 †20

HETZ, Stephen Paul. 2912 TITANIC AVE, SUMMIT SURGICAL OF EL PASO 79904 #023-12-1982 L2006 **GS** *020 †85

HEYDEMANN, Jacob Saml. 1300 MURCHISON DR, STE 310 79902 #048-15-1979 L1979 **ORS** *020 †40

HINOJOS, Ralu. 9398 VISCOUNT BLVD, STE 1B 79925 #048-14-2002 L2004 **FM** *020 †18

HO, Hoi. 4800 ALBERTA AVE 79905 #941-01-1975 L1986 **IM** *020 †20

HOFFER, Thomas Chas. 2400 TRAWOOD DR 79936 #020-12-1975 L1999 **DR** *020 †80,18

HOLLAND, Courtney Allen. ■ 79912 #038-45-2003 L2005 **ORS** *012

HOLLAND, David A. 1721 N LEE TREVINO DR, CARE CLINIC 79936 #048-14-1992 L1993 **EM** *020 †16

HOLLAND, David A. ■ 79912 #048-15-1993 L1994 **FM** *020 †18

HOOD, Howard Houston, III. 1625 MEDICAL CENTER ST 79902 #025-01-1977 L1983 **OBG EM** *020 †16

HOOKER, J Patrick. 8012 BIG BEND DR 79904 #048-02-1954 L1954 **NS N** *071 †25

HORN, Kathryn V. 9849 KENWORTHY ST 79924 #048-04-1984 L1985 **FM** *040 †18

HORTON, John Daniel. ■ 79911 #023-12-2004 L2006 **GS** *012

HOSAIN, Syed Abbas. ■ 79912 #704-03-1958 L1972 **OBG GS** *020

HOWARD, Robert Charles. 5005 N PIEDRAS ST, ARMY MEDICAL 79920 #024-07-2007 **TY** *012

HOWE, Jarett Kent. ■ 79912 #046-01-2006 **GS** *012

HSIEH, Russell Mike. 4800 ALBERTA AVE 79905 #422-01-2007 **EM** *012

HUANG, Christine. ■ 79912 #048-15-2008 *012

HUCHTON, Paul Jos. 1515 N OREGON ST 79902 #047-05-1958 L1963 **PD** *071 †55

HUGHES, Harold W. 4800 ALBERTA AVE, TEXAS TECH UNIVERSITY HSC 79905 #048-02-1986 L1987 **PUD** *020 †20

HUNKO, Gabriela. 6065 MONTANA AVE, STE A2 79925 #132-01-1991 L1996 **IM** *020 †20

IBARRA, Isela. 1512 N ZARAGOZA RD, STE A-1 79936 #048-15-2001 L2004 **PD** *020 †55

IBARRA, Sergio. 1625 MEDICAL CENTER ST 79902 #048-15-1989 L1990 **EM** *020 †16

IBARRA-MEDINA, Miguel H. 1900 N MESA ST 79902 #649-33-1983 L1987 **PD** *020 †55

IMURO, George Philip Lagu. 4800 ALBERTA AVE, DEPT OF INTERNAL MED 79905 #649-38-2002 L2007 **IM** *020

IPSON, Merle A. 4800 ALBERTA AVE, DEPT OF PEDIATRICS 79905 #048-15-1988 L1994 **NPM** *040 †55

IQBAL, Mohammad Javed. 1626 MEDICAL CENTER DR, 5TH FLOOR, STE 503 79902 #704-21-1992 L2004 **IM** *020 †20

ISAAC, David Wm. 3901 N MESA ST 79902 #039-05-1988 L1996 **PD** *020 †55

ISLAM, Nadim Bin. ■ 79912 #048-04-2001 L2004 **EM** *020 †16

ISLAS, Arthur Anthony. 9849 KENWORTHY ST, DEPT OF FAMILY & COMMUNITH 79924 #048-15-1998 L2001 **FSM** *012 †18

ISUANI, Hugo Emilio. 2600 N OREGON ST, STE 200 79902 #132-06-1967 L1977 **R NM** *020 †80

IVY, Roy, Jr. 1700 CURIE DR 79902 #048-02-1968 L1968 **OBG** *020 †30 ‡

IZQUIERDO, Miguel Armando. ■ 79912 #048-02-2007 *012

IZQUIERDO-FRAU, Omar L. 5005 N PIEDRAS ST, DEPT OF VET AFFAIRS 79920 #308-03-1978 L1981 **FM EM** *020 †18,16

JABALIE, Edward Nasif. 9398 VISCOUNT BLVD STE 1B 79925 #048-02-1957 L1957 **FM** *071 †18

JABOR, Mark A. 1700 N OREGON ST STE 755 79902 #048-15-1994 L2001 **PS** *020 †45,65

JACKSON, George Walker. 7430 REMCON CIR 79912 #048-02-1981 L1981 **FM OM** *020 †18

JACOBS, Homer Avery. 1700 CURIE DR STE 2000 79902 #021-01-1959 L1964 **OBG** *071 †30

JACOBS, Robert Kenan. 1201 E SCHUSTER AVE, STE 3A 79902 #033-05-1974 L1978 **GS** *020

JAMISON, Rodney Keith. 1600 MEDICAL CENTER ST, SOUTHWEST E N T STE 101 79902 #004-01-1974 L1996 **OTO GP** *020 †45

JANSS, William Cluff, Jr. 1626 MEDICAL CENTER ST, STE 500 79902 #005-14-1976 L1998 **FM IM** *020 †20,18

JASSO-MAGDALENO, Juan A. 1900 N OREGON ST, STE 312 79902 #649-01-1989 L1997 **NPM** *020 †55

JAVIER DE ROSAS, F. 2039 TRAWOOD DR # B 79935 #132-06-1968 L1977 **PD** *020 †55

JEDRZEJCZYK, Aneta. ■ 79925 #038-41-2007 **IM** *012

JESURUN, Carlos Antonio. 4800 ALBERTA AVE, TTUHSC 79905 #048-04-1973 L1974 **PD NPM** *040 †55

JI, Jianzhong. 4800 ALBERTA AVE 79905 #243-32-1992 **PD** *012

JIMENEZ, Mauricio Ernesto. 1501 N MESA ST, STE 2B 79902 #187-14-1982 L1996 **IM** *020 †20

JIMENEZ-SOTO, Jesus Raul. 2311 N MESA ST STE I 79902 #649-27-1980 L1986 **P** *020 †75

JIRON, R Vivian. ■ 79904 #048-13-1982 L1983 **FM** *020 †18

JOHN, Ann Katherine. ■ 79902 #048-02-2004 L2008 **AN** *012

JOHNSON, Chad Barrett. ■ 79912 #048-15-2005 **GS** *012

JOHNSON, Jeremy Scott. ■ 79912 #039-01-1997 L1998 **OBG** *020 †30

JOHNSON, Keith Randal. 10525 VISTA DEL SOL DR, STE 206 79925 #047-07-1998 L2002 **ORS** *020

JOHNSON, Robin Kimberly. ■ 79912 #020-02-2003 L2004 **PTH** *020

JOHNSON, Ryan C. 4800 ALBERTA AVE 79905 #018-75-2007, ▲ **OBG** *012

JOHNSON, Shawn Evette. ■ 79924 #048-12-2003 L2005 **ORS** *012

JOHNSTONE, John Hick. ■ 79936 #016-11-1936 L1946 **FM PD** *071

JONES-ALLEN, Angela S. 9201 DYER ST 79924 #566-01-1992 L1999 **FM** *020 †18

JORDAN, William Jefferson. ■ 79911 #048-14-2005 L2007 **ORS** *012

JORGENSEN, Anton Yang. ■ 79902 #041-02-2007 **ORS** *012

JOSEPH-VANDERPOOL, Jean R. 616 N VIRGINIA ST STE F 79902 #649-33-1982 L1990 **P PYG** *020 †75

JUGUILON, Crispin L, Jr. 1600 MONTANA AVE, EL PASO MHMR 79902 #748-10-1991 L1999 **P** *020 †75

JULIAN, Marilyn P. 1250 E CLIFF DR, STE 5B 79902 #748-11-1981 L1997 **IM** *020 †20

KAHN, Stuart Warren. 650 BELVIDERE ST, EL PASO PEDIATRIC ASSOC PA 79912 #048-12-1966 L1966 **PD OS** *020 †55

KAIM, Boris. 2311 N MESA ST 79902 #264-05-1962 L1976 **N SME** *020 †75 ‡

KAIP, Sherwood Ramsay. 2001 N OREGON ST 79902 #025-07-1956 L1961 **AN** *020 †05

KANG, Jian. 4800 ALBERTA AVE 79905 #243-47-1987 **PD** *012

KANG, Won Bok. 4800 ALBERTA AVE 79905 #583-03-1990 **EM** *012

KANLIC, Enes Mehmed. 4800 ALBERTA AVE, ORTHO DEPT 79905 #957-02-1977 L2000 **ORS** *020

KAO, Yin James. 5959 GATEWAY BLVD W, STE 120 79925 #048-14-1983 L1983 **AN** *020 †05

KAREH, Jorge. 1900 N OREGON ST STE 510 79902 #042-02-1985 L1995 **OBG GP** *020 ‡

KARP, Alan Jeffrey. 125 W HAGUE RD STE 590 79902 #048-12-1981 L1981 **GE IM** *020 †20

KATZ, Abraham J. 1201 E SCHUSTER AVE, STE 490 79902 #649-01-1977 L1988 **P** *020 †75

KAVONIAN, Gary. 10301 GATEWAY BLVD W 799, 1490A GEORGE DIETER DR.#27 79925 #649-33-1985 L1991 **IM** *020 †20

KEIVAN, Siamak. ■ 79912 #166-01-2004 *100

KERN, Billy Barker. ■ 79902 #021-01-1958 **FM OM** *071 †18

KESLING, Kimberly Lynn. 5005 N PIEDRAS ST STOP 36, WILLIAM BEAUMONT AMC 79920 #024-07-1990 L2004 **OSS** *020 †40

KHALSA, Ann Marie. 1505 MESCALERO DR 79925 #005-06-1987 L2006 **FM** *020 †18

KHAN, Farhan Masrur. ■ 79912 #704-04-1998 L2005 **P** *012

KHAN, Marryam Siddiqua. 4800 ALBERTA AVE, DEPARTMENT OF PEDIATRICS 79905 #704-02-1995 L2008 **PD** *012

KHAN, Mohammad Amjadullah. 4800 ALBERTA AVE 79905 #704-15-1996 **P** *012

KHANNA, Anubha. 5005 N PIEDRAS ST, DEPTARMENT OF PEDIATRICS 79920 #495-49-1995 L2006 **PD** *100 †55

KHARIDI, Viswanatha. 910 E REDD RD STE K, PMB222 79912 #495-09-1971 L1977 **N** *020

KHATEEB, Mazin A. 2311 N MESA ST, STE C 79902 #528-01-1968 L1979 **GS** *020

KHAUV, Keak Chy. 1700 CURIE DR STE 2100 79902 #018-03-2000 L2007 **IM** *020 †35

KIDD, Joseph Neal. 1600 MEDICAL CENTER ST, EL PASO SOUTHWESTERN 79902 #048-04-1968 L1968 **TS GS** *020 †85,90

KILHAM, Michael. 5005 N PIEDRAS ST 79920 #023-01-1970 L1977 **FM** *020 †18

KIM, Hojinglenn J. 1700 MURCHISON DR 79902 #048-15-1991 L1996 **AN** *020 †05

KIME, Lynn Ray. 2001 N OREGON ST, PROVIDENCE MEM HOSP PATH 79902 #007-02-1966 L1973 **PTH** *020 †50

KING, Barry Griffith, Jr. 3100 N LEE TREVINO DR 79936 #035-03-1968 L1970 **ORS** *020 †40

KING, Clinton Allen. 10657 VISTA DEL SOL DR 79925 #047-07-1973 L1975 **D PD** *020

KIRKS, Donald Ray. 5400 SUNCREST DR, STE B3 79912 #028-02-1968 L1968 **PDR DR** *030 †80

KLEIN, Terren David. 1755 CURIE DR, STE B 79902 #021-05-1988 L1989 **ORS** *020 †40

KLYSIK, Michal. ■ 79912 #048-15-2008 *012

KOKASH, Fares Atef. 4800 ALBERTA AVE, DEPT OF PEDIATRICS 79905 #875-01-1988 L2002 **CHN PD** *040 †55

KOLLI, Venkateswara Rao. 1250 E CLIFF DR, STE 4A 79902 #495-62-1981 L1994 **GE IM** *020 †20

KOOPMEINERS, Stephen H. ■ 79912 #001-02-1981 L1984 **PTH** *062 †50

KORZEC, Kenneth Richard. 5959 GATEWAY BLVD W, STE 160 79925 #016-01-1981 L1996 **OTO** *020 †45

KOSAREK, Cheryl A. 7300 REMCON CIR 79912 #048-14-1984 L1991 **D** *020 †15

KROMAH, Fatuma Aisha. ■ 79912 #041-14-2004 **GS** *012

KRONFOL, Rana Nabil. 650 BELVIDERE ST 79912 #605-01-1997 L2000 **PD** *020 †55

KUMAR, Sathees B. 1201 E SCHUSTER AVE STE 3B 79902 #495-31-1970 L1981 **PDC PD** *020 †55 ‡

KUNG, Alice Wei-Li. ■ 79912 #048-15-2006 L2006 **IM** *012

KUPETZ, Ira Sam. 10420 VISTA DEL SOL DR 79925 #021-06-1983 L1990 **DR** *020

LACERTE, Daniel. 4800 ALBERTA AVE, DIV NEUR SURG 79905 #067-04-1987 L2006 **NS** *020

LACY, Linda. 7430 REMCON CIR, STE B100 79912 #048-13-1987 L1989 **OBG** *020 †30

LAGUNAS, Yolanda. 7878 GATEWAY BLVD E, STE 103 79915 #048-12-1982 L1986 **OBG** *020 †30

LALUDE, Omosalewa O. 4800 ALBERTA AVE, TEXAS TECH UNIV INT MED 79905 #690-02-1995 L2006 **CD** *020 †20 ‡

LAM, M Tai. 1501 ARIZONA AVE, STE 2A 79902 #244-03-1973 L1979 **ID IM** *020 †20

LANDEROS, Mark M. 1700 CURIE DR, STE 1500 79902 #649-27-1987 L1999 **GS SO** *020 †85

LANZONA-FAMATIGAN, Maria. 1250 E CLIFF DR, STE 5A 79902 #748-01-1988 L2003 **IM** *020 †20

LARA, Michael D. 10201 GATEWAY BLVD W STE 1, RIO GRANDE SURGEONS, P.A. 79902 #048-02-1998 L2004 **GS** *020 †85

LARSON, Anita A. 5005 N PIEDRAS ST STOP 3, WILLIAM BEAUMONT AMC 79920 #027-01-1964 L1964 **IM OM** *020

LARSON, Steven Scott. 1201 E SCHUSTER AVE, STE 3A 79902 #048-15-1983 L1983 **GS** *020 †85

LATIFF, Guillermo Alfonso. 125 W HAGUE RD, STE 400 79902 #012-05-1985 L1998 **UP U** *020 †95

LAWRENCE, Joseph Franklin. 1625 MEDICAL CENTER ST 79902 #048-12-1965 L1965 **PTH** *020 †50

LAWSON, Mark E. 1625 MEDICAL CENTER ST 79902 #048-15-1990 L1991 **PD NPM** *020 †55

LAYUMAS, Catalino D. ■ 79934 #748-11-1966 L1981 **OS FM** *020

LEE, Howard Monroe, Jr. 1700 N OREGON ST, STE 790 79902 #047-06-1967 L1978 **NS** *020

LEE, Kenneth Amos. 5005 N PIEDRAS ST, DETP MCD/DSB-W BEAUMONT 79920 #047-07-1975 L1988 **MDM** *030

LEE, Llewellyn Vanorden. ■ 79912 #023-12-2001 L2007 **VIR** *020 †80

LEE, Sukhyung. 5005 N PIEDRAS ST, GENERAL SURGERY SERVICE 79920 #051-04-2003 L2005 **GS** *020

LEE, Young Ernest. 5005 N PIEDRAS ST, DEPT MED 79920 #024-07-2007 **IM** *012

LEECH, James Johnston. 5005 N PIEDRAS ST, WILLIAM BEAUMONT ARMY MEDI 79920 #048-13-1982 L1983 **NS** *062 †25

LEITCH, Walter Shad. ■ 79912 #023-12-2000 L2002 **IM** *100 †20

LE MAR, Homer Jess, Jr. 5005 N PIEDRAS ST STOP 3, WILLIAM BEAUMONT ARMY MED 79920 #028-03-1980 L1983 **END IM** *030 †20

LEMEZ, Alma. 4800 ALBERTA AVE, TX TECH U HLTH SCI CTR 79905 #957-08-1986 L2008 **FM** *020 †18

LEONG, Daniel. ■ 79907 #054-15-1964 **OS GP** *071

LEON SANCHEZ, Andres Rica. 4800 ALBERTA AVE, DEPT OF INTERNAL MED 79905 #737-06-2002 L2007 **IM** *100 †20

LEVANDOWSKI, Dale Howard. 5005 N PIEDRAS ST, WILLIAM BEAUMONT AMC 79920 #023-12-1997 L1998 **GS** *020 †75

LEVESQUE, Daniel Yuan. 1900 N OREGON ST, STE 314 79902 #048-15-2002 L2005 **IM** *020 †20

LEVINE, Johanan Sidney. 4800 ALBERTA AVE DEPT NEUR, TEXAS TECH UNIV HLTH SCI 79905 #035-46-1972 L1979 **N CHN** *020 †55,75 ‡

LEYVA, Rodolfo. 1729 WESTON BRENT LN STE A 79935 #049-01-1978 L1981 **PD** *020

LI, Deqing. 5005 N PIEDRAS ST, DEPT OF INTERNAL MED 79905 #243-22-1984 **IM** *012

LICON, Octavio. 10410 VISTA DEL SOL DR 79925 #649-01-1971 L1978 **ORS** *020 †40

LIM, William S. 5005 N PIEDRAS ST, WBAMC OPHTHALMOLOGY CLN 79920 #016-42-1999 L2001 **OPH** *020 †35

LIN, Yuezhen. 4800 ALBERTA AVE, DEPARTMENT OF PEDIATRICS 79905 #243-33-1987 L2007 **PD** *012

LINAN, Luis Enrique. 2400 TRAWOOD DR, STE 304 79936 #048-15-1989 L1990 **OBG** *020 †30

LIPTAKOVA, Helga Helga. 9870 GATEWAY BLVD N STE B7 79924 #286-12-1988 L1996 **PD** *020 †55

LIZARRAGA, Alejandro M. ■ 79902 #649-01-1966 L1978 **P** *020

LLAMAS, Luis. 2001 N OREGON ST, PROVIDENCE MEMORIAL HOPITA 79902 #649-01-1974 L1979 **PTH PCP** *020 †50 ‡

LLAMAS-SOFORO, Jorge F. ■ 79913 #649-27-1973 L1979 **OPH** *020 †35

LLOVERAS, Charlene E. 5001 N PIEDRAS ST, VA HEALTHCARE CENTER (111) 79930 #649-33-1994 L2002 **FM** *020 †18

LOAIZA QUINTERO, Jose Leo. 9849 KENWORTHY ST, TEXAS TECH UNIV-FAMILY PRA 79924 #264-05-1994 L2007 **FM** *020 †18

LODHI, Huma Yasmeen. 2260 TRAWOOD DR, PHYSICIANS HEALTHCARE ASSO 79935 #704-25-1991 L1999 **PD** *020 †55

LOEFFLER, Allison Melanie. ■ 79902 #056-05-2007 **OBG** *012

LOFLIN, James R. 8600 MONTANA AVE, EL PASO FIRE DEPARTMENT EM 79925 #048-02-1986 L1988 **EM** *040 †16

LOFTIN, Ryan Wade. ■ 79912 #048-02-2003 L2007 **OBG** *012

LONGORIA, Alfredo. 125 W HAGUE RD STE 150 79902 #649-14-1970 L1980 **GS VS** *020

LONGORIA, Rolando Rene. 10301 GATEWAY BLVD W 79925 #048-13-1978 L1978 **GE NTR** *020

LOPEZ, Arsenio L. 7848 GATEWAY BLVD E, EL PASO CANCER TREATMENT 79915 #748-02-1989 L1996 **ON** *020 †20

LOPEZ, Hector Manuel. 9849 KENWORTHY ST 79924 #048-02-2001 L2004 **FM** *020 †18

LOPEZ, Jose A. ■ 79912 #048-02-1999 L2001 **IM** *020

LOPEZ, Manuel De Jesus. 10470 VISTA DEL SOL DR, STE 208 79925 #649-07-1979 L1995 **NEP IM** *020 †20

LOPEZ-CORONADO, Anabel. 4800 ALBERTA AVE, HEALTH SCIENCE 79905 #649-33-2001 L2007 **IM** *020

LOPEZ-PO, Patricia. 700 S OCHOA ST, CENTRO DE SALUD LA FE 79901 #649-33-1987 L1998 **FM** *020 †18

LO PICCOLO, Philip Frank. 9513 DESERT HILLS LN 79925 #030-06-1967 L1980 **PD OS** *020 †55

LOUBRIEL VELEZ, Carlos. 4242 HONDO PASS DR, STE 101 79904 #042-01-1990 L1995 **OBG** *020 †30

LOWE, Ralph Stephen. ■ 79922 #048-13-1973 L1973 **AI IM** *020 †20,03

LOYA, Juan Francisco. 1724 WESTON BRENT LN 79935 #048-12-1992 L1993 **GS FM** *100

LOZANO, Hector. 5959 GATEWAY BLVD W 79925 #649-27-1985 L1993 **AN** *020

LOZANO, Javier E. 125 W HAGUE RD STE 400 79902 #649-01-1969 L1975 **U** *020 †95

LOZANO, Jesus Lorenzo. 1600 MEDICAL CENTR DR #410 79902 #649-01-1975 L1992 **PD** *020

LOZANO, Oscar. 1625 MEDICAL CENTER ST 79902 #649-01-1954 L1968 **OBG GP** *020 †71

LOZANO, Porfirio, Jr. 5001 N PIEDRAS ST, DEPT OF VETERANS AFFAIRS 79930 #028-79-1963, ▲ L1963 **IM** *020

LU, Yujuan. 5005 N PIEDRAS ST 79920 #243-43-1985 L2007 **IM** *012

LUGO, Andres Moran. ■ 79932 #649-01-1981 *100

LUGO, Esmeralda. ■ 79925 #048-14-2008 *012

LUKASIK, Adam Michal. ■ 79934 #055-02-2004 L2006 **IM** *020 †20

LUKOWSKI, John Luke. 1221 N COTTON ST 79902 #048-02-1954 L1954 **FM** *071 †18

LUMINARIAS, Victoria E. 5005 N PIEDRAS ST, STOP 36 79920 #748-01-1969 L1976 **PD** *020 †55

LUNA, Emilio. ■ 79912 #005-14-1996 L2004 **PD** *020 †55 ‡

LUNA, Jose. 8061 ALAMEDA AVE 79915 #056-06-1980 L1984 **FM** *020 †18

LUNDY, Ray Olva. 10555 VISTA DEL SOL DR, STE 120 79925 #047-07-1967 L1973 **HEM ON** *020 †20

LUO, Jun. 4800 ALBERTA AVE 79905 #243-76-1985 **PD** *012

LUTTER, Michelle Lea. ■ 79934 #046-01-2002 L2004 **OBG** *020 †30

LYMAN, Curtis Harold. 1801 N OREGON ST 79902 #048-02-1960 L1960 **FM OS** *020 †18

LYN, Heidi Anderson. 4800 ALBERTA AVE, DEPT OBG 79905 #048-04-1994 L1995 **OBG** *020 †30

LYN, Ian Thomas. 1600 MEDICAL CENTER ST, EL PASO SOUTHWESTERN 79902 #048-04-1994 L1995 **TS** *020 †85,90

LYON, Charles M. 1900 N OREGON ST, STE 400 79902 #033-05-1960 L1970 **GS UM** *020 †85

MABRY, M Dennis. ■ 79912 #048-14-1974 L1974 **EM** *075

MACCARIO, Micheline. ■ 79902 #165-04-1958 L1962 **N P** *071 †75

MACHEN, Michael Shaun. 5005 N PIEDRAS ST 79920 #023-12-1992 L2002 **ORS GP** *020 †40

MACHORRO, Angelica Imelda. 2260 TRAWOOD DR 79935 #048-15-2003 L2006 **PD** *020 †55

MAC KAY, John M, Jr. 4800 ALBERTA AVE, TEXAS TECH UNIVERSITY 79905 #038-43-1984 L1993 **EM** *020 †16

MAC PHAIL, Donald Clark. 2626 N MESA ST # 336 79902 #803-03-1951 L1967 **ORS** *071 †40

MADDOX, Robert Mc Lemore. 601 SUNLAND PARK DR, STE 2 79912 #048-02-1970 L1970 **OPH** *020 †35

MADKOUR, Amr Mohamed. ■ 79912 #048-15-2008 *012

MAGANA, Jorge Carlos. 5115 EL PASO DR 79905 #649-01-1956 L1966 **PD** *071 †55

MAGNANO, Aldo. 2001 N OREGON ST 79902 #132-01-1962 L1969 **PTH** *071 †50

MAHALE, Aarti Sunil. ■ 79912 #496-42-2000 EM *012

MAHBUBANI, Sunil Ramesh. 4800 ALBERTA AVE, DEPT OF EMERGENCY MED 79905 #048-15-2006 L2008 **EM** *012

MAIYEGUN, Sitratullah Ola. 4800 ALBERTA AVE, DEPARTMENT OF PEDIATRICS 79905 #690-02-1984 L2007 **PD** *012

MAJEED, Hashim A. 2300 MCKINLEY AVE 79902 #704-02-1990 L1995 **IM** *020 †20

MALDONADO, Cesar E. 10420 VISTA DEL SOL DR # 2, VISTA DEL SOL DIALYSIS 79925 #781-06-1980 L1998 **IM** *020

MALDONADO, Leonard. 5005 N PIEDRAS ST, WILLIAM BEAUMONT AMC 79920 #035-08-1946 L1988 **U** *071 †95

MALDONADO-MELENDEZ, H. 3260 N MESA ST 79902 #649-01-1974 L1991 **N** *020 †75

MALEKZADEH, Farzad. 4800 ALBERTA AVE 79905 #305-01-2001 L2005 **AN** *100

MALIK, Jamil Ayub. 5005 N PIEDRAS ST, CARDIOLOGY SERVICE 79920 #023-12-1995 L1997 **CD** *020 †20 ‡

MANEEVESE, Brian. ■ 79912 #048-15-2007 **EM** *012

MANI, Anju Arjan. 1625 MEDICAL CENTER DR, DEPT. OF PATHOLOGY 79902 #495-17-1995 L2002 **PTH** *020 †50

MANN, John Leroy. ■ 79912 #048-02-1964 L1964 **OPH** *071 †35

MANQUERO-BUTLER, Martha I. 1625 MEDICAL CENTER ST 79902 #649-33-1994 L2002 **FM** *020 †18

MANSFIELD, David J. 1755 CURIE DR, STE B 79902 #048-04-1996 L2000 **ORS** *020 †40

MANSFIELD, Lyndon Edwin. 4800 ALBERTA AVE 79905 #041-02-1968 L1984 **AI ALI** *020 †55,03

MARCELLO, Alton. 4800 ALBERTA AVE 79905 #038-45-2002 L2002 **OBG** *012

MARGOLIS, Michael J. ■ 79912 #048-02-2008 *012

MARGOLIS, Moises Eugenio. 200 S ALTO MESA DR 79912 #649-01-1968 L1975 **DR** *020

MAROS, Michael Andrew. 125 W HAGUE RD STE 500 79902 #048-14-1974 L1974 **ON IM** *020

MARQUEZ, Francisco Javier. 2616 N OREGON ST 79902 #649-27-1980 L1989 **P** *020 †75

MARQUEZ-SMITH, Teresa. 1250 E CLIFF DR, STE 4B 79902 #048-13-1991 L1994 **PD** *020

MARRANZINI, Benito A. ■ 79912 #308-02-1992 L2004 **END** *020 †20

MARSH, Kevin Lester. 5005 N PIEDRAS ST, WILLIAM BEAUMONT ARMY MEDI 79920 #035-09-2001 L2002 **PD** *020 †55

MARTELL, Gustavo Armando. 10301 GATEWAY BLVD W 79925 #048-02-1991 L1992 **OBG** *020 †30

MARTIN, Charmaine Alicia. 9849 KENWORTHY ST 79924 #048-02-1996 L2006 **FM** *020 †18 ‡

MARTIN, Gregory Edward. 1900 N OREGON ST STE 600 79902 #649-33-1987 L1997 **IM** *020 †20

MARTIN, Luis Alberto. ■ 79905 #048-02-2004 **IM** *020

MARTINEZ, Azalia Veronica. 1625 MEDICAL CENTER ST 79902 #048-15-1977 L1978 **FM EM** *020 †18

MARTINEZ, Daniel. ■ 79936 #649-01-1984 *020

MARTINEZ, Hector Raul. 1900 N OREGON ST STE 307 79902 #132-02-1960 L1969 **END IM** *020 †20

MARTINEZ, Ileana. 5823 N MESA ST 79912 #649-33-1992 L1998 **NEP** *020 †20

MARTINEZ, Luis Alberto. 4801 ALBERTA AVE, DEPT OF INTERNAL MEDICINE 79905 #275-01-1993 L2006 **IM** *020 †20

MARTINEZ, Renee Lucia. 4800 ALBERTA AVE, DEPT OF INTERNAL MED 79905 #682-03-2001 L2007 **IM** *020 †20

MARTINEZ, Robert Eric. ■ 79936 #048-15-2007 **EM** *012

MARTINEZ-CLARK, Gloria. 10201 GATEWAY BLVD W 79925 #042-03-1990 L1995 **OBG** *020 †30

MARTINEZ-LOPEZ, Jorge I. 4800 ALBERTA AVE 79905 #021-05-1950 L1950 **CD IM** *040 †20

MARTINEZ-ROSS, Juan Manue. ■ 79912 #023-12-2006 L2007 **IM** *012

MARWAH, Rajendra K. 1600 MEDICAL CENTER ST, STE 314 79902 #495-45-1971 L1981 **IM RHU** *020 †20 ‡

MARZOUK, Shaden. ■ 79932 #028-34-1998 L1998 **NS** *100

MASEL, David Lawrence. 3100 N LEE TREVINO DR 79936 #012-05-1985 L1995 **NS** *020 †25

MASIH, Namrata S. 4800 ALBERTA AVE, TX TECH U HLTH SCI CTR 79905 #495-43-1990 L1996 **PD** *020 †55

MASPONS, Aldo Rene. ■ 79936 #048-12-2006 L2006 **PD** *012

MASTER, Kiron Shyam. 200 S ALTO MESA DR 79912 #496-38-1991 L2001 **DR** *020 †20,80

MATABAN, Antonio A B. ■ 79938 #748-01-1957 L1970 **U** *020 †95

MATLOCK, John P. ■ 79912 #033-06-1990 L2001 **PTH PCP** *020 †50

MAURIELLO, Ginett Annina. 3329 MONTANA AVE, SALUD Y VIDA 79903 #067-03-1959 L1981 **GP** *020

MAXWELL, Amy Ann. 1801 N OREGON ST, RADIOLOGY DEPARTMENT 79902 #016-06-1997 L2006 **DR** *020 †80

MAY, Robert Paul. 720 ARIZONA AVE 79902 #048-12-1962 L1962 **PUD IM** *020 †20

MCCLENDON, Dixie Ann. ■ 79938 #048-14-2007 **TY** *012

MC CULLOUGH, Willis H. 1700 MURCHISON DR, STE 104 79902 #048-02-1959 L1959 **AN** *071 †05

MC DANALD, Eugene Chester. 2022 MURCHISON DR, STE 104 79902 #048-02-1973 L1973 **RHU IM** *020 †20

MC ELVAINE, Phillip Paul. 24OO MORCHISON ST 79930 #048-15-1979 L1979 **EM** *020

MC GEE, William Gordon. 1600 MEDICAL CENTER DR, STE 222 79902 #048-12-1958 L1958 **ATP CLP** *062 †50

MC GOVERN, Robert Gregory. 721 S OCHOA ST 79901 #035-01-1947 L1980 **PD OS** *030 †55

MCGRAW, Robert Pennington, III. 4800 ALBERTA AVE, HEALTH SCIENCE 79905 #048-15-2006 **AN** *012

MC LEAN, Joseph C. ■ 79912 #023-12-2003 L2005 **IM** *100 †20

MC LEAN, Susan Faye. 4800 ALBERTA AVE, HEALTH SCIENCES CNTR EL 79905 #051-04-1988 L1999 **GS** *020 †20

MC MASTERS, Robert Earl. ■ 79912 #048-02-1958 L1958 **N OS** *030

MC NEILL, Matthew Francis. ■ 79925 #025-07-2005 L2007 **IM** *012

MEDINA, Irma. 4800 ALBERTA AVE 79905 #649-33-1987 L2000 **PD** *020 †55

MEDINA, Josue Antonio. 7351 ALAMEDA AVE TRLR 21 79915 #048-15-2008 *012

MEDRANO, Rafael. 1700 N OREGON ST STE 570 79902 #048-04-1987 L1988 **CD** *020 †20

MEHTA, Nilesh. 6065 MONTANA AVE, STE A1 79925 #495-23-1986 L1992 **IM** *020 †20

MEIER, Donald Edward. 4800 ALBERTA AVE, DEPT OF SURGERY 79905 #047-06-1971 L1973 **PDS** *020 †85

MELGAR, Alberto. 1221 N COTTON ST STE 321, PANAMENCAN COMM HOSP 79902 #649-01-1956 L1960 **GE GS** *020 †85

MENA, Ascension Contveras. 907 CHELSEA ST STE 6 79903 #025-12-1982 L1984 **FM** *020 †18

MENDOZA, Joe. 1700 CURIE DR, STE 5900 79902 #039-01-1971 L1975 **OBG** *020

MENDOZA, Michelle Lee. 2300 MCKINLEY AVE, BIEN VIVIR SENIOR HEALTH 79930 #038-45-2001 L2004 **IM** *020

MENDOZA, Omar. 4636 CAPLES CIR 79903 #048-14-1999 L2001 **EM** *020 †16

MENDOZA CASTILLO, Rodin R. 1860 DEAN MARTIN DR, STE 101 79936 #649-31-1992 L2002 **PD** *020

MENDOZA SANCHEZ, Carlos. 812 N VIRGINIA ST STE 214 79902 #649-27-1993 *100

MENENDEZ-CORDOVA, Rogelio. 10470 VISTA DEL SOL DR 79925 #021-01-1972 L1979 **AI PUD** *055

MENJIVAR FLORES, Eduardo. 4800 ALBERTA AVE, DEPT EM 79905 #341-05-2002 **EM** *012 †20

MERLICH, Earle D. ■ 79904 #649-01-1965 L1974 **IM** *100

MERWORTH, Roy Warren. ■ 79930 #048-12-1959 L1959 **GP A** *071

MESHEL, William Norman. 10600 VISTA ALEGRE DR, # 4 79935 #010-03-1971 L1977 **IM EM** *020

METRIKIN, David Colin. 1733 WESTON BRENT LN, SOUTHWEST RETINA 79935 #836-01-1985 L1994 **OPH** *020 †20

MEZA, Aida Francisca. ■ 79912 #048-14-2004 L2006 **EM** *020

MEZA, Ana M. 1700 N OREGON ST, STE 515 79902 #048-03-1991 L1996 **IM** *020 †20

MEZA, Armando D. 4800 ALBERTA AVE 79905 #649-33-1988 L1992 **ID** *020 †20

MICHON, Joseph, Jr. ■ 79902 #023-07-1964 L1970 **OPH** *020 †35

MIDEZ, Jaime A. 10412 VISTA DEL SOL DR, STE 2A 79925 #231-05-1990 L1993 **IM** *020

MILES, Philip Austin. 8815 DYER ST STE 300, GYN PATH SERVICE 79904 #035-09-1964 L1977 **ATP GYN** *072 †30,50

MILLER, Brandon James. ■ 79912 #048-15-2005 **OBG** *012

MILLER, Jerry Winkler. 1700 N OREGON ST, STE 630 79902 #051-01-1976 L1987 **CD IM** *020 †20

MILLER, William Thad. 7132 N MESA ST 79912 #048-04-1966 L1966 **PS** *040 †65

MILLET, Lauren Christine. ■ 79912 #048-15-2008 *012

MILLETT, Fay Edward, Jr. 1900 N OREGON ST, STE 209 79902 #054-04-1962 L1968 **OPH PS** *071 †35

MINJARES, Jaime Raul. 5301 ALAMEDA AVE 79905 #649-27-1980 L1989 **IM EM** *020

MIRANDA, Blas Alberto Dia. 1015 N ZARAGOZA RD 79907 #649-27-1984 L2006 **IM** *020

MIRANDA RUEDA, Carlos. 5849 DIAMOND POINT CIR 79912 #649-27-1967 L1974 **GS** *030 †85

MISENHIMER, Gregory R. 1720 MURCHISON DR 79902 #048-15-1982 L1983 **ORS OSS** *020 †40

MITCHELL, Malcolm Stuart. ■ 79902 #008-01-1962 L1968 **ON IM** *050 †20

MITSUY IRIKURA, Leonardo. 4800 ALBERTA AVE 79905 #737-10-2004 **GS** *100

MOIN, Furqan. 1900 N OREGON ST, STE 312 79902 #704-16-1992 L2001 **NPM** *020 †55

MOKONCHU, Monique Charnge. 1600 MEDICAL CENTER ST, STE 102 79902 #012-21-1989 L2006 **OBG** *020 †30

MOLINA, Armando. 10501 VISTA DEL SOL DR 79925 #649-14-1969 L1985 **GS** *072

MOLINA, David. ■ 79936 #048-12-1998 **EM FM** *020

MOLINA, Melissa Ann. 1801 N OREGON ST 79902 #034-01-1997 L2000 **FM** *020 †18

MOLINARES, Vanina. ■ 79925 #264-25-2000 **IM** *012

MONDRAGON, Richard M. ■ 79902 #034-01-1991 L2005 **PTH** *020 †50

MONSIVAIS, Jose Jesus. 2400 TRAWOOD DR, STE 303 79936 #649-14-1971 L1986 **HS PMM** *020 †85

MONTANEZ, Tomy. ■ 79936 #649-33-1988 L1995 **FM** *020 †18

MONTELONGO, Juan A. 5832 CORONADO RIDGE DR, EL PASO TX 79912 79912 #048-15-1988 L1990 **IM** *020 †16

MONTERROSA, Ana Elizabeth. 4800 ALBERTA AVE 79905 #341-01-1982 **P** *012

MONTES, Rebecca. 125 W HAGUE RD, RIO GRANDE OB/GYN 79902 #048-02-2000 L2004 **OBG** *020

MONTOYA, Teodoro I. ■ 79912 #048-12-2006 **OBG** *012

MOORE, Debora Kay. 1700 N OREGON ST STE 560, OF THE SOUTHWEST 79902 #018-03-1992 L2003 **U** *020

MOORE, Robert Gene. 1700 N OREGON ST STE 560, SOUTHWEST 79902 #021-06-1987 L1988 **U** *020 †95

MOORTHY, Chetan S. 7040 N MESA ST, STE P 79912 #048-02-1991 L1993 **PDR** *020 †80

MORALES, Carlos Alfonso. 4800 ALBERTA AVE 79905 #264-05-1964 L1972 **PTH** *020 †55

MORALES, Carmela P. 1700 CURIE DR STE 48 79902 #048-12-1991 L1999 **GE** *020 †20

MORALES GONZALEZ, Angel M. 4800 ALBERTA AVE 79905 #649-52-2002 **GS** *012

MOREIRA, Gerardo Jose. 5821 DIAMOND POINT CIR 79912 #682-01-1981 L1992 **P** *020 †75

MORENO, Albert Jos. 5005 N PIEDRAS ST STOP 36, WILLIAM BEAUMONT AMC 79920 #005-14-1978 L1989 **NM IM** *040 †28

MORENO, Guillermo Enrique. ■ 79903 #847-10-1976 **CHP P** *071

MORENO, Joseph Angel. 5959 GATEWAY BLVD W, STE 120 79925 #048-15-1991 L1992 **AN** *020

MORENO, Robert Arnold. 2022 MURCHISON DR, STE 104 79902 #649-33-1984 L1990 **IM PM** *020

MORGADES, Juan. 827 E YANDELL DR 79902 #132-01-1958 L1972 **GS** *020 †85

MORRIS, Allister Kelly. 2616 N OREGON ST 79902 #047-06-1969 L1974 **P AN** *020 †05,75

MORTON, Richard Albert D. 10470 VISTA DEL SL DR #110 79925 #021-01-1957 L1963 **OTO A** *020 †45

MOSES, Lyndon Denny. ■ 79904 #048-02-1952 L1952 **GP** *072

MOTTA, Angelica J. ■ 79924 #048-02-2006 **IM** *012

MOUJAN, Pablo Miguel. 5005 N PIEDRAS ST, WILLIAM BEAUMONT AMC 79920 #132-01-1983 L2006 **AN** *020 †05

MROCHEK, Michael John. 1720 MURCHISON DR, I 79902 #047-06-1986 L1994 **PM OM** *020 †60

MUNOZ, Cruz Arturo. ■ 79903 #048-16-2006 **PD** *012

MUNOZ, Luis R. 2905 N STANTON ST 79902 #649-33-1990 L1996 **PD** *020 †55

MUNOZ, Oscar Carlos. 2820 N STANTON ST 79902 #264-13-1992 L2002 **IC CD** *020 †20

MURILLO, Carlos Andres. ■ 79902 #048-02-2000 L2007 **GS** *012

MURILLO, Tomas. 5959 GATEWAY BLVD W # 120 79925 #649-27-1965 L1977 **AN** *020

MURTAZA, Ghulam. 125 W HAGUE RD STE 260, RIO GRANDE OB GYN GROUP 79902 #704-01-1970 L1976 **OBG** *020 †30

MYERS, Keith Paul. ■ 79932 #023-12-2002 L2004 **PM** *020 †60

NADORRA, Rosario. 2022 MURCHISON DR STE 104 79902 #748-02-1976 L2002 **RHU IM** *020 †20

NAHOURAII, Richard A. ■ 79902 #008-01-1996 L1998 **GS** *020 †85

NAIR, Jyoti Govindan. 4800 ALBERTA AVE 79905 #495-48-1991 **PD** *012

NAJERA, Raul Abel. 745 S MESA HILLS DR, STE E 79912 #649-33-1981 L1986 **OM** *020 †18

NANDHAGOPALAN, Kugathasan. 7848 GATEWAY BLVD E, EL PASO CANCER CTR 79915 #495-95-1989 L2005 **HO** *020 †20

NANEZ, Gary. 5959 GATEWAY BLVD W, STE 160 79925 #034-01-1997 L2002 **OTO** *020 †45

NANG, Roberto Natividad. 5005 N PIEDRAS ST, STOP 36 79920 #049-01-1987 L1990 **PHP GP** *030 †70

NARAYAN, Rajeev. ■ 79912 #016-42-1997 **NEP IM** *020 †20

NASSOUR, Herbert Jim, III. 125 W HAGUE RD, STE 360 79902 #048-15-1988 **PS GS** *020 †85,65

NAVAR, Thomas R, Jr. 5400 SUNCREST DR, STE B3 79912 #649-01-1973 L1976 **AN** *020

NAVARRO, Teodoro C. ■ 79904 #748-01-1971 L1979 **U** *071

NAYLOR, Anthony Denis. 4800 ALBERTA AVE, TX TECH HSC EL PASO 79905 #917-26-1967 L1978 **R** *020 †80

NDUKA, Chinwe Celestina. 5301 ALAMEDA AVE STE 107, ECKLAND MED CLNC 79905 #690-04-1989 L1998 **FM** *020 †18

NEGRETE, Margaret. 5400 SUNCREST DR, STE B3 79912 #018-75-1989, ▲ L1992 **AN** *020

NEILL, Lynn W. 5400 SUNCREST DR, STE B3 79912 #048-02-1957 L1957 **AN** *020 †05

NEIMAN, Parviz. 5655 STARVIEW DR 79912 #517-05-1973 L1983 **DR** *020 †80

NEIRA, Carlos J. 5005 N PIEDRAS ST, WILLIAM BEAUMONT ARMY MED 79920 #682-01-1981 L1996 **ID** *020 †20

NELSON, Brian Keith. 6090 SURETY DR STE 412, TEXAS TECH UNIV REGIONAL 79905 #048-04-1975 L1975 **EM AM** *040 †16

NELSON, Erin Lynn. 6582 WIND RIDGE DR, UTHSCSA 79912 #035-09-1998 L2000 **OBG** *020 †30

NELSON, William J, Jr. 4800 ALBERTA AVE 79905 #048-02-1953 L1953 **NS** *071 †25

NEWLON, James Lewis, Jr. 5005 N PIEDRAS ST 79920 #005-12-2000 L2006 **OTO** *020 †45

NGUYEN, Khanh D. ■ 79922 #048-13-1990 L1992 **DR** *020 †80

NGUYEN, Tu Huu. ■ 79922 #941-01-1975 L1987 **PTH** *020 †50

NICHITA, Simona. 4800 ALBERTA AVE 79905 #781-01-1992 L2008 **PD** *012

NICKERSON, Mary Ann. 1700 N OREGON ST, STE 520 79902 #037-01-1977 L1980 **OBG** *020

NICKEY, Laurance Noyes. ■ 79912 #048-04-1955 L1955 **PHP PD** *071 †55

NIXON, Seigrid Nason. 5001 N PIEDRAS ST, EL PASO, VAHCS 79930 #041-09-1997 L1998 **IM** *020

NOBLE, Luis Salomon. 700 S MESA HILLS DR 79912 #649-52-1987 L1993 **REN GYN** *020 †30

NODLER, James Leonard. ■ 79902 #048-15-2008 *012

NOE, Michiel R. 1440 GEORGE DIETER DR, STE A 79936 #048-15-1993 L1994 **OBG** *020 †30

NORIEGA, Oscar Alberto. 9849 KENWORTHY ST, TEXAS TECH UNIVERSITY 79924 #005-02-1977 L1992 **FM** *020 †18

NOVOA, Julio Cesar. 2200 TRAWOOD DR, STE 308 79935 #047-07-1995 L1999 **OBG** *020

NOWAK, Paul Christopher. 1225 E CLIFF DR, BLDG3 79902 #048-12-1996 L1998 **PD** *020 †55

NUTIS, Dinorah Janet. 4800 ALBERTA AVE 79905 #649-33-1997 L2004 **IM** *040 †20

NUTIS, Mario. ■ 79924 #649-33-1998 L2003 **OBG** *100 †18

NUWAYHID, Bahij Suleiman. 4800 ALBERTA AVE, TEXAS TECH HSC 79905 #605-01-1968 L2005 **OBG** *040 †30

NUZZO, Michael Salvatore. ■ 79912 #033-06-2003 L2005 **ORS** *012

NWOSU, Azikiwe C. 4800 ALBERTA AVE, DEPT OF INTERNAL MEDICINE 79905 #690-04-1979 L1996 **NEP** *020

OBREGON, Jacinto Amaru. 4800 ALBERTA AVE 79905 #682-03-2001 **FP** *012

OCARANZA-FLORES, Hector I. 1801 N OREGON ST 79902 #649-33-1993 L1999 **PD** *020

OCHOA, Leah Marie. 5005 N PIEDRAS ST, MED CTR 79920 #023-12-2005 L2006 **ORS** *012

OCHOA, Reinaldo Rodriguez. 1755 CURIE DR, EL PASO SPECIALTY HOSPITAL 79902 #649-14-1997 L2002 **EM** *020 †16

OKADA, Ken. 10301 GATEWAY BLVD W, DEL SOL MED CTR DEPT SURGR 79925 #023-12-1991 L2001 **AN** *020 †05

O'KEEFE, Neil Thos. 5001 N PIEDRAS ST, DEPT OF VETERAN AFFAIRS VA 79930 #025-01-1961 L1975 **OPH** *020 †35

OKWUNWANNE, Kenneth Chukw. ■ 79912 #166-01-2000 L2001 **FM** *020

O'LEARY, John B. ■ 79912 #026-04-1951 **IM** *040 †20

OLIVA, Luis. 10420 MONTWOOD DR STE H 79935 #308-03-1984 L1989 **PD** *020 †55

OLIVARES, Robert Arnold. 5400 SUNCREST DR, STE B3 79912 #026-04-1978 L1982 **AN** *020 †05

OLIVARES, Robert Arnold, Jr. 5400 SUNCREST DR, STE B3 79912 #025-12-2003 L2007 **AN** *100

OLIVAS, Victor Jesus, Jr. ■ 79912 #048-12-2007 **GS** *012

OLIVER, Thomas George. 5005 N PIEDRAS ST STOP 23, WILLIAM BEAUMONT AMC 79920 #035-09-1995 L2003 **END IM** *020 †20

OMBABA, Jackson M. 4800 ALBERTA AVE, STERLING REGIONAL MEDICAL 79905 #038-41-2000 L2007 **GS** *100 †85 ‡

OPAWUMI, David Oluwole, Jr. ■ 79912 #033-05-2001 L2007 **NEP** *020 †20

ORELLANA, Miguel Alfredo. 10412 VISTA DEL SOL DR, STE 2A 79925 #319-04-1992 L2003 **IM** *100

ORELLANA CALDERON, Alan E. 4800 ALBERTA AVE, DEPT OF INTERNAL MED 79905 #341-01-1999 **PCC** *012 †20

ORONOZ, Joaquin F. ■ 79934 #042-01-1966 L1970 **OM FM** *030 †70

ORTEGA, Antonio M. 1400 N EL PASO ST, STE D 79902 #748-20-1986 L1996 **ID IM** *020 †20

ORTEGA, Deborah A. 6633 N MESA ST STE 101 79912 #048-02-1992 L1993 **MPD** *020 †05

ORTEGA, Pedro Ovidio A. 118 N HARRIS ST 79907 #275-01-1953 L1963 **GS GP** *030

ORTEGA, Rose Lorraine. 608 S SAINT VRAIN ST 79901 #048-13-2002 L2005 **PD** *020 †55

ORTIZ, Ivan A. ■ 79932 #048-02-1999 L2003 **AN** *020 †05 ‡

ORTIZ, Jorge Luis. 10501 VISTA DEL SOL DR, STE 112 79925 #042-01-2000 L2003 **PD** *020

OSUCHUKWU, George Amechi. 4800 ALBERTA AVE 79905 #690-02-2004 **IM** *012

OVALLE, Alejandro. ■ 79932 #649-33-2001 L2006 **IM** *020

OWENS, Brett Douglas. ■ 79912 #010-02-1998 L2003 **OSM** *020

PACHECO, Hector Octavio. 4800 ALBERTA AVE, TEXAS TECH UNIV ORTHOPEDIC 79905 #005-18-1991 L1998 **ORS** *020 †20

PACHECO BLANCO, Sergio. 1900 N OREGON ST, STE 410 79902 #649-02-1963 L1979 **NS** *020

PACHECO-SERRANT, Helson. 1700 N OREGON ST STE 660 79902 #042-01-1992 L1998 **NS** *020

PADILLA, Mario Marcos. 1300 MURCHISON DR STE 100 79902 #048-13-1980 L1980 **OBG** *020 †30

PAGE, Benjamin W. 5005 N PIEDRAS ST, STOP 36 79920 #036-01-1977 L1977 **P ADP** *020 †75

PAGE, Rianne Ashley. ■ 79912 #048-15-2008 *012

PALACIOS, Mariano. 2022 MURCHISON DR, STE 104 79902 #649-33-1983 L1991 **IM OS** *020

PALAFOX, Andrew Jos. 1720 MURCHISON DR, DEL NORTE ORTHOPAEDIC AND 79902 #048-15-1989 L1997 **ORS GS** *020 †40

PALAFOX, David Mario. 2501 N MESA ST 79902 #048-15-1980 L1980 **FM EM** *030 †18 ‡

PALLADINO, Humberto. 4800 ALBERTA AVE, DEPT OF SURGERY 79905 #132-11-2000 L2004 **GS** *012

PALOMINO, Adolfo H. 601 SUNLAND PARK DR, STE 6 79912 #649-01-1967 L1978 **EM FM** *020 †18

PANDO, Jary. 9849 KENWORTHY ST, TEXAS TECH UNIV-FAMILY PRA 79924 #275-02-1994 L2005 **FM** *020 †18

PANIAGUA, Julian Roberto. ■ 79912 #341-01-1987 L2007 **PD** *012

PAPAS, Constantine A. 6524 ROYAL RIDGE DR 79912 #418-01-1956 L1997 **VS GS** *071 †85

PARDO-RUIZ, Fernando Javi. 4800 ALBERTA AVE, TX TECH U HLTH SCI CTR 79905 #649-18-1980 L2005 **IM** *020 †20

PARISI, Sandro B. 1625 MEDICAL CENTER ST 79902 #016-42-1991 L1999 **DR** *020 †80

PARKS, Susan Lynne. 5005 N PIEDRAS ST, VA HEALTH CARE CENTER 79930 #048-13-1986 L1987 **OPH** *020 †35

PARRA, Guillermo. 3017 TRAWOOD DR 79936 #048-14-1984 L1985 **FM** *020

PARTOVI, Sirous N. ■ 79912 #048-02-1987 L1988 **EM** *020 †16,18

PARVEZ, Shabana. 10301 GATEWAY BLVD W 79925 #067-01-1994 L2007 **EM** *012 †18

PASTRANA, Raul Linage. 2001 N OREGON ST 79902 #649-01-1953 L1959 **OBG** *020

PATE, John Woodrow, Jr. 1700 CURIE DR STE 3500 79902 #048-02-1971 L1973 **FPS** *020 †45

PATEL, Jagdish. 11026 VISTA DEL SOL DR 79935 #495-22-1987 L1993 **PD** *020 †55

PATEL, Jignesh Devkaranbh. 11026 VISTA DEL SOL DR 79935 #495-22-1998 L2003 **PD** *020 †55

PATEL, Malini. ■ 79912 #048-15-2008 *012

PATEL, Vinaychandra. 1700 CURIE DR, SUITE 4800 SIERRA TOWER 79902 #919-05-1988 L1995 **GE** *020 †20

PATEL, Vipool R. 1250 E CLIFF DR, STE 2A 79902 #495-23-1988 L1996 **CD** *020 †20

PATTERSON, David S. 4420 LAZY WILLOW DR 79922 #048-02-1995 L1997 **RNR** *020 †80

PATTERSON MALDONADO, John. 9849 KENWORTHY ST, TEXAS TECH UNIV-FAMILY PRA 79924 #649-53-2001 **FP** *012

PAWLOWICZ, Ivan Noe. ■ 79912 #048-15-2004 **P** *012

PAYNE, Phileemon Eric. 4800 ALBERTA AVE, DEPT OF SURGERY 79905 #005-12-2004 **GS** *012

PAZMINO, Patricio A. 1704 N MESA ST 79902 #319-01-1974 L1984 **IM NEP** *020 †20 ‡

PEACOCK, Jack Baxter, Jr. 4800 ALBERTA AVE 79905 #036-01-1964 L1975 **GS CCM** *040 †85

PEAKE, Mark Franklin. 8820 GATEWAY BLVD N 79904 #048-13-1988 L1989 **D GP** *020 †20

PEASE, Howard Francis. 101 RIM RD # 300 79902 #036-07-1970 L1978 **CD IM** *020 †20

PEINADO FRAGOSO, Jesus. 4800 ALBERTA AVE 79905 #649-22-1996 **PD** *012

PEMA, Kanchan Mohan. 4800 ALBERTA AVE, TEXAS TECH HLTH SCI UNIV 79905 #836-05-1978 L1986 **RHU IM** *020 †20

PENA, Jacobo. ■ 79907 #048-14-2006 **FP** *012

PENA, Jennifer Marie. ■ 79912 #041-12-2008 *012

PENARANDA GOMEZ, Eribeth. 4800 ALBERTA AVE, TX TECH U HLTH SCI CTR 79905 #264-01-2000 L2007 **FM** *020 †18

PENA RUIZ, Miguel Angel. 4800 ALBERTA AVE, HEALTH SCIENCE 79905 #649-46-1996 L2007 **IM** *020 †20

PENNINCK, Johan J. 3100 N LEE TREVINO DR 79936 #165-04-1981 L1987 **ORS GS** *020 †40

PENON, Daniel Gomez. 12135 MONTWOOD DR STE 115 79936 #649-14-1980 L2002 **PD OS** *020 †55

PERALTA, Max A. 1733 CURIE DR STE 105 79902 #048-15-1998 L2000 **FM** *020 †18

PERALTA-KATENGELL, Ivania. 1700 N OREGON ST, STE 700 79902 #308-05-1990 L2005 **PD** *020 †18

PEREZ, Jose Francisco. 4800 ALBERTA AVE 79905 #275-01-1989 **IM** *012

PEREZ, Juan Rodrigo. 840 E REDD RD, BLDG 2 79912 #048-02-2001 L2004 **FM** *020 †18

PEREZ, Leida Pastora. 4800 ALBERTA AVE 79905 #935-05-1992 **IM** *012

PEREZ, Oscar Ernesto. 1400 N EL PASO ST 79913 L1978 **P** *020 †75

PEREZ, Ricardo Carbot. 9849 KENWORTHY ST, FAMILY PRACTICE CENTER 79924 #649-44-1988 L1995 **FM** *020 †18

PEREZ DIAZ, Susana Gema. 9849 KENWORTHY ST, TEXAS TECH UNIV-FAMILY PRA 79924 #275-01-1992 L2007 **FP** *012

PERSONETT, Becky Bea. 4421 EDGAR PARK AVE 79904 #017-20-1990 L1992 **FM** *020 †18

PESTER, Judith Ann Kubsch. 1625 MEDICAL CENTER ST 79902 #030-05-1969 L1981 **PTH DMP** *020 †50

PESTER, Thomas Lowell. 1700 MURCHISON DR, STE 211 79902 #030-05-1969 L1981 **GS** *020 †85

PETERSON, James Francis. ■ 79902 #019-02-1957 L1969 **PS GS** *071 †65

PETRI, Richard P, Jr. 5005 N PIEDRAS ST, WILLIAM BEAUMONT AMC 79920 #010-02-1991 L1994 **PM** *020 †60

PETTIT, Kimberly Ann Niel. ■ 79912 #010-02-2001 L2002 **D** *020 †15

PHAM, Tuan Anh. ■ 79912 #048-15-2008 *012

PHIFER, Sylvester Donald. ■ 79936 #047-07-1971 L1977 **R** *020

PHILIPS, David Andrew. ■ 79912 #035-09-2000 L2001 **CD** *020 †20

PHIPPS, Wendy D. 1221 N COTTON ST 79902 #048-15-1998 L2002 **OBG** *020 †30

PINAROC, Maria T Rubio. 11548 VISTA DEL SOL DR 79936 #748-02-1990 L1998 **IM GP** *020 †20

PINDAR, Wellington John. ■ 79912 #035-03-1959 L1965 **ORS** *071 †40

PINZON, Guillermo. 7878 GATEWAY BLVD E, STE 103 79915 #264-01-1959 L1969 **IM NM** *020 †28

PITCHFORD, William Arnold. 7430 REMCON CIR, BLDG A 79912 #048-12-1958 L1958 **FM** *020 †30

PITRE, Clarence A. ■ 79912 #048-12-1993 L1995 **OBG** *020

PLAVSIC, Branko M. 4800 ALBERTA AVE, TTUHSC-DEPT OF RADIOLOGY 79905 #957-01-1972 L1992 *020

PLOWDEN, John S. 125 W HAGUE RD, STE 440 79902 #012-01-1984 L1999 **PDC PD** *020 †55

PODILA, Sobha Rani. 5001 N PIEDRAS ST, VAHCS 79930 #495-50-1973 L2001 **IM PTH** *020 †20,50

PODILA, Sudhakar. 712 ESPADA DR 79912 #495-50-1978 L2001 **IM** *020 †20

POEHLMANN, Dwight Scott. 4800 ALBERTA AVE, OB/GYN DEPT 79905 #048-12-1988 L1990 **OBG** *020 †30
POEHLMANN, Kurt Stuermer. 6073 LOS PUEBLOS DR 79912 #048-12-1964 L1964 **FM GS** *020 †18
POLANCO, Daniel. 7430 REMCON CIR 79912 #048-15-1998 L2001 **IM** *020 †20
POLLAN, Alina. 4800 ALBERTA AVE 79905 #275-02-1987 L2008 **FP** *012
POLLARD, Kathleen Rose. ■ 79912 #048-15-2008 *012
POLLET, Randy Jos. 1725 BROWN ST 79902 #021-05-1973 L1973 **ORS** *020 †40
POLLOCK, Patrick James. ■ 79912 #023-12-1999 L2000 **ORS** *020
PONCE DE LEON, Georgina C. 5005 N PIEDRAS ST 79920 #048-16-1999 L2007 **PD** *020 †55
PONCEDELEON, Marcus C. 5005 N PIEDRAS ST, WILLIAM BEAUMONT AMC 79920 #048-16-1999 L2001 **N** *020
PONSFORD, John Anderson. ■ 79902 #048-02-1955 L1955 **AN** *071
PONTE, Enrique Nicanor. ■ 79912 #935-05-1971 L1988 **PD NPM** *020 †55
PORRAS, Enrique. 10470 VISTA DEL SOL DR, STE 108 79925 #715-01-1985 L1995 **IM GP** *020 †20
PORRAS, Jose Luis. ■ 79932 #056-06-1984 L1987 **IM** *020
PORRAS, Luis Fernando. 1700 N OREGON ST 79902 #649-01-1952 L1968 **GP OBG** *020
PORRES AGUILAR, Mateo. 4800 ALBERTA AVE 79905 #649-31-2005 **IM** *012
PORTILLO, Angelica C. ■ 79922 #649-14-1980 L1990 **IM** *020
PORTILLO, Raul M. 1625 MEDICAL CENTER ST 79902 #649-14-1977 L1983 **ON IM** *020 †20
POSNER, Matthew Adam. 5005 N PIEDRAS ST, WILLIAM BEAUMONT AMC 79920 #041-14-2006 L2007 **ORS** *012
POSTMA, Robert Alan. 1755 CURIE DR, STE A 79902 #048-13-1980 L1981 **EM** *030 †16
POTH, Roy Keith. 1625 MEDICAL CENTER ST 79902 #048-02-1968 L1968 **DR** *071 †80
POWELL, John Alexander. 5005 N PIEDRAS ST, STOP 23 79920 #023-12-1987 L1988 **IM** *020 †20
POWERS, Christopher J. 125 W HAGUE RD STE 260, TEXAS TECH UNIVERSITY HEAL 79902 #048-15-1998 L2001 **OBG** *020 †30
POWERS, Christopher R. ■ 79912 #021-05-1997 L1999 **IM** *020 †20
POWERS, Maya M. 7430 REMCON CIR, BLDG B 79912 #021-05-1997 L1999 **MPD** *020 †20,55
PRIETO, Jose, Jr. 11040 VISTA DEL SOL DR, STE C 79935 #005-11-1987 L1998 **PD** *020 †55
PRIETO-JIMENEZ, Carmen A. 4800 ALBERTA AVE, DEPT OF PEDIATRICS 79905 #341-04-1989 L2001 **PD** *020 †55
PROTZMAN, Scott Alan. 1720 MURCHISON DR 79902 #048-14-1994 L1995 **ORS** *020 †40
PURON, Luis Enrique. 4800 ALBERTA AVE, TX TECH U HLTH SCI CTR 79905 #275-02-1984 L2006 **FM** *020 †18
PUSCHETT, Mitchell Ivan. 6452 CALLE VISTA DR, MITCHELL PUSCHETT, MD PA 79912 #041-01-1992 L2002 **AN** *020 †05
QUADRI, Syed Obeidullah. ■ 79912 #496-21-1996 **P** *012
QUAN, Reagan Wei. 5005 N PIEDRAS ST, WILLIAM BEAUMONT ARMY MED 79920 #024-05-1998 L1999 **GS** *100 †85
QUESADA, Jaime A. 1900 N OREGON ST STE 610 79902 #341-01-1988 L1995 **PUD IM** *020 †20
QUEZADA, Oscar R. 10501 GATEWAY BLVD W 79925 #048-12-1997 L1999 **OBG** *020 †30
QUINONES, Iraham Axel San. 4800 ALBERTA AVE 79905 #649-33-2004 **IM** *012
QUINONEZ, Alner Miguel. 9849 KENWORTHY ST, TEXAS TECH UNIV-FAMILY PRA 79924 #270-03-2003 **FP** *012
QUINTANA, Joseph Anthony. 1700 N OREGON ST STE 570 79902 #649-27-1981 L1988 **CD** *020
QUIRARTE, Esteban. 5001 N PIEDRAS ST, VAHCC EL PASO 79930 #649-27-1986 L1995 **IM** *020 †20
RADENOVICH, Violeta. 1250 E CLIFF DR, STE 4D 79902 #737-06-1987 L1996 **PO** *020 †35
RADHAKRISHNAN, Hari. ■ 79912 #048-15-2008 *012
RAFIEI, Poyan. ■ 79932 #048-15-2008 *012
RAINEY, Gordon Kim. ■ 79912 #028-46-2001 L2003 **HO** *100
RAJA, Mohammad L. 1250 E CLIFF DR, STE 2A 79902 #649-33-1987 L1996 **CD EM** *020 †20
RAJAMOHANTY, Manjusha. 9849 KENWORTHY ST, TEXAS TECH UNIV-FAMILY PRA 79924 #496-05-1998 **IM** *012
RAJASHEKHAR, Sumithra. 1530 N LEE TREVINO DR 79936 #495-09-1965 L1977 **D** *020
RAJASHEKHAR, Tarikere P. 2001 N OREGON ST 79902 #495-33-1964 L1975 **PM** *020 †60
RAMIREZ, Amado, Jr. 10960 MONTWOOD DR, STE E 79935 #048-15-1998 L2001 **PD** *020 †55
RAMIREZ, Arthur Leonardo. 1515 N MESA ST 79902 #005-06-1977 L1985 **P** *020 †75
RAMIREZ, Jose Abel. 1250 E CLIFF DR, STE 4E 79902 #649-14-1982 L1989 **N** *020 †75
RAMIREZ, Luis A. 1400 GEORGE DIETER DR, STE 110 79936 #042-01-1982 L1988 **GE IM** *020 †20 ‡
RAMIREZ, Maria De Jesus. 1250 E CLIFF DR STE 3E 79902 #649-14-1972 L1981 **FM** *020
RAMIREZ, Ruben. 4800 ALBERTA AVE 79905 #649-33-2003 **IM** *012
RAMIREZ, Ruben Guillermo. 1250 E CLIFF DR STE 3E 79902 #649-14-1969 L1975 **GS EM** *020 †85
RAMON-LAMUS, Jose Antonio. 1225 E CLIFF DR STE 2B 79902 #264-01-1962 L1972 **AN** *071
RAMPY, Robbie June. 5005 N PIEDRAS ST, WBAMC CREDENTIALS OFFICE 79920 #649-33-1997 L2002 **IM** *020 †20 ‡
RANGEL, Lionel C. 2931 MONTANA AVE STE A 79903 #048-12-1997 L2001 **IM** *020 †20
RANKIN, David Alan. 5005 N PIEDRAS ST 79920 #020-02-2001 L2007 *020 †50
RAPP, Gary Stephen. 857 FOREST WILLOW CIR 79922 #048-02-1969 L1969 **R** *020 †80
RASKIN, Milton. 5959 GATEWAY BLVD W, STE 365 79925 #016-02-1954 L1968 **P N** *071 †75
RATHBUN, Donald. 1501 ARIZONA AVE STE 1C 79902 #048-02-1951 L1951 **N IM** *020
RAUDALES, Fernando F. 1700 CURIE DR STE 4300 79902 #451-01-1980 L1986 **NEP IM** *020 †20 ‡
RAVENSCROFT, Jenny L. 1900 N OREGON ST STE 31, TEXAS PA 79902 #048-13-2001 L2007 **NPM** *100 †55
RAYAS, Maria Socorro. ■ 79912 #048-13-2007 **PD** *012
REDDI, Renuka. 6544 BROOK RIDGE CIR 79912 #495-21-1966 L1973 **OBG** *071 †30
REDDY, Krishna. ■ 79902 #048-14-2008 *012
REED, Teresa Anne. 1400 GEORGE DIETER DR, STE 170 79936 #005-02-1982 L1994 **RO ADM** *020 †80
REEVES, Barbara Mudd. 4310 ALAMEDA AVE 79905 #048-12-1979 L1979 **FM** *020 †18
REEVES, Mark Richard. 910 E REDD RD, STE K167 79912 #649-27-1987 **PME PRS** *030
REEVES, Philip Lansing. 2001 N OREGON ST 79902 #048-12-1976 L1976 **AN** *020 †05
REFAEIAN, Manouchehr. 8900 VISCOUNT BLVD # 714 79925 #048-15-1993 L1994 **PM** *020 †60
REHA, Jeffrey Lee. 5005 N PIEDRAS ST, GENERAL SURGERY SERVICE 79920 #023-12-2006 L2007 **GS** *012
REISTER, Gary Everett. 2400 TRAWOOD DR, STE 100 79936 #038-43-1973 L1975 **DR GP** *020 †80
REITER, Dennis Joseph. 125 W HAGUE RD STE 340 79902 #048-78-1985, ▲ L1986 **OPH PS** *020
REMIREZ, Carlos Manuel. 6610 TARASCAS DR, 6024 AZTEC RD 79912 #649-14-1981 L1985 **FM OM** *020 †18
REPINE, Thomas Benton. 5005 N PIEDRAS ST 79920 #047-05-1998 L2000 **HO** *020 †20
RESTREPO, Bibiana Maria. 4800 ALBERTA AVE 79905 #264-17-1999 **PD** *012
REVILLA STILL, Rodolfo M. 1600 MEDICAL CENTER ST, STE 309 79902 #649-01-1965 L1992 **OBG** *020 †30
REYES, Kurt James. 5005 N PIEDRAS ST, DEPT MED/GME 79920 #048-13-2006 **IM** *012
REYNOLDS, Richard D. 125 W HAGUE RD STE 120 79902 #048-14-1997 L1999 **PS** *020 †65
RHODES, Miller Franklin. 4800 ALBERTA AVE, DEPT SURG 79905 #047-07-1973 L1994 **OTO** *020 †45 ‡
RIAZ, Uzma. 4800 ALBERTA AVE, TX TECH U HLTH SCI CTR 79905 #704-02-1990 **PD** *100
RICH, Nicolas, Jr. 2905 N STANTON ST 79902 #649-33-1982 L1989 **PD** *020 †55
RIGESTI, German J. 1700 N OREGON ST, STE 710 79902 #132-05-1990 L1995 **FM** *020 †18 ‡
RIOS, Angel Manuel. 1250 E CLIFF DR STE 3D 79902 #042-01-1988 L1993 **OBG** *020 †30 ‡
RIOS, Marino. 1714 N MESA ST 79902 #649-27-1971 L1978 **OTO PS** *020
RIVERA, Cynthia D. 5001 N PIEDRAS ST, VAHCS 79930 #048-15-1988 L1989 **P** *030 †75
RIVERA, Efrain, Jr. 5736 N MESA ST 79912 #048-04-1981 L1982 **AN IM** *020
RIVERA, Emmanuel. 1215 RIM RD 79902 #025-12-1985 L1993 **AN** *020
RIVERA, Manuel. 4800 ALBERTA AVE, REGIONAL ACADEMIC HEALTH C 79905 #649-14-1971 L1977 **IM** *020 †20
RIVERA, Nilda J. 1900 N OREGON ST STE 510, UNIVERSITY TOWERS 79902 #042-01-1989 L1994 **OBG GP** *020 †30 ‡
RIVERA, Ragene Ruth. 7848 GATEWAY BLVD E 79915 #048-04-1974 L1974 **HO** *020 †20
RIVERA, Raul. 5301 ALAMEDA AVE 79905 #048-02-1960 L1960 **GS GP** *075 †18
ROBBINS, Louis Stephen. 1700 MURCHISON DR STE 104 79902 #016-06-1961 L1961 **AN** *071 †05
ROBINSON, Arvin Edward. 4800 ALBERTA AVE, DEPARTMENT OF RADIOLOGY 79905 #051-04-1964 L1964 **DR PDR** *020 †80
ROBINSON, Charles H. ■ 79922 #047-06-1951 L1958 **R GP** *075 †80
ROBINSON, Estella. 10301 GATEWAY BLVD W 79925 #056-06-1985 L1989 **OBG** *020 †30
RODARTE, Galo Alonso. 24 BRONZE CREST LN 79902 #649-33-1992 L1997 **IM** *020 †20
RODARTE, Sergio M. ■ 79905 #649-27-1975 L1995 **PYG** *020
RODRIGUEZ, Angel Marcelo. 1717 N BROWN ST, STE 2B 79902 #649-18-1979 L1988 **P** *020 †75
RODRIGUEZ, Ariel. ■ 79912 #028-34-1954 L1974 **GS OS** *020 †85
RODRIGUEZ, Fausto A. 4800 ALBERTA AVE, DEPT PATHOLOGY 79905 #649-33-1984 L1997 **PTH** *020 †50
RODRIGUEZ, Francisco R. 1700 CURIE DR, STE 4300 79902 #042-01-1964 L1990 **U** *020 †95
RODRIGUEZ, Jose Luis. 700 S OCHOA ST 79901 #025-12-1982 L1983 **FM** *020 †18
RODRIGUEZ, Kim V. 9398 VISCOUNT BLVD, STE 2 79925 #048-14-1987 L1989 **PD** *020 †55
RODRIGUEZ, Luis Rodolfo. 1714 E YANDELL DR # B 79902 #649-02-1958 L1966 **IM** *020
RODRIGUEZ, Orestes Moldes. 1600 N OREGON ST STE 1A 79902 #042-03-1987 L1992 **GE IM** *020 †20
RODRIGUEZ, Simon Sergio. 4800 ALBERTA AVE, TEXAS TECH UNIV HEALTH SCI 79905 #649-33-2004 L2006 **IM** *012
RODRIGUEZ VALDES, Cesar. 4800 ALBERTA AVE 79905 #649-52-2005 L2007 **IM** *012
ROGERS, Booker T, Jr. ■ 79934 #048-12-1982 L1983 **AN** *020 †05
ROGERS, Cheryl Jan. 5001 N PIEDRAS ST, VA OUTPATIENT CLINIC 79930 #020-02-1982 L1985 **IM** *020
ROGERS, William Hardy. ■ 79912 #048-12-1966 L1966 **R GP** *020 †80
ROJAS, Jaime. ■ 79925 #048-12-2005 L2008 **GS** *100
ROJERO, Jorge Roberto. 10555 VISTA DEL SOL DR, STE 200 79925 #048-13-1981 L1981 **FM** *020 †18
ROLON, Juan Carlos. 1900 N OREGON ST, STE 305 79902 #726-01-1968 L1976 **OBG** *020
ROMERO-BELTRE, Plinio. ■ 79912 #308-01-1944 L1977 *071
ROMERO-RAMOS, Samuel F. 2311 N MESA ST, STE J 79902 #649-01-1974 L1980 **IM** *020 †20
RONCALLO, Ruben Rafael. 4500 N MESA ST 79912 #264-14-1986 L1999 **PD** *020
ROONEY, Richard C, Jr. 4646 N MESA ST 79912 #038-06-1995 L2005 **OSS** *020 †40
ROSARIO, Rey Francisco. 1700 CURIE DR STE 43, DALLAS NEPHROLOGY ASSOCIAT 79902 #042-02-2000 L2005 **NEP IM** *100 †20
ROSAS, Gilbert Arthur. 5400 SUNCREST DR, STE B3 79912 #048-02-1967 L1967 **AN** *020 †05
ROSAS BLUM, Eduardo Danie. 4800 ALBERTA AVE, DEPARTMENT OF PEDIATRICS 79905 #649-14-2005 **PD** *012
ROSEN, Andrew Phillip. 1600 MEDICAL CENTER DR, STE 307 79902 #048-12-1991 L1992 **OBG** *020 †30,18
ROSEN, Robert James. 1801 N OREGON ST 79902 #016-42-1968 L1974 **OPH** *020 †35
ROTH, Jason Eric. 5005 N PIEDRAS ST, WILLIAM BEAUMONT AMC 79920 #035-09-1998 L2000 **CD** *020 †20
ROVNER, Sergio Fernando. 10420 MONTWOOD DR STE H 79935 #132-01-1988 L1996 **IM END** *020 †20
ROY, Daniel Seth. 5005 N PIEDRAS ST 79920 #023-12-1994 L1995 **PD** *020 †55
RUFFIER, Jose Maria. 7878 GATEWAY BLVD E, STE 103 79915 #132-01-1975 L1986 **FM PTH** *020
RUFFIER, Juan Carlos. 10301 GATEWAY BLVD W 79925 #132-01-1965 L1983 **CD IM** *020
RUIZ, Augustin Martinez. 4904 ALAMEDA AVE 79905 #048-12-1954 L1954 **GP** *072
RUIZ, Javier. 1129 CALLE LOMAS DR, STE 104 79912 #048-12-1988 L1990 **AN** *020 †05
RYAN, Gary Thos. 1626 MEDICAL CENTER DR 79902 #018-03-1969 L1976 **GYN** *020 †30
SABAL, James. 5301 ALAMEDA AVE 79905 #025-01-1958 L1962 **FM** *071 †18 ‡
SABIDO, Delfin Viii M. 5005 N PIEDRAS ST, DEPT OF INTERNAL MEDICINE 79920 #748-02-1990 L1998 **HEM** *020 †20
SAENZ ALVARADO, Rodrigo. ■ 79912 #270-02-2000 L2007 **IM** *020 †20
SAHEBA, Ashit Indravadan. 6320 GATEWAY BLVD E 79905 #495-22-1979 L1986 **OM IM** *071 †70,20
SAINZ, Jorge G. 1801 N OREGON ST, UTHSCSA 79902 #048-13-1999 L2002 **CCP** *020 †55
SALADYGA, Anne Teresa. ■ 79912 #035-06-2005 L2007 **GS** *012
SALAZAR, Alex J. 601 E OVERLAND AVE 79901 #048-15-2001 L2003 **NS** *020
SALAZAR, Cesar Oswaldo. 10470 VISTA DEL SOL DR, STE 210 79925 #341-01-1984 L1994 **GE** *020 †20
SALCEDO, Jorge Alexis. 400 E ROBINSON AVE, STE A 79902 #451-01-1993 L2005 **FM** *020 †18
SALIB, Michael Fawzy Bish. 4800 ALBERTA AVE 79905 #915-04-1995 **P** *012
SALINAS LUNA, Vanessa Kar. 4800 ALBERTA AVE, DEPARTMENT OF PEDIATRICS 79905 #737-11-2001 **PD** *012
SALLOUM, Hassan Nasim. 4800 ALBERTA AVE 79905 #875-01-1982 L1995 **PD** *040 †55
SALTZSTEIN, Edward Cooper. 4815 ALBERTA AVE 79905 #016-06-1957 L1977 **GS** *020 †85
SAMANIEGO, Alvaro. 1208 MYRTLE AVE, OPPORTUNITY CENTER FOR THE 79901 #264-03-1955 L1973 **P** *020 †75
SAMONTE, Miguel, Jr. 11544 VISTA DEL SOL DR, BLDG A 79936 #748-01-1983 L1996 **AN PD** *020

■ = Address Information Privacy Protected

SANCHEZ, Carlos. ■ 79925 #649-07-1977 **P** *075
SANCHEZ, Ines Joan. ■ 79912 #042-01-1993 L2003 **HO** *020 †20
SANCHEZ IGLESIAS, Gervasio. 4800 ALBERTA AVE 79905 #275-03-1991 **PD** *012
SANDBERG, Kevin James. 7878 GATEWAY BLVD E # 403 79915 #048-04-1988 L1989 **PM OM** *020 †60
SAN MIGUEL, Francisco L. ■ 79924 #042-02-2003 L2005 **GS** *012
SAN MIGUEL, George Garcia. 125 W HAGUE RD STE 260 79902 #048-02-1978 L1978 **OBG** *020 †30
SANTILLAN, Alfredo Alejan. 4800 ALBERTA AVE, TX TECH U HLTH SCI CTR 79905 #649-52-2000 L2007 **GS** *100
SANTOSCOY, Robert. 1600 MEDICAL CENTER ST, EL PASO SOUTHWESTERN 79902 #048-14-1986 L1988 **PCS TS** *020 †90,85
SANTOS-CRUZ, Luis A. 125 W HAGUE RD, STE 180 79902 #042-01-1985 L1995 **PG** *020 †55
SARACINO, Dino Peter. ■ 79912 #748-17-1983 L2005 **GS** *071 †85
SARRE, Stefan Georg. ■ 79926 #016-43-1957 L1961 **CD IM** *062
SCHABACKER, Gary Walter. 1625 MEDICAL CENTER ST 79902 #016-11-1964 L1972 **SO** *020 †85
SCHAFFER, Michael G. 1700 N OREGON ST, STE 515 79902 #011-03-1988 L2004 **OBG** *020 †30 ‡
SCHECTER, David Robt. 1220 N OREGON ST 79902 #047-06-1969 L1971 **OPH** *020 †35
SCHER, Danielle Lauren. ■ 79912 #011-02-2007 **ORS** *012
SCHER, Marisela. 5001 N PIEDRAS ST 79930 #649-14-1974 L1979 **IM** *020
SCHICK, Martin E. ■ 79902 #035-03-1975 L1979 **AN** *075 †05
SCHLUSSELBERG, Danl Simon. 6090 SURETY DR, STE 101 79905 #048-12-1982 L1983 **DR** *050
SCHNEIDER, Robert Dale. 6730 WESTWIND DR 79912 #016-11-1960 L1969 **N** *020
SCHNURR, Thomas Steven. ■ 79903 #035-08-1995 **GP ADM** *030
SCHOLTENS, Paul Arthur. 1901 GRANDVIEW AVE 79902 #025-01-1960 L1981 **RO** *071 †80
SCHORR, Alan J. 700 S OCHOA ST 79901 #048-14-1986 L1987 **FM** *020 †18
SCHRIVER, John Parker. 5005 N PIEDRAS ST, WILLIAM BEAUMONT AMC 79920 #045-01-1989 L1993 **GS** *020 †85
SCHULTZ, Morris Aaron. ■ 79912 #048-02-1959 L1959 **ORS** *071 †40
SCHUSTER, Jeffrey David. 4800 ALBERTA AVE 79905 #048-13-1982 L1983 **PDC PD** *020 †55
SCHUSTER, Stephen A D. 1700 CURIE DR STE 2100 79902 #048-02-1965 L1965 **OPH** *020 †35
SCHYDLOWER, Manuel. 4800 ALBERTA AVE, HLTH SCIENCE CTR, DEPT PED 79905 #034-01-1971 L1978 **PD ADL** *040 †55
SCOTT, Thomas Shaver. 6380 MORGAN AVE STE E, EL PASO MEPSBLDG 6380 79906 #041-02-1968 L1983 **GS GP** *020
SCRAGG, William Harold. 4800 ALBERTA AVE, HEALTH SCIENCE CENTER 79905 #035-09-1957 L1976 **OBG** *040 †30
SCULLY, Thomas Jarvis. 5001 N PIEDRAS ST, EL PASO VA HCC 79930 #005-11-1963 L1969 **ORS** *071 †40
SEBESTA, Sean C. 9849 KENWORTHY ST 79924 #048-15-2002 L2005 **FM** *100 †18
SEE, Gladina M. 1801 N OREGON ST 79902 #748-08-1990 L1996 **IM** *020 †20
SEELIG, Deborah. 1733 CURIE DR, STE 203 79902 #043-01-1988 L1997 **PS OTO** *020 †45,65
SEENIVASAGAM, Makeswaran. 1801 N OREGON ST #220-04-1986 L2000 **MPD PD** *020 †20,55
SEGAPELI, Joseph Harry. 9398 VISCOUNT BLVD, STE 2 79925 #048-13-1981 L1982 **PD** *020 †55
SEGURA SANDOVAL, Maximino. ■ 79905 #649-01-1968 L1976 **GP** *071
SEIDENSTEIN, Carol M. 5005 N PIEDRAS ST 79920 #035-06-1963 L1969 **PD GP** *020
SEPULVEDA, Daniel Max. ■ 79902 #649-14-1964 L1968 **GE IM** *071
SERNA, Aime Diaz. 1400 N EL PASO ST, STE A 79902 #011-04-1998 L2001 **IM** *020 †20
SERNA, Jorge Humberto. 1700 CURIE DR STE 4300, EL PASO KIDNEY SPECIALIST 79902 #048-14-1997 L1999 **NEP** *020 †20,55
SERRANO, Carmen. 643 S MESA HILLS DR 79912 #042-01-1985 L1988 **N** *040 †75
SERRATO, Pedro. 4800 ALBERTA AVE 79905 #048-11-1996 L2000 **IM** *020 †20
SHAFFER, Christy Lyn. ■ 79912 #028-46-2003 L2007 **D** *020 †15
SHAHINIAN, Haroutioun. 1400 GEORGE DIETER DR, STE 270 79936 #913-38-1982 L1996 **HEM** *020 †20
SHAPIRO, Stephen Richard. 5001 N PIEDRAS ST, ELPASO VA HEALTH CARE 79930 #035-08-1960 L1968 **A IM** *030 †20,03
SHAW, Darinka Tsvetanova. 4800 ALBERTA AVE 79905 #198-04-1980 **PD** *012
SHEIKH, Shazia Farooq. 700 S OCHOA ST 79901 #704-21-1998 L2006 **IM** *020 †20
SHEPPARD, Frank James. 1225 E CLIFF DR STE 2B 79902 #748-09-1975 L1995 **CRS GS** *020 †10,85
SHERMAN, John Miller, III. 2900 PERSHING DR STE A 79903 #048-04-1963 L1963 **FM** *020 †18
SHIRSAT, Pratibha Kiran. 4800 ALBERTA AVE, CONTINUITY CARE CLINICS 79905 #496-38-1973 L1990 **PD** *020 †55
SHOWERY, Raymond Edward. ■ 79901 #048-02-1956 L1956 **GS OBG** *020
SHRODE, Paul W. 4505 ALBERTA AVE, MEDICAL EXAMINER'S OFFICE 79905 #048-15-1991 L1992 **FOP** *020
SHUKLA, Vani. 4800 ALBERTA AVE, HEALTH SCIENCES CENTER 79905 #496-02-1997 L2006 **IM** *100 †20
SIDES, Eric Everett. 1755 CURIE DR STE B 79902 #048-12-1991 L1992 **ORS** *020 †40
SILVA, Jose J. 1900 N OREGON ST, STE 200 79902 #649-14-1982 L1991 **IM N** *020 †20
SILVA, Naomi Nicole. ■ 79932 #010-01-2008 *012
SILVIA, Scott Keith. 6955 N MESA ST 108, SUNWEST MEDICAL PLAZA 79912 #042-03-1996 L1999 **FM** *020 †18
SIMPSON, Jana L. 1501 ARIZONA AVE STE 1A 79902 #048-13-1993 L1994 **D** *020
SIMPSON, Michael Homer. 1501 ARIZONA AVE STE 1A 79902 #048-12-1963 L1963 **D** *020 †15
SINGH, Anumeha. 4800 ALBERTA AVE 79905 #495-98-2004 **EM** *012
SINGH, Girvar. ■ 79912 #495-55-1964 L1978 **OPH** *020
SINGH, Heramb Kumar. 1155 N ZARAGOZA RD, STE C107 79907 #047-07-1985 L1994 **DR VIR** *020
SIRAJ, Sultana. ■ 79912 #160-02-1972 L1979 **PD** *071 †55
SKERRETT, Gregory Robert. ■ 79911 #030-06-2007 **GS** *012
SLADE, Dirk Lance. ■ 79912 #010-01-2000 L2008 **ORS** *020
SMART, John Forsyth. ■ 79936 #803-05-1958 L1974 **AN** *020
SMILEY, Hylas Emmett, III. 2001 N OREGON ST 79902 #038-41-1964 L1969 **R** *020 †80
SMITH, Christine Zaffater. 4800 ALBERTA AVE 79905 #021-06-1987 L1994 **PD** *072 †55
SMITH, Dean Eldon. 7430 REMCON CIR BLDG B 79912 #021-06-1987 L1993 **ORS OSS** *020 †40
SMITH, George F. ■ 79904 #010-02-1953 L1954 **OS PD** *050 †55
SMITH, Michael C. 4800 ALBERTA AVE, TEXAS TECH UNIV HEALTH SCI 79905 #048-15-1997 L1999 **EM** *020 †16

SMITH, William Odell, Jr. 5400 SUNCREST DR, STE B3 79912 #038-45-1985 L1992 **AN PME** *020 †05
SMOCK, Patrick Hunter. 5005 N PIEDRAS ST, ARMY MEDICAL 79920 #028-46-2002 L2005 **ORS** *020
SNYDER, Richard Donald. ■ 79925 #035-09-1957 L1959 **P** *071 †45
SOEGAARD, Antonio. 9870 GATEWAY BLVD N STE B1 79924 #042-01-1989 L1995 **OBG** *020 †30
SOLTERO REYES, Liliana. ■ 79912 #649-52-1999 **IM** *012
SONG, Angie Unchi. 1600 MEDICAL CENTER ST, SOUTHWEST EAR NOSE & 79902 #010-01-1993 L2003 **OTO** *020 †45
SONG, Daniel Joonho. ■ 79902 #023-12-2007 **TY** *012
SONGBANDITH, Virabandith. 3022 TRAWOOD DR, STE A 79936 #021-01-1996 L2000 **IMG** *020 †18
SOTO, Ediberto. 1801 N OREGON ST 79902 #042-03-1985 L1991 **CD IM** *020 †20
SOTO, Lucia F. ■ 79922 #048-02-2008 *012
SOZER, Sadri O. 1600 MEDICAL CENTER DR, STE 400 79902 #902-04-1991 L1995 **GS** *020 †65
SPALDING, Mary Carmen. 9849 KENWORTHY ST 79924 #048-02-1977 L1977 **FM** *020 †18
SPARKS, Rodney Jay. 4204 LOMA TAURINA DR 79934 #023-12-1998 L2002 **IM** *020 †20
SPERA, Thomas D. 2001 N OREGON ST 79902 #010-02-1982 L2004 **VIR RNR** *020 †80
SPIER, Curtis Jos. 7230 GATEWAY BLVD E, STE E 79915 #048-12-1960 L1960 **PME GP** *020 †05
SPIER, Eric Tomas. ■ 79902 #048-14-2002 L2005 **PM** *100 †60
SPIER, James Edward. 1600 MEDICAL CENTER ST, STE 101 79902 #048-02-1963 L1963 **OTO FPS** *071 †45
SPIER, Werner Emanuel. ■ 79902 #048-12-1955 L1955 **GYN** *071 †30
SPIVA, Deborah Anne. ■ 79906 #048-13-1973 L1973 **IM** *075 †20
SPURBECK, Maria Victoria. 125 W HAGUE RD, STE 390 79902 #048-15-1996 L2005 **PD** *020 †20
SPURBECK, William Wesley. 125 W HAGUE RD STE 170 79902 #048-15-1996 L2005 **PDS** *020 †85
SQUARE NUNEZ, Jaime Holbe. 4800 ALBERTA AVE, DEPT OF INTERNAL MED 79905 #649-19-2002 L2007 **IM** *020
STEEL, Samuel Lee. ■ 79934 #010-02-1994 L1996 **P** *100
STEINHAUER, Mark Henry. 700 W YANDELL DR 79902 #056-06-1982 L1998 **PM PMM** *020 †60
STILLEY, Mark A. 6905 MINERAL RIDGE DR 79912 #048-14-1993 L1994 **EM** *020 †18
ST-LO, Robert. 5959 GATEWAY BLVD W, STE 120 79925 #649-01-1967 L1977 **AN ICE** *020 †05
STOLAR, Jaime. 7500 VISCOUNT BLVD STE 193 79925 #649-01-1974 L1990 **EM GS** *020
STOREY ROJAS, Raul Enriqu. 4800 ALBERTA AVE 79905 #935-04-2002 **IM** *012
STOVALL, Robert M, Jr. 4800 ALBERTA AVE 79905 #049-01-1952 L1984 **AN** *071 †05
STRADER, Wilbur J, III. 1201 E SCHUSTER AVE, BLDG 7 79902 #017-20-1965 L1970 **END IM** *020 †20,28
STUMP, Robert Frank. 1625 MEDICAL CENTER ST 79902 #048-13-1998 L1999 **EM** *020 †16
SUAREZ, Claudia Emma. 4800 ALBERTA AVE, OB/GYN DEPT 79905 #649-02-1987 L2004 **OBG** *040 †30
SUCHOFF, Monica Lynne. 840 E REDD RD BLDG 3, DISCOVERY DEVLPMNTL CTR 79912 #048-12-1985 L1986 **PD** *020 †55
SULLIVAN, William Robt. 4800 ALBERTA AVE 79905 #019-02-1963 L1977 **OBG** *040 †18,30
SUNDERAJAN, Kirtana. ■ 79912 #048-15-2008 *012
SUNDRANI, Shanker. 10400 VISTA DEL SOL DR, STE 104 79925 #495-12-1977 L2001 **NS N** *020 †25,75
SUNG, Helen Minjung. 5005 N PIEDRAS ST 79920 #035-46-1995 L2001 **EM** *020 †16
SVARZBEIN, Leonardo. 2626 N MESA ST 79902 #132-02-1968 L1978 **NS** *071
SWANEY, Jerry James. 754A ESPADA DR 79912 #018-03-1965 L1974 **PHO ADL** *020 †55
SZEYKO, Gregory Harry. 2101 N OREGON ST, PROVIDENCE WOUND INSTITUTE 79902 #055-01-1971 L1976 **OS ID** *020 †20
TABATZKY, Christiane M. ■ 79912 #030-06-1981 L1988 **OTO FPS** *020 †45
TABER, Ben-Zion. ■ 79913 #024-01-1952 L1953 **OBG** *071 †30
TABER, David Owen. 1801 N OREGON ST 79902 #010-01-1963 L1972 **U** *020 †95 ‡
TABER, Jeffrey Everett. 2201 N STANTON ST, EL PASO UROLOGY CONSLT P.A 79902 #036-07-1992 L1997 **U** *020 †95 ‡
TACCIR-MACIAS, Claudia A. 4800 ALBERTA AVE, HEALTH SCIENCE 79905 #132-01-1979 **P** *012
TALAMAS, Emilia. ■ 79936 #649-52-1991 L2003 **PD** *020 †55 ‡
TAMEZ, Ernesto Marte. 6320 GATEWAY BLVD E 79905 #649-33-1981 L1994 **GP PD** *020
TAN, Esther Mayhong. 5005 N PIEDRAS ST, WILLIAM BEAUMONT ARMY MEDI 79920 #016-42-2004 L2006 **IM** *020 †20
TAN, Jeanette See. 10525 VISTA DEL SOL DR, STE 100 79925 #748-02-1989 L1995 **PUD** *020 †20
TARANGO, Miguel. 501 N YARBROUGH DR 79915 #649-27-1980 L1983 **FM** *020 †18
TARIN-GODOY, Bernardo C. 4615 ALAMEDA AVE 79905 #649-14-1982 L1987 **P** *020 †75
TATE, Robert Victor. ■ 79912 #039-01-1964 L1965 **GP GS** *071
TAVERAS, Juan Manuel. 1700 N OREGON ST, STE 570 79902 #308-05-1987 L1995 **CD IM** *020 †20
TAYLOR, Sabrina. ■ 79912 #010-02-2003 **EM** *012
TEMPLONUEVO, Raul Mendoza. 5001 N PIEDRAS ST 79930 #748-01-1966 L1980 **PUD IM** *020
TERREROS, Daniel Alvaro. 4800 ALBERTA AVE, TTUHSC DEPT OF PATHOLOGY 79905 #264-01-1973 L2007 **PTH** *020 †50
THEARD, Franz Carl. 1201 E SCHUSTER AVE STE 2B 79902 #010-01-1972 L1980 **OBG MFM** *020 †30
THERING, Harlan Robt. 125 W HAGUE RD STE 120 79902 #056-06-1960 L1979 **PS GS** *020 †85,65
THEUNE, Brian Thomas. 6201 LOS BANCOS DR 79912 #023-12-1994 L2002 **GS** *020 †85
THOMAS, John Perry, III. 9999 KENWORTHY ST STE A 79924 #048-02-1968 **FM A** *020 †18 ‡
THOMPSON, Richard Kenneth. 1501 ARIZONA AVE, MED CENTER SUITE 8-B 79902 #038-40-1963 L1970 **OBG** *071 †30
TING, Beatrice Thetgy. 3607 RIVERA AVE, PROJECT VIDA 79905 #209-01-1972 L1985 **PD OS** *020 †55
TOCYAP, Mary Lillian Dunu. 4800 ALBERTA AVE 79905 #748-02-1996 L2006 **PD** *020 †55
TODD, Luis. 1300 MEADOWVIEW DR 79925 #649-14-1984 L1991 **PD** *020 †55
TOLOUIAN, Ramin. ■ 79912 #517-08-1993 L2007 **NEP** *020
TOMASINO, Rodolfo. ■ 79902 #341-01-1966 L1976 **OBG** *020
TORRES, Jose. 2817 E YANDELL DR 79903 #048-14-1999 L2003 **GYN** *020
TORRES, Nancy Lorena. 2300 MCKINLEY AVE 79930 #024-01-2000 L2004 **IM** *020
TORZALA, Daniel Thomas, Jr. ■ 79912 #028-34-2001 L2003 **N** *020 †75
TRAN, Minh Van. 5001 N PIEDRAS ST, DEPT VETERAN AFFAIRS 79930 #942-01-1974 L1992 **IM** *020
TRAN, Therese H. 4800 ALBERTA AVE 79905 #018-75-2005, ▲ **OBG** *012
TRAYLOR, Michael T. 1250 E CLIFF DR, STE 2A 79902 #048-15-1975 L1975 **CD IM** *020 †20

TREJO, Octavio. 2001 N OREGON ST, PROVIDENCE MEM HOSP 79902 #048-13-1996 L1998 **PCP** *020 †50

TREPANIER, Donald Raymond. 5005 N PIEDRAS ST STOP 3, WILLIAM BEAUMONT ARMY MED 79920 #028-78-1956, ▲ L1956 **FM** *071

TREVINO, Marina. 4800 ALBERTA AVE, HEALTH SCIENCE 79905 #649-02-1997 L2007 **IM** *020 †20

TRIEU, Chuyen Le Hong. 4800 ALBERTA AVE 79905 #942-01-2001 L2007 **PD** *012

TRUBOWITSCH, Gregory. 1733 WESTON BRENT LN, SOUTHWEST RETINA 79935 #035-48-1987 L1992 **OPH** *020 †35

TRZMIELINA, Sonia Diniz D. 4800 ALBERTA AVE 79905 #187-03-1998 **FP** *012

TUBBS, William M. 2931 MONTANA AVE 79903 #048-04-1939 L1939 **GP** *072

TUNE, John Melvin. 125 W HAGUE RD STE 590 79902 #048-02-1976 L1976 **GE IM** *020 †20

TURES, John Francis. 1700 CURIE DR STE 4800 79902 #056-06-1970 L1976 **GE** *071 †20

TURNBULL, Gottlieb L. 5005 N PIEDRAS ST 79920 #010-03-1960 L1979 **NM PTH** *040 †28

TYROCH, Alan Henry. 4800 ALBERTA AVE, DEPT OF SURGERY 79905 #048-14-1990 L1997 **CCS TRS** *020 †85

TYROCH, Roxanne. 5005 N PIEDRAS ST, DEPT OF INTERNAL MEDICINE 79920 #003-01-1991 L1997 **IM** *020 †20

UDDIN, Mohammed Siraj. 1733 WESTON BRENT LN STE A 79935 #160-02-1968 L1991 **GE IM** *020 †20

UHRIG, Henry T. 4815 ALAMEDA AVE 79905 #035-09-1951 L1972 **R** *020

ULISSE, Keith Jos. ■ 79921 #010-01-1983 **AN** *020

UM, Seyoung. ■ 79912 #035-08-2002 L2004 **PD** *020

URIBE DUENAS, Armando. 5001 N PIEDRAS ST, MEDICINE SERVICE 79930 #649-14-1977 L1991 **IM** *020 †20

URQUIDEZ, Jose Antonio. 6320 COUGAR RDG 79912 #048-12-2002 L2004 **PM** *012

URQUIDI, Ulysses John. 9849 KENWORTHY ST 79924 #048-15-1999 L2002 **FM** *020 †18

URREA, Luis Hernando. 6211 EDGEMERE BLVD 79925 #264-05-1960 L1973 **GE IM** *020

URREA, Luis Hernando, II. 1700 MURCHISON DR 79902 #048-12-1990 L1991 **ORS OSM** *020 †40

URREA, Robert E. 6211 EDGEMERE BLVD STE 1 79925 #048-12-1991 L1997 **OSS** *020 †40

URTUBEY, Adriana. 1626 MEDICAL CTR, STE 503 79902 #264-10-1990 L2002 **IM** *020 †20

URUETA, Wilfrido. 5005 N PIEDRAS ST, DEPT OF INTERNAL MED 79920 #665-03-2005 **IM** *012

USEN, Stanley I O. 125 W HAGUE RD, STE 350 79902 #690-06-1982 L2004 **PD** *020 †55

VADI-LATIFF, V Helena. 5959 GATEWAY BLVD W, STE 120 79925 #011-02-1986 L1998 **AN** *020 †05

VALDIVIA, Rodolfo Carlos. 3710 ALAMEDA AVE 79905 #005-15-1962 L1975 *071

VALENZUELA, Manuel Franci. 4800 ALBERTA AVE 79905 #649-14-1994 L2005 **PD** *100

VALILIS, Panagiotis N. 1901 GRANDVIEW AVE 79902 #418-01-1985 L1995 **HEM** *020 †20

VALLS, Miguel. ■ 79912 #056-06-1946 L1946 **GP AM** *020

VANDSHEKARI, Nahid. 2300 MCKINLEY AVE 79930 #517-05-1992 L2003 **FM FPG** *020 †18

VANIAWALA, Vishwas Pravin. 4800 ALBERTA AVE, TX TECH U HLTH SCI CTR 79905 #495-89-1991 L2007 **PD** *012

VANN, Murray Mc Niece. 10400 VISTA DEL SL DR #204 79925 #062-01-1970 L1978 **U** *020 †95

VARGAS, Arturo Levaro. 2001 N OREGON ST DEPT PATH 79902 #649-01-1966 L1971 **PTH CLP** *020 †50 ‡

VARGAS, Miguel Angel. 4800 ALBERTA AVE, DEPT OF INTERNAL MED 79905 #649-01-1989 L2007 **IM** *020

VARGAS, Pedro. 1913 CUEVA DE ORO CT 79902 #048-12-1963 L1963 **CD IM** *020

VASALLO PEREZ, Javier Ale. 4800 ALBERTA AVE 79905 #275-01-1992 **IM** *012

VASQUEZ, Luis F. 2600 N OREGON ST 79902 #737-01-1965 L1985 **NS** *020 †25

VAUGHAN, Winston H. ■ 79903 #047-05-1936 L1957 **ORS** *071 †40

VAZQUEZ, Carlos Wm. 10460 VISTA DEL SOL DR, STE 300 79925 #042-01-1992 L1998 **OPH** *020 †35

VAZQUEZ, Genaro. 1900 N OREGON ST STE 610, EL PASO PULMONARY ASSOC 79902 #649-01-1969 L1976 **PUD CCM** *020 †20

VAZQUEZ-IBARRA, Jesus R. 10470 VISTA DEL SOL DR # 2 79925 #649-01-1965 L1975 **CD IM** *020

VAZQUEZ SANDOVAL, Alfredo. 4800 ALBERTA AVE, DEPT OF INTERNAL MED 79905 #649-52-2003 L2005 **PCC** *012 †20

VEGA, Ana Carolina. 4800 ALBERTA AVE, DEPARTMENT OF PEDIATRICS 79905 #264-15-2002 **PD** *012

VEGA, Carlos. ■ 79912 #649-07-1979 **AN** *100

VEGA, Oscar, Jr. 1600 MEDICAL CENTER ST, STE 214 79902 #048-13-1982 L1983 **AN PME** *020 †05

VEGA-RUIZ, Juan Angel. 125 W HAGUE RD, STE 370 79902 #649-27-1987 L1996 **PD** *020

VELASCO, Veronica Y. ■ 79912 #048-12-2004 **PTH** *012

VELAZQUEZ, Maria D. 1700 N OREGON ST STE 740 79902 #048-02-1997 L2000 **OBG** *020

VELEZ, Carlos A. 2820 N STANTON ST 79902 #264-05-1968 L1974 **CD IM** *020 †20

VENZOR, Jose, III. 10501 VISTA DEL SOL DR, STE 114 79925 #048-13-1991 L1993 **AI** *020 †20,03

VERA, Robert Wallace. 4800 ALBERTA AVE 79905 #048-12-1981 L1981 **OBG** *020 †30

VERMA, Kalpana M. 8061 ALAMEDA AVE, CENTRO SANVICENTE CLINIC 79915 #495-62-1983 L1995 **IM** *020 †20

VERWIEBE, Eric Gale. 5005 N PIEDRAS ST, WILLIAM BEAUMONT AMC 79920 #023-12-2005 L2007 **ORS** *012

VIADO, Emma Salcedo. 8061 ALAMEDA AVE, CENTRO SAN VICENTE 79915 #748-01-1976 L1987 **PD** *020 †55

VIESCA, Carlos Omar. 1755 CURIE DR, STE B 79902 #649-33-1996 L2002 **APM AN** *020

VIGIL, Jacob Patrick. 1625 MEDICAL CENTER ST 79902 #007-02-1984 L1993 **EM FM** *075 †18,16

VIGIL, Louis Fernando. 5959 GATEWAY BLVD W # 160 79925 #005-14-1978 L1982 **AN** *020

VILLA, Filomena Hazel Roc. 4800 ALBERTA AVE, DEPARTMENT OF PEDIATRICS 79905 #748-10-1986 **PD** *012

VILLALOBOS, Victor M. 6151 DEW DR, STE 410 79912 #048-13-1984 L1985 **FM** *020 †18

VILLANOS, Maria Theresa M. 4800 ALBERTA AVE, DEPARTMENT OF PEDIATRICS 79905 #748-13-1989 L2006 **PD** *100 †55

VILLAROJO, Lalaine Deleon. 5005 N PIEDRAS ST, DEPT OF PEDIATRICS 79920 #748-02-1990 L1998 **PD** *012

VILLARREAL, Jorge J. 3100 N STANTON ST, STE A 79902 #048-12-1986 L1987 **OBG FM** *020 †18,30

VILLARREAL, Jose Luis. 5652 N MESA ST 79912 #048-12-1990 L1991 **AN** *020 †05

VILLARREAL, Robert P. 5400 SUNCREST DR, STE B3 79912 #048-12-1978 L1978 **AN** *020 †05

VILORIO, Francisco L. 605 SPRING CREST DR 79912 #275-01-1953 L1964 **GP GS** *020

VINSON, Richard Patrick. 8820 GATEWAY BLVD N 79904 #021-05-1987 L1998 **D FM** *020 †18,15

VIVANCO, Cesar. 10460 VISTA DEL SOL DR, STE 302 79925 #737-06-1989 L2003 **ON** *020 †20

VOGLEWEDE, Daniel Chas. 125 W HAGUE RD, STE 400 79902 #649-14-1975 L1982 **U** *020 †95

VOGLEWEDE, Yasmin. 4815 ALAMEDA AVE 79905 #649-14-1975 **P** *100

WADDELL, Brad Edward. 5005 N PIEDRAS ST, WILLIAM BEAUMONT AMC 79920 #036-05-1989 L2007 **GS SO** *020 †85

WADE, William Hall. 2001 N OREGON ST 79902 #016-06-1951 L1960 **GP GS** *071 †85

WAGNER, Michel R. ■ 79912 #165-07-1992 L2000 **GS** *020 †85

WAGNER, Stanley Chas. 5001 N PIEDRAS ST, CARDIO SVC EL PASO VA HLTH 79930 #054-04-1966 L1976 **CD PDC** *020 †20

WALKER, Vernon Anthony. 7430 REMCON CIR, PHYSICIANS HEALTHCARE ASSO 79912 #048-12-1985 L1987 **FM** *020 †18

WALY, Farid A K. ■ 79936 #528-01-1960 L1975 **PD** *071

WANG, Benjamin Yong-Chen. 2001 N OREGON ST, PROVIDENCE HOSPITAL, RADIO 79902 #005-06-1994 L1998 **DR** *020 †80

WANG, Wansheng. 4800 ALBERTA AVE 79905 #243-62-1989 **PD** *012

WARRICK, Carrie Elizabeth. ■ 79912 #048-15-2005 **EM** *012

WASHBURN, Daniel Scott. ■ 79912 #023-12-1999 L2000 **OPH** *100 †35

WASIUDDIN, Roohi Urooj. 4800 ALBERTA AVE, DEPARTMENT OF PEDIATRICS 79905 #496-27-2002 L2008 **PD** *012

WATERMAN, Brian Robert. ■ 79932 #051-07-2007 **ORS** *012

WATERS, Sylvia Viktoria. 5005 N PIEDRAS ST, ANESTHESIA SERVICES 79920 #023-12-2000 L2005 *020

WATSON, Heather J. 1700 MURCHISON DR, STE 206 79902 #061-01-1974 L1978 **OBG** *020 †30

WATSON, Wayne Keith H. 9999 KENWORTHY ST, STE A 79924 #065-10-1974 L1978 **IM FM** *020 †20

WEBER, Michael Anthony. 5005 N PIEDRAS ST, WILLIAM BEAUMOUNT AMC 79920 #023-12-1996 L1998 *020 †85

WEEKS, Lyle David. 1700 N OREGON ST, STE 755 79902 #019-02-1965 L1975 **OTO** *020 †45

WEERATUNGE, Kumari Kushla. 4800 ALBERTA AVE, TX TECH U HLTH SCI CTR 79905 #220-01-2002 L2008 **PD** *020 †55

WEGLEITNER, Mark Jos. 7300 REMCON CIR, STE 300 79912 #026-04-1958 L1975 **OTO GP** *072 †45

WEINER, Sarah. ■ 79932 #869-07-1955 L1962 **FM GP** *071

WEINSTEIN, David Baer. 6955 N MESA ST, STE 101 79912 #035-08-1954 L1960 **A PD** *071 †55,03

WEISER, Susan Michelle. ■ 79912 #048-13-2008 **PD** *012

WELLS, Clinton Nelson. ■ 79912 #011-02-2001 L2007 **DR** *100 †80

WEST, Priscilla Ann. ■ 79934 #001-02-2006 L2008 **ORS** *012

WESTBROOK, Richard S. 3100 N LEE TREVINO DR 79936 #048-02-1973 L1973 **ORS** *020 †40

WETZEL, Patricia A. ■ 79912 #016-06-1988 L1989 **FM** *020 †18

WHITAKER, Derek Casper. ■ 79936 #051-04-1998 L1999 **ORS** *020 †40

WHITE, Kenneth Dale. 2001 N OREGON ST 79902 #048-15-1983 L1983 **EM** *020 †16

WIANT, Max Kenneth, Jr. 4625 ALABAMA ST STE B 79930 #041-12-1972 L1980 **FM ADM** *012

WIELAND, Kristina M. 9999 KENWORTHY ST, STE A 79924 #048-15-2003 L2006 **FM** *020 †18

WIESE, Steven Michael. ■ 79925 #048-15-2008 *012

WILLIAMS, Darryl Marlowe. 4800 ALBERTA AVE 79905 #048-04-1964 L1964 **HEM ON** *040 †20

WILLIAMS, Joseph Anthony. 5005 N PIEDRAS ST, WILLIAM BEAUMONT AMC 79920 #023-12-1997 L1997 **GE** *020 †20

WILSON, David Nicholas. ■ 79936 #048-15-2006 **OBG** *012

WILSON, Harry Lee. 2001 N OREGON ST 79902 #016-02-1973 L1993 **PTH PD** *020 †50,55

WINK, Jennifer Sue. 5005 N PIEDRAS ST, ATTN: CREDENTIAL OFFICE 79920 #016-42-1998 L2007 **PCC** *020 †20

WOJCIECHOWSKA, Joanna Mal. 4800 ALBERTA AVE 79905 #759-03-1983 L2006 **PD** *020 †55

WOLFE, Perry Talbott. 1515 N OREGON ST 79902 #649-33-1984 L1991 **FM OM** *020 †18

WONG, Ka Chun. 1400 GEORGE DIETER DR, STE 130 79936 #462-01-1972 L1982 **CD IM** *020 †20

WOO, Douglas King. 816 LAKESHORE DR, PROVIDENCE IMAGING CONSULT 79932 #012-01-1968 L1970 **DR** *020 †80

WOODY, Robert Craig. 10965 BEN CRENSHAW DR, BLDG 4A 79935 #048-12-1977 L1977 **N PD** *020 †55,75

WOO-TELLES, Argelia. 1030 N ZARAGOZA RD, STE V 79907 #048-14-1998 L2001 **FM** *020 †18

WU, John Henry. 5005 N PIEDRAS ST 7777, WILLIAM BEAUMONT ARMY MED 79920 #004-01-1995 L1996 **NEP** *020 †20

WYATT, Felicie Gretchen. 5005 N PIEDRAS ST, WILLIAM BEAUMONT AMC 79920 #038-43-2002 L2004 **IMG** *020 †20

YANG, Dongxiao. 4800 ALBERTA AVE 79905 #243-39-1985 **PD** *012

YEARY, Brandy Lynnette. 2931 MONTANA AVE, STE A 79903 #048-04-2003 L2005 **FM** *020 †18

YORK, John Carleton. 6633 N MESA ST, STE 101 79912 #048-02-1987 L1988 **AI** *020 †20,03

YOUNG, Robert Lindley. 1201 E SCHUSTER AVE, BLDG 7 79902 #007-02-1962 L1981 **END IM** *020 †20,28

YUSON, Olivia Ong. 4800 ALBERTA AVE, DEPARTMENT OF PEDIATRICS 79905 #748-19-1997 **PD** *012

YUSOOF, Syed A. 1601 N MESA ST 79902 #704-02-1988 L1995 **IM** *020 †20

ZABANAL, Rosario Cecilia. 8061 ALAMEDA AVE 79915 #748-08-1984 L1997 **PD** *020 †55

ZACCHILLI, Michael Anthon. ■ 79912 #024-16-2007 **ORS** *012

ZAHIR, Azhar. 1401 LOST PADRE MINE DR 79902 #704-01-1986 L1995 **IM** *020 †20

ZAKARIAN, Marianne L. ■ 79912 #048-02-1993 L1995 **OBG** *020 †30

ZALOZNIK, Arlene. 5005 N PIEDRAS ST, WM BEAUMONT AMC 79920 #041-07-1976 L1998 **ON HEM** *030 †20

ZALTZ, Charles. 10525 VISTA DEL SOL DR, STE 206 79925 #065-06-1961 L1977 **ORS** *020 †40

ZAMUDIO, Jose Manuel. 1201 E SCHUSTER AVE STE 5A 79902 #016-11-1992 L1995 **OBG** *020 †30

ZAYAS, Raul. 1742 N ZARAGOZA RD, STE A 79936 #042-02-1983 L1986 **FM** *020 †18

ZEIDAN, Sami. ■ 79902 #649-33-1979 L1987 **N CHN** *071

ZEPEDA, Hector. 10301 GATEWAY BLVD W 79925 #649-01-1978 L1996 **PTH** *020 †50

ZERBACH-CHAMBERLIN, K T. 125 W HAGUE RD STE 570 79902 #034-01-1988 L1989 **GS** *020 †85

ZHOU, Joseph Shengli. 4800 ALBERTA AVE 79905 #243-64-1983 **PD** *012

ZOLFOGHARY, Khosrow. 1700 N OREGON ST, STE 790 79902 #517-01-1951 L1961 **NS** *020 †20

ZUCKERMAN, Marc J. 4800 ALBERTA AVE 79905 #024-07-1977 L1984 **GE IM** *020 †20

ZUREK, Robert Chas. 1625 MEDICAL CENTER ST 79902 #035-15-1958 L1977 **IM PUD** *071 †20

ELDORADO — SCHLEICHER

BARLOW, Lloyd Hammon. PO BOX 715 76936 #049-01-1995 L2005 **FM** *020 †18

BRAME, Jim Bob. 305 MERTZON HWY 76936 #021-01-1963 L1964 **FM** *071 †18
PEASLEE, Deborah G. 3 SOUTH HACKBERRY, PEDIATRIC CLINIC 76936 #048-12-1984 L1985 **PD** *020 †55

ELECTRA – WICHITA

BANEZ, Alberto Quilop. 1207 S BAILEY ST 76360 #748-01-1972 L1980 **GP GS** *020 †85
BANEZ, Eloisa Yu. 1207 S BAILEY ST 76360 #748-01-1972 L1981 **IM FM** *020
DE LIZIO, Thomas S. 1207 S BAILEY ST 76360 #048-12-1995 L1996 **FM** *020 †18
ZAK, Margaret. 1207 S BAILEY ST, ELECTRA MEMORIAL HOSPITAL 76360 #759-11-1997 L2006 **FM** *020

ELGIN – BASTROP

BAILEY, Herbert Arthur. ■ 78621 #048-12-1945 L1945 **GE** *071
BEAUCHAMP, Richard Allen. ■ 78621 #048-13-1977 L1977 **PHP** *030
BIEL, William Trickey, Jr. 209 E 2ND ST 78621 #048-02-1977 L1979 **FM** *020
BROWN, Margaret Ellen. ■ 78621 #048-15-2004 L2007 **FM** *020
CULLEN, Roseanne. 515 N HWY 95 78621 #539-04-1971 L1981 **IM EM** *020
DARDEN, Mary Nancy. 196 BRINKLEY LN 78621 #048-04-1962 L1962 **P CHP** *020
ENGLISH, Karen Elaine. 214 HWY 290 78621 #021-06-1994 L1998 **PD** *020 †55
LERMA, Sammy. 428 S MAIN ST 78621 #048-02-1988 L1989 **FM** *020 †18
MOELLER, Benjamin A, Jr. ■ 78621 #047-06-1941 L1941 **IM** *071 †20
SHERMAN, Kenneth Brooks. 209 E 2ND ST 78621 #021-05-1974 L1976 **FM EM** *020 †16

ELSA – HIDALGO

RODRIGUEZ, Rene. ■ 78543 #048-16-1989 L1990 **FM** *020 †18

EMORY – RAINS

NELSON, Thomas Hutson. 215 DUFFY ST 75440 #021-01-1956 L1960 **FM** *071 †18
NICHOLSON, James Ernest. 886 E LENNON DR, STE 105 75440 #048-12-1959 L1959 **GP** *071
RODGERS, Jerry Wharton. 886 E LENNON DR STE 105, THE WELLNESS PLACE PLLC 75440 #048-12-1968 L1968 **FM OS** *020 †18
STANLEY, Ronald Truett. 650 E LENNON DR 75440 #048-04-1966 L1966 **FM** *020 †18

ENNIS – ELLIS

ABDULIAN, John Danl. 601 S CLAY ST, STE 108 75119 #028-34-1987 L2006 **GE** *020 †20
ANTHONY-WHITE, Ruby Lee. 601 S CLAY ST 75119 #036-01-1975 L1981 **OM IM** *020
BLAIR, Raymond Wesley, Jr. 2203 W LAMPASAS ST, STE 101 75119 #048-14-2004 L2007 **FM** *020 †18
CARRY, Melissa Moore. 802 W LAMPASAS ST 75119 #004-01-1983 L1989 **CD** *020 †20
COOK, Charles Wm, Jr. 800 S CHATFIELD ST 75119 #048-14-1990 L1991 **OBG** *020 †30
DAVISON, Barry Herron. 601 S CLAY ST STE 103 75119 #048-04-1972 L1972 **PD** *020 †55
FRANKLIN, Jay Olen. 802 W LAMPASAS ST 75119 #048-16-1981 L1981 **ICE CD** *020 †20
FUELBERTH, Norma Jean B. 805 W LAMPASAS ST 75119 #030-05-1983 L1991 **OBG** *020 †30
GIESSEL, Barton Elgin. 601 S CLAY ST, STE 107 75119 #048-02-1996 L1999 **FM** *020 †18 ‡
GRAYBURN, Paul Arthur. 802 W LAMPASAS ST 75119 #048-02-1981 L1981 **CD IM** *050 †20
HIBBS, Douglas Bain. 800 S CHATFIELD ST 75119 #048-12-1990 L1991 **IM** *020 †20
HOLT, Janie Leach. 911 S CLAY ST 75119 #021-06-1988 L1990 **PD** *020 †55
HYLAND, John Walton. 802 W LAMPASAS ST 75119 #028-02-1954 L1962 **CD IM** *020 †20
JASSIN, Basem M. 800 W LAMPASAS ST, STE B 75119 #008-01-1997 L2002 **OTO A** *020 †45 ‡
JINKS, Larry Alan. 802 W LAMPASAS ST 75119 #048-02-1981 L1981 **IM** *020 †20
JONES, Michael Wayne. 601 S CLAY ST STE 105 75119 #048-14-1987 L1988 **OBG** *020 †30
KANNAN, Lakshmipriya. 802 W LAMPASAS ST 75119 #495-59-1995 L2006 **HO** *020 †20
KATZ, Howard Martin. 800 S CHATFIELD ST 75119 #048-04-1972 L1973 **FM** *020 †18
KINZIE, William Boyd. 800 S CHATFIELD ST 75119 #048-04-1961 L1961 **FM** *071 †18
LAWS, Danny Blayne. 717 W LAMPASAS ST 75119 #005-12-1997 L1998 **FM** *020 †18
MILLER, Brian R. ■ 75119 #048-14-1989 L1990 **IM** *020 †20
RECTOR, Dale Freeman. ■ 75119 #018-03-1955 L1963 **CLP** *075 †50
SACKEY, Emmanuel E. 601 S CLAY ST 75119 #412-01-1987 L1997 **PD** *020 †55
SALGUERO, Jose J. 900 W ENNIS AVE STE 119 75119 #341-01-1988 L1998 **PD** *020 †55
SAMPSON, Cheryl Krames. ■ 75119 #048-12-1984 L1985 **IM** *020 †20
SILLS, Michael. 802 W LAMPASAS ST 75119 #010-01-1983 L1987 **CD** *020 †20
SILVERMAN, Robert Alan. 802 W LAMPASAS ST 75119 #051-04-1979 L1987 **IM** *020 †20
STOLER, Robert Craig. 802 W LAMPASAS ST 75119 #036-07-1990 L1991 **CD** *020 †20
SULLIVAN, John Michael. 802 W LAMPASAS ST 75119 #025-01-1997 L1998 **GS** *020 †85
SULLIVAN, Margaret Mary. ■ 75119 #048-13-2004 **IM** *100 †20
WILLIAMS, Kevin Alexander. 802 W LAMPASAS ST 75119 #035-01-1994 L1999 **ORS** *020
YOUNGBLOOD, Tonya J. 802 W LAMPASAS ST, ELLIS COUNTY MEDICAL ASSOC 75119 #048-16-1997 L2000 **FM** *020 †18

ERA – COOKE

BLOCK, Richard Edward. (COOKE COUNTY), 5335 COUNTY ROAD 398 76238 #048-02-1947 L1947 **IMG IM** *071

ESCAPEES – POLK

BLACK, David Elsey. 231 RAINBOW DR, PMB 13165 77399 #048-12-1973 L1975 **IM** *020
BOWMAN, Gary Wayne. 152 RAINBOW DR STE 5 77399 #048-02-1969 L1969 **AN** *040 †05
BRATTAIN, Paul Lowell. 249 RAINBOW DR, # 14987 77399 #017-20-1964 L1964 **AM ADM** *030 †70
BRIDGEMAN, John Francis. ■ 77399 #067-01-1957 L1958 **FM** *071 †18
BRYSON, Andrew Laird. ■ 77399 #011-03-1964 L1973 **CD IM** *020 †20
EISENHARDT, Otto Franz. ■ 77399 #001-02-1960 L1963 **P** *071
JOHNSON, Jay Taylor. ■ 77399 #040-02-1963 L1969 **PTH** *062 †50

KORN, John Thos. ■ 77399 #035-06-1958 L1964 **OBG** *071
PAISH, Donald Geo, Jr. 101 RAINBOW DR # 6622 77399 #035-03-1960 L1964 **ORS** *071 †40
POLMAN, Boris. ■ 77399 #016-11-1988 L1988 **IM** *020
ROHLFING, Walter A, III. 77399 #048-04-1970 L1971 **GS** *075 †85
SEVENTKO, Joseph Michael. ■ 77399 #035-20-1965 L1968 **ORS** *071 †40
SHIRLEY, Louis Alexander. ■ 77399 #027-01-1960 L1970 **OPH AM** *071 †35
STANFIELD, Melinda S. ■ 77399 #017-20-1969 L1969 **PD NPM** *071 †55
TAYLOR, Larry Raymond. 119 RAINBOW DR, STE 1961 77399 #039-01-1962 L1972 **P** *020
THOMPSON, Blair David. ■ 77399 #005-14-1966 L1967 **PTH DMP** *062 †50
WETCHER, Kenneth. 140 RAINBOW DR, # 4083 77399 #035-08-1967 L1970 **P** *020 †75 ‡
YETTER, Jos Frederick, III. ■ 77399 #017-20-1972 L1980 **FM PTH** *040 †50,18
ZIMMERMAN, Richard Wayne. 127 RAINBOW DR # 2749 77399 #016-11-1974 L1990 **IM** *020 †20

EULESS – TARRANT

AGUIRRE, Marco Alejandro. ■ 76039 #048-14-1999 L2003 **AN** *100 †05
ALCALEN, Erlinda Vidanes. ■ 76039 #748-02-1964 L1978 **OBG** *071
ARENIVAS, Lova Tiana. ■ 76040 #048-12-2004 **DR** *012
ARNOLD, Thomas Lee. 1504 WOODVINE DR, 1504 WOODVINE DRIVE 76040 #017-20-1962 L1968 **U** *020 †95
ASGHAR, Pamela. 350 W PARKWAY STE 120, WOMEN'S CARE OF MID CITIES 76040 #495-03-1981 L2005 **OBG** *020 †30
BOYD, Winford Craig. ■ 76039 #048-12-1961 L1961 **OM** *071
BRIDGFORD, Bettina. ■ 76040 #048-15-2007 **P** *012
BUCHANAN, Marty J. 469 W PARK WAY 76040 #048-13-1991 L1993 **IM** *020 †20
BUKSH, Stephen Rada. 469 WESTPARK WAY, STE 200 76040 #056-06-1996 L1999 **IM** *020 †20
CALANDRO, Mindy Leigh. ■ 76039 #048-02-2007 **PD** *012
CHANDY, Elizabeth. ■ 76040 #016-76-2002, ▲ L2005 **IM** *020 †20
CHANG, Dongkun J. ■ 76039 #048-13-2002 L2006 **PTH** *100 †50
CHAPMAN, Marc Edward. 469 WESTPARK WAY, STE 200 76040 #039-01-1989 L2000 **IM** *020 †20
CHIO, Ronald Lu. 469 WESTPARK WAY, STE 200 76040 #748-11-1993 L2003 **IM** *020 †20
COLIGADO, Eric J. 350 W PARKWAY, STE 121 76040 #048-14-1989 L1990 **PM** *020 †60
DAVILA, Samuel V. 469 WESTPARK WAY, NE TARRANT INTERNAL MEDICI 76040 #048-12-2005 L2008 **IM** *020
DIMBO, Regina K. ■ 76040 #048-02-2008 **012**
DRISKILL, Lance. ■ 76039 #036-05-2002 L2004 **VIR** *012 †80
EISEN, David Roy. 251 WESTPARK WAY, STE 302 76040 #011-02-1979 L1985 **CD** *020 †20
FRITZ, Katie Jane. ■ 76039 #030-06-2006 **GS** *012
HARRELD, Julie Lynn. ■ 76040 #048-12-2003 L2007 **DR** *012
HILL, Elizabeth Chavers. 601 W PARK WAY 76040 #028-78-1995, ▲ L1998 **FM** *020
HO, Roxanne Jui. ■ 76040 #048-12-2004 L2007 **IM** *100
HUSAIN, Asif. 2275 WESTPARK CT, STE 101 76040 #704-02-1972 L1983 **GS** *020 †85
HUSAIN, Tehmina. 2275 WESTPARK CT, STE 101 76040 #704-02-1972 L1983 **OBG** *020 †30
JAMES, Kevin Bernard. ■ 76039 #048-04-2001 L2006 **ORS** *100
JOHNSTON, Don Fredric. 350 WESTPARK WAY STE 204 76040 #048-12-1973 L1975 **ORS** *020 †40
JONES, Jonathan Owen. ■ 76039 #056-06-2005 L2006 **AN** *012
KARING, Michael V. 469 WESTPARK WAY, STE 200 76040 #048-02-1989 L1990 **IM** *020 †20
KELLEY, Gloria Ann. 469 WESTPARK WAY 76040 #021-05-1986 L1986 **IM** *020 †20
KHAN, Zohra Rashid C. 2275 WESTPARK CT, STE 102 76040 #704-06-1972 L1986 **P IM** *020
LUGGER, Jerry Lee. 461 WESTPARK WAY 76040 #038-40-1972 L1982 **PS EM** *020 †45,65
LUTTER, Michael Lee. ■ 76040 #048-12-2003 L2005 **P** *100
MARTIN, Bruce D. 350 WESTPARK WAY, STE 223 76040 #048-13-2000 L2004 **CCP** *020 †55
MAYOL-SHARP, Rebeca. 469 WESTPARK WAY, STE 200 76040 #048-12-1992 L1993 **IM** *020 †20
MILES, Brett A. ■ 76040 #048-12-2002 L2005 **OTO** *012
MISHKIN, David. ■ 76039 #005-16-1962 L1972 **AN** *071 †05
NGUYEN, Thuthuy T. 469 WESTPARK WAY, STE 200 76040 #048-15-1995 L1997 **IM** *020 †20
PHILLIPS, David J. ■ 76040 #048-14-2005 **OBG** *012
REAM, Gene Patrick. 307 WESTPARK WAY 76040 #048-02-1973 L1973 **D** *020 †15
ROBINSON, Brandy Rochelle. ■ 76040 #048-12-2005 L2007 **FP** *012
ROYBAL, Robert Edward. 493 WESTPARK WAY 76040 #021-01-1971 L1973 **ORS** *020 †40
STEELE, Darryl Newell. 800 N INDUSTRIAL BLVD, STE 101 76039 #062-01-1965 L1978 **FM OM** *020
STEPHENS, Maurice Leonard. ■ 76039 #004-01-1972 L1973 **GP GPM** *020
SULLIVAN, Paul Jeffrey. 350 W PARK WAY STE 100 76040 #010-03-1985 L1999 **DR** *020 †80
SUTTON, Lisa Michelle. ■ 76039 #048-12-2007 **PTH** *012
TAFEL, Robert Mathew. 469 WESTPARK WAY, STE 200 76040 #021-01-1966 L1971 **IM CD** *020 †20
TENORIO, Lulu L. ■ 76039 #048-12-2004 L2006 **DR** *012
THOMPSON, James Nicholas. 400 FULLER WISER RD # 300 76039 #038-40-1971 L1971 **OTO FPS** *030 †45
TURNER, Roy Wayne. 350 WESTPARK WAY STE 102, MID-CITIES OBSTETRICAL & G 76040 #021-05-1964 L1968 **GYN** *020 †30
UDOMRATN, Thienchai. ■ 76039 #891-02-1970 L1979 **IM HEM** *020 †20
WALKER, Jeffrey Allen. ■ 76040 #048-15-2006 **DR** *012
WINEGARDEN, Kristina K. ■ 76039 #048-16-2004 L2006 **OBG** *012
YAMAMOTO, Ronald Koji. 425 WESTPARK WAY 76040 #007-02-1969 L1975 **ORS OSM** *020 †40
YOON, Jinny. 601 WESTPARK WAY 76040 #583-01-1993 L2006 **PM** *020 †60
ZYCH-KOWALSKA, Anna T. 350 WESTPARK WAY STE 123 76040 #759-10-1964 L1991 **PD** *020 †55

FABENS – EL PASO

BARAHONA, Victor. 201 W. MAIN SUITE B 79838 #737-01-1970 L1980 **TS GS** *020
FARRIS, Kelly Edwin. PO BOX 3940, 101 POTASIO RD 79838 #056-06-1996 L1999 **FM** *020 †18
MARASOVICH, Steve Anthony. ■ 79838 #048-02-1961 L1961 **GYN** *020 †30

FAIR OAKS – BEXAR

BAUER, Kathryn Leigh. ■ 78015 #048-14-2008 *012

■ = Address Information Privacy Protected

BRIEGER, Donald Richmond. ■ 78015 #048-02-1964 L1964 **DR NM** *071 †80,28
DOUGHERTY, Thomas Butler. ■ 78015 #048-13-1981 L1982 **AN** *020 †05
GOLDBECK, Larry Omar. ■ 78015 #048-04-1958 L1958 **AN PUD** *020 †05
GRAVES, Virgil Boyd. ■ 78015 #048-02-1969 L1969 **DR RNR** *020 †80
HALLERMANN, Franz Josef. ■ 78015 #407-24-1956 L1969 **DR** *071 †80
HARRIS, Barbara Kay. ■ 78015 #048-13-2000 *100
MAANI, Elizabeth Varughes. ■ 78015 #023-01-2007 **IM** *012
MOK, William Lee Ling. ■ 78015 #048-13-1975 L1977 **AN** *020 †05
ORTIZ-CARRILLO, Salvador. ■ 78015 #847-03-1959 L1971 **IM** *071
PAUL, Leonard G. ■ 78015 #038-40-1951 L1961 **FM** *071 †18 ‡
SORRELLS, John Trenton. ■ 78015 #028-34-2005 L2008 **IM** *012

FAIRFIELD — FREESTONE

BERGER, Joseph Richard. 764 W COMMERCE ST 75840 #048-78-1994, ▲ L1996 **FM** *020
CLARK, Donald W. 125 NEWMAN ST 75840 #048-12-1960 L1960 **DR NM** *020
ELFARR, William A. 125 NEWMAN ST 75840 #048-02-1993 L1995 **U** *020 †95
GOLD, Daniel Mark. 125 NEWMAN ST 75840 #048-02-1984 L1985 **OPH** *020 †35
HEAD, Donald L. 125 NEWMAN ST 75840 #048-14-1984 L1985 **FM** *062 †18
JACKSON, James Don, Jr. 125 NEWMAN ST 75840 #012-21-1986 L1993 **GS** *020
KEECH, Daniel R. 125 NEWMAN ST 75840 #048-15-1996 L2000 **OTO** *020 †45
KELLER, John H, Jr. 125 NEWMAN ST 75840 #048-12-1953 L1953 **FM** *020 †18
KERBACHER, James J. 125 NEWMAN ST 75840 #048-13-1997 L2002 **FM** *020 †18
MORGAN, Alma Ruth. 125 NEWMAN ST 75840 #028-03-1973 L1992 **FM EM** *020 †18
NORTON, Court Bartlett. 125 NEWMAN ST 75840 #048-12-1974 L1976 **ORS** *020 †40
NWAFOR, Francis Oluchukwu. 125 NEWMAN ST 75840 #035-09-1991 L1999 **IM** *020 †95
ORMS, James M. 125 NEWMAN ST, EMERGENCY DEPARTMENT 75840 #048-14-1993 L1994 **FM OBS** *020 †18 ‡
SMITSON, Harold Leroy. 125 NEWMAN ST 75840 #048-12-1973 L1976 **DR** *020 †80
UPDEGROVE, John Dewey. 125 NEWMAN ST 75840 #048-02-1985 L1986 **PUD IM** *020 †20
VELTRI, Benjamin. 764 W COMMERCE ST 75840 #051-01-1982 L2004 **GS VS** *020 †85
WAGNER, Richard H. 125 NEWMAN ST 75840 #048-14-1992 L1993 **GS** *020

FAIRVIEW — COLLIN

BERG, Eric Christian. 691 OAKDALE CIR 75069 #041-07-1991 L1995 **AN** *020 †05
CRABB, Donald H. ■ 75069 #018-03-1947 L1948 **GP** *071
FADELE, Manita Soremekun. ■ 75069 #025-07-1992 L1997 **PD** *020
PETERS, Nick Paul. ■ 75069 #030-06-1991 L1995 **EM** *020 †16

FALFURRIAS — BROOKS

GALINDO, Carlos Xavier. ■ 78355 #048-02-2006 **FP** *012
LOZANO, Jose Manuel. 107 E ADAMS ST 78355 #649-14-1980 L1984 **FM** *020 †18
WILDER, Lowell Edgar. ■ 78355 #019-02-1945 L1948 **GP** *071 †18

FARMERS BRANCH — DALLAS

ELLIS, Malathi V. 9 MEDICAL PKWY, PLAZA 4, STE 308 75234 #036-08-2001 L2005 **OBG** *020 †30
GARCIA, Gonzalo H. 9 MEDICAL PKWY, PLAZA 4, STE 208 75234 #048-12-1992 L1993 **OBG** *020 †18
MARTINEZ, Ricardo J. 12879 JOSEY LN STE 100, RICARDO J MARTINEZ, M.D. 75234 #649-03-1986 L1996 **FM** *020 †18
MOLINA, Juan Carlos. 8 MEDICAL PKWY, PLAZA 2, SUITE 202 75234 #048-02-2003 L2006 **FM** *020 †18
PEPE, Paul Ernest. 13000 WILLIAM DODSON PKWY, CITY OF FARMERS BRANCH 75234 #005-02-1976 L1982 **EM PHP** *040 †20,16
SAVANI, Rashmin Chandulal. ■ 75244 #917-10-1982 L2007 **NPM PD** *020 †55

FERRIS — ELLIS

MEGNA, Robert James. 207 W 5TH ST 75125 #028-79-1985, ▲ L1987 **GP** *020

FISCHER — COMAL

ALDRED, Stephen Wayne. ■ 78623 #017-20-1977 L1980 **PTH** *030 †50
NGUYEN, Phuong. ■ 78623 #048-12-1991 **GS** *075
RAU, James Robt. ■ 78623 #047-06-1956 L1957 **GP** *072
WEISS, Kurt Guido. ■ 78623 #407-21-1956 L1964 **PTH** *071 †50

FLINT — SMITH

BABBITT, Gary D. 20208 STATE HIGHWAY 155 S, FAMILY PRACTICE 75762 #048-13-1984 L1986 **FM** *020 †18
BURSHE, Roger Andrew. 17911 BEDDINGFIELD RD 75762 #759-01-1986 L1997 **FM** *020 †18
CASEBOLT, Buford T. ■ 75762 #028-02-1951 L1951 **GS GP** *071 †85
DRAIN, Zachary Weylon. ■ 75762 #048-02-2006 **FM**
ELI, Alan M. 20208 STATE HIGHWAY 155 S 75762 #048-15-1999 L2002 **FM** *020 †18
GREEN, Michael Raymond. ■ 75762 #048-13-1975 L1975 **PD AI** *020 †55,03
STUCKEY, Danell Reiter. 20208 STATE HIGHWAY 155 S 75762 #048-14-2004 L2007 **FM** *020 †18

FLORENCE — WILLIAMSON

HOLDAMPF, Barry J. 301 BREWSTER ST 76527 #048-02-1993 L1994 **FM** *020 †18
MOON, Richard Sloan. ■ 76527 #048-13-1976 L1976 **FM** *062 †18

FLORESVILLE — WILSON

BISCHOFF, Timothy Alan. 1005 B ST, WILSON COUNTY MENTAL HLTH 78114 #048-14-1979 L1986 **P** *020 †75
CANTU, James. ■ 78114 #048-16-2008 *012
CHAVEZ, Harry Louis. 1303 HOSPITAL BLVD 78114 #005-18-1978 L1981 **FM** *020 †18
COATES, Glenn Coleman. 1707 HICKORY 78114 #048-02-1962 L1962 **FM** *071 †18
CURRIER, Daryl Clyde. 921 10TH ST STE 111 78114 #048-13-1976 L1976 **FM** *020 ‡
FAULKNER, Jeffrey Alan. ■ 78114 #048-02-1995 L1998 **OTO** *020 †45
FRYE, Emily E. 260 US HIGHWAY 181 N 78114 #048-13-1999 L2001 **FM** *020 †18
GEIBEL, Paul Tucker. 1303 HOSPITAL BLVD, STE 200 78114 #021-01-1983 L1989 **ORS** *020 †40
GURWITZ, Gregg. 1303 HOSPITAL BLVD, STE 200 78114 #048-12-1989 L1990 **ORS** *020 †40
HARRIS, Martha Jean. ■ 78114 #048-13-1975 L1975 **FM** *071 †18
KIETZKE, Karl Eugene. 1301 HOSPITAL BLVD 78114 #048-15-2000 L2002 **FM** *020 †18 ‡
KIZZART, Jerome Douglas. 1419 3RD ST 78114 #051-07-1982 L1988 **IM** *020 †20
NAYAK, Devraj Upendra. 497 10TH ST STE 101 78114 #495-17-1997 L2004 **CD** *020 †20
NAYAK, Hetal Devraj. ■ 78114 #495-17-1997 L2004 **AN** *020 †05
PARIMOO, Rahul. 260 US HIGHWAY 181 N 78114 #495-01-1996 L2004 **IM** *020 †20
RAO, Arun. 497 10TH ST, STE 101 78114 #495-01-1986 L2003 **HO** *030 †20
REBOLLAR, Caridad M. 2006 10TH ST, US HIGHWAY 181 78114 #042-01-1990 L1997 **NEP** *020 †20
ROJAS-WALSSON, Romeo. 499 10TH ST, CONNALLY MEMORIAL MEDICAL 78114 #649-01-1972 L1995 **FM** *020 †18
SALAZAR, Carlos E. 217 ABREGO LAKE DR 78114 #319-01-1968 L1985 **GS GP** *020 †85
SCHEPPLER, Steven Len. 1303 HOSPITAL BLVD 78114 #016-45-1979 L1980 **FM** *020 †18
SOKOLYK, Stephen Michael. 559 10TH ST, STE 1 78114 #048-12-1988 L1989 **CD** *020 †20

FLOWER MOUND — DENTON

ACETO, Thomas, Jr. ■ 75028 #041-02-1954 L1955 **END PD** *071 †55
ALLEN, Vicki J. 3424 LONG PRAIRIE RD 75022 #048-12-1994 L1995 **OBG** *020 †30
ATCHLEY, Michael R. 1001 CROSS TIMBERS RD, STE 1245 75028 #048-15-1990 L1991 **FM** *020 †20
ATEN, Monica Fonseca. ■ 75028 #270-01-1996 L2005 **PDI** *071 †55
AUERS, Leslie A Arrington. 3424 LONG PRAIRIE RD 75022 #048-15-1986 L1987 **OBG** *020 †30
AXLINE, Bradley Park. 3424 LONG PRAIRIE RD 75022 #038-44-1991 L1995 **OBG** *020 †30
BAJWA, Navjot. 4900 LONG PRAIRIE RD, STE 100 75028 #495-03-1984 L1998 **FM** *020 †18
BALARBAR, Melinda B. 1110 PARKER SQ 75028 #048-12-1997 L2000 **FM** *020 †18
BENNOS, Eric Sidaris. ■ 75022 #021-06-1982 L1984 **DR EM** *080
BODA, Himabindu Reddy. ■ 75022 #495-21-1998 L2005 **RHU** *020 †20
BOLTAN, David Dmitry. ■ 75028 #038-44-2005 L2008 **IM** *012
BOLTAN, Lindsay Elizabeth. ■ 75028 #038-44-2005 **IM** *012
BUCAN-KUREPA, Jelena. 3100 CHURCHILL DR, STE 310 75022 #957-01-1989 L1999 **IM** *020 †20
BURGESS, Kim Sherwin. 3535 FIREWHEEL DR STE D 75028 #048-04-1993 L1995 **PD** *020 †55
CHAZIKATTU, Anita Jacob. 2321 OLYMPIA DR 75028 #495-52-1982 L1990 **GE** *020 †20
CHU, Bobby. 1001 CROSS TIMBERS RD, STE 1240 75028 #004-01-1990 L1996 **IM** *020 †20
COFFMAN, Stewart Ross. 1701 MEADOW VISTA DR 75022 #048-04-1991 L1992 **EM** *020 †16
DAVIS, Randall Ivan. ■ 75028 #021-06-1997 L1998 **OBG** *020
DAVIS-HERR, Jacqueline. 3424 LONG PRAIRIE RD 75022 #048-15-2002 L2005 **OBG** *020
DAVOODI, Fariborz. 3101 CHURCHILL DR STE 315 75022 #048-12-1986 L1987 **FM** *020 †18
DEUSER, Tamra Kay. 2601 FLOWER MOUND RD, STE 133 75028 #047-06-1999 L2002 **FM** *020 †18
DHALIWAL, Harminder Singh. 4900 LONG PRAIRIE RD, STE 100A 75028 #495-29-1976 L1997 **PD** *020 †55
DHOOT, Shrikant R. 3101 CHURCHILL DR STE 200 75022 #495-56-1979 L1990 **PD** *020 †55
DUNHAM, Jocelyn B. 3700 FORUMS DR 75028 #048-14-1991 L1992 **FM** *020 †18
DUTTON, Karri D. 3871 LONG PRAIRIE RD 75028 #048-14-1990 L1994 **PD** *020 †55
EILERS, Steven Gerard. ■ 75022 #308-03-1981 L1985 **P** *020
ELLEPOLA, Achala Kumari. 1901 LONG PRAIRIE RD, STE 116 75022 #913-92-1987 L1998 **PD** *020
FITZGERALD, Marie Holman. 3051 CHURCHILL DR STE 130 75022 #048-14-1989 L1990 **AI** *020 †20,03
FITZGERALD, Ralph J. 3424 LONG PRAIRIE RD, STE 300 75022 #048-13-1989 L1990 **PD** *020 †55
FRANKLIN, Jonathan Doyal. 1708 NOBLE WAY, 4900 HARBOR COURT 75022 #017-20-1997 L2000 **EM** *020 †16
FRISBIE, Brenda. 1110 PARKER SQ 75028 #046-01-1999 L2002 **FM** *020 †18
GALUSHA, Andrea L. 3424 LONG PRAIRIE RD 75022 #048-15-1998 L1999 **OBG** *020 †30
GANAPATHIRAJU, Ajitha. ■ 75022 #495-11-1999 L2006 **IM** *020 †20
GARCIA, Conrad Manuel. 1001 CROSS TIMBERS RD 75028 #048-12-1977 L1977 **FM** *020
GARRETT, Tambra R. 3041 CHURCHILL DR, STE 200 75022 #048-12-1996 L1998 **FM** *020 †18
GEORGE, Susan. ■ 75028 #496-21-1998 L2008 **FM** *100 †18
GOLAB, Alexander. ■ 75028 #068-01-1962 L1977 **OBG** *020 †30
GROSS, Melvin. ■ 75028 #047-06-1961 L1962 **U** *075 †95
HARPAVAT, Kiran. 3101 CHURCHILL DR STE 200 75022 #495-30-1970 L1976 **PD** *020 †55
HARPAVAT, Sanjiv Sonny. ■ 75028 #024-01-2006 **PD** *012
HAUGHT, Courtney Ann. 3051 CHURCHILL DR 75022 #048-14-1998 L2002 **FM** *020 †18
HOANG, Thu Anh. 1001 CROSS TIMBERS RD, STE 1250 75028 #048-15-1995 L1997 **FM** *020 †18
HUDELSON, Mary Brandt. 3051 CHURCHILL DR STE 130 75022 #048-15-1987 L1988 **AI** *020 †20,03
KADI, James Steven. 3100 PETERS COLONY RD, PLASTIC & RESCONTRUCTIVE S 75022 #021-05-1989 L1990 **OTO** *020 †65
KANADIA, Kiran Bhikulal. 3101 CHURCHILL DR STE 200 75022 #495-19-1978 L1984 **PD** *020 †55
KELLY, Jill Sauser. 3535 FIREWHEEL DR, STE D 75028 #016-06-1997 L2000 **PD** *020 †55
KU, Barbara. ■ 75028 #048-15-2002 L2007 **IM** *100
LIMOSNERO, Odette N. 400 PARKER SQ STE 2 75028 #005-19-2000 L2003 **OBG** *020 ‡
LIN, Chung-Wu. ■ 75022 #244-02-1985 L1995 **HMP** *100 †50
LONG, James Robt. 2980 LONG PRAIRIE RD, STE E 75022 #047-06-1971 L1973 **FM** *020 †18
LUNGREN, Amy S. 3101 CHURCHILL DR, FLOWER MOUND WOMEN'S HEALT 75022 #048-12-1999 L2003 **OBG** *100
MADENWALD, Mark L. 1901 POINT DE VUE DR 75022 #048-02-1991 L1992 **EM** *020 †16

■ = Address Information Privacy Protected

MEYER, Ryan R. ■ 75028 #048-15-2000 L2007 **CCP** *100 †55
MONTIGUE, Beth Carlson. 3535 FIREWHEEL DR, STE D 75028 #048-12-1995 L1999 **PD** *020 †55
MORRISS, M Craig. ■ 75022 #048-12-1990 L1991 **DR** *020 †80
MURPHY, Sean Christopher. 5105 BALMORAL LN 75028 #016-06-2008 *012
MUZZARELLI, James Michael. 2628 LONG PRAIRIE RD SU 75022 #048-12-1998 L2001 **EM** *020 †16
NAYLOR, Debra Ann. 3041 CHURCHILL DR, STE 300 75022 #049-01-2001 L2004 **PD** *020 †55
NEURGAONKAR, Shrirang S. 3611 MORRISS RD, MODERN MEDICAL CLINIC 75028 #495-22-1984 L1994 **IM** *020 †20
NICHOLS, Wallace. ■ 75028 #038-06-1955 L1955 **PD** *071 †55
NOVAK, Jacob J. 2628 LONG PRAIRIE RD 75022 #048-15-1996 L1997 **EM** *020 †16
PAROSKI, Sylvie Helene. 3101 CHURCHILL DR, STE 212 75022 #005-11-1998 L2002 **OBG** *020 †30
PEREZ, Isaac. 3821 LONG PRAIRIE RD, STE 100 75028 #042-01-1990 L1997 **D** *020 †20,15
PETERSON, William Stanley. ■ 75028 #038-43-2001 L2002 **EM** *012
PHIPPS, Lowell F. 3101 CHURCHILL DR STE 310 75022 #048-15-1993 L1994 **FM** *020 †18
ROBERSON, Matthew Bruce. 3101 CHURCHILL DR STE 315 75022 #048-13-2000 L2002 **FM** *020 †18 ‡
ROSE, Gary Louis. 3424 LONG PRAIRIE RD 75022 #048-12-1975 L1975 **OBG** *020 †30
RUSSELL, Carl Lindsey. 2550 CROSS TIMBERS RD, STE 116 75028 #025-07-1981 L2002 **IM** *020 †20
SANTIAGO, Joseph Patrick. 1110 PARKER SQ 75028 #048-12-1997 L2000 **FM** *020 †18
SCHERER, David M. 3101 CHURCHILL DR, STE 220 75022 #048-16-1992 L1993 **CD** *020 †20
SCHUTE, Pamela Conner. ■ 75022 #005-15-1978 L1990 **OBS GYN** *075 †30
SEAMAN, Edwin Dwight. ■ 75022 #048-12-1960 L1966 **PTH NM** *071 †50,28
SELBY, George Walter. ■ 75022 #012-05-1953 L1953 **PD** *071 †55
SEYSAN-SABOUR, Roya V. 2261 OLYMPIA DR STE 100, FAMILY HEALTH CENTER 75028 #517-03-1981 L1994 **FM** *020 †18
SIMON, Kathryn Mary. 2200 MORRISS RD, STE 100 75028 #028-03-1982 L1985 **FM** *020 †18
SLEZAK, Sylvia. 3200 LONG PRAIRIE RD 75022 #286-03-1971 L1994 **FM** *020
SMITH, Landria Cecil. 6051 MORRISS RD 75028 #048-12-1944 L1945 **GP** *071
VAFAIE, Aimee Pooneh. 3535 FIREWHEEL DR 75028 #035-01-2001 L2004 **PD** *020 †55
VAN DELL, Harvey G. 400 PARKER SQ, STE 245 75028 #048-15-1998 L1999 **OBG** *020 †30
VENKATESH, Purnima. 3051 CHURCHILL DR, STE 130 75022 #021-06-1996 L2000 **AI** *020 †03,55
VILLALON, Raul, Jr. ■ 75022 #048-16-2000 L2007 **FM** *020 †18
WEIDNER, Carol A. 2724 THISTLEWOOD CT, DEPARTMENT OF ANETH & PAIN 75022 #048-14-1990 L1992 **AN** *020 †05
WRIGHT, Jack Marcus. 1001 CROSS TIMBERS RD, STE 1250 75028 #039-01-1981 L1995 **FM** *020 †18
WUST, Sven Kjellgren. 3051 CHURCHILL DR, STE 130 75022 #021-06-1996 L1999 **AI** *020 †20,03

FLOYDADA — FLOYD

AHMAD, Salman. 901 W CROCKETT ST 79235 #704-02-1990 L1995 **IM** *020 †20

FLUVANNA — SCURRY

DILLAHA, Carl A, Jr. 15556 COUNTY ROAD 2202 79517 #004-01-1951 L1953 **FM FPG** *020 †18

FORNEY — KAUFMAN

BEUTEL, Herbert Wm. ■ 75126 #048-04-1954 L1954 **GS CD** *071 †85
GARRISON, Robert Dale. 14812 MELODY LN 75126 #007-02-1997 L1999 **EM** *020 †16
HOBBS, Bobby R. 12415 SADDLE CLUB DR 75126 #010-03-1977 L1980 **IM** *020
KANANI, Pradip V. 410 PINSON RD 75126 #495-83-1977 L1986 **IM** *020 †20
KAY, Tim Eugene. 713 W BROAD ST STE 200 75126 #048-02-1989 L1990 **FM** *020 †18
MINER, Mary Susan. 785 VALLEY VIEW RD 75126 #649-01-1968 L1976 **PTH** *020
MOSS, Jason Tabias. ■ 75126 #048-15-2008 *012
REDDY, Jayaprakash N. 713 W BROAD ST STE 100, FORNEY PEDIATRIC & MEDICAL 75126 #495-37-1970 L1983 **IM** *020
REDDY, Jyothi J. 713 W BROAD ST, FORNEY PEDIATRIC&MEDICAL C 75126 #495-72-1970 L1982 **PD** *020 †55
SAGER, Rebecca A. ■ 75126 #048-13-2005 **PTH** *012
SMITH, Joseph Henry. ■ 75126 #025-01-1969 L1970 **PTH GP** *071
TOSCANO, Guido Rene. 11334 FM 740 75126 #319-01-1985 L1991 **IM** *020 †20
WALKER, Christine Z. 325 S BOIS D ARC ST 75126 #048-12-1948 L1948 **FM GP** *071 †18
WILSON, Wesley G. 713 W BROAD ST STE 200 75126 #048-78-1991, ▲ L1993 **FM** *020 †18

FORT DAVIS — JEFF DAVIS

GEORGE, Charles Edward. ■ 79734 #048-02-1957 L1957 **ORS** *072
WATKINS, William W. ■ 79734 #021-01-1937 L1937 **U** *071

FORT HOOD — BELL

ALAYON-VALERA, Juan B. USA MEDDAC 76544 #649-19-1976 **GP** *020
BAUER, Steven James. 36000 DARNALL LOOP, DARNALL ARMY COMMUNITY HOS 76544 #025-07-1999 L2004 **EM** *020 †16
BEAMAN, Nancy A. 36000 DARNALL LOOP, CARL R. DARNALL AMC 76544 #048-15-2001 L2003 **PTH** *020 †50
BRADY, Kerry M. 36000 DARNALL LOOP, USA MEDDAC 76544 #048-15-1990 L1991 **PTH** *020 †50
CAMPI, Jon Scott. 36000 DARNALL LOOP, MCXI-DCS-CR 76544 #033-05-1997 L1999 **OBG** *020 ‡
CARCHEDI, Lisa R. 36000 DARNALL LOOP, CARL DARNALL ARMY MED CTR 76544 #055-02-2000 L2007 **P** *100 ‡

CHANCE, John Randolph. 36000 DARNALL LOOP, USA MEDDAC 76544 #010-02-1997 L1998 **ORS** *020 †40
COFFMAN, Lydia A. 36000 DARNALL LOOP, DARNALL ARMY COMM HOSP 76544 #047-07-1978 L1978 **ORS** *020 †40
CONRAD, Stuart Allen. 36000 DARNALL LOOP, USA MEDDAC 76544 #027-01-1990 L2007 **CHP** *020 †75
CONROY, Corinne Marie. ■ 76544 #023-12-2000 L2002 **PD** *100 †55
CROLEY, Mark Holland. 36000 DARNALL LOOP, CARL R. DARNALL AMC 76544 #023-12-1992 L2008 **PD** *020 †55
DHAWAN, Aman. ■ 76544 #035-03-1999 L2000 **ORS** *020 †40
DODSON, Darrel Wayne. 36000 DARNALL LOOP, DEPARTMENT OF MEDICINE 76544 #010-01-1998 L2006 **IM CCM** *020 †20
ESTABROOK, Wm Wallace, III. 36003 WRATTEN DR, DARNALL ARMY COMM HOSP 76544 #024-16-1974 L1980 **P CHP** *020 †75
FILLMAN, Eric Paul. 36000 DARNALL LOOP, CR DARNALL ARMY MED CTR 76544 #023-12-1999 L2006 **PTH** *062 †50
FOSTER, Mark Stephen. 36000 DARNALL LOOP, USA MEDDAC 76544 #048-13-1982 L1983 **AM GP** *020 †35
FRIESEN, Clifford David. 36000 DARNALL LOOP, USA MEDDAC 76544 #005-12-1969 L1998 **AI A** *020 †55,03
FULLER, Everett Tomio. 36000 DARNALL LOOP BOX 31, DARNALL ARMY MEDICAL CENTE 76544 #010-02-2004 L2007 **EM** *020
GALLUP, Roger Arnold. 36000 DARNALL LOOP, USA MEDDAC 76544 #035-09-1991 L1993 **PCC** *020 †20
GERACCI, James Jay. 36000 DARNALL LOOP, CARL R. DARNALL ARMY MEDIC 76544 #023-12-1996 L1998 **FM** *020
GORSKE, Andrew Carl. 36000 DARNALL LOOP, DARNALL ARMY COMM HOSP 76544 #036-07-1995 L2005 **GE** *020 †20
GOURLEY, Eric Jerome. 36000 DARNALL LOOP, GENERAL SURGERY SERVICE 76544 #023-12-1997 L1999 **GS** *020 †85
HARTSTEIN, Bonnie Harriet. 36000 DARNALL LOOP, CARL R DARNALL ARMY MED CT 76544 #024-05-1997 L2002 **EM** *020 †16,55
HAWKINS, Eric Lynn. 36000 DARNALL LOOP, USA MEDDAC 76544 #023-12-1998 L1999 **EM** *020
HEROLD, Thomas J S. 36000 DARNALL LOOP, C.R. DARNALL ARMY MEDICAL 76544 #023-12-1994 L2005 **EM** *020
HILE, David Christopher. 36000 DARNALL LOOP BOX 31, CARL R DARNALL ARM MEDICAL 76544 #038-40-2002 L2006 **EM** *020 †16
HIRSCH, John Vladimir. 36000 DARNALL LOOP, BOX # 55 76544 #038-43-1998 L2008 **PAN** *020 †05
HUEBNER, Kermit David. 36000 DARNALL LOOP, CARL R. DARNALL ARMY MEDIC 76544 #038-44-1999 L2001 **EM** *020 †16
KOVAC, Christine Chorney. 36000 DARNALL LOOP, CARL R. DARNALL AMC 76544 #021-01-1995 L1997 **OBG** *020 †30
LAM, Peter Theinwin. 36000 DARNALL LOOP, CARL R DARNALL ARMY MED CT 76544 #209-01-1991 L2000 **NR PTH** *020 †28
LANGE, Christopher Lee. 36000 DARNALL LOOP, DARNALL ARMY COMMUNITY HOS 76544 #023-12-1997 L1998 **PFP** *020 †75
LARSEN, Wilma Ida. 36000 DARNALL LOOP, ATTN: CREDENTIAL OFFICE 76544 #023-12-1990 L1992 **OBG** *020 †30
LAZARUS, Donald Ray, Jr. 36000 DARNALL LOOP, CR DARNALL ARMY MED CTR 76544 #048-16-2002 L2004 **IM** *020 †20
LINKLATER, Derek Ryan. 36000 DARNALL LOOP, DEPT OF EMERGENCY MEDICINE 76544 #023-12-1999 L2003 **PEM** *012 †16
LUCAS, Glynda Williams. 36000 DARNALL LOOP, C.R. DARNALL ARMY MEDICAL 76544 #041-07-1992 L2004 **PD** *020 †55
LUND, Eric Thos. 36000 DARNALL LOOP, USA MEDDAC 76544 #023-12-1990 L1992 **GPM** *020 †70
MC CAIN, Gregory Thomas. 36000 DARNALL LOOP, ATTN CREDENTIAL OFFICE 76544 #023-12-2001 L2008 **PD** *020 †55
MCRAE, Scott Victor. 36000 DARNALL LOOP, USA MEDDAC 76544 #007-02-1993 L1996 **GE** *020 †20
MILLER, Colin Kelly. 36000 DARNALL LOOP, USA MEDDAC 76544 #018-03-1988 L1989 **ORS** *020 †40
PEACHER, John Jos. 36000 DARNALL LOOP, USA MEDDAC 76544 #649-14-1977 L1983 **AN** *020
PHILLIPS, Ben Kirk. 36000 DARNALL LOOP, DARNALL ARMY COMMUNITY HOS 76544 #023-12-1999 L2000 **P CHP** *100 †75
PILERI, Carl Louis. 36000 DARNALL LOOP, ATTN: CREDENTIAL OFFICE 76544 #030-06-2000 L2005 *020 †05
REDDING, Stephanie Denise. 36000 DARNALL LOOP, USA MEDDAC 76544 #023-12-1995 L2005 **FM** *020 †18
RITTER, Marylynn. 36000 DARNALL LOOP, PATHOLOGY B 76544 #011-03-1998 L2004 **PTH** *020
ROMEU VELEZ, Jorge L. 36000 DARNALL LOOP, USA MEDDAC 76544 #033-06-1998 L2006 **NPM** *020 †55
RONAY, Thomas Robert. 36000 DARNALL LOOP, BOX 12 76544 #026-04-2007 **FP** *012
SPANGLE, Karen Jones. 36000 DARNALL LOOP, DARNALL ARMY HOSPITAL 76544 #021-01-2000 L2005 **EM** *020 †16
STEVENS, Tracy Kendrew. 36000 DARNALL LOOP, USA MEDDAC 76544 #050-02-1996 L1998 **NPM** *020 †55
STONE, Kenneth Eric. 36000 DARNALL LOOP, CARL R. DARNALL ARMY MEDIC 76544 #018-03-1998 L2000 **CD** *020 †20
TAYLOR, Elizabeth S. 36003 DARNALL LOOP, CARL R. DARNALL ARMY MED C 76544 #021-01-1999 L2003 **P** *020
TUBB, Creighton Collins. 36000 DARNALL LOOP, CARL R. DARNALL ARMY MEDIC 76544 #048-12-1998 L2007 **ORS** *020 †40
VINSON, Frederick L. 36000 DARNALL LOOP, DARNALL ARMY COMMUNITY MED 76544 #039-01-1979 L1980 **OBG** *020 †30
WALLACE, David Michael. 36000 DARNALL LOOP, DARNALL ACH 76544 #023-12-1995 L1997 **FM** *020 †18
WIEMAN, Jason Scott. 36000 DARNALL LOOP, USA MEDDAC 76544 #023-12-1995 L1997 **GPM** *020 †70,18
WOOD, Brian Christopher. ■ 76544 #035-15-2007 **IM** *012
WOODSON, Justin Trevor. 36000 DARNALL LOOP, ATTN: CREDENTIAL OFFICE 76544 #023-12-1997 L1998 **GPM** *020 †70
WYNN, Michael Preston. 36000 DARNALL LOOP, CARL R DARNALL ARMY MEDIC 76544 #023-12-1994 L1996 **FM** *020 †18

ZEMZARS, Tamatha Frizzell. 36000 DARNALL LOOP, DARNALL ARMY COMMUNITY HOS 76544 #048-13-2002 L2004 *020 †55 **PD**

FORT SAM HOUSTON – BEXAR

AITA, John Scot. 3851 ROGER BROOKE DR, ATTN: CREDENTIAL OFFICE 78234 #030-05-2001 L2002 **GE** *012

ALLEN, Anthony Wayne. 3851 ROGER BROOKE DR, BROOKE ARMY MEDICAL CENTER 78234 #012-01-1992 L1993 **VIR** *020 †80

ALVAREZ, Johnny Dixon. 3851 ROGER BROOKE DR 78234 #748-10-1963 L1995 **GS** *030 †85

ANDERSON, Ian Scott. 3851 ROGER BROOKE DR, BROOKE ARMY MED CTR 78234 #010-02-2006 L2008 **AN** *012

BAKRIS, Nicholas C. 3851 ROGER BROOKE DR, STE 429-18 78234 #025-07-1989 L1991 **CD IM** *020 †20 ‡

BANKS, Kevin L. 3851 ROGER BROOKE DR 78234 #038-40-1997 L2000 **NM** *020 †95

BASKIN, Toney Wm. 3851 ROGER BROOKE DR, BROOKE AMC, BLDG 3600 78234 #021-05-1969 L1971 **CCS TRS** *020 †85

BATHINI, Prasantha. 3851 ROGER BROOKE DR, CARDIOLOGY SERVICE (MCHE-M 78234 #654-01-1997 L2005 **CD** *020 †20

BIEDIGER, Tracy L. 3851 ROGER BROOKE DR, MCHE-DD 78234 #021-01-1987 L1995 **D** *020 †15

BIRRIEL CARMONA, Tomas. 3851 ROGER BROOKE DR 78234 #847-04-1959 L1963 **AM FM** *071

BLACK, Ian Herrick. 3851 ROGER BROOKE DR, FORT SAM HOUSTON TX 78234 #041-14-1999 L2001 **AN** *020 †05

BLACKBOURNE, Lorne H. 3851 ROGER BROOKE DR, BROOKE ARMY MED CTR 78234 #051-01-1990 L1990 **CCS** *020 †85

BOLLES, Jonathan Andrew. 3851 ROGER BROOKE DR, ATTN: CREDENTIAL OFFICE 78234 #050-02-2001 L2003 **CD** *012

BONETA, Otto F. 2050 WORTH RD, USAMEDCOM 78234 #048-14-1989 L1990 **OM** *020 †70

BOYER, Dustin Lamar. 3851 ROGER BROOKE DR, BROOKE ARMY MEDICAL CENTER 78234 #023-12-1999 L2004 **RO** *100 †80

BRANSTETTER, Joanna Garna. 3851 ROGER BROOKE DR, ATTN CREDENTIAL OFFICE 78234 #023-12-2003 L2005 **ORS** *012

BRAVERMAN, Steven Edward. 2050 WORTH RD STE 102, US ARMY MEDICAL COMMAND 78234 #047-05-1987 L1989 **PM** *030 †60

BURNS, Travis Carter. 3851 ROGER BROOKE DR, ATTN: CREDENTIAL OFFICE 78234 #048-14-2004 L2006 **ORS** *012

BUTTERFIELD, Connie Ruth. ■ 78234 #019-02-1985 L1986 **OBG** *020 †30

CABOOT, Jason Blair. 2050 WORTH RD STE 26, HQ US ARMY MEDICAL COMMAND 78234 #041-02-2001 L2003 **PDP** *012 †55

CANCIO, Leopoldo Carlos. 3400 RAWLEY E CHAMBERS AVE, US ARMY INSTITUTE OF SURG 78234 #010-02-1987 L1988 **GS** *020 †85

CARDENAS, Ernesto. 3851 ROGER BROOKE DR, ATTN: CREDENTIAL OFFICE 78234 #042-02-2004 L2006 **OBG** *012

CARLIN, Kevin Jos. 3851 ROGER BROOKE DR, BROOKE ARMY MED CTR, BLDG 78234 #045-01-1983 L1987 **END IM** *020 †20

CARRIZALES, Arthur. 2991 GARDEN AVE, MCWETHY TROOP MEDICAL CLIN 78234 #026-04-1977 L1979 **FM AM** *020 †18

CASEY, Thomas Jos. 3851 ROGER BROOKE DR, BROOKE AMC, BLDG 3600 78234 #032-01-1986 L2007 **HMP** *020 †50

CASTRO, Candice Lee. 3151 SCOTT RD, MCCS-HMP SUITE 1229 78234 #011-04-1976 L1979 **GS** *040 †85

CAWTHON, Michael A. 3851 ROGER BROOKE DR 78234 #048-78-1978, ▲ L1978 **DR NM** *071 †20,28,80

CHANEY, Samuel Allen. 3851 ROGER BROOKE DR 78234 #038-40-1957 L1967 **OS** *030 †30

CHIN, Eric Joseph. 3851 ROGER BROOKE DR, MCHE-QD 78234 #051-01-2003 L2004 **EM** *012

CLARK, Kyra Powell. 3851 ROGER BROOKE DR, ATTN: CREDENTIAL OFFICE 78234 #041-14-2004 L2006 **IM** *020 †20

CLINKSCALES, Christopher. 3851 ROGER BROOKE DR, BROOKE ARMY MED CTR/ANEST 78234 #048-15-2002 L2007 **AN** *020 †05

COATES, Kevin Emerson. 3851 ROGER BROOKE DR, MCHE-QD 78234 #041-12-2003 L2005 **ORS** *012

COLLINS, Christopher Davi. 3851 ROGER BROOKE DR, BROOKE ARMY MED CNTR 78234 #048-14-2004 L2006 **D** *012

CONTRERAS, Maricela. 3851 ROGER BROOKE DR, ATTN MCHE-QD 78234 #005-11-1992 L2004 **DR** *020 †80

COTE, Lise Ann. 3851 ROGER BROOKE DR, ATTN:CREDENTIAL OFFICE 78234 #023-12-1987 L1989 **FM** *020 †18

CUNIOWSKI, Peter A. 3851 ROGER BROOKE DR, ATTN: CREDENTIAL OFFICE 78234 #024-05-2004 L2007 **EM** *020

CURLIN, Howard Lee. 3851 ROGER BROOKE DR, ATTN: CREDENTIAL OFFICE 78234 #047-20-1999 L2001 **OBG** *020 †30

DACUS, Jennifer. 3851 ROGER BROOKE DR, DEPT MED 78234 #048-13-2000 L2002 **HO** *012 †20

DAVIS, Andrew Scott. 3851 ROGER BROOKE DR, BROOKE AMC 78234 #035-09-2004 L2006 **OPH** *012

DEAL, Leonard E, Jr. 3851 ROGER BROOKE DR, ATTN: CREDENTIAL OFFICE 78234 #034-01-1992 L2004 **PCC** *020 †20

DEATON, Michael Allen. ■ 78234 #023-12-1993 L1994 **FM** *030 †18

DE LORENZO, Robert Allan. 3851 ROGER BROOKE DR, BROOKE ARMY MED CTR, BLDG 78234 #035-03-1990 L1997 **EM OS** *040 †16

DILLON, Christopher Alan. 3851 ROGER BROOKE DR, BROOKE ARMY MEDICAL CENTER 78234 #038-41-1988 L1999 **ADL AMI** *020 †55,20

DOOLEY, Sean Nathan. 3851 ROGER BROOKE DR, PULMONARY DISEASE SVC 78234 #047-20-2000 L2002 **PCC CCM** *012 †20

EASTRIDGE, Brian John. 3851 ROGER BROOKE DR, MCHE-SDI 78234 #023-01-1989 L1996 **GS** *020 †85

ELLIS, Michael Wayne. 3851 ROGER BROOKE DR 3600, MCH-MDI 78234 #038-06-1999 L2001 **ID** *020 †20

ENG, Terry L. 3851 ROGER BROOKE DR, BROOKE ARMY MC PED CLNC 78234 #023-12-1986 L1996 **PD** *020 †55

EVANS, Lee Andrew. 3851 ROGER BROOKE DR, ATTN CREDENTIAL OFFICE 78234 #036-05-2003 L2004 **U** *012

FICKE, James Robt. 3851 ROGER BROOKE DR, ATTN: CREDENTIAL OFFICE 78234 #023-12-1987 L1999 **ORS** *020 †40

FLETCHER, Andrew Scott. 3851 ROGER BROOKE DR, MCHE-QD 78234 #048-14-2003 L2005 **DR** *012

GENTLESK, Philip John. 3851 ROGER BROOKE DR, ATTN: CREDENTIAL OFC 78234 #010-02-1997 L2005 **ICE** *020 †20

GERHARDT, Robert T. 3851 ROGER BROOKE DR 78234 #011-02-1992 L1997 **EM AM** *020 †16

GILBERT, Bruce Curtiss. 3851 ROGER BROOKE DR, MCHE-QD 78234 #012-22-2003 L2005 **DR** *012

GLASSER, Jessie Sara. 3851 ROGER BROOKE DR, BOOKE AMY MED CTR DEPT MED 78234 #024-07-2005 L2006 **IM** *012

GOFF, Mitchell Jeremy. 3851 ROGER BROOKE DR, ATTN: CREDENTIAL OFFICE 78234 #056-06-2000 L2004 **OPH** *020 †35

GOKSEL, Denise L. 3851 ROGER BROOKE DR, ATTN: CREDENTIAL OFFICE 78234 #048-13-2003 L2005 **D** *012

GOLDMAN, Richard Alan. 3851 ROGER BROOKE DR 78234 #035-15-1971 L1972 **GS** *040 †85

GOULD, Stanley Farrell. 3851 ROGER BROOKE DR, DEPT OF OB/GYN 78234 #025-07-1975 L1976 **OBG** *040 †30

GRANVILLE, Robert Richey. 3851 ROGER BROOKE DR 78234 #040-02-1985 L2000 **ORS** *020 †40

GUERRERO, Arthur F. 3851 ROGER BROOKE DR, ATTN: CREDENTIAL OFFICE 78234 #023-12-2004 L2006 **IM** *100 †20

GUERRERO, Karen Tarm. 3851 ROGER BROOKE DR 78234 #023-12-2004 L2006 **D** *012

HACKER, Henry David. 3851 ROGER BROOKE DR, ATTN: CREDENTIAL OFFICE 78234 #035-20-1985 L2007 **OPH** *035

HALLIDAY, Alan Wood. 3851 ROGER BROOKE DR 78234 #041-14-1980 L1994 **N CN** *020 †75

HARFORD, David John. 3851 ROGER BROOKE DR, BROOKE ARMY MED CTR 78234 #023-12-1993 L1995 **PHO** *020 †55

HARRIS, Kenneth C. 3851 ROGER BROOKE DR, MCHE-AD 78234 #023-12-1987 L1997 **AN** *030 †05

HAUGER, Franklin Henry. 3851 ROGER BROOKE DR, ATTN: CREDENTIAL OFFICE 78234 #048-13-1994 L2006 **FM** *020 †18

HAYS, Allan Charles. 3851 ROGER BROOKE DR, DEPT EMERGENCY MEDICINE 78234 #012-01-1993 L1996 **AN** *020 †20

HELMRICK, Kevin Joseph. 2050 WORTH RD STE G-102 78234 #056-05-1997 L1998 **IM** *030 †20

HEWITSON, William C. 2250 STANLEY RD, UNIT 574 78234 #023-12-1991 L1992 **PHP OM** *040 †70 ‡

HILBERT, Douglas Raymond. 3851 ROGER BROOKE DR, ATTN: CREDENTIAL OFFICE 78234 #665-01-2001 L2007 **IM** *012

HOLCOMB, John Bradley. 3400 RAWLEY E CHAMBERS AVE 78234 #004-01-1985 L1998 **TRS CCS** *020 †85

HOLMES, Chad Kenneth. 3851 ROGER BROOKE DR, BROOKE ARMY MED CTR 78234 #023-12-2001 L2006 *020 †05

HOOVER, Aaron Zachary. 3851 ROGER BROOKE DR, ATTN: CREDENTIAL OFFICE 78234 #038-40-1998 L1999 **D** *020 †15

HORVATH, Lynn Longmore. 3851 ROGER BROOKE DR 3600, MCH-MDI 78234 #038-41-1997 L2007 **ID** *020 †20

HOSPENTHAL, Duane Russell. 3851 ROGER BROOKE DR, INF DISEASE MCHE-MDI 78234 #025-12-1991 L1993 **ID IM** *030 †20

HSU, Daniel Ping. 3851 ROGER BROOKE DR, ATTN CREDENTIAL OFFICE 78234 #023-12-1996 L1998 **PDP** *020 †55

HSU, Joseph Robert. 3851 ROGER BROOKE DR 78234 #021-01-1998 L2005 **ORS** *020 †40

HUDAK, Steven Jeffrey. 3851 ROGER BROOKE DR, ATTN: CREDENTIAL OFFICE 78234 #018-03-2004 L2006 **U** *012

HUEMAN, Kevin Geoffrey. 3851 ROGER BROOKE DR, ATTN: CREDENTIAL OFFICE 78234 #036-05-2003 L2005 **OTO** *012

HUMPHREYS, Christopher W. 3851 ROGER BROOKE DR, PULMONARY CLINIC 78234 #033-05-1998 L2006 **PCC** *020 †20

HUTTON, Robert Lee, Sr. 3851 ROGER BROOKE DR, BROOKE ARMY MEDICAL CENTER 78234 #023-12-2002 L2004 **PCP** *012 †50

JAMES, Bruce Lee. 3851 ROGER BROOKE DR, ATTN: CREDENTIAL OFFICE 78234 #023-12-2004 L2005 *100

JEHL, John Jos. 3851 ROGER BROOKE DR, BROOKE ARMY MED CTR, BLDG 78234 #048-12-1972 L1979 **FM** *020 †18

JENSEN, Ralph Evan. 3851 ROGER BROOKE DR, STE 429-18 78234 #010-01-2003 L2005 **IM** *020 †20

JIMENEZ, Santiago. 3851 ROGER BROOKE DR, ATTN: CREDENTIAL OFFICE, M 78234 #042-02-2004 L2005 *100

JOHNSON, Chatt Allan. 3851 ROGER BROOKE DR, BROOKE AMC 78234 #023-12-1993 L1995 **VS** *100 †85

JOHNSON, Erica Nicole. 3851 ROGER BROOKE DR, ATTN CREDENTIAL OFFICE 78234 #023-01-2003 L2005 **ID** *012 †20

KELLY, Joseph Francis. 3851 ROGER BROOKE DR, ATTN: CREDENTIAL OFFICE 78234 #024-07-2003 L2004 **GS** *012

KERCHIEF, Karl R. 3851 ROGER BROOKE DR 78234 #023-12-1982 L1987 **FM** *030 †18

KIRKPATRICK, Aaron David. 3851 ROGER BROOKE DR, MCHE-QD 78234 #032-01-2003 L2005 **DR** *012

KOCHAN, Christopher John. 3851 ROGER BROOKE DR, ATTN: CREDENTIAL OFFICE 78234 #023-12-1998 L2001 **AN** *020 †05

LACY, Gregory Lamont, II. 3851 ROGER BROOKE DR, BROOKE ARMY MEDICAL CENTER 78234 #021-01-2002 L2004 **U** *012

LAMB, Paul Brandon. 3851 ROGER BROOKE DR, ATTN: CREDENTIAL OFFICE 78234 #001-06-2005 L2007 **IM** *012

LANDES, Phillip Wm. 3851 ROGER BROOKE DR, BROOKE ARMY MEDICAL CENTER 78234 #051-07-1990 L2008 **PM PRS** *020 †60

LARSON, Brian Daniel. 3851 ROGER BROOKE DR 78234 #023-12-2005 L2007 **AN** *012

LAWINGER, Melanie T. 3851 ROGER BROOKE DR, BROOKE ARMY MED CTR 78234 #048-13-1992 L1993 **AN** *020 †05

LEATH, Charles Alexander. 3851 ROGER BROOKE DR, DEPT OF OB/GYN 78234 #045-01-1998 L2006 **GO OBG** *020 †30 ‡

LINFOOT, John Ardis, Jr. 3851 ROGER BROOKE DR, USAISR-TRAUMA/CRIT CARE 78234 #016-43-1992 L2005 **CCM** *020 †20

LONGENECKER, David Bruce. 3851 ROGER BROOKE DR, BROOKE AMC 78234 #023-12-1992 L1994 **OS** *020

LOUGEE, Douglas Alan. 3851 ROGER BROOKE DR, PEDIATRIC CLNC 78234 #049-01-1991 L1995 **PD** *020 †55

LOUNSBERY, Doreen Marie. 2050 WORTH RD STE 26 78234 #046-01-1984 L1986 IM IMG *030 †20

LUSK, Joanna Doreen. 3851 ROGER BROOKE DR 78234 #012-01-2000 L2001 PTH *020 †50

LYONS, Christina Jo. 3851 ROGER BROOKE DR, BROOKE ARMY MEDICAL CENTER 78234 #054-04-2002 L2004 D *020 †15

MAANI, Christopher V. 3851 ROGER BROOKE DR, FORT SAM HOUSTON TX 78234 #010-03-2002 L2007 AN *100

MADDOX, Craig Lynn. 3851 ROGER BROOKE DR, ATTN: CREDENTIAL OFFICE 78234 #016-45-2003 L2007 D *020

MARKELZ, Brian Paul. 3851 ROGER BROOKE DR, CREDENTIALS OFFICE 78234 #048-12-2004 L2006 IM *100 †20

MARTIN, Robert Russell. 3851 ROGER BROOKE DR, BROOKE ARMY MEDICAL CENTER 78234 #051-04-1983 L1990 GS TRS *020 †85

MARTINEZ OSORIO, Jorge Iv. 3851 ROGER BROOKE DR, BROOKE ARMY MED CENTER 78234 #264-03-1997 IM *012

MASON, Arthur D, Jr. BROOKE AMC INST SURG RES 78234 #028-02-1951 L1951 TRS *050

MC DERMOTT, Dustin Max. 3851 ROGER BROOKE DR, ATTN: CREDENTIAL OFFICE 78234 #039-01-2003 L2005 GS *012

MC FARLAND, Craig C. 3851 ROGER BROOKE DR, BROOKE ARMY MEDICAL CENTER 78234 #011-02-1998 L2006 AN *020 †05

MC LEAN, Scott D. 3851 ROGER BROOKE DR 78234 #023-12-1986 L2005 MG PD *020 †55,19

MC MULLIN, Neil Robert. 3851 ROGER BROOKE DR, ATTN: CREDENTIAL OFFICE 78234 #048-14-2003 L2005 GS *012

MICHAUD, Edward Conrad. 3851 ROGER BROOKE DR, BROOKE ARMY MEDICAL CENTER 78234 #033-06-1991 L1992 IM *020 †20

MILLS, Shane Jefferson. 3851 ROGER BROOKE DR, BROOKE ARMY MEDICAL CENTER 78234 #001-06-2000 L2000 GE *020 †20

MIRK, Anna Katherine. 3851 ROGER BROOKE DR, BROOKE ARMY MED CTR 78234 #011-02-2000 L2002 IMG *020 †20

MORALES, Kelly Joanne. 3851 ROGER BROOKE DR, ATTN: CREDENTIAL OFFICE 78234 #048-14-2003 L2005 OBG *020

MORRIS, Michael James. 3851 ROGER BROOKE DR, MDP/BROOKE ARMY MEDICAL CT 78234 #051-07-1987 L1998 PUD CCM *020 †20

MOSTELLER, David Allan. 3851 ROGER BROOKE DR, BROOKE ARMY MED CTR 78234 #023-12-2006 L2008 AN *012

MUNITZ, David William. 3851 ROGER BROOKE DR, BROOKE ARMY MED CTR 78234 #023-12-1998 L1999 AN *012 †55

MURRAY, Georgina Lee. ■ 78234 #051-04-1991 L1993 PTH *062

MYHAND, Rickey Cee. 3851 ROGER BROOKE DR, BROOKE ARMY MEDICAL CENTER 78234 #012-01-1988 L1991 HO *020 †20

NAUSCHUETZ, Karen K. 3851 ROGER BROOKE DR, BROOKE AMC/MCHE-PL 78234 #035-06-1984 L1990 PTH PCP *030 †50

NICHOLS, Donald Lee. 3851 ROGER BROOKE DR, STE 429-18 78234 #004-01-1987 L1989 FM OS *020 †18

NOVACK, Joseph John, III. 3851 ROGER BROOKE DR, BROOKE ARMY MED CTR 78234 #021-01-1999 PD *020 †55

O'BRIEN, Seth David. 3851 ROGER BROOKE DR, ATTN: CREDENTIAL OFFICE 78234 #010-02-1998 L2007 *020 †80

OKOH, Emuejevoke O. 3851 ROGER BROOKE DR, BROOKE ARMY MEDICAL CENTER 78234 #026-04-2003 L2005 GE *012 †20

ORTIZ, Adrian Noel. 3851 ROGER BROOKE DR, ATTN CREDENTIAL OFFICE 78234 #042-01-2000 L2003 PM *020

ORTIZ, Ana Alicia. 3851 ROGER BROOKE DR 78234 #042-01-1973 L1986 AI PDA *020 †55,03

OSCOS, Ana Bertha. 3851 ROGER BROOKE DR, ATTN CREDENTIAL OFFICE 78234 #048-13-1982 L1989 FM *020 †18

OWENS, Mark Frederick. 3851 ROGER BROOKE DR, BROOKE ARMY MEDICAL CENTER 78234 #023-12-1993 L1996 P *020 †75

PACKARD, Joshua Cade. 3851 ROGER BROOKE DR, BROOKE ARMY MEDICAL CENTER 78234 #023-12-2004 L2006 AN *012

PALACIOS, Raul G, III. 3851 ROGER BROOKE DR, DEPT OF RADIOLOGY 78234 #048-14-1999 L2000 VIR *012 †80

PALMER, John Middlemiss. 3851 ROGER BROOKE DR, ATTN CREDENTIAL OFFICE 78234 #023-12-1992 L2002 PDP *020 †55

PARKER, Mary Virginia. 3851 ROGER BROOKE DR, ATTN: CREDENTIAL OFFICE 78234 #023-12-1995 L1996 VS *020 †85

PASIPOULARIDES, Ares D. BROOKE ARMY MEDICAL CTR 78234 #026-04-1971 L1972 CD OS *050

PATTERSON, John Henry, Jr. ■ 78234 #039-01-1978 L1990 P *020

PAVEL, Carl Robert. 3851 ROGER BROOKE DR, ATTN: CREDENTIAL OFFICE 78234 #056-06-2004 L2006 PCC *012 †20

PHAM, Thang N. 3851 ROGER BROOKE DR 78234 #048-13-1993 L1994 IM *020 †20

PINTER, Robert Anthony. 2410 STANLEY RD, BROOKE ARMY MEDICAL CTR 78234 #038-41-1982 L1991 OM MG *020 †20,19,70

POLSKY, Muni Sheldon. 3851 ROGER BROOKE DR, ATTN: MCHE-SDU 78234 #020-12-1968 L1978 U *071 †95

PULCINI, Joseph Paul. 3851 ROGER BROOKE DR, BROOKE ARMY MED CTR, BLDG 78234 #023-12-2001 L2001 PCP *020 †50

RADVANY, Martin G. 3851 ROGER BROOKE DR, BROOKE ARMY MED CTR, BLDG 78234 #016-06-1991 L2000 VIR DR *040 †80

RAND, Elden Richard. 3851 ROGER BROOKE DR, ATTN: CREDENTIAL OFFICE 78234 #046-01-2000 L2005 CD *012 †20 ‡

RAYFIELD, John Charles. 3851 ROGER BROOKE DR # 4, ATTN CREDENTIAL OFFICE 78234 #023-12-1996 L2003 EM *020 †16

REEVES, C Stewart. 1750 GREELEY RD, BLDG 4011 78234 #019-02-1963 L1971 IM A *071 †20

REYNOLDS, Joel Charles. 3851 ROGER BROOKE DR, BROOKE ARMY MED CTR 78234 #027-01-1998 L1998 NEP *020 †20

RICHTER, Timothy Allen. 3851 ROGER BROOKE DR, BROOKE ARMY MED CTR 78234 #042-02-1998 L1999 GS *020

RIVERA-SANTIAGO, Hilda M. 3851 ROGER BROOKE DR, DEPT PEDS BROOKE ARMY MED 78234 #042-01-1986 L1995 PD *020 †55

ROHRER, Maryjo Katherine. 3851 ROGER BROOKE DR, BROOKE ARMY MEDICAL CENTER 78234 #023-12-1992 L2005 CD *020 †20

ROSS, Troy Wayne. 2050 WORTH RD, MEDCOM, USAMEDCOM, MCHO-Q 78234 #023-12-1997 L1998 PHP *020 †70

SANTIAGO-MARINI, Juan. 3851 ROGER BROOKE DR 78234 #042-01-1985 L1985 AM OM *020 †70

SAURI, Catherine Jo. 3851 ROGER BROOKE DR, FAMILY MED SVCS BAMC 78234 #010-02-1987 L1995 FM *020 †18

SCHULZE, Rafael Augusto. 3851 ROGER BROOKE DR, ATTN: CREDENTIAL OFFICE 78234 #042-01-2001 L2002 D *020 †15

SCOTT, Ethan Walter. 3851 ROGER BROOKE DR 78234 #001-02-2005 L2007 AN *012

SEDORY, David Marshall. 3851 ROGER BROOKE DR, BROOKE ARMY MEDICAL CENTER 78234 #038-06-2005 L2007 ORS *012

SETLIK, Robert Frank. 3851 ROGER BROOKE DR, DEPT OF HEME/ONC 78234 #035-06-2001 L2003 HO *100

SHEEHAN, Timothy D. 1200 STANLEY RD 78234 #010-02-1976 L1986 P GP *020 †75

SHIRANI, Khan Zafar Iqbal. 3851 ROGER BROOKE DR 78234 #704-04-1968 L1995 CCS GS *071 †85

SHRY, Eric Allen. 3851 ROGER BROOKE DR, BROOKE ARMY MEDICAL CENTER 78234 #028-02-1996 L2003 IC *020 †20

SHUMWAY, Nathan M. 3851 ROGER BROOKE DR, DEPT ONCOLOGY 78234 #005-76-2002, ▲ L2003 HO *012 †20

SIMMONS, John W, II. 3851 ROGER BROOKE DR, BROOKE AMC 78234 #048-16-2006 L2007 GS *012

SLIM, Ahmad Mohamad. 3851 ROGER BROOKE DR, ATTN: CREDENTIAL OFFICE 78234 #654-01-1999 L2006 CD *012 †20 ‡

SMITH, Charles Edward. 3851 ROGER BROOKE DR, ATTN: CREDENTIAL OFFICE 78234 #041-12-1990 L1997 APM *020 †05

SONG, Won Seuk. 3851 ROGER BROOKE DR, BROOKE ARMY MEDICAL CENTER 78234 #016-11-2001 L2007 NM *020

SPANGLER, Sean Alan. 3851 ROGER BROOKE DR, BROOKE ARMY MEDICAL CENTER 78234 #056-06-2002 L2004 CD *012 †20

STAFFORD, Elisabeth M. 3851 ROGER BROOKE DR 78234 #048-13-1981 L1985 ADL PD *020 †55

STENGEL, Joel. 3851 ROGER BROOKE DR 78234 #011-02-2002 L2004 GE *012 †20

STOCKINGER, Zsolt Thos. 1706 STANLEY RD STE 9, DMRTI 78234 #001-02-1992 L1992 TRS CCS *020 †85

STRAIGHT, Ann Marie. 3851 ROGER BROOKE DR, BROOKE ARMY MEDICAL CENTER 78234 #023-12-1998 L2000 PD *020 †55

STRAIGHT, Timothy Michael. 3851 ROGER BROOKE DR, STE 429-18 78234 #023-12-1998 L2000 ID *020 †20

SUMRALL, Richard Warren. 1706 STANLEY RD STE 91 78234 #036-07-1990 L1993 FM AM *040 †18 ‡

SUNDBORG, Michael John. 3851 ROGER BROOKE DR, BROOKE ARMY MEDICAL CENTER 78234 #023-12-1994 L1996 GO OBG *020 †30

SUTCLIFFE, Joseph B. 3851 ROGER BROOKE DR, BROOKE AMC 78234 #045-04-1990 L2007 P *020 †75,80

SWIECKI, Christopher W. 3851 ROGER BROOKE DR, ATTN:MCUC-MMD-QM 78234 #035-09-1996 L1997 *020 †85

THOMPSON, Jennifer C. 3851 ROGER BROOKE DR, ATTN: CREDENTIAL OFFICE 78234 #024-01-1992 L1993 ID IM *020 †20

TOLSON, Daniel Jacob. 3851 ROGER BROOKE DR, ATTN: CREDENTIAL OFFICE 78234 #023-12-2004 L2006 PD *100 †55

TORRES, Dawn Mcdowell. 3851 ROGER BROOKE DR, BROOKE ARMY MEDICAL CENTER 78234 #023-12-2001 L2003 GE *012

TROMBETTA, Leroy Jordan. 3851 ROGER BROOKE DR, BROOKE ARMY MED CTR 78234 #030-06-1997 L1998 GS *020 †85

UNSER, Stanley Henry. 3851 ROGER BROOKE DR, BROOKE ARMY MED CTR, BLDG 78234 #026-04-1982 L2007 FM GP *030 †18

URSONE, Richard Louis. 3851 ROGER BROOKE DR, BROOKE ARMY MEDICAL CENTER 78234 #048-14-2000 L2007 ORS *020 †40 ‡

VAN DEN BROEK, Jeffery W. 3851 ROGER BROOKE DR, BROOKE ARMY MEDICAL CENTER 78234 #048-78-2000, ▲ L2002 GE *012 †20

VAUGHAN, George Martin. 3851 ROGER BROOKE DR 78234 #048-02-1970 L1970 END IM *050 †20

VERBER, Gordon Michael. 3851 ROGER BROOKE DR, BROOKE ARMY MEDICAL CENTER 78234 #054-04-1977 L1999 AN CCA *020 †05

VILLACIS, Bernardo F. 3851 ROGER BROOKE DR, ATTN: CREDENTIAL OFFICE 78234 #319-03-1969 L1978 PD AI *020 †55

VYAS, Hansagauri B. 3851 ROGER BROOKE DR 78234 #495-23-1967 L1972 OS *020 †50

WAIBEL, Kirk Holden. 3851 ROGER BROOKE DR, BROOKE AMC, MCHE-QD, STE 4 78234 #048-13-1997 L1999 PD *020 †03,55

WALICK, Kristina Sinacori. 3851 ROGER BROOKE DR, ATTN: CREDENTIAL OFFICE 78234 #021-01-2002 L2007 OP *012

WILDE, Joseph Lee. 3851 ROGER BROOKE DR, BROOKE ARMY MED CTR 78234 #028-02-1993 L1994 D *020 †15

WILDE, Matthew Thomas. 3851 ROGER BROOKE DR, BROOKE ARMY MED CTR 78234 #023-12-2006 AN *012

WILSON, Robert Wm. 3851 ROGER BROOKE DR 78234 #040-02-1987 L1991 EM *020 †16

WOLF, Steven E. 3851 ROGER BROOKE DR, ATTN CREDENTIAL OFFICE 78234 #048-02-1990 L1991 GS *020 †85

WONDERLICH, David Anthony. 3851 ROGER BROOKE DR, ATTN: CREDENTIAL OFFICE 78234 #023-12-2004 L2006 GS *012

WONDERLICH, Kimberly Jann. 3851 ROGER BROOKE DR, BROOKE ARMY MED CNTR 78234 #023-12-2004 L2006 D *012

WOOL, Ronald Norman. 3851 ROGER BROOKE DR, BLDG 3600 78234 #023-12-1995 L1997 GE *020 †20

YORDAN, Raul. 3851 ROGER BROOKE DR, DEPT OB/GYN, RM 167-10 78234 #042-01-1981 L1988 GYN OBS *020 †30

YORK, Gerald Edward, II. 3851 ROGER BROOKE DR, BROOKE ARMY MEDICAL CENTER 78234 #047-20-1997 L2006 RNR *020 †80

ZACHER, Lisa Lynn. 3851 ROGER BROOKE DR, BROOKE ARMY MED CTR 78234 #046-01-1989 L1992 PCC IM *030 †20

ZAWACKI, Clorinda Kay. 3851 ROGER BROOKE DR, BROOKE ARMY MED CTR 78234 #023-12-1993 L1995 IM *020 †20

FORT STOCKTON – PECOS

GALLEGOS, Antonio. 5 PARK VILLA APT 4A 79735 #649-02-1970 L1977 GS *020

GEORGE, Cecil Ray. 511 N MAIN ST 79735 #048-13-1980 L1980 FM *020 †18 ‡

■ = Address Information Privacy Protected

JESSADAPAGORN, Napaporn. SANDERSON HWY, MEMORIAL HOSPITAL ANNER 79735 #891-01-1970 L1978 **PD** *020
MALLIK, Subodh Kumar. 2071 N MAIN ST 79735 #160-03-1992 L1998 **IM** *020 †20
MORALES, Felix G. 387 W I H 10, 2ND FL 79735 #048-15-2003 L2006 **FM** *020 †18
TALLEY, Sheri J. 1098 S FM 2037 79735 #048-13-1986 L1987 **FM** *020 †18
THAMMASITHIBOON, Prasert. 387 W INTERSTATE HIGHWY 10, STE 200 79735 #891-01-1970 L1978 **GS GP** *020 †85

FORT WORTH - TARRANT

AARON, Kimberly D. 801 7TH AVE 76104 #048-04-1991 L1992 **PD PEM** *030 †55
ABBOTT, Philip Don. 3700 RUFE SNOW DR 76180 #048-12-1961 L1961 **GYN** *020 †30
ABBOTT, Tommy Foy. 3658 RUFE SNOW DR 76180 #048-12-1961 L1961 **GYN** *020 †30
ABDO, Ellis Nick, III. 5701 BRYANT IRVIN RD # 302 76132 #027-01-1962 L1963 **GP** *020 †18
ABDUL-RAHIM, Aziz Samir. 1201 SUMMIT AVE 76102 #051-01-1983 L1989 **OPH** *020 †35
ABOLOYE, Pius Ayodele. ■ 76124 #047-07-1994 **FM** *100
ABRAHAMS, Harrison M. 1325 PENNSYLVANIA AVE #550 76104 #035-03-1997 L2003 **U** *020 †95
ACEVES, Jose Luis. 901 7TH AVE, STE 120 76104 #649-01-1985 L1995 **CHN** *020 †75,55
ACOSTA, Fernando, Jr. 901 7TH AVE STE 120, NEUROLOGY SERVICES 76104 #048-13-1999 L2005 **CN** *100
ADAMS, Kenneth Roy. 8825 RANDOM RD 76179 #048-12-1977 L1977 **EM** *020 †20,16
ADAMS, Robert C. 1500 S MAIN ST 76104 #028-79-1979, ▲ L1984 **OBG** *030
ADAMS, William Curtis. ■ 76109 #041-13-1947 L1989 **PD EM** *071 †55,16
ADNOT, John. 4200 S HULEN ST STE 400 76109 #011-04-1976 L1989 **D FM** *020 †18,15
AFOLABI, Oladapo O. 711 PENNSYLVANIA AVE 76104 #690-05-1994 L2003 **NEP** *020 †20
AFRINA, Mehvesh. 1500 S MAIN ST 76104 #496-27-2004 **P** *012
AGGARWAL, Ved V. 914 LIPSCOMB ST 76104 #496-09-1991 L1999 **APM** *020 †05
AGORO, Adesubomi B. 508 S ADAMS ST, STE 100 76104 #690-08-1986 L1997 **PUD IM** *020 †20
AGUIRRE, Yussein. ■ 76114 #048-12-2007 **FP** *012
AHMAD, Shujauddin M. ■ 76132 #704-01-1961 L1997 **TS CD** *071 †85,90
AHMED, Mohammed B. 900 8TH AVE 76104 #704-02-1961 L1978 **P PYG** *071 †75
AHTONE, Jeral Lee. 333 THROCKMORTON ST, APT 105 76102 #032-01-1975 L1994 **EM IM** *020
AKHTAR, Nasim. 1650 W ROSEDALE ST, STE 206 76104 #704-01-1966 L1975 **CD** *020 †20
AKWAR, Fergus T. ■ 76123 #048-02-2001 L2003 **FM** *100 †18
ALAM, Kanwal Zainab. 855 MONTGOMERY ST 76107 #704-01-1981 L2006 **P** *020
ALAME, Mariam Nehme. 1500 S MAIN ST, URGENT CARE CLINIC. JOHN P 76104 #605-03-1993 L2004 **FM** *020 †18 ‡
ALCANTARA, Enedina E. 1301 PENNSYLVANIA AVE, HARRIS METHODIST FORT WORT 76104 #748-01-1990 L2007 **IM** *020 †20
ALDRIDGE, Beverly Sidney. 801 7TH AVE 76104 #048-02-1981 L1981 **PD** *020 †55
ALEXANDER, John Stone. ■ 76132 #048-02-1954 L1954 **R** *071 †80
ALEXANDER, John W. ■ 76109 #054-04-1950 L1962 **PTH** *071 †50
ALEXIS, Althea Lynnette. 6100 HARRIS PKWY, STE 200 76132 #011-04-1990 L1992 **OBG** *020 †30
AL-FARRA, Sherif Taha. 855 MONTGOMERY ST 76107 #797-01-1989 L2002 **PCC** *020 †20
ALFORD, Brent T. 1325 PENNSYLVANIA AVE, STE 890 76104 #048-12-1995 L1997 **NS** *020 †25
ALI, Farida Yousuf. ■ 76123 #495-49-1989 L2004 **CHP** *020
ALI, Mohamed Ebadat. 1650 W ROSEDALE ST STE 203 76104 #704-02-1964 L1974 **PUD IM** *020
ALI, Tahir Syed. 6100 HARRIS PKWY STE 350 76132 #038-40-1995 L2002 **OTO** *020 †45
ALLEN, Jack Chas. 11801 S FREEWAY 76115 #005-12-1980 L1981 **FM** *020 †18
ALLEN, Terri Lee. 1199 8TH AVE 76104 #048-13-1981 L1981 **DR** *020 †80
ALLENDER, James Hudson. 801 7TH AVE 76104 #021-01-1978 L1983 **PDC CCP** *020 †55
ALLISON, Nanette N. 1500 S MAIN ST 76104 #048-78-2007, ▲ **P** *012
ALLSUP, Jessica Browning. 3731 HILLTOP RD 76109 #048-15-1992 L1993 **GP** *020
ALMENDRAL, Doroteo M. 1350 S MAIN ST STE 44 76104 #748-07-1967 L1977 **AN** *020
ALVARADO, Odilon P. 1001 12TH AVE, STE 160 76104 #048-13-1979 L1979 **IM** *020 †20
ALVAREZ, Mary Katherine. 5701 BRYANT IRVIN RD, STE 302 76132 #048-02-1993 L2004 **FM** *020 †18
ANDERSON, James Edward, Jr. 1650 W ROSEDALE ST, STE 201 76104 #047-05-1996 L2004 **TS** *020 †85,90
ANDERSON, Lee Edward. 1000 W CANNON ST 76104 #024-05-1977 L1979 **NEP CCM** *020 †20
ANDERSON, Lee Stewart. 1350 S MAIN ST, STE 3200 76104 #048-02-1974 L1974 **OPH** *020 †35
ANDERSON, Ralph Jos. 855 MONTGOMERY ST 76107 #065-06-1964 L1981 **GO** *020 †30
ANDERSON, Robert D. 6100 HARRIS PKWY, STE 1200 76132 #048-12-1986 L1987 **CD IM** *020 †20
ANDERSON, Ronald S. 4200 S HULEN ST STE 425 76109 #048-15-1987 L1988 **AN** *020 †05
ANDRES, David Wayne. 4916 OVERTON PLZ 76109 #017-20-1998 L2000 **AN** *020 †05
ANDREWS, Charles Edward. 950 W MAGNOLIA AVE 76104 #023-01-1975 L1980 **NEP IM** *020 †20
ANGELES, Fernando S M. 11797 S FRWY, STE 354 76115 #748-08-1961 L1977 **GS TS** *020 †85
ANTHONY, Philip Fowler. 901 HEMPHILL ST 76104 #048-04-1970 L1970 **OTO** *020 †45
ANTINONE, Ronald Louis. 901 TRAVIS AVE 76104 #030-06-1968 L1969 **OPH OS** *020 †35
ANWAR, Rubina. 950 W MAGNOLIA AVE 76104 #019-02-1983 L1986 **NEP IM** *020 †20
APPLEWHITE, Jeffrey C. 1300 W TERRELL AVE, STE 405 76104 #048-02-1995 L2001 **U** *020 †95
ARCE, Kevin. 1625 SAINT LOUIS AVE, FACIAL & ORAL SURGERY ASSO 76104 #026-08-2000 L2006 **OMF** *020
ARCE, Luis M. 8125 GERANIUM LN 76123 #319-03-1987 L1992 **FM** *020 †18
ARCHER, Kenneth Dean. 2400 WESTPORT PKWY # 1300 76177 #048-14-2002 L2004 **FM EM** *020 †18
ARCHER, Kerstin Ann. 801 7TH AVE, EMERGENCY DEPARTMENT 76104 #048-12-1982 L1983 **PD** *020 †55
ARCHIE, Ryan N. ■ 76109 #048-02-2008 *012
ARELLANO, Jose Bernardo. 1500 S MAIN ST, DEPT OF PEDIATRICS 76104 #187-06-1980 L1988 **NPM PD** *020 †55
ARGENBRIGHT, Keith Edward. 6100 HARRIS PKWY STE 340 76132 #021-01-1984 L1985 **FM** *020 †18
ARMSTRONG, George Nelson. 855 MONTGOMERY ST 76107 #048-12-1967 L1967 **ORS OFA** *040 †40
ARMSTRONG, John Mills, III. 911 6TH AVE 76104 #021-05-1975 L1975 **PTH** *020 †50
ARMSTRONG, John Royce. 911 6TH AVE 76104 #048-04-1959 L1960 **OPH** *020 †35
ARMSTRONG, Julian E. 6445 HARRIS PKWY, STE 100 76132 #035-46-1980 L1991 **GE IM** *020 †20
ARMSTRONG, Vanessa Claire. 333 THROCKMORTON ST 76102 #048-13-1997 L2001 **OBG** *071 †30
ARNOLD, Watson C, Jr. 901 7TH AVE, STE 410 76104 #048-12-1970 L1970 **NEP PD** *020 †55
ARONSON, Stuart Allan. 3800 HULEN ST, STE 100 76107 #038-06-1984 L1992 **DR** *020 †80
ARTIM, Richard Alleyne. 1301 PENNSYLVANIA AVE 76104 #007-02-1976 L1988 **ON HEM** *020 †20
ASHAI, Daud Hussain. 1001 COLLEGE AVE STE A 76104 #704-01-1985 L1997 **CCM IM** *020 †20
ASHFAQ, Mohammad. 1400 8TH AVE, BAYLOR ALL SAINTS 76104 #704-02-1993 L2001 **MPD** *020 †20,55
ASHMORE, Thaddeus H. 4916 OVERTON PLZ 76109 #048-13-1988 L1989 **AN** *020 †05
ASHRAF, Akber M. 1500 S MAIN ST 76104 #704-02-1986 L1996 **IM** *020 †20
ATCHESON, Robert Jones. 816 W CANNON ST 76104 #047-06-1954 L1960 **R NM** *072 †80
ATKINS, Lori R. 5801 OAKBEND TRL STE 180 76132 #048-02-1992 L1993 **OBG** *020 †30
ATKINSON, Denis Stuart. 1522 COOPER ST 76104 #048-02-1965 L1965 **CHP P** *020 †75
AUGUSTAT, Edwin Chas. 909 9TH AVE STE 401 76104 #021-05-1968 L1969 **OPH PS** *020 †35
AURIN, Fred Bawden. ■ 76102 #023-07-1942 L1943 **GS** *075 †85
AVERHART, Vernon Wendoth. 1650 W MAGNOLIA AVE, STE 212 76104 #028-02-1975 L1982 **OBG** *020 †30
AXTHELM, Dan Alan. 6100 HARRIS PKWY STE 380 76132 #030-05-1982 L1988 **RHU IM** *020 †20
BABBILI, Ananda Diwaker. ■ 76132 #654-01-1986 **FM EM** *020
BAEZ MARIN, Carlos R. PO BOX 27066 76127 #042-03-1990 L1995 **OBG** *020
BAHRAMI, Carlos S. ■ 76109 #048-78-1999, ▲ L2006 **NEP** *020 ‡
BAILEY, Eva Jo. 1401 HENDERSON ST 76102 #051-07-1983 L1989 **PTH** *020
BAILEY, Kenneth M. ■ 76102 #048-12-2000 L2008 **DR** *020 †80
BAILEY, Philip James. 855 MONTGOMERY ST 76107 #001-02-1974 L1983 **OBG** *020 †30
BAILEY, Susan Rudd. 5929 LOVELL AVE, FWAA 76107 #048-16-1981 L1981 **AI PDA** *020 †55,03
BAISDEN, Denise Lynn. 300, AEROSPAC MEDICINE DIVISION 76193 #055-02-1985 L1988 **AM** *062 †70
BAJAJ, Gurpreet Singh. 1307 8TH AVE, STE 603 76104 #038-43-1998 L2004 **ORS** *020 †40
BALCH, James Allen. ■ 76107 #048-12-1974 L1974 **PTH** *071 †50
BALLA, Rekha Hamilton. 1301 PENNSYLVANIA AVE, DIVISION OF NEONATOLOGY 76104 #495-27-1990 L2005 **PD** *020 †55
BALLARD, Amie Rebecca. ■ 76129 #048-12-2007 **PD** *012
BALLER, Donna Lynne. 4916 OVERTON PLZ 76109 #048-12-1981 L1983 **AN N** *020 †05
BAMBERGER, Charles. 420 S HENDERSON ST 76104 #231-01-1969 L1977 **U** *020 †95
BANNER, Mary Christine. 1522 COOPER ST 76104 #030-05-1988 L1997 **P** *020 †75
BANNOUT, Rim. 1500 S MAIN ST 76104 #011-02-1989 L1998 **CD IM** *020 †20
BANTA, Miguel B, Jr. 6333 AIRPORT FWY, STE 101 76117 #748-08-1963 L1971 **PME** *020 †05
BARBARO, Daniel John. 1125 COLLEGE AVE 76104 #035-09-1981 L1982 **ID** *020 †20
BARBEE, James Jos. 1500 S MAIN ST, 4TH FL 76104 #048-02-1973 L1973 **FM FSM** *020 †16,18
BARKER, Jerry L, Jr. 1001 12TH AVE, STE 200 76104 #048-12-1997 L1998 **RO** *020 †80 ‡
BARKER, Thomas Edward. ■ 76109 #048-02-1967 L1972 **P N** *071 †75
BARKLIS, Sam Steven. 1612 SUMMIT AVE STE 240 76102 #016-02-1946 L1970 **OS PA** *071
BARNES, Madge Lou. 1132 EVERMAN PKWY 76140 #036-08-1987 L1998 **FM** *020 †18
BARNHILL, Mary Anne. ■ 76102 #024-05-1993 L1995 **FP** *012
BARRETT, Robert Lou. 1201 8TH AVE 76104 #021-01-1964 L1964 **FM AM** *020 †18
BARRI, Yousri Mohamed H. 1400 8TH AVE 76104 #849-01-1979 L2002 **IM NEP** *020 †20
BARRINGTON, Royce Don. 1300 W TERRELL AVE, STE 320 76104 #048-02-1975 L1975 **OBG** *020 †30
BARRON, Melanie C. 900 8TH AVE, DEPT OF RHEUMATOLOGY 76104 #048-78-2000, ▲ L2004 **RHU** *012
BARRY, John. 300 W ROSEDALE ST, VA FT WOTH OUTPAT CLNC 76104 #047-07-1984 L1987 **IM GP** *020 †20
BARST, Geoffrey Stephen. 6316 RUFE SNOW DR 76148 #917-26-1970 L1978 **GP** *020
BARTLETT, Bryan Leonard. 1400 8TH AVE, FL 1 76104 #048-12-1980 L1980 **PTH** *020 †50
BASINGER, Alice Ann. 901 7TH AVE STE 120, COOK CHILDREN'S HOSPITAL 76104 #036-05-2000 L2006 **MG** *100 †55,19
BASU, Dhiman. 1001 12TH AVE STE 160, ADULT MEDICINE 76104 #495-39-1996 L2007 **RHU** *100 †20
BATISTE-MILTON, Sharlene. 900 8TH AVE 76104 #003-01-1991 L1996 **PTH** *020 †50
BATTINI, Vasantha Kumari. 1301 PENNSYLVANIA AVE 76104 #496-24-1993 L2000 **IM** *020 †20
BATTLE, Clinton Chas, Jr. 817 BAKER ST 76104 #024-07-1978 L1978 **IM** *020
BATTLES, Victor Earl. 2508 WILLING AVE 76110 #041-01-1978 L1980 **IM** *020 †20
BAUMER, Joan E Goforth. 1500 S MAIN ST, FAMILY PRACTICE 76104 #005-19-1977 L1998 **FM** *020 †18
BAUMER, Nathan Byran. 910 HOUSTON ST 76102 #005-19-1977 L1998 **EM FM** *040 †16
BAWEJA, Gurpreet Singh. 1300 W TERRELL AVE STE 5 76104 #495-05-1991 L2007 **IC** *020 †20
BAYOUTH, John M. 800 W MAGNOLIA AVE, STE A 76104 #048-02-1995 L1997 **GS** *020 †85
BEAM, Donald Timothy. 901 7TH AVE, STE 220 76104 #021-06-1999 L2006 **PHO** *020 †20,55
BEASLEY, Clifton H, Jr. 900 8TH AVE 76104 #028-02-1971 L1975 **OPH** *020 †18,35
BEATY, Rosalyn Brigette. 4255 AMON CARTER BLVD, MD 4100 76155 #047-07-1995 L1998 **GPM** *020 †70
BECHTEL, Philip Carter. 1325 PENNSYLVANIA AVE #890 76104 #048-02-1971 L1972 **NS** *020 †25
BEESON, Jeff K. ■ 76107 #048-78-2005, ▲ L2006 **EM** *012
BEGLEY, Grant F. 1500 S MAIN ST 76104 #021-01-1944 L1949 **U** *071 †95
BEHL, Ankur Rishi. 1500 S MAIN ST, JOHN PETER SMITH HOSP 76104 #039-01-2007 **ORS** *012
BEJAR, Manuel Eduardo. ■ 76116 #319-01-1952 L1961 **PD PDA** *071
BELFI, Kendra Lee Jensen. 909 9TH AVE, STE 300 76104 #048-12-1972 L1973 **IM IMG** *020 †20
BELL, David L. ■ 76102 #021-05-2002 L2006 **OMF** *020
BENJAMIN, Denis R. 801 7TH AVE 76104 #836-01-1968 L2000 **CLP PTH** *020 †50
BENNETT, Howard Mather. 1500 S MAIN ST 76104 #048-15-2004 L2007 **OBG** *012
BENSON, Bennett Norton. 1701 PENNSYLVANIA AVE 76104 #047-06-1963 L1971 **AN** *071 †05
BERENZWEIG, Harold Karl. 1201 SUMMIT AVE STE 500, NORTH TEXAS 76102 #035-19-1971 L1974 **GE IM** *030 †20
BERNHARD, Mark Hadley. 6100 HARRIS PKWY, STE 235 76132 #048-04-1984 L1986 **FM** *020 †18
BETHEA, James W, III. ■ 76109 #004-01-1967 L1975 **OTO** *071 †45
BETTES, Thomas N. 4255 AMON CARTER BLVD, AMERICAN AIRLINES MEDICAL 76155 #048-02-1982 L1983 **FM OM** *030 †70,18
BHAGAT, Neena. 1700 MISTLETOE BLVD 76104 #496-17-1994 L2006 **NEP** *020

■ = Address Information Privacy Protected

BHARGAVA, Anupama. 1500 S MAIN ST 76104 #495-99-1997 L2005 **FM** *100 †18
BHATIA, Rupinder Singh. 1220 W PRESIDIO ST 76102 #495-03-1993 L2001 **P CHP** *020
BHATIA, Subir Singh. 1350 S MAIN ST, BOWDEN EYE ASSOCIATES 76104 #038-43-1997 L2006 **OPH** *020
BIERBAUM, Walter F, III. ■ 76109 #004-01-2001 L2007 **PCP** *100 †50
BIRDWELL, Barbara Ann. 7100 OAKMONT BLVD, STE 101 76132 #048-13-1984 L1985 **FM** *020 †18
BIRDWELL, Henry V, Jr. ■ 76135 #048-02-1952 L1952 **GS GE** *071 †85
BIXLER, Glenn Geo. 1325 PENNSYLVANIA AVE, STE 250 76104 #048-13-1985 L1988 **PM** *020 †60
BLACK, Charles Thos. 901 7TH AVE 76104 #048-04-1979 L1979 **PDS GS** *020 †85
BLACK, Timothy Lee. 1433 W HUMBOLT ST 76104 #047-06-1979 L1987 **PDS** *020 †85
BLAIR, Roger Sproul. 1325 PENNSYLVANIA AVE #700 76104 #041-12-1969 L1973 **N** *020 †75
BLALOCK, Robert Jiles. 1500 S MAIN ST, JP SMITH HOSP/DPT PED 76104 #039-01-1973 L1992 **PD NPM** *020 †55
BLAZINA, Janice Fay. ■ 76133 #038-40-1978 L1983 **BBK CLP** *020 †50
BLISS, David Paul, Jr. 901 7TH AVE STE 210 76104 #028-03-1985 L1996 **PDS** *020 †85
BLOCK, Herbert E. ■ 76116 #010-01-1940 L1940 **ORS AM** *072 †40
BLOEMENDAL, Lee Chas. 1325 PENNSYLVANIA AVE, STE 720 76104 #048-04-1969 L1969 **GS VS** *020 †85
BLUE, Susan V Kelly. 800 8TH AVE 76104 #036-05-1969 L1973 **N** *020 ‡
BOEHLER, Lillian M. 4916 OVERTON PLZ 76109 #048-14-2003 L2007 **AN** *020
BOHNSACK, James Richard. 5701 BRYANT IRVIN RD, STE 202 76132 #028-03-1977 L1978 **FM** *020 †18
BOLAND, Gregory H. ■ 76102 #048-15-1987 L1990 **CHP** *075 †75
BOLLINGER, Bruce Alan. 800 12TH AVE STE 300 76104 #028-34-1981 L1987 **ORS** *030 †40
BOLUCH, John J. ■ 76180 #048-02-1951 L1951 **FM** *071 †18
BONHAM, Henry Edward E. 11801 SOUTH FWY 76115 #048-02-1967 L1967 **P CHP** *075 †75
BOONE, Melchor M, Jr. 855 MONTGOMERY ST 76107 #048-14-1989 L1990 **OBG** *020 †30
BOOTH, Elizabeth Anne. 2528 JACKSBORO HWY 76114 #021-01-1984 L1987 **PD** *020 †55
BORDELON, James Harold. 1001 12TH AVE, STE 200 76104 #021-05-1968 L1972 **ON HEM** *020 †20
BORDELON, Yvette Angele. ■ 76110 #021-06-2002 L2006 **HMP** *020 †50
BOREN, Darrell W. ■ 76133 #048-02-1953 L1953 **ADM GP** *071
BORG, Douglas Edward. 801 7TH AVE 76104 #028-03-1984 L1998 **PD** *020 †05,55
BORGE, A Norman. ■ 76117 #048-12-1964 L1964 **GP** *071
BORUM, Val F. ■ 76102 #021-01-1950 L1958 **AN** *071 †05
BOSTON, Don Wayne. ■ 76119 #048-12-1955 L1955 **FM GP** *071
BOTHWELL, James Mark. 1651 W ROSEDALE ST STE 200 76104 #035-45-1997 L2002 **OSM** *020 †40
BOULDEN, Kelly D. 4521 S HULEN ST 76109 #034-01-1995 L2002 **FM** *020 †18
BOWMAN, C Bradley. 800 5TH AVE, CORNEA ASSOCIATES OF 76104 #039-01-1989 L1994 **OPH** *020 †35
BOWMAN, Mitch Dee. 6451 BRENTWOOD STAIR RD 76112 #039-01-1985 L1986 **EM** *020 †16
BOWSER, Sondra Hoxie. 11801 SOUTH FWY 76115 #005-12-1972 L1982 **IM** *030 †20
BOX, James Jos. 6100 HARRIS PKWY 76132 #048-04-1973 L1974 **ORS** *020 †40
BOYD, James Luther. 6451 BRENTWOOD STAIR RD 76112 #048-12-1965 L1965 **OBG** *071 †30
BRADFORD, Laura Anne. 1400 8TH AVE 76104 #048-15-1992 L1993 **OBG** *020 †30
BRADSHAW, William Vinton. ■ 76109 #048-02-1963 L1963 **DR NR** *071 †80
BRANDENBERG, Karl Bruno. 6551 HARRIS PKWY, STE 200 76132 #033-05-1962 L1969 **OPH** *020 †35
BRANN, Benj Sandford, IV. 1301 PENNSYLVANIA AVE 76104 #001-02-1980 L1996 **NPM PD** *020 †55
BRANNON, John V. ■ 76132 #023-01-1951 L1953 **EM GP** *020
BRASHER, Warren K. 801 7TH AVE 76104 #048-02-1994 L1995 **PEM** *020 †55
BRATTON, Gregory C. ■ 76109 #048-13-2008 *012
BRAUN, Aaron Robert. ■ 76102 #030-05-2007 **TY** *012
BRAUNGARDT, Charles David. 1400 8TH AVE 76104 #048-04-1959 L1959 **GYN** *020 †30
BRENNAN, James Patrick. 950 W MAGNOLIA AVE 76104 #045-01-1967 L1972 **NEP IM** *020 †20
BRENNAN, Mary Carol. 6210 JOHN RYAN DR STE 101 76132 #021-05-1987 L1989 **PD** *020 †55
BREWINGTON, Jason Perry. 1500 S MAIN ST, DEPT OF FAMILY MEDICINE 76104 #047-07-2006 L2008 **FP** *012
BRIMMER, Robert Alvah, II. 6140 AVERY DR STE 62 76132 #048-02-1978 L1997 **P** *020 †75
BRINKER, Jared Zachary. ■ 76110 #048-15-2008 *012
BRISCOE, John Gilbert. 6100 HARRIS PKWY, STE 355 76132 #048-15-1985 L1986 **IM** *020 †20
BRONSTAD, Morris T, Jr. 1301 PENNSYLVANIA AVE 76104 #048-12-1948 L1948 **GP** *071
BROOKS, Clarence Jackson. 2200 EVANS AVE 76104 #010-03-1975 L1976 **FM** *020
BROOKS, Jennifer C. 909 9TH AVE, STE 101 76104 #010-03-1985 L1990 **OBG** *020 †30
BROOKS, Lloyd W. 1201 SUMMIT AVE, STE 500 76102 #048-78-1985, ▲ L1986 **IC CD** *020
BROOKS, Michael Edwin. 909 9TH AVE, STE 101 76104 #010-03-1984 L1990 **GS** *020 †85
BROOKS, Ralph Anthony. 1650 W ROSEDALE ST, STE 202 76104 #010-03-1983 L1988 **D** *020
BROTHERTON, Stephen L. 1651 W ROSEDALE ST, STE 200 76104 #048-12-1982 L1983 **ORS OSM** *020 †40
BROWN, David S. 901 7TH AVE STE 110, DEPARTMENT OF ORTHOPEDICS 76104 #048-12-1995 L1996 **ORS** *020 †40
BROWN, Frank Earle, Jr. 3800 HULEN ST, STE 100 76107 #048-02-1975 L1975 **GP DR** *020 †80
BROWN, Randal L. 855 MONTGOMERY ST 76107 #048-13-1998 L1999 **FM** *020 †18
BROWN, Robert W. ■ 76107 #021-01-1950 L1958 **CD** *071 †20
BROWN, Russell Glen. 750 8TH AVE, STE 530 76104 #035-06-1978 L1984 **P** *020 †75
BRUHL, Daniel Edward. 1201 SUMMIT AVE 76102 #048-04-1967 L1967 **OPH** *020 †35
BRUNER, Cavan Bryan. 1400 8TH AVE 76104 #048-02-1955 L1955 **FM** *071
BRYCE, Errol. 900 8TH AVE 76104 #649-38-1991 L1997 **IM** *020 †20
BUELL, Lisa Makovec. 6250 JOHN RYAN DR 76132 #056-05-1991 L1994 **FM** *020 †18
BUICE, James W. ■ 76185 #004-01-1953 L1964 **R** *071 †80
BULEY, Kenneth J. 6551 HARRIS PKWY STE 110 76132 #048-13-1992 L1993 **PM** *020 †60
BUMAGIN, Michael Saml. 7100 OAKMONT BLVD, STE 107 76132 #027-01-1968 L1969 **PS** *020 †65
BUNATA, Robert Emil. 801 W TERRELL AVE 76104 #016-06-1965 L1972 **HS** *072 †40
BURGE, Walworth Edward. 3800 HULEN ST, STE 100 76107 #021-06-1974 L1988 **DR** *020 †80
BURGOS, Hernan Enrique. 1065 W MAGNOLIA AVE 76104 #649-02-1962 L1965 **CHP P** *071
BURK, John Robt. 1521 COOPER ST 76104 #051-01-1970 L1975 **PUD SME** *020 †20
BURKE, Robert Arthur, Jr. 7100 OAKMONT BLVD STE 104 76132 #048-14-1988 L1994 **OBG** *020 †30
BURKE, Ronald G. 901 7TH AVE, STE 110 76104 #048-14-1989 L1990 **OP** *020 †40
BURKE, Sherri Ann. 3200 RIVERFRONT DR STE 103, FOREST PARK PEDS 76107 #048-78-1989, ▲ L1991 **PD** *020 †55
BURKETT, Joseph Hampton. 3840 HULEN ST 76107 #048-02-1981 L1985 **P ADP** *030 †75
BURKETT, Robert Judson. 800 8TH AVE STE 618 76104 #048-02-1962 L1962 **OTO** *020 †45
BURNETTE, Jason Odell. ■ 76137 #012-01-2008 *012
BURT, Napoleon. 801 7TH AVE, COOK CHILDREN'S MEDICAL CE 76104 #038-44-1988 L2002 **AN** *020 †05
BURTON, Alan G. 1500 S MAIN ST 76104 #048-13-1991 L1992 **EM** *020 †16,18
BURTON, Cary L. 5801 OAKBEND TRL, STE 100 76132 #048-04-1975 L1975 **OPH** *020 †35
BUSBY, Stephen Paul. PO BOX 11709 76110 #047-06-1974 L1978 **N** *020 †75
BUSCH, Edward Leonard. 1400 S MAIN ST STE 4 76104 #016-11-1955 L1962 **GS** *020 †85
BUSH, Tyronne A. 1500 S MAIN ST, JOHN PETER SMITH HOSPITAL 76104 #048-78-2005, ▲ L2006 **FP** *012
BUSSELL, Mark Hamilton. 7800 OAKMONT BLVD 76132 #016-11-1986 L1991 **PM** *020 †60
BUSSEY, Helen Jane. 800 5TH AVE STE 404 76104 #048-02-1972 L1972 **GS** *020 †85
BUSSEY, Joe Leverett. 1201 SUMMIT AVE 76102 #012-05-1954 L1958 **OPH** *071 †35
BYARLAY, Mark M. 1500 S MAIN ST, JOHN P SMITH HOSP 76104 #048-14-2002 L2005 **FM** *100 †18
BYRD, Alan Neil. 855 MONTGOMERY ST 76107 #048-02-1974 L1974 **FM** *020 †18
BYRD, William B. 6100 HARRIS PKWY 76132 #048-13-1998 L1999 **FM** *020 †18
CABACCANG SABATER, Nenita. 2400 LUDELLE ST, STE 2 76105 #748-07-1959 L1982 *020
CABALLERO, Roberto. 801 7TH AVE 76104 #649-30-1986 L1991 **CCP** *020 †55
CABANSAG, Remdios R. 11803 SO. FREEWAY,, STE 310B 76115 #748-07-1965 L1972 **OBG** *020
CADAMBI, Ajai. 750 8TH AVE, STE 400 76104 #048-12-1986 L1988 **ORS** *020 †40
CADORNA, Ernesto A. 1301 PENNSYLVANIA AVE, HARRIS METHODIST - FORT WO 76104 #748-10-1978 L2003 **IM** *020 †20
CAGLE, Jackson Edward. ■ 76109 #016-11-1956 L1961 **CD GS** *071 †85,90
CAIRE, Jacqueline Tyra. 1400 8TH AVE 76104 #021-05-1997 L1999 **DR** *020 †80
CAL, Stanley Xavier. 1500 S MAIN ST 76104 #035-47-1986 L1987 **IM** *020
CAMARILLO, Randal Matthew. ■ 76133 #048-14-2008 *012
CAMPBELL, John Kemp. 7100 OAKMONT BLVD 76132 #048-12-1974 L1976 **DR** *020 †80
CAMPBELL, Rowan S. 1500 S MAIN ST 76104 #048-12-2006 **FP** *012
CAMPBELL, Scott Weston. 4916 OVERTON PLZ 76109 #048-15-1999 L2003 **AN** *020 †05
CANAMAR, Oscar H. ■ 76109 #649-02-1957 **P GP** *071
CAPPEL, Joseph Ward, III. 5701 BRYANT IRVIN RD # 301 76132 #021-05-1975 L1978 **FM** *020 †18
CAPPER, David Paul. 3221 COLLINSWORTH ST # 160, COVENANT HOSPICE & PALLIAT 76107 #048-14-1982 L1983 **IM GP** *020 †20
CAPPER, Robert Sherman. 1500 S MAIN ST 76104 #038-40-1954 L1965 **CD** *071 †20
CARLTON, Charles Anthony. ■ 76104 #048-02-1977 L1977 **IM** *020 †20
CARPENTER, Scott Michael. ■ 76120 #048-14-2002 L2007 **AN** *020
CARR, Christian Lawrence. 1325 PENNSYLVANIA AVE, STE 200 76104 #048-04-1997 L2002 **GS** *020 †85
CARRINGTON, Frederick L. 6100 HARRIS PKWY, STE 140 76132 #048-02-1973 L1973 **OBG** *020 †30
CARTER, Elizabeth Wagner. 6100 HARRIS PKWY 76132 #048-02-1981 L1981 **FM FPG** *030 †18
CARTER, John Edward, Jr. ■ 76132 #016-76-1963, ▲ L1987 **FM** *071
CARTER, Willis Herbert. ■ 76116 #036-07-1947 L1954 **U** *071 †95
CASE, Christopher L. 901 7TH AVE STE 310, PED ARRHYTHMIA CTR 76104 #010-01-1982 L1996 **PDC PD** *020 †55
CASEY, Daniel Frederick. 1500 S MAIN ST, 4TH FL 76104 #028-03-1995 L1997 **FM** *020 †18
CASTANEDA, Antonio A. 1325 PENNSYLVANIA AVE, STE 777 76104 #048-12-1995 L1997 **GS** *020 †85
CASTANEDA, Carla Ann. ■ 76133 #048-12-1996 L2000 **IM** *020 †20
CASTELL, Allen James. 801 7TH AVE, ANESTHESIA DEPARTMENT 76104 #038-43-1991 L2003 **AN** *020 †05
CASTELLANOS, Ricardo. 1500 S MAIN ST 76104 #025-12-1978 L1979 **EM** *020 †16
CASTILLO, Carolyn Marie. 300 W ROSEDALE ST, VANTHCS FT WORTH OUTPATIEN 76104 #034-01-1984 L1988 **IM** *020 †20
CASTILLO, Eduardo Daniel. 1420 8TH AVE, STE 103 76104 #048-12-1997 L2005 **CRS** *020 †85
CAVAZOS, Ramiro David. 6100 HARRIS PKWY, STE B 76132 #048-02-1972 L1972 **PD** *020 †55
CAVENDER, Lundy E, Jr. 11803 SOUTH FWY 204 76115 #021-06-1981 L1990 **PD** *020 †55
CAWYER, John Curtis. ■ 76179 #004-01-2004 L2006 **EM** *020
CHACON, Monica Margarita. 901 7TH AVE STE 120, DEPARTMENT OF NEUROLOGY 76104 #008-01-1998 L2004 **CHN** *020
CHAE-KIM, Sang Hyup. 4916 OVERTON PLZ, PARKLAND HOSPITAL 76109 #048-16-2001 L2004 **AN** *100 †05
CHAMBERLAIN, Christina W. 1301 PENNSYLVANIA AVE, DEPARTMENT OF NEONATOLOGY 76104 #021-06-1998 L2001 **PD NPM** *020 †55
CHAMPION, John Edward. 800 8TH AVE STE 532 76104 #048-04-1974 L1974 **PD PHO** *020 †55
CHAN, Rafael C. 1001 12TH AVE, STE 200 76104 #748-02-1970 L1974 **RO** *020 †80 ‡
CHAPMAN, Darren Matthew. ■ 76109 #048-04-2001 L2007 **GS** *020
CHAPMAN, Martha Jean. ■ 76117 #048-02-1954 L1954 **GP CD** *020
CHARETTE, Vanessa S. 801 7TH AVE 76104 #005-18-1999 L2002 **PD** *020 †55
CHASE, Gerald Lynn. 6451 BRENTWOOD STAIR RD 76112 #021-05-1987 L1998 **EM** *020 †20,16
CHASE, Jerry Julius. ■ 76123 #021-05-1974 L1975 **IM** *020
CHASEN, Noah Nathan. ■ 76102 #048-02-2007 **TY** *012
CHELLAPPAN, Chandra P. ■ 76133 #048-16-2007 **OBG** *012
CHEN, Patrick. 1325 PENNSYLVANIA AVE, STE 610 76104 #495-52-1982 L2004 **PS** *020 †85,65
CHENG, Jungtung. 909 9TH AVE, STE 300 76104 #048-02-1988 L1989 **N IM** *020 †20
CHERIAN, Ruby. 801 7TH AVE, COOK CHILDRENS MEDICAL CEN 76104 #917-08-1995 L2000 **PD** *020 †55
CHERKASSKY, Michael. 1550 W ROSEDALE ST STE 418 76104 #913-52-1973 L1985 **IM** *020 †20
CHERRY, Judith S. ■ 76109 #048-78-1994, ▲ L1996 **P** *020 †75
CHESSOR, Alfredmy Gbassay. ■ 76123 #038-06-1998 L2001 **FP** *012
CHI, Lei. 4916 OVERTON PLZ, SUMMIT HEALTHCARE MGMT RES 76109 #243-44-1982 L1997 **AN** *020 †05
CHILCOAT, Jill K. 3800 HULEN ST, STE 100 76107 #048-13-1992 L1993 **DR** *020 †80
CHILCOAT, Ronald Gray, Jr. 815 PENNSYLVANIA AVE 76104 #048-13-1995 L1996 **VIR** *020 †80
CHILDERS, James Steven. 909 9TH AVE STE 300, THE FORT WORTH CLINIC, P.A 76104 #048-02-1986 L1987 **IM** *020 †20
CHILDS, Tilden L, III. 1350 S MAIN ST, STE 4150 76104 #021-01-1976 L1977 **DR** *020 †80
CHIN, Lincoln Fitzalbert. 1650 W ROSEDALE ST, STE 301B 76104 #566-01-1972 L1979 **N** *020 †75
CHIU, Joe Nyan. 108 E SEMINARY DR 76115 #407-10-1969 L1979 **FM PD** *020 †55,18

■ = Address Information Privacy Protected

CHO, Paul Henry. 1319 SUMMIT AVE 76102 #025-01-1991 L2001 NS *020 †25

CHOI, Maryanne. 4916 OVERTON PLZ, SUMMIT HEALTHCARE MGMT RES 76109 #033-06-1991 L1995 AN *020 †05

CHOUDHRY, Karamat. 909 9TH AVE STE 210 76104 #704-01-1960 L1972 TS VS *071 †85,90

CHOUDHRY, Zohra Anita. 1701 RIVER RUN STE 1010 76107 #048-14-1991 L1992 CHP †75

CHOUHAN, Rajendra Singh. 1650 W ROSEDALE ST STE 304 76104 #495-20-1970 L1977 U *020 †95

CHOW, Anita. 800 5TH AVE, STE 402 76104 #035-20-1994 L2004 GS *020 †85

CHU, Claire. 1500 S MAIN ST, JOHN PETER SMITH HOSPITAL 76104 #048-04-2005 OPH *012

CHU, Khoi Ba. 1201 S MAIN ST, STE C 76104 #011-04-1993 L1997 OBG *020 †30

CHUA, Marietta Montilla. 6857 DANIELDALE DR 76137 #748-01-1970 L1980 CHP *020

CHUNDURI, Krishnababu. 1650 W ROSEDALE ST, STE 301A 76104 #495-50-1972 L1981 N P *075

CICHOCKI, Jonathan J. 1400 S MAIN ST, STE 505 76104 #025-07-1976 L1981 OPH *020

CIMO, Michael L. ■ 76107 #048-14-2002 L2006 SP *100 †50

CINTRON, Ramon A. 855 MONTGOMERY ST 76107 #042-01-1992 L1995 FM *020 †18 ‡

CLARKE, Rohan Van Courtne. 1500 S MAIN ST, DEPT. OF MEDICINE 76104 #566-01-1997 L2008 GE *020 †20 ‡

CLASSEN, Ashley M. 1401 HENDERSON ST 76102 #048-78-1978, ▲ L1987 PME AN *020

CLAYTON, Irvin. 1100 W CANNON ST 76104 #021-01-1952 L1953 ORS *072 †40

COCHRUM, Brett Landon. 1525 MERRIMAC CIR STE 107 76107 #048-13-1986 L1987 EM FM *020 †18

COCHRUM, Jan Denver. 6100 HARRIS PKWY, EMERGENCY DEPT 76132 #048-12-1961 L1961 EM FM *020 †18

COERS, Carl Richard. 200 MED PL BLD 800 8TH AVE 76104 #027-01-1959 L1967 PS *020 †65

COFFEE, Charles C. 3609 BRIARHAVEN RD 76109 #048-02-1988 L1992 AN *020 †05

COFFEY, Robert Thos. 1400 S MAIN ST 76104 #048-02-1961 L1961 P *071

COFFMAN, Jamye. 801 7TH AVE 76104 #048-13-1987 L1990 PD *020 †55

COIMBRA, Caetano J Porto. 1420 8TH AVE STE 104 76104 #187-07-1980 L1994 NS *020 †25

COLE, James S. 7100 OAKMONT BLVD 76132 #048-14-1984 L1985 FM *020 †18

COLE, Reginald Allen. 1500 S MAIN ST 76104 #047-07-1984 L2003 N *020

COLEMAN, William Gregory. 1651 W ROSEDALE ST, STE 100 76104 #048-15-1984 L1985 ORS *020 †40

COLERIDGE, Samuel T. 2106 N MAIN ST 76164 #028-78-1971, ▲ L1992 FM EM *020 †18,16

COLES, Robert T N. 1500 S MAIN ST 76104 #067-01-1993 L1997 PD *020 †55

COLINA, Kenneth Forrester. 801 7TH AVE 76104 #048-04-1991 L1993 PD *020 †55

COLLEY, Sam Hague. 4916 OVERTON PLZ 76109 #048-15-1991 L1992 AN *020 †05

COLLINGE, Cory Alan. 800 5TH AVE, STE 200 76104 #020-02-1993 L1999 ORS *020 †40

COLLINS, Mark Francis. 1821 8TH AVE 76104 #048-14-1983 L1984 GS *020 †85

COLLISON, Robert Westin. 900 8TH AVE, PLAZA MEDICAL CENTER 76104 #030-06-1962 L1970 PTH *071 †50

COLQUITT, Catherine Amand. 909 9TH AVE STE 300, FORT WORTH CLN 76104 #048-12-1985 L1987 ID IM *020 †20

COMPERE, Dolphus E. 900 8TH AVE 76104 #048-04-1940 L1940 U *071 †95

CONCEPCION, Luzminda. 1500 S MAIN ST, DEPT OF PED NICU 76104 #748-10-1973 L2004 NPM PD *020 †55

CONCEPCION-LEVY, Maria D. ■ 76109 #022-07-1999 L1999 PD *020

CONNELLY, Kevin G. 6100 HARRIS PKWY, STE 285 76132 #048-12-1989 L1990 PUD *020 †20

CONRAD, Betty L. ■ 76132 #039-01-1944 L1946 GP IM *072

CONWAY, John Evert. 800 5TH AVE, STE 200 76104 #048-14-1983 L1985 ORS OSM *020 †40

COOK, Todd David. 1500 S MAIN ST, JOHN PETER SMITH HOSP 76104 #010-01-2007 ORS *012

COOKE, David Miller J. 1500 S MAIN ST, JOHN PETER SMITH HOSPITAL 76104 #016-43-1969 L1970 FM *020

CORDOVA, Joseph David. ■ 76107 #048-15-2003 L2005 FM *020 †18

CORLEY, David Dickson, Jr. 1300 W TERRELL AVE, STE 50 76104 #048-12-1987 L1988 CD *020 †20

COWAN, Gary Milton. 1350 S MAIN ST, STE 3200 76104 #048-12-1980 L1980 OPH *020 †35

COX, James Sidney. 6451 BRENTWOOD STAIR RD, STE 200 76112 #021-01-1975 L1976 EM FM *030 †18,16 ‡

COX, Virgil Munsey, Jr. ■ 76116 #048-02-1956 L1956 P *071 †75

CRANDALL, Ronald Owen. 3447 ALTA MESA BLVD STE 10 76133 #005-12-1983 L1984 FM *020 †18

CRAVENS, George F, III. 1412 S MAIN ST 76104 #048-12-1980 L1980 NS *020 †25

CRAWFORD, John Lloyd, Jr. 1325 PENNSYLVANIA AVE, STE 720 76104 #024-01-1977 L1984 GS CD *020 †85

CRAWFORD, Julie Heflin. 1533 MERRIMAC CIR, STE 100 76107 #048-14-1990 L1991 PD *020 †20

CRIBBS, Carey B. 801 7TH AVE, EMERGENCY DEPT 76104 #048-16-1985 L1986 PD *020 †55

CRIM, Randall D. 6500 HARRIS PKWY 76132 #048-14-2002 L2006 ON *020 †20

CROFFORD, Theodore W. 750 8TH AVE STE 4 76104 #048-02-1985 L1986 ORS GS *020 †40

CROWLEY, Kathleen. 1500 S MAIN ST, DEPT OB 76104 #048-04-1983 L1983 IM HEM *020 †20

CSAKY, Tihamer Zoltan. ■ 76107 #473-01-1939 OS *071

CUNNINGHAM, James Calvin. 901 7TH AVE, STE 420 76104 #048-02-1981 L1981 PDP PUD *020 †55

CUNNINGHAM, Linda L F. 855 MONTGOMERY ST 76107 #047-05-1982 L1984 PTH *040 †50

DAGEN, Jennifer D. 4916 OVERTON PLZ 76109 #048-13-2002 L2006 PAN *020 †05

DAILY, Herschel Byron. 4916 OVERTON PLZ 76109 #048-02-1977 L1977 AN *020

DALAL, Vinay. 1650 W MAGNOLIA AVE, STE 208 76104 #496-04-1996 L2002 AN *020

DALLAS, John S. 901 7TH AVE 76104 #047-06-1982 L1990 PDE P *050 †55

DALTON, John Howard. 1301 PENNSYLVANIA AVE 76104 #021-01-1972 L1972 PD *020 †55

DALTON, Mark David. 900 W MAGNOLIA AVE, STE 100 76104 #048-12-1970 L1970 GE *020 †20

DAMBRO, Mark Richard. 1650 W ROSEDALE ST STE 307 76104 #028-02-1979 L1988 FM *020 †18

DAMBRO, Nancy N. 901 7TH AVE, STE 420 76104 #024-07-1979 L1987 PDP *020 †55

DAMICO, Peter J. 6010 CURZON AVE 76116 #048-14-1986 L1988 FM *020 †18

DANI, Armand A. ■ 76107 #407-26-1944 L1969 PM D *020

DANIEL, Paxton Holt. 3800 HULEN ST, STE 100 76107 #048-14-1982 L1983 R *020 †80

DANIELL, Alfred Ronald. 1651 W ROSEDALE ST, STE 200 76104 #048-02-1961 L1961 IM OS *071 †20

DARNELL, Ruth P Little. ■ 76112 #048-12-1949 L1949 GP *071

DARROW, Eric Jon. 801 7TH AVE, DEPT OF ANESTHESIOLOGY 76104 #048-15-1991 L1993 AN *020 †05

DAVANLOO, Hedieh. 855 MONTGOMERY ST, UNT HEALTH SCIENCE CTR 76107 #408-11-1999 L2007 IM *020 †20

DAVDA, Rajesh Kumar. 1408 SAINT LOUIS AVE, TARRANT COUNTY NEPHROLOGY 76104 #048-16-1987 L1988 NEP IM *020 †20

DAVE, Arvinda Kiran. 801 7TH AVE, PICU OFFICE 76104 #495-23-1966 L1974 PD *020

DAVE, Virat Ramesh. ■ 76132 #048-16-2000 L2003 GE *020 †20

DAVENPORT, Norman Alan. 1400 8TH AVE 76104 #048-02-1977 L1977 IM CD *020 †20

DAVENPORT, Peter. ■ 76110 #048-02-2003 L2007 FP *012

DAVID, Fang Shen. 5801 OAKBEND TRL 76132 #048-12-1999 L2003 IM *020 †20

DAVID, James Kenneth. 816 W CANNON ST, RADIOLOGY ASSOCIATES 76104 #048-12-1998 L2003 DR *020 †80

DAVIDSON, James Eugene. 1651 W ROSEDALE ST 76104 #048-02-1975 L1975 IM *071 †20

DAVILA, Raymundo Eugenio. 1323 LEE AVE 76164 #649-01-1966 L1978 CD IM *020 †20

DAVIS, M Mc Kim. 900 8TH AVE, PLAZA MEDICAL CTR OF FORT 76104 #048-78-1978, ▲ L1978 EM *020 †16 ‡

DAVIS, Miles Wm. ■ 76116 #048-12-1960 L1960 FM *071 †18

DAVIS, Susan Lynn. 801 7TH AVE, MEDICAL CENTER 76104 #048-04-1987 L1988 CCP *020 †55

DAVIS, William K. 6501 N BEACH ST 76137 #048-15-1996 L1999 PD *020 †55

DEAN, Asad. 1001 12TH AVE, STE 200 76104 #048-12-1997 L2001 HO *020 †20

DEARDEN, Craig Lee. 1000 9TH AVE, STE C 76104 #048-15-1979 L1979 IM *020 †20

DEAS, Thomas Malcolm, Jr. 6445 HARRIS PKWY 76132 #021-06-1978 L1981 GE *020 †20

DEASON, Kristina J. 2630 WEST FWY, STE 126 76102 #019-02-1992 L1993 AN *020 †05

DE CASTRO, Constante R. 3500 CAMP BOWIE BLVD, 2ND FL 76107 #748-01-1980 L1989 PTH *020 †50

DE CASTRO, Maria M. 4445 OAK PARK LN STE 201 76109 #748-01-1980 L1989 PD *020

DECKER, Douglas Campbell. 1250 8TH AVE, STE 445 76104 #048-02-1980 L1980 OBG *020 †30

DE LEON, Frank Diaz. 1500 S MAIN ST, DEPT OF OB/GYN 76104 #049-01-1977 L1984 OBG *020 †20

DELGADO, Jackquelin. ■ 76135 #048-13-2006 OBG *012

DELL, Robert Vance. 1500 S MAIN ST, DEPARTMENT OF RADIOLOGY 76104 #019-02-1976 L1982 DR *020 †80

DEL ROSARIO, Edwin O. 855 MONTGOMERY ST 76107 #748-01-1986 L1993 IM *020 †20

DENSON, Toni L. 1500 S MAIN ST 76104 #048-14-1996 L2001 EM *020 †20

DENTON, James Gwyn. 800 8TH AVE STE 200 76104 #036-07-1974 L1976 PS HNS *020 †45,65

DEPORTER, Thomas Elden. 6300 RIDGLEA PL 76116 #047-20-1985 L1991 P *020 †75

DESAI, Ronak Kirti. ■ 76133 #048-02-2008 *012

DE TOLEDO, Luiz Carlos. 4255 BRYANT IRVIN RD, STE 105 76109 #187-30-1972 L1985 ORS HS *020 †40

DETWEILER, Jeffrey G. 6100 HARRIS PKWY 76132 #048-13-1983 L1989 PTH DMP *020 †50

DETWEILER, Rosemary Ellen. 6100 HARRIS PKWY 76132 #048-13-1983 L1989 PTH PCP *020 †50

DEWAR, Thomas Norman. 6445 HARRIS PKWY, STE 100 76132 #048-12-1986 L1987 GE IM *020 †20

DEWITT, Nathan William. ■ 76133 #047-06-2008 *012

DE WITT, Owen C. 935 W ROSEDALE ST STE 201 76104 #048-02-1982 L1988 ORS *020 †40

DE ZERN, Amy Elizabeth. ■ 76133 #023-07-2005 L2008 IM *012

DIEB, Thomas Mitchell. 1400 8TH AVE, FL 1 76104 #048-02-1977 L1977 PTH *020 †50

DIFFLEY, David Michael. 3800 HULEN ST, STE 100 76107 #023-07-1982 L1988 DR *020 †80

DILLEY, Frances Leone. 5701 BRYANT IRVIN RD, RD SUITE # 302 76132 #048-02-2002 L2004 FM *020 †18

DILLIN, Parker Linden. 900 12TH AVE 76104 #048-12-1979 L1979 ORS *020 †40

DINH, Hoang M. 1325 PENNSYLVANIA AVE, STE 680 76104 #048-12-2001 L2003 RHU *020

DIRKES, Kathryn. 76109 #016-06-1989 L1996 PDS GS *020 †85

DIRKS, Donald C. 1325 PENNSYLVANIA AVE, STE 100 76104 #019-02-1962 L1973 RO NM *071 †80

DISNEY, Jason R. 6100 HARRIS PKWY 76132 #048-13-1999 L2000 EM *020 †18

DIXSON, Suzanne. 1500 S MAIN ST, DEPARTMENT OF PEDIATRICS 76104 #048-02-1991 L1993 PD *020 †55

DJOKOVIC, Marija. 1002 MONTGOMERY ST STE 106, PSYCHIATRIC DEPARTMENT 76107 #957-02-1976 L2005 P *020 †75

DOENGES, Stephanie Dawn. 1500 S MAIN ST 76104 #038-40-2002 L2004 FM *020 †18

DOLLAHITE, Harry Anderson. 1401 8TH AVE 76104 #048-14-1982 L1983 ORS GS *020 †40

DONAHUE, David Jerome. 800 8TH AVE STE 220, SW NEUROLOGICAL SURGERY AS 76104 #047-06-1978 L1996 NS PD *020 †25

DONEGAN, Kerry Michael. 4351 BOOTH CALLOWAY RD, STE 208 76180 #056-05-1985 L1986 ORS *020 †40

DONOVAN, Mary Lynne. 1301 PENNSYLVANIA AVE 76104 #025-01-1981 L1986 OTO *020 †45

DONOVAN, Patrick Wm. 1011 COLLIER ST STE A 76102 #048-13-1988 L1989 PM *020 †60

DORY, Laurie Boquet. 901 TRAVIS AVE 76104 #047-06-1989 L1993 OPH *020 †45

DOSHI, Bipinchandra N. 3400 HULEN ST STE 105 76104 #495-23-1967 L1975 GS AS *020

DOSU, Babatunde Idowu. 1500 S MAIN ST, DEPT OF PEDIATRICS 76104 #690-08-1986 L1998 PD *020 †55

DOUGLAS, Gary Lee. ■ 76116 #021-05-1972 L1994 OP OS *071 †40

DOWLING, Robert A. 1300 W TERRELL AVE, STE 405 76104 #048-14-1982 L1983 U *020 †95

DOWLING, Robert Weber. ■ 76107 #038-06-1954 L1961 OBG *071 †30

DRECHSEL, Randy D. 300 W ROSEDALE ST, FW-OPC VA 76104 #048-14-1986 L1987 IM *020 †20

DRUMMOND-BORG, Lesley M. 1300 W LANCASTER AVE, STE 204 76102 #671-01-1971 L1988 CG *030 †19,55

DUCIC, Yadranko. 923 PENNSYLVANIA AVE, STE 100 76104 #065-09-1991 L1997 FPS OTO *020 †45

DUNCAN, Ray Bowman. 4456 OVERTON CREST ST 76109 #028-34-1962 L1967 AN *071 †05

DUNCAN, Tommy Brent. 1500 S MAIN ST 76104 #422-01-2002 L2006 FM *100 †18

DUONG, Huy. 6100 HARRIS PKWY 76132 #048-78-1993, ▲ L1994 PUD *020 †20

DURAND, John Lars. 1300 W TERRELL AVE, STE 50 76104 #003-01-1977 L1978 CD IC *020 †20

DY, Lina Tan. 1650 W ROSEDALE ST, STE 304 76104 #748-08-1971 L1977 PD *020 †20

DYSON, Maynard Campbell. 901 7TH AVE STE 420 76104 #051-01-1974 L1991 PDP PD *020 †55,03

DZURIK, Matthew Varnell. 601 7TH AVE #021-06-1999 L2006 PDC *020 †55

EADES, Ken S. 3309 MOSS HOLW 76109 #048-12-1969 L1975 R *020 †80

EAKIN, David Lance. 1400 8TH AVE, BAYLOR ALL SAINTS HOSP 76104 #048-02-1981 L1981 DR *020 †80

EAMES, Gretchen Marie. 901 W SEVENTH ST STE 22 76102 #018-03-1989 L1995 PHO *020 †55

EASTERLING, Larry Edward. 801 7TH AVE, PEDIATRIC INTENSIVE CARE U 76104 #021-06-1984 L1991 PD CCM *020 †55

EDEN, Billy Max. 1201 FAIRMOUNT AVE 76104 #039-01-1973 L1981 PUD IM *020 †20

■ = Address Information Privacy Protected

EDEN, Kimberly Tenpas. 5701 BRYANT IRVIN RD, STE 301 76132 #048-12-1998 L1999 **FM** *020 †18
EDWARDS, Layla Florencema. ■ 76179 #020-02-2005 L2008 **PD** *012
EDWARDS, Russell B. ■ 76132 #048-78-2006, ▲ **OBG** *012
EGER, Lynne Marie. 801 7TH AVE 76104 #005-02-1989 L1999 **PD PDI** *020 †55
EHL, Lisa Lynne. 6210 JOHN RYAN DR, STE 101 76132 #654-01-1991 L1996 **PD** *020 †55
EHRLICH, James Wilson. ■ 76132 #048-12-1957 L1957 **GP** *071
EICHENHOLZ, Philip Wm. 4916 OVERTON PLZ 76109 #036-07-1983 L1984 **AN CCA** *020 †20,05
ELBERT, Annette. 6100 HARRIS PKWY, STE 235 76132 #048-02-1991 L1997 **GS** *020 †85
ELDRIDGE, James K. 800 5TH AVE, STE 300 76104 #048-02-1999 L2002 **IM** *020 †20
ELLIOTT, Arvle S, II. 1533 MERRIMAC CIR, STE 100 76107 #048-12-1969 L1971 **PD** *020 †55
ELLIOTT, Peter John. 855 MONTGOMERY ST 76107 #039-01-1990 L1992 **OBG MFM** *020 †30
ELLIS, Dick G. 1000 MONTGOMERY ST 76107 #048-04-1952 L1952 **PDS UP** *071 †85
ELLIS, Thomas S. 1325 PENNSYLVANIA AVE, STE 890 76104 #048-14-1990 L1991 **NS** *020 †25
ELLIS, Vernon Geo. 8030 CAMP BOWIE W 76116 #065-06-1964 L1977 **FM** *020
ENGLAND, Michael John. 1250 8TH AVE STE 330 76104 #836-01-1979 L1998 **OBG** *020 †30
ENGLEKING, David Wayne. 11803 S FREEWAY 76115 #005-12-1974 L1979 **IM** *020 †20
EPPSTEIN, Roger S. 800 5TH AVE, STE 300 76104 #048-12-1990 L1991 **IM** *020 †20
EPPSTEIN, Stephen. ■ 76112 #048-12-1958 L1958 **IM** *072 †20
EREZ, Eldad. 901 7TH AVE STE 330, UNIV OF N TEXAS HEALTH SCI 76104 #550-03-1991 L2005 *100
ESTES, Ben Philip. 1309 S ADAMS ST 76104 #048-04-1947 L1947 **GS OS** *075
ETIER, Edgar Lee, Jr. 1400 8TH AVE 76104 #047-06-1944 L1944 **IM** *072
ETIER, Edgar Lee, III. 1307 8TH AVE STE 510 76104 #048-15-1983 L1983 **IM** *020
ETTER, Gary Lee. 3500 CAMP BOWIE BLVD 76107 #048-02-1980 L1980 **P** *020 †75 ‡
EUDALY, Harold B, Jr. 6300 RIDGLEA PL, STE 814 76116 #048-02-1958 L1958 **P** *020
EVANS, Curtis Ray. 6100 HARRIS PKWY, STE 355 76132 #039-05-1983 L1990 **IM** *020 †20
EVANS, John Paul. 3800 HULEN ST, STE 100 76107 #039-01-1994 L1996 **DR** *020 †80
EWIN, Christopher Scott. 5801 OAKBEND TRL, STE 260 76132 #021-01-1984 L1988 **FM GP** *020 †18
EWING, Scott Evan. ■ 76110 #048-78-2001, ▲ L2003 **CD IM** *020
EZUKANMA, Noble Uwaoma. 508 S ADAMS ST STE 100 76104 #308-03-1990 L1999 **CCM** *020 †20
FABUYI, Oyeyemi A. 508 S ADAMS ST STE 100, HEALTHFIRST MEDICAL GROUP 76104 #690-14-1994 L2004 **PCC** *020 †20
FAIRES, Raymond Alan. 1325 PENNSYLVANIA AVE, STE 325 76104 #048-04-1976 L1976 **PS CS** *020 †85,65
FAIREY, Ann Krulien. 1325 PENNSYLVANIA AVE, STE 740 76104 #045-01-1985 L1992 **NPM** *020 †55
FANG, Xiaoen. 4916 OVERTON PLZ 76109 #048-15-1990 L1992 **AN** *020 †05
FANNIN, Barbara Acuff. 1400 8TH AVE 76104 #048-12-1961 L1961 **GP PD** *020
FARRAR, Scott B. 4916 OVERTON PLZ 76109 #048-78-1991, ▲ L1992 **AN** *020 †05
FAWCETT, Henri Daniel. 1350 S MAIN ST, STE 4150 76104 #064-01-1975 L1982 **NM DR** *020 †28,80
FELPS, Kelly Erwin. 3308 DEEN RD, JPS DIAMOND HILL CLINIC 76106 #048-14-1982 L1983 **IM** *020 †20
FENDERSON, Patricia G. 1301 PENNSYLVANIA AVE 76104 #039-01-1992 L1997 **PTH** *020 †50
FENTON, Robert. 412 S HENDERSON ST 76104 #041-13-1964 L1970 **A** *020 †03
FENYES, David Anthony. 1400 8TH AVE 76104 #048-14-1998 L2003 **DR** *020 †80
FERREE, Edward Scott. ■ 76116 #048-78-1996, ▲ L2000 **IM** *020
FEWINS, John Leslie, Jr. 800 8TH AVE STE 336 76104 #041-14-1998 L2003 **OTO** *020 †45
FIEDERLEIN, Frederick J. ■ 76116 #008-01-1954 L1978 **N P** *071
FIERKE, Jay Lee. 3800 HULEN ST, STE 100 76107 #056-05-1972 L1976 **DR** *020 †80
FIGUEROA, Mayte Ideliz. 901 7TH AVE STE 310 76104 #035-47-1992 L2003 **PDC** *020 †55
FIKAR, Thomas Dean. 1400 8TH AVE, FL 1 76104 #048-12-1981 L1981 **DR** *075 †80
FINE, Gavin F. 801 7TH AVE 76104 #836-01-1989 L2004 **AN PAN** *020 †05
FIROUZBAKHT, Noushin A. 1325 PENNSYLVANIA AVE, STE 450 76104 #048-14-2003 L2005 **OBG** *020
FISHER, Keith Denton. 1350 S MAIN ST STE 3200, ST JOSEPH PROFESSIONAL BLD 76104 #035-01-1986 L1987 **OPH** *020 †35
FISHER, Suzanne D. 2000 EAGLE PKWY 76177 #048-13-1987 L1988 **PM** *020 †60
FISHER, Triwanna Lashawn. 1500 S MAIN ST 76104 #048-15-2005 L2007 **FP** *012
FITE, James Michael. 1125 S HENDERSON ST 76104 #048-02-1973 L1973 **OBG** *020 †30
FITZGERALD, Stephen D. 1420 8TH AVE, STE 103 76104 #048-04-1988 L1989 **CRS** *020 †85,10
FLEISHMAN, Ari Ian. 4916 OVERTON PLZ 76109 #048-02-1998 L1999 **AN** *020 †20,05
FLING, John Andrew. 855 MONTGOMERY ST 76107 #048-13-1978 L1978 **PD AI** *020 †55,03
FLORES, Alberto. 309 NW 25TH ST 76164 #056-06-1985 L1988 **IM** *020
FLOWERS, Brian Edward. 1201 SUMMIT AVE, OPHTHALMOLOGY ASSOCIATES 76102 #023-07-1993 L1998 **OPH** *020 †35
FLOWERS, Latosha Yvette. 1500 S MAIN ST 76104 #004-01-2001 L2004 **FM** *020 †18
FLOYD, Gary Warren. 801 7TH AVE # 104 76104 #048-02-1976 L1976 **PD PE** *030 †55
FONTES, Michael Angelo. 4916 OVERTON PLZ 76109 #030-06-1991 L1999 **AN** *020 †05
FOSTER, William E. 1500 S MAIN ST, JPS HEALTH NETWORK 76104 #048-12-1985 L1986 **AN** *020 †05
FOWLER, Gina M. 2755 MILLER AVE, COOK CHILDREN'S 76105 #048-78-2005, ▲ L2008 **PD** *012
FOWLER, Josephine R. 1500 S MAIN ST 76104 #306-01-1993 L2007 **FM OBS** *020 †18
FRANKEL, Mark Alan. 4916 OVERTON PLZ 76109 #048-02-1986 L1987 **AN IM** *020 †20,05
FRANKLIN, Gillian A. ■ 76107 #035-03-1991 **PTH** *012
FRANKS, Bert M. ■ 76116 #048-12-1960 L1960 **ADL** *071 †55
FREDRIC, Rhett Keyser. 1650 W ROSEDALE ST, STE 300 76104 #011-03-1966 L1972 **ON IM** *020 †20
FREEDMAN, Lyle Eric. 11803 S FWY STE 114 76115 #048-02-1978 L1982 **OPH** *020 †35
FREEMAN, Harold Paul, Jr. 6500 HARRIS PKWY, SW FORT WORTH CANCER CENTE 76132 #005-14-1985 L2002 **RO** *020 †80
FREEMAN, John Walter. 800 5TH AVE STE 505, MEDICAL CLINIC OF NORTH TE 76104 #048-02-1979 L1979 **OBG GP** *020 †30
FREESE, John Wilke. 1500 S MAIN ST, STE 303 76104 #023-07-1957 L1964 **GS SO** *071 †85
FREYER, Craig Alan. 3629 WESTERN CENTER BLVD, STE 201 76137 #016-11-1982 L1983 **FM** *020 †18
FRIEDMAN, James Martin. 1533 MERRIMAC CIR, STE 100 76107 #048-02-1972 L1973 **PD PDA** *020 †55
FROBERG, Paul K. 3800 HULEN ST, STE 100 76107 #048-13-1990 L1991 **DR** *020 †80
FROST, Andrew J. ■ 76116 #048-78-2008, ▲ *012
FULKERSON, Richard C. 1500 S MAIN ST 76104 #048-14-1986 L1987 **FM** *040 †18
FULLER, Philip S. 801 7TH AVE 76104 #048-02-1973 L1973 **PD** *020 †55
FULWADHVA, Urvi Pravin. ■ 76109 #024-05-2003 L2004 **FM** *020
FURBER, Edward Saxe. 1208 FAIRMOUNT AVE 76104 #407-10-1958 L1969 **P** *020 †75
FURNISS, Wilburn E. ■ 76109 #048-14-2007 **FP** *012
FUSSELMAN, Robert E. 3800 HULEN ST, STE 100 76107 #048-16-1983 L1983 **DR** *020 †80
GABELMAN, Charles G. 4740 E LANCASTER AVE 76103 #016-02-1944 L1973 **A** *071 †03
GABRIEL, John David. 4351 BOOTH CALLOWAY RD, STE 101 76180 #048-12-1978 L1978 **FM** *020 †18
GAGADAM, Dayaker R. 6701 OAKMONT BLVD 76132 #495-21-1982 L1997 **PCC** *020 †20
GAINES, Joseph Harvey, III. 7100 OAKMONT BLVD 76132 #021-05-1968 L1975 **ORS** *020 †40
GALANIS, Jennifer. ■ 76107 #048-13-2002 *100
GALLAHER, Caren E. 1307 8TH AVE 76104 #028-46-1987 L1993 **GS TRS** *072 †85
GALLIANI, Carlos Alberto. 801 7TH AVE 76104 #132-01-1975 L2000 **PP** *062 †50
GANACIAS, Jaclyn Leeann. ■ 76109 #019-02-2006 **FP** *012
GANDHI, Kanti Chhotalal. 4375 BOOTH CALLOWAY RD, STE 215 76180 #495-23-1971 L1981 **CD IM** *020 †20
GANDHI, Rajesh Ramesh. 1500 S MAIN ST, JPS HOSP OPC-303 76104 #035-03-1992 L2003 **TRS CCS** *020 †85 ‡
GARCIA, Amanda R. ■ 76107 #048-78-2007, ▲ *012
GARCIA, Arthur G. 1307 8TH AVE STE 507 76104 #048-12-1979 L1979 **OBG** *020
GARCIA, Felipe J, Jr. 1615 W OLEANDER ST, STE A 76104 #048-15-1987 L1989 **PM** *020 †60
GARCIA, Fernando. 1500 S MAIN ST, STE 303, OPC BUILDING 76104 #005-11-1992 L1998 **GS** *020 †85
GARCIA, Wilson Jose. 1201 5TH AVE 76104 #264-01-1965 L1975 **PM** *020 †60
GARCIA-THOMAS, Gabriela I. 3800 HULEN ST, STE 100 76107 #048-13-1991 L1992 **PDR** *020 †80
GARDNER, William Robt. 4545 BELLAIRE DR S, SUITE-9 76109 #048-04-1959 L1959 **FM** *071 †18
GARMER, Danny Joe. 1350 S MAIN ST, STE 4150 76104 #004-01-1986 L1991 **DR** *020 †80
GARNER, Gayla Beth. 8250 WINSCOTT PLOVER RD 76126 #028-46-1990 L1997 **EM** *020 †16
GARNETT, Richard W, Jr. 2707 AIRPORT FWY STE 216 76111 #051-01-1940 L1940 **P** *071 †75
GARRETSON, Melissa Jane. 801 7TH AVE, DEPT OF EMERGENCY MEDICINE 76104 #026-08-1993 L1996 **PD PEM** *020 †55
GARRETT, Christopher W. ■ 76179 #047-06-1997 L2004 **EM** *020 †16
GARRISON, Ferd Erwin, Jr. ■ 76107 #048-04-1959 L1959 **IM HEM** *075 †20
GARTMAN LAYNE, Sheila Ren. 1500 S MAIN ST, JOHN P SMITH HOSP 76104 #048-78-2006, ▲ **OBG** *012
GARZA, Mark Anthony. ■ 76107 #048-02-2004 L2008 **FP** *012
GASSER, Richard Chas. 816 W CANNON ST 76104 #018-03-1960 L1964 **R GP** *072 †80
GATES, Thomas Gerald. 1350 S MAIN ST, STE 4150 76104 #021-05-1986 L1991 **DR FM** *020 †80
GATHE, Joy Carole. 4916 OVERTON PLZ 76109 #005-02-1992 L1999 **AN** *020 †05
GAVINI, Udaya. 4701 BRYANT IRVIN RD N 76107 #495-37-2001 L2006 **IM** *020 †20
GEESBREGHT, John Michael. 1301 PENNSYLVANIA AVE 76104 #016-43-1970 L1973 **EM IM** *020 †16
GELVEZ, Javier. 801 7TH AVE 76104 #264-09-1990 L2001 **CCP** *020 †55
GENDRON, Ann Marie. 1300 W LANCASTER AVE # 101, SERVICES 76102 #032-01-1989 L1998 **PD** *020 †55
GEORGE, Josh O. 900 W MAGNOLIA AVE, STE 100 76104 #038-43-1999 L2002 **GE** *100 †20
GERARD, Cameron A. 4916 OVERTON PLZ 76109 #048-12-1989 L1991 **AN** *020 †05
GERK, Charles Anthony. ■ 76102 #007-02-2007 **FP** *012
GERSTLE, Ronald James. 816 W CANNON ST, RADIOLOGY ASSOCIATES 76104 #036-01-1999 L2006 **RNR** *020 †80
GEYER, Walter Leslie. ■ 76116 #004-01-1964 L1965 **GP** *071
GHAZALI, Sobia. ■ 76137 #704-25-1992 L1998 **IM** *020 †20
GIBBS, Johnny Manoon. ■ 76107 #011-04-2006 **ORS** *012
GIBLER, Sheridan Taylor. 6401 HARRIS PKWY STE 130 76132 #048-12-1966 L1966 **CD IM** *020 †20
GILES, Philip Wayne. 800 HEMPHILL ST 76104 #048-12-1972 L1972 **D** *020 †15
GILLETTE, Paul Crawford. 901 7TH AVE, STE 310 76104 #045-01-1969 L1973 **PDC** *030 †55
GILMAN, Jeffrey William. 801 7TH AVE, PEDIATRIC EMERGENCY MEDICI 76104 #030-06-1998 L2002 **PD** *020 †55
GLASS, Dudley Craig. 1500 S MAIN ST, 4TH FL 76104 #048-02-1977 L1977 **FM** *040 †18
GLEASON, Raleigh Rogerson. 1201 FAIRMOUNT AVE 76104 #048-12-1985 L1986 **PUD CCM** *020 †20
GLEIM, Gregory Paul. 1500 S MAIN ST 76104 #048-12-1980 L1980 **EM IM** *020 †20,16
GLENN, Rosalind Marie. 900 SOUTHLAND AVE 76104 #047-07-1978 L1986 **FM** *020 †18
GLOYNA, Robert Edward. 3800 HULEN ST, STE 100 76107 #048-12-1971 L1971 **DR NR** *020 †80
GLUCK, Franklin Bernard. 1550 W ROSEDALE ST, STE 314 76104 #165-04-1969 L1979 **END IM** *020 †20
GODBEY, Teresa E. 800 5TH AVE, STE 300 76104 #048-12-1984 L1986 **IM** *020 †20
GODFREY, Mark A. 833 TOWNE CT 76179 #048-14-1987 L1988 **FM** *020 †18
GOGGANS, Albert M. 1400 8TH AVE, BAYLOR ALL SAITS HOSPITAL 76104 #021-01-1944 L1950 **CD** *071 †20
GOGGIN, Daniel Anthony. 900 8TH AVE 76104 #048-02-1973 L1973 **P** *020 †75
GOLDMAN, Paul Jay. 1650 W ROSEDALE ST 76104 #038-06-1967 L1972 **IM** *075 †20
GOLDSTEIN, Robert Michael. 1400 8TH AVE 76104 #047-06-1981 L1988 **GS CCS** *020 †85
GONZALEZ, Gus Anthony. 800 W MAGNOLIA AVE 76104 #039-01-1997 L2007 **HO** *020 †20
GONZALEZ, Roberto Raul. 1500 S MAIN ST, JOHN P SMITH HOSP 76104 #308-05-2000 **FP** *012
GOOCH, Joel Robt. ■ 76109 #048-02-1972 L1972 **IM** *020 †20
GOODE, Stephen M. 200 W MAGNOLIA AVE, STE 100 76104 #048-12-1982 L1983 **OPH** *020 †35
GOODMAN, C Leroy. 800 8TH AVE STE 236 76104 #039-01-1964 L1971 **D** *020
GOPALAKRISHNAN, Prabhakara. 1500 S MAIN ST, DEPT OF INTERNAL MEDICINE 76104 #495-16-1999 L2004 **IM** *020
GORDON, Brent. 855 MONTGOMERY ST 76107 #011-75-1988, ▲ L1990 **FM OMM** *020
GORDON, Kimberly Lynn. 801 7TH AVE, EMERGENCY DEPARTMENT 76104 #048-15-1994 L1995 **PD** *020 †55
GOSSETT, Carl Wayne. 1500 S MAIN ST 76104 #048-15-1982 L1983 **EM** *020 †16
GOULD, David Lawrence. 1500 S MAIN ST, STE 303 76104 #035-08-1988 L1994 **U** *020 †95
GRACIA, Valentin. 700 SOUTH FWY 76104 #649-01-1952 L1957 **PS** *020 †65
GRACIA, Walter Dietrich. 1204 5TH AVE 76104 #048-02-1983 L1983 **PS HS** *020 †65
GRAHAM, Allan Lee. 7100 OAKMONT BLVD 76132 #016-11-1960 L1968 **TS** *071 †85,90
GRAHAM, Jack Monroe. ■ 76107 #048-14-1978 L1978 **OBS GYN** *020 †30

GRALINO, Bernard Jos. 1301 PENNSYLVANIA AVE 76104 #048-02-1968 L1968 **VIR DR** *020 †80

GRANADO, Elma Gonzales. 855 MONTGOMERY ST 76107 #748-01-1974 L1986 **P GP** *020 †75

GRANAGHAN, Richard T. 815 PENNSYLVANIA AVE 76104 #048-02-1984 L1985 **DR** *020 †80

GRANEK, Harold. 1021 WASHINGTON AVE 76104 #011-02-1976 L1980 **OPH** *020 †35

GRANGER, Mary Margaret. 901 7TH AVE, STE 220 76104 #004-01-1996 L2001 **PHO** *020 †55

GRANT, David A. 800 8TH AVE, STE 606 76104 #048-02-1951 L1951 **PS** *072 †85,65

GRANT, Jeanolivia D. PO BOX 27066, J STREET BUILDING 3000 76127 #041-02-1981 L1982 **OBG** *020 †30

GRANT, Karen M. 1201 8TH AVE STE A 76104 #048-12-1994 L1995 **FM** *020 †18

GRANT, Paul Anthony. 800 5TH AVE STE 410, BEN HOGAN CENTER 76104 #566-01-1966 L1977 **PME AN** *020

GRANT, Paul Anthony, Jr. ■ 76107 #048-12-1994 L1995 **CCS** *020

GRATCH, Jack Orrin. 5601 LOCKE AVE STE 101 76107 #041-77-1974, ▲ L1980 **NEP IM** *020

GRAVLEY, Daniel E. ■ 76109 #048-14-2003 L2007 **AN** *020

GRAY, David Wayne. 901 7TH AVE STE 110, NETWORK-ORTHOPAEDIC SERVIC 76104 #048-14-1986 L1987 **OP** *020 †40

GRAY, Joseph Henry Wicker. 6100 HARRIS PKWY 76132 #048-12-1961 L1961 **OPH** *020 †35

GREEN, A Christian. 800 12TH AVE, STE 100 76104 #048-12-1982 L1983 **AN** *020 †05

GREEN, Casey Brian. 1500 S MAIN ST, TRINITY SPRINGS PAVILION 76104 #048-02-2000 **P** *012

GREEN, Michael Lewis, Jr. 1420 8TH AVE STE 101 76104 #017-20-1996 L2003 **GS** *020 †85

GREEN, Michael Stanley. 1500 S MAIN ST 76104 #033-05-1976 L1981 **DR NM** *020 †80

GREEN, Peter Calder. 11803 SOUTH FREEWAY #206 76115 #065-06-1966 L1980 **IM OS** *075 †18

GREENE, Douglas Eugene. 855 MONTGOMERY ST 76107 #048-02-1981 L1981 **FM** *020 †18

GREER, Daria K. 900 W MAGNOLIA AVE, STE 201 76104 #048-15-1996 L1997 **FM** *020 †18

GREER, Morrell Clark, Jr. 1500 S MAIN ST 76104 #010-03-1972 L1978 **PD** *020 †55

GREGG, Susan. 1401 PENNSYLVANIA AVE 76104 #047-05-1979 L1988 **PTH** *020 †50

GRIFFIN, Robert Statham. 300 W ROSEDALE ST, DEPT VETERAN AFFAIRS OPC 76104 #048-12-1959 L1959 **IM** *020 †20

GRIMALDOS, Juan Pablo. 801 7TH AVE, COOK CHILDREN'S HOSPITAL 76104 #264-04-1992 L2002 **PAN** *020 †05

GRIMES, Elwyn Mancel. 1500 S MAIN ST, DEPT OF OBGYN 76104 #047-07-1968 L1969 **REN GYN** *030 †30

GRISSOM, David Byron. 1301 PENNSYLVANIA AVE 76104 #004-01-1992 L1999 **IM** *020 †20

GRUBBS, Randall Lee. 1301 PENNSYLVANIA AVE 76104 #047-05-1998 L2004 **NPM** *020 †55

GUDIMETLA, Sreenivas. 1300 W TERRELL AVE STE 500 76104 #048-13-1991 L1992 **CD** *020 †20

GUERRA, Martha Denise. 6618 FOSSIL BLUFF DR, STE 132 76137 #048-15-1994 L1997 **OBG** *020 †30

GUINAN, Robert Bruce. 6445 HARRIS PKWY, STE 100 76132 #048-12-1976 L1976 **GE IM** *020 †20

GUINN, Edward Wm. 5304 RAMEY AVE 76105 #048-02-1956 L1956 **GP OS** *020 ‡

GUINN, James Elvis. 1400 S MAIN ST STE 304 76104 #047-07-1941 L1946 **FM** *071

GUINN, Joseph Elvis. 7100 OAKMONT BLVD, STE 201B 76132 #041-07-1987 L1994 **VS** *020

GULATI, Annu Lallchand. 855 MONTGOMERY ST 76107 #495-96-1994 L2002 **FM** *020 †18 ‡

GULLEDGE, Wm Ralph, Jr. 1307 8TH AVE, STE 408 76104 #027-01-1971 L1977 **N** *020 †75

GUTHRIE, Lisa Gaye. 6401 HARRIS PKWY 76132 #048-12-1994 L1997 **PD** *020 †55

GUTHRIE, William Spurgeon. 6100 HARRIS PKWY, STE 345 76132 #048-12-1994 L1997 **IM** *020 †20

GUTTA, Kumar V R. 909 9TH AVE, STE 300 76104 #025-07-1989 L1996 **GE IM** *020 †20

GUZMAN, Daniel David. 801 7TH AVE 76104 #024-05-1997 L2000 **PD** *020

GUZMAN, Guillermo Antonio. 1319 SUMMIT AVE STE 330 76102 #048-12-1980 L1980 **N** *020 †75

HABER, Julian Stuart. 1300 W LANCASTER AVE, STE 101 76102 #011-02-1961 L1967 **PD** *020 †55

HACKMAN, Anne Marie. 901 7TH AVE, CARDIOLOGY ASSOCIATES 76104 #017-20-1987 L1990 **PDC PD** *020 †20,55

HADDEN, Timothy Bryan. 1300 W TERRELL AVE STE 500 76104 #039-01-1997 L2001 **IC** *020 †20

HADDOCK, Samuel Thompson. 801 7TH AVE 76104 #045-01-1995 L2000 **PD** *020 †55

HADEED, Sami K W. 901 7TH AVE STE 420, COOK CHILDREN'S MEDICAL CE 76104 #875-01-1980 L1990 **PD PDP** *020 †55

HADLEY, Lesca C. 1500 S MAIN ST, 4TH FL 76104 #048-15-1998 L1999 **FPG** *020 †18

HAEFELI, David C. 5445 BASSWOOD BLVD, STE 650 76137 #048-12-1982 L1983 **FM EM** *020 †18

HAFEEZ, Abdul. 950 W MAGNOLIA AVE 76104 #704-02-1988 L1997 **IM** *020 †20

HAFEEZ, Raheela Mahmood A. ■ 76137 #704-02-1988 L1999 **PD** *020 †55

HAFIZ, Zafar Ahmed. 4916 OVERTON PLZ 76109 #704-08-1973 L1987 **AN** *020

HAGEY-LEVERT, Rhonda L. 909 9TH AVE, STE 300 76104 #016-02-1985 L1992 **IM** *020 †20

HAHN, Marc B. 3500 CAMP BOWIE BLVD, EAD-864 76107 #018-75-1984, ▲ L2003 **AN PME** *040 †05

HAITHCOCK, Kelly Komaromy. 6551 HARRIS PKWY, STE 200 76132 #038-40-2002 L2006 **OPH** *020

HAJOVSKY, Brian A. 6100 HARRIS PKWY 76132 #048-15-1999 L2003 **OPH** *020 †35

HALKER, Raj Raghunath. 950 W MAGNOLIA AVE, DIVISION OF NEPHROLOGY 76104 #496-39-1998 L2007 **NEP** *020

HALL, James Albert. 3500 CAMP BOWIE BLVD # 714 76107 #048-12-1961 L1961 **P PYA** *071 †75

HALL, Thomas R. ■ 76106 #034-01-1980 L1981 **IM** *020 †20

HALLGREN, Sally Ann. 311 UNIVERSITY DR 76107 #048-78-1976, ▲ L1977 **NS PMM** *020

HALPENNY, Walter Hartley. 6401 HARRIS PKWY STE 100 76132 #048-14-1984 L1986 **PD** *020 †55

HAMILTON, Carl Leonard, III. 900 8TH AVE, PLAZA MEDICAL CENTER OF FO 76104 #048-02-1976 L1976 **EM IM** *020 †20,16

HAMILTON, Hinton H, III. 901 7TH AVE, STE 110 76104 #048-02-1970 L1970 **OP** *020 †40

HAMILTON, Stephen Joseph. 3301 STALCUP RD 76119 #048-16-2000 L2002 **FSM** *020 †18

HAMMONDS, Mark K. 6700 BUENOS AIRES DR 76180 #048-14-1989 L1990 **FM** *020 †18

HAMMONS, Douglas E. 3800 HULEN ST, STE 100 76107 #048-02-1995 L1999 **DR** *020 †80

HAMMONS, Matthew Austin. 800 8TH AVE STE 330 76104 #048-04-1999 L2005 **OPH** *020 †35

HAMPTON, Cynthia Robbins. 851 W TERRELL AVE 76104 #048-14-1985 L1986 **OBG** *020 †30

HANCOCK, Kenneth Chas. 1001 12TH AVE STE 20, TEXAS ONCOLOGY, P.A. 76104 #021-01-1978 L1987 **GO GYN** *020 †30

HANDLEY, James Mark. ■ 76179 #019-02-1955 L1955 **PTH** *072 †50

HANNAMAN, Mary R. 4775 SOUTH FWY 76115 #048-04-1983 L1984 **PM PMM** *020 †60

HANSON, Gregory Wayne. 6100 HARRIS PKWY, STE 240 76132 #048-15-1998 L2006 *020

HAQQANI, Muhammad Abdur R. 1500 S MAIN ST 76104 #704-16-1993 L2004 **P** *020 †75 ‡

HAQUE, Arshi Taban. 1500 S MAIN ST, JOHN PETER SMITH HOSPITAL 76104 #704-06-1995 L2006 **P** *100

HAQUE, Seema Yasmeen. 300 PENNSYLVANIA AVE, CLINIC 76104 #704-02-1991 L1999 **P PYG** *020 †75

HARALDSON, Samuel John. 2900 STADIUM DRIVE, DANIEL MEYER COLISEUM 76129 #005-15-2001 L2004 **FSM** *100 †16

HARDEE, Steven Harlan. 4504 BOAT CLUB RD, STE 800 76135 #027-01-1985 L1986 **FM** *020 †18

HARDIE, Robert Paul. 1300 W TERRELL AVE, STE 320 76104 #048-02-1974 L1974 **OBG** *020 †30

HARDT, Pattyann Amanda. ■ 76110 #048-02-2004 L2007 **OBG** *012

HARDWICK, Jack Franklin. 6100 HARRIS PKWY, PLAZA 130 76132 #048-02-1957 L1957 **FM IM** *020 †18

HARE, Richard Jos. 900 8TH AVE 76104 #048-13-1985 L1992 **PTH** *020 †50

HARGROVE, William Odell. 1500 S MAIN ST 76104 #021-01-1957 L1959 **IM** *071 †20

HAROONA, Ladi O. 508 S ADAMS ST, STE 100 76104 #690-08-1988 L2001 **CCM** *020 †20

HARRISON, David W. 900 8TH AVE 76104 #048-15-1998 L2002 **EM** *020

HARVEY, James M. 6601 DAN DANCIGER RD, STE 100 76133 #048-12-1990 L1991 **FM** *020 †18

HASH, Cecil Jackson, Jr. ■ 76107 #041-09-1968 L1969 **NS** *071 †25

HASSIBI, Saman M. 1400 8TH AVE, BAYLOR ALL SAINTS - RADIOL 76104 #048-02-1999 L2002 **R** *020 †80

HASSLER, Bert Graham. 1501 SUMMIT AVE 76102 #005-06-1955 L1956 **IM PUD** *071 †20

HAYDEN, Carlos Keith. 1350 S MAIN ST, STE 4150 76104 #048-02-1972 L1972 **DR** *020 †80

HAYNES, John H, III. 1500 S MAIN ST, JPS HEALTH NETWORK 76104 #021-06-1985 L1986 **FM OM** *030 †18 ‡

HAYWARD, Tamara Lynn. 6401 HARRIS PKWY 76132 #048-02-1999 L2002 **PD** *020 †55

HEAD, William Marshall. 900 8TH AVE 76104 #048-02-1954 L1954 **GP** *020

HEALEY, John Joseph, II. 1350 S MAIN ST, STE 4150 76104 #048-12-1993 L1994 **DR** *020 †80

HEFFERNAN, Jennifer Delia. 855 MONTGOMERY ST, UNT-HSC PCC 3RD FL 76107 #011-02-2001 L2005 **FM FPG** *020 †18

HEISTEIN, Jonathan Barry. 800 8TH AVE STE 240 76104 #033-06-1996 L2002 **PS** *020 †65

HENDERSON, Janet Lawson. 1325 PENNSYLVANIA AVE, STE 350 76104 #048-14-1982 L1983 **OBG** *020 †30

HENDRIX, Wm Clarence, Jr. ■ 76133 #048-02-1946 L1946 **OTO** *020 †45

HENRY, Linda Odeh. 801 7TH AVE, COOK CHILDRENS EMERG DEPT 76104 #048-13-1986 L1987 **PD PEM** *020 †55

HENRY, Raymond Lee. 1701 RIVER RVN RD, STE 508 76107 #048-12-1955 L1956 **AN OS** *071

HENRY, Robert, III. 920 E BERRY ST 76110 #048-13-1975 L1975 **OBG** *020 †30

HERD, James Francis. ■ 76107 #047-06-1962 L1964 **OBG** *071 †30

HERD, James P. 1250 8TH AVE STE 430 76104 #048-12-1987 L1989 **OBG** *020 †30

HERNANDEZ, Angel Wilfredo. 901 7TH AVE, STE 120 DEPT OF NEUROLOGY 76104 #042-02-1995 L2001 **CHN CN** *020 †75

HERNANDEZ, David Sergio. 1201 FAIRMOUNT AVE 76104 #048-02-2000 L2006 **PCC** *100 †20

HERNANDEZ, Omar. 1500 S MAIN ST, DEPT OF FAMILY PRACTICE 76104 #048-02-2005 **FP** *012

HERRERA, Rodolfo Alberto. 3230 RIVER LODGE TRL S 76116 #048-13-2003 L2006 **FSM** *020 †18

HERRIN, Lisa J. 2528 JACKSBORO HWY 76114 #048-14-1987 L1988 **PD** *020 †55

HERRING, Theodore Melvyn, III. 2011 S LAS VEGAS TRL 76108 #010-03-2000 L2003 **ORS** *100

HESS, Susan Lynn. 901 7TH AVE, STE 310 76104 #048-04-1985 L1986 **PDC** *020 †55

HEYM, Kenneth Matthew. 901 7TH AVE STE 220 76104 #047-05-1999 L2006 **PHO** *020 †55

HIBBS, Sarah Elizabeth. ■ 76123 #048-16-2005 L2006 **OBG** *012

HICKEY, Michael Steven. 1325 PENNSYLVANIA AVE, STE 777 76104 #021-01-1976 L1983 **TRS GS** *020 †85

HICKS, Charles E. ■ 76116 #048-04-1951 L1951 **FM** *071

HIGGINS, Jennifer Blackwe. 4916 OVERTON PLZ, SUMMIT HMR 76109 #048-13-2003 L2007 **AN** *020

HIGGINS, Kim E. ■ 76107 #048-78-2007, ▲ **FP** *012

HIGGS, Matthew Benjamin. ■ 76109 #048-15-2008 *012

HILL, Meredith Patricia. ■ 76112 #048-02-2004 **IM** *100

HINES, Terrance S. 1500 S MAIN ST 76104 #048-16-2006 L2007 **FP** *012

HINKLE, Kollier Joseph. 855 MONTGOMERY ST 76107 #045-01-2000 L2002 **FM** *020

HIRT, Darrell Lee. 1000 W CANNON ST 76104 #048-12-1981 L1981 **NP IM** *030 †20

HITZFELDER, Nancy J. 1300 W LANCASTER AVE, CHILD STUDY CENTER 76102 #048-02-1976 L1976 **PD OS** *020 †55

HODGSON, Robert Allan. 5445 BASSWOOD BLVD, STE 650 76137 #039-01-1982 L1983 **FM** *020 †18

HOFFMAN, Gerry Michael. 1250 8TH AVE STE 440 76104 #048-15-1976 L1976 **OBG** *020 †30

HOFFMAN, William Jos. 4916 OVERTON PLZ 76109 #016-43-1985 L1992 **AN** *020 †05

HOLCOMB, Robert Allen. 900 8TH AVE, PLAZA MEDICAL CENTER 76104 #048-12-1971 L1971 **EM** *020

HOLLAND, Teresa B. 801 7TH AVE, DEPARTMENT OF ANESTHESIA 76104 #055-01-1990 L1995 **AN** *020 †05

HOLLANDER, Ira Neil. 1300 W TERRELL AVE STE 405 76104 #048-12-1977 L1977 **U** *020 †95

HOLLINGER, Laura Elizabet. ■ 76109 #048-14-2008 *012

HOLLOWAY, Dyann. 801 7TH AVE, DEPT OF ANES 76104 #665-01-2001 L2006 **PAN** *020 †05

HOLM, Peter C. 1701 RIVER RUN, MEIER CLINICS FORT WORTH 76107 #048-02-1987 L1988 **P** *020

HOLMES, David Lawrence. 1250 8TH AVE STE 430 76104 #065-06-1976 L1981 **OBG** *020

HOLMES, John Robt. 900 8TH AVE 76104 #065-06-1953 L1980 **IM** *071

HOLSAPPLE, Cortell K, Jr. 1221 W LANCASTER AVE, ROBERT R DICKEY MD 76102 #021-01-1948 L1950 **IM** *071 †20

HOLT, Ernest Eugene. ■ 76109 #004-01-1939 L1944 **R RO** *071 †80

HOMER, Kevin. 11803 S FREEWAY, STE 210 76115 #048-12-1989 L1990 **PTH PCP** *020 †50

HOMER, Ladon W. 11801 SOUTH FWY 76115 #005-12-1965 L1975 **ATP CLP** *020 †50

HONEYCHURCH, Leslie F. ■ 76112 #016-42-1990 L1990 **P** *100

HONEYCUTT, Johnnie Harrel. 901 7TH AVE STE 120, DEPARTMENT OF NEUROSURGERY 76104 #004-01-1994 L2005 **NS** *020 †25

HOOKER, Glen Douglas. 1420 8TH AVE STE 103 76104 #065-06-1994 L2000 **CRS** *020 †85,10

HOOPER, Mickey L. 1250 8TH AVE STE 445 76104 #048-78-1997, ▲ L1998 *020

HOOT, William Rollins. 815 PENNSYLVANIA AVE, RADIOLOGY ASSOCIATES OF TA 76104 #048-12-1971 L1973 **DR** *020 †80

HOPKINS, Donald Harry. 1550 W ROSEDALE ST STE 410 76104 #048-02-1957 L1957 **FM** *020

HOPPER, Ken C. 1300 SUMMIT AVE, STE 600 76102 #048-02-1985 L1989 **P** *020 †75

HORNER, Douglas Branch. 801 7TH AVE 76104 #035-06-1976 L1979 **PD** *020

■ = Address Information Privacy Protected

HORSLEY, George Ernest. ■ 76134 #005-12-1945 L1951 **OTO OPH** *071 †45

HORSLEY, Sheila Kathleen. 11803 S FREEWAY STE 312, HUGULEY PROF BLDG 76115 #005-12-1979 L1980 **FM PHP** *020

HORSTMAN, William G. 815 PENNSYLVANIA AVE 76104 #028-02-1983 L2001 **DR** *020 †80

HORTON, Carl James, Jr. 4601 BOAT CLUB RD, STE 125 76135 #017-20-1998 L2004 **CD** *020 †20

HORTON, Stephen H. 1500 S MAIN ST 76104 #048-15-1999 L2001 **EM** *020 †16

HOUGH, Jerald P. ■ 76109 #021-01-1950 L1958 **DR** *071 †55,80

HOUSINI, Ihsan. 1401 PENNSYLVANIA AVE 76104 #875-01-1986 L1991 **PCP** *020 †50

HOWARD, Herbert H. ■ 76132 #039-01-1942 L1943 **IM AN** *071

HOWELL, Robert Michael. 6100 HARRIS PKWY STE 245 76132 #048-14-1986 L1988 **OBG** *020 †30

HOWREY, Richard Philip. 901 7TH AVE STE 220 76104 #025-01-1991 L1994 **PHO** *020 †55

HUBBARD, Richard Olen. 1325 PENNSYLVANIA AVE 76104 #039-01-1971 L1979 **NS PTH** *020 †25

HUBBELL, Carl Edward. 11803 S FREEWAY STE 312 76115 #048-12-1978 L1978 **PS** *020

HUCABY, Deborah S. 801 7TH AVE 76104 #048-12-1987 L1988 **PD** *020 †55

HUDGENS, H Stephen. 800 8TH AVE STE 510 76104 #048-12-1981 L1981 **TS** *020 †85,90

HUGHENS, H Kennon. 4916 OVERTON PLZ 76109 #021-06-1982 L1983 **AN** *020 †05

HUGHES, Charlece Scoma. 1307 8TH AVE, STE 408 76104 #048-78-2000, ▲ L2003 **N** *020 †75

HUGHES, William E, III. 801 7TH AVE 76104 #649-30-1981 L1988 **PN PD** *050 †55

HULL, Alan Robt. ■ 76109 #062-01-1962 L1968 **NEP IM** *071 †20

HUMMELKE, Melissa Dianne. 6451 BRENTWOOD STAIR RD 76112 #048-13-2002 L2005 **EM** *020 †16

HUMPERT, Natalie Marie. 3308 DEEN RD 76106 #028-78-2005, ▲ L2008 **FM** *100

HUMPHRIES, James Madison. 1661 EASTCHASE PKWY, CARE NOW CLINIC 76120 #048-12-1984 L1985 **FM** *020 †18

HUNNICUTT, Robert Weldon. 1400 8TH AVE 76104 #048-02-1972 L1972 **ORS** *062 †40

HUNT, Lyn Irene. 750 8TH AVE, STE200 76104 #048-02-1976 L1976 **OS** *020 †55

HUNT, Michael G. 1325 PENNSYLVANIA AVE, STE 110 76104 #048-04-1999 L2004 **OPH** *020 †35

HUNTER, Darlene Loucks. PO BOX 297400 76129 #048-12-1949 L1949 **GP** *020

HUNTZINGER, Howard James. ■ 76179 #048-13-1981 L1981 **FM** *020 †18

HUPERT, Mark Joseph. 1125 COLLEGE AVE 76104 #041-12-1993 L2001 **ID** *020 †20

HURSCHMAN, Alan Bruce. 1200 W MAGNOLIA AVE, STE 300 76104 #561-01-1986 L1990 **PM PME** *020

HUSS, Michael Garland. 4916 OVERTON PLZ 76109 #033-06-1991 L1995 **AN** *020 †05

HUSTON, Diana Arnouk. 801 7TH AVE 76104 #875-02-1989 L1995 **PD** *020 †55

HUTCHESON, Geo Oscar, Jr. 1301 PENNSYLVANIA AVE 76104 #048-02-1947 L1947 **PUD IM** *071

HUTCHESON, Richard Milam. 800 5TH AVE, STE 300 76104 #048-12-1981 L1981 **IM** *020 †20 ‡

HWANG, Pamela M. 7100 OAKMONT BLVD 76132 #048-12-1998 L2000 **DR** *020 †80

HYDE, Amber. ■ 76120 #104-01-2005 **FP** *012

HYER, Rex Lewis. 4916 OVERTON PLZ 76109 #047-06-1963 L1970 **AN** *020 †05

HYMAN, Joel C. 1307 8TH AVE STE 505, TARRANT DERMATOLOGY CONSUL 76104 #048-13-2000 L2004 **D** *020 †15

IGLESIA, Kim Angel. 815 PENNSYLVANIA AVE 76104 #048-16-1988 L1989 **PDR** *020 †80

IGLESIAS, Jose Luis. 901 7TH AVE 76104 #048-12-1992 L1993 **PDS** *020 †85

ILUYOMADE, Olakunle Olufe. 508 S ADAMS ST, STE 100 76104 #690-05-1992 L2007 **PCC** *020 †20

INDUKURI, Padmanabha Raju. 2707 AIRPORT FWY 76111 #495-58-1977 L1990 **P CHP** *020 †75

INGEBRIGTSEN, Norman A. 7500 GRAPEVINE HWY 76180 #048-02-1963 L1963 **FM** *020 †18

IRWIN, Peter James. 7100 OAKMONT BLVD STE 207 76132 #048-02-1989 L1990 **OBG** *020 †30

ISAAC, Marrisa Monique. ■ 76133 #048-14-2006 **P** *012

ISAACS, Emily Merrell. 909 9TH AVE, STE 300 76104 #008-02-1980 L1985 **RHU** *020 †20

ISABELL, Gene Paul, Jr. 1500 S MAIN ST, ORTHOPEDIC DEPARTMENT 76104 #048-14-2001 L2006 **OSM** *020

JABBAR, Kashif. ■ 76112 #704-01-2000 L2006 **IM** *020 †20

JACKSON, John Schooling. 900 W MAGNOLIA AVE, STE 100 76104 #020-02-1970 L1973 **IM OS** *020 †20

JACOBSON, Bruce Kelton. ■ 76180 #048-04-1954 L1954 **FM** *071 †18

JACOBSON, Kenneth Harris. 801 7TH AVE, COOK CHILDREN'S MEDICAL CE 76104 #035-47-1988 L2001 **AN** *020 †05

JAFRI, Syed Muhammed H. 1301 PENNSYLVANIA AVE, HOSPITAL MEDCINE ASSOCIATE 76104 #704-25-1991 L2006 **IM EM** *020 †20

JAGODA, Samuel, Jr. 300 W ROSEDALE ST, VA CLINIC 76104 #048-04-1956 L1956 **R** *020 †80 ‡

JAISWAL, Vilkesh Rama. 1500 S MAIN ST, DEPT OF PATHLGY 76104 #048-12-1998 L1999 **PTH** *020 †50

JAMAL, Karim Sadrudin. ■ 76132 #065-05-1990 L1994 **IM** *020 †20

JAMBOR, Christopher N. ■ 76107 #019-02-1978 L1981 **PD** *020 †55

JAMES, George. 4601 BOAT CLUB RD, STE 125 76135 #495-27-1991 L2005 **CD** *020 †20

JAPAS, Carlos Alberto. 11803 S FREEWAY STE 308 76134 #308-03-1979 L1987 **IM CCM** *020

JARRARD, Michael Robt. 2500 LOU MENK DR, BNSF MED OFFICER 76131 #048-12-1986 L2001 **OM** *030 †70

JAVED, Kausar. 1301 PENNSYLVANIA AVE 76104 #495-83-1999 L2005 **IM** *100 †20

JAYACHANDRAN, Asha Sarah. ■ 76116 #495-27-1990 L2003 **PD** *020 †55

JAYACHANDRAN, John V. 1300 W ROSEDALE ST 76104 #495-27-1990 L2003 **ICE** *020 †20

JENKINS, Thos Rodgers, Jr. ■ 76111 #010-01-1948 L1950 **R OS** *071 †80

JENSEN, Richard A. 3800 HULEN ST, STE 100 76107 #048-12-1988 L1990 **DR** *020 †80

JOGIMAHANTI, Sudha R. 5445 BASSWOOD BLVD, STE 650 76137 #495-70-1989 L1997 **FM** *020 †18

JOHNS, Delbert Alan. 1325 PENNSYLVANIA AVE, STE 350 76104 #048-02-1974 L1974 **GYN** *020 †30

JOHNSON, Charles. ■ 76179 #048-16-2008 *012

JOHNSON, Donald Rufus. 1111 5TH AVE 76104 #018-03-1977 L1983 **GE IM** *020 †20

JOHNSON, Fredric Dorhauer. 6100 HARRIS PKWY STE 205 76132 #048-02-1984 L1985 **FM** *020 †18 ‡

JOHNSON, Harold V, III. 800 8TH AVE STE 412 76104 #048-02-1968 L1968 **IM** *020 ‡

JOHNSON, James Danl. 1300 W TERRELL AVE STE 405 76104 #048-13-1973 L1973 **U** *020 †95

JOHNSON, John Edward, Jr. 1221 W LANCASTER AVE 76102 #048-02-1948 L1948 **IM IMG** *071 †20

JOHNSON, John Walker, III. 6100 HARRIS PKWY STE 225 76132 #039-01-1980 L1981 **U** *020 †95

JOHNSON, Shannon. 1701 RIVER RUN, MEIER CLINICS FORT WORTH 76107 #001-06-1996 L1999 **P** *020 †75

JOHNSON, Steven Edward. 800 5TH AVE, STE 300 76104 #048-12-1981 L1981 **IM** *020 †20

JOHNSTON, Dewey W. ■ 76132 #048-12-1949 L1949 **LM** *071 †20

JONES, Douglas Duane. 4200 S HULEN ST STE 425 76109 #051-04-1983 L1984 **AN** *020 †05

JONES, Freddie Ray. 1001 12TH AVE, STE 140 76104 #048-02-1970 L1970 **OPH GP** *020 †35

JONES, Mark Stinson. 6100 HARRIS PKWY, STE B 76132 #048-14-1995 L1997 **PD** *020 †55

JONES, Robert Lee Stinson. 6100 HARRIS PKWY, STE B 76132 #048-12-1966 L1966 **PD GP** *020 †55

JONES, Scott Jay. 900 8TH AVE, DEPARTMENT OF EMERGENCY ME 76104 #005-11-1991 L2006 **EM** *020 †16

JONES, Stuart Pannill. 1108 S HENDERSON ST 76104 #048-12-1960 L1960 **PD** *071 †55

JORDAN, David Curtis. 900 W MAGNOLIA AVE STE 201 76104 #048-12-1983 L1983 **FM** *020 †18

JORDAN, Jeffrey Warde. 4200 S HULEN ST STE 425 76109 #048-13-1976 L1976 **AN** *020 †05

JORDAN, Kirk Gerald. 1350 S MAIN ST, STE 1450 76104 #048-02-1991 L1992 **DR** *020 †80

JORNS, Kenneth Lloyd. 909 8TH AVE, STE C 76104 #021-01-1947 L1950 **GP GS** *071

JOSHI, Harshad Girish. ■ 76116 #010-03-2001 L2001 **IM** *020

JOSHI, Kaustubh Girish. ■ 76116 #033-05-2000 L2002 **PFP** *020 †75 ‡

JOSHI, Subhash Aniruddha. 5017 ALICIA DR 76133 #495-23-1975 L1983 **AI PD** *020

JUDGE, Linda O'Connell. 1199 8TH AVE 76104 #019-02-1980 L1982 **R** *020 †80

JUDSON, Jack Lynwood. 3301 N MAIN ST 76106 #008-01-1956 L1961 **GP AM** *020

JULIAO, Samuel. 1301 PENNSYLVANIA AVE 76104 #264-05-1973 L1983 **NPM** *020 †55

JURGENSEN, Karen Sue. 800 8TH AVE, STE 440 76104 #048-12-1976 L1983 **IM ID** *020 †20

JURGENSEN, Warren P. ■ 76103 #030-06-1950 L1968 **D P** *071 †75

KAHN, Anne Marie. 2630 WEST FWY STE 1 76102 #048-14-1998 L2000 **AN PAN** *020

KAMEN, Geoffrey Lee. 1500 S MAIN ST, JPS HEALTH NETWORK 76104 #550-02-2001 L2007 **FPG** *012 †18

KAMPINE, John Michael. 4916 OVERTON PLZ 76109 #056-06-1987 L1999 **AN** *020 †05

KAO, Yiling. 7100 OAKMONT BLVD 76132 #035-46-2001 L2006 **EM** *100 †16

KAPU, Nagarajani. 4916 OVERTON PLZ 76109 #048-02-1999 L2003 **AN** *020 †05

KARAKOURTIS, Paul H. 1500 S MAIN ST 76104 #048-14-1992 L1993 **EM** *020 †18

KARL, Cecilia. 300 W ROSEDALE ST, FWOPC OOFW 76104 #649-27-1986 L1997 **IM** *020

KASAL, Mumata Nataraj. ■ 76185 #495-09-1969 L1990 **R** *020

KASAL, Nataraj G. 1307 8TH AVE STE 406 76104 #495-09-1970 L1976 **GE IM** *020 †20

KASPAR, Melanie Sessions. 4916 OVERTON PLZ 76109 #048-12-1992 L1993 **AN** *020 †05

KAUFMAN, James Kevin. 1319 SUMMIT AVE 76102 #055-01-1994 L2000 **NS** *020 †25

KAUFMANN, Robert Alan. 800 5TH AVE STE 210 76104 #550-02-1984 L2004 **REN OBG** *020 †30

KAUR, Harminder Pal. 1500 S MAIN ST, JOHN P SMITH HOSP 76104 #913-07-1998 **P** *100

KAUSHIK, Satya Prakash. 617 TRAVIS AVE 76104 #495-41-1968 L1986 **PD AI** *020 †55

KAUTZ, Heather Mcreynolds. 1500 S MAIN ST 76104 #048-04-1997 L2000 **EM** *020 †16

KAUTZ, Kenneth Charles, Jr. 6451 BRENTWOOD STAIR RD, STE 200 76112 #048-04-1996 L2000 **EM** *020 †16

KAYSER, Scott W. 1500 S MAIN ST, DEPARTMENT OF RADIOLGY 76104 #048-14-1999 L2002 **DR** *020 †80

KAZA, Purnima. 2807 RANCH HOUSE DR E 76116 #496-24-1997 L2003 **FM** *020

KEATHLEY, Craig A. 1307 8TH AVE, STE 201 76104 #048-02-1997 L2004 **OBG** *020 †30 ‡

KEEN, Jack C. 5701 BRYANT IRVIN RD, STE 103 76132 #027-01-1967 L1983 **OBG** *020 †30

KELFER, Howard Michael. 901 7TH AVE STE 120 76104 #024-07-1976 L1982 **CHN PD** *020 †55,75

KELLEHER, Stephen Patrick. 1500 S MAIN ST, DEPT OF INTERNAL MEDICINE 76104 #024-01-1975 L2003 **IM** *020 †20

KELLER, Robert Tyson. 2751 GREEN OAKS RD 76116 #005-06-1982 L1988 **IM EM** *020 †20

KELLIE, Thomas E. ■ 76109 #803-05-1957 **OPH** *071 †35

KELLY, Allan Rowan. 929 COLLEGE AVE 76104 #048-12-1981 L1984 **IM ID** *020 †20 ‡

KELLY, Gordon B. 929 COLLEGE AVE 76104 #021-01-1951 L1954 **IM** *071

KELLY, Lee Roy Jos. 1400 8TH AVE 76104 #048-02-1955 L1955 **GS** *071 †85

KELLY, Marie Theresa. 2630 WEST FWY, STE 228 76102 #008-01-1974 L1976 **P OBG** *020 †30,75

KELLY, Robert Hart. 929 COLLEGE AVE 76104 #048-14-1981 L1981 **IM IMG** *020 †20 ‡

KELTON, Thomas Fowler. 4916 OVERTON PLZ 76109 #048-13-2003 L2007 **AN** *020

KEMP, Connie Susan. ■ 76133 #048-02-1977 L1978 **GP** *020

KENG, Jane Abigail. 750 8TH AVE STE 200, THE CHILDREN'S HOSPITAL 76104 #016-42-2001 L2007 **PG** *020 †55

KENNEDY, Jason Matthew. ■ 76132 #048-02-2004 **ORS** *012

KENNEDY, Shane W. 950 W MAGNOLIA AVE 76104 #048-12-1998 L2003 **NEP** *020 †20

KENT, Allen Sanders. 800 12TH AVE STE 200 76104 #048-14-1976 L1977 **ORS** *020 †40

KEY, Robert E. ■ 76109 #048-02-1951 L1951 **ORS** *071 †40

KHALAFI, Reza Seyed. 1650 W ROSEDALE ST STE 20 76104 #010-01-1987 L1994 **CD GS** *020 †85,90

KHALIFEH AL-SALEH, Ahmed. 1111 5TH AVE, DIGESTIVE HEALTH ASSOCIATE 76104 #875-02-1995 L2005 **GE** *020 †20

KHAMMAR, George S. 1017 12TH AVE 76104 #917-19-1987 L2002 **CD IC** *020 †20

KHAN, Ajaz Omer. 1500 S MAIN ST, JOHN PETER SMITH HOSP 76104 #496-27-1995 L2004 **FM** *100 †18

KHAN, Ali Aijaz. 1500 S MAIN ST, JOHN PETER SMITH HOSP 76104 #748-12-1992 L2004 **P** *100

KHAN, Fuad Asif. ■ 76137 #704-16-1999 L2003 **IM** *020

KHAN, Ghulam Zain-Ul-Din. 1500 S MAIN ST 76104 #704-15-1984 **P** *100

KHAN, Kassim. 1101 W ROSEDALE ST 76104 #028-46-1984 L1990 **OPH** *071 †35

KHAN, Riaz U. 1500 S MAIN ST, DEPARTMENT OF INTERNAL MED 76104 #704-09-1991 L1997 **GE** *020 †20

KHAN, Saba. ■ 76109 #704-16-1997 L2006 **IM** *020

KHAN, Shujaat Ali. 800 8TH AVE, STE 200 76104 #704-01-1966 L1975 **PS HS** *020 †65

KHAN, Sohail Ahmad. ■ 76133 #704-01-1979 L1992 **IM** *020 †20

KIM, Sang Y. 4504 BOAT CLUB RD 76135 #048-13-1998 L1999 **FM** *020 †18

KIM, Won Sup. 816 W CANNON ST, C/O RADIOLOGY ASSCOIATES 76104 #023-07-1978 L1987 **DR** *020 †80

KINCH, Robert. 1325 PENNSYLVANIA AVE #450 76104 #352-07-1943 L1990 **OBS** *071

KING, Dolores Kathryn. 2317 HANDLEY DR 76112 #038-41-1998 L2004 **MPD** *020 †20,55

KING, Joseph, III. 2317 HANDLEY DR 76112 #012-21-1998 L2004 **MPD** *020

KING-RANKINE, Marilyn. 909 9TH AVE STE 202, PLAZA 1 76104 #041-13-1978 L1985 **CD** *020 †20

KIRBY, Dana Sue. 5445 BASSWOOD BLVD, STE 650 76137 #047-20-1997 L2003 **FM** *020 †18

KIRCH, Linda Jeanne. 3437 W 7TH ST STE 270 76107 #048-13-1985 L1993 **AN** *020 †05

KIRK, Karen M. 3301 STALCUP RD 76119 #048-15-2001 L2004 **FSM PD** *020 †55

KLEINMAN, Samuel Eleazar. 801 7TH AVE 76104 #048-15-1988 L1989 **AN** *020 †05

■ = Address Information Privacy Protected

KLEUSER, Thomas Murnane. 1300 W ROSEDALE ST, STE B 76104 #048-02-1976 L1976 **ORS** *020 †40

KLINTMALM, Goran B G. 1400 8TH AVE 76104 #858-02-1976 L1985 **TTS GS** *020

KLYMIUK, Jadwiga Alina. 855 MONTGOMERY ST 76107 #759-10-1990 L2002 **P** *020

KNETEN, Craig Charles. 900 W MAGNOLIA AVE, STE 201 76104 #048-14-1996 L1997 **FM** *020 †18

KOBS, Tracy Le Neil. 855 MONTGOMERY ST 76107 #039-01-1957 L1965 **GYN** *020 †30

KOCH, Mark A. 1500 S MAIN ST, 4TH FL 76104 #048-13-1992 L1993 **FM** *040 †18

KOLAR, Donna E. 6100 HARRIS PKWY, STE 200 76132 #048-12-1984 L1985 **OBG** *020 †30

KONDZIELA, Sherry Ruth. 901 COLLEGE AVE 76104 #035-15-1989 L1993 **PM OS** *020 †60

KONZELMANN, Daniel J. 200 FELIKS GWOZDZ PL, OFFICE OF CHIEF MED EXAMIN 76104 #016-45-1992 L1998 **PTH** *020 †50

KOPPEL, Phillip R. ■ 76132 #005-16-1962 L1975 **GP** *075

KORENMAN, Michael Dean. 1821 8TH AVE 76110 #048-02-1974 L1974 **GS** *020 †85

KOSTOHRYZ, George, Jr. 4625 BOAT CLUB RD, STE 257 76135 #048-14-1977 L1978 **OTO** *020 †45

KOWALSKI, Peter Craig. 1814 8TH AVE B, PSYCHIATRIC MEDICINE ASSOC 76110 #039-01-1983 L1993 **CHP P** *020 †75

KRAUS, Vernon Jay. 900 COLLEGE AVE, STE C 76104 #038-41-1965 L1971 **OBG** *020 †30

KRAUSE, Frederick Wade. ■ 76104 #048-13-2004 **ORS** *012

KREBEL, Meredith Sanders. 801 7TH AVE, COOK CHILDRENS EMGY DEPT 76104 #048-12-1988 L1995 **PD PEM** *020 †55

KREBEL, Steven R. 801 7TH AVE, EMERG DEPT 76104 #048-12-1988 L1995 **PD PEM** *020 †55

KREUSEL, Roy Glenn. 1651 W ROSEDALE ST 76104 #048-14-1979 L1979 **OM** *020 †18

KROUSE, Marc Andrew. 200 FELIKS GWOZDZ PL 76104 #048-12-1977 L1977 **FOP PTH** *062 †50

KRUCKNER, Douglas Lee. 1500 S MAIN ST 76104 #033-06-2002 L2005 **FM** *020 †18

KUENSTLER, Kevin Andrew. 7630 N BEACH ST, STE 140 76137 #019-02-1995 L1996 **FM** *020 †18

KUENSTLER, Kristi Montgom. 3800 HULEN ST, STE 100 76107 #048-12-1994 L1995 **DR** *020 †80

KUKOLICH, Mary Kathryn. 1300 W LANCASTER AVE 76102 #035-20-1972 L1976 **CG PD** *020 †55,19

KUMAR, Prasanna. 3813 DIAMOND LOCH W, NORTH RICHLAND HILLS 76180 #495-37-1962 L1980 **FM FPG** *040 †18

KUMAR, Yuvaraj D. 800 8TH AVE, STE 406 76104 #048-12-1998 L2000 **IC** *020 †20

KUNERT, Raoul Thos. ■ 76109 #026-04-1963 L1972 **PTH** *071 †50

KUNKEL, Kelly Raymond. 1830 8TH AVE 76110 #048-02-1986 L1987 **PS FPS** *020 †85,65

KUNKEL, Raymond E. 2501 PARKVIEW DR, STE 600 76102 #016-43-1953 L1970 **AN FPG** *071 †05

KUO, Duy K. 815 PENNSYLVANIA AVE 76104 #048-12-1994 L1999 **DR** *020 †80

KURTZ, Stanley Morton. ■ 76116 #001-02-1958 L1962 **PTH** *020 †50

KUTZLER, Beatrice Grace. 4760 BARWICK DR, STE C 76132 #048-14-1987 L1989 **OBG** *020 †30

KUTZLER, Daniel E. 6100 HARRIS PKWY, STE 355 76132 #048-14-1987 L1988 **IM** *020 †20

LA, Samuel Seungkwon. 1350 S MAIN ST STE 4150 76104 #048-12-1998 L2003 **DR** *020 †80

LABOR, R Penny Megison. 3800 HULEN ST, STE 100 76107 #021-06-1990 L1995 **DR** *020 †80

LACKAN, Darren Wayne. 7241 HAWKINS VIEW DR 76132 #048-13-1999 L2003 **END** *020 †20

LACY, Joe N. 816 W CANNON ST 76104 #048-02-1986 L1989 **DR** *100 †40,80

LAGON, Manuel G. 901 8TH AVE 76104 #748-01-1956 L1967 **CRS** *020 †85,10

LAGON, Robert M. 4916 OVERTON PLZ 76109 #048-02-1993 L1997 **AN** *020 †05

LA GRONE, Columbus Lee. ■ 76109 #001-02-1953 L1957 **AN** *071 †05

LAI, Stephen. 901 7TH AVE, STE 310 76104 #033-05-1974 L1985 **PDC** *020 †55

LALANI, Inayat I. 4255 BRYANT IRVIN RD, STE 101 76109 #495-22-1961 L1972 **GS** *071 †85

LAMBERT, James Russell. 1400 8TH AVE 76104 #048-12-1960 L1960 **FPG** *071

LAMENSDORF, Hugh. ■ 76116 #021-01-1961 L1967 **U** *071 †95

LANDER, Stuart R. 1307 8TH AVE 76104 #048-13-1996 L1997 **CD** *020 †20

LANEY, Samuel Mark. 901 7TH AVE, STE 120 76104 #048-02-1984 L1985 **N** *020 †75

LANGHAM, Charles G, III. 1307 8TH AVE STE 201 76104 #048-02-1975 L1975 **OBG** *020

LANGSTON, Gary Wayne. 1500 S MAIN ST 76104 #005-12-1973 L2001 **EM FM** *020 †18,16

LANOUX, Michael Joel. 1199 8TH AVE 76104 #048-12-1988 L1989 **DR** *020 †80

LARSEN, David Thorsten. 1101 6TH AVE 76104 #048-12-1981 L1981 **DR** *020 †80

LASCANO, Charles Albert. ■ 76107 #264-08-1998 **FP** *012

LASHUS, Andrew Gordon. 901 7TH AVE STE 3 76104 #021-01-1990 L1999 **PDC PD** *020 †55

LASSITER, Alan Kent. 801 7TH AVE, COOK-FT WORTH CHILDRENS ME 76104 #048-02-1981 L1981 **MDM OS** *030 †55 ‡

LAUGHTON, Pierre Earl. 909 9TH AVE STE 3 76104 #028-34-1999 L2008 **IM** *020 †20

LAVINE, David Maurice. 800 8TH AVE STE 200 76104 #051-01-1972 L1972 **PS** *020 †65

LAWRENCE, Richard Burnett. 1550 W ROSEDALE ST STE 614 76104 #048-02-1974 L1974 **FM OM** *020 ‡

LAWRENCE, William David. 1601 8TH AVE, STE B 76104 #039-01-1985 L1989 **P** *020 †75

LAZARUS, Peter Simon. 801 7TH AVE, COOK CHILDREN'S MEDICAL CE 76104 #035-19-1973 L1976 **PD ID** *020 †55

LE, Linh T. 1210 ALSTON AVE 76104 #048-02-1995 L1998 **NEP** *020 †20

LEAHY, Ann Katherine. 801 7TH AVE, PICU OFFICE 76104 #539-02-1983 L1989 **PD** *020 †55

LE BLANC, Danielle Marie. 800 8TH AVE, STE 416 76104 #048-12-1999 L2005 **PS** *020 †65

LE BLANC, Raymond Arthur. 800 8TH AVE, STE 416 76104 #024-05-1971 L1976 **NS** *020

LECONEY, Thomas Ratcliffe. 3000 S HULEN ST, # 124-225 76109 #048-13-1985 L1986 **EM** *020 †16

LEDBETTER, Jason Seth. 900 8TH AVE 76104 #021-05-1998 L2001 **IM** *020 †20

LEE, David Frederick. 546 W SEMINARY DR STE A 76115 #048-12-1955 L1955 **FM** *020 †18

LEE, Derek Dongwoo. ■ 76137 #048-15-2007 **IM** *012

LEFLER, Hugh Talmage, Jr. ■ 76107 #036-01-1967 L1974 **GYN** *071 †30

LEHMAN, Dennis Lynn. 1555 MERRIMAC CIR STE 101, ATTN KIMBERLY DAGMIN 76107 #023-01-1962 L1964 **FM** *020 †18

LEHMANN, Claudio Straus. 1325 PENNSYLVANIA AVE, STE 680 76104 #231-01-1963 L1973 **RHU IM** *020

LEIFESTE, James Freeman. 4916 OVERTON PLZ 76109 #048-12-2002 L2006 **AN** *100

LEMONS, Steve Lee. 801 7TH AVE 76104 #039-01-1984 L1987 **PD** *020 †55

LENAMOND, Carrie Cherie. 6451 BRENTWOOD STAIR RD 76112 #048-12-2002 L2007 **EM** *020 †16

LESTER, Lynn Andrea. 833 TOWNE CT 76179 #035-08-1991 L1995 **IM** *020 †20

LEVY, Marlon F. 1400 8TH AVE, BLDG C 76104 #048-12-1985 L1986 **GS TTS** *020 †85

LEVY, Victor Y. 801 7TH AVE, COOK CHILDREN'S MEDICAL CE 76104 #027-01-1998 L2006 **NPM** *100 †55

LEWIS, Adolphus Ray. 4732 E LANCASTER AVE 76103 #048-78-1986, ▲ L1987 **FPG** *030

LIAO, Frank K. 6401 HARRIS PKWY 76132 #048-13-1996 L2002 **CD** *020 †85

LIAO, Lianxi Frank. 6401 HARRIS PKWY, STE 130 76132 #243-32-1989 L2002 **CD** *020 †20

LICHTMAN, David Michael. 1500 S MAIN ST, JOHN PETER SMITH HOSPITAL 76104 #035-08-1966 L1994 **ORS HS** *040 †40

LIEVANO, Gonzalo. 1500 S MAIN ST, STE 303 76104 #264-04-1988 L2002 **U** *020 †95

LILLI, Robert Harry. 6100 HARRIS PKWY 76132 #041-09-1982 L1988 **FM** *020 †18

LIN, Jeffrey Chaipui. 4300 RIDGEHAVEN RD 76116 #048-04-1992 L2000 **TS VS** *020 †85,90

LINDENMAYER, Brian Joseph. 1500 S MAIN ST, JPS HEALTH NETWORK 76104 #021-06-2006 L2008 **FP** *012

LINDER, Susan Kay. 2800 S HULEN ST, STE 203 76109 #048-12-1989 L1991 **PM PMM** *020 †60 ‡

LINDGREN, Matthew Jon. 1500 S MAIN ST 76104 #048-15-2003 L2005 **FM** *100 †18

LINDSAY, Robert A. 900 8TH AVE 76104 #048-14-1983 L1983 **AN** *030 †05

LINSKY, Richard Aaron. ■ 76132 #048-12-1999 L2001 **EM** *020 †16

LIPSCOMB, Thomas Stanley. 1400 COOPER ST 76104 #048-12-1964 L1964 **PDR DR** *020 †80

LIU, Jiangping. 1307 8TH AVE, STE 610 76104 #243-76-1983 L2002 **N** *020 †75

LIVINGSTON, Thomas S. 7100 OAKMONT BLVD 76132 #048-02-1982 L1983 **VIR** *020 †80

LIVINGSTONE, Keith S. 6601 DAN DANCIGER RD, STE 200 76133 #048-13-1983 L1983 **FM** *020 †18

LLOYD, Scott D. 1301 PENNSYLVANIA AVE, HOSPITAL MEDICINE ASSOCIAT 76104 #048-13-2000 L2003 **IM** *020 †20

LOBO, Charmaine R. ■ 76185 #048-04-1997 L2000 **FM** *020 †18

LOBO, Stephen Melvyn. 816 W CANNON ST, RADIOLOGY ASSOC OF TARRANT 76104 #024-01-2001 L2007 **AR** *100 †80

LOBSTEIN, Henry Philen. 1017 12TH AVE 76104 #048-04-1966 L1966 **CD OS** *020 †20

LO COCO, Salvatore John. 855 MONTGOMERY ST, OB/GYN DEPARTMENT 76107 #048-15-1988 L1989 **OBG** *020 †30

LODES, Kirk Jeremy. 4916 OVERTON PLZ 76109 #039-01-2001 L2005 **AN** *100 †05

LOFTIS, Jordan Lee. ■ 76132 #048-12-2005 **FP** *012

LOHLA, Evelyn Reyes. 1500 S MAIN ST, DEPT OF PEDIATRICS 76104 #748-10-1974 L1985 **NPM** *020 †55

LOIS, Manuel Rodriguez. 1500 S MAIN ST, DEPARTMENT OF MEDICINE 76104 #649-01-1985 L2003 **IM** *020 †20

LORIMER, Douglas David. 1000 9TH AVE 76104 #048-02-1976 L1976 **GS OS** *020 †85

LORIMER, Wishard S, Jr. 1600 TEXAS ST, HEALTH CARE CENTER 76102 #016-06-1944 **GS** *071 †85

LORIMER, Wishard Speer. 1400 8TH AVE 76104 #048-02-1974 L1974 **FM** *020

LOSS, Scott D. 1500 S MAIN ST, NORTH TX AFFILIATED MED GR 76104 #048-14-1987 L1988 **IM** *020 †20

LOUIS, James Eldon. 1050 5TH AVE, STE K 76104 #048-02-1964 L1964 **PD** *071 †55

LOVETT, Robert James. 6100 HARRIS PKWY 76132 #048-02-1972 L1972 **GS GP** *020 †85

LOWRY, William B. 3800 HULEN ST, STE 100 76107 #048-02-1982 L1983 **DR RNR** *020 †80

LUBRANO, Philip J. 1001 12TH AVE 76104 #048-13-1987 L1988 **AN** *020 †05

LUCENA, Jose. 1500 S MAIN ST, DEPT OF PEDS 76104 #748-02-1982 L1996 **PD NPM** *020 †55

LUGO, Teresa Del Carmen. 300 W ROSEDALE ST 76104 #042-02-1994 L2001 **IM** *020 †20

LUNA, Lydia Anita. 1307 8TH AVE STE 602 76104 #048-12-1980 L1982 **OBG** *020

LUNOW, David Ray. 1500 S MAIN ST 76104 #422-01-2002 L2006 **FM** *100 †18

LUTON, Thomas William. ■ 76109 #048-14-2003 L2004 **EM** *020

LYNCH, Fran Abraham. 1301 PENNSYLVANIA AVE 76104 #012-05-1999 L2002 **NPM** *020 †55

MABERRY, James Douglas. 1200 W ROSEDALE ST 76104 #048-12-1960 L1960 **D** *020 †15

MABERRY, Stephen D. 1200 W ROSEDALE ST 76104 #048-12-1992 L1993 **D DS** *020 †15

MACDONALD, Chas Henry N. 1701 RIVER RUN, STE 200 76107 #065-09-1958 L1977 **AN** *071

MACHI, Anthony Thomas. ■ 76109 #056-05-2007 *012

MACHI, Anthony Thos. 3131 SANGUINET ST, LENA POPE HOME, INC 76107 #056-06-1974 L2005 **P CHP** *020 †75

MACHOS, Robert J, Jr. 800 5TH AVE STE 300, MEDICAL CLINIC OF NORTH TE 76104 #048-12-1982 L1983 **IM** *020 †20

MACIAS, Carlos L. 4300 RIDGEHAVEN RD 76116 #048-14-1991 L1992 **TS** *020 †85,90

MACKEY, Steven James. 1651 W ROSEDALE ST, STE 100 76104 #017-20-1971 L1974 **ORS** *071 †40

MAEWAL, Hrishi Kesh. ■ 76123 #495-05-1964 L1976 **CD IM** *020

MAEWAL, Param. ■ 76134 #048-12-2002 L2005 **IM** *020 †20

MAIR, Kenneth A. 1325 PENNSYLVANIA AVE, STE 560 76104 #048-04-1991 L1992 **END** *020 †20

MALIK, Amir Zulfikar. 1017 12TH AVE 76104 #704-22-1984 L1998 **CD** *020 †20

MALIK, Muhammad Aslam. 855 MONTGOMERY ST 76107 #704-04-1963 L1974 **GS FM** *040

MALIK, Rabia Adeeb. 855 MONTGOMERY ST 2ND, JPS FAMILY MEDICINE DEPART 76107 #704-26-1999 L2007 **FM** *020 †18

MALIK, Sajeela. 1301 PENNSYLVANIA AVE 76104 #704-20-1989 L2000 **IM** *020 †20

MALIK, Saleem Iqbal. 901 7TH AVE STE 120, COOK CHILDRENS HOSPITAL 76104 #704-24-1991 L2003 **CHN** *020 †75,55

MALIK, Yasmin Melissa. 1500 S MAIN ST 76104 #704-20-1992 L2001 **IM** *020 †20

MALLETTE, Carol E. 1201 SUMMIT AVE, GASTRO ASSOC OF NORTH TEXA 76102 #048-16-2000 L2006 **GE** *020 †20

MALONE, James Donald. 1400 8TH AVE 76104 #021-01-1948 L1949 **P** *071 †75

MALTHESEN, Nolan S. 1500 S MAIN ST, JOHN PETER SMITH HOSPITAL 76104 #019-02-2006 **ORS** *012

MANDAL, Kathryn Koheli. 1301 PENNSYLVANIA AVE, TEXAS NEWBORN SERVICES 76104 #048-13-1999 L2006 **PD** *020 †55

MANDEL, Corey Seth. 901 7TH AVE STE 310 76104 #550-03-1997 L2003 **PDC** *020 †55 ‡

MANDELL, Susan Cohen. 1300 W LANCASTER AVE STE 1 76102 #048-14-1992 L1994 **PD** *020 †55

MANJUNATH, Prema. 1522 COOPER ST 76104 #495-33-1975 L1988 **CHP P** *020 †75

MANMADH-KUMAR, Puskoor. 2707 AIRPORT FWY, STE 203 76111 #495-57-1980 L1988 **P** *020

MANOV, Andrey Emanuilov. 1500 S MAIN ST, DEPT OF MEDICINE 76104 #198-01-1984 L1997 **IM** *020 †20

MANRIQUE, Julie Christine. ■ 76109 #048-02-2007 **TY** *012

MARCEL, Randy Jos. 4916 OVERTON PLZ 76109 #012-22-1991 L1992 **AN** *020 †05

MARCELLA, Joseph John. 1050 5TH AVE, SUTIE E 76104 #028-02-1977 L1983 **CD IM** *020 †20

MARCINCUK, Michelle C. 1500 S MAIN ST STE 3 76104 #035-01-1997 L1998 **OTO** *020 †45 ‡

MARGO, Theodore E. 1201 SUMMIT AVE, OPTHALMOLOGY ASSOCIATES 76102 #048-02-1989 L1990 **OPH** *020 †35

MARKS, Warren Alan. 901 7TH AVE, STE 120 76104 #048-15-1983 L1983 **CHN** *020 †55,75

MARLOWE, Brannon D. 4916 OVERTON PLZ 76109 #048-14-2002 L2005 **AN** *020 †05

MARRA, Diego E. 4421 OAK PARK LN 76109 #024-01-2001 L2006 D *100 †15
MARROW, William S. 1201 SUMMIT AVE 76102 #048-12-1952 L1952 GP *071
MARSHALL, James Dawson. 801 7TH AVE, COOK CHILDREN'S HOSPITAL 76104 #021-01-1989 L2002 CCP PA *020 †55
MARSHALL, R Larry. 855 MONTGOMERY ST, DIVISION OF RHEUMATOLOGY 4 76104 #047-06-1971 L1972 RHU IM *020 †18,20
MARTI, Alfredo Luis. 800 12TH AVE STE 100, MEDICAL CENTRE PAIN MANAGE 76104 #011-02-1982 L1992 AN *020 †05
MARTIN, Adriane K. 4625 BOAT CLUB RD 76135 #048-78-1999, ▲ L2001 *020
MARTIN, Justin L. 1300 W TERRELL AVE, STE 500 76104 #048-02-1998 L2001 IC *020 †20
MARTIN, Kristin K. ■ 76123 #039-79-2007, ▲ GS *012
MARTIN, Nelson W. 801 7TH AVE, ATTN: ANESTHESIOLOGY DEPT 76104 #048-12-1994 L1996 PAN *020 †05
MARTIN, Randall P. 4916 OVERTON PLZ 76109 #048-78-1982, ▲ L1983 AN *020
MARTIN, Steven Norman. 6201 SOUTH FWY, ALCON LABS HEALTH SERVICES 76134 #048-02-1973 L1973 EM OM *020 †16
MARTINEZ, Luis H. 1325 PENNSYLVANIA AVE, STE 325 76104 #048-12-1985 L1986 CCM IM *020 †20
MARVELLI, Thomas Lionel. 6273 GRANBURY RD 76133 #016-43-1978 L1985 OPH PO *020 †35
MASSEY, Michael Dennis. 5801 OAKBEND TRL, STE 200 76132 #040-02-1993 L1999 IM *020 †20
MASSINGILL, G Sealy. 1325 PENNSYLVANIA AVE, STE 450 76104 #048-14-1985 L1986 OBG *030 †30 ‡
MATHESON, Donald N. 1307 8TH AVE STE 607 76104 #048-02-1958 L1962 OTO *020 †45
MATHEWS, Reena Rachel. 1500 S MAIN ST, DEPT OF FAMILY MEDICINE 76104 #654-01-2004 FP *012
MATHIS, Nancy Jane Capps. 757 8TH AVE, STE B 76104 #048-12-1975 L1976 GP OS *020
MATOS, Willie R. ■ 76131 #042-01-1975 L1977 GP *020
MATTEI, Amity Smith. 1500 S MAIN ST, DEPT OF FAMILY MEDICINE 76104 #021-06-2002 L2004 FPG *020 †18
MATTHEWS, Jacquin Prewitt. 851 W TERRELL AVE 76104 #048-12-1989 L1993 OBG *020 †30
MAUK, Joyce Elizabeth. 1300 W LANCASTER AVE, CHILD STUDY CENTER 76102 #035-45-1982 L1998 PD DS *030 †55
MAUK, Richard Harold. 950 W MAGNOLIA AVE 76104 #038-40-1972 L1974 NEP IM *020 †20
MAUPIN, Doran Davis. ■ 76116 #048-02-1957 L1957 AN *071 †05
MAXWELL, Wm Worth, Jr. 1250 8TH AVE 76104 #048-04-1981 L1981 OBG *020 †30
MAXWELL HEES, Catherine J. 1250 8TH AVE, STE 435 76104 #048-02-1979 L1979 OBG *020 †30
MAY-MALONE, Lori Jan. 3800 HULEN ST, STE 100 76107 #048-12-2000 L2003 DR *020 †80 ‡
MAZADE, Marc A. 801 7TH AVE, PEDIA INFECTIOUS DISEASE D 76104 #048-02-1994 L2000 PDI *020 †55
MC ADAMS, Charles G. 4916 OVERTON PLZ 76109 #048-12-1986 L1987 AN *020 †05
MC ALPINE, David Bruce. 7100 OAKMORR BLVD, STE 102 76132 #836-01-1973 L1982 OBG *020
MC AULEY, Michael F, Jr. 3800 HULEN ST 76107 #048-12-1994 L1995 DR *020 †80
MC BRIDE, Kenneth W. 1300 W TERRELL AVE, STE 50 76104 #048-12-1984 L1985 CD ICE *020 †20
MC CALL, Norman Joel. 4060 SANDSHELL DR 76137 #048-02-1976 L1976 AM OM *020
MC CALL, Tyrone Lee. 800 5TH AVE, CORNEA ASSOCIATES OF 76104 #039-01-1996 L1997 OPH *020 †35
MC CALL, Victor Eugene. 800 5TH AVE STE 620 76104 #019-02-1961 L1966 R *071 †80
MC CALLUM, Jack Edward. 800 8TH AVE STE 2, SW NEUROLOGICAL SURGERY AS 76104 #012-05-1970 L1977 NS IM *020 †25
MC CARTHY, Terence J. 6451 BRENTWOOD STAIR RD, ROAD 200 76112 #048-02-1993 L1994 IM *020 †20
MC CARTY, James Richmond. 4305 S HULEN ST 76109 #048-04-1974 L1974 D DS *020 †15
MC DONALD, Cheryl K. 1125 COLLEGE AVE 76104 #048-12-1987 L1988 PUD PCC *020 †20
MC DONALD, Stuart D. 1521 COOPER ST 76104 #048-12-1987 L1988 PUD PCC *020 †20
MC DOUGALL, Peter Gordon. 6100 HARRIS PKWY STE 100 76132 #065-10-1975 L1977 GP *020
MC DOWELL, Albert Glenn. 1550 W MAGNOLIA AVE 76104 #048-02-1959 L1959 GP PS *020
MC GEHEE, Frank T, Jr. 1129 6TH AVE 76104 #012-05-1977 L1979 PD NPM *020 †55
MC GEHEE, Robert Neal. 1301 PENNSYLVANIA AVE 76104 #048-02-1966 L1966 TS GS *020 †85,90
MC GLOTHLIN, Jeffery C. 901 7TH AVE STE 120 76104 #048-12-1987 L1989 CHN PD *020 †55,75
MC GOWEN, Jeffrey Lee. 750 8TH AVE, STE 400 76104 #017-20-1999 L2004 ORS *020
MC GREGOR, Tamara Lynne. 1500 S MAIN ST, DEPT FP 76104 #048-12-1991 L1992 FM *020 †18
MCGUIRK, Megan G. 1325 PENNSYLVANIA AVE, PEDIATRIX MEDICAL GROUP OF 76104 #048-14-2002 L2007 NPM *012 †55
MC ILHERAN, George C, Jr. 1111 B 5TH AVE 76104 #048-12-1961 L1962 IM *071 †20
MC KELVEY, Robin Lee. ■ 76102 #038-45-2003 L2007 ID *100 †20
MC KENZIE, Randell Lynn. ■ 76109 #048-04-1976 L1976 DR IM *075 †20,80
MC LAUGHLIN, Emily B. 1200 W MAGNOLIA AVE, STE 110 76104 #047-20-1995 L2003 PS *020 †85,65
MC NAMARA, Brian Thompson. 1300 W ROSEDALE ST 76104 #064-01-1986 L1993 CD IM *020 †20
MC NEELY, Cynthia R. 6825 GREEN OAKS RD, HEALTHFIRST MEDICAL GROUP 76116 #048-14-1987 L1988 FM *020 †18
MC NEFF, John Elwood. 2919 MARKUM DR 76117 #048-12-1969 L1969 FM *071 †18
MC NEIL, Susan Elizabeth. 3100 BELLAIRE RANCH DR # 3 76109 #030-05-1988 L1997 FM *020 †18
MC REYNOLDS, David Bruce. 1500 S MAIN ST, STE 303OPC 76104 #007-02-1974 L1976 GS *020 †85
MC WHERTER, Jos Francis. 709 W LEUDA ST 76104 #048-12-1977 L1977 OBG *020 †30
MC WILLIAMS, Benj Aude. 1400 8TH AVE 76104 #048-02-1974 L1974 OBG *020 †30
MEGHANI, Karim M. 6701 OAKMONT BLVD 76132 #704-25-1988 L1992 PM *020 †60
MEHROTRA, Vinit. 1650 W ROSEDALE ST, STE 301 76104 #495-67-1997 L2006 CN *020
MEHTA, Shivang Ssarvottam. ■ 76123 #048-15-2008 *012
MEIDELL, Robert Steven. 1300 W TERRELL AVE, STE 50 76104 #025-01-1979 L1984 CD *020 †20
MENCHACA, John Albert. 6421 MCCART AVE 76133 #048-02-1967 L1967 PD PN *020 †55
MENDELSON, David James. 1500 S MAIN ST 76104 #040-02-1990 L1997 EM *020 †16
MENZIES, Robert D. 1500 S MAIN ST, JOHN PETER SMITH HOSPITAL 76104 #048-14-2003 L2006 FSM *020 †18

MERCER, Bradley S. 3200 RIVERFRONT DR, STE 103 76107 #048-14-1992 L1993 PD *020 †55
MERRILL, Berkeley Spiller. 5701 BRYANT IRVIN RD, STE 103 76132 #048-13-1973 L1973 OBG FM *020 †30
MERRILL, Nancy Bradley. ■ 76132 #021-05-1981 L1993 GP *020
MESSER, Larry Durward. 901 7TH AVE, STE 110 76104 #048-02-1972 L1972 ORS *020 †40
MESSING, Mark J. 1001 12TH AVE, STE 200 76104 #012-05-1984 L1990 GO GYN *020 †30
MEWIS, Beth Anne. 6100 HARRIS PKWY ST 345 76132 #056-06-1989 L1997 IM *020 †20
MEYERS, Steven Jay. 1651 W ROSEDALE ST STE 200 76104 #048-14-1996 L1999 FSM *020 †18
MIAN, Muhammad. 855 MONTGOMERY ST 76107 #704-04-1984 L2004 PYG *020
MICHELSEN, Luis Guillermo. 4916 OVERTON PLZ 76109 #264-10-1982 L2001 AN CD *020 †05
MIDDLEBROOK, Francis M. 76114 #048-02-1942 L1942 GP *075
MIDDLETON, Peter Alan. ■ 76162 #047-20-2004 FM *100
MIJARES, Carlos Javier. 1001 12TH AVE, STE 160 76104 #649-33-1980 L1989 IM *020
MILAM, Mary. 1307 8TH AVE, # 205 76104 #048-12-1975 L1975 ON HEM *020 †20
MILES, Charles Irby. ■ 76109 #048-02-1960 L1960 GP *020
MILES, William Keith. 800 8TH AVE STE 404 76104 #048-12-1965 L1965 OTO FPS *020 †45
MILEY, Robert Wm. ■ 76116 #016-11-1965 L1975 TS VS *071 †85,90
MILLER, Douglas Scott. 1307 8TH AVE, STE 505 76104 #048-02-1981 L1981 D *020 †15
MILLER, James Paul. 1433 W HUMBOLT ST 76104 #048-04-1981 L1981 PDS GS *020 †85
MILLER, Robert T. 2705 MUSEUM WAY 76107 #004-01-1955 L1962 ORS *071 †40
MILLION, Clark Bradley. 4916 OVERTON PLZ 76109 #039-01-1987 L1991 AN *020 †05
MILNE, Joseph C. 1651 W ROSEDALE ST, STE 200 76104 #048-04-1987 L1992 ORS OSM *020 †40
MIMS, Eric Blackistone. ■ 76104 #039-01-1990 L1992 IM *020 †20
MINTON, Ellis Langan. 1325 PENNSYLVANIA AVE #370 76104 #028-03-1963 L1966 OBG *020 †30
MINTON, Gordon H. 1500 S MAIN ST, DEPT OF ANESTHESIOLOGY 76104 #048-15-1989 L1990 AN *020 †20
MIRZA, Ambir Rauf. 1301 PENNSYLVANIA AVE, HOSPITALIST MEDICAL ASSOC 76104 #704-01-1997 L2003 IM *100
MITCHELL, Kent Landon. ■ 76107 #048-14-2003 L2005 PMM FSM *020 †18
MITCHELL, William Horace. 1651 W ROSEDALE ST, STE 200 76104 #048-12-1963 L1963 ORS *020 †40
MOELLENHOFF, Paul Coyle. ■ 76116 #028-03-1962 L1964 R *071 †80
MOGONYE, Jason Alan. 76108 #048-15-2006 L2007 FP *012
MOHAMMADI, Mehnaz Roshani. 1301 PENNSYLVANIA AVE, HOSPITAL MEDICINE ASSOCIAT 76104 #704-19-1994 L2004 IM *020
MOLENICH, Shirley Ann. 1650 W ROSEDALE ST, STE 301 76104 #003-01-1972 L1974 N *020 †75
MOLSON, Alan Howard. 1717 S MAIN ST 76110 #561-01-1972 L1984 OBG *020
MONTGOMERY, Randy Joe. 1350 S MAIN ST STE 2425 76104 #048-02-1985 L1986 OPH *020 †35
MOORE, Frank H. 1300 W TERRELL AVE STE 405 76104 #048-13-1991 L1992 U *020 †95
MOORE, Roger Wayne. 1301 PENNSYLVANIA AVE 76104 #048-04-1958 L1958 FM AM *030 †18
MORA, Venkata R. 300 W ROSEDALE ST, VETERANS ADMIN OUTPATIENT 76104 #495-70-1994 L2003 FM *020 †18 ‡
MORALES, Adrian Scott. 4916 OVERTON PLZ 76109 #048-12-2000 L2005 AN *020 †05 ‡
MORELAND, David Justin. 855 MONTGOMERY ST 76107 #021-05-1986 L1990 OBG *020 †30 ‡
MORENO, Sandra Gonzalez. 3301 STALCUP RD 76119 #048-13-2001 L2004 FM *020 †18
MOROHUNFOLA, Adunni Modup. 6138 WALRAVEN CIR STE B, TOTS & TYKES PEDIATRICS 76133 #690-07-1994 L2003 PD *020 †55
MORRIS, Laura Furniss. 3601 HULEN ST STE 1 76107 #048-14-1989 L1990 D *020 †15
MORRISSETTE, Dorris. 6100 HARRIS PKWY STE 100 76132 #047-07-1984 L1987 IM *020
MORROW, Julee Stokes. 6401 HARRIS PKWY STE 100 76132 #048-12-1984 L1987 PD *020 †55
MORTON, Dan Alan. 900 W MAGNOLIA AVE STE 100, NORTH TEXAS 76104 #048-12-1978 L1984 IM *020
MOSER, James Robt. 1555 MERRIMAC CIR 76107 #048-02-1970 L1970 P IM *020 †20
MOSES, Susan Margueritte. ■ 76107 #012-01-1976 L1977 AN *020
MOTLEY, Jennifer Lee. 5801 OAKBEND TRL STE 18 76132 #024-05-1999 L2003 OBG *020
MOTT, Lorren C. 1017 12TH AVE 76104 #048-02-1992 L1994 CD *020 †20
MUDALIAR, Chandramohan G. 1220 5TH AVE 76104 #495-16-1971 L1978 IM *020 †20
MUDDASANI, Pavani. 855 MONTGOMERY ST, 4TH FL 76104 #495-57-1991 L2006 GE *020 †20
MUELLER, Herbert Clem. 1200 WOODHAVEN BLVD 76112 #048-15-1977 L1979 IM *020
MUGHAL, Mohammad Iqbal. 951 W MAGNOLIA AVE 76104 #704-04-1970 L1977 IM *020 †20
MUJEEB, Amir. 1301 PENNSYLVANIA AVE 76104 #704-08-1991 L2006 IM *020 †20
MUMMERT, Diana Ioana. 1500 S MAIN ST, JOHN PETER SMITH HOSPITAL 76104 #781-04-1991 L2008 P *012
MUNDLURU, Giridhar. 800 8TH AVE STE 406 76104 #495-70-1981 L1988 IM CD *020 †20
MURCHISON, Lesley Caron. 3200 RIVERFRONT DR, STE 103 76107 #048-02-1985 L1986 PD *020 †55
MURPHEY, Donald K. 801 7TH AVE, INFECTIOUS DISEASES 76104 #048-13-1986 L1989 PDI PD *020 †55
MURPHY, James A, Jr. 900 W MAGNOLIA AVE, STE 201 76104 #048-14-1976 L1976 FM *020 †18
MURPHY, James Nolan, III. 1533 MERRIMAC CIR, STE 100 76107 #048-12-1966 L1966 PD *020 †55
MURPHY, Thomas Mead. 1522 COOPER ST 76104 #039-01-1968 L1991 CHP P *020 †75
MURRAY, Jeffrey C. 901 7TH AVE, STE 220 76104 #048-04-1988 L1989 PHO *020 †55
MURRAY, Matthew Michael. 801 7TH AVE 76104 #030-05-1986 L1992 PD PEM *020 †55
MURRAY, Natalie G Brand. 4916 OVERTON PLZ 76109 #495-06-1985 L1991 HEP GE *020 †20
MYDUR, Thippeswamy. 4916 OVERTON PLZ, NORTHSTAR ANESTHESIA P A 76109 #495-72-1982 L2001 AN *020 †05
NAIR, Chandrasekharan K P. 909 9TH AVE, STE 202 76104 #495-63-1971 L1984 CD *020 †20
NAIR, Sreekumaran. 909 9TH AVE, STE 208 76104 #495-63-1971 L1995 N *020 †75
NAMBURU, Venkat E. 7633 BELLAIRE DR S, STE 105 76132 #495-57-1983 L2002 GE IM *020 †20
NAMIREDDY, Vasanth Reddy. 6009 WESTCREEK DR 76133 #495-57-1979 L1991 FM *020 †18
NANA, Arvind Dahyabhai. 855 MONTGOMERY ST 76107 #048-02-1991 L1993 ORS OTR *020 †40
NANDI, Deipanjan. ■ 76116 #036-07-2008 *012
NARAYAN, Kalman. 813 HEMPHILL ST 76104 #495-16-1970 L1976 GE IM *020 †20
NARAYANAN, Radha. 5801 OAKBEND TRL, STE 200 76132 #039-01-1987 L1996 GE *020 †20
NATI, Carol. 1500 S MAIN ST 76104 #039-05-1985 L1987 P CHP *020 †75
NAWROCKI, Joseph Wm. 4500 S RIVERSIDE DR 76119 #026-04-1982 L1994 FM *020 †18

NAZARIAN, Manouchehr. 757 8TH AVE 76104 #517-01-1962 L1972 **TS GS** *020 †85,90
NEALY, Marcus Erskine. 1400 8TH AVE, BAYLOR ALL SAINTS DEPT. OF 76104 #048-12-1994 L1996 **AN** *020 †05
NEDRELOW, Jonathan Henry. 1325 PENNSYLVANIA AVE, AVE, #740 76104 #026-04-1998 L2004 **NPM** *020 †55
NEERUKONDA, Latha S. 601 W TERRELL AVE 76104 #495-50-1992 L2000 **ON** *020 †20
NEGRON, Angel G. 1001 12TH AVE STE 200, TEXAS ONCOLOGY, PA 76104 #042-01-1970 L1975 **ON IM** *020 †20
NELMS, Donald Kenneth. 1500 S MAIN ST 76104 #036-01-1964 L1969 **NPM PD** *020 †55
NELSON, Anna Lynn T. 801 7TH AVE, PICU OFFICE 76104 #048-14-1995 L1998 **PD** *074 †55
NELSON, Edward Reese, Jr. 800 5TH AVE, STE 300 76104 #048-12-1971 L1971 **IM** *020 †20
NELSON, William Brittain. 801 7TH AVE, PICU OFFICE 76104 #048-02-1980 L1980 **CCP PD** *020 †55
NESSLEIN, Lori Lee. 1301 PENNSYLVANIA AVE, DEPARTMENT OF NEONATOLOGY 76104 #028-46-1997 L2006 **NPM** *100 †55
NETHERY, David A. 6551 HARRIS PKWY STE 200 76132 #048-15-1996 L1999 **OPH** *020 †35
NEUMANN, John C. 4916 OVERTON PLZ 76109 #048-14-1987 L1988 **AN** *020 †05
NEVILLE, Heather Leigh. 6100 HARRIS PKWY, STE 140 76132 #048-13-2003 L2006 **OBG** *020
NEVILLE, Richard Burke. ■ 76110 #049-01-1983 L1990 **EM** *020 †16
NGUYEN, Binh D. 1127 OAKLAND BLVD 76103 #048-78-1998, ▲ L2000 **FM** *020
NGUYEN, Hoang Duc. 4916 OVERTON PLZ 76109 #018-03-1992 L1995 **DR** *020 †80
NGUYEN, Peter V. 711 PENNSYLVANIA AVE 76104 #048-14-1999 L2002 **NEP** *020 †20
NGUYEN, Trung Dinh. 5701 BRYANT IRVIN RD, STE 101 76132 #048-15-1992 L1993 **GS** *020
NGUYEN, Tuan Huu. 855 MONTGOMERY ST 76107 #048-02-1997 L1999 **FM** *020 †18
NICKELL, John Ambrose, Jr. 1201 FAIRMOUNT AVE 76104 #048-04-1961 L1961 **PUD CCM** *071 †20
NIELSON, Karen Lanette. 1300 W TERRELL AVE 76104 #048-04-1984 L1990 **RO** *020 †80
NIXON, Charles Thos. 4916 OVERTON PLZ 76109 #048-12-1979 L1979 **AN** *020 †05
NORMAN, Alan A. 1325 PENNSYLVANIA AVE, STE 110 76104 #048-04-1996 L2001 **OPH** *020 †35
NORMAN, James Lee. 1650 W MAGNOLIA AVE, STE 100 76104 #048-02-1971 L1971 **GS** *020 †85
NORVILLE, Scott V. 1500 S MAIN ST, DEPARTMENT OF MEDICINE 76104 #048-13-1993 L1994 **ID** *020 †20
NUGENT, John Lawrence E. 1001 12TH AVE, STE 200 76104 #048-12-1973 L1973 **HO** *020 †20
NWANKWO, Stella. 1500 S MAIN ST, JPS PHYSICIANS GROUP INC 76104 #690-04-1993 L2003 **IM** *020 †20
OBBINK, John Wm, Jr. 6401 HARRIS PKWY, STE 120 76132 #018-03-1990 L1996 **FM** *020 †18
O'CONNOR, Terence Michael. 4916 OVERTON PLZ 76109 #016-02-1975 L1980 **AN OBS** *020 †05
OEI, Kwan Kie. 3110 GREENE AVE 76109 #065-05-1972 L1978 **FM** *020
OGDEN, Steven Boyd. 750 8TH AVE STE 400 76104 #039-01-2002 L2007 **ORS** *020
OGUNMOLA, Nicholas A. 750 8TH AVE STE 200 76104 #690-05-1990 L2003 **PG PD** *020 †55
OHAN, Arthur H. 1132 EVERMAN PKWY 76140 #517-01-1957 L1969 **GS AS** *020
OHRI, Anjali. 1500 S MAIN ST 76104 #665-02-2005 L2007 **FP** *012
OLARTE, Jose L. 801 7TH AVE, CRITICAL CARE MEDICINE 76104 #264-19-1990 L1996 **PD** *020 †55
OLSON, N Kermit. 1500 S MAIN ST 76104 #016-06-1962 L1964 **IM NEP** *071 †20
OLTERMANN, Mark H. 1500 S MAIN ST, INTERNAL MEDICINE DEPARTME 76104 #048-02-1984 L1985 **CCM IM** *020 †20
OLVERA, Rebecca Elisa. 901 7TH AVE STE 220, PEDIATRIC HEMOTOLOGY/ONCOL 76104 #048-02-1997 L1998 **PHO** *020 †55
OOSTEN, Karen June. ■ 76137 #048-02-2007 **IM** *012
OPELLA, Christopher M. ■ 76107 #048-14-1997 L1998 **FM** *020 †18
O'REAR, John Wm. 2300 ROGERS AVE 76109 #047-06-1957 L1965 **OTO** *071 †45
ORTENBERG, Joseph Mark. 1300 W TERRELL AVE, STE 50 76104 #021-01-1993 L1999 **CD** *020 †20
ORTH, John S. ■ 76116 #023-01-1951 L1959 **AN AM** *071 †05
OSAFO-MENSAH, Kwaku A. 800 8TH AVE STE 432 76104 #005-11-1995 L2004 **PCC** *020 †20
OSBORN, James Rennie. 1300 W TERRELL AVE, STE 500 76104 #005-14-1960 L1970 **OS CD** *030 †20
O'SHEA, John Thos. 1000 MONTGOMERY ST 76107 #028-79-1965, ▲ L1972 **PTH HMP** *020
OSHMAN, Daniel Gregory. 801 7TH AVE, COOK CHILDRENS MED CTR 76104 #048-12-1977 L1977 **PDR DR** *020 †80
OSTRANSKY, David. 2801 S HULEN ST 76109 #028-79-1979, ▲ L1985 **PUD IM** *020
OSUNTOKUN, Bankole Olusey. 1433 W HUMBOLT ST, COOK CHILDREN'S MEDICAL CE 76104 #690-01-1985 L2006 **PG** *100 †55
OTERO, Angel L. 800 8TH AVE, STE 528 76104 #042-01-1968 L1975 **ORS** *020 †40
OVERTON, Marvin C, III. 6100 HARRIS PKWY 76132 #048-02-1961 L1967 **NS** *071
OWEN, Glenn P. 6451 BRENTWOOD DR 76112 #048-13-1987 L1990 **EM** *020 †18
OZAETA, Marcus S. 6210 JOHN RYAN DR 76132 #048-14-1996 L1999 **PD** *020 †55
PACE, Eugene Hillary. 1500 S MAIN ST 76104 #048-02-1981 L1982 **PTH** *020 †50
PACE, Thomas Jos. 2500 LOU MENK DR, BNSF 76131 #035-06-1989 L2004 **GPM** *030 †70
PACKWOOD, Eric Alan. 1325 PENNSYLVANIA AVE, STE 110 76104 #048-04-1995 L2000 **OPH PO** *020 †35
PAEK, Donald Robt. 5701 BRYANT IRVIN RD, STE 102 76132 #001-02-1973 L1983 **D** *020 †15
PAIK, Elaine. 1500 S MAIN ST, JOHN PETER SMITH HOSPITAL 76104 #422-01-2002 L2005 **FPG** *100 †18
PAILES, Nathan Allen. 4916 OVERTON PLZ, EXCEL ANESTHESIA, PA 76109 #039-01-1999 L2004 **AN** *020 †05
PALMAROZZI, Elizabeth Ann. 855 MONTGOMERY ST 76107 #048-78-1984, ▲ L1989 *020
PALMER, J Mark. 800 8TH AVE STE 426 76104 #048-04-1982 L1983 **OTO HNS** *020 †45
PARIKH, Maulik Paresh. 4916 OVERTON PLZ, NORTHSTAR ANESTHESIA 76109 #051-04-2002 L2006 **AN** *020 †05
PARKER, James F. 6100 HARRIS PKWY, STE 355 76132 #048-02-1982 L1985 **IM** *020 †20
PARKER, Leighton B, Jr. 1300 S UNIVERSITY DR, STE 511 76107 #035-20-1969 L1979 **NS** *020 †25
PARRA, Beatriz Alicia. 3000 J ST, FED MED CTR 76129 #935-02-1973 L1993 **IM** *020 †20
PARVEY, Harry Richard. 1500 S MAIN ST, DEPT OF RADIOLOGY 76104 #056-06-1977 L1979 **DR OS** *040 †80
PASCOE, Henry Richard. 5801 CURZON AVE, STE 1E 76107 #016-06-1962 L1965 **PTH** *020 †50
PATE, William Bart. 1500 S MAIN ST, 4TH FL 76104 #048-02-1968 L1968 **OBG** *020 †18
PATEL, Deepa Ramesh. ■ 76116 #048-04-2006 **FP** *012
PATEL, Imran. ■ 76132 #704-02-1989 L2005 **END** *020 †20
PATEL, Lincoln Rameshbhai. 7100 OAKMONT BLVD 76132 #038-43-1997 L2000 **VIR** *020 †80
PATEL, Nadeem. 1500 S MAIN ST, JPS PHYSICIANS GROUP, INC 76104 #704-02-1988 L1996 **IM** *020 †20
PATEL, Naresh H. 800 8TH AVE, STE 632 76104 #495-23-1982 L1994 **CD NM** *020 †20,28
PATEL, Parul Vinodkumar. 801 7TH AVE, COOK CHILDRENS PHYSICIAN N 76104 #048-13-2003 L2006 **PD** *020
PATEL, Premal P. 600 COMMERCE ST 76102 #048-13-2002 L2004 **FM** *100 †18
PATEL, Rahul Keshav. 855 MONTGOMERY ST 76107 #048-04-1998 L1999 **RHU IM** *020 †20
PATEL, Sonal R. 1500 S MAIN ST, JOHN PETER SMITH HOSPITAL 76104 #039-01-2003 L2005 **FM** *100 †18
PATRAS, Dorothy. 1425 PENNSYLVANIA AVE, FORT WORTH PATHOLOGY LAB 76104 #048-12-1956 L1956 **PTH OS** *071 †50
PATTON, Robyn Kramer. ■ 76108 #021-01-1996 L2007 **FM** *020 †18
PATTON, Steven. 4916 OVERTON PLZ 76109 #048-02-1990 L1991 **AN** *020 †05
PEARCE, Kenneth Blake. 6300 RIDGLEA PL, STE 100 76116 #021-01-1962 L1965 **AN OS** *020 †05
PEARSON, Todd Duncan. 801 7TH AVE, PEDIATRIC PALLIATIVE CARE 76104 #040-02-1980 L2007 **PD** *020 †55
PEDRO, Steven Douglas. 7833 OAKMONT BLVD 76132 #048-02-1970 L1970 **D GP** *020 †15 ‡
PEERWANI, Nizam. 200 FELIKS GWOZDZ PL 76104 #605-01-1976 L1977 **FOP** *020 †50
PEERWANI, Ziad. ■ 76120 #048-02-2005 L2005 **PTH** *012
PENA, Deogracias Rodolfo. 901 7TH AVE STE 410, COOK CHILDRENS SPECIALTY 76104 #748-02-1982 L1996 **PN PD** *020 †55
PENA B, Heriberto A. 3301 N MAIN ST 76106 #048-12-1958 L1958 **GP** *020
PENDER, John Teal. 1201 FAIRMOUNT AVE 76104 #048-12-1974 L1974 **PUD CCM** *020 †20
PENNY, Richard Edward. 6100 HARRIS PKWY, STE 345 76132 #048-02-1972 L1972 **IM** *020 †20
PENTECOST, Donald Eugene. 900 8TH AVE 76104 #048-12-1961 L1961 **OM GS** *020 †18
PEREZ, Gloria L. ■ 76111 #748-01-1961 L1982 **CD IM** *071 †20
PEREZ, Staci Dee. ■ 76102 #048-14-2008 *012
PERILMAN, Steven Kyle. 801 7TH AVE 76104 #048-12-1992 L1993 **PEM** *020 †55
PERKINS, Claude C. 1500 S MAIN ST 76104 #048-04-1997 L2001 **OBG** *020
PERRYMAN, William M. 11803 S FREEWAY 76115 #005-12-1974 L1976 **OBG** *020 †30
PESCHEL, Margie M Barnes. 1263 W ROSEDALE ST 76104 #048-12-1959 L1959 **BBK** *071 †50
PETERS, Justus Turner. ■ 76108 #030-06-2005 **FP** *012
PETTA, Lawrence Craig. 1400 8TH AVE 76104 #048-02-1969 L1969 **CRS GS** *071 †10,85
PETTEY, Thomas David. 6850 MANHATTAN BLVD, STE 410 76120 #027-01-1979 L1985 **OP** *075
PETTEY, William R. 6100 HARRIS PKWY, STE 390 76132 #048-12-1984 L1985 **GS** *020 †85
PFAFF, John K. 901 7TH AVE, STE 420 76104 #048-02-1984 L1985 **PDP** *020 †55
PHAM, Chinh Quoc. 1500 S MAIN ST 76104 #305-01-2003 **FM** *100
PHAM, Linda H. 1500 S MAIN ST, DEPT FM 76104 #048-14-2007 **FP** *012
PHAN, Huong Thien. 1500 S MAIN ST, JOHN PETER SMITH HOSPITAL 76104 #048-14-2004 L2007 **FM** *020 †18
PHAN, Linda Kay. 801 7TH AVE, COOK CHILDREN'S MEDICAL CE 76104 #048-13-2003 L2006 **PD** *100 †55
PHELPS, David R. 3800 HULEN ST, STE 100 76107 #048-12-1995 L1997 **DR** *020 †80
PHELPS, Stephanie Claire. ■ 76132 #048-12-1995 L1996 **IM** *020 †20
PHILIP, Shailaja M. 801 7TH AVE 76104 #048-04-1999 L2005 **PD** *020 †55
PHILLIPS, Alice Walker. 6210 JOHN RYAN DR, STE 101 76132 #048-04-1993 L1995 **PD** *020 †55
PHILLIPS, Greggory Kevin. 2401 WESTPORT PKWY, STE 140B 76177 #047-06-1988 L1989 **FM** *020 †18
PHILLIPS, Gregory Jos. 1050 5TH AVE, STE J 76104 #048-12-1974 L1979 **IM NTR** *020 †20
PHILLIPS, Michael Stephen. 3509 HULEN ST, STE 110 76107 #048-04-1975 L1975 **GYN GPM** *020
PHUC, Bao Vinh Nguyen. 1413 N BEACH ST, BEACH CLINIC 76111 #048-13-1997 L1999 **FM** *020 †18
PICKELL, Stuart C. 4545 BELLAIRE DR S, STE 9 76109 #048-12-1996 L2001 **MPD** *020 †20,55
PICKERING, Richard S. 3800 HULEN ST, STE 100 76107 #035-01-1971 L1977 **VIR R** *020 †80
PICKETT, Creighton A, III. 4916 OVERTON PLZ 76109 #048-15-1998 L1999 **AN** *020 †05
PIMENTEL, Brent Justin. ■ 76116 #048-13-1998 L2000 **FM PHP** *020 †18
PINILLA, Jorge. 1412 S MAIN ST 76104 #264-04-1985 L1996 **PUD** *020 †20
PINTO, Kirk J. 1325 PENNSYLVANIA AVE, STE 550 76104 #048-15-1990 L1991 **UP** *020 †95
PIRINELLI, Jeffrey J. 2630 WEST FWY STE 1, SUMMIT HEALTHCARE MGMT RES 76102 #048-16-1996 L1998 **AN** *020 †05
POCHE, Gerard. 1319 SUMMIT AVE, STE 200 76102 #048-04-1980 L1980 **AN** *020 †05
PODAWILTZ, Alan L. 3500 CAMP BOWIE BLVD, UNTHSC DEPT PSYCHIATRY 76107 #039-79-1995, ▲ L1997 **P** *030 †75
POMPA, Paul H. 2709 CALDER CT 76107 #048-12-1999 L2000 **EM FM** *020 †18
POQUIZ, Norberto Frias. ■ 76179 #748-08-1967 L1979 **AN** *020
POQUIZ, Raymund M. 6235 GRANBURY RD 76133 #048-12-1995 L1997 **PD** *020
PORTER, Alston Michael. 1400 8TH AVE, ALL SAINTS HOSPITAL 76104 #008-01-1980 L1985 **NPM PD** *020 †55
POWDERLY, Mary K. 801 7TH AVE 76104 #048-14-1999 L2002 **PD** *020 †55
POWELL, Karen Marie. ■ 76116 #046-01-1993 L1999 **FOP PTH** *062 †50
PREJEAN, Garrick C. 2400 NW 24TH ST 76106 #021-05-1987 L1989 **P** *072 †75
PRESLEY, Mark Brian. 6100 HARRIS PKWY, STE 320 76132 #048-02-1982 L1983 **ORS** *020 †40
PRESLEY, Norman Lee. ■ 76132 #048-04-1955 L1955 **R** *071 †80
PRESTON, Gregory. 801 7TH AVE, COOK CHILDRENS HLTH PLAN 76104 #025-07-1978 L2002 **CCP PD** *030 †55
PRICE, Earl Provine, Jr. ■ 76109 #048-04-1947 L1947 **FM GP** *071
PRICE, Karen A Bynum. ■ 76109 #048-12-1973 L1975 **P** *075 †75
PRICHARD, Edith V. 909 W MAGNOLIA AVE, STE 6 76104 #231-01-1974 L1992 **PD** *020 †55
PRIETO, Cecilia. 1500 S MAIN ST, DEPT OF PEDIATRICS 76104 #649-33-1979 L1994 **PD** *020 †55
PRITCHETT, S Suzanne Kay. 6100 HARRIS PKWY, STE 200 76132 #048-12-1984 L1986 **OBG** *020 †30
PROKELL, Peter J. 7100 OAKMONT BLVD 76132 #048-12-1997 L1998 **DR** *020 †80
PROSSER, Joseph Stephen. 1325 PENNSYLVANIA AVE, STE 800 76104 #028-34-1976 L2005 **IM CCM** *030 †20
PRUD'HOMME, Eck G, Jr. ■ 76116 #048-02-1952 L1952 **GP** *071
PUELMA, Raul Gaston. 3220 NORTH FWY 76111 #231-03-1955 L1967 **GS** *071 †85
PUGH, Billie Raymond. 6100 HARRIS PKWY STE 12 76132 #048-02-1972 L1972 **CD IM** *020 †20
PUMPHREY, John Andrew. 6100 HARRIS PKWY, STE 110 76132 #048-15-1986 L1987 **U GS** *020 †95
PUMPHREY, John David. 1821 8TH AVE 76110 #048-02-1957 L1957 **U** *071 †95
PURCELL, Norris Duane. 1814 8TH AVE STE B8 76110 #048-02-1966 L1966 **P PYA** *020 †75

■ = Address Information Privacy Protected

PURDY, Aaron G. 1500 S MAIN ST 76104 #048-02-2006 FP *012

PURGASON, James G. 7630 N BEACH ST, STE 140 76137 #048-13-1993 L1994 FM *020 †18

PURVIS, Kenneth Wayne. 6451 BRENTWOOD STAIR RD 76112 #048-02-1978 L1978 FM *020 †18

PUTEGNAT, Barry Burton, III. 816 W CANNON ST, RADIOLOGY ASSOCIATES 76104 #048-02-1996 L1999 PDR *020 †80

QUERALT, John. 815 PENNSYLVANIA AVE 76104 #048-12-1989 L1990 DR *020 †80

QURESHI, Muhammad Afzal. 3403 N BEACH ST, OF MEDICINE 76111 #704-01-1966 L1975 CD IM *020

QURESHI, Nikhat Afzal. 4255 BRYANT IRVIN RD, STE 102 76109 #704-01-1971 L1985 IM *020

QURESHI, Zaki Ahmed. 1500 S MAIN ST, JOHN P SMITH HOSP 76104 #496-22-2004 FM *100

RAGHAVAN, Arun Vijay. 900 8TH AVE, PLAZA MEDICAL CENTER OF FO 76104 #005-15-2002 L2006 EM *020 †16

RAJ, Jhansi M. 1617 W OLEANDER ST, STE A 76104 #495-21-1976 L1985 P ADM *020 †75

RAJAN, Betty J. 3601 HULEN ST STE 100 76107 #048-04-1994 L1996 D *020 †15

RAJU, Kosuri Bangar. 1001 12TH AVE STE 13 76104 #495-58-1973 L1985 IM *020 †20

RANA, Hetal Mahendra. 1500 S MAIN ST, FAMILY PRACTICE RESIDENCY 76104 #048-13-2004 L2005 FM *100 †18

RANA, Shital Manohar. 1500 S MAIN ST, DEPT OF FAMILY PRACTICE 76104 #496-60-2003 FP *012

RANELLE, Ann Elizabeth. 6100 HARRIS PKWY 76132 #028-78-2000, ▲ L2005 FM *020

RANELLE, Harold W. 5000 COLLINWOOD AVE 76107 #028-78-1968, ▲ L1968 OPH *020 †35

RANGINENI, Ramu. ■ 76123 #496-28-1996 L2004 IM *020

RANSOM, Elizabeth R. ■ 76109 #025-07-1989 L2007 OTO *020 †45

RANSOM, Scott. ■ 76109 #028-78-1988, ▲ L1989 OBG MDM *030 †30

RAO, Ashoo. 2528 JACKSBORO HWY 76114 #495-57-1980 L1988 PD *020 †55

RAPP, Thomas Earl. 6100 HARRIS PKWY 76132 #048-02-1965 L1965 ORS *020

RASTOGI, Shashi Prabha. 1550 W ROSEDALE ST STE 204 76104 #495-05-1966 L1990 OBG *020 †30

RATINO, Thomas Michael. 800 5TH AVE STE 410, BEN HOGAN CENTER 76104 #030-06-2002 L2007 APM *020 †05

RAULSTON, O Doak, Jr. 429 S BALLINGER ST 76104 #048-04-1960 L1960 ORS *020 †40

RAY, Julie C. 900 W MAGNOLIA AVE STE 201 76104 #048-02-1999 L2002 FM *020 †18

RAZACK, Abdool. ■ 76132 #064-01-1965 L1977 FM *072

RAZACK, Kerim F. 1521 COOPER ST, TEXAS PULMONARY CONSULTANT 76104 #048-02-1994 L1995 PCC *020 †20

READ, Martin D. 1300 W TERRELL AVE, STE 320 76104 #048-12-1986 L1987 OBG *020 †30

READ, Norman Leslie. 6717 GRAPEVINE HWY 76180 #566-01-1955 L1979 FM *071

READINGER, James Curtis. 6100 HARRIS PKWY, STE 345 76132 #048-13-1974 L1974 IM *020 †20

READINGER, Richard Ivan. 901 7TH AVE STE 310, COOK CHILDREN'S CARDIOLOGY 76104 #048-13-1971 L1971 PDC PD *020 †55

READINGER, Robert M. 1108 S HENDERSON ST 76104 #048-02-1999 L2002 PD *020 †55

REARDON, Ryan Scott. ■ 76123 #025-07-2004 ORS *012

REAVES, Larry Earl. 1400 8TH AVE 76104 #048-12-1978 L1978 PS HS *020 †65,85

REDDIX, Robert Nathaniel, Jr. 1500 S MAIN ST, JOHN PETER SMITH HOSPITAL 76104 #048-04-2001 L2003 ORS *100

REDDY, Gayatri Guduru. ■ 76102 #048-15-2003 L2006 IM *100 †20

REDDY, Guduru Ramana. 1650 W ROSEDALE ST, STE 206 76104 #495-58-1974 L1982 CD IM *020 †55,20

REDDY, Himabindu Bellam. 909 9TH AVE, STE 300 76104 #016-43-2003 L2003 PM *100

REDDY, Rajneesh Dharam. 2919 MARKUM DR 76117 #048-13-2003 L2005 FM *020 †18

REDDY, Sangameshwar Patel. 1500 S MAIN ST, 3RD FLOOR ENDOSCOPY CENTER 76104 #495-65-1988 L2001 GE *020

REDDY, Suchita D. 2919 MARKUM DR 76117 #495-56-1972 L1975 FM *020

REDROW, Mark Wm. 1001 12TH AVE, STE 200 76104 #048-02-1984 L1986 ON HEM *020 †20

REEB, Robert Jos, Jr. 815 PENNSYLVANIA AVE 76104 #048-02-1980 L1980 FM *020 †80

REED, Virginia Elizabeth. 1500 S MAIN ST 76104 #047-20-2002 L2004 FM *100 †18

REESE, William G. 3800 HULEN ST, STE 100 76107 #048-02-1995 L2000 DR *020 †80

REEVES, Ruth. 1500 S MAIN ST, JOHN P SMITH HOSP 76104 #661-02-2006 FP *012

RENAULT, Louis Joseph. 1500 S MAIN ST, STE 303 76104 #067-03-1962 L1977 OTO A *020

RENSHAW, Stephen Vance. 1500 S MAIN ST 76104 #021-01-1991 L1993 EM *020 †16

RETAMOZO, Luis Abel. 855 MONTGOMERY ST 76107 #649-14-1977 L1994 FM *020 †18

REYES, Rebecca Elliott. 1250 8TH AVE, STE 570 76104 #048-13-1990 L1991 OBG *020 †30

REYES-FLORES, Hernan. 3150 HORTON RD, FMC FTW/BOP 76119 #847-05-1977 L1979 IM ADM *020 †20

REYNOLDS, Lynne Marie. 801 7TH AVE, DEPT OF ANESTHESIA 76104 #005-12-1986 L2001 AN *020 †05

REZAIE, Morvarid. 900 8TH AVE 76104 #048-78-2006, ▲ L2008 IM *012

RHODES, Ray Norwood, Jr. 6100 HARRIS PKWY, STE 100 76132 #048-04-1974 L1974 PD *020 †55

RICHARDS, John Andrew. 556 8TH AVE 76104 #048-12-1971 L1971 ORS OSM *020 †40

RICHARDSON, John Marshall. ■ 76109 #048-12-1961 L1961 PD *071

RICHARDSON, Lorinda. 1301 PENNSYLVANIA AVE 76104 #023-01-1981 L1985 FM *020 †18

RICHIE-GILLESPIE, Mayme F. 855 MONTGOMERY ST 76107 #047-05-1986 L1987 OMO *020 †40

RIDLEY, Wade Clark, Jr. 709 W LEUDA ST 76104 #048-02-1986 L2001 OBG *020 †30

RIEHM, Laura Streater. 4200 S HULEN ST, STE 425 76109 #048-04-1992 L1993 AN *020 †05

RIGGS, Patrick Kelly. 5808 FOREST HIGHLANDS DR 76132 #048-14-1985 L1986 OPH *020 †35

RIHN, Jennifer Rachael. 855 MONTGOMERY ST 76107 #045-01-2000 L2002 IM *020

RILEY, David Michael. 1301 PENNSYLVANIA AVE, DEPARTMENT OF NEONATOLOGY 76104 #005-11-1997 L2002 NPM *020 †55

RINDFUSZ, David Wesley. 1500 S MAIN ST, DEPARTMENT OF OB/GYN 76104 #017-20-1976 L2005 OBG MFM *020 †30

RIOS, Matthew Lyle. 1500 S MAIN ST, DEPT. OF FAMILY MEDICINE 76104 #048-14-1997 L1999 FPG *020 †18

RIVERA, Frank James. 815 PENNSYLVANIA AVE 76104 #048-13-1982 L1983 DR GP *020 †80

RIVERS, Megan Nichole. ■ 76109 #048-15-2008 *012

ROBBINS, Randy L. 4916 OVERTON PLZ 76109 #048-15-1999 L2003 AN *100 †05

ROBERTS, Allen Lee. 6451 BRENTWOOD STAIR RD, STE 200 76112 #048-15-1993 L1994 EM *020 †16

ROBERTS, Dwayne Lee. 1201 SUMMIT AVE, OPHTHALMOLOGY ASSOCIATES 76102 #048-02-1996 L2004 OPH *020 †35

ROBERTS, Richard Arthur. 801 7TH AVE STE 120, COOK CHILDREN'S HOSPITAL 76104 #021-06-2000 L2007 NS *100

ROBERTS, Robert Clayton. 7100 OAKMONT BLVD 76132 #048-12-1982 L1987 DR *020 †80

ROBERTS, Rufus Alston, Jr. 1400 8TH AVE 76104 #048-04-1955 L1955 OPH *071 †35

ROBERTSON, Kathleen Mary. 1500 S MAIN ST, DEPARTMENT OF OB/GYN 76104 #026-04-1968 L1985 OBG OS *020 †30

ROBINSON, Irvin. ■ 76109 #051-01-1955 L1959 GE *071

ROBINSON, Kirsten K. 1325 PENNSYLVANIA AVE, PEDIATRIX MEDICAL GROUP 76104 #048-15-2001 L2004 PD *020 †55

ROBINSON, Roger R. 1701 RIVER RUN, STE 700 76107 #048-14-1988 L1989 P CHP *020 †75

ROBINSON, Valerie R. 1300 W LANCASTER AVE 76102 #048-15-1975 L1975 P CHP *020 †75 ‡

ROGERS, Audrey L. 3200 RIVERFRONT DR, FOREST PARK PEDIATRIC CLIN 76107 #048-12-1986 L1987 PD *020 †55

ROGERS, Janet Elaine. 1500 S MAIN ST 76104 #048-13-1994 L1996 EM *020 †16

ROGERS, Jeffrey B. 3200 RIVERFRONT DR, STE 103 76107 #048-12-1986 L1987 PD *020 †55

ROGERS, John Thos, Jr. 3200 RIVERFRONT DR 76107 #048-12-1960 L1960 PD *020 †55

ROGERS, Michael L. 409 REMUDA DR 76108 #007-02-1977 L1981 R *020 †80

ROGERS, Robert Jean. 5929 LOVELL AVE 76107 #048-12-1979 L1979 AI PDA *020 †55,03

ROHM, Fred Werner. 6100 HARRIS PKWY - ER 76132 #048-78-1991, ▲ L1992 EM *020 †18

ROJAS, Scott Edward. 1125 COLLEGE AVE 76104 #048-04-1994 L2002 ID *020 †20

ROSENTHAL, Harry, Jr. 1201 SUMMIT AVE 76102 #048-14-1983 L1983 OPH *020 †35

ROSS, Nealie Edward, Jr. 800 5TH AVE 76104 #048-02-1944 L1944 IM *071

ROSSER, Ethel Merryday. 1500 S MAIN ST, JOHN PETER SMITH HOSP 76104 #025-01-1948 L1949 OS *075

ROTEN, Lisa Michele. 901 7TH AVE 76104 #045-01-1993 L1999 PDC *020 †55

ROTH, Brett Alan. 1500 S MAIN ST 76104 #031-01-1989 L1999 EM OS *020 †16

ROY, Thomas Sherrard, II. 4916 OVERTON PLZ 76109 #064-01-1967 L1980 AN *020 †05

RUDOLPH, Timothy N. 1500 S MAIN ST 76104 #048-14-2005 L2006 FP *012

RUDY, Delbert Conson. 1325 PENNSYLVANIA AVE, STE 560 76104 #034-01-1978 L1986 U *020 †95

RUKAB, Tracy Marie. 6100 HARRIS PKWY, STE 320 76132 #048-14-1996 L2001 ORS OSM *020 †40

RUMALLA, Vishnu Kumar. 800 8TH AVE, STE 240 76104 #011-02-1996 L2004 PS *020 †85,65 ‡

RUSH, Stephen Lynn. 5321 BYERS AVE 76107 #048-02-1986 L1988 GS TRS *020 †85

RUSSELL, Stephen Maurice. 1401 PENNSYLVANIA AVE 76104 #005-02-1970 L1992 CLP PTH *071 †50

RUTLEDGE, Art Henry. 1650 W MAGNOLIA AVE 76104 #039-01-1944 L1947 IM *071

RUTLEDGE, Brian Culwell. 1650 W MAGNOLIA AVE 76104 #048-02-1978 L1978 IM *020

RUTLEDGE, David Michael. 6100 HARRIS PKWY, STE110 76132 #048-12-1994 L1995 GS *020 †85

RUTLEDGE, Peter Lloyd. 1050 5TH AVE, SUITE-A 76104 #048-02-1982 L1983 GS *020 †85

RUTLEDGE, Robb H. 1500 S MAIN ST 76104 #024-01-1949 L1958 GS *071 †85

RUXER, Robert Lloyd, Jr. 1001 12TH AVE, STE 200 76104 #051-04-1978 L1994 ON HEM *020 †20

RYALS, Brian Douglas. 901 7TH AVE, STE 120 76104 #039-01-1985 L1995 CHN PD *020 †75,55

RYAN, Langston Ray. 6100 HARRIS PKWY, STE 140 76132 #048-02-1979 L1979 OBG *020 †30

SADIQ, Syed Asfandyar. 1201 SUMMIT AVE STE 500, NORTH TEXAS 76102 #704-16-1990 L1996 IM *020 †20

SAENZ, Roberto Vela. 1400 8TH AVE 76104 #048-02-1975 L1975 ATP CLP *020 †50

SAIFEE, Nafees Fatima. 700 HEMPHILL ST 76104 #495-65-1969 L1975 FM *020

SAITIS, Juan. 909 W MAGNOLIA AVE, STE 6 76104 #231-01-1974 L1992 IM *020 †20

SALAZAR, Guillermo Jose. 1068 BOYINGTON DR, NAS-JRB 76127 #042-01-1979 L1993 AM OM *030 †70

SALMOND, Ronald. ■ 76107 #048-12-1982 L1983 NEP IM *020

SAMADI, Ramin. 1400 8TH AVE 76104 #517-08-1982 L2001 EM IM *020 †20,16

SAMUEL, Elizabeth. 5801 OAKBEND TRL, STE 200 76132 #495-31-1997 L2004 N *100 †75

SAMUELSON, Todd Erik. 1001 12TH AVE, STE 150 76104 #048-02-1986 L1987 HNS OTO *020 †45

SANCHEZ, Edmund Q. 1400 8TH AVE 76104 #025-07-1994 L2001 GS *020 †85

SANDERS, Joann Marie. 901 7TH AVE STE 220 76104 #028-34-1982 L1989 PHO PD *030 †55

SANDHU, Rajbir Kaur. 855 MONTGOMERY ST 76107 #495-29-1994 L2003 IM *020 †20

SANDSTAD, Julianne Seely. 1401 PENNSYLVANIA AVE, PATH ASSOCS TEXAS 76104 #026-04-1978 L1985 PTH *020 †50

SANKARAPANDIAN, Pankajam. 1001 PENNSYLVANIA AVE 76104 #495-42-1969 L1983 PD FM *020 †55

SARGENT, James Scott. 815 PENNSYLVANIA AVE 76104 #048-02-1973 L1973 DR *020 †80 ‡

SATYANARAYANA, M S. 11803 S FREEWAY 103 76115 #495-09-1970 L1978 PD PDC *020 †55

SCARLETT, Maxwell Curtis. 1700 PACIFIC PL 76112 #010-03-1971 L1976 EM FM *020

SCHAFFER, Richard Carl. 1400 8TH AVE 76104 #019-02-1946 L1957 PTH *071 †50

SCHMID, Wm Arthur, Jr. 1350 S MAIN ST, STE 4150 76104 #027-01-1977 L1981 DR NM *020 †80

SCHMIDT, Maria Elaine. 1420 8TH AVE 76104 #008-01-1983 L2005 DR *020 †80

SCHMIDT, Robert Herman. 750 8TH AVE, STE 400 76104 #051-01-1978 L1987 ORS *020 †40

SCHOOLER, Joe Frank. ■ 76112 #048-02-1955 L1956 PM ORS *072

SCHROEDER, Brian Toby. ■ 76109 #018-03-2002 L2007 FM *020 †18

SCHULTZ, Karen Denise. 901 7TH AVE STE 420, PEDIATRIC PULMONOLOGY 76104 #048-14-1997 L1999 PDP *020 †55

SCHULTZ, Steven M. 815 PENNSYLVANIA AVE 76104 #048-12-1984 L1985 DR *020 †80

SCHUSTER, Dennis Irwin. 747 8TH AVE 76104 #035-06-1973 L1977 PS *020 †65

SCHUSTER, Richard David. 556 8TH AVE 76104 #048-14-1995 L1996 ORS *020 †40

SCHUTTE, Deborah Ann. 901 7TH AVE, STE 310 76104 #030-05-1991 L2002 PDC *020 †55

SCHWARTZ, Burton W. TCU HEALTH CENTER, BOX 297400 76129 #041-02-1967 L1973 PD NPM *020 †55

SCHWARTZ, Judith A Parker. ■ 76116 #041-02-1970 L1973 OS *020

SCOTT, Carolyn Lea. ■ 76109 #048-12-1991 L1992 FM *020 †18

SCOTT, James Alan. 1325 PENNSYLVANIA AVE, STE 290 76104 #005-19-1981 L1986 PM PME *020 †60

SCROGGIE, William Beal. 6100 HARRIS PKWY 76132 #048-12-1964 L1964 PD *020 †55

SEELEY, Michael Paul. 1512 PENNSYLVANIA AVE, HARRIS OCCUPATIONAL HLTH 76104 #019-02-1978 L1979 OM *020 †18 ‡

SEGISMUNDO, Arturo Medina. 1301 PENNSYLVANIA AVE, HARRIS METHODIST HOSPITAL 76104 #748-01-1989 L2007 IM *020 †20

SEHAPAYAK, Georgina K. 1650 W ROSEDALE ST, STE 200 76104 #132-01-1964 L1971 CD IM *020 †20

SEHAPAYAK, Sommai. 1050 W ROSEDALE ST 76104 #891-02-1957 L1974 CRS *020 †10

SELLERS, Kara J. 1400 8TH AVE 76104 #048-13-1989 L1999 IM *020 †20

SELOD, Farooq Ibrahim. 800 8TH AVE 76104 #704-02-1966 L1973 ORS *020 †40

■ = Address Information Privacy Protected

SELOD, Sayeeda Anwar. ■ 76107 #704-02-1967 L1981 **BBK** *100
SENDKER, Jan A. 4916 OVERTON PLZ, PAAMG 76109 #048-16-1998 L2006 **AN** *020 †05
SENEVEY, Steven John. 1533 MERRIMAC CIR, STE 100 76107 #048-12-1965 L1965 **PD** *020 †55
SENTER, Paul Ross. 1325 PENNSYLVANIA AVE, STE 400 76104 #048-13-1982 L1983 **CRS** *020 †10,85
SERRANO, Jose N. ■ 76103 #264-01-1957 L1971 **P CHP** *071
SEWELL, John Holt. 1301 PENNSYLVANIA AVE 76104 #023-07-1948 L1952 **GS** *071 †85
SHABOUT, Nabeel Muhsen. 1325 PENNSYLVANIA AVE, STE 200 76104 #048-12-2000 L2004 **GS** *020 †85
SHAFFER, Howard Leslie. 6100 HARRIS PKWY, STE 350 76132 #048-13-1973 L1973 **OTO** *020 †45
SHAH, Kirit C. 1550 W ROSEDALE ST, STE 306 76104 #495-01-1975 L1998 **N** *020 †75
SHAH, Shehla Rizvi. ■ 76116 #704-06-1991 L2002 **PD** *020
SHAH, Syed N I H. 1017 12TH AVE 76104 #704-01-1985 L2000 **CD ICE** *020 †20
SHANK, Rebecca Sisk. 2945 SAN MARCOS DR 76116 #048-02-1983 L1990 **N** *020 †75
SHARMA, Rohit. ■ 76123 #048-12-2006 L2006 **IM** *012
SHASHIKUMAR, Kavitha. ■ 76132 #495-33-1996 L2002 **ID** *020 †20
SHEINBERG, Philip. 1101 W ROSEDALE ST 76104 #048-04-1953 L1953 **OPH** *071 †35
SHELTON, Joseph Houston. 900 W MAGNOLIA AVE, STE 100 76104 #048-04-2000 L2002 **GE** *020 †20
SHELTON, Mark Mc Gregor. 801 7TH AVE 76104 #048-16-1983 L1983 **PDI PD** *020 †55
SHENG, David Yiwei. 4916 OVERTON PLZ 76109 #243-16-1987 L2002 **AN** *020 †05
SHEPHERD, David L. 5344 QUAIL RUN ST 76107 #028-02-1991 L1997 **GS U** *020 †95
SHEPHERD, Richard Lee. ■ 76109 #017-20-1971 L1983 **VS** *071 †85,90
SHIDE, Kathleen L. 1450 8TH AVE 76104 #048-12-1996 L1997 **RO** *020 †80
SHIELDS, Thomas Lawrence. ■ 76102 #048-04-1940 L1940 **D** *071 †15
SHIN, James Y. 1500 S MAIN ST 76104 #048-13-1989 L1992 **NEP** *020 †20
SHORI, Sandeep K. 950 W MAGNOLIA AVE, NORTH FORT WORTH DIALYSIS 76104 #005-76-1997, ▲ L2001 **NEP** *020
SHROPSHIRE, Cameron E. 4619 CRESTLINE RD 76107 #048-02-1956 L1956 **AN** *020 †30,05
SHYN, Paul Bernard. 1350 S MAIN ST STE 4150, RADIOLOGY ASSO OF TARRANT 76104 #048-02-1985 L1986 **DR ATP** *020 †80
SI, Wei. 1301 PENNSYLVANIA AVE 76104 #243-47-1991 L2005 **SP** *100 †50 ‡
SIDEBOTTOM, Richard Alan. 1301 PENNSYLVANIA AVE 76104 #017-20-1977 L1981 **PD** *020 †55
SILVA, Roberto N. 3301 N MAIN ST 76106 #649-30-1976 L1977 *020
SILVA, Samuel. 4759 SOUTH FWY 76115 #649-02-1954 L1956 **GP OS** *020
SILVAS, Jose Ramon. 855 MONTGOMERY ST 76107 #048-13-1982 L1983 **P** *030 †75
SIMANI, Rose Serop. 855 MONTGOMERY ST STE 616, UNTHEALTH SCI CTR; OB/GYN 76107 #781-03-1989 L2005 **OBG** *020
SIMMONS, Sara Putnam. ■ 76109 #550-02-2005 L2005 **FP** *012
SIMPSON, Chanda Renee. 801 7TH AVE, DEPARTMENT OF NEONATOLOGY 76104 #048-02-1993 L1995 **NPM** *020 †55
SINGH, Indra Veer. 1201 FAIRMOUNT AVE 76104 #495-73-1988 L2004 **CCM** *020 †20
SINGH, Paul Shamsaer. ■ 76132 #048-13-2004 **OBG** *012
SIRIPONGWISHET, Paiboon. ■ 76155 #891-01-1985 L1996 **IM** *100 †20
SISODIYA, Kamlesh J. 1500 S MAIN ST, DEPT OF ANESTHESIOLOGY 76104 #048-13-1991 L1997 **APM** *020 †05
SIU, Benjamin Lawrence. 901 7TH AVE STE 310 76104 #014-01-1992 L2006 **PDC** *020 †55
SIY, Linda Marie. 855 MONTGOMERY ST 76107 #028-46-1990 L1991 **EM FM** *020 †18
SKINNER, Phillip Howard. 7900 VISTA RIDGE DR S 76132 #017-20-1973 L1977 **OPH** *020 †35
SKLAR, John Anthony. 2500 WEST FWY, STE 400 76102 #035-08-1985 L1992 **PM PMM** *020 †60
SLADE, Herbert Bryan. 3909 HULEN ST 76107 #035-15-1980 L1981 **IG PD** *050 †55,03
SLAGLE, Robert H. 4916 OVERTON PLZ 76109 #048-12-1985 L1986 **AN** *020 †05
SLEE, Barbara L. 1500 S MAIN ST, JPS HOSPITAL 76104 #018-03-1976 L1994 **FM** *040 †18
SLOAN, Frank Jay. 712 7TH AVE 76104 #048-12-2000 L2003 **PD** *020 †55
SLOANE, Robt Woodard, Jr. 1301 PENNSYLVANIA AVE 76104 #024-01-1968 L1975 **GS TS** *071 †85,90
SMITH, Clayton N. 6927 RIDGMAR MEADOW RD, STE 107 76116 #048-02-1960 L1960 **NS** *020
SMITH, David Craig. 1325 PENNSYLVANIA AVE 76104 #038-40-1977 L1988 **TRS GS** *020 †85
SMITH, Donald Lee. 855 MONTGOMERY ST 76107 #048-02-1968 L1968 **OBG** *020 †30
SMITH, James A. 1400 S MAIN ST STE 400, MHMR FO TARRANT COUNTY 76104 #048-02-1989 L1991 **P** *020 †75
SMITH, Jesse Ellis. 923 PENNSYLVANIA AVE, STE 100 76104 #048-12-1998 L2000 **FPS OTO** *020 †45
SMITH, John Houston. 300 W ROSEDALE ST, SURGERY CLINIC VA 76104 #048-12-1955 L1955 **GS** *020 †85
SMITH, Judson Paul. 1350 S MAIN ST STE 3100 76104 #048-02-1972 L1972 **OPH** *020 †35
SMITH, Kim Gilbert. 1301 PENNSYLVANIA AVE, DEPT OF NEONATOLOGY 76104 #048-12-1977 L1977 **NPM PD** *020 †55
SMITH, Mark Douglas. 7100 OAKMONT BLVD STE 108 76132 #021-05-1985 L1989 **OBG** *020 †30
SMITH, Robert Norwood, Jr. 11801 S FREEWAY 76115 #005-12-1969 L1978 **OBG** *020 †30
SMITH, Spencer Marion. 3800 HULEN ST, STE 100 76107 #036-07-1990 L1995 **DR** *020 †80
SMITH, Steven L. 1301 PENNSYLVANIA AVE, HOSPITAL MEDICINE ASSOCIAT 76104 #048-15-1989 L1990 **IM** *040 †20
SMITHSON, John Brantley. 1325 PENNSYLVANIA AVE, STE 200 76104 #001-02-1971 L1984 **GS** *020 †85
SMYTHE, Barbara Ann. 724 PENNSYLVANIA AVE 76104 #024-01-1984 L1992 **OPH** *020 †35
SOLANO, Olusegun Adedayo. 2400 NW 24TH ST 76106 #690-02-1980 L1991 **P** *020 †75
SOLOMON, Deepika Reddy. 4916 OVERTON PLZ 76109 #495-50-1995 L2002 **AN** *020 †05
SONG, Cheng C. 1001 12TH AVE, STE 154 76104 #048-02-1986 L1987 **OBG FM** *020 †30
SOPER, Keith Campbell. ■ 76137 #065-01-1949 L1965 **LM** *071 †40
SORGEN, Stephen Dale. 1300 W TERRELL AVE 76104 #021-01-1972 L1977 **RO** *020 †80
SOROKOLIT, Bob. 801 7TH AVE 76104 #065-01-1969 L1977 **PS HS** *020
SOROKOLIT, Walter Theo. 909 9TH AVE, STE 200 76104 #065-01-1959 L1978 **PS HS** *020
SOTMAN, Steven Bennett. 6100 HARRIS PKWY, STE 1210 76132 #021-01-1974 L1979 **ID IM** *020 †20
SOUSA, Monica Irene. 3900 BOAT CLUB RD 76135 #715-01-1982 L1997 **PD** *020 †55
SPEAKER, Jennifer L. 6825 GREEN OAKS RD 76116 #048-13-1993 L1994 **FM** *020 †18
SPROWLS, Larry Dwayne. 1301 PENNSYLVANIA AVE 76104 #048-13-1974 L1974 **OBG** *020 †30
STADTLER, Lindsay A. 6210 JOHN RYAN DR STE 10 76132 #024-07-1999 L2003 **PD** *020 †55
STANILAND, John Edward. 6100 HARRIS PKWY, STE 340 76132 #060-02-1991 L1995 **FM** *020
STARKS, Marion E. 4916 OVERTON PLZ 76109 #048-13-1988 L1993 *020 †05
STARK VANCS, Virginia I. 1325 PENNSYLVANIA AVE, STE 120 76104 #039-01-1987 L1996 **ON IM** *020 †20
STASIKOWSKI, Jacek Jan. 1307 8TH AVE STE 202 76104 #036-07-1968 L1976 **ORS** *020 †40
STECHER, Jack Alfred. 4916 OVERTON PLZ 76109 #054-04-1990 L1994 **AN** *020 †05
STEPHENSON, Gerald Robert. 1000 9TH AVE 76104 #023-07-1996 L2004 **GS** *020 †85
STERLING, Jeffrey Emery. 500 8TH AVE STE 110, DFW URGENT CARE 76104 #016-11-1991 L2003 **EM** *020 †16
STEVENER, Michael John. 1301 PENNSYLVANIA AVE, HARRIS METHODIST - FORT WO 76104 #048-12-1980 L1980 **NPM PD** *020 †55
STEVENS, Timothy Watson. 1500 S MAIN ST 76104 #028-02-1962 L1970 **IM CD** *040 †20
STEVENSON, Robert Nelson. 2001 W ROSEDALE ST 76104 #048-02-1974 L1974 **AN** *020 †05
STEWART, Richard Eugene. 855 MONTGOMERY ST, UNIV. OF NORTH TEXAS HSC 76107 #010-01-1984 L1992 **IC** *020 †20,28
STILES, Charles T. 6708 KINGSWOOD DR 76133 #048-13-1991 L1993 **EM** *020 †16
STOKDYK, Glenn A. ■ 76179 #056-06-1951 L1960 **DR NM** *071 †80
STOLAR, Stanley Harold. 900 8TH AVE 76104 #064-01-1958 L1977 **AN** *071
STOLTJE, Paul Alan. ■ 76122 #048-14-1990 L1991 **PDE** *020 †55
STOLTZ, Michael Lorson. 1210 ALSTON AVE 76104 #028-03-1970 L1973 **NEP IM** *020 †20
STONE, Mary E. 1301 PENNSYLVANIA AVE, ATTN: ADMINISTRATION 76104 #048-12-1992 L1995 **IM** *020 †20
STRANGE, Leslie C, III. 800 8TH AVE, STE 326 76104 #048-12-1970 L1970 **OTO** *020 †45
STRICKLAND, Kim L. ■ 76131 #048-78-2007, ▲ *012
STROCK, Louis Leighton. 800 8TH AVE, STE 606 76104 #048-02-1986 L1987 **PS** *020 †85,65
STRONG, Gary Bennett. 801 7TH AVE, COOK CHILDREN'S MEDICAL CE 76104 #047-05-1978 L1982 **PD** *020 †55
STUART, Anthony L. 4916 OVERTON PLZ 76109 #048-14-1990 L1991 **AN** *020 †05
STUDEY, Curtis Lauren. 1300 W TERRELL AVE 76104 #056-05-1982 L1987 **RO** *020 †80
STUNTZ, Richard Alan. 5701 BRYANT IRVIN RD # 201 76132 #048-14-1986 L1987 **FM** *020 †18
SUBA, Steven Antonio. 6100 HARRIS PKWY, STE 140 76132 #048-15-1984 L1985 **OBG** *020 †30
SUBRAMANIAM, Smita. 1500 S MAIN ST 76104 #495-30-1988 L2006 **IM** *020 †20
SUGIHARA, Theodore. 1001 12TH AVE, KAISER PERMANENTE' 76104 #035-09-1982 L1996 **A PD** *075 †03,55
SULLIVAN, George Harris. 750 8TH AVE 76104 #048-12-1959 L1959 **GYN** *071 †30
SUNKARA, Kishore. 2707 AIRPORT FWY, STE 216 76111 #495-58-1980 L1990 **P CHP** *020
SVOBODA, Leslie Ann. 1412 S MAIN ST 76104 #007-02-1991 L1994 **IM** *020 †20
SWARD-COMUNELLI, Susan L. 801 7TH AVE 76104 #028-02-1989 L1999 **NPM PD** *020 †55
SWAYDEN, Tracie D. 2801 S HULEN ST, STE 400 76109 #048-13-2002 L2004 *020
SWINK, James Edward. 5729 RIDGEROCK RD 76132 #048-12-1961 L1962 **ORS** *020 †40
SYED, Kamal A. 900 W MAGNOLIA AVE, STE 100 76104 #704-25-1988 L1993 **GE** *020 †20
SYED, Samira K. 6500 HARRIS PKWY 76132 #704-25-1989 L1994 **HO** *020 †20
SYEDA-MIAN, Mayanaz. 1400 S MAIN ST, ADULT MENTAL HEALTH CLINIC 76104 #704-02-1990 L2002 **P** *020
TACKETT, Leslie D. 1325 PENNSYLVANIA AVE 76104 #035-03-1994 L2004 **UP U** *020 †95
TAJON, El-Cid Organo. 1301 PENNSYLVANIA AVE 76104 #748-01-1990 L2006 **IM** *020 †20
TAKATA, Theodore Sunao. 1300 W TERRELL AVE, STE 50 76104 #023-01-1995 L1999 **ICE CD** *020 †20
TALBOYS, Paul Albert. ■ 76116 #010-01-1976 L1980 **AN EM** *020
TALENS, Evangeline T. 1301 PENNSYLVANIA AVE 76104 #748-01-1990 L2007 **IM** *020 †20
TALLANT, Arthur Nilon. 190 CONCHO TRL 76108 #048-12-1955 L1956 **OM FM** *075 †18 ‡
TAM, Vincent Kam Hung. 901 7TH AVE, COOK CHILDREN'S HOSPITAL 76104 #024-16-1982 L2002 **TS GS** *020 †85,90
TAN, Domingo Keng. 1001 COLLEGE AVE 76104 #048-13-1985 L1986 **GS VS** *020 †85
TANG, Baowei. ■ 76123 #243-71-1989 L2007 **RHU** *020 †20
TANNA, Rajendra Khetsi. 1000 COLLEGE AVE 76104 #495-28-1973 L1980 **AI PDA** *020 †55,03
TAPPER, Jay Brian. 801 7TH AVE, ANESTHESIA DEPARTMENT 76104 #048-02-1981 L1982 **AN EM** *020 †05
TARRIDE, Joseph, Jr. ■ 76116 #021-05-1952 L1960 **PTH GP** *071 †85,50
TATUM, Gail Douglas. 1500 S MAIN ST 76104 #021-01-1956 L1957 **GYN** *020 †30
TATUM, Larry Douglas. 1250 8TH AVE # 440 76104 #048-14-1979 L1979 **OBG** *020 †30
TATUM, Leslie. ■ 76108 #048-14-1982 L1983 **PTH** *020 †50
TATUM, Ross J. 3815 LISBON ST STE 200 76107 #048-02-1990 L1991 **CHP P** *020 †75
TAUB, Kent A. 1500 S MAIN ST 76104 #048-02-1993 L1994 **EM** *020 †16
TAYLOR, Stephen Maurice. 1000 MONTGOMERY ST 76107 #048-78-1985, ▲ L1986 **PMM OM** *071
TAYLOR, Suzanne Ruth. ■ 76137 #038-06-1981 L1990 **PTH** *020 †50
TEE, Cheow Meng. 1500 S MAIN ST 76104 #305-01-2004 L2008 **FP** *012
TEMPLETON, Erik Christian. 801 7TH AVE 76104 #048-13-2005 L2008 **PD** *012
TEOH, Doreen Lee. 801 7TH AVE 76104 #048-12-1994 L1998 **PD PEM** *020 †55
TERMINI, Benedict Anthony. ■ 76120 #023-01-1971 L1975 **CD IM** *062 †20 ‡
TERMINI, Trudy Elsmore. ■ 76120 #023-01-1975 L1975 **RHU IM** *020 †20
TERRELL, John Sandford. TCU HEALTH CENTER, BOX 297400 76129 #041-01-1960 L1960 **ADL** *020 †55
THEESFELD, Daniel Robt. 3000 ALEMEDA ST 76116 #016-42-1991 L1993 **AN PME** *020 †05
THIRUVENGADAM, A. ■ 76132 #495-42-1967 L1977 **CD IM** *020 †20
THOMAS, Henry W, Jr. ■ 76135 #048-02-1945 L1945 **FM** *071 †18
THOMAS, Howard Bertram. 1325 PENNSYLVANIA AVE, STE 690 76104 #067-01-1962 L1977 *100
THOMAS, Illtyd Reynolds. 1701 RIVER RUN, STE 508 76107 #352-05-1959 L1967 **AN** *020 †05
THOMAS, John Abraham. 1307 8TH AVE STE 603 76104 #048-12-1998 L2004 **ORS** *020 †40
THOMAS, Patrick Bruce. 1433 W HUMBOLT ST, PEDIATRIC SURGERY 76104 #045-01-1998 L2004 **PDS** *100
THOMAS, Vernon L. 11801 SOUTH FWY 76115 #005-12-1951 L1951 **GP** *071
THOMPSON, Linda Michele. 801 7TH AVE, COOK CHILDREN'S HOSPITAL 76104 #048-04-1999 L2002 **CCP** *100 †55
THOMPSON, Renika Katrice. 1500 S MAIN ST, DEPT OF FAMILY MEDICINE 76104 #019-02-2005 **FP** *012
THORNTON, Paul S. 901 7TH AVE STE 410, DEPARTMENT OF ENDOCRINOLOG 76104 #539-04-1984 L2003 **PDE** *020 †55
THURMAN, Addison E, Jr. 1300 W TERRELL AVE STE 405 76104 #039-01-1971 L1974 **U** *020 †95
THURMAN, Scott A. 1300 W TERRELL AVE, STE 405 76104 #048-02-1999 L2004 **U** *020 †95
TINLEY, Jason Christopher. ■ 76132 #012-01-2003 L2007 **ORS** *012
TOBEY, Martin Alan. 1300 W ROSEDALE ST 76104 #041-02-1970 L1972 **CD IM** *020 †20
TOBIAS, Brian. 855 MONTGOMERY ST 76107 #028-79-1986, ▲ L1994 **HS** *072

TODD, Joe Mack. 1300 W ROSEDALE ST, STE B 76104 #048-02-1975 L1975 **ORS** *020 †40
TODORA, Michael Anthony. 816 W CANNON ST 76104 #028-02-1998 L2003 **DR** *020 †80
TOLBERT, Suzanne Marie. 1301 PENNSYLVANIA AVE 76104 #048-12-1985 L1986 **FM** *020 †18
TOLER, Douglas Glen. 11801 SOUTH FWY 76115 #039-01-1979 L1982 **PTH** *020 †50
TOMBERLIN, Janice Kelly. 1300 W TERRELL AVE 76104 #048-13-1986 L1987 **RO** *020 †80
TONG, Jian. 801 7TH AVE, EMERGENCY DEPARTMENT 76104 #243-63-1986 L1997 **PEM PD** *020 †55
TONKIN, Allison Elizabeth. 815 PENNSYLVANIA AVE 76104 #024-05-1997 L2003 **DR** *020 †80
TOPPIN, Bruce E. 1301 PENNSYLVANIA AVE 76104 #051-01-1950 L1952 **GP GS** *071
TORRES, Kissi R. ■ 76120 #048-12-2006 **FP** *012
TORRES, Michelle. 923 PENNSYLVANIA AVE, STE 200 76104 #048-14-1999 L2002 **FM** *020 †18
TOUPS, Derwyn Matthew. ■ 76132 #048-02-1981 L1981 **DR** *062 †80
TRACY, John T. 1400 8TH AVE 76104 #048-04-1986 L1987 **EM** *020
TRAN, Dang-Quang Do. 1301 PENNSYLVANIA AVE, FOUNDATION DEPT 76104 #048-02-2001 L2004 **IM** *020
TRAN, Mytrang Thi. 855 MONTGOMERY ST 76107 #942-01-1988 L1999 **IM** *040 †20
TRAN, Yun Tzu. 1500 S MAIN ST, JOHN PETER SMITH HOSPITAL 76104 #048-12-2005 L2007 **FP** *012
TRELLO, Jodie Kathlene. 1400 S MAIN ST, STE 503 76104 #016-45-1992 L1993 **CHP** *020 †75
TREMBLAY, Normand Francis. 5929 LOVELL AVE 76107 #050-02-1970 L1977 **AI PD** *020 †05,55,03
TRIMBLE, Monty V. 7269 HAWKINS VIEW DR 76132 #048-13-1997 L2002 **OTO** *020 †45
TRIVEDI, Beena M. 2919 MARKUM DR 76117 #495-76-1986 L1997 **FM** *020 †18
TROTTER, Elliott R. 1301 PENNSYLVANIA AVE 76104 #048-13-1987 L1988 **FM** *020 †18
TROUTMAN, David G. 1301 PENNSYLVANIA AVE 76104 #048-15-1992 L1993 **IM** *020 †20
TROUTMAN, Edwin Glenn. 1000 MONTGOMERY ST 76107 #005-06-1952 L1959 **IM END** *020
TROUTMAN, Monte Eugene. 855 MONTGOMERY ST 76107 #016-76-1975, ▲ L1983 **GE IM** *030
TRUELSON, Thomas C. 6100 HARRIS PKWY, STE C 76132 #048-12-1988 L1989 **U** *020 †95
TUBERA, Butch Baclig. 3150 HORTON RD, FCI FT. WORTH 76119 #748-01-1986 L2003 **IM** *020
TUCKER, Garrett R, III. ■ 76110 #035-20-1963 L1971 **OM AM** *062 †95,70
TUKDI, Shakil Ahmed. 1301 PENNSYLVANIA AVE 76104 #704-02-1992 L2004 **P** *020 ‡
TULLOH, James Newton. 1701 RIVER RUN, STE 508 76107 #020-02-1955 L1962 **AN** *071 †05
TURBEVILLE, David F. 801 7TH AVE 76104 #001-02-1971 L1982 **NPM PD** *020 †55
TURNER, Jack L. 2426 WINTON TER W 76109 #021-01-1948 L1950 **OBG OS** *020 †30
TURNER, Kelly James. 1500 S MAIN ST 76104 #005-12-1998 L2002 **EM** *020 †16
TURNER, Robert Jos. 901 W LEUDA ST 76104 #021-05-1954 L1961 **SO OS** *071 †85
TURNER, William Clark. 1500 S MAIN ST 76104 #048-02-1995 L1999 **EM** *020 †16
UNINI, Fidelis Kanayo. 1550 W ROSEDALE ST, STE 206 76104 #690-04-1993 L2007 **IM** *020 †20
UPADHYAYA, Mahendra P. 6000 WESTERN PL, STE 300 76107 #495-74-1982 L2000 **PYG P** *020 †75
URSO, Richard S. 1400 8TH AVE 76104 #048-13-1988 L1989 **EM FM** *020 †18
URSPRUNG, Robert L. 1301 PENNSYLVANIA AVE 76104 #048-12-1998 L2001 **NPM** *020 †55
USHER, Kenneth Worthie. 1500 S MAIN ST 76104 #018-03-1981 L1985 **R** *020 †80
VALLURUPALLI, Vedavathy. 1500 S MAIN ST, NORTH TEXAS AFFILIATED MED 76104 #495-62-1993 L2002 **AN** *020
VAN ANTWERP, James D. ■ 76109 #019-02-1955 L1955 **P NM** *071 †75,28
VANCE, Wm Sterling, Jr. 1300 W TERRELL AVE, STE 50 76104 #048-12-1972 L1974 **CD IC** *020 †20
VANDEVYVER, Paul L. 801 7TH AVE 76104 #048-12-1988 L1989 **AN** *020 †05
VANKAWALA, Hasmukhlal C. 4916 OVERTON PLZ 76109 #209-01-1962 L1982 **AN** *020 †05
VAN SCOYK, Shelly Rene. ■ 76107 #048-78-2002, ▲ L2005 *100
VAN WYK, William Jacob. 803 W TERRELL AVE 76104 #048-02-1972 L1972 **ORS HS** *020 †40
VARA, Christopher Sean. 901 7TH AVE, UNIVERSITY OF UTAH 76104 #010-02-2000 L2007 **ORS** *100
VARGAS, Luis Antonio. 6601 DAN DANCIGER RD, STE 100 76133 #010-02-1997 L2001 **FM** *020
VAUGHAN, Michael S. 1500 S MAIN ST, DEPT OF MEDICINE 76104 #041-01-1967 L1977 **CD** *020 †20
VAUGHAN, William Glaze. 901 7TH AVE STE 210 76104 #012-01-1987 L1989 **PDS** *020 †85
VAUGHN, Stephen Bradley. ■ 76179 #305-01-2006 L2006 **AN** *012
VENKATAPPAN, Raj R. ■ 76180 #495-04-1957 L1978 **FM** *020 †18
VENKATAPPAN, Sumathi. ■ 76180 #048-13-1991 L1993 **DR** *020 †20,80
VERGHESE, Grace Mary. 1500 S MAIN ST 76104 #305-01-2007 **FP** *012
VERMETTE, Debra Null. 2501 PARKVIEW DR STE 600, VITAS HEALTHCARE OF TEXAS 76102 #048-12-1986 L1987 **FM** *020 †18
VERMETTE, Kenneth Norman. 7630 N BEACH ST, STE 140 76137 #048-12-1985 L1986 **FM** *020 †18
VERT, Deborah S. 801 7TH AVE 76104 #048-78-1995, ▲ L1996 **PD** *020 †55
VERTKIN, Gennady. 800 12TH AVE STE 100 76104 #913-15-1979 L2005 **AN CCM** *020 †05
VIGNESS, Richard Martell. 1307 8TH AVE, STE 601 76104 #048-14-1981 L1981 **TS VS** *020 †85,90
VINSON, Charles Eric. 1400 8TH AVE 76104 #004-01-1987 L1991 **EM** *020
VORIES, Andrew A. 1500 S MAIN ST, NORTH TEXAS AFFILIATED MED 76104 #048-13-1992 L1993 **OTO** *020 †45
VORIES, Patricia A. 4916 OVERTON PLZ 76109 #035-06-1992 L1999 **AN** *020 †05
VU, Chi Ha. 855 MONTGOMERY ST 76107 #021-05-1998 L2000 **FM** *020 †18
VUITCH, Milan Franklin. 1301 PENNSYLVANIA AVE 76104 #023-07-1981 L1987 **ATP PCP** *020 †50
VUONG, Nicholas M. 1500 S MAIN ST 76104 #048-13-2001 L2005 **AN** *020
VU-TRAN, Mylinh. 7100 OAKMONT BLVD 76132 #030-05-1985 L1989 **OBG** *020 †30
WADDELL, Gary M. 1101 6TH AVE 76104 #048-02-1992 L1996 **DR** *020 †80
WAGNER, Russell A. 855 MONTGOMERY ST 5TH FL, UNIVERSITY OF NORTH TEXAS 76107 #048-12-1987 L1988 **ORS OAR** *020 †40
WALDRON, Kerri Anne. ■ 76109 #011-04-2003 L2006 **IM** *020 †20
WALLACE, Ralph Perry. 2630 WEST FWY, STE 126 76102 #048-78-1980, ▲ L1980 **AN** *020 †05
WALRAVEN, Ellen Stockton. 909 9TH AVE, STE 300 76104 #048-04-1983 L1990 **ID IM** *020 †20
WALSH, Michael Jos. 4916 OVERTON PLZ 76109 #036-07-1992 L2003 **IM** *020 †05
WALSH, Patrick. 1622 8TH AVE, STE 120 76104 #048-02-1988 L1989 **DDL D** *020 †15
WALTER, Michael Capwell. 900 8TH AVE 76104 #024-01-1973 L1979 **U** *020 †95
WARD, David Lee. ■ 76107 #038-40-1979 L1998 **DR NM** *020 †70,80,28
WARD, Gregory Alan. 1319 SUMMIT AVE STE 200, DISORDERS 76102 #048-02-1990 L1996 **NS** *020 †25
WARD, Robert Logan. 6100 HARRIS PKWY, STE 345 76132 #048-02-1970 L1970 **IM** *020 †20
WARDLE, Bruce Edward. 544 W SEMINARY DR, SOUTHSIDE MEDICAL CLINIC 76115 #048-78-1983, ▲ L1983 **GP** *020
WARMINK, Corwin Alan. 801 7TH AVE, COOK CHILDREN'S 76104 #048-12-1997 L1999 **PD** *020 †55
WARREN, Robert Eric. 1201 SUMMIT AVE 76102 #048-02-1996 L1998 **OPH** *020 †35
WATEMBERG, Isaac Aaron. 855 MONTGOMERY ST 76107 #264-12-1986 L1997 **FM** *020 †18
WATKINS, Ingrid Kristen H. 4760 BARWICK DR STE C 76132 #048-14-1990 L1991 **OBG** *020 †30
WATKINS, Randall G. 801 7TH AVE, DEPARTMENT OF ANESTHESIA 76104 #048-15-2000 L2002 **PAN** *020 †05
WATSON, Keith Collins. 800 5TH AVE, STE 200 76104 #048-12-1974 L1974 **ORS** *020 †40
WATSON, Robert Kent. 1250 8TH AVE STE 440 76104 #048-13-1979 L1979 **OBG** *020 †30
WATTS, Barry Kent. 816 W CANNON ST, RADIOLOGY ASSOCIATES/TARRA 76104 #048-02-1976 L1976 **DR** *020 †80
WATTS, David C. 3800 HULEN ST, STE 100 76107 #048-14-1990 L1995 **DR** *020 †80
WAX, Martin Bruce. 6201 SOUTH FWY, MD: R231 76134 #005-06-1978 L2007 **OPH** *020 †35 ‡
WEBBER, Charles Eliot. 800 W MAGNOLIA AVE, STE A 76104 #041-02-1968 L1970 **GS TRS** *020 †85
WEBSTER, Charles Lon. ■ 76107 #021-01-1959 L1965 **NS** *071
WEEDEN, Steven Henry. 750 8TH AVE STE 400 76104 #048-14-1995 L1996 **ORS** *020 †40
WEST, Britton Reed. 1420 8TH AVE STE 103 76104 #021-01-1973 L1979 **CRS GS** *020 †10,85
WETTERMARK, Alfred Boyce. 1500 S MAIN ST 76104 #759-18-2001 L2008 **FPG** *100
WHALEY, Lawrence A. 1525 MERRIMAC CIR 76107 #048-14-1990 L1997 **IM PD** *020 †55,20
WHEELER, Joe Ellis. 1650 W ROSEDALE ST, STE 305 76104 #048-02-1964 L1964 **NS** *020
WHIPP, Harry Hughes. ■ 76135 #048-12-1967 L1967 **R** *020 †80
WHITBOURNE, Suzanne Karen. 1301 PENNSYLVANIA AVE 76104 #011-03-1996 L1999 **NPM** *020 †55
WHITE, James Bingham. ■ 76107 #048-12-1954 L1954 **PTH** *071 †50
WHITE, Richard Maurice. 909 W MAGNOLIA AVE STE 4 76104 #048-15-1977 L1982 **OBG** *020
WHITE, Robert Lloyd, II. ■ 76131 #039-01-1972 L1976 **FOP** *030 †50
WHITE, Ronald Nelson. 3109 6TH AVE STE A 76110 #050-02-1969 L1976 **FM** *020
WHITFIELD, John Aaron, Jr. 1307 8TH AVE STE 404 76104 #028-46-1984 L1985 **OBG** *020 †30
WHITLEY, Douglas Eugene. 1525 MERRIMAC CIR STE 107 76107 #048-12-1977 L1977 **EM FM** *020 †18,16
WHITNEY, Jeannette Ann. ■ 76107 #048-12-1992 L1993 **NPM** *020 †55
WHITWORTH, Mary Suzanne. 801 7TH AVE 76104 #048-02-1990 L1995 **PDI** *020 †55
WIDERHORN, Josef. 1307 8TH AVE STE 501, TEXAS HEART CLINIC 76104 #561-01-1980 L1992 **CD ICE** *020 †20
WIGGINS, Kenneth Marvin. 3625 CLUB GATE DR 76137 #048-12-1959 L1959 **CHP P** *071 †55,75
WIGGINTON, Stephen Andrew. 1201 SUMMIT AVE, OPHTHALMOLOGY ASSOCIATES 76102 #010-01-1995 L2000 **OPH** *020 †35
WIKOFF, Richard P. 6300 RIDGLEA PL, STE 100 76116 #048-12-1994 L2002 **GS** *020 †85
WILDE, David W. ■ 76137 #048-12-2005 **IM** *100
WILEY, Ruth. ■ 76133 #048-78-2004, ▲ L2007 **OBG** *012
WILLARD, John Edward. 1300 W TERRELL AVE, STE 50 76104 #021-01-1985 L1986 **CD IC** *020 †20
WILLCUTTS, Michael David. 901 7TH AVE STE 410, COOK CHILDREN'S MEDICAL CE 76104 #048-12-1992 L1993 **PD END** *020 †55
WILLIAMS, Delwin. 855 MONTGOMERY ST 76107 #048-12-1986 L1987 **P** *020 †75
WILLIAMS, James E. 2500 WEST FWY STE 300 76102 #021-05-1952 L1953 **PM** *071 †60
WILLIAMS, Martha Ann. 1500 S MAIN ST 76104 #048-13-1980 L1980 **GS** *020 †85,18
WILLIAMS, Wayne Glen. 855 MONTGOMERY ST 76107 #007-02-1975 L1976 **FM** *062 †18
WILLIS, Dan Alvin. 1325 PENNSYLVANIA AVE, STE 670 76104 #048-12-1974 L1974 **OPH GP** *020 †35
WILLIS, Virginia. ■ 76119 #020-02-1951 L1953 **AN** *071
WILLITS, Mark B. 1500 S MAIN ST, JOHN P SMITH HOSP 76104 #048-14-2002 L2006 **ORS** *020
WILSON, David Brooks. 1325 PENNSYLVANIA AVE, STE 560 76104 #020-12-1972 L1980 **END IM** *020 †20
WILSON, Diana E. 1325 PENNSYLVANIA AVE, STE 440 76104 #048-14-1985 L1991 **NS** *020 †25 ‡
WILSON, Richard Vance. ■ 76116 #025-01-1958 L1966 **ORS** *071 †40
WILSON, Stephen Lee. 1015 S HENDERSON ST 76104 #048-13-1975 L1983 **ORS HS** *020 †40
WILSON, Thomas Wm. ■ 76109 #016-02-1961 L1964 **PD** *020 †55
WILSON, Warren Dale. 800 8TH AVE, STE 220 76104 #012-05-1973 L1979 **NS** *020 †25
WINDHAM, William A. ■ 76107 #048-04-1986 L1987 **AN EM** *020 †05
WINN, James Russell. 1201 8TH AVE 76104 #048-02-1967 L1967 **FM IM** *020 †18
WINTER, A Scott. 855 MONTGOMERY ST 76107 #027-01-1976 L1977 **P ADM** *040 †75
WITHAM, William R. 1325 PENNSYLVANIA AVE, STE 200 76104 #048-15-2000 L2004 **GS** *020 †85
WITRYOL, Walter. 855 MONTGOMERY ST 76107 #008-02-1989 L2004 **PM** *020 †60
WITSCHY, James Kenton. 855 MONTGOMERY ST 76107 #048-13-1976 L1978 **P** *020 †75
WITT, Stacee Marie. 1500 S MAIN ST, JOHN PETER SMITH HOSPITAL 76104 #007-02-2003 L2007 **ORS** *012
WOLF, Todd Allen. 801 7TH AVE, EMERGENCY DEPT 76104 #305-01-1998 L2005 **PEM** *020 †55
WOLFF, William Shan. ■ 76109 #028-03-1965 L1970 **GS OS** *020 †85
WOOD, Robert C, Jr. 7100 OAKMONT BLVD 76132 #048-02-1988 L1989 **DR RNR** *020 †80
WOODLAND, Caroline E. 5701 BRYANT IRVIN RD, STE 304 76132 #048-78-1989, ▲ L1991 **FM** *020 †18
WORSHAM, Sidney Almon, III. 800 8TH AVE STE 626 76104 #048-02-1971 L1971 **U** *020 †95
WORSLEY, Jon Ben. 6401 HARRIS PKWY STE 100 76132 #048-12-1995 L1996 **PD** *020 †55
WRIGHT, Barbara A. 800 5TH AVE, STE 300 76104 #048-02-1986 L1989 **IM** *020 †20
WRIGHT, Patrick Beaumont. 1500 S MAIN ST, JPS DEPT ORTHOPEDICS 76104 #048-04-2005 **ORS** *012
WROTEN, B J. 801 W TERRELL AVE 76104 #048-02-1970 L1970 **HS** *020 †40
WROTEN, Eric Sanders. 801 W TERRELL AVE 76104 #048-02-2000 L2006 **ORS** *020
WU, Bo. 1500 S MAIN ST 76104 #243-70-1986 L2007 **P** *020
WU, Liancun. 1500 S MAIN ST, DEPT OF ANESTHLGY 76104 #243-47-1986 L2001 **AN** *020 †05
WU, Norman C. 4916 OVERTON PLZ 76109 #048-13-2001 L2005 **AN** *020 †05
WU, Sang Ling. 6100 HARRIS PKWY, LABORATORY 76132 #048-14-1998 L2002 **SP** *020
WU, Xiaoyan. 100 N LAMAR ST, TARRANT COUNTY MHMR 76102 #243-16-1983 L2001 **P** *020 †75
WYLIE, Mark William. 1651 W ROSEDALE ST, STE 100 76104 #048-12-1998 L2003 **OSS ORS** *020 †40
YACKULIC, Charles Fred. 1500 S MAIN ST 76104 #035-01-1973 L2000 **P** *020 †75
YANCY, Kerry Jo. 801 7TH AVE, COOK CHILDREN'S MEDICAL CE 76104 #048-12-1989 L1990 **PEM** *020 †55
YANES, Hector Osvaldo. 1400 8TH AVE 76104 #231-01-1962 L1972 **TS** *071 †85,90
YAQUINTO, James Jay. 815 PENNSYLVANIA AVE 76104 #048-12-1984 L1985 **R IM** *020 †80

■ = Address Information Privacy Protected

YARMCHUK, James. 300 W ROSEDALE ST 76104 #048-13-1991 L1993 FM *020 †18
YE, Yanping. ■ 76132 #243-45-1991 L2007 FPG *012 †18
YENTIS, Richard David. 4388 W VICKERY BLVD 76107 #041-01-1963 L1968 CHP *020 †75
YERGER, Nathan K. 1500 S MAIN ST, DEPT OF FAMILY MEDICINE 76104 #048-14-2006 FP *012
YIN, Zi. 815 PENNSYLVANIA AVE 76104 #036-07-2000 L2004 DR *020 †80
YOON, Sukhoon. ■ 76123 #035-01-1995 L2000 MPD PD *020 †20
YOUNG, John Gabbert. 6210 JOHN RYAN DR STE 109 76132 #048-13-1984 L1985 PD *020 †55
YOUNG, Richard. 1500 S MAIN ST, JOHN PETER SMITH HOSPITAL 76104 #048-13-1990 L1991 FM *040 †18
YOUNG, Richard Alan. 1500 S MAIN ST, 4TH FL 76104 #005-18-1983 L1984 FM *020 †18
YOUNGBLOOD, Marcus A. ■ 76126 #048-02-1960 L1960 AN *071
YOUREE, Bryan Eugene. 1125 COLLEGE AVE, TARRANT COUNTY INFECTIOUS 76104 #048-04-1999 L2006 ID *020 †20
YU, Michael Yihlin. ■ 76102 #025-01-2007 ORS *012
YURTTAS, Oguz. 3005 BELLAIRE RANCH DR 76109 #902-07-1997 L2005 *020 †20
ZAFAR, Mansoor. 1500 S MAIN ST 76104 #704-22-1994 P *100
ZAIDI, Nabila Shoeb. 3308 DEEN RD 76106 #704-09-1992 L2007 IM *100 †20
ZEH, Kim M. 1500 S MAIN ST 76104 #035-09-1982 L1986 EM GS *020 †16
ZERINGUE, Michael Paul. 1500 S MAIN ST, DEPT OF FAMILY MEDICINE 76104 #021-01-2005 L2007 FP *012
ZEY, George Wyatt. 1500 S MAIN ST, DEPARTMENT OF MEDICINE 76104 #048-02-1969 L1969 IM *020 †20
ZHANG, Shan. 4916 OVERTON PLZ 76109 #243-70-1985 L2002 AN *020 †05
ZIEGLER, Daniel Wayne. 1500 S MAIN ST, DEPARTMENT OF SURGERY 76104 #010-02-1980 L1981 GS CCS *020 †85
ZILBERG, Bernard. 1001 12TH AVE 76104 #836-02-1949 L1978 PD *020 †55
ZIMMERMAN, Sheryl F. 801 7TH AVE 76104 #049-01-1988 L2000 PD *020 †55
ZIMMERMANN, George Jay. 1000 9TH AVE, STE C 76104 #028-02-1971 L1978 GS *020 †85
ZWERNEMANN, Robert T. 6100 HARRIS PKWY 76132 #048-16-1995 L1996 OBG *020 †30

FRANKLIN – ROBERTSON

ROBERMAN, Lawrence M. 305 W GAY ST 77856 #048-13-1990 L1991 FM *020 †18

FRANKSTON – ANDERSON

MEEK, Bruce Weldon. ■ 75763 #016-06-1957 L1961 OBG *071 †30
YOUNG, Andrew Roland. ■ 75763 #028-78-1954, ▲ L1954 GP *071

FREDERICKSBURG – GILLESPIE

ADAMS, Kenneth Pogue. ■ 78624 #048-02-1954 L1954 FM *071 †18
ANDREASSIAN, Gregory D. 205 W WINDCREST ST, STE 220 78624 #048-13-1985 L1986 GS *020 †85
BACON, Celia Jan. ■ 78624 #048-13-1976 L1977 PTH *071 †50
BACON, James Leroy, Jr. ■ 78624 #028-34-1964 L1986 GP EM *071
BENTCH, Leonard H. 205 N BOWIE ST 78624 #048-13-1972 L1972 GE IM *020 †20
BRADEN, Michael Wm. 95 E HIGHWAY ST 78624 #048-13-1985 L1986 D *020 †15 ‡
BRAY, Andrea. 205 W WINDCREST ST 78624 #048-12-1997 L2000 PPR *020 †55
BRINGEWALD, Peter Robt. ■ 78624 #038-40-1964 L1972 OPH *020 †35
BURG, Charles Emil. 1308 S STATE HIGHWAY 16 78624 #048-02-1966 L1966 GP *020 †18
BURKHALTER, Archie Herman. ■ 78624 #048-12-1954 L1955 GP *071
BUSH, Roger Allen. ■ 78624 #018-03-1962 L1963 GP OM *071
CANTU, David A. 1305 N MILAM ST 78624 #048-12-1990 L1992 FM *020 †18
CANTU, Pamela Drake. 205 W WINDCREST ST 78624 #048-12-1990 L1991 IM *020 †20
CASILLAS, Ernest A. ■ 78624 #048-02-1963 L1963 P *071 †75
CLEMENTS, Arthur Morgan. ■ 78624 #028-02-1961 L1965 OPH *071 †35
COHN, Joseph Michael. 204 W WINDCREST ST 78624 #048-14-1996 L1998 ORS *020 †40
CORNETT, Karen Gruschkus. 200 W WINDCREST ST, STE 100 78624 #048-12-2000 L2003 FM *020 †18
COX, Alice D. 1308 S STATE HIGHWAY 16 78624 #039-01-1974 L1980 EM FM *020 †18
CRENWELGE, Wilbur Eugene. 1020 KERRVILLE HWY 78624 #048-02-1955 L1955 PD AN *071
CUNNINGHAM, Marshall Wade. 7 MEDICAL DR, STATE HIGHWAY 16 78624 #021-06-1979 L2004 PS HS *020 †65
DECHERD, George Michael. ■ 78624 #048-02-1957 L1957 U *071 †95
DULANEY, Jennifer Louise. 205 W WINDCREST ST 78624 #048-12-1994 L1995 OBG *020 †30
DULANEY, Richard Matthew. 205 W WINDCREST ST 78624 #048-12-1995 L1997 PD *020 †55
EDEN, Mark D. 200 W WINDCREST ST, STE 250 78624 #048-04-1988 L1989 FM *020 †18
ELLISON, Suzanne E. 200 W WINDCREST ST, C/O CORNERSTONE CLINIC 78624 #048-12-1980 L1980 FM *020 †18
FITZGERALD, John B. ■ 78624 #017-20-1956 L1964 TS GS *020 †85,90
FREEBORN, William Arthur. ■ 78624 #048-12-1972 L1972 U *020 †95
GAINER, Barbara Jeanne S. ■ 78624 #048-12-1966 L1969 DR *071 †80
GALLAGHER, Kevin M. 205 W WINDCREST ST, STE 140 78624 #048-78-2000, ▲ L2003 CD *030 †20
GARCIA, Ramon Antonio. 1020 KERRVILLE HWY 78624 #649-04-1970 L1973 FM EM *020 †18
GEORGE, Melissa A. 205 W WINDCREST ST 78624 #048-12-2003 L2006 IM *020 †20
GREENLEE, Ralph G, Jr. 110 N MILAM ST, STE 120 78624 #021-01-1966 L1969 N *020 †75
GREINER, Diane Zipprich. 205 W WINDCREST ST, STE 205 78624 #036-07-1993 L1994 CD *020 †20
HADDOCK, Eugene Peter. 205 W WINDCREST ST, STE 205 78624 #010-02-1966 L1972 CD *020 †20
HATCHETTE, James B, III. 1020 KERRVILLE HWY 78624 #021-05-1964 L1972 R *020 †80
HAUG, Yvonne Kay. 1305 N MILAM ST 78624 #048-13-1983 L1984 FM *020 †18
HAVRANEK, Russell Dean. 1009 S MILAM ST 78624 #030-05-1998 L1999 GE *020 †20
HOERMANN, Matthew J. 200 W WINDCREST ST STE 100 78624 #048-16-1991 L1992 FM *020 †18
HOERSTER, John Steven. 204 W WINDCREST ST 78624 #048-14-1981 L1981 ORS HS *020 †40
HOWARD, Felicia H. 205 W WINDCREST ST, STE 310 78624 #048-04-1995 L1996 MPD *020 †20,55
HOWARD-MCGRADY, Felicia K. 205 W WINDCREST ST, STE 310 78624 #016-43-1990 L1990 PD *020

HOWELL, Todd Rankin. 212C E AUSTIN ST 78624 #048-13-1983 L1984 FM EM *020 †18
HUGHES, Carl Paul. 205 S STATE HIGHWAY 16 78624 #048-12-1962 L1962 IM *071 †20
HUNTER, Malcolm E, Jr. ■ 78624 #051-04-1946 L1956 IM CD *020
HUTTON, John Thos. 715 BRYANT RD 78624 #048-04-1972 L1972 N *071 †75
JACKSON, Mell Chas, Jr. 205 W WINDCREST ST, STE 230 78624 #012-05-1975 L1984 IM CD *020 †20
JACOBS, Laura O'Gorman. 205 W WINDCREST ST, STE 205 78624 #048-04-1990 L1994 CD *020 †20
JOINER, Donald Richard. 205 W WINDCREST ST, STE 220 78624 #048-13-1995 L1996 VS *020 †85
JONES, Michael Churchill. 703 S ADAMS ST 78624 #048-13-1979 L1979 U *020 †95
KOTHMANN, John Radcliffe. 1308 S STATE HIGHWAY 16, FREDERICKSBURG CLINIC, PA 78624 #048-14-2001 L2004 FM *020 †18
LECLERC, Kenneth M. 205 W WINDCREST ST, STE 205 78624 #039-01-1993 L2002 CD *020 †20
LITTLE, Lucretia Ann. ■ 78624 #001-02-1964 L1968 P *020 †75
LOPEZ, Jose Antonio. 204 W SCHUBERT ST 78624 #737-06-1974 L1984 ON IM *020 †20
LOPEZ, Rochelle. ■ 78624 #042-01-1971 L1979 OPH OS *071 †35
MACHELL, Charles Heberton. 205 W WINDCREST ST, STE 205 78624 #048-02-1980 L1980 CD *020 †20
MAJORS, Michael James. 95 E HIGHWAY ST 78624 #048-13-1994 L1995 D *020 †15
MAPLE, Philip James. 1308 S STATE HIGHWAY 16 78624 #016-01-1980 L1982 IM *020 †20
MARR, William Lewis, III. ■ 78624 #048-02-1959 L1959 IM *071
MARTIN, Robert Otto. 1020 KERRVILLE HWY 78624 #048-13-1975 L1975 FM EM *020 †18
MASON, Richard Curtis. ■ 78624 #048-02-1976 L1979 FM *020 †18
MASSEY, Charles R, Jr. 103 GOEHMANN LN 78624 #048-13-1983 L1984 AN *020 †05
MAXWELL, William Clinton. 514 W AUSTIN ST 78624 #407-10-1967 L1970 PM *072 †60
MAYBEN, Jennifer K. 205 W WINDCREST ST 78624 #048-02-2001 L2004 IM *020
MEADOWS, John Cassius, Jr. 234 W MAIN ST # B 78624 #012-01-1945 L1951 IM *071 †20
MEEKS, Mark Alan. 415 S WASHINGTON ST 78624 #019-02-1991 L2004 AN *020 †05
MOORE, Jeff R. ■ 78624 #055-11-1953 L1961 PS HS *071 †85,65
OSTROWER, Victor Stanley. 1009 S MILAM ST 78624 #035-09-1965 L1974 IM GE *020 †20
PARTIN, James Ray. 205 W WINDCREST ST, STE 31 78624 #048-13-1976 L1976 IM N *020 †20
PEET, Jason N. 1308 S STATE HIGHWAY 16 78624 #048-13-1998 L1999 FM *020 †20
PEREZ, Jose Angel. 205 W WINDCREST ST, STE 205 78624 #048-12-1982 L1983 CD IM *020 †20
PLUENNEKE, Anne C. 755 S WASHINGTON ST 78624 #048-12-1998 L1999 OPH *020 †35
PORTO, Maurine Dion. 140 INDUSTRIAL LOOP 78624 #040-02-1981 L1987 PHP GP *030 †70
PURKHISER, Bradley R. 305 TANGLEWOOD DR 78624 #048-04-1983 L1984 IM *020 †20
RABINOWITZ, Abram Chas. 205 W WINDCREST ST, STE 205 78624 #048-13-1975 L1977 CD *020 †20
RAMSAY, John Paul. 200 W WINDCREST ST # 100 78624 #048-12-1980 L1980 FM *020 †18
RANDALL, Charles W. 1009 S MILAM ST 78624 #048-02-1988 L1990 GE IM *020 †20
ROBERTSON, Daniel Buford. 204 W WINDCREST ST 78624 #048-14-1978 L1978 ORS OSM *020 †40
ROCKWOOD, Andrew Paul. 213 E SAN ANTONIO ST 78624 #048-13-1985 L1987 U *020 †95
ROMAN GONZALEZ, Javier. 205 W WINDCREST ST, STE 205 78624 #042-01-1991 L1995 ICE *020 †20
ROMANICK, Peter Chas. 204 W WINDCREST ST 78624 #048-04-1980 L1982 ORS *075 †40
SANDERSON, John Nathaniel. 205 W WINDCREST ST, STE 205 78624 #047-06-1970 L1972 CD IM *020 †20
SMITH, Raymond Hiett. ■ 78624 #048-12-1975 L1976 FM AM *071 †18
SNOWDEN, Vernon L. ■ 78624 #005-11-1944 L1947 RHU GP *071
STAFFORD, Kristi Ann. 200 W WINDCREST ST 78624 #048-14-1996 L1997 FM *020 †18
STAUFFER, Jay Scott. 205 W WINDCREST ST, STE 220A 78624 #048-13-1987 L1988 GS *020 †85
STEIN, Edward F, Jr. 1020 KERRVILLE HWY 78624 #048-04-1952 L1952 GP GS *020
STEWART, Tim Paul. 1308 S STATE HIGHWAY 16 78624 #048-13-1985 L1986 FM *020 †18
STOTZ, Ronald Alvin. 1009 S MILAM ST, STE 4 78624 #048-02-1976 L1996 N *020 †75
STUMP, David Lee. 1009 S MILAM ST 78624 #017-20-1980 L1985 GE IM *020 †20
TELLE, James Thos. ■ 78624 #017-20-1963 L1969 DR *071 †80
TERRELL, Kenneth. 205 W WINDCREST ST, STE 340 78624 #048-13-1976 L1976 PUD IM *020 †20
THOMPSON, Nancy Kaye. 205 W WINDCREST ST, STE 31 78624 #048-14-1987 L1988 IM PD *020 †20,55
TOLAN, Gil Drake. 88 STAG TRL, HEART'S DELIGHT 78624 #005-11-1969 L1995 PHP NTR *050
TONTIPLAPHOL, Art Raphael. 205 W WINDCREST ST, STE 205 78624 #023-07-2000 L2004 CD *020 †20
TRAUGOTT, Richard Carl. ■ 78624 #038-40-1967 L1979 TS *020 †85,90
TYNAN, Leo Costello, III. 1308 S STATE HIGHWAY 16 78624 #048-12-1985 L1986 IM *020 †20
WALKER, Michael Lee. 206 W WINDCREST ST 78624 #048-04-1978 L1978 FPS OTO *020 †45
WALTON, Martha Ann. 755 S WASHINGTON ST 78624 #021-01-1979 L1986 OPH *020 †35
WEAVER, John Dudley. 1020 KERRVILLE HWY 78624 #048-13-1984 L1985 FM *020 †18 ‡
WEILBURG, Richard Daro. ■ 78624 #048-04-1964 L1964 GYN *071 †30
WESTFALL, John David. 415 S WASHINGTON ST 78624 #048-15-1996 L2000 AN *020 †05
WHITE, David Hopkins. 205 W WINDCREST ST, STE 205 78624 #048-13-1972 L1972 CD *020 †20
WOLTERS, Robert Wm. ■ 78624 #048-12-1971 L1971 OPH AM *020
ZURITA, Victor Franz. 1009 S MILAM ST 78624 #048-14-1989 L1990 GE *020 †20

FREEPORT – BRAZORIA

ALPHONSE, Michele. 2301 N BRAZOSPORT BLVD 77541 #041-09-1990 L1998 IM *020 †20,70
CALDWELL, John S, Jr. ■ 77541 #048-02-1945 L1945 GP *071
CROPPER, Kenneth Ross. ■ 77541 #048-02-1969 L1969 FM D *071
MC FADDEN, Sophia C. 2301 N BRAZOSPORT BLVD, HEALTH SERVICES, B-101 - D 77541 #042-01-1999 L2006 IM *020 †20
SALAZAR, Eugenio Jaime. 2301 N BRAZOSPORT BLVD, APT B101 77541 #025-12-1983 L1985 OM FM *020 †70,18
WEHMER, Ralph E, Jr. 1102 N BRAZOSPORT BLVD 77541 #048-14-1982 L1983 GPM *020 †18

FRESNO – FORT BEND

DAVIS, Alauna Nicole. ■ 77545 #048-04-2007 P *012

JENKINS, Megan Nicole. ■ 77545 #041-14-2007 L2007 **TY** *012
NEWBERRY, Travis R. ■ 77545 #048-14-2007 **OTO** *012
TALATI, Mihir. ■ 77545 #048-04-2005 L2007 **FP** *012
UDOM, Visitsunthorn. ■ 77545 #891-04-1973 L1977 **RHU IM** *074 †20

FRIENDSWOOD – GALVESTON

ADIO-ODUOLA, Titilola Ros. ■ 77546 #048-02-2008 *012
ALVES, Diana Jean. 807 S FRIENDSWOOD DR, STE 2 77546 #048-02-1965 L1965 **FM OS** *020
ANDREW, John G. ■ 77546 #048-12-1953 L1953 **ORS OS** *062 †40
ANDREWS, William Alan. 119 W PARKWOOD AVE 77546 #048-02-1979 L1980 **EM GS** *020 †16
ARMSTRONG, Martha. ■ 77546 #048-02-1999 L2002 **FM** *020 †18
AUSTIN, Michael Jos. 1009 MYRTLEWOOD DR 77546 #065-06-1974 L1978 **FM FPG** *020
BANG, Chu Ba. 705 IDLEWOOD DR 77546 #941-01-1967 L1978 **GP OBG** *071
BECKER, Teresa M. 347 E PARKWOOD AVE 77546 #038-43-1983 L1984 **IM EM** *020 †20
BIELAMOWICZ, Kevin James. ■ 77546 #048-12-2008 *012
BINDER, Michael Patrick. 128 W PARKWOOD AVE 77546 #048-15-1995 L1998 **PD** *020 †55
BOULTINGHOUSE, Oscar Wm. ■ 77546 #048-04-1981 L1982 **ORS** *020 †16
BROWN, George Thos. 215 E PARKWOOD AVE, STE A 77546 #048-02-1983 L1984
  OTO *020 †45
CASEY, Gregory N. ■ 77546 #048-13-1989 L1990 **CCP PD** *062 †55
CONWAY, Richard Mark. 807 S FRIENDSWOOD DR, STE 2 77546 #018-03-1965 L1968
  GP AM *020
DEAN, Emily G. 1306 SILVERLEAF DR 77546 #048-14-1998 L2001 **EM** *020 †16
DOMINGUEZ, Awilda M. ■ 77546 #042-01-1987 L1989 **PD** *020
DUGANO-DAPHNIS, Pamela D. 347 E PARKWOOD AVE 77546 #047-07-1996 L1998
  MPD IM *020 †20
EARLE, Robert Nelson. 1560 W BAY AREA BLVD, STE 305 77546 #048-14-1995 L1996
  P *020 †75
ELAFIFI, Bayoumi A. ■ 77546 #915-04-1958 L1975 **GS** *075
ESPANA, Kathrym Fernandez. 128 W PARKWOOD AVE, PEDIATRIC ASSOCIATES-FRIEN 77546
  #048-02-2004 L2007 **PD** *020 †55
GARRETT, Wm Edward, Jr. 133 N FRIENDSWOOD DR, ADVANCED SURGICAL WELLNESS 77546
  #047-07-1971 L1977 **GS EM** *020 †16,85
HAMEED, Khalid. ■ 77546 #704-01-1953 L1973 **PTH** *020 †50
HARISH, Seethamraju. ■ 77546 #495-65-1994 L2003 **PCC** *020
HART, John Alexander, Jr. ■ 77549 #021-01-1961 L1967 **OBG** *071
HAUSINGER, Sheryl Ann. 411 E PARKWOOD AVE 77546 #048-04-1983 L1983 **PD PEM** *020 †55
HEARN, Claude David. ■ 77546 #001-02-1965 L1972 **GS** *071 †85
HIGGINS, Napoleon B, Jr. 1560 W BAY AREA BLVD STE 1 77546 #047-07-1998 L2001
  P CHP *020 †75
HIJAZI, Nader Khalouk. ■ 77546 #575-01-1995 L2004 **PCC** *020 †20 ‡
HOANG, Tuquynh Nguyen. ■ 77546 #048-02-2004 **MPD** *012
HONG, Sung-Yun. 363 E PARKWOOD AVE 77546 #583-10-1974 L1984 **AN** *020
HUANG, Hai-Ning. ■ 77546 #244-03-1969 L1976 **IM** *071
HUANG, Kuangzoo Samuel. 355 E PARKWOOD AVE 77546 #036-01-1995 L1998 **FM** *020 †18
HUSAIN, Manik. ■ 77546 #495-19-1963 L1977 **OBG** *020
JONES, William P, Jr. ■ 77546 #047-06-1949 L1950 **FPG GP** *072
KEEPERS, Jerry May. 308 W PARKWOOD AVE, STE 106 77546 #048-13-1979 L1982
  AN PME *020
KHAN, Shahnaz. 807 S FRIENDSWOOD DR, STE 5 77546 #704-16-1980 L1992 **IM** *020 †20
KIM, Young Ju. 343 E PARKWOOD AVE 77546 #583-12-1973 L1979 **PD HEM** *020 †55
KUMAR, Alok. ■ 77546 #495-43-2002 **P** *012
MADHU, Purushoth. ■ 77546 #495-04-1997 L2002 **PD** *020 †55
MC GINNIS, Patrick Jos. 601 N CLEAR CREEK DR, CERNER CORPORATION 77546
  #020-12-1988 L1994 **AM IM** *020 †70
MELOCHE, Sara L. ■ 77546 #048-02-1989 L1990 **IM** *020 †20
MOLINA, Martha M. ■ 77546 #048-14-2007 **FP** *012
MOUKADDAM, Nidal Jihad. 1560 W BAY AREA BLVD, STE 110 77546 #605-01-1999 L2005
  P *100 †75
MOULTON, Darrell Lee. ■ 77546 #048-02-2004 **ORS** *012
MUECKE, Lee Norman. 133 N FRIENDSWOOD DR, # 305 77546 #048-02-1985 L1987
  PD GPM *020 †70
OCHSNER, Allison Becker. 355 E PARKWOOD AVE 77546 #041-02-1992 L1994 **FM** *020 †18
OLMOS, Xochitl Laura. ■ 77546 #035-01-2002 **PD** *100
PICCIONE, James M. 3010 HARVEST HILL DR 77546 #048-14-1985 L1993 **EM FM** *020 †18
POWERS, Jacquelyn Marie. ■ 77546 #048-02-2008 *012
ROESER, Mark Elliot. ■ 77546 #048-12-2007 **GS** *012
ROMEU, Hector J. ■ 77546 #275-01-1951 L1965 **FM OBG** *020
SHESHADRI, Ajay. ■ 77546 #048-12-2007 **IM** *012
SILVA, Gayani P. ■ 77546 #422-01-1991 L1997 **PD** *020 †55
SIM, Tommy Chua. 357 E PARKWOOD AVE, FM CTR ASTHMA & ALLRGC DIS 77546
  #748-01-1981 L1988 **AI MPD** *020 †55,03
SMILEY, Robert Hoyland. ■ 77546 #039-01-1956 L1972 **TS VS** *071 †85,90
SMITH, Mahalia D. 2227 LAKEWAY DR 77546 #048-02-1993 L1995 **IM** *020
SPUHLER, Wanda P. 2401 W PARKWOOD AVE STE B 77546 #047-06-1977 L1983 **GP** *020
STONE, Adam Laszlo. ■ 77546 #048-12-2005 **GS** *100
TAYLOR, Charman Lynn. ■ 77546 #048-02-1977 L1977 **P** *100
THINT, Monica Win. 411 E PARKWOOD AVE 77546 #209-01-1984 L1995 **PD** *020 †55
UKWADE, Philomena E. 401 E PARKWOOD AVE 77546 #690-06-1987 L1994 **IM** *020 †20
VAN ARSDALL, Melissa R. ■ 77546 #048-14-2006 **PD** *012

FRIONA – PARMER

ALEXANDER, Robert Snyder. 1307 CLEVELAND AVE 79035 #048-02-1962 L1962 **FM** *020 †18 ‡
DICKSON, Jeffrey S. 1307 CLEVELAND AVE 79035 #048-12-1998 L2001 **FM** *020 †18
JUBAY, Felipe Lawas, Jr. 1307 CLEVELAND AVE, FRIONA MED CLNC 79035
  #748-11-1972 L1994 **GP IM** *020
SPRING, Paul L. ■ 79035 #048-12-1944 L1945 **GP** *071

FRISCO – COLLIN

AHMED, Humera. 3880 PARKWOOD BLVD, STE 501 75034 #704-02-2001 L2007 **IM** *020 †20

ALANG, Jaspreet Singh. 3880 PARKWOOD BLVD, STE 304 75034 #495-14-1992 L2002
  IM *020 †20
ALEXANDER, Bruce John. 4500 HILLCREST RD, STE 120 75035 #017-20-1993 L1996
  FM *020 †18
ALEXANDER, Preston Clay. 4401 COIT RD STE 205 75035 #048-14-1983 L1983 **OBG** *020 †30
ALIMCHANDANI, Aneesha H. 9300 WADE BLVD STE 220 75035 #495-17-1992 L2004
  IM *020 †20
ALLEN, Mark Lee. 5575 WARREN PKWY, STE 116 75034 #048-13-1987 L1992 **U** *020 †95
ALLOJU, Murali. 4401 COIT RD, STE 201 75035 #495-57-1980 L1997 **GE** *020 †20
AMBAVARAM, Sukanya. 75035 #495-62-1994 L2007 **OM** *100
ANDERSON, Brady Edward. 4988 GOLFSIDE DR, BAYLOR UNIV MEDICAL CENTER 75035
  #048-15-2003 L2005 **GS** *012
ANGLIN, Beth V. 4401 COIT RD, STE 313 75035 #048-12-1993 L1994 **GS** *020 †85
BAILEY, Jennifer L. 4461 COIT RD STE 205 75035 #048-12-2000 L2003 **OBG** *020
BAILEY, Melissa Knox. 4401 COIT RD, SUITE 305, PAVILLION I 75035 #048-02-1995 L2004
  OBG *020 †20
BAIN, Deborah Z. 4851 LEGACY DR STE 601 75034 #048-13-1993 L1994 **PD** *020 †55
BARSIK, Tamara. 3880 PARKWOOD BLVD, STE 501 75034 #875-01-1990 L1998 **IM** *020 †20
BASS, Robert L. 4401 COIT RD STE 409 75035 #048-12-1988 L1989 **HS** *020 †40
BHARGAVA, Sharlaw. 5850 TOWN AND COUNTRY BLVD, STE 1202 75034 #495-77-1994 L2005
  CHP *020 †75
BHOJA, Ravi. ■ 75035 #012-22-2003 L2006 **AN** *100
BISHOP, Jennifer M. 5575 WARREN PKWY STE 115 75034 #048-13-2003 L2005 **FM** *020 †18
BOLIN, Jerry B. 3550 PARKWOOD BLVD, BLDG D 75034 #048-12-1996 L1999 **FM** *020 †18
BONDY, John David. 7589 PRESTON RD, TEXAS RADIOLOGY 75034 #048-12-1994 L1997
  DR *020 †30
BOSITA, Renato M. ■ 75034 #748-02-1960 L1972 **AN** *071 †05
BOYD, Suzette Lynn. 5575 WARREN PKWY STE 314 75034 #017-20-1995 L1996 **OBG** *020 †30
BRICKER, Eric Randolph. ■ 75034 #016-11-2004 L2007 **IM** *100 †20
BROCKMAN, Craig R, II. 4760 PRESTON RD STE 244 75034 #048-12-2001 L2003 **EM** *020 †16
BROWN, John Currier. ■ 75034 #017-20-1983 L1984 **EM** *020 †16
BUCH, Jeffrey Phillip. 5616 WARREN PKWY, STE 101 75034 #025-01-1980 L1985 **U** *020 †95
BULGER, Robert Raymond. 5575 WARREN PKWY, STE 310 75034 #026-08-1980 L1990
  PMM AN *020 †05
BURNS, William Cedric, II. 4401 COIT RD STE 407 75035 #048-12-1985 L1986
  OSM ORS *020 †40
CALDERON, Sheila F. 5729 LEBANON RD, B, #180 75034 #047-07-1980 L1981 **IM** *020
CARMAN, Christine Ann. 5575 WARREN PKWY 75034 #035-06-1992 L2001 **PS** *020 †55,65 ‡
CASE, Erin A. ■ 75034 #048-15-2003 L2006 **FM** *020 †18
CHACKO, Mona. 8200 STONEBROOK PKWY, PARKWAY, #100 75034 #495-58-1989 L2002
  FM *020 †18
CHAMPENA, Tito Alberto. ■ 75034 #341-01-1960 L1971 **P** *020 †75
CHECO, Pedro Elias. 3211 INTERNET BLVD STE 280 75034 #308-03-1985 L1990 **IM** *020 †20 ‡
CHINOY, Birjis D. 8000 WARREN PKWY STE 200 75034 #495-21-1990 L2003 **AI** *020 †20,03
COX, John Andrew. 4199 CHERRY RIDGE DR 75034 #030-06-1993 L2000 **IM** *020 †20
CULPEPPER, Guy Lee. 3550 PARKWOOD BLVD, BENT TREE FAMILY 75034 #048-14-1984 L1985
  FM *020 †18 ‡
CULVER, Jennifer L. 2595 DALLAS PKWY, STE 405 75034 #048-15-1995 L1996 **FM** *020 †18
DAVIS, Vicki Blackmon. 8680 W MAIN ST STE 1W 75034 #048-15-1981 L1981 **IM** *020 †20
DE LA PENA, Octavio A. 4401 COIT RD STE 201 75035 #649-31-1984 L1997 **GE** *020 †20
DEL VALLE, Francisco. ■ 75034 #847-08-1958 L1973 **IM** *020
DE VILLENEUVE, Allan Rene. 4500 HILLCREST RD, STE 140 75035 #048-12-1969 L1969
  PD *020 †55
DE YOUNG, George Gage. ■ 75034 #065-06-1963 L1978 **AN** *071 †05
DHANVANTRI, Vijaya Ramach. 3880 PARKWOOD BLVD, BLDG 5 75034 #496-39-1996 L2006
  IM *020 †30
DISRAELI, Phillip H. 8756 TEEL PKWY STE 3 75034 #048-04-1987 L1998 **FM UCM** *020 †18
DO, Vu Quoc. ■ 75035 #041-15-2002 L2007 **RNR** *012 †80
EKWEANI, Obiora Maduka. 3550 PARKWOOD BLVD, # A-205 75034 #690-02-1983 L2000
  IM EM *020 †20
ELLER, Richard F. 4401 COIT RD, STE 313 75035 #048-16-1990 L1991 **GS** *020 †85
ELLER, Thomas O, II. 4401 COIT RD STE 313 75035 #048-12-1984 L1995 **IM HOS** *020 †20 ‡
ELLIOTT, Tracy. 4401 COIT RD, STE 205 75035 #048-14-1998 L2002 **OBG** *020 †30
ELSAIE, Wahida Aly. ■ 75034 #915-02-1969 L1983 **P** *020
ENGELKING, Luke James. ■ 75034 #048-12-2007 L2007 **IM** *012
EVANS, Carolyn Ann. 4500 HILLCREST RD, STE 140 75035 #048-13-1979 L1979 **PD** *020 †55
FELDMAN, Jerald. 5575 WARREN PKWY 75034 #021-05-1954 L1955 **OPH** *071 †35
FERGUSON, Bryan J. 3550 PARKWOOD BLVD, BENT TREE FAMILY 75034 #048-04-1991 L1992
  FM *020 †18
FRANKUM, Wilbur Max. ■ 75034 #019-02-1981 L1989 **FM** *020 †18 ‡
FRIEDMAN, Bradley Ryan. 11560 TEEL PKWY, STE 100 75034 #021-01-2004 L2006
  FM *100 †18
GARZA, Alma D. 3550 PARKWOOD BLVD, BENT TREE FAMILY 75034 #048-12-1997 L1998
  FM *020 †18
GERLACHER, Gary Reagan. 3401 PRESTON RD, STE 11 75034 #048-04-1994 L1996
  PD *020 †55
GIBSON, Gerald P, Jr. 6001 JORDAN WAY 75034 #048-04-1995 L2003 **EM** *020 †16
GICHERU, Eugene Kangethe. 15726 FOX MEADOW LN 75035 #048-02-2002 L2004
  EM *100 †16
GILLEY, James Thos. 7589 PRESTON RD, STE 700 75034 #654-01-1987 L1995 **IM** *020
GLOGAU, Alexander Ives. 5575 WARREN PKWY, STE 106 75034 #035-08-1984 L1989
  ORS OTR *020 †40
GONZALES, Epichelle R. ■ 75034 #748-10-1995 L1999 **P** *100 †75
GONZALEZ-ROSALES, F. 4401 COIT RD STE 301 75035 #649-01-1979 L2000 **IM** *020 †20
GOODMAN, James Laurence. ■ 75034 #048-12-1970 L1970 **EM IM** *020 †16
GRAHAM, George Struby. 7589 PRESTON RD, TEXAS RADIOLOGY 75034 #030-06-1968 L1970
  R *020 †80
GREENBERG, Alan Mark. 4401 COIT RD, STE 205 75035 #048-14-1983 L1983 **OBG** *020 †30
GROSSLING, Higinia C. ■ 75035 #231-01-1954 L1970 **AN** *071
GUERRERO, Richard. ■ 75035 #048-15-2003 L2007 **IM** *100 †20
GUPTA, Raghav. 5575 WARREN PKWY, VISTA OPHTHALMOLOGY ASSOCI 75034
  #033-05-1997 L2001 **OPH** *020
GUSTOVICH, Carla Ann. 7589 PRESTON RD, STE 500 75034 #048-14-2000 L2003 **D** *020 †15
HALE, Janet Ames. ■ 75034 #004-01-1977 L1983 **SO** *071 †85
HAQ, Ehsan Ul. ■ 75034 #704-08-1963 L1973 **IM** *020

HAQ, Nadeem E. ■ 75034 #704-25-1993 L2004 **OPH** *020 †35
HARPER, Elise M. 4401 COIT RD, STE 205 75035 #048-04-1995 L1999 **OBG** *020 †30
HASSELL, Jeffrey S. 5575 WARREN PKWY, STE 116 75034 #048-12-1984 L1990 **U** *020 †95
HAWRONSKY, John W. 13542 LINCOLNSHIRE LN 75035 #024-07-1984 L1991 **FM** *020 †18
HAYS, Randall Lynn. 307 W MAIN ST, STE 135 75034 #021-06-1984 L2003 **EM** *020 †18
HERBERT, Frances B. 4401 COIT RD, STE 409 75035 #051-04-1992 L1998 **U** *020 †95
HERNANDEZ-SHEPPARD, Cassan. 301 W MAIN ST 75034 #048-14-1997 L1998 **FM EM** *020 †18
HESS, Guillermo. ■ 75035 #005-02-1976 L1990 **DR** *020 †80
HIGHTOWER, Leroy Wayne. ■ 75034 #048-12-1970 L1972 **GE IM** *020 †20
HILL, Jerron Carlyle. ■ 75034 #025-07-1990 L2002 **AN** *020 †05
HOANG, Thai Vinh. 3550 PARKWOOD BLVD, STE C306 STONEBRIAR PEDS 75034 #048-14-1998 L2001 **PD** *020 †55
HOLT, Catherine Anne. ■ 75035 #048-02-2002 L2005 **OBG** *020
HUQ, Syeda Fahmida. ■ 75034 #160-02-1984 **PM** *100
HURSEY, Kristina. 3550 PARKWOOD BLVD, STE 100 75034 #045-01-2002 L2005 **IM** *020 †20
INNES, Kristen Nelson. 3880 PARKWOOD BLVD 75034 #012-01-2000 L2005 **OBG** *020 †30
JEFFREY, Pamela Marie. 73 MILL POND DR 75034 #047-07-1985 L1986 **AN** *020 †05
JENKINS, Boyd R. 4500 HILLCREST RD STE 180, STONEBRIAR FAMILY PHYSICIA 75035 #048-14-1988 L1989 **FM** *020 †18
JENSEN, James Waldemar. ■ 75034 #028-34-1964 L1964 **OBG** *020 †30
JETT, Gary Kimble. 5575 WARREN PKWY STE 306 75034 #048-12-1978 L1978 **TS** *020 †85,90 ‡
JOHNSON, Bryan Garrett. 6842 W MAIN ST 75034 #019-02-1994 L2000 **IM** *020 †20
KANNAN, Subhasri. 9300 WADE BLVD STE 220 75035 #495-04-1995 L2003 **IM** *020 †20
KAPLAN, Seth David. 5575 WARREN PKWY STE 318 75034 #036-07-1996 L1999 **PD** *020 †55 ‡
KASMIERSKY, Valerie K. 5575 WARREN PKWY, STE 115 75034 #048-13-2001 L2003 **FM** *020 †18
KAVIKONDALA, Vijaya. 3880 PARKWOOD BLVD, STE 501 75034 #495-05-1990 L2005 **IM** *020 †20
KAYFAN, Farshid Daemi. 4851 LEGACY DR STE 301 75034 #001-02-1988 L1993 **EM** *020 †16
KHATAIN, Larissa Elizabet. ■ 75035 #048-12-2006 L2006 **OBG** *012
KIM, Nancy Y. 5575 WARREN PKWY, STE 115 75034 #048-12-1997 L2003 **U** *020 †95
KING, Kevin. 9801 CHAPEL TRL 75034 #048-12-1993 L1995 **AN** *012 †16
KNOLL, Victoria Dorothy. 5575 WARREN PKWY, STE 106 75034 #019-02-1997 L1998 **HS** *020 †40
KOURLIS, Harry A, Jr. 6023 ARBORETUM DR 75034 #010-02-1991 L1992 **TS** *020 †90,85
KUHNE, Robert Christopher. 4461 COIT RD, STE 309 75035 #048-02-1986 L1987 **OBG** *020 †30
KUMAR, Iresh. 7589 PRESTON RD STE 600 75034 #495-23-1994 L2004 **PD** *020 †55
KUNCHAM, Sreevani. 7227 PRESTON RD 75034 #495-62-1989 L2002 **IM** *020 †20
KUSI-MENSAH, Christian. ■ 75035 #198-04-1993 L2007 **FM** *020 †18
LA MASTERS, David Logan. 3211 INTERNET BLVD, STE 120 75034 #016-06-1977 L1985 **RNR DR** *020 †80
LATTA, Amy Marie. 3550 PARKWOOD BLVD, BENT TREE FAMILY 75034 #048-02-1999 L2001 **FM** *020 †18
LEE, Jun H. 3880 PARKWOOD BLVD STE 50 75034 #048-12-1993 L1994 **IM** *020 †20
LEE, Michael Ming-Jen. 4461 COIT RD STE 311 75035 #048-02-1990 L1993 **IM** *020
LESTZ, Leslie Katz. 5575 WARREN PKWY, STE 318 75034 #012-05-1998 L2001 **PD** *020 †55
LEW, Stephanie F. ■ 75035 #048-02-2001 L2004 **OBG** *100
LEWIS, Jerry Wayne. 5757 WARREN PKWY, # 110 75034 #039-01-1989 L1990 **AN** *020 †05
LIEMAN, Stephen Jay. 5575 WARREN PKWY, STE 116 75034 #048-04-1979 L1980 **U** *020 †95
LOFTIN, James Philip, Jr. 4401 COIT RD, STE 303 75034 #021-06-1975 L1982 **PUD IM** *020 †20
LONDON, Alan A. 4401 COIT RD STE 313 75035 #048-12-1994 L1996 **GS** *020 †85
LORENZO, Ana Cecilia Guaj. 4401 COIT RD STE 401 75035 #048-14-1992 L2007 **VS** *020 †85
MC INTIRE, Meredith Ann. 4461 COIT RD, PAVILLION II, STE 205 75035 #048-15-2003 L2007 **OBG** *020
MC NUTT, Joseph Wilson. 4401 COIT RD, PAVILLION 1 STE 407 75035 #004-01-1994 L1996 **ORS OSM** *020 †40
MCQUAID, Mark Allan. 1518 LEGACY DR, STE 120 75034 #048-12-1991 L1992 **GS VS** *020 †85
MEE, Mee. ■ 75034 #048-12-2004 †100
MEEHLHAUSE, Mark Gary. 5575 WARREN PKWY 75034 #018-03-1999 L2002 **FM** *020 †18
MEHENDALE, Neelesh H. 4401 COIT RD STE 411 75035 #021-05-1998 L1999 **OTO** *020 †45
MEHTA, Rinku Vakil. 45 PRISTINE POND DR 75034 #048-12-1999 L2008 **OBG** *020 †30
MERTEN, Jay Leonard. ■ 75034 #021-01-1971 L1976 **OPH** *020 †35
MEYER, Colin John. ■ 75034 #048-12-2003 *100
MORGAN, Mickey Dean. 5575 WARREN PKWY 75034 #048-13-1980 L1987 **GS** *020 †85
MOS, Amy K. 2595 DALLAS PKWY, PLANO WOMENS HEALTH CARE 75034 #048-15-2002 L2006 **OBG** *020
MOSHIER, Jason Harlon. 4500 HILLCREST RD, STE 140 75035 #051-07-1982 L1984 **PD** *020 †55
NAIL, Richard C. 4401 COIT RD, STE 203 75035 #048-12-1999 L2001 **PD** *020 †55
NAKPAIRAT, Sopon. ■ 75034 #891-01-1952 L1976 **U** *071 †95
NARAYANAN, Subashini. 3880 PARKWOOD BLVD, STE 501 75034 #495-72-1996 L2002 **IM** *020 †20
NEECE, Stephen Robt. 4401 COIT RD STE 403, U OF TX HSC SAN ANTONIO 75035 #048-14-1973 L1974 **NS** *020 †25
NELSON, Garrett S. ■ 75034 #048-15-2002 L2004 **GS** *100
NEUMANN, Scott E. 4461 COIT RD STE 411, CENTENNIAL MEDICAL PAVILIO 75035 #048-78-1999, ▲ L2001 **FM** *020
NEWTON, Christopher Lee. 4401 COIT RD, STE 203 75035 #048-12-1996 L1998 **PD** *020 †55
NGIAN, Yingying. 9662 AVALON DR 75035 #010-02-2001 L2004 **PD** *020 †55
NGUYEN, Minh Chinh. 4401 COIT RD STE 409, SUITE 106 75035 #035-08-1996 L2003 **GS** *100
NOYES, Christopher Thayer. 3550 PARKWOOD BLVD, STE 110 75034 #048-14-2000 L2002 **FM** *020 †18
ORRICK, Larry Richard. ■ 75034 #048-04-1976 L1976 **OBG IM** *020 †30
OUYANG, Luke Yen-Luan. 4401 COIT RD, STE 409 75035 #422-01-2001 L2005 **IM** *020
OWENS, Sherry L. ■ 75034 #039-01-1988 L1989 **PUD IM** *062 †20
PADEGAL, Vivek Anand. 4401 COIT RD, STE 303 75035 #495-33-1992 L1997 **PCC** *020 †20
PAYESTEH, David. ■ 75034 #048-15-2007 **AN** *012
PETROVSKI, Pauline. 4461 COIT RD STE 205 75035 #025-07-2000 L2004 **OBG** *020
RANKINS, Robert C. 8837 LEBANON RD STE 8 75034 #048-12-1994 L2000 **EM** *020 †16
REMBECKI, Richard Michael. 3550 PARKWOOD BLVD, STE G701 75034 #048-12-1989 L1992 **PDP** *020 †55
RICKS, James Ralph, III. 7548 PRESTON RD, STE 141 75034 #039-01-1967 L1976 **IM** *020 †18,20

RISAM, Satbirsingh M. 9300 WADE BLVD, STE 220 75035 #495-33-1990 L2002 **IM** *020 †20
RODGERS, Timothy Gale. 3880 PARKWOOD BLVD, STE 102 75034 #016-06-2002 L2005 **D** *020 †15 ‡
ROGENES, Vince Jonathan. 5575 WARREN PKWY, STE 116 75034 #056-06-1992 L1998 **U** *072 †95
ROGERS, Beverly A. 6434 SHADY OAKS DR 75034 #048-14-1989 L1990 **AN** *020 †05
RUPAREL, Jyotirbala N. ■ 75034 #495-22-1989 L1996 **PD** *020 †55
SASTRY, Vivek S. 3880 PARKWOOD BLVD, STE 501 75034 #495-37-1990 L1996 **IM** *020 †20
SCHLEGEL, John Dudley. ■ 75034 #048-12-1980 L1980 **ORS** *020 †40
SCHMITT, Eric John. 9191 KYSER WAY, BLDG 3 75034 #024-07-1999 L2005 **AI PDA** *020 †55,03
SCHWARTZ, Jay Paul. 4461 COIT RD, STE 315 75035 #016-06-1990 L1995 **PD** *020 †55
SCHWARTZ, Michael. 5575 WARREN PKWY, STE 106 75034 #048-06-1992 L1997 **ORS** *020 †40
SCOTT, Kirk Eugene. 5575 WARREN PKWY, STE 206 75034 #048-12-1999 L2002 **FPS** *020
SETOUDEH-MARAM, Shahriar. ■ 75035 #517-05-2000 L2007 **FM** *020 †18
SKILES, Roger Glynn. 5575 WARREN PKWY, STE 104 75034 #048-15-1982 L1983 **OTO HNS** *020 †45
SMART, Kenneth R, Jr. 4401 COIT RD, STE 309 75035 #048-16-1997 L2004 **PS** *020 †65
SMIGIEL, Mitchell. ■ 75034 #056-06-1967 L1976 **NS** *071 †25
SMITH, Julian Payne. ■ 75034 #035-01-1955 L1963 **GO GYN** *071 †30
SO-BOSITA, Juliet L. ■ 75034 #748-02-1963 L1969 **OBG** *071 †30
SOREMEKUN-SALAMI, Olutoyin. ■ 75034 #033-06-2003 L2007 **AN** *100
STOKES, Kathleen Dooley. 6930 PARKWOOD DR 75034 #033-05-1988 L1995 **PD** *020 †55 ‡
SURDACKI, Joseph Victor. 4401 COIT RD, STE 303 75035 #048-14-1988 L1989 **IM** *020 †20
TAYLOR, Geo De Laughter. ■ 75034 #004-01-1963 L1963 **GP** *071
THAKUR, Kalpana. 3880 PARKWOOD BLVD 75034 #495-92-1992 L2005 **IM** *020 †20
THARP, David Tilghman. 3550 PARKWOOD BLVD, STE 705 75034 #035-45-1974 L1993 **P CHP** *020 †75
TISCHENDORF, Sara Louise. 4500 HILLCREST RD STE 180 75035 #048-14-1996 L2000 **FM** *020 †18
TOMPKINS, Melissa Lasola. 4401 COIT RD, STE 303 75035 #748-02-1989 L1993 **PUD CCM** *020 †20
TREER, John Robert, Jr. 4401 COIT RD STE 409 75035 #048-12-1997 L1998 **IM** *020 †20
TRILLO, Gerardo Hernandez. 4461 COIT RD, STE 100 75035 #649-01-1980 L1990 **ON IM** *020 †20
VYZA, Anitha Y. 3880 PARKWOOD BLVD, STE 501 75034 #495-11-1992 L2000 **IM** *020 †20
WANG, Bo. 3880 PARKWOOD BLVD, STE 501 75034 #243-76-1985 L1998 **IM** *020 †20
WANG, Hui. 9300 WADE BLVD, STE 220 75035 #242-63-1995 L2005 **IM** *020
WEISBERG, Eric Lawrence. ■ 75034 #012-05-2003 L2005 **D** *020 †15
WELBORNE, Leslie Skinner. 4401 COIT RD STE 305, CENTENNIAL OB/GYN PA 75035 #048-02-1995 L1999 **OBG OCC** *020 †30
WIERSCHEM, Michael G. 4401 COIT RD, STE 409 75035 #048-12-1994 L1999 **U** *020 †95
WILLIAMS, Reed. 5400 DALLAS PKWY 75035 #048-12-1994 L1996 **IM** *100
WOOD, Kathryn Jo. 5575 WARREN PKWY, STE 208 75034 #048-13-1984 L1986 **OBG** *020 †30
WOODY, Jay R. 4851 LEGACY DR STE 3 75034 #048-12-1998 L1999 **EM** *020 †16
WU, Yiqun. 7227 PRESTON RD 75034 #243-29-1983 L2002 **FM** *020 †18
YEH, Chi-Hwa. 7227 PRESTON RD 75034 #048-02-1991 L1992 **FM GP** *020 †18

FULSHEAR – FORT BEND

CONDE, Arthur B. PO BOX 803, 8042 BOIS DARC LN 77441 #748-02-1957 L1967 **IM P** *071
HOSEY, Abner Benj. ■ 77441 #048-02-1956 L1956 **R** *020
SCHULTZ, Heidi Ann. 29818 FM 1093 RD, STE 200 77441 #048-14-1999 L2001 **FM** *020 †18 ‡

FULTON – ARANSAS

YORK, Thomas L. ■ 78358 #023-01-1951 L1952 **OM GP** *071

GAINESVILLE – COOKE

AGARWAL, Virendra K. 1902 HOSPITAL BLVD STE E, NTMC MEDICAL OFFICE BLDG 76240 #495-05-1975 L2003 **IM** *020 †20
ANWAR, Khawaja. 801 N GRAND AVE 76240 #704-01-1975 L1982 **CD IM** *020 †20
COLE, James Raymond. 413 E BROADWAY ST 76240 #048-12-1957 **GP OM** *020 †18
CROFT, Kevin Wallace. 2020 W HIGHWAY 82 76240 #030-06-1989 L1994 **OPH** *020 †35
CURRIER, Thomas Jos. 413 E BROADWAY ST 76240 #048-13-1977 L1993 **OBG** *020
GIBBS, Mark Eric. PO BOX 1239, 1625 N GRAND AVE 76241 #048-14-1996 L1997 **FM** *020 †18 ‡
GORDON, Stephen B. ■ 76240 #654-01-1984 L1995 **CLP** *020
HAILESELASSIE, Tsion E. 1902 HOSPITAL BLVD STE F 76240 #035-01-1997 L2003 **PD** *020
HENDRY, Marjorie H. ■ 76241 #041-07-1953 L1958 **PM IM** *071
JOHNSON, Curtis Harvey. 1511 LYNWOOD ST 76240 #048-14-2002 L2005 **EM** *020
JOLLY, Richard William. 1902 HOSPITAL BLVD, STE G 76240 #039-01-2001 L2004 **OPH** *020 †35
JOSEPH, Ezra S S. 1103 E CALIFORNIA ST 76240 #495-27-1955 L1975 **GS** *071
KHAIRA, Bhupinder S. 1016 RITCHEY ST 76240 #495-29-1979 L1987 **GS VS** *020 †85
KWAN, Patrick K. 801 N GRAND AVE 76240 #244-04-1973 L1982 **PD** *020
LEWIS, Douglas. 1900 HOSPITAL BLVD, EMERGENCY DEPT 76240 #048-02-1990 L1991 **EM** *020 †18
MC LAUGHLIN, Roane H. 1902 HOSPITAL BLVD STE B 76240 #048-16-1985 L1986 **OBG** *020 †30
MC LEROY, Robert Reagan. 1627 N GRAND AVE 76240 #021-01-1976 L1977 **FM** *020 †18
PIOTROWSKI, Daniel Scott. 1016 RITCHEY ST 76240 #005-12-1995 L1996 **FM** *020 †18
ROY, Lisa M. 1112 E CALIFORNIA ST 76240 #055-02-1997 L2005 **IM** *020
SALEM, Allen Jay. 1820 ONEAL ST STE 5 76240 #010-01-1986 L1999 **PUD IM** *020 †20
SCHACHAR, Leslie. 1925 N GRAND AVE 76240 #561-01-1971 L1976 **OPH** *020
SEARS, Larry Clay. 836 E CALIFORNIA ST 76240 #048-12-1977 L1977 **FM FPG** *020 †18
SEARS, V Glenn. 836 E CALIFORNIA ST 76240 #048-12-1975 L1978 **FM FPG** *020 †18 ‡
ZINDEL, Barry Lee. 426 N GRAND AVE 76240 #025-01-1964 L1973 **ORS** *020 †40

GALENA PARK – HARRIS

LAMBERT, Y Alan, Jr. 1609 LEGGETT DR 77547 #048-04-1952 L1952 **FM** *071 †18

MEDINA, Jose R. 1104 12TH ST 77547 #048-16-2002 L2003 **EM** *020 †16

GALVESTON – GALVESTON

AARSLAND, Asle. 301 UNIVERSITY BLVD, STE 2A 77555 #693-02-1984 L2007 *100

ABBASI, Hamid Reza. 301 UNIVERSITY BLVD, UNIV OF TEXAS MED BRANCH 77555 #409-10-1996 L2006 **NS** *012

ABDELHADI, Kareem Husam. UNIV OF TEXAS MED BRANCH, DEPT OF INT MED 77555 #575-01-2003 **IM** *012

ABDULLA, Nihal Essa. UNIV OF TEXAS MED BRANCH, DEPT OF INT MED 77555 #704-02-2000 L2008 **IM** *100 †20

ABDULLAH, Shaad Essa. 301 UNIVERSITY BLVD 77555 #704-02-2004 **IM** *012

ABOULEISH, Amr Ezzat. STE 2A, ROUTE 0591, UNIV OF TEXAS MEDICAL BRAN 77555 #048-14-1989 L1991 **AN PD** *020 †05

ABSTON, Sally. ■ 77550 #048-02-1962 L1962 **OS GS** *071 †85

ABU SAID, Ghassan Halim. 301 UNIV BLVD 77555 #913-96-2003 **IM** *012

ABU SHARIFEH, Tareq Moh'D. 301 UNIVERSITY BLVD, UTMB 77555 #575-01-1998 L2004 **IM** *020 †20

ADAMS, John Michael. UNIV OF TEXAS MED BRANCH, DEPT OF PSYCHIATRY 77555 #048-02-2003 L2008 **CHP** *012

ADAPALA, Prashanth. ■ 77551 #495-21-2000 L2008 **ON** *012 †20

ADEGBOYEGA, Patrick A. 301 UNIVERSITY BLVD, UNIVERSITY OF TEXAS MEDICA 77555 #690-08-1987 L1994 **PTH** *020 †50

AFZAL, Adnan. 301 UNIVERSITY BLVD, 5106 JOHN SEALY ANNEX 77555 #704-02-1991 L2001 **CD** *020 †20

AGUIAR, Savitri Gomes De. ■ 77550 #187-29-1999 L2008 **ID** *012 †20

AGUILAR, Lisa Marie. UNIV OF TEXAS MED BRANCH, DEPT OF PSYCHIATRY 77555 #048-02-2004 L2008 **P** *012

AHMAD, Masood. UTMB INT MED E53 77550 #495-51-1967 L1973 **CD** *020 †20

AHMED, Mub Basheer. ■ 77550 #422-01-2006 **PD** *012

AHMED, Sonya Sayed. 301 UNIVERSITY BLVD, UTMB/ORTHOPAEDICS 77555 #028-46-2003 L2008 **ORS** *012

AHSAN, Muhammad Azeem. 301 UNIVERSITY BLVD, DIV OF INF DISEASES 77555 #704-02-1988 L2002 **IM** *020 †20

AHUJA, Tejinder S. 301 UNIVERSITY BLVD, U T M B GALVESTON 77555 #495-90-1987 L1996 **NEP** *020 †20

AINSWORTH, Michael Alan. 301 UNIVERSITY BLVD 77555 #048-02-1981 L1981 **IM** *040 †20

AKINCI, Devrim. 301 UNIVERSITY BLVD, STE D62 77550 #902-05-1995 **VIR** *100

AL-FAWA'REH, Moh'D Dursi. 301 UNIVERSITY BLVD, UNIV OF TEXAS MED BRANCH-G 77555 #575-01-1995 L2007 **OSS** *100

ALI, Iftikhar A. 301 UNIVERSITY BLVD, UTMB EMERGENCY MEDICINE 77555 #048-15-1997 L2000 **EM** *020 †20

ALI JIWANI, Amyn Karim. 3.201 UNIVERSITY BLVD 77555 #704-16-1989 L2007 **PDC** *020 †55

AL-JUBEH, Jamal Mustafa. 301 UNIVERSITY BLVD, DEPT. OF PEDIATRICS 77555 #575-01-1992 L1997 **PDE** *020 †55

ALLEN, Stanley David. 301 UNIVERSITY BLVD, RT 792 77555 #048-02-1978 L1978 **ORS** *020 †40

ALLENSWORTH, Daniel C. 301 UNIVERSITY BLVD, U T M B GALVESTON 77555 #048-02-1955 L1955 **CD IM** *071

ALMOKAYYAD, Rami Mahmoud. 301 UNIV BLVD 77555 #575-02-2008 **IM** *012

ALONSO, Wilfred Jerome An. 301 UNIV BLV STE D62 77550 #748-10-2001 L2007 **FP** *020

ALPERIN, Jack Bernard. 301 UNIVERSITY BLVD, UNIVERSITY OF TEXAS MEDICA 77555 #047-06-1957 L1963 **HEM BBK** *040

AL TAANI, Jamal. 301 UNIV BLVD, STE D62 77555 #875-01-1994 L2007 **PDR** *100

ALY, Ashraf M. PEDIATRIC CARDIOLOGY, UNIV OF TEXAS MEDICAL BRAN 77555 #915-02-1978 L2002 **PDC** *020 †55

AMAR, Neil Kanth. ■ 77550 #048-02-2008 *012

AMOLE, Adewumi Olaolu Dav. 301 UNIV BLVD, STE D62 77555 #690-01-1987 **RNR** *012

ANANDAN, Sharadamani. 301 UNIVERSITY BLVD, REBECCA SEALY HOSPITAL 77555 #496-39-1994 L2004 **P** *020

ANAPARTHY, Rajeswari. ■ 77551 #495-58-2003 **IM** *012

ANDERS, D'Andrea Michelle. ■ 77550 #048-02-2007 **IM** *012

ANDERSON, Garland D. 301 UNIVERSITY BLVD, DEPT OF OB/GYN 77555 #017-20-1962 L1962 **FM OM** *020 †18

ANDERSON, Garland Douglas. 301 UNIVERSITY BLVD, OFFICE OF THE EXECUTIVE VI 77555 #047-06-1970 L1971 **OBG MFM** *030 †30

ANDERSON, Karl Elmo. UTMB-EWING HALL RTE J 09 77550 #023-07-1965 L1988 **GE IM** *040 †20

APARICIO, Sylvia Susana. 301 UNIVERSITY BLVD 77555 #024-01-2007 **PS** *012

ARENZON, Liliane. 606 UNIVERSITY BLVD 77550 #048-02-2004 L2007 **P** *012

ARISTIMUNO, Patricia. 301 UNIVERSITY BLVD, DIVISION OF NEPHROLOGY 77555 #132-01-1989 L1996 **NEP** *020 †20

ARIYO, Sarah H. 301 UNIV BLV, DEPT OF PEDS 77555 #048-12-2007 **PD** *012

ARNOLD, Benjamin Allen. ■ 77550 #048-02-2006 **AN** *012

ARONSON, Judith Field. 301 UNIVERSITY BLVD, STE 1022 77555 #036-01-1985 L1992 **PTH** *020 †50

ASHIZAWA, Tetsuo. 301 UNIVERSITY BLVD, DEPT NEURO-UTMB 77555 #572-20-1973 L1976 **N** *050 †75

ASSAD KOTTNER, Christian. 301 UNIV BLV STE D62 77550 #649-52-2004 **IM** *012

ASUNCION, Lloyd Patrick. ■ 77551 #014-01-2006 **MPD** *012

ATANASOV, Strahil T. 301 UNIVERSITY BLVD, DEPT OF INTERNAL MEDICINE 77555 #198-02-1983 L1996 **CHN** *020 †55,75

ATIVITAVAS, Touch. ■ 77551 #891-02-1995 **ON** *020 †20

AUNON, Serena Maria. 301 UNIVERSITY BLVD, JSA 4.112 77555 #048-14-2001 L2004 **AM** *020

AUSTER, Martin D. ■ 77550 #048-02-2000 **IM** *012

AUZENNE, Gregory. 301 UNIVERSITY BLVD, STE 2A 77555 #048-13-1999 L2003 **APM** *020 †05

AVERY, Andrew Nelson. 301 UNIVERSITY BLVD, UNIV OF TX MED BRANCH 77555 #048-02-1973 L1973 **OM PTX** *040 †20,70

AVERY, Eric Nelson. 301 UNIVERSITY BLVD, DEPT OF PSYCHIATRY, ROOM 1 77555 #048-02-1974 L1974 **P** *020

AYALA, Natalie. 301 UNIVERSITY BLVD #048-02-2007 **PD** *012

AZAM, Nasreen. 301 UNIVERSITY BLVD, PEDIATRIC NEPHROLOGY 77555 #919-03-1984 L2002 **PN** *020 †55

AZIZ, Sameh Nasseem. ■ 77550 #915-02-1998 L2007 **IMG** *100 †20

BAILEY, Byron James. 301 UNIVERSITY BLVD 77550 #039-01-1959 L1968 **OTO** *071 †45

BAJAJ, Mandeep. 301 UNIVERSITY BLVD, ROUTE 1060, UTMB 77550 #495-36-1989 L2001 **IM** *020 †20

BAKER, Jaqwiana Samia. 301 UNIVERSITY BLVD, UNIV OF TEXAS MED BRANCH 77555 #021-05-2006 **PD** *012

BANERJI, Soumo. ■ 77554 #048-04-2007 **GS** *012

BANEZ, Maria Norma Victor. 301 UNIV 77555 #748-01-2002 L2008 **PD** *012

BANTA, Brady J. BRANCH HOSPI, UNIV OF TEXAS MED 77555 #048-16-2000 L2004 **DR** *020

BARNHART, Charles C, Jr. ■ 77551 #048-02-1974 L1975 **P** *020 †75

BARNHART, Erin A. 301 UNIVERSITY BLVD, PATHOLOGY DEPARTMENT 77555 #048-14-2005 L2007 **PTH** *012

BARON, Samuel. UTMB-MICROBIOLOGY 77550 #035-19-1952 L1976 **ID IG** *050

BARTOS, David B. UNIV OF TEXAS MED BRANCH, DEPT OF INT MED 77555 #048-02-2001 L2008 **IM** *012

BARTZ, Roger Anthony. ■ 77550 #048-02-2007 **PD** *012

BASRAON, Sanmaan Kaur. 301 UNIV BVD 77555 #495-29-2005 **OBG** *012

BASS, Michael Joseph. ■ 77550 #016-45-2004 L2007 **PS** *012

BAUER, John Dryden. 301 UNIVERSITY BLVD, DIV. OF PLASTIC SURGERY 77555 #041-07-1993 L1998 **PS** *020 †65

BAUER, Valerie. 301 UNIVERSITY BLVD RT, UTMB DEPARTMENT OF SURGERY 77555 #048-02-1998 L2005 **CRS** *020 †85

BAXTER, Maria R Lake. ■ 77550 #048-02-1950 L1950 **IM OS** *071

BAYASI, Mohammed. 301 UNIVERSITY BLVD 77555 #875-01-2006 **GS** *012

BEACH, Patricia Jane. 301 UNIVERSITY BLVD 77555 #021-05-1979 L1982 **PD** *040 †55

BEACH, Robert Earl. 4.200 OLD JOHN SEALY, DIVISION OF NEPHROLOGY 77555 #021-05-1979 L1982 **NEP IM** *020 †20

BELALCAZAR, Ligia M. 301 UNIVERSITY BLVD 77555 #264-01-1986 L1997 **END** *020 †20

BELL, Tanvir Kaur. 301 UNIVERSITY BLVD, ROUTE 435 77555 #033-06-1995 L2003 **ID** *020 †20

BELLI, James Arthur. 301 UNIVERSITY BLVD, DEPT RAD 77550 #056-06-1957 L1959 **OS R** *071 †80

BENAVIDEZ, Marisol D. ■ 77554 #048-02-2004 L2007 **FM** *012

BERENSON, Abbey Belina. 301 UNIVERSITY BLVD, RT 587 77555 #048-04-1984 L1985 **ADL OBG** *020 †30

BERG, Leah E. UNIV OF TEXAS MED BRANCH, DEPT OF INT MED 77555 #048-02-2006 **IM** *012

BERILGEN, Jason Ertan. ■ 77550 #048-04-2004 L2007 **RO** *012

BERNARDY, Michelle Leigh. ■ 77551 #048-15-2005 L2008 **PD** *012

BERNIER, Geo Matthew, Jr. 1302 MARVIN GRAVES BLDG, 301 UNIVERSITY BLVD 77555 #024-01-1960 L1997 **HEM ON** *030 †20

BESSMAN, Joel David. 301 UNIVERSITY BLVD 77555 #035-01-1972 L1980 **IM HEM** *050 †20

BHAGIA, Vinita. ■ 77551 #496-07-2002 L2007 **END** *012

BHASKARAN, Archana. 301 UNIV BLVD 77555 #495-04-2004 **IM** *012

BHAYANA, Suverta. UNIV OF TEXAS MED BRANCH, DEPT OF INT MED 77555 #495-69-2002 **IM** *100

BHUTANI, Manoop S. 301 UNIVERSITY BLVD, STE 4.106 77555 #495-69-1988 L2002 **GE** *020 †20

BIDYASAR, Savita. 301 UNIV BLVD 77555 #496-03-2002 **IM** *012

BIRNBAUM, Yochai. 301 UNIVERSITY BLVD, 5.106 JOHN SEALY ANNEX, MC 77555 #550-01-1983 L2005 **CD IM** *040 †20

BITNER, Hubert Piotr. ■ 77551 #033-05-2005 **P** *012

BLACKWELL, Michele D. SUITE 126, 400 HARBORSIDE DRI 77555 #048-02-1994 L1996 **OBG** *030

BLACKWELL, Phyllis S W. 301 UNIVERSITY BLVD 77555 #021-01-1971 L1976 **R PD** *020 †80

BLACKWELL, Steven Jeffrey. 301 UNIVERSITY BLVD, ROUTE 724 77555 #021-01-1971 L1978 **PS CFS** *020 †65

BLACKWELL, Thomas Adrian. 301 UNIVERSITY BLVD, 4.112 JOHN SEALY ANNEX 77555 #048-02-1978 L1978 **IM EM** *030 †20,16

BLY, Keith Phillip. DEPT OF PEDIATRICS, 301 UNIVERSITY BLVD, RT C- 77555 #038-06-1993 L1996 **PD** *020 †55

BONDURANT, William Walton. 2200 MARKET ST STE 412 77550 #048-02-1962 L1962 **P** *020 †75

BONOAN, Louisea Marie Lag. 301 UNIVERSITY BLVD 77555 #748-01-1993 *100

BOOR, Paul Jos. 301 UNIVERSITY BLVD, STE 1022 77555 #024-07-1972 L1977 **PTH** *050 †50

BORAHAY, Mostafa Abdel-Az. BRANCH HOSPS, UNIV OF TEXAS MED 77555 #915-14-1998 **OBG** *012

BORQUAYE, Liliane A. 301 UNIVERSITY BLVD, JSA 2-A 77555 #412-01-1985 L2001 **AN** *020 †05

BOYARS, Michael Chas. UTMB E 61 PULMONARY DIV 77550 #024-05-1972 L1982 **PUD IM** *040 †20

BOYLE, Kristen Renee. ■ 77550 #048-02-2008 *012

BRADLEY, Selena C. 624 25TH ST, NOVA HEALTHCARE 77550 #048-02-1995 L1999 **PD** *020

BRAGA, Sashi Andrade. ■ 77551 #187-10-2000 **FP** *012

BRAHMA, Swatee. 301 UNIV BVD 77555 #495-38-2000 **IM** *012

BRAMLETT, Jason Lee. ■ 77550 #048-02-2005 **AN** *012

BRANDT, Taylor L. ■ 77550 #048-02-2008 *012

BRASIER, Allan Robt. 301 UNIVERSITY BLVD, UNIV OF TEXAS MED BRANCH 77555 #005-02-1983 L1992 **IM** *020 †20

BREITKOPF, Daniel Marc. 301 UNIVERSITY BLVD, CAMPUS RT 0587 77555 #035-08-1993 L1997 **OBG** *020 †30

BRENDEL, William B. ■ 77550 #048-02-2008 *012

BROOKS, Edward Gautier. 301 UNIVERSITY BLVD, CHILDRENS HOSP DEPT PEDS 77550 #048-15-1985 L1986 **PD IG** *020 †55,03

BROOKS, George Byron. 301 UNIVERSITY BLVD, TDCJ MANAGED CARE 77555 #051-04-1997 L2001 **GPM** *020

BROUSSARD, Brad Alan. 301 UNIVERSITY BLVD, DEPT OF INTERNAL MEDICINE 77555 #021-06-2003 L2006 **PCC** *012 †20

BROWN, Craig Douglas. 301 UNIVERSITY BLVD, FAMILY MEDICINE, UTMB 77555 #048-02-1971 L1971 **FM OM** *030 †70,18

BRYAN, George Thos. 301 UNIVERSITY BLVD, U TX MED BRCH DEAN EMERITU 77555 #047-06-1955 L1963 **PD PDE** *071 †55

BRYAN, John Alvis, Jr. 301 UNIVERSITY BLVD, U T M B GALVESTON 77555 #048-02-1993 **CHP** *100

BRYANT, Barbara Jean. 301 UNIVERSITY BLVD, ROUTE 717 77555 #048-02-2000 L2005 **BBK** *100 †50 ‡

BUI, Quynh-Uyen Thi. 301 UNIVERSITY BLVD, GERIATRICS DEPARTMENT 77555 #942-01-1991 L2003 **IMG** *020 †20

BUJOL KELLY, Erica Renee. DEPT. OF DERMATOLOGY, UNIV. OF TX. MEDICAL BRANC 77555 #021-05-1998 L2001 **D** *020 †15

BUKOWSKI, Radoslaw K. 301 UNIVERSITY BLVD, UNIVERSITY OF TX MED RANCH 77555 #759-04-1986 L1999 **OBG** *020 †30

BULLARD-BERENT, Debra B. 301 UNIVERSITY BLVD, STE 0462 77555 #040-02-1999 L2002 **PAN** *012

BUSATH, David Don. U TX MED BR PHYS BIOPH 77550 #049-01-1978 **OS** *050

BUYTEN, Jeffrey A. 301 UNIVERSITY BLVD J, MED BRANCH 77555 #048-12-2003 L2005 **OTO** *012

BYNO, Ashley Cramer. ■ 77554 #041-12-2006 L2006 **OBG** *012

BYNUM, James Alton. 515 POST OFFICE ST 77550 #048-02-2003 L2008 **ORS** *012

BYUN, Eun Kwang. 301 UNIV BLV STE D62 77550 #583-02-2000 **IM** *012

CABAN, Mabel E. 301 UNIVERSITY BLVD, ROUTE 165 77555 #042-01-1983 L2000 **PM** *050 †60

CADENAS, Jerson De Guzman. 301 UNIV 77555 #748-08-1998 **IM** *012

CAESAR, Rajani Ruth. ■ 77550 #660-07-2002 L2005 **N** *012

CALHOUN, William James. 301 UNIVERSITY BLVD, APICS DIVISION 77555 #041-14-1979 L1980 **PUD IM** *050 †20,03

CALLAS, Gerald. 301 UNIVERSITY BLVD 77550 #048-02-1967 L1967 **OS IM** *040

CALLENDER, David L. 301 UNIVERSITY BLVD, OFFICE PRESIDENT - STE 604 77555 #048-04-1984 L1985 **HNS OTO** *020 †45

CAMACHO, Alvin Carlos. UNIV OF TEXAS MED BRANCH, DEPT OF RADIOLOGY G-09 77555 #748-02-1995 **DR** *012

CAMACHO, Maria E. 301 UNIVERSITY BLVD, DEPT OF INTERNAL MED 77555 #264-01-1982 L2005 **IMG** *020

CAMORIANO, Gerardo D. AND VIS, DEPT OF OPHTHALMOLOGY 77555 #067-01-2006 **OPH** *012

CAMPBELL, Gerald Alan. 301 UNIVERSITY BLVD, STE 1022 77555 #048-12-1977 L1986 **NP ATP** *040 †50

CANCEMI, Mario Thomas. ■ 77550 #048-02-2004 L2008 **AN** *012

CANGELOSI, John J. 2227 POST OFFICE ST, LOFT 2 77550 #048-14-2005 L2007 **PTH** *012

CANO, Oscar. ■ 77550 #048-02-2004 L2008 **DR** *012

CAO, Li. 301 UNIVERSITY BLVD, DEPT OF 77555 #243-36-1982 **PCP** *100

CARDENAS, Victor J, Jr. 301 UNIVERSITY BLVD, DEPT OF INTERNAL MEDICINE 77555 #048-02-1983 L1983 **PUD IM** *020 †20

CARMICHAEL, Kelly D. 301 UNIVERSITY BLVD, UTMB CHILDRENS HOSP 3.220 77555 #048-02-1994 L1995 **ORS OP** *020 †40

CARPIN, Kimberly Marie. ■ 77554 #031-01-2005 **PS** *012

CARROLL, Amy Rae. BRANCH HOSPS, UNIV OF TEXAS MED 77555 #012-05-2005 **OBG** *012

CARTER, Dennis Lee. DEPT OF ANESTHESIOLOGY, UNIV OF TEXAS MED BRANCH 77555 #048-13-2007 **AN** *012

CARUSO, Jared Paul. 301 UNIVERSITY BLVD, CHILDREN'S HOSP ROUTE 0351 77555 #305-01-1995 L1999 **PD** *020 †55

CASEY, Kristin Leigh. ■ 77550 #048-02-2006 **DR** *012

CASOLA, Antonella. 301 UNIVERSITY BLVD, DEPT OF PEDIATRICS UTMB 77555 #561-31-1989 L2004 **PDI** *050 †55

CASS, Alvah Ray. 301 UNIVERSITY BLVD 77555 #041-12-1976 L1993 **FM** *040 †18

CESANI, Fernando. 301 UNIVERSITY BLVD, NUCLEAR-MED, 2ND FL RTE G- 77555 #042-01-1987 L1994 **DR** *020 †80,28

CHACHERE, Sheila Lynette. ■ 77553 #048-02-2001 L2003 **PD** *020 †55

CHALJUB, Gregory. 301 UNIVERSITY BLVD, DEPT OF RADLGY 77555 #016-43-1985 L1986 **DR NRN** *020 †80

CHALLAGULLA, Sabita. 301 UNIV BLVD 77555 #496-24-2003 **IM** *012

CHAMOUN, Antonio Joseph. 301 UNIVERSITY BLVD, DIV CARDIO UTMB RM 5.106 77555 #605-02-1994 L2001 **IC** *020 †20

CHAMPION, Stephanie Windl. ■ 77551 #048-02-2004 L2008 **OBG** *012

CHAN, Conner. 1720 24TH ST 77550 #048-02-2008 *012

CHANDLER, Stephanie Marie. 301 UNIVERSITY BLVD, UNIV OF TEXAS MED BRANCH 77555 #048-02-2006 **PD** *012

CHANG, Joseph Hsuanyee. 301 UNIVERSITY BLVD, UTMB 77555 #041-02-2002 L2007 **EM** *020 †16

CHEN, George Govern. ■ 77550 #048-02-2007 **IM** *012

CHEN, Harvey R. 301 UNIVERSITY BLVD, DIVISION OF CARDIOLOGY, JS 77550 #048-12-2002 L2005 **CD** *012 †20

CHEN, Lilly Liljing. ROUTE 0165, UTMB & ALVESTON, 77555 #035-48-1989 L1994 **N PM** *020 †75

CHENG, Sarah. ■ 77550 #048-02-2006 **PD** *012

CHENNAREDDYGARI, Swapna. 301 UNIV BLV STE D62 77550 #496-31-2000 **IM** *012

CHILVERS, Rebecca Ann. ■ 77550 #021-06-2003 **OBG** *100

CHO, Won-Suk. ■ 77554 #005-14-2000 L2006 **IM** *100

CHONMAITREE, Tasnee. MEDICAL BR, UNIVERSITY OF TEXAS 77555 #891-02-1973 L1981 **ID PD** *050 †55

CHORENS, Jose A. ■ 77551 #847-08-1958 L1967 **P** *071

CHU, Etem T. ■ 77550 #048-02-2008 *012

CHUNG, Dai H. 301 UNIVERSITY BLVD, CHILDRENS HOSP RM 3.220E 77555 #048-02-1988 L1999 **PDS** *020 †85

CHUNG, Stephanie Therese. 301 UNIV BLVD, STE D62 77555 #566-01-2003 **MPD** *012

CHUPP, Leslie E. 301 UNIVERSITY BLVD, UTMB 77555 #048-02-1988 L1989 **OBG** *020 †30

CLARK, Shannon Michelle. 301 UNIVERSITY BLVD, DEPT OF OB/GYN 77555 #020-02-2000 L2004 **OBG** *020 †30

COALE, George Buchanan. ■ 77554 #035-20-1958 L1961 **GYN** *071 †30

COCCO, Jennyfer Faridy. PLASTIC SURGERY, DIVISION OF 77555 #003-01-2004 **PS** *012

COGGESHALL, Richard Edwin. 200 UNIVERSITY BLVD 77550 #024-01-1956 **IM OS** *050

COHEN, Marvin Saml. 301 UNIVERSITY BLVD, ROUTE 591 77555 #550-04-1984 L1989 **AN** *020 †05

COLE, David W. ■ 77550 #004-01-1997 L1999 **GPM** *012

COLEMAN, James S. 1 QUINTANA PL 77554 #048-02-1993 L1995 **AN** *020 †05

COLMAN, Martin. UNV OF TX MEDICAL BRANCH, DEPT RAD 77555 #836-01-1964 L2000 **RO NM** *020 †28,80

COLMENTER, Heather Deann. DEPT OF ANESTHESIOLOGY, UNIV OF TEXAS MED BRANCH 77555 #048-02-2005 **AN** *012

CONLON, Julia Teresa. ■ 77554 #048-14-2007 **PD** *012

CONNER, Catherine Moler. ■ 77550 #048-02-2005 L2008 **PD** *012

CONNER, Chad Stephen. ■ 77550 #048-02-2004 L2008 **ORS** *012

CONTI, Vincent Roy. 301 UNIVERSITY BLVD, 6.120 JOHN SEALY ANNEX 77555 #024-07-1969 L1979 **TS GS** *020 †85,90

CONTRERAS, Juan Antonio. PO BOX 1439 77553 #048-02-2004 L2007 **IM** *100 †20

COOK, Barry Gregory. 301 UNIV BLVD, UNIV OF TEXAS MEDICAL BRAN 77555 #048-02-2003 L2006 **DR** *012

COOKE, Rhonda Kaylynn. 301 UNIVERSITY BLVD, UTMB - PATHOLOGY 77555 #011-04-2006 **PTH** *012

COOPER, James Kevin. ■ 77550 #048-02-2008 *012

COOPER, John T, Jr. ■ 77551 #048-13-1983 L1987 **FOP** *012

CORMACK, Trina S. 1411 13TH ST 77550 #048-15-1995 L1997 **P** *020 †18,75

CORTIELLA, Joaquin J, III. 301 UNIVERSITY BLVD, ROUTE 591 77555 #024-05-1981 L2003 **AN PD** *050

COSTANTINE, Maged Milad. 301 UNIVERSITY BLVD 77555 #605-01-2001 L2007 **OBG** *100

COUGHLIN, Andrew Michael. ■ 77550 #030-05-2008 *012

COUTURE, Susan E. 301 UNIVERSITY BLVD, DEPT OF EMERGENCY MEDICINE 77555 #048-02-1988 L1998 **IM PD** *020 †20,55

COWAN, Daniel Francis. 301 UNIVERSITY BLVD, STE 1022 77555 #067-01-1960 L1977 **ATP** *020 †50

COWAN, William Troy, Jr. 301 UNIVERSITY BLVD, U T M B GALVESTON 77555 #048-02-1980 L1980 **PTH** *020 †50

COZART, Jennifer Renee. ■ 77550 #048-02-2003 **GS** *012

CRIM, Jeremy Patrick. 301 UNIVERSITY BLVD, PATHOLOGY DEPARTMENT 77555 #048-02-2004 **PTH** *012

CUMMINGS, Julie E. ■ 77550 #048-02-2008 *012

CUNNINGHAM, Krista D. ■ 77550 #048-02-2008 *012

CUNNINGHAM, Paul Johnston. 1701 23RD ST 77550 #020-02-1955 L1960 **GS CRS** *071 †85

DAESCHNER, Charles Wm, Jr. 301 UNIVERSITY BLVD 77555 #048-02-1945 L1945 **OS PD** *071 †55

DAHER, Iyad Nassim. 301 UNIVERSITY BLVD, UNIV OF TEXAS MED BRANCH 77555 #605-01-1999 L2007 **CD** *100 †20

DANIELS, Jerry Claude. 32 ADLER CIR 77551 #048-02-1970 L1970 **RHU IM** *071

DAO, Minh Duy. BRANCH HOSPS, UNIV OF TEXAS MED 77555 #018-03-2007 **OBG** *012

DARG QUINONES, Ruth Guada. ■ 77550 #737-10-2004 **FP** *012

DAVENPORT, Louis Andrew. ■ 77550 #048-02-1999 **IPM** *012

DAVENPORT, Meredith Dough. 400 HARBORSIDE DR STE 126 77555 #048-02-1999 L2003 **OBG** *020 †30

DAVIS, Harry K. 2201 MARKET ST, STE 820 77550 #048-02-1949 L1949 **P FM** *071 †75,18

DAVIS, J Chad. 301 UNIVERSITY BLVD, UTMB GALVESTON 77550 #048-02-1994 L1997 **CCP** *020 †55

DAVIS, Michael J. 301 UNIVERSITY BLVD 77555 #047-07-1977 L1987 **CD IM** *020 †20

DAY, Barakah L. 301 UNIV BLV, UNIV TX MED BRANCH HOSP 77555 #048-13-2007 **PD** *012

DE GROOT, William John. 301 UNIVERSITY BLVD 77555 #010-02-1954 L1962 **PUD CD** *040 †20

DEISS, William Paul, Jr. 301 UNIVERSITY BLVD, U T M B GALVESTON 77555 #016-11-1945 L1968 **IM END** *072 †20

DELA CRUZ, Roberto Baylon, Jr. ■ 77550 #048-02-2006 **FP** *012

DELEON-MC QUATTER, Theresa. UNIV TX MED BRANCH-INT MED 77550 #048-02-2002 **IM** *100

DELOZIER, Kirby Blair. 303 ISLES END RD 77554 #027-01-1967 L1967 **DR RNR** *020 †80

DENG, Caishu. 301 UNIVERSITY BLVD 77555 #243-76-1986 L2002 **PCP** *100 †50

DENNISON, Matthew Stephen. ■ 77550 #048-02-2008 *012

DE PAZ, Cesar Eduardo. ■ 77550 #048-02-2008 *012

DE VALDENEBRO, Miguel. ■ 77555 #048-02-2003 L2008 **GS** *100

DHATT, Ajinder Singh. 301 UNIVERSITY BLVD 77555 #495-43-2002 L2006 **CHP** *012

DIAZ ARRASTIA, Conception. 301 UNIVERSITY BLVD, DEPT OF OB/GYN 77555 #033-06-1987 L1992 **OBG GO** *050 †30

DIAZ-ARRASTIA, Ramon F. 301 UNIVERSITY BLVD, DEPT OF OB/GYN 77555 #275-01-1952 L1969 **GS** *020 †85

DIETERICHS, Sonja Veronic. 700 UNIVERSITY BLVD, UNIV OF TEXAS MED BRANCH 77550 #048-02-2001 L2006 **OPH** *020

DILDY, Annola Kilai. 301 UNIVERSITY BLVD, UNIV OF TEXAS MED BRANCH 77555 #047-07-2005 **MPD** *012

DIMMICK, Joshua Ryan. 4.112 MCCOLLOUGH BLDG, 301 UNIVERSITY BLVD 77555 #048-14-2005 L2008 **D** *012

DIMMITT, Dean Bradshaw. ■ 77550 #048-02-2005 *100

DIPATRE, Pier Luigi. ■ 77555 #561-06-1985 L2007 **PTH** *020 †50

DIVEN, Dayna Gwinup. 301 UNIVERSITY BLVD, ROUTE 783 77555 #048-02-1986 L1987 **D** *020 †15

DIXON, Susan Frances. 301 UNIVERSITY BLVD, 7.104 JOHN SEALY ANNEX 77555 #001-02-1998 L2006 **OTO** *100

DIZON, Sammy Atienza. 301 UNIV BLVD 77555 #748-01-2002 L2007 **IM** *012

DOGUET, Lisa Michelle. UNIV OF TEXAS MED BRANCH, DEPT OF PSYCHIATRY 77555 #048-14-2006 L2007 **P** *012

DOMANSKI, Mark Christian. ■ 77550 #023-01-2006 **OTO** *012

DOMINGUEZ, Laura Isela. UNIV OF TEXAS MED BRANCH, DEPT OF INT MED 77555 #048-02-2007 **IM** *012

DOSHI, Poonam Nitin. ■ 77550 #048-02-2008 *012

DOSHI, Snehal Jitendra. UNIV OF TEXAS MED BRANCH, 301 UNIV BOULEVARD 77555 #422-01-2003 L2007 **NPM** *012 †55

DOTT, Sharon Gail. 301 UNIVERSITY BLVD, U T M B GALVESTON 77555 #048-02-1979 L1979 **P** *020 †75

DOULATRAM, Gulshan. 301 UNIVERSITY BLVD, OJS 2-A 77555 #495-59-1991 L2000 **APM** *020 †05

DOWNEY, Melinda Berna. 606 UNIVERSITY BLVD 77550 #048-02-2003 L2005 **PD** *100 †55

DREYER, Charles F. 301 UNIVERSITY BLVD, RM 1228 77555 #028-03-1979 L1984 **CHN N** *040 †55,75

DUARTE, Alexander Gomez. 5.112 JOHN SEALY ANNEX, UTMB, 301 UNIVERSITY BLVD 77555 #016-11-1989 L1995 **PUD IM** *020 †20

DUNN, Kimberly. 301 UNIVERSITY BLVD, U T M B GALVESTON 77555 #048-14-1990 L1992 **IM** *020

DUPONT, Andrew W. 301 UNIVERSITY BLVD, MC0764 77555 #048-14-1998 L2004 **GE** *020 †20

DUQUE, Wilbur Don Bayuga. 301 UNIVERSITY BLVD 77555 #748-10-2003 **FP** *012

DURHAM, Megan Rae. ■ 77555 #048-02-2007 **PD** *012

EANES, Robert Z. ■ 77551 #048-02-1960 L1960 **DIA PD** *040

EARHART, Angela Dawn. 301 UNIVERSITY BLVD, MAIL ROUTE 587 ATTN: SHERR 77555 #048-14-2002 L2006 **OBG** *100

EASTEP, Laura K. ■ 77550 #048-02-2006 **OBG** *012

EHDAIE, Sassan C. DEPT OF ANESTHESIOLOGY, UNIV OF TEXAS MED BRANCH 77555 #048-12-2007 **AN** *012

EL AMM, Chantal Antoine. 301 UNIV BLVD, ROUTE 0553 77555 #605-01-2003 L2004 **CD** *012 †20

ELEDRISI, Mohsen Saleh. 301 UNIVERSITY BLVD, 8-138 MRB 77555 #613-02-1992 L2000 **END** *020 †20

ELGHETANY, Mohamed Tarek. 301 UNIVERSITY BLVD, STE 1022 77555 #915-04-1979 L1987 PTH HMP *020 †50

ELIKAN, Lawrence Paul. ■ 77550 #048-02-2004 OTO *100

ELKON, Deborah. 301 UNIVERSITY BLVD, STE 2A 77555 #836-01-1984 L2006 *100

ELTORKY, Mahmoud Aly. 301 UNIVERSITY BLVD, STE 1022 77555 #915-03-1971 L2003 PTH PCP *020 †50

EMORY, Lee Evangeline. 1103 ROSENBERG ST 77550 #048-02-1969 L1969 PYG P *020 †75

ENGLISH, Paul Ward, II. 301 UNIVERSITY BLVD, DEPT OF EMERGENCY MEDICINE 77555 #048-02-1990 L1992 PUD *020 †20

EPSTEIN, Henry Fredric. 301 UNIVERSITY BLVD, UNIV. OF TEXAS MED. BRANCH 77555 #005-11-1969 L1978 OS *050

ESHAM, Adam Lester. ■ 77550 #038-44-2006 U *012

ESKUE, Kyle L. ■ 77550 #048-02-2006 PTH *012

ESPANA TENORIO, Jonathan. 301 UNIV BLVD 77555 #935-07-1999 OBG *012

ESPINOZA, Manuel George. DIV OF UROLOGY - RT 0540, UNIV OF TEXAS MED BRANCH 77555 #007-02-2002 U *012

ESSEX, Francis Xavier. ■ 77550 #030-06-1960 L1970 IM *071 †20

ESTELLA, Pedro. ■ 77551 #847-17-1982 CD *020

ETHRIDGE, Richard Thomas. ■ 77550 #048-02-2003 L2006 PS *012

EVANS, Ernest Burke. 301 UNIVERSITY BLVD, UTMB RT 0165 77555 #048-04-1947 L1947 ORS *071 †40

EVERS, Bernard Mark. 301 UNIVERSITY BLVD, GS DEPT #E33 77550 #047-06-1983 L1989 GS *050 †85

FABIAN, Roderic Harold. 301 UNIVERSITY BLVD, DEPT NEUROLOGY 77555 #048-02-1980 L1980 N CN *050 †75

FADHLI, Wameeth. 301 UNIV BLV 77555 #422-01-2004 MPD *100

FAGAN, Charles Jos. 301 UNIVERSITY BLVD, U T M B GALVESTON 77555 #016-11-1958 L1966 DR *071 †80

FAIRCHILD, Chad D. ■ 77550 #048-02-2008 L2008 *012

FANG, Xiang. BRANCH HOSPS, UNIV OF TEXAS MED 77555 #243-76-1985 N *012

FARMER, Lisa Rae. 301 UNIVERSITY BLVD, STE 2A 77555 #048-02-2001 L2005 AN *100 †05

FAROOQI, Waqar. ■ 77550 #704-02-1990 L1993 IM *075

FARROW, Buckminster John. 301 UNIVERSITY BLVD, UTMB 77555 #041-15-1999 L2006 GS *100

FATEMA, Aziza. UNIV OF TEXAS MED BRANCH, 4200 JOHN SEALY ANNEX 77555 #160-02-1999 L2008 NEP *012

FEERICK, Alan Emmet. ■ 77554 #539-02-1985 L1994 AN *020 †05

FEINSTEIN, Joshua Garth. 3007 AVENUE Q, U OF TX MEDICAL BRANCH 77550 #010-01-1997 L2001 EM *012 †16

FERGUSON, Edward C, III. 301 UNIVERSITY BLVD, U T M B GALVESTON 77555 #016-06-1950 L1951 OPH OS *071 †31

FINN, Nicola Jane. ■ 77554 #065-05-1992 L1999 DR *100 †80

FISCHER, Stefanie Ruthild. 301 UNIVERSITY BLVD, UTMB/DEPT. ANESTHESIOLOGY 77555 #409-10-1988 L1999 AN *100 †20,05

FISH, Jay Collie. 301 UNIVERSITY BLVD, DEPT GS 77550 #048-02-1958 L1958 GS *071 †85

FLEMMONS, Kevin D. 301 UNIVERSITY BLVD 77555 #048-02-2001 L2004 IM *020

FLEMMONS, Meghan Susanne. DEPT. OF OPTHAMOLOGY, 700 UNIVERSITY 77555 #048-02-2003 L2004 OPH *012

FLORES, Linda Patricia. ■ 77551 #048-02-1980 L1980 P *020

FLORES, Macarmina Acuna. UNIV OF TEXAS MED BRANCH, 301 UNIV BLVD 77555 #047-07-2003 NS *012

FONSECA, Rafael Antonio. SMITH PAVILION, 6.104 WAVERLY 77555 #308-05-2000 L2007 NPM *012

FONT, Jean Paul. 301 UNIVERSITY BLVD J, MEDICAL BR 77555 #042-01-2004 L2006 OTO *012

FORD, Josephine E Dean. 8502 SEAWALL BLVD # 101 77554 #048-02-1936 OS *071

FORD, Paul Matthew. DEPT OF ANESTHESIOLOGY, UNIV OF TEXAS MED BRANCH 77555 #048-02-2007 AN *012

FORESMAN, Ryan Neil. ■ 77550 #048-02-2008 *012

FOUGEROUSSE, Charles Emil. 517 UNIVERSITY BLVD 77550 #048-02-1962 L1963 GYN *071 †30

FOX, Karin A. ■ 77550 #048-13-2005 OBG *012

FRANKEL, Gerald Jos. 301 UNIVERSITY BLVD, UTMB DEPT OF UROLOGY 77555 #041-09-1969 L1985 U *020 †95

FRASER, John Jos. 301 UNIVERSITY BLVD, DIV EMERGENCY MED 77555 #048-02-1979 L1979 PD PEM *020 †55,70 ‡

FREEMAN, Wiyatta Bendu. ■ 77551 #048-15-2004 L2008 OBG *012

FRENKEL, Moshe Aaron. 301 UNIVERSITY BLVD, DEPT. OF FAMILY MEDICINE 77555 #550-02-1980 L2003 FM *018

FRIDLINGTON, Julie Lynn. ■ 77550 #048-02-2006 D *012

FUKE, Chris Taigo. 301 UNIVERSITY BLVD, JSA STE 2-A 77555 #024-07-2003 L2007 PMM *012

FULLER, Michael Alan. 301 UNIVERSITY BLVD, DEPT OF PSYCHIATRY 77555 #048-02-1984 L1989 P *040 †75

FUNSTON, Joe Sean. 301 UNIVERSITY BLVD, OF ANESTHESIOLOGY 77555 #048-02-1994 L1998 AN *020

FUTCH, Edward Downing. ■ 77550 #048-02-1945 L1945 CD IM *071 †20

GALLAGHER, James Jay. 815 MARKET ST, SHRINERS HOSPITALS FOR CHI 77550 #035-15-1992 L2007 CCS *020 †85

GALLITE, Dana Lynn. 301 UNIVERSITY BLVD, UNIV OF TEXAS MED BRANCH 77555 #038-44-2006 PD *012

GALVAN, Carlos Alberto. AND VIS, DEPT OF OPHTHALMOLOGY 77555 #005-11-2003 OPH *012

GAMILLA, Ann Kathleen Nob. UNIV OF TEXAS MED BRANCH, 4200 JOHN SEALY ANNEX 77555 #748-01-2000 L2008 NEP *012

GANCERES, Natalie M. 301 UNIVERSITY BLVD, DEPT OF ANESTHESIOLOGY 77555 #048-02-2002 L2006 APM *05

GARCIA, Pablo Reyna. ■ 77551 #048-02-1998 FM *100

GARCIA, Stephen D. 301 UNIVERSITY BLVD, UNIV OF TX MED BRANCH 77555 #048-02-2006 AN *012

GARCIA GALLEGOS, Jesus Ge. 301 UNIV BLVD 77555 #649-02-1996 FP *012

GARDNER, Angela Fulgham. 301 UNIVERSITY BLVD, ROUTE 1173 77555 #048-15-1986 L1987 EM *020 †16

GARDNER, Angela Racquel. 301 UNIV BLV STE 0462, INTERNAL MED DEPT 77555 #017-20-2005 IM *012

GARDNER, Frank H. 301 UNIVERSITY BLVD, U T M B GALVESTON 77555 #016-06-1945 L1975 HEM ON *072 †20

GARGES, Kim Jeffrey. 301 UNIVERSITY BLVD, DEPARTMENT OF ORTHOPAEDICS 77555 #021-01-1991 L2000 ORS *020 †40

GARZA GUTIERREZ, Gerardo. UNIV OF TEXAS MED BRANCH, DEPT OF INT MED 77555 #649-30-2002 L2008 PCC *012

GEARY, Cara Ann. 301 UNIVERSITY BLVD 77555 #036-01-1997 L2003 NPM PD *020 †55

GELMAN, Benjamin B. 301 UNIVERSITY BLVD, STE 1022 77555 #038-41-1983 L1989 PTH N *020 †50

GEOGHEGAN, Jennifer Ann. 301 UNIVERSITY BLVD, TEXAS MEDICA 77555 #003-01-2003 L2006 PS *012

GEORGE, William Kelley. 1802 MARKET ST 77550 #048-02-1952 L1952 IM *020

GEREZ MARTINEZ, Cesar. 301 UNIVERSITY BLVD, STE 417 77555 #649-19-2005 *100

GERIK, Susan Mabel. 301 UNIVERSITY BLVD 77555 #048-02-1994 L1996 PD *020 †55

GHOSH, Sidharth. ■ 77550 #048-02-2005 L2008 IM *012

GIBBONS, Ryan Fitz. ■ 77552 #047-05-2006 L2008 AN *012

GIBBONS, Stacey Lavoy. 301 UNIVERSITY BLVD, STE 2A 77555 #024-05-1988 L1999 AN *020

GIBLIN, Leonard James, III. ■ 77550 #048-02-2003 *012

GIBSON, Bernard Roy. 301 UNIVERSITY BLVD, RT 783 77555 #005-02-1971 L1973 D *020 †15

GIBSON, David C. 301 UNIVERSITY BLVD, UTMB ANESTHESIOLOGY DEPART 77555 #048-13-2004 L2008 AN *012

GIBSON, Jenee Jeri. ■ 77550 #048-02-2006 P *012

GIGLIO, Ginovante Anthony. ■ 77550 #048-02-2005 *100

GILL, Amanjit Singh. 301 UNIVERSITY BLVD 77555 #495-29-1994 L2007 *100

GILMER, Peachy R, Jr. ■ 77551 #847-01-1957 L1964 PTH CLP *071

GINN, Michaela Elizabeth. 301 UNIV BLV STE D62 77550 #305-01-2007 IM *012

GIOLMA, Marilyn Elizabeth. ■ 77550 #048-02-2008 *012

GLEINSER, David Michael. ■ 77551 #048-15-2007 OTO *012

GODLEY, Bernard Farrow. 301 UNIVERSITY BLVD, RT 1106 77555 #024-01-1989 L1997 OPH *020 †35

GOHIL, Mahendra Nandlal. DEPT OF RADIOLOGY UTMB 77550 #407-33-1963 L1977 DR OS *040 †28,80

GOLARDI, Natalia. UNIV TX MED BRANCH HOSPS, 301 UNIV BLV STE D62 77550 #913-91-1994 PTH *012

GOLD, Daniel Howard. 2302 AVENUE P 77550 #025-01-1966 L1977 OPH *071 †35

GOLDBLUM, Randall Mark. TEX U MED BRANCH HSP PED 77550 #048-02-1969 L1969 IG A *020 †55,03

GOLDMAN, Armond S. 301 UNIVERSITY BLVD, UNIVERSITY TEXAS 77555 #048-02-1953 L1953 IG PDA *071 †55,03

GOMEZ, Adriana. 301 UNIVERSITY BLVD, DEPT FM 77555 #935-01-2004 FP *012

GOMEZ, Guillermo Antonio. 301 UNIVERSITY BLVD 77555 #231-03-1979 L1998 GS *020 †85

GOMEZ, Monica M. ■ 77550 #048-02-2006 IM *012

GONZALEZ, Emilio B. 301 UNIVERSITY BLVD, U T M B DEPT RHEUM 77555 #726-01-1972 L1981 RHU IM *020 †20,03

GONZALEZ, Javier. BRANCH HOSPS, UNIV OF TEXAS MED 77555 #264-10-1997 N *012

GONZALEZ, Jose Luis. 301 UNIVERSITY BLVD, UTMB CHLDRNS HOSP 77555 #011-02-1976 L1979 PDE *040 †55

GOODACRE, Brian. C/O X-RAY DEPT G-09, UTMB 77555 #061-01-1985 L1994 DR *100 †80

GOODWIN, James Simeon. 301 UNIVERSITY BLVD, 3 324 JENNIE SEALY 77555 #024-01-1971 L1992 IG IMG *050 †20

GOODWIN, Jean P Mc Clung. ■ 77551 #024-01-1971 L1993 P PFP *020 †75

GOPALAKRISHNAMOORTHY, Mura. 301 UNIV BLVD 77555 #495-04-2005 IM *012

GORE, Dennis Carroll. 301 UNIVERSITY BLVD, EMERGENCY ROOM 77555 #048-02-1984 L1986 CCM GS *020 †20

GORENA, Amanda L. ■ 77550 #048-02-2008 *012

GORMAN, Blythe Kelley. 415 22ND ST, APT 2A 77550 #021-05-2005 PTH *012

GOTTUMUKKALA, Aruna. 301 UNIVERSITY BLVD, DEPT. OF PSYCHIATRY, 5222 77555 #495-11-1985 L2006 CHP *020 †75

GOYAL, Geetinder. 301 UNIV BLVD 77555 #496-43-2003 IM *012

GRANT, J Andrew. 301 UNIVERSITY BLVD, UNIV TX MED BRCH MRB 8.104 77555 #036-07-1966 L1973 AI IM *040 †20,03

GRAU-MASSANES, Manuel. ■ 77551 #847-01-1983 DMP *020

GRECULA, Michael Jos. UNIV TEXAS MED BRANCH, 6 136 MCCULLOUGH BLDG 77555 #038-44-1986 L1994 OAR ORS *020 †40

GREGORIO, Jason. 301 UNIV BLV STE D62 77550 #422-01-2007 PTH *012

GREIFENKAMP, Jonathan D. 301 UNIVERSITY BLVD, RT 553 77555 #048-02-2000 L2003 CD *020 †20

GROUP, Ashley Rae. ■ 77550 #048-02-2008 *012

GRUMBLES, Loretta L. 301 UNIVERSITY BLVD, RTE 460 77555 #048-02-1997 L2000 IM FM *040 †20

GUGLIUZZA, Kristene K. 301 UNIVERSITY BLVD, UNIV OF TEXAS MED BRANCH 77555 #016-11-1982 L1990 TTS GS *040 †85

GUIDRY, Jon Alvin. 301 UNIVERSITY BLVD, UNIV. OF TEXAS MEDICAL BRA 77555 #048-02-1991 L1993 P *020 †75

GUIDRY, Maria Theresa. 301 UNIVERSITY BLVD # 0165, THE UNIVERSITY OF TEXAS 77555 #748-16-1984 L1998 FM *020 †18

GUPTA, Kavita Omprakash. 301 UNIVERSITY BLVD, DEPT OF PEDIATRICS 77555 #495-37-2003 L2007 PD *012

GUPTA, Parantap. ■ 77551 #495-17-2002 L2007 IM *100 †20

GUTTIKONDA, Jyothsna. UNIV OF TEXAS MED BRANCH, 4200 JOHN SEALY ANNEX 77555 #495-59-1999 L2004 NEP *020

GUTTIKONDA, Sreedevi. 301 UNIV BLVD 77555 #495-21-2003 IM *012

GUTURU, Praveen. 301 UNIV BLV STE D62 77550 #495-11-2003 IM *012

HADDAD, Christopher A. 301 UNIV BLVD, ROUTE 0553 77555 #048-02-2003 L2003 CD *012 †20

HADDON, Robert. 301 UNIVERSITY BLVD, PREV. MED./COMMUNITY HEALT 77555 #023-01-1989 L2005 GPM †70,20

HADJIPAVLOU, Alexander. 301 UNIVERSITY BLVD, 6.136 MCCULLOUGH BLDG 77550 #418-01-1965 L1993 OSS *020 †40

HAEDGE, Philip William. UNIV OF TEXAS MED BRANCH, DEPT OF ANESTHESIOLOGY 77555 #048-13-2002 L2006 AN *020

HAGGARD, Mary E. 301 UNIVERSITY BLVD 77555 #048-02-1951 L1951 PHO *072 †55

HAHN, Dan W. 301 UNIVERSITY BLVD, UTMB GALVESTON 77555 #048-12-2004 L2008 AN *012

HAJI, Sara. ■ 77551 #048-02-2008 *012

HALEY, Susan L. ■ 77551 #048-14-2007 PTH *012

HANKINS, Gary D. 301 UNIVERSITY BLVD, 3.400 OLD JOHN SEALY HOS 77555 #051-04-1977 L1982 OBG MFM *020 †30

HANNIGAN, Edward Vincent. 301 UNIVERSITY BLVD, DEPT GYN 77550 #048-02-1970 L1970 GO ON †30

HANSEN, Karen Ann. 3828 URSULINE ST 77550 #048-02-1989 L1991 IM *020 †20

HANSUM, Christine Ann. BRANCH HOSPS, UNIV OF TEXAS MED 77555 #048-13-2005 OBG *012

HAQUE, Abida Khatoon. UTMB, DEPT PATH 77555 #495-21-1965 L1979 **PTH ATP** *020 †50

HAQUE, Waheedul. UTMB PSYCH BEHAVIORAL SCI 77550 #704-02-1962 L1979 **P** *020 †75

HAREN, Rachel Doll. ■ 77550 #048-02-2005 L2008 **PD** *012

HARIRAH, Hassan M. 301 UNIVERSITY BLVD, DIV OF MATERNAL-FETAL MEDI 77555 #915-07-1983 L2000 **OBG MFM** *040 †30 ‡

HARPER, William Fletcher. 301 UNIVERSITY BLVD 77555 #048-02-1970 L1970 **IM** *040 †20

HART, Umbert. ■ 77550 #308-01-1954 L1958 **GS** *020 †85

HASHMEY, Rayhan. 301 UNIVERSITY BLVD, U T M B GALVESTON 77555 #704-02-1989 L1995 **ID IM** *020 †20

HATCH, Sandra Sue. 301 UNIVERSITY BLVD, 1ST FL, MCCULLOUGH BLDG 77555 #048-14-1987 L1988 **RO** *020 †80

HAUCK, Erik Friedrich. 301 UNIVERSITY BLVD, UNIV OF TEXAS MED BRANCH 77555 #409-24-1999 L2008 **NS** *100

HAUPTMAN, Garrett Alan. ■ 77551 #011-03-2003 L2006 **OTO** *012

HAVEMANN, Eric Conrad. ■ 77550 #048-02-2007 **AN** *012

HAVER, Mary Claire. 301 UNIVERSITY BLVD, DEPT OB 77555 #021-06-1998 L2002 **OBG** *020 †30

HAVLEN, Pamela Ruth. 301 UNIVERSITY BLVD, BRANCH GALVESTON 77555 #048-02-1999 L2002 **IM** *020 †20

HAWKINS, Willie James. 715 19TH ST, GALVESTON COUNTY JAIL 77550 #048-02-1981 L1982 **FM** *020 †18

HAYES, Maureen. 301 UNIVERSITY BLVD, DEPT OF ANESTHESIOLOGY 77550 #045-01-1989 L2003 **APM** *020 †05

HEBELER, Joan Rochelle. 301 UNIVERSITY BLVD, UTMB 77555 #056-05-1958 L1963 **CHP PD** *040 †55,75

HENDERSON, Jerry Don. 300 STRAND ST, APARTMENT NUMBER 307 77550 #539-06-2001 L2004 **IM** *012

HENDERSON, Sherronda Moor. 301 UNIVERSITY BLVD 77555 #048-02-2003 L2007 **IM** *100 †20

HENLY, Walter S. ■ 77554 #023-07-1951 L1956 **CD TS** *071 †85,90

HERBERT-MALLET, Robin D. 301 UNIVERSITY BLVD, D/ PSYCHIATRY & BEHAV SCIE 77555 #048-13-1989 L1995 **CHP** *020 †75

HERMANN, Daniel Gene. ■ 77550 #048-02-2008 *012

HERNANDEZ, Antonia Maritz. ■ 77550 #048-02-2008 *012

HERNDON, David Newcomb. 815 MARKET ST 77550 #038-06-1974 L1982 **CCS TRS** *020 †85

HERRERA, David C. 301 UNIVERSITY BLVD, DEPT OF PREVENTIVE MEDICIN 77555 #048-02-1998 L2001 **GPM** *100 †16

HERSHMAN, John E. ■ 77550 #048-02-2008 *012

HEWLETT, Angela Lois. 301 UNIVERSITY BLVD, ROUTE 435 77555 #048-02-2002 L2005 **ID** *012 †20

HEYNE, Cynthia Contreras. 301 UNIVERSITY BLVD, ROUTE 591 77555 #048-02-2002 L2006 **CCA** *100

HILBERT, Lindsay Kay. 301 UNIVERSITY BLVD, UTMB-DEPT OF INTERNAL MEDI 77555 #048-02-2005 L2007 **IM** *012

HILD, Walther J. 301 UNIVERSITY BLVD 77550 #407-12-1949 **OS** *071

HILL, Alesha Jayne. 301 UNIVERSITY BLVD, ROUTE 193 77555 #048-02-2002 L2006 **CHP** *020 †20

HIRSCHFELD, Robt Magnus A. 301 UNIVERSITY BLVD 77555 #025-01-1968 L1991 **P** *030 †75

HO, Kihong. 301 UNIVERSITY BLVD J, MEDICAL BR 77555 #005-15-2005 **OTO** *012

HOANG, Thomas Tran. 301 UNIVERSITY BLVD, UTMB DIV OF UROLOGY 77555 #048-02-2003 **U** *100

HOFFMANN, Peter Robt. ■ 77550 #035-01-1975 L1977 **IM HEM** *030 †20

HOLASEK, Silvina Soledad. DEPT OF PSYCHIATRY, UNIV OF TEXAS MED BRANCH 77555 #132-12-2002 **P** *012

HOLDING, Julie Christine. ■ 77554 #048-02-2005 **PS** *012

HOLLAND, Owen Bryan. 301 UNIVERSITY BLVD, DEPT OF IM 77555 #048-02-1968 L1968 **IM END** *050 †20

HOLSTEIN, Gaylyn June. UNIV OF TEXAS MED BRANCH, DEPT OF PSYCHIATRY 77555 #048-02-2005 L2008 **P** *012

HORNSBY, Lawrence Gene. 28 S SHORE DR 77551 #027-01-1960 L1969 **FM** *020 †75

HOUSER, Christine Marie. 2109 POST OFFICE ST # 73 77550 #023-07-1996 L2002 **EM** *020 †16

HUANG, Frederick Szujuei. 301 UNIVERSITY BLVD 77555 #048-04-1994 L1995 **PHO PD** *020 †55

HUANG, Grace Yu-Tyng. ■ 77550 #048-02-2004 L2008 **AN** *012

HUANG, Ming-He. 301 UNIVERSITY BLVD, 5.106 JOHN SEALY ANNEX 77555 #243-45-1984 L2001 **CD** *020 †20

HUANG, Ted Tsung-Che. 326 MARKET ST 77550 #048-02-1965 L1969 **PS GS** *020 †85,65

HUDNALL, Stanley David. 301 UNIVERSITY BLVD, STE 1022 77555 #045-01-1978 L1992 **PTH CLP** *050 †50

HUGHES, Nancy L. 800 MECHANIC, UT MEDICAL BRANCH 77550 #048-02-1994 L1995 **IM** *020 †20

HUNDERUP, James Wellesley. ■ 77550 #051-07-1999 L2005 **EM** *020 †16

HUNTER, Glenn Colin. 301 UNIVERSITY BLVD #6.110, SECTION VASCU SURGER 77555 #836-02-1968 L2004 **VS GS** *020

HUSAIN, Shahid Javed. 301 UNIVERSITY BLVD, 5.112 JOHN SEALY ANNEX 77555 #704-21-1994 L2000 **PCC** *020 †20

HUSSAIN, Lubna. 301 UNIV BLV STE 0462, DEPT OF PEDS 77555 #048-15-2004 L2004 **PD** *012

HUSSAIN, Nasir. 4.174 JOHN SEALY HOSPITAL, DEPT OF INTERNAL MEDICINE 77555 #704-08-1983 L1994 **IM** *030 †20

HUSSEIN, Qaali. ■ 77550 #048-02-2008 *012

HUTTENBACH, Yve T. 301 UNIVERSITY BLVD, DEPT OF DERM 77555 #048-04-1998 L1999 **DMP** *020

HUYNH, Tran Cassandra. ■ 77550 #048-02-2006 **IM** *012

HWANG, Yong Gil. 301 UNIV BLVD 77555 #583-30-1999 **IM** *012

HYDE, Brannon Ray. 301 UNIVERSITY BLVD, ROUTE 534 77555 #048-02-2003 L2006 **GS** *012

IERO, Domenico. ■ 77551 #561-09-1952 L1963 **GP** *071

IGHANI-HOSSEINBAD, Farshid. ■ 77550 #048-15-2004 L2008 **OPH** *012

INDRIKOVS, Alexander Jose. 301 UNIVERSITY BLVD, STE 1022 77555 #308-02-1983 L1993 **PTH** *020 †50

ISENBERG, John Nevin. 301 UNIVERSITY BLVD, UTMB CHILDREN'S HOSPITAL 77555 #038-06-1970 L1979 **PD FM** *020 †55

ISHIHARA, Kanae. 301 UNIVERSITY BLVD, 4.200 JOHN SEALY ANNEX 77555 #030-06-1991 L2002 **NEP** *020 †20

IVEY, Frank Martin. 301 UNIVERSITY BLVD 77555 #048-02-1971 L1971 **ORS** *020 †40

IZAD, Alexander Arad. ■ 77551 #858-02-2001 L2007 **IM** *020

JACKSON, Grace Nightingal. ■ 77551 #048-04-2004 **PTH** *012

JACKSON, James T. 301 UNIVERSITY ROUTE 1173 77555 #048-02-1992 L1994 **IM EM** *020 †20

JACOBS, William Fredric. 301 UNIVERSITY BLVD, U T M B GALVESTON 77555 #048-02-1965 L1965 **CD IM** *071 †20

JACOBSON, Bradley. 301 UNIVERSITY BLVD 77550 #048-02-2006 **EM** *012

JADHAV, Siddharth Prafull. 301 UNIV BLV STE D62 77555 #496-26-2000 *100

JAFRI, Syed Fazle Ali. 301 UNIVERSITY BLVD, 4106 MCCULLOUGH BLDG 77555 #495-21-1982 L1999 **GE IM** *020 †20

JAHADI, Mohammad Reza. 301 UNIVERSITY BLVD 77555 #517-05-1966 L1975 **CRS GS** *040 †10

JAIN, Ajay. MEDICAL BR, UNIVERSITY OF TEXAS 77555 #305-01-2001 L2006 **PCC** *020

JAIN, Venu. ■ 77550 #495-29-1992 **OBG** *100

JAJORIA, Praveen. 301 UNIV BLVD 77555 #496-09-2001 **IM** *012

JAMAL, Naznin T. ■ 77551 #048-02-2008 *012

JAMES, Julia Maria. 301 UNIVERSITY BLVD, UNIV OF TX MED BRANCH HOSP 77555 #305-01-2004 L2008 **PD** *100

JAMES, Thomas N. 301 UNIVERSITY BLVD, U T M B GALVESTON 77555 #021-01-1949 L1988 **CD IM** *050 †20

JAMESON, Grace Klein. 121 TARPON AVE, STE 412 77550 #048-02-1949 L1950 **P CHP** *071 †75

JAYROE, Jason Brock. 301 UNIVERSITY BLVD, DEPT OF CARDIOLOGY 77555 #048-02-2003 L2006 **CD** *012 †20

JENICEK, John Andrew. 301 UNIVERSITY BLVD 77555 #016-11-1946 L1967 **AN PUD** *071 †05

JINKINS, A J, Jr. ■ 77551 #048-02-1965 L1965 **FM** *020

JINKINS, Julius L, Jr. ■ 77550 #048-02-1947 L1947 **GYN** *071 †30

JOHNSON, Claudine D. 400 HARBORSIDE DR STE 109 77555 #035-20-2002 L2005 **IM** *020 †20

JOHNSON, Clint Weston. ■ 77550 #048-15-2005 **ORS** *012

JOHNSON, Robert. 301 UNIVERSITY BLVD 77555 #023-12-1984 L2005 **PHP AM** *040 †70

JONES, Edgar F, III. 53 ADLER CIR, GALVESTON TEXAS 77551 77551 #048-02-1964 L1964 **GP FPG** *071 †18

JUBANG, Michael Jeremy. ■ 77550 #048-02-2007 L2008 **IM** *012

JURNALOV, Catalin Dumitru. 301 UNIVERSITY BLVD, DEPT OF OB-GYN 77555 #020-12-1992 L2001 **OBG OS** *020 †30

KALIA, Alok. 301 UNIVERSITY BLVD, UNIV TX MEDICAL BRANCH 77555 #495-27-1974 L1982 **PD PN** *020 †55

KALIMUDDIN, Malik Naz. 301 UNIVERSITY BLVD, RT 193 77555 #704-16-1983 L2006 **CHP** *012

KALU, Stella Uzumma. 301 UNIVERSITY BLVD, 3.320 CHILDREN'S HOSPITAL 77555 #690-04-2002 L2008 **PDI** *012 †55

KANG, Sundeep Singh. ■ 77550 #048-02-2007 **IM** *012

KANSAL, Neera. 301 UNIVERSITY BLVD, DIV OF EMERGENCY MEDICINE 77555 #048-14-1997 L1998 **MPD** *020 †20,55

KAPOOR, Kapil Gopal. UNIV OF TEXAS MED BRANCH, DEPT OF INT MED 77555 #038-40-2007 **IM** *012

KARNATH, Bernard M. 301 UNIVERSITY BLVD 77555 #048-02-1994 L1996 **IM** *020 †20

KASPER, Jared M. ■ 77550 #048-02-2008 *012

KASTURI, Krishna Sagar. 301 UNIV BLVD 77555 #495-21-2003 **IM** *012

KATHURIA, Manoj Kumar. 301 UNIV BLV STE D62 77550 #496-09-1988 *100

KATZMAN, Gregory Lewis. 301 UNIVERSITY BLVD, UNIVERSITY HOSPITAL CLINIC 77555 #017-20-1993 L2007 **RNR** *020 †80

KAY, Atrac Aryan. 301 UNIVERSITY BLVD 77555 #305-01-2006 **MPD** *012

KEARNEY, Joseph Patrick. 301 UNIVERSITY BLVD 77555 #048-02-1972 L1977 **ORS** *020 †40

KEENEY, Susan. RT 0526 UNIV TX MED BRANCH, DEPT PEDIATRICS 77555 #048-02-1982 L1983 **NPM PD** *050 †55

KELLS, Amy Frances. ■ 77554 #047-05-1993 L1994 **HS** *100 †85

KELLY, Brent Christopher. 301 UNIVERSITY BLVD, DEPT OF DERM 77555 #021-05-1999 L2002 **DMP** *100 †20,15

KELLY, Kyle A. ■ 77551 #048-02-2008 *012

KELSO, Harry Bertrand, Jr. 1 MOODY PLZ 77550 #048-02-1965 L1965 **IM** *020 †20

KELVER, Mae Ellen Meitzen. 301 UNIVERSITY BLVD, U.T.M.B 77555 #048-02-1979 L1979 **OBG REN** *020 †30

KENT, Thomas Andrew. U TX MED BRACH DPT N 77550 #019-02-1979 L1986 **N P** *050 †75

KESSEL, Ivan Leslie. 301 UNIVERSITY BLVD, MC 0711 77555 #836-01-1979 L2003 **RO** *020 †20

KHALIFE, Wissam Ibrahim. 301 UNIVERSITY BLVD, ROUTE 553 77555 #605-03-1999 L2006 **CD** *012 †20

KHAMAPIRAD, Tuenchit. 301 UNIVERSITY BLVD 77555 #891-01-1963 L1977 **PDR OS** *020 †80

KHARODAWALA, Murtaza Z. 301 UNIVERSITY BLVD J, MED BRANCH 77555 #025-07-2003 L2005 **OTO** *012

KILLEWICH, Lois Archer. 301 UNIVERSITY BLVD, RM 6.136 77555 #054-04-1984 L2004 **VS** *020 †85

KILLYON, Garry W. 815 MARKET ST, DIV OF PLASTIC SURGERY 77550 #047-07-1981 L2005 **PS** *020 †65 ‡

KIMBROUGH, Thomas Duke. 301 UNIVERSITY BLVD, GS DEPT #E42 77550 #048-02-1976 L1976 **GS** *020 †85

KING, James C, III. 301 UNIVERSITY BLVD, DEPT OF FAM MED 77555 #039-01-1976 L2003 **FM FPG** *040 †18

KING, William Henry. 301 UNIVERSITY BLVD, U T M B GALVESTON 77555 #010-03-1968 L1981 **AN** *071 †05

KINSELLA, John B. UTMB, DEPT OTO 77550 #539-04-1986 **OTO** *100

KINSKY, Michael P. 301 UNIVERSITY BLVD, JSA 2-A 77555 #048-02-1999 L2003 **AN** *100 †05

KLEIN, Gordon Leslie. UT MED BR, DEPT PED 77550 #035-46-1971 L1987 **PD GE** *050 †55

KLIMISCH, Justin John. ■ 77554 #048-02-2004 **ORS** *012

KNECHT, John George, III. 301 UNIV BLV STE D62 77550 #422-01-2007 **IM** *012

KNOX, Lynn K. 301 UNIVERSITY BLVD, STE 2A 77555 #048-12-1994 L1995 **AN** *020 †05

KOCHAR, Tina. 301 UNIV BLVD 77555 #496-43-2004 **IM** *012

KOMAK, Spogmai. ■ 77555 #048-02-2006 **GS** *012

KOUTROUVELIS, Aristides P. 301 UNIVERSITY BLVD 77555 #422-01-1993 L1998 **CCA** *020 †05

KROG, Benjamin John. 301 UNIVERSITY BLVD, DEPARTMENT OF ANESTHESIOLO 77555 #048-04-2005 L2007 **OBG** *100

KUMAR, Rajendra. 301 UNIVERSITY BLVD, DEPT RAD 77550 #495-36-1965 L1978 **DR NM** *040 †80,28

KUMAR, Sanjeev. 301 UNIVERSITY BLVD, APICS 77555 #495-03-1999 L2006 **PCC** *012 †20

KUMMERFELD, David Andrew. ■ 77550 #048-02-2008 *012

KUNAPULI, Sanjay. DEPT OF INT MED, UNIV OF TEXAS MED BRANCH 77555 #422-01-2003 **CD** *012

KUNCHARAPU, Indumathi. 301 UNIVERSITY BLVD, GALVESTON, DEPT OF FAMILY 77555 #495-57-1982 L1997 **FM** *020 †18

KUNIYOSHI, Sandra Midori. 301 UNIVERSITY BLVD, 9.128 JOHN SEALY ANNEX 77555 #005-12-1998 L2003 **N** *020 †75

LABUDA, Sarah. ■ 77551 #048-16-2007 **MPD** *012
LADNER, Stephen Stewart. DEPT OF RADIOLOGY G-09, UNIV OF TEXAS MED BRANCH H 77555 #048-02-1997 L2004 **RNR** *020
LA FORTE, Russell Andre. 606 UNIVERSITY BLVD 77550 #048-02-1992 L1993 **IM** *020 †20
LA FORTE, Suzanne C. 301 UNIVERSITY BLVD, DEPT. PEDIATRICS,DIV. GEN. 77555 #048-02-1994 L1998 **PD** *020 †55
LANE, Charles Joseph. UNIV OF TEXAS MED BRANCH, MED RESEARCH BLDG 8104 77555 #036-01-2004 **AI** *012 †20
LANGSJOEN, Hans Alfred. UTMB DEPT NEUR NOE 39 77550 #048-02-1974 L1974 **EM N** *020 †75
LANKFORD, Daniel Burgess. ■ 77550 #048-02-2007 **TY** *012
LAPPIN, Jacqueline A. 301 UNIVERSITY BLVD 77555 #539-03-1986 L1997 **GS** *020 †85
LARA, Theresa Christell. 301 UNIVERSITY BLVD, RT 195 77555 #048-02-2003 L2007 **P** *020
LAU, Daryl. ■ 77555 #067-01-1986 L1999 **IM** *020 †20
LAUNIKITIS, Robert A. 301 UNIVERSITY BLVD, UTMB/ORTHOPAEDICS 77555 #048-02-2003 L2008 **ORS** *012
LAW, Marianne Louise. ■ 77550 #051-01-2007 **OBG** *012
LEA, Alfred Scott. 301 UNIVERSITY BLVD, GRAVES BUILDING 4.318C 77555 #048-04-1975 L1976 **ID IM** *040 †20
LE BLANC, Alvin Louis. 220 BARRACUDA AVE 77550 #048-02-1955 L1955 **OBG** *040 †30
LEBOEUF, Jenny Lynn. ■ 77551 #021-05-2006 **DR** *012
LEE, Doris Anne. 301 UNIVERSITY BLVD 77555 #048-02-1967 L1967 **AN** *071 †05
LEE, Gabriel H. 301 UNIVERSITY BLVD 77555 #048-04-2005 L2007 **IM** *012
LEE, Jong O. 815 MARKET ST, STE 718 77550 #041-13-1996 L2004 **GS** *020 †85
LEE, Rayman Weimin. 301 UNIVERSITY BLVD, 5.112 J SEALY ANNX/RTE E61 77555 #036-01-1988 L1990 **PCC IM** *020 †20
LEE, Tammy Bohyun. BRANCH HOSPS, UNIV OF TEXAS MED 77555 #016-06-2002 L2007 **GS** *100
LEMON, Stanley Moncrief. 301 UNIVERSITY BLVD, OFF OF DEAN OF MEDICINE 77555 #035-45-1972 L2002 **ID IM** *050 †20
LENIHAN, Daniel John. 301 UNIVERSITY BLVD, UTMB 77555 #047-06-1988 L1998 **CD** *020 †20
LENIHAN, Merle Sharber. ■ 77551 #047-06-1988 L1998 **OBG** *020 †30
LEON, Luis A. 6511 STEWART RD STE 1 77551 #042-01-1958 L1965 **IM CCM** *020 †20 ‡
LEONARD, Morton H, Jr. 301 UNIVERSITY BLVD 77550 #048-02-1973 L1973 **DR** *020 †80
LEVIN, William Cohn. UNIV OF TEXAS MED SCH 77550 #048-02-1941 L1941 **HEM ON** *071 †20
LEVINE, Lyuba. 305 UNIVERSITY BLVD, #316 CLN SCI BLDG 77555 #422-01-1996 L2001 **OBG** *020 †30
LEVINE, Michael Jay. ■ 77551 #016-11-1966 L1984 **CHP** *020
LEVINE, Ruth Ellen. 301 UNIVERSITY BLVD 77555 #048-02-1987 L1988 **P** *040 †75
LEVY, Ronald Stuart. 301 UNIVERSITY BLVD, JSA 2-A 77555 #550-02-1988 L1998 **AN HS** *020 †05
LEWIS, Rebecca Ann. 301 UNIVERSITY BLVD, DEPT DERM 77550 #048-02-2003 L2006 **D** *100 †15
LI, Husong. 301 UNIVERSITY BLVD, DEPT ANESTHESIOLOGY UTMB 77555 #243-64-1985 L2002 **AN** *020
LICK, Scott Douglas. 301 UNIVERSITY BLVD, # E28 77555 #026-04-1987 L1994 **TS GS** *020 †85,90
LIEBERMAN, Steven Alex. 301 UNIVERSITY BLVD, 5.106 ADMINISTRATION BUILD 77555 #048-12-1985 L1987 **END IM** *020 †20
LIN, Di. ■ 77550 #048-02-2008 *012
LIN, Scott Hsin Sheng. ■ 77550 #048-02-2004 L2007 **GS** *100
LIN, Shwu-Fang. 301 UNIVERSITY BLVD, DEPARTMENT OF PEDIATRICS 77555 #132-01-1990 L2001 **PN** *020
LIN, Xi. DEPT OF NEUROLOGY, UNIV OF TEXAS MED BRANCH H 77555 #243-03-1991 L2007 **N** *010
LINARES, Hugo Alberto. 610 TEXAS AVE 77550 #132-01-1963 *050
LINDENBORN, Rachel Elizab. ■ 77550 #048-02-2008 *012
LINDGREN, Kjell Norwood. 301 UNIVERSITY BLVD, MC 1150 77555 #007-02-2002 L2006 **EM** *100 †16
LINDSEY, Ronald Wayne. 301 UNIVERSITY BLVD, 2316 REBECCA SEALY HOSP 77555 #035-01-1977 L1989 **OTR OSS** *020 †40
LIPSKY, Sharon Diane. 301 UNIVERSITY BLVD 77550 #048-02-1981 L1981 **DR** *020 †80
LITTON, Charles D. ■ 77550 #020-02-1960 L1966 **AN** *071 †05
LIU, Hanlin. 301 UNIVERSITY BLVD, GALVESTON, TX 77555-1110 77555 #243-46-1982 L2003 **OM CD** *020 †70
LIU, Xiushi. 301 UNIV BLVD, ROUTE 0553 77555 #243-92-1993 L2008 **CD** *012 †20
LIZARRALDE, Claudia Maria. UNIV TX MED BRANCH, DEPT PSYCH 77550 #429-01-1986 **CHP** *020
LOCKHART, Lillian Hoffman. 301 UNIVERSITY BLVD, DEPT PED CHILDRENS HOSP 77555 #048-02-1957 L1957 **OS HEM** *020 †55
LOERA, Jose Angel. DIV OF GERIATRIC MEDICINE, UNIV OF TX MEDICAL BRANCH 77555 #649-01-1970 L1982 **HEM ON** *020
LOGRONO, Roberto. 301 UNIVERSITY BLVD, U T M B GALVESTON 77555 #308-01-1982 L1997 **PTH** *075 †50
LONGO, Ginger Kay. 301 UNIVERSITY BLVD, RT 587 77555 #048-02-2002 L2005 **OBG** *100
LONGO, Monica. 301 UNIV BLV STE D62 77555 #561-09-1996 **OBG** *012
LONGWELL, John William. 301 UNIVERSITY BLVD, DEPT OF ANESTHESIOLOGY 77555 #048-02-1998 L2002 **AN** *020
LOOP, Karen Quintavell. ■ 77551 #051-04-2006 **PTH** *012
LOPEZ, Daniel Esteban. BRANCH HOSPS, UNIV OF TEXAS MED 77555 #016-11-2007 **GS** *012
LOUCKS, Emmakay Renee. 700 UNIVERSITY BLVD, UNIV OF TEXAS MED BRANCH 77550 #048-02-2001 L2005 **OPH** *100 †35
LOW, Brandon Ohara. ■ 77551 #048-02-2006 **ORS** *012
LUCIO, Emmanuel T. ■ 77551 #748-01-1988 L1997 **PTH** *100 †50
LUI, Charles Yan-Che. ■ 77555 #030-05-1980 L2006 **CD** *020 †20
LUKEFAHR, James Louis. 301 UNIVERSITY BLVD, DEPARTMENT OF PEDIATRICS 77555 #048-12-1978 L1978 **PD OS** *040 †55
LUNA, Maria Nichole. U OF TX MEDICAL BRANCH, 4.112 JOHN SEALY ANNEX 77555 #048-02-2003 L2006 **IM** *100 †20
LUTSCHG, Alexis L. 301 UNIVERSITY BLVD, STE 2A 77555 #048-14-2001 L2005 **AN** *020 †05
LYNLEY, Alexis Michel. 301 UNIVERSITY BLVD, DEPT OF ANESTHESIOLOGY- UT 77555 #054-04-1985 L1987 **AN** *020 †05
MAC GREGOR, Jan Marie. 301 UNIVERSITY BLVD 77550 #048-04-1986 L1987 **IM** *020 †20
MADAMBA, Alfredo Acaso. 301 UNIV BLV STE D62 77555 #748-01-1992 **RNR** *100
MAHON, Edward Lamar. ■ 77554 #047-05-1947 L1948 **ORS** *071 †40
MAITY, Smita. ■ 77551 #496-08-1997 L2003 **IM** *100 †20

MAKHLOUF, Michel Antonios. 301 UNIVERSITY BLVD, DEPT. OF OB/GYN MFM MC0587 77555 #045-01-1999 L2004 **OBG** *020
MALAKOUTI, Sam Sadegh. 301 UNIVERSITY BLVD, DEPARTMENT OF ANESTHESIOLO 77555 #517-10-1986 L1997 **APM** *020
MALHOTRA, Advitya. ■ 77551 #496-43-2002 **GE** *012 †20
MALHOTRA, Kavin. ■ 77554 #048-04-2006 **DR** *012
MALLETT, Joanne. ■ 77550 #048-02-1975 L1975 **GYN** *072 †30
MALLOY, Michael Howard. 301 UNIVERSITY BLVD 77555 #048-02-1973 L1973 **NPM PD** *050 †55
MALTEMPO, Melissa Anne. 301 UNIVERSITY BLVD, DEPT OF PEDIATRICS 77555 #035-06-2005 **PD** *012
MALTZ, Ashley. ■ 77550 #048-02-2007 **IPM** *012
MANICKAVASAGAM, Saraswathy. UNIV TX MED BRANCH HOSPS, 301 UNIV BLV STE D62 77550 #495-31-2001 **IM** *012
MARKAREWICZ, Carl R. 3011 AVENUE N 0 77550 #064-01-1977 **DR** *020
MARKOWITZ, Avi B. 301 UNIVERSITY BLVD, RM 4.164 77555 #005-02-1981 L1988 **ON IM** *020 †20
MARTIN, Jason Lee. 301 UNIV BLV STE D62 77550 #422-01-2007 **IM** *012
MARTIN, Julie Elizabeth. ■ 77550 #021-05-2005 L2008 **GS** *012
MARTINEZ, Carlos Heli. DEPT OF INT MED, UNIV OF TEXAS MED BRANCH 77555 #264-01-1986 **IPM** *012
MARTINEZ, Juan Gerardo. ■ 77550 #048-02-2004 L2007 **IM** *100 †20
MARTINEZ, Kelly Ann. ■ 77551 #019-02-2006 **OBG** *012
MARTINEZ, Sylvia Amador. ■ 77550 #048-02-2007 **IM** *012
MARTINEZ-TICA, Julian F. 301 UNIVERSITY BLVD OJS-2, DEPT OF ANESTHESIOLOGY, UT 77555 #737-01-1984 L1997 **AN** *020 †05
MARX, Marilyn. 301 UNIVERSITY BLVD, UNIV. OF TX MED BRANCH 77555 #016-01-1980 L1984 **GS** *020 †85
MASEL, Brent Ellis. 1528 POST OFFICE ST 77550 #016-43-1974 L1977 **N** *030 †75
MASEL, Todd Simon. ■ 77551 #048-02-2005 L2007 **N** *012
MAST, Christopher Glenn. 301 UNIVERSITY BLVD, MC 1123 77555 #038-41-1997 L2004 **FM** *020 †18
MAST, Kimberly Renee. 301 UNIVERSITY BLVD, MC 1167 77555 #038-41-1997 L2007 **IM** *020 †20
MATA, Carlos. ■ 77551 #048-02-2005 **PS** *012
MATALON, Reuben K. 301 UNIVERSITY BLVD, PROFESSOR OF PEDS 77555 #550-01-1959 L1997 **PD** *020 †55,19
MATEUS NINO, Julio Fernan. OB/GYN DEPARTMENT, UNIVERSITY OF TEXAS MEDICA 77555 #264-04-1994 L2007 **OBG** *020
MATHERNE, Ryan Joseph. ■ 77551 #021-05-2006 **D** *012
MATHERS, Charles Hood. ■ 77550 #048-02-2007 **IPM** *012
MATLOCK, Aaron G. ■ 77551 #048-02-2008 *012
MATTESON, Robert C. ■ 77550 #048-02-1986 L1987 **DR** *020 †80
MATTHEWS, Daniel Ted. ■ 77550 #048-02-1967 L1967 **DR** *030 †75
MAYHALL, C Glen. 301 UNIVERSITY BLVD, DIV OF INFECTIOUS DISEASES 77555 #048-04-1966 L1966 **ID IM** *062 †20
MAYNE, Jennifer Ruth. ■ 77550 #048-02-2007 **IM** *012
MAYNE, Joshua C. ■ 77550 #048-02-2008 *012
MCARTHUR, Monica Anne. 301 UNIVERSITY BLVD, UNIV OF TEXAS MED BRANCH 77555 #048-02-2006 **PD** *012
MCBRIDE, Latresha Johanna. ■ 77551 #010-03-2007 **PD** *012
MC CAMMON, Andrew Thomas. 301 UNIVERSITY BLVD, STE 2A 77555 #001-02-1998 L2006 **AN** *020 †05
MCCAULEY, Robert L. 815 MARKET ST 77550 #016-02-1977 L1987 **IM** *020 †65,85
MCCONNELL, Rachel Ivy. ■ 77551 #048-02-2005 L2007 **PD** *012
MC CORMICK, David Peter. 400 HARBORSIDE DR, UTMB 77555 #035-20-1968 L1986 **PD IM** *040 †55
MC DOWELL, Kelly N. CHILD/ADOLESCENT PSYCH, DIV OF 77555 #048-12-2004 L2008 **CHP** *012
MCKEE, Juliet Marie. 301 UNIVERSITY BLVD, DEPARTMENT OF 77555 #048-02-2000 L2003 **FM** *020 †18
MC KENDALL, Robert R. 301 UNIVERSITY BLVD, DPT NEUROLOGY 77550 #024-07-1969 L1985 **N IG** *050 †75
MC KENNA, John R. 200 UNIVERSITY BLVD, STE 922 77550 #048-02-1953 L1953 **GS** *071 †85
MC KINNEY, Kevin Hood. 301 UNIVERSITY BLVD, DEPT OF IM 77555 #048-02-1992 L1994 **END IM** *020 †20
MC KNIGHT, Monique Venita. BRANCH HOSPI, UNIV OF TEXAS MED 77555 #012-21-2003 L2007 **OBG** *020
MCKNIGHT, Techksell Meshe. ■ 77550 #010-03-2005 **IPM** *012
MC LARTY, Ewing Sinks, Jr. ■ 77550 #048-12-1953 L1953 **GP** *071
MC NEARNEY, Terry Ann. 301 UNIVERSITY BLVD, DIV RHEUMTLGY UTMB 77555 #028-34-1981 L1983 **RHU IM** *050 †20
MC NEEL, Linea Ann. 2200 MARKET ST, STE 412 77550 #007-02-1990 L1998 **P** *020 †75
MC QUITTY, Christopher K. 301 UNIVERSITY BLVD, JSA 2-A 77555 #019-02-1989 L1994 **AN** *020 †05
MCVAY, Travis James. DEPT OF ANESTHESIOLOGY, UNIV OF TEXAS MED BRANCH 77555 #048-14-2007 **AN** *012
MEDEIROS, Felipe Almada. ■ 77550 #187-43-2001 L2006 **IM** *020 †20
MEDLICOTT, Shaun A. ■ 77551 #060-02-1992 **PTH** *100
MEHLMAN, Karyl Norcross. 301 UNIVERSITY BLVD, RTE 595 77555 #016-06-1978 L1983 **N** *020 †75
MELTON, Bengi Biber. 301 UNIVERSITY BLVD 77555 #902-03-1991 L2004 **P** *020 †75 ‡
MELTON, Jennifer Leigh. ■ 77551 #021-05-2006 **OBG** *012
MERCADO, Anita C. 301 UNIVERSITY BLVD, RT # 460 77555 #048-02-1991 L1992 **IMG** *020 †20
MERLA, Ramanna. 301 UNIVERSITY BLVD 77555 #495-50-2001 L2007 **IM** *100 †20
MERRIMAN, David Joshua. ■ 77550 #048-12-2005 **ORS** *012
MEYER, Walter John, III. 301 UNIVERSITY BLVD, DEPT OF PSY UTMB 77555 #023-07-1968 L1975 **CHP** *050 †55,75
MEZA, Carlos A. 301 UNIVERSITY BLVD #048-16-1998 L2003 **IM** *020 †20
MICHAEL, Kendra Lashawn. 301 UNIVERSITY BLVD, UNIV OF TEXAS MED BRANCH 77555 #021-05-2006 **PD** *012
MICHELL, Michael W. UNIV OF TEXAS MED BRANCH, DEPT OF RADIOLOGY 77555 #048-02-2006 **DR** *012
MIDDLETON, Douglas M. ■ 77554 #048-12-1980 L1980 **GS EM** *020
MIDDLETON, Ellen Aurora. 301 UNIV BLV STE 0462, DEPT OF INTERNAL MEDICINE 77555 #048-02-2005 **IM** *012

MILESKI, William John. 301 UNIVERSITY BLVD, DEPARTMENT OF SURGERY 77555 #033-05-1983 L1990 **GS** *020 †85

MILLER, Kevin Burke. UNIV OF TEXAS MED BRANCH, DEPT OF INT MED 77555 #024-07-2004 **OPH** *012

MILLINGTON, Karmaine A. ■ 77550 #005-12-2004 L2008 **PTH** *012

MIRYALA, Ragini Prakash. 301 UNIVERSITY BLVD, UNIVERSITY OF TEXAS MEDICA 77555 #048-02-2005 L2008 **PD** *012

MISHRA, Deepti. 301 UNIVERSITY BLVD, RT 1128 UTMB GALVESTON 77555 #027-01-1996 L1999 **IM** *020 †20

MITCHEL, Dara Lynn. ■ 77550 #028-46-2005 **OBG** *012

MITTAL, Sahil. UNIV OF TEXAS MED BRANCH, DEPT OF INT MED 77555 #495-29-2001 **IM** *012

MIZE, William Lawrence. 301 UNIVERSITY BLVD, UTMB DEPARTMENT OF PEDIATR 77555 #048-04-1976 L1977 **PD DBP** *020 †55

MODI, Shreyas Ashwin. UNIV OF TEXAS MED BRANCH, DEPT OF INT MED 77555 #496-23-2001 L2008 **CD** *012 †20

MOHAMED, Gamal S. 301 UNIVERSITY BLVD STE J12-PATH 77550 #915-04-1981 **PTH** *020

MONROY, Anwar Eduardo. ■ 77551 #649-27-2003 **FP** *012

MONTERO, Froilan W. ■ 77550 #048-02-2008 *012

MONTIEL HURTADO, Carlos E. ■ 77551 #935-02-2001 **FP** *012

MONTOYA, Maria Elvira. UNIV OF TEXAS MED BRANCH, 4164 JOHN SEALY HOSP R-056 77555 #264-16-1997 L2007 **ON** *100

MOORE, Gradie Elizabeth. ■ 77550 #048-02-2008 *012

MOORE, Sheila Michelle. ■ 77550 #048-02-2007 *012

MORALES, Rolando. DIV OF PLASTIC SURGERY, UNIV OF TEXAS MED BRANCH H 77555 #048-02-2006 L2006 **PS** *012

MORENO, Eduardo Enrique. 301 UNIVERSITY BLVD, DEPARTMENT OF ANESTHESIOLO 77555 #048-13-2003 L2007 **AN** *012

MORETTIN, Luis B. 301 UNIVERSITY BLVD 77555 #132-01-1959 L1967 **R VIR** *040 †80

MORGAN, Jamison Dale. BRANCH HOSPS, UNIV OF TEXAS MED 77555 #040-02-2004 **OBG** *012

MOUNT, Jerry Ernest. 1701 TREMONT ST, 23RD 77550 #048-02-1962 L1962 **U** *020 †95

MOVVA, Sunil. UNIV OF TEXAS MED BRANCH, DEPT OF INT MED 77555 #495-04-2001 L2006 **IM** *100 †20

MOYNIHAN, Shannan. 301 UNIVERSITY BLVD, EWING HALL- 1.116 77555 #035-19-1999 L2003 **GPM** *020 †16,70

MUCOWSKI, Sara Jeanette. BRANCH HOSPS, UNIV OF TEXAS MED 77555 #041-15-2007 **OBG** *012

MUELLER, Martin. UNIV OF TEXAS MED BRANCH, DEPT OF ANESTHESIOLOGY 77555 #408-17-1998 L2007 **PAN** *100 †05

MUELLER, Rashmi N. ■ 77550 #496-15-1992 L2002 **AN** *020 †05

MUJEEB, Mehrukh. 301 UNIV BLCD 77555 #704-25-2002 **IM** *012

MUMMADI, Rajasekhara Redd. UNIV OF TEXAS MED BRANCH, DEPT OF INT MED 77555 #495-21-1998 **GE** *012 †20

MUMMADI, Srinivas Reddy. 301 UNIV BLVD 77555 #495-73-2003 **IM** *012

MUNN, Mary Bernadette. 301 UNIVERSITY BLVD, RT 587 77555 #021-01-1992 L2003 **OBG** *020 †30

MURTHY, Vijaya Laxmi. 301 UNIV BLV STE D62 77550 #496-35-2003 **IM** *012

MURUGAN, Thirumagal Anand. 301 UNIVERSITY BLVD, STE 417 77555 #495-04-2001 L2006 **PCC** *012 †20

MUSLIN, Sarah Shabot. ■ 77554 #048-02-2006 **AN** *012

MYERS, Martin Grosvenor. ■ 77554 #023-07-1967 L1970 **PD ID** *050 †55

MYERS, Wesley Thomas. ■ 77550 #048-02-2004 L2006 **PS** *012

NAGAMANI, Manubai. 301 UNIVERSITY BLVD, OB/GYN RM 3.108 J S ANNEX 77555 #495-42-1963 L1977 **OBG REN** *020 †30

NAGARAJ, Nandini. RT 0, 4106 JOHN MCCULLOUGH BLDG 77555 #496-22-2002 L2003 **GE** *012 †20

NAGIREDDY, Shanti Satya. 301 UNIVERSITY BLVD, ROUTE 193 77555 #495-58-1998 L2006 **CHP** *020 †75

NAIK, Shantanu Shreepad. 301 UNIVERSITY BLVD, UNIV OF TX MEDICAL BRANCH 77550 #654-01-2001 L2006 **PCC** *012

NANIWADEKAR, Ashutosh Sub. UNIV OF TEXAS MED BRANCH, DEPT OF INT MED 77555 #496-38-2001 **IM** *012

NAOUM, Joseph Joe. 301 UNIVERSITY BLVD, UTMB 77555 #047-05-1998 L2003 **VS** *100 †85

NASH, Michael Colquitt. ■ 77550 #048-02-2008 *012

NATH, Samir Kumar. 301 UNIVERSITY BLVD, UTMB DEPT OF INT MED DIV G 77555 #913-48-1980 L2004 **GE** *020 †20

NAUTA, Haring Jetse. 301 UNIVERSITY BLVD, UTMB DEPT NEURO SURG 77555 #038-06-1974 L1982 **NS** *020 †25

NAWGIRI, Ranjana Surendra. ■ 77554 #495-08-1985 L2006 **PTH** *100 †50

NEALON, William H. 301 UNIVERSITY BLVD, DEPT SURG 77550 #041-02-1979 L1985 **GS GE** *020 †85

NELSON, Cassandra. 301 UNIVERSITY BLVD, RM 3302 77555 #048-15-1999 L2002 **PD** *020 †55

NELSON, Robert J. 301 UNIVERSITY BLVD, U T M B GALVESTON 77555 #016-06-1958 L1983 **AN** *072

NELSON, Victor Allen. 301 UNIVERSITY BLVD, UTMB 77555 #056-06-1969 L1978 **IM FM** *020 †20

NESTI, Frances Ruth Darey. 301 UNIVERSITY BLVD, UT MEDICAL BRANCH 4 220 77555 #035-09-1967 L1995 **PD IM** *020 †55

NEWLANDS, Shawn David. 301 UNIV BLVD, JSA 7104 77555 #048-02-1990 L1999 **OTO HNS** *020 †45

NGUYEN, Audrey N. ■ 77550 #048-02-2006 **IM** *012

NGUYEN, Binh Thai. ■ 77551 #048-12-2007 **GS** *012

NGUYEN, Derrick Duong. ■ 77551 #048-13-2004 L2007 **ON** *012 †20

NGUYEN, Diane. ■ 77550 #048-02-2007 **IM** *012

NGUYEN, Donna. ■ 77550 #048-02-2008 *012

NGUYEN, Hoang Dang. 301 UNIVERSITY BLVD, UNIV OF TEXAS MED BRANCH 77555 #305-01-2004 L2007 **PD** *100

NGUYEN, Michael Thanh. 301 UNIVERSITY BLVD, DEPT. OF INTERNAL MEDICINE 77555 #048-12-2003 L2006 **IM** *100 †20

NGUYEN, Nga Anh. 301 UNIVERSITY BLVD, UTMB-DEPT OF PSYCHIATRY 77555 #941-01-1969 L1993 **CHP N** *050 †75

NGUYEN, Phuc Xuan. 301 UNIVERSITY BLVD, DEPARTMENT OF FAMILY PRACT 77555 #048-13-2000 L2003 **FM** *020 †18

NGUYEN, Tracy Uyentrang. 301 UNIVERSITY BLVD, OFC 1165 77555 #047-06-1993 L1996 **RHU** *020 †03,20

NIETO, David Michael. 301 UNIVERSITY BLVD, JSH, STE 2A 77555 #048-02-2003 L2007 **AN** *020

NOBLE, Ralph Wilferd, III. MAIL ROUTE 1119, PRIMARY CARE PAVILION 77555 #048-02-1975 L1975 **PD OS** *020 †55

NOLEN, Eric Dwayne. ■ 77550 #048-15-2003 **PTH FP** *012

NOPPAKUN, Nopadon. UNIV OF TX MED BRANCH, DEPT·DERM 77550 #891-04-1975 **D** *020 †15

NOWAK, David Edward. ■ 77550 #048-02-2007 *012

NOWICKI, Bogdan Jozef. 301 UNIVERSITY BLVD, DEPT OBGYN 77555 #759-07-1973 *100

NUSYNOWITZ, Martin L. U TX MED BRANCH, DEPT RAD 77550 #035-15-1958 L1972 **NM END** *020 †20,28

OANDASAN, Aileen P. SEALY HOSPITAL, 1.302 REBECCA 77555 #048-16-1995 L2001 **P** *020 †75

O'BOYLE, Michael. UTMB, DEPT PSYCHIATRY 77555 #027-01-1981 L1985 **P** *020 †75

OCHOA, Eliana Elisa. 301 UNIVERSITY BLVD, ROUTE 435 77555 #737-06-1999 L2007 **ID** *100 †20

O'DONELL, Alice Anne. 301 UNIVERSITY BLVD, UNIV TX MED BRANCH 77555 #004-01-1964 L1976 **FM PD** *040 †55

O'DWYER, Catherine Angela. 301 UNIVERSITY BLVD, # 2A 77550 #539-02-1987 L1995 **AN** *020 †05

OGRA, Swtantarta. 301 UNIV BLVD, # 351 77555 #495-08-1961 **OBG** *020

OJO, Folasade Mofoluso A. 301 UNIVERSITY BLVD, UTMB AT GALVESTON 77555 #690-02-1992 L2002 **IM** *020 †20

OJO, Olugbenga Babatunde. 301 UNIVERSITY BLVD, STE 202 77555 #690-02-1992 L2002 **IM** *020 †20

OLANO, Juan P. 301 UNIVERSITY BLVD, STE 1022 77555 #264-07-1987 L1999 **MM** *020 †50

OLSON, Gayle Lynn. 301 UNIVERSITY BLVD, 3400 JOHN SEALY ANNEX 77555 #030-06-1988 L1994 **OBG** *020 †30

OLVERA, David Adrian. ■ 77550 #048-02-2005 **AN** *012

ONIGU-OTITE, Edore Celest. 301 UNIV BLV STE D62, DEPT PSYCH 77550 #690-01-1991 L2008 **CHP** *012

OOMMEN, Jacob K. ■ 77550 #048-02-2004 **DR** *012

OOMMEN, Joseph. 301 UNIVERSITY BLVD, 9.128 JOHN SEALY ANNEX 77555 #039-01-2000 L2007 **N** *020 †75

OOMMEN, Smitha Elizabeth. 301 UNIV BLVD 77555 #495-27-2002 **IM** *012

ORIHUELA, Eduardo S. E-40, UNIV TX MED BRNCH UROL 77555 #737-06-1973 L1989 **U** *020 †95

ORTIZ, Waleska Del Carmen. UNIV OF TEXAS MED BRANCH, DEPT OF PSYCHIATRY 77555 #048-02-2004 L2008 **P** *012

OVERTURF, Steven Jeffrey. ■ 77550 #048-02-2008 *012

OWEN, Mary Jean. #118, 400 HARBORSIDE DRIVE 77555 #026-08-1980 L1981 **PD** *050 †55

PAAR, David P. 301 UNIVERSITY BLVD, FROST BANK BUILDING, SUITE 77555 #055-01-1984 L1992 **IM** *030 †20

PALMER, Lolita Vernette. BRANCH HOSPS, UNIV OF TEXAS MED 77555 #004-01-2004 **GS** *012

PANCHBHAVI, Vinod Kumar. 301 UNIVERSITY BLVD, RTE 165 77555 #495-21-1986 L2006 **ORS OFA** *020

PANDORF, Jesse John. 301 UNIVERSITY BLVD, UNIVERSITY OF TEXAS MEDICA 77555 #030-05-2006 **IM** *012

PANIAGUA, Oscar Alberto. 301 UNIVERSITY BLVD, RT 553 77555 #132-02-1995 L2006 **CD** *012 †20

PANOMITROS, Gregory Elias. 301 UNIVERSITY BLVD, DEPT OF ANESTHESIOLOGY 77555 #016-11-1993 L1998 **AN** *020 †05

PARKER, Katrina Lynn. 301 UNIV BLVD RM 3.270, UNIV OF TEXAS MEDICAL BRAN 77555 #025-07-1983 L2003 **PDE PD** *020 †55

PARKER, Sherrie Lynn. ■ 77551 #048-02-2004 **GS** *012

PASRICHA, Pankaj. 301 UNIVERSITY BLVD, UTMB GI DIV 77555 #495-36-1983 L1999 **GE IM** *050 †20

PASZTOR, Gabriella Ribarn. DEPT OF PSYCHIATRY, UNIV OF TEXAS MED BRANCH 77555 #473-04-1994 **P** *012

PATEL, Bipin Ishwarbhai. 6107 BROADWAY ST 77551 #495-23-1971 L1975 **IM** *020 †20

PATEL, Janak Ambubhai. DEPT-PD C71 U/T MED BRANCH 77550 #690-01-1981 L1990 **ID PD** *020 †55

PATEL, Nisha Babu. ■ 77550 #048-02-2008 *012

PATEL, Shalin Girish. ■ 77550 #048-16-2005 **IM** *012

PATTERSON, Joel Terrell. 301 UNIVERSITY BLVD, DIVISION OF NEUROSURGERY 77555 #048-02-1991 L1994 **NS** *020 †25

PATTON, Melissa Anne. UTMB - PATHOLOGY, 301 UNIV BLVD 77555 #048-14-2005 L2005 **PTH** *012

PELLEY, Ronald Peter. 301 UNIVERSITY BLVD, DEPT PTH 77550 #038-06-1976 **PTH** *020

PENDYALA, Swaroop. 210 MARKET ST, STE H204 77555 #495-27-1999 **IM** *100 †12

PERNAS, Francisco Guiller. 301 UNIVERSITY BLVD, MED BRANCH 77555 #011-02-2006 **OTO** *012

PERRI, Anthony Joseph, III. 301 UNIVERSITY BLVD, DEPARTMENT OF DERMATOLOGY 77555 #048-04-2004 L2007 **D** *012

PETERMAN, James Jacob, Jr. DEPT OF ANESTHESIOLOGY, UNIVERSITY OF TEXAS MEDICA 77555 #056-05-2001 L2005 **AN** *020 †05

PETERS, Clarence James. 301 UNIVERSITY BLVD, G.170 KEILER 77555 #023-07-1966 L1967 **OS IM** *050 †20

PFEIL, Thomas J, Jr. 4920 SEAWALL BLVD STE D 77551 #048-02-1993 L1994 **FM** *020 †18

PHAN, Hoang Minh. ■ 77550 #048-02-2004 L2007 **IM** *020

PHAN, Nghi Bao. ■ 77554 #048-15-2006 **MPD** *012

PHILIP, Sheena. CHILD/ADOLESCENT PSYCH, DIV OF 77555 #422-01-1997 **P** *100

PINSON, William Scott. ■ 77550 #048-02-2006 **AN** *012

POFFINBARGER, Kristel A. 606 UNIVERSITY BLVD 77550 #048-02-1992 L1993 **EM** *020 †16

POLIQUIT, Donna Mae Divin. ■ 77550 #048-02-2007 **PD** *012

PORTIER, Bryce Patrick. ■ 77550 #048-02-2008 *012

PORTNOY, Dmitry. 301 UNIVERSITY BLVD 2A, RR 591 77555 #913-06-1983 L1998 **AN** *020 †05

POUNDS, Lori Lynn. 301 UNIVERSITY BLVD, RM 6.110 77555 #041-13-1993 L2002 **VS** *020 †85

POWELL, Bethany Elise. 1 MOODY PLZ RM 430 77550 #473-02-1996 L2001 **FM** *020 †18

POWELL, Don Watson. 301 UNIVERSITY BLVD, 4.104 MCCULLOUGH, 0764 77555 #001-02-1963 L1992 **IM GE** *030 †20

PRAISOODY, Sankaman. BRANCH HOSPS, UNIV OF TEXAS MED 77555 #048-02-2005 **DR** *012

PRIMM, Patricia Ann. ■ 77550 #047-06-1980 L1983 **PD** *020 †55

PROUGH, Donald Sanderson. 301 UNIVERSITY BLVD, STE 2A 77555 #041-14-1973 L1992 **AN CCA** *050 †10

PRYS-PICARD, Curig Owen. 301 UNIV BLV STE D62 77550 #917-36-1993 **PCC** *012

PURCELL, Richard Kevin. 301 UNIVERSITY BLVD 77550 #048-02-1991 *100

PUSTILNIK, Stephen Merril. 301 UNIVERSITY BLVD, STE 1022 77555 #028-02-1992 L2003 **PTH** *020 †50

QAYUM, Ayesha M. PO BOX 868 77553 #048-02-2008 *012
QUACH, Steve Quan. 301 UNIVERSITY BLVD, UTMB 77555 #048-02-2001 L2004 IM *020 †20
QUINN, Francis B, Jr. UTMB, DEPT OTOLARYNGOLOGY 77555 #005-11-1953 L1982 OTO OS *071 †45
QURESHI, Mehreen Amer. 301 UNIVERSITY BLVD, UNIV OF TEXAS MED BRANCH 77555 #704-21-1998 L2007 CD *012 †20
RAIMER, Benny G. 301 UNIVERSITY BLVD, STE 5.118 ADMISTN BLDG 77555 #048-02-1974 L1974 PD *020 †55
RAIMER, David William. ■ 77551 #048-02-2007 IM *012
RAIMER, Sharon Smith. 301 UNIVERSITY BLVD, DEPT DERM 77555 #048-02-1972 L1972 D DMP *040 †15
RAJARAMAN, Chitra. ■ 77551 #495-42-1970 L1981 PTH *020 †50
RAJARAMAN, Srinivasan. 301 UNIVERSITY BLVD, STE 1022 77555 #495-66-1967 L1981 PTH CLP *020 †50
RAJI, Mukaila Ajiboye. 301 UNIVERSITY BLVD, JENNIE SEALY HOSPITAL 3.32 77555 #690-05-1987 L1999 IMG *020 †20
RAJU, Gottumukkala S. 301 UNIVERSITY BLVD, RT 764 77555 #495-11-1982 L2001 GE *020 †20
RALEY, Jennifer Rene. 400 HARBORSIDE DRIVE 77555 #048-14-1991 L1992 FM *020 †18
RAMIREZ, Kyralessa Beatri. 301 UNIV BLVD 77555 #308-05-2000 PD *012
RAMIREZ, Mark Adam. ■ 77550 #048-02-2004 L2007 D *012
RAMIREZ, Ruben Eduardo. 300 UNIVERSITY BLVD, UTMB 77555 #041-13-2005 L2007 OPH *012
RANGANATHAN, Govindaraj. 301 UNIVERSITY BLVD, STE 2A 77555 #495-16-1984 L2005 AN *020 †05
RANGASETTY, Umamahesh Cha. 301 UNIVERSITY BLVD, DIV OF CARDIOLOGY 77555 #496-35-1996 CD *012 †20
RANGEL CASTILLA, Leonardo. UNIV OF TEXAS MED BRANCH, 301 UNIV BLVD 77555 #649-04-2004 NS *012
RAO, Nikhil Gadahad. 415 22ND ST, APT 2C 77550 #051-01-2003 L2007 RO *012
RAPLEY, Jay Herbert. 301 UNIVERSITY BLVD 77555 #019-02-2003 L2007 ORS *012
RASMUSSEN, Amy Christine. ■ 77554 #048-02-2007 EM *012
RASMUSSON, Karen Ann. UNV OF TX MED DPT N 77550 #037-01-1976 L1982 N *071 †75
RASTOGI, Saurabh. UNIV OF TEXAS MED BRANCH, DEPT OF INT MED 77555 #495-45-2003 L2008 IM *100 †20
RATH, Paul Albert. ■ 77550 #048-02-2004 ORS *012
RATH, Stephen Anthony. 301 UNIVERSITY BLVD, ROUTE 591 77555 #048-02-2005 L2007 AN *020
READES, Rosalyn Nicole. 606 UNIVERSITY BLVD 77550 #048-02-2006 EM *012
REDDING, David Rogers. ■ 77550 #012-01-2002 L2004 AI *012 †20
REDDY, Nischita Kamireddy. ■ 77551 #495-50-2001 GE *012 †20
REEP, Gabriel Lynn. ■ 77550 #048-02-2008 *012
REEVES, Alexa Lynne. UNIV OF TEXAS MED BRANCH, 301 UNIV BLVD 77555 #054-04-2006 NS *012
REINER, Stacie Elise Beck. ■ 77550 #048-02-2005 AN *012
REINERTSON, Randal Corwin. STE 202, 400 HARBORSIDE DRIVE, 77555 #025-01-2001 L2005 IM *100
REINHART, Joshua Harold. 301 UNIVERSITY BLVD, DEPT MED 77555 #048-02-2007 IM *012
RESTO, Vicente Andres. 301 UNIVERSITY BLVD, UTMB, DEPT. OF OTOLARYNGOL 77555 #023-07-2000 L2007 OTO *100 †45
REUSS, Luis. 8TH MECHANIC STS SCI BLDG 77550 #231-01-1964 L1975 OS *050
REVAI, Krystal F Z. 301 UNIVERSITY BLVD, DEPARTMENT OF PEDIATRICS 77555 #473-01-1995 L2001 PD *020 †55
REZAEE, Ziba. ■ 77550 #048-02-2008 *012
REZAZADEH, Bahareh. UNIV OF TEXAS MED BRANCH, DEPT OF INT MED 77555 #048-02-2003 RHU *012 †20
RIASCOS CASTANEDA, Roy Fr. 301 UNIVERSITY BLVD, 0709 RADIOLOGY DEPT 77555 #264-18-1995 L2006 R RNR *040
RICCITELLO, Jon Michael. 301 UNIV BLVD, DEPT IM 77555 #067-01-2005 IPM *012
RICE, James Carter. 301 UNIVERSITY BLVD, 4.200 JOHN SEALY HOSPITAL 77555 #048-02-1984 L1987 NEP IM *020 †20
RICHARDS, Jeffrey S. 301 UNIVERSITY BLVD, DEPT OF ANESTHESIA, JSA 2- 77555 #048-02-1998 L2002 AN *020 †05
RICHARDSON, Carol Joan. 301 UNIVERSITY BLVD, UTMB PED 77550 #048-02-1970 L1970 NPM *040 †55
RICHARDSON, Gwyn. 301 UNIVERSITY BLVD, DEPT OF OB-GYN 77555 #048-02-2001 L2005 GO *020
RICHERSON, Katherine Loui. BRANCH HOSPS, UNIV OF TEXAS MED 77555 #038-40-2006 OBG *012
RICHTER, Adam Alston. ■ 77550 #048-02-2008 *012
RIDLEY, Ryan Wintrell. ■ 77555 #048-02-2006 OTO *012
RIEBEL, Heather Rose. 301 UNIV BLV STE 0462, DEPT OF PEDIATRICS 77555 #048-13-2006 PD *012
RIGOULET, Holly Annette. ■ 77550 #048-02-2007 P *012
RILEY, Clayton Hartwick. 301 UNIVERSITY BLVD, UTMB/ORTHOPAEDIC SURGERY 77555 #004-01-2006 ORS *012
RILEY-HAGAN, Margaret. 301 UNIVERSITY BLVD, U OF TX MEDICAL BRANCH 77555 #048-12-1988 L1990 PD FSM *020 †55
RIMA, Chamseddine H. 200 UNIVERSITY BLVD 77550 #605-01-1991 L1994 PD *020 †55
RIOUX, Ashley Paige. ■ 77550 #048-02-2008 *012
RIPSIN, Cynthia Marie. 301 UNIVERSITY BLVD 77555 #051-07-1997 L2006 FM *020 †18
RIVAS, Jorge Mauricio. 301 UNIVERSITY BLVD, PO BOX 65217 77555 #048-02-1997 IM *100
RIVERA, Karelys Diaz. ■ 77554 #048-02-2005 L2008 PD *012
ROBERSON, Eric Dwayne. 301 UNIVERSITY BLVD, U T M B GALVESTON 77555 #048-02-1995 L1997 IM *020 †20
ROBERTS, Norbert J, Jr. 301 UNIVERSITY BLVD, INFECTIOUS DISEASES, RT 08 77555 #035-19-1971 L1995 IM *020 †20
ROBINSON, Carolyn Jean. ■ 77550 #048-02-1976 L1976 NPM PUD *050 †55
ROBINSON, Nancy Ann. 301 UNIVERSITY BLVD, UNIVERSITY OF TEXAS MEDICA 77555 #011-03-1983 L1986 N PM *020 †75
ROBINSON, Sally Sue. 301 UNIVERSITY BLVD 77555 #048-02-1967 L1967 PD *020 †55
RODRIGUEZ, Gabriel. 301 UNIVERSITY BLVD, UTMB RTE 0540- 77555 #048-02-1994 L1995 U *040 †95
ROGERS, Patricia Ann. 301 UNIVERSITY BLVD 77555 #047-06-1981 L1985 PD *020 †55
ROMERO, Alicia Beatriz. 301 UNIV BLVD 77555 #935-03-2001 IM *012
ROMERO, Cecilia Maria. 301 UNIVERSITY BLVD, UTMB 77555 #034-01-1974 L1994 FM *030 †18

ROSANIO, Salvatore. 301 UNIVERSITY BLVD 77555 #561-17-1987 L2008 CD *100 †20
ROSE, Robert Marc. 301 UNIVERSITY BLVD 77555 #024-01-1961 L1978 P *030 †75
ROTH, Bela Peter. ■ 77551 #143-05-1969 L1975 EM IM *020 20,16
ROTHROCK, Robin Elizabeth. ■ 77554 #654-01-1997 L2005 FM *100 †18
ROUCE, Rayne Helen. ■ 77550 #048-02-2007 PD *012
ROUSE, Bobbye Muriel. U-TX MED HSP PED DEPT 77550 #048-12-1959 L1959 PD *020 †55
ROWEN, Judith Lynn. 301 UNIVERSITY BLVD, DEPT OF PEDIATRICS 77555 #023-01-1986 L1997 PD ID *020 †55
RUBIN, Sanford Alvin. U T M B, DEPT RAD 77550 #048-02-1966 L1966 DR PUD *040 †80
RUDDOCK, Nicole K. 301 UNIVERSITY BLVD, MC 0587 77555 #011-02-2002 L2006 OBG *100 †30
RUIZ, Claudia C. 301 UNIVERSITY BLVD, UNIV OF TEXAS MEDICAL BRAN 77555 #048-14-1999 L2003 NEP *020 †20
RUIZ PEREZ, Jaime. 301 UNIV BLVD 77555 #649-52-1999 FP *012
RUPP, Richard Earl. 301 UNIVERSITY BLVD 77555 #028-34-1986 L1995 ADL PD *040 †55
RUTLEDGE, Wayne Chandler. 301 UNIVERSITY BLVD, U T M B GALVESTON 77555 #305-01-1998 L2005 IM *100 †20
RZOUQ, Fadi Salem. 301 UNIV BLV STE D62 77550 #575-01-2006 IM *012
SAADE, George. 301 UNIV BLVD, UTMB DEPT OF OB-GYN 77555 #605-01-1985 L1991 OBG *020 †30
SAAVEDRA, Michael Carl. 301 UNIVERSITY BLVD 8-, UNIVERSITY OF TEXAS MEDICA 77555 #021-05-2003 L2003 AI *012 †20
SABOUNI, Moustafa Abdul W. ■ 77550 #875-02-1973 R RO *100
SACKEY, Kwesi. 301 UNIVERSITY BLVD, D/PED; DIV HEMATOLOGY-ONCO 77555 #412-01-1993 L1994 PD HEM *020 †20
SAEED, Kokab A. 400 HARBORSIDE, PRIMARY CARE PAVILLION 77555 #704-16-1979 L1993 PD *040 †55
SAEED, Muhammad Aslam. 301 UNIVERSITY BLVD, U T M B GALVESTON 77555 #704-17-1989 L2001 APM *020
SAGI, Sashidhar Varma. 301 UNIV BLV STE D62 77550 #495-58-1998 IM *012
SALAMEH, Mohammad S. ■ 77551 #575-01-1981 L1996 ON *020 †20
SALIASHVILI, Gocha. ■ 77551 #913-23-1987 L2003 CD *012 †20
SALINAS, Paul. 301 UNIVERSITY BLVD, DEPT OF SURGERY 77555 #048-14-2000 L2003 NS *012
SALINAS MALDONADO, Oscar. ■ 77557 #737-10-2004 FP *012
SAMI, Venkata Chalapathi. ■ 77554 #495-50-1992 L2007 IMG *100 †20
SAMRA, Manpreet. 301 UNIV BLVD 77555 #495-03-2005 IM *012
SAMUEL, Zita Susan. 1.302 REBECCA SEALY, 301 UNIVERSITY BOULEVARD 77555 #654-01-2001 L2007 P *100 †75
SAMUELS, Katrina Reja. ■ 77551 #010-03-2004 L2008 MPD *012
SANCHEZ, Alma J. ■ 77550 #048-02-2008 *012
SANCHEZ, Ramon L. 1501 BROADWAY ST 77550 #847-06-1971 L1983 D PTH *020 †50,15
SANDSTEAD, Harold Hilton. UTMB 300 UNIVERSITY BLVD, 1109 RM 3102C EWING HALL 77555 #047-05-1958 L1987 IM NTR *050 †20
SANFORD, Arthur Peter. 815 MARKET ST, RM 713 77550 #030-06-1991 L2003 GS CCS *020 †85
SAN MARTIN, Jose Eduardo. 301 UNIV BLVD, STE D62 77555 #341-03-2001 FP *012
SANSONE, Eve M. ■ 77554 #048-02-2001 L2002 PTH *012
SANTIAGO, Betty Ann. 301 UNIVERSITY BLVD, UTMB-CMC 77555 #033-05-1984 L1996 IM *020 †20
SARPONG, Kwabena Obeng. 301 UNIVERSITY BLVD, STE 119 AND 120 77555 #412-02-1997 L2005 PD *100 †55
SARRIA-DIAZ, Juan C. 301 UNIVERSITY BLVD, DIV OF INFECTIOUS DISEASE 77555 #264-07-1990 L1998 ID IM *040 †20
SARVAT, Bilal. 301 UNIVERSITY BLVD, UNIV OF TX MEDICAL BRANCH 77555 #704-02-1982 L2006 ID *100 †20
SATCHITHANANDAM, Laju. ■ 77550 #010-01-2003 L2003 DR *012
SAYEED, Syed M. SHRINER'S BURN HOSPITAL, 815 MARKET STREET 77555 #035-48-2003 CCS *100
SAYLE, Bettye Ann. ■ 77550 #048-02-1957 L1957 NM IM *020 †28
SCHMALSTIEG, Frank C. CHILD HEALTH CENTER, DEPT OF PEDIATRICS 77550 #048-02-1972 L1972 AI PD *050 †55,03
SCHNADIG, Vicki Jeanne. 301 UNIVERSITY BLVD, STE 1022 77555 #016-06-1975 L1982 PTH *040 †50
SCHNAIDERMAN TORRES, David. 301 UNIV BLV 77555 #737-10-2001 FP *012
SCHOPP, Jennifer G. ■ 77553 #048-02-2008 *012
SCHREIBER, Melvyn Hirsh. ROUTE # 0709, DEPT OF RADIOLOGY UTMB 77555 #048-02-1955 L1955 DR *020
SCOTT, Kelly Lynne. ■ 77550 #048-15-2006 GS *012
SCURRY, Murphy Townsend. 1501 BROADWAY ST 77550 #048-02-1958 L1958 IM END *071 †20
SEBASTIAN, Joseph. 301 UNIVERSITY BLVD 77550 #048-14-1998 IM *100
SEILER, Stephen Jacob. ■ 77550 #048-12-2006 DR *012
SELLIN, Joseph H. 301 UNIVERSITY BLVD, DIV GASTROENTEROLOGY-UTMB 77555 #035-46-1973 L1980 GE *020 †20
SEYBOLD, Herbert M. DIV OF UROLOGY, DEPT OF SURGERY 77551 #048-02-1951 L1951 U *071 †95
SHABOT, Joseph Marc. JOHN SEALY HOSP, DEPT MED 77550 #048-02-1973 L1973 IM *020 †20
SHACKELFORD, Brenna Mae. ■ 77550 #048-02-2008 *012
SHAH, Narayan R. 301 UNIVERSITY BLVD, DEPT OF OB GYN 77555 #495-23-1965 L1976 PHO PD *020 †20
SHAHINIAN, Vahakn Bedig. 301 UNIVERSITY BLVD, JSA 4.200 77555 #065-01-1994 L2002 NEP *050 †20
SHAIKH, Tufail Q. 301 UNIVERSITY BLVD, UNIVERSITY OF TEXAS MED BR 77555 #704-02-1981 L1994 OM *020 †70
SHANI, Raj. 301 UNIVERSITY BLVD, UTMB/ORTHOPAEDIC SURGERY 77555 #048-04-2007 ORS *012
SHANINA, Elena. BRANCH HOSPS, UNIV OF TEXAS MED 77555 #913-12-1990 N *012
SHARMA, Gulshan. 301 UNIVERSITY BLVD, JSA 5112 UTMB 77555 #495-43-1996 L2004 PCC IM *020 †20
SHARMA, Sarghi. 301 UNIVERSITY BLVD, REBECCA SEALY HOSP 77555 #495-43-1996 L2005 CHP *100 †75
SHARMA, Swati. 301 UNIVERSITY BLVD, RHEUMATOLOGY DIV 77555 #496-07-1998 RHU IM *012
SHATTUCK, Karen Elaine. 301 UNIVERSITY BLVD 77555 #048-02-1982 L1983 NPM PD *020 †55
SHAYANI, Payam. UTMB BOX 173788 77555 #048-02-2000 EM *100
SHEETS, Heather. ■ 77550 #048-02-2008 *012

SHEN, Jing. 301 UNIVERSITY BLVD J, BRANCH HOSPI 77555 #048-12-2002 L2007 **OTO** *100

SHEPHERD, Angela Jane. 301 UNIVERSITY BLVD 77555 #048-02-1982 L1983 **FM** *020 †18

SHERMAN, Jay Brian. 301 UNIVERSITY BLVD, U T M B GALVESTON 77555 #039-01-1984 L1988 **P** *020 †75

SHERWOOD, Edward R, III. 301 UNIVERSITY BLVD, DEPT OF ANESTHESIOLOGY 77555 #016-02-1994 L1998 **AN** *020 †05

SHOKAR, Gurjeet Singh. 301 UNIVERSITY BLVD, MC 1123 77555 #495-43-1988 L1999 **IM** *020 †18

SHOKAR, Navkiran Kaur. 301 UNIVERSITY BLVD 77555 #917-09-1992 L1999 **FM** *020 †18

SHOPE, Robert Ellis. 301 UNIVERSITY BLVD 77555 #035-20-1954 L1958 **OS** *030

SIDHU, Amrit K. 301 UNIV BLV STE 0462 77555 #496-36-1996 **PD** *012

SIERPINA, Victor Stephen. 301 UNIVERSITY BLVD, DEPT OF FAM MED 77555 #016-11-1979 L1996 **FM** *040 †18

SILVA, Helen Colleen. ■ 77550 #048-02-1985 L1986 **GS** *020 †85

SILVA, Michael B, Jr. ■ 77550 #048-02-1984 L1986 **VS** *020 †85

SILVA, Mireya. ■ 77551 #048-02-2004 L2008 **CHP** *012

SILVER, Brad Joseph. ■ 77550 #048-02-2008 *012

SILVER, Lori. BRANCH HOSPS, UNIV OF TEXAS MED 77555 #048-12-2004 L2008 **OBG** *012

SIMON, Chad Michael. ■ 77554 #021-05-2005 **OTO** *012

SINGH, Amanpal. 301 UNIV BLVD 77555 #495-36-2005 **IM** *012

SINGH, Harbhej. 301 UNIVERSITY BLVD, STE 2A 77555 #496-09-1981 L1994 **AN** *020 †05

SINGH, Jaswant. 301 UNIV BLVD 77555 #048-43-2004 **IM** *012

SINGH, Sonali. 700 UNIVERSITY BLVD 77550 #495-77-1996 L2007 **OPH** *100

SINGSON-CALDERON, Agnes. 301 UNIVERSITY BLVD, STE 2A 77555 #748-01-1966 L1983 **AN** *020 †05

SLOAN, Heather Aileen. ■ 77550 #048-13-2004 L2008 **OBG** *012

SMALLEY, Jason Michael. ■ 77550 #048-02-2008 *012

SMITH, Brian A. 301 UNIVERSITY BLVD, U T M B GALVESTON 77555 #023-07-1991 L1999 **OSM** *020 †40

SMITH, David English. ■ 77551 #028-02-1944 L1944 **PTH NP** *071 †50

SMITH, Douglas Frederick. 301 UNIVERSITY BLVD, STE 2A 77555 #065-10-1977 L2001 **AN** *020

SMITH, Huelen Everett, Jr. 3828 URSULINE ST 77550 #048-02-2003 L2007 **FM** *020

SMITH, Janice K. 301 UNIVERSITY BLVD 77555 #048-02-1982 L1983 **FM** *020 †18

SMITH, Lance S. 301 UNIVERSITY BLVD, STE 2A 77555 #048-12-1992 L1994 **CRS** *020 †10,85

SMITH, Leigh Russell, Jr. 401 UNIVERSITY BLVD, DEPT OF PEDIATRICS 77550 #048-02-1967 L1967 **PD** *020 †55

SMITH, Michael B. 301 UNIVERSITY BLVD, STE 1022 77555 #048-02-1984 L1985 **MM** *020 †50

SMITH, Nathaniel Hazen. 301 UNIVERSITY BLVD 0435, ARKANSAS DEPT HEALTH & HUM 77555 #048-04-1991 L1992 **ID** *020 †20

SMITH, Robert Glenn. ONE BAYLOR PLAZA, UTMB 301 UNIVERSITY BLVD 77555 #048-04-1986 L1987 **N IM** *020

SMITH, Tawana Lakesha. ■ 77551 #048-02-2005 **FP** *012

SMITH-PHILLIPS, Melissa M. ■ 77554 #048-02-2008 *012

SNODGRASS, Wayne R. 301 UNIVERSITY BLVD, DEPT PHARM 77550 #017-20-1972 L1988 **PA PD** *050 †55

SNYDER, Christen Elyse. ■ 77550 #048-15-2007 **OBG** *012

SNYDER, Edward James, III. 301 UNIVERSITY BLVD, ROUTE 764 77555 #048-02-1970 L1970 **GE HEP** *040 †20

SNYDER, Karen Dee. UNIV OF TEXAS MED BRANCH, DEPT OF PSYCHIATRY 77555 #048-02-2002 L2006 **CHP** *020 †75

SNYDER, Russell Robt. 301 UNIVERSITY BLVD, CAMPUS ROUTE 0587 77555 #048-14-1978 L1978 **OBG PTH** *020 †30

SOBELMAN, Douglas Scott. ■ 77550 #048-02-1993 *100

SOHN, Taylor Ashli. 301 UNIVERSITY BLVD, RT 542 77555 #023-07-1996 L2005 **GS** *020

SOLANKI, Daneshvari R. 301 UNIVERSITY BLVD 77555 #495-23-1968 L1979 **AN** *040

SOLER, Miguel Angel T. ■ 77554 #275-01-1951 L1969 **ORS** *071 †40

SOLOWAY, Roger David. 4-106 MCCULLOUGH BLDG UTMB 77550 #035-20-1961 L1989 **GE IM** *020 †20

SON, Hwajung. 301 UNIVERSITY BLVD J, MEDICAL BR 77555 #035-08-2006 **OTO** *012

SONSTEIN, Joseph. ■ 77550 #048-02-2005 **U** *012

SOOD, Gagan Kumar. 301 UNIVERSITY BLVD, 4.106 MCCULLOUGH BUILDING 77555 #495-90-1982 L2005 **GE** *020 †20

SPAK, K Edmund. 1818 BROADWAY ST 77550 #759-04-1952 L1971 **OPH** *071

SPEER, Alice Jean. 301 UNIVERSITY BLVD, RTE 566 77555 #048-04-1981 L1982 **IM** *020 †20

SPIRES, Albert Bryan, Jr. 1527 POST OFFICE ST 77550 #048-02-1955 L1955 **IM MDM** *071

SQUIRES, James Eugene. ■ 77550 #048-02-2008 *012

SRA, Karanpreet Kaur. 301 UNIVERSITY BLVD, UTMB-GALVESTON 77555 #048-02-2002 L2004 **D** *012

SRACIC, Julie Kristen. 301 UNIVERSITY BLVD, UTMB DEPT OF DERM 77555 #048-02-2004 L2006 **D** *012

SRESHTA, Joseph Nicholas. ■ 77550 #048-02-2007 **U** *012

SRIVASTAVA, Ruma. 301 UNIV BLV STE D62 77550 #495-98-2000 L2005 **PD** *100 †55

STAGER, Victoria. ■ 77550 #048-02-2007 **GS** *012

STANBERRY, Lawrence. 301 UNIVERSITY BLVD, DEPT OF PEDS UTMB 77555 #016-11-1977 L2003 **ID PD** *050 †55

STANLAKE, Melissa K. UNIV OF TEXAS MED BRANCH, DEPT OF PSYCHIATRY 77555 #048-14-2006 **P** *012

STARKEY, Jonathan M. ■ 77550 #048-12-2003 **IM** *100

STEPHENS, John Barry. ■ 77550 #017-20-2007 **PDM** *012

STEPHENSON, Kelly Waltner. 301 UNIVERSITY BLVD, U OF TX MEDICAL BRANCH 77555 #048-02-1997 L2002 **ORS** *020 †40

STIERNBERG, Douglas D. 301 UNIVERSITY BLVD 77550 #048-02-1949 L1949 **OPH OTO** *071 †35

STIERNBERG, Royall C. 301 UNIVERSITY BLVD 77550 #048-02-1944 L1944 **OPH A** *071 †45

STOBO, John David. 301 UNIVERSITY BLVD, U T M B 77555 #035-06-1968 L1999 **IG RHU** *030 †20

STONE, Michael Murphy. 301 UNIVERSITY BLVD, REBECCA SEALY HOSPITAL 77555 #048-13-1984 L1985 **P** *020 †75

STOUT, Landon Clarke, Jr. 301 UNIVERSITY BLVD, STE 1022 77555 #023-01-1957 L1973 **ATP** *072 †50

STRAWMYER, Thomas Reed. 301 UNIVERSITY BLVD 77550 #048-02-1984 L1985 **FM** *020 †18

STREET, Reagan Michelle. ■ 77550 #048-15-2005 **OBG** *012

SULEMANJEE, Nasir Ziauddi. 301 UNIVERSITY BLVD, STE 5.106 J.S.A. 77555 #704-25-1999 L2005 **CD** *012

SULLIVAN, Ronald Dayton. ■ 77550 #048-02-2003 **DR** *012

SUNKUREDDI, Prashanth Red. 301 UNIV BLV STE D62 77550 #422-01-2001 L2005 **RHU** *020

SUR, Sanjiv. 301 UNIVERSITY BLVD, INT MED/ALLERGY/IMMUNOLOGY 77555 #495-74-1979 L1998 **PDA IG** *020 †55,03

SWAMINATHAN, Sankar. 301 UNIVERSITY BLVD, U T M B GALVESTON 77555 #012-05-1984 L1996 **ID IM** *050 †20

SWEET, Laird A. 301 UNIV BLVD, ROUTE 0570, UNIV OF TEXAS MED BRANCH 77555 #048-02-1994 L1996 **IM** *020 †20

SWISCHUK, Leonard Edward. UTMB CHILD HLTH CTR C 65 77550 #060-01-1960 L1967 **PDR** *040 †80

SYBERT, Troy E. ■ 77555 #048-12-2001 L2003 **IM** *100

SYED, Sameet Zafar. 606 UNIVERSITY BLVD 77555 #048-02-2005 **AN** *012

SYED, Sujath Ali. 301 UNIVERSITY BLVD, ROUTE 193 77555 #496-37-1994 L2006 **CHP** *012

SZAUTER, Karen E. 301 UNIVERSITY BLVD, DIVISION OF GASTROENTEROLO 77555 #038-06-1983 L1991 **IM GE** *020 †20

SZUCS, Regina Piroska. 606 UNIVERSITY BLVD # 50 77550 #048-02-2005 L2005 **P** *012

SZYLLER, Alain Herbert. 301 UNIV BLVD 77555 #396-31-1984 **OBG** *012

TAKKAR, Chandandeep. 301 UNIV BLVD 77555 #495-03-2005 **IM** *012

TALLAVAJHULA, Sudha Sudha. 301 UNIVERSITY BLVD, MEDICAL BR 77555 #495-61-2002 **N** *012

TAN, Huaiyu. 515 POST OFFICE ST 77550 #048-02-2007 *012

TAN, Luke Kim Siang. 301 UNIVERSITY BLVD, DEPT OTOLARYNGOLOGY UTMB 77555 #825-01-1988 **OTO** *100

TANEJA, Shilpa. UNIV OF TEXAS MED BRANCH, DEPT OF INT MED 77555 #495-45-2003 L2008 **NEP** *012

TANG, Phong P. UNIV OF TEXAS MED BRANCH, DEPT OF INT MED 77555 #048-12-2006 **IM** *012

TANG, Yong. 301 UNIV BLVD, DIV OF INTERNAL MEDICINE 77555 #243-16-1996 **IM** *012

TANOUS, Helene Mary. 301 UNIVERSITY BLVD, U T M B GALVESTON 77555 #048-02-1967 L1975 **R** *071 †80

TAUBE, Justina P. 301 UNIV BLVD, RT 0787, UNIV OF TX MED BRANCH 77546 #048-02-1992 L1993 **OPH** *020

TESH, Robert Bradfield. 301 UNIVERSITY BLVD, STE 1022 77555 #041-02-1961 **PHP MM** *050

THEILER, Regan Nell. ■ 77550 #056-05-2003 L2007 **OBG** *100

THENAPPAN, Mahesh Viswana. ■ 77551 #048-02-2007 **IM** *012

THOMA, George Wm, Jr. 301 UNIVERSITY BLVD 77550 #041-01-1945 L1956 **PTH ON** *071 †50

THOMAS, Christopher R. 301 UNIVERSITY BLVD 77555 #048-04-1979 L1992 **CHP P** *040 †75

THOMAS, Shibu. 301 UNIVERSITY BLVD, DEPARTMENT OF INTERNAL MED 77555 #305-01-2001 L2005 **PCC** *012 †20

THOMPSON, Barbara Lynn. 301 UNIVERSITY BLVD, DEPT OF FAMILY MED 77555 #048-02-1971 L1971 **FM FPG** *040 †18

THOMPSON, Edward Ivins B. DEPT HBC&G UTMB F45 77550 #024-01-1960 L1962 **OS IM** *050

THOMPSON, James Chas. 301 UNIVERSITY BLVD, DEPT SURG 77550 #048-02-1951 L1951 **GS** *030 †85

THOMPSON, Spencer G. ■ 77551 #048-02-1951 L1951 **PD** *071 †55

THORLEY, Jeffrey Daynes. 6511 STEWART RD STE 1 77551 #035-01-1969 L1972 **IM IMG** *020 †20 ‡

TIBUNI, Susan M. 301 UNIV BLV STE 0462 77555 #048-13-2006 **IM** *012

TICHINDELEAN, Carmen. 301 UNIVERSITY BLVD 77555 #781-07-2002 L2004 **ID** *012 †20

TINCHER, Steven Wayne. 77551 #048-02-2008 *012

TOGNETTI, Stephanie Joann. ■ 77550 #048-02-2005 **IM** *012

TORRES, Marla Loren. ■ 77550 #042-01-2004 **GS** *012

TOWNSEND, Courtney M, Jr. 301 UNIVERSITY BLVD, UTMB / DEPT SURG 77555 #048-02-1969 L1969 **GS SO** *020 †85

TRAN, Mai Thi. 301 UNIVERSITY BLVD, UNIV OF TEXAS MED BRANCH 77555 #305-01-2003 L2008 **PD** *012

TRAVIS, Luther Brisendine. 301 UNIVERSITY BLVD, DEPT PED 77550 #012-01-1955 L1962 **DIA PN** *020 †55

TRIANA, Ana Catalina. 7303 OFFATS POINT CIR 77551 #264-04-1995 L2001 **FM** *020 †18

TRIFIRO, Richard. 1161 61ST ST STE 200, OUTPATIENT CLINIC 77551 #042-03-1985 L1997 **FM** *020 †18

TRIVEDI, Vinod. 301 UNIVERSITY BLVD, UTMB,DIV INFECTIOUS DISEAS 77555 #495-15-1996 L2005 **ID** *100 †20

TROTT, Amanda Ainsworth. ■ 77550 #422-01-2007 **PD** *012

TRUONG, Tri Dinh. ■ 77551 #396-35-1959 L1983 **GP** *071

TURLEY, Christine Bungay. 301 UNIVERSITY BLVD, U TX MED BRANCH RTE 0351 77555 #011-02-1988 L1997 **PD** *020 †55

TURNBOW, Benjamin James. ■ 77550 #028-03-2007 **ORS** *012

TURNER, William Clay. 301 UNIVERSITY BLVD, UNIV OF TEXAS MEDICAL BRAN 77555 #048-02-1974 L1974 **EM** *020 †16

TYCNER, Grazyna. 301 UNIV BLV STE 0462, UNIV TX MED BRANCH HOSPS 77555 #759-07-1993 L2008 **P** *012

UGALDE, Ana Lorena. 301 UNIV BLV STE 0462, UNIV TX MED BRANCH HOSPS 77555 #270-01-1997 **OBG** *012

UMEH, Chiamaka Nwamaka. 301 UNIVERSITY BLVD, UNIV OF TEXAS MED BRANCH 77555 #690-04-1999 L2008 **PD** *100 †55

URBAN, Randall J. 301 UNIVERSITY BLVD, DEPT OF IM 77555 #048-16-1982 L1983 **END** *020 †20

URIBE ACOSTA, Tomas Eduar. DEPT OF RADIOLOGY G-09, UNIV OF TEXAS MED BRANCH 77555 #264-04-1996 **RNR** *012

USTUNER, Evren. DEPARTMENT OF RADIOLOGY, UNIVERSITY OF TEXAS MEDICA 77555 #902-05-1997 *100

VADHERA, Rakesh B. 301 UNIVERSITY BLVD, UNIVERSITY OF TX MED. BRAN 77555 #495-45-1979 L1997 **AN** *020 †05

VALBUENA, Gustavo Adolfo. ■ 77551 #264-04-1994 L2006 **PTH** *100

VALE, Sandra Denise. UNIV OF TEXAS MED BRANCH, DEPT OF PSYCHIATRY 77555 #048-13-2004 L2007 **P** *012

VALENTINE, Vincent Gray. 301 UNIVERSITY BLVD, UNIV OF TX MED BRANCH/ JSA 77555 #021-05-1987 L1987 **PCC CCM** *020 †20

VALIKA, Batul. 301 UNIVERSITY BLVD, STE 115 77555 #016-01-2002 L2005 **END** *012 †20

VALLIERE, Jennifer L. ■ 77550 #048-02-2008 *012

VAN DELDEN, Peter R. 5714 AVENUE T 1/2 77551 #048-13-2005 L2008 **IM** *012

VANDERPLOEG, James M. 1.116 MAURICE EWING HALL, 301 UNIVERSITY BLVD. #018-03-1975 L1980 **AM OM** *020 †70

VAN KUIJK, Fredericus J. 700 UNIVERSITY BLVD, U OF TX MEDICAL BRANCH 77555 #660-05-1988 L1999 **OPH** *020 †35

VASUT, Brent J. DIV OF EMER MED RTE 1173, 301 UNIV BLVD 77555 #048-14-1994 L2001 **FM** *020 †18

VEASEY, Sparks P, III. 301 UNIVERSITY BLVD, STE 1022 77555 #048-02-1977 L1977 **PTH** *020 †50

VEITCH, Rachel Anne. 301 UNIV BLV STE 0462, DEPT OF IM 77555 #034-01-2004 L2004 **IM** *012

VELA, Robert C. 301 UNIVERSITY BLVD, UTMB 77555 #048-12-2004 L2006 **AN** *012

VENIEGAS, Crystal Joy. ■ 77550 #048-02-2008 *012

VERMA, Divya Ratan. 301 UNIV BLV STE 0462, DIV OF INTERNAL MEDICINE 77555 #496-50-2003 **IM** *012

VIATOR, Mickey James. 301 UNIVERSITY BLVD, U. T. BOX 15032 77555 #021-05-1978 L1978 **PD** *020 †55

VIBHAGOOL, Asda. 301 UNIV BLVD STE D62 ID 77550 #891-02-1981 **IM** *100 †20

VIBHAGOOL, Chitralada. 4122 MC COLLOUGH BLVD G83 77550 #891-01-1986 **D** *020 †15

VIDACIC, Aleksandra. 301 UNIV BLV STE D62 77550 #957-02-2002 **IM** *012

VIDAL, Ana Maria. 301 UNIVERSITY BLVD, UTMB-CMC HOSPITAL MEDICINE 77555 #264-05-1990 L2002 **IM** *020

VIEGAS, Steven Francis. 301 UNIVERSITY BLVD 77550 #024-05-1979 L1990 **ORS** *020 †40

VILLACIS, John Francisco. 301 UNIVERSITY BLVD, UTMB DEPT INTERNAL MEDICIN 77555 #048-15-1999 L2004 **AI** *020 †20,03

VILLARREAL, Diana. 1917 BROADWAY ST STE 2 77550 #048-02-1981 L1981 **P** *020 †75

VINCENT, James Stephen. 301 UNIVERSITY BLVD, UTMB DIV OF EMERGY MED 77555 #048-02-2000 L2002 **PEM** *020 †16 ‡

VINCENT, Kathleen. 301 UNIVERSITY BLVD 77550 #048-02-1998 L2002 **OBG** *050

VINETZ, Joseph Michael. 301 UNIVERSITY BLVD 77555 #005-18-1991 L1998 **IM ID** *050 †20

VITAL, Karla. 4200 JOHN SEALY ANNEX, 301 UNIVERSITY BLVD 77555 #011-03-1999 L2005 **NEP IM** *040 †20

VOGELPOHL, Elmer B, Jr. 301 UNIVERSITY BLVD 77550 #048-02-1954 L1954 **IM CD** *020

VOLPI, Elena. 301 UNIVERSITY BLVD, DEPT OF INT MED/GERIATRICS 77555 #561-15-1989 L2007 **IMG END** *020

VON MARENSDORFF, Hans M. 301 UNIVERSITY BLVD, DEPT OF INTERNAL MEDICINE 77555 #023-01-1985 L1991 **IM** *040 †20

VORNIK, Vadim D. 301 UNIVERSITY BLVD, STE 2A 77555 #913-11-1991 L2003 **AN** *020 †05

WACHER, Adam Jeffrey. 301 UNIVERSITY BLVD, JSA 2-A 77555 #048-02-1996 L2001 **AN** *020 †05

WAGNER, Donald Fred. 301 UNIVERSITY BLVD, U T M B GALVESTON 77555 #056-05-1970 L1972 **ORS** *071 †40

WAGNER, Karen Dineen. 301 UNIVERSITY BLVD, P DEPT #D29 77555 #035-48-1984 L1990 **CHP P** *020 †75

WAGNER, Richard Fahy, Jr. 301 UNIVERSITY BLVD, DEPT DERM 77550 #035-09-1980 L1988 **D PS** *020 †20,15

WAHBAH, Mary Michele. 301 UNIV BLV, UNIV TX MED BRANCH HOSP 77555 #048-02-2005 **PTH** *012

WAITS, Alicia Taskara. ■ 77550 #047-07-2003 L2007 **AN** *100

WALDROP, Kimberly Suzanne. BRANCH HOSPS, UNIV OF TEXAS MED 77555 #048-02-2004 **DR** *012

WALKER, David Hughes. 301 UNIVERSITY BLVD, STE 1022 77555 #047-05-1969 L1989 **PTH** *030 †50

WALLACE, John M. 1 UNIV OF TEXAS MED BR, DEPT MED 77555 #028-02-1950 L1962 **CD IM** *071 †20

WALLFISCH, Harry Kahn. 301 UNIVERSITY BLVD, ANESTHESIA DEPT/E91 77555 #021-05-1974 L1977 **AN CCA** *020 †05

WALLING, Dennis Michael. 4525 CADUCEUS PL 77551 #023-07-1987 L1996 **ID** *020 †20

WALSH, Catherine. 301 UNIVERSITY BLVD 77555 #048-02-2001 L2005 **CHP** *020

WANAMAKER, Michael Lee. 301 UNIVERSITY BLVD, STE 2A 77555 #048-02-2004 L2006 **ORS** *100

WANG, Liqiang. 301 U BLVD RT 0743, DEPT OF PATHOLOGY UTMB 77555 #243-32-1986 L2002 **PTH** *020 †50

WANG, Zhiqin. 301 UNIV BLV STE 0462, UNIV TX MED BRANCH HOSPS 77555 #243-71-1984 L2007 **PTH** *100 †50

WARD, Kristy K. 77551 #048-14-2005 **OBG** *012

WARE, David Lochridge. 301 UNIVERSITY BLVD E-53, DEPT INT MED/CARDIOLOGY 77555 #048-12-1982 L1983 **CD IM** *020 †20

WARNER, Meredith Ann. 301 UNIVERSITY BLVD, ORTHOPAEDIC SURGERY & REHA 77555 #041-02-1999 L2004 **ORS** *020 †40

WARNER, Stacey Lynn. UNIV OF TEXAS MED BRANCH, DEPT OF ANESTHESIOLOGY 77555 #048-02-2004 L2008 **AN** *012

WARREN, Michael Mark. RT 0540, DIVISION OF UROLOGY, 77555 #035-15-1963 L1971 **U** *040 †95

WATSON, Brandy Michad. DEPT OF ANESTHESIOLOGY, UNIV OF TEXAS MED BRANCH 77555 #025-07-2006 **AN** *012

WAYMACK, John Paul. 301 UNIVERSITY BLVD, U T M B GALVESTON 77555 #051-04-1978 L1990 **TRS** *020 †85

WEAVER, Donna Brotman. 400 HARBORSIDE DRIVE 77555 #041-07-1990 L1995 **FM** *020 †18

WEINDORFF, Kathleen Miche. 77550 #048-02-2005 L2008 **IM** *012

WEINMAN, Steven Alan. 301 UNIVERSITY BLVD, UTMB 429 BASIC SCI BLDG 77555 #028-02-1984 L1990 **IM** *020 †20

WEN, Tony Soo-Tung. 301 UNIVERSITY BLVD, DEPT OF OB/GYN 77555 #048-15-1988 L1989 **MFM OBG** *040 †30

WHITE, John F, III. 1 MOODY PLZ, 4TH FL 77550 #048-14-1990 L1991 **GS** *020 †85

WHITEHEAD, Robert Paul. 301 UNIVERSITY BLVD, DEPT INTERNAL MEDICINE/RT 77555 #023-01-1971 L1995 **ON IM** *050 †20

WIGG, Cindy Lou. 301 UNIVERSITY BLVD, UNIVERSITY OF TEXAS MEDICA 77555 #028-34-1980 L1985 **CHP P** *020 †75

WILD, Karla A. 13511 MOYENNE PL 77554 #048-02-1989 L1990 **PD** *020

WILDENFELS, Patience. ■ 77550 #048-21-2004 **GS** *100

WILKERSON, Michael Geo. 301 UNIV BLVD, 4.112 MC CULLOUGH BLDG 77555 #048-14-1984 L1985 **D** *040 †15

WILKES, Denise Marie. 301 UNIVERSITY BLVD, DEPT. OF ANESTHESIOLOGY 77555 #048-02-2002 L2006 **APM** *020

WILKEY, Donna Jean. 87 QUINTANA CIR 77554 #048-02-1974 L1974 **NM IM** *071 †20,28

WILLIAMS, Clarence E, II. STE 104, 400 HARBORSIDE DR. 77555 #048-02-2004 L2007 **FM** *100 †18

WILLIAMS, Courtney Geo. 301 UNIVERSITY BLVD, STE 2A 77555 #035-08-1988 L1993 **AN PME** *040 †05

WILLIAMS, Dannielle Erica. ■ 77550 #048-02-2008 *012

WILLIAMS, Felicia Nicole. ■ 77550 #036-01-2005 **GS** *100

WILLIAMS, William Geoff. 301 UNIVERSITY BLVD, U T M B GALVESTON 77555 #049-01-1984 L1985 **PS** *020 †65

WILLIAMSON, Mark A. 301 UNIVERSITY BLVD 77555 #048-02-1984 L1988 **P** *020 †30

WILLIS, Maurice. 301 UNIVERSITY BLVD, U OF TX MEDICAL BRANCH 77555 #012-21-1995 L1997 **ON** *100 †20

WILLIS, Wm Darrell, Jr. MARINE BIOMEDICAL INST 77550 #048-12-1960 L1960 **N** *050

WILSON, Charles Jos. 200 UNIVERSITY BLVD 77555 #048-02-1952 L1952 **D** *071 †15

WILSON, Stephen Kent. ■ 77551 #003-01-1977 L1991 **PTH** *050 †50

WIRT, Daniel P. 301 UNIVERSITY BLVD 77555 #016-43-1980 L1987 **PTH** *020 †50

WITLIN, Andrea G. 301 UNIVERSITY BLVD 77555 #041-77-1978, ▲ L1999 **MFM OBG** *071 †30 ‡

WITTICH, Gerhard R. 301 UNIVERSITY BLVD, DEPT OF RADIOLOGYUTMB G09 77555 #154-07-1976 L1994 **DR** *020 †80

WOLF, Dwight V. DEPT OF PSYCHIATRY, UNIV OF TEXAS MED BRANCH 77550 #048-02-1990 L1991 **CHP** *020 †75

WOLFE, Gregory Wayne. ROUTE #0709, DEPT OF RADIOLOGY 77555 #047-06-2003 L2007 **DR** *012

WONG, Brian Russell. 700 UNIVERSITY BLVD, UTMB DPT OPHTHALMOLOGY 77555 #048-02-1987 L1991 **OPH** *020 †35

WOODSIDE, Kenneth Jeffrey. 6.136 JSA 0534, 301 UNIVERSITY BOULEVARD 77555 #025-01-1999 L2005 **GS** *020

WOODSON, Lee Clinton. 301 UNIVERSITY BLVD, STE 2A 77555 #048-02-1987 L1989 **AN CCA** *040 †05

WORTLEY, Phillip Guy. ■ 77550 #048-02-2008 *012

WREN, Jennifer Lee. 301 UNIVERSITY BLVD, RT 193 77555 #048-02-2002 L2006 **CHP** *020

WRIGHT, Andrea Jennifer. ■ 77550 #048-02-2008 *012

XIA, Guangbin. ■ 77554 #243-58-1990 L2006 **N** *012

XIAO, Shu-Yuan. 301 UNIVERSITY BLVD, STE 1022 77555 #243-65-1984 L2001 **PTH** *020 †50

YANG, Chou. UNIV OF TEXAS MED BRANCH, DEPT OF ANESTHESIOLOGY 77555 #005-11-2003 L2007 **AN** *100

YNGVE, David Andrew. 301 UNIVERSITY BLVD, UNIVERSITY OF TX GALVESTON 77555 #017-20-1976 L1992 **OP ORS** *020 †40

YOO, Sonja L.. 301 UNIV BLV STE D62 77550 #028-78-2005, ▲ **OBG** *012

ZACHARIAH, Brian Stewart. 301 UNIVERSITY BLVD, DIV OF EMERGENCY MEDICINE 77555 #020-02-1986 L1990 **EM** *030 †16

ZAHAROPOULOS, Paul. 301 UNIVERSITY BLVD 77555 #418-02-1953 L1968 **PTH U** *020 †50

ZAUNBRECHER, Frederick M. 3828 URSULINE ST 77550 #021-05-1972 L1977 **IM PUD** *020 †20

ZHAO, Qing. 301 UNIV BLVD 77555 #243-92-1990 **PTH** *012

ZHOU, Wenhong. ■ 77551 #048-02-2008 *012

ZOMA, Willie D. 3-108 OCH MAIL ROUTE E-87, 301 UNIVERSITY BLVD 77555 #781-01-1979 L2003 **OBG** *020 †30

ZOMPA, Edward Anthony, II. 2027B 61ST ST, WEST ISLE URGENT CARE 77551 #048-02-1998 L1999 **EM** *020 †16

ZONOZY, Auzhand Yeganeh. ■ 77551 #048-02-2008 *012

ZUNIGA RODRIGUEZ, Renato. ■ 77551 #737-01-2005 **IM** *012

GARDEN RIDGE – COMAL

HAYS, Elizabeth Anne. ■ 78266 #048-16-1993 L1994 **PD** *020 †55

MILLER, James Grant. ■ 78266 #038-40-1977 L1988 **DR PD** *020 †55

NOVAK, Dain. ■ 78266 #836-01-1969 L1972 **FM** *100

WOOD, Rawson Lyman, III. ■ 78266 #023-12-1998 L1999 **GPM** *012 †70

GARDENDALE – ECTOR

APODACA, Don Sanchez. 7996 E US HIGHWAY 158 79758 #034-01-1974 L1976 **EM FM** *020

DAVIS, Glena J. ■ 79758 #048-78-2007, ▲ **OBG** *012

GARLAND – DALLAS

ABEL, Shawn D. 601 CLARA BARTON BLVD #250 75042 #048-13-1995 L1996 **PD** *020 †55

ADAMI, Bernard Frank. 2225 PEGGY LN 75042 #048-02-1972 L1972 **OBG** *020 †30

ADAMS, T Elwyn. 2300 MARIE CURIE DR 75042 #021-05-1957 L1962 **FM** *075 †50

ADCOCK, Jeffrey Fulton. 601 CLARA BARTON BLVD 75042 #005-19-1988 L1991 **FM** *020 †18

AGRAWAL, Kanti Lal. 700 WALTER REED BLVD, STE 205 75042 #495-36-1976 L1980 **CD CCM** *020 †20

AHMED, Naseer. 5533 NAAMAN FOREST BLVD 75044 #704-09-1966 L1972 **IM ON** *020

AKHAVI, Mahmood Sadat. 315 N SHILOH RD, STE 103 75042 #517-01-1968 L1977 **N** *020 †75

ALEXANDER, Summer Kristin. 601 CLARA BARTON BLVD # 34 75042 #048-14-2004 L2006 **FP** *012

ALLEN, Victor Lee. 3232 BROADWAY BLVD, STE C 75043 #048-02-1962 L1962 **FM** *020 †18

ANDERSEN, Robert L. 5345 N GEORGE BUSH FWY 75040 #048-15-1996 L1997 **FM** *020 †18

ANDERSON, Robert L. 5345 N GEORGE BUSH HWY 75040 #048-14-2006 L2008 **IM** *012

ARANT, Rebecca Rucker. ■ 75044 #039-01-2003 L2007 **EM** *012

ASLAM, Mohammed Kamran. 617 CLARA BARTON BLVD #102 75042 #048-12-2001 L2004 **CD** *012

AUBEL, Eric Brandon. ■ 75043 #048-15-2003 L2007 **AN** *012

BAILEY, Mark L. 700 WALTER REED BLVD, STE 311 75042 #048-04-1986 L1987 **GS VS** *020 †85

BALA, Mani. 7409 SUGARBUSH DR 75044 #495-36-1966 L1983 **PTH GP** *020 †50

BASCOM, Teresa Janelle. 1919 S SHILOH RD, STE 333 75042 #005-12-1996 L2000 **OBG** *020 †30

BASSEL, Paul S. 601 CLARA BARTON BLVD, STE 200 75042 #048-12-1991 L1993 **PD** *020 †55

BAUER, R David. 1130 BELT LINE RD, STE 135 75040 #035-01-1983 L1997 **OSS ORS** *020 †40

BEACH, Lynne Nabours. 621 CLARA BARTON BLVD #104 75042 #048-02-1985 L1988 **PD** *020 †55

BERGMAN, Mary M. 802 HOPKINS ST, PARKLAND 75040 #048-12-1988 L1990 **PD** *020 †55

BESHIRES, Eric Dene. 5345 N GEORGE BUSH HWY 75040 #048-16-1995 L1996 **FM** *020 †18

BINION, John T. 800 N SHILOH RD 75042 #048-12-1952 L1952 **IM CD** *071 †20

BIRDWELL, Russ D. 700 WALTER REED BLVD, STE 311 75042 #048-15-1996 L1997 **GS** *020 †85

BIXBY, R Richard. ■ 75043 #048-13-1994 L1996 **FM FPG** *020 †18

BOGUS, Houston, Jr. 601 CLARA BARTON BLVD, STE 300 75042 #047-07-1979 L1990 **GE IM** *020 †20

BOND, David Leeper. 601 CLARA BARTON BLVD, STE 340 75042 #048-04-1956 L1956 **GYN** *020 †30

BRADSHAW, Stacey T. 6850 N SHILOH RD 75044 #048-04-1990 L1991 **RNR** *020 †80
BRAGG, David Wayne. 5345 N GEORGE BUSH HWY 75040 #048-12-1984 L1985 **FM** *020 †18
BRENNER, Claire E. 618 CLARA BARTON BLVD, STE 2 75042 #048-12-1996 L2001 **ID** *020 †20
BRET, John Robt. 700 WALTER REED BLVD # 208 75042 #048-12-1981 L1981 **CD IM** *020 †20
BURGOS ORTA, Laura M I. 5506 BROADWAY BLVD 75043 #042-02-1999 L2002 **PD** *020 †55
CAMP, Roger Chapman. 705 WALTER REED BLVD 75042 #048-12-1969 L1969 **GE** *020 †20
CARLSON, David Wm. 4402 BROADWAY BLVD STE 1 75043 #048-14-1985 L1986 **FM** *020 †18
CARSON, Doyle Irvin. 777 WALTER REED BLVD STE 3 75042 #048-12-1960 L1960 **P** *020 †75
CHAMBERS, Nancey E. 777 WALTER REED BLVD, STE 102 75042 #021-06-1997 L1998 **IM** *020 †20
CHANDA, Ranjan. 617 CLARA BARTON BLVD, STE 102 75042 #495-36-2000 L2005 **IM PHP** *020 †20
CHANDLER, Becky L. 601 CLARA BARTON BLVD 75042 #048-12-1995 L1996 **FM** *020 †18
CHOWDHURY, Nur Shahanara. 1720 COMMERCE ST, CITYCARE CLINIC 75040 #039-01-2000 L2003 **FM** *020 ‡
CLARKE, Carlton Keith. 407 WEST I 30, BROADWAY MEDICAL CLINIC 75043 #566-01-1965 L1978 **FM** *020
CLARKE, Carlton Keith, II. 407 W 1-30 75043 #047-07-1997 L2002 **OBG** *020
CONSELMAN, Nicole Suzanne. 601 CLARA BARTON BLVD 75042 #048-14-1998 L2001 **FM** *020 †18
COOK, Allan Odell. 777 WALTER REED BLVD, MEDICAL PLAZA II, #B-10 75042 #048-14-1981 L1981 **TS GS** *020 †90,85 ‡
COTTRELL, Chris James. 700 WALTER REED BLVD 75042 #048-15-1999 L2005 **GS** *020 †85
COUCH, Carl E. 601 CLARA BARTON BLVD 75042 #011-03-1969 L1970 **FM** *030 †18
COWAN, Seth B. ■ 75043 #048-02-1953 L1953 **FM** *071 †18
COWART, Michael W. 700 WALTER REED BLVD, STE 306 75042 #048-15-1987 L1988 **OBG** *020
CURRY, Ana K Griffin. 700 WALTER REED BLVD # 204 75042 #048-16-1992 L1993 **IM** *020 †20
CURTIS, David Eugene. ■ 75042 #038-41-2001 **GS** *012
DANG, Tam Quang. 2901 BELT LINE RD STE A 75044 #048-13-1990 L1991 **AN** *020 †05
DASA, Sridevi Laxmi. 2300 MARIE CURIE DR, BAYLOR MED CTR AT GARLAND 75042 #038-44-1992 L1995 **EM** *020 †16
DAY, April M. 601 CLARA BARTON BLVD 75042 #048-12-2002 L2004 **FM** *020 †18
DAYIAN, Vahe Robert. 2636 W WALNUT ST, STE 100 75042 #065-01-1987 L1999 *020
DEARMORE, Roy Franklin. ■ 75041 #048-12-1958 L1960 **GP** *071
DE BUSK, James Bradford. 2300 MARIE CURIE DR 75042 #048-12-1966 L1966 **OBG** *020
DELIN, Jacquelyn B. 601 CLARA BARTON BLVD, STE 160 75042 #048-13-1999 L2003 **OBG** *100
DEMETRI, Leslie Robt. 2692 W WALNUT ST STE 109 75042 #048-02-1972 L1972 **FM** *020
DINH, Trong Hoang. ■ 75040 #941-01-1969 L1985 *100
DONICA, Stephen K. 3200 BROADWAY BLVD 75043 #048-14-1988 L1989 **AN** *020 †05
DUREN, Michael. 700 WALTER REED BLVD, STE 208 75042 #048-02-1966 L1966 **CD IM** *020 †20
ERWIN, Karl Wayne. ■ 75043 #050-02-1948 L1954 **AN** *071 †05
EVERETT, Charles Richard. 2201 FOREST LN 75042 #038-40-1958 L1962 **IM CD** *020
FERNANDO, Theophilus A. 2300 MARIE CURIE DR 75042 #220-01-1969 L1975 **PD** *020 †55
FEWIN, Lori Carlene. ■ 75040 #048-04-1991 L1992 **PD** *020 †55
FISCH, Jason P. 601 CLARA BARTON BLVD 75042 #048-16-1996 L1997 **FM** *020 †18
FISHER, Dale Christian. 6850 N SHILOH RD 75044 #048-04-1990 L1992 **RNR** *020 †80
FLEMING, Forney W, III. ■ 75043 #048-02-1969 L1969 **ORS** *071 †40
FLYNN, Robert E. 2300 MARIE CURIE DR 75042 #048-12-1997 L2000 **DR** *020 †80
FORSYTH, Earl Nelson, Jr. 800 N SHILOH RD, BAYLOR SENIOR HEALTH CENTE 75042 #048-04-1964 L1964 **IM GE** *020 †20
FOWLER, Stephen Rice. 1621 S JUPITER RD, CONCENTRA MEDICAL CENTERS 75042 #048-02-1990 L1991 **FM** *075 †18 ‡
FRANKO, Edward Robert, Jr. 2301 FOREST LN, STE 300 75042 #038-43-1986 L1992 **CRS GS** *020 †85,10
FRENKEL, Peter Alan. 700 WALTER REED BLVD, STE 208 75042 #048-12-1992 L1993 **CD** *020 †20
FULLERTON, Clifford T. 5345 N GEORGE BUSH HWY 75040 #048-12-1983 L1983 **FM** *020 †18
FULTON, Carl L. 1919 S SHILOH RD, STE 612 75042 #039-01-1979 L1984 **P PYG** *075
GABILONDO, Jorge C. 777 WALTER REED BLVD, STE 104 75042 #737-01-1971 L1975 **IM GE** *020 †20
GARCIA, Ramon Danilo. 2046 FOREST LN STE 130 75042 #308-01-1987 L1996 **IM** *020 †20
GARG, Nidhi. ■ 75044 #041-02-2000 L2003 **NEP** *020
GARNER, Lisa Anne. 3310 BROADWAY BLVD 75043 #048-04-1983 L1983 **D** *020 †15
GAROUTTE, Scott Allan. 2300 MARIE CURIE DR, BAYLOR MEDICAL CENTER GARL 75042 #018-03-1996 L1998 **DR** *020 †80
GEORGE, Betsy Ann. ■ 75043 #048-16-2003 L2006 **IM** *100 †20
GHOBRIEL, Aldo Anthony. 2241 PEGGY LN STE E 75042 #048-13-1998 L2004 **U** *020 †95
GILLEY, Lowell Dean. 1501 NORTHWEST HWY 75041 #020-12-1976 L1999 **GP** *020
GOEN, Rhonda A. 802 HOPKINS ST, GARLAND HEALTH CENTER 75040 #048-12-1993 L1995 **P** *020 †75
GRUMBERG, Alexander. 2231 PEGGY LN # A 75042 #561-17-1976 L1980 **PD** *020 †55
HAILEY, Amaha. ■ 75044 #048-13-1996 L2000 **FM** *020 †18
HALEY, Carlton Marshall. 1626 FOREST LN S STE B, GARLAND EYE ASSOCIATES, P. 75042 #048-12-2003 L2007 **IM** *100
HALEY, John Marshall. 1626 FOREST LN S 75042 #048-12-1968 L1968 **OPH** *020 †35
HAMPTON, Brenda J. 7150 N PRESDNT GRG BSH HWY, STE 203 75044 #048-15-1999 L2001 **FM** *020 †18 ‡
HARTMAN, Rachel Adena. 700 WALTER REED BLVD, STE 204 75042 #023-01-2003 L2006 **IM** *020 †20
HASHMI, Shakeb. 2300 MARIE CURIE DR 75042 #704-25-1992 L2000 **IM EM** *020 †20
HE, Guocheng. 2300 MARIE CURIE DR 75042 #243-21-1991 **FM** *100
HELLING, Cornelius J, Jr. 700 WALTER REED BLVD, STE 308 75042 #019-02-1967 L1970 **OBG** *020 †30
HENRY, James Warren, Jr. ■ 75043 #048-02-1952 L1952 **FM** *071 †18
HERBRANDSON, Clarence R. 601 CLARA BARTON BLVD, STE 340 75042 #026-04-1964 L2001 **FM GP** *020 †18
HOCKETT, Sheri Lynn. 2300 MARIE CURIE DR, RADIOLOGY DEPT 75042 #048-12-1978 L1978 **DR NR** *020 †80 ‡
HOLMES, Ronald Thyr. 2300 MARIE CURIE DR 75042 #024-07-1973 L1982 **PS GS** *071
HOOD, Mary K. 3641 BROADWAY BLVD, STE 200 75043 #048-12-1996 L1998 **FM** *020 †18
HOSS, Gary Vernon. 601 CLARA BARTON BLVD #300 75042 #012-05-1979 L1980 **IM** *020 †20
HOWSDEN, Floyd Lester. 1919 S SHILOH RD STE 300, LB 42 75042 #005-11-1967 L1977 **D** *020 †15
HUANG, Wentian. 2825 BELT LINE RD, STE 103 75044 #243-21-1982 L2005 **IM** *020
HUYNH, Dung Ngoc. 2110 RIVER CANYON LN 75041 #048-15-2006 L2008 **AN** *012
IGLESIAS, J. 310 E INTERSTATE 30, STE 100 75043 #847-04-1970 L1987 **P CHP** *074
INAGANTI, Kasturi. 601 CLARA BARTON BLVD, STE 300 75042 #495-65-1996 L2002 **RHU** *020 †20
IPE, George V. ■ 75043 #048-12-2007 L2007 *012
JACKSON, Jim Dwain. 777 WALTER REED BLVD # 102, BAYLOR SENIOR HEALTH CTR 75042 #048-02-1955 L1955 **IM** *071
JAIN, Jyoti. 6448 BROADWAY BLVD 75043 #495-20-1981 L1995 **PD** *020 †55
JENSE, Junitha. 4201 ABINGDON DR 75043 #495-98-1987 L2001 **FM** *020 †18
JIA, Qing. 601 CLARA BARTON BLVD # 30 75042 #243-47-1991 L2004 **END** *020 †20
JOHNSON, Christine L. 800 N SHILOH RD 75042 #048-02-1995 L1996 **PM** *020 †60
JOHNSTON, Walter Stuart. 700 WALTER REED BLVD, STE 311 75042 #048-12-1992 L1993 **GS** *020 †85
JONES, Kenneth Goss. ■ 75048 #004-01-1943 L1943 **ORS** *071 †40
JOY, Joyce Elizabeth. ■ 75043 #048-14-2003 L2007 **AN** *100
JUAREZ, Jyothi. 601 CLARA BARTON BLVD # 30 75042 #048-13-1999 L2002 **END** *012 †20
KAMAL, Lubna Shahid. 5506 BROADWAY BLVD, PEDIATRIC S CARE CLINIC 75043 #704-06-1983 L1997 **PD** *020 †55
KASSAB, Wafik M. 2241 PEGGY LN, STE B 75042 #330-04-1957 L1973 **PD GP** *020
KEEHN, Gordon Chas. 1626 FOREST LN S STE B 75042 #021-01-1987 L1991 **OPH** *020 †35
KERR, Jeffrey D. 601 CLARA BARTON BLVD, STE 340 75042 #048-15-1995 L1996 **FM** *020 †18
KETCHERSID, James Belton. 3200 BROADWAY BLVD, STE 350 75043 #048-12-1960 L1960 **PTH** *020 †50
KHAJAVI, Mehran. 1634 N JUPITER RD 75042 #517-08-1996 L2006 **IMG** *020 †18
KHAN, Yasmin. 802 HOPKINS ST, GARLAND HEALTH CENTER-PARK 75040 #704-06-1976 L1982 **IM CD** *020 †20
KITOWICZ, Agnieszka. 2201 FOREST LN 75042 #759-07-1997 L2007 **FM** *020 †18
KLEIN, Jeffrey Brett. 2241 PEGGY LN, STE A 75042 #016-42-1976 L1981 **ORS** *020 †40
KOPITA, Jeffrey Michael. 700 WALTER REED BLVD, STE 203 75042 #038-43-1989 L1995 **CCM PUD** *020 †20
KOTAS, Robert Andrew. 601 CLARA BARTON BLVD, STE 200 75042 #048-12-1999 L2001 **PD** *020 †55
KOUTRAS, Phoebus. 2300 MARIE CURIE DR, BAYLOR MED CTR AT GARLAND 75042 #418-01-1958 L1973 **TS VS** *072 †85,90
KRAUS, Daniel Morris. ■ 75044 #041-12-2005 **OBG** *012
KUKREJA, Suresh. 2241 PEGGY LN 75042 #495-36-1974 L1979 **PD PHO** *020 †55
KWONG, Stella S. 2825 BELT LINE RD STE 103 75044 #041-07-1973 L1981 **FM** *020 †18 ‡
LAMBERT, Cyrus Timothy. 601 CLARA BARTON BLVD, STE 340 75042 #048-02-1973 L1973 **FM** *040 †18
LANG, Kenneth Chas. 530 CLARA BARTON BLVD 75042 #038-40-1970 L1973 **FM** *020 †18
LEA, Rudy Nelson, Jr. ■ 75043 #036-08-1996 L2000 **FM** *020 †18
LEDAY, Temekka V. ■ 75043 #048-12-2008 *012
LEONE, Randolph T. 6850 N SHILOH RD 75044 #048-13-1989 L1990 **DR** *020 †80
LEVENTHAL, Milton. 700 WALTER REED BLVD 75042 #048-12-1957 L1957 **GS** *071 †85
LEVY, Alfred Evan. 601 CLARA BARTON BLVD 75042 #041-02-1978 L1979 **FM** *020 †18
LEWIS, William Wood. 1501 NORTHWEST HWY 75041 #048-12-1979 L1979 **FM EM** *020 †18
LI, Zhiyong. 315 N SHILOH RD STE 101 75042 #243-65-1986 L2000 **ON HEM** *020 †20
LICHLITER, Warren Eugene. 2301 FOREST LN, STE 300 75042 #048-02-1978 L1978 **CRS** *020 †10,85
LIMSENBEN, Johanna. 601 CLARA BARTON BLVD, STE 200 75042 #048-12-1999 L2002 **PD** *020 †55
LOSOYA, Gerardo. 1901 NORTHWEST HWY, STE 107 75041 #649-02-1981 L1991 **FM** *020 †18
LU, Xiaohui. 601 CLARA BARTON BLVD #340 75042 #243-76-1985 L2007 **FM** *100 †18
LUX, Nicholas Edward. 1919 S SHILOH RD STE 333 75042 #048-12-1985 L1986 **OBG** *020 †30
MADDOX, James Brougher. 777 WALTER REED BLVD # 200 75042 #048-12-1969 L1969 **OTO A** *020 †45
MAILLOUX, Raymond Jos. ■ 75044 #067-01-1968 L1977 **FM** *071
MALIK, Ayaz Ul-Haque. 777 WALTER REED BLVD, STE 303 75042 #704-03-1970 L1983 **NS** *020 †25
MARKS, Timothy N. 700 WALTER REED BLVD, STE 305 75042 #048-02-1989 L1993 **AN** *020 †05
MAXWELL, Michael C. 3232 BROADWAY BLVD, FAMILY HEALTH CARE 75043 #048-15-1991 L1992 **FM** *020 †18
MC COLLUM, Ronald Jos. 601 CLARA BARTON BLVD 75042 #048-12-1969 L1969 **FM** *020 †18
MC MILLIN, Kimberly Jo. 5345 N GEORGE BUSH HWY 75040 #048-14-1993 L1994 **FM** *020 †18
MC NABB, John Robt. 601 CLARA BARTON BLVD, STE 160 75042 #030-05-1975 L1985 **OBG** *020 †30
MCNEILL, Jennifer Lee. 700 WALTER REED BLVD, STE 301 75042 #048-13-1996 L2004 **GS** *020 †85
MC NEILL, Robert. 1530 FOREST LN S, STE D 75042 #038-06-2002 L2004 **GS** *020
MEADOR, Robert Joseph, Jr. 601 CLARA BARTON BLVD, STE 300 75042 #048-14-1996 L1998 **RHU** *020 †20
MEKHAIL, Mounir. 6714 CHRISTINA LN 75043 #915-04-1977 L1987 **AN** *020 †05
MENDEZ-TORRES, Leovares. 2046 FOREST LN, STE 130 75042 #308-01-1990 L1999 **IM** *020 †20
MERCER, John Wesley, Jr. 601 CLARA BARTON BLVD #340, GARLAND FAMILY PRACTICE CE 75042 #021-05-1997 L2001 **FM** *020 †18
MERIL, Allen. 2300 MARIE CURIE DR 75042 #035-46-1960 L1971 **ORS OS** *071 †40
MEYER, Beau Barron. 3501 SATURN RD STE 201 75041 #048-02-1984 L1985 **FM** *020 †18
MIGUEL, Nemesio L, Jr. 7409 SUGARBUSH DR 75044 #748-12-1983 L1994 **PTH** *020 †50
MILLER, Mark Raymond. 777 WALTER REED BLVD, STE 301 75042 #039-01-1989 L1994 **GE IM** *020 †20
MIROW, Sheldon Allan. 2825 BELT LINE RD, STE 103 75044 #035-46-1967 L1981 **PD** *020 †55
MITCHELL, Charles Bennett. ■ 75043 #038-06-1943 L1961 **PTH** *071 †50
MITTAL, Shashi. 601 CLARA BARTON BLVD # 34, GARLAND FAMILY PRACTICE CE 75042 #496-07-1988 L2004 **FM** *020 †18
MLCAK, Mark Stanton. 601 CLARA BARTON BLVD 75042 #048-13-1982 L1983 **FM** *020 †18 ‡
MOORE, Paul Terrence. 700 WALTER REED BLVD, STE LB12 75042 #021-01-1984 L1996 **N** *020 †75
MOORE, Sandra Velia. 530 CLARA BARTON BLVD, STE 200 75042 #048-14-1978 L1978 **GS** *020 †85
MOTEN, Humaira. ■ 75044 #704-25-1990 L1996 **IM** *020 †20
MURPHY, Mike Chas. 1813 CREEKSIDE CT 75040 #039-01-1984 L1997 **AN** *020 †05,55
NAGHMI, Rifat Pervaiz. 126 N INTERNATIONAL RD, # B 75042 #495-49-1979 L1999 **IM** *020 †20
NAGHMI, Subuhi. 126 N INTERNATIONAL RD, STE B 75042 #495-49-1980 L1999 **FM** *020 †18
NAIR, Krishnan. 601 CLARA BARTON BLVD, STE 300 75042 #067-01-1995 L1998 **IM** *020 †20

■ = Address Information Privacy Protected

NAIR, Rajasree Janaki. 601 CLARA BARTON BLVD #340 75042 #495-31-1994 L2003 **FM** *040 †18 ‡

NEWMAN, Keith D. 618 CLARA BARTON BLVD, TEXAS MEDICAL & SURGICAL 75042 #048-16-1987 L1993 **U** *020 †95

NGUYEN, Linh. 3555 W WALNUT ST, STE A 75042 #048-13-1990 L1991 **IM** *020 †20

NGUYEN, Thuy N. 3555 W WALNUT ST STE A 75042 #048-02-1993 L1995 **IM** *020 †20

NIAMATALI, Habiboola. 2010 S SHILOH RD, MEDICAL CENTER HOSP OF GAR 75041 #950-01-1966 L1981 **IM GP** *020

NICHOLSON, William D, IV. 700 WALTER REED BLVD, STE 301 75042 #048-01-1996 L2001 **GS** *020 †85

NICHOLSON, William Daniel, III. 700 WALTER REED BLVD # 301 75042 #048-12-1971 L1971 **GS** *020 †85

NOAH, Terrence D, Jr. 2300 MARIE CURIE DR 75042 #047-06-1979 L1980 **EM** *020 †16

OKTAY, Halil Ilhan. 2300 MARIE CURIE DR 75042 #902-01-1947 L1962 **IM HEM** *071

OLIVARES, Jairo R. 777 WALTER REED BLVD, STE 201 75042 #264-02-1981 L1995 **ON IM** *020 †20

ORTIZ, Raynaldo R. 700 WALTER REED BLVD, STE 305 75042 #048-02-1989 L1991 **AN** *020

OSUAGWU, Chukwuma C. 617 CLARA BARTON BLVD # 10 75042 #048-12-2003 L2006 **IM** *020 †20

PAGE, Richard Alan. 3260 SOUTHERN DR STE E 75043 #028-34-1982 L1998 **AI PD** *020 †55,03

PARIKH, Dhaval Harin. ■ 75040 #048-02-2008 #012

PATEL, Akash Arvind. 1919 S SHILOH RD, SUITE 300 LB 42 75042 #036-07-2001 L2005 **D** *020 †15

PATEL, Pankaj. 802 HOPKINS ST 75040 #495-48-1981 L1994 **IM ID** *020 †20

PAYSEUR, Shannon Braud. 565 W INTERSTATE 30 75043 #047-07-2001 L2005 **FM** *020 †18

PENA RODRIGUEZ, Cesar B. 2046 FOREST LN STE 13 75042 #308-11-1989 L2003 **IM** *020 †20

PERRY, Maurice Clifton. 2300 MARIE CURIE DR 75042 #048-12-1959 L1959 **PTH** *020 †50

PETTIT, Michael James. ■ 75043 #048-13-1999 L2002 **DR** *020 †80

PICKENS, Glynn J. 2241 PEGGY LN, STE A 75042 #048-02-1990 L1991 **U** *020 †95

PINN, Michael. 3112 N JUPITER RD STE 213 75044 #836-02-1976 L1981 **FM** *020 †18 ‡

POOLE, Carol Ann. 2300 MARIE CURIE DR 75042 #021-06-1987 L1991 **OBG** *020 †30

PRASAD, Raghavendra S. 4105 ABINGDON DR 75043 #496-01-1972 L1994 **FM OBG** *020 †18

PRATHER, Irene. 601 CLARA BARTON BLVD 75042 #048-15-1979 L1979 **FM EM** *020 †18

QUINONES-BENJAMIN, Ramon. 2692 W WALNUT ST, STE 209 75042 #042-01-1973 L1992 **GS FM** *020 †85

RAINWATER, Noble Bryan. 1621 S JUPITER RD STE 101, CONCENTRA MEDICAL CENTERS 75042 #048-15-1986 **OM** *020 †20

RAJ, Hans J. 601 CLARA BARTON BLVD, STE 340 75042 #048-14-2002 L2005 **FM** *100 †18

REDDY, Sashidhar N. 777 WALTER REED BLVD, STE 201 75042 #048-02-1994 L2006 **HO** *020 †20

RESTREPO, Hector Dario. 2300 MARIE CURIE DR 75042 #264-04-1967 L1981 **AN** *020 †05

REYES, Cynthia Elaine. 802 HOPKINS ST, GARLAND HEALTH CTR 75040 #048-02-1981 L1981 **PD** *020 †55

RICHARDS-CARTY, Cherri Jo. ■ 75043 #010-03-1973 L1979 **DR NM** *020

RIGNEY, Mark Edward. ■ 75040 #048-02-1992 L2002 **FM** *020 †18

RIOS, Walter. 2601 FOREST LN 75042 #649-38-1991 L2002 **FM** *100 †18

ROCKEL, Thomas Hastings. 700 WALTER REED BLVD, STE 307 75042 #024-07-1961 L1980 **N CHN** *071 †55,75

RODERICK-ROSEBERRY, R H. 601 CLARA BARTON BLVD, STE 250 75042 #048-15-1990 L1991 **PD** *020 †55

RODRIGUEZ, Freddy Angel. 3050 S 1ST ST, STE 215 75041 #176-01-1969 L1975 **GS** *020

ROMAN-LATORRE, Jorge. 621 CLARA BARTON BLVD, STE 102 75042 #231-01-1966 L1997 **NEP IM** *020 †20

RORRIE, Kendra A. 601 CLARA BARTON BLVD, STE 300 75042 #048-12-1999 L2003 **D** *020 †15

ROSEN, Myron H. 601 CLARA BARTON BLVD, STE 200 75042 #048-12-1993 L1995 **PD** *020 †55

RUBANE, Carter Frank. 2241 PEGGY LN, STE D 75042 #021-01-1965 L1975 **OTO** *071 †55

SADLER, Jane S Samaan. 5345 N GEORGE BUSH HWY 75040 #048-16-1991 L1992 **FM** *020 †18

SALTER, Wm Richard, Jr. 1919 S SHILOH RD, STE 333 75042 #048-15-1988 L1989 **OBG** *020 †30

SARLES, Harry Eugene, Jr. 777 WALTER REED BLVD, STE 301 75042 #048-02-1979 L1979 **GE** *020 †20

SCHADE, C M. 2300 MARIE CURIE DR 75042 #011-02-1976 L1978 **PME AN** *020 †05

SEIFERT, John Dupont. 1901 NORTHWEST HWY, STE 200 75041 #056-06-1965 L1968 **OTO** *071 †45

SENTER, Donald Fred. 760 N SHILOH RD 75042 #048-12-1965 L1965 **AI A** *020 †03

SHAH, Dhiren L. 700 WALTER REED BLVD, STE 205 75042 #495-92-1976 L1983 **CD** *020 †20

SHAH, Stephanie Hugghins. 2692 W WALNUT ST, STE 207 75042 #021-01-2000 L2003 **GE** *100 †20

SHARMA, Nirupma. 5506 BROADWAY BLVD 75043 #495-47-1993 L2002 **NPM** *020 †55

SHARP, Carey Blythe. 7502 SPICEWOOD DR 75044 #048-04-2003 L2005 **FM** *020 †18

SHUMATE, Bill G. 5345 N PRESDNT GRG BSH HWY, BUSH FRWY 75040 #048-12-1994 L1995 **FM** *020 †18

SIDDIQUI, Sadia Sajid. 802 HOPKINS ST, GARLAND HEALTH CENTER 75040 #704-02-1996 L2006 **FM** *020 †18

SIEGEL, Robert M. ■ 75044 #012-05-1949 L1950 **GPM IG** *071 †55

SLJIVICH, Milan. 760 N SHILOH RD, ALLERGY CLN OF GARLAND 75042 #726-01-1987 L1998 **AI** *020,03

SLOAN, Chas Matteson, Jr. 2692 W WALNUT ST STE 203 75042 #048-16-1983 L1983 **PMM AN** *020 †05

SMITH, Daniel Alan. 601 CLARA BARTON BLVD, STE 300 75042 #048-04-1999 L2004 **D** *100 †15

SMITH, Jordan Lindsey. ■ 75043 #048-14-2007 **OBG** *012

SMITH, Roderic Alan. 5345 N GEORGE BUSH HWY 75040 #028-34-1977 L1979 **FM** *020 †18

SNYDER, Cheryl Ann. 2300 MARIE CURIE DR 75042 #004-01-1979 L1984 **OPH** *020 †35

SOLIS, Rolando M. 621 CLARA BARTON BLVD, STE 102 75042 #748-08-1963 L1971 **CD** *072

SPLANN, Frank Freeman, Jr. 2241 PEGGY LN, STE E 75042 #047-06-1962 L1969 **U** *020 †95 ‡

SRUBAR, Bernard Frank. PO BOX 461484 75046 #048-12-1974 L1974 **FM** *020

STEPHANIAN, Edic. 700 WALTER REED BLVD, STE 311 75042 #005-06-1987 L1994 **VS** *020 †85

STEWART, Ewa K. 2376 LAVON DR STE 130 75040 #048-02-1994 L2000 **PD** *020 †55

SUTTON, James Edward. 700 WALTER REED BLVD # 204 75042 #047-06-1989 L1991 **IM** *020 †20

TABADA, Arlo Wee Sit. ■ 75040 #748-29-1992 *100

TAMIM, Marwan Yahya. 517 W INTERSTATE 30, # C 75042 #605-01-1972 L1977 **OBG** *020 †30

TANG, Hue M. ■ 75043 #048-13-2006 **OBG** *012

TAYLOR, Darlene S. 2300 MARIE CURIE DR, MEDICAL DIRECTOR -MSS 75042 #048-14-1987 L1988 **IM** *030 †20

TAYLOR, William R. 7145 N PRESDNT GRG BSH HWY 75044 #048-02-1985 L1986 **EM** *020

THACH, Thao Thanh. 325 N SHILOH RD, STE 103 75043 #035-09-1996 L2003 **OPH** *020

THIGPEN, David C. 700 WALTER REED BLVD, STE 204 75042 #048-12-1999 L2003 **IM** *100 †20

THOMPSON, Lewis R, Jr. ■ 75043 #005-06-1954 L1967 **ORS OS** *071 †40

THOMPSON, Steven Howard. 2696 W WALNUT ST, VISTA HOSPITAL 75042 #035-09-1994 L2000 **IM** *020 †20

THOTA, Archana. 617 CLARA BARTON BLVD, LSIMA #102 75042 #495-11-1992 L2000 **IM** *020 †20

THWAITES, Richard David. 2300 MARIE CURIE DR 75042 #422-01-2002 **FM** *100

TINGLE, Leslie Earle. 601 CLARA BARTON BLVD, STE 340 75042 #048-02-1975 L1975 **FM FPG** *040 †18

TOWNSEND, John S, IV. 2301 FOREST LN STE 100 75042 #048-16-1988 L1990 **GP FOP** *020

TRAN, Justin Chau Ngoc. 3401 SATURN RD, STE 201 75041 #048-13-1999 L2003 **FM** *020

TRAN, Van Thi. 3465 W WALNUT ST STE 225 75042 #941-01-1972 L1979 **GP OBG** *020 †18

TROENDLE, David M. ■ 75043 #048-12-2007 **PD** *012

TROMBELLO, Michael John. 2300 MARIE CURIE DR 75042 #021-01-1975 L1976 **DR NM** *020 †80

TROSTEL, Robert Rhoads. 777 WALTER RD BLVD #STE400 75042 #048-12-1962 L1962 **OBG** *020 †30

TROSTEL, Steven Glen. 777 WALTER REED BLVD, STE 400 75042 #048-15-1992 L1994 **OBG** *020 †30

TULANON, Paitoon. 2301 FOREST LN, STE 300 75042 #891-02-1972 L1985 **CRS** *020 †10,85

UDDIN, Muhammad Razi. 2719 BELT LINE RD 75044 #704-02-1989 L2002 **PD** *020 †55

VAANDRAGER, Johan. 306 W WALNUT ST 75042 #660-03-1958 L1963 **FM** *071 †18

VALLARINO, Anthony Alexis. 601 CLARA BARTON BLVD 75042 #005-76-2005, ▲ L2006 **FP** *012

VARWANI, Musa. 700 WALTER REED BLVD, STE 204 75042 #577-01-1990 L2006 **IM** *020 †20 ‡

VENGALIL, Marina Tomy. 306 N SHILOH RD 75042 #495-63-1994 L2000 **N** *020 †20

VO, Duc P. 7150 N GEORGE BUSH HWY, STE 100 75044 #048-12-1995 L1998 **HS** *020 †40

VU, Thong Tien. 3465 W WALNUT ST, STE 225 75042 #941-01-1964 L1979 **FM** *020 †18

WEINGARDEN, Gary Irwin. 2300 MARIE CURIE DR 75042 #025-01-1980 L1982 **CD** *020 †20

WEPRIN, Lawrence Scott. 7150 N PRESDNT GRG BSH HWY, STE 202 75044 #016-11-1966 L1972 **OTO HNS** *020 †45

WHITCOMB, Larry Dale. 2696 W WALNUT ST 75042 #005-12-1979 L1980 **GS** *020 †85

WINANDY, Joan Margaret. ■ 75042 #016-11-1958 L1965 **R NM** *072 †80

WINN, William Eugene, Jr. 2300 MARIE CURIE DR 75042 #014-01-1998 L2000 **DR** *020 †80

WIPRUD, John Michael. 601 CLARA BARTON BLVD 75042 #056-06-1990 L1998 **FM** *020 †18

WYATT, Joseph Robt. 7150 N PRESDNT GRG BSH HWY, STE 200 75044 #047-05-1989 L1995 **OTO** *020 †45

WYLL, Allison Nicole. 7150 N GEORGE BUSH HWY, STE 200 75044 #048-14-1998 L2003 **OTO** *020 †45

WYLL, Shelby Allan. 1626 FOREST LN S, STE C 75042 #048-12-1968 L1968 **OPH** *020 †35

YAU, Franklin Seelai. 700 WALTER REED BLVD, STE 311 75042 #048-12-1996 L1997 **VS** *020 †20,85

ZAHEDI, Mojdeh. 2300 MARIE CURIE DR 75042 #517-11-2000 **FP** *012

ZERBY, Ashli Rhea. ■ 75044 #048-15-2005 L2006 **AN** *012

ZHANG, Jinsong. 2300 MARIE CURIE DR 75042 #243-47-1991 **FP** *012

ZOYS, George N. 2241 PEGGY LN, STE A 75042 #048-13-1995 L1996 **ORS** *020 †40

GARRISON – NACOGDOCHES

SNIDER, L W. 3292 BRUSH PRAIRIE RD, L.W. SNIDER, MD. 75946 #021-05-1955 L1956 **FM GS** *071 †18

GATESVILLE – CORYELL

ALBORNOZ, Debra Kay M. ■ 76528 #308-12-1985 L1996 **FM** *020 †18

BAILEY, Ralph C. 1507 W MAIN ST 76528 #021-01-1949 L1950 **FM** *071 †18

BIERWIRTH, Matthew B. 227 MEMORIAL DR 76528 #048-13-1991 L1994 **PD** *020 †55

CHEN, Scott Huei-Shung. 1507 W MAIN ST 76528 #385-02-1965 L1973 **CD** *020 †20

CURTIS, David Geo. 1916 HIGHWAY 36 BYP N, LANE MURRAY UNIT 76596 #030-05-1986 L1989 *020

DELANEY, Robert M. ■ 76528 #012-01-1950 L1951 **GP** *020

DWYER, Kevin W. 227 MEMORIAL DR 76528 #048-13-1991 L1992 **DR** *020 †80

FLOYD, William Forrest. 1507 W MAIN ST 76528 #048-02-1956 L1956 **FM EM** *030 †18

GALT, Sheryl Dubois. ■ 76528 #003-01-1994 L1997 **IM** *020 †20

GOLLADAY, Elizabeth Carol. ■ 76528 #051-04-1991 L1994 **MFM OBG** *040 †30

GWIN, Chester Samuel. ■ 76528 #005-12-2003 **PTH** *100

HALL, Sharon Roberta. 1507 W MAIN ST 76528 #028-34-1987 L2005 **EM FM** *020 †18

HAMM, Darren E. 227 MEMORIAL DR 76528 #048-02-1991 L1992 **EM** *020 †18

LEININGER, Larry Wayne. 227 MEMORIAL DR 76528 #041-13-1973 L1992 **FM ADM** *020 †18

MACIK, Felicia Kay. 227 MEMORIAL DR 76528 #048-78-1995, ▲ L1997 **FM** *020 †18

MAYNARD, Timothy Douglas. 227 MEMORIAL DR 76528 #048-12-1980 L1980 **FM** *020 †18

PHILLIPS, Barry Edsel. 1507 W MAIN ST 76528 #051-01-1974 L1975 **EM** *020

READ, Elaine Hope. 227 MEMORIAL DR 76528 #067-01-1947 L1978 *020

VANCE, Kerry Dean. 227 MEMORIAL DR 76528 #028-46-1980 L1989 **FM EM** *020 †18

GAUSE – MILAM

SMITH, Maurice Camp. ■ 77857 #005-02-1954 L1955 **NS** *071 †25

GEORGETOWN – WILLIAMSON

ACKER, Stephen Eugene. ■ 78633 #021-01-1965 L1965 **RO NM** *071 †80 ‡

ALTHAUS, Sean R. ■ 78633 #035-06-1966 L1967 **OTO** *071 †45

ASCHENBECK, Randal Lane. ■ 78628 #048-15-2007 **DR** *012

BAECHTEL, William Robt. ■ 78633 #048-04-1957 L1957 **OBG** *071 †30

BARENBERG, Kathryn Grace. 4945 WILLIAMS DR 78633 #048-13-2004 L2007 **IM** *020 †20

BARTSCHMID, Albert H, III. 1904 RAILROAD ST 78626 #048-12-1978 L1978 **ORS** *020 †40

BASTA, Lucy Giorgione. ■ 78633 #561-11-1979 L1983 **IM GP** *071

BENHAMMOU, Rania Oukhmano. 1524 LEANDER RD, SAN GABRIEL SQUARE 78628 #125-01-2000 L2007 **PD** *020 †55

BENOLD, Douglas Mac. 2100 SCENIC DR 78626 #048-04-1947 L1947 **FM GP** *071 †18
BENOLD, Stephen Douglas. 2001 SCENIC DR 78626 #048-12-1975 L1975 **MDM FPG** *071 †18
BERG, Paul Andrew. 2100 SCENIC DR, GEORGETOWN MEDICAL CENTER 78626 #048-13-1989 L1990 **FM EM** *020 †18
BINGMAN, Kenneth R. ■ 78633 #036-07-1958 L1962 **NEP IM** *071 †20
BLAINE, Alva L Lockhart. ■ 78633 #048-12-1946 L1950 **PD** *071
BLATNER, Adam. ■ 78633 #005-02-1963 L1984 **CHP P** *071 †75
BOHMFALK, Thomas Chas. 2100 SCENIC DR, GEORGETOWN MEDICAL CENTER 78626 #048-12-1976 L1976 **FM** *020 †18
BOYD, William Jos. ■ 78628 #561-17-1975 L1983 **DR FM** *020
BRACKEN, Jessica Nicole. ■ 78628 #030-05-2004 L2008 **OBG** *012
BRAY, James E. 603 W UNIVERSITY AVE 78626 #048-13-1998 L2002 **FSM** *020 †18
BRIGGS, Michaelanne E. 701 SAN GABRIEL VILLG BLVD 78626 #048-14-2002 L2005 **GS** *100
BRIGGS, Rambie Le. 4945 WILLIAMS DR, SCOTT & WHITE CLINIC 78633 #048-04-1966 L1966 **GE IM** *071 †20
BRISTER, Susan Catherine. 4945 WILLIAMS DR 78633 #048-04-2000 L2004 **MPD** *020 †20,55 ‡
BURGEST, Sean Gregory. 3613 WILLIAMS DR, BAYLOR COLLEGE OF MEDICINE 78628 #038-41-2001 L2004 **APM** *020 †05
BURT, Howard. 1520 LEANDER RD STE A 78628 #048-02-1954 L1954 **D** *071 †15
CAIN, William Curtis. 1512 LEANDER RD, AUSTIN ORAL & MAXILLOFACIA 78628 #048-15-2004 L2007 **GS** *100
CALLAS, James M. 205 ALYSSA DR 78633 #048-02-1998 L2002 **DR** *020 †80
CASEY, Erin Suzanne. ■ 78628 #012-05-2002 L2006 **PD** *020 †55
CHANG, Hui-Chu J. 4945 WILLIAMS DR 78633 #035-09-2001 L2007 **IM** *020 †20
CHANG-STREPKA, Judy Yuan. 4945 WILLIAMS DR 78633 #048-02-2006 **OPH** *012
CHAPARALA, Dilip Kumar. ■ 78628 #495-58-1974 L1984 **P CHP** *020 †75
CHOI, Mi Y. 501 S AUSTIN AVE, BLDGE 2 78626 #583-13-1981 L1999 **IMG** *020 †20
CLARK, Jennifer L. 4945 WILLIAMS DR 78633 #048-13-2000 L2003 **IM** *020 †20
CLAY-PO, Yolanda Yvonne. 2118 SCENIC DR 78626 #048-02-1996 L1999 **IM** *020 †20
CONNER, Johnathan Charles. 2000 SCENIC DR 78626 #048-14-1999 L2006 **EM** *020
CORTEZ, Manuel Joaquin. ■ 78633 #028-34-1959 L1963 **P** *072 †75
CURNUTTE, Matthew Barret. ■ 78633 #048-14-2003 L2005 **EM** *012
DARNALL, Christopher K. 3121 NORTHWEST BLVD, GEORGETOWN SLEEP CENTER, P 78628 #027-01-2002 L2008 **CN** *100
DE VILLEZ, David Lee. 4500 WILLIAMS DR, STE 212 PMB 403 78633 #017-20-1968 L1975 **PME** *071 †05
DIETLEIN, Jon F. 311 RIVER BEND DR 78628 #048-02-1985 L1986 **OPH IM** *020 †35
DOWNS, Haskell Edward. ■ 78633 #048-12-1952 L1952 **IM** *071 †20
DUGALL, John Callan. 4945 WILLIAMS DR 78633 #016-06-1966 L1994 **CD** *020 †20
ENGLISH, Christopher Sean. 1904 RAILROAD ST 78626 #048-02-1999 L2002 **ORS** *020 †40 ‡
ENGVALL, William Ray. ■ 78633 #048-02-1959 L1959 **AN OS** *071 †05
ERICKSON, Harold M, Jr. ■ 78626 #040-02-1964 L1973 **CHP** *071 †75
ESPIRITU, Armando J. ■ 78633 #748-08-1964 L1976 **CD IM** *020
FAIN, Jerry D. 2000 SCENIC DR 78626 #048-02-1987 L1988 **HO IM** *020 †20
FANE, Larry Ralph. 1500 W UNIVERSITY AVE #103, LONE STAR CIRCLE OF CARE 78628 #018-03-1967 L1970 **PD MDM** *020 †55
FIEDLER, Benjamin P. 701 E UNIVERSITY AVE 78626 #048-02-1993 L1996 **FM** *020 †18 ‡
FLACHS, Lisa S. 128 HAZELTINE DR, PEDIATRICS 78628 #048-15-1995 L1996 **PD** *020 †55
FOMBY, Elizabeth Wilson. 4945 WILLIAMS DR, SCOTT & WHITE CLINIC 78633 #019-02-1993 L2001 **FM** *020 †18
FRANCIS, Thachil Abraham. 104 KEYSTONE CV 78633 #495-37-1960 L1970 **IM CD** *071 †20
FRANKLIN, Scott William. 1520 LEANDER RD STE B 78628 #048-14-1995 L2002 **OTO** *020
FRIEDLAND, Thomas M. 2000 SCENIC DR 78626 #067-01-2003 L2007 **EM** *012
GHALEB, Aline. 4945 WILLIAMS DR 78633 #649-33-1990 L2001 **GE** *020 †20
GIPSON, Adana Milliken. 1524 LEANDER RD, SAN GABRIEL PEDIATRICS 78628 #048-12-1993 L1994 **PD** *020 †55
GRAY, Macaria C. ■ 78626 #748-01-1959 L1973 **PD** *072
GRAY, Sharette Kirsten. ■ 78626 #023-12-1996 L1998 **P CHP** *020 †75
GREVE, Sheryl Ann. ■ 78633 #004-01-1978 L1979 **PYA P** *074
GUPTA, Abhilasha. 1229 LEANDER RD 78628 #495-92-1994 L2002 **IM** *020 †20
HAAS, Harry D. 119 CRYSTAL SPRINGS DR 78633 #019-02-1962 L1996 **IM** *020 †20
HAGLUND, Sogol. ■ 78628 #048-16-2007 **IM** *012
HALL, Brian Terry. ■ 78633 #016-06-2001 L2007 **EM** *020 †16
HARDNER, Gerald J. ■ 78633 #010-02-1960 **U** *071 †95
HART, Kathryn D. ■ 78628 #048-02-1988 L1989 **FM** *020 †18
HAUGHEY, Adam J. ■ 78626 #048-14-2008 *012
HAYES, Diana Frances. ■ 78628 #917-06-1965 L1985 **IM PUD** *071
HEARNE, Christopher B. 4945 WILLIAMS DR, GEORGETOWN 78633 #048-04-1979 L1980 **IM** *020 †20
HERMOSA, Joseph Paul. 3613 WILLIAMS DR, STE 404 78628 #048-02-2000 L2002 **IM** *020
HEXSEL, Felippe Augusto. ■ 78633 #187-27-1953 L1976 **GP** *071
HIGHTOWER, Stephen Frank. 4945 WILLIAMS DR 78633 #034-01-1982 L2007 **IMG IM** *020 †20
HILDING, Ronald Frederick. ■ 78628 #049-01-1965 L1966 **P** *020 †75
HINDS, Frank C. 1500 W UNIVERSITY AVE, STE 103 78628 #048-14-2002 L2006 **OBG** *020
HOHF, Jerome C. ■ 78633 #038-06-1943 L1951 **GS U** *071 †85
HOSSALLA, Doris E. 1524 LEANDER RD 78628 #038-40-1980 L1981 **PD** *020 †55
HOVANKY, Kim T. 1526 LEANDER RD 78628 #048-15-1990 L1991 **AI IM** *020 †20,03 ‡
JOLLY, Michael. ■ 78628 #048-12-2004 L2006 **IM** *012 †20
JONES, Willis T, Jr. ■ 78633 #048-02-1950 L1950 **AN** *071
JOSE, Manuel Cruz. 4945 WILLIAMS DR 78633 #014-01-1981 L1999 **IM EM** *020 †20
JUNG, Harry Harper, III. 345 LOGAN RANCH RD 78628 #048-15-1981 L1981 **AN** *020 †05
KELLEY, John L. ■ 78628 #048-02-1966 L1966 **FM** *071 †18
KELLY, William Lee. ■ 78633 #048-04-1962 L1962 **GYN** *071 †30
KENDALL, Reginald Jos. ■ 78633 #054-04-1977 L1978 **OBG** *020 †30
KLEIN, David Gary. ■ 78628 #034-01-1985 L2005 **GS** *020 †85
KLEIN, Donald Raymond. ■ 78633 #038-40-1957 L1962 **PS** *071 †65
KLOTT, Carlo Lee. 508 S ROCK ST, INFIRMARY 78626 #028-03-1985 L1987 **EM GP** *020
LANDES, Ronald Gale. ■ 78626 #056-06-1973 L1978 **NS GS** *100
LATIMER, Jeffrey Robt. ■ 78627 #048-12-1980 L1980 **EM IM** *020 †20
LAWLESS, Harold Lee. ■ 78633 #007-02-1954 L1958 **GP** *071
LEONARD, Russell J. ■ 78628 #016-06-1945 L1947 **GPM GS** *072 †85,90
LONG, Jack Calhoun Scott. 1900 SCENIC DR STE 3318 78626 #023-07-1968 L1970 **U** *020 †95
LONGWELL, Sidney Marshall, Jr. 2000 SCENIC DR 78626 #021-05-2001 L2007 **EM** *100 †16
LOWERY, Daniel Dennis. 29013 TURNBERRY CT 78628 #007-02-1979 L1999 **PUD IM** *020 †20
MABERY, Jared Blaine. 2000 SCENIC DR 78626 #048-16-1998 L1999 **EM** *020 †16
MAHAFFEY, Andrew Glenn. 2000 SCENIC DR, STE 204 78626 #048-16-1983 L1983 **OBG** *020 †30
MANNING, Robert Thos. ■ 78633 #019-02-1954 L1954 **IM** *072 †20
MARTIN, David Ward. 1900 SCENIC DR, APT 2208 78626 #023-12-1987 L1998 **GS** *020 †85
MARTIN, Douglas Wayne. 4945 WILLIAMS DR 78633 #048-15-1980 L1980 **OTO EM** *020 †45
MARYMONT, Jesse Henry, Jr. ■ 78633 #035-15-1954 L1974 **NM CLP** *071 †28,50
MC CULLOUGH, James Allen. ■ 78633 #048-02-1969 L1975 **FM** *071 †18
MEYERS, Thomas Patterson. ■ 78633 #047-06-1968 L1978 **TS** *020 †85,90
MILLER, Kevin L. 101 W COOPERATIVE WAY, STE 101 78626 #048-15-1998 L2001 **D** *020 †15
MULCAHEY, Tom L. 2000 SCENIC DR 78626 #048-15-1986 L1987 **AN** *020 †05
NACOL, Michael Saml Edwin. 1229 LEANDER RD 78628 #048-15-1980 L1980 **IM FM** *020 †20
NICKLEBUR, Scott A. 2000 SCENIC DR 78626 #048-15-1999 L2001 **EM** *020 †20,16
OTTO, Richard Elmer. 908 ROCKMOOR DR 78628 #048-02-2001 L2004 **FM** *020 †18
PALAZZO, Lori Lynn. 10 SPRING ST # 102, COMPASS BANK BUILDING 78626 #021-05-1986 L2007 **IM** *020 †20
PANKRATZ, Natacha Pheem. 1500 W UNIVERSITY AVE, LONE STAR CIR OF CARE PEDS 78628 #056-05-2000 L2005 **PD** *020 †55
PARKHURST, Gregory D. ■ 78628 #016-06-2003 L2005 **OPH** *100
PEARCE, Richard Wiley. 2100 SCENIC DR, GEORGETOWN MEDICAL CENTER 78626 #021-01-1968 L1971 **FM** *020 †18
PENNINGTON, Jay Burton. 2000 SCENIC DR, GEORGETOWN HOSPITAL 78626 #048-15-1986 L1987 **AN** *020 †05
PHAM, Connie Lanphuong. 2118 SCENIC DR 78626 #048-02-1989 L1990 **IM** *020 †20
PICKENS, Steven G. 603 W UNIVERSITY AVE, STE 110 78626 #048-02-1988 L1989 **PD** *020 †55
POLICH, John J. ■ 78633 #018-03-1950 L1952 **PD** *071 †55
PRICE, Paula Holland. 103 THOUSAND OAKS BLVD 78628 #048-15-1987 L1988 **PD NTR** *020 †55
RABIDEAU, Alan Leonard. 2000 SCENIC DR 78626 #046-01-1992 L1999 **FM** *020 †18
RAGSDALE, Keith. ■ 78633 #028-78-2001, ▲ L2005 **AN** *020 †05
RAMSEY, David Alan. 603 W UNIVERSITY AVE, STE 110 78626 #048-02-1977 L1977 **PD** *020
REA, Jeffrey Harwood. ■ 78628 #023-01-2002 L2004 **EM** *020 †16
REDDY, Anitha Chinnapu La. ■ 78628 #496-40-1998 L2007 **FM** *020
REDDY, Ramadevi M. ■ 78628 #495-57-1991 L1999 **IM** *020 †20
RIPLEY, Lucius A, III. 1500 W UNIVERSITY AVE, STE 103 78628 #048-13-1980 L1980 **P** *020 †75
SATHIANATHAN, Kumar. 3613 WILLIAMS DR 78628 #495-45-1988 L1999 **ID** *020 †20
SAYRE, William Horace. ■ 78633 #048-02-1970 L1970 **AN** *071 †05
SCHMICKRATH, Richard Chas. 1011 CR 104 78626 #007-02-1973 L1977 **PTH** *020 †50
SCHRIER, Jana Jones. 2000 SCENIC DR 78626 #048-02-1983 L1983 **OBG** *020 †30
SCHWERTNER, Belinda C. 1900 SCENIC DR, STE 2222 78626 #048-02-1997 L2000 **OBG** *020 †30
SCHWERTNER, Charles J. 1904 RAILROAD ST 78626 #048-02-1997 L2000 **ORS** *020 †40
SCRUGGS, Jessica Michele. ■ 78628 #048-16-2008 *012
SHALLIN, Anthony W. 3613 WILLIAMS DR 78628 #048-04-1991 L1992 **IM** *020 †20
SHEFFIELD, Roy Sherrill. ■ 78633 #048-12-1945 L1945 **IM CD** *071 †20
SHEPHERD, James Lloyd. 701 E UNIVERSITY AVE 78626 #048-02-1958 L1958 **FM** *071 †18
SHEPHERD, James M. 2000 SCENIC DR 78626 #048-02-1984 L1985 **EM** *020 †18
SHEPHERD, Jane. 2001 SCENIC DR 78626 #048-02-1984 L1985 **IM** *020 †20
SHERMAN, John Vaneff. 603 W UNIVERSITY AVE, STE 122 78626 #048-14-1995 L1999 **OBG** *020 †30
SHERMAN, Vincent Anthony. 2000 SCENIC DR 78626 #048-02-1989 L1990 **OBG** *020 †30
SHIFLEY, Jennifer Mary. 4945 WILLIAMS DR 78633 #048-13-2000 L2003 **FM** *020 †18
SMITH, Lewis Garvey, III. 2000 SCENIC DR, CENTER 78626 #035-01-1993 L1998 **RO** *020 †80
SNOOK, Murray A. 908 ROCKMOOR DR 78628 #048-14-1989 L1990 **FM** *020 †18
SOBHANI, Boback B. 2000 SCENIC DR 78626 #048-04-1993 L2001 **FM** *020 †18
SOTO, Leroy Theoforo. 3721 WILLIAMS DR 78628 #005-02-1981 L1983 **EM PD** *020
SPOOR, Daniel Harry. ■ 78627 #048-02-1958 L1958 **AI IM** *030 †70
STAEBEL, Craig A. 950 W UNIVERSITY AVE, STE 207 78626 #048-16-2000 L2001 **PS** *020 †65
STARR, David Stanley. ■ 78628 #143-07-1971 L1977 **TS** *020
STERN, Robert Chas. 2000 SCENIC DR 78626 #048-02-1981 L1981 **PTH IM** *020 †20,50
STONE, Sarah L. ■ 78628 #048-16-2007 **P** *012
STUMP, Bonnie Snead. 2804 GABRIEL VIEW DR 78628 #048-04-1979 L1979 **OBG** *020 †30
TADLOCK, Hugh Mac Arthur. 316 STARVIEW DR 78628 #048-13-1982 L1983 **IM** *020 †20 ‡
TANNOUS, Jeanet N. 25 WATERS EDGE CIR # 91 78626 #048-16-1994 L1995 **PD** *020 †55
TARUN, Ricardo D. ■ 78633 #748-08-1967 L1979 **IM GE** *020 †20
TARVIN, Charles Thornton. ■ 78633 #048-02-1963 L1963 **GYN** *071 †30
TAYLOR, Thomas F. ■ 78628 #019-02-1953 L1953 **GP** *071
THOMPSON, Don Michael. 2000 SCENIC DR 78626 #048-13-1993 L1997 **IM** *020 †20
THOMPSON, James B. 105 WILDWOOD DR, STE 201 78633 #048-02-1989 L1990 **FM** *020 †18
TOPEK, Nathan Harold. ■ 78633 #048-04-1948 L1948 **NTR GYN** *071 †30
TORRES, Jorge Francisco. ■ 78633 #649-01-1950 L1980 **OBG** *071 †18
TRAVIS, Wade R. ■ 78633 #048-04-1997 L1998 **PD** *020
VERA-BURKHALTER, Cheryl D. ■ 78628 #048-13-2004 L2007 **FM** *100 †18
VOSS, Daniel Stephen. 2100 SCENIC DR, GEORGETOWN MEDICAL CENTER 78626 #048-02-1985 L1986 **FM OBS** *020 †18
WALLOOPPILLAI, Dharshini. 902 N AUSTIN AVE 78626 #917-29-1991 L1997 **IM** *020 †20
WATERBURY, Richard Chas. ■ 78633 #018-03-1965 L1966 **AN** *071 †05
WEIR, Michael Ross. 303 RIDGE RUN DR, DEPT OF PEDIATRICS 78628 #048-02-1969 L1970 **PD** *020 †55
WHARTON, Lawrence Hay. ■ 78633 #048-02-1956 L1956 **P** *071
WILLIS, John Gregory. 2100 SCENIC DR, GEORGETOWN MEDICAL CENTER 78626 #048-04-1983 L1985 **FM** *020 †18

GIDDINGS – LEE

BIRNBAUM, Laura M. ■ 78942 #048-13-2002 L2004 **FM** *020 †18
BURNS, Charles Minton. ■ 78942 #048-02-1956 L1956 **GP** *020
JATZLAU, Amy Joanne. 189 S MANSE AVE 78942 #048-16-2001 L2004 **PD** *020 †55

GILMER – UPSHUR

BULLER, David Warren. 602 TITUS ST, STE 120 75644 #021-06-1985 L1988 **FM** *020 †18
BURKE, Eunice Cook. 711 TITUS ST, GILMER PRIMARY CARE CLINIC 75644 #021-05-1987 L1993 **IM** *020 †20

■ = Address Information Privacy Protected

CROW, Howard Graham. ■ 75644 #048-04-1944 L1944 **P** *071
CROW, Louise Calvert. ■ 75644 #048-04-1944 L1944 **PD PHP** *071
EDMONDSON, Charles T. ■ 75644 #004-01-1951 L1951 **R** *020 †80
FOSTER, Eugene Ralston. 200 N MONTGOMERY ST 75644 #048-02-1959 L1960 **FM** *020 †18
HOLLEY, Everett D. 712 N WOOD ST, ER MEDICAL DIRECTOR 75644 #048-14-2001 L2003
    FM *020 †18
HUFF, William Kenneth. 711 TITUS ST, EAST TEXAS MEDICAL CTR 75644 #048-13-1981 L1981
    IM *020 †20
KING, Lewis R, II. 602 TITUS ST 75644 #048-04-1991 L1992 **FM** *020 †18
LAPERRIERE, Maurice. 712 N WOOD ST 75644 #067-03-1972 L1982 **EM** *020
MC KENZIE, John Marshall. 710 TITUS ST 75644 #021-06-1981 L1983 **FM** *020 †18
MURRY, Rucker Steven. 602 TITUS ST STE 100 75644 #004-01-1980 L1983 **FM IMG** *020 †18
PARNELL, Billy J. 705 BUFFALO ST 75644 #021-01-1947 L1948 **R** *071 †80
TIVIDAD, Santos. ■ 75644 #748-01-1961 L1978 **AN** *071
UPENDRAN, Ilanko. 711 TITUS ST, ETMC PHYSICIANS CLINIC 75644
    #495-99-1993 L2004 *020 †20
WARDEN, Don Page. ■ 75645 #048-12-1955 L1955 **IM PUD** *071
WARDEN, Lenore Sponsler. ■ 75645 #048-12-1955 L1955 **FM** *071

GIRARD – KENT

WOODWARD, Harold Loyd. ■ 79518 #048-02-1977 L1977 **EM GP** *030

GLADEWATER – GREGG

BOURDON, Lynn Louis, Jr. 1600 BROADWAY AVE 75647 #048-04-1961 L1961 **FM** *020 †18 ‡
DAVIDSON, Robert Michael. 307 W UPSHUR AVE 75647 #028-34-1986 L1987 **IM** *020 †28,20
HOLLAS, William Joseph. 1600 BROADWAY AVE, GOOD SHEPHERD FAMILY HEALT 75647
    #048-14-1995 L1997 **FM** *020 †18
HUNT, Warren H, III. 307 W UPSHUR AVE 75647 #021-01-1953 L1955 **IM CD** *020 †20
MC KENZIE, Charles Benj. ■ 75647 #047-06-1957 L1959 **GP** *071
SKIPPER, Kenneth Hilton. 1600 BROADWAY AVE 75647 #038-06-1974 L1979 **FM** *020 †18
VADASZ, Andrew George. 1600 BROADWAY AVE, GOOD SHEPHERD HEALTH CENTE 75647
    #473-01-1990 L1997 **CHN PD** *020 †55,75

GLEN ROSE – SOMERVELL

CARPENTER, Bruce David. 409 GLENWOOD ST STE 500 76043 #048-02-1980 L1980
    FM *020 †18
COKER, Aimee L. 1008 NE BIG BEND TRL 76043 #048-14-1999 L2001 **FM** *020 †18
DAVIS, Michael Lee. 409 GLENWOOD ST STE 500 76043 #048-02-1974 L1974 **FM** *020 †18
HAY, Michael Thomas. ■ 76043 #048-12-1999 L2001 **ORS** *020
PATEL, Deepak Hirabhai. 408 GLENWOOD ST 76043 #033-05-1992 L1998 **CD** *020 †20
RIGGS, Michael Gwynn. ■ 76043 #048-02-1972 L1972 **IM** *020
SCHMIDT, Paul Alan. 1021 HOLDEN ST 76043 #048-16-1981 L1981 **FM PLM** *020 †18
SCHNEIDER, Mark Wm. 1008 NE BIG BEND TRL, BOX 728 76043 #048-13-1979 L1979
    FM *020 †18

GOLDTHWAITE – MILLS

CHILDRESS, Marvin A. ■ 76844 #039-01-1945 L1948 **GP** *071
JONES, Charles Eric. ■ 76844 #048-02-1957 L1957 **FM** *020 †18
THOMPSON, James Merwyn. PO BOX 508, 320 CO RD 235 76844 #048-04-1971 L1971
    FM GYN *071 †18

GOLIAD – GOLIAD

WILLIAMS, Raymond Delano. 414 W NORTH ST, P O BOX 1204 77963 #048-02-1966 L1966
    GS *020 †85

GONZALES – GONZALES

BILIR, Sule P. 228 SAINT GEORGE ST 78629 #048-16-1984 L1985 **FM** *020 †18
COLE, William F. 102 N SAINT JOSEPH ST 78629 #048-04-1966 L1966 **ORS** *071 †40
ESKA, Terry Fuller. 73 PARK ROAD 11 N 78629 #023-07-1973 L1976 **IM FM** *020 †20 ‡
MEDELLIN, Roland A. 228 SAINT GEORGE ST, GONZALES COMM HLTH CTR 78629
    #043-01-1990 L1991 **FM** *020 †18
PRICE, James Cullen. ■ 78629 #047-05-1945 L1947 **GP OS** *071
RIVAS, Humberto. 1110 N SARAH DEWITT DR, SIEVERS MED CLNC 78629 #270-02-1987 L1993
    PD *020
THUNDIYIL, Mary T. 2550 N SARAH DEWITT DR 78629 #561-13-1968 L1977 **PD** *020 †55
VAZ, Garth Olstein. 1110 N SARAH DEWITT DR 78629 #011-03-1988 L1993 **FM OBS** *020 †18
VOGE, Victoria Mae. 15068 FM 766 78629 #649-01-1971 L1996 **OM AM** *020 †70
WILLIAMSON, Robert Arthur. 1605 N SARAH DEWITT DR 78629 #048-02-1972 L1972
    FM EM *020

GOODFELLOW AIR FORCE BASE – TOM GREEN

AGUIRRE, Jose Carlos. 271 FORT RICHARDSON AVE 76908 #166-02-2002 L2002 **GS** *020 †18
COCKE, Brian Thomas. 271 FORT RICHARDSON AVE, 17 MDG/SGQ 76908 #143-11-2002 L2006
    FM *020
ELMER, Kathleen Beverly. 271 FORT RICHARDSON AVE, 17TH MEDICAL GROUP 76908
    #023-12-1989 L1990 **D** *020 †15 ‡
ENDO, Toru. PO BOX 44132 76908 #024-07-2006 L2006 **IM** *012

GOULDBUSK – COLEMAN

MC BRAYER, Harvard L, Jr. ■ 76845 #048-12-1966 L1966 **FM** *020

GRAHAM – YOUNG

BEHR, Donald Arthur. 820 MONTGOMERY RD, STE 206 76450 #048-02-1981 L1982
    GS *020 †85
BROWN, Peter Stanley. 1339 EAST ST 76450 #021-01-1979 L1980 **FM** *020 †18
CAWLEY, Dora Elisa. 820 MONTGOMERY RD 76450 #048-15-1983 L1983 **PD** *020 †55
CAWLEY, James Erich. 820 MONTGOMERY RD, STE 203 76450 #048-15-1983 L1983
    OBG U *020 †30
CHARTRAND, Daniel James. 1301 MONTGOMERY RD 76450 #028-34-2002 L2003 **EM** *020
GILBERTSON, Jeffrey K. 1301 MONTGOMERY RD, P O BOX 1627 76450 #048-15-1999 L2001
    FM *020 †18
GLENN, Sunny Jean. ■ 76450 #048-02-2005 **OBG** *012
HUFFMAN, Hal Davis. 1339 EAST ST 76450 #048-14-1981 L1981 **FM** *020 †18
JONES, Steven K. 1339 EAST ST 76450 #048-13-1998 L1999 **FM** *020 †18
KOBERG, Frederick Johnson. 1416 QUAIL RUN, SOUTHWEST MEDICAL ASSOCIAT 76450
    #048-02-1971 L1971 **UCM GP** *020
LUCAS, John F, III. 1339 EAST ST 76450 #048-12-1995 L1996 **FM** *020 †18
MARTIN, William Patrick. 1339 EAST ST 76450 #048-15-1998 L1999 **FM** *020 †18
MITCHELL, Gerald John. 1301 MONTGOMERY RD 76450 #005-12-1973 L1974
    IM OS *020 †20,70
NESBITT, Lynn Royce. 1301 MONTGOMERY RD, GRAHAM REGIONAL MEDICAL CT 76450
    #048-02-1966 L1966 **GP** *020
REED, Peter W. 1339 EAST ST 76450 #048-15-2001 L2002 **FM** *020 †18

GRANBURY – HOOD

AIKIN, Penelope Tanisha. 606 S HARBOR CT, AND PEDIATRICS, PA 76048 #038-44-1997 L2001
    MPD *020 †55,20
ANDREWS, Ernest Chas. ■ 76049 #048-02-1958 L1958 **GS** *071 †85
AOGAICHI, Keiko. ■ 76049 #033-06-1977 **IM** *062
ARBABI, Kathryn Miller. 1308E PALUXY RD STE 203 76048 #051-04-2000 L2004 **OBG** *020
BHALOO, Salim S. 1308 PALUXY RD, STE 303 76048 #048-78-1998, ▲ L2001 **IM AI** *020
BONNELL, Wendy Michelle. ■ 76049 #048-14-1999 L2002 **PD** *020 †55
BUCHANAN, Christopher T. 1209 MEDICAL PLAZA CT 76048 #048-12-1998 L2004 **U** *020 †95 ‡
BURCH, John Edward, Jr. PO BOX 2427 76048 #011-02-1970 L1986 **OBG** *100 †30
COUNTS, Hasmer, Jr. ■ 76049 #048-02-1960 L1960 **OS GS** *071
DE SUTTER-SIMPSON, Alison. 805 HILL BLVD 76048 #654-01-1985 L1998 **PD** *020 †55
DODD, Lloyd Earl. 1310 PALUXY RD, LAKE GRANBURY MEDICAL CENT 76048
    #048-04-1973 L1973 **AM FM** *020 †70,16,18
ELLIS, Christopher J. 2121 E HIGHWAY 377, LAKE GRANBURY PRIMARY CARE 76049
    #048-16-1996 L1997 **IM** *020 †20
FINDLAY, David J. 1310 PALUXY RD 76048 #048-13-1992 L2001 **AN PME** *020 †05
GEORGE, Darren Keith. 303 W PEARL ST 76048 #048-78-1992, ▲ L1994 **FM** *020
GILLESPIE, Robert Samuel. ■ 76048 #048-02-1997 L2003 **PN** *020 †55 ‡
HAGOOD, Clyde Otis. ■ 76049 #021-01-1956 L1975 **UM GS** *071 †85
HARMER, Jon-Paul. 1308 PALUXY RD, LONE STAR PAIN MEDICINE 76048 #048-13-1997 L2002
    APM *020 †05
HOWSER, Donald Marvin, III. 1212 MEDICAL PLAZA CT, COMPREHENSIVE OB/GYN 76048
    #018-03-2001 L2001 **OBG** *020 †30
JENNINGS, Ruston Ladd. 1318 PALUXY RD, GRANBURY INTERNAL MEDICINE 76048
    #048-14-1996 L1997 **IM** *020 †20
KELLEHER, James Matthew. 2121 E HIGHWAY 377 76049 #043-01-1987 L2004 **FM** *020 †18
KILLOUGH, John Harvey. ■ 76049 #008-01-1945 L1958 **CD IM** *071 †20
KNOWLES, Perry Dean. 201 PENINSULA CT 76048 #048-12-1983 L1983 **FM** *020 †18
KRONE, Peter Kennedy. 1208 MEDICAL PLAZA CT 76048 #004-01-1992 L2002 **GS** *020 †85
KRZEMINSKI, Stephen G. 1305 PALUXY RD, STE A 76048 #016-76-1994, ▲ L1999 *020
KUNKEL, Kevin P. ■ 76048 #048-15-2003 L2004 **GS** *100
LASTER, Jerry L. 1308 PALUXY RD, STE 203 76048 #048-12-1984 L1985 **GS CCM** *020 †85
LEE, Robert Louis. 805 HILL BLVD, UNIT103 76048 #048-13-1994 L1996 **FM** *020 †18
LOHMEYER, James Scott. 2310 VIENNA DR 76048 #021-06-1981 L1985 **AN** *020 †05
LOUDEN, Keith Ward. 1204 MEDICAL PLAZA CT 76048 #048-13-1995 L1997
    ORS OSM *020 †40
MARK, Corey Justin James. 1308 PALUXY RD STE 303, LAKE GRANBURY MED CTR 76048
    #065-05-2000 L2006 *020
MARKS, Roger Edward. ■ 76049 #035-03-1946 L1950 **OS** *071
MC COMBS, Kyle Patton. 1310 PALUXY RD 76048 #048-02-1997 L1998 **IM** *020 †20
MC CURDY, Mark A. 1312 PALUXY RD 76048 #048-04-1994 L1996 **U** *020 †95
MILLER, John David. ■ 76049 #048-12-1956 L1961 **AN** *020 †05
MOORE, George Henry. 8120 CLEBURNE HWY 76049 #048-02-1961 L1961 **GP** *050
MOORE, Thomas Dickson. ■ 76049 #039-01-1954 L1969 **OS PD** *030 †55
MOYER, James Thos. ■ 76049 #048-02-1969 L1969 **EM AM** *020 †18
MUELLER, Nicole Alison. 1201 MEDICAL PLAZA CT, GRANBURY EYE CLINIC 76048
    #018-75-1999, ▲ L2003 **OPH** *020
NILES, Christopher J. 801 MALLARD POINTE DR, RIVER VALLEY ANESTHESIA, P 76049
    #011-02-1996 L2005 **AN** *020 †05
PATEL, Amit Indravadan. 1212 MEDICAL PLAZA CT 76048 #033-06-1999 L2006 **OBG** *020 †30
POWERS, Laura Goins. 1305 PALUXY RD STE B 76048 #048-14-2000 L2003 **MPD** *020 †55
PRESNALL, Dixon. 1314 PALUXY RD 76048 #048-12-1965 L1965 **R** *071 †80 ‡
SALAS, Abel A. 602 E HIGHWAY 377 76048 #048-02-1974 L1974 **FM** *020
SEGLER, Dana Franklin. ■ 76049 #048-12-1965 L1965 **OBG** *062 †30
SINAY, Lenito John Yanos. 1308E PALUXY RD, STE 300 76048 #748-02-1989 L2007
    IM PUD *020 †20
SMITH, Jennifer Ann. 1308 PALUXY RD, STE 300 76048 #048-16-2003 L2005 **FM** *020 †18
SMITH, Oren Rudolph. 710 PALUXY RD 76048 #021-01-1959 L1979 **OPH** *071 †35
SMITH, Richard Eugene. ■ 76048 #023-07-1961 L1963 **IM ON** *071 †20
SNELL, Timothy Earl. 1308 PALUXY RD, LONE STAR PAIN MEDICINE 76048 #049-01-1999 L2004
    APM *020 †05
STEINMANN, David B. 1540 SOUTHTOWN DR, STE 104 76048 #048-02-1994 L1995
    PD *020 †55
STROUD, Michael Bryant. 1540 SOUTHTOWN DR STE 107 76048 #048-04-1965 L1965
    D PTH *020 †50,15
WATTS, Shannon L. 1540 SOUTHTOWN DR, STE 104 76048 #048-12-1993 L1994 **PD** *020 †55
WOOD, Roy Claude, Jr. ■ 76048 #048-04-1969 L1969 **AN FM** *020
WRIGHT, Delia I. 1305 PALUXY RD STE B 76048 #048-14-1998 L1999 **PD** *020 †55

■ = Address Information Privacy Protected

ZARA, Joshua. 1308 PALUXY RD STE 300 76048 #035-46-1976 L1992 **GE IM** *020 †20

GRAND PRAIRIE – DALLAS

ALMAND, James Raymond. 200 N CARRIER PKWY, STE 110 75050 #020-02-1955 L1956 **FM PHP** *020 †18

ARMANI, Abraham. 801 GREENVIEW DR 75050 #048-12-2000 L2002 **GS** *020

BEADLE, Eric Joseph. 4116 S CARRIER PKWY, STE 250 75052 #048-02-2003 L2006 **FM** *020 †18

BERNARDEZ-TAN, Ruth A. 2985 N HIGHWAY 360, STE 140 75050 #748-01-1987 L1995 **PD** *020 †55

BERZINSKAS WELLER, Egle E. 2210 N STATE HIGHWAY 360 75050 #025-07-2000 L2005 **OBG** *100 †30

BROWN, Deandre Antoine. ■ 75052 #019-02-2006 **IM** *012

BROWN, Herschel L. 4116 S CARRIER PKWY # 280, PMB 716 75052 #039-01-1991 L1996 **EM** *020 †16

BUTLER, Amy Nicole. ■ 75052 #048-14-2004 **CD** *012 †20

BUTLER, Jason Robert. ■ 75052 #010-01-2007 **FP** *012

CALENE, James Glenn. ■ 75050 #016-06-1955 L1957 **PD PDA** *030 †55

CAPINO, Antonia Gan. 929 W PIONEER PKWY, STE A 75051 #748-02-1970 L1978 **PD** *020 †55

COLE, Rhea. 820 S CARRIER PKWY 75051 #048-12-1988 L1991 **FM** *020 †18

CORLEY-DANIELS, April Jan. ■ 75054 #045-01-2003 **FM** *100

CROCHET, John R, Jr. ■ 75052 #048-02-2005 L2007 **OBG** *012

CUNNIGHAM, Mara L. ■ 75054 #005-76-2006, ▲ L2008 **FP** *012

DANHOF, Ivan Edward. 222 SW 2ND ST STE 201, NORTH TX MED ASSOC 75051 #048-12-1962 L1962 **GE** *072

DELL, Charles Ross. 401 COLLEGE ST 75050 #048-12-1975 L1975 **FM** *020

DESIO, Francis Anthony J. 200 N CARRIER PKWY, STE 100 75050 #028-78-1953, ▲ L1961 **FM** *071

DI LENA, Reynold James. 2737 SHERMAN ST 75051 #010-02-1978 L1986 **GYN OBS** *020 †30

DI PASCUALE, Mario Antoni. 75051 #935-01-1996 **TY** *012

FISHER, Aileen. ■ 75052 #011-04-1995 L1999 **P** *020 †75

FLEISCHER, Richard S. 3950 S CARRIER PKWY, CARENOW MEDICAL CENTERS 75052 #005-14-1983 L1997 **FM** *020 †18

FLORY, Frank C. 2304 BARDIN RD 75052 #048-02-1959 L1959 **GP** *020 †16

FRIEDMAN, Paul C. 2709 HOSPITAL BLVD 75051 #048-13-1973 L1976 **EM IM** *020 †16

GUNES, Seval. 4927 LAKE RIDGE PKWY, STE 170 75052 #409-10-1989 L1991 **AN PME** *020 †05

HOSLER, James P. 2717 OSLER DR STE 101 75051 #025-01-1974 L1979 **GE IM** *020 †20 ‡

HULSEY, Meredith E. ■ 75052 #048-78-2003, ▲ L2007 **PTH** *012

HYDE, Burt Eugene. 2304 BARDIN RD 75052 #030-05-1956 L1960 **GP** *020

JANGA, Sireesha. 2530 SARA JANE PKWY # 9 75052 #495-62-2000 L2005 **IM** *020 †20

KLEIN, Heather Leigh. ■ 75054 #048-14-2008 *012

KORUTHU, Gincy. ■ 75052 #048-02-2007 **N** *012

KRAM HOLDEN, Martin. 530 S CARRIER PKWY, STE 220 75051 #286-07-1991 L1998 **P** *020

LAN, Cynthia Tzeching. ■ 75050 #056-06-2002 L2005 **HO** *012 †20

LENZ, Adam C. ■ 75052 #048-12-2003 L2004 **AN** *012

LOPEZ, Ana Isabel. 4927 LAKE RIDGE PKWY # 100 75052 #048-13-1994 L1996 **FM** *020 †18

LUCENTE, James Ray. ■ 75050 #048-12-2001 **GS** *100

MANAHAN, Alberto T. 929 W PIONEER PKWY, STE D 75051 #748-02-1965 L1977 **OTO FPS** *020 †45

MANDADAPU, Srinivasa Rao. 2530 SARA JANE PKWY # 1 75052 #495-50-1994 L2004 **IM** *020

MC CURLEY, Lee R. 775 W WESTCHESTER PKWY, STE 102 75052 #048-12-1985 L1986 **FM** *020 †18

MCKISSACK, Melanie Lenise. ■ 75052 #048-12-2008 *012

MEGWA, Joseph Maduabuchi. 530 S CARRIER PKWY STE 220 75051 #690-01-1979 L2004 **FM EM** *020 †18 ‡

MILMO, Daniel. ■ 75050 #048-12-2008 *012

MIRANDA CATURAY, Epifania. 2715 OSLER DR 75051 #748-10-1973 L1995 **PD** *020 †55

MONTANI, Norberto J C. 200 N CARRIER PKWY STE 109 75050 #132-01-1964 L1970 **IM** *020

MORRIS, Arnold J. 2304 BARDIN RD 75052 #048-13-1979 L1979 **FM PME** *071

MORURI, Susan N. ■ 75052 #048-02-2008 *012

NJO, Lucas. 4927 LAKE RIDGE PKWY, STE 170 75052 #041-13-1985 L2002 **AN** *020 †20,05

NOLEN, Michael Glenn. 817 W HIGHWAY 303 STE 190 75051 #039-01-1988 L1989 **GS** *020 †85

PARIKH, Navinchandra C. 200 N CARRIER PKWY, STE 107 75050 #495-01-1959 L1973 **FM** *020

PARUCHURI, Radha Kumari. ■ 75050 #495-58-1990 **FP** *012

PERALTA, Victor Hugo. 2100 N HWY 360, STE 220 75050 #737-01-1969 L1975 **FM OM** *020 †70 ‡

PHAM, Nhan Chi. ■ 75052 #048-04-1987 L1988 **IM** *020

PHILLIPS, James R. ■ 75050 #048-02-1949 L1949 **PD OS** *071 †55

PHILLIPS, Roycerene M H. ■ 75050 #048-02-1950 L1950 **GP GPM** *071

READ, Edwin P. 1902 WESTMINSTER DR 75050 #048-02-1950 L1950 **EM** *071 †18

REDDY, Srilatha Arrem. 615 SMALL ST, STE 108 75050 #495-57-1996 L2001 **FM** *020 †18

ROBERTSON, Jeffrey A. 507 W CROSSLAND BLVD 75052 #048-04-1983 L1983 **GP LM** *020

SCHULTZ, Jennifer Elaine. ■ 75052 #048-02-2004 L2007 **OBG** *012

SIMS, Michael D. 4116 S CARRIER PKWY # 250 75052 #048-04-1996 L1997 **FM** *020 †18

SIMS, Shannon Warner. 4927 LAKE RIDGE PKWY, BAYLOR HEALTH CENTER 75052 #048-14-1996 L1997 **FM** *020 †18

STRACHAN-BATSON, Jill A. ■ 75052 #012-21-1996 L2006 **FM** *020 †18

SYRQUIN, Abraham. 517 N CARRIER PKWY STE A 75050 #649-01-1962 L1967 **GS VS** *020 †85

TERRELL, John David. ■ 75052 #004-01-2006 **U** *012

TRUONG, Tuan Anh. ■ 75052 #048-12-2007 **GS** *012

VILLANO, Kathryn Slott. ■ 75054 #045-01-2002 L2006 **OBG** *100 †30

WEST, Penny C. 4927 LAKE RIDGE PKWY, STE 100 75052 #001-06-1989 L1992 **IM** *020 †20

WHITCOMB, Donald Craig. 2461 ROBINSON RD BLDG A 75051 #005-12-1977 L1978 **FM** *020 †18

WIEGMAN, Ralph Thane. 643 S GREAT SOUTHWEST PKWY, STE 102 75051 #048-12-1978 L1978 **OBG** *020 †30

WOOD, Sara Ellen. ■ 75054 #004-01-2006 **PD** *012

XIQUES, Pablo L. 2502 E MAIN ST STE 204 75050 #275-01-1964 L1975 **GP** *020

GRAND SALINE – VAN ZANDT

INGRIM, Richard Lynn. 801 N WALDRIP ST 75140 #649-07-1980 L1984 **FM** *020

MASSEY, Warner Barron. 709 N WALDRIP ST # 8 75140 #048-12-1969 L1969 **GP NM** *020 †50,28

MUHAMMAD, Ashfaque Ghulam. 735 N WALDRIP ST, PHOENIX MEMORIAL HOSPITAL 75140 #704-16-1990 L2007 **IM** *020 †20

ROMACK, Anthoni Re. 104 W FRANK ST 75140 #048-12-1983 L1983 **P** *020 †75

GRANDVIEW – JOHNSON

HINES, Dwight Allen, II. 203 S 3RD ST, HUGULEY MEDICAL ASSOCIATES 76050 #048-02-1992 L1994 **EM** *020 †18

HOUGLUM, Arvid J. ■ 76050 #026-04-1951 L1985 **PHP FM** *071 †70,18

GRANGER – WILLIAMSON

HALL, Terri Ann. ■ 76530 #048-15-1986 L1987 **EM** *020 †16

SKROVAN, Clarence Chas. ■ 76530 #048-02-1964 L1964 **GPM PHP** *071 †70

SKROVAN, Susan Sandstrom. ■ 76530 #048-02-1961 L1961 **PD** *071 †55

GRANITE SHOALS – BURNET

JOHNSON, Alvis F, Jr. ■ 78654 #048-02-1946 L1946 **PD PDC** *071 †55

GRAPELAND – HOUSTON

CUTSHAW, Edward Geo. 102 S MAIN ST 75844 #047-06-1958 L1962 **GP** *020

GRAPEVINE – TARRANT

ACHARYA, Ashish Ashutosh. 1650 W COLLEGE ST 76051 #048-04-1999 L2006 **ID** *100 †20

ALLAUDIN, Amina R. 1650 W COLLEGE ST 76051 #704-02-1983 L1996 **FM** *020 †18

ALLEN, Katrina E. 1625 LANCASTER DR 76051 #048-12-1998 L2000 **OBG** *020 †30

ALVI, Mona. ■ 76092 #704-21-1996 **CHP** *020

AMMONS, David Harlan. 1600 W COLLEGE ST, STE 140 76051 #048-12-1971 L1974 **TS** *020 †85,90

ANDERSON, Thomas Carl. 1643 LANCASTER DR STE 202, TEXAS ONCOLOGY PA 76051 #016-11-1974 L1993 **ON HEM** *020 †20

ARCA, Sandra Hancock. 3801 WILLIAM D TATE AVE, STE 200 76051 #048-14-1992 L1993 **PD** *020 †55

ASH, Steven Patterson. 1601 LANCASTER DR, STE 170 76051 #048-02-1986 L1987 **U** *020 †95

AURORA, Vikas. 1643 LANCASTER DR STE 202 76051 #048-02-2001 L2007 **IM** *100

BASCO, Michael Angelo. 4100 HERITAGE AVE, STE 102 76051 #005-18-1987 L1989 **OBG** *020 †30

BAZALDUA, Carlos. 2020 W STATE HIGHWAY 114, STE 200 76051 #048-12-1992 L1993 **IM** *020 †20

BOND, James R, Jr. 1615 LANCASTER DR, STE 107 76051 #048-04-1986 L1987 **D** *020 †15

BONNET, James Vincent. 1600 W COLLEGE ST STE 140 76051 #048-02-1980 L1980 **ORS** *020 †40

BROOKS, Harold Lloyd. 2701 N GRAPEVINE MILS BLVD 76051 #039-01-1963 L1965 **CD** *040

CABLE, Melanie Kay. ■ 76099 #004-01-1974 L1975 **OPH** *074 †35

CANNON-SMITH, Tracy L. ■ 76051 #025-01-1995 L2005 **U** *020 †95

CAPELO, Roderick Marcus. 2020 W STATE HIGHWAY 114, STE 110 76051 #048-12-1999 L2005 **ORS** *020

CAPILI, Carleo Abaya. 1501 W NORTHWEST HWY 76051 #748-02-1974 L1982 **GP GS** *020 ‡

CAPILI, Regina Rodriguez. 1501 W NORTHWEST HWY 76051 #748-02-1979 L1982 **FM** *020 †18

CASALY, Joseph S. 1245 S MAIN ST, STE 120 76051 #008-02-1984 L1999 **N PMM** *020 †75

CASH, Robert Lindsey, Jr. 1600 W COLLEGE ST, STE 110 76051 #048-02-1980 L1980 **PUD** *020 †20

CHAI, Jinping. ■ 76051 #243-39-1985 L2003 **IM** *020 †20

CHEN, Henry I-Ting. 1600 W COLLEGE ST, STE 185 76051 #035-20-1998 L2004 **PTH PCP** *020 †20

CHUDNOW, Robert Steven. 1643 LANCASTER DR, STE 304 76051 #025-07-1990 L1994 **CHN** *020 †75

CLARK, Edward Deallen. 1600 W COLLEGE ST, STE LL10 76051 #039-01-1995 L1997 **OBG** *020 †30

COPE, Angela Malcolm. 1625 LANCASTER DR 76051 #048-15-1990 L1991 **OBG** *020 †30

COULTER-SMITH, Barbara A. 1625 LANCASTER DR 76051 #018-75-1989, ▲ L1998 **OBG** *020 †30

COWEN, Alan Ephraim. 1600 W COLLEGE ST, STE 1101 76051 #012-01-1978 L1979 **OBG** *020 †30

COX, Clifton L. 1600 W COLLEGE ST STE 320 76051 #048-04-1990 L1992 **CRS** *020 †85,10

DAVIDSON, Nettie Nichole. 2020 W HIGHWAY 114, STE 200 76051 #012-01-2000 L2004 **IM** *020 †20

DAVIDSON, Scott D. 1601 LANCASTER DR, STE 170 76051 #048-02-1994 L2000 **U** *020 †95

DAVIS, Steven Gabe. 1650 W COLLEGE ST 76051 #017-20-1986 L1990 **ID IM** *020 †20

DEMARTINI, Robert Vincent. 1600 W COLLEGE ST, STE 490 76051 #035-09-1987 L1988 **IM** *020 †20

DOTTI, Michael Wm. 1602 LANCASTER DR, STE 102 76051 #023-12-1983 L1993 **FM** *020 †18

DRAKE, William Neil. 1602 LANCASTER DR, STE 102 76051 #025-12-1992 L1995 **FM** *020 †18

DRINKARD, Lee Campbell. 2020 W STATE HIGHWAY 114, STE 220 76051 #055-01-1987 L1997 **HO IM** *020 †20

DURRETT, Lenard Roy. 210 N PARK BLVD, STE 107 76051 #048-02-1982 L1983 **PME AN** *020 †05

ELDERS, Gregory Jay. 2535 IRA E WOODS AVE 76051 #025-01-1999 L2004 **ORS** *100 †40

ELIESON, Melvin J. 1600 W COLLEGE ST, STE 690 76051 #048-02-2000 L2005 **GS** *020 †85 ‡

ELLIOTT, Robert Larry. 1600 W COLLEGE ST STE 440 76051 #001-02-1983 L1994 **GS** *020 †85

ENTY, Don Arthur. 1600 W NORTHWEST HWY 76051 #048-15-1981 L1981 **AN PMM** *020 †05

FERRIS, John Steven. 1604 LANCASTER DR 76051 #016-43-1976 L1976 **IM** *020 †20

FLOWERS, Julia Collette. 1600 W COLLEGE ST, STE 540 76051 #024-01-1993 L1998 **OBG** *020 †30

FOWLER, Robert W. 2303 IRA E WOODS AVE, FOWLER SPORTS MEDICINE 76051 #048-12-1988 L1989 **FM FSM** *020 †18

FREY, Patrick Robert. 1600 W COLLEGE ST, STE 190 76051 #019-02-1994 L1999 **U** *020 †95
FRUCHTER, Michael Stanley. ■ 76051 #305-01-1983 L1985 **P FM** *020
FUTSCHER, Eric Robt. 1600 W COLLEGE ST STE L 76051 #649-14-1977 L1993 **FM** *020 †18
GHAFFAR, Faryal Abdul. 1600 W COLLEGE ST, STE 280 76051 #704-02-1991 L2000
  PD PDI *020 †55
GHALI, Fred E. 1325 W NORTHWEST HWY 76051 #048-12-1993 L1995 **D PDD** *020 †15,55
GIBBS, Courtney L. 1625 LANCASTER DR 76051 #048-15-1998 L2001 **OBG** *020 †30
GLADNEY, Samuel L. 1600 W COLLEGE ST STE 210 76051 #004-01-1970 L1971 **GP** *071
GORDON, Martyn D. 1604 LANCASTER DR 76051 #048-02-1983 L1983 **IM** *020 †20
GRAHAM, Alexander. 1034 MOCKINGBIRD DR 76051 #065-06-1960 L1977 **FM** *071
GRAVES, Nathan Lynn. 1601 LANCASTER DR, STE 170 76051 #039-01-1980 L1981 **U** *020 †95
GREGORY, William M. 1650 W COLLEGE ST, GRAPEVINE RADIOLOGY ASSOCI 76051
  #048-13-1995 L1997 **DR** *020 †80 ‡
HAGMAN, Joseph E. 1650 W COLLEGE ST 76051 #048-15-1990 L1991 **DR VIR** *020 †80
HALUSZKA, Mary Ousley. 1600 W COLLEGE ST STE 190 76051 #023-12-1982 L2003
  U *040 †95
HARRIS, Howard W. 4100 HERITAGE AVE, STE 102 76051 #048-12-1997 L2003 **ORS** *020
HASSANI, Dahlia Mehrnoosh. 1650 W COLLEGE ST 76051 #016-11-2002 L2007 **EM** *100 †16
HATCHER, Alexander H. 1650 W COLLEGE ST 76051 #048-14-1994 L1997 **EM** *020 †16
HOGAN, Chad A. 1280 S MAIN ST STE 100, HOGAN MEDICAL FOR YOUR FAM 76051
  #048-12-1997 L2000 **FM** *020 †18
HOPKINS, Eric E. 1600 W NORTHWEST HWY 76051 #048-13-1999 L2002 **PD** *020 †55 ‡
HORODA, Michael Johnathan. ■ 76051 #039-01-1986 L1987 **IM IMG** *072
HOUSTON, Jody W. 2020 W STAT HGHWY 114 #300 76051 #048-13-1999 L2006 **GE** *020 †20
JAYSON, Hal Terry. 1600 W COLLEGE ST STE 100 76051 #048-13-1982 L1983 **DR** *020 †80
JOHNSON, Bill J. 1601 LANCASTER DR STE 20 76051 #048-15-1981 L1981 **IM** *020 †20
KANE, Judith P. 315 W WALL ST STE 100 76051 #021-01-1982 L1983 **P** *020 †55,75
KAPPLER, Sherri Lynn. 1650 W COLLEGE ST, DEPARTMENT OF NICU 76051
  #016-42-1996 L2005 **NPM** *020 †55 ‡
KEEBLE, Tony Dion. 5301 WILLIAM D TATE AVE 76051 #048-12-1985 L1986 **FM** *020 †18
KHAN, Anila I. ■ 76051 #704-06-1987 L1996 **IM** *020 †20
KHAN, Rehan A. 210 N PARK BLVD, STE 107 76051 #704-02-1990 L1996 **IM** *020 †20
KILGUS, Andrew Henry. 1600 LANCASTER DR, STE 103 76051 #016-11-1962 L1983
  PD A *071 †55
KOGAN, James B. 1650 W COLLEGE ST, DEPT OF RADIOLOGY 76051 #048-12-1994 L1995
  DR *020 †20
KOTSANIS, Constantine A. 2020 W HIGHWAY 114, STE 260 76051 #418-01-1976 L1983
  OTO AI *020 †45
KUSHWAHA, Alok P. 1650 W COLLEGE ST BOX 24 76051 #048-13-1995 L1996 **IM** *020 †20
LABOR, Phillips Kirk. 1643 LANCASTER DR 76051 #021-06-1991 L1999 **OPH** *020 †35
LACEY, Stephen Ward. 2020 W STATE HIGHWAY 114, CONSULTANTS 76051
  #028-02-1981 L1985 **GE IM** *020 †20
LANCASTER, Edgar L, Jr. 1600 LANCASTER DR, STE 110 76051 #048-02-1951 L1951 **FM** *071
LAUREL, Valerie Lynn. 1650 W COLLEGE ST 76051 #048-12-1993 L1994 **ID** *020 †20
LEE, Karla Jan. 1600 W COLLEGE ST 76051 #048-13-1991 L1993 **CD** *020 †20
LEVITAN, David Ross. 2020 W STATE HIGHWAY 114, CONSULTANTS 76051 #038-40-1997 L2001
  GE *100 †20
LOCKARD, Daniel T, Jr. 1600 W COLLEGE ST STE 540 76051 #048-02-1984 L1988
  OBG *020 †30
LOPEZ, Monica Edith. 1625 LANCASTER DR 76051 #048-12-2003 L2006 **OBG** *020
LWIN, Thida. ■ 76051 #209-01-1991 L2005 **PTH** *100 †50
MAHAN, Kerry Elizabeth. 3900 GRAPEVINE MILLS PKWY, UNIT 1323 76051 #055-01-1988 L2005
  IM *020 †20
MALONE, Gary Louis. 1450 HUGHES RD, STE 108 76051 #048-02-1979 L1979
  PYA P *020 †75 ‡
MAYSE, Richard Allen. 811 IRA E WOODS AVE 76051 #048-02-1980 L1980 **PUD OS** *020 †20
MC COY, Michael Wayne. 811 IRA E WOODS AVE 76051 #021-05-1987 L1989 **PD** *020 †55
MEHTA, S Neil. 1650 W COLLEGE ST 76051 #060-01-1991 L1997 **GE IM** *020 †20
MENDEZ, Angelo Carlos. 1600 W COLLEGE ST STE 340 76051 #048-12-1983 L1983
  OBG *020 †30 ‡
MILLER, Andrew H. 2020 W STATE HIGHWAY 114, STE 280 76051 #048-12-1983 L1983
  CD IM *020 †20
MILLER, Van Strickland. 1643 LANCASTER DR, STE 304 76051 #048-02-1986 L1987
  CHN *040 †75,55
MITCHELL, Michael Ronald. 2020 W STATE HIGHWAY 114, STE 280 76051 #048-02-1982 L1983
  CD *020 †20
MOHABEER, Ajay Jagarnath. ■ 76051 #917-08-1983 L1998 **GP OM** *020
MONG, Michael A. 1600 W COLLEGE ST, STE 390 76051 #048-12-1984 L1985 **OPH PD** *020 †35
MOORE, Philip Alan. 1600 W COLLEGE ST STE LL20 76051 #048-12-1978 L1978
  GS PHL *020 †85
MOSER, Doreen A. 1600 W COLLEGE ST, STE 260 76051 #048-78-1990, ▲ L1994
  OBG *020 †30
MOUSTAPHA, Ali Issam. 2020 W STATE HIGHWAY 114, STE 280 76051 #605-01-1995 L2005
  IC *020 †20
MUSSO, Nick Frank, Jr. 1650 W COLLEGE ST, BAYLOR REGIONAL MEDICAL CE 76051
  #306-01-1985 L1992 **FM** *020 †18
NASH, Lisa Ann. ■ 76051 #023-07-2004 L2007 **PD** *100 †55
NEAL, Kerry Doyle. 1600 W COLLEGE ST, STE 1101 76051 #047-06-1982 L1986 **OBG** *020 †30
NEW, Troy Gerald, Jr. 1600 W COLLEGE ST STE 340 76051 #001-02-1993 L1997 **OBG** *020 †30
NGUYEN, Todd Thang Quoc. 3333 SPRUCE LN 76051 #048-02-2002 L2008 **IM** *020 †20
O'BRIEN, Cherie Hsu. 1600 W COLLEGE ST, STE 410 76051 #035-03-1987 L1998 **N** *020 †75
OSBORNE, John Andrew. 3801 WILLIAM D TATE AVE, STE 850 76051 #041-02-1990 L1997
  CD GPM *020 †20
PAGE, John Kevin. 1604 LANCASTER DR 76051 #004-01-1992 L1997 **IM** *020 †20
PARMEKAR, Suneeta Sandeep. ■ 76051 #496-38-1994 **FM** *012
PATE, Perry Glenn. 1650 W COLLEGE ST 76051 #048-12-1976 L1989 **ID IM** *020 †20
PAUL, Vincent Ivan. 2355 E GRAPEVINE MILLS CIR 76051 #065-01-1986 L1997 **FM** *020 †18
PAYNE, Gerald G, Jr. 1600 W COLLEGE ST, STE 210 76051 #048-12-1982 L1983
  OBG MFM *020 †30
PETERS, Pat Andrew. 2535 IRA E WOODS AVE 76051 #048-13-1983 L1983 **ORS** *020 †40
PETERS, Theodore Thos. 2535 IRA E WOODS AVE 76051 #048-12-1979 L1979
  HS ORS *020 †40
PHAM, Daniel Ha. 3105 IRA E WOODS AVE, STE 120 76051 #048-04-1992 L2000
  FM OM *020 †18 ‡
PITTARD, Carlton Duwain. 1280 S MAIN ST SU 76051 #048-02-1957 L1957 **GP OBG** *020
PONDER, John Coleman. 1600 W COLLEGE ST, STE 270 76051 #048-04-1979 L1980
  OTO HNS *030 †45

PRENTISS, Adrienne Lynn. 1600 W COLLEGE ST, STE 510 76051 #016-43-1995 L1999
  FM *020 †18
PROST, Henry M. 2020 W HIGHWAY 114, STE 320 76051 #048-14-1997 L1999 **END** *020 †20
PUGACH, Jeff Lawrence. 1600 W COLLEGE ST, STE 190 76051 #033-06-1991 L2001
  U *020 †95
PUMMILL, Charles Lawrence. 1600 W COLLEGE ST STE 100 76051 #048-02-1959 L1959
  DR FM *020 †18,80
PUPPALA, Jagadish. 1643 LANCASTER DR, STE 203 76051 #496-24-1992 L1999 **CD** *020 †20
PURGETT, Thomas Jaye. 1600 W COLLEGE ST, STE 690 76051 #016-11-1986 L1988
  GS *020 †85
RASHDAN, Iyad. 2020 W STATE HIGHWAY 114, STE 280 76051 #875-01-1986 L2000
  CD *020 †20
REIDLAND, Kenneth E. ■ 76051 #048-04-1949 L1949 **ORS OS** *071 †40
RIELA, Anthony Richard. 1643 LANCASTER DR, STE 304 76051 #033-05-1979 L1990
  CHN OS *020 †55,75
RITTER, Timothy Edward. 2020 W HIGHWAY 114, STE 300 76051 #048-12-1987 L1988
  GE IM *020 †20
ROBERGE, Natalie Anne. 1600 W COLLEGE ST, STE 270 76051 #048-12-1988 L1989
  OTO *020 †45
ROBERT, Rebecca Maring. 1600 W COLLEGE ST, STE 1101 76051 #048-02-1994 L1996
  OBG *020 †30
ROBERT, Wm Pierre, III. 1600 W COLLEGE ST, STE 60 76051 #048-02-1991 L1992 **PD** *020 †55
ROST, Timothy Joel. 1600 W COLLEGE ST STE 340 76051 #048-02-1984 L1985 **OBG** *020 †30
ROUGHNEEN, Patrick Thos. 1600 W COLLEGE ST, STE 555 76051 #917-13-1982 L1992
  TS *020 †85,90
SANDHU, Sawroop. 2093 BRENTCOVE DR, ATT:DIANE JONES 76051 #495-22-2002 L2008
  FM *020 †18
SATHYAPRAKASH, Roopa. 2020 WEST STATE, HIGHWAY 114 STE 320 76051
  #495-72-1996 L2006 **END** *020 †20
SCHROEDER, Timothy G. 1600 W COLLEGE ST STE 110 76051 #048-12-1990 L1992
  PCC *020
SCOTT, Anthony Mark. 1600 W COLLEGE ST, STE 60 76051 #048-02-1984 L1986 **PD** *020 †55
SHORI, Vanita Devi. 1600 LANCASTER DR, COOK CHILDREN'S HEALTH CAR 76051
  #025-12-1998 L2001 **PD** *020 †55
SIMMONS, Janie Milburn. 122 N MAIN ST 76051 #034-01-1991 L1995 **IM** *020 †20
SIMS, Michael Neil. 1600 W COLLEGE ST, STE 540 76051 #048-02-1974 L1974 **OBG** *020 †30
SMITH, Jeffrey A. 2020 W STATE HIGHWAY 114, CONSULTANTS 76051 #048-02-1995 L2001
  GE *020 †20
SO, Gerald Mendoza. 1643 LANCASTER DR, STE 304 76051 #036-05-1990 L1998
  CHN CN *072 †55,75
SOLOMON, Martin David. 1600 W COLLEGE ST, STE 470 76051 #016-43-1982 L1990
  N IM *020 †20,75
SPADY, David Keith. 2020 W STATE HIGHWAY 114, CONSULTANTS 76051 #005-12-1976 L1980
  GE *050 †20
STERN, Richard Leo. 901 W WALL ST 76051 #048-12-1998 L1999 **RHU** *020 †20
STOREY, Donald Francis. 1650 W COLLEGE ST 76051 #035-01-1995 L2004 **ID** *020 †20
TALEB ZADEH, Abas. 1340 S MAIN ST STE 180, MAIN STREET MEDICAL CLINIC 76051
  #517-01-1951 L1979 **GS** *020
TAN, Simon Sy. 2020 W HIGHWAY 114, STE 310 76051 #748-01-1987 L2001 **N** *020
TANG, Mary Yuh. 2549 SPRINGHILL DR 76051 #016-06-1990 L1996 **IM EM** *020 †20
TAUNTON, Oscar David, Jr. 4100 HERITAGE AVE, STE 102 76051 #001-02-1989 L1999
  ORS *020 †40
TAYLOR, Bernard Gyewu. ■ 76051 #412-01-1997 L2006 **IM** *100 †20
THELEMAN, Kevin P. 1643 LANCASTER DR, STE 203 76051 #048-15-1998 L1999 **IC** *100 †20
TROTTER, Brooks Payne. 1604 LANCASTER DR 76051 #048-15-1983 L1983 **IM** *020 †20
VALLEJO-CRAIG, Pamela. 2020 W HIGHWAY 114, STE 200 76051 #048-12-2003 L2005
  IM *020 †20
VERA, Richard L. 1615 LANCASTER DR STE 150 76051 #048-02-1991 L1992 **APM** *020 †05
WAI, Robert Bingtak. 1600 W COLLEGE ST, STE 540 76051 #047-06-1990 L1994 **OBG** *020 †30
WEATHERALL, Marcus Lesly, Jr. ■ 76051 #048-12-2008 *012
WEBER, James J. 2020 W STATE HIGHWAY 114, CONSULTANTS 76051 #048-12-1987 L1988
  GE *020 †20
WILSON, Steve I. 1650 W COLLEGE ST 76051 #243-16-1988 L2002 **APM** *020 †05
WINTERS, Mary Lynn. 315 W WALL ST, STE 100 76051 #004-01-1984 L1991 **P AN** *020 †75
WITT, Clarke. 1340 S MAIN ST 76051 #030-05-1968 L1974 **CHP P** *020
WOOMER, Scott F. 1650 W COLLEGE ST, DEPT OF RADIOLOGY 76051 #048-12-1994 L1996
  R NM *020 †80,28
WRIGHT, Randall A. 1600 W COLLEGE ST STE 440 76051 #048-13-1993 L1995 **GS** *020 †85
YATES, Judy L. 2020 W HIGHWAY 114, STE 200 76051 #048-12-1996 L1997 **IM** *071 †20
ZATKALIK, Shane E. 1650 W COLLEGE ST 76051 #048-12-2001 L2002 **EM** *020 †16

GREENVILLE – HUNT

ABERNETHY, Joan Lea. 3005 JOE RAMSEY BLVD E 75401 #026-04-1997 L1998 **OPH** *020 †35
ADKISSON, Mike Allen. 4818 WELLINGTON ST, STE 1 75402 #048-02-1962 L1962 **PD** *071 †55
ANDERSON, William Douglas. 4215 JOE RAMSEY BLVD E 75401 #047-06-1985 L1988 **EM** *020
ANDRE, Karen Kaden. 3900 JOE RAMSEY BLVD E 75401 #048-12-1980 L1980
  PS OPH *020 †16
ATA, Ahmad Saeed. 4501 JOE RAMSEY BLVD E, STE 200 75401 #704-20-1989 L1999
  N *020 †75
BAHM, Sandy Bernard, II. 4215 JOE RAMSEY BLVD E 75401 #048-04-1969 L1969 **ORS** *020 †40
BAREIKA, Arturas. 4101 WESLEY ST STE C, WESLEY MED PLAZA 75401 #913-49-1991 L2004
  IM RHU *020
BAREIKIENE, Violeta. ■ 75402 #913-96-1989 L2004 **IM** *020 †20
BLEIER, Joseph T. 4215 JOE RAMSEY BLVD E, EMERGENCY DEPARTMENT 75401
  #048-15-1993 L1994 **EM** *020 †20
BRUN, Gloria Rodarte. 5604 WESLEY ST, STE 103 75402 #048-15-1989 L1994 **P CHP** *020 †75
BURING, David Myron. ■ 75402 #048-12-1965 L1965 **OBG** *071 †30
CLARK, Alan S. 4211 JOE RAMSEY BLVD E, STE 100 75401 #048-04-1997 L1998 **FM** *020
COKER, Jerry Clyde. ■ 75402 #048-12-1960 L1960 **OBG** *071 †30
DENHAM, Claude A. 4215 JOE RAMSEY BLVD E 75401 #048-02-1982 L1983 **ON** *020 †20
DEUELL, Robert Franklin. 4211 JOE RAMSEY BLVD E, STE 100 75401 #051-04-1983 L1986
  FM *075 †18
DONSKY, Alan Stuart. 4211 JOE RAMSEY BLVD E, STE 108 75401 #048-02-1998 L2005
  ICE *020 †20

EBRAHIM, Moushira Anwar. 4818 WELLINGTON ST, STE 8 75402 #915-04-1979 L1993 PTH *020 †50

ELLINGTON, Timothy David. 4211 JOE RAMSEY BLVD E, STE 100 75401 #048-02-1980 L1980 IM *020 †20

ENGELMAN, David Ream. 4211 JOE RAMSEY BLVD E, STE 101 75401 #012-05-1969 L1970 CD *020 †05

FANOUS, Amira Boulos. ■ 75402 #915-04-1985 L2005 PTH *020

FAROOQ, Hassan. 3900 JOE RAMSEY BLVD E, STE 7 75401 #704-04-1992 L1998 IM *020 †20

FRY, David Kent. 4211 JOE RAMSEY BLVD E 75401 #030-06-1978 L1992 PD EM *020 †55

GAMBOA, Gloria Danielle. 4724 WELLINGTON ST, INSTACARE, INC 75401 #048-04-1995 L1996 FM *020 †18

GRAHAM, Camille Alicia. 4000 MEDICAL PKWY 75401 #024-01-1996 L2001 OTO *020 †45

GRAY, Peter Frederick. 4215 JOE RAMSEY BLVD E 75401 #007-02-1975 L1977 FM FPG *020 †18

HAGGARD, Jeffrey Cole. 4215 JOE RAMSEY BLVD E 75401 #039-01-1994 L1997 EM *020 †16

HAMID, Syed Adnan. 4215 JOE RAMSEY BLVD E, PRESBYTERIAN HOSPTIAL OF G 75401 #704-25-1991 L2004 IM *020 †20

HENDRICKS, Joel Ray. 4215 JOE RAMSEY BLVD E 75401 #048-12-1980 L1986 GS *020 †85

HERMAN, Wesley Kent. 3005 JOE RAMSEY BLVD E 75401 #037-01-1976 L1981 OPH OS *020

HURST, Edward Palm. 3900 JOE RAMSEY BLVD E 75401 #048-02-1981 L1981 OPH GS *035

JUSTICE, Barry Lynn. 4818 WELLINGTON ST, STE 1 75402 #048-02-1979 L1982 PD *020 †55

KADEN, Van G. 301 DIVISION ST 75401 #048-12-1951 L1951 GS *071 †85

KALRA, Gurjeet Singh. 4702 WESLEY ST STE C 75401 #495-74-1978 L1988 P *062

KERBY, Troy Wayne. 4215 JOE RAMSEY BLVD E, DEPARTMENT OF RADIOLOGY 75401 #305-01-2001 L2006 DR *020 †80

KHALFE, Wajiuddin. 301 DIVISION ST 75401 #704-16-1991 L1996 IM *020 †20

KHAN, Kaneez Rukia. PO BOX 1908, GREENVILLE COMMUNITY HEALT 75403 #495-21-1996 L2005 MPD *020 †20,55

KNODERER, William R. ■ 75402 #822-01-2002 *020

KOGER, Linton M. 4211 JOE RAMSEY BLVD E, STE 100 75401 #048-14-1997 L1998 FM *020 †18 ‡

KORNU, Paul. 2706 AILEEN BLVD, SUITE-B 75402 #891-01-1966 L1975 IM *020

KOWALCZYK, Teresa. 4221 RIDGECREST RD, STE 109 75402 #759-12-1988 L1998 OBG *020 †30

KRAVEN, Thomas. 4215 JOE RAMSEY BLVD E 75401 #033-05-1976 L1992 OS UM *020 †85

KWELLER, Howard Evan. 4004 MEDICAL PKWY 75401 #035-47-1978 L1980 GP *020 ‡

MADSEN, Leah Patterson. 4211 JOE RAMSEY BLVD E, STE 100 75401 #034-01-1997 L1998 FM *020 †18

MARROY, Larry James. 4215 JOE RAMSEY BLVD E 75401 #021-05-1965 L1988 AN *020 †05

MATTHEWS, George Philip. 3005 JOE RAMSEY BLVD E 75401 #038-43-1987 L1996 OPH *020 †35

MC CRARY, Dee Gordon, Jr. 4101 WESLEY ST 75401 #048-12-1975 L1975 FM *020 †18

MOOLAMALLA, Praveen. 3900 JOE RAMSEY BLVD E 75401 #496-24-1989 L1997 P *020

MORRIS, John Wm. 3900 JOE RAMSEY BLVD E 75401 #048-12-1947 L1947 OPH OTO *072

PATTERSON, Patrice A. 4818 WELLINGTON ST STE 1 75402 #048-13-1995 L1998 PD *020 †55

PENLAND, Heath R. 301 DIVISION ST, GLEN OAKS HOSP 75401 #048-12-2001 L2006 P PYG *100 †75

PHILIP, Mohan Parayil. 4221 RIDGECREST RD STE 107 75402 #495-31-1994 L2003 PCC SME *020 †20

PRATUMRAT, Pairoj. 3900 JOE RAMSEY BLVD E, STE E 75401 #891-04-1971 L1985 OBG *020 †30

RIEDWEG, Edward Albert. 301 DIVISION ST DEPT IM 75401 #060-01-1965 L1975 OS IM *075 †20

RINNER, Steven Eric. 4805 WESLEY ST, NRI-NORTHEAST TEXAS 75401 #035-06-1967 L1973 NEP IM *020 †20

RIPP, Thomas Victor. 4000 MEDICAL PKWY 75401 #016-43-1975 L1984 OTO A *020 †45

RONAGHAN, Joseph Edward. 4221 RIDGECREST RD, STE 105 75402 #021-01-1977 L1991 GS EM *020 †85

SANDIN, James Howard. ■ 75402 #048-12-1964 L1964 U *071 †95

SCHROEDER, George E. 4215 JOE RAMSEY BLVD E 75401 #048-02-1999 L2002 EM *020 †16

SHAH, Iqtidar Ul-Hassan. 4004 MEDICAL PKWY 75401 #704-01-1958 L1973 GS *020 †85

SIDDIQUI, Farrah Naz. 4000 MEDICAL PKWY, ALLERGY ENT CLINIC OF NE T 75401 #704-25-1999 L2006 OTO *020 †45

SILES, Fernando M. 2405 STONEWALL ST 75401 #737-06-1973 L1984 CHP P *020

SMITH, Perry Mathews. 4211 JOE RAMSEY BLVD E, STE 100 75401 #048-12-1978 L1978 IM *020 †20

THOMAS, Maxine J. PO BOX 8645 75404 #048-13-1983 L1985 FM *020 †18 ‡

THURMOND, Frederick Allen. 301 DIVISION ST 75401 #034-01-1998 L2000 CD *020 †20

TRISARNSRI, On-Anong. 4818 WELLINGTON ST, STE 8 75402 #891-01-1971 L1981 PTH *020 †50

TYLER, Earl Day. 4215 JOE RAMSEY BLVD E, HUNT MEMORIAL HOSPITAL 75401 #048-15-1975 L1976 DR *020 †80

UPATHAM, Suvij. 3900 JOE RAMSEY BLVD E 75401 #891-03-1971 L1977 OBG IM *020 †30

USMAN, Asim R. 4215 JOE RAMSEY BLVD E, MEDICAL STAFF OFFICE 75401 #704-25-1992 L2001 IM *020 †20

VORA, Neil M. 4000 MEDICAL PKWY 75401 #048-14-1997 L2003 OTO *020 †45

WRIGHT, Mark L. 4215 JOE RAMSEY BLVD E 75401 #048-13-1987 L1988 IM *020 †20

WU, Min-Sheng. 4215 JOE RAMSEY BLVD E 75401 #385-01-1966 L1975 AN *020

ZAPATA, Malissia Denise. 4221 RIDGECREST RD, STE 109 75402 #033-05-1999 L2004 OBG *020

ZEB, Mohiudin Aurang. 3900 JOE RAMSEY BLVD E, STE 7 75401 #704-02-1971 L1984 IM CD *020 †20

ZIAI, Elham. 4211 JOE RAMSEY BLVD E 75401 #016-11-1998 L2006 FM *020 †18 ‡

GROESBECK — LIMESTONE

DOUPNIK, Ladislav. 625 MCCLINTIC DR 76642 #286-11-1960 L1978 GP EM *071

FANNIN, Kenneth Ray. 701 MCCLINTIC DR 76642 #048-02-1960 L1971 GS *071 †85

HOESCHELE, Mark J. 701 MCCLINTIC DR 76642 #048-12-2000 L2002 FM *020 †18

KENNEDY, Forrest Lynn. 76642 #028-78-1955, ▲ L1955 LM *071

LOMENZO, Ken Gerard. 701 MCCLINTIC DR 76642 #422-01-1998 L2001 FM *020 †18

MATLOCK, Robert C. 204 W TRINITY ST 76642 #048-02-1996 L1997 FM *020 †18

RAHAMAN, Sheer. 701 MCCLINTIC DR 76642 #539-04-1960 L1977 FM *020

GROVES — JEFFERSON

LEE, Kwang-Su. 5500 39TH ST, RENAISSANCE HOSPITAL 77619 #583-09-1972 L1977 AN *020 †05

LONGUET, Roy Harvey. 77619 #048-04-1975 L1976 R *020 †80

PEINERT, Robt Alfred, Jr. 5500 39TH ST 77619 #385-05-1970 L1983 ORS OSS *020 †40

PURGHOL, Marwan. 5502 39TH ST, STE 103 77619 #875-01-1985 L2000 N *020

STEWART, John Harlan. 4000 TWIN CITY HWY, STE 307 77619 #048-02-1979 L1979 PTH *020 †50

GUN BARREL CITY — HENDERSON

ASPEGREN, Todd Alan. 100 MUNICIPAL DR 75156 #039-01-1987 L1996 FM *020 †18

CHUONG, Jen-Mann. 2310 W MAIN 75156 #385-09-1967 L1973 A *020

EDWARDS, Albert Owen. 519 N GUN BARREL LN, STE C 75156 #048-04-1992 L1993 OPH *020 †35

EHRHARDT, Ralphana L. 519 N GUN BARREL LN, STE C 75156 #048-02-1985 L1986 OPH *030 †35

GILES, William R. 100 MUNICIPAL DR, STE 200 75156 #048-14-2001 L2005 MPD *020

LEMMON, Kenneth Paul. 126 W MAIN ST 75156 #048-14-1975 L1975 FM *020 †18

MC MULLEN, Susan Clymer. 100 MUNICIPAL DR, ETMC FIRST PHYS CLINIC 75156 #003-01-1989 L2007 FM *020 †18

MIDDENDORF, Robert Chas. 519 N GUN BARREL LN, STE C 75156 #028-34-1964 L1971 OPH *020 †35

SHRADER, Karen Elizabeth. 429 N GUN BARREL LN # 111 75156 #048-14-1982 L1983 FM *020

SMITH, Charles Byron. 801 W MAIN ST 75156 #048-04-1967 L1967 GP EM *071 FM *020

SPITZER, Shari Jo. 100 MUNICIPAL DR, STE 100 75156 #038-44-1994 L1996 FM *020 †18

WOOD, T Stacy. 519 N GUN BARREL LN, STE C 75156 #048-15-1984 L1985 OPH *020 †35

WOOD, Thomas Preston. 519 N GUN BARREL LN, STE C 75156 #048-12-1955 L1955 OPH *020 †35

GUNTER — GRAYSON

FERRELL, John Carl. PO BOX 354, 206 MAPLE ST 75058 #048-13-1984 L1985 EM *020

HALE CENTER — HALE

FREEMAN, Ray W. 502 W STEVENSON 79041 #048-12-1950 L1950 FM GS *071 †18

JORDAN, Jack Grundy. 203 W 4TH, HI-PLAINS HOSPITAL 79041 #048-12-1952 L1952 FM *020 †18

HALLETTSVILLE — LAVACA

BATES, Jeffrey Charles. 1400 N TEXANA ST, LAVACA MEDICAL CENTER 77964 #422-01-1997 L2001 EM PCC *020

BIGGS, Jackson Turk. ■ 77964 #048-12-1976 L1977 P *020 †75

CIBOROWSKI, Crayton Edwin. 1400 N TEXANA ST 77964 #021-01-1973 L1974 FM EM *020 †18

CONNER, Barbara Nell. 316 S MAIN ST 77964 #019-02-1974 L1976 FM FPG *020 †18 ‡

LAVALLEE, Barry Dennis A. ■ 77964 #062-01-1988 FM *100

REASONER, Brian Michael. 1406 N TEXANA ST STE D 77964 #019-02-1995 L1999 MPD PD *020 †20,55

THOMPSON, Carleton K, Jr. 1406 N TEXANA ST 77964 #048-12-1968 L1968 GE IM *020 †20

WILKINSON, Maurice G. 1400 N TEXANA ST 77964 #048-15-1976 L1976 GP EM *020

HALLSVILLE — HARRISON

BRYK, Scott Gregory. ■ 75650 #048-13-1997 L1998 VIR *100 †80

BURROW, Rebecca Jane. 2878 A B CARTER RD 75650 #048-13-1986 L1987 MDM FM *030 †18

EAKIN, Donald Glenn. 9401 FM 449 75650 #048-13-1977 L1977 EM *020 †16

HORTMAN, Gregory S. 135 WHISTLER LN 75650 #048-15-1998 L2001 PD *020

HALTOM CITY — TARRANT

HISER, Gregory Mark. ■ 76137 #045-01-2005 *100

KRISHNARAJ, K N P. 6101 DENTON HWY, STE D 76148 #495-16-1961 L1978 FM PD *071 †55,18

MANNE, Murali Krishna. ■ 76137 #495-37-2001 L2006 IM *020 †20

NGUYEN, Huy Le. 2919 MARKUM DR 76111 #021-05-1993 L1997 MPD PD *020 †55,20

TANWAR, Meena Kumari. 5221 DILLON CIR 76137 #048-15-2008 *012

TENNANT, Thomas B. 6340 N BEACH ST 76137 #048-13-1995 L1996 FM *072 †18

HAMILTON — HAMILTON

CRAIG, William S. 400 N BROWN ST, HAMILTON GENERAL HOSPITAL 76531 #048-14-2005 L2007 FP *012

HORNE, Monte H. 303 N BROWN ST, ASSOCIATES 76531 #048-02-1998 L1999 FM *020 †18

KILLIAN, Luke M. 303 N BROWN ST, ASSOCIATES 76531 #048-12-1997 L1999 FM *020 †18

LEE, James R. 303 N BROWN ST, ASSOCIATES 76531 #048-12-1994 L1995 FM *020 †18 ‡

LENGEFELD, Robbye Kaye. 303 N BROWN ST, ASSOCIATES 76531 #048-16-2001 L2003 FM *020 †18

MORGAN, Hardy. 1615 COUNTY ROAD 113 76531 #048-13-1973 L1973 FM FPG *020 †18

TAN, Ping Ngi. 302 N BROWN ST 76531 #244-02-1972 L1978 IM *020

WILLIAMSON, George Danl. 5087 E HIGHWAY 22 76531 #495-33-1963 L1976 ORS *020 †40

HAMLIN — JONES

SMITH, Marshall Leroy. ■ 79520 #048-04-1945 L1945 GP *071

SUNKAVALLI, Krishna R V. 350 NW AVENUE F, HAMLIN MEDICAL CLINIC 79520 #495-11-1965 L1983 **GP GS** *020

WHITE, Chad L. 350 NW AVENUE F 79520 #048-02-1999 L2001 **FM** *020 †18

HAMSHIRE – JEFFERSON

ANDRES, Leonidas Salvador. HAMSHIRE RD 77622 #748-08-1973 L1979 **FM GS** *020

HARKER HEIGHTS – BELL

ADLER, Jeffrey Brian. ■ 76548 #041-13-2006 L2008 **EM** *012

ALI, Yasmeen. 200 NOLA RUTH BLVD 76548 #160-02-1987 L1998 **PD** *020 †55

ANDERSON, Devry Calvin. ■ 76548 #041-02-2000 L2004 **FP** *012

ANDERSON, Mark Ian. ■ 76548 #055-01-1999 L2000 **U** *020 †95

BIER, Scott Albert. ■ 76548 #041-15-2004 L2007 **EM** *020

BISHOP, Raymond H, Jr. ■ 76548 #048-02-1952 L1952 **IM** *071 †20

BLOOMQUIST, Luke Robert. ■ 76548 #041-13-2007 **FP** *012

BONILLA, David Josue. ■ 76548 #042-03-2001 L2005 **OBG** *020 †30

BUNCH, Edward Earl. 2110 KANGAROO TRL 76548 #030-06-1979 L1988 **PD ADL** *020

BYRNE, Robert Wendel. ■ 76548 #011-04-2006 L2007 **FP** *012

CAIN, Ruby Jean. ■ 76548 #036-01-1979 L1989 **D** *020

ELEMUREN-OGUNMUYIWA, I. 740 S AMY LN STE 101 76548 #130-01-1991 L1997 **FM** *020 †18

ELLIS, Charles Thompson. ■ 76548 #047-06-1970 L1992 **ORS** *020

FALKNER, Cathy Luganda. ■ 76548 #017-20-1999 **FM** *100

FLAGG, Artemus, II. ■ 76548 #024-05-2002 L2006 **GS** *100

GIBBONS, Mark Daniel. ■ 76548 #045-04-1996 L1998 **OTO** *020 †45

HAWLEY, Jason Stuart. ■ 76548 #023-12-2001 L2002 **N** *020 †75

HELLUMS, John Sherwood. ■ 76548 #048-14-2005 L2006 **EM** *012

HUBERT, Jeffrey K. ■ 76548 #048-78-1994, ▲ L1995 **FM** *020 †18

HUGHES, Matthew Edward. 1503 CHARDONNAY DR 76548 #011-03-1996 L1999 **EM** *020 †16

IVANY, Buffy Granger. ■ 76548 #048-13-2001 L2001 **FM** *100 †18

IVANY, Christopher George. ■ 76548 #048-13-2001 L2002 **CHP** *020

IZU, Jerry Kiyoshige. ■ 76548 #023-12-2000 L2007 **OBG** *020 †30

JOHNSON, Ray Monroe. 200 NOLA RUTH BLVD 76548 #039-01-1965 L1991 **PD PSM** *020 †55

KENNEDY, David Wilson. ■ 76548 #035-01-1991 L1996 **HEM** *020 †20 ‡

KLESNEY, Deanna Marie. ■ 76548 #033-06-2007 **EM** *012

LAKY, Joan Carol Trost. ■ 76548 #051-04-1987 L1988 **FM** *020 †18

LEVSKY, Marc Elliott. ■ 76548 #016-06-2000 L2006 **EM** *020 †16

MARTIN, Deandra Aaron. ■ 76548 #039-01-2007 **FP** *012

MARTINEK, Lawrence. ■ 76548 #422-01-1985 L1989 **IM** *020

MASULLO, Lawrence N. 220 TEPEE DR 76548 #048-14-2002 L2006 **EM** *020 †16

MCARTHUR, Todd Jeffrey. ■ 76548 #023-12-2005 L2006 **EM** *012

MILLER, Joel Alexander. ■ 76548 #028-03-2006 L2007 **EM** *012

NUNLEY, James Christie. ■ 76548 #035-01-1999 L2001 **GS** *020 †85

OH, John Songyong. ■ 76548 #035-09-1998 L2007 **GS** *020 †85

ORGAN, Robert Jean-Luc. 200 NOLA RUTH BLVD 76548 #011-02-1997 L2004 **PD** *020 †55

OSORO, Harrison Makori. 112 QUAPAW DR 76548 #577-01-1994 L2001 **FM** *020 †18

PAREKH, Dina Suryakant. ■ 76548 #023-12-2001 L2003 **PD** *020 †55

PASCUAL, Fernando Jordan. ■ 76548 #748-02-1955 L1965 **FM** *071 †81

PATEL, Paresh Ram. ■ 76548 #023-12-2001 L2007 **EM** *020 †16

QUINTANILLA, Jose Homero. ■ 76548 #649-04-1976 L1989 **PD** *071

RILEY, George Richard. ■ 76548 #041-02-1961 L1962 **GP** *071

RISTEDT, David Eric. ■ 76548 #023-12-1995 L1997 **EM** *020 †18

SALINAS, Ruben. ■ 76548 #023-12-1999 L2000 **FM** *020 †18

SEE, Craig Stephen. ■ 76548 #035-15-1999 L2001 **GS** *020 †85

SIGEL, Jay Barton. 3810 QUAIL HOLLOW RD 76548 #023-01-1976 L1993 **FM EM** *020 †18

SKLAR, Lisa C. ■ 76548 #041-77-2005, ▲ L2005 **IM** *012

SOTO, Mayra I. ■ 76548 #042-01-1979 L1984 **FM** *020

STREET, Luther, Jr. 200 NOLA RUTH BLVD STE B 76548 #012-01-1971 L1974 **PD NEP** *020 †55

TRICKEY, David Nathaniel. ■ 76548 #047-05-2005 L2007 **EM** *012

TUCKER, Leo D, II. ■ 76548 #048-78-1985, ▲ L1988 **IM** *020

UNWIN, Brian Keith. 2109 GRIZZLY TRL 76548 #023-12-1988 L1999 **FPG** *040 †18

WALTER, Jack Ryan. ■ 76548 #005-12-2000 L2002 **U** *020 †95

WERTIN, Thomas Michael. ■ 76548 #023-12-2000 L2001 **GS** *020 †85

YADAV, Neera. 200 NOLA RUTH BLVD 76548 #496-10-1993 L2005 **PD** *020 †55

YUNGMANN, Lisa Meredith. ■ 76548 #023-01-2002 **EM** *020

HARLINGEN – CAMERON

ABANTO, Pedro Ruben. 2102 TREASURE HILLS BLVD, DEPT OF MED 78550 #649-38-2002 **IM** *012

AGUERO-VAZQUEZ, Claudia. 2222 BENWOOD ST 78550 #048-14-1998 L1999 **FM** *020 †18

AGUILAR, Homer Olivo. 321 S 13TH ST 78550 #005-02-1975 L1976 **FM** *020 †18

ALANIZ, Pedro F. 1702 N ED CAREY DR 78550 #048-02-2002 L2007 **AN** *100

ALANIZ, Ricardo A. 1821 S SESAME SQ, STE 17 78550 #048-02-2000 L2002 **FM** *020 †18

ALEXANDER, Linda Marie. 2101 PEASE ST 78550 #048-02-1983 L1983 **END IM** *020 †20

ALI, Mir Shujaat. 2101 PEASE ST 78550 #704-25-1992 L1997 **PD** *020 †55

ALLISON, Richard F. 1301 S RANGERVILLE RD 78552 #045-01-1942 L1951 **PUD OS** *072

ALPERIN, Jeremy Ethan. 2101 PEASE ST 78550 #050-02-1966 L1978 **OTO** *062 †45

ARANEDA, Marco Adolfo. 2121 PEASE ST, STE 101 78550 #429-01-1989 L2003 **ON HO** *020 †20

ARCHE-REYES, Carlos A. 5501 S EXPRESSWAY 77, HARLINGEN HOSPITALIST GROU 78550 #042-01-1987 L1993 **IM** *020 †20

ARENAL, Angela Christine. 1702 N ED CAREY DR, HARLINGEN ANESTHESIA ASSOC 78550 #352-04-1960 L1991 **AN** *074 †05

ARGUELLES, Ramon F. 2101 PEASE ST, STE 101 78550 #308-02-1982 L1997 **RO** *020 †80

BARNARD, John L, Jr. ■ 78552 #016-06-1951 L1952 **OS ORS** *071 †40

BASSETT, Rick Wm. 1601 TREASURE HILLS BLVD 78550 #038-41-1978 L1983 **ORS** *020 †40

BATTA, Anil K. 2306 CAMELOT PLAZA CIR 78550 #495-03-1983 L1997 **PD** *020 †55

BENAVIDES, Antonio V. 5501 S EXPRESSWAY 77, STE 301 78550 #048-12-1989 L1990 **GS** *020 †85

BENAVIDES, Henry Anthony. 2121 PEASE ST STE 3D 78550 #048-13-1984 L1985 **OBG** *020 †30

BERBERIAN, Bruce Michael. 2101 PEASE ST 78550 #012-05-1990 L1997 **DR** *020 †80

BERKOWITZ, Richard Alan. 1515 N ED CAREY DR 78550 #016-42-1976 L1982 **OPH OS** *020 †35

BERNARDONI, Alberto. 1706 TREASURE HILLS BLVD, SU CLINICA FAMILIAR 78550 #935-03-1968 L1995 **PD** *020 †55

BETANCOURT, Alejandro J. 2121 PEASE ST, STE 304 78550 #042-02-1992 L2001 **NS** *020 †25

BHATLA, Anshu. 2101 PEASE ST 78550 #496-07-1989 L1996 **IM** *020 †20

BHATLA, Brajesh. 4402 E SESAME DR 78550 #495-36-1985 L1996 **NEP IM** *020 †20

BLAKE, Hugo Guillermo. 2310 N ED CAREY DR, STE 1-A 78550 #649-01-1973 L1976 **CD IM** *020 †20

BOTHWELL, Timothy C. 721 W HARRISON AVE 78550 #048-14-1986 L1987 **FM** *020 †18

BRAZA, Mariejane Malinao. 2102 TREASURE HILLS BLVD, DEPT OF MED 78550 #748-11-2000 **IM** *012

BRIN, Edward Neal. 1702 N ED CAREY DR 78550 #008-01-1974 L1977 **AN OS** *020 †05

BUTTERS, Harry Emerson. 2101 PEASE ST 78550 #048-02-1975 L1975 **R** *020 †80

CALERO, Juan P. 510 VICTORIA LN, STE 1 78550 #264-05-1987 L2004 **CCM** *100 †20

CALO, Luis. 2200 HAINE DR, PA 78550 #042-03-1981 L1984 **FM** *075 †18 ‡

CAMACHO, Maria Teresa. 2101 PEASE ST 78550 #176-01-1988 L2002 **PD** *020 †55

CAMPBELL, James Chas. 2200 HAINE DR, PA 78550 #040-02-1977 L1979 **D** *020 †15

CANTU, Uvaldo, Jr. 2230 HAINE DR 78550 #048-12-1983 L1987 **OBG** *020 †30

CARTER, James G. ■ 78552 #018-03-1952 L1953 **AN** *071 †05

CARTER, Samuel C. ■ 78550 #047-06-1943 L1958 **IM TS** *071

CASTILLO, James W. 2121 PEASE ST, STE 1G 78550 #011-02-2002 L2005 **IM PLM** *020 †20

CASTRO, Hector Jose. 733 NANTUCKET DR 78550 #042-44-1991 L2003 **IM END** *020 †20

CAVUSOGLU, Ihsan M. 1301 S RANGERVILLE RD 78552 #902-10-1956 L1967 **PUD OS** *020

CHEN, Hao. 2101 PEASE ST 78550 #243-61-1991 **FP** *012

CHOWDARY, Vijaya Seshu K. 2101 PEASE ST 78550 #495-19-1974 L1983 **IM** *020 †20

CINTRON, Miguel. 1717 N ED CAREY DR 78550 #042-01-1974 L1992 **OBG** *020 †30

CLARK, Bliss Watson. 5501 S EXPRESSWAY 77 78550 #012-01-1981 L1990 **ORS** *020 †40

CLARK, Thomas Alan. 709 CORONADO VLG BOX 138 78550 #011-02-1967 L1978 **TS GS** *020 †85,90

COBOS, Jose A. 1601 TREASURE HILLS BLVD 78550 #649-31-1983 L1996 **ORS** *020 †40

COHEN, Jose. 1717 N ED CAREY DR 78550 #132-02-1974 L1982 **OBG** *020 †30

COHN, Aaron I. 2929 CYPRESS DR, UNIV/COLORADO HEALTH SCI C 78550 #048-02-1987 L1993 **AN** *071 †05

COLLIER, Robert Oran. 1901 BELL ST STE B 78550 #048-02-1971 L1971 **P** *020 †75

CONCHA, Lourdes B. 2200 HAINE DR, PA 78550 #748-01-1994 L2004 **END** *020 †20

CORNWELL, Margie Wagner. 2026 E TYLER AVE 78550 #048-13-1981 L1982 **PTH** *020 †50

COSTA LUNA, Cesar Anibal. 1206 S F ST 78550 #042-01-1970 L1990 **PD** *020 †55

DAHM, Lawrence John. 2101 PEASE ST, P O BOX 2918 78550 #048-12-1976 L1976 **PTH** *020 †50

DANIELSON, Maia Serena. 1710 N ED CAREY DR 78550 #051-07-1997 L2001 **FM** *020 †30

DAVENPORT, Dewitt Shelton. 2026 E TYLER AVE 78550 #048-13-1981 L1981 **PTH** *020 †50

DEAL, Eugene Chandler. ■ 78550 #051-01-1973 L2003 **PUD A** *020 †20

DEBENEDETTO, Richard B. PO BOX 530269 78553 #048-15-1994 L1996 **IM** *020 †20

DELATORRE, Luis. 1706 TREASURE HILLS BLVD, SU CLINICA FAMILIAR 78550 #048-02-2004 L2007 **PD** *020 †55

DE OLIVEIRA, Luciana Fons. ■ 78550 #187-03-2000 **IM** *012

DE SOUZA, Gerard A. 1702 N ED CAREY DR 78550 #496-15-1976 L2001 **AN** *020 †05

DHURJON, Leland Menon. 1205 N ED CAREY DR 78550 #566-01-1981 L1999 *020

DIGGINS, William Lawrence. ■ 78550 #067-01-1958 L1981 **FM** *071

DILL, Maria G. 1301 S RANGERVILLE RD, RGSC/STHCS 78552 #048-13-1986 L1990 **FM UM** *030 †18 ‡

DIMARIA, Chaylah Joy. ■ 78550 #008-02-2007 **FP** *012

DIX-EMPERADOR, Lisa Maria. 597 W SESAME DR, STE C 78550 #041-13-1989 L2002 **CD** *020 †20

DOMINGUEZ, Roland Jos. 321 S 21ST ST, HARLINGEN PEDIATRICS 78550 #048-04-1987 L1988 **PD** *020 †55

DONES VAZQUEZ, Jose G. 2121 PEASE ST STE 304 78550 #042-03-1995 L2002 **NS** *020 †25

DOUGHERTY, Joseph Chas. 1901 BELL ST, STE A 78550 #035-20-1960 L1971 **NEP IM** *020 †20

DUDLEY, Samuel W. ■ 78552 #048-16-1999 L2002 **PD** *020 †55

DYER, Stephanie Jo. 5501 S EXPRESSWAY 77 78550 #031-01-1991 L1997 **AN** *020 †05

DYKSTRA, Mandie Lee. 2222 BENWOOD ST 78550 #048-14-2003 L2005 **FM** *020 †18

EDWARDS, Walter T. ■ 78552 #048-04-1950 L1950 **EM** *071 †16,15

EGUIA, Luis E. 2200 HAINE DR, PA 78550 #176-01-1987 L2002 **ICE CD** *020 †20

ERNST, Joseph Jacob. 2200 HAINE DR 78550 #048-13-1979 L1979 **U** *020 †95

EVANS, Jason. ■ 78552 #041-13-2003 L2008 **P** *100

EVANS, Michael David. 2310 N ED CAREY DR, STE 1-A 78550 #035-09-1981 L1987 **CD IM** *050 †20

FARLEY, Norma Jean. ■ 78552 #048-13-1994 L1996 **FOP** *020 †50

FENNEGAN, Francis Michael. 5505 S EXPRESSWAY 77 # 300, PROFFESIONAL BLDG 78550 #036-01-1961 L1968 **NS** *071 †25

FERRIS, John Ackel, Jr. 2200 HAINE DR, VALLEY DIAGNOSTIC CLINIC 78550 #021-01-1953 L1955 **IM** *071 †18

FISCH, Stanley Irving. 321 S 21ST ST, HARLINGEN PEDIATRICS 78550 #035-46-1970 L1973 **PD CHP** *020 †55

FISHER, Charles Franklin. 2101 PEASE ST 78550 #048-13-1981 L1981 **DR GP** *020 †80

FISHER, William Augustus. 1720 N ED CAREY DR 78550 #041-13-1948 L1973 **PD PDA** *072 †55

FLORES, Eduardo D. 2310 N ED CAREY DR, STE 1-A 78550 #024-01-1985 L1986 **CD IM** *020 †20

FLORES, Jorge Humberto. 4402 E SESAME DR 78550 #048-14-1996 L1999 **NEP** *020 †20

FOLSOM, Charles Tandy. 632 N ED CAREY DR STE 400 78550 #039-01-1965 L1966 **FM** *020 †50

FORMAN, David Michael. 2121 PEASE ST, STE305 78550 #011-02-1990 L1994 **AN PMM** *020 †05

FOX, Charles D, Jr. ■ 78550 #048-12-1968 L1968 **GS** *020 †85

FUENTES, Daniel A. 2101 PEASE ST 78550 #023-07-1994 L2001 **VIR** *020 †80

FULLER, Terry W. 2121 PEASE ST STE 2C 78550 #048-04-1985 L1996 **N** *020 †75

GARCIA, Alfredo. 1722 S CAROLINA ST 78550 #042-01-1977 L1984 **END IM** *020 †20

GARCIA, Cesar H. 2102 TREASURE HILLS BLVD, DEPT OF MED 78550 #048-13-2006 **IM** *012

GARCIA, Cynthia Anna. 5505 S EXPRESSWAY 77, STE 200 78550 #048-04-1988 L1990 **PM IM** *030 †20,60

GARCIA, Gustavo. 2101 PEASE ST, STE 1G 78550 #649-45-1991 L2004 **IM** *020 †20

GARCIA, Jose Luis. ■ 78552 #649-02-1983 L2004 *100

GARCIA, Juan Marcos. 512 VICTORIA LN STE 7 78550 #048-14-1994 L1996 **FM** *020 †18

GARCIA, Stephanie Herrera. 5505 S EXPRESSWAY 77, STE 203 78550 #048-14-1992 L1993 **FM** *020 †18
GARCIA-VAZQUEZ, Fernando. 418 E TYLER AVE STE B 78550 #042-02-1996 L2000 **MPD** *020 †20
GARZA, Juan Joel. 2310 N ED CAREY DR, STE 1-A 78550 #048-02-1997 L1999 **IC CD** *020 †20
GARZA, Maribelle. 321 S 21ST ST, HARLINGEN PEDIATRICS 78550 #048-13-1990 L1992 **PD** *020 †55
GHAFOORI, Giovanna. 1649 SAM HOUSTON ST 78550 #005-02-1991 L1998 **PS** *020 †85,65
GIL, Victor Hugo. 1717 TREASURE HILLS BLVD 78550 #041-13-1999 L2006 **DR** *020
GOGIA, Poonam. 1706 TREASURE HILLS BLVD 78550 #496-07-1989 L1995 **IM** *020 †20
GONZALEZ, Luis Alfredo. 802 S LOOP 499 STE 4 78550 #341-03-1990 L2000 **FM** *020 †18
GONZALEZ, Tomas A. 2101 PEASE ST 78550 #048-14-1991 L1994 **P** *020 †75
GOULDY, John Price. ■ 78550 #039-01-2001 L2002 **P** *020
GRANNUM, Carol Verita. 1706 TREASURE HILLS BLVD 78550 #035-01-1993 L1998 **PD** *020 †55
GRANNUM, Errol Olwyn. 1645 TREASURE HILLS BLVD 78550 #008-01-1993 L1998 **OPH** *020
GRAYSON, Guy Howard. 1911 LUBBOCK ST, STE C 78550 #005-06-1985 L1991 **PHO** *020 †55
GREEN, Wayne Donovan. 2121 PEASE ST, STE 602 78550 #033-05-1994 L2005 **GE** *020 †20
GUERRA, Hector, Jr. 2101 PEASE ST 78550 #048-12-1997 L1998 **EM** *020 †16
HALE, Jennifer Marie. ■ 78550 #010-02-2004 L2006 **FM** *100 †18
HALE, Matthew Heath. 2102 TREASURE HILLS BLVD 78550 #001-02-2002 L2004 **FM** *020 †18
HALL, Christopher Michael. ■ 78550 #030-05-2002 L2004 **FM** *020 †18
HALL, Haywood. 1327 E WASHINGTON AVE, # 314 78550 #048-04-1986 L1994 **EM** *020 †16
HALLOUM, Ammar Mohamed-Al. 510 VICTORIA LN, STE 1 78550 #875-01-1997 L2006 **PCC** *020 †20 ‡
HANLEY, James Francis. 1706 TREASURE HILLS BLVD 78550 #008-02-1975 L1981 **IM IMG** *040 †20
HANSEN, Christopher Hans. 2101 PEASE ST 78550 #048-12-1971 L1971 **GS** *020 †85
HARGREAVES, Sara E. ■ 78550 #048-13-2008 *012
HARRIS, Max Young. ■ 78550 #048-02-1960 L1960 **IM** *071
HATCHER, Robert Lee. ■ 78552 #048-04-1966 L1967 **END IM** *071 †20
HAYDEN, Mark Marvin. ■ 78550 #054-04-1974 L1995 **EM FM** *020 †18,16
HERNANDEZ, Roberto Jesus. 2101 PEASE ST 78550 #649-30-2001 L2005 **IM** *020 †20
HERRING, Beverly A. ■ 78550 #048-14-1987 L1988 **IM** *020
HILMY, Ashraf A. 2121 PEASE ST STE 604 78550 #915-04-1981 L1985 **GS VS** *020 †05,85
HILMY, Mahmoud Shereef. 2310 N ED CAREY DR 1A, HEART CLINIC 78550 #495-36-1977 L1984 **CD IM** *020 †20
HOLDER, Robert Fred. 2106 HALE AVE 78550 #048-02-1995 L2000 **FM** *020 †18
HOWE, John Bruce. 2113 HAINE DR 78550 #026-04-1982 L1988 **OPH** *020 †35
HUGHSTON, Mitchell Brock. 1713 TREASURE HILLS BLVD, STE 1D 78550 #048-15-1985 L1987 **OBG** *020 †30
HUNTER, Susan Delores. 2306 CAMELOT PLAZA CIR 78550 #016-06-1993 L1996 **OBG** *020 †30
HYDE, David C. ■ 78552 #048-04-1990 L1992 **OPH** *020 †35
IJAZ, Beena. 1706 TREASURE HILLS BLVD 78550 #704-09-2000 L2007 **IM** *020
INFANTE, Noemi. 2306 CAMELOT PLAZA CIR 78550 #048-02-2001 L2005 **OBG** *020
JACKSON, Robert Carl. 2101 PEASE ST 78550 #056-05-1945 L1957 **GS GP** *020 †85,90
JAMES, Oral Cobley. 1806 RUNNELS ST 78550 #566-01-1987 L2002 **GE IM** *020 †20
KEILLOR, Herman Jos. 1801 N ED CAREY DR 78550 #048-12-1969 L1969 **ORS GP** *020 †40
KLEIN, Garner Franklin. 2101 PEASE ST, VALLEY HEALTHCARE NETWORK 78550 #048-02-1958 L1958 **CD IM** *071 †20
KLUG, Thomas Jos. ■ 78550 #038-41-1954 L1961 **GS** *071 †85
KOTTA, Shridhar. 2200 HAINE DR, PA 78550 #495-52-1991 L1996 **IM** *020 †20
KRISHNARAJAH, Amirthan. 1301 S RANGERVILLE RD, SOTH TEXAS HEALTH CARE SYS 78552 #220-04-1985 L1999 **IM** *020 †20
KUYE, Mogbolahan Olugbemi. ■ 78550 #690-02-2000 L2006 **IM** *020 †20 ‡
LAWLER, Marion R, Jr. 2121 PEASE ST, STE 207 78550 #048-04-1963 L1963 **TS GS** *020 †85,90
LAYIWOLA, Femi Rasheed. 5501 S EXPRESSWAY 77, HARLINGEN MEDICAL CENTER 78550 #690-05-1992 L2006 **IM** *020 †20
LEE, Donald Geo. 1702 N ED CAREY DR, HARLINGEN ANES ASSOC 78550 #017-20-1966 L1971 **AN** *020 †05
LEIBERT, Bruce Alan. 2222 BENWOOD ST 78550 #025-07-1984 L1996 **FM** *020 †18
LESTER, Louis Fredrick, II. 1702 N ED CAREY DR, HARLINGEN ANESTHESIA ASSOC 78550 #048-15-1985 L1986 **AN** *020 †05
LIGHTNER, Teresa Kreps. 3225 W COBBLESTONE CRK DR 78550 #017-20-1985 L1992 **IM** *020 †20
LOPEZ, Cynthia. 1706 TREASURE HILLS BLVD, SU CLINICA FAMILIAR 78550 #048-13-1997 L1998 **PD** *020 †55
LOPEZ, Leticia Livia. 1706 TREASURE HILLS BLVD 78550 #048-04-1992 L1995 **PD** *020 †55
LOPEZ, Ruben Montelongo. 2121 PEASE ST, STE 207 78550 #025-01-1991 L1995 **TS** *020 †85
LOVGREN, Robert Ellsworth. ■ 78552 #030-05-1939 L1939 **OTO** *071 †45
LOYA, Francisco. 5501 S EXPRESSWAY 77 78550 #048-12-1998 L2001 **IM** *020 †20
LOZANO, Diana. 5505 S EXPRESSWAY 77, STE 203 78550 #017-20-1993 L1996 **IM** *020 †20
LOZANO, Jorge Federico. 2101 PEASE ST, ATTN: MEDICAL STAFF SERVIC 78550 #048-13-2002 L2005 **IM** *100 †20
LUGO, Ivelisse. 1022 S F ST, # B 78550 #042-01-1977 L1994 **FM** *020 †18
MAGOON, Sheila Marie. 2202 S 77 SUNSHINE STRIP, STE H 78550 #041-09-1985 L1995 **FM** *030 †18
MAKAI, Balazs. 5501 S EXPRESSWAY 77, HARLINGEN MEDICAL CENTER 78550 #473-03-1996 L2005 **AN** *020 ‡
MALDONADO, Carlos Emilio. 2200 HAINE DR, PA 78550 #016-76-1987, ▲ L1994 **DR** *020
MALDONADO, Juan Antonio. 2106 HALE AVE 78550 #048-12-1996 L1997 **FM** *020 †18
MARIN, Elena Longoria. 1706 TREASURE HILLS BLVD 78550 #024-05-1983 L1986 **PD** *030 †55
MARTINEZ, Daniel. 597 W SESAME DR 78550 #018-03-1993 L2004 **TS** *020 †85,90
MARTINEZ, Dora Alicia. ■ 78550 #048-13-2007 **FP** *012
MARTINEZ, Ruben Davila. 2306 CAMELOT PLAZA CIR 78550 #048-04-1977 L1978 **OBG** *020 †30
MASON, Edward Louis. 3118 PINEHURST DR 78550 #016-11-1974 L1991 **FM** *020 †18
MAUNEY, Dorila Edelmira. 321 S 21ST ST, HARLINGEN PEDIATRICS 78550 #726-01-1981 L1991 **PD** *020 †55
MC CORMICK, Erin Kathleen. 2121 PEASE ST, STE 403 78550 #010-01-1990 L1997 **U** *020 †95
MC CRACKEN, Ann Goodwin. 2121 PEASE ST, STE 204 78550 #021-01-1983 L2000 **GS CRS** *020 †85
MC KENNA, William Robt. 1713 TREASURE HLS BLVD #1B 78550 #048-15-1977 L1977 **AI IM** *020 †20,03
MC KISSICK, Jeffrey R. 2222 BENWOOD ST 78550 #048-15-2001 L2003 **FM** *020 †18
MC MILLIN, Reagan Ben. 1205 N ED CAREY DR, BOX 531848 78550 #048-13-1982 L1990 **OPH** *020 †35
MC ROBERTS, Marcus L, III. 1622 N ED CAREY DR 78550 #048-02-1984 L1985 **P** *020
MEADOWS, Donald Chapman. 1515 N ED CAREY DR 78550 #001-02-1969 L1983 **OPH** *020 †35
MENDEZ, Jarod. 1710 N ED CAREY DR, A HLTH SPECIALIST FOR HER 78550 #042-03-1993 L2001 **OBG** *020 †30
MERCADO, Ivette Yolanda. ■ 78550 #042-03-1992 L1995 **HEM ON** *030 †20
MILD, Charles Franklin. 2200 HAINE DR, PA 78550 #649-19-1980 L1989 **CD IM** *020 †20
MINOR, Robert C. 1713 TREASURE HILLS BLVD, STE 2D 78550 #048-02-1987 L1989 **IM** *020 †20
MINTO, Lester John. 613 W SESAME DR 78550 #649-14-1976 L1982 **FM** *020 †18
MIRANDA, Larry M. 608 N ED CAREY DR, CHILDRENS CLNC OF HARLIGEN 78550 #748-10-1973 L1991 **PD** *020 †55 ‡
MITCHELL, Francis. 512 VICTORIA LN, STE 7 78550 #051-04-1978 L1978 **FM** *020 †18
MOORE, Jacob J. ■ 78550 #048-12-2002 L2006 **OPH** *100
MORENO, Carlos Ignacio. ■ 78552 #264-13-1982 L2000 **IM** *020 †20
MORON, David. 1401 S RANGERVILLE RD 78552 #048-13-1984 L1988 **P** *020 †75
MOSLENER, Matthew David. 2222 BENWOOD ST 78550 #041-02-2006 **FP** *012
MOVVA, Prasad V. 922 E TYLER AVE 78550 #495-11-1992 L1998 **FM GP** *020 †18
MOYER-DIENER, David D. 2101 PEASE ST, VALLEY EMERGENCY PHYSICIAN 78550 #048-04-2000 L2004 **EM** *020 †16
MUNIZ, Leofredo Garcia. 2014 PEASE ST 78550 #048-02-1958 L1958 **FM GP** *020
NATHAN, Julia Irene. 1017 EBONY DR 78550 #005-19-1984 L1993 **EM IM** *020 †20
NEASMAN, Farley Berry. 2200 HAINE DR, PA 78550 #011-02-1977 L2000 **CD** *020 †20
NESMITH, Dorothy Shelton. ■ 78550 #010-01-1998 L2002 **PM** *020 †60
NGUYEN, Lauren Patrick. 2101 PEASE ST 78550 #005-06-1995 L2002 **DR** *020 †80
NGUYEN, Tan Duong. 1901 N ED CAREY DR STE 200 78550 #016-11-1994 L2000 **OTO** *020 †45
NICOLOSI, Joseph Vincent. 1702 N ED CAREY DR, HARLINGEN ANESTH ASSOC 78550 #051-07-1988 L1997 **AN PAN** *020 †05
NUNEZ, Rafael A. 1327 E WASHINGTON AVE, # 106 78550 #308-03-1999 L2004 **IM** *020
NUNNERY, Eugene, Jr. 1713 TREASURE HILLS BLVD, STE 2D 78550 #028-02-1977 L1981 **RHU IM** *020 †20
ODOM, Mary Kathleen. ■ 78550 #048-12-1971 L1971 **GP** *071
O'DONNELL, Brian M. 597 W SESAME DR, STE B 78550 #048-13-1999 L2001 **FM** *020 †18
OHABOR, Constantine Iwedi. ■ 78550 #690-01-1989 L2006 **IM** *020 †20
ONETO, Miguel Alejandro. 2101 PEASE ST 78550 #132-07-1992 L2002 **VIR** *020 †80
OORJITHAM, Edward G. 1205 N ED CAREY DR, STE 2C 78550 #039-01-1992 L1994 **FM OTO** *020 †18
PACKARD, John P. ■ 78550 #018-03-1943 L1946 **U** *071
PADILLA, Juan Moises. 2121 PEASE ST, STE 304 78550 #042-01-1991 L2008 **NS** *020 †25
PADULA-SUAREZ, Luis E. 2310 N ED CAREY DR, STE 1-A 78550 #935-01-1989 L1997 **CD** *020 †20
PAGAN-ARCHE, Roxana. 2200 HAINE DR, PA 78550 #042-03-1988 L1994 **FM** *020 †18
PALLAPATI, Joel J J. 1706 TREASURE HILLS BLVD, SU CLINICA FAMILIAR 78550 #495-62-1984 L1997 **IM** *020 †20
PALLAPATI, Leela. 1706 TREASURE HILLS BLVD 78550 #495-21-1992 L2004 **FM** *020 †18
PALLARES, Jerry X. 2101 PEASE ST 78550 #048-04-1993 L1994 **VIR** *020 †80
PALLARES, Victor Alberto. 1702 N ED CAREY DR 78550 #011-02-1989 L1993 **AN** *020 †05 ‡
PANGILINAN, Evangelino G. 1242 N 77 SUNSHINE STRIP 78550 #748-08-1966 L1979 **P** *020
PAPILLA, Francisco Reyes. 321 S 21ST ST, HARLINGEN PEDIATRICS 78550 #748-20-1999 L2004 **PD** *020 †55
PARADA, Victoria Anaite. 2200 HAINE DR, PA 78550 #429-02-1998 L2003 **N** *020 ‡
PARTIN, John A. 1706 N ED CAREY DR 78550 #048-13-1999 L2001 **FM** *020 †18
PATTERSON, Seth Fleming. 2222 BENWOOD ST 78550 #045-04-2002 L2005 **FM** *040 †18
PEAN, Joseph Leslie. 1713 TREASURE HILLS BLVD, STE 2A 78550 #649-20-1980 L1989 **CCM** *020 †20
PEREZ, Nolan E. 512 VICTORIA LN, STE 2 78550 #048-13-1998 L2002 **GE** *020 ‡
PERRY, Cynthia A. 1706 TREASURE HILLS BLVD 78550 #048-15-1996 L1999 **IM** *020 †20
PETERS, Jason Edward. ■ 78550 #001-06-2004 L2006 **FM** *020 †18
PHILLIPS, Jason R. 1801 N ED CAREY DR, STE E 78550 #048-02-1998 L2004 **GE** *020 †20
PIMENTEL, Carlos X. 2310 N ED CAREY DR, STE 1-A 78550 #319-04-1986 L1995 **IM CD** *020 †20
PIRTLE, Thomas Emmett, III. 2101 PEASE ST 78550 #048-02-1978 L1978 **RO DR** *020 †80
PON, Marcelino. 1301 S RANGERVILLE RD 78552 #737-01-1967 L1996 **FM EM** *020 †18
POSADA, Juan Diego. 2310 N ED CAREY DR, STE 1-A 78550 #264-16-1986 L1997 **CD** *020 †20
POSADA, Rolando. 512 VICTORIA LN STE 7 78550 #048-13-1996 L1999 **FM** *020 †18
POULOS, Savvas Kostas. 2121 PEASE ST, STE 207 78550 #041-09-1985 L1995 **HS ORS** *020 †40
QUINTANA-GUERRERO, Ofsman. 2310 N ED CAREY DR, STE 1-A 78550 #682-01-1982 L1995 **CD IM** *020 †20
QUINTANILLA, Eleazar. 2102 TREASURE HILLS BLVD, RAHC INTERNAL MED RES 78550 #649-45-1988 **IM** *012
RAJHUNS DSILVA, Roma Ruha. 2101 PEASE ST 78550 #495-08-1993 **FP** *012
RAMA, Adolfo Rosales. 2200 HAINE DR, PA 78550 #748-11-1970 L1982 **GS CD** *020 †85
RAMIREZ, Guadalupe D. 512 VICTORIA LN, STE 7 78550 #048-13-1995 L1998 **IM** *020 †20
RAMOS, Arnulfo. HARLINGEN STATE TB HOSP 78552 #649-01-1953 L1961 **GP OS** *075
REDDY, Chandrasekhar T. 1706 TREASURE HILLS BLVD 78550 #495-57-1979 L1995 **IM** *020 †20
REDDY, Surapureddy S. 1821 S SESAME SQ, STE 8 78550 #495-21-1979 L2000 **PD** *020 †55
REDMOND, Susan Lee. 1713 TREASURE HILLS BLVD, STE 1D 78550 #016-45-1983 L1987 **OBG** *020 †30
REYNOSO, Luis Alberto. 2200 HAINE DR, PA 78550 #737-01-1986 L1996 **IM** *020 †20
RICKERHAUSER, Nancy M. 2222 BENWOOD ST 78550 #041-13-1992 L1997 **FM OBS** *020 †18 ‡
RINGHEANU, Mihaela. 2101 PEASE ST 78550 #781-01-1995 L2003 **PG** *020 †55
RIZVI, Syed Hassan Mehdi. 2101 PEASE ST, VBMC 78550 #704-02-1992 L1999 **PD** *020 †55
ROA, Donald Caroro. 2306 CAMELOT PLAZA CIR, STE C 78550 #748-01-1994 L2003 **CD** *020 †20
RODRIGUEZ, Reynaldo. 1702 N ED CAREY DR 78550 #048-04-1977 L1977 **AN** *020 †05
ROQUE, Jorge A. 3214 BANYON CIR 78550 #649-04-1988 L1997 **FM** *020 †18
RUIZ, Peter A. ■ 78550 #048-13-2006 **FP** *012
SAAVEDRA, Dinah Canonigo. 1706 TREASURE HILLS BLVD 78550 #748-11-1995 L2003 **PD** *020 †55
SACA, Rodolfo Antonio. 2121 PEASE ST STE 601 78550 #649-14-1979 L1985 **NPM PD** *020 †55

■ = Address Information Privacy Protected

SALVATORE, Kathleen A. 2407 HAINE DR 78550 #048-14-1992 L1993 **P** *020 †75
SANCHEZ, Gerardo De Jesus. 2101 PEASE ST 78550 #649-02-1981 L1986 **NPM PD** *020 †55
SANCHEZ, Maribel. ■ 78550 #048-14-2006 **FP** *012
SANDOVAL, Jose Toribio. 2101 PEASE ST 78550 #005-11-1977 L1980 **FM** *020 †18
SANTOS, Antonio Lopez. ■ 78550 #748-01-1956 L1976 **GS** *071 †85
SANUSI, Oladayo A L. 1901 BELL ST STE F 78550 #690-02-1994 L2005 **IM NEP** *020 †20 ‡
SCHWARTZ, Stephen Lloyd. 1919 N ED CAREY DR 78550 #017-20-1971 L1974 **D** *020 †15
SCOTT, Mary Lynn. 721 W HARRISON AVE 78550 #047-06-1990 L2003 **FM** *020 †18
SEUDEAL, Indal M. 1300 E HARRISON AVE 78550 #165-03-1985 L1995 **PUD** *020 †20
SHENKENBERG, Todd David. 2121 PEASE ST, STE 201 78550 #048-04-1980 L1981 **HEM ON** *020 †20
SHEPPERD, Catherine. 1702 N ED CAREY DR 78550 #048-02-1970 L1970 **AN** *020 †05
SHERIFF, Mohammad Usman. 2121 PEASE ST, STE 407 78550 #495-33-1990 L2002 **CD IM** *020 †20
SIMPSON, Michael Earl. 1702 N ED CAREY DR 78550 #010-03-1988 L2000 **AN** *020 †05
SIX, Eric Geo. 5505 S EXPRESSWAY 77, STE 306 78550 #775-01-1972 L1984 **NS** *020 †25
SKYE, George E, II. 1620 N ED CAREY DR 78550 #039-01-1976 L1980 **R NR** *071 †80
SMITH, Brian Randal. 601 W SESAME DR, TEXAS DEPARTMENT HEALTH 78550 #048-12-1976 L1990 **PHP** *030 †70
SMITH, Ray Fortner. 707 W SESAME DR 78550 #048-13-1978 L1978 **FM** *020 †18
SOMERVILLE, Robt Russell. 712 N 77 SUNSHINE STRIP, STE 27 78550 #016-06-1959 L1967 **OTO A** *020 †45
SORENSON, Julie Diana. 2301 MARIPOSA LN 78550 #041-02-1982 L1986 **IM** *020 †20
SOSA, Estela. 1616 S CAROLINA ST, STE A 78550 #048-02-1987 L1989 **OBG** *020 †30
SOUFFRANT-CHERIVAL, G M. 1706 TREASURE HILLS BLVD 78550 #649-14-1978 L2005 **IM** *020 †20
SPECK, George Wm. 2121 PEASE ST, STE 203 78550 #048-02-1972 L1972 **GYN** *020 †30
SPECK, Lena Teresa. 2121 PEASE ST STE 203 78550 #048-14-2000 L2004 **OBG** *020
SREENIVAS, Rashmi. 2610 EMERALD LAKE DR 78550 #048-04-2008 *012
SUBHANI, Muhammad. 2121 PEASE ST STE 2F, HARLINGEN NEONATOLOGY ASSO 78550 #704-02-1990 L1999 **PD** *020 †55
SUGUNAN, Kunnath P. ■ 78550 #495-44-1969 L1979 **FM** *020 †18
SUGUNAN, Unnyampath. 1706 TREASURE HILLS BLVD 78550 #495-44-1965 L1984 **PD** *020 †20
SUITER, Sally Ann. ■ 78552 #048-02-1996 L1998 **PD** *020
TAW, William Whellyan. 2101 PEASE ST 78550 #048-13-1991 L1997 **R** *020 †80
TAYLOR, Eric, Jr. 2310 N ED CAREY DR, STE 1-A 78550 #023-07-1992 L1999 **CD** *020 †20
TEETER, Carmelita Ana. 1601 TREASURE HILLS BLVD 78550 #048-04-1996 L2002 **ORS OSM** *020 †40
TELLO, Miguel Angel. 2222 BENWOOD ST 78550 #048-02-2004 L2006 **FM** *020 †18
THOMAS, John W. ■ 78550 #048-12-2005 L2008 **FP** *012
TOLAND, George Jefferson, Jr. 2226 HAINE DR 78550 #048-02-1960 L1960 **PD** *020 †55
TORKILDSEN, Wm Halvard. 5505 S EXPRESSWAY 77, STE 205 78550 #048-13-1974 L1974 **IM CCM** *020 †20
TORRES, Frank. 721 W HARRISON AVE, SAN BENITO MED ASSOCS 78550 #048-12-1997 L2001 **FM** *020 †18
TRAPP, Enrique. 1401 S RANGERVILLE RD 78552 #649-01-1952 L1959 **IM DIA** *020
TRUJILLO, Nicolas E. 608 N ED CAREY DR 78550 #264-13-1983 L2001 **PD** *071
VALDEZ, Adela S. 2102 TREASURE HILLS BLVD, THE UNIV OF TX HLTH SCI CT 78550 #048-04-1980 L1981 **FM** *040 †18
VALLADARES, Jose L. 2121 PEASE ST, STE 101 78550 #737-01-1980 L2002 **HO** *020 †20
VARGAS, Donald. 1901 PEASE ST 78550 #682-01-1968 L1979 **ORS** *040 †20
VASQUEZ, Alberto E. 1706 TREASURE HILLS BLVD 78550 #737-06-1986 L1998 **PD** *020 †55
VELA, Leonel. 2102 TREASURE HILLS BLVD, UTHSC AT SAN ANTONIO 78550 #048-04-1983 L1991 **PHP** *020 †70
VELAZQUEZ, Victor A. 2226 HAINE DR 78550 #308-04-1988 L1992 **GP** *020
VIETO, Roberto J. 1401 S RANGERVILLE RD, SOUTH TX HEALTHCARE CLINIC 78552 #649-14-1974 L1982 **END IM** *020 †20
VILLORANTE, Editha Emily. 2101 PEASE ST 78550 #748-08-1984 L2008 **FP** *012
VINAI, Modini. 2101 PEASE ST, PICU 78550 #495-33-1995 L2006 **CCP** *020 †55
VU, Loan T. 1702 N ED CAREY DR 78550 #048-14-2002 L2006 **AN** *020 †05
WALKER, Christopher L. ■ 78550 #048-13-2005 L2007 **FP** *012
WALTHER, Jay Ronald. 628 N ED CAREY DR 78550 #048-12-1970 L1982 **IMG IM** *020 †20,15
WANG, Benny Yaohsien. 1702 N ED CAREY DR, HARLINGEN ANES ASSOC 78550 #056-06-2002 L2007 **AN** *020
WEATHERS, Jerry Don. ■ 78552 #039-01-1977 L1982 **CHP EM** *020
WELLINGTON, Earl Crosby. 1629 TREASURE HILLS BLVD, STE B5 78550 #035-15-1968 L1976 **IM PUD** *020
WERTH, James Laree. 5118 PALM VALLEY DR S 78552 #018-03-1965 L1992 **OTO A** *071 †45 ‡
WHITE, Darryl G. 2222 BENWOOD ST 78550 #048-12-1990 L1992 **FM** *020 †18
WILES, Jack. ■ 78550 #048-12-1950 L1950 **U** *020
WILLIAMS, Aldon Brydon. 2121 PEASE ST, STE 305 78550 #011-02-1990 L1995 **APM** *020 †05
WING, Richard James. 601 W SESAME DR, TDH-PH REGION 11 78550 #056-06-1988 L1991 **IM** *020 †20
YAMAGUCHI, Jonathan H. 1401 S RANGERVILLE RD, BLDG 503 78552 #035-09-1982 L1983 **GP** *020
YARDLEY, David E. 1821 S SESAME SQ, STE 5 78550 #016-43-1980 L1999 **CD IC** *020 †20
ZHU, Shanjian. ■ 78550 #243-16-1999 L2002 **IMG** *100 †20

HARPER — GILLESPIE

TAYLOR, Lynne J P. ■ 78631 #021-01-1950 L1950 **PUD DR** *071

HASKELL — HASKELL

CADENHEAD, Charles Wayne. 1417 N 1ST ST, HASKELL CLINIC 79521 #048-13-1975 L1975 **FM** *020
CADENHEAD, James F, Jr. 1417 N 1ST ST, HASKELL CLINIC 79521 #047-05-1945 L1947 **FM GS** *071

HAWKINS — WOOD

GUSTAFSON, Don Harral. ■ 75765 #048-12-1963 L1963 **EM GS** *020 †85,16

HOFFMAN, William W. ■ 75765 #016-06-1951 L1958 **U** *071 †95

HEARNE — ROBERTSON

CHMIELEWSKI, Zbigniew A. 709 BARTON ST 77859 #759-11-1981 L1996 **IM** *020 †20
HUDDLESTON, Ronald Wayne. 709 BARTON ST 77859 #048-12-1962 L1962 **GP** *071 †18
KENNAMER, Kenan Kay. 709 BARTON ST 77859 #048-12-1961 L1961 **GP EM** *020 †18
MINSON, Matthew Alan. 807 POST OAK ST 77859 #048-02-1990 L1991 **AN** *020
THADAREDDY, Venkat. 709 BARTON ST, ST JOSEPH-HEARNE FAMILY ME 77859 #495-65-1975 L1995 **IM** *020

HEATH — ROCKWALL

DILLARD, Andrew Gene. 1717 WEISKOPF DR 75032 #048-12-1960 L1960 **GYN** *071 †30
FINCHER, Timothy Roland. 6435 S FM 549, ROCKWALL EYE ASSOCIATES 75032 #004-01-1999 L2006 **OPH** *020 †35
FOOTE, Lindsey L. 6435 S FM 549 STE 2 75032 #048-12-2001 L2003 **FM** *020 †18
GOODWYN, Regina G. 210 CEDAR TREE LN 75032 #048-12-1990 L1991 **EM FM** *020 †18
HALLORAN, Philip Bradley. ■ 75032 #055-01-1968 L1971 **GS** *072 †85
HOWARD, James R. 75032 #048-02-1977 L1977 **FM** *075 †16,18
HUBENAK, Roxanne F. ■ 75032 #048-15-1991 L1992 **EM** *020 †16
JOHNSON, Todd Christian. 6435 S FM 549, STE 201 75032 #018-03-1990 L1995 **ORS** *020 †40
KERN, Jack Alan. 201 LAURENCE DR 75032 #017-20-1961 L1965 **ORS OS** *020 †40
LENSCH, David B. 6435 S FM 549, STE 201 75032 #048-12-1986 L1987 **FM** *020 †18
MUNS, Gregory James. 6435 S FM 549 STE 2 75032 #048-12-1984 L1985 **FM** *020 †18
ROLAND, John Robt. 807 FAITH TRL 75032 #048-13-1986 L1990 **FM EM** *020 †18

HEBBRONVILLE — JIM HOGG

GLENDENNING, Fletcher C. 205 S SMITH AVE 78361 #048-12-1951 L1951 **FM** *020 †18
GUTIERREZ, Jose Alvar, Jr. PO BOX 129, 473 ST HWY 285 78361 #649-02-1974 L1977 **FM** *020 †18

HELOTES — BEXAR

ABOUCHAHINE, Sahar. ■ 78023 #305-01-2002 *100
ALI, Syed S. ■ 78023 #704-16-1985 L1997 **EM IM** *020 †20
ALLNUTT, Richard A, III. ■ 78023 #038-41-1979 L1980 **CLP FM** *030
BALZEN, Jace. ■ 78023 #048-02-2008 *012
BAUMHOLTZ, Michael Aaron. ■ 78023 #041-02-2000 L2006 **PS** *012 †85 ‡
BENSLIMANE, Samia. ■ 78023 #048-13-2004 L2006 **IM** *100 †20
BERNAL, Vanessa Bernal. ■ 78023 #048-13-2003 L2006 **IM** *020 †20
BERRY, John Nathan. ■ 78023 #023-12-2003 L2005 **DR** *012
BURROW, Jamey Walcott. ■ 78023 #027-01-2004 **ORS** *012
CANTU, Michelle L. ■ 78023 #048-14-2005 **P** *012
CARLIN, Carrie Lynn. ■ 78023 #028-34-2003 L2004 **DR** *012
CARPENTER, Lydia. ■ 78023 #024-01-2002 L2003 **D** *012
CAVAZOS, Nilda Alicia. ■ 78023 #048-13-2004 L2007 **FM** *020
CLEMENSHAW, Michael Neill. ■ 78023 #023-12-2005 L2006 **DR** *012
CONLEY, Maria Ann. ■ 78023 #005-12-2004 L2005 **CD** *012 †20
DAHAGAM, Chaitanya Krishn. ■ 78023 #001-02-2006 **GS** *012
D'ASARO, George Earl. ■ 78023 #048-11-1961 L1967 **GP OS** *071
DAVIDS, Neil Brian. ■ 78023 #023-12-2007 **EM** *012
DAVIS, Kenneth Reed. ■ 78023 #011-04-1978 L1998 **AN PD** *020 †55,05
ERANKY, Yasoda. ■ 78023 #495-11-1969 L1982 **DR** *020 †80
FIELDER, Layne Marc. ■ 78023 #051-07-2007 **TY** *012
FITZGERALD, Brian Michael. ■ 78023 #023-12-2008 *012
FRANZEN, Kimberly Lynn. ■ 78023 #030-05-2003 L2004 **GS** *012
FRECKLETON, Michael Wayne. 15123 CHINQUAPIN, STE 130 78023 #016-06-1989 L1995 **DR** *020 †80
FREY, Michael Earl. 78023 #048-13-2002 L2004 **GPM** *020 †70
GIDEON, Wendy Lea. 12274 BANDERA RD, STE 106 78023 #048-16-1999 L2002 **PD** *020 †55
GINGERICH, Troy Curtis. ■ 78023 #020-02-2004 **AN** *012
GONZALEZ, Lorelei Arlene. ■ 78023 #048-13-2004 L2008 **PD** *012
GRABOW, Thomas William. 11864 BANDERA RD 78023 #048-02-1975 L1975 **OPH** *020 †35
HACKLEY, Allen Roger. 11217 CAVE CRK 78023 #038-40-1976 L1980 **EM IM** *020
HAGGERTY, Charles Justin. ■ 78023 #016-43-2003 L2005 **ORS** *012
HAHN, Henry Bentley. ■ 78023 #051-04-2007 **PD END** *030 †55
HALLMARK, Kelly Renee. ■ 78023 #048-14-2005 **PTH** *012
HANDS, Kathleen Elaine. ■ 78023 #665-01-2001 L2006 **END** *100
HEADLEY, Catherine M. ■ 78023 #054-04-2002 L2006 **D** *020 †15
HOOVER, Jacob. ■ 78023 #028-34-2005 L2007 **IM** *012
HOWARTH, William Roberts. ■ 78023 #023-12-2008 *012
HUMPHREY, Julia Louise. ■ 78023 #039-01-2006 L2007 **DR** *012
JARVIS, Bruce W. 11844 BANDERA RD BOX 706 78023 #026-04-1953 L1965 **CLP HEM** *071 †50
JONES, Christy Wilea. ■ 78023 #010-03-1995 L1998 **PD** *020 †55
KAERCHER, Raymond W. 12274 BANDERA RD STE 221 78023 #048-13-1995 L1997 **GS** *020
KATSELNIK, Daniel. ■ 78023 #048-13-2005 **IM** *012
KOHN, Annemarie Susie. ■ 78023 #016-43-2003 L2008 **PD** *020 †55
KU, Paul Tehwei. ■ 78023 #048-15-2002 L2007 **EM** *020
LOMBOY, Juanito Quinones. ■ 78023 #305-01-2007 **FP** *012
LOVE, Joseph D. ■ 78023 #041-77-2004, ▲ L2006 **GS** *012
LOWERY, William Jeffrey. ■ 78023 #004-01-2005 L2007 **OBG** *012
MARRERO, Jorge Arzola. ■ 78023 #035-06-1999 **U** *012
MC DONOUGH, Robert C. ■ 78023 #012-05-1997 L1998 **U** *020 †95
MEFFORD, Michael Benjamin. ■ 78023 #045-04-1995 L2000 **CHP** *020 †75
MORRIS, Amber Ann. ■ 78023 #016-42-2005 L2007 **OBG** *020
NANDISH, Shailesh Solur. ■ 78023 #496-39-1993 L2007 **CD** *012 †20
NGUYEN, Son Van. ■ 78023 #048-13-1994 L1997 **FM** *020 †18
OCHOA, Oscar. ■ 78023 #048-12-2001 L2008 **GS** *100

PACHECO, Daniel. ■ 78023 #042-02-2005 L2008 **DR** *012
PARKER, Ashley N. ■ 78023 #048-13-2007 **OBG** *012
PARKER, Jason Anthoney. ■ 78023 #048-13-2005 **OBG** *012
PATEL, Nilesh Arvind. ■ 78023 #033-06-1999 L2005 **GS** *020 †85
PATTERSON, Gregory. ■ 78023 #047-20-1983 L1988 **IM** *020
PERUCCA, Philip James. ■ 78023 #005-02-1971 L1973 **GE IM** *030 †20
PETRICEK, Travis G. ■ 78023 #048-14-2004 **GS** *012
PURSIFULL, Nathan F. ■ 78023 #016-06-2006 **GS** *012
RATCLIFFE, Temple Andrew. ■ 78023 #041-12-2003 L2005 **IM** *020 †20
RISPOLI, Damian Mark. ■ 78023 #023-12-1992 L2007 **OAR** *020 †40
ROGERS, Jonathan Matthew. ■ 78023 #665-01-2000 L2003 **AN** *100 †05
RYDER, Robert Geo. PO BOX 617 78023 #016-11-1954 L1955 **GP AM** *071
SANDERS, William Edward. ■ 78023 #048-02-1974 L1974 **ORS HS** *020 †40
SANTHANAM, Ravi. ■ 78023 #495-94-1992 L2005 **IM** *020 †20
SKIPPER, Gail Christine. ■ 78023 #023-12-2005 L2007 **P** *012
STERNAMAN, Edward Carl. ■ 78023 #308-13-2001 L2005 **IM** *020 †20
SULLIVAN, C Daniel. ■ 78023 #056-06-1982 L1983 **IM MDM** *020 †20
TAMAYO, Laura R. 12274 BANDERA RD, STE 106 78023 #048-13-1999 L2002 **PD** *020 †55
TREVINO, Juan Jose. ■ 78023 #048-04-1975 L1975 **FM** *040 †18
VRANA, Michael S. ■ 78023 #048-13-2006 **ORS** *012
VROON, Tiffany L. ■ 78023 #001-06-1994 L1997 **PD** *072 †55
WANG, Yubao. ■ 78023 #243-57-1987 L2006 **HO** *012 †20
WOOSLEY, Homer E, Jr. ■ 78023 #004-01-1951 L1975 **GS AM** *071 †85
YANASE, David J. 11844 BANDERA RD 78023 #048-15-1993 L1994 **D** *020 †15
ZENG, Rong. ■ 78023 #048-16-2002 L2004 **DR** *100 †80

HEMPHILL — SABINE

FRANKS, Julia Dorene. ■ 75948 #048-14-2008 *012
GORE, William Stanley. ■ 75948 #048-04-1973 L1974 **ON IM** *071 †20
NEAL, Michael Douglas. PO BOX 1948, 2200 HWY 83 75948 #048-13-1985 L1986 **GP EM** *020
WINSLOW, Grover Cleveland. ■ 75948 #048-12-1953 L1953 **FM** *020

HEMPSTEAD — WALLER

BABU, Suresh K. 350 HIGHWAY 290 E, STE 5 77445 #495-09-1993 L1996 **IM** *020 †20

HENDERSON — RUSK

BRASWELL, Marlin T. 300 WILSON ST 75652 #021-05-1942 L1948 **GP** *071
BUCKELEW, Daryl Q. 300 WILSON ST 75652 #048-13-1993 L1999 **GE** *020 †20
CAHILL, Jeffrey Paul. 325 WILSON ST 75652 #023-01-1977 L1977 **FM** *020 †18
CAMAZINE, Brian Michael. 300 WILSON ST, HENDERSON MEMORIAL HOSPITA 75652 #024-01-1986 L1994 **GS TS** *020 †85
CLAGUE, John Rogers. 610 N HIGH ST 75652 #048-13-1982 L1983 **U GP** *020
CRAIG, David Clark. 1600 US HIGHWAY 79 S, DAVID C CRAIG MD 75654 #065-06-1968 L1977 **OPH** *020
CURTIS, Michele Sprechman. 511 N HIGH ST, THOMAS E CURTIS MD PA 75652 #048-04-1988 L1989 **FM** *020 †18
CURTIS, Thomas Edwin. 300 WILSON ST 75652 #048-04-1988 L1989 **FM** *020 †18
DEESE, Julian V. 300 WILSON ST 75652 #039-01-1975 L1980 **GE** *020 †20
HAUSMANN, Jan M. 317 WILSON ST, HENDERSON MEM CLINIC 75652 #047-06-1971 L2004 **IM** *020 †20
HAY, Meredith Alane. 511 N HIGH ST 75652 #028-46-2000 L2003 **FM** *020 †18 ‡
HENDERSON, Charles Carey. ■ 75653 #048-12-1945 L1945 **OS GS** *071 †85
HEYNS, William Petsch, Jr. 300 WILSON ST 75652 #048-13-1974 L1978 **PTH PCP** *020 †50
HUGHES, Bill Geo. 300 WILSON ST 75652 #012-05-1975 L1976 **GE IM** *020 †20
KHALIFA, Ahmed. 300 WILSON ST 75652 #915-03-1951 L1973 **ATP** *020 †50
LADAGE, Frederick Sanford. 325 WILSON ST 75652 #004-01-1972 L1976 **FM GP** *020 †18
MANN, James H. ■ 75652 #048-04-1953 L1953 **GP AS** *071
MC CLELLAND, James Pat. 300 WILSON ST 75652 #048-04-1955 L1955 **R** *071 †80
MC CRADY, William M. 511 N HIGH ST 75652 #048-14-1982 L1983 **FM PD** *030 †18
MELVIN, John Thames. 300 WILSON ST, HENDERSON MEMORIAL HOSPITA 75652 #011-03-1980 L1983 **DR** *020 †80 ‡
MORRIS, Alfred Eugene. 511 N HIGH ST 75652 #048-12-1954 L1955 **FM** *071 †18
OLOFINLADE, Olusola. 300 WILSON ST 75652 #690-01-1987 L2001 **GE** *020 †20
PAI, Yogesh Govindaraya. 105 N HIGH ST 75652 #496-38-1993 L1996 **PD** *020 †55
PERRICONE, Charles M. 511 N HIGH ST 75652 #048-12-1984 L1985 **FM** *020 †18
RASLAN, Saleem. 100 ZEID BLVD STE A 75652 #875-01-1998 L2005 **IM** *020 †20
ROBERSON, William B, Jr. 300 N HIGH ST A, GOOD SHEPHERD FAMILY HLTH 75652 #048-78-1994, ▲ L2004 **FM** *020 †18
SKARDA, Shayne Taylor. 300 WILSON ST 75652 #034-01-1998 L2001 **GE** *020 †20
SPRINGFIELD, Harold James. 119 S MARSHALL ST 75654 #048-02-1960 L1960 **GP** *071
STARLING, Mary Joyce. 300 WILSON ST 75652 #048-13-1990 L1991 **FM** *020 †18
TORRES, William H. 300 WILSON ST 75652 #048-12-1988 L1989 **GE** *020 †20
VOZZA-ZEID, Brenda. 100 ZEID BLVD, STE A 75652 #422-01-1995 L1998 **IM** *020 †20
WALGAMA, Upali Sanath. 321 WILSON ST 75652 #220-01-1966 L1977 **IM** *020 †20
WILKERSON, Bill. 300 N HIGH ST 75652 #048-12-1960 L1960 **FM GS** *020 †18
WILLIAMS, Sue Ann. 105 N HIGH ST 75652 #007-02-1974 L1978 **OBG** *020 †30
ZEID, Yasser F. 105 ZEID BLVD 75652 #915-04-1988 L1997 **OBG** *020 †30

HENRIETTA — CLAY

GREER, Thomas David. 102 S ARCHER ST, BOX 360 76365 #048-02-1964 L1964 **FM AM** *020 †18 ‡
NOE, Paula Michelle. ■ 76365 #048-12-2005 L2008 **IM** *012
PARKEY, J Robert. 305 S ARCHER ST, P O BOX 389 76365 #048-02-1994 L1996 **FM OS** *020 †18
SCHAFFNER, Leroy. 303 S ARCHER ST 76365 #048-12-1959 L1959 **GP GS** *071
WOLFE, Mitchell C. 310 W SOUTH ST 76365 #048-02-1994 L2000 **FM** *020 †18

HEREFORD — DEAF SMITH

ADAMS, Stenneth Cameron. 300 WITHERSPOON AVE, TRENTON SURGICAL ASSOC., P 79045 #010-03-1993 L2007 **GS** *020 †85
DOTSON, Rodney Norman. 335 MILES ST 79045 #847-04-1967 L1972 **GP PD** *020
GREGG, John Thos. 300 WITHERSPOON AVE 79045 #007-02-1980 L1989 **GS VS** *020 †85 ‡
GUY, Eric C. 110 N 25 MILE AVE 79045 #048-02-1995 L2000 **IM** *020 †20
JOHNSON, Howard Raymond. 300 WITHERSPOON AVE, HEREFORD HLTH CLNC 79045 #039-01-1964 L1965 **GP** *020
MC BRAYER, Duffy E, Jr. 79045 #048-12-1964 L1964 **FM** *075 †18
MIMS, Arthur Trow. ■ 79045 #048-12-1945 L1945 **GS** *071 †85
PAYNE, Gerald Gene. 801 E 3RD ST 79045 #048-12-1964 L1964 **FM** *020 †18
REVELL, Timothy John. 801 E 3RD ST 79045 #005-15-1979 L1982 **GP** *020
RUSH, Clyde Edward. 801 E 3RD ST 79045 #017-20-1943 L1949 **GS TS** *071 †85,90
SERNA, Linda Sherri. ■ 79045 #005-02-1976 L2003 **GS** *020 †85

HEWITT — MCLENNAN

BENNETT, Robert S, Jr. 76643 #048-14-1983 L1983 **EM** *020
COONEY, Edward Anthony. 510 N HEWITT DR, SCOTT & WHITE HEWITT CLINI 76643 #041-09-1980 L1987 **FM** *040 †18
KITSON, Sandra. 510 N HEWITT DR 76643 #056-06-1995 L2005 **FM** *020 †18
SHARP, James Glenn. 510 N HEWITT DR 76643 #048-13-1985 L1986 **FM** *020 †18
WALTER, Robert Wayne. ■ 76643 #012-01-1969 L1970 **PTH** *071 †50

HICO — HAMILTON

HARRIS, Jimmy N. 507 W FIRST ST, N TEXAS MED TRANS INC. 76457 #048-12-1987 L1988 **IM PD** *020 †55,20

HIDALGO — HIDALGO

PUIG, Carlos E. ■ 78557 #048-12-2004 **FM** *100
RODRIGUEZ, Rene Lenardo. ■ 78557 #649-19-1980 **OS GS** *020
TOVAR C, Felipe De Jesus. ■ 78557 #649-02-1966 **PD** *020

HIDE A WAY — SMITH

BOWN, Kenneth Winston. 1624 MORNINGSIDE TRL 75771 #064-01-1967 L1977 **FM** *071 †18
EVANS, Arthur F, III. ■ 75771 #048-04-1969 L1969 **NS** *071 †25
GATTI, Robert Roy. ■ 75771 #039-01-1955 L1958 **FM** *071 †18
LEINART, Oliver S, Jr. ■ 75771 #048-04-1946 L1946 **FM** *071

HIGHLAND VILLAGE — DENTON

CALLAHAN, Sean Michael. ■ 75077 #048-12-2007 *012
CONGER, Marla Rae. 2280 HIGHLAND VILLAGE RD, STE 130 75077 #025-07-1983 L1987 **PD OS** *020 †55
GOMEZ, Rebecca K. 2940 FM 407 STE 302 75077 #048-13-2000 L2002 **FM** *020 †18
HAMBRICK, Brent Allen. ■ 75077 #039-01-1988 L1989 **EM** *020 †18
HAYES, Cornelius John. ■ 75077 #010-01-1954 L1959 **IM** *071 †20
KELKAR, Kalpana Pemmaraju. 2280 HIGHLAND VILLAGE RD, STE 130 75077 #007-02-2001 L2003 **PD** *020 †55
NEELY, Wanda Fairye. 2250 FM 407 STE 108, PMB 207 75077 #048-04-1955 L1955 **OPH** *071 †35
PATEL, Jyoti Narendra. ■ 75077 #495-76-1974 L1982 **P** *020
PRABHAKAR, Meenakshi S. ■ 75077 #495-59-1993 L1997 **ID** *020 †20
WU, Ching-Tsung. ■ 75077 #385-02-1960 L1970 **PD GP** *072 †55

HIGHLANDS — HARRIS

ABDELSAYED, Dallal W. 607 E WALLISVILLE RD 77562 #915-02-1978 L1984 **FM** *030 †18
STANFIELD, Peter. 610 S MAIN ST 77562 #847-03-1975 L1980 **PME P** *020

HILLISTER — TYLER

LAWRENCE, Derry Clee. PO BOX 459, PR 8495 #353 77624 #048-12-1970 L1970 **BBK PD** *020

HILLSBORO — HILL

BAILEY, Colin R. 1323 E FRANKLIN ST, STE 105 76645 #048-14-1993 L1994 **FM** *020 †18
BAUERSCHLAG, Jason R. 1323 E FRANKLIN ST, STE 105 76645 #048-16-1998 L1999 **FM OBS** *020 †18
BEYER, Carol Buturla. 1323 E FRANKLIN ST 76645 #048-02-1978 L1978 **PD** *020 †55
BEYER, David Henry. 213 DELMORE DR 76645 #023-01-1948 L1966 **P AM** *071 †70
BROWN, Robert W. 117 JANE LN 76645 #048-13-2004 L2007 **FM** *020
CHARLES, Michael Sheldon. 1323 E FRANKLIN ST STE 101 76645 #422-01-1985 L1989 **GS** *020 †85
DYKES, Thomas Lane. 1323 E FRANKLIN ST, STE 105 76645 #048-04-1945 L1945 **OBG** *071
DYKES, Thomas Lane, Jr. 1323 E FRANKLIN ST, STE 105 76645 #048-14-1981 L1981 **OBG** *020 †30
EARHART, James M, Jr. 1323 E FRANKLIN ST 76645 #048-15-1986 L1987 **FM** *020 †18
ERWIN, John Preston, Jr. 1323 E FRANKLIN ST STE 105 76645 #048-02-1964 L1968 **FM** *071 †18
FLOY, Paul Stephen. 1323 E FRANKLIN ST 76645 #018-03-1993 L1996 **FM** *020 †18
GIBNEY, Richard Lee. 1507 HILLVIEW DR 76645 #030-06-1972 L1974 **NEP** *020 †20
JOHNSON, John Meade. 1323 E FRANKLIN ST STE 105 76645 #048-02-1967 L1967 **FM PHP** *071 †18

KHAN, Nasir. 101 CIRCLE DR 76645 #704-16-1990 L2003 **IMG** *020 †18
MARSHALL, Wesley C. ■ 76645 #048-15-2004 L2005 **FM** *020 †18
PRATT, Franklin Glade. ■ 76645 #030-05-1964 L1974 **R** *071 †80
RISINGER, Brian J. 101 CIRCLE DR 76645 #048-14-1991 L1993 **DR** *020 †80
SHAW, Timothy John. 101 CIRCLE DR 76645 #028-03-1978 L2006 **GS TS** *020 †85
SKELTON, David Boyd. 1323 E FRANKLIN ST STE 105 76645 #048-02-1975 L1975 **FM OBS** *020 †18
TEAGUE, Christopher W. 1323 E FRANKLIN ST, STE 105 76645 #048-13-1997 L1998 **FM** *020 †18 ‡
ZERDECKI, John Wells. 201 OLD BRANDON RD 76645 #028-02-1973 L1977 **OPH** *071 †35

HITCHCOCK – GALVESTON

SOUZA, Shiloe Nicole. ■ 77563 #048-15-2007 **OBG** *012
VON HOESSLIN, Hermann. ■ 77563 #409-20-1989 **IM** *100

HOCKLEY – HARRIS

HELFRICH, Craig M. ■ 77447 #048-13-1996 L1998 **GP** *020
PUANA, Lynn Welch. ■ 77447 #030-06-2002 **IM** *100
PUANA, Rudolph Burton. ■ 77447 #030-06-2002 L2006 **CCA** *020 †05

HOLLY LAKE RANCH – WOOD

BOLTON, M Graham. ■ 75765 #048-04-1951 L1951 **FM** *071 †18
GUSKY, Jeffrey Starr. 964 CLEAR WATER TRL 75765 #054-04-1982 L1983 **GS** *020

HONDO – MEDINA

BADRAN, Nidal J. 3100 AVENUE E 78861 #575-01-1990 L1996 **IM** *020 †20
BEERAM, Sridhar. 606 31ST ST 78861 #495-21-1994 L2006 **HO** *100 †20
DE LA CRUZ, Antonio C. 2912 AVENUE E 78861 #748-08-1969 L1997 **GP** *020
DULLNIG, Mitchell Max. 3100 AVENUE E 78861 #048-14-1985 L1986 **IM** *020
FINK, John Mark. 78861 #025-01-1974 L1982 **OBG** *020 †30
FITTS, James M. 125/114 P.R. 4303 78861 #048-02-1985 L1986 *020
FITZGERALD, Robt Theodore. 78861 #001-02-1955 L1969 **NS AM** *071 †25
HUTSON, Miles Austin. 3200 AVENUE E 78861 #016-11-1976 L1977 **FM** *020 †18
MEYER, John Walter. 3200 AVENUE E 78861 #021-01-1973 L1975 **FM OS** *020 †18 ‡
ROWLAND, Richard Spencer. 3200 AVENUE E 78861 #048-13-1995 L1996 **FM** *020 †18
WINDROW, Matthew J. 3200 AVENUE E 78861 #048-15-1996 L1997 **FM** *020 †18
WINDROW, Zachary Robert. 3200 AVENUE E 78861 #048-13-1994 L1995 **FM** *020 †18

HONEY GROVE – FANNIN

ROMERO, Calixto A, Jr. 906 COUNTY ROAD 2770, WADLEY TOWER 75446 #016-02-1970 L1976 **CD IM** *040 †20

HOOKS – BOWIE

SMOLARZ, Casey Michael. ■ 75561 #048-02-2007 **EM** *012

HORIZON CITY – EL PASO

DAYS, Alison L. 12583 DARRINGTON RD 79928 #008-01-1999 L2003 **PD** *020 †55
HERNANDEZ GARCIA, Juan Ca. 335 BARREL CACTUS DR 79928 #649-33-2007 *100
SULLENGER, Lauri M. ■ 79928 #048-15-2008 *012

HORSESHOE BAY – LLANO

BROOKS, Theron Edgar, III. ■ 78657 #048-12-1963 L1963 **PD** *020 †55
COLUMBUS, Donald Gordon. ■ 78657 #065-06-1973 L1983 **OBG** *020 †30
DETENBECK, Lee Clark. 413 LIGHTHOUSE DR 78657 #048-02-1964 L1964 **ORS** *071 †40
DICKSON, Jesse Hamilton. ■ 78657 #048-12-1959 L1960 **ORS** *071 †40
JOHNSON, Dale Franklin. PO BOX 7935 78657 #048-04-1942 L1942 **PD** *072 †55
KNOX, Cecil Byron, Jr. ■ 78657 #048-02-1947 L1947 **GP GS** *071
LITTLE, Stephen B. ■ 78657 #048-13-1982 L1983 **EM FM** *020 †16
SAKOW, Nolan Keith. ■ 78657 #649-14-1980 L1982 **DR ATP** *020 †50,28
SARTAIN, Peggy Ann. ■ 78657 #048-02-1959 L1959 **ON PD** *071 †55
SCANLON, Hugh Aloysius. ■ 78657 #026-04-1963 L1983 **FM** *071 †18
THIGPEN, Joe E. ■ 78657 #048-04-1950 L1951 **GP** *072
TIZIANI, Joseph James, Jr. ■ 78657 #025-01-1960 L1961 **P** *020 †75
WHITE, Thomas De Witt. ■ 78657 #048-14-1981 L1981 **FM** *020 †18
WILLOUGHBY, William A. 414 LIGHTHOUSE DR 78657 #007-02-1949 L1975 **OPH** *071 †35

HOUSTON – FORT BEND

GONZALEZ, Sonia M. ■ 77053 #048-04-2006 **FP** *012
LE, Bao. ■ 77053 #048-78-2005, ▲ L2007 **IM** *012

HOUSTON – HARRIS

ABADEER, Rania. PO BOX 20708, DEPT OF PATHOLOGY 77225 #048-14-2003 **PTH** *012
ABAYA, Bernardino Flores. 6720 BERTNER ST 77030 #748-02-1984 L1992 **NEP IM** *020 †20
ABBAS, Farhat. ■ 77030 #704-02-1984 **U** *100
ABBAS, Rukhsana Moiz. 15821 FM 529 RD, # 149 77095 #704-16-1982 L1997 **PTH** *100

ABBASI, Elham Hafshejani. 800 PEAKWOOD DR STE 6F 77090 #517-20-1996 L2003 **IM** *100 †20
ABBASI, Maaz Ahmed. 1 BAYLOR PLZ 77030 #704-25-2001 L2007 **CCM** *100 †20
ABBRUZZESE, James Lewis. 1515 HOLCOMBE BLVD, BOX 426 77030 #016-02-1978 L1986 **ON HEM** *020 †20
ABDALLA, Eddie Kaleel. 1515 HOLCOMBE BLVD, THE UNIV OF TX MD ANDERSON 77030 #025-01-1993 L1999 **GS** *020 †85
ABDALLA, Nageeb Girgis. 1100 W 34TH ST 77018 #915-04-1974 L1997 **FM** *020 †18
ABDEL FATTAH, Amr Adel H. ■ 77054 #915-04-1995 **CHP** *100
ABD EL-MALEK, Hany Samir. 6565 FANNIN ST # B452 77030 #915-02-1988 L2005 **AN CCA** *020 †05
ABDELMELEK, Lourice K. 5420 DASHWOOD DR STE 100 77081 #915-04-1981 L1996 **FM** *020 †18
ABDEL-MESSIH, Emile Fares. 7447 HARWIN DR, STE 109 77036 #915-03-1971 L1982 **GP** *020
ABDELRAHMAN, Nidal M J. 6565 FANNIN ST B452, DEPT OF ANESTHESIOLOGY 77030 #704-01-1995 L2000 **AN** *020 †05
ABDO, George Joe. 800 PEAKWOOD DR STE 58 77090 #048-02-1967 L1967 **R** *020 †80
ABDUL-ALIM, Bilal. ■ 77004 #048-04-1977 L1977 **GP** *020
ABDUL GAWI, Mochammad. ■ 77057 #506-18-1976 *100
ABDULLA, Cedela. 7737 SOUTHWEST FWY, STE 420 77074 #539-06-2003 **FP** *012
ABDULLAH, Saad A Dakhil. 8181 FANNIN ST, APT 1314 77054 #528-01-1984 *100
ABDULLATIF, Mariam Lantin. ■ 77025 #048-14-2008 *012
ABEDI, Fouad M. ■ 77066 #048-15-2008 *012
ABEDIN, Saeid. 909 FROSTWOOD DR, STE 227 77024 #517-01-1972 L1983 **OPH** *020 †35
ABENE, Michael Vincent. 6565 FANNIN ST MS 587 77030 #021-05-1989 L1994 **SME** *020 †75
ABOU-CHACRA, Grace Issam. 6411 FANNIN ST, 7TH FL 77030 #605-01-1995 *100
ABOUGHALI, Wael Ata. 6410 FANNIN ST, STE 250 77030 #048-12-2002 L2005 **FM** *100
ABOULEISH, Ezzat I A. ■ 77059 #330-04-1953 L1983 **AN** *071
ABOULFOTOUH, Frieda Kamel. ■ 77025 #048-04-2006 **P** *012
ABOU-SLEIMAN, Joseph E. 8303 GULF FWY, STE 101 77017 #048-14-2000 L2004 **FM** *020 †18
ABRAHAM, Asha Caroline. PO BOX 20708 77225 #495-52-2004 **IM** *012
ABRAHAM, Johns V. ■ 77059 #048-14-1992 **AN** *100
ABRAHAM, Selwin John. 1709 DRYDEN RD STE 550, BCM FACULTY CENTER 77030 #005-12-2006 **IM** *012
ABRAHAM, Susan Catherine. ■ 77004 #041-01-1994 L2007 **PTH** *020 †50
ABRAHAM, Vinu Mathew. 1504 TAUB LOOP, BAYLOR COLLEGE OF MED 77030 #495-63-2002 L2002 **PCC** *012 †20
ABRAHIM, Alber R. 10851 SCARSDALE BLVD, STE 130 77089 #915-04-1979 L1998 **FM** *020 †18
ABRAMOVICI, Adi Rosablima. 1709 DRYDEN RD, BAYLOR COLLEGE OF MEDICINE 77030 #035-03-2006 **OBG** *012
ABRAMOWITZ, Joel. 925 GESSNER RD STE 310 77024 #035-08-1976 L1980 **ON HEM** *020 †20
ABRAMS, Jacki. 6720 BERTNER ST, DEPARTMENT OF PATHOLOGY 77030 #041-13-1983 L1989 **PTH PD** *020 †50
ABRAMS, Marvin Jacob. 17376 NORTHWEST FWY 77040 #065-01-1962 L1977 **FM** *020
ABRAMS, Stephanie Renee. ■ 77096 #048-14-2000 L2006 **PG** *100 †55
ABRAMS, Steven Allen. 1100 BATES AVE, RM 7066 77030 #038-40-1982 L1987 **NPM** *050 †55
ABRAMSON, Steven Ilan. 6431 FANNIN ST 5.020, UT HSC MEDICAL SCHOOL 77030 #836-01-1994 L2003 **AN** *020 †05
ABRAMSON, Stuart Lee. 6621 FANNIN ST, RM FC330.01 77030 #048-04-1984 L1985 **IG OS** *050 †03,55
ABREHA, Amanuel Misghina. 440 BENMAR DR, STE 1205 77060 #366-01-1988 L2005 **IM** *020 †20
ABRUZZO, Lynne Victoria. 1515 HOLCOMBE BLVD, UT M.D. ANDERSON CANCER CE 77030 #016-02-1986 L2000 **PTH** *020 †50,19
ABUELEM, Tarek M.T.. 1 BAYLOR PLZ, BAYLOR COLL MED 77030 #575-01-2001 **NS** *012
ABU-FARSAKH, Hussam A R. 1200 MOURSUND ST 77030 #584-01-1986 L1991 **BBK** *020 †50
ABUSHULLAIH, Basel A. PO BOX 53211 77052 #797-03-1987 L1993 **PD** *020 †55
ABUSHULLAIH, Samer A. PO BOX 53211 77052 #797-03-1992 **ON** *020 †20
ABUZAHRA, Mohammed Marwan. 1709 DRYDEN RD, BAYLOR COLLEGE OF MEDICINE 77030 #605-01-2002 L2005 **CD** *012 †20
ABUZAITOUN, Omar Rebhi. 6621 FANNIN ST, DEPT OF ALLERGY & IMMUNOLO 77030 #575-01-1990 L1997 **AI** *100 †55,03
ACEVEDO, Guillermo De F. 96 BERRY RD 77022 #264-04-1964 L1972 **GP PTH** *020 †50
ACEVEDO, Jose Guillermo. 2450 FONDREN RD STE 102, HILLCROFT MEDICAL CLINIC 77063 #308-11-1987 L1997 **OM** *020 †20
ACEVEDO LOHNER, Luisa M. 4801 WOODWAY DR, STE 350W 77056 #132-07-1978 L1986 **P CHP** *020 †75
ACHARI, Amrit Naryana. 8915 GAYLORD ST 77024 #495-24-1964 L1975 **N** *020 †75
ACHARI, Arup. 1707 SUNSET BLVD, MEDICAL CLINIC OF HOUSTON 77005 #048-02-1991 L1992 **CD** *020 †20
ACHARI, Madhureeta. 8915 GAYLORD ST 77024 #048-14-1992 L1994 **N NRN** *020 †75
ACHARYA, Deepak. 6540 BELLOWS LN 77030 #048-04-2005 L2008 **IM** *012
ACHKAR, Katafan. 1415 LA CONCHA LN 77054 #875-01-1989 L1995 **NEP** *020 †20
ACHOUH, Paul Elias. ■ 77054 #605-02-1996 *100
ACHOUR, Hela. ■ 77055 #895-01-1996 **IM** *012
ACOSTA, Alisa A. 1205 BOMAR ST 77006 #048-14-2001 L2004 **PN** *012 †55
ACOSTA, Luis Silvio. 17203 RED OAK DR, STE 201 77090 #264-02-1967 L1976 **NEP END** *020 †20
ADACHI, Javier Antonio. 1515 HOLCOMBE BLVD, UNIT 402 77030 #737-06-1990 L2005 **ID** *100
ADACHI, Roberto. 2121 W HOLCOMBE BLVD, RM 403D 77030 #737-06-1990 L1995 **PUD CCM** *050 †20
ADAM, Ervin. ■ 77096 #286-02-1951 L1973 **OS IMG** *071
ADAM, Karolina. 7900 FANNIN ST, STE 2600 77054 #041-07-1983 L1983 **MFM OBG** *020 †30
ADAM, Kenneth Stuart. 3000 WESLAYAN ST, STE 347 77027 #065-01-1961 L2000 **P** *020
ADAM, Octavian Remus. ■ 77096 #781-01-2002 L2007 **N** *020
ADAM, Vlasta. ■ 77096 #286-02-1950 L1972 **IMG ID** *071
ADAMS, Harold Kenneth. 12950 EAST FWY, STE 100 77015 #041-09-1990 L1996 **AN** *020 †05
ADAMS, James Meryyn, Jr. 1200 MOURSUND ST 77030 #048-04-1970 L1970 **PD** *020 †55
ADAMS, John James. 4141 NORTH FWY, STE 100 77022 #048-04-1963 L1963 **OS GP** *020
ADAMS, Joseph A. 11301 FALLBROOK DR 77065 #035-06-1991 L1992 **PO** *035
ADAMS, Phillip R. 4126 SOUTHWEST FWY 77027 #048-14-1976 L1976 **TS GS** *020 †85,90
ADAMS, Ronnie Lasalle, II. 1919 NORTH LOOP W, STE 218 77008 #048-12-2000 L2006 **GS** *020 †85 ‡
ADAMS, Sasha Danielle. ■ 77031 #045-01-2002 L2005 **GS** *012
ADCOCK, Lisa Mae. 1 BAYLOR PLZ, NEWBORN SECTION OF PEDIATR 77030 #021-05-1988 L1994 **PD NPM** *020 †55

ADDEL-HAY, Liliane Emile. 6621 FANNIN ST, MC 1-1481 77030 #605-02-1990 L1998 PD *020 †55

ADEKUNLE-OJO, Aderonke O. 6621 FANNIN ST STE 165, CHILDREN'S HOSP.MC1/1481 77030 #690-02-1989 L1998 PD *020 †55

ADELAJA, Ibironke V. ■ 77089 #048-16-2006 L2008 GS *012

ADELMAN, Maria Milner. ■ 77096 #913-36-1942 L1974 PTH *071

ADELS, Morton Julian. ■ 77056 #048-04-1956 L1956 OBG *071 †30

ADELSON, Marcia. ■ 77005 #024-05-1978 L1981 IMG *020 †75

ADESINA, Adekunle M. 1 BAYLOR PLZ, DEPARTMENT OF PATHOLOGY 77030 #690-01-1980 L2002 NP *020 †50

ADESINA, Olutomisin M. 8777B S GESSNER DR 77074 #690-01-1980 L2002 PD *020 †55

ADESOMO, Jerry Adebayo. 3101 RICHMOND AVE STE 250 77098 #010-03-1976 L1980 OBG *020 †30

ADEWUYA, Oladapo Adedamol. ■ 77089 #690-05-1994 FM *100

ADEYINKA, Olasunkanmi W. 6410 FANNIN ST STE 250, UT PHYSICIANS 77030 #690-02-1986 L1993 FM *020 †18

ADHAM, Besma I. 5615 KIRBY DR, STE 440 77005 #036-01-1984 L1990 NPM PD *020 †55

ADHAM, Walid Khalid. 3018 HOLLY HALL ST 77054 #048-14-2000 L2003 RNR *020 †80 ‡

ADHAM, Yousef Hilmi. 2476 BOLSOVER ST # 213 77005 #915-03-1956 P *100

ADICKES, Mark Stephen. 6400 FANNIN ST, STE 1620 77030 #024-01-2000 L2006 OSM *020

ADKINS, Alvin Thos. 5757 WOODWAY DR, STE 200 77057 #048-04-1954 L1956 PD *071 †30

ADKINS, James Marshall. 11800 ASTORIA BLVD 77089 #048-04-1962 L1962 GYN *020 †30

ADLER, Douglas Graham. 6431 FANNIN ST 4.234, GASTROENTEROLOGY 77030 #035-20-1995 L2004 GE *020 †20

ADLER, Michael T. 6431 FANNIN ST, DEPT OBG 77030 #048-14-2006 OBG *012

ADLER, Michelle Renee. 6621 FANNIN ST CC1210, TX CHILDRENS HOSPITAL 77030 #005-18-2001 L2001 GPM *020 †18,70

ADMIRAND, Joan H. ■ 77019 #036-05-1998 L2004 HMP *020 †50

ADRADA CRUZ, Beatriz Elen. 1 BAYLOR PLZ 77030 #264-07-1991 RNR *100

ADROGUE, Horacio Esteban. 1709 DRYDEN RD, 9TH FLOOR, 09.10 77030 #048-15-1997 L2003 NEP *020 †20

ADROGUE, Horacio Jose. 1709 DRYDEN RD, STE 925 77030 #132-01-1965 L1979 NEP IM *050 †20

ADROGUE, Julia V. 1709 DRYDEN RD, ATTENTION: CARDIOLOGY 77030 #913-99-1995 L2005 CD *012

ADUSUMILLI, Srijhansi. ■ 77070 #495-11-1993 L2004 IM *020

ADYANTHAYA, Ajit V. 11914 ASTORIA BLVD, STE 410 77089 #495-17-1967 L1973 CD *020 †20

AFIF, Claude Michel. ■ 77025 #605-02-1992 ID *100

AFIFI, Mohamed Amin. ■ 77042 #915-04-1959 L1977 *100

AFONSO, Natasha Susana. ■ 77002 #021-01-2008 *012

AFSHARKHARGHAN, Vahid. 1 BAYLOR PLZ BCM286, THROMBOSIS RESEARCH SECTIO 77030 #902-05-1991 L1999 ON *020 †20

AFZAL, Haider. ■ 77059 #704-02-1994 L2006 FM *100

AGA, Donnie W. 1221 MCKINNEY ST, STE 40300 77010 #048-14-1994 L1996 IM *020 †20

AGA, Irene Eseesemarie. 5656 KELLEY ST RM 2LD80001, OB/GYN-LBJ HOSPITAL 77026 #019-02-2003 L2007 OBG *100

AGARWAL, Piyush Kumar. 1515 HOLCOMBE BLVD U, UT MD ANDERSON CANCER CENT 77030 #035-20-2000 L2004 U *020

AGARWAL, Rajiv. 6431 FANNIN ST 77030 #048-12-1999 L2002 CD *100 †20

AGARWAL, Suneal K. ■ 77024 #048-02-2008 *012

AGBOOLA, Iyabode Abiodunm. ■ 77081 #035-19-2005 L2008 OBG *012

AGGARWAL, Ajay Kumar. 5314 DASHWOOD DR 77081 #495-45-1987 L1993 AN PME *020 †05

AGGARWAL, Anjali. 1 BAYLOR PLZ 77030 #495-30-1989 L2008 FP *012

AGGARWAL, Shalini. ■ 77041 #495-41-1993 L2007 CHP *012

AGGARWAL, Ved Parkash. 8000 N STADIUM DR, HUMAN SERVICES 77054 #495-12-1958 L1972 PD *020 †55

AGGARWAL, Vinod. 2111 HOLLY HALL ST APT 10 77054 #496-38-1988 *100

AGHA, Naureen Imtiaz. 1 BAYLOR PLZ 77030 #704-02-2001 L2006 IM *020 †20

AGOMO, Emelike Uchechi. ■ 77045 #010-03-2008 OPH *012

AGOSTON, Ildiko. 6550 FANNIN ST MS SM677, BAYLOR COLLEGE OF MEDICINE 77030 #473-01-1996 L2001 CD *075 †20

AGRAWAL, Anoop. ■ 77004 #028-46-1998 L2002 MPD *020 †20,55

AGRAWAL, Anurag. ■ 77005 #495-36-1995 L2006 PCC *020 †20

AGRAWAL, Dipti. 6560 FANNIN ST STE 1540, INFECTIOUS DISEASES ASSOC 77030 #024-05-1996 L1998 ID *020 †20

AGRAWL, Girish G. 800 PEAKWOOD DR, STE 5E 77090 #496-38-1993 L2002 DR *020 †80

AGRIS, Joseph. 6560 FANNIN ST STE 1730 77030 #035-03-1968 L1976 PS TRS *020 †65

AGU, Johnson Izuchukwu. 4605 POST OAK PLACE DR, STE 217 77027 #690-04-1987 L1999 IM *020 †20

AGUILAR, David. 6431 FANNIN ST, UNIVERSITY OF TEXAS HSC 77030 #048-04-1996 L2003 CD *100 †20

AGUILAR, Eugenio A, III. 6410 FANNIN ST, STE 927 77030 #048-15-1979 L1979 PS OTO *020 †45,65

AGUILAR, Francia V. 2411 FOUNTAIN VIEW, STE 200 77057 #748-01-1971 L1978 AN *020

AGUILAR, Jorge. ■ 77030 #048-14-2005 L2007 AN *012

AGUILAR, Lesly Giselle. ■ 77030 #451-01-1996 L2007 N *100

AGUILAR, Martha B. 6909 GREENBRIAR ST 77030 #048-14-1994 L1997 RHU *020 †20

AGUILAR, Phillip M. 1616 CLEAR LAKE CITY BLVD, STE 109 77062 #048-14-1994 L1995 FM *020 †18

AGUILERA DIAZ, Dolly Grac. 1515 HOLCOMBE BLVD UNIT 8, DIVISION OF PEDIATRICS 77030 #264-04-1998 L2000 PHO *012 †55

AGUIRRE, Francisco Delfin. 5990 AIRLINE DR STE 1 77076 #176-01-1966 L1981 OBG *030

AGUIRRE, Jose William. ■ 77083 #264-05-1997 FP *012

AGUOCHA, Nnenna Nkechinye. ■ 77072 #012-05-2008 *012

AGUSALA, Kartik. ■ 77030 #048-04-2008 *012

AGUSALA, Ravinder. 11111 JONES RD, STE 1 77070 #495-65-1969 L1981 CD IM *020 †20

AGYEMANG, Eleanor Mary. 7737 SOUTHWEST FWY STE 42, RES PRGM 77074 #048-14-2005 L2008 FP *012

AHAMAD, Anesa Waheda. 1515 HOLCOMBE BLVD, UNIT 097 RADIATION ONCOLOG 77030 #566-01-1994 L2004 RO *020 †80

AHEARN, Mark C. 2115 ELMEN ST, B 77019 #024-07-1990 L2002 EM *020 †16

AHLSCHIER, Allan Dee. 1239 WYNDEN OAKS GARDEN DR 77056 #021-01-1966 L1970 DR EM *100

AHLUWALIA, Anu. 1300 MOURSUND ST, MEDICAL SCHOOL 77030 #048-02-1990 L1991 P *020 †75

AHMAD, Alya Malik Zaman. 6441 HIGH STAR DR 77074 #048-13-1998 L2002 PD *020

AHMAD, Amna. ■ 77030 #704-02-2003 IM *012

AHMAD, Anwar. 1315 ST JOSEPH PKWY, CARDIOLOGY ASSOCIATES 77002 #704-25-1988 L1994 CD *020 †20

AHMAD, Ataurrabb. 11301 FALLBROOK DR, STE 204 77065 #021-05-1995 L2000 GS *020 †85

AHMAD, Fahd Aqeeb. 6621 FANNIN ST RM A170, MC1-1000 77030 #028-03-2006 PD *012

AHMAD, Hussain. ■ 77059 #704-21-1986 L1998 IM *020 †20

AHMAD, Kaashif Aqeeb. ■ 77054 #704-25-2000 L2002 NPM *012 †55

AHMAD, Neelofur Rahman. 810 PEAKWOOD DR, STE D 77090 #016-06-1988 L1999 RO *020 †80 ‡

AHMAD, Arsalan. ■ 77030 #704-02-1995 L2007 SP *012

AHMED, Bashir. 1201 WILCREST DR, APT 86 77042 #160-02-1996 *100

AHMED, Bilal. PO BOX 20708, DEPT OF INT MED 77225 #704-25-2003 L2008 IM *012

AHMED, Faiz. 11760 FM 1960 RD W 77065 #495-33-1975 L1993 N *020

AHMED, Masroor. 77079 #704-02-1990 L1999 APM *020 †05 ‡

AHMED, Nabil Mohamed. 77025 #915-02-1995 L2006 PHO *050 †55

AHMED, Nasiya N. ■ 77004 #048-14-2002 L2007 IMG *020 †20

AHMED, Nisar. 18220 TOMBALL PKWY 77070 #704-02-1965 L1974 GE IM *020 †20

AHMED, Saleha R. 1631 NORTH LOOP W STE 400 77008 #704-01-1987 L1995 IM *020 †18

AHMED, Salmaan Nazir. 902 FROSTWOOD DR STE 275 77024 #005-06-2001 L2005 RNR *020 †80

AHMED, Saud Iqbal. ■ 77025 #704-01-2000 ID *012 †20

AHMED, Shazia Saman. ■ 77004 #012-01-2003 L2007 IM *100

AHMED, Sheikh Ejaz. 1631 NORTH LOOP W STE 400 77008 #704-16-1979 L1989 CD IM *020 †20

AHN, Sangmin. ■ 77004 #583-02-2002 L2006 PM *012

AHRAR, Kamran. 1515 HOLCOMBE BLVD, UNIT 325 77030 #005-06-1993 L2000 VIR *020 †80

AHUJA, Anoop S. 6624 FANNIN ST 77030 #038-06-1995 L2000 OTO *020 †45

AIKU, Idorenyin Leslie. 15770 BELLAIRE BLVD APT 26 77083 #690-12-2002 L2007 FP *012

AINSWORTH, Joseph Thos. ■ 77256 #021-01-1942 L1949 GP *071

AIREWELE, Gladstone. 6621 FANNIN ST CC1510, TEXAS CHILDREN'S CANCER CE 77030 #690-06-1986 L1999 PHO *020 †55

AIYER, Viswanathan C. 1315 ST JOSEPH PKWY, STE 302 77002 #048-12-1997 L2004 AN *020 †05

AJANI, Dilawar. 7777 SOUTHWEST FWY, STE 636 77074 #704-08-1980 L1992 IM *020

AJANI, Jaffer A. 1515 HOLCOMBE BLVD BOX 78 77030 #495-19-1973 L1980 ON *020 †20

AJATTA, Frank Olusegun. 4545 POST OAK PLAC DR #130 77027 #690-08-1991 L2002 IM *020 †20

AJAYI, Abimbola Temitayo. 1007 EDGEBROOK DR 77034 #690-05-1984 L2001 PD *020 †55

AJIM, Alice Amah. 2000 CRAWFORD ST STE 730 77002 #690-02-1992 L2001 IM IMG *020 †20

AJIM, Ayo Ayodeji. 2000 CRAWFORD ST, STE 1118 77002 #690-02-1991 L2001 EM IM *020 †20

AJMANI, Chandra Prabha. 12121 RICHMOND AVE, STE 409 77082 #495-45-1970 L1975 PM *020 †60

AJMANI, Surainder Kumar. 12121 RICHMOND AVE STE 409 77082 #495-45-1966 L1974 IM IMG *020 †28,20

AKAY, Mehmet Hakan. ■ 77025 #902-07-1992 L2006 TS *012 †85

AKCAN, Ayse. ■ 77030 #902-07-1996 PN *100

AKERMAN, Tamar Fay. PO BOX 20708 77225 #048-04-2004 L2007 RHU *012 †20

AKHTAR, Adeeba. 8830 LONG POINT RD STE 20 77055 #160-03-1994 L2005 IMG *100 †18

AKHTAR, Nadeema. 4414 NAVIGATION BLVD, MHMRA 77011 #704-06-1977 L1984 P *020 †75

AKINS, Todd Drake. 12326 GAYLAWOOD DR, UNIV OF TX HSC HOUSTON 77066 #048-15-2000 L2002 AN *100

AKTHAR, Waheeduddin. ■ 77072 #495-57-1974 L1979 IM EM *020

ALADE, Kiyetta Hanan. 6621 FANNIN ST, MC 1-1481 77030 #011-03-2002 L2007 PEM *012 †55

ALAGKIOZIDIS, Ioannis. ■ 77030 #418-02-2002 OBG *012

ALAKAYI, Molly. 2727 W HOLCOMBE BLVD 77025 #905-01-1986 L2005 FM *020 †18

ALAM, Anjum A. 3805 HIGHWAY 6 S 77082 #704-06-1967 L1977 RO FM *020 †80

ALAM, Mahboob. ■ 77054 #704-25-2002 L2008 CD *012 †20

ALANI, Wayne O. 12121 RICHMOND AVE 77082 #048-13-1983 L1989 ORS *020 †40

ALANIS, Audencio. 2001 HERMANN DR, STE 220 77004 #649-02-1979 L1986 GS AS *020 ‡

ALANIZ, John M. 17070 RED OAK DR STE 305 77090 #048-04-1975 L1976 OBG *020

ALAPAT, Philip M. 1504 TAUB LOOP 77030 #048-15-1999 L2001 PCC *020 †20

AL-ASADI, Mazen. 1221 MCKINNEY ST, STE 40300 77010 #875-01-1988 L2001 GE *020 †20

ALAVI SERESHKI, Mary M. 16125 CAIRNWAY DR STE 110 77084 #048-14-1983 L1983 FM *020 †18

ALAWAMI, Amel Hussain. 1 BAYLOR PLZ 77030 #797-03-1995 PD *100 †55 ‡

AL-AWAMI, Yusra H. ■ 77052 #797-03-1987 IM *100 †20

ALBA, Frances Maria. PO BOX 20708, UNIV TX MED SCH 77225 #034-01-2007 GS *012

AL-BAHRANI, Husam Edeen A. 17202 RED OAK DR STE 307 77090 #528-01-1968 L1974 ORS OSM *020 †40

ALBAKSHY, Faiz Radhy. 1 BAYLOR PLZ 77030 #797-03-1983 CD *100 ‡

ALBARRACIN, Constance T. 1515 HOLCOMBE BLVD 77030 #748-01-1984 L2003 PTH *020 †50

AL-BASSAM, Mahdi Saleh. 7737 SW FWY STE 9 77074 #605-01-1971 L1973 CD IM *020 †20

ALBERS, Kenneth O. 909 DAIRY ASHFORD ST # 216 77079 #048-02-1968 L1968 FM *020 †18

ALBERT, Jeffrey Martin. ■ 77004 #047-05-2008 *012

ALBERTO, Paul Christian. 4505 POST OAK PLACE DR, STE 130 77027 #748-01-1992 L2001 IM *020 †20

ALBIN, Jorge. 1919 LA BRANCH ST, ASSOCIATES 77002 #048-14-1982 L1983 DR *020 †80

ALBINA, Bernard Zacharia. 1315 ST JOSEPH PKWY, ORTHOPAEDIC ASSOCIATES 77002 #605-02-1964 L1971 ORS *020 †40

ALBO, Daniel. 2002 HOLCOMBE BLVD, MICHAEL E. DEBAKEY VAMC 77030 #924-01-1991 L2000 GS *020 †85

ALBRECHT, Steffen. ■ 77030 #067-06-1985 PTH *020 †50

ALBRIGHT, James Thomas. 6550 FANNIN ST, STE 2001 77030 #041-09-1996 L2003 OTO PDO *020 †45

ALBRIGHT, Steven Benjamin. ■ 77024 #048-12-2008 *012

ALBUERNE, Luis Mario. 2900 WESLAYAN ST 77027 #847-01-1977 L1986 DR R *020 †80

ALBUQUERQUE, Sheila Marya. 2727 W HOLCOMBE BLVD, 4TH FLOOR ADMINISTRATION 77025 #495-52-1997 L2006 RHU *100 †18

ALCABY, Joseph D. 1 BAYLOR PLZ 77030 #550-02-1980 D *020

ALCORN, Roosevelt. 2636 S LOOP W STE 700 77054 #025-12-1974 L1979 PD *020

ALDAMA-LUEBBERT, Alfonso. 6720 BERTNER ST 77030 #048-04-1974 L1977 NS *020 †25

ALDAPE, Kenneth Dean. 1515 HOLCOMBE BLVD BOX 85, MDACC-DEPT OF PATHOLOGY 77030 #005-02-1991 L2001 NP *020 †50

ALDINGER, Keith Alan. 1315 ST JOSEPH PKWY #16061, ST JOSEPH INT MED ASSOC 77002 #018-03-1973 L1974 IM END *020 †20

AL-DOSSARY, Fahad S. ■ 77056 #797-03-1989 L1993 **PDI** *100 †55

ALEGAILY, Khalid Ahmad. ■ 77288 #797-03-1992 L1998 **PD** *100 †55

ALEXANDER, Charlotte B. 7777 SOUTHWEST FWY, HOUSTON ORTHOPAEDIC 77074 #048-02-1980 L1980 **ORS HS** *020 †40

ALEXANDER, James K. 2002 HOLCOMBE BLVD, HOUSTON VAMC-SECTION 111B 77030 #024-01-1946 L1955 **CD IM** *071 †20

ALEXANDER, Jamile Yasmin. 6624 WAKEFOREST AVE 77005 #010-02-1987 L1989 **R RNR** *020 †20

ALEXANDER, Jessica Aronow. ■ 77019 #048-13-1984 L1993 **AN PME** *071 †05

ALEXANDER, Lauren Ashley. ■ 77030 #048-04-2008 *012

ALEXANDER, Raymond T. 1315 ST JOSEPH PKWY, STE 1101 77002 #048-04-1979 L1979 **IM EM** *020 †20

ALEXANDER, Richard M. 7737 SOUTHWEST FWY STE 200 77074 #035-15-1976 L1983 **TS** *020 †85,90

ALEXANDER, Steven Thomas. ■ 77030 #495-37-2004 **FP** *012

ALEXANDER, Victoria L. 10370 RICHMOND AVE, STE 1125 77042 #048-14-1990 L1991 **IM** *020 †20

ALEXANIAN, Raymond. 1515 HOLCOMBE BLVD # 1 77030 #024-01-1955 L1964 **HEM** *071 †20

AL-FAHL, Mohammed-Tarek. 17202 RED OAK DR STE 307 77090 #033-06-1996 L2001 **OSM** *020 †40

AL-FARIS, Nafisah Ahmed. ■ 77030 #797-03-1992 **PD** *100 †55

AL-FAYYADH, Majid I M. ■ 77030 #797-01-1989 L2000 **PDC** *100 †55

ALFORD, Bobby Ray. 1 BAYLOR PLZ, CHANCELLOR'S OFFICE NA102 77030 #048-04-1956 L1956 **NO HNS** *030 †45

ALFORD, Eugene Landon. 6560 FANNIN ST, STE 704 77030 #048-13-1986 L1987 **FPS OTO** *020 †45

ALFORD, Jack Allen. ■ 77071 #048-04-1955 L1955 **GP OM** *071

ALFORD, Margo Hilliard. 5656 KELLEY ST, LYNDON B JOHNSON HOSPITAL 77026 #035-08-1972 L1975 **PHP PD** *012

ALFREY, Clarence Powhatan. 6620 MAIN ST, 12TH FL 77030 #048-04-1955 L1955 **HEM IM** *071 †20

ALHABBAL, Ghassan Adnan. ■ 77030 #010-02-1991 **OSM** *100

AL-HAJ, Iman Hassan. ■ 77072 #916-01-1992 L2005 **GS** *020

AL-HIMYARY, Ali Jafar S. 6624 FANNIN ST, 19TH FL 77030 #584-01-1989 L1997 **PUD CCM** *020 †20

AL-HOUSSEINI, Ali. 1 BAYLOR PLZ 77030 #605-01-2003 **OBG** *012

ALI, Abdul. 8830 LONG POINT RD, STE 507 77055 #495-21-1965 L1976 **CD** *020 †20

ALI, Afroze. 6630 DE MOSS DR, PEOPLE'S HEALTH CENTER 77074 #495-21-1982 L1995 **IM IMG** *020 †20

ALI, Amna Irshad. PO BOX 20708, DEPT OF PSYCH 77225 #704-02-2001 **P** *012

ALI, Asif. 8830 LONG POINT RD, STE 507 77055 #048-14-2002 L2006 **CD** *012

ALI, Asra. 7737 SW FWY, STE 760 77074 #048-14-1997 L1998 **D** *020 †15

ALI, Fazal Mahmoud. ■ 77054 #704-02-1988 **DR** *100

ALI, Mohamed Salah-Eldin. 2411 FOUNTAIN VIEW DR, STE 200 77057 #915-04-1995 L2003 **AN** *020 †05

ALI, Mohammed B. ■ 77054 #495-74-1984 L1993 **CCM** *020 †20

ALI, Mohammed Khalil. ■ 77036 #330-03-1957 L1972 **PUD CD** *071

ALI, Muntaz. 233 W PARKER RD 77076 #064-01-1966 L1977 **GP** *071

ALI, Sabiha J. 16303 BROOKFORD DR 77059 #495-21-1978 L1985 **N** *040

ALI, Shezi Zulekha. 6624 FANNIN ST, STE 1240 77030 #704-25-1993 L2002 **IM** *020 †20

ALI, Sibtain H. 4407 YOAKUM BLVD, STE 77006 #704-21-1989 L2002 **NEP** *020 †20

ALI, Vaseem. 6431 FANNIN ST STE 3204, UNIV OF TX MEDICAL SCHOOL 77030 #495-21-1965 L1976 **OBG** *020 †30

ALIANELL, Samuel John. 17080 RED OAK DR 77090 #035-15-1989 L1993 **PM** *020 †60

ALIDON, Zenaida Pardillo. 1315 ST JOSEPH PKWY, STE 1703 77002 #748-09-1974 L2005 **NPM PD** *020 †55

ALIPUI VANLARE, Celestine. 4545 POST OAK PLACE DR, STE 130 77027 #412-01-1985 L1997 **IM** *020 †20

ALJAWADI, Georgia. ■ 77074 #048-78-2007, ▲ *012

AL-JURDI, Rayan Kamal. 1 BAYLOR PLZ 77030 #605-01-1998 **P** *100 †75

AL-KARADSHEH, Amer. 8830 LONG POINT RD STE 502 77055 #575-01-1989 L1995 **END** *020 †20

ALKHATIB, Amer 'Ahmad Rif. 6431 FANNIN ST STE 1.150, AT HOUST 77030 #575-01-2002 L2006 **IM** *100 †20

AL-KHURAISHI, Amir Rashee. 8830 LONG POINT RD, STE 507 77055 #919-02-1997 L2004 **GE** *012 †20

ALKURAYA, Fowzan Sami. 14781 MEMORIAL DR # 2321 77079 #797-01-1999 L2000 **MG** *020 †55,19

ALKURAYA, Khawla Sami. 14781 MEMORIAL DR 77079 #797-01-1994 L1994 **PTH** *100 †50

ALKUS, Pelin. ■ 77024 #048-15-2007 **IM** *012

ALLADICE, Tova Liana. 8200 WEDNESBURY LN STE 360 77074 #010-02-1995 L1999 **PM** *020 †60

AL-LAHAM, Aref. PO BOX 542286 77254 #781-04-1982 **U OBG** *100

AL-LAHIQ, Maha K. 11914 ASTORIA BLVD, STE 550 77089 #797-03-1985 L1996 **IM** *020

ALLBRITTON, R Ellen. 18333 EGRET BAY BLVD, STE 305 77058 #048-14-1995 L1996 **P** *020 †75

ALLEN, Bradley Scott. 6431 FANNIN ST, MSB 1.214 77030 #016-42-1981 L2003 **TS** *020 †85,90

ALLEN, Carl Eugene. ■ 77030 #038-40-2002 L2002 **PHO** *012 †55

ALLEN, Coburn H. 6621 FANNIN ST 1-1481 77030 #048-04-1994 L1997 **PDI** *020 †55

ALLEN, Deidra Deshun. 15003 FM 529 RD, STE A 77095 #048-02-2002 L2005 **FM** *020 †18

ALLEN, Herbert C, Jr. 7515 MAIN ST 77030 #051-04-1941 L1952 **NM IM** *071 †28

ALLEN, Joseph Yang. 6621 FANNIN ST, RM A-165 77030 #048-12-1998 L2001 **PEM** *020 †55

ALLEN, Marian Charlotte. 837 FM 1960 RD W, STE 105 77090 #048-04-1985 L1986 **FM** *020 †18

ALLEN, Matthew Wade. ■ 77005 #024-01-2003 **RO** *012

ALLEN, Robert L. 12121 RICHMOND AVE, STE 109 77082 #048-02-1988 L1993 **DR** *020 †80

ALLEN, Sarah Elizabeth. 1709 DRYDEN RD, STE 625 77030 #020-02-1985 L2005 **ID IM** *020 †20

ALLEN, Timothy. 11800 ASTORIA BLVD 77089 #001-02-1997 L2006 *020 †05

ALLEN-DICKERSON, Blythe L. 2004 LEELAND ST 77003 #007-02-2002 L2007 **GPM** *020 †70

ALLEY, Steven S. 6400 FANNIN ST 77030 #048-13-1996 L1998 **PD** *020 †55

ALLEYNE, Paul Andre. ■ 77056 #035-48-1999 L2002 **EM** *020 †16

ALLIBONE, George Wm. ■ 77019 #836-02-1971 L1980 **DR** *071 †80

ALLISON, Ana G Ruiz. 4009 BELLAIRE BLVD, STE K 77025 #042-01-1982 L1990 **IM END** *020

ALLISON, Andrew Eblen. 6431 FANNIN ST 1134, OF TEXAS-HOUSTON 77030 #048-02-2006 **AN** *012

ALLISON, Arthur Polk, Jr. 205 HOLLOW TREE LN 77090 #048-02-1957 L1957 **EM FM** *020 †16,18

ALLISON, James Eblen. 4101 GREENBRIAR ST, STE 100 77098 #048-04-1973 L1973 **PD ID** *020 †55

ALLISON, Paul Mark. 6720 BERTNER ST, MC 4- 265 77030 #017-20-1981 L1990 **PTH BBK** *020 †50

ALLISON, Sara Elizabeth. 2002 HOLCOMBE BLVD 11, HOUSTON VA MEDICAL CENTER 77030 #030-05-2002 L2006 **P** *020

ALLISON, Sean Christian. ■ 77062 #001-02-2003 L2007 **OPH** *100

ALLOJU, Manohar. 12549 GULF FWY 77034 #048-02-1976 L1978 **EM GS** *020 †16

ALLON, Michael A. 10901 KATY FWY 77079 #048-15-1990 L1991 **OBG** *020 †30

ALLON, Moshe. 1234 NASA PKWY 77058 #654-01-1986 L1992 **N IM** *020

AL-MARASHI, Fatma Hassan. 8830 LONG POINT RD STE 502 77055 #517-05-1986 L1997 **IM END** *020 †20 ‡

ALMENDAREZ, Yvette M. 1 BAYLOR PLZ, BAYLOR COLL MED 77030 #048-04-2005 L2008 **PD** *012

ALMOOSA, Khalid Faeq. 6431 FANNIN ST, MSB 1274 77030 #539-06-1995 L2007 **PCC** *020 †20

ALMOUSA, Eyas N. ■ 77054 #575-01-1988 L1995 **IM** *100 †20

ALMULLAHASSANI, Ameer. ■ 77047 #875-01-2002 **N** *012

ALO, Kenneth M. 837 FM 1960 RD W, STE 105 77090 #048-16-1989 L1990 **APM AN** *020 †05

ALO, Melanie Jeanne. 6621 FANNIN ST STE A300 77030 #048-04-1985 L1986 **AN** *020 †05

ALOBAIDI, Mohammad Tarik. 9220 KIRBY DR, STE 700 77054 #010-03-1999 L2004 **DR** *020 †80

ALOIA, Natalie. 7501 PARK PLACE BLVD 77087 #005-14-1996 L2003 **PD** *020 †55

ALOIA, Thomas Anthony. 1515 HOLCOMBE BLVD, BOX 444 77030 #005-14-1996 L2003 **GS** *020 †85

ALOMRANI, Ahmed Nasser. ■ 77030 #797-01-1994 L1998 **PDC** *020 †55

ALONSO, Carol A. ■ 77025 #048-14-2006 **D** *012

ALONSO, Guy T. ■ 77025 #048-14-2006 **PD** *012

ALOUDAT, Sarah Ibrahim. ■ 77030 #575-01-2002 **IM** *012

ALOUSI, Amin Majid. 1515 HOLCOMBE BLVD, MD ANDERSON - UNIT 423 77030 #025-07-1997 L2006 **ON** *020 †20,55

ALP, Mehmet Serdar. 6410 FANNIN ST, STE 1020 77030 #902-03-1986 L1994 **NS** *020

ALPER, Ali Yilmaz. ■ 77058 #902-10-1956 L1967 **AN** *071

ALPERT, Jack Nathaniel. 6624 FANNIN ST, ALPERT & SERMAS 77030 #024-07-1964 L1970 **N** *020 †75 ‡

ALPERT, Lesley C. 6565 FANNIN ST 77030 #024-07-1979 L1982 **ATP** *020 †50

ALPIZAR, Ignacio Asterio. ■ 77071 #275-01-1960 L1976 **AN** *071

ALQUIZA, Dionisio R, Jr. 2002 HOLCOMBE BLVD, V A MEDICAL CENTER 77030 #748-11-1973 L1990 **P GP** *020

ALRAHWAN, Amin David. 18300 SAINT JOHN DR, ST. JOHN HOSPITAL PATHOLOG 77058 #875-01-1994 L2003 **SP** *100 †50

ALREFAI, Ali Hussein. ■ 77057 #575-02-1993 L2001 **CN** *020 †75

AL-SAADI, Mukhtar Ahmed A. 1 BAYLOR PLZ 77030 #528-01-2002 **GS** *012

AL-SABBAGH, Mouhamad R. 6410 FANNIN ST STE 1260 77030 #875-02-1978 L1991 **IM NTR** *020 †20

AL-SALMI, Qasem Ahmed. 6621 FANNIN ST # 3-2571 77030 #695-01-1994 **PDP** *100

AL-SAYED, Moeenaldeen. 1 BAYLOR PLZ, DPT MOL & HUMAN GENETICS 77030 #797-01-1991 L1998 **MG** *020 †55,19

AL-SENANI, Fahmi Mohammed. 6431 FANNIN ST, STE 7044 77030 #797-01-1992 L2001 **N** *100 †75

AL-SERAIHY, Amal Salman. ■ 77054 #797-02-1991 **PHO** *100 †55

AL-SHAER, Moutasim Homod. 11301 FALLBROOK DR STE 130, CYFAIR CARDIOVASCULAR ASSO 77065 #575-01-1994 L2007 **IM VM** *020 †20 ‡

AL-SHALATONI, Hashim M. 5656 KELLEY ST # 1EC73029 77026 #704-21-1995 L2004 **VN** *100

ALSHANTI, Mohammad Sami. 3330 HILLCROFT ST STE D 77057 #704-16-1990 **EM** *020 †16

ALSHARIFI, Nasreen A G. 3701 KIRBY DR, STE 660 77098 #528-01-1969 L1983 **FM** *020 †18

ALSHEHABI, Muna Sadeq. 1 BAYLOR PLZ, DEPT FM 77030 #155-01-2001 **FP** *012

ALSINA, Carlos Roberto. ■ 77057 #132-01-1963 L1973 **P** *020

ALSTOT, Barbara Gayle. ■ 77025 #048-04-1997 **AN** *100

ALTAHER, Ghada Hisham. 12970 EAST FWY, STE I10 77015 #528-01-1985 L2004 **OPH** *020

ALTAMIRA, David A. 7777 SOUTHWEST FWY, STE 640 77074 #048-04-1990 L1991 **PS** *020 †65

ALTINGER, Hans Peter. 7620 BELLFORT ST 77061 #407-16-1951 L1961 **GYN** *020 †30

ALTMAN, Carolyn Ann. 6621 FANNIN ST 19345C, PEDIATRIC CARDIOLOGY 77030 #041-12-1986 L1994 **PDC** *020 †55

ALTMAN, Michael Alan. 6410 FANNIN ST, STE 250 77030 #048-15-1985 L1987 **FM** *020 †18

ALTOBELLI, Mary Elisabeth. ■ 77030 #048-04-2007 **PD** *012

ALTSCHULER, Milton. 4550 POST OAK PLACE DR 77027 #048-02-1959 L1959 **P** *071 †75

ALUKAL, Joseph Paul. ■ 77030 #036-01-2001 L2001 **U** *100

ALVARADO, Maria D. 11800 ASTORIA BLVD 77089 #042-01-1983 L1995 **AN** *020 †05

ALVARADO, Yesid. ■ 77030 #264-11-1994 L2007 **IM** *100 †20

ALVAREZ, Braulio Antonio. 7707 FANNIN ST, STE 250 77054 #649-01-1965 L1973 **PUD IM** *020

ALVAREZ, Hernan, Jr. ■ 77046 #048-02-1952 L1954 **CD** *071

ALVAREZ, Luis Alfonso. 4888 LOOP CENTRAL DR, STE 510 77081 #048-12-1965 L1965 **P** *020 †75

ALVAREZ, Matilde A. ■ 77007 #275-01-1942 **OBG** *074

ALVAREZ, Paulino Antonio. 6550 FANNIN ST STE 1001 77030 #132-11-2001 **IM** *012

ALVAREZ, Ricardo Hugo. 6431 FANNIN ST STE 1.150, AT HOUST 77030 #132-03-1990 L2007 **HO** *012 †20

ALVAREZ, Roberto F. 9511 HUFFMEISTER RD, STE 100 77095 #048-12-1988 L1989 **FM** *020 †18

ALZAGA FERNANDEZ, Ana Gra. ■ 77007 #649-19-2006 **IM** *012

AL-ZAGHRINI, Ghassan J. 2500 FONDREN RD STE 270 77063 #605-01-1992 L1996 **CD** *020 †20

AMADOR, Melissa S. ■ 77075 #048-14-2007 **MPD** *012

AMAJOH, Nwanyieze I. PO BOX 20708, DEPT OF OB/GYN 77225 #038-45-2005 **OBG** *012

AMATO, Robert J. 6560 FANNIN ST, DEPT OF UROLOGY - STE 2050 77030 #048-78-1983, ▲ L1983 **ON** *020

AMAYA, Rene Anthony. 902 FROSTWOOD DR STE 279 77024 #048-12-1995 L2002 **PDI** *020 †55

AMBANI, Dipika Sanjay. 7777 SOUTHWEST FWY, DIPIKA S AMBANI MD PLLC 77074 #496-46-1996 L2006 **OBG** *020

AMEDE, Francis Joseph. 6565 FANNIN ST, THE METHODIST HOSPITAL 77030 #422-01-1991 L2005 **CCM** *020 †20

AMEEN, Ray Charles. 8831 LONG POINT RD STE 204 77055 #048-04-1944 L1944 **GP OS** *071

AMELL-RUSSO, Juan Ramon F. 17400 RED OAK DR, STE 107 77090 #308-01-1973 L1979 **IM CD** *020 †20

AMES, Frederick Carl. 1515 HOLCOMBE BLVD 77030 #048-02-1969 L1969 **ON GS** *020 †85

AMES, Maria Del Rosario. PO BOX 60830, ODESSA REGIONAL HOSPITAL 77205 #748-02-1974 L2000 **PD NPM** *020 †55

AMESUR, Sandeep Nirmal. 3388 SAGE RD, UNIT 2601 77056 #033-06-1994 L2004 **DR** *020 †80

AMIEL, Gilad Eliyahu. 3610 GLEN HAVEN BLVD 77025 #550-04-1993 *100

AMIN, Hesham Mahmoud. 1515 HOLCOMBE BLVD 77030 #915-02-1982 L2002 **HMP** *020 †50

AMIN, Ila Rameschandra. ■ 77064 #495-23-1971 L1982 **GP** *020

AMIN, Rajesh Surendra. 6565 FANNIN ST MS D281, RADIOLOGY DEPT. 77030 #021-06-1996 L1998 **DR** *020 †80

AMIN-SANKAR, Zatul H. 302 W GULF BANK RD 77037 #566-01-1959 L1983 **AN** *020 †05

AMIR, Offer. ■ 77096 #550-04-1989 L1999 **IM** *020 †20

AMJADI, Rojan. 915 GESSNER RD, STE 870 77024 #048-13-1994 L1995 **PS** *020 †65

AMR, Ziad Ahmadsami. 1919 LA BRANCH ST, ST JOSEPH HOSPITAL 77002 #575-01-2000 L2006 **GS** *100 †85

AMRIKACHI, Mojghan. ■ 77030 #902-05-1991 L2000 **SP** *020 †50

AN, Andrea Hyeyong. 18333 EGRET BAY BLVD, STE 650 77058 #035-09-2000 L2005 **CN** *100

AN, Young C. ■ 77057 #048-13-2005 **AN** *012

ANAGNOSTOPOULOS, Athanassi. 1515 HOLCOMBE BLVD, BOX 423 77030 #418-01-1990 *050

ANANABA, Ijeoma Elewachi. ■ 77025 #012-05-2006 **MPD** *012

ANAND, Bhupinderjit Singh. 2002 HOLCOMBE BLVD, VA MEDICAL CENTER 77030 #495-03-1967 L1993 **GE IM** *020 †20

ANAND, Sujatha. 10028 WEST RD 77064 #495-04-1999 L2006 **FM** *100 †18

ANANDAM, Jaishreelin Leel. 6621 FANNIN ST, RM A-170 77030 #047-07-2007 **PD** *012

ANANDU, Darshan Priya. 7333 NORTH FWY, STE 401 77076 #048-13-1989 L1990 **GE** *020 †20

ANANWORANICH, Jintanat. ■ 77054 #891-07-1992 **ALI** *100 †03,55

ANCHONDO, Homero Rene. 909 FROSTWOOD DR, STE 364 77024 #649-27-1965 L1977 **NS** *071 †25

ANCONA-SCHULTZ, Deborah M. 3310 RICHMOND AVE 77098 #035-19-1988 L1996 **RNR** *020 †80

ANDERLINI, Paolo. 1515 HOLCOMBE BLVD # 24 77030 #561-09-1986 L1997 **ON** *020 †20

ANDERSON, Anne E. 1102 BATES AVE, FEIGIN CENTER MC3-6365 77030 #048-02-1987 L1988 **N** *020 †75

ANDERSON, Christopher M. ■ 77047 #018-03-1998 L2002 **PDS** *012 †85

ANDERSON, Clifford E, Jr. 6524 SAN FELIPE ST # 106 77057 #048-02-1966 L1966 **PYA P** *071

ANDERSON, Eli Theodore. 12102 BISSONNET ST 77099 #048-04-1976 L1976 **P** *020

ANDERSON, Heather Lea. ■ 77004 #048-04-2006 **PD** *100

ANDERSON, Hildreth V, III. 6431 FANNIN ST, STE 1246 77030 #012-05-1980 L1989 **CD IM** *020 †20

ANDERSON, Karen Yvonne. 4101 GREENBRIAR ST, STE 330 77098 #048-04-1980 L1981 **NEP** *020 †20

ANDERSON, Marcus R. 6431 FANNIN ST 1.134, OF TEXAS-HOUSTON 77030 #048-14-2007 L2008 **IM** *012

ANDERSON, Matthew L. 6620 MAIN ST 77030 #008-01-1995 L2000 **OBG** *020 †30

ANDERSON, Nancy Louise. ■ 77005 #048-04-1979 L1980 **DR** *074 †80

ANDERSON, Timothy Wm. 1200 BINZ ST STE 630 77004 #035-06-1974 L1979 **CD IM** *020

ANDERSSON, Borje Sven. 1515 HOLCOMBE BLVD, UNIT 423 77030 #858-02-1977 L1983 **HEM IM** *020

ANDING, Robert Glenn. 7900 FANNIN ST, STE 4000 77054 #021-05-1985 L1989 **OBG** *020 †30

ANDINO, Cesar Augusto. 6565 DE MOSS DR STE 100 77074 #451-01-1983 L1997 **FM** *020 †18

ANDINO, Lizmarie. ■ 77004 #042-03-2003 L2007 **SP** *012 †50

ANDRABI, Tayab Reza Shah. 1515 HOLCOMBE BLVD 77030 #704-20-1984 L1993 **AN** *020 †05

ANDRADE, Roberto Agustin. 2015 THOMAS ST, THOMAS ST CLINIC 77009 #319-04-1995 L2003 **ID** *020 †20

ANDRADE ALTUVE, Javier En. ■ 77054 #935-01-2001 L2004 **GS** *012

ANDRASSY, Richard John. 6431 FANNIN ST, UTHSC HOUSTON 77030 #051-04-1972 L1975 **PDS TRS** *020 †85

ANDREEFF, Michael. 1515 HOLCOMBE BLVD, BOX 448 77030 #407-10-1968 L1991 **HO** *050

ANDREOPOULOU, Eleni. 1515 HOLCOMBE BLVD, UNIT 1354 77030 #418-04-1994 L2007 **ON** *100

ANDREWS, Joan Patchett. 4110 BELLAIRE BLVD, STE 210 77025 #010-02-1992 L1999 **PD GP** *020 †55

ANDREWS, Linda Boerger. 1 BAYLOR PLZ # 350 77030 #039-01-1989 L1993 **P** *030 †75

ANDREWS, William Ross. 6411 FANNIN ST, ROBERTSON 653 77030 #065-06-1982 L2008 **CCM AN** *020 †05

ANDROPOULOS, Dean Barbara. 6621 FANNIN ST, WT 19345H 77030 #005-18-1984 L1998 **PD** *020 †05,55

ANG, Kie Kian. 1515 HOLCOMBE BLVD BOX 97 77030 #165-04-1975 L1987 **RO** *020 †80

ANGEL, Jorge. ■ 77027 #264-01-1953 L1962 **NS** *071 †25

ANGEL, Tiffany Alyse. 7737 SOUTHWEST FWY STE 350 77074 #048-14-1997 L1998 **D** *020 †15

ANGELINI, Paolo. 6624 FANNIN ST, STE 2780 77030 #561-03-1968 L1974 **CD IM** *020

ANGELO, Christopher S. 1740 W 27TH ST, STE 221 77008 #028-79-1968, ▲ L1969 **FM** *020

ANGLIN, Larry Wayne. 600 N DAIRY ASHFRD #MC2021 77079 #021-01-1972 L1974 **OM PHP** *020 †70

ANGUAY, John Christopher. ■ 77047 #023-01-2004 **GS** *020

ANGUIANO, Grizelda Morale. ■ 77054 #048-14-2006 L2008 **PD** *012

ANHALT, Melvyn Alan. 915 GESSNER RD STE 720 77024 #001-02-1964 L1968 **U** *020 †95

ANIGBOGU, John Chike. 11000 FONDREN RD, BLD # A 77096 #048-02-1991 1996 **PRS PM** †60

ANKOMA-SEY, Victor. 6410 FANNIN ST STE 225, LIVER ASSOCIATES OF TEXAS 77030 #412-01-1987 L1996 **GE HEP** *050 †20

ANMUTH, David M. 7707 FANNIN ST STE 195 77054 #041-13-2002 L2007 **AI** *020 †55,03

ANNAMALAI, Palaniappan. ■ 77030 #016-11-2000 L2003 **VIR** *100 †80

ANNAMANENI, Amit. 800 PEAKWOOD DR, STE 4E 77090 #495-21-1983 L1996 **PUD CCM** *020 †20

ANNAMBHOTLA, Suman. ■ 77004 #001-02-2005 L2008 **GS** *012

ANNIGERI, Shivayogi C. 2002 HOLCOMBE BLVD, VA MED CTR 77030 #495-72-1978 L1988 **IM** *020

ANSARI, Safdar Abbas. 1 BAYLOR PLZ 77030 #704-25-2003 **IM** *100

ANTANI, Rupa Rashmikant. ■ 77003 #917-01-2000 L2003 **CN** *012

ANTHIS, Cynthia Neitzey. 3755 GRAMERCY ST 77025 #048-04-1992 L1993 **FM** *020 †18

ANTHIS, Joel Norman. 18220 TOMBALL PKWY STE 185 77070 #048-04-1995 **OTO** *020 †45

ANTHUMANICKAM VENKATESH, S. 2411 FOUNTAIN VIEW DR, STE 200 77057 #495-16-1990 L2004 **AN** *020 †05

ANTOINE-TAYLOR, Mercella. 3701 KIRBY DR, STE 600 77098 #566-01-1996 L2007 **FM** *100

ANTON, James Michael. PO BOX 20345, TEXAS MED CTR MC 1-226 77225 #010-02-1998 L2003 **AN** *020 †05 ‡

ANTON, Rose Cecelie. 1 BAYLOR PLZ, DEPT PTH 77030 #045-01-1994 L1997 **PTH** *020 †50

ANTONETTI, Carlos C. 515 W LITTLE YORK RD 77091 #275-01-1943 L1966 **IM OS** *020

ANWAR, Sadaf. 11920 ASTORIA BLVD STE 390 77089 #704-02-1997 L2004 **FM** *020

ANWAR, Zahida Riffat. 6431 FANNIN ST # 5020 77030 #917-18-1981 *020

ANZALONE, Mary Lynn. 1885 OLD SPANISH TRL, JOSEPH A. JACHIMCZYK FOREN 77054 #021-05-1991 L2004 **PTH** *020 †50

APARASU, Anuradha. 4545 POST OAK PLACE DR, STE 130 77027 #495-21-1995 L2006 **IM** *020 †20

APONTE, Miriam Del Carmen. 2211 NORFOLK ST STE 104 77098 #715-01-1977 L1984 **P** *020 †75

APPEL, Michael Frederick. 6624 FANNIN ST STE 2500 77030 #048-04-1961 L1961 **GS** *020 †85

APPEL, Stanley Hersh. 6560 FANNIN ST STE 802, METHODIST NEUROLOGICAL INS 77030 #035-01-1960 L1976 **N OS** *020 †75

APPELL, Rodney Alan. 6560 FANNIN ST, STE 2100 77030 #041-02-1973 L2002 **U** *020 †95

APPIAH, William Opoku. 211 HIGHLAND CROSS DR 77073 #010-03-2004 L2007 **EM** *020

APPLEYARD, Joan. 6909 GREENBRIAR ST 77030 #011-02-1988 L1994 **RHU** *020 †20

APPLING, Maria Morazzani. 7580 FANNIN ST STE 335 77054 #048-04-1979 L1979 **OBG** *071 †30

APPLING, Walter Douglas. 2500 TANGLEWILDE ST, STE 160 77063 #048-04-1977 L1977 **OTO HNS** *020 †45

AQUINO, Laura. 2411 FOUNTAIN VIEW DR #200, 1 77057 #048-12-1978 L1978 **BBK AN** *020 †05

AQUINO, Marcus M. 1213 HERMANN DR, STE 530 77004 #495-52-1978 L1988 **CRS** *020 †10,85

ARA, Mary M. ■ 77035 #048-14-2008 †012

ARAB, Samer Nimr. 1 BAYLOR PLZ, BAYLOR COLL OF MED 77030 #575-02-2003 **GS** *012

ARAI, David Andrew. 1313 HERMANN DR 77004 #016-11-1988 L1994 **EM** *020 †16

ARAMAYO, Willy Lizandro. 150 W PARKER RD, STE 110 77076 #176-01-1969 L1975 **FM GS** *020

ARANA, Antonio. 1221 MCKINNEY ST, STE 40300 77010 #847-11-1971 L1978 **N** *071 †75

ARANI, Mohsen. 1709 DRYDEN RD STE 667, BAYLOR COLLEGE OF MEDICINE 77030 #473-04-1996 L2007 **HO** *012 †20

ARAP, Wadih. 1515 HOLCOMBE BLVD, BOX 1374 77030 #187-04-1983 L2000 **ON HO** *050

ARAT, Anil. 1 BAYLOR PLZ, DEPT OF RADIOLOGY STE 165 77030 #902-05-1994 L2007 **RNR** *100

ARAUJO, John Charles. 1515 HOLCOMBE BLVD, BOX 438 77030 #016-43-2000 L2003 **ON** *020 †20

ARAUZ, Julio Cesar. 3100 BROADWAY ST STE 104E, CLINICA FAMILIAR 77017 #682-01-1984 L1994 **FM** *020 †18 ‡

ARBAB, Farinaz. 12141 RICHMOND AVE 77082 #517-01-1989 L2004 **PTH PCP** *020 †50

ARCENEAUX, Matthew Steven. 11800 ASTORIA BLVD 77089 #048-02-1990 L1991 **AN** *020 †05

ARCHER, Kathleen Frances. 1229 CAMPBELL RD 77055 #003-01-1981 L1982 **OPH PS** *020 †35

ARCHIBONG, Emma Virginia. ■ 77025 #036-07-2007 **PD** *012

ARCILLA, Juanita Rivera. 11000 FONDREN RD 77096 #748-08-1970 L1986 **PM** *020

ARDALI, Bedia Muzaffer. ■ 77063 #902-03-1949 L1967 **PUD IM** *074

ARDOIN, Charles D, Jr. 9301 SOUTHWEST FWY, STE 480 77074 #048-14-1989 L1990 **FM** *030 †18

ARDUINO, Roberto Claudio. 6431 FANNIN ST 77030 #132-01-1982 L1994 **ID** *020

ARELLANO, Victor-Hugo. ■ 77041 #319-01-1977 L1985 **EM IM** *020 †16

AREM, Ridha. 7501 FANNIN ST, STE 730 77054 #895-01-1976 L1983 **END IM** *020 †20

ARENARE, Brian Anthony. 1400 EL CAMINO VILLAGE DR 77058 #008-01-1983 L1998 **GPM** *020 †70

ARENE, Ifeoma Nwakaego. 12834 WILLOW CTR, STE E 77066 #690-02-1994 L2002 **CHP** *020 †75

ARENIVAR, Leroy. ■ 77005 #048-14-2007 **P** *012

ARFA, Kenneth Scott. 5225 YARWELL DR 77096 #048-12-1987 L1988 **P PFP** *020 †75

ARFAI, Parviz. 7777 SOUTHWEST FWY STE 724 77074 #517-01-1961 L1971 **PS HS** *020 †65

ARGUELLO, Pedro Miguel. 9190 OLD KATY RD, STE 102 77055 #319-03-1982 L1997 **GE IM** *020 †20

ARIAS, Cesar Augusto. 6431 FANNIN ST, MSB 2.112 77030 #264-18-1992 L2007 **ID** *012 †20

ARIAS, Waleska Enid. 6621 FANNIN ST, MC 2-3450 77030 #042-02-1996 L1998 **CCP** *020

ARIBI, Ahmed Mohmmed. 1711 OLD SPANISH TRL, APT 428 77054 #613-02-1996 L2005 **IM** *100 †20

ARKUS, Robert Leslie. 7500 BEECHNUT ST STE 2100 77074 #041-02-1969 L1975 **GE IM** *020

ARLINGHAUS, Kimberly A. 2002 HOLCOMBE BLVD, 116MH 77030 #048-04-1986 L1987 **P** *020 †75

ARMADA, Michelle Marie. ■ 77030 #042-02-2005 L2008 **EM** *012

ARMAND, Ray. 1140 BUSINESS CENTER DR, STE 370 77043 #517-01-1990 L2004 **HMP** *020

ARMISTEAD, Paul Michael. 1515 HOLCOMBE BLVD, UNIT 438 77030 #036-01-2002 L2005 **ON** *012 †20

ARMITAGE, Lisa Yvonne. 6431 FANNIN ST, MSB1.122 77030 #048-14-1998 L2003 **ID** *100 †55,20

ARMSTEAD, Sumiko Iesha. ■ 77071 #048-04-2007 **IM** *012

ARMSTRONG, Davill. 6826 W MONTGOMERY RD 77091 #033-06-1974 L1979 **IM CD** *020

ARMSTRONG, Dawna Lavina. 6621 FANNIN ST, STE B1 77030 #062-01-1961 L1977 **NP** *020

ARMSTRONG, Joanne C. 2807 NOTTINGHAM ST, DEPT OBGYN, BAYLOR COLLEGE 77005 #033-05-1988 L1999 **OBG** *020 †30

ARMSTRONG, Richard M. 6501 FANNIN ST NB302, NEUROLOGY ASSOC. 77030 #062-01-1961 L1977 **N** *030

ARMSTRONG, Robin L. 4545 POST OAK PLACE DR, STE 130 77027 #048-02-1998 L2001 **IM** *020 †20

ARMSTRONG, Ryan N. ■ 77006 #048-13-2003 L2006 **DR** *012

ARNAL, Luisa Eugenia. ■ 77077 #935-01-2000 L2006 **PDI** *100 †55

ARNAOUT, Diane. ■ 77007 #048-13-2007 **PD** *012

ARNETT, Frank C, Jr. 6431 FANNIN ST, DEPT INT MED 77030 #038-41-1968 L1985 **RHU** *050 †20

ARNOLD, W Thos. 6448 FANNIN ST 77030 #048-02-1944 L1944 **GE IM** *071

ARNOULT, Jeffrey Blake. 1220 AUGUSTA DR, STE 100 77057 #048-14-1976 L1976 **OPH** *020 †35

AROCHA, Bernardino A. 3005 HULDY ST 77098 #011-02-1982 L1983 **IM** *020

ARONSON, Charles. ■ 77063 #836-01-1944 L1978 **OTO** *071

ARORA, Anita. ■ 77004 #021-05-2005 L2006 **D** *012

ARORA, Harvinder Singh. 6720 BERTNER ST RM P355, EPISCOPAL HOSPITAL 77030 #495-36-2002 L2006 **CD** *012

ARORA, Mukand Lal. 8300 HOMESTEAD RD 77028 #495-45-1963 L1977 **P PD** *020

ARPINO, Grazia. 1 BAYLOR PLZ, BAYLOR COLL OF MED 77030 #561-31-1997 **HO** *012

ARREDONDO, Odette. ■ 77004 #048-02-1997 L2002 **IM** *020 †18

ARRIBAS, Elsa Maria. 1515 HOLCOMBE BLVD 77030 #042-01-1996 L2001 **DR** *020 †80

ARRINGTON, Amy Sharon. 6621 FANNIN ST, RM A170 77030 #048-04-2007 **PD** *012

ARROYO, Jesus Manuel. 9910 ORCHARD CT 77054 #042-01-2002 L2004 **EM** *020 †16

ARSHAD, Syed. 710 FM 1960 RD W 77090 #704-02-1989 L2001 **IM** *020 †20

ARUFFO, Roy N. ■ 77005 #041-01-1957 L1974 **PYA P** *072

ARUN, Banu Kaniye. 1515 HOLCOMBE BLVD # 56, UT/MD ANDERSON CANCER CENT 77030 #902-07-1989 L1998 **HO** *020

ARUNKUMAR, Radha. 1400 HOLCOMBE BLVD UNIT 4, MD ANDERSON CANCER CENTER 77030 #495-04-1987 L2005 **AN** *020 †05

ASALY, Abidel-Rahim. 6431 FANNIN ST 77030 #550-04-1988 **IC CD** *100

ASANO, Ichiko. 6431 FANNIN ST, MSB 5 020 77030 #572-46-1997 **AN** *100 †05

ASBURY, James. 2617C W HOLCOMBE BLVD, STE 431 77025 #047-06-1995 L2001 **AN** *020

ASGHAR, Ali. 2002 HOLCOMBE BLVD, MENTAL HEALTH CARE LINE 77030 #495-57-1974 L1984 **P** *020

ASGHARALI, Ali Abbas. 2002 HOLCOMBE BLVD 77030 #036-05-2000 L2003 **PYG** *020 †75

ASHE, Herbert John, Jr. 1221 MCKINNEY ST, STE 40300 77010 #021-05-1980 L1985 **OTO** *030 †45

ASHKENAZI, Shabtai-Shai. ■ 77071 #550-01-1977 L1990 *020

ASHMORE, Edward Lane. 7401 MAIN ST 77030 #010-03-1981 L1985 **AN** *020

ASHOK KUMAR, A J. 1515 HOLCOMBE BLVD BOX 57, DEPT OF RADIOLOGY 77030 #495-04-1967 L1994 **R** *020 †80

ASHRAF, Deeba Ruxana. 2800 S MACGREGOR WAY, STE 3E 77021 #048-14-2002 L2007 **CHP** *020

ASHRAF, Madiha. 6550 FANNIN ST STE 1001 77030 #704-25-2005 **IM** *012

ASHRAF, Noman. 1709 DRYDEN RD STE 550, BCM FACULTY CENTER 77030 #704-25-2003 **IM** *012

ASHRITH, Guha. PO BOX 20708, UNIV TX MED SCH AT HOUSTON 77225 #495-52-2002 L2008 **IM** *100 †20

ASHTON, Carol Marie. 2002 HOLCOMBE BLVD, VA MEDICAL CENTER 77030 #048-02-1980 L1980 **IM IMG** *050 †20

ASIMACOPOULOS, P John. 2476 BOLSOVER ST STE 526 77005 #418-01-1967 L1982 **TS** *020 †85

ASKENASY, Erik P. ■ 77054 #048-14-2005 **GS** *012

ASKEW, Linda Lee G. ■ 77057 #048-14-1986 L1989 **P** *020 †75

ASLAM, Muhammed Javed. 14340 TORREY CHASE BLVD 77014 #704-01-1961 L1977 **HEM IM** *071 †50,20

ASLAM, Saima. 1 BAYLOR PLZ, BAYLOR COLL OF MED 77030 #704-25-1999 L2005 **ID** *100 †20

ASSASSI, Shervin. 6431 FANNIN ST 5.264 77030 #409-05-1999 L2005 **RHU** *020 ‡

ASSEF, Rosalyn Sarmiento. 5757 WOODWAY DR, STE 200 77057 #001-02-1989 L1999 **PD** *020 †55

ASSOUAD, Mario. 6560 FANNIN ST, STE 2204 77030 #875-02-1990 L1997 **NEP IM** *020 †20

ASTORINO, Lauren Diane. 6720 BERTNER ST 77030 #048-04-1983 L1984 *020

ASUMUGHA, Kingsley N. 11003 RESOURCE PKWY, STE 104 77089 #004-01-1988 L1994 **OBG** *020 †30

ATASHBAND, Armita. ■ 77098 #048-15-2006 **IM** *012

ATER, Joann Lynnette M. 1515 HOLCOMBE BLVD, DEPT PEDIATRICS BOX 87 77030 #028-02-1977 L1988 **PHO** *020 †55

ATER, Stewart Bruce. 7737 SOUTHWEST FWY, STE 955 77074 #028-02-1976 L1989 **CHN PD** *020 †55,75

ATHANASSIOU, Nicolas. 6565 FANNIN ST STE B452, ANESTHESIOLOGY 77030 #418-01-1986 L2002 **AN** *020 †05

ATHAR, Nishath. 1709 DRYDEN RD STE 1100, DEPT OF OB-GYN 77030 #036-07-2002 L2006 **OBG** *040

ATHAR, Parveen. 6431 FANNIN ST, DEPT. OF NEUROLOGY 77030 #027-01-1993 L2003 **N** *020 †75

ATHARI, Mohammad. 2321 SOUTHWEST FWY 77098 #517-01-1970 L1976 **N** *020 †75

ATHEY, Patricia Ann. 1 BAYLOR PLZ, DEPARTMENT OF RADIOLOGY 77030 #048-04-1970 L1970 **DR** *020 †80

ATKINSON, Jonnae Olivia. ■ 77054 #010-01-2005 **FP** *012

ATLURU, Narayana Rao. 17150 EL CAMINO REAL, STE E 77058 #495-50-1970 L1978 **AN** *020 †05

ATMAKURI, Satyaprakas P. ■ 77082 #012-05-2000 L2005 **IC** *100 †20

ATMAR, Robert L. 1504 TAUB LOOP 77030 #048-04-1981 L1982 **ID IM** *020 †20

ATRI, Ashutosh. ■ 77054 #495-93-2005 **P** *012

ATTALA, Mohamed Naguib E. 1515 HOLCOMBE BLVD UNIT 42, UT MD ANDERSON CANCER CENT 77030 #915-02-1976 L1999 *020

ATTALLAH, Antonious Safwa. 1709 DRYDEN RD STE 550, BCM FACULTY CENTER 77030 #033-05-2006 **IM** *012

ATTIA, Samuel Labib. 6624 FANNIN ST STE 1460 77030 #915-03-1966 L1975 **U** *020 †95

ATTISHA, Walid K. 902 FROSTWOOD DR, STE 275 77024 #048-04-2001 L2004 **RNR** *020 †80

ATWAL, Diana Tej. 6630 DE MOSS DR, PEOPLES CLINIC 77074 #024-05-2001 L2005 **FM** *020 †18

AUER, David Edgar. 12121 RICHMOND AVE, STE 301 77082 #028-03-1991 L1995 **FM** *020 †18

AUGUST, Todd Robt. ■ 77007 #035-20-1979 L1981 **IM** *020 †20,16

AUSTIN, Robert Fleming. 5737 CULLEN BLVD, STE 200 77021 #047-07-1963 L1975 **PD** *020

AUSTIN, Sharon Gunter. 7011 SOUTHWEST FWY, MHMRA MENTAL HEALTH DIVISI 77074 #025-07-1991 L2005 **P** *020

AVENDANO, Amilcar. 17080 RED OAK DR 77090 #429-02-1986 L1994 **CD** *020 †20

AVERETT, Lauren Marie. ■ 77005 #048-04-2003 L2006 **HO** *012 †20

AVERY, Parnell Napoleon. 1213 HERMANN DR 77004 #047-07-1962 L1971 **GS FM** *075

AVES, Teodulo Manuel. 9055 KATY FWY, STE 418 77024 #028-02-1989 L1990 **AN** *020 †05

AVILA, Justo S, Jr. 5990 AIRLINE DR 77076 #748-01-1957 L1977 **ORS** *071 †40

AVILES, Francisco. 2139 SOUTHGATE BLVD, HOUSTON VAMC 77030 #042-01-1967 L1973 **P** *020 †75

AWAD, Ketti. 6624 FANNIN ST STE 1210 77030 #035-09-2000 L2003 **IM** *020 †20

AWAD, Sally Henin. 6431 FANNIN ST 417, DEPT EMERGENCY MEDICINE 77030 #048-12-1995 L2000 **EM** *020 †16

AWAD, Samir Samuel. 6550 FANNIN ST, STE 1661 77030 #041-02-1993 L2000 **GS** *020 †85

AWADALLA, Hany Mohamedahm. ■ 77054 #915-04-1995 *100

AWAIS, Ahmed. PO BOX 20708 77225 #704-25-2002 **IM** *012

AWAIS, Muhammad. PO BOX 20708 77225 #704-25-2005 **IM** *012

AWOBOKUN, Oluyemisi O. 4545 POST OAK PLACE DR, STE 130 77027 #690-01-1987 L2005 **RHU** *100 †20

AXLER, Maxwell L. 9432 OLD KATY RD, STE 200 77055 #065-05-1969 L1977 **FM FSM** *020 †18

AYALA, Alberto Gabriel. 1515 HOLCOMBE BLVD BX 85 77030 #649-02-1962 L1967 **PTH** *030 †50

AYALA, Gladys Patricia. ■ 77054 #035-03-2007 **IM** *012

AYALA, Gustavo Enrique. 1 BAYLOR PLZ # 286A 77030 #726-01-1989 L1999 **PTH** *020 †50

AYANBULE, Oluwafunmil. PO BOX 20708, DEPT OF SURGERY 77225 #016-11-2006 **GS** *012

AYCOCK, Phillip Douglas. 710 FM 1960 RD W 77090 #048-04-1962 L1962 **P** *071

AYENSU-COKER, Leslie Efe. 6550 FANNIN ST STE 880, BAYLOR COLLEGE OF MED 77030 #048-12-2000 L2005 **OBG** *100

AYOOLA, Angelina Ibiwari. 11811 FM 1960 RD W 77065 #690-01-1983 L2000 **FM** *020 †18

AYOUB, Mohammed. ■ 77062 #495-21-1986 L2000 **CHP** *075

AYRES, Nancy Ann. 6621 FANNIN ST, TX CHILDRENS HOSPITAL 77030 #048-15-1977 L1977 **PDC** *055

AYYAR, Geetha P. ■ 77024 #048-14-1999 L2005 **DR** *100 †80

AYYAR, Subramanyam M. 1631 NORTH LOOP W, STE 220 77008 #048-14-1994 L1999 **GS** *020 †85

AZAD, Jaspaul S. 902 FROSTWOOD DR, STE 168 77024 #048-02-1999 L2005 **GE** *020 †20

AZAR, Nicole. 12141 RICHMOND AVE 77082 #605-01-1987 L1995 **AN** *020

AZARI, Parinaz. ■ 77006 #422-01-2006 **PM** *012

AZEEMUDDIN, Shakeela. 10707 W BELLFORT ST 77099 #495-65-1978 L1987 **PD** *020 †55

AZEEMUDDIN, Syed Khaja. 10707 W BELLFORT ST 77099 #495-65-1974 L1982 **HEM PD** *020

AZIMPOOR, Ali Faghani. 8830 LONG POINT RD STE 103 77055 #517-03-1965 L1975 **NS** *020 †20

AZIMPOOR, Farzad. ■ 77024 #048-02-2007 L2007 **IM** *012

AZIZ, Nasim Akhtar. ■ 77062 #704-06-1965 L1982 **OBG** *071

AZIZZADEH-FARD, Ali. 6410 FANNIN ST, STE 450 77030 #048-04-1998 L2003 **GS VS** *020 †85

AZZAM, Jamil Teofilo. 1504 TAUB LOOP, BEN TAUB GEN HOSP 77030 #605-01-1958 L1970 **PD PDA** *040 †55

BAAKLINI, Walid A. 6624 FANNIN ST STE 1900 77030 #605-01-1993 L1997 **PCC** *020

BABA, Mohammad. 2060 SPACE PARK DR, STE 406 77058 #875-01-1988 L1995 **PCC IM** *020 †20

BABAIAN, Richard J. 1515 HOLCOMBE BLVD 1373, DEPT OF UROLOGY, UNIT 77030 #010-02-1972 L1979 **U** *071 †95

BABBAR, Harsh. ■ 77030 #495-45-1998 L2008 **PCC** *012 †20

BABBER, Parikshet Ahuja. 211 HIGHLAND CROSS DR, STE 275 77073 #422-01-2000 L2005 **IM** *020 †20

BABBITT, Kriste E. ■ 77004 #048-14-2008 *012

BABCOCK, James Chapman. ■ 77005 #048-04-1981 L1982 **EM** *020 †16

BABER, Harold Truman. 17070 RED OAK DR, STE 401 77090 #004-01-1968 L1969 **FM** *020 †18

BABIERA, Gildy Vallarta. 1515 HOLCOMBE BLVD, BOX 444 77030 #035-09-1991 L1997 **GS** *020 †85

BABINEAUX, Michael James. ■ 77004 #021-05-2008 *012

BABINEAUX, Tyeshia V. ■ 77089 #048-02-2004 L2007 **PD** *020

BACANI, Eugenio Martin. 12345 KATY FWY, URGENT CAR FACILITY 77079 #048-12-1985 L1986 **FM** *020 †18

BACANI, Marcial Judebarba. 6565 FANNIN ST 77030 #048-02-1983 L1985 **AN** *020 †05

BACHOURA, Alex G. ■ 77054 #048-14-2007 **GS** *012

BACHYNSKY, Nicholas. 5314 DASHWOOD DR 77081 #047-06-1971 L1973 **IM END** *075

BACINO, Carlos Alberto. 6701 FANNIN ST, STE 1560 77030 #132-01-1980 L1994 **CG PD** *020 †55,19

BACKES, Susan. 4550 POST OAK PLACE DR, STE 252 77027 #021-05-1979 L1982 **P** *020 †75

BACKLAS, Daniel R. ■ 77007 #847-04-1981 L1988 **DR** *020 †80

BACKLAS, Purnima Lama. 6505 PICKENS ST, UNIT 1 77007 #495-39-1976 L1990 **DR PTH** *020

BACON, Robert John. BEN TAUB GEN HOSP 77030 #047-07-1947 L1953 **U** *071 †95

BACON, Robert John, Jr. 3100 WESLAYAN ST STE 350 77027 #047-07-1975 L1978 **P** *020

BADAR, Tehmina A. 7500 BEECHNUT ST STE 250 77074 #048-02-1993 L1995 **PCC SME** *020 †20

BADEA, Anda Roxana. 7322 SOUTHWEST FWY, STE 160 77074 #781-01-1990 L2005 **FM** *020 †18

BADGWELL, Christy Michele. 1 BAYLOR PLZ, BAYLOR COLL MED 77030 #048-04-2006 **D** *012

BAERENSTECHER, John G. 921 GESSNER RD, ANES DEPT STE 226 77024 #048-14-1991 L1993 **AN** *020

BAERENSTECHER, Karen H. 6565 FANNIN ST 77030 #048-14-1993 L1994 **IM** *020 †20

BAGREE, Ameena. PO BOX 20708 77225 #495-02-2005 **DR** *012

BAGWELL, Shannon Huffer. 211 HIGHLAND CROSS DR, STE 275 77073 #048-14-2004 L2007 **EM** *020

BAHRAMI, Armita. 1 BAYLOR PLZ, DEPT OF PATHOLOGY 77030 #517-01-1995 L2007 **PTH** *012

BAHRANI, Mahmoud Abdul H. ■ 77024 #528-01-1961 **PD OS** *020 †55

BAI, Yu. 6431 FANNIN ST, DEPT OF PATHOLOGY UTHSC-H 77030 #243-47-1987 L2005 **BBK** *150 †50

BAIG, Basith Mirza. 8945 LONG POINT RD, STE 125 77055 #704-02-1984 L1991 **CD IM** *020 †20,55

BAIG, Imran. 13259 EAST FWY I10 77015 #704-25-1992 L1998 **PD** *020 †55

BAIG, Mukarram A. 11840 FM 1960 RD W 77065 #704-25-1989 L1998 **CD IM** *020 †20

BAIG, Naghma Kaifi. 6565 FANNIN ST 77030 #704-02-1987 L1998 **AN** *020

BAIK, Annie K. ■ 77005 #043-01-2004 L2006 **OPH** *012

BAILARD, Neil Stephane. 6550 FANNIN ST STE 1003, DEPT OF ANESTHESIOLOGY 77030 #005-06-2001 L2005 **AN** *100 †05

BAILE, Walter Franklin. 1515 HOLCOMBE BLVD, UNIT 135 77030 #561-14-1972 L1994 **P** *020 †75

BAILEY, Amanda Michelle. ■ 77054 #004-01-2007 **PD** *012

BAILEY, Amber Jo. ■ 77054 #039-01-2004 **PD** *100

BAILEY, Franchelle Yvette. ■ 77091 #048-04-1993 L1994 **IM** *020 †20

BAILEY, Harold Randolph. 6550 FANNIN ST STE 2307 77030 #048-12-1968 L1968 **CRS** *020 †85,10

BAILEY, Jason Richard. ■ 77004 #048-14-2004 L2007 **GS** *012

BAILEY, Margaret Carey. ■ 77065 #047-06-1964 L1968 **IM** *071 †20

BAILEY, Pamela Jean. 6621 FANNIN ST 1-1481, TEXAS CHILDRENS HOSP 77030 #048-14-1987 L1994 **PD** *020 †20

BAILEY, Regina Anastasia. ■ 77047 #010-01-2008 *012

BAILEY, Richard Wardell. ■ 77054 #048-04-1996 **FM** *100

BAINBRIDGE, Terry C. ■ 77096 #061-01-1987 L1990 **PTH ON** *020 †50

BAIRD, James D. 2727 W HOLCOMBE BLVD, SURGERY DEPT, 3A 77025 #048-04-2000 L2005 **GS** *020 †85

■ = Address Information Privacy Protected

BAIRD, John Mathis. 1616 FOUNTAIN VIEW DR #511 77057 #048-02-1963 L1963 **U GS** *020 †95

BAIRD, Maryam Hakimzadeh. 7900 FANNIN ST, STE 4000 77054 #048-04-2001 L2005 **OBG** *020 †30

BAIRD, Samuel Howard. 6720 BERTNER ST, 2-270 77030 #048-13-1970 L1971 **RNR R** *020 †80

BAJOYO, Aries Palmejar. 4545 POST OAK PLACE DR, STE 130 77027 #748-14-1992 L2006 **IM** *020 †20

BAJWA, Kulvinder S. 7737 SOUTHWEST FWY, STE 965 77074 #048-13-1995 L2000 **GS** *020 †85

BAJWA, Mohsin Kalim. 411 LANTERN BEND DR, STE 235 77090 #704-20-1982 L1995 **PCC CCM** *020 †20

BAKAEEN, Faisal Ghazi. 2002 HOLCOMBE BLVD, MICHAEL E. DEBAKEY VA MEDI 77030 #917-03-1994 L2004 **TS** *020 †85,90

BAKER, Annmarie Rose. 6431 FANNIN ST, SCHOOL A 77030 #048-13-2004 **PD** *100

BAKER, Ashley Ann. ■ 77054 #048-04-2007 **PD** *012 †55

BAKER, Benton, III. 2600 NORTH LOOP W, STE 453 77092 #048-04-1974 L1974 **OBG U** *071 †30

BAKER, Byron Wycke. 6720 BERTNER ST 77030 #048-04-1981 L1983 **AN** *020 †05

BAKER, Carol Jane. 6701 FANNIN ST 77030 #048-04-1968 L1968 **ID PD** *050 †55

BAKER, Dudley D, IV. 13215 DOTSON RD, STE 200 77070 #048-02-1987 L1988 **OBG** *020 †30

BAKER, Ellen S. ■ 77062 #035-20-1978 L1980 **AM IM** *030 †20

BAKER, Kelty R. 6560 FANNIN ST, STE 1260 77030 #048-04-1993 L1994 **HEM** *020 †20

BAKER, Kemba Pili. 15655 CYPRESSWOOD MEDCL DR 77014 #048-02-2004 L2007 **PD** *020 †55

BAKER, Macarthur Leon. ■ 77075 #021-05-2005 **AN** *012

BAKER, Tahirih Taj. 1111 AUGUSTA DR, DEPT OF FAMILY PRACTICE 77057 #018-03-1986 L1988 **FM** *020 †18

BAKER, Tanner B. ■ 77054 #048-14-2008 *012

BAKER, Timothy Jos. 2002 HOLCOMBE BLVD, VAMC 77030 #048-14-1989 L1990 **P** *020 †75

BAKER, Treneth Paul. 2727 W HOLCOMBE BLVD 77025 #028-46-1995 L1998 **GS** *020 †85

BAKHSHI, Tiki. 6431 FANNIN ST, UT HEALTH SCI CTR OB/GYN 77030 #011-02-1996 L2005 **OBG** *020 †30

BAKHT, Farid Raif. 2500 FONDREN RD STE 270 77063 #065-01-1980 L1981 **FM** *020 †18

BALA, Natarajan. 2060 SPACE PARK DR 77058 #495-61-1975 L1983 **GE IM** *020 †20

BALACHANDRAN, Diwakar D. 1515 HOLCOMBE BLVD, UNIT 403 77030 #016-06-1995 L2003 **PCC IM** *020 †20

BALAGOT, Oliver A. 2002 HOLCOMBE BLVD 77030 #748-08-1965 L1982 **FM** *020 †18

BALAGURA, Saul. ■ 77006 #264-05-1964 L1988 **NS OS** *071 †25

BALAKRISHNAN, Priya V. 3925 TENNYSON ST 77005 #495-53-1993 L2000 **NEP** *020 †20

BALAKRISHNAN, Vasantha. 12522 DORWAYNE CT, GALENA PARK MEDICAL CLINIC 77015 #495-04-1971 **PTH** *074

BALASUBRAMANIAM, Swarna. 2222 MARONEAL ST, UNIT 922 77030 #026-08-1992 L2007 **CRS** *020 †85,10

BALASUBRAMANYAM, Ashok. 1 BAYLOR PLZ, DIVISION OF ENDOCRINOLOGY 77030 #495-52-1983 L1994 **END IM** *050 †20

BALAT, Isam Yusuf A. 1200 BINZ ST STE 1100 77004 #048-02-1973 L1973 **OBG ID** *020 †30

BALAZS, Andrea Erika. 6621 FANNIN ST, CC 1020.05 77030 #473-01-1984 L2005 **PD PDE** *020 †55

BALDEO, Noli Cantuba. ■ 77030 #048-16-2008 *012

BALDWIN, Bonnie J. 7737 SOUTHWEST FWY, STE 201 77074 #048-04-1985 L1986 **PS** *020 †65

BALDWIN, Robert T. 7737 SOUTHWEST FWY STE 2 77074 #048-04-1985 L1986 **TS CD** *020 †85,90

BALERDI, Maria Josefa. ■ 77068 #429-02-1986 L1994 **PTH** *100

BALETTE, Jules. 17030 NANES DR, STE 110 77090 #341-01-1963 L1970 **GS GP** *071

BALEVA, Jasmin M. 4545 POST OAK PLACE DR, STE 130 77027 #748-02-1993 L2000 **MPD** *020 †20,55 ‡

BALL, Daniel Webster, III. 6560 FANNIN ST, STE 600 77030 #028-02-1987 L1989 **GE** *020 †20

BALL, Valdesha Lechante. ■ 77047 #047-07-2005 **P** *012

BALLA NDZIE, Sylvain Domi. ■ 77054 #408-14-1997 **FP** *012

BALLANTYNE, Christie M. 6565 FANNIN ST # A601 77030 #048-04-1982 L1983 **CD IM** *050 †20

BALLO, Matthew Tibor. 1515 HOLCOMBE BLVD, BOX 97 77030 #038-06-1995 L2000 **RO** *020 †80

BALLOUK, Fayez. ■ 77025 #875-02-1982 L1992 **BBK** *020 †50

BALSAVER, Ashok Mukund. 6565 FANNIN ST 77030 #495-01-1959 L1968 **ATP CLP** *020 †50

BAN, A Vu. 9938 BELLAIRE BLVD, STE B 77036 #941-01-1959 L1980 **GP** *020

BANCROFT, Gregory Nelson. ■ 77059 #048-04-2003 **PS** *012

BANDHAKAVI, Subhadra. 10594 FUQUA ST, SOUTHBELT CLINIC 77089 #495-11-1988 L2002 **IM** *020 †20

BANDI, Venkata D. 1504 TAUB LOOP, PULMONARY DEPARTMENT 77030 #495-50-1981 L1990 **PCC IM** *020 †20

BANDYOPADHYAY, Arindam. 12141 RICHMOND AVE 77082 #495-02-1989 L2005 **END** *020 †20

BANERJEE, Mitali. ■ 77025 #048-04-2008 *012

BANEZ, Eugenio Inis. 1502 TAUB LOOP, 4TH FL 77030 #748-02-1972 L1978 **PTH** *075 †50

BANFIELD, Edison Hamilton. 2914 BLODGETT ST 77004 #010-03-1954 L1959 **GP** *072 †85

BANFIELD, Michael Dewitt. 15 E GREENWAY PLZ 77046 #010-03-1953 L1954 **GP** *071 †18

BANG, Hoon Yul. ■ 77030 #048-04-2008 *012

BANG, Jennifer Kristy. 1801 NORTH LOOP W, STE 45 77008 #048-02-2003 L2006 **FM** *020 †18

BANG, Leng. 1 BAYLOR PLZ, BAYLOR COLL OF MED 77030 #011-03-2002 L2007 **CHP** *100

BANGERT, Carolyn Anne. 6655 TRAVIS ST STE 980, UT HOUSTON DEPT DERM 77030 #048-12-2002 L2006 **D** *020 †15

BANGERT, Scott David. ■ 77035 #003-01-2005 L2006 **D** *012

BANKER, Amina Kothari. PO BOX 20708 77225 #704-02-1983 **IM** *100

BANKS, Kristine Elizabeth. ■ 77054 #038-43-2006 **ORS** *012

BANKS, William Skidmore. 7777 SOUTHWEST FWY, STE 804 77074 #048-02-1962 L1962 **OPH** *020 †35

BANNER, Edward A, Jr. 6720 BERTNER ST 77030 #026-04-1982 L1984 **AN** *020 †05 ‡

BANSAL, Vivek. ■ 77054 #048-04-2006 *012

BAPAT, Avinash Narayan. 11914 ASTORIA BLVD, STE 400 77089 #496-38-1969 L1985 **CD IM** *020 †20

BAPAT, Shahsultan Avinash. ■ 77062 #496-38-1969 L1986 **PM** *071 †60

BAPTISTA, Edward Gumapac. 6400 FANNIN ST, STE 2210 77030 #048-14-1996 L1997 **CD** *020 †20

BARAKAT, Ayman. 6431 FANNIN ST STE 1134, AT HOUST 77030 #875-01-2002 L2007 **IM** *012

BARAKAT, Omar. 6624 FANNIN ST STE 1200, TRANSPLANTATION & GENERAL 77030 #875-02-1985 L1997 **GS** *020

BARAKAT, Ruchdi. 6431 FANNIN ST STE 1.150, AT HOUST 77030 #875-01-2002 L2007 **NEP** *012 †20

BARANOWSKA-DACA, Elzbieta. 205 HOLLOW TREE LN 77090 #759-06-1986 L2002 **NEP** *020 †20

BARBANDI, Mazen. ■ 77024 #048-02-2008 *012

BARBARO, Tina Grace. ■ 77006 #028-34-2006 **OBG** *012

BARBER, Michael James. 6655 TRAVIS ST, STE 700 77030 #024-05-1998 L1999 **P** *020 †20

BARCENAS LEVY, Camilo G. 4407 YOAKUM BLVD, STE B 77006 #682-01-1968 L1975 **NEP IM** *020 †20

BARCES, Pastor Vicente. ■ 77072 #132-05-1972 **FM** *100

BARCIO, Michelle Garcia. 17070 RED OAK DR, STE 405 77090 #048-14-1999 L2003 **OBG** *020 †20

BARDWIL, Michael Ferris. 909 FROSTWOOD DR, STE 234 77024 #048-14-1982 L1983 **GS VS** *020 †85

BARELI, Lee Hagar. ■ 77054 #048-04-2008 *012

BARER, Jorge M. 7900 FANNIN ST, STE 3500 77054 #649-01-1967 L1975 **PD GP** *020 †55

BARGER, Philip Murray. 6565 FANNIN ST MS 524, WINTERS CTR FOR HEART FAIL 77030 #038-06-1989 L1992 **CD** *050 †20

BARHORST, Mark D. 9920 CYPRESSWOOD DR 77070 #048-16-1988 L1989 **AN PME** *020 †05

BARKER, Charles Holt. 1502 TAUB LOOP, MHMRA OF HARRIS CO. 77030 #021-01-1968 L1971 **P** *020 †75

BARKLEY, John M. 12951 SOUTH FWY 77047 #048-04-1999 L2001 **DR** *020 †80

BARLOW, Mark S. 2060 SPACE PARK DR, STE 310 77058 #048-14-2000 L2005 **PS** *020 †65 ‡

BARLOW, Sarah E. 6701 FANNIN ST STE 1010, TEXAS CHILDREN'S HOSPITAL 77030 #048-12-1989 L2007 **PG PD** *020 †55

BARLOW, Thomas Ray. 17080 RED OAK DR 77090 #048-14-1975 L1976 **AN** *020 †05

BARNARD, Michael A. 18220 STATE HIGHWAY 249, STE 390 77070 #836-01-1969 L1977 **WD** *020 †20

BARNES, Carlin Denise. 2101 CRAWFORD ST, STE 308 77002 #048-16-1994 L2000 **CHP** *020 †75

BARNES, Douglas Agna. 6977 MAIN ST, SHRINERS HOSP FOR CHILDRN 77030 #048-04-1973 L1974 **OP** *020 †40

BARNES, Frank Lister, II. 4126 SOUTHWEST FWY, STE 1410 77027 #048-04-1960 L1960 **ORS** *020 †40

BARNES, Johnson P, Jr. 4126 SOUTHWEST FWY, STE 1410 77027 #021-01-1969 L1970 **GS** *020 †85

BARNES, Rhonda Jonelle. 4405 GRIGGS RD 77021 #047-06-2000 L2002 **FM** *100 †18 ‡

BARNES, Ruby Preeti. ■ 77025 #048-04-2008 *012

BARNES, Stephen Anthony. ■ 77098 #025-01-1991 L1998 **GS SO** *020 †85

BARNETT, Ben Jos. 4115 SWARTHMORE ST, CENTER AT HOUSTON 77005 #048-02-1991 L1992 **ID** *020 †20

BARNETT, Marcus Duane. 11302 FALLBROOK DR, STE 202A 77065 #048-02-1984 L1991 **OBG** *020 †30

BARNUM, Bruce Edward. 6624 FANNIN ST, 20TH FL 77030 #048-04-1978 L1978 **CD** *020 †20

BARNWELL, Lyndon Forbess. 1504 TAUB LOOP, BEN TAUB HOSPITAL 77030 #047-07-1997 L1999 **IM** *020

BARON, Jason Dennis. 5500 GUHN RD, STE 100 77040 #048-02-1967 L1967 **CHP P** *020

BARR, Jeffrey Vincent. ■ 77054 #048-14-2004 **P** *012

BARR, Robert Halasi. 6410 FANNIN ST 77030 #048-02-1963 L1963 **GO** *071 †30

BARR, Sarah Nicole. ■ 77006 #048-04-2007 **PD** *012

BARR, Yael. ■ 77059 #550-02-1995 **IPM** *012

BARRADA, Mohamed Ismail. 902 FROSTWOOD DR, STE 215 77024 #330-02-1961 L1984 **OBG MFM** *075 †30

BARRATT, Michael Reed. NASA/JSC JOHNSON SPACE CTR, MEDICAL OPNS SD26 77058 #016-06-1985 L1992 **AM IM** *050 †20,70

BARRATT, Michelle S. 6410 FANNIN ST, STE 500 77030 #016-06-1985 L1991 **PD ADL** *020 †55

BARRENO, Ramon Xavier. 6431 FANNIN ST, SCHOOL A 77030 #048-14-2006 **PD** *012

BARRENO-CANALES, Ramon. 9055 KATY FWY STE 418 77024 #649-27-1972 L1979 **AN** *040

BARRERA, Alfonso. 915 GESSNER RD, STE 825 77024 #649-30-1977 L1979 **PS HS** *020 †45,65

BARRETO, Andrew David. 2212 NAOMI ST 77054 #036-05-2002 L2006 **VN** *100 †75

BARRETT, Bernard M, Jr. 6624 FANNIN ST STE 2200 77030 #011-02-1969 L1976 **PS** *020 †65 ‡

BARRETT, Richard Michael. 3730 KIRBY DR STE 700 77098 #041-09-1968 L1978 **P CHP** *075

BARRIENTOS, Silvio Proto. ■ 77087 #737-01-1960 L1971 **AN CCA** *020

BARRIGA, Juan Carlos. 1740 W 27TH ST, STE 304 77008 #319-01-1988 L2001 **PCC** *020 †20 ‡

BARRIOS, Roberto Jose. 6565 FANNIN ST, THE METHODIST HOSP PATH DP 77030 #649-01-1969 L1992 **PTH ATP** *020 †50

BARRON, Bruce Jonathan. 6431 FANNIN ST STE 2132, DEPT OF NUCLEAR MEDICINE 77030 #011-04-1975 L1981 **PD NM** *020 †55,28

BARROSO, Alberto Oswaldo. 6560 FANNIN ST, STE 600 77030 #187-03-1966 L1980 **GE IM** *020 †20

BARROSO, Stephen R. 7600 BEECHNUT ST 77074 #048-02-1990 L1991 **AN** *020 †05

BARRY, Yvonne Nanette. 14027 MEMORIAL DR PMB 252, MEMORIAL - SPRBRANNEO CONS 77099 #030-05-1981 L1986 **NPM PD** *020 †20

BARSHES, Neal R. 7818 VICKIJOHN DR 77071 #016-11-2001 L2004 **GS** *012

BART, Jerome Barry. 2727 W HOLCOMBE BLVD, 4TH FL 77025 #024-01-1963 L1969 **HEM IM** *020 †20

BARTH, Justine Leanna. 1504 TAUB LOOP, DEPT OF GEN MED/GERTCS 77030 #048-04-1992 L1994 **IM IMG** *020 †20

BARTH, Merle Henry. 12951 SOUTH FWY 77047 #017-20-1967 L1973 **DR R** *020 †80

BARTIMMO, Ernest E, Jr. 915 GESSNER RD STE 100 77024 #010-02-1967 L1973 **IM PUD** *020 †20

BARTLETT, Allison Humes. 1 BAYLOR PLZ, MS BCM320 77030 #028-02-2002 L2008 **PDI** *012 †55

BARTLETT, Brenda Lee. ■ 77004 #023-01-2006 L2007 **IM** *012

BARTON, Kimberly Taylor. ■ 77063 #048-12-1997 L1999 **PD** *020 †55

BARTSCH, Heather Renee. ■ 77009 #048-04-2007 **MPD** *012

BARZI, Afsaneh. 4545 POST OAK PLACE DR, STE 130 77027 #517-01-1996 L2005 **IM** *020 †20

BASDEN, Edwin Herbert. 1401 ST JOSEPH PKWY, DEPT OF PATHOLOGY 77002 #033-05-1972 L1974 **PTH** *050

BASHIR, Jamil. 3333 ALLEN PKWY, UNIT 1408 77019 #060-01-1991 *100

BASIT, Saleha. ■ 77043 #495-21-1964 L1976 **PTH** *020

BASKIN, David Stuart. 6560 FANNIN ST STE 900 77030 #035-47-1978 L1985 **NS** *020 †25

BASLER, Elizabeth A. 7505 MAIN ST, STE 300 77030 #048-04-1985 L1986 **D** *020 †15

BASS, Barbara Lee. 6550 FANNIN ST, STE 1661A 77030 #051-01-1979 L2006 **GS** *020 †85

BASS, Barry Fenroy. 6411 FANNIN ST, STE 470 77030 #836-02-1961 L1970 **AN** *020 †05

BASS, Heather Shepherd. PO BOX 20708, DEPT OF FAMILY MEDICINE 77225 #048-12-2005 L2008 **FP** *012

BASSILI, Hosni Risk. 920 FROSTWOOD DR 77024 #330-02-1964 L1978 **AN** *020

BASSILI, Lisa Michelle. ■ 77002 #048-15-2002 L2006 **AN** *020
BAST, Robert Clinton, Jr. 1515 HOLCOMBE BLVD BOX 92 77030 #024-01-1971 L1994 **ON HEM** *050 †20
BASU, Abhijeet George. 6400 FANNIN ST, STE 3000 77030 #038-40-1999 L2003 **IC** *020 †20
BASU, Chandrasekh. 1709 DRYDEN RD 77030 #024-07-1999 L2005 **PS** *020 †65
BASU, Margaret Henderson. 2211 NORFOLK ST, STE 628 77098 #048-04-2002 L2006 **P** *020 †75
BATES, Jeffrey T. 1 BAYLOR PLZ, C/O BAYLOR CLGE OF MED 77030 #048-12-1994 L1995 **IM** *020 †20
BATHIJA, Neera. 8191 SOUTHWEST FWY, STE 106 77074 #496-09-1978 L1992 **IM** *020 †20
BATMANIS, Elizabeth. ■ 77005 #048-04-1954 L1954 **PD** *072 †55
BATMANIS, Michael. 2001 BANKS ST 77098 #048-02-1959 L1959 **AN** *020
BATSAKIS, John Geo. ■ 77004 #025-01-1954 L1982 **PTH PCH** *071 †50
BATTAGLIA, Carl Jos. 17080 RED OAK DR 77090 #024-07-1966 L1976 **AN OBG** *020 †30,05
BATTAGLIA, Frank Jos. 12337 JONES RD, STE 350 77070 #048-04-1979 L1979 **OBG** *020 †30
BATTE, Gerald Littleton. 1811 BERING DR STE 160 77057 #021-05-1959 L1966 **P** *071
BATTLE, Robert Mc Ree. 9910 LONG POINT RD 77055 #048-02-1965 L1965 **GP P** *020
BAUER, Ross Karl. ■ 77057 #033-06-1993 L1997 **EM** *020
BAUM, Alan Carl. 651 BERING DR, UNIT 1905 77057 #048-02-1968 L1972 **OPH** *020
BAUM, Laura Marie. ■ 77087 #048-16-2005 **OBG** *012
BAUM, Lawrence Owen, III. ■ 77025 #048-02-2003 **U** *012
BAUMANN, Donald Peter, Jr. 1515 HOLCOMBE BLVD, DEPT. OF PLASTIC SURGERY, 77030 #035-08-1998 L2005 **PS** *020 †65
BAUMGARTNER, James Edmund. 6410 FANNIN ST STE 830 77030 #025-01-1985 L1992 **NS** *020 †25
BAUTISTA, Arturo. 6621 FANNIN ST 77030 #176-03-1959 L1982 **PD** *020 †55
BAUTISTA, Edilberto M. 4126 SOUTHWEST FWY, STE 1220 77027 #748-02-1967 L1974 **PUD IM** *020 †18
BAVARE, Charudatta Shrika. 6550 FANNIN ST, THE METHODIST HOSP 77030 #496-38-2000 **GS** *012
BAVISHI, Dipti. 7777 SOUTHWEST FWY STE 544 77074 #495-44-1987 L1997 **GE** *020 †20
BAVISHI, Nilesh S. 7777 SOUTHWEST FWY STE 544 77074 #308-11-1985 L1997 **CD** *020 †20
BAWEJA, Kanwarpreet Singh. 6431 FANNIN ST, STE 4.148 77030 #495-36-2000 L2006 **NEP** *100 †20
BAXT, John Henry. 7603 S LINPAR CT 77040 #011-03-1967 L1971 **DR** *020 †80
BAXTER, Aaron James. 1 BAYLOR PLZ 77030 #665-01-2006 **DR** *012
BAXTER, Donald Ervin. 7401 MAIN ST 77030 #012-01-1969 L1970 **ORS** *020 †40
BAXTER, Thomas Leroy, III. 6560 FANNIN ST STE 1408 77030 #041-02-1970 L1978 **IM** *020 †20
BAYER, Timothy Lee. 2002 HOLCOMBE BLVD 77030 #048-12-1975 L1979 **P** *020 †75
BAYLES, Spencer. ■ 77096 #019-02-1944 L1956 **P** *071 †75
BAYONA, Jose. 6431 FANNIN ST, UNIV OF TX-HEALTH SCIENCE 77030 #042-01-1980 L1998 **FM** *020 †18
BAYS, Janis A. 1 BAYLOR PLZ 77030 #048-04-1988 **AN** *100
BAZE, Elizabeth Faye. 6550 FANNIN ST, STE 1501 77030 #048-12-1999 L2003 **OPH** *020 †35
BEACH, Robyn Alexander. ■ 77079 #048-12-1999 L2004 **SP** *100 †50
BEADLE, Beth Michelle. 6723 BERTNER ST, DEPT OF RADIATION ONCOLOGY 77030 #016-06-2004 L2004 **RO** *012
BEAHM, Elisabeth Kirstin. 1515 HOLCOMBE BLVD, UNIT 443 77030 #016-42-1987 L1996 **PS** *020 †65
BEALE, Daniel J. ■ 77019 #048-02-2001 *100
BEALE, Estela M. 1515 HOLCOMBE BLVD, MD ANDERSON CANCER CENTER- 77030 #132-01-1961 L1990 **P CHP** *020
BEAN, Samuel Franklin. 1200 BINZ ST, STE 1110 77004 #048-02-1962 L1962 **D** *020 †15
BEARD, Earl Francis. 6624 FANNIN ST, STE 2000 77030 #016-06-1948 L1954 **CD** *071 †20
BEARD, Lisa Fisher. ■ 77006 #001-06-2004 L2008 **OBG** *012
BEARD, Lise M. 4710 STILLBROOKE DR 77035 #048-14-1992 L1993 **FM** *020 †18
BEARD, Mary Beth. 6550 FANNIN ST, BETH BEARD MARY 77030 #048-13-1979 L1979 **PS HS** *020
BEARDEN, James Martin. ■ 77070 #038-40-1964 L1964 **OM ORS** *071
BEARDSLEY, Robert Mclain. ■ 77008 #048-04-2008 *012
BEASLEY, Anitra Danielle. ■ 77024 #048-04-2004 L2008 **OBG** *012
BEASLEY, R Palmer. PO BOX 20186 77225 #024-01-1962 L1966 **GPM IM** *030 †20,70
BEATTY, Jill M. 211 HIGHLAND CROSS DR, GULF COAST PHYSICIAN ADMIN 77073 #048-13-2000 L2003 **EM** *020 †16
BEATY, Stacy Gerald. 6431 FANNIN ST, STE 6.143 77030 #048-14-2003 L2006 **ORS** *012
BEAUDET, Arthur Louis. 1 BAYLOR PLZ STE T619 77030 #008-01-1967 L1972 **MG PD** *040 †55,19
BEBERNISS, Ronald Michael. 12345 KATY FWY 77079 #048-04-1973 L1973 **EM** *020
BECA, Sorin Gheorghe. ■ 77058 #781-04-1992 L2008 **END** *012 †20
BECK, Belinda Kari. ■ 77004 #048-14-2003 L2006 **OBG** *100
BECK, Daniel A. UNIV TEX AFFIL HOSP 77030 #869-04-1972 **PD** *050
BECK, Dennis Alan. 7026 OLD KATY RD, STE 276 77024 #048-04-1971 L1971 **DR** *020 †80
BECK, Jason. ■ 77054 #048-14-2008 *012
BECKER, Frederick F. M D ANDERSON HOSP PATH 77030 #035-19-1956 L1976 **PTH** *050 †50
BECKER, Natasha Sarkari. ■ 77081 #020-12-2004 L2006 **GS** *012
BECKER, Steven Victor. 10405 TOWN AND COUNTRY WAY, STE 402 77024 #062-01-1974 L1977 **FM** *020 †18
BECKINGER, Rhodora Javier. ■ 77054 #048-14-2008 *012
BECKMAN, Bradley Irwin. 909 FROSTWOOD DR STE 105 77024 #048-02-1978 L1978 **D** *020 †15
BECKMANN, Nicholas Marc. 6431 FANNIN ST, MSB 2.130 77030 #019-02-2005 L2005 **DR** *012
BEDFORD, Joe Albert. 6431 FANNIN ST, STE JJL308N 77030 #010-03-1977 L1983 **FM** *020 †18
BEDI, Deepak Gobind Singh. 1515 HOLCOMBE BLVD, BOX 57 77030 #577-01-1976 L1983 **DR OS** *020 †80
BEDIKIAN, Agop Yervant. 1515 HOLCOMBE BLVD BOX 430, DEPT OF MELANOMA 77030 #605-01-1971 L1976 **ON IM** *020 †20
BEDNARZ-PRASHAD, Audrey J. PO BOX 20098 77225 #048-14-1999 L2002 **IM** *020
BEDNER, Tom David. ■ 77096 #048-04-1966 L1966 **GE IM** *020 †20
BEDOYA ALVAREZ DE TOLEDO, . 1709 DRYDEN RD STE 550, BCM FACULTY CENTER 77030 #737-06-2004 **IM** *012
BEDROSIAN, Isabelle. 1515 HOLCOMBE BLVD # 444, DEPT SURGICAL ONCOLOGY 77030 #016-06-1994 L2001 **GS** *020 †85
BEECH, Thomas R, II. ■ 77007 #048-15-1993 L1994 **GS EM** *020
BEG, Khurshid Alam. ■ 77070 #160-02-1983 L1998 **IM** *020 †20
BEGHTOL, Carter Vance. ■ 77043 #030-05-1962 L1971 **OM GP** *071
BEHAINE, Jorge O. 1315 CALHOUN ST STE 1404 77002 #264-04-1965 L1977 **EM AM** *020
BEHAZIN, Azar. ■ 77008 #048-04-2004 **IM** *100 †20
BEHAZIN, Nancy Soraya. ■ 77008 #048-15-2008 *012
BEHL, Jyoti. ■ 77047 #495-37-2002 L2007 **FM** *100
BEINART, Garth Aubrey. 1515 HOLCOMBE BLVD, UNIT 10 77030 #048-04-2001 L2003 **ON** *020
BELANGER, Yasmin Natasha. ■ 77030 #048-04-2006 **OBG** *012
BELCHEVA, Anna Belcheva. 920 FROSTWOOD DR, STE 780 77024 #048-13-1998 L2001 **ON** *020 †20
BELL, Alfreda Lynette. 1221 MCKINNEY ST, STE 40300 77010 #048-04-1997 L1999 **FM** *020 †18
BELL, Carlton Bruce. 6411 FANNIN ST 77030 #048-04-1989 L1990 **IM** *020 †20
BELL, Gina Lynne. 7001 CORPORATE DR, STE 120 77036 #005-12-1995 L2007 **FM** *020 †18
BELL, Katherine Ann. 7515 MAIN ST, STE 770 77030 #011-02-1998 L2000 **D** *020 †15
BELL, Nicholas Pat. 6565 FANNIN ST NC-205, DEPT OF OPHTHALMOLOGY 77030 #011-02-1998 L2000 **OPH** *020 †35
BELL, Robert Steven. 11325 FALLBROOK DR 77065 #003-01-1976 L1991 **ORS** *020 †40
BELLAH, Gordon, Jr. 2060 SPACE PARK DR STE 204 77058 #048-12-1978 L1978 **PD** *020 †55
BELLAN, Phillip Martin. 7474 S KIRKWOOD RD STE 104 77072 #062-01-1976 L1979 **FM** *020
BELLARD, Bobby Joseph. ■ 77007 #047-07-2006 **GS** *100
BELLER, Suha A. 1300 MOURSUND ST, 1ST FL RECP AREA 77030 #902-10-1967 L1976 **P PYG** *071 †75
BELLOWS, Warren Sylvanus. 6560 FANNIN ST 77030 #048-12-1974 L1974 **GS** *072 †85
BELMONT, John Wm. 6701 FANNIN ST 77030 #048-04-1981 L1981 **PD** *020 †55,19
BELORGEY, Laura Monique. 1 BAYLOR PLZ, BAYLOR COLL OF MED 77030 #014-01-2003 L2007 **CN** *012
BELTRAN, Jose L. ■ 77057 #048-14-2007 **GS** *012
BELTRAN, Priscilla L. 1801 KNOLL ST 77080 #048-02-1983 L1983 **FM** *020 †18
BELZ, Irving. 2901 BISSONNET ST 77005 #047-06-1961 L1969 **P** *030 ‡
BENAVIDES, David A. 909 FROSTWOOD DR STE 251 77024 #048-02-1988 L1989 **OSS ORS** *020 †40
BENDRE, Manali Sachin. PO BOX 20708, DEPT OF CLIN PATH 77225 #495-22-1999 L2007 **PTH** *012
BENDRE, Sachin Vilas. 6431 FANNIN ST, SCHOOL A 77030 #495-22-1995 **PDE** *012 †55
BENEDICT, Claude R. 6431 FANNIN ST 77030 #220-01-1973 L1983 **CD IM** *050 †20
BENEDICT, William Francis. 1515 HOLCOMBE BLVD BOX 42, M D ANDERSON CANCER CENTER 77030 #035-03-1968 L1972 **OS** *050
BENEKE, Anita E Glikman. 9090 GAYLORD ST STE 101 77024 #048-04-1975 L1975 **FM AN** *050
BEN-GALIM, Peleg Joseph. 1 BAYLOR PLZ, BAYLOR COLL OF MED 77030 #550-01-1994 **OSS** *100
BENHAMOU, Elias. 2411 FOUNTAIN VIEW DR, STE 222 77057 #396-34-1985 L1992 **PME AN** *020 †05
BENJAMIN, Peter. ■ 77005 #067-01-1955 L1977 **PD** *020 †55
BENJAMIN, Robert Stephen. 1515 HOLCOMBE BLVD, BOX 450 77030 #035-19-1968 L1974 **ON** *020 †20
BENJAMINS, Laura Jane. 6431 FANNIN ST, UNIVERSITY OF TEXAS MEDICA 77030 #025-07-1998 L1999 **ADL** *020 †55
BENNETT, James B. 7401 MAIN ST 77030 #020-02-1969 L1976 **HS ORS** *020 †40
BENNETT, James Michael. 7401 MAIN ST, UHZ SPORTS MEDICINE INSTIT 77030 #020-02-1999 L2005 **OSM** *020
BENNY, Benoy Varkey. 1709 DRYDEN RD, STE 725 77030 #894-01-1999 L2006 **PM** *100 †60
BENNY, Rose Santiago. 6463 HILLCROFT ST, MID MICHIGAN MED CTR 77081 #748-10-2001 L2006 **PD** *020
BENREY, M Jaime. 6624 FANNIN ST, STE 2310 77030 #649-01-1969 L1975 **CD** *020 †20
BENSLER, James Michael. 6720 BERTNER ST, M/C 1-133 77030 #054-04-2003 L2006 **CD** *012 †20
BENSON, Arthur B, Jr. 13111 EAST FWY 77015 #048-02-1960 L1969 **GP** *071
BENSON, George Sinclair. 6414 FANNIN ST, STE G150 77030 #041-01-1969 L1977 **U** *020 †95
BENTLIF, Philip Sidney. ■ 77056 #352-03-1956 L1961 **GE** *071 †20
BENTON, Christopher Brent. ■ 77096 #048-04-2005 **IM** *012
BENTZ, Alan Elliott. 710 FM 1960 RD W, EMERGENCY DEPARTMENT 77090 #005-02-1992 L1998 **EM** *020 †16
BENYESH-MELNICK, Matilda. 701 N POST OAK RD, STE 216 77024 #550-01-1952 L1982 **P** *071
BENZ, Matthew Steven. 6560 FANNIN ST STE 750 77030 #025-01-1997 L2003 **OPH** *020 †35
BERAN, Miloslav. 1515 HOLCOMBE BLVD, MDACC 77030 #858-02-1977 L1980 **ON HEM** *020
BERARDINUCCI, Don L. 17070 RED OAK DR, STE 407 77090 #065-05-1991 L1998 **U** *020 †95
BERCAW, Jennifer L. ■ 77005 #021-06-2004 **OBG** *012
BERENS, Pamela Donovan. 6410 FANNIN ST # 3503.604, DEPT OF OB/GYN 77030 #026-04-1989 L1993 **OBG** *040 †30
BERG, Carolyn Michelle. ■ 77003 #048-04-2006 **GS** *012
BERG, Howard Siebert. ■ 77040 #048-02-1963 L1963 **PTH GP** *071 †50
BERG, Jonathan Sanford. 1 BAYLOR PLZ 77030 #036-01-2003 L2006 **MG** *100 †19
BERG, Stacey Lynn. 6621 FANNIN ST MC, TEXAS CHILDREN'S HOSPITAL 77030 #041-12-1985 L1994 **PHO** *020 †55
BERGER, David Hyman. 2002 HOLCOMBE BLVD, SURGERY 112 77030 #035-08-1984 L1991 **GS OS** *020 †85
BERGER, Mark Benj. 6550 FANNIN ST, STE 2403 77030 #048-04-1981 L1981 **PUD IM** *020 †20
BERGERON, Jennifer Lynn. ■ 77054 #048-04-2008 *012
BERGERON, Jimmie Leon. 17030 NANES DR STE 201 77090 #012-05-1968 L1970 **IM** *020 †20
BERGERON, John. 1961 W T C JESTER BLVD 77008 #048-14-1992 L1993 **GP** *020
BERGLAND, John M, III. 2306 ELLA LEE LN 77019 #023-07-1962 L1967 **IM PUD** *071 †20
BERGMAN, Eldo Wm. 11271 RICHMOND AVE, STE 101 77082 #038-43-1972 L1978 **CHN PD** *020 †55
BERGMAN, Mary Ann Conklin. 6624 FANNIN ST STE 1900, ST LUKES MEDICAL TOWER 77030 #038-43-1973 L1979 **PD NPM** *020 †55
BERK, Morris E. ■ 77024 #836-02-1948 L1978 **DR** *020
BERKMAN, Norman Lee. 7580 FANNIN ST STE 100 77054 #041-12-1963 L1967 **IM** *020 †20
BERKOVICH, Alexander. 6565 FANNIN ST 77030 #913-16-1980 L1999 **AN** *020
BERKOWITZ, Shaina M. ■ 77054 #048-14-2006 **AN** *012
BERLINER, Kenneth Gregory. 15769 NORTH FWY 77090 #035-03-1992 L1997 **ORS** *020 †40
BERMAN, Louis. 1200 BINZ ST STE 830 77004 #836-01-1957 L1977 **RHU IM** *020 †20
BERMAN, Philip Leonard. 909 FROSTWOOD DR STE 104 77024 #035-09-1982 L1983 **CD IM** *020 †20
BERMUDEZ, Ovidio Felix. ■ 77025 #275-01-1959 L1974 **GP** *071
BERNAL, Antonio. 1213 HERMANN DR STE 515 77004 #847-01-1964 L1977 **GE** *020 †20
BERNAL, Christine Bea. 6621 FANNIN ST 77030 #748-01-1996 **PPR** *100

■ = Address Information Privacy Protected

BERNARD, David Wm. 6565 FANNIN ST, TMH MS 205 77030 #041-07-1992 L1999 CLP PCH *020 †50

BERNARD, Robert John. 11413 WHIPPOORWILL RD 77024 #051-04-1983 L1985 NEP *020 †20

BERNARDI, Ronald John. ■ 77030 #041-12-2004 PHO *012

BERNARDO, Marializa V. 1570 S DAIRY ASHFORD ST, STE 116 77077 #748-01-1987 L1994 NEP *020 †20

BERNICKER, Eric H. 1707 SUNSET BLVD, MEDICAL CLINIC OF HOUSTON 77005 #048-04-1990 L1991 ON *020 †20

BERNINI, Juan C. 6701 FANNIN ST 77030 #270-01-1984 L1996 PHO *020 †55

BERNSTAM, Elmer Victor. 7000 FANNIN ST STE 600 77030 #025-01-1995 L2003 IM *020 †20

BERNSTEIN, Howard Robt. 9090 GAYLORD ST, STE 101 77024 #917-08-1964 L1977 FM OM *020 ‡

BERREST, Maria P. PO BOX 20708, UNIV TX MED SCH AT HOUSTON 77225 #649-01-1985 AN *100

BERRIOS, Nelson Antonio. 7777 SW FWY STE 900 77074 #042-01-1978 L1986 N *020 †75

BERRY, Charles Alden. ■ 77042 #005-02-1947 L1963 AM GPM *020 †70

BERRY, Jennifer Y. 2111 WELCH ST 77019 #048-02-1998 L2002 FM *020 †18

BERRY, John Bruce. 6720 BERTNER ST 77030 #048-04-1969 L1969 NS *020 †25

BERRY, Suzanne C. 6565 FANNIN ST 77030 #048-13-1997 L2000 AN *020 †05

BERSHAD, Eric Michael. ■ 77096 #025-07-2002 L2008 N *100 †75

BERTHELOT, Cindy Noel. 1515 HOLCOMBE BLVD, BOX 434 77030 #048-12-2006 L2007 IM *012

BERTINI, John E, Jr. 1315 ST JOSEPH PKWY, STE 1502 77002 #048-14-1982 L1983 U *020 †95

BERTLES, Ann Marie. PO BOX 20708, DEPT OF OB/GYN 77225 #011-04-2005 OBG *012

BERTOLINO, Paul David. ■ 77030 #048-02-2005 DR *012

BERTONI, Mario Erninio. 8968 KIRBY DR 77054 #561-01-1967 L1976 DR OS *020 †80

BERTUCH, Alison Ann. 6621 FANNIN ST, 14TH FL # CC141000 77030 #035-45-1993 L1999 PHO *020 †55

BERY, Tarang. 2450 FONDREN RD, STE 314 77063 #495-12-1982 L1993 AN *020

BERZIN, Edward. 6560 FANNIN ST STE 1804 77030 #048-04-1994 L1997 PS *020 †65

BESA, Pelayo De Carcer. 1515 HOLCOMBE BLVD 77030 #231-01-1981 L1991 RO *020 †80

BESTAK, Marc. ■ 77055 #035-15-1972 L1973 PHO PD *020 †55

BEST BOURGEOIS, Kelly Den. ■ 77005 #048-14-1989 L1991 AN *020 †05

BETTEGA, Paulo Roberto. 2801 GESSNER DR 77080 #187-08-1970 L1984 P CHP *020 †75

BEUTNAGEL, James R. 5810 BOLERO POINT CIRCL CT 77041 #048-02-1982 L1983 EM FM *020 †18

BEVEN, Gary Edward. 2101 NASA PKWY, MAIL CODE SD12 77058 #038-06-1989 L2006 PFP P *020 †75

BEVERS, Michael Wayne. 6624 FANNIN ST, STE 2590 77030 #048-01-1990 L1991 OBG GO *020 †30

BEVERS, Therese B. 1515 HOLCOMBE BLVD, UNIT 1322 77030 #048-13-1987 L1988 FM PHP *020 †18

BEYER, Alvin, Jr. ■ 77025 #048-02-1944 L1944 P *071 †75

BHADSAVLE, Siraj Ashok. 1 BAYLOR PLZ, BAYLOR COLL MED 77030 #035-03-2004 L2005 AN *100

BHAGWATH, Gayathri. 2002 HOLCOMBE BLVD, PRIMARY CARE CLINIC 77030 #495-37-1995 L2006 IM *020 †20

BHAKTA, Kushal Yagnesh. 6621 FANNIN ST, MC WT6-104 77030 #048-04-2000 L2006 NPM *100 †55 ‡

BHALLA, Karan Surinder. 6431 FANNIN ST, UTHSC DIV OF CARDIOLOGY 77030 #496-38-1998 L2006 CD *012

BHALLA, Prabha. 11914 ASTORIA BLVD, STE 460 77089 #495-36-1970 L1983 OPH OS *020

BHALLA, Rajinder K. 2045 SPACE PARK DR, STE 100 77058 #495-36-1970 L1980 CD AMI *020 †20

BHAMIDIPATI, Sujatha. 7600 BEECHNUT ST 77074 #495-65-1986 L2003 AN *020 †05

BHARDWAJ, Manoj Kumar. 1 BAYLOR PLZ, BAYLOR COLL OF MED 77030 #495-37-2003 L2008 IM *012

BHARDWAJ, Neeta Rani. 11710 FM 1960 RD W 77065 #495-41-1981 L1987 PD NPM *020 †55

BHARDWAJ, Rakesh. 714 FM 1960 RD W, STE 206 77090 #495-36-1980 L1983 AN *020 †05

BHARDWAJ, Rishi Raj. 3701 KIRBY DR, STE 600 77098 #495-37-2003 L2007 IM *012

BHARGAVA, Peeyush. 4059 GLEN COVE DR 77021 #495-73-1997 L2003 NM *020 †28 ‡

BHARKSUWAN, Sammuel. 17070 RED OAK DR, STE 506 77090 #035-19-1995 L1998 OBG *020 †30

BHARWANI, Lavina D. 1709 DRYDEN RD, STE 650 77030 #048-04-1997 L2003 ON *020 †20

BHASKARA, Achala Na. 6431 FANNIN ST STE 1.150, AT HOUST 77030 #030-06-2004 L2007 IM *100 †20

BHASKARAN, Vatsala. 11550 FUQUA, STE 560 77034 #495-59-1980 L1982 P *020 †75

BHAT, Leena S. 1900 SAINT JAMES PL, STE 600 77056 #048-04-1994 L2000 D *020 †15

BHAT, Suprabha. 7500 BEECHNUT ST, STE 266 77036 #495-37-1991 L1999 N *020 †75

BHATIA, Devinder Singh. 710 FM 1960 RD W 77090 #004-01-1991 L2000 TS VS *020 †85,90

BHATIA, Harmohinder S. 1140 CYPRESS STATION DR 77090 #495-08-1970 L1979 CD IM *020 †20

BHATIA, Ramona. 1709 DRYDEN RD STE 550, BCM FACULTY CENTER 77030 #016-06-2007 IM *012

BHATT, Bhavesh. 607 TIMBERDALE LN, STE 201 77090 #048-14-1995 L1997 IM *020 †20

BHATTACHARJEE, Meenakshi. 6621 FANNIN ST, STE B1 77030 #495-08-1978 L1996 NP *020 †50

BHATTACHARJEE, Modhush. 6431 FANNIN ST # MSBI-3122, INTRNL MED DEPT/UNIV OF TX 77030 #495-27-1978 L2003 IM *075 †20

BHATTACHARYA, Gayatri. ■ 77072 #495-38-1969 L1974 FM *020

BHOJANI, Faiyaz Ali. 910 LOUISIANA ST, STE 1022 77002 #704-02-1984 L1993 OM IM *020 †70,20 ‡

BHOJANI, Rehal Abbas. ■ 77056 #048-12-2007 FP *012

BHUCHAR, Vinod Kumar. 1631 NORTH LOOP W STE 100 77008 #495-08-1970 L1976 HO IM *020 †20

BHUTANI, Anjali. ■ 77059 #495-69-1987 L2002 IM *020 †20

BHUVA, Parita. ■ 77025 #048-15-2006 N *012

BIBB, Christopher Odell. 1515 HOLCOMBE BLVD, BOX 37 77030 #001-02-2001 L2007 PCH *100 †50

BICKEL, Perry E. 6431 FANNIN ST, MSB 4202 77030 #048-12-1988 L2008 END *050 †20

BICKHAM, Jacqueline G. 1515 HOLCOMBE BLVD # 431, UN MD ANDERSON CANCER CENT 77030 #048-15-1989 L1990 P *020 †20

BICQUART, Celine. ■ 77004 #048-14-2007 TY *012

BIDANI, Akhil. 4800 CALHOUN ST, N207 ENGG BLDG I 77204 #048-02-1981 L1981 PUD CCM *050 †20

BIDANI, Sudha A. 6621 FANNIN ST 77030 #496-38-1966 L1974 AN *020 †05

BIDIWALA, Khurshid. ■ 77084 #495-17-1975 L1985 PD *020 †55

BIDROS, Rafi Sirop. 1401 ST JOSEPH PKWY, GWS 3RD FLOOR 77002 #021-05-2001 L2008 PS *012 †85

BIER, Dennis Martin. 1100 BATES AVE, CHILDRENS NUTRITION RES CT 77030 #033-05-1966 L1996 PDE NTR *050 †55

BIGGS, Thomas Morgan. 1315 ST JOSEPH PKWY, STE 900 77002 #048-04-1958 L1958 PS *071 †65

BIKKINA, Ravi Shankar. 810 PEAKWOOD DR, STE 107 77090 #033-05-1998 L2001 DR *020 †80

BILES, Ervin Wiley. 1635 NORTH LOOP W 77008 #048-04-1946 L1946 R NM *071 †80

BILICILER-DENKTAS, Gurur. ■ 77005 #902-07-1992 L2005 PDC *020 †55

BILLINGS, Winetta Carol. ■ 77083 #048-14-1981 L1981 FM *020 †18

BILLUPS, James Thos. ■ 77098 #048-02-1932 L1932 GS *071

BILOW, Ronald Martin. ■ 77030 #016-42-1996 L2001 DR *020 †80

BINA, Said. 11850 FM 1960 RD W 77065 #517-08-1973 L1983 GS CD *020 †85

BINDAL, Ajay Kumar. 7737 SOUTHWEST FWY, STE 230 77074 #016-06-1990 L1996 NS *020 †25

BINDER, Gary L. 6620 MAIN ST 77030 #561-01-1968 L1974 OBG *020 †30

BING, Arlys W. ■ 77079 #048-04-1953 L1953 GP OM *071

BIONDO, Mario. 902 FROSTWOOD DR, STE 150 77024 #561-14-1957 L1967 OBG *071

BIRAN, Haim. M D ANDERSON HOSP INST 77030 #550-01-1968 L1977 ON IM *050

BIRCHANSKY, Sherri Beth. 6621 FANNIN ST, TEXAS CHILDREN'S HOSPITAL 77030 #011-02-1986 L2008 PDR *020 †80

BIRD, John Andrew. ■ 77030 #048-13-2003 L2008 AI *012 †55

BIRDSALL, Holly Hyde. 2002 HOLCOMBE BLVD 77030 #048-04-1984 L1986 OTO IG *030 †45

BIRKEN, Randolf A. 11070 RED OAK DR 77090 #024-05-1976 L1977 GYN *020 †30

BISHARA, Maher. 8830 LONG POINT RD STE 408 77055 #875-01-1983 L1989 IM NEP *020 †20

BISHOP, James Oliver. 6550 FANNIN ST, STE 1501 77030 #048-04-1969 L1969 OPH *071 †35

BISHOP, John Ollie. 7401 MAIN ST 77030 #048-04-1973 L1973 ORS OFA *020 †40

BISHOP, Leigh Carlton. 2002 HOLCOMBE BLVD, MED VA MEDICAL CENTER 77030 #048-02-1980 L1980 P *040 †75

BISHOP, Rachel Dara. 1200 BINZ ST STE 1410 77004 #021-01-1998 L2000 IM *020 †20

BISWAS, Jonmenjoy. 6410 FANNIN ST STE 6 77030 #048-16-2004 L2008 IM *100

BIVENS, Nathan H. ■ 77056 #007-02-1959 L1976 AN *071 †05

BJORNSSON, Bjorn Logi. 1 BAYLOR PLZ, DEPT PATHOLOGY 77030 #484-01-1983 PTH *100

BLACHER, Eric J. 11302 FALLBROOK DR STE 107 77065 #005-19-1977 L1985 U *020 †95

BLACK, Dawn Dickson. 7900 FANNIN ST, STE 4811 77054 #048-02-1990 L1991 OBG *030 †30

BLACK, Peter Colin. 1515 HOLCOMBE BLVD, UNIT 1373 77030 #409-32-1997 L2007 U *020

BLACK, Richard Glynn. 6410 FANNIN ST 77030 #065-01-1960 L1989 AN OS *020 †05

BLACKBURN, David Chambers. 1313 HERMANN DR, PARK PLAZA HOSPITAL 77004 #011-04-1979 L1980 RO *020 †80

BLACKBURN, Edward A, Jr. 7777 WEST ST, STE 820 77093 #048-02-1948 L1948 OTO *071 †45

BLACKBURN, N Theresa N. 5429 ASHBY ST 77005 #048-02-1970 L1970 P CHP *020 †75

BLACKER, H Martin. 6550 FANNIN ST, PAIN CNTRL & FUNCTL RESTOR 77030 #030-05-1959 L1979 NS *071 †25

BLACKLOCK, Jerry Bob. 6560 FANNIN ST STE 944 77030 #027-01-1979 L1985 NS *020 †25

BLACKMON, Ana Lia. 6560 FANNIN ST, SCURLOCK TOWER, STE 1950 77030 #048-12-1994 L2001 IM *020 †20

BLACKMON, Shanda Jo. 6550 FANNIN ST, STE 1661A 77030 #012-21-1998 L2003 TS *020 †85

BLACKSTONE, William Oscar. 8850 LONG POINT RD 77055 #045-01-1973 L1974 EM *020

BLAILOCK, Zack Robert. 7600 BEECHNUT ST, 2ND FL 77074 #048-04-1963 L1963 PTH *071 †50

BLAIN, James M. ■ 77007 #048-12-1951 L1951 CD *072

BLAIR, Carol Lynn. 14781 MEMORIAL DR, # 2501 77079 #003-01-1979 L1980 P *020

BLAIR, Hugh Thos. 1919 LA BRANCH ST 77002 #048-04-1968 L1968 PUD IM *020 †20

BLAIR, Robert Kendrick. 5929 CRAB ORCHARD RD 77057 #048-02-1937 L1937 OS GP *071

BLAIR, Robert Kendrick. 1221 MCKINNEY ST, STE 40300 77010 #048-02-1971 L1971 ORS *020 †40

BLAKE, Donald Cary. ■ 77059 #025-01-1983 L1995 DR NM *020 †28,80

BLAKE, Pamela Young. 1631 NORTH LOOP W STE 640, MEMORIAL HERMANN NORTHWEST 77008 #010-02-1990 L2006 N *020 †75

BLAKELY, Richard Walter. 9301 SOUTHWEST FWY, # 5000 77074 #048-04-1968 L1968 IM *030 †20

BLAKKOLB, Christi Lynn. ■ 77054 #016-43-2005 GS *012

BLAKLEY, Gail. 5151 KATY FWY, STE 150 77007 #048-02-1979 L1979 OM PTX *020 †70

BLANCHARD, Lawrence D. 6720 BERTNER ST # O 520, MC1-226 77030 #048-14-1994 L1998 AN *020 †05

BLANCO, Ernesto Ignacio. 1707 COLQUITT ST 77098 #048-04-2002 L2005 U *100

BLANEY, Susan Marie. 6701 FANNIN ST 77030 #038-43-1984 L1995 PHO PD *020 †55

BLASS, Christina Marie. 6655 TRAVIS ST, STE 980 77030 #021-01-2005 L2007 D *100

BLAUE, Barrett Randall. 1819 CRAWFORD ST STE 1708, CHRISTUS ST JOSEPH HOSP 77002 #048-14-2005 OBG *012

BLAUSTEIN, Alvin Stephen. 2002 HOLCOMBE BLVD 77030 #035-46-1970 L1972 CD IM *050 †20

BLAZEK, Allison M. 5151 KATY FWY, STE 100 77007 #048-14-1997 L2001 MPD *020 †20,55

BLAZER, Dan German, III. 1515 HOLCOMBE BLVD 1402, DEPT. OF SURGICAL ONCOLOGY 77030 #036-07-1999 L2006 GS *100

BLAZO, Maria A. 3701 KIRBY DR STE 600 77098 #048-13-1993 L1994 MG *020 †18,19

BLEDSOE, Christopher S. 77063 #048-14-2005 AN *012

BLEIBERG, Efrain. 2801 GESSNER DR 77080 #649-02-1976 L2005 CHP PYA *020 †75 ‡

BLEVINS, Kelly W. 7401 MAIN ST 77030 #048-14-1994 L1996 ORS *020 †40

BLEYER, Werner A. 1515 HOLCOMBE BLVD, MD ANDERSON CANCER CTR 77030 #035-45-1969 L1990 PHO ON *030 †55

BLEYZER, Gedaly. ■ 77024 #913-04-1952 L1986 P *071

BLIEDEN, Lauren Sasha. ■ 77007 #048-04-2007 TY *012

BLINDER, Joshua Jacob. ■ 77030 #041-01-2003 L2003 PDC *012 †55

BLIZZARD, Cynthia A. ■ 77024 #048-14-1984 L1985 IM *074 †20

BLOCH, Solomon. 11807 BUNKER HILL CIR 77024 #836-02-1952 L1981 R *071 †80

BLOCHER, Thomas Anthony. 2411 FOUNTAIN VIEW DR #175 77057 #048-02-1975 L1975 P ADM *071 †75

BLOCK, Joseph Harmon, Jr. 411 W 21ST ST 77008 #048-02-1963 L1963 OPH OS *071

BLOCKER, William P, Jr. 6550 FANNIN ST, STE 1421 77030 #048-12-1944 L1944 PM IM *071 †60

BLOEBAUM, Ronald Matthew. 1140 CLEAR LAKE CITY BLVD, STE A 77062 #017-20-1997 L2004 AI *020 †20,03

BLOMQUIST, Gustav Arthur. ■ 77027 #047-05-2004 L2007 DR *012

BLOOM, Daniel Gordon. ■ 77096 #048-12-2007 L2008 IM *012

BLOOM, Elizabeth Stroh. 1515 HOLCOMBE BLVD 77030 #016-06-1990 L1992 **RO** *020 †80 ‡

BLOOM, Kim. 6550 FANNIN ST, SM-2403 77030 #005-11-1974 L1977 **PUD IM** *020 †20

BLOOM, Leon. 8830 LONG POINT RD, STE 207 77055 #065-01-1956 L1976 **ORS** *071 †40

BLOOM, Martin Lorne. 8830 LONG POINT RD STE 207 77055 #065-01-1979 L1980 **ORS** *020 †40

BLOOM, Samuel. ■ 77024 #035-19-1936 L1972 **IM A** *071 †03,20

BLOOME, David Mitchell. 7401 MAIN ST 77030 #048-12-1996 L2000 **ORS** *020 †40

BLOOME, Michael Allyn. 8945 LONG POINT RD, STE 111 77055 #016-11-1967 L1974 **OPH** *020 †35

BLOUNT, Farris, Jr. 2000 CRAWFORD ST STE 1400, ST JOSEPH PROF BLDG 77002 #048-14-1984 L1985 **FM** *020 †18

BLOW, Benjamin James. ■ 77054 #048-02-2007 **IM** *012

BLUM, Philip Stuart. 11914 ASTORIA BLVD, HOUSTON NEUROLOGICAL 77089 #048-04-1990 L1995 **N** *020 †75

BLUM, Sonja. ■ 77030 #048-14-2006 L2008 **N** *012

BLUMBERG, Norman. ■ 77071 #836-01-1950 L1980 **GS CRS** *020

BLUMENREICH, B Joy. 4230 AMHERST ST 77005 #035-06-1979 L1980 **FM ADM** *020 †18

BLUMENSCHEIN, George R, Jr. 1515 HOLCOMBE BLVD, UNIT 432 77030 #048-14-1994 L1998 **ON** *020 †20

BLURTON, Matthew S. 6720 BERTNER ST, MC 2.270 77030 #048-04-2000 L2006 **AR** *020 †80

BOARDMAN, Dennis Richard. 4110 BELLAIRE BLVD, STE 210 77025 #030-06-1980 L1983 **PD** *020 †55

BOATRIGHT, Dowin Hugh. ■ 77004 #048-04-2008 *012

BOBINO, Desiree Marlene. 2727 W HOLCOMBE BLVD, 2ND FLR NEUROLOGY CLINIC 77025 #048-04-2000 L2005 **N** *100 †75

BOBO, Kimberly A. 6624 FANNIN ST, STE 1800 77030 #048-14-1998 L2002 **OBG** *020 †30

BOCCALANDRO, Cristina S. 6431 FANNIN ST STE 4042 77030 #935-01-1992 L2002 **END IM** *020 †20

BOCCHINI, Claire Elizabet. ■ 77054 #048-04-2005 **PD** *012

BOCELL, James Russell. 6560 FANNIN ST, STE 400 77030 #048-04-1973 L1973 **ORS** *071 †40

BODAGALA, Siva Ramaiah. 1504 TAUB LOOP 77030 #495-62-1981 L2002 **DR** *020 †80

BODAMER, Olaf Alrich. 77096 #409-10-1992 **MG** *100 †19

BODELL, Benson. ■ 77095 #016-42-1948 L1972 **AN** *071 †05

BODENHEIMER, Carol F. 1333 MOURSUND ST, TIRR 77030 #041-13-1991 L2006 **PM** *020 †60

BODEY, Gerald Paul. 1515 HOLCOMBE BLVD, M D ANDERSON HOSP BOX 402 77030 #023-07-1960 L1966 **ID IM** *071 †20

BODIE, Shamanique Shamona. PO BOX 20708 77225 #016-06-2004 L2008 **OBG** *012

BODIN, James Andrew, Jr. 4200 PORTSMOUTH ST 77027 #048-14-1993 L1994 **FM** *020 †18

BODIWALA, Ravi Kishor. ■ 77030 #012-01-2005 **DR** *012

BODURKA, Diane C. 1515 HOLCOMBE BLVD, DEPT ONCOLOGY 77030 #010-02-1990 L1994 **GO** *020 †30

BOECK, Ryan Alexander. ■ 77054 #048-04-2008 *012

BOEHME, Christopher L. 2800 S MACGREGOR WAY, U TX HOUSTON HEALTH SCI CE 77021 #048-14-2001 L2005 **P** *020

BOEHME, Elizabeth Yardley. 3400 BISSONNET ST, STE 100 77005 #023-07-1985 L1988 **IM** *020 †20

BOERKOEL, Cornelius F, III. 6701 FANNIN ST 77030 #038-06-1993 L1998 **PD** *020 †55,19

BOGAEV, Roberta Camden. 6770 BERTNER ST, STE C355K 77030 #051-01-1992 L1999 **CD** *020 †20

BOGITCH, Ray Michael. 77035 #048-12-2003 **N** *100

BOGLE, Melissa Anne. 3700 BUFFALO SPEEDWAY, STE 700 77098 #048-14-1999 L2000 **D** *020 †15

BOGOMOLNY, Yefim. 6431 FANNIN ST 5.020, UT-HOUSTON MEDICAL SCHOOL 77030 #913-86-1976 L2003 **AN** *100

BOHAN, Kenneth E. ■ 77063 #047-06-1944 L1944 **PD** *071 †55

BOHAN, Timothy Patrick. 1213 HERMANN DR, STE 740 77004 #011-02-1980 L1988 **CHN PA** *040 †75,55

BOHNN, Byron James. 7026 OLD KATY RD, STE 276 77024 #048-02-1966 L1966 **R DR** *020 †80

BOHNN, Jules Henry. 1215 BARKDULL ST 77006 #048-12-1960 L1960 **P PYA** *075

BOHORQUEZ R, Julio Cesar. ■ 77077 #264-01-1966 L1979 **GP** *071

BOIN, Marc Howard. 7600 BEECHNUT ST, DEPT OF ANESTHESIOLOGY 77074 #048-14-1989 L1989 **AN** *020 †05

BOISAUBIN, Eugene V. 6431 FANNIN ST, MSB 1.150 77030 #028-03-1971 L1975 **IM** *040 †20

BOLIO, Carlos Miguel. ■ 77027 #649-01-1997 *074

BOLIVER-CAMPBELL, Robin E. 1707 CALUMET ST, CENTRAL METROPOLITAN MEDIC 77004 #038-45-1993 L1997 **IM** *020

BOLLARD, Catherine Mary. 6621 FANNIN ST, MC 3-3320 77030 #671-01-1991 L2004 *020

BOLLINE, Stephen Clifford. 4110 BELLAIRE BLVD, STE 210 77025 #021-05-1975 L1978 **PD** *020 †55

BOLLINENI, Srinivas. 1504 TAUB LOOP, DEPT CCM 77030 #495-70-2000 **CCM** *012

BOLOURI, Marjan Sedigha. ■ 77030 #048-04-2008 *012

BOLTON, William David. 1515 HOLCOMBE BLVD 77030 #048-15-1999 L2007 **TS** *100 †85

BOMGAARS, Lisa Rochelle. 6701 FANNIN ST 77030 #038-40-1990 L1997 **PHO** *020 †55

BONAR, James Peter. ■ 77092 #038-43-1992 L2000 **CCS** *020 †85

BOND, Rodney H. ■ 77096 #143-08-1974 **IM ON** *040

BOND, William Michael. 7474 S KIRKWOOD RD, STE 104 77072 #048-14-1981 L1981 **FM** *020 †18

BONFANTE MEJIA, Eliana Es. PO BOX 20708 77225 #264-04-1992 L2006 **R RNR** *100 †80

BONIUK, Milton. 6550 FANNIN ST, STE 1501 77030 #064-01-1956 L1963 **OPH** *040 †35

BONMATI ORTEGA, Carmen. 12951 SOUTH FWY 77047 #847-04-1982 L1988 **DR** *020 †80

BONNELL, William F Jr. 2505 WORDSWORTH ST 77030 #048-04-2000 L2003 **PEM** *020 †55

BONNEN, James G. 11914 ASTORIA BLVD, STE 300 77089 #048-02-1992 L1993 **NS** *020 †25

BONNER, Francis M, III. 17070 RED OAK DR, STE 205 77090 #048-04-1971 L1971 **OTO** *020 †45

BONNER, Marian Edith. 714 FM 1960 RD W STE 206, ROSE IMAGING SPECIALISTS 77090 #036-07-1987 L1999 **DR** *020 †80

BOOKER, Oscar Julian. ■ 77047 #048-04-2003 L2008 **CD** *012 †20

BOOM, Julie Newport. 6701 FANNIN ST CCC1540, TEXAS CHILDRENS HOSPITAL 77030 #048-04-1992 L1994 **PD** *020 †55

BOOM, Marc Louis. 6565 FANNIN ST, D200 77030 #048-04-1992 L1994 **IM IMG** *030 †20

BOON, John Reynolds. ■ 77025 #048-04-2003 **GS** *100

BOONE, Barry Danl. 7401 MAIN ST 77030 #048-02-1991 L1994 **OSM** *020 †40

BOONE, Carroll Robt. 7401 MAIN ST 77030 #048-12-1972 L1975 **ORS** *020 †40

BOONE, Timothy B. 6560 FANNIN ST, SCURLOCK TOWER STE 2100 77030 #048-14-1985 L1987 **U GS** *020 †95

BOONE SUELL, Mary Nell. 6621 FANNIN ST 2-2261, TEXAS CHILDRENS HOSPITAL 77030 #048-04-1998 L2001 **PHO** *020 †55

BOOSER, Daniel James. 1515 HOLCOMBE BLVD, UNIT 1354 77030 #008-01-1967 L1979 **IM ON** *020 †20

BOOTIN, Debra Mucasey. 7400 FANNIN ST, STE 900 77054 #048-04-1986 L1987 **PD** *020 †55

BOOZALIS, Jane E. 6720 BERTNER ST 77030 #019-02-1985 L1989 **AN IM** *020 †05

BOOZALIS, Steve Theodore. 7401 MAIN ST 77030 #048-02-1984 L1985 **AN** *020 †05

BOPARAI, Jasmine. 2002 HOLCOMBE BLVD, THE VA MEDICAL CENTER 77030 #496-07-1997 L2006 **END** *020 †20

BORDEN, Starr. 10497 TOWN AND COUNTRY WAY, STE 360 77024 #011-02-1975 L1978 **FM** *020 †18 ‡

BORDON, Alicia Raquel. 1631 NORTH LOOP W, STE 550 77008 #132-08-1991 L2001 **IM** *020

BORGER, Jules Hirsch. 3400 BISSONNET 77005 #048-04-1956 L1957 **OPH** *071 †35

BORGES, Rafael Geovanny. 2807 LITTLE YORK RD, STE 110 77093 #308-01-1979 L2000 **FM** *020 †20

BORGHERO, Yerko Orestes. ■ 77019 #231-03-1998 **RO** *100 †80

BOROCHOFF, Jerome Lloyd. 800 W SAM HOUSTON PKWY S, STE 201 77042 #028-03-1969 L1971 **GP OS** *020

BOROVOY, Jacobo. 4543 POST OAK PLACE DR, STE 209 77027 #649-13-1990 L1994 **PD PG** *100 †55

BORRELL, Leo James. 4150 WESTHEIMER RD STE 103 77027 #012-05-1967 L1971 **CHP P** *020 †75

BORRMANN, Deborah Kay. ■ 77059 #048-02-1982 L1983 **PD** *074

BORSATO, Garry Wayne. 2222 MARONEAL ST, UNIT 1615 77030 #065-06-1989 *100

BORSKI, Thomas Greg. 2727 W HOLCOMBE BLVD 77025 #048-04-1995 L2001 **OTO** *020 †45

BORSOS, Bela. ■ 77057 #407-07-1948 L1952 **FM** *071

BORTHAKUR, Gautam. 1515 HOLCOMBE BLVD, UNIT 428 77030 #495-18-1985 L1996 **HEM** *100 †20

BORTOLOTTI, Lorenzo E. 13125 EAST FWY 77015 #048-14-1996 L1999 **IM** *020 †20

BOSWELL, Hillary Brooke. 6624 FANNIN ST, STE 1800 77030 #038-40-2001 L2005 **OBG** *100

BOTAS, Modesto. ■ 77096 #275-01-1953 L1966 **IM** *071

BOTERO, Rafael Claudino. 6410 FANNIN ST STE 370, TEXAS LIVER CENTER 77030 #264-03-1974 L2004 **IM HEP** *020 †20

BOTSFORD, Lindsay Kathryn. ■ 77025 #048-04-2007 *012

BOTTO, Juan-Manuel A. 1213 HERMANN DR STE 570, PULMONARY & INT MED ASSOC 77004 #737-06-1985 L1999 **PUD IM** *020 †20

BOTZ, Gregory Harnett. 1515 HOLCOMBE BLVD, BOX 112 77030 #010-01-1990 L1998 **AN** *020 †20

BOU ARAM, Boura'A Abdul K. 6621 FANNIN ST, RM MC 77030 #605-01-2001 L2002 **NPM** *012 †55

BOUCKENOOGHE, Alain R. 2002 HOLCOMBE BLVD 77030 #165-04-1985 L1997 **ID GP** *020 †20

BOUJAOUDE, Lina Chafic. ■ 77005 #605-02-1994 L2007 **PD** *020

BOULAFENDIS, Demetrio. 8830 LONG POINT RD, STE 606 77055 #561-01-1957 L1968 **TS** *071 †85

BOURGEOIS, Keith Alan. 1315 ST JOSEPH PKWY, STE 1601 77002 #021-05-1983 L1985 **OPH** *020 †35

BOURGEOIS, Yolonda Marie. ■ 77059 #021-05-1989 L1992 **EM** *020 †16

BOUSHY, Samuel Fadlo. 7777 SW FRWY NO 744 77074 #021-01-1957 L1964 **PUD IM** *071 †20

BOUTHAINA, Dabaja. 1515 HOLCOMBE BLVD, UNIT 097 77030 #605-03-1991 L2006 **RO** *100

BOUTON, Michael Steven. 902 FROSTWOOD DR STE 166 77024 #048-15-1984 L1986 **GS** *020 †85 ‡

BOUTROS, Boutros A. 12121 RICHMOND AVE STE 117 77082 #915-03-1964 L1976 **OBG** *020

BOUTROS, George. 3310 RICHMOND AVE 77098 #065-06-1970 L1977 **R** *020 †80

BOUTROS, Sean G. 6410 FANNIN ST STE 732 77030 #048-04-1998 L2005 **PS** *020 †65

BOWDEN, John B. 2200 SOUTHWEST FWY, STE 333 77098 #048-14-1988 L1989 **D** *020 †15

BOWDEN, Mary Talley. 8850 LONG POINT RD 77055 #012-01-1998 L2000 **OTO** *020 †45

BOWERS, Theron C, Jr. 2002 HOLCOMBE BLVD, MENTAL HEALTH CARE LINE 77030 #048-04-1987 L1988 **P** *020 †75

BOWMAN, Albert Boyd. 1930 EL DORADO BLVD 77062 #048-02-1966 L1966 **GP** *071

BOWMAN, Zebulon Lynn. ■ 77041 #036-07-1977 L1994 **OPH** *020 †35

BOYAREDDIGARI, Prasanth R. 211 HIGHLAND CROSS DR #275 77073 #048-16-2003 L2005 **EM** *020

BOYD, David B. 810 PEAKWOOD DR, STE 200 77090 #048-02-1987 L1988 **DR** *020 †80

BOYD, Heidi Annette. ■ 77062 #048-02-1997 *100

BOYD, Matthew L. 18220 STATE HIGHWAY 249 77070 #048-16-1982 L1983 **AN** *020 †05

BOYD, Nakeisha L. 6770 BERTNER ST, TEXAS HEALTH INSTITUTE 77030 #021-05-2002 L2007 **AN** *100 †05

BOYD, Robert Allen. 4110 BELLAIRE BLVD, STE 210 77025 #019-02-1969 L1972 **PD** *071 †55

BOYE, Adolfo E. 5644 LAWNDALE ST 77023 #231-02-1965 L1975 **PTH FM** *020 †50

BOYER, Anthony Francis. ■ 77005 #048-14-2008 *012

BOYER, Jean-Marc Jacques. 6410 FANNIN ST, STE 470 77030 #396-37-1984 L1996 **AN** *030

BOYLAN, Frances. ■ 77054 #539-04-1974 L1987 *100

BOYLSTON, Wm Harrison, Jr. 2900 WESLAYAN ST, STE 540 77027 #021-05-1961 L1969 **CHP P** *020 †75

BOYNTON, James Franklin. 12727 KIMBERLEY LN STE 300 77024 #048-14-1998 L2002 **PS HS** *020 †65

BOZINOVSKI, Jovan. 1 BAYLOR PLZ, MS BCM 390 77030 #065-05-1998 L2005 **CD** *100

BOZKURT, Biykem. 2002 HOLCOMBE BLVD, MEDVAMC-CARDIOLOGY 3C306A 77030 #902-10-1989 L1994 **CD IM** *020 †20

BRACEY, Arthur W, Jr. 6720 BERTNER ST MC4-265, ST. LUKE'S EPISCOPAL HOSPI 77030 #010-02-1976 L1981 **PTH BBK** *020 †50

BRACK, Amanda Whittenburg. 915 GESSNER RD, STE 350 77024 #048-02-2003 L2006 **PD** *020 †55

BRACKETT, Julienne. 6621 FANNIN ST, DEPT OF PEDS HEMA & ONCOLO 77030 #041-01-2003 L2008 **PHO** *012 †55

BRADEN, Albert Henry, III. 3400 BISSONNET ST, STE 100 77005 #048-14-1977 L1977 **IM** *020 †20

BRADEN, David J. 3400 BISSONNET ST, STE 100 77005 #048-02-1953 L1953 **IM** *071

BRADLEY, Burke Thompson. 7401 MAIN ST 77030 #048-02-1990 L1991 **AN** *020 †05

BRADLEY, Ishmeal Earl. 99 SUNSET BLVD, MARTEL COLLEGE 77005 #048-12-2007 **IM** *012

BRADLEY, Raymond L, Jr. 9034 WESTHEIMER RD STE 339 77063 #048-04-1946 L1946 **OBG** *071 †30

BRADLEY, Richard Neville. 5656 KELLEY ST, STE 1EC93006 77026 #010-02-1994 L1997 **EM OS** *030 †16

BRADY, Jett R. 6565 FANNIN ST MS D281, DEPT OF RADIOLOGY 77030 #048-14-1991 L1992 **DR** *020 †80,28

BRADY, Kimberly K. 915 GESSNER RD STE 540 77024 #048-04-1991 L1993 **OBG** *020 †30
BRAHMBHATT, Nimeet Ramesh. 1 BAYLOR PLZ, DEPT OF INTERNAL MEDICINE 77030 #038-43-2004 **IM** *012
BRAHMBHATT, Reshma Raj. ■ 77054 #048-04-2008 *012
BRAITEH, Fadi Samir. 1515 HOLCOMBE BLVD, UNIT 10 77030 #605-02-1998 L2004 **HO** *012 †20
BRAKE, Mary Catherine. ■ 77054 #036-08-2007 **MPD** *012
BRALY, Walter Grant. 7401 MAIN ST 77030 #048-02-1979 L1979 **OFA** *020 †40
BRAMS, Matthew Niel. 550 WESTCOTT ST STE 520 77007 #048-14-1987 L1988 **P CHP** *020 †75
BRANDAU, George Henry. ■ 77019 #021-01-1942 L1943 **GS** *071
BRANDMAN, Craig Joel. PO BOX 19189 77224 #035-08-1973 L1974 **IM** *020
BRANDON, Thomas Reynolds. 3730 KIRBY DR STE 1200 77098 #048-04-1965 L1965 **P** *020 †75
BRANDT, Mary Lynn. 6621 FANNIN ST, CLINICAL CARE CENTER 650.0 77030 #048-04-1982 L1984 **PDS CCM** *020 †85
BRANNAN, Stephen Kyle. ■ 77058 #048-12-1985 L1986 **P** *050 †75
BRANSFORD, Paris. 6911 ALMEDA RD STE 101 77021 #047-07-1963 L1971 **GS GP** *075
BRANT, Carol Richman. 6431 FANNIN ST 77030 #048-46-1985 L1985 **DR IM** *020
BRAUCHLE, Randall Walter. 2500 TANGLEWILDE ST, STE 160 77063 #048-02-1997 L2000 **OTO** *020 †45
BRAUER, Raymond Oliver. 1315 CALHOUN ST STE 940 77002 #005-12-1943 L1948 **PS** *071 †65
BRAUN, Michael Compton. 6431 FANNIN ST 3.124, UNIV OF TX HSC 77030 #041-01-1990 L2001 **PN** *050 †55
BRAUN, Ursula K M. 2002 HOLCOMBE BLVD, BLDG T110 #132 (39A) 77030 #409-10-1993 L1999 **IMG** *020 †20
BRAUNSDORF, Dell H. 2000 WEST LOOP S, UNITED BEHAVRL HLTH 77027 #048-02-1989 L1994 **P** *020 †10
BRAVERMAN, Richard M. 6621 FANNIN ST, MC 2-2521 77030 #023-07-1984 L1986 **PDR** *020 †80
BRAVO, Cesar A. 8830 LONG POINT RD STE 408 77055 #737-03-1967 L1977 **NEP IM** *020 †20
BRAY, Collin Douglas. 1 BAYLOR PLZ 77030 #048-14-2000 L2002 **DR** *100 †80
BRAY, Rachel Rosenthal. 14730 BARRYKNOLL LN 77079 #048-14-2000 L2003 **PD** *020 †55 ‡
BRAZILE, Daphne C. ■ 77004 #047-07-1994 **CHP** *100
BREE, Alanna Flath. 6621 FANNIN ST, CC620.16 77030 #016-45-2000 L2006 **D** *020 †15
BREE, Douglas Ray. 6560 FANNIN ST, STE 620 77030 #016-45-2000 L2006 **IC** *020 †20
BREINHOLT, John Philip. 1 BAYLOR PLZ 77030 #049-01-2000 L2008 **PDC** *012 †55 ‡
BRELSFORD, Harold J. PO BOX 20347 77225 #048-04-1951 L1951 **ORS** *020 †40
BRENER, Daniel Michael. 3730 KIRBY DR, STE 700 77098 #048-04-1974 L1974 **P PYA** *020 †75
BRENER, Zidella M Seibel. ■ 77030 #048-02-1935 L1935 **CHP** *072
BRENNAN, Brian William. ■ 77030 #021-01-2008 *012
BRENNAN, Thomas S. ■ 77024 #016-43-1989 L1987 **NEP IM** *020 †20
BRENNER, Jennifer Wendi. PO BOX 20708, UNIV TX MED SCH 77225 #016-43-2003 L2005 **GE** *012 †20
BRENNER, Malcolm Keith. 6621 FANNIN ST, MC 3-3320 77030 #917-22-1975 L2002 **PD** *020
BRENNER, Ralph Larry. 6411 FANNIN ST 7TH FL 77030 #048-02-1965 L1965 **OPH** *071 †35
BRESALIER, Robert Scott. 1515 HOLCOMBE BLVD, UNIT 436 77030 #016-02-1978 L2004 **GE IM** *050 †20
BRESCIA, Samuel Timothy. 1 BAYLOR PLZ, BAYLOR COLLEGE OF MED 77030 #048-13-2002 L2002 **PDC** *012
BRESSLER, Fred Jay. 6624 FANNIN ST STE 2550 77030 #016-11-1984 L1991 **FPS OTO** *020 †45
BREWER, Earl Johnson, Jr. ■ 77027 #048-04-1954 L1954 **PD RHU** *071 †55
BREWER, Eileen Doyle. 6621 FANNIN ST 77030 #028-02-1971 L1977 **NEP PD** *050 †55
BREWER, Pamela Yvonne. 2002 BINZ ST STE B 77004 #010-03-1984 L1991 **FM** *020 †18
BREWER, Raymond Larry. 4200 PORTSMOUTH ST 77027 #048-04-1951 L1951 **OPH** *071 †35
BREWSTER, Abenaa Marcia. 1515 HOLCOMBE BLVD, BOX 236 77030 #024-01-1995 L2002 **ON** *020 †20
BREWTON, Gary Wm. 1745 W ALABAMA ST 77098 #048-04-1981 L1981 **IM** *020 †20
BRIAN, Michael John. ■ 3020 77030 #143-07-1980 *100
BRICKER, Michelle Breaux. 11850 FM 1960 RD W 77065 #048-14-1990 L1991 **AN** *020 †05
BRICKMAN, Solomon Sam. 11730 FM 1960 RD W 77065 #065-01-1963 L1978 **D** *020
BRIDGES, James Patrick. 4545 POST OAK PLACE DR, STE 130 77027 #048-14-1995 L1996 **IM** *020 †20
BRIDGES, Margaret E. 6560 FANNIN ST, STE 1404 77030 #045-01-1973 L1979 **GE IM** *020 †20
BRILL, Laura Ann. 7037 CAPITOL ST, MAGNOLIA CLINIC 77011 #038-40-1984 L1988 **OBG** *071 †30
BRINDLEY, Paul Claunch. 7777 SOUTHWEST FWY, STE 820 77074 #048-02-1965 L1965 **OTO FPS** *020 †45 ‡
BRINK, Paul A. ■ 77057 #836-04-1984 **CD** *020
BRINKER, Mark Robt. 7401 MAIN ST 77030 #021-01-1987 L1993 **ORS** *020 †40
BRINKLEY, Michele Goldman. 18220 TOMBALL PKWY, STE 370 77070 #048-16-1989 L1990 **FM** *020 †18 ‡
BRINSMADE, Alan B. ■ 77056 #869-05-1955 L1960 **P** *071
BRISCOE, Donald Anthony. 424 HAHLO ST 77020 #051-01-1992 L2002 **FM** *020 †18
BRISSETT, Anthony Edwin. 6550 FANNIN ST STE 1727, BAYLOR COLLEGE OF MEDICINE 77030 #025-07-1996 L2003 **OTO** *020 †45
BRITTON, Jeffrey Donald. 11757 KATY FWY STE 1540 77079 #048-02-1974 L1974 **OM FM** *020 †70
BROADDUS, Russell Ray. 1515 HOLCOMBE BLVD, DEPT PATH BOX 85 77030 #048-14-1994 L1998 **ATP** *020 †50
BROADWELL, Anita Ward. 6900 FANNIN ST, STE 665 77030 #048-02-1982 L1983 **ON IM** *020 †20,05
BROBBEY, Gwendolyn E. 2900 SMITH ST, STE 101 77006 #412-01-1974 L1981 **PD PHP** *020 †55
BROCK, Gary T. 6411 FANNIN ST 77030 #048-12-1985 L1986 **OP** *020 †40
BROCK, Patricia Ann. 1504 TAUB LOOP 77030 #020-02-1983 L1985 **GS** *020 †85
BROCK, Paul W, Jr. 6560 FANNIN ST, STE 1100 77030 #001-06-1984 L1994 **AN** *020 †05
BROCKMAN, H Le Roy. ■ 77077 #045-01-1944 L1953 **GS TS** *071 †85
BROD, Staley Armstrong. 6431 FANNIN ST # 7044, DEPT. UNIV OF TX HLTH SCIE 77030 #048-43-1981 L1992 **N IM** *020 †20,75
BRODSKY, Harris Elliot. ■ 77030 #048-02-2007 L2007 **TY** *012
BROOKS, Dandrea Lynne. 7400 FANNIN ST STE 1118 77054 #012-21-1990 L1993 **OBG** *020 †30
BROOKS, Jacel Craig. ■ 77047 #001-02-2006 **PD** *012

BROOKS, John David. ■ 77082 #021-05-1957 L1967 **R** *020
BROOKS, Thomas Cleveland. 3317 MONTROSE BLVD # 1121 77006 #048-04-1944 L1944 **OS** *075
BROOKS-CARTER, Gizelle. 6620 MAIN ST 77030 #035-01-1997 L2005 **OBG** *020 †30
BROSNAN, Patrick Gerald. 6431 FANNIN ST, UT MED SCH # 3122 MSB 77030 #010-02-1968 L1974 **END PD** *040 †55
BROUGH, Royce D, Jr. ■ 77007 #048-13-1973 L1975 **EM** *020
BROUSSARD, Ashley Elizabe. 6431 FANNIN ST 1.134, OF TEXAS-HOUSTON 77030 #021-01-2007 **IM** *012
BROUSSARD, Dwane Gerard. 9055 KATY FWY, STE 200 77024 #016-45-1993 L1994 **FM** *020 †18
BROUSSARD, Marjorie Andre. 1 BAYLOR PLZ, DEPT FM 77030 #935-03-2001 **FP** *012
BROWDER, Dan Preston. 6431 FANNIN ST, UNIV OF TEXAS MED SCH 77030 #048-04-2001 L2006 **FM** *020 †18
BROWN, Anthony Edward. 7550 OFFICE CITY DR, GULFGATE HEALTH CENTER 77012 #048-04-2001 L2004 **FM** *020 †18
BROWN, Arthur Morton. 1 BAYLOR PLZ # PHYSIOL 77030 #062-01-1956 L1975 **OS** *040
BROWN, Ayanna Janell. ■ 77054 #048-02-2004 L2006 **CHP** *012
BROWN, Barrett Shytles. 7401 MAIN ST 77030 #048-04-2001 L2005 **OSM** *020
BROWN, Barry Merle. 12335 KINGSRIDE LN # PMB28 77024 #041-01-1963 L1969 **P** *075 †75
BROWN, Brigitte Berengere. ■ 77094 #021-05-1993 L2007 **IM** *020 †20
BROWN, Chester Wayne. 6621 FANNIN ST 77030 #038-41-1993 L1997 **MG PD** *050 †19,55
BROWN, Christopher Patric. ■ 77056 #036-08-2005 L2007 **PD** *100
BROWN, Cortney Michelle. ■ 77054 #021-01-2000 L2005 **OBG** *100 †30
BROWN, Dale, Jr. 6620 MAIN ST 77030 #048-02-1964 L1965 **OBG** *020 †30 ‡
BROWN, David Lee. 1400 HOLCOMBE BLVD, UNIT 409 77030 #026-04-1978 L1980 **AN PME** *020 †05
BROWN, Deborah Lynn. 6655 TRAVIS ST, STE 400 77030 #041-01-1987 L2003 **PD** *020 †55
BROWN, Dennis Graeme. 909 FROSTWOOD DR STE 221 77024 #048-04-1968 L1974 **N GP** *020 †20
BROWN, Ervin Benj. 6624 FANNIN ST STE 2410 77030 #007-02-1977 L1982 **GS** *020 †85
BROWN, Ethan T. 15881 FM 529 RD STE A, MEDICAL DIRECTOR 77095 #048-02-1993 L1994 **EM** *020 †16
BROWN, Jacqueline E. 5751 BLYTHEWOOD ST, STE 700 77021 #048-12-1980 L1980 **OBG PHP** *020 †30
BROWN, Jeffrey Stuart. 909 DAIRY ASHFORD ST # 205 77079 #016-42-1976 L1979 **END IM** *020 †20
BROWN, Jessica Karwowski. 6565 FANNIN ST, PHYSICIAN ORGANIZ, ANESTHE 77030 #048-14-2000 L2004 **AN** *020 †05
BROWN, Jody Jim. ■ 77030 #048-13-1996 L1996 **AN** *100
BROWN, John Robt. ■ 77018 #048-02-1948 L1948 **GP** *071
BROWN, Karen Ann. 1900 YORKTOWN ST 77056 #065-01-1980 **AN** *100 †05
BROWN, Karen Susan. 820 GESSNER RD STE 750 77024 #048-04-1985 L1991 **P** *020 †75
BROWN, Mark. 2727 W HOLCOMBE BLVD, MEDICAL CENTER ANESTHESIA 77025 #039-01-1983 L1984 **AN** *020 †05
BROWN, Michael G. 17070 RED OAK DR STE 101 77090 #048-04-1982 L1983 **HS GS** *020 †85
BROWN, Philip M. ■ 77030 #048-15-1989 L1990 **PA LM** *030
BROWN, Powel Harris. 1 BAYLOR PLZ, BCM600 77030 #035-19-1985 L1996 **IM ON** *020 †20
BROWN, Richard W. 7600 BEECHNUT ST, 2ND FL 77074 #048-01-1989 L1994 **PTH** *050 †50
BROWN, Robert T. 7026 OLD KATY RD, STE 276 77024 #048-13-1983 L1983 **R DR** *020 †80
BROWN, Stephen Dale. 1200 BINZ ST, STE 580 77004 #048-02-1997 L2002 **ORS** *020 †40
BROWN, Steven Dunning. 5656 KELLEY ST, UNIVERSITY OF TEXAS MED 77026 #048-02-1983 L1983 **PUD CCM** *020 †20
BROWN, Susan Smith. 18220 TOMBALL PKWY, STE 400 77070 #048-12-1986 L1987 **IM** *020 †20
BROWN, Tricia Jean. 18220 STATE HWY 249, STE 360 77070 #048-04-1998 L1999 **D** *020 †15
BROWN, William Knox. ■ 77027 #051-01-1947 L1948 **IM** *071 †20
BROWN, William Ross. 77002 #051-04-2007 **IM** *012
BROWNE, Lorna Patricia. 6621 FANNIN ST 2-2521, TEXAS CHILDREN'S HOSPITAL 77030 #539-06-1999 **PDR** *100
BROWNE, Shirley Annette. 6500 HORNWOOD DR 77074 #048-14-1977 L1978 **AN** *020
BROWNFIELD, Shaylon V. 1140 WESTMONT DR, STE 340 77015 #048-13-2001 L2005 **OBG** *020
BROWNHILL, Robert Lee. 7777 SOUTHWEST FWY, STE 554 77074 #048-04-1955 L1955 **ORS** *020 †40
BROWNING, John Caleb. ■ 77005 #048-02-2001 L2004 **D** *100 †55,15
BROWN-PRICE, Tonya M. 2101 CRAWFORD ST, STE 214 77002 #035-09-1990 L1992 **PD IM** *020 †55
BROXTON, Kyrel Darice. 1250 CYPRESS STATION DR 77090 #011-03-1980 L1982 **PD** *020 †55
BRUBAKER, Latha Mary. 12345 KATY FWY, CONCENTRA 77079 #305-01-1999 L2007 **FM** *020 †18
BRUCE, Suzanne. 1900 SAINT JAMES PL, STE 650 77056 #048-04-1981 L1981 **D** *020 †15
BRUCKNER, Brian Allen. ■ 77004 #011-03-1997 L1999 **GS** *100 †85
BRUERA, Eduardo. 1515 HOLCOMBE BLVD, UNIT 008 77030 #132-04-1980 L2003 *100
BRUNELLI, Luca. 6431 FANNIN ST 3.200, THE UNIV OF TX MED SCH HST 77030 #561-07-1988 L2004 **PD NPM** *050 †55 ‡
BRUNER, Christine Roberts. 7737 SOUTHWEST FWY STE 420, PRACTICE RESID 77074 #036-05-2002 L2004 **FM** *020 †18
BRUNER, Janet M. 1515 HOLCOMBE BLVD 77030 #038-43-1979 L1985 **ATP NP** *020 †50
BRUNER, Terrence Weston. 1709 DRYDEN RD, BAYLOR COLLEGE OF MED 77030 #036-05-2002 **PS** *012
BRUNETTI PIERRI, Nicola. 1 BAYLOR PLZ 77030 #561-31-1997 **MG** *100 †19
BRUNICARDI, Francis Charl. 1709 DRYDEN RD STE 1500, BAYLOR COLLEGE OF MEDICINE 77030 #033-06-1980 L1996 **GS TRS** *020 †85
BRUNNER, John Franklin. 1 BAYLOR PLZ, DEPT RAD 77030 #038-06-2006 **DR** *012
BRYAN, Richard Armond. 1415 NORTH LOOP W, STE 820 77008 #048-02-1974 L1974 **DR** *020 †80
BRYAN, William Jay. 6560 FANNIN ST STE 400 77030 #048-04-1975 L1975 **ORS** *020 †40
BRYANT, Jess Oldham. 821 PEAKWOOD DR STE 203 77090 #048-12-1957 L1957 **GYN** *071 †30
BRYANT, Kenny Wayne. 77021 #001-02-2003 L2006 **DR** *012
BRYANT, Ronald. 8307 KNIGHT RD 77054 #001-02-1997 L2000 **IM** *020 †20
BRYSON, Trenton D. ■ 77054 #048-14-2008 *012
BU ARAM, Sawsan Khodor. ■ 77025 #605-01-1997 **OPH** *100
BUCCI, Mary Kara. 1515 HOLCOMBE BLVD BX 97 77030 #025-01-1998 L2006 **RO** *020 †80
BUCHANAN, Gary Stephen. 10370 RICHMOND AVE, STE 1125 77042 #048-04-1988 L1989 **IM** *020 †20
BUCHANAN, Jason Nicholas. 6630 DE MOSS DR 77074 #048-04-2002 L2005 **FM** *020 †18

BUCHHOLZ, Thomas Arthur. 1515 HOLCOMBE BLVD BX 97, DEPT RADIATION ONCOLOGY 77030 #024-07-1988 L1997 **RO** *020 †80

BUCHMILLER, Brett Lee. 7017 ALMEDA RD, PMB 270 77054 #049-01-1997 L2000 **AI** *012 †55,20

BUCHSBAUM, Mona S. 3310 RICHMOND AVE 77098 #048-04-1990 L1991 **DR** *020 †80

BUCK, David S. 3701 KIRBY DR STE 600 77098 #048-04-1990 L1991 **FM** *020 †18

BUCK, John Eric. 16 FM 1960 RD W, CYPRESS CREEK MEDICAL CENT 77090 #048-13-1995 L1996 **EM** *020 †16

BUCK, John Gregory. 5850 ROGERDALE RD 77072 #025-07-1991 L1997 **PTH** *030 †50

BUCKLE, Rosemary. 1315 ST JOSEPH PKWY, ORTHOPAEDIC ASSOCIATES 77002 #048-14-1989 L1990 **ORS** *020 †40

BUCKLEY, Robyn Fader. 1707 SUNSET BLVD 77005 #048-14-1999 L2003 **IM** *020 †20

BUCKWOLD, Frederick J. 2 GREENWAY PLZ, STE 500 77046 #065-10-1973 L1978 **MDM IM** *030 †20

BUDOFF, Jeffrey Evan. 6620 MAIN ST, STE 1300 77030 #035-20-1991 L1999 **HS** *020 †40

BUECHLER, Robert B. 17030 NANES DR, STE 210 77090 #048-13-1982 L1990 **OTO** *020 †45

BUENCAMINO, Lucy Ann. 15655 CYPRESSWD MED DR 77014 #038-43-1982 L1984 **IM** *020 †20 ‡

BUENO-BELLO, Agnes C. ■ 77074 #748-10-1971 **CHP P** *020

BUERGLER, John Martin. 6550 FANNIN ST, STE 1901 77030 #016-02-1992 L1996 **CD** *020 †20

BUESCHER, Ronald Ray. 10021 S MAIN ST STE B3 77025 #048-04-1980 L1980 **GP OM** *020

BUESO, Fernando R. 1315 ST JOSEPH PKWY, STE 1507 77002 #561-17-1967 L1978 **OBG** *020 †30 ‡

BUESO, Gerardo. 5711 ALMEDA RD 77004 #561-19-1972 L1980 **END IM** *020 †20

BUESO-RAMOS, Carlos E. 1515 HOLCOMBE BLVD 77030 #451-01-1982 L1993 **HMP PTH** *020 †50

BUFORD, Deena Louise. 13501 KATY FWY, RM W2-108 77079 #047-07-1984 L1991 **OM IM** *020 †70

BUFORD, Reginald C. 13111 EAST FWY STE 106 77015 #038-41-1982 L1990 **PS** *020

BUGGS, Colleen. 6621 FANNIN ST, CLINICAL CARE CENTER 1020 77030 #024-01-1998 L2006 **PDE** *020 †55

BUHAY, Caroline. 1709 DRYDEN RD STE 550, BCM FACULTY CENTER 77030 #048-04-2007 **IM** *012

BUHLER, Scott Anthony. ■ 77019 #021-05-2007 **ORS** *012

BUI, Dana Thuy. ■ 77054 #048-14-2008 *012

BUI, Dat Duc. 11717 HIGHLAND MEADOW DR, STE 300 77089 #048-15-1999 L2002 **IM HOS** *020 †20

BUI, Duc Thi. 17322 RED OAK DR 77090 #048-14-1992 L1994 **AN** *020 †05

BUI, Hoanh. 8200 WILCREST DR 77072 #941-01-1964 L1980 **FM** *071

BUI, Michael-Quoc Hung. ■ 77059 #048-02-2003 L2007 **CD** *012 †20

BUI, Thao P. 1515 HOLCOMBE BLVD BOX 42, MD ANDERSON CANCER CTR 77030 #048-12-1991 L1992 **AN** *020 †05

BUI, Trang Anh. 3400 BISSONNET ST, STE 100 77005 #039-01-1996 L1999 **IM** *020 †20

BUIE, Joseph. 8831 LONG POINT RD STE 300 77055 #048-15-1995 L1998 **FM** *020 †18 ‡

BUJA, Louis Maximilian. 7000 FANNIN ST STE 1715, UTHSC AT HOUSTON 77030 #021-01-1967 L1974 **ATP CD** *030 †50

BUJNOCH, Louis John. 714 FM 1960 RD W, STE 206 77090 #048-14-1976 L1976 **DR NM** *020 †80

BUJOSA, Carlos Miguel. ■ 77057 #275-01-1953 L1963 **AS GP** *071

BULAN, Glenn Edgar. 7710 BEECHNUT ST, TEXAS EYE INSTITUTE 77074 #035-09-1995 L2005 **OPH** *020 †35

BULL, Joan M Carlson. 6431 FANNIN ST 1.150, ONCOLOGY DIVISION 77030 #005-11-1966 L1981 **ON IM** *050 †20

BULLARD, Arlean M. 15655 CYPRESSWOOD MEDCL DR, STE 110 77014 #004-01-1998 L2001 **FM** *020

BULLOCK, Ada Jemison. 7505 FANNIN ST STE 510 77054 #028-02-1978 L1984 **CHP** *030 †75

BULLOCKS, Jamal M. 6624 FANNIN ST, STE 2260 77030 #010-02-2001 L2006 **PS** *100

BUNGO, Michael Wm. 1133 JOHN FREEMAN BLVD, STE 403 77030 #033-05-1975 L1981 **CD IM** *020 †20

BUQUING, Joey Oliver. 6624 FANNIN ST, STE 1400 77030 #748-10-1985 L1997 **NEP** *020 †20

BURBRIDGE, Gail Everett. 1200 BINZ ST 77004 #030-05-1972 L1974 **GS** *020 †85

BURDINE, John Alton, Jr. ■ 77024 #048-02-1961 L1961 **NM** *071 †28

BURGER, David Lawrence. 4606 BRYN MAWR LN 77027 #048-12-1979 L1980 **EM** *020 †16

BURGER, Jan Andreas. PO BOX 301402, DEPT OF LEUKEMA UNIT 428 77230 #409-05-1994 *100

BURGERT, Susan Jo. 6441 MAIN ST 77030 #021-05-1989 L1991 **ID** *020 †20

BURGESS, Patricia Ann. 2424 W HOLCOMBE BLVD, MEDICAL CENTER ANESTHESIA 77030 #048-02-1997 L1999 **AN** *020

BURIAN, Daniel Francis. 18220 TOMBALL PKWY, METHODIST WILLOWBROOK HOSP 77070 #041-12-1996 L2003 **EM** *020 †16

BURK, Kathryn J. ■ 77030 #048-14-2008 *012

BURKE, Douglas K. 2000 CRAWFORD ST STE 1405 77002 #048-14-1997 L2000 **NEP IM** *020 †20

BURKE, Gene Edberne. 3637 W ALABAMA ST, STE 100 77027 #048-04-1956 L1956 **IM OS** *071

BURKE, Luke Ignatius. 1631 NORTH LOOP W, STE 620 77008 #035-48-1993 L1996 **OTO SME** *020 †45

BURKE, Patrick Brazier. ■ 77005 #048-14-2004 **MPD** *012

BURKE, Thomas Wm. 1515 HOLCOMBE BLVD BOX 43 77030 #021-01-1978 L1988 **GO GYN** *020 †30

BURKHEAD, James M, III. 7900 FANNIN ST STE 2 77054 #048-14-1989 L1990 **OBG** *020 †30

BURKHOLDER, Henry Leroy. ■ 77030 #035-03-2007 **PD** *012

BURNAZIAN, Geo Ghazaros. 1200 BINZ ST, STE 530 77004 #781-01-1966 L1976 **IM ID** *020 †20

BURNETT, Edmund L. 7710 BEECHNUT ST 77074 #005-12-1953 L1959 **OPH** *071 †35

BURNETT, Leanne. 17000 EL CAMINO REAL, STE 205 77058 #048-04-1986 L1987 **N** *020 †75

BURNS, Allassia Yvette. 6431 FANNIN ST 4.202, INTERNAL MED-ENDOCRINOLOGY 77030 #048-14-1999 L2002 **END** *020 †20

BURNS, David Erin. 902 FROSTWOOD DR STE 307 77024 #065-05-1978 L1985 **RHU IM** *020 †20

BURNS, Jami Nicole. ■ 77002 #028-46-2005 **AN** *012

BURNS, John Thos. 14903 EL CAMINO REAL 77062 #048-02-1968 L1968 **ORS** *020 †40

BURNS, Kevin Matthew. ■ 77035 #048-13-2006 **PTH** *012

BURNS, Sophia Lewis. 19770 KINGSLAND BLVD, STE 240 77094 #024-07-1989 L1992 **OBG** *020 †30

BURPEAU, John A. 1200 BINZ ST STE 1410 77004 #048-14-1992 L1993 **IM** *020 †20

BURROUGHS, Kelli Valencia. 1819 CRAWFORD ST STE 1708, JOSEPH HOSPITAL 77002 #045-01-2005 **OBG** *012

BURROW, Trey Cullen. ■ 77006 #048-14-2007 **AN** *012

BURRUSS, John Wm. 1 BAYLOR PLZ # 350, BAYLOR COLLEGE OF MEDICINE 77030 #048-04-1992 L1994 **P** *030 †75

BURT, Kristina L. ■ 77021 #048-12-2001 L2004 **PTH** *100 †50

BURTON, Allen Wade. 1400 HOLCOMBE BLVD, UTMD ANDERSON CANCER CENTE 77030 #048-04-1991 L1995 **PME AN** *020 †05

BURTON, Gregory Keith. 1200 BINZ ST, STE 480 77004 #025-07-1989 L1991 **PM** *020 †60

BURTON, Joe Edward. 13501 KATY FWY, RM W2-104 77079 #047-06-1969 L1998 **AM OM** *030 †70,18

BURYANEK, Jamie Jay. ■ 77021 #046-01-2001 L2002 **PCP** *100 †50

BURZYNSKI, Stanislaw R. 9432 OLD KATY RD, STE 200 77055 #759-06-1967 L1973 **IM** *020

BUSAIDY, Naifa L. 1515 HOLCOMBE BLVD, UNIT 435 77030 #048-04-1997 L2004 **END** *020 †20

BUSCH, Carrie Elizabeth. ■ 77059 #048-16-2008 *012

BUSCH, Gerald Irwin. 2424 W HOLCOMBE BLVD STE 1 77030 #048-12-1981 L1981 **P CHP** *020 †75

BUSH, Amanda Jo. ■ 77230 #048-02-2005 **OBG** *012

BUSH, Barbara Elizabeth. 6550 MAPLERIDGE ST, STE 101A 77081 #048-04-1981 L1981 **IM** *020 †20

BUSHONG, Craig Patton. 3355 W ALABAMA ST, STE 125 77098 #048-02-1984 L1987 **CHP P** *020 †75

BUSTAMANTE, Pedro Manuel. ■ 77007 #048-04-2006 **P** *012

BUTCHER, Larry Ray. 6431 FANNIN ST STE JJL308, DEPT OF FAMILY PRACTICE 77030 #048-14-1981 L1981 **FM** *020 †18

BUTLER, Charles Edward. 1515 HOLCOMBE BLVD BOX 44, DEPT OF PLASTIC SURGERY 77030 #041-01-1990 L2000 **PS** *020 †85,65

BUTLER, Debbie Knowles. 17080 RED OAK DR 77090 #005-14-1990 L2002 **DR** *020 †80

BUTLER, Edward Brian. 6565 FANNIN ST DB137, METHODIST HOSPITAL 77030 #010-02-1982 L1989 **RO** *020 †80

BUTLER, Ian John. 6431 FANNIN ST, HLTH SCI CTR/STE 7044 77030 #143-01-1965 L1976 **CHN PD** *040 †75

BUTLER, James Arthur. ■ 77024 #067-01-1959 L1974 **EM GS** *071 †85

BUTLER, James Elmer. 4126 SOUTHWEST FWY, STE 1400 77027 #048-02-1962 L1962 **ORS OS** *020 †40

BUTLER, Kymberly Nicol. 818 RINGOLD ST, ACRES HOME 77088 #041-09-1997 L1999 **FM** *020 †18

BUTLER, Max Camille. 2405 S GESSNER RD, STE B 77063 #048-02-1958 L1958 **FM** *020 †18

BUTLER, Patricia Mary. 6431 FANNIN ST # 304 77030 #919-01-1965 L1978 **CHP P** *030 †75

BUTLER, William Thos. 1 BAYLOR PLZ, SUITE BCMC-177A 77030 #038-06-1958 L1966 **IG** *030

BUTNER, Robert Westbrook. 6400 FANNIN ST 18TH FL 77030 #023-07-1968 L1974 **OPH** *020 †35

BUTT, Ghazala Roohi. 6565 FANNIN ST, PHYSICIAN ORGANZ, ANESTHES 77030 #704-02-1971 L1992 **AN** *020 †05

BUTTAR, Gurdip Singh. 6565 DE MOSS DR STE 230 77074 #495-10-1979 L1993 **P** *020

BUTTON, Jeanne Helen. 2727 W HOLCOMBE BLVD, KELSEY-SEYBOLD CLINIC 77025 #028-02-2002 L2006 **PM** *100 †60

BUTTS, Donald Ray. 800 PEAKWOOD DR STE 2C 77090 #048-02-1962 L1970 **CRS** *020 †10

BUZAID, Antonio Carlos. 1515 HOLCOMBE BLVD 77030 #187-11-1982 L1992 **ON IM** *020 †20

BUZDAR, Amanullah. 1515 HOLCOMBE BLVD, # 1354 77030 #704-04-1967 L1975 **ON IM** *020 †20

BUZI, Adva. ■ 77025 #048-04-2008 *012

BUZNEGO, Evaristo. 8522 JENSEN DR 77093 #275-01-1954 L1971 **FM** *071

BYBEE, Joseph David. 6720 BERTNER ST 77030 #028-02-1960 L1963 **IM ID** *020 †20

BYRNE, Michael Edward. 8823 S RICE AVE 77096 #048-13-1973 L1974 **AM PD** *020

BYRNE, Roger Patrick. 2450 FONDREN RD STE 130 77063 #048-15-1991 L1992 **FPS** *020

CABANILLAS, Maria Eugenia. 2323 MCCLENDON ST 77030 #042-01-1998 L2001 **IM** *020 †20

CABANILLAS ESCALONA, F. 6723 BERTNER ST, M.D. ANDERSON HOSP & TUMOR 77030 #042-01-1970 L1975 **ON** *050 †20

CABRERA, Juan Alberto. 6431 FANNIN ST # 148 77030 #737-01-1978 L1984 **PTH** *100

CABRERA-DIAZ, Gilberto. ■ 77089 #341-01-1973 **FM** *100

CABRERA MEZA, Gerardo A R. 6621 FANNIN ST MC, TEXAS CHILDREN HOSP 77030 #429-01-1973 L1995 **PD NPM** *020

CACAYORIN, Edwin Domingo. 6431 FANNIN ST MS 2.100, DEPARTMENT OF RADIOLOGY 77030 #748-08-1971 L1992 **DR** *075 †80

CACERES PRENDES, Mariano. 5310 IRVINGTON BLVD STE B 77009 #341-01-1967 L1986 **GP** *020 †85

CADENAS, Julio Cesar. 6545 SOUTHWEST FWY 77074 #264-05-1964 L1984 **OM END** *071

CAEIRO, Juan P. 6624 FANNIN ST STE 1410 77030 #132-02-1990 L2005 **ID** *020 †20

CAESAR, Franchelle Lyrett. 4545 POST OAK PLACE DR, IPC- THE HOSPITALIST COMPA 77027 #020-02-2004 L2007 **IM** *020 †20

CAESAR, Larry Winston. 1213 HERMANN DR, STE 770 77004 #048-04-2005 L2007 **PD** *012

CAFRI, Carlos Jose. 6431 FANNIN ST, UTMSH/DIV OF CARDIOLOGY 77030 #132-08-1984 **CD** *100

CAGLE, Philip Theo. 6565 FANNIN ST, MAIN BLDG ROOM 227 77030 #047-06-1981 L1983 **PTH PUD** *020 †50

CAHILL, Catherine Wynne. ■ 77004 #056-06-2007 **ORS** *012

CAIN, James Alton, III. 3310 RICHMOND AVE 77098 #048-02-1981 L1981 **R EM** *020 †80

CAIRO, Michelina Marie. ■ 77025 #010-02-2005 **IM** *012

CALABRESE, Donna Marie. 1515 HOLCOMBE BLVD, UNIT 112 77030 #048-14-1985 L1986 **PUD CCM** *020 †20

CALDER, Cynthia T. 7401 MAIN ST 77030 #012-05-1985 L1989 **AN** *020 †05

CALDERA, Plinio Antonio. 17080 RED OAK DR 77090 #048-14-1996 L1997 **ORS** *020 †40

CALDERON, Darrell Yarritu. ■ 77018 #025-01-1994 L1996 **EM** *020 †16

CALDERON, Enrique Eduardo. PO BOX 20708, DEPT OF OPTHALMOLOGY 77225 #905-02-2004 **OPH** *012

CALDERON, Marcos. 7000 FANNIN ST STE M40, HOUSTON MEDICAL IMAGING CN 77030 #649-01-1964 L1973 **NM IM** *020 †28

CALDERON, Reynaldo. 2424 W HOLCOMBE BLVD 77030 #048-04-1978 L1978 **PD** *020

CALDWELL, Krista D. 6621 FANNIN ST, MC1-1481 77030 #048-04-2003 L2006 **PEM** *012 †16

CALHOUN, Krystin Renee. 2300 OLD SPANISH TRL, APT 2070 77054 #422-01-2004 **N** *012

CALI, Joseph Robt, Jr. 1631 NORTH LOOP W, STE 490 77008 #030-06-1987 L1992 **CRS GS** *020 †85,10

CALLAWAY, Heather C. 6431 FANNIN ST STE JJL495, UNIV OF TEXAS MEDICAL SCHO 77030 #007-02-1999 L2003 **PD** *020 †55

CALLEGARI, Eugenio G. 920 FROSTWOOD DR 77024 #737-06-1964 L1972 **AN** *020 †05

CALVILLO, Octavio Jorge. 5225 KATY FWY STE 105 77007 #649-01-1969 L1984 **APM** *020 †05

CALVO, Russell David, Jr. 11325 FALLBROOK DR 77065 #048-14-1978 L1978 **ORS EM** *020 †40

■ = Address Information Privacy Protected

CALZADA, Gabriel. ■ 77054 #048-04-2002 **OTO** *100

CAMACHO, Luis Hernando. 920 FROSTWOOD DR, STE 780 77024 #264-19-1988 L2001 **HO** *020 †20

CAMATI, Mirian. ■ 77007 #187-08-1977 L2002 **FM OBG** *020 †18

CAMBOR, Charles Glenn. 4200 MONTROSE BLVD STE 470 77006 #007-02-1953 L1971 **PYA P** *020 †75

CAMERON, Bruce Molloy. 6624 FANNIN ST STE 2600, ST LUKES MEDICAL TOWER 77030 #048-02-1944 L1944 **ORS** *071 †40

CAMERON, Charles. 77030 #048-14-2007 **PD** *012

CAMERON, Susan M. ■ 77006 #048-14-2007 **EM** *012

CAMP, John Frederick. ■ 77030 #051-04-2004 L2008 **AN** *012

CAMPAGNA, Maria-Claudia. 1 HERMANN CIRCLE DR, # 4093 77030 #264-06-1987 L1997 **IM** *020 †20

CAMPAGNARO, Erica Leigh. 1515 HOLCOMBE BLVD, UNIT 10 77030 #021-05-2000 L2004 **ON** *020 †50

CAMPANA, Roger Enrique. ■ 77063 #048-15-2008 *012

CAMPBELL, Aaron Wayne. 77054 #048-14-2004 L2006 **OBG** *012

CAMPBELL, Caleb Robert. ■ 77030 #048-04-2008 *012

CAMPBELL, Joslyn Lynn. 1415 LA CONCHA LN 77054 #048-02-1996 L2000 **NEP** *020 †20

CAMPBELL, Judith Rochelle. 1 BAYLOR PLZ RM 302A, DEPARTMENT OF PEDIATRICS 77030 #048-04-1985 L1986 **PD ID** *020 †55

CAMPBELL, Julian Roderick. 6431 FANNIN ST # 5-020 77030 #917-07-1984 L1995 *020

CAMPBELL, Katrin Ann. 6621 FANNIN ST 2-1495, TEXAS CHILDREN'S HOSPITAL 77030 #035-06-2001 L2006 **PAN** *100 †20

CAMPBELL, Michael F. 6550 FANNIN ST, STE 2403 77030 #048-14-1999 L2001 **NEP** *020 †20

CAMPBELL, Patricia F. 6431 FANNIN ST 77030 #051-07-1991 L1995 **PEM PD** *020 †55

CAMPBELL, Price C. 11914 ASTORIA BLVD 77089 #016-06-1950 L1950 **U** *071

CAMPBELL, Winfield M, Jr. ■ 77025 #048-02-2003 **ORS** *020

CAMPBELL, Zeromeh Lorelei. ■ 77004 #010-03-2007 **PD** *012

CAMPO, Jose Angel. 10211 PIPING ROCK LN 77042 #132-01-1960 L1973 **AN** *071 †05

CAMPO OSORIO, Marcela. ■ 77098 #264-05-2000 **ID** *012 †20

CAMPOS, Carlos J. ■ 77056 #847-01-1972 **AN** *100

CAMPOS, Luis A. 925 GESSNER RD, STE 630 77024 #803-03-1969 L1974 **CD IM** *020 †20

CAMPOS, Luis Talavera. 920 FROSTWOOD DR, STE 780 77024 #737-06-1969 L1975 **ON IM** *020 †20

CAMPOS, Robert James. 1333 MOURSUND ST 77030 #847-01-1947 L1962 **N PM** *071

CAMPOS-LOPEZ, Carlos J. 6621 FANNIN ST 77030 #132-01-1990 L2002 **AN** *020 †05

CAMPOS-RECIO, Jorge. 2411 FOUNTAIN VIEW DR, STE 200 77057 #231-01-1961 L1975 **AN** *020 †05

CANALES, John Fierros. 6720 S BELT PKWY W, CARDIOLOGY FELLOWSHIP OFFI 77085 #028-02-2003 L2006 **CD** *012 †20

CANDELARIA, Rosalind Rosi. ■ 77023 #047-06-2004 L2007 **DR** *012

CANFIELD, Steven Eric. 6431 FANNIN ST 6.018, UT MD ANDERSON CANCER CENT 77030 #041-02-1996 L2004 **U** *020

CANGIR, Ayten. 1515 HOLCOMBE BLVD 77030 #902-03-1955 L1971 **PHO ON** *071 †55

CANLAS, Donna Natividad. 1200 BINZ ST, STE 290 77004 #748-02-1985 L1997 **FM** *020 †18

CANNELLA, Steven Jeffrey. 1631 NORTH LOOP W, STE 200 77008 #048-02-1984 L1987 **AN** *040 †05

CANNON, Bryan C. 6621 FANNIN ST 19-345C 77030 #048-12-1995 L1997 **PDC** *020 †55 ‡

CANNON, Christopher P. ■ 77008 #054-04-1992 L2004 **ORS** *020 †40

CANO, Pedro Juan. 1515 HOLCOMBE BLVD, MC 4009; BOX 37 77030 #847-16-1983 L2002 **BBK** *020 †20

CANPOLAT, Cengiz. ■ 77081 #902-10-1984 **PHO** *020

CANSECO, Elvia Isela. ■ 77071 #048-02-2008 *012

CANTU, Dora Elia. 1740 W 27TH ST, STE 180 77008 #048-14-1989 L1990 **OPH** *020 †35

CANTU, Jose A. 77025 #048-14-2005 L2007 **IM** *012

CANTU, Michael R. 7823 AUTUMN HOLLOW LN 77041 #048-04-1999 L2001 **EM** *020 †16

CAO, James Tich Huu. 3304 MILAM ST, STE A 77006 #941-01-1972 L1982 **ON IM** *020 †20

CAO, Khoa Tien. 10904 SCARSDALE BLVD, STE 150 77089 #048-02-1996 L1999 **FM** *020 †18

CAO, Long B. ■ 77084 #048-02-2008 *012

CAO, Piergiorgio. 1300 MOURSUND ST DEPT CDS 77030 #561-17-1972 **TS** *050

CAO, Xiaoyan Shelley. ■ 77054 #025-01-2006 **GS** *012

CAPELLI, Christopher C. ■ 77005 #056-05-1989 L1999 **IM** *071

CAPLAN, Charles Howard. 925 GESSNER RD STE 400, MEDICAL PLAZA 4 77024 #005-11-1973 L1981 **CD IM** *020 †20

CAPLAN, Harold Eli. ■ 77096 #048-02-1954 L1954 **OPH** *071 †35

CAPLAN, Richard Edward. 6560 FANNIN ST STE 1008 77030 #048-12-1980 L1980 **GS** *020 †85

CAPLAN, William D. 710 FM 1960 RD W, NICU 77090 #048-04-1988 L1991 **NPM PD** *020 †55

CAPLOVITZ, Coleman D. 6550 FANNIN ST STE 2403 77030 #048-02-1947 L1947 **IM CD** *071 †20

CAPRIOTTI, Robert John. 2530 W HOLCOMBE BLVD 77030 #041-09-1963 L1980 **PS OTO** *020 †45

CARABELLO, Blase Anthony. 2002 HOLCOMBE BLVD, BLVD (111MCL) 77030 #041-13-1973 L1975 **CD IM** *020 †20

CARAM, Pedro Mario. 909 FROSTWOOD DR, STE 207 77024 #048-14-1985 L1986 **NS** *020 †25

CARANDANG, Virgilio C. 1631 NORTH LOOP W STE 430 77008 #748-10-1973 L1978 **FM** *020 †18

CARAWAY, Michael Derek. 2727 TUDOR MNR 77082 #048-02-1996 L1997 **EM** *020 †16

CARAWAY, Nancy P. 1515 HOLCOMBE BLVD 77030 #048-13-1985 L1987 **ATP PCP** *020 †50

CARBAJAL, Jael Gijon. 6431 FANNIN ST 5.020 77030 #048-14-2001 L2006 **AN PAN** *100 †05

CARD, George Gary. 7777 SOUTHWEST FWY, STE 820 77074 #048-04-1971 L1971 **OTO** *020 †45

CARDAMA, Alfonso Quintas. ■ 77025 #847-05-1994 **HO** *012 †20

CARDENAL, Jorge Vivas. 1919 NORTH LOOP W STE 260 77008 #264-04-1969 L1981 **OBG** *020 †30

CARDINALLI-STEIN, Andria. 915 GESSNER RD STE 100, MEMORIAL CITY MED 77024 #035-20-2001 L2005 **IM** *020

CARDON, Aaron Lynn. ■ 77006 #048-04-2008 *012

CARDONA, Emilio R. 7515 MAIN ST, STE 600 77030 #429-01-1971 L1976 **P ADP** *020 †75

CARDONE, Gabriella. ■ 77025 #649-31-1995 L2001 **PEM** *100 †55

CARDUS, Bettina I. 2801 GESSNER DR 77080 #048-16-1988 L1999 **IM** *020 †20

CARILLO, Julius Anthony. ■ 77030 #039-01-2007 **GS** *012

CARKACI, Selin. 1515 HOLCOMBE BLVD 77030 #902-21-2002 *100

CARLINI, Maria Estel. 7777 SW FWY STE 740 77074 #034-01-1993 L1995 **ID** *020 †20

CARLO, Waldemar Francisco. 1 BAYLOR PLZ, BAYLOR COLL OF MED 77030 #041-01-2004 L2004 **PDC** *012 †55

CARLOS, Leticia Quintos. ■ 77069 #748-01-1958 L1976 **FM** *071

CARLSON, Victor. 1919 LA BRANCH ST 77002 #048-02-1963 L1963 **R** *071 †80

CARLTON, Carter Eugene. 6560 FANNIN ST, STE 2100 77030 #048-04-1955 L1955 **U** *071 †95

CARLYLE, Dennis Ronald. 1611 NORTH BLVD 77006 #016-06-1970 L1973 **DR** *020 †80

CARLYLE, Susan J H. 7600 FANNIN ST 77054 #016-06-1970 L1971 **AN** *071 †05 ‡

CARMENATES, Olga. 7737 SOUTHWEST FWY, STE 410 77074 #270-02-1986 L1995 **FM** *020 †18

CARMICHAEL, Don B. 710 FM 1960 RD W 77090 #048-02-1987 L1988 **AN** *020 †05

CARMONA, Robert Agustin. 710 FM 1960 RD W 77090 #062-01-1963 L1976 **AN** *020

CARNEY, Richard Grady. 7400 FANNIN ST, STE 1090 77054 #048-13-1975 L1975 **IM** *020 †20

CAROOM, Cyrus T. 1 BAYLOR PLZ, BAYLOR COLL MED 77030 #048-04-2007 **GS** *012

CARPENTER, Frank E. 2001 NASA PKWY, BLDG 37 77058 #019-02-1974 L1977 **P AM** *020 †75

CARPENTER, Larry Steven. 2457 S BRAESWOOD BLVD, ST. LUKE'S DIAGNOSTIC CENT 77030 #048-02-1984 L1985 **RO** *020 †80

CARPENTER, Robert J, Jr. 6624 FANNIN ST STE 2720, ST LUKES MED TWR 77030 #048-04-1973 L1973 **OBG MFM** *020 †30

CARPIO, Cynthia A. 13114 FM 1960 RD W, STE 200 77065 #048-14-1992 L1993 **IM** *020 †20

CARRANZA, Jose. 6431 FANNIN ST JL-454, MEM HERMANN HOSP 77030 #649-01-1962 L1981 **P PA** *020

CARRASCO, Daniel A. 6655 TRAVIS ST, STE 100 77030 #048-14-1998 L2005 **D** *100 †15

CARRICK, Matthew M. 1504 TAUB LOOP RM 4B31002, BEN TAUB GENERAL HOSPITAL 77030 #048-15-1999 L2003 **GS** *020 †05

CARRIE, James Ross Gordon. 2002 HOLCOMBE BLVD, DEPT PSYCH VA HOSP 77030 #919-03-1955 L1976 **P N** *071

CARRIER, Brian Patrick. ■ 77004 #021-06-2006 **DR** *012

CARRIER, David Allen. 6565 FANNIN ST, THE METHODIST HOSP MS D281 77030 #010-02-1984 L1990 **RNR** *020 †80

CARRILLO MARQUEZ, Maria A. ■ 77030 #935-07-2000 **PDI** *012 †55

CARRION, Victor Rafael. 2411 FOUNTAIN VIEW DR #200 77057 #042-02-2002 L2006 **AN** *020 †05

CARROLL, Derrick Lynn. ■ 77016 #047-07-2002 **FM** *100

CARROLL, James Michael. 215 WESTHEIMER RD, LEGACY COMMUNITY HEALTH 77006 #021-05-1994 L2007 **IM** *020 †20

CARROLL, Kelley W. 13707 STATE HIGHWAY 249 77086 #010-01-2002 L2005 **FM** *100 †18

CARROLL, L Natalie. 2305A SOUTHMORE BLVD 77004 #047-07-1974 L1978 **OBG GP** *020 †30

CARROLL, Rebecca May. ■ 77054 #016-42-2006 **AN** *012

CARRUM, George. 6565 FANNIN ST M964, CELL AND GENE THERAPY 77030 #048-04-1987 L1988 **IM** *020 †20

CARRUTHERS, Jacqueline R. 7333 NORTH FWY, STE 330 77076 #048-13-1996 L1999 **IM** *020

CARSON, Arch Irwin, IV. 1200 HERMANN PRESSLER DR, RAS-1030 77030 #038-40-1990 L1992 **OM PTX** *030 †70

CARTER, Anthony Neill. ■ 77047 #048-04-2008 *012

CARTER, Beth A. 6621 FANNIN ST, CCC 1010.00 77030 #016-06-1997 L2003 **PG HEP** *020 †55

CARTER, James Curtis, Jr. 6565 FANNIN ST, BLDG B452 77030 #028-02-1993 L1999 **AN** *020 †05

CARTER, Jane Elizabeth. 2411 FOUNTAIN VIEW DR #200 77057 #048-01-1985 L1995 **AN** *020 †05

CARTER, Jerome Oliver. 1333 MOURSUND ST 77030 #001-02-2001 L2004 **PM** *071 †60

CARTER, Joseph Gene. ■ 77074 #048-02-2005 L2007 **FP** *012

CARTER, Macharia Tuere. 1 BAYLOR PLZ, BAYLOR COLLEGE OF MEDICINE 77030 #001-06-2001 L2005 **PD** *020 †55

CARTER, Patrick Michael. 1221 MCKINNEY ST, STE 40300 77010 #016-01-1982 L1994 **FM FPG** *030 †18

CARTER, R Edward. ■ 77057 #048-02-1951 L1951 **PM IM** *071

CARTER, Scott C. ■ 77074 #048-14-2001 L2003 **DR** *100 †30

CARTER, Tracy Lynn. 18220 TOMBALL PKWY, STE 400 77070 #038-41-1997 L2001 **MPD** *020 †20,55

CARTWRIGHT, Thomas J. 17080 RED OAK DR 77090 #048-02-1990 L1991 **ORS** *020 †40

CARVOUNIS, Petros Euthymi. 6550 FANNIN ST, STE 1501 77030 #917-09-2000 L2005 **OPH** *100 †35

CASAL, Roberto Fernando. 6431 FANNIN ST STE 1.150, AT HOUST 77030 #132-01-1998 **PCC** *012 †20

CASAR, Jose Gregorio. 6550 FANNIN ST STE 2321 77030 #649-31-1980 L1987 **PUD IM** *020 †05

CASEY, Brett Mikal. 1716 SUNSET BLVD 77005 #048-13-1987 L1993 **PTH** *020 †50,19

CASH, Camille Geneva. 1315 ST JOSEPH PKWY, STE 1305 77002 #048-04-1995 L1999 **PS** *020 †85,65

CASILLAS, Gaston Lhebrard. 1213 HERMANN DR STE 460 77004 #042-02-1985 L1998 **CRS GS** *020 †85,10

CASKEY, Charles Thos. 1825 PRESSLER ST STE 205, IMM 77030 #036-07-1963 L1972 **IM OS** *071 †20,19

CASS, Darrell Lorne. 6621 FANNIN ST, STE 650 77030 #005-14-1991 L2001 **PDS GS** *020 †85

CASSADY, Christopher Ian. 6621 FANNIN ST, MC2-2521 77030 #005-14-1990 L2001 **PDR** *020 †80

CASSCELLS, Saml Ward, III. 7000 FANNIN ST, RM 795 77030 #024-01-1979 L1994 **CD** *020 †20

CASSIDY, Crystal Colleen. 8007 PAGEWOOD LN 77063 #048-14-1997 L1998 **EM** *020

CASSIDY, John Wayne. 1 BAYLOR PLZ, STE 600 77056 #038-41-1980 L1988 **P N** *030 †75 ‡

CASSO, Araceli. 17555 EL CAMINO REAL 77058 #048-12-1986 L1987 **CHP P** *020 †75

CASSO, Daniel. 2020 NASA RD 1, STE 260 77058 #048-12-1984 L1987 **PS HS** *020 †65

CASTAGNINI CASTRO, Luis A. 1 BAYLOR PLZ, BAYLOR COLL OF MED 77030 #737-06-2002 **PDI** *012 †55

CASTANEDA, Manuel Franco. 232 E CROSSTIMBERS ST # E 77022 #649-01-1960 L1984 **OBG** *020 †16

CASTANER, Maricel Del Car. 1709 DRYDEN RD STE 550, BCM FACULTY CTR 77030 #042-01-2005 L2008 **IM** *012

CASTIGLIONE-RICHMOND, Anna. PO BOX 20708, DEPT OF PATHOLOGY & LAB 77225 #025-07-2006 **PTH** *012

CASTILLO, Brian Ceniza. ■ 77025 #048-02-2007 **FP** *012

CASTILLO, Elisa R. 5900 CHIMNEY ROCK RD, STE Y 77081 #048-14-2001 L2004 **PD** *020 †55

CASTILLO, Joseph Arthur. 11738 FM 1960 RD W 77065 #048-04-1976 L1976 **OBG** *020

CASTILLO, Joseph Xavier. 1111 AUGUSTA DR 77057 #047-07-1981 L1997 **GPM** *020

CASTILLO, Leticia C. 6621 FANNIN ST WT6-006, TEXAS CHILDREN'S HOSPITAL 77030 #649-01-1977 L2007 **PD CCM** *020 †55

CASTILLO, Luis Enrique G. 607 TIMBERDALE LN, STE 200 77090 #737-06-1975 L1980 **ID** *020 †20

CASTILLO, Maynard L. ■ 77034 #748-12-1985 **PD** *100

■ = Address Information Privacy Protected

CASTILLO, Noel M. 6411 FANNIN ST 7TH FL, HERMANN EYE CENTER 77030 #748-01-1986 **OPH** *100

CASTILLO, Robert Manuel. 4302 CENTER ST 77007 #649-04-1978 L1982 **GP AN** *020

CASTILLO, Teodoro A. 1333 MOURSUND ST, INSTIT. FOR REHABILITATION 77030 #748-10-1988 L1998 **PM SCI** *020 †60

CASTILLO, Theresa Ortega. 13215 DOTSON RD, STE 200 77070 #048-13-2002 L2006 **OBG** *100

CASTILLO SALAZAR, Ivan Gu. ■ 77030 #264-19-1988 L2007 **OPH** *100

CASTRIOTTA, Richard James. 6431 FANNIN ST, STE 1.266 77030 #561-01-1973 L1999 **PUD SME** *020 †20

CASTRO, Melinda J. 11914 ASTORIA BLVD STE 9, DEPT. OF ANESTHESIA 77089 #048-12-1984 L1985 **AN** *020 *05

CASTRO, Timothy, Jr. 710 FM 1960 RD W 77090 #012-01-1981 L1991 **AN** *020 †05

CASTROW, Fred F. II. 1511 ORCHARD PARK DR 77077 #048-02-1961 L1961 **D DMP** *071 †15

CATALDO, Vince David. 1515 HOLCOMBE BLVD UNIT 1, M.D. ANDERSON CANCER CTR 77030 #021-05-2002 L2006 **HO** *012 †20

CATE, Thomas Randolph. 1 BAYLOR PLZ MS 280, BAYLOR CLGE OF MED 77030 #047-05-1959 L1975 **IM ID** *071 †20

CATHEY, Ginger Nicole. 7900 FANNIN ST, STE 4000 77054 #021-06-1999 L2001 **OBG GYN** *020 †30

CATLIN, Francis Irving. 6621 BERTNER ST 77030 #023-07-1948 L1972 **OTO** *071 †45

CATO, Larry Wayne. 1919 LA BRANCH ST 77002 #048-14-1995 L1998 **AN** *020

CATON, Michael T. 7600 BEECHNUT ST 77074 #048-12-1992 L1993 **AN** *020 †05

CAUDILL, John Wilhite, Jr. 5757 WOODWAY DR, STE 200 77057 #048-04-1970 L1970 **PD** *020 †55

CAUDLE, Abigail Suzanne. PO BOX 301402, MD ANDERSON CANCER CENTER 77230 #036-01-2000 L2007 **SO** *100 †85

CAUSEY, Jamie Christine. ■ 77019 #048-14-2007 **MPD** *012

CAVAZOS, Christina M. ■ 77006 #036-07-2001 L2007 **RNR** *020 †80

CAVAZOS, Jorge M. 1709 DRYDEN RD STE 550, BCM FACULTY CTR 77030 #048-04-2005 L2007 **IM** *012

CAVAZOS, Juan L. 2150 HIGHWAY 6 S, STE 100 77077 #048-12-1990 L1991 **EM** *020 †16

CAVAZOS, Ninfa. ■ 77085 #048-02-1945 L1945 **CHP IMG** *020 †50

CAVINESS, Alison Chantal. 6621 FANNIN ST, EMERGENCY DEPARTMENT 77030 #024-01-1993 L1996 **PD** *020 †55

CAWOOD, Charles David, Jr. 6560 FANNIN ST, STE 1270 77030 #020-02-1961 L1966 **U** *071 †95

CEBRUN, Hazel Christine. 211 HIGHLAND CROSS DR, STE 275 77073 #048-14-1997 L2002 **EM** *020 †16

CECH, David Allen. 6560 FANNIN ST STE 1200 77030 #035-08-1978 L1985 **NS** *020 †25

CEGIELSKI, Catherine L. ■ 77040 #048-14-1994 L1997 **IM** *020

CEN, Putao. ■ 77054 #243-21-1999 L2007 **HO** *012 †20

CENDALES-BEHAINE, Linda. ■ 77095 #649-40-1994 L2007 **HS TTS** *100

CENSULLO, Michael L. 6431 FANNIN ST, MSB 5.020 77030 #010-02-1997 L2004 **VIR** *020 †80

CERNY, Jeffrey L. 1515 HOLCOMBE BLVD, UT-MD ANDERSON CANCER CENT 77030 #048-14-2001 L2005 **AN** *100 *05

CERVANTES-VAZQUEZ, Mario. 1 BAYLOR PLZ, RM 286A 77030 #649-01-1979 L1990 **PTH** *020 †50

CERVERA, Roberto De Alba. 1 BAYLOR PLZ, BAYLOR COLL OF MED 77030 #649-14-2000 L2008 **GS** *012

CESPEDES, Benedicto C. ■ 77040 #748-02-1948 L1970 **DR RO** *020 †80

CESTA, Mark Andrew. 10370 RICHMOND AVE, STE 1125 77042 #003-01-2001 L2004 **CCA** *020 †16

CEZEAUX, Gus Edward, Jr. 5615 KIRBY DR, STE 850 77005 #048-04-1962 L1962 **AN** *071 †05

CHACK, Alissa Catherine. 6621 FANNIN ST RM A170, MC1-1000 77030 #056-06-2006 L2004 **PD** *012

CHACKO, Kristina Rachel. ■ 77054 #048-04-2006 **IM** *012

CHACKO, Mariam Renate. 6621 FANNIN ST, ADOLESCENT MEDICINE & 77030 #495-08-1974 L1984 **ADL PD** *040 †55

CHACKO, Ranjit Cherian. 6655 TRAVIS ST, STE 590 77030 #220-01-1971 L1977 **P PYG** *020 †75

CHADDA, Prabhujeet Kaur. 7737 SOUTHWEST FWY STE 300 77074 #495-92-1971 L1983 **NPM PD** *050

CHADHA, Harparminder S. 1635 NORTH LOOP W, MEMORIAL NOWTHWEST HOSPITA 77008 #495-54-1972 L1998 **EM** *020 †16

CHADHA, Naiyer. 5757 WOODWAY DR STE 200, POST OAK PEDS 77057 #495-54-1975 L1998 **PD NPM** *020 †55

CHAFEY, David Holmes. ■ 77007 #042-02-2005 **ORS** *012

CHAHADEH, Hassan H. 5225 KATY FWY, STE 105 77007 #875-01-1985 L1994 **APM EM** *020 †05

CHAI, Samantha Jene-Hee. ■ 77004 #035-20-2004 L2008 *100

CHAINAKUL, Weera. ■ 77098 #039-01-2006 L2006 **GS** *012

CHAKRAVORTY, Jaya. ■ 77062 #495-67-1970 *075

CHAMBERS, Beth Amanda. ■ 77030 #048-04-2005 **P** *012

CHAMBERS, Jeffrey Jason. ■ 77004 #048-14-2004 L2006 **EM** *020

CHAMBERS, Kimberly Ann. 6431 FANNIN ST, STE 6.270 77030 #025-12-1996 L1999 **EM** *020 †16

CHAMBERS, Mark Dashiell. ■ 77025 #048-02-1955 L1955 **PTH** *071 †30,50

CHAMILOS, Georgios. PO BOX 20708, UNIV TX MED SCH AT HOUSTON 77225 #418-01-1996 **ID** *012

CHAMMA, Nicolau J. 2211 NORFOLK ST, STE 517 77098 #187-26-1981 L1996 **GP OM** *020 †70

CHAMPAGNE, Laura L. 9055 KATY FWY 77024 #048-14-1991 L1992 **P** *020 †75

CHAMPION, P Kay, Jr. 11301 FALLBROOK DR, STE 100 77065 #016-06-1964 L1968 **END IM** *071 †20

CHAMPLIN, Richard Eugene. 1515 HOLCOMBE BLVD, UNIT 423 77030 #016-02-1975 L1990 **ON HEM** *050 †20

CHAN, Andrea Anpei. ■ 77025 #041-14-2007 **GS** *012

CHAN, Andy Sungkin. 6720 BERTNER ST 77030 #024-05-1998 L2002 **PM** *020 †60

CHAN, Chinglin Lillian. 2500 FONDREN RD STE 170 77063 #048-04-1983 L1983 **FM** *020 †18

CHAN, Chung-Yin Stanley. 6550 FANNIN ST, HOSP (HOUSTON) 77030 **TY** *012

CHAN, Edward Kaiwah. 7737 SOUTHWEST FWY STE 850, 20/20 EYE CLINIC & OPITCAL 77074 #048-04-1983 L1983 **OPH** *020 †35

CHAN, Edward Y H. ■ 77083 #048-02-2007 **GS** *012

CHAN, Eric Kayfung. 6823 STAFFORDSHIRE ST 77030 #048-15-2003 L2005 **AN** *020

CHAN, Evelyn Cheeyin. 1515 HOLCOMBE BLVD ST 1.122, UNIV OF TX MEDICAL CENTER 77030 #048-06-1989 L1994 **IM OS** *020 †20

CHAN, Frank S M. 9129 MESA DR, LAKE FOREST MEDICAL CLINIC 77028 #065-06-1981 **IM** *020

CHAN, Galant Au. ■ 77083 #048-04-2007 *012

CHAN, Kin Yee. 907 BAY AREA BLVD STE B 77058 #048-02-1989 L1990 **FM OS** *020 †18

CHAN, Kwai Tung. 3601 N MACGREGOR WAY, DEPT PM&R QUENTON MEASE HP 77004 #539-06-1991 L1999 **FM** *020 †60

CHAN, Lawrence Chin Bong. 1 BAYLOR PLZ, DEPT OF MEDICINE 77030 #462-01-1966 L1974 **END IM** *050 †20

CHAN, Lillian Wai Lan. 2500 FONDREN RD, STE 270 77063 #051-04-1953 L1956 **PD** *020

CHAN, Ling Ling. 6565 FANNIN ST, MS 033 77030 #825-01-1991 **RNR** *100

CHAN, Lisa L. 13727 CEDAR POINT DR 77070 #048-13-1995 L1997 **IM** *020 †20

CHAN, Robert Ching. ■ 77054 #047-05-2007 *100

CHAN, See Wai. 6621 FANNIN ST WT6-145, SEC OF NEONATOLOGY, DEPT P 77030 #023-07-1995 L2006 **NPM** *020 †55

CHAN, Yie S. ■ 77041 #048-15-2003 L2008 **AN** *020

CHANA, Harminder Singh. 5990 AIRLINE DR STE 160, CYPRESSWOOD CLINIC ASSOC 77076 #577-01-1972 L1978 **GP PD** *020

CHANDAWARKAR, Aarti Rajiv. 6621 FANNIN ST, CC-1570 77030 #496-38-1993 L2002 **PD** *020 †20

CHANDRA, A Chitra. 5656 KELLEY ST, DEPT OF RADIOLOGY 77026 #495-59-1973 L1983 **R** *020

CHANDRA, Prakash. 1709 DRYDEN RD STE 550, BCM FACULTY CENTER 77030 #495-36-2004 **IM** *012

CHANDRAKAR, Chandra. 7737 SOUTHWEST FWY STE 505 77074 #495-09-1959 L1982 **OBG** *071 †30

CHANDRAKAR, Kunjeelal. 5314 DASHWOOD DR 77081 #495-19-1962 L1982 **GS** *020 †85

CHANDRASEKHAR, Krishna. 11914 ASTORIA BLVD STE 370 77089 #495-59-1967 L1981 **PUD OS** *020 †20

CHANDRASEKHAR, Shobana. 1504 TAUB LOOP, 3LD 77030 #495-04-1990 L2006 **AN PME** *020 *05

CHANDY, Binoy Mathew. ■ 77030 #041-02-1997 L1998 **PDO** *012

CHANEY, Kara Dawn. 13114 FM 1960 RD W, STE 200 77065 #048-12-2003 L2006 **PD** *020 †55

CHANEY, Michael Joe. 17070 RED OAK DR STE 400 77090 #048-02-1975 L1975 **PS** *020 †65

CHANG, Andrew Hin. 6720 BERTNER ST MC2-270, ST. LUKE'S EPISCOPAL HOSPI 77030 #023-07-2001 L2007 **RNR** *100 †80

CHANG, Ching-Yen Joseph. 7900 FANNIN ST, STE 1800 77054 #024-01-1989 L1996 **NO OTO** *020 †45

CHANG, Chung Che. 6565 FANNIN ST MS 205, DEPT PATHOLOGY 77030 #244-08-1983 L2004 **HMP** *020 †50

CHANG, Claire Huang Cao. 1200 BINZ ST STE 1220, PLAZA MEDICAL CENTER 77004 #048-04-1995 L2000 **OPH** *020 †20

CHANG, David Woosuk. 1515 HOLCOMBE BLVD # 443, MD ANDERSON CANCER CTR 77030 #056-05-1987 L1998 **PS HS** *020 †65

CHANG, David Zongsheng. 1515 HOLCOMBE BLVD UNIT 4, UT MD ANDERSON CANCER CENT 77030 #032-01-1998 L2004 **HO** *020 †20

CHANG, Eric Lin. 1515 HOLCOMBE BLVD, BOX 97 77030 #024-01-1994 L1999 **RO** *020 †80

CHANG, George Jaeshik. 1515 HOLCOMBE BLVD, UNIT 444 77030 #005-14-1995 L2004 **CRS GS** *020 †85,10

CHANG, Hui-Ming. 7000 FANNIN ST, STE 795 77030 #244-02-1980 L1993 **PME PLM** *020 †05

CHANG, Jennifer Tenye. ■ 77059 #035-01-2008 *012

CHANG, Jenny Chee Ning. 6550 FANNIN ST, STE 701 77030 #917-03-1989 L2002 *020

CHANG, Joe Yujiao. 1515 HOLCOMBE BLVD, UNIT 97 77030 #243-16-1985 L2002 **RO** *020 †80

CHANG, Karen Delysia. 6410 FANNIN ST STE 500 77030 #566-01-1979 **PD** *100 †55

CHANG, Kiran Najam. 6431 FANNIN ST 1134, OF TEXAS-HOUSTON 77030 #704-01-2003 **DR** *012

CHANG, Lee Cin. ■ 77006 #048-12-2003 L2007 **AN** *020

CHANG, Lisa Y. 1919 S BRAESWOOD BLVD 77030 #041-02-1995 L2002 **PD** *020 †55

CHANG, Marvin Clinton. 6200 SAVOY DR, STE 150 77036 #048-14-1988 L1989 **AN PMM** *020 †05

CHANG, Michael L. 2138 MCCLENDON ST 77030 #005-02-1996 L1998 **EM** *020 †16

CHANG, Paula. ■ 77071 #048-16-2008 *012

CHANG, Peggy Doncaster. 2101 NASA RD 1 BLDG 8, MAILCODE SD22 77058 #048-14-1988 L1991 **PD** *020 †20

CHANG, Peter. 4126 SOUTHWEST FWY 77027 #048-14-1981 L1981 **CD IM** *020 †20

CHANG, Peter Shun-Hsien. 6431 FANNIN ST, MSB 5.020 77030 #048-14-2002 L2007 **AN** *100

CHANG, Peter Taejin. 6550 FANNIN ST, STE 1501 77030 #001-02-1999 L2004 **OPH** *020 †35 ‡

CHANG, Sandy. 1515 HOLCOMBE BLVD, DEPT OF MOLECULAR GENETICS 77030 #035-20-1997 L2004 **PTH** *020

CHANG, Shirong. 1 BAYLOR PLZ, SURGERY EDUCATION OFFICE 77030 #048-04-2003 **GS** *012

CHANG, Shu-Mai Kuo. ■ 77056 #385-03-1954 L1971 **PD PDA** *071 †55,03

CHANG, Su-Min. 6550 FANNIN ST 77030 #132-01-1992 L2000 **CD** *050 †20

CHANG, Terence Min-Yee. 7737 SOUTHWEST FWY, STE 400 77074 #048-02-2005 L2007 **FP** *012

CHANG, Victor Yonguor. ■ 77030 #048-04-2006 **IM** *012

CHANG, Yupo J. 5858 WESTHEIMER RD, STE 306 77057 #048-12-1998 L1999 **FM** *020 †18

CHANG-GODINICH, Anne En-I. 13300 HARGRAVE RD, STE 300 77070 #048-04-1995 L1996 **OPH** *020 †35

CHANIN, Katia. 3701 KIRBY DR STE 60, BAYLOR FAMILY PRACTICE CTR 77098 #649-52-2001 L2006 **FM** *020 †18

CHAO, Grace Chen. 6621 FANNIN ST 77030 #048-02-1989 L1990 **GPM PD** *020 †55

CHAO, K S Clifford. 1515 HOLCOMBE BLVD, BOX 97 77030 #244-01-1982 L2003 **RO** *020 †80

CHAPMAN, Alan Jesse, Jr. 9055 KATY FWY, STE 400 77024 #048-04-1979 L1979 **ID IM** *020 †20

CHAPMAN, Gregory S. 3310 RICHMOND AVE 77098 #048-14-1976 L1976 **DR IM** *020 †80

CHAPMAN, Lawrence E, Jr. ■ 77004 #048-02-1955 L1955 **GP** *071

CHAPMAN, Michael Christop. 9 SUNSET BLVD 77005 #030-05-2006 **PD** *012

CHAPPELL, Christine. ■ 77079 #038-40-1998 L2001 **PD** *020 †55

CHAPPELL, Phylliss M. 6440 COMMUNITY DR 77005 #038-06-1980 L1994 **RNR FM** *020 †18,80

CHARALAMPOUS, Kanellos D. 6100 HILLCROFT ST STE 150 77081 #048-04-1958 L1960 **P** *071 †75

CHARANIA, Zubeida Shabbar. 6604 SW FWY, MEDIC CLINIC 77074 #704-08-1976 L1985 **GP** *020 †20

CHARBONNEAU, Patrick C. 211 HIGHLAND CROSS DR, STE 275 77073 #027-01-1999 L2008 **EM** *020 †16

CHARLTONOUW, Kristofer M. ■ 77096 #024-01-2002 L2007 **GS** *100 †85

CHARNOV, Jeffrey Hal. 5 DUNNAM LN 77024 #005-15-1988 L1989 **AN** *020 *05

CHARNSANGAVEJ, Chusilp. 1515 HOLCOMBE BLVD # -57 77030 #891-04-1972 L1983 **DR AR** *020 †80

CHASEN, Beth Annah. 6431 FANNIN ST, DEPARTMENT OF RADIOLOGY 77030 #048-04-1999 L2004 **DR** *100 †80,28

CHASEN, Marvin Harvey. 1200 MOURSUND ST, DEPT RAD 77030 #038-40-1973 L1977 R *020 †80

CHATHA, Rupinder K. 902 FROSTWOOD DR STE 166 77024 #048-12-1993 L1994 NEP *020 †20

CHATHAMPALLY, Yashwant G. 6431 FANNIN ST 451, DEPT OF EMERGENCY MEDICINE 77030 #035-08-1996 L2006 EM *020 †16

CHATZIIOANNOU, Sofia N. 1 BAYLOR PLZ, RADIOLOGY DEPARTMENT 77030 #418-01-1991 L1997 NM *050 †28

CHAU, Arthur Fitzgerald. 6550 MAPLERIDGE ST, STE 108 77081 #021-05-1989 L1996 ORS *020 †40

CHAUDHRY, Imtiaz A. 6720 BERTNER ST 77030 #049-01-1994 L2001 OPH PS *020 †35

CHAUDHRY, Mohammad R. ■ 77056 #704-01-1958 L1974 IM PA *030

CHAUHAN, Sonia. 7777 SW FWY STE 310, PEDIATRIX MEDICAL GROUP 77074 #495-49-1991 L2005 NPM *020 †55

CHAUPIN, Damian V. 710 FM 1960 RD W 77090 #737-01-1971 L1979 VS PHL *020

CHAUVIN, Sara Nunez. 1885 OLD SPANISH TRL, EXAMINERS OFFICE 77054 #021-05-1997 L2004 PTH *020 †50

CHAVA, Praveen. ■ 77070 #495-50-2002 FP *012

CHAVA, Ramakrishna V. 530 N SAM HOUSTON PKWY E, STE 100 77060 #495-50-1992 L2000 IMG *100 †18

CHAVDA, Jay. 7737 SOUTHWEST FWY, STE NO300 77074 #495-22-1973 L1984 OTO A *020

CHAVEZ, Anthony. 7580 FANNIN ST STE 300 77054 #049-01-1977 L1980 OBG *020 †30

CHAVEZ, Armando. 11040 EAST FWY 77029 #048-04-1994 L1995 IM *020

CHAVEZ-FRAZIER, Arianne E. ■ 77005 #028-02-2003 L2007 D *012

CHAWLA, Bandana Narang. 6550 MAPLERIDGE ST STE 225, STE 225 77081 #048-12-1998 L2000 IM *020 †20

CHAWLA, Munish. 1415 NORTH LOOP W, STE 820 77008 #048-13-1992 L1993 DR *020 †80

CHECKLES, Nicholas Saml. 1315 ST JOSEPH PKWY # 1002 77002 #038-41-1956 L1977 PM OS *071 †60

CHEDRAWI, Aziza. 6624 FANNIN ST, MC 2-2521 77030 #605-01-1992 L1999 CHN *020 †75,55

CHEE, Maria Victoria. 8900 LAKES AT 610 DR 77054 #048-02-1995 L1998 IM *020 †20

CHEEK, William R. 6621 FANNIN ST # 3-3435, CLINICAL CARE CTR #950 77030 #028-02-1951 L1960 NS *040 †25

CHEEMA, A Rashid. 7707 FANNIN ST, STE 250 77054 #704-01-1961 L1970 OS IM *020 †55

CHELIUS, Daniel. ■ 77054 #048-04-2005 OTO *012

CHELU, Laura. 1 BAYLOR PLZ, BAYLOR COLL OF MED 77030 #781-03-2000 L2008 OBG *012

CHELU, Mihail Gabriel. ■ 77035 #781-03-2000 IM *012

CHEMALY, Roy Fouad. 1515 HOLCOMBE BLVD, #402 INFECTIOUS DISEASE 77030 #605-02-1992 L2002 ID *020 †20

CHEN, Aeneid L J. 10701 VINTAGE PRESERVE PKW 77070 #048-16-1989 L1990 OBG *020 †30 ‡

CHEN, Alex Min-Hin. 4331 BRIGHTWOOD DR 77068 #048-12-2002 L2005 FM *020 †18

CHEN, Alice Jean. 1 BAYLOR PLZ, DEPARTMENT OF PATHOLOGY 77030 #048-04-2002 L2007 BBK *100 †50

CHEN, Andy. 211 HIGHLAND CROSS DR, STE 275 77073 #041-02-1997 L2000 EM *020 †16

CHEN, Antai. ■ 77079 #244-02-1968 P N *020

CHEN, Anthony Yenshen. ■ 77030 #048-14-2008 *012

CHEN, Caleb. 7777 SOUTHWEST FWY, STE 736 77074 #048-04-1995 L1997 NEP *020 †20

CHEN, Catherine Peishin. ■ 77054 #048-04-2007 AN *012

CHEN, Cheng D. 9180 BELLAIRE BLVD, STE E 77036 #244-06-1982 L1997 IM *020 †20

CHEN, Chu-Huang. 6565 FANNIN ST MS A-601, BAYLOR COLLEGE OF MEDICINE 77030 #244-01-1978 L1998 CD *050 †20

CHEN, Jacqueline P. ■ 77054 #048-14-2005 MPD *100

CHEN, Jocelyn C. ■ 77054 #048-14-1994 L1996 FM *020 †18

CHEN, Julia Han. ■ 77090 #048-13-2006 AN *012

CHEN, Karen. 1515 HOLCOMBE BLVD # 112 77030 #035-03-1993 L1998 CCA *020 †05

CHEN, Lei. ■ 77021 #243-52-1983 L2008 HMP *100 †50

CHEN, Leon L. ■ 77054 #048-04-2008 *012

CHEN, Liqian. 6720 BERTNER ST, DEPT OF CV ANES MC 1 77030 #243-16-1983 L1999 AN *020 †05

CHEN, Lisa. 800 PEAKWOOD DR STE 2C 77090 #035-01-1992 L2000 CRS *020 †85,10

CHEN, Maurice Gerard. ■ 77030 #665-01-2000 L2000 NPM *012 †55

CHEN, Min C. 710 FM 1960 RD W 77090 #048-04-1994 L1996 FM *020 †18

CHEN, Ming King. 9288 BELLAIRE BLVD 77036 #244-01-1966 L1977 OBG *020

CHEN, Peng. 1709 DRYDEN RD 77030 #243-21-1987 L2007 NS *020

CHEN, Phebe C. 12141 RICHMOND AVE, DEPT OF RADIOLOGY 77082 #048-04-1985 L1986 DR PD *020 †55,80

CHEN, Sharon Wenwen. 1709 DRYDEN RD STE 550, BCM FACULTY CENTER 77030 #035-46-2006 IM *012

CHEN, Su Sin. ■ 77098 #495-02-1990 L2006 PP *100

CHEN, Tso Ming. 2002 HOLCOMBE BLVD 77030 #048-15-2005 L2007 IM *012

CHEN, Yayan. 6565 FANNIN ST M227 77030 #243-32-1987 L2007 HMP *012 †50

CHEN, Yongfang. 9160 BELLAIRE BLVD, STE E 77036 #243-33-1989 L2002 FM *020 †18

CHENAULT, David Isaac. 17070 RED OAK DR STE 205, O.R.L. ASSOCIATES P.A 77090 #038-41-1974 L1976 OTO *020 †45

CHENG, Angela. ■ 77054 #011-03-2004 GS *012

CHENG, Christine S. 1302 WAUGH DR # 818 77019 #048-02-1998 L2000 FM *020 †18

CHENG, Jed-Sian N. 6431 FANNIN ST, MED SCH AT HOUSTON 77030 #048-14-2007 GS *012

CHENG, Jie. 6624 FANNIN ST STE 1710,) 77030 #243-45-1982 L2002 ICE *020

CHENG, Jose S. 6630 DE MOSS DR 77074 #748-02-1962 L1972 IM END *020 †20

CHENG, Le-Beng C. 6630 DE MOSS DR, HARRIS COUNTY HOSPITAL DIS 77074 #748-01-1962 L1972 PD *020 †55

CHENG, Mingfang Annie. 1200 BINZ ST STE 1350 77004 #243-45-1982 L2003 IM *020 †20

CHENG, Pay-Zen. 6065 HILLCROFT ST 77081 #385-02-1957 L1977 GP GS *071 †85

CHENG, Thanh Chi. 10370 RICHMOND AVE, STE 1125 77042 #047-05-1995 L1998 EM *020 †16

CHEONG, Benjamin Y. 6720 BERTNER ST, MC2.270 77030 #917-06-1994 L2004 CD *020 †20

CHEPKO, James Douglas. 5900 NORTH FWY, STE 143 77076 #041-09-1976 L1978 FM *020 †16

CHEPYALA, Sreesudha. 1 BAYLOR PLZ, DEPT FM 77030 #672-04-2002 FP *012

CHERCHES, Igor M. 7505 MAIN ST, STE 290 77030 #048-04-1990 L1992 N *020 †75

CHEREM, Lazaro. 6421 FANNIN ST 77030 #649-14-1973 L2000 NEP IM *020 †20

CHERIAN, Jessy. 5515 DARSCHELLE DR 77069 #048-04-1992 L1995 IM *020 †20

CHERN, Joshua Jiachuh. ■ 77025 #048-04-2004 NS *012

CHERNOSKY, Debra Lynn. 4646 WILD INDIGO ST, STE 100 77027 #048-14-1985 L1986 D *020 †15

CHERNOSKY, Marvin Ernest. 6410 FANNIN ST, STE 703 77030 #021-01-1952 L1957 D *071 †15

CHERNYSHEV, Oleg Yuryevic. ■ 77026 #913-06-1996 N *012

CHERUKURI, Raja. ■ 77054 #496-33-2004 FP *012

CHERUVU, Silaja. 13806 ROSEBRANCH CT 77059 #048-15-2008 *012

CHEUK, Vasco. ■ 77007 #011-02-2002 L2005 EM *020 †16

CHEUNG, Kim Kum. 6431 FANNIN ST 3.020, UNIV OF TX-HOUSTON HLTH SC 77030 #021-01-1983 L1995 PD *012

CHEUNG, Min. 1515 HOLCOMBE BLVD BOX 97, UT MD ANDERSON CANCER CENT 77030 #035-01-1997 L2002 RO *020 †80

CHEVEZ-BARRIOS, Patricia. 6565 FANNIN ST, METHODIST HOSP STE M227 77030 #649-01-1984 L1997 PTH OPH *020 †50

CHEVRAY, Pierre-Yves M. 1515 HOLCOMBE BLVD UNIT 44 77030 #023-07-1994 L2001 PS *020 †65

CHHEDA, Gitesh D. ■ 77054 #021-05-2004 DR *012

CHI, T Linda. 1515 HOLCOMBE BLVD, UNIT 57 77030 #048-04-1979 L1995 R IM *020 †20,80

CHIA, Angela. 6400 FANNIN ST, STE 2110 77030 #048-04-1997 L2000 PD *020 †55

CHIANG, Christina C. ■ 77057 #048-02-2006 EM *012

CHIANG, Joseph Shute. 1515 HOLCOMBE BLVD, TICAL CARE, BOX 042 77030 #017-20-1985 L1990 AN *020 †05

CHIANG, Stephen Brian. 12951 SOUTH FWY, RMI PHYSICIAN SERVICES 77047 #016-11-2001 L2004 NM *020 †28

CHIANG, Yung Carol. ■ 77274 #244-04-1985 L1994 DR *020 †50,80

CHIAO, Elizabeth Yu. 2002 HOLCOMBE BLVD, VETERANS AFFAIRS MEDICAL C 77030 #035-20-1998 L2004 ID *100 †20

CHIGULLAPALLY, Raghavendri. ■ 77098 #495-65-2003 IM *012

CHIKEOBI, Chuma Jideofo. ■ 77030 #041-01-2007 PS *012

CHILAKAPATI, Madhuri. 2727 W HOLCOMBE BLVD, KELSEY-SEYBOLD 77025 #035-06-2000 L2005 OPH *020 †35

CHILDERS, David Omer, Sr. 7580 FANNIN ST STE 230 77054 #021-05-1955 L1967 PD *020 †55

CHIMENTI, Jeffrey S. 7908 N SAM HOUSTON PKWY W, STE 200 77064 #048-04-1988 L1989 OTO *020 †45

CHIN, Gilbert B. 1819 CRAWFORD ST, DEPT LABOR DELIVERY 77002 #048-14-1990 L1991 AN *020 †05

CHIN, Hsiao Yang. 2727 W HOLCOMBE BLVD, RADIOLOGY DEPT 77025 #048-04-1990 L1991 DR *020 †80

CHIN, Peter Anthony. 6621 FANNIN ST, MC-1495 77030 #894-01-1991 L2006 AN PAN *020 †05

CHING, Charles Ling. ■ 77096 #048-04-1957 L1965 IM CD *020

CHING, Christine Denise. ■ 77098 #036-07-2000 L2007 GS *100

CHINNAPPAN, Raj. ■ 77054 #048-04-2008 *012

CHINTAGUMPALA, Murali M. 6621 FANNIN ST 77030 #495-04-1982 L1992 PHO PD *020 †55

CHINTALA, Venkatalakshmi. 1515 HOLCOMBE BLVD UNIT 42, UT MD ANDERSON CANCER CENT 77030 #495-11-2000 L2006 IM *100 †20

CHINTAMANENI, Aparajitha. 6431 FANNIN ST STE 7.044 77030 #496-23-1996 L2005 CN *100

CHISOLM, Olethia Elise. 2727 W HOLCOMBE BLVD, KELSEY-SEYBOLD CLINIC 77025 #041-09-1993 L1994 IM OS *020 †20

CHITTALURU, Sudha Naga. 12015 LOUETTA RD, STE 200 77070 #495-57-1992 L1999 IM *020 †20

CHITTY, Dudley Anne. 6431 FANNIN ST, MEMORIAL HERMANN HOSPITAL 77030 #048-14-2001 L2005 AN *100 †05

CHIU, David. 6560 FANNIN ST, STE 802 77030 #008-01-1991 L1997 N *020 †75

CHIU, So-Khim Tan. ■ 77024 #385-02-1949 L1964 GYN *072 †30

CHIU, Wen Jung. 1515 HOLCOMBE BLVD BOX 42 77030 #385-02-1947 L1965 AN *071 †05

CHO, Jeong Hee. 6565 FANNIN ST M227 77030 #583-08-1986 PTH *012

CHO, Nai G Chang. 920 FROSTWOOD DR 77024 #583-03-1968 L1975 AN *020

CHO, Sungjoon. ■ 77054 #056-06-2004 L2008 PM *012

CHOHAN, Lubna. 6431 FANNIN ST STE 3.604, DEPT OF OB-GYN 77030 #038-41-2001 L2005 OBG *020 †20

CHOI, Benjamin. ■ 77030 #048-04-2008 *012

CHOI, Chi Si. 2711 LITTLE YORK RD # 215 77093 #583-06-1970 L1979 CD IM *020

CHOI, Grace Rhim. ■ 77025 #016-06-2002 L2002 PDC *012 †55

CHOI, Hae-Sun. 2002 HOLCOMBE BLVD 77030 #583-13-1979 L1992 DR NM *020 †28,80

CHOI, Jeanie Mcintyre. 6431 FANNIN ST STE 2.026 77030 #048-14-2003 L2008 DR *012

CHOI, Judy Miyoung. ■ 77030 #035-20-2007 GS *012

CHOI, Lorraine. ■ 77098 #035-08-2003 GS *012

CHOI, Seungtaek Lee. 1515 HOLCOMBE BLVD, BOX 1202 77030 #035-20-2000 L2006 RO *100 †80

CHOI, You Suk. ■ 77002 #583-10-2003 IM *012

CHOKSI, Asit Jaykant. 800 PEAKWOOD DR STE 6F 77090 #496-38-1979 L1986 ON HEM *020 †20

CHON, Hye Sook. 1 BAYLOR PLZ, DEPT OBG 77030 #583-12-1997 OBG *012

CHON, Steven Kichan. 714 FM 1960 RD W STE 302 77090 #048-02-2004 L2006 FM *020 †18

CHON, Susan. 1515 HOLCOMBE BLVD, DEPT OF DERM UNIT 434 77030 #005-11-1997 L2004 D *020 †15

CHONG, Edward Ming-Tai. ■ 77079 #048-02-2006 P *012

CHONG, Ilsong. 1919 NORTH LOOP W STE 250 77008 #048-14-1992 L1997 IM IMG *020 †20

CHONG, Joseph Chung Wah. 9250 BELLAIRE BLVD STE A 77036 #462-01-1982 L1987 IM *020 †30

CHONG, Karen. 5445 BRAESVALLEY DR # 706E 77096 #060-02-1994 MG *100 †55,19

CHONG, Michelle Hyunjoo. ■ 77030 #048-14-2008 *012

CHOO, Eugene M. ■ 77054 #048-04-2005 L2008 IM *012

CHOO, Joshua Hyosung. 6320 MAIN ST 77005 #048-04-2006 GS *012

CHOO, Sik. 3100 WESLAYAN ST, STE 372 77027 #583-02-1970 L1977 IM ON *020

CHOPRA, Lucky Atul. 8307 KNIGHT RD 77054 #048-06-1992 L1994 DR *020

CHOPRA, Yash. 1333 MOURSUND ST 77030 #495-14-1971 L1988 AN *020 †05

CHORLEY, Joseph Nathaniel. 6621 FANNIN ST, ADOLESCENT MEDICINE & 77030 #048-04-1992 L1995 PD *020 †55

CHOU, Eunice Wu Mei. 5314 DASHWOOD DR 77081 #385-02-1962 L1974 A *071 †55,03

CHOUDHRY, Kiran Siddique. 6621 FANNIN ST STE 1020, DEPT OF PEDIATRICS-ENDOCRI 77030 #704-25-2001 L2003 PDE *012 †55

CHOUEIRI, Michel Bernard. 7950 N STADIUM DR, APT 232 77030 #605-01-2005 IM *012

CHOWDHURY, Reezwana. 1709 DRYDEN RD STE 550, BCM FACULTY CENTER 77030 #035-19-2006 IM *012

CHRASTIL, Brenda Marie. ■ 77027 #030-05-2004 L2007 D *012

CHRIST, John Ernest. 6560 FANNIN ST, STE 1402 77030 #048-04-1973 L1973 PS GS *075 †65

CHRISTENSEN, Cecil Marvin. 1200 BINZ ST, STE 1430 77004 #649-03-1963 L1965 ORS *020 †40

CHRISTOFORIDES, Christos. 7515 MAIN ST STE 800 77030 #418-01-1960 L1981 AN *020 †05

CHRISTOPHERSON, M B. 1140 BUSINESS CENTER DR, STE 390 77043 #048-04-1971 L1971
GYN *020 †30
CHRONISTER, Justin Edward. ■ 77079 #048-14-2008 *012
CHRONOWSKI, Gregory. ■ 77030 #041-02-1998 L2006 RO *012
CHU, Albert Yu-Ping. 1885 OLD SPANISH TRL 77054 #035-06-1999 L2005 FOP *100
CHU, Ching-Chiang. 15655 CYPRESSWD MED DR, STE 400 77014 #244-01-1987 L1999
N *020 †75
CHU, Danny. ■ 77030 #024-07-1997 L2006 TS *020 †85,90
CHU, David Heungwon. ■ 77021 #035-19-2005 L2005 IM *100
CHU, Kim-Thu. 8200 WEDNESBURY LN, STE 225 77074 #011-02-1994 L1998 OBG *020
CHU, Mongthuy Thi. 3327 MEMORIAL CREST BLVD 77007 #011-02-1996 L1998 FM *020 †18
CHU, William B. ■ 77056 #048-14-2001 L2005 PD *020 †55
CHU, William Chang-Wei. 3030 POST OAK BLVD # 202 77056 #429-01-1980 L1981 DR *020
CHU, Yvonne Ifang. 6550 FANNIN ST, STE 1501 77030 #048-04-1999 L2003 OPH *020 †35
CHUA, Annabelle Nancy. 6621 FANNIN ST, PEDI RENAL DEPT. 77030 #036-05-1999 L2005
PN *100 †55
CHUA, Carlos. 710 FM 1960 RD W STE 220, DEPT OF NEONATOLOGY 77090
#748-01-1972 L2002 NPM PD *020 †30
CHUA, Karen Sui Geok. ■ 77025 #825-01-1988 PM *100
CHUANG, Hsi-Sheng. 4331 BRIGHTWOOD DR, STE 201 77068 #385-03-1966 L1977 N *020 †75
CHUANG, Vincent P. 1515 HOLCOMBE BLVD 77030 #385-02-1965 L1978 DR *020 †80
CHUANWALA, Shaista. 8615 ARRANMORE LN 77095 #704-02-1973 L1984 P *020
CHUAPETCHARASOPON, C. 7224 STAFFORDSHIRE ST 77030 #891-04-1979 DR *020
CHUGHTAI, Omar Rasheed. ■ 77004 #704-01-2001 L2007 SP *100
CHUN, Sang Hoon. 6500 NORTH FWY STE 117 77076 #583-04-1966 L1983 U *020
CHUN, Yun. ■ 77025 #035-09-1999 L2006 GS *020 †85
CHUNDRU, Ravi K. 845 FM 1960 RD W STE 101 77090 #048-14-1997 L1998 OPH *020 †35
CHUNDRU, Sunitha. ■ 77072 #035-08-2001 *100
CHUNG, Taylor. 6621 FANNIN ST, MC2-2521 77030 #041-01-1987 L1999 PDR *020 †80
CHUO, Liyun. 7011 SW FWY 77074 #048-02-1990 L1993 P *020 †75
CHUONG, Ching-Fong James. 7500 BEECHNUT ST, STE 308 77074 #244-02-1977 L1985
REN GYN *020 †30
CIANCA, John Christopher. 3440 RICHMOND AVE 77046 #035-03-1988 L1993 PM *020 †60
CIARAVINO, Michael Edward. 3700 BUFFALO SPEEDWAY #850 77098 #011-03-1991 L1997
PS *020 †65
CICERI, Elisa. BAYLOR COLL OF MED, DEPT RAD 77030 #561-03-1988 RNR *100
CICERO LEBRIJA, Alejandra. 6431 FANNIN ST, JJL STE 310 77030 #649-13-1999 *100
CID, Emma. 6431 FANNIN ST 77030 #011-02-1987 L1992 CD IM *020 †20
CIMO, Philip L. 909 FROSTWOOD, STE 221 77024 #048-02-1967 L1967 HEM *020 †20
CINTRON, Nitza M. 811 BRADWELL DR 77062 #048-02-1995 L1997 IM *030 †20
CISEK, Lawrence James, Jr. 6521 FANNIN ST STE 660CCC 77030 #023-07-1990 L2000
UP *020 †95
CITARDI, Martin Jason. 6431 FANNIN ST 5.036, DEPARTMENT OF OTOLARYNGOLO 77030
#023-07-1991 L2008 OTO *020 †45
CITRON, Deborah Riley. 1 BAYLOR PLZ, DEPT OF PATHOLOGY 77030 #021-05-1993 L1998
PTH *020 †50
CIVITELLO, Andrew Brian. 1200 BINZ ST STE 1290, DELGADO CARDIO ASSOCS 77004
#048-14-1995 L1998 CD IC *020 †20
CLAGHORN, James Lesley. 1010 WAVERLY ST 77008 #035-03-1961 L1965 P PA *020 †75
CLANTON, Lemuel J, Jr. ■ 77041 #047-01-1992 L1997 PM *020 †60
CLANTON, Thomas Oscar. 6431 FANNIN ST, MSB6 156 77030 #048-04-1976 L1976
OSM OFA *020 †40
CLARDY, Christina J. 938 E TIDWELL RD 77022 #047-07-1976 L1983 AN *020
CLARK, Dana Lynn. 1100 W 34TH ST 77018 #005-14-1990 L1993 FM *020 †18
CLARK, David W. ■ 77003 #048-14-2005 OTO *020
CLARK, Gary David. 6621 FANNIN ST, CC1250 77030 #021-05-1982 L1995 CHN PD *050 †75,55
CLARK, John Rodney, Jr. 5622 E SAM HOUSTON PKWY N 77015 #048-04-2001 L2004
PD *020 †55
CLARK, Jonathan Bailey. 1 BAYLOR PLZ, NSBRI STE NA 425 77030 #023-12-1980 L1981
N AM *020 †75,70
CLARK, Laurie Susan. 4101 GREENBRIAR ST, STE 100 77098 #036-05-1981 L1987 PD *020 †55
CLARK, Monica. 6431 FANNIN ST STE JJL-310, UNIVERSITY OF TEXAS AT HOU 77030
#016-11-1997 L2007 GPM *012
CLARK, Pamela. ■ 77057 #048-14-2008 *012
CLARK, Sharonda N. ■ 77054 #048-14-2008 *012
CLARK, William D. 2312 TIDWELL RD 77093 #036-01-1969 L1975 GP CLP *020 †50
CLARKE, Norma Veronica L. 2801 GESSNER DR 77080 #566-01-1981 L2003 CHP P *020 †75
CLARKE, William Paschal. 9301 SW FWY STE 245 77074 #048-21-1973 L1974 EM *020 †16
CLAUSEN, Roy Elwood, Jr. ■ 77084 #005-11-1944 L1952 N P *071 †75
CLAUSS, Paul Oliver David. 11914 ASTORIA BLVD, STE 570 77089 #041-09-1954 L1960
FM *071
CLAVIJO, Jaime Alberto. 7737 SOUTHWEST FWY STE 5 77074 #649-30-1991 L2001
PCC *020 †20
CLAYMAN, Gary Lee. 1515 HOLCOMBE BLVD BOX 06, UT M D ANDERSON CANCER CEN 77030
#038-44-1986 L1989 HNS *020 †45
CLAYTON, Charles Thos. 1346 CAMPBELL RD 77055 #048-12-1978 L1978 DR *020 †80
CLAYTON, Victoria Louise. 8830 LONG POINT RD, STE 706 77055 #048-14-1978 L1978
IM IMG *020
CLEARMAN, Rebecca Ruth. 5219 CAROLINE ST 77004 #048-04-1984 L1985 PM OS *020 †60
CLEARY, Thomas Geo. UNIVERSITY OF TEXAS 77030 #028-02-1971 L1978 PD *050 †55
CLEMENT, Earl Jay, II. 8011 GLENFOREST CT, FAMILY PRACTICE 77061 #047-07-1999 L2005
FM *020 †18
CLEMENT-CORMIER, Yvonne. ■ 77019 #048-04-1986 L1988 AN *020
CLEMMONS, John Benj. 1213 HERMANN DR STE 420 77004 #010-03-1975 L1981
GE IM *020 †20
CLEVELAND, Benny Ray. 11914 ASTORIA BLVD, STE 360 77089 #001-02-1958 L1965
GS CRS *071 †85
CLIFTON, Guy Lynn. 6431 FANNIN ST, STE 7.130 77030 #048-02-1975 L1977 NS *020 †25
CLOTEAUX, Christopher D. 6624 FANNIN ST, STE 1900 77030 #048-13-2000 L2003 IM *020 †20
CLOWER, Matthew Simpson. ■ 77054 #048-14-2008 *012
CLYBURN, Terry Alan. 6431 FANNIN ST, MSB 6150 77030 #048-02-1979 L1979 ORS *020 †40
COALE, John M. 7600 FANNIN ST 77054 #048-14-1992 L1994 AN *020 †05
COAN, John David. ■ 77030 #051-04-1968 L1974 DR *071 †80
COATE, Dallas Eugene. 7737 SOUTHWEST FWY, STE 400 77074 #017-20-1977 L1993
OBS FM *040 †18

COATS, Alfred Cornell. ■ 77024 #048-04-1962 L1962 OS *050
COATS, David K. 6550 FANNIN ST, STE 1501 77030 #048-15-1987 L1988 OPH *020 †35
COBB, Gerald Barton. 211 HIGHLAND CROSS DR #275 77073 #048-12-1982 L1983
IM EM *020 †20
COBURN, Amy Grossman. 6624 FANNIN ST STE 2100 77030 #048-04-1985 L1989
OPH *020 †35
COBURN, Michael. 6560 FANNIN ST, STE 2100 77030 #035-19-1982 L1983 U *020 †95
COCHINWALA, Asif. 1740 W 27TH ST, STE 201 77008 #704-02-1987 L1994 RHU *020 †20
COCHRAN, Jaimie N. 1900 YORKTOWN ST, #680 77056 #048-02-1952 L1952 P *071
COCHRAN, John R. 5656 KELLEY ST, 1 EC 93006 UT HOUSTON MED 77026
#048-15-1988 L1989 PD CCP *020 †55
COCHRAN, Susan M. 6550 FANNIN ST, STE 2339 77030 #048-14-1991 L1993 IM *020 †20
COCKRILL, Tonya Christine. ■ 77035 #048-14-2004 RHU *012 †20
COE, William A. ■ 77005 #048-15-1975 L1975 DR *020 †80
COFFEY, Donna Marie. ■ 77025 #270-01-1991 L2002 PTH *020
COFRESI-AVILES, Mariame. 2323 S SHEPHERD DR STE 110 77019 #042-01-1967 L1971
P *020 †75
COGGINS, Steven S. 6720 BERTNER ST 77030 #048-02-1988 L1989 AN *020 †05
COHAN, Leslie C. 7580 FANNIN ST STE 235 77054 #048-04-1982 L1983 OBG *020 †30
COHAN, Sandra Rochelle. ■ 77098 #012-21-2007 PD *012
COHAN, Steven Andrew. ■ 77096 #048-04-1996 FM *100
COHAN, Stuart K. ■ 77096 #035-15-1949 L1955 PD *071 †55
COHEN, Alan Marshall. 6431 FANNIN ST, DEPT OF RADIOLOGY, MSB 2.1 77030
#038-06-1972 L1995 DR *062 †80
COHEN, Benjamin E. 1315 ST JOSEPH PKWY, STE 920 77002 #024-01-1969 L1978
PS HS *020 †65,85
COHEN, Brian David. ■ 77004 #028-46-2003 L2006 AN *020
COHEN, Dan Chaim. ■ 77030 #048-04-2006 IM *012
COHEN, Janice Mateo. ■ 77004 #028-46-2004 L2008 PM *012
COHEN, Joel Steven. 13300 HARGRAVE RD, STE 300 77070 #021-01-1973 L1977
OPH PTH *020 †35
COHEN, Joshua Bernard. ■ 77006 #048-02-2007 IM *012
COHEN, Kelli A. 1 BAYLOR PLZ, BAYLOR CLG OF MED 77030 #048-13-1991 L1998
PDR *020 †80
COHEN, Kenneth Eric. 909 FROSTWOOD DR, STE 126 77024 #048-13-1984 L1985 PD *020 †55
COHEN, Lisa Fox. 1 BAYLOR PLZ, RM 286A 77030 #048-12-1994 L1996 PTH *020 †50
COHEN, Philip Randolph. 100 UH HEALTH CTR, UNIV OF HOUSTON HLTH CTR 77204
#035-09-1983 L1984 D DMP *020 †15
COHEN, Victor Kichk. 1515 HOLCOMBE BLVD, BOX 422 77030 #067-01-1995 L2002
ON *100 †20
COHEN, William Zachary. 7007 NORTH FWY STE 205 77076 #023-01-1981 L1982 FM *030 ‡
COHN, Cal K. 8200 WEDNESBURY LN, STE 270 77074 #035-20-1967 L1975 P *020 †75
COHN, William Ettlinger. 1101 BATES AVE, SURGICAL ASSOCIATES OF 77030
#048-04-1986 L1987 TS *020 †85,90
COKER, Lacy Elizabeth. ■ 77054 #048-14-2008 *012
COKER, Newton Jasper. 6550 FANNIN ST # 1727, DEPTARTMENT OF OTO 77030
#012-01-1976 L1983 OTO NO *071 †45
COLASURDO, Giuseppe N. 6431 FANNIN ST 3.220 77030 #561-25-1985 L1991
PD PDP *020 †55
COLBY, Steven Thos. ■ 77080 #048-14-1984 *100
COLE, Letha Birkholtz. 2430 SUNSET BLVD 77005 #048-02-1984 L1985 CHP P *020 †75
COLE, Patrick Dale. ■ 77025 #048-12-2004 GS *012
COLE, Rhonda Audrey. 2002 HOLCOMBE BLVD, VAMC 111D 77030 #028-02-1984 L1987
GE IM *020 †20
COLEBY, Craig Alan. 6565 FANNIN ST # 1290, MED/PEDS PR 77030 #056-06-2004 L2006
MPD *012
COLEMAN, Christopher L. ■ 77084 #048-04-1987 *100
COLEMAN, Glenda L. 8100 GREENBRIAR ST, STE 250 77054 #043-01-1987 L1993
IMG *020 †20
COLEMAN, Kelly Marissa. 10375 RICHMOND AVE, STE 1575 77042 #048-02-2002 L2006
PD *020
COLEMAN, Ralph Franklin. 11732 S WILCREST DR 77099 #001-02-1962 L1976 GP EM *020
COLEMAN, Robert Louis. 1515 HOLCOMBE BLVD, UNIT 1362 77030 #030-06-1987 L1992
GO *020 †30
COLEN, John Sherman. ■ 77004 #041-12-2005 U *012
COLLACO, Christopher R. 9494 SOUTHWEST FWY, STE 650 77074 #048-02-1999 L2002
AI *020 †20,03
COLLARD, Charles D. 6720 BERTNER ST 77030 #048-04-1991 L1992 AN *020 †05
COLLARD, Quentin L. 7400 FANNIN ST, STE 900 77054 #048-14-1989 L1991 PD *020 †55
COLLAZO, Jesus Carlos. ■ 77036 #275-01-1949 L1968 P *071 †18
COLLETTI, Laura Ann. 6431 FANNIN ST, DIVISION OF GENERAL MEDICI 77030
#024-05-1980 L1991 IM *020 †20
COLLIER, Samuel James. ■ 77008 #048-14-2007 L2007 P *012
COLLINS, Clyde Aulgin. ■ 77092 #035-06-2006 IM *012
COLLINS, Donald R. 1315 ST JOSEPH PKWY, STE 900 77002 #048-14-1987 L1988 PS *020 †65
COLLINS, Evan Douglas. 6550 FANNIN ST, STE 2525 77030 #048-15-1990 L1997 HS *020 †40
COLLINS, George P. ■ 77059 #048-04-1953 L1953 AN *071 †05
COLLINS, James Allen. 7600 FANNIN ST, THE WOMAN'S HOSPITAL OF TE 77054
#048-04-1959 L1963 IM *020 †20
COLLINS, N Perryman, Sr. 7737 SOUTHWEST FWY, STE 420 77074 #048-04-1955 L1955
GS TS *020 †85,90
COLMAN, Howard. 1515 HOLCOMBE BLVD, DEPT./NEURO-ONCOLOGY, BOX 77030
#028-02-1997 L2001 N *020 †75
COLMAN, June Williams. 1140 WESTMONT DR, STE 340 77015 #047-07-1993 L1996
OBG *020 †30
COLMAN, Ronald Cornelius. 1200 BINZ ST STE 700, DIAGNOSTIC CLINIC OF HOUST 77004
#047-07-1992 L1999 GE *020 †20
COLOMB, Camille Marie. 6621 FANNIN ST, STE A300 77030 #021-05-1988 L1993 PAN *020 †05
COLOMBOWALA, Ilyas Kaizar. 1 BAYLOR PLZ, SECTION OF CARDIOLOGY 77030
#048-04-2002 L2004 CD *012 †20
COLOME, Maria I. 3317 ROBINHOOD ST 77005 #649-06-1984 L1991 D DMP *020 †50,15
COLOMER-MENDOZA, Alberto. 6431 FANNIN ST STE 1.150, AT HOUST 77030
#042-02-2003 L2006 PCC *012 †20
COLQUHOUN, Joseph. ■ 77030 #917-20-1949 L1965 DR *071 †80
COLQUHOUN, Tiffany Raynor. 77007 #048-02-2000 L2007 PDO *020 †45
COLTON, Lara M. 6550 FANNIN ST STE SM1001, METHODIST ACADEMIC MEDICIN 77030
#048-14-2002 L2005 IM *100 †20

COLWELL, Nathan Wayne. 810 PEAKWOOD DR, STE 107 77090 #048-02-1964 L1964 DR *020 †18,80

COMAIR, Youssef G. 1709 DRYDEN RD 77030 #605-02-1982 L2008 NS *020 †25

COMBS, Meaghan Ann. ■ 77056 #021-01-2008 *012

COMEAUX, Guy Louis. 7401 MAIN ST 77030 #021-05-1971 L1973 AN *020 †05

COMEAUX, Tamyra Y. 11811 FM 1960 RD W STE 104 77065 #012-21-1996 L2000 OBG *020 †30

COMPTON, Brandi Antoinett. ■ 77056 #048-14-2008 *012

COMSTOCK, Eric G. 6910 BELLAIRE BLVD # NO-12 77074 #048-04-1958 L1958 OM PTX *020

CONANT, Charles Norman. 7600 BEECHNUT 2ND FL PATH 77074 #038-06-1958 L1969 PTH BBK *071 †50

CONDARA, Harold A, Jr. 925 GESSNER RD 77024 #048-14-1985 L1986 CD IM *020 †20

CONDE, Allan Arthur. 12727 KIMBERLEY LN 77024 #048-02-1995 L1997 AN *020 †05

CONDEFER, William Thomas. 6550 FANNIN ST, STE 2403 77030 #033-05-1993 L2000 PCC *020 †20

CONDRON, Michael Robert, II. 6431 FANNIN ST, DEPARTMENT OF PATHOLOGY UT 77030 #047-07-2004 PTH *012

CONDRON, Suzanne Marie. 17150 EL CAMINO REAL, BAY AREA PED ASSOC PA 77058 #048-04-2001 L2004 PD *020 †20

CONE, Stephen M. 7900 FANNIN ST, STE 4000 77054 #048-04-1989 L1991 OBG *020 †30

CONKLIN, George Taylor. 1200 BINZ ST, DIAGNOSTIC CLINIC OF 77004 #035-45-1969 L1972 HEM IM *020 †20

CONKRIGHT, Kendra Jo. 1 BAYLOR PLZ, MED/PEDIATRICS PROGRAM 77030 #016-11-2006 MPD *012

CONLAY, Lydia Ann. 1709 DRYDEN RD, STE 1700, MS: BCM 120 77030 #021-06-1976 L2004 AN NTR *020 †05

CONLEY, Adam Michael. ■ 77054 #048-14-2008 *012

CONLEY-HARVEY, Cherice M. 1111 AUGUSTA DR, DEPT INTERNAL MEDICINE 77057 #018-03-1997 L2000 IM *020 †20

CONLON, Charles Lee. 7777 SOUTHWEST FWY, STE 744 77074 #048-02-1975 L1975 HO HEM *020 †20

CONLON, Rosemary Moore. 6411 FANNIN ST 77030 #048-02-1975 L1975 PD *020 †55

CONNALLY, Michael J. 6431 FANNIN ST, DEPT ORS 77030 #048-14-2007 ORS *012

CONNELLY, James W. 2002 HOLCOMBE BLVD 77030 #021-01-1952 L1964 R *020 †80

CONNELLY, John Henry. 6720 BERTNER ST MC4-265, ST LUKES PATHOLOGY DEPT 77030 #021-06-1984 L1986 PTH *020 †20

CONNELLY, Michael Wm. 7900 FANNIN ST, STE 3300 77054 #048-14-1991 L1993 PD *020 †55

CONNELLY, Rosina Avila. 6621 FANNIN ST, CCC 1540.00 77030 #935-01-1998 L2006 PD *100 †55

CONNER, Benjamin Norman. 3120 SOUTHWEST FWY, GREATER HOUSTON RADIOLOGY 77098 #011-02-1984 L1986 DR *020 †80

CONNER, John Stanley. ■ 77025 #048-04-1958 L1958 OBG *071 †30

CONNOLLY, Terence Patrick. 6624 FANNIN ST 77030 #539-04-1968 L1976 R DR *020 †80

CONNOLLY, Timothy Adrian. 6624 FANNIN ST, STE 1730 77030 #010-02-1998 L2002 PCC *100 †20

CONOLEY, Patrick Mcmillan. 2727 W HOLCOMBE BLVD 77025 #048-04-1976 L1976 DR *020 †80 ‡

CONRAD, Alexis April. 7550 KIRBY DR, APT 822 77030 #041-14-2005 OBG *012

CONRAD, Charles A. 1515 HOLCOMBE BLVD BOX 4, DEPT OF NEURO-ONCOLOGY 77030 #048-14-1988 L1989 P *020 †75

CONRAD, Larry Paul. 1200 BINZ ST STE 1230 77004 #036-05-1969 L1975 OTO PS *020 †45

CONROW, David Scott. 6565 FANNIN ST MS D281, THE METHODIST HOSPITAL 77030 #004-01-1995 L1998 DR *020 †80

CONSIDINE, James Francis. 1775 SAINT JAMES PL # 200 77056 #033-05-1960 L1962 P *071

CONSTANTACOS, Cathrine. 6621 FANNIN ST STE 1020 77030 #418-01-2002 L2007 PDE *012 †55

CONTE, Maurice S. 4309 YOAKUM BLVD 77006 #561-11-1964 L1976 GP A *071

CONTRERAS, Janice E. ■ 77019 #048-02-2003 L2007 *100

COOGAN, Sheila Marie. 6410 FANNIN ST, STE 450 77030 #048-14-1991 L1993 VS *020 †85

COOK, Candance Lynne. ■ 77045 #048-14-1998 *100

COOK, Craig Elton. ■ 77030 #048-14-2008 *012

COOK, Elise Donaville. 1515 HOLCOMBE BLVD 77030 #005-02-1988 L1989 FM GPM *020 †18

COOK, James Ergle, Jr. 9090 GAYLORD ST, STE 101 77024 #048-04-1960 L1960 FPG OS *071

COOK, Patrick Jos. 1707 SUNSET BLVD, MEDICAL CLINIC OF HOUSTON 77005 #048-04-1979 L1979 CD IM *020 †20

COOK, Paul Cameron. 920 FROSTWOOD DR, STE 720 77024 #048-14-1982 L1983 U *020 †95

COOK, Paul Issa. 6400 FANNIN ST, STE 1900 77030 #048-14-1988 L1989 OBG *020 †30

COOK, Steven J. 4101 GREENBRIAR ST, STE 100 77098 #048-14-1991 L1992 PD *020 †55

COOK, William Andrew. 3801 KIRBY DR STE 300 77098 #036-01-1972 L1978 D *020 †15

COOKE, Jonathan Edward. 1709 DRYDEN RD STE 550, BCM FACULTY CENTER 77030 #016-06-2007 IM *012

COOKE, Shanon M. 1123 AUTREY ST # 2 77006 #048-14-2003 L2007 AN *020

COOKE, Vera. ■ 77054 #048-14-2008 *012

COOLEY, Denton A. 1101 BATES AVE, SURGICAL ASSOCIATES OF 77030 #023-07-1944 L1944 TS *020 †85,90

COOPER, Bruce T. 12814 WILLOW CTR STE B 77066 #048-02-1986 L1987 PS *020

COOPER, Constance D. 7900 FANNIN ST, STE 4500 77054 #021-01-1995 L1999 OBG *020 †30

COOPER, Griffin L, Jr. ■ 77021 #010-03-1945 L1947 GP *075

COOPER, James Bryan. 1140 CLEAR LAKE CITY BLVD, STE A 77062 #048-15-1977 L1977 A AI *020 †55,03

COOPER, Jason Edward. 7900 FANNIN ST, STE 4811 77054 #021-05-1996 L2000 OBG *020 †30

COOPER, John Robert, Jr. 6720 BERTNER ST, STE 0-520 77030 #021-01-1972 L1978 AN CCA *020 †05 ‡

COOPER, Johnny O'Neal. ■ 77068 #041-77-1972, ▲ L1980 IM *071

COOPER, Lisa Marie. 12141 RICHMOND AVE 77082 #048-13-2002 L2006 EM *020 †16

COOPER, Ryan S. 1709 DRYDEN RD STE 550, BCM FACULTY CENTER 77030 #048-14-2006 IM *012

COORG, Rohini Kusum. 6431 FANNIN ST, SCHOOL A 77030 #048-13-2007 PD *012

COPELAND, Lynn R. 800 PEAKWOOD DR, DIGESTIVE SPECIALISTS OF 77090 #039-01-1975 L1991 GE IM *020 †20

COPE-YOKOYAMA, Sandy D. ■ 77077 #048-04-2002 L2008 PP *012

COPPEDGE, Woodrow William. 6260 WESTPARK DR, STE 300 77057 #048-13-1996 L2001 P ADP *012

CORBETT, Sean Thomas. 6621 FANNIN ST, SCOTT DEPT OF UROLOGY 77030 #539-04-2000 L2007 UP *020

CORBOY, Jane Ellen. 3701 KIRBY DR, STE 600 77098 #048-04-1982 L1983 FM EM *020 †18

CORBUT, David Ignatius. 1011 RUELL ST 77017 #048-14-1981 L1981 TS VS *020 †85,90

CORDES, Brett Mccormack. 1 BAYLOR PLZ, DEPT OF OTORHINOLARYNGOLOG 77030 #021-05-2004 OTO *012

CORDOBA SENTIES, Alfonso. 17203 RED OAK DR STE 101, SURGICAL ARTS BLDG 77090 #649-01-1969 L1978 GS VS *020

CORDOVA, Francisco Jose. 6431 FANNIN ST, UTHSC DIV OF CARDIOLOGY 77030 #042-01-2003 L2005 CD *012 †20

COREY, Seth Joel. 1515 HOLCOMBE BLVD, DEPT OF PEDS MD ANDERSON 77030 #021-01-1982 L2006 PD PHO *050 †55

CORKE, Patricia Perry. 18333 EGRET BAY BLVD, STE 305 77058 #048-02-1968 L1968 P N *020 †75

CORKRAN, Tina T. 13231 CHAMPION FOREST DR, STE 230 77069 #048-14-2002 L2004 FM *020 †18

CORLEY, Ryan Jackson. ■ 77054 #048-15-2007 TY *012

CORMIER, Janice Nicole. 1515 HOLCOMBE BLVD BOX 444, DEPT SURG 77030 #024-16-1991 L1999 GS *020 †85

CORN, Paul Gettys. 1515 HOLCOMBE BLVD, UNIT 1374 77030 #010-02-1993 L2005 ON *020 †20

CORNEJO, Santiago Martin. ■ 77008 #003-01-2006 DR *012

CORNELL, Robert John. 1315 ST JOSEPH PKWY, STE 1700 77002 #035-01-1997 L2003 U *020 †95

CORORVE, Alan Eli. 7707 FANNIN ST, STE 250 77054 #016-11-1965 L1972 IM CD *020

CORPENING, Thomas N. 1740 W 27TH ST, STE 309 77008 #023-01-1950 L1957 IM AI *020

CORRALES MEDINA, Vicente. 2247 SOUTH BLVD 77098 #737-11-1997 ID *012 †20

CORREA, Armando G. 6621 FANNIN ST, CC-1540.00 77030 #649-52-1987 L1991 PD PDI *020 †55

CORRIERE, Joseph N, Jr. 1220 HOLCOMBE BLVD # 127, ANDERSON CANC 77030 #033-05-1963 L1974 U *030 †95

CORRIGAN, Esther Maria. ■ 77009 #056-06-2001 L2006 OBG *020

CORRY, David B. 1 BAYLOR PLZ STE 520B, BAYLOR COLLEGE OF MEDICINE 77030 #048-12-1988 L2000 IM PCC *020 †20

CORTES, Christopher J. 1315 ST JOSEPH PKWY, STE 1107 77002 #048-12-1997 L1998 PCC *020 †20

CORTES, Jose Antonio. 1515 HOLCOMBE BLVD, UNIT 87 77030 #429-01-1990 L2002 CCP *020 †55

CORTES-FRANCO, Jorge E. 1515 HOLCOMBE BLVD # 428 77030 #649-01-1989 L1996 IM HO *050

CORTEZ, Roland. 7915 FM 1960 RD W, STE 108 77070 #048-02-1996 L1998 R NR *020 †80

COSELLI, J Stapleton. 6770 BERTNER ST, STE C350 77030 #048-02-1977 L1977 TS GS *020 †85,90

COSELLI, Michael Pool. 6566 FANNIN ST, STE 1608 77030 #048-02-1983 L1983 GS *020 †85

COSIO, Carmen Cecilia. 6621 FANNIN ST, WT 6-006 TEXAS CHILD HOSP 77030 #429-02-1984 L1993 CCP PD *020 †55

COSS BU, Jorge Antonio. 6621 FANNIN ST, CRIT CARE SCT /MC 2-3450 77030 #649-52-1986 L2003 CCP *020 †55

COSTA, Felix A. 17115 RED OAK DR 77090 #737-01-1957 L1972 GP CHP *075

COSTELLOE, Colleen Mary. 1515 HOLCOMBE BLVD # 273, UT MD ANDERSON CANCER CTR 77030 #048-14-1997 L2001 DR *020 †80

COTA SCHWARZ, Ana Lucia. ■ 77054 #649-30-2005 PTH *012

COTLAR, David Michael. 7777 SOUTHWEST FWY, STE 946 77074 #048-04-1973 L1973 PD *020 †55

COTLER, Howard Bruce. 1200 BINZ ST, STE 670 77004 #041-02-1979 L1986 OSS TRS *020 †40

COTRONEO, Christopher Mic. 1 BAYLOR PLZ, MED /PEDS PROGRAM MS: BCM 77030 #035-45-2005 MPD *012

COTTINGHAM, Karen Louise. 6565 FANNIN ST 77030 #054-04-1979 L1983 IM ON *020 †20

COTTON, Ronald Timothy. ■ 77004 #048-04-2006 GS *012

COUCH, Charles Earl. 9470 LONG POINT RD 77055 #038-06-1956 L1980 FM GP *071

COUCH, Robert Barnard. 1 BAYLOR PLZ, MS: BCM-280 77030 #047-05-1956 L1966 ID IM *050 †20

COUCH, William Higgins. 1140 CYPRESS STATION DR, NORTHWEST DIAGNOSTIC CLINI 77090 #048-02-1973 L1973 IM *020 †20

COULTER, Stephanie. 6565 FANNIN ST, STE 2780 77030 #048-14-1991 L1999 IM *020 †20

COURIEL, Daniel Ricardo. 1515 HOLCOMBE BLVD, UNIT 423 77030 #132-01-1987 L2000 HEM ON *020 †20

COUROUCLI, Xanthi Ioanna. 1 BAYLOR PLZ, BAYLOR COLLEGE OF MEDICINE 77030 #418-01-1987 L1998 NPM *020 †55

COUTTS-VAN DIJK, Louisa C. 3701 KIRBY DR, STE 100 77098 #660-07-1985 L1995 FM *040 †18

COVELER, Lewis Alvin. 6565 FANNIN ST 77030 #041-12-1970 L1978 AN *020 †05

COVERDALE, John H. 1 BAYLOR PLZ 77030 #671-01-1980 L1988 P *020 †75

COVERT, Charles Betts. 800 BERING DR STE 202 77057 #048-04-1971 L1971 P *020 †75

COVINGTON, Karl K. 465 W PARKER RD, STE 100A 77091 #025-12-1982 L1985 GP IM *020

COVINSKY, Michael Harvey. 6565 FANNIN ST 77030 #048-04-1997 L2004 PTH *020 †50

COWAN, Katherine A. 2800 S MACGREGOR WAY, HARRIS CTY PSYCH CTR 77021 #048-02-1982 L1983 P *020 †75

COWAN, Laura E. 1 BAYLOR PLZ, BAYLOR COLL MED 77030 #048-13-2007 PTH *012

COWAN, Mary Alice Lindsey. 7400 FANNIN ST STE 750 77054 #048-04-1979 L1979 OBG *020 †30

COWART, Marolyn Maurine. ■ 77227 #048-02-1956 L1956 FM *071

COWLES, Charles E. 6431 FANNIN ST, # 5.020 77030 #048-14-2004 L2006 AN *012

COWMAN, Dan Chas. 3310 RICHMOND AVE 77098 #005-11-1981 L1987 DR *020 †80

COX, Charles S, Jr. 6431 FANNIN ST, STE 5.236 77030 #048-02-1988 L1989 CCS *020 †85

COX, Colleen Lance. 3739 FARBER ST 77005 #048-04-1994 L1996 IM *020 †20

COX, James D. 1515 HOLCOMBE BLVD # 97, UT MD ANDERSON CANCER CTR 77030 #035-45-1965 L1989 RO *030 †80

COX, James F, Jr. 150 W PARKER RD, STE 707 77076 #048-02-1946 L1948 GP *071

COX, Margo Ann. ■ 77005 #024-07-1973 L1982 NPM PD *071 †55

COX, Robert Irvin. 7777 SOUTHWEST FWY, UROLOGY CLINIC ASSOCIATES 77074 #021-01-1955 L1962 U *071 †95

CRADDOCK, John Anthony. 6621 FANNIN ST, TEXAS CHILDREN'S HOSPITAL 77030 #023-12-1995 L1997 PHO *012 †55

CRADDOCK, John Walton, Jr. 2500 TANGLEWILDE ST, STE 160 77063 #048-14-1995 L1996 OTO HNS *020 †45

CRAGO, Rex Morrell. 8100 GREENBRIAR ST 77054 #016-11-1961 L1969 IM OM *071 †20

CRAIG, Alanna Leslie. 7403 BULL CREEK RD 77095 #048-13-1990 L1991 AN *020 †05

CRAIG, Ann Marie. 5151 EDLOE ST, APT 14308 77005 #041-01-1985 L2005 PD PEM *020 †55 ‡

CRAIG, Jason A. 1919 LA BRANCH ST, ST JOSEPH HOSPITAL 77002 #048-15-2004 **AN** *012
CRAIG, John Anthony. ■ 77005 #048-02-2004 L2006 **AN** *012
CRAIGEN, William J. 6701 FANNIN ST 77030 #048-04-1988 L1991 **OS** *020 †55,19
CRAM, Lorie Fox. 1910 JOHN RALSTON RD 77013 #048-14-1995 L1997 **FM** *020 †18
CRAMER, Alan Thos. 6565 FANNIN ST 77030 #048-04-1963 L1963 **PS FPS** *020 †65
CRAMER, F Michael. ■ 77024 #048-13-1977 L1977 **FOP HEM** *020 †50
CRAMER, W Owen. 1315 CALHOUN ST STE 1106 77002 #048-14-1976 L1976 **GS** *020 †85
CRANDELL, Sharon Sue. 6431 FANNIN ST, UNIV TX MED SCH DEPT PED 77030 #028-02-1974 L1978 **PD NPM** *040 †55
CRANE, Christopher Haydon. 1515 HOLCOMBE BLVD, DEPT RAD 77030 #051-01-1993 L1999 **RO** *020 †80
CRANE, Patrice Eileen. 915 GESSNER RD, STE 350 77024 #048-02-1985 L1988 **PD** *020 †55
CRAVEN, Judith Lynn B. ■ 77021 #048-04-1974 L1974 **AN** *030
CRAWFORD, Elisabeth W S. ■ 77063 #048-02-1939 L1939 **OPH** *071 †35
CRAWFORD, Heather Paige. 6431 FANNIN ST, SCHOOL A 77030 #010-03-2004 **MG** *012 †55
CRAWFORD, Janeana. 6431 FANNIN ST, MSB 1.122 77030 #025-07-1994 L1999 **MPD PD** *020
CRAWFORD, Michael P. ■ 77030 #048-02-2006 **GS** *012
CRAWSHAW, Steven Lytle. 5333 WESTHEIMER RD, STE 560 77056 #041-14-1979 L1997 **GS** *020 †85
CREED, Rosella Ann. ■ 77021 #048-14-2007 **IM** *012
CREIXELL, Ramon. 12121 RICHMOND AVE, STE 121 77082 #048-14-1996 L1998 **FM** *020 †18
CREO, Joseph Perfecto. ■ 77098 #305-01-2000 L2007 **AN** *100 †20,05
CRIBBS, Marc Garret. ■ 77006 #036-08-2004 **MPD** *012
CRIEP, Leo H. 8830 LONG POINT RD STE 406 77055 #041-12-1972 L1979 **IM** *071
CRISOSTOMO, Abigail Herna. 6431 FANNIN ST, STE JJL310 77030 #748-01-2003 *100
CRISTOBAL, Ricardo. 1 BAYLOR PLZ NA-102, DEPT OF OTOLARYNGOLOGY 77030 #847-11-1993 L2003 **NO** *012
CRISTOFANILLI, Massimo. 1515 HOLCOMBE BLVD, DIV OF MEDICINE, BOX 424. 77030 #561-17-1986 L1997 **ON** *020 †20
CRITELLI, Paul A. ■ 77054 #048-14-2008 *012
CRITTENDON, Ivory. ■ 77007 #040-02-2004 L2006 **PDC** *012 †55
CROFOOT, Gordon E, Jr. 3701 KIRBY DR STE 1230 77098 #016-06-1974 L1977 **IM** *020
CROFT, Steven Michael. 7777 SOUTHWEST FWY STE 506 77074 #048-14-1986 L1987 **N** *020 †75
CROMBY, James W. 6486 BURGOYNE RD, STE 211 77057 #917-04-1956 L1980 *020
CROMMETT, John Wilson. 6431 FANNIN ST, MSB 7.154B 77030 #001-02-1994 L2000 **CCM IM** *020 †20
CRONIN, Ernest Dattner. 1315 CALHOUN ST STE 920 77002 #048-02-1971 L1971 **PS OTO** *020 †45,65
CROOCK, Alan David. 3601 N MACGREGOR WAY, DEPT OF FAM & COMM MED 77004 #836-01-1975 L1990 **RHU IM** *020 †20
CROSBY, Melissa Ann. 1515 HOLCOMBE BLVD BOX 443, MD ANDERSON CANCER CTR 77030 #036-01-2000 L2005 **PS** *020 †65
CROSS, Cartrell James. PO BOX 66288 77266 #048-04-1973 L1973 **PUD IM** *020 †20
CROSS, Chadrick Antony. ■ 77054 #016-11-2003 **GS** *012
CROUCH, Carter Craig. 7401 MAIN ST 77030 #021-01-1976 L1977 **ORS HS** *020 †40
CROUCH, Michael Avery. 3701 KIRBY DR, STE 100 77098 #005-11-1977 L1990 **FM EM** *020 †18
CROUSE, Heather Lyne. 6621 FANNIN ST, TEXAS CHILDENS HOSPITAL 77030 #036-01-2002 L2005 **PEM** *012 †55
CROWE, James Earl. 6431 FANNIN ST, DEPT OF RADIOLOGY 77030 #036-05-1966 L2005 **PDR** *020 †80
CROWSON, Cathie Clair. ■ 77004 #048-14-1984 **FM** *020
CRUMB, Charles Kenneth. 7777 SOUTHWEST FWY STE 736 77074 #028-03-1968 L1973 **NEP IM** *020 †20
CRUMBIE, David Anthony, Jr. 1 BAYLOR PLZ, BAYLOR COLL MED 77030 #036-08-2000 L2007 **OSM** *012
CRUMP, Monica Elayne. ■ 77044 #041-15-2002 L2007 **PM** *020 †60
CRUZ, Andrea Tania. 6621 FANNIN ST MC, TEXAS CHILDREN'S HOSPITAL 77030 #047-05-2001 L2004 **PDI** *012 †55
CRUZ, Nestor. 1214 ELGIN ST 77004 #264-01-1956 L1978 **AN PMM** *072 †05
CRUZ, Suzanna. 6720 BERTNER ST 77030 #048-13-1994 L1995 **EM** *020 †16
CRUZ, Vergel V. 5102 N MAIN ST STE B 77009 #748-01-1960 L1969 **GS** *071
CUA, Beatriz S. 6431 FANNIN ST, STE 3.234 77030 #748-10-1987 L1997 **CCP** *020 †55
CUADRADO, Luis Felipe. 6565 FANNIN ST 77030 #847-09-1955 L1971 **AN** *020 †05
CUANO, Rumulo Lavarez. ■ 77074 #748-01-1972 *075
CUBB, Anthony. 1200 TEXAS ST, HEALTH SERVICES UNIT 77002 #270-01-1981 L1993 **IM** *020 †20
CUCHAPIN, Regina T. ■ 77071 #048-12-2004 L2007 **IM** *100 †20
CUELLAR, Alberto D. 17080 RED OAK DR 77090 #048-02-1984 L1985 **ORS OAR** *020 †40
CUERVO, Jaime. 6710 CAPITOL ST 77011 #264-04-1966 L1976 **GE IM** *020 †20
CUEVO, Enrique Guison. 1111 AUGUSTA DR 77057 #748-01-1985 L1996 **FM** *020 †18
CUKIER, Jean. 7400 FANNIN ST, STE 1280 77054 #028-03-1974 L1981 **PS** *020 †65,85 ‡
CULBERSON, John W. 2002 HOLCOMBE BLVD, EXTENDED CARE (110) 77030 #033-05-1992 L1996 **FM** *020 †18
CULBERT, Steven Jerry. 1515 HOLCOMBE BLVD, DEPT OF PEDIATRICS M.D. AN 77030 #005-11-1970 L1976 **PHO PD** *040 †55
CULOTTA, Ralph J. ■ 77017 #021-01-1948 L1953 **GS TS** *071 †85
CULTRERA, Jennifer Lyn. 1515 HOLCOMBE BLVD, UNIT 10 77030 #011-02-2003 L2006 **HO** *012 †20
CUMAGUN, Victorino Gaffud. 4126 SOUTHWEST FWY STE 930 77027 #748-02-1967 L1975 **GS FM** *020
CUMBER, Salimah Fidaali. 1826 WIRT RD 77055 #704-25-1993 L2000 **FPG** *020
CUNADO, Carlos. 1313 HOLLAND ST, STE C 77029 #132-03-1975 L1998 **CHN** *020
CUNNINGHAM, Gene C, Jr. 6720 BERTNER ST 77030 #039-01-1967 L1972 **DR GP** *020 †80
CUNNINGHAM, Glenn Ross. 6624 FANNIN ST, STE 1240 77030 #039-01-1966 L1973 **IM END** *020 †20
CUNNINGHAM, Jennifer Lori. 8403 LORRIE DR 77025 #048-04-1999 L2003 **PCC** *100
CUNNINGHAM, Leigh Erin. ■ 77081 #048-14-2007 *012
CUNNINGHAM, Matthew. ■ 77019 #011-03-2007 **IM** *012
CUNNINGHAM, Michelle. 1709 DRYDEN RD STE 800 77030 #048-04-2001 L2005 **IMG** *020 †20
CUNNINGHAM, Paul York. ■ 77081 #048-04-2001 L2005 **CD** *012 †20
CUPIC, Zoran. 909 FROSTWOOD DR STE 251 77024 #165-04-1966 L1974 **ORS** *030 †40
CURB, Dolph Lange. ■ 77074 #048-02-1934 L1934 **GE** *071 †20
CURLEY, Steven Alan. 1515 HOLCOMBE BLVD, BOX 444 77030 #048-14-1982 L1983 **SO AS** *020 †85
CURRY, Choladda Vejabhuti. 1 BAYLOR PLZ, RM 213-B 77030 #891-02-1999 L2006 **HMP** *100 †50
CURRY, Daniel Joseph. 6621 FANNIN ST, ST., MCC1230.00 77030 #016-01-1996 L2008 **NS** *020
CURRY, Jonathan Lee. ■ 77005 #016-43-1998 L2004 **PTH** *100 †50
CURTIS, Amarinthia E. ■ 77005 #036-01-2003 L2008 **RO** *012
CURTIS, Bill B, II. 5656 KELLEY ST # 1EC 77026 #048-15-1987 L1988 **EM** *020 †16
CURTIS, Michele Groark. 5656 KELLEY ST, LBJ HOSPITAL, UT OB/GYN 77026 #048-15-1988 L1989 **OBG** *020 †30
CURTIS, Peter John. 12121 RICHMOND AVE 77082 #917-02-1966 L1980 **GS VS** *072
CURTIS, Regina M. 1919 LA BRANCH ST 77002 #038-06-1984 L1987 **AM OM** *020 †70 ‡
CUTLER, Debra A. 2727 W HOLCOMBE BLVD, KELSEY-SEYBOLD CLINIC P.A. 77025 #047-05-1977 L1980 **PD PUD** *020 †55
CUTRER, William Ben. ■ 77074 #020-12-2003 L2006 **CCP** *012 †55
CYKOWSKI, Matthew D. ■ 77069 #048-13-2003 *100
CYPRUS, Gerald Steven. 1709 DRYDEN RD STE 650 77030 #028-34-1967 L1968 **ON HEM** *020 †20
CZELUSTA, Kim-Lan T. 1 BAYLOR PLZ # MS350 77030 #048-04-1999 L2003 **P** *020 †75
CZERNIAK, Bogdan. 1515 HOLCOMBE BLVD 77030 #759-08-1973 L1993 **BBK** *020 †50
DAAS, Maher. 6624 FANNIN ST, 19TH FL 77030 #875-01-1987 L2002 **IM PCC** *020 †20
DACCAK, Munzer M C. ■ 77024 #396-06-1951 L1991 **GE** *071
DACI, Kuang. 1709 DRYDEN RD STE 550, BCM FACULTY CENTER 77030 #187-04-2005 **IM** *012
DACSO, Clifford Clark. 6560 FANNIN ST, STE 1150 77030 #048-04-1975 L1976 **IM ID** *020 †20 ‡
D'ADDESIO, Joseph Paul. 11800 ASTORIA BLVD, EMERGENCY DEPT 77089 #035-03-1977 L1995 **EM** *020 †20,16
DAHLBERG, Carl G Wolfe. 6624 FANNIN ST STE 1730, PCCS 77030 #048-04-1986 L1988 **PUD CCM** *020 †20
DAHM, Lida I Swafford. 8850 LONG POINT RD 77055 #021-01-1962 L1969 **AN PME** *020 †05
DAHOUI, Hanane. 6431 FANNIN ST, STE JJL310 77030 #605-02-2004 *100
DAI, Cheng-Ti. 11999 KATY FWY, STE 220 77079 #067-01-1982 L1983 **PME AN** *020 †05
DAI, Zhihao. 8208 GULF FWY, STE 101 77017 #243-75-1984 L2005 **IM** *100 †20
DAICHMAN, Ricardo. 6424 FANNIN ST 77030 #132-01-1961 L1968 **P** *071 †75
DAIGLE, Caroline Elizabet. ■ 77073 #048-14-2008 *012
DAILEY, Natalie Janinemir. ■ 77004 #024-01-2005 **MPD** *012
DAILEY, Warren Bertrand. 2626 S LOOP W, STE 320 77054 #047-07-1975 L1980 **FM** *020 †18
DAILY, Leon J, Jr. 9015 MANHATTAN DR 77096 #048-02-1964 L1964 **OBG** *020 †30
DAILY, Louis. 2523 MARONEAL ST 77030 #048-02-1943 L1943 **OPH** *071 †35
DAILY, William Hart. 6431 FANNIN ST, MSB 5020 77030 #048-13-1983 L1983 **AN** *020 †05
DAIRI, Nada. 6431 FANNIN ST, STE 1.264 77030 #875-02-1991 L2002 **PCC** *020 †20
DALAL, Shalini. 1515 HOLCOMBE BLVD, #008 DPT-PALLIATIVIE CARE 77030 #495-73-1991 L2004 **IM** *020 †20
DALBY, Jessica Willow. ■ 77054 #048-04-2008 *012
DALE, John Wesley. 5629 FM 1960 RD W 77069 #048-04-1963 L1963 **CHP P** *020 †75
DALESSANDRO, David Paul. 1 BAYLOR PLZ, BAYLOR COLL OF MED 77030 #039-01-2006 L2007 **N** *012
DALEY, Mary Denise. 1515 HOLCOMBE BLVD, UT MD ANDERSON 77030 #064-01-1983 L1997 **AN** *020 †05
DALIANI, Danai. ■ 77054 #418-01-1987 L1996 **ON IM** *020 †20
DALLAS, Nikolaos Andreas. 7777 KNIGHT RD, MAIL UNIT 0173 77054 #016-06-2004 L2006 **GS** *012
DALTON, Stephen Calhoun. 1415 NORTH LOOP W STE 820 77008 #048-12-1981 L1981 **DR R** *020 †80
DALY, David Thos. 2727 W HOLCOMBE BLVD 77025 #030-06-1987 L2003 **OTO** *020 †45
D'ANDREA, Mark Anthony. 12811 BEAMER RD 77089 #042-02-1985 L1989 **RO PMM** *020 †80
DANEK, Lisa Catherine. 3701 KIRBY DR STE 600, DEPT OF FAMILY & COMM MEDI 77098 #035-03-1996 L2000 **FM** *020 †18
DANG, Anh Tu. 1120A DENNIS ST 77004 #048-04-1987 L1988 **IM** *020 †20
DANG, Han Hoang. 7007 NORTH FWY, STE 240 77076 #048-14-2000 L2002 **NEP** *020
DANG, Hung Tan. 10838 BEECHNUT ST 77072 #048-14-1993 L1994 **IM** *020 †20 ‡
DANG, Joseph. 17070 RED OAK DR, STE 101 77090 #048-14-1994 L1996 **PM** *020 †60
DANG, Linh Mai. 1 BAYLOR PLZ, DEPT OF PATHOLOGY MC 315 77030 #028-46-2006 **PTH** *012
DANG, Michael Minh. 13629 BAY FRONT DR 77077 #048-13-1985 L1986 **EM IM** *020 †20
DANG, Minh Phuong D. 6431 FANNIN ST, UNIV OF TEXAS MED SCH 77030 #004-01-1999 L2007 **FM** *020
DANGLER, Lori Ann. 1515 HOLCOMBE BLVD # 409, DEPT OF ANESTHESIOLOGY 77030 #012-01-1993 L2007 **AN OS** *020 †05
DANI, Radhika N. ■ 77005 #048-04-2004 L2007 **P** *012
DANIEL, David William. ■ 77054 #048-04-2008 *012
DANIEL, Jamuna Varughese. 6540 BELLOWS LN # 507 77030 #048-04-2000 L2003 **IM** *100 †20
DANIEL, Suresh. 6624 FANNIN ST 19TH FL, ST LUKE'S MEDICAL TOWER 77030 #495-27-1984 L1996 **PCC SME** *020 †20
DANIEL, Timothy Dilon. 2002 HOLCOMBE BLVD, M E DEBAKEY HOUSTON VAMC 77030 #024-01-2000 L2003 **IM** *020 †20 ‡
DANIELSON, Jerry Dan. 13111 EAST FWY 77015 #068-01-1973 L1978 **FM** *020
DANILA, Cristina Ileana. 6431 FANNIN ST 1134, OF TEXAS-HOUSTON 77030 #781-05-1996 **IM** *012
DANNENBAUM, Mark J. ■ 77005 #048-14-2002 L2008 **NS** *012
DANNER, Carrie Adele. ■ 77054 #048-14-2006 **PD** *012
DANSON, Heather Louise. PO BOX 20708, UNIV TX MED SCH 77225 #007-02-2007 **OBG** *012
DANZIGER, Danny Howard. 2450 FONDREN RD, STE 310 77063 #048-04-1981 L1981 **PD** *020 †55
DAO, Daniel T. 909 FROSTWOOD DR 77024 #048-04-1987 L1988 **AN** *020 †05
DAO, Linda Nghi. ■ 77065 #048-15-2005 L2005 **PTH** *012
DAOURA, Nicolas. 7777 SOUTHWEST FWY, STE 105 77074 #396-12-1994 L2003 **IM ID** *020 †20
DARCOURT RIZO PATRON, Jorg. 6431 FANNIN ST, STE 1.150, AT HOUST 77030 #132-01-2000 L2006 **HO** *012 †20
D'ARCY, Daniel Paul. 13111 EAST FWY 77015 #918-01-1971 L1986 **EM** *020 †16
DARGAN, Maday Benitez. 8076 EL RIO ST 77054 #048-14-1989 L1990 **PTH BBK** *020 †50
DARK, Brittany L. PO BOX 20708, LYNDON B JOHNSON HOSP 77225 #012-21-2006 **OBG** *012
DARMADI, Daniel Haryanto. 2060 SPACE PARK DR 77058 #028-34-1995 L2001 **GE IM** *020 †20
DAROUICHE, Rabih Omar. 2002 HOLCOMBE BLVD, VETERANS AFFAIRS MED CTR 77030 #605-01-1984 L1988 **ID IM** *020 †20
DARRIGRANDI, Hector C. 6565 FANNIN ST 77030 #231-01-1965 L1972 **AN** *020
DARSEY, Susan L Bowen. 800 BERING DR STE 420 77057 #048-02-1965 L1969 **P** *020 †75
DARVISHI, Roham. 2002 HOLCOMBE BLVD 77030 #517-20-1994 L2005 **IM** *040 †20
DAS, Aparajita. 1709 DRYDEN RD STE 550, BCM FACULTY CENTER 77030 #033-06-2006 **IM** *012

DAS, Bhaguanti Shah. 1313 HERMANN DR 77004 #495-01-1963 L1972 **OBG** *020 †30
DAS, Bidhan Bihari. ■ 77035 #008-01-2007 L2007 **GS** *012
DAS, Biman Behari. 7800 FANNIN ST, STE 111 77054 #495-32-1959 L1969 **AN** *071 †05
DAS, Dolon Chapa. 6560 FANNIN ST, STE 1532 77030 #048-04-1998 L2002 **NEP IM** *020 †20
DAS, Prajnan. 1515 HOLCOMBE BLVD, UNIT 97 77030 #024-01-1999 L2004 **RO** *020 †80 ‡
DAS, Rituparna. 1 BAYLOR PLZ, BAYLOR COLL OF MED 77030 #012-01-2006 **N** *012
DASTGIR, Amer. ■ 77054 #048-02-2001 *100
DAUMAS-BRITSCH, Lilette. 12755 WOODFOREST BLVD 77015 #048-13-1986 L1988 **GP** *020 ‡
DAUNNO, Dominick Stevan. 1708 ELMEN ST 77019 #048-14-1992 L1993 **GPM** *020 †20
DAUSER, Robert C. 1709 DRYDEN RD 77030 #025-01-1977 L1994 **NS** *020 †25
DAVENPORT, Crystal Michel. ■ 77021 #048-14-2007 **PD** *012
DAVER, Naval Gustad. 1709 DRYDEN RD STE 550, BCM FACULTY CTR 77030 #495-01-2004 **IM** *012
DAVEY, Richard James, Jr. ■ 77006 #035-45-1969 L2006 **OS HEM** *050 †20
DAVID, Cynthia Lee. 1515 HOLCOMBE BLVD, BOX 57 77030 #041-02-1972 L1984 **PDR DR** *050 †80
DAVID, Elizabeth H. 5656 KELLEY ST, ANNEX BLDG 77026 #012-01-1979 L2001 **P** *020 †75
DAVIDOW, Alison B. 5701 WOODWAY DR, STE 202 77057 #048-12-1995 L1997 **FM** *020 †18
DAVIDOW, Joseph Franklin. 5701 WOODWAY DR STE 202 77057 #065-05-1969 L1977 **GP** *020
DAVIDSOHN, Carminia E. 13114 FM 1960 RD W, STE 200 77065 #748-02-1987 L1995 **IM** *020 †20
DAVIDSON, Christina Marie. 6431 FANNIN ST STE 3640, OB/GYN 77030 #048-14-2000 L2004 **OBG** *020
DAVIDSON, James Douglas. 8230 ANTOINE DR 77088 #065-05-1959 L1978 **FM** *071
DAVIDSON, Joyce Eileen. 2801 GESSNER DR 77080 #028-46-1979 L2002 **P CHP** *020 †75
DAVIDSON, Mary E. 10370 RICHMOND AVE, STE 1125 77042 #048-02-1992 L1994 **EM FM** *020 †18
DAVIDSON, Michael Kevin. 1315 ST JOSEPH PKWY, STE 1503 77002 #048-02-1997 L1998 **FM** *020 †18
DAVIDSON, Regina Denise. ■ 77034 #048-02-2004 L2007 **AI** *012 †55
DAVIES, Albert Owen. 1200 MOURSUND ST, DEPT IM 77030 #049-01-1975 L1984 **CCM IM** *020 †20
DAVIES, Michael Arwyn. ■ 77025 #048-14-2001 L2004 **ON** *020
DAVIES, Peter John A. 6431 FANNIN ST RM 5.104, DEPT INTEGRATIVE BIOLOGY/P 77030 #011-02-1972 L1982 **DR** *050
DAVIES, Thomas Llewelyn. 8762 LONG POINT RD, STE 101 77055 #917-08-1967 L1977 **OBG** *020
DAVILA, David D. 12814 WILLOW CTR 77066 #048-78-1998, ▲ L2004 **GS** *020
DAVILA, Marta Ligia. 1515 HOLCOMBE BLVD # 436, MD ANDERSON CANCER CTR 77030 #024-01-1988 L2005 **GE HEP** *020 †20
DAVIS, Angela Maria. 915 GESSNER RD STE 500 77024 #017-20-1995 L1999 **D** *020 †15
DAVIS, Anu Bhalla. 6431 FANNIN ST 4.202, U OF TX HEALTH SCIENCE CEN 77030 #048-02-2001 L2005 **END** *100
DAVIS, Arlene Naomi. ■ 77025 #041-02-2004 L2004 **NPM** *012 †55
DAVIS, Barry Robt. 1200 HERMANN PRSLR DR #801 77030 #005-18-1977 L1984 **PHP IM** *050 †70
DAVIS, Carl Cuthbert, Jr. 1200 BINZ ST 77004 #027-01-1975 L1977 **GS VS** *020 †16,85
DAVIS, Carla Mc Guire. 7707 FANNIN ST, STE 195 77054 #036-07-1997 L2001 **AI** *020 †55,03
DAVIS, Cornelius, III. 7515 MAIN ST, STE 550 77030 #036-07-1989 L2003 **TS** *020 †85,90
DAVIS, Deborah Kinney. 1919 S BRAESWOOD BLVD, 5TH FL 77030 #051-01-1994 L2001 **PD** *020 †55
DAVIS, Deidre Elizabeth. ■ 77054 #048-04-2005 **P** *012
DAVIS, Erica Chon. ■ 77021 #048-04-2007 **OTO** *012
DAVIS, Garth Philip. 6560 FANNIN ST STE 738 77030 #048-04-1996 L2001 **GS** *020 †85
DAVIS, Garvin Henderson. 2051 MACARTHUR ST 77030 #023-07-1998 L2003 **OPH** *020 †35
DAVIS, Georganna. 6560 FANNIN ST, STE 724 77030 #048-16-2003 L2007 **D** *020 †15
DAVIS, George M. 710 FM 1960 RD W 77090 #048-14-1994 L1999 **EM** *020 †16
DAVIS, Glenn Roderick. 1250 CYPRESS STATION DR, STE B 77090 #048-04-1997 L1998 **IM MPD** *020 †20,55
DAVIS, Jan Kathryn. 909 FROSTWOOD DR STE 327 77024 #048-14-1979 L1979 **PD** *020 †55
DAVIS, Jason A. 1 BAYLOR PLZ 77030 #048-14-2004 L2006 **ORS** *012
DAVIS, Jay B. 6560 FANNIN ST, STE 1408 77030 #048-02-1992 L1996 **IM** *020 †20
DAVIS, Jeffrey Robert. 2101 NASA PKWY 77058 #005-18-1980 L1988 **AM OM** *030 †70 ‡
DAVIS, John Warren. 1515 HOLCOMBE BLVD, DEPT. OF UROLOGY, UNIT 137 77030 #051-01-1994 L2000 **U** *020 †95
DAVIS, Kent Gregory. 11301 FALLBROOK DR STE 320 77065 #048-04-1993 L1995 **OTO** *020 †45
DAVIS, Larry Joe. 4299 SAN FELIPE ST, STE 300 77027 #048-12-1977 L1977 **IM** *020 †20,50
DAVIS, Lesley Robin. 1315 ST JOSEPH PKWY, STE 1200 77002 #048-15-2003 L2007 **OBG** *020
DAVIS, Lisa Renee. 3701 KIRBY DR 77098 #048-04-1997 L2000 **FM** *020 †18
DAVIS, Lloyd John. 6720 BERTNER ST 77030 #039-01-1969 L1972 **DR OS** *020 †80
DAVIS, Monica M. 1515 HOLCOMBE BLVD, DEPT OF ANESTHESIOLOGY 77030 #048-13-1998 L2002 **AN** *020
DAVIS, Nathan Andrew. ■ 77054 #048-14-2008 *012
DAVIS, Nora J. 17000 EL CAMINO REAL STE 3 77058 #048-02-1992 L1993 **P** *020
DAVIS, Paul Lawson, Jr. ■ 77030 #036-05-1968 L2007 **DR** *020 †80
DAVIS, Rachel A. ■ 77025 #048-14-2005 **OBG** *012
DAVIS, Robert. 6560 FANNIN ST STE 738 77030 #836-01-1963 L1975 **GS VS** *020 †85
DAVIS, Shawn Barrett. 8470 HIGHWAY 6 N 77095 #048-12-1998 L1999 **FM EM** *020 †18
DAVIS, Shawn Christina. 8470 HIGHWAY 6 N 77095 #047-07-1997 L2006 **IM** *020 †20
DAVIS, William D. 2405 S GESSNER RD, STE B 77063 #048-14-1996 L1997 **FM** *020 †18
DAVIS-ROBERSON, Susie A. 11301 FALLBROOK DR, STE 304 77065 #048-14-1979 L1979 **FM EM** *020 †18
DAVY, Susan Mary. 710 FM 1960 RD W 77090 #016-11-1975 L1980 **PTH BBK** *020 †50
DAWAMNEH, Mohamad F. ■ 77036 #875-01-1979 L1990 **PCP PTH** *020 †50
DAWES, Derek S. ■ 77018 #048-14-2005 **IM** *012
DAWSON, Donald Clair. ■ 77063 #048-02-1952 L1952 **GP GS** *071
DAWSON, John Rapier. ■ 77005 #048-04-2007 **ORS** *012
DAWSON, Peter Sutherland. 1631 NORTH LOOP W, STE 500 77008 #067-01-1964 L1978 **OPH** *020 †35
DAWSON, Rebeca Corrales. 8830 LONG POINT RD, STE 805 77055 #264-01-1961 L1978 **FM P** *020
DAY, Heather M. ■ 77030 #065-10-1989 L1993 **RHU** *020 †20
DAYTON, Harvey Hugh, Jr. 1320 QUITMAN ST, CADWALDER-QUITMAN CLINIC 77009 #048-02-1975 L1982 **CD IM** *050 †20,05
DE, Jitakshi Chandrakant. ■ 77054 #036-07-1999 L2007 **MGP** *012 †50
DEAN, Andrea Renata. PO BOX 20708, DEPT OF INTERNAL MEDICINE 77225 #025-07-2005 L2008 **IM** *012
DEAN, Stewart M. 17080 RED OAK DR 77090 #048-14-1984 L1985 **ORS** *020 †40
DE ANCHONDO, Silvia S. 909 FROSTWOOD DR, STE 364 77024 #649-27-1969 L1979 **PM** *071
DEAN-COLOMB, Windy Marie. PO BOX 20708, UT MD ANDERSON CTR 77225 #016-11-2001 L2007 **HO** *012 †20
DEATON, Ashley Brooks. ■ 77024 #048-14-2005 **P** *012
DEATON, Benjamin Andrew. 14623 SUN HARBOR DR 77062 #048-15-2002 L2005 **AN** *020 †05
DEAVER, John Edward. 2450 LOUISIANA ST, STE 400 77006 #018-03-1981 L1991 **MFM OBG** *020 †30
DEAVERS, Michael Thos. 1515 HOLCOMBE BLVD 77030 #021-05-1989 L1997 **ATP CLP** *020 †50
DE BAKEY, Michael Ellis. 6565 FANNIN ST, STE A974 77030 #021-01-1932 L1948 **TS** *071 †85,90
DE BAUCHE, Thomas Leon. 11301 FALLBROOK DR, STE 130 77065 #038-43-1975 L1979 **CD IM** *020 †20
DE BENDER, John Jeffrey. 4151 SOUTHWEST FWY STE 715 77027 #028-34-1973 L1978 **ORS** *020 †40
DEBIANE, Labib Gilles Sel. 1 BAYLOR PLZ 77030 #605-01-2005 **GS** *012
DEBNAM, James Matthew. 1515 HOLCOMBE BLVD, UNIT 370 77030 #021-01-1996 L2007 **RNR** *020 †80
DE BROECK, Julius Anthony. 5870 HIGHWAY 6 N STE 106 77084 #048-04-1981 L1981 **FM** *020 †18
DE CARO, Louis. 6624 FANNIN ST, STE 2100 77030 #132-01-1972 L1983 **TS** *020
DE CUERVO, Julia. 6710 CAPITOL ST 77011 #264-04-1967 L1979 **FM OBG** *020
DEETLEFS, Elias Albertus. 1635 NORTH LOOP W, MEMORIAL HOSPITAL NORTHWES 77008 #836-04-1981 L1992 **IM** *020 †20
DE FELICE, Clement A. 6550 FANNIN ST, STE 2021 77030 #847-11-1982 L1988 **CD IM** *020 †20
DE FOY, Walter Josin. 705 BYRNE ST 77009 #048-02-1967 L1967 **P** *071 †75
DE FRANCESCO, Fred Louis. 6430 FM 1960 RD W # 118 77069 #561-17-1957 L1979 **ORS** *071 †40
DEGAFFE, Guenet Hailu. ■ 77031 #034-01-2005 **PD** *012
DEGIOANNI, Jos Jean Chas. 1919 LA BRANCH ST 77002 #016-06-1973 L1975 **AM EM** *020 †70,16
DE GOLOVINE, Serge. 1709 DRYDEN RD STE 550, BCM FACULTY CTR 77030 #132-01-2002 **IM** *012
DEGROOT, John Frederick. 1515 HOLCOMBE BLVD, UNIT 431 77030 #048-02-1998 L2002 **N** *020
DE GUZMAN, Marietta M. 6701 FANNIN ST 77030 #748-01-1985 L2002 **PD** *020 †55
DE IPOLYI, Peter Denis. 1315 ST JOSEPH PKWY, STE 1800 77002 #024-05-1967 L1971 **GS SO** *020 †85
DEISTER, Diana Dawn. ■ 77030 #048-13-2007 **P** *012
DEJARNETTE, Tracie M. 2627 CAROLINE ST 77004 #047-07-1991 L2000 **CHP PFP** *074
DEJOHN, Carla Nicole. ■ 77025 #048-02-2006 L2006 **PD** *012
DE JOHN, Charles Saml. 3801 KIRBY DR, STE 730 77098 #048-02-1976 L1976 **P PYG** *020 †75
DEKA, Kamal. 6121 HILLCROFT ST STE J 77081 #495-78-1977 L1995 **ID PD** *020
DEKMEZIAN, Roupen Hagop. 1919 LA BRANCH ST 77002 #605-01-1978 L1985 **PTH** *020 †50
DEKOVICH, Alexander A. 1515 HOLCOMBE BLVD, UNIT 436 77030 #025-07-1974 L2004 **GE IM** *020 †20
DE LA COTERA JULE, Rodrigo. 714 FM 1960 RD W, STE 300 77090 #341-03-2001 L2005 **IM** *020 ‡
DE LA CRUZ, Kim Insua. ■ 77025 #748-02-2000 L2007 **TS** *012
DE LA CRUZ, Maxine Grace. ■ 77025 #748-02-2000 **IMG** *100 †20
DE LA GARZA, Gabriel Omar. ■ 77030 #048-04-2008 *012
DELAHOUSSAYE, Peggy M. 1140 BUSINESS CENTER DR, STE 370 77043 #048-14-1983 L1983 **PTH** *020 †50
DELANO, Benjamin Arthur. 6431 FANNIN ST, RM 4.020 77030 #041-13-2003 L2006 **GS** *012
DE LAS CASAS, Cesar A. 1515 HOLCOMBE BLVD 77030 #737-06-1994 L2003 **ON** *020 †20
DE LA TORRE, Jorge. 2001 KIRBY DR, STE 503 77019 #275-01-1960 L1976 **P PYA** *020 †75
DE LAUGHTER, Michael C. ■ 77096 #048-04-2001 L2003 **ICE** *012
DEL CASTILLO, Francisco J. 2919 CANAL ST 77003 #275-01-1954 L1975 **OM FM** *072
DEL CASTILLO, Hector, Sr. 1313 HERMANN DR 77004 #649-01-1950 L1956 **GYN OS** *020 †30
DEL CASTILLO, Hector, Jr. 1213 HERMANN DR STE 220 77004 #048-14-1978 L1978 **OBG OS** *020 †30
DELCID, Ricardo Eligio. ■ 77054 #048-14-2007 **P** *012
DELCLOS, George Luis P. 6550 FANNIN ST, SM-2403 77030 #847-01-1981 L1983 **OM PUD** *040 †20,70
DELCLOS, Luis. MD ANDERSON CANCER CTR 77030 #847-01-1950 L1962 **RO** *071 †80
DELCLOS, Marc E. 1515 HOLCOMBE BLVD, BOX 97 77030 #048-04-1992 L1993 **RO** *020 †80
DELEMOS, David Michael. 6621 FANNIN ST, MC-1-1481 77030 #048-12-1994 L1996 **PD** *020 †55
DE LEON, Cira Jane. 6500 HORNWOOD DR 77074 #048-02-1976 L1976 **P ADP** *020
DE LEON-SCAGLIA, Berta C. 6969 GULF FWY, STE 340 77087 #924-01-1990 L2004 **FM** *020 †18
DELERY, Clotaire D. 5503 FORESTHAVEN DR 77066 #021-05-1955 L1962 **DR RO** *071 †80
DEL FABBRO, Egidio G. 1515 HOLCOMBE BLVD UNIT 8, UT MD ANDERSON CANCER CTR 77030 #836-01-1990 L2005 **IM PLM** *020 †20
DELGADILLO, Pedro Alcides. 300 W LITTLE YORK RD, STE 130 77076 #649-01-1970 L1973 **GS** *020
DELGADO, Alejandro F. 2539 S GESSNER RD STE 6 77063 #048-15-1977 L1977 **FM** *020 †18
DELGADO, Armando. 9200 WESTHEIMER RD 77063 #649-01-1971 L1975 **FM** *020 †05 ‡
DELGADO, Mitzi. 18 RIVER HOLLOW LN 77027 #649-14-1972 L1980 **PTH GP** *020
DELGADO, Reynolds Mc Munn. 6624 FANNIN ST, STE 2180 77030 #048-12-1991 L1992 **CD** *020 †20
DELGADO, Victor Manuel. 1603 LORRAINE ST 77009 #649-02-1952 L1960 **GP** *071
DELGADO GUAY, Marvin Omar. 1515 HOLCOMBE BLVD, DIV OF PALLETIVE CARE 77030 #429-02-1999 L2002 **IMG PLM** *100 †20
DELHEY, Karen Ann. ■ 77030 #025-01-1986 L1991 **U** *020 †95
DEL JUNCO, Gerard W, Jr. 8076 EL RIO ST, BROWN AND ASSOCIATES MEDIC 77054 #007-02-1974 L1981 **PTH** *020 †50 ‡
DEL MONTE, John, Jr. 1515 HOLCOMBE BLVD BOX 10, UT MD ANDERSON CANCER CENT 77030 #005-02-2002 L2006 **ON** *012 †20
DELPASSAND, Ebrahim S. 9701 RICHMOND AVE, STE 122 77042 #517-01-1982 L1990 **NM PTH** *020 †28
DEL RIO, Delia. 4151 SOUTHWEST FWY, STE 300 77027 #132-01-1958 L1974 **GP PTH** *071

■ = Address Information Privacy Protected

DEL VALLE, Rene. 4545 POST OAK PLACE DR, STE 130 77027 #042-03-1993 L1998 IM *020 †20

DEMIAN, Nagi Mtanios. 6431 FANNIN ST, U OF TX MED SCH AT HOUSTON 77030 #048-14-2003 L2007 OMF *020

DEMINA, Olga. ■ 77025 #913-15-1991 L2007 CHP *020

DEMMLER, Gail Josephine. 1 BAYLOR PLZ, INFECTIOUS DISEASE SUBSECT 77030 #048-15-1977 L1977 PD ID *050 †55

DEMPSEY, Peter Jos. 1515 HOLCOMBE BLVD, UNIT 1350 77030 #028-34-1966 L2004 DR NM *020 †80

DENFIELD, George Hilton. 6565 FANNIN ST, TEXAS MEDICAL CENTER 77030 #025-12-1983 L1987 AN *020 †05

DENFIELD, Susan. 6621 FANNIN ST, TX CHILDRENS HOSP 77030 #025-12-1983 L1987 PDC PD *020 †55

DENKTAS, Ali Emin. 6431 FANNIN ST 1246, UTHSC HOUSTON 77030 #902-07-1991 L2005 CD *020 †20

DENNISON, Andrew Cullen. ■ 77006 #041-01-2004 L2004 PM *012

DENSON, Susan Ellen. 6431 FANNIN ST STE 3.256, UNIV TX MED SCH 77030 #048-12-1972 L1976 PD NPM *020 †55

DENSON, Tamika Sherell. ■ 77007 #047-07-2003 L2006 IM *020 †20

DERMAN, Howard S. 6560 FANNIN ST, DEPT OF NEURO STE 802 77030 #016-01-1974 L1977 N *020 †75

DE ROTH, Georgine. ■ 77098 #067-01-1999 L2004 FM *020 †18

DERRICK, John Rafter. 17225 EL CAMINO REAL, STE 344 77058 #021-01-1946 L1959 TS *072 †85,90

DERVAY, Joseph Paul. 2101 NASA PKWY 77058 #035-15-1984 L1994 EM AM *020 †16,70

DESAI, Anupa Kalidas. 6720 BERTNER ST, MC3-261 77030 #048-02-2004 L2007 NM *020 †28

DESAI, Devak Girish. 77054 #012-01-2007 IM *012

DESAI, Hemlata J. 6621 FANNIN ST, STE MC1-1481 77030 #495-23-1971 L1979 PD *020

DESAI, Kirit. 7777 SOUTHWEST FWY, STE 942 77074 #495-23-1971 L1979 CD IM *020

DESAI, Moreshwar S. 6621 FANNIN ST, WT6-006 77030 #496-38-1993 L2004 CCP *100 †55

DESAI, Mounang Praful. 710 FM 1960 RD W 77090 #001-06-1996 L1997 EM *020 †16

DESAI, Rakesh Jayantilal. 820 GESSNER RD STE 750 77024 #495-76-1986 L1992 CHP *020 †75

DESAI, Reshma Piyush. 6431 FANNIN ST, SCHOOL A 77030 #048-16-2005 PD *012

DESAI, Samir Prakash. 2002 HOLCOMBE BLVD, HOUSTON VA MEDICAL CENTER 77030 #025-07-1995 L2004 IM *020 †20

DESAI, Snehal Subodh. ■ 77071 #048-04-2006 RO *012

DESAI, Svetang Vijay. 1709 DRYDEN RD STE 550, BCM FACULTY CTR 77030 #047-06-2005 IM *012

DESAI, Thrity R. 4560 FM 1960 RD W, STE 101 77069 #704-04-1979 L1985 PD *020 †55

DESALOMS, Armando. 2800 S MACGREGOR WAY 77021 #132-01-1964 L1972 P *020 †75

DE SANTOS, Luis Alonso. 1415 NORTH LOOP W, STE 820 77008 #847-04-1969 L1976 R *020 †80

DE SCIOLI, Kelly Ryann. 77004 #048-04-2005 PD *012

DESHPANDE, Salil V. ■ 77006 #048-04-1998 L1999 IM *030 †20

DESILVA, Ranil Nishan. 1709 DRYDEN RD STE 550, BCM FACULTY CTR 77030 #041-13-2005 L2008 IM *012

DES NOYERS, Michel. 77090 #649-14-1970 L1979 *100

DE SOUZA, Jonas Araujo. PO BOX 20708, DEPT OF INT MED 77225 #187-09-2003 IM *012

DE SOUZA, Rowena Anne. ■ 77006 #047-07-2003 GS *100

DES RUISSEAUX, Paul W. 2077 S GESSNER RD, STE 225 77063 #065-09-1957 L1982 PS *020

DES VIGNES-KENDRICK, Mary. 8000 N STADIUM DR, SERVICES 77054 #047-07-1978 L1982 PHP PD *030 †55

DESWAL, Anita. 2002 HOLCOMBE BLVD, VA MEDICAL CENTER 77030 #495-36-1987 L1998 CD *020 †20

DETER, Russell Lee, II. 1200 MOURSUND ST, DEPT OBGYN 77030 #048-04-1963 L1963 OBS *050

DETTER, Timothy J. 12121 RICHMOND AVE, STE 121 77082 #048-15-1998 L2001 FM *020 †18

DEUELL, Brian P. ■ 77054 #048-14-2008 *012

DEUTSCH, Allen. 2727 W HOLCOMBE BLVD, DEPARTMENT OF ORTHOPAEDICS 77025 #035-46-1994 L2000 ORS *020 †40

DEV, Rony. 1515 HOLCOMBE BLVD - UNIT 77030 #018-75-2000, ▲ L2004 PLM *100

DE VALLE, Oscar Louis. 2028 WIRT RD 77055 #306-01-1987 L1993 FM *020 †18 ‡

DE VALLE, Rodrigo Victor. 2028 WIRT RD 77055 #275-01-1948 L1976 FM R *020

DE VILLALOBOS, Diego H. 1515 HOLCOMBE BLVD, UNIT 112 77030 #132-07-1981 L2002 CCA *020 †05

DEVILLE, Karen Thompson. 5615 KIRBY DR, STE 440 77005 #048-02-1988 L1990 NPM PD *020 †55

DEVIN, Clinton James. ■ 77005 #047-05-2002 L2007 ORS *100

DEVIN, Jessica. ■ 77005 #047-05-2002 L2007 END *100 †20

DEVINE, Catherine Ellen. 1515 HOLCOMBE BLVD, UNIT 1273 77030 #048-14-1999 L2003 DR *020 †80

DEW, Laura Ilene. 7401 MAIN ST 77030 #011-03-1990 L1994 AN *020 †05

DEWITT, Susan Jane. 710 FM 1960 RD W, HOUSTON NORTHWEST HOSPITAL 77090 #048-14-1984 L1986 NPM PD *020 †55

DEY, Mahua. ■ 77019 #048-04-2007 *012

DE YBARRONDO, Lisa E. 5656 KELLEY ST RM 1EC93006, LBJ HOSPITAL PEDIATRICS 77026 #048-02-1989 L1993 PD *020 †55

DHADWAL, Ajay Kapoor. ■ 77004 #917-30-1994 L2001 VS *012

DHALIWAL, Amandeep Singh. 6540 BELLOWS LN APT 210 77030 #067-01-2004 IM *100 †20

DHANANI, Karim Zul. ■ 77088 #048-02-2007 IM *012

DHANANI, Shiraz P H. 8830 LONG POINT RD STE 404 77055 #495-22-1972 L1982 CD IM *020 †20

DHANANI, Zulfikarali K. 8240 ANTOINE DR STE 212 77088 #803-05-1970 L1977 FM *020

DHANJI, Devanshi Talib. 8900 LAKES AT 610 DR 77054 #048-04-1999 L2003 OBG *020 †30

DHEKNE, Ramesh D. 6720 BERTNER ST, STE 3-261 77030 #495-56-1966 L1975 NM IM *020 †28

DHESI, Manjit K. 7440 FM 1960 RD W 77070 #918-01-1975 L1981 GP *020

DHESI, Tarsem S. 7440 FM 1960 RD W 77070 #917-08-1973 L1980 GP *020

DHINGRA, Atul K. 8097 EL MUNDO ST 77054 #048-13-1995 L1996 EM *020 †16

DHINGRA, Hari Mohan. 2002 HOLCOMBE BLVD, VA MC 77030 #495-41-1968 L1981 ON HEM *020 †20

DHINGRA, Rakesh Kumar. 5392 W 34TH ST 77092 #034-01-1978 L1979 FM OS *020

DHIR, Anita Gupta. ■ 77004 #035-09-2001 L2006 IM *020

DHIR, Prajay. 2855 GRAMERCY ST 77025 #024-05-2001 L2006 OPH *020

DHOLAKIA, Nizar Ali. 6560 FANNIN ST, STE 1640 77030 #704-16-1984 L1993 ID IM *020 †20

DHOTHER, Sukhjinder Singh. 18220 STATE HIGHWAY 249 77070 #917-07-1985 L1997 AN *020 †05

DIAMONON, James Samaniego. 14027 MEMORIAL DR 276 77079 #748-01-1956 L1967 GS *071

DIAZ, Dolores. 5614 E SAM HOUSTON PKWY N 77015 #048-14-1989 L1991 OPH *020 †35

DIAZ, Eduardo M, Jr. 1515 HOLCOMBE BLVD, STE 69 77030 #048-04-1989 L1990 OTO HNS *020

DIAZ, Eduardo Manuel. 1631 NORTH LOOP W STE 620 77008 #275-01-1956 L1972 OTO *020 †45

DIAZ, Iver. 18300 SAINT JOHN DR 77058 #132-02-1966 L1976 PTH *020 †50

DIAZ, J Jesus. 2101 CRAWFORD ST STE 208 77002 #649-03-1966 L1973 PD GS *020 †55

DIAZ, Orlando Manuel. 1 BAYLOR PLZ 360, BAYLOR COL OF MED RADIOLOG 77030 #264-02-1985 L2003 *020 †80

DIAZ, Salvador Flores. 6720 BERTNER ST 77030 #649-02-1973 L1986 AN *020 †05

DIAZ, Sheridan M. 1515 HOLCOMBE BLVD BOX 10, UNIV OF TX MD ANDERSON 77030 #067-01-1979 L1993 IM ON *020

DIAZ, Victor Alberto. 11200 WESTHEIMER RD, STE 700 77042 #649-02-1972 L1995 FM OM *030 †18

DIAZ DE VIVAR DAUMAS L, An. 1 BAYLOR PLZ, DEPT OF PATHOLOGY MC 315 77030 #726-01-2002 PTH *012

DIAZ-MARCHAN, Pedro J. 1504 TAUB LOOP, RADIOLOGY DEPARTMENT MRI 77030 #042-01-1985 L1991 DR *020 †80

DIAZ SAMIA, Ramon. ■ 77089 #649-02-1963 L1968 AN *020

DICHOSO, Carmelo C. 7777 SOUTHWEST FWY STE 736 77074 #748-01-1966 L1974 NEP IM *020

DICKASON, Nancy W. 4110 BELLAIRE BLVD, STE 210 77025 #048-04-1995 L1997 PD *020 †55

DICKENS, Diana L. 13114 FM 1960 RD W, STE 100 77065 #048-14-1987 L1989 AI *020 †55,03

DICKERSON, Cristin A. ■ 77005 #048-14-1989 L1990 DR *020 †80

DICKERSON, Heather Anne. 6621 FANNIN ST, MC 19345-C 77030 #024-05-1997 L2004 PDC *020 †55

DICKEY, Burton Fuller. 2002 HOLCOMBE BLVD MS 151 77030 #008-02-1980 L2006 PUD IM *050 †20

DICKEY, Juan Rayner. 2500 TANGLEWILDE ST, STE 160 77063 #048-04-1960 L1960 OTO *020 †45

DICKEY, William James. 8300 HOMESTEAD RD, STE 5 77028 #012-01-1957 L1962 IM *020

DICKINSON, Jan Elizabeth. 6431 FANNIN ST 77030 #143-06-1981 MFM *020

DICKINSON, Robert Stanley. 2727 W HOLCOMBE BLVD, M&M STE , THIRD FLOOR 77025 #048-04-1976 L1976 IM *020 †20

DICKSON, Jerry Ervin. 8945 LONG POINT RD STE 101 77055 #048-02-1967 L1967 D DMP *020 †15

DICKSON, Kyle Farr. 6431 FANNIN ST, UNIV TX 77030 #005-18-1989 L1990 ORS *040 †40

DIEBER, Joseph Michael. ■ 77006 #028-34-2005 L2008 DR *012

DIEKER, Carrie Alissa. ■ 77054 #048-14-2008 *012

DIERSCHKE, Nicole Dawn. ■ 77004 #048-14-2004 OBG *012

DIEZ, Blanca. 18333 EGRET BAY BLVD, STE 560 77058 #649-01-1973 L1978 P *020

DIEZ, Jose Guillermo. 1709 DRYDEN RD, STE 900 77030 #264-04-1989 L1998 CD IC *040 †20

DI FERRANTE, Nicola Mario. ■ 77030 #561-17-1948 ORS *050

DIKE-ODIMGBE, Patricia E. 2424 HAMILTON ST STE 410 77004 #005-14-1973 L1976 PD *020 †55 ‡

DI LEO, Joseph Salvador. 1919 S BRAESWOOD BLVD # MC 77030 #021-05-1958 L1962 PD *020

DI LEO, Steven Joseph. 1221 MCKINNEY ST, STE 40300 77010 #048-04-1993 L1994 DR *020 †80

DILLARD, Kristin J. ■ 77042 #048-12-2005 PD *012

DILLINGHAM, Kieron M. ■ 77054 #048-14-2005 L2007 IM *012

DILLON, John Lowell. 2701 LIGHTHOUSE DR 77058 #649-01-1972 L1974 FM *020

DI LORENZO, Daniel John. 6560 FANNIN ST 9 77030 #024-01-1999 L2001 NS *012

DIMALIBOT, Alfonsa Gracia. 6510 LAWNDALE ST 77023 #748-21-1990 L2006 FM *100 †18

DIMINO, Rakhi Chaudhuri. 1510 MCDUFFIE ST 77019 #038-40-2002 L2005 OBG *020 †30

DIMITRIJEVIC, Milan R. ■ 77081 #957-03-1955 N OS *020

DIMMOCK, David Paul. 1 BAYLOR PLZ, NAB2015 77030 #917-24-1998 L2007 MG *100 †19,55

DINERSTEIN, Stevan L. 6560 FANNIN ST, STE 2204 77030 #048-12-1973 L1973 IM NEP *020 †20

DING, Bryan Charhoa. ■ 77025 #048-04-2005 L2007 ORS *012

DING, Yiling. 5850 ROGERDALE RD 77072 #243-24-1982 L2004 DMP PTH *100 †50

DINGES, Malcolm Dan, Jr. 6700 BELLAIRE BLVD 77074 #004-01-1948 L1950 GP GS *071

DINGLE, Bridgette Marie. 6431 FANNIN ST, AT HO 77030 #012-21-2006 PD *012

DINH, Tri A. 6550 FANNIN ST STE 901 77030 #048-04-1992 L1994 GYN GO *020 †30

DINH, Tue Anh. 6560 FANNIN ST, STE 800 77030 #048-14-1989 L1999 PS *020 †65

DINNEY, Colin Padraic N. 1515 HOLCOMBE BLVD 77030 #062-01-1982 L1991 U OS *020

DIREKLY, Kenneth M. 7900 CAMBRIDGE ST # 28-1A 77054 #048-13-2003 L2004 EM *020

DISHOP, Megan Katherine. 6621 FANNIN ST, STE B1 77030 #036-05-1997 L2003 PP *020 †50

DISTEFANO, Michael C. 6621 FANNIN ST 1-1481, TEXAS CHILDREN'S HOSPITAL, 77030 #048-04-2002 L2005 PEM *012 †55

DISU, Saka Rotimi. 1200 HERMANN PRESSLER DR, RM 1014W 77030 #690-02-1989 L2007 GPM OM *012

DITTMAN, Sol Louis. ■ 77024 #048-02-1947 L1947 FM *071 †18

DIVITA, Eugene Chas. 520 POST OAK BLVD STE 390 77027 #051-04-1957 L1958 P *071 †75

DIWAN, Abdul Hafeez. 1515 HOLCOMBE BLVD BOX 85, MD ANDERSON -DEPT OF PATHO 77030 #704-25-1991 L2003 PTH *020 †18

DIWAN, Pranav Mohan. 6431 FANNIN ST 1.134, OF TEXAS-HOUSTON 77030 #035-08-2007 IM *012

DIWAN, Sharafali Y. ■ 77065 #704-02-1989 L1994 ID *075 †20

DIXON, Darrell Russell. 2600 NORTH LOOP W STE 453, SYSTEM MED DIRECTOR 77092 #049-01-1974 L1995 FM *030 †18

DO, Doan Thuy. ■ 77044 #048-14-2007 FP *012

DO, Huy Tran. 16314 REDWICKE LN 77084 #048-16-1999 L2000 AN *100 †55

DO, Thanh V. 4545 POST OAK PLACE DR, STE 130 77027 #048-13-1991 L1994 IM *020 †20

DO, Y Hoang. 6524 SAN FELIPE ST # 110 77057 #941-01-1975 L1976 OPH GP *020 †35

DOAK, Carolyn Mary. ■ 77025 #048-02-1978 L1978 IM *020

DOAN, David T. ■ 77025 #048-14-2008 *012

DOAN, Quynhthu Nguyen. ■ 77054 #048-04-2006 OBG *012

DOAN, Thuy T. 3701 KIRBY DR, STE 600 77098 #048-14-1998 L2001 FM *020 †18

DOBBS, Herman A, Jr. ■ 77005 #048-04-1952 L1952 GS TS *071 †85

DOBBS, Stuart Myron. 6560 FANNIN ST, STE 600 77030 #012-01-1975 L1977 GE IM *020 †20

DOCKINS, Richard Orval. 800 BELL ST, CORP EMB 3171A 77002 #004-01-1980 L1991 OM IM *030 †20,70

DOCKRAY, Lee Raymond. 15322 COPPER GROVE DR 77095 #048-15-1983 L1983 PD *020 †55

DOCTOR, Shreenath V. 5300 SAN JACINTO ST STE 14 77004 #048-02-1992 L1993 P *020

DOCTOR, Uday V. 7505 MAIN ST, STE 150 77030 #048-13-1983 L1983 AN *020 †05 ‡

DODD, Gerald D, Jr. M D ANDERSON TUMOR INST 77030 #041-02-1947 L1959 R *071 †80

DODD, Sara Miller. ■ 77025 #048-14-2004 L2007 EM *020

DODDS, Charles Richey. 6431 FANNIN ST 1134, OF TEXAS-HOUSTON 77030 #048-14-2006 AN *012

DODSON, Steven Richard. 3630 WAKEFOREST ST 77098 #026-04-1974 L1979 FM R *071 †18,80

DOERR, Clinton Harold. 6624 FANNIN ST STE 1730 77030 #048-04-1995 L1997 PCC SME *020 †20

DOERR, Cynthia Ann. ■ 77027 #030-05-1989 L1995 ID PD *071 †55

DOERR, Harold Kenneth. 6550 FANNIN ST STE 1003 77030 #048-14-1987 AN GS *100

DOGAN, Oya. 2411 FOUNTAIN VIEW DR 77057 #902-10-1987 L2001 AN *020 †05

DOGGETT, Jerry Lloyd. 6624 FANNIN ST, 17TH FL 77030 #048-04-1958 L1958 GS TS *071 †85,90

DOHADWALA, Mustafa Mustan. ■ 77084 #023-07-2007 L2007 IM *012

DOHERTY, Christy. ■ 77030 #048-04-2006 D *012

DOHERTY, Sean David. FANNIN ST, HOSP (HOUSTON) 77030 #048-04-2007 TY *012

DOKAINISH, Hisham. 6620 MAIN ST, OFC 11A08 77030 #065-10-1995 L2004 CD *020

DOLAN, Jean T. 911 WORTHSHIRE ST 77008 #048-02-1993 L1995 GS *020

DOLCE, Donald Louis, Jr. ■ 77019 #048-14-2008 *012

DOLLE, Donna Suzanne. 2060 SPACE PARK DR, STE 304 77058 #048-02-1993 L1994 IM *020 †20

DOLSON, George Michael. 2002 HOLCOMBE BLVD, RENAL 111-J VAMC 77030 #028-34-1979 L1980 NEP IM *020 †20

DOMASK, A Madeline. 9055 KATY FWY, STE 200 77024 #048-02-1987 L1988 IM *020 †20

DOMINGO, Robert Padolina. ■ 77054 #048-04-2008 *012

DONALD, Robert Louis. ■ 77024 #048-04-1955 L1955 IM *071

DONALDSON, Emilie Elaine. 1 BAYLOR PLZ, BAYLOR COLLEGE OF MEDICINE 77030 #021-05-2003 L2004 ACA *012

DONARUMA-KWOH, Marcella. ■ 77024 #048-04-2001 L2006 PEM *100 †55

DONCASTER, Malcolm L. 6621 FANNIN ST 77030 #048-02-1960 L1960 PD *020 †55

DONDLINGER, Tarsy Pokorny. 2450 FONDREN RD STE 310, PINEY POINT PEDIATRIC ASS 77063 #048-14-1996 L2000 PD *020 †55

DONEKER, Thomas Geo, Jr. 1111 AUGUSTA DR 77057 #048-02-1990 L1992 IM *020 †20

DONELSON, Richard Kenneth. ■ 77007 #005-06-1966 L1976 PHP PUD *020

DONG, Jennifer Stacey. 837 FM 1960 RD W, STE 105 77090 #065-05-1991 L2000 *020

DONLEY, Sara Elizabeth. ■ 77019 #048-04-2007 IM *012

DONNELL, Malcolm Thos. 2411 FOUNTAIN VIEW DR #200 77057 #048-04-1981 L1981 AN *020 †05 ‡

DONOVAN, Donald Thos. 6501 FANNIN ST, BAYLOR OTOLARYNGOLOGY 77030 #048-04-1976 L1976 OTO HNS *020 †45

DONOVAN, William Francis. 5225 KATY FWY, STE 625 77007 #016-43-1968 L1975 ORS OM *020 †40

DONOVAN, William Henry. 1333 MOURSUND ST, TIRR 77030 #035-03-1966 L1980 PM *020 †60

DONSKAYA, Sofiya I. 11222 RICHMOND AVE, STE 145 77082 #913-99-1977 L1997 P *020 †75

DOODY, Rachelle Smith. 6550 FANNIN ST, STE 1801 77030 #048-13-1983 N *020 †75

DORA, Jonathan Jos. 6560 FANNIN ST, STE 760 77030 #048-04-1968 L1968 PS *020 †65

DORFAN, Herbert Isaac. 6560 FANNIN ST STE 1616 77030 #048-12-1964 L1969 P *020 †75 ‡

DORFMAN, Scott Russell. 6621 FANNIN ST 2.2521, TEXAS CHILDREN'S HOSPITAL 77030 #048-12-1988 L1989 DR *020 †80

DORSCH, Ernst Rudolf. 915 GESSNER RD STE 850 77024 #035-03-1971 L1978 GE IM *020 †20

DORSEY, Kenneth Eugene. 1221 MCKINNEY ST, STE 40300 77010 #010-03-1972 L1997 D AM *020 †15

DOSEKUN, Akinsansoye. 6431 FANNIN ST 77030 #690-02-1975 L1992 NEP *020

DOSHI, Ankur Arvind. 920 FROSTWOOD DR, STE 570 77024 #048-02-1996 L1998 IM *020 †20

DOSSEY, Joe Ed. 920 FROSTWOOD DR, STE 740 77024 #048-04-1965 L1965 GS OS *071 †85

DOUBLEDAY, C William. 515 POST OAK BLVD, STE 535 77027 #048-14-1981 L1981 D *020 †15

DOUGHERTY, Anne Hamilton. 6431 FANNIN ST 1.246, DIVISION OF CARDIOLOGY 77030 #048-02-1978 L1978 CD IM *020 †20

DOUGHTY, Cara Boyles. ■ 77025 #028-02-2000 L2003 PEM *100 †55

DOUGLAS, Brian Claude. 6624 FANNIN ST STE 2560 77030 #065-01-1974 L1978 GE IM *020 †20

DOUGLAS, Glen Alan. 800 BELL ST, 3180J 77002 #004-01-1969 L1981 OM AM *030

DOUGLAS, William Ian. 6431 FANNIN ST, PEDIATRIC CARDIOVASCULAR S 77030 #005-14-1988 L2008 PDC *020 †85,90

DOWDY-WESTMARK, Kaye Ann. 1200 BINZ ST, STE 1430 77004 #011-03-1988 L1995 RNR *020 †80

DOWLEN, Joseph Ronald. 710 FM 1960 RD W 77090 #048-13-1974 L1974 EM *020 †16

DOWNEY, Cara Ryan. ■ 77025 #048-04-2007 PS *012

DOWNEY, Helen T. 6411 FANNIN ST 77030 #048-02-1982 *020

DOWNEY, Sally Ann. 7777 SOUTHWEST FWY, STE 310 77074 #048-02-1981 L1981 NPM PD *020 †55

DOYLE, Peter Dillon. 6411 FANNIN ST 5.020, THE UNIV OF TEXAS MED SCH 77030 #048-14-1988 L1989 AN *040 †05 ‡

DOYLE, Timothy Kevin. 6550 FANNIN ST, STE 1723 77030 #048-12-1986 L1987 ICE CD *020 †20

DRAGOI, Ioana Ana. 6463 HILLCROFT ST 77081 #781-02-1990 L2005 PD *020 †55

DRAIN, Brighid Natasha. 1 BAYLOR PLZ 77030 #062-01-2005 FP *012

DRAKE, Niles Harris. ■ 77054 #004-01-2005 PD *012

DRAKSHARAM, Babu. 906 WAYSIDE DR 77011 #495-50-1970 L1976 P *020

DRAZNIN, Tacie Heath. ■ 77096 #016-06-1976 L1982 PD *075 †55

DREESSEN, Philip Ray. 4101 GREENBRIAR ST, STE 100 77098 #048-04-1967 L1967 PD *020 †55

DREHER, Beverly A. 7026 OLD KATY RD, STE 276 77024 #048-02-1990 L1991 DR *020 †80

DRELL, William Kadison. 909 FROSTWOOD DR STE 258 77024 #039-01-1983 L1984 P *020 †75

DREWERY, Helen Kay. 1504 TAUB LOOP 77030 #917-19-1988 *100

DREWRY, Sandra Jan. 6360 W SAM HOUSTON PKWY N, STE 200 77041 #048-12-1965 L1965 IM NEP *020 †20

DREWS, Ashley Logan. 6550 FANNIN ST, STE 1001 77030 #048-04-1992 L1997 ID *020 †20

DREYER, Sherlene Annette. 6431 FANNIN ST, M S B 2-100 77030 #048-13-1984 L1986 NPM PD *020 †55

DREYER, William Jeffrey. 6621 FANNIN ST, MC 19345C 77030 #011-03-1981 L1988 PDC *050 †55

DREYER, Zoann Eckert. 6621 FANNIN ST, CC1410.00 77030 #005-19-1982 L1988 PHO PD *040 †55

DRIVER, Larry C. 1515 HOLCOMBE BLVD, BOX 42 77030 #048-13-1980 L1980 AN PME *020 †05

DRONAVALLI, Goutham. ■ 77054 #495-37-2001 L2006 IM *100 †20

DROOBY, Ala'Ud-Din Sobhy. ■ 77063 #869-05-1952 L1980 P *071

DROSDECK, Patricia R. ■ 77062 #035-09-1960 OS *074

DRTIL, Alexander F. 915 GESSNER RD, STE 585 77024 #048-14-1987 L1988 ICE *040 †20

DRTIL, Shannon Hendry. 6565 FANNIN ST, TEXAS MEDICAL CENTER 77030 #048-14-1988 L1990 AN *020 †05

DRUTZ, Jan Edwin. 6621 FANNIN ST, TEXAS CHILDREN'S HOSPITAL 77030 #020-02-1968 L1972 PD *040 †55

DRYDEN, Allison Kelly. ■ 77030 #048-14-2008 *012

DRYDEN, Damla K. 6624 FANNIN ST, STE 1800 77030 #028-02-1997 L2001 OBG *020 †30

DRYDEN, Mark Joseph. 1515 HOLCOMBE BLVD, BOX 57 77030 #025-07-1995 L2000 DR *020 †80

DRYDEN, Natalie Janet. 6624 FANNIN ST, MEDICAL CLINIC OF HOUSTON 77030 #048-02-2000 L2003 IM *020 †20

DSOUZA, Daniel Keith. 1500 S DAIRY ASHFORD ST, SUITE #197 "A" 77077 #048-14-1988 L1989 FM *020 †18

DSOUZA, Viveka Frances. 3701 KIRBY DR, STE 100 77098 #495-52-1999 L2005 FM *100 †18

DUARTE, Jaime Enrique. 3016 CANAL ST 77003 #264-01-1995 L2002 FM *020

DUBE, Clarence Oscar. 6411 FANNIN ST 77030 #048-02-1963 L1963 GP UM *020

DUBEY, Swapan. 6431 FANNIN ST 431, DEPT EMERGENCY MEDICINE 77030 #048-13-1996 L1999 EM *020 †16

DUBIN, Gerald Harvey. ■ 77006 #035-15-1970 L1971 P *074

DU BOIS, Raymond N, Jr. 1515 HOLCOMBE BLVD, UNIT 118 77030 #048-13-1985 L1987 IM GE *020 †20

DU BOSE, Ralph Keller. 6565 FANNIN ST 77030 #048-02-1976 L1976 AN *020 †05

DUBRAWSKY, Chagai. 18220 STATE HIGHWAY 249 77070 #550-01-1964 L1976 IM *020

DUCHINI, Andrea. 1709 DRYDEN RD STE 8.4 77030 #561-06-1988 L2000 GE *040 †20

DUCHMAN, Stanley Mathias. 13300 HARGRAVE RD, STE 500 77070 #046-01-1994 L1995 IC CD *020 †20

DUDNEY, Newton E. 1300 BAY AREA BLVD, BLDG B 77058 #048-02-1949 L1950 FM OM *071

DUFFY, James Desmond. 6565 FANNIN ST, THE METHODIST HOSPITAL 77030 #775-01-1979 L2005 P N *020 †75

DUFFY, Jennie Ann Ozog. 6560 FANNIN ST, STE 724 77030 #048-04-1978 L1978 D PDD *020 †15 ‡

DUFFY, Patrick Edward. ■ 77054 #030-06-2002 L2008 VS *012

DUGAS, Mark J. 1709 DRYDEN RD, STE 1700 77030 #048-78-1995, ▲ L1999 AN GS *020 †05

DUKE, James Henry, Jr. 6431 FANNIN ST # 4168 77030 #048-12-1960 L1960 GS *020 †85

DUKE, Penelope Kerstin. 11250 FALLBROOK DR, CY-FAIR SURGERY CENTER 77065 #028-46-1988 L1989 AN *020 †05

DULSKI, Joy Ellen. 6431 FANNIN ST 77030 #016-01-2005 L2007 PD *012

DUMAS, Carlos A. 4755 ALDINE MAIL RD 77039 #132-04-1983 L1996 FM *040 †18 ‡

DUMITRU, Adrian C. 6560 FANNIN ST STE 2020 77030 #781-01-1988 L1997 APM *020 †05

DUMLER, Thomas Lee. 18220 TOMBALL PKWY, DEPT RADIOLOGY/METHODIST W 77070 #028-02-1979 L1981 DR *020 †80

DUNA, George F. 6620 MAIN ST, STE 1375 77030 #605-01-1988 L1996 RHU *020 †20

DUNBAR, Burdett Sheridan. 6621 FANNIN ST, MC 21495 77030 #016-11-1963 L1988 AN *020 †05

DUNCAN, James Michael. 2101 NASA PKWY, MAIL CODE SD 77058 #019-02-1977 L2001 PUD CCM *030 †20

DUNCAN, John Michael, Jr. 1101 BATES AVE, SURGICAL ASSOCIATES OF 77030 #048-04-1971 L1971 TS VS *020 †85,90

DUNCAN, Newton Oran, III. 6550 FANNIN ST STE 2001, TEXAS EAR, NOSE & THROAT C 77030 #048-04-1978 L1978 PDO OTO *020 †45

DUNCAN, Scott Wm. 920 FROSTWOOD DR, DEPT OF ANESTHESIOLOGY 77024 #051-04-1990 L1994 AN *020 †05

DUNN, Esther Talacki. 424 HAHLO ST, HOUSTON COMMUNITY HEALTH C 77020 #048-14-1986 L1987 OPH *020 †35

DUNN, Ralph O, Jr. 6699 CHIMNEY ROCK RD, 2ND FL 77081 #025-01-1951 L1956 OPH *071 †35

DUNN, Randall Clifford. 7900 FANNIN ST # 4400 77054 #048-04-1980 L1981 REN OBG *020 †30

DUNN, Steven Hutson. 800 PEAKWOOD DR, STE 6C 77090 #048-04-1986 L1987 OPH *020 †35

DUNNINGTON, Joel Sullivan. 1515 HOLCOMBE BLVD, DIAGNOSTIC IMAGING 0368 77030 #048-14-1981 L1981 DR *020 †80

DUONG, Can H. 6500 NORTH FWY, STE 110 77076 #048-12-2002 L2006 OBG *020

DUONG, Su Duy. 1502 TAUB LOOP, MHMRA OF HARRIS COUNTY/NPC 77030 #941-01-1971 L1991 P *040

DUPONT, Herbert L. 6720 BERTNER ST, MC1-164 77030 #012-05-1965 L1973 ID IM *030 †20

DUPREE, Dixie K. ■ 77065 #048-12-1977 L1977 AN *100

DURAIRAJ, Gopalasamy. 12141 RICHMOND AVE 77082 #495-95-1970 L1983 IM EM *020 †20

DURAL, Ali Tarkan. 800 PEAKWOOD DR, DIGESTIVE SPECIALISTS OF 77090 #902-04-1991 L1995 GE IM *020 †20

DURAL, Ayse. 2727 W HOLCOMBE BLVD 77025 #902-21-1991 L1998 PM *020 †60

DURAND, Jean-Bernard. 1515 HOLCOMBE BLVD, # 449 77030 #056-06-1988 L1997 CD IM *020 †20

DURAND SANCHEZ, Ana Vella. ■ 77063 #649-03-2004 PM *012

DURAYAPPAH, Siryalatha. 8762 LONG POINT RD, STE 106 77055 #220-01-1971 L1979 IM *020

DURHAM, Cecil Gabriel. 1919 HAROLD ST APT B 77098 #048-02-1965 L1965 DR R *020

DU ROY, Robert Mignon. ■ 77063 #007-02-1945 L1945 OM *071

DURRANI, Ayaz Mahmud. 7777 SOUTHWEST FWY # 1068 77074 #704-02-1958 L1976 U EM *020 †95

DURRANI, Neelofer S. 1631 NORTH LOOP W, STE 410 77008 #704-15-1982 L1994 OBG *020 †30

DURRANI, Omar Hayat. 915 GESSNER RD, STE 720 77024 #021-01-1998 L2005 U *020 †95

DURRETT, Ray Robt. 1200 BINZ ST STE 1180 77004 #036-07-1963 L1969 IM NEP *071 †20

DURYEA, Teresa Kay. 6621 FANNIN ST, TX CHILDREN'S HOSP. 77030 #030-05-1984 L1991 PD *020 †55

DUTTA, Ankhi. 1 BAYLOR PLZ, BAYLOR COLL OF MED 77030 #495-02-2000 PD *012

DUTTA, Puja Manojit. ■ 77054 #496-46-2004 FP *012

DUVIC, Madeleine. 1515 HOLCOMBE BLVD, BOX 434 77030 #036-07-1977 L1984 D IM *020 †15,20

DYER, Carmel Bitondo. 6431 FANNIN ST 77030 #048-04-1988 L1989 **IMG** *020 †20

DYK, Aleksandra Maria. ■ 77030 #028-34-2005 L2008 **IM** *012

DYKOSKI, Laurie K. ■ 77025 #048-13-2005 **AN** *012

EACHEMPATI, Sriranjini. 7333 NORTH FWY, STE 122 77076 #495-04-1969 L1981 **PD** *020

EADON, Michael Thomas. 1709 DRYDEN RD STE 550, BCM FACULTY CENTER 77030 #016-01-2006 **IM** *012

EAPEN, Georgie Alex. 1515 HOLCOMBE BLVD BOX 4, DEPT OF PULM MED 77030 #690-06-1990 L1998 **PCC** *020 †20

EARDLEY, Warren Arthur. 6621 FANNIN ST 77030 #048-04-1961 L1961 **PD** *071 †55

EARLE, Edward. ■ 77019 #048-02-1964 L1964 **CRS GS** *020 †10,85

EARLE, Philip Norman. 5353 RICHMOND AVE, APT 2 77056 #064-01-1976 L1977 **GP** *020

EARTHMAN, Thomas Phillip. 77098 #028-34-1962 L1965 **END IM** *071 †20

EATON, Wentworth Guy. 16300 KUYKENDAHL RD 77068 #048-02-1961 L1961 **GYN** *020

EBAUGH, Albert Lipscomb. ■ 77030 #048-04-1963 L1963 **P OS** *071

EBELING, Robert Lee, III. ■ 77030 #048-02-2008 *012

EBERLE, Kathleen Hummel. 11914 ASTORIA BLVD, HOUSTON NEUROLOGICAL 77089 #048-04-1998 L2000 **N** *020 †75

ECHEVERRI, Luis G. 7737 SOUTHWEST FWY STE 506 77074 #264-01-1982 L1997 **TS** *020 †90,85

ECHO, Anthony. 1 BAYLOR PLZ, DIV OF PLASTIC SURGERY 77030 #031-01-2005 **PS** *012

ECHOLS, Ben H. 2616 S LOOP W STE 235 77054 #035-06-1975 L1980 **GE IM** *020

ECHOLS-ELLIOTT, Sabrina M. 3701 KIRBY DR, STE 100 77098 #016-06-1996 L2000 **FM** *020 †18

ECKHOFF, Christina M. ■ 77005 #048-04-1979 L1979 **PD** *075 †55

ECKHOFF, Paul Gregory. 3550 WILLOWBEND BLVD 77054 #048-14-1979 L1979 **FM** *075 †18

ECKMAN, Christian D. 1504 TAUB LOOP, DEPARTMENT OF MEDICINE 77030 #048-04-1994 L1997 **IM** *020 †20

ECO, Lourdes C. ■ 77005 #011-02-2002 L2008 **IM** *020 †20

ECROYD, Lisa Marie. ■ 77008 #048-12-2007 **PD** *012

EDDINGS, Jill Marie. 1919 S BRAESWD BLVD 5TH FL, TCPA 77030 #048-04-2004 L2007 **PD** *020 †55

EDDINS-FOLENSBEE, F. 1 BAYLOR PLZ, BAYLOR COLLEGE OF MED 77030 #048-04-1983 L1983 **CHP P** *020 †75

EDEIKEN-MONROE, Beth Sue. 1515 HOLCOMBE BLVD 77030 #041-02-1973 L1979 **R** *050 †80

EDELMAN, Jonathan Samuel. 1 BAYLOR PLZ, BAYLOR COLL OF MED 77030 #550-02-2000 L2003 **ACA** *012

EDELMAN, Mark H. 9055 KATY FWY, STE 304 77024 #048-04-1988 L1989 **PS** *020 †85,65

EDELSTEIN, David Wm. 2727 W HOLCOMBE BLVD 77025 #026-04-1978 L1991 **ORS** *020 †40

EDELWEISS, Marcia. 1515 HOLCOMBE BLVD, UNIT 53 77030 #187-02-1998 L2004 **SP** *020 †50

EDERY, Benjamin. 7737 SOUTHWEST FWY STE 750 77074 #264-05-1969 L1978 **D** *020

EDGE, Arveitta Y. ■ 77030 #048-14-2008 *012

EDGERTON, Mary Elizabeth. ■ 77030 #041-07-1994 L2006 **PTH** *020 †50

EDISON, Bruce David. ■ 77024 #035-15-1967 L1974 **OTO** *071 †45

EDMOND, Jane Covington. 6550 FANNIN ST, STE 1501 77030 #048-04-1985 L1986 **OPH PD** *020 †35

EDMONDS, Joseph Lindsay. 6550 FANNIN ST STE 2 77030 #019-02-1993 L2000 **PDO** *020 †45

EDMONDSON, Everton A. 6560 FANNIN ST, STE 2202 77030 #035-19-1980 L1986 **OS IM** *020 †75

EDMONSON, Sarah Ruth. 3701 KIRBY DR STE 600 77098 #048-12-1996 L1998 **FM** *050 †18 ‡

EDMONSOND, Megan Ann. ■ 77096 #048-04-2007 **IM** *012

EDMUNDSON, Herbert Paine. 7324 SOUTHWEST FWY, STE 1050 77074 #048-13-1984 L1985 **N** *020 †75

EDWARDS, Angelina Ruth. 6431 FANNIN ST 1.134, OF TEXAS-HOUSTON 77030 #048-15-2007 **IM** *012

EDWARDS, Betty Jo. 10130 LOUETTA RD, STE G 77070 #048-02-1976 L1976 **OBG** *020 †30

EDWARDS, Creighton Lewis. 6620 MAIN ST 77030 #048-12-1960 L1960 **GO GYN** *020 †30

EDWARDS, Jocelyn R. 6720 BERTNER ST 77030 #048-14-1994 L1996 **AN** *020 †05

EDWARDS, Kirk D. 920 FROSTWOOD DR, STE 1200 77024 #048-02-1988 L1989 **FM** *020 †18

EDWARDS, Mark L. 12121 RICHMOND AVE, STE 224 77082 #048-14-1988 L1989 **PCC** *020 †20

EDWARDS, Morven Spencer. 1 BAYLOR PLZ, DEPARTMENT OF PEDIATRICS 77030 #048-04-1973 L1973 **PDI PD** *050 †55

EDWARDS, Stephen Jawahar. 6431 FANNIN ST, SCHOOL A 77030 #048-15-2005 L2008 **PD** *012

EDWARDS, Thomas Bradley. 7401 MAIN ST 77030 #021-05-1995 L2003 **ORS** *020 †40

EDWARDS, William Thos. 710 FM 1960 RD W 77090 #048-14-1975 L1976 **EM FM** *020 †18,16

EFFENHAUSER, Rainer Klaus. 1515 HOLCOMBE BLVD 77030 #056-05-1989 L1993 **FP** *012 †70

EFTEKHARI, Farzin. 1515 HOLCOMBE BLVD, BOX 57 77030 #517-01-1967 L1981 **DR PDR** *040 †80

EGBE, Joyce Ego Eziashi. ■ 77071 #690-06-1991 L2007 **PD** *020 †55

EGBUNIKE, Augustine. 7111 HARWIN DR STE 200 77036 #654-01-1983 L1996 **FM** *020 †18

EGBUNIKE, Margaret C. 8610 MARTN LTHR KNG JR, S CENTRAL HOUSTON CHC 77033 #690-01-1983 L1997 **FM** *020 †18

EGGINK, Berthe Joanne. ■ 77059 #660-07-1989 **NPM** *100 †55

EGLER, Rachel Anne. 6621 FANNIN ST, CC1510.00 77030 #035-03-1999 L2005 **PHO** *100 †55

EGWIM, Chukwuma Ikechukwu. 6431 FANNIN ST, MSB 4.234 77030 #690-04-1998 **GE** *012

EHIEMUA, Shade Bethena. ■ 77054 #048-14-2005 L2005 **CHN** *012

EHNI, Bruce Loyal. 6560 FANNIN ST, STE 1200 77030 #048-04-1976 L1976 **NS** *020 †25

EHRLICH, Lisa L. 6624 FANNIN ST STE 121 77030 #048-02-1993 L1997 **IM** *020 †20

EICHELBERGER, John F. 1707 SUNSET BLVD, MEDICAL CLINIC OF HOUSTON 77005 #048-02-1982 L1983 **IM** *020

EICHER, Susan A. 6501 FANNIN ST, BAYLOR OTOLARYNGOLOGY 77030 #048-04-1988 L1990 **OTO** *020 †45

EICHHORN, Ralph David. ■ 77056 #035-19-1942 L1951 **GE IM** *071 †20

EIDMAN, Dan Kelly. 6624 FANNIN ST STE 1510 77030 #048-04-1975 L1975 **ORS** *020 †40

EIFEL, Patricia Jeanne. 1515 HOLCOMBE BLVD, UNIT 1202 77030 #005-11-1977 L1984 **RO GYN** *040 †80

EIFLING, Michael Dennis. 1 BAYLOR PLZ 77030 #007-02-2001 L2007 **CD** *012 †20

EIGENBRODT, Edwin Hixson. 6431 FANNIN ST, M S B 2-100 77030 #016-02-1959 L1966 **PTH** *040 †50

EIGENRAUCH-KARPEN, Heidi. 1100 BATES AVE, CNRC-SUITE 10070 77030 #033-06-1994 L2000 **NPM PD** *020 †55

EISELE, Volker. 4110 BELLAIRE BLVD, STE 204 77025 #409-16-1971 L1975 **AN** *020 †05

EISEMANN, Michael Louis. 6550 FANNIN ST, STE 2119 77030 #041-02-1972 L1977 **PS OTO** *020 †45,65

EISENBERG, Michael. 4545 POST OAK PLACE DR, STE 130 77027 #305-01-2001 L2005 **IM** *020 †20

EISENSTAT, David Daniel. 1515 HOLCOMBE BLVD 77030 #065-01-1985 **PHO** *100 †55

EISNER, Diana. 2030 NORTH LOOP W STE 125 77018 #048-12-1977 L1977 **PD NPM** *020 †55

EISSA, Mona A. 6655 TRAVIS ST 77030 #915-02-1981 L1995 **ADL** *100 †55

EKERUO, Wesley Obioma. ■ 77025 #036-07-2004 **U** *012

EKIZIAN, Michael Armen. ■ 77077 #048-12-2001 **IM** *012

EKNOYAN, Garabed. 1 BAYLOR PLZ, BAYLOR COLLEGE OF MEDICINE 77030 #605-01-1961 L1968 **NEP** IM *020 †20

EKPENYONG, Ursula Uduak. ■ 77083 #048-14-2002 L2005 **AN** *020 †05

ELAYDA, Macarthur Abique. 6720 BERTNER ST 77030 #748-02-1972 **CD PHP** *050

ELBAZ, Alain E. 13300 HARGRAVE RD, STE 400 77070 #067-02-1987 L1998 **ORS** *020 †40

EL-BEHEARY, Mohamed Ezzat. 6565 FANNIN ST, CARDIOLOGY, F1003 77030 #915-02-1994 L2001 **IM** *020 †20

EL-DAFASHY, Diaa Y. ■ 77059 #915-02-1986 L2000 **OBG** *020

ELDER, Christopher L. 3040 FM 1960 RD E, STE 111 77073 #041-15-1999 L2003 **PM** *020 †60

ELDIN, Karen Wiedemann. ■ 77081 #048-04-2001 L2005 **PTH** *020 †50

ELDRIDGE, Charles P, Jr. 6447 MAIN ST 77030 #036-01-1960 L1966 **R** *071 †80

ELENBERG, Ewa. 6621 FANNIN ST MC32482, TEXAS CHILDREN'S HOSPITAL 77030 #759-10-1983 L1997 **PD PN** *020 †55

ELERIAN, Lamia Fikry. 277 W GRAY ST 77019 #915-04-1986 L1991 **NPM** *020 †55

ELFAR, Mohamed Soliman Ah. ■ 77057 #915-11-1992 L2008 **GS** *012

ELFARRA, Rola Mahmoud. 2002 HOLCOMBE BLVD 77030 #024-07-1998 L2001 **IM** *020 †20

EL HAFI, Salah Eddine. 925 GESSNER RD, STE 630 77024 #396-06-1974 L1984 **CD IM** *020 †20

ELHAJ, Fareed. ■ 77006 #048-04-2002 L2005 **END** *012 †20

ELHAJ, George Eid. 810 PEAKWOOD DR STE 202 77090 #165-01-1972 L1978 **IM END** *020

ELHAJ, Mona. ■ 77006 #048-14-2007 **IM** *012

EL-HAKAM, Lisa Michael. ■ 77059 #048-02-2003 L2008 **CHN** *012

ELIDEMIR, Okan. 6621 FANNIN ST, CC 1040 00 77030 #902-04-1992 L1998 **PDP** *020 †55

ELK, Jerome Rael. 920 FROSTWOOD DR, MEMORIAL CITY HOSPITAL 77024 #836-02-1974 L1988 **AN** *020 †05

EL KHOURY, Ramy. PO BOX 20708, UNIV TX MED SCH 77225 #539-06-2005 **N** *012

ELKOUSY, Hussein Adel. 7401 MAIN ST 77030 #036-07-1995 L2002 **ORS OSM** *020 †40

ELLEDGE, Richard Moffet. 6620 MAIN ST 77030 #048-14-1981 L1981 **ON IM** *020 †20

ELLERHORST, Julie Ann. 1200 JACKSON BLVD, U. T. M.D. ANDERSON CANCER 77006 #048-04-1984 L1987 **ON IM** *020 †20

ELLINGTON, Owen Bernardo. 17314 FM 149 STE 100 77064 #041-14-1975 L1988 **AN ID** *020

ELLIOTT, Danielle Denine. ■ 77030 #048-04-1997 L2003 **PTH** *020 †50

ELLIOTT, Donald Allison. ■ 77263 #048-04-1961 L1962 **PD OS** *071 †55

ELLIOTT, Tricia C. 1221 MCKINNEY ST, STE 40300 77010 #048-02-1996 L2003 **FM** *020 †18

ELLIS, Amy Elizabeth. ■ 77025 #048-14-2006 **P** *012

ELLIS, Byron Keith. 7777 SW FWY, STE 420 77074 #028-02-1996 L2003 **IM** *020 †20

ELLIS, Dan Beckley. 77054 #048-04-2006 **AN** *012

ELLIS, Denise M. ■ 77004 #048-14-1997 **P** *100

ELLIS, Lee Marshall. 1515 HOLCOMBE BLVD BOX 106, MD ANDERSON CANCER CTR 77030 #051-01-1983 L1991 **GS ON** *020 †85

ELLIS, Rosegenee. 211 HIGHLAND CROSS DR, STE 275 77073 #047-07-2003 L2006 **IM** *020 †20

ELLIS, Tamara L. ■ 77006 #048-13-2005 **GS** *012

ELLISON, Dayna L. PO BOX 20708, DEPT OF OB/GYN 77225 #048-14-2005 **OBG** *012

ELLSWORTH, Warren Aldrich, IV. 1 BAYLOR PLZ, DIV OF PLASTIC SURGERY 77030 #048-04-2004 **PS** *012

EL-NAGGAR, Adel Kamel. 1515 HOLCOMBE BLVD # 85 77030 #915-04-1970 L1987 **PTH** *020 †50

ELSAHLY, Hana Mohammed. 1 BAYLOR PLZ, DEPT OF MVM RM 225D 77030 #605-01-1994 L2002 **ID** *020 †20

ELSAYEM, Ahmed F O. 1515 HOLCOMBE BLVD, DEPT OF PALLIATIVE CARE, B 77030 #848-01-1985 L2001 **IM** *020 †20

EL-SERAG, Hashem Beshir. 2002 HOLCOMBE BLVD, HOUSTON VA MED CENTER 152 77030 #613-01-1991 L2000 **GE** *020 †20

ELTON, Richard John. 1515 FANNIN ST # 5020 77030 #917-01-1984 *075

ELVAMBUENA, Ma Eden N. 4545 POST OAK PLACE DR, STE 130 77027 #748-01-1992 L2003 **IM** *020 †20

EL-ZIMAITY, Hala M. ■ 77030 #915-04-1982 L1993 **PTH** *020 †50

EMEREUWAONU, Ikechukwu Uz. 1 BAYLOR PLZ 77030 #690-06-2001 L2008 **FP** *012

EMERSON, Deanna Doro. ■ 77069 #048-02-1968 L1968 **CHP P** *020 †75

EMERSON, Joseph Jordan. ■ 77030 #048-04-2008 *012

ENABULELE, Christopher E. PO BOX 741061 77274 #913-92-1970 *020

ENAD-DE GUZMAN, Deborah S. 5615 KIRBY DR STE 440 77005 #748-11-1982 L1995 **NPM** *020 †55

ENCISO, Josephine Martina. 6621 FANNIN ST 550-05, BAYOR COLLEGE OF MEDICINE 77030 #003-01-1996 L2003 **NPM** *020 †55

ENDE, M J. ■ 77027 #048-13-1977 L1982 **DR** *020

ENDOM, Erin E. 6621 FANNIN ST STE A210, TEXAS CHILDREN'S HOSPITAL 77030 #048-14-1988 L1989 **PD** *020 †55

ENG, Cathy. 1515 HOLCOMBE BLVD, BOX 426 77030 #041-09-1994 L2002 **HO** *020 †20

ENG, Christine May. 1 BAYLOR PLZ, NAB 2015 77030 #021-01-1983 L2001 **CMG CG** *020 †55,19

ENG, Robert G. ■ 77099 #048-15-1996 L1997 **EM** *020 †16

ENGELHARDT, Erin Kristin. 6350 MAIN ST 77005 #048-12-2007 **PD** *012

ENGELHARDT, Hugo T, Jr. ■ 77005 #021-01-1972 L1972 **OS** *040

ENTMAN, Mark Lawrence. 6565 FANNIN ST, METHODIST HOSP DEPT MED 77030 #036-07-1963 L1971 **CD IM** *050 †20

EPNER, Daniel Evan. 2002 HOLCOMBE BLVD, HOUSTON VA MED CTR 77030 #048-04-1986 L1987 **ON IM** *030 †20

EPNER, Linda Chiou. 6565 FANNIN ST 200, CULLEN EYE INST 77030 #048-04-1986 L1987 **OPH** *020 †35

EPPLE, Heinrich. ■ 77004 #409-33-1995 L2007 **AN** *020

EPPS, Howard Robt. 7401 MAIN ST, FONDREN ORTHOPEDIC GRP 77030 #023-07-1989 L1996 **ORS OP** *020 †40

EPSTEIN, Hayley Lynne. ■ 77019 #048-14-2008 **P** *012

EPSTEIN, Michael Jerry. 6620 MAIN ST 77030 #035-08-1964 L1971 **HS** *040 †40

ERAJ, Ummeed A. 7620 BELLFORT ST 77061 #577-01-1980 L1997 **OBG** *020

ERANA, Rodrigo. 6701 FANNIN ST 77030 #649-31-1993 L2002 **PHO** *020 †55

ERASMUS, Jeremy John. 1515 HOLCOMBE BLVD, MD ANDERSON CANCER CTR 77030 #836-01-1982 L2000 **DR** *020 †80

ERDBERG, Mindel Ruth. ■ 77024 #869-05-1942 L1943 **P CHP** *071 †75

ERFANI, Seamae. 6621 FANNIN ST, STE A 77030 #422-01-2001 L2005 **PD** *020 †55
ERGUN, Gulchin Ayshe. 6560 FANNIN ST STE 1160 77030 #038-06-1984 L1998 **GE IM** *020 †20
ERGUVAN-DOGAN, Basak. 1515 HOLCOMBE BLVD 77030 #902-05-1997 *100
ERHO, Benedict Lucky. ■ 77083 #690-01-1985 L2002 **GS** *100
ERICKSON, Kent. 401 GREENS RD 77060 #902-10-1991 L2002 **FM EM** *020 †18
ERICKSON, Peter Edward. 6410 FANNIN ST # 325 77030 #065-01-1974 L1976 *020
ERICSSON, Arthur Dale. ■ 77030 #025-01-1957 L1969 **N OS** *071 †75
ERICSSON, Charles Derwin. 6431 FANNIN ST, DEPT OF MED DIV OF INFECTI 77030 #024-01-1970 L1975 **ID IM** *040 †20
ERIE, Susan Therese. 9055 KATY FWY, STE 200 77024 #016-11-1991 L1992 **FM** *020 †18
ERLICHMAN, Jasmin. 3737 DACOMA ST 77092 #048-04-1991 L1993 **CHP** *020
ERMAC, Alfredo Tumarao, Jr. 7825 HIGHWAY 6 N, STE 101 77095 #048-02-1996 L2000 **FM** *020 †18
ERMIS, Peter Ryan. ■ 77019 #048-13-2005 **MPD** *012
ERNST, Randy Devereux. 1515 HOLCOMBE BLVD, MD ANDERSON CANCER CTR 77030 #048-02-1990 L1992 **DR AR** *020 †80
ERSOY, Mukerrem Yesim. 6431 FANNIN ST 1134, AT HOUST 77030 #902-19-1998 L2007 **IM** *100 †20
ERTAN, Atilla. 6560 FANNIN ST, STE 2208 77030 #902-03-1963 L1991 **GE IM** *020 †20
ERWIN, Gary Edward. 810 PEAKWOOD DR STE 101 77090 #048-02-1970 L1970 **ON IM** *020 †20
ERWIN, Wendell Dwight. 6621 FANNIN ST 77030 #048-04-1966 L1966 **ORS** *071 †40
ESAKOWITZ, Leonard. ■ 77025 #836-01-1977 L1981 **PD** *020
ESANGBEDO, Ivie Doris. ■ 77054 #690-02-2004 L2007 **PD** *012
ESCALANTE, Carmelita P. 1515 HOLCOMBE BLVD, UNIT 437 77030 #021-05-1985 L1987 **IM** *020 †20
ESCALANTE-GLORSKY, Susana. 6620 MAIN ST, STE 1510 77030 #035-47-1986 L2000 **GE** *020 †20
ESCOBAR, Miguel Antonio. 6655 TRAVIS ST, STE 400 77030 #264-08-1989 L2002 **HEM IM** *050 †20
ESCUDIER, Susan M. 7515 MAIN ST, STE 740 77030 #048-04-1985 L1986 **ON HEM** *020 †20
ESKANDARI, Farahnaz. ■ 77030 #517-08-1994 **FP** *012
ESMAELI-AZAD, Bita. 1515 HOLCOMBE BLVD # 441, DEPT OF HEAD AND NECK SURG 77030 #016-42-1990 L1998 **OPH** *020 †35
ESPER, Nancy. 7580 FANNIN ST, STE 100 77054 #875-01-1995 L2002 **IM** *020 †20
ESPINOZA, Erica Marie. ■ 77025 #048-02-2007 *012
ESPINOZA, Maria Del Carme. 1007 EDGEBROOK DR 77034 #048-14-1999 L2002 **PD** *020
ESPIRITU, Edgardo T. 12339 MAIN ST 77035 #748-02-1964 L1975 **FM** *020 †85
ESPIRITU, Ernesto T. 737 W CAVALCADE ST, STE A 77009 #748-02-1973 L1981 **FM EM** *020
ESPIRITU, Mario S. 10700 NORTH FWY STE 385 77037 #748-07-1960 L1972 **OM FM** *020
ESQUENAZI, Rafael Camhi. 1140 WESTMONT DR, STE 320 77015 #649-01-1971 L1977 **NEP IM** *020 †20
ESTEP, Jerry D. 6550 FANNIN ST, STE 1901 77030 #048-04-1999 L2002 **CD** *020 †20
ESTES, Susie M. 9539 HUFFMEISTER RD, ENDOCRINE AND PSYCHIATRY C 77095 #048-02-2001 L2006 **END** *020
ESTEVA, Francisco J. 1515 HOLCOMBE BLVD # 1354, M.D. ANDERSON CANCER CENTE 77030 #847-13-1988 L1998 **ON HEM** *050 †20
ESTEY, Elihu Harris. 1515 HOLCOMBE BLVD, DEPT LEUKEMIA 77030 #023-07-1972 L1979 **IM N** *020 †20
ESTRADA-Y-MARTIN, Rosa M. 6431 FANNIN ST STE 1.266, UNIV OF TX HLTH SCI CTR 77030 #429-01-1985 L2000 **PCC** *040 †20
ESTRERA, Anthony L. 6410 FANNIN ST, HPB 450 77030 #048-12-1993 L1999 **TS VS** *020 †85,90
ESTROV, Zeev. 1515 HOLCOMBE BLVD, MD ANDERSON CANCER CENTER 77030 #550-02-1973 L1996 **IM** *050 †20
ETEROVIC, Erna B. 1200 MOURSUND ST, DEPT PUD 77030 #231-01-1966 L1978 **PUD PDC** *050
ETHERIDGE, Whitson B, II. 4407 YOAKUM BLVD, STE B 77006 #048-04-1971 L1971 **NEP IM** *020 †20
ETTER, Elegy Leon. 1315 ST JOSEPH PKWY, STE 1102 77002 #048-02-1982 L1983 **GS** *020 †85
EUBANKS, Billy Ray. 700 LOUISIANA ST 77002 #021-01-1962 L1962 **U** *071 †95
EUBANKS, Leigh Ellen. 1900 SAINT JAMES PL, STE 650 77056 #021-01-1987 L1993 **D** *020 †20,15
EUSCHER, Elizabeth D. ■ 77030 #048-04-1997 L2004 **PTH** *020 †50
EVANGELISTA, Monaliza S. ■ 77047 #048-02-2007 **MPD** *012
EVANS, Charity Hassie. ■ 77054 #016-42-2007 **GS** *012
EVANS, Desiree Lynell. 5737 CULLEN BLVD, STE 200 77021 #021-01-1999 L2002 **PD** *020 †55
EVANS, Donnie. 1141 SOUTHWEST FWY, STE 200 77027 #005-11-1987 L1989 **IM** *020 †20
EVANS, Douglas Brian. 1515 HOLCOMBE BLVD BOX 444, M D ANDERSON CANCER CENTER 77030 #024-05-1983 L1989 **SO GS** *020 †85
EVANS, Harry Launius. 1515 HOLCOMBE BLVD, UT MD ANDERSON CANCER CTR 77030 #011-03-1974 L1978 **PTH DMP** *020 †50
EVANS, Patricia W. 7401 FANNIN ST, MSB 3.142 77030 #048-16-2000 L2003 **PD** *020 †55 ‡
EVANS, Peter Shelby. ■ 77077 #018-03-1990 L1999 **EM** *020 †16
EVANS, Randolph Warren. 1200 BINZ ST STE 1370 77004 #048-04-1978 L1978 **N** *020 †75
EVANS, Richard Arthur. 1011 AUGUSTA DR, STE 210 77057 #021-01-1971 L1975 **PMM PM** *020 †85
EVANS, Scott E. 1515 HOLCOMBE BLVD, UNIT 403 77030 #048-13-1999 L2005 **PCC** *100 †20
EVERSON, Lloyd Kermit, Jr. 16825 NORTHCHASE DR, STE 1300 77060 #024-01-1969 L1996 **ON HEM** *030 †20
EWER, Michael S. 1515 HOLCOMBE BLVD, BOX 43 77030 #869-01-1970 L1975 **CD IM** *020 †20
EWTON, April Anne. ■ 77005 #048-04-1994 L1996 **HMP** *020 †50
EX, David A. ■ 77025 #048-16-1992 L1993 **DR** *020 †80
EYPE, Sheila M. 6431 FANNIN ST 1.134, OF TEXAS-HOUSTON 77030 #048-14-2007 **IM** *012
EZELL, Robert Floyd. 7777 SOUTHWEST FWY NO-328 77074 #017-20-1970 L1972 **FM** *020 †18
EZENWABACHILI, Obiajulu C. 7737 SOUTHWEST FWY, STE 620 77074 #913-12-1984 L2000 **IM** *020 †20
EZIEFULE, Akwugo Adanna. 9311 MEADOW BRANCH CT 77095 #048-15-2008 *012
EZZEDDINE, Richard Joseph. ■ 77030 #048-04-2006 *012
FABRE, Louis Fernand, Jr. 5847 SAN FELIPE ST, STE 2000 77057 #048-04-1969 L1969 **P N** *050 †75
FADEL, Bahaa M. 6624 FANNIN ST, STE 2380 77030 #605-02-1986 L1993 **CD IM** *020 †20
FADEM, Stephen Zale. 11111 BROOKLET DR, STE 100 77099 #039-01-1973 L1974 **NEP IM** *020 †20
FADERL, Stefan. 1515 HOLCOMBE BLVD, DEPT OF LEUKEMIA, UNIT 428 77030 #409-16-1990 L1999 **ON** *020 †20
FADIL, Ahmed A. 6431 FANNIN ST, STE 1-27 77030 #915-02-1988 L1995 **PCC** *020 †20

FADULU, Sunday O. 1221 MCKINNEY ST, STE 40300 77010 #048-13-1998 L2002 **FM** *020
FAELDONEA-SERUELO, Rhyl A. 6431 FANNIN ST 308, UNIV OF TEXAS MED SCH 77030 #748-14-1999 L2008 **FP** *012
FAGAN, Elizabeth A. 4848 LOOP CENTRAL DR # 700, ENCYSIRE PHARMACEUTICALS 77081 #917-19-1975 L1994 **IM GE** *050
FAHIM, Danny Kamal. ■ 77030 #025-01-2005 L2005 **NS** *012
FAHNBULLEH, Augustus. 7333 NORTH FWY, STE 308 77076 #610-01-1988 L2003 **ID** *020 †20
FAHR, Linda N Meyers. 1707 SUNSET BLVD 77005 #018-03-1968 L1974 **R** *020 †80
FAHY-CHANDON, Bridget N. 6565 FANNIN ST SM1661, DEPARTMENT OF SURGERY 77030 #005-15-1997 L2006 **GS** *020 †85
FAIN, Robert Henry, Jr. 7401 MAIN ST 77030 #048-04-1980 L1980 **ORS** *020 †40
FAINSTEIN, Victor. 6560 FANNIN ST, STE 1540 77030 #649-01-1973 L1979 **ID IM** *020 †20
FAIR, Elizabeth Ann. ■ 77019 #048-02-2001 L2005 **EM** *020 †16
FAIRLEY, Robert Ryan. 7900 CAMBRIDGE ST, APT 21-10 77054 #048-14-2004 *100
FAIRWEATHER, David Atilla. 1140 WESTMONT DR STE 520 77015 #025-07-1997 L2003 **GS** *020 †85
FAIZ, Fayaz Ahmed. 11760 FM 1960 RD W 77065 #704-02-1970 L1979 **N** *020 †75
FAIZ, Saadia A. 6431 FANNIN ST, STE 1.274 77030 #048-14-1999 L2002 **PCC** *100 †20
FAIZ, Zaitoon. 11760 FM 1960 RD W 77065 #704-02-1971 L1979 **PDC PD** *075 †55
FAKHOURY, Khoulood F. 6621 FANNIN ST, CLINICAL CARE CTR, CC1040. 77030 #575-01-1985 L1994 **PD PDP** *020 †55
FAKHRI, Samer. 6410 FANNIN ST STE 1200, DEPT. OF OTOLARYNGOLOGY 77030 #067-01-1998 L2005 *020
FALBEY, Francis B, Jr. 7401 MAIN ST 77030 #048-15-1988 L1989 **AN** *020 †05 ‡
FALCHOOK, Gerald Steven. 1515 HOLCOMBE BLVD UNIT 10, MD ANDERSON CANCER CTR 77030 #021-05-2001 L2004 **ON** *012
FALGOUT, Jovita Peresich. 7630 BELLFORT ST 77061 #021-05-1955 L1964 **PD** *071 †55
FALIAKOU, Eleni C. ■ 77054 #418-01-1987 L1992 **GS** *100
FALIK, Ruth. 1 BAYLOR PLZ, BAYLOR COLLEGE OF MEDICINE 77030 #026-19-1978 L2000 **IM CD** *040 †20
FALKENSAMMER, Christine. ■ 77054 #154-02-1999 L2008 **PDC** *012 †55
FAMAKINWA, Olufenwa Juani. ■ 77030 #048-14-2008 *012
FAN, Chiao-Ya Grace. 9630 CLAREWOOD DR, STE A5 77036 #048-04-1999 L2002 **FM** *020 †18
FAN, Jinping. ■ 77054 #243-43-1986 L2005 **CD** *012 †20
FAN, Leland Lane. 6701 FANNIN ST, CLINICAL CARE CENTER 77030 #048-04-1973 L1973 **PDP CCP** *020 †55
FANALE, Michelle Anne. 1515 HOLCOMBE BLVD # 429, UT MD ANDERSON CANCER CTR 77030 #033-05-1999 L2002 **ON HEM** *020 †20
FANAROF, Gerald. 12121 RICHMOND AVE, STE 111 77082 #836-01-1968 L1978 **GE IM** *020 †20
FANG, Bingshuang. 17322 RED OAK DR 77090 #243-57-1982 L2000 **AN** *020 †05
FANG, Kaisen. 11920 ASTORIA BLVD, STE 210 77089 #005-06-1985 L1993 **IM** *020 †20
FANG, Weitsuen Daniel. 6720 BERTNER ST, MC 2-270 77030 #048-04-1996 L1998 **VIR** *020
FANN, William Edwin. 1 BAYLOR PLZ, BAYLOR COLLEGE OF MEDICINE 77030 #001-02-1959 L1977 **P PA** *071 †75
FANNING, Tina Varley. 1515 HOLCOMBE BLVD APT 53 77030 #038-43-1979 L1979 **PTH** *020 †50
FANT, Michael Edward. 6431 FANNIN ST, DEPT OF PEDIATRICS MSB 3.2 77030 #047-05-1980 L1987 **NPM PD** *020 †55
FARAG, Wafaa Youssef. 1648 RICHMOND AVE 77006 #915-02-1984 L2002 **P CHP** *020 †75
FARAGHER, Ian Godwin. 6550 FANNIN ST STE 2307 77030 #143-02-1984 **CRS** *100
FARBER, Eileen S. 2211 NORFOLK ST, STE 140 77098 #048-14-1984 L1991 **P** *020
FARBER, Harold J. 6621 FANNIN ST 1040.00, PULMONARY MEDICINE SERVICE 77030 #035-48-1987 L2007 **PDP PD** *020 †55
FARELLA, Angelina. 17150 EL CAMINO REAL 77058 #305-01-1995 L1999 **PD** *020 †55
FARESI, Mariano Martin. ■ 77047 #132-01-1996 L2006 **CRS** *012 †85
FARHA, Peter F. 1631 NORTH LOOP W, STE 160 77008 #605-01-1976 L1981 **ON IM** *020 †20
FARID, Yasser Refaat. 6723 BERTNER ST, U TX-M D ANDERSON CANCER C 77030 #915-02-1994 L2002 **OMO** *100
FARINAS, Carlos A. 4101 GREENBRIAR ST STE 200 77098 #042-01-1985 L1991 **DR** *020 †20,80
FARIS, Arthur Monroe, Jr. 1313 HERMANN DR 77004 #048-02-1966 L1966 **OBG** *071 †30
FARIZANI, Forough. 6400 HILLCROFT ST, HILLCROFT PHYSICIANS PA 77081 #028-78-1994, ▲ L1997 **FM** *020
FARLEY, Arthur John. 403 HEIGHTS BLVD 77007 #048-02-1967 L1967 **PYA CHP** *020 †75
FARLEY, Elizabeth Anne. ■ 77004 #048-14-2007 **IM** *012
FARMER, Christopher Micha. ■ 77054 #048-14-2008 *012
FARMER, John Alan. 1 BAYLOR PLZ, 5TH FL 77030 #048-12-1974 L1976 **CD** *020
FARMER, Kathryn Loren. 6655 TRAVIS ST, STE 820 77030 #048-14-1987 L1988 **D** *071 †15
FARNIE, Mark Alexander. 6410 FANNIN ST, STE 600 77030 #048-14-1987 L1988 **IM PD** *020 †55,20
FARO, Constance Joneen. 7400 FANNIN ST STE 840 77054 #030-06-2002 L2006 **OBG** *020
FARO, Sebastian. 7400 FANNIN ST, STE 840 77054 #030-06-1975 L1983 **OBG ID** *020 †30
FAROOQ, Naveed Umer. 3007 ACORN WOOD WAY 77059 #048-11-1986 L1996 **ID** *020 †20
FARR, Michael Henry. 7600 FANNIN ST, PATHOLOGY DEPT 77054 #048-04-1971 L1971 **PTH** *020 †50
FARRELL, Edward Monroe. 7800 FANNIN ST STE 201 77054 #649-14-1978 **GS** *020
FARRIS, Kevin Wayne. 6431 FANNIN ST 308 77030 #020-12-2005 L2007 **FP** *012
FASAKIN, Yemi Muyiwa. 2002 HOLCOMBE BLVD, VA ER 77030 #011-02-2004 L2007 **IM** *100 †20
FASHE, Juan Olivas. 7003 CECIL ST # 11 77030 #737-01-1978 **TS** *020
FASON, Fred Lanier. ■ 77054 #048-04-1960 L1960 **P** *071 †75
FASULLO, Frank Joseph, Jr. 17047 EL CAMINO REAL, STE 105 77058 #048-14-1994 L1995 **FM** *020 †18 ‡
FASULO, Mark. ■ 77054 #048-14-2006 L2008 **IM** *012
FATEH HYDER, Syed Mohamme. ■ 77025 #496-27-2004 **FP** *012
FATEMI, Omid. 1709 DRYDEN RD STE 550, BCM FACULTY CENTER 77030 #051-01-2007 **IM** *012
FATHALLA, Waseem Mahmoud. ■ 77063 #875-01-1993 L1997 **CHN** *020 †75,55
FATTOR, Ron Arthur. 5656 KELLEY ST, LBJ HOSPITAL, PATHOLOGY 77026 #048-04-1983 L1983 **PTH** *050
FAUST, Eric Jos Barelas. 4407 YOAKUM BLVD, STE B 77006 #048-14-1988 L1989 **NEP IM** *020 †20
FAUSTINELLA, Fabrizia. 6431 FANNIN ST 1.122, UT-HOUSTON MEDICAL SCHOOL 77030 #561-15-1986 L1998 **IM** *020 †20
FAYAD, Luis Eduardo. 1515 HOLCOMBE BLVD, BOX 429 77030 #319-04-1985 L1995 **ON** *020 †20

FAYLE, Robert W. 7600 FANNIN ST 77054 #048-14-1976 L1976 **N** *020 †75

FAZ, Gabriel T. ■ 77030 #048-14-2008 *012

FAZLANI, Mushtaq Ahmed. 2323 WIRT RD, 12211 PINE BROOK DRIVE 77055 #704-01-1961 L1979 **GP OS** *020

FEARMONTI, Regina Marie. 1400 HOLCOMBE BLVD, FC 12.3000 77030 #016-43-2001 L2006 **GS SO** *100

FECILE, Marylynn. 6621 FANNIN ST 3-332, TEXAS CHILDREN'S HOSPITAL 77030 #041-14-1995 L2002 **PHO** *020 †55

FEDDER, Larry Leo. 6700 BELLAIRE BLVD 77074 #869-07-1951 L1963 **IM CD** *071 †20

FEELEY, Thomas Wm. 1400 HOLCOMBE BLVD, UNIT 409 77030 #024-05-1972 L1998 **AN CCA** *040 †05

FEENEY, Marissa Laurette. 1885 OLD SPANISH TRL, HCME 77054 #016-45-1997 L2004 **PTH FOP** *020 †55

FEIG, Barry W. 1515 HOLCOMBE BLVD, MD ANDERSON CNCR CTR #444 77030 #035-15-1984 L1991 **GS** *020 †85

FEIG, Daniel I. 1102 BATES AVE, RENAL SECTION MC3-2482 77030 #054-04-1995 L2001 **PN PD** *050 †55

FEIGIN, Ralph David. 6621 FANNIN ST, TEXAS CHILDREN'S HOSPITAL 77030 #024-05-1962 L1977 **PD ID** *030 †55

FEIGON, Judith Tova. 7515 MAIN ST, STE 650 77030 #048-13-1976 L1981 **OPH** *020 †35

FELBERG, Mary Williamson. 6621 FANNIN ST 77030 #016-11-1992 L1997 **AN** *020 †05

FELDER, John Matthew. ■ 77054 #048-04-2008 *012

FELDMAN, Bernard Harry. 1740 W 27TH ST STE 215 77008 #030-05-1963 L1964 **U** *020 †95

FELDMAN, David Neil. ■ 77030 #035-15-1994 L2004 **BBK** *020 †50

FELDMAN, Evan Michael. ■ 77047 #035-45-2005 **PS** *012

FELDMAN, James Maxwell. 915 GESSNER RD STE 950, MEMORIAL CITY CARDIOLOGY A 77024 #030-06-1999 L2000 **CD** *030 †20

FELDMAN, Marc Howard. 9055 KATY FWY, STE 200 77024 #038-43-1994 L1998 **FM FSM** *020 †18

FELDMAN, Robert Malcolm. 6400 FANNIN ST, 18TH FL 77030 #016-42-1986 L1995 **OPH OS** *020 †35

FELDMAN, Zeev Tuvia. 6560 FANNIN ST STE 944 77030 #550-02-1988 *100

FELDMAN, Jennifer Marie. 6431 FANNIN ST, MSB 3.140B 77030 #017-20-1997 L2002 **ADL** *100 †55

FELTON, Erik W. 6550 FANNIN ST, SMITH TOWER, SUITE 1003 77030 #048-12-1999 L2003 **AN** *020 †05

FENG, Felicia Ann. 2500 FONDREN RD, STE 160 77063 #021-05-1996 L2000 **IM** *020 †20

FENG, Jianwei. 9888 BELLAIRE BLVD STE 154 77036 #243-46-1987 L2003 **CD** *020 †20

FENG, Yi. ■ 77065 #025-07-2001 L2005 **AN** *020 †05

FENIG, David Michael. ■ 77025 #041-01-2001 L2003 **U** *100

FENNER, Charles Edwin. 6411 FANNIN ST 77030 #048-02-1959 L1960 **D** *071

FERGUSON, Angela K. ■ 77059 #048-02-2001 L2007 **PS** *100

FERGUSON, Emma C. ■ 77070 #048-04-2000 L2005 **DR** *100 †80

FERGUSON, James Elvin. 6411 FANNIN ST 77030 #048-13-1980 L1980 **EM** *020 †16

FERGUSON, James Jos, III. ■ 77030 #041-01-1979 L1987 **CD IM** *020 †20

FERGUSON, Laura E. 5656 KELLEY ST, LBJ HOSPITAL 77026 #048-14-1985 L1987 **PD** *020 †55

FERGUSON, Robert E, Jr. 1515 HOLCOMBE BLVD, PLASTIC SURGERY, FC8.2000 77030 #051-01-2001 L2007 **PS** *020

FERNANDES, Caraciolo J. 6621 FANNIN ST 77030 #495-01-1986 L1999 **NPM** *020 †55

FERNANDEZ, Antonio. ■ 77024 #264-01-1966 L1976 **P N** *020

FERNANDEZ, Esperanza. 13111 EAST FWY, STE 212 77015 #308-03-1987 L1995 **FM** *020 †18

FERNANDEZ, Fabio E. 6701 FANNIN ST 77030 #048-05-1959 L1971 **CHN** *020 †55,75

FERNANDEZ, Fernando D. ■ 77054 #748-10-1989 **AN** *020

FERNANDEZ, Isairis Prieto. 1007 EDGEBROOK DR 77034 #847-04-1970 L1977 **PD** *020

FERNANDEZ, Natalie R. 1300 MOURSUND ST 77030 #748-01-1984 **CHP** *100

FERNANDEZ, Nelson A. 4888 LOOP CENTRAL DR, STE 700 77081 #035-47-1977 L1982 **PUD IM** *030 †20

FERNANDEZ, Orlando Pedro. 1007 EDGEBROOK DR 77034 #847-04-1970 L1977 **OBG** *020

FERNANDEZ, Sara Louise. ■ 77054 #048-04-2004 **IM** *100 †20

FERNANDEZ-KLINE, Blanca E. 3701 KIRBY DR STE 600, BAYLOR COLLEGE OF MEDICINE 77098 #025-12-2000 L2000 **FM** *100 †18

FERNANDEZ-VARGAS, Carlos. 7777 SOUTHWEST FWY, STE 1036 77074 #231-01-1966 L1973 **RO** *075

FERNBACH, Donald Jos. ■ 77005 #010-01-1952 L1958 **HEM PD** *071 †55

FERRAJOLI, Alessandra. 1515 HOLCOMBE BLVD, BOX 428 77030 #561-15-1988 L2000 **ON** *020 †20

FERRARA, Joseph Michael. ■ 77025 #035-15-2003 L2007 **N** *100

FERRARI, Carlos Abel. 915 GESSNER RD, STE 375 77024 #132-02-1972 L1984 **GS** *020 †85

FERRARIO, Lara. 6431 FANNIN ST, UT-HOUSTON DEPT ANESTH 77030 #561-03-1993 L2005 **AN** *100 †05

FERRELL, Bethany V Mc Vey. 5425 POLK ST STE J, (MC 1906) 77023 #048-02-1999 L2001 **GPM** *030 †70

FERRENDELLI, James A. 6411 FANNIN ST 77030 #007-02-1962 L1996 **N PA** *030 †75

FERRER, Kathleen Teresa. 6701 FANNIN ST CC1210, SECTION OF RETROVIROLOGY 77030 #033-06-1999 L2003 **MPD** *020 †55

FERRIS, Marley Samuel. 2411 FOUNTAIN VIEW DR, STE 200 77057 #048-12-2003 L2007 **AN** *100

FERRO, Pieretta Sbavaglia. 1 BAYLOR PLZ, BYLOR COLLEGE MED 77030 #561-17-1953 L1965 **R GP** *020

FERRY, George Douglass. 6621 FANNIN ST, 3-3391 77030 #048-04-1964 L1964 **PG PD** *062 †55

FERSON, David Zbigniew. 1515 HOLCOMBE BLVD 77030 #759-10-1982 L1996 **AN** *020 †05

FETZER, David Thomas. ■ 77054 #048-14-2008 *012

FEUER, Hugh Scott. ■ 77005 #035-08-1996 L2000 **EM** *020 †16

FEUER, Laurie Beth. 3400 BISSONNET ST, STE 100 77005 #035-08-1997 L2000 **IM** *020 †20

FIEDLER, Ryan E. ■ 77002 #048-14-2007 **IM** *012

FIELDER-MOORE, Jean. ■ 77035 #048-12-1944 L1945 **OPH** *071

FIELDS, Clive Kevin. 9055 KATY FWY, STE 200 77024 #048-14-1988 L1989 **FM ADM** *020 †18

FIELDS, Harold Jack. 9055 KATY FWY, STE 200 77024 #919-05-1960 L1974 **FM** *050 †18 ‡

FIELER, John T, Jr. 2727 ALLEN PKWY STE A 77019 #021-05-1982 L1985 **FM** *075 †18

FIESTA, Matthew P. ■ 77030 #048-14-2008 *012

FIFE, Caroline E. 6411 FANNIN ST 77030 #048-16-1984 L1985 **FM UM** *020 †18

FIGHALI, Sayid Fuad. 6624 FANNIN ST STE 2000 77030 #605-01-1979 L1984 **CD** *020 †20

FIGUEREDO, Giovanna. ■ 77025 #264-12-1991 **FP** *012

FILAK, Christa Lynn. 6400 FANNIN ST, STE 2110 77030 #016-42-1998 L2001 **PD** *020 †55

FILIPOWICZ, Ewa Anna. ■ 77079 #759-03-1988 L2007 **PTH** *100

FILLMAN, Stephen Douglas. 1140 CYPRESS STATION DR, NORTHWEST DIAGNOSTIC CLINI 77090 #048-02-1976 L1976 **IM** *020 †20

FILLMORE, Scott J. 13300 HARGRAVE RD, STE 505 77070 #037-01-1987 L1991 **PM** *020 †60

FINCH, Christie J. 1 BAYLOR PLZ, BAYLOR CLG OF MED-PATHLGY 77030 #048-14-1993 L1994 **PTH PCP** *020 †50

FINCH, Jennifer L. 4407 YOAKUM BLVD, STE B 77006 #048-14-1998 L2000 **NEP IM** *020 †20

FINCH, Stephanie Amber. ■ 77054 #048-14-2008 *012

FINE, Paul Martin. 1504 TAUB LOOP 77030 #010-01-1971 L1977 **OBG U** *020 †30

FINEGOLD, Milton J. 6621 FANNIN ST, TX CHILDREN'S HOSPITAL 77030 #035-45-1960 L1979 **PP HEP** *020 †50

FINIANOS, Antoine Nafez. 6431 FANNIN ST 1134, OF TEXAS-HOUSTON 77030 #605-01-2003 **IM** *012

FINK, Aaron Harlan. 4550 POST OAK PLACE DR 77027 #048-04-1982 L1983 **CHP P** *020 †75

FINKEL, Howard Zelig. 6560 FANNIN ST, STE 1740 77030 #041-09-1969 L1974 **ORS** *020 †40

FINKEL, Kevin Wm. 6431 FANNIN ST, MSB 4 148 77030 #048-14-1987 L1994 **NEP** *020 †20

FINKELSTEIN, Barney. 8081 GREENBRIAR ST 77054 #041-01-1960 L1966 **R** *071 †80

FINKELSTEIN, Jeremy Paul. 6565 FANNIN ST, STE M-196 77030 #023-01-1994 L1995 **EM** *020 †16

FINKOWSKI DE RIVERA, J. 5615 KIRBY DR, STE 440 77005 #024-01-1983 L1988 **NPM** *020 †55

FINNILA, Christopher J. 1707 SUNSET BLVD, MEDICAL CLINIC OF HOUSTON 77005 #048-04-1998 L1999 **IM** *020 †20

FINNILA, Lara Baranov. 4101 GREENBRIAR ST, STE 100 77098 #048-14-1999 L2002 **PD** *020 †55

FIORE, Nicholas Arthur. 11302 FALLBROOK DR, STE 308 77065 #305-01-1999 L2006 **HS** *020 †85

FIORITO, Diego Evasio. 1 BAYLOR PLZ, BAYLOR COLLGE MED PATH DEP 77030 #132-04-1985 L1996 **PTH PCP** *020 †50

FIRPO, Patrice Danielle. 7900 FANNIN ST, STE 4811 77054 #041-13-1996 L1998 **OBG** *020 †30

FIRST, Kenneth Robt. 1100 HERCULES AVE, STE 100 77058 #024-01-1983 L1989 **ORS OSM** *020 †40

FISCH, Michael Jordan. 1515 HOLCOMBE BLVD, UNIT 241 77030 #051-01-1990 L2001 **ON PLM** *020 †20

FISCHER, Craig Leland. 2101 NASA PKWY, MAIL CODE SA STE A2 77058 #019-02-1962 L1971 **PTH NM** *030 †50,28,18

FISCHER, Craig Peter. 6431 FANNIN ST, STE 4294 77030 #048-14-1992 L2001 **GS** *020 †85

FISCHER, Harald E. ■ 77035 #409-19-1967 L1975 **BBK** *062 †50

FISCHER, John Henry, II. 6720 BERTNER ST, ST LUKE'S EPISCOPAL HOSPIT 77030 #048-04-1994 L1996 **DR** *020 †80

FISCHER, Martin Stanley. 6624 FANNIN ST, STE 2000 77030 #035-09-1963 L1970 **RHU IM** *020 †20

FISCHER, Ronald Peter. 6431 FANNIN ST # 4.286, DEPT. OF SURGERY 77030 #038-41-1961 L1983 **TRS GS** *071 †85

FISCHER, Stanton Pollard. 6624 FANNIN ST, STE 1900 77030 #041-01-1956 L1965 **PUD IM** *071 †20

FISH, Richard David. 6624 FANNIN ST, STE 2220 77030 #048-12-1982 L1983 **CD IM** *020 †20

FISHER, Anna Lee. ■ 77019 #005-14-1976 L1979 **AM EM** *020

FISHER, Brandon W. 1364 RM 1960 RD W STE 10 77090 #048-15-2001 L2006 **DR** *020 †80

FISHER, Christine Megan. ■ 77025 #016-42-2006 **RO** *012

FISHER, Colette Elise. 4501 GROVEWAY DR, PEDIATRIC ASSOCIATES 77087 #025-07-2003 L2006 **PD** *100 †55

FISHER, John David. 7737 SOUTHWEST FWY, STE 100 77074 #048-14-1987 L1989 **GS** *020 †85

FISHER, Mark Bradley. ■ 77030 #025-07-2001 L2007 **U** *100

FISHER, Richard Gilbert. 1 BAYLOR PLZ # BCM360, DEPT RAD 77030 #048-02-1963 L1963 **VIR R** *040 †80

FISHER, Ronald Evan. 6565 FANNIN ST, DEPT OF RADIOLOGY 77030 #048-04-1991 L2002 **NM** *020 †28

FISHER, Stanley P. 6560 FANNIN ST, DEPT OF NEURO STE 802 77030 #041-15-2000 L2002 **N** *020 †75

FISHER, William Edward. 1709 DRYDEN RD STE 1500, BAYLOR COLLEGE OF MEDICINE 77030 #038-41-1990 L1998 **GS** *020 †85

FISHER, William Frederick. 17000 EL CAMINO REAL 77058 #011-03-1975 L1979 **EM** *020 †16

FISHERMAN, Alan Mark. 2500 CITYWEST BLVD, STE 1150 77042 #048-02-1975 L1975 **MDM PMM** *030

FISHKIND, Avrim Brett. 1333 MOURSUND ST 77030 #023-07-1991 L1996 **P** *020 †75

FISHMAN, Amiram Moshe. 6550 FANNIN ST STE 701 77030 #550-02-1985 L1993 **OBG** *020

FISHMAN, Douglas Shawn. 6701 FANNIN ST 10TH FL, CLINICAL CARE CENTER 77030 #550-02-2000 L2006 **PG** *100 †55

FISHMAN, Irving Joshua. 6624 FANNIN ST STE 1980 77030 #067-01-1971 L1978 **U** *020 †95

FISHMAN, Lawrence B. 6421 FANNIN ST 77030 #062-01-1984 **PDO** *020 †45

FISHMAN, Marvin Allen. 6621 FANNIN ST 77030 #016-11-1961 L1979 **CHN** *020 †55,75

FITKO, James. 6360 W SAM HOUSTON PKWY N, STE 200 77041 #016-06-1978 L1993 **OM IM** *030 †20,16,70

FITTON, Conar Patrick. ■ 77054 #021-01-2006 **IM** *012

FITZGERALD, Nancy E. 1515 HOLCOMBE BLVD # 368, DIAGNOSTIC IMAGING 77030 #038-45-1991 L2001 **DR PDR** *020 †80

FITZGERALD, Ray Munn. 17080 RED OAK DR 77090 #048-02-1971 L1971 **ORS** *020 †40

FITZGIBBONS, Stella Jones. 6565 FANNIN ST 77030 #048-04-1980 L1981 **IM** *020 †20

FLACK, James Norton. 1 BAYLOR PLZ # 350 77030 #048-13-1986 L1988 **P** *020 †75

FLAM, Gary Howard. 6720 BERTNER ST 77030 #005-14-1987 L1991 **AN** *020 †05

FLANAGAN, Kathy C. 2211 NORFOLK ST STE 505 77098 #048-14-1985 L1988 **P** *020 †75

FLEMING, Gloria E R M. ■ 77052 #048-02-1957 L1957 **EM** *071

FLEMING, James John. ■ 77079 #048-14-1984 L1986 **GS** *020 †85

FLEMING, Jason B. ■ 77005 #047-06-1990 L1993 **GS** *020 †85

FLEMING, Mark Albert. 4515 IVANHOE ST 77027 #019-02-1968 L1971 **R OS** *020 †80

FLEMING, William H. 7777 SOUTHWEST FWY STE 900 77074 #028-34-1975 L1979 **N** *020 ‡

FLICK, Sarah Robinson. 7011 SOUTHWEST FWY, MHMRA OF HARRIS COUNTY 77074 #048-02-1986 L1987 **CHP P** *030 †75

FLORENCE, Lewis. 7444 HARRISBURG BLVD 77011 #048-04-1953 L1953 **OBS GP** *020

FLORES, Gary Wm. 7401 MAIN ST 77030 #048-04-1985 L1986 **AN** *020 †05

FLORES, Imelda M F Caoili. ■ 77083 #748-01-1991 **PTH** *100

FLORES, Miguel Juan. 710 FM 1960 RD W 77090 #048-13-1976 L1977 **FM** *020 †18

FLORES, Ricardo Jose. 6621 FANNIN ST CC15100, TEXAS CHILDREN'S HOSP 77030 #042-01-2004 **PHO** *012 †55

FLORES, Roberto C. 4414 NAVIGATION BLVD, MHMR RIPLEY CLINIC 77011 #748-01-1974 L1994 **P** *020

FLORES, Sara Kristine. ■ 77025 #048-04-2006 **P** *012

FLORES, Serina Marie. 210A HAWTHORNE ST 77006 #048-02-2000 L2004 **IM** *020 †20

FLORES, Steven Edward. 6620 MAIN ST, 13TH FLOOR, DEPT ORTH SURG 77030 #048-04-2001 L2006 **OSM** *100

FLORES FIGUEROA, Jose. ■ 77033 #649-03-2000 **ID** *012

FLORES-SANDOVAL, Felipe N. 6624 FANNIN ST STE 2280 77030 #429-01-1973 L1981 **U** *020 †95

FLOREZ, Luisa Fernanda. 1885 OLD SPANISH TRL, EXAMINER DEPT 77054 #264-07-1990 L2004 **FOP** *012

FLOURNOY, Jamie Nicole. 6431 FANNIN ST, JJL431 77030 #051-07-2004 L2006 **EM** *020

FLOWERS, C E Blanton. 2323 S SHEPHERD DR STE 110 77019 #048-04-1983 L1984 **P** *020 †75

FLOWERS, Larry. 110 CYPRESS STATION DR, STE 113 77090 #047-07-1982 L1986 **P** *020 †75

FLOYD, Craig Monroe. 7600 BEECHNUT ST 77074 #048-14-1981 L1981 **PTH** *020 †50

FLOYD, John Robert. ■ 77021 #001-02-2000 **NS** *100

FLOYD, William Norman, Jr. 7505 MEMORIAL WOODS DR 77024 #021-01-1966 L1967 **IM R** *020 †80

FLURRY, Mitchell Duncan. ■ 77054 #048-14-2008 *012

FOGARTY, James Patrick. 11800 FM 1960 RD W 77065 #048-02-1978 L1978 **ORS** *020 †40

FOGELMAN, David Randal. 1515 HOLCOMBE BLVD, UNIT 426 77030 #035-46-1998 L2007 **HO** *020 †20

FOGIEL, Barbara Rose. 915 GESSNER RD, STE 800 77024 #550-02-1998 L2002 **OBG** *020 †30

FOLCINI, Matias Eugenio. 2520 BROADMEAD AVE, APT 920 77025 #132-14-2004 *100

FOLDES, Cara Allison. 1504 TAUB LOOP, BEN TAUB GEN HOS 77030 #035-47-1997 L2003 **IM** *040 †20

FOLEY, Richard James. 607 TIMBERDALE LN STE 201 77090 #016-11-1977 L1982 **NEP IM** *020 †20

FOLLEN, Michele. 1515 HOLCOMBE BLVD # 193, BME CENTER 77030 #025-01-1980 L1988 **GO OBG** *020 †30

FONG DE LOS SANTOS, Yoland. 1 BAYLOR PLZ, DEPT PATH 77030 #649-52-2001 **PTH** *100 †50

FONSECA, Orlando G. ■ 77024 #048-14-2002 L2007 **IM** *020

FONSECA, Oscar A. 1213 HERMANN DR STE 338 77004 #341-01-1959 L1971 **IM END** *020

FONT, Elso. ■ 77072 #847-04-1968 **PTH** *020

FONT, Ramon L. 6550 FANNIN ST, STE 1501 77030 #275-01-1956 L1979 **ATP OS** *020 †50

FONTENOT, James Thos. 17400 RED OAK DR 77090 #649-14-1972 L1976 **FM** *020

FOOX, Ivor Wilfred. 4524 HIGHWAY 6 N 77084 #836-01-1969 L1977 **GP** *020

FORBIS, Samuel Earl. ■ 77059 #021-01-1959 L1959 **R** *020

FORD, Dinsdale Washington. 7737 SOUTHWEST FWY, STE 580 77074 #010-03-1976 L1981 **OBG** *020

FORD, Donald P. 5000 MONTROSE BLVD 77006 #048-04-1950 L1950 **OPH** *071 †35

FORD, Kenneth Bowen, Jr. 101 BROAD OAKS CIR 77056 #048-02-1969 L1969 **ORS** *020 †40

FORD, Patrick Vaughn. 6720 BERTNER ST, STE 3-261 77030 #048-13-1982 L1983 **NM** *020 †28

FORD, Ralph Vernon. ■ 77027 #048-04-1946 L1946 **IM** *071 †20

FORD, Richard Jos. 1515 HOLCOMBE BLVD BOX 72, CANCER CTR 77030 #038-06-1974 L1977 **IG PTH** *050 †50

FORDAN, Steve Vincentesto. 7147 HARMONY CV 77036 #048-04-2003 L2006 **END** *012 †20

FORDIS, C Michael. 1709 DRYDEN RD, STE 534 77030 #005-18-1975 L1980 **IM** *020

FORGASON, Burt Lanier. 14441 MEMORIAL DR STE 6 77079 #048-14-1985 L1986 **FM** *020 †18

FORINGER, John Richard. 105 DREW ST 77006 #048-14-1996 L1998 **NEP** *020 †20

FORMAN, Arthur David. 1515 HOLCOMBE BLVD, DEPT OF NEURO-ONCOLOGY-BOX 77030 #041-09-1976 L1988 **N ON** *020 †75

FORNAGE, Bruno D. 1515 HOLCOMBE BLVD, DIAGNOSTIC IMAGING DIVISIO 77030 #396-27-1974 L1992 *020

FORNER, Thomas Dewitt. ■ 77024 #048-14-1985 L1986 **IM** *020

FOROOZAN, Rod. 6550 FANNIN ST, STE 1501 77030 #035-46-1997 L2003 **OPH** *020

FORRESTER, Gene D. 607 TIMBERDALE LN, STE 201 77090 #048-02-1990 L1991 **NEP** *020 †20

FORSTALL, Peter George. 6720 BERTNER ST, CARDIOLOGY EDUCATION 77030 #054-04-2002 L2006 **CD** *012 †20

FORTES, Paul F. 12727 KIMBERLEY LN, AESTHETIC CENTER FOR 77024 #048-04-1990 L1991 **PS GS** *020 †65,85

FORTIN-MAGANA, Romeo. 6655 HILLCROFT ST STE 109 77081 #341-01-1960 L1981 **PD** *020

FORTUN, Jorge Andres. ■ 77030 #025-01-2004 *100

FOSHEE, Sarah Lynn. 3111 UNIVERSITY BLVD 77005 #048-02-1992 L1993 **AN** *020 †05

FOSSELLA, Frank Vito. 1515 HOLCOMBE BLVD, BOX 80 77030 #048-04-1982 L1983 **ON** *020 †20

FOSTER, Dianne J. 818 RINGOLD ST 77088 #048-02-1987 L1990 **PD** *020 †55

FOSTER, Paul Jos. 8285 EL RIO ST, STE 170 77054 #038-41-1987 L1995 **PD** *020

FOSTER, Samuel Burk. 6621 FANNIN ST 77030 #025-01-2001 L2006 **AI** *050 †55,03

FOSTER, William Joseph, Jr. 6410 FANNIN ST, STE 920 77030 #036-07-1999 L2004 **OPH** *020 †35 ‡

FOTE, Barnabas Talla. ■ 77054 #409-41-2004 **GPM** *012

FOWLER, Elizabeth Sanchez. 10718 NORCHESTER VILG DR D 77070 #048-02-2001 L2004 **PD** *020 †55

FOWLER, Grant C. 6431 FANNIN ST, SUITE JJL 324 77030 #048-14-1984 L1985 **FM FSM** *040 †18 ‡

FOWLER, Nathan Hale. 1515 HOLCOMBE BLVD, UNIT 429 77030 #048-02-2001 L2007 **HO** *100

FOWLER, Robert Skead. ■ 77009 #048-13-1979 L1980 **GP** *020

FOX, Brigitte M G. 77005 #048-02-1996 L1999 **IM** *020 †20

FOX, Janice Marie. 77056 #025-12-1973 L1978 **P** *020

FOXHALL, Lewis Emory. 1515 HOLCOMBE BLVD UNT 220, UT MD ANDERSON CANCER CTR 77030 #048-04-1976 L1976 **FM** *030 †18

FRACE, William Jeffrey. 710 FM 1960 RD W DEPT ANES 77090 #048-02-1980 L1980 **AN** *020 †05

FRACHTMAN, Richard Julian. 920 FROSTWOOD DR 77024 #048-02-1977 L1977 **DR** *020 †80

FRACHTMAN, Steven Jay. ■ 77030 #048-02-2006 **IM** *012

FRADKIN, Robbie Jean. ■ 77071 #048-02-2004 L2007 **CHP** *012

FRAGOSO, Veronica Garcia. ■ 77093 #048-14-2008 **FM** *100

FRAM, Lewis Bertrand. 12335 KINGSRIDE LN, # 137 77024 #048-02-1964 L1964 **U** *071 †95 ‡

FRANCIS, Anita Marie. 5315 FM 1960 RD W, STE B 77069 #005-14-1996 L2008 **OBG** *020 †30

FRANCIS, Mark Douglas. 12025 LOUETTA RD 77070 #048-04-1982 L1983 **GS** *020

FRANCIS, William Raleigh. 4126 SOUTHWEST FWY, STE 1620 77027 #048-04-1973 L1973 **ORS OSS** *020 †40

FRANCISCO, Gerard E. 1333 MOURSUND ST, E103 77030 #748-02-1989 L1997 **PM OS** *050 †60

FRANCO, Juan M. 1315 ST JOSEPH PKWY, STE 1202 77002 #048-14-2001 L2005 **OBG** *020 †30

FRANCO, Luis Miguel. 6621 FANNIN ST, CC-1560 77030 #264-04-2000 **MG** *012 †20

FRANCO, Miguel A, Jr. 1201 DAIRY ASHFORD ST, STE 200 77079 #035-19-1979 L1981 **IM PUD** *020 †20

FRANCO RIVERA, Patricia. PO BOX 20708, UNIV TX MED SCH 77225 #264-04-2002 **DR** *012

FRANGOGIANNIS, Nikolaos. ■ 77030 #418-01-1990 L1999 **CD** *020 †20

FRANGOS, Stephen A. 1500 LOUISIANA ST, RM 1614 77002 #023-12-1983 L1989 **OM** *030 †70

FRANK, Christopher M. 6720 BERTNER ST RM P332, EPISCOPAL HOSPITAL 77030 #035-01-2001 L2005 **ICE** *012

FRANK, Steven Jay. 1515 HOLCOMBE BLVD, BOX 97 77030 #012-05-2000 L2002 **RO** *100 †80

FRANKE, Fritz Oswald A. 2603 AUGUSTA DR # 805 77057 #154-07-1970 L1977 **P CHP** *020 †75

FRANKEL, Norman Bruce. 6560 FANNIN ST, STE 600 77030 #035-46-1965 L1971 **GE IM** *020 †20

FRANKEL, Ryan Evan. ■ 77004 #024-07-2002 L2002 **U** *012

FRANKLIN, Daniel J. 2500 TANGLEWILDE ST, STE 160 77063 #048-04-1981 L1982 **OTO** *020 †45

FRANKLIN, Joshua Charles. ■ 77006 #011-03-2007 L2007 **TY** *012

FRANKLIN, Letitia Tsion. 1313 HERMANN DR, STE 270 77004 #048-02-2003 L2007 **AN** *020

FRANKLIN, Robbi Lyle. ■ 77054 #048-02-2004 **NS** *012

FRANKLIN, Robert R. 7900 FANNIN ST STE 4000 77054 #048-02-1953 L1953 **GYN** *020 †30

FRANKLIN, Wayne Jay. ■ 77098 #005-14-1997 L2002 **CD** *100 †20

FRANKLIN, William Clyde. 7737 SOUTHWEST FWY STE 625 77074 #048-04-1956 L1956 **IM** *020

FRANKS, Robert Cecil. 6410 FANNIN ST, STE 1400 77030 #047-05-1958 L1969 **PD PDE** *071 †55

FRANZ, Robert Geo. 21175 STATE HWY 249, PMB 303 77070 #039-01-1959 L1959 **FM** *040

FRASER, Charles D. 6621 FANNIN ST, MC WT 19345H 77030 #048-02-1984 L1985 **TS** *020 †85,90

FRASER, Ronald L. 12121 RICHMOND AVE STE 425 77082 #065-09-1960 L1977 **ORS** *020 †40

FRATES, Ralph Coryell, Jr. 5656 KELLEY ST, DIVISION OF EMERGENCY MEDI 77026 #021-01-1969 L1974 **GPM** *020 †55,70

FRAZIER, Bryant John. 2500 FONDREN RD, STE 270 77063 #024-16-1997 L2000 **FSM** *020 †18

FRAZIER, Johnnie Jeanne P. 6431 FANNIN ST STE 3140, UNIV OF TEXAS MED SCHOOL 77030 #048-15-1976 L1978 **PD ID** *020 †55

FRAZIER, Oscar Howard. 1101 BATES AVE, SURGICAL ASSOCIATES OF 77030 #048-04-1967 L1967 **TS TTS** *020 †85,90

FRAZIER, Roderick N. 1213 HERMANN DR, STE 845 77004 #047-06-1981 L1982 **GP** *020

FRAZIER, Winfred Taylor. ■ 77054 #048-04-2008 *012

FRED, Herbert Leonard. 5656 KELLEY ST 77026 #023-07-1954 L1954 **IM** *040 †20

FREDRICKS, Simon. ■ 77007 #016-42-1952 L1958 **PS** *020 †65

FREDRICKSON, Becky Jo. 1740 W 27TH ST 77008 #048-04-2000 L2002 **OPH** *020 †35

FREEDMAN, Leon David. 909 FROSTWOOD DR, STE 126 77024 #035-09-1972 L1974 **PD** *020 †55

FREEDMAN, Ralph Stuart. 1515 HOLCOMBE BLVD # 440 77030 #836-01-1965 L1977 **GYN IG** *020 †30

FREEMAN, Asha Marie. 6431 FANNIN ST, AT HO 77030 #041-13-2005 **PD** *012

FREEMAN, Bobbie Jo. ■ 77266 #048-14-2004 L2008 **AN** *012

FREEMAN, Brandi Kaye. ■ 77054 #048-04-2008 *012

FREEMAN, Christopher John. ■ 77054 #035-03-2004 L2007 **EM** *020

FREEMAN, Gary Cornielious. 12827 GULF FWY, GULF FREEWAY ORTHOPEDICS P 77034 #048-04-1964 L1964 **ORS HS** *020 †40

FREEMAN, Phillip Neal. 1140 BUSINESS CENTER DR, STE 200 77043 #020-02-1983 L1986 **PS OS** *020 †65

FREEMAN, Scott B. 6431 FANNIN ST, DEPT OF ANES 5.020 77030 #048-12-2001 **AN** *100

FREET, Daniel James. 6431 FANNIN ST, STE 1400 77030 #018-03-1995 L1997 **PS** *020 †65

FREIREICH, Emil J. 1515 HOLCOMBE BLVD, STATION 55 77030 #016-11-1949 L1965 **HO IM** *050 †20

FREMAUX, Richard Leon. 5656 KELLEY ST 77026 #021-05-1969 L1970 **RNR DR** *020 †80

FRENCH, Jessica Renee. ■ 77006 #048-14-2008 *012

FRENCH, Shannon L. ■ 77025 #048-16-2000 L2007 **PD** *100 †55

FRENCH-BLOOM, Katy Elizab. 1419 MONTROSE BLVD # 505 77019 #021-01-2003 L2007 **ACA** *012

FRENCH-ROSAS, Lindsey Nic. ■ 77004 #003-01-2008 *012

FRENGER, Fred Paul, Jr. ■ 77079 #048-13-1974 L1974 **GP P** *020

FRENZEL, Elizabeth Conrad. 1515 HOLCOMBE BLVD, UTMDACC EMPLOYEE HEALTH 63 77030 #036-01-1989 L1990 **GPM** *100 †70

FRENZEL, John Carroll. 1220 HOLCOMBE BLVD, UNIT 1243 77030 #048-04-1989 L1990 **AN MDM** *020 †05

FRETWELL, Roslyn C. 7600 BEECHNUT ST 77074 #045-01-1980 L1983 **AN** *040 †05

FREW, Kelly Becker. 1 BAYLOR PLZ, DEPT OF ANESTHIOLOGY 77030 #048-04-2005 **AN** *012

FRIAS, Angelica S. 2402 WESTGATE ST STE 200 77019 #231-03-1967 L1975 **P CHP** *020 †75

FRIDAY, Renee Yvette. 2050 SPACE PARK DR 77058 #041-12-1988 L2003 **PDC** *020 †55

FRIEBEN, Ryan William. ■ 77021 #048-14-2008 *012

FRIEDLAND, Joan Angert. 2002 HOLCOMBE BLVD 77030 #016-11-1960 L1965 **IM** *040

FRIEDLAND, Sigmund Wm. 1200 BINZ ST STE 300 77004 #016-02-1968 L1968 **IM CD** *071 †20

FRIEDMAN, Alan Wm. 1707 SUNSET BLVD, MEDICAL CLINIC OF HOUSTON 77005 #048-14-1986 L1993 **RHU IM** *020

FRIEDMAN, Claire Leslie. 6500 HORNWOOD DR 77074 #048-04-1992 L1995 **CHP** *020 †75

FRIEDMAN, Ellen Mae. 6501 FANNIN ST, BAYLOR OTOLARYNGOLOGY 77030 #035-46-1975 L1991 **PDO** *020 †45

FRIEDMAN, Elliott Robert. ■ 77030 #021-01-2003 L2006 **DR** *012

FRIEDMAN, Gary Kanter. 11757 KATY FWY 77079 #048-04-1968 L1968 **IM** *020 †20,70

FRIEDMAN, Janice Elaine G. 7011 SOUTHWEST FWY, MHMRA 77074 #048-02-1965 L1970 **P OBG** *020

FRIEDMAN, Jeffrey David. 6560 FANNIN ST, STE 800 77030 #048-04-1985 L1993 **PS** *020 †85,65

FRIEDMAN, Morton. 13111 EAST FWY 77015 #869-02-1963 L1971 **AN** *020

FRIEDMAN, Paul M. 7515 MAIN ST, STE 240 77030 #047-06-1996 L2001 **D** *020 †15

FRIEDMAN, Richard Alan. 6621 FANNIN ST, TCH-WT-19345C 77030 #041-12-1980 L1988 **PDC PD** *050 †55

FRIEDMAN, Robert Harry. 920 FROSTWOOD DR STE 580 77024 #048-02-1965 L1965 **OBG** *020 †30

FRIEDMAN, Zvi. 1313 HERMANN DR # 407 77004 #550-01-1968 L1979 **NPM** *020 †55

FRIEDMANN, Craig Henry. 600 N DAIRY ASHFORD ST, MA 3046 77079 #035-01-1986 L1990 **OM IM** *030 †20,70

FRIEL, Michael Thomas. ■ 77054 #021-01-2003 L2007 **GS** *012

FRIERSON, James N. 2403 CAROLINE ST 77004 #048-02-1952 L1952 **OM** *071

■ = Address Information Privacy Protected

FRIES, John Geo. ■ 77057 #012-01-1955 L1959 **HNS** *071 †85

FRIGINI, Luiz Alexandre R. 1 BAYLOR PLZ, BAYLOR CM - DEPT. OF RADIO 77030 #187-14-1994 L2005 **DR** *020 †80

FRITZ, Traci Renae. ■ 77009 #048-02-2007 L2008 *012

FROMBERG, Henry Fielding. 6565 FANNIN ST 77030 #048-04-1956 L1956 **AN** *020

FROME, Adam Immanuel. 6565 FANNIN ST # 1290, MED/PEDS PR 77030 #048-13-2004 L2007 **IM** *012 †20

FROMM, Geri-Lynn. 1515 HOLCOMBE BLVD 77030 #016-06-1981 L1989 **GO GYN** *020 †30

FROMM, Robert E, Jr. 2219 DORRINGTON ST 77030 #016-06-1981 L1986 **IM CCM** *020 †20,70,16

FROMMER, Pedro. 10023 S MAIN ST STE C9 77025 #231-01-1973 L1978 **NEP IM** *020 †20

FRONTERA, Joel Ernesto. 77004 #042-01-2003 L2008 **SCI** *012

FROST, Adaani Ethel. 6620 MAIN ST, MAIL STOP 621 77030 #063-01-1973 L1991 **IM PUD** *020 †20

FROST, James Dahle, Jr. 6565 FANNIN ST DEPT EEG 77030 #048-04-1962 L1962 **N** *050

FROST, Louis B. 7322 SOUTHWEST FWY STE 160 77074 #048-14-2001 L2003 **GPM GP** *020

FROST, Scot Jos. 18220 TOMBALL PKWY STE 330 77070 #048-02-1981 L1981 **ORS OSM** *020 †40

FRUHMAN, Gary. ■ 77071 #035-19-2004 L2006 **OBG** *012

FRUMIN, Marshall Stewart. 7777 SOUTHWEST FWY STE 344 77074 #047-06-1970 L1981 **ORS OSM** *020 †40

FRUMOVITZ, Michael M. 1515 HOLCOMBE BLVD, UNIT 1362 77030 #005-14-1997 L2001 **OBG** *020

FRUTHALER, Carolyn Sue. 2223 WEST LOOP S, HARRIS CO. PUBLIC HEALTH & 77027 #021-05-1983 L1987 **OBG PHP** *062 †30

FRYE, Cathlyne Ellen. ■ 77030 #048-02-1978 L1978 **AN** *020 †05

FRYE, Richard Eugene. 6431 FANNIN ST, MSB 7.109 77030 #010-02-1998 L2007 **CHN** *020 †75,55 ‡

FU, Jack Brian. 1302 WAUGH DR 77019 #048-12-2002 L2006 **PM** *100 †60

FU, Siqing. PO BOX 301439, 1515 HOLCOMBE UNIT 1364 77230 #243-52-1985 L2005 **HO** *012 †20

FUCHIGAMI, Kevin David. 2900 RICHMOND AVE 77098 #016-06-1988 L1991 **DR** *020 †80

FUENTES, Francisco. 6431 FANNIN ST 77030 #847-08-1969 L1975 **CD IM** *020 †20

FUENTES-BLACK, Sharon M. ■ 77048 #048-02-2003 L2007 **PTH** *100

FUENTEZ, Irene Hernandez. 412 TELEPHONE RD, EASTOOD HEALTH CLINIC 77023 #048-04-1980 L1980 **IM** *020 †20

FUERST, Jan Fredric. 909 FROSTWOOD DR STE 311 77024 #048-12-1971 L1971 **D** *020 †15

FUEYO MARGARETO, Juan. 1515 HOLCOMBE BLVD, STE 316 77030 #847-12-1984 L2000 *100

FUJII, Mavis Dorothy. 18333 EGRET BAY BLVD, EGRET BAY NEUROLOGY PA 77058 #061-01-1980 L1989 **N** *020 †70

FUJISE, Kenichi. 6431 FANNIN ST, DIVISION OF CARDIOLOGY 77030 #572-01-1987 L1993 **CD IM** *020 †20

FUKAMI, Norio. ■ 77002 #572-12-1992 L2005 **GE** *020 †20

FUKSHANSKY, Mikhail. 1515 HOLCOMBE BLVD, BOX 42 77030 #035-48-1999 L2004 **APM** *020 †60

FUKUDA, Tomiko. 6410 FANNIN ST STE 1535 77030 #056-06-2002 L2006 **ORS** *020

FULFORD, Robert Alan. 3701 KIRBY DR, STE 436 77098 #065-05-1961 L1975 **ORS** *020 †40

FULLER, Gregory N. 1515 HOLCOMBE BLVD 77030 #048-04-1987 L1988 **NP** *020 †50

FULLER, Lillian Mary. 1515 HOLCOMBE BLVD, M D ANDERSON CANCER CENTER 77030 #065-06-1947 L1958 **RO** *071 †80

FULLER, Lisa Rodney. 6621 FANNIN ST, WT 6-104 77030 #021-05-1998 L2004 **PD** *020 †55

FULLER, Tracy Ann. 6720 BERTNER ST STE 0-520, TEXAS HEART INSTITUTE 77030 #025-07-2001 L2006 **IM** *100 †05

FULTON, Stephanie Carol. 1740 W 27TH ST STE 301 77008 #048-13-1981 L1981 **OBG** *020 †30

FULWEBER, Robert Cyril. 1515 HOLCOMBE BLVD STE 1562 77030 #011-03-1964 L1971 **CD** *020 †20

FUNG, Derrick Syho. ■ 77025 #048-04-2008 *012

FUNG, Kathleen Blue. 6621 FANNIN ST RM A170, MC1-1000 77030 #048-12-2006 **PD** *012

FUNG, Kee-Bun. 2002 HOLCOMBE BLVD, X-RAY DEPARTMENT 77030 #244-03-1963 L1975 **DR** *020 †80

FUNG, Philip H. ■ 77054 #048-12-2006 **IM** *012

FURIAN, Lucrezia. 6431 FANNIN ST, DEPT IMMLGY & ORGAN TRNAPL 77030 #561-11-2001 **GS TTS** *100

FURNO, Robert Kangil. 6431 FANNIN ST 417, UT HOUSTON MEDICAL SCHOOL/ 77030 #056-06-2001 L2006 **EM** *020 †16

FURR, Erin Elizabeth. ■ 77025 #016-42-2002 L2007 **N** *100

FURSE, Robert Austen. 7777 SOUTHWEST FWY, STE 1004 77074 #048-04-1977 L1977 **ON IM** *020 †20

FUSTOK, Abdelkader. 4126 SOUTHWEST FWY, STE 1030 77027 #396-18-1973 L1979 **PS HS** *020

GAALLA, Amar K. 2727 W HOLCOMBE BLVD 77025 #048-14-1993 L1994 **DR** *020 †80

GABBARD, Glen Owens. 6655 TRAVIS ST STE 500 77030 #016-01-1975 L2002 **P PYA** *040 †75

GABBAY, Kenneth Heskel. 6621 FANNIN ST, # 3-2353 77030 #035-45-1961 L1986 **IM OS** *020

GABBAY, Myrna. ■ 77024 #065-09-1969 L1973 **D** *020

GABEL, Catherine Leo. 2500 FONDREN RD, STE 270 77063 #048-14-1991 L1992 **OBG** *020 †30

GABER, Ahmed Osama. 6550 FANNIN ST DEPT OF, SMITH TOWER, STE SM1661A 77030 #915-04-1976 L2006 **GS** *020 †85

GABER, Lillian Wadie. ■ 77005 #915-02-1976 L2008 **PTH** *020 †50

GABLER, Kelly Ann. 7737 SOUTHWEST FWY, STE 420 77074 #048-14-2005 L2007 **FP** *012

GADHIA, Vandana Mohanbhai. 1711 OLD SPANISH TRL, APT 402 77054 #048-04-2005 **IM** *012

GADICHERLA, Sonal M. ■ 77054 #495-09-2001 **IM** *012

GADIRAJU, Prasad D. 7600 BEECHNUT ST 77074 #495-65-1975 L1997 **AN** *020 †05

GAER, Edward Allen. 12121 RICHMOND AVE STE 216 77082 #056-05-1964 L1987 **N P** *020 †75

GAGEL, Robert Francis. 1515 HOLCOMBE BLVD, BOX 433 77030 #038-40-1971 L1982 **END IM** *030 †20

GAGLIARDI, Michael. 6431 FANNIN ST 4232, UNIVERSITY OF TEXAS HLTH S 77030 #030-06-1964 L1971 **GE IM** *020

GAHREMANPOUR, Amir Ali. ■ 77054 #517-05-1998 L2007 **IM** *020 †20

GAHUNIA, Sareena Lani. ■ 77021 #003-01-2005 **PD** *012

GAINES, Larry Strawder. 1201 GROSS ST 77019 #045-01-1966 L1982 **RO AM** *071 †80

GAITANARU, Daniela M. 6550 FANNIN ST STE 2421, SMITH TOWER 77030 #781-05-1990 L1998 **PCC** *012

GAITZ, Charles Milton. 6565 FANNIN ST 77030 #048-02-1946 L1946 **PYG P** *071 †75

GAITZ, Jeffrey Preston. 6565 FANNIN ST, STE 206 77008 #048-02-1977 L1977 **N** *020 †75

GAKHAR, Anju. ■ 77083 #496-09-1980 *074

GALATI, Joseph S. 6624 FANNIN STE 1990, LIVER SPECIALISTS OF TEXAS 77030 #422-01-1987 L1995 **HEP GE** *020 †20

GALE, Stephen. 6431 FANNIN ST STE 4.276, DEPARTMENT OF SURGERY 77030 #016-11-1996 L2007 **GS** *100 †85

GALER, Chad Edward. 1515 HOLCOMBE BLVD 77030 #018-03-2001 L2008 **OTO** *020 †45

GALE-ROWE, Margaret A. 5425 POLK ST STE J 77023 #065-09-1987 L2003 **GPM** *030 †70

GALFIONE, Matthew Richard. ■ 77030 #048-04-2007 *012

GALFIONE, Ronald Richard. 6560 FANNIN ST, STE 1012 77030 #048-14-1974 L1974 **IM** *020 †20

GALICIA, Dalia G. ■ 77025 #048-04-2003 L2005 **AI** *012 †20

GALINDO, Denis Leo. 1140 CYPRESS STATION DR, NORTHWEST DIAGNOSTIC CLINI 77090 #048-02-1975 L1975 **IM** *020 †20

GALLAGHER, Hugh Gerald. 6410 FANNIN ST 77030 #539-05-1983 L1994 **AN PMM** *020

GALLAGHER, John Chas. 2 CHELSEA BLVD 77006 #001-02-1958 L1962 **IM** *020

GALLAS, Stacey E. 1919 S BRAESWOOD BLVD, TX CHILDRENS PED ASSOC 77030 #048-04-1993 L1995 **PD** *020 †55

GALLEGOS, Phillip. ■ 77004 #654-01-2007 *012

GALLENTINE, Kathleen Anne. 5615 KIRBY DR STE 410 77005 #048-04-1977 L1978 **P** *020 †75

GALLER, Greg Wayne. 6720 BERTNER ST 77030 #019-02-1986 L1994 **GE IM** *020 †20

GALLOWAY, Robert Edward. 1200 BINZ ST, STE 1025 77004 #008-01-1973 L1977 **IM** *020 ‡

GALVADO-NETO, Antonio L. 6540 BELLOWS LN # 1301-B 77030 #187-21-1992 L2006 **SP** *100

GALVAN, Linda Anna. 9555 W SAM HSTN S #225 77099 #048-12-1985 L1993 **EM GS** *020 †16

GAMBELLO, Michael John. 6431 FANNIN ST, MSB 3144A 77030 #035-45-1993 L2002 **PD MG** *020 †19,55

GAMBLE, Henry Floyd, III. ■ 77235 #010-03-1968 L1979 **ORS HS** *020 †40

GAN, Sew-Hock. 6918 CORPORATE DR STE A10 77036 #244-02-1971 L1983 **FM** *020

GANC, Jaime. 6776 SW FWY STE 630 77074 #649-01-1962 L1973 **P CHP** *020 †75

GANDHI, Kiran Mukesh. 7777 SOUTHWEST FWY STE 808 77074 #495-17-1979 L1986 **IM** *020 †20

GANDHI, Samita. ■ 77054 #495-03-2000 **P** *012

GANIM, Mazen. 6400 FANNIN ST, STE 2210 77030 #048-14-1990 L1993 **IM** *020 †20

GANIM, Ricky Paul. 6410 FANNIN ST, STE 1425 77030 #048-14-1998 L2005 **IC** *020 †20

GANJU, Malini K. ■ 77025 #495-51-1985 **NM** *100

GANNON, Catherine M. 6621 FANNIN ST, MC: WT6-104 77030 #041-02-1990 L2006 **NPM** *020 †55

GANNON, Michael John. 11452 SPACE CENTER BLVD 77059 #065-06-1970 L1978 **FM** *020

GANTELA, Swaroop. ■ 77082 #048-04-1998 *100

GAO, Cuiying. ■ 77025 #243-32-1990 *100

GAO, Shuwei. 1515 HOLCOMBE BLVD, BOX 437 77030 #243-47-1983 L1998 **IM** *020 †20

GAOS, Carlos Maldonado. ■ 77007 #649-31-1982 **CD IM** *100

GARABELLI, Lauren Elizabe. 6621 FANNIN ST RM A170, MC1-1000 77030 #036-05-2006 **PD** *012

GARABELLI, Paul James. 1709 DRYDEN RD STE 550, BCM FACULTY CENTER 77030 #036-05-2006 **IM** *012

GARB, Ronald. 820 GESSNER RD STE 750 77024 #539-04-1965 L1991 **P** *020 †75

GARBER, Alan Joel. 6550 FANNIN ST, COSMETIC DAYSURGERY CT 77030 #041-13-1968 L1974 **IM END** *072

GARCIA, Aimee Dinorah. 2002 HOLCOMBE BLVD 2C-110 77030 #033-05-1994 L1995 **IMG** *020 †20

GARCIA, Alvaro Rene. 13111 EAST FWY 77015 #649-02-1984 L1990 **FM OM** *020 †18

GARCIA, Antonio. 5310 IRVINGTON BLVD 77009 #341-01-1964 L1973 **PD OS** *020

GARCIA, Charles Albert. 12970 EAST FWY, STE I10 77015 #021-01-1969 L1969 **OPH** *020 †35

GARCIA, Daniel. 5402 E SAM HOUSTON PKWY N 77015 #048-02-1998 L1999 **FM** *020 †18

GARCIA, Delfino F. 1707 SUNSET BLVD, MEDICAL CLINIC OF HOUSTON 77005 #024-05-1992 L1996 **IM** *020 †20

GARCIA, Eugenia. 6510 HILLCROFT ST 77081 #048-02-2001 L2004 **PD** *020 †55

GARCIA, Guillermo. 800 PEAKWOOD DR, STE 8B 77090 #048-14-1999 L2005 **GS** *020 †85

GARCIA, Habacuc D. 1635 NORTH LOOP W, MEDICAL STAFF OFFICE 77008 #048-02-2001 L2005 **EM** *100 †16

GARCIA, Isabel Tiongson. ■ 77005 #048-02-2004 L2008 **FM** *012

GARCIA, Jonas. 318 HERMANN DR STE 830 77004 #048-14-1978 L1978 **CD IM** *020 †20

GARCIA, Jorge A. 6624 FANNIN ST, STE 2310 77030 #042-01-1973 L1977 **IC CD** *020 †20

GARCIA, Jose. 6431 FANNIN ST # 3256 77030 #026-04-1978 L1988 **NPM** *020 †20

GARCIA, Jose Jorge. 920 FROSTWOOD DR 77024 #649-01-1961 L1967 **PD HEM** *071 †55

GARCIA, Jose Manuel. 2002 HOLCOMBE BLVD, DIV OF ENDOCRINOLOGY-VAMC 77030 #132-09-1997 L2000 **END IM** *020 †20

GARCIA, Juan Ignacio. 2900 WESLAYAN ST STE 540 77027 #132-01-1976 L1980 **CHP P** *020 †75

GARCIA, Juan Pacheco. 11511 VETERANS MEMORIAL DR, STE 200 77067 #649-02-1983 L1988 **FM** *020 †18

GARCIA, Laura Elena. ■ 77054 #048-04-2008 *012

GARCIA, Miguel Antonio. ■ 77059 #264-02-1963 L1972 **AN** *020

GARCIA, Priscilla J. ■ 77054 #048-04-2004 L2008 **AN** *012

GARCIA, Shawn Marie. ■ 77096 #048-04-2005 **PD** *100

GARCIA, Tony. 6431 FANNIN ST # 5.020, UNIV TX DEPT ANES 77030 #048-14-2001 L2005 **AN** *100 †05

GARCIA-GONZALEZ, Efrain. 302 HAMILTON ST, SAN JOSE CLINIC 77002 #042-01-1955 L1964 **CD IM** *071 †20

GARCIA MANERO, Guillermo. 1515 HOLCOMBE BLVD, BOX 428 77030 #847-06-1991 L2000 **HEM** *020 †20

GARCIA-MENCHACA, Pablo. ■ 77025 #649-03-1988 **AI** *020

GARCIA-MOWATT, Ibrahim. 427 W 20TH ST STE 704 77008 #649-14-1976 L1982 **ID IM** *020

GARCIA POPA-LISSEANU, Mari. 1 BAYLOR PLZ #847-13-2001 L2007 **AI** *012 †55

GARCIAPRATS, Anthony J. 6621 FANNIN ST, STE A-150 77030 #048-04-2002 L2005 **PD** *100 †55

GARCIA-PRATS, Jos Arthur. 6621 FANNIN NEON OFF 77030 #021-01-1972 L1975 **PD NPM** *040 †55

GARCIA-TORRES, Francisco. 1221 MCKINNEY ST, STE 40300 77010 #041-02-1971 L1979 **GE IM** *072 †20

GARD, Don Allan. ■ 77098 #048-04-1963 L1963 **PS SO** *071 †65

GARDEN, Adam Seth. 1515 HOLCOMBE BLVD BOX 97, UT MD ANDERSON CANCER CTR 77030 #035-08-1984 L1990 **RO IM** *020 †80

GARDEN, Fae Greenberg. 6431 FANNIN ST, STE 2330 77030 #035-20-1985 L1988 **PM** *020 †60

GARDINER, Carolyn L. 6431 FANNIN ST 1.122 77030 #048-14-1990 L1991 **IM** *020 †20

GARDNER, Donald Franklin. 909 FROSTWOOD DR STE 224 77024 #016-11-1973 L1983 **END IM** *050 †20

GARDNER, Jerad Michael. 6565 FANNIN ST M227 77030 #021-01-2006 **PTH** *012

GARDNER, Susan Elizabeth. 17030 NANES DR, STE 105 77090 #047-06-1975 L1980 PD *020 †55

GAREWAL, Davinder Singh. 6431 FANNIN ST, STE 5-020 77030 #539-06-1981 *100

GARG, Ambica. ■ 77054 #496-02-1998 OBG *012

GARG, Ravin Jain. PO BOX 20708, UT MD ANDERSON CTR 77225 #016-02-2003 L2007 HO *012 †20

GARG, Renu. 1919 NORTH LOOP W, STE 200 77008 #023-01-1982 L1983 PD *020 †55 ‡

GARRETT, Christopher R. ■ 77025 #539-04-1988 L1993 HO *020 †20

GARRETT, John Jones. 2855 GRAMERCY ST 77025 #048-04-1965 L1965 OPH *071

GARRETT, Laura Margaret. ■ 77054 #048-14-2007 TY *012

GARRETT, Marshall Lee, Jr. 10655 STEEPLETOP DR 77065 #030-06-1978 L1990 AN *020 †05

GARRETT, Nan M. ■ 77056 #048-04-1998 L1999 DR *100 †80

GARRIDO, Doris. 1200 BINZ ST STE 180, HOUSTON ALLERGY AND 77004 #048-14-1993 L1994 AI *020 †55,03

GARRIDO, Ramon. 1200 BINZ ST 77004 #275-01-1954 L1966 A PDA *020 †55,03

GARRIGA-PRIDA, Jose E. ■ 77096 #030-06-1947 L1948 P *020 †75

GARRISON, Catherine M. 6431 FANNIN ST, UNIV TX MED SCH AT HOUSTON 77030 #048-14-2003 GS *100

GARRISON, Susan Janette. 10021 S MAIN ST, STE B1 77025 #045-01-1979 L1981 PM *020 †60

GARTSMAN, Gary Marshall. 7401 MAIN ST 77030 #016-02-1975 L1981 ORS HS *020 †40

GARY, Alinda Patrice. 2801 GESSNER DR 77080 #035-19-2002 L2006 P *020

GARYALI, Anil. ■ 77054 #495-51-1993 L2006 IMG *100

GARZA, Daniel R. 2990 RICHMOND AVE STE 428 77098 #048-13-1997 L1998 P *020 †75

GARZA, David Albert. 7026 OLD KATY RD, STE 276 77024 #048-04-1999 L2004 DR *020 †80

GARZA, James Edward. 1322 SPACE PARK DR, STE B150 77058 #048-12-1993 L1997 FM *020 †18

GARZA, Jim S. 3700 BUFFALO SPEEDWAY, STE 350 77098 #048-04-1975 L1975 TS GS *020 †85,90

GARZA, Jonathan A. 6431 FANNIN ST, STE 7.111 77030 #035-01-2003 L2006 CN *012

GARZA, Juan Leonel. 1710 W 25TH ST 77008 #048-13-1994 L1996 IM *020 †20

GARZA, Marco G. 6431 FANNIN ST DEPT O, JJL 451 77030 #048-14-1999 L2002 EM *020 †16

GARZA, Mario, Jr. 11037 FM 1960 RD W, STEEPLECHASE PEDIATRIC 77065 #048-14-1984 L1986 PD *020 †55

GARZA, Richard. 11914 ASTORIA BLVD # 140A 77089 #048-04-1985 L1986 GS VS *020 †85

GARZA, Robert E. 4605 N BRAESWOOD BLVD, # 203-CC 77096 #048-04-1995 L1999 P *020 †75

GARZA, Rodolfo. 11914 ASTORIA BLVD, STE 140A 77089 #649-02-1954 L1963 GS *020 †85

GARZA-LEAL, Hector. ■ 77083 #649-30-1979 L1984 *020

GASPARD, Gregory Paul. ■ 77062 #048-12-2004 L2007 IM *012 †20

GASTEAZORO, Jorge Jose. ■ 77068 #451-01-1951 L1973 IM GP *072

GASTON, William Robert. 6550 FANNIN ST, STE 1025 77030 #048-04-1962 L1962 CD *020 †20

GATENO, Jaime. 6550 FANNIN ST, STE 2237 77030 #041-07-1992 L1994 OS *040

GATENO, Kristen. 2002 HOLCOMBE BLVD, VA MEDICAL CENTER 77030 #041-07-1992 L2001 IMG *100 †20

GATES, Keith Saxton. ■ 77035 #048-14-2006 EM *012

GATHE, Joseph Clayton, Jr. 4900 FANNIN ST 77004 #048-04-1981 L1981 ID IM *072 †20

GATOURA, Georgia Marie. 2217 PINE VALLEY DR 77019 #048-04-1977 L1978 GP *020

GATTA, Smitha. 125 E 16TH ST 77008 #496-20-2000 L2004 FM *020 †18

GAUTHIER, Polly King. 6720 BERTNER ST, DEPT PATH 77030 #048-14-1993 L1994 SP *020 †50

GAVAGAN, Thomas Francis. 3701 KIRBY DR, STE 600 FMLY COMM MED/BCM 77098 #038-45-1982 L2002 FM PHP *020 †70,18

GAY, Andre Nicolas. ■ 77079 #048-04-2008 L2008 *012

GAYATHRI, Yedatore V. ■ 77025 #495-33-1980 L1994 AN *020 †05

GAYED, Isis Wadie. 1515 HOLCOMBE BLVD, MD ANDERSON CANCER CENTER 77030 #848-01-1986 L1997 NM *020 †28

GAYTAN, Thelma. ■ 77054 #048-04-2008 *012

GAZA-LAPUS, Carmeltia. 7600 BEECHNUT ST 77074 #748-01-1967 L1975 AN *020 †05

GBAANADOR, Gbaranen Bm. 8449 W BELLFORT ST 77071 #048-04-1981 L1988 GS GP *020 †85

GE, Shuping. 6621 FANNIN ST, MC 19345 C 77030 #243-46-1986 L2006 PD *020 †55

GE, Yimin. ■ 77058 #243-49-1982 L2006 PTH *100 †50

GEBARA, Simon Amine. 2500 FONDREN RD, STE 20 77063 #605-02-1985 L1995 IM *020 †20

GEBHARD, Thomas Andrew. ■ 77007 #048-14-2007 TY *012

GEE, Jerry Brooksher, II. 5615 KIRBY DR STE 440 77005 #021-01-1989 L1996 NPM *040 †55

GEE, Sandra Burkhead. 50 BRIAR HOLLOW LN, STE 296 77027 #048-14-1989 L1990 CHP *020 †75

GEEVARGHESE, Debbie A. ■ 77054 #048-14-2007 IM *012

GEI, Alfredo Francisco. 6550 FANNIN ST, STE 901 77030 #270-01-1988 L2001 OBG *020 †30

GEIBEL, Eric T. 7026 OLD KATY RD, STE 276AZA 77024 #048-02-1987 L1988 DR *020 †80

GEIS, Richard Clarence. 6560 FANNIN ST, STE 1612 77030 #048-04-1961 L1961 TS VS *020 †85,90

GELBARD, Alexander H. ■ 77004 #021-01-2006 OTO *012

GELFAND, Yuri Michael. ■ 77084 #048-12-2006 OTO *012

GELTEMEYER, Abby M. 6431 FANNIN ST 3.142 77030 #048-02-2001 L2006 MPD *100 †55

GEMOETS, Thomas H. ■ 77071 #048-04-1956 L1956 IM CD *075

GEMPEL, Hayley M. ■ 77054 #048-14-2008 *012

GENSBURG, Ronald Scott. 1415 NORTH LOOP W, STE 820 77008 #017-20-1982 L1985 R VIR *020 †80

GENTRY, Clare Nicole. ■ 77025 #012-05-2001 L2003 ID *020

GENTRY, Erika Lynn. 3601 N MACGREGOR WAY 77004 #048-14-1996 L1997 FM *020 †18

GENTRY, Layne Oral. 6720 BERTNER ST RMB525, ST LUKES HOSPITAL 77030 #040-02-1965 L1973 ID *020 †20

GENTRY, Ronnie A. 6560 FANNIN ST, STE 1950 77030 #048-14-1992 L1993 IM *020 †20

GEORGE, Brannon Edward. ■ 77054 #048-14-2008 *012

GEORGE, Camille Jacob. 4126 SOUTHWEST FWY STE 300 77027 #021-01-1991 L1993 ORS OSM *020 †40

GEORGE, Dornechia Elverna. ■ 77054 #048-04-2006 D *012

GEORGE, Edward Albert. 2323 CLEAR LAKE CITY BLVD, STE 108-PMB 77062 #064-01-1964 L1973 ORS *020 †40 ‡

GEORGE, Elias. ■ 77030 #048-04-2008 *012

GEORGE, Judith Mabel. 3715 LATMA DR 77025 #048-04-2008 *012

GEORGE, Michael Samir. 17080 RED OAK DR 77090 #038-06-1999 L2005 ORS OSM *020 †40

GEORGES, Danae. ■ 77030 #048-02-1999 L2004 CHP *020

GERBER, Gregory Collins. 8303 SOUTHWEST FWY STE 455 77074 #045-01-1983 L1983 PM *020 †60

GERBER, Robert Mark. 2002 HOLCOMBE BLVD, VETERANS AFFAIRS MED CENTE 77030 #048-04-1982 L1983 P *020 †75

GERDES, John Richard. 9000 WESTHEIMER RD 77063 #048-12-1959 L1959 GYN *020 †30

GERGES, Ann N. 6621 FANNIN ST WT6-104, DEPT NEONATOLOGY 77030 #011-02-2002 L2005 PD *100 †55

GERGUIS, Steven S. 7026 OLD KATY RD, STE 276 77024 #048-02-1999 L2005 DR *020 †80

GERHARDS, Ronald S. 7600 BEECHNUT ST 77074 #048-04-1983 L1985 AN *020 †05

GERSHENSON, David Marc. 1515 HOLCOMBE BLVD 77030 #047-05-1971 L1979 GO *020 †30

GERSHENWALD, Jeffrey Evan. 1515 HOLCOMBE BLVD, DEPT OF SURGICAL ONCOL UN 77030 #035-20-1990 L1995 SO GS *020 †85

GERTLER, Ralph. 6621 FANNIN ST 77030 #409-05-1998 L2004 AN *100 †05

GERTZBEIN, Stanley David. 6565 FANNIN ST 77030 #065-01-1966 L1978 OSS *020 †40

GHADIALLY, James A. 3262 WESTHEIMER RD, # 313 77098 #068-01-1975 L1984 ORS *020 †40

GHADIRI, Niloufar. ■ 77059 #517-06-1994 L2006 IM *100 †20

GHAFIR, Mohamad Samer. 12121 RICHMOND AVE, STE 109 77082 #875-01-1981 L1991 DR *020 †80

GHALI-HANA, Hany Fayez. 1515 HOLCOMBE BLVD, BOX 349 77030 #915-04-1993 L2005 PUD *020 †20

GHARBAOUI, Idriss Seddik. 6431 FANNIN ST 77030 #655-01-1987 L2004 HS OP *020

GHAURI, Rana. 11811 FM 1960 RD W # 15 77065 #048-16-1998 L2000 OPH *020 †35

GHAZZAWI, Omar Amin. ■ 77023 #605-01-1961 L1976 PD *020 †55

GHEBRANIOUS, Amir Ramsis. 10950 RESOURCE PKWY, STE A 77089 #915-03-1984 L1995 IM *020 †20

GHELBER, Diana. ■ 77025 #781-02-1987 P *012

GHELBER, Oscar. ■ 77025 #781-02-1987 L2007 *100

GHERARDINI, Giulio. 6621 FANNIN ST # 330, TEXAS CHILDRENS HOSP 77030 #561-23-1988 PS *012

GHISTA, Anamika D. ■ 77030 #054-04-2001 IM *100

GHOBRIAL, Salah Yosri. 411 LANTERN BEND DR, STE 235 77090 #330-02-1957 L1971 PUD *020 †20

GHODSIZAD, Ali. ■ 77030 #409-38-2001 *100

GHORAYEB, Bechara. 8830 LONG POINT RD STE 806, SPRING BRANCH PROF BLDG 77055 #605-01-1970 L1986 OTO NO *020

GHORAYEB, Ghassan R. ■ 77058 #024-05-2006 L2006 OPH *012

GHORBANI, Rhonda P. 6431 FANNIN ST, UTHMS PATHOLOGY 77030 #035-03-1993 L1997 PTH *020 †50

GHOSH, Alokananda. ■ 77062 #048-04-2004 L2006 IM *012

GHOSH, Lisa Chacko. 4755 ALDINE MAIL ROUTE, ALDINE COMMUNITY HEALTH CE 77039 #495-45-1993 L2003 FM *020 †18

GHOSH, Subrata. 6624 FANNIN ST, STE 1740 77030 #495-39-1983 L2002 NS *020 †25

GHOSH, Utpal. 2002 HOLCOMBE BLVD, MAILCODE: 111PC 77030 #495-45-1989 L2000 IM *020 †20

GHULMIYYAH, Labib Makram. ■ 77006 #605-01-2000 L2008 OBG *100 †30

GHUSN, Husam F. 2002 HOLCOMBE BLVD, VAMC 77030 #605-01-1982 L1989 END IM *020 †20

GIACOBBE, Lauren Elisabet. 6565 FANNIN ST, SEE-48-0211 77030 #048-14-2006 OBG *012

GIAM, Patrick Yean-Yong. 7401 MAIN ST 77030 #048-04-1984 L1988 AN *020 †05

GIANCOLA, Angela Anna. 77019 #011-03-2004 L2007 D *012

GIANGIULIO, Maria. ■ 77054 #048-04-2000 *100

GIANNONI, Carla Marie. 6501 FANNIN ST, BAYLOR OTOLARYNGOLOGY 77030 #048-04-1990 L1997 OTO PDO *020 †45

GIANNUKOS, Nicholas John. 7200 NORTH LOOP E 77028 #048-02-1967 L1967 P *020

GIARDINO, Angelo Peter. 2450 HOLCOMBE BLVD STE 34L, TEXAS CHILDREN'S HOSPITAL 77021 #041-01-1987 L2005 PD *020 †55 ‡

GIBB, Graham K. 6550 FANNIN ST STE 2307 77030 #065-01-1993 CRS *100 †85,10

GIBBONS, Cecelia M. 10701 VINTAGE PRESERVE PKW 77001 #048-02-1990 L1991 FM *020 †18

GIBBONS, Don Lynn, Jr. 1515 HOLCOMBE BLVD, UNIT 10 77030 #035-46-2004 L2007 HO *020

GIBBS, Barbara Jenkins. ■ 77019 #048-02-1977 L1977 DR OS *071 †80

GIBBS, Harry Robt. 1515 HOLCOMBE BLVD # 70 77030 #024-01-1974 L1990 CD IM *020 †20

GIBBS, Jerry Manut. ■ 77019 #011-03-2003 L2006 DR *012

GIBBS, Kirsten Inglee. ■ 77021 #047-05-2008 *012

GIBSON, Diane Lankford. 6565 FANNIN ST B452 77030 #048-04-1986 L1987 AN *020 †05 ‡

GIBSON, Donald, II. 9889 BELLAIRE BLVD STE 134 77036 #048-14-1987 L1989 IM *020 †20

GIBSON, Donald Melvin. 902 FROSTWOOD DR, STE 144 77024 #048-04-1978 L1979 CD TS *020 †85,90

GIBSON, Fredrick Jack. 8830 LONG POINT RD 77055 #048-02-1958 L1958 GP *071

GIBSON, Rachele Anne. 1709 DRYDEN RD STE 550, BCM FACULTY CENTER 77030 #021-05-2007 IM *012

GIBSON, Tobias Quintin. ■ 77025 #027-01-2003 L2004 AN *100

GIDLEY, Paul Wm. 1515 HOLCOMBE BLVD, UNIT 441 77030 #048-14-1990 L1992 NO OTO *020 †45

GIDVANI, Bhakti J. 1201 DAIRY ASHFORD ST, STE 200 77079 #496-38-1991 L2000 PUD SME *020 †20

GIDWANI, Rima Ramesh. ■ 77005 #048-13-2006 IM *012

GIEP, Tung Nguyen. 10655 STEEPLETOP DR 77065 #045-01-1987 L2000 NPM *020 †55

GIESECKE, Noel Martin. 6720 BERTNER ST, MC 1-226 77030 #048-02-1985 L1986 AN CCA *020 †05

GIESLER, Carl Frederick. 6620 MAIN ST, STE 1450 77030 #016-06-1970 L1971 OBG IM *020 †30

GIESSEL, William U. 215 MILBY ST 77003 #048-02-1949 L1949 OM *071 †70

GIFFORD, Loring Arden. 2503 ROBINHOOD ST, STE 100C 77005 #048-12-1965 L1966 P *075 †75

GIGLI, Irma. 2121 W HOLCOMBE BLVD 77030 #132-02-1957 L1974 D AI *030 †15

GIGLIO, Auro Del. 1515 HOLCOMBE BLVD 77030 #187-04-1985 L1989 ON *020 †20

GIGLIO, John K. 1635 NORTH LOOP W 77008 #048-14-1986 L1987 FM *020 †18

GILANI, Hussain Ahmed. ■ 77006 #048-02-2007 IM *012

GILBERT, Billy Ray. ■ 77021 #048-12-2005 *012

GILBERT, Janet M. 6565 FANNIN ST 77030 #048-14-1989 L1990 AN *020

GILBERT, Mark Richard. 1515 HOLCOMBE BLVD, BOX 431 77030 #023-07-1982 L2001 IM N *020 †20,75

GILBERT, Susan W. 13259 I 10 E 77015 #038-06-1978 L1984 PS *071 †65

GILBERT-LEWIS, Kidada Nat. ■ 77074 #048-02-2002 L2006 PCP *012

GILBERTSON, Eva Labelle. ■ 77010 #041-13-1941 L1943 DR *071 †80

GILCHRIST, Alasdair Grant. 1740 W 27TH ST, STE 234 77008 #917-23-1962 L1978 OTO *020

GILCREASE, Michael Zane. 1515 HOLCOMBE BLVD 77030 #047-05-1991 L1994 **BBK** *020 †50

GILDEN, Mark. 2002 HOLCOMBE BLVD 77030 #016-11-1964 L1980 **IM** *020 †20

GILDENBERG, Philip Leon. ■ 77005 #041-13-1959 L1975 **NS OS** *071 †25

GILGER, Mark Alan. 6701 FANNIN ST 77030 #030-06-1980 L1987 **PG** *020 †20

GILGER, Michael Alan. ■ 77030 #048-04-2008 *012

GILL, Brijesh Singh. 6431 FANNIN ST 4.276 77030 #001-02-1997 L2000 **CCS** *020 †85

GILL, Kuljit S. 26 ARBOR BEND DR 77070 #048-02-1994 L2000 **OPH** *020

GILL, Paul S. 6431 FANNIN ST STE 4152, UNIV OF TEXAS MED SCH 77030 #021-06-2001 L2008 **PS** *012 †85

GILLENWATER, Ann Marie. 1515 HOLCOMBE BLVD, RM 69 77030 #051-01-1987 L1989 **HNS OTO** *020 †45

GILLESPIE, John Chas. 3120 SOUTHWEST FWY, GREATER HOUSTON RADIOLOGY 77098 #020-02-1979 L1985 **DR** *020 †80

GILLESPIE, Susan Lanelle. 6621 FANNIN ST, CCC 1210 77030 #038-06-1997 L2006 **PD** *020 †20

GILLESS, Clyde Harmon, Jr. 1250 CYPRESS STATION DR, F.M. 1960 PEDIATRIC CENTER 77090 #048-14-1978 L1978 **PD** *020 †55

GILLIAM, Vanessa A. 6431 FANNIN ST, AT HO 77030 #048-14-2006 **PD** *012

GILLILAND, Mark Douglas. 6624 FANNIN ST STE 2260 77030 #019-02-1977 L1979 **PS HS** *020

GILLIS, David Black, Jr. 77058 #036-01-1964 L1964 **GPM AM** *020 †05,70

GILLIS, Latricia T. ■ 77077 #048-04-2005 L2008 **FP** *012

GILLMAN, Cyril Eustace. 211 HIGHLAND CROSS DR #275 77073 #051-01-1999 L2004 **EM** *020 †16

GILMER, Wm Somerville. 1213 HERMANN DR STE 745 77004 #048-04-1983 L1983 **N CN** *020 †20

GILMORE, Arlette J. 2727 W HOLCOMBE BLVD, RADIOLOGY DEPT 77025 #048-02-1996 L1998 **DR** *020 †80

GILMORE, Clarence E, IV. 1504 TAUB LOOP 77030 #048-14-1993 L1994 **AN** *020

GILMORE, Stevan Marc. 2437 BAY AREA BLVD, # 163 77058 #036-05-1998 L2001 **GPM** *020 †16,70

GILMORE, V Hugh. 9401 SOUTHWEST FWY # 319 77074 #048-14-1976 L1976 **FM MDM** *030 †18

GINSBERG, Emily Lisa. ■ 77021 #024-07-2005 L2005 **AN** *012

GINSBERG, Lawrence David. 17115 RED OAK DR STE 109, RED OAK PSCHIATRY ASSOC 77090 #011-02-1981 L1985 **P ADM** *020

GINSBERG, Lawrence Edward. 1515 HOLCOMBE BLVD, DEPT DR BOX 57 77030 #016-42-1982 L1994 **DR N** *020 †80

GINZBURG, Eugenia I. 5100 SAN FELIPE ST, STE 182 77056 #913-15-1969 L1985 **NPM PD** *020 †20

GIORDANO, Giovanni G. 6411 FANNIN ST 77030 #561-07-1987 **OPH** *020

GIORDANO, Sharon Hermes. 1515 HOLCOMBE BLVD BOX 424, MD ANDERSON CANCER CENTER 77030 #023-07-1996 L1999 **ON** *020 †20

GIORDANO, Thomas P. 2015 THOMAS ST, THOMAS STREET CLINIC 77009 #023-07-1996 L2000 **ID** *020 †20

GIORGBERIDZE, Irakli. 6550 FANNIN ST, STE 1723 77030 #913-23-1985 L2005 **ICE** *020 †20

GIRALT, Sergio A. 1515 HOLCOMBE BLVD, MD ANDERSON CANCER CENTER 77030 #935-01-1983 L1991 **ON HEM** *020 †20

GIRARD, Louis Jos. 4126 SOUTHWEST FWY, STE 1428 77027 #048-02-1944 L1944 **OPH** *071 †35

GIRARD, Pierrette Marie. 9851 MEADOWGLEN LN, VILLA 16 77042 #067-02-1985 *100

GIRARDET, Rebecca G. 2500 BOLSOVER ST 77005 #003-01-1992 L1995 **PD** *020 †55

GIRAY-BELLEZZA, Nilgun. ■ 77025 #024-07-1982 L2000 **P** *020 †75

GIRGAWY, Essam Agaiby. 800 PEAKWOOD DR, STE 8A 77090 #915-02-1980 L2003 **ID** *020 †20

GIRGIS, Adel Selim. 920 FROSTWOOD DR 77024 #915-02-1961 L1977 **AN** *020 †05

GIRGIS, Kamel Zaki. 6720 BERTNER ST 77030 #330-02-1957 L1967 **AN** *071 †05

GIRGIS, Michael Mina. ■ 77041 #422-01-2003 L2006 **FM** *020 †18

GIRTANNER, Robert Edward. 6550 FANNIN ST 77030 #869-01-1969 L1971 **GO ON** *075 †30

GITTESS, Franklin Harold. 1020 HOLCOMBE BLVD, STE 505 77030 #035-46-1964 L1972 **P PYA** *071 †75

GIULIAN, Dana John. 8275 EL RIO ST, STE 130 77054 #035-20-1978 L1984 **N** *020

GIVEON, Ron. 6624 FANNIN ST, STE 1730 77030 #048-02-1993 L1998 **IM** *020 †20

GLADISH, Gregory Wayne. 1515 HOLCOMBE BLVD, UNIT 0371 77030 #021-06-1993 L1999 **DR** *020 †80

GLANDON-HYUN, Angela C. 6621 FANNIN ST, MC 1-1481 77030 #038-40-2001 L2005 **PD** *020 †55

GLAS, Mary Margaret. ■ 77030 #010-02-2002 L2005 **CCP** *012 †55

GLASS, George Stuart. 4600 POST OAK PLACE DR, STE 307 77027 #016-06-1967 L1974 **P ADP** *020 †75

GLASS, Henry G. ■ 77098 #001-02-1952 L1955 **GS TS** *071 †85

GLASS, Nancy Lee. 1 BAYLOR PLZ 77030 #048-04-1978 L1978 **AN PD** *020 †55,05

GLASS, Sharifa Nanyamka. ■ 77004 #041-15-2008 *012

GLEASON, Wallace A, Jr. 6431 FANNIN ST G420 77030 #026-04-1969 L1977 **PD GE** *040 †55

GLEZEN, William Paul. 1 BAYLOR PLZ 77030 #016-11-1956 L1975 **ID PD** *050 †55

GLINKOWSKI, Tadeusz. 14770 MEMORIAL DR 77079 #759-09-1959 L1975 **GP** *071

GLISSON, Bonnie Sue. 1515 HOLCOMBE BLVD 77030 #038-40-1979 L1996 **ON IM** *050 †20

GLOBER, Gary Alan. 1515 HOLCOMBE BLVD, GI ONCOLOGY/DIGESTIVE DIS 77030 #005-14-1962 L1990 **GE IM** *020 †20

GLOMBICKI, Alan Paul. 6550 FANNIN ST, STE 2301 77030 #016-11-1981 L1982 **GE IM** *050 †20

GLORSKY, Steven Lane. 6620 MAIN ST STE 151 77030 #035-47-1986 L2001 **GS TRS** *020 †85

GLOVER, Chris Darrel. 6621 FANNIN ST, DEPT OF ANESTH-STE A200 77030 #048-04-2000 L2004 **PAN** *100 †05 ‡

GLOVER, Katrina Yvonne. 1515 HOLCOMBE BLVD, UNIT 426 77030 #048-12-1997 L2004 **ON** *020

GNAIM, Charlie I. 6431 FANNIN ST, STE 1.240A 77030 #048-14-2002 L2005 **CD** *012 †20

GO, Chi Hiong Uy. 4545 POST OAK PLACE DR, STE 130 77027 #748-08-1993 L2000 **IM** *020 †20

GOAL, Jay C. 2807 LITTLE YORK RD 77093 #048-13-1987 L1990 **FM** *020 †18

GOBRAN, Amani R. 13111 EAST FWY STE 308 77015 #048-04-1988 L1989 **OTO HNS** *020

GODDARD, Julie A. ■ 77030 #048-04-2004 **OTO** *012

GODDARD-FINEGOLD, Jan. 6621 FANNIN ST, TEXAS CHILDREN'S HOSPITAL 77030 #041-01-1974 L1978 **PD CHN** *020 †55

GOEDDE, Lisa Marie. 2727 W HOLCOMBE BLVD 77025 #048-14-1994 L1996 **FM** *020

GOEL, Nisheeth Kumar. 6720 BERTNER ST, CARDIOLOGY EDUCATION, 1-13 77030 #027-01-2001 L2006 **CD** *012

GOEL, Shefali. 6431 FANNIN ST STE 1.150, AT HOUST 77030 #495-90-1999 L2007 **NEP** *020

GOENS, Ray Winston. 9042 CRANLEIGH CT 77096 #048-02-1945 L1945 **IM** *071

GOEPFERT, Helmuth. 1515 HOLCOMBE BLVD, MD ANDERSON HSOPITAL 77030 #231-01-1962 L1972 **HNS OTO** *071 †45

GOETZ, Joseph Sam. 4664 BEECHNUT ST 77096 #005-14-1978 L1990 **OPH** *020 †35

GOETZ, Margaret Amelia. 6621 FANNIN ST 77030 #048-12-1980 L1980 **PD** *020 †55

GOFFMAN, Joel Henry. 9090 GAYLORD ST 77024 #023-01-1967 L1972 **OPH** *020

GOFRAN, Anita. ■ 77030 #010-03-2001 L2007 **NEP** *020

GOGOLA, Gloria Romeo. 6977 MAIN ST, UNIV OF TEXAS-HOUSTON SCH 77030 #001-02-1993 L1995 **HS ORS** *012

GOGOLA, Jon Ramon. 920 FROSTWOOD DR, STE 610 77024 #001-02-1993 L1998 **OBG** *020 †30

GOH, Alvin Chunchin. ■ 77054 #016-06-2005 **U** *012

GOKASLAN, Ayse Gul. 6560 FANNIN ST STE 1002 77030 #902-10-1983 L1989 **ID IM** *020 †20

GOKULAKRISHNAN, Ganga. PO BOX 20708, UNIV TX MED SCH AT HOUSTON 77225 #495-42-1995 **NPM** *012 †55

GOLD, Irving Lazar. 7777 SOUTHWEST FWY, STE 1052 77074 #781-01-1976 L1982 **NEP IM** *020 †20

GOLD, Joshua Michael. 6560 FANNIN ST STE 1248 77030 #067-01-1968 L1977 **IM** *020

GOLDBAUM, Stephanie. 9105 N WAYSIDE DR 77028 #065-09-2000 L2003 *100

GOLDBERG, Isaac Meir. 1111 HERMANN DR UNIT 11B 77004 #048-14-1981 L1981 **FM** *020 †18

GOLDBERG, Jacobo. 7500 BEECHNUT ST, STE 352 77074 #649-01-1972 L1977 **PD** *020 †55

GOLDBERG, Leonard Harry. 7515 MAIN ST, STE 240 77030 #836-03-1967 L1981 **D OS** *020 †15

GOLDBERG, Seymour Hy. 7800 FANNIN ST, STE 204 77054 #550-01-1975 L1983 **PD** *020

GOLDENBERG, Daniel S. 12180 GREENSPOINT DR # 229 77060 #422-01-1995 **N** *100

GOLDFARB, Brian Scott. 211 HIGHLAND CROSS, STE 275 77073 #035-09-2002 L2005 **IM** *100 †20

GOLDFARB, David. ■ 77035 #048-04-2007 **GS** *012

GOLDFARB, Richard Alan. 6560 FANNIN ST, STE 1440 77030 #048-04-1977 L1978 **U** *020 †95

GOLDMAN, Alica Maria. 1 BAYLOR PLZ, DEPARTMENT OF NEUROLOGY 77030 #286-03-1989 L2002 **N** *020 †75

GOLDMAN, Eugene Jerome. 7500 BEECHNUT ST, STE 388 77074 #016-06-1957 L1964 **U** *071 †95

GOLDMAN, Stanford Milton. 6431 FANNIN ST, STE 2-100 77030 #035-46-1965 L1994 **DR NM** *040 †80,28

GOLDSMITH, Ian Lance. 1 BAYLOR PLZ, DEPT OF NEUROLOGY, NB302 77030 #035-15-1994 L2002 **N** *020 †75

GOLDSTEIN, Alexander, Jr. 6720 BERTNER ST 77030 #048-04-1961 L1961 **AN** *071 †05

GOLDSTEIN, Mark Thos. 77079 #021-06-1983 L1986 **AN** *020 †05

GOLDSTEIN, Steven Saul. 11914 ASTORIA BLVD 77089 #016-02-1969 L1976 **N IM** *020 †20,75

GOLDSTEIN, Stuart Leonard. 6701 FANNIN ST 77030 #035-01-1990 L1993 **PN** *020 †55

GOLI, Sadasivareddy. 5990 AIRLINE DR, STE 250 77076 #495-58-1994 L2002 **IM** *020 †20

GOLLAS, Adrian. 6431 FANNIN ST, SCHOOL A 77030 #649-31-1994 L2002 **PD** *100

GOMBERAWALLA, Asim Mustaf. ■ 77054 #048-04-2008 *012

GOMBERAWALLA, Harshada. 6550 MAPLERIDGE ST, GOMBERWALLA HARSHADA 77081 #495-17-1973 L1992 **PD** *020

GOMBOS, Dan S. 1515 HOLCOMBE BLVD BOX 44, PLASTIC SURG DEPT/OPTHALMO 77030 #005-11-1994 L2002 **OPH OS** *020 †35

GOMES, Heidi Sophia. 6701 FANNIN ST CC-1210, TEXAS CHILDREN'S HOSP 77030 #001-02-1995 L1998 **PD** *020 †55

GOMEZ, Efrain A. ■ 77096 #737-01-1956 L1978 **P** *071 †75

GOMEZ, Enrique Miguel. ■ 77054 #042-02-2003 L2007 **SP** *012 †50

GOMEZ, Lida Janeth. ■ 77056 #649-02-1986 L2003 **AN** *020

GOMEZ, Luis Solon. 1 BAYLOR PLZ 77030 #264-04-1959 L1973 **R DR** *071 †80

GOMEZ, Miguel Angel, III. 902 FROSTWOOD DR, STE 144 77024 #048-04-1991 L1992 **TS GS** *020 †90,85

GOMEZ, Pablo Walter. ■ 77054 #042-02-2003 L2007 **PTH** *100 †50

GOMEZ ESQUIVEL, Rene Dani. 6431 FANNIN ST, MSB 1.150 77030 #649-30-2001 L2008 **MPD** *012

GONCHARUK, Viktor. 1515 HOLCOMBE BLVD, DEPT OF PATHOLOGY 77030 #913-18-1984 L2003 **DMP** *020 †50

GONDI, Sreedevi. ■ 77025 #020-02-2004 L2007 **IM** *100 †20

GONSOULIN, Morna L. ■ 77005 #048-12-1995 L1997 **FOP** *020 †50

GONZALES, Carlos Alberto. 915 GESSNER RD, STE 250 77024 #049-01-1983 L1995 **OPH** *020 †16,35

GONZALES, Edmond T, Jr. 6621 FANNIN ST STE 660, DEPARTMENT OF UROLOGY 77030 #021-01-1965 L1974 **U** *020 †95

GONZALES, Nicole Renee. 6431 FANNIN ST, MSB 7.118 77030 #048-14-2000 L2005 **VN** *100 †75

GONZALEZ, Arturo Gabriel. 1919 LA BRANCH ST, CHRISTUS ST JOSEPH HOSP 77002 #649-14-1994 **GS** *012

GONZALEZ, Aurora. 1315 ST JOSEPH PKWY, STE 1507 77002 #048-12-1996 L1998 **OBG** *020 †30

GONZALEZ, Carlos Jose. 11030 FALLBROOK DR, STE 304 77064 #030-06-1981 L1982 **GP** *020

GONZALEZ, Carmen Esther. 1515 HOLCOMBE BLVD, MD ANDERSON CANCER CTR 77030 #042-01-1998 L1998 **NM** *020 †20,28

GONZALEZ, David A. 3310 RICHMOND AVE 77098 #649-02-1959 L1965 **CD IM** *071

GONZALEZ, Domingo Gil, Jr. 1631 NORTH LOOP W STE 250 77008 #048-12-1983 L1983 **CD IM** *020 †20

GONZALEZ, Guillermo. 2002 HOLCOMBE BLVD 77030 #649-03-1979 L1993 **AN** *020

GONZALEZ, Hugo Rene. 13125 EAST FWY 77015 #048-02-1965 L1965 **FM OM** *071

GONZALEZ, Jessica. ■ 77054 #024-05-2007 **MPD** *012

GONZALEZ, Jorge Mario. 6550 FANNIN ST STE 2317 77030 #429-01-1977 L1982 **IM PUD** *020

GONZALEZ, Juan Manuel. 3500 LITTLE YORK RD, STE A3 77093 #429-01-1979 L1988 **NEP IM** *020 †20

GONZALEZ, Julian J. 13125 EAST FWY 77015 #048-02-1993 L1994 **FM OM** *020 †18

GONZALEZ, Monica Andrea. ■ 77021 #048-14-2000 L2006 **DR** *100 †80 ‡

GONZALEZ, Pedro Luis. ■ 77054 #042-02-2005 L2008 **DR** *012

GONZALEZ, Penelope. 4545 POST OAK PLACE DR, STE 130 77027 #649-35-1990 L2003 **IM** *020 †20

GONZALEZ, Rafael Eduardo. 1709 DRYDEN RD, MS: BCM 620, SUITE 9.91 77030 #042-01-2000 L2003 **IC** *100 †20

GONZALEZ, Ricardo Jorge. 1515 HOLCOMBE BLVD, UNIT 444 77030 #011-04-1997 L2004 **GS** *020 †85

GONZALEZ, Ricardo Rene. 6560 FANNIN ST, STE 1270 77030 #005-11-1999 L2006 **U** *020 †95

GONZALEZ-ANGULO, Ana M. 1515 HOLCOMBE BLVD, UNIT 1354 77030 #264-07-1995 L2003 **ON** *020 †20

GONZALEZ BERJON, Jose Mig. 6565 FANNIN ST MS 205 77030 #649-31-2006 **PTH** *012

GONZALEZ DE LEON, Cesar. 1515 HOLCOMBE BLVD, BOX 10 77030 #649-02-1986 **ON IM** *100

■ = Address Information Privacy Protected

GONZALEZ VERA VALL, Oscar. 6671 SOUTHWEST FWY, STE 450 77074 #726-01-1973 L1982 OBG *020 †30

GOOD, Amy Bennett. ■ 77030 #028-46-2004 L2004 NPM *012 †55

GOOD, Edward Fitz Simons. ■ 77058 #045-01-1964 L1972 N AM *071 †75

GOODFRIEND, Barry H. 6550 FANNIN ST, STE 1200 77030 #048-02-1959 L1959 IM *071

GOODGAME, Richard Wilder. 1 BAYLOR PLZ, RM 525-D 77030 #023-07-1975 L1979 ID IM *020

GOODINE, Glenda. 11452 SPACE CENTER BLVD 77059 #064-01-1977 L1978 FM *020 ‡

GOODLY, Joseph Lawrence. 6410 FANNIN ST, STE 1020 HARMAN PROFESSION 77030 #021-01-1993 IM *100

GOODMAN, Amber E. 2222 MARONEAL ST UNIT 1345 77030 #048-14-2006 PD *012

GOODMAN, Heather S. 1 BAYLOR PLZ BCM-350, BAYLOR COLLEGE OF MEDICINE 77030 #048-04-1994 L1996 P *020 †75

GOODMAN, Jerry Clay. 6565 FANNIN ST 77030 #048-04-1975 L1975 NP N *020 †75

GOODMAN, Lawrence Albert. ■ 77059 #056-05-1976 L1978 AN *020 †05

GOODNIGHT, Sheila Jean. 2002 HOLCOMBE BLVD, VAMC 111-I 77030 #048-15-1984 L1985 PUD IM *020 †20

GOODPASTOR, Sarah Elizabe. ■ 77098 #048-13-2007 IM *012

GOOSEY, John Douglas. 1220 AUGUSTA DR, STE 100 77057 #045-01-1979 L1983 OPH *020 †35

GOPAL, Jayashree. ■ 77030 #495-04-1991 END *100 †20

GOPAL, Srihari. 3701 KIRBY DR, STE 100 77098 #033-06-1995 L1998 FM EM *020 †18

GOPALAKRISHNA, G S. 6701 FANNIN ST, # 1110 77030 #495-09-1969 L1977 GE PD *020 †55

GOPALAKRISHNAN, Thandava. 10594 FUQUA ST 77089 #495-04-1987 L1998 IM *020 †20

GOPALANI, Salim. 1631 NORTH LOOP W STE 260 77008 #048-04-1994 L1994 IM *020 †20

GOPINATH, Shankar Prakash. 1709 DRYDEN RD 77030 #495-09-1981 NS *100

GORBATIY, Vladislav. ■ 77230 #012-05-2005 U *012

GORDON, Craig S. 915 GESSNER RD, STE 625 77024 #024-05-1974 L1979 GE *020 †20

GORDON, Gene Stephen. 5000 MONTROSE BLVD STE 1 77006 #036-07-1972 L1978 P *020 †75

GORDON, Harvey Lawrence. 6560 FANNIN ST, STE 1406 77030 #035-19-1959 L1964 U *071 †95

GORDON, Michael James. 6400 FANNIN ST, STE 3000 77030 #038-40-1971 L1978 CD *020 †20

GORDON, Robert Morris. ■ 77057 #035-19-1962 L1969 N *071 †75

GORDON, William Edward. ■ 77025 #021-01-2003 L2006 CCP *012 †55

GORE, Cheryl Ann. 6621 FANNIN ST 77030 #422-01-1994 L1998 AN *020 †05

GOREN, David. 4201 BELLAIRE BLVD 77025 #550-01-1994 HS *100

GORENA, Maria E. ■ 77096 #048-04-2003 L2007 AN *100

GORENA, Michael A. ■ 77096 #048-04-2003 L2008 PAN *012

GOSS, John A, Jr. 1709 DRYDEN RD, STE 1500 77030 #030-06-1988 L1998 GS *020 †85

GOSS, Zuleika Murritt. ■ 77054 #027-01-2008 *012

GOSSETT, Garland Wm. 2000 CRAWFORD ST STE 132 77002 #010-03-1985 L1990 GE IM *020

GOSSETT, Shannon Michelle. 2310A DORRINGTON ST 77030 #048-02-2000 L2003 AN *020 ‡

GOSSEY, John Travis. 3701 KIRBY DR, STE 600 77098 #016-06-2002 L2005 GP *020 †20

GOSUICO, Amelia Delacruz. ■ 77279 #748-02-1972 L1980 ON FM *020

GOTSCHALL, Ann Bulman. 3701 KIRBY DR STE 600, MEDICINE 77098 #048-04-1986 L1988 IM *020 †20

GOTTESMAN, Mark Jesse. 7580 FANNIN ST STE 330 77054 #048-02-1978 L1978 OBG *020 †30

GOTTLIEB, Harold Elliot. 1315 CALHOUN ST STE 1605 77002 #561-17-1980 L1985 IM *020 †20

GOTTLIEB, Lewis Ravenet. 4000 NORTH FWY, STE 222 77022 #048-14-1984 L1985 P *020

GOTTSCHALK, Lewis Isaac. 13700 VETERANS MEMORIAL DR 77014 #836-02-1979 L1997 AN *040 †05

GOTTSCHALK, Stephen. 6621 FANNIN ST MC, TEXAS CHILDREN'S CANCER CE 77030 #409-07-1992 L2001 PHO *020 †55

GOTTUMUKKALA, Vijaya N. 1400 HOLCOMBE BLVD # 409, DEPT OF ANESTH & PAIN MED 77030 #495-11-1985 L2007 AN *020 †05

GOUGER, Donald Thos. PO BOX 6834 77265 #035-03-1965 L1966 OPH *075

GOULD, Kenneth Geo, Jr. ■ 77069 #036-07-1954 L1966 IM PUD *071 †20

GOULD, Kenneth Lance. 6431 FANNIN ST, STE MSB 4256 77030 #038-06-1964 L1980 CD IM *020

GOULDIN, Edmund N. ■ 77042 #051-04-1949 L1958 IM HEM *071 †20

GOVEA, Christopher John. 2900 RICHMOND AVE 77098 #048-04-1999 L2000 DR *020 †80

GOVINDAIAH, Asha. 920 FROSTWOOD DR, STE 780 77024 #495-33-1992 L2003 HO *020

GOYAL, Kanu Shri. ■ 77082 #038-06-2007 L2007 ORS *012

GOYTIA, Robin Nestor. 5447 VALKEITH DR, HOUSTON 77096 #048-13-2002 L2005 ORS *100

GOYTIA, Veronica Karen. ■ 77070 #422-01-2001 L2004 PDI *012 †55 ‡

GRABOIS, Martin. 1709 DRYDEN RD, STE 725 77030 #041-13-1966 L1973 PM PMM *020 †60

GRACIA, Joette Michele. 1100 W 34TH ST 77018 #048-02-1997 L2001 FM *020 †18

GRAF, Jeanine Marie. 6621 FANNIN ST 6006 77030 #038-40-1988 L1995 CCP *020 †55

GRAFF, Homer L, Jr. ■ 77024 #048-04-1951 L1952 OTO A *071

GRAHAM, Akili H. 2519 RUTH ST 77004 #047-07-1995 L1999 FM *020 †18

GRAHAM, Amy Denise. ■ 77009 #048-14-2007 AN *012

GRAHAM, Brett Harrison. 6701 FANNIN ST, MEDICAL GENETICS 77030 #012-05-1998 L2003 MG PD *050 †55,19

GRAHAM, Charles Richard. ■ 77018 #005-06-1961 L1975 EM FM *020

GRAHAM, David P. 2002 HOLCOMBE BLVD, MENTAL HEALTH CARE LINE 77030 #048-04-1999 L2005 P *020

GRAHAM, David Yates. 6550 FANNIN ST STE 1122 77030 #048-04-1966 L1969 GE *050 †20

GRAHAM, Gregory Dane. 5900 POST OAK PLACE DR 77027 #409-04-1978 L1980 P *020 †75

GRAHAM, John Kirkland. 717 SAGE RD 77056 #021-01-1963 L1972 PS OTO *020 †45,65

GRAHAM, Monica Joyce. 2519 RUTH ST, GRAHAMTIME FAMILY MEDICINE 77004 #047-07-1997 L1999 FM *020 †18

GRAHAM, William Robt. 1502 TAUB LOOP, DEPT OF MEDICINE 77030 #048-12-1981 L1981 IM *020

GRAICHEN, Maria Villa. 1707 SUNSET BLVD, MEDICAL CLINIC OF HOUSTON 77005 #048-02-1990 L1995 DR *020 †80

GRAIR, Deborah B. ■ 77054 #665-02-2005 *100

GRAMZE, Nickalaus Lane. 6431 FANNIN ST 1.134 77030 #003-01-2007 MPD *012

GRANADA, Juan Fernando. 6550 FANNIN ST, STE 2021 77030 #264-16-1994 L2005 IC *020 †20

GRANATH, Emily T. ■ 77030 #048-14-2008 *012

GRANBERRY, Warren Malcolm. 6624 FANNIN ST STE 2600 77030 #021-01-1957 L1964 ORS HS *040 †40

GRANCHI, Thomas Stephen. 1504 TAUB LOOP, EMERGENCY CENTER 77030 #038-40-1988 L1989 GS *020 †85

GRANDA-FRANCO, Enrique B. 8200 WEDNESBURY LN, STE 102 77074 #847-04-1969 L1974 FM IM *020

GRANGER, John Michael. ■ 77004 #038-43-2003 L2003 ID *012 †20

GRANIER, L Gonzalo. 7707 FANNIN ST, STE 250 77054 #409-21-1971 L1978 IM *020 †20

GRANMAYEH, Elaine Sima. ■ 77024 #048-13-2002 L2008 DR *100 †80

GRANMAYEH, Masood. 902 FROSTWOOD DR, STE 275 77024 #517-01-1966 L1975 R *020 †80

GRANT, Howard. 2646 S LOOP W STE 400 77054 #047-07-1975 L1978 EM *020

GRANTCHAROVA, Elena P. 6431 FANNIN ST STE 4152, UNIV OF TEXAS MED SCH 77030 #035-19-1997 L2000 PS *020

GRANVILLE, George Ellis. 2002 HOLCOMBE BLVD 77030 #048-02-1944 L1944 IM *020 †20

GRANVILLE, Laura Ann. 1 BAYLOR PLZ, CULLEN BLDG RM 286A 77030 #048-02-2000 L2004 SP *100 †50

GRANWEHR, Bruno Palma. 1515 HOLCOMBE BLVD, UNITE 402 77030 #018-03-1999 L2005 ID IM *020 †20

GRAS, Hector Ricardo. 8850 LONG POINT RD 77055 #132-04-1956 L1973 AN *071

GRASU, Roxana Marilena. 1515 HOLCOMBE BLVD, MD ANDERSON CANCER CENTER 77030 #781-02-1989 L2003 AN *020 †05

GRATE, Isaac, Jr. 11811 PEPPERDINE LN 77071 #047-07-1978 L1983 EM GP *020 †16

GRAUBARD, Lucy L. 7500 BEECHNUT ST STE 352 77074 #048-02-1995 L1997 PD *020 †55

GRAUBART, Emily Bedrick. 4126 CHILDRESS ST 77006 #016-06-2004 L2005 OPH *012

GRAVES, Jeffery Justin. 6550 FANNIN ST, HOSP (HOUSTON) 77030 #019-02-2007 L2008 TY *012

GRAWE, Glenda Hazel. 6621 FANNIN ST, TEXAS CHILDREN'S HOSPITAL 77030 #049-01-1996 L2006 PEM *100 †55

GRAY, James Mitchell. 100 UH HEALTH CTR, HEALTH CENTER 77204 #048-04-1956 L1956 IM AM *020

GRAY, Karen Jane. ■ 77047 #047-07-2002 L2006 END *012 †20

GRAY, Kathy J. 205 HOLLOW TREE LN 77090 #048-15-1990 L1991 EM *020

GRAY, Paul Milton, Jr. ■ 77004 #048-04-1963 L1963 R DR *071 †80

GRAY, Richard Earl. 8081 GREENBRIAR ST 77054 #021-05-1967 L1969 PTH *062 †50

GRAZZIUTTI, Monica L. 6431 FANNIN ST, 1 228 JFB 77030 #132-04-1982 L2006 ID *100

GREASER, Michael Christop. ■ 77030 #048-14-2008 *012

GREELEY, Christopher S. 6431 FANNIN ST 77030 #051-01-1992 L2007 PD *040 †55

GREEN, Carol Joy. 6624 FANNIN ST, 19TH FL 77030 #010-01-1984 L1985 PD PEM *020 †55

GREEN, David M. ■ 77062 #048-02-1999 L2007 ORS *100

GREEN, Demetris Allen. ■ 77057 #048-04-1992 L1993 IM *075

GREEN, Linda K. 2002 HOLCOMBE BLVD, VA MED CTR LAB SVC 113 77030 #048-13-1982 L1983 PTH PCP *020 †50

GREEN, Louis Harry. ■ 77030 #048-02-1947 L1947 GS *071 †85

GREEN, Marjorie Catherine. 1515 HOLCOMBE BLVD, BOX 1354 77030 #048-02-1995 L2000 ON *020 †20

GREEN, Mary Trotter. 6624 FANNIN ST, STE 2105 77030 #048-04-1982 L1983 OPH *020 †35

GREEN, Paige M. ■ 77057 #048-02-2002 L2007 DR *100 †80

GREEN, Tanisha Dionne. 1315 ST JOSEPH PKWY, STE 302 77002 #021-01-2001 L2005 AN *020

GREEN, Valerie Sarena. 1885 OLD SPANISH TRL 77054 #305-01-2001 L2006 FOP *100

GREENBERG, Cindy Alicia. 7515 MAIN ST, STE 770 77030 #011-02-1986 L1989 D DMP *020 †15

GREENBERG, Stephen Baruch. 1709 DRYDEN RD, STE 500 77030 #023-01-1970 L1974 IM ID *040 †20

GREENE, Anshula. ■ 77007 #048-13-2001 L2003 PD *020 †55

GREER, Jeannette M. 2450 FONDREN RD STE 311 77063 #048-14-1988 L1989 D *020 †15

GREGG, Frederick Parker. 6720 BERTNER ST, DEPT RAD 77030 #048-02-1970 L1970 DR *020 †80 ‡

GREGG, James Parker. ■ 77027 #048-02-2002 GS *100

GREGORIC, Igor D. 1101 BATES AVE, SURGICAL ASSOCIATES OF 77030 #957-03-1979 L2000 TS GS *020 †85,90

GREGORY, Lloyd J, Jr. ■ 77019 #048-04-1947 L1947 PUD OM *072

GREGORY, R Frederick. 6448 FANNIN ST, DIAGNOSTIC CLINIC OF HOUST 77030 #035-01-1961 L1963 IM END *071 †20

GREISS, Isis M. ■ 77005 #330-04-1957 L1973 PD *071 †55

GRELLHESL, Dana M. ■ 77054 #048-14-2008 *012

GRESIK, Mary Victoria. 6621 FANNIN ST, STE B1 77030 #016-43-1970 L1978 PTH *020 †50

GREVE, Marion Jos. ■ 77056 #024-01-1945 L1948 IM CD *071 †20

GRIECO, Gustavo. 4126 SOUTHWEST FWY 77027 #935-07-1984 L1992 CD *020 †20

GRIFFIN, George Edward. 1919 LA BRANCH ST 77002 #047-07-1968 L1972 GS *020 †85

GRIFFIN, Ian James. 1 BAYLOR PLZ, DEPT OF NEONATOLOGY 77030 #917-05-1989 L2001 NPM *020

GRIFFIN, Lance Wayland. ■ 77004 #048-14-2008 *012

GRIFFIN, Paul Andrew. 1200 BINZ ST, STE 1430 77044 #048-12-1969 L1969 ORS *020 †40

GRIFFITH, Donald Paul. 2002 HOLCOMBE BLVD, UROLOGY SERVICE, VAMC, HOU 77030 #048-04-1963 L1963 U *020 †95

GRIFFITH, John Dorland. 1300 MOURSUND ST 77030 #047-06-1955 L1979 P PA *020 †75

GRIFFITHS, James J. 6410 FANNIN ST, STE 260 77030 #048-14-1991 L1993 PTH MDM *030

GRIFFITHS, Suzel Ehrmann. 1115 S BRAESWOOD BLVD, MED CTR CLNC 77030 #396-31-1968 L1981 PHP *020

GRIFFON, Robert Jackson. 13630 BEAMER RD, STE 107 77089 #021-05-1960 L1971 GYN *071

GRILLO, Ricardo Paris. 2028 WIRT RD 77055 #024-04-1960 L1972 PD *020 †55 ‡

GRIMES, Kevin A. ■ 77025 #048-14-2002 L2006 ID *020 †20

GRIMES, Sandra R. 3311 YUPON ST, APT 601 77006 #048-13-1987 L1988 P *020

GRIMMER, Daniel Luke. 6720 BERTNER ST, ST. LUKE'S EPISCOPAL HOSPI 77030 #018-03-1987 L1992 ATP NP *020 †50

GRINER, Enid S. 5511 AUSTIN ST 77004 #047-07-1986 L1990 *020

GRINO, Placido B. ■ 77025 #847-12-1978 L1986 END EM *020 †20

GRINSTEAD, William C, III. 7737 SOUTHWEST FWY, STE 780 77074 #048-12-1986 L1987 CD *020 †20

GRISALES, Tamara. ■ 77054 #048-14-2007 OBG *012

GRISSOM, Larry Allan. 810 PEAKWOOD DR STE 107 77090 #048-14-1978 L1978 DR GP *020 †80

GRISSOM, Ruth Busche. 1709 DRYDEN RD STE 1700, BAYLOR COLLEGE OF MEDICINE 77030 #048-04-2001 L2005 AN *012

GRITZ, Barry Frank. 6420 RICHMOND AVE, STE 355 77057 #048-04-1987 L1988 P *020 †75

GROEN, Alfred Leonard. 2411 FOUNTAIN VIEW DR, STE 200 77057 #660-03-1985 L1991 AN *020 †05

GROFF, Geoffrey Allen. 9055 KATY FWY, STE 200 77024 #649-14-1984 L1996 FM EM *020 †18

GROFF, Janet Yvonne. 6431 FANNIN ST, JJL 324 77030 #048-02-1980 L1980 PHP *050 †18,70

GROH, Jesse Brookshire. 6621 FANNIN ST RM A170, MC1-1000 77030 #048-04-2006 PD *012

GROPPI, Kelly Lynn. ■ 77021 #048-14-2007 TY *012

GROS, Michael Louis. 12337 JONES RD, STE 350 77070 #048-04-1976 L1983 **OBG** *020 †30
GROSE, Nellie Poh Kee. 230 WESTCOTT ST STE 208 77007 #068-01-1968 L1974 **FM** *020 †18
GROSS, Ronald Leon. 6550 FANNIN ST, STE 1501 77030 #055-01-1982 L1983 **OPH** *020 †35 ‡
GROSSHANS, David Randall. 1515 HOLCOMBE BLVD, ANDERSON CANC 77030 #007-02-2004 L2004 **RO** *012
GROSSHEIM, Lisa Freeman. 6431 FANNIN ST JJL431 77030 #048-14-1994 L1995 **EM** *020 †16
GROSSMAN, Herbert Barton. 1515 HOLCOMBE BLVD, DEPT OF UROLOGY UNIT 1373 77030 #041-13-1970 L1995 **U** *020 †95
GROSSMAN, James Ellsworth. 12345 KATY FWY 77079 #048-04-1993 L1996 **IM UCM** *020 †20
GROSSMAN, Neal Jay. 12606 W HOUSTON CENTR BLVD, STE 200 77082 #011-02-1974 L1976 **PD** *020 †55
GROSSMAN, Robert Geo. 6560 FANNIN ST STE 944, DEPT OF NEUROSURGERY 77030 #035-01-1957 L1963 **NS** *020 †25
GROSSMARINO, Vanessa. ■ 77054 #048-14-2008 *012
GROTTA, James Chas. 6431 FANNIN ST ST 7.044 77030 #051-01-1971 L1979 **N** *020 †75
GROVER, Pawan. 7500 BEECHNUT ST, STE 280 77074 #033-06-1989 L1991 **PME AN** *020 †05
GROVER, Rajeev. 2045 SPACE PARK DR, STE 100 77058 #048-14-1992 L1993 **CD** *020 †20
GROVER, Tejpal. 1515 HOLCOMBE BLVD UNIT 04 77030 #039-01-1995 L1996 **IM** *020 †20
GROVER, Tina Marie. 1504 TAUB LOOP 77030 #039-01-1995 L1996 **PD** *020 †55
GROVES, Morris D. 1515 HOLCOMBE BLVD, NEURO-ONCOLOGY/BOX 431 77030 #048-04-1986 L1987 **N LM** *050 †75
GRUBB, Laura Katherine. ■ 77025 #010-01-2000 L2006 **PD** *020 †55
GRUBBS, Elizabeth Gardner. 1515 HOLCOMBE BLVD UNIT 4, U OF TX MDA CANCER CENTER 77030 #036-07-1999 L2006 **GS** *100
GRUBER, Nelson Peter. 2800 S MACGREGOR WAY # 2D- 77021 #048-14-1984 L1986 **P PYG** *020 †75 ‡
GRUMMON, Charissa Ann. ■ 77021 #048-14-2007 *012
GRUNERT, George M. 7900 FANNIN ST, STE 4000 77054 #048-04-1973 L1973 **GYN REN** *020 †30
GRUNEWALDT, Hardy. ■ 77099 #187-02-1954 L1973 **GP** *072
GRUNFELD, Jonathan Franz. 1515 HOLCOMBE BLVD 77030 #050-02-1996 L1998 **OS** *100
GU, Yan. 8076 EL RIO ST 77054 #243-71-1989 L2004 **SP** *020 †50
GUADAGNOLO, Beverly A. 1515 HOLCOMBE BLVD, UNIT 97 77030 #024-01-2001 L2006 **RO** *010 †20
GUAJARDO, Mario. 7600 BEECHNUT ST, 2ND FL 77074 #649-02-1959 L1969 **PTH** *071 †50
GUANA, Pedro. 12141 RICHMOND AVE 77082 #264-01-1960 L1974 **PM** *071 †60
GUARDIOLA, Amalia. ■ 77054 #042-01-2002 L2005 **PD** *100 †55
GUDARO, Irfan Hussain. 1919 LA BRANCH ST 77002 #704-16-2002 **GS** *100
GUDIBANDA SIVASANKARA VENK, . 1400 HOLCOMBE BLVD - UNIT, ANDERSON CAN 77030 #495-62-1997 L2004 **PMM** *012
GUEHRING, Jme Thos. 2450 FONDREN RD STE 310 77063 #048-04-1968 L1968 **PD** *071 †55
GUELER, Alfredo Claudio. 5420 DASHWOOD DR STE 302 77081 #048-14-1978 L1979 **EM IM** *020 †16
GUERRA, Carlos, Jr. 9701 RICHMOND AVE, STE 200 77042 #048-14-1989 L1990 **P CHP** *020 †75
GUERRA, Nicolas Noel. 6621 FANNIN ST RM A170, MC1-1000 77030 #048-04-2006 **PD** *012
GUERRA-CARDUS, Laura Elen. ■ 77019 #048-04-2005 *100
GUERRERO, Jorge. 6710 CAPITOL ST 77011 #048-14-1985 L1985 **FM** *020
GUERRERO, Marlon Alex. ■ 77006 #047-07-2003 L2008 **GS** *012
GUERRERO, Milton Alonso. 8303 SOUTHWEST FWY, STE 120 77074 #264-02-1988 L1995 **FPG** *020
GUERRERO, Thomas Michael. 1515 HOLCOMBE BLVD, RADIATION ONCOLOGY - BOX 9 77030 #005-14-1997 L2002 **RO** *020 †80
GUERRERO-RAMIREZ, Luis E. 2055 S GESSNER RD, STE 250 77063 #264-04-1967 L1974 **GPM P** *075
GUERRIERO, William Graham. 6560 FANNIN ST STE 1554 77030 #048-12-1963 L1963 **U TTS** *020 †95
GUERRINI, Joseph Bernard. 530 N BELT DR E STE 100 77060 #561-23-1973 L1978 **FM FPG** *020 †18
GUGENHEIM, Joseph J. 7401 MAIN ST 77030 #016-06-1972 L1973 **ORS OP** *020 †40
GUHA, Sushovan. 1515 HOLCOMBE BLVD # 436, DEPT OF GI MED & NUTRIT 77030 #495-53-1988 L2005 **IM GE** *050 †20
GUHA-THAKURTA, Nandita. ■ 77030 #495-96-1989 L2007 **RNR** *100 †80
GUIBERTEAU, Milton Jerome. 1919 LA BRANCH ST, ASSOCIATES 77002 #048-04-1971 L1971 **DR NM** *020 †80,28
GUICE, Marcus L. 1200 BAKER ST, HARRIS CNTY SHERIFFS OFF 77002 #035-06-1975 L1979 **IM** *030
GUILAK, Hooshang. 902 FROSTWOOD DR, STE 237 77024 #517-01-1953 L1972 **END IM** *071
GUILAK, Nahid Toufigh. ■ 77024 #517-01-1955 L1972 **PD** *071 †55
GUILLERMAN, Robert Paul. 6720 BERTNER ST 77030 #028-02-1994 L2002 **PDR** *020 †80
GUILLIAMS, Stephen Edward. 12121 RICHMOND AVE, STE 203 77082 #048-14-1974 L1974 **OBG** *020
GUILLORY, Charleta. 6621 FANNIN NEWBORN OFFICE, TEXAS CHILDREN'S HOSPITAL 77030 #021-05-1974 L1981 **NPM** *020 †55
GUINEE, Vincent Florence. 1515 HOLCOMBE BLVD # -01 77030 #035-20-1959 L1974 **PHP IM** *071 †70
GUIRGUIS, Nabil Yacoub Sh. 1300 MOURSUND ST, HOUSTON PSYCHIATRY 77030 #915-03-1990 L2005 **CHP** *020 †20
GUITREAU, Joseph Ray, Jr. 1504 TAUB LOOP, BEN TAUB INTERNAL MED. DEP 77030 #021-06-1996 L1998 **IM** *020 †20
GUKHOOL, Jason A. 211 HIGHLAND CROSS DR, STE 275 77073 #028-46-1999 L2006 **OS IM** *020 †20,16
GULE, Maria Kristine. PO BOX 20708 77225 #539-06-2005 **GS** *012
GULL, Humara Shireen. 11815A ADEL RD 77067 #704-06-1990 L1996 **NM** *020 †28,20
GULLETT, Ashley Edith. ■ 77054 #048-14-2008 *012
GULLETT, James Ralph. 7900 FANNIN ST, STE 4000 77054 #048-04-1970 L1970 **OBG** *020 †30
GUMBERT, Sam D. ■ 77005 #048-14-2006 **AN** *012
GUMMATTIRA, Pushpa K. 2800 S MACGREGOR WAY, CENTER 77021 #495-09-1976 L1988 **P** *020
GUNASEKERA, Nishani C. 2411 FOUNTAIN VIEW DR #200, GREATER HOUSTON ANESTHESIO 77057 #220-01-1992 L2003 **AN** *020
GUNAWAN, Anthony. 920 FROSTWOOD DR STE 690 77024 #165-04-1976 L1981 **CD IM** *020 †20
GUNDEL, Robert Ellsworth. ■ 77040 #041-01-1945 **OM** *071
GUNDLACH, Marney. 6701 FANNIN ST, CCC 1540.00 77030 #025-01-2001 L2006 **PD** *020 †55 ‡
GUNN, Albert Edward. 1515 HOLCOMBE BLVD 77030 #539-05-1967 L1973 **IM IMG** *030 †20

GUNN, Angelyn. 837 FM 1960 RD W, STE 105 77090 #048-04-2000 L2001 **AR** *100 †80
GUNN, Debra Clark. 7900 FANNIN ST, STE 4000 77054 #028-02-1978 L1982 **OBG** *020
GUNN, Emily W. 6410 FANNIN ST, STE 480 77030 #048-14-1998 L2002 **MPD** *020 †55,20
GUNN, Gary B. ■ 77042 #048-15-2004 L2007 **RO** *012
GUNN, Sheila Kaye. 6621 FANNIN ST, CCC-1020.05 77030 #039-01-1984 L1986 **PDE** *020 †55
GUNTUPALLI, Jayarama S. 6431 FANNIN ST 77030 #495-21-1971 L1989 **NEP IM** *050 †20
GUNTUPALLI, Kalpalatha K. 1709 DREYDEN RD, STE 950 77030 #495-21-1971 L1989 **PCC IM** *020 †20
GUNTUPALLI, Saketh Ram. ■ 77025 #048-14-2005 **OBG** *012
GUO, Chuanhai. ■ 77025 #243-32-1990 L2007 **PTH** *100 †50
GUO, Ying. 1515 HOLCOMBE BLVD BOX 8, M.D. ANDERSON CANCER CENTE 77030 #243-94-1985 L2000 **PM** *020 †60
GUPTA, Arpan. ■ 77006 #048-04-2008 *012
GUPTA, Kaushal K. 11230 AIRLINE DR, # 1 77037 #495-08-1975 L1981 **IM** *020 †20
GUPTA, Monesha Lalit. 6431 FANNIN ST, MSB 3-130 77030 #495-01-1988 L1997 **PD PDC** *020 †55
GUPTA, Monica Patel. 6431 FANNIN ST, INTERNAL MEDICINE DEPARTME 77030 #048-02-2003 L2006 **CD** *012
GUPTA, Richa. ■ 77005 #495-18-1996 L2002 **IM** *020 †20
GUPTA, Sandeep. 11914 ASTORIA BLVD STE 370 77089 #495-45-1987 L1995 **PUD IM** *020 †20
GUPTA, Sanjay. 1515 HOLCOMBE BLVD 77030 #495-14-1987 L2003 *020 †80
GUPTA, Swati Kaushal. 7710 BEECHNUT ST, STE 210 77074 #496-38-1992 L2002 **CD** *020 †20
GURIN, David M. 6621 FANNIN ST STE 310, MAIL CODE 2-1495 77030 #048-02-1993 L1994 **AN** *020 †05
GUSHIKEN, Francisca C. 1 BAYLOR PLZ, BCM 286 RM N1302 77030 #737-06-1990 L1999 **HEM** *020 †20
GUSS, Jennifer Eve. 3601 N MACGREGOR WAY, DISTRICT MC 2707; RESIDENC 77004 #010-01-1996 L2002 **MPD** *020 †20,55
GUSTAFSON, Paul Robt. ■ 77096 #050-02-1977 L1983 **ON IM** *020 †20
GUSTAFSON, Robert Everett. 9090 GAYLORD ST, STE 106 77024 #018-03-1945 L1956 **PD PDA** *071 †55
GUSTAFSON, Steven A. 1515 HOLCOMBE BLVD UNIT 72, MD ANDERSEN CANCER CTR 77030 #018-75-1996, ▲ L2005 **PCH** *012
GUSTAFSON, Wesley C, Jr. 8720D S GESSNER DR 77074 #048-02-1961 L1961 **FM OS** *020 †18
GUSTAVSON, Lillian P. ■ 77006 #048-02-1963 L1963 **HEM PD** *071 †55
GUTHRIE, Agnes Maria D. 6431 FANNIN ST # 2134 77030 #759-03-1963 L1967 **DR EM** *020 †20
GUTIERREZ, Augusto E. 1919 LA BRANCH ST 77002 #275-01-1957 L1967 **RO** *071 †80
GUTIERREZ, Jose Asuncion. 7500 BEECHNUT ST STE 214 77074 #264-02-1967 L1975 **P PYG** *020 †75
GUTIERREZ, Maria C. 1 BAYLOR PLZ, DEPT PATH BAYLOR CLGE MD 77030 #264-01-1979 L1999 **PTH** *040 †50
GUTIERREZ, Orlando David. 5656 KELLEY ST, LBJ EC93006 77026 #649-04-2001 L2006 **FM** *100 †18
GUTSTEIN, Howard Bruce. 1515 HOLCOMBE BLVD, UNIT 110 77030 #023-07-1982 L1999 **AN** *020 †05
GUTTERMAN, Jordan Udell. 1515 HOLCOMBE BLVD, UNIT 950 77030 #051-04-1964 L1971 **ON HEM** *050 †20
GUTTIN, Jorge. 6624 FANNIN ST, STE 2220 77030 #649-01-1968 L1975 **CD** *020 †20
GUY, Elizabeth Sy-Siong. 1504 TAUB LOOP, PULMONARY & CRITICAL CARE 77030 #748-02-1983 L1999 **PUD IM** *020 †20
GUYDEN, Jamie Lynn. 3726 DACOMA ST 77092 #033-05-2003 L2006 **PM** *020
GUYNN, Robert Wm. 1300 MOURSUND ST STE 206 77030 #023-07-1967 L1973 **P** *040 †75
GUZICK, Norman David. 7777 SOUTHWEST FWY STE 956 77074 #048-02-1972 L1972 **D DMP** *020 †15
GUZMAN, Horacio Jose. 11914 ASTORIA BLVD, STE 500 77089 #649-14-1969 L1975 **OTO** *020 †45
GUZMAN, Nicizaki. 18220 TOMBALL PKWY, STE 400 77070 #649-01-1980 L1995 **FM** *020 †18
GUZMAN AGUAYO, Nelio. PO BOX 270708 77225 #649-19-2004 **MPD** *012
GUZON, Marielou R. 6035 AIRLINE DR STE 1 77076 #748-08-1973 L1984 **PD** *020
GWISE, Peter Joseph. ■ 77014 #067-01-1971 L1973 **PS GS** *020
GWOZDZ, Jennifer Susan. 3402 HIGHWAY 6 S STE D 77082 #917-02-1975 L1978 **GP** *020
HA, Caroline Ann. ■ 77096 #048-12-2008 *012
HA, Christina Pham. ■ 77094 #048-02-2008 *012
HAAS, Eric Mitchell. 6560 FANNIN ST, STE 600 77030 #048-14-1997 L1998 **CRS GS** *020 †85,10
HABASHY, Labib Mishricky. 14903 EL CAMINO REAL 77062 #330-01-1957 L1967 **OBG** *071
HABER, Leslie A Marsh. 6565 FANNIN ST 77030 #048-04-1984 L1986 **HEM PTH** *020 †50
HABER, Steven Earl. 11757 KATY FWY STE 1540 77079 #048-14-1986 L1987 **PUD IM** *020 †20
HABIB, Jubran Bishara. 2002 HOLCOMBE BLVD 77030 #605-01-1981 L1989 **CD IM** *020 †20
HABIB, Vivian Makram. 4545 POST OAK PLACE DR, STE 130 77027 #422-01-2000 L2003 **IM** *020 †20
HACK, Maryann. 5126 CAREW ST 77096 #048-12-1981 L1981 **AN** *020 †05
HACKEN, Joan Beck. 2002 HOLCOMBE BLVD, DEPT RADIOLOGY 77030 #035-01-1973 L1980 **DR** *020 †80
HACKER, Jerriann. 6720 BERTNER ST 77030 #048-04-1967 L1967 **GS** *020 †05
HADAD, Anibal Raul. 150 FM 1959 RD 77034 #132-02-1971 L1986 **GS VS** *020 †85
HADDAD, John Lawrence. 6565 FANNIN ST, STE D281 77030 #035-47-1987 L1993 **DR** *020 †80
HADDAD, Rudy Morshed. ■ 77030 #048-02-2003 L2003 **CD** *012 †20
HADDOCK, A J. 2925 W T C JESTER BLVD 77018 #048-02-1963 L1963 **FM** *020 †18
HADLEY, Arthur Twining. 11777 KATY FWY STE 270 77079 #021-01-1972 L1982 **FM GPM** *020 †70,18 ‡
HADNOTT, William Hicks, III. 1200 BINZ ST, STE 1430 77004 #048-02-1998 L2003 **ORS** *020 †40
HADSAITONG, Damrong. ■ 77072 #891-03-1970 L1975 **GS EM** *075 †85
HADSAITONG, Tussanee S. ■ 77072 #891-03-1971 L1974 **AN** *020 †05
HAFEEZ, Tahir. 8876 GULF FWY, STE 215 77017 #422-01-2000 L2007 **NEP** *020 †20 ‡
HAFFAR, Anan Ahmad M. ■ 77005 #875-01-1975 L1980 **PD ID** *020 †55
HAFKIN, Jonas Scott. ■ 77096 #048-04-2006 **AN** *012
HAGAN, Katherine B. ■ 77025 #048-14-2005 L2008 **AN** *012
HAGBERG, Carin A. 6431 FANNIN ST 5.020, PROFESSOR 77030 #048-14-1988 L1989 **AN** *040 †05
HAGEMEISTER, F B. 1515 HOLCOMBE BLVD, UNIT 429 77030 #048-12-1972 L1976 **ON IM** *050 †20
HAGSTROM, Garry Lee. 1200 BINZ ST STE 1180 77004 #017-20-1973 L1977 **NEP IM** *071 †20
HAHN, Karin Marie. 1515 HOLCOMBE BLVD, UNIT 241 77030 #065-01-1994 L1998 **ON** *020 †20

■ = Address Information Privacy Protected

HAIDER, Lubna Syed. 6624 FANNIN ST, STE 1730 77030 #048-04-2001 L2003 **IM** *020

HAIDER, Syed H. 6431 FANNIN ST # 3-236 77030 #704-01-1988 L2003 **PD NPM** *020 †55

HAIDET, Paul Matthew. 2002 HOLCOMBE BLVD, HOUSTON VA MED. CTR. 77030 #041-14-1991 L1994 **IM** *020

HAIRSTON, John Chance. 6431 FANNIN ST, DIV OF UROLOGY 77030 #048-14-1995 L2002 **U** *020 †95

HALASWAMY, Hanagavadi S. ■ 77082 #495-09-1960 L1998 **FM** *020 †55,18

HALAT, Anthony John. ■ 77030 #048-14-2002 L2005 **IM** *100 †20

HALBERDIER, John Edward. 7050 LAKEVIEW HAVEN DR 77095 #048-02-1972 L1973 **FM** *020

HALBERDIER, Louis S, Jr. 15655 CYPRESSWOOD MEDCL DR, STE 110 77014 #048-02-1968 L1968 **FM** *020 †18

HALDANKAR, Pradnya Sachid. 1 BAYLOR PLZ, BAYLOR COLL MED 77030 #496-44-1999 **AN** *012

HALDEMAN, Sandra Regenie. 7580 FANNIN ST, STE 335 77054 #048-02-1994 L1998 **OBG** *020 †30

HALE, Kathryn Ann. 6550 FANNIN SMITH TOWER, STE 1225 77030 #039-01-1972 L1993 **PUD IM** *020 †20

HALEVY, Amir. 6565 FANNIN ST B-501 77030 #048-04-1987 L1988 **IM** *050 †20

HALEY, Ronald Anthony. 2600 S LOOP W, STE 155 77054 #047-07-1966 L1968 **FM** *020

HALF, Elizabeth Emily. 6431 FANNIN ST 4.234, UNIV OF TEXAS MED SCH DEPT 77030 #550-02-1992 L2007 **GE** *100

HALL, Ara Schlaman. ■ 77071 #048-14-2006 **PD** *012

HALL, David Lee. 3701 KIRBY DR, STE 100 77098 #048-02-1991 L1992 **FM** *020 †18

HALL, David P. 211 HIGHLAND CROSS DR 77073 #048-13-1986 L1988 **IM** *020 †20

HALL, Jason Jennings. ■ 77005 #036-05-2002 L2005 **PS** *012 †85

HALL, Jennie F. 2002 HOLCOMBE BLVD, DEPT OF PSYCHIATRY 77030 #048-14-1991 L1993 **P** *020 †75

HALL, Kris Benjamin. ■ 77005 #021-05-1995 L2004 **FM** *020

HALL, Rahn Garner. 2646 S LOOP W, STE 575 77054 #048-04-1980 L1983 **OBG** *020

HALL, Robert Jos. 6624 FANNIN ST STE 2480 77030 #035-06-1948 L1965 **CD** *071 †20

HALL, Stuart R. 6621 FANNIN ST, WT19354H 77030 #048-04-1998 L2000 **AN** *020 †05

HALLADAY, Jeffrey Paul. 909 FANNIN ST, STE 3500 77010 #005-18-2006 L2007 **IM** *012

HALLEVI, Hen. PO BOX 20708, UNIV TX MED SCH AT HOUSTON 77225 #550-04-2000 **VN** *100

HALLMAN, Charles Harlow. 1101 BATES AVE, SURGICAL ASSOCIATES OF 77030 #048-04-1984 L1986 **TS** *020

HALLMAN, Grady Lamar. 1101 BATES AVE, SURGICAL ASSOCIATES OF 77030 #048-04-1954 L1954 **TS** *020 †85,90

HALLORAN, Vickey C. 5629 FM 1960 RD W STE 225 77069 #010-02-1951 L1977 **PD A** *071 †55

HALLOUSH, Ruba Abdalla. ■ 77025 #575-02-2000 L2006 **SP** *100 †50

HALPERN, Barbara Cutting. ■ 77096 #005-11-1944 L1945 **PD ON** *071 †55

HALPERN, Betty Anne. 5300 N BRAESWOOD BLVD, # 324 77096 #048-04-1980 L1980 **IM** *020 †20

HALPHEN, John M. 6411 FANNIN ST 77030 #048-13-1995 L1997 **IMG** *100 †18

HALPIN, Robert Edward. 2450 FONDREN RD, STE 310 77063 #048-12-1980 L1980 **PD** *020 †55

HALTER, Dale Geo. 902 FROSTWOOD DR STE 208 77024 #017-20-1974 L1981 **RHU IM** *020 †20

HALTON, Heather Lynn. ■ 77006 #021-01-2008 *012

HALVORSON, Peter S. 13114 FM 1960 RD W, STE 200 77065 #048-02-1989 L1992 **FM** *020 †18

HAMAD, Nidal M. 6720 BERTNER ST 77030 #048-21-1978 L1985 **CD IM** *020 †20

HAMAKER, Justin Charles. ■ 77054 #048-04-2008 *012

HAMAT, Howard B. 275 LANTERN BEND DR # 200 77090 #065-01-1990 L1997 **GE** *020 †20

HAMBERGER, Arthur Donald. 909 FROSTWOOD DR, STE 152 77024 #035-46-1969 L1975 **RO IM** *020 †20,80

HAMBURG, Sol. 12121 RICHMOND AVE STE 115 77082 #048-01-1981 L1983 **OPH** *020 †35

HAMEL, Todd Leland. 10028 WEST RD, STE 102 77064 #048-14-1997 L2005 **FM** *020 †18

HAMID, Basem. 1515 HOLCOMBE BLVD, UNIT 409 77030 #875-01-1995 L2006 **OS** *020 †20,75

HAMID, Monira. 3301 MERRICK ST 77025 #704-25-1992 L2004 **GS CRS** *020 †85

HAMILL, Marshall Bowes. 6565 FANNIN ST, STE NC205 77030 #048-04-1979 L1979 **OPH** *020 †35

HAMILL, Raymond Dennis. 1707 SUNSET BLVD, MEDICAL CLINIC OF HOUSTON 77005 #048-04-1969 L1969 **IM HEM** *020 †20

HAMILL, Richard James. 2002 HOLCOMBE BLVD, MS 111G 77030 #025-07-1978 L1986 **ID IM** *040 †20

HAMILTON, Alan Scott. ■ 77030 #048-13-2007 **IM** *012

HAMILTON, Carlos R, III. 1415 NORTH LOOP W, STE 820 77008 #048-02-1994 L1995 **VIR** *020 †80

HAMILTON, Carlos Robt, Jr. 6431 FANNIN ST 77030 #048-04-1966 L1966 **END** *020 †20

HAMILTON, Dale James. 6550 FANNIN ST, STE 1001 77030 #028-34-1978 L1980 **END DIA** *020 †20

HAMILTON, David Douglas. ■ 77005 #048-14-2004 **GS** *012

HAMILTON, Dixie Glaze, Jr. ■ 77095 #048-02-1952 L1952 **GYN** *071 †30

HAMILTON, Emily Rebecca. ■ 77004 #048-14-2006 **AN** *012

HAMILTON, Henry Kendall. PO BOX 980339 77098 #048-02-1969 L1969 **ORS** *071 †40

HAMILTON, Jon-Paul. 4200 MONTROSE BLVD, STE 540 77006 #048-14-1995 L1996 **P** *020 †75

HAMILTON, Jos De Vance, II. 1 BAYLOR PLZ # BCM350 77030 #048-04-1975 L1975 **P** *030 †20

HAMILTON, Lesley Elizabet. ■ 77054 #048-16-2004 L2008 **PTH** *012

HAMILTON, Stanley Ralph. 1515 HOLCOMBE BLVD, BOX 85 77030 #017-20-1973 L2001 **ATP CLP** *050 †50

HAMILTON, Steven M. 6624 FANNIN ST STE 1650 77030 #048-14-1982 L1983 **PS** *020 †65

HAMILTON-AUGUST, Yolanda. 6431 FANNIN ST, UNIVERSITY OF TEXAS 77030 #045-01-1990 L2000 **GE IM** *020 †20

HAMILTON-SPENCE, Erin C. ■ 77030 #048-02-2002 L2008 **NPM** *012

HAMMILL, Hunter Adrian. 7400 FANNIN ST, STE 1160 77054 #035-01-1976 L1988 **OBG ID** *020 †30

HAMMOND, Jeremy John. ■ 77096 #143-02-1970 L1977 **IM** *050 †20

HAMMOND, Molly E. 17150 EL CAMINO REAL 77058 #048-15-1995 L1997 **PD** *020 †55

HAMNER, Ellen Jean. ■ 77054 #048-04-2008 *012

HAMOUDI, Walid H. 1515 HOLCOMBE BLVD 77030 #528-01-1976 L1999 **BBK** *020

HAMOUIE, Sabine Yasmin. 77095 #875-02-1988 *100

HAMSIOGLU, Feryal. ■ 77054 #902-07-1989 **GE** *100

HAMZA, Zainab Tahar. 75074 BISSONNET ST 77074 #563-01-2001 L2005 **FM** *100 †18

HAN, Holly Crisp. ■ 77008 #048-04-2005 **P** *012

HAN, Jin Yong. ■ 77054 #726-01-2001 **FP** *012

HAN, Liz Ye. ■ 77006 #024-05-2000 L2006 **OBG** *100

HAN, Noel Mathew. 15655 CYPRESSWD MED DR 77014 #048-14-1992 L1993 **FM** *020 †18

HAN, Xiang-Yang. 1515 HOLCOMBE BLVD BOX 84 77030 #243-16-1984 L2001 **IM** *020 †50

HAN, Yong Suk. 6621 FANNIN ST, STE A/LK MCI-1481 77030 #026-08-1991 L1994 **PD HOS** *020 †55

HANAFY, Khalid Amin. ■ 77005 #048-14-2004 L2007 **N** *012

HANANEL, Alan Elan. 12121 RICHMOND AVE, STE 112 77082 #048-13-1994 L2000 **U** *020 †95

HANANIA, Nicola Alexander. 1504 TAUB LOOP, DEPT OF MEDICINE, 6TH FLOO 77030 #575-01-1984 L1995 **CCM PUD** *020 †20

HANASONO, Matthew M. 1515 HOLCOMBE BLVD 443, DEPARTMENT OF PLASTIC SURG 77030 #005-11-1997 L2004 **PS OTO** *020 †45,65

HANBY, Daniel Edgar. 8830 LONG POINT RD, STE 605 77055 #021-01-1962 L1971 **PD GP** *020 †55

HANCOCK, George Gray, Jr. 2500 FONDREN RD, STE 270 77063 #048-04-1968 L1968 **OM** *020 †70

HANCOCK, John Austin. ■ 77006 #048-14-2006 **DR** *012

HANDY, Beverly Carol. 1515 HOLCOMBE BLVD, BOX 37 77030 #048-14-1992 L1993 **PCH** *020 †50

HANFLING, Marcus Jay. 1504 TAUB LOOP, BEN TAUB PEDIATRIC CLINIC 77030 #016-06-1979 L1983 **PEM PD** *040 †55

HANIF, Muhammad. 18220 TOMBALL PKWY, STE 210 77070 #704-02-1983 L2000 **PCC IM** *020 †20

HANIF, Muzamil. ■ 77005 #704-26-1997 L2008 **DR** *020 †28,80

HANISSIAN, Talynn Aram. 4501 GROVEWAY DR 77087 #047-06-1984 L1990 **PD** *020 †55

HANKA, Valerie Lynne. ■ 77062 #020-12-1996 **FM** *100

HANKINS, Christopher L. 6540 BELLOWS LN 77030 #048-02-1982 L1983 **HS PTH** *020 †50

HANKINS, Linda L. 3310 RICHMOND AVE 77098 #048-14-1985 L1986 **DR** *020 †80

HANNA, Edward Adeeb. 8100 GREENBRIAR ST 77054 #330-01-1953 L1968 **GS TS** *071 †85,90

HANNA, Ehab Y. 1515 HOLCOMBE BLVD # 441, UT MD ANDERSON CANCER CTR 77030 #915-04-1982 L2004 **OTO HNS** *020 †45

HANNA, George P. 6431 FANNIN ST, UTHSCH 77030 #048-12-1991 L1992 **CD** *020 †20

HANNAH, Christina D. ■ 77077 #048-13-2001 L2006 **SP** *100

HANRAHAN, Lawrence Martin. 2929 ALLEN PKWY STE 2000, ACCENTURE 77019 #038-41-1988 **OS** *062

HANSEN, Carlos Enrique. 6206 DASHWOOD DR 77081 #132-02-1960 L1977 **GP HS** *020 †85

HANSER, Donald Sheldon. 427 W 20TH ST 77008 #065-01-1972 L1976 **GP** *020

HANSLIK, Paul A. 7600 BEECHNUT ST 77074 #048-13-1987 L1988 **PME AN** *020 †05

HANSON, Darrell Scott. 6620 MAIN ST, STE 1300 77030 #048-04-1995 L1997 **ORS** *020 †40

HANSON, George. 9337B KATY FWY # 101 77024 #412-01-1985 L1992 **IM** *020 †05

HANSON, Gregory Wm. 7401 MAIN ST 77030 #048-04-1975 L1975 **ORS** *020 †40

HANSON, Hugh H. ■ 77004 #048-02-1943 L1943 **CD** *075 †20

HANSON, Imelda Celine. 6621 FANNIN ST 330.01, BAYLOR COLLEGE OF MEDICINE 77030 #048-12-1978 L1978 **PDA IG** *040 †55,03

HANSON, Laura Ann. ■ 77030 #048-04-2008 *012

HANSON, Miriam Louise. 1900 SAINT JAMES PL, STE 600 77056 #048-04-2003 L2007 **D** *020 †15

HANSON, Sonali Gosain. 5110 BUFFALO SPEEDWAY, STE 200 77005 #048-04-1995 L1997 **D** *020 †15

HANSON, Travis Wade. 17080 RED OAK DR 77090 #028-02-1997 L2002 **ORS** *020 †40

HAQUE, Md Anwarul. 1200 HERMANN PRESSLER DR, STE 1014 77030 #160-08-1980 L2007 **GPM** *100

HAQUE, Mohammad Aynal. 8830 LONG POINT RD, STE 204 77055 #160-01-1978 L1992 **FM EM** *020 †18 ‡

HAQUE, Sajid Azeem. 6431 FANNIN ST 1.274, PULMONARY MEDICINE 77030 #048-02-1997 L2002 **PCC** *020 †20

HAQUE, Shareque Azeem. 6565 FANNIN ST 77030 #048-02-1991 L1992 **AN** *020 †05

HARATI, Yadollah. 6550 FANNIN ST, STE 1801 77030 #517-01-1970 L1976 **N PTH** *020 †75

HARBERG, Beryl L. 1000 UPTOWN PARK BLVD # 61 77056 #004-01-1950 L1962 **TS CD** *020 †85,90

HARBISON, Matthew Trevor. ■ 77007 #048-14-2002 L2008 **MPD** *100 †20,55

HARBOTT, Mark John. 1709 DRYDEN RD 77030 #836-01-1996 L2005 **AN** *100 †05

HARBOUR, William Thos. 10660 MILLS RD 77070 #027-01-1964 L1965 **GP** *020

HARDARSON, Hordue Snaevar. ■ 77005 #484-01-1995 **PDI** *100 †55

HARDEE, Eric Paul. 830 FM 1960 RD W, STE 7 77090 #048-04-1992 L2002 **DR** *020 †80

HARDER, Stephen James. ■ 77054 #048-04-2006 **IM** *012

HARDIKAR, Sulabha Vasant. 8000 N STADIUM DR, HOUSTON DEPT OF HEALTH 77054 #495-17-1954 L1980 **PHP** *030

HARDIKAR, Vasant Vasudeo. 1504 TAUB LOOP 77030 #495-01-1951 L1977 **AN** *071

HARDIN, Cheryl Lynette. 6001 GULF FWY BLDG C2, TEXAS CHILDREN'S PEDIATRIC 77023 #011-03-1987 L1989 **PD** *020 †55

HARDWICK-SMITH, Susan. 6410 FANNIN ST, STE 825 77030 #048-04-1995 L1997 **OBG** *020 †30

HARDY, Lawrence Frederick. 7401 MAIN ST 77030 #048-02-1981 L1983 **AN** *020 †05

HARDY, Shannon Leigh. ■ 77005 #048-02-2007 **OBG** *012

HARE, Joanie Yvonne. 7900 FANNIN ST, STE 2600 77054 #001-02-1989 L1995 **OBG MFM** *020 †30

HARIHARAN, Radhika R. 3601 N MACGREGOR WAY 77004 #495-59-1984 L1998 **IMG** *020 †20

HARLAND, Jan. 1313 HERMANN DR 77004 #048-13-1982 L1983 **AN** *020

HARMON, Nika Elizabeth. 921 GESSNER RD, EMERGENCY DEPARTMENT 77024 #041-14-2000 L2003 **EM** *020

HARMS, Konrad P. 1819 CRAWFORD ST STE 1708 77002 #048-14-1998 L2000 **OBG** *020 †30

HAROLD, Cecil Glenn. ■ 77021 #048-02-1957 L1957 **GS** *020 †85

HARPER, John B, Jr. ■ 77077 #041-13-1952 L1955 **R** *071 †80

HARPER, R A. 2800 S MACGREGOR WAY 77021 #048-14-1984 L1987 **CHP P** *040 †75

HARPER, Richard Andrew. 2800 S MACGREGOR WAY 77021 #039-01-1984 L1985 **OPH** *040 †35

HARPER, Richard Louis. 6560 FANNIN ST, NEUROSURGICAL GROUP OF 77030 #048-04-1971 L1971 **NS** *020 †25

HARRELL, Antwar Melvin. 4545 POST OAK PLACE DR # 1 77027 #021-06-2000 L2004 **IM GPM** *020 †20

HARRELL, Barry Lynn. 2120 ASHLAND ST 77008 #048-02-1969 L1969 **D** *020 †15

HARRELL, James Earl. 1 BAYLOR PLZ 77030 #004-01-1962 L1972 **OS DR** *071 †80

HARRELL, John S. 1709 DRYDEN RD STE 725 77030 #048-13-2002 L2007 **PM** *020 †60

HARRELL, Luther, Jr. 8000 N STADIUM DR, 3RD FL 77054 #047-07-1976 L1981 **OBG** *030

HARRING, Theresa Rebecca. ■ 77047 #048-04-2008 *012

HARRIS, Annette O. 7505 MAIN ST STE 300 77030 #048-04-1989 L1990 **D** *020 †15

HARRIS, Bernard Anthony. ■ 77059 #048-15-1982 L1983 **IM** *050

HARRIS, Canaan Lavelle. 1315 ST JOSEPH PKWY, STE 1810 77002 #010-02-1976 L1982 **OTO** *020 †45

HARRIS, Darryl Clarence. 12704 NORTH FWY 77060 #047-07-1990 L2002 **OBG** *020 †30

HARRIS, Homer E. ■ 77079 #047-07-1945 L1945 **D** *071 †15

HARRIS, James M. 1315 ST JOSEPH PKWY, STE 1502 77002 #048-12-1984 L1985 **U** *020 †95

HARRIS, Leah Waldrop. ■ 77007 #024-07-2003 L2003 **OBG** *012

HARRIS, Leslie L. 6621 FANNIN ST # 6-104, TEXAS CHILDS HOSP MC 77030 #048-14-2000 L2004 **NPM PD** *020 †55

HARRIS, Lindsey Dufour. 1220 AUGUSTA DR, STE 100 77057 #048-14-2000 L2002 **OPH** *020 †35 ‡

HARRIS, Mary Elizabeth. ■ 77006 #024-05-2003 L2007 **PD** *100

HARRIS, Norma E Fallis. PO BOX 540248 77254 #060-01-1956 L1963 **R IM** *071 †20,80

HARRIS, Paul P. 17070 RED OAK DR STE 505 77090 #033-05-1990 L1996 **OBG** *020

HARRIS, Richard Lowell. 6560 FANNIN ST, STE 2204 77030 #048-04-1978 L1978 **ID IM** *020 †20

HARRIS, Rudolph John. 4009 BELLAIRE BLVD, STE K 77025 #048-12-1956 L1956 **GP** *020

HARRIS, Toi Blakley. 1 BAYLOR PLZ, PSYCHIATIY DEPT 77030 #028-46-1992 L1994 **P** *020 †75

HARRISON, Lyndall F. 2727 W HOLCOMB BLVD 4TH FL 77025 #048-14-1986 L1988 **AI PD** *020 †55,03

HARRISON, William Thos. 6565 FANNIN ST 77030 #048-04-1945 L1945 **IM** *071

HARRYKISSOON, Rajesh I. 6431 FANNIN ST, MSB 1.150 77030 #048-12-2000 L2004 **PCC** *012 †20

HART, Jacqueline Spoerer. 4126 SOUTHWEST FWY, STE 1700 77027 #048-02-1961 L1961 **ON IM** *020

HART, Justin Patrick. 1515 HOLCOMBE BLVD, ANDERSON CANC 77030 #036-07-2005 **RO** *012

HART, Stephen F. 2101 NASA RD 1, MEDICAL OPERATIONS S026 77058 #048-16-1990 L1993 **GPM** *020 †70

HARTAS, Georgios Aristote. ■ 77002 #781-08-1998 L2003 **PDC** *100

HARTING, Mandy Sue. ■ 77019 #048-14-2004 L2007 **D** *012

HARTING, Matthew Tihen. 6431 FANNIN ST, UT MED SCHOOL-DEPT OF SURG 77030 #048-14-2003 **GS** *012

HARTSHORNE, Wendy Joanne. 7737 SOUTHWEST FWY, STE 700 77074 #051-01-1993 L1997 **OBG** *072 †30

HARTWELL, Elizabeth A. 1400 LA CONCHA LN 77054 #048-14-1987 L1989 **CLP BBK** *030 †50

HARVEY, Aaron Matthew. 6565 FANNIN ST M227 77030 #048-02-2007 **PTH** *012

HARVEY, Benjamin Dain. 18220 STATE HIGHWAY 249 77070 #048-02-1991 L1992 **AN** *020 †05

HARVEY, Debra Kay. 6550 FANNIN ST, STE 2435 77030 #048-14-1987 L1988 **FM** *040 †18

HARVEY, Edythe Pennal. 2801 GESSNER DR 77080 #048-15-1983 L1983 **P ADP** *040 †75

HARVEY, Sarah Alums. 2450 FONDREN RD, STE 310 77063 #048-04-1994 L1996 **PD** *020 †55

HARVEY, William R. 6431 FANNIN ST # 5020 77030 #836-02-1982 **AN** *020

HARVIN, William Hartman. 7027 FANNIN ST 77030 #048-14-1986 L1988 **ORS** *012

HARWELL, William S. 7777 SW FWY STE C46 77074 #001-01-1951 L1958 **DR RO** *071 †80

HASAN, Ayesha Hafsa. 6431 FANNIN ST, DEPT ADL/PEDS 77030 #704-25-2001 **ADL** *012

HASAN, Ferhat Moin. 11914 ASTORIA BLVD, STE 420 77089 #704-09-1977 L1990 **OBG** *020 †30

HASAPES, Joseph Philip. 1221 MCKINNEY ST, 40300 77010 #035-01-1989 L1996 **DR** *020 †80

HASHAM-JIWA, Nadya A. 11920 ASTORIA BLVD, STE 150 77089 #048-78-2001, ▲ L2006 **ON** *020

HASHEMI, Kattayoon. 909 FROSTWOOD DR, STE 227 77024 #010-02-1990 L1995 **OPH** *020 †35

HASITAVEJ, Rasmee. ■ 77058 #891-02-1951 L1970 **GP PD** *072 †55

HASNAIN, Syed Zafar. 902 FROSTWOOD DR, STE 253 77024 #704-02-1989 L2001 **IM** *020 †20

HASSAN, Amir Ali. 11914 ASTORIA BLVD, STE 330 77089 #704-16-1984 L1993 **END** *020 †20

HASSAN, Laila Amirali. 11914 ASTORIA BLVD, STE 330 77089 #704-16-1986 L1993 **PTH** *020 †20

HASSAN, Saamir Anwar. 6540 BELLOWS LN 77030 #048-04-2005 **IM** *012

HASSAN, Saffana Nilufer. 1631 NORTH LOOP W, STE 480 77008 #001-02-1999 L2003 **AI** *020 †20,03

HASSAN, Seema I. 10878 WESTHEIMER RD # 164 77042 #704-16-1987 **IM** *100

HASSANEIN, Hossam Mahmoud. 8181 FANNIN ST 77054 #915-02-1993 *100

HASSAN GHALYAIE, Nasrin. 1 BAYLOR PLZ 77030 #517-01-2002 **GS** *012

HASSENBUSCH, Samuel J, III. 1400 HOLCOMBE BLVD, RM FC7.2000 77030 #023-07-1978 L1993 **NS** *020 †25

HATFIELD, Bradley D. ■ 77056 #048-14-2006 **DR** *012

HATTAR, Lana Nweiser. 1 BAYLOR PLZ, BAYLOR COLL MED 77030 #575-01-2002 L2004 **PG** *012 †55

HATTINGH, Pieter Wilhelm. 6431 FANNIN ST # 5-020 77030 #836-04-1975 **AN** *100

HAU, Thomas L. 6565 FANNIN ST M196, METHODIST HOSPITAL 77030 #021-01-1997 L2002 **EM** *020

HAUFRECT, Dale Blair. 2476 BOLSOVER ST, BOX 220 77005 #016-42-1971 L1973 **N** *075

HAUFRECT, Eric Jay. 6550 FANNIN ST, STE 2221 77030 #048-04-1973 L1973 **OBG** *020 †30

HAUN, Lara Kristine. 77024 #028-34-2005 **OBG** *012

HAUPT, Bisong. 6565 FANNIN ST M227 77030 #243-71-1982 L2007 **SP** *100 †50

HAUS, Loren Wilson. 13430 NORTHWEST FWY, STE 950 77040 #019-02-1941 L1949 **GYN** *020 †30

HAUSER, Harris Milton. 7500 BEECHNUT ST, STE 266 77074 #048-04-1955 L1955 **N P** *020 †75

HAUSKNECHT, Mark John. 6400 FANNIN ST STE 3000 77030 #048-04-1980 L1980 **CD** *020 †20

HAUSNER, Richard Jeffrey. 9597 JONES RD 800 77065 #035-15-1971 L1978 **PTH** *020 †50

HAVRAN, Laurie A. ■ 77061 #048-14-1987 L1989 **FP** *020 †55

HAWILA, Munah Jack. 8830 LONG POINT RD, STE 712 77055 #605-01-1975 L1977 **U** *020 †95

HAWKINS, Edith P. ■ 77063 #012-05-1959 L1975 **PP PTH** *071 †50

HAWKINS, Kimberly Denise. 1140 WESTMONT DR, STE 430 77015 #047-07-1997 L2001 **OBG** *020 †30

HAWKINS, Laura Mary. ■ 77005 #068-01-1985 L1999 **PD** *020 †55

HAWKINS, Lee Roy. 2101 CRAWFORD ST, STE 214 77002 #048-12-1991 L1992 **PD** *020 †55

HAWKINS, Marla Anne. ■ 77098 #001-02-2003 L2005 **PHO** *012 †55

HAWKINS, Mary Katherine. 1 BAYLOR PLZ 77030 #048-15-2007 **PD** *012

HAWKINS, Shannon Michelle. 1709 DRYDEN RD, STE 1100 77030 #017-20-2002 L2006 **OBG** *100

HAWKINS, W Rex. 18220 STATE HIGHWAY 249, STE 140 77070 #012-05-1959 L1965 **OPH** *020 †35

HAWKINS, Wendy J. 11321 FALLBROOK DR 77065 #023-07-1991 L1996 **IM** *020 †20

HAXHILLARI, Arian. 1315 ST JOSEPH PKWY, STE 1400 77002 #120-01-1992 L2006 **FM** *100 †18

HAY, Raymond Mc Iver. 6550 MAPLERIDGE ST STE 108 77081 #021-05-1966 L1973 **ORS** *020 †40

HAYCOCKS, Neil George. ■ 77025 #051-04-2005 L2007 **PTH** *012

HAYES, Shannon Kelley. 7400 FANNIN ST, STE 730 77054 #048-04-2000 L2003 **PD** *020 †55

HAYES, Shelley Alene. 520 POST OAK BLVD STE 780 77027 #048-04-1983 L1983 **P** *020 †75 ‡

HAYES, Teresa Gray. 2002 HOLCOMBE BLVD, VA 111 H HEMATOLOGY-ONCOL 77030 #035-19-1982 L1983 **ON IM** *020 †20

HAYES-JORDAN, Andrea A. 6431 FANNIN ST, MSB 5.254 77030 #032-01-1991 L2005 **GS** *020 †85

HAYKAL, Hani Abdul Azia F. 6565 FANNIN ST, THE METHODIST HOSPITAL, MS 77030 #605-01-1978 L1991 **DR NR** *020 †20

HAYMAN, Linda A. 1707 SUNSET BLVD, MEDICAL CLINIC OF HOUSTON 77005 #021-05-1973 L1975 **DR** *050 †80

HAYMOND, Morey Wm. 1100 BATES AVE, RM 7062 77030 #028-02-1969 L1997 **PDE END** *030 †55

HAYNIE, Thomas Powell. 1515 HOLCOMBE BLVD 77030 #048-04-1956 L1956 **NM ON** *071 †28,20

HAYSOM, Howard Henry. 211 HIGHLAND CROSS DR #275 77073 #064-01-1976 L1977 **EM FM** *020 †20

HE, Guoxiang. 4040 BROADWAY ST 77087 #243-21-1983 L1997 **FM** *020 †18

HE, Hongying. PO BOX 20708, DEPT OF RADIOLOGY 77225 #035-46-2005 **DR** *012

HE, Ming S. ■ 77006 #048-12-2004 **HO** *012 †20

HEADRICK, Charles B. ■ 77024 #048-02-1953 L1953 **FM** *071

HEALEY, Katherine. ■ 77008 #048-14-2002 L2005 **EM** *020

HEALY, Catherine Mary. 1 BAYLOR PLZ RM 302, BAYLOR COLLEGE OF MEDICINE 77030 #539-02-1991 **PDI** *100

HEALY, John A. PO BOX 20708, UNIV TX MED SCH 77225 #048-14-2007 **GS** *012

HEALY, Richard O. 1 HERMANN CIRCLE DR, # 4093 77030 #539-04-1970 L1999 **FM U** *020 †95,18

HEAPS, Brian Richard. ■ 77035 #051-04-2006 **OBG** *012

HEARD, John Gregory. ■ 77098 #048-12-1966 L1966 **R** *071 †80

HEARD, Michael Joseph. 6624 FANNIN ST, STE 1800 77030 #012-05-1991 L2000 **OBG REN** *020 †30 ‡

HEATH, Karina Annelise. ■ 77061 #737-06-1995 **FP** *012

HEBENSTREIT, Charles G. ■ 77054 #048-14-2008 *012

HEBERT, Adelaide Ann. 6655 TRAVIS ST, STE 980 77030 #021-01-1980 L1981 **D EM** *020 †15

HECHT, Stephen Gregory. 6431 FANNIN ST, JJL 445 77030 #038-40-1986 L1992 **EM IM** *040 †20,16

HECK, Kent Alan. 6720 BERTNER ST MC4-265 77030 #021-01-1988 L1994 **PTH** *020 †50

HEDDEN, Elizabeth A. 11550 FUQUA ST, STE 560 77034 #048-02-1988 L1998 **CHP** *020 †75

HEDDINGS, Hazel Jeannette. 1703 GRAY ST, DAYBREAK CLINIC 77003 #051-01-1977 L1999 **FM** *020 †18

HEDRICK, Thomas Day. 3314 ALBANS RD 77005 #048-04-1976 L1976 **DR** *020 †80

HEERENSPERGER, Timothy E. 15775 PARK TEN PL 77084 #048-14-1987 L1988 **AN** *020 †05

HEFFELMAN, Craig Semple. 5314 DASHWOOD DR 77081 #649-01-1973 L1976 **ORS PMM** *071

HEFNER, James Donald. 5656 KELLEY ST, LBJ HOSPITAL 77026 #047-05-1955 L1977 **EM OBG** *020 †30

HEGARTY, Paul Kevin. 7777 GREENBRIAR ST 77030 #539-02-1994 *100

HEGGENESS, Michael Holte. 6620 MAIN ST 77030 #011-02-1984 L1990 **ORS** *020 †40

HEIDELBERGER, Ruth. 6431 FANNIN ST, DEPT OF NEUROBIOLOGY UTHMS 77030 #035-48-1993 *050

HEILMAN, Alan Edward. 7401 MAIN ST 77030 #048-04-1983 L1985 **ORS** *020 †40

HEILSTEDT, Heidi Ann. 1102 BATES AVE, RM 235 77030 #025-07-1994 L2000 **MG** *020 †55,19

HEIMBERGER, Amy Beth. 1515 HOLCOMBE BLVD, DEPT OF NEUROSAURG #442 77030 #028-02-1995 L2003 **NS** *020 †25

HEIN, Perry Dayle. 9339 NORTH LOOP E 77029 #048-02-1976 L1976 **EM** *020 †16

HEIN, Walter Raymond. JOHNSON SPACE CTR SD 22 77058 #048-04-1954 L1954 **GPM AM** *030 †85

HEINE, Jon Edward. 925 GESSNER RD STE 400, MEDICAL PLAZA 4 77024 #028-03-1971 L1978 **CD IM** *020 †20

HEINEMANN, Jeffrey John. 1313 HERMANN DR, STE 270 77004 #048-02-1996 L2000 **AN** *020 †05

HEINLE, Jeffrey Stephen. 6621 FANNIN ST, WT19345H 77030 #041-12-1987 L1996 **TS** *020 †85,90

HEINLE, Sheila Kim. 6624 FANNIN ST, STE 2480 77030 #041-12-1986 L1996 **CD IM** *020 †20

HEIRD, William Carroll. 1100 BATES AVE 77030 #047-05-1964 L1965 **NTR PD** *050 †55

HELD, Barbara I. 6550 FANNIN ST, STE 2221 77030 #035-08-1997 L2001 **OBG** *020 †30

HELEKAR, Bharati Santosh. 1 BAYLOR PLZ, BAYLOR COLLEGE OF MED 77030 #496-15-1985 L2005 **PTH** *100 †50

HELGASON, Agust Hordur. 7600 BEECHNUT ST 77074 #484-01-1953 L1967 **PTH DMP** *071 †50

HELLER, Lior. 6624 FANNIN ST, STE 2260 77030 #550-01-1989 L2003 *020

HELLERSTEIN, Lewis Jan. 1140 WESTMONT DR, TEXAS ONCOLOGY, P.A. 77015 #007-02-1964 L1968 **ON HEM** *020 †20

HELMCAMP, Jeffrey K. 6431 FANNIN ST STE 2.026 77030 #048-13-2002 L2005 **DR** *100 †80

HELMER, Drew Anthonie. 2002 HOLCOMBE BLVD 111PC0 77030 #035-01-1997 L1999 **IM** *050 †20

HELMER, Kenneth S. 5656 KELLEY ST, LBJ HOSPITAL, DEPT. OF SUR 77026 #048-14-1998 L2004 **GS** *100 †85

HELWIG, Glenn Alvin. ■ 77008 #016-42-1973 L1974 **OBG** *071 †30

HEMENWAY, Shawn Gabriel. 6431 FANNIN ST, SCHOOL A 77030 #054-04-2007 **PD** *012

HEMSTREET, George P, IV. 6431 FANNIN ST, UNIV TEXAS HLTH SCIENCE 77030 #001-02-1999 L2004 **IC** *020 †20

HENAO, Sergio. 902 FROSTWOOD DR STE 135 77024 #264-03-1965 L1973 **P CHP** *020 †20

HENAO, Wanda Juanita. 902 FROSTWOOD DR, STE 135 77024 #048-02-1968 L1973 **P** *020 †75

HENCE, Reginald D. ■ 77054 #048-14-2007 **IM** *012

HENDERSON, Brian Porter. 2411 FOUNTAIN VIEW DR, STE 200 77057 #055-02-2001 L2006 **AN** *020 †05

HENDERSON, Hattie Elaine. ■ 77063 #038-45-1998 L2003 **DR** *012

HENDERSON, Janet Lee. 6431 FANNIN ST 3.140 77030 #005-12-1992 L1998 **PD NDP** *020

HENDERSON, Kimberly. 2000 CRAWFORD ST, STE 1325 77002 #010-03-1985 L1992 **AN PME** *020 †05

HENDERSONTUCKER, Raven. ■ 77021 #048-14-2008 *012

HENDLEY, Katie Leighanne. PO BOX 20708, UNIV TX MED SCH 77225 #048-14-2006 **N** *012

HENNARD, Georges Marcel. ■ 77008 #869-05-1948 L1979 **ORS GP** *071

HENNESSY, Bryan Thomas Jo. PO BOX 301439, UNIT 1364 77230 #539-04-1997 L2007 **ON** *100

HENRIKSEN, Linda Lucille. 18220 TOMBALL PKWY, STE 400 77070 #048-02-1969 L1969 **PD** *020

HENRY, Charles S. 7777 SOUTHWEST FWY, STE 304 77074 #048-14-1999 L2001 **NEP** *020 †20

HENRY, Mark Howard. 1200 BINZ ST STE 1200 77004 #036-07-1992 L1997 **HS** *020 †40

HENRY, Michelle Fern. ■ 77054 #048-04-2008 *012

HENSON, Helene Kosieracki. 2002 HOLCOMBE BLVD 117 77030 #048-14-1985 L1986 **PM** *030 †60

HEPTULLA, Rubina A. ■ 77030 #495-45-1990 L2002 **PDE PD** *020 †55

HERBST, Roy S. 1400 HOLCOMBE BLVD BX 432, MD ANDERSON CANCER CENTER 77030 #035-20-1991 L1999 **ON** *012 †18

HERD, James Alan. ■ 77025 #061-01-1956 L1982 **IM** *071

HERESI, Gloria. 6431 FANNIN ST #1739, DEPT PD 77030 #231-01-1975 L1996 **PD** *020 †55

HERGENROEDER, Albert Chas. 6621 FANNIN ST 1710.00, TEXAS CHILDRENS HOSPITAL 77030 #041-12-1980 L1987 **ADL PSM** *030 †55

HERLIHY, James Patrick. 6624 FANNIN ST STE 1730, SLEEP MEDICINE CONSULTANTS 77030 #010-02-1984 L1995 **PUD CCM** *020 †20

HERMAN, Robert Alan. 915 GESSNER RD, STE 850 77024 #024-07-1972 L1979 **GE IM** *020 †20

HERMANN, William Joseph. 921 GESSNER RD, CLINICAL LABS 77024 #025-07-1971 L1977 **CLP PTH** *020 †50

HERMANTO, Ulrich. 1515 HOLCOMBE BLVD, ANDERSON CANC UNIT 97 77030 #035-47-2002 L2007 **RO** *020 †20

HERMOSO, Marcos R F. 2411 FOUNTAIN VIEW DR #200 77057 #748-01-1988 L1996 **AN** *020 †05

HERNANDEZ, Alfred Joe, Jr. 1200 BINZ ST STE 650 77004 #048-02-1968 L1968 **GE PLM** *020 †20

HERNANDEZ, Carlos F. 2211 NORFOLK ST, STE 460 77098 #649-30-1983 L1997 **P** *020

HERNANDEZ, Eduardo A. 6624 FANNIN ST, STE 2780 77030 #042-01-1994 L2000 **CD** *020 †20

HERNANDEZ, Jose Alberto. 6621 FANNIN ST 2-2521, DIAGNOSTIC IMAGING 77030 #264-04-1992 L2003 **VIR PDR** *020 †18

HERNANDEZ, Jose M. ■ 77079 #048-13-2004 L2006 **AN GP** *100

HERNANDEZ, Rose Mary. 5615 KIRBY DR, STE 440 77005 #048-13-1986 L1987 **NPM** *020 †55

HERNANDEZ JIMENEZ, Isaac. ■ 77063 #649-03-2005 L2006 **PM** *012

HERNANDEZ MALAGON, Maria. 77030 #264-05-1998 **ID** *012

HERNANDEZ-NUNEZ, Aquileo. 11914 ASTORIA BLVD STE 540 77089 #264-04-1965 L1985 **GS VS** *020 †85

HERNDON, Erica Arvette. ■ 77068 #048-12-2007 **OBG** *012

HERNDON, John W. 6624 FANNIN ST 77030 #048-04-1953 L1953 **OTO** *020 †45

HERNE, Kelly L. 7737 SW FWY STE 53 77074 #048-14-2000 L2001 **D** *020 †15

HERPIN, Callie H. 6440 HILLCROFT ST, STE 304 77081 #016-45-1997 L1998 **FM** *100

HERRERA, Anthony Joseph. ■ 77030 #048-04-2008 *012

HERRERA, Carlos R. 7737 SOUTHWEST FWY, STE 700 77074 #024-01-1983 L1984 **IM** *020 †20

HERRERA, Elizabeth. 6565 FANNIN ST, PHYSIC ORGANIZ, SUITE B452 77030 #023-01-1989 L2002 **CCA** *020 †05

HERRERA, Hector John. 7401 MAIN ST 77030 #048-02-1987 L1988 **AN** *020 †05

HERRERA, Jose Raul, Jr. ■ 77098 #341-01-1950 L1960 **R** *071 †80

HERRING, T Melvyn, Jr. 5090 RICHMOND AVE #117 77056 #005-12-1968 L1974 **OBG** *071 †30

HERRINGTON, Bruce. ■ 77030 #021-05-2004 L2008 **PTH** *012

HERSHBERGER, Robert L. ■ 77030 #036-07-1951 L1953 **IM** *071

HERSHKOWITZ, Leonard. 7500 BEECHNUT ST, STE 135 77074 #048-07-1970 L1975 **N** *020 †75

HERSMAN, Jessica. ■ 77054 #048-14-2008 *012

HERTEL, Paula Marie. 6701 FANNIN ST, TEXAS CHILDREN'S HOSPITAL 77030 #026-04-1998 L2001 **PG** *100 †55

HERZ, Ralph. 915 GESSNER RD, STE 100 77024 #048-04-1965 L1977 **GP** *040

HERZOG, Cynthia E. 1515 HOLCOMBE BLVD, MD ANDERSON CANCER CENTER 77030 #048-02-1985 L1987 **PD PHO** *071 †55

HESLOP, Helen Elisabeth. 6565 FANNIN ST M964 77030 #671-01-1980 L2001 **PHO HEM** *050

HESS, Charles Gustavus. 1820 W 43RD ST, #2 77018 #048-02-1959 L1959 **PD** *020

HESS, Patricia A. ■ 77018 #048-14-2004 L2007 **CHP** *012

HESSE, Clyde Everett. ■ 77058 #048-04-1957 L1957 **PD** *071

HESSEL, Amy Clark. 1515 HOLCOMBE BLVD, UNIT 441 77030 #011-03-1994 L1995 **OTO HNS** *020 †45

HESSELBACHER, Sean Eric. ■ 77019 #051-07-2004 L2004 **PCC** *012 †20

HESTER, Jeane Porter. ■ 77056 #039-01-1967 L1973 **IM ON** *071

HETHERINGTON, Geo Wm, Jr. 2539 S GESSNER RD STE 8 77063 #048-02-1964 L1964 **D** *020 †15

HEW, Jane. 2411 FOUNTAIN VIEW DR, STE 200 77057 #035-09-1993 L2006 **AN** *020 †05

HEWITT, Ryan Joseph. ■ 77057 #048-14-2008 *012

HEYMACH, John Victor, Jr. 1515 HOLCOMBE BLVD, DEPT OF THNMO, UNIT 432 77030 #005-11-1998 L2005 **HO** *020 †20

HEYNE, Joseph D. 1 BAYLOR PLZ, BAYLOR COLL MED 77030 #048-14-2003 L2008 **GS** *012

HEYNE, Kirk Edward. 1707 SUNSET BLVD, MEDICAL CLINIC OF HOUSTON 77005 #048-04-1981 L1982 **ON HEM** *020 †20

HIATT, Peter Montez. 6621 FANNIN ST, CLINICAL CARE CTR 77030 #018-03-1980 L1986 **PDP PD** *020 †55

HICKEY, Janet Marie. ■ 77035 #048-02-2002 **P** *100

HICKMAN, Glenda Gail. 6565 FANNIN ST M796, THE METHODIST HOSPITAL 77030 #048-02-1997 L2001 **MPD** *020 †55,20

HICKMAN, Jennifer A. 5110 BUFFALO SPEEDWAY, STE 200 77005 #048-14-2003 L2006 **D** *020 †15

HICKMAN, Timothy N. 920 FROSTWOOD DR STE 720 77024 #028-34-1990 L2002 **REN OBG** *020 †30

HICKS, John Bernard. 6621 FANNIN ST, STE B1 77030 #064-01-1958 L1963 **IM OS** *071

HICKS, Lindsey D. ■ 77054 #048-14-2008 *012

HICKS, M John. MCI-2261, TX CHILDRENS HOSP DEPT PAT 77030 #011-02-1988 L1992 **ATP** *020 †50

HICKS, Marshall Edward. 1515 HOLCOMBE BLVD BOX 325, DPT RADIOLOGY 77030 #020-12-1982 L2000 **VIR** *020 †80

HIDALGO, Carlos Hugo. 19515 TOMBALL PKWY #56 77070 #649-30-1975 L1980 **FM** *075 †18

HIGGINBOTHAM, Chandra G. 2000 CRAWFORD ST, STE 860 77002 #021-05-1987 L1991 **OBG** *030

HIGGINBOTHAM, Jeffrey Nor. ■ 77066 #048-14-2004 L2005 **AN** *012

HIGGIN-BOTHAM, Kimberly B. 1515 HOLCOMBE BLVD, UNIT 10 77030 #048-14-2002 L2005 **ON** *012 †20

HIGGINBOTHAM, Warren H. 2002 HOLCOMBE BLVD 77030 #021-01-1946 L1952 **P** *071

HIGGINS, John Patrick. 6431 FANNIN ST, RM 1.254 77030 #143-05-1990 L2007 **CD IM** *020 †20

HIGGS, Lawrence Michael. ■ 77062 #017-20-1962 L1970 **CD IM** *071 †20

HIGHSTEAD, Richard Grant. ■ 77062 #048-02-2006 L2008 **GS** *012

HIGHTOWER, Ann Susan. 7026 OLD KATY RD, STE 276 77024 #048-02-1984 L1985 **DR** *020 †80

HIGHTOWER, Curtis Errol. 1400 HOLCOMBE BLVD BOX 409, CTR 77030 #038-06-1984 L1999 **AN** *020 †05

HIGHTOWER, Erica E. ■ 77054 #048-14-2004 L2007 **IM** *012 †20

HIGUERA, Stephen. 1 BAYLOR PLZ, DEPT PS 77030 #042-02-2002 **PS** *012

HILDRETH, David H. 6560 FANNIN ST STE 400 77030 #047-06-1977 L1984 **ORS** *020 †40

HILL, Carey Stratton. 1100 HOLCOMBE BLVD, BOX 221 77030 #047-06-1954 L1963 **PMM PLM** *072

HILL, Charles Adrian. ■ 77235 #048-04-1956 L1956 **DR NM** *071 †80

HILL, Charles M, Jr. 800 PEAKWOOD DR STE 7F 77090 #048-02-1969 L1969 **GP** *020 †18

HILL, Frank Douglass. 4101 GREENBRIAR ST STE 100 77098 #048-04-1954 L1954 **PD** *020 †55

HILL, Jason Bradley. ■ 77030 #021-05-2006 **MPD** *012

HILL, Karen Elizabeth. 5420 DASHWOOD DR STE 103 77081 #038-41-1992 L1996 **IM PD** *020 †55,20

HILL, L Leighton. 1 BAYLOR PLZ 77030 #021-05-1952 L1960 **PN PD** *071 †55

HILLAR, Marian. TEX SOUTHERN U BIOL DEPT 77004 #759-07-1962 **OS ON** *040

HILLERT, Arthur W. 7555 CHERRY PARK DR 77095 #048-13-1997 L1998 **FM** *020 †18

HILLERT, Carlotta A. 7555 CHERRY PARK DR 77095 #048-13-1997 L1998 **FM** *020 †18

HILLIARD, Harriet Nailor. 15655 CYPRESSWOOD MEDCL DR, STE 100 77014 #027-01-1987 L1991 **FM** *020 †18

HILLIARD, Robert L, Jr. 2000 CRAWFORD ST, STE 1220 77002 #048-13-1994 L1995 **OBG** *020 †30

HILLIER, Yvonne. 2727 W HOLCOMBE BLVD, MEDICAL CENTER ANESTHESIA 77025 #048-02-1989 L1993 **AN** *020

HILLSON, Sarah. ■ 77008 #917-10-2000 **IM** *100 †20

HILMERS, David C. 6701 FANNIN ST, STE 1540.00 77030 #048-04-1995 L1997 **MPD** *020 †20,55

HIMES, Ryan Wallace. ■ 77054 #654-01-2003 L2006 **PG** *012 †55

HINCK, Vincent C. BAYLOR COLLEGE OF MEDICINE, DEPARTMENT OF RADIOLOGY 77030 #035-09-1953 L1973 **R** *040 †20

HINCKLEY, Lisa Kay. 1701 HERMANN DR, UNIT 3201 77004 #046-01-1993 L2000 **RNR** *020 †80

HINDS, William Lawyer. 6448 FANNIN ST 77030 #035-15-1954 L1962 **DR OS** *071 †80

HINES, Merrill Odom, III. ■ 77008 #021-05-2000 L2006 **FOP** *012

HINESTROZA, Howard. 6621 FANNIN ST 77030 #035-47-2001 L2006 **PD** *020 †55

HINITT, Steven A. 200 N DAIRY ASHFORD ST 77079 #048-14-1999 L2002 **FM** *020 †18

HINKLEY, Clark Miller. ■ 77030 #036-01-1961 L1967 **OBG** *071 †30

HINOJOSA, Derly. ■ 77054 #048-14-2008 *012

HINOJOSA, Jaime H. ■ 77054 #048-14-2008 *012

HINTON, Warren Edward. 810 PEAKWOOD DR, STE 107 77090 #027-01-1968 L1968 **R** *020 †80

HIPPS, William Michael. 11914 ASTORIA BLVD, TEXAS EYE INSTITUTE 77089 #012-07-2001 L2005 *020 †35

HIRANI, Kamal Harnam. ■ 77004 #495-01-1996 L2005 **IM** *062 †20

HIROSE, Yoko. 4954 GLENMEADOW DR 77096 #035-19-1981 L1983 **AN FPS** *020 †05

HIRSCH, Douglas J. 921 GESSNER RD, DEPT. OF ANESTHESIOLOGY 77024 #422-07-1991 L1997 **AN** *020 †05

HIRSCH, Ellyn Adrian. 7900 FANNIN ST, STE 3500 77054 #024-05-1989 L1997 **PD** *020 †55

HIRSCHFELD, Jacobo. 2807 LITTLE YORK RD, YORK PLAZA HOSP 77093 #132-01-1963 L1968 **PD** *020

HIRSCH-GINSBERG, Cheryl F. 1515 HOLCOMBE BLVD, UNIT 37 77030 #020-02-1981 L1987 **PTH** *020 †50

HIRSHBERG, Richard M. 1111 HERMANN DR, UNIT 9B 77004 #048-04-1959 L1959 **NS** *071 †25

HITCHINS, Lisa D. 1201 DAIRY ASHFORD ST, STE 200 77079 #021-01-1996 L2006 **D** *020 †15

HITE, Stanley Jack. 7777 SOUTHWEST FWY, STE 756 77074 #012-01-1959 L1966 **NS** *072 †25

HITE, Suzanne Marie. 1111 AUGUSTA DR 77057 #048-12-1978 L1995 **PD** *020 †55

HIXSON, Rosetta Dawn. PO BOX 20708 77225 #011-03-1999 **GS** *100

HO, Andrew M. 1200 BAKER ST, MEDICAL DIVISION 77002 #048-04-1993 L1994 **IM** *020 †20

HO, Benjamin Shing Chiu. 4101 GREENBRIAR ST, STE 100 77098 #048-14-2004 L2007 **PD** *020

HO, Ching. 17070 RED OAK DR STE 209 77090 #462-01-1953 L1977 **GS** *071 †85

HO, Cynthia Diem-Thuy. 4545 POST OAK PLAC DR #130 77027 #048-02-1999 L2002 **FM** *020 †18

HO, David Shucheung. 6560 FANNIN ST, STE 1554 77030 #048-13-1989 L1995 **U** *020 †95

HO, Hong Hung. ■ 77083 #005-11-2006 **TY** *012

HO, Linus. 1515 HOLCOMBE BLVD #426, DEPT. OF GI MEDICAL ONCOLO 77030 #005-11-1991 L1999 **HO ON** *020 †20

HO, Michael Dinghwa. 7710 BEECHNUT ST, STE 206 77074 #028-02-1986 L1992 **AN PD** *020 †55,05

HO, Minh Ngoc. ■ 77072 #048-15-2005 **PD** *012

HO, Minh Vuong. 902 FROSTWOOD DR STE 155 77024 #941-01-1970 L1977 **FM** *020 †18

HO, Philip Levy. ■ 77030 #048-04-2007 **GS** *012

HO, Stephen. 1917 ASHLAND ST 77008 #748-01-1974 L1982 **IM PD** *020

HO, Tam V. 1200 BINZ ST, STE 690 77004 #048-14-1995 L1997 **NEP** *020 †20

HO, Tang. ■ 77030 #023-07-2003 L2008 **OTO** *012

HO, Tram N. 12924 BELLAIRE BLVD, STE 101 77072 #048-04-1995 L1997 **IM** *020 †20

HO, Trieu Quang. 6431 FANNIN ST STE 1.150, AT HOUST 77030 #048-16-2002 L2007 **CD** *012 †20

HO, Winston. 6400 FANNIN ST, STE 2020 77030 #048-04-1991 L1994 **PD** *020 †55

HOAGLAND, Janet G. 3400 BISSONNET ST STE 185 77005 #021-01-1982 L1985 **DR OS** *020

HOANG, An Ngoc. 6431 FANNIN ST, UNIV OF TEXAS MED SCH 77030 #048-14-2006 **U** *012

HOANG, Dinh Ngoc. 6988 WILCREST DR 77072 #840-01-1965 L1979 **FM** *020

HOANG, Giao Ngoc. 8282 BELLAIRE BLVD STE 144 77036 #941-01-1969 L1978 **IM HEM** *020 †20

HOANG, Linda Karen. 1 BAYLOR PLZ, DEPT OF ANESTH SM1003 77030 #048-13-2003 L2007 **AN** *020

HOANG, Long B. 12438 FM 1960 RD W 77065 #048-04-1999 L2003 **MPD** *100 †20

HOANG, Nancy Tran. 10655 STEEPLETOP DR, CYPRESS FAIRBANKS HOSP 77065 #048-16-2000 L2002 **FM** *100 †18 ‡

HOANG, Thanh K. 11210 BELLAIRE BLVD, STE 126A 77072 #048-15-1993 L1996 **FM** *020 †18

HOBDAY, Christopher David. 6550 FANNIN ST STE 901, TMHPO OB/GYN DEPARTMENT 77030 #036-01-2004 L2008 **OBG** *012

HOBERMAN, Brian Jay. 7600 BEECHNUT ST, EMERGENCY DEPARTMENT 77074 #048-02-1999 L2002 **EM** *020 †16

HOC, Ba Chu. 12600 SCARSDALE BLVD STE A 77089 #941-01-1969 L1983 **GP** *020

HOCHHAUSER, Leo. 6431 FANNIN ST, DIAG IMAGING U OF TX HOUST 77030 #409-23-1971 L1999 **RNR R** *020 †80

HOCHMAN, Fredric Lyone. 6560 FANNIN ST, STE 600 77030 #062-01-1974 L1979
GE IM *020 †20
HOCHMAN, Joel F Simon. 540 HEIGHTS BLVD 77007 #048-04-1966 L1966 P PMM *072 ‡
HODGE, Patrick Nathaniel. ■ 77080 #048-14-1973 L1976 EM FM *020
HOEFER, David Wayne. 7825 HIGHWAY 6 N, STE 101 77095 #048-02-1996 L1998 FM *020 †18
HOEFNER, Bambi Lynn. 3275 W ALABAMA ST STE B, RIVER OAKS PEDS PA 77098
#048-15-1999 L2003 PD *020 †55
HOEKMAN, Robert Eugene. 4126 SOUTHWEST FWY 77027 #018-03-1967 L1972 ORS *020 †40
HOERMANN, Karen Lee. 1707 SUNSET BLVD, MEDICAL CLINIC OF HOUSTON 77005
#048-04-1996 L1999 IM *020 †20
HOFF, Ana O. 1515 HOLCOMBE BLVD, UNIT 435 77030 #187-33-1991 L1998 END *020 †20
HOFFMAN, Abigail Weil. 6550 FANNIN ST, THE METHODIST HOSPITAL 77030 #021-01-2007
GS *012
HOFFMAN, Alan S. 6624 FANNIN ST STE 2380 77030 #048-04-1985 L1986 IM OS *020 †20
HOFFMAN, Benjamin Haskell. 1001 FANNIN ST, STE 4000 77002 #035-47-1983 L2002
OM IM *030 †20,70
HOFFMAN, Joel Aaron. 7401 MAIN ST 77030 #048-04-1979 L1979 AN *020 †05
HOFFMAN, Lynn Preston. 6560 FANNIN ST 77030 #048-04-1975 L1975 GYN *020 †30
HOFFMAN, Neville Elliot. 6410 FANNIN ST 77030 #143-06-1966 L1977 GE *050
HOFSTETTER, Wayne Lewis. ■ 77025 #048-05-06-1993 L2005 TS *020 †85,90
HOGAN, Patrick J. 6624 FANNIN ST, STE 2220 77030 #010-02-1970 L1973 CD IC *020 †20
HOGAN, Walter L. 4101 GREENBRIAR ST STE 100 77098 #001-02-1957 L1962
OBG REN *071 †30
HOGAN, William Jos, Jr. 4101 GREENBRIAR, STE 100 77098 #028-34-1987 L1996
PD PM *020 †55
HOGE, Ann Theresa. 1515 HOLCOMBE BLVD, ANDERSON CANC 77030 #056-06-2003 RO *012
HOHL, James F. 77009 #039-01-1944 L1946 D IM *071
HOHLT, Russell W. 6431 FANNIN ST 1134, UNIV OF TEXAS-HOUSTON 77030 #048-14-2006
IM *012
HOLANDA, Alexandre Alcant. 1 BAYLOR PLZ 77030 #187-10-1999 FM *020
HOLBERT, Anthony W. ■ 77089 #048-04-2008 *012
HOLBROOK, John Lowell. ■ 77025 #047-05-1983 L1988 ORS HS *020 †40
HOLD, Michael Daniel. ■ 77043 #048-02-2003 L2007 OBG *020
HOLDEMAN, Nicky R. 4901 CALHOUN RD 77004 #048-15-1987 L1988 OPH *040
HOLDEN, Mark Davis. 14703 EAGLE VISTA DR, DEPT OF INTERNAL MEDICINE 77077
#048-02-1985 L1986 IM *020 †20
HOLDER, Ashley Margaret. ■ 77098 #048-04-2008 *012
HOLDER, Kenneth Alan. 1515 HOLCOMBE BLVD, DEPT AN 77030 #048-14-1976 L1976
AN IM *020 †05
HOLDER, Pamela Dawn. 8076 EL RIO ST, BROWN & ASSOC 77054 #048-16-1981 L1981
PTH PCP *020 †50
HOLLAND, Peter Marc. 2727 W HOLCOMBE BLVD 77025 #035-09-1969 L1977 OPH *071 †35
HOLLAND, Venessa A. 7515 MAIN ST STE 510 77030 #048-12-1982 L1983 D PUD *012 †20,70
HOLLEMAN, Marsha Cline. 3701 KIRBY DR STE 622 77098 #048-04-1982 L1983 FM *020 †18
HOLLENBECK, Timothy C. 6431 FANNIN ST, UNIV TX MED SCH AT HOUSTON 77030
#048-14-2003 L2006 GS *100
HOLLERAN, Linda Marie. 5870 HIGHWAY 6 N STE 100 77084 #048-04-1981 L1981 FM *030 †18
HOLLEY, Laurie Sisemore. 6720 BERTNER ST, DEPT OF PATHOLOGY 6720 BER 77030
#048-14-1993 L1994 FOP *020 †50
HOLLIER, Larry H, Jr. 6701 FANNIN ST 77030 #021-01-1991 L1996 PS *020 †65
HOLLIER, Lisa Marie. 5656 KELLEY ST, LBJ GENERAL HOSPITAL 77026 #021-01-1991 L1996
OBG *020 †30
HOLLINGER, F Blaine. 1 BAYLOR PLZ, BCM-385 77030 #019-02-1962 L1970 HEP ID *071
HOLLINGSWORTH, Gary Lyn. 8076 EL RIO ST, BROWN & ASSOC MED LABS 77054
#048-04-1976 L1977 PTH OS *020 †50
HOLLINS, Blanchard T. 4315 LOCKWOOD DR STE 1 77026 #047-07-1953 L1958 OBG *020 †30
HOLMAN, Katherine Marie. 1709 DRYDEN RD STE 550, BCM FACULTY CENTER 77030
#035-01-2006 IM *012
HOLMAN, Paul Joseph. 6560 FANNIN ST, STE 944 77030 #025-07-1997 L2006 NS *020 †25
HOLMES, Allen Alexander. ■ 77025 #048-14-2003 L2006 AN *100
HOLMES, Andrea Martha Eli. 6431 FANNIN ST 2.112, UNIV OF TX HLTH SCI CTR 77030
#539-03-1996 ID *012
HOLMES, Frankie Ann. 909 FROSTWOOD DR, STE 221 77024 #051-04-1976 L1981
ON IM *020 †20
HOLMES, Holly M. 1515 HOLCOMBE BLVD, UNIT 437 FC 2.3064 77030 #048-14-2000 L2006
IM IMG *020
HOLMES, Sally Ann. 2002 HOLCOMBE BLVD, SCI 128/VAMC 77030 #047-06-1990 L2005
PM SCI *020 †60
HOLMES, Terence Shayne. 4126 SOUTHWEST FWY, STE 1000 77027 #048-02-1977 L1977
IM *020 †20
HOLMSTEN, Charles Gustav. 7545 S BRAESWOOD BLVD 77071 #048-02-1969 L1969 GP *020
HOLMSTEN, Walter R. 8303 SOUTHWEST FWY # 12 77074 #048-02-2000 L2004
FM OM *020 †18
HOLOYE, Paul Yvan Leon. 6624 FANNIN ST, STE 1610 77030 #165-01-1965 L1972
ON IM *020 †20
HOLSINGER, Erin Eanes. 5757 WOODWAY DR, STE 200 77057 #048-04-1995 L1997
PD *020 †55
HOLSINGER, F Christopher. 1515 HOLCOMBE BLVD, UNIT 441 77030 #047-05-1995 L1997
OTO HNS *020 †45
HOLSTE, Catherine Sanesi. 7400 FANNIN ST STE 1050, C/L HALSTON WOMENS CARE 77054
#048-04-1994 L1995 OBG *020 †30
HOLT, Jessica Bunce. 820 GESSNER RD, STE 1560 77024 #048-02-2003 L2007 P *020
HOLT, Marston Shaun. 1100 HERCULES AVE, STE 100 77058 #038-43-1998 L2004
ORS *100 †40
HOLZ, Eric Robt. 6550 FANNIN ST STE 1501 77030 #048-04-1989 L1991 OPH *035
HOLZMANN-PAZGAL, Galit. 6431 FANNIN ST, DEPARTMENT OF PEDIATRICS 77030
#016-06-1994 L2006 PD ID *030 †55
HOMS GUILLOTY, Maritza. 1221 MCKINNEY ST, STE 40300 77010 #042-01-1981 L2002
OTO *045
HOMSI, Jade. ■ 77002 #875-01-1995 L2001 IM *100
HOMSY, Paul T. 1315 ST JOSEPH PKWY, STE 1500 77002 #048-14-1984 L1985 OM *020 †75,70
HONEY, Robert Edmund. ■ 77005 #048-14-2008 *012
HONEYCUTT, Gregory Robert. 1 BAYLOR PLZ, DEPT IM 77030 #048-04-2006 IM *012
HONG, David Sanghyun. 1515 HOLCOMBE BLVD BOX 43, MD ANDERSON CENCER
CENTER 77030 #035-46-1999 L2002 ON *100 †20
HONG, Jennifer Lynne. ■ 77096 #048-04-2007 PD *012

HONG, Soran. 2000 CRAWFORD ST STE 900 77002 #583-08-1974 L1999 IM *020 †20
HONG, Thomas Edward. 6400 FANNIN ST, STE 3000 77030 #048-04-1998 L2005 ICE *020 †20
HONG, Waun Ki. 1515 HOLCOMBE BLVD BOX 80, MD ANDERSON CANCER CTR 77030
#583-01-1967 L1984 PTH IM *020 †20
HONNY, Yaa Amoah. 6718 HIGHWAY 6 S 77083 #008-02-1994 L2000 IM *020 †20
HOOD, James Furniss. 2990 RICHMOND AVE, STE 142 77098 #048-02-1966 L1966
ORS *020 †40
HOOKS, Penny Jo Friduss. 5555 MORNINGSIDE DR # 211A 77005 #048-02-1975 L1975
P PYA *020 †05,75
HOOTS, William Keith. 6655 TRAVIS ST STE 400 77030 #036-01-1975 L1980 PHO PD *020 †55
HOOVER, Soraya N. 150 W PARKER RD STE 705 77076 #915-02-1961 L1978 OTO A *020
HOPE, Julia C. 915 GESSNER RD, STE 100 77024 #048-02-1992 L1993 IM *020 †20
HOPKINS, Bobbi J. 6621 FANNIN ST STE 1250, CLINICAL CARE CENTER 77030
#028-03-2001 L2006 CN *100 †75
HOPKINS, Eldon G. 1140 BUSINESS CENTER DR, STE 200 77043 #048-12-1994 L2000
ORS *020 †40
HOPKINS, Victoria. ■ 77002 #043-01-2001 L2007 FM *020 †18
HORANY, Melvin. ■ 77024 #048-04-1948 L1948 FM *071 †18
HORMANN, Mark D. 6431 FANNIN ST, JJL 495 77030 #048-14-1993 L1995 PD *040 †55
HORN, Kim J. 1740 W 27TH ST STE 209 77008 #048-14-1985 L1989 NEP IM *020 †20
HOROVITZ, Alan Gary. ■ 77054 #048-14-1981 L1981 PTH *071 †50
HOROVITZ, Marc Edward. 6701 FANNIN ST 77030 #005-06-1976 L1993 PHO PD *020 †55
HORST, David Andrew. 6621 FANNIN ST, WT6-104 77030 #048-04-1997 L2003 NPM *020 †55
HORTOBAGYI, Gabriel N. 1515 HOLCOMBE BLVD # 1354 77030 #264-01-1970 L1975
ON IM *030 †20
HORTON, Terach Marie. 6701 FANNIN ST 77030 #012-05-1992 L2004 PHO *020 †55
HORVATH, Andrea Marianne. 4110 BELLAIRE BLVD, HOUSTON PED ASSOC STE 210 77025
#005-11-1994 L1997 PD *020 †55
HORVATH, Thomas Bela. 2002 HOLCOMBE BLVD, EXEC OFC (11) DEBAKEY VAMC 77030
#143-02-1965 L1976 P IM *030 †75
HORWITZ, Barry Lee. 8945 LONG POINT RD, STE 111 77055 #048-02-1969 L1969
OPH *071 †35
HORWITZ, Melton Jay. 6624 FANNIN ST 77030 #048-02-1966 L1966 OTO NO *020 †45
HOSING, Chitra. 1515 HOLCOMBE BLVD, DEPT OF BMT BOX 423 77030 #496-07-1985 L1999
ON *020 †20
HOSKIN, Ronald Antonius. 6563 W BELLFORT ST 77035 #005-06-1983 L1984 FM *020 †18
HOU, Jason Ken. ■ 77096 #016-06-2003 L2006 GE *012 †20
HOU, Jyh-Gong. 2002 HOLCOMBE BLVD, MAIL 127PD 77030 #244-05-1990 L2001 N *020 †75
HOUSTON, Gregory Kevin. 1415 NORTH LOOP W STE 820, MEMORIAL RADIOLOGY
ASSOC 77008 #016-11-1978 L1984 R *020 †20
HOVANETZ, Melissa Stanton. PO BOX 20708, DEPT OF PATHOLOGY 77225 #048-14-2005
PTH *012
HOWARD, Annette M. 6655 TRAVIS ST STE 780 77030 #041-12-1989 L1994 N *020
HOWARD, Christopher M. ■ 77059 #048-16-2001 L2005 MPD *020 †20,55
HOWARD, Gregory L. 10655 STEEPLETOP DR 77065 #048-14-1992 L1993 AN *020 †05
HOWARD, Jennifer Lauren. ■ 77030 #051-04-2004 L2008 PM *012
HOWARD, Lillian G. 11700 FM 1960 RD W 77065 #048-04-1989 L1990 FM FPG *020 †18
HOWARD, Tamara Lee. ■ 77004 #048-02-2007 PD *012
HOWARTH, Cathryn Barbara. 2501 ADDISON RD 77030 #917-05-1963 L1986 PHO PD *020 †55
HOWELL, Daniel L, Jr. ■ 77030 #048-13-2001 CRS *012 †85
HOWELL, Greg Allen. 1635 NORTH LOOP W, DEPT OF EMERGENCY MEDICINE 77008
#027-01-1990 L1995 EM *020 †16
HOWELL, Jimmy Frank. 6560 FANNIN ST STE 1824 77030 #048-04-1957 L1957
TS VS *020 †85,90
HOXHAJ, Shkelzen. 1 BAYLOR PLZ, MS-BCM 285 77030 #035-09-1998 L2007
EM IM *020,16
HOY, Jennifer Frances. UTMS RM JFB 1 724 77030 #143-03-1977 ID *100
HOYER, David R, Jr. 211 HIGHLAND CROSS DR, STE 275 77073 #039-01-1981 L1982
EM OS *020
HOYLE, James Cranford. 1221 MCKINNEY ST, STE 40300 77010 #036-05-1972 L1978
ADL PD *030 †55
HOYOS, Gabriel Eduardo. 7580 FANNIN ST STE 300 77054 #048-13-1979 L1979 OBG *020 †30
HRACHOVY, Richard Allan. 6565 FANNIN ST 77030 #048-02-1974 L1974 N *020 †75
HRGOVCIC, Martin Jozo. 6447 MAIN ST 77030 #957-01-1953 L1970 IM ON *020
HSIEH, Georgia Rose. 1919 LA BRANCH ST 77002 #048-04-1980 L1980 EM *020 †16
HSIEH, Michael. ■ 77030 #041-02-2001 L2007 UP *012
HSU, Adam Yuanheng. ■ 77030 #016-42-2002 L2006 OPH *100
HSU, Charles. 9110 BELLAIRE BLVD, STE C 77036 #033-05-1991 L2001 PD *020 †55
HSU, David Wei Hau. 921 GESSNER RD 77024 #048-02-2002 L2005 EM *020 †16
HSU, Deborah Chiungwen. 6621 FANNIN ST STE A-210 77030 #036-01-1994 L1996
PD PEM *020 †55
HSU, Elias I. 1 BAYLOR PLZ, DEPT OF UROLOGY 77030 #035-19-2002 L2008 U *012
HSU, Hsiu-Bun. 2002 HOLCOMBE BLVD 77030 #048-78-2000, ▲ L2002 PM *020 †60
HSU, Jean Enid. ■ 77054 #048-04-2003 L2007 GS *012
HSU, Katharine Han-Kuang. 1 BAYLOR PLZ RM 357E, 1200 MOURSUND 77030
#242-03-1939 L1960 PD *071
HSU, Ming-Cheia. 11311 COLOMA LN 77024 #244-04-1967 L1974 AN *020
HSU, Patrick Weite. 1515 HOLCOMBE BLVD, UNIT 443 77030 #033-06-2003 L2008 PS *012
HSU, Peter Wang. 1515 HOLCOMBE BLVD # 409 77030 #024-05-1992 L2000 AN *020 †05
HSU, Sigmund H. 1515 HOLCOMBE BLVD, BOX 431 77030 #043-01-1995 L2002 IM *020
HSU, Yu To. 10416 ROCKLEY RD 77099 #385-01-1964 L1978 FM PTH *020 †50
HSU-WONG, Sylvia. 6620 MAIN ST STE 1425, BAYLOR CLINIC DPT OF DERM 77030
#048-04-1989 L1997 D *020 †15 ‡
HU, Andy Ting. ■ 77019 #048-04-2001 PD *100
HU, Grace Tingcol. 11811 FM 1960 RD W STE 100 77065 #048-04-1993 L1995 PD *020 †55
HU, Guiying. 1221 MCKINNEY ST, STE 40300 77010 #243-85-1985 L2002 ON *020 †20
HU, H Chung-Tai. 1250 CYPRESS STATION DR, STE B 77090 #038-41-1972 L1988
FM OS *020 †18
HU, Han-Hwa. ■ 77089 #244-03-1972 N *020
HU, Mimi I-Nan. 1400 HOLCOMBE BLVD, UNIT 435 77030 #048-14-2000 L2002 END *100
HUA, Frank Qiang. 15655 CYPRESSWOOD MEDCL DR, STE 100 77014 #243-16-1983 L1996
IM *020 †20
HUAN, Duong Hong. ■ 77041 #840-01-1967 GP *020
HUANG, Henry Darchon. 1709 DRYDEN RD STE 550, BCM FACULTY CENTER 77030
#048-12-2007 IM *012

HUANG, James. 6621 FANNIN ST 77030 #048-04-1991 L1993 **PHO PD** *050 †55
HUANG, James Kin Ming. ■ 77072 #385-03-1953 L1971 **PM** *071 †60
HUANG, Jaou-Chen. 6431 FANNIN ST, MSB 3-604 77030 #244-02-1980 L1993 **OBG** *020 †30
HUANG, Ming-Yang. 2727 W HOLCOMBE BLVD, RADIOLOGY 77025 #041-02-1995 L2001 **DR** *020 †80
HUANG, Monica L. 6720 BERTNER ST, DEPT. OF RADIOLOGY MC 2-27 77030 #048-04-1994 L1995 **DR** *020 †80
HUANG, Nancy Nan. ■ 77005 #242-03-1941 L1955 **PUD ID** *072 †55
HUANG, Steven Chihhow. ■ 77077 #048-12-2004 **AN** *012
HUANG, William Yumin. 1100 W 34TH ST, NORTHWEST HEALTH CENTER 77018 #016-06-1980 L1983 **FM** *020 †18
HUANG, Zai-Feng. 7900 CAMBRIDGE ST 77054 #243-45-1983 L2005 **IM** *100 †20
HUBBARD, Hopethe H. ■ 77054 #048-04-2004 L2007 **IM** *100 †20
HUBENTHAL, Erica A. ■ 77077 #048-04-2005 L2008 **PD** *012
HUBER, Astrid. 7333 NORTH FWY STE 262 77076 #409-23-1967 L1976 **GP FM** *071
HUCKABY, Henry Lafayette. 2619 HOLMAN ST 77004 #047-07-1965 L1973 **PS GS** *075
HUDSON, Christie Anne. 4410 NAVIGATION BLVD 77011 #048-04-2002 L2005 **PD** *020
HUERTA, Alfredo, Jr. 7825 HIGHWAY 6 N, STE 107 77095 #048-02-1996 L1998 **FM** *020 †18
HUFFMAN, Richard Jules. 7600 BEECHNUT ST 77074 #048-02-1980 L1980 **AN** *020 †05
HUG, Verena. 6655 TRAVIS ST STE 960 77030 #869-02-1972 L1978 **END IM** *020 †20
HUGE, Donald Sehrt. 2500 CITYWEST BLVD # 1150 77042 #048-04-1957 L1957 **MDM U** *030
HUGG, Terry Wayne. 17115 RED OAK DR STE 109 77090 #048-04-1971 L1971 **P CHP** *020 †75
HUGHART, Marsha Sue. 1201 DAIRY ASHFORD ST 77079 #039-01-1980 L1981 **IM** *020 †20
HUGHES, Dennis Patrick. 1515 HOLCOMBE BLVD, UNIT 853 77030 #008-01-1996 L2006 **PHO** *020 †55
HUGHES, Douglas Eugene. 6431 FANNIN ST STE 1.150, AT HOUST 77030 #010-03-2004 L2007 **DR** *012
HUGHES, John Irison. 2727 W HOLCOMBE BLVD, MAIN CAMPUS 77025 #011-04-1975 L1981 **GE OS** *020 †20
HUGHES, Peter Anthony. 7401 MAIN ST 77030 #048-02-1983 L1983 **AN** *020 †05
HUGHES, T M, III. 12121 RICHMOND AVE 77082 #048-02-1982 L1983 **U** *075 †95
HUH, Joseph. 2002 HOLCOMBE BLVD 77030 #056-06-1990 L2002 **TS** *020 †85,90
HUH, Winston Wook. 1515 HOLCOMBE BLVD, UNIT 87 77030 #020-12-1997 L1999 **PHO** *020 †55
HUH, Yang Ok. 1515 HOLCOMBE BLVD 77030 #583-01-1974 L1984 **CLP BBK** *020 †50
HUI, Gloria Chi Man. 920 FROSTWOOD DR 77024 #014-01-1981 L1982 **CD IM** *020 †20
HULL, John G. ■ 77019 #023-07-1945 L1950 **IM** *071 †20
HULME, Jonathan Russell. 17215 RED OAK DR, STE 110 77090 #048-04-1979 L1980 **OBG** *020 †30
HUMAYUN, Vasif Ali. ■ 77059 #495-65-1984 L1995 **IM** *020 †20
HUME, Orne Scott. 12121 RICHMOND AVE STE 226 77082 #035-20-1966 L1974 **OBG PHP** *071 †30
HUME, Thaddeus Wm. 2000 CRAWFORD ST STE 1510 77002 #010-03-1973 L1978 **ORS** *020 †40
HUMPHREY, Tamara Shantrel. ■ 77054 #028-34-2005 **N** *012
HUMPHRIES, James C. 18100 SAINT JOHN DR, STE 380 77058 #047-06-1984 L1992 **U** *020 †95
HUNDAL, Mandeep. 6431 FANNIN ST 1134, UNIV OF TEXAS - HOUSTON 77030 #495-36-2002 **IM** *012
HUNDLEY, Richard Zol. 1313 HERMANN DR 77004 #001-02-1954 L1958 **OBG OS** *071
HUNG, Richard Teson. 6624 FANNIN ST, STE 1480 77030 #048-04-1993 L1998 **OTO** *020 †45
HUNG, Scott H. 10950 RESOURCE PKWY, STE A 77089 #048-14-1991 L1994 **FM GS** *020 †18
HUNT, Allison Selby. 6550 FANNIN ST, STE 2221 77030 #048-16-2003 L2007 **OBG** *100
HUNT, Kelly. 1515 HOLCOMBE BLVD, DEPT OF SURG ONCOLOGY-BOX 77030 #047-06-1986 L1994 **GS SO** *020 †85
HUNTER, Jeffrey Thomas. ■ 77072 #011-03-1998 L2000 **D** *020
HUNTER, Jill Vanessa. 6621 FANNIN ST, MC2-2521 77030 #917-20-1975 L2006 **RNR** *020 †80
HUNTER, Oliver C, Jr. 6411 FANNIN ST 77030 #048-02-1963 L1963 **CD IM** *020 †20
HUNTER, Robert Brookshire. ■ 77019 #048-02-1980 L1980 **OM P** *030 †75,70
HUNTER, Robert Lee, Jr. 6431 FANNIN ST, MSB 2 136 DEPT PATH 77030 #016-02-1965 L1999 **CLP** *030 †50
HURDISS, Lawrence Wesley. 9220 KIRBY DR, STE 700 77054 #035-15-1971 L1981 **DR** *020 †80
HURT, R Wayne. 1315 ST JOSEPH PKWY, MED PL 1 STE 1708 77002 #048-04-1966 L1966 **NS** *020 †25
HURTADO, Eric Alec. 6560 FANNIN ST STE 2100 77030 #010-01-2001 L2005 **OBG OS** *020 †30
HURTADO, Sandra Maria. 7900 FANNIN ST, STE 4000 77054 #041-01-1990 L2001 **OBG** *020 †30
HURWITZ, Alan Joel. ■ 77006 #048-13-1979 L1979 **P** *071 †75
HURWITZ, Edward Jay. 5110 BUFFALO SPEEDWAY, STE 200 77005 #048-02-1966 L1966 **D** *020 †15
HURWITZ, Raye Carol. 6565 FANNIN ST 77030 #048-04-1978 L1978 **IM PD** *020 †20
HURWITZ, Richard L. 6701 FANNIN ST 77030 #035-03-1975 L1985 **PHO PD** *050 †55
HUSAIN, Shaista A. 1315 ST JOSEPH PKWY, STE 1109 77002 #704-09-1975 L1991 **OTO FPS** *020 †45
HUSNI, Rola Najib. 1515 HOLCOMBE BLVD BOX 47, INFECTIOUS DISEASES DEPT 77030 #605-01-1991 L1997 **ID** *020
HUSSAIN, Ayub. 18220 TOMBALL PKWY STE 310 77070 #704-21-1987 L2001 **GE** *020 †20
HUSSAIN, Khozema B. 6620 MAIN ST, STE 1475 77030 #704-02-1990 L2002 **GE** *020 †20
HUSSEIN, Adnan J. 427 W 20TH ST, STE 705 77008 #915-06-1980 L1997 **FM** *020 †18
HUST, Robert Geoffrey. 6400 FANNIN ST, STE 3000 77030 #048-04-1978 L1978 **CD** *020 †20
HUSTON, David Paul. 1 BAYLOR PLZ, BCM 285 STE 672E 77030 #036-05-1973 L1980 **IG AI** *050 †20,03
HUSTON, Sarah Elizabeth. ■ 77030 #048-04-2006 **PD** *012
HUTCHENS, Jerome Enos. 2605 POTOMAC DR 77057 #048-02-1956 L1956 **P GP** *071
HUTCHINS, Susan Diane. 607 TIMBERDALE LN STE 201 77090 #048-04-1992 L1993 **IM** *020 †20
HUTTON, George Joseph. 6501 FANNIN ST 77030 #047-05-1996 L1997 **N** *020 †75
HUTTON, Jill Christensen. 6624 FANNIN ST STE 1800 77030 #047-05-1996 L1997 **OBG** *020 †30
HUYNH, Keith A. 10720B FM 1960 RD W 77070 #048-15-1992 L1994 **IM** *020 †20
HUYNH, Khanh D. 902 FROSTWOOD DR, STE 275 77024 #011-02-1994 L1997 **RNR R** *020 †80
HUYNH, Phan Tuong. 6720 BERTNER ST MC2-270 77030 #051-01-1989 L1995 **DR** *020 †80
HUYNH, Son Luke. 3120 SOUTHWEST FWY, GREATER HOUSTON RADIOLOGY 77098 #048-14-1996 L1997 **DR** *020 †80
HUYNH, Tam Thi T. 6540 BELLOWS LN # 507 77030 #067-01-1990 L2000 **VS** *020 †85
HWANG, Gwangyi Y. 1 BAYLOR PLZ, DEPT OBG 77030 #048-04-2005 **OBG** *012
HWANG, Jessica Park. 1515 HOLCOMBE BLVD, UNIT 437 77030 #048-14-1996 L1998 **MPD** *020 †20
HWANG, Kevin O. 6431 FANNIN ST, MSB 1.122 77030 #048-02-1998 L2005 **IM** *050 †20
HWANG, Long Shong. 1919 LA BRANCH ST 77002 #244-02-1968 L1982 **AN** *020 †05
HWANG, Lu-Yu. 1515 HOLCOMBE BLVD 77030 #244-02-1975 **ID PD** *040
HWANG, Rosario Frances. 1515 HOLCOMBE BLVD, BOX 444 77030 #023-01-1993 L2000 **SO** *020 †85
HWU, Katherine. 6621 FANNIN ST 1130.03, TEXAS CHILDREN'S HOSPITAL 77030 #041-01-1987 L1993 **PDE PD** *020 †55
HWU, Patrick. ■ 77005 #041-07-1987 L2004 **IM ON** *020 †20
HWU, Wen-Jen. 1515 HOLCOMBE BLVD, UNIT 430 77030 #005-15-1982 L2005 **ON IM** *020 †20
HYATT, Jerry Lee. 17202 RED OAK DR 77090 #039-01-1972 L1977 **ORS** *020 †40
HYBARGER, Glen R. ■ 77030 #048-13-2008 *012
HYDE, Kenneth John. 1220 AUGUSTA DR, STE 100 77057 #005-12-1983 L1989 **OPH OS** *020 †35
HYMAN, Barry Noel. 7707 FANNIN ST, STE 250 77054 #036-07-1963 L1971 **IM OPH** *020 †35,20 ‡
HYMAN, David J. 1502 TAUB LOOP, BEN TAUB GENERAL HOSPITAL 77030 #035-19-1981 L1982 **IM GPM** *020 †20,70
HYMES, Sharon. 1515 HOLCOMBE BLVD, UNIT 434 77030 #048-04-1976 L1983 **D IM** *020 †20,15
HYNES-O'CONNOR, Margarita. ■ 77072 #132-05-1969 L1978 **PD** *020 †55
HYSLOP, Thomas. 2223 WEST LOOP S 77027 #035-45-1964 L1979 **GPM PHP** *071 †70
HYUN, David Yungdam. 1 BAYLOR PLZ, RM 302A 77030 #038-40-2002 L2005 **PDI** *012
HYUN, John. 7026 OLD KATY RD, STE 276 77024 #048-12-1998 L2001 **DR** *020 †80
IACOBAS, Ionela. 6621 FANNIN ST CC15100, TEXAS CHILDREN'S HOSP 77030 #781-08-2002 **PHO** *012 †55
IBARRA, Bartolome N, Jr. ■ 77062 #748-02-1958 L1974 **OM GP** *020
IBARRA, Francis Roberto. 2424 W HOLCOMBE BLVD, MEDICAL CENTER ANESTHESIA 77030 #048-14-1987 L1988 **AN** *020 †05
IBARRA, Herminia Chan. ■ 77062 #748-02-1958 L1983 **RO IM** *071
IBARRA, Segundo Sergio. 2801 GESSNER DR 77080 #726-01-1992 L1999 **CHP P** *020 †75
IBARRA ROVIRA, Juan Jose. 1 BAYLOR PLZ 77030 #726-01-2000 **DR** *012
IBRAHEIM, Nashaat B. 12121 RICHMOND AVE, STE 306 77082 #915-04-1982 L1997 **FM** *020 †18
IBRAHIM, Adel Asaad Saad. ■ 77081 #915-03-1994 L2008 **IMG** *012 †18
IBRAHIM, Fatima. 800 PEAKWOOD DR, STE 6D 77090 #495-59-1986 L2005 **N** *020 †75
IBRAHIM, Morhaf. PO BOX 20708 77225 #875-01-2004 **IM** *012
IBRAHIM, Nuhad Khalil. 1515 HOLCOMBE BLVD, MDACC BOX 1354 77030 #528-01-1980 L1992 **ON IM** *020 †20
ICE, Mary Frances. 714 FM 1960 RD W STE 206 77090 #042-01-1997 L1999 **DR** *020 †80
IDELCHIK, Gary Michael. 6720 BERTNER ST RM P355, EPISCOPAL HOSPITAL 77030 #048-12-2002 L2006 **CD** *012 †20
IDICULA, Sindhu A. 1 BAYLOR PLZ 350, BAYLOR COLL OF MED 77030 #048-02-2005 **P** *012
IFEJIKA, Nneka Lotea. ■ 77007 #036-01-2003 L2007 **PM** *100
IGAL, Victor S. 921 FM 1960 RD W, STE 101 77090 #021-01-1958 L1960 **OBG** *071
IGARASHI, Makoto. 1200 MOURSUND ST 77030 #572-20-1952 **OTO AM** *050
IGLEHART, Sharon Lynette. 14359 TORREY CHASE BLVD #G, PSYCHIATRIC AFFILIATES OF 77014 #025-07-1982 L1988 **CHP** *020
IGLESIA, Angel De La. 150 W PARKER RD 77076 #847-04-1946 L1961 **OBG** *071
IGLESIAS, J V. 17203 RED OAK DR, STE 202 77090 #264-03-1964 L1973 **GS VS** *020 †85,90
IGNACIO, Craig. 6431 FANNIN ST STE 5.020, UNIV OF TX MEDICAL SCHOOL 77030 #305-01-1990 L1996 **AN** *020 †05
IGNATIUS, Jasmin A. ■ 77030 #048-78-2007, ▲ **IM** *012
IKE, John O. 7500 BEECHNUT ST STE 152 77074 #690-04-1986 L1995 **IM NEP** *020 †20
IKEN, Richard Jay. 10375 RICHMOND AVE, STE 1575 77042 #028-03-1978 L2005 **PD** *020 †55
IKO, Ojiugo M. ■ 77077 #690-04-1988 L1996 **IM HEM** *071 †20
ILIESCU, Cezar A. 6431 FANNIN ST 1246, UNIV OF TEXAS MEDICAL SCHO 77030 #781-01-1994 L2008 **IC** *012
ILIESCU, Gloria Diana. 6431 FANNIN ST STE 1.150, AT HOUST 77030 #781-01-2000 L2007 **IM** *020 †20
ILKIW, Roma L. ■ 77082 #060-01-1981 L1990 **PD CD** *020 †55
ILLNER, Anna. 6720 BERTNER ST, MC 2-270 77030 #048-02-1994 L2006 **RNR** *020 †80
ILLOH, Kachikwu Oseloka. 6431 FANNIN ST, STE 7019 77030 #690-03-1991 L2006 **N EP** *020 †75
ILLOH, Orieji C. 6431 FANNIN ST, DEPT OF PATHOLOGY AND LAB 77030 #690-03-1991 L2006 **PTH BBK** *020 †50
IMPERIAL, Valentino R. 8945 LONG POINT RD STE 112 77055 #748-01-1958 L1978 **AN** *020
IMSAIS, William Khalil. 1504 TAUB LOOP, BEN TAUB GENERAL HOSPITAL 77030 #021-05-2002 L2007 **MEM** *020 †20
IMTIAZ, Farhina Khan. 11811 FM 1960 RD W, STE 104 77065 #012-21-1996 L2000 **OBG** *020 †30
INALA, Rao. 8200 WEDNESBURY LN STE 380 77074 #495-11-1964 L1978 **GS** *020 †85
INAMDAR, Nikhil V. 11914 ASTORIA BLVD, STE 360 77089 #917-28-1983 L1994 **GE** *020 †20
INAMPUDI, Rajitha. ■ 77004 #048-04-2005 **PD** *012
INBODY, Steven Bryce. 7505 MAIN ST STE 125 77030 #016-06-1983 L1985 **N** *020 †75
INCALCATERRA, James. 1300 BAY AREA BLVD, STE B 77058 #048-12-1972 L1976 **GP** *020 †18
INCAVO, Stephen Jos. 6550 FANNIN ST STE 2500, METHODIST CENTER FOR ORTHO 77030 #035-15-1983 L2006 **ORS** *020 †40
INFANTE, Ernesto. 6410 FANNIN ST STE 1014, UT PHYSICIANS 77030 #847-04-1964 L1972 **N CN** *020 †75
INFANTE DE LA ROSA, Rosa. PO BOX 20708 77225 #737-06-1991 **ID** *100
ING, Frank Fai. 6621 FANNIN ST, MC19345C 77030 #035-48-1985 L1995 **PDC** *020 †55
INGLE, Ashwin Prabhakar. 7600 BEECHNUT ST 77074 #917-08-1996 L2002 **AN** *020 †05
INGLESE, Marc John. ■ 77007 #011-03-2003 L2006 **D** *012 †20
INGLIS, Kristen J. ■ 77030 #048-12-1995 L1998 **GS** *020 †85
INGRAHAM, Annette Blanton. 18100 HOSPITAL BLVD, STE 350 77058 #048-02-1990 L1991 **PD** *020 †55
INGRAM, Alice Michelle. ■ 77073 #036-08-1996 L1999 **FM** *020 †18
INGRAM, Jelani Deaomari. ■ 77054 #048-14-2008 *012
INGRAM, Laverne Dorothy. 5656 KELLEY ST, LBJ GEN HOSP/UNIVERSITY OF 77026 #051-07-1981 L1991 **DR** *020
INJAC, Alexander Nelson. 4101 GREENBRIAR ST, STE 100 77098 #010-02-1996 L1999 **PD** *020 †55
INSULL, William, Jr. 1709 DRYDEN RD RM 808 77030 #023-07-1949 L1978 **IM CD** *050

INTERIANO, Benjamin. 7737 SOUTHWEST FWY, STE 640 77074 #341-01-1967 L1989 IM PUD *020 †20

INTERIANO, Jose Carlos. 1631 NORTH LOOP W STE 440 77008 #341-01-1982 L1990 PD PDA *020 †55

INTODY, Zsofia. 6621 FANNIN ST RM A170, MC1-1000 77030 #473-01-1997 PD *012

IONESCU-MATIU, Irina A. 7737 SOUTHWEST FWY STE 670 77074 #781-01-1971 L1987 PD *020 †55

IQBAL, Kiran. ■ 77054 #704-06-2005 P *012

IQBAL, Uzma. 11302 FALLBROOK DR, STE 202B 77065 #704-06-1993 L2005 HO *020 †20

IRANI, Adel Dinshaw. 6410 FANNIN ST, STE 450 77030 #048-02-1989 L1997 TS VS *020 †85,90

IRANI, Katie D. 3601 N MACGREGOR WAY 77004 #495-01-1957 L1971 PM *062 †60

IRBY, Juanetta M. 8000 N STADIUM DR, DEPT. HEALTH AND HUMAN SER 77054 #048-13-1986 L1987 IM *020

IRR, William George. 6624 FANNIN ST, ALPERT & SERMAS 77030 #055-01-1991 L1995 N OS *020 †75

IRVINE, Timothy E. 411 LANTERN BEND DR, STE 240 77090 #048-13-1997 L1999 FM *020 †18

IRVING, Sandra Jean. 13114 FM 1960 RD W, STE 200 77065 #048-14-1999 L2002 FM *020 †20

IRWIN, John Francis. 7900 FANNIN ST STE 4000 77054 #048-04-1972 L1972 OBG *020 †20

ISAAC, John C. 13300 HARGRAVE RD, STE 500 77070 #048-12-1994 L1997 IC CD *020 †30

ISAACS, George. 1200 BINZ ST, DIAGNOSTIC CLINIC OF 77004 #011-02-1963 L1970 N *020 †75

ISACHIEVICI, Diana. PO BOX 20708, UNIV TX MED SCH AT HOUSTON 77225 #781-02-2000 P *012

ISART, Fernando A. 2925 W T C JESTER BLVD, STE 1 77018 #270-02-1984 L1992 PD *020 †55

ISENHOWER, Dominique E. 7400 FANNIN ST STE 900 77054 #048-04-1998 L2000 PD *020 †55

ISENSEE, Laura Marie. ■ 77057 #048-04-1982 L1983 N *020 †75

ISIKLAR, Zekeriya U. ■ 77054 #902-05-1985 OTR *100

ISMAIL, Nadia June. 1504 TAUB LOOP, BAYLOR COLLEGE OF MEDICINE 77030 #048-13-1999 L2005 IM *020 †20

ISSA, Jean-Pierre Jean. 1515 HOLCOMBE BLVD, UNIT 428 77030 #605-01-1987 L1989 ON *050 †20

ITTMAN, Michael Murrey. ■ 77030 #038-06-1983 L1998 PTH *020 †50

IVAN, Doina. ■ 77005 #781-01-1994 L2002 SP *100

IVERSEN, Robert Christian. ■ 77004 #048-14-2007 IM *012

IVEY, Richard Todd. 6620 MAIN ST 77030 #021-06-1993 L1996 OBG *020 †30

IYENGAR, Puneeth. ■ 77054 #035-46-2005 RO *012

IYENGAR, Sridhar Sampath. 10500 FORUM PLACE DR 77036 #495-33-1978 L1988 DR NM *020 †28,80

IYER, Revathy. 1515 HOLCOMBE BLVD # 57, IM UNIV OF TX MD ADSN HOSP. 77030 #021-05-1988 L1991 DR *020 †80

IZADDOOST, Shayan Alireza. ■ 77024 #048-04-2003 PS *012

IZADYAR, Shahram. 1 BAYLOR PLZ, BAYLOR COLL OF MED 77030 #517-01-1999 N *012

IZAWA, Jonathan Iwao. 1515 HOLCOMBE BLVD, BOX 110 77030 #065-06-1994 L2000 U *020

JABARA, Benjamin James. ■ 77021 #021-01-2008 †012

JABBOURY, Khaled Wadi. 12121 RICHMOND AVE, STE 100 77082 #528-03-1977 L1984 ON HEM *020

JABLONSKI, Richard Danl. 1200 BINZ ST, DIAGNOSTIC CLINIC OF 77004 #038-06-1972 L1977 END IM *020 †20

JAC, Jaroslaw. 6560 FANNIN ST STE 2050 77030 #759-10-1990 L1995 HO *020 †20

JACKSON, Courtney Carol. 1 BAYLOR PLZ, BAYLOR COLL OF MED 77030 #021-01-1999 L2000 HMP *012 †20,50

JACKSON, Daniel. ■ 77025 #028-34-1941 L1949 IM PUD *071 †20

JACKSON, David Wayne. 1917 ASHLAND ST 77008 #048-13-1985 L1986 PTH *020 †50

JACKSON, George Barry. 920 FROSTWOOD DR, STE 510 77024 #019-02-1963 L1973 OBG AN *020 †05,30

JACKSON, Gilchrist Lewis. 2727 W HOLCOMBE BLVD MC3 77025 #020-02-1974 L1977. GS HNS *020 †85

JACKSON, Ira J. ■ 77004 #035-19-1943 L1949 NS OS *071 †25

JACKSON, Joseph Harold. 1 BAYLOR PLZ, BAYLOR COLL OF MED 77030 #048-15-2005 AN *012

JACKSON, Richard Allen. 6560 FANNIN ST STE 1130 77030 #048-12-1971 L1971 IM *020 †20

JACKSON, Robert Andrew. 4126 SOUTHWEST FWY, STE 600 77027 #048-02-1959 L1959 IM *071

JACKSON, Robert Evan. 6550 FANNIN ST, STE 2323 77030 #048-02-1981 L1982 IM *020 †20

JACKSON, Shaun Chadrick. ■ 77030 #048-04-2003 L2008 PMM *012

JACKSON, Thomas F. ■ 77219 #012-01-1949 L1960 R RO *071 †80

JACKSON, Timothy Albert. 1515 HOLCOMBE BLVD, DEPT. OF ANESTHESIOLOGY & 77030 #024-01-2000 L2005 AN *100 †05

JACOB, Matteethra G. 8520 KNIGHT RD 77054 #035-01-1976 L1978 IM CD *020 †20

JACOB, Meenu. 2002 HOLCOMBE BLVD 77030 #495-45-1985 L2003 FPG FM *020 †18

JACOB, Sonia Sara. 4006 INVERNESS DR 77019 #048-46-1998 L2002 IC *020 †20

JACOBE, Russel Lee, Jr. ■ 77027 #048-04-1964 L1964 OTO *071 †45

JACOBS, Aleda Anne. 1 BAYLOR PLZ, DEPT OF DERM 77030 #035-45-1999 L1999 D *100

JACOBS, Mark Alan. 7900 FANNIN ST, STE 4000 77054 #048-04-1977 L1977 OBS GYN *020 †30

JACOBS, Mark Steven. 4888 LOOP CENTRAL DR, STE 510 77081 #048-14-1978 L1978 P *020 †75

JACOBS, Warren M. 7550 FANNIN ST 77054 #021-01-1942 L1950 OBG OS *071 †30

JACOBSON, Herbert S. ■ 77024 #048-02-1952 L1953 PS *071 †85,65

JACOBSON, Kalen L. 1515 HOLCOMBE BLVD, MAILSTOP 402 77030 #048-13-1987 L1989 IM *020 †20

JACOBSON, Sheila Werch. 902 FROSTWOOD DR STE 228 77024 #048-16-1988 L1989 N *020 †75

JACOBSON, Stuart A. 920 FROSTWOOD DR, STE 760 77024 #048-04-1987 L1988 CD *020 †20

JADHAV, Meenakshi J. 11800 ASTORIA BLVD 77089 #495-17-1969 L1982 AN *020

JAFARNIA, Kourosh. 17080 RED OAK DR 77090 #048-13-1996 L1999 ORS HS *020 †40 ‡

JAFFE, Norman. 1515 HOLCOMBE BLVD, STE 87 77030 #836-01-1956 L1979 OS PD *020 †55

JAFFE, Penny Arline. 2015 THOMAS ST, THOMAS STREET CLINIC 77009 #035-20-1981 L1989 ID IM *020 †20

JAFFE, Stephen Elliot. ■ 77054 #305-01-1999 L2004 P *100 ‡

JAFFEE, Alvin. 6621 FANNIN ST 77030 #012-05-1963 L1968 PD *020 †55

JAFFEE, Noah Wayne. 1200 POST OAK BLVD STE 10 77056 #048-04-1992 L1994 DR *020 †80

JAFRI, Syed Mohammed Raza. ■ 77030 #048-05-2007-2003 L2003 GE *012 †20

JAIMES, Jill Li. ■ 77030 #048-04-2000 L2003 PEM *100 †55

JAIMES, Michael A. ■ 77030 #048-04-2000 L2003 VIR *012 †55,80

JAIN, Aarthi Yelundur. 6720 BERTNER ST 77030 #048-14-1990 L1997 AN *020 †05

JAIN, Ajay. 902 FROSTWOOD DR, STE 188 77024 #496-03-1995 L2001 IM *020 †20 ‡

JAIN, Ajay Kumar. ■ 77030 #495-45-1998 PG *012 †55

JAIN, Amit. ■ 77054 #495-36-2004 L2006 IM *012

JAIN, Anjali. 6776 SOUTHWEST FWY, STE 450 77074 #495-45-1975 L1981 PM PME *020 †60

JAIN, Anudeep. 810 PEAKWOOD DR, STE 107 77090 #048-14-1989 L1990 DR *020 †80

JAIN, Manas. 6431 FANNIN ST 6018, UNIV OF TEXAS MED SCH 77030 #016-06-2004 U *012

JAIN, Narendar Kumar. 77065 #495-45-1977 L1984 IM EM *020 †05

JAIN, Rajul Krishna. PO BOX 20708, UNIV TX MED SCH 77225 #048-12-2001 L2003 HO *012

JAIN, Ranu. 6431 FANNIN ST 77030 #495-30-1988 L2003 AN *020 †05

JAIN, Sonali. 1 BAYLOR PLZ 77030 #495-73-1999 GS *012

JAIN, Surendra Kumar. 6624 FANNIN ST, STE 2320 77030 #495-36-1975 L1980 CD IM *020 †20

JALAL, Diana Ibrahim. 6431 FANNIN ST 4.148, UNIV OF TEXAS MEDICAL SCHO 77030 #575-01-1998 L2004 NEP *020 †20

JALAL, Prasun Kumar. 1709 DRYDEN RD, STE 1500 77030 #495-02-1990 L2008 GE *100 †20

JALAL, Sohail. 915 GESSNER RD STE 585 77024 #704-01-1982 L1992 CD IM *020 †20

JALALI, Mehri. ■ 77024 #517-06-1988 L2002 PTH *100 †50

JAMAIL, Michael S. PO BOX 20708, DEPT PSYCH 77225 #048-14-1987 P *100

JAMAL, Amin Rahim. 7777 SOUTHWEST FWY, STE 802 77074 #308-10-1985 L1999 IM END *020 †20

JAMALUDDIN, Ahmed Unnisa. 3230 S DAIRY ASHFORD ST 77082 #495-65-1982 L1989 CD *020 †20

JAMES, Paul Jerrall. 2101 CRAWFORD ST, STE 304 77002 #047-07-1986 L1988 GS *020 †85

JAMES, Teddy C. 12739 WOODFOREST BLVD, STE B 77015 #060-01-1975 L1978 GP *020

JAMES, Thomica Julia. 1919 LA BRANCH ST DEPT OF, CHRISTUS ST JOSEPH 77002 #010-03-1999 L2002 EM *020 †16

JAMMAL, Cory T. 7600 BEECHNUT ST, 2ND FL 77074 #048-13-1983 L1986 PTH *020 †50

JAMSHIDI-NEZHAD, Mohammad. 13900 BEECHNUT ST STE D 77083 #018-75-1993, ▲ L2001 GS VS *020 †85

JAN, Connie S. 1615 HERMANN DR, UNIT 1311 77004 #048-04-2000 L2003 PD *020 †55

JANEK, Kyle Lee. 7600 BEECHNUT ST 77074 #048-02-1983 L1983 AN *020 †05

JANES, Olen Gaynor, II. 7777 SOUTHWEST FWY # 53 77074 #048-04-1961 L1961 GYN GO *040

JANESE, Woodrow Wm. 13303 CHAMPION FOREST DR, STE 4 77069 #035-15-1968 L1984 NS N *020 †25

JANI, Alap Rajni. ■ 77030 #048-04-2008 *012

JANJAN, Nora Anita. 1515 HOLCOMBE BLVD BOX 97 77030 #003-01-1979 L1980 RO PME *071 †80

JANKI, Patricia N. 13601 WOODFOREST BLVD 77015 #048-02-1995 L1996 FM OM *020 †18 ‡

JANKOVIC, Joseph. 6550 FANNIN ST, STE 1801 77030 #003-01-1973 L1977 N *020 †75

JANNAPUREDDY, Madhukaran. ■ 77030 #048-04-2008 †012

JANOWITZ, David H. 7007 NORTH FWY STE 145, DAVID H JANOWITZ MD 77076 #048-04-1984 L1985 OBG *020 †30

JANSA, Arthur M. 6410 FANNIN ST STE 1100, UT ORTHOPAEDICS 77030 #048-02-1950 L1950 ORS *030 †40

JANSSEN, Bryan L. ■ 77054 #048-14-2008 *012

JANUARY, Bruce Edward. 1800 BERING DR, STE 200 77057 #047-06-1992 L1999 OPH *020 †35 ‡

JANZ, Brian A. ■ 77030 #038-43-2001 L2001 PS *012

JARA, Delma Irene. 1140 BUSINESS CENTER DR, STE 403 77043 #033-05-1995 L2001 GS *020 †85

JARJOUR, Imad Tawfik. 6621 FANNIN ST CC1250, TEXAS CHILDREN'S HOSPITAL 77030 #875-01-1981 L2005 CHN OS *020 †55,75

JAROLIMEK, Amanda M. 6431 FANNIN ST 2.100, MED SCHOOL 77030 #048-14-1993 L1994 DR *020

JAROLIMEK, Lubor. 4126 SOUTHWEST FWY 77027 #048-14-1993 L1994 ORS *020

JARRELL, Jill Ann. ■ 77027 #012-05-2003 L2007 MPD *020 †20,55

JARRETT, Alan. 8850 LONG POINT RD 77055 #047-06-1969 L1971 OPH *020 †35 ‡

JARRIEL, William Scott. 5615 KIRBY DR STE 440, MEDICAL CENTER NEONATAL AS 77005 #048-12-1983 L1983 NPM *020 †55

JARRIN, Ileana Leonor. ■ 77036 #319-03-1982 L1997 IM *020

JARROUGE, Elie G. ■ 77004 #035-06-2008 *012

JASPER, Jill Marie. 6621 FANNIN ST, STE A210 77030 #018-03-1999 L2002 PEM *100 †55

JASSER, Joseph William. 6360 W SAM HOUSTON PKWY N, STE 200 77041 #038-40-1998 L2007 IM OM *030 †20

JASTROW, Kenneth Michael. PO BOX 20708, DEPT OF GEN SURG 77225 #305-01-2005 GS *012

JAVADI, Massoud. 4229 VILLANOVA ST 77005 #048-04-2002 L2004 IM *100 †20

JAVED, Lubna. ■ 77074 #704-01-2001 L2004 IMG *012 †18

JAVED, Maqsood. 11914 ASTORIA BLVD, STE 185 77089 #704-15-1981 L1990 PUD IM *020 †20

JAVLE, M M. 1515 HOLCOMBE BLVD, UNIT 426 77030 #495-01-1991 L2007 ON *020 †20

JAWDAT, Imtihan Ma'An. 6720 BERTNER ST 77030 #528-01-1969 L1986 CD IM *020 †20

JAYANTY, Satya Vikram. 909 FROSTWOOD DR STE 302 77024 #495-11-1975 L1983 GE IM *020 †20

JAYARAMAN, Gnananandh. ■ 77030 #495-42-1995 L2001 PCC *012 †20

JAYASINGHE, Chandra P. ■ 77024 #220-01-1981 L1998 AN *020 †05

JAYNE, Christopher J. 7580 FANNIN ST, STE 335A 77054 #035-06-1996 L1999 OBG *020 †30

JEA, Andrew H. 6621 FANNIN ST, CCC 1230.01, 12TH FLOOR 77030 #011-02-1999 L2007 NS *020

JEAN-LOUIS, Frantz. 6035 AIRLINE DR STE 7 77076 #649-20-1984 L1996 PD NPM *020 †55

JEAN-PIERRE, Claudel D. 6550 FANNIN ST, SMITH TOWER SUITE 901 77030 #038-45-1997 L2007 OBG *020 †30

JEDLICKA, Leigh Ann. ■ 77054 #048-04-2006 IM *012

JEFFCOAT, Sheila R. 921 GESSNER RD, DEPT OF ANESTHESIOLOGY 77024 #048-13-2001 L2005 AN *020 †05

JEFFERIES, Craig Michael. 1201 DAIRY ASHFORD ST, STE 200 77079 #048-14-1991 L1992 FM *020 †18

JEFFERIES, Johnny Lynn, Jr. 6621 FANNIN ST, MC 19345-C 77030 #047-06-1996 L2003 CD *100 †20,55

JEFFERSON, John Robertson, III. ■ 77030 #048-14-2008 *012

JEFFERSON, Larry S. 6621 FANNIN ST, WT6-006 77030 #039-01-1976 L1982 PD PUD *020 †55

JEFFRESS, Isabelle F. 6431 FANNIN ST # 3.142, UT MEDICAL SCHOOL 77030 #048-14-1995 L1996 MPD *020 †55,20

JEFFRIES, Maggie Ann. 1515 HOLCOMBE BLVD, UNIT 409 77030 #041-15-2003 L2007 AN *020

JEHAIMI, Cayce Taher. 6431 FANNIN ST STE 3.122 77030 #613-02-2000 L2008 PDE *012 †55

JELINEK, Katherine A. ■ 77007 #048-12-2007 L2007 GE *020 †20

JEMISON, Mae Carol. ■ 77259 #035-20-1981 L1988 GP AM *030

JENKINS, Danl Edwards, III. 7438 HARRISBURG BLVD 77011 #047-06-1971 L1972 **OPH PS** *020 †35
JENKINS, Mark Andrew. 6100 MAIN ST MS 760, STUDENT HEALTH SERVICE 77005 #048-14-1987 L1988 **IM** *012
JENNINGS, Anthony J. 15827 SYLVAN LAKE DR 77062 #048-16-1984 L1985 **R** *020 †80
JENNINGS, Jennifer Shinae. ■ 77062 #048-13-2003 **NS** *012
JENNINGS, Marisa Leigh. ■ 77005 #048-14-2008 *012
JENNINGS, Paul Ernest. 4126 SOUTHWEST FWY, STE 1400 77027 #048-14-1984 L1985 **ORS OSM** *020 †40
JENSEN, Corey Tyler. ■ 77021 #038-41-2005 L2006 **DR** *012
JENSEN, Craig Louis. 6621 FANNIN ST, MC 1010.00 77030 #049-01-1983 L1988 **PG NTR** *050 †55
JENSEN, Jack Edward. 9180 OLD KATY RD 77055 #019-02-1976 L1978 **ORS OSM** *020 †40
JENSEN, Kenneth Myron. 3465 W ALABAMA ST 77027 #035-20-1955 L1964 **R DR** *071 †80
JERMYN, Rita Anne. ■ 77004 #035-15-2007 **MPD** *012
JEROUDI, Ahmad Mohamed. ■ 77024 #048-12-2007 **IM** *012
JERUSS, Jacqueline Sara. 1515 HOLCOMBE BLVD, DEPT. OF SURGICAL ONCOLOGY 77030 #050-02-1997 L2005 **GS** *100 †85
JETER, Melenda Dionne. 1515 HOLCOMBE BLVD, MDACC-RADIATION ONCOLOGY 77030 #051-01-1997 L2002 **RO** *020 †80
JETTON, Jennifer Garcia. ■ 77030 #048-04-2004 L2007 **PN** *012 †55
JEU, Mary C. 1313 HERMANN DR # 270, PARK PLAZA DEPT ANES 77004 #748-01-1964 L1969 **AN** *071 †05
JEUDY, Wilner Emmanuel. 8313 SOUTHWEST FWY, STE 201 77074 #048-14-1997 L1998 **FM** *020 †18
JEZIC, Goran A. 1200 BINZ ST STE 670 77004 #048-14-1992 L1993 **PM** *020 †60
JHAVERI, Pavan Mukesh. ■ 77054 #048-04-2008 *012
JHINGRAN, Anuja. 1515 HOLCOMBE BLVD BOX 97 77030 #048-15-1988 L1989 **RO** *020 †80
JHINGRAN, Satish Gopal. 6411 FANNIN ST #495-05-1960 L1972 **NM END** *071 †28
JIA, Zaishui. 9110 BELLAIRE BLVD, STE C 77036 #243-32-1987 L1997 **PD** *020 †55
JIANG, Yong-Hui. 1 BAYLOR PLZ, T617 DEPT MOLEC HUMAN GEN 77030 #243-16-1987 L2007 **MG** *100 †55,19
JIH, Ming Hwey. 7515 MAIN ST, STE 240 77030 #005-06-1999 L2003 **D** *020 †15
JIMENEZ, Alfredo. 18100 SAINT JOHN DR # 240, CLEAR LAKE ENT 77058 #275-01-1974 L1993 **OTO** *020 †45
JIMENEZ, Carlos Alberto. 1515 HOLCOMBE BLVD # 403, MDACC 77030 #264-01-1987 L2000 **IM** *020 †20
JIMENEZ, Marcela. ■ 77021 #264-21-2000 L2003 **SP** *012
JIMENEZ, Pedro Alfredo. 6411 FANNIN ST #275-01-1945 L1976 **OTO** *071 †45
JIMENEZ, Tomas David. ■ 77007 #042-01-2003 L2005 **DR** *012
JIMENEZ VASQUEZ, Camilo. 1400 HOLCOMBE BLVD, MD ANDERSO 77030 #264-04-1995 L2007 **END** *100 †20
JIN, Wenwu. ■ 77054 #038-06-2003 **U** *012
JING, Min. 6720 BERTNER ST MC2-270, ST LUKE'S EPISCOPAL HOSPIT 77030 #048-14-1991 L1992 **DR** *020 †80
JIRALERSPONG, Sao. 1515 HOLCOMBE BLVD, UNIT 10 77030 #048-04-2001 L2006 **ON** *012 †20
JISTEL, James R. 1313 HERMANN DR, STE 270 77004 #048-12-1985 L1986 **AN** *020 †05
JIWANI, Ali Zul. ■ 77054 #048-04-2008 *012
JOCSON, Maria A L. 710 FM 1960 RD W STE 220 77090 #748-02-1983 L1999 **PD** *062 †55
JOE, John Christopher. 3701 KIRBY DR, STE 600 77098 #048-16-1988 L1989 **FM MDM** *030 †18
JOHAL, Amandeep Kaur. ■ 77030 #495-43-2003 *100
JOHN, Susan D. 6431 FANNIN ST, MSB 2.130B 77030 #048-02-1984 L1985 **R PDR** *020 †80
JOHNSON, Andrew Benjamin. 9711 RIDDLEWOOD LN 77005 #048-14-1997 L1998 **P** *020 †75
JOHNSON, Anitra L. 1 BAYLOR PLZ, BAYLOR COLL OF MED 77030 #048-04-2002 L2006 **OBG** *100
JOHNSON, Anthony. 6620 MAIN ST STE 1450, UNIVERSITY OF NORTH CAROLI 77030 #055-75-1980, ▲ L2008 **OBG MFM** *020 †19
JOHNSON, Cheryl Karen. 12121 RICHMOND AVE, STE 226 77082 #038-43-1994 L1997 **FM** *020 †18
JOHNSON, Christopher N. ■ 77054 #048-04-2008 *012
JOHNSON, Christopher R. 2424 W HOLCOMBE BLVD STE 1 77030 #011-03-1996 L1999 **P** *020 †75
JOHNSON, Clemmie Eubanks. ■ 77018 #047-07-1946 L1948 **OBG GP** *071
JOHNSON, Craig David. 6560 FANNIN ST, STE 600 77030 #017-20-1971 L1972 **GE IM** *020 †40
JOHNSON, Danny Ray. 4040 BROADWAY ST 77087 #048-12-1985 L1986 **FM PTH** *020
JOHNSON, Ewan Douglas. ■ 77082 #048-02-2004 **HO** *012
JOHNSON, Faye Marie. 1515 HOLCOMBE BLVD, BOX 432 77030 #048-14-1996 L1998 **ON IM** *050 †20
JOHNSON, Fritz Mahin. ■ 77024 #019-02-1965 L1966 **TS CD** *071 †85,90
JOHNSON, Garfield, III. 915 GESSNER RD, STE 225 77024 #025-01-2000 L2005 **OTO** *020 †45
JOHNSON, Glen Royce. 2636 S LOOP W STE 925 77054 #010-03-1972 L1975 **FM** *030 †18
JOHNSON, Glover O L, Jr. 7789 SOUTHWEST FWY, STE 390 77074 #047-07-1966 L1974 **CD IM** *020
JOHNSON, Karen Elaine. 6621 FANNIN ST 77030 #048-04-1981 L1984 **NPM PD** *020 †55
JOHNSON, Kerry Wayne. 2060 SPACE PARK DR, STE 212 77058 #048-15-1984 L1985 **OBG** *020
JOHNSON, Keyne Kristin. ■ 77054 #041-12-2001 **NS** *020
JOHNSON, Kimberly Mae. ■ 77025 #005-02-2004 L2004 **PDC** *012 †55
JOHNSON, Laura Ann. 6621 FANNIN ST 77030 #048-14-1996 L1997 **PD NPM** *020 †55
JOHNSON, Lectoy T. ■ 77021 #010-03-1956 L1960 **AN PUD** *071 †05
JOHNSON, Luckett. 2600 S LOOP W, STE 100 77054 #048-04-1976 L1979 **FM** *020
JOHNSON, Mark Edward. 6620 MAIN ST, 13TH FL 77030 #048-12-1979 L1993 **ORS** *020 †40
JOHNSON, Nia Ermyn. 6720 BERTNER ST, MC 4-217 77030 #041-13-2005 L2008 **EM** *012
JOHNSON, Olendruff Lerey. 5445 ALMEDA RD, STE 305 77004 #047-07-1981 L1984 **IM EM** *020 †20
JOHNSON, Pamela Lashmet. 12303 WESTHEIMER RD STE B, DAIRY ASHFORD MED CLC 77077 #016-11-1989 L2006 **OBG** *050 †30,70
JOHNSON, Patrick R. 1415 NORTH LOOP W, STE 820 77008 #048-16-1989 L1990 **DR** *020 †80
JOHNSON, Paul Edwin. 2002 HOLCOMBE BLVD, 112 D 77030 #036-05-1967 L1974 **OTO GE** *040 †45
JOHNSON, Peter Arnold. ■ 77030 #048-04-2004 L2005 **P** *012
JOHNSON, Peter Haan. 1515 HOLCOMBE BLVD, DEPT. OF MED.ONCOLOGY- UNI 77030 #020-12-2001 L2004 **ON** *020
JOHNSON, Philip Carl, III. 6431 FANNIN ST 1.122 77030 #048-04-1979 L1979 **IM ID** *020 †20

JOHNSON, Robert R. ■ 77062 #049-01-1951 L1952 **GP OM** *071 †70
JOHNSON, Sara Michelle. ■ 77054 #048-14-2004 **GS** *012
JOHNSON, Stacie Nicole. ■ 77033 #048-04-2006 **IM** *012
JOHNSON, Tametra Lynette. ■ 77075 #021-05-2006 **OBG** *100
JOHNSON, Ty R. 7600 BEECHNUT ST 77074 #048-14-2001 L2005 **AN** *020 †05
JOHNSON, William K. 17203 RED OAK DR STE 103 77090 #048-14-1988 L1989 **GS** *020 †85
JOHNSON, Yvette Renee. 6621 FANNIN ST WT6-104, SECTION OF NEONATOLOGY 77030 #028-02-1987 L2005 **GPM** *020 †55
JOHNSON-CALDWELL, Jennifer. 2450 LOUISIANA ST, STE 400 77006 #048-13-1996 L1998 **IM** *020 †20
JOHNSTON, Robt Alexander. 1707 SUNSET BLVD 77005 #023-07-1956 L1962 **IM END** *071
JOHNSTON, Smith L, III. 1515 HOLCOMBE BLVD 77030 #012-05-1981 L1993 **AM IM** *062 †70
JOHNSTONE, Edwin Enoch. 2323 S SHEPHERD DR STE 908 77019 #048-04-1964 L1964 **P** *050 †75
JOLIAT, Jonathan Michael. ■ 77098 #021-01-2008 *012
JOLIVET, David A. 16630 IMPERIAL VALLEY DR, STE 115 77060 #048-04-1982 L1982 **GP** *020
JON, Cindy Kam-Tai. 6431 FANNIN ST 3.244 77030 #048-14-2000 L2003 **PDP** *100
JONASCH, Eric. 1515 HOLCOMBE BLVD, # 1374 77030 #001-07-1992 L2002 **HO** *020 †20
JONES, Alisha Jenai. 1 BAYLOR PLZ, DEPT OF INTERNAL MED/PEDS 77030 #048-04-2005 **MPD** *012
JONES, Claudette Louise. 2626 S LOOP W STE 120 77054 #047-07-1975 L1978 **IM** *020
JONES, Clay Travis. 6621 FANNIN ST, MC-WT 6104 77030 #021-05-2003 L2006 **PD** *100 †55
JONES, Daniel M. 1515 HOLCOMBE BLVD 77030 #038-06-1994 L1999 **PTH** *020 †50
JONES, Danny Brigman. 6565 FANNIN ST, NC 205 77030 #036-07-1962 L1972 **GPM** *030 †35
JONES, Derek L. 7731 SOUTHWEST FWY, STE 202 77074 #048-12-1993 L1998 **ORS** *020 †40
JONES, Edith Irby. 2601 PROSPECT ST 77004 #004-01-1952 L1960 **IM** *020
JONES, Elizabeth B. 6431 FANNIN ST JJL448 77030 #021-06-1986 L1999 **EM** *020 †20,16
JONES, Eric Alan. 6621 FANNIN ST STE 660, DIV OF PEDIATRIC UROLOGY 77030 #054-04-1993 L2001 **U** *020 †95
JONES, Gisele Anjanique. 10655 STEEPLETOP DR 77065 #021-05-1994 L1995 **IM** *020 †20
JONES, Holly June. 7515 MAIN ST, STE 670 77030 #038-43-1992 L1997 **RHU** *020 †20
JONES, James Harvey. 902 FROSTWOOD DR, STE 275 77024 #027-01-1965 L1969 **DR NM** *020 †80
JONES, Jeffrey Allen. 2101 NASA RD 1, FLIGHT MEDICINE, SD 2 77058 #048-04-1984 L1993 **AM U** *020 †70,95
JONES, Jerry Wayne. 4209 W ALABAMA ST 77027 #048-13-1974 L1974 **EM IM** *020 †16
JONES, Jim Aubrey. 6431 FANNIN ST 1134, OF TEXAS-HOUSTON 77030 #021-05-2006 **IM** *012
JONES, John Kerrison. 6550 FANNIN ST, STE 2001 77030 #917-19-1965 L1966 **PDO OTO** *020
JONES, John Marcus. 1213 HERMANN DR STE 660 77004 #021-01-1971 L1977 **NS GS** *020 †25
JONES, Julia Leigh. 7505 MAIN ST, STE 290 77030 #021-01-1987 L1991 **N** *020 †75
JONES, Julie Anne. 3601 N MACGREGOR WAY, SBC 001 77004 #048-02-1979 L1979 **PD PHP** *030 †15
JONES, Kevin Lee. 7600 BEECHNUT ST 77074 #048-14-1990 L1991 **AN** *020 †05
JONES, Mason Daniel. ■ 77019 #048-02-2001 L2006 *100 †18
JONES, Melissa Sue. 6621 FANNIN ST RM A170, MC1-1000 77030 #048-04-2006 **PD** *012
JONES, Myrtle Oates. 6565 DE MOSS DR STE 232 77074 #020-02-1982 L1993 **OBG** *020 †30
JONES, Neema Aisha. 1415 LA CONCHA LN 77054 #048-14-2003 L2007 **NEP** *012 †20
JONES, Peter Howard. 6565 FANNIN ST, MS A601 77030 #048-04-1977 L1982 **IM** *020 †20
JONES, Roy Bradley. 1515 HOLCOMBE BLVD # 423, BLOOD/MARROW TRANSPLANT DE 77030 #036-07-1975 L2002 **IM** *020 †20
JONES, Stacey Nicole. 509 W TIDWELL RD STE 100 77091 #048-14-1998 L1999 **FM** *020 †18
JONES, Stanley C. 7500 BEECHNUT ST, STE 150 77074 #048-12-1969 L1970 **OSS ORS** *020 †40
JONES, Stephanie. 1 BAYLOR PLZ, DEPT OF ANESTHESIOLOGY 77030 #048-04-2004 L2008 **AN** *012
JONES, Tamisha Elise. ■ 77021 #048-04-2007 **PD** *012
JONES, Thomas Louis. ■ 77047 #048-02-2004 L2007 **ORS** *012
JONES, Wilbur Lindsey. 7731 SOUTHWEST FWY, STE 202 77074 #048-12-1968 L1968 **ORS** *020 †40
JONES, Wm Patterson, III. 18100 UPPER BAY RD, STE 206 77058 #027-01-1977 L1980 **AN** *020 †05
JONG, Kevin Yao. 1919 NORTH LOOP W, STE 220 77008 #048-04-1992 L1996 **OPH** *020 †35
JONG, Sue Tsen. 6410 FANNIN ST 77030 #048-04-1992 L1993 **PD** *020 †55
JONSSON, Steinn. 2002 HOLCOMBE BLVD 77030 #484-01-1977 L1980 **PUD IM** *020 †20
JOO, Sang Bai. 7007 NORTH FWY, STE 225 77076 #583-03-1966 L1977 **GP** *071
JOOMA, Nuruddin. ■ 77030 #021-01-2001 L2005 **HO** *012
JORDAN, John Gibbons. ■ 77030 #036-01-2007 **IM** *012
JORDAN, Michelle Dana. ■ 77021 #047-07-2004 **AN** *012
JORDAN, Paul Howard, Jr. ■ 77004 #016-02-1944 L1965 **GS** *071 †85
JORDAN, Paulette L. ■ 77071 #047-07-1981 L1988 **PD** *020
JORDON, Robert E. 6655 TRAVIS ST STE 980 77030 #035-06-1965 L1984 **D IG** *020 †15
JORGENSEN, Jeffrey Lee. 6565 FANNIN ST 77030 #005-11-1994 L1998 **PTH** *020 †50
JOSE, Cherrie Lynn. ■ 77009 #048-15-2007 **TY** *012
JOSELEVITZ, Joel. 5225 KATY FWY, STE 105 77007 #649-44-1984 L1992 **PM PMM** *020 †60
JOSEPH, Linda Mary. 2002 HOLCOMBE BLVD, ANESTHESIOLOGY DEPT. 77030 #495-32-1988 L2006 **AN** *020 †05 ‡
JOSEPH, Richard Wayne, Jr. ■ 77004 #012-05-2004 L2007 **IM** *020 †20
JOSEPH, Rohan Abraham. 6550 FANNIN ST, THE METHODIST HOSP 77030 #496-36-2004 **GS** *012
JOSEPH, Sindhu Liz. ■ 77083 #048-13-2007 **IM** *012
JOSEPH, Usha Anna. 5656 KELLEY ST, UNIVERSITY OF TX LBJ GEN 77026 #495-16-1971 L1979 **ON NM** *050 †28
JOSHI, Reeti Kautilya. PO BOX 20708 77225 #495-01-2005 **IM** *012
JOSHI, Rupali Narendra. 7737 SOUTHWEST FWY, RES P 77074 #496-46-2000 L2007 **FM** *020 †18
JOSON, Lisa Ann. 14340 TORREY CHS BLVD #160, CORNERSTONE PSY ASSOC 77014 #048-14-1997 L1998 **CHP** *020 †75
JOUDAH, Fady Ahmad. 2002 HOLCOMBE BLVD, EMERGENCY ROOM VA HOSPITAL 77030 #012-01-1996 L1999 **IM** *020 †20
JOYNER, Jamil Prentice. ■ 77054 #048-04-2005 L2008 **PD** *012
JOYNER, Roy E. ■ 77024 #012-01-1950 L1955 **OM GPM** *071 †70
JULAPALLI, Meena Rao. ■ 77004 #048-04-2005 **PD** *012
JULAPALLI, Venodhar Rao. 800 PEAKWOOD DR, STE 7E 77090 #048-04-1999 L2004 **IM** *020 †20

■ = Address Information Privacy Protected

JULAPALLI, Vinay Rao. 1701 HERMANN DR, UNIT 2004 77004 #048-13-1997 L2001 **IC** *012 †20
JUMSHYD, Ali. ■ 77096 #704-02-1960 L1981 **DR** *071 †80
JUMSHYD, Junaid. ■ 77096 #704-16-1992 **IM** *100
JUNEJA, Harinder Singh. 6431 FANNIN ST, UTHSC AT HOUSTON 77030 #495-36-1971 L1981 **HEM ON** *040 †20
JUNG, Peter Yijoon. 915 GESSNER RD, STE 760 77024 #048-04-1999 L2002 **PD** *020 †55
JUNG, Woo Nahm. 915 GESSNER RD, STE 760 77024 #583-06-1969 L1982 **PD GP** *071 †55
JURNEY, Sara F. 6410 FANNIN ST STE 825, COMPLETE WOMEN'S CARE CENT 77030 #048-14-2000 L2004 **OBG** *020
JUSTINO, Henri. 6621 FANNIN ST 19345-C, PEDIATRIC CARDIOLOGY 77030 #067-01-1994 L2004 **PDC PD** *020 †55
JYOTHULA, Soma Sundara Sh. 1504 TAUB LOOP, BAYLOR COLLEGE OF MED 77030 #495-36-2001 L2003 **PCC** *012 †20
KAALE, Robert Lee. 18300 SAINT JOHN DR 77058 #048-02-2002 L2005 **EM** *020 †16
KAANDERS, Johannes H. 6723 BERTNER ST 77030 #660-07-1984 **RO** *020
KADAKIA, Rajan Avinash. 11920 ASTORIA BLVD, STE 400 77089 #051-04-2001 L2002 **IC** *012
KADAKIA, Rupin Avinash. 11840 FM 1960 RD W 77065 #048-04-1994 L2003 **CD IC** *020 †20
KADEN, Andreas. ■ 77054 #048-14-2008 *012
KADIA, Tapan. 1515 HOLCOMBE BLVD # 421, ANDERSON CANC 77030 #033-06-2001 L2004 **ON** *012
KADIYALA, Himabindu. 2002 HOLCOMBE BLVD, VA MEDICAL CENTER 111PC 77030 #495-50-1987 L1996 **IM** *020 †20
KADMON, Dov. 6560 FANNIN ST, STE 2100 77030 #550-01-1972 L1986 **U** *020 †95
KAESLER, Kelly. 8830 LONG POINT RD STE 807 77055 #047-06-1968 L1969 **OS** *020 †95
KAESTNER, Gottfried R. ■ 77096 #407-33-1959 L1967 **ORS** *071 †40
KAFOGLIS, William Stathis. 3838 HILLCROFT ST 77057 #020-02-1959 L1967 **ORS** *072
KAGARUKI, Robin Lyn. ■ 77082 #030-05-1995 *100
KAHAN, Allayne Valerie. ■ 77096 #016-06-1967 L1979 **PTH** *050 †50
KAHAN, Barry Donald. 6431 FANNIN ST, MSB STE 60240 77030 #016-02-1965 L1977 **GS TTS** *020 †85
KAHAN, Kara L. 4950 MEMORIAL DR 77007 #048-14-2000 L2003 **CHP** *020 †75
KAHANEK, Natalie Renee. ■ 77025 #048-14-2008 *012
KAHN, Andrew Mark. 6431 FANNIN ST, MSB 4.107 77030 #024-05-1975 L1981 **NEP** *050 †20
KAILA, Vijaya Lakshmi. 7333 NORTH FWY STE 401 77076 #495-62-1988 L1996 **GE IM** *020 †20
KAILASAM, Jayasree. 1213 HERMANN DR STE 350 77004 #495-59-1993 L1998 **IM** *020 †20
KAKASCIK, Aimee Gretchen. ■ 77081 #028-79-2003, ▲ L2008 **PAN** *012
KAKVAN, Mohamed. 2909 HILLCROFT ST, STE 250 77057 #517-01-1952 L1974 **GS PTH** *071 †85
KALASKAR, Anupama Shashik. 6431 FANNIN ST 77030 #049-01-2004 **PDI** *012 †55
KALCHOFF, William Pete. 7731 SW FWY STE 201, SUITE 201 77074 #028-34-1972 L1978 **TS** *020 †85
KALDIS, Teresa P. 6550 FANNIN ST, SMITH TOWER, STE 2501 77030 #048-14-1995 L1996 **IM PM** *020 †20,60
KALE, Arundhati Subhash. 6621 FANNIN ST, TX CHILDREN'S HOSPITAL 77030 #495-65-1981 L1993 **PN PD** *020 †55
KALHOR, Neda. ■ 77040 #517-08-1997 L2008 **SP** *100 †50
KALIA, R Elizabeth. 18100 HOSPITAL BLVD, STE 350 77058 #495-08-1974 L1980 **PD** *020 †55
KALIFE-CANAVATI, Gerardo. 6624 FANNIN ST STE 2480 77030 #649-02-1989 L1997 **CD** *020 †20
KALINA, Jeffrey Earl. 710 FM 1960 RD W 77090 #028-34-1994 L1996 **EM** *020 †16
KALISH, Mark David. 915 GESSNER RD STE 720 77024 #047-07-1970 L1977 **U** *020 †95
KALISH, Raime Beth. 2812 RICE BLVD, 2812 RICE BLVD. 77005 #048-14-1997 L1998 **AN** *020 †05
KALISKY, Zvi. 2990 RICHMOND AVE, STE 142 77098 #550-01-1968 L1976 **PM** *020 †60
KALKONDE, Mrunal Yogeshwa. 1 BAYLOR PLZ, DEPT OF PATHOLOGY MC 315 77030 #495-83-2003 **PTH** *012
KALKONDE, Yogeshwar Vidya. 1 BAYLOR PLZ, BAYLOR COLL OF MED 77030 #495-19-1996 **N** *012
KAM, Laurence. 931 GESSNER RD 77024 #836-01-1973 L1981 **AN** *020 †05
KAMAT, Aparna Ashish. 1515 HOLCOMBE BLVD, UNIT NUMBER 440 77030 #496-38-1994 L2002 **OBG** *020 †30
KAMAT, Ashish Madhav. 1515 HOLCOMBE BLVD, UNIT 1373 77030 #496-38-1994 L2002 **U SO** *020 †95
KAMBLE, Madhuri V. 1502 TAUB LOOP, NEURO PSYCHIATRIC CENTER 77030 #496-07-1989 L2000 **CHP** *020 †75
KAMBLE, Rammurti. 6565 FANNIN ST, M979 77030 #495-92-1991 L2006 **HEM** *020 †20
KAMDAR, Ankur Ashwin. 6621 FANNIN ST, MC 3-2290 77030 #048-04-2002 **PPR** *012 †55
KAMDAR, Shobhana Jagat. 4654 HIGHWAY 6 N, STE 307 77084 #495-22-1971 L1977 **PD** *020
KAMENETSKY, Luda. 1315 ST JOSEPH PKWY, STE 1101 77002 #913-06-1986 L1997 **IM** *020 †20
KAMINSKY, Dave. ■ 77030 #021-05-1936 L1942 **GP** *071
KAMINSKY, Robert Isadore. 2342 UNDERWOOD ST 77030 #048-04-1968 L1968 **U GP** *020 †95
KAMINSKY, Steven. 6431 FANNIN ST, MSB 2-100 77030 #048-02-1970 L1970 **OS PDS** *020 †80
KAMPAL, Rony. ■ 77054 #048-12-2003 L2006 **IM** *020 †20
KAN, Pui-Hung Peggy. 6624 FANNIN ST, STE 1510 77030 #048-02-1979 L1979 **PD** *074 †55
KANCHERLA, Vikas S. 10130 LOUETTA RD 77070 #048-15-2002 L2007 **AI** *020 †55
KANDPAL, Sangeeta. ■ 77030 #495-45-1990 L1995 **NPM** *012 †55
KANDYIL, Roshini Moosari. ■ 77019 #048-14-2001 L2007 **AI** *012
KANE, Walter. 10370 RICHMOND AVE, STE 1125 77042 #048-14-1996 L1998 **EM FM** *020 †18 ‡
KANG, Elisabeth Min. ■ 77030 #031-01-2006 **EM** *012
KANG, Jane Jeesun. ■ 77004 #021-05-2000 L2003 **P** *020 †75
KANT, Andrew Peter. 17080 RED OAK DR 77090 #016-43-1972 L1973 **ORS** *020 †40
KANTARJIAN, Hagob M. 1515 HOLCOMBE BLVD BOX 61 77030 #605-01-1979 L1983 **ON** *020 †20
KANUNGO, Anuradha. ■ 77054 #495-13-1986 L2006 **ATP HMP** *020 †50 ‡
KAO, Christina Chen-Yu. ■ 77005 #048-04-2001 L2007 **PCC** *012
KAO, Lillian Shiowyu. 5656 KELLEY ST, STE 30S62008 77026 #025-01-1996 L2003 **GS** *020 †85
KAPADIA, Mohammed Minhas. 1300 MOURSUND ST, 226, UNIV TX HOUSTON MED SCH 77030 #704-02-1986 L2004 **P** *012
KAPADIA, Zehra. 1140 WESTMONT DR, STE 200 77015 #704-02-1998 L2005 **ON** *020
KAPASI, Abbas A. 17030 NANES DR, STE 105 77090 #880-01-1974 L1979 **PD** *020 †55
KAPLAN, Alan Leslie. 6550 FANNIN ST STE 901 77030 #035-01-1955 L1963 **GYN GO** *020 †30
KAPLAN, Brian H. 6560 FANNIN ST, STE 600 77030 #048-04-1984 L1985 **GE IM** *020 †20
KAPLAN, Kevin Alan. ■ 77057 #048-13-2007 L2007 *012
KAPLAN, Martin L. 1200 BINZ ST STE 300, DIAGNOSTIC CLINIC OF HOUST 77004 #035-19-1964 L1971 **PUD IM** *020 †20
KAPLAN, Michael A. 6624 FANNIN ST 77030 #048-04-1990 L1993 **HNS OTO** *020 †45
KAPLAN, Sheldon Lee. 1 BAYLOR PLZ, DEPARTMENT OF PEDIATRICS 77030 #028-03-1973 L1977 **PDI** *050 †55
KAPLAN, Walid. 6701 FANNIN ST 77030 #875-01-1988 L1994 **PD PDE** *050 †55
KAPOOR, Ashish. 17030 NANES DR STE 214 77090 #495-45-1991 L1997 **IM** *020 †20
KAPOOR, Shalini. 1315 ST JOSEPH PKWY, STE 1205 77002 #067-01-1994 L1998 **OPH** *020 †35
KAPOOR, Vinay. 1502 TAUB LOOP, OF HARRIS COUNTY 77030 #495-73-1976 L2000 **CHP EM** *020 †75
KAPUSTA, Mario Osvaldo. 5585 WESLAYAN ST 77005 #132-03-1973 L1978 **TS PHL** *020 †85,90
KAR, Biswajit. 6624 FANNIN ST STE 2180 77030 #495-73-1983 L2002 **IC** *020 †20
KARACAN, Ismet. 1 BAYLOR PLZ 77030 #902-01-1953 L1973 **OS P** *071 †75
KARAKOC, Tayfun. ■ 77007 #902-07-1994 L2004 **P** *020 †75
KARAM-HAGE, Maher A. 1155 PRESSLER ST, CPB, UNIT 1330 77030 #429-02-1993 L2007 **ADP P** *020 †75
KARAS, Tomer Zachariah. 2001 HOLCOMBE BLVD # 2706 77030 #048-14-1998 L2000 **TS** *020 †85,90
KARAVITI, Lefkothea P. 1 BAYLOR PLZ, BAYLOR COLLEGE OF MEDICINE 77030 #418-01-1977 L1991 **PD** *020 †55
KARIM, Amin H. 10021 S MAIN ST, STE B1 77025 #704-02-1977 L1981 **CD IC** *020 †20
KARIM, Shahnaz Amin. 10021 S MAIN ST, STE B-ONE 77025 #704-16-1983 L1999 **PM** *020 †60
KARIMJEE, Najmuddin K. 12015 LOUETTA RD STE 200 77070 #048-02-1989 L1992 **IM** *020 †20
KARIMZADEHNAJAR, Kaveh. PO BOX 20708 77225 #517-08-2000 **IM** *012
KARISTINOS, Anastassios. 1504 TAUB LOOP, BEN TAUB HOSPITAL 77030 #418-02-1993 L2005 **OSM** *100
KARLBERG, Helena Ingrid. 7600 BEECHNUT ST 77074 #858-05-1979 L1988 **AN** *020 †05
KARMALI, Shahzeer. ■ 77004 #060-01-2002 *100
KARMEL, Catherine. 1213 HERMANN DR STE 630 77004 #016-42-1991 L1995 **OBG** *020 †30
KARNEZIS, Stellios. ■ 77030 #048-04-2008 *012
KARNI, Amir. 13111 EAST FWY, STE 110 77015 #048-04-1996 L1997 **GS** *020 †85
KARNI, Simon. 13111 EAST FWY STE 110 77015 #550-02-1974 L1980 **GS** *020 †85
KAROTKIN, Lester. ■ 77024 #048-02-1940 L1940 **IM** *071 †20
KARP, Daniel D. 1515 HOLCOMBE BLVD # 432 77030 #036-07-1973 L2004 **ON HEM** *020 †20
KARPEN, Douglas. 6430 HILLCROFT ST, STE 115 77081 #028-79-1974, ▲ L1975 **GP** *020
KARPEN, Saul Jos. 1 BAYLOR PLZ, BAYLOR COLLEGE OF MEDICINE 77030 #035-47-1989 L2000 **PG** *020 †55
KARPINOS, Marianna. 8900 LAKES AT 610 DR, HUMAN RESOURCES 77054 #048-04-2002 L2006 **N** *100
KASAB, Enas Hilmy Salem. ■ 77054 #025-07-2003 L2008 **FM** *100 †18
KASEB, Ahmed Omar Riad. ■ 77054 #915-02-1998 L2007 **HO** *100
KASHYAP, Rohit Kumar. 411 LANTERN BEND DR, STE 240 77090 #305-01-1996 L2002 **FM** *020 †18
KASIRAJAN, Lakshmipriya. 6431 FANNIN ST 1.150, UTHSC HOUSTON 77030 #495-42-1995 L2004 **PCC** *020 †20
KASPER, Douglas Victor. ■ 77030 #005-12-1998 L2000 **EM** *020 †16
KASRA ZARMANDIL, Pour. ■ 77030 #517-01-1967 **GS CD** *020
KASS, Jeffrey Block. ■ 77056 #048-04-1975 L1976 **R** *020 †80
KASS, Joseph Shimon. 6501 FANNIN ST 302, BAYLOR COLLEGE OF MEDICINE 77030 #048-04-2001 L2004 **N** *020 †75
KASSAW, Kristin A. 6655 TRAVIS ST STE 700 77030 #048-04-1997 L1999 **P** *020 †75
KASSIOTIS, Christos Micha. 7900 CAMBRIDGE ST, APT 21-10 77054 #418-01-1996 L2005 **CD** *012 †20
KASSIS, Christelle Emile. PO BOX 20708, UNIV TX MED SCH 77225 #605-03-2003 **ID** *012 †20
KASSIS, Edmund Salim. ■ 77030 #041-12-1999 L2002 **TS** *012 †85 ‡
KASSOUF, Wassim. 1515 HOLCOMBE BLVD, UNIT 1373 77030 #067-01-1998 L2005 **U** *100 †95
KATCHEVES, Alexander Stev. ■ 77021 #023-01-2005 **N** *012
KATEI, George K. 7102 LONG POINT RD 77055 #412-01-1987 L1996 **IM** *020 †20
KATIC, Alain. 1010 WAVERLY ST 77008 #048-02-1991 L2000 **P** *020 †75
KATKIN, Julie Pamela. 6621 FANNIN ST, CLINICAL CARE CENTER 77030 #048-04-1985 L1986 **PDP** *050 †55
KATRANA, David John. 909 FROSTWOOD DR, STE 260 77024 #016-06-1974 L1979 **PS** *020 †65
KATTA, Rajani. 6620 MAIN ST 77030 #048-04-1994 L1998 **D** *020 †15
KATZ, Allan Robt. 6431 FANNIN ST # 3282 77030 #051-04-1967 L1975 **OBG** *020 †30
KATZ, Charles Darrell. 6624 FANNIN ST 77030 #048-04-1985 L1986 **OTO FPS** *020 †45
KATZ, Debra Miriam. 7011 SOUTHWEST FWY, MHMRA OF HARRIS COUNTY 77074 #010-01-1985 L1995 **CHP P** *020 †75
KATZ, Jeffrey. 6410 FANNIN ST STE 1111, UNIVERSITY OF TEXAS PHYSIC 77030 #836-02-1975 L1981 **AN** *020 †05
KATZ, Marcia Fay. 6620 MAIN ST, STE 11B15 77030 #024-05-1984 L1996 **PCC** *020 †20
KATZ, Matthew Harold. 1515 HOLCOMBE BLVD, UT MD ANDERSON CANCER CENT 77030 #035-09-1999 L2006 **GS** *100
KATZ, Michael Louis. ■ 77025 #654-01-2006 **IM** *012
KATZ, Philip Bernard. 800 PEAKWOOD DR, STE 5E 77090 #035-09-1977 L1978 **DR** *020 †80
KATZ, Ruth Louise. 1515 HOLCOMBE BLVD BOX 53 77030 #836-01-1969 L1980 **ATP** *020 †50
KATZ, Stephen Mark. 6431 FANNIN ST, MSB 6246 77030 #048-04-1977 L1977 **ON GS** *050 †85
KATZ, Tracy M. 6431 FANNIN ST 1.134, OF TEXAS-HOUSTON 77030 #048-14-2007 **IM** *012
KAU, Vincent W. 12121 RICHMOND AVE, STE 110 77082 #048-15-2001 L2005 **IM** *020 †20
KAUFFMAN, Christopher Ray. ■ 77007 #048-04-2008 *012
KAUFFMAN, Julia Anne. ■ 77054 #028-02-2008 *012
KAUFMAN, Daniel Andrew. 4101 GREENBRIAR ST STE 325 77098 #021-01-1969 L1974 **P** *020 †75 ‡
KAUFMAN, Ira H. ■ 77004 #035-20-1953 L1954 **OPH** *071 †35
KAUFMAN, Ira Saul. 5757 WESTHEIMER RD, # 346 77057 #035-08-1970 L1977 **ORS** *020 †40
KAUFMAN, Raymond H. 6550 FANNIN ST, STE 901 77030 #023-01-1948 L1956 **GYN PTH** *020 †30
KAUL, Kuldip Kumar. 2060 SPACE PARK DR STE 400 77058 #495-51-1974 L1982 **DIA END** *020
KAUR, Amandeep. 6431 FANNIN ST 308 77030 #495-29-2004 **FP** *012
KAUR, Berneet. 1885 EL PASEO ST, APT 833 77054 #048-14-2003 L2008 **N** *100
KAUR, Harmeet. 1515 HOLCOMBE BLVD BOX 57 77030 #496-07-1985 L2001 **DR** *020 †80
KAUR, Harpreet. 6431 FANNIN ST, # 7-044/MSB 77030 #495-43-2001 L2007 **N** *012
KAUR, Kiran Navdeep. ■ 77054 #021-01-2007 **IM** *012
KAVANAGH, John Jos. 1515 HOLCOMBE BLVD, GYN MEDICINE BOX 401 77030 #041-02-1975 L1980 **ON IM** *020 †20
KAVIN, Ian Allen. 902 FROSTWOOD DR, STE 227 77024 #836-01-1962 L1979 **PD A** *020 †55
KAW, Madhukar. 12121 RICHMOND AVE, STE 424 77082 #495-51-1987 L2000 **GE IM** *020 †20

■ = Address Information Privacy Protected

8719

KAWASAKI, Gilo. DEPT OF COMMUNITY MEDICINE, BAYLOR COLLEGE OF MEDICINE 77030 #021-01-1985 L1989 **IM** *074 †20

KAY, David Cyril. 1313 CAMPBELL RD STE C 77055 #016-11-1958 L1980 **P ADP** *071 †75

KAY, Thomas M. 1313 CAMPBELL RD, STE C 77055 #048-13-1997 L1998 **FM** *020 †18

KAYLANI, Zayd Sirri. 1631 NORTH LOOP W, STE 650 77008 #605-01-1967 L1977 **GE IM** *020

KAYNAK, Husnu Evren. PO BOX 20708 77225 #902-07-2002 **IM** *012

KAZMI, Syed Mohammad Ali. PO BOX 20708 77225 #704-25-2004 **IM** *012

KEARLEY, Jennifer Olivia. 1 BAYLOR PLZ, BAYLOR COLL OF MED 77030 #012-05-2003 **PP** *012

KEARNEY, Debra Lynn. 6621 FANNIN ST, STE A 77030 #016-06-1980 L1981 **PTH PP** *020 †50

KEARNS, Richard Jos. 7401 MAIN ST 77030 #010-02-1975 L1984 **ORS** *020 †40

KEATING, Anna R. 1515 HOLCOMBE BLVD, PEDIATRICS, UNIT 87 77030 #048-14-1997 L1999 **PHO** *020,55

KEATING, Michael Joseph. 1400 HOLCOMBE BLVD, BOX 428 77030 #143-02-1966 L1975 **ON HEM** *020

KEATON, Toni Eliece. 2101 CRAWFORD ST, STE 309 77002 #047-07-1993 L1998 **IM** *020 †20

KEATS, Arthur Stanley. ■ 77030 #041-01-1946 L1955 **AN PA** *071 †05

KEATTS, James Griffin. 12970 EAST FWY 77015 #004-01-1965 L1969 **OPH OS** *075

KEBRIAEI, Partow. 1515 HOLCOMBE BLVD, UNIT 423 77030 #048-14-1997 L1998 **HO** *020 †20

KEDZIERSKA, Katarzyna J. ■ 77030 #048-04-2002 L2008 **RNR** *012 †80

KEE, Patrick Han-Chee. ■ 77030 #143-01-1994 *012

KEE, Spencer Stephen. 1220 HOLCOMBE BLVD # 1243 77030 #775-01-1981 L2000 **AN** *020

KEELER, Elizabeth A. ■ 77005 #048-14-2001 L2003 **OBG** *020

KEELER, Harvey Saml Grant. 7710 BELLAIRE BLVD 77036 #065-01-1963 L1976 **GP** *020

KEELER, Martin H. 5230 ARIEL ST, 5230 ARIEL ST 77096 #035-09-1953 L1977 **P** *020 †75

KEENMON, Corinna Maria. ■ 77025 #048-02-2005 **P** *012

KEICHIAN, Andres Hugo. 3003 S LOOP W, STE 505 77054 #132-01-1964 L1974 **N** *020 †75

KEIL, Christie S. ■ 77030 #048-14-2008 *012

KEIR-GARZA, Jennifer L. 11914 ASTORIA BLVD, STE 140B 77089 #048-14-1993 L1995 **OTO** *020 †45

KEITEL, Wendy Anne. 1 BAYLOR PLZA-IN RES CTR 77030 #036-07-1977 L1982 **ID IM** *050 †20

KEITH, George Thos, Jr. 8830 LONG POINT RD, STE 603 77055 #047-06-1980 L1982 **PUD IM** *020 †20

KELAHER, James Edmund. 6620 MAIN ST STE 1375, BAYLOR CLINIC 77030 #030-06-1994 L1995 **IM** *020 †20,70

KELLAWAY, Judianne. 6400 FANNIN ST 18TH FL, HERMANN EYE CENTER 77030 #048-14-1987 L1989 **OPH IM** *040 †35

KELLER, Francis Xavier. ■ 77030 #034-01-1979 L1981 **AN** *020 †05

KELLER, Glen Elmer. 11302 FALLBROOK DR, STE 308 77065 #004-01-1955 L1970 **FM** *071 †18

KELLER, Michael Glen. 11302 FALLBROOK DR STE 104, CY FAIR MEDICAL PROF BLDG 77065 #004-01-1981 L1984 **IM FM** *020 †18

KELLER, Richard. 6431 FANNIN ST STE 1.150, AT HOUST 77030 #048-15-2004 L2007 **IM** *012 †20

KELLER, Wayne Francis. 17750 CALI DR, MD & ASSOC., PLLC 77090 #048-02-1962 L1962 **P ADP** *020

KELLERMANN, Alan Scott. ■ 77024 #021-01-1971 L1972 **FM OS** *020 †18

KELLERMAYER, Richard. 1 BAYLOR PLZ, TEXAS CHILDREN'S HOSPITAL 77030 #473-03-1997 **PG** *012 †55

KELLEY, Janice Marie. 18220 TOMBALL PKWY 77070 #023-01-1978 L1980 **IM GP** *020

KELLY, Anita A. ■ 77080 #048-14-1986 L1987 **FM** *020 †18

KELLY, Crystal. ■ 77054 #048-02-2007 **OBG** *012

KELLY, Daniel Mitchell. 3809 MAIN ST 77002 #030-06-1968 L1969 **FM OM** *075 †18

KELLY, Erin Colleen. ■ 77030 #048-14-2008 *012

KELLY, Kathryn A. ■ 77024 #048-16-1988 L1989 **FM** *062 †18

KELLY, Lindsey Kathryn. ■ 77054 #048-14-2008 *012

KELLY, Marise. 900 BROADWAY ST 77012 #649-30-1981 L1996 **FM** *020 †18

KELLY, Michael Vernon, II. 17070 RED OAK DR STE 303 77090 #048-12-1971 L1971 **PS GS** *020

KELLY, Roy Jackson. 77079 #030-05-1954 L1965 **AM PHP** *071 †70

KELLY, Scott D. ■ 77006 #048-14-2007 *012

KELLY, Todd Lawrence. 1515 HOLCOMBE BLVD, BOX 112 77030 #048-14-1995 L1999 **CCA** *020 †05

KELSEY, John Roger. ■ 77057 #048-04-1945 L1945 **GE IM** *071 †20

KELSEY, Mavis Parrott. ■ 77024 #048-12-1936 L1936 **IM** *071 †20

KEMP, Bonnie Lucas. 1515 HOLCOMBE BLVD 77030 #048-04-1987 L1988 **DMP** *020 †50

KEMP, Katherine I. 1707 SUNSET BLVD, MEDICAL CLINIC OF HOUSTON 77005 #048-04-1966 L1966 **DR** *020 †80

KEMP, Kelvin D. ■ 77054 #048-14-2008 *012

KEMPER, James W. 11118 WICKWOOD DR 77024 #017-20-1952 L1956 **RHU IM** *071 †20

KENDRICK, James B. 1631 NORTH LOOP W STE 200 77008 #048-04-1986 L1988 **ORS** *020

KENDRICK, James Barton. 1631 NORTH LOOP W STE 600 77008 #027-01-1960 L1968 **ORS** *071 †40

KENJURA, Bryan C. ■ 77018 #048-14-2002 L2005 **IM** *020 †20

KENNAMER, Debra Leigh. 1515 HOLCOMBE BLVD BOX 409, MD ANDERSON CANCER CENTER 77030 #048-02-1980 L1980 **AN** *020 †20

KENNEDY, Curtis Edward. 6621 FANNIN ST, WT 6-006 77030 #048-04-1997 L1999 **CCP** *020 †55

KENNEDY, Douglas Wm. 8240 ANTOINE DR 77088 #065-01-1956 L1977 **PD** *071 †55

KENNEDY, Kathleen Ann. 6431 FANNIN ST, MSB 3.228 77030 #028-34-1980 L1987 **NPM** *020 †55

KENNEDY, Kenneth R. 1221 MCKINNEY ST, STE 40300 77010 #048-04-1986 L1987 **FM** *020 †18

KENNY, Thomas Paul. 6431 FANNIN 5 020 77030 #539-02-1983 L1996 **AN** *040 †20

KENT, David S. 915 GESSNER RD, STE 720 77024 #048-14-2002 L2007 **U** *020

KERAGA, Gloria Theresa. 3303 FM 1960 RD W, STE 250 77068 #035-09-1978 L1981 **P** *020

KERN, Susan B. 8850 LONG POINT RD 77055 #048-13-1983 L1984 **GP PM** *020 ‡

KERR, George Roderick. 6655 TRAVIS ST 77030 #064-01-1955 L1978 **NTR PD** *050 †55

KERSTMAN, Eric Lee. 1333 MOURSUND ST, MHH/TIRR 77030 #035-08-1991 L2005 **AM** *020 †60,70

KERTESZ, Naomi Joan. 6621 FANNIN ST, MC 19345-C PED CARDIOLOGY 77030 #016-06-1989 L1997 **PDC ICE** *012

KERWIN, Joseph Peter. 1150 GEMINI ST STE A22, LOCKHEED MISSILES SPACE CO 77058 #016-06-1957 **AM OS** *030

KESHWANI, Nazmudin. 7048 BISSONNET ST 77074 #917-01-1978 L1982 **FM** *020 †18

KESSLER, Frederick B. 6621 FANNIN ST 77030 #048-02-1956 L1956 **HS GS** *071 †85

KESSLER, Michael Scott. 6655 TRAVIS ST 77030 #035-19-1972 L1974 **PD** *020 †55

KETONEN, Leena. 1515 HOLCOMBE BLVD - UNIT, UT MD ANDERSON CANCER CENT 77030 #374-01-1969 L1999 **R** *050

KETTERER, Cynthia Lee. 14770 MEMORIAL DR, STE 100 77079 #048-14-1992 L1997 **GS** *020

KEVORKIAN, Charles Geo. 6624 FANNIN ST, STE 2330 77030 #143-07-1973 L1979 **PM** *020 †60

KEW, Yvonne. 1504 TAUB LOOP, DEPT. OF NEUROLOGY, 2ND FL 77030 #035-46-1998 L2004 **N** *020 †75

KEWALRAMANI, Chanda H. 2405 S GESSNER RD, STE B 77063 #048-13-1993 L1995 **FM** *020 †18

KEY, James Everett, II. 6624 FANNIN ST STE 2100, MED CTR OPHTHALMOLOGY 77030 #048-04-1970 L1970 **OPH** *020 †35

KEYS, Lindsey L. ■ 77054 #048-14-2008 *012

KHAIRALLA, Hanan Abdulmaj. 6431 FANNIN ST, STE 1.150 77030 #797-03-1998 L2008 **IM** *100

KHAKOO, Aarif Yusuf. 1515 HOLCOMBE BLVD, UNIT 449 77030 #035-01-1999 L2005 **CD** *100 †20

KHALADKAR, Bhanu R. 7600 BEECHNUT ST 77074 #495-28-1976 L1979 **AN** *020 †05

KHALAF, Mohammad Nabeel. 1315 ST JOSEPH PKWY, STE 1703 77002 #875-01-1990 L2001 **NPM** *020 †55

KHALIFA, Ahmed Anwar H. 6411 FANNIN ST 77030 #915-07-1974 L1990 **OM PM** *020 †70

KHALIFEH, Ibrahim Mustafa. ■ 77030 #875-01-1999 L2005 **SP** *100 †50

KHALIL, Abraham Kazem. ■ 77030 #048-12-2006 **AN** *012

KHALIL, Kamal Ghaleb. 6410 FANNIN ST, STE 480 77030 #330-02-1961 L1975 **TS VS** *020 †85,90 ‡

KHALIL, Mohamed Ahmed. ■ 77289 #915-02-1969 L1977 **N** *071

KHALIL, Momtaz Ayoub. ■ 77025 #915-04-1963 **ORS** *050

KHALIL, Samia Nazir. 6431 FANNIN ST STE 5020, UNIV OF TX MED SCH - HOUST 77030 #915-02-1964 L1975 **AN** *020 †05

KHALIL, Sherif Kamal. 902 FROSTWOOD DR, HOUSTON EYE AND LASER 77024 #048-14-1999 L2003 **OPH** *020 †35

KHALILI TABRIZI, Hessam. ■ 77054 #517-01-1997 L2007 **FP** *012

KHALYL-MAWAD, Janine F. 7207 GESSNER DR, LABORATORY CORP OF AMERICA 77040 #605-02-1976 L1985 **DMP** *100 †50

KHAN, Abdul Hannan. 11301 FALLBROOK DR 77065 #160-01-1978 L1995 **PUD IM** *020

KHAN, Abdul-Jabbar Asim. 1415 LA CONCHA LN 77054 #704-20-1991 L1998 **NEP** *020 †20

KHAN, Adnan Ahmed. 1 HERMANN MUSEUM CIRCLE DR 77004 #004-01-2003 L2008 **PMM** *012

KHAN, Ahmad A. 1504 TAUB LOOP, BEN TAUB GENERAL HOSPITAL 77030 #010-01-2004 L2007 **IM** *100 †20

KHAN, Amer Ahmad. 7777 SOUTHWEST FWY, STE 304 77074 #038-44-1997 L2002 **NEP** *020 †20

KHAN, Amir M. 6431 FANNIN ST, UT HOUSTON MC/STE 3.234 77030 #704-25-1989 L2000 **NPM** *020 †55

KHAN, Asadullah. 4545 POST OAK PLACE DR, STE 130 77027 #704-25-1998 L2003 **IM** *020 †20

KHAN, Asma. ■ 77041 #704-16-1994 **FP** *012

KHAN, Ataur-Rehman Rizwan. 8830 LONG POINT RD, STE 401 77055 #704-21-1994 L2003 **CD** *020 †20

KHAN, Attiya Shaheen. 8830 LONG POINT RD, STE 401 77055 #704-06-1975 L1981 **CD IM** *020 †20

KHAN, Danish Muhammad. ■ 77025 #704-25-2003 **IM** *012

KHAN, Faraz Masood. 18220 TOMBALL PKWY, FL 4 77070 #704-25-1996 L2006 **IM** *020 †20

KHAN, Farheen. 6431 FANNIN ST, JJL #324 77030 #704-08-1992 L2004 **FM** *100 †18

KHAN, Gulam Murtuza. 8830 LONG POINT RD, STE 202 77055 #495-21-1975 L1996 **GP** *020

KHAN, Hana K. ■ 77040 #048-04-2006 **DR** *012

KHAN, Jessica Santiago. 8449 W BELLFORT ST, STE 140 77071 #748-02-1989 L1998 **IM ID** *020 †20

KHAN, Junaid Ahmad. 2050 SPACE PARK DR 77058 #704-02-1982 L2000 **IM** *020 †20

KHAN, Kashif Zafar. 9321 KIRBY DR 77054 #704-02-1993 L2007 **OM FM** *020 †18

KHAN, Laeeq Ahmad. 17202 RED OAK DR, STE 303 77090 #704-01-1964 L1976 **PD** *020 †55

KHAN, Mohammad Yousaf. 6410 FANNIN ST, STE 230 77030 #654-01-1998 L2006 **HO** *020 †20

KHAN, Muniba Masood. 1 BAYLOR PLZ, BAYLOR COLL OF MED 77030 #704-25-1999 **FM** *020

KHAN, Nasim Farhat. 8303 GULF FWY, STE 101 77017 #704-02-1961 L1983 **CHP P** *020

KHAN, Rashid. 1000 N POST OAK RD, STE G100 77055 #704-02-1988 L1998 **NEP** *020 †20

KHAN, Rashid Hasan. 1709 DRYDEN RD, STE 635 77030 #704-02-2001 L2006 **IM** *020 †20

KHAN, Rubina Fareed. 6677 ROOKIN ST 77074 #704-02-1987 L1994 **PD** *020 †55

KHAN, Salman A. 4407 YOAKUM BLVD, STE B 77006 #704-02-1987 L1994 **NEP** *020 †20

KHAN, Sardar Amir Daud. 714 FM 1960 RD W STE 201 77090 #704-01-1970 L1980 **GE** *020

KHAN, Shahab Abdurrehman. 1631 NORTH LOOP W, STE 100 77008 #704-01-1983 L2007 **HO** *020 †20

KHAN, Sonya. ■ 77089 #048-02-2006 **IM** *012

KHAN, Talat Ishaq. 1401 ST JOSEPH PKWY 77002 #704-20-1999 L2005 **AN** *020 †05

KHAN, Tareq Obaid. 6720 BERTNER ST 77030 #495-65-1975 L1981 **AN** *020 †05

KHAN, Ziad Umar. ■ 77025 #704-33-2005 **IM** *012

KHANDWALLA, Hashim Mohamm. 4545 POST OAK PLACE DR, STE 130 77027 #704-25-1998 L2003 **IM** *020 †20

KHAN-JALAL, Yasmeen S. 915 GESSNER RD, STE 585 77024 #048-14-1992 L1995 **OTO** *020 †45

KHANUM, Aida Zarina. 5001 NAVIGATION BLVD, EL CENTRO DE CORAZON 77011 #704-25-1998 L2004 **PD** *100 †55

KHARE, Kamayani. PO BOX 20708, UNIV TX MED SCH 77225 #039-01-2005 **N** *012

KHATER, Noha Ibrahim. PO BOX 20708 77225 #915-02-1996 **OPH** *100

KHATRI, Bhakti D. 1707 SUNSET BLVD, MEDICAL CLINIC OF HOUSTON, 77005 #048-13-1999 L2002 **IM** *020 †20

KHATTAK, Ashbala. PO BOX 20708, DIV OF OPHTHALMOLOGY 77225 #704-09-2002 **OPH** *012

KHAVARI, Rose. ■ 77021 #048-02-2005 **U** *012

KHAWAJA, Lubna Ubaid. 4545 POST OAK PLACE DR, STE 130 77027 #704-25-1991 L2002 **PD IM** *020 †55,20

KHAWLI, Fadi A. 920 FROSTWOOD DR, STE 620 77024 #605-01-1986 L1992 **PUD** *020 †20

KHERA, Harish Chandra. 7500 BEECHNUT ST STE 375 77074 #495-05-1963 L1975 **GS GP** *020 †85

KHERA, Mohit. ■ 77021 #048-13-2000 L2007 **U** *020

KHERADMAND, Farrah. 1 BAYLOR PLZ, STE 520B 77030 #010-01-1989 L2000 **IM** *020 †20

KHIN, Sanda. 1 BAYLOR PLZ 77030 #209-01-1995 L2006 **IMG** *100 †18

KHOKHAR, Ather Rafiq. 1140 WESTMONT DR, STE 320 77015 #021-05-1994 L1997 **NEP** *020 †20

KHOO, Andrew Kian Ming. 1515 HOLCOMBE BLVD 77030 #825-01-1987 **PS** *020

KHORSANDI, Mark Darius. 3726 DACOMA ST 77092 #011-75-1999, ▲ L2007 **HS** *020

KHOSHDEL, Abbas. 9105 N WAYSIDE DR 77028 #517-08-1976 L1994 **FM** *020 †18

KHOSLA, Uday Mohan. 1709 DRYDEN RD, STE 9.11 77030 #038-41-1999 L2001 **NEP** *020 †20

KHOURI, Issa F. 1515 HOLCOMBE BLVD, DIVISION OF CANCER MEDICIN 77030 #561-17-1983 L1990 **ON HEM** *050 †20

KHOURY, Alexander Fuad. ■ 77005 #605-01-1986 L1990 **CD IM** *020 †20

KHOURY, Mary Ann. 820 GESSNER RD, STE 1200 77024 #039-01-1987 L1990 **OM** *020

KHRAISH, Gina Hanna. 1415 LA CONCHA LN, TION ASSOCIATES, PA, KIDNE 77054 #048-04-1999 L2002 **NEP** *020 †20

KHUDDUS, Umme Hani. 1 BAYLOR PLZ, DEPT FM 77030 #496-21-2000 **FP** *012

KHURANA, Hema. 6565 FANNIN ST M227 77030 #496-03-2002 **PTH** *012

KIBERT, Leonard Geo. 5990 AIRLINE DR, STE 160 77076 #041-12-1984 L1992 **IM** *020 †20

KIBIRIGE, Mustapha. 2000 CRAWFORD ST, STE 842 77002 #034-01-1993 L1999 **OPH** *020

KIDD, Thornton Lenoir. 1140 CLEAR LAKE CITY BLVD, STE A 77062 #048-02-1957 L1957 **AI PDA** *020 †55,03

KIDDER, Benjamin Glenn. ■ 77027 #027-01-2005 **N** *012

KIEBACK, Dirk G. 6620 MAIN ST, STE 1450 77030 #409-12-1980 **GO GYN** *020

KIELHOFNER, Marcia Ann. 6624 FANNIN ST STE 1410 77030 #028-46-1984 L1989 **ID IM** *020 †20

KIENSTRA, Andrew Joseph. 6621 FANNIN ST, MC1481 77030 #016-45-1996 L2000 **PD** *020 †55

KIENSTRA, Kirsten Anderso. 6621 FANNIN ST WT6-104, NEONATOLOGY, W TOWER 6 FLR 77030 #028-02-1997 L2003 **NPM** *020 †55

KIES, Merrill Stephen. 1515 HOLCOMBE BLVD, BOX 432 77030 #016-43-1973 L1978 **ON IM** *020 †20

KIKUCHI, Kerry Lloyd. 211 HIGHLAND CROSS DR 77073 #035-09-2000 L2004 **EM** *020 †16

KILBURN, Lindsay Baker. 6621 FANNIN ST, MC 3-3320 77030 #051-07-2001 L2007 **PHO** *100 †55

KILIC, Gokhan. ■ 77030 #902-07-1990 L2008 **OBG** *020 †30

KILLEFER, Heidi Noelle. ■ 77054 #026-08-2005 **PD** *012

KILLIAN, James Mahony. 6501 FANNIN ST MS 302 77030 #056-06-1958 L1969 **N** *020 †75

KILLINGER, Robert Peter. 5757 WOODWAY DR, STE 200 77057 #051-01-1962 L1969 **PD OS** *020 †55

KILLORAN, Peter Vincent. ■ 77004 #032-01-2007 **AN** *012

KILPATRICK, Charles C. 5656 KELLEY ST, LYNDON B. JOHNSON HOSPITAL 77026 #048-14-1999 L2003 **OBG** *020 †30

KIM, Angela. 1515 HOLCOMBE BLVD # 443, UT MD ANDERSON CANCER CENT 77030 #005-14-1994 L2004 **OPH** *020 †35

KIM, Cheor Jung. 150 W PARKER RD, STE 106 77076 #583-09-1970 L1974 **N FM** *071

KIM, Christopher Yongku. 6431 FANNIN ST, UTHSC DIV OF CARDIOLOGY 77030 #038-41-2004 L2008 **CD** *012

KIM, Chung Yul. 17150 EL CAMINO REAL 77058 #583-02-1963 L1975 **AN** *071

KIM, Daniel Juhun. 1 BAYLOR PLZ, DEPT OF ANESTH SM1003 77030 #048-12-2002 L2006 **AN** *020 †05

KIM, Daniel Yul. 211 HIGHLAND CROSS DR #275 77073 #048-02-1995 L1998 **IM** *020 †20

KIM, Dong Hoon. 6410 FANNIN ST STE 7.146, DEPT OF NEUROSURGERY 77030 #583-02-1977 L1985 **PD** *020 †55

KIM, Dong Soo. 6500 NORTH FWY STE 116 77076 #583-09-1967 L1982 **IM NEP** *020 †20

KIM, Douglas Jhoongoo. ■ 77096 #038-43-2004 L2007 **PTH** *012

KIM, Edward O. ■ 77025 #041-12-1999 **IM** *100

KIM, Edward Sanghyun. 1515 HOLCOMBE BLVD 77030 #016-06-1996 L1998 **ON** *020 †20

KIM, Edward Thomas. 1709 DRYDEN RD STE 550, BCM FACULTY CENTER 77030 #016-42-2007 **IM** *020 ‡

KIM, Eugene S. 6621 FANNIN ST, MC -CCC/650 77030 #035-01-1996 L2005 **PDS** *020 †85

KIM, Euishin Edmund. 1515 HOLCOMBE BLVD, UNIT 1264 77030 #583-02-1966 L1981 **NM R** *020 †80,28

KIM, Gyu Wha. 6322 AIRLINE DR 77076 #583-09-1972 L1978 **FM** *020 †18

KIM, Han-Seob. 1504 TAUB LOOP, BEN TAUB HOSP 77030 #583-02-1959 L1971 **ATP PCP** *020 †50

KIM, Hee Joon. ■ 77054 #048-14-2006 **OPH** *012

KIM, Hyung Wook. 6518 COTORRA COVE CT 77041 #048-15-2002 L2005 *020

KIM, In Gon. 5135 ALDINE MAIL RD, STE 100 77039 #583-09-1972 L1977 **FM** *020 †18

KIM, Jeffrey Joongmyung. 6621 FANNIN ST, MC19345-C 77030 #016-11-1999 L2006 **PDC** *100 †55

KIM, Jeri. 1515 HOLCOMBE BLVD, GU MEDICAL ONCOLOGY-BOX 42 77030 #005-06-1993 L1999 **ON** *020 †20

KIM, Jin. 6720 BERTNER ST 77030 #048-02-1996 L2000 **EM** *020 †16

KIM, Joanne Y. 925 GESSNER RD, STE 480 77024 #048-13-1992 L1993 **N** *020 †75

KIM, Joseph D. ■ 77057 #024-05-1997 L2000 **EM** *100

KIM, Joy Young. 1709 DRYDEN RD, BAYLOR COLLEGE OF MEDICINE 77030 #051-04-2007 **OBG** *012

KIM, Kevin Bumsoo. 1515 HOLCOMBE BLVD BOX 430, UT M.D. ANDERSON CANCER CT 77030 #016-11-1995 L2002 **ON** *020 †20

KIM, Michael D. 6440 HILLCROFT ST, STE 100 77081 #583-03-1965 L1978 **FM** *020 †18

KIM, Poong. 902 FROSTWOOD DR STE 178 77024 #583-02-1972 L1984 **OBG** *020

KIM, Richard. 6431 FANNIN ST, MSB 4-268 77030 #023-01-1998 L2003 **U** *020 †95

KIM, Rira Jun. ■ 77077 #048-16-2004 L2004 **PD** *020

KIM, Si Whang. ■ 77024 #583-02-1959 **U** *020

KIM, Stella Kyungmee. 1515 HOLCOMBE BLVD, UNIT 441 77030 #024-01-1996 L2003 **OPH** *020 †35

KIM, Tae Whang. 6621 FANNIN ST, STE A300 77030 #010-03-1989 L1998 **AN** *020 †05

KIM, Tony. 2411 FOUNTAIN VIEW DR # 20, GREATER HOUSTON ANESTHESIO 77057 #033-06-1997 L2001 **AN** *020 †05

KIM, Yong Sik. 818 RINGOLD ST, ACRES HOME HEALTH CENTER 77088 #583-12-1985 L2005 **FM** *020 †18

KIM, Young Il. 12121 RICHMOND AVE, STE 101 77082 #583-02-1959 L1975 **CD IM** *020 †20

KIM, Young Sun. 150 W PARKER RD, STE 106 77076 #583-09-1970 L1974 **GP AN** *071

KIMBALL, William Brice, Jr. 6565 FANNIN ST MS D281, C/O THE METHODIST HOSPITAL 77030 #048-02-1969 L1969 **DR** *020 †80

KIMBROUGH, Richard Lee. 2855 GRAMERCY ST 77025 #048-02-1971 L1971 **OPH** *020 †35

KIMYAIASADI, Arash. 7515 MAIN ST, STE 240 77030 #023-07-1999 L2003 **D DS** *020 †15

KINALSKA-SKRZYPCZAK, M. 4101 GREENBRIAR ST, STE 100 77098 #759-11-1981 L1986 **PD** *020 †55

KINCEY, Jordana Michelle. ■ 77024 #047-07-2007 **OBG** *012

KING, Brent Russell. 6431 FANNIN ST 6.270, DEPT OF EMERGENCY MEDICINE 77030 #048-14-1983 L1983 **EM** *020 †55,16

KING, Carroll Joan. 1515 HOLCOMBE BLVD, UNIT 87 77030 #016-06-1993 L1999 **CCP** *020 †55

KING, Christopher Michael. ■ 77035 #048-04-2004 **N** *012

KING, Daniel Albert. ■ 77018 #048-04-1982 L1983 **AN** *020 †05

KING, David Ellroy. 6565 FANNIN ST # D281 77030 #048-04-1983 L1984 **RNR R** *020 †80

KING, Frances Allene. 7600 FANNIN ST 77054 #028-02-1978 L1982 **SO GS** *071 †85

KING, Gloria S. ■ 77071 #048-02-1997 L1998 **FM** *020 †18

KING, Harry Richard. 4200 PORTSMOUTH ST 77027 #016-06-1961 L1991 **TS VS** *020 †85,90

KING, Pamela Marie. 4727 WESTHEIMER RD 77027 #048-04-1978 *100

KING-CASAS, Katherine Yud. 6621 FANNIN ST, STE A-170 77030 #028-02-2003 L2006 **PDI** *012 †55

KINNER, Beatriz Morales. ■ 77057 #649-01-1960 L1975 **PTH** *062 †50

KINTNER, Katherine Marie. ■ 77054 #048-02-2008 *012

KIRBY, Henry Burrell. ■ 77030 #048-02-1965 L1965 **IMG ID** *071 †20

KIRBY, Robert Gene. 711 LOUISIANA ST 77002 #048-13-1983 L1987 **OPH** *020 †35

KIRBY, Stella L. 2700 WOODLAND PARK DR 77082 #048-14-1994 L2003 **IM** *020 †20

KIRBY, Wendy L. BAYLOR COLL OF MED, DEPT PSYCH 77030 #048-04-1995 L1996 **CHP** *020 †75

KIRK, John Wm. 6560 FANNIN ST STE 1654, HOUSTON CARDIOVASCULAR ASS 77030 #023-07-1971 L1983 **CD IM** *020 †20

KIRKBY, Valerie St Claire. 2727 W HOLCOMBE BLVD, UT HSC/DEPT OF RADIOLOGY 77025 #010-03-1986 L1992 **DR** *020 †80

KIRKHAM, James Earl. 908 TOWN AND COUNTRY BLVD, STE 650 77024 #048-04-1955 L1955 **P** *020

KIRKHAM, Stuart G. 6550 FANNIN ST STE 2625 77030 #143-03-1990 **HS** *100

KIRKLAND, John L, III. 6701 FANNIN ST 77030 #036-01-1968 L1975 **PDE** *050 †55

KIRKLAND, Rebecca G Trent. 6621 FANNIN ST, STE 1540 77030 #036-07-1968 L1975 **PD END** *020 †55

KIRKPATRICK, Joel Brian. 6565 FANNIN ST # 205 77030 #028-02-1962 L1972 **NP ATP** *020 †50

KIRSHON, Brian. 7900 FANNIN ST, STE 2600 77054 #836-01-1980 L1985 **OBG MFM** *020 †30

KISER, Charler R. ■ 77025 #048-15-2000 L2004 **FM** *020

KISH, Erin Carroll. ■ 77009 #047-06-2003 L2008 **ADL** *012 †55

KISHIGAMI, Shinobu. 7737 SOUTHWEST FWY, RES P 77074 #572-14-2002 **FP** *012

KISS, George Michael. 5656 KELLEY ST, LBJ-EC930006 77026 #035-09-1993 L2004 **EM** *020 †16

KIT, Malon. ■ 77024 #048-02-1977 L1977 *020

KITAGAWA, Seiji. 6621 FANNIN ST MC, TEXAS CHILDREN'S HOSP 77030 #572-20-1974 L1978 **PD GE** *020 †55

KITE, Lisa Lea. 3222 RICE BLVD 77005 #048-02-2002 L2004 **EM GP** *100

KITTEN, Clifford M. 830 FM 1960 RD W, STE 3 77090 #048-15-1975 L1975 **TS GS** *020 †85,90

KJOME, Kimberly Leigh. 1300 MOURSUND ST 77030 #048-14-2004 L2007 **P** *012

KLEBUC, Michael John A. 6560 FANNIN ST STE 300 77030 #068-01-1993 L2000 **PS** *020 †65

KLEIMAN, Neal Stephen. 6565 FANNIN ST, F-1090 77030 #035-01-1981 L1982 **CD** *020 †20

KLEIN, Harvey Lynn. 6560 FANNIN ST STE 1234 77030 #048-02-1968 L1968 **U** *020 †95

KLEIN, Ira. 10565 KATY FWY, STE 305 77024 #035-19-1970 L1975 **GE IM** *020

KLEIN, Mervyn Joel. 1111 AUGUSTA DR, C/O KELSEY SEYBOLD CLINIC 77057 #038-41-1966 L1967 **IM PUD** *020 †20

KLEIN, Milton Saml. 6400 FANNIN ST 77030 #005-18-1972 L1979 **CD IM** *020 †20

KLEIN, Nora Joan. 906 WAYSIDE DR 77011 #035-46-1970 L1983 **PD ID** *020 †55

KLEINERMAN, Eugenie Sue. 1515 HOLCOMBE BLVD, BOX 173 77030 #036-07-1975 L1984 **IG PHO** *010 †55

KLEINMAN, Isaac. 3701 KIRBY DR, STE 600 77098 #048-12-1955 L1955 **FM EM** *071 †16,18

KLEINMAN, Michael H. 7500 BEECHNUT ST, STE 240 77074 #048-12-1983 L1983 **GS SO** *020 †85 ‡

KLEINMANN, Guy. ■ 77025 #550-03-1992 *100

KLEPPE, Soledad. 1 BAYLOR PLZ 77030 #132-07-1996 **MG** *100

KLEYNERMAN, Vladimir E. 2411 FOUNTAIN VIEW DR #200 77057 #913-21-1968 L1996 **AN** *020 †05

KLIMA, Marcella. ■ 77030 #286-02-1959 L1970 **ATP DMP** *071 †50

KLIMA, Tomas. 6720 BERTNER ST 77030 #286-13-1962 L1969 **PTH PD** *071 †50

KLINE, Allen Haber. 3838 HILLCROFT ST, STE 215 77057 #048-04-1955 L1955 **PD** *020 †55

KLINE, Mark W. 6621 FANNIN ST, CCC 1210 77030 #048-04-1981 L1981 **ID PD** *040 †55

KLISH, William John. 6701 FANNIN ST, GI HEP & NUTRITION 77030 #056-05-1967 L1975 **PG NTR** *040 †55

KLOPCIC, Corrie Elizabeth. 6621 FANNIN ST, DEPT OF PEDIATRICS 77030 #056-05-2004 L2007 **PEM** *012 †55

KLUCZNIK, Richard Paul. 6565 FANNIN ST, MS 204 77030 #024-07-1983 L1992 **RNR R** *020 †80

KNAFO, Elizabeth. 1313 HERMANN DR 77004 #067-02-1990 L1998 **FM** *020 †18

KNAPP, Foster Anthony. ■ 77006 #016-06-1974 L1978 **DR** *100

KNAPP, Geo Stanford, III. 327 KICKERILLO DR 77079 #047-06-1961 L1972 **AN IM** *020

KNAPP, John Andrew. ■ 77024 #048-04-1953 L1953 **PD OS** *071 †55

KNEITZ, Joel Steve. 6624 FANNIN ST, STE 1240 77030 #048-14-1995 L1996 **MPD** *020 †20

KNIGHT, Louis Elmer, Jr. 17200 RED OAK DR STE 203 77099 #048-12-1975 L1975 **OBG GYN** *020 †30

KNIGHT, Richard James. 6550 FANNIN ST, SM 1661 A 77030 #021-01-1983 L1989 **GS TTS** *020 †85

KNIGHT, Vernon. 29 LANA LN 77027 #024-01-1943 L1966 **ID IM** *050 †20

KNIGHT, William Powell. 18220 STATE HIGHWAY 249 77070 #048-04-1969 L1969 **AN** *071 †05

KNOLLE, Jon Warren. 5656 KELLEY ST, DEPT OB 77026 #021-01-1963 L1964 **OBG** *071 †30

KNOWLES, William Roy. ■ 77024 #048-04-1954 L1954 **D** *071 †15

KNOX, Daryl Keith. 1502 TAUB LOOP, NEURO-PSYCHIATRIC CENTER 77030 #056-05-1978 L1980 **P** *020 †75

KNUDSON, Edward C. 10912 EAST FWY 77029 #011-03-1973 L1976 **R** *040 †80

KO, Tien C. 6431 FANNIN ST, MSB 4-608 77030 #005-14-1986 L1993 **GS** *020 †85

KOBAYASHI, Katsuhiro. 1515 HOLCOMBE BLVD U 77030 #572-67-1993 L2007 **VIR** *100

KOBER, Dana Lee. 1 BAYLOR PLZ, BAYLOR COLL OF MED 77030 #028-46-2002 L2006 **CHP** *012

KOBS, Darcey Gus, III. 5850 ROGERDALE RD, QUEST DIAGNOSTICS 77072 #048-02-1989 L1990 **PTH GP** *020 †50

KOCH, Douglas Donald. 6550 FANNIN ST, STE 1501 77030 #024-01-1977 L1978 **OPH** *020 †35

KOCH, Elizabeth Rose. ■ 77025 #019-02-1981 L1982 **DR** *020 †80

KOCH, Krista Diane. ■ 77096 #048-15-2007 **OBG** *012

KOCH, Paul C. ■ 77023 #035-19-1978 L1979 **AM EM** *020

KOCH, Stephen Matthew. 6431 FANNIN MSMB 5.020 77030 #003-01-1981 L1991 **IM** *020 †20

KOCHAR, Harmohinder Singh. 1740 W 27TH ST, STE 110 77008 #495-03-1978 L1991 **IM PUD** *020 †20

KOCHIS, George Paul. 5300 SAN JACINTO ST STE 12 77004 #025-07-1948 L1977 **PYA P** *020 †75

KOCIENIEWSKA, Danuta K. 6431 FANNIN ST 5.020 77030 #759-01-1983 L2002 **AN** *020

KODALI, Udayini. 275 LANTERN BEND DR, STE 200 77090 #495-11-1997 L2005 **GE** *020 †20

KODURI, Kalyani. 2002 HOLCOMBE BLVD, VETERANS ADMINISTRATION 77030 #495-21-1988 L2002 **IM** *020 †20

KODURI, Vijay Kumar. 2616 S LOOP W, STE 430 77054 #495-21-1982 L1997 **IM** *020 †20

KOECK, William K. ■ 77005 #048-14-2002 L2008 **OP** *012

KOENIG, Mary Kay. ■ 77025 #422-01-2002 **CHN** *100

KOEPPEN, Hartmut. ■ 77005 #409-05-1984 L1990 **HMP** *050 †50

KOERNER, Michael Matthias. 6620 MAIN ST STE 11B06 77030 #409-25-1981 **CD CCM** *020

KOGELNIK, Horst Dieter. ■ 77025 #154-07-1967 **RO R** *011

KOGUTT, Marvin Stuart. 6621 FANNIN ST, TEXAS CHILDREN'S HOSPITAL 77030 #048-02-1967 L1967 **PDR DR** *020 †80

KOHEN, Refail. 77071 #902-01-1947 L1962 **DR** *100

KOHUTIAK, Vladimir. ■ 77005 #759-02-1931 **P** *071

KOKA, Vijay Kishore. 8876 GULF FWY, STE 215 77017 #495-27-1995 L2004 **NEP** *020 †20

KOKANOVIC, Obrad Stevan. ■ 77025 #056-05-2005 **IM** *012

KOKKINIS, Hippocrates. 8951 RUTHBY ST STE 9 77061 #418-01-1953 L1959 **GYN** *071 †30

KOLEY, Grace Kimberly. 6431 FANNIN ST, DEPARTMENT OF RADIOLOGY 77030 #030-06-1987 L1994 **IM** *020 †80

KOLIMAS, Robert Jos. 2002 HOLCOMBE BLVD # 127 77030 #016-11-1981 L1982 **N CN** *020 †75

KOLLE, Bracken S. 2411 FOUNTAIN VIEW DR, STE 200 77057 #048-04-2004 L2006 **AN** *012

KOLLER, Charles Asa. 3774 PLUMB ST 77005 #038-40-1973 L1986 **HEM ON** *050 †20

KOLLER, Kim Livingston. 910 LOUISIANA ST, STE 1014 77002 #051-01-1982 L1993 **OM IM** *020 †20,70

KOLOMEYEVSKAYA, Nonna Vla. 1709 DRYDEN RD, BAYLOR COLLEGE OF MEDICINE 77030 #035-03-2007 **OBG** *012

KOLPAKCHI, Anna L. 2002 HOLCOMBE BLVD, VETERAN ADMIN MED CTR 77030 #913-15-1975 L1986 **IM IMG** *020 †20

KOLSTAD, Kaare, Jr. 6550 FANNIN ST, STE 2500 77030 #008-02-1992 L1998 **OSM** *020 †40

KOLTZ, David A. ■ 77096 #048-12-1999 L2008 **RNR** *100 †80

KOMAKI, Ritsuko. 1515 HOLCOMBE BLVD, BOX 97 77030 #572-36-1969 L1992 **RO** *020 †80

KOMANDURI, Krishna V. 1515 HOLCOMBE BLVD, BMT BOX 900 77030 #026-04-1991 L2003 **IM** *020 †20

KOMORN, Robert Melvin. 6560 FANNIN ST STE 1726 77030 #025-01-1964 L1970 **OTO HNS** *020 †45

KONE, Bhavani P S S. 2411 FOUNTAIN VIEW DR, STE 200 77057 #495-57-1991 L2005 **CD** *020 †05

KONES, Richard. ■ 77054 #035-19-1964 L1969 **IM CD** *071

KONG, Amanda L. ■ 77098 #043-01-2002 L2003 **GS** *100 †85

KONG, Keng He. ■ 77025 #825-01-1986 **PM** *100

KONG, Lingkun. 6565 FANNIN ST M227 77030 #243-44-1988 **SP** *012

KONOPLEV, Sergej Naumovit. 1515 HOLCOMBE BLVD, UNIT 072 77030 #913-01-1990 L2007 **HMP** *100 †50

KONTOYIANNIS, Dimitrios P. 1515 HOLCOMBE BLVD, BOX 402 77030 #418-01-1989 L1998 **ID** *020 †20

KONZEN, Benedict S. 1515 HOLCOMBE BLVD, BOX 8 77030 #038-43-1993 L2001 **PM N** *020 †60

KOO, Hoonmo Lee. ■ 77054 #048-14-2000 L2004 **ID** *012 †20

KOO, Suzzane Jean. 921 GESSNER RD STE 226, METROWEST ANESTHESIA CARE 77024 #019-02-2000 L2007 **AN** *020 †05

KOPAS, Lisa Mona. ■ 77025 #048-04-2003 L2005 **PCC** *012 †20

KOPECKY, Charles R. 2260 W HOLCOMBE BLVD # 200 77030 #048-14-1985 L1986 **P PMM** *020 †75

KOPEL, Allyson Jones. 5110 BUFFALO SPEEDWAY, STE 200 77005 #048-14-2001 L2006 **D** *020 †15

KOPETZ, Edmund Scott. 1515 HOLCOMBE BLVD, UNIT 426 77030 #023-07-2001 L2004 **ON** *020 †20

KOPINITZ, Edward Albert. 2615 WAUGH DR # 600 77006 #048-02-1965 L1965 **AN** *071

KORAB, Yamen Saade. 3701 KIRBY DR, STE 600 77098 #605-01-2003 L2007 **FM** *100

KORBLING, Martin Johannes. 1515 HOLCOMBE BLVD, ANDERSON CNCR CTR BOX 68 77030 #409-10-1974 L1993 **HEM ON** *020

KORHONEN, Matti Olavi. 12121 RICHMOND AVE STE 215 77082 #374-03-1967 L1980 **OBG PTH** *020 †50,30

KORMEIER, Lucy Caudill. 2500 FONDREN RD 77063 #048-14-1989 L1990 **END IM** *020 †20

KORNBLAU, Steven Mitchell. 1515 HOLCOMBE BLVD, UNI TX MD ANDERSON CAN CTR 77030 #048-02-1985 L1986 **HEM ON** *050 †20

KORNGUTH, David Gregory. 1515 HOLCOMBE BLVD, ANDERSON CANC 77030 #024-05-2001 L2005 **RO** *100 †80

KORNGUTH, Linda Junjeh. ■ 77096 #024-05-2001 L2005 **FM** *100 †18

KOROMA, Dennis Matthew S. ■ 77072 #902-05-1992 **PD** *100

KORSAH, Kenneth Nana Amu. 5420 DASHWOOD DR, STE 202 77081 #409-25-1968 L1976 **OBG** *020 †30

KORTH, Juliana Milhari. PO BOX 20708 77225 #187-87-1998 **FM** *100

KOSAKI, Kenjiro. ■ 77054 #572-20-1989 **PD MG** *100 †19

KOSHMAN, Robert Wm. 915 GESSNER RD, STE 560 77024 #060-01-1970 L1982 **ORS** *020

KOSHY, Santhosh K G. 1504 TAUB LOOP, CARDIOLOGY; BTGH 77030 #495-31-1991 L2006 **CD** *100 †20 ‡

KOSHY, Sheeba. 1515 HOLCOMBE BLVD, -UNIT 429 77030 #024-05-1999 L2002 **ON** *100 †20

KOSIR, Roman. ■ 77018 #957-03-1997 *100

KOSKINEN, Deborah Lee. 6621 FANNIN ST 77030 #041-07-1982 L1987 **PD** *020

KOSOY, Jerome. 7505 FANNIN ST, STE 300 77054 #041-02-1964 L1969 **OTO FPS** *071 †45

KOSRIRUKVONGS, Panida. 6411 FANNIN ST 77030 #891-02-1979 **OPH** *100

KOSTEN, Thomas Richard. 2002 HOLCOMBE BLVD # 110R, RESEARCH (151) 77030 #035-20-1977 L2007 **P** *050 †75

KOSURI, Murali Mohan. 9105 N WAYSIDE DR, SETTEGAST HEALTH CENTER 77028 #495-57-1970 L1979 **FM EM** *020 †18 ‡

KOTHARI, Amit Jagdish. ■ 77077 #024-07-2007 **IM** *012

KOTHARI, Pulin S. ■ 77077 #048-13-1996 L1997 **PTH** *020 †50

KOTHARI, Shirish M. ■ 77024 #495-22-1963 L1973 **DR RO** *071 †80

KOTHARI, Sunil. 1333 MOURSUND ST, E103 77030 #048-14-1995 L1996 **PM** *020 †50

KOTHARI, Usha Dilip. 7040 LAWNDALE ST A, LAWNDALE PED CLINIC 77023 #496-07-1971 L1980 **PD GP** *100

KOTT, Edward Tyrrell. 7207 GESSNER DR, LABORATORY CORP OF AMERICA 77040 #048-14-1975 L1975 **PTH PCP** *020 †50

KOTT, Marylee Mueller. 6431 FANNIN ST 2.270, UNIV OF TEXAS MEDICAL SCHO 77030 #048-14-1977 L1978 **ATP PCP** *020 †50

KOTT, Sarah T. ■ 77030 #048-14-2006 **PTH** *012

KOVACEV, Ted Armstrong. 1919 LA BRANCH ST 77002 #422-01-2005 **GS** *012

KOVACS, Julia Ann. 1213 HERMANN DR, STE 430 77004 #003-01-1995 L1997 **IM** *020 †20

KOVAL, Michael S. ■ 77054 #048-14-2008 *012

KOVANCI, Ertug. 6550 FANNIN ST STE 801 77030 #902-10-1992 L2004 *020 †30

KOVITZ, Craig Adam. 18100 SAINT JOHN DR, STE 320 77058 #035-47-1997 L1998 **ON** *020 †20

KOWALSKI, Alicia M. 1220 HOLCOMBE BLVD, BOX 1243 77030 #048-14-1998 L1998 **AN** *020

KOYYALAGUNTA, Dhana L. 1400 HOLCOMBE BLVD, U.T. M.D. ANDERSON CANCER 77030 #495-01-1986 L2000 **AN** *020 †05

KOZAK, Jeffrey Alan. 7401 MAIN ST 77030 #048-04-1982 L1983 **ORS** *020 †40

KOZAR, Rosemary Ann. 6431 FANNIN ST 4-284, UNIV OF TX HOUSTON 77030 #041-13-1986 L1988 **GS CCS** *020 †85

KRAFT, Irvin A. 6720 BERTNER ST 77030 #035-19-1949 L1957 **P CHP** *020 †75

KRAINAK, Jacquelyn Rose. ■ 77030 #048-14-2008 *012

KRAJCA, Justin Ashley. ■ 77054 #048-14-2008 *012

KRAJCER, Zvonimir. 6624 FANNIN ST, STE 2780 77030 #957-01-1970 L1976 **IM** *020 †20

KRAJEWSKI, Kenneth John. 2800 S MACGREGOR WAY 77021 #030-06-1976 L1982 **P** *020 †75

KRAKAUR, Richard B. ■ 77056 #035-01-1948 L1958 **PTH CLP** *071 †50

KRAMER, Donald Louis. 4120 SOUTHWEST FWY STE 230 77027 #041-02-1981 L1994 **AN PME** *020 †05

KRAMER, Larry Allen. 6431 FANNIN ST 2100, DEPT OF RADIOLOGY/MEDICAL 77030 #016-11-1985 L1990 **DR** *020 †80

KRAMER, Stephen James. 5847 SAN FELIPE ST STE 200 77057 #051-04-1967 L1973 **P** *020 †75

KRANCE, Robert Allen. 1102 BATES AVE, STE 1120 77030 #016-43-1970 L1998 **HEM PD** *020 †55

KRASKO, Anatoli N. 909 FROSTWOOD DR, STE 302 77024 #913-98-1983 L2003 **PCC** *020 †20

KRATSCHMER, Robert C, III. 2707 FERNDALE ST 77098 #048-15-1999 L2002 **PS HS** *020 †65

KRAUS, Gary Edward. 12121 RICHMOND AVE, STE 324 77082 #035-48-1986 L2004 **NS** *020 †25

KRAUSE, James Harold. 3400 BISSONNET ST, STE 220 77005 #039-01-1958 L1964 **OPH** *020

KRAUSE, James Michael. 1140 CYPRESS STATION DR, STE 200 77090 #038-40-1972 L1975 **IM** *020 †20

KRAUTER, Susan Elaine. 1905 HOLCOMBE BLVD 77030 #039-01-1983 L1998 **IM PLM** *020 †20

KRAVITZ, Seth Paul. 18220 TOMBALL PKWY, STE 400 77070 #005-02-1980 L1983 **PD** *020 †55

KRAY, Kenneth T. 1140 CLEAR LAKE CITY BLVD, STE A 77062 #016-11-1976 L1987 **AI PDA** *020 †55,03

KREBS, Michael A. 8945 LONG POINT RD STE 123 77055 #041-01-1972 L1978 **PM OM** *020 †60

KREIDIEH, Imad Abdallah. ■ 77082 #915-04-1981 *020

KREINER, Laura Ann. ■ 77070 #048-14-2008 *012

KREMER, Ronald Henry. ■ 77030 #003-01-1976 L1977 **EM** *020 †16

KREMER, Wolf Peter. ■ 77030 #409-22-2002 L2006 **ACA** *012

KREML, Stephanie. ■ 77005 #048-04-2004 L2008 **GS** *012

KREUZER, Stefan Werner. 909 FROSTWOOD DR STE 251 77024 #048-13-1995 L1998 **ORS** *020 †40

KRIDEL, Russell Wm Hayes. 6655 TRAVIS ST STE 900 77030 #038-41-1975 L1976 **FPS OTO** *020 †45 ‡

KRIEZELMAN, Justin David. ■ 77020 #550-02-2002 L2003 **EM** *012

KRISEMAN, Yana Leah. ■ 77056 #048-04-2007 **TY** *012

KRISHNA, Chandan. ■ 77058 #048-02-2006 **NS** *012

KRISHNA, Linda L. ■ 77005 #039-01-1992 L1995 **FM** *020 †18

KRISHNA, Sistla Bala. 7737 SOUTHWEST FWY, STE 805 77074 #495-21-1973 L1980 **IM IMG** *020 †20 ‡

KRISHNAMURTHY, Barathi. 6431 FANNIN ST 308, UNIV OF TEXAS MED SCH 77030 #496-28-1999 **FP** *012

KRISHNAMURTHY, Rajesh. 6621 FANNIN ST 2-2521, RADIOLOGY DEPARTMENT 77030 #495-16-1993 L2003 **PDR** *020 †80

KRISHNAMURTHY, Savitri. 1515 HOLCOMBE BLVD, DEPT CYTOPATHOLOGY BOX 053 77030 #495-02-1986 L1999 **SP** *020 †50

KRISHNAN, Lee Ann. 9 E GREENWAY PLZ, STE 2950 77046 #048-12-1993 L1999 **FOP PTH** *062 †20

KRISHNAN, Ramesh. 915 GESSNER RD STE 720 77024 #048-12-1993 L1999 **U** *020 †95

KRISHNAN, Sunil. 1515 HOLCOMBE BLVD, UNIT 097 77030 #495-27-1995 L2004 **IM** *020 †20,80

KRISHNAN, Venkataraman. ■ 77096 #495-38-1987 **AI** *020 †55

KRISTIANSEN, Sonja B. 9055 KATY FWY STE 450 77024 #048-15-1989 L1990 **REN** *020 †30

KROGER, Edward John, II. 1301 MCKINNEY ST, STE 5100 77010 #048-12-1985 L1986 **IM LM** *020 †20

KROLL, Michael Howard. 2002 HOLCOMBE BLVD, VA MEDICAL CENTER 77030 #035-20-1981 L1990 **IM HEM** *050 †20

KROLLS, Tanya Kristine. ■ 77025 #048-14-2007 **P** *012

KRONBERG, Esta Lynn. 7500 BEECHNUT ST STE 228 77074 #048-13-1981 L1981 **D** *020 †15

KRONFORST, Kenny Delbarco. 6431 FANNIN ST, SCHOOL A 77030 #048-14-2006 L2007 **PD** *012

KRONOWITZ, Steven Jerome. 1515 HOLCOMBE BLVD BOX 62, MD ANDERSON CANCER CTR-PLA 77030 #011-02-1992 L2000 **PS** *020 †65,85

KRUCKE, Gus William. 6431 FANNIN ST 1.122, U OF TX MEDICAL SCHOOL 77030 #001-06-1988 L1991 **IM** *020 †16,20

KRUSE, Gina Rae. ■ 77054 #048-04-2008 *012

KRYGIER, Jeffrey Edward. ■ 77030 #010-02-2002 L2007 **OMO** *012

KUANG, Jo K. 710 FM 1960 RD W 77090 #244-02-1968 L1976 **AN** *020 †05

KUBAN, Deborah Ann. 1515 HOLCOMBE BLVD # 1202, DEPT RADIATION ONCOL. 77030 #012-01-1981 L2002 **RO** *020 †80

KUBRUSLY, Luiz Ferando. PO BOX 20334 77225 #187-76-1979 **TS** *020

KUDISCH, Marc. 7777 SOUTHWEST FWY, STE 716 77074 #561-17-1984 L1992 **GE IM** *020 †20

KUEHNLE, Ingrid. 1102 BATES AVE STE 1120 77030 #409-10-1993 L1999 **PHO** *020 †55

KUERER, Henry Mark. 1515 HOLCOMBE BLVD, BOX 106 77030 #035-08-1992 L1997 **SO** *020 †85

KUHL, Kristine R. ■ 77007 #048-14-2005 **IM** *012

KUHN, George T. 1315 ST JOSEPH PKWY, STE 1202 77002 #048-14-1982 L1983 **OBG GP** *020 †30

KULIEV, Agadadash. 10575 KATY FWY, STE 435 77024 #913-19-1994 L2005 **IM** *020 †20 ‡

KULKARNI, Madan Vasant. 810 PEAKWOOD DR, STE 107 77090 #496-38-1973 L1986 **DR NM** *020 †28,80

KULKARNI, Pratibha R. 902 FROSTWOOD DR STE 293 77024 #495-53-1979 L1992 **IM** *020 †20

KUMAR, Kasturi Aswani. 233 W PARKER RD 77076 #495-27-1973 L1978 **N** *071 †75
KUMAR, Kumuda. 6411 FANNIN ST 77030 #496-39-2002 **FM** *100
KUMAR, Meena. ■ 77025 #048-02-2007 **GS** *012
KUMAR, Rajeev. 2424 W HOLCOMBE BLVD, STE 204 77030 #068-01-1991 L2005 **N** *020 †75
KUMAR, Ramon N. 6720 BERTNER ST 77030 #048-12-2004 L2007 **CD** *012 †20
KUMAR, Ravindra. 909 FROSTWOOD DR STE 230 77024 #495-45-1974 L1994 **IM** *020 †20
KUMAR, Rukmini D. 8200 WEDNESBURY LN, STE 112 77074 #495-65-1975 L1987 **PD** *020
KUMAR, Satheesha S. 1315 ST JOSEPH PKWY, CARDIOLOGY ASSOCIATES 77002
  #495-09-1971 L1980 **CD IC** *020 †20
KUMAR, Vikas. ■ 77030 #495-24-2000 L2006 *100
KUMARAVEL, Malarvizhi Man. PO BOX 20708 77225 #495-16-1994 **PTH** *012
KUMASHI, Padmavati R. 800 PEAKWOOD DR, STE 7H 77090 #495-96-1994 L2005 **ID** *020 †20
KUMENDA, Thomas Obwengi. 2002 HOLCOMBE BLVD, MC 111PC 77030 #577-01-1990 L2003
  FM *020 †18
KUN, Amy Rachel. 6621 FANNIN ST, TEXAS CHILDREN'S HOSPITAL 77030 #047-06-2002 L2008
  PHO *012
KUNA, Kalyan Gupta. ■ 77025 #030-06-2004 **AN** *012
KUNDI, Azam Khan. 1221 MCKINNEY ST, STE 40300 77010 #704-25-1992 L1997 **IM** *020
KUNDRA, Vikas. 1515 HOLCOMBE BLVD BOX 368, UT MD ANDERSON CANCER CENT 77030
  #024-01-1995 L2002 **DR** *020 †80
KUNG, Shirley H. 211 HIGHLAND CROSS DR, STE 275 77073 #048-14-2000 L2004 **EM** *100 †16
KUNIK, Mark E. 2002 HOLCOMBE BLVD, VA MED CTR # 110T-152 77030 #048-04-1987 L1988
  P *020 †75
KUNISHIGE, Joy Hisako. 6655 TRAVIS ST STE 980, U. OF TEXAS DEPARTMENT OF 77030
  #011-03-2003 L2004 **D** *012
KUO, Edward L. 4602 WASHINGTON AVE STE B, WASHINGTON AVE FAM PRACT 77007
  #048-12-1997 L1998 **FM** *020 †18
KUO, Eugene Chin. 6410 FANNIN ST, STE 1535 77030 #016-01-2001 L2006 **OSS** *100
KUO, Sheng-Han. 1 BAYLOR PLZ, DEPT OF NEUROLOGY 77030 #244-02-2004 **N** *012
KUPFERMAN, Michael Elliot. 1515 HOLCOMBE BLVD, UNIT 441 77030 #041-01-1999 L2005
  OTO *100 †45
KUPOR, Lary Richard. 1315 ST JOSEPH PKWY, STE 1709 77002 #024-01-1967 L1974
  NEP IM *040 †20
KURIAN, Anju S. ■ 77054 #035-15-2003 L2007 **EM** *020
KURIAN, Babin. PO BOX 20708, DEPT OF INTERNAL MEDICINE 77225 #048-13-2004 **IM** *012
KURIE, Jonathan Meigs. 1515 HOLCOMBE BLVD BOX 80, DEPT THORACIC ONCOLOGY 77030
  #036-08-1983 L1993 **ON IM** *020 †20
KURLANDER, Harold Michael. 925 GESSNER RD, STE 480 77024 #048-04-1977 L1978
  N NRN *020 †75
KURRELMEYER, Karla Marie. 6620 MAIN ST, STE 1225 77030 #026-04-1993 L1997
  CD IM *020 †20
KURTEK, Richard William. 10655 STEEPLETOP DR, CYPRESS FAIRBANKS MEDICAL 77065
  #041-12-2000 L2007 **EM** *020
KURZROCK, Razelle. 1515 HOLCOMBE BLVD 77030 #065-01-1978 L1984 **HEM ON** *050 †20
KUSHWAHA, Anne Marie. 1515 HOLCOMBE BLVD 77030 #048-13-1992 L1998 **DR** *020 †80
KUSNOOR, Anita Vijay. ■ 77054 #048-04-2004 L2007 **IM** *100 †20
KWAK, Larry W. 1515 HOLCOMBE BLVD, UNIT 429 77030 #016-06-1982 L2005 **IG** *050 †20
KWAN, Justin Yuanping. 6550 FANNIN ST STE 1801, DEPT OF NEUROLOGY 77030
  #035-06-2000 L2004 **N** *020 †75
KWAN, Mary S K. 6700 BELLAIRE BLVD, STE 600 77074 #385-02-1968 L1976 **IM PM** *071
KWATER, Piotr Antoni. 1515 HOLCOMBE BLVD BOX 42, MD ANDERSON CANCER CTR 77030
  #759-01-1988 L1988 **AN** *020 †05
KWOH, Christopher H. 1415 LA CONCHA LN 77054 #048-04-2000 L2006 **NEP** *020 †20
KWOK, Stephanie Iwei. ■ 77030 #048-04-2008 *012
KWON, Michael Chil. ■ 77046 #005-15-2001 L2001 **RNR** *100 †80
KWONG, Raymond Po. 7111 HARWIN DR, STE 210 77036 #048-13-1984 L1985 **FM** *020
KYLE, William Buck. ■ 77054 #035-20-2006 **PD** *012
KYLES, Regina Faye. 1010 LAMAR ST, STE 210 77002 #048-02-1984 L1985 **IM** *020
KYRIAKIDES, Polina. 6431 FANNIN ST, MSB 2-100 77030 #418-02-1988 L2006 **DR VIR** *020 †80
KYRITSIS, Athanassios P. 1515 HOLCOMBE BLVD, BOX 100 77030 #418-01-1978 L1990
  N *020 †75
LA, Bao-Quoc Huy. 12121 RICHMOND AVE, STE 315 77082 #048-12-1995 L1998 **OBG** *020 †30
LABANCA, Francisco. 1 BAYLOR PLZ, DEPT OBG 77030 #132-11-1999 **OBG** *012
LABARTHE, Darwin Raymond. ■ 77056 #035-01-1965 L1967 **GPM** *050 †70
LABIS, John Scott. 6565 FANNIN ST MS D281, RADIOLOGY DEPARTMENT 77030
  #048-04-1998 L1999 **DR** *100 †80
LABORDE, Stephen Van. 1333 WEST LOOP S, STE 1425 77027 #021-01-1997 L2002
  D DS *020 †15
LABORIE, Wendy Y. 277 W GRAY ST 77019 #026-04-1998 L2001 **MPD** *020 †55,20
LABOW, Sam Stanley. 5314 DASHWOOD DR 77081 #065-09-1961 L1977 **PS OS** *075
LABRIOLA, Joanne E. 6410 FANNIN ST, STE 1535 77030 #041-12-2001 L2007 **ORS** *100
LACAYO, Humberto Jose. 7333 NORTH FWY, STE 430 77076 #682-01-1961 L1982 **IM** *071
LACERAS, Alexander Fabi. 6431 FANNIN ST STE JJL310 77030 #748-25-1984 *100
LACOUR, Audrey Turner. 12600 BISSONNET ST, STE E1 77099 #048-02-2002 L2005
  FM *020 †18
LACOUR, Douglas W, Jr. 1250 CYPRESS STATION DR 77090 #048-04-1997 L2000 **PD** *020 †55
LACOUR, Robin Ann. ■ 77074 #021-06-2002 L2004 **OBG** *012
LAFLEUR, Jay Lance. ■ 77054 #048-15-2007 **TY** *012
LA FRANCESCA, Saverio. ■ 77004 #561-12-1985 **CD** *020
LAFUENTE, Javier Antonio. 6560 FANNIN ST, STE 1612 77030 #270-01-1981 L1993
  TS GS *020 †85,90
LA GRONE, Don Michael. 2246 BISSONNET ST 77005 #048-02-1970 L1970 **P CHP** *020 †75
LAHAM, Federico Ricardo. ■ 77025 #132-01-2001 **PDI** *012 †55
LAHART, Christopher J. 2015 THOMAS ST 77009 #016-43-1982 L1983 **IM OS** *020 †20
LAHORI, Ramachandra J. 710 FM 1960 RD W 77090 #016-06-1991 L1998 **AN** *020 †05
LAHOTI, Amit. 1400 HOLCOMBE BLVD, UNIT 437 77030 #048-13-1998 L2001 **NEP** *100 †20
LAHOTI, Sandeep. 6624 FANNIN ST STE 1700, MEDICAL CLINIC OF HOUSTON 77030
  #048-12-1990 L1994 **GE** *020 †20
LAHOTI, Sheela. 2500 BOLSOVER ST, THE CHILDRENS ASSMNT CTR 77005
  #011-02-1991 L1995 **PD** *020 †55
LAI, Eda Ho. ■ 77025 #048-15-2007 *012
LAI, Eugene C. 6550 FANNIN ST STE 1801, DEPARTMENT OF NEUROLOGY 77030
  #048-04-1986 L1987 **N** *040 †75
LAI, James Chaolung. 12000 RICHMOND AVE, STE 208 77082 #048-12-1990 L1991
  AN PME *020 †05

LAI, Jenny M. 6550 FANNIN ST, SMITH TOWER, STE 2501 77030 #048-12-1992 L1993
  PM *020 †60
LAI, King Ong. 714 FM 1960 RD W, STE 206 77090 #385-02-1960 L1971 **AN OBG** *071
LAI, Meiyu Tammy. 2227 SOUTHGATE BLVD 77030 #048-04-1993 L1994 **PM** *020 †60
LAI, Raymond Kai-Chi. 1515 HOLCOMBE BLVD 77030 #060-01-1992 L2000 **HMP** *020 †50
LAI, Yi-Chen. 6621 FANNIN ST WT6-006, TEXAS CHILDREN'S HOSPITAL 77030
  #041-12-1998 L2006 **CCP** *020 †55
LAING, Susan Tiukinhoy. 6431 FANNIN ST, MSB 1-246 77030 #748-02-1991 L1992
  CD PD *020 †20
LAIRD, Martha A. ■ 77096 #649-13-1984 L1991 **PHP OBG** *020 †30
LAKHANI, Nuruddin B. ■ 77074 #704-25-1992 **PD** *100
LAKHANI, Salim Abdullah. 1801 NORTH LOOP W, STE 50 77008 #704-02-1984 L1993
  IM IMG *020 †20
LAKHIA, Ragini Dinesh. 1140 BUSINESS CENTER DR 77043 #495-76-1969 L1976 **PTH** *020 †50
LAKKIS, Clair Lisa. 6431 FANNIN ST, MSB 1150 77030 #048-14-2001 L2004 **PCC** *012 †20
LAKKIS, Nasser. 6550 FANNIN ST, STE 1901 77030 #605-01-1986 L1994 **CD IM** *020 †20
LAL, Rajiv. 6431 FANNIN ST STE 4.148, UNIVERSITY OF TX MEDICAL S 77030
  #495-36-2000 L2006 **NEP** *020
LALANI, Seema Rashid. 6701 FANNIN ST 77030 #704-25-1994 L2002 **MG PD** *020 †19,55
LALL, Arun. 4126 SOUTHWEST FWY, STE 440 77027 #496-09-1979 L1998 **AN** *020
LALLANDE, Beverly Jean. 1300 MOURSUND ST, DEPARTMENT OF CHILD AND AD 77030
  #048-14-2004 L2007 **P** *012
LALLY, Kevin Patrick. 6431 FANNIN ST STE 5.258, UTHSC AT HOUSTON 77030
  #021-01-1980 L1991 **PDS CCM** *020 †85
LALLY, Pamela Fischer. ■ 77005 #041-01-1980 L1988 **PD** *020 †55
LAM, Andy. ■ 77098 #048-04-2007 **AN** *012
LAM, Bach Nguyen. 18100 UPPER BAY RD, STE 206 77058 #048-15-1986 L1988 **AN** *020
LAM, Chee Kong. 6431 FANNIN ST, STE 5.020 77030 #671-01-1995 L2006 *100
LAM, Fong Wilson. ■ 77004 #048-12-2003 L2006 **CCP** *012 †55
LAM, Kim Thien. ■ 77054 #048-15-2007 **OBG** *012
LAM, Michael Kaijia. 7789 SOUTHWEST FWY, STE 530 77074 #048-12-1994 L1998
  OPH *020 †35
LAM, Vinh Dao. ■ 77082 #422-01-2004 L2007 **FM** *020
LAMBERT, Jeffery Curtis. 15655 CYPRESSWOOD MEDCL DR, STE 110 77014
  #048-14-1985 L1986 **FM** *020 †18
LAMBERT, Laura Ann. 1400 HOLCOMBE BLVD, UNIT 444 77030 #024-01-1996 L2003
  GS *020 †85
LAMBERT, Mark Edward. 7737 SOUTHWEST FWY, STE 780 77074 #017-20-1969 L1976
  CD *020 †20
LAMKI, Lamk Mohamed. 6431 FANNIN ST, MSB 2 132 77030 #539-04-1965 L1979
  NM IM *020 †28
LAMKI, Neela. 1 BAYLOR PLZ 77030 #539-04-1966 L1979 **R** *040 †80
LAMMING, Christopher Edwa. 1 BAYLOR PLZ, BAYLOR COLL OF MED 77030 #917-12-1991
  PD *012
LAMOTHE IZURIETA, Mario R. 2727 W HOLCOMBE BLVD 77025 #649-01-1985 L1995
  IM *020 †20
LAMPING, Dorothy R. 5630 N ELDRIDGE PKWY, STE 350 77041 #048-02-1984 L1985
  FM *020 †18
LAN, Shaun Xiao. ■ 77025 #048-04-2007 *012
LANDERS, Maurice Bernard. 1315 ST JOSEPH PKWY, STE 1205 77002 #025-01-1963 L1997
  OPH *071 †35
LANDES, Marjorie Therese. 2002 HOLCOMBE BLVD, MICHAEL E DE BAKEY VA HOSP 77030
  #033-05-1968 L1977 **P** *020 †20
LANDIS, Dennis Michael D. 1 BAYLOR PLZ STE NB302, BAYLOR COLLEGE OF MEDICINE 77030
  #024-01-1971 L2007 **N** *030 †20,75
LANDIVAR, Carlos Jorge. 7737 SOUTHWEST FWY STE 660 77074 #176-01-1968 L1975
  OBG *020
LANDON, Genie. ■ 77005 #048-04-1980 L1980 **PTH** *020 †50
LANDON, Glenn Carey. 1221 MCKINNEY ST, STE 40300 77010 #016-43-1975 L1986
  ORS *040 †40
LANDRAU, Carmen Waleska. 6431 FANNIN ST STE 1.150, AT HOUST 77030
  #042-02-2002 L2006 **CD IM** *012
LANDRY, Trela Monique. 2101 NASA PKWY # SD-13 77058 #048-02-1997 L2000
  MPD *020 †20,55
LANE, Angela R. ■ 77025 #048-14-2008 *012
LANE, Deanna L. 1515 HOLCOMBE BLVD, UNIT 1350 77030 #048-14-1999 L2005
  DR OS *020 †80 ‡
LANE, George H, Jr. 17263 #048-04-1950 L1950 **ORS** *071 †40
LANE, John Christopher. 14903 EL CAMINO REAL 77062 #048-12-1990 L1991 **FM** *020 †18 ‡
LANERI, John Philip, Jr. 829 PEAKWOOD DR 77090 #048-02-1966 L1966 **U** *071 †95
LANG, Frederick Frank, Jr. 1515 HOLCOMBE BLVD, DEPT OF NEUROSURGERY UNIT 77030
  #008-01-1988 L1996 **NS** *020 †25
LANG, Michael Leslie. ■ 77096 #836-02-1975 L1994 **AN PME** *020 †05
LANG, Thang Vu. 2500 FONDREN RD, STE 270 77063 #016-06-1994 L1997 **GE** *020 †20
LANGE, Allison Michele. ■ 77054 #056-06-2005 L2008 **PD** *100
LANGE, Campbell M. 5757 WOODWAY DR, STE 200 77057 #048-14-1979 L1979 **PD** *020 †55
LANGFORD, Christoph P. 1216C WELCH ST, EMERGENCY DEPARTMENT 77006
  #048-13-1991 L1996 **EM** *020 †16
LANGFORD, Lauren Ann. 1515 HOLCOMBE BLVD, BOX 85 77030 #048-02-1978 L1978
  NP P *020 †50
LANGHAM, Camille Bridget. 4801 WOODWAY DR, STE 369W 77056 #048-14-1988 L1989
  IM *020
LANGLEY, Rhet Rollins. ■ 77030 #048-14-2008 *012
LANGLINAIS, Brandon James. ■ 77004 #048-04-1999 L2004 **DR** *012
LANGSTON, Claire. 6621 FANNIN ST, STE B1 77030 #041-02-1967 L1981 **PP** *040 †50
LANIER, Jeffrey Day. 2855 GRAMERCY ST 77025 #048-02-1966 L1966 **OPH** *020 †35
LANKFORD, Jeremy Edward. ■ 77054 #016-02-2007 **PD** *012
LANO, Elizabeth Anne. 1515 HOLCOMBE BLVD 77030 #048-14-1989 L1991 **DR** *020 †80
LANTIN, Regina M. 6431 FANNIN ST 3.126, DEPT OF PEDIATRICS 77030 #748-01-1988 L1995
  PDC *020 †55
LANYS, Shane G. 7739 W BELLFORT ST 77071 #065-06-1977 L1982 **FM** *020
LANZA, Frank Leo. 7777 SOUTHWEST FWY STE 708 77074 #048-02-1962 L1962
  GE IM *020 †05
LAOWATTANA, Somchai. 1 BAYLOR PLZ, MS:NB302 77030 #891-01-1992 L2006 **N** *020 †75
LAPIN, Herman. 1315 ST JOSEPH PKWY 77002 #048-01-1958 L1958 **IM** *020 †20
LAPIN, Stephen L. 6560 FANNIN ST, STE 1440 77030 #048-04-1986 L1987 **U** *020 †95

■ = Address Information Privacy Protected

LA PINTA, Chas Keith, Jr. 2101 NASA RD 1, BLDG 41SD25 77058 #038-06-1965 L1967 AM GPM *030

LAPUERTA, Brittney Mc Dan. 6720 BERTNER ST 77030 #048-14-2000 L2004 AN *020

LAPUERTA, Leopoldo, Jr. 1315 ST JOSEPH PKWY # 950 77002 #048-12-1988 L1989 PS HS *020 †65,85

LARA, Humberto A. 8076 EL RIO ST 77054 #649-02-1970 L1976 PTH *020 †50

LARKIN, John Stuart. ■ 77021 #048-14-2008 *012

LARRAZOLO, Oscar Gabriel. 6431 FANNIN ST, SCHOOL A 77030 #005-12-2007 PD *012

LARREY, Richard Morris. 11734 FM 1960 RD W 77065 #028-02-1974 L1979 ORS *020 †40

LASICS, Brooke. 4110 BELLAIRE BLVD, STE 210 77025 #048-12-2002 L2005 PD *020 †55

LASKOWSKI, Tadeusz Z. 2050 NORTH LOOP W STE 226 77018 #759-08-1954 L1964 U *071 †95

LASTER, Rebecca Bautista. 5900 CHIMNEY ROCK RD, STE Y 77081 #048-78-2004, ▲ L2007 PD *020 †55

LATIFI, Haleema Tasneem. 3701 KIRBY DR STE 600, FAMILY & COMM MEDICINE 77098 #495-57-1986 L2003 FM *020 †18 ‡

LATIMER, Lonniejay. ■ 77030 #048-14-2008 *012

LATIMER, Patrice. 1100 W 34TH ST, NORTHWEST HEALTH CENTER 77018 #025-01-1996 L1997 FM *020 †18

LATORRE, Juan Manuel. 1333 MOURSUND ST, THE INSTITUTE FOR REHABILI 77030 #264-04-1994 L2003 SCI PM *020 †60

LATTHE, Bharat Baburao. 530 N BELT DR E, STE 100 77060 #495-01-1982 L1998 FM FPG *020 †18

LATTIMORE, Joseph S. ■ 77094 #048-04-1946 L1946 OBG *020 †30

LAU, Ching Ching. 6621 FANNIN ST, MC 3-3320 77030 #024-01-1993 L1995 PHO PD *050 †55

LAU, David Lc. 6410 FANNIN ST STE 450 77030 #025-07-2001 L2007 VS *012 †85

LAU, Lewis Kah Sin. ■ 77030 #917-18-1988 IM *100

LAU, Melvin K. ■ 77019 #048-13-2004 L2007 GE *012 †20

LAU, Yiukeung. ■ 77080 #048-14-1998 L2005 ON *050 †20

LAUCIRICA, Rodolfo. 1 BAYLOR PLZ DEPT PTH 77030 #308-07-1983 L1992 PTH *020 †50

LAUGHLIN, Misty D. ■ 77027 #048-16-1988 L1989 EM *020 †18,16

LAURSEN, Kerry A. 2202 W ALABAMA ST, STE B 77098 #048-13-2001 L2003 FM *020 †18

LAUTERBURG, Bernhard Hans. 1200 MOURSUND ST 77030 #869-02-1970 L1979 GE PA *050 †20

LAUZON, John Parry, Jr. 7401 MAIN ST 77030 #048-02-1966 L1966 AN *020 †05

LAVENDER, Edward James. 710 FM 1960 RD W 77090 #917-01-1970 L1977 FM GP *020 †18

LAVIS, Victor Ralph. 6431 FANNIN ST, MSB 6.100 77030 #005-11-1962 L1976 IM END *020 †55

LAW, Elizabeth Marie. 17150 EL CAMINO REAL 77058 #038-40-2000 L2004 PD *020 †55

LAW, Samuel Wm, II. 6560 FANNIN ST 77030 #048-04-1975 L1976 OBG *020 †30

LAWHON, Thomas James. 7500 BEECHNUT ST, STE 262 77074 #048-02-1971 L1971 GS GP *020 †85

LAWRENCE, David D. 1415 NORTH LOOP W, STE 820 77008 #050-02-1960 L1968 DR VIR *071 †80

LAWRENCE, David Dubrul. 1415 NORTH LOOP W, STE 810 77008 #048-02-1981 L1981 R VIR *020 †20

LAWRIE, Gerald Murray. 1315 ST JOSEPH PKWY, STE 1306 77002 #143-03-1969 L1975 CD *020

LAWSON, Nicholette Michel. ■ 77025 #048-04-2008 *012

LAYMAN, Richard M. 3930 KIRBY DR STE 108 77098 #048-14-2004 L2007 AN *012

LAZAR, Alexander J. 1515 HOLCOMBE BLVD BOX 85, ANDERSON CANCER CENTER 77030 #048-12-2000 L2004 DMP *100 ‡

LAZARZ, Donald Thos. 4151 SOUTHWEST FWY, STE 715 77027 #048-04-1958 L1958 ORS *020 †40

LE, Anne Thi. 7900 FANNIN ST, STE 3700 77054 #048-12-1999 L2006 CRS GS *020 †85 ‡

LE, Charles Nguyenthanh. 1709 DRYDEN RD STE 550, BCM FACULTY CTR 77030 #028-34-2006 IM *012

LE, Daniel D. 10515 BELLAIRE BLVD, FAMI CARE MED CLNC 77072 #048-14-1993 L1996 IM *020 †20

LE, David Dung. 900 WAYSIDE DR, CY-FAIR MEDICAL CLINIC 77011 #941-01-1972 L1980 FM *020 †18 ‡

LE, Haiyen Truong. 12020 FM 1960 RD W, STE 700 77065 #048-14-1997 L1998 PD *020 †55

LE, Hoang Linh. ■ 77089 #048-15-2006 GS *012

LE, Houng Thien. PO BOX 301439, UNIT 1350 77230 #063-01-1995 L2005 *100 †80

LE, Hung Huy. 9798 BELLAIRE BLVD, STE A 77036 #048-04-1992 L1993 OPH *020 †35

LE, Huong T. 837 FM 1960 RD W, STE 105 77090 #048-04-1989 L1990 FM *020 †18

LE, Mai Oanh Hoang. 6431 FANNIN ST, UNIV TX MED SCH 77030 #048-14-2006 P *012

LE, Minh Huy. 5704 S GESSNER DR STE D 77036 #048-02-1989 L1992 IM *020 †20

LE, Nham Hong. 6550 FANNIN ST, THE METHODIST HOSPITAL 77030 #021-05-2007 GS *012

LE, Nhuai Christine. 2060 SPACE PARK DR, STE 304 77058 #023-01-1994 L1998 IM *020 †20

LE, Ninh Huy. 5704 S GESSNER DR STE D 77036 #941-01-1968 L1982 PD GP *020

LE, Ott. ■ 77030 #048-02-2002 L2006 DR *100 †80

LE, Phi-Nga Jeannie. 2600 GESSNER DR, STE 250 77080 #048-13-2001 L2004 FM *020 †18

LE, Quan H. 10515 BELLAIRE BLVD STE J 77072 #048-14-1997 L1998 IM *020 †20

LE, Quoc Duc. 837 FM 1960 RD W, STE 105 77090 #048-14-1996 L1998 FM *020 †18

LE, Richard A. 11918 VETERANS MEMORIAL DR 77067 #048-02-1995 L2000 IM *020 †20

LE, Roger P. 13111 EAST FWY, STE 108 77015 #048-02-1994 L1999 U *020 †20

LE, Thomas Trong. 6918 CORPORATE DR, STE A12 77036 #941-01-1970 L1991 IM EM *020 †20

LE, Trung N. 1919 NORTH LOOP W STE 410 77008 #048-13-1988 L1994 FM *020 †18

LE, Vinh T. 11034 SCARSDALE BLVD, STE A 77089 #048-02-1996 L1999 DR VIR *020 †80

LEACH, Fredrick Sebastian. 6560 FANNIN ST, STE 2100 77030 #005-11-1990 L1996 U *020 †95

LEACH, Gary Russell. 1631 NORTH LOOP W, STE 150 77008 #041-02-1966 L1983 RO U *020 †95,80

LEACH, Neville Gary. ■ 77041 #065-09-1960 L1977 GS TS *071

LEACHMAN, Dewitt Richard. 6624 FANNIN ST, STE 2780 77030 #048-12-1977 L1977 CD IM *020 †20

LEAHY-SNYDER, Elizabeth A. ■ 77057 #035-45-1986 L1990 PD IM *020 †20,55

LEAL, Juan. 1917 ASHLAND ST 77008 #264-04-1962 L1970 AN *071 †05

LEAMING, Katherine Jennif. ■ 77098 #035-09-2004 L2007 PEM *012 †55

LEASS, Donald Leon. 17070 RED OAK DR STE 105 77090 #023-01-1970 L1975 PD NPM *020 †55

LEATH, Robert M. 6535 SOUTHWEST FWY 77074 #048-02-1987 L1988 FM EM *020 †18

LEAVENS, Milam Edmund. 1515 HOLCOMBE BLVD BOX 69 77030 #048-04-1948 L1948 NS *071 †25

LEAVITT, Lewis A, III. 2608 YORKTOWN PL 77056 #048-14-1981 L1981 EM *020 †16

LE BLANC-MATHEWS, Kelly N. 6565 FANNIN ST 77030 #048-02-1999 L2004 AN *020

LEBOVITZ, Russell Martin. ■ 77019 #028-02-1982 L1982 PTH *020

LEBRON, Diana. 6621 FANNIN ST CC1710, TEXAS CHILDRENS HOSPITAL 77030 #033-06-1989 L2005 N *020 †75,55

LEBWOHL, Jason Marc. 211 HIGHLAND CROSS DR, STE 275 77073 #033-05-2002 L2006 EM *020 †16

LECHIN, Alex E. 11914 ASTORIA BLVD, STE 670 77089 #935-01-1986 L1993 PCC SME *020 †20

LE CONEY, Richard H. 3120 SOUTHWEST FWY, STE 400 77098 #048-02-1977 L1978 EM *020 †16

LEDBETTER, Abbe Alzu, Jr. 4544 POST OAK PLACE DR, STE 390 77027 #048-02-1960 L1960 IM A *020 †20

LEDER, Archie Allen. ■ 77057 #048-02-1954 L1954 CD IM *071 †20

LEDERER, Martha Anne. ■ 77005 #048-14-2008 *012

LEDLIE, William Boyer. 6410 FANNIN ST 77030 #048-02-1975 L1975 FM ADM *020 †18

LEDOUX, John Francis. 6431 FANNIN ST, UTHSC DIV OF CARDIOLOGY 77030 #001-06-2002 L2005 IC *012

LEE, Andrew Kwangson. 11301 FALLBROOK DR STE 328, HOUSTON TOTAL ORTHO & HAND 77065 #010-03-1992 L1997 ORS HS *020 †40

LEE, Barbara. 4299 SAN FELIPE ST, STE 300 77027 #143-03-1984 L2006 CCA IM *020 †20

LEE, Benjamin P. 2323 CLEAR LAKE CITY BLVD, STE 180-177 77062 #422-01-1998 L2007 IM *020 †20

LEE, Brendan Honleung. 1 BAYLOR PLZ 630E, DEPT MOLECULAR/HUMAN GENET 77030 #035-08-1993 L1995 PD MG *050 †19,55

LEE, Carl Edward, II. 1315 ST JOSEPH PKWY, STE 1202 77002 #048-04-1999 L2003 OBG *020 †30

LEE, Charles John. 1919 CRAWFORD ST, MGJ-12 77002 #048-14-1993 L1994 AN GP *020 †05

LEE, Chenwei. 6565 FANNIN ST 77030 #024-01-1995 L2001 VIR *020 †80

LEE, Chin Hyun. 7333 NORTH FWY, STE 310 77076 #583-02-1974 L1982 OBG *020

LEE, Chok K. 1200 BINZ ST, STE 875 PLAZA MED CTR 77004 #035-46-1981 L1982 IM *020 †20

LEE, Christen-Jennifer An. ■ 77030 #048-04-2008 *012

LEE, Cora D. ■ 77094 #048-13-2000 L2003 AN *020 †05

LEE, Daniel W, III. ■ 77030 #048-14-2003 PD *012

LEE, Daria B. 8830 LONG POINT RD, STE 407 77055 #048-04-1989 L1990 PUD *020 †20

LEE, David Anson. 6400 FANNIN ST, 18TH FL 77030 #024-05-1980 L2007 OPH *020 †35

LEE, David Aubrey. 6565 FANNIN ST, 6565 FANNIN ST STE 1760 77030 #021-05-1970 L1972 PS OTO *020 †45,65 ‡

LEE, David Dong Han. ■ 77059 #583-01-1958 L1976 FM PMM *071 ‡

LEE, Dean Anthony. 6621 FANNIN ST 77030 #005-12-1996 L2003 PHO PD *050 †55 ‡

LEE, Diana King. 77025 #048-02-2003 L2008 AN *012

LEE, Edward Ilho. ■ 77030 #048-04-2006 PS *012

LEE, Eric Ted. 6630 DE MOSS DR 77074 #048-12-2004 L2007 FM *100 †18

LEE, Helen Hyunsun. 6431 FANNIN ST STE 4.148, RENAL DISEASES & HYPERTENS 77030 #048-12-1999 L2002 NEP *020 †20

LEE, Henry Shih. 6431 FANNIN ST, UT MED SCHLMSB 2100 77030 #016-06-1991 L1996 DR *020 †80

LEE, Jeffrey Edwin. 1515 HOLCOMBE BLVD # 444, DEPT SURG ONC POB 301402 77030 #005-11-1984 L1991 GS SO *020 †85

LEE, Jeffrey Heebum. 1515 HOLCOMBE BLVD 77030 #048-02-1989 L1990 GE *020 †20

LEE, Jeffrey Yee. 8945 LONG POINT RD STE 212 77055 #048-14-1976 L1976 IM IMG *020 †20

LEE, Jennifer Catherine. ■ 77019 #035-45-2005 PD *100

LEE, John. 1313 HERMANN DR 77004 #048-14-1995 L2000 DR *020 †80

LEE, Jonathan Glen. 1200 BINZ ST STE 1430 77004 #021-06-1983 L1989 ORS *020 †40

LEE, Joon Sang. 237 NORTH LOOP W 77008 #583-03-1969 L1977 DR *020 †80

LEE, Justin M. ■ 77006 #048-04-2004 L2008 AN *012

LEE, Kay Lynn. 8200 WEDNESBURY LN, STE 495 77074 #048-02-1978 L1978 FM *020 †20

LEE, Kenneth Jiannhung. 7500 BEECHNUT ST, STE 150 77074 #036-07-1999 L2005 OSS *020

LEE, Kyung Po. ■ 77077 #583-01-1973 L1977 GS *020 †85

LEE, Margaret Yu. ■ 77063 #048-13-2002 L2006 IM *020

LEE, Ming Sheng. 1515 HOLCOMBE BLVD 77030 #244-04-1976 L1988 HEM ON *020

LEE, Patricia Clement. 2060 SPACE PARK DR STE 200 77058 #048-14-1981 L1985 ID D *020 †50

LEE, Paul Sung. PO BOX 20708, U TX MED SCH DEPT RAD 77225 #041-15-2006 DR *012

LEE, Peter Y. PO BOX 20708 77225 #048-12-2000 L2005 AN *020

LEE, Po Wen. 8951 RUTHBY ST STE 1 77061 #244-02-1968 L1973 FM PD *020 †18

LEE, Roger. ■ 77025 #048-14-2008 *012

LEE, Shayna Patrice. 3520 SOUTHMORE BLVD 77004 #048-13-1985 L1986 P *020

LEE, Susan C. 1 BAYLOR PLZ, DEPT OF ANESTH SM1003 77030 #048-13-2003 L2005 AN *020

LEE, T H. 2007 BLALOCK RD 77080 #941-01-1967 L1977 FM OS *071

LEE, Tri Richard. 1221 MCKINNEY ST, STE 40300 77010 #035-03-1992 L2000 END *020 †20

LEE, Walter. 17420 NORTHWEST FWY 77040 #025-01-1986 L1995 GP *020

LEE, Yong-Duck Chung. 7333 NORTH FWY, STE 220 77076 #583-09-1970 L1979 U *020 †55

LEE, Yongok Eugenia. ■ 77071 #583-03-1953 L1982 OPH FM *020

LEE, Youngna Jenny. 6621 FANNIN ST, ONCOLOGY 77030 #035-47-1998 L2005 PHO *100 †55

LEE, Yung. 211 HIGHLAND CROSS DR # 2 77073 #048-02-2004 L2007 EM *020

LEEDS, Leroy J. 7550 FANNIN ST, STE 146 77054 #035-06-1964 L1968 GYN *020 †30

LEEDS-RICHTER, Shelly. 7900 FANNIN ST 77054 #048-04-1997 L2001 OBG *020 †30

LEE-DUKES, Gwendolyn. 100 UH HEALTH CTR, UNIVERSITY OF HOUSTON 77204 #019-02-1972 L1979 CHP P *020 †75

LEETH, Angela Marie. ■ 77007 #048-02-2004 HO *012 †20

LEEVES, Jane A. 1801 LEXINGTON ST 77098 #048-14-1987 L1988 CHP P *020 †75

LEFFLER, Thomas Edward. 2727 W HOLCOMBE BLVD, ORTHO 2ND FLR 77025 #016-06-1970 L1976 ORS *020 †40

LEGALL, Michelle Evette. ■ 77044 #047-07-2002 L2007 FM *100

LEGENDRE, Kevin E. 8411 W BELLFORT ST, STE 100A 77071 #048-14-1989 L1990 DR *020 †80

LEGGETT, Philip Lloyd. 800 PEAKWOOD DR, STE 8B 77090 #048-02-1980 L1980 GS GE *020 †85

LEGGINGTON, Robert B, Jr. 4407 YOAKUM BLVD, STE B 77006 #048-02-2000 L2003 NEP *020

LEGHA, Sewa Singh. 6624 FANNIN ST STE 1440 77030 #495-08-1970 L1977 ON IM *071 †20

LEHANE, Daniel E, Jr. 6550 FANNIN ST, STE 1101 77030 #035-06-1966 L1973 ON IM *020 †20

LEIBMAN, Bryan Derek. 1701 HERMANN DR UNIT 1406 77004 #048-04-1995 L1998 U *020 †20

LEIBOWITZ, Julian Lazar. 6410 FANNIN ST 77030 #035-46-1975 L1985 PTH *050

LEICHMAN, Joshua Gregory. 6431 FANNIN ST, MSB 1-246 77030 #005-06-2001 L2006 CD *012 †20

LEIFESTE, Homer F. 1313 HERMANN DR 77004 #048-02-1943 L1943 U *071 †95

LEIGHTON, William Rado, Jr. 6565 FANNIN ST 77030 #048-14-1997 L2001 AN *020 †05

LEIMAN, Basil Colin. ■ 77279 #836-01-1976 L1985 **AN** *075 †05
LEIMAN, David Gary. ■ 77024 #422-01-2007 **AN** *012
LEISER, Alfred E. ■ 77046 #056-05-1946 L1956 **END IM** *071 †20
LEIVA, Jorge Ignacio. 1631 NORTH LOOP W, STE 220 77008 #649-04-1991 L1998 **GS** *020 †85
LEJA, Monika Jacqueline. ■ 77030 #016-43-2001 L2005 **CD** *100 †20
LEKE, Efua Bonnie. 1709 DRYDEN RD, BAYLOR COLLEGE OF MEDICINE 77030 #010-02-2007 **OBG** *012
LEKETAMBO, Awungjia Camer. 1709 DRYDEN RD STE 550, BCM FACULTY CENTER 77030 #041-13-2006 **IM** *012
LELAND CANTU, Jessica Ann. ■ 77047 #048-04-2007 **OBG** *012
LEMAIRE, Chad Michael. ■ 77054 #048-04-2006 **P** *012
LE MAIRE, Scott A. 1 BAYLOR PLZ, BCM 390 77030 #016-06-1992 L1999 **TS GS** *050 †85,90
LEMAK, Leslie Louis. 3465 W ALABAMA ST # 27705 77027 #025-07-1947 L1953 **R** *071 †80
LEMAK, Margaret Anne. 3801 KIRBY DR STE 300 77098 #048-14-1981 L1981 **D** *020 †15
LEMAK, Noreen Appleberry. ■ 77056 #025-07-1947 L1951 **N** *071
LEMESHKO, Sergy V. ■ 77054 #048-04-2005 **DR** *012
LEMKE, Daniel Spencer. 6621 FANNIN ST, MCI-1481 77030 #048-04-2002 L2005 **PEM** *012 †55
LEMLEY, Sherry J. 211 HIGHLAND CROSS DR #275 77073 #048-04-2002 L2004 **FM** *020 †18
LEMMING, Sandra E. 9055 KATY FWY, STE 200 77024 #048-04-1999 L2002 **FM** *020 †18
LEMMONS, Benjamin David. 9301 SOUTHWEST FWY, # 245 77074 #048-02-1983 L1985 **EM** *020
LEMOS, Marilyn Brock. 6624 FANNIN ST, STE 1900 77030 #047-05-1977 L1979 **PD** *020 †55
LEMOS, Ruben. 1221 MCKINNEY ST, STE 40300 77010 #264-05-1973 L1981 **OPH OS** *020 †35
LENGE DE ROSEN, Veronica. 1 BAYLOR PLZ, BAYLOR COL OF MED 77030 #132-01-1996 **DR** *012
LENGYEL, Mircea Ioan C. 12704 NORTH FWY 77060 #016-43-1953 L1965 **CRS** *020 †10
LENNINGTON, Jennifer N. ■ 77025 #048-04-2002 L2005 **PN** *012 †55
LENT, William Allen. 1200 BINZ ST STE 930 77004 #048-14-1979 L1979 **IM** *020 †20
LENTINO, Eduardo Pedro. 8345 LONG POINT RD 77055 #132-01-1967 L1977 **GS** *075 †85
LENTZ, America Alicia. 6624 FANNIN ST STE 1900 77030 #048-13-2001 L2004 **IM** *020 †20
LENZ, Matthew L. 1707 SUNSET BLVD, MEDICAL CLINIC OF HOUSTON 77005 #048-04-1984 L1987 **PA IM** *020 †20
LENZI, Renato. 1515 HOLCOMBE BLVD, BOX 302 77030 #561-17-1977 L1990 **ON IM** *020 †20
LEONARD, Denise Ione. 17010 SUGAR PINE DR, STE B 77090 #011-04-1988 L2007 **OBG** *020 †30
LEONARD, Tommy, Jr. 6621 FANNIN ST, MC-WT6-104 77030 #012-01-1973 L2000 **PD NPM** *020 †55
LEONARDO, Grace Cheng. 11037 FM 1960 RD W, STEEPLECHASE PEDIATRIC 77065 #748-11-1991 L2003 **PD** *020 †55
LEONG, Khai Pang. 1 BAYLOR PLZ, BAYLOR COLL OF MED 77030 #825-01-1987 **ALI** *100
LEONG, Mimi. 1709 DRYDEN RD, STE 1600 77030 #041-07-1994 L2005 **PS** *020 †85,65
LEONG-KEE, Susan Margaret. 6620 MAIN ST STE 1450, BAYLOR CLINIC 77030 #048-02-2003 L2007 **OBG** *020
LEONHARDT, Lara Michelle. ■ 77056 #422-01-2004 L2007 **PD** *020
LERMA, Juan. 9700 BISSONNET ST, STE 2500 77036 #048-13-1991 L1992 **IM** *020 †20
LERMAN, Steven Elliot. 12424 GREENSPOINT DR 77060 #028-02-1984 L1988 **OM** *050 †70
LERNER, Marvin Wolfe. 7777 SOUTHWEST FWY STE 820 77074 #048-02-1963 L1963 **OTO** *020 †45
LERNER, Seth P. 6560 FANNIN ST, STE 2100 77030 #048-04-1984 L1985 **U** *020 †95
LESAGE, Gene David. 6431 FANNIN ST, U TX HOUSTON MED SCH 77030 #028-46-1977 L1984 **GE HEP** *020 †20
LESEM, Michael David. 1010 WAVERLY ST 77008 #048-14-1981 L1981 **P** *020 †75
LESSER, Jary Marshall. 1300 MOURSUND ST, INSTITUTE 77030 #048-12-1973 L1974 **P** *020 †75
LESTER, Malisa Siri. PO BOX 20708, DEPT OF RADIOLOGY 77225 #048-14-2005 **DR** *012
LESTER, Matthew T. ■ 77054 #048-02-2006 **IM** *012
LETOURNEAU, Phillip Andre. ■ 77005 #021-05-2007 **GS** *012
LETSOU, George Vasilios. 6410 FANNIN ST, STE 450 77030 #035-01-1983 L1995 **TS GS** *020 †85,90
LEUNG, Kathryn Suetwa. 6701 FANNIN ST 77030 #040-02-1995 L2002 **PHO** *020 †20,55
LEUNG, Kevin Kinman. 6431 FANNIN ST, DEPT OF 77030 #016-11-2002 L2007 **GE** *012 †20
LEUNG, Michael P. 10701 VINTAGE PRESERVE PKW 77001 #048-04-1998 L2002 **OBG** *020 †30
LEUNG, Stephanie Kawing. ■ 77062 #048-13-2007 **PD** *012
LEV, Israel Eli. 1 BAYLOR PLZ, BAYLOR COLL OF MED 77030 #550-02-1990 **IC** *020
LEVAR, Joshua Michael. ■ 77025 #048-15-2008 *012
LEVARO-PANO, Fernando. 4126 SOUTHWEST FWY, STE 330 77027 #649-01-1990 L2001 **GS** *020
LEVENBACK, Charles F. 1515 HOLCOMBE BLVD BOX 440, MD ANDERSON CANCER CTR 77030 #035-47-1983 L1989 **GO GYN** *020 †30
LEVEQUE, Christopher M. 6565 FANNIN ST, F-102 METHODIST HOSP 77030 #021-05-1981 L1986 **CLP BBK** *020 †50
LEVEQUE, Jennifer Jo. 1 BAYLOR PLZ, DEPT OF DERMATOLOGY 77030 #021-01-2003 L2004 **D** *012
LEVERETT, Howard Arthur. 1603 DRISCOLL ST 77019 #048-04-1965 L1965 **FM** *020
LEVETOWN-BLUM, Marcia. ■ 77019 #051-04-1986 L1989 **PLM CCP** *040 †55
LEVIN, Bernard. 1515 HOLCOMBE BLVD, MD ANDERSON HOSP BOX 203 77030 #836-01-1964 L1985 **GE ON** *020 †20
LEVIN, Sherri S. 920 FROSTWOOD DR STE 550 77024 #048-14-1984 L1986 **OBG** *020 †30
LEVIN, Victor Alan. 1515 HOLCOMBE BLVD, BOX 431 77030 #056-05-1966 L1989 **N ON** *020 †75
LEVINE, Aaron Martin. 11914 ASTORIA BLVD, STE 540 77089 #041-12-1971 L1979 **PM PMM** *020 †60 ‡
LEVINE, Jonathan Neal. 6565 FANNIN ST MS 33, THE METHODIST HOSPITAL 77030 #035-09-1994 L1999 **RNR** *020 †80
LEVINE, Mark Elliot. 5602 LYONS AVE 77020 #048-14-1996 L2002 **FM** *020 †18
LEVINE, Robert L. 6431 FANNIN ST, STE MSB7.142 77030 #035-15-1980 L1987 **EM CCM** *020 †20,16
LEVINS, John P. 1201 DAIRY ASHFORD ST, STE 200 77079 #048-14-1984 L1986 **IM** *020 †20
LEVISON, Judith E. 3220 PLUMB ST 77005 #024-07-1976 L2000 **OBG** *020 †30
LEVY, Alejandro Gustavo. ■ 77035 #042-03-2003 **PHO** *012 †55
LEVY, Bruce Andrew. 6410 FANNIN ST, STE 1460 77030 #048-02-1986 L1988 **N** *020
LEVY, Freda Lynne. 6565 FANNIN ST 77030 #048-12-1985 L1987 **NEP IM** *020 †20
LEVY, Naomi Jaeger. 7500 BEECHNUT ST STE 352 77074 #048-14-1999 L2002 **PD** *020 †55
LEVY, Steven Jay. 13111 EAST FWY 77015 #041-77-1970, ▲ L1977 **IMG** *020 †20
LEVY, Steven Robt. 10375 NORTHWEST FWY, LONE STAR CHILDRENS MED 77092 #649-02-1982 L1986 **PD** *020

LEWEN, Gregory David. 6400 FANNIN ST, STE 1800 77030 #016-42-2003 L2007 **OPH** *100
LEWEN, Merrill Sue. 12727 KIMBERLEY LN 77024 #038-06-1990 L2006 **OBG** *020 †30
LEWINSKI, Uri Haim. M D ANDERSON TUMOR INST 77030 #869-02-1964 **ON HEM** *020
LEWIS, Glen Edward. ■ 77027 #048-04-1959 L1959 **U** *020
LEWIS, Jessica Koh. 1221 MCKINNEY ST, STE 40300 77010 #051-04-1972 L1982 **PUD PD** *020 †55
LEWIS, Jimmie Earl, Jr. 1221 MCKINNEY ST, STE 40300 77010 #048-04-1994 L1995 **IM** *020 †20
LEWIS, John Mance. 4901 CALHOUN RD 77004 #048-14-1975 L1975 **N** *020 †75
LEWIS, John Milton. ■ 77024 #048-04-1955 L1955 **CD** *071 †20
LEWIS, John Walter. 4901 CALHOUN RD, COLLEGE OF OPTOMETRY 77004 #048-02-1967 L1967 **OPH** *040 †35
LEWIS, Kay L Riffle. 15 GREENWAY PLZ UNIT 20J, 1300 MOURS UND 77046 #036-07-1964 L1969 **P PD** *020 †55
LEWIS, Mark A. 1709 DRYDEN RD STE 550, BCM FACULTY CTR 77030 #048-04-2005 **IM** *012
LEWIS, Richard Alan. 6550 FANNIN ST, STE 1501 77030 #025-01-1969 L1979 **OPH MG** *020 †35
LEWIS, Roy Sheldon. 915 GESSNER RD, STE 280 77024 #036-01-1994 L1996 **OTO** *020 †45
LEWIS, Valerae Olive. 1515 HOLCOMBE BLVD, BOX 408 77030 #024-01-1993 L2000 **OMO ORS** *020 †40
LEWITTON, Michael. 6560 FANNIN ST, STE 1440 77030 #035-01-1994 L1996 **U** *020 †95
LEY, Carolyn Anne. ■ 77030 #019-02-2006 **GS** *012
LEYVA, Astrud Lorraine Oc. ■ 77071 #048-02-2007 **IM** *012
LI, Benjamin T. 1 BAYLOR PLZ 350, BAYLOR COLL OF MED 77030 #033-05-2007 **P** *012
LI, George C. 6400 FANNIN ST, STE 3000 77030 #048-04-1984 L1985 **IC CD** *020 †20
LI, Jennifer Yeonghua. ■ 77054 #048-04-2005 L2005 *100
LI, Jianyi. 6565 FANNIN ST M227 77030 #243-20-1991 L2006 **NP** *012
LI, Joyce. ■ 77025 #016-11-2003 L2006 **PEM** *012 †55
LI, King Chuen Peter. 6565 FANNIN ST D280 77030 #065-01-1981 L2007 **DR** *020 †80
LI, Spencer Chun-Yueh. 915 GESSNER RD, STE 625 77024 #048-02-1987 L1988 **GE IM** *020 †20
LI, Yujing. 2727 W HOLCOMBE BLVD, MEDICAL CENTER ANESTHESIA 77025 #243-46-1987 L2002 **APM** *020 †05
LI, Zizhuang. 1200 HERMANN DR, PRESSLER W-1014 77004 #243-36-1983 L2003 **AN** *100
LIAO, Zhongxing. 1515 HOLCOMBE BLVD BOX 97, RADIATION ONCOLOGY 77030 #243-76-1982 L1998 **RO** *020 †80
LIAW, Shih-Ning. 6431 FANNIN ST, SCHOOL A 77030 #005-14-2002 L2005 **PD** *020
LICHTARGE, Olivier. 1 BAYLOR PLZ # T921, BAYLOR CLG MDCN MDL & HUM 77030 #005-11-1990 L2000 **END IM** *050 †20
LICHTIGER, Benjamin. 1515 HOLCOMBE BLVD UNIT 24 77030 #132-01-1964 L1971 **BBK CLP** *020 †50
LIDSKY, Martin David. 1709 DRYDEN RD # 09-42, DEPT OF INTERNAL MED 77030 #010-01-1954 L1964 **RHU IM** *020
LIEBER, Ira Howard. 17115 RED OAK DR, STE 120 77090 #041-09-1979 L1980 **CD IM** *020 †20
LIEBERMAN, Michael W. 6565 FANNIN ST B490, THE METHODIST HOSP 77030 #041-12-1967 L1989 **PTH OS** *050 †50
LIEBIG, Catherine Ann. 1 BAYLOR PLZ, STE 404D 77030 #028-34-2003 L2006 **GS** *012
LIEGEL, Joyce M. 110 CYPRESS STATION DR, STE 128 77090 #048-14-1985 L1996 **P** *020
LIFSCHITZ, Carlos Hugo. 6621 FANNIN ST MC, TEXAS CHILDRENS' HOSPITAL 77030 #132-01-1973 L1980 **PD GE** *050 †55
LIFSCHITZ, Lucia Veronica. ■ 77005 #048-04-2008 *012
LIGGAN, Deborah Y. ■ 77060 #048-16-1996 **FM** *100
LIGHT, David W, IV. 5632 PIPING ROCK LN, DEPT OF RADIOLOGY 77056 #048-02-1998 L2000 **DR** *020 †80
LIGHT, James Keith G. 1315 CALHOUN ST, STE 1506 77002 #836-01-1963 L1978 **U** *020 †95,28
LIGHT, Robert Alan. 6447 MAIN ST 77030 #048-02-1976 L1976 **U** *020 †95
LIGON, Ralph Edwin. 5656 KELLEY ST, LBJ GEN HOSPITAL-DEPT SURG 77026 #004-01-1967 L1998 **GS VS** *071 †85
LIKOVER, Larry Lee. 909 FROSTWOOD DR STE 353 77024 #048-04-1975 L1975 **ORS** *020 †40
LILLIBRIDGE, Scott R. ■ 77005 #023-12-1981 L1983 **FM** *020 †18
LILLY, Ralph Burton. 6410 FANNIN ST STE 1423 77030 #064-01-1964 L1968 **N OS** *020 †75
LIM, Alice. 7814 BELLAIRE BLVD 77036 #048-16-1994 L1996 **FM** *020 †18
LIM, Arthur. ■ 77225 #048-04-2007 **GS** *012
LIM, Beng-Hai. 1707 BRITTMOORE RD 77043 #825-01-1985 L1995 **HS** *020
LIM, David Joonbeom. 915 GESSNER RD, STE 685 77024 #038-44-1987 L1995 **U UP** *020 †95
LIM, John Mah. 915 GESSNER RD, STE 250 77024 #048-13-1982 L1983 **OPH** *020 †35 ‡
LIM, Marcy L. 6400 FANNIN ST, STE 2210-B 77030 #748-02-1990 L1996 **CD IM** *020 †20
LIM, Sherry. ■ 77030 #050-02-1998 L2005 **GS** *020 †85
LIM, Stanley Wyeyan. 1 BAYLOR PLZ, DEPARTMENT OF RADIOLOGY 77030 #035-09-1999 L2002 **DR** *100 †80
LIMA, Marcos Jose G. 1515 HOLCOMBE BLVD 77030 #187-02-1986 L1998 **ON** *020
LIMBRICK, Erikka Shandrea. ■ 77026 #048-13-2002 L2007 **AN** *100
LIN, Albert Pochen. ■ 77005 #005-14-2002 L2006 **IM** *100
LIN, Alison. 7777 SOUTHWEST FWY, STE 804 77074 #048-04-1992 L1993 **OPH** *020 †35
LIN, Carole. 6621 FANNIN ST, MAIL CODE 2-1495 77030 #016-43-1998 L2005 **AN** *020 †05
LIN, Chao-Ming. ■ 77030 #243-46-1952 L1984 **GP** *020
LIN, Dorothy Shih-Cheng S. ■ 77030 #243-46-1952 L1984 **NM** *071 †80,28
LIN, Edward Hueiguo. 1515 HOLCOMBE BLVD # 426, MDA CANCER CENTER 77030 #243-72-1986 L2000 **HO** *020 †20
LIN, Hsuan-Ju Lavinia. ■ 77054 #048-13-2005 **AN** *012
LIN, James Matthew. 9111 LAKES AT 610 DR, APT 213 77054 #035-06-2003 **ORS** *012
LIN, Jennifer Elaine. ■ 77005 #048-04-2008 *012
LIN, Jiejian. 1315 ST JOSEPH PKWY, STE 1710 77002 #243-21-1984 L1998 **ID** *020 †20
LIN, Joe C. 5209 SAGECIRCLE ST S 77056 #048-14-1991 L1993 **AN** *020 †05
LIN, Linda Hershyuan. 845 FM 1960 RD W, STE 101 77090 #016-06-1999 L2005 **OPH** *020 †35
LIN, Patrick Pohtseng. 1515 HOLCOMBE BLVD, UNIT 408 77030 #005-11-1990 L1998 **ORS** *020 †40
LIN, Pei. 1515 HOLCOMBE BLVD, 72 DEPT OF HEMA 77030 #243-24-1982 L2003 **HMP** *020 †50
LIN, Peter Hsin Hung. 1709 DRYDEN RD, FACULTY CENTER, SUITE 1500 77030 #016-42-1992 L2003 **GS** *020 †85
LIN, Ted Taiku. ■ 77099 #048-02-2008 *012
LIN, Thomas Chihtau. 1919 LA BRANCH ST 77002 #048-04-1990 L1991 **IM** *020 †20
LIN, Tony Jiann. 6624 FANNIN ST, STE 1900 77030 #048-04-1990 L1992 **IM** *020 †20
LIN, Wei. PO BOX 20708, UT MD ANDERSON CTR 77225 #024-01-2004 L2004 **HO** *012
LIN, Wendy Yar-Wen. ■ 77025 #016-06-2005 **PM** *012
LIN, Yung-Chang. ■ 77054 #244-04-1987 **ON** *020

■ = Address Information Privacy Protected

LIN, Yvonne Gail. ■ 77004 #005-15-2001 L2007 **OBG** *100

LINARES, Adriana Catalina. 6630 DE MOSS DR 77074 #264-04-1988 L2007 **FM** *100 †18

LINDBERG, Robert Dery. ■ 77005 #016-06-1959 L1963 **RO OS** *071 †80

LINDBERG, Scott Andrew. 6565 FANNIN ST 77030 #048-04-2001 L2005 **AN** *020 †05

LINDE, Stuart Allen. 2525 NORTH LOOP W, STE 220 77008 #836-02-1966 L1978 **AN** *020

LINDEMANN, Kenneth C, Jr. 16945 NORTHCHASE DR, STE 303 77060 #035-06-1985 L2003 **IM** *020 †20

LINDLEY, Gene Ray. 6447 MAIN ST 77030 #021-01-1954 L1954 **PUD IM** *071

LINDSAY, Amy Elizabeth. ■ 77064 #048-14-2002 L2006 **N** *020

LINDSAY, Christopher S. 3405 EDLOE ST, STE 200 77027 #065-06-1994 L1999 **ORS** *100

LINDSAY, Thomas Rambo. 211 HIGHLAND CROSS DR 77073 #051-04-2000 L2004 **EM** *020 †16

LINDSEY, Angela A. ■ 77027 #048-02-1997 **GS** *100

LINDSEY, James Norris. 6550 FANNIN ST, STE 961 77030 #048-02-1979 L1979 **P** *020

LINDSEY, John Wm. 6431 FANNIN ST, DEPT NEUROLOGY STE 7.044 M 77030 #024-01-1987 L1994 **IM** *020 †75

LING, James J. 6560 FANNIN ST STE 802, SCURLOCK TOWER 77030 #048-04-2002 L2006 **IM** *100

LINGLE, Robert Johnston, II. 6431 FANNIN ST, UTHSC DIV OF CARDIOLOGY 77030 #048-02-2003 L2007 **CD** *012 †20

LINK, Richard E, Jr. 6560 FANNIN ST STE 2100 77030 #005-11-1997 L1998 **U** *020 †95

LINTNER, David M. 6560 FANNIN ST STE 400 77030 #035-45-1986 L1992 **OSM** *020 †40

LINVILLE, Cain Robert. PO BOX 20708, UNIV TX MED SCH 77225 #028-03-2007 **GS** *012

LIOTTA, Domingo. 6621 FANNIN ST 77030 #132-02-1950 L1968 **CD GS** *020

LIOU, Aimee. ■ 77054 #028-02-2002 L2002 **PDC** *012 †55

LIPA, Joan Elizabeth. 1515 HOLCOMBE BLVD, BOX 062 77030 #065-06-1992 L2000 **GS** *020 †65

LIPPMAN, Howard Roy. 17070 RED OAK DR STE 407, NORTHWEST UROLOGY ASSOC 77090 #003-01-1986 L1987 **U** *020 †95

LIPPMAN, Scott Michael. 1515 HOLCOMBE BLVD # 432, UTMD ANDERSON CANCER CTR 77030 #023-07-1981 L1988 **ON** *012 †20

LIPSHULTZ, Larry I. 6560 FANNIN ST, SCURLOCK TOWER #2100 77030 #041-01-1968 L1975 **U** *050 †95

LIPSKI, Ian. 1400 HOLCOMBE BLVD # 409, DEPT OF ANESTHESIOLOGY/PAI 77030 #048-14-1999 L2003 **AN** *020 †05

LIS, Thaddeus William. 11800 ASTORIA BLVD 77089 #056-06-1988 L1996 **AN CCA** *020 †05

LISCUM, Kathleen R. 1504 TAUB LOOP, BEN TAUB GENERAL HOSP 77030 #048-04-1988 L1993 **GS CRS** *040 †85,10

LISMAN, Kevin A. 6560 FANNIN ST, STE 3000 77030 #048-12-1995 L1998 **CD** *020 †20

LISS, Shelly Emanuel. 7777 SOUTHWEST FWY, C-68 77074 #048-04-1961 L1961 **PM OS** *071 †60

LISSE, Scott A. 6560 FANNIN ST, SCURLOCK TOWER, SUITE 1130 77030 #048-04-1989 L1990 **IM** *020 †20

LISTER, Barbara J. 6565 FANNIN ST 77030 #048-04-1980 L1980 **RHU** *020 †20

LITOWSKY, David. ■ 77096 #025-01-1955 L1960 **IM** *071 †20

LITTLE, Hugh Robinson. ■ 77081 #016-11-2002 L2004 **EM** *100

LITTLE, Kim Jingming. ■ 77003 #048-04-2005 L2008 **PD** *012

LITTLE, Stephen H. 6550 FANNIN ST, STE 1901 77030 #065-10-1997 L2004 *100

LITTLES, Charita Shenee. 7322 SOUTHWEST FWY, STE 160 77074 #047-07-1995 L2003 **FM** *020 †18

LITTLETON, James Troy. ■ 77035 #048-04-1997 *100

LITTON, Jennifer K. 1515 HOLCOMBE BLVD, UNIT 1354 77030 #024-16-2000 L2003 **ON** *020 †20

LIU, Elizabeth Ann. ■ 77065 #048-14-1982 L1983 **R** *020

LIU, Fred H Y. ■ 77065 #242-22-1949 L1962 **PUD** *071

LIU, Henghsiao Edward. 6340 MAIN ST 77030 #048-12-2007 **IM** *012

LIU, James H. 17070 RED OAK DR, STE 205 77090 #048-04-1992 L2000 **PDO GS** *020 †45

LIU, Jing. 1515 HOLCOMBE BLVD, BOX 053 77030 #243-03-1982 L1999 **PCP** *020 †50

LIU, Jinsong. ■ 77005 #243-16-1983 L2006 **PTH** *020 †50

LIU, Joseph H. 17322 RED OAK DR 77090 #048-02-1990 L1995 **APM** *020

LIU, Lesley Lynn. ■ 77054 #019-02-2004 **MPD** *012

LIU, Qi. ■ 77054 #243-16-1988 L2002 **ON** *100 †20

LIU, Roy Min. ■ 77004 #016-11-1997 L2001 **GS** *020

LIU, Wei. 5445 LA BRANCH ST 77004 #243-45-1982 L1998 **AN** *020 †05

LIU, Wenli. 1515 HOLCOMBE BLVD, BOX 437 77030 #243-76-1988 L1999 **IM** *020 †20

LIU, Xiaoqing. 7777 SOUTHWEST FWY, STE 1036 77074 #243-26-1982 L2006 **P** *020 †75

LIVELO, Reynaldo Ferrer. ■ 77066 #748-08-1968 *100

LIVESAY, James Jinkins. 1101 BATES AVE, STE P514 77030 #048-04-1973 L1973 **TS VS** *020 †85,90

LIVESAY, John Nessly. 7600 FANNIN ST 77054 #048-14-1983 L1983 **AN** *020 †05

LIVESAY, William Rugeley. ■ 77063 #048-02-1946 L1946 **IM CD** *071 †20

LIVESAY, William Scott. 7614 RIVER POINT DR 77063 #048-12-1972 L1973 **GYN OS** *020 †30

LIVINGSTON, Christopher K. 6431 FANNIN ST STE 4.150, DIV OF PLASTIC SURG-UTMC 77030 #020-02-1996 L1998 **PS HS** *020 †65

LIVINGSTONE, Ronald A. 9099 WESTHEIMER RD STE 107 77063 #918-01-1963 L1976 **OBG** *071

LIVORSI, Daniel Joseph. ■ 77030 #016-11-2005 L2006 **IM** *012

LLERENA, Jose. ■ 77042 #737-06-1983 L1998 **DR** *020 †80

LLOYD, John Morgan, III. 7580 FANNIN ST STE 310 77054 #048-02-1981 L1981 **OBG** *020 †30

LLOYD, Kenneth Scott. 6550 FANNIN ST, STE 2403 77030 #010-02-1984 L1987 **PUD IM** *020 †20

LLOYD, Ralph Roland, III. 6720 BERTNER ST 77030 #004-01-1979 L1979 **AN** *020

LO, Huayying. ■ 77082 #048-12-2008 L2008 *012

LOBLEY, Kelly Bruce. 15655 CYPRESSWOOD MEDCL DR, STE 100 77014 #048-04-1985 L1986 **PD** *020 †55

LOBOPRABHU, Sheila M. 6655 TRAVIS ST, BAYLOR COLLEGE OF MEDICINE 77030 #495-96-1993 L1998 **P** *020 †75

LOCK, Kin Shing. 12606 W HOUSTON CENTR BLVD, STE 200 77082 #048-02-1986 L1987 **PD** *020 †55

LOCK, Richard Cheuk. 12121 RICHMOND AVE STE 413 77082 #048-14-1991 L1994 **IM** *020 †20

LOCKE, James Perry. 2101 NASA PKWY, MAILCODE: SD13 77058 #056-05-1994 L1998 **EM AM** *020 †16,70

LOCKHART, Christopher R. 8307 KNIGHT RD, # K 77054 #048-14-1991 L1992 **IM** *020 †20

LODATO, Robert Francis. 6431 FANNIN ST # 274 77030 #023-07-1978 L1985 **PUD CCM** *020 †20

LODHI, Sundus A. ■ 77096 #048-14-2003 L2006 **NEP** *012 †20

LOE, Hardy Douglas, Jr. ■ 77098 #048-02-1955 L1955 **PHP** *071

LOEB, Robert S. 9220 KIRBY DR, STE 700 77054 #065-01-1988 L2001 **R** *020 †80

LOFTIS, Laura L. 6621 FANNIN ST, WT 6-006 77030 #048-16-1990 L1991 **CCP PD** *020 †55

LOFTON, Latanya Denise. ■ 77054 #001-06-2003 L2005 **SCI** *012

LOGAN, James Scott. CODE SD24 NASA/JSC 77058 #039-01-1978 L1982 **AM** *020 †70

LOGHIN, Catalin. 6431 FANNIN ST, CARDIOLOGY DIV, RM MSB 1.2 77030 #781-02-1985 L2001 **CD** *020 †20

LOGHIN, Monica Elena. 1515 HOLCOMBE BLVD, DEPT NEURO-ONCOLOGY UNIT 4 77030 #781-02-1983 L2006 **N** *020 †75

LOGOTHETIS, Christopher J. 1515 HOLCOMBE BLVD 77030 #418-01-1974 L1978 **ON IM** *020 †20

LOKHANDWALA, Abbas F. 6624 FANNIN ST, STE 2510 77030 #704-16-1989 L1996 **NEP IM** *020 †20

LOMAX, James Welton, II. 1 BAYLOR PLZ # MS350 77030 #048-04-1971 L1971 **P PYA** *040 †75

LOMBANA, Fernando. 2323 WIRT RD, STE F 77055 #264-04-1982 L1987 **FM PD** *020 †55 ‡

LOMBARD, Earl Joseph, II. 7900 FANNIN ST, STE 2100 77054 #047-07-1991 L1995 **OBG** *020 †30

LOMBARD, Richard Jos. 6909 LYONS AVE STE B, LYONS MEDICAL CLINIC 77020 #048-12-1990 L1992 **FM** *020 †18

LOMO, Adjetey Kwaku. 601 WAYSIDE DR, STE B 77011 #412-01-1973 L1994 **PD** *020 †55

LOMONACO, John Jos, Jr. 1009 MISSOURI ST 77006 #048-14-1990 L1994 **PS** *020 †85,65

LONCAREC, Sonja K. 2010 FM 1960 RD, WESTFIELD EMERGENCY CENTER 77073 #957-01-1954 L1972 **OM GS** *020

LONCARICH, David Patrick. 6500 FANNIN ST, STE 1006 77030 #005-06-1992 L2001 **ORS** *020 †40

LONDON, Jeffrey Chas. 7401 MAIN ST, DEPARTMENT OF RADIOLOGY 77030 #048-14-1983 L1983 **DR** *020 †20

LONDONO OBREGON, Camila. 6431 FANNIN ST, AT HO 77030 #319-07-2003 **PD** *012

LONG, John Kendall. 1200 BINZ ST STE 1275 77004 #048-14-1975 L1975 **PS GS** *020 †65

LONG, John Mallory. 4101 GREENBRIAR ST STE 100 77098 #048-04-1963 L1963 **PD** *020 †55

LONG, Scott Wesley. ■ 77062 #048-02-2008 *012

LONG, Walter K. 5718 BELLAIRE BLVD 77081 #012-05-1953 L1954 **GS EM** *040

LONGANO, Frank Joseph. ■ 77081 #038-06-2004 L2007 **IM** *100 †20

LONGHINI, Luca. 6411 FANNIN ST 7TH FL, HERMANN EYE CTR 77030 #561-22-1990 **OPH** *100

LONGMIRE, Stephen. 1504 TAUB LOOP 77030 #048-04-1980 L1982 **AN OBG** *050 †05

LONGO, Eric S. ■ 77006 #048-14-2002 L2007 **MSR** *012 †80 ‡

LONGO, Lara Ann. 7500 SAN FELIPE ST, STE 200A 77063 #048-14-1995 L1996 **FM OM** *020 †18 ‡

LONGO, Marc Narciso. 7500 SAN FELIPE ST STE 200 77063 #048-14-1990 L1991 **OPH OS** *020 †35

LOO, Chee Siew. 909 FROSTWOOD DR STE 224 77024 #825-01-1985 L2004 **IM END** *020 †20

LOPAS, Carol Laverne. ■ 77061 #165-04-1959 L1967 **OBG** *020 †30

LOPEZ, Alberto Gerardo. 6624 FANNIN ST, STE 2780 77030 #005-11-1979 L1984 **P** *030 †75

LOPEZ, Alfredo Ruben. 1 BAYLOR PLZ, DEPT OF ANESTH SM1003 77030 #048-14-2002 L2007 **ACA** *012

LOPEZ, George Arthur. 6550 FANNIN ST, STE 1801 77030 #005-02-1995 L2002 **N** *020 †75

LOPEZ, J Alberto. 6624 FANNIN ST, STE 2780 77030 #935-01-1984 L1991 **CD ICE** *020 †20

LOPEZ, Lina Maria. 1300 MOURSUND ST, PSYCHIATRY DEPT. 77030 #264-16-1994 L2006 **CHP** *100

LOPEZ, Michelle Ann. ■ 77019 #048-04-2006 **PD** *012

LOPEZ, Miguel Angel. ■ 77071 #649-33-1991 L2001 **FM** *100 †18

LOPEZ, Randolph A. 17070 RED OAK DR, STE 101 77090 #035-03-1998 L2005 **HS** *100

LOPEZ, Rodolfo Avelino. ■ 77059 #748-01-1963 L1981 **DR** *030 †80

LOPEZ, Suzanne Marie. 6431 FANNIN ST, MSB 3.242 77030 #017-20-1987 L1991 **NPM** *020 †55

LOPEZ, Ulysses Co. 4545 POST OAK PLACE DR, STE 130 77027 #748-01-1988 L1997 **IM** *020 †20

LOPEZ AYALA, Gustavo Andr. ■ 77030 #649-14-2002 **FP** *012

LOPEZ GODOY, Francisco Gu. ■ 77061 #341-06-1996 **FP** *012

LOPEZ-MIRANDA, Beatriz. 1221 MCKINNEY ST, STE 40300 77010 #847-15-1988 L2001 **PDR** *020 †10

LOPEZ-SANCHEZ, Moises. ■ 77089 #649-01-1953 L1963 **IM** *071

LOPEZ-TERRADA, Dolores H. 6621 FANNIN ST, STE B1 77030 #847-08-1987 L2000 **PTH** *020 †20

LOPOSZKO, Joseph. ■ 77267 #561-01-1951 L1955 **P** *020

LOQUIAS, Jesus Arthur Pel. ■ 77054 #748-10-2000 **FM** *100

LORCH, Steven Michael. 6431 FANNIN ST, MSB 3.126 77030 #012-05-2001 L2007 **PDC** *100 †55

LORD, Brian. 1140 WESTMONT DR STE 425 77015 #035-08-1976 L1994 **U** *020 †95

LORENTE-DINNBIER, Lorenzo. 800 PEAKWOOD DR STE 4D 77090 #847-08-1968 L1975 **N** *020 †75

LORENZO, Pablo. 40 FM 1960 RD W # 185 77090 #649-01-1971 L1975 **EM** *020

LORIGAN, James Gerard. ■ 77027 #539-04-1978 L1989 **DR** *020

LORIN, Martin Irving. 6621 FANNIN ST 77030 #035-19-1959 L1978 **PD PUD** *040 †55

LOTFI, Djamchid. 6621 FANNIN ST, STE 1550 77030 #917-20-1963 L1989 **N IM** *020 †20

LOTLIKAR, Prashant Y. 3707 DUMBARTON ST, DEPT OF CARDIOVASCULAR ANE 77025 #048-02-1991 L1992 **AN** *020 †05 ‡

LOTZ, Dawid Gabriel. ■ 77096 #836-04-1981 **AN** *100

LOTZE, Eberhard Conrad. 7900 FANNIN ST 77054 #048-04-1965 L1965 **GYN** *020 †30

LOTZE, Peter M. 7900 FANNIN ST, STE 4000 77054 #048-04-1994 L1999 **OBG** *020 †30

LOTZE, Timothy E. 6621 FANNIN ST STE 1250 77030 #048-13-1995 L1999 **CHN** *020 †55,10

LOU, Eugene Chunlin. 909 FROSTWOOD DR STE 340 77024 #048-04-1994 L1997 **ORS** *020 †40

LOUIS, Alfred Robt. 8109 CULLEN BLVD, STE E 77051 #047-07-1968 L1970 **FM GS** *020 ‡

LOUIS, Chrystal Ursula. 6621 FANNIN ST, MC 3-3320 77030 #021-01-2001 L2007 **PHO** *100 †55

LOUIS, Penelope Terhune. 6624 FANNIN ST, 19TH FL 77030 #002-02-1981 L1986 **PD** *020 †55

LOUTFI, Rabih Habib. 1504 TAUB LOOP, BEN TAUB GENERAL HOSPITAL 77030 #605-01-2002 L2006 **PCC** *012 †20

LOVE, Almer Ray, II. 2002 HOLCOMBE BLVD, MC PC111 77030 #024-05-2000 L2005 **IM** *100

LOVE, David A. 820 GESSNER RD, STE 750 77024 #048-04-1996 L2000 **P** *020 †75

LOVE, Latanya Jones. 6431 FANNIN ST, STE 3.142 77030 #048-02-2000 L2002 **MPD** *020 †55,20

LOVITT, Steven M. 7505 MAIN ST, STE 290 77030 #048-04-1995 L1999 **N** *020 †75

LOVOI, Joseph J. ■ 77090 #048-14-2008 *012

LOW, Morton David. 1200 HERMANN PRESSLER DR 77030 #065-05-1960 L1991 **OS N** *030

LOW, Richard Christensen. 14441 MEMORIAL DR STE 12 77079 #036-01-1973 L1976 **PD** *020 †55 ‡

LOWE, Chyrl Lynn. 6565 FANNIN ST 77030 #048-04-1977 L1978 **AN** *020 †05

LOWE, Thomas Elton, Jr. 1919 LA BRANCH ST 77002 #021-01-1962 L1963 **FM ADM** *020

LOWE, Walter Richard. 6620 MAIN ST, 13TH FL 77030 #048-14-1983 L1983 **ORS OSM** *020 †40

LOWENTHAL, Elizabeth Dawn. 6621 FANNIN ST, # CC1570 77030 #048-04-2000 L2003 **PD** *020 †55

LOWRY, Adam Wayne. 6621 FANNIN ST 77030 #012-05-2005 L2007 **PD** *012

LOWRY, Angus M. ■ 77006 #048-13-2002 L2004 **AN** *012 †20

LOYA, Aslam M. 11914 ASTORIA BLVD, STE 125 77089 #704-02-1991 L1997 **IM** *020 †20

LOYA, Georgina. 7825 HIGHWAY 6 N, STE 107 77095 #048-02-1995 L1998 **FM** *020 †18

LOYA, Mohammed Altaf. ■ 77089 #704-02-1992 L2004 **PYG** *020 †75

LOYA, Munir M.. 11914 ASTORIA BLVD STE 125 77089 #704-02-1998 L2004 **IM** *020

LOYALKA, Pranav. 6720 BERTNER ST, MC1-133 77030 #028-03-1997 L2002 **IC** *020 †20

LOYD, Herbert Melton. 6560 FANNIN ST STE 500 77030 #021-05-1959 L1967 **DR** *071 †80

LOYER, Evelyne Madeleine. MD ANDERSON CANCER CTR, DEPT RAD 77030 #396-31-1984 L1989 **DR** *020 †80

LOZANO, Martha Ruth. 12739 WOODFOREST BLVD # A 77015 #649-30-1983 L1987 **PD** *020 †55

LOZANO, Pablo. 6624 FANNIN ST STE 2000, KELSEY-SEYBOLD CLINIC 77030 #649-14-1978 L1993 **CD IM** *020 †20

LU, Bee Sun. 3935 WESTHEIMER RD, STE 238 77027 #748-01-1963 L1972 **IM** *020

LU, Bening Tan. 12060 BELLAIRE BLVD, STE D 77072 #748-01-1972 L1976 **PD** *020 †55

LU, Bing. 710 FM 1960 RD W 77090 #243-16-1987 L1996 **AN** *020 †05

LU, Charles. 1400 HOLCOMBE BLVD UNIT 4 77030 #008-01-1991 L1999 **ON** *050 †20

LU, Christopher Paul-Shie. ■ 77071 #048-14-2004 L2007 **FM** *020 †18

LU, Hsin Huang. 2457 S BRAESWOOD BLVD, RADIATION ONCOL CTR 77030 #056-05-1982 L1984 **RO** *020 †80 ‡

LU, Huifang. ■ 77030 #243-47-1988 L2005 **RHU AI** *100 †20,03

LU, Karen Hsieh. 1500 HOLCOMBE BLVD BOX 440, GYNECOLOGIC ONCOLOGY DEPT 77030 #008-01-1991 L1999 **OBG** *020 †30

LU, Lee Bach. 1504 TAUB LOOP, BEN TAUB GENERAL HOSPITAL 77030 #048-04-1994 L1997 **IM** *020 †20

LU, Shitze. 6410 FANNIN ST, STE 1228 77030 #048-04-1994 L1997 **IM** *020 †20

LU, Thomas. 1313 HERMANN DR, PARK PLAZA HOSPITAL 77004 #035-09-1996 L2001 **DR VIR** *020 †80

LU, Tzu Chiau. 2912 ELLA LEE LN 77019 #385-02-1964 L1970 **P** *020 †75

LU, Wen-Hsiung. ■ 77024 #244-02-1963 L1974 **PD PN** *071 †55

LUBEN, Debra Lynn. 1221 MCKINNEY ST, STE 40300 77010 #028-46-1991 L1997 **PD** *020 †55

LUBETKIN, Sanford Jay. 7737 SOUTHWEST FWY, STE 780 77074 #010-02-1977 L1979 **CD IM** *020 †20

LUCAS, Michael James. 5656 KELLEY ST, LYNDON BAINES JOHNSON HOSP 77026 #005-14-1981 L1986 **OBG** *020 †30

LUCAS, Quincy Marso. 4545 POST OAK PLACE DR, STE 130 77027 #016-42-1998 L2008 **IM** *020

LUCAS, William Frederick. 17750 CALI DR, TEXAS CYPRESS CREEK HOSP 77090 #048-12-1961 L1961 **GP** *030

LUCCI, Anthony. 6550 FANNIN ST STE 1628, BAYLOR COLLEGE OF MEDICINE 77030 #048-15-1991 L1993 **GS** *020 †85

LUCCI, Anthony Peter. 7500 SAN FELIPE ST, STE 1050 77063 #561-17-1958 L1963 **OBG** *020 †30

LUCHI, Robert J. 1 BAYLOR PLZ # M320 77030 #041-01-1952 L1971 **IMG IM** *071 †20

LUCKETT, Floyd E, III. 2317 FANNIN ST 77002 #048-04-1983 L1983 **IM** *020

LUDWICK, James Joseph. 12606 W HOUSTN CNTR #220, W HOUSTONN ENT & SLEEP CTR 77082 #038-43-1999 L2004 **OTO** *020 †45

LUDWIG, Joseph Aloysius. ■ 77005 #018-03-1998 L2006 **IM** *020 †20

LUDWIG, Michelle Suzanne. 1515 HOLCOMBE BLVD, ANDERSON CANC 77030 #012-05-2005 **RO** *012

LUEHR, Susan L. 8524 HIGHWAY 6 N BOX 342 77095 #048-14-1992 L1993 **AN** *020 †05

LUENGAS, Jorge. 1801 NORTH LOOP W, STE 30 77008 #048-14-1994 L1997 **FM** *020 †18

LUERSSEN, Thomas George. 1709 DRYDEN RD 77030 #017-20-1976 L2008 **NS PD** *020 †25

LUETHCKE, Rebecca Good. 915 GESSNER RD, STE 540A 77024 #048-04-1984 L1986 **OBG** *020 †30

LUFSCHANOWSKI, Roberto M. 6624 FANNIN ST, STE 2780 77030 #132-01-1960 L1968 **CD** *020 †20

LUGO-FARIA, Merlin D. 301 HAMILTON ST, SAN JOSE COMM CLC 77002 #042-01-1961 L1974 **FM GPM** *071 †70,18

LUINA, Alejandro. ■ 77004 #042-03-2003 L2007 **SP** *012 †50

LUKEMAN, John Milton. 1515 HOLCOMBE BLVD, DEPT PATH 77030 #051-04-1945 L1955 **PTH** *071 †50

LUKENS, Frank Jesse. 444 FM 1959 RD, STE A 77034 #429-02-1995 L2003 **GE** *020 †20

LUMICAO, Tomas G. 3701 KIRBY DR, STE 100 77098 #748-10-1975 L1995 **FM** *020 †18

LUMMIS, Frederick R, Jr. ■ 77019 #048-02-1956 L1956 **GE IM** *075 †20

LUMSDEN, Alan Boyd. 6560 FANNIN ST, STE 1006 77030 #919-03-1982 L2003 **VS** *020 †85

LUMSDEN, Robt Macken, II. 5656 KELLEY ST 77026 #005-02-1963 L1994 **HS** *040 †40

LUNA, Hortencia G. 5656 KELLEY ST 77026 #049-01-1982 L1983 **EM PD** *062 †16

LUNA, Jeffrey Thomas Pagt. 6723 BERTNER ST 77030 #748-01-1997 **OMO** *012

LUNA, Mario A. 1515 HOLCOMBE BLVD BX 85 77030 #649-14-1959 L1965 **PTH** *020 †50

LUNA, Raymond. ■ 77054 #048-14-2008 *012

LUNN, William Wilburn, II. 1709 DRYDEN RD, STE 950 77030 #048-12-1990 L1991 **PCC** *020 †20

LUONG, Trung Trent. ■ 77089 #048-12-2006 **IM** *012

LUPER, William E. 8850 LONG POINT RD 77055 #048-12-1960 L1960 **CLP IM** *020 †50

LUPO, Pamela Jean. ■ 77059 #048-04-2007 **PD** *012

LUPSKI, James R. 6701 FANNIN ST 77030 #035-19-1985 L1989 **PD MG** *020 †55,19

LUTSCHG, Kenneth William. 7026 OLD KATY RD 77024 #021-06-1994 L1995 **DR** *020 †80

LUU, Nguyen Trong. 211 HIGHLAND CROSS DR, STE 275 77073 #048-02-2002 L2005 **IM** *020 †20

LUU, Phong T. 6630 DE MOSS DR 77074 #048-14-1993 L1995 **IM** *020 †20

LUU, Phuong Que. ■ 77086 #048-15-2008 *012

LUU NGUYEN, Anh Kim. 8411 W BELLFORT ST 77071 #941-01-1978 L1984 **AN** *020

LUX, Melanie Plunkett. 6977 MAIN ST, CHILDREN 77030 #048-04-1992 L1993 **AN** *020 †05

LUX, Thomas R. 6431 FANNIN ST, MSB 1122 77030 #048-14-1990 L1991 **IM** *020 †20

LUYIMBAZI, David Tebukya. ■ 77004 #035-09-2005 **GS** *012

LUYKX, Ruth Atlas. 14441 MEMORIAL DR STE 1 77079 #165-06-1978 L1985 **CHN N** *020

LY, Linda Lananh. ■ 77005 #048-14-2007 *012

LY, Peter-Danh Cong. ■ 77005 #048-14-2006 **P** *012

LYMAN, Mary Joanna. 12606 W HOUSTON CENTR BLVD, STE 260 77082 #048-14-2000 L2003 **PD** *020 †55

LYMAN, Richard Dwight. ■ 77059 #048-12-1961 L1962 **EM** *071

LYN, Michelle Anderson. 6621 FANNIN ST, MCI-1481 77030 #035-06-1988 L1994 **PD PEM** *020 †55

LYNCH, Edward Conover. 6550 FANNIN ST, THE METHODIST HOSPITAL 77030 #028-02-1956 L1962 **HEM** *030 †20

LYNCH, Garrett Rushing. 6620 MAIN ST, STE 1375 77030 #048-04-1974 L1981 **ON** *020 †20

LYNCH, Mary L. 2727 GRAMERCY ST, KELSEY-SEYBOLD CLINIC PA 77025 #030-06-1979 L1988 **PTH IM** *020 †20,50

LYNCH, Patrick Michael. 1515 HOLCOMBE BLVD # 78 77030 #030-06-1983 L1988 **GE IM** *020 †20

LYNCH, Richard Harold. ■ 77224 #030-05-1960 L1965 **GS CD** *020 †85

LYNCOOK, Richard Xavier. 1250 CYPRESS STATION DR 77090 #008-01-1999 L2007 **MPD** *020 †20,55

LYOS, Andrew Thos. 6560 FANNIN ST STE 1530 77030 #025-01-1987 L1995 **PS FPS** *020 †45,65

LYPKA, Michael Alexander. ■ 77004 #005-06-2003 L2004 **PS** *012

LYUKSYUTOVA, Olga I. ■ 77025 #048-02-2006 **AN** *012

MA, Tony S. 2002 HOLCOMBE BLVD, SECTION OF CARDIOLOGY (111 77030 #062-01-1983 L1987 **CD IM** *020 †20

MAALOUF, Jeanne Kathleen. 6621 FANNIN ST, MC 2-1495 77030 #048-13-2002 L2006 **PAN** *020

MABADEJE, Adetayo Saida. 7777 SOUTHWEST FWY 77074 #690-02-1995 L2007 **AN PME** *020 †05

MABATAH, Augustine Kanebi. 8300 HOMESTEAD RD 77028 #048-02-1991 L1992 **OPH** *020 †35

MABRIE, Herman James. 150 W PARKER RD STE 506 77076 #047-07-1973 L1979 **OTO HNS** *020

MACALUSO, Annamaria. ■ 77024 #048-14-2008 *012

MACAPINLAC, Homer Aquino. 1515 HOLCOMBE BLVD BOX 83, U.T. M.D. ANDERSON CANCER 77030 #748-10-1983 L2002 **NM** *020 †28

MACCATO, Maurizio L. 7900 FANNIN ST, STE 2600 77054 #048-04-1984 L1988 **OBG ID** *020 †30

MAC FARLANE, Deborah F. 1515 HOLCOMBE BLVD, BOX 434 77030 #671-01-1985 L2003 **D** *020 †15

MAC GREGOR, Mark G. 830 GEMINI ST 77058 #048-02-1986 L1987 **IM** *020 †20

MACHELEDT, Janet Elaine. 1140 BUSINESS CENTER DR, STE 360 77043 #048-14-1986 L1987 **ON HO** *020 †20

MACHKHAS, Hazem. 2500 FONDREN RD, STE 260 77063 #605-01-1990 L2004 **N** *020 †75

MACIA, Jennifer Lynn. 7500 BEECHNUT ST, STE 352 77074 #012-05-1996 L1999 **PD** *020 †55

MACIAS, Charles Gilbert. 6621 FANNIN ST STE A165, NC 1-1481 77030 #048-12-1991 L1993 **PD** *020 †55

MACIAS SEPULVEDA, Catalina. 1 BAYLOR PLZ 77030 #649-52-2001 **FM** *100

MACICEK, Scott Lawrence. ■ 77007 #021-05-2004 **PDC** *012

MAC INERNEY, Douglas M. 1313 HERMANN DR, PARK PLAZA HOSPITAL 77004 #048-02-1990 L1991 **DR** *020 †80

MACK, David R. 13300 HARGRAVE RD, STE 400 77070 #048-04-1990 L1991 **ORS** *020 †40

MACK, Marie F. 18220 TOMBALL PKWY, STE 400 77070 #048-04-1990 L1991 **D** *020 †15

MACK, William Harold. 4151 SOUTHWEST FWY, STE 300 77027 #047-07-1964 L1967 **PD** *020

MACKAY, Bruce. 1515 HOLCOMBE BLVD BOX 85 77030 #803-03-1956 L1970 **PTH** *075 †50

MAC KENZIE, Kenneth Roy. 6410 FANNIN ST 77030 #062-01-1961 L1988 **P OS** *030 †75

MACKEY, David Craig. 1515 HOLCOMBE BLVD, DEPARTMENT OF ANESTHESIOLO 77030 #028-03-1979 L1990 **AN PMM** *020 †20,05

MAC LEAN, Robert Appleby. ■ 77024 #035-20-1962 L1968 **PHP PUD** *071

MAC MAHON, Andrew Ernest. 2503 DRISCOLL ST 77019 #008-01-1964 L1969 **PD** *020 †55

MACNEIL, Kara Bannerman. PO BOX 20708, DEPT OF OB/GYN 77225 #011-03-2004 L2008 **OBG** *012

MACRIS, Michael Peter. 1631 NORTH LOOP W, STE 240 77008 #012-01-1984 L1986 **TS VS** *020 †85,90

MADABHUSHI, Ranga R. 7600 BEECHNUT ST 77074 #495-50-1980 L1993 **AN** *020 †05

MADAN, Anand. 6431 FANNIN ST, UNIV OF TEXAS HLTH SCI CTR 77030 #495-29-1994 L2006 **GE IM** *020 †20 ‡

MADAN, Anita. PO BOX 20708, UNIV TX MED SCH AT HOUSTON 77225 #665-01-2004 **N** *012

MADAN, Niti. 6431 FANNIN ST 4.148, UNIV OF TEXAS HEALTH SCIEN 77030 #495-29-1997 L2006 **NEP** *012

MADAN, Pankaj. 1 BAYLOR PLZ 77030 #495-36-2003 **IM** *012

MADAN, Veena. 6500 HORNWOOD DR 77074 #496-02-1968 L1978 **AN** *020

MADANAT, Faik Farah. ■ 77025 #575-01-1983 *100

MADANAT, Faris Farah. ■ 77096 #605-01-1973 **PD** *100 †55

MADDOX, Billy Ray. 8850 LONG POINT RD 77055 #048-04-1957 L1957 **NM** *020

MADDOX, Henry E, III. 7777 SOUTHWEST FWY, STE 820 77074 #048-02-1953 L1953 **OS OTO** *071 †45

MADDURI, Nirupama S. 6621 FANNIN ST, SUITE CCC 1530 77030 #028-46-1998 L2005 **PD** *100

MADEWELL, John Edward. 1515 HOLCOMBE BLVD, BOX 1273 77030 #039-01-1969 L1983 **DR** *020 †80

MADJID, Mohammad. 6770 BERTNER ST, MC 2-255 77030 #517-01-1997 **IM** *012

MADJIDI, Azita. 1 BAYLOR PLZ, DIV OF PLASTIC SURGERY 77030 #396-22-1989 L2003 **PS** *012

MADJITEY, George Eric. 2000 CRAWFORD ST, STE 1310 77002 #010-03-1976 L1982 **OBG** *020 †30

MADKAN, Bandana Wendy. 6655 TRAVIS ST, STE 980 77030 #012-01-2004 L2005 **D** *012

MADOFF, David Craig. 1515 HOLCOMBE BLVD, UNIT 325 77030 #041-12-1995 L2000 **DR** *020 †80

MADRID, Francisco Andres. 2002 HOLCOMBE BLVD 77030 #275-01-1943 L1966 **FM** *071 †18

MADRIZ, Omar I. 920 FROSTWOOD DR 77024 #048-04-1995 L2000 **CRS GS** *020 †85,10

MADU, Clara Chinaemerem. ■ 77041 #010-03-2002 L2006 **IM** *100 †20

MAFFET, Mark Wm. 6620 MAIN ST STE 1325, DIV OF ORTHOPEDIC SURGERY 77030 #048-04-1989 L1990 **ORS** *020 †40

MAGANTI, Rashmi M.. ■ 77030 #496-39-2000 L2007 **RHU** *012 †20

MAGAT, Elaine Magdaraog. ■ 77030 #748-01-1997 **PM** *012

MAGEE, Mary L. 1919 LA BRANCH ST 77002 #048-02-1946 L1946 **GYN** *071 †30

MAGEE, Wendy C. 11003 RESOURCE PKWY # 104 77089 #048-04-1994 L1996 **D DS** *020 †15

MAGHNIE, Afif Ali. ■ 77057 #649-14-1980 *020

MAGID, Jonathan Marc. 1707 SUNSET BLVD, MEDICAL CLINIC OF HOUSTON, 77005 #048-12-1999 L2002 **IM** *020 †20

MAGID, Mannie Lionel. 5420 DASHWOOD DR, STE 100 77081 #836-01-1969 L1979 **FM GP** *020

■ = Address Information Privacy Protected

MAGILL, Linda S. 2424 W HOLCOMBE BLVD, MEDICAL CENTER ANESTHESIA 77030
#048-14-1987 L1988 **AN** *020 †05

MAGLIOLO, Albert M. 701 SAN JACINTO ST 77002 #048-02-1945 L1945 **OS GP** *071

MAGNUS-LAWSON, Saml Benj. 1315 ST JOSEPH PKWY, STE 1704 77002 #690-01-1973 L1983
IM NEP *072 †20

MAGUADOG, Gloria D. 4800 W 34TH ST 77092 #048-14-1999 L2002 **P** *020

MAHAJAN, Anita. 1515 HOLCOMBE BLVD, BOX 097 77030 #067-01-1992 L2002 **RO** *020 †80

MAHAJAN, Sushma Gupta. ■ 77024 #495-36-1966 L1975 **PTH** *071 †50

MAHER, James Arthur, Jr. 2727 W HOLCOMBE BLVD 77025 #051-04-1974 L1978
IM GE *020

MAHER, Michael R. 77095 #021-06-2004 **AN** *012

MAHESHWARI, Bani. ■ 77004 #048-04-2008 *012

MAHESHWARI, Praveen. ■ 77030 #495-77-2002 *100

MAHESHWARI, Shail. ■ 77004 #048-16-2005 L2007 **IM** *012

MAHFOUD, Caroline W. 6621 FANNIN ST, CHILDRENS TX HOSP/MC 3 248 77030 #605-01-1987
PN *100

MAHMARIAN, John Jos. 6550 FANNIN ST, STE 677 77030 #035-09-1980 L1981 **CD IM** *050 †20

MAHMOOD, Hammad. 1 BAYLOR PLZ 77030 #704-25-2002 **FM** *100

MAHMOODUDDIN, Faisal. ■ 77054 #030-06-2005 **AN** *012

MAHMOODUDDIN, Salma. 7600 BEECHNUT ST 77074 #495-21-1971 L1981 **PTH** *050

MAHONEY, Donald H. 6621 FANNIN ST, TEXAS CHILDRENS HOSPITAL 77030
#021-01-1972 L1977 **PD HEM** *020 †55

MAHONEY, Stephen E. 12606 W HOUSTON CENTR BLVD, STE 110 77082 #048-12-1988 L1989
D DMP *020 †15

MAHVASH, Armeen. 1515 HOLCOMBE BLVD, UNIT 325 77030 #048-04-1999 L2004
VIR *020 †80

MAHZARI, Frank. 6624 FANNIN ST, STE 1900 77030 #048-12-2002 L2004 **IM** *020 †20

MAI, Rene Alphonse. ■ 77025 #048-15-2008 *012

MAIDENBERG, Robert Owen. 9090 GAYLORD ST STE 101 77024 #065-06-1961 L1976
FM A *020 ‡

MAIER, Robert Chris. 5656 KELLEY ST, CHIEF OF OB/GYN SERVICES 77026
#048-12-1965 L1965 **OBG** *040 †30

MAIERS, Michael Joseph. 1 BAYLOR PLZ, DEPT RAD 77030 #016-42-2006 L2008 **DR** *012

MAILLARD, Alberto A J. 6410 FANNIN ST STE 1508 77030 #048-02-1972 L1972
HNS OTO *020 †45

MAISLOS, Francisco R. 7737 SOUTHWEST FWY STE 520 77074 #132-02-1969 L1976
CD IM *020 †20

MAISLOS, Steven Daniel. 7737 SOUTHWEST FWY, STE 900 77074 #048-14-1998 L2004 **U** *020

MAJID, Abdul. 7035 HIGHWAY 6 S, EXCEL CLINIC 77083 #704-01-1981 L2005 **PD NPM** *020 †55

MAJID, Hashir. 1504 TAUB LOOP, BAYLOR COLLEGE OF MED 77030 #704-25-2001
PCC *012 †20

MAJID, Ruckshanda. 4545 POST OAK PLACE DR, STE 130 77027 #704-25-1998 L2004
PCC *012 ‡

MAJID, Tanweer Hussain. PO BOX 20708 77225 #704-25-2001 **GS** *012

MAJMUNDAR, Nishith U. 11920 ASTORIA BLVD STE 290 77089 #495-48-1991 L2003
N *020 †75

MAJMUNDAR, Sweta N. 11920 ASTORIA BLVD, STE 290 77089 #495-48-1991 L2003 **N** *020 †75

MAKHLOUF, Rita Antonios. 7777 SW FWY STE 310, PEDIATRIX MED GRP 77074
#605-01-1988 L1994 **PD NPM** *020 †55

MAKULSKI, Darlene Debra. 1333 MOURSUND ST, TIRR 77030 #048-14-2000 L2004
PM *020 †60

MALATHUM, Kumthorn. 6431 FANNIN ST # 1728 77030 #891-04-1986 **ID** *100

MALDONADO, Rolando Rene. 548 WAUGH DR 77019 #048-02-2000 L2003 **FM** *020 †18

MALHI, Nadeem Ashraf. 14903 EL CAMINO REAL 77062 #048-15-1999 L2005 **FM** *020

MALHOTRA, Reenu. ■ 77005 #495-03-1993 L2007 **PTH** *100 †50

MALIK, Amir S. 6410 FANNIN ST, STE 1020 77030 #704-20-1988 L2001 **NS** *020 †25

MALIK, Fardina. 7777 GREENBRIAR ST, APT 1020 77030 #160-01-2002 **IM** *012

MALIK, Hatim Gulamali. 12015 LOUETTA RD, STE 200 77070 #495-47-1965 L1981 **NS** *020 †25

MALIK, Henna Mukhtar. 10375 RICHMOND AVE STE 1 77042 #305-01-2004 L2008 **IM** *100 †20

MALIK, Imrana Alam. 1515 HOLCOMBE BLVD, UNIT 112 77030 #016-43-1998 L2002
PCC *100 †20

MALIK, Saira Maliha. ■ 77054 #016-11-2003 L2008 **PD** *020 †55

MALIK, Shaista. 3701 KIRBY DR STE 60, BAYLOR FAMILY PRACTICE CTR 77098
#704-25-2001 L2006 **FM** *100 †20

MALIK, Zaid Bin Hussain. 12031 SWORDS CREEK RD 77067 #704-02-1999 L2006
CHP *100 †75

MALINENI, Vasavi. 11914 ASTORIA BLVD, TEXAS EYE INSTITUTE 77089 #021-05-1998 L2004
OPH *020 †35

MALINI, Srini. 8200 WEDNESBURY LN, STE 320 77074 #495-33-1969 L1973 **R DR** *020 †80

MALINOW, Ana Maria. 6701 FANNIN ST 77030 #038-06-1989 L1998 **PD** *020 †55

MALKINA, Svetlana. 2800 S MACGREGOR WAY, HARRIS COUNTY PSYCHIATRIC 77021
#913-01-1979 L2003 **P** *020

MALLADI, Vivek Reddy. ■ 77021 #048-04-2008 *012

MALLAMPALLI, Antara. 1504 TAUB LOOP 6TH FL, PULMONARY SECTION 77030
#016-06-1992 L2004 **PCC** *020 †20

MALLELA, Vijaya Lakshmi. 4755 ALDINE MAIL ROUTE, ALDINE COMMUNITY HEALTH CE 77039
#495-58-1978 L1994 **FM** *020 †18

MALLERICH, Melvin Justin. 2000 CRAWFORD ST # 1710 77002 #021-05-1948 L1956
AN OS *020

MALLERY, Marcelle. ■ 77025 #048-04-2004 **DR** *012

MALLETTE, Lawrence Edward. 8200 WEDNESBURY LN, STE 380 77074 #047-05-1970 L1975
END IM *020 †20

MALLICK, Shahid Qaiyum. 7737 SOUTHWEST FWY, STE 940 77074 #704-02-1987 L1995
PCC *020 †20

MALLORY, Geo Barron, Jr. 6621 FANNIN ST 77030 #035-46-1974 L2002 **PDP PD** *020 †55

MALONE, Diana M. 710 FM 1960 RD W 77090 #048-02-2000 L2003 **FM** *020 †18

MALONE, Robert Steven. 6565 FANNIN ST RM D-281 77030 #028-34-1984 L1986
OS DR *020 †80

MALPHRUS, Amy Denise. 6621 FANNIN ST, STE 1710 77030 #039-01-2000 L2005
CHN *100 †75

MALPICA, Anais. 1515 HOLCOMBE BLVD 77030 #935-01-1984 L1992 **PTH** *020 †50

MALSEED, Lynn Marie. 7011 SOUTHWEST FWY, MHMRA OF HARRIS CO 77074
#048-02-1977 L1977 **CHP P** *020

MALVEAUX, Karen Willie. 13111 EAST FWY 77015 #048-14-1985 L1986 **AN PME** *020 †05

MALYA, Ramachandra. 7333 NORTH FWY, STE 127 77076 #495-09-1978 L1993 **NEP** *020 †20

MALYA, Rohith Ramachandra. ■ 77030 #048-04-2008 *012

MAMEDOVA, Farrah Vagif. 11037 FM 1960 RD W, STEEPLECHASE PEDIATRIC 77065
#913-19-1999 L2005 **PD** *012

MAMMEN, Joshua. 1515 HOLCOMBE BLVD, DEPARTMENT OF SURGICAL ONC 77030
#024-05-1999 L2007 **GS** *100 †85

MANCHANDIA, Alpa Manohar. ■ 77004 #021-06-2003 **OBG** *100

MANCIAS, Pedro. 6410 FANNIN ST, STE 1025 77030 #048-14-1988 L1993 **CHN** *020 †75

MANCINI, Ralph Michael. 909 FROSTWOOD DR STE 132 77024 #038-40-1972 L1976
PM *020 †60

MANDAL, Binita. 1140 CLEAR LAKE CITY BLVD, STE A 77062 #011-02-2000 L2003
AI *020 †20,03

MANDAVA, Pitchaiah. 2002 HOLCOMBE BLVD 77030 #048-02-1997 L1999 **N** *020 †75

MANDYAM, Srinand Anandam. ■ 77005 #048-15-2006 **AN** *012

MANESS, Gerald Winston. 2050 NORTH LOOP W, STE 130 77018 #048-04-1957 L1957
FM A *020 †18

MANESS, Karen Diane. 4536 HIGHWAY 6 N, PRIMARY CARE ASSOCIATES 77084
#048-14-1991 L1992 **FM** *020 †18

MANGAL, Rakesh Kumar. 7900 FANNIN ST, STE 4400 77054 #021-01-1988 L1993
GYN REN *020 †20

MANGALPALLY, Kiran Kumar. ■ 77025 #495-65-2000 L2007 **IM** *100 †20

MANGAT, Harpreet Singh. 2727 W HOLCOMBE BLVD, DEPT. OF FAMILY MEDICINE 77025
#422-01-2001 L2006 **FM** *020 †18

MANGINI, Oscar R. 12141 RICHMOND AVE 77082 #132-02-1960 L1976 **PTH CLP** *020 †50

MANGUBA-GIBBS, Rosemary. 10655 STEEPLETOP DR, CENTER 77065 #748-01-1988 L1998
NPM *020 †55

MANHAS, Amit Hari. ■ 77098 #048-04-2002 L2005 **CD** *012 †20

MANIAN, Prasad. 6624 FANNIN ST STE 1730 77030 #495-22-1986 L1992 **PUD CCM** *020 †20

MANIKDIYIL, Babith Joseph. ■ 77047 #495-53-1998 L2000 **PCC** *100 †20

MANLANGIT, Ebba Marie Ban. 6431 FANNIN ST 77030 #748-01-2003 **FP** *012

MANN, Charanjeev Kaur. 18100 SAINT JOHN DR 77058 #048-02-1991 L1995 **IM** *020 †20

MANN, David Guye. 6621 FANNIN ST STE A300, MAIL CODE 2-1495 77030 #041-15-2002 L2008
PAN *020 †05

MANN, Michael Richard. 2500 FONDREN RD, STE 300 77063 #016-06-1995 L2000
ORS *020 †40 ‡

MANN, Paul Michael. 5115 MAIN ST, MANN EYE INSTITUTE 77002 #021-05-1969 L1970
OPH EM *020 †35

MANN, Sidney F R. ■ 77068 #836-01-1972 *100

MANNER, Charles Elmer. 1213 HERMANN DR, STE 855 77004 #023-01-1975 L1978
HEM ON *020 †20

MANNING, A Erin. 6560 FANNIN ST 77030 #048-04-1997 L2001 **OBG** *020 †30

MANNING, Everald O. 4825 ALMEDA RD, RHEUMATIC DISEASE CLINIC 77004
#048-04-2000 L2003 **FM** *020 †18

MANNING, Gary Michael. 6565 FANNIN ST 77030 #048-04-1981 L1982 **AN** *020 †05

MANNING, John Thos, Jr. 1515 HOLCOMBE BLVD, UTMD ANDERSON CANCER CTR 77030
#036-01-1972 L1979 **PTH** *020 †50

MANNING, Shelley Delois. 3601 N MACGREGOR WAY, MLK CLINIC 77004 #024-07-1982 L1984
IM *020 †20

MANNS, Melantha Dorthea. 6431 FANNIN ST 1134, OF TEXAS-HOUSTON 77030 #047-07-2006
IM *012

MANOR, Davida Elizabeth. 2302 MILFORD PL 77014 #011-02-2000 L2004 **EM** *020 †16

MANSELL, Peter Wm Anson. 6723 BERTNER ST 77030 #917-20-1962 L1982 **ON** *030

MANSFIELD, Paul Furman. 1515 HOLCOMBE BLVD BOX 106 77030 #041-02-1983 L1989
SO *020 †85 ‡

MANSO, Gilberto. 7211 REGENCY SQUARE BLVD, STE 200 77036 #048-02-1969 L1969
FM NTR *020 †18

MANSOOR, Zia. 6431 FANNIN ST 77030 #704-02-1986 L2003 **AN** *020

MANSOURI, Roshanak. ■ 77030 #048-04-2008 *012

MANSURI, Irfan. ■ 77059 #704-16-1991 L2003 **FM** *020 †18

MANUEL, William S, IV. 6624 FANNIN ST STE 1730, MEDICAL CENTER ASSOCIATES 77030
#048-14-2001 L2004 **IM** *100

MANZI, Suzanne Marie. ■ 77054 #422-01-2005 **PM** *012

MANZONI RIART, Adriana Ma. 1 BAYLOR PLZ 77030 #726-01-2004 **GS** *012

MANZULLO, Ellen Frances. 1515 HOLCOMBE BLVD # 437 77030 #048-14-1986 L1987
IM *020 †20

MAO, Alice R. 550 WESTCOTT ST STE 520 77007 #048-14-1987 L1988 **P CHP** *020 †75

MAO, Chi Chiang. 427 W 20TH ST STE 220 77008 #048-14-1981 L1981 **IM** *020 †20

MAO, Daniel Yc. 3002 ASHFORD OAK DR, EMTEL 77082 #047-07-1999 L2002 **EM** *020 †16

MAO, Xun. 7500 BEECHNUT ST STE 225, METROPLUS PEDIATRICS, PA 77074
#243-72-1983 L1983 **PD** *020

MAO, Zhi. ■ 77054 #048-12-2004 L2008 **NEP** *012 †20

MAOR, Moshe Heinz. 1515 HOLCOMBE BLVD BOX 97 77030 #550-01-1965 L1976
RO *020 †80 ‡

MAPA, Meilani C. ■ 77054 #038-44-2003 L2007 **PM** *100

MAPP, Anna Levon. 2000 CRAWFORD ST 77002 #048-02-2001 L2006 **OPH** *020

MAPP, Michael Wallace. 2000 CRAWFORD ST, STE 842 77002 #038-06-1994 L1999 **OPH** *020

MARANGELL, Lauren B. 6410 AUDEN ST, BAYLOR COLLEGE OF MEDICINE 77005
#048-04-1987 L1994 **P** *030 †75

MARASIGAN, Brian Lim. ■ 77006 #028-46-2003 L2006 **ACA** *012

MARCAL, Leonardo Pimentel. 1515 HOLCOMBE BLVD, UNIT 1350 77030 #187-14-1997 L2005
DR *100 †80

MARCELLI, Marco. 2002 HOLCOMBE BLVD, BLDG 211 77030 #561-15-1980 L1994
IM END *020 †20

MARCELLUS, John Elias. 4888 LOOP CENTRAL DR, STE 510 77081 #027-01-1992 L1993
CHP *020 †75

MARCIN, Patrick Christoph. ■ 77021 #048-14-2008 *012

MARCOE, Malcolm. 7777 SOUTHWEST FWY, STE 1032 77074 #065-05-1957 L1963 **U** *071 †95

MARCONTELL, Jerry Clark. 6447 MAIN ST 77030 #048-04-1963 L1963 **GYN** *071 †20

MARCOS RAYMUNDO, Luis Aug. 6431 FANNIN ST 1134, OF TEXAS-HOUSTON 77030
#737-06-2004 **IM** *012

MARCUS, Caroline Anne. ■ 77054 #048-04-2007 **PD** *012

MARCUS, Donald Martin. 1 BAYLOR PLZ, BAYLOR COLLEGE OF MEDICINE 77030
#035-01-1955 L1980 **RHU IM** *040 †20

MARGINEAN, Esmeralda C. ■ 77098 #781-04-1993 L2003 **PCP** *100 †20

MARGOLIN, Judith Frances. 6701 FANNIN ST 77030 #038-41-1985 L1994 **PHO** *020 †55

MARGOLIS, Kenneth Joel. 211 HIGHLAND CROSS DR, STE 275 77073 #041-15-1999 L2004
OS *020

MARGULIS, Vitaly. ■ 77054 #048-12-2001 L2002 **U** *012

MARIAN, Ali J. 1 BAYLOR PLZ, JEWISH BLDG. ROOM 519D 77030 #517-01-1980 L1991 CD IM *050 †20

MARICICH, Stephen Michael. 1 BAYLOR PLZ, MS 225 RM T807 77030 #038-06-2000 L2006 CHN *100 †75

MARIE, Nathalie Antoinett. ■ 77081 #011-02-2004 L2007 P *012

MARIN, Rudolph Moncivais, Jr. 548 WAUGH DR 77019 #048-14-2000 L2003 FM *020 †18 ‡

MARISCALCO, Mary Michele. 6621 FANNIN ST 6-006 77030 #038-41-1981 L1984 CCP *020 †55

MARKHAM, Betty Susann. 15655 CYPRESSWOODS MDCL DR 77014 #025-07-1977 L1982 D *020 †15

MARKMAN, Maurie. 1515 HOLCOMBE BLVD, UNIT 121 77030 #035-19-1974 L2006 ON IM *020 †20

MARKO, Michael W. 5314 DASHWOOD DR 77081 #039-01-1969 L1974 OBG *071 †30

MARKS, Kevin Troy. 12121 RICHMOND AVE, STE 200 77082 #047-07-2000 L2003 GE *020 †20

MARKUS, Ramsey Fuad. 6560 FANNIN ST STE 802, BAYLOR DERMTLGY 77030 #028-46-1995 L2000 D *020 †15

MARLIN SWARTZ, Sarah Jane. ■ 77096 #048-04-2002 L2005 PN *012

MARMELL, Howard Michael. 11914 ASTORIA BLVD 77089 #035-01-1967 L1975 N PM *020 †75

MARNOY, Robert Sheldon. ■ 77027 #024-05-1954 L1980 OM OBG *071 †30

MAROM, Edith Michelle. 1515 HOLCOMBE BLVD, RADIOLOGY DEPT - BOX 57 77030 #550-02-1992 L2007 R *020 †80

MARQUES, Erik Scott. 6431 FANNIN ST, STE 1400 77030 #033-05-1994 L2002 HS *020 †85,65

MARQUEZ, Lucila. ■ 77019 #048-04-2005 PD *012

MARQUIS, Alexander F. 9432 OLD KATY RD STE 200 77055 #048-02-1995 L1996 FM *020 †18

MARR, Rita F. 2002 HOLCOMBE BLVD, VETERANS AFFAIRS MED CTR 77030 #048-14-1987 L1989 CD IM *074 †20

MARSHALL, Christy Leigh. ■ 77030 #048-14-2006 GS *012

MARSHALL, Gailen D, Jr. 6431 FANNIN ST, 4.044MSB 77030 #048-02-1984 L1989 IM IG *020 †20,03

MARSHALL, June G. 7333 NORTH FWY STE 120 77076 #035-19-1979 L1983 OBG *040 †30

MARSHBURN, Thomas Henry. 2101 NASA PKWY, MAIL CODE CB NASA/JSC 77058 #036-05-1989 L1994 EM AM *030 †16

MARTAINDALE, Sarah R. PO BOX 20708, UNIV TX MED SCH 77225 #048-13-2006 DR *012

MARTIN, Barry Alan. 12401 S POST OAK RD 77045 #010-03-1977 L1979 GP FM *020

MARTIN, Christopher Drake. 2801 GESSNER DR, THE MENNINGER CLINIC 77080 #048-04-2001 L2005 P *100 †75

MARTIN, Debra Zlatkis. 7900 FANNIN ST STE 1650, 1502 TAUB LOOP 77054 #048-15-1981 L1981 P *020 †75

MARTIN, Don E. 8866 GULF FWY, MANAGED MEDICAL PLANS 77017 #048-04-1949 L1949 GP *020

MARTIN, James Francis. 6431 FANNIN ST STE 4-268 77030 #048-14-1986 L1987 GS *020

MARTIN, Kistreia Marche. 1 BAYLOR PLZ, DEPT OF ANESTHESIOLOGY 77030 #047-06-2004 L2008 AN *012

MARTIN, Michael C. ■ 77054 #048-14-2007 IM *012

MARTIN, Raymond A. 8200 WEDNESBURY LN, STE 111 77074 #035-06-1968 L1977 N *020 †75

MARTIN, Stacey Kathleen. ■ 77054 #048-14-2006 ORS *012

MARTIN, Talitha Lisamarie. ■ 77067 #035-01-2008 *012

MARTIN, Thomas L. ■ 77077 #048-04-1951 L1951 GYN *071 †30

MARTINELLI, Paul Thomas. 6655 TRAVIS ST, STE 840 77030 #048-14-2001 L2004 D *100 †15

MARTINEZ, Carlaann. ■ 77021 #034-01-2002 OBG *100 †30

MARTINEZ, Fernando. 6723 BERTNER ST, UNIV TX MD ANDERSON CTR 77030 #264-05-1986 L2004 PCH *012

MARTINEZ, Ivvanee Escobar. ■ 77025 #007-02-2006 OBG *012

MARTINEZ, James Michael. 6655 TRAVIS ST, STE 560 77030 #048-02-1997 L1998 P *020 †75

MARTINEZ, Joaquin Gerardo. 12036 AIRLINE DR 77037 #649-04-1977 L1997 *020

MARTINEZ, Joseph Lionel. ■ 77004 #034-01-2003 L2003 NS *012

MARTINEZ, Melissa. 6655 TRAVIS ST STE 560, BAYLOR COLLEGE OF MEDICINE 77030 #048-04-2001 L2005 P *020 †75

MARTINEZ, Michelle L. 2530 W HOLCOMBE BLVD 77030 #048-13-1998 L2006 PD *020 †55

MARTINEZ, Nina Leyson. ■ 77083 #033-06-2007 IM *012

MARTINEZ, Sylvia. 6565 FANNIN ST, THE METHODIST HOSP 77030 #048-14-2006 GS *012

MARTINEZ-CAMACHO, Alvaro. ■ 77004 #025-07-2005 L2008 IM *012

MARTINEZ VIERA, Hector G. 2530 W HOLCOMBE BLVD 77030 #056-06-1964 L1976 FPS *020 †45

MARTYNOWICZ, Marek A. 6624 FANNIN ST, 19TH FL 77030 #759-12-1990 L2001 PCC *020 †20

MARU, Dipen Maheshbhai. ■ 77025 #495-48-1993 L2006 SP *020 †50

MARUGG, Crista Angeli. 6720 BERTNER ST 77030 #660-08-1993 L2000 AN *105

MARVIN, Robert G. 6431 FANNIN ST, M.S.B. 4.170 77030 #067-01-1989 L1994 CCS *020 †85

MARX, Arlene Cecile. 3310 RICHMOND AVE 77098 #038-41-1985 L1990 DR *020 †40

MARYMONT, John Victor. 6620 MAIN ST STE 1325, ORTHOPEDIC SURGERY DEPT 77030 #047-05-1986 L1995 ORS *020 †40

MASELLI CACERES, Diego Jo. 6431 FANNIN ST 1134, OF TEXAS-HOUSTON 77030 #429-02-2004 IM *012

MASON, Chawla Latoya. 1709 DRYDEN RD, STE 1700 77030 #021-01-2002 L2007 AN *100 †05

MASON, David La Ron. 2060 SPACE PARK DR, STE 402 77058 #040-02-1992 L1998 GS *012

MASON, Gary I. 7777 SOUTHWEST FWY, STE 934 77074 #035-19-1973 L1978 OPH *020 †35

MASOZERA, Nicholas M. 2002 HOLCOMBE BLVD, PC111 77030 #905-01-1986 L2003 IM *020 †20

MASSARELLI, Erminia. 6550 FANNIN ST STE 1001 77030 #561-31-1997 IM *012

MASSEY, Gloria Susan. 11302 FALLBROOK DR, STE 107 77065 #001-06-1979 L1996 U *071 †95

MASSIN, Edward Krauss. 6620 MAIN ST STE 1520, ST. LUKE'S DIAG CATH LAB, 77030 #028-02-1965 L1971 CD PDC *020 †20

MASSON, Marcos Vincent. 4126 SOUTHWEST FWY STE 330 77027 #016-01-1985 L1992 HS ORS *020 †40

MASSUM-KHANI, Gholam Ali. 6624 FANNIN ST, STE 2480 77030 #517-01-1971 L1978 CD ICE *020

MASTER, Gynette Carol. 11914 ASTORIA BLVD, STE 680 77089 #048-14-1981 L1981 OPH *071 †35

MASTERS, Kenneth H. ■ 77007 #046-01-2007 *012

MASTERSON, Jessicalyn. PO BOX 20708, UNIV TX MED SCH 77225 #035-46-2003 L2006 HO *012 †20

MASTOURI, Nasim. ■ 77030 #517-12-2001 IM *012

MASTROBATTISTA, Joan M. 6431 FANNIN ST, DEPT OF OB/GYN, SUITE 3.03 77030 #033-05-1988 L1992 OBG *020 †30

MASUD, Faisal N. 6565 FANNIN ST STE B452, THE METHODIST HOSP ANES 77030 #704-20-1989 L1997 CCA OS *020 †05

MATAMOROS, Aurelio. 1515 HOLCOMBE BLVD, BOX 57 77030 #007-02-1978 L1980 DR *020 †80

MATEJOWSKY, Rebecca T. 2002 HOLCOMBE BLVD, VAMC VETERANS HOSPITAL 77030 #048-12-1994 L1996 DR *020 †80

MATEO, Harvey Chan. ■ 77025 #748-02-2000 IM *100

MATERSON, Richard Stephen. ■ 77077 #011-02-1965 L1976 PM PMM *071 †60

MATHEW, Annie. ■ 77096 #495-27-1953 L1975 GP CD *020

MATHEW, Mathen. ■ 77096 #495-22-1967 L1976 AN *071

MATHEW, Ninan T. 1213 HERMANN DR 77004 #495-31-1962 L1972 N *020

MATHEW, Paul. 1515 HOLCOMBE BLVD, BOX 1374 77030 #690-02-1985 L1995 HEM ON *020 †20

MATHEW, Shirley E. 12121 RICHMOND AVE STE 108 77082 #048-02-1994 L1998 OPH *020

MATHEW, Sonia Flaten. 3701 KIRBY DR, STE 100 77098 #026-08-1997 L2000 FM *020 †18

MATHEWS, Vasilios. 7401 MAIN ST 77030 #035-01-1996 L2003 OAR ORS *020 †40

MATHIAS, John Robt. 7580 FANNIN ST STE 305, OF HOUSTON 77054 #041-13-1968 L1989 GE IM *020

MATHIJSEN, Stephanie E. 14781 MEMORIAL DR STE 170 77079 #021-01-1991 L2000 P *020

MATHIS, Kenneth Bradford. 6550 FANNIN ST, STE 2500 77030 #048-12-1985 L1986 ORS †40

MATHUR, Disha. 6400 FANNIN ST, STE 2020 77030 #495-41-1996 L2007 PD *020 †55

MATHUR, Nitin. 1 BAYLOR PLZ 77030 #018-03-2002 L2004 CD *012 †20

MATHUR, Virendra Singh. 6624 FANNIN ST, STE 2480 77030 #495-05-1957 L1975 CD IM *020 †20

MATHURIA, Nilesh Sudhir. 1709 DRYDEN RD, STE 992 77030 #048-16-2002 L2004 CD *012 †20

MATHURIN, Emile. 7333 NORTH FWY, STE 100 77076 #649-30-1983 L1993 PM *020 †55,60

MATIN, Surena F. 1515 HOLCOMBE BLVD, UNIT 1373 77030 #035-20-1994 L2002 U *020 †95

MATOBA, Alice Yukiko. 6550 FANNIN ST, STE 1501 77030 #008-01-1977 L1983 OPH *050 †35

MATOCHA, John Chas. 123 N POST OAK LN, STE 420 77024 #048-14-1979 L1979 GPM GP *020 †70 ‡

MATORIN, Philip Andrew. 12121 RICHMOND AVE, STE 304 77082 #048-02-1990 L1991 OTO *020 †45

MATTA, Eduardo Jose. 6431 FANNIN ST 2.132, DEPART. OF DIAGNOSTIC & IN 77030 #021-01-2001 L2007 AR *020 †80

MATTEER, Nancy Plange. 2002 HOLCOMBE BLVD 111D, BAYLOR COLLEGE OF MEDICINE 77030 #041-15-2003 GE *012 †20

MATTERN, Jeremy Keith. ■ 77007 #820-02-2001 FM *030

MATTEWAL, Amarbir Singh. ■ 77054 #495-36-2000 L2004 PCC *012 †20

MATTHEWS, Annette Grace. 6618 CORAL RIDGE RD 77069 #048-04-1979 L1979 PD *020 †55

MATTHEWS, Hugh Randall. 2214 BARTLETT ST 77098 #048-14-1977 L1978 P CHP *020 †75

MATTHEWS, Leah Michelle. 5622 E SAM HOUSTON PKWY N 77015 #010-02-1997 L1998 PD *020 †55

MATTIOLI, Federico Luis. 3700 BUFFALO SPEEDWAY, STE 325 77098 #048-15-1996 L2000 OPH *020

MATTIOLI, Martha Luisa. 3413 CANAL ST 77003 #132-01-1966 L1979 FOP FM *072

MATTOX, Kenneth Leon. 1 BAYLOR PLZ 77030 #048-04-1964 L1964 TS TRS *030 †85,90

MATUS, Heidi Leanne. ■ 77098 #048-14-2008 *012

MATUSZCZAK, Maria. 6431 FANNIN ST 5.020 77030 #165-03-1982 L2004 PAN *012

MATZUK, Martin Matthew. 1 BAYLOR PLZ 77030 #028-02-1989 L1993 PTH *020 †50

MAUK, Paul Martin. 915 GESSNER RD STE 850 77024 #048-04-1980 L1981 GE IM *020 †20

MAUS, Erik Alberto. 6411 FANNIN ST, HYPERBARIC MED 77030 #649-31-1996 L2007 IM *100 †20

MAUSKAR, Anant Nilkanth. 8300 HOMESTEAD RD, STE 5 77028 #495-28-1961 L1977 FM IM *071 †18

MAVLIGIT, Giora. 1515 HOLCOMBE BLVD, CLINICAL IMMUNOLOGY BOX 41 77030 #550-01-1965 L1973 ON *071 †20

MAWAD, Michel Elie. 12951 SOUTH FWY 77047 #605-02-1976 L1985 R RNR *020 †80

MAWJI, Fatima Amirali I. 1919 LA BRANCH ST 77002 #495-01-1973 L1982 AN *020 †05

MAX, Ernest. 6550 FANNIN ST STE 2307 77030 #231-01-1961 L1974 CRS *071 †10,85

MAXWELL, Rebecca Helena. 6260 WESTPARK DR, STE 250 77057 #048-04-2000 L2003 P *020 †75 ‡

MAY, Stephen A. 6540 BELLOWS LN # 602 77030 #048-13-2000 L2005 SP *100 †50

MAY, Thaddaeus David. ■ 77098 #019-02-2007 MPD *012

MAYEKAR, Maya Shailesh. 902 FROSTWOOD DR, STE 293 77024 #496-38-1976 L1979 FM *020 †18

MAYES, Gary Brent. ■ 77079 #021-01-1973 L1974 FM P *020 †80

MAYES, Maureen Davidica. 6431 FANNIN ST # 5.270, HEALTH SCIENCE CENTER 77030 #051-07-1976 L2002 RHU IM *050 †20

MAYES-ELDEN, Chanda Lajai. 1300 MOURSUND ST 77030 #019-02-2005 L2008 P *012

MAYFIELD, Nicholas D. 2727 GRAMERCY ST STE 200 77025 #021-01-2002 L2006 OPH *020

MAYHEW, Amy Marie. ■ 77035 #035-45-2007 *012

MAYMI, Carmen Laura. 6603 APPLE VALLEY LN, . 77069 #042-01-1985 L1992 AN PME *040 †05

MAYO, Carlos O. 4200 PORTSMOUTH ST 77027 #737-06-1980 L1997 OBG *020

MAYOR, Jesus. 302 W GULF BANK RD, 302 W GULF BANK RD 77037 #308-03-1983 L1987 GP PD *020 †55

MAYORGO, Gilbert. 6910 BELLAIRE BLVD STE 8 77074 #048-02-1985 L1987 PTH *020

MAYS, Steven Randolph. 6655 TRAVIS ST, STE 600 77030 #048-13-1994 L1996 D *020 †15

MAZCURI, Riaz Shahbehram. 6300 HILLCROFT ST, STE 310 77081 #704-02-1979 L1986 P *020 †20

MAZE, Gregory L. 17115 RED OAK DR, STE 109 77090 #048-13-1997 L2003 P *020 †75

MAZHAR, Khurram Mirza. ■ 77030 #016-01-2006 IM *012

MAZIQUE, Edward Houston. 7706M KING ST L 77028 #010-03-1976 L1981 IM *020 †20

MAZIQUE, Emory Edwin. 5009 CAROLINE ST STE 105 77004 #047-07-1962 L1966 IM *020

MAZLOOM, Ali. ■ 77054 #048-04-2008 *012

MAZOW, Jack Bernard. ■ 77096 #048-02-1947 L1947 A *071 †20,03

MAZOW, Malcolm Lowell. 2855 GRAMERCY ST 77025 #048-02-1961 L1961 OPH PD *020 †35 ‡

MAZUMDAR, Nirmal Kumar. 10103 FONDREN RD STE 460 77096 #495-15-1959 L1978 FM GS *020

MAZUR, Erik Christian. ■ 77054 #048-04-2007 OBG *012

MAZUR, Lynnette Joan. 6431 FANNIN ST STE 3-230, UNIV OF TX MED SCH DEPT PD 77030 #649-03-1981 L1990 PD *040 †55

MAZZEI, Walter Robert. 404 OXFORD ST # 5130 77007 #016-45-2004 L2008 CD *012 †20

MAZZIOTTI, Mark Victor. 6621 FANNIN ST, STE 650 77030 #041-01-1993 L2001 PDS *020 †85

MBAWUIKE-NEZE, Pauline C. 8527 W BELLFORT ST, STE A 77071 #032-01-1994 L1997 FM *020 †20

MBOGUA, Caroline Mayor. 1213 HERMANN DR E445 77004 #010-03-1987 L1992 IM PD *020 †20,55

MC ALEER, Maryfrances. 1515 HOLCOMBE BLVD UNIT 97, UNIV OF TX M D ANDERSON 77030 #041-02-2001 L2006 **RO** *100 †80

MC ALEVY, Merlene F. 1111 AUGUSTA DR 77057 #030-05-1971 L1974 **PD** *020 †55

MC ALISTER, Wade Prince. 548 WAUGH DR 77019 #048-15-1996 L2002 **OSM OAR** *020

MC ALLISTER, Hugh A, Jr. 6720 BERTNER ST 77030 #036-01-1966 L1985 **PTH CD** *020 †50

MCALLISTER, Joshua R. ■ 77089 #048-02-2008 *012

MC AMIS, Robert James. 13111 EAST FWY 77015 #048-12-1955 L1955 **OM** *020

MCARTHUR, Benjamin Allen. ■ 77096 #048-04-2008 *012

MC BATH, James M. 1213 HERMANN DR, STE 810 77004 #048-14-1984 L1985 **GS** *020 †85

MC BRIDE, James R, Jr. 7580 FANNIN ST STE 335 77054 #021-05-1974 L1975 **OBG** *020 †30

MC BRIDE, Janie A. 1515 HOLCOMBE BLVD 77030 #048-14-1987 L1988 **BBK** *020 †50

MC BRIDE, John Cecil. 1919 LA BRANCH ST, DEPT OF OB/GYN 77002 #010-03-1969 L1974 **OBG** *020

MC BRIDE, Richard Leslie. 902 FROSTWOOD DR STE 210 77024 #060-01-1961 L1977 **OBG** *071

MC CABE, Marshall E. ■ 77079 #035-19-1946 L1978 **IM** *071 †20

MC CALLUM, Wm Geo Becks. ■ 77019 #025-12-1980 L1982 **EM** *071 †20,16

MC CANDLESS, Robert Gail. 12951 SOUTH FWY 77047 #048-02-1959 L1959 **DR** *071 †80

MC CANN, Michael T. 7505 MAIN ST, STE 150 77030 #048-12-1987 L1988 **APM AN** *020 †05

MC CANTS, David S. 1 BAYLOR PLZ, BAYLOR COLLEGE OF MEDICINE 77030 #048-12-2003 L2006 **IM** *100 †20

MCCANTS, Naomi Lee. 8951 RUTHBY ST STE 1 77061 #048-12-2003 L2006 **FM** *020 †18

MC CARTHY, James Joseph. 6431 FANNIN ST 445, DEPT OF EMERGENCY MEDICINE 77030 #016-43-1998 L2001 **EM** *020 †16

MC CARTHY, John Jos. 6550 FANNIN ST STE 1001 77030 #048-04-1976 L1976. **HEM IM** *040 †20

MCCARTHY, Marissa. ■ 77006 #011-02-2004 L2008 **PM** *012

MCCARTHY, Megan Elizabeth. 1 BAYLOR PLZ, DEPT OBG 77030 #035-47-2007 **OBG** *012

MC CARVER, Charles Truitt. 4009 BELLAIRE BLVD, BEST CARE CLINIC 77025 #048-02-1958 L1958 **GP** *071

MCCAULEY, Mark David. ■ 77057 #048-04-2006 **IM** *012

MC CLAIN, Kenneth Louis. 6701 FANNIN ST, CC1510.00 77030 #016-02-1973 L1986 **PHO PD** *020 †55

MCCLAM, Michael Lewis. 1 BAYLOR PLZ, DEPT. OF PSYCHIATRY, BCM 3 77030 #048-04-2002 L2005 **P** *020 †75

MCCLAM, Tamela Denise. ■ 77030 #048-04-2008 *012

MCCLANAHAN, Leslie Rena. ■ 77054 #048-14-2008 *012

MC CLELLAN, Robert Ensign. 10370 RICHMOND AVE STE 200 77042 #049-01-1975 L1989 **OS** *020 †85

MCCLELLAND, Myles Christo. ■ 77004 #654-01-2007 **IM** *012

MC CLENDON, Edward Bruce. 11830 FM 1960 RD W 77065 #048-14-1978 L1978 **GP** *020

MC CLINTOCK, Hoyt Mingus. 6621 FANNIN ST 77030 #048-04-1955 L1955 **PD** *071 †55

MC CLOSKEY, Sharon Syers. 920 FROSTWOOD DR, STE 610 77024 #048-02-1997 L2001 **OBG** *020 †30

MC CLUGGAGE, Charles Wade. 6720 BERTNER ST, MC2-2170 77030 #023-01-1969 L1980 **RNR DR** *020 †80

MCCLUNG, Amy Ayres. 1709 DRYDEN RD, STE 10.5 DEPT OF DERMA 77030 #048-02-2005 **D** *012

MC CLUNG, Tony Spurgeon. 1213 HERMANN DR, STE 520 77004 #048-02-1976 L1976 **U** *020 †95

MCCLURE, Aaron. ■ 77006 #048-78-2004, ▲ L2008 **AN** *012

MC CLURE, Toinette Anita. 714 FM 1960 RD W STE 107 77090 #048-02-2000 L2004 **AN** *020

MC COLLOSTER, Patrick J. 1615 N MAIN ST 77009 #021-05-1987 L1990 **FM** *020 †18

MC COLLUM, Charles H, III. 6550 FANNIN ST, STE 1661 77030 #048-02-1959 L1959 **VS GS** *040 †85,90

MC CONNELL, Kristin D. 6624 FANNIN ST, STE 1550 77030 #048-04-1998 L1999 **N** *020 †75

MCCONNELL, Stephen David. ■ 77054 #048-14-2008 *012

MCCORMICK, Lynn Marie. ■ 77054 #048-04-2008 *012

MC CORMICK, Theron G. 6621 FANNIN ST 77030 #021-05-2000 L2003 **AI** *020 †55,03 ‡

MC COY, Jack Chas. ■ 77062 #048-02-1967 L1968 **GP OM** *075

MC CRARY, John A, III. 1315 ST JOSEPH PKWY, STE 1205 77002 #048-12-1962 L1962 **OPH** *020 †35

MCCRAY, Courtney Jane. ■ 77019 #048-14-2008 *012

MC CREERY, Charles John. 6560 FANNIN ST, STE 620 77030 #539-03-1986 L1997 **CD** *020 †20

MC CREERY, Kathryn Mary. 1102 BATES AVE 77030 #539-06-1986 L1999 **OPH** *020 †35

MC CULLOCH, Patrick C. 6620 MAIN ST STE 1325, DEPT. OF ORTHOPEDIC SURGER 77030 #005-02-2000 L2006 **OSM** *100

MC CULLOUGH-AVES, M Alice. ■ 77057 #048-04-1948 L1948 **PD** *075

MC CUTCHEON, Conrad Kyle. 1740 W 27TH ST STE 234 77008 #048-02-1987 L1988 **OTO** *020 †45

MC CUTCHEON, Ian E. 1515 HOLCOMBE BLVD # 442 77030 #067-01-1984 L1992 **NS** *020

MC DERMOTT, Terry Lee. ■ 77095 #048-13-2005 **FP** *012

MCDONALD, Alden Joseph. ■ 77030 #024-01-2004 L2007 **CD** *012 †20

MC DONALD, Anuradha. 6701 FANNIN ST 77030 #048-04-1992 L1994 **PD** *020 †55

MC DONALD, Meghan Claire. 6621 FANNIN ST, BAYLOR COLLEGE OF MEDICINE 77030 #056-06-1986 L1989 **NPM PD** *020 †55

MC DONALD, Robert Emmett. 1740 W 27TH ST, STE 315 77008 #048-12-1978 L1978 **U** *020 †95

MC DONNELL, Hilda Ines. 5600 S WILLOW DR, STE 117 77035 #132-01-1975 L1997 **PD** *020

MC DONNELL, Timothy James. 1515 HOLCOMBE BLVD BOX 089, DEPT OF MOLECULAR PATHOLOG 77030 #028-02-1986 L1991 **PTH** *050 †50

MC ELMURRY, Stephen E. 1140 BUSINESS CENTER DR, STE 400 77043 #048-04-1973 L1974 **GS** *020 †85

MC ENERY, Kevin Wm. 1515 HOLCOMBE BLVD BOX 57, MD ANDERSON CANCER CENTER 77030 #010-02-1986 L1996 **DR** *050 †80

MC GEE, Angela Denise. 2727 W HOLCOMBE BLVD 77025 #012-21-1994 L1996 **GE** *020 †20

MC GEE, Clifton E, Jr. 4414 NAVIGATION BLVD, MHMRA OF HARRIS COUNTY 77011 #048-02-1993 L1994 **CHP** *020

MC GINNIS, Michael R. 5901 LONG DR, CLINIC 77087 #048-14-1986 L1987 **CHP** *020

MC GINTY, Nicole. 7500 BEECHNUT ST, STE 270 77074 #048-14-1994 L1996 **FM** *020 †18

MCGOVERN, Susan Lynne. 1515 HOLCOMBE BLVD, ANDERSON CANC 77030 #016-06-2005 **RO** *020

MC GOWAN, Thomas. 902 FROSTWOOD DR, STE 261 77024 #024-07-1973 L1980 **PUD IM** *020 †20

MC GRANN, Monica A. ■ 77005 #048-16-2002 L2005 **PD** *100

MC GRAW, Pamela Yount. 909 FROSTWOOD DR, STE 126 77024 #036-01-1994 L1996 **PD** *020 †55

MC GRAW-WALL, Becky L. 7501 FANNIN ST, STE 710 77054 #048-12-1984 L1985 **OTO PSH** *020 †45

MC GREGOR, Gregor Iain. M D ANDERSON HOSP INST 77030 #065-06-1971 **GS** *050

MC GREGOR, Jacqueline C. 3642 UNIVERSITY BLVD STE 2 77005 #048-02-1993 L1998 **CHP** *020 †75

MC GUIRE, Sean Eric. 6431 FANNIN ST STE 1.150, AT HOUST 77030 #048-04-2004 L2005 **RO** *012

MC GUIRK, Christopher M. 18220 TOMBALL PKWY, STE 200 77070 #048-12-1999 L2003 **OBG** *020 †30

MC HARGUE, Mary Ellen. 427 W 20TH ST, STE 300 77008 #001-06-1999 L2003 **AN** *020

MCHUGH, Catherine. ■ 77030 #023-12-2007 **OTO** *012

MC HUGH, Thomas Philip. 800 PEAKWOOD DR STE 8C 77090 #025-07-1983 L1991 **PS GS** *020 †65 ‡

MC INTYRE, Brenda Harvey. 5615 KIRBY DR, STE 440 77005 #048-04-1986 L1987 **NPM** *020 †55

MC KANE, Brice William. 2530 W HOLCOMBE BLVD 77030 #048-13-1998 L2005 **PS** *100 †65

MC KAY, Andrew K. 10926 EAST FWY 77029 #024-05-1992 L1996 **AN** *020 †05

MC KAY, Siripoom V. 6701 FANNIN ST 77030 #048-04-1993 L1995 **END** *020

MC KAY, William James. 1504 TAUB LOOP, EMERGENCY DEPT., URGENT CA 77030 #034-01-1974 L1981 **EM GP** *020 †16

MC KECHNIE, John Chas. 6560 FANNIN ST, STE 600 77030 #048-04-1959 L1959 **GE IM** *071 †20

MC KEE, Bryce Ross. 9099 WESTHEIMER RD, STE 107 77063 #041-12-1961 L1973 **AN** *071 †05

MCKEE-GARRETT, Tiffany M. 6701 FANNIN ST 77030 #048-14-1993 L1994 **PD** *020 †55

MC KEEVER, Clark Dickson. 902 FROSTWOOD DR, STE 288 77024 #041-02-1962 L1968 **ORS** *020 †40

MC KEEVER, Grant Rexford. 902 FROSTWOOD DR, STE 309 77024 #041-02-1962 L1968 **ORS** *020 †40

MC KELLAR, Aida. 2425 UNDERWOOD ST 77030 #605-01-1949 L1977 **P** *020

MC KELVEY, Eugene Mowry. 6701 FANNIN ST 77030 #023-07-1960 L1973 **ON IM** *030 †20

MC KELVY, Brandy Jo. 6431 FANNIN ST 1.274, UT HSC AT HOUSTON 77030 #048-14-1999 L2005 **PCC IM** *020

MCKENNEY, Allyson Louise. ■ 77030 #048-14-2006 **MPD** *012

MC KENZIE, Emmett D. 6621 FANNIN ST, TEXAS CHILDREN'S HOSPITAL 77030 #048-04-1991 L1992 **TS** *020 †85,90

MCKENZIE, Laurie Evenson. 920 FROSTWOOD DR, STE 720 77024 #011-03-1997 L2001 **OBG REN** *020 †30

MC KEOWN-BIAGAS, Cecilia. 7322 SOUTHWEST FWY, STE 550 77074 #001-02-1989 L1991 **FM** *020 †20

MC KINNEY, Michael Dean. 7000 FANNIN ST, STE 1721 77030 #048-02-1976 L1976 **FM** *020 ‡

MCKINNEY, Polawyn C. ■ 77059 #048-02-2006 **IM** *012

MCKNIGHT, Aisha Jenelle. ■ 77025 #047-07-2007 **PS** *012

MC KOWEN, Robert Lee. 12121 RICHMOND AVE STE 412 77082 #051-04-1978 L1987 **TS** *020 †85,90

MC LAUCHLIN, Greg Stewart. 7505 MAIN ST, STE 290 77030 #048-04-1999 L2003 **N** *020

MCLAUGHLIN, Leah C. ■ 77025 #048-14-2008 *012

MC LAUGHLIN, Peter. 1515 HOLCOMBE BLVD, BOX 429 77030 #024-07-1974 L1980 **ON HEM** *050 †20

MC LAURIN, Scott Sutton. 6720 BERTNER ST 77030 #048-16-1984 L1987 **AN** *020 †05

MC LELLAN, Michelle A. 12727 KIMBERLEY LN 77024 #004-01-1989 L1990 **AN** *020 †05

MC LEMORE, Joe Ed. ■ 77024 #048-02-1960 L1960 **OBS** *071 †30

MC LENAN, Dilicia Holder. 6621 FANNIN ST, W TOWER 6TH FL RM B06104 77030 #187-04-1979 L1998 **NPM PD** *020 †55

MC MAHON, Colin Joseph. 6621 FANNIN ST # MC2-2280 77030 #539-04-1994 L2004 **PD** *020 †55

MC MANNIS, Suzanne Imherr. ■ 77059 #016-01-1987 L1987 **PD** *020 †55

MC MANUS, Calvin C. 4141 NORTH FWY, STE 100 77022 #021-05-1963 L1969 **OBG** *020 †30

MC MANUS, Samuel Prescott. 1415 NORTH LOOP W, STE 810 77008 #027-01-1959 L1972 **R** *071 †80

MC MILLAN, Dean Riley. 163 ALDINE BENDER RD 77060 #027-01-1965 L1973 **FM** *020

MC MILLAN, Mae Frances. 100 SANDMAN ST 77007 #047-07-1959 L1960 **CHP OS** *020 †30

MC MONIGAL, Kathleen Anne. 2101 NASA RD 1 SD, NASA-JSC 77058 #026-04-1978 L1994 **PTH** *062 †50

MC MORRIS, Clyde, Jr. 1315 ST JOSEPH PKWY, STE 1701 77002 #038-06-1997 L1998 **FM** *020 †18

MC MULLEN, Faber Francis. 6000 BRITTMOORE RD 77041 #048-04-1956 L1956 **CD IM** *071 †20

MC MURTREY, Marion John. 1515 HOLCOMBE BLVD 77030 #023-07-1959 L1967 **TS CD** *071 †85

MC NAIR, Douglas Scott. 1200 MOURSUND ST, DEPT PAT 77030 #026-04-1978 L1982 **CLP IM** *062 †50

MC NAMARA, Patrick James. 1512 W ALABAMA ST 77006 #041-09-1983 L1985 **IM** *020 †20

MC NEEL, Day Pattison, Jr. 1740 W 27TH ST 77008 #048-04-1963 L1963 **NS** *071 †25

MC NEELY, John Wallace. 6400 FANNIN ST, STE 1500 77030 #048-14-1979 L1979 **AN** *020 †05

MC NEES, Sandra Willis. 4126 SOUTHWEST FWY 77027 #048-02-1993 L1994 **DR** *020 †80

MC NEESE, Catherine C. 807 PEDEN ST 77006 #048-14-2000 L2002 **DMP** *012

MC NEESE, Margaret Carter. 6431 FANNIN ST, MSB G400 77030 #048-02-1971 L1971 **PD OS** *030 †55

MC NEIL, Cynthia Diane. 3003 S LOOP W, STE 410 77054 #048-14-1988 L1989 **OBG** *020 †30

MCNEIL, Jonathon Chase. ■ 77054 #048-04-2006 **PD** *012

MC NEILL, Dave Etheldred. 1140 CYPRESS STATION DR, STE 200 77090 #048-02-1972 L1972 **IM** *020 †20

MC NUTT, Michelle Kathlee. ■ 77035 #048-13-2004 **GS** *012

MC PHERSON, Alice R. 6550 FANNIN ST, STE 1501 77030 #056-05-1951 L1958 **OPH** *020 †35

MC PHERSON, David Dugald. 77004 #060-01-1978 L2007 **CD IM** *050 †20

MC PHERSON, Mona Lynn. 6621 FANNIN ST WT6-006 77030 #001-02-1992 L1999 **CCP** *020 †55

MCQUITTY, Elizabeth Burns. ■ 77030 #048-04-2008 *012

MC RAE, Stephen Efrem. ■ 77005 #051-01-1997 L2007 **VIR** *020 †80

MC REYNOLDS, Edwards U. 1640B NORFOLK ST 77006 #048-02-1967 L1967 **CHP P** *020 †75

MC REYNOLDS, Geo Walter. 7777 SOUTHWEST FWY STE 820 77074 #048-02-1969 L1969 **OTO** *020 †45

MC REYNOLDS, John Weldon. 5151 KATY FWY # 117 77007 #048-04-1954 L1954 **GP** *071

MC WILLIAMS, Robt Barton. 7600 FANNIN ST 77054 #048-13-1974 L1988 **REN OBG** *020 †30

MEACHEM, Francesca Tanei. 1 BAYLOR PLZ, DEPT OF ANTHESIOLOGY 77030 #036-01-2005 **AN** *012

MEADOR, John Henry. 2500 FONDREN RD, STE 270 77063 #048-02-1960 L1960 GS VS *020 †85

MECKLAI, Almas A. 18220 TOMBALL PKWY, STE 335 77070 #704-02-1971 L1981 GP EM *020 ‡

MEDAA, Ramzy Georges. 1 BAYLOR PLZ 77030 #875-02-1999 GS *012

MEDEIROS, Leonard J. 1515 HOLCOMBE BLVD 77030 #024-16-1980 L1999 HEM PTH *020 †50

MEDELLIN, Hector L. 902 FROSTWOOD DR STE 275 77024 #649-01-1959 L1969 DR *020 †80

MEDINA, Glorimar. ■ 77025 #042-02-2003 AN *100

MEDINA, Leo Montillano. ■ 77077 #748-08-1991 *100

MEDINA, Matias Relos. T233 W PARKER RD 77076 #748-07-1966 L1977 EM *020

MEDINA-MARQUIS, Maricruz. 1635 NORTH LOOP W, MEMORIAL HERMANN NW 77008 #048-02-2000 L2002 EM *020 †16

MEDIWALA, Sanjay Navin. 2002 HOLCOMBE BLVD, HOUSTON VA MEDICAL CENTER 77030 #048-04-2000 L2003 END *012 †20

MEDLEY, Hansa Ben. 8989 WESTHEIMER RD, STE 314 77063 #495-34-1981 L1992 IM *020 †20

MEDLEY, Leslie E. 77030 #048-04-2005 AN *012

MEDRANO, Francisco Daniel. 4545 POST OAK PLACE DR, STE 130 77027 #041-13-2001 L2005 MPD *020 †20

MEDRANO, Jose Navarro. 1333 MOURSUND ST 77030 #847-06-1954 L1971 AN *020

MEDRANO-KREIDLER, Juan C. 7400 FANNIN ST STE 800 77054 #176-01-1974 L1978 OBG *020 †30

MEEK, Susan Bieber. 4126 SOUTHWEST FWY 77027 #016-42-1980 L1988 OPH *020

MEEKS, Derek W. ■ 77054 #048-14-2005 L2006 GS *100

MEEKS, Evan Granville. ■ 77007 #048-14-2008 *012

MEERZA, Syed Fazle Ali. 12779 JONES RD STE 108 77070 #160-02-1959 L1979 CD IM *020

MEGDAL, Martin L. 9034 WESTHEIMER RD # 400 77063 #660-03-1957 L1960 P CHP *071 †75

MEGHJI, Abdulrasul G. 10701 VINTAGE PRESERVE PKW 77001 #495-56-1981 L2000 FM *020 †18

MEHAFFEY, Mark James. 7314 MAIN ST, MARK J. MEHAFFEY, M.D.,P.A 77030 #012-01-1995 L1998 EM *020 †16

MEHANNA, Raja Michel. 1709 DRYDEN RD STE 550, BCM FACULTY CENTER 77030 #605-02-2005 IM *012

MEHDI, Syed Hassan. 6624 FANNIN ST STE 1900 77030 #704-16-1992 L2006 IM *020 †20

MEHLHOFF, Thomas Lynn. 7401 MAIN ST 77030 #048-04-1982 L1983 ORS HS *020 †40

MEHLING, Blair Marlin. ■ 77025 #060-01-1993 L1999 PS *020

MEHRA, Manjul. 6500 HORNWOOD DR 77074 #495-12-1965 L1984 P *020

MEHRA, Rakesh Chand. 1515 HOLCOMBE BLVD BOX 24 77030 #917-01-1977 L1992 HEM IM *020 †20

MEHRA, Vikram. 10101 SOUTHWEST FWY # 310 77074 #048-13-1993 L1994 P PYG *020 †75

MEHRAN, Reza John. 1515 HOLCOMBE BLVD # 445 77030 #067-01-1986 L2005 GS *020 †85

MEHTA, Hansa Bhupendra. 710 FM 1960 RD W 77090 #496-38-1968 L1976 AN *020 †05

MEHTA, Kalpana Navnit. 1504 TAUB LOOP 77030 #495-22-1969 L1984 P *020

MEHTA, Kanubhai Paragji. 1631 NORTH LOOP W STE 460 77008 #917-07-1957 L1974 CD IM *062 †20

MEHTA, Meena M. 77005 #495-22-1963 L1974 PS *020 †18

MEHTA, Niraj N. 5656 KELLEY ST, STE 4PO-30012 77026 #048-14-1993 L1995 IM *020 †20

MEHTA, Parth Subhash. 6621 FANNIN ST, CC 1410.00 77030 #035-48-2000 L2006 PHO *100 †20

MEHTA, Rangda Dilipkumar. 6910 BELLAIRE BLVD, STE 13 77074 #495-48-1979 L1982 FM *020 †20

MEHTA, Reena S. ■ 77025 #028-46-2007 PD *012

MEHTA, Seema. 77054 #047-06-2004 L2004 PG *012 †55

MEHTA, Sheilendra Suresh. 7500 BEECHNUT ST STE 240, SUITE 240 77074 #048-14-1997 L2005 GS AS *020 †85

MEHTA, Snehal Dilipkant. 902 FROSTWOOD DR STE 275 77024 #495-01-1980 L1985 DR AR *020 †80

MEINER, Sean T. ■ 77071 #048-14-2008 *012

MEISCH, Richard Alden. 1300 MOURSUND ST 77030 #026-04-1971 L1989 P PA *050

MEISLER, Irwin M. 8951 RUTHBY ST, STE 4E 77061 #048-04-1950 L1950 FM *071 †18

MEIXNER, Susan Turnquist. 5615 KIRBY ST STE 516 77005 #048-14-1983 L1983 P PYA *020 †75

MEJIA PEREZ, Rodrigo E. 1515 HOLCOMBE BLVD, DEPT OF PEDIATRICS BOX 87 77030 #264-10-1985 L1995 PD CCP *020 †55

MELANCON, Suzanne Michell. ■ 77054 #021-05-2007 PD *012

MELARTIN, Riku. 1919 LA BRANCH ST, PO BOX 9 77002 #913-01-1994 GS *100

MELENDEZ, Johnny. 1315 ST JOSEPH PKWY, STE 1703 77002 #042-03-1992 L1997 NPM *020 †55

MELGAREJO BRAVO, Nicolas. 6431 FANNIN ST 1134, UNIV OF TEXAS - HOUSTON 77030 #264-01-2003 IM *012

MELHEM, Ziad Ibrahim. 6400 FANNIN ST, STE 1900 77030 #605-01-1997 L2004 OBG *020

MELILLO, Anthony Stephen. 1051 PINELOCH DR STE 100 77062 #056-06-1986 L1995 ORS OSM *020 †40

MELISSINOS, Emmanuel G. 6410 FANNIN ST, STE 1220 77030 #418-01-1969 L1979 PS *020 †65

MELLON, Matthew Birk. ■ 77004 #035-19-2005 L2005 ORS *012

MELNIKOV, Vladimir. 6431 FANNIN ST 51020, DEPT ANESTHLGY 77030 #913-96-1981 L2005 *100

MELTON, Danielle Hemard. 6431 FANNIN ST STE G510 77030 #048-04-2002 L2005 PM *100

MELTZER, Steven Dale. 7900 FANNIN ST, STE 3600 77054 #048-04-1974 L1974 OBG *020 †30

MEMON, Abdul Qadir. 403 COACHMAN LN, 403 COACHMAN LANE 77024 #704-08-1969 L1977 AN *020 †05 ‡

MEMON, Amir Abdul-Ghaffar. 800 PEAKWOOD DR STE 7B 77090 #704-08-1993 L1999 NEP IM *020 †20

MEMON, Jamil Ahmed. 11914 ASTORIA BLVD, STE 185 77089 #704-17-1984 L2003 IM *020 †20 ‡

MENA, Gabriel Eduardo. 1515 HOLCOMBE BLVD, ANESTHESIOLOGY DEPT #409 77030 #264-04-1996 L2005 AN *020 †05

MENCER, Melanie Lynn. 1213 HERMANN DR, STE 430 77004 #047-07-1996 L1999 FM *020 †18

MENDELL, Henry E. 6565 DE MOSS DR STE 222 77074 #048-02-1947 L1947 IM *071 †20

MENDELOW, Arthur Lipman. 77068 #836-01-1957 L1979 ORS *071 †40

MENDELSOHN, John. 1515 HOLCOMBE BLVD BOX 91 77030 #024-01-1963 L1998 ON IM *050 †20

MENDELSON, Inez Rachel. ■ 77024 #917-08-1953 L1981 CHP *071

MENDEZ, Donna Reyes. 6621 FANNIN ST, MC 11481 77030 #048-02-1992 L1994 PD *020 †55

MENDEZ, Hector Ricardo. ■ 77054 #451-01-2004 OBG *012

MENDEZ, Ruben. ■ 77054 #048-14-2008 *012

MENDEZ-CANCEL, Rodolfo. 1400 EL CAMINO VILLAGE DR 77058 #042-01-1992 L1995 IM *020

MENDIA, Enrique. 6500 HORNWOOD DR 77074 #429-01-1970 L1984 P *020

MENDIOLA, Monica L. ■ 77054 #048-04-2006 OBG *012

MENDIOLA, Victor A. 7333 NORTH FWY STE 250 77076 #275-01-1960 L1972 GP *020

MENDIOLA, Victor O. 7333 NORTH FWY, STE 250 77076 #048-14-1993 L1994 FM *020 †18

MENDOZA, Jason Anthony. 6701 FANNIN ST 77030 #016-01-2001 L2007 PD *100 †55

MENDOZA, Jorge Salvador. 2102 BAUER DR 77080 #429-01-1984 L2002 PD *020 †55

MENDOZA, Laura. ■ 77024 #048-13-1997 L2000 PD *100

MENNINGER, Roy W. 2801 GESSNER DR 77080 #035-20-1951 L1956 P *020 †75

MENNINGER, W Walter. 2801 GESSNER DR 77080 #035-20-1957 L1959 P PFP *072 †75 ‡

MENSH, Brett Daren. ■ 77009 #048-01-1993 L1994 *100

MENTZ, Henry A, III. 4400 POST OAK PKWY, AESTHETIC CENTER FOR 77027 #021-05-1984 L1991 PS OTO *020 †45,65

MENTZER, John Frank. ■ 77062 #038-40-1970 L1976 FM *020

MERAIKIB, Basem Mohamed A. PO BOX 20708, UNIV TX MED SCH AT HOUSTON 77225 #915-04-1996 PTH *100

MERCER, David Wayne. 5656 KELLEY ST, DEPT OF SURGERY 77026 #056-05-1986 L1993 GS *020 †85

MEREDITH, Afsa. 6806 BINTLIFF DR 77074 #496-38-1961 L1973 IM CD *020

MERELLO, Augusto. 3139 W HOLCOMBE BLVD # 810 77025 #132-01-1957 L1982 DR NM *071 †28,80

MERHAV, Hadar. 6410 FANNIN ST, STE 470 77030 #550-01-1984 L2004 GS AS *020

MERIANO, Frank V. 6560 FANNIN ST, STE 1008 77030 #048-04-1986 L1987 GE *020 †20

MERIC, Funda. 1515 HOLCOMBE BLVD BOX 44, MD ANDERSON CANCER CENTER 77030 #008-01-1991 L1999 GS *020 †85

MERINO, Orlando Rodolfo. 1919 LA BRANCH ST 77002 #231-02-1964 L1975 RO *020 †80 ‡

MERKEL, Manasa. 5314 DASHWOOD DR, LABORATORY BELLAIRE HOSPIT 77081 #836-02-1960 L1978 PTH *020 †50

MERKELZ, Kurt Philip. 777 N POST OAK RD, 3RD FL 77024 #048-14-1994 L1999 PMM FPG *020 †20

MERKL, Christopher O. 2116 BISSONNET ST 77005 #048-14-1988 L1989 P PYG *020 †75

MERKLE, Maryhaven. 1400 HOLCOMBE BLVD, UNIT 437 77030 #048-04-1988 L1996 IM *020 †20

MEROUEH, Chady Mohamad Ali. 1515 HOLCOMBE BLVD, BOX 053 77030 #605-03-2001 L2005 PTH PCP *100 †50

MERRIKH, Hooman Kirk. ■ 77057 #104-01-2006 *100

MERRILL, Joseph Melton. 3701 KIRBY DR STE 600, BAYLOR COLLEGE OF MEDICINE 77098 #024-01-1948 L1971 IM CD *020 †20

MERRIMAN, George J, Jr. 6720 BERTNER ST 77030 #048-04-1940 L1940 FM *071 †18

MERSZEI, Justin David. 6560 FANNIN ST STE 2204 77030 #005-06-1999 L2001 NEP *020 †20

MERTEN, Michael. ■ 77054 #409-24-1993 IM *100 †20

MERTENS, Benny Frank. ■ 77070 #054-04-1965 L1966 PTH *030 †50

MERY, Amin G. 650 W BOUGH LN, STE 164 77024 #048-13-1998 L2000 AI *020 †20,03

MESBAH, Rozita. 2424 W HOLCOMBE BLVD, MEDICAL CENTER ANESTHESIA 77030 #409-33-1990 L2001 AN *020 †05

MESHBERGER, Scott Douglas. 2727 W HOLCOMBE BLVD, RADIOLOGY DEPT 77025 #048-04-1993 L1994 DR *020 †80

MESTRY, Kaustubh Sudhir. 1 BAYLOR PLZ, DEPT FM 77030 #495-01-2002 FP *012

METHUKU, Aparna. ■ 77041 #495-37-1999 L2008 IM *071 †20

METRY, Denise Walker. 6621 FANNIN ST 620.16 77030 #048-14-1995 L2000 D *020 †15

METTAUER, Mark M. 830 FM 1960 RD W, STE 3 77090 #048-16-1997 L1998 TS *020 †85,90

METWALLI, Adam Riad. 1515 HOLCOMBE BLVD, UNIT 1373 77030 #036-05-2000 L2005 U *100 †20

METZ, Paul S. 909 FROSTWOOD DR, STE 262 77024 #048-13-2001 L2005 GS *020

METZLER, Patti Reddell. 411 BAY AREA BLVD 77058 #048-06-1985 L1988 PD *020 †55

MEYER, B Christoph. 8200 WEDNESBURY LN, STE 360 77074 #035-01-1989 L1996 OSS *020 †40

MEYER, Jeffrey A. 1200 HERMANN PRESSLER DR, UNI TEXAS SCH PUB HLTH LIB 77030 #048-14-1988 OS *030

MEYER, Jennifer Kathleen. 1707 SUNSET BLVD 77005 #035-46-1998 L2001 IM *020 †20

MEYER, John Stirling. 2321 SOUTHWEST FWY 77098 #067-01-1948 L1969 N *020 †75

MEYER, Larissa Alejandra. ■ 77096 #024-01-2002 L2004 OBG *100

MIA, Abul Quasem. ■ 77044 #495-02-1949 L1978 GP *071

MIAN, Amir Shabbir. ■ 77062 #704-04-2000 L2007 AN *100 †05

MIAN, Asad Iqbal. 1 BAYLOR PLZ 77030 #704-25-1997 L2007 MG *100

MIAN, Ayesha Irshad. 2801 GESSNER DR 77080 #704-25-1998 L2004 P CHP *100 †75

MICHAEL, Mini. 6621 FANNIN ST, MC 3-2482 77030 #495-31-1991 L2004 PN *100 ‡

MICHALAK, David Wayne. ■ 77055 #048-13-2003 L2007 FM *100 †18

MICHELETTI, Gildo Anthony. 1213 HERMANN DR STE 540 77004 #048-02-1973 L1974 D *020 †15

MIDDLEMAN, Amy Beth. 6621 FANNIN ST 1710.00, CLINICAL CARE CENTER 77030 #041-01-1990 L1997 ADL *020 †55

MIDDLETON, Lavinia P. 1515 HOLCOMBE BLVD UNIT 85, U.T. M.D. ANDERSON CANCER 77030 #010-01-1993 L1999 SP *020 †50

MIELES, Luis Alberto. 6410 FANNIN ST, STE 470 77030 #264-01-1974 L2003 GS *020 †85

MIESZ, Andrew. 2801 LITTLE YORK RD 77093 #759-03-1952 L1971 GS CRS *020

MIETTINEN, Sari Tellervo. 1919 NORTH LOOP W, STE 140 77008 #048-04-2003 L2006 PD *020 †55

MIETZSCH, Ulrike. ■ 77025 #408-30-2001 L2007 NPM *012 †55

MIGDAL, Michael Robert. 1515 HOLCOMBE BLVD -434, DEPT OF DERMATOLOGY 77030 #049-01-1997 L2003 D *020 †15

MIGLIORE, Philip Jos. 3602 GRENNOCH LN 77025 #041-12-1956 L1962 CLP *071 †50

MIGUEL, Breno Loureiro. ■ 77024 #187-32-1990 L2002 OBG *020 †30

MIHALICK, Michael Joseph. 6624 FANNIN ST, STE 2310 77030 #017-20-1969 L1976 CD IM *020 †20

MIHALO, Robert Matthew. 1515 HOLCOMBE BLVD BOX 04, TEXAS MEDICAL CENTER 77030 #025-07-1972 L1975 AN AM *020 †20

MIKATI, Issam. 2002 HOLCOMBE BLVD # 111B, VA MEDICAL CENTER CARDIOLO 77030 #605-01-1990 L1994 CD *020 †20

MIKESKA, Heather A. 7737 SOUTHWEST FWY STE 42, RES PRGM 77074 #048-14-2006 FP *012

MIKHAIL, Adib R. 17200 RED OAK DR 77090 #915-04-1964 L1974 P *020 †75

MILAM, John Danl. 6431 FANNIN ST, DEPT. OF PATHOLOGY & LAB. 77030 #021-05-1960 L1966 PTH BBK *020 †20

MILAM, Michael Robert. ■ 77054 #020-12-2001 L2007 OBG *100

MILAM, Rebecca Ashley. ■ 77054 #020-22-2003 L2007 DR *100 †80

MILANI, Rodolfo Edmundo. ■ 77098 #132-04-1941 L1959 AN *071

MILAS, Luka. M D ANDERSN HSP TUMOR INST 77030 #957-01-1963 L1985 *020

MILBOURNE, Andrea M. 1515 HOLCOMBE BLVD BOX 440, DEPT OF GYNECOLOGIC ONCOLO 77030 #014-01-1992 L2002 OBG *020 †30

MILES, Brian Jason. 7026 OLD KATY RD, STE 276 77024 #048-02-2000 L2006 **RNR** *020 †80
MILES, Brian John. 6560 FANNIN ST STE 2100 77030 #025-01-1974 L1994 **U** *020 †95
MILEUR, Mason W. ■ 77003 #048-14-2007 **IM** *012
MILEWICZ, Allen L. 6621 FANNIN ST, STE 650 77030 #035-19-1981 L1987 **PDS CCS** *020 †85
MILEWICZ, Dianna Mc Gooke. 6431 FANNIN ST, U OF T HEALTH CTR 77030 #048-12-1984 L1987 **IM** *050 †20,19
MILLAN, Marcela. ■ 77005 #024-07-2001 L2006 **PD** *020 †55
MILLAR, Sarah J. ■ 77035 #048-02-2006 **EM** *012
MILLAS, Stefanos George. ■ 77025 #048-12-2003 **GS** *012
MILLER, Aaron M. 800 PEAKWOOD DR, STE 6C 77090 #048-15-2001 L2005 **PO OPH** *020 †35
MILLER, Billy Jack. ■ 77004 #048-14-2001 L2002 **EM** *020 †16
MILLER, Bradley E. ■ 77098 #048-13-2004 L2008 **PCC** *012
MILLER, Courtney Nicole. ■ 77054 #048-15-2006 **IM** *012
MILLER, David Howard. 6550 FANNIN ST STE 2339 77030 #048-04-1971 L1971 **IM** *020 †20
MILLER, Douglas Jay. 6621 FANNIN ST, WT 17417B 77030 #550-02-1993 L2007 **AN** *020 †05
MILLER, Earl Lewis. 211 HIGHLAND CROSS DR #205 77073 #016-42-1999 L2002 **EM** *020 †16
MILLER, Gary Evan. 530 WELLS FARGO DR STE 110 77090 #048-02-1960 L1960 **P ADP** *020 †75 ‡
MILLER, Geoffrey. 6701 FANNIN ST 77030 #539-03-1972 L1992 **P** *020 †75
MILLER, Harold Jay. 6620 MAIN ST STE 1450, DEPT. OF OB/GYN 77030 #021-05-1960 L1966 **OBG OS** *020 †30
MILLER, Howard. 7600 FANNIN ST 77054 #048-02-1988 L1989 **AN** *020 †05
MILLER, Jason Harris. 6655 TRAVIS ST STE 980, DEPARTMENT OF DERMATOLOGY 77030 #035-09-2002 L2005 **D** *012
MILLER, John W. 902 FROSTWOOD DR, HOUSTON EYE AND LASER 77024 #048-14-1985 L1986 **OPH** *020 †35
MILLER, Jonna C. 7400 FANNIN ST STE 1050, HWCA 77054 #048-14-1996 L1999 **OBG** *020 †30
MILLER, Lane Ray. 6720 BERTNER ST 1-133, EPISCOPAL HOSPITAL 77030 #422-01-1997 L2001 **IC** *020 †20
MILLER, Morris Chas. ■ 77098 #067-01-1948 L1977 **GE** *071
MILLER, Nava. 7900 FANNIN ST, STE 3500 77054 #035-46-1997 L2000 **PD** *020 †55
MILLER, Norman. ■ 77057 #836-01-1957 L1979 **AN** *071
MILLER, Robert Allen. ■ 77096 #048-13-1970 L1970 **OPH** *071 †35
MILLER, Robert Harold. 5615 KIRBY DR STE 600 77005 #021-01-1973 L1978 **OTO HNS** *030 †45
MILLER, Shane Michael. ■ 77054 #048-04-2005 **PD** *012
MILLER, Steven D. 6431 FANNIN ST 4.276 77030 #039-01-1999 L2002 **TS** *012 †85
MILLER, Susan Maria. 6560 FANNIN ST STE 1150 77030 #028-03-1983 L1984 **FM** *020 †18
MILLER, Vicki Elizabeth. 1818 MEMORIAL DR, STE 200 77007 #048-12-1995 L1996 **FM** *020 †18
MILLER, Wm Farrington. 1661 TANGLEWOOD BLVD 77056 #048-04-1978 L1979 **AM GP** *050 †70
MILLER-HANCE, Wanda C. 6621 FANNIN ST 19345, TEXAS CHILD HOSP PED 77030 #056-05-1981 L1984 **AN PDC** *020 †55,05
MILLER-MILES, Kimberly R. 7900 FANNIN ST, STE 4000 77054 #048-02-2000 L2005 **OBG** *020
MILLIKAN, Randall Eugene. 1515 HOLCOMBE BLVD, BOX 427 77030 #011-02-1988 L1994 **ON** *050 †20
MILLS, Gordon Brent. 1515 HOLCOMBE BLVD, UNIT 950 77030 #060-01-1977 L1996 **GO** *050
MILLS, Jesse Nelson. ■ 77005 #018-03-2001 L2002 **U** *100
MILLS, Vern Andreas. 4545 POST OAK PLAC DR #130 77027 #054-04-1977 L1994 **PUD IM** *020 †20
MILLS, Virginia M. 3914 LEELAND ST 77003 #048-02-1991 L1992 **FM** *020 †18
MILONE, Jennifer Melissa. ■ 77077 #011-03-2007 **P** *012
MILTON, Roger Peter, Jr. ■ 77004 #010-03-1992 L1998 **FOP** *020
MIMS, Martha P. 1504 TAUB LOOP, DEPT. OF MEDICINE/ONCOLOGY 77030 #048-04-1998 L2001 **ON** *020 †20
MIMS, Sharon G. ■ 77096 #048-13-2005 **ORS** *100
MIMS, Thos Jefferson, Jr. 6624 FANNIN ST STE 2340, ST LUKES TOWER 77030 #021-06-1976 L1985 **NS** *020 †25
MINEO, Michael Thomas. 6560 FANNIN ST, STE 1900 77030 #048-14-1999 L2002 **U** *020 †95
MINER, Edward Christian. 6720 BERTNER ST, ST. LUKE'S EPISCOPAL HOSPI 77030 #028-02-2002 L2006 **CD** *012 †20
MINKES, Robert K. 6624 FANNIN ST, HOUSTON PEDIATRIC 77030 #021-01-1992 L2006 **PDS GS** *020 †85
MINKOWITZ, Harold Sydney. 921 GESSNER RD, ANESTHESIOLOGY AND PAIN 77024 #836-01-1988 L1997 **AN** *020 †05
MINTZ, A Aaron. 6621 FANNIN ST 77030 #048-02-1948 L1948 **PD** *040 †55
MINTZ, Max Ronald. 8240 ANTOINE DR STE 209 77088 #048-04-1965 L1965 **PD** *020 †55 ‡
MINTZ-HITTNER, Helen. 6410 FANNIN ST, STE 920 77030 #048-04-1969 L1969 **PO NPM** *050 †35
MIQDADY, Mohamad-Iqbal S. 5757 WESTHEIMER RD # 3231 77057 #575-02-1993 L2000 **PG** *020 †20
MIR, Mohsin Rehman. ■ 77004 #055-01-2006 **D** *012
MIRABI, Batool. 1709 DRYDEN RD, STE 725 77030 #517-01-1969 L1975 **PM** *020 †60
MIRABI, Mohsen. 7515 MAIN ST STE 600 77030 #154-07-1968 L1974 **P** *020 †75
MIRANDA, Fernando Enrique. 4141 SOUTHWEST FWY, STE 400 77027 #041-14-1997 L2003 **GS** *020 †85
MIRANDA, Matias. 6720 BERTNER ST 77030 #737-01-1957 L1972 **AN** *020
MIRANDA, Roberto Nicolas. 1515 HOLCOMBE BLVD, DEPT OF HEMATOPATHOLOGY, U 77030 #737-06-1983 L2007 **PTH HMP** *020 †50
MIRANDA, Victor Matias. 10370 RICHMOND AVE, STE 1125 77042 #048-02-1981 L1982 **EM** *071
MIRAVITE, Jaime V. ■ 77056 #748-24-1988 L1996 **FM** *020 †18
MIRELES, Jamir Encarnacio. ■ 77073 #748-08-1988 L2007 **FM** *020 †18
MIRO, Ramon Ernesto. 1740 W 27TH ST 77008 #341-01-1971 L1985 **OBS GYN** *020 †30
MIRZA, Humayun. 8945 LONG POINT RD STE 125 77055 #704-02-1985 L2003 **CD** *020 †20
MIRZA, Qasim Mohammad. 1 BAYLOR PLZ 77030 #704-01-2001 L2007 **PCC** *012 †20
MIRZAIETHRANE, Madjid. 6624 FANNIN ST, 20TH FL 77030 #902-03-1991 L2001 **CD** *020 †20
MISELLATI, Adnan Azzam. ■ 77054 #613-02-1999 **FP** *012
MISHAW, Clifford Owen. 6410 FANNIN ST STE 410 77030 #048-14-1979 L1979 **PD** *020 †55
MISRA, Arunima. 8945 LONG POINT RD STE 106 77055 #048-12-1994 L1996 **CD** *100 †20
MISRA, Sanghamitra Moulik. 10375 RICHMOND AVE, STE 1575 77042 #048-16-2003 L2006 **PD** *100 †55
MITCH, William Evans, II. 1709 DRYDEN RD, STE 925 77030 #024-07-1967 L2003 **NEP IM** *050 †20

MITCHEL, Shannon Marie. ■ 77025 #048-13-2007 **GS** *012
MITCHELL, Adam Michael. 1504 TAUB LOOP, RM 81.001 77030 #048-04-2002 L2005 **IM** *040 †20
MITCHELL, Alfred Tennyson. 18100 SAINT JOHN DR STE 2 77058 #005-18-1989 L1995 **PS** *020
MITCHELL, Bartley David. ■ 77004 #048-04-2008 *012
MITCHELL, Dana Faye. 6624 FANNIN ST STE 1400, KIDNEY ASSOCIATES, PLLC 77030 #021-05-2000 L2006 **NEP** *020 †20
MITCHELL, Derrick Anthony. 211 HIGHLAND CROSS DR, STE 275 77073 #023-07-2002 L2005 **EM** *020
MITCHELL, Donald Davis. 77074 #048-02-1945 L1945 **PD** *072 †55
MITCHELL, Jerry Ray. 6565 FANNIN ST, MAIL STATION F-504 77030 #047-05-1968 L1977 **IM** *050
MITCHELL, Sheri Lorraine. 1213 HERMANN DR, STE 670 77004 #021-01-1987 L1990 **PD** *020 †55
MITCHELL, Tamara Andrea. 810 PEAKWOOD DR, STE 107 77090 #030-06-1990 L1992 **DR** *020 †80
MITCHELL-TAPPING, George. ■ 77009 #048-15-1998 L2000 **AN** *020
MITCHEM, Lafrabya Nataka. ■ 77025 #045-04-2005 **EM** *012
MITRA, Shrabanee. 818 RINGOLD ST 77088 #048-13-1991 L2005 **FM** *020 †18
MITSCHKE, Michael C. 915 GESSNER RD, STE 900 77024 #048-02-1989 L1990 **CD** *020 †20
MITSUI, Masao. 1515 HOLCOMBE BLVD 77030 #385-05-1965 L1973 **PD IM** *075
MITTENDORF, Elizabeth Ann. 1400 HOLCOMBE BLVD, FC 12 3000 77030 #038-06-1996 L2005 **GS** *020 †85
MIZRAHI, Eli. 1 BAYLOR PLZ - NB302, DEPT OF NEUROLOGY 77030 #011-02-1975 L1982 **N CHN** *050 †55,75
MO, Benjamin Pui-Nin. ■ 77041 #243-21-1956 L1975 **AN** *071 †05
MOAKE, Joe Lawrence. 1709 DRYDEN RD STE 675, BAYLOR FACULTY CENTER-BCM 77030 #023-07-1967 L1973 **HEM IM** *050
MOBLEY, David Frank. 915 GESSNER RD, STE 725 77024 #047-06-1968 L1970 **U** *020 †95
MOCHARLA, Raman. 12121 RICHMOND AVE, STE 10 77082 #017-20-1993 L1998 **RNR** *020 †80
MODELSKI, Michael A. 150 W PARKER RD STE 204 77076 #352-07-1960 L1965 **CD IM** *071
MODI, Dipaben Dhananjay. 4545 POST OAK PLACE DR, STE 130 77027 #495-89-1992 L2005 **IM** *020
MODI, Gunjan M. ■ 77054 #048-04-2008 *012
MODI, Sapna Vinod. ■ 77054 #048-04-2008 *012
MODI, Shivani M. ■ 77054 #048-12-2004 L2007 **IM** *100 †20
MODY, Dina. 6565 FANNIN ST M227 77030 #496-38-1979 L1982 **PTH PCP** *020 †50
MOE, Olive Irene. ■ 77024 #041-07-1946 L1948 **GP OM** *071
MOELLER, Benjamin James. 6431 FANNIN ST 1134, OF TEXAS-HOUSTON 77030 #036-07-2006 **RO** *012
MOELLER, Frederick Gerard. 1300 MOURSUND ST 77030 #048-14-1985 L1986 **P PA** *020 †75
MOELLER, Molly Kathleen. ■ 77035 #036-07-2006 **PD** *012
MOENCH, Howard C. 1313 HERMANN DR 77004 #005-06-1963 L1975 **RO** *020 †80
MOGHIMI, Michael Hooman. ■ 77030 #048-14-2008 *012
MOGLOVKIN, Emily Meryl. ■ 77030 #048-14-2008 *012
MOHAMED, Shaffin Ali. 5773 WOODWAY DR, STE 465 77057 #035-03-1989 L1995 **AN PME** *020
MOHAMMAD, Fawzi Tawfic. ■ 77025 #042-02-2006 **DR** *012
MOHAMMED, Basim Soliman. ■ 77058 #915-04-1993 L1999 **SP** *100 †50
MOHAMMED, Shujauddin. 12121 RICHMOND AVE STE 214 77082 #495-21-1977 L1984 **CD IM** *020 †20
MOHAN, Pammi Venkatesh. 1 BAYLOR PLZ, BAYLOR COLLEGE OF MEDICINE 77030 #495-04-1991 L2006 **NPM** *100
MOHAN, Uma Yanamadala. 11302 FALLBROOK DR STE 105 77065 #495-21-1983 L1992 **GE** *020 †20
MOHANTY, Aaron. 6410 FANNIN ST, STE 1020 77030 #495-13-1986 L2007 *100
MOHI, Shagufta Zahid. 9210 HIGHWAY 6 S, STE C 77083 #704-02-1983 L1999 **PD** *020 †55
MOHINDRA, Prita Khanna. 1515 HOLCOMBE BLVD BOX 42, DEPT OF ANESTHESIOLOGY & C 77030 #496-07-1973 L1977 **AN CD** *020 †20
MOHIUDDIN, Imran Taj. 6560 FANNIN ST STE 1006 77030 #024-07-1997 L1999 **VS VIR** *020 †85
MOHNEY, John Leroy. 2304 FULTON ST 77009 #016-76-1969, ▲ L1969 **GP** *020
MOHSENIN, Amir. ■ 77054 #048-14-2008 *012
MOHYUDDIN, Tayyab. ■ 77054 #704-01-2000 L2002 **CD** *012 †20
MOIEL, Richard Herbert. 610 JACKSON HILL ST 77007 #021-01-1960 L1969 **NS** *071 †25
MOISE, Kenneth Jos, Jr. 6620 MAIN ST 77030 #021-05-1981 L1986 **MFM OBG** *072 †30
MOISE, Ovidiu Laurian L. 1631 NORTH LOOP W, STE 240 77008 #781-01-1993 L2004 **AN** *100 †05
MOISI, Marc Daniel. 6560 FANNIN ST STE 900, METHODIST HOSPITAL 77030 #035-19-2005 **NS** *012
MOK, Henry. 1515 HOLCOMBE BLVD, ANDERSON CANC 77030 #048-04-2005 **RO** *012
MOKADDEM, Bilal Mahmoud. 4407 YOAKUM BLVD, STE B 77006 #915-02-1981 L1995 **NEP IM** *020 †20
MOKRYNKA, Dian Joy. 2500 FONDREN RD, STE 270 77063 #035-09-1990 L1994 **OBG** *020 †30
MOLDOVAN, Stanton I. 6550 FANNIN ST STE 2415 77030 #041-02-1967 L1974 **N P** *020 †75 ‡
MOLINA, Claudia Patricia. ■ 77089 #429-02-1994 L2007 **SP** *020 †50
MOLINA-LAMAS, Eduardo. 7600 FANNIN ST 77054 #132-01-1970 L1975 **AN** *071 †05
MOLLDREM, Jeffrey Joel. 1515 HOLCOMBE BLVD, UNIT 900 77030 #026-04-1990 L1999 **HEM** *020 †20
MOLONY, Donald Andrew. 6431 FANNIN ST 77030 #005-18-1978 L1981 **NEP IM** *040 †20
MOMENI, Mazdak. 1 BAYLOR PLZ, DEPT OBG 77030 #517-01-2002 **OBG** *012
MOMOH, Adeyiza Olutoyin. 1 BAYLOR PLZ, BAYLOR COLL OF MED 77030 #016-06-2004 L2007 **PS** *012
MONCAYO, Rafael Eduardo. 7737 SOUTHWEST FWY, STE 420 77074 #264-09-1997 **FP** *012
MONDERSON, Thesselon W. ■ 77096 #010-03-2002 L2008 **HSO** *012
MONDSHINE, Raymond Henry. ■ 77074 #048-04-1956 L1956 **PD** *071 †55
MONGA, Manju. 6431 FANNIN ST, STE 3.268 77030 #065-05-1986 L1991 **OBG** *020 †30
MONGA, Trilok Nath. 2002 HOLCOMBE BLVD 77030 #495-01-1960 L1993 **PM** *020 †60
MONGA, Uma. ■ 77005 #495-05-1960 L1993 **RO IM** *020 †80
MONGE, Tania V. PO BOX 20708, UNIV TX MED SCH 77225 #048-14-2007 **OBG** *012
MONHEIT, Jacqueline G. 1 BAYLOR PLZ, DEPARTMENT OF PATHOLOGY 77030 #264-02-1979 L1984 **PTH ATP** *020 †50 ‡
MONLA, Yumna Tarek. 8830 LONG POINT RD, STE 502 77055 #605-01-1985 L1991 **END** *020 †50
MONMOUTH, Michael Anthony. 2020 NASA RD 1, STE 200 77058 #024-01-1983 L1989 **ORS OSM** *020 †40

MONROE, Matthew T. 4126 SOUTHWEST FWY, STE 1430 77027 #759-10-1965 L1975 CD IM *020 †20

MONSALVEZ, Jose Gabriel. 4126 SOUTHWEST FWY # 1100 77027 #231-01-1966 L1976 GS AS *020

MONT, Jay L. 6666 HARWIN DR, STE 480 77036 #011-02-1989 L1990 IM *020

MONTAGUE, Eleanor M Dino. ■ 77056 #041-07-1950 L1959 RO *071 †80

MONTAGUE, Laura J. ■ 77027 #023-07-1952 L1954 OBG *074

MONTALVA, Marcelo R. 5615 KIRBY DR, STE 850 77005 #231-01-1970 L1975 AN *020 †05

MONTALVO, Justo. 6624 FANNIN ST, 19TH FL 77030 #737-06-1987 L1997 PCC IM *020 †20

MONTALVO CHEN, Rolf Omar. 4755 ALDINE MAIL RD, ALDINE COMMUNITY HEALTH CE 77039 #319-07-2001 L2006 FM *100

MONTANES, Patricia. 1919 NORTH LOOP W, STE 140 77008 #264-04-1976 L1986 PD IM *020 †55

MONTEALEGRE, Alvaro Ignac. ■ 77030 #270-02-2001 L2007 OBG *100

MONTERO, Alberto Jose, Jr. 1515 HOLCOMBE BLVD, DIVIDIOSN OF ONCOLOGY 77030 #048-02-1999 L2002 ON *100 †20

MONTERO, Alfredo C. 2002 HOLCOMBE BLVD, VA HOSPITAL/ 111-B 77030 #847-04-1952 L1964 CD IM *040

MONTES, Joseph A. 6671 SW FWY, STE 110 77074 #048-14-1985 L1986 FM DIA *020 †18

MONTES, Leigh. 77090 #048-04-1996 L2002 TS *020 †85

MONTES, Martin. ■ 77030 #737-06-1997 L2003 ID *020 †20

MONTESINOS, Walter R. 14919 WAYBRIDGE DR 77062 #847-13-1977 L1988 GP GS *020

MONTGOMERY, Baxter D. 10480 MAIN ST 77025 #048-02-1990 L1991 CD IM *020 †20

MONTGOMERY, C Hunter. ■ 77057 #051-01-1953 L1959 OM IM *071 †70,20

MONTGOMERY, Hal Edwin. 6692 SOUTHWEST FWY 77074 #048-02-1957 L1957 GP *020

MONTGOMERY, Jos Saml, III. 11302 FALLBROOK DR STE 307 77065 #048-04-1977 L1977 OBG *020 †30

MONTOYA, Guillermo. 3138 MOSSY ELM CT 77059 #264-01-1963 L1972 GP *020

MONTOYA, Melissa Marina. 77024 #305-01-2007 FP *012

MONTOYA, Roberto. 1631 NORTH LOOP W STE 625 77008 #264-04-1965 L1975 PS HS *020 †70

MONTOYA JIMENEZ, Fernando. 12727 KIMBERLEY LN 77024 #264-04-1968 L1976 AN *020 †05

MONZON, Federico Alberto. ■ 77096 #649-01-1992 L2008 PTH *020 †50

MOODY, Frank Gordon. 6431 FANNIN ST STE 4164 77030 #035-20-1956 L1983 GS AS *040 †85

MOODY, Joe Marshall. ■ 77056 #040-06-1947 L1955 R RO *071 †80

MOOLA, Farhad O. 1 BAYLOR PLZ 77030 #068-01-1997 HS *100

MOON, Duck Gi. 10131 HAMMERLY BLVD 77080 #583-03-1972 L1978 GP *020 †50

MOON, Teresa Lynn. ■ 77005 #048-15-2005 AN *012

MOONAT, Sunita. 810 PEAKWOOD DR STE 103 77090 #495-30-1969 L1974 GYN *020 †30

MOONAT, Suresh Chandra. 810 PEAKWOOD DR STE 103 77090 #495-20-1970 L1974 FM *020 †18

MOORE, Byron H. ■ 77019 #048-12-2006 PTH *012

MOORE, Charles Henry. 17115 RED OAK DR, STE 120 77090 #045-01-1979 L1981 CD IM *020 †20

MOORE, Charles Mortimer. 810 PEAKWOOD DR STE 104 77090 #021-01-1956 L1974 FM GP *020 †18

MOORE, Charles Robert. 926 N WILCREST DR, INT EYECARE VISION CTR 77079 #047-06-1962 L1963 OPH *020 †35

MOORE, Charles Robert. 6431 FANNIN ST STE 6.018 77030 #021-05-2003 U *012

MOORE, Frederick Alan. 6550 FANNIN ST SM1661, DEPT OF SURGERY 77030 #041-12-1979 L1981 GS *020 †85

MOORE, Jack. 7550 FANNIN ST 77054 #021-01-1949 L1952 GYN *071 †30

MOORE, Jeffrey G. 1515 HOLCOMBE BLVD, CYTOPATHOLOGY BOX 053 77030 #016-43-1990 L1999 PCP *020

MOORE, Kristin Ann. 7707 FANNIN ST, STE 195 77054 #048-02-1980 L1980 AI *020 †20,03

MOORE, Laura Jane. 6550 FANNIN ST, STE 1661A 77030 #048-14-2000 L2005 CCS *100 †85

MOORE, Melissa Inez. 8314 SOUTHWEST FWY 77074 #048-14-1999 L2002 FM *020

MOORE, Milton Donald, Jr. 9350 KIRBY DR STE 100A 77054 #047-07-1980 L1985 D *020

MOORE, Nakita M. ■ 77021 #048-16-2007 P *012

MOORE, Norman Hall. 427 W 20TH ST STE 712 77008 #048-02-1958 L1958 FM *020 †18

MOORE, Portia Lynette. ■ 77054 #048-14-2005 L2007 PD *012

MOORE, Robert Alan, Jr. 2424 W HOLCOMBE BLVD, MEDICAL CENTER ANESTHESIA 77030 #048-04-1976 L1976 AN PME *020 †05

MOORE, Robert Henry. 6621 FANNIN ST 104000 77030 #048-02-1980 L1980 PDP *020 †55

MOORE, Sandra Harlene. 77079 #047-07-1973 L1975 AN PHP *074 †05

MOORE, Sarah E. ■ 77019 #048-12-2007 PD *012

MOORE, Sarah Lynn Guyton. ■ 77005 #048-12-1989 L1990 GP *020

MOORE, Stacey Denise. ■ 77027 #038-41-2000 L2007 PDS *012

MOORE, Valerie C. 7777 SOUTHWEST FWY, STE 310 77074 #020-12-1981 L1986 NPM PD *020 †55

MOORE, Warren H. 6720 BERTNER ST, STE 3-261 77030 #036-01-1977 L1981 NM IM *020 †20,28

MOORE, William Patrick. 701 N POST OAK RD STE 216 77024 #048-02-1956 L1956 CHP P *020 †75 ‡

MOORE, William T. ■ 77005 #048-02-1953 L1953 P *020 †75 ‡

MOOREHEAD, Will Earl. 5600 S WILLOW DR, STE 206 77035 #047-07-1969 L1989 ORS *075 †40

MOORE-JONES, Dominic. 1919 LA BRANCH ST 77002 #539-02-1957 L1966 IM *071

MOORHEAD, John Cary. 7908 N SAM HOUSTON PKWY W, STE 200 77064 #048-04-1989 L1995 OTO *020 †45

MOORHEAD, Louise Cope. 7438 HARRISBURG BLVD 77011 #011-03-1973 L1973 OPH *020 †35

MOPARTY, Ravi Kumar. ■ 77089 #495-21-1990 L2001 IM *020 †20

MORA, Melissa Kay. 1 BAYLOR PLZ, BAYLOR COLL OF MED 77030 #048-02-2003 NPM *012 †55

MORA, Ricardo. 7600 BEECHNUT ST 77004 #016-11-1994 L1997 AN CCA *020 †05

MORADI, Mahmood. 920 FROSTWOOD DR STE 625, ASSOCIATION 77024 #048-15-1990 L1991 NS *020 †25

MORALES, Adam F. ■ 77007 #048-14-2007 TY *012

MORALES, David Luis Simon. 6621 FANNIN ST, MC WT19345H 77030 #008-01-1995 L2004 TS *020 †85,90

MORALES, Miguel. 2409 ALDINE MAIL ROUTE 77039 #016-11-2000 L2003 FPG *020 †18

MORALES, Percy Francisco. ■ 77025 #028-02-2004 L2007 IM *012

MORAN, Ana Isolina. 1 BAYLOR PLZ, BCM 268 ROOM 1318N 77030 #737-06-1997 L2004 ID *100 †20

MORAN, Cesar Augusto. 1515 HOLCOMBE BLVD 77030 #429-01-1981 L2002 PTH *020 †50

MORAN, Cynthia H. 11222 RICHMOND AVE, STE 200 77082 #036-08-1986 L1988 FPG EM *020 †18

MORAN, John Richard. 2855 GRAMERCY ST 77025 #045-01-1995 L2000 OPH *020 †35

MORAN, Wilmer, Jr. 2600 S LOOP W 77054 #047-07-1968 L1973 DR EM *030

MOREANO, Walter F. 12605 EAST FWY, STE 510 77015 #737-01-1968 L1984 GS OS *020 †30

MOREIRA, Wendel Santos. ■ 77054 #187-32-1998 L2001 CD *100 †20

MORELL, Guillermo Juan. 9350 KIRBY DR STE 110, OMNI DIALYSIS CENTER 77054 #042-01-1985 L1988 NEP IM *020 †20

MORELLO, Frank A, Jr. 1515 HOLCOMBE BLVD, BOX 325 77030 #048-14-1994 L1995 VIR *020 †80

MORENO, Carlos Americo. 6431 FANNIN ST, DEPT OF FAM & COMM MED 77030 #024-01-1977 L1978 FM *040 †18

MORENO, Claudia Patricia. ■ 77054 #048-14-2008 *012

MORENO, Maria I L. 6720 BERTNER ST 77030 #275-01-1952 L1958 AN *071

MORENO, Orlando. ■ 77057 #847-05-1960 L1964 P *075

MORENO VERA, Mauricio Ale. 1515 HOLCOMBE BLVD, UNIT 441 77030 #231-03-1998 L1999 P *075

MORETTI, Paolo Maria. 1 BAYLOR PLZ 77030 #561-11-1990 MG *100

MORETTO, Matthew Christop. ■ 77030 #048-04-2008 *012

MORGAN, Avolonne Bianca. 1801 NORTH LOOP W, STE 40 77008 #048-14-2008 *012 PD *020 †55

MORGAN, Christine E. 2101 NASA PKWY, KELSEY SEYBOLD JSC CLC 77058 #048-04-1991 L1992 FM OM *020 †18

MORGAN, Christopher Killo. ■ 77098 #048-14-2008 *012

MORGAN, Galin Lewis. 1221 MCKINNEY ST, STE 40300 77010 #048-04-1986 L1987 DR *020 †80

MORGAN, Glenn Lynwood. 17070 RED OAK DR, STE 301 77090 #021-05-1987 L1991 OBG *020 †30

MORGAN, Julie S. 7600 BEECHNUT ST, MEMORIAL HERMANN SOUTHWEST 77074 #048-15-2004 L2007 EM *020

MORGAN, Laura Marie. ■ 77030 #048-14-2008 *012

MORGAN, Lisa A. ■ 77019 #048-14-2006 AN *012

MORGAN, Meredith Victor. 6411 FANNIN ST 77030 #048-04-1974 L1974 OBG *020 †30

MORICE, Rodolfo Carlos. 1515 HOLCOMBE BLVD BOX 76, UNIV TX ANDERSON CANCR CTR 77030 #270-01-1974 L1982 PUD *020 †20

MORIN, Gilles R. ■ 77069 #067-03-1953 L1953 P *071

MORIN, Lee M. 2101 NASA RD 1, JSC-CB 77058 #035-19-1981 L1983 OM AM *020 †70

MORITZ, Burt E, IV. 1 BAYLOR PLZ 77030 #048-02-1992 L1994 OSM *020

MORKAS, Muffaddalsiraj. 925 GESSNER RD STE 310 77024 #704-02-1995 L2007 HO *020 †20

MORMAN, Mark Bradley. 1502 TAUB LOOP, NEUROPSYCHIATRIC CTR 77030 #048-14-1992 L1993 CHP *020 †75

MORONEY, John William. ■ 77008 #016-43-2002 L2004 OBG *020

MORON MURILLO, Fanny Emil. 1 BAYLOR PLZ, BCM 360 77030 #264-01-1992 L2007 *020

MORRIS, Brenda Hook. 6431 FANNIN ST 3.226, DEPARTMENT OF PEDIATRICS 77030 #048-02-1987 L1988 NPM PD *020 †55

MORRIS, Charles Jay. 1333 WEST LOOP S STE 1100 77027 #048-13-1983 L1983 FM LM *030 †18

MORRIS, Michael W. 5990 AIRLINE DR STE 110 77076 #836-01-1968 L1978 GS AS *020

MORRIS, Randall Emmett. 915 GESSNER RD, STE 900 77024 #048-15-1984 L1985 CD *020 †20

MORRIS, Robert Keith, Jr. 1819 CRAWFORD ST, # 1708 77002 #021-05-1974 L1977 OBG *020 †30

MORRIS, Russell R. ■ 77018 #048-14-2001 AN *020

MORRISON, Catherine Anne. ■ 77007 #045-01-2005 GS *012

MORRISON, Daniel Peter. ■ 77005 #024-07-1962 L1970 PM R *071 †60

MORRISON, John Troth. 2120 ASHLAND ST 77008 #005-15-1977 L2005 D *020 †15 ‡

MORRISON, Laura Jo. 1709 DRYDEN RD, 8TH FL 77030 #038-06-1997 L2002 IM IMG *020 †20

MORRISON, Leon Macmillan. ■ 77082 #036-05-1995 L1998 AN *020 †05

MORRISON, Tara Mc Donald. 11914 ASTORIA BLVD, STE 500 77089 #036-05-1996 L1998 OTO *020

MORRISON, William Henry. 1515 HOLCOMBE BLVD, BOX 97 77030 #023-07-1978 L1988 IM RO *020 †20,80

MORROW, Achilia S. 3701 KIRBY DR, STE 600 77098 #024-01-2002 L2006 IM *100 †20

MORROW, Edwin Jos, Jr. 4126 SOUTHWEST FWY STE 800 77027 #048-04-1947 L1947 IM *071

MORROW, Phuong Khanh Huyn. 1515 HOLCOMBE BLVD, BOX 1354 77030 #048-14-2000 L2003 ON *100 †20

MORROW, Robert B. 7600 BEECHNUT ST, ADMINISTRATION OFFICE 77074 #048-14-1987 L1988 FM *030 †18

MORSI, Hesham. ■ 77030 #915-11-1991 L2006 RNR *100 †80

MORTAZAVI, Ali. 6624 FANNIN ST STE 2000 77030 #517-01-1979 L1993 CD IM *020 †20

MORTENSON, Melinda Moon. 1515 HOLCOMBE BLVD, MD ANDERSON CANCER CENTER 77030 #005-19-1999 L2006 GS *100

MOSBACHER, Diane. 712 MAIN ST STE 2200 77002 #048-04-1983 L1983 P *020 †75

MOSBY, Richard Allen. 2305 SOUTHMORE BLVD, MEDCARE 77004 #048-13-1970 L1970 DR *075 †80

MOSELEY, James Bruce, Jr. 6560 FANNIN ST, STE 400 77030 #048-12-1983 L1983 ORS OSM *020 †40

MOSES, Ron Lee. 6624 FANNIN ST, STE 1480 77030 #023-07-1993 L1998 OTO *020 †45

MOSIER, Dennis Ramon. 1 BAYLOR PLZ, DEPT NEURO NB 302 77030 #011-03-1989 L1993 N *020 †75

MOSQUERA, Ricardo Alberto. ■ 77005 #649-30-1994 L2000 PDP *012 †55

MOSS, Timothy James. ■ 77025 #018-03-2008 *012

MOTAPARTHI, Kiran. ■ 77030 #048-04-2007 *012

MOTEN, William M. ■ 77027 #024-01-1949 L1957 D *071 †15

MOTHNER, Brent A. 6621 FANNIN ST STE A-210 77030 #048-14-2002 L2005 PD *020

MOTIL, Kathleen Jean. 1100 BATES AVE, CHILDRENS NUTRITION RES CT 77030 #041-07-1973 L1982 GE PD *020 †55

MOTIWALA, Nisrin Hatim. 14027 MEMORIAL DR 77079 #704-16-1996 L2006 PTH *100

MOTT, Antonio Reddick. 6621 FANNIN ST 19345-C, TEXAS CHILDRENS HOSPITAL 77030 #012-01-1989 L1999 PDC *020

MOUGOURIS, Taso. 4545 POST OAK PLACE DR, STE 130 77027 #422-01-1998 L2004 IM *020 †20

MOULDER, Stacy Lynn. 1515 HOLCOMBE BLVD 77030 #027-01-1995 L2005 HO *020 †20

MOULIK, Mousumi. 6431 FANNIN ST, MSB, UTHSC 77030 #495-36-1990 L1996 PDC *100 †55

MOULOPOULOS, Lia Angela. ■ 77031 #418-01-1985 L1991 R *100

MOUMNEH, Ghada Abdalleh. ■ 77082 #605-01-1995 L2004 PP *020 †50

MOURA, Roberto Abdalla. 1720 DRYDEN RD, STE 216 77030 #187-20-1960 L1968 OPH *071 †35

MOURE, Antonio. ■ 77019 #847-05-1952 L1964 NS *075 †25

MOURE, Jean M Buchanan. ■ 77019 #352-07-1956 L1962 N *072

MOUSSAOUI, Ali M. 7324 SOUTHWEST FWY, STE 1050 77074 #605-01-1991 L1997 N *020 †75

MOUTON, David Eugene. 1111 AUGUSTA DR, KELSEY-SEYBOLD CLINIC WEST 77057 #021-05-1965 L1970 IM NM *062 †28,20

MOUZOON, Melanie Ehni. 7900 FANNIN ST, STE 2100 77054 #048-14-1982 L1983 PD HOS *020 †55

MOWBRAY, Hillary Shane. 6431 FANNIN ST, SCHOOL A 77030 #048-16-2004 L2007 PD *020

MOYE, Jerry Walter. 1250 CYPRESS STATION DR 77090 #051-01-1964 L1969 PD AM *020 †55

MOYE, Lemuel Alexander. 1100 HERMAN PRESSLER, SCHOOL OF PUBLIC HEALTH 77030 #017-20-1978 L1984 GPM *020

MOYER, Virginia Ann. 6701 FANNIN ST, STE 1540 77030 #048-04-1977 L1978 PD *040 †55

MOYLETT, Bernadine Howard. 1 BAYLOR PLZ RM 302A 77030 #539-06-1991 AI *100

MSHVILDADZE, Medea O.. ■ 77025 #913-23-1990 L2006 AN *100 †05

MUELLER, Brigitta Ursula. 6701 FANNIN ST 77030 #869-02-1985 L2003 PD *020 †55

MUELLER, Eric J. ■ 77054 #048-14-2007 IM *012

MUELLER, Ernest O H, Jr. 17000 EL CAMINO REAL, STE 105J 77058 #048-02-1969 L1969 PTH *020 †50

MUFFOLETTO, Anthony J. 7500 BEECHNUT ST, HOUSTON ORTHOPAEDIC 77074 #048-13-1991 L2000 ORS *020 †40

MUGHAL, Naveed A. 18220 TOMBALL PKWY, STE 350 77070 #917-05-1986 L2000 MPD *020 †55

MUHAMMAD, Shahid. 2727 W HOLCOMBE BLVD, KELSEY-SEYBOLD CLINIC 77025 #704-02-1986 L1995 END *020 †20

MUI, Bong Quy. 13480 VETERANS MEMORIAL DR 77014 #941-01-1972 L2006 FM OS *020 †18

MUKANA, Nsuela. ■ 77071 #041-14-2006 *012

MUKERJI, Shraddha Siddhar. 1 BAYLOR PLZ 77030 #496-38-1998 PDO *012

MUKHI, Vicky S. ■ 77021 #048-13-2004 L2007 DR *012

MUKHOPADHYAY, Arun K. 11914 ASTORIA BLVD # 580 77089 #495-02-1965 L1974 GE IM *020

MUKHOPADHYAY, Madhuri. ■ 77001 #048-14-2003 END *012

MULANOVICH, Victor. 1515 HOLCOMBE BLVD UNIT 1, MD ANDERSON CANCER CENTER 77030 #737-06-1990 L2005 ID IM *012

MULCHANDANI, Hargobind J. ■ 77081 #495-16-1951 L1977 GP *071

MULDER-YUAN, Marijn G. 1919 S BRAESWOOD BLVD, FIFTH FLOOR 77030 #660-05-1989 L2001 PD PEM *020 †20

MULKEY, Anna Deborah. 1515 HOLCOMBE BLVD, BOX 437 77030 #010-02-1999 L2002 IM *020 †20

MULLANS, Elizabeth Anne. 1233 WEST LOOP S STE 1050 77027 #028-46-1993 L1995 D *020 †15

MULLENS, Michael. 6431 FANNIN ST, UNIV TX MED SCH AT HOUSTON 77030 #048-14-2003 L2003 AN *012

MULLICK, Seema Sanjeev. 6448 FANNIN ST, DIAG CLINIC OF HOUSTON 77030 #495-08-1987 L1995 PTH PCP *020 †50

MULLINS, Charles Edward. 6621 FANNIN ST, TEXAS CHILDREN'S HOSPITAL 77030 #010-01-1958 L1969 PDC *012

MULLINS, Harold. ■ 77021 #047-07-1961 L1965 IM *071

MULUKUTLA, Venkatacha. 1 BAYLOR PLZ, DEPT OF INTERNAL MED/PEDS 77030 #048-04-2005 MPD *012

MUNCY, Debra M. 211 HIGHLAND CROSS DR #275 77073 #048-14-1988 L1989 EM *020 †16

MUNDANTHANAM, George J. 1 BAYLOR PLZ, DEPT OF ORTHO SURGERY 77030 #033-05-2003 L2008 ORS *012

MUNDEN, Martha Mappus. 6621 FANNIN ST 2.2521, TEXAS CHILDREN'S HOSPITAL 77030 #045-01-1988 L1995 DR *020 †80

MUNDY, Daniel O. 6410 FANNIN ST STE 200 77030 #048-04-1993 L1994 OBG *020 †30

MUNDY, Stephanie B. 6624 FANNIN ST STE 1240, ST. LUKE'S MEDICAL CLINIC 77030 #048-04-1993 L1994 IM *020 †20

MUNIZ, Antonio Eugenio. 6431 FANNIN ST 432, U OF T HOUSTON MEDICAL SCH 77030 #021-05-1991 L2007 EM PE *040 †16

MUNIZ, Henry. 4407 YOAKUM BLVD, STE B 77006 #011-02-1974 L1984 NEP *020 †20

MUNK, Zev Moshe. 902 FROSTWOOD DR, STE 222 77024 #067-01-1974 L1978 AI IM *020 †20,03

MUNNUR, Uma. 1504 TAUB LOOP 3RD FL, DEPARTMENT OF ANESTHESIA 77030 #495-57-1989 L1998 AN *020 †05

MUNOZ, Judith A. 1221 MCKINNEY ST, STE 40300 77010 #264-04-1988 L1997 FM *020 †18

MUNOZ RIVAS, Flor. 6621 FANNIN ST, CLINICAL CARE CTR STE 1150 77030 #429-02-1991 L1998 PD ID *050 †55

MUNOZ SOLARES, Carlos E. 6560 FANNIN ST STE 1720 77030 #429-01-1966 L1975 IM END *020 †28

MUNTZ, James Edwin. 6550 FANNIN ST STE 2339 77030 #048-04-1975 L1976 IM *020 †20

MUPPIDID, Sridevi. 8303 SOUTHWEST FWY, STE 120 77074 #496-24-1996 L2002 PD *020 †55

MURAD, Ferid. 1825 PRESSLER ST STE 530, U. OF TEXAS HOUSTON HEALTH 77030 #038-06-1965 L2000 PA IM *012

MURAKAMI, Shun Ichi. 1515 HOLCOMBE BLVD, BOX 0011 77030 #572-07-1964 N *020

MURDOCK, Horace David. 1315 CALHOUN ST STE 1702 77002 #047-07-1972 L1974 TS *020 †85

MURPHEY, Michael David. ■ 77005 #422-01-2001 P *100

MURPHY, Edward Chas. 6550 FANNIN ST STE 1720 77030 #016-06-1971 L1972 NS *020 †20

MURPHY, Thomas James. 11452 SPACE CENTER BLVD 77059 #064-01-1976 L1978 FM *020 ‡

MURPHY, Wm Alexander, Jr. 1515 HOLCOMBE BLVD UNIT 57, UT MD ANDERSON CANCER CTR 77030 #041-14-1971 L1994 DR *020 †80

MURR, Marilyn Gay. 1221 MCKINNEY ST, STE 40300 77010 #048-04-1983 L1983 FM *020 †50

MURRA, Lourdes Maria. 15003 FM 529 RD, STE A 77095 #021-05-1994 L2006 FM IM *020 †20,18

MURRA-SACA, Salvador E. 11302 FALLBROOK DR, STE 205 77065 #649-14-1982 L1994 N *020 †75

MURRAY, Barbara Elizabeth. 6431 FANNIN ST, MSB 2.112 DIV OF ID 77030 #048-12-1973 L1981 ID *030 †20

MURRAY, James Lee. 1515 HOLCOMBE BLVD, BOX 422 77030 #017-20-1972 L1983 ON IG *020 †20

MURRAY, Mark Andrew. 10370 RICHMOND AVE, STE 1125 77042 #005-12-1993 L1995 IM *020 †20

MURRAY, Mark D. 10370 RICHMOND AVE, STE 1125 77042 #048-14-1997 L2004 GE *020 †20

MURRAY, Patrick Joseph. 1709 DRYDEN RD, 12TH FL 77030 #035-15-2002 L2007 OSM *012

MURTAGH, Blaithnead Mary. 6431 FANNIN ST, UTHSC DIV OF CARDIOLOGY 77030 #539-05-1997 L2001 CD *100 †20

MURTHY, Bhamidipati V R. 6431 FANNIN ST 4.148, DIV OF RENAL DISEASE AND H 77030 #495-45-1999 L2001 IM *020 †20

MURTHY, Jayasimha N. 6431 FANNIN ST, MSB 1.274 77030 #495-52-1996 L2005 PCC *012

MURTHY, Ravi. 1515 HOLCOMBE BLVD 77030 #495-52-1988 L2004 VIR *020 †80,20 ‡

MURTI, Meena. 6431 FANNIN ST 77030 #048-04-2004 L2007 PD *020 †55

MURUGASU, Belinda. 6431 FANNIN ST 77030 #825-01-1981 PN *020

MUSCAL, Eyal. 6621 FANNIN ST, MC 3-2290 77030 #041-02-2000 L2007 PPR *100 †55

MUSGROVE, Kathryn H. 915 GESSNER RD, STE 250 77024 #048-14-1984 L1985 OPH PD *020 †35

MUSHER, Daniel Michael. 2002 HOLCOMBE BLVD, INFECTIOUS DISEASE SECTION 77030 #035-01-1963 L1971 ID IM *050 †20

MUSHIN, Uriel. 902 FROSTWOOD DR, STE 163 77024 #550-02-1979 L1986 VS GS *020 †85

MUSHTAQ, Aliya Naaz. 6550 FANNIN ST 1001 77030 #577-01-2005 IM *012

MUSSA, Firas Fuad. 1709 DRYDEN RD STE 1500, DEPARTMENT OF SURGERY 77030 #528-01-1995 L2005 VS *100 †85

MUSTAFA, Muhammad S. 4903 W SAM HOUSTON PKWY N, STE C 77041 #704-22-1985 L1997 N *075

MUTH, Elizabeth Helen. 1 BAYLOR PLZ, DEPT OF PEDIATRICS 77030 #048-04-2006 MPD *012

MUTHAPPA, Poovamma B. 14027 MEMORIAL DR STE 252 77079 #495-09-1978 L1989 PD *020 †55

MUTHUSWAMY, Bhuvana. 1 BAYLOR PLZ, MS: BCM 621 77030 #496-01-1990 L1999 IM *020 †20

MUYLAERT, Stephanie Julli. ■ 77030 #048-14-2008 *012

MUZQUIZ-DRUMMOND, Sylvia. 7011 SOUTHWEST FWY 77074 #649-30-1990 L1997 P *020 †75

MUZZAFFAR, Tariq. ■ 77007 #495-51-1997 L2008 HMP *020

MYERS, Dana Leigh. 6560 FANNIN ST, STE 738 77030 #024-05-1993 L1998 GS *020

MYERS, Darryn Lancaster. 12141 RICHMOND AVE 77082 #005-14-1995 L2004 EM *020 †16

MYERS, Delbert Dennis. 6621 FANNIN ST 77030 #017-20-1967 L1973 PD *020 †55

MYERS, Irving L. 50 BRIAR WAY 77027 #038-40-1960 L1963 P *020

MYERS, James Wm. 3313 CASON ST 77005 #025-01-1963 L2001 GS OS *020 †85

MYERS, Jeffrey Nicholas. 1515 HOLCOMBE BLVD, HEAD AND NECK SURGERY 77030 #041-01-1991 L1998 OTO *020 †45

MYERS, Larry Gene. 920 FROSTWOOD DR 77024 #048-02-1967 L1967 OBG *071 †30

MYERS, Tara Jo. 10370 RICHMOND AVE, STE 1125 77042 #048-14-1983 L1983 IM *020 †20

MYGDAL, Kristen Lem. ■ 77046 #048-02-2001 L2007 IM *080

MYNDERSE, Amy Terry. 6624 FANNIN ST, MEDICAL CLINIC OF HOUSTON 77030 #048-04-2002 L2005 IM *100 †20

MYONES, Barry. 6621 FANNIN ST MC, TEXAS CHILDRENS HOSPITAL 77030 #035-03-1977 L1992 PD PPR *020 †55

NAAMAN, Adam. ■ 77055 #035-46-1971 L1975 GS VS *071 †85

NABI, Faisal. ■ 77082 #048-15-2000 L2006 CD *100 †20

NACHIMSON, Joel Edward. 800 PEAKWOOD DR, STE 7J 77090 #048-13-1987 L1988 EM FM *020 †18

NADEEM, Sahba Q. 11914 ASTORIA BLVD STE 355 77089 #704-02-1982 L1994 IM HO *020 †20

NADEEM, Saiyyeda. 1 BAYLOR PLZ 77030 #704-26-2000 NM *012

NADEEM, Tania. 1 BAYLOR PLZ MS 350 77030 #704-25-2001 L2007 CHP *012

NADER-EFTEKHARI, Shahla. 6431 FANNIN ST STE 3604, DEPT OB/GYN 77030 #917-05-1970 L1982 END REN *020

NADERI, Sahar. ■ 77030 #048-04-2008 *012

NAEINI, Ramin Morshedzade. 1 BAYLOR PLZ 77030 #517-01-2002 DR *012

NAFTOLIN, Leigh Z. 2400 AUGUSTA DR, STE 105 77057 #065-06-1963 L1976 FM *020

NAG, Pratip K. 6621 FANNIN ST, STE A210 77030 #016-42-2003 L2006 PD *020

NAGABHUSHAN, Kukkalli K. 211 HIGHLAND CROSS DR, STE 275 77073 #495-99-1992 L2001 EM *020

NAGEL, Georgia Anna. PO BOX 20708, DEPT OF INT MED 77225 #935-01-2003 FP *012

NAGUEH, Sherif F. 6550 FANNIN ST STE 1901, METHODUS DEBAKEY CARDLGY 77030 #915-02-1986 L1996 CD IM *020 †20

NAHMIAS, Larry Michael. 18333 EGRET BAY BLVD, STE 560 77058 #017-20-1975 L1990 P PFP *020 †75

NAIDOO, Elton Rex. ■ 77054 #048-14-2008 *012

NAIK, Bindi Jayendra. ■ 77006 #048-16-2003 L2006 GS *012

NAIK, Ojas Ajit. 1709 DRYDEN RD STE 550, BCM FACULTY CENTER 77030 #021-06-2006 IM *012

NAIK, Sagar Arvind. 6720 BERTNER ST, DEPT OF RADIOLOGY 77030 #048-04-1999 L2000 DR *020 †80

NAIK, Satish Shrinivas. 830 GEMINI ST 77058 #038-44-1996 L2000 IM *020 †20

NAIK, Sunil Shanker. 11821 EAST FWY, STE 135 77029 #496-01-1980 L1997 IM *020 †20

NAING, Aung. 1400 HOLCOMBE BLVD, UNIT 422 DIV CANCER 77030 #902-05-1997 L2006 HO *020 †20

NAIR, Bas. 17776 S H 249 6 77064 #495-31-1968 L1980 PD FM *020

NAIR, Bindu Balachandran. 10370 RICHMOND AVE, STE 1125 77042 #496-32-1998 L2005 FM *040 †18

NAIR, Jeethy Parameswaran. 1919 LA BRANCH ST 77002 #495-37-1999 FM *100

NAIR, Lekshmi. ■ 77007 #016-06-2001 L2007 DR *020 †80

NAJAM, Lubna Younis. 12000 WILCREST DR STE 206 77031 #704-01-1974 L1979 PD *020 †55

NAJAM, Muhammad Younis. 12000 MURPHY RD # NO-206 77031 #704-01-1974 L1977 PD *020 †55

NAJARI, Bobby Baback. ■ 77030 #048-04-2008 *012

NALLUSAMY, Selvrani. 2727 W HOLCOMBE BLVD, 4TH FL 77025 #495-61-1996 L2005 HO *100 †20

NAMMOUR, Nicolas Maher. 6501 FANNIN ST MS NB302, DEPT. OF NEUROLOGY 77030 #605-03-1998 L2007 CN *020 †75

NANDA, Baljit Kaur. ■ 77005 #495-41-1962 L1970 ATP *020 †50

NANDA, Roz. 6400 FANNIN ST, STE 1900 77030 #016-42-1991 L1995 OBG *020 †30

NANDETY, Rao K. 6692 SOUTHWEST FWY, MEDICLINIC 77074 #495-50-1960 L1978 CD IM *062

NANDWANI, Shams Sherali. 710 FM 1960 RD W 77090 #704-02-1987 L1999 PD *020 †55

NANNINI, Esteban Carlos. 1515 HOLCOMBE BLVD, UT M.D. ANDERSON CANCER C 77030 #132-04-1992 ID *100

NAPLES, Joseph John. 6565 FANNIN ST B452, DEPT OF ANESTH 77030 #028-34-1969 L1980 AN *020 †05

NAQVI, Kiran. 7600 BEECHNUT ST, CAPE COD HOSPITAL 77074 #704-02-2001 L2007 IM *100 †20

NAQVI, Shagufta Naz. 12121 RICHMOND AVE, STE 208 77082 #704-02-1992 L2005 ON *020 †20

NARANG, Harcaran Singh. 8240 ANTOINE DR, STE 102 77088 #495-69-1991 L2002 IM *020 †20

■ = Address Information Privacy Protected

NARANG, Nisha. 3720 W ALABAMA ST 77027 #495-03-1999 **IM** *020

NARASIMHAN, Supriya. ■ 77054 #495-96-2002 L2004 **ID** *012 †20

NARAYAN, Rakesh. 11800 ASTORIA BLVD 77089 #025-07-1993 L2001 **AN** *020 †05

NARAYANA, Narayana P. 1315 ST JOSEPH PKWY, STE 1210 77002 #495-09-1971 L1983 **GE IM** *020 †55,20

NARCISSE, Victor Joseph. 1709 DRYDEN RD, 8TH FL 77030 #048-04-1997 L2002 **IM** *020 †20

NART, Armando. 7600 BEECHNUT ST, 2ND FL 77074 #048-04-1982 L1983 **PTH FOP** *020 †50

NARULA, Harminder Singh. 1885 OLD SPANISH TRL 77054 #495-02-1973 L1982 **FOP NP** *062 †20

NARVIOS, Aida Bangue. 1515 HOLCOMBE BLVD UNIT 07 77030 #748-09-1977 L1995 **BBK** *020 †50

NARWANI, Ajay Mohan. 6431 FANNIN ST # 196 77030 #496-21-2002 L2002 **PMM** *012

NASCIMBENE, Angelo. ■ 77030 #561-03-2001 **IM** *012

NASH, Edward A. 17270 RED OAK DR, STE 200 77090 #048-14-2002 L2006 **PM** *020 †60

NASH, Marianne Elizabeth. ■ 77005 #048-14-2007 **P** *012

NASHED-GUIRGUIS, Heidi M. 9105 N WAYSIDE DR 77028 #048-02-2000 L2004 **FM** *020 †18 ‡

NASIR, Aisha. 4545 POST OAK PLACE DR, STE 130 77027 #704-06-1997 L2004 **IM** *020

NASIR, Nadim, Jr. 6560 FANNIN ST STE 620 77030 #048-12-1986 L1987 **ICE CD** *020 †20

NASSAR, George M. 1415 LA CONCHA LN 77054 #605-01-1988 L1997 **NEP IM** *020 †20

NASSER, Dean A. 11914 ASTORIA BLVD STE 670, TX INSTI. OF CHEST & SLEEP 77089 #011-02-1998 L2004 **PCC** *020 †20

NASSER, Maher Mohammad. 6624 FANNIN ST, STE 1710 77030 #915-02-1970 L1979 **CD IM** *020 †20

NASSIF, George M. PO BOX 590668 77259 #048-12-2000 L2003 **PCC** *012 †20

NASSIF, Nadim Sami. 1631 NORTH LOOP W, STE 500 77008 #028-34-1995 L1999 **OPH** *020 †35

NATALI, Dalila. PO BOX 20708, 7044 MSB 77225 #042-01-2003 **CN** *012

NATELSON, Ethan Allen. 6550 FANNIN ST, SMITH TOWER STE 1001 77030 #048-04-1966 L1972 **HEM** *040 †20

NATES, Joseph Luis. 1515 HOLCOMBE BLVD, BOX 112 77030 #264-12-1981 L2000 **AN** *020

NATH, Rahul Kumar. 2201 W HOLCOMBE BLVD, STE 225 77030 #016-06-1988 L1998 **PS** *020 †65

NATHANI, Muhammed. 2727 W HOLCOMBE BLVD 77025 #704-02-1987 L1997 **GE IM** *020 †20

NATHO, Lorraine Ruth. ■ 77054 #067-01-1995 L1995 *020

NAVANEETHAN, Priya. 15850 EXPORT PLAZA DR, DIVISION OF IMMIGRATION HE 77032 #028-46-2001 L2004 **PCC** *012

NAVARIJO, Joseph P. 6624 FANNIN ST STE 2480 77030 #048-13-1993 L1994 **CD** *020 †20

NAVARRO, Fernando Andres. 6431 FANNIN ST, MSB 3.140 77030 #264-04-1995 L2005 **PG** *020 †55

NAVARRO, Romel Lustina. 10807 JONES RD, # 131 77065 #748-02-1993 L2000 **END** *020 †20

NAWAR, Diyaa Mohammad Has. 424 HAHLO ST, BRAZOS FAMILY MEDICINE 77020 #915-04-1996 L2005 **FM** *100 †18

NAWAR, Mohamed Abdelhamid. ■ 77054 #915-02-1996 L2004 **CD** *100

NAWASIRIPONG, Opas. ■ 77025 #891-04-1992 L2004 **N EM** *020

NAYAK, Atasu Kumar. 6624 FANNIN ST, LUKE'S TOWER 77030 #495-13-1987 L2004 **IC** *020 †20

NAYAR, Vikram Vadasseri. ■ 77054 #023-01-2003 **NS** *012

NAYEEMUDDIN, Inayath F. 7011 SW FWY, SWCSC-MHMRA 77074 #495-51-1989 L1997 **P** *020

NAYGANDHI, Yamini Bharat. 11302 FALLBROOK DR, STE 201 77065 #495-13-1986 L2002 **IM** *020 †20

NAZARANI, Mehboob A. 7324 SOUTHWEST FWY, STE 640 77074 #704-16-1990 L1997 **P** *020 †75

NAZARIO, Javier A. ■ 77035 #024-01-2004 L2007 **DR** *012

NAZARIO, Lizette Arlene. 1515 HOLCOMBE BLVD, DEPT BIOIMMUNOTHERAPY, BOX 77030 #042-01-1988 L1992 **ON** *020 †20

NAZERI, Alireza. ■ 77056 #517-01-1997 L2007 **IM** *100 †20

NDUBUEZE, Chinonyerem N. 4545 POST OAK PLACE DR, STE 130 77027 #690-04-1989 L2001 **IM** *020 †20

NEAL, Cheryl L. ■ 77007 #048-14-2004 L2007 **P** *012

NEAL, Mary Tonry. 7900 FANNIN ST 77054 #021-05-1979 L1981 **GYN** *020 †30

NEAL, Ryan Christopher. 6565 FANNIN ST STE B160 77030 #047-07-1991 L1992 **CD IM** *020 †20

NEASON, Chau Le. 13730 PEAR WOODS CT 77059 #048-14-2002 L2006 **IM** *100 †20

NEBGEN, Denise. 6550 FANNIN ST, STE 2201 77030 #016-06-1997 L1999 **OBG GYN** *020 †30

NEBLETT, Charles Robt. 6560 FANNIN ST STE 1748 77030 #048-04-1965 L1965 **NS** *020 †25

NEELA, Sangeeta. ■ 77082 #048-12-2005 **DR** *012

NEELAPU, Sattva Swarup. 1515 HOLCOMBE BLVD, BOX 903 77030 #495-53-1992 L2005 **IM ON** *020 †20

NEELY, Amber Elaine. ■ 77025 #048-14-2005 L2006 **P** *012

NEFF, Nancy Elaine. 1615 N MAIN ST 77009 #048-04-1975 L1975 **IM** *071 †20

NEIMAN, Abigail Rebecca. 8830 LONG POINT RD, STE 105 77055 #035-46-1992 L2000 **RHU** *020 †20

NEIMAN, Melissa. ■ 77006 #048-02-1983 L1983 **NS** *020 †25

NEISH, Steven Richard. 6621 FANNIN ST, TEXAS CHILDREN'S HOSPITAL 77030 #046-01-1983 L2003 **PDC PD** *020 †55

NELLIMARLA, Kusuma. PO BOX 20708, UNIV TX MED SCH AT HOUSTON 77225 #495-11-2002 **PD** *100

NELSON, Ann. 17030 NANES DR STE 105 77090 #005-19-1986 L2008 **PD** *020 †55

NELSON, Bruce R. 6655 TRAVIS ST STE 840, HOUSTON MEDICAL CENTER 77030 #048-14-1985 L1986 **DS D** *020 †15

NELSON, David G. 9511 HUFFMEISTER RD, STE 100 77095 #048-15-1988 L1989 **FM** *020 †18

NELSON, David Paul. 6621 FANNIN ST, TX CHILDRENS HOSP 77030 #016-02-1989 L2005 **PD P** *020 †55

NELSON, Elaine Kay. 6621 FANNIN ST, MC 1-1481 77030 #048-02-2004 L2007 **PEM** *012 †55

NELSON, Elizabeth A. 6620 MAIN ST, STE 1225 77030 #048-04-1992 L1995 **IM** *020 †20

NELSON, Flavia. 6431 FANNIN ST STE 7044, MSB MED SCHOOL BUILDING 77030 #649-27-1991 L2003 **N** *020 †20,75

NELSON, Jonathan C. 1400 HOLCOMBE BLVD # 444, DEPT. OF SURGICAL ONCOLOGY 77030 #048-14-2002 L2007 **GS** *100 †85

NELSON, Sarah C. 6431 FANNIN ST, MSB 1.150 77030 #048-14-2001 L2004 **END** *100 †20

NELSON, Vincent Gordon. 6565 FANNIN ST 77030 #016-02-1998 L2002 **AN** *020 †05 ‡

NEMECEK, John Joseph. 4900 FANNIN ST 77004 #016-45-1981 L1982 **GP** *020

NEMETH, Nicole Lea. 1515 HOLCOMBE BLVD, UNIT 443 77030 #011-04-2002 L2007 **PS** *020

NEMITZ, Randall Alan. 7600 BEECHNUT ST 77074 #048-14-1983 L1984 **AN** *020 †05

NEMOTO, David Takuma. 902 FROSTWOOD DR 77024 #021-01-1990 L1995 **GE** *020 †20

NERO, Tavares Delietric. 2411 FOUNTAIN VIEW DR, STE 200 77057 #021-05-2003 L2007 **AN** *020

NETOSKIE, Mark John. 1980 POST OAK BLVD, STE 1900 77056 #048-14-1986 L1987 **PD** *030 †55 ‡

NETREBA, James L. ■ 77065 #048-14-1997 L1998 **PTH** *100 †50

NETSCHER, David Terence J. 6624 FANNIN ST STE 2730 77030 #836-01-1977 L1986 **PS HS** *020 †65,85

NETSCHER, Ruth Evans. 3000 RICHMOND AVE, STE 425 77098 #836-01-1977 L1986 **P** *074 †75

NEUL, Jeffrey Lorenz. ■ 77025 #016-02-2000 L2006 **CHN** *050 †75

NEVILLE, Shannon Kate. ■ 77009 #011-03-2002 L2008 **OBG** *100

NEVINS, Christopher Lloyd. 1707 SUNSET BLVD, MEDICAL CLINIC OF HOUSTON 77005 #012-05-1993 L1996 **IM** *020 †20

NEW, Bonnie Arline. 2211 NORFOLK ST STE 920 77098 #048-04-1976 L1977 **OM IM** *020 †70

NEW, Pamela Zyman. 6560 FANNIN ST STE 944, DEPT OF MED DIV OF NEUROLO 77030 #016-06-1976 L1985 **N IM** *020 †75

NEWALL, German. 4400 POST OAK PKWY, AESTHETIC CENTER FOR 77027 #010-02-1986 L1992 **PS** *020 †65

NEWMAN, Lonzetta L. 1515 HOLCOMBE BLVD, UNIT 437 77030 #005-14-1997 L1999 **IM** *020 †20

NEWMARK, Michael Ede. 2727 W HOLCOMBE BLVD, KELSEY-SEYBOLD CLINIC 77025 #035-01-1972 L1981 **N** *020 †20

NEWSOME, Reginald James. ■ 77003 #048-13-2006 L2008 **AN** *012

NEWTON, Lesley Kittredge. 2826 TANGLEY RD 77005 #007-02-1980 L1987 **N IM** *020 †20,75

NEWTON, Thomas Richard. 800 PEAKWOOD DR, STE 2C 77090 #048-13-1995 L2002 **CRS** *020 †85,10

NG, Amelia Wong. 1200 BINZ ST STE 690 77004 #748-01-1994 L2001 **PCC** *020 †20

NG, Bernard Soo Kian. 2002 HOLCOMBE BLVD, MAILSTOP 151B 77030 #825-01-1992 L2004 **RHU AI** *020 †20,03

NG, Chaan Soong. 1515 HOLCOMBE BLVD, UNIT 57 77030 #917-28-1989 L2004 *020

NGO, Dieu Rick Quang. 915 GESSNER RD, STE 240 77024 #048-13-1998 L2002 **GS** *020 †85

NGO, Jamie Anthao. 12060 BELLAIRE BLVD, STE D 77072 #048-16-2001 L2004 **PD** *020

NGO, Khanh Ngoc. 8955 HIGHWAY 6 N, STE 120 77095 #048-16-2000 L2002 **FM** *020 †18 ‡

NGO, Lieu Bich. 6431 FANNIN ST 431 77030 #048-02-2004 L2006 **EM** *020

NGO, Thu H. 1504 TAUB LOOP 77030 #048-04-1995 L2002 **PTH** *020

NGO, Thuy Vi. ■ 77066 #048-04-2007 **IM** *012

NGO, Vinh Doan. ■ 77025 #048-02-2007 **EM** *012

NGUYEN, Alex P. 1213 HERMANN DR, STE 855 77004 #048-14-1999 L2004 **ON** *020

NGUYEN, Alexander L. 837 FM 1960 RD W, STE 105 77090 #048-14-1996 L1997 **IM** *020 †20

NGUYEN, Anh P. 4120 SOUTHWEST FWY, STE 100 77027 #048-02-1993 L1997 **AN** *020

NGUYEN, Anh Thi. 105 DREW ST 77006 #027-01-1987 L1988 **ID** *020 †20

NGUYEN, Anh Thuy. 1515 HOLCOMBE BLVD, BOX 42 77030 #048-12-1991 L1992 **AN** *020 †05

NGUYEN, Anh Truong. 4545 POST OAK PLACE DR, STE 130 77027 #048-14-1996 L1998 **IM** *020 †20

NGUYEN, Anh Tu D. ■ 77082 #067-01-1996 L2005 **PCC** *100 †20

NGUYEN, Anhquan Thinh. 6720 BERTNER ST RM P355, EPISCOPAL HOSPITAL 77030 #005-15-2001 L2005 **IC** *012

NGUYEN, Anhtu Hoang. ■ 77007 #048-15-2001 L2005 **AN** *020

NGUYEN, Bay Van. 2060 SPACE PARK DR STE 114 77058 #048-13-1977 L1977 **GP PD** *020 ‡

NGUYEN, Bich Van. 11034 SCARSDALE BLVD, STE B 77089 #941-01-1971 L1987 **GP** *020

NGUYEN, Bich-May Dinh. ■ 77071 #048-04-2008 *012

NGUYEN, Binh Thai. 1415 LA CONCHA LN 77054 #051-07-1999 L2003 **NEP** *020 †20

NGUYEN, C Thu. 8200 WEDNESBURY LN, STE 230 77074 #067-06-1995 L2000 **OTO PSH** *020 †45

NGUYEN, Canh V. 6431 FANNIN ST, MSB 5.020 77030 #048-16-2002 L2006 **AN** *020 †05

NGUYEN, Chanh M. 6431 FANNIN ST 1.134 77030 #048-14-2005 L2008 **IM** *012

NGUYEN, Charles. ■ 77049 #048-04-2003 **OBG** *100

NGUYEN, Chau D. 7111 HARWIN DR STE 201, HARWIN MEDICAL CENTER 77036 #048-13-1997 L2001 **OBG** *020 †30

NGUYEN, Chau Ngoc. 4126 SOUTHWEST FWY 77027 #941-01-1969 L1996 **GP** *020 †18

NGUYEN, Chieu Dinh. 650 N SAM HOUSTON PKWY W 77067 #048-02-1990 L1992 **GS** *020 †85

NGUYEN, Christopher Van. 6565 FANNIN ST 77030 #021-01-2003 L2005 **CD** *012 †20

NGUYEN, Chuong Van. 15655 CYPRESSWOOD MEDCL DR, STE 100 77014 #047-06-1985 L1988 **FM** *020 †18

NGUYEN, Cuong Ta. 10422 CHELSEA BROOK LN, ATTN CREDENTIALING 77089 #016-45-1989 L1997 **PD** *020

NGUYEN, Dang Minh. ■ 77064 #048-04-2004 L2007 **GE** *012

NGUYEN, Doan Khac. 11301 FALLBROOK DR STE 100 77065 #016-11-1994 L1995 **ORS** *020 †40

NGUYEN, Doanh. ■ 77036 #048-14-2007 L2007 **IM** *012

NGUYEN, Dongchau. 6624 FANNIN ST, SLMT, SUITE 2000 77030 #041-02-1993 L2000 **CD** *040 †20

NGUYEN, Duong D. 8989 WESTHEIMER RD STE 213 77063 #942-01-1965 L1993 **P** *020

NGUYEN, Dzung An. 7601 W SAM HOUSTON PKWY S, STE 850 77072 #942-01-1969 L1979 **GP** *020

NGUYEN, Giao Quynh. 1701 WEBSTER ST STE B 77003 #941-02-1975 L1982 **GYN OBS** *074

NGUYEN, Hai K. 11509 VETERANS MEMORIAL DR, STE 600 77067 #048-02-1989 L1990 **PD** *020

NGUYEN, Hai N. 810 PEAKWOOD DR 77090 #048-13-1997 L1998 **DR** *020 †80

NGUYEN, Hang Xuan. ■ 77054 #048-04-2008 *012

NGUYEN, Hanh Thi-Bich. 710 FM 1960 RD W 77090 #048-14-1996 L2000 **AN** *020 †05

NGUYEN, Hayley Thu. 5151 KATY FWY STE 100 77007 #048-02-2002 L2004 **FM** *020 †18

NGUYEN, Hoa Khanh. ■ 77067 #048-16-2007 **IM** *012

NGUYEN, Hoanglan. ■ 77067 #048-78-2005, ▲ **IM** *012

NGUYEN, Hung Thanh. 11810 FM 1960 RD W 77065 #038-45-2000 L2003 **IM** *020 †20

NGUYEN, Hung V. ■ 77025 #048-02-1999 L2005 **FM** *020

NGUYEN, Huy Anh. ■ 77041 #048-12-2004 **IM** *100

NGUYEN, Huy Khac. 13727 CEDAR POINT DR 77070 #048-14-1996 L1997 **FM** *020 †18

NGUYEN, Huyen Thi Bich. 7550 OFFICE CITY DR 77012 #942-01-1977 L1995 **IM** *020 †20

NGUYEN, Jackie T. PO BOX 20708, DEPT OF PATHOLOGY 77225 #048-78-2004, ▲ L2007 **PTH** *012

NGUYEN, Janet Sue. 6621 FANNIN ST RM A170, MC1-1000 77030 #048-04-2006 **PD** *012

NGUYEN, Janette. 11301 FALLBROOK DR STE 202 77065 #654-01-2000 L2007 **IM** *012

NGUYEN, Jennifer Dinh. 1709 DRYDEN ST 1700 77030 #048-13-1993 L1994 **AN** *020 †05

NGUYEN, Jennifer Thanhthi. 17030 NANES DR STE 206 77090 #021-05-2001 L2005 **OBG** *020

NGUYEN, John S. 1602 ERWIN RD 77039 #048-04-2002 L2005 **CD** *012 †20

NGUYEN, John Tuan. 3262 WESTHEIMER RD 77098 #048-14-2001 L2006 **PS** *012 †85

NGUYEN, Jon Dzung. 6550 FANNIN ST, SM1661A 77030 #048-02-2003 L2008 **GS** *012

NGUYEN, Joseph Vinh. ■ 77083 #048-15-2002 L2006 **RNR** *012 †80

NGUYEN, Khanh. ■ 77025 #048-14-1999 L2004 **D** *020

NGUYEN, Khanh Pc. 18220 TOMBALL PKWY, STE 400 77070 #048-02-2002 L2005 **IM** *020

NGUYEN, Khanh Q. 11618 ALDINE WESTFIELD RD, WESTFIED MEDICAL CLINIC 77093 #941-01-1966 L1979 **FM OM** *020 †18

NGUYEN, Khanh Thithuy. 6624 FANNIN ST, 19TH FL 77030 #048-04-1992 L1997 **IM** *020 †20

NGUYEN, Khanhtrang Thi. 11920 ASTORIA BLVD 77089 #048-16-1996 L2000 **IM** *020 †20

NGUYEN, Khoa D. 5858 WESTHEIMER RD, STE 306 77057 #048-02-1999 L2000 **FM** *020 †18

NGUYEN, Khoa Trong. 17070 RED OAK DR, STE 509 77090 #048-13-1990 L1997 **GS TRS** *020 †85

NGUYEN, Khoi-Nguyen Teres. ■ 77083 #028-46-2006 **FP** *012

NGUYEN, Le Thanh. 8100 CAMBRIDGE ST 77054 #942-01-1992 L2007 **FM** *020 †18

NGUYEN, Linh Trang Quan. 4039B GRAMERCY ST 77025 #048-14-1999 L2003 **AN** *020

NGUYEN, Liz Ha. ■ 77054 #048-04-2001 **GS** *100

NGUYEN, Loc Tan. 4331 BRIGHTWOOD DR, CORNERSTONE HEALTHCARE CTR 77068 #941-01-1977 L1995 **IM CCM** *020 †05,20

NGUYEN, Loc Tien. ■ 77095 #048-02-2004 **AN** *012

NGUYEN, Loi Phi. 8989 WESTHEIMER RD, STE 212 77063 #011-03-1986 L1988 **CD IM** *020 †20

NGUYEN, Long Phan. 4151 SOUTHWEST FWY, STE 410 77027 #941-01-1974 L1984 **AN** *020

NGUYEN, Mai Phuong. 710 FM 1960 RD W 77090 #021-05-1994 L1998 **EM** *020 †16

NGUYEN, Maria T. 11811 FM 1960 RD W, STE 155 77065 #048-14-1994 L1995 **ID** *020 †20

NGUYEN, Marilyn Quynh. ■ 77003 #048-12-2006 **PS** *012

NGUYEN, Minh Chi. 837 FM 1960 RD W, STE 105 77090 #016-11-1982 L1984 **DR** *020 †80

NGUYEN, Minh T. ■ 77054 #048-16-2004 **GS** *012

NGUYEN, My-Linh A. 77005 #048-16-1993 L1994 **FM** *020 †18

NGUYEN, Nghia Chi. 4545 POST OAK PLAC DR #130 77027 #005-06-2003 L2006 **IM** *020 †20

NGUYEN, Nghia D. 6431 FANNIN ST, MSB 2.137 77030 #048-02-1989 L1990 **PTH** *020 †50

NGUYEN, Ngoc Xuan. 8819 BEAWOOD DR 77083 #941-01-1969 L1993 **PM GP** *020 †60

NGUYEN, Nhu Nguyen Thi. ■ 77066 #654-01-2003 L2007 **FM** *100 †18

NGUYEN, Nhu Quynh. 8200 WILCREST DR, STE 9 77072 #048-16-1999 L2003 **OPH GP** *020 †35

NGUYEN, Nicole Nhan T. 14770 MEMORIAL DR, STE 100 77079 #048-02-1999 L2002 **FM** *020 †18

NGUYEN, Pamela Phuong. 10961 NORTHWEST FWY 77092 #048-14-1999 L2001 **FM** *020 †18

NGUYEN, Peter Tuan. 1709 DRYDEN RD, MS BCM 620 77030 #048-15-2003 L2005 **NEP** *012 †20

NGUYEN, Phi Phu. 9798 BELLAIRE BLVD 77036 #048-14-1991 L1993 **PS** *020

NGUYEN, Phong Hoai Thu. 2430 FRY RD, STE 100 77084 #048-14-1997 L1998 **IM** *020 †20

NGUYEN, Phuc Duc. 818 RINGOLD ST, ACRES HOME CLINIC HARRIS C 77088 #039-01-2001 L2004 **FM** *020

NGUYEN, Phung Dinh. 2905 MILAM ST 77006 #941-01-1973 L1982 **AI IM** *020 †20,03

NGUYEN, Phuong-Dung Julie. 7501 FANNIN ST STE 750 77054 #048-02-1989 L1990 **IM PUD** *020 †20

NGUYEN, Quan Dinh. 4545 POST OAK PLACE DR, STE 130 77027 #942-01-1989 L2002 **IM** *020 †20

NGUYEN, Son Kim. 1120A DENNIS ST 77004 #038-41-1984 L1985 **AN** *020 †05

NGUYEN, Sun Binh. ■ 77096 #048-15-2007 **PD** *012

NGUYEN, Susie Le. 11810 FM 1960 RD W 77065 #038-45-2000 L2003 **IM** *020 †20 ‡

NGUYEN, Tai N. 11920 ASTORIA BLVD, STE 300 77089 #048-15-1994 L1995 **IM** *020 †20

NGUYEN, Thanh. 11914 ASTORIA BLVD, STE 300 77089 #048-15-1993 L1994 **U** *020 †95

NGUYEN, Thanh Minh. ■ 77054 #038-40-2002 L2004 **PDE** *012 †55

NGUYEN, Thanh Van. 4545 POST OAK PLACE DR, STE 130 77027 #941-01-1967 L1977 **FM** *071

NGUYEN, Thengoc Dinh. 9200 WESTHEIMER RD STE 30 77063 #048-14-2004 L2007 **FM** *020

NGUYEN, Thieu V. 7500 BEECHNUT ST, STE 291 77074 #048-14-1991 L1992 **CD** *020 †20

NGUYEN, Thu Thi. 11509 VETERANS MEMORIAL DR, STE 600 77067 #047-06-2000 L2002 **PD** *012 †55

NGUYEN, Thuan Khac. 13727 CEDAR POINT DR 77070 #048-14-1995 L1996 **IM** *020 †20

NGUYEN, Thuan T. 12060 BELLAIRE BLVD, STE A 77072 #048-14-1991 L1992 **GE IM** *020

NGUYEN, Thuan Van. 2900 TRAVIS ST, MEDICAL PLAZA, STE. #C 77006 #941-02-1970 L1982 **GS TRS** *020

NGUYEN, Thuy K. 3221 FANNIN ST 77004 #048-04-1994 L1995 **OPH** *020 †35

NGUYEN, Thuy P. 18220 TOMBALL PKWY, STE 400 77070 #048-02-1993 L1994 **PD** *020 †55

NGUYEN, Thuyen Troung. ■ 77083 #048-02-2004 L2007 **IM** *100

NGUYEN, Thy Phuong. ■ 77006 #048-04-2006 **N** *012

NGUYEN, Timothy. 1709 DRYDEN RD 77030 #048-15-1988 L1989 **FM** *020 †18

NGUYEN, Tinh A. 2499 ELLA BLVD 77008 #048-02-1993 L1995 **FM** *020 †18

NGUYEN, Tom T. 7737 SOUTHWEST FWY, STE 250 77074 #048-04-1983 L1983 **OBG** *020 †30

NGUYEN, Tra Thanh. ■ 77083 #941-01-1969 L1981 **GP** *020

NGUYEN, Tri Hoaiduc. 6655 TRAVIS ST STE 650, HOUSTON MEDICAL CENTER BLD 77030 #028-46-1993 L2003 **DS IM** *020 †15

NGUYEN, Trung Chanh. 6621 FANNIN ST WT6-006, TEXAS CHILDREN'S HOSPITAL 77030 #051-01-1995 L2003 **CCP** *020 †55

NGUYEN, Tu-Lan Dinh. ■ 77089 #048-14-2006 **P** *012

NGUYEN, Tuan Hoang. 12060 BELLAIRE BLVD, STE D 77072 #003-01-1993 L1996 **PD** *020 †55

NGUYEN, Tue Duc. 1701 WEBSTER ST STE B 77003 #941-01-1975 L1982 **EM** *020 †16

NGUYEN, Van Duy. 211 HIGHLAND CROSS DR # 2 77073 #041-13-1999 L2008 **IM** *020 †20

NGUYEN, Van Hoang. 1 BAYLOR PLZ, DEPT OF ANESTHESIOLOGY 77030 #051-01-2006 **AN** *012

NGUYEN, Van Van. 17010 SUGAR PINE DR 77090 #048-02-1987 L1989 **OBG** *020 †30

NGUYEN, Vian Hien. ■ 77025 #048-04-2007 **OBG** *012

NGUYEN, Viet H. 1120A DENNIS ST 77004 #048-13-1996 L1997 **FM** *020 †18

NGUYEN, William L N. 4126 SOUTHWEST FWY, STE 600C 77027 #048-13-1992 L1993 **IM** *020

NICHAMAN, Milton Zalman. ■ 77096 #024-07-1957 L1958 **PHP NTR** *050

NICHOLAS, Dianne E. 4200 PORTSMOUTH ST 77027 #048-02-1991 L1992 **IM** *020

NICHOLS, Buford L, Jr. 1 BAYLOR PLZ, BAYLOR COLLEGE OF MEDICINE 77030 #008-01-1960 L1964 **NTR GE** *030 †55

NICHOLS, Julieana. 1102 BATES AVE 3-2305, ACADEMIC GENERAL PEDIATRIC 77030 #048-02-1997 L2000 **PD** *020 †55

NICHOLS, Mark L. 915 GESSNER RD STE 280 77024 #048-02-1987 L1988 **OTO NO** *020 †45

NICHOLS, Scott David. ■ 77004 #005-11-2006 **RO** *012

NICHOLS, Susan Spencer. 1922 TRIWAY LN 77043 #048-14-1991 L1995 **PD** *020

NICHOLS, Thomas Duncan. 2424 W HOLCOMBE BLVD # 103 77030 #048-13-1977 L1977 **D** *020 †15

NICHOLSON, Merickston L. ■ 77054 #869-07-1956 L1981 **IM ON** *071

NICHOLSON, Veronika Anna. 1515 HOLCOMBE BLVD 77030 #010-03-1988 L1989 **IM PD** *020 †20,55

NICOLAIDIS, Stephen C. ■ 77025 #067-01-1991 L1998 **HS** *020 †65

NICOME, Roger Kenrick. 6621 FANNIN ST, MC 1-1481 77030 #048-04-2004 L2007 **PD** *100

NIEFIELD, Stewart Lee. 6560 FANNIN ST, STE 1130 77030 #048-04-1980 L1981 **IM** *020 †20

NIELSEN, Anton Peter. 13300 HARGRAVE RD, STE 500 77070 #036-07-1977 L1982 **CD IM** *020 †20

NIETO, Jose Felipe. 3208 BROADWAY ST 77017 #649-04-1972 L1980 **P GP** *020

NIETO, Mario Edmundo. ■ 77021 #047-05-2008 *012

NIETO, Yago. 1515 HOLCOMBE BLVD, UNIT 423 77030 #847-11-1990 L2006 *020 †20

NIGRO, James Francis. 5110 BUFFALO SPEEDWAY, STE 200 77005 #048-04-1988 L1995 **OS D** *020 †55,15

NIGRO, Marjory Gonzalez. 5110 BUFFALO SPEEDWAY, STE 200 77005 #187-31-1988 L1999 **D** *020 †15

NIHILL, Michael Robt. 6621 FANNIN ST, MC 19345C 77030 #143-03-1960 L1972 **PDC PD** *020 †55

NIKKO, Anthony Phan. 5151 SAN FELIPE ST, STE 1440 77056 #048-12-1996 L1998 **D** *020 †15

NIKOLAIDIS, Andreas C. 6621 FANNIN ST 77030 #048-13-1996 L2001 **PD** *020 †55

NIKOLAIDIS, Melissa Orteg. ■ 77030 #048-04-2007 **AN** *012

NIKOLINAKOS, Petros Georg. 1515 HOLCOMBE BLVD, UT MD ANDERSON CANCER CENT 77030 #473-04-1996 L2007 **HO** *012 †20

NIMETZ, Gary Jack. 77056 #048-04-1960 L1960 **PD** *020 †55

NINIAN, Gregory M. 13111 EAST FWY 77015 #060-01-1975 L1978 **FM** *020

NIRANJAN, Iyer. 11914 ASTORIA BLVD STE 370 77089 #495-16-1990 L1997 **PCC** *020 †20

NIRKEN, Milton Harry. 6720 BERTNER ST 77030 #048-01-1966 L1966 **PD** *020 †55

NISH, M Joan. ■ 77024 #021-05-1951 L1965 **AN** *071

NISHIKAWA, Akira. 12121 RICHMOND AVE, STE 211 77082 #572-20-1977 L1984 **CD IM** *020 †20

NISHINO, Michiya. ■ 77030 #048-04-2008 *012

NISNISAN, Josier Mariano. 12121 RICHMOND AVE, STE 401 77082 #748-18-1991 L2002 **IM** *020 †20

NITHIANANTHAM, Sowmini. 4950 MEMORIAL DR, CHILD ADOLESCENT & ADULT P 77007 #496-35-1995 L2004 **CHP** *100 †75

NITISHIN, Arnold. ■ 77096 #048-02-1961 L1961 **NM D** *020 †15,28

NIX, Bobby R. ■ 77054 #048-14-2008 *012

NIXON, Richard Gene. 10555 NORTHWEST FWY, STE 140 77092 #048-04-1983 L1985 **ORS OSM** *020 †40

NJOROGE, Kimberley K. ■ 77025 #018-75-2002, ▲ L2004 **ACA** *012

NOEBELS, Jeffrey Lloyd. 1 BAYLOR PLZ, DEPARTMENT OF NEUROLOGY 77030 #008-01-1981 L1987 **N** *050 †75

NOEL, Michael Lee. 9055 KATY FWY, STE 200 77024 #017-20-1980 L1987 **FM** *020 †18

NOEL, Richard L. 530 WELLS FARGO DR STE 110, ALTERNATIVE SVCS NETWORK 77090 #048-02-1988 L1990 **P PYG** *020 †75

NOLAND, Amy Sumner. ■ 77025 #048-04-2007 **EM** *012

NOLASCO, Alan Eugene. 3400 BISSONNET ST, STE 165 77005 #048-14-1998 L2001 **FM** *020 †18

NOLEN, David D. ■ 77030 #048-14-2008 *012

NOLLA, Jose Miguel. 2727 W HOLCOMBE BLVD, KELSEY-SEYBOLD CLINIC 77025 #010-02-2000 L2005 **ORS HS** *020

NOON, George Paul. 6565 FANNIN ST 77030 #048-04-1960 L1960 **CD** *020 †85,90 ‡

NOONAN, Timothy Michael. 19770 KINGSLAND BLVD, STE 300 77094 #016-43-1999 L2004 **ORS OFA** *020 †40

NOORBAKSH, Sarah. 8945 LONG POINT RD 77055 #048-14-1983 L1983 **FM** *020 †18

NORD, Kristi Elizabeth. 1709 DRYDEN RD STE 550, BCM FACULTY CENTER 77030 #041-14-2006 **IM** *012

NORGA, Koenraad Karel. 6621 FANNIN ST 3-332, TEXAS CHILDREN'S HOSPITAL 77030 #165-04-1993 **PHO** *100 †55

NORI, Priya. ■ 77030 #035-46-2007 **IM** *012

NORMAN, Jennifer Kay. ■ 77054 #039-01-2003 L2004 **CHN** *012

NORMAN, Michael Atkinson. 1709 DRYDEN RD STE 1500, BAYLOR COLLEGE OF MEDICINE 77030 #012-05-1997 L2007 **GS** *100 †85

NORMAN, Peter Harold. ■ 77005 #048-01-1977 L1996 **AN** *020 †05

NOROSKI, Lenora Mendoza. 6621 FANNIN ST, ALLERGY/IMMUNOLOGY 77030 #035-20-1989 L1994 **ALI PD** *020 †55

NORRIS, Christopher J. 6431 FANNIN ST STE 1.150, UTHSC AT HOUSTON 77030 #048-14-2002 L2005 **NEP** *012 †20

NORRIS, J Gavin. 2900 RICHMOND AVE 77098 #001-02-1997 L2001 **N** *020

NORRIS, John Edward. 7505 MAIN ST, STE 290 77030 #016-06-1952 L1957 **RHU IM** *071 †20

NORRIS, Morgan Edward, III. 6400 FANNIN ST STE 2130 77030 #051-04-1996 L2002 **PS HS** *020 †65

NORSWORTHY, Nilufer Bozde. ■ 77018 #902-03-1992 **IM** *012

NORTH, Jamie Lenee. PO BOX 20708, DEPT OF OB/GYN 77225 #047-07-2005 **OBG** *012

NORTH, Luceil Bauer. 6431 FANNIN ST STE 2.132, UT HOUSTON MED.SCH 77030 #012-01-1956 L1967 **DR** *071

NORTHROP, Jennifer Lynn. 1 BAYLOR PLZ S407, BAYLOR COLLEGE OF MEDICINE 77030 #054-04-1997 L2002 **MG** *020 †19,55

NORTHRUP, Hope. 6431 FANNIN ST, DEPT OF PEDS/UNIV TX MED 77030 #045-01-1983 L1988 **MG PD** *050 †55,19

NORTON, Ralph Elmer. 810 PEAKWOOD DR, STE 107 77090 #048-04-1970 L1970 **DR** *020 †80

NORTON, Stacy L. 13215 DOTSON RD, STE 200 77070 #048-15-1993 L1994 **OBG** *020 †30

NOSAVILLE, Yury J. 7737 SOUTHWEST FWY STE 880 77074 #913-16-1970 L1981 **OBG** *020 †30

NOSE, Yukihiko. 1 BAYLOR PLZ, BAYLOR COLLEGE OF MEDICINE 77030 #572-29-1957 **OS TS** *030

NOSER, Elizabeth Anne. 6411 FANNIN ST STE R1681.4, ROBERTSON PVIL 77030 #048-14-1998 L2003 **N** *020

NOSRATI, Neda. ■ 77024 #048-04-2008 *012

NOTTA, Nasreen Janatali. 1111 AUGUSTA DR 77057 #704-25-1995 L2004 **IM ID** *020 †20

NOTTEBOHM, Guillermo A. 8830 LONG POINT RD, STE 408 77055 #132-01-1962 L1968 **NEP** *020 †20

NOTTINGHAM, John David. 2060 SPACE PARK DR # 210 77058 #048-12-1964 L1964 **P** *071 †75

NOUREDDINE, Ghassan A. 6550 FANNIN ST STE 2421 77030 #605-01-1990 L1995 **PCC** *020 †20

NOURI, Kent Harold. ■ 77004 #048-04-2004 **PM** *012

NOVAK, Irwin Sam. 1213 HERMANN DR STE 745 77004 #048-02-1974 L1974 **N P** *020 †75

NOVAKOSKI, Maryann. ■ 77025 #035-09-1981 L1985 **PTH** *075 †50

NOVICK, Howard. 8300 BISSONNET ST STE 590 77074 #561-01-1970 L1975 **GYN** *020 †30

NOVY, Stanley Barnett. 3465 W ALABAMA ST 77027 #048-02-1969 L1969 **DR** *071 †80

NOWITZ, Leslie Jacob. 5420 DASHWOOD DR, STE 100 77081 #836-01-1968 L1978 **FM** *020

NOWLIN, Donald Henderson. 7777 SOUTHWEST FWY, STE 940 77074 #048-02-1958 L1958 **ORS** *072 †40

NOWZARADAN, Younan. 4009 BELLAIRE BLVD STE K 77025 #517-01-1970 L1976 **GS VS** *020 †85

NUCHTERN, Jed Gregory. 6701 FANNIN ST # 650 77030 #024-01-1985 L1995 **PDS** *020 †85

NUDELMAN, Rodolfo Jose. 1 BAYLOR PLZ 77030 #132-01-2002 **PTH** *012

NUGENT, Alan William. 6621 FANNIN ST, MC 19345-6 77030 #143-02-1991 L2005 **PDC** *020

NUILA, Ricardo. ■ 77054 #048-04-2006 **IM** *012

NUILA CROUSE, Edward J. 2050 NORTH LOOP W STE 224 77018 #341-01-1973 L1983 **OBG** *020 †30

NUILA-CROUSE, Richard. 1631 NORTH LOOP W, STE 570 77008 #341-01-1976 L1986 **OBG** *020 †30

NUNEZ RODRIGUEZ, Cesar Au. 1515 HOLCOMBE BLVD, DEPT OF PEDIATRICS UNIT 87 77030 #264-06-1982 L2005 **PHO** *020

NURUDDIN, Zakia. 15655 CYPRESSWOOD MEDCL DR, STE 100 77014 #160-02-1985 L1999 **FM** *020 †18

NUTTING, Arni C. 6621 FANNIN ST, TEXAS CHILDREN'S HOSPITAL 77030 #060-02-1999 L2007 **PDC** *100

NWACHIE, Comfort Ada. 1 BAYLOR PLZ, DEPT FM 77030 #690-06-1988 **FP** *012

NWORA, Emmanuel Mbanefo. 8303 SOUTHWEST FWY # 9 77074 #048-02-2000 L2005 **FM** *020 †18

NWOSU, Onamma Chikamnene. 4545 POST OAK PLACE DR, STE 130 77027 #690-04-1992 L2005 **FM** *020

OAKES, Joanne Louise. 6431 FANNIN ST STE 6.262, DEPT OF EMERGENCY MEDICINE 77030 #048-12-1996 L2002 **EM** *020 †16

OAKES, Walter Harris. 9321 KIRBY DR, COUCENTRA MEDICAL CENTER 77054 #065-01-1960 L1976 **OM PM** *020 †85

OAKMAN, Jerry Dennis. 12015 LOUETTA RD, STE 300 77070 #027-01-1973 L1974 **GP** *020

OATES, Jay Cartwright. 7401 MAIN ST 77030 #048-04-1975 L1975 **ORS OFA** *020 †40

OATES, Scott Douglas. 1515 HOLCOMBE BLVD 77030 #038-40-1989 L1998 **HS** *020 †65

OBASANJO, Olugbenga O. ■ 77083 #690-01-1994 **FM** *020 †70

OBENOUR, Wm Hypes, Jr. 7401 MAIN ST 77030 #036-07-1966 L1970 **IM PUD** *020 †20

OBEROI, Asra. 7322 SOUTHWEST FWY, STE 160 77074 #048-15-1993 L1994 **IM END** *020 †20

OBERTON, Selby Brent. ■ 77005 #048-02-2006 **IM** *012

O'BRIEN, Christopher J. ■ 77054 #041-02-2005 **IM** *012

O'BRIEN, Herbert Lewis. 710 FM 1960 RD W 77090 #060-01-1965 L1977 **PD** *020 †55

O'BRIEN, Jennifer Jane. ■ 77025 #048-14-2007 *012

OBRIEN, Kelly M. ■ 77098 #048-13-2004 L2007 **IM** *100 †20

O'BRIEN, Mary Frances. 900 THREADNEEDLE ST, C/O CONDEA VISTA CO 77079 #025-07-1987 L1990 **PD** *074 †55

O'BRIEN, Richard Fry. 920 FROSTWOOD DR 77024 #048-04-1955 L1955 **GP** *075

O'BRIEN, Susan Mary. 1515 HOLCOMBE BLVD BOX 61, UNIT 428 77030 #033-05-1980 L1987 **ON** *050 †20

OBUKOFE, Christie Emuobo. 1140 WESTMONT DR, STE 520 77015 #038-43-1989 L1993 **OBG** *020 †30

OBUOBI, Alice. 6621 FANNIN ST, NEONATOLOGY DEPT. 77030 #412-01-1990 L2007 **PD NPM** *040 †55

OCAMPO, Catherina B. 6621 FANNIN ST 77030 #748-02-1995 L2003 **PDC** *020 †55

OCERA, Hermes Capulong. PO BOX 58960 77258 #748-07-1970 L1977 **PME GS** *020

OCHOA, Blanca E. ■ 77005 #005-02-2000 L2002 **D** *012 †20

OCHOA, Lyssa N. ■ 77054 #048-04-2003 **GS** *012

OCHOA, Melissa. 6655 TRAVIS ST STE 500 77030 #048-04-2003 L2006 **CHP** *012

OCHOA, Theresa Jean. ■ 77063 #737-06-1997 **PDI** *100

O'CONNOR, Pamela Marie Ap. 1 BAYLOR PLZ, BAYLOR COLL OF MED 77030 #539-05-1993 **NPM** *100

O'CONNOR, Steven John. 4200 PORTSMOUTH ST 77027 #030-05-1989 L1994 **PTH** *020 †50

O'CONNOR, Terence D. 7026 OLD KATY RD, STE 276 77024 #048-04-1991 L1992 **DR** *020 †80

O'CONNOR, Teresia M. 6621 FANNIN ST, CCC 1540.00 77030 #056-05-1999 L2002 **PD** *050 †55

ODETUNDE, Olufunke A. 2626 S LOOP W, STE 310 77054 #690-02-1985 L1996 **FM** *020 †18

ODILI, Uzochukwu Chinedu. ■ 77071 #048-14-2007 **GS** *012

ODLE, M David. 6621 FANNIN ST 77030 #041-12-1962 L1968 **AN PAN** *071 †05 ‡

ODOM, Leroy. 2000 CRAWFORD ST STE 1300 77002 #035-08-1976 L1980 **GE IM** *020 †20

O'DONNELL, Elizabeth C. 1315 ST JOSEPH PKWY # 1703 77002 #748-02-1978 L1987 **PD NPM** *020 †55

O'DONNELL, Manus James. 6560 FANNIN ST 77030 #539-01-1955 L1967 **CD IM** *071

O'DONOVAN, Donough John. 6621 FANNIN ST, TEXAS CHILDRENS HOSPITAL 77030 #539-06-1990 L2000 **NPM** *100

O'DRISCOLL-O'MALLEY, Mary. 109 N POST OAK LN, STE 445 77024 #539-01-1967 L1981 **P** *074 †75

ODUFUYE, Olajumoke Olufun. 1 BAYLOR PLZ, BAYLOR COLL OF MED 77030 #690-02-1998 **PD** *012

O'DWYER, Joseph Michael. 6410 FANNIN ST, STE 1228 77030 #048-14-1989 L1990 **IM** *020 †20

OEI, Benjamin E. 10370 RICHMOND AVE, STE 1125 77042 #048-13-1987 L1988 **EM FM** *020 †18

OERMANN, Christopher M. 6701 FANNIN ST 77030 #028-03-1989 L1997 **PDP** *020 †55

OETAMA, Betty Kalianda. 8076 EL RIO ST 77054 #506-01-1975 L2003 **HMP** *020 †50

OGAWA, Yoshiko. ■ 77004 #572-03-1999 L2007 **AI** *100 †20,03

OGBAA, Ikenna Kalu. ■ 77030 #033-06-2002 L2005 **IM** *100 †20

OGBONNAYA, Kalu Irem. 9888 BISSONNET ST, STE 160 77036 #035-46-1983 L1985 **IM** *020

OGBURN, H Michael. 7777 SOUTHWEST FWY # 1052 77074 #020-02-1973 L1979 **NEP IM** *020 †20

OGDEN, Angela Kent. 6621 FANNIN ST # 33320, C/O RESEARCH HEMATOLOGY 77030 #020-02-1982 L1988 **PHO** *050 †55

OGEBE, Ori Sarah. 1 BAYLOR PLZ, MS 350 77030 #690-01-2000 L2003 **CHP** *012

OGGERO, Kelly Steven. 2060 SPACE PARK DR STE 100 77058 #048-14-1985 L1986 **GS SO** *020 †85

OGHALAI, John Steven. 6501 FANNIN ST, BAYLOR OTOLARYNGOLOGY 77030 #056-05-1994 L1996 **OTO** *020 †45

OGUEJIOFOR, Albert I. 8200 WEDNESBURY LN, STE 280 77074 #690-02-1985 L1999 **IM** *020 †20 ‡

OGUNJIMI, Kemi. ■ 77021 #038-45-2006 **OBG** *012

OH, Jeong Hoon. 1515 HOLCOMBE BLVD, UNIT 437 77030 #187-04-1988 L2002 **IM** *020 †20

OH, Julia Linda. 1515 HOLCOMBE BLVD UNIT 1 77030 #016-11-1999 L2005 **RO** *100 ‡

OH, Seunghee. ■ 77021 #048-02-2005 **FP** *012

OH, Yun Whan. 1515 HOLCOMBE BLVD, BOX 432 77030 #043-01-1988 L2001 **IM ON** *020 †20

OHANIAN, Sevak T. 10575 KATY FWY, STE 417 77024 #048-14-1995 L1998 **N** *020 †75

OHIKU, Elizabeth. 3737 DACOMA ST, NORTHWEST CLINIC 77092 #016-11-1999 L2007 **CHP** *020 †75

OHMAGARI, Norio. ■ 77025 #572-81-1997 L2001 **ID** *100

OJEAS, Harry S. 2060 SPACE PARK DR 77058 #042-01-1990 L1992 **GE** *020 †20

OJEIH, Chris Henry Uche. 5656 KELLEY ST 77026 #690-01-1985 L1999 **FM FPG** *020 †18

OJUKWU, Juliana Uzoma. ■ 77089 #690-06-1987 L1992 **PD** *020 †55

OKAFOR, Andrew Obunike. 12210 ASHLEY CIRCLE DR W D 77071 #690-04-1984 L1994 **IM** *020 †20 ‡

OKAFOR, Chinwe Jane. ■ 77072 #048-02-2007 **IM** *012

OKAFOR, Nnaemeka Gene. ■ 77025 #028-03-2003 L2007 **EM** *020

OKAFOR, Tania Ijeoma. 4545 POST OAK PLACE DR, STE 130 77027 #010-01-2000 L2004 **FM** *020

OKCU, Mehmet Fatih. 6701 FANNIN ST, TEXAS CHILDRENS CANCER CTR 77030 #902-10-1989 L1997 **PHO** *020 †55

OKEKE, Adaeze Christine. 3701 KIRBY DR STE 600, PRACTICE AND COMMUNITY MED 77098 #042-01-2001 L2004 **FM** *020

OKEKE, Obianuju Christine. 7500 BEECHNUT ST, STE 290 77074 #690-04-1986 L1996 **RHU** *020 †20

OKELE, Humphrey Enyinnaya. ■ 77082 #165-04-1994 *071

OKERBERG, Kristen A. 6431 FANNIN ST 1.246, UTMSH, DIV OF CARDIOLOGY 77030 #048-13-1998 L2001 **ICE** *020 †20

OKEREKE, Phyllis Chizomam. 1315 ST JOSEPH PKWY, STE 1205 77002 #690-04-1975 L2000 **OPH** *020

OKEZIE, Okezie Ndubisi. ■ 77003 #001-02-2000 L2003 **APM** *020 †60

OKHUYSEN, Pablo Christian. 6410 FANNIN ST, UNIV OF TX MSB 2.112 77030 #649-14-1988 L1993 **ID IM** *040 †20

OKHUYSEN-CAWLEY, Regina S. 1515 HOLCOMBE BLVD, PEDIATRIC CRITICAL CARE, U 77030 #649-14-1984 L1992 **PD** *020 †55

OKI, Yasuhiro. ■ 77002 #572-03-1998 **ON** *100 †20

OKOH, Jennifer Onaiwu. 1 BAYLOR PLZ 77030 #690-06-1995 **FP** *012

OKONJI, Catherine Uche. 12121 RICHMOND AVE, STE 420 77082 #048-04-2001 L2003 **IM** *020

OKORIE-AWA, Chinyere N. 9888 BISSONNET ST, STE 160 77036 #690-10-1995 L2003 **FM** *100

OKORO, Chijioke V. 1919 NORTH LOOP W 77008 #010-03-1981 L1989 **IM EM** *020

OKOSE, Peter Chukwuemeka. 1006 FEDERAL RD 77015 #690-01-1981 L1992 **IM** *020 †20

OKPALO, Maria Adanne. ■ 77083 #016-11-1995 L2002 **OBG** *020 †30

OKPARA, Robert Alachebere. 3601 N MACGREGOR WAY, MARTIN LUTHER KING HLTH CE 77004 #409-10-1970 L1997 **HEM IM** *020 †20

OLAFISOYE, Olawole Oladel. 1 BAYLOR PLZ, BAYLOR COLL OF MED 77030 #690-01-2002 **GS** *100

OLAGUNDOYE, Olasupo A. 6431 FANNIN ST JJL324 77030 #690-05-1988 L1996 **FM** *020 †18

OLDHAM, Karen Pacella. ■ 77027 #010-01-1968 L1970 **IM** *020 †20

OLDHAM, Sandra A A. 6431 FANNIN ST STE 2.026, DEPT OF RADIOLOGY 77030 #011-02-1973 L1995 **DR** *020 †80

OLEAR, Margaret Zeria. 16125 CAIRNWAY DR, STE 100 77084 #690-01-1982 L1999 **IM** *020 †20

OLIFANT, David Mitchell. 810 PEAKWOOD DR, STE 170 77090 #011-03-1980 L1982 **DR** *020 †80

OLIVARES, Juan. ■ 77046 #048-12-2008 *012

OLIVE, Anthony P. 6701 FANNIN ST, SUITE CCC1010-00 77030 #048-14-1989 L1990 **PG** *020 †55

OLIVER, Carolyn Jean. ■ 77024 #048-02-1977 L1977 **FM** *075 ‡

OLIVER, Dwight H. 6431 FANNIN ST, M S B 2-100 77030 #048-13-1993 L1995 **PTH** *020 †50

OLIVERO, Juan Jose. 6560 FANNIN ST, STE 2206 77030 #429-01-1970 L1975 **NEP IM** *020 †20

OLIVERSON, Thomas John. 7600 BEECHNUT ST 77074 #048-04-2000 L2004 **AN** *020 †05

OLMO, Jaime A. 3700 CANAL ST, CLINICA SAN LUCAS INC 77003 #847-05-1956 L1959 **FM** *071

OLSAN, Russell Geo. 3630 WAKEFOREST ST 77098 #018-03-1968 L1974 **R** *020 †80

OLSEN, Alex Bryan. ■ 77043 #048-15-2007 L2007 **GS** *012

OLSEN, Randall James. 6565 FANNIN ST, B250 77030 #030-05-2003 L2007 **HMP** *020 †50

OLSEN, Roy W. 6565 FANNIN ST STE 107 77074 #048-04-1952 L1952 **GP OS** *020

OLSON, Kelly Ann. ■ 77006 #048-04-2006 **PD** *012

OLSON, Krista Lee. 6501 FANNIN ST, BAYLOR OTOLARYNGOLOGY 77030 #048-04-1997 L1999 **OTO** *020 †45

OLSON, Laura Elaine. ■ 77006 #048-14-2007 **FP** *012

OLSON, William Marvin. 1313 HERMANN DR, PARK PLAZA HOSPITAL 77004 #016-11-1972 L1978 **PTH** *020 †50

OLSSON, Scott Edwin. 8830 LONG POINT RD STE 308 77055 #035-08-1993 L2004 **TS** *020 †85,90

OLUTIMEHIN, Omobolaji Hel. 5656 KELLEY ST 113, LBJ HOSPITAL UNIV OF TEXAS 77026 #690-02-1985 L2004 **FM** *020

OLUTOYE, Olutoyin A. 6621 FANNIN ST STE 310, DEPT ANESTHESIOLOGY 77030 #690-05-1990 L2001 **AN** *020 †05

OLUTOYE, Oluyinka O. 6621 FANNIN ST, STE 650 77030 #690-05-1988 L2001 **PDS** *020 †85

O'MAHONY, Christine Ann. 6550 FANNIN ST STE 1661 77030 #041-07-1995 L2005 **GS** *020 †85

O'MALLEY, Bert Wm. 1 BAYLOR PLZ # M613 77030 #041-12-1963 L1973 **OTO END** *050

O'MALLEY, William Francis. 10655 STEEPLETOP DR, HARRIS COUNTY 77065 #035-08-1992 L1995 **EM** *020 †16

OMER, Shuab. ■ 77025 #495-51-1999 L2002 **TS** *012

OMESSI, Elan Mishael. 6720 BERTNER ST, DEPT OF RADIOLOGY MC2-270 77030 #005-11-1989 L1994 **DR** *020 †80

ONDO, William Geo. 6550 FANNIN ST, STE 1801 77030 #051-04-1991 L1996 **N** *020 †75

O'NEAL, Shannon M. 6621 FANNIN ST RM A170, MC1-1000 77030 #048-14-2006 **PD** *012

O'NEIL, Anita Louise. 1313 HERMANN DR # 270 77004 #048-04-1976 L1977 **AN** *020 †05

O'NEIL, Gregory John. 7600 FANNIN ST 77054 #048-04-1976 L1977 **AN** *020

O'NEILL, Daniel Benedict. 2020 NASA RD 1, STE 200 77058 #048-04-1983 L1983 **ORS** *020 †40

ONGKASUWAN, Julina. ■ 77047 #023-01-2004 **OTO** *012

ONN, Amir. ■ 77096 #550-01-1994 *100

ONSI-ABDEEN, Ali. 150 W PARKER RD STE 206 77076 #915-03-1964 L1976 **GS** *020

ONUEKWUSI, Chinelo I. 6431 FANNIN ST, AT HO 77030 #048-12-2006 **PD** *012

ONUFER, Jane Ann. 1515 HOLCOMBE BLVD 77030 #024-07-1992 L1997 **DR RNR** *020 †80

ONWUCHEKWA, Jean Ifeyinwa. ■ 77005 #048-12-2006 **IM** *012

■ = Address Information Privacy Protected

OOI, Seng Kah. ■ 77080 #048-02-1964 L1971 **PS GP** *071 †65

OOLUT, Joseph James. 6431 FANNIN ST STE 1.150, AT HOUST 77030 #048-14-2003 L2006 **NEP** *012 †20

OOMMEN, Biju. 2636 S LOOP W, STE 210 77054 #495-99-1998 L2003 **IMG** *020 †20

ORAMASIONWU, Gloria E. ■ 77054 #048-04-2003 L2003 **PDI** *012 †55

ORD, Justin Christopher. ■ 77019 #005-15-2002 **DR** *012

ORDONEZ, Nelson. 6723 BERTNER ST, DEPT PATH 77030 #264-01-1970 L1978 **ATP** *020 †50

ORE, Victor Raul. 7333 NORTH FWY 77076 #737-01-1959 L1974 **GP GS** *071

OREILLY, Michael Scott. 1515 HOLCOMBE BLVD, MD ANDERSON CANCER CENTER 77030 #424-07-1989 L2002 **RO** *020 †80

OREJUELA, Francisco Javie. 5656 KELLEY ST RM 2LD80001, RM 2LD8000A LBJ HOSP 77026 #264-04-1991 L2002 **OBG** *020 †30

ORELLANA, Renan A. 6621 FANNIN ST WT-6006 77030 #341-01-1996 L2000 **PD CCP** *050 †55

ORENGO, Antonio. 11040 EAST FWY 77029 #561-10-1955 L1977 **GP CLP** *020 †50

ORENGO, Ida F. 1709 DRYDEN RD, STE 1050 77030 #048-04-1987 L1988 **D** *020 †15

ORENGO, Luis Antonio, Jr. ■ 77030 #042-02-2006 **PM** *012

ORENGO-NANIA, Silvia D. 6550 FANNIN ST, STE 1501 77030 #048-04-1987 L1988 **OPH** *020 †35

ORETTE, Austin. 6550 MAPLERIDGE ST, STE 218 77081 #690-04-1985 L1996 **FM** *020 †18

ORIA, Horacio Enrique. 8830 LONG POINT RD STE 506 77055 #132-07-1973 L1982 **GS OS** *020 ‡

ORIA, Richard A. 12121 RICHMOND AVE, STE 109 77082 #048-12-1985 L1986 **DR** *020 †80

ORIAHI, Emmanuel Nkonye. 8145 HIGHWAY 6 S, STE 108 77083 #048-04-1993 L1994 **IM** *020 †20

ORKIN, Alan Jay. ■ 77056 #027-01-1977 L1981 **OBG REN** *020 †30

ORLANDER, Philip Robt. 6410 FANNIN ST, STE 600 77030 #165-01-1976 L1983 **END IM** *020 †20

ORMAN, Benjamin Franklin. 9009 WEST LOOP S, ARAMCO MEDICAL CLINIC 77096 #036-07-1962 L1966 **IM PUD** *020 †20

ORNELAS, Abby. ■ 77030 #048-14-2008 L2008 *012

ORNELAS, Jacob D. ■ 77030 #048-14-2008 *012

OROSCO, Luis R. 7900 FANNIN ST STE 2300 77054 #048-02-1992 L1993 **AN** *020 †05

ORREGO, Carlos Mario. 6550 FANNIN ST, CARDIO ASSOC 77030 #264-16-1993 L2007 **IM** *100 †20

ORSON, Frank Mc Nair. ■ 77005 #048-04-1977 L1977 **OS IG** *050 †20,03

ORSON, Lillian K. 9220 KIRBY DR, STE 700 77054 #048-04-1981 L1982 **DR** *020 †80

ORTEGA, Cesar Antonio. 3313 ORLANDO ST 77093 #041-13-2000 L2003 **PD** *020 †55

ORTEGA, E M. 1919 NORTH LOOP W, STE 115 77008 #649-19-1984 L1993 **OBG** *020 †30

ORTEGA MORA, Juan Antonio. 3313 ORLANDO ST 77093 #649-01-1968 L1975 **FM PD** *020

ORTEZ, Gustavo Adolfo C. 6925 HARRISBURG BLVD 77011 #649-01-1963 L1969 **GP** *020 ‡

ORTIZ, Victoria G. 5535 MEMORIAL DR # F 858 77007 #048-13-2003 L2006 **D** *012 †20

ORTIZ LARA, Jose Salvador. 8850 LONG POINT RD 77055 #649-26-1968 L1978 **AN** *020

ORTIZ-PEREZ, Tamara. 1 BAYLOR PLZ, DEPT RAD 77030 #042-01-2006 **DR** *012

ORTIZ-TORO, Jaime. 2002 HOLCOMBE BLVD, VA MED CTR 77030 #847-10-1967 L1969 **IM** *020

ORZECK, Eric A. 8181 N STADIUM DR 77054 #051-01-1965 L1969 **END NM** *020 †20

OSADIYA, Adekemi Olubunmi. 7550 OFFICE CITY DR 77012 #690-02-1988 L2002 **FM** *020 †18

OSARENKHOE, Ilevba Uwaila. 6431 FANNIN ST, AT HO 77030 #010-03-2005 L2008 **PD** *012

OSBORN, Ronald B. 2411 FOUNTAIN VIEW DR, STE 202 77057 #048-14-1992 L1993 **AN** *020 †05

OSBORN, Timothy Craig. 710 FM 1960 RD W 77090 #018-03-1994 L2000 **AN** *020 †05

OSBORNE, Charles Kent. 1 BAYLOR PLZ, RM BCMC335A 77030 #028-03-1972 L1977 **ON** *050 †20

OSES, Joaquin Manuel. ■ 77036 #275-01-1954 L1962 **P** *071 †75

OSHER, William Jacob. ■ 77024 #035-08-1945 L1972 **IM CD** *072 †20,28

OSMANSKA-JAC, Dagmara. 6550 FANNIN ST, STE 2403 77030 #759-10-1990 L1997 **IM** *020 †20

OSTERMAIER, Kathryn Klish. 1504 TAUB LOOP, PEDIATRIC CLINIC 77030 #048-04-1996 L1999 **PD** *020 †55

OSTERMAN, Debra M. 1200 BAKER ST, RM ICS 210 77002 #048-14-1988 L1989 **P PFP** *020 †75

OSTERMEYER, Britta. 2001 HOLCOMBE BLVD UNIT 23 77030 #409-38-1992 L2003 **P** *020 †75

OSTROSKY-ZEICHNER, Luis. 6431 FANNIN ST, BLDG JFB 77030 #649-62-1995 L2002 **ID** *020

OSTROWSKI, Mary L. 1313 HERMANN DR, PARK PLAZA HOSPITAL 77004 #024-07-1980 L1992 **PTH** *020 †50

O'SULLIVAN, Paul John Pat. 1515 HOLCOMBE BLVD # 371 77030 #539-06-1996 *100

OSWALD, Alice Lam. 1709 DRYDEN RD STE 1700 77030 #048-04-2003 L2006 **AN** *020

OTEY, Theodore T. 4306 S MACGREGOR WAY, STE B 77021 #047-07-1985 L1992 **IM** *020 †20

OTHEE, Gurdeep Singh. 211 HIGHLAND CROSS DR, STE 275 77073 #038-44-1996 L2006 **EM** *020 †16

OTT, David Alan. 1101 BATES AVE, SURGICAL ASSOCIATES OF 77030 #048-04-1972 L1972 **TS VS** *020 †85,90

OTT, John P, Jr. 2500 FONDREN RD, STE 270 77063 #048-12-1987 L1988 **IM** *020 †20

OU, Richard J. 12121 RICHMOND AVE, STE 407 77082 #048-04-1999 L2003 **OPH** *020 †35

OUYANG, Jeannette Chang. ■ 77030 #016-11-2003 L2004 **ID** *012 †55

OVERMAN, Michael James. 1515 HOLCOMBE BLVD, UNIT 426 77030 #023-07-2000 L2004 **ON** *020 †20

OVERSTREET, John W, Jr. ■ 77027 #021-01-1943 L1953 **GS TS** *071 †85,90

OVERTON, Dennis James. 6411 FANNIN ST 77030 #917-01-1985 *100

OVERTON, Mark Winston. 1 BAYLOR PLZ 350, BAYLOR COLL OF MED 77030 #048-16-2004 **P** *012

OWEN, William R. 3272 WESTHEIMER RD, STE 18 77098 #024-01-1949 L1955 **CD IM** *071 †20

OWENS, Cabe Michael. 1601 FANNIN ST 77002 #048-02-1991 L1992 **AN** *075

OWENS, Donald Wilburn. 1111 AUGUSTA DR 77057 #048-02-1961 L1961 **D DMP** *020 †15

OWENS, James W M, Jr. 6621 FANNIN ST, DEPT OF PEDIATRICS 77030 #054-04-1998 L2006 **CN** *100

OWENS, John Carl. 6550 FANNIN ST 77030 #048-04-1957 L1957 **IM CD** *071

OWENS, Judith Jo. 3700 BUFFALO SPEEDWAY, STE 350 77098 #048-04-1987 L1988 **OTO PDO** *020 †45

OWENS, Katherine Conry. 1302 WAUGH DR 77019 #048-14-2002 L2006 **AN** *100 †05

OXSPRING, Harry Hollis. 7676 HILLMONT ST STE 101 77040 #048-13-1980 L1980 **AN** *020 †05

OYEDE, Christopher Olu Ab. ■ 77083 #690-01-1980 L2003 **P** *020

OZA, Virendra H. 7600 BEECHNUT ST 77074 #919-03-1965 L1976 **AN PMM** *020 †05

OZAKI, Claire Fujiye. 6624 FANNIN ST, STE 1200 77030 #030-05-1984 L1992 **GS** *020 †85

OZDOGAN, Cenk. 3738 NOTTINGHAM ST 77005 #902-10-1995 L2002 **AN** *020 †05

OZER, Kerem. ■ 77054 #902-10-2002 L2008 **END** *012 †20

OZERDEM, Ugur. 1 BAYLOR PLZ, DEPT MED 77030 #902-05-1993 **IM** *100

OZKAN, Efe. ■ 77098 #902-05-2001 *100

OZKAN, Orhan Seref. 2450 LOUISIANA ST, STE 400-144 77006 #902-05-1991 L2002 *020 †80

OZKAN, Yonca. 1 BAYLOR PLZ 77030 #902-05-1997 L2008 *100

PABBISETTY NAGA, Swarajyal. 6431 FANNIN ST STE JJI32, U OF TX HEALTH SCIENCE CEN 77030 #495-70-1990 L2006 **FM** *020 †18

PACE, Patrick Wheat. ■ 77019 #048-14-1999 L1999 **GS** *020

PACHA, Ahmad M Rajab. 17030 NANES DR STE 207 77090 #875-01-1972 L1978 **GE IM** *020 †20

PACHECO, Susan E. 6621 FANNIN ST, FC 330.01 77030 #042-01-1985 L1997 **ALI** *020 †55,03

PACHECO, Vitor Hugo. 1 BAYLOR PLZ, BAYLOR COLL MED 77030 #187-10-2000 L2003 **CN** *012

PACKARD, Bruce Douglas. 600 N DAIRY ASHFORD ST, WC 02 2064 77079 #018-03-1985 L2003 **GPM** *020 †18

PADILLA, David. 5445 ALMEDA RD STE 445, AMICHAI MEDICAL 77004 #048-13-2001 **ID PMM** *100

PADILLA, Guillermo. 2502 CANAL ST 77003 #649-02-1952 L1958 **FM** *020

PADILLA, Julia F. ■ 77089 #048-02-1994 L1996 **IM** *020

PADULA, Anthony. 6431 FANNIN ST, UNIV TX DEPT PATH 77030 #561-17-1995 L2005 **HMP** *020 †50

PAGANI, John Jos. 3310 RICHMOND AVE 77098 #005-14-1976 L1980 **DR** *020 †80

PAGE, Suzanne E. 2900 WESLAYAN ST, STE 620 77027 #048-13-1989 L1990 **PM** *020 †60

PAGLIARO, Lance C. 1515 HOLCOMBE BLVD BOX 55, MD ANDERSON CANCER CTR 77030 #035-03-1987 L1992 **ON HEM** *050 †20

PAHLAVAN, Shane Mohammad. ■ 77030 #048-02-2006 **OTO** *012

PAHLAVAN, Silen. 1213 HERMANN DR STE 755 77004 #305-01-2001 L2005 **PD** *020 †55

PAHLAVAN, Sogol. ■ 77007 #048-04-2002 L2005 **PD** *100 †55

PAINTER, Joseph T. 1515 HOLCOMBE BLVD 77030 #048-02-1949 L1950 **ON IM** *071 †20

PAINTER, Timothy Joe. 1415 NORTH LOOP W, STE 820 77008 #048-02-1995 L2000 **DR** *020 †80

PAL, Sunita. ■ 77054 #048-04-2008 *012

PALACIO, Herminia. 2223 WEST LOOP S 77027 #035-47-1987 L2001 **IM** *020 †20

PALACIOS, Carlos J. 7333 NORTH FWY, STE 430 77076 #682-01-1989 L1997 **IM** *020 †20

PALAMATTAM, Jessy R. 1 BAYLOR PLZ, BAYLOR COLL OF MED 77030 #035-08-2004 L2007 **CCP** *012 †55

PALARCA, Carlo Torralba. ■ 77007 #748-29-2004 **EM** *012

PALAU, Leonardo A. 800 PEAKWOOD DR STE 8A 77090 #319-04-1985 L1997 **ID IM** *020 †20

PALAZZI, Debra Lynn. 1 BAYLOR PLZ, RM 302A 77030 #036-01-1998 L2004 **PDI** *020 †55

PALLEGAR, Sanjay Rajashek. 6624 FANNIN ST, STE 1990 77030 #496-35-1994 L2004 **IM** *020 †20

PALMER, Richard Earle, Jr. 12345 JONES RD STE 101 77070 #048-14-1979 L1979 **P** *020 †75

PALMER, Robert Leldon. 1800 SAINT JAMES PL, STE 150 77056 #048-13-1981 L1981 **OTO** *020 †45

PALMER, Sue Mary. 1200 BINZ ST, STE 540 77004 #003-01-1975 L1986 **MFM DIA** *020 †30

PALOMINO, Rossana Cecilia. 4501 GROVEWAY DR, PEDIATRIC ASSOCIATES 77087 #024-01-1995 L1998 **PD** *020 †55

PALUMBO, Carl Frank, II. 950 CAMPBELL RD, BIENVILLE ORTHOPAEDIC SPEC 77024 #021-01-1996 L2006 **ORS** *020 †40

PAN, Jenny Szuchin. ■ 77030 #048-04-2007 **IM** *012

PAN, Wei. 6720 BERTNER ST STE 0520, DEPT OF CV ANES 77030 #243-16-1983 L2002 **AN** *020

PANDE, Swati. 17030 NANES DR STE 105 77090 #496-07-1982 L1989 **PD** *020 †55

PANDIT, Lavannya Mundayat. ■ 77098 #048-12-2000 L2000 **PCC** *012 †20

PANDIT, Rahul. 6624 FANNIN ST, STE 2100 77030 #016-01-1998 L2003 **OPH OS** *020 †35

PANDYA, Aashish Mahesh. 4407 YOAKUM BLVD, STE B 77006 #048-14-2002 L2007 **IM** *100 †20

PANDYA, Hina Thekdi. PO BOX 6845 77265 #038-40-1992 L1995 **IM** *020 †20

PANDYA, Pulin K. 515 W LITTLE YORK RD 77091 #495-22-1969 L1979 **U** *020 †95

PANDYA, Rajendra Gijubhai. 12025 LOUETTA RD, STE B 77070 #495-76-1983 L1992 **ID IM** *020 †20

PANIAGUA, David. ■ 77025 #270-01-1986 L1999 **CD IC** *020 †20

PANIAGUA, Raul A. 7600 BEECHNUT ST, MEMORIAL HERMANN SW 77074 #341-01-1964 L1968 **AN** *020 †05

PANTHAYI, Sreelatha. ■ 77025 #495-66-1984 L2003 **AN** *100 †05

PAO, Winnie Chiwah. ■ 77096 #016-06-2004 L2004 **N** *012

PAPADAKES, Nicholas Geo. ■ 77024 #018-03-1960 L1980 **ORS** *071 †40

PAPADIMITRAKOPOULOU, Vas. 1515 HOLCOMBE BLVD UNIT 4, CTR/DEPT OF THORACIC/HEAD& 77030 #418-03-1988 L1997 **ON** *020 †20

PAPADOPOULOS, C N. ■ 77024 #048-04-1958 L1960 **AN** *020

PAPADOPOULOS, John N. 1515 HOLCOMBE BLVD, MD ANDERSON CANCER CENTER 77030 #048-15-2002 L2008 **U** *100

PAPADOPOULOS, Nicholas E. 1515 HOLCOMBE BLVD, UNIT 430 77030 #418-01-1966 L1978 **ON** *020

PAPANDREOU, Christos N. 1515 HOLCOMBE BLVD BOX 13, MD ANDERSON CANCER CENTER 77030 #418-01-1980 L2000 **IM** *020 †20

PAPASOZOMENOS, Sozos C. 6431 FANNIN ST, DEPT OF PATHOLOGY&LAB MEDI 77030 #418-02-1969 L1985 **NP ATP** *050 †50

PAPASOZOMENOS, Theognosia. ■ 77071 #048-14-2004 **OBG** *100

PAPP, Otto Akos. 920 FROSTWOOD DR STE 760 77024 #473-04-1952 L1972 **CD** *071

PAPPA, Afreen Siddiqui. 3701 KIRBY DR, STE 600 77098 #048-14-1992 L1993 **FM** *020 †18

PAPPAS, Stephen C. 6720 BERTNER ST MC1-187, TEXAS LIVER INSTITUTE, SLE 77030 #065-05-1977 L2003 **HEP** *020

PAPPO, Alberto. 6621 FANNIN ST CC1510, TEXAS CHILDREN'S CANCER CE 77030 #649-13-1984 L1989 **PD PHO** *020 †55

PARASHER, Punit Singh. 6431 FANNIN ST, UTHSC DIV OF CARDIOLOGY 77030 #035-09-2004 L2004 **CD** *012 †20

PARAZYNSKI, Scott Edward. NASA JOHNSON SPACE CENTER, MAIL CODE CB 77058 #005-11-1989 L1993 **IM** *020

PARDO, Jorge H. 2711 LITTLE YORK RD 77093 #264-01-1955 L1980 **GP GS** *020

PAREDES, Abel. 915 GESSNER RD STE 350 77024 #429-01-1970 L1975 **PD ID** *020 †55

PARE-MONDERSON, Anna Sabr. ■ 77096 #308-04-1994 L2007 **IMG** *012

PARGHI, Chirag. ■ 77054 #048-04-2006 L2008 **IM** *012

PARIKH, Aruna Dinesh. 8850 LONG POINT RD 77055 #495-22-1970 L1976 **PTH CLP** *020 †50

PARIKH, Manish Ramesh. 4545 POST OAK PLACE DR, STE 130 77027 #048-16-1999 L2001 **MPD** *020 †55,20

PARIKH, Mihir J. 818 RINGOLD ST, ACRES HOME 77088 #048-14-1994 L1996 **FM** *020 †18

PARIKH, Mina Ashvin. 5901 LONG DR, SECSC-MHMRA OF HARRIS COUN 77087 #495-76-1972 L1994 **P** *020

8738

■ = Address Information Privacy Protected

PARIKH, Ramesh Ramanlal. 7707 FANNIN ST, STE 205 77054 #495-01-1962 L1970 **P** *020 †75
PARIKH, Sameer Ashok. ■ 1504 TAUB LOOP, GEN. MEDICINE DEPT. ,ROOM 77030 #496-38-2001 L2005 **IM HOS** *020 †20
PARIKH, Shreya Ranchhod. ■ 77054 #048-02-2004 L2007 **END** *012 †20
PARK, In Sook. 6621 FANNIN ST 77030 #583-02-1973 L1975 **PD PDC** *020 †55
PARK, Jin Sup. 1221 MCKINNEY ST, STE 40300 77010 #583-02-1973 L1977 **DR** *020 †80
PARK, Joon Il. 8850 LONG POINT RD 77055 #583-01-1970 L1982 **IM** *020 †20
PARK, Min Sung. 1515 HOLCOMBE BLVD, UNIT 010 77030 #041-01-2003 L2007 **HO** *012 †20
PARK, Quocdai D. ■ 77006 #048-14-2005 L2008 **IM** *012
PARK, Seung Kyoon. 1 BAYLOR PLZ, DEPARTMENT OF RADIOLOGY 77030 #583-02-1963 L1975 **R** *020 †80
PARKE, Robert Barton, Jr. 6501 FANNIN ST, BAYLOR OTOLARYNGOLOGY 77030 #048-04-1973 L1974 **HNS OTO** *020 †45
PARKER, Bruce Robt. 6621 FANNIN ST, DEPT RADIOLOGY 2-2521 77030 #024-01-1963 L1995 **PDR DR** *020 †80
PARKER, Cora Barbara. 7444 HARRISBURG BLVD 77011 #048-02-1979 L1979 **OBG** *020
PARKER, David William. ■ 77054 #048-14-2008 *012
PARKER, George Wayne. 2411 FOUNTAIN VIEW DR, GREATER HOUSTON ANESTHESIA 77057 #048-14-2003 L2007 **AN** *020
PARKER, Jason Matthew. 6431 FANNIN ST 1134, UNIV OF TEXAS-HOUSTON 77030 #048-14-2006 **IM** *012
PARKER, Sterling Glenn. ■ 77077 #016-06-1942 L1948 **ORS** *071 †40
PARKER, Warren Dennis. 6560 FANNIN ST STE 1200, NEUROSURGICAL GROUP OF 77030 #048-04-1968 L1968 **NS** *020 †25
PARKERSON, Geo Robt, III. 3701 KIRBY DR STE 600, DEPT OF FAMILY & COM MEDIC 77098 #036-07-1981 L2000 **ID** *020 †18,20
PARKS, Donald Harry. 6431 FANNIN ST, STE 1400 77030 #065-06-1970 L1976 **PS** *040 †65
PARMAR, Stavan Pankaj. ■ 77094 #048-16-2004 **GS** *012
PARRA, Cesar Augusto. 1821 WIRT RD 77055 #264-19-1989 L2000 **PD** *020 †55
PARRISH, Robert Gene. 6560 FANNIN ST, STE 1506 77030 #048-04-1981 L1981 **NS** *020 †25
PARRY, Rachel Amy. 2727 W HOLCOMBE BLVD, DERMATOLOGY DEPT 77025 #036-07-1994 L2005 **D** *020 †15
PARSLEY, Brian Strake. 6620 MAIN ST, STE 1300 77030 #048-14-1983 L1984 **OAR ORS** *040 †40
PARSONS, James Theodore. 150 W PARKER RD, 405 PARKWAY TOWERS PROF BL 77076 #004-01-1955 L1958 **GS TS** *071 †85,90
PARSONS, Janet R. ■ 77065 #048-02-1982 L1983 **U** *020
PARSONS, Kenneth Clinton. ■ 77027 #025-01-1970 L1993 **PM** *071 †60
PARSONS, Ward Chester. 12700 N FEATHERWOOD DR 77034 #021-05-1973 L2002 **DR** *020 †80
PARTA, Mark Jos. ■ 77098 #021-01-1988 L2008 **ID** *020 †20
PARTI, Avinash Chandra. 6969 GULF FWY STE 370 77087 #495-29-1963 L1982 **IM** *020
PARTIDA, Angela E. 2323 S SHEPHERD DR, STE 1106 77019 #048-04-2003 L2007 **P** *100
PARULEKAR, Suhas Gajanan. 1515 HOLCOMBE BLVD 77030 #495-17-1967 L2000 **OS DR** *020 †80
PARVEN, Stephen Gil. 3120 SOUTHWEST FWY, GREATER HOUSTON RADIOLOGY 77098 #048-13-1982 L1983 **DR** *020 †80
PASHA, Raza. 12121 RICHMOND AVE, STE 304 77082 #038-06-1996 L2001 **OTO** *020 †45
PASKOW, James Andrew. 600 KENRICK DR, STE E10 77060 #033-06-1986 L1990 **FM PMM** *020 †18
PASKOWITZ, James Joseph. 2323 S SHEPHERD DR # 1012 77019 #051-04-2002 L2006 **P** *020 †75
PASTORE, Yves Dominique. 6621 FANNIN ST 77030 #869-04-1992 **PHO** *100
PATCHELL, Larry Leander. 3120 SOUTHWEST FWY, STE 530 77098 #039-01-1972 L1983 **DR EM** *020 †80
PATE, David Chas. 6720 BERTNER ST, B-111 77030 #048-04-1982 L1984 **IM** *030 †20
PATE, Janet Christine. 3838 HILLCROFT ST, STE 215 77057 #048-04-2001 L2004 **PD** *020 †55
PATE, Jennifer Elizabeth. ■ 77030 #048-02-2000 L2004 **P** *020 †75
PATEK, Alison Marie. ■ 77054 #048-14-2008 *012
PATEL, Akash J. ■ 77054 #048-04-2007 **GS** *012
PATEL, Anil Bhailalbhai. 4605 POST OAK PLACE DR 77027 #495-48-1990 L2001 **IMG** *020 †20
PATEL, Anisha Bipin. ■ 77054 #048-04-2008 *012
PATEL, Ankit Mukesh. ■ 77007 #033-06-2004 L2004 **PM** *012
PATEL, Ashish Ramesh. 1515 HOLCOMBE BLVD, M.D. ANDERSON CANCER CENTE 77030 #008-01-2000 L2000 **TS** *012 †85
PATEL, Atisha Girish. 2260 W HOLCOMBE BLVD, # 116 77030 #048-04-2004 L2007 **HO** *012 †20
PATEL, Bela. 6431 FANNIN ST, MSB 1.274 77030 #048-14-1993 L1994 **PCC** *020 †20
PATEL, Binita. 6621 FANNIN ST, TXCH A210 77030 #048-13-2000 L2003 **PEM** *100 †55
PATEL, Chirag Yashvantkum. ■ 77054 #041-02-2003 L2008 **GS** *100
PATEL, Devang Suresh. 2411 FOUNTAIN VIEW DR, STE 200 77057 #422-01-2002 L2007 **AN** *100 †05
PATEL, Dhruv Chandrakant. ■ 77054 #305-01-1999 L2004 **PD** *020
PATEL, Dilipbhai Jivabhai. ■ 77095 #496-16-1980 †100
PATEL, Dinesh M. 2801 LITTLE YORK RD 77093 #495-23-1971 L1979 **IM CD** *020 †20
PATEL, Falgun. ■ 77054 #048-04-2006 L2006 **PEM** *012 †55
PATEL, Falguni. 1709 DRYDEN RD, STE 1700 77030 #495-22-1986 L1997 **AN** *020 †05
PATEL, Harsadbhai D. 7333 NORTH FWY STE 401 77076 #495-23-1970 L1978 **GE** *020 †20
PATEL, Hemantkumar S. 2002 HOLCOMBE BLVD, MHCL-116 77030 #495-23-1984 L1992 **P PFP** *020 †75
PATEL, Hiten Bhaskar. ■ 77059 #041-15-2008 *012
PATEL, Jayshree H. 5990 AIRLINE DR STE 250 77076 #495-23-1968 L1980 **GP A** *020
PATEL, Julie Yogesh. 1 BAYLOR PLZ 672E, BAYLOR COLLEGE OF MEDICINE 77030 #021-05-2000 L2005 **AI** *020 †20,03
PATEL, Kavita Shah. ■ 77077 #048-04-1997 L1999 **IM** *020 †20
PATEL, Ketan Natubhai. ■ 77073 #016-42-2005 **PD** *012
PATEL, Kiranchandra M. 15419 ROCKY OAK CT, THE PEARLAND CLINIC 77059 #495-33-1989 L1998 **FM** *020 †18
PATEL, Krina Kirit. 6431 FANNIN ST 1.134, OF TEXAS-HOUSTON 77030 #048-12-2007 **IM** *012
PATEL, Maneesh N. 11717 HIGHLAND MDW DR #300 77089 #495-48-1991 L1998 **IM** *020 †20
PATEL, Mayank Chandulal. 11914 ASTORIA BLVD, STE 370 77089 #495-22-1992 L2002 **PUD** *020 †20
PATEL, Megha Suresh. ■ 77095 #048-04-2008 *012
PATEL, Minal M. 3701 KIRBY DR, STE 600 77098 #539-06-1984 L2002 **FM GPM** *020 †70,18
PATEL, Mukesh R. 11920 ASTORIA BLVD, STE 280 77089 #495-23-1986 L2002 **IM** *020 †20

PATEL, Nihar V. ■ 77007 #048-13-2005 **AN** *012
PATEL, Nilam Chiman. 6431 FANNIN ST, JLL 431 77030 #001-06-2004 L2006 **EM** *020
PATEL, Nimisha Anant. ■ 77005 #035-19-1992 L1996 **OPH** *020 †35
PATEL, Niraj Chandrakant. 1 BAYLOR PLZ, RM 302A 77030 #020-02-2000 L2006 **AI** *012
PATEL, Niraj Ramesh. ■ 77266 #048-04-2008 *012
PATEL, Nirav Arvin. ■ 77054 #048-04-2008 *012
PATEL, Nishant R. 1 BAYLOR PLZ 350, BAYLOR COLL OF MED 77030 #048-16-2006 **P** *012
PATEL, Parag Dhirubhai. 1709 DRYDEN RD STE 550, BCM FACULTY CTR 77030 #919-05-2003 *012
PATEL, Pareshkumar. 1631 NORTH LOOP W, STE 250 77008 #005-14-1993 L2002 **IC** *020 †20
PATEL, Payal Satish. ■ 77030 #001-02-2007 **IM** *012
PATEL, Pinakin R. 921 FM 1960 RD W, STE 115B 77090 #495-22-1982 L1992 **IM N** *020 †20
PATEL, Pooja Nilesh. 6431 FANNIN ST 1134, UNIV OF TEXAS - HOUSTON 77030 #495-23-2003 **IM** *012
PATEL, Raina. 14703 EAGLE VISTA DR, EAGLES TRACE MEDICAL CENTE 77077 #048-13-1997 L1999 **IM** *020
PATEL, Rajeev Jayendra. 1709 DRYDEN RD STE 550, BCM FACULTY CTR 77030 #048-04-2005 **IM** *012
PATEL, Rajnikant R. 8200 WEDNESBURY LN STE 290 77074 #495-23-1978 L1985 **IM EM** *020 †16,20
PATEL, Ranjan S. 13668 WESTHEIMER RD 77077 #495-23-1971 L1979 **FM** *020 ‡
PATEL, Rupal Somabhai. 1709 DRYDEN RD, STE 925 77030 #048-04-1998 L2000 **NEP** *020 †20
PATEL, Sachin. ■ 77054 #048-04-2008 *012
PATEL, Sachin Pramod. ■ 77030 #011-04-2005 **IM** *012
PATEL, Sandip Pravin. ■ 77054 #048-04-2008 *012
PATEL, Sanjeet Girish. ■ 77054 #048-04-2008 *012
PATEL, Shaila S. 6411 FANNIN ST 77030 #495-17-1973 L1980 **PD** *020 †55
PATEL, Shalin Dinesh. 1631 NORTH LOOP W, STE 460 77008 #048-02-2001 L2006 **NEP** *020
PATEL, Shatishkumar Y. 8200 WEDNESBURY LN, STE 295 77074 #577-01-1990 L2000 **NEP** *020 †20
PATEL, Shil Kiritkumar. ■ 77054 #016-42-2004 **IM** *012
PATEL, Shital Mahendra. 1 BAYLOR PLZ, BMC 280 RM 221D 77030 #055-01-1997 L2003 **ID MPD** *050 †55,20
PATEL, Shital Suryakant. 837 FM 1960 RD W STE 105 77090 #036-05-2001 L2005 **MPD** *020 †55,20
PATEL, Shreyaskumar R. 1515 HOLCOMBE BLVD, UNIT 450 77030 #495-23-1982 L1990 **ON IM** *012 †20
PATEL, Silka Govind. 6431 FANNIN ST STE 3214 77030 #036-01-2007 **OBG** *012
PATEL, Sunil Mohan. 1515 HOLCOMBE BLVD BOX 10, U TEXAS MD ANDERSON CANCER 77030 #041-12-2002 L2004 **ON** *012 †20
PATEL, Tejash. 2727 W HOLCOMBE BLVD, 4TH FL 77025 #005-14-1998 L2004 **IM** *020 †20
PATEL, Tracy. ■ 77021 #665-01-2004 L2004 **PDE** *012
PATEL, Vandna S. 8000 N STADIUM DR 6TH FL, NEIGHBORHOOD SVCS MDHHS 77054 #495-23-1982 L1990 **PD** *020
PATEL, Varsha Vishnubhai. ■ 77090 #825-01-1976 L1979 **IM** *020 †20
PATEL, Vikramkumar D. 2060 SPACE PARK DR, STE 210 77058 #495-22-1978 L1984 **GYN OBG** *020 †30
PATEL, Vinod Kantibhai. ■ 77041 #539-06-1968 L1977 *020
PATEL, Vinodkumar T. 5135 ALDINE MAIL RD, NORTHSIDE CLNC STE 400 77039 #917-01-1975 L1980 **GP** *020
PATEL, Vipulkumar G. 2050 SPACE PARK DR 77058 #495-23-1992 L2000 **IM** *020 †20
PATEL, Vitthalbhai H. 4151 SOUTHWEST FWY 77027 #495-20-1963 L1982 **GS GP** *072
PATHAN, Asad Zaheeruddin. 5656 KELLEY ST 77026 #048-04-2008 L1993 **IM** *020 †20
PATIL, Deena A. 2411 FOUNTAIN VIEW DR, STE 200 77057 #495-98-1996 L2004 **AN** *020 †05
PATIL, Minakshi J. PO BOX 20708 77225 #496-26-1991 L2003 **AN** *020 †05
PATIL, Prabhuguouda B. 150 W PARKER RD, STE 206 77076 #495-37-1966 L1975 **CD IM** *075
PATINO, Maria Olga. 9220 KIRBY DR, STE 700 77054 #264-04-1989 L2004 **DR** *020 †80
PATLAN, John T, Jr. 1515 HOLCOMBE BLVD, BOX 437 77030 #048-13-1996 L1998 **IM PD** *020 †55,20
PATNI, Reena. 1709 DRYDEN RD, STE 10.5 77030 #048-04-2002 L2005 **D** *012 †20
PATOLIA, Dolar S. 7400 FANNIN ST, STE 755 77054 #495-22-1989 L1999 **OBG** *020 †30
PATOLIA, Shreekant. 1315 ST JOSEPH PKWY, STE 1200 77002 #495-89-1986 L1997 **IM** *020 †20
PATRICK, Joseph James. 1728 BISSONNET ST # 100 77005 #005-02-1974 L1985 **TS GS** *020 †85
PATRINELY, James Randall. 3730 KIRBY DR, STE 900 77098 #047-05-1980 L1982 **OPH PS** *020 †35
PATRON, Douglas Jay. 4100 CLINTON DR, BLDG 19 77020 #010-01-1988 L1995 **OM IM** *030 †70,20
PATRONE, Louis Nelson. ■ 77024 #847-04-1972 L1978 **OBG** *075
PATRONELLA, Christopher K. 12727 KIMBERLEY LN, AESTHETIC CENTER FOR 77024 #048-02-1982 L1983 **PS** *020 †85,65
PATSCH, Wolfgang Peter. 1 BAYLOR PLZ 77030 #154-02-1971 L1988 **IM** *020 †20
PATT, Bradford Stewart. 7777 SOUTHWEST FWY STE 820, HOUSTON EAR NOSE & THROAT 77074 #021-05-1986 L1988 **FPS OTO** *020 †45
PATT, Richard B. 6720 BERTNER ST 77030 #654-01-1981 L1994 **PMM PME** *020 †05
PATTEN, Bernard M. 6550 FANNIN ST, STE 1801 77030 #035-01-1966 L1973 **N IM** *071 †75
PATTEN, Edward Lee. 2900 ELGIN ST 77004 #048-04-1977 L1978 **GS NTR** *020
PATTERSON, Bruce C. 1221 RICHMOND AVE STE 121 77006 #048-14-1985 L1986 **FM** *020 †18
PATTERSON, Guy K. 2323 S SHEPHERD DR STE 950 77019 #048-02-1977 L1977 **PYA P** *020 †75
PATTINSON, Terrence James. 2101 NASA PKWY, NASA/JOHNSON SPACE CENTER 77058 #026-04-1977 L1994 **AM EM** *020
PAUEKSAKON, Paisit. ■ 77025 #891-06-1987 L1999 **PTH** *020 †50
PAUKERT, Martin T. ■ 77054 #048-14-2008 *012
PAUL, Mary Steinhardt. 6621 FANNIN ST 330.01, ALLERGY AND IMMUNOLOGY 77030 #048-14-1989 L1990 **PD AI** *020 †03,55
PAUL, Mini Mary. 3701 KIRBY DR, STE 6.021 77098 #048-14-1996 L1999 **IM** *020 †20
PAUL, Paulose J. 6723 BERTNER ST 77030 #060-02-1996 *100
PAUL, Sumita. 14806 VIA DEL NORTE DR 77083 #495-83-1984 L2001 **CD** *020 †20
PAULING, Fred Wm. 830 FM 1960 RD W, STE 3 77090 #048-12-1958 L1958 **TS** *020 †85,90
PAULINO, Arnold D. 6565 FANNIN ST DB1-077, RADIATION ONCOLOGYDEPT. 77030 #048-14-1989 L1990 **RO** *020 †80
PAULINO, Evangelina C. ■ 77099 #748-07-1956 L1981 **GP** *071
PAULOS, Leon Ernest. 6620 MAIN ST, BAYLOR CLINIC 11TH FLOOR 77030 #049-01-1973 L2007 **ORS OS** *020 †40

PAULOSE, Nidhy Sarah. ■ 77054 #035-03-2004 L2007 **PDP** *012 †55
PAULSON, Benjamin Stanley. ■ 77047 #036-07-2004 **GS** *012
PAULUS, David Dare, Jr. 1515 HOLCOMBE BLVD BOX 57 77030 #039-01-1955 L1962 **R** *071 †80
PAVLOV, Oleg Feodorovich. 7900 CAMBRIDGE ST 77054 #913-06-1974 **W** *100
PAWELEK, Timothy R. ■ 77025 #048-14-2006 **AN** *012
PAYAN, Maria Cristina. 837 FM 1960 RD W, STE 105 77090 #048-04-1996 L1998 **DR** *020 †80
PAYNE, Margaret Lee. 1213 HERMANN DR, STE 770 77004 #048-12-1979 L1982 **PD** *020 †55
PAYNE, Steven M. 12779 JONES RD, STE 108 77070 #048-04-1990 L1991 **FM** *020 †18
PAYSSE, Evelyn Annette. 6550 FANNIN ST, STE 1501 77030 #005-02-1989 L1996 **OPH PO** *020 †35
PAZ, Pedro Francisco. ■ 77028 #021-01-2008 *012
PEACOCK, Cynthia Lou. 1709 DRYDEN RD, STE 5.86B 77030 #048-04-1995 L1996 **MPD** *020 †20,55
PEAKE, Dwight Edward. 1709 DRYDEN RD 77030 #051-04-1984 L1990 **EM IM** *020 †20,16
PEAKES, Waverly Ford. 3412 UNIVERSITY BLVD 77005 #039-01-1999 L2003 **OBG** *020 †30
PEARCE, Adrian C. 6431 FANNIN ST # -20 77030 #917-07-1975 *100
PEARCE, Jason R. ■ 77074 #048-14-2008 *012
PEARCE, Patricia R Denton. ■ 77021 #035-03-1950 L1964 **P** *071 †75
PEARLMAN, Michael Leslie. 6431 FANNIN ST, SCHOOL A 77030 #007-02-2004 **CHN** *012
PEARSALL, Gurney Fields. 7900 FANNIN ST STE 3100 77054 #047-07-1966 **PD** *020 †55
PEARSALL, Gurney Fields. 2951 CHIMNEY ROCK RD, STE A 77056 #047-07-1992 L1998 **FM GS** *020 †18
PEARSALL, Lisa R. 7900 FANNIN ST, STE 2100 77054 #047-07-1985 L1992 **OBG** *020 †20
PEARSALL, Marina. 2951 CHIMNEY ROCK RD 77056 #913-99-1981 L1998 **IM** *020 †20
PEARSEY, David Lee. 7324 SOUTHWEST FWY # 10 77074 #048-04-1962 L1962 **OTO** *020
PEARSON, Gregory William. 915 GESSNER RD, STE 860 77024 #048-04-1998 L2002 **D** *020 †15
PEARSON, Katherine. ■ 77018 #048-78-2007, ▲ *012
PECK, Evan Rouleau. ■ 77063 #051-01-2005 **PM** *012
PEDDAREDDIGARI, Vijay Gop. 1515 HOLCOMBE BLVD, UNIT 10 77030 #495-70-1996 L2006 **HO** *012 †20
PEDEN, Eric K. 6560 FANNIN ST, STE 1006 77030 #048-12-1993 L1995 **VS** *020 †85
PEDERSEN, Arthur Thomas. 6448 FANNIN ST 77030 #016-02-1962 L1970 **AI IM** *071 †20,03
PEDLEY, Chad A. 2411 FOUNTAIN VIEW DR, STE 200 77057 #048-14-2001 L2005 **AN** *020 †05
PEDRICK, Clayton B. 7600 FANNIN ST 77054 #021-05-1990 L1994 **AN** *020 †05,30 ‡
PEDROSA, Michael Macedo. ■ 77077 #035-03-2002 L2007 **DR** *020 †80
PEERHBOY, Zehra Mansur. 7200 NORTH LOOP E 77028 #704-06-1969 L1985 **P LM** *020
PEGANYEE, Sukhdev Singh. 1315 ST JOSEPH PKWY STE 15 77002 #649-14-1969 L1972 **FM** *020 †20
PEGRAM, Samuel Bruce. 1213 HERMANN DR STE 470 77004 #038-40-1980 L1981 **RHU IM** *020 †20
PEIL, Ralph Graham. 12880 SOUTH FWY 77047 #048-02-1967 L1967 **DR** *020 †80
PEIXOTO, Magdalena B. ■ 77025 #048-14-2005 L2007 **P** *012
PELINI, David Chas. ■ 77024 #024-05-1980 L1981 **EM** *020 †16
PELLENBERG, Rod Evan. ■ 77095 #021-01-2007 **PD** *012
PELLICENA, Alexandra. 1631 NORTH LOOP W, STE 410 77008 #038-06-1997 L1999 **OBG** *020 †20
PELLOSKI, Christopher E. 1515 HOLCOMBE BLVD, UNIT 97 77030 #016-06-2001 L2006 **RO** *100
PELTIER, Elaine Coleman. 1200 BINZ ST, STE 1000 77004 #048-04-1990 L1992 **AN** *020 †05
PENDLETON, James Henry. 3402 DOWLING ST, STE 102 77004 #048-02-1954 L1954 **GP** *020
PENMETSA, Santhi. 6630 DE MOSS DR, PEOPLES HEALTH CENTER 77074 #496-23-1993 L2000 **IM** *020 †20
PEPPLE, Kathryn Lynn. ■ 77025 #048-04-2008 *012
PERACHA, Waseem. 11302 FALLBROOK DR, STE 110 77065 #704-02-1989 L2000 **NEP EM** *020 †20
PERCY, Lea June. ■ 77005 #021-01-1992 L1996 **AN** *020 †05
PEREIRA, Faria Agnes. 3501 BRADFORD ST 77025 #035-19-1996 L1999 **PEM** *020 †55
PEREZ, Dolores Margarita. 6720 BERTNER ST 77030 #649-02-1975 L1986 **AN** *020 †05
PEREZ, Esther Perurena. 2015 THOMAS ST 77009 #275-01-1956 L1973 **P** *071
PEREZ, Marco Rafael. 1515 HOLCOMBE BLVD, DEPARTMENT OF ANESTHESIA, 77030 #042-01-2003 L2008 **PMM** *012
PEREZ, Martin G. 10375 RICHMOND AVE, STE 1575 77042 #048-13-1997 L2001 **IM** *020 †20
PEREZ, Mayra C. 6565 FANNIN ST, SEE-48-0211DEPT OF FAM MED 77030 #048-14-2006 **FP** *012
PEREZ, Tiffany Anne. PO BOX 20708, UT MD ANDERSON CTR 77225 #021-05-2003 **HO** *012
PEREZ-GARCIA, Gonzalo Jos. ■ 77027 #048-04-2006 **P** *012
PEREZ-MASUELLI, Carmen. 1140 CYPRESS STATION DR, NORTHWEST DIAGNOSTIC CLINI 77090 #035-47-1994 L2000 **RHU** *020 †20
PERIN, Emerson C. 6624 FANNIN ST, STE 2220 77030 #187-02-1983 L1991 **CD IM** *020 †20
PERKINS, Christopher Heat. 1 BAYLOR PLZ, DEPT OF ORTHO SURGERY 77030 #048-04-2006 **ORS** *012
PERKINS, George Howard. 1515 HOLCOMBE BLVD, MAILBOX 97/RADIATION/ONCOL 77030 #036-01-1993 L2001 **RO** *020 †80
PERKISON, William B. 910 LOUISIANA ST, STE 1006 77002 #048-02-1994 L1996 **FM OM** *030 †70,18 ‡
PERLES, Zeev. 6621 FANNIN MC 2 2280, PEDIATRIC CARDIOLOGY DEPT 77030 #550-01-1990 **PDC** *100
PERONA, Marissa Santos. 18100 SAINT JOHN DR, STE 350 77058 #748-16-1985 L2001 **PD** *020 †55
PERONE, Nicola. 1631 NORTH LOOP W STE 560 77008 #561-17-1965 L1971 **GYN** *020 †30
PERRAULT, Daniel Lee. ■ 77030 #048-04-2008 *012
PERRIER, Nancy D. PO BOX 301402, UTMD ANDERSON CANCER CTR 77230 #021-05-1993 L2004 **GS** *020 †85
PERROTTE, Paul. 1515 HOLCOMBE BLVD, BOX 110 77030 #067-02-1991 L1998 *020
PERRY, Andrew Mccormick. 6621 FANNIN ST, SECTION OF EMERGENCY MEDIC 77030 #048-04-2004 L2007 **PEM** *012 †55
PERRY, Bruce Duncan. 1102 BATES AVE 77030 #016-06-1984 L1993 **CHP P** *050 †75
PERRY, Carlton James. 2707 FERNDALE ST 77098 #048-02-1989 L1990 **PS** *020 †85,65
PERRY, Eula Faye Davis. ■ 77004 #010-03-1961 L1964 **PD** *020
PERRY, Gabriel. 2 WARRENTON DR 77024 #550-01-1966 L1975 **OBG** *020 †30
PERRY, John Leonard. 10907 WICKWILD ST, HUNTERS CREEK VILLAGE 77024 #020-02-1946 L1952 **GS TS** *071
PERRY, Levi Vincent. 1919 LA BRANCH ST 77002 #010-03-1961 L1964 **CD IM** *020 †20

PERSSE, David Edward. 500 JEFFERSON ST 15TH FL 77002 #010-02-1989 L1993 **EM** *030 †16
PERSYN, Danette M. 2476 BOLSOVER ST, # 20 77005 #048-04-1998 L2001 **FP** *012
PERVEEN, Shamsa. 7035 HIGHWAY 6 S, EXCEL CLINIC 77083 #704-06-1984 L2006 **FM** *020 †18
PESAH, Yakov Iosifovich. ■ 77096 #048-04-2007 *012
PESEK, Matthew K. 6431 FANNIN ST, SCHOOL A 77030 #048-14-2007 **PD** *012
PESIKOFF, Richard Bernard. 6500 HORNWOOD DR 77074 #035-19-1964 L1970 **CHP P** *020 †75
PETAK, Steven Michael. 7400 FANNIN ST, TEXAS INST FOR 77054 #016-11-1979 L1981 **END LM** *020 †20
PETER, Charles S, Jr. 13111 EAST FWY 77015 #021-01-1954 L1966 **GS** *020 †85
PETER, Philip. 6640 FANNIN ST, STE 2340 77030 #021-01-1968 L1977 **NS** *020 †25
PETEREK, William Henry. 1300 BAY AREA BLVD, BLDG B 77058 #048-02-1970 L1970 **FM** *071
PETERKIN, George A, III. 2500 FONDREN RD, STE 250 77063 #048-04-1984 L1986 **GS VS** *020 †85
PETERO, Virgilio Garcia, Jr. ■ 77004 #748-10-1995 *100
PETERS, Alonzo. 5990 AIRLINE DR STE 240 77076 #028-34-1978 L1980 **FM EM** *050 †18
PETERS, Douglas K. 13125 EAST FWY 77015 #048-04-1993 L1994 **FM** *020 †18
PETERS, Kenneth Walker. 6720 BERTNER ST 77030 #027-01-1975 L1982 **GS** *020 †85
PETERS, Lori Ann. ■ 77025 #048-04-2007 *012
PETERS, Sarah L. 6565 FANNIN ST, MED/PEDS PR 77030 #048-04-2003 **MPD** *100 †20,55
PETERS, Tricia Lyzanne. ■ 77096 #048-04-2008 *012
PETERSON, Amanda L. PO BOX 20708, DEPT PATHOLOGY 77225 #048-14-2006 **PTH** *012
PETERSON, David Frederick. 7600 BEECHNUT ST 2ND FL, MEMORIAL HERMAN SOUTHWEST 77074 #016-11-1966 L1973 **PTH PCH** *071 †50
PETERSON, Joelle G. ■ 77054 #048-04-2007 **TY** *012
PETERSON, Jon Lee. 902 FROSTWOOD DR, STE 302 77024 #048-14-1977 L1977 **FM** *020 †18
PETERSON, Robert Dickey. 17070 RED OAK DR STE 500 77090 #048-02-1973 L1973 **PS** *020 †65
PETERSON, Stefanie Lynn. 1 BAYLOR PLZ, BAYLOR COLLEGE OF MED 77030 #028-34-2003 **NPM** *012 †55
PETHE, Rajeev. 17422 JACKSON PINES DR 77090 #495-28-1992 L1996 **EM IM** *020 †16,20
PETKOVA, Anelia Todorova. 7630 BELLFORT ST 77061 #198-01-1979 L1993 **IM EM** *020
PETROPOULOS, Demetrios. 1515 HOLCOMBE BLVD 77030 #418-01-1986 L2003 **PHO** *020 †55
PETTAWAY, Curtis Alvin. 1515 HOLCOMBE BLVD, MD ANDERSON CANCER CENTER 77030 #041-13-1983 L1984 **U** *020 †95
PETTIFORD, Janine Nicole. ■ 77025 #028-34-2005 **GS** *012
PETTIT, Charles Robt. 150 GESSNER RD # 14 77024 #005-15-1968 L1994 **OTO** *020 †45
PEUNGJESADA, Silanath. ■ 77054 #891-07-1995 L2008 *100
PEVEY, James Keith. 5151 KINGFISHER DR 77035 #048-04-1957 L1957 **ORS OSM** *020 †40
PEVOW, Frederick Merrill. 13259 EAST FWY 77015 #021-01-1963 L1970 **OTO** *071 †45
PFEIFFER, William Raymond. 1415 NORTH LOOP W STE 82 77008 #048-14-1981 L1981 **DR** *020 †80
PFISTER, Irma Hernandez. 4545 POST OAK PLACE DR, STE 130 77027 #021-05-1996 L2007 **IM** *020 †20
PFLUGFELDER, Stephen Carl. 6550 FANNIN ST, STE 1501 77030 #035-15-1981 L2001 **OPH** *020 †35
PHALAK, Ashok H. 6500 HORNWOOD DR 77074 #495-97-1971 L1980 **EM FM** *020 †16
PHAM, Baothang Ngoc. 1500 S DAIRY ASHFORD ST, STE 198 77077 #021-06-2003 L2005 **FM** *020 †18
PHAM, Chi Manh. 12303 WESTHEIMER RD, STE B 77077 #941-01-1973 L1982 **FM EM** *020
PHAM, Chuong Hoang. 11730 FM 1960 RD W 77065 #048-02-1993 L1997 **OBG** *020 †30
PHAM, Cuong Tien. 6431 FANNIN ST 1134, OF TEXAS-HOUSTON 77030 #661-02-2006 **IM** *012
PHAM, Cuong Vanphu. 6431 FANNIN ST JJL324 77030 #016-45-2002 L2005 **FM** *020 †18
PHAM, Cynthia Baokhue. 1221 MCKINNEY ST, STE 40300 77010 #048-04-1997 L2000 **DR** *020 †80
PHAM, Diemphuong Doan. 2499 ELLA BLVD, ELLA FAMILY MEDICINE 77008 #048-02-1996 L1998 **FM** *020 †18
PHAM, Duke R. 1 BAYLOR PLZ MS 360, BAYLOR RADIOLOGY DEPARTMEN 77030 #048-12-2000 L2005 **DR** *020 †80
PHAM, Dung Q. ■ 77054 #048-04-2005 **U** *012
PHAM, George Giao. 911 BELLAIRE BLVD, 223 77036 #941-01-1967 L1988 **P** *071
PHAM, Hai Hong. 6112 BELLAIRE BLVD, STE E 77081 #941-01-1975 L1982 **FM EM** *020 †18
PHAM, Hoang Ngoc. 4545 POST OAK PLACE DR, STE 130 77027 #019-02-1992 L2002 **IM** *020 †20
PHAM, Huong Diem. ■ 77099 #422-01-2001 **OBG** *100
PHAM, Huy Quang. 6565 FANNIN ST 77030 #048-04-1994 L1998 **AN** *020 †05
PHAM, Khoa V. 1504 TAUB LOOP 77030 #942-01-1978 L1996 **FM** *020 †18
PHAM, Tien. 5314 DASHWOOD DR 77081 #941-01-1963 L1977 **GP** *020
PHAM, Tony Aichi. 1 BAYLOR PLZ RM M822, MAILSTOP BCM 130 77030 #048-04-1993 L2007 **P** *050 †75
PHAM, Trung S. 13119 VETERANS MEM DR, MEMORIAL BLVD 77014 #048-14-1991 L1992 **CD** *020 †20
PHAN, Alexandria T. 1515 HOLCOMBE BLVD, BOX 426 77030 #005-15-1997 L2001 **ON** *020 †20
PHAN, Huy Thanhhoang. ■ 77054 #048-14-2008 *012
PHAN, Nguyen Duc. 837 FM 1960 RD W, STE 105 77090 #048-15-2001 L2004 **IM** *020
PHAN, Phillip Cuong. 1515 HOLCOMBE BLVD, ANDERSON CAN 77030 #048-04-1999 **APM** *100
PHAN, Thaibinh Tran. 8828 RIVERWELL CIR W 77083 #422-01-2007 *100
PHAN, Vincent Chau. 7500 BEECHNUT ST, HOUSTON ORTHOPAEDIC 77074 #048-02-1995 L1996 **ORS HS** *020 †40
PHARIES, Hugh Scott. 3737 DACOMA ST 77092 #048-02-1974 L1983 **P CHP** *020 †75
PHATAK, Darshan Ramesh. ■ 77054 #033-05-2000 L2006 **FOP** *020 †50 ‡
PHELPS, Benjamin Ryan. 6701 FANNIN ST, CCC 1210 77030 #036-07-2003 L2007 **PD** *100 †55
PHELPS, Christopher I. 6431 FANNIN ST, STE 6.142MSB 77030 #048-13-2004 L2007 **ORS** *012
PHI, Anthony Hoang. 13119 VETERANS MEMORIAL DR 77014 #048-14-1991 L1993 **IM** *020 †20
PHILBROOK, Lisa. 2525 NORTH LOOP W 77008 #048-13-1987 L1988 **AN** *020
PHILIP, Annie. 1200 BINZ ST, STE 700 77004 #048-13-1998 L2001 **ID** *020 †20
PHILIP, Maria. ■ 77054 #048-14-2008 *012
PHILLIPS, Alfred Jon. 909 FROSTWOOD DR, STE 126 77024 #028-02-1966 L1969 **PD** *020 †55
PHILLIPS, James Lawrence. 1 BAYLOR PLZ M108, BAYLOR COLLEGE OF MEDICINE 77030 #038-06-1958 L1994 **PD** *030 †55
PHILLIPS, John M. 6410 FANNIN ST 77030 #035-20-1944 L1952 **DR** *071 †80
PHILLIPS, Lee Garrit. ■ 77054 #048-14-2008 *012
PHILLIPS, Michelle Theres. ■ 77004 #048-04-2008 *012
PHILLIPS, Paula Jane. 1229 CAMPBELL RD 77055 #048-13-1984 L1985 **OPH** *020 †35

PHILLIPS, William Anthony. 6701 FANNIN ST CC67001 77030 #016-02-1978 L1988 ORS *020 †40

PHUAH, Allan K. 5555 SAN FELIPE ST, STE 800 77056 #048-02-1995 L1998 IM *020 †20

PHUC, Do Van. 3005 FANNIN ST 77004 #938-01-1952 L1979 GP *072

PHUNG, Man Kien. 6431 FANNIN ST 1.134, OF TEXAS-HOUSTON 77030 #038-45-2007 MPD *012

PICHANICK, Adney M E. 1315 ST JOSEPH PKWY, STE 1703 77002 #836-02-1965 L1979 NPM PD †55

PICKARD, Laurens Russell. 6560 FANNIN ST, STE 1612 77030 #048-02-1970 L1970 TS VS *020 †85,90

PICKETT, Jackson B, III. ■ 77006 #008-01-1968 L1969 N *020 †75

PICKETT, Taylor King. 800 PEAKWOOD DR, STE 4B 77090 #001-02-1988 L2006 TS GS *020 †90,85

PICKRON, Thomas Bartley. 6560 FANNIN ST, STE 600 77030 #001-06-1999 L2005 CRS *020 †85,10

PIDALA, Mark Jos. 6550 FANNIN ST, STE 2307 77030 #038-41-1990 L1998 CRS *020 †85,10

PIEDRA, Pedro Antonio. 1 BAYLOR PLZ, DEPT OF MOLCLE VIRLGY 77030 #011-04-1981 L1988 ID PD *050 †55

PIEGARI, Michael John. ■ 77081 #305-01-2002 L2006 OBG *020

PIELOP, Josie Amley. ■ 77024 #048-04-2001 L2005 D *012 †15

PIELOP, William Christian. 915 GESSNER RD, STE 760 77024 #048-02-1999 L2002 PD *020 †55

PIERANTONI, Hector Ruben. 1315 ST JOSEPH PKWY # 1703 77002 #042-01-1980 L1987 PD NPM *020

PIERCE, Robert Ronald. 7515 MAIN ST, STE 500 77030 #028-34-1958 L1966 N *071 †75

PIHAPAUL, Sarina Anne. PO BOX 20708, UNIT 421 77225 #021-05-2002 HO *012 †20

PILISZEK, Theodore S. 17200 STATE HIGHWAY 249, STE 100 77064 #917-19-1963 L1981 FM EM *020

PILLAI, Anush Sasidharan. 424 HAHLO ST, HOUSTON COMMUNITY HEALTH C 77020 #048-78-2001, ▲ L2003 FM *020

PILLAI, Manu. ■ 77025 #035-08-2002 L2004 CD *012 †20

PILLER, Linda Beth. ■ 77096 #048-14-1986 L1987 PTH *020

PINCKNEY, Cwanza Aretha. ■ 77025 #048-02-2004 L2007 EM *020

PINCKNEY, James Samuel, II. ■ 77054 #048-04-2008 *012

PINELL, Phillip M. 7900 FANNIN ST, STE 2600 77054 #048-04-1987 L1988 OBG *020 †30

PINELL-MIDENCE, Octavio C. 1200 MOURSUND ST, DEPT PSYCH 77030 #682-01-1956 L1970 P *040 †75

PINERA, Jorge Andres. 5322 W BELLFORT ST, STE 118 77035 #275-01-1960 L1964 FM P *072 †18

PINES, Stuart Shever. ■ 77074 #035-15-1953 L1980 IM *071

PINGITORE, Pasquale R. 2900 NORTH LOOP W, STE 1300 77092 #067-01-1974 L1982 FM *030 †18

PINSKY, Jay Royston. ■ 77057 #038-45-2007 AN *012

PINTO PATARROYO, Gineth P. 1 BAYLOR PLZ, DEPT MED 77030 #264-27-2000 IM *012

PINYAN, Amanda Leigh. 1709 DRYDEN RD STE 550, BCM FACULTY CENTER 77030 #012-01-2007 IM *012

PIOT, Didier Ferdinand. ■ 77004 #065-09-1970 L1979 GP ID *071

PIOVANETTI, Omar Nai. 77054 #042-03-2002 OPH *012

PIPKIN, Michael Lee. 3730 KIRBY DR, STE 700 77098 #048-04-1973 L1973 PYA P *020 †75

PIRALI, Shiraz W. 3805 HIGHWAY 6 S 77082 #704-02-1987 L1994 IM *020 †20

PIRAT, Aras. 2222 MARONEAL ST, UNIT 234 77030 #902-03-1995 *100

PIRICS, Michael Lander. ■ 77069 #048-04-2008 *012

PISKLAK, Paul Vincent. ■ 77035 #048-14-2008 *012

PISTERS, Katherine Mary W. 1515 HOLCOMBE BLVD, BOX 80 77030 #065-05-1985 L1994 ON IM *050 †10

PISTERS, Louis Leon. 1515 HOLCOMBE BLVD, DEPARTMENT OF UROLOGY 77030 #065-06-1986 L1991 U *020 †95

PISTERS, Peter Wm Theodor. 1400 HOLCOMBE BLVD, UTMD ANDERSON CANCER CTR 77030 #065-06-1985 L1994 AS CRS *020 †85

PITCHER, John David, III. ■ 77005 #048-04-2008 *012

PITTMAN, Carmen V. ■ 77030 #048-14-2008 *012

PITTMAN-WALLER, Virginia. 1 HERMANN MUSEUM CIRCLE DR 77004 #048-13-1997 L1998 PS *020

PITTS, Richard Edwin. 11914 ASTORIA BLVD, TEXAS EYE INSTITUTE 77089 #048-02-1972 L1972 OPH *020 †35

PIVALIZZA, Evan Graham. 6431 FANNIN ST STE 5.020, UNIVERSITY OF TEXAS MEDICA 77030 #836-02-1985 L1997 AN *020 †55

PIVALIZZA, Penelope June. 6621 FANNIN ST, DEPARTMENT OF NEUROLOGY, 77030 #836-02-1983 L1997 PD *020 †55

PLACENCIA, Frank Xavier. ■ 77054 #048-04-2002 NPM *012 †55

PLAGER, Carl. 1515 HOLCOMBE BLVD, BOX 450 77030 #035-08-1968 L1976 ON IM *071 †20

PLASENCIA, Carlos Manuel. 3315 DELANO ST, SCHCHC - RIVERSIDE 77004 #007-02-1988 L1992 FM *020 †18

PLAVIDAL, Ferdinand Jos. 7580 FANNIN ST STE 335 77054 #021-05-1972 L1973 OBG *020 †30

PLEITEZ, Milvia Yadira. 6560 FANNIN ST STE 802, DEPT OF NEUROLOGY 77030 #048-14-1990 L1997 N *020 †75

PLESSALA, Richard Anthony. 5 N POST OAK LN, STE 2250 77024 #028-34-1960 L1962 PD *075 †55

PLIMACK, Elizabeth Rosenb. 1515 HOLCOMBE BLVD, UNIT 10 77030 #035-19-2002 L2005 ON *012 †20

PLON, Sharon Emma. 6701 FANNIN ST 77030 #024-01-1987 L1995 PD *020 †19

PLUMB, Richard Leon. 7400 FANNIN ST, STE 730 77054 #023-01-1956 L1960 PD *020 †55

PLUMMER, Paula Coe. 12000 RICHMOND AVE # 222 77082 #048-14-1979 L1979 FM OM *020

PNEUMATICOS, Spiros G. 6560 FANNIN ST, STE 1900 77030 #418-01-1989 L1998 ORS GS *020 †40

POA, Edward. 2801 GESSNER RD 77080 #016-06-1999 L2003 P *020 †75

POAGE, Jan Johnson. 2323 S SHEPHERD DR, STE 1106 77019 #048-04-1983 L1991 P CHP *020 †75

PODET, Ethan Jeffrey. 1315 ST JOSEPH PKWY, CARDIOLOGY ASSOCIATES 77002 #048-04-1982 L1983 CD IM *020 †20

PODOBA, Elizabeth C. 11302 FALLBROOK DR, STE 101 77065 #759-01-1974 L1982 OBG *020

PODOLL, Amber Suzanne. 6431 FANNIN ST 4.148 77030 #038-40-2002 L2004 NEP *012 †20,55

PODOLOFF, Donald Alan. 1515 HOLCOMBE BLVD, DIVISION OF DIAGNOSTIC IMA 77030 #035-08-1964 L1975 NM DR *020 †80,28

POGRIBNA, Ulana. ■ 77007 #021-01-2007 *012

POHIL, Richard John. 1201 DAIRY ASHFORD ST 77079 #025-07-1980 L1984 PUD IM *020 †20

POHL, John Michael. 1415 NORTH LOOP W, STE 820 77008 #016-43-1988 L1995 DR *020 †80

POHLMANN, Rebecca Anne. ■ 77054 #048-14-2008 *012

POINDEXTER, Alfred N, III. 6620 MAIN ST 77030 #047-07-1968 L1972 REN OBG *040 †30

POINDEXTER, Christine E. ■ 77064 #010-01-1992 L1997 IM *020 †20

POINDEXTER, David Perrin. 11790 FM 1960 RD W, HEALTH SOUTH REHABILITATIO 77065 #038-40-1975 L1982 PM PRS *020 †60

POJAS, Romeo R. PO BOX 20708, UNIV TX MED SCH AT HOUSTON 77225 #748-07-1977 P *100

POKALA, Hari Prasadarao. 17202 RED OAK DR STE 305 77090 #495-59-1970 L1981 GE IM *020 †20

POKORNY, Patsy S Ferrell. 7800 FANNIN ST STE 300, KELSEY-SEYBOLD CLNC 77054 #019-02-1967 L1977 OBG ADL *071 †30

POLDER, Kristel Dawn. ■ 77030 #048-14-2005 L2008 D *012

POLIAK, Martin. 1707 SUNSET BLVD, MEDICAL CLINIC OF HOUSTON 77005 #286-13-1984 L1997 IM *020 †20

POLIAK, Nina Mihajlovna. 1 BAYLOR PLZ, BAYLOR COLL OF MED 77030 #409-33-1999 PD *012

POLK, Tommy Allen. 17080 RED OAK DR 77090 #004-01-1972 L1976 AN *020 †05

POLL, Jed T. ■ 77047 #056-06-2004 L2008 *100

POLLACK, Jo M. 909 FROSTWOOD DR, STE 129 77024 #048-04-1993 L1994 GS *020 †85

POLLARD, Jack A. 1111 AUGUSTA DR, KELSEY SEYBOLD WEST CLINIC 77057 #048-12-1989 L1990 OBG *020 †30

POLLOCK, Darren Ronald. 7777 SW FWY, STE 604 77074 #011-02-1996 L1998 CRS *020 †85,10

POLLOCK, Howard Jos. 13111 EAST FWY 77015 #025-01-1966 L1972 DR *020 †80

POLLOCK, Raphael Etomar. 1400 HOLCOMBE BLVD # 444, UTMD ANDERSON CANCER CTR 77030 #028-34-1977 L1985 GS GO *020 †85

POLLO PALACIOS, Walter. 800 PEAKWOOD DR STE 7D 77090 #132-01-1959 L1974 CD *020 ‡

POLO, Mario Javier. ■ 77054 #042-01-2003 DR *012

POLSANI, Venkateshwar Rao. 4545 POST OAK PLACE DR, STE 130 77027 #495-65-2000 L2005 IM *100 †20

PONCE DE LEON, Eddy G. 7737 SW FWY STE 520 77074 #275-01-1960 L1972 GP GS *020

PONDER, Roy Craig. 6560 FANNIN ST STE 1148 77030 #048-12-1967 L1967 OSS *020 †40

PONG, Somkiat L. 2060 SPACE PARK DR 77058 #891-04-1973 L1981 PUD CCM *020 †20

PONNURU, Bhaskara M. 17150 EL CAMINO REAL, ANESTHESIA ASSOCIATES, LLP 77058 #495-50-1970 L1980 AN *020 †05

PONNURU, Lalitha Sree. ■ 77059 #495-50-1978 L1984 PD *075

PONNURU, Sagarika. ■ 77059 #048-04-2008 *012

POO, Ivan B. 9720 JONES RD STE 240 77065 #275-01-1960 L1971 FM AN *020

POOL, James Lewis. 1709 DRYDEN RD STE 632, BAYLOR FACULTY CTR 77030 #039-01-1972 L1977 IM PA *020 †20

POOL, Sam Lee. ■ 77058 #039-01-1963 L1968 AM GP *050

POOL, Stanley Joel. 8951 RUTHBY AIRPORT ST 5 77061 #836-02-1972 L1978 FM OM *020 †18

POON, Kenneth Kehn-Yao. ■ 77019 #004-01-2004 MPD *012

POON, Selina. ■ 77004 #021-01-2004 ORS *012

POONAWALA, Ashiqueali I. 18220 TOMBALL PKWY, STE 210 77070 #704-02-1983 L1997 IM *020 †20

POONIA, Disha. 10961 NORTHWEST FWY 77092 #048-16-2000 L2002 FM *020 †18

POOR, Evelyn Shearer. 2219 DORRINGTON ST 77030 #051-07-1982 L1993 PUD IM *020 †20

POPAT, Keyuri Uday. 1400 HOLCOMBE BLVD BOX 409 77030 #495-96-1991 L2000 AN *020 †05

POPAT, Uday Rameshchandra. 1515 HOLCOMBE BLVD, UNIT 423 DEPT BLD & MARROW 77030 #495-96-1984 L2000 IM HO *020 †20

POPATIA, Tajdin Razac. 5445 LA BRANCH ST 77004 #880-01-1974 L1984 AN *020 †05

POPE, Linda D. 3405 EDLOE ST, STE 300 77027 #038-40-1980 L1981 OPH OS *020

POPEK, Anthony J. 10497 TOWN AND COUNTRY WAY, STE 360 77024 #048-14-1986 L1987 FM *020 †18

POPEK, Edwina J. 6621 FANNIN ST, STE B1 77030 #018-75-1981, ▲ L1982 PTH PP *020 †50

POPLACK, David Gerson. 6621 FANNIN ST, & HEMATOLOGY SERVICE 77030 #024-05-1970 L1995 PHO PD *030 †55

POPOVICH, Jovan. 6550 FANNIN ST, STE 2500 77030 #957-02-1978 L1995 RHU IMG *020 †20

PORAT, Eyal E. 6410 FANNIN ST STE 450, UTHSC - HOUSTON 77030 #550-04-1991 L2005 *100

PORCHE, Vivian L Harris. 1515 HOLCOMBE BLVD BOX 42, ANESTHESIOLOGY DEPT 77030 #048-14-1985 L1989 AN *071 †05

PORRAS, Ciro Jorge. 6510 HILLCROFT ST STE 200 77081 #649-22-1980 L1986 PD FM *020 †55

PORRAS, Guillermo. 6720 BERTNER ST 77030 #429-01-1949 L1968 GP IM *020

PORSA, Esmaeil. 6431 FANNIN ST STE MSB, U OF TX MEDICAL SCHOOL 77030 #048-13-1993 L1994 IM *020 †20

PORTELA, Jesus. 232 E CROSSTIMBERS ST # E 77022 #847-04-1959 L1980 GP PD *020

PORTER, Dean Priest. 7710 BEECHNUT ST STE 100 77074 #036-01-1989 L1991 OPH *020 †35

PORTER, Geoffrey Allan. 1515 HOLCOMBE BLVD, BOX 106 77030 #065-05-1992 L1998 GS *020 †08

PORTER, Robert Hale. 7777 SOUTHWEST FWY, SOUTHWEST NEPHROLOGY 77074 #051-04-1972 L1977 NEP IM *071 †20

PORTER, Thomas Wm, III. 6550 FANNIN ST, 11TH FL 77030 #025-01-1989 L1992 IM PD *020 †20,55

PORTNOY, Benjamin Lee. 1200 BINZ ST STE 1025 77004 #038-06-1970 L1973 ID IM *020 †20

PORTNOY, Luba. 11800 ASTORIA BLVD 77089 #913-06-1983 L2000 AN *020 †05

PORTOCARRERO, Mario J. 6565 DE MOSS DR, STE 110 77074 #682-01-1984 L1995 PD *020 †20

PORTUGAL, David Alexander. 7737 SOUTHWEST FWY, STE 780 77074 #048-14-1992 L1994 CD IM *020 †20

POSEY, Audrey Fern. 1315 ST JOSEPH PKWY, STE 302 77002 #048-04-1960 L1960 AN *071 †05

POSEY, Douglas Harris. 1885 OLD SPANISH TRL 77054 #025-07-1976 L2000 PTH *020 †50

POSEY, John Alton, Jr. 6560 FANNIN ST STE 1130 77030 #048-02-1975 L1975 IM *020 †20

POSEY, Kristi J. 2116 BISSONNET ST 77005 #048-14-1990 L1991 N *020 †75

POST, Cheri Ann. 6363 WOODWAY DR, STE 850 77057 #048-14-1978 L1980 FM *020 †18

POTHULURI, Saritha. 714 FM 1960 RD W, STE 302 77090 #028-46-1994 L2002 IM *020 †20

POTOCKI, Lorraine. 6621 FANNIN ST STE 1560, MCCC1560 77030 #024-05-1987 L1996 PTH *020 †50,19

POTSIC, Bradley John. ■ 77004 #011-03-2007 TY *012

POTTS, John Rex. 6431 FANNIN ST, UNIV OF TEXAS MEDICAL SCHO 77030 #039-01-1977 L1991 GS *020 †85

POTYLCHANSKY, Elena. 1709 DRYDEN RD 77030 #913-01-1986 L1998 AN *020 †05

POTYLCHANSKY, Yury. 1400 HOLCOMBE BLVD, UNITE 409 77030 #913-09-1986 L1996 AN *020 †05

POUZAR, Joe E. 14903 EL CAMINO REAL, CLEAR LAKE FAMILY PHYSICIA 77062 #048-04-1987 L1988 FM *020 †18

POUZAR, Linda Porter. 14903 EL CAMINO REAL 77062 #048-04-1987 L1988 FM *020 †18

■ = Address Information Privacy Protected

POVEDA, Antonio. 1111 AUGUSTA DR, KELSEY-SEYBOLD CLINIC PA 77057 #264-06-1968 L1978 IM *020

POWASER, Peter Allen. 1 BAYLOR PLZ, RM 286A 77030 #048-04-1997 L2002 PTH *020 †50

POWELL, David R. 6621 FANNIN ST, MC 32482STE 800 77030 #033-05-1977 L1987 PD *020 †55

POWELL, David William. 7737 SOUTHWEST FWY, STE 760 77074 #021-01-1993 L1996 D *020 †15

POWELL, N Berkeley, Jr. 4200 WESTHEIMER RD STE 288 77027 #036-07-1974 L1978 PS HS *020 †65 ‡

POWELL, Shanti I. 4934 BEECHNUT ST 77096 #495-16-1970 L1997 FM *020 †18 ‡

POWELL, Suzanne Z. 6565 FANNIN ST # 205, DEPT PATH 77030 #055-01-1988 L1998 NP *020 †50

POWELL, William E. ■ 77058 #035-45-1960 L1965 OBG *071 †30

POWELLS, Janice Ruth S. 8300 BISSONNET ST STE 300 77074 #016-43-1974 L1977 PD ADL *020

POWER, Robert Walter. 6621 FANNIN ST, STE A300 77030 #048-12-1989 L1990 AN *020 †05

POWERS, Brian Coyne. 6565 FANNIN ST, STE 1270 77030 #048-04-1977 L1978 U *020 †95

POWERS, Jason Z W. 907 W ALABAMA ST 77006 #048-15-1997 L1999 FM *020 †18 ‡

POWERS, Martin Peter. 6565 FANNIN ST M227 77030 #025-01-2004 L2008 PTH *012

POWERS, William Edward. 6565 FANNIN ST 77030 #016-01-1985 L1991 EM AM *020 †70,16

POWITZKY, Amy Brooke. 1707 SUNSET BLVD, MEDICAL CLINIC OF HOUSTON 77005 #038-43-1997 L2003 DR *100 †80

POWITZKY, Eric S. 6624 FANNIN ST STE 1430 77030 #048-04-1996 L2002 OTO *020 †45

POWNER, David James. 6431 FANNIN ST, MSB 7.154 77030 #011-03-1970 L2003 CCM IM *020 †20

POYTHRESS, Edward Lee. 1504 TAUB LOOP, DEPT OF INTERNAL MEDICINE 77030 #051-01-1993 L1996 IMG *020 †20

PRABHAKAR, Anand Mohan. ■ 77006 #041-01-2004 L2004 DR *012

PRABHU, Manjeshwar R. 2020 NORTH LOOP W STE 1 77018 #495-04-1975 L1984 P *020 †75

PRABHU, Maya Ramakrishna. 4615 POST OAK PLACE DR, STE 205 77027 #495-37-1979 L1984 AN *020 †05

PRABHU, Sujit Sequeira. 1515 HOLCOMBE BLVD, BOX 442 77030 #495-72-1987 L2003 NS *020 †25

PRAKASH, Eva. 211 HIGHLAND CROSS DR, STE 275 77073 #035-08-1992 L1999 EM *020 †16

PRAKASH, Rahul. 11302 FALLBROOK DR, STE 110 77065 #495-45-1989 L1992 NEP IM *020 †20

PRAKASH, Siddharth Kumar. ■ 77030 #048-04-2001 L2003 CD *012

PRAMUDJI, Christina Marie. 915 GESSNER RD, STE 720 77024 #001-02-1996 L1998 U *020 †95

PRANKE, Don Wallace. ■ 77005 #016-11-1944 L1955 U *071 †95

PRASAD, Amit. ■ 77054 #048-04-2008 *012

PRASAD, Ar S. 6776 SOUTHWEST FWY # 40 77074 #048-13-1994 L1998 IM *020

PRASHAD, Sandhya Jyoti. ■ 77021 #048-04-2007 P *012

PRATER, Lawrence Bertram. 1313 HERMANN DR 77004 #010-03-1971 L1975 OBG *071 †30

PRATT, Craig Murdoch. 6620 MAIN ST, STE 1225 77030 #005-15-1971 L1979 IM CD *020 †20

PRAVER, Howard Smith. 9200 WESTHEIMER RD 77063 #048-04-1961 L1961 OBG *020 †30

PRAVINKUMAR, S. Egbert. 1515 HOLCOMBE BLVD # 112, UT MD ANDERSON CANCER CTR 77030 #495-16-1991 L2007 *020

PREMKUMAR, Muralidhar Heb. 1 BAYLOR PLZ 77030 #496-39-1996 NPM *012

PRESBITERO, Jade Araneta. ■ 77042 #748-10-1983 TS *020

PRESBITERO, Julia V. 6410 FANNIN ST 77030 #748-02-1944 L1975 AN *071 †05

PRESS, Gregory Michael. 6431 FANNIN ST STE 451, DEPT. OF EMERGENCY MEDICIN 77030 #048-14-2000 L2004 EM *020 †16

PRETI, Alejandro. 6560 FANNIN ST, STE 1224 77030 #132-01-1985 L1994 ON IM *020 †20

PREUSS, Charles Wayne. 12205 WEST RD 77065 #048-15-1985 L1985 *075

PRIBIL, Stefan G. 6410 FANNIN ST, STE 1115 77030 #035-06-1980 L2006 NS *020 †25

PRICE, Harry Roger. 920 FROSTWOOD DR, STE 780 77024 #017-20-1966 L1969 ON IM *020 †20

PRICE, Jack Fredrick. 6621 FANNIN ST 77030 #039-01-1994 L2003 PDC *020 †55

PRICE, Kristen Joyce. 1515 HOLCOMBE BLVD, BOX 042 77030 #021-05-1985 L1988 PUD IM *020 †20

PRICE, Mark A. 1200 BINZ ST, STE 1040 77004 #048-04-1991 L1992 D DS *020 †15

PRICE, Steven Louis. 1919 NORTH LOOP W STE 640 77008 #048-04-1976 L1976 P *020

PRICE, Todd Marshall. 915 GESSNER RD, STE 620 77024 #039-05-1983 L1986 ID IM *020 †20

PRIETO, Victor G. 1515 HOLCOMBE BLVD, DEPT OF PATH UNIT 85 77030 #847-22-1986 L2001 ATP DMP *020 †50

PRINCE, Joseph Edward. 6550 FANNIN ST, STE 1236 77030 #028-03-1994 L1996 PCC *020 †20

PRINCE, Whitney S. 1709 DRYDEN RD STE 550, BCM FACULTY CTR 77030 #048-14-2005 IM *012

PRITCHETT, Allison M. 1 BAYLOR PLZ RM 523D 77030 #056-05-1996 L2003 CD *020 †20

PRO, Barbara. 1515 HOLCOMBE BLVD BOX 68, DEPT OF LYMPHOMA/MYELOMA 77030 #561-17-1988 L1999 ON *020 †20

PROBST, Francis Joseph, III. ■ 77030 #025-01-2001 L2007 MG *100

PROFIT, Jochen. 6621 FANNIN ST, DIVISION OF NEONATOLOGY, W 77030 #409-05-1997 L2005 NPM *100 †55

PROLER, Meyer Leon. 1001 TEXAS ST, STE 1400 77002 #048-04-1962 L1962 CN ON *062 ‡

PROMECENE-COOK, Pamela A. 6431 FANNIN ST STE 3.204 77030 #048-14-1992 L1993 OBG *020 †20

PROPST, Christina B. 7900 FANNIN ST, STE 3500 77054 #021-01-1998 L2000 PD *020 †55

PROVENZANO, Mark P. 950 CAMPBELL RD 77024 #048-04-1982 L1983 ORS *020 †40

PRUESSNER, Harold Trebus. 7737 SOUTHWEST FWY 77074 #048-02-1948 L1948 FM FPG *071 †18

PRUITT, Currissa L. ■ 77041 #048-14-2004 FM *100

PTASZYNSKI, Konrad Maciej. 1515 HOLCOMBE BLVD, UT MD ANDERSON CANCER CTR 77030 #759-08-1981 SP *100

PU, Shou-Jin. PO BOX 20708, UNIV TX MED SCH AT HOUSTON 77225 #244-02-1977 *100

PU, Yi-Wen. ■ 77004 #244-08-2001 PM *012

PUCEK, Mark Douglas. 1414 S LOOP W STE 200, HOUSTON CTR FOR OCCUPAT. M 77054 #048-14-1982 L1983 FM *020 †18

PUDUVALLI, Vinaykumar K. 1515 HOLCOMBE BLVD, BOX 431 77030 #495-33-1989 L1997 N *020 †75

PUESAN, Mirna. 7127 NORTH LOOP E 77028 #308-11-1986 L1997 OM IM *020 †20

PUGH, Martha Elanor. 9339 NORTH LOOP E 77029 #001-02-1965 L1967 PM *071 †60

PUGH, William Clyde. 7600 BEECHNUT ST, 2ND FL 77074 #016-02-1980 L1987 PTH *020 †50

PUIG, Carlos J. 24 GREENWAY PLZ, STE 950 77046 #016-76-1972, ▲ L1977 EM *020 †16

PULAKHANDAM, Sreelatha. 1300 MOURSUND ST 77030 #496-01-1993 L2003 CHP *020 †75

PULIDO, Michael A. 1315 ST JOSEPH PKWY, STE 302 77002 #048-02-1999 L2003 AN *020 †05

PULLIAM, Albert Leon. 1313 HERMANN DR 77004 #025-01-1974 L1977 IM *020

PUNDIT, Mahesh. 970 CAMPBELL RD, WEST HOUSTON SURGICARE 77024 #917-07-1984 L1994 AN *020 †05

PUPPALA, Dileep Kumar. 11301 FALLBROOK DR STE 210 77065 #495-58-1994 L2002 PCC SME *020 †20

PURNELL, Howard Goodloe. 14909 NORTHWEST FWY 77040 #048-02-1955 L1955 GS *071

PUROHIT, Maulik P. ■ 77054 #048-12-2006 PM *012

PURUGGANAN, Ronaldo V. 1515 HOLCOMBE BLVD 77030 #048-14-1996 L1999 AN *020 †05

PURYEAR, Lucy J. 2211 NORFOLK ST, STE 628 77098 #048-04-1992 L1994 P *020 †75

PUSKOOR, Rohit Venkat. ■ 77054 #048-04-2008 *012

PUSTILNIK, Terri Behrman. 1515 HOLCOMBE BLVD, UNIV TX MD ANDERSON 77030 #028-02-1992 L1997 OBG *020 †30

PUSZTAI, Lajos. 1155 PRESSLER ST, CENTER, BOX 1354 77030 #473-01-1987 L1997 ON *020 †20

PUTHENPARAMBIL, Larry Mic. ■ 77054 #048-04-2008 *012

PUTNAM, Joe B, Jr. 1515 HOLCOMBE BLVD, UNIV TX MD ANDERSON CANCER 77030 #036-01-1979 L1988 TS CD *020 †85,90

PUTTERMAN, Bart David. 6560 FANNIN ST, STE 1980 77030 #048-04-1984 L1985 OBG *020 †30

PYEATT, Amber D. ■ 77030 #048-04-2005 L2008 PD *012

PYLES, Jocelyn Marie. 5602 LYONS AVE, LYONS HEALTH CENTER 77020 #036-01-1983 L1985 GP PHP *020

QADEER, Asaf R. 7333 NORTH FWY STE 111 77076 #704-01-1970 L1988 EM *020

QADIR, Maqbol. 1315 ST JOSEPH PKWY, STE 1703 77002 #704-02-1989 L2003 PD NPM *020 †55

QADRI, Nabil Saleem. 6431 FANNIN ST, STE 2.132 77030 #048-15-2002 L2003 RNR *012

QAYYUM, Abdul. PO BOX 20708, UNIV TX MED SCH AT HOUSTON 77225 #704-04-1988 P *100

QAZILBASH, Muzaffar H. 1400 HOLCOMBE BLVD # 423, STEM CELL TRANSPLANTATION 77030 #704-02-1987 L2002 HEM *020 †20

QUADEER, Arshi Abdul. ■ 77054 #048-14-2003 NEP *012 †20

QUADEER, Tahseen H. 6410 FANNIN ST, STE 200 77030 #704-06-1976 L1992 OBG *020 †30

QUADRI, Yasmeen. ■ 77055 #704-02-1985 L2000 FM *020 †18

QUAN, Angel. 17070 RED OAK DR STE 402 77090 #341-01-1957 L1981 OBG *020

QUAST, Don Carlfred. 1213 HERMANN DR STE 560 77004 #048-04-1958 L1958 TS GS *020 †85,90

QUAYLE, William Henry. 2855 GRAMERCY ST, 77025 77025 #028-03-1973 L1981 OPH *020 †35

QUESADA, Emilio T. 1504 TAUB LOOP 77030 #132-01-1984 L1994 U GS *100

QUESADA, Jorge Roberto. 1200 BINZ ST, STE 910 77004 #649-01-1973 L1979 ON IM *020 †20

QUILEZ, Joaquin Burillo. 7777 SOUTHWEST FWY, STE 354 77074 #847-01-1959 L1973 OBG *020 †30

QUINN, Andrew M, Jr. 6720 BERTNER ST 77030 #048-02-1988 L1989 AN *020 †05

QUINONES, Miguel A. 6620 MAIN ST, STE 1225 77030 #042-01-1968 L1974 CD IM *020 †20

QUINONEZ, Ricardo Alejand. 6621 FANNIN ST, MC 1-1481 77030 #429-01-1997 L2005 *100 †55

QUINTANA, Oscar F. 4000 FULTON ST 77009 #048-14-1994 L1998 AN *020 †05

QUINTOS, Olivia F G. 17322 RED OAK DR 77090 #748-01-1964 L1976 AN *020

QUIROGA, Walter Salvador. ■ 77054 #048-04-2008 *012

QUIROS, Ruben. 6431 FANNIN ST, STE MSB 3.140A 77030 #715-01-1986 L2002 PG PD *020 †55

QURESHI, Rafia. ■ 77098 #495-65-1966 L1986 PM *100

QURESHI, Waqar Ahmed. 1709 DRYDEN RD 77030 #917-28-1983 L1998 GE *020 †20

RAAB, Stacey. ■ 77035 #048-14-2007 *012

RAAD, Issam Inaam. 1515 HOLCOMBE BLVD 77030 #605-01-1982 L1989 ID *020 †20

RABAGO, Erwin C. 350 N SAM HOUSTON PKWY E 77060 #748-10-1971 L1975 FM *020

RABB, Mary Frances. 6431 FANNIN ST RM 5020 77030 #021-05-1987 L1992 AN *020 †05

RABER, Adele Pleta. 1504 TAUB LOOP 77030 #065-06-1974 L1981 PD PUD *020 †55

RABER, Martin Newman. 1515 HOLCOMBE BLVD, BOX 426 77030 #165-04-1975 L1979 ON HEM *020 †20

RABIE, Trevor. 2808 MILAM ST, STE F 77006 #836-02-1976 L1983 PUD IM *020 †20

RABIN, Karen Ruth. 6621 FANNIN ST, CC 1410.00 77030 #005-02-1998 L2006 PD *020 †55

RACHAL, Henry, III. ■ 77003 #038-06-2005 AN *012

RACHAL, Lindy Thaddeus. 1200 BINZ ST, STE 480 77004 #048-14-1983 L1983 GE IM *020 †20

RACHLIN, Lillian. ■ 77005 #041-07-1942 L1943 GS *071 †85

RADACK, James Henry. 11111 WILCREST GREEN DR, STE 210 77042 #048-02-1982 L1983 EM FM *020 †20

RADAIDEH, Majdi Morshed. 2002 HOLCOMBE BLVD, MICHAEL E. DEBAKEY VA MEDI 77030 #575-02-1996 L2004 *100 †80

RADCLIFFE, Ann Humphreys. 1707 SUNSET BLVD, MEDICAL CLINIC OF HOUSTON, 77005 #048-04-1993 L1994 IM *020 †20

RADCLIFFE, Randal Barry K. ■ 77062 #539-04-1955 L1974 DR *074

RADELAT, Paul Bernard. 1300 POST OAK BLVD, STE 2500 77056 #021-05-1957 L1964 PTH FOP *020 †50

RADHAKRISHNAN, Ravi. ■ 77025 #048-15-2002 L2005 GS *012

RADOFF, Russell Neil. 1707 SUNSET BLVD, MEDICAL CLINIC OF HOUSTON 77005 #048-02-1996 L1999 IM *020 †20

RAE, Sharon. 1919 S BRAESWOOD BLVD, 5TH FL 77030 #048-12-1970 L1970 PD *020 †55

RAFANAN, Marilyn A. 16111 CAIRNWAY DR STE 170 77084 #748-16-1983 L1995 FM *020 †18 ‡

RAFATI, Danny Salah. ■ 77025 #048-02-2007 *012

RAFATI, Joyce Cigarroa. ■ 77025 #048-04-2007 AN *012

RAFATI, Tarek Salah. ■ 77019 #048-02-2005 L2008 FP *012

RAGAB, Magda M. 1221 MCKINNEY ST, STE 40300 77010 #915-03-1981 L1997 PD *020 †55

RAGAVENDRAN, Annapurni B. 7601 FANNIN ST, INTRACARE HOSP 77054 #495-54-1981 L1994 P *020 †75

RAGHAVAN, Archana Susan. ■ 77006 #048-04-2005 AN *012

RAGHAVAN, Rajeev. ■ 77006 #048-04-2005 L2007 IM *012

RAGHUTHAMAN, Ayyam P. 7737 SOUTHWEST FWY STE 915 77074 #495-04-1967 L1976 GE *050 †20

RAGOUILLIAUX, Corinne J. ■ 77062 #396-19-1992 L2003 NPM *100 †55

RAHBAR, Mehran. ■ 77005 #517-01-1986 L2002 APM *020 †05

RAHIM, Enayet. 2060 SPACE PARK DR, STE 406 77058 #160-02-1976 L2006 IM *020 †20

RAHIM, Malik Tariq. 6431 FANNIN ST, UTHSC DIV OF CARDIOLOGY 77030 #704-01-2001 L2004 CD *012 †20

RAHLFS, Thomas Frederick. 1515 HOLCOMBE BLVD # 409, DEPT OF ANESTHESIOLOGY 77030 #048-04-1981 L1981 AN *020 †05

RAHMAN, Abul Hashem M W. 7322 SOUTHWEST FWY, STE 160 77074 #160-02-1982 L2006 IM *020

■ = Address Information Privacy Protected

RAHMAN, Ersalan Ahmad. 12970 EAST FWY, STE I10 77015 #051-04-1999 L2003 **OPH** *020 †35
RAHMAN, Hashim. ■ 77024 #016-11-1998 *100
RAHMAN, Naheed. 11037 FM 1960 RD W, STEEPLECHASE PEDIATRIC 77065 #495-15-1971 L1982 **PD** *020 †55
RAHMAN, Syed Shah Noor Ur. 6410 FANNIN ST STE 1430 77030 #308-11-1985 L1993 **NEP IM** *020 †20
RAI, Mallika. ■ 77027 #495-33-1970 L1975 **FM** *020 †18
RAI, Nilima. ■ 77056 #496-14-1985 L1994 **FM** *020 †18
RAICHMAN, Jorge Arnaldo. 7500 BEECHNUT ST STE 214 77074 #132-01-1976 L1982 **P ADP** *020 †75
RAIJMAN, Isaac Langsam. 6620 MAIN ST, STE 1510 77030 #649-01-1984 L1990 **GE** *020 †20
RAIMER, Lauren Allison. ■ 77047 #048-04-2008 *012
RAINE, David B. ■ 77030 #048-02-1953 L1953 **IM** *071
RAINE, Michael Bennett. 6448 FANNIN ST 77030 #048-02-1957 L1957 **CD IM** *071 †20
RAINE, Susan Patricia. 1709 DRYDEN RD, STE 1100 77030 #048-04-2001 L2005 **OBG** *020 †30
RAINOW, Alex. 77054 #035-03-2007 **IM** *012
RAINUSSO GUAINAZZO, Nino. 6621 FANNIN ST, TEXAS CHILDREN'S HOSPITAL 77030 #737-06-2000 L2003 **PDP** *012 †55
RAISSI SHABARI, Farshad. ■ 77098 #517-01-1998 L2004 **IM** *100 †20
RAISZADEH, Ramin. 6500 FANNIN ST, STE 1006 77030 #048-04-1998 L2004 **ORS** *100 †40
RAIZEN, Yuval. 77007 #048-04-2008 *012
RAIZNER, Albert Edwin. 6550 FANNIN ST, STE 2021 77030 #035-08-1967 L1974 **CD** *020 †20
RAIZNER, Michael Evan. 6550 FANNIN ST STE SM2021 77030 #048-04-1998 L2002 **IC** *020 †20
RAJAEE, Soroosh. ■ 77077 #517-05-1964 **OBG** *100
RAJAGOPALAN, Lakshmy S. 710 FM 1960 RD W # 220 77090 #495-28-1977 L1989 **PD NPM** *020 †55
RAJENDRAN, Suresh Kumar. 444 FM 1959 RD 77034 #495-08-1986 L1992 **GE** *020 †20
RAJKOVIC, Aleksandar. 6620 MAIN ST 77030 #038-06-1992 L1998 **MG** *020 †30
RAJU, Manthena Anji. 17150 EL CAMINO REAL STE E, ANESTHESIA ASSOCIATES, LLP 77058 #495-50-1970 L1978 **AN** *020
RAKEL, Robert Edwin. 3701 KIRBY DR STE 600 77098 #038-41-1958 L1985 **FM** *040 †18
RAKERS, Karen Lynn. 915 GESSNER RD, STE 100 77024 #028-34-2002 L2006 **FM** *020 †18
RAKKHIT, Ronjay. ■ 77054 #045-01-2003 L2006 **HO** *012 †20
RALEY, Marvin Ray. ■ 77006 #048-02-1975 L1975 **PD** *040 †55
RALPH, Ronald Bert. 1200 BINZ ST STE 1180 77004 #048-02-2000 L2003 **NEP** *020 †20
RALSTON, Alvin Jackson. 18220 STATE HIGHWAY 249 77070 #021-05-1990 L1993 **AN** *020 †05
RAM, Gita. ■ 77054 #048-04-2008 *012
RAMA, Jennifer Ann. 1 BAYLOR PLZ, DEPT OF PULMONOLOGY/PEDS 77030 #422-01-2003 **PDP** *012 †55
RAMACHANDRAN, Asha Rani. 15655 CYPRESSWOOD MEDCL DR, KELSEY SEYBOLD CLINIC 77014 #894-01-1999 L2005 **PD** *020 †55
RAMADAS, Elangovan. 7011 SW FWY, MHMRA 77074 #495-04-1981 L2005 **P CHP** *020 †75
RAMAKRISHNAN, Vasuki. 12831 WOODLITE LN, A AND B LABS 77015 #495-04-1975 L1980 **PD** *071
RAMAN, Jay K. 1631 NORTH LOOP W, STE 220 77008 #495-31-1966 L1981 **GS VS** *020 †85
RAMAN, Krishna K. 11302 FALLBROOK DR, STE 110 77065 #495-45-1988 L2002 **NEP** *020 †20
RAMAN, Sanjeev Murthi. 1504 TAUB LOOP, BAYLOR COLLEGE OF MED 77030 #495-01-2001 L2003 **PCC** *012 †20
RAMASWAMI, Nalini. 11914 ASTORIA BLVD, STE 330 77089 #495-59-1992 L2004 **END** *020 †20
RAMBEAU, John Corwin. 8305 KNIGHT RD 77054 #024-07-1957 L1963 **R OS** *071 †80
RAMCHANDANI, Mahesh K. 1315 ST JOSEPH PKWY # 1306 77002 #917-03-1982 L1993 **TS** *020 †85,90
RAMCHATESINGH, Jacqueline. 4410 NAVIGATION BLVD, STE 278 77011 #306-01-1997 L2006 **PD** *020 †55
RAMESH, Gowrappala S. 915 GESSNER RD, STE 650 77024 #495-35-1973 L1981 **GE** *020 †20
RAMI, Topan. 6560 FANNIN ST, STE 620 77030 #005-14-1998 L2000 **IM** *020 †20
RAMIN, Susan Marie. 6431 FANNIN ST STE 3.036, DEPT OBG & RPRDCTV SCI 77030 #026-04-1984 L1986 **OBG MFM** *040 †30
RAMIREZ, Adriane A. 6431 FANNIN ST, AT HO 77030 #048-14-2006 **PD** *012
RAMIREZ, Andrea Anne. 6621 FANNIN ST, MC 3-2290 77030 #033-06-2003 **PPR** *012 †55
RAMIREZ, Araceli. 12303 WESTHEIMER RD, STE B 77077 #048-14-1998 L2001 **FM** *020 †18
RAMIREZ, Ariel. ■ 77030 #429-01-1981 **N** *100
RAMIREZ, Eduardo S. 211 HIGHLAND CROSS DR, STE 275 77073 #042-02-1990 L1993 **IM** *020 †20
RAMIREZ, Fanny Elena. 1315 ST JOSEPH PKWY, STE 1309 77002 #264-03-1982 L1996 **FM** *020 †18 ‡
RAMIREZ, Irma. 1515 HOLCOMBE BLVD, PEDIATRICS, BOX 87 77030 #042-01-1967 L1979 **PHO** *071
RAMIREZ, John Perez. 7109 LAWNDALE ST, STE B 77023 #048-04-1984 L1986 **FM** *020
RAMIREZ, Manuel Carrillo. 2001 KIRBY DR STE 1109, MANUEL C RAMIREZ MD 77019 #048-02-1963 L1963 **P CHP** *020
RAMIREZ, Manuel L, III. 6550 FANNIN ST # 1200 77030 #649-33-1986 **IMG** *100
RAMIREZ, Marina L. 1221 MCKINNEY ST, STE 40300 77010 #048-02-1985 L1986 **PD** *020 †55
RAMIREZ, Mario Bentiz. TEX RESEARCH INST SCI PSY 77011 #264-01-1965 **P** *020
RAMIREZ, Mildred M. 6431 FANNIN ST, MC 3.604 77030 #042-01-1987 L1991 **OBG** *020 †30
RAMIREZ, Pedro. 1515 HOLCOMBE BLVD 77030 #035-46-1994 L1999 **OBG** *020 †30
RAMIREZ-AMAYA, Rene. 710 FM 1960 RD W, STE 220 77090 #341-01-1980 L2001 **NPM PD** *020 †55
RAMIZ, Naila. 800 PEAKWOOD DR, STE 7G 77090 #160-02-1993 L2002 **IM** *020 †20
RAMOCKI, Melissa Beth. 6621 FANNIN ST CC1250, TEXAS CHILDREN'S HOSPITAL 77030 #016-02-2003 L2007 **CHN** *012
RAMONDETTA, Lois Michelle. 1515 HOLCOMBE BLVD, DEPT GYN ONC, BOX 1362 77030 #033-06-1993 L1998 **OBG** *020 †30
RAMOS, Antonio J. 1302 N SHEPHERD DR 77008 #048-14-1998 L2000 **IM** *020 †20
RAMOS, Carlos A. 6565 FANNIN ST M964, THE METHODIST HOSPITAL 77030 #770-02-1994 L2007 **HO** *100 †20
RAMOS, Carlos Canales. 7900 FANNIN ST 77054 #048-04-2000 L2002 **OBG** *020
RAMOS, German Augusto. 3311 CANAL ST 77003 #264-02-1981 L1998 **FM** *020 †18
RAMOS, Lesley A. 1709 DRYDEN RD STE 550, BCM FACULTY CTR 77030 #048-14-2005 L2007 **IM** *012
RAMOS, Oscar Roberto. 1 BAYLOR PLZ, BAYLOR COLLEGE OF MED 77030 #649-01-1956 L1966 **PTH HEM** *030 †50
RAMOS GONZALEZ, Juan M. PO BOX 20708, DEPT OF RADIOLOGY 77225 #042-02-2002 L2003 **DR** *012
RAMOS-PATEL, Damitra Damo. ■ 77096 #048-04-2006 **MPD** *012

RAMRAJ, Ramya. 1 BAYLOR PLZ, BAYLOR COLL OF MED 77030 #495-94-2002 L2008 **PD** *012
RAMSEY, Edward Earl, Jr. 10005 S MAIN ST 77025 #048-14-1993 L1994 **AN** *020
RAMSEY, Peter James. 1504 TAUB LOOP 77030 #028-03-2002 L2005 **GE** *012 †20
RAMSHESH, Priya V. 2727 W HOLCOMBE BLVD 77025 #495-01-1994 L2005 **HEM** *100 †20
RAMU, Jayanthi Belakere. 15010 MEMORIAL DR 77079 #305-01-2003 L2008 **FM** *020 †18
RANA, Prachi. 5001 WOODWAY DR, UNIT 1706 77056 #496-07-1991 L1999 **IM** *020 †20
RANA, Sanila. 4126 SOUTHWEST FWY, STE 1000 77027 #048-13-1993 L1994 **IM** *020 †20
RANA GAITE, Jaime Manuel. 920 FROSTWOOD DR, STE 760 77024 #132-03-1964 L1976 **CD IM** *071 †20
RANA-PATEL, Kiran. 2727 W HOLCOMBE BLVD, KELSEY-SEYBOLD CLINIC - OR 77025 #305-01-1999 L2005 **SCI** *020 †60 ‡
RANCE, Ronald Michael. 427 W 20TH ST STE 503 77008 #561-17-1978 L1982 **GE IM** *020 †20
RANDALL, David Crow. 12930 EAST FWY 77015 #048-02-1991 L1992 **ORS** *020 †40
RANDEL, Wilmer H, Jr. ■ 77098 #035-19-1945 L1948 **IM** *072 †20
RANDHAWA, Simrat Kaur. 2380 S MACGREGOR WAY 77021 #048-16-2004 L2007 **AN** *020
RANDLE, Lucious, Jr. 1213 HERMANN DR STE 415 77004 #048-04-1979 L1979 **OPH** *020 †35
RANDLE, Sonja L. 1300 MOURSUND ST, UNIVERSITY OF TEXAS MEDICA 77030 #048-14-1985 L1986 **CHP P** *040
RANDOLPH, Brion Vincent. 1709 DRYDEN RD STE 5550, BCM 620 77030 #045-04-2003 L2006 **HO** *012 †20
RANEY, Kenneth C. ■ 77030 #048-14-2008 *012
RANEY, Rance Wilson. 7908 N SAM HOUSTON PKWY W, STE 200 77064 #048-04-1991 L1993 **OTO** *020 †45
RANGAN, Kasthuri. 17030 NANES DR, STE 210 77090 #495-04-1972 L1981 **OTO HNS** *020 †45
RANGANATHAN, Padmini. ■ 77005 #495-59-1971 L1979 **PHO** *075 †55
RANGARAJ, Gopikishan Rao. ■ 77025 #495-65-1983 L1996 **IM** *020 †20
RANGDAENG, Samreung. 6565 FANNIN ST 77030 #891-03-1982 L1989 **PTH** *020 †50
RANGEL, Remberto. 1213 HERMANN DR STE 700 77004 #275-01-1952 L1973 **PM IM** *020 †60
RANGAKULNUWAT, Somrak. 6621 FANNIN ST, TX CHILDRENS HOSP/MC3 257 77030 #891-03-1984 **PDP** *020
RANKIN, John Sedgwick. ■ 77054 #048-04-2008 *012
RANKIN, Roger Noel Lee. 17322 RED OAK DR 77090 #056-06-1978 L1978 **AN EM** *020
RANKIN, William Earl. 1300 BAY AREA BLVD, # B 77058 #048-02-1957 L1958 **OBG** *071 †30
RANSDELL, Brian Lee. 6655 TRAVIS ST, STE 980 77030 #048-04-2003 L2006 **D** *020 †15
RAO, Anuradha T.N. 6431 FANNIN ST 77030 #496-07-1994 *100
RAO, Bangra Kulur B. 1631 NORTH LOOP W STE 510 77008 #495-14-1971 L1977 **PUD IM** *020 †20
RAO, Bhavana. 9717 CYPRESSWOOD DR, APT 1926 77070 #495-98-2004 *012
RAO, Brinda Ramakrishna. 2900 RICHMOND AVE, UT MD ANDERSON CANCER CENT 77098 #048-16-2001 L2007 **DR** *100 †80
RAO, Ganesh. 1515 HOLCOMBE BLVD, UNIT 442 77030 #003-01-1998 L2006 **NS** *100
RAO, Harish Pulipaka. 4545 POST OAK PLAC DR #130 77027 #048-01-2002 L2007 **IM** *020 †20
RAO, Jyoti. 2060 SPACE PARK DR 77058 #495-11-1987 L1997 **GE IM** *020 †20
RAO, Metram J. 17400 RED OAK DR 77090 #495-57-1967 L1981 **CD IM** *020 †20
RAO, P Syamasundar. 6431 FANNIN ST, MSB 3-130 77030 #495-11-1965 L2002 **PDC PD** *020 †55
RAO, Purnima Iyer. 1111 AUGUSTA DR, KELSEY-SEYBOLD 77057 #021-05-1999 L2003 **OBG** *020 †30
RAO, Silpa. PO BOX 20708 77225 #495-37-2005 **FP** *012
RAO, Srinivas P. 12121 RICHMOND AVE, STE 109 77082 #048-04-1989 L1990 **DR** *020 †80
RAO, Sudhir R. ■ 77054 #422-01-2002 L2007 **APM** *100 †05
RAO, Vasanthi G. 2002 HOLCOMBE BLVD, MICHEAL E. DEBAKEY VA MEDI 77030 #495-33-1971 L1979 **DR** *020 †80
RAO, Vemulapalli Kesava. 7800 FANNIN ST, STE 111 77054 #496-01-1970 L1978 **AN** *020
RAOOF, Humaira Syed. 8900 LAKES AT 610 DR 77054 #495-65-1969 L1977 **PD** *020 †55
RAPHAEL, Jean Leclerc, II. 6621 FANNIN ST, STE 1540.00 77030 #024-01-2001 L2006 **PD** *100 †55
RAPHAEL, Pedro. 7000 FANNIN ST, KELSEY-SEYBOLD CLNC PA 77030 #275-01-1954 L1967 **DR** *100 †10
RAPINI, Ronald Peter. 6655 TRAVIS ST, STE 980 77030 #038-40-1978 L1984 **D DMP** *020 †15
RAPP, Kadisha B. ■ 77042 #023-01-2000 L2007 **EM ESM** *020 †16 ‡
RAPPAPORT, Norman Harvey. 6560 FANNIN ST, STE 1812 77030 #041-09-1975 L1980 **PS HS** *020 †65 ‡
RASEKH, Abdi. 6624 FANNIN ST STE 2480, HALL GARCIA CARDIOLOGY 77030 #396-36-1990 L1998 **ICE IC** *040 †20
RASHEED, Nasir. 11811 FM 1960 RD W, STE 198 77065 #704-02-1989 L1997 **IM PD** *020 †20
RASHID, Asif. 1515 HOLCOMBE BLVD 77030 #847-04-1961 L1999 **ATP** *020 †50
RASHID, Haroonur. 6624 FANNIN ST STE 2000, SLMT, 20TH FLOOR 77030 #704-20-1985 L1998 **CD IM** *020 †20
RASHID, Misba Abdul. ■ 77072 #496-40-1995 L2007 **FM** *100
RASHTI, Edward Jos. 5207 BRAESHEATHER DR 77096 #048-02-1961 L1962 **N SME** *020 †75
RASO, Enrique. #2002, 200I HOLCOMBE BLVD 77030 #847-04-1961 L1975 **NS** *071 †25
RATHI, Nisha. 6431 FANNIN ST MS 31.150 77030 #016-11-1999 L2002 **PCC** *100 †20
RATINOV, Gerald. 1315 ST JOSEPH PKWY, STE 1004 77002 #026-04-1959 L1965 **N** *020 †75
RATLIFF, William M. 1631 NORTH LOOP W STE 645 77008 #048-02-1985 L1986 **GS** *020 †85
RATNANI, Mohammad I. 6565 FANNIN ST, # 452 B 77030 #704-16-1990 L2003 **CCM** *020 †20
RATY, Sally Radelat. 1504 TAUB LOOP, BEN TAUB GENERAL HOSPITAL 77030 #048-04-1988 L1989 **AN** *020 †05
RAUCH, Ronald Arthur. 6621 FANNIN ST, MAIL CODE 2-2521 77030 #048-04-1979 L1979 **DR N** *020 †75,80
RAVAL, Bharat. 6431 FANNIN ST, DEPARTMENT OF RADIOLOGY 77030 #905-01-1971 L1983 **DR** *020 †80
RAVANDI-KASHANI, Farhad. 1400 HOLCOMBE BLVD, DEPT OF LEUKEMIA - UNIT 42 77030 #917-29-1987 L1998 **ON** *020 †20
RAVANFAR, Parisa. 1709 DRYDEN RD STE 550, BCM FACULTY CENTER 77030 #028-34-2008 *012
RAVDEL, Arnold. 7333 NORTH FWY STE 290 77076 #836-01-1960 L1978 **ORS GS** *020
RAVELO, Elihut. 8951 RUTHBY ST STE 9 77061 #275-01-1952 L1971 **FM** *020
RAVICHANDRAN, Guruswami K. 6300 HILLCROFT ST, STE 210 77081 #495-04-1975 L1979 **P OS** *020
RAWAL, Bhumi Balmukund. PO BOX 20708, DEPT OF RADIOLOGY 77225 #001-02-2004 **DR** *012
RAWALT, Rebecca Elizabeth. ■ 77082 #030-05-2005 L2008 **PD** *012
RAWRA, Fahd. PO BOX 20708 77225 #704-02-2003 **P** *012
RAY, Alak. 1631 NORTH LOOP W STE 460 77008 #495-46-1977 L1985 **NEP IM** *020

RAY, Priscilla. 6624 FANNIN ST STE 2120 77030 #048-04-1974 L1974 **P PFP** *020 †75

RAY, Sterling Haywood, III. PO BOX 88109 77288 #048-12-2003 L2005 **IM** *100

RAYMER, Lindsay Michele. ■ 77079 #048-14-2004 **P** *012

RAYMOND, Austin Kevin. 1515 HOLCOMBE BLVD, DEPT PATH BOX 85 77030 #035-20-1976 L1983 **PTH** *020 †50

RAZA, Syed Asad. 902 FROSTWOOD DR, STE 275 77024 #704-22-1987 L2004 *020 †80

RAZA, Umara Ali. 6550 FANNIN ST STE 1001 77030 #704-25-2005 **IM** *012

RAZAK, Razaali. 902 FROSTWOOD DR, STE 227 77024 #704-16-1982 L1996 **PD** *020 †55

RAZAVI, Mehdi. 6624 FANNIN ST, STE 2480 77030 #041-07-1995 L2004 **CD** *020 †20

RAZEGHI, Peter. 6431 FANNIN ST STE 1.150, AT HOUST 77030 #409-25-1999 L2007 **CD** *012 †20

RAZZACK, Jamal. 902 FROSTWOOD DR STE 267 77024 #704-02-1989 L1997 **PCC SME** *020 †20

REA, John Edward, III. 7737 SW FWY, STE 201 77074 #021-01-1971 L1978 **TS GS** *020 †85,90

READ, Steven Mitchell. 6431 FANNIN ST, MSB 5.020 DEPT OF ANES. 77030 #048-14-2003 L2006 **AN** *100

READINGER, A Beckworth. 6655 TRAVIS ST STE 980 77030 #048-02-2002 L2006 **D** *020 †15

REAM, Justin. ■ 77054 #048-04-2008 *012

REARDON, Michael Joseph. 6560 FANNIN ST, STE 1006 77030 #048-04-1978 L1978 **TS VS** *020 †85,90

REARDON, Patrick Ray. 6560 FANNIN ST, STE 1836 77030 #048-04-1983 L1983 **GS** *020 †85

REBELES, Sonia Abril. 5656 KELLEY ST, UNIVERSITY OF TEXAS HOUSTO 77026 #048-13-2003 L2006 **OBG** *100

RECHICHI, Angela. 6411 FANNIN ST 77030 #561-11-1953 L1980 **IM** *071 †20

RED, Anita D. PO BOX 4238 77210 #048-14-2006 **P** *012

REDDICK, Max Edward. 902 FROSTWOOD STE 247 77024 #028-02-1967 L1973 **D DMP** *020 †15 ‡

REDDY, Adhikari Lata. 77021 #039-01-2007 **IM** *012

REDDY, Bal. 4755 ALDINE MAIL ROUTE 77039 #048-14-2002 L2005 **FM** *020

REDDY, Deepa Ramireddi. ■ 77081 #048-12-2005 L2005 **IM** *012

REDDY, Devender D. 427 W 20TH ST STE 700 77008 #495-21-1975 L1987 **CD IM** *020

REDDY, Gurunath Thota. 275 LANTERN BEND DR # 200 77090 #495-21-1981 L1986 **GE** *020 †20

REDDY, Kandakatla Raj S. 1515 HOLCOMBE BLVD, DEPT OF PALLIATIVE CARE,UN 77030 #495-65-1982 L1994 **PLM AN** *020 †05

REDDY, Kota J. 7710 BEECHNUT ST, STE 220 77074 #495-49-1985 L1997 **CD** *020 †20

REDDY, Madhavi A. 6550 MAPLERIDGE ST, STE 201 77081 #048-04-1996 L1998 **FM** *020 †18

REDDY, Malladi Sudhakar. 2045 SPACE PARK DR, STE 180 77058 #495-21-1968 L1993 **IM** *020 †20

REDDY, Manoj A. 2604 QUENBY AVE 77005 #048-04-1997 L2000 **RO** *020 †80

REDDY, Padma Pagadi. 11226 SOUTHWEST FWY 77031 #495-57-1997 L2004 **FM** *020 †18

REDDY, Pushpa Yaratha. 15514 CONIFER BAY CT, CLEARLAKE INTEGRATED HEALT 77059 #495-98-1994 L2001 **IM** *020

REDDY, Raghu M. ■ 77070 #496-39-1995 L2004 **PCC** *100 †20

REDDY, Ravi R. 7333 N FREEWAY, SUITE 401 77076 #495-65-1973 L1980 **GE** *020 †20

REDDY, Rekha Goli. ■ 77064 #496-01-1994 L2001 **AN** *020

REDDY, Saraswati P. 1315 ST JOSEPH PKWY, STE 1800 77002 #495-33-1988 L1994 **ON** *020 †20

REDDY, Sreelatha. 7737 SW FWY STE 968, AND LIVER CLINIC, P.A. 77074 #495-21-1992 L2001 **GE** *020 †20

REDDY, Sudarsana K. 9898 BISSONNET ST STE 152 77036 #495-16-1957 L1976 **GP** *020

REDDY, Swaroop A V N. 2002 HOLCOMBE BLVD 77030 #495-65-1972 L1983 **IM** *020

REDDY, V Janardhana. 17150 EL CAMINO REAL, STE E 77058 #495-50-1970 L1975 **AN** *020

REDDY, Vanitha Venkataswa. ■ 77056 #496-22-2001 L2006 **IM** *020

REDDY, Yogesh Puttappa. ■ 77054 #496-39-1999 L2007 **FM** *012

REDEL, Carol Ann. 6701 FANNIN ST 77030 02-01-1986 L1991 **PD** *020 †55

REDELL, Michele Simmons. 6621 FANNIN ST 3-3320, TEXAS CHILDRENS CANCER CEN 77030 #054-04-1998 L2002 **PHO** *020 †55

REDMON, Agile Hugh, Jr. 7505 FANNIN ST, STE 515 77054 #048-04-1948 L1948 **A** *071 †03

REDMOND, Daniel Clarke. ■ 77024 #048-02-1959 L1959 **GS** *074 †85

REDMOND, Frank Austin. 5749 SAN FELIPE ST 77057 #038-43-1982 L1996 **EM** *020 †16

REDONDO, Maria Jose. ■ 77005 #847-13-1992 L2008 **END** *020

REDWINE, Michael Dwain. 6431 FANNIN ST STE 2.130 77030 #048-02-1973 L1973 **DR NM** *020 †20,28,80

REDWINE, William Allen. 6624 FANNIN ST STE 2400 77030 #048-12-1969 L1971 **GS** *020 †85

REECE, Gregory Paul. 1515 HOLCOMBE BLVD, UNIT 443 77030 #021-06-1982 L1990 **PS GS** *020 †85,65

REECE, William Edward. 2411 FOUNTAIN VIEW DR # 2 77057 #005-02-1977 L2007 **AN PD** *020 †55,05

REED, Bethany A. PO BOX 20708, DEPT OF OB/GYN 77225 #048-15-2004 L2007 **OBG** *012

REED, Brian Christopher. 3701 KIRBY DR STE 600, BAYLOR FAMILY AND COMM MED 77098 #025-01-1999 L2002 **FM** *020 †18

REED, Joel E. 1213 HERMANN DR, PULMONARY & INTERNL MEDCN 77004 #016-06-1950 L1959 **PUD IM** *071 †20

REED, Jon Allison. 1 BAYLOR PLZ, DEPT OF PATH BCM-315 77030 #041-14-1989 L1999 **DMP** *020 †50

REED, Kenneth. 6431 FANNIN ST 77030 #060-01-1974 L1978 **P** *020 †75

REED, Linnie Mae. 6910 BELLAIRE BLVD STE 9, MAILING: P.O. BOX 27495 77074 #047-06-1977 L1983 **FM** *020

REED, Valerie Ibom. 1515 HOLCOMBE BLVD, BOX 97 77030 #036-07-2003 L2008 **RO** *012

REEDER, Desirae J. ■ 77035 #048-14-2007 **P** *012

REESE, Merrick Hogan. 16825 NORTHCHASE DR 77060 #048-12-1963 L1963 **ON HEM** *030 †20

REESE, Rachel B. ■ 77079 #048-14-2007 **PD** *012

REEVES, Keith O. 6550 FANNIN ST, STE 2201 77030 #048-04-1970 L1970 **OBG** *020 †30

REEVES, William John, Jr. 10121 WINDMILL LAKES BLVD 77075 #040-02-1958 L1969 **IM ON** *020

REFUERZO, Jerrie Selga. 6431 FANNIN ST, STE 3.270 77030 #025-07-1996 L2008 **OBG** *020 †30

REGAN, Victoria L. 6410 FANNIN ST, STE 722 77030 #048-14-1987 L1988 **PD** *020 †55

REHMAN, Hafeez Ur. ■ 77024 #704-02-1990 *062

REHMAN, Javed. 6624 FANNIN ST STE 1900 77030 #048-02-2002 L2005 **IM** *020

REHMAN, Qaiser. 11301 FALLBROOK DR, STE 126 77065 #704-25-1993 L2006 **RHU IM** *020 †20

REHMAN, Zahida. 3701 KIRBY DR STE 600 77098 #704-21-1987 L2002 **IM** *020 †20

REICH, Lydie. ■ 77096 #286-07-1976 L1996 **P** *020 †75

REICHMAN, Eric F. 6431 FANNIN ST, EMERGENCY DEPT 77030 #056-06-1993 L2003 **EM** *040 †16

REID, Karlene Claudia. 1 BAYLOR PLZ, BCM 286, N1319 77030 #566-01-1991 L2003 **ID** *020 †20

REILLY, Christopher L. 12121 RICHMOND AVE, STE 312 77082 #917-18-1990 L1996 **GS** *020 †85

REILLY, Edward Leo. 1300 MOURSUND ST # 267, UT MEDICAL SCHOOL AT HOUST 77030 #033-05-1961 L1973 **P ADP** *040 †75

REINOEHL, Pamela Jean. ■ 77024 #007-02-1993 L1996 **PD** *020 †55

REISMAN, Neal Robt. 6624 FANNIN ST, STE 1600 77030 #041-13-1973 L1980 **PS HS** *020 †85,65

REISS, Ahn P. 7789 SOUTHWEST FWY, STE 510 77074 #035-08-1995 L1999 **OBG** *020 †30

REITER, Alexander Arie. 7900 FANNIN ST, STE 2600 77054 #561-01-1972 L1989 **MFM OBG** *020

REITMAN, Charles Alan. 6620 MAIN ST, STE 1300 77030 #048-04-1995 L1997 **OSS OTR** *020 †40

REJAIE, Babak. 902 FROSTWOOD STE 275, MEMORIALHERMANN/MEMORIAL C 77024 #654-01-1998 L2007 **PDR** *020 †80

REJAIE, Iraj. ■ 77024 #517-06-1962 L1975 **PS** *071 †85,65

REMENCHIK, Alexander P. 8799 NORTH LOOP E STE 250 77029 #016-02-1951 L1974 **IM CD** *020 †20

REMMERS, Paul August. 1 BAYLOR PLZ, MS BCM 621 77030 #048-02-1983 L1983 **IM** *020 †20

REMUS, Luis Enrique, III. ■ 77030 #021-01-1995 L2001 **FOP** *100

REN, Dewei. 8282 CAMBRIDGE ST 77054 #243-45-1982 *100

REN, Jie. ■ 77081 #243-72-1986 L2003 **AN** *020

RENDON GARCIA, Juan Jesus. 6550 FANNIN ST, THE METHODIST HOSP 77030 #649-19-2004 **GS** *020

RENNER, Robert Allen. 1221 MCKINNEY ST, STE 40300 77010 #048-04-1968 L1968 **U** *020 †95

RENOM LLONCH, Montserrat. ■ 77025 #847-12-1991 L1997 **PD** *020 †55

RENSIMER, Edward Robt. 915 GESSNER RD, STE 525 77024 #041-13-1975 L1979 **ID IM** *020 †20

RENTIERS, Paul Kenneth. 1919 NORTH LOOP W STE 170 77008 #060-01-1966 L1977 **OPH** *020 †35

RESETKOVA, Erika. ■ 77004 #286-03-1984 L2004 **PTH** *020 †50

RESTREPO, Cristian. 1213 HERMANN DR, STE 278 77004 #264-03-1965 L1967 **P PYA** *020 †75

RESTREPO, Margo Kaliner. 1213 HERMANN DR, STE 880 77004 #048-14-1974 L1974 **P PYA** *020 †75 ‡

REUBEN, Jeffrey David. 4126 SOUTHWEST FWY, STE 700 77027 #038-06-1981 L1987 **ORS** *020 †40

REUL, George John, Jr. 1101 BATES AVE, SURGICAL ASSOCIATES OF 77030 #056-06-1962 L1971 **TS VS** *020 †85,90

REUL, Ross M. 1101 BATES AVE, SURGICAL ASSOCIATES OF 77030 #048-04-1993 L1995 **TS** *020 †85,90

REVEILLE, John Duffin. 6431 FANNIN ST RM 5270, UNIV OF TEXAS MEDICAL SCHO 77030 #023-07-1977 L1987 **RHU OS** *050 †20

REVERDIN, Alexandra Kathr. 6431 FANNIN ST 3.228 77030 #869-04-2000 **PDP** *012

REX, John Howard. 2617C W HOLCOMBE BLVD, PMB 114 77025 #048-04-1982 L1985 **ID IM** *020 †20

REYES, Erasmo A. ■ 77054 #048-14-2008 *012

REYES, Louis C. 8541 GULF FWY, FAIR PARK MEDICAL CLINIC 77017 #737-01-1959 L1979 **GS OS** *071

REYES, Maria A. 13111 EAST FWY 77015 #042-01-1998 L2001 **FM** *020 †18 ‡

REYES, Oscar Louis. ■ 77057 #649-14-1977 *075

REYNOLDS, George E S, III. 17150 EL CAMINO REAL 77058 #048-04-1972 L1972 **PD** *020 †55

REYNOLDS, Jason Miller. 1 BAYLOR PLZ 77030 #048-12-2002 L2006 **PD** *100 †55

REYNOLDS, Timothy James. 7710 BEECHNUT ST, STE 220 77074 #027-01-1984 L1999 **CD EM** *020 †20

REYSER, Julia. 3601 N MACGREGOR WAY, 4TH FLOOR GERIATRIC CLINIC 77004 #913-19-1995 L2005 **FM** *020 †18

REZA, Syed H. 7333 NORTH FWY, STE 210 77076 #704-02-1972 L1993 **N** *020

RHEE, Edward Jiwook. 1415 LA CONCHA LN 77054 #016-06-1996 L2001 **NEP** *020 †20

RHEE, Yong Whan. 9501 LONG POINT RD, STE R 77055 #583-02-1969 L1979 **IM** *020 †20

RHETT, Esi M. ■ 77021 #033-06-2007 **AN** *012

RHINES, Laurence David. 1515 HOLCOMBE BLVD, BOX 442 77030 #024-01-1993 L2001 **NS** *020 †25

RHO, Seung Kook. 15655 CYPRESSWOOD MEDCL DR, STE 400 77014 #583-02-1970 L1979 **N P** *071 †75

RHOADS, Jon Marc. 6431 FANNIN ST, DEPT. OF PEDIATRICS/GASTRO 77030 #023-07-1980 L2006 **PD** *050 †55

RHODES, Frederick A, III. 11800 ASTORIA BLVD 77089 #048-04-1986 L1988 **AN** *020 †05

RHODES, Jennifer L. 1 BAYLOR PLZ, BAYLOR COL OF MED 77030 #048-04-1998 L2001 **PD** *020 †55

RHODES-MORRIS, Helen E. 1515 HOLCOMBE BLVD, DEPARTMENT OF GYNECOLOGIC 77030 #048-15-1988 L1989 **GYN** *020 †30

RIAZ, Mohammad. 12121 RICHMOND AVE, STE 208 77082 #704-02-1990 L1996 **ON** *100 †20

RIBBLE, John Chas. 6410 FANNIN ST 77030 #048-12-1955 L1955 **PD IM** *040 †20

RIBELLES, Elisa. 920 FROSTWOOD DR 77024 #048-02-1980 L1980 **IM** *020 †20

RIBELLES, Jacqueline L T. 2131 KIRBY DR, STE 93 77019 #048-02-1955 L1955 **GP** *071

RIBELLES, Jose Antonio. 77019 #847-01-1945 L1955 **GS TS** *071

RIBEN, Michael Warren. ■ 77005 #041-01-1994 L2004 **PTH** *020

RICARDO, Arlene Esther. 7789 SOUTHWEST FWY STE 400 77074 #035-06-1993 L1995 **GS** *020 †55

RICE, David Christopher. 1515 HOLCOMBE BLVD # 445, M.D. ANDERSON CANCER CENTE 77030 #539-03-1991 L2002 **TS** *020 †85,90

RICE, Jacqueline Nicole. 211 HIGHLAND CROSS DR, STE 275 77073 #001-02-2003 L2006 **EM** *020 †16

RICE, Lawrence. 6550 FANNIN ST, STE 1001 77030 #012-05-1974 L1977 **HEM HO** *020 †20

RICE, Liston Mc Leod. 3742 TANGLEY RD 77005 #048-12-1980 L1980 **EM** *020 †20,16

RICE, Marilyn K Mattison. ■ 77036 #038-40-1965 L1970 **IM** *020 †20

RICE, Terry Wynne. 1504 TAUB LOOP 77030 #020-02-1984 L2003 **IM EM** *040 †20

RICE, Theresa Cachuela. 1102 BATES AVE 77030 #748-01-1959 L1981 **GS EM** *071

RICH, Donna C. 6411 FANNIN ST 77030 #048-02-1993 L1994 **PS** *020 †65

RICHARD, Paul Stephen. ■ 77030 #021-01-2008 *012

RICHARDS, David Matthew. ■ 77005 #025-07-2006 **IM** *012

RICHARDS, Kristy L. 1515 HOLCOMBE BLVD UNIT 10 77030 #005-11-2001 L2003 **ON** *020

RICHARDS, Marrie Byrne. 3400 BISSONNET ST STE 297 77005 #048-04-1974 L1974 **GP** *020

■ = Address Information Privacy Protected

RICHARDSON, James Daron. 8100 GREENBRIAR ST 77054 #051-01-1977 L1986 **DR** *075 †80
RICHARDSON, Karen A. 10370 RICHMOND AVE, STE 1125 77042 #048-14-1996 L1998 **FM EM** *020 †18
RICHEY, Stephen Lane. 6431 FANNIN ST, ASSISTANT CHIEF OF SERVICE 77030 #021-05-2004 L2007 **IM HO** *012 †20
RICHMOND, Camilla Ann. ■ 77006 #016-06-2004 L2007 **PD** *020 †55
RICKLING, Sylvia. 1221 MCKINNEY ST, STE 40300 77010 #048-14-1990 L1991 **DR** *020 †80
RICKMAN, Frank D. 6400 FANNIN ST, STE 3000 77030 #020-02-1968 L1973 **IM CD** *020 †20
RICKS, Ann Marie. ■ 77227 #048-04-2007 L2008 **OBG** *012
RICKS, John P. 1200 POST OAK BLVD, STE 426 77056 #027-01-1966 L1970 **DR** *020 †80
RICKS, Richard Kenneth. 7777 SOUTHWEST FWY 77074 #048-04-1958 L1958 **TS GS** *071 †85,90
RIEBER, Alyssa Gosney. ■ 77063 #001-02-2001 L2003 **ON** *020
RIED, Hubert Leo. 11303 CHIMNEY ROCK RD 77035 #010-02-1946 L1952 **PD PHO** *071 †55
RIEDEL, Bernhard Joachim. 1515 HOLCOMBE BLVD, UNIT 42 77030 #836-06-1987 L2005 *020
RIENIETS, Cynthia Youmans. 3000 RICHMOND AVE, RIVER OAKS IMAGING & DIAGN 77098 #048-02-1992 L1993 **DR** *020 †20
RIERA GONZALEZ, Gregorio. 1 BAYLOR PLZ 77030 #935-08-2000 **OBG** *100
RIGGS, John W. 5656 KELLEY ST, LBJ HOSP 77026 #048-14-1986 L1987 **OBG** *020 †30
RIGGS, Shirley Ann. 6624 FANNIN ST, STE 2430 77030 #048-04-1974 L1974 **HEM IM** *020 †20
RIGGS, Stuart. 6624 FANNIN ST 77030 #048-02-1953 L1953 **ID IM** *071 †20
RIGO, Mark Steven. ■ 77069 #038-40-1976 L1985 **EM PD** *020 †55
RIHA, Karel. 6431 FANNIN ST, MSMB 5-020 77030 #286-09-1985 L1997 **AN** *020
RILEY, Lizabeth E. 3701 KIRBY DR, STE 600 77098 #048-02-1992 L1996 **FM** *020 †18
RILEY, Wayne Joseph. 1 BAYLOR PLZ RM 181A, BAYLOR COLLEGE OF MEDICINE 77030 #012-21-1993 L1996 **IM** *020 †20
RILEY, William John. 4126 SOUTHWEST FWY, STE 1210 77027 #016-02-1960 L1969 **N CHN** *020 †75
RIMAWI, Mothaffar F. 1 BAYLOR PLZ, BREAST CENTER, BCM600 77030 #575-01-1997 L2005 **ON** *100 †20
RINANDO, James Michael. ■ 77006 #048-14-2006 **AN** *012
RIOS, Adan. 1200 BINZ ST, STE 1490 77004 #715-01-1970 L1977 **ON IM** *020 †20
RIOS, Danielle Rae. 6621 FANNIN ST RM A170, MC1-1000 77030 #003-01-2006 **PD** *012
RIOS, Enrique Heberto. ■ 77054 #048-04-1983 L2004 **NPM** *020 †55
RIOS, Felipe. 8208 GULF FWY, STE 101 77017 #649-02-1969 L1977 **CD** *020
RIOS-SIERRA, Carlos E. 8945 LONG POINT RD, STE 112 77055 #429-01-1987 L1988 L2001 **AN** *020
RIQUELME, John F. 6720 BERTNER ST 77030 #231-02-1966 L1971 **AN CCA** *020 †05
RISHI, Kirtee. 6565 FANNIN ST M227 77030 #496-07-1996 L2008 **NP** *012
RISIN, Semyon Aron. ■ 77005 #913-32-1964 L2002 **PTH** *020 †50
RISKIN, Arieh. ■ 77035 #550-01-1987 **NPM** *100
RISSER, William Leigh. 6431 FANNIN ST, DEPT OF PEDIATRICS 77030 #008-01-1972 L1978 **PD OS** *030 †55
RITTER, Marcella Blake. ■ 77030 #048-13-1980 L1980 **OBG** *071 †30
RIVAS, Ricardo A. 710 FM 1960 RD W, HOUSTON NW MEDICAL CENTER 77090 #048-12-1986 L1987 **PD** *020 †20
RIVAS Y ZEPEDA, Agustin. 17202 RED OAK DR 77090 #649-17-1952 L1964 **GS TS** *071
RIVENES, Shannon M. 6621 FANNIN ST, CARDIOLOGY 77030 #003-01-1993 L1999 **PDC** *020
RIVERA, Andreana L. 1 BAYLOR PLZ, DEPT PATHOLOGY 77030 #048-04-2004 **NP** *012 †55
RIVERA, Carlos John. 7580 FANNIN ST, STE 210 77054 #024-01-1983 L1991 **CHN PD** *020
RIVERA, Carlos Roberto. 2727 W HOLCOMBE BLVD 77025 #048-02-2001 L2004 **IM** *020 †20
RIVERA, Edgardo. 6550 FANNIN ST SM1001, THE METHODIST HOSPITAL 77030 #042-01-1990 L1992 **ON** *020 †20
RIVERA, Efrain. ■ 77054 #048-14-2008 *012
RIVERA, Frieda J. 6550 FANNIN ST # 1200 77030 #042-03-1987 L1994 **PN** *020 †55
RIVERA, Idalia R. 13630 BEAMER RD, STE 108 77089 #042-01-1987 L1994 **PD** *020 †55
RIVERA, Jorge Luis. ■ 77021 #042-01-2003 **OPH** *012
RIVERA, Marie Lourdes. 1 BAYLOR PLZ, BAYLOR COLL OF MED 77030 #042-02-2004 L2006 **NP** *012 †50
RIVERA, Victor M. 6501 FANNIN ST, # NB100 77030 #649-01-1965 L1973 **N** *020 †75
RIVERA-OPIO, Norma M. 6411 FANNIN ST 77030 #042-01-1991 L2001 **IM** *020 †20
RIVERA SERRANO, Carlos Ma. 1 BAYLOR PLZ 77030 #264-21-2003 L2006 **GS** *100
RIVERO, Maria Teresa. 2060 SPACE PARK DR, STE 308 77058 #048-15-1984 L1985 **OBG** *020 †30
RIVIELLO, James John, Jr. 6621 FANNIN ST, CC#1250 77030 #024-07-1978 L2007 **P CHN** *020 †55,75
RIZK, Edward G. 5351 INSTITUTE LN 77005 #018-03-1946 L1959 **PD** *071 †55
RIZK, Magdy Wadie. 12121 RICHMOND AVE, STE 317 77082 #915-02-1966 L1982 **OBG** *020 †30
RIZVI, Murtaza. ■ 77054 #023-01-2001 L2006 **PS** *012
RIZVI, Rabab. ■ 77030 #704-20-2002 L2006 **P** *012
RIZVI, Sara B. 11037 FM 1960 RD W, B-2 77065 #048-13-2000 L2003 **PD** *020 †55
RIZVI, Zaufishan. 902 FROSTWOOD DR STE 253 77024 #704-02-1994 L2001 **FM** *020 †18
RIZZO, Gina Teresa. 18100 SAINT JOHN DR, NASSAU BAY 77058 #048-14-1986 L1987 **GYN** *071 †30
RO, Jae Yun. 1515 HOLCOMBE BLVD 77030 #583-01-1969 L1985 **PTH CLP** *050 †50
RO, Jungsil. 8100 GREENBRIAR ST, STE 250 77054 #583-08-1972 L1985 **ON IM** *020 †20
RO, Won Suk Bobby. ■ 77007 #048-02-2001 L2005 **AN** *020 †05
ROACH, Dorothy Jean. 530 WELLS FARGO DR STE 116 77090 #048-12-1980 L1980 **REN OBG** *020 †30
ROARK, David Tuxworth. 2500 TANGLEWILDE ST, STE 160 77063 #048-02-1971 L1971 **OTO** *020 †45
ROBA, Anteneh Tesfaye. 710 FM 1960 RD W, HOUSTON NORTHWEST MEDICAL 77090 #781-04-1982 L1993 **EM** *020 †16
ROBB, Geoffrey Lawrence. 1515 HOLCOMBE BLVD, BOX 443 77030 #011-02-1974 L1992 **PS HS** *020 †45,65
ROBBEN, Christopher Paul. 6560 FANNIN ST, STE 1950 77030 #035-19-1982 L1983 **IM** *020 †20
ROBBINS, Richard James. 6550 FANNIN ST STE 1001 77030 #030-06-1975 L2006 **IM END** *050 †20
ROBERSON, Monica L. 7400 FANNIN ST, STE 930 77054 #048-13-1999 L2003 **OBG** *020
ROBERSON, Saulette Raquel. ■ 77004 #036-05-2005 L2007 **IM** *012
ROBERTS, Candace E. 7550 FANNIN ST 77054 #048-04-1983 L1983 **OS DR** *020 †80
ROBERTS, Edward Brooke. 12930 EAST FWY 77015 #051-04-1994 L1999 **OTR** *020 †40
ROBERTS, Edward Roy. 6700 BELLAIRE BLVD 77074 #048-02-1963 L1963 **AN** *020

ROBERTS, Erica Allyson. ■ 77008 #048-14-2004 L2008 **OBG** *012
ROBERTS, Jess Clifton. 1 BAYLOR PLZ, DEPT OF OTOLARYNGOLOGY 77030 #027-01-2006 **OTO** *012
ROBERTS, Robert. 6550 FANNIN ST STE SM677, BAYLOR COLLEGE 77030 #064-01-1966 L1984 **CD** *030
ROBERTS, Seth Howard. 6720 BERTNER ST MC2-270, ST. LUKE'S EPISCOPAL HOSPI 77030 #048-04-2002 L2007 **DR** *100 †80
ROBERTSON, Carolyn Lee. ■ 77021 #035-03-2008 *012
ROBERTSON, Claudia Sue. 1 BAYLOR PLZ, BAYLOR COLLEGE OF MEDICINE 77030 #048-04-1975 L1975 **CCM IM** *020 †20
ROBERTSON, John Marion. 7400 FANNIN ST, STE 1130 77054 #048-12-2002 L2004 **PDP** *012 †55
ROBERTSON, Nathaniel, Jr. 507 N SAM HOUSTON PKWY E, STE 245 77060 #004-01-2001 L2005 **FM** *020
ROBESON, Julie. 7007 NORTH FWY, STE 240 77076 #048-14-1985 L1987 **NEP IM** *040 †20
ROBINETT, Amber Johnson. ■ 77029 #048-12-2005 L2008 **PD** *012
ROBINS, Owen Hill. 6565 DE MOSS DR 77074 #025-01-1957 L1963 **GPM IM** *020 †20
ROBINSON, Celia Nicole. ■ 77004 #010-02-2007 **GS** *012
ROBINSON, Daniel D. 8830 LONG POINT RD, STE 605 77055 #048-13-1982 L1983 **PD** *020 †55
ROBINSON, David. 6431 FANNIN ST 449, UT-HOUSTON MEDICAL SCHOOL 77030 #035-03-1993 L1999 **EM** *050 †16
ROBINSON, David Jonathan. 6431 FANNIN ST 449, DEPT OF EMERGENCY MEDICINE 77030 #047-06-1974 L1977 **DR** *020 †80
ROBINSON, Elbert Floyd. 6560 FANNIN ST STE 1810 77030 #024-01-1961 L1967 **NS** *020 †25
ROBINSON, Emily Katheryn. ■ 77005 #048-14-1993 L2000 **GS** *020 †85
ROBINSON, Jubilee Brown. 7900 FANNIN ST 77054 #038-41-1993 L2000 **OBG** *020 †30
ROBINSON, Lawrence H. 6431 FANNIN ST # 2130 77030 #048-12-1971 L1971 **PDR R** *040 †80
ROBINSON, Matthew M. ■ 77058 #048-13-1990 L1990 **U** *020 †95
ROBINSON, Shay E. ■ 77004 #048-14-2006 **AN** *012
ROBINSON, Theresa Lynn. 7580 FANNIN ST 77054 #048-15-1984 L1985 **OBG** *020 †30
ROBLEDO, Jaime D. 12335 KINGSRIDE LN # 108 77024 #649-52-1991 L1998 **AN** *020 †05
ROBSON, Joseph P. 1919 LA BRANCH ST 77002 #048-14-2002 L2006 **EM** *020 †16
ROCA, Alberto N. 920 FROSTWOOD DR, MEMORIAL CITY 77024 #737-01-1963 L1968 **PTH** *020 †50
ROCA, German. 3016 CANAL ST 77003 #264-02-1957 L1979 **IM GP** *071
ROCHA, Donna Kundert. 2800 S MACGREGOR WAY, HARRIS COUNTY PSYCHIATRIC 77021 #048-14-1996 L1998 **P** *020
ROCHA, Maryesther Moore. ■ 77005 #048-14-2002 L2005 **PD** *020 †55
ROCHA, Samuel S. 13111 EAST FWY, STE 203 77015 #048-02-1969 L1969 **FM N** *020 †18
ROCHELLE, Donald Glenn. 6624 FANNIN ST STE 2780 77030 #048-04-1955 L1955 **CD** *071 †20
ROCHEN, Jeffrey L. 1221 MCKINNEY ST, STE 40300 77010 #048-04-1987 L1988 **END** *020 †20
ROCHEN, Shari Dawn. 10575 KATY FWY, STE 435 77024 #030-06-1988 L1995 **IM** *020 †20
ROCK, Craig Steven. 6624 FANNIN ST, STE 1600 77030 #033-06-1986 L1993 **PS** *020 †65
RODDY, Louis H. 1315 ST JOSEPH PKWY, STE 1005 77002 #048-15-1976 L1976 **PUD** *020 †20
RODEN, Rudolph G. ■ 77004 #065-05-1955 L1977 *040
RODEY, Glenn Eugene. 6565 FANNIN ST, # B154 77030 #038-40-1961 L1999 **IG CLP** *050
RODGERS, L Rodney. 5508 BRIAR DR 77056 #048-02-1943 L1943 **IM** *071 †20
RODON AHNERT, Jordi. 5505 CHAUCER DR 77005 #847-12-2000 *100
RODRIGUEZ, A Arturo. 1515 HOLCOMBE BLVD, DEPT OF GEN INTERNAL MEDIC 77030 #649-31-1983 L2007 **IM** *020
RODRIGUEZ, Adib F. 77030 #429-01-1980 L1989 **PD** *100 †55
RODRIGUEZ, Alberto M L R. 6431 FANNIN 1.728 JFB 77030 #737-06-1991 L1999 **ID** *100 †20
RODRIGUEZ, Angel Augusto. ■ 77054 #042-03-2002 L2004 **HO** *012 †20
RODRIGUEZ, Diana Leticia. 6621 FANNIN ST, CC 1250 77030 #048-14-1987 L1988 **CHN** *020 †75,55
RODRIGUEZ, Edwin. 7026 OLD KATY RD, STE 276 77024 #042-01-1998 L2003 *020 †80
RODRIGUEZ, Hector B. 1221 MCKINNEY ST, STE 40300 77010 #025-12-1994 L1998 **IM** *020
RODRIGUEZ, Joel Abelardo. 77098 #048-04-2004 **GS** *012
RODRIGUEZ, Jose Esteban. 2500 FONDREN RD STE 210 77063 #042-03-1980 L1989 **OSS ORS** *020 †40
RODRIGUEZ, Libsen J. 6431 FANNIN ST # 1.728 77030 #935-07-1988 L1999 **ID** *100
RODRIGUEZ, Margot Bazan. ■ 77030 #005-06-1979 L1981 **DR** *020
RODRIGUEZ, Maria Alma. 1515 HOLCOMBE BLVD BOX 68 77030 #048-14-1979 L1979 **ON IM** *020 †20
RODRIGUEZ, Marisa. ■ 77054 #048-04-2008 *012
RODRIGUEZ, Michael Steven. 7026 OLD KATY RD, STE 276 77024 #011-04-1997 L2001 **VIR** *020 †80
RODRIGUEZ, Nidra Ivonne. 6655 TRAVIS ST STE 400HMC, GULF STATES HEMOPHILIA AND 77030 #042-01-1998 L2006 **PHO** *020 †55
RODRIGUEZ, Radames. 6431 FANNIN ST 1134, UNIV OF TEXAS - HOUSTON 77030 #042-01-2005 **IM** *012
RODRIGUEZ, Ramon Agustin. ■ 77077 #275-01-1954 L1969 **GYN** *071
RODRIGUEZ, Victor Frank. 8850 LONG POINT RD 77055 #038-40-1983 L1990 **FM EM** *020 †20
RODRIGUEZ, Victor M. 6565 DE MOSS DR, STE 232 77074 #042-01-1972 L1996 **OBG** *020 †30
RODRIGUEZ-BARRADAS, Maria. 2002 HOLCOMBE BLVD, VAMC-INFECTIOUS DIS SECT 77030 #935-01-1983 L1992 **ID IM** *020 †20
RODRIGUEZ-BIGAS, Miguel A. 1515 HOLCOMBE BLVD, BOX 444 77030 #042-01-1982 L2001 **GS SO** *020 †85
RODRIGUEZ-GOMEZ, Salvador. ■ 77243 #649-01-1952 L1971 **PS GS** *071
RODRIGUEZ GONZALEZ, V. 2201 W HOLCOMBE BLVD, STE 305 77030 #042-01-1989 L1993 **IM END** *020 †20
RODRIGUEZ-RIGAU, Luis J. 7400 FANNIN ST, TEXAS INST FOR 77054 #847-12-1974 L1977 **REN END** *020 †20
RODRIGUEZ-VEGA, Luisa M. ■ 77007 #042-01-1998 L2004 **PDE** *100 †55
ROEDER, Max Byerly. 810 PEAKWOOD DR, STE 107 77090 #038-40-1959 L1962 **DR RNR** *071 †80
ROEHL, Kendall Renee. ■ 77089 #048-02-2003 L2007 **PS** *012
ROEHM, John Otto F. 12951 SOUTH FWY, HOUSTON RADIOLOGY ASSOC 77047 #041-03-1957 L1965 **VIR** *020 †20
ROEHR, Jadwiga Joanna. 11302 FALLBROOK DR STE 303 77065 #759-12-1970 L1985 **OBG** *020 †30
ROESER, Andrew C. ■ 77098 #048-04-2002 **NS** *012
ROESSLER, Robert Louis. 2476 BOLSOVER ST, STE 445 77005 #035-01-1945 L1964 **P** *071 †75
ROFF, Nathalie Ho. ■ 77006 #048-14-1994 L1996 **IM** *020
ROGERS, Amber Presson. ■ 77021 #048-04-2007 **PD** *012

ROGERS, James Michael. 17350 STATE HGHWY 249 #358 77064 #048-14-1979 L1979 **P** *020 †75

ROGERS, Joanne Lavette. 4126 SOUTHWEST FWY, STE 600F 77027 #048-13-1989 L1991 **FM** *020 †18 ‡

ROGERS, John Chas. 6620 MAIN ST STE 1250 77030 #018-03-1975 L1988 **FM GPM** *040 †70,18

ROGERS, Mark Randall. 12000 RICHMOND AVE, STE 370 77082 #048-14-1985 L1986 **OSM ORS** *020 †40

ROGERS, Ryan William. 6550 FANNIN ST STE 1501 77030 #016-42-1998 L2005 **OPH** *075 ‡

ROGG, Elizabeth Watkins. 1200 BINZ ST, STE 300 77004 #010-02-1977 L1982 **ON IM** *071 †20

ROGGENKAMP, Kristin M. ■ 77007 #048-14-2006 **OBG** *012

ROHATGI, Pooja Rani. ■ 77054 #048-04-2008 *012

ROHDE, Gert. 5771 ENID ST, NOVA HEALTH CARE CENTERS 77009 #048-78-1999, ▲ L2001 **FM OM** *020 †18

ROHREN, Eric Michael. 1515 HOLCOMBE BLVD, UNIT 1264 77030 #026-08-1996 L1996 **NR** *020 †80,28

ROIG ROJAS, Ingrid Lidia. 1 BAYLOR PLZ 77030 #737-06-2004 **IM** *012

ROISMAN, Evelyn. 7900 FANNIN ST, STE 3500 77054 #035-06-1969 L1971 **IM** *020

ROJAS, Ana M. ■ 77054 #048-13-2002 L2005 **NPM** *012

ROKES GAGLIUFFI, Christoph. PO BOX 20708, UNIV TX MED SCH 77225 #737-06-2001 **PHO** *012 †55

ROLDAN JIMENEZ, Carlos J. 6431 FANNIN ST JJL445, UTHSC-HOUSTON 77030 #264-03-1992 L2002 **EM** *020 †16

ROLLINS, Lois Rae. 1110 NASA PKWY STE 307 77058 #039-01-1965 L1972 **GYN** *020

ROLNICK, Carmen L. 6411 FANNIN ST 77030 #042-01-1985 L1985 **PD** *020

ROLNICK, Richard Harold. 909 FROSTWOOD DR STE 261 77024 #429-01-1981 L1985 **PM IM** *020 ‡

ROLSTON, Kenneth V Isaac. 1515 HOLCOMBE BLVD, UNIT 402 77030 #495-08-1974 L1983 **ID IM** *020 †20

ROMA, Andres Anibal. ■ 77030 #132-01-1999 L2003 **SP** *012

ROMAGUERA, Jorge E. 1515 HOLCOMBE BLVD # 429 77030 #042-01-1982 L1988 **IM HO** *050 †20

ROMAIN, Zaneta Danette. ■ 77054 #048-04-2003 **U** *012

ROMAN, Ana Estela. 6560 FANNIN ST, STE 1406 77030 #924-01-1977 L1989 **PUD IM** *020 †20

ROMAN, Ernest T. 1214 ELGIN ST 77004 #649-30-1986 L1989 **IM** *020

ROMAN CAMARGO, Jorge. 6431 FANNIN ST, DEPT OBG 77030 #264-01-1992 **OBG** *020

ROMANO, Olivia Brooke. ■ 77098 #048-14-2008 *012

ROMAN-PAVAJEAU, Jaime Lui. 1 BAYLOR PLZ, BAYLOR COLL OF MED 77030 #264-12-1990 L2007 **TS** *012 †85

ROMERO, Carlos Enrique. 4126 SOUTHWEST FWY 77027 #319-03-1969 L1975 **AN** *020

ROMERO, Edgar J. 1315 ST JOSEPH PKWY, STE 1703 77002 #935-01-1993 L2001 **NPM** *020 †55 ‡

ROMERO, Julia I. 18220 STATE HWY 249, STE 260 77070 #042-01-1982 L1992 **OBG** *020 †30

ROMO-FRITZ, Julie A. 18220 TOMBALL PKWY, STE 370 77070 #048-14-1989 L1990 **FM** *020 †18 ‡

RONCO, Juan Jose. 6431 FANNIN ST # 1.274 77030 #132-01-1980 **CCM** *020 †20

RONEN, Pinky. 920 FROSTWOOD DR, STE 530 77024 #550-02-1989 L1997 **OBG** *020 †30

ROONGTA, Suresh M. 6624 FANNIN ST, STE 1440 77030 #495-01-1964 L1978 **N** *020 †75

ROOS, Linda J. 9119 S GESSNER DR, STE 201 77074 #048-02-1986 L1987 **PM PMM** *020

ROOSTH, Thomas Malcolm. 12880 SOUTH FWY 77047 #048-04-1969 L1969 **DR** *062 †80

ROOT, Lawrence Gordon. 1315 ST JOSEPH PKWY, STE 1500 77002 #048-12-1975 L1975 **P PYG** *020 †75

ROPER, Pamela R. 1315 CALHOUN ST STE 920 77002 #048-04-1981 L1981 **PS** *020

ROSALES, Marguerite F M. 1515 HOLCOMBE BLVD UNIT 4, UT MD ANDERSON CAN CER CEN 77030 #021-01-1988 L1991 **ON HO** *020 †20

ROSALES, Oscar Rafael. 6400 FANNIN ST STE 2220, MEDICAL CENTER HEART CONSU 77030 #264-04-1983 L1991 **CD IM** *020 †20

ROSA-RUIZ, Samuel. ■ 77062 #308-03-1978 L1979 **GS** *020

ROSAS, Alejandro E. 2411 FOUNTAIN VIEW DR #200, GREATER HOUSTON ANESTH 77057 #649-14-1979 L1983 **AN** *020 †05

ROSE, Franklin A. 6624 FANNIN ST STE 2200 77030 #007-02-1977 L1981 **PS HS** *020 †65

ROSE, Harris Samuel. 6431 FANNIN ST STE 6.132 77030 #024-01-2003 L2006 ORS *012

ROSE, James Ellington. 6560 FANNIN ST, STE 944 77030 #048-02-1968 L1968 **NS OS** *020 †25

ROSE, Johnnie Lee. 2101 CRAWFORD ST STE 205 77002 #048-04-1977 L1977 **N** *020

ROSE, Stacey Elaine. ■ 77006 #048-04-2007 *012

ROSE, Stephen Lawrence. PO BOX 73289 77273 #023-07-1982 L1983 **DR** *020 †80

ROSEMAN, Stephen Conrad. 6565 FANNIN ST 77030 #048-04-1993 L1994 **AN** *020 †05

ROSEN, Alan. 17080 RED OAK DR 77090 #836-01-1984 L1997 **ORS HS** *020 †40

ROSEN, Alan David. 6560 FANNIN ST STE 708 77030 #048-02-1965 L1965 **OBG** *020 †30

ROSEN, Daniel Gustavo. 1 BAYLOR PLZ, DEPT OF PATHOLOGY MC 315 77030 #132-01-1993 **PTH** *020

ROSEN, Joseph Bradley. 77002 #039-09-2007 **PDP** *012 †55

ROSEN, Theodore. 6620 MAIN ST STE 1425 77030 #025-01-1974 L1976 **D** *020 †15

ROSEN, Wayne Stephen. 6550 FANNIN ST, STE 2307 77030 #065-05-1991 **GS** *100 †85,10

ROSENBAUM, Ralph Steve. 1 BAYLOR PLZ, GENERAL INTERNAL MED 77030 #048-02-1976 L1976 **IM** *020 †20

ROSENBAUM, Sean Max. 6620 MAIN ST 77030 #048-02-2001 L2004 **FM** *020

ROSENBERG, Bernard Allan. 14340 TORREY CHS BLVD #160 77014 #048-04-1978 L1978 **P ADM** *020 †75

ROSENBERG, Harvey S. 6410 FANNIN ST 77030 #048-04-1949 L1950 **PTH** *030 †50

ROSENBERG, Wade Ronald. 6560 FANNIN ST, STE 1750 77030 #048-14-1981 L1981 **VS GS** *020 †85

ROSENBLATT, Kevin Paul. ■ 77057 #048-12-2000 L2004 **ATP OS** *050

ROSENBLEET, Jodi Ann. 6621 FANNIN ST, TEXAS CHILDREN'S HOSPITAL 77030 #041-13-2000 L2007 **PHO** *100 †55 ‡

ROSENFELD, Bernard Lloyd. 7400 FANNIN ST STE 910 77054 #024-07-1971 L1980 **OBG** *020 †30

ROSENFELD, Scott Bernard. 6621 FANNIN ST, CLINICAL CARE CENTER CC670 77030 #048-13-2001 L2007 **OP** *100

ROSENFIELD, David Barry. 6560 FANNIN ST, DEPT OF NEURO STE 802 77030 #016-11-1970 L1977 **N OS** *020 †20

ROSENKRANTZ, Milton P. 16630 IMPERIAL VALLY DR #1, U.S. HEALTHWORKS 77060 #048-04-1975 L1975 **ORS** *020 †40 ‡

ROSENTHAL, Benjamin Perry. 14730 BARRYKNOLL LN 77079 #048-02-1963 L1963 **PD PDA** *020 †55 ‡

ROSENTHAL, David Ira. 1515 HOLCOMBE BLVD, RADIATION ONCOLOGY 77030 #011-02-1984 L1992 **RO OTO** *020 †80

ROSENTHAL, Harry Max. 14730 BARRYKNOLL LN 77079 #048-02-1967 L1967 **PD** *020 †55

ROSENTHAL, Morris W. 14730 BARRYKNOLL LN 77079 #048-02-1951 L1951 **PD AM** *020 †55

ROSENTHAL, Paul Gilbert. 14730 BARRYKNOLL LN 77079 #048-02-1957 L1957 **PD AM** *020 †55

ROSENTHAL, Stuart Hanley. 8945 LONG POINT RD, STE 112 77055 #025-01-1966 L1973 **RHU IM** *020 †20

ROSS, John Burnett. 7600 FANNIN ST, ATTN: ADMINISTRATION 77054 #048-02-1973 L1973 **OBG** *020 †30

ROSS, Merrick Ira. 1515 HOLCOMBE BLVD # 106 77030 #016-11-1980 L1988 **GS** *020 †85

ROSS, Patti Jayne. 6431 FANNIN ST STE 3282, DEPT. OB/GYN 77030 #021-01-1972 L1976 **OBS** *040 †30

ROSS, Robert Marshal. 3333 RICHMOND AVE, FL 2 77098 #065-10-1972 L1977 **PUD OM** *020 †20

ROSS, Ronald Charles. 12345 KATY FWY 77079 #049-01-1973 L1974 **EM OM** *020 †70,16

ROSS, William A. 1515 HOLCOMBE BLVD # 436, GI MEDICAL & NUTRITION 77030 #005-15-1982 L1986 **GE IM** *020 †20

ROSSANO, Joseph William. 1615 HERMANN DR, UNIT 1433 77004 #003-01-2001 L2007 **PDC** *012 †55

ROSSELL ANZUETO, Maria A. 7900 FANNIN ST STE 3500 77054 #429-02-1991 L1997 **PD** *020 †55

ROSSEN, Roger Downey. 1200 MOURSUND ST 77030 #038-06-1961 L1968 **AI IM** *050 †03

ROSSI, G Martin. 915 GESSNER RD, STE 550 77024 #132-01-1978 L1986 **N IM** *020 †20

ROSSMAN, Lucho Loiseau. 6431 FANNIN ST, MSB 2.100 77030 #048-04-1998 L2006 **VIR** *100 †80

ROSSMANN, Susan Norton. 1400 LA CONCHA LN, GULF COAST REG BLOOD CTR 77054 #048-04-1989 L1990 **PTH BBK** *030 †50

ROTH, David B. ■ 77005 #048-04-1988 L1989 **PTH** *100 †50

ROTH, David Robt. 6621 FANNIN ST, STE CCC270 77030 #005-06-1978 L1980 **UP U** *020 †95

ROTH, Forrest S. ■ 77019 #028-34-2002 **PS** *012

ROTH, Jack Alan. 1515 HOLCOMBE BLVD, DEPT OF THORACIC SURG-109 77030 #023-07-1971 L1986 **TS ON** *050 †85,90

ROTH, Maximo. 1140 WESTMONT DR, STE 505 77015 #048-04-1959 L1959 **GS OS** *020

ROTHENBERG, Gayle Anne. 2000 BERING DR, STE 260 77057 #048-14-1978 L1979 **OS AN** *020

ROTHENBERG, Philip Burton. 6560 FANNIN ST 77030 #016-06-1964 L1970 **PS** *071 †65

ROTMAN, Harris. 11914 ASTORIA BLVD STE 340 77089 #047-06-1962 L1969 **D** *020 †15

ROUAH, Emilie. ■ 77096 #836-01-1977 L1980 **PTH NP** *040 †20

ROUND, Mary Ella. 6720 BERTNER ST 2-270, RADIOLOGY DEPT 77030 #048-04-1987 L1988 **DR** *020 †80

ROUNTREE, Carl Barth. 1740 W 27TH ST STE 213 77008 #021-01-1970 L1973 **D A** *020 †15

ROUNTREE, Susan Dykman. 6550 FANNIN ST STE 1801, DEPT. OF NEUROLOGY 77030 #004-01-1979 L1992 **N EM** *020 †16,75

ROUSSEAU, Raphael Fitzger. 1 BAYLOR PLZ, BAYLOR COLL OF MED 77030 #396-31-1998 **PHO** *100

ROUSSELL, William G. 2900 RICHMOND AVE, RIVER OAKS IMAGING 77098 #264-01-1965 L1975 **DR** *020

ROUTH, Lisa Carole. 7505 FANNIN ST, STE 120 77054 #048-16-1986 L1987 **P** *020 †75

ROWE, Guillermo. 7580 FANNIN ST STE 300 77054 #649-01-1969 L1975 **OBG END** *020 †30

ROW, Margaret B. 1515 HOLCOMBE BLVD, BOX 437 77030 #010-01-1994 L1995 **IM EM** *020 †20

ROWLAND, Lisa P. 18220 TOMBALL PKWY 77070 #048-02-1994 L1998 **PD** *020 †55

ROWLEY, Matthew Thomas. 1 BAYLOR PLZ, DEPT OF ANESTHIOLOGY 77030 #035-09-2005 **AN** *012

ROY, Angshumoy. 1 BAYLOR PLZ, DEPARTMENT OF PATHOLOGY 77030 #495-02-2000 **PTH** *012

ROY, Anjali. ■ 77054 #495-15-2000 L2007 **DR** *100 †80

ROY, Bhaskar Kumar. 902 FROSTWOOD DR STE 253 77024 #495-36-1974 L1980 **END IM** *020 †20

ROY, Rendentor Antonio. 6540 BELLOWS LN # 603 77030 #748-01-1992 L2002 **NEP** *020 †20

ROYAL, Richard Eldon. 1515 HOLCOMBE BLVD # 444, MD ANDERSON CANCER CTR 77030 #040-02-1988 L2001 **SO GS** *020 †85

ROZNER, Marc A. 1400 HOLCOMBE BLVD, MAIL CODE 0409 77030 #051-04-1990 L1998 **AN OS** *020 †05

RUBASHKIN, Boris. 9525 KATY FWY STE 312 77024 #913-69-1969 L1982 **P** *020

RUBEN, Saul. 6087 WOODWAY DR 77057 #048-13-1993 L1994 **DR** *020 †80

RUBENCHIK, Illana Aviva. 6411 FANNIN ST 77030 #836-01-1988 L1997 **PTH** *020 †50

RUBENFELD, Sheldon. 7515 MAIN ST, STE 690 77030 #010-02-1971 L1974 **END IM** *020 †20

RUBENSTEIN, Edward B. ■ 77030 #041-09-1981 L1982 **IM** *050 †20

RUBENSTEIN, Wm Stuart. 2050 NORTH LOOP W STE 220 77018 #016-42-1965 L1969 **OTO** *071 †45

RUBIN, Howard Stanton. 6400 FANNIN ST, STE 3000 77030 #048-02-1974 L1974 **IC CD** *020 †20

RUBIN, Paul T. 7737 SOUTHWEST FWY 77074 #035-08-1989 L1994 **AN IM** *020 †05

RUBIN, Richard Alan. 7515 MAIN ST, STE 670 77030 #048-04-1984 L1984 **RHU IM** *020 †20

RUBIN, Robert Jay. 6560 FANNIN ST, STE 1130 77030 #048-04-1977 L1978 **IM** *020 †20

RUBIN, Shari Paulette. ■ 77025 #048-02-2006 **IM** *012

RUBIO, Nancy Beth. 2002 HOLCOMBE BLVD, DEPT OF PSYCHIATRY (116-A) 77030 #048-14-1986 L1987 **P ADM** *020 †75

RUDNER, Lanny Joseph. 7054 #048-04-2006 **ORS** *012

RUGER, Erica Patrice. ■ 77071 #048-12-2006 **OBG** *012

RUGGIERO, Jaclyn Estelle. ■ 77054 #033-05-2007 **PD** *012

RUIBAL, Calixto J. 7109 LAWNDALE ST, STE B 77023 #275-01-1967 L1981 **GP** *020

RUIZ, Joseph Raymond. 4200 PORTSMOUTH ST 77027 #035-20-1986 L1989 **AN** *020 †05

RUIZ, Monica Isabella. ■ 77006 #048-12-2006 **PTH** *012

RUIZ, Pedro. 1300 MOURSUND ST, THE UNIV OF TX HEALTH SCIE 77030 #396-06-1964 L1981 **P** *040 †75

RUIZ, Richard Stranahan. 6411 FANNIN ST, 7 JONES 77030 #048-02-1957 L1957 **OPH** *020 †35

RUMBAUT, Edith Gonzalez. 2727 W HOLCOMBE BLVD, KELSEY SEYBOLD CLINIC 77025 #048-04-1994 L2001 **PM** *020 †60

RUNGTA, Manish. 1 BAYLOR PLZ 77030 #033-05-1998 L2002 **GE** *020 †20

RUOFF, Chad M. ■ 77046 #038-45-2007 **IM** *012

RUPPE, Mary Denise. 6431 FANNIN ST, MSB 4.202 77030 #035-46-1998 L2005 **END** *050 †20

RUSHFORD, Frederick E. 13300 HARGRAVE RD, STE 505 77070 #042-01-1980 L1982 **END IM** *020 †20

RUSHTON, Jennifer R. ■ 77054 #048-04-2004 **PTH** *012

RUSSELL, Donald Jos. ■ 77024 #017-20-1963 L1966 **N IM** *071 †75

RUSSELL, Jonathan R. 10130 LOUETTA RD, STE G 77070 #030-06-1996 L2000 **OBG** *020 †30

RUSSELL, Matasha Levette. 6431 FANNIN ST 324 77030 #048-02-2002 L2005 **FM** *020 †18

RUSSO, Charles Eugene. 1220 AUGUSTA DR, STE 100 77057 #048-02-1960 L1960 **OPH** *072 †35

RUSSO, Penni Melissa. 1631 NORTH LOOP W STE 220, ASSOCIATION 77008 #048-14-2000 L2005 **GS** *100 †85

RUST, Megan Mary. 6565 FANNIN ST, M227 77030 #030-06-1999 L2003 **PCP** *020 †50

RUSTIN, Terry Aubrey. 7505 FANNIN ST, STE 510 77054 #040-02-1974 L1980 **OS IM** *020 †20

RUTHERFORD, Huey Douglas. 12951 SOUTH FWY 77047 #048-02-1970 L1970 **R** *020 †80

RUTLEDGE, Michael L. 7600 BEECHNUT ST, 2ND FL 77074 #048-04-1983 L1984 **PTH** *075 †50

RUTTMAN, Cameron Rey. ■ 77079 #019-02-2000 L2007 **GS** *020 †85

RYAN, Denise Mary. 211 HIGHLAND CROSS DR, STE 275 77073 #035-46-2000 L2003 **EM** *020 †16

RYAN, James Vincent. 6448 FANNIN ST 77030 #539-02-1952 L1969 **IM** *071

RYAN, Kathleen Haller. 1111 AUGUSTA DR 77057 #048-04-1981 L1981 **IM** *020 †20

RYTTING, Michael Edward. 1515 HOLCOMBE BLVD, PEDIATRICS UNIT 87 77030 #025-01-1990 L1994 **PHO PD** *020 †20,55

RZASNICKI, Michael Clark. 18220 TOMBALL PKWY, STE 390 77070 #048-04-1995 L1997 **FM** *020 †18

SAADEDDIN, Amer Adnan. PO BOX 20708 77225 #528-01-1985 **P** *100

SABALESKY, Doreen A. 7515 MAIN ST STE 680 77030 #048-14-1987 L1988 **P** *020 †75

SABATES, Felix Nabor, Jr. ■ 77047 #028-46-1988 L1992 **OPH EM** *020 †35

SABBAGH, Amer. 1140 BUSINESS CENTER DR 77043 #875-02-1980 L1993 **GS VS** *020 †85

SABER, Elie Nagib. 1213 HERMANN DR, STE 700 77004 #605-02-1994 L1999 **NEP** *020 †20

SABER, Jackline. 1 BAYLOR PLZ 77030 #118-01-1987 L2007 **FP** *012

SABICHI, Anita Lyn. 1515 HOLCOMBE BLVD, UNIT 236 DEPT/CLNCL CANCER 77030 #007-02-1987 L1998 **ON** *020 †20

SABIR, Sharjeel Hussein. 6550 FANNIN ST, HOSP (HOUSTON) 77030 #048-04-2007 L2008 **TY** *012

SABLOFF, Bradley Scott. 1515 HOLCOMBE BLVD, BOX 56 77030 #067-01-1992 L2000 **DR** *020 †80

SABONGHY, Eric Peter. 915 GESSNER RD, STE 560 77024 #048-14-1998 L2000 **ORS** *020 †40

SABONGHY, Magdy Michel. ■ 77079 #915-04-1965 L1978 **AN** *020 †05

SABONGHY, Nagwa. ■ 77079 #330-04-1968 L1978 **FM** *020 †18

SACHDEV, Ritu M. 2002 HOLCOMBE BLVD 111D, BAYLOR COLLEGE OF MEDICINE 77030 #495-45-1999 L2001 **GE** *012 †20 ‡

SACHDEVA, Kanwardeep Sing. 6431 FANNIN ST 1134, UNIV OF TEXAS - HOUSTON 77030 #495-03-2001 **IM** *012

SACHS, Ian Lee. 6560 FANNIN ST, STE 600 77030 #016-06-1972 L1973 **GE IM** *020 †20

SACKS, Bethany C. 1701 HERMANN DR, UNIT 3201 77004 #035-47-1999 L2007 **GS** *020 †85

SACKS, Justin Michael. 1515 HOLCOMBE BLVD, MC 1402 77030 #035-47-1998 L2007 **HS** *100

SADA, David Michael. ■ 77025 #035-45-2005 L2008 **GS** *100

SADBERRY, Faye Elayne. 5901 LONG DR, BAYLOR COLLEGE OF MEDICINE 77087 #048-12-2000 L2005 **CHP** *020 †75

SADEGHI, Navid. 6431 FANNIN ST, DEPT IM 77030 #517-01-1999 L2007 **IM** *100 †20 ‡

SADEGHI, Payman. ■ 77024 #308-06-2000 L2005 **N** *100

SADEGHI, Sarmad. ■ 77005 #517-01-1998 **IM** *012

SADEGHPOUR, Eghteder O. 909 FROSTWOOD DR STE 256 77024 #517-06-1969 L1981 **ORS HS** *020 †40

SADHWANI, Sheela Harish. 1615 N MAIN ST, CASA DE AMIGOS CLINIC 77009 #495-19-1969 L1974 **FM FPG** *071 †18

SADIGHI, Zsila S. ■ 77054 #048-14-2005 **CHN** *012

SADOCK, Victoria A. 6621 FANNIN ST 1-1481, TEXAS CHILDREN'S HOSPITAL 77030 #035-19-1996 L2003 **PD** *020 †55

SADRE-MASHAYEKH, Mahin. 3801 KIRBY DR, STE 730 77098 #517-01-1960 L1988 **P** *020 †75

SAENZ, Henry. 6630 DE MOSS DR, PEOPLES CLINIC HEALTH CTR 77074 #682-01-1957 L1968 **IM** *071

SAETTONE, Eduardo C. 6716 HILLCROFT ST, STE 1 77081 #847-01-1967 L1974 **IM PUD** *071

SAFAHIEH, Sina Mohammad. ■ 77024 #048-02-2008 *012

SAFAR, Hossam. ■ 77230 #125-01-1981 L1999 **IM** *020 †20

SAFDAR, Amar. 1515 HOLCOMBE BLVD 77030 #704-02-1989 L2005 **IM ID** *020 †20

SAFDAR, Naueen S. 5555 SAN FELIPE ST, STE 800 77056 #704-06-1988 L1997 **IM** *020 †20

SAFDAR, Zeenat. 6620 MAIN ST STE 11B09, PULMONARY&CRITICAL CARE SE 77030 #704-16-1991 L2006 **PCC** *050 †20

SAFI, Hazim Jawad. 6431 FANNIN ST # 1-220 77030 #528-01-1970 L1981 **TS GS** *020 †85,90

SAFRO, Ivor Lawrence. 920 FROSTWOOD DR STE 530 77024 #836-01-1955 L1977 **OBG END** *071 †30

SAGBINI RADI, Jose C. 17203 RED OAK DR STE 201 77090 #264-02-1965 L1974 **GS** *020

SAGGI, Bobby Hemant. 6410 FANNIN ST, STE 470 77030 #020-12-1994 L2005 **TTS GS** *020 †85

SAHA, Suparna. 1 BAYLOR PLZ, BAYLOR COLL OF MED 77030 #005-06-2006 **AN** *012

SAHAI, Achal. 1709 DRYDEN RD STE 550, BCM FACULTY CENTER 77030 #021-01-2007 **IM** *012

SAHAI, Sunil Kumar. 1515 HOLCOMBE BLVD, UNIT 437 77030 #048-02-1997 L1999 **MPD EM** *020 †55,20

SAHI, Farzana Noor. 7777 SW FWY, STE 640 77074 #704-02-1985 L1996 **GPM** *020 †20

SAHIN, Aysegul A. 1515 HOLCOMBE BLVD 77030 #902-03-1980 L1988 **ATP PTH** *050 †50

SAINI, Scott. 1200 BINZ ST STE 175, HOUSTON FAMILY PRACTICE 77004 #065-05-1993 L1999 *020 †18

SAJADI, Cyrus. 2605 POTOMAC DR 77057 #517-05-1973 L1982 **P** *020 †75

SAJID, Mansoor Ahmed. ■ 77002 #704-20-1985 L2007 **PTH** *100 †50

SALAHUDEEN, Abdulla K. 1515 HOLCOMBE BLVD, GIM, AT & EC/RENAL DIVISIO 77030 #495-31-1976 L2006 **IM NEP** *020 †20

SALAS DE ARMAS, Ismael Al. 1 BAYLOR PLZ 77030 #935-07-2001 **GS** *012

SALAZAR, Gentil. 9055 KATY FWY, STE 306 77024 #264-01-1965 L1974 **CHP P** *020

SALAZAR, Joel Adam. 2002 HOLCOMBE BLVD, MICHAEL E DEBAKEY VA MEDIC 77030 #048-14-1999 L2003 **IMG** *020 †20

SALAZAR, Jorge Douglas. ■ 77006 #054-04-1994 L2006 **TS** *020 †85,90

SALBER, Patricia Rae. 4888 LOOP CENTRAL DR # 700, UNIVERSAL AMERICAN CORP 77081 #005-02-1978 L1979 **IM EM** *030 †20,16

SALCEDO, Christophe C. 1631 NORTH LOOP W, STE 635 77008 #048-15-1993 L1994 **GS** *020 †85

SALCEDO, Eva Samella Salv. ■ 77071 #748-31-2002 **FP** *012

SALEEM, Abdus. 6565 FANNIN ST, MS #205 77030 #704-01-1952 L1976 **HMP** *020 †50

SALEEM, Agha S. 1919 NORTH LOOP W, STE 299 77008 #048-13-1989 L1992 **PUD** *020 †20

SALEEM, Sadia. 1709 DRYDEN RD STE 550, BCM FACULTY CENTER 77030 #704-25-2004 **IM** *012

SALEEM, Shahzadi. 2002 HOLCOMBE BLVD 77030 #704-06-1954 L1976 **PM PTH** *071 †50,60

SALEH, George Youssef. 7600 BEECHNUT ST, 2ND FL 77074 #605-02-1984 L1989 **DMP** *020 †50

SALEHI, Ali Asghar. 427 W 20TH ST, STE 401 77008 #517-06-1975 L1985 **DR** *020 †80

SALEK, Ata. 8830 LONG POINT RD, STE 207 77055 #875-01-1977 L1986 **FM** *020 †18

SALEM, Bashar. 6431 FANNIN ST STE 1.150, AT HOUST 77030 #875-02-2001 L2006 **IM** *100 †20

SALEM, Khaled Ibrahim. 7600 BEECHNUT ST 77074 #915-04-1990 L2000 **AN PME** *020 †05

SALEM, Noha Adel. 902 FROSTWOOD DR, STE 227 77024 #915-03-1987 L1997 **PD** *020 †55

SALEM, Philip Adeeb. 6624 FANNIN ST STE 1630 77030 #605-01-1965 L1977 **ON GP** *030

SALINAS, Ezequiel David. ■ 77035 #048-14-2002 **CCP** *012

SALINAS, Jeanmarie K. 11914 ASTORIA BLVD, STE 575 77089 #048-14-1984 L1988 **OBG** *020 †30

SALINAS, Joseph Andrew. 7900 FANNIN ST STE 2100 77054 #048-04-1992 L1994 **OBG** *020 †30

SALINAS, Vannessa Emmanue. ■ 77054 #048-04-2008 *012

SALMERON, Eva T. 6431 FANNIN ST, UTMSB BUILD G510 77030 #048-04-1988 L1989 **PM** *020 †20,60

SALMERON, Geraldine. 1709 DRYDEN RD, 8TH FL 77030 #048-04-1975 L1975 **IMG RHU** *020 †20

SALMERON, Marie. 11811 FM 1960 RD W, STE 100 77065 #847-03-1986 L1996 **PD** *020 †55

SALMONSEN, Paul Clarke. 6411 FANNIN ST 77030 #048-04-1968 L1968 **OPH** *020 †35

SALTER, James Edward, Jr. 920 FROSTWOOD DR, PATHOLOGY DEPT. 77024 #027-01-1986 L1992 **PTH PCP** *020 †50

SALVATO, Patricia Denise. 4126 SOUTHWEST FWY, STE 1700 77027 #048-14-1981 L1981 **IM** *020 †20

SAM, Kathy U. ■ 77030 #048-04-2006 **IM** *012

SAMAD, Abdul. ■ 77099 #305-01-1985 *074

SAMAHA, Ameed Nassif. 7530 BROMPTON ST 77025 #605-01-1992 **OPH** *100

SAMAL, Aditya Kumar. 11811 FM 1960 RD W, STE 175 77065 #495-13-1983 L2002 **CD** *020 †20

SAMANI, Kaveh. ■ 77056 #517-05-1996 L2007 **IM** *100 †20

SAMANIEGO, Felipe. 1515 HOLCOMBE BLVD, UNIT 429 77030 #024-01-1983 L2000 **ON IM** *020 †20

SAMANO, A Francisco J. ■ 77252 #649-01-1973 L1988 **GE IM** *050

SAMANT, Meghana Suhas. 6463 HILLCROFT ST 77081 #496-15-1996 L2000 **PD** *020 †55

SAMAVEDI, Venkata Anuradh. 10594 FUQUA ST 77089 #495-57-1989 L2008 **IM** *020 †20

SAMI, Mirwat Shehzad. ■ 77030 #704-25-2002 **IM** *012

SAMI, Shehzad. ■ 77030 #704-25-2000 L2007 **IM** *020 †20

SAMIUDDIN, Zishan. 2015 THOMAS ST, THOMAS STREET CLINIC 77009 #495-65-1982 L1992 **P ADP** *020 †75

SAMO, Tobias Chas. 6560 FANNIN ST STE 1540 77030 #016-42-1978 L1979 **ID** *020 †20

SAMORA-MATA, Joann F. 7400 FANNIN ST STE 1050 77054 #048-02-1990 L1991 **OBG** *020 †30

SAMPAT, Keeran Ravin. ■ 77030 #051-01-2005 **MPD** *100

SAMSON, Susan L. 1 BAYLOR PLZ, ALKEK NS 20 77030 #065-05-2000 L2006 **END IM** *050 †20

SAMUELS, Barry Ivan. 1515 HOLCOMBE BLVD # 0368 77030 #025-01-1965 L1974 **DR OS** *020 †80

SAMUELS, David A. 6560 FANNIN ST STE 1654 77030 #024-01-1973 L1979 **CD IM** *020 †20

SAMUELS, Douglas Scott. 4550 POST OAK PLACE DR, STE 248 77027 #048-14-1979 L1979 **CHP P** *020

SAMUELS, Joshua A. 6431 FANNIN ST, DEPT NEPHROLOGY/MSB 4.148 77030 #048-04-1995 L1996 **PN** *020 †20,55

SAMUELS, Melvin Lawrence. ■ 77024 #041-02-1947 L1956 **ON IM** *071 †20

SAMUELS, Tracey Eileen. 7400 FANNIN ST STE 1050 77054 #048-14-1986 L1987 **OBG** *020 †30

SAMWAYS, Justyn S. 412 HADLEY ST 77002 #048-14-1996 L1999 **EM** *020 †16

SANCHEZ, Armando G. 900 WAYSIDE DR 77011 #649-14-1980 L1987 **IM OM** *020

SANCHEZ, Benny Juarez. 10694 JONES RD, STE 150 77065 #030-06-1984 L1988 **IM PME** *020

SANCHEZ, Carmen Irene. ■ 77002 #021-05-2004 L2007 **MPD** *012

SANCHEZ, Charles W. ■ 77054 #048-14-2008 *012

SANCHEZ, Demetrio Enrique. 4200 PORTSMOUTH ST 77027 #649-26-1981 **OS IG** *020

SANCHEZ, John Michael. ■ 77025 #048-14-1985 L1986 **FM** *020 †18

SANCHEZ, Judith Imelda. ■ 77030 #005-14-2000 L2007 **OBG** *020 †30

SANCHEZ, Laura Jennifer. ■ 77018 #048-16-2008 *012

SANCHEZ, Michael Anthony. ■ 77043 #021-05-2008 *012

SANCHEZ, Natalia Ninon. 6400 HILLCROFT ST 77081 #048-14-2000 L2003 **MPD** *020 †20,55 ‡

SANCHEZ, Rafael G. 11914 ASTORIA BLVD STE 270 77089 #726-01-1968 L1977 **GE IM** *020

SANCHEZ, Ramiro. 5724 CHIMNEY ROCK RD, OUTPATIENT CLINICAL CARE P 77081 #649-14-1978 L1994 **FM** *020 ‡

SANCHEZ-BURGOS, Teodoro Y. 7737 SOUTHWEST FWY STE 670 77074 #649-06-1970 L1982 **PD ID** *020 †55

SANDBERG, Eric Thowald. 2727 W HOLCOMBE BLVD, SUTIE 4B 77025 #036-05-1987 L1991 **AI** *020 †55,03

SANDER, Kathy Lee. 7900 FANNIN ST STE 2100 77054 #003-01-1997 L2001 **OBG** *020 †30

SANDERLIN, Damien Brough. 8240 ANTOINE DR, STE 107 77088 #047-07-2000 L2003 **FM** *020

SANDERS, Marc R. 3405 EDLOE ST, STE 300 77027 #048-04-1989 L1993 **OPH** *020 †35

SANDERS, Mark J. 6431 FANNIN ST, JJL 495 77030 #048-14-1991 L1992 **MPD** *020

SANDERS, Mark Steven. 4126 SOUTHWEST FWY, STE 1730 77027 #035-08-1981 L1986 **ORS GS** *020 †40

SANDERSON, Terry Allen. 1500 WEST LOOP N, STE 137 77008 #048-02-1963 L1963 **OM GS** *020 †85

SANDHU, Amrick Singh. 6431 FANNIN ST 1.134, OF TEXAS-HOUSTON 77030 #495-37-2006 **IM** *012

SANDLER, Carl Michael. 1515 HOLCOMBE BLVD BOX 127, UNIV OF TEXAS MD ANDERSON 77030 #024-07-1971 L1977 **DR AR** *020 †80

SANDLES, Everett Lorenzo. 5622 E SAM HOUSTON PKWY N 77015 #041-09-1995 L1998 **PD** *020 †55

SANDLIN, Marlin Elijah. 12951 SOUTH FWY 77047 #048-04-1979 L1980 **R** *020 †80

SANDOVAL, Elizabeth. ■ 77054 #048-14-2007 **EM** *012

SANDOVAL, Lucia Dorothy. 2727 W HOLCOMBE BLVD 77025 #007-02-1984 L1995 **FM** *020 †18

SANDOVAL, Stephen D. 6560 FANNIN ST, STE 400 77030 #048-12-2002 L2007 **ORS** *100

SANDOVAL MARTINEZ, Luis A. 1 BAYLOR PLZ, BAYLOR COLL OF MED 77030 #649-14-2002 **OBG** *012

SANDS, Mary Elizabeth. 810 PEAKWOOD DR STE D, HOUSTON NW RADIOTHERAPY 77090 #048-04-1991 L1993 **RO** *020 †80 ‡

SANDS, Thomas Trey. ■ 77002 #021-05-2004 **GS** *012

SANFORD, David Bruce. 6624 FANNIN ST, STE 1610 77030 #048-14-1988 L1989 **ON HEM** *020 †20

■ = Address Information Privacy Protected

SANGALE, Zaina Misigo. ■ 77003 #038-43-2003 **PTH** *100
SANGANI, Mahendra. ■ 77098 #495-01-1968 L1978 *020
SANGER, Philip A. 4299 SAN FELIPE ST STE 300 77027 #048-15-1975 L1975 **PUD** *020 †20
SANGHVI, Anup. 5645 HILLCROFT ST STE 203 77036 #495-28-1995 L1999 **IM FM** *020 †18
SANKARANARAYANAN, V. 12000 RICHMOND AVE STE 215 77082 #495-42-1977 L2003 **N CN** *020
SANON, Saurabh. 8333 BRAESMAIN DR APT 1 77025 #495-83-2005 **IM** *012
SANTALA, Samuel Martin. ■ 77062 #041-14-2002 L2007 **SP** *020
SANT'AMBROGIO, Sara. ■ 77019 #048-14-1996 L1998 **PCP** *020 †50
SANTIAGO, Hector Luis. 7600 FANNIN ST 77054 #038-06-1988 L1992 **AN** *020 †05
SANTIAGO, Lumarie. ■ 77025 #042-01-2001 L2007 **DR** *020 †80
SANTIBANEZ-WOOLRICH, A L. 723 SHOTWELL ST 77020 #649-01-1959 L1977 **GP GS** *020
SANTOS, Cynthia W. 1300 MOURSUND ST, UT HOUSTON MEDICAL SCHOOL 77030 #048-14-1986 L1987 **CHP P** *020 †75
SANTOS, George D. 5151 SAN FELIPE ST, STE 1470 77056 #048-14-1986 L1987 **P ADP** *020 †75
SANTOS, Lisa Diane. 1200 BINZ ST, STE 1030 77004 #048-15-1984 L1985 **PS** *020 †65
SANTOS, Luviza J. 4545 POST OAK PLACE DR, STE 130 77027 #748-16-1987 L1996 **IM** *020 †20
SANTOS, Ray Eric. 18100 SAINT JOHN DR, STE 300 77058 #048-15-1986 L1987 **ORS** *020 †40 ‡
SANTOS, Xiomara Marie. 1709 DRYDEN RD STE 1100, BAYLOR COLLEGE OF MEDICINE 77030 #042-01-2005 **OBG** *012
SANTOS-MENDOZA, Norma. 8850 LONG POINT RD 77055 #748-01-1965 L1979 **PM** *020
SAPIRE, Kenneth Joel. 1515 HOLCOMBE BLVD, UNIT 409 77030 #836-02-1982 L1993 **AN PD** *020 †55,05
SAPRID, Jose Solomon R. ■ 77070 #748-13-1982 L1985 *020
SAQER, Rizk Abdulaziz. 11037 FM 1960 RD W, STE B1 77065 #613-01-1982 L1997 **AN** *020
SAQUIN, Asteria Rimando. 6510 HILLCROFT ST STE 200 77081 #748-10-1973 L1981 **PD GP** *020 †55
SARABIA, Michael Joseph. 6720 BERTNER ST MC4-217 77030 #048-14-1995 L1998 **EM** *020 †16
SARAF, Neelima Pradeep. 2121 HEPBURN ST, APT 509 77054 #495-41-1977 L1988 **OBG** *075
SARAF, Pradeep Govind. 2121 HEPBURN ST, APT 509 77054 #495-98-1972 L1979 **U GS** *020
SARANATHAN, Kasturirangan. 7737 SOUTHWEST FWY, STE 970 77074 #495-04-1970 L1980 **CD IM** *020 †20
SARAVANAKUMAR, Shahthi. 5622 E SAM HOUSTON PKWY N 77015 #495-42-1990 L1999 **PD** *020 †55
SARDINA, Alexander Jose. 3120 SOUTHWEST FWY, GREATER HOUSTON RADIOLOGY 77098 #048-04-1995 L1997 **DR** *020 †80
SARDINAS, Alfredo. 12121 RICHMOND AVE STE 425 77082 #649-14-1974 L1982 **ORS** *020 †40
SARGENT, Albert John. ■ 77008 #035-45-1973 L2003 **P CHP** *020 †55,75
SARGENT, Rachel Lynn. ■ 77098 #033-06-2001 L2001 **HMP** *100 †50
SARIDEY, Sai Kaumudi. 1 BAYLOR PLZ 77030 #495-11-2001 **NEP** *012 †20
SARINO, Maria Carmen Arce. 4545 POST OAK PLACE DR, STE 130 77027 #748-01-1991 L1997 **IM** *020 †20
SARKAR, Sonali. ■ 77054 #496-34-1999 **P** *100
SARKARI, Bahadur. 17625 EL CAMINO REAL STE 1 77058 #495-01-1967 L1987 **CHP P** *020 †75
SARKISS, Mona Girgiss. 1515 HOLCOMBE BLVD, UNIT 42 77030 #915-02-1989 L2001 **AN** *020 †05
SARMA, Satyam. ■ 77021 #041-02-2003 L2007 **CD** *012 †20
SARNA, Achal. 6720 BERTNER ST MC2-270, ST. LUKE'S EPISCOPAL HOSPI 77030 #016-06-1999 L2001 **DR** *100 †80
SARON, Irvin Jack. 11302 FALLBROOK DR, STE 206 77065 #836-01-1965 L1979 **U** *020 †95
SARRAFIAN, Myrna. 6410 FANNIN ST STE 1010 77030 #048-14-1988 L1989 **IM** *020 †20
SARRAJ, Amrou. PO BOX 20708, UNIV TX MED SCH 77225 #875-01-2005 L2006 **N** *012
SARRIS, Andreas Helias. 1515 HOLCOMBE BLVD BOX 68, DEPT OF HEMATOLOGY 77030 #008-01-1981 L1992 **ON HEM** *020 †20
SARTORI, Michele. 6624 FANNIN ST STE 2250 77030 #561-13-1978 L1989 **CD** *020 †20
SARWAR, Iftikhar. 1917 ASHLAND ST 77008 #704-02-1984 L1995 **IM** *020 †20
SASA, Ghadir Suleiman Iss. 6621 FANNIN ST CC15100, TEXAS CHILDREN'S HOSP 77030 #575-02-2002 **PHO** *012 †55
SASSO, Robert Donald. 1919 LA BRANCH ST 77002 #715-01-1964 L1974 **GS** *020 †85
SASSOON, Phyllis. 1515 HOLCOMBE BLVD 77030 #495-35-1964 L1978 **AN** *071 †05
SASTRY, Rathni N. 11914 ASTORIA BLVD STE 450 77089 #495-59-1970 L1976 **PD** *020 †55
SATHEESCHANDRAN, C V. 7011 SOUTHWEST FWY, MHMRA 77074 #495-44-1980 L1993 **P** *020
SATHYAMOORTHY, Kumaran. 1 BAYLOR PLZ, BAYLOR COLL MED 77030 #035-08-2006 **U** *012
SATIJA, Pankaj Shiv. 1 BAYLOR PLZ 77030 #495-17-1998 L2004 **N** *012
SATITPUNWAYCHA, Pon. 11301 FALLBROOK DR STE 101 77065 #891-01-1962 L1978 **GS** *020 †85
SATO, Erika Aki. ■ 77046 #028-03-2006 **GS** *012
SATTERWHITE, Terry Keith. 615 GLENCHESTER ST 77079 #036-05-1968 L1974 **ID IM** *071 †20
SATYAN, Krishna Bindigana. ■ 77008 #007-02-2004 **NS** *012
SAUCEDA, Francisco B. ■ 77073 #048-14-1989 L1990 **FM** *020 †18
SAUCEDO, James Matthew. ■ 77054 #048-04-2008 *012
SAULS, Clifford Dan. 7600 FANNIN ST, 2ND FL 77054 #048-04-1974 L1974 **NP P** *050 †50
SAUNDERS, Ann Elizabeth. 1300 MOURSUND ST, HEALTH SCIENCE CENTER 77030 #065-06-1973 L1988 **CHP** *040 †75
SAUNDERS, Robert L, Jr. 650 W BOUGH LN, STE 164 77024 #027-01-1972 L2001 **AI** *020 †20,03
SAVRICK, Mark Danl. 714 FM 1960 RD W, STE 206 77090 #048-12-1989 L1990 **AN** *020 †05
SAVRICK, Patti Lynne. 7400 FANNIN ST, STE 900 77054 #048-12-1989 L1990 **PD** *020 †55
SAW, Margaret. 4200 PORTSMOUTH ST 77027 #209-01-1961 L1974 **FM IMG** *020
SAWAF, Nabih Wahid. ■ 77057 #875-01-1978 **NM DR** *020
SAWAYA, Raymond. 1515 HOLCOMBE BLVD # 442, DEPT OF NEUROSURGERY 77030 #605-02-1974 L1991 **NS OS** *020 †25
SAWERIS, Jocelyne M. 6431 FANNIN ST, AT HO 77030 #048-14-2005 **PD** *012
SAWWAF, Ziyad Wahid. ■ 77057 #875-01-1964 **DR R** *020
SAX, Steven Lawrence. 6565 FANNIN ST 77030 #048-04-1981 L1982 **DR** *020 †80
SAYEED, Ahmed. 7095A HIGHWAY 6 N 77095 #704-02-1961 L1979 **PTH** *020 †50
SAYEED, Amina. 920 FROSTWOOD DR, STE 510 77024 #048-14-1995 L1996 **OBG** *020 †30
SAYEED, Fatima. 7095A HIGHWAY 6 N 77095 #704-02-1967 L1981 **GP** *020
SAZAMA, Kathleen J. 1515 HOLCOMBE BLVD # 800, MD ANDERSON CANCER CTR 77030 #010-02-1976 L2001 **CLP BBK** *020 †50
SCAFIDI, Ana Maria. ■ 77005 #048-02-2000 L2003 **IM** *020
SCAGLIA, Fernando. 1 BAYLOR PLZ, BCM225 77030 #132-03-1991 L1998 **MG** *020 †19,55
SCAGLIA, Julio Fernando. 7109 LAWNDALE ST, STE B 77023 #924-01-1983 L1998 **PD PDE** *020 †55
SCALLY, Michael Chas. 8707 KATY FWY, STE C 77024 #024-01-1980 L1981 **GPM END** *020
SCARANO, Victor Richard. 6560 FANNIN ST STE 832 77030 #041-02-1961 L1995 **PFP TS** *062 †85,90,75 ‡
SCARBOROUGH, Terry Kent. 6410 FANNIN ST, STE 1400 77030 #034-01-1993 L2002 **GS** *020 †85
SCARDINO, Gerard Anthony. 4414 NAVIGATION BLVD 77011 #021-05-1982 L1986 **P** *020 †75
SCEPANSKY ROFF, Mary K. 6624 FANNIN ST, STE 2180 77030 #048-14-1981 L1981 **OBG** *020
SCEUSI, Eric Louis. PO BOX 20708, UNIV OF TX MED SCH 77225 #033-05-2007 **GS** *012
SCHAAF, Christian Patrick. 1 BAYLOR PLZ, DEPT MG 77030 #409-10-2005 **MG** *012
SCHACHEL, Priti R. 1819 CRAWFORD ST 77002 #048-13-1999 L2002 **OBG** *020 †30
SCHAFFER, Don Minchen. 7900 FANNIN ST, STE 3300 77054 #048-04-1976 L1976 **PD** *020 †55
SCHAPIRA, Daniel. 7107 LAWNDALE ST 77023 #649-01-1969 L1987 **OPH** *020 †35
SCHAPIRO, Robert Neil. ■ 77021 #065-05-2001 **NS** *100
SCHAROLD, Mary Louise. 2301 WESTHEIMER RD 77098 #048-04-1968 L1968 **P PYA** *020 †75
SCHATTE, Edith D. 1111 AUGUSTA DR 77057 #048-14-1986 L1987 **OPH** *071 †35
SCHATTE, Marcus Ross. 4200 PORTSMOUTH ST 77027 #048-02-1979 L1979 **OPH** *071 †35
SCHEA, Randi Andrew. ■ 77056 #056-05-1988 L1993 **RO** *071 †80
SCHECTER, Marc Gregory. 6621 FANNIN ST, CC.1040.00 77030 #048-02-2000 L2002 **PDP** *100 †55
SCHEFFEY, Eric Heston. 9343 NORTH LOOP E STE 600, E HARRIS CO ORTHOC ASSN 77029 #048-13-1976 L1976 **ORS** *020
SCHEFFLER, Margaret Dorot. 6621 FANNIN ST RM A170, MC1-1000 77030 #041-15-2006 **PD** *012
SCHEINBAUM, Karen Robyn. 1705 JACKSON ST 77003 #035-46-1987 L1992 **DR** *020 †80
SCHEININ, Scott A. 1315 ST JOSEPH PKWY, STE 1306 77002 #048-04-1986 L1987 **TS** *020 †85,90
SCHELLINGERHOUT, David. 1515 HOLCOMBE BLVD, M D ANDERSON CANCER CTR U 77030 #836-03-1993 L2007 **DR** *020 †80
SCHENK, Leah Michelle. 7900 FANNIN ST # 4400 77054 #018-03-1990 L1998 **REN OBG** *020 †30
SCHERER, Elena. PO BOX 20708 77225 #781-05-1980 **AN** *100
SCHEUERLE, Angela E. 6410 FANNIN ST, STE 1400 77030 #011-04-1988 L1995 **PD** *020 †19,55
SCHIERMAN, Steven Wm. 17070 RED OAK DR STE 101 77090 #035-01-1987 L1995 **PS** *020
SCHIESS, Mya Caryn. 6431 FANNIN ST 7.044, UNIV OF TX-HOUSTON MED SCH 77030 #034-01-1980 L1985 **N PA** *020 †75
SCHIFFMAN, Jade Stacy. 2726 BISSONNET ST, # 240-229 77005 #035-15-1975 L1976 **OPH N** *020 †75,35 ‡
SCHILLACI, Harold Gene. ■ 77079 #048-04-1957 L1957 **U** *020 †95
SCHILLING, Helen Maria. 17320 RED OAK DR, STE 104 77090 #020-02-1986 L1988 **PM** *020 †60
SCHINDLER, William Jos. 7600 FANNIN ST 77054 #048-04-1974 L1974 **OS END** *071
SCHLAIN, Israel. 6630 DE MOSS DR 77074 #132-01-1953 L1964 **IM** *020
SCHLEGEL, Julie Ann Miley. ■ 77025 #048-12-2002 L2005 **PD** *020
SCHLEGEL, Todd Thos. 2101 NASA PKWY, MAIL CODE SK3 77058 #026-04-1989 L1993 **IM** *020 †20
SCHLESINGER, Alan E P. 6621 FANNIN ST 2-2521, TEXAS CHILDREN'S HOSPITAL 77030 #008-01-1980 L1995 **DR PD** *020 †80
SCHLESINGER, Paula M C. 2727 W HOLCOMBE BLVD 77025 #008-01-1982 L1986 **PD** *020 †55
SCHLETTE, Ellen J. 1515 HOLCOMBE BLVD 77030 #048-14-1994 L1996 **HMP** *020 †50
SCHMALSTIEG, Linda Ash. 5925 KIRBY DR STE E # 55 77005 #048-04-1976 L1976 **CHP P** *020 †75
SCHMALTZ, Kristen M. ■ 77077 #048-13-1995 L1998 **PD** *020
SCHMELER, Kathleen Marie. ■ 77008 #041-15-2000 L2005 **OBG** *100
SCHMIDT, Jimmy Douglas. 710 FM 1960 RD W 77090 #048-04-1967 L1967 **D DMP** *020 †15
SCHMIDT, Rosa Michelle. 1504 TAUB LOOP, DEPT MED 77030 #048-04-1995 L1996 **ADL** *020 †20
SCHMITT, Alexis Udall. 2002 HOLCOMBE BLVD, EMERGENCY DEPT. 77030 #003-01-1998 L2002 **IM** *020 †20
SCHMULEN, Arthur Carl. 6560 FANNIN ST, STE 600 77030 #021-05-1973 L1974 **GE IM** *020 †20
SCHNEE, Mark J M. 6624 FANNIN ST, STE 2310 77030 #919-05-1972 L1977 **CD** *020 †20
SCHNEIDER, Adam Michael. 6550 FANNIN ST STE 2525, BAYLOR COLL MED 77030 #143-05-2000 **HSP** *012
SCHNEIDER, Franz Emil. 2060 SPACE PARK DR 77058 #429-02-1985 L1992 **GE IM** *020 †20
SCHNEIDER, Gabrielle M. 1 BAYLOR PLZ 350, BAYLOR COLL OF MED 77030 #036-01-2004 L2008 **P** *012
SCHNEIDER, Karen M. 6410 FANNIN ST STE 350 77030 #048-13-1997 L1998 **OBG** *020 †30
SCHNEIDER, Laurie. 2800 S MACGREGOR WAY 77021 #048-15-1991 L1992 **P** *020 †75
SCHNEIDER, Michael David. 1 BAYLOR PLZ RM 506D, BAYLOR COLLEGE OF MEDICINE 77030 #041-01-1976 L1987 **IM** *020
SCHNEIDERMAN, Jacob. ■ 77096 #550-02-1972 L1982 **TS GS** *050
SCHNICK, John Crews. 2500 FONDREN RD, STE 270 77063 #048-02-1973 L1973 **FM** *020 †18
SCHNIDER, Geoffrey. 7580 FANNIN ST STE 310 77054 #836-01-1974 L1977 **OBG** *020 †30
SCHNIEDERJAN, Joseph Paul. ■ 77035 #048-13-2004 **DR** *012
SCHOCK, Larry W. 1313 HERMANN DR, PARK PLAZA HOSPITAL 77004 #048-02-1993 L1995 **DR** *020 †80
SCHOLL, Robert J. 800 PEAKWOOD DR STE 5E 77090 #048-04-1994 L1999 **PDR** *020 †80
SCHOOLAR, Joseph Clayton. 5300 SAN JACINTO ST, STE 180 77004 #016-02-1960 L1964 **P** *030 †75
SCHOPPA, Derek Michael. 6720 BERTNER ST 77030 #048-14-1995 L1997 **AN** *020 †05
SCHRADER, Shannon Ray. 4101 GREENBRIAR ST STE 200 77098 #020-02-1989 L1990 **FM** *020 †18
SCHREIBER, Douglas K. 11750 FM 1960 RD W, DOUGLAS K SCHREIBER MD 77065 #048-02-1989 L1990 **AI** *020 †20,03
SCHRODER, Steven Jeffrey. ■ 77030 #048-04-2008 *012
SCHROEDER, Ann Frances. 6431 FANNIN ST, SCHOOL A 77030 #048-14-2003 **PD** *100 †55
SCHROEDER, Barbara C. 7900 FANNIN ST, STE 4000 77054 #048-13-1991 L1992 **OBG** *020 †30
SCHROEDER, Megan. ■ 77027 #048-12-1998 **PD** *100 †55
SCHROEDER, R J. 902 FROSTWOOD DR STE 242 77024 #048-02-1960 L1960 **FM GP** *020
SCHROTH, George. 6431 FANNIN ST, RM 1256 77030 #062-01-1969 L1979 **IC** *020 †20
SCHULMAN, Brian J. 11914 ASTORIA BLVD 77089 #836-01-1968 L1978 **N** *020 †75
SCHULTZ, Brian Robert. 6621 FANNIN ST, TEXAS CHILDREN'S HOSPITAL 77030 #023-07-2002 L2006 **PEM** *012 †55

■ = Address Information Privacy Protected

SCHULTZ, Herman J. ■ 77030 #048-02-1952 L1952 **D** *071 †15

SCHULTZ, Roger Wayne. 1201 DAIRY ASHFORD ST 77079 #016-06-1984 L1985 **IM** *020 †20

SCHULTZ, Stanley Geo. 6431 FANNIN ST, JJL 410 77030 #035-19-1956 **OS** *050

SCHULZ, Paul Ernest. 1 BAYLOR PLZ, DEPT NEURO NB-302 77030 #024-05-1984 L1988 **NUP N** *050 †50

SCHULZE, Christopher B. 6720 BERTNER ST, ST LUKES EPISCOPAL HOSP 77030 #048-04-1983 L1983 **EM** *020

SCHUSTERMAN, Mark Asher. 6624 FANNIN ST, STE 1420 77030 #020-02-1980 L1988 **PS FPS** *020 †85,65

SCHUTZE, Gordon Edward. 6621 FANNIN ST, # CC1210 77030 #048-15-1984 L1986 **PD PDI** *030 †55

SCHWABE, Aloysia L. 6621 FANNIN ST, MAIL CODE WT 21-329 77030 #048-13-1995 L1999 **PM** *020 †60

SCHWAIGER, Ernest Polack. ■ 77056 #028-79-1937, ▲ L1941 *071

SCHWANECKE, Rebecca P. 8200 WEDNESBURY LN, STE 110 77074 #748-01-1958 L1971 **PD NPM** *020 †55

SCHWARTZ, David Louis. 1515 HOLCOMBE BLVD, UNIT 97 77030 #005-14-1994 L2006 **RO** *050 †80

SCHWARTZ, Diane Alyse. ■ 77063 #048-15-2006 **GS** *012

SCHWARTZ, Harold Robt. 6720 BERTNER ST 77030 #048-02-1945 L1945 **IM** *075

SCHWARTZ, Helene Louise K. 1401 ST JOSEPH PKWY 77002 #048-04-1975 L1976 **PTH** *020 †50

SCHWARTZ, Jan R Miller. 902 FROSTWOOD DR, STE 153 77024 #041-12-1968 L1972 **D** *020 †15

SCHWARTZ, Jim Taub. 1709 DRYDEN RD 77030 #048-04-1967 L1967 **GE** *020 †20

SCHWARTZ, Mary Rebecca. 6565 FANNIN ST, M.S. 205 77030 #028-02-1978 L1979 **PTH PCP** *020 †50

SCHWARZ, Peter Jos. 6560 FANNIN ST, STE 1008 77030 #016-11-1987 L1991 **GE IM** *020 †20

SCHWARZWALD, Heidi Lynn. 6701 FANNIN ST, STE 1210 77030 #038-41-1996 L1998 **PD** *020 †55

SCHWEPPE, Henry Irving. 6720 BERTNER ST 77030 #048-02-1954 L1954 **PUD IM** *071 †20

SCIARD, Didier. ■ 77077 #165-03-1982 L2004 *100

SCOBERCEA, Razvan George. ■ 77054 #016-11-2003 L2008 **ORS** *012

SCOTT, Allison Cooper. 6977 MAIN ST, SHRINERS HOSPITAL FOR CHIL 77030 #048-14-1984 L1985 **ORS FOP** *020 †40

SCOTT, Benjamin Henry. 7500 BEECHNUT ST STE 256 77074 #065-05-1943 L1977 **GP** *071

SCOTT, Bradford G. 1 BAYLOR PLZ, BAYLOR COLLEGE OF MEDICINE 77030 #048-12-1994 L2000 **GS** *020 †85

SCOTT, Daryl Armstrong. 1 BAYLOR PLZ, RM 633E 77030 #018-03-2000 L2005 **MG** *100 †55,19

SCOTT, Korrin Jean. ■ 77006 #048-14-2008 *012

SCOTT, Larry Dee. 6431 FANNIN ST, UNIV TEXAS MED SCHL 77030 #047-05-1969 L1976 **GE IM** *020 †20

SCOTT, Patricia A. 7401 KATY FWY, JULIANNA POOR MEMORIAL CC 77024 #048-14-1988 L1989 **CHP** *071 †75

SCOTT, Paul Martin. 7500 BEECHNUT ST STE 256 77074 #065-09-1971 L1977 **OPH** *020 †35 ‡

SCOTT, Philip Dell. 845 FM 1960 RD W STE 101 77090 #048-04-1975 L1975 **OPH** *020 †35

SCOTT, Stephen M. 7550 OFFICE CITY DR, HARRIS COUNTY HOSPITAL DIS 77012 #048-04-1999 L2003 **IM** *020 ‡

SCOTT, Vincent J. ■ 77025 #048-14-2008 *012

SCOTT-GURNELL, Kathy C. 3610 WILLOWBEND BLVD, STE 1000 77054 #048-02-1990 L1991 **CHP P** *020 †75

SCOUROS, Maria Anna. 1220 BLALOCK RD STE 300 77055 #917-28-1973 L1980 **ON HO** *020 †20

SCRUGGS, Adrianne Rochell. 15655 CYPRESSWOOD MEDCL DR, STE 100 77014 #047-07-2002 L2005 **IM** *020 †20

SCRUGGS, Corey Jaimar. 6565 FANNIN ST 10TH FL, CORONARY CARE UNIT 77030 #047-07-2002 L2004 **IM** *100 †20

SCURRIA, Maria Sandra. 1213 HERMANN DR, STE 650 77004 #027-01-1979 L1980 **FM** *020 †18 ‡

SDRINGOLA-MARANGA, S. 6431 FANNIN ST, MSB 1.242 77030 #561-15-1990 L2001 **CD** *020 †20

SEABERG, John Paul. 6431 FANNIN ST, STE 6.142 77030 #039-01-2004 L2007 **ORS** *012

SEABERG, Karen M. 6431 FANNIN ST, UNIV TX MED SCH AT HOUSTON 77030 #048-14-2000 L2005 **DR** *100 †80

SEALE, Michael M. 1301 FRANKLIN ST 77002 #048-02-1985 L1988 **FM** *020 †18

SEALOCK, Robert Jay. ■ 77025 #048-14-2007 **IM** *012

SEARS, David Alan. 1 BAYLOR PLZ, DEPT OF MEDICINE 77030 #040-02-1959 L1969 **HEM IM** *071 †20

SEARS, Ernest Simon, Jr. 6624 FANNIN ST, STE 1440 77030 #048-12-1969 L1974 **N** *020 †75

SEAY, Timothy. 211 HIGHLAND CROSS DR, STE 275 77073 #048-13-1989 L1994 **EM** *020 †16

SECRIST, Wendy Camron. 7600 FANNIN ST, RADIOLOGY DEPT. 77054 #048-04-1994 L1998 **DR** *020 †20

SEDENO-SUAREZ, Heriberto. 12121 RICHMOND AVE, STE 110 77082 #847-06-1975 L1977 **FM** *020 †18

SEDGWICK, Emily Lorraine. 12880 SOUTH FWY 77047 #005-02-1996 L2003 **DR** *020 †80

SEDOTAL, Royce Leon. 8945 LONG POINT RD, STE 115 77055 #039-01-1968 L1970 **GP** *020

SEEBORG, Filiz O. 6621 FANNIN ST FC, TEXAS CHILDRENS HOSPITAL 77030 #902-01-1990 L2006 **AI** *020 †55,03

SEEFELDT, Steven Garrett. 1221 MCKINNEY ST, STE 40300 77010 #020-12-1994 L1998 **IM** *020 †20

SEGEL, Joseph. 1500 S DAIRY ASHFRD #198 77077 #836-01-1954 L1979 **FM** *020 †18

SEGER, John Jos. 6624 FANNIN ST, STE 1910 77030 #048-14-1979 L1979 **CD** *020 †20

SEGHERS, Victor Jules. 6621 FANNIN ST 2-2521, TEXAS CHILDREN'S HOSPITAL 77030 #048-04-2001 L2007 **PDR** *100 †80

SEGUROLA, Santiago Ricard. 6431 FANNIN ST 1.134, OF TEXAS-HOUSTON 77030 #042-01-2007 **IM** *012

SEHGAL, Moushumi. 6621 FANNIN ST WT6-006, TEXAS CHILDREN'S HOSPITAL 77030 #496-38-1996 L2001 **CCP** *020 †55

SEHNE, Erika Maria. ■ 77030 #048-04-2008 *012

SEHORN, Timothy Jamison. 7515 MAIN ST STE 350 77030 #048-14-1996 L2001 **GS** *020

SEIDEL, Shelley Lynn. ■ 77005 #048-14-2003 **GS** *100

SEILHEIMER, Dan Keith. 6621 FANNIN ST, CC 1040.00 77030 #048-04-1972 L1972 **PDP PD** *030 †55

SEIPEL, Timothy John. 1 BAYLOR PLZ, BAYLOR COLLEGE OF MEDICINE 77030 #048-15-2003 L2004 **DR** *012

SEKERAK, Robin Joyce. 2002 HOLCOMBE BLVD 77030 #038-40-1992 L2000 **PM GP** *020 †60

SEKILI, Selim Mehmet. 12121 RICHMOND AVE STE 402 77082 #016-11-1987 L1991 **CD IM** *020 †20

SEKULA-GIBBS, Shelley. 2050 SPACE PARK DR 77058 #048-02-1979 L1982 **D FM** *020 †18,15

SELEM, Joseph. ■ 77054 #042-02-2005 L2005 **OPH** *012

SELINA, Paul Gregory. 7127 NORTH LOOP E, U.S. HEALTH WORKS 77028 #060-01-1994 L1996 **DR** *020 †18,80

SELINKO, Vera Lidia. 1515 HOLCOMBE BLVD 77030 #011-03-1981 L1982 **DR** *020 †80

SELL, Stewart. 6431 FANNIN ST # 2136 77030 #041-12-1960 L1984 **CLP PTH** *050 †50

SELLA, Avishay. ■ 77030 #550-02-1977 L1987 **ON** *100

SELLECK, Sarah E. 1709 DRYDEN RD, 8TH FL 77030 #048-14-1994 L1996 **IMG** *020 †20

SELLERS, Sherry L. 6701 FANNIN ST 77030 #048-15-1990 L1992 **PD** *020 †55

SELLIN, Rena. 1515 HOLCOMBE BLVD BOX 15 77030 #035-46-1974 L1980 **END IM** *020 †20

SELOUAN, Roger-Raymond Ra. 1 BAYLOR PLZ, DEPT RAD 77030 #605-02-2005 **DR** *012

SELZMAN, Andrew A. 915 GESSNER RD, STE 720 77024 #048-13-1989 L1990 **U** *020 †95

SELZMAN, Harold Martin. 1315 ST JOSEPH PKWY # 1005 77002 #048-04-1962 L1962 **IM NEP** *020 †20

SEN, Ami Divecha. 9337B KATY FWY # 242 77024 #048-04-1990 L1991 **IM** *020 †20

SEN, Filiz. ■ 77030 #902-19-1990 L2002 **PTH** *020 †50

SEN, Rohan. 1709 DRYDEN RD STE 550, BCM FACULTY CENTER 77030 #011-02-2006 **IM** *012

SENDOS, Anusuya N. 6550 MAPLERIDGE ST, STE 210 77081 #495-04-1969 L1981 **PD FM** *020

SENDOS, Lavanya Navakoti. 6431 FANNIN ST, STE JJL310 77030 #495-16-2004 *100

SENDOS, Sendasaperu Navak. ■ 77030 #024-05-2005 **DR** *012

SENTER, Cedric H, Jr. 2101 NASA PKWY, MAIL CODE SD2 77058 #034-01-1984 L2000 **FM** *020 †18

SEPLOWITZ, Rhoda Gail. ■ 77096 #035-09-2004 L2008 **P** *012

SEPTIMUS, Joshua David. 6560 FANNIN ST STE 1130, ASSOCIATES IN MEDICINE, PA 77030 #048-04-2000 L2002 **IM** *020 †20

SEPULVEDA, Felix. 5615 KIRBY DR, STE 850 77005 #737-01-1962 L1968 **AN PD** *020 †05

SEPULVEDA, Karla A. 2727 W HOLCOMBE BLVD 77025 #048-14-1999 L2002 **DR** *100 †80

SEPULVEDA, Raul. 17080 RED OAK DR 77090 #649-02-1962 L1972 **NS NRN** *020 †25

SEPULVEDA, Walfrido. 2525 MURWORTH DR STE A14 77054 #042-01-1988 L1994 **CHP** *020

SEREATAN, Washington F. 915 GESSNER RD, STE 360 77024 #036-05-1996 L1999 **NEP** *020

SERLIN, Scott Benjamin. PO BOX 20708, DEPT OF RADIOLOGY 77225 #036-07-2003 **DR** *012

SERMAS, Angelo. 6624 FANNIN ST, ALPERT & SERMAS 77030 #048-04-1978 L1979 **N** *020 †75

SERNA, Dorothy C. ■ 77041 #011-04-1994 L1997 **IM** *020 †20

SERNA, Samuel. 1 BAYLOR PLZ, DEPT OF RADIOLOGY BCM 360 77030 #048-04-2002 L2005 **RNR** *012 †80

SERPA ALVAREZ, Jose Augus. 2015 THOMAS ST, THOMAS STREET HEALTH CENTE 77009 #737-06-1999 L2008 **ID** *012 †20

SERRANO GUERRERO, Juan H. 1200 BINZ ST STE 1195 77004 #737-01-1971 L1975 **OBG** *020

SESHADRI, Lakshmi. 7737 SOUTHWEST FWY, STE 970 77074 #025-12-1997 L2001 **IM** *020 †18

SESSIONS, Josephine W. 1315 ST JOSEPH PKWY, STE 1700 77002 #048-14-1975 L1975 **N** *030 †75

SESSIONS, Leslie Howard. ■ 77092 #004-01-1974 L1974 **FM** *020 †18

SESSOMS, Sandra Lee. 6550 FANNIN ST, STE 2500 77030 #048-04-1978 L1978 **RHU IM** *020 †20

SETH, Nikesh Dilip. ■ 77004 #003-01-2006 **AN** *012

SETH, Vineet. ■ 77082 #048-15-2005 **DR** *012

SETHI, Manu. ■ 77030 #496-02-1994 L2000 **AN** *100 †05

SETHNA, Jerri P. 530 WELLS FARGO DR, STE 119 77090 #495-96-1977 L1988 **P AN** *020

SETO, Elaine Singwah. ■ 77054 #048-04-2007 **PD** *012

SETTONNI, Loretta Campbel. 2256 W HOLCOMBE BLVD 77030 #038-06-1994 L2007 **DR** *020 †80

SETTOON, Charles Eugene. 6565 FANNIN ST 77030 #021-05-1987 L1991 **AN PME** *020 †05 ‡

SETYADI, Hedy Gracia. ■ 77054 #048-04-2007 **IM** *012

SEU, Young Hwan. ■ 77040 #583-02-1957 L1975 **AN** *071

SEUNG, Kim. 2801 GESSNER DR 77080 #048-04-1998 L2002 **P** *020

SEUNGDAMRONG, Jason. ■ 77068 #048-12-2006 **EM** *012

SEUNGDAMRONG, Shatchai. ■ 77068 #891-02-1964 L1973 **PD GS** *020 †55

SEUTTER, Ryan Neal. 2431 DORRINGTON ST, UNIT A 77030 #026-04-2001 L2005 **CD** *012

SEWIELAM, Ahmed Ibrahim. 1221 MCKINNEY ST, STE 40300 77010 #915-02-1993 L2003 **PM PME** *020 †60 ‡

SEYEDAIN, Maryam. ■ 77057 #048-14-1991 L1994 **GE** *020 †20

SFONDOURIS, John Lewis. ■ 77054 #048-04-2008 *012

SHABOT, Myron Michael. 7737 SW FWY, STE 200 77074 #048-12-1970 L1970 **GS CCS** *030 †85

SHADLE, Kathleen Sue. 1631 NORTH LOOP W STE 150, RADIATION ONCOLOGY ASSOCIA 77008 #003-01-1988 L1992 **RO** *020 †20,80

SHADMAN, Omar. 17150 EL CAMINO REAL 77058 #001-06-1999 L2003 **AN** *020

SHAFER, Jessica Ann. 6621 FANNIN ST 300, TEXAS CHILDREN'S CANCER CE 77030 #035-08-2000 L2006 **PHO** *100 †55

SHAFF, Denise Lorraine. 8830 LONG POINT RD 77055 #836-01-1977 L1979 *074 ‡

SHAFI, Mehnaz A. 1709 DRYDEN RD STE 800, BAYLOR COLLEGE OF MEDICINE 77030 #704-25-1989 L2003 **GE** *020 †20

SHAFIE, Taghi. 4200 PORTSMOUTH ST 77027 #517-06-1973 L1979 **N** *020 †20

SHAH, Aashish Kiran. 5656 KELLEY ST RM 2LD80001, DEPARTMENT OF OB/GYN-LBJ H 77026 #048-13-1998 L1999 **OBG** *020

SHAH, Ami Navnit. 1515 HOLCOMBE BLVD, FC 12.000, BOX 0444 77030 #016-11-2003 L2006 **GS** *012

SHAH, Anjali R. ■ 77070 #025-01-2006 L2006 **TY** *012

SHAH, Anjan Mahendra. 6621 FANNIN ST, WEST TOWER, ROOM 19345 77030 #039-01-1999 L2004 **PDC** *012 †20,55

SHAH, Ashish Bhavesh. ■ 77054 #008-02-2002 L2003 **PDC** *012 †55

SHAH, Beejal Ashok. ■ 77054 #033-05-2003 L2008 **END** *012 †20

SHAH, Binal Satish. 1 BAYLOR PLZ, PEDIATRIC PULMONOLOGY 77030 #024-05-2003 **PDP** *012 †55

SHAH, Chaitanya Bhupendra. 11302 FALLBROOK DR, STE 302 77065 #495-23-1987 L2007 **CD IC** *020 †20

SHAH, Chirayu Jashvant. ■ 77054 #048-04-2005 **IM** *012

SHAH, Daulat. 17115 RED OAK DR 77090 #704-04-1968 L1983 **GS** *075

SHAH, Dhruvil Rashmikant. ■ 77054 #048-04-2008 *012

SHAH, Dipan Jogendra. 6550 FANNIN ST 77030 #056-06-1994 L2008 **CD** *020 †20

SHAH, Farah. 6560 FANNIN ST, STE 724 77030 #048-14-1989 L1990 **D OS** *020 †15

SHAH, Gopi Alpesh. 6550 FANNIN ST STE 2021 77030 #495-23-1992 L2000 **CD** *020 †20

SHAH, Jatin Jashwantlal. 1515 HOLCOMBE BLVD, UNIT 429 77030 #038-40-2001 L2007 **HO** *100

SHAH, Jay Bakul. ■ 77054 #035-01-2002 L2004 **U** *100
SHAH, Kirtikumar T. ■ 77096 #495-22-1962 L1973 **GE IM** *071 †20
SHAH, Kokila Navin. 9314 CULLEN BLVD, SUNNYSIDE HEALTH CTR 77051 #495-17-1969 L1980 **GP** *020
SHAH, Komal B. 1515 HOLCOMBE BLVD, UTMD ANDERSON CANCER CENTE 77030 #048-04-2000 L2007 **RNR** *100 †80
SHAH, Manish Ishwar. 6621 FANNIN ST MC, TEXAS CHILDREN'S HOSPITAL 77030 #005-15-2001 L2004 **PEM** *100 †55
SHAH, Mona Dhiraj. ■ 77054 #023-01-2001 L2007 **PHO** *100 †55
SHAH, Mona Mahendra. ■ 77059 #048-02-2006 L2007 **GS** *012
SHAH, Monisha. 6621 FANNIN ST, MC 1-1481 77030 #016-42-2001 L2005 **PEM** *012 †55
SHAH, Nihita Pravin. 1 BAYLOR PLZ, DEPT OF FAM MED 77030 #496-38-2001 **FP** *012
SHAH, Nina. ■ 77054 #035-19-2002 L2007 **HO** *012 †20
SHAH, Nishant Raj. 1709 DRYDEN RD STE 550, BCM FACULTY CENTER 77030 #016-06-2006 **IM** *012
SHAH, Nurun Nessa. 2800 S MACGREGOR WAY RM 77021 #160-01-1977 L1983 **P** *020 †75
SHAH, Pallay Jitendra. 6431 FANNIN ST, STE JJL 310 77030 #495-23-1989 *100
SHAH, Pankaj K. 8200 WEDNESBURY LN, STE 300 77074 #495-76-1976 L1991 **PUD CCM** *020 †20
SHAH, Parin Pradipkumar. 211 HIGHLAND CROSS DR #275 77073 #016-42-2001 L2005 **EM** *100
SHAH, Prachi Edlagan. 6621 FANNIN ST, CC 1530 77030 #048-04-1998 L2006 **PD** *020 †55
SHAH, Rameshchandra D. 11800 ASTORIA BLVD 77089 #496-38-1965 L1992 **AN** *020
SHAH, Ranjan Prafull. 77071 #495-17-1969 L1979 **IM END** *020
SHAH, Riddhi Manoj. 1709 DRYDEN RD STE 550, BCM FACULTY CENTER 77030 #495-17-2004 **IM** *012
SHAH, Satishchandra C. ■ 77031 #495-22-1965 L1976 **PTH** *100 †50
SHAH, Seema. 6560 FANNIN ST, STE 2204 77030 #042-01-1983 L1986 **ID IM** *020 †20 ‡
SHAH, Shalin Jyotindra. ■ 77030 #035-46-2002 **RO** *100
SHAH, Sonali Niranjan. 6431 FANNIN ST, MSB 3.244 77030 #039-01-2006 L2006 **MPD** *012
SHAH, Sweta Santosh. ■ 77054 #021-05-2005 **MPD** *012
SHAH, Tejal Bipin. ■ 77057 #041-13-2007 **IM** *012
SHAH, Umair Adnan. 2223 WEST LOOP S, HARRIS CNTY PUB HLTH & ENV 77027 #038-43-1996 L1998 **IM** *030 †20
SHAH, Usha R. 1917 ASHLAND ST, THE HEIGHTS HOSPITAL 77008 #495-96-1972 L1978 **PTH** *062 †50
SHAH, Vikas Satish. ■ 77030 #033-05-2000 L2005 **CCP** *100 †55
SHAH, Vishal Michael. 1024 LA RUE ST 77019 #048-12-2002 L2005 **OSM** *012
SHAH, Yogesh P. 2800 S MACGREGOR WAY 77021 #495-76-1977 L1983 **DR** *020 †80
SHAHAM, Iraj. 1917 ASHLAND ST 77008 #517-01-1965 L1975 **AN PME** *020
SHAHAR, Julio. 13111 EAST FWY, STE 304 77015 #132-01-1962 L1989 **PUD** *020 †20
SHAHAR, Karen Hedva. ■ 77054 #048-04-2004 **RO** *012
SHAHED, Joohi. 6550 FANNIN ST STE 1801 77030 #048-04-2000 L2004 **N** *020 †75
SHAHEEN, Hanan. 2800 S MACGREGOR WAY 77021 #875-01-1982 L1992 **CHP** *020 †75
SHAHEN, Ali Reza. 77019 #305-01-1999 L2007 **AN** *100
SHAHJAHAN, Munir. 6565 FANNIN ST M227 77030 #160-02-1990 **PTH** *012
SHAHZAD, Atif. 275 LANTERN BEND DR, STE 200 77090 #305-01-2001 L2007 **GE** *100
SHAHZAD, Mian Mohammed Kh. ■ 77054 #305-01-2003 L2007 **OBG** *012
SHAIB, Yasser Hani. 2002 HOLCOMBE BLVD, 3A-320 77030 #605-01-1995 L2005 **IM** *020 †20
SHAIBANI, Aziz. 6624 FANNIN ST STE 1670 77030 #528-02-1983 L1993 **N CN** *020 †75
SHAIKH, Kamran A. ■ 77054 #048-04-2004 L2006 **IM** *100 †20
SHAIKH, Muhammad Y. 11327 BISSONNET ST, BISSONNET MEDICAL CTR PA 77099 #704-16-1987 L1997 **IM** *020 †20
SHAKHASHIRO, Akram. 8945 LONG POINT RD, STE 203 77055 #875-01-1992 L2001 **IM** *020 †20
SHALAN, Nabeel Kamal. 5615 MORNINGSIDE DR # 405 77005 #575-01-1998 L2004 **IM** *100 †20
SHALEK, Elaine Chudleigh. ■ 77068 #048-04-1953 L1953 **PTH CLP** *071 †50
SHALIN, Sara Christine. ■ 77092 #048-04-2007 **PTH** *012
SHAMBURGER, Amber Dawn. 1819 CRAWFORD ST STE 1708 77002 #048-14-2004 L2008 **OBG** *012
SHAMIM, Samiya Fatima. ■ 77054 #704-02-2002 L2008 **PD** *100
SHAMSI, Manazir. 6311 FULTON ST 77022 #704-02-1960 L1975 **P ADM** *020 †75
SHAMSZAD, Pirouz. 6621 FANNIN ST RM A170, MC1-1000 77030 #010-01-2006 **PD** *012
SHAN, Kesavan. 7737 SOUTHWEST FWY, FREEWAY #780 77074 #917-20-1990 L1997 **CD** *020 †20
SHANDERA, Wayne Xavier. 1504 TAUB LOOP, 2-001 DEPT OF MED 77030 #023-07-1977 L1982 **IM ID** *040 †20
SHANI, Tara Hari. 1631 NORTH LOOP W STE 470 77008 #495-16-1973 L1978 **FM** *020 †18
SHANKAR, K. J.. 6770 BERTNER ST C1000 77030 #495-04-2000 L2006 **IM CD** *020
SHANMUGAM, Balasubramanian. ■ 77077 #495-37-2000 L2008 **ID** *012 †20
SHANNON, Rhonda L. 6720 BERTNER ST, DEPT OF PATHOLOGY 77030 #048-14-1984 L1986 **PTH** *020 †50
SHANNON, Vickie Rene. 1515 HOLCOMBE BLVD, BOX 403 77030 #028-02-1983 L1985 **PUD CCM** *020 †20
SHANOFF, Henry Melvin. 7707 FANNIN ST 77054 #065-01-1948 L1976 **IM CD** *071
SHANTI, Ihsan F. 5300 N BRAESWOOD BLVD, # 376 77096 #704-01-1988 L1998 **APM** *020 †05 ‡
SHAPIRO, Lorie M. 909 DAIRY ASHFORD ST, STE 205 77079 #048-14-1983 L1983 **END IM** *020 †20
SHAPIRO, Stuart Alan. 2600 S GESSNER RD, STE 107 77063 #048-04-1978 L1978 **FM OM** *020 †18 ‡
SHARAF, Ambreen. 6535 SOUTHWEST FWY 77074 #704-02-1999 L2006 **FM** *020 †18
SHARAFKHANEH, Amir. 2002 HOLCOMBE BLVD, BLDG 1001111 77030 #517-01-1990 L1999 **PCC SME** *050 †20
SHARER, Randall J. 211 HIGHLAND CROSS DR, STE 275 77073 #048-14-1998 L2003 **OS** *020 †20,16
SHARIF, Farhana Imran. ■ 77027 #704-25-1989 L1996 **PD** *020 †55
SHARMA, Bhavana. 6621 FANNIN ST RM A170, MC1-1000 77030 #051-04-2006 **PD** *012
SHARMA, Jagdish Chandra. 17506 RED OAK DR 77090 #495-05-1962 L1973 **N** *020
SHARMA, Kapil. 77005 #067-01-2000 L2007 **TS** *100
SHARMA, Kishore J. 77095 #495-29-1972 L1977 **PD** *020 †55
SHARMA, Morali Divatia. 1 BAYLOR PLZ, # 527E 77030 #495-23-1983 L1994 **IM END** *040 †20
SHARMA, Namrata. ■ 77004 #305-01-2003 L2002 **NEP** *012 †20
SHARMA, Saumya. 6431 FANNIN ST, UTHSC DIV OF CARDIOLOGY 77030 #305-01-2000 L2007 **ICE** *012

SHARMA, Sumeet K. 6699 CHIMNEY ROCK RD, CONSULTANTS PA 77081 #048-14-1996 L1999 **OPH** *020 †35
SHARMA, Timothy Lesley D. 7505 FANNIN ST 77054 #917-25-1965 L1968 **P ADP** *071 †75 ‡
SHARMAN, Ralph Stoddard. ■ 77005 #048-04-1970 L1970 **DR** *020 †80
SHARON, Elad. ■ 77096 #048-04-2003 L2006 **ON** *012
SHATTUCK, Brandy Lynne. ■ 77025 #035-03-2007 **PTH** *012
SHAULY, Yaacov. 6431 FANNIN ST 77030 #550-02-1985 **OPH** *020
SHAW, Andrew David. 1515 HOLCOMBE BLVD UNIT 11, DEPT OF CRITICAL CARE 77030 #917-20-1992 L2004 *020
SHAW, Carl R. 6621 FANNIN ST 1-1481, TEXAS CHILDREN'S HOSPITAL 77030 #048-04-1998 L2004 **PEM** *020 †55
SHAW, Charles Mullican. 2002 HOLCOMBE BLVD 77030 #048-04-1971 L1971 **P** *020
SHAW, Daphne Nizza. 14730 BARRYKNOLL LN 77079 #048-04-1997 L2000 **PD** *020 †55
SHAW, Leroy Bert. 8309 KNIGHT RD 77054 #048-04-1955 L1955 **FM GPM** *020 †18
SHAW, Marsha Rosaura. 6431 FANNIN ST 1134, OF TEXAS-HOUSTON 77030 #012-01-2006 **IM** *012
SHAW, Thomas L. 6621 FANNIN ST 3RD FL, CHILDREN'S HOSPITAL 77030 #048-04-2001 L2006 **PAN** *100 †55
SHAW-RICE, Judi. 2201 W HOLCOMBE BLVD, STE 320 77030 #045-01-1989 L1992 **IM** *020 †20
SHAYE, Alexandra Nicole. ■ 77030 #021-06-2002 L2002 **SP** *100 †50
SHCHELOCHKOV, Oleg Anatol. 1 BAYLOR PLZ 77030 #913-41-1997 L2003 **MG** *012 †55
SHEARER, Sarah A. 4407 YOAKUM BLVD, STE B 77006 #048-14-1985 L1986 **NEP IM** *020 †20
SHEARER, William Thos. 6621 FANNIN ST, MC FC330.01 77030 #028-02-1970 L1978 **AI PDA** *020 †55,03
SHEEHAN, Andrea M. ■ 77008 #048-04-2000 L2003 **HMP** *100 †50 ‡
SHEEHAN, William Luther. 11914 ASTORIA BLVD STE 6, UROLOGY ASSOCIATION 77089 #048-04-1960 L1960 **U** *071 †95
SHEENA, Helene Rae. 1111 AUGUSTA DR, KELSEY SEYBOLD CLINIC WEST 77057 #021-01-1991 L1995 **PD** *020 †55
SHEENA, Kamal Salim. 6720 BERTNER ST 77030 #017-20-1954 L1960 **GS CRS** *071 †85
SHEENA, Ronnie Abraham. 6560 FANNIN ST STE 1130 77030 #021-01-1990 L1993 **IM** *020 †20
SHEETS, Jessica Katherine. 6565 FANNIN ST MS D281, RADIOLOGY DEPARTMENT 77030 #048-02-1996 L1998 **DR** *020 †80
SHEFFIELD, James Kermit. ■ 77005 #045-01-1994 L2007 **N** *020 †75
SHEIKH, Mansoora Ahmed. 7322 SOUTHWEST FWY, STE 160 77074 #704-02-1976 L2005 **IM IMG** *020 †20
SHEIKH HAMAD, David. 1709 DRYDEN RD, STE 925 77030 #550-01-1981 L1995 **NEP IM** *020 †20
SHEINBAUM, Roy. 6431 FANNIN ST STE 5.018, DEPT OF ANESTHESIA 77030 #065-06-1984 L1993 **AN** *020 †05
SHEINBEIN, Courtney Adam. ■ 77004 #048-12-2003 L2007 **RO** *012
SHELBURNE, Julia Tyson. 6431 FANNIN ST 3.142, DEPARTMENT OF PEDIATRICS 77030 #048-04-1999 L2003 **PD** *020 †55
SHELBURNE, Samuel Ainslie, III. 1 BAYLOR PLZ, BCM 286 RM N1319 77030 #048-02-1998 L2001 **ID** *100 †20
SHELBY, Harold Thos. 1709 DRYDEN RD 77030 #010-03-1969 L2006 **GE IM** *020 †20
SHELDON, Gerald Murray. 5800 WOODWAY DR, APT 102 77057 #065-01-1962 L1977 **OPH** *020 †35
SHELFORD, Edwina M. ■ 77025 #041-07-1969 L1986 **AN** *020 †20,05
SHELTON, Michael W. 1221 MCKINNEY ST, STE 40300 77010 #048-14-1993 L1995 **FM** *072 †18
SHEN, Andy E. 6565 FANNIN ST 77030 #654-01-2005 **FP** *012
SHEN, Michelle Choutwin. ■ 77030 #048-13-2002 **GS** *012
SHEN, Steven Sijiu. 6565 FANNIN ST M239, DEPT OF PATHOLOGY 77030 #243-52-1984 L2002 **SP** *020 †50
SHEN, Yang. 1709 DRYDEN RD, STE 1050 77030 #048-04-2005 L2005 **D** *012
SHENAQ, Jihad M. 7737 SOUTHWEST FWY, STE 950 77074 #528-01-1987 L1994 **PS** *020 †85,65
SHENAQ, Salwa A. 2002 HOLCOMBE BLVD, VA MEDICAL CTR 77030 #915-02-1972 L1978 **AN CD** *030 †05
SHENG, Kai. 710 FM 1960 RD W STE 22 77090 #004-01-2000 L2003 **PD** *020 †55 ‡
SHENOI, Rohit P. 6621 FANNIN ST STE A210, MC 1-1481 77030 #496-38-1988 L1998 **PEM PD** *020 †55
SHENOUDA, Christian Nicho. ■ 77019 #539-04-2006 **PM** *012
SHENOY, Arundathi V. ■ 77021 #048-04-2004 L2007 **IM** *100 †20
SHENOY, Balkunje Vasudev. 7333 NORTH FWY, STE 100 77076 #495-37-1964 L1976 **CD IM** *020 †20
SHENOY, Vikram. ■ 77030 #048-04-2008 *012
SHEPARD, Paul E. 7825 HIGHWAY 6 N, STE 101 77095 #048-14-1997 L1999 **FM** *020 †18
SHEPPARD, Gary Jerome. 7777 SOUTHWEST FWY STE 636 77074 #048-02-1991 L1992 **IM** *020 †20
SHER, Michael. 3120 SOUTHWEST FWY, GREATER HOUSTON RADIOLOGY 77098 #048-14-1985 L1986 **R** *020 †80
SHERLOCK, Kevin Edward. ■ 77070 #918-01-1968 L1981 **FM EM** *020
SHERMAN, Neil Edward. 909 FROSTWOOD DR, STE 152 77024 #028-02-1976 L1988 **RO ON** *020 †80
SHERMAN, Steven Ira. 1515 HOLCOMBE BLVD, ANDERSON CNCR CTR BOX 15 77030 #023-07-1985 L1994 **END** *020 †20
SHERWANI, Kamran. 11840 FM 1960 RD W 77065 #704-20-1987 L1997 **CD IM** *020 †20
SHERWOOD, Barbara Anne. 9797 MEADOWGLEN LN 77042 #306-01-1987 *100
SHETH, Anil Uttamchand. 915 GESSNER STE 360 77024 #496-38-1974 L1979 **NEP IM** *020 †20
SHETH, Kala Rajendra. ■ 77030 #495-22-1964 *100
SHETH, Rajendra Dahyabhai. ■ 77030 #495-22-1960 L1990 **GP UCM** *020
SHETH, Rita. 6701 FANNIN ST 77030 #496-38-1987 L1998 **PN** *020 †55
SHETH, Rucha A. 10655 STEEPLETOP DR, CY-FAIR MED CENTRE HOSP 77065 #496-38-1972 L1981 **PTH** *062 †50
SHETLAR, Debra Jane. 2002 HOLCOMBE BLVD EYE112C, MICHAEL E DEBAKEY VA MED 77030 #048-14-1984 L1985 **OPH ATP** *020 †35,50
SHETTY, Mahesh Kalappa. 7600 FANNIN ST 77054 #495-37-1983 L1995 **DR** *020 †80 ‡
SHETTY, Rajesh A. 1709 DRYDEN RD STE 5.57, BAYLOR COLLEGE OF MEDICINE 77030 #496-36-1995 L2008 **PCC** *012 †20
SHETTY, Shakunthala. 6621 FANNIN ST 77030 #495-09-1991 L2000 **AN** *020 †05
SHEVCHEK, Rachel Beth. ■ 77025 #048-04-2008 *012
SHI, Hong. 1313 HERKIMER ST 77008 #243-33-1982 L2003 **PM** *020 †60
SHI, Susan S. 6560 FANNIN ST, STE 1980 77030 #016-06-2003 L2007 **OBG** *100
SHIELDS, Julia Diane. ■ 77054 #048-14-2008 *012

SHIH, Cheryl Swon. ■ 77030 #048-04-2008 *012
SHIH, Eugene. 9220 KIRBY DR, STE 700 77054 #035-08-1993 L2001 **RNR** *020 †80
SHIH, Hue-Teh. 12335 KINGSRIDE LN, PMB 103 77024 #244-04-1980 L1988 **CD IM** *020 †20,55
SHIM, Wan Joo. 1 BAYLOR PLZ 77030 #583-03-1978 **CD** *020
SHIMADA, Kazuhito. 100 CYBERONICS BLVD, STE 201 JAXA HOUSTON 77058 #572-23-1983 L1995 **AM OTO** *030 †70
SHIN, David Dongryun. 6550 FANNIN ST, STE 2435 77030 #014-01-1993 L1998 **VS GS** *020 †85
SHIN, Ki Y. 1515 HOLCOMBE BLVD, UNIT 08 77030 #048-04-1994 L1998 **PM** *020 †60
SHINAWI, Marwan Suleman. 1 BAYLOR PLZ, BAYLOR COLLEGE OF MEDICINE 77030 #550-03-1996 L2005 **MG** *100 †19
SHINN, Mary N. 1200 BINZ ST, STE 1190 77004 #048-14-1984 L1985 **PS** *020 †65
SHIPMAN, Hope Daneda. 9055 KATY FWY, STE 100 77024 #048-14-1982 L1983 **END IM** *020 †20
SHIPPY, Angela A. 6720 BERTNER ST, STE P536 77030 #048-02-1996 L1998 **IM** *020 †20
SHIRLEY-DAVIS, Diane M. 18220 TOMBALL PKWY STE 185 77070 #016-45-1995 L2001 **OTO** *020 †45
SHIRVANI, Shervin Mohajer. ■ 77024 #036-07-2006 L2007 **IM** *012
SHIRZADI, Shahin. 7500 BEECHNUT ST, STE 135 77074 #048-15-1995 L1997 **CN** *020 †75
SHIUE, Harncherng. ■ 77025 #048-12-2003 **CD** *012 †20
SHIVANNA, Binoy. 1 BAYLOR PLZ, BAYLOR COLL OF MED 77030 #495-09-1994 **NPM** *012 †55
SHIVDASANI, Vandana Subas. 6621 FANNIN ST STE 1020, DEPT OF PEDIATRICS-ENDOCRI 77030 #496-36-2001 L2007 **PDE** *012
SHIVER, Tiana M. 6655 TRAVIS ST STE 960 77030 #048-13-1986 L1987 **END IM** *020 †20
SHIVSHANKER, K. 7737 SOUTHWEST FWY STE 840 77074 #495-73-1975 L1979 **GE IM** *020 †20
SHKEDY, Clive I. 909 FROSTWOOD DR STE 152 77024 #836-01-1987 L1994 **RO** *020 †80
SHOAIB, Arif Mohammad. 2411 FOUNTAIN VIEW DR, STE 217 77057 #704-16-1990 L2002 **CHP** *020 †75
SHOEMAKER, James Gerard. 7324 SW FREEWAY NO 375 77074 #048-13-1976 L1976 **FM** *020
SHOENFELD, Norman Alan. 10625 TELGE RD 77095 #032-01-1980 L2004 **VS GS** *020 †85
SHOHET, Jason Matthew. 6701 FANNIN ST 77030 #024-05-1993 L2000 **PHO** *020 †55
SHOOK, Joan Elizabeth. 6621 FANNIN ST # 13420, TEXAS CHILDRENS HOSP 77030 #038-41-1981 L1984 **PD** *030 †55
SHOOK, Ryan Seth. 1709 DRYDEN RD STE 550, BCM FACULTY CTR 77030 #048-12-2006 **IM** *012
SHOSS, Adrienne Beth. ■ 77096 #048-02-2003 L2004 **D** *012
SHOSS, Joseph. 7600 FANNIN ST 77054 #048-04-1949 L1950 **PD PDA** *071 †55
SHOSS, Samuel. 4200 PORTSMOUTH ST 77027 #021-01-1962 L1965 **OPH** *071 †35
SHOYEB, Abu Hasnat. 6431 FANNIN ST, UTHSC DIV OF CARDIOLOGY 77030 #160-02-1988 **CD** *012 †20
SHPALL, Elizabeth Joan. 1515 HOLCOMBE BLVD # 423, BLOOD/MARROW TRANSPLANTATI 77030 #038-41-1980 L2002 **ON** *020 †20
SHPANER, Alexander. ■ 77054 #005-18-2002 L2004 **GE** *012 †20
SHPATS, Helen. 2314 DORRINGTON ST, UNIT D 77030 #048-14-1999 L2000 **GP** *020
SHREWSBERRY, Cecil Rosco. ■ 77030 #048-14-2008 *012
SHROFF, Kapil Rajendra. ■ 77054 #028-34-2006 L2008 **DR** *012
SHU, Sally Fieming. 11301 FALLBROOK DR, STE 310 77065 #036-01-1977 L1982 **OTO** *020 †45
SHU, Tung. 6431 FANNIN ST 77030 #048-02-1996 L2002 **U** *020 †95
SHUBERT, Edward Elmer. 17115 RED OAK DR STE 121 77090 #060-01-1966 L1977 **OPH** *020
SHUJAUDDIN, Faheem Fatima. 12121 RICHMOND AVE STE 214 77082 #495-65-1983 L1990 **IM EM** *020 †20
SHUKLA, Neeta Urmil. 2411 FOUNTAIN VIEW DR #200 77057 #495-01-1988 L2002 **AN** *020
SHUKLA, Vershalee. ■ 77030 #068-01-2003 **RO** *012
SHULLENBERGER, C C. ■ 77096 #017-20-1939 L1949 **HEM IM** *071 †20
SHULMAN, Robert Jay. 1100 BATES AVE, STE 8072 77030 #016-42-1976 L1979 **PD GE** *050 †55 ‡
SHULTS, Justin Craig. 6431 FANNIN ST, MSB 5.020 77030 #048-14-2002 L2006 **AN** *100 †05
SHULZ, Sue Lynn. 6565 FANNIN ST 77030 #048-04-1988 L1990 **AN** *020 †05
SHUMAN, Michelle Lynn. 9055 KATY FWY, STE 420 77024 #019-02-1997 L1998 **PD** *020 †55
SHURAIH, Mossaab. 6431 FANNIN ST STE 1.150, AT HOUST 77030 #875-02-2001 L2005 **IM** *100 †20
SHUREIQI, Imad. 1515 HOLCOMBE BLVD, MC 236 CLN CANCER PREV 77030 #875-01-1985 L1999 **ON IM** *020 †20
SHUTKO, Candice E. 2411 FOUNTAIN VIEW DR, STE 200 77057 #048-13-2002 L2006 **AN** *100
SICKLER, Robert Wilan. 6560 FANNIN ST, STE 1900 77030 #048-06-1987 L1991 **AN** *071 †05
SIDDIKI, Saba Khan. 6431 FANNIN ST 3.242 77030 #704-25-1999 L2007 **PD** *100 †55
SIDDIQ, Danish Mumtaz. 1709 DRYDEN RD STE 550, BCM FACULTY CENTER 77030 #704-25-2005 **IM** *012
SIDDIQI, Asma H. 1250 CYPRESS STATION DR 77090 #704-02-1989 L1995 **PD** *020 †55
SIDDIQI, Khuram Hissam. ■ 77005 #704-26-2002 L2007 **IM** *020
SIDDIQI, Mohammad I. 17320 RED OAK DR, STE 210 77090 #048-46-1994 L1997 **EM** *020 †16
SIDDIQI, Naila Farooq M. 17320 RED OAK DR STE 21 77090 #704-04-1994 L2000 **PD** *020 †55
SIDDIQI, Nikhat Zohra. 13323 DOTSON RD, STE 100 77070 #065-01-1986 L1994 **IM** *020 †20
SIDDIQI, Shah Naweed. 13323 DOTSON RD, STE 100 77070 #917-03-1987 L1993 **NS** *020 †25
SIDDIQUA, Tahrin. ■ 77084 #048-15-2006 **PD** *012
SIDDIQUI, Gazala. 6431 FANNIN ST, MSB 3.104 77030 #495-92-1992 L2005 **OBG** *020
SIDDIQUI, Hina Farooq. 6431 FANNIN ST, UTHSC DIV OF CARDIOLOGY 77030 #704-02-1995 L2007 **ICE** *020 †20
SIDDIQUI, Iqbal Mustafa. 77054 #048-04-1998 L2002 **FM** *100 †18
SIDDIQUI, Mohammad Haroon. 12121 RICHMOND AVE, STE 307 77082 #915-03-1982 L1993 **PD** *020
SIDDIQUI, Nighat Islam. ■ 77007 #704-18-1984 L1999 **PD** *100 †55
SIDDIQUI, Salman Hamid. 1200 POST OAK BLVD, APT 1614 77056 #704-25-2000 **IM** *012
SIDDIQUI, Saqib Armughan. 4126 SOUTHWEST FWY, STE 1620 77027 #143-07-1989 L2005 **ORS** *100
SIDDIQUI, Shakeel A. 6621 FANNIN ST STE A300, MAIL CODE 2-1495 77030 #496-22-1991 L2001 **PAN** *020 †05
SIDDIQUI, Shakil Ahmad. 3737 DACOMA ST, MHMRA OF HARRIS CTY 77092 #704-08-1990 L2000 **P CHP** *020
SIDHU, Gurnaib. 6566 KELLEY ST, LBJ HOSP ER 77026 #495-65-1976 L1995 **IM** *020
SIDHU, Jasvinder Singh. 6550 FANNIN ST, STE 1901 77030 #025-01-1996 L2003 **ICE CD** *020 †20
SIDHU, Trepanjeet Kaur. 6431 FANNIN ST 308, UNIV OF TEXAS MED SCH 77030 #496-38-2002 **FP** *012
SIDIQ, Homayon. 6620 MAIN ST STE 1505, DISEASE 77030 #704-25-1992 L1997 **GE** *012 †20

SIE, Evelyn Tjhioe. 8850 LONG POINT RD 77055 #506-02-1968 L1979 **PTH** *020 †50
SIEBERT, William Terry. 1315 ST JOSEPH PKWY, STE 1710 77002 #048-04-1972 L1972 **ID HEM** *020 †20
SIEDENTOP, Carrie E. ■ 77040 #407-11-1945 L1958 **GP AN** *071
SIEFKER-RADTKE, Arlene O. 1515 HOLCOMBE BLVD, BOX 1374 77030 #023-07-1996 L2001 **ON** *020 †20
SIEGEL, Candace. 830 GEMINI ST 77058 #048-14-1976 L1976 **PD** *020 †55
SIEGEL, Jacob. ■ 77024 #016-42-1944 L1951 **AI IM** *071 †03
SIEGEL, Michael Marvin. 7700 SAN FELIPE ST, STE 420 77063 #024-07-1972 L1973 **PD HEM** *030 †55
SIEGEL, Michel. 7700 SAN FELIPE ST, STE 420 77063 #010-01-1996 L2002 **OTO** *020
SIEGELMAN, Michael Harris. 1504 TAUB LOOP 77030 #035-19-1961 L1966 **IM** *020 †20
SIEGLER, Samuel Lewis, II. 1200 BINZ ST STE 1300, PLAZA MEDICAL CENTER 77004 #028-34-1987 L1988 **FM OM** *020 †18
SIELING, Michael S. 17150 EL CAMINO REAL 77058 #048-02-1992 L1993 **AN** *020 †05
SIELSKI, Lori Ann. 6701 FANNIN ST 77030 #033-06-1987 L1997 **PD** *020 †55
SIEMS, Courtney Elizabeth. ■ 77004 #021-01-2005 L2008 **FP** *012
SIENKO, Anna Elizabeth. 6565 FANNIN ST, THE METHODIST HOSPITAL 77030 #759-01-1983 L1994 **ATP** *020 †50
SIGIREDDI, Gurunath R. 6565 FANNIN ST 77030 #495-65-1983 L1993 **AN** *020 †05
SIHRA, Lyra A. 8945 LONG POINT RD STE 212 77055 #048-14-1994 L1995 **IM** *020 †20
SIKKA, Natalie Ann. 1 BAYLOR PLZ, BAYLOR COLL OF MED 77030 #035-06-1999 L2005 **PG** *020 †55
SIKORA, Andrew Gregory. ■ 77005 #035-46-2000 L2007 **OTO** *100 †45
SILAPUNT, Sirunya. ■ 77030 #891-01-1995 L2005 **D** *012
SILAY, Yavuz Selim. 6550 FANNIN ST, DEPT NEURO 77030 #902-03-2000 *100
SILBERMAN, Reuben. ■ 77056 #836-01-1951 L1978 **GS** *020
SILLER, Barry S. 2223 DORRINGTON ST 77030 #048-04-1988 L1989 **OBG GO** *030 †20
SILLOS, Elaine Maria D. 6621 FANNIN ST, WT06104 77030 #187-08-1979 L2003 **NPM PD** *020 †55
SILVA, Elvio G. 1515 HOLCOMBE BLVD BOX 85 77030 #132-03-1969 L1979 **ATP** *050 †50
SILVA, Guilherme Vianna. ■ 77035 #187-03-1994 L2004 **IC** *012 †20 ‡
SILVA, Illeana Daniella. ■ 77040 #048-13-2007 **PD** *012
SILVA CARMONA, Manuel De. 1 BAYLOR PLZ, BAYLOR COLL OF MED 77030 #649-30-2002 L2007 **PD** *012 †55
SILVER, Gregory Adam. 6431 FANNIN ST STE 5.196 77030 #048-02-2006 L2008 **AN** *012
SILVERBLATT, Julian. ■ 77056 #038-41-1948 L1954 **IM PUD** *071 †20
SILVERMAN, Louis F. 7777 SOUTHWEST FWY, STE 460 77074 #025-07-1961 L1969 **GS TS** *020 †85,90
SILVERMAN, Paul Marshall. 1515 HOLCOMBE BLVD BOX 368, DIAGNOSTIC RADIOLOGY 77030 #024-16-1977 L2000 **DR** *020 †80
SILVERMAN, Seth Warren. 5300 MEMORIAL DR, STE 510 77007 #033-06-1979 L1980 **PFP** *020 †75
SILVERMAN, Sheppy John. 6560 FANNIN ST STE 2200 77030 #062-01-1957 L1961 **OPH** *020 †35
SILVERSTEIN, Marc David. 6550 FANNIN ST STE 1661, THE METHODIST HOSPITAL 77030 #035-01-1977 L2006 **IM IMG** *030 †20
SIM, Christopher Siang Ch. 4331 BRIGHTWOOD DR 77068 #624-01-1975 L1979 **FM PD** *020
SIM, Sue Jin. 7207 GESSNER DR, LABORATORY CONCEPTS OF 77040 #583-01-1978 L1996 **SP** *020 †50
SIM, Woon Ki. 902 FROSTWOOD DR, STE 186 77024 #583-02-1978 L1996 **FM FSM** *020 †18
SIMI, Warren Wm. 4126 SOUTHWEST FWY STE 400 77027 #048-13-1972 L1972 **PUD IM** *020
SIMMONS, Clyde Wilton, Jr. 920 FROSTWOOD DR STE 730 77024 #048-04-1970 L1970 **PS** *020 †65
SIMMONS, Jeane Raycheal. 4126 SOUTHWEST FWY 77027 #048-16-1992 L1994 **OBG** *020 †30
SIMMONS, Natasha Charlese. ■ 77025 #028-34-2004 L2007 **FM** *012
SIMMONS, Sherolyn D. 8415 W BELLFORT ST # 150 77071 #047-07-1983 L1985 **AN** *020
SIMMS, Uca F. ■ 77090 #021-01-1943 L1970 **AN** *071 †05
SIMON, Frederick. 1229 CAMPBELL RD 77055 #065-01-1965 L1977 **OPH** *071 †35
SIMON, Lawrence Mariano. ■ 77054 #048-04-2003 **OTO** *012
SIMON, Mark Christopher. 2411 FOUNTAIN VIEW DR # 2 77057 #048-13-2003 L2007 **AN** *020
SIMON, Terry Lee. 7515 MAIN ST, STE 340 77030 #048-04-1977 L1977 **OBG** *020 †30
SIMONETTA, Alexander Bono. 6431 FANNIN ST, DEPARTMENT OF RADIOLOGY 77030 #051-04-1992 L1998 **RNR** *020 †80
SIMONICH, Stephen Donald. 6431 FANNIN ST RM 6.144, UT MEDICAL SCHOOL HOUSTO 77030 #048-02-1995 L2005 **OSM** *020 †40
SIMOTAS, Alexandra. 11302 FALLBROOK DR STE 301 77065 #048-14-1994 L1999 **OBG** *020 †30
SIMPSON, Bobby Jack. ■ 77069 #048-02-1964 L1964 **OBG** *071 †30
SIMPSON, Ericka Portley. 6560 FANNIN ST, DEPT OF NEURO STE 802 77030 #048-14-1995 L1997 **N** *020 †75
SIMPSON, Leo. 9265 BUFFALO SPEEDWAY, ST LUKES EPISCOPAL HOSPITA 77025 #495-36-1997 L2005 **CD** *012 †20
SIMPSON, Richard Kendall. 6560 FANNIN ST STE 944, BAYLOR COLLEGE OF MEDICINE 77030 #045-01-1982 L1989 **NS** *020 †20
SIMPSON, Sherri Marie. 2002 HOLCOMBE BLVD 77030 #047-07-2002 L2007 **CHP** *100
SIMPSON, Steve Allen. 1709 DRYDEN RD STE 550, FACULTY CENTER, BCM 620 77030 #035-09-2004 L2005 **CD** *012 †20
SIMPSON, Tiffani M. ■ 77025 #048-14-2005 L2008 **FP** *012
SIMS, Catherine Ferguson. 2411 FOUNTAIN VIEW DR # 2 77057 #005-14-1977 L2002 **AN** *020
SIMS, Leslie R. ■ 77054 #048-14-2008 *012
SIMS, Robert Erwin. 1 BAYLOR PLZ, DEPARTMENT OF RADIOLOGY 77030 #045-04-1981 L1982 **DR** *020 †80
SINACORI, Mina Karam. 920 FROSTWOOD DR, STE 740 77024 #035-19-1998 L2002 **OBG** *020 †30 ‡
SINCLAIR, Jan P. ■ 77004 #671-02-1987 **AI** *100
SINEGAL, Monica Lynn. 11000 FONDREN RD STE A 77096 #048-02-1992 L1994 **FM** *020 †18
SINGH, Amit Tej. ■ 77027 #048-04-2008 *012
SINGH, Amrita. ■ 77030 #048-04-2008 *012
SINGH, Gita. 1 BAYLOR PLZ 77030 #496-26-1999 **FP** *012
SINGH, Harbans. ■ 77059 #048-04-1992 L1993 **DR** *020 †80
SINGH, Hardeep. 2002 HOLCOMBE BLVD, VA MEDICAL CENTER 152 77030 #495-36-1994 L1997 **IM** *020 †20
SINGH, Kamaljit Singh. 12838 ASHTON LAKE LN 77041 #495-29-1980 L1999 **NPM** *020 †55
SINGH, Karanbir. 6565 FANNIN ST STE 452, PHYS ORGANIZ, ANESTHESIOLO 77030 #654-01-1996 L2003 **AN** *020 †05

SINGH, Navneet. 6431 FANNIN ST, MSB 4.148 77030 #048-16-2001 L2005 **NEP** *020 †20
SINGH, Ruhi. ■ 77041 #048-04-2007 **IM** *012
SINGH, Sanjay Kumar. 6565 FANNIN ST, D281 77030 #048-04-1988 L1989 **DR RNR** *020 †80
SINGH, Supriya. PO BOX 20708 77225 #495-05-2003 **IM** *012
SINGHAL, Geeta Rani. 6621 FANNIN ST, STE A210 77030 #039-01-1994 L1998 **PD** *020 †55
SINGHAL, Nita Israni. 9105 N WAYSIDE DR 77028 #495-22-1992 L2006 **FM** *020 †18
SINGLA, Neeta S. 11111 JONES RD STE 3 77070 #496-07-1980 L1992 **PCC** *020 †20
SINGLETARY, Sonja Eva. 1515 HOLCOMBE BLVD, BOX 4444 77030 #045-01-1977 L1985 **GS** *020 †85
SINGLETON, Edward B. 6621 FANNIN ST 77030 #048-02-1946 L1946 **PDR** *071 †80
SIROTA, Paul Gunnar. 2500 FONDREN RD, HILLCROFT MIEDICAL CLINIC 77063 #048-02-1967 L1968 **R** *020 †80
SISON, Blandina Caducoy. 837 FM 1960 RD W, STE 105 77090 #748-08-1973 L1996 **FM** *020 †18 ‡
SITTENFELD, Oscar M. 6431 FANNIN ST STE 7044 77030 #270-01-1982 **N** *100
SITTON, Clark W. ■ 77006 #048-13-1993 L1995 **DR** *020 †80
SIVASANKARAN, Sujatha. ■ 77025 #495-42-1994 **OBG** *012
SIZER, Kurt Clement. 1515 HOLCOMBE BLVD, UT MD ANDERSON UNIT 24 77030 #024-05-1989 L2005 **BBK HMP** *062 †20
SJOBLOM, Matthew David. ■ 77054 #048-04-2008 *012
SKAGGS, Ray Hamilton. 77006 #048-02-1945 L1945 **IM CD** *071 †20
SKAKUN, Gary Blaine. 6550 FANNIN ST STE 2307 77030 #060-02-1978 L1984 **CRS** *020 †10,85
SKARIA, George P. ■ 77005 #048-02-2001 L2005 **AN** *100 †05
SKARIBAS, Ioannis Mihail. 7600 BEECHNUT ST 77074 #418-02-1991 L1999 **AN PMM** *020 †05
SKATTEBOL, Atle. ■ 77054 #035-06-1992 **OS** *020
SKELLENGER, Mark Edward. 445 BAY AREA BLVD 77058 #048-04-1976 L1976 **VS DS** *020 †85
SKELTON, Hillary Alaine. ■ 77030 #048-14-2008 *012
SKELTON, James M, Jr. ■ 77057 #048-02-1972 L1972 **IM** *020
SKELTON, Thomas S. 1 BAYLOR PLZ, BAYLOR COLL MED 77030 #048-14-2007 **GS** *012
SKIBA, William Edward. 17115 RED OAK DR STE 109, RED OAK PSYCHIATRIC ASSOCI 77090 #048-16-1986 L1987 **P** *020 †75
SKIBBER, John Michael. 1400 HOLCOMBE BLVD UNIT 44, UT MD ANDERSON CANCER CTR 77030 #048-02-1981 L1989 **GS SO** *020 †80
SKOLKIN, Mark D. 6720 BERTNER ST, MC2-270 77030 #016-11-1980 L1981 **DR** *020 †80
SKOLNICK, Alan Wm. 915 GESSNER RD, STE 720 77024 #016-42-1965 L1971 **U** *020
SKOR, Arnold Barry. 829 PEAKWOOD DR, STE 101 77090 #048-02-1969 L1969 **IM OS** *020 †20
SKORACKI, Roman Jan. 1515 HOLCOMBE BLVD, BOX 443 77030 #060-02-1996 L2001 *020
SKORUPSKI, Josh Chandler. ■ 77054 #550-03-2002 L2008 **MG** *012
SLADE, Stephen Glenn. 3900 ESSEX LN, STE 101 77027 #048-14-1978 L1980 **OPH** *020 †35
SLATER, Jeremy Daniel. 6431 FANNIN ST, STE 7019 77030 #041-12-1986 L2004 **N SME** *020 †75
SLAUGHTER, Rustin Timothy. 6260 WESTPARK DR STE 150 77057 #039-01-1998 L2002 **P** *020
SLAWIN, Kevin Mark. 6560 FANNIN ST, STE 2100 77030 #035-01-1986 L1993 **U OS** *020 †95
SLESNICK, Timothy Charles. 6621 FANNIN ST, MC 19345-C 77030 #048-04-2001 L2007 **PD** *100 †55
SLOMKA, Myron B. ■ 77024 #048-12-1960 L1960 **OS LM** *071
SLOMOVITZ, Brian Matthew. 1515 HOLCOMBE BLVD BOX 440, MD ANDERSON CANCER CENTER 77030 #033-05-1998 L2002 **GO OBG** *020 †30
SLOPIS, John M. 1515 HOLCOMBE BLVD BOX 4, MD ANDERSON CANCER CENTER 77030 #048-14-1983 L1989 **PD** *020 †55,75
SMALKY, Kathleen Anne. 6620 MAIN ST, STE 11A06 77030 #048-12-1986 L1987 **IM** *020 †20
SMALLING, Richard Warren. 6431 FANNIN MSMB 1 246 77030 #048-14-1975 L1975 **CD** *050 †20
SMECK, Jane Ann. 920 FROSTWOOD DR 77024 #048-12-1981 L1981 **EM** *020
SMELLEY, James Alfred. 1740 W 27TH ST STE 180 77008 #048-02-1962 L1962 **OPH** *071 †35
SMILEY, Samuel Neil. 1415 NORTH LOOP W STE 820, STE 820 77008 #048-12-1983 L1983 **DR** *020 †80
SMIRNAKIS, Stelios M. 1 BAYLOR PLZ, RM 5517 77030 #024-01-1997 L2000 **N** *050 †75
SMITH, Aimee Lynn. ■ 77007 #041-14-2005 **OBG** *012
SMITH, Alfred Emanuel. 802 BRIARBROOK DR 77042 #048-02-1956 L1956 **GS** *020 †85
SMITH, Ann Charisse. 1504 TAUB LOOP, GENERAL INTERNAL MEDICINE 77030 #024-01-1996 L1999 **IM** *020 †20
SMITH, Barry Saml. 1709 DRYDEN RD, STE 725 77030 #041-02-1969 L1985 **PM** *030 †60
SMITH, Bruce K. 1315 ST JOSEPH PKWY, STE 940 77002 #048-16-1986 L1987 **PS HS** *020 †65 ‡
SMITH, Cedrick Dwayne. 2004 LEELAND ST 77003 #048-02-1997 L1999 **GS** *020
SMITH, Christopher K. 1140 BUSINESS CENTER DR, STE 200 77043 #048-15-1994 L1999 **ORS** *020 †40
SMITH, Christopher P. 6560 FANNIN ST, STE 2100 77030 #016-06-1994 L1999 **U** *020 †95
SMITH, Claudius Gregory. 800 PEAKWOOD DR STE 5F 77090 #051-04-1976 L1982 **OBG** *020 †30
SMITH, Dean Ward. 1200 BINZ ST STE 580, DEAN SMITH, MD, PA 77004 #028-03-1995 L2001 **HS ORS** *020 †40
SMITH, Ellen Ware. 6550 FANNIN ST, HOSP (HOUSTON) 77030 #048-16-2007 **TY** *012
SMITH, Frances A. 7900 FANNIN STE 2100, KELSEY-SEYBOLD CLINIC PA 77054 #048-04-1981 L1981 **OBG** *020 †30
SMITH, Frank Edward. 1709 DRYDEN RD, #659 BAYLOR FACULTY CTR 77030 #060-01-1960 L1964 **ON IM** *020 †20
SMITH, Frank Rees. 3702 DEL MONTE DR 77019 #035-01-1962 L1979 **OM PHP** *071 †20
SMITH, Gregory Lantz. 7941 KATY FWY # 524 77024 #028-03-1974 L1982 **PS** *020 †85,65
SMITH, Harry Jerome. 14400 WESTMONT DR, STE 200 77015 #038-45-1987 L1996 **HO** *020 †20
SMITH, Holly Dawn. 6431 FANNIN 77030 #048-14-1996 L1998 **MPD** *020 †20,55
SMITH, Hubert Leland, Jr. 2925 W T C JESTER BLVD 77018 #025-01-1964 L1967 **FM** *020 †18
SMITH, Ivonne. 7900 FANNIN ST, STE 4811 77054 #048-15-1994 L1996 **OBG** *020 †30
SMITH, John Herbert. 12121 RICHMOND AVE, STE 106 77082 #038-40-1963 L1969 **IM PUD** *020
SMITH, Justin Gil. ■ 77054 #048-14-2008 *012
SMITH, Katherine Elizabet. ■ 77030 #048-04-2005 L2008 **PD** *012
SMITH, Keely Garrett. 6431 FANNIN ST, STE 3.226B 77030 #048-14-2001 L2005 **MPD** *100 †55,20
SMITH, Keith Davis. 7400 FANNIN ST, TEXAS INST FOR 77054 #041-12-1959 L1971 **END IM** *020 †20
SMITH, Keitha Renee. 9055 KATY FWY STE 460 77024 #004-01-1990 L1996 **OTO** *020
SMITH, Kelly J. 6411 FANNIN ST 77030 #048-14-2001 L2005 **AN** *020 †05
SMITH, Kenneth Randall. ■ 77007 #001-02-2004 L2005 **OPH** *012

SMITH, Kerrington David. ■ 77005 #035-20-2000 L2007 **GS** *100 †85
SMITH, Kevin Raynard. 6410 FANNIN ST, STE 810 77030 #048-14-1986 L1987 **OTO FPS** *020 †45
SMITH, Kimberly Connelly. 6431 FANNIN ST, JJL 480 77030 #048-02-1984 L1987 **PD** *040 †55
SMITH, Kristina Bess. ■ 77054 #048-04-2006 **PD** *012
SMITH, Lakesha Shonra. ■ 77054 #016-45-2002 L2007 **AN** *100
SMITH, Latisha Antoinette. 6431 FANNIN ST RM MSB5-020, UNIV TX HEALTH SCI CTR HOU 77030 #041-09-1983 L1998 **UM IM** *020 †20
SMITH, Melissa O'Toole. ■ 77005 #048-14-1996 L1997 **DR** *020 †80
SMITH, Michael Dean. 900 WAYSIDE DR I 77011 #048-02-1979 L1979 **AN EM** *020 †20
SMITH, Paul Joseph. ■ 77030 #048-04-2008 *012
SMITH, Phillip Paul. 6560 FANNIN ST, STE 2100 77030 #038-41-1984 L2004 **OBG** *020 †30
SMITH, Pliny Cleland. 12951 SOUTH FWY 77047 #048-02-1969 L1969 **R** *071 †80
SMITH, Rhonda Glynn. 4101 GREENBRIAR ST, STE 100 77098 #048-04-1981 L1981 **PD** *020 †55
SMITH, Richard Myrl, Jr. 77027 #027-01-1960 L1963 **AN** *071 †05
SMITH, Stacey Leigh. 2222 MARONEAL ST UNIT 134 77030 #048-14-2004 **OTO** *012
SMITH, Stephanie Marie. 6624 FANNIN ST, MEDICAL CLINIC OF HOUSTON 77030 #048-04-2001 L2004 **IM** *020
SMITH, William Wayne. ■ 77030 #048-04-1960 L1960 **GS** *020 †85
SMITH, Zachary J. 12121 RICHMOND AVE STE 116 77082 #048-14-2000 L2003 **IM** *020
SMITHERMAN, Hannah Fouts. 6621 FANNIN ST 77030 #048-04-1998 L2001 **PEM** *020 †55
SMITHERMAN, Jay S. 2727 W HOLCOMBE BLVD, KELSEY SEYBOLD CLINIC 77025 #048-04-2002 L2004 **IM** *020 †20
SMITHERMAN, Robert Kent. 1504 TAUB LOOP, INTERNAL MEDICINE 77030 #048-04-1998 L2001 **IM** *020 †20
SMITHERMAN, Wendy L. ■ 77025 #048-04-2004 L2008 **P** *012
SMITH SHENOUDA, Tina Anne. ■ 77019 #539-04-2005 **FP** *012
SMITHWICK, Orla Mary. 6411 FANNIN ST 77030 #539-05-1989 L2000 **EM** *100 †16
SMOLARZ, Joseph Ryan. ■ 77025 #048-02-2004 L2006 **OTO** *012
SMYTH, Shane Joseph. ■ 77030 #539-05-1998 L2006 **CN** *100 †75
SMYTHE, Cheves Mc Cord. 6410 FANNIN ST 77030 #024-01-1947 L1970 **IMG IM** *071 †20
SNEIGE, Nour A. MD ANDERSON HOSP, SURGICAL PATHOLOGY 77030 #875-01-1972 L1981 **PTH** *030 †50
SNELL, Jamaal Tremaine. ■ 77054 #048-04-2008 *012
SNYDER, Hal. ■ 77025 #048-02-1942 L1942 **GS** *071 †85
SNYDER, Michael Jesse. 6550 FANNIN ST, STE 2307 77030 #021-06-1986 L1998 **CRS** *020 †10,85
SOBIESK, Paul Jacob. 1315 ST JOSEPH PKWY, STE 302 77002 #021-05-1991 L1992 **AN** *020 †05
SOBOCINSKI, Robert S. ■ 77079 #035-06-1953 L1973 **FM EM** *071
SOBOLEVSKY, Irene V. 2727 W HOLCOMBE BLVD, KEISEY-SEYBOID CLINIC 77025 #913-93-1982 L1997 **IM** *020 †20
SOCKRIDER, Marianna M. 6621 FANNIN ST, CLINICAL CARE CTR 77030 #028-46-1983 L1988 **PDP PD** *030 †55
SODERBERG, Britt Linnea. ■ 77030 #024-07-2004 L2007 **PD** *012 †55
SODERSTROM, Charles E. 1415 NORTH LOOP W STE 820 77008 #048-12-1990 L1992 **DR** *020 †80
SODERSTROM, Mary Stream. ■ 77030 #048-12-1990 L1992 **P** *020 †75
SODHI, Amik. 1709 DRYDEN RD STE 550, BCM FACULTY CENTER 77030 #495-36-2004 **IM** *012
SOECHTING, Marsha F. ■ 77005 #048-04-1984 L1986 **OPH** *071 †35
SOH, Lay-Tin. ■ 77054 #825-01-1984 **ON** *020
SOHAL, Guljeet Kaur. 1615 N MAIN ST 77009 #654-01-2002 L2006 **FM** *020 †18
SOHEILI, Pejman. 6565 FANNIN ST 77030 #035-09-1994 L2006 **CCM** *100 †20
SOKOLOW, Harry I. 4100 WESTHEIMER RD, STE 148 77027 #048-02-1988 L1989 **FM** *020 †20
SOLCHER, Dean Clarence. 1200 BINZ ST STE 700, DIAGNOSTIC CLINIC OF HOUST 77004 #048-02-1961 L1965 **GE IM** *020 †20
SOLCHER, Patrick V. 1200 BINZ ST, DIAGNOSTIC CLINIC OF 77004 #048-14-1994 L2003 **IM** *020 †20
SOLETSKY, Susan. 6977 MAIN ST, SHRINERS HOSPITAL 77030 #035-20-1989 L1994 **AN GP** *020 †05
SOLIMAN, Ahmed Mohamed. ■ 77082 #915-03-2000 **IM** *012
SOLIMAN, Pamela Therese. ■ 77005 #051-04-1999 L2005 **OBG** *100
SOLIS, George Patrick. 909 FROSTWOOD DR STE 162 77024 #028-02-1972 L1976 **OBG** *020 †30
SOLIS, Miguel Angel, Jr. 6431 FANNIN ST STE JSL308, U TX HSC-FP 77030 #649-30-2002 L2007 **FM** *100
SOLIS, Robert Thos. 6720 BERTNER ST 77030 #008-01-1965 L1969 **IM PUD** *020 †20
SOLIS-BOO, Eva F V. 7707 CANAL ST 77012 #847-04-1969 L1976 **FM** *020
SOLIZ, Amil J. 12345 KATY FWY 77079 #048-14-1983 L1983 **FM** *020 †18
SOLIZ, Jose M. 9822 CYNTHIA ANN CT 77025 #048-14-2002 L2005 **AN** *100 †05
SOLLENNE, Nicholas P, III. 1707 SUNSET BLVD, MEDICAL CLINIC OF HOUSTON 77005 #048-02-1983 L1984 **IM** *020 †20
SOLOMON, Eric Harry. 2900 RICHMOND AVE, RIVER OAKS IMAGING 77098 #836-02-1975 L1981 **DR** *020 †80
SOLOMON, Stuart Lowell. 6560 FANNIN ST 77030 #048-13-1978 L1978 **CD IM** *071 †20
SOLOMOS, Nicholas J. 1221 MCKINNEY ST, STE 40300 77010 #048-14-1989 L1990 **FM** *020 †18
SOLTES, George Don. 6565 FANNIN, F 303. 77030 #048-04-1988 L1989 **VIR** *020 †80
SOMERS, William H. ■ 77063 #035-09-1950 L1955 **R** *071 †80
SOMERVILLE, Laura L. 7707 FANNIN ST, STE 195 77054 #048-13-1986 L1992 **AI IM** *020 †20,03
SONABEND, Michael Lee. 1 BAYLOR PLZ, DEPT OF DERMATOLOGY 77030 #024-05-2003 L2006 **D** *012 †15
SONG, Brian June. ■ 77084 #048-02-2008 *012
SONG, Sara Ann. ■ 77025 #039-01-2005 **FP** *012
SONI, Sachin. PO BOX 20708 77225 #495-73-2004 **IM** *012
SONI, Samit Dilip. ■ 77030 #048-04-2008 *012
SONIK, Simon. 9660 HILLCROFT 77096 #836-01-1957 L1978 **FM** *071
SONWALKAR, Smita Subodh. 12141 RICHMOND AVE 77082 #495-83-1984 L2001 **AN** *020 †05
SOO, Chiu-Shiung. 8850 LONG POINT RD, SPRING BRANCH MEDICAL CENT 77055 #385-01-1965 L1980 **DR** *020 †80
SOOD, Anil Kumar. 1515 HOLCOMBE BLVD, DEPT OF GYN ONCOLOGY 77030 #036-01-1991 L2002 **OBG GO** *030 †30
SOON, Chao Yang. 1 BAYLOR PLZ 77030 #671-01-1997 **IC** *012
SOPARKAR, Sidhartha C. 3730 KIRBY DR, STE 900 77098 #024-16-1990 L1994 **OPH** *020 †35

■ = Address Information Privacy Protected

SORBERA, Brenda C. ■ 77054 #023-01-1991 L1993 **IM** *020 †20
SORKIN, Tatiana Azarova. 1315 ST JOSEPH PKWY, STE 302 77002 #913-32-1989 L2005 **AN** *020 ‡
SORLEY, David C. 2411 FOUNTAIN VIEW DR # 2 77057 #048-12-1998 L1999 **AN** *020
SOROF, Jonathan Michael. ■ 77005 #041-01-1989 L1995 **PN** *020 †55
SOROKA, Selic. 6206 DASHWOOD DR 77081 #132-01-1954 L1964 **IM P** *020
SOROKA, Sergio Adolfo. 7600 BEECHNUT ST, 2ND FL 77074 #132-01-1981 L1985 **PTH** *020 †50
SOSA RODRIGUEZ, Javier Ed. ■ 77025 #935-06-2002 **FP** *012
SOSTMAN, Henry Dirk. 6565 FANNIN ST, DUNN TOWER STE 200 77030 #008-01-1976 L2006 **DR NM** *030 †80,28
SOTELO, Elsa P. ■ 77054 #048-14-2005 **PTH** *012
SOTELO, Tiffany Michelle. 6431 FANNIN ST, UNIV OF TEXAS MED SCH 77030 #010-01-2001 L2006 **U** *100
SOTO, Jose Raul. 7789 SW FWY STE 420 77074 #042-01-1975 L1982 **CD IC** *020 †20
SOTO, Wigberto. 11914 ASTORIA BLVD 77089 #042-01-1989 L1996 **OBG** *020
SOTOMAYOR, Jose F. 6532 CANAL ST # B 77011 #737-01-1967 L1974 **GP FM** *020 †50
SOUCHON, Eduardo Antonio. 6431 FANNIN ST, M S B 4.020 77030 #935-01-1968 L1976 **GS SO** *040 †85
SOUDERS, Christopher M. 1806 CHERRYHURST ST 77006 #048-04-1998 L2001 **EM** *020 †16
SOULE, Robert Marion, Jr. 8309 KNIGHT RD 77054 #048-02-1978 L1979 **EM** *020 †16
SOUTHARD, Robert Ellis. ■ 77025 #001-06-2001 **GS** *012
SOUTHERLAND, Sean Patrick. ■ 77054 #048-14-2008 *012
SOUTHERN, Jeanne. 4544 POST OAK PLACE DR, STE 287 77027 #048-04-1985 L1986 **GP PMM** *020
SPAETH, Maya C. 1 BAYLOR PLZ, BAYLOR COLL MED 77030 #060-02-2000 L2002 **HSP** *012
SPAFFORD, Andrew. 13231 CHAMPION FOREST DR, STE 230 77069 #048-13-1996 L1998 **FM** *020 †18
SPAIN, Charles Adkin. ■ 77006 #048-02-1954 L1954 **R** *071 †80
SPANGLER, Gary W, Jr. 17000 EL CAMINO REAL, STE 201B 77058 #048-15-2000 L2002 **FM** *020 †18 ‡
SPANKUS, Elizabeth M. ■ 77024 #048-14-1978 L1979 **PS OTO** *071 †45,65
SPANN, Stephen Jimmie. 3701 KIRBY DR 77098 #048-04-1975 L1975 **FM MDM** *040 †18
SPARKS, John Wesley. 6431 FANNIN ST # 3.242 77030 #024-01-1972 L1991 **NPM PD** *050 †55
SPAULDING, Glenn Francis. ■ 77059 #016-11-1984 L1989 **IM** *050
SPEARS, Neal M. 11219 BOTTLEBRUSH CT, EAST COMMONS PLACE 77095 #048-13-1999 L2002 **PD** *020 †55
SPECK, Laura Michelle. ■ 77006 #048-02-2007 **IM** *012
SPECTOR, Ivan Charles. 3100 WESLAYAN ST STE 350 77027 #048-14-1983 L1983 **P** *020 †75 ‡
SPEDALE, Jeanne Howell. 5110 BUFFALO SPEEDWAY, STE 200 77005 #021-05-1994 L1997 **D** *020 †15
SPEER, Michael Emery. 6621 FANNIN ST, WT 6 - 104 77030 #048-04-1968 L1968 **NPM** *040 †55
SPELLER, Charles Kirby. 6610 HARWIN DR, STE 180 77036 #047-07-1966 L1971 **ORS** *020
SPENCER, John Paul. ■ 77041 #016-11-1970 L1975 **CD IM** *075 †20
SPENCER, William Hall, III. 6550 FANNIN ST, STE 1901 77030 #036-07-1965 L1972 **CD** *020 †20
SPIEGEL, Aldona Jedrysiak. 6560 FANNIN ST STE 800 77030 #065-09-1994 L1998 **PS** *020 †65
SPIEGEL, Felix. ■ 77019 #035-19-1989 L2001 **GS EM** *020 †85
SPIEL, Helen Ruth. 2727 W HOLCOMBE BLVD 77025 #048-02-1980 L1989 **N** *020 †75
SPILLER, William F. ■ 77019 #048-02-1945 L1945 **D** *071 †15
SPINDLER, Joseph S. 6655 TRAVIS ST, STE 960 77030 #847-04-1972 L1977 **RHU IM** *020
SPINKS, Adiaha Idara. 6621 FANNIN ST CC-1530, TEXAS CHILDREN'S HOSPITAL 77030 #047-07-1999 L2005 **DBP** *100 †55
SPINN, Matthew Paul. 6431 FANNIN ST, UTHSC HOUSTON MEDICAL SCHO 77030 #048-14-2003 L2006 **GE** *012 †20
SPINNER, Stanley Warren. 909 FROSTWOOD DR, STE 126 77024 #048-13-1982 L1983 **PD** *020 †55
SPITZ, Margaret Ruth. 1515 HOLCOMBE BLVD 77030 #836-01-1966 L1978 **PHP** *050
SPIVAK, Hadar. 1200 BINZ ST, STE 1470 77004 #550-02-1989 L1998 **GS** *020 †85
SPIWAK, Alana Ruth. 4119 MONTROSE BLVD STE 300 77006 #025-01-1980 L1982 **PYA P** *020 †75
SPJUT, Harlan Jacobson. 7401 MAIN ST 77030 #049-01-1946 L1962 **ATP CLP** *071 †50
SPONENBERG, Susan Leah. 1111 AUGUSTA DR, KELSEY SEYBOLD CLINIC 77057 #048-04-1979 L1979 **PD** *020 †75
SPRABERY, Scott Ellis. 2211 NORFOLK ST STE 403 77098 #027-01-1995 L1997 **CHP P** *020 †75
SPRAGUE, Donald Eldon. 2101 NASA RD 1, NASA/JSC CLINIC SD32 77058 #649-01-1972 L1973 **AM AI** *020 †18,70
SPRAWKA, Nicole M. ■ 77004 #048-12-2004 **OBG** *012
SPRINGER, Arthur Jonathan. 1707 SUNSET BLVD, MEDICAL CLINIC OF HOUSTON 77005 #035-09-1975 L1980 **CD IM** *020 †20
SPRINGER-TOLLETT, Melanie. 6410 FANNIN ST, STE 1460 77030 #048-14-1991 L1992 **IM** *020 †20
SPROCKEL, Dennis Garyjose. ■ 77047 #048-14-2006 **GS** *100
SPROTT, Annie L. ■ 77047 #048-14-2008 *012
SRAJ, Shafic Abdullah. 1709 DRYDEN RD, 12TH FL 77030 #605-01-2001 **HSO** *012
SREENARASIMHAIAH, V. 915 GESSNER RD, STE 360 77024 #028-46-1996 L2004 **NEP** *020
SREJIC, Una. 1515 HOLCOMBE BLVD, BOX 42 77030 #061-01-1992 L1997 **AN** *020 †05
SRESHTA, Dominic Gregory. 7737 SOUTHWEST FWY STE 800 77074 #495-52-1992 L2000 **IM** *020 †20
SRINIVASAN, Anand. 1 BAYLOR PLZ, DEPT OF ORTHO SURGERY 77030 #041-02-2005 **ORS** *012
SRIRAM, Pankajam Manalath. 7575 KIRBY DR APT 1207 77030 #495-09-1965 L1975 **P GP** *020
SRIRAMA, Rohith. ■ 77004 #051-07-2002 L2007 **AN** *100 †05
SROKOWSKI, Tomasz Pawel. 1515 HOLCOMBE BLVD BOX 001 77030 #028-02-2003 L2006 **HO** *012
SROUR, Ahmad Mohamad. ■ 77054 #605-04-2004 **GS** *012
SRUNGARAM, Ramesh K. 11811 FM 1960 RD W STE 175 77065 #495-57-1975 L1987 **TS** *020 †85
SSENGOBA, Anisa Seana. 3701 KIRBY DR STE 600 77098 #038-06-2001 L2008 **FM** *100 †18
STABE, Susan. 830 GEMINI ST 77058 #048-02-1979 L1979 **PD** *020 †55
STACK, Austin G. 6431 FANNIN ST, MSB 4148 77030 #539-04-1991 L2003 **NEP** *020
STADE, Eileen Carol. 8200 WEDNESBURY LN STE 485 77074 #048-04-1978 L1978 **IM** *071 †20
STADNYK, Alexander Nestor. 6624 FANNIN ST, STE 1450 77030 #060-01-1981 L1988 **PUD IM** *020 †20
STAERKEL, Gregg Allen. 1515 HOLCOMBE BLVD, UNIT 53 77030 #048-02-1983 L1983 **PCP PTH** *020 †50

STAEWEN, Robert S. 3310 RICHMOND AVE 77098 #048-12-1987 L1988 **DR R** *020 †80
STAFFORD, Donald R. 1140 BUSINESS CENTER DR, STE 200 77043 #048-02-1993 L1995 **ORS** *020 †40
STAFFORD, James Benj. 6550 FANNIN ST STE 2500 77030 #048-12-1975 L1975 **PS HS** *020 †85,65
STAFFORD, John R. ■ 77005 #048-02-1960 L1960 **P** *071 †75
STAFFORD, Novarro C. 5740 W LITTLE YORK RD #281 77091 #010-03-1965 L1968 **AN** *020 †05
STAFFORD, Novarro C. 5746 W LITTLE YORK RD 77091 #047-07-1985 L1988 **PD** *020
STAHL, Nicole K. 6431 FANNIN ST, MED SCH AT HOUSTON 77030 #048-14-2007 **P** *012
STAINBACK, Raymond F, III. 6624 FANNIN ST, STE 2480 77030 #048-04-1987 L1989 **CD IM** *020 †20
STAIR, Matthew Allen. ■ 77006 #048-12-2004 L2007 **DR** *012
STAL, Samuel. 6621 FANNIN ST, MC-CC610.10 77030 #016-43-1974 L1981 **PS HNS** *020 †45,65
STAMATAKIS, Lambros. 1 BAYLOR PLZ, DEPT OF UROLOGY 77030 #023-01-2005 **U** *012
STAMATIOU, Eleftherios S. 1707 SUNSET BLVD, MEDICAL CLINIC OF HOUSTON 77005 #418-02-1962 L1973 **CD IM** *020
STAMBULIE, Roberto. 800 PEAKWOOD DR 77090 #021-01-1960 L1967 **OBG** *071 †30
STANA, Roman. 6565 FANNIN ST 77030 #286-04-1985 L2000 **AN** *020 †05
STANASEL, Irina. ■ 77030 #048-04-2008 *012
STANCEL, Gregory A. ■ 77096 #048-14-2005 L2007 **PTH** *012
STANIETZKY, Nir. 6720 BERTNER ST, ST LUKE'S EPISCOPAL HOSPIT 77030 #065-01-1997 L2003 **DR** *020 †80
STANOSHECK, Kyle Douglas. 7600 BEECHNUT ST 77074 #030-06-2000 L2004 **AN** *020 †05
STANTON, James P. ■ 77042 #010-02-1952 L1978 **GE IM** *071 †20
STARBRANCH, Eileen K. 2600 GESSNER DR STE 280 77080 #048-04-1968 L1969 **P CHP** *020 †75 ‡
STARIKOV, Roman Solomon. ■ 77041 #048-16-2003 L2004 **OBG** *020
STARK, Ann Carol Robbins. 6621 FANNIN ST WT6-104, SECTION OF NEONATOLOGY 77030 #024-01-1971 L2004 **NPM PD** *050 †55
STARKE, Jeffrey Robt. 1 BAYLOR PLZ, BAYLOR COLLEGE OF MEDICINE 77030 #035-45-1980 L1983 **PD** *020 †55
STASNEY, Charles Richard. 6550 FANNIN ST STE 2001 77030 #048-04-1969 L1969 **OTO** *020 †45
STAVINOHA, Michael Wayne. 1631 NORTH LOOP W, STE 655 77008 #048-02-1984 L1985 **GE IM** *020 †20
STAVINOHA, Randal Ray. 1221 MCKINNEY ST, STE 40300 77010 #048-02-1991 L1992 **ISM IM** *020 †20
STAVIS, Monte I. 909 FROSTWOOD DR STE 334 77024 #024-05-1975 L1980 **OPH OS** *020 †35
STAYER, Stephen Alexander. 6621 FANNIN ST STE A300, MAIL CODE 2-1495 77030 #048-12-1984 L1985 **AN CCM** *020 †05,55
STEELE, Kenya. 2000 CRAWFORD ST, STE 900 77002 #048-02-2000 L2003 **FM** *020 †18
STEELY, Robert Lee. 4126 SOUTHWEST FWY, STE 1230 77027 #048-02-1993 L1995 **PS** *020 †85,65
STEHLIN, John S, Jr. 1315 ST JOSEPH PKWY, STE 1818 77002 #056-06-1947 L1957 **GS ON** *071 †85
STEIN, Fernando. 6621 FANNIN ST # 2-3450, WEST TOWER STE 440 77030 #429-01-1975 L1980 **CCP PD** *020 †55
STEIN, Jay Harold. 1 BAYLOR PLZ STE 181A, BAYLOR COLLEGE OF MEDICINE 77030 #047-06-1960 L1975 **NEP** *030 †20
STEIN, Joshua Daniel. 1709 DRYDEN RD 12TH FL, BAYLOR COLLEGE OF MEDICINE 77030 #035-20-2001 L2007 **OSM** *012
STEIN, Ned Barry. 7777 SOUTHWEST FWY, STE 514 77074 #036-05-1973 L1978 **U** *020 †95
STEINBACH, Thomas Leo. 8303 SOUTHWEST FWY, STE 120 77074 #649-02-1962 L1968 **GE IM** *071
STEINBAUER, Jeffrey Robt. 6620 MAIN ST, STE 11D28 77030 #019-02-1977 L1991 **FM** *020 †18
STEINBERG, Joel Larry. 1300 MOURSUND ST, RM 359 77030 #016-11-1974 L1993 **P** *050 †75
STEINBERGER, Emil. 6411 FANNIN ST 77030 #018-03-1955 L1971 **REN END** *071
STEINBIS, Emily Sue. 6320 MAIN ST 77005 #048-04-2006 **OBG** *012
STEINER, Alton Louis. 1315 ST JOSEPH PKWY, STE 1705 77002 #035-01-1962 L1980 **IM END** *020
STEINER, Martin Roth. 8303 SOUTHWEST FWY, STE 835 77074 #011-03-1967 L1972 **N** *020 †75
STEINERT, Dejka Marida. 1515 HOLCOMBE BLVD, BOX 450 77030 #004-01-1999 L2002 **ON** *100 †20
STEINKULLER, Joan Sommers. 1504 TAUB LOOP 77030 #010-01-1967 L1979 **PD PEM** *040 †55
STEINKULLER, Paul G. 6550 FANNIN ST, STE 1501 77030 #010-01-1967 L1977 **OPH** *020 †35
STELIGA, Matthew Allen. ■ 77006 #056-06-2001 L2007 **TS** *012 †85
STELLING, Michael Wm. 1919 S BRAESWD BLVD 5TH FL, TC PEDIATRIC ASSOCIATES 77030 #016-06-1971 L1994 **PDE DIA** *012
STELLY-SEITZ, Charlotte M. 1213 HERMANN DR STE 675 77004 #048-04-1984 L1985 **PM PD** *020 †60,55
STEMMLER, Cristina. 5644 WESTHEIMER RD, # 900 77056 #132-01-1972 L1981 **FM PMM** *020 †18
STENOIEN, Randall A. 713 COLQUITT ST, INNOVATIVE RADIOLOGY 77006 #048-13-1984 L1985 **DR** *020 †80
STEPANIAK, Philip Carey. ■ 77058 #038-44-1983 L1987 **EM AM** *020 †16
STEPHANOU, Nicholas James. 1315 CALHOUN ST, NJ STEPHANOU MD PA 77002 #039-01-1965 L1974 **OBG** *072
STEPHEN, Matthew David. ■ 77054 #048-16-2003 L2006 **PDE** *012 †55
STEPHEN, Michael J. PO BOX 20708, DEPT OF INTERNAL MEDICINE 77225 #048-14-2005 **IM** *012
STEPHENS, Brett Walker. 6431 FANNIN ST STE 1.134, AT HOUST 77030 #048-14-2003 L2006 **NEP** *012 †20
STEPHENS, Edward M. 2626 S LOOP W STE 600 77054 #048-04-1978 L1978 **GS** *020 †16
STEPHENS, Jerry Ham. 2727 W HOLCOMBE BLVD, 4TH FL 77025 #048-02-1954 L1954 **D** *074 †15
STEPHENS, Nicholas Adam. ■ 77030 #048-14-2006 **GS** *100
STEPHENS, Tanya Washingto. 1515 HOLCOMBE BLVD, BOX 57 77030 #018-03-1994 L2001 **DR** *020 †80
STERLING, Leroy Louis, Jr. 4126 SOUTHWEST FWY, STE 1120 77027 #007-02-1979 L1982 **CD IM** *020 †20
STERN, Jon Karl. 7500 BEECHNUT ST STE 350 77074 #048-12-1974 L1974 **D PD** *020 †15,55
STERN, Juan Forgach. 1213 HERMANN DR STE 720 77004 #649-01-1969 L1976 **U** *020 †95
STERN, Lawrence David. 1315 ST JOSEPH PKWY, STE 1605 77002 #048-12-1976 L1980 **CD IM** *071 †20

STERN, Steven Emery. 17070 RED OAK DR STE 201C 77090 #048-04-1975 L1975 **OBG** *020 †30 ‡

STEUBER, Charles Philip. 6621 FANNIN ST, CC1410.00 77030 #028-34-1967 L1973 **PHO PD** *020 †55

STEVENS, Paul Michael. 3030 POST OAK BLVD, UNIT 412 77056 #050-02-1958 L1967 **PUD OM** *071 †20

STEVENS, Tobey Alan. 7900 FANNIN ST 77054 #048-14-2002 L2006 **OBG** *020

STEVENSON, Catherine Dyer. 4203 MONTROSE BLVD, STE 440 77006 #047-20-1999 L2003 **P** *020 †75

STEVENSON, Ricardo. PO BOX 20708, UNIV TX MED SCH AT HOUSTON 77225 #231-03-1998 **OPH** *100

STEWARD, Ryan Goodson. ■ 77019 #048-13-2007 **OBG** *012

STEWART, David Alexander. ■ 77054 #048-14-2008 *012

STEWART, David James. 1515 HOLCOMBE BLVD, UNIT 432 77030 #065-05-1974 L1978 **IM ON** *050

STEWART, Donald S. ■ 77030 #048-12-2002 L2006 **ORS** *012

STEWART, John Michael. ■ 77007 #051-01-1993 L2004 **FOP** *020

STEWART, Julie Nicole. 1 BAYLOR PLZ, BAYLOR COLL MED 77030 #048-04-2006 **U** *012

STEWART, Michael Scott. ■ 77054 #048-04-2008 *012

STEWART, Robert Hampton. 2855 GRAMERCY ST 77025 #048-02-1964 L1968 **OPH OS** *020 †35

STEWART, William Colby. 1220 AUGUSTA DR, STE 100 77057 #654-01-1992 L2001 **OPH** *020 †35

STEYNERS, Frank Jose. 1200 BINZ ST, STE 180 77004 #847-04-1959 L1964 **A** *020 †55,03

STIERNBERG, Charles M. 919 MILAM ST, STE 1830 77002 #048-02-1978 L1978 **OTO HNS** *020 †45

STINEBAUGH, Bobby J. 6550 FANNIN ST, COSMETIC DAYSURGERY CT 77030 #048-04-1957 L1964 **NEP IM** *071 †20

ST JOHN, Martha Wolfram. 11757 KATY FWY, STE 380 77079 #048-14-2002 L2004 **P** *020

ST LAURENT, Matthew J. 18220 STATE HIGHWAY 249, STE 300 77070 #048-16-1992 L1993 **GS AS** *020 †85

ST MICHEL, Christina Menz. ■ 77080 #048-04-2003 L2006 **FM** *020 †18

STOCKMAN, Patricia. 14903 EL CAMINO REAL 77062 #048-02-1986 L1987 **FM** *020 †18

STOCKS, Gregory Wm. 7401 MAIN ST 77030 #048-12-1989 L1988 **ORS** *020 †40

STOECKELHUBER, Beate M. ■ 77025 #409-16-1990 **DR** *020

STOECKER-SIMON, Dawn Eile. 1707 SUNSET BLVD 77005 #039-01-2000 L2003 **IM** *020 †20

STOLAR, Andrea Gail. 2801 GESSNER DR, THE MONNINGER CLINIC 77080 #048-04-1990 L1991 **P** *030 †75

STOLZMANN, Ewelina Maria. 1213 HERMANN DR STE 700 77004 #759-04-1962 L1989 **PM** *020

STONE, Faith Marie. 5511 AUSTIN ST 77004 #047-07-1983 L1988 **OBG PD** *020

STONE, John S. 5511 AUSTIN ST 77004 #047-07-1956 L1959 **OBG** *020

STONE, Marvin Allen. 4550 POST OAK PLACE DR, STE 341 77027 #035-09-1968 L1984 **P PFP** *030 †75

STONE, Sabrina Jill. ■ 77025 #048-02-2005 **IM** *012

STONECIPHER, Harlin Keith. 1313 HERMANN DR 77004 #039-01-1963 L1964 **CD IM** *020 †20

STONER, Paul S, Jr. 2101 NASA PKWY, FLIGHT MED CLINIC/SD13 77058 #041-13-1982 L2004 **AM OM** *020 †70

STOOL, Edward Wm. 1200 BINZ ST STE 1260 77004 #021-01-1970 L1972 **PUD** *020 †20

STOREY, Carol M. 920 FROSTWOOD DR, STE 610 77024 #048-02-1985 L1986 **OBG** *030 †30

STOREY, Michael A. 150 FM 1959 RD 77034 #048-12-1989 L1995 **GS** *020 †85

STOUT, Bob Edmondson. 919 MILAM ST, STE 1830 77002 #048-02-1958 L1958 **OTO** *071 †45

STOVER, John W. ■ 77036 #048-04-1949 L1950 **IM GP** *071

STRAJA, Alexander Mircea. 6560 FANNIN ST 77030 #781-01-1954 L1971 **PME AN** *071

STRATHEARN, Lane. 6621 FANNIN ST, CC 1530 77030 #143-05-1992 L2007 *050

STRAUCH, Elizabeth M. 1905 HOLCOMBE BLVD, HOUSTON HOSPICE 77030 #048-04-1988 L1989 **IM** *020 †20

STRAUSS, Gerald Z. 3120 SOUTHWEST FWY, STE 400 77098 #065-01-1955 L1978 **GS** *071

STRAWN, John Robt. ■ 77005 #048-04-1956 L1956 **IM HEM** *071 †20

STRAX, Richard. 1919 LA BRANCH ST, ASSOCIATES 77002 #035-19-1976 L1978 **VIR DR** *020 †80

STREET, James Earl. 6565 FANNIN ST 77030 #048-02-1960 L1960 **AN PUD** *071 †45

STREET, Jerry Neville. 1140 BUSINESS CENTER DR, STE 202 77043 #041-13-1979 L1980 **ORS** *020 †40

STREITMANN, Michael J. 5009 CAROLINE ST, STE 105 77004 #048-13-1992 L1993 **PS OTO** *020 †45,65

STRIBLING, Rise Jo. 6550 FANNIN ST STE 1661, SUITE 1661 77030 #039-01-1988 L1992 **GE HEP** *020 †20

STRICKLAND, Carol A. 1315 ST JOSEPH PKWY, STE 1606 77002 #048-12-1990 L1991 **IM** *020 †20 ‡

STRICKLAND, James Leland. 6431 FANNIN ST, UTHSC DIV OF CARDIOLOGY 77030 #048-14-1999 L2002 **ICE** *020 †20

STRICKLER, Virginia Leigh. PO BOX 809045 77280 #047-20-1999 L1999 **P** *100

STRICKMAN, Neil Edward. 6624 FANNIN ST, STE 2480 77030 #035-15-1977 L1978 **CD IM** *020 †20

STRIMPEL, Patricia Alice. 1 BAYLOR PLZ, BAYLOR COLL OF MED 77030 #654-01-2006 L2006 **N** *012

STROBEL, Nathanie H. 6431 FANNIN ST, STE 3.228 77030 #048-14-1998 L2001 **MPD** *020 †55

STROEHLEIN, John R. 1515 HOLCOMBE BLVD, UNIT 436 77030 #020-02-1967 L1977 **GE IM** *020 †20

STROEHLEIN, Kristina B. 35 TIEL WAY 77019 #759-03-1964 L1977 **PTH** *020 †50

STROH, Brandon C. ■ 77024 #026-04-1998 L1999 **DR** *020 †80,28

STROHMEYER, James Arthur. 1919 LA BRANCH ST 77002 #011-02-1971 L1972 **AN** *020 †05

STROM, Eric Alan. 1515 HOLCOMBE BLVD, UT MD ANDERSON CANCER CENT 77030 #016-06-1982 L1990 **RO IM** *020 †20,80

STRONG, Louise C Connally. 1515 HOLCOMBE BLVD, BOX 209 77030 #048-02-1970 L1970 **CG** *050

STROTHER, Douglas Ray. 6621 FANNIN ST, MC3-3320 77030 #030-05-1982 L1994 **PHO PD** *020 †55

STROUD, Daniel Garber. 830 FM 1960 RD W, STE 3 77090 #021-01-1979 L1990 **TS GS** *020 †85,90

STROUSE, Christopher J. 6431 FANNIN ST, STE 5.020 77030 #048-14-2005 L2007 **AN** *012

STRUM, Angela Kay. ■ 77003 #048-04-2006 **OTO** *012

STUART, H James. 6411 FANNIN ST 77030 #048-02-1959 L1959 **P ADP** *071 †75

STUART, Mark A S. 17270 RED OAK DR, STE 200 77090 #836-01-1966 L1977 **ORS** *020 †40

STUART, Michael Henry. ■ 77025 #048-02-1996 **P** *100

STUBBERS, Sheena Yvette. 6565 FANNIN ST, INTERNAL MEDICINE GROUP 77030 #048-14-1996 L1998 **IM** *040 †20

STUBBLEFIELD, Samuel Culb. 6621 FANNIN ST WT6-006 77030 #048-04-2004 L2007 **PD** *020 †55

STUBER, Frank. 6431 FANNIN ST STE 5-020 77030 #409-12-1988 *100

STUCKEY, Daniel Edward. 1980 POST OAK BLVD, STE 1900 77056 #048-04-1975 L1975 **FM MDM** *030 †18

STURGIS, Erich Madison. 1515 HOLCOMBE BLVD, UNIT 441 77030 #010-02-1990 L1998 **HNS OTO** *020 †45

STURM, Renea Michelle. ■ 77006 #048-04-2008 *012

STUTEVILLE, Joseph E. ■ 77059 #005-11-1971 L1980 **OM AM** *020 †70

SU, Alex M. 9055 KATY FWY STE 200, VILLAGE FAMILY PRACTICE 77024 #048-04-1997 L1999 **FM** *020 †18

SU, Di. 7600 BEECHNUT ST, EMERGENCY DEPARTMENT 77074 #051-04-2002 L2005 **EM** *020 †16

SU, Henry Yienghow. 6410 FANNIN ST STE 200 77030 #048-14-1989 L1990 **OBG** *020 †30

SU, Jack Meng. 6701 FANNIN ST 77030 #005-02-1994 L2001 **PHO** *020 †55

SU, Jackson. 1400 HOLCOMBE BLVD # 409, MOACC-FACULTY CTR 77030 #048-14-2001 L2005 **AN PME** *100 †05 ‡

SU, Paul Chao Ling. ■ 77036 #244-04-1973 L1982 **P** *050

SU, Spencer Henry. 10023 S MAIN ST, STE C9 77025 #048-15-2002 L2007 **NEP** *020 †20

SU, Young Y. 6431 FANNIN ST, U TX HOUSTON 77030 #043-01-1998 L2004 **CCA** *020

SUAREZ, Hugo. 7109 LAWNDALE ST, STE B 77023 #187-30-1985 L1995 **FM** *020 †18

SUAREZ, Jorge Antonio. 8090 WESTHEIMER RD, DOCTORS CARE CLINIC N, PA 77063 #187-30-1983 L1992 **FM** *020 ‡

SUAREZ, Jose Ignacio. 6501 FANNIN ST 77030 #264-04-1988 L2007 **N NS** *020 †75

SUAREZ, Marta Pilar. 6431 FANNIN ST MSB3124, MED SCH-HOUSTON 77030 #042-01-2002 L2006 **PN** *012

SUAREZ, Martha Concepcion. ■ 77075 #048-14-2006 **FP** *012

SUAREZ ALMAZOR, Maria Eug. 1515 HOLCOMBE BLVD # 437, UT MDANDERSON CANCER CTR 77030 #132-01-1979 L2006 **RHU** *100

SUBRAMANIAN, Anuradha. ■ 77025 #028-46-2000 L2007 **GS** *100 †85

SUBRAMANIAN, Shyamsunder. 1709 DRYDEN RD, STE 9.50 77030 #496-38-1994 L2005 **PCC SME** *020 †20

SUBRAMANYAM, Geetha. 17300 EL CAMINO REAL #102A 77058 #495-33-1979 L1983 **FM FPG** *018

SUBRAMANYAM, Sumitra. ■ 77054 #048-14-2008 *012

SUCHER, Joseph Frank. 6550 FANNIN ST STE 1661, SMITH TOWER 77030 #028-03-1995 L1997 **GS CCS** *020 †85

SUCHOWIECKY, David. 7505 FANNIN ST, STE 350 77054 #649-01-1973 L1978 **P PD** *020

SUELL, Douglas Michael, Jr. 7900 FANNIN ST STE 3300 77054 #048-04-1997 L2000 **PD** *020 †55

SUFFIELD, Jill J. ■ 77025 #048-14-2006 **AN** *012

SUFIAN, David Paul. 9339 NORTH LOOP E 77029 #028-78-1964, ▲ L1970 **GS VS** *071

SUH, Grace Kyungeun. ■ 77007 #008-01-2003 L2007 **HO** *012 †20

SUHADY, Tony. ■ 77030 #409-21-1991 **IM** *100

SUHR, Melanie Ann. 7200 NORTH LOOP E 77028 #048-12-1977 L1977 **P PFP** *020 †75

SUKI, Samer Said. 800 PEAKWOOD DR, STE 6F 77090 #605-01-1987 L1991 **ON HEM** *020 †20

SUKI, Wadi Nagib. 1415 LA CONCHA LN 77054 #605-01-1959 L1960 **IM NEP** *020 †20

SUKIN, Steven Wayne. 1 BAYLOR PLZ 77030 #024-07-1996 L2002 **U** *020 †95

SUKKAR, Samir Mohammed. 1616 CLEAR LAKE CITY BLVD, STE 102 77062 #021-05-1992 L1994 **PS GS** *020 †65

SUKUMARAN, Anakara V. 6565 FANNIN ST B452, DEPT. OF ANESTHESIOLOGY 77030 #495-44-1967 L1980 **AN** *020 †05

SULAK, Laura Eve. 6720 BERTNER ST 77030 #048-13-1984 L1985 **PTH** *020 †50

SULEK, Marcelle. 6501 FANNIN ST, BAYLOR OTOLARYNGOLOGY 77030 #048-04-1977 L1977 **OTO PDO** *020 †45

SULEMAN, Waseem. 6411 FANNIN ST, MEM HERMANN HLTHCARE SYS 77030 #704-02-1996 **FM** *100

SULIBURK, James William. 6431 FANNIN ST, MSB, SUITE 4.276 77030 #039-01-2001 L2003 **GS** *012

SULLIVAN, John Philip, Jr. ■ 77095 #048-02-2007 **P** *012

SULLIVAN, Thomas James. 7026 OLD KATY RD, STE 276 77024 #041-12-1969 L1971 **R** *020 †80

SULMAN, Erik Philip. 1515 HOLCOMBE BLVD, UNIT 97 4403 JONATHAN ST 77030 #041-13-2003 **RO** *012

SUMERLIN, Donald James. SUITE 810, 1415 N LOOPWEST 77008 #048-04-1965 L1965 **R** *071 †80

SUMMERS, Kathy Lynn. 7400 FANNIN ST, STE 1085 77054 #017-20-1984 L1986 **OBG** *020 †30

SUMPTER, Kristi. 12850 JONES RD STE 105 77070 #048-78-1995, ▲ L2000 **CS GS** *020

SUN, Xiaoping. 1515 HOLCOMBE BLVD, DEPT OF LAB MEDICINE UNIT 77030 #243-43-1984 L2003 **PTH** *020 †50

SUNDBECK, Lindsey K. 1 BAYLOR PLZ 350, BAYLOR COLL OF MED 77030 #048-13-2004 **P** *012

SUNDER, Laxman. 8208 GULF FWY STE 101 77017 #048-13-1999 L2002 **IM** *020 †20

SUNDERESWARAN, Lalitha L. 902 FROSTWOOD DR STE 172 77024 #495-33-1987 L1995 **CD** *020 †20

SUNG, Chung-Shin. 6624 FANNIN ST, STE 2320 77030 #036-07-1973 L1975 **CD IM** *020 †20

SUNNY, Jamie Anita. ■ 77054 #048-14-2004 L2008 **AN** *012

SUPKIS, Daniel E, Jr. ■ 77024 #048-14-1982 L1983 **AN** *020 †05

SUPPATKUL, Marisa. 1300 MOURSUND ST, UTMSI - CHILD 77030 #048-02-2002 L2005 **CHP** *020 †75

SUPSUPIN, Emilio Patacsil. ■ 77030 #748-16-1996 **RNR** *100

SUPTUESAT, Alisara. ■ 77005 #891-04-1990 **RNR** *100

SUR, Nilanjana. 10161 HARWIN DR, STE 106 77036 #495-47-1990 L2000 **PCP** *020 †50

SURABHI, Venkateswar Rao. 6431 FANNIN ST, MSB 2.130 77030 #495-57-2000 **DR** *100

SURAPANENI, Usha Rani. 8610 MARTN LTHR KNG JR, JR. BLVD 77033 #495-72-1992 L2007 **FM** *020 †18

SURESH, Maya S. 6550 FANNIN ST STE 1003, BAYLOR COLLEGE OF MEDICINE 77030 #495-65-1969 L1980 **AN** *020 †05

SURH, Linda Christine. 1200 MOURSUND ST, DEPT PED 77030 #067-01-1980 **OS PD** *050 †55

SURI, Anuj. PO BOX 20708, DEPT OF OB/GYN 77225 #047-06-2006 **OBG** *012

SUROVIK, Jamie Goodall. ■ 77007 #048-13-2006 **D** *012

SURYAM, Kodali. 4200 PORTSMOUTH ST 77027 #496-01-1971 L1978 **TS GS** *050 †85,90

SUSARLA, Sarat Chandra. 7400 FANNIN ST, STE 1130 77054 #048-02-2002 L2006 **PDP** *012 †55

SUSNOW, Lawrence Irving. 6402 MERCER ST 77005 #005-02-1973 L1997 IM *020 †20

SUSSMAN, Howard Michael. 8945 LONG POINT RD, STE 115 77055 #035-08-1959 L1972 IM GE *020 †20

SUSSMAN, Norman Leslie. 1709 DRYDEN RD STE 1500, MAIL STOP 390 77030 #836-01-1976 L1985 HEP GE *020 †20

SUTARIA, Sapna Bharat. 6621 FANNIN ST, STE A210MC 77030 #048-16-2001 L2004 PD *020 †55

SUTER, Bernhard. 6621 FANNIN ST RM A170, MC1-1000 77030 #409-02-2000 PD *012

SUTER, Robert Eduard. 211 HIGHLAND CROSS DR, STE 275 77073 #018-75-1989, ▲ L1991 EM *020 †16

SUTTER, Donna J. 2211 NORFOLK ST STE 705 77098 #048-02-1984 L1986 P *020 †75

SUTTER, Kari. ■ 77006 #011-02-2002 L2008 RHU *012 †20

SUTTON, Anthony M. ■ 77021 #048-14-2007 *012

SUTTON, Fred Milton, Jr. 1709 DRYDEN RD STE 800, BAYLOR COLGE OF MED 77030 #025-01-1979 L1980 GE IM *040 †20

SUTTON, Jeffrey P. 1 BAYLOR PLZ NA-425 77030 #065-01-1982 L1987 P CHP *050 †75

SUTTON, John Jason. ■ 77030 #048-14-2008 *012

SUTTON, Mark Allen. 6560 FANNIN ST, STE 1270 77030 #054-04-1992 L1998 U GS *020 †95 ‡

SUTTON, Phillip Gordon. 17203 RED OAK DR STE 203 77090 #048-02-1974 L1974 GS *020 †85

SUTTON, Richard Evan. 2015 THOMAS ST, THOMAS ST CLINIC 77009 #005-11-1989 L1999 ID *020 †20

SUTTON, Vernon Reid. 6701 FANNIN ST, 16TH FL CLINICAL CARE CTR 77030 #020-12-1992 L1999 MG CG *020 †20

SUZAWA, Hilary Su-Yin. 3601 N MACGREGOR WAY, MLK CLINIC 77004 #048-04-2001 L2005 MPD *100 †20,55 ‡

SUZ RUIZ, Maria Del Pilar. PO BOX 20708, UNIV TX MED SCH 77225 #264-04-1999 L2005 AN *012

SVATEK, Mandie Tibball. 6431 FANNIN ST, DEPARTMENT OF PEDIATRICS 77030 #048-02-2002 L2005 PD *020 †55

SVATEK, Robert Scott. ■ 77030 #048-02-2002 L2004 U *100

SVOBODA, Sarah Lynn. 1635 NORTH LOOP W 77008 #030-05-1998 L1999 EM *020 †16

SWAFFORD, Joseph. 1515 HOLCOMBE BLVD # 433 77030 #010-03-1978 L1984 CD IM *020 †20

SWAFFORD, Melba W. 6550 FANNIN ST STE 1003, 9115 RIDDLEWOOD LANE 77030 #010-03-1979 L1983 AN *040 †05

SWAIM, Laurie Sue. 6431 FANNIN ST # MSB3-204, UT MED SCHOOL 77030 #039-01-1989 L1993 OBG *020 †30

SWANN, Alan Craig. 6431 FANNIN ST # 5236 77030 #048-12-1972 L1981 P *050 †75

SWANSON, David Allen. 1515 HOLCOMBE BLVD, DEPT UROLOGY-UNIT 1373 77030 #041-01-1967 L1976 U SO *072 †95

SWANSON, Dixie Cobb. 6621 FANNIN ST 77030 #048-04-1978 L1978 PD *020 †55

SWANZY, Elisabeth E. ■ 77006 #048-13-2006 RO *012

SWARR, Daniel Todd. ■ 77047 #041-01-2007 PD *012

SWATE, Tommy Ernest. 10900 NORTHWEST FWY, STE 127 77092 #021-01-1971 L1975 OBG P *020 †30

SWEENEY, Alex Daniel. ■ 77004 #048-04-2008 *012

SWEENEY, Michael Sandlin. 6560 FANNIN ST, STE 1824 77030 #048-04-1976 L1976 TS *020 †85,90

SWENSON, Richard Terry. 6550 MAPLERIDGE ST STE 120 77081 #048-04-1967 L1967 GP *020

SWICK, Todd Jay. 7500 SAN FELIPE ST, STE 525 77063 #035-48-1974 L1980 N SME *020 †75 ‡

SWINFORD, Rita D. 6431 FANNIN ST STE 3.236A, PEDIATRICS DIV OF NEPHROLO 77030 #035-48-1990 L1998 PN *020 †55

SWISHER, Stephen Gauger. 1515 HOLCOMBE BLVD BOX 109, DEPT THORACIC SURG 77030 #005-18-1986 L1994 TS *020 †85,90

SY, Jama Suarez. 6540 BELLOWS LN, # 602 77030 #748-29-1998 L2006 CCP *012 †55

SY, Wilben Herrera. PO BOX 20708 77225 #748-01-1995 OPH *100

SYED, Athar Hamid. 2000 CRAWFORD ST, STE 777 77002 #495-01-1969 L1979 N *020 †75

SYED, Ghyasuddin. 11800 ASTORIA BLVD 77089 #704-02-1982 L2002 *020 †05 ‡

SYED, Misha Fatima. 6411 FANNIN ST, 7TH FLOOR, JONES PAVILION 77030 #048-04-2001 L2005 OPH *100 †35

SYED, Shabnam Athar. ■ 77030 #495-01-1969 L1980 R *020 †80

SYED, Shahid Hussain. 800 BELL ST, RM 3180 77002 #704-08-1974 L1997 GP *020 †70

SYED, Tanveer F. 12121 RICHMOND AVE STE 225, WESTCHASE HEALTH CLINIC 77082 #495-65-1991 L1998 IM *020 †20

SYMMANS, William Fraser. 1515 HOLCOMBE BLVD 77030 #671-02-1986 L2000 CLP *020 †50

SZALAI, Gabor. 1709 DRYDEN RD STE 9.92, SECTION OF CARDIOLOGY 77030 #473-01-1996 L2006 IC *012 ‡

SZELEI-STEVENS, Kathleen. ■ 77079 #021-05-2001 L2002 BBK *020

SZIGETI, Kinga. 1 BAYLOR PLZ MS NB302, THE NEUROSENSORY CENTER 77030 #473-03-1994 L2007 MG *100

SZIGETI, Reka Gabriella. 1 BAYLOR PLZ, DEPARTMENT OF PATHOLOGY 77030 #473-03-1997 PTH *012

SZKLARUK, Janio. 1515 HOLCOMBE BLVD BOX 368, MD ANDERSON CANCER CENTER 77030 #041-01-1993 L2001 DR *020 †80

SZWAST, Anita Louise. ■ 77025 #041-12-1999 L2003 PDC *100 †20,55

TA, Uyen Hoang. 2500 FONDREN RD, STE 130 77063 #021-05-1997 L2001 OBG *020 †30

TABCHY, Adel Bassam. 1515 HOLCOMBE BLVD, UT MD ANDERSON CANCER CENT 77030 #605-01-2001 L2007 HO *012 †20

TABER, Larry Holmes. 1 BAYLOR PLZ, MICROBIOLOGY ROOM 221D 77030 #048-04-1960 L1966 ID PD *050 †55

TABIBI, Wasae Seyed. 6624 FANNIN ST, STE 1400 77030 #048-14-1991 L1992 NEP *020 †20

TABOADA, Carlos Francisco. 2727 W HOLCOMB BLVD 4TH FL 77025 #275-01-1946 L1962 IM ON *071 †20

TABOADA, Jorge Luis. ■ 77054 #048-14-2002 L2007 DR *100 †80

TABOR, Debra Diane. 6565 FANNIN ST, TEXAS MEDICAL CENTER 77030 #048-02-1991 L1992 AN *020 †05

TABRIZI, Ali Reza. 14027 MEMORIAL DR 77079 #517-08-1973 L1982 GE IM *020 †20

TADDEO, Terrance A. ■ 77058 #038-43-1992 L1996 AM *020 †70

TADROS, Magdy Khalil. 11880 FM 1960 RD W 77065 #915-05-1979 L1997 FM *020 †18

TADROS, Nazmi Aziz. 1709 DRYDEN RD, MEDICAL TOWERS 77030 #915-02-1952 L1974 OM *071 †70

TAEGEL, Edwin Jackson. 909 FROSTWOOD DR, STE 256 77024 #048-04-1965 L1965 ORS *020 †20

TAEGTMEYER, Heinrich. 6431 FANNIN ST, DIV OF CARDIOLOGY 77030 #407-05-1968 L1983 CD IM *050 †20

TAFFET, George Efrem. 1709 DRYDEN RD, STE 850 77030 #043-01-1982 L1987 IMG *050 †20

TAGAROPULOS, Demetrio. 820 RICHMOND AVE 77006 #715-01-1971 L1977 U *020 †95

TAGGART, Melissa W. 1515 HOLCOMBE BLVD UNIT 0, UT MDACC DEPT OF PATHOLOGY 77030 #021-05-2001 L2008 SP *100 †50

TAGHADOSI, Maryam. 2600 NORTH LOOP W 163 77092 #308-12-1987 L1994 PD *020 †55

TAGHECHIAN, Shaya. 6431 FANNIN ST, UNIV OF TEXAS MED SCH 77030 #012-05-2006 U *012

TAHER, Majdi Majid A. 1200 BINZ ST, STE 460 77004 #704-16-1988 L2004 IM *020 †20

TAIT, Eric Steven. 2000 CRAWFORD ST, STE 1400 77002 #048-04-2003 L2006 IM *020 †20

TAITEL, Arthur Larry. 6545 SOUTHWEST FWY, CONCENTRA MEDICAL CENTERS 77074 #056-06-1964 L1971 GS *020 †85

TAKASE, Kouji. 6728 HIGHWAY 6 S 77083 #048-04-1981 L1982 FM *020 †18

TAKASHIMA, Masayoshi. 6501 FANNIN ST, BAYLOR OTOLARYNGOLOGY 77030 #048-04-1996 L2005 OTO *020 †20

TAKEI, Hidehiro. 6565 FANNIN ST, THE METHODIST HOSP PATH 77030 #572-76-1990 L2006 NP PCP *020 †50

TAKENAKA, Katrin Yasuko. 6540 BELLOWS LN 77030 #048-14-1996 L1997 EM *020 †16

TALAKKOTTUR, Charles Davi. PO BOX 20708 77225 #654-01-2004 L2007 MPD *100

TALEGHANY, Ahmad S. 6550 MAPLERIDGE ST STE 216 77081 #517-01-1968 L1976 CD IM *020 †20

TALIEH, Leila. 915 GESSNER RD, STE 870 77024 #048-16-1991 L1992 IM *020 †20

TALIEH, Mohammad. 8945 LONG POINT RD STE 2 77055 #517-01-1960 L1974 GS GP *071

TALLACKSON, Donald Bert. 12335 KINGSRIDE LN, # 339 77024 #045-01-1989 L1994 AN *020 †05

TALMAGE, Edward A. 12121 RICHMOND AVE, STE 403 77082 #035-09-1952 L1965 PME PMM *071

TALPAZ, Moshe. 1515 HOLCOMBE BLVD 77030 #550-01-1975 L1981 ON IG *020 †20

TALPUR, Rakhshandra. 1515 HOLCOMBE BLVD 77030 #704-08-1991 D *020 †20

TALUKDAR, Rudranath. 13300 HARGRAVE RD, STE 190 77070 #495-39-1988 L2003 ON *020 †20

TALWALKAR, Sameer S. ■ 77054 #496-44-2001 L2004 HMP *012

TAM, Alda L. 1515 HOLCOMBE BLVD, UNIT 325 77030 #061-01-2000 L2006 VIR *100 †80

TAMBOLI, Pheroze. 1515 HOLCOMBE BLVD 77030 #704-02-1989 L1999 SP *020 †50

TAMERISA, Ravi V. ■ 77024 #495-50-1971 L1977 AN PME *020 †05

TAMM, Eric Peter. 1515 HOLCOMBE BLVD, UNIT 0368 77030 #033-06-1991 L1997 DR *020 †80

TAN, Daniel Tiangleng. 10101 SOUTHWEST FWY, STE 510 77074 #039-05-1988 L1993 P *020 †75

TAN, Earl Eng Chow. 1919 LA BRANCH ST 77002 #244-02-1972 L1977 FM *020

TAN, Eng K. 6540 BELLOWS LN # 604 77030 #825-01-1989 N *100

TAN, Faye Chiou. 3601 N MACGREGOR WAY, DEPT PMTR 77004 #048-04-1990 L1991 PM *020 †60

TAN, Filemon K. 6431 FANNIN ST 5.270, DIVISION OF RHEUMATOLOGY 77030 #048-14-1990 L1992 RHU IM *020 †20

TAN, Grace B. 8150 SOUTHWEST FWY STE C 77074 #917-07-1983 L1997 FM *030 †18

TAN, Miguel Nokeng. 1631 NORTH LOOP W, STE 460 77008 #748-01-1976 L1993 NEP OM *020 †20

TAN, Robert See-Hoong. 2002 HOLCOMBE BLVD 110, EXTENDED CARE-MEDVAMC 77030 #825-01-1983 L1998 FM FPG *020 †18

TAN, Seang Beng. TEXAS MEDICAL CENTER, STE 2625 77030 #825-01-1981 ORS *100

TANAKA, Maria Florencia. 1 BAYLOR PLZ 77030 #132-14-2002 IM *012

TANAKAWA, Nobuo. ■ 77007 #572-29-1971 L1977 PUD PD *050 †55

TANDON, Nitin. 6410 FANNIN ST STE 10 77030 #495-73-1993 L2006 NS *020

TANG, An Thien. ■ 77084 #048-04-2003 L2006 IM *020 †20

TANG, Hsiao Chiang. 13111 EAST FWY 77015 #270-01-1999 L2003 IM *020 †20

TANG, Hsin-Yi Amy. ■ 77030 #048-02-2006 MPD *012

TANG, James. 11302 FALLBROOK DR STE 304 77065 #005-11-1975 L1981 PS HS *020 †65

TANG, Jose B, Jr. 1631 NORTH LOOP W STE 635 77008 #748-11-1965 L1972 GS *020 †85

TANG, Rosa Ana. 4901 CALHOUN RD 77004 #737-06-1974 L1975 OPH N *020 †35 ‡

TANG, Timothy Tai Thien. 12579 RICHMOND AVE, STE 800 77082 #048-02-1992 L1994 IM *020 †20

TANNERYA, Richard G. 2472 BOLSOVER ST, STE 363 77005 #065-01-1973 L1979 GP OS *020

TANNIR, Nizar M. 1515 HOLCOMBE BLVD, BOX 427 77030 #605-01-1979 L1984 ON HEM *020 †20

TANOUS, Thomas Louis. ■ 77065 #048-14-2004 ORS *012

TANYI, Janos Laszlo. 1 BAYLOR PLZ, DEPT OBG 77030 #473-04-1993 L2008 OBG *012

TAO, Xiang. 7737 SOUTHWEST FWY, STE 310 77074 #243-76-1985 L2001 RHU *020 †20

TAPIA, Carl D. 6621 FANNIN ST, CC 1540 77030 #048-04-2002 L2005 PD *020 †55 ‡

TARAIF, Suad. ■ 77030 #155-01-1996 L2003 PCP *100 †50

TARNOW, Jay Dennis. 1001 WEST LOOP S, STE 215 77027 #035-46-1972 L1979 CHP P *020 †75

TARRAND, Jeffrey James. 1515 HOLCOMBE BLVD 77030 #051-01-1981 L1988 MM OS *020 †50

TARRAND, Nancy Marshall. ■ 77096 #051-01-1985 L1990 P *020 †75

TARRANT, Marvin Rowan, II. 13111 EAST FWY, STE 206 77015 #048-04-1967 L1967 FM FPG *020 †18

TARRANT, William Paul. ■ 77021 #048-14-2007 PTH *012

TARTELL, Robert M. 7474 S KIRKWOOD RD STE 104 77072 #016-01-1975 L1980 FM GP *030

TARVER, Cynthia P. 11454 SPACE CENTER BLVD, STE B 77059 #048-13-1989 L1990 OTO *020 †45

TARVER, William J. 2101 NASA PKWY, MAIL CODE SD-13 77058 #048-13-1989 L1990 AM OM *020 †70

TASTARD, Luz Viviana. 1333 MOURSUND ST 77030 #264-01-1989 L2004 PM *020 †60

TATEVIAN, Nina. 6621 FANNIN ST, MC 1-2261 77030 #913-15-1973 L2001 PP ATP *020 †50

TATSUI, Claudio Esteves. 6540 BELLOWS LN APT 507 77030 #187-08-1999 NS *020

TATUM, James Kent. ■ 77003 #048-02-2003 L2005 DR *012

TAUL, E Jay. 7030 BRETSHIRE DR 77016 #021-05-1958 L1961 GP *071

TAUSEND, Harold Jack. ■ 77019 #048-02-1941 L1941 IM *071 †20

TAVACKOLI, Shahin. 925 GESSNER RD, STE 630 77024 #048-02-1998 L1999 CD *020 †20

TAVAKOLI-TABASI, Shahriar. ■ 77021 #902-19-1992 L1999 ID *020 †20

TAVEE, Winston D. ■ 77004 #028-46-2001 L2002 EM *012

TAVEL, Linda Lee. 7407 NORTH FWY, STE 939 77076 #048-14-1983 L1983 FM PLM *020 †18

TAVYEV, Yana Jane. ■ 77030 #048-04-2003 NDN *012

TAWAKKOL, Samer Nader. 12121 RICHMOND AVE, STE 408 77082 #025-07-1989 L2001 ORS OAR *020 †40

TAYLOR, Addison A, III. 1709 DRYDEN RD RM 06.30, BAYLOR COLLEGE OF MED 77030 #028-03-1970 L1977 PA IM *050 †20

TAYLOR, Alan Chas. ■ 77035 #048-14-1977 L1977 EM GP *075 †16

TAYLOR, Barbara L H. ■ 77004 #048-04-1963 L1974 **P CHP** *071 †75
TAYLOR, Harold Newell. 12727 KIMBERLEY LN 77024 #018-03-1947 L1954 **IM** *071
TAYLOR, Jennifer Marie. ■ 77007 #048-14-2004 **U** *012
TAYLOR, Joe Robt. 1919 LA BRANCH ST 77002 #048-12-1976 L1976 **IM** *072
TAYLOR, Kristal Dawn. ■ 77006 #047-06-2007 **OBG** *012
TAYLOR, Michael David. 6621 FANNIN ST, MC 19345-C 77030 #056-05-2001 L2006 **PDC** *100 †55
TAYLOR, Sharonda Alston. ■ 77047 #023-07-2002 L2007 **ADL** *012
TAYLOR, Thomas Vincent. 1315 ST JOSEPH PKWY, STE 1800 77002 #917-08-1968 L1997 **GS** *020
TAYLOR, Tiffany A. ■ 77054 #048-14-2006 L2008 **PD** *012
TAYLOR, Wade Wm, Jr. 12727 KIMBERLEY LN 77024 #649-14-1979 L1986 **AN PME** *020 †05
TAYLOR-COX, Barbara J. 12606 W HOUSTON CENTR BLVD, STE 280 77082 #048-14-1985 L1986 **PD** *020 †55
TAYYAN, Nawar Marwan. 11920 ASTORIA BLVD, STE 220 77089 #605-01-1996 L2001 **CD IC** *020 †20
TCHARMTCHI, Mohammad H. 6621 FANNIN ST 2-3450, SECTION OF CRITICAL CARE M 77030 #154-07-1988 L1999 **PD CCP** *020 †55
TEETERS, Van Wayne. 1200 BINZ ST, VITREORETINAL CONSULTANTS 77004 #048-02-1967 L1967 **OPH OS** *071 †35
TEH, Bin Lin. 2002 HOLCOMBE BLVD, VETERANS AFFAIRS MEDICAL C 77030 #143-05-1993 L2005 **DR** *020 †80
TEH, Bin Sing. 6565 FANNIN ST, STE DB1-077 77030 #143-05-1990 L1999 **RO** *020 †80
TEICH, Andrew Franklin. ■ 77030 #035-01-2006 L2008 **PTH** *012
TEICHGRAEBER, Davis Chris. ■ 77025 #048-02-2004 L2007 **DR** *012
TEICHGRAEBER, John Flynn. 6431 FANNIN ST, STE 5.254 77030 #012-05-1978 L1983 **PS HNS** *020 †45,65
TEITEL, Edward Ray. ■ 77096 #048-13-1978 L1978 **GS MDM** *030 †85
TEJADA, Carlos T. ■ 77027 #737-01-1969 **OBG** *020
TEJANI, Mehul Navin. 23 SUNSET BLVD 77005 #048-04-2007 L2007 **IM** *012
TEJWANI, Ajay. ■ 77054 #021-01-2008 †012
TELLEZ, Maria Emilia. 6621 FANNIN ST 77030 #649-30-1995 L2002 **PD** *020 †55
TENARO, Leslie J. 1201 DAIRY ASHFORD ST 77079 #012-05-1984 L1995 **D** *020 †15
TENCZYNSKI, Theodore F. 1631 NORTH LOOP W STE 155 77008 #033-05-1972 L1976 **ON IM** *020
TENN, Andrew Gordon. ■ 77025 #005-19-2004 **DR** *012
TENNANT, Lucile B. ■ 77266 #048-12-1991 L1992 **PP** *020 †50
TENNEY, Meaghan Elizabeth. ■ 77054 #011-02-2004 L2008 **OBG** *012
TENNYSON, Kenneth Barniel. 1917 ASHLAND ST 77008 #027-01-1967 L1971 **DR R** *020 †80
TERAN, Jose M, Jr. 6621 FANNIN ST, TEXAS CHILDREN'S HOSPITAL 77030 #429-02-1985 L1995 **PDP PD** *020
TERAN, Julio C. 5161 SAN FELIPE ST, STE 320 77056 #682-01-1968 L1984 **CD IM** *020 †20
TERASAWA, Masashisa. 7000 FANNIN ST 77030 #572-50-1973 **CD IM** *050 †20
TERASHIMA, Keita. 6621 FANNIN ST CC15100, TEXAS CHILDREN'S HOSP 77030 #572-58-1998 **PHO** *012 †55
TEREFFE, Welela. ■ 77002 #035-19-2000 L2005 **RO** *100 †80
TERLONGE, Delouis, Jr. 6621 FANNIN ST 1570, TEXAS CHILDREN'S HOSPITAL 77030 #048-04-2000 L2003 **PD** *020 †55
TERNENY, Orlando Julio M. 6624 FANNIN ST, CARDIOLOGY ASSOCIATES PA 77030 #935-02-1964 L1971 **IM OS** *071 †20
TERRADAS MIARNAU, Maria D. ■ 77054 #847-12-1987 **CCP** *100
TERREL, Jeffrey Wm. 1919 LA BRANCH ST, ST JOSEPH HOSPITAL 77002 #048-04-1973 L1973 **PTH** *020 †50
TERRELL, Correna L. ■ 77030 #048-04-1993 L1998 **DR** *020 †80
TERRELL, John Butler, Jr. 902 FROSTWOOD DR, STE 171 77024 #048-04-1965 L1965 **OS IM** *020 †20
TERRILL, Louise A Bednar. 9105 N WAYSIDE DR 77028 #019-02-1973 L1980 **IM** *020
TERRY, Jaimie Elizabeth. 1200 BINZ ST, STE 630 77004 #016-06-1989 L1990 **GS** *020 †85
TERUYA, Jun. 6621 FANNIN ST, TX CHILDRENS HOSP MC1-2261 77030 #572-29-1979 L2002 **CLP BBK** *020 †50
TEW, Brian Haralson. 1200 SMITH ST, 400 CITICORP CENTER 77002 #048-13-1978 L1978 **FM** *020
TEW, Stephen Alter. 3400 BISSONNET ST STE 206 77005 #048-13-1975 L1975 **PYA P** *020 †75
TEWANI, Sonia Kamlesh. ■ 77030 #024-05-2008 †012
TEXTER, Karen Marie. 6621 FANNIN ST 19345-C, TEXAS CHILDRENS HOSPITAL 77030 #048-04-2001 L2007 **PDC** *020 †55
THACKER, Seema. 3737 DACOMA ST, NORTH WEST MHMRA 77092 #495-08-1985 L1996 **P** *020 †75
THAI, Nguyen Sam. 8250 BELLAIRE BLVD STE 1 77036 #941-01-1977 L1985 **PD** *020
THAI, Ryan T. 2808 MAIN ST, STE F 77006 #048-13-1999 L2000 **FM** *020 †18
THAKAR, Dilip R. 1400 HOLCOMBE BLVD, BOX 409 77030 #495-92-1983 L1993 **AN** *020 †05
THAKER, Anil P. 915 GESSNER RD STE 100, MEDICAL PLAZA 3 77024 #305-01-2001 L2006 **IMG** *020
THAKER, Kamlesh Babubhai. 6565 FANNIN ST STE B452, METHODIST HOSPITAL, ANESTH 77030 #495-23-1979 L1985 **CCM AN** *020,05
THAKKAR, Harish N. 9220 HIGHWAY 6 S, STE E 77083 #495-22-1984 L1996 **IM** *020 †20
THAKKAR, Heena Narendra. 1740 W 27TH ST STE 305 77008 #496-38-1969 L1975 **PD** *020 †55
THAKKAR, Kalpesh Harshad. 6621 FANNIN ST, CCC 1010 77030 #048-15-2001 L2004 **PG** *100 †55
THAKKAR, Shilpa Narendra. ■ 77019 #048-14-2006 **PD** *012
THAKUR, Rajiv Prithviraj. 2001 HERMANN DR, STE 205 77004 #028-03-1994 L2000 **VIR** *020 †80
THALLER, Richard Michael. 9055 KATY FWY, STE 420 77024 #028-03-1969 L1974 **PD GP** *020 †55
THAM, Yee Lu. 6620 MAIN ST STE 1385, BAYLOR COLLEGE OF MEDICINE 77030 #143-05-1992 L2001 **ON** *020 †20
THAPAR, Mohinder Kumar. 6431 FANNIN ST 3.126, UNIV OF TX MEDICAL SCHOOL 77030 #495-29-1962 L1979 **PDC PD** *020 †20
THAPAR, Renu Kapur. 12121 RICHMOND AVE STE 114 77082 #495-45-1964 L1982 **P PYG** *020 †75
THARAPPEL-JACOB, Reena An. 1051 PINELOCH DR STE 600 77062 #305-01-2001 L2005 **OBG** *020 †30
THAVER, Ghulam Hussain. ■ 77069 #704-25-2001 L2007 **DR** *012 †28
THAYER, Patricia Sowder. 920 FROSTWOOD DR, STE 610 77024 #048-04-1993 L1994 **OBG** *020 †30

THEKDI, Apurva Arvind. 6550 FANNIN ST, STE 2001 77030 #028-02-1997 L2008 **OTO** *020
THERIAULT, Rachel Leigh. ■ 77004 #048-04-2004 L2007 **IM** *012 †20
THERIAULT, Richard L. 1515 HOLCOMBE BLVD, BOX 424 77030 #028-79-1973, ▲ L1984 **ON IM** *020
THIAGARAJAN, Perumal. 6431 FANNIN 5292 MSB, UNIV TX MED SCH DEPT HEM 77030 #495-95-1974 L1998 **HEM IM** *020 †20
THIAGARAJAN, Ram. 902 FROSTWOOD DR, STE 215 77024 #048-12-1992 L1994 **CD** *020 †20
THIESSEN, Craig Peter. 12121 RICHMOND AVE, STE 109 77082 #062-01-1975 L1978 **DR** *020 †80
THIGPEN, Matthew A. ■ 77025 #048-13-2005 **GS** *012
THIRUMALAIRAJ, Jayakumar. 7737 SOUTHWEST FWY STE 830 77074 #495-42-1974 L1982 **VS** *020 †20
THIRUMURTHI, Selvi. ■ 77098 #011-04-2000 L2005 **GE** *100 †20
THOLANY, Alice. 1919 S BRAESWOOD BLVD, 5TH FL 77030 #048-14-1999 L2004 **PD** *020 †55
THOLANY, Justin Joseph. 1415 NORTH LOOP W, STE 820 77008 #033-05-1998 L2004 **DR** *020 †80
THOMANN, Ariel Jose. ■ 77024 #048-04-1963 L1963 **OM AM** *030 †70
THOMAS, Andrew. ■ 77066 #759-08-1952 L1973 **FM OBG** *071
THOMAS, Angela C. ■ 77035 #048-04-1994 L1997 **FM** *020 †18
THOMAS, Ann E. 6621 FANNIN ST STE A210, MC 1-1481 77030 #035-15-2003 L2006 **PEM** *012 †55
THOMAS, Christine G. 6431 FANNIN ST, SCHOOL A 77030 #048-14-2007 **PD** *012
THOMAS, Debi Ann. 1515 HOLCOMBE BLVD, DEPT OF LEUKEMIA UNIT 428 77030 #008-02-1992 L1998 **HO** *050 †20
THOMAS, Elson Mathew. ■ 77054 #048-13-2006 **IM** *012
THOMAS, Eric J. 6431 FANNIN ST 1.122, UT HOUSTON MEDICAL SCHOOL 77030 #048-12-1989 L1990 **IM** *050 †20
THOMAS, Erica Lynn. ■ 77001 #001-02-2005 L2008 **PD** *012
THOMAS, George, Jr. ■ 77096 #035-08-2002 L2006 **AN** *020
THOMAS, Georgia Anne. 1515 HOLCOMBE BLVD # 218 77030 #038-40-1973 L1983 **OM ADM** *020 †20
THOMAS, James Herman, Jr. ■ 77227 #048-02-1981 L1981 **FM R** *020
THOMAS, John Russell. 1313 HERMANN DR 77004 #020-02-1945 L1951 **PTH** *071
THOMAS, Justin K. ■ 77054 #048-14-2008 †012
THOMAS, Kelly Latreece. 1 BAYLOR PLZ, BAYLOR COLLEGE OF MEDICINE 77030 #048-04-2004 L2007 **IM** *100 †20
THOMAS, Mathew T. ■ 77054 #048-16-2001 L2005 **EM** *020 †16
THOMAS, Melanie Byrne. 4259 LEHIGH AVE 77005 #024-05-1996 L2001 **ON** *020 †20
THOMAS, Melissa Susan. ■ 77030 #020-02-2003 **CN** *012
THOMAS, Milton Moore. 2 RIVERWAY, STE 1200 77056 #035-08-1977 L1981 **IM** *020 †20
THOMAS, Patricia Elizabet. ■ 77081 #021-05-2003 L2008 **PDC** *012 †55
THOMAS, Sandhya Sara. ■ 77025 #048-14-2006 **IM** *012
THOMAS, Sellers J, Jr. ■ 77056 #021-01-1948 L1951 **GS TS** *071 †85
THOMAS, Sindhu Mariam. 6431 FANNIN ST STE 1.134, AT HOUST 77030 #048-14-2003 L2006 **NEP** *012 †20
THOMAS, Stephen Michael. 15655 CYPRESSWOOD MEDCL DR, STE 100 77014 #024-05-1998 L2001 **FM** *020 †18
THOMAS, Steven Martz. 12121 RICHMOND AVE, STE 312 77082 #048-04-1986 L1987 **GS** *020 †85
THOMAS, Sutha. 1818 MEMORIAL DR, STE 200 77007 #495-99-1989 L2005 **PD** *020
THOMAS, Valencia Dorchell. 1515 HOLCOMBE BLVD BOX 434, DEPT OF DERMATOLOGY 77030 #016-02-2000 L2008 **D** *100 †15
THOMAS, Zachariah. 6720 BERTNER ST 77030 #496-40-1994 L2002 **CCA AN** *020 †05
THOMAS BAHAR, Valerie. 7737 SOUTHWEST FWY, STE 320 77074 #048-12-1989 L1991 **OBG** *020 †30
THOMAZY, Vilmos Antal. 1504 TAUB LOOP 77030 #473-04-1977 L2003 **PTH** *020 †50
THOMPSON, David Allan. 6550 FANNIN ST STE 2307 77030 #064-01-1974 L1978 **CRS** *020 †10,85
THOMPSON, Dorothy. 5615 KIRBY DR, STE 440 77005 #917-14-1977 L1995 **PD** *020 †55
THOMPSON, Jeffrey Brian. 1120 NASA PKWY, STE 205 77058 #048-14-2001 L2004 **EM** *020 †16
THOMPSON, Katherine H. 7400 FANNIN ST STE 700 77054 #056-06-1990 L1996 **CG CCG** *020 †55,19
THOMPSON, Matthew Martin. 6655 TRAVIS ST # 590, DEPT OF PSYCHIATRY 77030 #048-02-1997 L1999 **PYG** *020 †75
THOMPSON, Melissa L. 2424 W HOLCOMBE BLVD, MEDICAL CENTER ANESTHESIA 77030 #048-13-1990 L1991 **AN** *020 †05
THOMPSON, Patrick Andrew. 6621 FANNIN 1410.0 77030 #048-04-2001 L2007 **PHO** *020 †55
THOMPSON, Paul Melville. 13111 EAST FWY 77015 #055-01-1991 L1994 **DR** *020 †80
THOMPSON, Peter Kempner. 7600 FANNIN ST 77054 #048-02-1964 L1964 **GYN** *071 †30
THOMPSON, Rachel Jane A. 7400 FANNIN ST STE 1050 77054 #048-04-1980 L1980 **OBG** *020 †30
THOMPSON, Randall Leslie. 14441 MEMORIAL DR STE 3 77079 #016-02-1940 **OS** *071
THOMPSON, Saween Kaur. 6410 FANNIN ST, STE 170 77030 #048-04-1996 L1997 **DR** *020 †80
THOMPSON, Steven Douglas. 2211 NORFOLK ST STE 737 77098 #048-02-1975 L1975 **ORS** *020 †40
THOMPSON, William Raymond. 1313 HERMANN DR STE 270 77004 #048-02-1979 L1979 **AN** *020 †05
THOMSON, Cole Taggart. 909 FROSTWOOD DR STE 336 77024 #035-46-2000 L2006 **GE** *020 †20
THOMSON, Hugh K. 2525 NORTH LOOP W, STE 412 77008 #048-02-1989 L1991 **AN** *020 †05
THONG, Weng Yu. 714 FM 1960 RD W, STE 206 77090 #143-05-1993 L2003 **AN** *020 †05
THORNE, F G. 6720 BERTNER ST 77030 #065-09-1985 L1997 **AN** *020 †18
THORNTON, Carmen M. 18220 TOMBALL PKWY, STE 400 77070 #048-02-1988 L1990 **OBG** *020 †30
THORNTON-MOTT, Wanda L. 6624 FANNIN ST, STE 1800 77030 #048-04-1977 L1977 **OBG** *020 †30
THOSANI, Nirav Chandrakan. ■ 77025 #495-76-2004 **IM** *012
THOTA, Chandralatha N. 906 WAYSIDE DR 77011 #495-65-1973 L1977 **GP** *020
THRASH, John Francis. 10000 MEMORIAL DR, STE 200 77024 #048-04-1981 L1981 *020
THUAN, Tran Van. ■ 77069 #941-01-1964 L1979 **GP** *020
THUKRAL, Sucheta. 7777 SOUTHWEST FWY, STE 756 77074 #496-07-1964 L1977 **PM OS** *020 †60
THURMAN, Douglas Randolph. 275 LANTERN BEND DR # 200 77090 #048-14-1983 L1983 **GE** *020 †20

THURSTON, Andrew Lawton. ■ 77054 #048-04-2008 *012

TIEU, Kenneth Khiem. ■ 77007 #041-14-2005 **GS** *012

TILLIS, Cea Chenea. 6431 FANNIN ST 3232 77030 #021-05-2004 L2007 **NPM** *012

TILNEY, Vanessa Kristina. 4545 POST OAK PLACE DR, STE 130 77027 #048-02-1999 L2003 **MPD** *020 †20

TIMMINS, Audra Elisabeth. 6620 MAIN ST 77030 #048-04-1996 L1998 **OBG** *020 †30

TIMMINS, Katherine S. 4407 YOAKUM BLVD, STE B 77006 #048-15-1991 L1992 **NEP IM** *020 †20

TING, Joseph Chao. 1400 HOLCOMBE BLVD # 409, DEPT OF ANESTH PAIN MED 77030 #028-78-2000, ▲ L2005 **AN PME** *020 †05

TINKER, Arlene. 2510 WASHINGTON AVE 77007 #035-15-1994 L2006 **FM** *020 †18

TINTNER, Roni. 6560 FANNIN ST, DEPT OF NEURO STE 802 77030 #011-03-1980 L1981 **N** *020 †75

TIN-U, Caesar K. 6411 FANNIN ST 77030 #209-01-1985 L1999 **HO IM** *020 †20

TIPPETT, Jason Clint. ■ 77054 #048-14-2008 *012

TITUS, Patrick A. ■ 77091 #010-03-1953 L1961 **FM OBG** *020

TIWARI, Pinky Sajala. 6624 FANNIN ST STE 2190 77030 #021-01-1990 L1996 **N CN** *020 †75

TJIA, Imelda Michelle. 6621 FANNIN ST STE A300, MC2-1495 77030 #048-14-1995 L1999 **AN** *020 †05

TJOA, Weilie. 1315 ST JOSEPH PKWY, STE 1007 77002 #048-14-1982 L1984 **OBG** *020 †30

TO, Brandon Nghia. 3648 FM 1960 RD W, STE 104 77068 #021-05-1997 L2003 **EM** *020 †16

TODD, Josh Weber. 1709 DRYDEN RD STE 550 77030 #012-01-2004 L2006 **CD** *012 †20

TODD, Samual R. 6550 FANNIN ST STE 1661A 77030 #048-15-1996 L2001 **GS TRS** *020 †85

TOKUNAGA, Chris Chikazu. 2002 HOLCOMBE BLVD STOP 11 77030 #305-01-1985 L1993 **P ADM** *020 †15

TOLAND, Dennis Merrit. 11301 FALLBROOK DR, STE 214 77065 #048-13-1973 L1973 **GE IM** *020

TOLL, Julie K. 1111 AUGUSTA DR, KELSEY SEYBOLD 77057 #048-14-1987 L1990 **FM** *020 †18

TOLPIN, Daniel Aryeh. 1 BAYLOR PLZ, DEPT OF ANESTH SM1003 77030 #041-02-2004 L2008 **AN** *012

TOM, Cindy Waytoon. 6720 BERTNER ST RM P355, EPISCOPAL HOSPITAL 77030 #005-15-2002 L2008 **CD** *012 †20

TOM, Donald. 7600 BEECHNUT ST 77074 #048-13-2001 L2003 **AN** *020 †05

TOMA, George Badeah. ■ 77054 #021-01-2002 L2005 **AN** *012

TOMA, Maha B. 1707 BRITTMOORE RD 77043 #528-01-1985 L1998 **IM** *020 †20

TOMJANOVICH, Nichole R. 2323 S SHEPHERD DR STE 101 77019 #048-02-2002 L2006 **P** *020 †75

TOMM, Karl Elmer. 6560 FANNIN ST STE 1846 77030 #016-06-1965 L1971 **GS TS** *020 †85,90

TOMPSON, Matthew L. 6560 FANNIN ST, STE 600 77030 #048-14-1998 L2001 **GE** *020 †20

TOOMBS, Barry Donald. 6720 BERTNER ST 77030 #048-02-1974 L1974 **DR VIR** *020 †80

TOPKARA, Veli Kemal. 1709 DRYDEN RD STE 550, BCM FACULTY CTR 77030 #902-05-2004 L2005 **IM** *012

TOPPELL, Kenneth Lawrence. 1213 HERMANN DR STE 570 77004 #012-05-1968 L1975 **PCC IM** *020 †20

TORN, Secily Whittenberg. 915 GESSNER RD, STE 760 77024 #048-02-1999 L2002 **PD** *020 †55

TORO BOTERO, Hugo Mario. 9105 N WAYSIDE DR STE 100 77028 #264-20-1989 L1997 **IM** *020 †20

TORRANCE, Shaunna A. ■ 77006 #048-14-2008 *012

TORRE-AMIONE, Guillermo. 6550 FANNIN ST STE 1901, THE METHODIST HOSPITAL 77030 #649-30-1985 L1993 **CD IM** *020 †20

TORRES, Ana M Botello. 3527 ELLA BLVD 77018 #048-02-1996 L1998 **MPD** *020 †20

TORRES, Arturo Alejo. 6 CHELSEA BLVD STE A 77006 #005-06-1979 L1987 **CHP P** *030 †75

TORRES, Cherie Aimee. 6630 DE MOSS DR 77074 #042-01-1997 L2000 **PD OS** *050 †55

TORRES, Elvis. 12000 RICHMOND AVE, STE 220 77082 #011-75-1991, ▲ L1996 **OBG** *020 †30

TORRES, Laura. 6621 FANNIN ST STE A300, TEXAS CHILDREN'S HOSPITAL 77030 #024-01-1988 L1992 **AN** *020 †05,55

TORRES, Lora Lisa. 3303 FM 1960 RD W, STE 420 77068 #048-02-1996 L2000 **PD** *020

TORRES, Mylin Ann. 1515 HOLCOMBE BLVD, ANDERSON CANC 77030 #005-11-2003 **RO** *012

TORRES, Nora Upina. 13018 WOODFOREST BLVD, STE A 77015 #748-08-1973 L1980 **PD** *020 †55

TORRES CABALA, Carlos Ant. ■ 77030 #737-05-1994 L2006 **DMP** *012 †50

TORRES PEREZ, Harrys Anto. 6431 FANNIN ST 1134, UNIV OF TEXAS-HOUSTON 77030 #935-06-1995 **IM** *012

TORREY, Susan Beth. 6621 FANNIN ST, TEXAS CHILDREN'S HOSPITAL 77030 #008-02-1989 L2007 **EM PD** *050 †55,16

TOSTO, Sebastian Thos, Jr. 2727 W HOLCOMBE BLVD, KELSEY-SEYBOLD CLINIC 77025 #033-06-1992 L2006 **MPD** *020 †20

TOTH, Robert Stephen. 4519 YOAKUM BLVD 77006 #048-04-1976 L1976 **LM FM** *071

TOTORICA, Marcelo. 1315 ST JOSEPH PKWY, STE 1507 77002 #011-04-1999 L2003 **OBG** *020 †20

TOTZ, Robert Stahl. 909 FROSTWOOD DR, STE 203 77024 #048-02-1970 L1970 **D** *020 †15

TOUNG, David Dara. ■ 77030 #048-04-2007 L2008 **IM** *012

TOUNG, James Shihchun. 7908 N SAM HOUSTON PKWY W, STE 200 77064 #051-01-2000 L2005 **OTO** *020 †45

TOVAR, T Jose Antonio. ■ 77074 #264-01-1957 L1970 **AN PD** *071

TOW, Adela May Peh-Er. 1 BAYLOR PLZ 77030 #825-01-1987 **PM** *100

TOWBIN, Jeffrey Allen. 6621 FANNIN ST, TX CHILDRENS HOSP PED CARD 77030 #038-41-1982 L1987 **PDC OS** *020 †55

TOWHIDI, Ali Akbar. 7777 SOUTHWEST FWY STE 358 77074 #517-01-1951 L1973 **GS PS** *071 †85

TOWNS, Graham C. 1709 DRYDEN RD STE 550, BCM FACULTY CENTER 77030 #048-02-2006 **IM** *012

TOY, Eugene Chuck. 1819 CRAWFORD ST STE 1708, ST JOSEPH'S HOSPITAL 77002 #048-04-1986 L1987 **OBG** *020 †18,30

TOZZI, Federico. 6550 FANNIN ST 77030 #561-19-2003 **GS** *012

TRABANINO, Jose Guillermo. 2500 FONDREN RD, STE 270 77063 #341-01-1971 L1980 **GE** *020 †20

TRABANINO-CALDERON, R. ■ 77006 #341-01-1973 *100

TRABER, Peter Geo. 6620 MAIN ST, STE 1225 77030 #025-07-1981 L2006 **GE IC** *030 †20

TRACHTENBERG, Barry Herma. ■ 77030 #048-13-2005 L2007 **IM** *012

TRAIN, Louis M. 2626 S LOOP W, STE 555 77054 #065-01-1962 L1977 **FM** *020 †18

TRAN, Alan Dinh. 13734 STATE HWY 249, STE B 77086 #048-14-1992 L1993 **FM** *020 †18

TRAN, Benson D. ■ 77040 #048-02-2008 *012

TRAN, Charles Quang. 7737 SOUTHWEST FWY STE 42, RES PRGM 77074 #048-02-2004 L2008 **FP** *012

TRAN, Chau My. ■ 77011 #748-10-2004 **FP** *012

TRAN, Connie K. 3 WINDERMERE LN 77063 #048-16-1991 L1993 **AN** *020 †05

TRAN, Dat Quoc. 1 BAYLOR PLZ 77030 #021-01-2001 L2004 **AI** *100 †55,03

TRAN, Duyen My. 17115 RED OAK DR, STE 207 77090 #048-13-2000 L2003 **IM** *020 †20 ‡

TRAN, Giang Dong. 2002 HOLCOMBE BLVD, DEPT. OF ANESTHESIOLOGY 77030 #941-01-1975 L1982 **AM** *020

TRAN, Giang L. 5656 KELLEY ST 1EC900, LBJ GENERAL HOSPITAL 77026 #048-12-1998 L2000 **IM** *020 †20

TRAN, Ha. 9115 BELLAIRE BLVD, STE 121 77036 #941-01-1968 L1982 **PTH** *020

TRAN, Hien Lan. 12141 RICHMOND AVE 77082 #051-07-1997 L2000 **EM** *020 †16

TRAN, Hiep Huu. 1709 DRYDEN RD STE 1700, BCM ANESTHESIOLOGY 77030 #048-15-2003 L2006 **AN** *020

TRAN, Joe Q. 6701 FANNIN ST, BAYLOR COLLEGE OR MEDICINE 77030 #048-04-2000 L2003 **PD** *020 †55

TRAN, Khoa Dinh. 10311 N ELDRIDGE PKWY, STE B4 77065 #041-01-1999 L2004 **OTO** *020 †45 ‡

TRAN, Ky-Dieu T. ■ 77030 #019-02-2008 *012

TRAN, Lee Thien. ■ 77054 #048-04-2004 L2008 **OPH** *012

TRAN, Mai Kim. ■ 77054 #048-14-2008 *012

TRAN, Michael H. 12121 RICHMOND AVE, STE 10 77082 #039-01-1989 L2001 **DR EM** *020 †80

TRAN, Minh A. 902 FROSTWOOD DR, STE 188 77024 #048-14-1998 L2001 **PCC** *020 †20

TRAN, Nicole N. 7400 FANNIN ST, STE 1050 77054 #048-15-2000 L2004 **OBG** *020 †30

TRAN, Paul Chi Tien. 2918 MILAM ST 77006 #941-01-1965 L1979 **FM IM** *075 †18

TRAN, Thao Minhphuong. 6550 FANNIN ST, STE 2501 77030 #026-04-1995 L1999 **PM** *020 †60

TRAN, Thinh Hoang. 6565 FANNIN ST, M101 77030 #026-04-1992 L1996 **IM** *020 †20

TRAN, Thuyvan Thi. 5615 KIRBY DR, STE 440 77005 #016-42-1996 L2002 **NPM** *020 †55

TRAN, Tinh Van. 2420 DUNLAVY ST 77006 #048-14-1968 L1978 **PM FM** *020 †18

TRAN, Tony T. 8535 DAWNRIDGE DR 77071 #048-12-1997 L2001 **CD** *020 †20

TRAN, Tranbetty Thai. ■ 77034 #016-06-2005 **IM** *012

TRAN, Tuan Q. 6624 FANNIN ST STE 1730 77030 #048-13-1997 L1999 **IM** *020 †20

TRAN, Tuyen Viet. 6624 FANNIN ST STE 1900, SUITE 1900 77030 #048-02-1986 L1987 **IM** *020 †20

TRAN, Vu Phi. ■ 77057 #048-02-2005 **AN** *012

TRANVAN, Que. 1315 CALHOUN ST 77002 #941-01-1971 L1986 **OBG** *075

TRANVINH, Eric. ■ 77054 #048-12-2008 *012

TRAPANI, Leonard V. 1400 HOLCOMBE BLVD, BOX 409 77030 #561-17-1990 L2002 **CCA** *020

TRASK, Todd Wilson. 6560 FANNIN ST STE 944, SCURLOCK TOWER 77030 #036-01-1989 L1996 **NS** *020 †25

TRAUTMANN, Johan Karl. 17150 EL CAMINO REAL, STE E 77058 #836-04-1984 L1994 **AN** *020 †05

TRAUTNER, Barbara Wells. 1 BAYLOR PLZ, RM N1319 77030 #051-01-1995 L1996 **ID** *020 †20

TRAUTNER, Paul Kevin. ■ 77005 #047-05-1992 *075

TRAUTWEIN, Lynn Marie. 6621 FANNIN ST, TEXAS CHILDRENS HOSPITAL 77030 #048-04-1987 L1988 **PDR DR** *020 †80

TRAVIS, Lewie Lorenz, Jr. 77082 #048-04-1958 L1958 **ID IM** *071 †20

TREADAWAY, Joe Paul. 6550 FANNIN ST, STE 961 77030 #048-02-1972 L1972 **P FM** *020 †18,75

TREADWELL-DEERING, Diane. 6621 FANNIN ST 77030 #048-02-1981 L1981 **CHP P** *040 †75

TREAT, Elmer Lawrence. 2550 HOLLY HALL ST, MACGREGOR MEDICAL ASSOCIAT 77054 #039-01-1967 L1995 **GS GE** *071 †85

TREMAINE, Brian Nathan. 11321 FALLBROOK DR, DIABETES CENTERS OF AMERIC 77065 #005-18-1996 L1999 **IMG** *100 †20

TRENT, Jonathan C, II. 1515 HOLCOMBE BLVD, UNIT 450 77030 #048-14-1995 L1998 **ON** *020 †20

TRENTALANGE, Mark John. 2424 W HOLCOMBE BLVD, MEDICAL CENTER ANESTHESIA 77030 #035-09-1986 L1993 **AN** *020 †05

TREVINO, Ann Christine. 5402 E SAM HOUSTON PKWY N 77015 #048-15-1999 L2001 **FM OBS** *020 †18

TREVINO-BEENE, Eliza. 4560 FM 1960 RD W, STE 101 77069 #048-02-2000 L2003 **PD** *020 †55

TREXLER, Nowice A. ■ 77054 #048-14-2007 **IM** *012

TRICE, Torri Janet Na. ■ 77075 #011-03-2002 L2005 **OBG** *100

TRILLOS, Donaldo. 6624 FANNIN ST, STE 2320 77030 #264-01-1966 L1976 **CD IM** *020 †20

TRIMBLE, Robert Hugh. 8307 KNIGHT RD 77054 #048-02-1963 L1963 **R** *030

TRINCA, Kimberly Anne. ■ 77080 #048-04-2007 L2008 **TY** *012

TRINH, Charles Cuong. 1 BAYLOR PLZ, DEPT OF RADIOLOGY 77030 #047-06-1994 L1995 **VIR** *020 †80

TRINH, Cuong. 11772 BELLAIRE BLVD 77072 #048-14-1991 L1992 **IM** *020

TRINH, Hoang Lan Thi. ■ 77089 #941-02-1973 **FM** *100

TRINH, Thuyhanh Thi. ■ 77054 #048-04-2002 L2005 **FM** *100 †18

TRINH, Vinh Quang. 6306 GULFTON ST, # 101 77081 #941-01-1964 L1979 **GP** *020

TRIPATHY, Uttam. 6560 FANNIN ST STE 1836 77030 #495-13-1986 L2005 **TS** *020 †85,90

TRIVEDI, Nalinchandra K. 710 FM 1960 RD W 77090 #495-23-1958 L1980 **FM** *071

TRIVEDI, Prasad M. 6720 BERTNER ST 77030 #495-19-1973 L1978 **AN** *071 †05

TRIVEDI, Rachna D. PO BOX 20708, UT MD ANDERSON CTR 77225 #041-02-2004 L2007 **HO** *012 †20

TRIVEDI, Sandhya. 11000 RICHMOND AVE, STE 330 77042 #965-01-1983 L1990 **P CHP** *020 †75

TROJAN, Jarka. 2002 HOLCOMBE BLVD, VA MED CTR 77030 #286-02-1956 L1975 **FM IM** *020 †20

TROLLEY, Gregory Charles. 1709 DRYDEN RD STE 550, BCM FACULTY CENTER 77030 #020-12-2007 **IM** *012

TRONCOSO, Patricia. 1515 HOLCOMBE BLVD, DEPT OF PATH BOX 85 77030 #016-02-1978 L1986 **ATP** *020 †50

TROTTER, Kaela Jill. 6431 FANNIN ST, UNIV TX MED SCH AT HOUSTON 77030 #048-14-2003 **AN** *020

TROVER, Barton C, II. ■ 77005 #024-05-1979 L1980 **OBG** *020 †30

TRUJILLO, Edilberto. 5600 S WILLOW DR STE 114 77035 #132-01-1964 L1976 **GP GS** *020

TRUMBLE, Theodore J, II. 6550 FANNIN ST 77030 #048-14-1990 L1992 **IMG** *072 †20

TRUONG, Angela T. ■ 77005 #067-01-1994 L2001 **APM** *020 †05

TRUONG, Dam-Thuy. ■ 77005 #942-01-1969 L2000 **AN** *020 †05

TRUONG, Elizabeth. ■ 77054 #048-14-2008 *012

TRUONG, Luan Dinh. 6565 FANNIN ST, MS 205 77030 #041-14-1979 L1981 **CLP** *020 †50

TRUONG, Mylene T. 1515 HOLCOMBE BLVD BOX 57, MD ANDERSON CANCER CTR 77030 #067-01-1991 L1997 *020 †80

TRUONG, Tho Quy. 1 BAYLOR PLZ 77030 #016-11-2003 **RHU** *012 †20

TSAI, Chundar. 1200 BINZ ST, STE 1100 77004 #017-20-1995 L1997 **OBG** *020 †30

TSAI, Felix Wang. 6431 FANNIN ST 77030 #016-06-1996 L1996 **TS** *020 †85,90

TSAI, Hwai Jer. 8191 SOUTHWEST FWY STE 115 77074 #244-04-1967 L1978 **OBG** *020 †30

TSAI, Jamie Gilbert. ■ 77004 #048-12-2004 L2006 **DR** *012

TSAI, January Y. ■ 77002 #025-01-2005 L2005 **AN** *012

TSAKIRI, Sophia. 6431 FANNIN ST STE 3230, UNIVERSITY OF TEXAS, MEDIC 77030 #418-01-1990 L2003 **NPM** *020 †55

TSAO, Anne Szui. 1515 HOLCOMBE BLVD BOX 10, ANDERSON CANCER CENTER 77030 #016-02-1998 L2001 **ON** *020 †20

TSAO, Calvin Nienfong. 7850 PARKWOOD CIR DR, STE A-6 77036 #048-13-2003 L2005 **FM** *020 †18

TSAO, Jerry Y. 7850 PARKWOOD CIR DR, STE A-6 77036 #048-13-1993 L1994 **FM** *020 †18

TSAO, Kuojen. ■ 77005 #019-02-1998 L2007 **PDS** *100 †85

TSCHIRHART, Monica Jenett. ■ 77004 #048-14-2008 **FP** *012

TSE, Edward Kin-Chow. 9129 MESA DR 77028 #051-01-1979 L1983 **IM** *020 †20

TSIHIRA-SENGAL, Huda I. 8145 HIGHWAY 6 S, STE 108 77083 #915-09-1984 L1993 **PD** *020 †55

TSIHLIAS, John. 1515 HOLCOMBE BLVD, UT MD ANDERSON CANCER CTR 77030 #065-01-1991 L1998 **U** *020

TSOUNIAS, Emmanouil. ■ 77002 #781-02-1997 **PD** *100

TSUCHIDA, Douglas Seibi. 915 GESSNER RD, STE 815 77024 #065-01-1970 L1977 **PD** *020 †18

TU, Janet Chen. 1 BAYLOR PLZ, BAYLOR COLLEGE OF MEDICINE 77030 #048-04-1999 L2002 **HO** *012 †20

TU, John Tho Huu. ■ 77084 #308-03-2000 *100

TU, Naiwen Diane. 1 BAYLOR PLZ, DEPARTMENT OF PEDIATRICS, 77030 #023-07-2003 L2006 **PD** *100 †55

TU, Namhuong Thi. 2411 FOUNTAIN VIEW DR, STE 200 77057 #048-12-1991 L1995 **AN** *020 †05

TU, Shiming. 1515 HOLCOMBE BLVD, BOX 427 77030 #028-02-1987 L1993 **ON IM** *020 †20

TUAZON, Divina Manucdoc. 7500 BEECHNUT ST STE 250 77074 #748-10-1990 L2004 **PCC IM** *020

TUBERGEN, David Gerard. 1515 HOLCOMBE BLVD, UT MD ANDERSON CANCER CENT 77030 #025-01-1961 L1993 **ON IG** *030 †55

TUBERQUIA, Julio Cesar. ■ 77019 #264-03-1961 L1974 **OBG** *071

TUCKER, James Drew. ■ 77006 #048-13-1982 L1983 **P** *020 †75

TUCKER, Jeffery James. 6431 FANNIN ST RM 6.144, UT DEPARTMENT OF ORTHOPAED 77030 #021-01-1971 L1972 **ORS** *020 †40

TUCKER, Jeremy Scott. ■ 77096 #024-01-2004 **PD** *100

TUCKER, Laurel Ellis. 10497 TOWN AND COUNTRY WAY, STE 360 77024 #017-20-1993 L1998 **FM** *020 †18

TUCKER, Sheldon M. ■ 77030 #016-11-1944 L1948 **GP** *071

TUCKER, Stephen Brent. 6655 TRAVIS ST, STE 820 77030 #005-06-1973 L1979 **D** *020 †15

TUFT, Daniel Stephen. 1177 WEST LOOP S 77027 #007-02-1967 L1993 **A PUD** *020 †03

TULLOCH, Brian Robt. 1200 BINZ ST, DIAGNOSTIC CLINIC OF 77004 #917-30-1965 L1978 **END DIA** *020

TUMA, Samir. 1213 HERMANN DR STE 850 77004 #550-01-1969 L1978 **NEP IM** *020

TUMBUSCH, Katherine J. 1919 LA BRANCH ST 77002 #048-14-2001 L2005 **OBG** *012

TUMMALA, Sudhakar. 1515 HOLCOMBE BLVD #495-50-1993 L2001 **N CN** *020 †20,75

TUNG, Celestine Shauching. ■ 77005 #048-04-2003 L2007 **OBG** *100

TUNG, Daniel Shinje. 8830 LONG POINT RD, STE 502 77055 #025-01-2001 **END** *020

TUNG, Irene Tintin. ■ 77036 #048-04-2007 **PD** *012

TUNG, Poyee Pansy. 6431 FANNIN ST STE 1.228 77030 #005-14-1995 L2006 **CD IM** *020 †20

TURELL, David Jos. 6565 FANNIN ST 77030 #035-15-1954 L1960 **IM CD** *072 †20

TURIY, Yuliya. ■ 77025 #010-01-2006 **PD** *012

TURNER, Denise Buchanan. 9211 WEST RD, STE 143 77064 #048-04-1978 L1979 **FM FPG** *020 †18

TURNER, Dwan Marie. 18220 TOMBALL PKWY, STE 400 77070 #019-02-1996 L1998 **OBG** *030 †30

TURNER, Eddie Joe. ■ 77085 #047-06-2004 **FP** *012

TURNER, John Andrew. 830 GEMINI ST 77058 #039-01-1990 L1991 **IM** *020 †20 ‡

TURNER, Krista Lea. 6550 FANNIN ST 77030 #048-02-1999 L2005 **GS CCS** *020 †85

TURNER, Marsha M. 11811 FM 1960 RD W, STE 100 77065 #048-16-1993 L1995 **PD** *020 †55

TURNER, Teri Lee. 6701 FANNIN ST, STE 1540 77030 #039-01-1991 L1993 **PD OS** *040 †55

TURNQUEST, Dexter Godfrey. 17070 RED OAK DR STE 507 77090 #011-04-1989 L1991 **GS** *020 †85

TURRENTINE, Mark Allen. 1111 AUGUSTA DR, WEST CLINIC 77057 #028-03-1990 L1993 **OBG** *030

TUSA, Theodore S, Jr. 1919 LA BRANCH ST 77002 #048-04-1949 L1949 **GS** *071 †85

TUTTLE, Lee Lyman D, Jr. 77019 #048-04-1956 L1956 **GS TS** *071 †85,90

TUTTLE, William Sharp. 902 FROSTWOOD DR, HOUSTON EYE AND LASER 77024 #020-02-1956 L1960 **OPH** *020 †35

TWEARDY, David J. 1 BAYLOR PLZ, BCM 286 N1319 77030 #024-01-1978 L2000 **ID IM** *050 †20

TWEMLOW, Stuart W. 2801 GESSNER DR 77080 #671-01-1966 L2006 **P PYA** *020 †75

TWIFORD, Thomas Wm, Jr. ■ 77074 #048-14-1974 **DR** *020 †80

TWINING, James Anderson. 17150 EL CAMINO REAL 77058 #016-11-1965 L1970 **PD** *020 †55

TWOMEY, Jeremiah John. 4151 SOUTHWEST FWY, STE 610 77027 #539-04-1959 L1968 **IM OM** *020 †20

TY, Maryann O. 2500 CITYWEST BLVD STE 775 77042 #748-01-1981 L1988 **P** *020 †75

TY, Ramon C, Jr. 7737 SOUTHWEST FWY, STE 565 77074 #748-02-1978 L1986 **CD IM** *020 †20

TYAGI, Avishkar. 1709 DRYDEN RD STE 550, BCM FACULTY CENTER 77030 #011-04-2007 **IM** *012

TYRING, Stephen Keith. 2060 SPACE PARK DR, STE 200 77058 #048-02-1983 L1983 **D ID** *020 †15

TYSON, Jon Edward. 6431 FANNIN ST, MSB 2-106 77030 #021-01-1968 L1975 **NPM PD** *050 †55

TZAN, Chyan-Song J. 1709 DRYDEN RD, DEPT OF ANESTHESIOLOGY 77030 #244-01-1986 L2000 **AN** *020 †05

UBESIE, Kanayo E. 7737 SOUTHWEST FWY, STE 819 77074 #048-12-1988 L1989 **OBG** *020 †30

UBHAYAKAR, Kiran Madhav. ■ 77095 #048-02-2007 **MPD** *012

UDAYAMURTHY, Yasodara B. 15655 CYPRESSWD MED DR, STE 100 77014 #495-66-1979 L1984 **IM** *020

UDDEN, Mark Myers. 1 BAYLOR PLZ # MED, BAYLOR COL OF MED 77030 #048-12-1977 L1977 **HEM IM** *040 †20

UDDIN, Said. 11301 FALLBROOK DR, STE 120 77065 #704-16-1988 L1999 **RHU** *020 †20

UDOETUK, Sade. ■ 77054 #041-01-2008 *012

UEBERSCHAR, Elisabeth. 5615 MORNINGSIDE DR, DIAGNOSTIC CLINIC OF HOUST 77005 #068-01-1977 L1986 **DR** *020 †80

UENO, Naoto Tada. 1515 HOLCOMBE BLVD, UNIT 1354 77030 #572-54-1989 L1993 **ON** *020 †20

UGBARUGBA, Steven C. 11302 FALLBROOK DR STE 306 77065 #690-06-1988 L2003 **GE** *020 †20

UGOLINI, Valentina. 13300 HARGRAVE RD, STE 500 77070 #561-17-1977 L1980 **CD IM** *020 †20

UKANI, Hanif. ■ 77030 #060-02-1998 L2004 **HS** *100

ULANDAY, Jocelyn B. 2002 HOLCOMBE BLVD #748-02-1975 L1992 **P** *020 †75

ULLRICH, Korey R. 6431 FANNIN ST, STE 1.150 77030 #048-14-2005 L2007 **IM** *012

UMARU, Samuel. ■ 77054 #690-03-1997 **CCP** *012 †55

UPCHURCH, Timothy Purnell. 6431 FANNIN ST, MSB 7044 77030 #048-14-2001 L2005 **VN** *100 †75

UPTMORE, David Joseph, Jr. 6655 TRAVIS ST, STE 980 77030 #048-14-2003 L2006 **D** *020 †15

URALIL, Annie. 1501 PECH RD 77055 #561-17-1977 L1991 **PM** *020

URALIL, Sherene Elizabeth. ■ 77054 #048-14-2008 *012

URIBE-BOTERO, Gonzalo. 6655 HILLCROFT ST, STE 100 77081 #264-03-1962 L1974 **BBK PTH** *020 †50

URISTA, Moctezuma S. 6633 HILLCROFT ST STE 123 77081 #649-01-1956 L1971 **PTH** *071 †50

URREA BOTERO, Gabriel Alb. 1 BAYLOR PLZ 77030 #264-06-1987 **FP** *012

URRUTIA-MARTINEZ, Jose A. 6560 FANNIN ST, STE 600 77030 #649-14-1978 L1989 **GE** *020 †20

USHER, Kim Ann. ■ 77008 #894-01-2002 L2007 **FP** *012

USSERY, Fred Monroe, III. 1213 HERMANN DR, STE 380 77004 #048-12-1974 L1974 **OPH OS** *071 †35

UTHMAN, Margaret. 6431 FANNIN ST 77030 #004-01-1982 L1988 **PTH** *020 †50

UWAYDAH, Nema Ibrahim. ■ 77059 #051-04-1996 L1999 **FM OBG** *020 †18

UY, Carmelita Santos. 2002 HOLCOMBE BLVD #748-02-1972 L1980 **AN** *020 †05

UYEDA, Jesse Kitanishi. 8876 GULF FWY, STE 215 77017 #048-04-1991 L1992 **NEP** *020 †20

UYEKI, James Veldehiroy. ■ 77098 #035-19-1997 L2004 **ON** *012 †20

UZELMEIER, William Jos. 7026 OLD KATY RD, STE 276 77024 #048-02-1992 L1993 **VIR** *020 †80

UZOAGA, Enyibuaku Rita. 9119 S GESSNER DR, STE 305 77074 #048-02-2002 L2004 **FM** *020 †18

UZOIGWE, Ekene Ifeyinwa. PO BOX 20708, UNIV TX MED SCH 77225 #024-05-2006 **PTH** *012

UZONI-BOECKER, Catherine. 6431 FANNIN ST # 5020 77030 #836-01-1977 L1987 **AN** *020 †55

UZQUIANO, Nelson Enrique. 7737 SOUTHWEST FWY STE 870 77074 #176-01-1974 L1977 **OBG** *020 †30

VACHHANI, Bhupatrai G. 6503 ANTOINE DR 77091 #495-99-1976 L1982 **IM** *020 †20

VACHHANI, Shital Bhupatra. ■ 77054 #048-02-2005 **AN** *012

VACHRIS, Timothy P. 7737 SOUTHWEST FWY STE 42, RES PRGM 77074 #048-14-2005 L2008 **FP** *012

VADEN, Reggie Adele. 2727 W HOLCOMBE BLVD, KELSEY SEYBOLD CLINIC 77025 #004-01-1993 L1999 **CRS** *020 †10,85

VADHAN, Saroj Govindji. 1515 HOLCOMBE BLVD, BOX 24 77030 #495-01-1978 L1986 **IG ON** *020 †20

VADUGANATHAN, Periyanan. 11914 ASTORIA BLVD, STE 100 77089 #495-66-1980 L1994 **CD IM** *020 †20

VAID, Amit Raizada. 6624 FANNIN ST STE 190, BAYLOR COLLEGE OF MEDICINE 77030 #035-09-2002 L2005 **IM** *100 †20

VAIDYA, Parish Subhash. 6620 MAIN ST, STE 1350 77030 #041-13-2003 L2007 **PM** *100

VAILLANT, Brian David. ■ 77007 #456-05-2003 L2003 **N** *100

VAJPAYEE, Archna. 8307 KNIGHT RD 77054 #027-01-2001 L2003 **FM** *020 ‡

VAKAMUDI, Sudha. 5314 DASHWOOD DR 77081 #495-62-1974 L1981 **AN** *020

VAKIL, Manoj Bhagubhai. 6503 ANTOINE DR 77091 #495-17-1972 L1982 **IM EM** *020 †20

VAKLAVAS, Christos. PO BOX 20708 77225 #418-02-2001 **IM** *012

VALADKA, Alex B. 6410 FANNIN ST, STE 1020 77030 #016-02-1987 L1993 **NS** *020 †25

VALBUENA MORA, Jose R. ■ 77054 #935-03-1996 **HMP** *100

VALDERRABANO, Miguel V. 6550 FANNIN ST STE 1901, CARDIOLOGY DEPT 77030 #847-13-1994 L2006 **ICE** *020 †55

VALDES, Cecilia T. 7900 FANNIN ST # 4400 77054 #048-04-1983 L1983 **OBG REN** *020 †30

VALDES, Ignacio Herman. 4010 BLUE BONNET BLVD #202 77025 #048-12-1998 L1999 **P** *020 †75

VALDES, Luis German. ■ 77017 #275-01-1946 L1963 **GS TS** *071 †85

VALDEZ, Luis. ■ 77054 #737-06-1990 **ID** *100 †20

VALDEZ, Peter. ■ 77277 #649-14-1964 L1971 **GP** *071

VALDEZ, Rafael Nunez. 1315 ST JOSEPH PKWY STE 14, JOSEPH HOSPITAL 77002 #649-02-1990 L2008 **FM** *100

VALDEZ VARGAS, Tulio Albe. 6701 FANNIN ST 61022 77030 #264-04-1997 L2000 **PDO** *100 †45

VALDIZAN, Maria C. 620 UNDERHILL ST 77092 #737-01-1982 **FM** *100

VALENA, Nelson Valer. ■ 77004 #041-12-1992 L1994 **PM** *020 †60

VALENCIA, Gabriel Adrian. 7737 SOUTHWEST FWY 77074 #025-01-2004 **FP** *012

VALENSON, Arnold A. 11914 ASTORIA BLVD, STE 280 77089 #035-46-1974 L1979 **ORS OSM** *020

VALENTINE, Alan David. 1515 HOLCOMBE BLVD, UNIT 431 77030 #048-14-1986 L1987 **P** *020 †75

VALENZUELA, Rafael E. 728 E TIDWELL RD 77022 #308-01-1970 L1980 **FM EM** *020

VALERO, Vicente. 1515 HOLCOMBE BLVD, UNIT 1354 77030 #649-02-1980 L1987 **ON IM** *020 †20

VALLBONA, Carlos. 3701 KIRBY DR, STE 600 77098 #847-01-1950 L1962 **PD PM** *040 †55

VALLEJO, Jesus G. 6621 FANNIN ST, MC-2371 77030 #048-04-1989 L1990 **PD** *020 †55

VAN, Livia. ■ 77054 #048-04-2008 *012

VAN, Thanh. 909 FROSTWOOD DR, STE 152 77024 #048-02-1998 L2001 **RO** *020 †80

VANASSE, Louise G. 6431 FANNIN ST 3.123, UNIVERSITY OF TEXAS MEDICA 77030 #067-06-1989 L1993 **PDE** *020 †55

VANBIBER, Russell Carl. 2500 FONDREN RD, STE 270 77063 #048-13-1983 L1983 **FM** *020 †20

VAN BUREN, Charles Thos. 6431 FANNIN ST, RM 6240 77030 #041-01-1972 L1977 **TTS GS** *020 †85

VAN BUREN, George, II. ■ 77025 #048-14-2003 L2007 **GS** *012

VANCE, Kelly Ellen. 1 BAYLOR PLZ MS 350, BAYLOR COLLEGE OF MEDICINE 77030 #020-12-2001 L2004 **P** *100 †75

VANCE, Leonel Kevin. 1400 HOLCOMBE BLVD - UNIT, ANDERSON CAN 77030 #027-01-1996 L1997 **PMM** *012 †05

VAN DEN VEYVER, Ignatia B. 1709 DRYDEN RD, STE 1100 77030 #165-08-1986 L1994 **OBG CG** *050 †19

VANDERLICK, Mary Ellen. 6624 FANNIN ST STE 1550, ALPERT & SERMAS NEURO ASSC 77030 #021-06-1993 L1998 N *020 †75

VANDERWEIDE, David Gordon. 12827 GULF FWY 77034 #048-04-1988 L1989 ORS OSM *020 †40

VANEK, Natalie N. 6431 FANNIN ST, # JFB1728 77030 #048-14-1991 L1992 ID *020 †20

VAN EPS, Randolph George. ■ 77030 #660-07-1994 *100

VAN HORN, Gage, III. 6410 FANNIN ST STE 1014 77030 #048-04-1963 L1963 N *040 †75

VANIK, Richard Kenneth. 7777 SOUTHWEST FWY, STE 500 77074 #016-11-1977 L1984 PS HS *020 †85,65

VAN-LIAW, Phong N. 6621 FANNIN ST 77030 #035-20-1999 L2003 PD *020 †55

VAN RIET, Lieven. 2121 KIRBY DR, UNIT 19 77019 #165-02-1958 L1964 OPH *071 †35

VAN SANTEN, Enrique C. 4200 PORTSMOUTH ST, BAYOU CITY MEDICAL CTR 77027 #649-01-1961 L1974 PTH *071 †50

VAN SICKLE, Mary Lou. 7777 SOUTHWEST FWY, STE 620 77074 #048-13-1985 L1989 OBG *020 †30

VANZANT, Robert Courtenay. 10497 TOWN AND COUNTRY WAY, STE 360 77024 #048-04-1974 L1974 FM *020 †18

VAQUERO, Carlos F. 7007 GULF FWY, STE 136 77087 #649-01-1966 L1975 GYN *020 †30

VARADHACHARY, Atul. 2 HOUSTON CTR STR 3500, MC KINSEY & CO 77010 #495-96-1987 IM *030

VARADHACHARY, Gauri. 1515 HOLCOMBE BLVD, BOX 426 77030 #495-96-1991 L1997 HO IM *020 †20

VARADY, Andrew Gabor. 10694 JONES RD STE 150 77065 #048-14-1981 L1982 DR EM *020 †80

VARGA, Karoly. 6131 FANNIN ST 77030 #473-01-1993 *100

VARGAS, Gonzalo. 7737 SOUTHWEST FWY 77074 #264-05-1970 L1978 TS *020 †85,90

VARGAS, Rosalba Elena. ■ 77025 #021-01-2007 PD *012

VARGHEESE, Ajay K. 6565 FANNIN ST 77030 #048-04-1999 L2003 AN *020 †20

VARGHESE, Freemu K. 1200 BINZ ST, DIAGNOSTIC CLINIC OF 77004 #495-93-1980 L1991 NEP IM *020 †20

VARGHESE, Jeena Mary. PO BOX 20708, DEPT OF INT MED 77225 #496-33-2003 IM *012

VARGHESE, Nisha. ■ 77030 #048-04-2008 *012

VARGHESE, Shaun Sam. ■ 77030 #048-14-2008 *012

VARGO, Thomas Andrew. 6621 FANNIN ST, TEXAS CHILDREN'S HOSPITAL 77030 #005-14-1963 L1970 PDC *062 †55

VARMA, Datla Gopala K. 1515 HOLCOMBE BLVD, M.D. ANDERSON HOSPITAL 77030 #495-11-1975 L1989 DR NM *020 †28,80

VARNER, Holly Knudsen. 1322 SPACE PARK DR # A194 77058 #048-15-1990 L1991 N *020 †75

VARNER, Kevin Eugene. 6560 FANNIN ST STE 400 77030 #048-04-1992 L1994 ORS *020 †40

VARNHOLT, Heike. 14781 MEMORIAL DR, # 2256 77079 #409-38-2000 L2001 PTH *100 †14

VARON, Jacob. 7400 FANNIN ST STE 1175 77054 #649-01-1975 L1983 PS HS *020

VARON, Joseph. 2219 DORRINGTON ST 77030 #649-01-1987 L1994 CCM PUD *020 †20

VARTANIAN, Levon R. 710 FM 1960 RD W, EMERGENCY 77090 #048-14-1994 L1997 EM *020 †16

VARTIAN, Carl Victor. 7777 SOUTHWEST FWY, STE 740 77074 #035-08-1979 L1984 ID IM *071 †20

VARTIVARIAN, Shahe E. 7777 SOUTHWEST FWY, STE 105 77074 #605-01-1981 L1988 ID IM *020

VARUGHESE, Annie Thos. 17203 RED OAK DR STE 103 77090 #012-01-1989 L1995 IC *020 †20

VARUGHESE, Jamie. ■ 77021 #048-04-2005 PD *012

VARUGHESE, Roopa. ■ 77064 #495-79-1998 L2006 PD *020

VASANTHI, Mary. 7011 SOUTHWEST FWY #495-95-1984 L1994 P *020 †75

VASCOE, Jerran Sutherlin. ■ 77062 #048-04-2008 *012

VASQUEZ, Ricardo Javier. ■ 77098 #042-01-2006 PM *012

VASQUEZ DONADO, Andres F. ■ 77054 #264-12-2004 IM *012

VASUDEVA, Boosupalli. 11920 ASTORIA BLVD, STE 290 77089 #496-39-1992 L2006 CHN *100 †75

VASUDEVAN, Deepa A. 1776 YORKTOWN ST STE 150 77056 #495-21-1994 L1998 FM *020 †18

VATSALA, Srinivaschari. 6560 FANNIN ST STE 1840, SCURLOCK TOWER 77030 #495-04-1958 L1979 OBG *030

VAUGHN, David D. ■ 77098 #023-07-1992 L2002 DR IM *020 †80

VAUGHN, Heather Lee. 6621 FANNIN ST 1-1481, TEXAS CHILDREN'S HOSPTIAL 77030 #011-02-1999 L2003 *020 †55

VAUGHTERS, Ann Byron Robe. ■ 77006 #051-01-2007 L2007 *012

VAUTHEY, Jean Nicolas. 1515 HOLCOMBE BLVD BOX 444, CENTER 77030 #869-05-1979 L1998 GS *020 †85

VAVASSEUR, Chantee D. 5901 LONG DR 77087 #048-14-1989 L1990 P *020 †75

VAWDA, Salma. 6441 HIGH STAR DR, CHRISTUS SOUTHEST HEALTH C 77074 #704-06-1985 L1997 PD *020 †55

VAZ, Roy Thomas Harold. ■ 77077 #496-34-2003 IM *100

VAZ, Vikram Joseph. ■ 77077 #048-02-2007 *012

VAZIRINIA, Negar. 1213 HERMANN DR STE 755 77004 #048-02-1992 L1994 PD *020 †55

VAZQUEZ, Eduardo Genaro. ■ 77030 #048-14-2004 L2004 AN *012

VAZQUEZ, Silverio Miguel. ■ 77042 #275-01-1944 L1964 FM IM *071

VECCHIO, Rosario. 6431 FANNIN ST # 4.020 77030 #561-04-1982 *100

VEERASAMY, Anitha D.. 1220 BLALOCK RD 77055 #496-23-2001 L2005 FM *020 †18

VEGA, Ana E. ■ 77025 #048-14-1996 L1997 PTH *020 †50

VEGA, Javier Antonio. 6630 DE MOSS DR 77074 #042-01-1997 L1999 IM *020 †20

VEGA VAZQUEZ, Francisco. 1 BAYLOR PLZ 77030 #847-04-1992 L2006 HMP *100 †50

VEJLANI, Fehmida. 10300 CYPRESSWOOD DR # 12 77070 #704-02-1995 L2002 IM *020 †20

VELA, Oscar. ■ 77006 #048-14-2002 L2004 EM *020

VELARDE, Samuel. ■ 77081 #132-01-1950 L1975 PTH *020

VELASCO, Alfredo Bellon. 1 BAYLOR PLZ, MS BCM350 77030 #649-01-2001 P *100

VELASCO, Ariel M. 915 GESSNER RD, STE 360 77024 #748-08-1989 L1996 NEP IM *020 †20

VELASQUEZ, William S. 7737 SOUTHWEST FWY, STE 575 77074 #737-01-1968 L1977 IM HEM *030 †20

VELAZQUEZ, Francisco J. 6431 FANNIN ST STE 1.150, AT HOUST 77030 #042-01-2002 L2005 IM *100 †20

VELEV, Nikolai Stilianov. PO BOX 20708 77225 #198-01-1992 ID *012

VELEZ, Jorge Bernardo. 1221 MCKINNEY ST, STE 40300 77010 #010-03-1994 L2000 FSM *020 †18

VELEZ, Maria Eugenia. 2002 HOLCOMBE BLVD 77030 #042-01-1976 L1990 IM GE *020 †20

VELEZ PESTANA, Luis Ivan. 2260 W HOLCOMBE BLVD, STE 311 77030 #042-01-1994 L2002 AN *020 †05

VELLEKOOP, Lijda. ■ 77006 #660-07-1973 L1979 HO *020 †20

VELOZ, Ruben Dario. ■ 77019 #048-13-2000 L2003 EM FM *020 †18 ‡

VEMULAPALLI, Sushma. 1515 HOLCOMBE BLVD, UNIT 422 77030 #496-35-2000 L2007 IM *020 †20

VENABLE, Henry Donn. 1313 HERMANN DR, STE 270 77004 #039-01-1983 L1998 AN *020 †05

VENEGAS, Karen A. 4550 POST OAK PLACE DR 77027 #042-01-1982 L1985 P PD *020 †55,75

VENKATESH, Srinivasa Rao. 11301 FALLBROOK DR, STE 210 77065 #495-33-1975 L1982 PUD IM *020 †20

VENNIX, Michael J. 6620 MAIN ST, STE 1225 77030 #048-04-1988 L1989 PM *020 †60

VENTA, Luz A. 6550 FANNIN ST STE 701, METHODIST BREAST CARE CENT 77030 #016-02-1983 L2002 R *020 †80

VENTURA, Karyna Golda C. ■ 77030 #748-02-1995 L2001 PCP *020 †50

VENYAH, Titus Kofi. 711 BAY AREA BLVD, STE 500 77058 #025-12-2001 L2003 FM FPG *020 †18

VERA, Robyn Bell. ■ 77006 #016-76-2006, ▲ IM *012

VERANI, Regina C. 6535 FANNIN ST, # F-905 77030 #187-13-1969 L1977 ATP *062 †50

VERCHERE, Sherien H. 6431 FANNIN ST 5020, UNIVERSITY OF TEXAS MEDICA 77030 #915-04-1988 L1997 PAN *020 †05

VERDUZCO, Monica. ■ 77021 #048-04-2005 PM *012

VERDUZCO, Rafael. 9720 JONES RD, STE 240 77065 #649-02-1970 L1974 FM *020 †18 ‡

VERGHESE, Roy. ■ 77096 #495-37-1979 AN *100

VERM, Ray Alan. 6560 FANNIN ST, STE 600 77030 #048-04-1971 L1971 GE IM *020 †20

VERMA, Amit. 6565 FANNIN ST, DEPARTMENT OF NEUROLOGY, S 77030 #495-03-1992 L1999 CN *020 †75

VERMA, Dharmendra. 6431 FANNIN ST, MSB 4.234 77030 #496-09-2001 L2006 GE *012 †20

VERMA, Dushyant. 1515 HOLCOMBE BLVD, BOX 428 77030 #495-69-1987 L2006 IM *020 †20

VERMA, Neeta. 190 HEIGHTS BLVD 77007 #048-16-1996 L1997 FM *020 †18

VERMA, Rajiv. 1515 HOLCOMBE BLVD, UNIT 325 77030 #495-45-1997 L2007 VIR *100

VERNER-COLE, Elizabeth A. ■ 77054 #048-14-2006 OPH *012

VERSALOVIC, James. 6621 FANNIN ST, STE B1 77030 #048-04-1995 L2002 PTH *020 †20

VERSTOVSEK, Gordana. 2002 HOLCOMBE BLVD, DEPT OF PATH VA MED CTR 77030 #957-01-1992 L2001 PTH PCP *020 †50

VERSTOVSEK, Srdan. 1515 HOLCOMBE BLVD BOX 428, MD ANDERSON CANCER CTR 77030 #957-01-1992 L1999 HO *020 †20

VETERE, Stephanie Anne. ■ 77006 #045-01-2005 P *012

VEURINK, Ryan J. 6431 FANNIN ST, STE 6.144 77030 #048-14-2005 ORS *012

VIAMONTE, Carlo A. ■ 77005 #048-04-2003 OTO *012

VICENCIO-GARAYGAY, Jan P. ■ 77059 #748-02-1970 L1978 IM *071 †14

VICK, Giles Wesley, III. 6621 FANNIN ST, TEXAS CHILDREN'S HOSPITAL 77030 #036-07-1979 L1987 PDC PD *050 †55

VICROY, Theresa Gay. 6431 FANNIN ST, STE 1012 77030 #028-02-1984 L1987 IM *020 †20

VIDAEFF, Cristian A. 7600 BEECHNUT ST 77074 #781-01-1977 L2001 OBG MFM *020 †30

VIDAL, Camille Chantal. ■ 77025 #048-04-2004 L2008 OBG *012

VIDAL, Marieberta. 6431 FANNIN ST STE 1.150, AT HOUST 77030 #042-01-2002 L2005 IM *100 †20

VIERLING, Donna Marie. 2300 MCCUE RD, APT 245 77056 #011-02-1979 L2007 GE *020 †20

VIERLING, John Moore. 1709 DRYDEN STE 1500, BAYLOR LIVER HEALTH 77030 #005-11-1972 L2007 IM GE *050 †20

VIETS, Jayne M. 4606 FM 1960 RD W, STE 400 77069 #048-14-1994 L1996 MPD *020 †20,55

VIETS, Joseph L. 1709 DRYDEN RD, STE 1700, MC:BCM 120 77030 #019-02-1976 L1985 AN *020 †05

VIJ, Meena. 2002 HOLCOMBE BLVD, VA MEDICAL CENTER 77030 #495-41-1976 L1983 DR *020 †80

VIJAYAN, Hemalatha. 8191 SOUTHWEST FWY, STE 118 77074 #495-42-1976 L1994 IM *020 †20

VIJE, Hadassah N. 10655 STEEPLETOP DR, CY-FAIR MEDICAL CNTR 77065 #048-15-1993 L1995 AN *020 †20

VIKRAM, Raghunandan. 1515 HOLCOMBE BLVD, UNIT 1350 77030 #495-98-1998 *100

VILCHEZ, Regis Antonio. 1 BAYLOR PLZ, BCM 286 RM N1319 77030 #270-02-1991 L1998 ID IM *050 †20

VILES, Robert Prentiss. 7600 BEECHNUT ST 77074 #048-04-1972 L1972 AN MDM *030 †05

VILLA, Xavier. 6701 FANNIN ST 77030 #308-04-1985 L1999 PG CCP *020 †55

VILLALOBOS, Enrique. 2028 WIRT RD 77055 #264-01-1960 L1975 FM *071

VILLANUEVA-MEYER, J R. 9220 KIRBY DR, STE 700 77054 #649-14-1982 L1993 NM DR *020 †28

VILLAREAL, Julian Trevino. 13125 EAST FWY 77015 #649-02-1960 *100

VILLARREAL, Graciela. 1504 TAUB LOOP 5TH FL, RM 5IP61007 77030 #048-12-1988 L1990 PD *020 †55

VILLARREAL, Rodolfo L, Jr. 1415 NORTH LOOP W, STE 820 77008 #048-02-1967 L1967 R *020 †80,28

VILTZ, Anna Louise. 7011 SOUTHWEST FWY, CENTER 77074 #048-02-1991 L1993 CHP *020 †75

VINCENT, Toicha A. 1111 AUGUSTA DR, INTERNAL MEDICINE DEPT. 77057 #025-12-2003 L2006 IM *020 †20

VINDEKILDE, Soren John. 7037 CAPITOL ST 77011 #056-05-1975 L1982 OBG PHP *020 †70,30 ‡

VINE, Bernard Geo. 1631 NORTH LOOP W 77008 #024-01-1956 L1960 GS HNS *071 †85

VINH, Baominh Philip. ■ 77004 #048-14-2007 AN *012

VINNERKVIST, Anders Nils. 6410 FANNIN ST, STE 450 77030 #858-02-1991 *100

VINTA, Malavika. 6431 FANNIN ST, MSB 1.150 77030 #035-03-2001 L2004 NEP *020 †20

VIOLA, Carlos Alberto. ■ 77060 #132-01-1950 L1975 GS GP *075

VIOLA, George Michael. ■ 77004 #132-10-2002 ID *012 †20

VIRANI, Salim Shahbuddin. 2801 GESSNER DR 77080 #704-25-1998 L2005 CD *012 †20

VIRGADAMO, Vincenzo. 6624 FANNIN ST STE 2160 77030 #561-12-1969 L1976 N *020

VISUS, Maria Carmen. 18100 SAINT JOHN DR, STE 280 77058 #026-04-1990 L1998 IM *020 †20

VISWANATHAN, Ashwin. ■ 77004 #048-04-2003 L2005 NS *012

VISWANATHAN, Chitra. 6540 BELLOWS LN # 903 77030 #048-04-2000 L2002 DR *100 †80

VISWESWARAN, Aparna. ■ 77005 #051-07-1996 DR *100 †80

VITAL, Carlos James. 1313 HERMANN DR 77004 #021-05-1999 L2005 AI *020 †20,03

VITAL, Mark Christopher. 915 GESSNER RD, STE 250 77024 #048-12-1997 L1998 OPH *020 †35

VITENAS, Povilas, Jr. 11914 ASTORIA BLVD, STE 470 77089 #021-01-1982 L1990 PS HS *020 †65

VITERI, Alfredo Luis. 915 GESSNER RD, STE 450 77024 #319-03-1968 L1971 GE IM *020 †20

VITTONE, Alicia Beatriz. 2800 S MACGREGOR WAY 77021 #132-01-1975 L2004 P *020 †75

VIVEKANATHAN, K. 11720 FM 1960 RD W, NORTHWEST HOUSTON CARDIOLO 77065 #495-04-1988 L2003 **IC** *020 †20
VIZIROV, Leila. 1631 NORTH LOOP W, STE 480 77008 #913-19-1981 L2003 **FM** *020 †18 ‡
VLAHAKOS, Victor. 1740 W 27TH ST STE 30 77008 #048-02-1974 L1974 **IM** *020 †20
VO, Hoa Kim. 6030 S RICE AVE STE A 77081 #038-44-1997 L2000 **IM** *020 †20
VO, Hong Xuan. ■ 77030 #048-14-2008 *012
VO, Jacqueline Diemthy. 1200 BINZ ST, STE 1130 77004 #038-44-1998 L2005 **RHU IM** *020 †20
VO, Jane Thu. 3701 KIRBY DR STE 60, BAYLOR FAMILY PRACTICE CTR 77098 #016-11-2002 L2005 **FM** *020 †18
VODNALA, Srinivas. 11301 FALLBROOK DR, STE 210 77065 #495-37-1994 L2003 **PUD** *020 †20
VOELKER, Heidi Michelle. ■ 77025 #001-02-1994 L1997 **PHO** *020 †55
VOGEL, Susan Michelle. 902 FROSTWOOD DR, STE 190 77024 #035-15-1987 L1988 **IM** *020 †20
VOHRA, Vinona. 17115 RED OAK DR, STE 201 77090 #495-03-1962 L1976 **PD** *020 †55
VOIGT, Robert John. 4212 SAN FELIPE ST, STE 517 77027 #649-14-1972 L1975 **FM** *020 †16
VOLATE, Rupa Puttappa. 6624 FANNIN ST, STE 2000 77030 #495-33-1994 L2006 **CD** *020 †20
VOLLERO, Hilda Tawil. ■ 77024 #605-01-1966 L1981 **CHN PD** *020
VOLLERO, Robert Anthony. 502 TIMBER TERRACE RD 77024 #008-01-1967 L1981 **U GS** *020 †85,95
VOLLMER, Dennis George. 6431 FANNIN ST, DEPT OF NEUROSURGERY 77030 #048-13-1979 L1997 **NS** *020 †25
VOLOYIANNIS, Theodoros. 6550 FANNIN ST STE 2307, UNIV OF TX HSC AT HOUSTON 77030 #418-02-1998 L2005 **CRS** *020 †85
VOLPI, John Julius. 6560 FANNIN ST, STE 902 77030 #048-04-2003 L2007 **IM** *100
VOLPINI, Kaelin Colleen. ■ 77025 #048-14-2008 *012
VON-MASZEWSKI, Marian E. 1114 AUGUSTA DR, 11 TOWNHOUSE 77057 #048-14-1998 L2004 **AN** *100 †05
VON NOORDEN, Gunter K. 6550 FANNIN ST, STE 1501 77030 #407-23-1954 L1972 **OPH** *071 †35
VOTANOPOULOS, Konstantinos. 1 BAYLOR PLZ 77030 #418-02-1996 L2007 **GS** *100 †85
VRABEC, Jeffrey Thos. 6501 FANNIN ST, BAYLOR OTOLARYNGOLOGY 77030 #016-06-1986 L1993 **OTO NO** *020 †45
VU, Anh-Tu Thi. 7502 CROTON RD 77036 #048-02-1998 L2001 **PD** *020 †55
VU, Christopher Dong. ■ 77030 #048-04-2008 *012
VU, Dac T. 8278 BELLAIRE BLVD STE A 77036 #048-12-1993 L1994 **IM** *020 †20
VU, Hao Trong. ■ 77072 #048-15-2008 *012
VU, Joseph H. 1709 DRYDEN RD, STE 1700 77030 #047-06-1993 L1997 **AN** *020 †05
VU, Khanh D. 1515 HOLCOMBE BLVD, BOX # 428 77030 #048-14-1999 L2002 **IM** *020 †20
VU, Loi Tien. 8278 BELLAIRE BLVD, STE A 77036 #941-01-1965 L1978 **AN** *020
VU, Quan A. ■ 77082 #048-14-1993 L1994 **AN** *020 †05
VU, Quang A. 6540 BELLOWS LN # 402 77030 #048-14-1994 L1997 **MPD PD** *020 †55,20
VU, Rosabelle Via. ■ 77086 #048-14-2007 **PD** *012
VU, Steven Kien. 19002 TEBROC CT 77094 #021-01-2000 L2005 **AN** *020 †05
VU, Tammy H. 12121 RICHMOND AVE, STE 414 77082 #048-02-2000 L2004 **OBG** *020 ‡
VU, Thinh H. ■ 77043 #048-16-2001 L2006 **RNR** *100 †80
VU, Thuan Trong. 1415 NORTH LOOP W, STE 820 77008 #038-40-1999 L2005 **DR** *020 †80
VU, Tuan A. 4200 PORTSMOUTH ST 77027 #048-02-1993 L1995 **IM** *020 †20
VULLAGANTI, Mithila. ■ 77030 #001-06-2006 **IM** *012
VUONG, Madelyn P. ■ 77007 #048-16-2000 L2003 **DR** *020 †80
VUTPAKDI, Akom. 510 W TIDWELL RD 77091 #891-02-1963 L1972 **DR** *071 †80
VYAS, Anuja Sanghvi. 6620 MAIN ST STE 1450, DEPT. OF OBGYN 77030 #035-19-2003 L2007 **OBG** *020
VYAS, Kishorchandra L. ■ 77056 #495-23-1969 L1976 **PTH** *020 †50
VYAS, Nilesh Balvantray. 11920 ASTORIA BLVD, STE 280 77089 #495-23-1986 L2006 **IM** *020 †20
WADDELL, Caroline Cook. ■ 77024 #021-05-1965 L1970 **HEM IM** *071 †20
WADDELL, Delmar Wm. 1213 HERMANN DR STE 444 77004 #048-02-1967 L1967 **A** *071
WADDELL, Louis Clyde, Jr. 6447 MAIN ST 77030 #021-01-1964 L1973 **IM OM** *071 †20,70
WADE, Walter H, III. 2002 HOLCOMBE BLVD, SPINAL CORD INJURY CARE LI 77030 #016-11-1981 L1993 **GPM** *020 †60
WADERA, Pramodh Kumar. 7600 BEECHNUT ST 77074 #495-11-1978 L1982 **AN PME** *020 †05
WAER, Robert S. ■ 77006 #048-12-1989 L1990 **OBG** *020 †30
WAFELMAN, Leontien S. ■ 77098 #660-01-1988 L1992 **NPM PD** *100 †55
WAGER, Sharon Freeman. 714 FM 1960 RD W, STE 303 77090 #048-12-1989 L1993 **FPG** *020 ‡
WAGLE, Rohan Ravindra. ■ 77030 #048-04-2008 *012
WAGNER, David Richard. ■ 77040 #021-01-1969 L1972 **AN** *020
WAGNER, Jennifer Kathleen. ■ 77047 #017-20-2008 *012
WAGNER, Milton Lee. 6621 FANNIN ST 77030 #048-02-1955 L1955 **PDR** *071 †80
WAGNER, Nils. ■ 77054 #409-10-1993 **AN** *100
WAGNERBARTAK, Nicolaus A. ■ 77006 #041-01-2004 L2007 **DR** *012
WAGUESPACK, Steven Gerard. 1515 HOLCOMBE BLVD 77030 #048-14-1994 L2002 **PDE** *020 †20,55
WAHED, Mohammed Amer. 6431 FANNIN ST # 2.294, DEPARTMENT OF PATHOLOGY 77030 #160-10-1988 L2003 **PTH** *100 †50
WAI, Shannon San San. 1 BAYLOR PLZ, BAYLOR COLL OF MED 77030 #919-03-2002 **PD** *012
WAIDHOFER, William. 10611 GRANT RD 77070 #048-02-1976 L1976 **D** *020 †15
WAINWRIGHT, David John. 6431 FANNIN ST, STE 1400 77030 #065-01-1978 L1980 **PS OS** *020 †65
WAISMAN, Margaret. 4101 GREENBRIAR ST STE 115 77098 #021-01-1968 L1973 **D DS** *020 †15
WAIT, Coleman Farris. 2905 SACKETT ST 77098 #048-04-1984 L1986 **LM** *075
WAKIL, Joe Y. ■ 77005 #048-04-1990 *100
WAKIL, Sonya Salih. 17750 CALI DR, CYPRESS CREEK HOSPITAL 77090 #048-13-1988 L1989 **CHP PD** *020 †75
WALBURN, David James. 3275 W ALABAMA ST 77098 #048-13-1976 L1976 **PD** *020 †55
WALCOTT, Debbieann E. 1221 MCKINNEY ST, STE 40300 77010 #036-05-1993 L1996 **IM** *020 †20
WALCZAK, Marek. ■ 77041 #759-04-1988 L2007 **IM** *100 †20
WALDMAN, Terry Irvin. 6565 FANNIN ST 77030 #020-02-1970 L1978 **AN** *020 †05
WALDRON, Jimmie Franklin. 7777 SOUTHWEST FWY, STE 820 77074 #047-06-1956 L1963 **OTO A** *020 †45
WALDROP, Tracie Michelle. 6565 FANNIN ST M227 77030 #048-02-2004 L2007 **PTH** *012
WALES, Dirk Oliver. ■ 77019 #038-45-1988 L1999 **IM** *020 †20
WALI, Ashutosh. 1709 DRYDEN RD, MEDICAL TOWERS #1700 77030 #496-09-1980 L1999 **AN** *020 †05
WALI, Gouher. 8830 LONG POINT RD, STE 210 77055 #704-16-1981 L1998 **FM** *020 †18
WALI, Sharmilla Kaw. 6677 ROOKIN ST 77074 #495-51-1989 L2001 **PD** *020
WALKER, Brian D. 6624 FANNIN ST STE 1730 77030 #919-02-1971 L1975 **PUD IM** *020 †20
WALKER, Candice Estelle. ■ 77027 #048-12-2007 **OBG** *012
WALKER, David C. 6565 FANNIN ST 77030 #048-04-1987 L1989 **AN** *020 †05
WALKER, David Gregory. 8408 BELLAIRE BLVD 77036 #048-12-1982 L1983 **FM** *020 †18
WALKER, Paul W. 1515 HOLCOMBE BLVD BX 8, MD ANDERSON CANCER CTR 77030 #060-01-1983 L2003 **PLM FM** *020
WALKER, Peter Anthony, Jr. PO BOX 20708, DEPT OF SURGERY 77225 #028-34-2006 **GS** *012
WALKER, Rebecca Johnson. 6701 FANNIN ST 77030 #048-12-1973 L1975 **PD** *020 †55
WALKER, Richard Wendell, Jr. ■ 77058 #035-46-1974 L1981 **OBG** *020
WALKER, Steven Eugene. 4545 POST OAK PLACE DR, STE 130 77027 #048-14-2003 L2007 **MPD** *020 †20
WALKER, William Easton. 6410 FANNIN ST 77030 #803-05-1968 L1979 **TS VS** *020 †85,90
WALKES, Joncecil Martin. 6560 FANNIN ST, STE 1006 77030 #005-14-1996 L2000 **TS** *020 †85,90
WALKUP, Jimmie Lee. 1213 HERMANN DR STE 345 77004 #048-12-1963 L1963 **U** *020 †95
WALL, Alexis Jacob. ■ 77069 #048-04-2005 **GS** *012
WALL, Matthew J, Jr. 1 BAYLOR PLZA SURGERY DEPT 77030 #048-04-1984 L1985 **TS** *040 †85,90
WALLACE, Brian Edward. ■ 77054 #048-14-2006 **AN** *012
WALLACE, Elizabeth Marie. ■ 77079 #060-02-1984 L1999 *020
WALLACE, James Oran. 6624 FANNIN ST STE 2400 77030 #020-12-1973 L1980 **GS** *020 †85
WALLACE, Jenny R. 6655 TRAVIS ST, STE 980 77030 #048-14-2004 L2007 **D** *012
WALLACE, Michael Jeffrey. 1515 HOLCOMBE BLVD BOX 325, UT MD ANDERSON CANCER CENT 77030 #048-14-1990 L1991 **VIR** *020 †80
WALLACE, Sidney. 1515 HOLCOMBE BLVD 77030 #041-13-1954 L1967 **DR R** *071 †80
WALLING, Vernon Ray, II. 5151 SAN FELIPE ST 77056 #048-14-1981 L1981 **CHP** *020 †75
WALLIS, Robert Randolph. 11800 ASTORIA BLVD 77089 #048-02-1972 L1972 **FM OM** *071 ‡
WALLS, Endia Nichelle. 4405 GRIGGS RD 77021 #028-03-2000 L2002 **FM** *020 †18
WALMSLEY, James Albert. 15907 EDGEWOOD DR 77059 #048-02-1959 L1959 **GP** *020 †18
WALMSLEY, Robert P. 6624 FANNIN ST, STE 2750 77030 #048-04-1982 L1983 **CD IM** *020 †20
WALPOLE, Ben. ■ 77005 #016-01-1940 L1946 **FM** *071
WALSH, Garrett Lyndon. 1515 HOLCOMBE BLVD, UNIT 445 77030 #065-05-1983 L1990 **TS CD** *040 †85,90
WALTER, Joseph Antony, III. ■ 77006 #048-14-1975 L1975 **ORS** *020 †40
WALTER, Tameka Michelle. ■ 77054 #048-04-2006 **AN** *012
WALTERS, Elbert Lane. 7600 FANNIN ST 77054 #048-04-1972 L1972 **AN** *020 †05
WALTERS, Karina Joanne. ■ 77035 #048-12-2001 L2002 **EM** *020 †16
WALTERS, Ronald Stewart. 1515 HOLCOMBE BLVD BOX 424 77030 #030-05-1976 L1981 **ON IM** *030 †20
WALTON, Brian Leroy. 6720 BERTNER ST MCI-133, DEPT CARDIOLOGY EDUCATION 77030 #019-02-1997 L2001 **IC** *020 †20
WALTON, Harold Jose. 11452 SPACE CENTER BLVD 77059 #264-04-1986 L1997 **IM** *020 †20
WAN, Christine. ■ 77099 #048-15-2008 *012
WAN, Qiang. ■ 77081 #243-72-1986 L2006 **NM** *100 †28
WANCHOO, Ruchi Jaikrishan. ■ 77054 #495-17-1982 **N** *012
WANEBO, Jacqueline Elise. 7900 FANNIN ST STE 3300 77054 #051-01-1992 L1995 **PD** *020 †55
WANG, Brian Shihning. 7501 FANNIN ST STE 710, EMPLOYEE PHYSICIAN, HOUSTO 77054 #036-05-2002 L2007 **OTO** *020
WANG, David. ■ 77057 #048-04-2000 L2003 **EM** *020
WANG, Fan. ■ 77018 #243-63-1983 L2005 **OBG** *100
WANG, Janet Luyu. 1709 DRYDEN RD STE 550, BCM FACULTY CENTER 77030 #048-04-2006 **IM** *012
WANG, Jay. ■ 77004 #005-06-2002 L2005 **HO** *012 †20
WANG, Jennifer. 1709 DRYDEN RD STE 550, BCM FACULTY CENTER 77030 #048-04-2007 **IM** *012
WANG, Jeremy Chengyuh. 18333 EGRET BAY BLVD, STE 200 77058 #035-19-1998 L2005 **NS SCI** *020
WANG, Jian. 2002 HOLCOMBE BLVD, EXT 110 77030 #243-46-1985 L2006 **FM IMG** *020 †18
WANG, Jimin. 9888 BELLAIRE BLVD, STE 122 77036 #243-38-1986 L2003 **IM RHU** *020 †20
WANG, Lin. 8303 SOUTHWEST FWY, STE 120 77074 #243-33-1991 L2004 **IM** *020
WANG, Lisa Lynn. 6701 FANNIN ST 77030 #036-01-1993 L1999 **PHO** *020 †55
WANG, Michael L. 1515 HOLCOMBE BLVD, UNIT 429 77030 #243-46-1985 L1998 **ON** *020 †20
WANG, Miranda Onyin. 1910 JOHN RALSTON RD, STE 200 77013 #055-01-2003 L2006 **FM** *020 †18
WANG, Nan. 6400 FANNIN ST, STE 1800 77030 #048-04-1996 L1997 **OPH** *020 †35
WANG, Run. 6410 FANNIN ST, STE 6.018 77030 #243-71-1983 L2002 **U** *020 †95
WANG, Sherry Chenyu. 6620 MAIN ST, MAIL STATION 621 77030 #048-04-1999 L2002 **IM** *020 †20
WANG, Steve L. 6431 FANNIN ST # 5.020, UTHSC-HOUSTON 77030 #048-14-1999 L2004 **AN** *020 †05 ‡
WANG, Tzu Chiang. 9600 BELLAIRE BLVD, STE 232 77036 #244-02-1975 L1980 **IM** *020 †20,16
WANG, Vincent H. ■ 77077 #385-02-1968 L1974 **IM CD** *071
WANG, Wei Lien. ■ 77004 #024-07-2002 L2002 **PTH** *100 †50
WANG, Xin. 9750 BELLAIRE BLVD, STE 180 77036 #243-46-1990 L2003 **PM** *020 †60
WANG, Yanlin. ■ 77025 #243-67-1989 L2006 **NEP** *012 †20
WANG, Yun. 1200 BINZ ST, STE 690 77004 #243-54-1984 L2002 **FM** *020 †18
WANG, Zhiqiang. 6565 FANNIN ST M227 77030 #243-46-1986 **PTH** *012
WANGLER, Michael Francis. 6621 FANNIN ST RM A170, MC1-1000 77030 #048-04-2006 **PD** *012
WANIA, Darius Furrokh. 10792 BELLAIRE BLVD STE B 77072 #704-02-1988 L1995 **IM** *020 †20
WAQAR, Tahira. 7600 BEECHNUT ST 77074 #704-24-1991 L2003 **AN** *020
WARD, John Francis, III. 1515 HOLCOMBE BLVD, DEPARTMENT OF UROLOGY - UN 77030 #010-02-1991 L2006 **U GS** *020 †95
WARD, Kimberley Morine. ■ 77025 #035-01-2001 L2006 **D** *100 †15
WARD, Mark Allen. 6621 FANNIN ST, MC 1-1000 77030 #048-04-1981 L1981 **PD PE** *040 †55
WARD, Michael Cullen. ■ 77058 #048-02-2003 **PD** *020
WARDAK, Marium Altaf. ■ 77004 #048-02-2007 **AN** *012
WARDHAN, Swapna. 2002 HOLCOMBE BLVD, VETERANS HOSPITAL 77030 #495-14-1993 L1999 **IM** *020 †20
WARE, Drue Neeley. 6431 FANNIN ST, RM MSB 4 164 77030 #048-14-1985 L1986 **GS** *071 †85
WARE, James Everett. 427 W 20TH ST STE 710 77008 #048-12-1961 L1961 **FM OM** *020 †18
WARE, Steve Alan. 900 BROADWAY ST, BROADWAY CLINIC 77012 #048-13-1979 L1979 **P** *020 †75

■ = Address Information Privacy Protected

WARFIELD, Brett Henry. ■ 77041 #047-07-1993 L2004 **AN** *020 †05

WARFIELD, Sharita. ■ 77041 #025-07-1995 L2004 **EM** *020 †16

WARNEKE, Kimberly Anne. 2800 S MACGREGOR WAY 77021 #048-14-1998 L2002 **P** *020 †75

WARNEKE, Michael Larry. 11920 ASTORIA BLVD, STE 300 77089 #048-14-1979 L1979 **IM** *020 †20

WARNER, Ben F. 10600 FONDREN RD STE 200 77096 #048-14-1994 **PTH** *100

WARNER, Mark T. ■ 77018 #048-14-2005 **DR** *012

WARNER, Noranna Burridge. 6431 FANNIN ST 77030 #047-06-1975 L1982 **RHU IM** *020 †20

WARNOCK, Kenneth M, II. 18220 TOMBALL PKWY, STE 330 77070 #048-14-1998 L1999 **ORS** *020 †40

WARRAK, Elia Lutfallah. 2855 GRAMERCY ST, HOUSTON EYE ASSOCIATES 77025 #605-01-1990 **OPH** *100

WARREN, Joshua J. 1300 MOURSUND ST, RM 173 77030 #048-15-2004 L2006 **CHP** *012

WARREN, Marcia Patricia. 1 BAYLOR PLZ 77030 #041-13-1990 L1994 **PD** *020 †55

WARREN, Robert Wells. 6621 FANNIN ST, MC3-2290 77030 #028-02-1978 L1989 **PD RHU** *020 †55,03

WARRINGTON, Curtis David. 920 FROSTWOOD DR 77024 #011-03-1966 L1973 **OS** *020 †05

WARSHAW, Herman Eugene. ■ 77096 #048-04-1957 L1957 **OTO** *071 †45

WARWICK, Eric Tad. 6630 DE MOSS DR 77074 #048-15-2000 L2004 **FM** *020 †18 ‡

WASHINGTON, Courtney Reno. ■ 77023 #047-07-2007 **TY** *012

WASHINGTON, Mary Ann. 1140 WESTMONT DR, STE 320 77015 #056-06-1986 L1991 **NEP IM** *020 †20

WASKO, Carina Ann. 1 BAYLOR PLZ, DEPT OF DERMATOLOGY 77030 #041-14-2003 L2007 **D** *100 †15

WASSEF, Adel Attallah. 2800 S MACGREGOR WAY 77021 #915-04-1978 L1986 **P** *020 †75

WATCHA, Mehernoor F. 6621 FANNIN ST, DEPT. ANESTHESIOLOGY 77030 #496-38-1972 L1993 **AN PD** *020 †55,05

WATERHOUSE, Timothy B. 4100 MILAM ST 77006 #010-02-1993 L1997 **OBG** *020 †30

WATERS, Lindsay L. ■ 77054 #048-14-2008 *012

WATKINS, Herbert Leonard. 1221 MCKINNEY ST, STE 40300 77010 #035-01-1990 L1993 **U** *020 †95

WATKINS, Lowell Andrew. 427 W 20TH ST, HEIGHTS EYE CENTER 77008 #048-14-1982 L1983 **OPH GP** *020 †35

WATKINS, Michael W. ■ 77054 #048-14-2008 *012

WATKINS, Ulysses Wesby, Jr. 14215 S POST OAK RD 77045 #010-03-1975 L1980 **FM** *020

WATKINS, Winston Eugene. 2000 CRAWFORD ST, STE 1400 77002 #048-02-1984 L1985 **IM** *020 †20

WATSON, Alfred B, Jr. 1504 TAUB LOOP 77030 #012-05-1963 L1978 **DR AM** *020 †70,80

WATSON, James Chestnut. 5445 ALMEDA RD, STE 200 77004 #010-03-1964 L1966 **FM GPM** *020 †18

WATSON, La Donna. 12000 RICHMOND AVE STE 330, PEDIATRICIANS OF WEST HOUS 77082 #048-02-1979 L1979 **PD** *020 †55

WATSON, Larry Cordell. 2060 SPACE PARK DR STE 100 77058 #048-02-1972 L1972 **GS** *020 †85

WATSON, Virginia Emily. ■ 77024 #048-02-2003 L2006 **GS** *100

WATSON-MILLET, Marilyn K. 2411 FOUNTAIN VIEW DR, STE 200 77057 #010-03-1984 L1994 **AN** *020 †05

WATTANAMANO, Pornthep. 2600 GESSNER DR, STE 190 77080 #891-01-1988 L2003 **ID IM** *020 †20

WEAKLEY, Sarah M. ■ 77035 #048-14-2007 **GS** *012

WEAKLEY, Suzanne. 18220 STATE HWY 249, STE 130 77070 #048-02-1972 L1972 **A IM** *020 †20,03

WEATHERS, Susan Wheeler. 1 BAYLOR PLZ, DEPARTMENT OF RADIOLOGY 77030 #035-01-1977 L1980 **DR RNR** *020 †80

WEAVER, Ralph Maurice. 8989 WESTHEIMER RD, COLLINS FISHER RADY ASSOCS 77063 #048-04-1972 L1972 **DR** *020 †80

WEAVER, Robert A. 9432 OLD KATY RD, STE 200 77055 #048-12-1988 L1989 **IM** *020

WEAVER, Seymour M, III. 4007 BELLAIRE BLVD, STE GG 77025 #048-04-1977 L1978 **D DS** *020 †15 ‡

WEAVER, Sterling Harrisbe. 13111 EAST FWY, STE 109 77015 #051-01-1994 L1998 **OBG** *020 †30

WEBB, David Michael. ■ 77056 #012-01-2008 *012

WEBB, Fonda Delores. ■ 77003 #047-07-2008 *012

WEBB, John Quincy A, Jr. 5090 RICHMOND AVE, PMB 131 77056 #047-07-1966 L1974 **OPH** *020

WEBB, Judith T. ■ 77042 #028-03-1972 L1974 **EM** *074

WEBB, Nancy E R. 1221 MCKINNEY ST, STE 40300 77010 #048-04-1974 L1975 **OPH** *020 †35

WEBB, Sala Suzette. ■ 77025 #051-04-2005 L2008 **P** *012

WEBER, Donna Marie. 1515 HOLCOMBE BLVD # 429, MD ANDERSON CANCER CENTER 77030 #016-45-1988 L1995 **ON** *020 †20

WEBER, John Edward. 6666 HARWIN DR, STE 220 77036 #041-12-1945 L1946 **OBG OS** *071 †30

WEBER, Randal S. 1515 HOLCOMBE BLVD, UNIT 441 77030 #047-06-1976 L1986 **OTO HNS** *020 †45

WEBSTER, Cecil Ray, Jr. ■ 77005 #048-04-2007 **P** *012

WECHSLER, Adriana H. 7737 SW FWY STE 405, SW MEMORIAL HOSP 77074 #041-02-1991 L1997 **IM** *040 †20

WECHSLER, Barbara Cecile. 6621 FANNIN ST, TEXAS CHILDREN'S HOSPITAL 77030 #041-13-1977 L2008 **PM** *020 †60

WEDDINGTON, Lloyd Damon. 2000 CRAWFORD ST STE 900 77002 #012-21-1995 L2003 **IM** *020 †20

WEE, Kee Young. 810 PEAKWOOD DR STE 107 77090 #035-06-1996 L2001 **R NM** *020 †80,28

WEEDEN, Kenneth Carl. ■ 77024 #048-02-1958 L1958 **AN** *020

WEEDIN, John William. ■ 77005 #005-18-2006 **U** *012

WEGLEIN, Daniel Gideon. ■ 77059 #048-12-2007 **ORS** *012

WEGRYN, Tara Lee. 6400 FANNIN ST STE 2295 77030 #011-03-1982 L1992 **N** *020 †75

WEI, Andy C. 3838 HILLCROFT ST, STE 215 77057 #048-04-1994 L1997 **PD** *020 †55

WEI, Chik-Fong. 6400 FANNIN ST STE 2210-B 77030 #048-02-1988 L1989 **CD** *020 †20

WEI, Christine Gotuaco. 1 BAYLOR PLZ, DEPARTMENT OF PEDIATRICS 77030 #748-02-1990 L2000 **NPM PD** *020 †55

WEIBEL, Jorge. 6 CHELSEA BLVD, HEADACHE & PAIN CLINIC 77006 #231-02-1947 L1963 **N PMM** *012

WEIDMAN, Elliott Russell. 7400 FANNIN ST, TEXAS INST FOR 77054 #062-01-1971 L1979 **END REN** *020

WEIDMAN, Joseph Lorenzo, II. ■ 77030 #048-04-2008 *012

WEIDO, Anthony J. 7707 FANNIN ST, STE 195 77054 #048-02-1990 L1991 **AI PDA** *020 †20,03 ‡

WEIHE, Elizabeth Kristine. ■ 77004 #048-04-2006 L2008 **DR** *012

WEIKERT, Mitchell Patrick. 6550 FANNIN ST, STE 1501 77030 #048-04-1998 L2003 **OPH** *100 †35

WEIL, Jacqueline A. 2234 HILSHIRE TRAIL DR 77080 #048-14-1994 L1995 **FM** *020 †18

WEIL, Stuart M. 6624 FANNIN ST STE 2140 77030 #048-14-1984 L1986 **NS** *020 †25

WEILBAECHER, Donald G. 6565 FANNIN ST MS 205, METHODIST HOSPITAL 77030 #021-05-1966 L1977 **PTH CD** *020 †50

WEILER, David Lee. 1415 NORTH LOOP W, STE 810 77008 #025-01-1973 L1977 **R** *020 †80

WEINBERG, Elizabeth F. 4203 MONTROSE BLVD, STE 375 77006 #048-04-1991 L1995 **P** *020 †75

WEINBERG, Jacob. 6621 FANNIN ST, TEXAS CHILDREN'S HOSPITAL 77030 #023-07-1999 L2006 **ORS** *100

WEINBERG, Jeffrey Steven. 1515 HOLCOMBE BLVD, DEPT OF NEUROSURG-UNIT 442 77030 #035-19-1993 L2001 **NS** *020 †25

WEINBERG, John Kenneth. 10370 RICHMOND AVE, STE 1125 77042 #035-20-1985 L1991 **EM GS** *020 †85

WEINDEL, Michael David. 1 BAYLOR PLZ, DEPARTMENT OF PATHOLOGY 77030 #654-01-2007 **PTH** *012

WEINER, Bradley Kenneth. 6550 FANNIN ST STE 2500, DEPT OF ORTHOPAEDICS 77030 #038-44-1991 L2006 **ORS** *020 †40

WEINER, Bruce Roger. 12930 EAST FWY 77015 #038-06-1968 L1977 **ORS** *020 †40

WEINER, Joslyn Beth. 1504 TAUB LOOP, SECTIN GEN MED 77030 #048-04-1995 L1997 **IM** *040 †20

WEINER, Morris A. 6565 FANNIN ST M204Q, THE METHODIST HOSPITAL 77030 #030-06-1977 L1978 **DR** *020 †80

WEINERT, Mary Frances. 6560 FANNIN ST STE 1540 77030 #048-04-1989 L1990 **ID** *020 †20

WEINPEL, Joseph Bryant. ■ 77047 #048-14-2005 **MPD** *012

WEINSTEIN, Phillip. 902 FROSTWOOD DR, STE 262 77024 #065-01-1970 L1977 **FM FSM** *020

WEINSTOCK, Yitzchak Etan. ■ 77096 #035-46-2003 **OTO** *012

WEIR, Raymond Urban. 6431 FANNIN ST, UNIVERSITY OF TEXAS - HOUS 77030 #005-02-1994 L2008 **RNR** *020 †80

WEISBERG, Alec David. 6720 BERTNER ST, RM P-322 (M/C 1-133) 77030 #047-05-2004 L2007 **CD** *012 †20

WEISENBURGER, Kathleen E. 1140 CYPRESS STATION DR, NORTHWEST DIAGNOSTIC CLINI 77090 #051-04-1985 L1986 **IM** *020 †20

WEISMAN, Leonard Emil. 1504 TAUB LOOP RM WT6-104, DEPT OF PEDS 77030 #048-04-1974 L1994 **NPM PD** *030 †55

WEISS, James Dana. 2500 WEST LOOP S, STE 530 77027 #016-42-1986 L1993 **PM** *020 †60

WEISS, Katherine Jean. ■ 77030 #048-03-2006 **PD** *012

WEISS, Stephen Joel. 7907 OAKINGTON DR 77071 #561-01-1969 L1976 **ORS** *020

WELBORN, Mark Gregory. 7505 MAIN ST, STE 290 77030 #048-04-1983 L1983 **N** *020 †75

WELCH, Beatrice. 12141 RICHMOND AVE 77082 #048-04-1953 L1953 **FM** *071

WELLBORNE, Frank R. 909 FROSTWOOD DR STE 362 77024 #018-75-1978, ▲ L1981 **RHU IM** *020 †20

WELLINGHOFF, Vanessa T. ■ 77081 #048-13-2004 L2007 **IM** *020

WELLS, Allison Michelle. ■ 77024 #048-04-2006 L2006 **AN** *012

WELLS, Kenneth Douglas. 1001 LOUISIANA ST, STE 1047 77002 #048-14-1986 L1987 **FM OM** *030 †18

WELLS, Linda Marie. 1 BAYLOR PLZ, DEPT PTHLGY CLG OF MED 77030 #005-12-1998 L2001 **PTH** *020 †50

WELLS, Robert Jeffrey. 1515 HOLCOMBE BLVD UNIT 87, UT MD ANDERSON CANCER CENT 77030 #005-18-1972 L2004 **PHO PD** *030 †55

WELSH, Francis Joseph. 1504 TAUB LOOP, BEN TAUB GENERAL HOSPITAL 77030 #041-02-1999 L2003 **GS** *100 †85

WELTGE, Arlo Frederick. 6431 FANNIN ST 417, UTH-HSC DEPT EM 77030 #048-14-1978 L1978 **EM OM** *020 †70,16 ‡

WEN, Chi-Pang. 1301 MCKINNEY ST, ROOM 2711 GULF TOWER 77010 #385-02-1966 L1976 **FM OM** *020 †70,18

WENDENBURG, Hans Otto. 17070 RED OAK DR, STE 503 77090 #048-02-1969 L1969 **NS FM** *030

WENDERFER, Scott Edward. 6431 FANNIN ST, PEDIATRICS, RM 3.126 77030 #038-41-2001 L2003 **PN** *050 †55 ‡

WENDT, Elaine A. 3601 N MACGREGOR WAY 77004 #048-04-1995 L1998 **MPD** *020 †20,55

WENDT, Juliet Bixby. 1 BAYLOR PLZ, BAYLOR COLLEGE OF MEDICINE 77030 #048-04-1979 L1983 **NM PD** *020 †55,28

WENGER, Joy Marie. ■ 77006 #028-03-2003 **PHO** *012 †20

WENKER, Olivier Charles. 1515 HOLCOMBE BLVD, OFF OF TECH DISCVRY UT 355 77030 #869-07-1983 L1996 **AN CCA** *030

WENZEL, Lisa Rose. ■ 77054 #036-05-2004 L2008 **PM** *012

WERAGODA, Ramal M. 6431 FANNIN ST 1.134, OF TEXAS-HOUSTON 77030 #048-14-2007 **IM** *012

WERCH, Angel. 6550 MAPLERIDGE ST, STE 210 77081 #132-01-1958 L1966 **OBG** *071 †30

WERCH, Jochewed B. 1504 TAUB LOOP, DEPT PATH 77030 #132-01-1960 L1968 **CLP BBK** *020 †50

WERNER, Brian Charles. 1 BAYLOR PLZ, DEPT OF ANESTHESIOLOGY 77030 #035-01-2006 **AN** *012

WERTMAN, Bradley Gray. 7600 FANNIN ST, STE 200 77054 #048-04-1973 L1973 **PTH** *020 †50

WESSON, David E. 6621 FANNIN ST CC650 77030 #065-01-1973 L1998 **PDS** *020 †85

WEST, Barbara. 6621 FANNIN ST 104000 77030 #048-14-1986 L1987 **PD PUD** *020 †55

WEST, Henry Earl. ■ 77004 #047-07-2004 **OBG** *012

WEST, Hugh Nole, III. 5110 SAN FELIPE ST, UNIT 282W 77056 #048-02-1971 L1971 **DR** *020 †80

WEST, O Clark. 6431 FANNIN ST, RADIOLOGY DEPT, MSB 2.100 77030 #028-02-1986 L1997 **DR** *020 †80

WESTBROOK, Mark D. 15655 CYPRESSWOOD MEDCL DR, STE 110 77014 #048-14-1982 L1983 **FM** *020 †18 ‡

WESTERMAN, Eric Lane. 6550 FANNIN ST, STE SM1001 77030 #048-04-1972 L1972 **ID IM** *020 †20

WESTHEIMER, Donald Nagel. 6565 FANNIN ST, TEXAS MEDICAL CENTER 77030 #048-02-1971 L1971 **AN** *020 †05

WESTIN, Jason Robert. ■ 77009 #011-03-2002 L2006 **IM** *020 †20

WESTMARK, Richard M. 18333 EGRET BAY BLVD, STE 200 77058 #011-03-1988 L1995 **NS** *020 †25

WESTMORELAND, Jack Coogan. ■ 77035 #048-04-1954 L1954 **GP** *071

WESTNEY, Ouida L. 6431 FANNIN ST STE 6.018 77030 #023-07-1992 L1999 **U** *020 †95

WESTON, Brian Roy. ■ 77056 #539-06-1999 L2007 **GE** *100 ‡

WESTON, Peter Vernon. ■ 77005 #836-01-1958 L1969 **GYN** *071 †30

WEXLER, Stephan Eric. 2001 HOLCOMBE BLVD # 3404 77030 #048-13-1978 L1978 **PS EM** *020 †65

WEYAND, Anna Melissa. ■ 77004 #048-04-2008 *012

WHALEN, George Edward. 7737 SOUTHWEST FWY STE 860 77074 #056-06-1959 L1975 **GE IM** *020

WHARTON, James Taylor. 1515 HOLCOMBE BLVD # 351 77030 #048-02-1963 L1964 **GO GYN** *020 †30

WHEATLEY, Marsha Kaye. 2626 WESTHEIMER RD, STE 213 77098 #048-14-1983 L1983 **P** *020 †75

WHEELER, Brandi Jlaan. ■ 77030 #048-04-2003 **PD** *100

WHEELER, Edward John. 11914 ASTORIA BLVD, STE 510 77089 #048-02-1986 L1988 **PM** *020 †60

WHEELER, James Martin. 4100 MILAM ST 77006 #048-04-1981 L1983 **REN OBG** *020 †30

WHEELER, Kevin D. 915 GESSNER RD, STE 240 77024 #048-04-1986 L1987 **GS** *020 †85

WHEELER, Susan Hirschhorn. 909 FROSTWOOD DR, STE 104 77024 #048-04-1986 L1987 **CD** *020 †20

WHEELER, Thomas Michael. 1 BAYLOR PLZ, MS BCM315 77030 #048-04-1977 L1977 **OS** *040 †50

WHELAN, Jeffery M. 1221 MCKINNEY ST, STE 40300 77010 #048-04-1985 L1986 **ORS OSM** *020 †40

WHELER, Jennifer Jane. ■ 77006 #035-20-1999 L2007 **ON** *100 †20

WHIPP, Stephen Vinh. 1819 CRAWFORD ST STE 1708, JOSEPH HOSPITAL 77002 #048-14-2005 **OBG** *012

WHISENNAND, Hartwell H. 2476 BOLSOVER ST 77005 #048-02-1968 L1968 **TS GS** *020 †85

WHITE, Arthur C. 1 BAYLOR PLZ 77030 #024-01-1952 L1957 **ID IM** *040 †20

WHITE, Arthur C, Jr. 1 BAYLOR PLZ, DEPT MEDICINE 77030 #017-20-1982 L1990 **ID IM** *040

WHITE, Blackman Lee, Jr. 808 TRAVIS ST STE 837 77002 #048-04-1960 L1960 **OBG** *020 †30

WHITE, Charles Lee, III. 16825 NORTHCHASE DR 77060 #003-01-1978 L1984 **NP ATP** *020 †50

WHITE, Crystal Dawn. ■ 77054 #048-04-2008 *012

WHITE, Daniela Maria. 5225 KATY FWY STE 650 77007 #781-01-1992 L2001 **P CHP** *020 †75

WHITE, Dezra. 2101 CRAWFORD ST STE 312 77002 #048-02-1968 L1968 **OBG** *020 †30

WHITE, Heather M. ■ 77008 #048-14-1985 L1986 **GE IM** *020 †20

WHITE, Lucile Elizabeth. ■ 77005 #016-02-2001 L2007 **D** *020 †15

WHITE, Marlon D. 13215 DOTSON RD, STE 200 77070 #048-02-1987 L1988 **OBG** *020 †30

WHITE, Martin Ray. 1707 SUNSET BLVD, MEDICAL CLINIC OF HOUSTON 77005 #048-04-1977 L1977 **IM HEM** *020 †20

WHITE, Najia Hassen. 815 WALKER ST STE 837 77002 #048-04-1961 L1961 *071

WHITE, Neill Richard. 1504 TAUB LOOP 77030 #048-04-2002 L2006 **MPD** *100 †55,20

WHITE, Neva N. 6431 FANNIN ST, JJL 495 77030 #048-14-1998 L2007 **PD** *020 †55

WHITE, Richard Hall. 6692 SOUTHWEST FWY 77004 #048-12-1969 L1969 **GP OS** *020 †18

WHITE, Robert Elliott. 2121 SAGE RD, STE 180 77056 #048-02-1965 L1965 **P** *020 ‡

WHITE, Robert Erickson. 2405 S GESSNER RD, STE B 77063 #048-02-1960 L1960 **FM** *020

WHITEHEAD, Christin M C. ■ 77025 #539-04-1958 L1963 **AN** *071

WHITEHEAD, William Eiji. 1709 DRYDEN RD 77030 #048-02-2003 L2007 **AN** *100

WHITEHEAD, William Ernest. 6621 FANNIN ST, STE 1230.01 77030 #048-14-1996 L2007 **NS** *020

WHITELEY, Laura Lingle. 902 FROSTWOOD DR STE 190, MEMORIAL HEALTH AND WELLNE 77024 #048-14-1999 L2003 **MPD** *020 †55,20

WHITE-SATCHER, D'Juanna O. 1 BAYLOR PLZ, TX CL CC 1540 77030 #024-01-1991 L2004 **PD ADL** *020 †55

WHITESIDE, Sheila Joyce. 5901 LONG DR 77087 #018-03-1991 L1993 **CHP** *020 †75

WHITFIELD, Jarvis Brandon. ■ 77021 #047-07-1954 L1957 **GP GS** *071

WHITFIELD, Kristin L. ■ 77015 #048-14-2004 L2007 **PG** *012 †55

WHITING, Carman Hall. 6431 FANNIN ST, JJL STE 324 77030 #043-01-1999 L2002 **FM** *020 †18

WHITLOCK, Leslie Edwin. 1919 LA BRANCH ST 77002 #010-03-1962 L1967 **OBG** *071 †30

WHITMAN, Gary Jacob. 1515 HOLCOMBE BLVD, BOX 301439 # 1350 77030 #038-06-1986 L2007 **DR** *020 †80

WHITMIRE, Gerald Allen. 7515 MAIN ST STE 590B 77030 #048-13-1979 L1981 **OBG** *020

WHITMIRE, Rogers O'Neil. 7515 MAIN ST, STE 590 77030 #025-12-1973 L1975 **OBG** *020 †30

WHITNEY, Anne Piott. ■ 77054 #048-04-2008 *012

WHITNEY, Simon N. 3701 KIRBY DR, STE 100 77098 #035-19-1979 L2000 **FM** *040 †18

WHITNEY, Stephen Everett. 6621 FANNIN ST, STE A 210/MC 1-481 77030 #048-04-1979 L1980 **PD HOS** *020 †55

WHITSELL, Robert Earl. 3000 RICHMOND AVE, STE 540 77098 #019-02-1960 L1965 **ORS** *020 †40

WHITSETT, Jeffrey Clay. 1237 CAMPBELL RD 77055 #039-01-1986 L1991 **OPH** *020 †35

WHITTAKER, Carla Jewel. ■ 77047 #048-15-1992 **OBG** *100

WHITTINGTON, Horace G. 1502 TAUB LOOP, NEURO PSYCHIATRIC CENTER 77030 #048-04-1952 L1952 **P LM** *020 †75

WIBLE, Elissa Fory. ■ 77054 #021-01-2004 L2008 **N** *012

WIECK, Gretchen K. 6431 FANNIN ST, UNIVERSITY OF TEXAS HEALTH 77030 #012-05-1998 L2005 **CN** *100 †75

WIEMER, D Robert. 6560 FANNIN ST STE 1760 77030 #048-04-1965 L1965 **PS** *020 †65 ‡

WIENER, Isidoro Bercovich. 902 FROSTWOOD DR, STE 265 MEM PROF BLDG 1 77024 #649-01-1976 L1983 **GS VS** *020

WIENER, Thomas C. 2323 CLEAR LAKE CITY BLVD, STE 152 77062 #048-12-1987 L1988 **PS HS** *020 †65

WIERDA, William G. 1515 HOLCOMBE BLVD # 428 77030 #016-42-1993 L2002 **HO IM** *020 †20

WIESENBORN, Scott T. ■ 77021 #048-14-2006 L2007 **EM** *012

WIESENTHAL, Joseph. ■ 77277 #048-04-1945 L1945 **IM** *071

WIGDER, Matthew W. ■ 77096 #048-14-2001 L2003 **PD** *020 †55

WIGFALL, Preston Allen. ■ 77256 #041-02-1981 L1983 **IM** *020 †20

WIGGINS, Michele K. 11850 FM 1960 RD W 77065 #048-14-1993 L1994 **APM** *020 †05

WIGGINS, Xavier Gayle. ■ 77015 #024-05-2004 **FM** *100

WILBUR, Jennette L. ■ 77006 #048-04-2004 L2007 **FM** *100 †18

WILDE, Henry Dayton. 6550 FANNIN ST 77030 #021-01-1957 L1958 **ORS** *072 †40

WILEY, Sara Kay. 4110 BELLAIRE BLVD, STE 210 77025 #039-01-1997 L2002 **PD** *020 †55

WILFONG, Angus. 6621 FANNIN ST 77030 #068-01-1986 L1991 **CHN CN** *020 †55

WILHELM, Ginger Winford. 6431 FANNIN ST JJL-445, DEPT. OF EMERGENCY MEDICIN 77030 #048-02-1979 L1979 **EM** *020 †16

WILHELMUS, Kirk Robt. 6550 FANNIN ST, STE 1501 77030 #047-05-1975 L1981 **OPH EP** *020 †35 ‡

WILKENFELD, Jerome S. 8850 LONG POINT RD 77055 #021-01-1964 L1965 **PTH** *020 †50

WILKERSON, James A, Jr. 8806 LONG POINT STE 101 77055 #048-04-1985 L1986 **FM** *020 †18

WILKERSON, Robert Gray. 8153 LONG POINT RD 77055 #048-02-1967 L1967 **P CHP** *020

WILKING, Andrew Pray. 6357 EDLOE ST 77005 #035-01-1978 L1988 **RHU PD** *020 †55

WILKING, Marilyn Nash. 4101 GREENBRIAR ST, STE 100 77098 #035-47-1977 L1982 **PD** *020 †55

WILKINS, Robert Benson. 2855 GRAMERCY ST 77025 #048-02-1964 L1964 **OPH PS** *020 †35

WILKS, Jonathan Andrew. ■ 77054 #048-04-2005 **GS** *012

WILLARD, Julie Anne. ■ 77054 #048-04-2008 *012

WILLERSON, James Thornton. 6431 FANNIN ST # 1150 77030 #048-04-1965 L1965 **CD IM** *050 †20

WILLIAMS, Arthur Love. ■ 77002 #047-07-1966 L1974 **IM** *020 †20

WILLIAMS, Austin Oscar. 5420 DASHWOOD DR STE 301 77081 #033-06-1994 L1996 **IM** *020 †20

WILLIAMS, Brian Jeremy. ■ 77054 #048-04-2008 *012

WILLIAMS, Candace Yvonne. ■ 77073 #025-01-2004 **GS** *012

WILLIAMS, Christian Edwar. ■ 77054 #012-21-2005 **PD** *012

WILLIAMS, Colville T. 2424 HAMILTON ST STE 300 77004 #566-01-1987 L1995 **NEP IM** *020 †20

WILLIAMS, Cynthia L. 1707 SUNSET BLVD, MEDICAL CLINIC OF HOUSTON 77005 #048-14-2000 L2003 **IM** *020 †20

WILLIAMS, Dana Steeves. ■ 77005 #036-07-1955 L1963 **GP OS** *071 †55

WILLIAMS, Daniel Mark. ■ 77096 #048-14-2007 **EM** *012

WILLIAMS, Ebony. 6431 FANNIN ST, JJL 495 77030 #047-07-2002 L2005 **PD** *020 †55

WILLIAMS, Eric Andrew. 6621 FANNIN ST WT6, TEXAS CHILDREN'S HOSPITAL 77030 #036-07-1996 L1999 **CCP** *020 †55

WILLIAMS, Francesca M. ■ 77025 #035-19-2000 **OBG** *100

WILLIAMS, Francis M. 6909 GREENBRIAR ST, RHEUMATOLOGY ASSOCIATES OF 77030 #048-14-1992 L1993 **RHU IM** *020 †20

WILLIAMS, Gwendolyn A. 830 GEMINI ST 77058 #048-02-1983 L1983 **PD** *020 †55

WILLIAMS, Kelcey Laura. ■ 77054 #036-08-1997 L2003 **SCI** *100 †60

WILLIAMS, Kristin Noelle. 6624 FANNIN ST, ALPERT & SERMAS 77030 #025-07-2001 L2003 **OBG** *020

WILLIAMS, Leo Jos. 1919 LA BRANCH ST 77002 #048-04-1957 L1957 **PTH** *071 †50

WILLIAMS, Lyal Gordon. 6565 FANNIN ST 77030 #021-01-1960 L1966 **AN** *071

WILLIAMS, Marion J. 2727 W HOLCOMBE BLVD 77025 #048-12-1953 L1953 **TS VS** *071 †85,90

WILLIAMS, Michelle N. 1515 HOLCOMBE BLVD, UNIT 085 77030 #011-03-2000 L2006 **PTH SP** *020 †50

WILLIAMS, Patricia K. ■ 77005 #048-14-2000 **NPM** *012 †55

WILLIAMS, Richard P, Jr. 1323 ROSEWOOD ST 77004 #020-12-1966 L1971 **GPM EM** *020 †16,70

WILLIAMS, Robert Leon. ■ 77098 #035-03-1946 L1972 **P N** *071 †75

WILLIAMS, Robin Jacquet. 5656 KELLEY ST, EMERGENCY MED DEPT 77026 #048-02-1986 L1989 **PD** *020 †55

WILLIAMS, Rolfe M. 2411 FOUNTAIN VIEW DR, STE 200 77057 #048-14-1989 L1990 **AN** *020 †05

WILLIAMS, Russel Herndon. 9190 KATY FWY, STE 101 77055 #048-12-1991 L1995 **U OS** *020 †95

WILLIAMS, Susan Patricia. 1709 DRYDEN RD, 8TH FL 77030 #017-20-1995 L1997 **IM** *020 †20

WILLIAMS, Temple W, Jr. 6565 FANNIN ST 77030 #048-04-1959 L1959 **ID IM** *071 †20

WILLIAMS, Teresa Renee. ■ 77099 #047-07-2007 **FP** *012

WILLIAMS, Terry Raymond. 4126 SOUTHWEST FWY # 1520 77027 #035-06-1971 L1976 **U GS** *020 †95

WILLIAMS, Victoria R. 9301 SOUTHWEST FWY, STE 5000 77074 #048-13-1998 L2007 **FM** *020 †18

WILLIAMSON, Ava A. PO BOX 20708, UNIV OF TX MED SCH 77225 #048-13-2006 **PD** *012

WILLIAMSON, Jack B. 7401 MAIN ST 77030 #048-02-1987 L1989 **OSS GS** *020 †40

WILLIAMSON, Robert Arthur. 6501 FANNIN ST, BAYLOR OTOLARYNGOLOGY 77030 #005-14-1995 L2007 **OTO** *020 †45

WILLIAMSON, Warren Joe. ■ 77096 #048-04-1954 L1954 **GP** *020

WILLIAMSON, William Danl. 6655 TRAVIS ST, STE 880 77030 #021-05-1974 L1978 **PD** *020 †55

WILLIAMS-WATSON, Kimberly. 1801 NORTH LOOP W STE 40 77008 #048-16-1995 L1997 **PD** *020 †18

WILLINGHAM, Simone Davis. 2101 NASA RD 1, MAIL CODE: SD32 77058 #010-03-1998 L2001 **FM** *020 †18

WILLIS, Samuel Eric. ■ 77007 #048-04-2002 L2006 **FM** *020 †18

WILLMAN, Krista Yvonne. 1919 S BRAESWOOD BLVD, 5TH FL 77030 #005-18-1996 L2005 **PD** *020 †55

WILLS, Kyle Stanley. PO BOX 4093 77210 #030-05-1980 L1984 **P OS** *020

WILLS, Patrick Wayne. 2000 CRAWFORD ST, STE 900 77002 #041-14-1975 L1977 **IM** *020

WILLS, Rebecca Enola. 2000 CRAWFORD ST, STE 900 77002 #005-06-1973 L1974 **GP** *020

WILMOT, Ivan. ■ 77021 #012-05-2002 L2004 **PDC** *012 †55

WILSON, Bridget Dean. 7373 ARDMORE ST APT 14 77054 #024-05-2007 **FP** *012

WILSON, Cornelius A. 902 NORMANDY ST STE 100, PEDIATRIC CLINIC 77015 #033-05-1988 L1992 **MPD** *020

WILSON, David Leon. 211 HIGHLAND CROSS DR, STE 275 77073 #010-03-1999 L2002 **EM** *020

WILSON, Erik Browning. 6431 FANNIN ST, STE 4170 77030 #048-04-1996 L1997 **GS** *020

WILSON, Hilton H. ■ 77004 #010-03-1956 L1963 **AN** *071

WILSON, Howard King. 1200 BINZ ST, STE 1410 77004 #038-41-1975 L1978 **END IM** *020 †20

WILSON, James Michael. 6624 FANNIN ST, STE 2480 77030 #021-01-1990 L1993 **CD** *020 †20

WILSON, Joe Bob. 1200 BINZ ST STE 300, DIAGNOSTIC CLINIC OF HOUST 77004 #048-12-1961 L1961 **R** *071 †20

WILSON, Kathleen Russ. 6621 FANNIN ST 1530, BAYLOR CLG MEYER CTR 77030 #007-02-1973 L1976 **PD** *020 †20

WILSON, Kelly Elizabeth. 7400 FANNIN ST, STE 930 77054 #007-02-1992 L1995 **OBG** *020 †30

WILSON, Leslie Evelyn. 6410 FANNIN ST STE 600 77030 #021-05-1996 L2003 **RHU IM** *020 †20

WILSON, Matthew Hunter. 1 BAYLOR PLZ, ALKEK, N520 77030 #047-05-2001 L2007 **NEP** *100

WILSON, Pamela D. 2476 BOLSOVER ST STE 424 77030 #048-14-1994 L1995 **AN** *020

WILSON, Todd David. ■ 77004 #048-14-2003 **GS** *012

WIMALAWANSA, Sunishka Mai. ■ 77054 #048-04-2008 *012

WIMAN, Stephanie E. 3100 RICHMOND AVE, STE 500 77098 #041-01-1994 L1995 **FM** *020 †18

WIMBERLEY, David W. 7401 MAIN ST 77030 #048-12-1997 L2004 **ORS** *020 †40

WIMBERLY, David M. 17150 EL CAMINO REAL, STE E 77058 #048-14-1987 L1989 **AN** *020 †05

WIN, Htut Kyaw. 1 BAYLOR PLZ 77030 #209-01-1995 L2005 **CD** *100 †20

WINAKER, Kenneth Lee. 3737 DACOMA ST 77092 #035-08-1970 L1975 **P** *020 †75

WINFIELD, Kevin Scott. 2060 SPACE PARK DR, STE 102 77058 #048-04-1995 L1997 **IM** *020 †20

WINGARD, Peggy. 100 CYBERONICS BLVD, CYBERONICS INC 77058 #048-12-1981 L1982 PAN *012

WINKEL, Erwin C, III. 1140 CYPRESS STATION DR, STE 303 77090 #048-04-1989 L1990 U *020 †95

WINKEL, Erwin Charles, II. 710 FM 1960 RD W 77090 #048-04-1959 L1959 U *071 †95

WINKELMANN, Tara Lyn. 1819 CRAWFORD ST 77002 #048-13-2004 L2008 OBG *012

WINKELSTEIN, Abraham. 800 PEAKWOOD DR, STE 6H 77090 #010-02-1991 L1997 GE *020 †20

WINSLOW, Kathryn Anne. ■ 77027 #023-01-2007 OBG *012

WINSTON, Barry David. 1140 CYPRESS STATION DR, STE 306 77090 #048-13-1973 L1973 GE *020 †20

WINSTON, Donald Skeer. 5615 MORNINGSIDE DR, STE 1000 77005 #028-46-1975 L1978 TRS GS *020

WINSTON, Erin L. ■ 77030 #048-13-2004 L2007 DR *012

WINSTON, Leland Alfred. 6560 FANNIN ST, STE 400 77030 #048-02-1973 L1973 ORS *020 †40

WINSTROM, Margit Mary. 4126 SOUTHWEST FWY, STE 1210 77027 #041-07-1968 L1970 FM *020 †18

WINTER, Ronald Stephen. 9105 N WAYSIDE DR, CLINIC 77028 #048-13-1984 L1986 FM *020 †18

WINTERS, Alan Jos. 5314 DASHWOOD DR 77081 #035-08-1966 L1973 GYN END *071 †30

WINTERS, William L, Jr. 6550 FANNIN ST 77030 #016-06-1953 L1968 CD IM *020 †40

WINTZ, Ruth L Lachar. 7007 NORTH FWY, STE 240 77076 #048-04-1997 L2006 IM NEP †20

WITHERS, Benjamin F. 12000 LAWNDALE ST, MEDICAL DEPARTMENT 77017 #030-05-1973 L1994 OM AM *030 †70 ‡

WITHERS, Edward Hodges. 6550 FANNIN ST, STE 2427 77030 #048-02-1971 L1971 PS *020 †85,65

WITT, Raymond R. ■ 77056 #047-05-1953 L1958 GS TS *071 †85

WITTENBERG, Susan Elaine. 6411 FANNIN ST 7TH FL 77030 #048-14-2000 L2005 OPH *100 †35

WITTIG, Linda Beth. 3540 W DALLAS ST, JUVENILE PROBATON DEPT 77019 #048-12-1981 L1981 CHP PD *020 †55,75

WITTMAN, Ian Geoffrey. ■ 77054 #048-04-2008 *012

WOEHLER, Thomas Richard. ■ 77007 #017-20-1964 L1971 A IM *071 †20,03

WOEHRMANN, Amy L. ■ 77005 #048-02-1992 L1993 EM *020 †16

WOERNER, Audrey Claire. 6431 FANNIN ST, AT HO 77030 #048-14-2006 MG *012

WOHLFAHRT, Douglas Wayne. 11281 RICHMOND AVE, # J-112 77082 #048-04-1974 L1977 OBG FM *020

WOJCIECHOWSKI, Zbigniew J. 6565 FANNIN ST, ANESTHESIOLOGY, B452 77030 #759-01-1975 L1994 AN CD *020 †05

WOJCIK, Ewa Marie. 1515 HOLCOMBE BLVD 77030 #759-07-1982 L1992 PTH *020 †50

WOLDESENBET, Mesfin. 7777 SOUTHWEST FWY, STE 310 77074 #366-01-1989 L2003 NPM *100 †55

WOLENS, Jeoffrey Kless. 2727 GRAMERCY ST STE 225 77025 #048-13-1994 L1997 PD *020 †55

WOLF, Charles Lee. ■ 77090 #048-02-1957 L1957 OM *071

WOLF, Cyril. 902 FROSTWOOD DR STE 290 77024 #836-01-1968 L1977 FM *020 †18

WOLF, David Alexander. MAIL CODE 594 NASA/JOHNSN 77058 #017-20-1982 L1982 AM *030

WOLF, David Scott. 6431 FANNIN ST STE 4.234, UTHSC AT HOUSTON 77030 #048-14-2005 L2008 GE *012 †20

WOLF, Dwayne A. ■ 77095 #048-02-1993 L1994 PTH *072 †50

WOLF, John Eaton, Jr. 1709 DRYDEN RD, STE 1050 77030 #048-02-1965 L1965 D *020 †15

WOLF, Judith Kay. 1515 HOLCOMBE BLVD BOX 67, MD ANDERSON CANCER CENTER 77030 #038-44-1986 L1988 OBG *020 †30

WOLF, Varina L. ■ 77025 #048-12-2002 PD *012

WOLFE, Steven Bennett. 6621 FANNIN ST, BAYLOR PEDIATRIC CARDIOLOG 77030 #025-07-1988 L1994 PDC PD *020 †55

WOLFF, Johannes Ernst Ale. 1515 HOLCOMBE BLVD, UNIT 87 77030 #409-32-1986 L2007 *100

WOLFF, Robert Alan. 1400 HOLCOMBE BLVD, BLVD. FC11.2018 77030 #035-03-1986 L1998 IM HEM *050 †20

WOLINSKY, Jerry Saul. 6410 FANNIN ST, STE 1025 77030 #016-11-1969 L1983 N *050 †75 ‡

WOLK, David Jonathan. 1919 LA BRANCH ST, ASSOCIATES 77002 #010-02-1983 L1985 DR *020 †20

WOLLASTON, Dianne E. 5773 WOODWAY DR # 259 77057 #048-14-1993 L1994 RHU *020 †20

WOLSKI, Irene E. 5858 WESTHEIMER RD, STE 708 77057 #048-14-1989 L1990 P *020

WOMBLE, Brooke Leanne. ■ 77005 #048-04-2008 *012

WONG, Adrian Alexander. PO BOX 20708, UNIV TX MED SCH 77225 #048-13-2006 DR *012

WONG, Christina Waiyun. 3300 BELLEFONTAINE ST # 45 77025 #048-14-2003 L2006 PD *100

WONG, Daniel R. ■ 77030 #065-01-1999 L2007 TS *100

WONG, Franklin C. 1515 HOLCOMBE BLVD 77030 #016-42-1986 L1990 NM N *020 †28,75

WONG, Harry Y. 6560 HORNWOOD DR 77074 #048-02-1995 L1998 FM *020

WONG, Jamie. 6500 FANNIN ST, STE 1100 77030 #024-07-1994 L1999 OPH *020 †35

WONG, John Eu Li. ■ 77005 #048-01-1995 HEM ON *020 †20

WONG, Patrick Lupyin. ■ 77025 #016-42-2005 L2005 PM *012

WONG, Ping Fai. 6400 FANNIN ST, STE 2210 77030 #462-02-1987 L1995 IM *020 †20

WONG, Siew Min. 1 BAYLOR PLZ, DEPT OF GASTROENTEROLGY 77030 #067-01-2002 GE *012 †20

WONG, Stephanie L. 15655 CYPRESSWOOD MEDCL DR, STE 100 77014 #048-12-1992 L1994 PD *020 †55

WONG, Tien P. 6560 FANNIN ST, STE 750 77030 #048-04-1987 L1988 OPH OS *020 †35

WONG, Timothy S. ■ 77024 #048-12-1986 L1987 AN *020 †05

WONG-DOMENECH, Maria T. 5708 W LITTLE YORK RD 77091 #308-04-1984 L1991 PD *020 †55

WONGSA, Peggy. 11302 FALLBROOK DR STE 305 77065 #891-01-1977 L1996 PD NPM *020 †55

WONGSA, Voravit. 11302 FALLBROOK DR, STE 105 77065 #891-01-1979 L1996 GS *020 †85

WOO, Cynthia Lynne. 13111 EAST FWY, EAST HOUSTON REGIONAL MEDI 77015 #027-01-1988 L1989 DR *020 †80

WOO, Shiao Yuo. 1515 HOLCOMBE BLVD UNIT 97, UTMD ANDERSON CANCER CTR 77030 #624-01-1972 L1988 RO PHO *020 †55,80

WOOD, Amy G. 7515 MAIN ST, STE 770 77030 #041-13-1996 L1997 D *020 †15

WOOD, Barry Payne. ■ 77019 #048-02-1954 L1954 R *071 †80

WOOD, Christopher G. 1515 HOLCOMBE BLVD, UT-M.D. ANDERSON CANCER CT 77030 #016-06-1989 L1997 U *050 †95

WOOD, Edwin C. 3642 UNIVERSITY BLVD STE 2 77005 #010-01-1950 L1972 PYA P *020 †75

WOOD, Hilaire Candace. 7900 FANNIN ST, OBSTETRICS AND GYNECOLOGIC 77054 #001-06-2004 OBG *012

WOOD, Lori Anne. 1515 HOLCOMBE BLVD, DEPT OF GENITOURINARY ONCO 77030 #065-05-1992 L1998 HEM *020 †20

WOOD, R Patrick. 6624 FANNIN ST, STE 1200 77030 #035-45-1979 L1991 GS TTS *020 †85

WOOD, Ying-Ying Y. 6463 HILLCROFT ST 77081 #048-13-1989 L1992 PD *020 †55

WOODARD, Le Chauncy D. 3601 N MACGREGOR WAY 77004 #048-02-1997 L2000 IM *020 †20

WOODBURY, Suzanne Linda. 6621 FANNIN ST, MC WT21-329 77030 #047-06-2000 L2004 PM *020 †60

WOODHAM, Robert Lee. 4888 LOOP CENTRAL DR, STE 510 77081 #048-02-1977 L1978 P ADM *020 †75

WOODMAN, Scott Eric. PO BOX 20708, UT MD ANDERSON CTR 77225 #035-46-2004 L2007 HO *012 †20

WOODRUFF, Amy L. 6624 FANNIN ST STE 2720 77030 #048-04-1995 L1996 CD *020 †20

WOODS, George Wm. 7401 MAIN ST 77030 #004-01-1965 L1973 ORS *020 †40

WOODS, Karen L. 6560 FANNIN ST, STE 600 77030 #028-46-1983 L1985 GE IM *020 †20

WOODS, Rashida Halima. ■ 77096 #047-07-2007 PD *012

WOODWARD, Rell Madison. 7550 FANNIN ST 77054 #048-04-1976 L1976 OBG *020 †30

WOODWARD, Wendy Ann. 6723 BERTNER ST 77030 #041-02-2000 L2005 RO *100 †80

WOOLEY, Robert Franklin. 3630 WAKEFOREST ST 77098 #048-02-1959 L1959 R *071 †80

WOOLFOLK, Donna. 6410 FANNIN ST, STE 200 77030 #048-12-1986 L1987 OBG *020 †30

WOON, Cybele Chi-Jan. 1237 CAMPBELL RD 77055 #048-04-1990 L1991 OPH *020 †35

WOOTEN, Florence D. 2000 CRAWFORD ST STE 1200 77002 #047-07-1983 L1986 OPH *020 †35

WOOTEN, Michelle O. 8119 MEADOW CREST ST, STE 1003 77071 #048-02-1992 L1993 AN *020

WOOTTON, Susan Haldane. 6431 FANNIN ST, MSB 6.132 77030 #012-01-1997 L2007 PDI *100 †55

WORCHEL, Albert. 8200 WEDNESBURY LN STE 295 77074 #048-04-1959 L1959 GP *071

WORD, Bonnie Marie. 6701 FANNIN ST 77030 #028-02-1982 L2004 PD ID *074 †55

WORSHAM, Austen Winfield. ■ 77004 #048-14-2008 *012

WORTH, Jordan Frederick. 1200 BINZ ST STE 775 77004 #065-01-1966 L1976 IM GE *020

WORTH, Laura Lynn. 1515 HOLCOMBE BLVD UNT 853, DEPT OF PEDIATRICS - UNIT 77030 #048-14-1990 L1991 PHO *020 †55

WORTHAM, Jonathan Maurice. ■ 77004 #048-04-2008 *012

WORTHING, Louie F. 17070 RED OAK DR, STE 307 77090 #048-02-1973 L1973 PS GS *020 †65

WRAY, Curtis Jackson. 1515 HOLCOMBE BLVD UNIT 4, SURGICAL ONCOLOGY 77030 #020-12-1998 L2005 GS *100 †85

WRAY, Nelda Ann Park. 2002 HOLCOMBE BLVD 152 77030 #048-04-1972 L1972 IM PUD *030 †20

WRIGHT, Adam Christopher. 2411 FOUNTAIN VIEW DR, STE 200 77057 #048-02-1996 L2000 AN *020 †05

WRIGHT, Booker Taliaferro. 9211 KENILWORTH ST 77024 #025-01-1972 L1978 ORS *020 †40

WRIGHT, Crystal Clay. ■ 77005 #048-04-2002 L2006 AN *100 †05

WRIGHT, James Robt, III. 14340 TORREY CHASE BLVD, STE 325 77014 #048-14-1975 L1975 P ADM *020 †75

WRIGHT, Jennifer Anne. ■ 77096 #048-02-2002 L2008 HO *012 †20

WRIGHT, John David. 6560 FANNIN ST, STE 1270 77030 #048-02-1960 L1960 U *071 †95

WRIGHT, John Paul. 10602 CHEVY CHASE DR 77042 #048-15-1977 L1977 AN *020 †05

WRIGHT, Lawrence Allison. 3100 TIMMONS LN, STE 150 77027 #048-04-1968 L1968 OPH *020 †35

WRIGHT, Libbyette Elaine. 915 GESSNER RD, STE 640 77024 #048-16-1990 L1992 D *020 †15

WRIGHT, Paula Evon. 4410 NAVIGATION BLVD, STE 278 77011 #018-03-1999 L2002 PD *020 †55

WRIGHT, Stanley Eugene. ■ 77024 #048-13-2007 OBG *012

WRIGHT, Thomas Raney. ■ 77021 #010-03-1967 L1967 OPH *020

WRIGHT-BOWERS, Debra S. 6431 FANNIN ST, AT HO 77030 #048-12-2006 PD *012

WU, Eileen Wanying. ■ 77001 #048-02-2005 ORS *012

WU, Ina. ■ 77277 #048-04-2008 *012

WU, Naixing. 12141 RICHMOND AVE 77082 #243-16-1983 L2000 AN *020 †05

WU, Stanley Genjen. 11302 FALLBROOK DR, STE 308 77065 #048-14-1996 L2001 FM *020 †18

WU, Sylvia. 4126 SOUTHWEST FWY 77027 #048-02-1991 L1992 IM *020 †20

WUPPER, Jo Lee. ■ 77266 #030-05-1978 L1984 OPH *020

WYLIE, William Jerome. 9200 WESTHEIMER RD 77063 #021-05-1959 L1964 IM *071

WYNE, Kathleen. 5550 FANNIN ST, SM1001 77030 #016-02-1990 L1993 END *050 †20

WYNNE, Abigail Guerrero. 7737 SOUTHWEST FWY, RES P 77074 #048-12-2006 FP *012

WYNNE, David M. 1709 DRYDEN RD STE 550, BCM FACULTY CENTER 77030 #048-12-2006 DR *012

WYNNE-DUNCAN, Gracia. 7400 FANNIN ST, STE 1050 77054 #048-14-1996 L2000 OBG *020 †30

WYSE, Roberta Louise. 3701 KIRBY DR STE 600, BAYLOR COLLEGE OF MEDICINE 77098 #010-01-1978 L1982 PD *020 †55

XELLER, Charles Fred. 3000 RICHMOND AVE, STE 540 77098 #035-08-1979 L1989 ORS HS *020 †40

XIE, Chen. 2727 W HOLCOMBE BLVD 4C 77025 #011-02-1994 L2000 OTO *020 †45

XU, Baiyang. 1885 OLD SPANISH TRL 77054 #243-44-1982 L2003 FOP *100

XU, Jianzhang. 2500 FONDREN RD, STE 270 77063 #243-16-1983 L1994 FM *020 †18

XU, Xudong. 9160 BELLAIRE BLVD, STE E 77036 #243-33-1984 L2004 FM *020 †18

XYDAKIS, Antonios M. ■ 77025 #418-03-1995 END *100 †20

XYDAS, Nicolas P. 6500 NORTH FWY STE 1 77076 #048-12-1990 L1995 OBG *020 †30

YA, Aung Thu. 4545 POST OAK PLACE DR, STE 130 77027 #209-01-1995 L2005 IM *100 †20

YACOUB, Joseph Mikhail. ■ 77062 #915-04-1959 L1978 *020

YACOUB, Odile Francoise. 11800 ASTORIA BLVD 77089 #396-21-1971 L1978 AN *020 †05

YADAV, Rajesh Ramashankar. 1515 HOLCOMBE BLVD, UNIT 008 77030 #021-05-1992 L1999 IM PM *020 †60

YAGNIK, Vivek C. 6720 BERTNER ST MC-270, ST. LUKE'S EPISCOPAL HOSPI 77030 #048-04-1996 L1998 DR *020 †80

YAKOOB, Tasneem Paliwala. 6720 BERTNER ST 77030 #048-13-2001 L2003 IM *020

YALAMANCHILI, Devi. 2101 CRAWFORD ST 77002 #495-50-1969 L1977 PD GP *020

YALAMANCHILI, Rajasekhara. 11111 JONES RD STE 6 77070 #495-65-1973 L1985 FM *020 †18

YALLAMPALLI, Sasidhar. ■ 77030 #048-04-2007 *012

YAMOAH, Edward Hammond. 1 BAYLOR PLZ, BAYLOR COLL OF MED 77030 #005-02-2006 AN *012

YAMPEY, Moises. ■ 77096 #726-01-1957 L1972 PHP GP *071

YANCEY, Linda S. 800 PEAKWOOD DR, STE 8A 77090 #048-15-2000 L2004 ID *100 †20

YANG, Deborah Jin. 1709 DRYDEN RD, STE 1050 77030 #048-04-2004 L2007 D *012

YANG, Elizabeth L. 1500 S DAIRY ASHFRD #197B 77077 #048-14-1988 L1989 FM *020 †18

YANG, Eric Yota. ■ 77025 #016-06-2006 IM *012

YANG, Frank Young. 8111 SOUTHWEST FWY 77074 #048-04-1984 L1985 AN *020 †05

YANG, Jeong Soon. 6500 NORTH FWY, KIM & YANG'S CLINIC 77076 #583-09-1970 L1982 PD *074 †55

YANG, Lien-Yen. ■ 77030 #244-04-1988 U *100

YANG, Serena. 6621 FANNIN ST, BAYLOR CLG OF MED ACAD GEN 77030 #012-05-1998 L2001 PD *050 †55

YANG, Shawn Xiangdong. 7600 BEECHNUT ST 77074 #243-95-1990 L2004 AN *020,05

YANG, Stanley S. 1919 NORTH LOOP W, STE 200 77008 #048-14-1995 L1998 IM *020

YANG, Stephen Siehon. 6431 FANNIN ST, MSB G.510 77030 #041-15-2001 L2005 PM *100 †60

YANG, Victor W. 1631 NORTH LOOP W, STE 510 77008 #016-06-1984 L1987 GE IM *020 †20

YANG, Wei Tse. 1515 HOLCOMBE BLVD 77030 #825-01-1987 L2006 *100

YANKELOVE, Samuel Jay. 8800 KATY FWY, STE 107 77024 #023-01-1976 L1980 OPH *020 †35

YANOSIK, Justin Edward. 6330 MAIN ST 77005 #048-04-2007 AN *012

YAO, David. 1709 DRYDEN RD, MS: BCM 620, STE 9.91 77030 #048-15-2001 L2004 CD *012

YAO, James C. 1515 HOLCOMBE BLVD, UT MDACC BOX 426 77030 #048-04-1995 L1997 ON *050 †20

YAO, Joyce H. 1221 MCKINNEY ST, STE 40300 77010 #048-02-1987 L1988 OBG *020 †30

YAO, June. 4407 YOAKUM BLVD, STE B 77006 #243-21-1987 L2006 NEP *100 †20

YAO, Sheng-Kun. 9110 BELLAIRE BLVD, STE E 77036 #243-78-1983 L1997 IM CD *020 †55

YAO, Tai. 10792 BELLAIRE BLVD, ALIEF MEDICAL CLINIC 77072 #243-16-1952 L1982 FM *020

YAP, Hwee Yong. ■ 77056 #917-04-1971 L1977 ON IM *020 †20

YARISH, Robert Scott. 10565 KATY FWY STE 100 77024 #056-05-1978 L1987 PS GS †016,65

YASKO, Alan Wm. 1515 HOLCOMBE BLVD 77030 #016-06-1984 L1991 OMO *020 †40

YATSU, Frank Michio. 6431 FANNIN ST STE 7044, UTMSH 77030 #038-06-1959 L1984 N *030 †75

YAWN, David Houston. 1 BAYLOR PLZ, DEPT PATH 77030 #048-04-1969 L1969 PTH BBK *020 †50

YAZBEK, Naji Fadlallah. ■ 77054 #605-01-1996 L1998 CD *100 †20

YAZDANI, Hossein. ■ 77055 #517-01-1973 L1997 GP *020

YAZDANI-KACHOOEI, Parvin. 6701 FANNIN ST #517-06-1975 L1982 PD PDE *020 †55

YBALLE, Anunciacion S. ■ 77056 #748-11-1965 L1973 PTH *071

YBARRA, Christie A. 1 BAYLOR PLZ, MS 350 77030 #048-04-2003 L2007 P *100

YBARRA, Richard J. 10130 LOUETTA RD, SUTIE L 77070 #048-04-1984 L1985 EM FM *020 †18

YE, Dongjiu. 1515 HOLCOMBE BLVD, DEPT OF PATHOLOGY 77030 #243-21-1986 L2003 PTH *012 †50

YE, Ying. 1 BAYLOR PLZ, DEPT OF PATH BCM 77030 #243-16-1983 L2004 PTH *100 †50

YEAKLEY, Joel Wallis. 6431 FANNIN ST RM 2130, UTHSC DEPT OF RADIOLOGY 77030 #048-02-1965 L1965 DR *020 †20

YEDURURI, Sireesha. 1 BAYLOR PLZ, BAYLOR COLL OF MED #495-21-1999 PDR *100

YEE, Donald L. 6701 FANNIN ST 77030 #048-04-1997 L2003 PHO *020 †55 ‡

YEE, Gene Woo. 12121 RICHMOND AVE STE 121 77082 #048-13-1977 L1978 GP OM *020 †16

YEE, Helen Shen. 77054 #048-04-2004 PM *012

YEE, Kimberly A. ■ 77030 #035-15-2001 L2007 CRS *100 †85

YEE, Richard Willington. 6400 FANNIN ST 18TH FL, UNIVERSITY EYE ASSOCIATES 77030 #048-13-1979 L1979 OPH *020 †35

YEE YOUNG, Anthony. 4331 BRIGHTWOOD DR 77068 #064-01-1973 L1977 GP *020 ‡

YEH, Belinda Min Chu. 8880 BELLAIRE BLVD, STE H 77036 #244-02-1981 L1990 PD *020 †55

YEH, Chun-Sung. ■ 77004 #244-02-1966 L1984 *020

YEH, Edward Tu-Hsing. 1515 HOLCOMBE BLVD # 449, DEPT OF CARDIOLOGY 77030 #005-19-1980 L1993 CD RHU *020 †20

YELIN, Frank Sheppard. ■ 77024 #061-01-1964 L1971 NS *071 †25

YELLAPRAGADA, Sarvari Ven. ■ 77025 #495-04-2000 L2007 HO *012 †20

YEN, Jennifer L. ■ 77081 #048-14-2006 P *012

YEN, Kimberly Guo. 6550 FANNIN ST, STE 1501 77030 #025-01-1995 L2002 OPH *020 †35

YEN, Michael Tzechien. 6550 FANNIN ST, STE 1501 77030 #025-01-1996 L2002 OPH *020 †35

YEN, Terry A. 6621 FANNIN ST, PEDIATRIC EMERGENCY MEDICI 77030 #048-04-1997 L1999 PD *020 †55 ‡

YEOMAN, Mark Allen. 925 GESSNER RD STE 400 77024 #041-01-1970 L1971 CD IM *020

YEOMANS, Edward Roberts. 5656 KELLEY ST, DEPT OF OB AND GYN 77026 #030-06-1980 L1992 MFM OBG *040 †30

YERRAMSETTI, Rama Rao. 902 FROSTWOOD DR STE 222 77024 #496-24-1987 L2000 AI PD *03,55

YETMAN, Robert Jos. 6431 FANNIN ST, DEPT PED 77030 #021-06-1984 L1987 PD *040 †55

YEUNG, Cecil S T. 1103 BANKS ST 77006 #065-01-1979 L1987 HNS FPS *020 †45

YEUNG, Saiching Jim. 1515 HOLCOMBE BLVD, BOX 437 77030 #028-34-1991 L1992 END IM *020 †20

YI, Donna Maria. 2801 GESSNER DR 77080 #047-07-1983 L2000 P *020 †75

YIN, Dwight Edward. ■ 77059 #048-12-2003 L2006 PD *020 †20

YIN, Zhengnan. ■ 77025 #243-64-1987 FP *012

YING, Anita Kuo. 6621 FANNIN ST STE 1020, DEPT OF PEDIATRICS-ENDOCRI 77030 #036-07-1999 L2008 END *100 †20,55

YIP, Eddie King-Shiu. 2424 W HOLCOMBE BLVD, MEDICAL CENTER ANESTHESIA 77030 #244-03-1969 L1975 AN *020

YLLANA-SHEPPERD, Aurora V. 2202 W ALABAMA ST STE B 77098 #048-02-2001 L2004 FM *020 †18

YOCKEY, Fredericka C. ■ 77098 #396-31-1978 L1982 OPH *040

YOFFE, Boris. 2002 HOLCOMBE BLVD BLDG 1, VAMC, 77030 #550-03-1974 L1991 IM GE *020 †20

YOFFE, Galina. 7515 MAIN ST, STE 220 77030 #550-02-1976 L1990 PD GP *020 †55

YOFFE, Rona. 1 BAYLOR PLZ, BAYLOR COLL OF MED 77030 #048-14-2002 L2005 PDE *012 †55

YOHO, Jason Allen. 6431 FANNIN ST, UTHSC DIV OF CARDIOLOGY 77030 #055-01-2002 CD *012

YONATH, Hagith. 1 BAYLOR PLZ T619, BAYLOR COLL OF MED 77030 #550-10-1996 L2007 MG *100 †19

YOO, John K. 11454 SPACE CENTER BLVD, STE B 77059 #048-04-1992 L1993 OTO *020 †45

YOON, Mike Tai. 7333 NORTH FWY, STE 311 77076 #583-01-1968 L1975 PM PME *020 †20

YORK, Byron Parker, Jr. 4126 S W FREEWY 1200 77027 #048-04-1959 L1959 ORS *071 †40

YORKE, Rebecca Frances. 2504 ELMEN ST, BAYLOR COLLEGE OF MEDICINE 77019 #048-02-1997 L2001 PTH *020

YOSHOR, Daniel. 6620 MAIN ST, STE 1350 77030 #016-02-1993 L1999 NS GS *020 †25

YOSOWITZ, Edward E. 6624 FANNIN ST STE 1800 77030 #017-20-1967 L1968 GYN *020 †30

YOSOWITZ, Julie Anne. 6701 FANNIN ST 77030 #048-04-1994 L1996 PD *020 †30

YOSOWITZ, Philip. 7515 MAIN ST # NO-730 77030 #005-14-1968 L1977 PS *020 †85,65

YOU, Mingjian. 1515 HOLCOMBE BLVD UNIT 72, DEPT HEMATOPATHOLOGY-UTMDA 77030 #243-43-1986 L2007 HMP *100

YOUENS, Harry Thos, Jr. 12141 RICHMOND AVE 77082 #048-02-1963 L1963 OPH FPS *020 †35

YOUNAS, Shiraz Ahmad. 1 BAYLOR PLZ, DEPT OF ORTHO SURGERY 77030 #704-25-1999 L2008 ORS *012

YOUNES, Anas. ■ 77027 #875-01-1983 L1992 PTH *020 †20

YOUNES, Houssam Khaled. 1 BAYLOR PLZ, BAYLOR COLL OF MED 77030 #902-07-2003 GS *012

YOUNES, Mamoun. 1 BAYLOR PLZ, BAYLOR COLL MED DEPT PATH 77030 #875-02-1981 L1992 ATP GP *020 †50

YOUNG, Amy Elise. 6620 MAIN ST, STE 1450 77030 #027-01-1990 L1996 OBG *020 †30

YOUNG, Cynthia Okhuyse. ■ 77095 #048-14-1986 L1988 GP *020

YOUNG, Danielle Zandrae. 2411 FOUNTAIN VIEW DR #200 77057 #028-34-2002 L2006 AN *020 †05

YOUNG, David Allan. 6621 FANNIN ST STE A-300, ANESTHESIOLOGY, MC2-1495 77030 #011-02-1994 L2000 AN PAN *020 †05

YOUNG, Donald Claude, III. 427 W 20TH ST, STE 210 77008 #649-14-1976 L1979 GP OM *020

YOUNG, Edward John. 2002 HOLCOMBE BLVD, VETERANS AFFAIRS M C 77030 #023-01-1968 L1969 ID IM *020 ‡

YOUNG, James Henry, Jr. 2000 CRAWFORD ST, STE 780 77002 #047-07-1975 L1978 CD IM *020

YOUNG, John Wm. ■ 77069 #047-06-1963 L1969 PS *072 †85,65

YOUNG, Kavon Lynette. ■ 77047 #048-14-2001 FP *012

YOUNG, Lisa Woo. 10655 STEEPLETOP DR 77065 #048-14-1988 L1989 AN *020 †05

YOUNG, Mitchell Alan. 1118 BARKDULL ST 77006 #048-04-1977 L1978 CHP PFP *020 †75

YOUNG, Ozora Frances. ■ 77005 #048-12-1957 L1957 FM *071 †18

YOUNG, Reed Bates. 6550 FANNIN ST STE 1640 77030 #048-02-1983 L1983 N *020 †75

YOUNG, Ronald Lloyd. 6620 MAIN ST 77030 #869-01-1969 L1971 GYN REN *020 †30

YOUNGBLOOD, Sloan Curry. ■ 77096 #048-04-2007 AN *012

YOUNGBLOOD, Todd Jeffrey. 1140 CYPRESS STATION DR 77090 #048-02-2002 L2005 FM *020 †18

YOUNIS, Antoine Georges. 6624 FANNIN ST STE 2420 77030 #605-02-1971 L1975 CD IM *020 †20

YOUNIS, George Antoine. 6624 FANNIN ST STE 2420 77030 #048-12-1998 L2003 CD IC *020 †20

YOUNKER, Thomas Dirk. ■ 77025 #012-01-1979 L1985 AN *020 †05 ‡

YOUNT, Greschen Ann. 1919 LA BRANCH ST, DEPT OF OB/GYN 77002 #048-13-1983 L1983 OBG *020 †20

YOUSEFI, Pouran. 3701 KIRBY DR, STE 600 77098 #517-08-1994 L2000 FM *020 †18

YRIGOYEN, Edmundo D. 427 W 20TH ST, STE 708 77008 #847-06-1977 L1982 IM *020 †20

YU, Bernard C Y. 9600 BELLAIRE BLVD, STE 211 77036 #244-04-1980 L1995 OPH *020 †35

YU, Peirong. 1515 HOLCOMBE BLVD, BOX 443 77030 #243-78-1984 L2002 PS *020 †65

YU, Sherman C. 6431 FANNIN ST, MSB 4.290 77030 #048-04-2000 L2005 GS *100 †85 ‡

YU, Tsekuan. 1515 HOLCOMBE BLVD, BOX 1202 77030 #048-14-2000 L2005 *100 †80

YUAN, Mike Nanyong. 9889 BELLAIRE BLVD, STE 128 77036 #243-67-1982 L1999 N *020 †75

YUDOFSKY, Beth Ellen. 1 BAYLOR PLZ, BAYLOR COLLEGE OF MEDICINE 77030 #035-01-1976 L1993 P *020 †75

YUDOFSKY, Stuart Chas. 1 BAYLOR PLZ # 350 77030 #048-04-1970 L1970 P *030 †75

YUDOVICH, Martin. 4501 GROVEWAY DR, PEDIATRIC ASSOCIATES 77087 #649-01-1969 L1975 PD *020 †55

YUE, Joyce Wonkai. ■ 77081 #051-01-2006 PD *012

YUEN, Carrie Haulai. 1515 HOLCOMBE BLVD 77030 #030-06-1995 L2006 PHO *020 †20,55

YUKSEL, Eser. 6624 FANNIN ST, STE 2260 77030 #902-05-1984 L2003 *020

YUN, Kenneth S. ■ 77019 #028-34-2004 U *012

YUNG, W K Alfred. 1515 HOLCOMBE BLVD # 431, UD M D ANDERSON CENCER CTR 77030 #016-02-1975 L1981 N ON *020 †75

YUSUF, Shabana. 6621 FANNIN ST, MC WT6-104 77030 #495-14-1996 L2004 PD *020 †55

YUSUF, Syed Wamique. 1515 HOLCOMBE BLVD # 449, MD ANDERSON CANCER CTR 77030 #704-02-1986 L2001 CD IM *020 †20

YUSUF, Tony Edward. 6431 FANNIN ST 77030 #605-01-1993 L2002 GE *100 †20

ZAAFRAN, Sherif Z. 18220 STATE HIGHWAY 249 77070 #048-14-1995 L1996 AN *020 †05

ZABCIK-DE WITT, Carol E. 17030 NANES DR STE 206 77090 #048-02-1985 L1986 GYN *020 †30

ZABREK, Edward Martin. 920 FROSTWOOD DR STE 540 77024 #023-01-1978 L1982 OBG *020 †30

ZACHARIAS, Nikolaos M. 1709 DRYDEN RD, STE 1100 77030 #418-01-1995 L2005 OBG MFM *020

ZAFAR, Ghazal Iftikhar. ■ 77027 #704-25-2003 FP *012

ZAFAR, Muhammad Behzad. 1709 DRYDEN RD STE 550, BCM FACULTY CENTER 77030 #704-25-2003 IM *012

ZAFARNIA, Mohammade E. 8830 LONG POINT RD STE 808 77055 #517-03-1965 L1977 GE IM *020 †20

ZAGARS, Gunars. 1515 HOLCOMBE BLVD, M D ANDERSON CANCER CENTER 77030 #143-03-1971 L1984 OS *020 †80

ZAGE, Peter Eric. 1515 HOLCOMBE BLVD, DEPT. OF PEDIATRICS, UNIT 77030 #035-01-1999 L2005 PD *020 †55

ZAHARIA, Adrian. ■ 77054 #781-01-2003 FP *012

ZAHEER, Amer. 1200 BINZ ST, STE 500 77004 #704-21-1990 L1997 IM *020 †20

ZAHEER, Irum. 6550 FANNIN ST STE 1001 77030 #704-20-2001 IM *012

ZAHRA, Hadi. ■ 77006 #030-05-2005 L2005 RO *012

ZAIDI, Saleem Akbar. 6565 FANNIN ST, STE B452 77030 #704-16-1987 L1998 CCA *020 †05

ZAIDI, Syed Fakhar-E-Alam. 6431 FANNIN ST, DEPT OF PATHOLOGY 77030 #704-02-1989 PTH *100

ZAIDI, Syed Navaid. 12135 BISSONNET ST, STE D 77099 #704-02-1989 L2005 FM FPG *020 †18

ZALESKI, Henri I, Jr. 6550 FANNIN ST STE 2423 77030 #048-04-1970 L1970 ON IM *020 †20

ZAMAN, Fiaz. 800 PEAKWOOD DR, STE 6C 77090 #028-46-1995 L1997 OPH *020 †35

ZAMBRA, Alejandro. 5644 LAWNDALE ST 77023 #924-01-1975 L1978 FM PTH *020

ZAMORA, Gus. ■ 77054 #048-14-2007 OBG *020

ZAMORA, Luis F. 800 PEAKWOOD DR STE 2C 77090 #231-01-1968 L1976 CRS GS *071 †85,10

ZAMORA, Noe. ■ 77018 #048-14-2002 L2005 IM *100

ZAND, Behrouz. ■ 77004 #030-05-2007 OBG *012

ZANDERS, Mary Josephine. 12121 RICHMOND AVE STE 104 77082 #021-01-1982 L1990 OBG *020 †30

ZANE, Alan Irving. ■ 77007 #025-07-1960 L1973 OTO *071 †45

ZANIEWSKI-SINGH, Michelle. 17070 RED OAK DR STE 309 77090 #056-05-1977 L1981 END IM *020 †20 ‡

■ = Address Information Privacy Protected

ZANNIKOS, Symeon Vasilios. ■ 77062 #048-13-2008 *012
ZAPATA-CABRERA, Vicente. 1910 JOHN RALSTON RD, STE 100 77013 #737-06-1970 L1978
   OBG *020 †30
ZARIN, David Paul. 17070 RED OAK DR, STE 205 77090 #038-41-1974 L1976 OTO *020 *45
ZARIN, Jerald Lawrence. 2425 WEST LOOP S, STE 1000 77027 #035-46-1966 L1972
   PD MDM *020 †55
ZARNOW, Beth Ann. ■ 77047 #048-04-2008 *012
ZARRABI, Jalil. 7109 LAWNDALE ST, STE B 77023 #517-01-1966 L1975 GP PD *020 †55
ZARRABI, Maryam. 6630 DE MOSS DR 77074 #517-01-1966 L1975 PD END *020 †55
ZARRAGA, Ignatius Gerardo. 1 BAYLOR PLZ 77030 #748-02-2001 L2005 CD *012 †20
ZARRAGA, Walfredo A. 6550 FANNIN ST # 1200 77030 #748-02-1977 L1994 IM *020 †20
ZARRIN-KHAMEH, Neda. ■ 77096 #517-01-1997 L2007 PTH *100
ZARZOUR, David Paul. ■ 77068 #048-02-2006 AN *012
ZARZOUR, Gamil Youssef. 11302 FALLBROOK DR # 10 77065 #915-02-1970 L1977
   PD *020 †55
ZATORSKI, Jeffrey. 1313 HERMANN DR 77004 #017-20-1961 L1965 IM *071 †20
ZATORSKI, Jeffrey J. 800 PEAKWOOD DR STE 5E 77090 #048-02-1993 L1996 DR *020 †80
ZAVALA, Victoria A. 2411 FOUNTAIN VIEW DR, STE 200 77057 #016-45-2002 L2006
   AN *005
ZAVALETA, Eric M. ■ 77030 #048-16-2007 TY *012
ZAVALETA, Jose F. 7737 SOUTHWEST FWY, STE 415 77074 #341-01-1964 L1982 IM END *020
ZAW, Moe Oo. 7141 SOUTHWEST FWY 77074 #209-03-1991 L1998 IM *020 †20
ZAYYANI, Najah Rashed. 6565 FANNIN ST # B503 77030 #605-01-1977 L1981 GE *020 †20
ZEBIAN, Rami Camille. ■ 77054 #605-04-2003 IM *012
ZEFO, Nancy. 11800 ASTORIA BLVD 77089 #023-12-1981 L1990 R *020 †80,28
ZEGARRUNDO, Rolando. 6859 S GESSNER DR 77036 #176-01-1968 L1977 PD *020
ZELAYA, Ana Sofia. ■ 77022 #270-03-1996 FP *012
ZELISKO, Michael B. ■ 77025 #048-14-2005 AN *012
ZELITT, David L. 14732 PERTHSHIRE RD 77079 #048-02-1987 L1988 DR *020 †80
ZELLER, Robert S. 7580 FANNIN ST STE 760, SUITE 210 77054 #035-06-1963 L1971
   CHN PD *020 †55,75
ZELUFF, Barry James. 6624 FANNIN ST STE 1410 77030 #048-04-1978 L1978 ID IM *020 †20
ZEMO, Sessunu Michael. ■ 77036 #048-04-2008 *012
ZENALI, Maryam J. PO BOX 20708, DEPT OF PATHOLOGY 77225 #048-14-2006 PTH *012
ZENGER, Elmer. ■ 77080 #040-02-1951 GP *020
ZENNER, George O, III. 5757 WOODWAY DR, STE 260 77057 #048-14-1986 L1987 FM *020 †18
ZENNER, George Otto, Jr. 5757 WOODWAY DR, STE 260 77057 #048-02-1960 L1960
   FM *071 †18
ZEON, Zae Young. 6500 NORTH FWY STE 107 77076 #583-01-1973 L1979 GP *020
ZEPEDA, David Edward. 6624 FANNIN ST, STE 1800 77030 #048-13-1974 L1979 OBG *020 †30
ZEPEDA, Luis E. 8101 AIRPORT BLVD, STE A 77061 #429-01-1985 L1996 FM *020 †18
ZERDA, Barbara E. ■ 77059 #048-14-2008 *012
ZERTUCHE SANCHEZ, Aurora. 1 BAYLOR PLZ 77030 #649-30-2001 PD *012
ZERWAS, John Mc Call. 2411 FOUNTAIN VIEW DR # 2 77057 #048-04-1980 L1981
   AN GS *020 †05
ZEVALLOS, Jose Pedro. ■ 77025 #033-05-2005 OTO *012
ZHANG, Jin Xiu. 2727 W HOLCOMBE BLVD 77025 #035-08-1998 L2005 GE *020 †20
ZHANG, Lily. 1 BAYLOR PLZ, BAYLOR COLL OF MED 77030 #048-12-2004 L2006 CD *012 †20
ZHANG, Wenyong William. ■ 77025 #035-20-2004 L2006 MGP *012
ZHANG, Yi. 6560 FANNIN ST STE 900, NEUROSURGERY 77030 #048-04-1998 L2007 NS *020
ZHAO, Bihong. ■ 77054 #243-76-1982 L2006 PTH *100 †50
ZHOU, Shao Feng. 6431 FANNIN ST 5.156, UT MEDICAL SCHOOL HOUSTO 77030
   #243-72-1983 L2003 AN *020 †05
ZHOU, Wei. 1709 DRYDEN RD, STE 1500 77030 #035-09-1998 L2005 VS *100 †85
ZHOU, Xiaodong. 7500 BEECHNUT ST, STE 225 77074 #243-72-1983 L2000 OBG *020 †30
ZHUKOVSKY, Donna S. 1515 HOLCOMBE BLVD BOX 008, UNIV TX ANDERSON CANCER
   CT 77030 #067-01-1982 L2001 ON PLM *020 †20
ZIAFAT, Ebrahim. 515 W LITTLE YORK RD, STE A 77091 #517-01-1959 L1974 PD EM *020
ZIETZ, Barry L. 12121 RICHMOND AVE STE 272 77082 #048-14-1985 L1986 PD *020 †55
ZIMMERMAN, Geoffrey A. ■ 77079 #047-05-2002 L2006 OBG *100
ZIMMERMAN, Gretchen Mary. 7515 MAIN ST, STE 350 77030 #041-09-1980 L1982 GS *020 †85
ZIMMERMAN, Janice L. 6550 FANNIN ST STE 1001 77030 #048-04-1983 L1983
   IM CCM *020
ZIMMERMAN, Stanley Jay. 7707 FANNIN ST, STE 250 77054 #048-12-1955 L1955
   END NM *020 †20
ZINNER, Cindy Marie. 1905 HOLCOMBE BLVD, HOUSTON HOSPICE AND PALLIA 77030
   #020-12-1988 L2005 MPD IM *020 †20,55
ZINNER, Ralph Goldman. 1515 HOLCOMBE BLVD, BOX 432 77030 #010-02-1993 L1999
   ON *020 †20
ZIONTS, Michael Allan. 1221 MCKINNEY ST, STE 40300 77010 #021-01-1964 L1966 IM *020
ZISMAN, Devy. ■ 77096 #550-03-1990 RHU *100
ZISMAN, Eliyahou. ■ 77096 #550-01-1990 AN *100
ZOGHBI, Huda Yahya. 1 BAYLOR PLZ, MS-225 77030 #047-07-1979 L1980 CHN PD *050 †55,75
ZOGHBI, William Antoine. 6550 FANNIN ST MS SM677 77030 #047-07-1979 L1980 CD *020 †20
ZOIS, Ismene N. 1529 W 18TH ST, QUALITY CARE FAMILY CLINIC 77008 #048-14-1993 L1995
   FM *020 †18
ZOLDHELYI, Pierre. 6770 BERTNER ST, TEXAS HEART INSTITUTE 77030 #561-11-1985 L1993
   CD IM *020
ZORRILLA, Karen Lisa. 902 FROSTWOOD DR, STE 227 77024 #048-04-1993 L1995
   PD *020 †55
ZOUZOU, Ahmad Maher. ■ 77054 #875-03-1998 L2006 IM *100 †20
ZU, Youli. 6565 FANNIN ST MS 205, PATH DEPT METHODIST HOSP 77030 #243-28-1982 L2005
   PTH HMP *020 †50
ZUBER, Muzamil Mohamed. 1 BAYLOR PLZ, BAYLOR COLL OF MED 77030
   #577-01-1999 L2008 CCP *012
ZUCCONI, James Peter. 233 W PARKER RD 77076 #847-04-1984 L1989 PD *020
ZUCKERBROD, Stewart Lee. 5420 DASHWOOD, STE 101 77081 #048-04-1983 L1985
   OPH *020 †35
ZUNIGA, Arturo. 3313 W OREM DR 77045 #048-12-1983 L1986 FM EM *020 †18
ZUNIGA, Charlotte T. 4101 GREENBRIAR ST, STE 200 77098 #048-14-1999 L2002 PD *020 †55
ZUNIGA, Dario. 6550 MAPLERIDGE ST STE 217 77081 #451-01-1967 L1976 GS VS *020
ZUNIGA, Efrain Nazario. ■ 77045 #649-02-1958 OS *071
ZURAWIN, Robert K. 6620 MAIN ST 77030 #048-04-1977 L1978 GYN GP *020 †30
ZURAWSKI, Glenn Francis. 1515 HOLCOMBE BLVD, BOX 42 77030 #035-15-1977 L1999
   AN *020 †05

ZURITA SAAVEDRA, Amado Ja. 1515 HOLCOMBE BLVD # 137 77030 #847-14-1993 *100
ZURI-YAFI, Mohammad I A. 6431 FANNIN ST, STE 3.123 77030 #875-01-1992 L2000
   PDE *020 †55
ZWEIDLER-MC KAY, Patrick. ■ 77030 #041-13-1997 L2006 PHO *020 †55
ZWEIGHAFT, Ronald Melvin. 7500 SAN FELIPE ST, STE 525 77063 #048-12-1974 L1978
   N GPM *020 †75
ZWELLING, Leonard Alan. 1515 HOLCOMBE BLVD, BOX 525 77030 #036-07-1973 L1984
   IM *050 †20
ZWILLMAN, Michael Evan. 6565 FANNIN ST, DEPT. ANESTHESIA & CRIT. C 77030
   #305-01-1988 L2006 IM *020 †20
ZYKORIE, Stuart. 17070 RED OAK DR, STE 407 77090 #035-08-1972 L1980 U *020 *95

HUBBARD – HILL

JAVIER, Ricardo R. 112 NW 2ND ST 76648 #748-01-1961 L1972 GS GP *020
RYMAN, James Lowell. 105 NW 8TH ST 76648 #048-14-2004 L2006 FM *020 †18
RYMAN, Jesse Merle, Jr. 701 NE 5TH ST 76648 #048-02-1965 L1965 GP *020

HUFFMAN – HARRIS

GLENNEY, Mary Elizabeth. ■ 77336 #016-11-1966 OS *075
HART, Lara Renee. ■ 77336 #041-15-2008 *012

HUGHES SPRINGS – CASS

ARNOLD, David Wayne I. ■ 75656 #048-12-1986 *100
SHARP, Kathleen E. 201 E 2ND, GLENN GARRETT CLINIC 75656 #025-07-1999 L2003
   FM FSM *020 †18

HUMBLE – HARRIS

ANDERSON, Kenneth Carl. ■ 77345 #021-01-1970 L1978 OBG AM *071 †30
ANDREW, Wm Harvey, Jr. ■ 77338 #048-12-1946 L1946 R *020 †80
ANDRUS, Peter Leverett. 20035 W LAKE HOUSTON PKWY, STE 100 77346 #041-01-1971 L1976
   PD GPM *072 †55 ‡
ARIYARATNA, Savitri J. 8484 WILL CLAYTON PKWY 77338 #220-02-1979 L1996 FM *020 †18
ASKEW, Julius Bolden, Jr. 18951 N MEMORIAL DR 77338 #048-04-1969 L1969 PTH *020 †50
ATLURU, Suseela Devi. 18955 N MEMORIAL DR, STE 290 77338 #495-50-1974 L1981
   OBG U *020 †30
BALES, Randolph Craig. 2310 1/2 ATASCOCITA RD, & CORRECTIONS DEPT. 77396
   #048-02-1971 L1971 EM *020
BALTZ, Richard Patrick. 9816 MEMORIAL BLVD, STE 120 77338 #048-02-1975 L1977
   ON IM *020 †20
BANKER, Parendra P. 18955 N MEMORIAL DR, STE 470 77338 #495-23-1976 L1982
   GE IM *020 †20 ‡
BARRY, David Howe. 8484 WILL CLAYTON PKWY 77338 #016-06-1971 L1976 PD *020 †55
BATISTE, Yvette. 9816 MEMORIAL BLVD, STE 204 77338 #048-02-1993 L1995 FM *020 †18
BEAUVAIS, Jane L. 18955 N MEMORIAL DR # 260 77338 #048-14-1993 L1995 IM *020 †20
BERNELL, Julie Ann. 18955 N MEMORIAL DR, STE 350 77338 #048-04-1992 L1993
   OBG *020 †20
BINA, Massoud. 18955 N MEMORIAL DR, STE 400 77338 #517-01-1970 L1990 N NP *020 †75
BODIN, John Eric. 18951 N MEMORIAL DR 77338 #048-04-1976 L1980 EM GPM *071 †16
BREAZEALE, Jennifer H. 2755 W LAKE HOUSTON PKWY 77339 #027-01-1999 L2003
   OBG *020
BREMER, Malcolm H. 18955 N MEMORIAL DR, STE 550 77338 #041-09-1967 L1975
   VS TS *020 †85,90 ‡
BROOKS, George Alfred. 1806 HUMBLE PLACE DR 77338 #011-02-1983 L1983 FM *020
BUENDIA, Acxitl. ■ 77346 #341-01-1966 L1976 OBG FM *072
CARLSON, Carolyn Brandt. 8484 WILL CLAYTON PKWY, KELSEY-SEYBOLD CLINIC 77338
   #048-04-1994 L1996 PD *020 †55
CARLYLE, David Chas. 18951 N MEMORIAL DR 77338 #048-02-1974 L1974 EM *071 †16
CASTILLO, Cesario A. ■ 77338 #048-14-1998 L2001 FM *020 †20
CASTILLO, Gregg Ceniza. 14954 MESA DR, STE 107 77396 #048-14-2004 L2006 FM *020 †18
CATTERSON, Allen Duane. 18951 N MEMORIAL DR 77338 #007-02-1955 L1963
   OM AM *071 †70
CHARLES, Robt Edward, Jr. 18951 N MEMORIAL DR 77338 #047-06-1975 L1981 PTH *020 †50
CLARK, Garth A. ■ 77338 #048-02-1987 L1990 IM *075
COFFMAN, Mark Robt. 18951 N MEMORIAL DR 77338 #048-04-1976 L1976 OPH *020 †35
COLOSIMO, Lee Ralph. 19411 MCKAY BLVD, STE 250 77338 #041-12-1973 L1982
   TS *020 †85,90
CORREDOR, Frank J. 18951 N MEMORIAL DR 77338 #048-14-1993 L1994 PTH *020 †50
COTE, Jessica Marie. ■ 77396 #048-02-2007 OBG *012
CRAWFORD, Ranessa L. 18951 N MEMORIAL DR, EMERGENCY GROUP PHYSICIANS 77338
   #048-14-2002 L2005 EM *020 †16
CROSS-SHOKES, Paula G. 2755 W LAKE HOUSTON PKWY 77339 #010-01-1985 L1987
   FM *020 †18
CUADRA, Fernando Luis. 1420 FM 1960 BYPASS RD E, STE #103 77338 #737-03-1991 L1997
   IM *020 †20
DARA, Anil A. 18955 N MEMORIAL DR, STE 200 77338 #275-02-1979 L1998 IM GE *020 †20
DIAZ, Ismael, Jr. 5510 ATASCOCITA RD STE 260 77346 #048-14-1998 L2002 FM *020 †18
DICKERSON, Karen D. 18951 N MEMORIAL DR 77338 #048-16-1992 L1993 GP *020
DO, Thong M. 18455 W LAKE HOUSTON DR, STE 190 77346 #048-14-1990 L1996
   IM PD *020 †55
EVANS, Don Lee. ■ 77339 #030-05-2002 L2006 RNR *012 †80
FANG, Wenjing. 18951 N MEMORIAL DR 77338 #243-46-1985 L1999 PTH *020 †50
FARRIOR, Mark Alan. 18951 N MEMORIAL DR 77338 #021-01-1996 L1999 PD *020 †55
FEDORUK, Christopher D. 18951 N MEMORIAL DR, ER DEPT 77338 #024-07-1999 L2005
   EM *020
FILLEY, Mark Jason. 18951 N MEMORIAL DR, EMERGENCY DEPARTMENT 77338
   #048-14-1995 L1999 EM *020 †16
FRASCHINI, Giuseppe. 9816 MEMORIAL BLVD, STE 120 77338 #561-14-1970 L1978
   ON IM *020 †20

GARCIA, Gilbert M. 104 E MAIN ST 77338 #048-15-1995 L1996 **PD** *020 †55

GILFOIL, Mason P., Jr. 18350 TIMBER FOREST DR, STE 100 77346 #021-05-1974 L1976 **PD** *020 †55

GLENN, Christopher J. 18955 N MEMORIAL DR, STE 350 77338 #048-14-1992 L1994 **OBG** *072 †30

GRAUMLICH, David Charles. 900 ROCKMEAD DR, STE 125 77339 #038-40-1968 L1974 **DR** *020 †80 ‡

GRUESKIN, James Michael. 18951 N MEMORIAL DR 77338 #018-03-1994 L2006 **EM** *020

HANSON, Anthony K. 18955 N MEMORIAL DR # 300 77338 #412-01-1986 L1995 **NEP** *020 †20

HARPER, Henry Osler, Jr. 10203 BIRCHRIDGE DR, STE 400 77338 #048-02-1972 L1972 **EM** *071

HARPER, Purvis Eugene. 18350 TIMBER FOREST DR, STE 100 77346 #048-02-1978 L1978 **PD ADL** *020 †55

HOANG, Huong Q. 18700 W LAKE HOUSTON PKWY, STE A104 77346 #048-04-1996 L1998 **FM** *020 †18 ‡

HOFFMAN, Robert Dean. 18955 N MEMORIAL DR, STE 340 77338 #048-02-1990 L1991 **OTO HNS** *020 †45

HOKE, Bob. ■ 77346 #039-01-1958 L1980 **P OM** *071 †70,75

HUSBY, Richard Todd. 18951 N MEMORIAL DR, ER DEPT 77338 #016-11-1985 L1993 **EM** *071 †16

IMPERIAL, Valerie C. ■ 77396 #061-01-2005 L2008 *100

JACKS, Alisa Suit. 2755 W LAKE HOUSTON PKWY 77339 #048-14-1993 L1995 **PD** *020 †55

JACKSON, Adrianna Janell. ■ 77346 #023-07-2007 **IM** *012

JACOB, Mohan. 18955 N MEMORIAL DR, STE 440 77338 #495-73-1975 L1983 **CD IM** *020 †20

JAYARAM, Turuvekere H. 9950 MEMORIAL BLVD STE 102 77338 #495-09-1972 L1983 **IM PUD** *020 †20

JEAN-PIERRE, Veronica. 18842 S MEMORIAL DR, STE 203 77338 #038-45-1998 L2005 **END** *020 †20

JOHN, Reji. 12203 PINELANDS PARK LN 77346 #495-72-1998 L2004 **NEP** *100 †20

JOHNSON, Terri D. ■ 77338 #048-04-2008 *012

JOSEPH, Philmore Josley. 18955 N MEMORIAL DR, STE 250 77338 #048-12-1971 L1973 **ORS** *020 †40

JYOTHI, Achi Napeena. 7820 FM 1960 RD E STE 206 77346 #495-57-1985 L2000 **FM** *020 †18

KENDALL, William Roland. ■ 77346 #038-40-1959 L1975 **AN PME** *071 †05

KERR, Ronald James. 601 ROCKMEAD DR 77339 #021-01-1978 L1986 **ORS** *020

KHAN, Mohammad Omer. 18955 N MEMORIAL DR, STE 300 77338 #704-02-1990 L2000 **ID** *020 †20

KHUSHALANI, Ashok I. ■ 77338 #496-38-1975 L1979 **CHP P** *020 †75

KNOWLES, Kurt James. 77339 #426-01-1985 L2001 **PTH** *020 †50

KORTHAUER, Ken Mason. 601 ROCKMEAD DR 77339 #048-02-1980 L1980 **ORS** *020 †40

KRAUSE, Ira. 18838 S MEMORIAL DR, STE 104 77338 #048-04-1989 L1990 **U** *020 †95

KREIT, Nadia Ibrahim. 18951 N MEMORIAL DR 77338 #875-01-1979 L1997 **PD** *020 †55

KUNTHUR, Anuradha. 18951 N MEMORIAL DR 77338 #495-70-1997 L2004 **IM** *020

KUO, Mu Erh. 18955 N MEMORIAL DR, STE 550 77338 #244-03-1948 L1976 **GP** *020

LADLEY, David Mark. ■ 77338 #016-45-1982 L1985 **FM** *075 †18

LAMPRECHT, Kathy Byers. 18951 N MEMORIAL DR 77338 #039-01-1980 L1981 **PTH** *020 †50 ‡

LATEEF, Ahmad Hasan. 19506 HIGHWAY 59 N, STE 320 77338 #704-20-1988 L2005 **AN** *020 †05 ‡

LEE, Yates P. 8484 WILL CLAYTON PKWY 77338 #048-02-1995 L1999 **FM** *020 †18

LLOYD, Alan Todd. 9810 FM 1960 RD W, STE 280 77338 #049-01-1984 L1994 **P** *020 †75

MAGEE, Douglas L. 8484 WILL CLAYTON PKWY 77338 #048-14-1987 L1988 **IM** *020 †20

MALICAN, Jude Patrick. 18951 N MEMORIAL DR, MEMORIAL HERMANN NORTHEAST 77338 #028-34-1985 L2007 **EM** *020 †16

MANN, Paul Michael, II. 18850 S MEMORIAL DR 77338 #048-14-1999 L2004 **OPH** *020 †35

MARTINEZ MIRANDA, Iadara. ■ 77396 #649-03-2004 *100

MATOS, Karen. 19333 HIGHWAY 59 N STE 14 77338 #042-02-2000 L2003 **PD** *020 †55

MAUPIN, Roger Alan. 900 ROCKMEAD DR 77338 #016-11-1963 L1969 **DR** *071 †80

MC GINNESS, John E, III. ■ 77347 #048-14-1985 L1988 **IM** *075

MEHTA, Navnit Ratilal. 9816 MEMORIAL BLVD STE 107 77338 #495-22-1969 L1979 **FM** *020 †18

MEHTA, Tejas Navnit. 9816 MEMORIAL BLVD, STE 107 77338 #041-13-2003 L2005 **IM** *100 †20

MOCEGA, Ena E. 18951 N MEMORIAL DR 77338 #275-01-1961 L1970 **NP PCP** *071 †50

MORENO, Rogelio Albert. ■ 77346 #715-01-1993 **P** *100

MOULTRIE, Jane Murray. 2350 ATASCOCITA RD, PAM LYCHNER STATE JAIL 77396 #016-06-1988 L1995 **IM ID** *020 †20

MUNOZ OSORIO, Jesus A. 9950 MEMORIAL BLVD, STE 203 77338 #649-01-1979 L1994 **NPM PD** *020

NATHAN, Ranga S. 9816 MEMORIAL BLVD, STE 206 77338 #495-04-1972 L1978 **GE IM** *020 †20

NGUYEN, Khanh Duc. 9816 MEMORIAL BLVD STE 202 77338 #048-13-2002 L2006 **N** *020 †75

NGUYEN, Lan Kelly. ■ 77396 #047-06-2002 L2006 **PM** *020 †60

NGUYEN, Thai Duc. 9816 MEMORIAL BLVD, STE 202 77338 #941-01-1977 L1986 **N** *020

NIZIOL, Charles. ■ 77339 #048-02-1979 L1979 **EM GP** *020 †16

NWOKEJI, Cordell Okezie. 18838 S MEMORIAL DR # 104 77338 #010-03-2000 L2005 **U** *020 †95

O'CONNOR, Daniel Brian. 18951 N MEMORIAL DR, ER DEPT 77338 #048-14-1973 L1974 **EM** *020 †16

OHIA, Ekanem Offiong. 8484 WILL CLAYTON PKWY, KELSEY-SEYBOLD CLINIC 77338 #690-05-1981 L2003 **FM** *020 †18

OKOLOISE, Richard E. 5324 ATASCOCITA RD, STE T 77346 #048-02-2003 L2006 **EM** *020

ORTEGA, Jose M. 18955 N MEMORIAL DR # 480 77338 #048-14-1987 L1988 **GS** *020 †85

PALWAI, Prashanth Reddy. 18955 N MEMORIAL DR, STE 490 77338 #495-62-1994 L2004 **RHU** *020 †20

PANDYA, Kirit K. 18955 N MEMORIAL DR, STE 430 77338 #495-22-1961 L1992 **U** *020 †95

PARIANI, Harish Kumar H. ■ 77346 #495-19-1974 L1979 **GP OM** *020

PATEL, Vasishta Manubhai. 18955 N MEMORIAL DR, STE 230 77338 #917-25-1976 L1983 **N IM** *020 †20,75

PATTON, Eve Lynnette. 18838 S MEMORIAL DR # 101 77338 #010-03-1989 L1991 **FM** *020 †18

PEREZ, Carmen Josefa. 22999 HIGHWAY 59 N, STE 136 77339 #042-01-1991 L1995 **IM** *020 †20

PETTIT, George Walter. 18951 N MEMORIAL DR, NORTHEAST MEDICAL CENTER H 77338 #048-04-1981 L1981 **EM IM** *020 †16,20

QAYUM, Maryam Margaret. 9802 FM 1960 BYPS W #100 77338 #021-05-1993 L1998 **PM** *020 †60

RAKLA, Fakhruddin A. 9950 MEMORIAL BLVD STE 102 77338 #704-02-1983 L1992 **CCM PUD** *020

RAMOS, Gonzalo. ■ 77396 #737-06-2001 L2007 **IMG** *020 †20

RECIO-FELICIANO, Salvador. 22999 HIGHWAY 59 N, STE 136 77339 #042-02-1991 L1995 **IM** *020 †20

REISCHMANN, Barbara Faye. 18951 N MEMORIAL DR 77338 #019-02-1970 L1971 **EM** *020 †16

REVANA, Madaiah. 9950 MEMORIAL BLVD STE 201 77338 #495-09-1971 L1977 **CD IM** *020 †20

RIANON, Nahid Jamal. ■ 77396 #160-03-1992 L2007 **FM** *100

RIDGE, Laresa Annette. 1712 1ST ST E 77338 #048-14-2000 L2003 **FM** *020 †18

RITTENHOUSE, Ralph A. 18838 S MEMORIAL DR, STE 103 77338 #016-43-1960 L1975 **FM P** *020 †18 ‡

RODRIGUEZ, Melissa. 19333 HIGHWAY 59 N, STE 145 77338 #048-14-2001 L2004 **PD** *020 †55

ROWE, Hoon. ■ 77396 #583-01-1973 L1977 **IM** *020 †20

ROY, Pradeep Kumar. 2330 TIMBER SHADOWS DR 77339 #496-38-1978 L1987 **P PFP** *020 †75

RUMALLA, Srinivas Kumar. 18955 N MEMORIAL DR, STE 260 77338 #495-57-1991 L1996 **IM** *020 †20

RUMALLA, Sunita. 18955 N MEMORIAL DR, STE 260 77338 #021-06-1992 L1994 **IM** *020 †20

SAMUEL, Asha Kasturi. 18955 N MEMORIAL DR # 360 77338 #495-42-1973 L1984 **HEM** *020 †50

SAMUEL, Embaty J R. 18955 N MEMORIAL DR, STE 360 77338 #495-04-1974 L1984 **CD IM** *020 †20

SCHEMPP, Rosemary. 8484 WILL CLAYTON PKWY, KELSEY-SEYBOLD CLINIC 77338 #048-14-1991 L1992 **IM** *020 †20

SCHETTLER, Heinrich G. 18842 S MEMORIAL DR # 202 77338 #048-04-1975 L1975 **OBG** *020 †30

SESSIONS, Jerry Lee. 18951 N MEMORIAL DR, ER DEPT 77338 #040-02-1980 L1982 **EM** *020 †16

SEWARD, Richard E. 2350 ATASCOCITA RD, TDCJPAM LYCHNER STATE JAIL 77396 #048-15-1979 L1980 **P CHP** *020 †75

SHAH, Arunkumar J. 9810 FM 1960 BYPASS RD W, SUITE 115 77338 #496-38-1969 L1980 **GE IM** *020

SHELBY, Amelia Ruthdesire. ■ 77346 #010-03-2001 L2005 **FM** *100 †18

SHRUM, K Ray. 18700 W LAKE HOUSTON PKWY, STE A105 77346 #051-07-1996 L2001 **OPH** *020 †35

SINGLETON, David L. 9745 FM 1960 BYPASS RD W 77338 #048-14-1992 L1993 **IM PD** *020

SLOAN, Sonya Myles. ■ 77396 #048-02-1999 L2007 **ORS** *100

SMITH, Mark Thos. 18350 TIMBER FOREST DR, STE 100 77346 #048-02-1975 L1975 **PD** *020 †55

SMITH, Steven Jeffrey. 22999 HIGHWAY 59 N STE 218 77339 #038-40-1975 L1980 **D IM** *020 †15

SMOOT, Cynthia M. 18350 TIMBER FOREST DR 77346 #048-16-1999 L2002 **PD** *020 †55

SORGEN, Norman Mark. 18955 N MEMORIAL DR, STE 560 77338 #024-05-1973 L1976 **GS** *020 †85

SRINIVASAMURTHY, N. 1712 1ST ST E, STE M 77338 #495-09-1973 L1979 **PD CHP** *020 †55

STEEN, Anna Frances. ■ 77346 #048-13-2005 **GS** *100

STOKES, George Nicholas. 18955 N MEMORIAL DR 77338 #048-14-1979 L1979 **FM** *020 †18

STRAKA, Philip Jos. 9810 FM 1960 RD W, STE 165 77338 #016-06-1992 L1999 **PS** *020 †65

SUNWOO, Changwon Justin. ■ 77346 #583-05-1942 L1971 **P** *071

TAYI, Ravichandarrao Venk. ■ 77346 #308-14-1997 L2006 **FM** *100

TRICHE, Millicent Paige. ■ 77396 #028-34-2002 L2006 **OBG** *020

TROWBRIDGE, John Parks. 9816 MEMORIAL BLVD STE 205 77338 #038-06-1976 L1977 **CD PMM** *020

VASSALLO, Keith David. 8484 WILL CLAYTON PKWY 77338 #048-14-1995 L1998 **IM** *020 †20

VEGA, Charles Edward. ■ 77396 #048-04-2007 **ORS** *012

VENKATESH, Athi P. 2313 TIMBER SHADOWS DR 77339 #495-95-1992 L2003 **P** *020 ‡

VERMA, Neeru None. ■ 77339 #048-16-2003 L2006 **P** *100

VILLAFANI, J Mario. 18955 N MEMORIAL DR # 320 77338 #048-12-1991 L1996 **GS** *020 †85

VILLAFANI, Mario F. 8710 WINSTON FALLS CT 77396 #176-02-1964 L1981 **AN** *020 †05

WANG, Jeff Chi Chao. 9816 MEMORIAL BLVD, STE 107 77338 #048-02-1996 L1998 **IM** *020 †20

WASHINGTON, Labaron T. 18951 N MEMORIAL DR 77338 #048-12-1994 L1996 **PTH** *020 †50

WESSELS, Robert A. 18951 N MEMORIAL DR 77338 #048-04-1982 L1983 **PTH** *020 †50 ‡

WHITE, Jerry Allen. 2350 ATASCOCITA RD, UTMB 77396 #048-12-1959 L1959 **PHP GP** *020 †70

WILLIAMSON, Thomas James. 2755 W LAKE HOUSTON PKWY 77339 #038-40-1997 L2000 **IM** *020 †20

ZIA, Mohammad. 18955 N MEMORIAL DR, STE 300 77338 #704-02-1989 L2000 **NEP** *020 †20

HUNT – KERR

AHLGREN, E Warner. 135 MARYMEADE DR 78024 #035-06-1962 L1966 **AN PUD** *071 †05

BACON, Dan Wallace. ■ 78024 #048-02-1955 L1955 **FM OBG** *020 †18

GRAVES, Ghent, Jr. HIGHWAY 39, CASITA 78024 #048-04-1955 L1955 **IM PUD** *071 †20

KILLIAN, Thomas Jos. ■ 78024 #021-01-1965 L1972 **OTO A** *020 †45

RAGAN, Jesse Dietzel. PO BOX 765, HIGHWAY 39 & MAUK RD 78024 #048-04-1958 L1958 **PD** *071 †55

RODRIGUEZ, Vincent John. PO BOX 308 78024 #005-02-1985 L1987 **FM** *075

HUNTINGTON – ANGELINA

HARRISON, Natasha Nicole. ■ 75949 #048-02-2005 L2005 **IM** *012

HUNTSVILLE – WALKER

ADAMS, Glenda Marie. 3009A HIGHWAY 30 W 77340 #048-02-1976 L1976 **PHP OS** *030

ANTWI, Stephen Kwaku. 77340 #048-02-1999 L2003 **MPD** *020

ATKINS, Billy Jack. 260 IH 45 S, STE A 77340 #048-02-1967 L1967 **OBG FM** *020 †30,18 ‡

BHURIWALA, Aliakbar. 1524 11TH ST STE B, PLUS CARE 77340 #704-02-1991 L1996 **IM** *020 †20

BOYLE, Lawrence Patrick. 130 MEDICAL CENTER PKWY #9 77340 #048-12-1972 L1987 **GS** *020 †85

CHANG, Shao-Jen. ■ 77340 #048-14-1995 L1997 **MPD PD** *020 †20,55

COLE, Thomas Carroll, Jr. 1203 AVENUE J 77340 #036-07-1973 L1974 **GP** *020

CONWELL, Halford Roger. 2800 LAKE RD 77340 #038-41-1955 L1956 **AM GP** *020

DAO, Hung Trong. 829 10TH ST, HUNTSVILLE CLINIC, INC. 77320 #941-01-1971 L1982 **FM PTH** *020

DEAHL, Timothy J. 260 IH 45 S, STE B 77340 #048-12-1988 L1989 **OBG** *020 †30 ‡

DEVINE, Johnnie Colon. ■ 77340 #047-06-1961 L1965 **OBG** *071

FERNANDEZ, Roberto. 2507 LAKE RD 77340 #048-02-1999 L2002 **FM** *020 †18

FICKLEN, David R. 102 MEDICAL PARK LN STE A, 521 I-45 SO. SUITE #4 77340 #048-02-1995 L1998 **IM** *020 †20

GAINES, Sheri Cording. ■ 77340 #048-14-1990 L1991 **CHP** *020 †75

GOPALANI, Anisa Faruk. 130 MEDICAL CENTER PKWY, STE 10 77340 #048-02-2001 L2006 **APM** *020 †60

HANNA, James Michael. 130 MEDICAL CENTER PKWY, STE 3 77340 #048-02-1976 L1976 **D** *020 †15

HEATH, Dalton D. 129 MEDICAL PARK LN 77340 #048-02-1988 L1990 **ORS** *020 †40

HEBERT, Michelle M. 110 MEMORIAL HOSPITAL DR, HUNTSVILLE MEMORIAL HOSP 77340 #048-02-1996 L1996 **PTH** *020 †50

HILL, Tom D. 4030 SAM HOUSTON AVE, STE A 77340 #048-14-1989 L1991 **FM** *020 †18

HINES, John Stanley. 130 MEDICAL CENTER PKWY, STE 2 77340 #048-02-1976 L1976 **IM** *020 †20

HSIAO, Glenda Read. ■ 77340 #048-14-1995 L2001 **MPD PD** *020 †20,55

JULYE, Ernestine Amoi. FARM ROAD 2821, TX DEPT OF CRIMINAL JUSTIC 77349 #016-11-1994 L2002 **IM** *020 †20

KELLEY, Michael Frederick. 3009 HIGHWAY 30 W, HEALTH SERVICES DIVISION 77340 #005-18-1978 L1984 **PHP** *018,70

KHAN, Nabeel Munfaet Ali. 119 MEDICAL PARK LN, STE A 77340 #704-22-1996 L2002 **IM** *020 †20

KNIGHT, John D. 100 MEDICAL CENTER PKWY, STE 1000 77340 #048-14-1992 L1993 **MPD** *020 †20,55

KNUTH, David Paul. 2507 LAKE RD 77340 #048-04-1973 L1974 **FM** *020 †18

KOEHL, Michael Frank. 100 MEMORIAL HOSPITAL DR 77340 #048-02-1965 L1965 **PTH** *020 †50

LEGGETT, Joe Edward. ■ 77340 #048-02-1974 L1974 **P** *075

LIMSIACO, Marciano Salvio. 1212 12TH ST 77340 #748-11-1975 L1989 **P** *030

LINTHICUM, Lannette C. 3009A HIGHWAY 30 W, TX DEPT CRIMINAL JUSTICE 77340 #023-01-1983 L1986 **IM** *020 †20

MAHAFFEY, Robert Karl. 2507 LAKE RD 77340 #048-02-1975 L1975 **FM** *020 †18

MAHESRI, Murtaza I. 1524 11TH ST STE B 77340 #704-02-1990 L1996 **IM** *020 †20

MALEK, Gholamreza. 100 MEMORIAL HOSPITAL DR 77340 #048-04-1994 L2000 **DR** *020 †80

MALIK, Sajid Zahir. 2804 LAKE RD STE 7 77340 #048-13-1991 L1992 **N** *020

MARTIN, Jerry Darrell. 129 MEDICAL PARK LN 77340 #048-02-1978 L1978 **ORS** *020 †40

MC GEHEE, Frank Owen. 1909 22ND ST 77340 #021-01-1965 L1966 **OPH** *035

MCKEEVER, Gregory C. 100 MEDICAL CENTER PKWY, STE 1000 77340 #048-13-1995 L1996 **FM** *020 †18

MONDAY, Chas Woodrow, Jr. 130 MEDICAL CENTER PKWY, STE 6 77340 #048-02-1966 L1966 **GS** *020 †85

MONTGOMERY, Curtis Edward. 956 ELKINS LK 77340 #005-18-1978 L1995 **OBG** *020 †30

NATHAN, Pradan Anbu. 3009A HIGHWAY 30 W, STE 169 77340 #495-42-1976 L1984 **P PFP** *020 †20

NELSON, Lan Albin. 610A NORMAL PARK DR 77320 #056-05-1971 L1981 **FM ON** *062 †18

NGUYEN-KHOA, Nhan-Anh. ■ 77320 #396-32-1959 L1979 **GP** *071

NICHOLS, Charles Gardner. PO BOX 7103 77342 #035-09-1961 L1962 **P** *071

NIEWENHOUS, Theodore H. ■ 77340 #041-13-1954 L1991 **GP** *071

OLSON, Karin E. 260 INTERSTATE 45 S 77340 #048-02-1994 L1993 L1997 **MPD** *020

PAGE COLEMAN, Jill Marie. 643 INTERSTATE 45 S 77340 #048-02-1997 L2003 **GP** *020

PEVEY, Willard Joel. ■ 77340 #021-05-1957 L1969 **OBG** *071 †30

PRIER, David A. 100 MEDICAL CENTER PKWY 77340 #048-14-1986 L1987 **PD IM** *020 †20,55

QUAN, Lawrence. 100 MEMORIAL HOSPITAL DR 77340 #001-02-1975 L1979 **FM EM** *020 †18

RAINES, Charles Anion. 1528 AVENUE J, SAM HOUSTON STATE UNIV 77340 #048-02-1973 L1974 **GP** *020

REX, David L. 110 MEMORIAL HOSPITAL DR, HUNTSVILLE MEMORIAL HOSP 77340 #048-13-1986 L1987 **DR** *020 †80

ROLLINS, Lowell G, Jr. 100 MEDICAL CENTER PKWY, STE 1000 77340 #048-04-1990 L1991 **FM** *020 †18

SCHULTE, Jayne R. 100 MEDICAL CENTER PKWY, STE 1000 77340 #048-14-1992 L1994 **MPD** *020 †20,55

SELASSIE, Mhrete Ab Gebre. 2840 LAKE RD STE 4 77340 #017-20-1959 L1977 **IM** *071

SHUKLA, Urmil Raghudeo. 130 MEDICAL CENTER PKWY, STE 10 77340 #495-01-1982 L1997 **GS VS** *020 †85

SIMS, Stephen M. 133 MEDICAL PARK LN, STE B 77340 #048-02-1978 L1978 **AN PME** *020 †05

SINGH, Gurpreet Dipu. 2507 LAKE RD 77340 #048-12-1997 L2002 **OPH** *020 †35

SMALL, Lawrence Wayne. 521 INTERSTATE 45 S STE 12 77340 #048-02-1977 L1977 **CD IM** *020

SMITH, Marcus Darnell. ■ 77342 #010-03-1998 L2004 **IM** *020

TAYLOR, Richard W. 2804 LAKE RD 77340 #067-01-1973 L1977 *100

TORONJO, Walter Daivd. 521 IH 45 S, STE 11 77340 #048-07-1978 L1978 **FM** *020 †18

TOWLER, Henry Howell, Jr. 130 MEDICAL CENTER PKWY, STE 1 77340 #012-05-1966 L1979 **OTO A** *020 †45

TREMOR, Isnardo. 2507 LAKE RD, HUNTSVILLE FAMILY CLINIC L 77340 #748-10-1973 L1996 **FM** *020 †18

VICKERS, Frank Allen. PO BOX 1499, VICKERS MEDICAL OFFICE 77342 #048-02-1961 L1961 **FM** *020

VILAYTHONG, Jill Ngeun. ■ 77340 #048-12-2007 **IM** *012

VINCENT, Bobby Melvin. 264 FM 3478 RD, ESTELLE UNIT 77320 #021-01-1984 L1987 **IM** *020

WARD, Jesse Scott. 129 MEDICAL PARK LN 77340 #048-02-1997 L2000 **ORS** *020 †40

WELLS, Darrel Richard. 14 STATE HWY 75 N 77320 #048-12-1978 L1978 **EM FM** *020 †16,18

WELLS, Lawrence Harold. 2507 LAKE RD 77340 #048-13-1980 L1980 **FM** *020 †18

WILLIAMS, Betty Jean. 1697 FM 980 RD, ELLIS UNIT MEDICAL DEPARTM 77320 #047-05-1972 L1973 **FM OS** *020 †20

WILLIAMS, Robert Lewis. 3009A HIGHWAY 30 W 77340 #048-14-1995 L1996 **IM UM** *020 †20

YAP, Romeo Sy. ELLIS II PSYCHIATRIC CTR, TEXAS DEPT OF CORRECTION 77340 #748-11-1976 L1988 *020

HURST – TARRANT

ACEVEDO, Antonio. 729 W BEDFORD EULESS RD, STE 203 76053 #649-02-1971 L1975 **AN** *020

AL-HAFIDH, A-Salam Nuri. 1709 PRECINCT LINE RD 76054 #528-01-1976 L1987 **IM PD** *020 †55,20

ANDREWS, Charley J, III. 556 W BEDFORD EULESS RD, STE C 76053 #021-05-1975 L1977 **OPH** *020 †35

BELL, John David. 117 E HARWOOD RD, MID CITIES DIALYSIS CENTER 76054 #048-02-1969 L1969 **NEP IM** *020 †20

BRONSTEIN, Antonia Loiz. 1832 NORWOOD PLZ 76054 #042-03-1981 L1984 **PD** *020 †55

BUCHANAN, Jennifer Nicole. ■ 76053 #048-14-2003 **MPD** *100 †20,55

BZOSTEK, Barry David. 731 MARTIN RD, COOK CHILDRENS 76054 #035-15-1970 L1974 **PD** *020 †55

CAMPERLENGO, Nicholas V. ■ 76054 #016-45-1993 L1998 **PYG** *020

CASTANEDA, Jorge Alberto. ■ 76054 #048-12-2002 L2006 **FM** *100 †18

CHOWDHURY, Prosanti K. 6316 PRECINCT LINE RD 76054 #039-01-1988 L1990 **PD** *020 †55

COUTOUMANOS, Julia C. 731 MARTIN RD 76054 #048-12-1993 L1994 **PD** *020 †55

DEITCHMAN, Michael J. 731 MARTIN RD, COOKS CHILDREN'S 76054 #048-02-1994 L1997 **PD** *020 †55

FARRIS, Douglas R. 1733 PRECINCT LINE RD, NORTHEAST TARRANT DERMATOL 76054 #048-13-1993 L1999 **D** *020 †20,15

FAWZY, Magda H. 6316 PRECINCT LINE RD 76054 #915-02-1976 L1996 **PD EM** *075 †55

FIERRO, Randolph Brian. 1612 HURST TOWN CENTER DR, SURGICAL HOSPITAL 76054 #048-12-1991 L2006 **APM** *020 †18

FLEISCHER, Martin. ■ 76054 #005-15-1962 L1966 **R NM** *071 †80,28

GUTHRIE, Aubrey Elton, II. ■ 76054 #048-04-1959 L1959 **FM** *071 †18

HABBU, Ranganath Sakharam. 1050 W PIPELINE RD STE 202 76053 #495-01-1977 L1989 **P** *020

HARRELL, Ronald Robt. ■ 76053 #048-02-1956 L1956 **GPM OM** *020 †70

HU, Gang. 1872 NORWOOD DR 76054 #036-07-1998 L2003 **OPH** *020 †35

KAGELER, Woody Vernon. 828 W HARWOOD RD 1118, TARRANT COUNTY CLG 76054 #048-02-1971 L1971 **PUD CCM** *030 †20

KELLY, Derek Keith. ■ 76053 #048-12-2007 **EM** *012

MOORE, Anjanette R. 6316 PRECINCT LINE RD 76054 #048-13-2002 L2006 **PD** *100 †55

MOY, Leland Eric. 729 W BEDFORD EULESS RD, STE 203 76053 #003-01-1986 L1987 **AN** *05

NGUYEN, Tho Quoc. 1733 PRECINCT LINE RD 76054 #048-12-1989 L1990 **D** *020 †20,15

NOVOTNY, Jerome Douglas. 600 E HURST BLVD, BELL HELLICOPTER 76053 #048-04-1983 L1983 **EM FM** *020 †18

OUSEPH, Florence. 1717 PRECINCT LINE RD, STE 207 76054 #495-27-1975 L1981 **P OS** *020 †75

RANELLE, Brian D. 1872 NORWOOD DR 76054 #028-78-1972, ▲ L1973 **OPH** *020 †35

REDDY, Dharam Prabhakar. 25041 NORWOOD 76054 #495-21-1978 *100

RISK, William. 809 W HARWOOD RD, STE 204 76054 #048-02-1960 L1960 **U** *020

ROE, Elise M. ■ 76053 #048-14-2005 **GS** *012

SANDHU, Gurcharan Singh. ■ 76054 #495-02-1952 L1979 **OPH PHP** *071

SINGLETON, Wright W. 121 NE LOOP 820 76053 #048-15-1990 L1991 **OM IM** *020

STEELE, John Gilbert. 1444 PRECINCT LINE RD 76053 #048-12-1961 L1961 **ORS** *072 †40

SUMNER, Stephanie. 6316 PRECINCT LINE RD 76054 #048-14-1990 L1991 **PD** *020 †55

THOMASON, James L. 769 LONESOME DOVE TRL 76054 #048-14-1984 L1987 **P** *020 †75

TROUM, Stephen Jay. 729 W BEDFORD EULESS RD, STE 112 76053 #036-05-1991 L2000 **HS GS** *020 †85

VALIS, Debra Ann. 6316 PRECINCT LINE RD 76054 #048-15-1986 L1987 **PD** *020 †55

WIRTHLIN, Laurie Sue. 6316 PRECINCT LINE RD 76054 #004-01-1987 L1992 **PD** *020 †55

HUTTO – WILLIAMSON

CASTILLO, Cathy A. 151 EXCHANGE BLVD, STE 500 78634 #048-14-2000 L2005 **FM** *020 †18

CHANG, Franklin. 120 ED SCHMIDT BLVD 78634 #048-04-1995 L1996 **FM** *020 †18

COHEN, Dinna Orina. 120 ED SCHMIDT BLVD 78634 #048-14-1990 L1991 **FM** *020 †18

COHEN, Nathan Ralph. 120 ED SCHMIDT BLVD 78634 #048-02-1987 L1988 **IM PD** *020 †55,20

FERRELL, Angelle W. 151 EXCHANGE BLVD, AUSTIN REGIONAL CLINIC 78634 #048-04-1999 L2006 **PD** *020 †55

HUDGINS, John Robt. 1985 COUNTY ROAD 105 78634 #048-02-1984 L1985 **IM OM** *030 †20

KIM, Yoonsin. 120 ED SCHMIDT BLVD 78634 #005-76-2003, ▲ L2006 **FM** *020 †18

LUTTRELL, Brady Lynn. 151 EXCHANGE BLVD, STE 500 78634 #019-02-2004 L2007 **FM** *020 †18

STONE, Mark Alan. 120 ED SCHMIDT BLVD 78634 #048-02-1996 L1998 **FM** *020 †18

IDALOU – LUBBOCK

BISBEE, Robert J. 113 WALNUT ST, IDALOU COMM HLTH CTR 79329 #048-15-1994 L1995 **IM** *020 †20

INGLESIDE – SAN PATRICIO

JIMENEZ, Prospero, Jr. OXY-CHEM 78362 #048-02-1946 L1946 **OM GP** *071

LEWIS, Claude Hugh. ■ 78362 #028-79-1961, ▲ L1962 **GP** *071

PARKER, Sandra Kay. 327 CORAL SEA RD, STE 165 78362 #048-13-1999 L2002 **FM** *100 †18

PERRY, Alton Rhodes, Jr. ■ 78362 #048-04-1961 L1961 **FM IM** *020

RUTKOWSKI, John A. ■ 78362 #048-16-1987 L1988 **EM FM** *020 †18

ZAFRA, Mildred Pulido. 2334 STATE HIGHWAY 361, STE 114 78362 #748-08-1988 L1998 **PD** *020 †55

INGRAM – KERR

COOK, Thomas E. ■ 78025 #048-04-1952 L1952 **PD A** *071 †55

SEARLE, Noel Bonham. ■ 78025 #048-04-1954 L2002 **GE IM** *071 †20

IOWA PARK – WICHITA

CONKLIN, Jeremy Henry. 310 W ALAMEDA ST 76367 #022-75-2005, ▲ L2008 *020

KALMANOV, Alexander M. 2101 FM 369 N, JAMES J ALLRED UNIT 76367 #913-69-1965 L1992 **FM** *020

SOELL, Erwin Frederick. PARK CLINIC 76367 #028-02-1957 L1960 **FM** *071 †18

STUTTE, Lawrence Dean. 310 W ALAMEDA ST 76367 #039-01-1980 L1982 **FM** *020 †18

■ = Address Information Privacy Protected

WEBB, John A. ■ 76367 #004-01-1952 L1959 **GS CLP** *071 †50

IRAAN – PECOS

FRANKS, Edwin Ray. 305 W 5TH ST 79744 #048-02-1959 L1959 **FM GS** *020

IRVING – DALLAS

AAKER, Benjamin. ■ 75039 #030-05-2005 **EM** *012
ABRAHAM, Suma M. 2021 N MACARTHUR BLVD, STE 520 75061 #048-12-1995 L1997 **IM** *020 †20
ABUNDO, Frank James. 5001 STATESMAN DR 75063 #561-17-1963 L1966 **P N** *020
ADDINGTON, Stefanie Lynn. 2021 N MACARTHUR BLVD, STE 515 75061 #048-02-1999 L2004 **END** *020 †05
AEBERSOLD, Ronald Robt. 2001 W PARK DR 75061 #004-01-1966 L1969 **IM IMG** *071 †20
ALBORNOZ, Ludwig L. ■ 75063 #264-10-1987 **PTH** *100
ALCAZAR-PESANTE, Lisa G. 5001 STATESMAN DR 75063 #048-02-1987 L1989 **PD** *020 †55
ALI, Basit. 5401 GREEN PARK DR, # 202 75038 #035-75-1996. ▲ L2005 **FPG** *100
ALI, Fathi I. 5001 STATESMAN DR 75063 #613-01-1990 L2006 *100
ALLEN, Putul Murarka. 8615 FREEPORT PKWY, STE 225 75063 #048-12-1996 L1999 **PD** *020 †55
ALSHARABI, Ghazwan M.. ■ 75063 #875-01-1996 L1999 **PCP** *100 †50
ALTER, Lawrence Jos. 7200 STATE HIGHWAY 161, STE 200 75039 #048-02-1979 L1984 **U** *020 †95
AMADEO, Marco. 5001 STATESMAN DR 75063 #605-02-1957 L1980 **P** *020
ANANDKUMAR, Muthusamy. 7918 N MACARTHUR BLVD 75063 #496-28-1998 L2006 **FM** *100 †18
ANDERSON, James M. 1110 COTTONWOOD LN STE 100 75038 #048-02-1987 L1988 **FM** *020 †18
ANDERSON, Paula Ann. 8400 ESTERS BLVD STE 19 75063 #048-14-1998 L2006 **PTH** *020 †50
ANDREWS, Sasha Elizabeth. ■ 75039 #048-04-2007 **OBG** *012
ANGELO, Concordia A. 1901 N MACARTHUR BLVD 75061 #748-01-1961 L1981 **PM** *071
APONTE, Dorian Y.. ■ 75063 #042-01-2005 L2008 **P** *012
ARDAMAN, Thuy-Dung. 8400 ESTERS BLVD STE 190, CARIS DIAGNOSTICS INC 75063 #048-02-1988 L1989 **PTH PCP** *020 †50
ARNOLD, Christina A. ■ 75063 #048-12-2006 **PTH** *012
ARNOLD, Michael Andrew. ■ 75063 #048-12-2008 *012
ASHFORD, Jason S. ■ 75063 #048-12-2005 **GS** *012
ASKARI, Mary Anne, Jr. 7200 STATE HIGHWAY 161, STE 100 75039 #048-14-1989 **PD** *020 †55
AUBRY, Alvin Jos, Jr. 6800 N MACARTHUR BLVD 75039 #021-01-1972 L1982 **AI PD** *020 †55,03
AYOUB, Lisa Michelle. ■ 75063 #048-12-2008 *012
AZHAR, Muhammad Faheem. ■ 75038 #704-21-1987 L1997 **IM** *020 †20
BAGSHAHI, Hossein. ■ 75062 #305-01-2004 L2004 **GS** *012
BAILEY, Steven Hugh. ■ 75062 #047-07-2005 **GS** *012
BAKER, Stuart Brian. 220 LAS COLINAS BLVD E, VHA INC 75039 #023-07-1974 L1975 **IM RHU** *030 †20
BALANI, Jyoti Parmanand. ■ 75038 #496-39-1997 L2005 **PTH** *100 †50
BALFANZ, Phillip Eugene. ■ 75038 #048-02-2007 **P** *012
BALIS, Amy Frances. 2001 N MACARTHUR BLVD, STE 240 75061 #048-12-1993 L1994 **DR** *020 †80
BALLARD, Lauri M. 1305 MEADOW CREEK DR # 212 75038 #048-12-1999 L2002 **IM** *020 †20
BANG, Linda Sanghee. 400 W IH 635 FWY STE 200 75063 #018-03-2000 L2002 **IM** *020 †20
BARNES, William Wayne. 5001 STATESMAN DR 75063 #005-06-1963 L1964 **OTO HNS** *071 †45
BASHOUR, Jennifer Min-Wen. 400 W IH 635 FWY STE 200 75063 #048-04-2000 L2003 **IM** *020 †20
BAYLESS, Robert Eugene. 2120 N MACARTHUR BLVD, STE 100 75061 #028-03-1983 L1984 **ORS OSM** *020 †40
BEAUBRUN, Yvon Michel. ■ 75063 #440-01-1955 L1979 **OBG** *071 †30
BELL, Michael Alexander. 1901 N MACARTHUR BLVD, DEPARTMENT OF EMERGENCY ME 75061 #422-01-2004 L2007 **EM** *020
BELL, Steven Arnold. 2021 N MACARTHUR BLVD, MEDICAL & SURGICAL CLINIC 75061 #038-41-1967 L1997 **IM IMG** *020 †20
BENJAMIN, Ramsis. 5001 STATESMAN DR 75063 #016-01-1994 L1996 **N ON** *020
BERDECIO, Eduardo T. 5001 STATESMAN DR 75063 #176-02-1968 L1988 **P** *020 †75
BERGESTUEN, Deidi A. ■ 75063 #048-12-1994 L1995 **IM** *020 †20
BERNAL, Amparo. 1800 N BRITAIN RD 75061 #264-02-1980 L1995 **IM** *020 †20
BERNSTEIN, Louis David. 3989 N BELT LINE RD 75038 #048-12-1970 L1995 **OM IM** *062 †20
BESEIKRI, Naeima K.. 5001 STATESMAN DR 75063 #613-01-1992 L2006 *100
BHATT, Anand Dilip. 400 W IH 635 FWY STE 250 75063 #016-11-2002 L2005 **PD** *020 †55
BIARD, Maria N. 1110 COTTONWOOD LN STE 100 75038 #065-09-1988 L1996 **FM** *020 †18
BLACK, Alison Adams. 440 W IH 635 FWY STE 365, LAS COLINAS DERMATOLOGY, P 75063 #048-12-1991 L1992 **D** *020 †15
BOWER, Kevin Rudy. 1901 N MACARTHUR BLVD, BAYLOR MED CTR EM DEPT 75061 #016-06-1981 L1984 **EM** *020 †16
BRAUD, Jason James. ■ 75060 #021-06-2006 L2008 **DR** *012
BRONSON, Ted Paul. 1110 COTTONWOOD LN, STE 105 75038 #056-05-1973 L1975 **CD IM** *020 †20
BROPHY, Michael Haas. 800 W AIRPORT FWY, STE 1015 75062 #048-12-1973 L1973 **P OBS** *020 †75
BROWNING, Pritha Chitkara. 400 W IH 635 FWY STE 200 75063 #048-12-1998 L2001 **IM** *020 †20
BROWNING, Travis G. ■ 75061 #048-12-2003 L2005 **DR** *012
BRUCE, Mark. ■ 75038 #048-34-1983 L1990 **EM** *020
BUIE, James Scott. 2311 TEXAS DR 75062 #048-02-1975 L1975 **PTH** *020 †50
BURNETT, Glenn Edward, II. 1901 N MACARTHUR BLVD, BAYLOR-IRVING HOSPITAL 75061 #039-01-1992 L1995 **IM** *020 †20
BURTON, Erik V. ■ 75061 #021-06-2004 **N** *012
CABANSAG, Dean Allan. 4545 FULLER DR, STE 340 75038 #005-12-1995 L2002 **FM** *020 †18
CANCHOLA, Daniel R. 6420 N MACARTHUR BLVD, STE 130 75039 #048-13-1997 L1999 **FM** *020 †18
CANO, Adriana. 701 TUSCAN, STE 265 75039 #048-12-1986 L1987 **NEP IM** *020 †20
CANTRELL, David M. 1901 N MACARTHUR BLVD, INPATIENT UNIT 4TH FLOOR 75061 #048-15-1996 L1997 **IM** *020 †20

CARAG WEST, Myrna B. 219 S O CONNOR RD 75060 #748-08-1966 L1979 **IM PUD** *020
CARLISLE, James Lou, Jr. ■ 75038 #047-07-2006 **PM** *012
CARMICHAEL, Kristen Riche. 6750 N MACARTHUR BLVD, STE 309 75039 #048-14-2000 L2004 **OBG** *020 †30
CARTER, Brett Wilson. ■ 75063 #027-01-2005 L2005 **DR** *012
CASIANO, Elizabeth R. ■ 75063 #043-01-2004 L2008 **OBG** *012
CASTANO, Claudia. 1901 W IRVING BLVD 75061 #048-12-1996 L1998 **GP** *020 ‡
CAVANAUGH, Sean X. 7415 LAS COLINAS BLVD, STE 100 75063 #048-15-2000 L2003 **RO** *020
CEDERBERG, Kevin Bradley. ■ 75061 #010-02-2004 L2007 **DR** *012
CHADALAWADA, Poornima. 1156 HIDDEN RDG 75038 #496-31-1999 L2006 **IM** *100
CHAGARLAMUDI, Anita. ■ 75061 #495-13-1991 *100
CHAHAL, Ravinder Singh. ■ 75063 #018-03-2006 L2007 **AN** *012
CHAN, Danny. ■ 75038 #028-34-1999 L2007 **VIR** *100 †80 ‡
CHANDER, Subhash. 127 S MAIN ST, M D PAIN CENTER 75060 #495-29-1973 L1977 **AN OS** *020 †05
CHANDRASEKHARA, Darshna. 1110 COTTONWOOD LN 75038 #048-14-1998 L2001 **OBG** *020
CHAO, Sam. ■ 75061 #005-19-2004 L2006 **DR** *012
CHAO, Tamara Tinmay. ■ 75061 #005-19-2004 L2006 **OBG** *012
CHAPPELL, Tenesha Richole. 2021 N MACARTHUR BLVD #520 75061 #048-02-1998 L2001 **IM** *020 †20
CHARTON, Justin Wayne. ■ 75039 #004-01-2005 **OPH** *012
CHEMMALAKUZHY, Jacob. 701 TUSCAN, STE 240 75039 #028-46-1998 L2006 **IC** *020 †20
CHEN, Nancy. ■ 75063 #016-11-2007 **IM** *012
CHENAULT, Carrie Bess. ■ 75062 #048-15-2001 L2006 **PTH** *020 †50
CHENNUPATI, Subbarao S. 1444 GARDENIA ST 75063 #495-58-1971 L1979 **AN OS** *020
CHIU, Michael Joseph. 701 TUSCAN STE 265 75039 #025-01-1988 L1990 **IM** *020 †20
CHOI, Duck Kyun. 5001 STATESMAN DR 75063 #583-10-1973 L1978 **DR** *020
CHOWDHERY, Robina Naz. ■ 75038 #038-43-2005 **IM** *012
CLARK, David Frederick. ■ 75062 #048-12-2008 *012
CLIFFORD, Edward James. 2001 N MACARTHUR BLVD, STE 255 75061 #048-12-1986 L1987 **GS** *020 †85
CLUFF, Douglas M. 400 W IH 635 FWY STE 210 75063 #048-15-1998 L2001 **FM** *020 †18
COCHRAN, John Walter. 1302 LANE ST STE 900 75061 #045-01-1964 L1971 **OTO** *020 †45
COHEN, Evelyn. 4545 FULLER DR, MEDICAL DOCTOR ASSOCIATES 75038 #016-42-1975 L1976 **R NM** *020 †80
COMBS CANTRELL, Deborah T. 1901 N MACARTHUR BLVD 75061 #048-02-1986 L1987 **N** *020 †75
CONOLEY, Megan Jane. 6750 N MACARTHUR BLVD #150 75039 #048-13-1999 L2003 **MPD** *020 †20,55
COOK, Jeannine Rozas. 2023 W PARK DR 75061 #021-05-1984 L1987 **PD** *020 †55
COOPER, Daniel E. 2401 E AIRPORT FWY, TEXAS STADIUM 75062 #048-12-1984 L1986 **ORS** *020 †40
CORBIN, Nicol S. ■ 75061 #048-13-2001 L2007 **UP** *012
COX, Jennifer Ann. ■ 75063 #027-01-1997 L2005 **PHO** *100 †55
CRAWFORD, Lindsay Michele. ■ 75063 #048-04-2007 **ORS** *012
CRIM, Randall Wayne. 2001 N MACARTHUR BLVD, STE 275 75061 #048-12-1984 L1987 **CRS** *020 †85,10
CRONSON, Harold Andrew. 4925 N O CONNOR RD, STE 120 75062 #048-15-1982 L1983 **P** *020 †75
CROOK, Terri Carole. 8400 ESTERS BLVD STE 190, PATHOLOGY PARTNERS INC 75063 #004-01-1995 L1997 **ATP** *062 †50
CROW, Nannette Foglia. 7200 STATE HIGHWAY 161, STE 100 75039 #001-06-1986 L1990 **PD** *020 †55
CUMP, Norma Gonzalez. 1302 LANE ST STE 2010 75061 #016-11-1987 L1992 **FM PD** *020 †18
CURLEE, Chad A. ■ 75062 #048-78-2007. ▲ *012
CURTIS, Amy Valette. ■ 75062 #003-01-2006 **D** *012
CWIKLA, Mark Jos. 2001 N MACARTHUR BLVD, STE 444 75061 #048-02-1979 L1979 **NS** *020 †25
DAIGLE, Scott Jos. 5001 STATESMAN DR 75063 #021-06-1990 L1990 **FM** *020
DANI, Dhimant Lalitchandr. ■ 75039 #495-23-1997 L2006 **N** *012 †20
DATTATREYA, Rajiv. 1110 COTTONWOOD LN, STE 100 75038 #495-53-1985 L2000 **IM END** *020 †20
DAVE, Sachin Bhupendrabha. ■ 75063 #495-22-2000 L2003 **CN** *012
DAY, Robert Clay. 2001 N MACARTHUR BLVD # 24, IRVING RADIOLOGICAL ASSOC 75061 #011-03-1980 L1982 **DR** *020 †80
DAYAL, Yogeshwar. 8400 ESTERS BLVD, STE 190 75063 #495-36-1961 L1972 **PTH IM** *050 †50
DEEMS, David Alexander. 1110 COTTONWOOD LN 75038 #004-01-1988 L1990 **FM** *020 †18
DELWOOD, Linda Jean. ■ 75063 #048-12-1985 L1987 **AN IM** *020 †20,05
DEMARIE, Bryan Keith. 349 LAS COLINAS BLVD E, STE A 75039 #021-06-1987 L2000 **IM** *020 †20
DEOL, Navtej S. ■ 75039 #065-06-1990 L1995 **FM** *020 †18
DESAI, Anil Ishwarbhai. 1425 GREENWAY DR, STE 480 75038 #654-01-1998 L2002 **IM** *020 †20
DESAI, Nilesh Kundanlal. ■ 75063 #048-16-2003 L2006 **DR** *012
DE SOYZA, Devinda. 1625 N STORY RD, STE 140 75061 #048-13-1997 L1999 **NEP** *020 †20
DHARIA, Tushar Dilip. ■ 75063 #048-12-2003 L2005 **GE** *012 †20
DHARMA, Shashikala. 4301 N MACARTHUR BLVD, STE 107 75038 #048-15-1985 L1986 **OPH** *020 †35 ‡
DIAZ, Thomas E. 3501 N MACARTHUR BLVD, STE 410 75062 #048-14-1987 L1988 **FM** *020 †18
DICKERSON, Harold Joe. 2001 N MACARTHUR BLVD, STE 240 75061 #048-02-1971 L1971 **DR** *020 †80
DICKEY, Elizabeth S. 7200 STATE HIGHWAY 161, STE 100 75039 #017-20-1982 L1983 **PD** *020 †55
DICKEY, William Thos. 800 W AIRPORT FWY, STE 416 75062 #048-12-1970 L1970 **PTH** *020 †50
DINAKARAN, Sivavasavi Kum. ■ 75063 #496-37-2000 L2006 **IM** *100
DOMINIQUE, Colette M. 3501 N MACARTHUR BLVD, STE 500 75062 #021-06-2000 L2004 **OBG** *020
DOUGLAS, Howard Thos. 391 LAS COLINAS BLVD E, STE 130-614 75039 #048-02-1978 L1978 **FM** *075
DUARTE, Jose F. ■ 75063 #275-01-1962 L1975 *020
DU BOIS, Kenneth Guinn. 1923 W PARK DR 75061 #048-12-1961 L1961 **FM** *071 †18
DUJON, Edgardo Beson. ■ 75038 #748-02-1966 L1974 **PDS** *020
DUJON, Teresita F. ■ 75038 #748-02-1966 L1974 **AN** *005
EARGLE, Central L, Jr. 140 N MACARTHUR BLVD 75061 #012-01-1965 L1981 **FM** *071 †18
ECHT, Gregory Allen. 7415 LAS COLINAS BLVD, STE 100 75063 #017-20-1985 L1989 **RO** *020 †80

EDELMAN, Gerald. 2001 N MACARTHUR BLVD, STE 630 75061 #007-02-1985 L1993 **IM ON** *020 †20

EDENHOFFER, Ildiko G. 9947 N MACARTHUR BLVD, STE 100 75063 #473-01-1988 L1995 **PD** *020 †55

EISENBERG, Robert Steven. 1430 N MACARTHUR BLVD, STE 107 75061 #016-42-1975 L1981 **OPH** *020

ELMORE, Stephanie Hurn. 1701 W WALNUT HILL LN, STE 200 75038 #048-14-1994 L1995 **FM** *020 †18

EMBREY, Jeffrey R. 1901 N MACARTHUR BLVD, BAYLOR MEDICAL CTR AT IRVI 75061 #048-12-1982 L1983 **PTH CLP** *020

ENNIS, Gregory Philip. 2001 W AIRPORT FWY STE 105 75062 #017-20-1971 L1973 **EM** *020

ESCOBAR, Jose Fernando. ■ 75063 #048-15-2000 L2006 **TS** *012

EVANS, Kurt James. 400 W IH 635 FWY STE 310 75063 #034-01-1976 L1987 **U** *020 †95

FANOUS, Elia. 3501 N MACARTHUR BLVD, STE 500 75062 #048-15-2001 L2005 **OBG** *020 †30

FAUST, Bruce M. 2001 N MACARTHUR BLVD #048-12-1963 L1963 **ORS** *071 †40

FEFERMAN, Robert S. 1901 GATEWAY DR 75038 #654-01-1986 L1997 **END IM** *020 †20

FERNANDES, Neil James. ■ 75063 #048-12-2004 L2006 **DR** *012

FERNANDES, Neville F. 701 TUSCAN STE 110 75039 #775-01-1991 L1998 **GE** *020 †20

FERNANDES, Valentino F J. 2001 N MACARTHUR BLVD, STE 660 75061 #775-01-1987 L2003 **PCC CCM** *020 †20

FERRIS, Caroline J. ■ 75014 #539-04-1996 L2006 **AN CCA** *020 †05

FINE, Jeffrey Steven. 2021 N MACARTHUR BLVD #225 75061 #021-01-1986 L2007 **GE** *020 †20

FOOS, Marcus James. 2021 N MACARTHUR BLVD #150 75061 #048-15-2001 L2003 **IM** *020 †50

FOWERS, Michelle Burnside. 400 W IH 635 FWY STE 635, NORTH TEXAS HEALTH CARE AS 75063 #049-01-1999 L2002 **PD** *020 †55

FRANCIS, David George. ■ 75063 #495-52-1989 L2004 **AN** *020 †05

FRANZ, Jerry Louis. 4425 W AIRPORT FWY 75062 #020-12-1971 L1973 **PME PMM** *020 †85,90

FRITZ, Rodney R. 1110 COTTONWOOD LN, STE 105 75038 #048-12-1982 L1983 **TS** *020 †85,90

FROST, Natalie Kay. ■ 75063 #048-12-2004 L2007 **PD** *100 †55

FURMAN, Allan Jonathan. 6750 N MACARTHUR BLVD, MEDICAL & SURGICAL CLINIC 75039 #065-06-1992 L1995 **FM** *020 †18

GAILLARD, David H, Jr. 5001 STATESMAN DR 75063 #001-02-1967 L1970 **DR R** *020 †80

GAMAN, Walter N. 1110 COTTONWOOD LN, STE 200 75038 #062-01-1975 L1985 **FM IMG** *020 †18

GAO, Wei. 1451 W AIRPORT FWY, STE 2 75062 #243-45-1984 L2000 **FM** *020 †18

GARCIA, Jose Enrique. ■ 75063 #748-01-1994 L2006 **AN** *100

GARCIA, Raymond Lloyd. 2015 W PARK DR 75061 #041-13-1967 L1977 **D** *020 †15

GARRISON, Robin Evan. ■ 75039 #056-06-2000 **AN** *100

GATTINENI, Jyothsna. ■ 75063 #495-16-1994 **PN** *012

GEORGE, Jessie. ■ 75039 #048-02-2002 L2005 **NEP** *012 †20

GERKE, Calvin Glenn, Jr. ■ 75039 #036-07-1997 L2007 *020

GIBBONS, David. ■ 75062 #539-04-1986 L1997 **PTH** *100 †50

GICHERU, Sidney Kambo. 10106 STAUBACH DR 75063 #048-12-1996 L1999 **OPH** *020 †35

GILBERT, Francis Monroe. ■ 75062 #048-04-1954 L1954 **PD** *071

GILLEAN, John Alex, III. 6363 N HIGHWAY 161, STE 450 75038 #004-01-1977 L1985 **IM** *030 †20

GILMAN, Alex S. 2425 TEXAS DR, HEARTHSTONE ASSISTED LIVIN 75062 #041-78-2000, ▲ L2003 *020 †20

GIRSON, Mark Saml. 2001 N MACARTHUR BLVD #240, IRVING RADIOLOGICAL ASSOCI 75061 #836-01-1981 L1988 **R RNR** *020 †80

GONZALES, Mae P. 3204 N MACARTHUR BLVD, STE B 75062 #748-01-1982 L1993 **FM** *020 †18

GONZALES, Peter C W. 3204 N MACARTHUR BLVD # B 75062 #748-01-1982 L1990 **N CN** *020 †55,75

GOOTOS, Peter John, II. 1333 CORPORATE DR, STE 230 75038 #048-12-1989 L1992 **AN CCA** *020 †05

GOSDIN, Gary Robt. 1302 LANE ST, STE 400 75061 #048-12-1973 L1973 **TS** *020 †85,90

GOTTSCHALK, Hilton Philli. ■ 75062 #048-13-2005 **ORS** *012

GRASTY, Betty Chung. 701 TUSCAN STE 235 75039 #011-03-1998 L2001 **IM** *020 †20

GREENBERG, Mark S. 400 W LYNDON B JOHNSON FWY, STE 330 75063 #048-12-1985 L1986 **OSM ORS** *020 †40

GREGORY, David Kermit. 440 W LYNDON B JOHNSON FWY, STE 415 75063 #048-13-1980 L1980 **OPH** *020 †35

GRIFFIN, Kellie Marie. ■ 75061 #021-05-2003 L2007 **AN** *100

GROSS, Leonard. 1110 COTTONWOOD LN, STE L100 75038 #021-01-1969 L1984 **DR NM** *020 †80,28

GROSSMAN, Erik Robert. ■ 75061 #024-05-1998 L2001 **IM** *020 †20

GRUBE, Steven M. ■ 75038 #048-12-2003 L2006 **PDI** *012 †55

GUEVARA, Raul A. 701 TUSCAN, STE 280 75039 #748-02-1990 L2002 **N OPH** *071

GUINN, Latoya Charlette. ■ 75063 #048-02-2007 **PTH** *012

GULIZIA, James Martin. 8400 ESTERS BLVD STE 190 75063 #030-05-1994 L2006 **PTH OS** *020 †50

GUPTA, Paula A. ■ 75038 #048-12-2004 L2007 **DR** *012

GUPTA, Puneet Kumar. ■ 75038 #048-12-2004 L2004 **N** *012

GURUMURTHY, Manisha Balas. ■ 75063 #496-38-2001 L2006 **IM** *100 †20

GUZMAN, Hernando. ■ 75063 #264-04-1968 L1982 **FM** *020 ‡

HAAS, Derek Anthony. 7501 LAS COLINAS BLVD 75063 #017-20-1997 L2001 **OBG** *020

HADEN, James Russell. ■ 75063 #048-13-1998 L2000 **AI** *100 †20,03

HAN, Michelle M. 400 W INTERSTATE HWY 635, STE 250 75063 #048-04-1994 L1996 **PD** *020 †55

HANDEL, Maximo. 222 LAS COLINAS BLVD W, STAFF CARE INC 75039 #132-01-1956 L1974 **P CHP** *071

HANSON, Chad Michael. ■ 75063 #048-12-2004 L2006 **ORS** *012

HANSON, John Russell. 3501 N MACARTHUR BLVD, STE 350 75062 #056-06-1990 L1993 **OBG** *020

HAQUE, Anwar. ■ 75038 #166-03-2000 L2006 **FM** *020

HARRISON, Myron Crandall. 5959 LAS COLINAS BLVD, RM 3310 75039 #026-04-1974 L1995 **EM OM** *020 †16,70

HASSAN, Luann Kay. 4301 N MACARTHUR BLVD, STE 201 75038 #048-13-1992 L1993 **OBG** *020 †20

HAVEMANN, James Frederick. 400 W IH 635 FWY STE 210, NORTH TX HEALTHCARE ASSOCI 75063 #048-12-2001 L2004 **FM** *020 †18

HAYNES, Scotty Jack. ■ 75063 #047-06-2004 L2008 **DR** *012

HAYS, Lowell Bradford. 349 LAS COLINAS BLVD E 75039 #048-12-1992 L1993 **IM** *020 †20

HAZEN, Richard Ward. 2001 N MACARTHUR BLVD, STE 660 75061 #011-03-1988 L1989 **PCC** *020 †20

HEDA, Shashank Brijmohan. ■ 75063 #495-83-1990 **IM** *071

HEIDBRINK, Peter Jay. 2001 N MACARTHUR BLVD, STE 450 75061 #048-04-1973 L1974 **PUD CCM** *020 †20

HEIDENHOFER, Roland M. PO BOX 143333 75014 #041-13-1977 L1994 **GP EM** *020 †16

HELLER, Susan Holland. 2021 N MACARTHUR BLVD, MEDICAL & SURGICAL CLINIC 75061 #048-12-1990 L1992 **PD** *020 †55

HELMER, Richard Earle, IV. ■ 75063 #048-02-2000 L2004 **TS** *012 †85

HENDRICKS, William Andrew. 2105 W AIRPORT FWY 75062 #048-02-1957 L1957 **GP EM** *071 †85

HERBIG, Kathleen Suzanne. 75061 #048-12-2004 **PS** *012

HERNANDEZ, Antonio V. ■ 75063 #264-01-1956 L1962 **OBG** *020 †30

HERNANDEZ, Maria Consuelo. ■ 75063 #649-14-1990 L1996 **PD ADL** *030

HIJAZI, Bishr M. ■ 75038 #875-01-1994 L2001 **HS** *100 ‡

HOFFMAN, Steven A. 701 TUSCAN, STE 200 75039 #048-12-1982 L1983 **OBG** *020 †30

HOLLAND, Karen Dorothy. 2021 N MACARTHUR BLVD, MEDICAL & SURGICAL CLINIC 75061 #048-02-1973 L1973 **PD** *020 †55

HOLMES, Brian Joseph. 2001 N MCARTHR BLVD, STE 240 75061 #048-14-1993 L2000 **DR** *020 †80

HOLT, Jonathan Donoho. 207 MOSS HILL RD 75063 #048-02-2004 L2006 **EM** *100

HOMBAL, Shiril. ■ 75063 #495-72-1973 L1993 **PTH** *020 †50

HONIG, Kevin Michael. 400 W LBJ FWY STE 3 75063 #033-05-2002 L2008 **ORS** *012

HOUSE, John Michael. 7200 N HIGHWAY 161, STE 200 75039 #039-01-1983 L1988 **U** *020 †95

HSU, Shan-Shan Huang. 4770 REGENT BLVD, QUEST DIAGNOSTIC INC 75063 #385-01-1964 L1973 **PTH PCP** *071 †50

HUANG, Alfred C. 117 N MACARTHUR BLVD 75061 #048-12-1996 L1998 **FM** *020 †18 ‡

HUBER, Wolfgang Karl. ■ 75039 #407-23-1957 L1962 **PA P** *071

HUGGINS, Sam. 2001 N MACARTHUR BLVD, STE 205 75061 #048-12-1951 L1951 **OTO** *071 †45

HUGHES, Diane. 3626 N MACARTHUR BLVD #200 75062 #047-06-1997 L1998 **OBG** *020 †30

HUI, Mei Y. ■ 75061 #048-12-2005 **FP** *012

HURLEY, Jefferson B. 701 TUSCAN, STE 125 75039 #048-12-1992 L1993 **CRS** *020 †85,10

HURT, Walter Grear. 6750 N MACARTHUR BLVD, STE 151 75039 #047-05-1997 L2003 **ORS** *020 †40

HUTTON, William Louis, Jr. 1255 CORPORATE DR, 3RD FL 75038 #048-12-1966 L1973 **OPH** *071 †35

IBRAHIM, Tariq Musa. ■ 75062 #048-12-2006 **GS** *012

IRELAND, Jack Eaton. 2021 N MACARTHUR BLVD, MEDICAL & SURGICAL CLINIC 75061 #048-12-1964 L1964 **GP A** *020 †18

ISRAEL, Robert Warren, Jr. 2001 N MCARTHR BLVD, STE 500A 75061 #048-15-1980 L1980 **IM** *020 †20

IVERSEN, Brianna Leigh. ■ 75062 #048-14-2007 **EM** *100

JACOBSON, James Michael. 5525 N MACARTHUR BLVD, STE 850 75038 #018-03-1974 L1991 **END IM** *030 †20 ‡

JAEGER, Claire P. 7200 STATE HIGHWAY 161, STE 300 75039 #062-01-1985 L1997 **FM** *020 †18

JAIN, Vikas Chandra. 400 W LYNDON B JOHNSON FWY, STE 420 75063 #021-05-1996 L2002 **CD** *020 †20

JAISWAL, Sapna Jagdish. ■ 75062 #496-50-1999 L2004 **FM** *100 †18

JEWELL, Lee. 1901 N MACARTHUR BLVD 75061 #025-01-1962 L1968 **IM** *071

JHANDIYA, Faisal Q. 1425 GREENWAY DR, IPC- HOSPITALIST COMPANY 75038 #704-16-1983 L2002 **IM** *020 †20

JOHNSON, D Marina. 433 LAS COLINAS BLVD E 75039 #005-14-1978 L1985 **END IM** *020 †20

JOHNSTON, Louis C. 5100 N O CONNOR BLVD, SUITE200 75039 #048-12-1956 L1956 **IM GP** *071

JOHNSTON, Richard C. 349 LAS COLINAS BLVD E 75039 #048-15-1975 L1975 **IM** *020 †20

JONES, Bradley Scott. 400 W IH 635 FWY STE 100 75063 #048-12-1999 L2001 **IM** *020 †20

JONES, Jamira Truvillyn. ■ 75063 #025-07-2004 L2007 **EM** *100

JOSEPH, Asha. ■ 75063 #836-02-1998 L2008 **NEP** *012 †20

JOYNER, Edwin M, Jr. 1901 N MACARTHUR BLVD 75061 #001-02-1963 L1967 **IM** *020

KAMINSKI, Ken Joseph. 1050 LAKE CAROLYN PKWY, APT 3320 75039 #033-06-2006 **ORS** *012

KANDIMALA, Geetha Bhavani. ■ 75038 #495-50-2001 L2003 **CN** *012

KAPADIA, Lav Anupam. 400 W LYNDON B JOHNSON FWY, IRVING COPPELL EAR NOSE 75063 #028-46-1994 L1995 **OTO PDO** *020 †45

KAPIL, Kamna. 1110 COTTONWOOD LN, STE 100 75038 #065-09-1996 L1999 **FM** *020 †18

KARIMI, Prameela. ■ 75063 #495-58-1994 L2002 **NPM** *100 †55

KARJEKER, Mukhtiaar H. 6750 N MACARTHUR BLVD #210 75039 #836-02-1974 L1978 **FM IMG** *020 †18

KARSAN, Naznin. ■ 75062 #060-02-1997 **OTO FPS** *020

KARSAR, Naznin. ■ 75062 #060-02-1997 L2007 *100

KATZMAN, Steven M. 701 TUSCAN STE 110, TX DIGESTIVE DISEASE CONSU 75039 #649-14-1980 L1987 **GE IM** *020 †20

KAY, Joan P. 2021 N MACARTHUR BLVD, STE 150 75061 #048-12-1997 L2000 **PD** *020 †55

KAZEWYCH, Mark Alexander. 2120 N MACARTHUR BLVD #100, IRVING ORTHOPEDICS 75061 #038-44-1995 L2002 **ORS** *020 †40

KECHEJIAN, Sarkis John. 421 E AIRPORT FWY, STE 201 75062 #024-05-1963 L1970 **CD** *020 †20

KEDZIERSKI, Rafal Michal. ■ 75060 #048-12-2004 L2008 **DR** *012

KEGLOVITS, Michael Jos. 1901 N MACARTHUR BLVD 75061 #048-12-1954 L1954 **FM GP** *072

KEILSON, Gerald R. 2001 N MACARTHUR BLVD, STE 400 75061 #048-02-1953 L1953 **OBG** *020 †30

KELLEY, Jared Lee. 1915 W PARK DR, OF IRVING, P.A. 75061 #048-02-1978 L1978 **OBG** *020 †30

KELSALL, Peter John. 612 N STORY RD # 106107 75061 #919-03-1968 L1981 **FM OS** *020

KENNEDY, A Alexander John. ■ 75063 #035-03-2001 L2004 **EM** *020 †16

KERANS, Adrian R F F. 1451 W AIRPORT FWY STE 1 75062 #917-18-1975 L1978 **FM** *020 †18

KETHA, Sumana. 1901 W PARK DR 75061 #495-50-1991 L1999 **IM** *020 †20

KETHLEY, Jerold D. ■ 75061 #048-12-1950 L1950 **GS** *071

KHALIFAH, Anthony Paul. 1901 N MACARTHUR BLVD, BAYLOR IRVING HOSPITAL 75061 #047-05-2004 L2007 **IM** *100 †20

KHAN, Rabia Awan. 6750 N MACARTHUR BLVD, STE 100 75039 #704-09-1982 L1987 **N** *020 †75

KHAN, Tariq Nawaz. ■ 75061 #704-25-1999 L2007 **GS** *100 †85

KHATOON, Nazia. 1800 N BRITAIN RD 75061 #704-02-1997 L2007 **FM** *100 †18

KHATRI, Ismail A. ■ 75062 #704-02-1995 L2000 **N IM** *020 †75

KIELHORN, Alden Franz. 8400 ESTERS BLVD, STE 190 75063 #030-06-1975 L2004 **PTH** *020 †50

KIZILBASH, Ali M. 701 TUSCAN, STE 240 75039 #704-25-1990 L1996 **CD** *020 †20

KLEIN, Diane Fiorelli. 440 W INTERSTATE HWY 635, STE 355 75063 #048-13-1980 L1980 **OPH** *020

KNESEVICH, Maryann. 102 DECKER CT, STE 250 75062 #017-20-1981 L1990 **P** *020 †75

KOLLI, Shalini. ■ 75039 #495-65-1997 L2006 **IM** *020 †20

KORKMAS, Frederick Jos. 2023 W PARK DR 75061 #048-02-1953 L1953 **OBG OS** *020

KORKMAS, Maurice V. 2023 W PARK DR 75061 #048-02-1951 L1951 **GYN** *071 †30

KOSURI, Subba Raju. ■ 75063 #495-50-1984 L1998 **CD** *020 †20

KOTHA, Vani. ■ 75063 #495-21-1999 L2007 **END** *020

KREISBERG, Suzanne H. 4770 REGENT BLVD 75063 #048-15-1984 L1990 **PTH PCP** *020 †50

KRUM, Theodore J. 6750 N MACARTHUR BLVD, STE 309 75039 #048-02-1986 L1987 **OBG** *020 †30

KUDESIA, Sudhir Swarup. ■ 75063 #495-05-1971 **FM** *100

KUTLER, Mark Lawrence. 2001 N MACARTHUR BLVD 75061 #048-13-1980 L1980 **R** *020 †80

KWON, Bobby Young. ■ 75060 #048-12-2004 L2008 **AN** *012

LAI, Wen S. 6800 N MACARTHUR BLVD, LAS COLINAS MEDICAL CENTER 75039 #048-12-1994 L1995 **IM** *020 †20

LAKHANPAL, Sharad. 3200 N MACARTHUR BLVD, STE 104 75062 #495-05-1974 L1987 **RHU IM** *020 †20

LAM, Tukien Michael. ■ 75062 #016-02-1993 L1994 **IM** *071 †20

LARRISON, Deborah Marlain. ■ 75039 #021-06-2005 **OTO** *012

LAURIAT, Sandra Marie. 1625 N STORY RD, STE 140 75061 #048-12-1992 L1998 **NEP IM** *020 †20

LE, Sy Q. 7501 LAS COLINAS BLVD, # 200A 75063 #048-02-1988 L1989 **REN OBG** *020 †30

LEDIG, Erik Otto. ■ 75063 #048-02-2007 **EM** *012

LEE, Ethan. ■ 75063 #048-12-1997 *100

LEE, James S. 1335 N BELT LINE RD, STE 13 75061 #583-10-1966 L1984 **GP PTH** *020

LEE, Laura Anne. ■ 75063 #048-12-1996 *100

LEE, Michael Robert. ■ 75063 #021-05-2005 L2007 **OTO** *020

LEE, Sandy L. 1901 N MACARTHUR BLVD 75061 #021-01-1997 L2001 **IM** *020 †20

LEE, Stacy Lane. ■ 75063 #021-05-2006 **DR** *012

LEE, Won Joon. 811 N O CONNOR RD 75061 #583-01-1972 L1978 **GP** *020

LEVY, Richard Simon. 6750 N MACARTHUR BLVD, STE 151 75039 #021-01-1990 L1996 **ORS** *020 †40

LEWIS, Howard. 7415 LAS COLINAS BLVD 75063 #011-04-1980 L2006 **RO** *020 †80

LEWIS, Jeremy Jason. ■ 75063 #038-45-2006 **NS** *012

LI, Lucy. 2015 W PARK DR 75061 #024-07-1999 L2003 **D** *020 †15

LIANG, Alexander Shihyun. 1625 N STORY RD, STE 140 75061 #048-12-1997 L1999 **NEP IM** *020 †20

LIEBMAN, Jacob. 421 E AIRPORT FWY, P O BOX 120964 75062 #869-01-1965 L1980 **PTH** *020 †50

LIESMANN, Jean Elizabeth. 5001 STATESMAN DR 75063 #019-02-1974 L1977 **ON IM** *020 †20

LINGVAY, Ildiko. ■ 75063 #781-01-1998 L2002 **END** *100 †20

LITZ, Craig Edward. 6800 N MACARTHUR BLVD 75039 #051-04-1984 L1997 **PTH HMP** *020 †50

LIVINGSTON, Jeff M. 3501 N MACARTHUR BLVD, STE 500 75062 #048-12-1999 L2002 **OBG** *020 †30

LLOYD, Robert Ashley. ■ 75038 #056-05-1964 L1971 **FM MDM** *071 †18

LO, David Chihang. 2001 N MACARTHUR BLVD, BAYLOR UNIVERSITY MEDICAL 75061 #048-12-2002 L2006 **FM** *020 †60

LOCKWOOD, Richard Larry. 3626 N MACARTHUR BLVD 75062 #048-04-1983 L1984 **AN** *075

LOGAN, Adina Manuela. 701 TUSCAN, STE 145 75039 #781-01-1991 L1998 **IM** *020 †20

LUJAN, Giovanni Mario. 8400 ESTERS BLVD, STE 190 75063 #341-01-1993 L2004 **PTH** *020

LUNT, Peter Geo. ■ 75038 #869-04-1982 L1986 **AN** *020 †20,05

MACARTHUR, John Ward. ■ 75063 #035-01-2008 L2008 *012

MACKANJEE, Harshavadan R. ■ 75038 #836-05-1976 **NPM** *020

MAHALDAR, Antra. ■ 75039 #496-17-1998 L2005 **HO** *012 †20

MAHAN, Joel Brennan. 1845 E NORTHGATE DR, BOX 529 75062 #048-13-2007 **FP** *012

MAHATMA, Mahendra. 4301 N MACARTHUR BLVD, STE 107 75038 #917-18-1981 L1990 **GE PUD** *020 †20

MAJERES, Kevin Daryl. 320 DECKER DR 75062 #048-12-2001 L2003 **P** *020 †75

MALLET, Maryrita Kaiser. 3021 GATEWAY DR, STE 290 75063 #048-16-1992 L1993 **P** *020 †75

MALY, Ronald Francis. ■ 75061 #030-06-1962 L1968 **GP** *020 †70

MANICKAM, Sathya. ■ 75061 #495-94-1993 *100

MANN, Simardeep Kaur. ■ 75038 #038-44-2005 L2007 **P** *012

MANNING, Melvin Ray, Jr. 6750 N MACARTHUR BLVD, STE 151 75039 #005-18-1993 L1995 **PM** *020 †60

MANNING, Tessa Leigh. ■ 75060 #048-12-2008 *012

MARAMREDDY, Haritha. ■ 75063 #495-70-1995 L2005 **CHP** *020 †75 ‡

MARKER, Allison Elizabeth. ■ 75038 #001-02-2004 **OBG** *012

MARKER, Bradley Tyler. ■ 75038 #001-02-2004 **GS** *012

MARROQUIN, Patricia. 1110 COTTONWOOD LN, STE 200 75038 #048-02-2000 L2003 **OBG** *020 †30

MARSHALL, Sarah E. ■ 75060 #048-14-2006 **PD** *012

MARSHALL, William W. ■ 75061 #048-12-1993 *100

MARTIN, Lisa Pehosh. 2001 N MACARTHUR BLVD, STE 450 75061 #004-01-1998 L2004 **FM** *020 †18

MASKAL, Steven Leslie. 7200 N HIGHWAY 161, STE 300 75039 #048-12-1991 L2001 **GS** *020 †85

MASON, Camille Lillian. 2001 N MACARTHUR BLVD, STE 655 75061 #049-01-1999 L2007 **D DS** *100 †15 ‡

MASON, Jeffrey Cole. 2021 N MACARTHUR BLVD #325, MEDICAL & SURGICAL CLINIC 75061 #016-11-1986 L1989 **FM** *020 †18

MATHEW, Abraham T. ■ 75060 #495-37-1990 **CCP** *100

MATIN, Sina. 2001 N MACARTHUR BLVD, STE 255 75061 #051-04-1993 L2000 **GS** *020 †85

MATTHEWS, Edwin Curtis. 349 LAS COLINAS BLVD E, STE A 75039 #035-03-1990 L1998 **IM** *020 †20

MAXEY, John Anthony. 701 TUSCAN STE 205 75039 #654-01-1985 L1992 **OBG** *020 †30

MAXEY, Samuel Alvin. ■ 75063 #021-05-1963 L1987 **PTH** *071 †50

MC CABE, Jerome Francis. 8411 STERLING ST 75063 #038-41-1994 L2006 **DR** *020 †80

MC COLM, Vincent Nguyen. 6750 N MACARTHUR BLVD, STE 150 75039 #048-12-2002 L2006 **MPD** *020 †20,55

MC NALLY, Rand A. ■ 75061 #048-12-1988 *100

MENDEZ, Juan Manuel, Jr. 7750 N MACARTHUR BLVD, STE 120 PMB 345 75063 #005-15-1977 L1979 **IM OM** *020 †20,70

MEYER, Carissa Shea. 6750 N MACARTHUR BLVD #150 75039 #048-12-2000 L2004 **PD** *020 †55 ‡

MEYERSON, Lawrence B. 2021 N MACARTHUR BLVD, STE 300 75061 #038-40-1965 L1971 **D DS** *020 †15

MILLER, Alan Newton. ■ 75061 #048-12-1954 L1954 **PD** *071 †55

MITTAL, Vineeta Sitaram. ■ 75063 #496-38-1992 L2003 **PD** *100 †55

MOGHE, Chandrakant B. ■ 75062 #495-45-1987 L1990 **AN** *100

MOIKEHA, David H. 6800 N MACARTHUR BLVD 75039 #014-01-1993 L2004 **EM** *020 †16

MOLINA, Hector Oscar. 1901 W IRVING BLVD 75061 #048-12-1996 L1997 **EM** *020

MORGAN, Clark Robert. ■ 75060 #048-12-2006 **AN** *012

MORGAN, Galon Cory. ■ 75039 #048-12-2005 **DR** *012

MULLER, Jennifer Lynn. ■ 75063 #048-02-2007 **OBG** *012

MULLINS, James Byron, II. 7449 LAS COLINAS BLVD, STE 100 75063 #004-01-1989 L1999 **OTO FPS** *020 †45

MUNSHI, Nikhil Vilas. ■ 75062 #035-01-2003 L2006 **CD** *012

MURPHY, Thomas Patrick. 3950 N STORY RD, # 314B 75038 #048-12-1954 L1954 **PD** *020 †55

MURTHY, Jyoti S.. 3204 N MACARTHUR BLVD, SUITE-A 75062 #495-73-1989 L2004 **PD** *020 †55

MYERS, John H. ■ 75063 #048-15-1991 L1994 **EM** *020 †16

MYLES, Angela M. 1901 N MACARTHUR BLVD 75061 #004-01-1999 L2003 **OBG** *020

NACHIMSON, Harold Irwin. ■ 75063 #048-12-1963 L1963 **FM** *071 †18

NARASIMHAN, Gomathy. ■ 75038 #495-59-1996 *100

NARCISSE, Zania Bailey. ■ 75062 #047-07-2005 L2005 **PM** *012

NATOUR, Nahille I. 2021 N MACARTHUR BLVD, STE 500 75061 #048-16-2001 L2004 **OBG** *020 †30

NENE, Sudhanshu Yeshwant. ■ 75063 #496-24-1989 **P** *100

NERO, Alecia C. ■ 75063 #048-12-2004 L2004 **MPD** *012

NGUYEN, Anh Tat. ■ 75062 #048-16-2007 **GS** *012

NGUYEN, Casey K. 1420 N MACARTHUR BLVD 75061 #048-12-2001 L2003 **FM** *020 †18

NGUYEN, Charles M. ■ 75060 #048-12-2007 **IM** *012

NGUYEN, Huong G. ■ 75039 #048-16-2007 **AN** *012

NGUYEN, Nam Phong. 7415 LAS COLINAS BLVD, STE 100 75063 #165-03-1983 L1999 **RO IM** *020 †20,80

NGUYEN, Vananh T. 5001 STATESMAN DR, STAFF CARE INC 75063 #056-06-1998 L2001 **DR** *020 †80

NOH, Jung Ja. 2001 N MACARTHUR BLVD, STE 340 75061 #583-01-1968 L1974 **AI** *020 †55,03

NOLES, John Gray. 2121 CREEKSIDE CIR S 75063 #021-06-1999 L2001 **AN** *020 †05

OBERLIN, Donald Leigh. ■ 75038 #048-12-1957 L1957 **R** *071

OEI, Ho-Bing Patrick. ■ 75063 #018-03-2003 L2005 **RHU** *012 †20

OKHAI, M Farouk. ■ 75038 #919-02-1977 L1981 **OBG** *020 †30

OKORONKWO, C. 1711 W IRVING BLVD, STE 151 75061 #690-04-1988 L1997 **IM** *020 †20

O'NEIL, Kevin Patrick. 2001 N MACARTHUR BLVD #540 75061 #035-03-1993 L1997 **OBG** *020 †30

ORLINO, Angela Mae. ■ 75014 #038-40-1998 L2005 **MPD** *020 †20,55

OROURKE, Terence Leonard. ■ 75039 #041-02-1990 L1993 **FM** *020 †18

OVERBECK, John Douglas. 701 TUSCAN, STE 240 75039 #048-12-1984 L1986 **CD IM** *020 †20

PADDA, Manmeet Singh. ■ 75063 #495-29-1996 L2003 **GE** *100

PAK, Yong Tae. 2120 N MACARTHUR BLVD 75061 #039-01-2001 L2005 **PM** *100 †60

PANDOVE, Sandeep. ■ 75060 #495-29-1990 L2002 **IM** *020 †20

PANGTAY, Dennis. 2021 N MACARTHUR BLVD, MEDICAL & SURGICAL CLINIC 75061 #649-19-1981 L1985 **FM** *071 †18

PARDEN, Stephen Roy. 5001 STATESMAN DR, STAFF CARE INC 75063 #001-06-1986 L1987 **GS TS** *020 †85

PARKER, Ralph R. 701 TUSCAN STE 225 75039 #048-12-1990 L1991 **GS VS** *020 †85

PATEL, Jigar Bhadresh. 7942 N GLEN DR # 30 75063 #001-02-2004 L2006 **EM** *100

PATEL, Milan Manu. 5001 STATESMAN DR 75063 #017-20-1999 L2004 **P** *100

PATEL, Namrata Mahendra. ■ 75039 #048-15-2007 **OBG** *012

PATEL, Shakuntala M. 1508 CAMINO LAGO, 1508 CAMINOLAGO,IRVING,TX7 75039 #495-22-1968 L1981 **IM** *020 †20

PATTISAPU, Ramakrishna V. 2001 N MACARTHUR BLVD # 20 75061 #048-13-1980 L1986 **GS** *020 †85

PAYNE, Michael Stephen, Jr. 2001 N MACARTHUR BLVD, STE 630 75061 #016-01-1999 L2004 **RO** *020 ‡

PENCE, Ludlow Mays. ■ 75061 #048-04-1941 L1941 **N** *071 †75

PENNICK, Harriet O Graves. 3501 N MACARTHUR BLVD, STE 100 75062 #041-13-1977 L1980 **PD** *020 †55

PENTA, Mrudula. ■ 75063 #005-11-2006 L2006 **OTO** *012

PEREZ, Maria Carmina C. 1625 N STORY RD, STE 140 75061 #748-02-1993 L2001 **NEP** *020 †20

PEVETO, Shannon Wincy. 701 TUSCAN STE 285, PEDIATRIC CENTER OF LAS CO 75039 #048-12-2000 L2002 **PD** *020 †55

PHAM, Henri T. 6750 N MACARTHUR BLVD, MEDICAL & SURGICAL CLINIC 75039 #048-04-1991 L1997 **U** *020 †95

PHAM, Hien Q. 6750 N MACARTHUR BLVD, STE 250 75039 #048-02-1995 L1996 **FM** *020 †18

PHILIPS, Kay Lynn. 2021 N MACARTHUR BLVD #520, INTERNAL MEDICINE ASSOC OF 75061 #047-06-1998 L2006 **IM** *020 †20

PHILLIPS, Leslie A. 2001 N MACARTHUR BLVD #540 75061 #048-12-1997 L1998 **OBG** *020 †30

PHILLIPS, Rita Cathy. 1425 GREENWAY DR, STE 480 75038 #041-13-1982 L1983 **IM** *020 †20

PHUONG, Viet. ■ 75038 #048-12-2008 *012

PILLAI, Saji. 701 TUSCAN STE 265 75039 #496-20-1999 L2005 **IM** *020 †20

PITTMAN, Michael Ray. 9400 N MACARTHUR BLVD, STE 124-606 75063 #048-12-1984 L1985 **P** *040 †75

POBEE, Kojo Abaka. 7750 N MACARTHUR BLVD, STE 120-253 75063 #412-01-1988 L1999 **IM IMG** *020 †20

POSEY, Rebecca Z. 1901 N MACARTHUR BLVD 75061 #048-13-1985 L1989 **EM** *020 †16

POSVAR, Brandon Heath. ■ 75060 #048-14-2006 **OPH** *012

POUNDS, Merle Roland. 2105 W AIRPORT FWY, STE 109 75062 #048-12-1965 L1967 **GS** *071

POWELL, Charles Lee. 1110 COTTONWOOD LN, HEALTHCARE ASSOCIATES OF I 75038 #021-06-1998 L2005 **FM** *020 †18

PROCHERA, Charles Walter. 6750 N MACARTHUR BLVD, STE 206D 75039 #016-11-1977 L1980 **PUD** *020 †20

RADUAZO, Phillip Anthony. ■ 75063 #025-07-2005 L2007 **DR** *012

RAIN, Thomas Edwin. 2001 N MACARTHUR BLVD, STE 255 75061 #048-12-1973 L1978 **GS** *020 †85

RAKHEJA, Dinesh. ■ 75039 #495-36-1993 L2006 **PP** *100 †50

RAMAKRISHNAN, Nagarajan. ■ 75063 #495-16-1989 L1995 **CCM SME** *020 †20

RAMEY, Helen Jo Toma. 2021 N MACARTHUR BLVD, MEDICAL & SURGICAL CLINIC 75061 #039-01-1960 L1967 **DR PDR** *020 †80

RAMIREZ, Albert. ■ 75039 #048-12-2002 L2006 **PM** *020

RAMOS, Maria Angelica. ■ 75062 #042-01-1997 L2004 **END IM** *020 †20

RAMOS, Shelley Bruce. 701 TUSCAN, STE 200 75039 #048-15-1994 L1997 **OBG** *020 †30

RAROQUE, Henry G, Jr. 701 TUSCAN STE 280 75039 #748-02-1982 L1989 **N** *020 †75

RATHKAMP, Quynh Tiem-Kim. 6750 N MACARTHUR BLVD, STE 150 75039 #021-01-1995 L1999 **MPD** *020 †20,55

RAVAL, Gargi Dinker. ■ 75063 #010-01-1999 L2006 **PM** *020 †60

REDDICK, Sybil Rochelle. 2300 VALLEY VIEW LN, STE 870 75062 #018-03-1991 L1995 **PM** *020

REHMAAN, Munaimaa. ■ 75063 #495-77-2004 **IM** *012

REID, Roy Moran, Jr. ■ 75061 #048-12-1965 L1966 **GS** *020 †85

RIVERA, Julio Robert. 2001 N MACARTHUR BLVD, STE 255 75061 #048-15-1996 L2001 **GS** *020 †85

ROBERTS, R Mills. 2120 N MACARTHUR BLVD, STE 100 75061 #048-02-1990 L1991 **ORS OSM** *020 †40

ROBIOU, Cristian Ivan. 8400 ESTERS BLVD STE 19 75063 #308-02-1987 L2004 **ATP** *020 †50

ROCHON, Roy B. 6750 N MACARTHUR BLVD, MEDICAL & SURGICAL CLINIC 75039 #047-07-1982 L1989 **GS** *020 †85

RODRIGUEZ-FRIAS, Edmundo. ■ 75039 #737-06-2002 **IMG** *012 †20

ROGERS, Nicholas Alan. ■ 75038 #017-20-2005 **IM** *012

ROMANELLI, Enid Samara. 1141 KINWEST PKWY, STE 100 75063 #048-02-1996 L2000 **FM IM** *020 †20,18

ROMERO, Robert. ■ 75062 #649-01-1957 L1960 **AN** *071

ROOT, Walter Wade. ■ 75063 #005-18-2005 L2007 **P** *012

ROTHKOPF, Michael. 701 TUSCAN, STE 240 75039 #008-01-1972 L1977 **CD IM** *020 †20

ROYER, Thomas Clayton. 6363 N HIGHWAY 161 75038 #041-01-1967 L1968 **EM GS** *030 †85

RUBIN, Allen W. 701 TUSCAN STE 110, TX DIGESTIVE DISEASE CONSU 75039 #041-02-1967 L1974 **GE IM** *020 †20

RUTHERFORD, Stephanie M. 6750 N MACARTHUR BLVD, ST 150 75039 #048-12-1999 L2002 **PD** *020 †55

SAFAVI, Shahriar Shahri. 2001 N MACARTHUR BLVD, STE 650 75061 #047-06-1970 L1977 **GE IM** *020 †20

SAKOVICH, Stephen Peter. 3501 N MACARTHUR BLVD, BDLG.500 75062 #048-15-1982 L1983 **OBG** *020 †30

SAKURAI, Yoshio. ■ 75062 #572-15-1987 **CCP** *100

SALAZAR, Adrian. ■ 75039 #048-12-2005 **IM** *012

SAMPSON, Joann Marcella. ■ 75014 #010-03-1997 L2004 **PD** *020 †55

SAMUEL, Diana Tressa. ■ 75039 #305-01-2001 **CHP** *012

SANDERS, Steven B. 2120 N MACARTHUR BLVD, STE 100 75061 #048-15-1990 L1991 **ORS OAR** *020 †20

SARVA, Rajendra. ■ 75038 #495-50-1974 L1983 **GE** *020 †20

SAUNDERS, Timothy Charles. ■ 75063 #016-42-2006 L2008 **EM** *012

SAVCENKO, Michal. 1110 COTTONWOOD LN, STE 105 75038 #286-03-1987 L2004 **TS VS** *020 †85,90

SCANKS, Keira Nicole. ■ 75039 #048-02-2007 **IM** *012

SCHAEFER, Jason Ryan. ■ 75063 #048-12-2007 **EM** *012

SCHILLING, John F, Jr. ■ 75061 #048-12-1966 L1966 **IM** *071 †20

SCHLEIER, Sue E. 701 TUSCAN, STE 285 75039 #048-12-1988 L1989 **PD** *020 †55

SCHORN, Larry Wayne. 1110 COTTONWOOD LN, STE 210 75038 #048-12-1973 L1973 **TS** *020 †85,90

SCHOTT, Thomas Michael. 400 W LBJ FWY STE 330 75063 #023-07-1988 L1995 **ORS OSM** *020 †40

SEYFETDINOVA, Natalya. 2021 N MACARTHUR BLVD, MEDICAL & SURGICAL CLINIC 75061 #048-12-2002 L2005 **PD** *020 †55

SHAH, Mahasukhlal H. 5001 STATESMAN DR 75063 #495-17-1963 L1976 **N** *072 †75

SHAH, Neela Gada. 2021 N MACARTHUR BLVD, STE 520 75061 #048-14-2003 L2005 **IM** *020 †20

SHAH, Nirav Jayprakash. ■ 75039 #005-06-2007 *012

SHAH, Zafar Ali. 1901 N MACARTHUR BLVD 75061 #495-03-1960 L1977 **TS OS** *071 †85

SHARIF, Folasade Adenike. 4026 N STORY RD # 73 75038 #047-05-2001 L2004 **PD** *100 †55

SHARMA, Meenu. 5001 STATESMAN DR 75063 #495-90-1991 L2001 **IM** *100 †20

SHARMA, Richa. ■ 75063 #913-48-1995 L2004 **IM** *012

SHELTON, Christopher M. 2021 N MACARTHUR BLVD, STE 150 75061 #048-15-1995 L1996 **FM** *020 †18

SHELTON, Gregory Scott. ■ 75063 #048-12-2006 **OBG** *012

SHILLING, Steven L. 1110 COTTONWOOD LN, STE 105 75038 #048-12-1987 L1988 **CD** *040 †20

SHIRVANI, Ali R. 7200 STATE HWY 161, STE 200 75039 #048-04-1993 L1995 **U** *020 †95

SHIVNANI, Anand Thanwar. 2001 N MACARTHUR BLVD, STE 630 75061 #016-06-2001 L2006 **RO** *020 †80

SHLIPAK, Louis. 1901 N MACARTHUR BLVD 75061 #048-02-1956 L1956 **IM** *020 †20

SHUPE, James Grant. 9400 N MACARTHUR BLVD, STE 124-606 75063 #049-01-1988 L1989 **PFP P** *020 †75

SILAS, Tanisha Elizabeth. ■ 75062 #005-19-2006 **OBG** *012

SINGH, Sandeep. 1425 GREENWAY DR 75038 #495-90-1998 L2005 **NEP** *012 †20

SINGHAL, Anuradha Vijay. 8400 ESTERS BLVD 75063 #495-19-1994 L2005 **PTH** *100 †50

SINGHANIA, Neil Abe. ■ 75039 #048-04-2002 L2007 **AI** *020 †20,03

SMITH, Shawna Denise. ■ 75038 #041-09-1988 L2002 **IM** *020 †20

SMITH, Trisha E. 400 W IH 635 FWY STE 210, NORTH TEXAS HEALTH CARE AS 75063 #048-13-1996 L1998 **FM** *020 †18 ‡

SNELLINGS, Mary Bielecki. 909 LAKE CAROLYN PKWY, STE 220 75039 #048-02-1989 L1990 **IM** *020 †20

SOHN, Eunmee. 1333 CORPORATE DR, STE 200 75038 #583-08-1983 L1988 **P** *020 †75

SONAWALA, Rinarani Sunil. ■ 75062 #496-38-2000 L2005 **PG** *020 †55

SONES, Laura J. ■ 75062 #048-02-2008 *012

SORENSEN, Kathleen Ann. ■ 75062 #017-20-2002 L2007 **RNR** *012 †80

SPENGLER, Adam L. ■ 75063 #048-14-2007 *012

STADLER, Ronney Francis. 701 TUSCAN, STE 125 75039 #048-04-1997 L2000 **CRS GS** *020 †85,10

STANTON, Elbert Harvey. ■ 75060 #048-12-1956 L1956 **GP** *075

STARNES, Willis Leslie. 3204 N MACARTHUR BLVD 75062 #048-02-1981 L1981 **PD** *020 †55

STAUD, Jennifer L. 701 TUSCAN STE 20 75039 #048-15-2000 L2005 **OBG** *100

STEWART, Michael Lee. 2001 N MACARTHUR BLVD #240 75061 #048-02-1969 L1969 **DR** *020 †80

STROUT, Bradley Cameron. ■ 75063 #005-19-1999 L2004 **NR** *100 †80 ‡

SU, Charles Y. 1901 N MACARTHUR BLVD 75061 #048-14-1991 L1993 **EM IM** *020 †20,16

SUEZ, Daniel. 1115 KINWEST PKWY STE 100 75063 #396-35-1977 L1986 **AI PD** *020 †03,55

SUHLER, Richard J. 2001 N MACARTHUR BLVD, STE 240 75061 #048-12-1989 L1990 **RNR** *020 †80

SUNDERLAND, Margaret C. 2001 N MACARTHUR BLVD, STE 630 75061 #040-02-1982 L1988 **ON HEM** *020 †20

SUTTLE, Karen S T. 2021 N MACARTHUR BLVD, STE 115 75061 #836-02-1984 L1998 **FM** *020 †18

SWANSON, Philip Harold. 2001 N MACARTHUR BLVD 75061 #026-04-1980 L1984 **GS VS** *020 †85

SYED, Samaha. 4713 N O CONNOR RD 75062 #704-06-2000 L2006 **IM** *020 †20

SZUSZKIEWICZ, Magdalena M. ■ 75063 #023-01-2000 L2005 **END** *012 †20

TAYLOR, Judy Wilcox. 1440 N MACARTHUR BLVD, STE 103 75061 #048-02-1983 L1983 **GYN** *020 †30

TAYLOR, Marcia L. ■ 75063 #048-12-2005 **OBG** *012

TAYLOR, Wm Nathaniel, Jr. ■ 75062 #011-02-1981 L1982 **PM** *020

TCHETGEN, Marieblanc Nana. 7200 STATE HWY 161, STE 200 75039 #023-07-1993 L2002 **U** *020 †95

TELLA, Prabhav Koti Hanum. ■ 75063 #495-11-1999 L2007 **APM** *020 †20

THEILEN, Frank W. 400 W LBJ FWY, IRVING COPPELL EAR NOSE 75063 #048-02-1982 L1983 **OTO A** *020 †45

THEILEN, George B, III. 1302 LANE ST STE 700 75061 #048-12-1980 L1980 **OBG** *020 †30

THOMASON, Timothy Sean. 2021 N MACARTHUR BLVD, STE 225 75061 #048-12-2002 L2005 **OTO** *020

TIMON, Stephen Jay. 400 W LBJ FWY, STE 330 75063 #021-01-1997 L2003 **OSS** *020 †40

TISHERMAN, Darryl Barton. 2021 N MACARTHUR BLVD, BLVD, #150 75061 #041-02-1964 L1995 **FM** *020 †18 ‡

TOLEDO ACEVEDO, Zulma I. ■ 75039 #042-02-2000 L2007 **PD** *020

TORBIAK, Carl William. ■ 75038 #062-01-1990 L1996 **DR** *020 †80

TORRES, Carlos Manuel. 8400 ESTERS BLVD STE 190, CARIS PATHOLOGY 75063 #649-52-1989 L1998 **ATP** *020 †50

TRAN, Maryanne Thu. ■ 75039 #028-46-2005 **DR** *012

TRAN, Trung D. 7200 STATE HWY 161, STE 100 75039 #048-12-1993 L1994 **PD** *020 †55

TRAPASSO, Robert Louis. 8400 ESTERS BLVD STE 190 75063 #035-12-1976 L2004 **PTH** *020 †50

TREAT, Kristina Spakovsky. ■ 75063 #048-12-2003 L2007 **PTH** *100 †50

TRIMBLE, George Alan. 391 LAS COLINAS BLVD E, STE 130-718 75039 #048-02-1976 L1976 **P** *020

TSAI, Ray. ■ 75039 #016-06-2002 L2008 **PD** *020 †55

TSAY, Bing Shubing. 400 W LBJ FWY STE 330, ALLSTAR ORTHOPEDICS 75063 #048-04-1992 L2001 **ORS** *020 †40

TYLOCK, Gary Richard. 3100 N MACARTHUR BLVD 75062 #038-40-1980 L1982 **OPH** *020 †35

TYPHAIR, Sara L. 1425 GREENWAY DR, STE 480 75038 #048-15-1999 L2001 **FM** *020 †18

UDDIN, Fatema Sultana. ■ 75063 #048-12-2006 **IM** *012

UPDAHYAY, Sujata Anoop. ■ 75063 #495-49-1989 L1999 **IM** *020 †20

UPPALAPATI, Padhavathy. 701 TUSCAN, STE 240 75039 #495-70-1990 L2000 **CD** *020 †20

VAJJA, Manohar Prasad. ■ 75063 #495-11-2000 L2007 **PM** *020 †20

VALDEZ, Cristina V. 3501 N MACARTHUR BLVD, STE 400 75062 #649-14-1978 L1995 **FM** *020 †18 ‡

VALLERA, Raymond Anthony. 701 TUSCAN STE 110, TX DIGESTIVE DISEASE CONSU 75039 #038-45-1990 L1996 **GE** *020 †20

VALLIANI, Farida. ■ 75063 #704-16-1986 L1995 **IM** *020 †20

VAN DUYNE, Charles Pearce. 440 W LBJ FWY, STE 455B 75063 #035-03-1977 L1986 **OBG** *020 †30

VAN WRIGHT, Aaron, III. ■ 75063 #004-01-1992 L1997 **P** *020 †75

VASANI, Sugam Bipinchandr. ■ 75038 #496-59-2001 L2005 **GS** *100

VATTAM, Sreenadha Reddy. ■ 75039 #495-62-1993 L2005 **PM** *100 †60

VAUGHAN, James W. ■ 75063 #048-12-2007 L2007 **PTH** *012

VEGA, Damaris. ■ 75063 #042-02-2002 L2005 **END** *020 †20

VELA, Ricardo. ■ 75062 #048-02-2003 L2007 **FM** *020

VENTIMIGLIA, Joseph Byron. 909 LAKE CAROLYN PKWY, STE 220 75039 #036-07-1993 L1996 **FM** *020 †18

VIKTORIN, Gina. 6750 N MACARTHUR BLVD, STE 150 75039 #048-12-1996 L1999 **PD** *020 †55

VILLALBA, Veronica. 6750 N MACARTHUR BLVD, STE 207 75039 #048-02-1998 L2002 **OBG** *020 †30

VINSON, David W. 121 N MACARTHUR BLVD 75061 #048-04-1981 L1981 **ADL EM** *020 †18,16

VOWELL, Billy Sam. ■ 75062 #048-12-1959 L1959 **FM** *071 †18

WAGUESPACK, Keith Alan. 7200 STATE HWY 161, STE 200 75039 #048-12-1999 L2003 **U** *020 †95

WALDRON, Michael James. 6800 N MACARTHUR BLVD 75039 #048-12-1973 L1973 **PTH CLP** *020 †50

WALKER, Geoffrey Scott. 1625 N STORY RD, STE 140 75061 #917-05-1972 L1980 **NEP IM** *020

WARMINSKI, Johnathan D. ■ 75060 #048-12-2008 *012

WATSON, Angela Michele. ■ 75060 #048-02-2004 **OBG** *012

WEBSTER, Frank Craig. 8710 FREEPORT PKWY, STE 200 75063 #048-12-1988 L1989 **P** *020 †75

WEISBERG, Robert J. 2001 N MACARTHUR BLVD, STE 630 75061 #016-42-1969 L1976 **ON HEM** *020 †20

WEIX, Patrick Michael. 7429 LAS COLINAS BLVD, STE 101 75063 #048-12-1997 L1998 **OBG** *020 †30

WELCH, Babu Guai. ■ 75014 #010-03-1997 L2005 **RNR** *020

WELTER, Kimberly Rose. ■ 75063 #004-01-2004 L2007 **PTH** *100

WESTKAEMPER, John Gerard. 2120 N MACARTHUR BLVD, STE 100 75061 #041-01-1990 L1991 **HS** *020 †40

WHETSTONE, Michael Ricci. 7433 LAS COLINAS BLVD, STE 100 75063 #048-15-1983 L1983 **PS GS** *020 †65

WHITAKER, Robert Roy. 2001 N MACARTHUR BLVD, STE 425 75061 #016-11-1972 L1974 **OPH** *020 †35

WHITAKER, Roy, Jr. 2001 N MACARTHUR BLVD, MEDICAL & SURGICAL CLINIC 75061 #036-01-1981 L1986 **OPH** *020 †35

WHITE, Cheryl Ann. 2001 N MACARTHUR BLVD, STE 320 75061 #024-01-1997 L2003 **PS** *020

WILKINS, Bernard A, Jr. ■ 75063 #047-07-1970 L1979 **ORS** *020

WILKOFSKY, Steven Ira. 701 TUSCAN STE 110 75039 #035-08-1976 L1978 **GE IM** *020 †20

WILLIAMS, Neil Paul. 400 W LBJ FWY, IRVING COPPELL EAR NOSE 75063 #039-01-1987 L1988 **OTO HNS** *020 †20

WILLIAMS, Tammi M. 2021 N MACARTHUR BLVD, MEDICAL & SURGICAL CLINIC 75061 #048-13-1998 L2001 **PD** *020 †55

WIRTH, Nancy Ellen. 1125 EXECUTIVE CIR 75038 #025-01-1986 L1987 **PM P** *020 †60

WITT, Michael P. 1901 N MACARTHUR BLVD, INPATIENT CARE UNIT 75061 #048-12-1998 L2000 **IM** *020 †20

WOHL, Eric L. 2001 N MACARTHUR BLVD #450, ERIC L. WOHL, MD 75061 #048-13-1989 L1990 **IM** *020 †20

WOLLENMAN, John David. 2001 N MACARTHUR BLVD, STE 540 75061 #048-12-1974 L1974 **OBG** *020 †30

WON, Douglas Sung. 2120 N MACARTHUR BLVD 75061 #048-12-1998 L2004 **OSS** *020

WOO, Juan Antonio. ■ 75063 #048-12-2008 *012

WORNER, David E. 2021 N MACARTHUR BLVD, MEDICAL & SURGICAL CLINIC 75061 #048-15-1996 L1999 **FM** *020 †18

WYRICK, Christine Clark. ■ 75039 #038-41-2001 L2007 **CCA** *012

YALAMANCHILI, Kanthi. ■ 75039 #048-16-2001 L2004 **GE** *012

YANG, Kenneth J. 1901 N MACARTHUR BLVD 75061 #048-12-1999 L2003 **GE** *012 †20

YANG, Qinghua. 8400 ESTERS BLVD STE 19, PATHOLOGY PARTNERS 75063 #243-29-1983 L2003 **PTH** *020 †50

YEPES, Armando. 1110 COTTONWOOD LN, STE 105 75038 #264-10-1992 L2004 **CD IC** *020 †20

YOUNG, John David, Jr. 2001 N MACARTHUR BLVD, STE 500A 75061 #051-01-1980 L1981 **IM** *020 †20

ZAHN, Jennifer Ann. ■ 75039 #021-05-2005 **PM** *012

ZAVALETA, John Jos. 3501 N MACARTHUR BLVD, STE 350 75062 #048-12-1981 L1981 **OBG** *020 †30

ITASCA — HILL

WILLIS, Kathryn W. ■ 76055 #048-12-1951 L1951 **PD OS** *072 †55

WINDMILLER, Joan. FILES VALLEY RD 76055 #048-12-1958 L1958 **PD PHO** *072 †55

JACKSBORO — JACK

CHOKSHI, Sushil B. 217 W BELKNAP ST 76458 #495-23-1966 L1979 **GP GS** *020 †85

GARCIA, Carmelo Atangan. 717 MAGNOLIA ST 76458 #748-01-1963 L1975 **FM EM** *020

JAMAL, Syed M A. 717 MAGNOLIA ST, FAITH COMMUNITY HOSPITAL 76458 #704-25-1990 L1995 **IM FM** *020 †20

SHORT, James Wm. ■ 76458 #048-02-1963 L1963 **GP FM** *020

JACKSONVILLE — CHEROKEE

BENNETT, Daniel C. 501 S RAGSDALE ST, EAST TEXAS MED CTR 75766 #005-12-1993 L1997 **DR** *020 †80

BIEM, Henry B. ■ 75766 #068-01-1968 L1978 *020

BONE, Mary Alice. 466 S BONNER ST 75766 #048-12-1955 L1955 **PHP** *075

BONSUKAN, Eulogio O. 126 COUNTY ROAD 4212, HIGHWAY 135 75766 #748-01-1966 L1977 **GS VS** *020

CAMPBELL, Todd Alan. 501 S RAGSDALE ST, ETMC - JACKSONVILLE 75766 #039-01-1993 L1998 **DR** *020 †80

CARR, Jeffrey Glenn. 2026 S JACKSON ST 75766 #005-14-1988 L1994 **CD IM** *020 †20

CARSON, Billy Dan. 2026 S JACKSON ST, FAMILY PRACTICE 75766 #048-14-1998 L1999 **FM** *020 †18

CHACKO, Aparna R. 2026 S JACKSON ST 75766 #496-22-1993 L2002 **HO** *020 †20

CLAYTON, Harold Boyd. ■ 75766 #048-15-1980 L1981 **FM** *020

COOPER, Melvin Wayne. 203 NACOGDOCHES ST, STE 240 75766 #048-02-1969 L1973 **CD IM** *040 †20

COOPER, Wayne Douglas. 203 NACOGDOCHES ST, STE 240 75766 #010-01-1973 L1974 **OBG** *020 †30

CRAIG, Randall Gordon. 2025 S JACKSON ST, TRINITY MOTHER FRANCIS HOS 75766 #039-01-1975 L1985 **GPM** *012 †18

CRAWFORD, Joe D. ■ 75766 #021-05-1951 L1952 **OBG** *020 †30

DANEL, Joe Randolph. 1242 COUNTY ROAD 1515, 1242 CRI515 75766 #039-01-1961 L1972 **GP** *020

DAVENPORT, Paul Stuart. 946 S BOLTON ST 75766 #048-02-1976 L1981 **D** *020 †15

FELTS, Frank T. 2026 S JACKSON ST 75766 #048-16-1983 L1983 **GS VS** *020 †85

FIELD, Timothy Edward. 203 NACOGDOCHES ST STE 300 75766 #048-16-1981 L1981 **OBG** *020

GASTILLO, Frank L. E501 S RAGSDALE ST 75766 #748-02-1960 L1977 **GS U** *020 †85

GASTILLO, Norma D Lazaro. 470 S BONNER ST 75766 #748-02-1961 L1977 **GYN** *072 †30

GOEL, Satish. 203 NACOGDOCHES ST, STE 275 75766 #496-09-1990 L1998 **PD** *020 †55

GUILLERMO, Romeo Dungca. 205 E COMMERCE ST 75766 #748-02-1960 L1977 **R NM** *071 †80

HARKINS, Jimmy Blaine. 501 S RAGSDALE ST 75766 #048-02-1973 L1973 **PTH** *020 †50

HOBUS, Paul A. 501 S RAGSDALE ST, ETMC JACKSONVILLE 75766 #048-02-1987 L1992 **AN** *020

JOHNSON, Christopher R. 203 NACOGDOCHES ST STE 370 75766 #048-16-1995 L1999 **MPD PD** *020 †20,55

KOTHEIMER, Gregory Conrad. 203 NACOGDOCHES ST, STE 240 75766 #038-40-1973 L1976 **IM** *020 †20

KRAUSE, Theresa L. 203 NACOGDOCHES ST STE 370 75766 #048-15-1999 L2003 **MPD** *020 †20,55

KULAGA, Andrew D. 2026 S JACKSON ST 75766 #048-12-1982 L1983 **PTH** *020 †50

LESCHPER-VERHELLE, Kendra. 2026 S JACKSON ST, FAMILY PRACTICE 75766 #654-01-1990 L1995 **IM** *020 †20

LOW, James R. 203 NACOGDOCHES ST, STE 360 75766 #048-12-1988 L1989 **IM** *020 †20

MC CLUSKY, Oliver Edwin. 2026 S JACKSON ST 75766 #048-02-1970 L1970 **MDM IM** *020 †20

MILAWSKI, William. 2026 S JACKSON ST 75766 #065-06-1961 L1980 **FM** *020

NILES, Chad Reed. 2026 S JACKSON ST 75766 #031-01-1998 L2000 **DR** *020 †80

PARRISH, Todd A. 2026 S JACKSON ST 75766 #048-12-1993 L1995 **ORS** *020 †40

PERRY, Malcolm Oliver, III. 203 NACOGDOCHES ST STE 260 75766 #035-20-1987 L1992 **U** *095

PONTIUS, Jill. 5656 N JACKSON ST, HWY 69 N 75766 #056-06-1987 L1989 **P** *020 †75

RACE, Mark Christopher. 203 NACOGDOCHES ST, STE 350 75766 #048-14-1982 L1983 **PM OS** *020 †60

RAGLAND, Jane. 546 S RAGSDALE ST 75766 #048-02-1995 L1999 **MPD PD** *020 †20,55

RALSTON, Leslie W. ■ 75766 #048-12-1949 L1949 **R** *071 †80

REDDY, Ravinder Baimeedi. 2026 S JACKSON ST, ST LUKE'S EPISCOPAL HOSPIT 75766 #495-21-1996 L2003 **CD IM** *020 †20

SAADE, Guillermo Alfonso. 203 NACOGDOCHES ST 75766 #341-01-1965 L1977 **IM DIA** *072

SELF, Stanley D. 5656 N JACKSON ST 75766 #048-02-1987 L1988 **P** *020 †75

SESSIONS, Craig E. 2026 S JACKSON ST 75766 #048-15-1994 L1995 **ORS** *020

SESSIONS, Roger C. 2026 S JACKSON ST 75766 #048-02-1983 L1983 **ORS** *020 †40

SMITH, Robert W, Jr. 2026 S JACKSON ST 75766 #048-15-1993 L1995 **CD IC** *020 †20

TOLLESON, Tad Rex. 2026 S JACKSON ST 75766 #048-14-1993 L1994 **IC** *020 †20

TURNER, Delber Boyce. 203 NACOGDOCHES ST STE 200 75766 #048-04-1966 L1967 **IM PUD** *020 †20

VIERKANT, Matthew Arlyn. 2026 S JACKSON ST 75766 #048-13-1991 L1992 **IM** *020 †20

WASSON, James Louis. 2026 S JACKSON ST 75766 #011-04-1990 L1994 **OBG** *020 †30

WEAVER, Austin Allison. 2026 S JACKSON ST, DIRECT CARE 75766 #048-13-1979 L1979 **FM** *020 †18

WEAVER, Craig C. 2026 S JACKSON ST, FAMILY PRACTICE 75766 #048-02-1987 L1988 **FM** *020 †18

WICK, Jeffrey P. 305 W RUSK ST 75766 #048-12-1993 L2003 **OPH** *020 †35

WILLIAMS, Lucia. 203 NACOGDOCHES ST STE 300 75766 #028-34-1984 L1985 **OBG** *020 †30

WONNACOTT, James Brian. 203 NACOGDOCHES ST, STE 265 75766 #064-01-1972 L1978 **FM EM** *020 †18 ‡

YEAGER, Daren P. 2026 S JACKSON ST 75766 #048-14-1997 L1998 **OBG** *020 †30

JASPER — JASPER

ACHARIYAKOSOL, Archana. 605 W GIBSON ST 75951 #891-01-1966 L1977 **GS** *071 †85

BIDWELL, Peter Alexander. 1007 DICKERSON DR 75951 #065-06-1965 L1978 **FM** *020

BOTROS, Maged Ramzy. 215 E WATER ST 75951 #330-04-1965 L1985 **U** *020

BOTTORFF, Melvin K. 1275 MARVIN HANCOCK DR, WOMENS HLTHCARE 75951 #004-01-1960 L1960 **GYN** *020 †30

BOYLES, Rick A. 1002 DICKERSON DR 75951 #048-13-1993 L1994 **FM** *020 †18

DICKERSON, Joe Wesley. 1002 DICKERSON DR 75951 #048-02-1941 L1941 **GP** *071

GILLESPIE, Thomas Eugene. 1275 MARVIN HANCOCK DR 75951 #539-02-1961 L1969 **R** *071 †80

GILLILAND, Martin Edward. 315 W HOUSTON ST 75951 #422-01-1985 L1993 **FM OBS** *020 †18 ‡

GUTIERREZ, Charles John. 605 W GIBSON ST 75951 #005-14-1994 L2000 **GS** *020 †85

HEALING, Robert Dyson. 4239 US HIGHWAY 190 W 75951 #649-01-1974 L1983 **FM PD** *020 †20

KHURSHID, Munwwer. 1276 S PEACHTREE 75951 #704-02-1992 L1998 **N CN** *020 †75

MISHRA, Durba. 1273 S PEACHTREE ST 75951 #495-79-1992 L2000 **IM** *020 †20

PEARSON, Lynn Lanier. 208 CRAIG ST 75951 #005-15-1963 L1967 **ORS OSM** *020 †40

PETERS, Carol Lynne. 315 W HOUSTON ST, COMPLETE HEALTHCARE 75951 #005-12-1986 L2005 **OBG REN** *020 †30

PHAM, Richard D. 315 W HOUSTON ST 75951 #048-02-1995 L1997 **FM** *020 †18

POPEJOY, Lee Tarence, II. 162 E LAMAR ST 75951 #021-05-1961 L1964 **GP OTO** *020

RATH, Kalyan K. 1273 S PEACHTREE ST 75951 #495-79-1986 L1996 **PD GP** *020 †55

RIGGINS, Richard R. 1276 S PEACHTREE ST 75951 #021-06-1991 L1998 **FM** *020 †18

SCHNEIDER, Rebecca Marie. 315 W HOUSTON ST 75951 #654-01-2001 L2005 **FM PD** *020 †20

SETABUTR, Chaninthorn A. 605 W GIBSON ST 75951 #891-02-1969 L1980 **PD** *020 †55

SETABUTR, Dhave. 201 CRESTWOOD DR 75951 #048-15-2008 *012

SINGH, Geeta. 300 MARVIN HANCOCK DR 75951 #495-12-1988 L1997 **FM** *020 †18 ‡

SINGH, Saurabh. 300 MARVIN HANCOCK DR 75951 #495-12-1987 L1993 **IM** *020 †20 ‡

SPENCER, James Berthold. 676 COUNTY ROAD 233, RR 1 BOX 537 75951 #048-02-1967 L1967 **GP** *020

STAGGEMEIER, Dale August. ■ 75951 #654-01-2001 L2005 **FM** *020 †18

SYKES, Walter P. 1275 MARVIN HANCOCK DR, CHRISTUS JASPER MEMORIAL 75951 #039-01-1949 L1950 **FM OS** *071 †18

THOMAS, C Bryce. PO BOX 1930 75951 #048-02-1960 L1960 **GP EM** *071

TIMMONS, Wm Thorpe, Jr. ■ 75951 #048-04-1975 L1975 **OBG FM** *020

WHITING, Ralph Edward. 315 W HOUSTON ST 75951 #040-02-1960 L1996 **OBG FM** *071 †30

JEFFERSON — MARION

DE WARE, Jesse M, III. 202 W HENDERSON ST 75657 #048-04-1940 L1940 **GP** *071

SANDERS, William Robt. ■ 75657 #048-02-1968 L1968 **P** *072

SIMMONS, Donald Rae. 903 N WALCOTT ST, GLENN GARRETT CLINIC 75657 #039-01-1999 L2001 **FM** *020 †18

WEBER, Michael Jensen. 210 BEREA 2 75657 #005-12-1967 L1976 **EM FM** *020 †18

WYATT, David Erin. ■ 75657 #048-15-2007 **AN** *012

JOHNSON CITY — BLANCO

MC KEE, Paul Jay. 780 RANCH ROAD 2721, CAMA 78636 #001-02-1967 L2006 **AN** *020 †05

SPEAKMAN, Walter F. ■ 78636 #039-01-1945 L1954 **P** *071 †75

JONESVILLE — HARRISON

SIEBENLIST, Bud Roger. ■ 75659 #005-12-1965 L1988 **FM DR** *020

JOSHUA — JOHNSON

BROWNING, James Monroe. 113 WOOD OAK DR 76058 #005-12-1974 L1975 **OM EM** *020 †18

FRANK, Harold D. 1529 S BROADWAY ST 76058 #649-14-1962 L1964 **FPG FM** *072

HOFFMAN, John Gregory. 3517 SW WILSHIRE BLVD 76058 #048-14-1997 L1998 **FM** *020 †18

MEELHUYSEN, Delbe Thomas. PO BOX 345 76058 #005-12-1987 L2007 **IM EM** *020 †20

MILLER, Robert Michael. 3517 SW WILSHIRE BLVD 76058 #005-12-1980 L1995 **FM OBG** *020 †18

SAADE, Raja Habib. PO BOX 910, JOSHUA FAMILY MED CARE 76058 #048-16-2000 L2003 **FM** *020 †18

JOURDANTON — ATASCOSA

BICKFORD, John Robert. 1901 HIGHWAY 97 E, STE 120 78026 #429-02-1990 L1998 **PD PEM** *020 †55

■ = Address Information Privacy Protected

BLACKMON, E Barton, Jr. 1901 HIGHWAY 97 E STE 230 78026 #045-01-1978 L2005 **OBG** *020 †30
BURDETT LANGE, Kathleen M. ■ 78026 #048-02-1987 L1990 **LM OS** *020
CLEMENCE, Elliott Irving. 1901 HIGHWAY 97 E STE 210 78026 #024-07-1986 L1996 **ORS** *020
DONNELL-KOWALIK, Jennifer. 256 MEDICAL DR 78026 #048-14-1997 L1998 **OBG** *012 †18
FORD, Janice Latecher. 1905 HIGHWAY 97 E 78026 #010-03-2000 L2008 **MPD** *020 †20,55
HAMNER, Ronald Wayne. 1720 HIGHWAY 97 E 78026 #047-05-1978 L1982 **NEP IM** *020
MC FARLAND, Michael Allen. 1105 OAK ST STE A 78026 #048-13-1984 L1985 **FM D** *020 †18
MONTEMAYOR, Lenibet Miria. ■ 78026 #737-09-1997 L2005 **IM** *020
MORGAN, Lana K. 1901 HIGHWAY 97 E STE 120 78026 #048-13-1984 L1986 **PD** *020 †55
SYED, Nasir Sultan. 1901 HIGHWAY 97 E, STE 110 78026 #704-08-1986 L2003 **IM** *020 †20

JUNCTION – KIMBLE

BANAHAN, Benj Franklin. 2101 MAIN ST 76849 #021-01-1957 L1997 **EM FM** *071 †16,18
HERBERT, Carol Ann. 109 REID RD 76849 #048-13-1986 L1996 **FM** *020 †18
MARTINEZ, Alberto Noe. 109 REID DR 76849 #005-11-1982 L1983 **FM** *020 †18
MECKLEY, Arnold Hugh. ■ 76849 #051-04-1955 L1959 **OPH** *071 †35
TRUONG, Thao Minh. 109 REID RD, JUNCTION MEDICAL CLINIC 76849 #048-04-1995 L1997 **FM** *020 †18 ‡

JUSTIN – DENTON

CLARKE, Diane. ■ 76247 #047-06-1986 L1992 **IM** *020 †20
SCHNEIDER, Daniel Jacob. 8054 SMITH RD 76247 #005-14-1958 L1987 **PHP GPM** *050

KARNES CITY – KARNES

BIELA, Timothy A. ■ 78118 #048-13-2002 L2007 **NPM** *012 †55
DESEQUERA, Gerardo. 810 COMMERCE ST, WACKENHUT CORRECTIONS 78118 #748-11-1990 L1997 **FM** *020 †18
ZARAGOZA, Fernando Leonel. 1092 HIGHWAY 80 78118 #048-12-2001 L2005 **AN** *100 †05

KATY – FORT BEND

ADKISSON, Cameron D. ■ 77494 #048-02-2008 *012
ALAGUGURUSAMY, S. 5602 MEDICAL CENTER DR, KATY MEDICAL CENTER 77494 #495-42-1968 L1977 **EM U** *020 †20
ALI, Shamim. 5618 MEDICAL CENTER DR, STE 109 77494 #704-08-1980 L2003 **IM** *020 †18
ALLPORT, Frederick Wm. ■ 77494 #068-01-1958 L1967 **P CHP** *020 †75
ALVEAR, Joel. 1260 PIN OAK RD STE 218 77494 #048-14-1998 L2001 **FM** *020 †18
ANDREWS, Sarah E. 23920 KATY FWY, STE 330 77494 #048-02-1990 L1991 **OBG** *020 †30
ARMSTRONG, Rachel Jean. 5602 MEDICAL CENTER DR 77494 #064-01-1976 L1979 **EM** *030 †16
BEALL, Rakel Chandra. ■ 77494 #048-04-2007 *012
BLAKLEY, Olga Pavlovna. ■ 77494 #913-61-1986 L2004 **AN** *020 †05 ‡
BOOTH, Earnest. ■ 77494 #048-12-1951 L1951 **PTH** *071 †50
BUI, Cory Khoiquoc. ■ 77494 #005-15-2003 L2006 **FM** *020 †18
CHUNG, Moo John. 1331 W GRAND PKWY S, STE 230 77494 #039-01-1999 L2002 **IM** *020 †20 ‡
DEL CASTILLO, Gilbert. 1260 PIN OAK RD, STE 202 77494 #649-14-1980 L1987 **AN** *020
FLAX, Ira Lynwood. 5602 MEDICAL CENTER DR 77494 #051-04-1974 L1976 **GE IM** *020 †20
GONIK, Morris. 1260 PIN OAK RD, STE 203 77494 #025-12-1979 L1983 **OBG** *020
GONZALEZ, Alexander. 23920 KATY FWY, STE 560 77494 #048-14-2000 L2003 **PD** *020 †55
GRAJEDA, Miguel Angel. ■ 77494 #429-01-1972 *074
GUARDIA, Rene Walter. ■ 77494 #176-03-1985 L2004 **PD** *020 †55
HIENAMAN, Mary E. 23232 KINGSLAND BLVD 77494 #048-15-1990 L1991 **OBG** *020 †30
HOLT, Byron Busby. 23232 KINGSLAND BLVD 77494 #048-02-1965 L1965 **OBG** *020 †30
HOLT, Todd Miles. 23232 KINGSLAND BLVD 77494 #048-02-2001 L2005 **OBG** *020 †30
HUTSELL, Robert Allen. 23920 KATY FWY, STE 200 77494 #048-14-1999 L2002 **AN** *020 †05
JACKSON, Clemis Laraine. 1334 PIN OAK RD 77494 #048-02-1987 L1989 **FM** *020 †18
JANECKI, Andrzej. 5618 MEDICAL CENTR DR S100 77494 #759-04-1977 L1999 **GE** *020 †20
JENKINS, Taryll Lamont. 23920 KATY FWY, STE 440 77494 #047-07-2002 L2006 **OBG** *020
JOHNSON, Edwina. ■ 77494 #012-05-1993 L1995 **IM** *020
JOSEPH, Sheldon W. ■ 77494 #026-04-1949 L1955 **OS PD** *071 †55
KLINKE, William Bernard. 1331 W GRAND PKWY S, STE 160 77494 #048-12-1973 L1976 **OTO** *020 †45
KOY, Robert Dudley. 5602 MEDICAL CENTER DR, MEMORIAL HERMAN KATY 77494 #021-05-1974 L1975 **PTH** *020 †50
LE, Hung V. 2830 COMMERCIAL CENTR BLVD, STE 102 77494 #048-12-1992 L1993 **IM** *020 †20
LONGE, Ucheoma Nebechi. ■ 77494 #690-06-2000 **FP** *012
MC CULLAGH, Malachy S. ■ 77494 #065-06-1964 L1977 **FM** *075
MEHTA, Mukesh N. 1331 W GRAND PKWY S, STE 230 77494 #495-48-1998 L1999 **IM** *020 †20
MONROY, Grace A. ■ 77494 #748-01-1990 L1996 **PD** *020 †55
MONTANO, Nazly C. ■ 77494 #264-12-1988 L2002 **PD** *020
MONTOYA, Cecilia Lopez De. 23410 TROPHY LN 77494 #264-04-1968 L1976 **DR** *020
MONTOYA, Sergio Andres. ■ 77494 #048-02-2005 **IM** *100
MOREIRA, Alvaro Francisco. ■ 77494 #682-01-1958 L1969 **P** *071 †75
MORENO, Francisco Eugen. 23920 KATY FWY STE 3 77494 #649-01-1971 L1978 **PD** *020
MOULD, David Carter. ■ 77494 #019-02-1990 L1995 **AN** *020 †05
NOOR, Saba S. 1260 PIN OAK RD STE 209 77494 #704-25-1992 L2004 **FM** *020 †18
NORRIS, James Ted, Jr. ■ 77494 #048-14-2000 L2004 **AN** *020
OLEY, Thomas John. 5618 MEDICAL CENTER DR, STE 205 77494 #048-02-1971 L1971 **ORS** *020 †40
PATRONELLA, Allyson T. 23920 KATY FWY, STE 330 77494 #048-13-1992 L1993 **OBG** *020 †30
PICOLOS, Michalis K. ■ 77494 #018-01-1996 L2002 **END** *100 †20
RIOS, Gaddiel David. 23920 KATY FWY, STE 500 77494 #024-07-1998 L2005 **FM** *020 †18
ROCKMAN, Steven Ian. 23920 KATY FWY, STE 540 77494 #035-46-1975 L1984 **OBG NPM** *020 †30
SAVAGE, Walter P. ■ 77494 #033-05-1960 L1974 **P** *071
SCHMIDT, Kristin Noelle. 23920 KATY FWY, STE 330 77494 #048-14-1996 L2000 **OBG** *020 †30

SCHULINGKAMP, Robt Harold. ■ 77494 #021-05-1959 L1959 **GP OS** *071
SCHUMACHER, Brooke Ann. 1260 PIN OAK RD, STE 110 77494 #016-43-1990 L1994 **OBG** *020 †30
SHARMA, Sumeet Kumar. 77494 #422-01-1999 L2006 **PDC** *020 †55
SINGH, Manvinder. 23920 KATY FWY, STE 340 77494 #035-09-1987 L2007 **REN GYN** *020 †30
SOBARZO, Arturo Jose. 5602 MEDICAL CENTER DR 77494 #649-27-1972 L1985 **AN** *075
SOBARZO, Maria Milian. 23920 KATY FWY STE 330 77494 #048-16-1985 L1987 **OBG** *020 †30
SOLIS, Ramon A, Jr. 1331 W GRAND PKWY S, STE 230 77494 #048-14-1987 L1988 **IM** *020 †20 ‡
TAL, Jacob. 23920 KATY FWY, STE 460 77494 #550-02-1976 L1980 **OBG** *020 †30 ‡
WEAVER, Phil Jefferson. 1336 PIN OAK RD, RADIANT IMAGING & DIAG 77494 #048-02-1967 L1967 **DR GP** *020 †80
WIEGREFFE, James Weldon. ■ 77494 #048-02-1959 L1959 **FM** *071 †18

KATY – HARRIS

ADAMS, John R. 21700 KINGSLAND BLVD, MEDICAL COLLEAGUES OF 77450 #048-02-1997 L2000 **IM** *020 †20
AHMED, Amina J. 707 S FRY RD, STE 495 77450 #704-02-1985 L1997 **NEP** *020 †20
AHMED, Syed Viqar. 6840 S MASON RD, # 100 77450 #495-21-1989 L1996 **IM** *020 †20
AKHTAR, Asif. 707 S FRY RD STE 380, INTERVENTIONAL CARDIOLOGY 77450 #704-02-1990 **IC** *100 †20
AL-KHUSH, Ahmad-Rabia. 705 S FRY RD, STE 225 77450 #875-01-1986 L2001 **FM GE** *020 †18
ALLISON, Leslie James. 21238 KINGSLAND BLVD, MONARCH MEDICAL CLINIC 77450 #063-01-1988 L1995 **FM D** *020
ANDERSON, Blake Lew. 701 S FRY RD STE 230 77450 #035-01-1998 L2003 **OTO HNS** *020 †45
ANDERSON, Tiffany M. 21700 KINGSLAND BLVD STE 2 77450 #048-14-2002 L2006 **OBG** *020
ASADUDDIN, Adil. 701 S FRY RD, STE 225 77450 #048-02-1999 L2002 **IM** *020 †20
BANDOLON, Pura K. ■ 77450 #748-09-1964 L1972 **OBG** *020 †30
BARBEE, Michael J. ■ 77449 #048-02-2008 *012
BARTSCH, Edward Fred. 5207 E 5TH ST 77493 #048-02-1962 L1962 **GP** *020
BHATT, Harshada Rajendra. 830 S MASON RD STE B6 77450 #495-22-1969 L1981 **PD** *020
BING, Mark Lyndon. 21700 KINGSLAND BLVD 77450 #029-01-1979 L1980 **IM PHP** *020 †20
BING, Paul E. 21700 KINGSLAND BLVD, MEDICAL COLLEAGUES OF 77450 #048-15-1990 L1991 **PCC** *020 †20
BLOSS, Robert Scott. 21700 KINGSLAND BLVD, HOUSTON PEDIATRIC 77450 #048-12-1974 L1977 **PDS** *020 †85
BONNOR, Ricardo Mauricio. 21720 KINGSLAND BLVD, STE 303A 77450 #048-02-1999 L2003 **GS** *020 †85
BOOKERT, Jasmine Brandi. 22531 GUSTON HALL LN 77449 #010-03-2005 L2005 **EM** *012
BROWNE, Katherine S. 705 S FRY RD, STE 120 77450 #048-04-2002 L2005 **PD** *020 †55
CAMPBELL, Nancy Gayle. 21660 KINGSLAND BLVD, KELSEY-SEYBOLD CLN 77450 #048-04-1990 L1991 **FM** *020 †18
CARLYLE, Trenton A. 21222 KINGSLAND BLVD 77450 #048-04-1996 L2001 **ORS** *020 †40
CASTELLANOS, Mario Eduard. ■ 77491 #048-12-2006 **OBG** *012
CHANG, Elena Erie. ■ 77450 #048-12-2008 *012
CHEN, Anna Jie. 705 S FRY RD, STE 320 77450 #039-01-1999 L2002 **PD** *020 †55
CHUAN, Joseph. 1803 PARKLAKE VLG, DEPT ANESTHESIOLOGY 77450 #048-04-2000 L2004 **AN** *020 †05
CLARKE, Roy Adrian. 705 S FRY RD, STE 120 77450 #028-02-1999 L2002 **PD** *020 †55
COHEN, Adam Seth. 705 S FRY RD, STE 120 77450 #012-05-1999 L2002 **PD** *020 †55
COLE, Nichole Fleming. 705 S FRY RD, STE 235 77450 #021-05-1998 L2000 **OBG** *020 †30
COROVESSIS, Catherine C. 21700 KINGSLAND BLVD 77450 #048-13-1998 L2002 **OBG** *020 †30
CRISWELL, Allen Ross. 707 S FRY RD, ORTHOPAEDIC ASSOCIATES 77450 #041-13-1971 L1973 **ORS** *020 †40
CURRIE, William Alexnder. 21700 KINGSLAND BLVD, MEDICAL COLLEAGUES OF 77450 #649-30-1980 L1982 **GE IM** *020 †20
CZELUSTA, Adam James. 707 S FRY RD STE 395 77450 #048-02-1999 L2003 **D** *020 †15
DASILVA, Omololu Adetokun. ■ 77450 #035-20-2005 **PD** *012
DAWSON, Jabon Ramon. 701 S FRY RD, ANESTHESIOLOGY DEPT 77450 #001-02-1984 L1985 **AN** *020 †05
DEHLAVI, Afshan H. 705 S FRY RD, STE 120 77450 #048-16-2004 L2007 **PD** *020 †55
DIAS, Wenceslaus P C. ■ 77450 #495-97-1972 L1977 **GS GP** *020 †85
DIAZ CASILLAS, Jose M. 507 PARK GROVE LN 77450 #042-03-1984 L1992 **N** *020 †75
DOMINY, Donald Dean, III. ■ 77450 #048-12-2006 **ORS** *012
DUFF, Diana D. 701 S FRY RD, STE 100 77450 #048-04-1994 L1997 **OBG** *020 †30
EDWARDS, G Russell. 1331 W GRAND PKWY N, STE 240 77493 #048-04-1987 L1988 **OBG** *020 †30
EDWARDS, Laura Denise. 848 DOMINION DR STE 200 77450 #048-02-1975 L1975 **FM** *020 †18
ELLSWORTH, Donald P, Jr. 20214 BRAIDWOOD DR, STE 215 77450 #045-04-1986 L2003 **FM** *040 †18
FARMER, Charles E. ■ 77450 #021-05-1951 L1993 **GP GS** *020
FERNANDEZ, Douglas Keith. 1331 W GRAND PKWY N, STE 350 77493 #023-12-1981 L1993 **GE IM** *020 †20
FOTOUH, Asmaa Tohami. 777 S FRY RD, STE 207 77450 #915-02-1977 L1987 **PD** *020 †55
FOX-JAKOB, Tracy. 707 S FRY RD, STE 490 77450 #048-12-1987 L1988 **OTO** *020 †45
FREEMAN, Christian M. 777 S FRY RD, STE 207 77450 #048-14-2002 L2005 **PD** *020 †55
GAGLIARDI, Joseph M, Jr. ■ 77450 #041-02-1960 L1961 **ORS** *071 †40
GALLAS, Mennen Theo. 777 S FRY RD, STE 102 77450 #016-42-1991 L1998 **PS** *020 †85,65
GARDNER, Samuel Thomas. ■ 77450 #039-01-1998 L2002 **EM** *020
GARTZMAN, Steven Howard. 701 S FRY RD, C/O EMERGENCY DEPARTMENT 77450 #005-06-1993 L1998 **EM** *020 †16
GERSON, Lester Paul. 21720 KINGSLAND BLVD, IMAGING DE 77450 #048-02-1965 L1965 **R** *020 †80
GIBBS, Lynn Ralph. 810 S MASON RD STE 201 77450 #048-02-1976 L1980 **FM EM** *020 †16
GIDDINGS, Shelleyanne E. 21660 KINGSLAND BLVD, KELSEY-SEYBOLD CLNC PA 77450 #041-14-1988 L1991 **PD** *020 †55
GIEZENTANNER, Anita L. 701 S FRY RD 77450 #048-14-1985 L1987 **AN** *020 †05
GILLICK, Roy Harry. 830 S MASON RD STE A4 77450 #065-06-1959 L1977 **FM** *020
GONZALEZ, Luis Alfonso. ■ 77450 #649-30-1978 *100
GORDON, Elizabeth Ann. 5550 S PEEK RD 77450 #025-07-1993 L1997 **PD** *020 †55 ‡
GUZEL, Volkan Bilgin. 21222 KINGSLAND BLVD 77450 #902-09-1992 L2005 **ORS** *100
HABER, Harold Norman. 539 S MASON RD 77450 #065-01-1956 L1976 **FM** *072

HADEN-PINNERI, Kathryn. ■ 77450 #048-12-1997 L2005 **FOP** *020 †50
HAIKAL, Rahim. 21660 KINGSLAND BLVD 77450 #118-01-1980 L1994 **FM** *020 †18
HANCOCK, Mark S. 21222 PARK MOUNT DR 77450 #048-13-1993 L1997 **AN** *020 †05
HANEY, Helen Marie. 705 S FRY RD, STE 120 77450 #038-06-1985 L1998 **PD** *020 †55
HATE, Rahul Udaykumar. ■ 77450 #035-20-2006 **PD** *012
HICKS, Benfard Earl. 21660 KINGSLAND BLVD, KELSEY-SEYBOLD CLINIC 77450 #048-14-1977 L1977 **PD** *020 †55
HORMAZDI, Bomi Khodabax. 701 S FRY RD, SUTIE 110 77450 #496-38-1971 L1977 **PD** *020 †55 ‡
HORNUNG, Joseph L. 701 S FRY RD, ANESTHESIOLOGY DEPT 77450 #048-14-1994 L1997 **AN** *020 †05
HOTZE, Steven Forrest. 20214 BRAIDWOOD DR, STE 215 77450 #048-14-1976 L1976 **A** *020
HOVIS, Todd Michael. 21720 KINGSLAND BLVD, STE 305 77450 #048-04-1989 L1991 **OPH** *020 †35
HSU, Branden. 1331 W GRAND PKWY N, STE 340 77493 #048-04-1997 L1999 **HO IM** *020 †20
IFTIKHAR, Huma Irfan. 20903 KINGSLAND BLVD 77450 #704-02-1989 L2001 **FM** *020 †18
IFTIKHAR, Irfan. 20903 KINGSLAND BLVD 77450 #704-02-1989 L1994 **IC CD** *020 †20
JARQUIN, Armando Jose. 21312 PROVINCIAL BLVD 77450 #649-14-1983 L1994 **FM** *020 †18
JOHNS, Joseph B. 705 S FRY RD, STE 325 77450 #048-13-1998 L2002 **OBG** *020 †30
KALAPATAPU, Viswanath. 1331 W GRAND PKWY N, STE 230 77493 #654-01-1997 L2006 **IM** *020 †20
KANTAMANI, Anuradha. 701 S FRY RD STE 105 77450 #495-65-1989 L1997 **GE** *020 †20
KARIBIAN, Alan V. ■ 77450 #048-12-1994 L1996 **PPR** *100 †55
KENDALL, Kevin Edward. 22028 HIGHLAND KNOLLS DR, # D 77450 #048-13-1994 L1995 **IM** *020 †20
KHALAF, Tareq Hanna. 462 S MASON RD 77450 #605-01-1971 L1978 **RHU IM** *074 †20
KHAN, Azmat Syed. 21214 KINGSLAND BLVD 77450 #704-06-1991 L2006 **IMG** *020 †20
KHAWAJA, Mubarak A. 707 S FRY RD, STE 375 77450 #704-08-1987 L1997 **PUD** *020 †20
KING, John Q T, Jr. 873 S MASON RD, STE 310 77450 #047-07-1972 L1975 **OBG** *020
KISCH, Agnes I. 707 S FRY RD, STE 275 77450 #473-04-1982 L1994 **PD** *020 †55
KNOPP, Victor C. 2211 N FRY RD, STE N 77449 #048-13-1983 L1983 **FM** *020 †18
KUAN, Shu-Chin. 21234 KINGSLAND BLVD 77450 #187-54-1985 L1992 **PD PN** *020 †55
LALANI, Shamim. 707 S FRY RD, STE 360 77450 #704-02-1986 L1995 **IM** *020 †20
LEARNED-BURTON, Lori J. 21720 KINGSLAND BLVD, STE 305 77450 #048-04-1994 L2003 **OPH** *020 †20
LEE, Jin Soo. ■ 77450 #583-02-1974 L1984 **HO IMG** *050 †20
LEE, Timothy Chenan. 2102 CHERRINGTON DR 77450 #048-04-2001 L2003 **GS** *012
LENTSCH, Kirsten Ann. 3030 S MASON RD 77450 #038-40-1998 L2001 **PD** *020 †55
LEVIN, Raymond Coleman. 430 S MASON RD STE 101 77450 #065-01-1959 L1977 **FM** *071
LIN, Selina. 1331 W GRAND PKWY N, STE 240 77493 #048-02-1989 L1990 **OBG** *020 †30
LO, Carson Tan. 1331 W GRAND PKWY N, STE 310 77493 #748-10-1985 L1996 **IM ID** *020 †20
LONGHI, Enrique Horacio. ■ 77493 #132-01-1953 L1968 **GP** *071
LUETHCKE, David Ross. 701 S FRY RD STE 200 77450 #048-04-1984 L1986 **PS** *020 †65
MADDIRALA, Sunil David. ■ 77450 #654-01-2002 L2003 **CCP** *012
MAMMEN, Anju A. 777 S FRY RD, STE 207 77450 #041-15-2001 L2007 **PD** *020 †55
MAMMEN, George P. 1331 W GRAND PKWY N, STE 130 77493 #495-31-1973 L1980 **CD IC** *020 †20
MARTINEZ, Isabel. 511 PARK GROVE LN 77450 #011-02-1977 L1978 **FM OS** *020 †18
MC CULLAGH, Kelly A. 21700 KINGSLAND BLVD, STE 202 77450 #048-15-1990 L1991 **OBG** *020 †30
MC GARVEY, William C. 21222 KINGSLAND BLVD 77450 #041-02-1989 L1994 **ORS OFA** *020 †40
MC GLEW, Hilda. ■ 77450 #305-01-1984 L1988 **FM** *020 †18
MEHRA, Naveen K. ■ 77449 #048-13-2007 **AN** *012
MEHTA, Rajen Kanu. 1331 W GRAND PKWY N, STE 130 77493 #048-02-1992 L1998 **IM CD** *020 †20
MENDELSON, Edward Gerald. 21402 PROVINCIAL BLVD 77450 #065-01-1964 L1977 **OBG** *020
MIRO-QUESADA, Miguel V. 705 S FRY RD, STE 230 77450 #023-07-1969 L1984 **ON HEM** *020 †20
MOELLER, David Jos. 21720 KINGSLAND BLVD, IMAGING D 77450 #048-02-1981 L1981 **DR NRN** *020 †80
NASH, Stewart Maikidi. 6810 CRYSTAL POINT DR 77449 #048-15-2008 *012
NAYAR, Arun G. 21720 KINGSLAND BLVD, STE 305 77450 #048-46-1991 L1993 **OPH** *020 †35
NELMS, Donald Cade. 705 S FRY RD, STE 320 77450 #048-14-1981 L1981 **PD** *020
NGUYEN, Nha Van. 701 S FRY RD 77450 #048-02-1989 L1990 **AN PME** *020 †05
NGUYEN, Nhan Huynh Trung. ■ 77450 #048-12-1999 L1999 **GS** *100
NGUYEN, Thomas A T. ■ 77449 #048-14-2008 *012
NGUYEN, Thomas T. 701 S FRY RD, STE 227 77450 #048-14-1994 L1995 **FM** *020
NOOR, Sohail. 705 S FRY RD, STE 470 77450 #704-25-1992 L1996 **IM** *020 †20
NOVICK, Sherry Lauren. 430 S MASON RD 77450 #021-01-2001 L2005 **D** *020 †15
ODHAV, Anil C. 1331 W GRAND PKWY N, STE 130 77493 #965-01-1989 L1999 **IM** *020 †20
PADERANGA, Robert C. ■ 77450 #748-07-1962 *100
PADWICK, Luke. 701 S FRY RD, CHRISTUS ST. CATHERINE HOS 77450 #048-12-1997 L2002 **EM** *020 †16
PAPPADAS, John T. 707 S FRY RD, STE 475 77450 #048-12-1984 L1985 **OBG** *020 †30
PARHIZGAR, Alireza. ■ 77450 #517-05-2000 L2007 **IM** *020 †20
PATEL, Hema C. ■ 77450 #422-01-1998 L2002 **IM** *020 †20
PAYNE, Norris Sheldon. 21660 KINGSLAND BLVD 77450 #048-12-1978 L1978 **PD** *020 †55
PEZZIA, Willy. 714 S PEEK RD 77450 #737-01-1968 L1975 **IM PUD** *020 †20
PIMENTEL, Severino M, Jr. 21304 PROVINCIAL BLVD 77450 #048-13-1996 L1998 **FM** *020 †18 ‡
RAMIREZ-NIETO, Maria C. 707 S FRY RD, STE 350 77450 #042-01-1985 L1993 **N PM** *020
RECHTER, Alan J. 707 S FRY RD, STE 255 77450 #030-06-1994 L1996 **ORS** *020 †40
REDDY, Pallavolu N. 20911 KINGSLAND BLVD, PARAGON PRIMARY CARE PHYSI 77450 #495-70-1982 L1999 **IM** *020 †20
REININGER, David Wright. 1331 W GRAND PKWY N, STE 230 77493 #048-02-1978 L1978 **IM IMG** *020 †20 ‡
RENAZCO, Marco Antonio. 707 S FRY RD, STE 465 77450 #048-16-1997 L2001 **P** *020 †75
RIHAL, Pardeep Singh. 705 S FRY RD, STE 115 77450 #025-07-1991 L1997 **AI** *020 †20,03
RODGERS, Bruce Allen, Jr. 603 PARK GROVE LN 77450 #048-14-2001 L2007 **HS** *020
ROMAN, Joe, III. 707 S FRY RD, STE 355 77450 #048-14-1985 L1986 **OBG** *020 †30
ROMERO, Fernando Antonio. 701 S FRY RD STE 120 77450 #048-14-1985 L1987 **OPH PO** *020 †35
SABBAGH, Roula. 21660 KINGSLAND BLVD, KELSEY-SEYBOLD CLINIC 77450 #875-02-1980 L1993 **PD** *020 †55

SAJJA, Prasuna. 707 S FRY RD, STE 394 77450 #495-16-1997 L2005 **FM** *020 †18
SALAZAR, Robert A. 707 S FRY RD STE 485 77450 #748-02-1989 L1997 **PUD CCM** *020 †20
SALVO GONZALEZ, Valeska L. ■ 77450 #048-14-2003 L2006 **PD** *100 †55
SARGENT, Michael G. 21937 KATY FWY 77450 #671-01-1970 L1980 *020
SHAH, Archana Kanti. 705 S FRY RD, STE 120 77450 #048-04-1995 L1998 **PD** *020 †55
SHEIKH, Wasim A. 701 S FRY RD 77450 #704-21-1982 L1998 **IM** *020 †50,20
SHERIDAN, David Paul. 20214 BRAIDWOOD DR, STE 215 77450 #003-01-1985 L2002 **FM** *020 †18
SHIN, David Joseph. 22511 KATY FWY STE 400 77450 #836-01-1976 L1979 **FM IMG** *020
SINCLARE, Ross G. ■ 77450 #060-01-1958 L1978 *020
SIVASUBRAMANIAN, Parijatha. ■ 77450 #048-15-2008 *012
SMITH, Patricia Amanda. 705 S FRY RD 77450 #054-04-1997 L2001 **OBG** *020 †30
SPANGLER, Henry Burton. 21720 KINGSLAND BLVD, IMAGING D 77450 #047-06-1964 L1968 **DR RO** *040 †80
SPENCER, Jose Arturo. ■ 77450 #007-02-1980 L1982 **DR** *020 †80
SPENCER, Steven Craig. 701 S FRY RD, STE 103 77450 #048-02-1987 L1988 **FM** *020 †18
STOUT, Tamara A. 707 S FRY RD, STE 280 77450 #048-12-2002 L2005 **FM** *020 †18
SUBRT, Paul. 1331 W GRAND PKWY N, STE 370 77493 #048-02-1980 L1981 **D** *020 †15
SUNEJA, Randeep. 701 S FRY RD 77450 #495-45-1983 L1992 **CD IM** *020 †20
TAMBOLI, Sanober Meer. 607 S MASON RD 77450 #704-02-1987 L1996 **AI** *020 †55,03
TAMERISA, Radha Ann. 1331 N GRAND PKWY, STE 350 77493 #305-01-1997 L2003 **GE** *020 †20
TRAN, Vanhien Cong. 701 S FRY RD STE 115 77450 #019-02-1996 L1998 **GS** *020
TRINH, Trang Thuy. 21720 KINGSLAND BLVD 77450 #048-14-1993 L1994 **FM** *020 †20
UBALDO, Hector. 462 S MASON RD STE 100 77450 #308-11-1989 L1996 **IM FM** *020 †20
UNNISSA, Ifthekar. 21542 KINGSLAND BLVD 77450 #495-21-1981 L1992 **PD** *020 †55
VANDONGEN, Danique L. 21720 KINGSLAND BLVD, STE 102 77450 #035-20-2003 L2007 **PM** *020
VILCHEZ, Denis Alberto. 21718 BARCAN CIR 77450 #649-14-1982 *100
WAINSCOTT, Brenda Lee. 21700 KINGSLAND BLVD # 201 77450 #048-14-1996 L1999 **IM** *020 †20
WALLACE, Patrick Joseph. 701 S FRY RD, STE 115 77450 #016-02-1989 L1994 **GS SO** *020 †85
WANI, Manish K. 707 S FRY RD, STE 250 77450 #048-04-1994 L2001 **OTO** *020 †45
WASSERMAN, Matthew W. 21222 KINGSLAND BLVD 77450 #048-04-1999 L2005 **ORS** *020 †40
WEXLER, Michael Louis. 705 S FRY RD STE 120 77450 #016-42-1969 L1972 **PD** *020 †55
WHITFORD, Randolph Peck. 21830 KINGSLAND BLVD, STE 102 77450 #048-13-1979 L1979 **OPH** *020 †35
WIGGINS, Raymond Lavelle. 810 S MASON RD, STE 301 77450 #048-14-2001 L2003 **GS** *020
YEE, Lansing Wayne. 21660 KINGSLAND BLVD 77450 #048-02-1981 L1981 **FM** *020 †18

KAUFMAN — KAUFMAN

ABELLO-RIVERO, Angelina A. 874 W HIGHWAY 243 STE 115 75142 #748-08-1970 L1979 **OBG** *020
ASTUDILLO, Gerardo. 503 W HIGHWAY 243 75142 #649-02-1990 L2003 **OBG** *020
BALL, James Andrew. 1987 COUNTY RD STE 279 75142 #048-02-1948 L1948 **PD** *071 †55
CHAMPINE, Michael J. 709 W HIGHWAY 243, STE B 75142 #048-13-1988 L1990 **ORS OAR** *072 †40
DAILEY, Jimmy W. 850 W STATE HIGHWAY 243 75142 #048-13-1996 L1997 **FM A** *020 †18
DENGLE, Shashank K. 874 W HIGHWAY 243, PRES PROF BLDG STE 111 75142 #495-01-1975 L1987 **CD IM** *020 †20
FORTNER, William Jay. 101 N HOUSTON ST, STE 1 75142 #048-02-1968 L1968 **FM PHP** *020 †18
GRIMM, Martha Anne. 850 W STATE HIGHWAY 243 75142 #003-01-1997 L1998 **EM** *020 †16
HEAFER, Harold Arthur. 101 N HOUSTON ST 75142 #007-02-1983 L1986 **FM EM** *020 †18
LEWIS, Charles Turner, III. 1011 W GROVE ST 75142 #048-04-1990 L1992 **PD** *020
MARSH, Peter Hyatt. 874 W HIGHWAY 243, STE 106 75142 #048-04-1981 L1982 **FM OM** *020 †18 ‡
MC MAHON, Stephen Ray. 874 W HIGHWAY 243 STE 108 75142 #048-12-1976 L1976 **IM** *020 †20
MOHAN, Prabha. 709 W HIGHWAY 243 STE C 75142 #495-74-1989 L1996 **IM** *020 †20
ONG, Gene Djin Sing. 850 W STATE HIGHWAY 243 75142 #409-04-1970 L1975 **PTH** *020 †50
REODICA, Rowena Evasco. 850 W STATE HIGHWAY 243 75142 #748-08-1968 L1977 **GP** *020
RIVERO, Manuel Soriano. 874 W HIGHWAY 243, STE 102 75142 #748-08-1969 L1979 **IM END** *072
SMITH, Charles B. 874 W HIGHWAY 243 75142 #048-13-1994 L1996 **FM** *071 †18
SPITZER, Stuart K. 874 W HIGHWAY 243, STE 107 75142 #048-12-1993 L1994 **GS** *020 †85
TWAY, Mona Sue C. 850 W STATE HIGHWAY 243 75142 #039-01-1976 L1981 **DR FM** *020
ZALETA, Sara L. 874 W HIGHWAY 243 75142 #048-12-2000 L2004 **MPD** *020 †20,55 ‡

KEENE — JOHNSON

ALEXANDER, James E. PO BOX 588 76059 #047-06-1943 L1949 **IM** *071 †20
ALLEN, Charles Guy. ■ 76059 #005-12-1948 L1950 **GP** *071
BARTON, Bret Max. ■ 76059 #005-12-1999 L1999 **PTH** *071
CABANSAG, John C. 111 S OLD BETSY RD 76059 #748-07-1955 L1972 **IM P** *020
DE ROMANETT, Linda Elaine. ■ 76059 #005-12-1982 L1983 **IM** *020
FREELAND, Harold Eugene. ■ 76059 #048-12-1959 L1959 **FM** *072
KAYLOR, Marietta June. ■ 76059 #005-12-1966 L1982 **FM GP** *075 †18
KIMBROW, Nancy Leona. 212 S OLD BETSY RD 76059 #005-12-1979 L1983 **FM** *020 †18
LEE, Victor Ralph. ■ 76059 #021-05-1956 L1964 **EM GP** *071
MEDINA, Amante De Leon. ■ 76059 #748-07-1966 L1976 **FM GPM** *071
MILLER, Janice Arlene. ■ 76059 #005-12-1980 L1998 **FM** *020 †18
STAGG, Ruth E Anderson. ■ 76059 #005-12-1945 L1978 **GP** *071
VARGA, Laszlo. 208 WOODLAWN DR, AND NEUROLOGY 76059 #067-01-1959 L1985 **P N** *062 †75

KELLER — TARRANT

ABERCROMBIE, David M. ■ 76248 #034-01-1982 L1983 **EM** *020 †16
ALAVI, Ali. 5112 POSTWOOD DR 76248 #051-01-1996 L2001 **U** *020 †95

ALEXANDER, Lawrence N. ■ 76248 #048-02-1965 L1965 **EM OM** *071 †85
ALLEN, James Young, Jr. 4140 HERITAGE TRACE PKWY, FAMILY HEALTH CARE 76248 #048-13-1972 L1972 **FM** *020 †18
AMIN, Yama. 606 SAN CLEMENTE DR 76248 #048-13-2000 L2003 **EM** *020
BALLARD, Kimberly Sue. 1006 KELLER PKWY, STE 103 76248 #048-02-1997 L2000 **PD** *020 †55
BARLOW, Laura Lynn. ■ 76248 #017-20-1995 **PTH** *100
BENSON, Rochelle A. ■ 76248 #048-02-1993 L1996 **PD** *075 †55
BRIDGES, William C. 8553 N BEACH ST 76248 #048-12-1997 L1998 **PM** *020 †60
BROWNING, Richard Marlin. ■ 76248 #048-12-1975 L1975 **OBG** *020 †30
BUSIGO, Jason Pete. ■ 76248 #042-01-2000 L2005 **DR** *020 †80
CHACON, Francisco. 3529 HERITAGE TRACE PKWY, STE 137 76248 #048-14-1998 L1999 **FM** *020 †18
CONNER, Byron Felton. 1300 MESA TRL 76248 #048-15-1994 L1995 **FM** *020 †70,18
DODA, Tobin. ■ 76248 #048-14-1991 *100
DOMAGAS, Benjamin Tinio. 451 E PRICE ST, KELLER MEDICAL CLINIC 76248 #748-07-1964 L1978 **IM** *020 †20
FRICKER, Timothy Jay. 230 N RUFE SNOW DR, CHILDREN'S MEDICAL CENTER 76248 #016-43-1998 L2001 **PD** *020 †55
FULLER, Gregory Michael. 816 KELLER PKWY STE 102 76248 #004-01-1987 L1990 **FM** *020 †18
GAGNON, Maurice Robt. 1141 KELLER PKWY, STE A 76248 #050-02-1972 L1979 **OBG** *020 †30
GANACIAS-ACUNA, Edna F. ■ 76248 #748-08-1967 L1975 **AN** *020
GOMEZ, Omar A. 230 N RUFE SNOW DR 76248 #048-16-1994 L1995 **PD** *020 †55
GREEN, Roddy D. 1141 KELLER PKWY STE B, CORNERSTONE FAMILY & SPORT 76248 #048-12-1998 L2003 **FM** *020 †18
GREENBERG, Ana Cadena. ■ 76248 #649-52-2000 **FP** *012
HOANG, Mai Vu-Quynh. ■ 76248 #048-02-1997 L1999 **FM** *020 †18
KALLAL, Kevin John. 240 N RUFE SNOW DR 76248 #016-45-1983 L1990 **FM** *020 †18
KELLEY, Zachary Lamar. ■ 76248 #054-04-2003 L2008 **ORS** *012
KILIANSKI, Joseph R, Jr. 1141 KELLER PKWY, STE A 76248 #048-16-1987 L1988 **OBG** *020 †30
KOSANKE, Kristin Lynn. 230 N RUFE SNOW DR, CHILDREN'S MEDICAL CTR-DAL 76248 #039-01-1997 L2000 **PD** *020 †55
KRIEG, Debra P. 4100 HERITAGE TRACE PKWY, STE 116 76248 #048-13-2001 L2003 **FM** *020 †18
KUSHWAHA, Shari M. 1670 KELLER PKWY, STE 170 76248 #048-13-1995 L2003 **PD** *020 †55
LANDSTROM, Donald L. ■ 76248 #016-11-1966 L1967 **N NP** *071 †75
LEFFEL, Alicia Renee. 240 N RUFE SNOW DR, KID CARE PEDIATRICS 76248 #048-02-1996 L1997 **PD** *020 †55
LEWIS, Chad Eric. ■ 76248 #017-20-1999 L2004 **CRS** *020 †85
LIU, Kevin S. 601 S MAIN ST, STE 200 76248 #048-04-1998 L1999 **FM** *020 †18
LOFTIS, James Stewart. ■ 76248 #012-16-1956 L1956 **FM** *071 †18
MAKOWSKI, Glenn Joseph. 4224 HERITAGE TRACE PKWY, STE 304 76248 #048-13-1997 L1999 **OMF** *020
MALIK, Nadia. ■ 76248 #704-02-1999 L2008 **IM** *100 †20
MANGHAM, Huong Pham. 1006 KELLER PKWY, STE 103 76248 #048-12-1999 L2002 **PD** *020 †55
MAYFIELD, Mark Stanley. 940 KELLER PKWY STE 12 76248 #048-02-1985 L1988 **FM** *020 †18
MENDEZ, Michelle Yvette. ■ 76248 #042-01-2001 L2005 **SCI** *100
MILLER, Jan Estes. 4100 HERITAGE TRACE PKWY 76248 #034-01-1995 L2007 **FM** *020 †18
MORGAN, Royce Harvey. 2209 BEACON HILL DR 76248 #039-01-1954 L1992 **GP OM** *020
NAIR, Thamilarasi R. ■ 76248 #495-42-1972 **P** *062
OBENG, Joseph. ■ 76248 #412-01-1999 L2004 **IM** *020
OGBUE, Patrick Okwudili. ■ 76248 #690-06-1990 L2004 **AN** *020 †05
O'LEARY, Christa E. 601 S MAIN ST, STE 200 76248 #048-78-1997, ▲ L1998 **FM** *020 †18
PLACKIS, Cynthia. ■ 76248 #049-01-1983 L1987 **EM** *020 †16
RAJU, Gopal S. ■ 76248 #495-09-1959 L1971 **GS FM** *071
RIGGS, Haiqiong Wu. ■ 76248 #019-02-2003 L2007 **AN** *020
RUMALLA, Smita Kasat. 816 KELLER PKWY STE 10 76248 #033-06-1997 L2004 **FM** *020 †18
SATYA, Ramadass. ■ 76248 #495-62-1977 L2007 **VIR** *100 †28
SCHULER, Christopher M. ■ 76248 #038-44-2001 L2007 **HMP** *100
SNEAD, Jonathan C, II. 4120 HERITAGE TRACE PKWY, STE 208 76248 #048-15-2001 L2003 **OBG** *020 †30
SWEGLER, Erica Williams. 816 KELLER PKWY STE 102 76248 #048-14-1983 L1983 **FM** *020 †18
TERK, Jason Victor. 1006 KELLER PKWY, STE 103 76248 #048-02-1993 L1997 **PD** *020 †55
TOLAR, Roger L, Jr. 1141 KELLER PKWY 76248 #048-13-1991 L1993 **FM** *020 †18
VAUGHAN, Thomas Henry, Jr. 1141 KELLER PKWY, STE A 76248 #048-02-1976 L1976 **OBG** *020 †30
WHITE, Michael Alan. 1141 KELLER PKWY, STE A 76248 #048-15-1984 L1985 **OBG** *020 †30
WIMMER, Patrick J. ■ 76248 #048-12-1991 L1992 **EM** *020 †16
YOK, Sara Ran. 1006 KELLER PKWY STE 103 76248 #048-04-2002 L2005 **PD** *020 †55
YOUNGMAN, De Lyle Roy. ■ 76248 #030-05-1957 L1977 **ORS AM** *071 †40

KEMAH – GALVESTON

GHOSH, Sunanda. ■ 77565 #048-12-2004 **GS** *012
GHOSH, Sunil Kumar. ■ 77565 #495-02-1955 L1980 *020
LEWANDOWSKI, Eric M. ■ 77565 #048-13-1986 L1992 **AN** *020 †05
LOYNES, Richard James S. 1026 ASPEN RD, C/O GULF COAST EMERGENCY P 77565 #065-06-1974 L1977 **EM** *020 †16
MOSLEY, Grenville Ross. ■ 77565 #671-01-1958 L1979 **EM FM** *071 †18,16

KEMPNER – LAMPASAS

HEPLER, Timothy John. ■ 76539 #023-12-2005 L2007 **FP** *012

KENEDY – KARNES

DAY, Ancie Fred. RR 1 78119 #048-12-1955 L1955 **GP** *071
DUGI, Daniel David, Jr. 113 W MAIN ST, DETAR MEDICAL CENTER-KENED 78119 #048-13-1980 L1980 **FM** *020 †18
MITCHELL, Rayford Benard. 3313 S HIGHWAY 181, STE C 78119 #048-12-2004 L2005 **FM** *020 †18

RAMIREZ, Roberto. 3349 S HIGHWAY 181, STE 4 78119 #048-04-1985 L1986 **FM** *020 †18
SALDANA, Joel. 3349 S HIGHWAY 181 STE 2 78119 #048-02-1986 L1987 **FM** *020 †18
SEAWORTH, John Fortune. 3349 S HIGHWAY 181 78119 #028-02-1976 L1979 **CD** *020 †20

KENNEDALE – TARRANT

WATT, John Everett. ■ 76060 #041-01-1962 L1970 **P PYA** *020 †75

KERENS – NAVARRO

SPEAK, Kenneth Edwin. ■ 75144 #005-15-1962 L1975 **GP** *071

KERMIT – WINKLER

CHOUDHARY, Niraj. 814 MYER LN 79745 #495-15-1996 L2001 **IM** *020 †20
CHOUDHARY, Smriti Dubey. 828 MYER LN 79745 #495-96-1999 L2004 **IM** *020

KERRICK – DALLAM

MATHEWS, Gary W. STATE LINE ROAD 79051 #048-13-1984 L1985 **GP** *020

KERRVILLE – KERR

ALLEN, William Marion. 695 HILL COUNTRY DR 78028 #048-13-1973 L1973 **ORS** *020 †40
APPLING, J Scott. ■ 78028 #019-02-1992 L1995 **FM** *020 †18
ATCHISON, Martin V. ■ 78028 #048-12-1944 L1945 **ORS** *071 †40
AVERY, Christopher M. 420 WATER ST, STE 105B 78028 #048-13-1981 L1981 **AN ORS** *020 †05
BALLAY, Charles Joseph, II. 1331 BANDERA HWY, STE 1 78028 #021-06-2001 L2007 **OTO** *020 †45
BARNETT, John Mathis. 218 SIDNEY BAKER ST 78028 #048-02-1975 L1975 **RO EM** *020 †80
BARRINGTON, Rebecca E. 694 HILL COUNTRY DR 78028 #048-16-1990 L1991 **ON HO** *020 †20
BAUGHMAN, Donald Ray. ■ 78028 #018-03-1954 L1955 **R NM** *071 †80
BENNETT, Allen. ■ 78028 #011-02-1976 L1977 **D** *020 †15
BERG, Timothy A. 710 WATER ST STE 60 78028 #036-05-1984 L1996 **GS TRS** *020 †85
BOONE, George Daniel. 710 WATER ST 78028 #048-12-1980 L1980 **IM ADM** *020 †20
BOONE, James Carroll. PO BOX 293370 78029 #048-12-1984 L1985 **IM** *020 †20
BOREN, Paul Goodwyn. ■ 78028 #039-01-1962 L1963 **FM** *071
BOWERS, Robert Graves. 201 GUY GRIGGS PROF BLDG, ROBERT G BOWERS JR MD PA 78028 #048-12-1957 L1957 **OPH** *071 †35
BOYCE, Theodore Ralph. 1331 BANDERA HWY, STE 3 78028 #005-15-1966 L1969 **FM** *071 †18
BRADLEY, Harold Franklin. PO BOX 291741 78029 #012-01-1965 L1970 **AN** *071 †05
BROCK, Thomas Wm. 721 THOMPSON DR, KERRVILLE STATE HOSPITAL 78028 #016-01-1973 L1985 **IM** *020 †20
BRYSON, David Lyman. 721 THOMPSON DR, KERRVILLE STATE HOSP 78028 #008-01-1963 L1976 **OS** *030
BUTLER, Jack. ■ 78028 #048-02-1955 L1955 **PHP** *071 †70
BYRD, William C, Jr. ■ 78028 #036-05-1950 L1955 **IM** *071
CAMMACK, J Thomas. 1331 BANDERA HWY, MEDICAL SURGICAL SPECIALIS 78028 #048-13-1987 L1989 **U** *020
CHANCELLOR, Jon E. 151 ASHLEY DR, CARE CLINICS, PA 78028 #048-14-2002 L2005 **FM FSM** *020 †18
CHATHAM, Valerie Daniels. 3600 MEMORIAL BLVD, SOUTH TX VET HLTHCARE 78028 #048-13-1985 L1987 **IM** *020 †20
CHEDZOY, Nancy E Alvarez. 601 CLAY ST 78028 #028-46-1999 L2003 **OPH** *020 †35
CHENE, Janet Lea. 144 FAIRWAY DR STE A 78028 #308-11-1986 L1996 **FM EM** *040 †18
CHICA, Gerardo A, II. 2210 BANDERA HWY, UNIT C 78028 #048-15-1997 L2002 **IM** *020 †20
CLAYPOOL, Harry A. ■ 78028 #048-12-1955 L1959 **R** *072 †80
CLAYTON, Eugene N, III. 710 WATER ST 78028 #048-12-1989 L1990 **AN** *020 †05
COATES, Greig W. ■ 78028 #048-16-1990 *100
COLGIN, Murray Merchant. 710 WATER ST STE 606 78028 #048-02-1984 L1985 **IM** *020 †20
COLLINS, Frederick Gene. ■ 78028 #030-05-1947 L1947 **OTO** *071 †45
CONROY, Normabelle Helmen. ■ 78028 #016-42-1947 L1951 **P PFP** *072
CRAVEY, Russell S. 1001 WATER ST, STE E-100 78028 #048-16-1993 L1994 **OPH** *020 †35
CROZIER, Emily. ■ 78028 #048-12-2008 *012
DAVIS, Christopher Thomas. 710 WATER ST 78028 #048-13-2002 L2006 **AN** *020 †05
DAVIS, John Dillard. 220 WESLEY DR, FAMILY PRACTICE 78028 #048-12-1974 L1974 **FM** *020 †18
DE LEON, Mark Christopher. 694 HILL COUNTRY DR 78028 #023-12-1994 L2000 **HO** *020 †20
DENKE, Margo Ann. 710 WATER ST 78028 #024-01-1981 L1987 **IM END** *020 †20
DE VANEY, George Thos. 721 THOMPSON DR, KERRVILLE STATE HOSPITAL 78028 #048-12-1957 L1957 **GE IM** *071
DODD, George Emmet, Jr. ■ 78028 #048-02-1942 L1943 **IM** *071
DONALD, Clarence W, Jr. 710 WATER ST 78028 #012-01-1963 L1973 **PD** *071
DUCKER, Thomas E. 1331 BANDERA HWY, GUADALUPE PHYS GRP 78028 #048-12-1988 L1991 **GE** *020 †20
EASTIN, Kirsten Olsson. 105 DEERWOOD DR 78028 #048-12-1992 L1994 **P** *020 †75
EASTMAN, Harry Jerome. 3600 MEMORIAL BLVD, KERRVILLE VA MEDICAL CENTE 78028 #048-12-1964 L1964 **IM GE** *020 †20
FANNIN, Heather Fay. 500 THOMPSON DR 78028 #048-13-1986 L1987 **P** *020 †75
FARIAS-DANIELS, Geraldine. 721 THOMPSON DR 78028 #048-04-1984 L1987 **P** *020
FINLEY, Olivia Isabelle. ■ 78028 #010-03-1978 L1984 **GP** *075
FITZGERALD, Mark R. 401 JUNCTION HWY 78028 #048-12-1995 L1996 **FM** *020
FONTENOT, Michael Scott. 315 W MAIN ST 78028 #048-12-1985 L1994 **PD** *020 †55
FOSTER, Mirelle J. 710 WATER ST 78028 #048-14-1998 L2002 **PM** *020 †60
FRITZSCH, Ralph J. 251 CULLY DR STE C 78028 #048-12-1993 L1995 **U** *020 †95
GABATIN, Jose Q. 721 THOMPSON DR 78028 #748-01-1955 L1975 **P GP** *071 †75
GAGNON, Lori I Braveman. 260 CULLY DR 78028 #654-01-1999 L2005 **FM** *100 †18 ‡
GAGNON, Michael James. 1001 WATER ST STE J-100, THE HILL COUNTRY CENTER FO 78028 #654-01-1999 L2005 **RO** *020 †80

■ = Address Information Privacy Protected

GANGAI, Mauro Pat. ■ 78028 #024-07-1956 L1975 **U** *020 †95
GARDNER, Sandra E. 3600 MEMORIAL BLVD, KERRVILLE VA MEDICAL CENTE 78028 #021-01-1991 L1995 **GPM** *020 †20
GATLIN, Coley C. 710 WATER ST 78028 #048-13-1997 L2001 **FSM** *020 †18
GIVEN, Brian V. 710 WATER ST, STE 606 78028 #048-16-1995 L1996 **GS** *020 †85
GIVEN, Tami Hammond. 218 SIDNEY BAKER 78028 #048-16-1994 L1995 **OBG** *020 †30
GOHLKE, Marvin H. ■ 78028 #048-02-1951 L1951 **FM** *071 †18
GOLDSTEIN, Janine Lee. 819 WATER ST, STE 300 78028 #021-06-1990 L1996 **CHP** *020
GRAHAM, James Lee. 708 HILL COUNTRY DR, STE 300A 78028 #649-19-1981 L1984 **FM** *020 †18
GRAHAM, Loyd Alton. 3600 MEMORIAL BLVD, KERRVILLE VA HOSPITAL 78028 #048-04-1982 L1983 **IM** *020 †20
GREGORY, George Wm. ■ 78028 #007-02-1967 L1972 **TS GS** *071 †85,90
GRIFFITH, Karl E. 321 HUNTSBERRY RIDGE RD, DEPT OF ANESTH 78028 #048-02-1983 L1983 **AN** *020 †05
GRIMM, John H. ■ 78029 #035-15-1949 L1950 **R AM** *071 †80
GROCKI, Michael Stephen. 176 FAIRWAY DR 78028 #048-15-1999 L2005 **IM** *020
GUERRA, Michael Edward. 1724 KAMIRA 78028 #048-16-1985 L1986 **OPH** *020 †35
HAGEMEIER, Karl F, III. 1331 BANDERA HWY 78028 #048-04-1982 L1983 **GS** *020 †85
HALE, Tyson D. 320A WATER ST 78028 #048-02-1999 L2001 **DR** *020 †80
HARDEE, Thos Leonard, Jr. ■ 78028 #021-01-1960 L1971 **P** *071 †75
HARPER, Benjamin L. 710 WATER ST, EMERGENCY DEPT 78028 #048-14-1998 L1999 **FM EM** *020 †18
HARRELSON, George Wm, Jr. ■ 78028 #004-01-1965 L1971 **P GP** *071
HARRISON, Gunyon M. ■ 78028 #051-01-1946 L1957 **PD PUD** *020 †55
HAWKINS, Theron Chas. 710 WATER ST 78028 #048-04-1956 L1956 **U** *020 †95
HEACOCK, Allen K. ■ 78028 #048-12-1960 L1960 **P GP** *020
HOLLAND, Kathleen M. 1436 SIDNEY BAKER ST 78028 #048-13-1979 L1981 **PD NPM** *020 †55
HURLEY, Cathy Ann. 710 WATER ST STE 60 78028 #048-02-1985 L1987 **IM** *071 †20
JACKSON, Donald Everett. ■ 78028 #048-04-1958 L1958 **GS VS** *071 †85
JAHED, Abdul Zahed. ■ 78028 #118-02-1978 L1997 **IM** *020 †20
JAMES, Kimberly Dawn. 819 WATER ST, STE 300 78028 #048-02-2001 L2006 **CHP** *020
JOHNSON, James Ernest, Jr. ■ 78028 #048-02-1955 L1955 **P** *071 †75
JOHNSON, Richard Benj, Jr. 710 WATER ST, STE 300 78028 #048-14-1978 L1978 **IM** *020 †20
JOHNSON, Roger Stanley. 983 LANDMARK DR 1 78028 #026-04-1951 L1961 **LM GS** *071 †85
JOHNSTON, Maurice B. 721 THOMPSON DR 78028 #041-12-1941 L1951 **GPM AM** *071 †70
KAVANAGH, Joseph Terrence. 3600 MEMORIAL BLVD, DEPT OPH 78028 #917-12-1991 L2001 **OPH** *020 †35
KILGORE, Henry Earl, Jr. 3600 MEMORIAL BLVD # 50-2 78028 #048-12-1962 L1962 **GS** *020 †85
KING, Alan Edward. 3600 MEMORIAL BLVD, SOUTH TX VETERANS HLTH 78028 #035-09-1962 L1969 **GS** *020 †85
KNIGHT, John Albert, Jr. 1331 BANDERA HWY, STE 2 78028 #048-04-1967 L1967 **OBG** *020 †30
KOCAY, Paul H. 1331 BANDERA HWY, STE 2 78028 #048-12-1982 L1983 **OBG** *020 †30
LAYNE, Ottis Langley, Jr. 710 WATER ST 78028 #048-04-1970 L1970 **EM ADM** *020 †16
LAYTON, Ernest G, Jr. 251 CULLY DR, STE A 78028 #048-16-1990 L1992 **PS** *020 †65
LEE, James Arthur. 3600 MEMORIAL BLVD, VA MED CTR 78028 #016-43-1966 L1974 **P ADM** *071
LENNHOFF, Michael. 721 THOMPSON DR 78028 #649-01-1962 L1975 **P IM** *071
LEWIS, Charles Ernest. 711 HILL COUNTRY DR 78028 #048-13-1975 L1975 **ORS** *020 †40
LIGGETT, Charles Lee. ■ 78028 #041-02-1944 L1951 **GYN OBS** *071 †30
LINDNER, Milton J, Jr. 3600 MEMORIAL BLVD, VA HOSP 78028 #649-05-1963 L1968 **OPH** *071 †35
LIONE, John Gabriel. ■ 78028 #035-08-1944 L1969 **GPM** *071 †70
LIVELY, Michael Shawn. 710 WATER ST 78028 #048-02-2003 L2006 **EM** *020 †16
LLANOS, Arturo R. 420 WATER ST, STE 103 78028 #048-02-1987 L1988 **FM** *020 †18 ‡
MABAQUIAO, Gaudioso L. 721 THOMPSON DR 78028 #748-07-1971 L1981 **IM OBG** *020
MAC KAY, Robert Carroll. ■ 78028 #021-01-1957 L1957 **PTH** *071 †50
MALAKOFF, Mary Louise. ■ 78028 #654-01-1996 **P** *071
MARQUE, Melvin Joseph, III. 710 WATER ST, SID PETERSON MEMORIAL HOSP 78028 #021-05-1998 L2006 **EM** *020 †16
MARSH-ROSS, Elinor E. ■ 78028 #030-06-1942 L1948 **GP PM** *071
MARTIN, Michael Winfield. 3600 MEMORIAL BLVD, MEDICAL CENTER 78028 #048-02-1976 L1976 **IM** *020 †20
MASSEY, Lisa Gaye. 420 WATER ST STE 105B 78028 #048-04-1981 L1982 **AN** *020 †05
MATEY, Douglas Andrew, Jr. PO BOX 291411, 1331 BANDERA HWY SUITE 3 78029 #034-01-1974 L1980 **OBG** *020 †30
MATTHEIS, Kenneth Robt. ■ 78028 #030-06-1966 L1966 **NS** *075 †25
MATTHEWS, Jeffery Ray. 721 THOMPSON DR, KERRVILLE STATE HOSPITAL 78028 #039-01-1991 L1992 **P** *020 †75
MC BRIDE, Kenneth Bernard. 721 THOMPSON DR, KERRVILLE STATE HOSPITAL 78028 #024-01-1963 L1970 **IM END** *071 †20
MC KENZIE, Gregory Gene. 710 WATER ST 78028 #048-04-1978 L1979 **IM** *071 †20
MEHENDALE, Anand Wasudeo. 222 SIDNEY BAKER S STE 500 78028 #495-28-1976 L1981 **N ADM** *020 †75
MELCHER, Linette Bell. PO BOX 294029 78029 #048-02-1994 L1996 **N** *020 †75
MELUCCI, Michael B. 710 WATER ST STE 402 78028 #033-06-1979 L1998 **CD IM** *020 †20
MERIWETHER, John C. 315 W MAIN ST 78028 #021-06-1986 L1989 **PD** *020 †55
MERRITT, Vivin Earl. 154 WHARTON RD 78028 #048-04-1973 L1973 **GS** *071 †85
MILOY, David R. 1001 WATER ST, STE D-100 78028 #048-15-1994 L2002 **IM** *020 †20
MITCHELL, Robert Eugene. 695 HILL COUNTRY DR 78028 #019-02-1980 L1981 **ORS** *020 †40
MOHAR, Dale Elliott. 708 HILL COUNTRY DR, STE 400 78028 #048-13-1990 L1991 **AI** *020 †20,03
MONTGOMERY, Richard F, Jr. 501 JEFFERSON ST, STE 2 78028 #048-13-1977 L1983 **OS OTO** *074 †45
MOODY, Austin R, II. 420 WATER ST, STE 108 78028 #048-13-1982 L1983 **N** *020 †75
MORRIS, Donald Clinton, Jr. 695 HILL COUNTRY DR, STE C 78028 #048-14-1996 L2001 **ORS** *020 †40
MORRIS, William E. 710 WATER ST 78028 #048-13-1974 L1974 **IM** *020 †20
MOSS, Sue. 1422 SIDNEY BAKER 78028 #048-14-1985 L1986 **P** *020 †75
MURRMANN, Don Neil. 843 SIDNEY BAKER 78028 #017-20-1978 L1981 **IM** *020 †20
NOONAN, Thomas A, Jr. ■ 78028 #048-78-1977, ▲ L1982 **GP GS** *072
NORSTROM, Craig Wilbur. ■ 78028 #060-01-1955 L1961 **NS OS** *071 †25
O'DONNELL, Wm Chas, Jr. 220 WESLEY DR, MEDICAL ARTS PLAZA 78028 #048-12-1973 L1974 **FM** *020 †18
PARKER, Wade M. ■ 78028 #048-02-1952 L1952 **PTH** *071 †50
PEARCE, Carolyn Jean. ■ 78028 #021-01-1986 L1987 **NEP HEM** *071 †20
PELTON, Kelly Crews. 708 HILL COUNTRY DR, STE 400 78028 #048-16-1995 L1998 **IM** *020 †20
PERRYMAN, Teri Lyn. 218 QUINLAN ST, # 382 78028 #048-14-1995 L1996 **PD** *020 †55
PETERSON, Evan Hugo, Jr. 232 W LACEY OAK PKWY 78028 #026-04-1964 L1985 **FM** *071 †18
PETTY, Larry Dean. ■ 78028 #048-12-1965 L1965 **AN** *071 †05
PHILLIPS, Theresa S. 306 WESLEY DR, STE B 78028 #048-13-1994 L1995 **N** *020
POIRIER, Robert Harold. 1446 SIDNEY BAKER ST 78028 #056-06-1965 L1973 **OPH** *071 †35
POPE, Henry David. ■ 78028 #021-01-1955 L1957 **FM** *071 †18
PRICE, Gerald Allen. 710 WATER ST STE 706 78028 #048-13-1994 L1995 **MPD** *020
PRIOUR, Donald James. 961 WATER ST 78028 #048-02-1972 L1972 **OPH** *020 †35 ‡
PRIOUR, Harlan Lary. 710 WATER ST 78028 #036-07-1975 L1975 **OBG** *020
PRUNEDA, Joe M, III. 320A WATER ST 78028 #048-02-1988 L1989 **DR** *020 †80
QUINTANILLA, Jaime. 402 RIVERHILL BLVD 78028 #649-02-1954 L1959 **CHP P** *020 †75
RECTOR, William Raymond. 705 WATER ST 78028 #048-02-1967 L1967 **DR OS** *020 †80
REHER, Vicky L. 721 THOMPSON DR 78028 #048-13-1993 L1994 **P** *020 †75
REYNOLDS, Robert M. 710 WATER ST 78028 #048-04-1985 L1986 **AN FM** *020 †18,05
ROBINSON, Julie Anne. 819 WATER ST, STE 300 78028 #048-13-1987 L1988 **P** *020
ROSE, J Lee. ■ 78028 #048-14-1986 L1987 **EM** *020 †18
ROSSON, Dorothy Annette. 3600 MEMORIAL BLVD, KERRVILLE VAMC 78028 #048-02-1986 L1987 **IM** *020 †20
ROTH, Georgia White. 151 ASHLEY DR 78028 #048-13-1985 L1986 **FM** *020 †18
ROUSE, Lisa A. 707 HILL COUNTRY DR # 106 78028 #048-14-1987 L1988 **FM** *020 †18
SANTIAGO-YOUNG, Odemaris. 176 FAIRWAY DR 78028 #042-02-1989 L1991 **RHU IM** *020 †20
SCHLABACH, Michael Ray. 1331 BANDERA HWY, STE 1B 78028 #048-02-1978 L1978 **IM GPM** *020 †20
SCHROEDER, Klaus M. 1001 WATER ST, STE J-100 78028 #409-33-1989 L1996 **IM** *020 †20
SCOTT, Deborah A. 3600 MEMORIAL BLVD, VA MEDICAL CENTER 78028 #048-13-1986 L2001 **IM** *020 †20
SHAW, Donna Marie. 3600 MEMORIAL BLVD, MENTAL HEALTH CLINIC 78028 #004-01-1980 L1980 **P** *020 †75
SHAW, Milton Don. 3600 MEMORIAL BLVD 78028 #048-13-1978 L1978 **IM IMG** *020 †20
SHORT, Stephen Lynn. ■ 78028 #048-02-1978 L1978 **ID IM** *020 †20
SIMES, Edward Lee. 819 WATER ST, STE 300 78028 #048-04-1975 L1975 **P** *020 †75
SINCLAIR, Thomas Albert. ■ 78028 #048-04-1946 L1946 **GYN** *071 †30
SMITH, Thomas Gillispie, III. 710 WATER ST, STE 300 78028 #048-02-1997 L2002 **U** *020 †95
SMITHDEAL, Charles David. 317 SIDNEY BAKER ST S, STE 400 78028 #047-06-1958 L1960 **PS** *071 †45
SNYDER, Alvin Eugene. ■ 78028 #005-15-1966 L1967 **FM PHP** *071 †18
SPECK, Fred L. ■ 78028 #048-02-2008 *012
SPECK, Fred Louis, Jr. 401 JUNCTION HWY 78028 #048-02-1977 L1977 **D OS** *020 †15
SPROUSE, David Robt. 220 WESLEY DR, FAMILY PRACTICE 78028 #048-13-1986 L1987 **FM** *020 †18
STEVENSON, Robert Neal. 721 THOMPSON DR, KERRVILLE STATE HOSP 78028 #048-13-1975 L1978 **P** *020 †75
STOBBE, William Robt. ■ 78028 #047-06-1960 L1961 **P** *072 †75
SWANZY, Jack Martin. 3600 MEMORIAL BLVD, DEPARTMENT OF VETERAN'S AF 78028 #048-13-1977 L1977 **IM** *020 †20
SWINDELL, Samuel Waddy. ■ 78028 #048-12-1954 L1954 **GS** *071
THOMAS, Rex E. 707 HILL COUNTRY DR STE 10 78028 #048-02-1951 L1951 **AN** *071
THURMOND, Jack A. ■ 78028 #045-01-1953 L1962 **OPH** *071 †35
TOLOZA, Eileen Marie. 710 WATER ST, EMERGENCY DEPARTMENT 78028 #005-15-2001 L2004 **EM** *020 †16
TRAEGER, Rodney Saml. ■ 78028 #048-02-1970 L1970 **U** *020 †95
TRUE, Janet Elaine. 721 THOMPSON DR 78028 #019-02-1979 L1989 **P** *020 †75
TRUELOCK, Kerri Lee. 218 SIDNEY BAKER 78028 #048-13-2001 L2005 **OBG** *020 †30
TUCKER, Karsten G. 220 WESLEY DR, FAMILY PRACTICE 78028 #048-02-1998 L2001 **FM** *020 †18
VINAS, Joseph Francis. 251 CULLY DR, SURGICAL ASSOCIATES OF KER 78028 #048-02-1973 L1973 **GS** *020 †85
WALLIN, John David. ■ 78028 #008-01-1962 L1965 **NEP IM** *040 †20
WAMPLER, M Gatlin. 1331 BANDERA HWY, STE 2 78028 #048-13-1990 L1991 **OBG** *020 †30
WATSON, Rebecca T. 1331 BANDERA HWY STE 3 78028 #048-12-1996 L1998 **MPD** *020 †20,55
WAYNER, Matthew John, III. 708 HILL COUNTRY DR, STE 300 78028 #048-13-1986 L1992 **OPH** *020 †35
WELLS, James Dowling. 420 WATER ST, STE 104 78028 #048-02-1974 L1974 **IM** *020
WHEATLEY, Kenneth K, Jr. ■ 78029 #048-04-1977 L1978 **R OS** *020 †80
WILLIAMS, Charles Hood. 819 WATER ST, STE 300 78028 #048-02-1954 L1954 **AN ADM** *020 †05
WILLIAMS, Christopher E. 936 JUNCTION HWY 78028 #048-12-1999 L2000 **FM** *020 †18
WILLIAMS, Margaret J. 819 WATER ST, STE 300 78028 #021-06-1981 L1985 **P CHP** *020 †75
WILSON, Kathleen Rose. 710 WATER ST, STE 507 78028 #654-01-2000 L2004 **IM** *020 †20
WINKLER, David C. 1331 BANDERA HWY STE 3 78028 #048-13-1999 L2002 **IM** *020
WOODWARD, Debra Epps. ■ 78028 #048-14-1986 L1987 **FM** *020 †18
WORTHINGTON, Marion M. 721 THOMPSON DR 78028 #917-28-1962 L1966 **P OS** *030 †50,75
WRIGHT, Douglas Edwin. 1001 WATER ST, STE E - 200 78028 #048-15-1986 L1987 **GE** *020 †20
YOUNG, James Alan. 176 FAIRWAY DR 78028 #048-04-1991 L1992 **IM** *020 †20
YOUNGBLOOD-MCKENZIE, B. 710 WATER ST 78028 #048-13-1991 L1992 **AN** *020 †05
ZUBER, Randolph Clark. GRIGGS PROF BLDG STE 300 78028 #048-02-1967 L1967 **U** *020 †95

KILGORE – GREGG

BROCKWAY, Jason K. 1718 S HENDERSON BLVD 75662 #048-02-1995 L1996 **FM** *020 †18
CIBELE, Francisco. 2019 S HENDERSON BLVD # 3 75662 #132-02-1966 L1974 **GS GP** *020 †85
DENNIS, Michael Howard. ■ 75662 #048-12-1980 L1981 **FM** *075 †18
DENNY, Phil Dozier, Jr. 1612 S HENDERSON BLVD 75662 #048-13-1986 L1987 **EM** *020 †18
ECHOLS, Robert B. 1612 S HENDERSON BLVD 75662 #028-02-1950 L1952 **FM** *071
FORTSON, Wayne Everett. 2019 S HENDERSON BLVD 75662 #004-01-1973 L1977 **FM** *020
HOLLAND, Jill Diane. 1711 S HENDERSON BLVD, STE 400 75662 #048-14-2002 L2004 **FM** *020 †18
LANGLEY, Clark Wynn. 1718 S HENDERSON BLVD 75662 #039-01-1998 L2001 **FM** *020 †18
LANKA, Surya Prakash. 2019B S HENDERSON BLVD, STE 12 75662 #495-99-1986 L1993 **IM** *020

MC SHAN, Michael Wade. 1711 S HENDERSON BLVD, STE 300 75662 #048-02-1975 L1975 **FM EM** *020 †16 ‡

MILLER, Mark D. 1718 S HENDERSON BLVD 75662 #048-13-1992 L1993 **FM** *020 †18

PATEL, Atulkumar R. 1612 S HENDERSON BLVD 75662 #495-23-1985 L1993 **IM** *020 †20

REDMON, Jonathan L. 1718 S HENDERSON BLVD 75662 #048-14-1998 L2000 **GS** *100 †85

REPASKY, James Edmund. 1718 S HENDERSON BLVD 75662 #048-12-1979 L1979 **FM** *020 †18

RUSSELL, Patrick T. 22596 FM 2767 E, MOTHER FRANCES HOSPITAL 75662 #048-14-1996 L1998 **IM** *020 †20

SLUSHER, Kevin Dale. 1612 S HENDERSON BLVD, JAKE M MAJORS MD 75662 #021-06-1990 L1994 **OBG** *075

WHITE, Gary C. 2019 S HENDERSON BLVD, STE 4 75662 #308-10-1989 L1998 **FM** *020 †18

WHITMER, Wade Wyatt. 1718 S HENDERSON BLVD # 4 75662 #048-13-1983 L1983 **ORS** *020 †40

WOLCOTT, John Kevin. 5174 FM 1252 W 75662 #048-13-1984 L1987 **FM** *020 †18

ZAPATA SUAREZ, Juan Raul. 316 N HENDERSON BLVD # A 75662 #649-01-1967 L1972 **GP IM** *020

KILLEEN — BELL

ABD EL-REHEIM, Fayza. 2201 S CLEAR CREEK RD, METROPLEX HOSP PATH DEPT 76549 #915-07-1972 L1983 **ATP CLP** *020 †50

ALI, Sayed Karar. ■ 76542 #035-48-2003 L2006 **IM** *020 †20

ALLRED, Robert Lewis. 2300 S CLEAR CREEK RD 76549 #039-01-1963 L1971 **ORS OAR** *020 †40

ALVARADO, Nivea I. 2201 S CLEAR CREEK RD 76549 #042-01-1983 L1992 **PD** *020 †55

ASAMOAH, Osei Kwame, Jr. 2201 S CLEAR CREEK RD 76549 #005-14-2004 L2007 **EM** *020

AVERITT, William M. 3801 SCOTT AND WHITE DR 76543 #048-78-1990, ▲ L1991 **FM** *020 †18

BACA, Katrina May. 3801 SCOTT AND WHITE DR 76543 #034-01-1999 L2002 **PD** *020 †55

BARATANG, Ramil T. 3106 S W S YOUNG DR #B-201, CEDAR CREST CLINIC 76542 #748-10-1991 L2005 **CHP P** *020

BARNETT, Frederick M. 2201 S CLEAR CREEK RD 76549 #041-14-1985 L1995 **DR** *020 †80

BEAL, Terry Jackman. 2117 CLEAR CREEK RD 76549 #025-07-1971 L1979 **ORS EM** *020 †40

BLANKENSHIP, Lilian V. 2804 S W S YOUNG DR 76542 #748-11-1972 L1978 **PD** *020 †55

BURNETT, Tiffany Nicole. ■ 76542 #010-01-2003 L2004 *100

BUZZARD, Aaron Keith. ■ 76549 #048-13-2004 L2005 **EM** *020

CARLSON, Derek Mikel. ■ 76542 #022-75-2007, ▲ **EM** *012

CASHION, Wm Richard, Jr. 2207 CLEAR CREEK RD # 310, AUSTIN HEART 76549 #048-02-1966 L1966 **CD IM** *020 †20

CASTELLANOS, Luis G. 3106 S W S YOUNG DR, STE B204 76542 #048-16-1995 L1997 **OBG** *020 †30

CAVANAUGH, Regina K. 2201 S W S YOUNG DR, STE 116A 76543 #048-14-1992 L1993 **CHP** *020 †75

CHAFFER, Sheldon C, II. 2201 S W S YOUNG DR, STE 101B 76543 #048-14-2000 L2002 **NEP** *100 †20

CHANG, Austin W. 401 W JASPER DR 76542 #048-02-1999 L2002 **OPH** *020 †35

CHEEMA, Kausar Sayeed. ■ 76542 #704-04-1970 L1987 **PD** *020 †55

CHITWOOD, Charles J. ■ 76544 #048-12-1997 L2002 **FM** *020 †18

CHOWDHURY, Zinia. ■ 76542 #160-01-1992 L2004 **FM** *020

CHUNG, Byung Ho. 2301 S CLEAR CREEK RD, STE 212 76549 #583-02-1958 L1979 **GS VS** *020 †85,90

COLBERG, Pedro Nelson. 2201 S STAN SCHLUETER LOOP 76549 #649-01-1952 L1954 **GP D** *020

COLES, Stuart L. 3801 SCOTT AND WHITE DR 76543 #048-16-1985 L1986 **PD** *020 †55

COLON, Hector F. 2105 S CLEAR CREEK RD 76549 #042-01-1983 L1995 **N** *020 †75

DAVIS, Amanda Dawn. ■ 76542 #011-05-2005 L2007 **EM** *012

DAY, Charles Ryon. 2301 S CLEAR CREEK RD, STE 216 76549 #001-02-1986 L1997 **PS** *020 †85,65

DAY, Phillip Lee. 2201 S CLEAR CREEK RD, METROPLEX HOSP 76549 #048-15-1977 L1977 **PTH PCP** *050

DRIGALLA, Jessica Wallace. 3801 SCOTT AND WHITE DR 76543 #048-13-2003 L2006 **PD** *100 †55

EASTES, Gary Dean. 2301 S CLEAR CREEK RD, STE 208 76549 #048-12-1971 L1971 **U** *020 †95 ‡

ELMORE, Omega Faye. 2900 TRIMMIER RD 76542 #024-07-1983 L1989 *020

ESTERS, John Robt. 2207 S CLEAR CREEK RD, STE 202 76549 #010-03-1976 L1989 **OPH** *020 †35

FAROOQI, Manzoorul S. 3004 S W S YOUNG DR 76542 #704-08-1973 L1996 **PD** *020 †55

FERNANDEZ-REYES, Ernesto. 2301 S CLEAR CREEK RD, STE 126 76549 #649-01-1964 L1983 **IM** *071

FOULKS, Charles Jerome. 2201 S W S YOUNG DR, STE 101B 76543 #047-06-1975 L1978 **NEP IM** *020 †20

FOWLER, Miranda Cheryl. ■ 76549 #039-01-2006 L2008 **FP** *012

FREEMAN, Edward Boyd. 2127 S CLEAR CREEK RD 76549 #016-42-1992 L1993 **P** *020

FRITZ, Jed Stewart. 3801 SCOTT AND WHITE DR 76543 #048-16-1992 L1993 **FM** *020 †18 ‡

GARDNER, Jed R. 3801 SCOTT AND WHITE DR 76543 #048-16-1988 L1997 **FM** *020 †18

GELZER, Ronald Le Roy. 2900 TRIMMIER RD, RAPID RESPONSE HEALTH SERV 76542 #023-12-1983 L1995 **FM** *020 †18

GERDES, Paul Douglas. 3801 SCOTT AND WHITE DR 76543 #048-02-1983 L1983 **FM** *020 †18

GIFFORD, David Bailey. ■ 76543 #005-06-1967 L1968 **RHU** *020 †20

GLASSBERG, Eric Allen. 3801 SCOTT AND WHITE DR 76543 #035-08-2002 L2005 **FM** *020 †18

GODO, Charles Mawuli. 2301 S CLEAR CREEK RD, METROFLEX HOSPITAL 76549 #412-02-1993 L2004 **IM** *020 †20

GOHL, Monty Lee. 2111 S CLEAR CREEK RD 76549 #005-12-1969 L1976 **GS EM** *020 †85

GOWAN, Alan Clay. 2207 S CLEAR CREEK RD, STE 101 76549 #028-78-1999, ▲ L2002 **ON** *020 †20

GRIMES, Gil Charles. 3801 SCOTT AND WHITE DR 76543 #048-12-1995 L2001 **FM** *020 †18

HADLOCK, Daniel Canfield. 2207 S CLEAR CREEK RD, STE 101 76549 #041-01-1966 L1990 **HO PLM** *020 †20 ‡

HELLUMS, Deborah Brooks. 401 W JASPER DR 76542 #048-04-2002 L2006 **MPD** *020 †20,55

HINOJOSA, Camille Zavalet. 3801 SCOTT AND WHITE DR 76543 #048-16-2000 L2005 **GPM** *020 †70

HO, Kun-Tzeng. ■ 76541 #385-02-1962 L1973 **PD PDC** *020 †55

HOMSI, Omar. 2301 S CLEAR CREEK RD, STE 226 76549 #875-01-1980 L1997 **PD PDI** *020 †55

HOUSE, Charles Harold. ■ 76543 #005-12-1959 L1962 **GP** *071

JAMPALA, Vijayababu. 2201 S CLEAR CREEK RD, 2201 SOUTH CLEARCREEK ROAD 76549 #495-50-1981 L1988 **CHP P** *020 †75

JOSEPH, John Anthony, II. 3801 SCOTT AND WHITE DR, SCOTT & WHITE KILLEEN CLNC 76543 #048-14-1983 L1983 **FM EM** *020 †18 ‡

JUAREZ, John, Jr. 2201 S CLEAR CREEK RD 76549 #048-12-1980 L1980 **DR** *020 †20,28,80

JUNDT, Jeffrey Wm. 2301 S CLEAR CREEK RD #206 76549 #016-11-1980 L1985 **RHU IM** *062 †20

KEMPER, Eddie Paul. 2207 S CLEAR CREEK RD, STE 201 76549 #005-12-1983 L1997 **OBG** *020 †30

KERNAN, Philip M, Jr. ■ 76541 #051-01-1954 L1954 **OBG AM** *071 †30

KHWAJA, Shamsuddin. 2105 S CLEAR CREEK RD 76549 #704-08-1982 L2004 **N IM** *020 †75

KIM, Cheung Ki. 3106 S W S YOUNG DR, STE B203 76542 #583-06-1966 L1995 **FM PD** *020 †18

KIM, Gemma. 3801 SCOTT AND WHITE DR 76543 #654-01-2003 L2006 **FM** *020 †18

KINDLE, Kenneth R. 3801 SCOTT AND WHITE DR 76543 #048-78-1989, ▲ L1990 **FM** *020 †18

KING, Dennis Maurice. 3106 S W S YOUNG DR, STE B202 76542 #048-02-1970 L1970 **CHP P** *020 †75

KIRKPATRICK, Michael O. 1002 WALES DR, STE 8 76549 #004-01-1980 L1982 **FM** *020 †18

KLINE, James Lee. 2207 SCHOTTISCHE LN 76542 #051-04-2003 *100

KOTT, Daniel Francis. ■ 76542 #016-43-1963 **OBG** *071 †30

KUHNS, David Wallace. ■ 76549 #041-13-1985 L1988 **EM** *020 †16

LEONARDO, Pablo Be. 2301 S CLEAR CREEK RD, STE 202 76549 #748-07-1962 L1982 **IM** *020

LEWIS, Rory Howard. 2301 S CLEAR CREEK RD, STE 204 76549 #035-09-1990 L1998 **ORS** *020 †40

LOBAUGH, Mark Leland. 2111 S CLEAR CREEK RD 76549 #016-42-1986 L2002 **OBG** *020 †30

LOPEZ, Arthur G, Jr. 2121 S CLEAR CREEK RD 76549 #748-01-1974 L1983 **OTO GS** *020

LOUIS, William Geo. 2301 S CLEAR CREEK RD 76549 #048-04-1978 L1984 **OBG** *020

LUNA-BANIQUED, Zita O. 2201 S CLEAR CREEK RD 76549 #748-01-1972 L1982 **DR** *020 †80

MACEY, Harry Buford, Jr. 401 W JASPER DR, KINGS DAUGHTERS CLINIC 76542 #048-12-1958 L1958 **GYN** *071 †30

MARES, Adolph, Jr. 2207 CLEAR CREEK RD, STE 203 76549 #048-04-1987 L1990 **CD IM** *020 †20

MARIENFELD, Carla Beth. ■ 76542 #048-04-2007 **P** *012

MARTEN-ELLIS, Gerard L. 2301 S CLEAR CREEK RD, STE 116 76549 #042-01-1979 L1984 **OPH** *020 †35

MAXWELL, Shane R. 3801 SCOTT AND WHITE DR 76543 #048-15-1994 L1995 **FM** *020 †18

MAYER, Henry August, Jr. 1010 W JASPER DR 76542 #048-15-1976 L1988 **ORS OSM** *020 †20

MC COLLOUGH, Randy F. 2207 S CLEAR CREEK RD, STE 304 76549 #048-02-1986 L1987 **CD** *020 †20

MCINTYRE, Jacquelene M. 3816 S CLEAR CREEK RD, STE A 76549 #036-01-1989 L1992 **IM** *020

MC NANEY, Joseph Wm. ■ 76541 #035-09-1959 **AM PHP** *072

MILLER, Luke Michael. ■ 76542 #023-12-2003 L2005 **FM** *020 †18

MITCHELL, Charles Walter. ■ 76543 #005-12-1979 L1981 **EM** *020 †16

MITCHELL, Karen-Mae L. ■ 76543 #023-07-1996 L2002 **PTH** *050

MOCZYGEMBA, Richard Wayne. ■ 76542 #048-13-1984 L1988 **CHP** *020 †75

MORALES, Freddie Miguel. 2301 S CLEAR CREEK RD, STE 126 76549 #042-01-1980 L1984 **IM PUD** *020 †20

NAIR, Shyamala P. 2201 S W S YOUNG DR, STE 111B 76543 #495-31-1970 L1976 **PD** *071 †55

NARAYANAN, Mohanram. 2201 S W S YOUNG DR, STE 101B 76543 #495-08-1984 L1990 **NEP IM** *020 †20 ‡

NOWLIN, Thomas Peyton, IV. ■ 76549 #048-02-2000 L2007 **OTO** *020 †45

OANDASAN, Dulce Maria S. 3801 SCOTT AND WHITE DR 76543 #748-21-1986 L2007 **FM** *020 †18

OAS, Lute Geo. 2207 S CLEAR CREEK RD, STE 101 76549 #048-14-1992 L1993 **RO** *020 †80

PARK, Saung Zin. 2301 S CLEAR CREEK RD, STE 230 76549 #024-07-1994 L2004 **VS** *020 †85,90

PHILLIPS, Matthew. 2207 S CLEAR CREEK RD, STE 304 76549 #025-01-1980 L1997 **CD** *020 †20

RABSATT, Latasha Alexis. ■ 76542 #048-02-2008 *012

RAMANI, Hemalkumar Chandu. 2201 S CLEAR CREEK RD, METROPLEX HEALTH SYSYTEM 76549 #495-23-1999 L2005 **IM** *020

REBECCA, George S. 2123 S CLEAR CREEK RD 76549 #010-02-1975 L1993 **CD** *020 †20

REED, Larry Douglas. SUITE 108, 4520 E. CENTRAL TX. EXPWY, 76543 #048-12-1963 L1963 **P GP** *020

RENSBERRY, Matthew Duane. ■ 76542 #038-40-2007 **FP** *012

RIEDEL, David C. 2301 S CLEAR CREEK RD, STE 226 76549 #048-16-1989 L1990 **CHP** *020 †75

RISHI, Alka Shrikant. 2207 S CLEAR CREEK RD, STE 303 76549 #495-20-1968 L1993 **OBG** *020 †30

RISHI, Shrikant K. 2207 S CLEAR CREEK RD, STE 303 76549 #495-20-1967 L2002 **OTO** *020 †45

ROBLES, Zenaida F. 502 W JASPER DR 76542 #748-01-1958 L1977 **GP** *020

ROMAN, Lauren Suzanne. ■ 76549 #035-06-2005 L2007 **FP** *012

ROMERO-FIGUEROA, Arturo. 2201 S W S YOUNG DR, STE 114B 76543 #042-02-1988 L1992 **OBG** *020

SEGHERS, Victor Koenraad. 2115 S CLEAR CREEK RD 76549 #165-04-1968 L1974 **CD IM** *020 †20

SHETH, Minesh Punjalal. 2201 S CLEAR CREEK RD, METROPLEX HOSPITAL 76549 #495-48-1995 L2004 **IM** *020

SHIRLEY, Cynthia A. 2300 S CLEAR CREEK RD, STE 202 76549 #048-13-1997 L2006 **OBG** *020 †30

SIEBENLIST, James Barry. 2111 S CLEAR CREEK RD 76549 #005-12-1961 L1968 **OBG** *071 †30

SMITH, Darryl Richard. 4204 E STAN SCHLUETER LOOP, KILLEEN MED DIAGNOSTIC CTR 76542 #048-13-1986 L1987 **IM** *071 †20

SMITH, Steven Lynn. 3801 SCOTT AND WHITE DR 76543 #048-02-1977 L1977 **FM** *020 †18

SPENCER, Edward E. 502 W JASPER DR 76542 #048-14-1985 L1986 **FM** *020 †18

STANCEY, Corina Alina. 401 W JASPER DR 76542 #038-43-1997 L2005 **OPH** *020 †35

STEELE, Donald Ray. ■ 76544 #005-14-1966 L1969 **D DS** *071

STRELETZ, Deborah Albrech. 1002 WALES DR, STE 8 76549 #023-12-2000 L2007 **FM** *020 †18

SUBRAMANIAN, Mani. 2207 S CLEAR CREEK RD, STE 302 76549 #495-42-1971 L1983 **HO IM** *020 †20

SUKUMAR, Latha. 2301 S CLEAR CREEK RD, STE 112 76549 #495-04-1976 L1993 **IM** *020 †20

SUKUMAR, Sundaram. 2301 S CLEAR CREEK RD, STE 112 76549 #495-04-1976 L1993 **IM** *020 †20

SUVUNRUNGSI, Precha. 2109 S CLEAR CREEK RD 76549 #891-01-1964 L1972 **IM** *020

THOMAS, James W. 403 N GRAY ST 76541 #048-04-1951 L1951 **OS** *071

TUGGLE, Roger Dale. 1002 WALES DR, STE 8 76549 #047-06-1978 L1990 **OTO** *020 †45

VANCURA, Stephen Jos. 2201 CLEAR CREEK RD 76549 #019-02-1976 L1981 **DR** *020 †80

WARD, Erica Leigh. 3801 SCOTT AND WHITE DR 76543 #048-16-2003 L2006 **PD** *020 †55

WEST, Paul M. 3106 S W S YOUNG DR, # B204 76542 #048-13-1989 L1990 **OBG** *020 †30

WHITTEN, Rondald Joiner. 2300 E RANCIER AVE, STE 3 76543 #007-02-1954 L1955 **GP OS** *071

WILSON, Mark Danl. 401 W JASPER DR 76542 #048-02-1979 L1979 **FM A** *020 †18

WINKLER, Richard Edward. 401 W JASPER DR 76542 #014-01-1982 L1991 **FM GS** *071

WOOD, Harold Lee. PO BOX 938 76540 #047-06-1955 L1959 **PD PDC** *020

ZAPATA, Hugo. ■ 76549 #176-01-1965 L1977 **OBG** *071

ZHAO, Xiaotuan. 2301 S CLEAR CREEK RD, STE 102 76549 #243-49-1983 L2005 **GE** *020 †20

KINGSBURY – GUADALUPE

LAW, Paul Foster. ■ 78638 #048-13-1975 L1975 **AN** *071 †05

MOORING, John Wesley. ■ 78638 #048-13-2007 **PTH** *012

KINGSLAND – LLANO

BRANNEN, Mac. ■ 78639 #048-02-1955 L1955 **D** *071 †15

FREDERICK, John Wilson. 2112 W RANCH ROAD 1431, STE 5 78639 #048-14-1985 L1986 **FM** *020 †18

GOOLSBY, Charles Donahoo. ■ 78639 #012-05-1964 L1964 **OBG** *040

JORDAN, Jack. ■ 78639 #048-12-1954 L1969 **GP** *071

MILLER, Grady Franklin. 2112 W RANCH ROAD 1431, STE 5 78639 #039-79-1997, ▲ L1999 **FM** *020 †18

PANNELL, Harlan Clay. 531 ELLEN WILLIAMS LOOP 78639 #007-02-1960 L1974 **FM AM** *020 †18

PRUESSNER, Janice Lee. 2112 W RANCH ROAD 1431, STE 5 78639 #048-14-1985 L1987 **FM** *020 †18

RUSSELL, Kimberly A L. 2112 W RANCH ROAD 1431, STE 5 78639 #048-13-1993 L1994 **FM** *020 †18

STEVENSON, Harold R. ■ 78639 #048-12-1949 L1949 **FM GS** *071 †18

KINGSVILLE – KLEBERG

ANDAYA, Alfredo R, Jr. 1311 GENERAL CAVAZOS BLVD, STE J 78363 #748-10-1975 L1993 **PD** *020

AQUINO, Andres D. 1311 GENERAL CAVAZOS BLVD 78363 #748-01-1954 L1974 **PTH** *071 †50

BORROMEO-OBALLO, Erlinda. 1311 GENERAL CAVAZOS BLVD, STE 303 78363 #748-01-1961 L1980 **OS IM** *020

BOYD, Martin Alan. 1311 GENERAL CAVAZOS BLVD, STE 305 78363 #048-02-2002 L2007 **OBG** *020

BRUSCHETTA, Humberto R. 500 E CAESAR AVE 78363 #649-14-1981 L1996 **END IM** *020 †20

CHO, Unam. 1311 GENERAL CAVAZOS BLVD 78363 #422-01-1996 L2004 **PD** *020 †55

CHOUCAIR, Wassim Khaled. 1311 GENERAL CAVAZOS BLVD, STE 203 78363 #035-01-1994 L2002 **CD** *020 †20

DIAZ DE LEON, David. ■ 78363 #048-14-2005 **PD** *012

EKANAYAKE, Surendranath P. 1311 GENERAL CAVAZOS BLVD, STE 305 78363 #422-01-1994 L2007 **OBG** *020 †30

FERNANDEZ, Soledad Seludo. 506 E RAGLAND AVE 78363 #748-01-1955 L1969 **IM** *020

FOSTER, William Edward. ■ 78363 #048-02-1962 L1962 **FM EM** *071 †18

FRANKLIN, Carolyn R. 1300 GENERAL CAVAZOS BLVD 78363 #048-13-1983 L1983 **FM** *020 †18

GEDDES, James Douglas. 1311 GENERAL CAVAZOS BLVD, STE F 78363 #062-01-1976 L1982 **IM** *020 †20

GRAJEDA, Hector. PO BOX 5028 78364 #649-33-1993 L2005 **PD** *020 †55

HEMMERT, Jerome Kermit. 1300 GENERAL CAVAZOS BLVD 78363 #649-14-1981 L1987 **FM OM** *020 †18

HEMMERT, Teresa M. 227 W KLEBERG AVE 78363 #649-14-1982 L1985 **FM** *020

HOOPER, Ray Gilbert. 1311 GENERAL CAVAZOS BLVD 78363 #621-01-1955 L1961 **U** *020 †95

HUMPHREY, Joseph Thomas. 78363 #016-42-2006 L2007 *012

MARTIN, Benson L. ■ 78363 #048-02-1957 L1957 **GYN** *071 †30

MC CUTCHON, Frederick J. 1311 GENERAL CAVAZOS BLVD 78363 #021-01-1953 L1958 **FM** *071 †95

MC KINSTRY, Scott William. 1311 GENERAL CAVAZOS BLVD, STE 203 78363 #028-02-1993 L1999 **CD** *020 †18

MURPHY, Robert Ray. 510 E CAESAR AVE 78363 #047-06-1971 L1977 **IM** *020

OBALLO, Felino Canendo. 1311 GENERAL CAVAZOS BLVD, STE 303 78363 #748-01-1963 L1980 **GS** *020 †85

O'RYAN, Julio C. 415 S 6TH ST 78363 #847-06-1971 L1975 **PD** *020 †55

PATEL, Anilkumar C. 1018 S 14TH ST 78363 #495-22-1988 L1997 **PD** *020 †55

RAMEY, Lindell E. 1300 GENERAL CAVAZOS BLVD 78363 #048-04-1942 L1946 **GP OS** *071

REYES, Georgino Rafael. 5444 CYPRESS CRK 78363 #308-01-1960 L1977 **PD** *071 †55

RODRIGUEZ, Octavio J. 1021 SENATOR CRLS TRN BLVD 78363 #048-14-1993 L1994 **FM** *020 †18

SHOEMAKER, Edward Stanton. 611 E KLEBERG AVE, COASTAL BEND WOMENS 78363 #048-02-1973 L1973 **OBG** *020 †30

SMITH, Raleigh Arnold. 593 N COUNTY RD 1070 78363 #048-12-1979 L1979 **GS** *020 †85

STALLWORTH, Angela Lafaye. 78363 #001-06-2003 L2005 **FM** *012 †18

STROMAN, Pamela Ramirez. ■ 78363 #048-14-2005 L2008 **FP** *012

TALABI, Adetola. 1300 GENERAL CAVAZOS BLVD 78363 #690-01-1991 L1997 **CCA** *020 †05

UGARTE, Jose M. 1300 GENERAL CAVAZOS BLVD 78363 #847-05-1968 L1974 **FM IM** *020 †18

KINGWOOD – HARRIS

ABELL, Creed W. 800 ROCKMEAD DR STE 208, RADIOLOGY BUSINESS MANAGEM 77339 #048-02-1984 L1990 **DR** *020 †80

ABOGUNDE, Eneze Doris. ■ 77339 #008-02-2007 **AN** *012

ADAME, Jessie. 1442 KINGWOOD DR # 123 77339 #048-14-1990 L1991 **FOP PTH** *020

ADAMS, John Quincy. 1075 KINGWOOD DR, STE 150 77339 #048-15-1985 L1986 **AN** *020 †05

AMINA, Shazia. ■ 77345 #704-20-1993 L2005 **FM** *020 †18

ANDREWS, James Todd. 22999 HIGHWAY 59 N, STE 246 77339 #048-14-1991 L1992 **OTO** *020 †45

ARIF, Abdus Salam. 22999 HIGHWAY 59 N 77339 #704-20-1989 L1999 **AN** *020 †05

BALASUBRAMANIAN, Anand. 24042 HIGHWAY 59 N 77339 #495-66-1992 L2004 **IM** *020 †20

BANERJEE, Amitabha. 800 ROCKMEAD DR STE 208, C/O BAYTOWN RADLGY ASSOC 77339 #060-01-1981 L1990 **DR NM** *020 †80,28

BARNHART, David Andrew. 20035 W LAKE HOUSTON PKWY 77346 #048-04-1970 L1970 **PD** *020 †55

BARNSFATHER, Kris Ellen. 611 ROCKMEAD DR, STE 100 77339 #020-02-2002 L2006 **OBG** *020

BASALDUA, Martin. 22999 HIGHWAY 59 N, STE 272 77339 #048-13-1980 L1981 **FM** *020 †18

BAUMGARNER, Rebekah Jean. 22999 HIGHWAY 59 N 77339 #048-14-1993 L1994 **FM** *020 †18

BEAVER, Patricia Faye. 601 ROCKMEAD DR 77339 #060-02-1979 L1986 **ORS** *020 †40

BECKNER, Gregory Mitchell. 350 KINGWOOD MEDICAL DR, CARE FOR WOMEN 77339 #048-14-1983 L1983 **OBG** *020 †30

BELAKERE, Ramegowda. ■ 77345 #305-01-2002 L2007 **FM** *020 †18

BERTOLINO, Gerard A. 22999 HIGHWAY 59 N, KINGWOOD MEDICAL CENTER 77339 #021-05-1984 L1989 **PTH** *020 †50

BERWIND, Robert Theodore. 22999 HIGHWAY 59 N STE 182 77339 #041-02-1965 L1976 **U** *020

BISCETTE, Shan M. 20031 W LAKE HOUSTON PKWY, NORTHEAST WOMENS HLTH 77346 #048-02-1999 L2003 **OBG** *020 †30

BOYD, Noel C. 611 ROCKMEAD DR, STE 100 77339 #048-04-1997 L2002 **OBG** *020 †30

BROWNING, Jennifer Miller. 22999 HIGHWAY 59 N 77339 #048-02-1995 L1997 **OBG** *020 †30

CAVNAR-JOHNSON, Mary E. 22710 PROFESSIONAL DR, STE 202 77339 #048-13-1986 L1987 **FM** *020

CHARY, Achi Pandu Ranga. 22999 HIGHWAY 59 N, STE 232 77339 #495-21-1982 L2000 **NEP** *100 †20

CHEUNG, Min-Yuen Cynthia. ■ 77345 #048-04-2007 *012

CHIN, Soopeen. 20035 W LAKE HOUSTON PKWY 77346 #048-04-1992 L1993 **PD** *020 †55

CHINEN, Javier. ■ 77339 #737-06-1991 L2008 **AI** *020 †55,03

CLARK, Charles Kenley. 22999 HIGHWAY 59 N, STE 108 77339 #048-12-1972 L1980 **OPH** *020 †35

CLEGG, Thomas Joe. 22999 HIGHWAY 59 N, STE 246 77339 #048-02-1979 L1979 **OTO** *020 †45

COON-NGUYEN, Elizabeth An. 22710 PROFESSIONAL DR, STE 201 77339 #048-15-2001 L2003 **FM** *020 †18

COX, Ashley Michelle. 20035 W LAKE HOUSTON PKWY, STE 100 77346 #048-04-2005 L2007 **PD** *012

CUBBERLEY, Thomas Ward. 800 ROCKMEAD DR, STE 208 77339 #025-07-1979 L1984 **DR** *020 †80

DANG, Hai Phuc. 800 ROCKMEAD DR, STE 210 77339 #048-14-1992 L1994 **DR** *020 †80

DANIELS, Allan Harold. 22710 PROFESSIONAL DR, STE 202 77339 #005-06-1997 L2001 **MPD** *020 †20,55

DAVID, David R. ■ 77345 #048-16-1982 L1983 **FM** *020 †18 ‡

DE JESUS, Anibal. 22999 HIGHWAY 59 N 77339 #042-01-1994 L1996 **AN** *020 †05

DHEKNE, Rasika Ramesh. 22999 HIGHWAY 59 N, DEPT PATH 77339 #495-17-1970 L1976 **PTH** *020 †50

DI MAALA, James E. ■ 77345 #048-02-2006 **DR** *012

DOBBS CURLING, Susan Gale. 22999 HIGHWAY 59 N 77339 #048-14-1983 L1983 **AN PME** *020 †05

DOSSMAN, Robin. 1442 KINGWOOD DR, # 118 77339 #048-13-1993 L1994 **P** *020 †75

DOUTHIT, Thomas Eugene. ■ 77345 #039-01-1954 L1956 **GYN** *071 †30

EDUARTE, Winlove Pabellan. 800 ROCKMEAD DR STE 210 77339 #748-11-1968 L1979 **DR NM** *020 †80,28

ELLIOTT, Kim. 22999 HIGHWAY 59 N STE 282 77339 #048-04-1983 L1984 **IM** *020 †20

ELLISON, William Joseph. 22999 HIGHWAY 59 N 77339 #048-02-2001 L2004 **AN** *020 †05

EL-ZAIM, Haissam Sohail. ■ 77345 #048-02-2002 L2007 **ORS** *012

EPSTEIN, Neal Edward. 800 ROCKMEAD DR STE 208 77339 #035-46-1975 L1979 **DR** *020 †80

FEUER, Randall. 350 KINGWOOD MEDICAL DR, CARE FOR WOMEN 77339 #048-04-1981 L1982 **OBG** *020 †30

FLETCHER, Stephen Alan. 22999 HIGHWAY 59 N 77339 #048-78-1979, ▲ L1979 **NS** *020

FRANCISCO, Gregory M. ■ 77339 #028-03-1999 L2001 **ICE** *012 †20

GACAD-GILLEY, Aurora M. 20035 W LAKE HOUSTON PKWY, STE 100 77346 #748-01-1967 L1980 **PD ADL** *020 †55

GALLACHER, Bernard P. 22999 HIGHWAY 59 N 77339 #067-01-1979 L1996 **AN CCA** *020 †05

GARNEPUDI, Mary Jemmibai. ■ 77345 #495-58-1973 L1990 **OBG** *020

GOHEL, Gautam V. 800 ROCKMEAD DR, STE 208 77339 #495-37-1988 L1996 **DR** *020 †80

GOKHALE, Anita V. 22999 HIGHWAY 59 N 77339 #495-98-1985 L1997 **AN GP** *020 †05

GRACE, Jarrott S. ■ 77345 #048-14-2005 L2008 **AN** *012

GRAHAM, Walter E. 1331 NORTHPARK DR, EMERGENCY CENTER 77339 #048-14-1987 L1988 **AN** *020 †05

GRANGER, Wayne Hanson. ■ 77339 #048-02-1941 L1941 **NM R** *071 †80,28

GREEN, William B. 22999 HIGHWAY 59 N 77339 #048-13-1987 L1988 **AN PD** *020 †05,55

GRIDLEY, Asahel Lee. ■ 77339 #048-02-2008 *012

GROGAN, Wendell Arthur. 22999 HIGHWAY 59 N, STE 169 77339 #016-06-1980 L2005 **SME N** *020 †75

GROSS, Stephanie Lynn. 1850 W LAKE HOUSTON PKWY, STE 190 77339 #048-04-1992 L1993 **FM** *020 †18

HARRIS, Steven Lewis. 2802 KINGS FOREST DR, CDC/HOUSTON QUARANTINE STA 77339 #048-13-1977 L1977 **PHP MDM** *030 †16

HARVEY, Gregory Paul. 22999 HIGHWAY 59 N, ORTHOPAEDIC ASSOCIATES 77339 #035-09-1983 L1991 **ORS OSM** *020 †40

HASSEL, Kathleen J Bangs. 20035 W LAKE HOUSTON PKWY, STE 100 77346 #048-04-2000 L2003 **PD** *020 †55

HEALD, James Cameron. 2001 LADBROOK DR 77339 #025-01-1961 L1967 **P PYA** *020 †75

HEAPE, Angela Nicole. ■ 77339 #048-04-2008 *012

HELLER, Carl S. 22999 HIGHWAY 59 N, STE 272 77339 #035-15-1980 L1981 **FM** *020 †18

HERNANDEZ, Chris. 22999 HIGHWAY 59 N 77339 #048-02-1999 L2002 **EM** *020 †16

HERRERA, Carlos Ang. ■ 77345 #748-08-1983 L1997 **HEM** *020

HOLLINGSWORTH, Hunter R. 350 KINGWOOD MEDICAL DR, CARE FOR WOMEN 77339 #048-12-1991 L1992 **OBG** *020 †30

HUNT, Madeline A. 22999 HIGHWAY 59 N, STE 230 77339 #048-14-1994 L1995 **FM** *020 †18

ILISKOVIC, Natasha. ■ 77339 #957-11-1988 L2007 **CD IM** *020 ‡

JACKSON, Todd Lincoln. ■ 77339 #056-06-2006 L2007 **OPH** *012

■ = Address Information Privacy Protected

JARRETT, James Michael. 22999 HIGHWAY 59 N 77339 #048-14-1992 L1993 **AN** *020 †05
JOHNSON, Erik Scott. 1331 NORTHPARK DR 77339 #048-02-1999 L2002 **FM** *020
KHAN, Faraz Adil. 800 ROCKMEAD DR, STE 208 77339 #048-14-1996 L2002 **DR VIR** *020 †80
KHOURY, Pierre Nassif. 22710 PROFESSIONAL DR, STE 100 77339 #605-02-1991 L1998 **HO** *020 †20
KING, Leslie Harris. 22999 HIGHWAY 59 N 77339 #048-12-1982 L1983 **AN EM** *020 †05
KNAPP, Michael E. 800 ROCKMEAD DR, STE 208 77339 #048-15-1995 L1997 **DR RNR** *020 †80
KOSSOY, Kent Ian. 22999 HIGHWAY 59 N, STE 188 77339 #028-03-1985 L1991 **GS CRS** *020 †85,10
LAIRD, Aaron C. ■ 77339 #048-14-2007 **EM** *012
LAROSE, Claude. 22999 HIGHWAY 59 N STE 290 77339 #065-09-1956 L1978 **AI IM** *020 †03
LASTOCZY, Frank Michael. 22999 HIGHWAY 59 N 77339 #016-42-1993 L1997 **AN** *020 †05
LE, Dewey. 77339 #048-78-2003, ▲ 2008 **N** *020
LEACH, Thomas Michael. 611 ROCKMEAD DR 77339 #048-02-1973 L1973 **PD** *030 †55
LECAVALIER, Marcel. 1102 KINGWOOD DR STE 20 77339 #649-14-1968 L1973 **FM AN** *071
LECOMPTE, Brian Eric. 24042 HIGHWAY 59 N, FAMILY HEALTH CLINIC 77339 #021-06-1980 L1986 **PS** *020 †65
LEE, Jody Sui. 2019 RED MAGNOLIA CT 77339 #048-14-1994 L1999 **DR** *020 †80
LEHMAN, Craig Allen. 2411 FOREST GARDEN DR 77345 #019-02-1968 L1975 **DR AM** *020 †80 ‡
LITTLE, Raymond Wendell. 2627 CHESTNUT RIDGE DR, STE 100 77339 #024-05-1992 L2000 **IC** *020 †20
LOAR, Christopher Morton. 22999 HIGHWAY 59 N, STE 180 77339 #028-02-1982 L1983 **N CN** *020 †75 ‡
LONGLEY, Neill Byron. 800 ROCKMEAD DR STE 208 77339 #048-12-1956 L1965 **DR** *020 †80
LU, Dai. 22999 HIGHWAY 59 N 77339 #243-16-1987 L1998 **AN** *020 †05
LUGO-MIRO, Victor I. 3036 NORTHPARK DR 77339 #042-01-1981 L1989 **ADL PD** *020 †55
LUU, Kham David. 22999 HIGHWAY 59 N, STE 214 77339 #048-02-1989 L1994 **PCC IM** *020
MAHAN, Miles E. 20031 W LAKE HOUSTON PKWY, STE 200 77346 #048-15-1992 L1993 **OBG** *020 †30
MANLONGAT, George G. 22710 PROFESSIONAL DR, STE 201 77339 #048-14-1994 L1995 **FM** *020 †18
MANN, Chandler Robt. 24018 HIGHWAY 59 N 77339 #031-01-1990 L1992 **AN** *020 †05
MANN, Louise T. 22999 HIGHWAY 59 N, CARE FOR WOMEN 77339 #031-01-1989 L1993 **OBG** *020 †30
MARRUFO, Benito V. 2755 W LAKE HOUSTON PKWY 77339 #048-04-1996 L1997 **IM** *020 †20
MC COIG, Edward Lloyd. 22710 PROFESSIONAL DR, STE 201 77339 #048-14-1979 L1979 **IM** *020
MC LAUGHLIN, Eric Luther. ■ 77345 #035-09-2001 L2004 **EM** *020
MENDOZA, Ernest Jonas San. 22710 PROFESSIONAL DR, STE 202 77339 #748-10-2000 L2005 **FM** *020
MOHSIN, Shaheen A. 611 ROCKMEAD DR STE 600 77339 #704-16-1979 L1996 **PD** *020 †55
MOORE, Walter Parker, III. 22999 HIGHWAY 59 N, STE 246 77339 #048-12-1988 L1989 **OTO A** *020 †45
MORAGNE, John Edward. 1075 KINGWOOD DR, STE 150 77339 #039-01-1986 L1992 **AN** *020 †05
MORKOWSKI, Hanna Maria. ■ 77339 #759-04-1980 L2007 **FM** *100 †18
MORKOWSKI, Jerzy Jozef. ■ 77339 #048-13-2000 L2005 **PTH** *020 †50
MORROW, Robert John. 2202 RUNNING SPRINGS DR 77339 #048-12-1973 L1973 **OBG** *020 †30
MOSSADEGH, Mahsa. 22999 HIGHWAY 59 N STE 154 77339 #038-40-1998 L2003 **GS** *020 †85
MUENCH, Laura Jacobson. 800 ROCKMEAD DR STE 208 77339 #021-05-1993 L2005 **DR** *020 †80
MUSCAT, Joseph O. 601 ROCKMEAD DR 77339 #048-13-1989 L1990 **ORS** *020 †40
NORVELL, Oxana V. 1442 KINGWOOD DR, # 207 77339 #913-09-1998 **FP** *012
NOVOSAD, Bryan Jos. 2601 W LAKE HOUSTON PKWY, KINGWOOD URGENT CARE 77339 #048-02-1977 L1977 **FM** *020 †18
NUNEZ, George, Jr. ■ 77339 #048-12-1990 L1991 **GE** *020 †20
NUNNERY, Angela Yvette. 22710 PROFESSIONAL DR, STE 202 77339 #048-12-1985 L1986 **FM** *020 †18
OHEN, Omonele A. ■ 77339 #048-14-2006 **AN** *012
OWENS, Rochelle R. ■ 77345 #048-14-1987 L1988 **FM** *020 †18
OZARDA, Ahsen Turgut. ■ 77339 #902-01-1940 L1966 **RO NM** *071 †80
PATEL, Sumant U. 800 ROCKMEAD DR, STE 125 77339 #495-17-1973 L1980 **DR** *020 †80
PAYNE, William David, Jr. ■ 77345 #027-01-2005 **PTH** *012
PENN, Hyman. 611 ROCKMEAD DR STE 600 77339 #048-13-1982 L1983 **PD** *020 †55
PHELAN, James Harry. 2325B TIMBER SHADOWS DR 77339 #048-04-1974 L1974 **FM** *020 †18
PLUMMER, Amy Hallgarth. 611 ROCKMEAD DR, STE 100 77339 #048-04-1992 L1993 **OBG** *020 †30
POTHULURI, Nomita Jairaj. 2300 GREEN OAK DR STE 150 77339 #004-01-1998 L2001 **FM** *020
QADRI, Ahmed Kabir. 22999 HIGHWAY 59 N 77339 #704-02-1984 L2006 **IM** *020 †20
RABIN, Vicki Rose. 2300 GREEN OAK DR, STE 300 77339 #021-05-1986 L1989 **D** *020 †15
REDONDO, Anne Catherine. 22999 HIGHWAY 59 N 77339 #048-12-1988 L1989 **AN** *020 †05
REED, Jonathan Grant. 800 ROCKMEAD DR, STE 208 77339 #016-43-1980 L1990 **R** *020 †80
ROBERTS, Dennis D. ■ 77339 #048-14-2005 L2007 **AN** *100
RODRIGUEZ, Luis Hernando. 1543 GREEN OAK PL, STE 200 77339 #264-01-1956 L1974 **IM HEM** *020
ROSEN, Robert Terry. 24042 HIGHWAY 59 N 77339 #035-06-1968 L1971 **U** *020 †95
RUSSO, Lawrence Justus. ■ 77345 #021-05-1970 L1970 **ORS** *020 †40
SANCHEZ-RAMOS, Raul A. 22999 HIGHWAY 59 N, STE 272 77339 #649-03-1977 L1993 **FM** *020 †18
SETHI, Gurdeep. 22710 PROFESSIONAL DR, STE 100 77339 #495-43-1985 L1998 **HO** *020 †20
SHAPPARD, Robert Douglas. ■ 77345 #065-10-1985 L1992 **FM** *020
SHAW, Kelvin Sanjeev. 1850 W LAKE HOUSTON PKWY, STE 150 77339 #048-13-1998 L2003 **AI** *020 †20,03
SHERICK, Kurt James. 2110 FOREST FALLS DR 77345 #017-20-1985 L1986 **P** *012
SIMPSON, Jerry Gordon. ■ 77345 #012-01-1965 L1969 **OM PHP** *030 †70
SIMS, Paul Edward, Jr. 22999 HIGHWAY 59 N 77339 #051-04-1994 L2005 **AN** *020 †05
SIROPAIDES, Michael P. 22999 HIGHWAY 59 N, STE 154 77339 #041-13-1981 L1988 **CD IM** *020 †20
STANISLAW, Scott Richard. 601 ROCKMEAD DR 77339 #041-07-1993 L1998 **ORS** *020 †40 ‡
STANLEY, William Anthony. 611 ROCKMEAD DR, STE 600 77339 #048-02-1973 L1973 **PD IM** *020 †55
SUNKUREDDI, Krishna Vr. 1210 STONEHOLLOW DR 77339 #495-62-1978 L1993 **CHP PYG** *020 †75

TAYI, Sudha. 2313 TIMBER SHADOWS DR, STE 200 77339 #495-04-1974 L1985 **P** *020
THOTA, Venkatasujatha N.. 23423 HIGHWAY 59 N, APT 1115 77339 #495-21-1990 L2008 **OBG** *100
TIU, Alexander L. 22999 HIGHWAY 59 N STE 214 77339 #748-01-1986 L1991 **PUD IM** *020 †20
TIU, Nenita U. 22999 HIGHWAY 59 N, STE 214 77339 #748-01-1986 L1991 **PD** *020 †55
TORRES, Fernando G. 2001 LADBROOK DR 77339 #048-02-1989 L1990 **P CHP** *020
TRAN, An Duc. 22999 HIGHWAY 59 N 77339 #048-02-1991 L1992 **AN** *020 †05
TRAN, Huy Quoc. 800 ROCKMEAD DR 77339 #021-01-1996 L2007 **DR** *020
UDDIN, Shakeel. 22999 HIGHWAY 59 N 77339 #704-16-1980 L1993 **CD IM** *020 †20
URIBE-TORRES, Brenda. 350 KINGWOOD MEDICAL DR, CARE FOR WOMEN 77339 #005-14-1992 L1996 **OBG** *020 †30
URQUHART, Bradford A. 22999 HIGHWAY 59 N, ORTHOPAEDIC ASSOCIATES 77339 #048-12-1968 L1993 **ORS** *020 †40
VELA, Alejandro Hinojosa. 22999 HIGHWAY 59 N 77339 #048-02-2001 L2005 **AN** *020 †05
VILLACRES, David Fernando. 3407 RIVERS EDGE TRL 77339 #048-13-1988 L1990 **PM** *020 †60
WARREN, Ray E. 2601 W LAKE HOUSTON PKWY 77339 #039-01-1966 L1967 **IM** *020 †55
WEED, David Herman. 2755 W LAKE HOUSTON PKWY 77339 #038-40-1975 L1986 **PD** *020 †55 ‡
WIEMAN, Matthew Scott. ■ 77345 #024-05-2002 L2002 **AN** *100
WILLIAMS, Gwenevere E. 1801 KINGWOOD DR, STE 170 77339 #047-20-1985 L1990 **PM** *020 †60
WILLIAMS, Jakeen E. 2755 W LAKE HOUSTON PKWY 77339 #021-05-2002 L2005 **PD** *020 †55
WILLS, Harold D. 22999 HIGHWAY 59 N 77339 #048-04-1996 L1999 **IM FM** *020
WILSON, Michael Ernest. 800 ROCKMEAD DR, STE 208 77339 #048-12-1968 L1968 **DR NM** *020 †80
YOM, Sun Y. 22999 HIGHWAY 59 N, KINGWOOD MED CTR RADIOLGOY 77339 #048-13-1985 L1986 **DR** *020 †80
YOUNG, Danna Lynn. 22999 HIGHWAY 59 N 77339 #021-01-1998 L2002 **EM** *020 †16
YOUNG, Melissa G. 4435 KINGWOOD DR, KINGS CROSSING 77339 #048-13-1986 L1987 **GP** *020
ZAVALA, Sharon Kaye. 350 KINGWOOD MEDICAL DR, CARE FOR WOMEN 77339 #048-04-1992 L1996 **OBG** *020 †30
ZUAZU, Gregorio B. 800 ROCKMEAD DR, STE 208 77339 #847-06-1971 L1976 **PDR R** *050 †80

KIRBYVILLE – JASPER

TAN, Erlinda Mercado. 211 FM 82 75956 #748-01-1974 L1978 **FM** *020
ZAFAR, Usman. 205 E LAVIELLE ST 75956 #704-01-1979 L1994 **IM** *020 †20

KNOX CITY – KNOX

DUKE, Ezekiel L. 712 E SOUTH 5TH ST 79529 #048-15-2004 L2006 **FM** *020 †18
SANCHEZ-BARRETTO, Shirley. 712 SE 5TH ST, BOX 519 79529 #748-10-1971 L1985 **NPM PD** *020

KOUNTZE – HARDIN

HOOKS, Henry Allen. 501 MONROE ST 77625 #048-02-1955 L1955 **GP PHP** *071 †18
STEELE, George Mack, Jr. ■ 77625 #048-02-1970 L1970 **FM GP** *071
WINBERG, Jana Marie. 805 HIGHWAY 69 S 77625 #034-01-1999 L2002 **FM** *020 †18

KRUM – DENTON

DOYLE, Robert Lawrence. ■ 76249 #023-01-1964 L1964 **U** *071 †95
HILL, Norwood Oakley. ■ 76249 #048-04-1961 L1961 **HEM ON** *072

KYLE – HAYS

BURGUM, David Leland. ■ 78640 #048-02-1962 L1962 **N P** *020 †75
FRIES, Barbara A. ■ 78640 #028-34-1965 L1967 **N** *020 †75
GRADY, Michael Joseph. 181A KIRKHAM CIR, CORRIDOR PRIMARY CARE 78640 #048-14-1995 L1996 **PD** *020 †55
HARRISON, Sue Ann. 181A KIRKHAM CIR, CORRIDOR PRIMARY CARE 78640 #048-14-1984 L1986 **PD** *020 †55 ‡
HEATLY, Maurice Dean. ■ 78640 #048-04-1939 L1939 **P** *071
HUMPHREY, Jill Suzanne. 181A KIRKHAM CIR, CORRIDOR PRIMARY CARE 78640 #023-01-2003 L2006 **PD** *020 †55
MILLER, Michelle Edwards. 181A KIRKHAM CIR, CORRIDOR PRIMARY CARE 78640 #048-04-2001 L2005 **PD** *100
OSINA, Rachel Jean. 181A KIRKHAM CIR, CORRIDOR PRIMARY CARE 78640 #048-15-2001 L2005 **PD** *020
RODRIGUEZ, Sarah Chance. 211 ELMHURST, APT E 78640 #048-02-2001 L2006 **OTO** *020 †45
SYED, Faisal Mohammed. 78640 #704-25-1996 L2007 **CD** *020 †20

LA COSTE – MEDINA

KOHLLEPPEL, Shelley R. ■ 78039 #048-14-2007 **FP** *012

LA FERIA – CAMERON

JUAREZ, Elizabeth. ■ 78559 #048-14-2004 L2007 **IM** *020 †20
MC ALLISTER, Patrick R. PO BOX 6811, 108 CHELO 78559 #048-02-1980 L1980 **PTH** *020 †50

LA GLORIA – STARR

SMITH, Alvin Marine. 1 MILE N STATE HIGHWAY 755 78591 #048-12-1969 L1969 **OBG** *071 †30

LA GRANGE – FAYETTE

ANDERSON, Charles Wiley. 543 N JACKSON ST 78945 #048-14-1986 L1987 **FM EM** *020 †18
CHORENS, Albert L. 2 SAINT MARKS PL, STE 130 78945 #048-14-1991 L1992 **GS** *020 †85
DOBBS, Robert Mays. ■ 78945 #012-05-1958 L1970 **U** *071 †95
JUNO, Russell Joseph, III. 2 SAINT MARKS PL, STE 130 78945 #048-14-1999 L2006 **GS** *020
JUNO, Shannon Marie. 2 SAINT MARKS PL, STE 140 78945 #048-14-2000 L2006 **OBG** *020 †30 ‡
LEWIS, Raymond. ■ 78945 #027-01-1957 L1969 **D** *071
LINDEN, Barry Eugene. 353 E PEARL ST 78945 #048-14-1983 L1983 **OTO HNS** *020 †45
MC BROOM, William M. 1253 N VON MINDEN ST 78945 #048-14-1976 L1976 **FM** *020 †18
MELEAR, Jason Michael. 2 SAINT MARKS PL 78945 #048-15-1996 L1997 **ON** *020 †20
PARMLEY, Van Sam. 78945 #021-01-1939 L1940 **AN GP** *071 †05
PIERATT, William H. 1 SAINT MARKS PL 78945 #048-78-1992, ▲ L1993 **IM** *020 †20
PRABA, Anant Chelva. 2 SAINT MARKS PL STE 130 78945 #048-04-1993 L1994 **GS CCS** *020 †85
SMALLEY, Robert Hamilton. PO BOX 825 78945 #048-12-1967 L1971 **R** *075 †80
STAHL, David M. ■ 78945 #048-04-1952 L1952 **U OS** *071 †95
STIFFLER, Thomas Andrew. 3517 CREAMER CREEK RD 78945 #028-03-1976 L1994 **OBG** *071 †30
THOMAS, Walter Neal. 403 E GUADALUPE ST 78945 #048-02-1967 L1967 **OBG** *020 †30
WHITE, Daniel Allen. 2 SAINT MARKS PL, STE 130 78945 #048-13-1974 L1974 **GS** *020 †85

LA JOYA – HIDALGO

KINDE, Paul James. PO BOX 1380, VISTA ST, LA JOYA, TX 7856 78560 #025-07-2000 L2003 **FM** *020

LA MARQUE – GALVESTON

ANDERSON, Benno Du Menil. 421 OAK ST 77568 #048-02-1968 L1968 **FM GP** *071 †18
ARCENEAUX, Cassandra N. 1207 OAK ST 77568 #048-02-2002 L2005 **GPM** *020 †18
BONILLAS, Robert Granillo. ■ 77568 #003-01-2000 L2002 **PS** *012
BUI, Anne Thu-Anh. ■ 77568 #048-02-2005 **IM** *012
CLARK-WRONSKI, Julianna M. ■ 77568 #048-02-2008 *012
FRADKIN, Aaron. 6409 MEMORIAL DRIVE, THE EYE CLINIC OF TEXAS 77568 #048-02-1955 L1955 **IM** *071
GINZEL, Andrew William. ■ 77568 #048-02-2005 **DR** *012
GUIDRY, Harlan M. 1207 OAK ST, GALVESTON COUNTY HLTH DIST 77568 #048-02-1987 L1988 **PHP FM** *030 †18
HENSON, Louise M. PO BOX 939, 2000 TEXAS AVE SUITE 200 77568 #048-02-1999 L2002 **FM** *020
JIMENEZ-RAMIREZ, Carlos J. ■ 77568 #042-02-2001 L2001 **CCS** *012
KOESTER, Herman Lott. 1310 HIGHWAY 3 77568 #048-02-1955 L1955 **PTH** *071 †50
REID, Bradley Joseph. ■ 77568 #048-12-2006 **AN** *012
SAUER, Heather Louise. ■ 77568 #028-34-2006 **P** *012

LA PORTE – HARRIS

ASHBY, George Perry. 410 E FAIRMONT PKWY, STE A 77571 #649-02-1983 L1988 **FM OM** *020 †70,18
BHATT, Sapankumar Subhash. 404 W FAIRMONT PKWY, LA PORTE INTERNAL MEDICINE 77571 #496-41-1997 L2004 **IM** *020
COBHAM, David Allan. 1007 S BROADWAY ST 77571 #011-02-1990 L1993 **FM** *020 †18 ‡
HANSEN, Douglas Brayshaw. PO BOX 1489 77572 #035-45-1955 L1964 **CHP PYA** *071 †75
HOLLE, Henry Bernard. 2411 CRESCENT DR 77571 #035-01-1954 L1955 **GS SO** *020 †85
JOHNSTON, Robert D. 1309 W FAIRMONT PKWY, STE L 77571 #048-16-1987 L1988 **FM** *020 †18
LEE, Harvey Bryan. 1309 W FAIRMONT PKWY, LEE CHIROPRACTIC CLINIC 77571 #062-01-1972 L1977 **IM** *100
MOCK, Presley Joe, Jr. 1200 HIGHWAY 146 S STE 250 77571 #048-02-1964 L1964 **FM** *020 †18 ‡
MOOSA, Abdool Sattar. 1007 S BROADWAY ST 77571 #836-01-1970 L1984 *040
MOOSA, Abdul R. 1007 S BROADWAY ST 77571 #422-01-1988 L1993 **FM** *020 †18
NGUYEN, Erin Hoai. 1309 W FAIRMONT PKWY, STE L 77571 #422-01-2004 L2007 **FM** *100 †18
PATEL, Dilipkumar C. 404 W FAIRMONT PKWY 77571 #495-23-1989 L1991 **IM** *020 †20
PATEL, Rakesh Ramanbhai. 10611 W FAIRMONT PKWY 77571 #048-14-1995 L1997 **FM** *020 †18
RODRIGUEZ, Adriana M. ■ 77571 #048-12-2005 L2007 **PD** *012
SANDERS, John Kerry. 1309 W FAIRMONT PKWY, STE X 77571 #048-02-1972 L1972 **GS** *020
STANTON, James Michael. 1309 W FAIRMONT PKWY, STE X 77571 #048-04-1974 L1975 **OM FM** *020 †70
UDDIN, Rahman Sahadat. 10407 W FAIRMONT PKWY, STE B 77571 #495-16-1987 L1988 **PD** *020 †55
WATSON, James Jay. 425 SHADYLAWN ST 77571 #048-12-1990 L1991 **GS** *020

LA VERNIA – WILSON

COY, John Ross. ■ 78121 #047-06-1966 L1966 **R OS** *020
EKMARK, Roderick David. ■ 78121 #048-02-2005 **P** *012
GARCIA, Salvador Juan. ■ 78121 #042-01-1974 L1976 **GP** *020
RIVERA, Susan Yvette. 14114 US HIGHWAY 87 78121 #041-15-2001 L2006 **OBG** *100
WHITE, Torree Michelle. ■ 78121 #040-02-2005 **EM** *012

LACKLAND AIR FORCE BASE – BEXAR

ABRAHAMIAN, Greg Avedis. 2200 BERGQUIST DR, LACKLAND AFB TX 78236 #048-13-1992 L1994 **GS** *020 †85
ADAMS, Karla Elizabeth. 2200 BERGQUIST DR STE 1, 59TH MED WING/MMNP 78236 #023-12-2006 L2007 **PD** *012

AGAN, Brian K. 2200 BERGQUIST DR STE 1, WHMC/CMC 78236 #007-02-1996 L1997 **IM** *020 †20
AGUILAR, Raul Alfonso. 2200 BERGQUIST DR STE 1, WILFORD HALL MED CTR 78236 #026-04-1978 L1980 **FM FPG** *020 †18
AGURS, Latanya Delvina. 2200 BERGQUIST DR STE 1, 59TH MED WING/MMNP 78236 #012-05-2006 L2007 **PD** *012
AHRENDT, Dale Michael. 2200 BERGQUIST DR STE 1, WHMC 78236 #046-01-1994 L1997 **PD** *020 †55
AKERS, Kevin Scott. 2200 BERGQUIST DR, WILFORD HALL USAF MED CTR 78236 #047-06-2003 L2004 **ID** *012 †20
ALLAN, Patrick Francis. 2200 BERGQUIST DR, WHMC/CMC 78236 #016-01-1998 L2006 **PCC** *020 †20
ALLEY, Joshua Benjamin. 2200 BERGQUIST DR STE 1, 59 MDW 78236 #051-01-2002 L2004 **GS** *020 †85
ALMALEH, Michael David. 2200 BERGQUIST DR STE 1, ATTN: CREDENTIAL OFFICE 78236 #024-05-1999 L2006 **CD** *020 †20
ANDERSON, Joan Nicole. 2200 BERGQUIST DR STE 1, 59TH MEDICAL WING/MKAA 78236 #005-12-1996 L1997 **AN** *100
ANDREASON, Kurt Weldon. 2200 BERGQUIST DR STE 1, 859TH MSGS/MCST 78236 #023-12-1998 L1999 **OPH** *020 †35
ANUSAVICE, Jenniferjil Le. 2200 BERGQUIST DR STE 1, 59TH MED WING/MMNP 78236 #011-03-2005 L2007 **PD** *012
ARNER, David Mark. 2200 BERGQUIST DR, DEPT OF INTERNAL MEDICINE 78236 #023-12-2006 L2007 **IM** *012
ARROYO, Ramon A. 2200 BERGQUIST DR STE 1, LACKLAND AFB, WHMC/CMC 78236 #042-01-1982 L1992 **IM** *020 †20
ASHER, Charles A. 2200 BERGQUIST DR, DEPT OF EMERGENCY MED 78236 #017-20-2006 L2008 **EM** *012
ASKEW, Adrienne W. 2200 BERGQUIST DR STE 1, WILFORD HALL MED CTR 78236 #023-12-1997 L2000 **OBG** *020 †30
AVERY, Eleanor Elizabeth. 2200 BERGQUIST DR STE 1, 59 MDOS/MMCN 78236 #036-08-1988 L1990 **N IMG** *020 †20,75
AVILA, Maria V. 2200 BERGQUIST DR, WILFORD HALL MEDICAL CENTE 78236 #264-01-1966 L1975 **CHP P** *075
BAILEY, William Harold. 2200 BERGQUIST DR STE 1, CREDENTIALS OFFICE 78236 #021-01-1976 L1977 **CD IM** *020 †18,20
BAQUERO, Jeannie A. 2200 BERGQUIST DR STE 1, WILFORD HALL MED CTR 78236 #048-16-1996 L1998 **END** *020 †20
BARKER, James A. 2200 BERGQUIST DR STE 1, WILFORD HALL MED CTRGCMC 78236 #023-12-1987 L1990 **PHO** *020 †55 ‡
BARR, Jeffrey Mark. 2200 BERGQUIST DR STE 1 78236 #035-48-2007 **IM** *012
BARR, Jeffrey William. 2200 BERGQUIST DR STE 1 78236 #017-20-1999 L2006 **AN PMM** *020 †05
BASKIN, Darrell E. 2200 BERGQUIST DR STE 1WH, ATTN CREDENTIAL OFFICE LAC 78236 #048-04-2003 L2004 **OPH** *012
BATES, Christopher Wayne. 2200 BERGQUIST DR STE 1, WHMC/CMC 78236 #023-12-2005 L2006 **IM** *020
BATTS, Travis Carlos. 2200 BERGQUIST DR STE 1, WILFORD HALL MED CTR 78236 #036-01-2004 L2006 **IM** *020 †20
BAUGH, Laura Marie. 2200 BERGQUIST DR STE 1, 59 MDWGSGHC 78236 #017-20-2002 L2004 **CN** *020 †75
BECK, Rachel Lenore. 2200 BERGQUIST DR STE 1, 759 MSGS/59MDW DEPT OF CAR 78236 #032-01-1998 L2005 **CD IM** *020 †20
BEECHIE, Carla Anne. 2200 BERGQUIST DR, 59 MDW 78236 #028-02-1971 L1983 **PD** *030 †55
BENINATI, William. 2200 BERGQUIST DR STE 1, WHMC/CMC 78236 #023-12-1988 L1990 **SME PCC** *020 †20
BINI, John Kennedy. 2200 BERGQUIST DR STE 1, ATTN:CREDENTIAL OFFICE 78236 #048-15-1999 L2005 **GS** *020 †85
BOATMAN, Erik Alfred. 2200 BERGQUIST DR STE 1, 59TH MDW/CMC 78236 #033-06-1999 L2005 **AN** *040 †05
BOETTCHER, Elizabeth Dee. 2200 BERGQUIST DR STE 1, WHMC/CMC 78236 #047-05-1993 L2005 **U** *020 †95
BOLIN, Kurt Robert. 2200 BERGQUIST DR STE 1, 59 MEDICAL OPERATIONS GP (78236 #011-04-2000 L2002 **FM** *020 †18
BOSTON, Mark Eugene. 2200 BERGQUIST DR STE 1, ATTN: CREDENTIALS OFFICE 78236 #003-01-1994 L2007 **PDO** *020 †45
BOWERS, Steven Paul, Jr. 59 SSS/SGCQ 78236 #012-05-1995 L2004 **GS** *040 †85
BOWSER, Andrew Neale. 2200 BERGQUIST DR STE 1, WILFORD HALL MED CTR 78236 #035-15-1995 L2008 **VS** *020 †85
BRENNAN, Joseph Anthony. 2200 BERGQUIST DR STE 1, WHMC/CMC 78236 #024-07-1986 L2003 **OTO GS** *020 †45
BRIGGS, Jonathan Wayne. 2200 BERGQUIST DR STE 1, 59TH MEDICAL WING 78236 #023-12-1996 L1997 **OPH AM** *020 †35
BRIGHT, William A. 2200 BERGQUIST DR STE 1, ATTN: CREDENTIAL OFFICE 78236 #048-15-2000 L2000 **OPH** *012
BROSCH, Lorie C. 2200 BERGQUIST DR STE 1, 59TH MDW/CMC 78236 #030-06-1977 L1980 **GPM** *020 †70,18
BROSTROM, Lisa Danielle. 2200 BERGQUIST DR 78236 #048-04-2000 L2002 **PS** *020 †85
BRUDNAK, Daniel M. 2200 BERGQUIST DR STE 1, WHMC/CMC 78236 #048-14-1991 L1992 **FM** *020 †18
BURGESS, Deborah Narkun. 2200 BERGQUIST DR, STE 1 78236 #023-12-1985 L1993 **NEP IM** *030 †20
BUSH, David Michael. 2200 BERGQUIST DR STE 1, WHMC/CMC 78236 #023-07-1995 L2005 **PDC** *020 †55
BYRNES, Joseph P M. 2200 BERGQUIST DR STE 1, WHMC/CMC 78236 #016-11-1977 L1979 **CCM AN** *020 †05
CALABRIA, Christopher W. 2200 BERGQUIST DR, STE 1 78236 #023-01-2001 L2008 **AI** *020 †55,03
CANBY-HAGINO, Edith D. 2200 BERGQUIST DR STE 1, 59TH MDW/CMC 78236 #005-06-1993 L1999 **U** *020 †95
CANNON, Jeremy Wynne. 2200 BERGQUIST DR STE 1, ATTN: CREDENTIAL OFFICE 78236 #024-01-1998 L2000 **GS** *100 †85
CAPENER, Dale Clifton. 2200 BERGQUIST DR STE 1 78236 #023-12-2003 L2007 **AN** *020
CARPENTER, Matthew Trent. 2200 BERGQUIST DR STE 1, WILFORD HALL MEDICAL CENTE 78236 #041-02-1987 L2006 **RO** *020 †20,80
CARRIZALES, Scott C. 2200 BERGQUIST DR STE 1, 59 MEDICAL OPERATIONS GP (78236 #023-12-1996 L1998 **D** *012 †18

CEVEY, Renee. 2200 BERGQUIST DR STE 1, 59 MDW, WILFORD HALL MEDIC 78236 #028-02-2000 L2002 **PD** *020 ‡

CHACKO, Kalapurackal J. 2200 BERGQUIST DR STE 1, WHMC/CMC 78236 #495-63-1970 L1985 **PD** *020 †55

CHARLTON, Michael T. 2200 BERGQUIST DR STE 1, (S 78236 #023-12-1998 L2007 **ORS** *020

CHEN, Stephen Russell. 2200 BERGQUIST DR STE 1, WHMC/CMC 78236 #023-12-2000 L2006 **VIR** *100 †80

CHO, Jason Ju Hyeon. 2200 BERGQUIST DR STE 1, WILFORD HALL MED CTR 78236 #035-15-1996 L1999 **PD** *020 †55

CHRISTOPHER, Geo Winston. 2200 BERGQUIST DR STE 1, 59TH MDW/CMC 78236 #051-01-1978 L1980 **ID** *020 †20

CHUNG, Paul Woochul. 2200 BERGQUIST DR STE 1, 59TH MED WING/MMNP 78236 #016-06-2002 L2004 **PD** *020 †55

CLOUSE, William Darrin. 2200 BERGQUIST DR, STE 1 78236 #026-08-1994 L2004 **VS** *020 †85

COGDILL, Jason Matthew. 2200 BERGQUIST DR STE 1, ATTN: CREDENTIAL OFFICE 78236 #018-03-2004 L2005 **IM** *020 †20

CONDIE, David Reed. 2200 BERGQUIST DR STE 1, 579 MDTS/MTRD WILFORD HALL 78236 #023-12-1991 L1994 **DR VIR** *020 †55,80

CONGER, Nicholas Galen. 2200 BERGQUIST DR STE 1, 59TH MDW/CMC 78236 #048-14-1997 L1998 **ID** *020 †20

COPP, David Dean. 2200 BERGQUIST DR STE 1, WHMC/CMC 78236 #023-12-1992 L1995 **GS** *020 †85

COPPOLA, Christopher Paul. 2200 BERGQUIST DR STE 1, WHMC/CMC 78236 #023-07-1994 L2002 **PDS** *020 †85

COTANT, Casey Lee. 2200 BERGQUIST DR STE 1, ATTN: CREDENTIAL OFFICE 78236 #049-01-2002 L2007 **NEP** *020 †20

COX, James Glenn. 2200 BERGQUIST DR STE 1, WHMC/CMC 78236 #048-12-1993 L1994 **AN** *020 †05

CRESSLER, Dana Keith. 1515 TRUEMPER ST, 37 MDG 78236 #023-12-1998 L2000 **FM** *020 †18

CRUZ-ZENO, Elvin Josel. 2200 BERGQUIST DR STE 1, ATTN:CREDENTIAL OFFICE 78236 #023-12-2000 L2006 **AN** *020 †05

CULTON, Lisa Karen. 2200 BERGQUIST DR STE 1, WHMC/CMC 78236 #048-14-1999 L2003 **PTH** *100 †50

DALRYMPLE, Monica Anna. 2200 BERGQUIST DR STE 1, 59 MDW/MTRD 78236 #008-01-1996 L2006 **DR** *020 †80

DAMASCO, Leo Alexandro. 2200 BERGQUIST DR STE 1, 59TH MED WING/MMNP 78236 #023-12-2006 L2008 **PD** *012

DANG, Tam Q. 2200 BERGQUIST DR, SAN ANTONIO UNIF SVC HLTH 78236 #048-12-2007 **TY** *012

DANIEL, Lynnell Marie. 2200 BERGQUIST DR STE 1, ATTN CREDENTIAL OFFICE LAC 78236 #021-06-2000 L2006 **AN** *020

DELMAR, Judith Ann. 2200 BERGQUIST DR STE 1, ATTN CREDENTIAL OFFICE 78236 #048-13-1979 L1980 **IM R** *020 †20

DENTCHEV, Dimitar Iliev. 2200 BERGQUIST DR STE 1, 59 MEDICAL WING/MCOA 78236 #198-04-1987 L2003 **AN** *020 †05

DETMERING, Donald Gregory. 2200 BERGQUIST DR STE 1, WHMC/CMC 78236 #020-12-1999 L2006 **FM** *020 †18

DEYKIN, Brad Ashley. 2200 BERGQUIST DR STE 1 78236 #021-06-2001 L2003 **EM** *020 †16

DILLON, Jeffrey David. 2200 BERGQUIST DR STE 1, WILFORD HALL MED CTR 78236 #049-01-2003 L2003 **AN** *020

DOLAN, Matthew James. 2200 BERGQUIST DR STE 1 78236 #032-01-1985 L1988 **ID** *020 †20

DONNELLY, Devin Lawrence. 2200 BERGQUIST DR STE 1, WILFORD HALL MED CTR 78236 #051-04-1989 L1992 **OBG** *020 †30

DOOLEY, Yashika Trenise. 2200 BERGQUIST DR STE 1, ATTN: CREDENTIAL OFFICE 78236 #024-01-2000 L2007 **OBG** *020

DUDENHOEFER, Eric James. 2200 BERGQUIST DR STE 1, WHMC/CMC 78236 #016-43-1994 L1996 **OPH** *020 †35

DUFFY, Daniel Hugh. 2200 BERGQUIST DR STE 1, WHMC/CMC 78236 #023-12-1997 L2004 **NM** *020 †80,28

DUGINSKI, Thomas Michael. 2200 BERGQUIST DR STE 1, 59TH MEDICAL WING /MMCN 78236 #026-04-1982 L2002 **N CN** *020 †75

EADIE, James Stowe. 2200 BERGQUIST DR STE 1, ATTN:CREDENTIAL OFFICE 78236 #024-01-2000 L2000 **EM** *030 †16

EBERHARDT, Lisa Marie. 2200 BERGQUIST DR, STE 1 78236 #048-14-2004 **OBG** *012

EDELL, Thomas Alan. 2200 BERGQUIST DR, STE 1 78236 #019-02-1992 L2002 **AN PME** *020 †05

ELDER, Jamison Wendell. 2200 BERGQUIST DR STE 1, 59 MDW/MCOA 78236 #023-12-1999 L2003 **AN** *020 †05 ‡

ELLER, Robert Lafitte. 2200 BERGQUIST DR STE 1, LACKLAND AFB 78236 #047-05-2000 L2002 **OTO** *020 †45

EMERY, Robert Lewis. 2200 BERGQUIST DR STE 1, WHMC/CMC 78236 #023-12-2001 L2003 **DR** *012

ENGLAND, Ron Willard, II. 2200 BERGQUIST DR STE 1, 59 MDOS/SGOMA 78236 #023-12-1997 L1998 **AI** *020 †20,03

EPPINGER, Michael John. 2200 BERGQUIST DR STE 1, CREDENTIALS MANGER 78236 #025-01-1991 L1993 **TS** *020 †85,90

ESTRADA, Jorge Alberto. 2200 BERGQUIST DR STE 1, WHMC/CMC 78236 #341-01-1974 L1998 **IM** *020 †20

EWING, Christopher A. 2200 BERGQUIST DR STE 1, 59TH MDW/CMC 78236 #018-03-1998 L2004 **EM** *020 †16

FACKLER, Sarah Ann Marie. 2200 BERGQUIST DR, 59TH MED WING 78236 #038-44-2004 L2004 **END** *012 †20

FAUBION, Matthew Duane. 2200 BERGQUIST DR STE 1, WHMC/CMC 78236 #039-01-1998 L2001 **PFP** *020 †75

FAUX, Brian Michael. 2200 BERGQUIST DR STE 1, WHMC/CMC 78236 #041-15-2000 L2008 **N** *020 †55,75

FEIG, James Augustine. 2200 BERGQUIST DR STE 1, WHMC/CMC 78236 #023-12-1994 L1995 **FOP** *020 †50

FERGUSON, Earl Edward, III. 2200 BERGQUIST DR STE 1, WHMC/CMC 78236 #016-43-1994 L1996 **PS** *020 †85,65

FERRE, Robinson Mark. 2200 BERGQUIST DR STE 1, ATTN: CREDENTIAL OFFICE 78236 #056-06-2003 L2003 **EM** *020 †16

FIECHTNER, Bridget Kaye. 2200 BERGQUIST DR STE 1, WILFORD HALL MED CTR 78236 #026-08-2000 L2008 **IM** *020 †20

FISHER, Charles Ray, Jr. 2200 BERGQUIST DR STE 1, 59TH MDW 78236 #028-03-1987 L1989 **GPM AM** *020 †70,18

FISK, Andrea Denise. 2200 BERGQUIST DR, 59 MEDICAL WING 78236 #026-04-1998 L1999 **OBG** *020

FLYNN, Julianne. 2200 BERGQUIST DR STE 1, WHMC/CMC 78236 #016-02-1996 L1998 **OS** *020 †20,75

FOODY, William Francis, Jr. 2200 BERGQUIST DR STE 1, WHMC/CMC 78236 #051-04-1993 L2006 **GE** *020 †20

FOSTER, Jerry James. 2200 BERGQUIST DR STE 1, 59TH MDW 1ET 78236 #038-40-1965 L1979 **PD** *020 †55

FRANKLIN, Kevin James. 2200 BERGQUIST DR STE 1, 59 MEDICAL WING 78236 #023-12-1993 L1995 **GE** *020 †20

FRASER, Christina V. 2200 BERGQUIST DR STE 1 78236 #048-12-1998 L2005 **OBG** *020 †30

FREEMAN, John Edward. 2200 BERGQUIST DR STE 1, WHMC/CMC 78236 #352-07-1963 L1977 **RO** *071 †80

FRENIA, Douglas Scott. 2200 BERGQUIST DR STE 1, WHMC/CMC 78236 #023-12-1999 L2001 **PCC** *020 †20

FRINK, Spencer James. 2200 BERGQUIST DR STE 1, WILFORD HALL MED CTR 78236 #023-12-1990 L1993 **ORS** *020 †40

FROHM, Robert Max. 2200 BERGQUIST DR STE 1, CREDENTIALS OFFICE 78236 #021-01-2003 L2003 **AN** *020

FRY, Lon A. 2200 BERGQUIST DR, STE 1 78236 #048-78-1995, ▲ L1996 **AN** *020 †05

FRYLING, Maliwan. 2200 BERGQUIST DR STE 1, WHMC/CMC 78236 #891-02-1969 L1983 **FM** *030 †18

GALLAGHER, Joseph Patrick. 2200 BERGQUIST DR STE 1, WHMC/CMC 78236 #041-13-1999 L2001 **GE** *020 †20

GARCIA, Amy D. 2200 BERGQUIST DR, DEPT OF PEDS 78236 #048-13-2007 **PD** *012

GARZA, Juan. 2200 BERGQUIST DR STE 1, WHMC/CMC 78236 #023-12-1997 L1998 **RHU** *020 †20

GIBSON, William Allen. 2200 BERGQUIST DR STE 1, WHMC/CMC 78236 #041-12-1986 L2002 **EM** *020 †55,16

GILL, Howard Elmo, III. 2200 BERGQUIST DR STE 1 78236 #051-07-1987 L1988 **PM PMM** *020 †60

GILL, Stephen Aaron. 2200 BERGQUIST DR STE 1, WHMC/CMC 78236 #023-12-1996 L1998 **PCP** *020 †50

GILLETTE, Robert Kurt. 2200 BERGQUIST DR STE 1, WILFORD HALL MED CTR 78236 #025-07-1977 L2008 **NPM PD** *020 †55

GILSON, Robert T. 2200 BERGQUIST DR STE 1, CREDENTIALS OFFICE 78236 #048-14-1988 L2007 **D IM** *020 †20,15

GLANTON, Christopher W. 2200 BERGQUIST DR, STE 1 78236 #048-12-1997 L1999 **NEP IM** *020 †20

GONZALEZ, Erika Gabriela. 2200 BERGQUIST DR STE 1, 59 MEDICAL OPERATIONS GP (78236 #048-02-2002 L2004 **AI** *012 †55

GONZALEZ, Jeannette Ellen. 2200 BERGQUIST DR STE 1, DEPT OF PEDS 78236 #048-14-2000 L2002 **PD NPM** *020 †55

GONZALEZ, Michael George. 2200 BERGQUIST DR STE 1, WHMC/CMC 78236 #048-14-2000 L2007 **EM** *020 †16

GOOCH, John Mark. 2200 BERGQUIST DR STE 1, WHMC/CMC 78236 #020-02-1992 L1994 **OPH** *020 †35

GOOD, Robert Brian. 2200 BERGQUIST DR STE 1, WHMC/CMC 78236 #023-12-1990 L1992 **RNR** *020 †80

GORDON, Michael Chas. 2200 BERGQUIST DR STE 1, WHMC/CMC 78236 #005-06-1986 L2000 **OBG MFM** *071 †30

GOROSPE, Jose Brian. 2200 BERGQUIST DR STE 1, WHMC/CMC 78236 #023-12-2005 L2006 **IM** *020

GOWDER, Daniel Wade. 2200 BERGQUIST DR, STE 1 78236 #012-01-2004 L2004 **EM** *020

GRAU, Thomas Chas. 2200 BERGQUIST DR STE 1, 759 MAOS MMM 78236 #033-06-1986 L1988 **IM** *040 †20

GREEN, C Bruce. 2200 BERGQUIST DR STE 1, WHMC/CMC 78236 #056-06-1978 L1980 **FM AM** *030 †70,18

GREENE, Jeffery Parnell. 2200 BERGQUIST DR STE 1, WHMC/MMNP 78236 #010-03-1996 L1997 **PD** *020 †55

GREER, Barry James. 2200 BERGQUIST DR STE 1, WILFORD HALL MED CTR 78236 #023-12-1999 L2001 **DR** *100 †80 ‡

GROGAN, Patrick Mark. 2200 BERGQUIST DR STE 1, WHMC/CMC 78236 #023-12-1996 L2004 **N** *020 †75

GUTKE, Gregory Doxey. 2200 BERGQUIST DR STE 1, 59TH MDW/CMC 78236 #023-12-2002 L2002 **GPM** *020 †70

GUTTA, Himabindu. 2200 BERGQUIST DR STE 1, WILFORD HALL MED CTR 78236 #048-13-2004 **IM** *100 †20

HADDOCK, Gerald Ray. 2200 BERGQUIST DR STE 1, ATTN CREDENTIAL OFFICE 78236 #005-76-2001, ▲ L2006 **AN** *020 †05

HAKIM, Samuel. 2200 BERGQUIST DR STE 1, WHMC/CMC 78236 #035-03-1989 L2008 **U** *020 †95

HAMID, Nadeem Abdul. 2200 BERGQUIST DR STE 1, LACKLAND AFB, WHMC/CMC 78236 #024-07-2000 L2002 **PAN** *020

HANSON, Ryan Douglas. 2200 BERGQUIST DR STE 1, WHMC/CMC 78236 #021-01-2002 L2007 **AN** *100

HARDIN, Charles K. 2200 BERGQUIST DR STE 1, 59 MDW 78236 #028-03-1982 L1992 **PS GS** *020 †85,65

HAYGOOD, Tamara M. 2200 BERGQUIST DR STE 1, WILFORD HALL MED CTR 78236 #048-14-1988 L1989 **DR** *020 †80

HAYWOOD, Betty. 2200 BERGQUIST DR STE 1, WHMC/CMCQ 78236 #007-02-1968 L1975 **AN** *020

HENDERSON, James H, II. 2200 BERGQUIST DR STE 1, 59TH MDW 78236 #039-05-1985 L1988 **PUD SME** *030 †20

HINKLE, Mary K. 2200 BERGQUIST DR, WILFORD HALL 78236 #024-07-2003 L2004 **ID** *012 †20

HIVNOR, Chad Mitchell. 2200 BERGQUIST DR STE 1, 59TH MDW 78236 #048-13-1998 L1999 **D** *020 †15

HOGAN, Brian Keith. 2200 BERGQUIST DR STE 1, 59MDW-MMIM 78236 #021-01-2002 L2004 **ID** *012 †20

HOLCK, David E. 2200 BERGQUIST DR STE 1, WHMC/PSSE DEPT OPH 78236 #023-12-1987 L1989 **OPH** *020 †35

HOLDER, Allen Daxter. 2200 BERGQUIST DR STE 1, WHMC/CMC 78236 #047-20-2000 L2007 **EM** *020

HORLBECK, Drew Michael. 2200 BERGQUIST DR STE 1, WHMC/CMC 78236 #016-11-1994 L1996 **OTO** *020 †45

HORNE, Brandon Robert. 2200 BERGQUIST DR, STE 1 78236 #023-12-2000 L2003 **ORS** *020

HORNE, Stefanie Kristine. 2200 BERGQUIST DR STE 1, WHMC/CMC 78236 #023-12-2001 L2002 **OTO** *012

HOWELL, Della Livesay. 2200 BERGQUIST DR STE 1, WHMC/CMC 78236 #051-04-1998 L2000 **PHO** *020 †55

HRNCIR, David Eugene. 2200 BERGQUIST DR STE 1, WHMC/CMC 78236 #048-12-1980 L1981 **AI PD** *020 †55,70,03

HSING, Andrew Yitzu. 2200 BERGQUIST DR STE 1 78236 #024-05-2003 L2005 **PCC** *012 †20

HUNTER, Leslie Marie. 2200 BERGQUIST DR STE 1, WHMC/CMC 78236 #023-12-1989 L1999 **PD** *020 †55

IDDINS, Bart O. 2200 BERGQUIST DR STE 1, 59 MDW-CV 78236 #048-13-1991 L1992 **D** *020 †15

JACKSON, Julia Christine. 2200 BERGQUIST DR STE 1, WHMC/CMC 78236 #023-12-2001 L2001 **CHP** *020 †75

JAFFEE, Michael Scott. 2200 BERGQUIST DR STE 1, WHMC/CMC 78236 #051-01-1992 L1998 **N** *020 †75

JARNAGIN, Kyle Forrest. 2200 BERGQUIST DR STE 1, WHMC/CMC 78236 #023-12-2005 L2006 **IM** *020

JENKINS, Donald Howard. 2200 BERGQUIST DR STE 1, WHMC/CMC, 59TH MDW 78236 #023-12-1988 L1990 **TRS CCS** *020 †85

JENNE, Joel Wayne. 2200 BERGQUIST DR STE 1, WHMC/CMC 78236 #021-01-1999 L2006 **ORS** *100 †40

JOE, Keith Jeremy. 2200 BERGQUIST DR STE 1, 859 MSGS/MCSO 78236 #023-12-2002 L2004 **ORS** *012

JOHNSON, Charles Edward. 2200 BERGQUIST DR STE 1, WILFORD HALL MED CTR 78236 #021-01-1994 L1996 **DR** *020 †80

JOHNSON, James E, Jr. 2200 BERGQUIST DR, 59 MSGS/MCOA 78236 #048-16-1998 L2000 **AN** *020 †05

JOHNSON, Lori A. 2200 BERGQUIST DR STE 1, WILFORD HALL MED CTR 78236 #035-01-1994 L1997 **PD** *020 †55

JOHNSON, Robert Keyirce. 2200 BERGQUIST DR STE 1, WHMC/CMC 78236 #048-12-1978 L1978 **PD** *020 †55

JONES, Benjamin Lyman. 2200 BERGQUIST DR, SAN ANTONIO UNIF SER HLTH 78236 #023-12-2007 **TY** *012

JONES, David Scott. 2200 BERGQUIST DR STE 1, WILFORD HALL MED CTR/MMNP 78236 #007-02-1999 L2001 **PG PD** *020 †55

JONES, Lyell Keen, Jr. 2200 BERGQUIST DR STE 1, DEPT OF NEUROLOGY 78236 #036-05-2000 L2001 **CN** *020 †75

JONES, Mc Clure Kenneth. 2200 BERGQUIST DR, STE 1 78236 #039-01-1998 L2005 **AN** *020 †05

JONES, Woodson Scott. 2200 BERGQUIST DR STE 1, WHMC/CMC 78236 #048-02-1990 L1991 **PD** *020 †55

KACPROWICZ, Robert Frank. 2200 BERGQUIST DR STE 1, 59TH MEDICAL WING 78236 #016-06-1996 L2002 **EM** *040 †16

KADERBEK, Eric Wayne. 2200 BERGQUIST DR, MEDICAL CENTER/MC 78236 #023-12-2003 **AN** *020

KEARNEY, Patricia Riordan. 2200 BERGQUIST DR STE 1, WHMC/CMC 78236 #048-13-1990 L1998 **PD** *020 †55

KENDALL, Brian Scott. 2200 BERGQUIST DR STE 1, WHMC/CMC 78236 #023-12-1990 L1998 **PTH** *020 †50

KERECMAN, Jay Daniel. 2200 BERGQUIST DR, NEONATOLOGY/WILFORD HALL M 78236 #023-12-1995 L2008 **NPM PD** *020 †55

KING, James Anthony. 2200 BERGQUIST DR STE 1, 59 MDW/MSGS 78236 #056-05-1983 L1996 **EM GS** *030 †85,16

KING, Jeremy Alan. 2200 BERGQUIST DR STE 1, LACKLAND AFB 78236 #028-34-1999 L2001 **OBG** *020 †30

KING, Nevra Sisli. 2200 BERGQUIST DR STE 1, WILFORD HALL MED CTRQ 78236 #902-07-1993 L2003 **NS** *012

KING, Scott Alexander. 2200 BERGQUIST DR STE 1, WHMC/CMC 78236 #023-12-2002 L2007 **AN** *020 †05

KOBAYASHI, Ky Masami. 2200 BERGQUIST DR STE 1, WILFORD HALL MED CTR 78236 #007-02-1995 L2006 **HS** *020 †40

KOEBBE, Christopher James. 2200 BERGQUIST DR STE 1, ATTN: CREDENTIAL OFFICE 78236 #038-41-2000 L2008 **NS** *100

KOLKEBECK, Thomas Edward. 2200 BERGQUIST DR STE 1, 59 MDW 78236 #023-12-1995 L2007 **EM** *020 †16

KOST, Edward Robt. 2200 BERGQUIST DR STE 1, ATTN: CREDENTIAL OFFICE 78236 #023-12-1989 L2002 **OBG GO** *020 †30 ‡

KOSTUR, Gregory Daniel. 2200 BERGQUIST DR STE 1, WHMC/CMC 78236 #023-12-1999 L2002 **PD** *020 †55

KOWALSKI, Robert John, Jr. 2200 BERGQUIST DR STE 1, WHMC NEUROSURGERY 78236 #011-04-1998 L2006 **NS** *020

KOZIOL, Steven Anthony. 2200 BERGQUIST DR STE 1, WHMC/CMC 78236 #051-01-2000 L2002 **U** *012

KRUGER, Robert M. 2200 BERGQUIST DR STE 1, 759 MDOS/MMIM 78236 #050-02-1992 L1999 **IMG IM** *020 †20

KYU, Win Wah. 2200 BERGQUIST DR STE 1, WHMC/CMC 78236 #209-01-1986 L2001 **PD** *020 †55

LANDRUM, Michael Leroy. 2200 BERGQUIST DR STE 1, WHMC/CMC 78236 #028-03-1999 L2001 **ID** *100 †20

LARSON, Steven Paul. 2200 BERGQUIST DR STE 1, LACKLAND AFB, WHMC/CMC 78236 #016-01-1999 L2004 **GE** *020 †20

LASHELL, Mark Stephen. 2200 BERGQUIST DR STE 1, WILFORD HALL MED CTR MMIA 78236 #019-02-1997 L1999 **AI** *012 †55

LAUDIE, Matthew Aaron. 2200 BERGQUIST DR 78236 #023-12-2002 L2004 **AN** *020 †05

LAWSON, Richard Weldon. 2200 BERGQUIST DR STE 1PSP, WILFORD HALL MEDICAL CENTE 78236 #048-04-1970 L1970 **PD** *072 †55

LEMONS, Douglas Van. 2200 BERGQUIST DR STE 1, ATTN CREDENTIAL OFFICE LAC 78236 #019-02-2000 L2006 **AN** *020 †05

LESTER, Michelle. 2200 BERGQUIST DR STE 1, WHMC/CMC 78236 #019-02-2002 L2004 **IM** *020

LIN, John Chaochun. 2200 BERGQUIST DR STE 1, WILFORD HALL MED CTR 78236 #051-01-1998 L2006 **CCP** *020 †55

LIPPSTONE, Matthew Brian. 2200 BERGQUIST DR STE 1, 59 MDQ 78236 #041-02-2002 L2007 **EM** *020 †16

LISANTI, Christopher J. 2200 BERGQUIST DR STE 1, WHMC/CNC 78236 #023-12-1987 L2008 **DR** *020 †80

LLOYD, Jeremy Douglas. 2200 BERGQUIST DR STE 1, WHMC/CMC 78236 #048-02-1997 L1998 **EM** *020

LOTTERMAN, Seth Aaron. 2200 BERGQUIST DR STE 1, ATTN: CREDENTIAL OFFICE 78236 #035-46-2003 L2005 **EM** *020

LOWE, James David. 2200 BERGQUIST DR STE 100 78236 #023-12-1996 L2007 **VIR** *020 †80

LUNDBERG, Doris I. 2200 BERGQUIST DR STE 1, WHMC/CMC 78236 #024-07-1974 L1978 **IM** *020 †20

LYNCH, John Patrick. 2200 BERGQUIST DR STE 1, 59TH MDW/CMC 78236 #034-01-1993 L1994 **GPM** *020 †18,70

LYONS, Robert Allan. 2200 BERGQUIST DR STE 1, WHMC/CMC 78236 #038-43-2001 L2002 **OPH** *020 †35

MACKINNON, Andrew Ian. 2200 BERGQUIST DR STE 1, WILFORD HALL MED CTRGCMC 78236 #056-06-2000 L2000 **CD** *020 †20

MAGALLANES, Orlando R. 2200 BERGQUIST DR STE 1, ATNN:CREDENTIAL OFFICE 78236 #048-13-1994 L1994 **EM** *020 †16

MALDONADO-MONTALVO, Maribe. 2200 BERGQUIST DR STE 1 78236 #042-01-2006 L2007 **PD** *012

MANNING, John Lawrence. 2200 BERGQUIST DR STE 1, WHMC/CMC 78236 #048-02-1984 L1985 **FM** *020 †18

MARCONI, Vincent Charles. 2200 BERGQUIST DR STE 1, VINCENT MARCONI 78236 #023-07-2000 L2008 **ID** *020 †20

MASON, Phillip E. 2200 BERGQUIST DR STE 1, WHMC/CMC 78236 #048-12-1999 L2002 **EM** *020 †16

MASTERSON, Brian Jos. 2200 BERGQUIST DR STE 1, WHMC/CMC 78236 #024-01-1988 L1988 **AM** *020 †20,75

MATCHETTE, Michael Wolfe. 2200 BERGQUIST DR STE 1, ATTN: CREDENTIAL OFFICE 78236 #048-13-2002 L2008 **DR** *020 †80

MATHIS, Derek Andrew. 2200 BERGQUIST DR STE 1, WILFORD HALL MED CTR 78236 #051-07-1999 L2000 **PTH** *020 †50

MATURO, Stephen Charles. 2200 BERGQUIST DR STE 1, WHMC/CMC 78236 #023-12-2001 L2002 **OTO** *012

MC CAFFERTY, Randall R. 2200 BERGQUIST DR STE 1, 59 MDW 78236 #023-12-1993 L2006 **NS OS** *020 †25

MC DANIEL, Joseph Lynn. 2200 BERGQUIST DR STE 1, WHMC/CMC 78236 #047-20-1997 L1998 **EM** *020 †16

MC DOWELL, Laveta L. 2200 BERGQUIST DR STE 1, 59 MDW 78236 #048-14-1997 L1998 **NEP** *020 †20

MC FARLAND, Ross William. 2200 BERGQUIST DR STE 1, ATTN: CREDENTIAL OFFICE 78236 #025-07-1998 L2008 **HO** *020 †20

MC GILL, Kenneth Wayne. 2200 BERGQUIST DR STE 1, WHMC/CMC 78236 #654-01-1982 L1984 **FM** *020 †18

MCHUGH, Ryan Scot. 2200 BERGQUIST DR STE 1, 59TH MED WING/MMNP 78236 #048-13-2006 **PD** *012

MEIER, Adam W. 2200 BERGQUIST DR, STE 1 78236 #003-75-2007 ▲ **OBG** *012

MENDEZ, Evelyn. 2200 BERGQUIST DR STE 1, 59 MDW/CMC 78236 #042-01-1979 L1982 **PD** *020 †55

MESSIER, Stephen Elliott. 2200 BERGQUIST DR STE 1, WHMC/CMC 78236 #050-02-1998 L2000 **PD** *020 †55

MEYER, Karl Lee. 2200 BERGQUIST DR STE 1, WHMC/CMC 78236 #048-13-1998 L1999 **GS** *020

MEYER, Michael Thomas. 2200 BERGQUIST DR STE 1, WILFORD HALL MED CTR 78236 #056-05-1995 L2007 **CCP** *020 †55

MILHOAN, Kirk Alan. 2200 BERGQUIST DR STE 1, ATTN: CREDENTIALS OFFICE 78236 #041-02-1996 L2005 **PDC AM** *020 †55

MILLARE, Giovanni G. 2200 BERGQUIST DR STE 1, ATTN: CREDENTIAL OFFICE 78236 #748-18-1988 L1997 **FM** *020 †18,80

MILLER, Lee Anthony. 2200 BERGQUIST DR, STE 1 78236 #021-06-2000 L2006 **OTO** *020 †45

MOELLENHOFF, Michael E. 2200 BERGQUIST DR STE 1, WHMC/CMC 78236 #035-09-1994 L1995 **AN** *020

MOLL, Jeremy David. 2200 BERGQUIST DR STE 1, 59TH MED WING/MMNP 78236 #028-34-2005 L2007 **PD** *012

MOORE, Andrew Erle. 2200 BERGQUIST DR STE 1, 859 MSGS/MC50 78236 #048-16-1997 L2006 **ORS AM** *020 †40

MOORE, Janelle Lynn. 2200 BERGQUIST DR 78236 #023-12-2002 **ID** *020

MOORE, Meredith Linn. 2200 BERGQUIST DR STE 1, 59TH MEDICAL OPERATIONS G 78236 #045-04-1998 L2000 **AI** *012 †55

MOORE, Nicole Ninette. 2200 BERGQUIST DR STE 1, 59 MDW/MMCU 78236 #023-12-1994 L2005 **P** *020 †75

MOORE, Scott Alan. 2200 BERGQUIST DR STE 1, ATTN: CREDENTIAL OFFICE 78236 #047-05-1994 L1995 **CD** *020 †20

MORRIS, Michael Scott. 2200 BERGQUIST DR STE 1, WHMC/CMC 78236 #041-01-1998 L1999 **U** *020 †95

MORROW, Benjamin David. 2200 BERGQUIST DR, WILFORD HALL MED CTR/SGMII 78236 #041-14-2006 L2008 **IM** *012

MOTLEY, Garrick Lydell. 2200 BERGQUIST DR STE 1 78236 #024-01-1997 L2000 **U** *100

MUCK, Andrew Evan. 2200 BERGQUIST DR STE 1, ATTN: CREDENTIAL OFFICE 78236 #023-07-2004 L2007 **EM** *020

MUELLER, Deborah Lynn. 2200 BERGQUIST DR STE 1, MEDICAL CENTER 78236 #045-01-1992 L1997 **CCS** *020 †85

MURDOCH-CUENCA, Monica D. 2200 BERGQUIST DR STE 1, WILFORD HALL USAF MED CTR 78236 #016-42-1998 L2005 **PD** *020 †55

MURDOCK, Alan Dietrich. 2200 BERGQUIST DR STE 1, 859TH SURG OPS 78236 #001-02-1994 L1997 **TRS CCS** *020 †85

NAGY, Christopher James. 2200 BERGQUIST DR STE 1, WHMC/CMC 78236 #021-01-2001 L2005 **AN** *020 †05

NAVEJAR, Chrissy A. 2200 BERGQUIST DR 78236 #048-78-2006, ▲ L2007 **IM** *012

NELSON, Douglas Alan. 2200 BERGQUIST DR STE 1, ATTN: CREDENTIALS OFFICE 78236 #023-12-1996 L2005 **HO** *020 †20

NEUHAUSER, Katerina Maria. 2200 BERGQUIST DR STE 1 78236 #023-12-1993 **PHP** *100

NEWLON, Heather Renee. 2200 BERGQUIST DR STE 1 78236 #027-01-2005 L2007 **D** *012

O'BRIEN, Sean Patrick. 2200 BERGQUIST DR, DEPT OF ORTHO SURG 78236 #023-12-2002 L2004 **ORS** *100

ODUNSI, Adedayo. 2200 BERGQUIST DR, STE 1 78236 #690-01-1984 L1996 **NEP** *012 †20

OKSOL, Bruce Allen. 2200 BERGQUIST DR STE 1, WHMC/CMC, 59TH MDW 78236 #005-06-1977 L1980 **AM PD** *030 †55

OKULICZ, Jason Frank. 2200 BERGQUIST DR STE 1, WHMC/CMC 78236 #033-05-2002 L2004 **ID** *012 †20

OMER, Preston Sutherland. 2200 BERGQUIST DR STE 1, 59TH MED WING/MMNP 78236 #030-05-2005 L2007 **PD** *012

ONG, Bruce Anthony. 2200 BERGQUIST DR STE 1, 59TH MED WING/MMNP 78236 #012-22-2004 L2006 **PD** *100

OSSWALD, Michael Bernhard. 2200 BERGQUIST DR, 59 MDW/MMIH/STE 1 78236 #024-05-1989 L1994 **HO IM** *020 †20

OSSWALD, Sandra Shanglie. 2200 BERGQUIST DR STE 1, WHMC/CMC 78236 #024-05-1989 L1996 **D** *020

OTT, Christopher Joseph. 2200 BERGQUIST DR, DEPT OF ANESTHESIOLOGY 78236 #003-01-2003 **AN** *012

OTTO, Hans Frederick. 2200 BERGQUIST DR STE 1, WILFORD HALL MED CTR MMIA 78236 #038-40-2001 L2001 **AI** *012 †20

OTTOLINI, Martin Gerard. 2200 BERGQUIST DR STE 1, 59 MDW 78236 #025-07-1984 L1988 **PD ID** *050 †55

PALEKAR, Nicole Anil. 2200 BERGQUIST DR STE 1, WHMC/CMC 78236 #011-02-2000 L2006 **GE** *020 †20

PANDAY, Vasudha Aruna. 2200 BERGQUIST DR STE 1 78236 #041-02-2001 L2001 **OPH** *020 †35

PARK, Myung Soo. 2200 BERGQUIST DR STE 1, WHMC/CMC 78236 #035-08-1995 L2000 **CCS** *020

PAVLIK, Emily Nell. 2200 BERGQUIST DR STE 1, WILFORD HALL MED CTRGCMC 78236 #041-02-2004 L2006 **EM** *020

PELLETIER, Joseph P. 2200 BERGQUIST DR, STE 1 78236 #016-42-1991 L1994 **BBK** *020 †20,50

PELSZYNSKI, Mary Margaret. 2200 BERGQUIST DR STE 1, 59 MDW/CMC 78236 #023-12-1986 L1989 **PD PHO** *020 †55

PENDER, Bradley R. 2200 BERGQUIST DR STE 1, WHMC/CMC 78236 #048-02-1993 L2001 **AN** *020 †05

PERRY, William Brian. 2200 BERGQUIST DR STE 1 78236 #036-07-1990 L1991 **CRS GS** *020 †85,10

PETERSON, Johnr Douglas. 2200 BERGQUIST DR, EDU DEPT OF INTERNAL MED 78236 #021-01-2006 L2008 **IM** *012

PHALEN, James Arthur. 2200 BERGQUIST DR STE 1, 859 MDOS/MMNP 78236 #023-12-1996 L1998 **DBP PD** *020 †55

PHILLIPS, Timothy Martin. 2200 BERGQUIST DR STE 1, ATTN: CREDENTIAL OFFICE 78236 #023-12-2001 L2003 **U** *020

PLOTT, Eric Vincent. 2200 BERGQUIST DR STE 1, 759TH MDOS/MMIG 78236 #023-12-2002 L2004 **GE** *012 †20

POULIN, John Joseph. 2200 BERGQUIST DR STE 1, 59TH MED WING/MMNP 78236 #023-12-2006 L2008 **PD** *012

PROPST, Anthony Mark. 2200 BERGQUIST DR STE 1, 59TH MDW/CMC, WHMC 78236 #036-01-1992 L2000 **OBG REN** *020 †30

QUINN, James Mc Clintock. 2200 BERGQUIST DR STE 1, WHMC/CMC 78236 #035-01-1988 L1991 **ALI IM** *020 †20,03

RAMIREZ, Alexies. 2200 BERGQUIST DR STE 1, WHMC/CMC 78236 #021-01-1999 L2006 **CD** *012 †20

RAMOS, Rolando Ysadt. 2200 BERGQUIST DR STE 1 78236 #308-05-1986 L2001 **PTH** *020

RAMPTON, Marcus James. 2200 BERGQUIST DR, SAN ANTONIO UNIF SER 78236 #035-45-2007 **TY** *012

RASMUSSEN, Todd Erik. 2200 BERGQUIST DR STE 1, WILFORD HALL USAF MED CTR 78236 #026-08-1993 L1995 **VS** *020 †85

RAUTIOLA, Joel Lloyd. 2200 BERGQUIST DR STE 1, WHMC/CMC 78236 #024-05-1979 L1999 **DR** *020 †80

REGULES, Jason Allen. 2200 BERGQUIST DR 78236 #023-12-2002 L2004 **ID** *012 †20

REICH, Stephen Scott. 2200 BERGQUIST DR STE 1, WHMC/CMC 78236 #025-07-1998 L2006 **ICE** *020 †20

REILLY, Charles Daniel. 2200 BERGQUIST DR STE 1, ATTN:CREDENTIAL OFFICE 78236 #023-12-1997 L1998 **OPH** *100 †35

RENGEL, Jeffrey Michael. 2200 BERGQUIST DR, 59 MCDA 78236 #021-01-2001 L2003 **AN** *020 †05

RESTON, Rocky Russell. 2200 BERGQUIST DR STE 1, 59 MDW 78236 #023-12-1998 L2000 **AN** *020 †05

RETZLOFF, Matthew G. 2200 BERGQUIST DR STE 1, 59 MDW 78236 #048-12-1994 L1995 **OBG REN** *020 †30

RICHARDSON, Mark Worden. 2200 BERGQUIST DR STE 1, WHMC/CMD 78236 #023-12-1988 L2008 **OTR** *020 †40

RIDDLE, Gregory Allen. 2200 BERGQUIST DR STE 1, WHMC/CMC 78236 #001-06-1994 L1995 **FM FSM** *071 †18

RIRIE, David Wendell. 2200 BERGQUIST DR STE 1, WHMC/CMC 78236 #023-12-1989 L2001 **HO ON** *020 †20

ROBERTS, Sanford Eugene. 2200 BERGQUIST DR STE 1, WHMC/CMC 78236 #023-12-1993 L1995 **OPH** *020 †35

ROBINS, Richard Judd. 2200 BERGQUIST DR, STE 1 78236 #023-12-2004 L2005 **ORS** *012

RODRIGUEZ, Jose E. 2200 BERGQUIST DR STE 1, ATTN: CREDENTIAL OFFICE 78236 #042-01-1982 L1985 **FM** *020 †18

RODRIGUEZ, Rechell Gandia. 2200 BERGQUIST DR STE 1, MMIM 78236 #023-12-1997 L2000 **IM** *020 †20

ROGERS, Lisa Anne. 2200 BERGQUIST DR STE 1, WILFORD HALL MED CTR 78236 #004-01-2003 L2007 **AN** *020

ROKE, Daniel Mark. 2200 BERGQUIST DR STE 1, WHMC/CMC 78236 #050-02-1997 L2003 *020 †05

ROMICK, Benjamin G. 2200 BERGQUIST DR STE 1, 59 MDW 78236 #018-03-2001 L2002 **CD** *012 †20 ‡

ROSTOMILY, Robert Cullen. 2200 BERGQUIST DR STE 1, WHMC/CMC 78236 #038-06-1987 L1989 **NS** *020 †25

ROTENBERG, Joshua S. 2200 BERGQUIST DR STE 1, 859 MDOS MMNP 78236 #043-01-1995 L2005 **PD** *020 †75,55

ROUX, Napoleon Pangan. 2200 BERGQUIST DR, WILFORD HALL MEDICAL/MCOA 78236 #023-12-2004 L2006 **AN** *012

RUMSEY, Christopher A. 2200 BERGQUIST DR STE 1 78236 #022-75-2007, ▲ **OBG** *012

SAN DIEGO, Jerry William. 2200 BERGQUIST DR STE 1, WHMC/CMC 78236 #048-15-1998 L2000 **PTH** *020

SAUER, Samual Wade. 2200 BERGQUIST DR, DEPT MED 78236 #023-12-1996 L1997 **IM** *012 †70

SCHMID, Carrie Ann. 2200 BERGQUIST DR STE 1, WILFORD HALL MED CTR 78236 #023-12-2002 L2004 **MG** *020 †55

SCHMID, Josef F, III. 2200 BERGQUIST DR STE 1, WHMC/CMC 78236 #036-05-1992 L2002 **FM** *020 †18

SCHMITZ, Matthew Robert. 2200 BERGQUIST DR STE 1, ORTHOPAEDICS 78236 #016-43-2004 L2006 **ORS** *012

SCHREIER, Jorgina Santos. 2200 BERGQUIST DR STE 1, ATTN CREDENTIAL OFFICE 78236 #187-03-1966 L1979 **PD** *020 †55

SCLAFANI, Joseph James, Jr. 2200 BERGQUIST DR, SAN ANTONIO UNIF SER HLTH 78236 #035-48-2007 **TY** *012

SCOTT, Weston Price. 2200 BERGQUIST DR STE 1, WHMC/CMC 78236 #021-01-1980 L1988 **FM OS** *030 †18

SEAY, Thomas Marion. 2200 BERGQUIST DR STE 1 78236 #020-12-1987 L2007 **VIR R** *100 †95,80

SELBY, Dale Marcus. 2200 BERGQUIST DR STE 1, WHMC/CMC 78236 #023-12-1997 L1998 **HMP** *020 †50

SENECHAL, James Daffin. 2200 BERGQUIST DR STE 1, WHMC.CMC 78236 #051-04-2002 L2004 **FM** *020 †18

SHAH, Zulfiqar Ali. 2200 BERGQUIST DR STE 1, ATTN: CREDENTIAL OFFICE 78236 #305-01-2001 L2006 **IM** *020 †20

SHIMOTSU, Gary Wilson. 2200 BERGQUIST DR STE 1, WHMC/CMC 78236 #048-12-1978 L1978 **IM** *020 †20

SHOOR, Daniel Abram. 2200 BERGQUIST DR STE 1, 37TH AEROSPACE MEDICINE SQ 78236 #023-12-1996 L1997 **AM OM** *020 †70

SHUE, Philip Michael. 2200 BERGQUIST DR STE 1, WHMC/CMC 78236 #038-45-1984 L1985 **GPM** *020 †75

SIEDLECKI, Chung Man. 2200 BERGQUIST DR STE 1, ATTN: CREDENTIAL OFFICE 78236 #023-12-1991 L1993 **GPM** *020 †70,18

SIMPSON, Michael Patrick. 2200 BERGQUIST DR, DEPT OF EMERGENCY MEDICINE 78236 #023-12-2006 L2008 **EM** *012

SKY, Karen Melanie. 2200 BERGQUIST DR, WILFORD HALL INTERNAL MEDI 78236 #005-12-2002 L2005 **IM** *100 †20

SLADKY, John Henry. 2200 BERGQUIST DR 78236 #056-06-1999 L2007 **N** *020 †75

SLAWINSKI, Kimberly Ann. 2200 BERGQUIST DR STE 1, 59TH MEDICAL WING 78236 #023-12-1984 L1988 **OPH** *020 †35

SLOAN, Steven Brett. 2200 BERGQUIST DR STE 1, WHMC/CMC 78236 #023-12-1994 L1995 **D** *020 †15

SMITH, Benjamin D. 2200 BERGQUIST DR STE 1, WHMC/CMC 78236 #008-01-2001 L2003 **RO** *020 †80

SMITH, David Lawrence. 2200 BERGQUIST DR, STE 1 78236 #023-12-1988 L2001 **SO CCS** *020 †85

SMITH, David Meade. 2200 BERGQUIST DR, 59 MDW/MRDO 78236 #048-13-1997 L1998 **GS** *020

SORENSEN, Richard Allan. 2200 BERGQUIST DR STE 1, ATTN CREDENTIAL OFFICE 78236 #047-07-1998 L2007 **EM** *020 †16

SORGE, David Glenn. 2200 BERGQUIST DR STE 1, WHMC/CMC 78236 #049-01-1988 L1989 **DR** *020 †80

STAMM, Jason Andrew. 2200 BERGQUIST DR STE 1, 59TH MDW/CMC 78236 #041-14-2001 L2002 **IM** *020

STEELE, John Joseph, III. 2200 BERGQUIST DR, STE 1 78236 #023-12-1998 L2007 **NS** *020

STINNER, Daniel Joseph. 2200 BERGQUIST DR, DEPT OF ORTHOPAEDIC SURG 78236 #016-02-2006 L2008 **ORS** *012

STONE, Alan Barth. 2200 BERGQUIST DR STE 1, WHMC/CMC 78236 #023-12-1990 L1996 **DR** *020 †50,80

STORMO, James Edward. 2200 BERGQUIST DR STE 1, WILFORD HALL MED CTR 78236 #023-12-2001 L2006 **AN** *020 †05

STRUBLE, Erika Jean. 2200 BERGQUIST DR STE 1, WHMC/CMC 78236 #023-12-1999 L2000 **HO** *100 †20

SWASEY, Drew Napier. 2200 BERGQUIST DR STE 1, WHMC/CMC 78236 #023-12-2002 L2002 **AN** *012

SWICK, John Thomas, II. 2200 BERGQUIST DR STE 1, WILFORD HALL MED CTR 78236 #051-04-2003 L2008 **AN** *020

TAFT, Wesley William. 2200 BERGQUIST DR STE 1, 59TH MED WING/MMNP 78236 #016-11-2006 **PD** *012

TAKAO, Richard Tsuyoshi. 2200 BERGQUIST DR STE 1, WHMC/SGHC 78236 #040-02-1972 L1985 **PD ADL** *020 †55

TALARCZYK, Matthew Robert. 2200 BERGQUIST DR STE 1, WHMC/CMC 78236 #056-05-1998 L2000 **PS** *020 †85,65

TANKERSLEY, Michael S. 2200 BERGQUIST DR STE 1, WHMC/CMC 78236 #047-06-1993 L1995 **AI** *020 †55,03

TESSIER, Christopher Mich. 2200 BERGQUIST DR, DEPT IM 78236 #024-07-2006 L2007 **IM** *012

THAXTON, Robert Edwin. 2200 BERGQUIST DR STE 1 78236 #023-12-1996 L1997 **EM** *040 †16

THOMAS, Linda Patricia. 2200 BERGQUIST DR STE 1, WILFORD HALL MED CTR 78236 #038-41-1997 L1998 **PDR** *020 †80

THOMAS, Nicole Marie. 2200 BERGQUIST DR STE 1 78236 #003-01-1996 L1998 **PD** *020 †55

THOMAS, Roger Shawn. 2200 BERGQUIST DR STE 1, WHMC/CMC 78236 #023-12-2005 L2006 **GS** *100

TRAVIS, Thomas W. ■ 78236 #023-12-1986 L1987 **FM** *020 †70

TULLY, Charla C. 2200 BERGQUIST DR STE 1, INTERNAL MED PRGRM 78236 #039-79-2007, ▲ **IM** *012

TYREE, Kreangkai. 2200 BERGQUIST DR STE 1, WILFORD HALL MEDICAL CENTE 78236 #023-12-1998 L2000 **PD** *020 †55

TYREE, Melissa R. 2200 BERGQUIST DR STE 1, WIFORD HALL MEDICAL CENTER 78236 #023-12-1998 L2007 **PD** *020 †55

URBAN, Derek Kurt. 2200 BERGQUIST DR STE 1, WHMC/CMC 78236 #038-40-1993 L1995 **DR** *020 †80

VALENTA, Jerome Clement, Jr. 2200 BERGQUIST DR STE 1, ATTN: CREDENTIAL OFFICE 78236 #048-02-1975 L1975 **FM** *020 †18

VANDEKIEFT, Michael W. 2200 BERGQUIST DR STE 1, WHMC/CMC 78236 #035-08-1997 L1998 **IM** *020 †20

VENTICINQUE, Steven G. 2200 BERGQUIST DR STE 1, 59TH MDW/CMC 78236 #011-03-1994 L2002 **AN** *020 †05

VOIGT, Charles Virgil. 2200 BERGQUIST DR STE 1, LACKLAND AFB, WHMC/CMC 78236 #046-01-2000 L2006 **DR** *100 †80

VROON, Brian Anton. 2200 BERGQUIST DR STE 1, 59 MDW 78236 #025-01-1994 L1995 **OBG** *020 †30

WALKER, Daniel Reuben. 2200 BERGQUIST DR STE 1, MEDICAL CENTER 78236 #023-12-1999 L2001 **PTH** *012

WALLER, Stephen Glenn. 2200 BERGQUIST DR STE 1, WILFORD HALL MED CTR 78236 #023-12-1983 L2004 **OPH AM** *040 †35

WARD, Jane Ballard. 2200 BERGQUIST DR STE 1, WILFORD HALL MED CTR 78236 #023-12-1983 L1999 **OPH PD** *030 †35

WEISENBURGER, Irene Nmi. 2200 BERGQUIST DR, DEPT ENDO 78236 #010-02-2002 **END** *012

WELCH OCHSNER, Audra L. 2200 BERGQUIST DR STE 1, MMCU 78236 #048-15-1998 L1999 **P** *020 †75

WELD, Kyle Jones. 2200 BERGQUIST DR STE 1, WHMC/CMC 78236 #047-05-1995 L1997 **U** *020 †95

WEMPE, Joseph Matthew. 2200 BERGQUIST DR STE 1, 859 MDTS/MTLP 78236 #046-01-1984 L2007 **DMP** *020 †50

WERNER, Mark Eric. 2200 BERGQUIST DR STE 1, 59 MDW/ SGHC 78236 #023-12-1989 L1995 **ORS** *020 †40

WEST, Kevin Bruce. 2200 BERGQUIST DR STE 1, WHMC/CMC 78236 #005-06-1974 L2005 **AM FM** *020 †18,70

WESTPHALL, Johann S. 1515 TRUEMPER ST, 37TH MDG/SGPF 78236 #023-12-1996 L1997 **GPM** *020 †70

WHEELER, John Charles, III. 2200 BERGQUIST DR STE 1 78236 #045-01-2000 L2002 **ORS** *012

WHITE, Kevin Michael. 2200 BERGQUIST DR STE 1, ATTN: CREDENTIAL OFFICE 78236 #023-12-2001 L2001 **AI** *012

WIEDENHOEFER, James F. 2200 BERGQUIST DR STE 1, WHME/CMC 78236 #020-02-1998 L2001 **OBG** *020 †30

WILHELM, Christopher John. 2200 BERGQUIST DR STE 1, 59TH MED WING/MMNP 78236 #023-12-2005 L2007 **PD** *012

WILLIAMS, Carl Lee. 2200 BERGQUIST DR STE 1, WHMC/CMC 78236 #017-20-1979 L2000 **FM** *020 †18

WILSON, Lynn Marie. 2200 BERGQUIST DR STE 1, WHMC/CMC 78236 #036-05-1999 L2005 **EM** *020

WISCO, Oliver Jayme. 2200 BERGQUIST DR, ATTN: CREDENTIAL OFFICE 78236 #041-77-2002, ▲ L2003 **D** *012

WONG, Kondi. 2200 BERGQUIST DR STE 1, WHMC/CMC 78236 #023-12-1988 L2004 **NP PTH** *020 †50

WOOD, David A. 2200 BERGQUIST DR STE 1, WHMC/CMC 78236 #048-02-1995 L1996 **DR** *020 †80

WOODS, Jon Bentley. 2200 BERGQUIST DR STE 1, WILFORD HALL MED CTR 78236 #023-12-1995 L1996 **PD PDI** *020 †55

WRIGHT, Denise. 2200 BERGQUIST DR STE 1, WHMC/CMC 78236 #007-02-1994 L1997 **HMP** *020 †50

YAMAGUCHI, Kent Takao. 2200 BERGQUIST DR STE 1, WHMC/CMC 78236 #005-02-1972 L1973 **PS HS** *020 †45,65 ‡

YOUNG, David G, III. 2200 BERGQUIST DR STE 1, WILFORD HALL MEDICAL CENTE 78236 #005-06-1977 L1978 **IM AM** *020 †20

YOUNG, Joshua Yusak. 2200 BERGQUIST DR STE 1, 0059 MEDICAL OPERATIONS GP 78236 #005-12-2003 L2005 **GS** *020

ZIMMERMAN, Michelle K. 2200 BERGQUIST DR STE 1, WHMC/CMC 78236 #041-01-1998 L1999 **PTH** *020

LAGO VISTA – TRAVIS

BRIGGS, Robert Cornelius. ■ 78645 #023-07-1959 L1960 **IMG PM** *071

KYTE, Paul David. 6502 LOHMANS CROSSING RD 78645 #048-14-1981 L1981 **FM** *020 †18

QUINLIVAN, Wm Leslie Gray. 3404 AMERICAN DR APT 330, 4 78645 #917-25-1946 L1961 **GYN** *020

STEARNS, Michael Quentin. ■ 78645 #010-02-1984 L1986 **N** *075 †75

TSITLAKIDIS, Constantina. ■ 78645 #035-09-2000 L2003 **IM** *100 †20

LAGUNA VISTA – CAMERON

PEREDO, Luzviminda K. ■ 78578 #041-13-1976 L1979 **IM PUD** *020

LAJITAS – BREWSTER

CALOMENI, John A. ■ 79852 #048-13-1982 L1983 **EM** *020 †16

LAKE DALLAS – DENTON

BOULDIN, Carole-Anne. ■ 75065 #048-16-2005 **AN** *012

JONES, Lajuan Kinette. ■ 75065 #048-02-1998 L2008 **PHO** *100 †55

SEXTON, Gerald David. ■ 75065 #041-13-1988 *100

LAKE JACKSON – BRAZORIA

AGGARWAL, Sanjay K. ■ 77566 #917-08-1988 L1997 **PCC** *020 †20

AMIN, Alkesh C. 215 OAK DR S, STE G 77566 #495-23-1987 L1994 **IM** *020 †20

BARADHI, Nabil Shakeib. 215 OAK DR S, STE L 77566 #051-04-1986 L1990 **CD** *020 †20

BAUTISTA, Lina Tapiador. 106 N PARKING PL 77566 #748-01-1960 L1977 **GP** *071

BENNETT, Donald Neill. 215 OAK DR # B 77566 #048-02-1973 L1973 **OBG** *030 †30

BERTHEAU, Julius Herman. 229 PARKING WAY ST 77566 #041-01-1965 L1967 **FM OM** *020 †18

BLAKE, Philmore Alexander. 188 ABNER JACKSON PKWY 77566 #023-07-1993 L1999 **U** *020 †95

BOTTENFIELD, Gerald Wayne. 54 FLAG LAKE PLZ 77566 #025-07-1974 L1983 **PD** *020 †55

BROCINER, Ronald L. 100 MEDICAL DR 77566 #035-06-1981 L1983 **DR** *020 †80

BUI, Liem Phuong. 101 PARKING WAY ST, STE A 77566 #941-01-1972 L1976 **GP** *020

BURNS, William Edward, Jr. 201 OAK DR S STE 101 77566 #048-13-1976 L1976 **IM FM** *020 †18

CHANG, Tai-Li. 207 BANYAN ST 77566 #023-07-2008 *012

CHRETIEN, Leo T. 104 CIRCLE WAY ST 77566 #048-04-1990 L1993 **EM IM** *020

COLLINS, Hubert Vincent. 100 MEDICAL DR, BRAZOSPORT REG HEALTH SYS 77566 #047-07-1980 L2000 **AN** *020 †05

CREEL, Nicholas Barry. 215 OAK DR S STE A 77566 #048-14-1973 L1974 **OBG** *020

CROW, Wayne Nathan. 77566 #048-13-1977 L1977 **DR** *020 †80

DALAL, Rajesh V. 192 ABNER JACKSON PKWY 77566 #495-23-1987 L1996 **IM** *020 †20

DAVE, Amish Mahendra. 100 MEDICAL DR, UTMB 77566 #048-02-2002 L2005 **DR** *020 †20

DRISCOLL, Alisa Marie. 77566 #048-13-2001 L2006 **U** *020

FALCON, Emerardo, Jr. 100 MEDICAL DR, RM B 77566 #048-13-1982 L1983 **ON IM** *020 †20

FEAVER, Brian J. 201 THAT WAY ST 77566 #065-10-1987 L1995 **FM OS** *020 ‡

FISHER, James Allen. ■ 77566 #048-12-1954 L1954 **GP OS** *071

FLAKE, Raymond E. ■ 77566 #048-04-1949 L1950 **OM IM** *071 †20

FREEDMAN, Craig Kevin. 100 MEDICAL DR, BRAZOSPORT MEMORIAL HOSPIT 77566 #023-01-1990 L1991 **DR** *020 †80

FUCHS, James Donald. 100 MEDICAL DR 77566 #048-04-1976 L1977 **DR** *020 †80

FUGLER, Richard Clark. 56 FLAG LAKE PLZ 77566 #001-02-1996 L1998 **GS** *020

GIBBERMAN, Jeffrey Bruce. 222 PARKING WAY ST, FAMILY REHAB MED ASSOC 77566 #035-08-1993 L1995 **PM PRS** *020 †60

GILLILAND, Michael Paul. 215 OAK DR S STE D 77566 #048-13-1979 L1979 **OBG EM** *020 †30

GOLD, Judith. 450 THIS WAY ST STE B 77566 #781-01-1986 L1995 **NEP IM** *020

GRADY, Frank Jos. 103 PARKING WAY ST 77566 #008-01-1965 L1970 **OPH** *020 †35

GRADY, Jonathan Patrick. ■ 77566 #048-02-2007 L2007 **TY** *012

HARDOIN, Richard Allen. 54 FLAG LAKE PLZ 77566 #025-07-1975 L1978 **PD** *020 †55

HARRIS, Scott Loren. 215 OAK DR S STE L 77566 #048-13-1982 L1983 **CD IM** *020 †20

HARTLEY, Lawrence J. 504 AOK DR 77566 #038-06-1953 L1960 **PTH** *071 †50

HOFFMAN, Frank Jos. 201 OAK DR S, STE 104 77566 #048-02-1978 L1978 **ORS** *020 †40

HUDSON, Samuel Lewis. 120 FLAG LAKE DR, STE 1 77566 #048-13-1979 L1979 **ORS** *020

IMPERIAL, Arturo Domingo. 100 MEDICAL DR 77566 #748-01-1962 L1974 **GS HS** *020 †85

IMPERIAL, Josefina Delfin. 201 THAT WAY ST, CHILDREN'S CLINIC 77566 #748-01-1962 L1974 **PD** *071 †55

JAIN, Rakesh. ■ 77566 #495-38-1986 L1991 **P** *020 †75

JESS, Raymond Carl. 100 MEDICAL DR 77566 #048-02-1966 L1966 **OBG OS** *020 †30

JORDAN, Ray Calvin. 134 S PARKING PL 77566 #048-02-1958 L1960 **OPH** *020 †35

KATTEGUMMULA, Ranga R. 215 OAK DR S, STE K 77566 #495-21-1975 L1984 **IM** *020 †20

KHAN, Mohammad Afzal. 129 CIRCLE WAY ST, STE A 77566 #027-01-2000 L2006 **IM** *020 †20

KILBOURN, Laurie G. 100 MEDICAL DR DEPT AN, BRAZOSPORT MEM HOSP 77566 #048-02-1988 L1992 **AN** *020 †05

KILIAN, Robert Jack. 131 CIRCLE WAY ST, STE B 77566 #048-02-1967 L1972 **ORS** *020 †40

KRELL, Blair William. 214 PARKING WAY ST 77566 #048-02-1997 L2001 **N** *020 †75

LAROCHE, Howard G, Jr. 201 OAK DR S STE 201 77566 #048-14-1987 L1991 **N** *020 †75

LE, Khanh Ngoc. 109 PARKING WAY ST, THE GI CENTER 77566 #021-01-2000 L2002 **GE** *100 †20

LE BOEUF, Lawrence Von. 100 MEDICAL DR 77566 #048-12-1962 L1962 **EM** *020

LEIDLEIN, Jane H. 109 CIRCLE WAY ST 77566 #048-14-1992 L1993 **OPH OS** *020 †35

LOCKETT, Lillian Doris. 135 OYSTER CREEK DR, STE E 77566 #030-06-1988 L1992 **OBG** *020 †30

LUNSFORD, Thomas Mason. 215 OAK DR S STE F 77566 #048-02-1970 L1970 **OTO FPS** *020 †45

MARAIST, Donald Joseph. ■ 77566 #028-34-1962 L1970 **OBG** *071 †30

MARSHALL, Jana Katherine. 215 OAK DR S, STE I 77566 #048-04-1995 L1997 **FM** *020 †18

MARTINEZ, Edgar Ivan. 100 MEDICAL DR 77566 #042-03-1988 L1998 **AN OBG** *020 †05

MARTINEZ, Henry Enoc. 201 OAK DR S, STE 202 77566 #042-02-1996 L2002 **GS** *020

MAXWELL, John Andrew. 125 CIRCLE WAY ST 77566 #048-16-1991 L1992 **RNR** *020 †80

MAY, Henry King. ■ 77566 #048-02-1944 L1944 **GP OS** *071

MC DONALD, Richard. ■ 77566 #017-20-1942 L1952 **PTH** *071 †50

MC DOWELL, Ansel Lewis. ■ 77566 #048-02-1955 L1955 **OM GS** *030 †85

MC FADDEN, Brett Aaron. 129 CIRCLE WAY ST, STE A 77566 #041-12-1999 L2005 **IM** *020 †20

MEAH, Nizam Mohammad. 109 PARKING WAY ST 77566 #160-01-1984 L1994 **GE** *020 †20

MEYERS, Bruce Paul. 201 OAK DR S STE 207 77566 #048-02-1971 L1971 **OTO** *020 †45

NELMS, William Harold. 126 POST OAK RD 77566 #048-02-1956 L1956 **IM** *071 †20

NGUYEN, Ngoc-Diep Thi. 101 PARKING WAY ST, STE A 77566 #941-01-1971 L1978 *074

OANDASAN, Oscar Cortez. 201 OAK DR S, STE 102 77566 #048-10-1965 L1979 **GP R** *020

O'LEARY, John Clarence. ■ 77566 #048-02-1946 L1946 **R** *071 †80

PANT DHODAPKAR, Anupama. 100B MEDICAL DR 77566 #495-01-1990 L2004 **HO** *020 †20

PATEL, Nilesh J. 201 OAK DR S, STE 204 77566 #048-94-1986 L1994 **CHP** *020 †75

PATEL, Rikin S. ■ 77566 #048-13-2005 L2008 **IM** *012

PAUL, Ronald Ernest. 56 FLAG LAKE PLZ 77566 #036-07-1961 L1963 **OBG** *020 †30

PELTIER, Frank Adolph. 215 OAK DR S, STE C 77566 #048-02-1978 L1978 **D** *020 †15

PISARSKI, Gregory P. 215 OAK DR S, STE J 77566 #048-14-1989 L1991 **PS** *020 †65,85

PLANA, Juan Carlos. 215 OAK DR S STE L 77566 #264-04-1995 L2005 **CD** *100 †20

POOTHULLIL, John M. 201 OAK DR S STE 106 77566 #495-31-1968 L1976 **A PD** *020 †55,03

RESNICK, Harvey. 201 OAK DR S, STE 107 77566 #062-01-1964 L1966 **FM** *020 †18 ‡

ROBINSON, Cyrus Miles. 201 OAK DR S, STE 108 77566 #004-01-1969 L1976 **U** *071 †95

RYAN, Lucy Haberthier. 135 OYSTER CREEK DR, STE W 77566 #048-13-1992 L1994 **PD** *020 †55

SABBAGH, Mouin Fayez. 106 CIRCLE WAY ST 77566 #915-02-1978 L1994 **IM** *020 †20

SABRSULA, Irvin Frank, Jr. 135 OYSTER CREEK DR STE S 77566 #048-14-1978 L1978 **FM** *020 †18 ‡

SHAH, Alpesh Rasiklal. 215 OAK DR S, STE L 77566 #495-23-1992 L1999 **CD** *020 †20

SINHA, Anil Kumar. 201 OAK DR S 77566 #048-16-1991-1990 L1998 **GS** *020 †85

SNYDER, Wallace Mc Clure. ■ 77566 #048-02-1954 L1954 **OS R** *071 †80

STEELE, Kevin Charles. ■ 77566 #048-14-2004 L2006 **FM** *020 †18

STRICKLAND, Alan Douglas. ■ 77566 #048-04-1974 L1974 **GE PD** *071 †55

SWEATT, William H. 104 CIRCLE WAY ST STE B 77566 #023-07-1995 L1996 **GE** *020 †20

THOMAS, Antony B. 215 OAK DR S, STE I 77566 #495-13-1986 L1997 **FM PD** *020 †18

THOMPSON, Robert Pool, Jr. 201 OAK DR S, STE 108 77566 #048-13-1984 L1990 **GS** *020 †85

THOMPSON, Sanford Rodgers. 201 OAK DR S STE 104, THOMPSON ORTHOPEDIC CLNC 77566 #048-02-1970 L1970 **ORS** *020 †40

VAVICH, Joel Mitchell. 135 OYSTER CREEK DR STE B 77566 #023-07-1970 L1982 **PD** *020

WANG, Pei Lien. 215 OAK DR S, STE W 77566 #038-40-1973 L1984 **PD** *020 †55

WILLIAMS, Milton Craig. 52 FLAG LAKE PLZ 77566 #048-02-1971 L1971 **P** *020

LAKE KIOWA – COOKE

CALDWELL, James Wm. ■ 76240 #048-12-1959 L1959 **PM** *071 †60

LAKE WORTH – TARRANT

JAIN, Rashmi. 3900 BOAT CLUB RD 76135 #016-42-2002 L2006 **PD** *100 †55

YEE, Wayne Wong. 3900 BOAT CLUB RD 76135 #048-13-1981 L1981 **PD** *020 †55

LAKEHILLS – BANDERA

HARRIS, Edmund Dennis. ■ 78063 #025-07-1980 L1989 **DR** *020 †80

LAKEWAY – TRAVIS

ADENI, Shubha. 900 RR 620 S STE C201 78734 #495-33-1982 L2002 **PD** *020 †55
ARCHULETA, Michael E. 1100 LAKEWAY DR, STE 101 78734 #048-15-1989 L1991 **FM LM** *071
BENNETT, Brent L. 2300 LOHMANS SPUR STE 106 78734 #048-02-1982 L1983 **IM** *020 †20
COHN, Robert Leon. ■ 78734 #048-12-1954 L1954 **AN** *071 †05
CORNET, Jo Ann Margaret. ■ 78734 #038-06-1956 L1974 **PD PHO** *071 †55
CUNNINGHAM, Mary Ana. 1313 RR 620 S, STE 201 78734 #048-14-1997 L1998 **D** *020 †15
DE VERE, Ronald. 1200 LAKEWAY DR, STE 8 78734 #062-01-1968 L1974 **N** *020 †75
GAERTNER, James S. ■ 78734 #048-14-1991 L1992 **FM** *020 †18
GANDARILLAS, Manuel P. ■ 78738 #275-01-1951 L1969 **GS GYN** *071 †18
GEIBEL, Roger S. 218 CAPRI 78734 #021-01-1950 L1954 **GP U** *072
GRAHAM, Douglas Troy. ■ 78734 #038-44-2000 L2007 **AN** *020 †05
HARTJEN, Ruth Helen. ■ 78734 #041-07-1996 L2004 **EM** *020 †16
JOHNSON, George Lester. ■ 78734 #048-02-1955 L1955 **GP GS** *071
LAZAR, Jeffrey David. ■ 78738 #025-01-1974 L1975 **PA IM** *050 †20
MANICOM, Ronald Edward. 1200 LAKEWAY DR, STE 8 78734 #048-04-1961 L1961 **NS** *020 †25
MAYES, Gordon Worth. ■ 78734 #048-02-1957 L1957 **ORS** *071 †40
MILLS, William C, Jr. ■ 78734 #048-02-1943 L1943 **FM** *071
POHL, James Keller. 801 RR 620 S, STE 101 78734 #048-12-1975 L1979 **PUD IM** *020 †20
REDDY, Shobha Dharam. 317 RANCH ROAD 620 S, STE 100 78734 #495-21-1978 L2006 **IM OS** *020 †20
ROBITAILLE, Doris M. 1411 RR 620 S 78734 #048-13-1988 L1989 **FM** *020 †18
STEWART, John J, Jr. ■ 78734 #036-07-1966 L1970 **OPH** *071 †35
STRAMA, Thomas. ■ 78734 #011-02-1967 L1968 **GYN** *071 †30
VAGSHENIAN, Gregory Simon. ■ 78734 #041-01-1973 L1995 **P GP** *020 †75
WEINER, Max B. ■ 78734 #035-06-1934 **GP** *071
WHITTENBERG, Cynthia. 107 RANCH RD 620 S, STE 102-D5 78734 #048-04-1993 L1994 **IM FM** *020 †20

LAMESA – DAWSON

BROWN, Lisa Lovette. 1510 N BRYAN AVE 79331 #016-11-1991 L1995 **FM** *020 †18
BUTTERY, James M. ■ 79331 #048-02-1950 L1950 **GP OBG** *071
CHAMALES, Michael Hood. 1600 N BRYAN AVE 79331 #048-02-1974 L1974 **D** *020
CHOWPAKNAM, Griengsak. 1016 N 17TH ST 79331 #891-03-1972 L1979 **PD GP** *020 †55 ‡
COCHRAN, Phillip Douglas. 1600 N BRYAN AVE 79331 #048-15-1999 L2000 **FM** *020 †18
LEE, Yung Kee. 1600 N BRYAN AVE 79331 #583-04-1959 L1974 **GP GS** *020 †18 ‡
LUONG, Binh M. ■ 79331 #048-12-1998 L1999 **GP** *020
MC KAY, James Vernon. 1600 N BRYAN AVE 79331 #048-02-1942 L1943 **GP** *071
OGEDA, Fidel Lopez. 1510 N BRYAN AVE 79331 #048-12-2003 L2006 **FM** *020
QUADEER, Mohammed Abdul. 1600 N BRYAN AVE 79331 #495-21-1959 L1977 **EM GP** *020 ‡
SMILEY, David Neil. 1600 N BRYAN AVE 79331 #048-02-1956 L1956 **GS GP** *071 †85

LAMPASAS – LAMPASAS

BANDAS, Lynn M. 608 N KEY AVE 76550 #048-16-1993 L1994 **DR** *020 †80
BISHOP, Alton Arnold. 76550 #048-02-1956 L1956 **GP GS** *020 †18
CAIN, James E, III. 207 W AVENUE E 76550 #048-04-1994 L1996 **FM** *020 †18
CAIN, Robin Gruen. 207 W AVENUE E 76550 #048-14-1995 L1996 **FM** *020 †18
ELLISON, Stephen R. 1962 FM 1478 76550 #048-13-1995 L1996 **EM** *020 †16
FARCUS, Gerald Leo. ■ 76550 #028-03-1971 L1974 **AN** *020 †05
HIGGINS, John T. 1004 1/2 S KEY AVE 76550 #649-14-1980 L1989 **FM** *020 †15
JOHNSTON, Samuel Iredell. ■ 76550 #048-02-1954 L1955 **CRS** *071
KERLEY, Thomas K. 608 N KEY AVE, SETON HIGHLAND LAKES HEALT 76550 #048-15-1991 L1992 **FM** *020 †18
LANE, Mark Steven. 207 W AVENUE E 76550 #048-15-1984 L1985 **FM** *020 †18
MALAVE, Ernesto. 305 S KEY AVE 76550 #042-03-1983 L1994 **FM** *020
PATTESON, Morris K, Sr. 207 W AVENUE E, FAMILY MEDICINE CLINIC 76550 #048-02-1945 L1945 **FM** *071
PATTESON, Morris K, Jr. 207 W AVENUE E, FAMILY MEDICINE CLINIC 76550 #048-14-1974 L1974 **FM PD** *020 †18
PERRY, Robert R. 207 W AVENUE E 76550 #048-14-1994 L1995 **FM** *020 †18
WINEGAR, Robert Frank, II. 608 N KEY AVE 76550 #048-13-1973 L1973 **DR NM** *020 †80
ZIDD, Edward Alan. ■ 76550 #048-12-1970 L1970 **FM** *020 †18,16

LANCASTER – DALLAS

BADER, Elliott. 2500 W PLEASANT RUN RD, STE 210 75146 #836-01-1950 L1978 **GS GE** *020
BELLOMO, Joseph Francis. 2700 W PLEASANT RUN RD, STE 340 75146 #035-19-1982 L1987 **CD IM** *020 †20
BROWN, Steven W. ■ 75134 #048-13-2002 **NS** *012
CHAKMAKJIAN, Souren K. 2700 W PLEASANT RN RD #240, MIDWAY PARK PROFESSIONAL B 75146 #605-01-1966 L1968 **PD PDC** *020 †55
CHESTER, Catherine Payne. 2600 W PLEASANT RUN RD 75146 #048-12-1955 L1955 **AI PD** *071 †03
CHIMATA, Yugandhar Prasad. 2500 W PLEASANT RUN RD 75146 #496-35-1997 L2003 **NEP** *020 †20
CUADROS, Maria M. 2500 W PLEASANT RUN RD, STE 215 75146 #737-05-1989 L2000 **FM** *020 †18
DANDE, Ratna Silpa. 2500 W PLEASANT RUN RD, STE 100 75146 #495-50-1997 L2005 **NEP** *020 †20
DISCH, Ralph C. 2600 W PLEASANT RUN RD 75146 #035-08-1949 L1957 **GS** *071 †85
DOTI, Anthony Ralph. 2500 W PLEASANT RUN RD, STE 215 75146 #654-01-1996 L1999 **IM** *020

FLASDICK, Rudolf Monroe. 2600 W PLEASANT RUN RD 75146 #021-01-1952 L1960 **IM OM** *020
GAMIL, Wafer Soliman. 2500 W PLEASANT RUN RD, STE 215 75146 #915-02-1987 L1998 **IM** *020 †20
GORREPATI, Navaneeta K. 2700 W PLEASANT RUN RD, STE 1104 75146 #495-58-1976 L1985 **CD IM** *050 †20
HARVEY, Heidi Lynne. 2500 W PLEASANT RUN RD, STE 210 75146 #064-01-1994 L1996 **FM** *100
ISSA, Ghadir A. 2700 W PLEASANT RUN RD, STE 220 75146 #048-14-1992 L1994 **PD** *020 †55
JUAREZ, Maria Isabel. 2600 W PLEASANT RUN RD 75146 #847-11-1990 L1996 **HO** *020 †20
KOTTAPALLI, Mahesh Babu. 2500 W PLEASANT RUN RD, STE 215 75146 #496-37-1999 L2005 **ID** *020 †20
LYDEN, Sandra Diane. ■ 75146 #422-01-2002 L2002 **FOP** *100
MAXWELL, Garrett Wortham. ■ 75146 #048-02-1959 L1959 **IM FM** *071
MC GRIFF, Lloyd. 354 W PLEASANT RUN RD 75146 #047-07-1979 L1994 **GS** *020
MEHR, Chris. ■ 75146 #047-07-2002 L2006 **FM** *100 †18
NYSTROM, Robert Elmer. ■ 75146 #016-06-1947 L1952 **OPH** *071 †35
OGWU, Austin I. 2505 W BELT LINE RD, ALPHA MED CTR 75146 #915-03-1983 L1996 **IM** *020 †20
OLATUNJI, Michael O. 2500 W PLEASANT RUN RD, STE 215 75146 #048-02-2002 L2005 **IM** *100 †20
OLUSANYA, Oladele O. 2500 W PLEASANT RUN RD, STE 200 75146 #690-01-1976 L1999 **FM OBG** *020 †18 ‡
OWO, Toks Akin. 2600 W PLEASANT RUN RD, MEDICAL CENTER AT LANCASTE 75146 #690-01-1982 L2000 **IM PD** *020 †20
SEJOUR-WHITE, Jeannette N. 2700 W PLEASANT RUN RD, STE 300 75146 #011-03-1997 L1999 **PD** *020 †55
SHARDA, Gireesh. 2500 W PLEASANT RUN RD, STE 100 75146 #048-15-1998 L2000 **PM** *020 †60
SHIELDS, Wilma Farrington. ■ 75146 #028-02-1943 L1961 **PTH IM** *071 †50
SKYIEPAL, Mark Denning. 2500 W PLEASANT RUN RD, SITE 215 75146 #048-02-1991 L1992 **GS** *020 †85
TENNY, John Ramsey. 2700 W PLEASANT RUN RD, STE 210 75146 #028-03-1980 L1981 **ORS** *020 †40
VELUSAMY, Latha. 2500 W PLEASANT RUN RD, STE 100 75146 #495-94-1996 L2007 **NEP** *020 †20
WALLIS, Harold Ford. 2500 W PLEASANT RUN RD, STE 220 75146 #048-13-1976 L1980 **OBG** *020 †30

LANEVILLE – RUSK

BROWN, David M. ■ 75667 #048-15-1993 L1994 **EM FM** *020

LANTANA – DENTON

HAYNES, William A. ■ 76226 #005-12-1978 L1993 **EM** *071 †16
PATEL, Meenakshi P. ■ 76226 #495-23-1977 L1982 **P** *020
PATEL, Piyush Vallabhbhai. ■ 76226 #495-23-1974 L1982 **CD IM** *020
WOLBRINK, Alex Mark. ■ 76226 #018-03-1995 L2004 **OS** *020 †70

LAREDO – WEBB

ACEVEDO, Eliud. 1405 JACAMAN RD, STE 101 78041 #042-03-1988 L1992 **OBG** *020 †30
AGUIRRE, Jesus I-Burgos. 7210 MCPHERSON RD, STE 2200 78041 #649-02-1973 L1977 **GP** *020
AGUIRRE, Marisa I. ■ 78041 #048-13-1998 L2002 **FM** *062 †18
ALDAPE, Adolfo Alejandro. 5702 MCPHERSON RD, UNIT 20 78041 #038-43-1996 L2000 **MPD** *020 †55,20
ALDARONDO-ANTONINI, N. 6410 MCPHERSON RD STE 103, DERMAT SPECIALS OF LAREDO 78041 #024-16-1993 L2000 **D** *020 †15
ALLEN, William Randall. 10710 MCPHERSON RD, STE 100 78045 #027-01-1972 L1977 **PN** *020 †55
ALVAREZ, Avelino Claro. ■ 78041 #308-11-1985 L1989 **PD** *020 †55
ALVAREZ, Norberto. 78045 #649-02-1994 L2007 **FM** *100 †18
AMARAL, Jennifer Ramos. 10710 MCPHERSON RD, STE 100 78045 #042-02-1999 L2005 **PD** *100
ANGUIANO, Richard. 1310 JUNCTION DR STE A 78041 #005-18-1991 L1997 **DR** *020 †80
BECERRA, Enrique H. 4151 LOOP 20, STE 203 78043 #005-14-1984 L1999 **OBG** *020 †30
BENAVIDES, Enrique F. 1020 E HILLSIDE RD 78041 #649-02-1975 L1978 **OBG** *020 †30
BENAVIDES, Enrique F, III. 1020 E HILLSIDE RD 78041 #048-02-1998 L2000 **OBG** *100 †18,30
BENAVIDES, Luis Manuel. 506 GALE ST 78041 #048-13-1978 L1978 **FM FPG** *020 †18
BENAVIDES, Melissa A. 10700 MCPHERSON RD 78045 #048-02-1998 L1999 **FM** *020 †18
BENAVIDES, Oscar. 209 W VILLAGE BLVD, STE 11 78041 #649-14-1980 L1991 **FM** *020
BERLIOZ, Jose Ludovico. ■ 78041 #451-01-1986 L1998 **NPM** *020 †55
BLANCO, Alex Joseph. 9901 MCPHERSON RD, STE 102 78045 #048-14-1998 L2001 **FM** *020 †18
BOCANEGRA, Ruben D. 4151 LOOP 20, STE 101B 78043 #649-30-1983 L1995 **FM OBS** *020 †18
BROWN, Nyda Williams. 827 UNION PACIFIC BLVD, PMB 71-188 78045 #012-01-1963 L1963 **P OS** *020 †75
BUITRON, Paul Raymond. 220 W HILLSIDE RD STE 13 78041 #649-04-1975 L1978 **OTO** *020
CALIXTO, Eutimio. 1700 E SAUNDERS ST 78041 #042-01-1982 L1990 **GS** *020
CAMERO, Joseph Porfirio. 1710 E SAUNDERS ST, STE B370 78041 #056-06-1983 L1986 **N** *020
CAMPOS, Sara. 1501 E BUSTAMANTE ST, STE D 78041 #048-13-1991 L1993 **PD** *020
CANALES, Elsa Salazar. 7210 MCPHERSON RD, STE 205 78041 #048-02-1998 L2004 **GE** *020 †20
CANTU, Cynthia G. 9901 MCPHERSON RD, STE 102 78045 #048-14-1998 L2004 **FM** *020 †18
CANTU, Dennis David. 1710 E SAUNDERS ST, # B650 78041 #048-04-1978 L1978 **FM** *020 †20
CANTU, Roberto J. 702 GALVESTON ST 78040 #649-02-1967 L1975 **ORS** *020 †40
CANTU, Xavier Raul. 313 W VILLAGE BLVD STE 104 78041 #649-02-1982 L1985 **FM** *020 †18
CANTU-WILLMAN, Raul S. 201 COLORADO ST 78041 #649-02-1968 L1974 **GS GP** *020
CARDENAS, Melchor Pablo. 904 CORPUS CHRISTI ST 78040 #649-52-1988 L1999 **FM** *020 †18 ‡

■ = Address Information Privacy Protected

CARDENAS MENDOZA, Jorge A. PO BOX 1835, 1500 PAPPAS ST 78044 #649-06-1960 L1969 P *071

CASAS ZARAGOZA, Carlos N. 1700 E SAUNDERS ST 78041 #649-02-1989 L1996 IM *020 †20

CASTANEDA, Fernando A. 4151 LOOP 20 STE 102 78043 #048-14-1993 L1997 PD *020

CASTANEDA, Flavio. 1710 E SAUNDERS ST 78041 #649-30-1982 L2004 VIR R *050

CASTANEDA, Pedro, Jr. 1003 GARFIELD ST 78040 #649-02-1972 L1974 PD ADL *020

CASTILLON, Richard. 1710 E SAUNDERS ST # 200A 78041 #048-02-1996 L2000 OBG *020 †30

CAVAZOS, Miguel A, Jr. 1616 LOGAN AVE 78040 #048-02-1968 L1968 PD NPM *071 †55

CAVAZOS, Patricia E. 1616 LOGAN AVE 78040 #048-13-1999 L2004 PD *020 †55

CHAFFIN, Craig Erick. ■ 78043 #048-02-1980 L1981 P *020

CHAPA, Jose S. 5823 NORTHGATE LN 78041 #649-02-1953 L1963 GS *071 †85

CHEEMA, Shafiq-Ur-Rehman. 1710 E SAUNDERS ST, STE B675 78041 #704-01-1997 L2004 NEP *100 †20

CHHINA, Satbir S. 10710 MCPHERSON RD, STE 100 78045 #495-03-1985 L2001 NPM *020 †55

CIGARROA, Carlos Gonzalez. 702 E CALTON RD, STE A 78041 #024-01-1987 L1992 CD *020 †20

CIGARROA, Joaquin G, Jr. 1710 E SAUNDERS ST, 55TH FLOOR TOWER B 78041 #024-01-1947 L1950 IM *020 †20

CIGARROA, Leonides G, Jr. 1710 E SAUNDERS ST, STE B460 78041 #649-30-1992 L1997 FM *020 †18

CIGARROA, Ricardo G. 1710 E SAUNDERS ST, MEDICAL TOWER B 5TH FL 78041 #024-01-1984 L1988 CD *020 †20

CLARKE, Cheryl C. ■ 78045 #566-01-1991 L1999 OBG *020 †30

CLELAND, Timothy P. 1006 E HILLSIDE RD, STE 2 78041 #048-15-1990 L1991 OPH *020 †35

CLICK, Maurice A, Jr. 1710 E SAUNDERS ST, STE B660 78041 #048-14-1984 L1985 FM *020 †18

COMPEAN, Rene Rolando. 6828 SPRINGFIELD AVE STE 3, DEL MAR PROFESSIONAL PLAZA #048-13-1985 L1986 FM *020 †18

CRUZ, Carlos. 8607 MCPHERSON RD, STE 101 78045 #048-12-1984 L1985 OBG *020 †30

CRUZ, David H. 1811 N ARKANSAS AVE 78043 #048-13-1994 L1997 FM *020 †18

DEAYALA, Rafael Emilio. 1710 E SAUNDERS ST, STE B485 78041 #048-12-1986 L1987 OBG *020 †30

DE CALDERA, Beatriz G. 4151 LOOP 20, STE 101B 78043 #649-30-1994 L2004 FM *020

DE GONZALEZ, Blanca Cantu. ■ 78043 #649-02-1953 L1959 PTH IMG *071

DIAZ, Horacio Alberto. 3527 LOOP 20, STE 110 78043 #649-54-1988 L1998 FM *020 †18

DUNHAM, Edward Kellogg. ■ 78045 #035-01-1968 L1970 IM AI *071 †20,03

EAST, Paul. ■ 78041 #917-30-1968 L1969 LM PHP *030 †70

ELIZONDO-CANTU, Oscar L. ■ 78043 #649-02-1943 L1959 AN *075

ESPINOSA, Carlos Andres. 6801 MCPHERSON RD, STE 223 78041 #042-03-1992 L1998 NEP *020 †20

ESTEBAN MARIA, Jacinto. NORTHGATE LN C STE 118 78041 #649-01-1963 L1979 GS *020

FAZ-GUEVARA, Eliud A. 4001 MCPHERSON AVE, STE 104 78041 #649-02-1972 L1981 CHP P *020

FERNANDEZ, Caroline. 1710 E SAUNDERS ST, TOWER B STE B490 78041 #748-11-1991 L2000 IM *020 †20

FERNANDEZ, Eduardo B. 7210 MCPHERSON RD, STE 210 78041 #042-01-1987 L1997 U *020 †95

FERNANDEZ, Martin Pablo. ■ 78040 #649-52-1995 L2007 DMP *100 †50

FLORES, Angelica. 1515 PAPPAS ST, GATEWAY COMM HLTH CTR 78041 #048-04-1987 L1988 IM *062 †20

FLORES, Ildefonzo. 1520 E SAN PEDRO ST, STE 101 78041 #048-12-1984 L1985 IM *020 †20

FLORES-SALAZAR, Maximo. 10700 MCPHERSON RD, DOCTORS HOSP LAREDO ER 78045 #649-02-1970 L1987 GS *100

FLORES-VEGA, Carlos H. 2359 E SAUNDERS ST, CLINIC 78041 #649-02-1956 L2003 IM CD *071

GALAN, Anthony R. 6801 MCPHERSON RD, STE 330 78041 #308-02-1989 L1999 GE *020 †20

GALO, Michael Vincent. 702 GALVESTON ST 78040 #021-01-1966 L1967 ORS *020 †40

GARCIA, Adolfo G. 1710 E SAUNDERS ST, STE B675 78041 #649-02-1971 L1977 NEP IM *020 †20

GARCIA, Enrique T. 1710 E SAUNDERS ST, # B250 78041 #048-04-1986 L1987 OTO *020 †45

GARCIA, George Victor. ■ 78040 #048-12-1957 L1957 GP OBG *075

GARCIA, Jose Gerardo. 1500 PAPPAS ST, BLDG 664 78041 #649-02-1957 L1964 P AM *020 ‡

GARCIA, Jose Maria W. 413 INTERAMERICA BLVD, PMB 070-361 78045 #649-14-1981 L1991 CD IM *020 †20

GARCIA, Jose R. 6801 MCPHERSON RD, STE 327 78041 #048-02-1994 L1996 IM *020 †20

GARCIA, Manuel Garcia. 1620 LANE ST 78043 #649-02-1958 L1967 R *020

GARCIA, Maria Aurora. 6550 SPRINGFIELD AVE, STE 101 78041 #025-01-1997 L2001 OBG *020 †30

GARCIA-CAVAZOS, Rogelio. 2309 E SAUNDERS ST 78041 #649-02-1995 L2003 RHU *020 †20

GARCIA-RAMOS, Gustavo A. 6551 STAR CT, LAREDO VA OUTPATIENT CLC 78041 #649-45-1988 L1998 FM *020 †20

GARRASTEGUI BIGAS, Juan J. 1710 E SAUNDERS ST, STE B170 TOWER B 78041 #042-01-1989 L2001 IM *020 †20

GARZA, Amando F, III. 1519 E BUSTAMANTE ST # A 78041 #649-02-1983 L1988 PD CHN *020 †55

GARZA, Arturo Alberto. 10700 MCPHERSON RD 78045 #649-02-1986 L1995 GS *020 †85

GARZA, Arturo O. 1710 MCPHERSON RD, STE 120 78041 #649-30-1980 L1982 EM GP *020

GARZA, Carlos. 220 W HILLSIDE RD, STE 5A 78041 #649-14-1977 L1987 GS VS *020

GARZA, Daniel. 6801 MCPHERSON RD, STE 336 78041 #649-30-1981 L1988 CHN PD *020 †55,75

GARZA, Isaias, Jr. 6262 MCPHERSON RD, STE 110 78041 #649-30-1982 L1986 FM *020 †18

GARZA, Jose Manuel. 7807 MCPHERSON RD STE 2E 78045 #048-14-1979 L1979 GP EM *020 †16

GARZA, Rebecca Uribe. 121 CALLE DEL NORTE, STE 104 78041 #016-06-1974 L1982 PD *020 †55

GARZA-DIAZ, Armando. PO BOX 3112 78044 #649-14-1976 FM *100

GAUNTLETT, Hughenna L. ■ 78045 #005-12-1951 L1951 GS *071 †85

GODINES, Reynaldo. 6801 MCPHERSON RD, STE 339 78041 #048-12-1975 L1975 GE IM *020 †20

GOMEZ-REJON, Julio C. 6828 SPRINGFIELD AVE 78041 #649-02-1956 L1959 IM P *075

GOMEZ-VAZQUEZ, Eduardo. 7210 MCPHERSON RD, STE 115 78041 #048-13-1992 L1993 FM *020 †18

GOMEZ-VAZQUEZ, Jorge. 7210 MCPHERSON RD, STE 115 78041 #048-13-1992 L1993 FM *020 †18

GOMEZ-VAZQUEZ, Jose. 7210 MCPHERSON RD, STE 115 78041 #048-13-1985 L1986 AN *020 †05

GOMEZ-VAZQUEZ, Roberto. 7210 MCPHERSON RD STE 115 78041 #649-14-1976 L1985 GS *020 †20

GONZALEZ, Dagoberto, Jr. 5711 MCPHERSON RD STE 100 78041 #048-16-1996 L1997 OBG *020 †30

GONZALEZ, Juan Carlos. ■ 78045 #048-02-2005 L2006 N *012

GONZALEZ, Manuel J. 1101 CORPUS CHRISTI ST 78040 #649-30-1974 L1975 VS GS *020 †85

GONZALEZ, Victor M. 1502 LOGAN AVE, STE 206 78040 #649-30-1976 L1983 GE IM *020

GUAJARDO, Arturo. 1710 E SAUNDERS ST, TOWER B SUITE 385 78041 #649-30-1998 L2004 FM *020 †20

GUTIERREZ, Jose Santiago. 6930 SPRINGFIELD AVE 78041 #649-33-1981 L1986 OBG *020 †30

GUTIERREZ, Oscar V. 702 E CALTON RD, STE 201A 78041 #048-12-1987 L1989 IM *020

GUTIERREZ, Salvador Luis. PO BOX 826 78042 #275-01-1949 L1977 IM *020

GUZMAN-GONZALEZ, Octavio. 6826 SPRINGFIELD AVE, STE 101 78041 #649-14-1980 L1994 CD IM *020

HABER, Milton. 6801 MCPHERSON RD, STE 220 78041 #649-02-1974 L1987 IM *020

HALL, Anthony Darwin. ■ 78043 #649-14-1978 L1983 UCM *071

HINOJOSA, Armando Roberto. 2309 E SAUNDERS ST, CENTER INC 78041 #016-45-1998 L1999 IM *020

HOCHMAN, Michael Avery. 5313 MCPHERSON RD 78041 #016-11-1993 L1999 OPH *020 †35

HOLZKNECHT, Philip. 6801 MCPHERSON RD STE 217, FAMILY ORTHOPEDICS OF S. T 78041 #010-02-1987 L2002 ORS *020 †40

HUANG, Benson Y. 1710 E SAUNDERS ST B290 78041 #748-10-1983 L1994 IM PCC *020 †20

HUDSON, Robert Donald. 121 CALLE DEL NORTE, STE 102 78041 #048-04-1978 L1978 D *020 †15

JACQUES, Emilio, Jr. 5823 NORTHGATE LN 78041 #649-02-1982 L1991 GP PHP *020

JOHNSON, Leonard W. 220 N ZAPATA HWY STE 11 78043 #019-02-1964 L1965 CD IM *071 †20

JONES, Kenneth Neil. ■ 78045 #048-02-1979 L1979 AN PMM *071

JOVEL-BARRIERE, Manuel. 10700 MCPHERSON RD, DOCTOR'S HOSPITAL OF LARED 78045 #341-01-1980 L1987 RO *020

KANDELL, Thomas William. 220 N ZAPATA HWY STE 11A 78043 #649-01-1974 L1976 IM UCM *072 †20

KEENE, Gladys Cronfel. 500 E MANN RD 78041 #048-02-1965 L1966 A PD *020 †55,03

KEENE, Roger Hampton. 500 E MANN RD, STE 2 78041 #649-02-1965 L1966 OTO *020 †45

KULUBYA, Edwin S. 1700 E SAUNDERS ST, ANESTHESIA DEPARTMENT 78041 #010-03-1982 L2000 AN *020 †20

LANG, Lester Wilson. 904 CORPUS CHRISTI ST 78040 #048-02-1967 L1967 FM EM *020

LARA, Esther A Dominguez. 313 MANOR RD 78041 #341-01-1977 L1984 PM *075

LAWSON, Shirley Keith. 1515 LOGAN AVE 78040 #048-02-1969 L1969 GP *071

LAZOFSON, Kenneth Alan. 1700 E SAUNDERS ST, LAREDO MEDICAL CENTER 78041 #041-13-1990 L1996 DR *020 †80

LEAL, Francisco Alonzo. 1420 LOGAN AVE 78040 #649-02-1968 L1973 CD IM *020 †20

LESSNER, Daniel I. 220 N ZAPATA HWY, STE 11 78043 #035-15-1984 L1985 FM *071 †18

LEVINE, Alan Saml. ■ 78045 #011-02-1961 L1963 FM P *020 †75,18

LIGHTNER, Oscar Newton. 6826 SPRINGFIELD AVE, STE 102 78041 #649-30-1978 L1983 FM *020 †18

LOPEZ, Victor Manuel. 10700 MCPHERSON RD 78045 #649-19-1977 L1986 AN OS *020

LOSTETTER, Alvin Chas. ■ 78040 #048-12-1969 L1969 AN *075

LOZANO, Francisco Gerardo. 1209 SAN DARIO AVE, # 7-195 78040 #649-52-1984 L1992 PD *020 †55

MADDOX, Robert Kelley. 322 PLYMOUTH LN 78041 #048-02-1965 L1975 GS *020 †85

MALDONADO, Jose Roel. 6826 SPRINGFIELD AVE, STE 203 78041 #649-02-1996 L2004 FM *020 †18 ‡

MANDELL, Marshall. ■ 78041 #035-08-1946 L1951 A RHU *075 †03

MANGUAL, Rafael Arcangel. 1405 JACAMAN RD STE 1 78041 #042-03-1997 L2000 FM *020 †18

MARINA, Doina Fiorentina. 6801 MCPHERSON RD STE 338 78041 #781-01-1968 L1996 OBG *071 †30

MAROUF, Lina M. 1006 E HILLSIDE RD, STE 2 78041 #605-01-1982 L1989 OPH *020 †35

MARTINEZ, Arturo Antonio. 7210 MCPHERSON RD, STE 200 78041 #649-30-1985 L1989 *020

MARTINEZ, Edwin Roberto. 10710 MCPHERSON RD, STE 105 78045 #042-03-1995 L2002 CD *020 †20

MARTINEZ, Emanuel Ernesto. 7210 MCPHERSON RD, STE 200 78041 #649-30-1982 L1989 PD *020

MARTINEZ, Robert A. 706 SHILOH DR 78045 #048-02-1995 L1998 PD *020 †55

MARTINEZ-MARTINEZ, Z. PO BOX 451244 78045 #649-02-1966 L1975 GS *071 †85

MATA, Virgilio H. ■ 78041 #649-01-1958 L1961 OBG *071 †30

MEDEROS, Ivan Alejandro. 1710 E SAUNDERS ST, STE B375 78041 #036-05-1988 L1995 GS *020 †85

MENCHACA, Diego Francisco. 1203 WELBY CT, STE 2 78041 #649-30-1980 L1998 FM *020 †18

MENDOZA, Louis F, Jr. 1801 GUST ST # 2 78041 #649-02-1971 L1974 IM PUD *020

MENDOZA, Luis O. 2202 SANTA MARIA AVE 78040 #649-02-1969 L1971 GP *020

MIRANDA, Eduardo. 2344 LAGUNA DEL MAR CT, STE 104 78041 #649-14-1981 L1999 ON HEM *020 †20

MIRELES AUDIFFRED, Raul. 7210 MCPHERSON RD STE 210 78041 #649-02-1971 L1977 U *020 †95

MOLINA, Edgar L. 4151 BOB BULLOCK LOOP, STE 201 78043 #748-02-1990 L1996 PD PDI *020 †55

MOLINA, Esteban Alejo. 802 GALVESTON ST 78040 #649-02-1968 L1975 OBG *020 †30

MOLINA, Jose E. 1302 HENDRICKS AVE 78040 #649-02-1968 L1974 GS *020 †85

MOLINA, Jurairat. 4151 BOB BULLOCK LOOP, STE 201 78043 #891-03-1987 L2001 AI *020 †03,55

MONIOT, Alfred L. ■ 78045 #010-02-1971 L1980 DR NM *071 †20,28,80

MONTALVO, Juan F. 6423 MCPHERSON RD, STE 13 78041 #048-14-1992 L1994 OBG *020 †30

MORALES-VELAZQUEZ, C A. 1515 LOGAN AVE 78040 #649-01-1953 L1961 AN GP *020

MOREAU, Yvel Pascal. 1710 E SAUNDERS ST, STE B450 78041 #033-05-1993 L2004 ORS *020

MORENO, Efren A. 6262 MCPHERSON RD, STE 208 78041 #042-02-1981 L1989 PS HS *020

NAJERA LOZANO, Miguel E. 801 CORPUS CHRISTI ST 78040 #649-02-1967 L1975 GS VS *020 †85

NGO, Peter T. 1710 E SAUNDERS ST # B350 78041 #748-01-1992 L2001 END IM *020 †20

NIMCHAN, Ralph. 6801 MCPHERSON RD, STE 226 78041 #950-01-1968 L1974 CD IM *020 †20

NTAKIRUTIMANA, Eliel. 1710 E SAUNDERS ST, STE 384 78041 #649-38-1980 L1992 AN *020 †05

ORCES, Carlos. 1219 CORPUS CHRISTI ST 78040 #319-04-1988 L1998 RHU *020 †20

ORONOZ, Joaquin F, Jr. 10710 MCPHERSON RD STE 202 78045 #023-12-1991 L2000 ORS *020 †40

PELLEGRIN, Alfredo Garcia. 820 LAREDO ST 78040 #649-02-1968 L1970 **PD** *020
PENA, Francisco I. 2801 MUSSER ST 78043 #649-14-1977 L1981 **GP** *020
PEREZ, Evelia Nanez. ■ 78043 #649-02-1961 L1965 **AN** *071
PEREZ, Sigifredo. 2001 CEDAR AVE 78040 #649-02-1959 L1967 **OBG** *071 †30
PINEDA, Jesus Sergio. 7210 MCPHERSON RD, STE 220 78041 #048-02-1983 L1985 **FM** *020
POPP, Roseanne Mary. 1515 LOGAN AVE 78040 #048-13-1994 L1995 **FM** *020
POSLIGUA, Lorena Elizabet. ■ 78041 #319-03-1998 L2007 **SP** *100
POTTS, Fred Ernest, III. ■ 78040 #048-13-1977 L1977 **AN** *020 †05
PUEBLITZ, Siegfried. 10700 MCPHERSON RD 78045 #649-01-1977 L1992 **PTH** *020 †50
PUIG, John Valentine, II. 9652 MCPHERSON RD, STE 12 78045 #048-13-1999 L2001 **FSM FM** *020 †18
RAFATI, Salah A K. 5401 SPRINGFIELD AVE 78041 #605-01-1971 L1975 **DR** *020 †80
RAJPUT, Mohammad S A. 2359 E SAUNDERS ST 78041 #704-02-1962 L1993 **GP P** *020
RAMONET, Jorgelina. 5823 NORTHGATE LN STE 2018 78041 #132-01-1967 L1981 **CD IM** *071
RAMOS, Augusto Gueco. 1700 E SAUNDERS ST 78041 #748-01-1979 L1997 **ATP** *020 †50
RAMOS, Baltazar R, III. 1601 MUSSER ST 78043 #048-13-1973 L1973 **PD** *020 †55
RAMOS-SORIANO, Asuncion G. 1710 E SAUNDERS ST, STE B380 78041 #748-02-1986 L1996 **PD PG** *020 †55
RANGEL, Manuel Sigfrido. ■ 78041 #649-31-1983 L1992 **IM** *020
RECTO, Allan Lim. 1710 E SAUNDERS ST, STE B475 78041 #748-10-1989 L2000 **PD** *020 †55
RECTO, Gesina Nietes. 6801 MCPHERSON RD, STE 214 78041 #748-14-1991 L2000 **PD** *020 †55
REDA, Hassan Khalil. 1420 LOGAN AVE 78040 #605-01-1995 L2000 **TS CD** *020 †85,90
REGALADO, Maria M. 10700 MCPHERSON RD 78045 #748-01-1991 L2002 **NEP** *020 †20
REID, F Theodore, Jr. ■ 78041 #067-01-1954 L1960 **P** *071 †75
RENDON, Juan Manuel. ■ 78045 #649-02-1970 **GP GS** *020
REYES, Mateo. 3527 LOOP 20 STE 107 78043 #048-02-1997 L1998 **FM** *020 †18
REZA TRUJILLO, Cesar. 10700 MCPHERSON RD, DOCTORS HOSPITAL OF LAREDO 78045 #649-02-1978 L2001 **AN** *020
RODRIGUEZ, Francisco, IV. PO BOX 440087 78044 #048-04-1995 L1997 **TS** *020 †85,90
RODRIGUEZ, Antonio C. 8607 MCPHERSON RD, STE 100 78045 #048-04-1994 L1997 **PD** *020 †55
RUIZ, Edmundo J. 500 E MANN RD 78041 #649-02-1951 **P** *071
SALAZAR ZUNIGA, Abel E. 1303 CALLE DEL NORTE, STE 100 78041 #649-02-1967 L1975 **DR NM** *020
SALINAS, Antonio. 8607 MCPHERSON RD, STE 101 78045 #048-12-1984 L1985 **OBG** *020 †30
SALINAS, Guillermo. 1700 E SAUNDERS ST 78041 #048-02-1969 L1972 **DR NRN** *020 †80,28
SALZMAN, Arie. 1710 E SAUNDERS ST # B670 78041 #550-02-1993 L2000 **ORS** *020 †40
SANCHEZ, Homero R. 6262 MCPHERSON RD, STE 209 78041 #048-13-1976 L1979 **P CHP** *020
SANCHEZ R, Wilfrano Angel. 6801 MCPHERSON RD STE 112 78041 #649-02-1966 L1974 **OBG** *020
SANCHEZ-VILLASENOR, F. 1710 E SAUNDERS ST, STE B370 78041 #649-03-1990 L1997 **N** *020 †75
SANDE LOURO, Ramon Angel. 5502 SAN BERNARDO AVE, STE 600 78041 #264-02-1962 L1994 **GS OM** *020 †85
SANTOS, Arthur Dwayne. 1420 LOGAN AVE, STE 3 78040 #005-12-1976 L1996 **TS GS** *020 †90,85
SANTOS, Renan Rodriguez. 1515 LOGAN AVE 78040 #649-14-1972 L1985 **AN GP** *020
SARWAL, Abha. ■ 78045 #016-42-2002 L2005 **IM** *020 †20
SCHAIN, Richard Joel. ■ 78045 #035-19-1954 L1995 **N PD** *071 †75,55
SLOMAN-MOLL, Erik Robt. 7210 MCPHERSON RD STE 100 78041 #024-07-1990 L1998 **OTO HNS** *020
SOMERVILLE, Judson J. 6801 MCPHERSON RD, STE 334 78041 #048-14-1988 L1989 **PME AN** *020 †05 ‡
SORIANO, Andres Omar. 1710 E SAUNDERS ST, STE A140 78041 #319-03-1998 L2005 **ON** *020 †20
SORIANO, Ramon Manuel G. 1710 E SAUNDERS ST, STE B380 78041 #748-02-1978 L1996 **ORS** *020 †40
SOSA, Fernando. 7210 MCPHERSON RD, STE 117 78041 #048-13-1998 L2001 **PD** *020
SPENCER, Debbie Patricia. ■ 78045 #023-01-1997 L2002 **OBG** *020
SUED, Jaime Alejandro. 7614 ROCIO DR 78041 #308-02-1989 L1999 **APM** *020 †05
TADROS, Nabil. 1700 E SAUNDERS ST, PATHOLOGY DEPT 78041 #915-02-1957 L1972 **PTH** *020 †50
TOMASEVIC, Mira. 313 W VILLAGE BLVD, STE 104 78041 #957-01-1970 L1985 **PTH AN** *020
TREVINO, Alfredo, Jr. 1006 E HILLSIDE RD 78041 #048-02-1970 L1970 **OPH** *020 †35
TREVINO, Manuel R. 1712 VIOLETA CT 78041 #649-02-1971 L1975 **PD** *020
TREVINO, Rodolfo. ■ 78045 #649-30-1986 **PD CCP** *020
TREVINO, Victor Danl. 101 W VILLAGE BLVD 78041 #649-23-1977 L1985 **FM EM** *020
TULA, Cesar Jorge. 1710 E SAUNDERS ST # A1460 78041 #132-02-1970 L1982 **ON HEM** *020 †20
UNZEITIG, Gary Walter. 6801 MCPHERSON RD, STE 106 78041 #016-06-1978 L1983 **OS ON** *020 †85
UNZEITIG, Jane Elizabeth. 6801 MCPHERSON RD, STE 106 78041 #016-06-1978 L1983 **AI PD** *020 †55,03
VALENZUELA-RENDON, Jorge. 1215 SAN DARIO AVE, STE 4-271 78040 #649-02-1981 *100
VALLS, Patrick Louis. 1303 CALLE DEL NORTE, STE 100 78041 #048-02-1986 L1987 **DR** *020 †80
VARELA, Humberto Jose. 506 GALE ST 78041 #649-30-1975 L1977 **FM** *020 †18
VASQUEZ, Winder Nelson. 500 E MANN RD 78041 #132-01-1970 L1979 **IM CCM** *020 †20
VELA, Jorge. 1710 E SAUNDERS ST # B270 78041 #649-02-1972 L1982 **TS** *020
VELASCO, Carlos Ricardo. 2007 S ZAPATA HWY, P O BOX 3397 78046 #649-02-1995 L2005 **FM** *020
VILLARINO, Miguel. 4151 BOB BULLOCK LOOP, STE 103 78043 #649-16-1979 L1997 **FM** *020 †18
VILLARREAL, Gustavo E. 1020 CORPUS CHRISTI ST 78040 #649-02-1979 L1983 **FM** *020 †18
VILLARREAL, Luis Federico. 4619 SAN DARIO AVE # 310 78041 #048-14-2002 L2004 **FM** *020
VILLARREAL, Osvaldo. ■ 78043 #048-13-2003 L2007 **PD** *020 †55
VILLARREAL, Roberto Luis. 6553 METRO CT, STE A 78041 #649-02-1976 L1979 **PDC PD** *020 †55
VILLEGAS, Roberto, Jr. 10710 MCPHERSON RD, # 204 78045 #649-02-1980 L2003 **NPM PD** *020 †55
VOGT, Louis Bennett. 220 N ZAPATA HWY STE 11A 78043 #005-15-1962 L1963 **LM** *071
WELSH, Esperanza C. 410 E HILLSIDE RD, # 503 78041 #649-12-1998 L2005 **DMP** *100 †15
WESSIGK-DE LA CRUZ, Mildre. 6551 STAR CT 78041 #649-14-1999 **IM** *020 †20 ‡
WILKINSON, Stephen S. ■ 78045 #040-02-1982 L2006 **EM FM** *020 †18,16

WONG, Sunny. ■ 78045 #024-07-1983 L1987 **GE IM** *020 †20
WOOD, Percy H, Jr. 413 INTERAMERICA BLVD # 1, C/O BORDER CROSSINGS 78045 #047-06-1949 L1954 **P** *071 †75
WRIGHT, Frank David. 1700 E SAUNDERS ST 78041 #649-30-1992 L1998 **M** *071 †18
ZAFFIRINI, Luis Alberto. 5835 NORTHGATE LN 78041 #649-30-1973 L1976 **OPH** *020 †35
ZAFFIRINI, Rodolfo G, Jr. 5835 NORTHGATE LN, # B 78041 #021-01-1964 L1966 **OPH** *020 †35
ZAMARRON, Eloy. 6801 MCPHERSON RD, STE 109 78041 #649-02-1980 L1994 **FM** *020 †18
ZAMBRANO, Gerardo Javier. ■ 78046 #005-11-2008 *012
ZUNIGA-GOLDWATER, Adonis. 7210 MCPHERSON RD, STE 102 78041 #649-30-1984 L1990 *020

LAUGHLIN AIR FORCE BASE – VAL VERDE

ALI, Arif N. ■ 78843 #016-02-2007 **RO** *012
DILEO, Roy Jos. ■ 78843 #023-12-1991 L1999 **EM** *020 †16
FILES, Douglas Scott. 590 MITCHELL BLVD, BLDG 375 78843 #025-07-1994 L1995 **GPM** *020 †20,70
PISATURO, Alexander M. ■ 78843 #035-09-2003 L2004 **IM** *020

LEAGUE CITY – GALVESTON

AGRAHARKAR, Aruna M. 212 GULF FWY S STE G3 77573 #495-21-1976 L1998 **IMG IM** *020 †20
AGRAHARKAR, Mahendra L. 212 GULF FWY S STE G3 77573 #495-21-1975 L1998 **IM NEP** *020 †20
AHMED, Syed. 1301 LINK RD 77573 #495-21-1980 L1987 **P** *020 †75
ANDERSON, Jessica Brooks. ■ 77573 #048-02-2004 L2008 **MPD** *012
ANDERSON, William Ed. ■ 77573 #018-03-1973 L1974 **FPG** *075
AQUINO, Brian Christopher. 302 HIGHWAY 3 S, CLEAR CREEK CLINIC PA 77573 #495-52-1983 L1990 **FM OBS** *020 †18
ARMEN, Glenn Chas. 201 ENTERPRISE AVE STE 900 77573 #051-04-1982 L1983 **FM** *020 †18
BABU, Rajesh V. ■ 77573 #048-15-2000 L2002 **PCC** *012 †20 ‡
BAGGETT, Ronald Wayne. 3016 CLOVERDALE DR 77573 #048-02-1965 L1965 **EM** *020 †85
BAILEY, Rahn Kennedy. 614 W MAIN ST, STE D101 77573 #048-02-1990 L1991 **P PFP** *020 †75
BAKER, Olen C. ■ 77573 #048-15-2004 L2006 **CHP** *012
BASSO, Victor Jay. ■ 77573 #025-07-1967 L1973 **OPH** *071 †35
BAUER, Peter Allan. ■ 77573 #026-08-1985 L1987 **GPM** *020 †70
BERNO, Michael Gerard. 1150 DEVEREUX DR 77573 #048-14-1996 L1997 **CHP** *020 †75
BROWNE, George William. ■ 77573 #033-06-2003 L2006 **AI** *012 †20
BURNS, Sean Thomas. ■ 77573 #048-12-2006 **ORS** *012
CALAF, Salvador Federico. ■ 77573 #048-02-2008 *012
CHANG, Peter. PO BOX 1357 77574 #051-04-2001 L2006 **PS** *020
CHAUDHARI, Swetanshu. ■ 77573 #005-14-2001 L2001 **GS** *100 †85
CHEEMA, Bushra Iqbal. ■ 77573 #704-04-1996 L2006 **ON** *012 †20
COLE, Richard Wayne. ■ 77573 #004-01-1999 L2003 **GPM** *012 †16
CONLEY, Peter James. ■ 77573 #028-34-2004 L2006 **MPD** *012
COONFIELD, Kimberly Joy. ■ 77573 #048-14-2007 **IM** *012
COTTINGHAM, John Thomas. ■ 77573 #048-02-2004 L2006 **FM** *020
DANG, Michelle. ■ 77573 #048-14-2007 **AN** *012
DAYAL, Gauri. 201 ENTERPRISE AVE, STE 900 77573 #048-04-1999 L2002 **FM** *020 †18
DE CASTRO, Patricia. ■ 77573 #264-10-1980 *100
DETMER, Thomas David. 190 GULF FWY S, STE B2 # 144 77573 #025-07-1982 L1983 **P** *020 †75
DIAZ, Roberto Jose. ■ 77573 #048-13-2005 L2007 **GS** *100
DOWLING, James Peter Fitz. ■ 77573 #048-02-2006 **FP** *012
EWERT, Anne Catherine. ■ 77573 #048-15-2006 **PD** *012
EWERT, Patricia Bohn. 1100 GULF FWY S, STE 230 77573 #048-02-2003 L2005 **FM** *100 †18
EYZAGUIRRE, Eduardo J. ■ 77573 #737-06-1990 L2001 **PTH** *020 †50
FAN, Xinqing. ■ 77573 #243-32-1991 L2005 **GE** *012 †20
FAY, James Michael. ■ 77573 #048-15-2004 **AN** *012
FLORES, Lisa R. ■ 77573 #048-13-2005 **OBG** *012
GIVENS, John Dewey. ■ 77573 #016-11-1954 L1955 **OM GP** *030 †85
GOHARKHAY, Nima. ■ 77573 #154-07-1998 L2005 **OBG** *020
GONZALEZ, William Edward. PO BOX 958, TX 77 77574 #048-02-1961 L1961 **DR** *020 †80
GRAS, Ann Marie. ■ 77573 #048-02-2006 **P** *100
GUDERIAN, Gerard L. 1100 GULF FWY S, STE 230 77573 #048-15-1994 L1995 **FM** *020 †18
GUPTA, Meera Rani. ■ 77573 #017-20-2001 L2008 **AI** *100 †20,55,03
HEAD, Philip Allen, Jr. 311 GREEN OAKS DR 77573 #048-02-1991 L1994 **IM OS** *020
HINH, Peter Phuc. ■ 77573 #048-15-2006 **U** *012
HO, Sze-Key. PO BOX 1357 77574 #572-10-1963 L1973 **P** *071
HUSAIN, Amina. ■ 77573 #038-44-2004 L2004 **OPH** *012
HUSSEIN, Hanan. ■ 77573 #473-02-2003 L2008 **FM** *100 †18
JAGAN MOHAN, Sathyanarayan. ■ 77573 #495-61-2001 L2006 **GE** *012
JAIN, Prem Lata. 2047 W MAIN ST, STE A2 77573 #495-03-1959 L1967 **FM** *020 †18
JAIN, Sangeeta. ■ 77573 #495-85-1988 L2005 *020
JANOE, Jack Wayne. 201 ENTERPRISE AVE, STE 800 77573 #048-02-1974 L1974 **FM FSM** *020
KEELEN, David Martin. ■ 77573 #048-02-2008 *012
KO, Kathleen Huei-Huei. 201 ENTERPRISE AVE, STE 900 77573 #048-12-2000 L2003 **FM** *020 †18 ‡
KOSTY, John Walter. 3023 MARINA BAY DR, STE 101 77573 #041-01-1978 L1987 **ORS** *020 †40
KOZA, Joseph. 77574 #422-01-2003 **EM** *020
LEW, Cynthia. ■ 77573 #048-13-1987 L1988 **FM** *071 †18
LISKA, Kristie L. ■ 77573 #048-13-2004 L2007 **IM** *100
LLOYD, Jim O. ■ 77573 #039-79-1996, ▲ L1997 **P** *020 †75
LU, Aojing. ■ 77573 #048-13-2008 *012
MAGLIOLO, Michael Anthony. 2450 S SHORE BLVD, STE 215 77573 #048-02-1976 L1976 **OBG** *020 †30 ‡
MAGRINAT, Gaston Juan. 2951 MARINA BAY DR STE 130 77573 #847-11-1971 L1979 **CD IM** *020
MARCOM, George Weldon. 302 HIGHWAY 3 S, CLEAR CREEK CLINICPA 77573 #048-12-1961 L1961 **FM** *071 †18
MARETH, David R. ■ 77573 #048-14-2005 **AN** *012

MARKEY, John Chas, Jr. 2450 S SHORE BLVD, SUITE 200 MARINA PLAZA BL 77573 #021-05-1971 L1977 **GS** *020 †85

MARROQUIN, Guillermo. ■ 77573 #264-10-1977 **OPH** *100

MCCRAY-GARRISON, Rispba. ■ 77573 #048-02-2006 **IM** *012

MC ELROY, Sandra Neskorik. 612 W MAIN ST STE C 77573 #048-14-1985 L1987 **P** *020

MIRCEA, Aurel Emilian. 2951 MARINA BAY DR, # 130-524 77573 #781-01-1961 L1978 **FM FPG** *071

MOKKALA, Sandhya Rani. 212 GULF FWY S, STE G3 77573 #495-70-1991 L2000 **IM** *020 †20

MOORE, Walter D, Jr. 2154 COVE PARK DRIVE 77574 #048-04-1952 L1953 **PTH NM** *071 †50,28

MOREIRA, Alvaro G. ■ 77573 #048-02-2006 **PD** *012

MOREIRA, Marcia. ■ 77573 #048-02-2007 **PD** *012

MURRAY, Manuela J. ■ 77573 #264-16-2002 L2008 **PD** *012

NAJAM, Sabeen. ■ 77573 #704-25-2002 L2007 **IM** *100 †20

NINAN, Mathews. 302 HIGHWAY 3 S, CLEAR CREEK CLINIC PA 77573 #422-01-2002 L2005 **FM** *020 †18

NISHI, Shawn Pua Eiko. ■ 77573 #048-02-2005 L2008 **IM** *012

NOVICK, Steven Louis. ■ 77573 #023-07-1993 L1998 **DR** *020 †80

OKORODUDU, Daniel Esimaju. ■ 77573 #048-02-2008 *012

PALACIO URAN, Diana Maria. ■ 77573 #264-03-1992 L2006 **PDR** *100

PEDRAZA CARDOZO, Sandra L. ■ 77573 #264-10-1997 **FP** *012

PHILLIPS, Linda G. 651 FM 270 RD, STE I 77573 #016-02-1978 L1989 **PS GS** *020 †85,65

POLSEN, Charles Geo. 2525 S SHORE BLVD, 2525 SO SHORE BLVD 77573 #035-09-1991 L1993 **PS** *020 †65

POWELL, Danny Walter. ■ 77573 #007-02-2004 **AN** *012

POWELL-DUNFORD, Nicole C. ■ 77573 #023-12-2001 L2002 **FM** *020 †18

QIU, Suimin. ■ 77573 #243-64-1984 L2005 **SP** *100 †50

RASHEED, Shama. 1150 DEVEREUX DR, DEVEREUX TEXAS TREATMENT N 77573 #048-14-1999 L2002 **CHP** *020 †75

RIOS, Javier Antonio. ■ 77573 #048-02-2004 L2007 **FP** *012

RITTGER, Kevin Duane. 2525 S SHORE BLVD 77573 #056-06-1993 L1995 **EM** *020

ROBINSON, Bernice Louise. ■ 77573 #033-06-2000 L2004 **OBG** *100

ROESER, Theodore P. 2095 W MAIN ST STE B 77573 #048-02-1976 L1977 **FM** *020 †18

ROGOSA, Victor Jos. ■ 77573 #035-46-1968 L1986 **FM** *071 †85

SAEED, Mohammad Akhtar. 1100 GULF FWY S, STE 230 77573 #704-16-1979 L1987 **CHP P** *020 †75

SAYERS, Stephen Chas. ■ 77573 #016-45-1982 L1983 **FM OBG** *020

SCOTT, Robin L. ■ 77573 #048-14-1987 **P** *050

SEEGER, Grant R. ■ 77573 #037-01-2004 L2007 **RO** *012

SHAH, Avni. ■ 77573 #048-16-2007 **PD** *012

SHAH, Neel Lalit. ■ 77573 #016-06-2005 L2008 **IM** *012

SHUTTLESWORTH, Jennifer L. ■ 77573 #048-02-2005 **PTH** *012

SINGH, Sharmila Devi. ■ 77573 #048-02-2005 L2008 **IPM** *012

SOOD, Sonia. 1100 GULF FWY S, STE 230 77573 #496-07-1989 L2005 **FM** *020 †18 ‡

SRINIVASAN, Padmavathi Ne. ■ 77573 #048-16-2001 L2006 **RNR** *020 †80

SRINIVASAN, Ramesh. ■ 77573 #048-16-2002 **GE** *012 †20

STOECKER, Maggie Marie. ■ 77573 #048-12-2007 **PTH** *012

TEER, Janice M. 302 HIGHWAY 3 S, CLEAR CREEK CLINIC PA 77573 #048-15-1991 L1992 **FM** *020 †18

THOMAS, Lauree. ■ 77573 #056-05-1979 L1981 *020

TIRANDAZ, Houshmand. 109 MARSHALL ST 77573 #517-01-1967 L1985 **P** *020

TONG, Chester Kit. ■ 77573 #385-03-1963 L1972 **IM ON** *020

ULERT, Izaak Alan. ■ 77573 #396-05-1938 L1942 **GS GP** *072

UPITIS, Janis. ■ 77573 #407-04-1949 L1958 **R** *071

VANDAELE, Francoise T. 2450 S SHORE BLVD, STE 215 77573 #396-02-1976 L1982 **OBG** *020 †30

VELUVOLU, Anuja. ■ 77573 #021-06-2005 **IM** *100

VILLARRUBIA, Carolyn T. 1150 DEVEREUX DR 77573 #021-05-1962 L1970 **CHP P** *020 †55

WALCOTT, Farzana. ■ 77573 #048-02-2008 *012

WATKINS, Bernard Neal. 302 HIGHWAY 3 S, CLEAR CREEK CLINIC PA 77573 #048-02-1967 L1967 **GP** *020

WONG, Howard Leland. ■ 77573 #048-02-2007 **P** *012

WRIGHT, Amber Elizabeth. ■ 77573 #048-15-2007 **P** *012

WU, Jing. ■ 77573 #243-69-1993 **N** *012

YANG, Jack. ■ 77573 #243-92-1982 L2004 **PCP** *020

YOLLAND, Michael David. ■ 77573 #048-14-2007 **AN** *012

ZAMORA, Alvaro Francisco. 2911 S SHORE BLVD, STE 190 77573 #021-05-1994 L1996 **FM** *020 †18

LEANDER – WILLIAMSON

ALDRED, Brian Neil. ■ 78641 #016-11-1993 L2008 **EM** *020 †16

ANDERSON, William Jos. ■ 78641 #048-02-1977 L1984 **HS** *020 †40

AZADI, Sohail B. 502 CRYSTAL FALLS PKWY, STE B 78641 #048-13-1998 L2007 **PD** *020 †55

MANSOLO, Ron Michael. 902 CRYSTAL FALLS PKWY 78641 #048-14-1995 L1996 **FM** *020 †18

MAULDIN, Allen Lee. 2701 S HIGHWAY 183 STE B 78641 #048-13-1982 L1983 **FM** *020 †18

PAI, Mizar Anita. ■ 78641 #048-16-2001 L2002 **AN** *074

VESPER, Rachel Corpus. ■ 78641 #048-04-1985 L1988 **EM GP** *020

ZALLES, Maria Carola. ■ 78641 #132-01-1984 L2008 **PTH** *020 †50

LEESBURG – CAMP

BARTON, Charles Dean. ■ 75451 #048-02-1976 L1976 **EM** *071 †20,16

LEON VALLEY – BEXAR

MARTINEZ, Carlo Obet. ■ 78238 #028-02-2005 **GS** *012

VAZQUEZ, Bianca Julissa. ■ 78238 #042-02-2005 **GS** *012

LEONARD – FANNIN

CANTRELL, William, III. 700 E FANNIN ST 75452 #048-02-1960 L1960 **FM GP** *020 †18

LEVELLAND – HOCKLEY

AHMADI, Hamid. 1900 COLLEGE AVE 79336 #517-01-1973 L1993 **R NM** *020 †80

BABB, Franklyn C. 103 JOHN DUPREE DR 79336 #048-15-1997 L1998 **FM** *020 †18

BAILEY, Michael G. 1804 COLLEGE AVE 79336 #048-13-1987 L1988 **FM** *020 †18

BURWICK, Frank C. 1900 COLLEGE AVE 79336 #409-12-1968 L1993 **IM PD** *020 †20,55

CHONG, Somchai. 1000 FM 300 79336 #891-01-1966 L1979 **OBG FM** *020

HUGHES, Charles Von Oden. 116 JOHN DUPREE DR STE A 79336 #051-04-1982 L1983 **FM** *020 †18 ‡

HUSKEY, Stephanie A. ■ 79336 #048-15-2001 **IM** *020

JACKSON, Ronny L. ■ 79336 #048-02-1995 L1995 **EM** *020 †16

MADURA, Judith Marie. 1000 FM 300, SOUTH PLAINS RURAL HEALTH 79336 #016-45-1991 L2001 **PD IM** *020 †55

MALOUF, Cathy S. 817 HOUSTON ST 79336 #048-15-1995 L1996 **IM** *020 †20

MANNING, George Smith. ■ 79336 #040-02-1975 L1992 **FM** *020 †18

NELSON, Robert Chas. ■ 79336 #030-05-1967 L1968 **GP** *020

PAULSEL, John Thos. 1900 COLLEGE AVE 79336 #048-04-1975 L1975 **IM** *020 †20

PHAM, Luu Phuong Thi. 1000 FM 300 79336 #941-01-1965 L1981 **FM** *020 †18

SMILEY, Evelyn Joy King. 1000 FM 300 79336 #048-02-1957 L1957 **GP** *020

TAN, Alfred Wm Thos. 1804 COLLEGE AVE 79336 #506-01-1959 L1975 **FM FPG** *020 †18 ‡

VICHUGSANANON, Deena. 116 JOHN DUPREE DR STE E 79336 #016-11-2004 L2007 **PD** *020

WEAVER, Harry T, Jr. 1804 COLLEGE AVE 79336 #048-15-1987 L1988 **GS** *020 †85

WIRI, Suvipa. 116 JOHN DUPREE DR 79336 #891-03-1974 L1982 **PD NPM** *020 †55

WIRI, Weerachai. 116 JOHN DUPREE DR 79336 #891-03-1971 L1982 **GS** *020 †85

YOUNG, G Jeffrey. 103 JOHN DUPREE DR 79336 #048-15-1987 L1988 **FM EM** *020 †18

LEWISVILLE – DENTON

ADAMS, Scott C. ■ 75067 #021-06-2004 L2007 **DR** *012

AHMAD, Salman. 396 W MAIN ST # 100 75057 #704-01-1989 L1996 **AN** *020 †05

ALBRITE, James P. 1422 W MAIN ST, STE 200 75067 #275-01-1943 L1973 **OTO A** *071 †45

ANDERSON, Samuel J. ■ 75067 #020-02-1943 L1944 **IM** *071

APTE, Udita. 535 W PURNELL RD, STE 180 75057 #496-31-1999 L2006 **FM** *020 †18

BADARACCO, Susan M. 2280 HIGHLAND VILLAGE RD, STE 130 75077 #048-13-1995 L1997 **PD** *020 †55

BAKER, Bruce H. 1600 WATERS RIDGE DR, STE A 75057 #048-14-1984 L1985 **NEP IM** *020 †20

BALKUNDI, Dhruvraj. 500 W MAIN ST, NICU 75057 #495-21-1986 L2004 **NPM** *020 †55

BARTH, Thomas Leslie. 500 W MAIN ST 75057 #048-13-1973 L1973 **OPH** *075

BATTISTE, James Douglas. ■ 75067 #048-12-2008 *012

BERESFORD, Kenneth Wayne. 751 HEBRON PKWY, STE 220 75057 #030-05-1975 L2000 **FM** *020 †18

BESHAY, Joseph Emmanuel. ■ 75067 #036-08-2001 L2008 **NS** *012

BESHAY, Victor Emmanuel. ■ 75067 #036-08-2001 L2005 **OBG** *100 †30

BESTE, Timothy A. 800 S STEMMONS FWY 75067 #048-13-1985 L1986 **FM** *020 †18

BOILS, Christie Lynn. ■ 75056 #025-07-2007 **PTH** *012

BORGFELD, Bryan J. 500 W MAIN ST, STE 300 75057 #048-02-1988 L1989 **GS** *020 †85

BOWMAN, William Paul. 401 N VALLEY PKWY, STE 400 75067 #062-01-1973 L1983 **PHO** *020 †55

BRAMHALL, Thomas Cunning. 324 W MAIN ST STE 100 75057 #004-01-1990 L1996 **OTO HNS** *020 †45

BURGESS, Michael Clifton. 500 W MAIN ST 75057 #048-14-1977 L1977 **OBG** *020 †30

BURGESS, Richard Chipman. 500 W MAIN ST, PATHOLOGY DEPARTMENT 75057 #048-12-1975 L1975 **PTH** *020 †50

CANTRELL, Jeffery S. 500 W MAIN ST, STE 200 75057 #048-02-1987 L1989 **ORS** *020 †40

CARLOS, Maria A. 500 W MAIN ST, MEDICAL CENTER OF LEWISVIL 75057 #748-02-1987 L2004 **PD** *020 †55

CARRUTH, Alan Wayne. 396 W MAIN ST STE 100 75057 #048-12-1981 L1981 **AN** *020 †05

CASTRO, Harvey. 500 W MAIN ST FRNT EM, LEWISVILLE MEDICAL CENTER 75057 #048-02-2002 L2006 **EM** *020

CHANDI, Cherry. 2016 FM 407 STE 370 75077 #495-08-1992 L2002 **IM** *020 †20

CHANDRA, Archana. 502 N VALLEY PKWY, STE 1 75067 #495-30-1989 L1999 **FM** *020 †18

CHEBROLU, Srivasa Bhushan. 1600 WATERS RIDGE DR, STE A 75057 #495-21-1993 L2005 **NEP** *020 †20

CLARKE, Delphia M. 1550 LAKEWAY DR STE 300 75057 #048-13-1983 L1986 **OP** *020 †80

CLAYTON, Lisa Kay. 105 KATHRYN DR, STE 700 75067 #012-05-1988 L1992 **P** *020 †75

COLLINS, Rebecca Norton. 328 W MAIN ST 75057 #036-08-1988 L1990 **OBG** *020 †30

CONNALLY, Parchelle D. 1422 W MAIN ST STE 200, DENTON PHYSICAL MEDICAL PA 75067 #016-11-1987 L1995 **PM PMM** *020 †60

CONYERS, James Alan. 500 W MAIN ST STE 300 75057 #048-12-1975 L1975 **GS SO** *020 †85

COOKE, David Hume, Jr. 475 ELM ST, STE 100 75057 #048-14-1979 L1979 **N** *020 †20,75

CORBITT, Danny Keith. 500 W MAIN ST, STE 200 75057 #048-02-1979 L1979 **ORS** *020 †40

CORLETT, Richard Harold. 1422 W MAIN ST, STE 100A 75067 #048-02-1978 L1978 **FM** *062 †18

COSTA, Dennis James. 2790 LAKE VISTA DR 75067 #056-06-1984 L1989 **HEM ON** *020 †20

COSTELLO, Louis Edward. 190 CIVIC CIR, STE 250 75067 #020-12-1991 L1992 **CHP P** *020 †75

COX, James Tudor. 1850 LAKEPOINTE DR, STE 400 75057 #010-01-1990 L1992 **GE** *020 †20

CRUZ, Pamela U. 751 HEBRON PKWY, STE 150 75057 #748-10-1991 L2001 **IM** *020 †20

DAMON, Jerry Henry. 500 W MAIN ST 75057 #048-02-1960 L1961 **GP** *072

DAVIDSON, Barbara C. ■ 75067 #048-12-1994 L1995 **FM** *020 †18

DESAI, Emmanuel F. 500 W MAIN ST 75057 #495-23-1972 L1977 **IM** *020 †20

DHALIWAL, Hardeep S. 535 W PURNELL RD STE 160 75057 #495-89-1981 L1987 **IM** *020 †20

DIAZ, Raul. 541 W MAIN ST, STE 150 75057 #847-06-1975 L1999 **U** *020 †20

DICKSON, Kent Farr. 500 W MAIN ST, STE 200 75057 #007-02-1992 L1993 **HS ORS** *020 †40

DOBSON, Peter Grant. 396 W MAIN ST STE 100 75057 #003-01-1992 L1996 **AN** *020

DOHERTY, Thomas Wm. ■ 75067 #654-01-1984 L1989 **IM** *020 †20

ELIEFF, Steven Lewis. 1850 LAKEPOINTE DR, STE 200 75057 #038-40-1991 L1995 **OPH** *020 †35

ELKINS, William N, III. ■ 75056 #048-15-2001 L2008 **RNR** *020 †80

ETTINGER, Mark Raymond. ■ 75077 #021-05-2005 **NS** *012

EVANICH, John David. 500 W MAIN ST, STE 200 75057 #048-12-1995 L2001 **ORS** *020 †40

EVANS, Michael B. 324 W MAIN ST STE 100 75057 #048-15-2001 L2006 **OTO** *020 †45

FAGAN, Gary D. 751 HEBRON PKWY 75057 #048-14-1990 L1991 **FM EM** *020 †16

FIGUEROA, Ivan. ■ 75067 #042-02-2003 L2007 **PM** *020

FLIEDNER, Thomas Sample. 560 W MAIN ST, STE 200 75057 #033-05-1990 L1993 OBG *020 †30

FRANKLIN, Stanley Felix. 541 W MAIN ST STE 180 75057 #047-06-1975 L1977 OBG *020 †30

GAJRAJ, Noor Mahamood. 2702 SIR ECTOR LN, NOOR GAJRAJ, MD 75056 #917-19-1983 L1999 AN PME *105

GARZA, Aimee C. 405 E STATE HIGHWAY 121 75057 #048-13-2002 L2007 CN *100

GEORGE, Elizabeth. ■ 75056 #422-01-1998 L2003 IM *020 †20

GIESLER, Brady G. 500 W MAIN ST, STE 200 75057 #048-12-1987 L1988 ORS OSS *020 †40

GOGIA, Rajendra S. ■ 75067 #495-30-1978 L1993 PM *020 †60

GOUVION, Michael David. 405 STATE HIGHWAY 121 BYP, BLDG A 75067 #005-14-2000 L2002 DR *020 †80

GRODZIN, Charles Jason. 475 ELM ST 1 75057 #016-01-1990 L2000 PCC *020 †20

GUPTA, Rakesh. 541 W MAIN ST STE 180 75057 #048-02-1986 L1987 OBG *020 †30

GUPTA, Sangeeta. 2141 S EDMONDS LN 75067 #495-36-1990 L1995 PD *020 †55

HANNA, Magdy Riad. ■ 75067 #915-07-1988 L2004 FM *100

HANSEN, Robert Hartvig, III. ■ 75056 #048-12-2007 GS *012

HARMAN, Bruce Alan. 1165 S STEMMONS FWY, STE 264 75067 #048-15-1992 L1993 IM *020 †20

HASHMI, Hasan Farid. 328 W MAIN ST, STE 200 75057 #704-02-1978 L2007 CRS GS *020 †85,10

HAYNIE, David Powell. 614 S EDMONDS LN STE 101, CARDIOVASCULAR SPECIALISTS 75067 #048-14-1983 L1983 CD IM *020 †20

HEERWAGEN, James Robt. 500 W MAIN ST STE 200 75057 #038-44-1985 L1986 ORS OSM *020 †40

HEW, Michael Yimloy. 500 W MAIN ST, D201 75057 #021-05-1994 L2000 PTH BBK *020 †50

HODGE, Julia. 751 HEBRON PKWY, STE 240 75057 #048-14-1988 L1989 PD *020 †55

HOLT, Mark Walker. 1165 S STEMMONS FWY, STE 114 75067 #048-12-1976 L1978 PD *020 †55

HUNTER, David Maddox. 2601 S STEMMONS FWY, STE 110 75067 #021-05-1963 L1973 OPH AM *020 †35

HUTCHINS, Leslie Marian. ■ 75067 #048-12-2008 *012

IDEMUDIA, Smart O. 560 W MAIN ST, STE 205 75057 #048-02-1991 L1995 IM *020

ILAHI, Zainab. 2790 LAKE VISTA DR 75067 #048-14-1997 L2005 RO *020 †80

JIWANI, Laila Noorruddin. 713 HEBRON PKWY, STE 232 75057 #035-19-2001 L2007 PD *020 †55

JOHNSON, Jack Leegon, Jr. 560 W MAIN ST STE 100 75057 #027-01-1983 L1989 FM *020 †18

JONES, Gary Roy. ■ 75077 #048-02-1963 L1963 GYN *071 †30

JULKA, Manjula. 1175 DIANE CIR 75067 #496-38-1995 L2004 FM *020 †18

KALAYANAMIT, Tul. 190 CIVIC CIR, STE 235 75067 #036-01-1991 L1994 PCC IM *020 †20

KAUR, Rominder. 2016 FM 407 STE 370 75057 #495-03-1986 L1996 IM *020 †20

KEN, James Geekeung. 405 STATE HIGHWAY 121 BYP, STE A160 75067 #005-18-1987 L1997 DR *020 †80

KENNEDY, Patrick Lee. 614 S EDMONDS LN, STE 101 75067 #048-12-1980 L1980 CD IM *020 †20

KERR, Ronald Neal. 2790 LAKE VISTA DR 75067 #048-12-1979 L1979 ON HEM *020 †20

KHAN, Jalil A. 502 N VALLEY PKWY, STE 1 75067 #704-21-1987 L1995 IM *020 †20

KHAN, Najam Hasan. 614 S EDMONDS LN, STE 210 75067 #704-02-1983 L1995 IM *020 †20

KHAN, Rabia J. 2852 VISTA VIEW DR 75067 #704-16-1982 L1997 IM *020 †20

KIMBLE, Michael Lee. ■ 75077 #051-04-2003 L2005 EM *100 †16

KNIGHT, J Thomas. 500 W MAIN ST 75057 #048-12-1981 L1981 DR N *020 †80

KOPPEL, Lowell Barry, Jr. 751 HEBRON PKWY STE 100, TRINITY WEST URGENT CARE 75057 #048-13-1999 L2002 FM *020 †18

KREMER, Edward Norris. 1175 DIANE CIR, STE 101 75067 #048-12-1977 L1977 IM CD *020 †20

KU, W Stephen. 1850 LAKEPOINTE DR, STE 200 75057 #017-20-1988 L1992 OPH *020 †35

LEE, Andrew Yiu. 405 HIGHWAY 121 BYP, STE 160 75067 #005-14-1994 L1999 VIR *020 †80

LEUNG, Steven James. 1165 S STEMMONS FWY, STE 114 75067 #011-03-1996 L1998 PD *020 †55

LIM, Simon Sewon. 540 SURF ST 75067 #042-02-1991 L2001 FM *020 †18

LINDEN, Bruce Leonard. 2300 HIGHLAND VILG RD #600 75077 #048-15-1982 L1983 FM *020 †18

LIPTON, John Stuart. 591 W MAIN ST 75057 #048-13-1985 L1987 PS GS *020 †65

LOFTIS, Sonya F. 751 HEBRON PKWY, STE 240 75057 #048-14-1999 L2001 PD *020 †55

LYDE, Carolyn B. 324 W MAIN ST, STE 200 75057 #048-02-1995 L1986 D *020 †15

MARSDEN, Cindi. 328 W MAIN ST 75057 #048-02-1986 L1987 OBG *020 †30

MATHEWS, Sunil. 405 E STATE HIGHWAY 121 75057 #495-28-1990 L2001 N CN *020 †75

MC ADAMS, Lisa Marie. ■ 75077 #048-14-1985 L1987 GPM *020 †70

MC DEARMONT, Scott R. 500 W MAIN ST, STE 300 75057 #048-12-1996 L1998 GS *020 †85

MEHTA, Nimisha Apurva. 475 ELM ST STE 201 75057 #495-48-1986 L2003 IM *020 †20

MENDONCA, Dureshahwar Jav. 190 CIVIC CIR STE 235 75067 #704-16-1990 L1999 PCC *020 †20

MENDONSA, Robert E, Jr. 500 W MAIN ST 75057 #048-02-1992 L1993 ORS *020 †40

MINTON, Bryan Howard. 1422 W MAIN ST STE 100A 75057 #004-01-1995 L2001 FM *020 †18 ‡

MINTON, Gregory Allen. ■ 75077 #030-05-1981 L1981 FPS *075

MULLER, Cynthia Ruby. 2560 KING ARTHUR BLVD, STE 124-108 75056 #737-06-1995 L2003 IM FM *020 †20

MYINT, Twinkle A. 1850 LAKEPOINTE DR, STE 300 75057 #048-14-1994 L1995 IM *020 †20

NEWTON, Dennis E, III. 324 W MAIN ST, STE 200 75057 #048-02-1968 L1968 D *071 †15

NGUYEN, Duy X. 2141 S EDMONDS LN 75067 #048-15-1990 L1991 PD *020 †55

OGDEN, J Glen. 2141 S EDMONDS LN 75067 #048-15-1990 L1991 PD *020 †55

OGIN, Gary Arthur. 301 W ROUND GROVE RD, STE 104 75067 #034-01-1976 L1985 PME AN *020 †05

OLUWOLE, Olawole S. 1010 S EDMONDS LN, STE 105 75067 #690-01-1982 L2002 IM *020 †20

OWENS, David. 571 W MAIN ST STE 200 75057 #048-12-1991 L1993 OBG *020 †30

PASSMORE, James Albert. 291 E ROUND GROVE RD 75067 #048-04-1968 L1968 OPH *020 †35

PATEL, Manoj Kumar. 535 W PURNELL RD STE 160 75057 #046-01-1996 L1999 IM *020 †20

PEAK, Sandra C. 713 HEBRON PKWY, STE 232 75057 #048-13-1995 L1997 PD *020 †55

PEAKE, Herschel S, Jr. 405 HWY 121 BYP, BLDG A 75067 #048-12-1965 L1965 VIR R *020 †80

PERI, Usha Naga. 1600 WATERS RIDGE DR, STE A 75057 #495-21-1992 L1998 NEP IM *020 †20

PERRY, Franklin D. 570 S EDMONDS LN STE 110 75067 #034-01-1973 L1974 OTO *071 †45

PHILIP, Annie J. 502 S OLD ORCHARD LN # 126 75057 #048-12-1995 L1997 PD *020 †55

PHILIP, Priya Mathew. 1165 S STEMMONS FWY, STE 264 75067 #495-37-1994 L2002 FM *020 †18 ‡

PIERCE, Lisa Yvette. 105 KATHRYN DR, STE 300 75067 #039-01-1992 L1993 CHP *020 †75

PIWONKA, Thomas E. 500 W MAIN ST 75057 #048-16-1986 L1987 AN *020 †05

PRATHO, Scott Mason. 500 W MAIN ST 75057 #048-15-1984 L1985 FM EM *020 †18

PRINCE, Mark R. 571 W MAIN ST STE 100 75057 #048-14-1993 L1994 AN *020

PRINGLE, Timothy Craig. 560 W MAIN ST, CENTRAL OHIO VASCULAR SERV 75057 #038-06-1995 L2007 VS *020 †20

PURI, Nidhi. ■ 75067 #028-34-2005 PD *012

RAMPOLDI, James Moses. 190 N VALLEY PKWY STE 203, #203 DENTON CTY HELTH DEPT 75067 #737-01-1954 L1971 GP GYN *020

RANDHAWA, Tejpal Singh. ■ 75077 #305-01-2001 L2005 IM *020 †20

RAVINDRAN, Jayaraman. 475 ELM ST, STE 100 75057 #495-61-1978 L1995 N SME *020 †75

REDDY, Renuka K. 500 W MAIN ST 75057 #495-65-1987 L1998 NPM *020 †55

REYES, Miguel Angel, Jr. 405 HWY 121 BYP, BLDG A 75067 #021-01-2001 L2007 DR *020 †80

REYNOLDS, Lizabeth. 405 STATE HIGHWAY 121 BYP, STE A160 75067 #049-01-1978 L1983 R PD *020 †80

RICHARDSON, David C. ■ 75077 #048-04-1974 L1975 OBG *071 †30

SALMON, Thomas H. 405 E STATE HIGHWAY 121 75057 #048-13-1991 L1992 N *020 †75

SANDERS, Barry. 560 W MAIN ST STE 106 75057 #035-06-1973 L1978 GE *020 †20

SANTOS, Raul A. 614 S EDMONDS LN, STE 101 75067 #048-02-1999 L2006 CD IC *020 †20

SCHLEGEL, Harold F. 500 W MAIN ST 75057 #048-12-1953 L1953 GP *072

SCHWOB-FERRARA, M F. ■ 75077 #024-01-1956 OS HEM *071 †55

SHAH, Sharfuddin. ■ 75056 #704-01-1958 L1969 IM DIA *071

SHAH, Varsha Dilip. 535 W PURNELL RD, STE 180 75057 #495-76-1976 L1981 FM *020 †18

SHEPHERD, Timothy Scott. 314 W MAIN ST 75057 #005-12-1978 L1979 FM EM *020 †18

SHOVLIN, Patrick W, III. 500 W MAIN ST, STE 300 75057 #048-15-1993 L1994 GS *020 †85

SIGLER, Martin Tristram. 405 HWY 121 BYP, BLDG A 75067 #001-02-2000 L2002 DR *020 †80

SIMMONS, Calvin T, II. 1175 DIANE CIR, STE 101 75067 #048-04-1973 L1974 FM A *020 †18

SMITH, William Seward, Jr. 502 S OLD ORCHARD LN, STE 126 75057 #048-02-1959 L1960 PD *020 †55

SNOOK, Russell Wm. 1850 LAKEPOINTE DR STE 200 75057 #721-01-1992 L1999 OPH *020 †35

STREBECK, Sarah Lois. 1422 W MAIN ST 75067 #027-01-1991 L2002 P *020 †75

SULLIVAN, Timothy Patrick. 405 STATE HIGHWAY 121 BYP, STE A160 75067 #024-07-1985 L2001 DR *020 †80

SWANHOLM, Dale Gregory. 2300 HIGHLAND VILLAGE RD, STE 600 75077 #048-12-1972 L1975 FM *020 †18

SWANSON, Susan Lynn. 291 E ROUND GROVE RD 75067 #048-12-1987 L1988 OPH *020 †35

TANNA, Bhavna Nitin. 1175 DIANE CIR, STE 101 75067 #496-38-1987 L1999 FM *020 †18

TARIQ, Mohammad J. 1850 LAKEPOINTE DR STE 100 75057 #704-21-1986 L1996 PME *020 †05

TASA, Laura Ann. 405 STATE HIGHWAY 121 BYP, STE A160 75067 #048-04-2000 L2004 DR *020 †80

TAVAREKERE, Anuradha R. 724 W MAIN ST, STE 160 75067 #495-33-1992 L1999 IM *020 †20

THAPAR, Pankaj. 396 W MAIN ST # 100 75057 #495-45-1981 L1998 AN CCM *020 †05

THEIN, Yee Yee. 860 HEBRON PKWY, STE 204 75057 #209-01-1990 L2000 P *020 †75

THIBEAUX, Albert, Jr. 500 W MAIN ST 75057 #021-05-1962 L1979 R *020 †80

THUMMALA, Maheshwar Reddy. 500 W MAIN ST, MEDICAL CENTER OF LEWISVIL 75057 #495-65-1984 L2000 PD NPM *020 †55

TILLEY, John Michael. 2300 HIGHLAND VILG RD #600 75077 #048-12-1981 L1981 FM *020 †18

TORRES, Marcela D. 401 N VALLEY PKWY, STE 400 75067 #737-06-1990 L1999 PHO *020 †55

TOVAR, Rudolph Manuel. 560 W MAIN ST, STE 200 75057 #048-02-1972 L1972 OBG *020 †30

TREECE, Chad Edward. 500 W MAIN ST 75057 #048-15-2002 L2007 GS *020 †85

VASAVADA, Nishendu. 560 W MAIN ST, STE 101 75057 #495-23-1972 L1978 P *020 †75

WAHI, Ravi K. 396 W MAIN ST STE 100 75057 #495-41-1979 L1998 AN CCA *020 †05

WALDMAN, Mark B. 751 HEBRON PKWY, STE 100 75057 #048-12-1994 L1995 FM *020 †18

WATERS, William Jos. 405 HIGHWAY 121 BYP, BLDG A 75067 #048-12-1980 L1980 DR *020 †80

WATSON, Mildred Elaine. 1278 FM 407 STE 109 75077 #308-07-1982 L1990 FM *072 †18

WHITTEMORE, Anthony Roe. 405 HWY 121 BYP, STE 150 75067 #011-02-1978 L2000 R *040 †20

WILLENBORG, Michael J. 500 W MAIN ST 75057 #048-14-1997 L2002 ORS *020 †40

WILLIAMS, Shirley Ann. 614 S EDMONDS LN STE 101, CARDIOVASCULAR SPECIALISTS 75067 #018-03-1977 L1984 CD IM *020 †20

WILLIAMSON, Richard W, Jr. 500 W MAIN ST, STE 200 75057 #048-02-1969 L1969 ORS *020 †40

ZAHALUK, David William. 751 HEBRON PKWY, STE 100 75057 #065-01-1990 L1996 FM *020 †18

ZULQARNAIN, Muhammad. 1850 LAKEPOINTE DR, STE 100 75057 #704-01-1987 L2005 APM *020 †05

LIBERTY – LIBERTY

BROWN, Arthur Reese. 720 TRAVIS ST 77575 #048-02-1967 L1967 FM *020 ‡

CALLENS, Don Shannon. 720 TRAVIS ST, LIBERTY MEDICAL SURGICAL C 77575 #048-02-2004 L2006 FM *020 †18

CARD, Robert Justin. 1353 N TRAVIS ST 77575 #021-01-1974 L1979 CD *020 †20

DALEY, Rebecca W. 720 TRAVIS ST 77575 #048-78-1997, ▲ L1998 OMM *020

DARK, Sheri Lynne. 1409 N TRAVIS ST 77575 #048-14-1995 L1996 FM *020 †18

JESSURUN, Carlos Ruben. 1353 N TRAVIS ST 77575 #048-02-1991 L1992 CD *020 †20

KHAN, Kamran Ahmad. 1353 N TRAVIS ST 77575 #704-24-1993 L2003 IM *020 †20

MESA, Andres. 1353 N TRAVIS ST 77575 #264-18-1989 L1998 CD IC *020 †20

OSTMAN, Robert Amos. 1353 N TRAVIS ST 77575 #048-13-1976 L1976 EM GP *020

RODRIGUEZ, Jenny Kristine. ■ 77575 #048-02-2008 *012

RODRIGUEZ, Sergio Luis. 1353 N TRAVIS ST 77575 #275-01-1960 L1972 FM GP *075

TALOSIG, Socorro Aggabao. 1353 N TRAVIS ST 77575 #748-01-1970 L1979 PD *020 †55

TREISTMAN ZIGHELBOIM, B. 1353 N TRAVIS ST 77575 #737-06-1966 L1972 CD IM *020 †20

LIBERTY HILL – WILLIAMSON

BUCKLEY, Mary Lou. ■ 78642 #041-01-1947 L1948 AN *071 †05

COLEMAN, William Edward. ■ 78642 #048-12-1962 L1962 FM *071 †18

RODEGHERO, James A. ■ 78642 #028-34-1952 L1953 FM *071 †18

UMSTATTD, Laura J. ■ 78642 #048-02-2008 *012

LILLIAN – JOHNSON

REEVES, David Alvis. ■ 76061 #048-02-1974 L1974 AN *071 †05

LINDALE – SMITH

BEALL, Virginia B. 1440 S MAIN ST 75771 #048-12-1988 L1989 **OPH PO** *020 †35
BRAUN, Patricia A Denton. GENERAL DELIVERY 75771 #048-12-1966 L1966 **FM OS** *020
BROOKS, Melita Lang. 3203 S MAIN ST #048-02-1991 L1992 **FM** *020 †18
BROWN, Jonathan T. ■ 75771 #048-12-2008 *012
BUTLER, Kathleen V. 2416 S MAIN ST, LINDALE PEDIATRICS 75771 #048-02-1998 L2001
   PD *020 †55
DAVIS, Anthony D. 2410 S MAIN ST 75771 #048-15-1998 L1999 **FM** *020 †18 ‡
FOWLER, Roger Neal. 3203 S MAIN ST #004-01-1977 L1981 **FM** *020 †18
HANEY, David Geo. 16658 FOX RUN LN 75771 #026-04-1957 L1964 **OPH** *071 †35
LAWTON, Willis Hill. 20131 FM 16 W 75771 #068-01-1971 L1996 *020
MC DANIEL, James Russell. ■ 75771 #048-02-1967 L1967 **ORS GP** *071 †40
PENNELL, Curtis Jeffrey. 1440 S MAIN ST 75771 #021-06-1991 L1993 **OPH** *020 †35 ‡
RICHARDSON, Gene Allan. ■ 75771 #048-04-1957 L1957 **R** *071 †80
VERA, Eleazar, Jr. 2410 S MAIN ST 75771 #048-13-1989 L1990 **FM** *020 †18
WHITNEY, Clayton Everett. 1440 S MAIN ST 75771 #048-12-1981 L1981 **OPH OS** *020 †35

LINDEN – CASS

ALBEIGE, Hassan. 402 N KAUFMAN ST 75563 #875-01-1987 L1995 **IM EM** *020 †20
BLACKBURN, James David. 404 N KAUFMAN ST 75563 #048-02-1961 L1961 **GS GP** *020 †85
LEGROW, Reginald Bruce. 402 N KAUFMAN ST, GLENN GARRETT CLINIC 75563
   #064-01-1974 L1982 **GP** *020
LEGROW, Robert. 404 N KAUFMAN ST 75563 #048-14-2003 L2006 **FM** *020 †18
WITHERSPOON, Robert G. 402 N KAUFMAN ST, GLENN GARRETT CLINIC 75563
   #048-02-1975 L1975 **OBG** *072

LITTLE ELM – DENTON

FLORES, John Gerard. 730 E ELDORADO PKWY 75068 #048-12-1993 L1994 **IM** *020 †20
WOLF, Jill E. 730 E ELDORADO PKWY 75068 #048-14-1993 L1995 **IM** *020 †20

LITTLEFIELD – LAMB

CHATWELL, J W. 2401 HALL AVE 79339 #048-12-1954 L1954 **FM** *071 †18
FAIN, Jesse Randel. 401 W 6TH ST 79339 #048-12-1954 L1955 **GP** *071
HINCKLEY, Herbert M. STAR ROUTE H CI 79339 #048-12-1953 L1953 **GP** *071
KLEIN, Barney Isadore, Jr. 1500 S SUNSET AVE 79339 #048-02-1962 L1962 **GP** *020
KLEIN, Kelly Lockwood. 1600 S SUNSET AVE 79339 #048-15-1995 L1996 **FM OBS** *020 †18
LENTZ, Jason B. 1600 S SUNSET AVE 79339 #048-15-2004 L2006 **FM** *020 †18
MOLINA, Isabel. 1600 S SUNSET AVE 79339 #048-15-2001 L2002 **FM** *020
WALKUP, Robert D. 1600 S SUNSET AVE 79339 #048-15-2000 L2001 **FM** *020 †18 ‡

LIVE OAK – BEXAR

ALMENDAREZ, Valentin, Jr. 12709 TOEPPERWEIN RD, STE 309 78233 #048-16-1992 L1994
   OBG *020 †30
ALVAREZ, Flavio H. 11481 TOEPPERWEIN RD, STE 1202 78233 #264-18-1989 L1998
   NEP *020 †20
ARASTU, Raiqua S. 11515 TOEPPERWEIN RD, STE 202 78233 #495-21-1975 L1986
   A PD *020 †55,03
BAUMAN, Wendall C, Jr. 12501 JUDSON RD STE 201 78233 #023-12-1983 L1993 **OPH** *020 †35
BERGMAN, Randy Norman. 12602 TOEPPERWEIN RD, STE 100 78233 #011-02-1979 L1983
   IM *020 †20
BRINKMAN, Frank Peter. 12107 TOEPPERWEIN RD, STE 1 78233 #021-06-1973 L1973
   EM *020 †85
BROWN, Lance Fortson. 12412 JUDSON RD, NORTHEAST METHODIST HOSPIT 78233
   #035-01-1991 L2000 **EM** *020 †16
CANNON, Jeffrey Alexander. 11901 TOEPPERWEIN RD, STE 1201 78233 #048-12-2001 L2004
   FM *020 †18
CUDA, Darryl D. 12709 TOEPPERWEIN RD # 101 78233 #023-12-1986 L1998 **ORS** *020 †40
DABAS, Basel. 12501 JUDSON RD, STE 102 78233 #875-01-1988 L1997 **HO IM** *020 †20
FISCHER, Richard Emil. 12709 TOEPPERWEIN RD, STE 203 78233 #048-13-1980 L1985
   GS *020 †85
FORSETH, Barbara J. 12602 TOEPPERWEIN RD, STE 100 78233 #048-13-1995 L1996
   IM *020 †20
GARCIA, John Jos. 12315 JUDSON RD, STE 118 78233 #048-02-1988 L1993 **FM UCM** *020
GARZA, Joseph A. 12602 TOEPPERWEIN RD, STE 201 78233 #048-14-2000 L2004 **OBG** *020
GONZALEZ, Virnalisis M. 12602 TOEPPERWEIN RD, STE 114 78233 #042-01-1994 L2006
   D *020 †15 ‡
GRAHAM, Christopher W. 12709 TOEPPERWEIN RD # 110 78233 #047-05-1987 L1994
   U *020 †95
GRODRIAN, Wayne Edward. ■ 78233 #017-20-1942 **GP** *071
HALL, Gary Marvin. 12709 TOEPPERWEIN RD, STE 203 78233 #048-12-1981 L1981
   GS *020 †85
HLA, Tin Aung. 12501 JUDSON RD 78233 #209-01-1987 L1998 **IM** *020 †20
HOCKLEY, Alfred John, III. 12602 TOEPPERWEIN RD 78233 #041-13-1981 L1996
   D AM *020 †15
HORVATH, Robert Andrew. 12315 JUDSON RD, STE 210 78233 #028-34-1968 L1978
   IM END *020
HUFFINGTON, Paul E, Jr. ■ 78233 #023-01-1960 L1972 **AN** *071 †05
JAMES, Jocelyn Leah. 12602 TOEPPERWEIN RD, STE 207 78233 #055-01-1983 L1984
   FM *020 †15
JOHNSON, Rinna Conol. 12602 TOEPPERWEIN RD # 114 78233 #023-12-1991 L2002
   D *020 †20
KAPOOR, Brijesh. 11481 TOEPPERWEIN RD 1202, RENAL ASSOCIATES, P.A. 78233
   #496-09-1993 L2007 **NEP** *020 †20 ‡
KUJAWA, Ples Latson. 12709 TOEPPERWEIN RD, STE 101 78233 #048-13-1983 L1983
   ORS *020 †40
MANGAT, Harmeet Singh. 12602 TOEPPERWEIN RD, STE 100 78233 #495-29-1979 L1985
   IM *020 †20

MARTIN, Jack Lee. 12709 TOEPPERWEIN RD, STE 205 78233 #035-01-1975 L2008
   IM CD *020 †20
MARTIN-AREVALO, De Andra. 11481 TOEPPERWEIN RD, STE 1202 78233 #048-04-1991 L1993
   NEP *020 †20
MARTINEZ, Raul Gerardo. 12412 JUDSON RD 78233 #048-13-1994 L1996 **PMM AN** *020 †05
MORRIS, Kay. 12315 JUDSON RD, STE 318 78233 #048-13-1977 L1979 **GYN** *020 †30
MOSS, Jesse, Jr. 12602 TOEPPERWEIN RD, STE 211 78233 #018-03-1981 L1988
   OTO PSH *020 †45
NARVAEZ, Roberto M. 12412 JUDSON RD 78233 #030-06-1978 L1988 **IM GE** *020 †20
NEAL, Thomas Ward. 12702 TOEPPERWEIN RD, STE 120 78233 #048-04-1973 L1973 **FM** *020
NGUYEN, Huyen T. 12501 JUDSON RD STE 202 78233 #048-13-1992 L1995 **IM** *020 †20
OCHOA, David Albert. 11485 TOEPPERWEIN RD, STE 1 78233 #048-14-1986 L1987
   FM *020 †18
OLIVER, Michael Edwin. 12709 TOEPPERWEIN RD # 204 78233 #011-02-1979 L1982
   N *020 †75
PARSONS, William Thos. 12602 TOEPPERWEIN RD # 114 78233 #045-01-1975 L1978
   D *020 †15 ‡
PIPKIN, Charles S. 12709 TOEPPERWEIN RD, STE 302 78233 #048-02-1983 L1983
   OSS GS *020 †40
PITTARD, Aaron B. 11601 TOEPPERWEIN RD 78233 #048-12-2001 L2006 **OPH** *020
QURESHI, Mohammed Arshad. 11901 TOEPPERWEIN RD #1401 78233 #704-02-1991 L2005
   PUD CCM *020 †20
RAZA, Syed Nayyar. 12705 TOEPPERWEIN RD, MEDICAL ONCOLOGY SAN ANTON 78233
   #704-02-1990 L2002 **HO IM** *020 †20
REYES, Cesar. 12709 TOEPPERWEIN RD, STE 309 78233 #649-01-1974 L1983 **OBG** *020 †30
RILEY, Arie T. 12412 JUDSON RD, 139483585 78233 #023-12-1986 L1993 **EM** *020 †16
RITCHIE, John David. ■ 78233 #025-07-2007 **GS** *012
ROBERTSON, Valorie R. 12412 JUDSON RD 78233 #048-13-1992 L1994 **FM** *020 †18
RODRIGUEZ, Jesus L. 12702 TOEPPERWEIN RD, STE 132 78233 #048-16-2000 L2003
   PD *020 †55
RUIZ, Heine. 12602 TOEPPERWEIN RD, STE 100 78233 #737-06-1992 L2006 **IM** *075 †20
SADLER, Randall Kent. 12602 TOEPPERWEIN RD, STE 201 78233 #048-12-1982 L1983
   OBG *020 †20
SCHULZE, Brian E. 12709 TOEPPERWEIN RD # 101 78233 #048-14-1994 L1995 **ORS** *020 †40
SKOP, Ingrid Ruth. 12602 TOEPPERWEIN RD, STE 201 78233 #028-02-1992 L1993
   OBG *020 †30
SLEDGE, Scott L. 12709 TOEPPERWEIN RD, STE 101 78233 #048-12-1985 L1986
   OAR OSM *020 †40
SMITH, Joshua Augustus. 12413 JUDSON RD, STE 120 78233 #005-12-1955 L1957
   EM GS *071 †85
STOLL, John F. 12412 JUDSON RD, NORTHEAST METHODIST HOSPIT 78233
   #048-12-1982 L1983 **DR OS** *020 †80
TAJKHANJI, Moiz Abbas. 12414 TOEPPERWEIN RD 78233 #495-33-1988 L1994 **FM** *020 †18 ‡
TALAFUSE, David W. 11901 TOEPPERWEIN RD, STE 1201 78233 #048-13-1985 L1986
   FM *020 †20
TUCHSEN, George Randolph. 12709 TOEPPERWEIN RD STE 2 78233 #048-14-1989 L1990
   GS *020 †85
VALDEZ, Ronald Anthony. 12709 TOEPPERWEIN RD, STE 309 78233 #048-02-1983 L1983
   OBG *020 †30
VANOVER, Randall Mark. 12602 TOEPPERWEIN RD, STE 100 78233 #025-07-1981 L1982
   IM EM *020 †20
VILLARREAL, Marcus S. 12107 TOEPPERWEIN RD, STE 1 78233 #048-02-1981 L1981
   GP EM *020 †16
WILCOX, Rex E. 12709 TOEPPERWEIN RD, STE 101 78233 #048-02-1982 L1983 **ORS** *020 †40
ZAMAN, Fahim. 11481 TOEPPERWEIN RD 78233 #704-02-1989 L2006 **NEP IM** *020 †20

LIVINGSTON – POLK

BA, Aung. 1717 HIGHWAY 59 LOOP N 77351 #209-03-1982 L1998 **IM EM** *020 †20
BRAWNER, Marlo. 400 OGLETREE DR, LIVINGSTON PEDIATRIC CLINI 77351
   #005-18-1998 L2003 **PD** *020 †55
BRUNING, Karla B. 300 BYPASS LN, STE 200 77351 #048-16-1997 L1998 **FM** *020 †18
BUESCHER, David C. 219 EASTWOOD AVE 77351 #048-13-1992 L1994 **FM** *020 †18
BUI, Hunganh Buu. 1930 U S HIGHWAY 190 W, LIVINGSTON MEDICAL CLINIC 77351
   #305-01-2001 L2005 **FM** *020 †18
CHERIPARAMBIL, Kuruvila. 1717 HIGHWAY 59 LOOP N 77351 #495-28-1981 L2000
   CD IM *020 †20
COSTELLO, Cory Nathan. ■ 77351 #035-09-1996 L2000 **FM** *100 †18
COX, Steve Ryan. 601 OGLETREE DR, STE B 77351 #048-15-1984 L1985 **GS** *020 †85
DABNEY, Joseph T, Jr. ■ 77351 #021-01-1947 L1949 **FM** *071
EVANS, Kerry Lane. 1717 HIGHWAY 59 LOOP N 77351 #020-02-1995 L1998 **FM EM** *020 †18
FELD, Steven Leigh. 1717 HIGHWAY 59 LOOP N # A 77351 #048-12-1980 L1991
   CD IM *020 †20
GUPTA, Aditya. 309 HIGHWAY 59 LOOP S, CALVARY MEDICAL CLINIC 77351
   #495-45-1998 L2003 **IM** *020
INGRAM, Chester Wm. 505 N DREW AVE 77351 #001-02-1975 L1981 **FM** *020 †18
JACOBS, Carol L. 400 OGLETREE DR 77351 #048-13-1993 L1994 **PD** *020 †55
KANAAN, Elias T. 601 OGLETREE DR, STE C 77351 #605-02-1993 L1997 **IM** *020 †20
KATARI, Singaraju. 604 S WASHINGTON AVE 77351 #495-58-1969 L2001 **PD** *020 †55
KETHINENI, Nirmala. ■ 77351 #495-09-1999 L2005 **IM** *100 †20
KURUVILLA, Anita. 400 W CHURCH ST, PINEYWOODS DIAGNOSTIC CLIN 77351
   #495-44-1987 L2001 **IM** *020 †20
LAURORA, Kenneth Joseph. 400 BYPASS LN, STE 111 77351 #033-05-1999 L2003 **IM** *020
LOUGHRAN, James Patrick. 1717 HIGHWAY 59 LOOP N 77351 #039-05-1990 L2005
   FM *020 †18 ‡
LUNA, Raymond J. 219 EASTWOOD AVE 77351 #034-01-1981 L1983 **FM** *020 †18
NELLSCH, Verner Owen. ■ 77351 #019-02-1978 L1999 **OBG** *020 †30
NELSON, James Charles, Jr. 602 E CHURCH ST 77351 #308-11-1990 L2000 **FM** *020
NEUMAN, Raymond Aubry. 1930 U S HIGHWAY 190 W 77351 #048-12-1981 L1981 **FM** *020
PEAKE, Robert Lee. ■ 77351 #017-20-1960 L1968 **END IM** *071 †20
PHILLIPS, Frederick L. 410 E CHURCH ST, STE C 77351 #016-11-1942 L1960 **PD** *071 †55
REDDY, S Chandra Bose. 414 S WASHINGTON AVE, RAJ MEDICAL CENTER 77351
   #495-65-1980 L2003 **PDC** *020 †55
SARATHY, Rama. 309 LOOP DR 59, CALVARY MED CLNC 77351 #913-92-1976 L2002
   PD *020 †55

SHAW, Timothy Shane. 601 OGLETREE DR, STE D 77351 #305-01-2000 L2005 **ORS** *020 †40
SLOMINSKI, Henry Francis. ■ 77351 #030-06-1957 L1957 **FM PHP** *071
SMITH, Charlene. 410 E CHURCH ST STE A 77351 #048-13-1982 L1983 **OPH IM** *020 †35
SWEARINGEN, Robert E. 571 STATE PARK ROAD 56, INDIAN HEALTH SVC 77351
  #048-04-1953 L1953 **GP GS** *020
TOLLS, Ronald Melchior. 739 OAKDALE LOOP, P O BOX 1758 77351 #048-02-1966 L1995
  GS SO *020 †85
WAECHTER, Frank Edward, III. 403 OGLETREE DR STE 200 77351 #030-05-1975 L2005
  OBG *020 †30
WALKER, Frank S, Jr. 1717 HIGHWAY 59 LOOP N 77351 #048-12-1985 L1986 **CRS GS** *020
WATSON, Jeffrey Alan. 602 E CHURCH ST 77351 #016-42-1985 L1996 **IM** *020
WOOD, Jerry Dewayne. 219 EASTWOOD AVE 77351 #048-13-1981 L1981 **FM** *020 †18 ‡
WOODROME, Robert Gale. 340 PAN AMERICAN DR STE B4 77351 #048-13-1999 L2001
  FM *020 †18
YOUSSEF, Souad Sleiman. ■ 77351 #605-03-2000 L2006 **ID** *020 †20
ZOND, Alan Gray. 3872 FM 350 S 77351 #041-77-1992, ▲ L1998 **FM** *020

LLANO – LLANO

FORRISTER, Sonja Zirkel. 102 E YOUNG ST 78643 #048-14-1987 L1988 **FM** *020 †18
GRIMSHAW, Randall J. 102 E YOUNG ST 78643 #048-14-1987 L1988 **FM** *020 †18
MANTHEIY, Joseph Richard. 200 W OLLIE ST 78643 #048-16-1984 L1985 **FM** *020 †18
MARTIN, Wayne Robt. 200 W OLLIE ST 78643 #007-02-1968 L2007 **FM** *020 †18
NGUYEN, Lan Thanh. 102 E YOUNG ST 78643 #048-03-1987 L1992 **GS** *020 †85
THOMAS, Griffith M. 102 E YOUNG ST 78643 #048-14-1982 L1983 **GS GP** *020 †18
TUCKER, Kelly Rush. 102 E YOUNG ST 78643 #048-14-1985 L1986 **FM** *020 †18

LOCKHART – CALDWELL

ABCEDE, Hilda Maderal. 1013 W SAN ANTONIO ST 78644 #748-10-1968 L1988 **PD** *020
BLACK, Angela Pilcher. 300 S COLORADO ST, STE A 78644 #048-13-1997 L2003 **PD** *020 †55
KIRTLEY, Randall Wesley. 300 S COMMERCE ST, STE B 78644 #048-02-1984 L1985
  FM *020 †18 ‡
MOHANDAS, Arjun. 300 S COLORADO ST STE D, INTERNAL MEDICINE 78644
  #495-27-1991 L1991 **IM** *020 †20
MOHANDAS, Renu. 300 S COLORADO ST, STE D 78644 #495-27-1991 L1999 **IM** *020 †20
RODRIGUEZ-INIGO, Pedro A. ■ 78644 #275-01-1944 L1968 **IM** *071
ROMANEK, Barton James. 109 W SAN ANTONIO ST 78644 #065-10-1975 L1978 **FM** *020 ‡
SILVA, Marcelino Sinense. ■ 78644 #048-09-1971 L1976 **GP** *020
WALES, Philip Arthur. ■ 78644 #048-02-1943 L1943 **IMG** *071
WHEELER, Kimberly M. 1009 W SAN ANTONIO ST 78644 #048-13-2003 L2005 **FM** *020 †18
WILBURN, Darrell Eddie. 1400 INDUSTRIAL BLVD 78644 #030-05-1986 L1989 **IM** *020

LOCKNEY – FLOYD

MANGOLD, Gary Bedford. 320 N MAIN ST 79241 #048-15-1976 L1976 **FM** *020 †18 ‡
STENNETT, Kevin T. 320 N MAIN ST 79241 #048-15-1987 L1988 **FM OBS** *020 †18
STEWART, Kevin L. PO BOX 37 79241 #048-12-1988 L1989 **FM** *020 †18

LONE OAK – HUNT

KALER, Lawrence Wm. ■ 75453 #040-02-1991 L1993 **DR** *020 †80

LONGVIEW – GREGG

AGOSTINI, Anthony J. 709 HOLLYBROOK DR, STE 2301 75605 #041-78-1997, ▲ L2005
  IC *020 †20
ALBERS, Jason A. 2101 W LOOP 281 75604 #048-02-1999 L2002 **FM** *020 †18
ALZAGA, Donna Morato. 703 E MARSHALL AVE STE 10, INTERNAL MEDICINE ASSOC. O 75601
  #748-02-2001 L2007 **IM** *020 †20
ANDREWS, Mary Uffelman. 804 MEDICAL DR STE I 75605 #021-05-1969 L1973 **OPH** *020 †35
ARCHER, Julia Jefferes. 703 E MARSHALL AVE, INTERNAL MEDICINE 75601
  #048-15-1992 L1993 **IM** *020 †20
ARCHER, Timothy Frank. 433 HAMPTON CT 75605 #023-12-1986 L2002 **EM** *020 †16
BAGLEY, Jimmie Curtis. ■ 75603 #048-02-1957 L1957 **FM** *071 †18
BAILEY, Shirley Sidwell. 305 N 5TH ST 75601 #048-02-1967 L1967 **PD** *020
BECK, Dennis Ray. 703 E MARSHALL AVE STE 4002 75601 #048-15-1984 L1985 **AN** *020 †05
BECK, Stephen J. 901 WALNUT HILL DR 75605 #048-13-1979 L1979 **D** *020 †15
BELL, Joseph Webster. 709 HOLLYBROOK DR, STE 4500 75605 #048-13-1984 L1986
  IM IMG *020 †20
BENEFIELD, Sabrina. 707 HOLLYBROOK DR 75605 #021-06-1997 L2001 **OBG** *020 †30
BERG, Lamont S. 703 E MARSHALL AVE 75601 #048-02-1994 L2005 **AN** *020 †05
BIANCA, Joseph Frank. 804 MEDICAL DR, STE 8 75605 #021-05-1968 L1969 **GYN** *020 †30
BLADES, Carrie Marie. 700 E MARSHALL AVE, EMERGENCY DEPARTMENT 75601
  #021-06-2002 L2005 **EM** *020 †16
BOLDT, Lyle Dean. 700 E MARSHALL AVE, DEPARMENT OF RADIOLOGY 75601
  #017-20-1964 L1984 **EM** *071 †18
BRAZELL, Donald Scott. 2101 W LOOP 281 75604 #048-14-1989 L1990 **FM GPM** *020 †18
BRAZELL, Lynn Allen. 703 E MARSHALL AVE, STE 5007 75601 #048-14-1990 L1992
  OBG *020 †20
BRIMMER, Sushama Sharma. 2021 W LOOP 281, LONGVIEW INTERNAL MEDICINE 75604
  #021-05-1999 L2003 **MPD** *020
BROCK, Bobby C. 1809 W LOOP 281 75604 #048-02-1988 L1989 **FM** *020 †18
BROWN, David Lane. 911 W LOOP 281 STE 111 75604 #048-02-1989 L1991 **CHP P** *020 †75
BROWN, O Wharton, III. 707 HOLLYBROOK DR 75605 #021-05-1975 L1978 **PD** *020 †55
BROWNE, Lewis Austin. 806 MEDICAL DR, STE 100 75605 #048-02-1980 L1980 **FM** *020 †20
BUCKNER, Edwin E. ■ 75601 #021-01-1953 L1955 **FM OS** *071 †18
BURKE, Benjie Llewellyn. 703 E MARSHALL AVE, STE 4006 75601 #021-05-1987 L1993
  AN *020 †20
BURKE, Wendy Jaye. 201 WOODCREEK DR 75605 #010-02-1974 L1976 **P** *020 †75

BURT, Nancy Ann. 701 E MARSHALL AVE, MEDICAL PLAZA I, SUITE 407 75601
  #030-05-1995 L1999 **N** *020
BUTLER, Bradley G. 703 E MARSHALL AVE, STE 4006 75601 #048-16-2001 L2003
  AN AM *020 †05 ‡
CAMP, Mark Arnold. 815 N 4TH ST STE C 75601 #039-01-1986 L1987 **CCM PUD** *020 †20
CAMPBELL, Harold Edison. 1107 E MARSHALL AVE 75601 #049-38-1993 L2006 **FM** *100 †18
CAMPBELL, John Curran. 700 E MARSHALL AVE, RADIOLOGY DEPT ATTN DR CAM 75601
  #048-14-1997 L1998 **DR** *020 †80
CAPERS, Daniel Gregory. 2300 BILL OWENS PKWY # 824 75604 #048-12-1973 L1975
  AM GYN *020
CARY, Robert Watson. 2901 N 4TH ST 75605 #048-13-1980 L1980 **FM OM** *020 †18
CHAIKIN, Samantha Jane. 705 E MARSHALL AVE, STE 1002 75601 #028-79-1994, ▲ L1998
  PD *020 †55
CHASTAIN, Oscar Jack, III. 701 E MARSHALL AVE, STE 504 75601 #048-04-1980 L1980
  TS *020 †85,90
CHIKKAMUNIYAPPA, Shylashre. 700 E MARSHALL AVE 75601 #496-39-1998 L2006
  PTH HMP *020 †50
CHOW, Thomas S. 703 E MARSHALL AVE, STE 3004 75601 #048-04-1990 L1991 **NS N** *020
CLARK, Emmette Anderson. 707 HOLLYBROOK DR 75605 #048-02-1976 L1976 **PD** *071 †55
COLEMAN, Solon Lycurgus. 701 N 6TH ST 75601 #001-02-1956 L1960 **IM** *071 †20
COLQUITT, John Adam. 703 E MARSHALL AVE, STE 4006 75601 #048-12-1981 L1981
  AN *020 †05
COLQUITT, Landon A. ■ 75601 #048-02-1950 L1950 **ORS** *071 †40
COODY, Michael Wayne. 700 E MARSHALL AVE, GOOD SHEPHERD MEDICAL CENT 75601
  #021-05-1986 L2002 **EM FM** *020 †18
COOK, Byron Floyd, III. 703 E MARSHALL AVE, STE 4003 75601 #048-02-1976 L1976
  GS *020 †85
COPPEDGE, John Ronald. 703 E MARSHALL AVE # 4003 75601 #048-12-1975 L1975
  GS *020 †85
CORINALDI, Chalene A. 700 E MARSHALL AVE, GOOD SHEPHERD MEDICAL CENT 75601
  #041-13-1999 L2003 **EM** *020 †16
COUCH, Linda Sue. 1300 N 4TH ST 75601 #051-01-1998 L2003 **ON** *020 †20
COWAN, Alan Lee. 709 HOLLYBROOK DR STE 5601 75605 #048-02-2002 L2007 **OTO** *020 †20
CRUMPLER, Charles Prentic. 402 N 7TH ST 75601 #048-12-1976 L1976 **CD IM** *020 †20
DANIELS, Wendell David. 515 N 3RD ST 75601 #048-04-1976 L1976 **IM RHU** *020 †20
DANTONI, John Thos, Jr. 2901 N 4TH ST 75601 #021-05-1991 L2002 **PD** *020 †55
DAVIS, Donna Phipps. 1107 E MARSHALL AVE 75601 #048-15-1995 L1998 **PD** *020 †55
DECKELBOIM, Gary Glenn. 330 E LOOP 281 75605 #035-08-1984 L1992 **OPH IM** *020 †35
DE HAVEN, Thomas J. 1705 JUDSON RD 75601 #048-12-1985 L1986 **OPH** *020 †35
DEVULAPALLI, Sita M. 903 WALNUT HILL DR, STE 1 75605 #495-11-1990 L1997 **IM** *020 †20
DICKSON, Robert L. 700 E MARSHALL AVE, DEPARTMENT OF EMERGENCY ME 75601
  #048-13-2001 L2004 **EM** *020 †16
DIPASQUALE, John T. 700 E MARSHALL AVE, DEPARMENT OF RADIOLOGY 75601
  #048-12-1992 L1994 **EM** *020 †16
DOERRFELD, David Wm. 701 E MARSHALL AVE, STE 512 75601 #018-03-1987 L1998
  OBG *020 †30
DRAYER, Irving Jerome. 701 E MARSHALL AVE, IRVING J DRAYER M D 75601
  #048-02-1962 L1962 **GS VS** *071 †85
DUNCAN, Lewis Alvin. 1300 N 4TH ST, LONGVIEW CANCER CENTER 75601
  #021-01-1970 L1973 **ON HEM** *020 †20
DUNNAHOO, Christopher L. ■ 75604 #048-12-2002 L2006 **EM** *020 †16
DUQUELLA, Gregory Woodlee. 700 E MARSHALL AVE 75601 #024-07-1997 L2004
  MPD *020 †20
DUVALL, Charles Darren. 4777 US HIGHWAY 259 75605 #048-16-1994 L1996 **DR** *020 †80
EARNEST, Carl Richard. 703 E MARSHALL AVE, INTERNAL MEDICINE 75601
  #039-01-1995 L1999 **IM** *020 †20
EDWARDS, Gregory Ashton. 703 E MARSHALL AVE, STE 5008 75601 #021-05-1997 L2002
  U *020 †95
ELDER, Jack Donald, Jr. 709 HOLLYBROOK DR STE 3401 75605 #048-02-1965 L1965
  ORS *020 †40
ELHALWAGI, Baher Mohamed. 703 E MARSHALL AVE, STE 3008 75601 #915-02-1987 L1997
  PCC *020 †20
ELKINS, Oliver Wayne. ■ 75602 #021-05-1938 L1946 **GP** *071
ENGLAND, Richard Wayne. ■ 75601 #048-02-1973 L1973 **FM** *072 †18
ENGLISH, Richard Dean. 1300 N 6TH ST STE 104, LONGVIEW OCCUP MED CLN 75601
  #048-04-1974 L1975 **OM GP** *020 †70
ERICKSTAD, Mark David. 703 E MARSHALL AVE STE 500 75601 #048-12-1986 L1987
  GS U *020 †95
ERWIN, David Randolph. 2901 N 4TH ST 75605 #048-02-1979 L1979 **DR** *020 †80
FARR, James Edward, Jr. ■ 75605 #045-01-1968 L1978 **CD IM** *020
FERRELL, John Milton, Jr. 703 E MARSHALL AVE, STE 5008 75601 #048-12-1968 L1968
  U *020 †95
FITZGERALD, Lynn F. 701 E MARSHALL AVE, STE 403 75601 #016-11-1993 L1999
  NS GS *020 †25
FLETES, James Robt. 700 E MARSHALL AVE 75601 #649-02-1979 L1981 **PTH** *020 †50
FLORY, Kenneth Marshall. 703 E MARSHALL AVE, INTERNAL MEDICINE 75601
  #048-13-1975 L1975 **IM** *020 †20
FONTENOT, Jonathan Wayne. 707 HOLLYBROOK DR, 707 HOLLYBROOK 75605
  #021-05-1994 L2000 **ORS** *020 †40
FORD, Doris E. 805 MEDICAL CIRCLE DR 75605 #305-01-1999 L2003 **FM** *020 †18
FOSTER, Will S, Jr. ■ 75601 #020-02-1969 L1970 **AN OS** *071 †05
FRASE, Larry Lynn. 1300 N 4TH ST, LONGVIEW CANCER CENTER 75601 #048-12-1983 L1983
  ON HEM *020 †20
FUSELER, Laura Jane. 709 HOLLYBROOK DR 75605 #021-06-1998 L2002 **IM** *020 †20
GASIC, Andrei Claudio. 1400 N 4TH ST 75601 #041-07-1986 L1987 **GE IM** *020 †20
GATSON, April. 103 W LOOP 281, STE 750 75605 #004-01-1998 L2001 **FM** *020 †18
GAY, Charles Edward, Jr. 805 MEDICAL CIRCLE DR 75601 #047-06-1957 L1960 **FM** *071 †18
GERBER, Terry Lynn. 402 N 7TH ST 75601 #048-02-1998 L2004 **CD** *020 †20
GLOWCZWSKI, Alan C. 700 E MARSHALL AVE 75601 #048-14-1989 L1990 **DR** *020 †80
GOR, Henry. 707 HOLLYBROOK DR, DIAGNOSTIC CLC OF LONGVIEW 75605
  #048-02-1975 L1975 **OBG** *020 †30
GRAHAM, Timothy E. 2901 N 4TH ST 75605 #048-12-1987 L1988 **DR** *020 †80
GRECO, Anthony Vincent. 901 WALNUT HILL DR 75605 #065-01-1990 L1995 **D** *020 †15
GREGORY, Johnasan M. 709 HOLLYBROOK DR, STE 5603 75605 #048-13-1984 L1985
  IM *020 †20
GREIFENKAMP, John Edward. 709 HOLLYBROOK DR, STE 4500 75605 #020-12-1971 L1973
  IM *020 †20

GUILLORY, Michael Bruce. 3209 N 4TH ST STE 100 75605 #021-05-1977 L1978 **OPH** *020 †35
GUPTA, Sandeep Kumar. 700 E MARSHALL AVE, GOOD SHEPHERD MEDICAL CENT 75601 #305-01-2001 L2005 **EM** *020 †16
HALL, John Lee. 1701 CENTENARY DR 75601 #048-12-1966 L1966 **P** *020 †75
HAMER, Richard Allen. 701 E MARSHALL AVE 75601 #001-02-1985 L1987 **N** *020 †75
HAROLD, James Gregory. 1300 N 6TH ST 75601 #048-15-1989 L1990 **P** *020 †75
HARRINGTON, Luther G. 700 E MARSHALL AVE 75601 #048-13-1976 L1986 **EM FM** *020 †18,16
HARRISON, Donald E. ■ 75607 #067-01-1952 L1956 **IM** *071
HATZIS, Gregory P. 615 N 3RD ST, STE 2 75601 #048-12-2003 L2004 **OMF** *020 ‡
HAVENS, William Orvil. ■ 75604 #048-02-1960 L1960 **R** *071
HAWNER, Philip Pierre. 703 E MARSHALL AVE # 4008 75601 #051-04-1991 L1997 **PS** *020 †65
HENRY, Rodney Lee. 402 N 7TH ST 75601 #048-12-1980 L1980 **CD IC** *020 †20
HERBECK, Gregory Eugene. 707 HOLLYBROOK DR 75605 #048-02-1978 L1978 **PD** *020 †55
HILLIARD, George M, III. 409 N 6TH ST 75601 #048-04-1958 L1958 **ORS** *071 †40
HILTON, Martin E. 709 HOLLYBROOK DR 75605 #048-15-2002 L2007 **ORS** *020
HIPKE, Matt E. 911 WALNUT HILL DR 75605 #048-14-1988 L1989 **AMI IM** *020 †20
HOLCOMB, Marvin B. 703 E MARSHALL AVE, STE 4003 75601 #048-12-1984 L1986 **GS** *020 †85
HOLMAN, Todd Read. 1009 N 4TH ST, STE A 75601 #048-14-1981 L1981 **AI A** *020 †55,03
HOO, Yin Shan. 703 E MARSHALL AVE, STE 3004 75601 #048-02-1989 L1991 **IM** *020
HOUGH, Steven Jerald. 703 E MARSHALL AVE, STE 4006 75601 #048-02-1979 L1979 **AN** *020 †05
HOWARD, Walter Kim. 700 E MARSHALL AVE, GOOD SHEPHERD MEDICAL CENT 75601 #048-16-1983 L1983 **DR NM** *020 †80
HOWES, Timothy Howes. 2901 N 4TH ST 75605 #021-06-1986 L1991 **U** *020 †95
HUDSON, Michael R. 707 HOLLYBROOK DR, DIAGNOSTIC CLINIC OF LONGV 75605 #048-16-1987 L1989 **PD** *020 †55
HUFFMAN, Larry Wayne. 701 N 6TH ST, PRIMARY CARE ASSOCIATES 75601 #048-02-1976 L1976 **FM** *020 †18
HUNTER, Carla Noll. 707 HOLLYBROOK DR 75605 #048-13-1983 L1983 **PD** *020 †55
HUNTER, Philip S. 2101 W LOOP 281 75604 #048-13-1983 L1983 **FM** *020 †18
HUTCHESON, Elizabeth K. 707 HOLLYBROOK DR 75605 #048-12-1997 L1998 **OBG** *020 †30
IHIONKHAN, Ehimare C. 730 E MARSHALL AVE # 3007 75601 #690-06-1990 L2000 **NPM PD** *020 †55
IRELAND, Raymond Jos. 700 E MARSHALL AVE 75601 #048-02-1969 L1969 **OPH** *020 †35
IVEY, Dorothy Lynn. 805 MEDICAL DR 75605 #048-14-1995 L1997 **FM** *020 †18 ‡
JACKSON, Frank Richie, Jr. 805 MEDICAL DR 75605 #048-04-1961 L1961 **FM** *020 †18
JACOBS, Gary Robt. 703 E MARSHALL AVE, STE 4008 75601 #048-14-1975 L1975 **PS** *020 †65
JACOBSON, Edward Earl. 1111 N 6TH ST 75601 #048-02-1974 L1974 **OBS GYN** *020 †30
JAMISON-BLAIR, Diane E. 709 HOLLYBROOK DR, STE 4500 75605 #021-06-1993 L2003 **MPD** *020 †20
JENKINS, David K. 707 HOLLYBROOK DR 75605 #048-02-1989 L1990 **ORS** *020 †40
JOHNSON, Gid Roger. 703 E MARSHALL AVE STE 500, MEDICAL PLAZA BLDG. 75601 #048-02-1974 L1974 **U** *071 †95
JOHNSON, Joseph Olen. ■ 75604 #048-02-1959 L1959 **OBG** *071 †30
JONES, Dan C. 700 E MARSHALL AVE, GOOD SHEPHERD WELLNESS CEN 75601 #048-12-1970 L1970 **IM** *071 †20
KAMALI, Kayvan. 701 E MARSHALL AVE, MEDICAL PLAZA 1, SUITE 405 75601 #422-01-1996 L2003 **IM** *020 †20
KEATON, Jerry Alan. 700 E MARSHALL AVE 75601 #039-01-1980 L1992 **DR** *020 †80
KELLEY, Janet L. 703 E MARSHALL AVE, STE 5007 75601 #048-16-2000 L2003 **OBG** *020 ‡
KELLY, Gene Paul. 2901 N 4TH ST, EMERGENCY DEPARTMENT 75605 #048-13-1998 L2001 **EM** *020 †16
KING, Brian E. 700 E MARSHALL AVE, DEPARMENT OF RADIOLOGY 75601 #048-12-1993 L1996 **EM** *020 †16
KING, Craig Kent. 3209 N 4TH ST STE 1 75605 #048-12-1980 L1980 **OPH** *020 †35
KIRK, Louis John, III. 1107 E MARSHALL AVE 75601 #048-13-1975 L1975 **OBG** *020 †30
KISER, Roger Wm. 709 HOLLYBROOK DR, STE 4500 75605 #048-02-1968 L1968 **PUD IM** *020
KLINGENBERG, Christopher. 700 E MARSHALL AVE, GOOD SHEPHERD HEALTH SYSTE 75601 #048-02-2004 L2007 **EM** *020
KODALI, Sayoji Venkata. 703 E MARSHALL AVE, STE 4006 75601 #495-98-1973 L1982 **AN CCA** *020 †05
KORNMAN, Moyne Treat. 804 MEDICAL DR STE F 75605 #048-04-1994 L1996 **BBK** *020 †50
KORNMAN, Scott Elbert. 2901 N 4TH ST, LRMC DEPARTMENT OF PATHOLO 75605 #048-04-1994 L1996 **FOP** *020 †50
KOYA, Rama. 1300 N 4TH ST, LONGVIEW CANCER CENTER 75601 #495-50-1985 L2000 **HO** *020 †20
KRAL, Jonathan J. 700 E MARSHALL AVE, EMERGENCY DEPARTMENT 75601 #016-06-1993 L1997 **EM** *020 †16
LANGFORD, Michael D. 409 N 6TH ST 75601 #048-12-1991 L1992 **ORS** *020 †40
LEATH, Michael Carter. 801 N 4TH ST 75601 #048-02-1974 L1974 **FM IM** *020 †20
LEATHERMAN, Geo Frederick. 402 N 7TH ST 75601 #048-12-1980 L1980 **CD** *020 †20
LEE, Chul Woo. ■ 75605 #583-01-1958 L1971 **AN** *071 †05
LEEDY, Liesel E. 703 E MARSHALL AVE, STE 4002 75601 #048-14-1992 L1993 **AN** *020 †05
LE JEUNE, John Edward. 805 MEDICAL DR 75605 #048-12-1977 L1977 **FM** *020 †18
LEWIS, Perry Carter. 701 E MARSHALL AVE, STE 200 75601 #048-13-1989 L1990 **GE** *020 †20
LIN, Paul L. 707 HOLLYBROOK DR, DIAGNOSTIC CLINIC OF LONGV 75605 #048-12-1995 L1996 **OBG** *020 †30
LITTLE, Earle Elvis. NL 37 LAKE CHEROKEE 75603 #004-01-1955 L1960 **R RO** *071 †80
LITTLEJOHN, Mark C. 709 HOLLYBROOK DR 75605 #048-02-1988 L1989 **OTO** *020 †45
LITTLEJOHN, Stephen G. 409 N 6TH ST 75601 #048-02-1992 L1993 **ORS** *020 †40
LIU, Edward C. 707 HOLLYBROOK DR STE 500, 707 HOLLYBROOK 75605 #048-02-1978 L1978 **ORS** *020 †40
LOCKHART, Jonathan Clay. 2020 BILL OWENS PKWY STE 1 75604 #048-13-1994 L1995 **P** *020 †75
LOFTIS, John R, Jr. 1705 JUDSON RD 75601 #004-01-1944 L1949 **OPH** *071 †35
LUCAS, Franz Julius. ■ 75601 #407-04-1947 L1960 **AN** *071
LUCAS, John Richard. 1111 N 6TH ST 75601 #048-02-1966 L1966 **GYN GP** *020 †30
MACK, John Benj. 703 E MARSHALL AVE, STE 4003 75601 #048-04-1987 L1989 **GS** *020 †85
MARSHALL, Berry Neil. 800 PADON ST 75601 #048-02-1957 L1957 **GP** *071
MARSHALL, G Kenneth. 717 N 4TH ST 75601 #028-03-1974 L1977 **FM** *020 †18
MARTIN, Andrew J. 700 E MARSHALL AVE 75601 #048-02-1998 L2005 **VIR** *020 †80
MARTIN, Charles Randall. 703 E MARSHALL AVE STE 30 75601 #048-02-1987 L1989 **PUD CCM** *020 †20
MARTIN, Laura Mc Alpin. 703 E MARSHALL AVE, STE 4002 75601 #047-05-1985 L1989 **AN** *020 †05
MARTIN, Rodney Brown. 901 PEGUES PL 75601 #021-05-1968 L1969 **OTO** *020 †45
MARTIN, Theresa Clark. 707 HOLLYBROOK DR 75605 #048-02-1993 L1994 **OBG** *020 †30
MARTINEZ, Catherine Meiti. 709 HOLLYBROOK DR, STE 3400 75605 #011-03-1993 L2004 **PCC** *020 †20
MASSENBURG, Bryan E. 700 E MARSHALL AVE 75601 #048-15-1999 L2000 **FM** *020 †18
MAULDIN, James E, Jr. 2904 N 4TH ST, STE 101A 75605 #048-04-1981 L1981 **OBG** *020 †30
MC CASH, Wray B. ■ 75601 #048-02-1952 L1952 **D** *071 †15
MC CLURE, Ken E, Jr. 701 E MARSHALL AVE STE 310 75601 #036-08-1996 L2003 **IM** *020
MC CRARY, Kevin W. 700 E MARSHALL AVE 75601 #048-13-1992 L1998 **R RNR** *020 †80
MC CRORY, Kathleen A. 705 E MARSHALL AVE, STE 1002 75601 #048-78-1995, ▲ L1996 **PD** *020 †55
MC DANIEL, Robert Carral. 2101 W LOOP 281 75604 #048-02-1968 L1968 **GP CLP** *020 †50
MC DONALD, De Ward D. 717 N 4TH ST 75601 #048-12-1955 L1955 **GP** *020
MC DONALD, Glenn A. 425 N FREDONIA ST, STE 100A 75601 #048-14-1990 L1991 **NEP IM** *020 †20
MC GEE, Mary Katherine. 425 N FREDONIA ST, STE 100B 75601 #048-02-1984 L1986 **NEP IM** *020 †20
MC GREDE, Henry C, Jr. ■ 75603 #048-12-1945 L1945 **GYN** *071 †30
MC QUAID, Kevin James. 410 N 4TH ST 75601 #010-02-1984 L1994 **PTH** *020 †50
MEEK, Craig A. 700 E MARSHALL AVE, EMERGENCY DEPARTMENT 75601 #048-12-1992 L1993 **EM** *020 †16
MEEK, Suzanne M. 700 E MARSHALL AVE, GOOD SHEPHERD HOSPITAL 75601 #048-12-1993 L1994 **EM** *020 †16
MENDENHALL, Brian William. 700 E MARSHALL AVE 75601 #048-13-1994 L1998 **EM** *020 †16
MERRITT, Daniel B, Jr. 703 E MARSHALL AVE # 4003 75601 #048-16-1996 L1998 **GS** *020 †85
MESCHKE, Michael Allen. ■ 75605 #048-13-1973 L1973 **OM GPM** *030 †70 ‡
MIAN, Abbas Raza. 701 E MARSHALL AVE, STE 412 75601 #704-09-1997 L2006 **IM** *020 †20
MITCHELL, Oliver Clayton. 1511 JUDSON RD, STE A 75601 #021-05-1961 L1966 **OTO OS** *020
MORRIS, Michael W. 805 MEDICAL DR 75605 #048-12-1997 L1998 **FM** *020 †18
MORTON, Allen Ross. 2024 VILLA LN 75604 #027-01-1987 L1994 **AN PME** *020 †05
MORTON, Margaret Lucius. 707 HOLLYBROOK DR, 707 HOLLYBROOK 75605 #027-01-1990 L1994 **OBG** *020 †30
MORTON, Randy Loren. 3209 N 4TH ST, STE 300 75605 #048-02-1983 L1983 **GS** *020 †85
MOULDS-MERRITT, Christine. ■ 75601 #048-16-1992 L1993 **GS** *020 †85
MUIRHEAD, Joel Thomas. 1205 N 6TH ST, HEATON EYE ASSOCIATES 75601 #027-01-1993 L2003 **OPH** *020 †35
MULLIKIN, Gerald G. ■ 75601 #048-12-1948 L1948 **AN** *071 †05
NAYINI, Krishna Reddy. 402 N 7TH ST 75601 #495-21-1968 L1980 **CD IM** *020 †20
NAYINI, Rama Devi. 915 N 4TH ST 75601 #495-21-1973 L1981 **PUD** *020 †20
NEWKIRK, Charles Floyd. 2901 N 4TH ST 75605 #048-13-1972 L1972 **CD** *020 †20
NICHOLS, James A. 700 E MARSHALL AVE, GOOD SHEPHERD MEDICAL CENT 75601 #048-12-1991 L1993 **EM** *020 †16
NORMAN, Wayman Bowers. ■ 75601 #048-12-1946 L1946 **OTO** *071 †45
OZMENT, Angela Christine. 700 E MARSHALL AVE, DEPARMENT OF RADIOLOGY 75601 #048-12-1995 L2001 **EM** *071 †16
PACKARD, Teresa Faye. 703 E MARSHALL AVE, STE 3000 75601 #048-15-1990 L1991 **OBG** *020 †30
PARKS, Garland Leon. ■ 75605 #039-01-1967 L1984 **GP OM** *071
PARSI, Pake. 700 E MARSHALL AVE 75601 #517-01-1964 L1976 **OBG** *071 †30
PARVEEN, Rozina. 701 E MARSHALL AVE STE 4 75601 #160-01-1994 L2007 **IM** *020 †20
PAYNE, Gregory N. 700 E MARSHALL AVE, DEPARMENT OF RADIOLOGY 75601 #048-12-1992 L1994 **IM** *020 †20,16
PELTZER, Marc Yves. 2901 N 4TH ST 75605 #005-02-1986 L1993 **R** *020 †80
PERKINS, William David. 701 E MARSHALL AVE 75601 #027-01-1984 L1988 **N** *020 †75
PHILLIPS, Deborah Kay. 703 E MARSHALL AVE, STE 3005 75601 #048-13-1989 L1990 **D** *020 †15
PIERSON, Donald Arthur. 2901 N 4TH ST 75605 #048-02-1973 L1973 **FM** *020 †18
PISTONE, Joseph A. 700 E MARSHALL AVE, GOOD SHEPHERD MED CTR EMGY 75601 #042-02-1998 L2001 **FM EM** *020 †18
PLAN, Alejandro Barba. 903 WALNUT HILL DR STE 2 75605 #748-01-1979 L1992 **END IM** *020 †20
PRICE, Clinton Conell. 2300 BILL OWENS PKWY 75604 #048-02-1988 L2002 **P CHP** *020 †75 ‡
PRICE, Kellous A. 800 PADON ST, P O BOX 3587 75601 #048-15-1997 L2003 **OTO** *020 †45
PULIPAKA, Uma Prabha. 701 E MARSHALL AVE, STE 502 75601 #495-62-1990 L2002 **N CN** *020 †75
RANGU, Srinivas Goud. 703 E MARSHALL AVE, INTERNAL MEDICINE 75601 #495-98-1992 L2000 **IMG** *020 †20
RANKIN, Ted Leroy. 700 E MARSHALL AVE 75601 #048-12-1959 L1959 **PTH** *071 †50
RASHEED, Kareem S. 703 E MARSHALL AVE, STE 4006 75601 #495-33-1974 L1984 **AN** *020 †05
RASHEED, Meena. 3211 N 4TH ST 75605 #495-94-1975 L1985 **AN** *020
REDDY, Rekha Salguti. 2131 S MOBBERLY AVE 75602 #496-01-1989 L2002 **IM** *020
REDDY, Sanjay Gopala. 703 E MARSHALL AVE, STE 1001 75601 #496-33-1997 L2008 **IM** *100
REDDY, Venkateshwar S. 425 N FREDONIA ST, STE 100A 75601 #495-33-1988 L1998 **NEP IM** *020 †20
REESOR, Kenneth Eugene. 409 N 6TH ST 75601 #020-12-1984 L1992 **ORS** *020 †40
REMENCHIK, Ellen Jean. 707 HOLLYBROOK DR, DIAGNOSTIC CLINIC OF LONGV 75605 #048-16-1984 L1985 **IM OM** *020 †70,20
RIDDLE, Napoleon Brannon. 605 N 6TH ST 75601 #021-05-1956 L1957 **FM GP** *020
ROBERTS, Karen Louise. 707 HOLLYBROOK DR 75605 #048-12-1979 L1979 **PD** *020 †55
ROBERTS, Michael C. 703 E MARSHALL AVE, STE 4006 75601 #048-15-1996 L1998 **AN** *020 †05
ROE, Lawrence H, Jr. 703 E MARSHALL AVE, INTERNAL MEDICINE 75601 #046-01-1984 L1997 **IM** *020 †20
ROGERS, Jason. ■ 75605 #016-42-2002 L2005 **EM** *100
ROTZLER, William H. 707 HOLLYBROOK DR STE S400 75605 #048-02-1983 L1983 **OTO** *020 †45
SADLER, David Lee. 701 E MARSHALL AVE, STE 504 75601 #048-12-1974 L1974 **TS GS** *020 †85,90
SAFARIMARYAKI, Shahrokh. 3211 N 4TH ST, STE A 75605 #654-01-1987 L1999 **P CHP** *020
SAIKIN, George Michael. 709 HOLLYBROOK DR, STE 4500 75605 #048-02-1978 L1978 **IM** *020
SANSOME, Robert Jos. 703 E MARSHALL AVE, INTERNAL MEDICINE 75601 #048-13-1973 L1976 **IM** *020 †20
SAWYER, James Watson. 701 E MARSHALL AVE, STE 310 75601 #001-02-1976 L1978 **IM** *020 †20

■ = Address Information Privacy Protected

SCHOTTSTAEDT, Margaret Wa. 1805 S MOBBERLY AVE, BEACON HOSP 75602 #048-04-1976 L1979 **PLM ON** *020 †20 ‡

SCOTT, Ronald Alan. 402 N 7TH ST 75601 #048-14-1983 L1983 **CD IM** *020 †20

SCOTT, Thomas Lane. ■ 75602 #051-04-1979 L1979 **IM** *020 †20

SCRIBNER, Anita Neill. 709 HOLLYBROOK DR, STE 4500 75605 #048-13-1994 L1997 **ID** *020 †20

SHAKAMURI, Shobha. 425 N FREDONIA ST, STE 100A 75601 #495-21-1974 L1985 **NEP IM** *020

SHARMA, Neeraj Roshanlal. 1300 N 4TH ST, LONGVIEW CANCER CENTER 75601 #495-96-1988 L2001 **ON HEM** *020 †20

SHEA, Jeffrey M. 709 HOLLYBROOK DR STE 4500 75605 #048-14-1988 L1989 **PCC** *020 †20

SHEN, Hong I. 3100 N 4TH ST, SHEN MED ASSOC 75605 #048-13-1998 L1999 **FM** *020 †18

SHIRLEY, Robert M. ■ 75604 #048-15-2003 L2008 **GS** *012

SIGTENHORST, Georg D. 701 E MARSHALL AVE, STE 504 75601 #048-12-1987 L1988 **TS** *020 †85,90

SINGH, Rajeev. 709 HOLLYBROOK DR STE 2301, HOUSTON CARDIOVASCULAR CON 75605 #495-92-1990 L2000 **CD** *020 †20

SKARDA, Cori Elena. 701 E MARSHALL AVE, STE 310 75601 #034-01-2000 L2003 **IM** *020 ‡

SLADE, Theodore Leigh. 701 E MARSHALL AVE STE 410 75601 #048-02-1976 L1976 **NS** *020 †25

SLONE, Rodney Bayron. 703 E MARSHALL AVE, INTERNAL MEDICINE 75601 #048-12-1979 L1979 **GO** *020 †20

SMITH, Alex J. 2021 W LOOP 281 75604 #048-02-1993 L1996 **IM** *020

SMITH, George R. ■ 75605 #048-12-1989 L1990 **IM** *020 †20

SMITH, Larry Lamar. 2901 N 4TH ST 75605 #048-06-1981 L1985 **D** *020 †15

SMITH, Raelanda Elaine. 1107 E MARSHALL AVE 75601 #021-01-1997 L1999 **PD** *020 †55

SOMERVILLE, Stephen P. 709 HOLLYBROOK DR, STE 5600 75605 #048-12-1976 L1980 **PTH** *020 †50

SOMMERHALDER, Alberto P. 700 E MARSHALL AVE 75601 #132-01-1968 L1977 **DR NM** *020 †28,80

SREEMANNARAYANA, Jampana. 1603 JUDSON RD 75601 #495-62-1975 L1985 **IM** *020 †20

STANLEY, Jordan Gay. 409 N 6TH ST 75601 #021-06-1994 L1995 **ORS** *020 †40

STEPHENS, William C. 1705 JUDSON RD 75601 #021-05-1951 L1955 **OTO** *071 †45

STEPHENSON, Georgia Spenc. 1705 JUDSON RD 75601 #048-02-1998 L2002 **OPH** *020 †35

STEPHENSON, Wm Kenneth. 409 N 6TH ST 75601 #048-12-1968 L1968 **ORS GP** *071 †40

STETZNER, Larry Chas. PO BOX 7444 75607 #026-04-1974 L1984 **OM FM** *020 †70,18

STEVENS, Alexander C. ■ 75601 #048-02-1952 L1952 **GS** *071 †85

SUITS, Jason P. 703 E MARSHALL AVE, STE 4003 75601 #048-16-1999 L2004 **GS** *020 †85

TARBUTTON, George Lester. ■ 75605 #027-01-2002 L2007 **GPM** *020

TAYLOR, Bernard Wm. 1300 N 4TH ST, LONGVIEW CANCER CENTER 75601 #048-14-1986 L1987 **RO GS** *020 †80

TAYLOR, Harold R. 2901 N 4TH ST 75605 #048-12-1984 L1986 **EM** *020

TAYLOR, Michael Byron. 2901 N 4TH ST 75605 #048-02-1978 L1978 **EM** *020

TAYLOR, Thomas Griffin. 409 N 6TH ST 75601 #048-12-1977 L1977 **ORS** *020 †40

THARP, Warren B. 915 PEGUES PL 75601 #021-01-1946 L1949 **PD AI** *071

THOMSON, Mary E. 323B N HIGH ST 75601 #048-15-1991 L1992 **IM** *071

TIBILETTI, Francis James. 701 E MARSHALL AVE, STE 309 75601 #048-15-1987 L1988 **OBG** *020 †30

TOBIN, Timothy Michael. 709 HOLLYBROOK DR, STE 4500 75605 #028-03-1989 L2000 **IM** *020 †20 ‡

TOMPKINS, Robert T. 703 E MARSHALL AVE, INTERNAL MEDICINE 75601 #048-13-1991 L1992 **IM** *020 †20

UPCHURCH, Stan D. 700 E MARSHALL AVE, DEPARMENT OF RADIOLOGY 75601 #048-12-1992 L1994 **EM** *020 †16

URETSKY, Gordon Glenn. 2901 N 4TH ST 75605 #048-14-1981 L1981 **FM EM** *020 †18

VAN BURKLEO, Julia M B. 703 E MARSHALL AVE, STE 5007 75601 #048-12-1957 L1957 **GYN** *020

VAN SICKLE, Herman Ray. 700 E MARSHALL AVE 75601 #048-02-1963 L1963 **GP** *071

WADLEY, Byron Richard. 1800 W LOOP 281, STE 204 75604 #048-02-1981 L1981 **P AN** *020 †05,75

WALDROP, Mylynda C. 705 E MARSHALL AVE, # 1002 75601 #048-14-2000 L2003 **PD** *020

WALLIS, Mark S. 6 DOCTOR CIR 75605 #048-13-1988 L1989 **D** *020 †15

WALTER, Stephen L. 410 N 4TH ST 75601 #048-13-1996 L1998 **HMP** *020 †50

WALTRIP, Alexandra F. ■ 75605 #020-02-1999 L2000 **GS** *100

WALTRIP, Todd J. 703 E MARSHALL AVE STE 400 75601 #048-04-1994 L2000 **GS** *020 †85

WARDEN, Russell Page. 709 HOLLYBROOK DR, STE 4500 75605 #048-02-1981 L1981 **IM** *020 †20

WASSEF, Joseph Soliman I. 3400 W MARSHALL AVE, STE 426 75604 #915-04-1977 L1992 **CHP** *020 †75

WATKINS, Sanford Eugene. 709 HOLLYBROOK DR STE 4500 75605 #030-06-1998 L2006 **IM** *100

WHEELER, Robert Mc Kinney. 707 HOLLYBROOK DR 75605 #048-04-1979 L1979 **OBG** *020 †30 ‡

WHITE, Faber Allen, III. 700 E MARSHALL AVE, EMERGENCY DEPARTMENT 75601 #004-01-2001 L2005 **ESM** *100 †16

WILLIAMS, Charles Randall. 804 MEDICAL CIR DR 75605 #048-02-1980 L1980 **ORS** *020 †40

WILLIAMS, Mark Johnston. 703 E MARSHALL AVE STE 4002 75601 #048-13-1986 L1988 **AN PME** *020 †05

WILLIAMS, Paul Brian. 703 E MARSHALL AVE, STE 5008 75601 #021-06-1994 L1999 **U** *020 †95

WITT, David R, II. 805 MEDICAL DR 75605 #048-14-1997 L1998 **FM** *020 †18 ‡

WOMACK, Stephen Lee. 906 N 6TH ST 75601 #039-01-1978 L1996 **PD** *020 †55

WOOD, Johnny D. 703 E MARSHALL AVE, STE 3000 75601 #048-13-1989 L1990 **OBG** *020 †30

WOODSON, James Thomas. 700 E MARSHALL AVE, DEPT OF EMERGENCY MED 75601 #039-01-1999 L2002 **EM** *020 †16

YANCEY, Christopher A. 709 HOLLYBROOK DR 75605 #048-14-1990 L1991 **OBG** *020 †30

YU, Adam Jing-Cheng. 703 E MARSHALL AVE, STE 3008 75601 #244-05-1988 L1996 **PCC IM** *020 †20

ZVOLANEK, Ervin Edward. ■ 75604 #048-12-1965 L1965 **R** *071 †80

LORAINE – MITCHELL

TERRY, Joseph Crane. 901 S KINDRED 79532 #048-02-1947 L1947 **FM** *071

LORENA – MCLENNAN

BENHAM, Melisa B. ■ 76655 #048-13-1985 L1986 **IM** *020 †20

SIMON, H Jos. ■ 76655 #007-02-1943 L1944 **P N** *071

SMITH, Robert Bruce. ■ 76655 #048-02-1962 L1962 **P** *071 †75

LOS FRESNOS – CAMERON

HAMAMCY, Tharwat M. RR 3 BOX 339A 78566 #330-03-1966 L1982 **GS** *075

KOKERNOT, Robert H. ■ 78566 #048-04-1950 L1950 **GPM EM** *075 †70,18

LOUISE – WHARTON

OCHOA, Robert Anthony. ■ 77455 #048-02-2004 **GS** *012

LUBBOCK – LUBBOCK

ABOUTALEBI, Sina. ■ 79416 #048-15-2005 **D** *012

ADAMS, Edna Patricia. ■ 79414 #036-05-2001 L2006 **PD** *020

AGLER, Karen S. 6104 AVENUE Q SOUTH DR 79412 #048-16-1984 L1985 **IM** *020 †20

AJMAL, Shajeea. ■ 79424 #048-15-2008 *012

AKIN, Russell Scott. 3601 4TH ST STOP 9400, TEXAS TECH DERMATOLOGY 79430 #048-15-2005 L2007 **D** *012

AKINS, Robin Scott. 3601 4TH ST, RM 1A115 79430 #048-15-2001 L2004 **RO** *012

AL-ALAMI, Bachar A. 3813 22ND ST STE E 79410 #264-08-1985 L1992 **PD** *020

ALALAWI, Raed Hashim. ■ 79416 #695-01-1997 L2003 **IM** *100

AL AYOUBI, Mohamad. 3506 21ST ST STE 60 79410 #875-02-1998 L2004 **IM** *020

ALI, Mohammed Hyder. ■ 79414 #048-15-2006 L2006 **IM** *012

ALI, Muhammed Fa. 5501 50TH ST, # 1204 79414 #033-05-1996 L2004 **ICE** *020 †20

AL-KHARRAT, Houssam M. 2424 50TH ST, RM 300 79412 #875-01-1995 L1998 **GE** *020 †20

ALKUL, Mohamed Jamil. 3606 21ST ST, STE 102 79410 #875-01-1979 L1994 **PD** *020 †55

ALLAS, Jose Maria E O. 3801 50TH ST STE 5 79413 #748-01-1982 L1991 **FM GS** *020 †18

ALLEN, Ted Wayne. 3611 22ND PL 79410 #048-04-1966 L1966 **GS** *020 †85

ALLISON, Kevin Lee. 3812 24TH ST 79410 #030-05-1985 L1990 **OPH** *020 †35 ‡

ALTAMIMI, Hamed A. ■ 79424 #575-01-1992 L2007 **GE** *020 †20 ‡

ANDERSON, Jared Dean. ■ 79414 #048-15-2008 *012

ANDERSON, Paul Jos. 4302 22ND PL 79410 #010-01-1988 L1995 **RO** *020 †80

ANSLEY, Leslie R. ■ 79424 #048-15-1952 L1952 **GYN** *071

ANURAS, Jitra. 4828 11TH ST 79416 #891-01-1968 L1985 **AI IM** *020 †20,03

ARANDIA ANTELO, Luis F. 4020 21ST ST, STE 2 79410 #132-03-1982 L1995 **PD** *020

ARCHIBALD, Rowena. 25 BRIERCROFT OFFICE PARK 79412 #017-20-1980 L2004 **OM** *020 †70

ARENTZ BROWN, Suellen Can. HEALTH SCIENCE, TEXAS TECH UNIV 79430 #048-02-2004 **GS** *012

ARLEDGE, Patricia R. 3519 22ND PL 79410 #048-15-1994 L2000 **PS** *020 †15

ARMSTRONG, Michael Keeth. 3525 19TH ST 79410 #048-02-1966 L1966 **DR** *020 †80

ARNOLD, Robert N. ■ 79424 #048-02-1949 L1949 **GYN** *071 †30

ARONOFF, David Randall. 7727 QUAKER AVE, A FAMILY UROLOGY & GYNECOL 79424 #011-04-1991 L2001 **U** *020 †95

ARREDONDO, Esteban R. 3601 4TH ST STOP 8182, TEXAS TECH UNIVERSITY HSC 79430 #048-15-2003 L2007 **GS** *100

ARREDONDO, Rachel A. ■ 79407 #048-15-2005 **AN** *100

ARVANDI, Aliakbar. HEALTH SCIENCE, TEXAS TECH UNIV 79430 #517-03-1993 **CD** *012 †20

ARZE, Annelise Ximena. ■ 79414 #176-03-2001 **P** *012

ASH, Weldon Lloyd. 2424 50TH ST RM 203 79412 #048-02-1966 L1966 **FM P** *020 ‡

ASMUSSEN, Maurice Dwayne. ■ 79407 #048-15-1987 L1990 **PD** *020 †55

ATKINSON, Billy Don. 4102 24TH ST 79410 #048-02-1982 L1983 **OBG** *020 †30

ATTAR, Monzer. 3425 22ND PL 79410 #605-01-1962 L1968 **GE IM** *020

ATTAYA, Eman Nabil. ■ 79407 #048-15-2005 L2007 **DR** *012

ATTAYA, Hesham Nabil. ■ 79407 #048-15-2008 *012

ATTAYA, Nabil Mostafa. 4102 24TH ST STE 403 79410 #330-03-1964 L1976 **CD IM** *020 †20

AURINGER, Michael Paul. 5915 82ND ST 79424 #048-14-1984 L1988 **FM** *020 †18

AZATIAN, Ashot G. 3615 19TH ST 79410 #913-38-1986 L2002 **P** *020 †75

BACCHI-SMITH, Donna. 3017 19TH ST 79410 #038-41-1981 L1985 **PD PHP** *040 †55

BADGWELL, Jon Michael. 3601 4TH ST, STOP 8182 79430 #048-04-1971 L1971 **AN PD** *020 †05

BAIDWAN, Rajvinder Singh. ■ 79424 #048-15-2008 *012

BAKDASH, Mohammad Marwan. 4515 MARSHA SHARP FWY, GRACE CLINIC 79407 #875-01-1970 L1974 **IM END** *020 †20 ‡

BAKER, Charles Eugene. 3601 4TH ST 79430 #048-04-1957 L1957 **ORS** *071 †40

BAKER, Chas Richard F, Jr. DEPARTMENT OF SURGERY, TEXAS TECH HEALTH SCIENCES 79430 #023-07-1961 L1969 **GS TRS** *071 †85

BAKER, James Deuon. ■ 79424 #048-12-1962 L1962 **AN** *020 †05

BAKER, Laura Kyle. 3601 4TH ST, TEXAS TECH UNIVERSITY 79415 #048-15-1981 L1981 **FM** *020 †18

BAKER, Robert Edward. 3506 21ST ST 79410 #048-12-1958 L1958 **OPH** *020 †35

BALCH, Michael Tol. 3805 22ND ST, STE B 79410 #048-02-1976 L1976 **IM** *020 †20

BALDWIN, Nevan Geo. 3601 21ST ST 79410 #035-06-1983 L2001 **NS** *020 †25

BALE, Bradley Field. 3506 21ST ST 79410 #020-12-1974 L2007 **FM CD** *020 †18

BALL, Corey D. 3601 4TH ST, DEPT OF INTERNAL MED 79430 #048-15-2003 L2005 **NEP** *012 †20

BANISTER, Melinda Dawn. 3601 4TH ST STOP 8312 79430 #030-05-1998 L2003 **GS** *020 †85

BANISTER, Ronald Earl. 3601 4TH ST, ANESTHESIOLOGY DEPARTMENT 79430 #021-01-1998 L2000 **AN** *020 †05

BARKER, Craig W. 7202 SLIDE RD STE 100 79424 #048-15-1998 L1999 **FM** *020 †18

BARRANDA, R L. ■ 79413 #748-07-1965 L1976 **PD** *020 †55

BARRETT, George C. 2420 QUAKER AVE 79410 #036-05-1952 L1952 **R** *071 †80

BARROW, Boone. 3601 4TH ST 79430 #048-15-1998 L1999 **FM FSM** *020 †18

BARTEE, Barry Kyle. 3234 64TH ST 79413 #048-15-1999 *100

BARTON, Charles D. 3615 19TH ST 79410 #030-05-1975 L1985 **EM FM** *020 †18,16

BASIT, Shazia. 3601 4TH ST 79430 #704-16-1996 **P** *012

BATRA, Subhash Chand. 2424 50TH ST RM 201 79412 #495-45-1979 L1995 **GE IM** *020 †20

BATRA, Swaran Lata. 416 FRANKFORD AVE 79416 #495-69-1979 L1995 **IM** *020 †20

BAYOUTH, Charles Victor. 3509 22ND ST 79410 #048-02-1997 L1998 **GS** *020 †85
BECEIRO, Jose R. 3801 50TH ST 79413 #847-05-1964 L1974 **END IM** *020 †20
BECK, George Preston. 4601 18TH ST 79416 #048-02-1955 L1955 **AN AM** *071 †05
BECK, Howard Wilbanks. 6102 82ND ST 79424 #048-02-1986 L1987 **U** *020 †95
BECK, Suzanne Adams. 3502 22ND ST 79410 #048-02-1986 L1987 **AI PDA** *020 †03,55
BEHNKE, Carolyn M. 3420 22ND PL 79410 #048-02-1988 L1990 **AN** *020 †05
BELLE-HENRY, Christina. 3614 23RD ST 79410 #001-06-1997 L1998 **OBG** *020 †30
BELLO-REUSS, Elsa Noemi. 3601 4TH ST STOP 9410 79430 #231-01-1964 L1989 **NEP** *050
BELLOTTE, Brent William. THOMPSON HALL 79430 #055-01-2001 L2003 **OPH** *020 †35
BELTZ, Louis Jos, Jr. 3420 22ND PL 79410 #023-12-1990 L2003 **AN GP** *020 †05
BENNETT, Kelly A. 3601 4TH ST, STE 1C143 79430 #048-16-1995 L1996 **FM** *020 †18
BENSON, Kenneth Herbert. 6102 82ND ST 79424 #048-15-1975 L1976 **U** *020 †95
BERGFELD, Scott Doug. 3821 22ND PL, STE A 79410 #030-05-1981 L1993 **FM FPG** *020 †18
BERK, Steven L. 3601 4TH ST, STOP 6207 79430 #024-05-1975 L2002 **IM ID** *040 †20
BERMAN, Daniel Winter. 602 INDIANA AVE, EMERGENCY CENTER 79415 #035-46-1999 L2001 **EM** *020 †16
BETHI, Siddharth. 3601 4TH ST, STOP 8413 79430 #496-50-2000 **IM** *012
BETHUNE, Kimberly M. ■ 79423 #048-15-1993 L1994 **END** *100 †20
BETTS, William B. 3502 9TH ST STE 240, UNIVERSITY MEDICAL CENTER 79415 #048-13-1988 L1989 **NS VN** *020
BHATIA, Narinder P Singh. 3601 4TH ST, DEPT OF PEDIATRICS STOP 94 79430 #495-45-1984 L1998 **CCP** *020 †55
BHATT, Rajat Suresh. 3601 4TH ST, TEXAS TECH. 79430 #496-46-1999 L2007 **IM** *020
BICKLEY, Lynn S. 3601 4TH ST MS 8326 79430 #035-45-1982 L2003 **IM GPM** *040 †20
BILTOFT, Emily Christine. ■ 79410 #048-15-2008 L2008 *012
BIRCHFIELD, Vance. 602 INDIANA AVE, EMER DEPT 79415 #048-15-1996 L1997 **FM** *020 †18
BIRD, Colin Patrick. ■ 79424 #048-15-2007 **GS** *012
BIRKHOLZ, Christopher Jam. ■ 79413 #048-15-2008 *012
BISHARA, Angele. ■ 79424 #915-02-1970 L1975 **AN PME** *075
BISHARA, Nabil Ghabriel. 6610 QUAKER AVE 79413 #915-02-1962 L1976 **ORS PM** *071
BITTLE, Chas Carroll, Jr. 3601 4TH ST, TTUHSC DEPT OF PHARMACOLOG 79430 #048-13-1984 L1986 **FM IM** *030
BLACKWELL, David Eric. 3601 4TH ST, TTUHSC MS8340 79430 #036-05-1973 L1976 **OS** *020
BLACKWOOD, William Dean. 2424 50TH ST, RM 302 79412 #048-02-1955 L1955 **GE IM** *071 †20
BLANCAS-TIEMANN, Kirk. ■ 79416 #048-15-2005 L2008 **FP** *012
BLANCO, Holly Michelle. ■ 79413 #048-15-2008 *012
BLANN, David W. 2102 OXFORD AVE 79410 #048-15-1995 L1996 **OBG** *020 †30
BLANN, Melissa M. 2424 50TH ST, RM 303 79412 #048-15-1997 L1998 **PTH** *020 †50
BLISS, Shannon Dee. ■ 79416 #048-15-2006 **IM** *012
BLOCK, Steven Clark. 3610 24TH ST, LUBBOCK DIGESTIVE DISEASE 79410 #048-04-1982 L1983 **GE IM** *020 †20
BLOOM, Robert Franklin. 3413 20TH ST 79410 #016-43-1973 L1978 **GS D** *020 †15
BODHIREDDY, Surender R. 2424 50TH ST, RM 303 79412 #495-65-1979 L1997 **PTH NP** *020 †50
BOLOTAULO, Claire Aileen. HLTH SCIENCES, TEXAS TECH UNIV 79430 #748-01-1999 **FP** *012
BOLTON, Jack A, Jr. 3601 4TH ST STOP 8182, TEXAS TECH UNIVERSITY HSC 79430 #048-15-1990 L1992 **AN** *020 †05
BOOP, James Jeffrey. 3008 50TH ST STE F 79413 #035-09-1983 L1987 **OPH** *020
BOOTHE, William David. 4020 21ST ST STE 3 79410 #048-15-1979 L1979 **OPH** *020 †35
BORIS, Glenn Jos. 3204 44TH ST, STE 107 79413 #056-06-1969 L1975 **PD** *062 †55
BORNO, Mounir Y. 4802 N LOOP 289 79416 #915-02-1982 L1995 **CD** *020 †20
BOSE, Sanjay. ■ 79416 #495-36-1992 L1997 **IM** *020 †20
BOSSCHER, Hemmo A. 3505 22ND PL 79410 #660-06-1987 L1997 **APM AN** *020 †05
BOSWELL, David Louis. 3601 4TH ST, DEPT OF ANESTHESIOLOGY 79430 #048-15-2005 L2007 **AN** *012
BOSWELL, Mark Vance. 3601 4TH ST STOP 8182, TX TECH UNIVERSITY HSC 79430 #038-06-1984 L2006 **AN PME** *020 †05
BOTROS, Ramzi Guergeus. ■ 79424 #330-02-1955 L1967 **OBG GS** *071
BOURGEOIS, Michael Jos. 3601 4TH ST, TTMC PEDIATRICS 79430 #021-06-1975 L1979 **PD PDE** *040 †55
BOWMAN, Thomas A. ■ 79413 #048-15-2005 L2008 **PD** *012
BOYD, Allison Lea. ■ 79416 #048-15-2008 *012
BOYD, Robert Clinton. 4601 50TH ST, STE 112 79414 #048-13-1980 L1980 **AN** *020
BOYD, Susan A. ■ 79493 #048-15-1992 **OBG** *100
BOYNTON, Steven E. 4515 MARSHA SHARP FWY 79407 #048-15-1995 L1996 **FM** *020 †18
BRACKEEN, Amy Rocky. 3601 22ND ST 79410 #048-16-2002 L2004 **D** *020 †15
BRADLEY, Jason T. 3514 21ST ST 79410 #048-15-1999 L2001 **IC** *020 †20 ‡
BRADLEY, Jay C. 105 N YORK AVE 79416 #048-15-2003 L2005 **OPH** *100
BRADSHAW, Todd Wesley. ■ 79416 #048-15-2008 *012
BRANDI, Luis Hristianis. 3601 4TH ST, DEPT PTH 79430 #422-01-2005 **PTH** *012
BRATVOLD, Jared Michael. ■ 79423 #037-01-2006 **GS** *012
BRICKER, Donald Lee. 4202 78TH ST, # 13 79423 #035-20-1959 L1969 **TS** *071 †85,90
BRIDWELL, Travis. 4102 24TH ST, STE 100 79410 #035-06-1956 L1962 **IM** *071
BRINDLEY, George West. 3601 4TH ST STOP 9436, DEPARTMENT OF ORTHOPAEDICS 79430 #048-02-1981 L1981 **ORS** *020 †40
BRISTOL, Benjamin Lee. ■ 79424 #008-02-1993 L1999 **FOP** *100 †50
BRITTON, Carl Lee, Jr. 3502 82ND ST 79423 #034-01-1991 L1993 **U** *020 †95
BRITTON, Charles H, III. ■ 79423 #048-12-1998 **GS** *100
BROCK, Eric Randall. 3601 4TH ST, DEPT OF ORTHO SURG 79430 #048-15-2004 **ORS** *012
BROGAN, Walter Chas. 5109 82ND ST, UNIT7 79424 #055-01-1986 L1991 **CD** *020 †20
BROOME, Edward Lindsay. 2215 NASHVILLE AVE 79410 #048-02-1972 L1972 **OBG** *020 †30
BROSELOW, Andrew Martin. 4102 24TH ST 79410 #048-15-1995 L1997 **OBG** *020 †30
BROSELOW, Robert Joel. 4009 19TH ST, STE E 79410 #041-09-1966 L1972 **GYN P** *020 †30
BROTHERS, Jorge R. 3805 22ND ST STE A 79410 #649-01-1970 L1986 **U** *020 †95
BROTHERS, Teresa Mouret. 8008 SLIDE RD STE 37B 79424 #649-01-1970 L1986 **CHP** *020
BROTMAN, Lawrence Danl. 3601 4TH ST, 2B-112 79430 #025-01-1964 L1983 **R** *020 †80
BROWN, Byron Linus. 3508 22ND PL 79410 #048-12-1980 L1980 **AN GP** *020 †05
BROWN, Cynthia Ruth. 3420 22ND PL 79410 #048-15-1986 L1987 **AN** *020 †05
BROWN, Paul F. 3506 21ST ST, STE 400 79410 #048-15-1987 L1988 **CHN N** *020 †75
BRUENING, Brian James. 4005 24TH ST 79410 #034-01-1985 L1987 **DR** *020 †80
BRUNER, Lia Pierson. 3601 4TH ST STOP 8143, DEPT OF FAMILY & COMMUNITY 79430 #024-01-2001 L2006 **FM** *020 †18
BUCHOK, Stephen Jos, Jr. 3601 4TH ST, MS 8103 79430 #048-13-1986 L1987 **P** *100 †05
BUESSELER, John Aure. ■ 79413 #056-05-1944 L1970 **MDM OPH** *071 †35
BURGETTE, Phillip L. 2424 50TH ST STE 20 79412 #028-46-1983 L2001 **OBG** *020
BURGUENO, Jorge Enrique. 3601 4TH ST 79430 #275-04-1995 **IM** *012
BURKE, Edward Bland. ■ 79423 #007-02-1958 L1959 **PD PHP** *071
BURKE, James. 3506 21ST ST 79410 #352-10-1969 L1981 **ORS** *020 †40
BURKE, Joanna L. 4102 24TH ST, STE 300 79410 #048-15-1999 L2002 **OBG** *020 †30
BURKHOLDER, Duncan Mark. 4515 MARSHA SHARP FWY 79407 #048-02-1983 L1983 **OBG** *020 †30
BURLEY, Ronnelle. 3711 22ND ST, STE B 79410 #011-04-1994 L1996 **OBG** *020 †30
BURRELL, James Harold. 3615 19TH ST 79410 #048-02-1972 L1972 **IM IMG** *020 †20
BUSCEMI, Dolores M. 3601 4TH ST, MAIL STOP 8300 79430 #048-15-1992 L1993 **IM** *020 †20
BUSCHMAN, Job Owen. 3509 22ND ST, SWAT SURGICAL ASSOCIATES 79410 #048-15-1982 L1983 **GS CRS** *020 †85
BUSE, Stephen L. 4515 MARSHA SHARP FWY 79407 #048-15-1996 L2000 **FM** *020 †18
BUSHAN, Naga S. 5220 80TH ST 79424 #495-65-1981 L1990 **RHU IM** *020 †20
BUSTI, Anthony James. 3601 4TH ST, TX TECH UNIV HLTH SCI CTR 79430 #048-15-2001 *100
BUTLER, Dana Andrew. 3307 82ND ST, UNIT J 79423 #048-15-1982 L1983 **P** *020 †75
BUTLER, Mary Rebecca. 4000 24TH ST 79410 #048-15-1986 L1988 **OBG** *020 †30
BUTLER, Rebecca Denise. ■ 79424 #048-15-2007 **PD** *012
BUTLER, Thomas C. 3601 4TH ST 79430 #047-05-1967 L1988 **IM** *050 †20
CABRERA, Leopoldo A. 3624 50TH ST STE D 79413 #748-08-1982 L1996 **PD** *020 †55
CALMES, James Michael. 5220 80TH ST 79424 #048-15-1980 L1980 **RHU** *020 †20
CAMP, Tammy M. 3601 4TH ST, TEXAS TECH UNIV HLTH SCI C 79430 #048-15-1994 L1995 **PD** *020 †55
CAMPBELL, Samuel Joe. 3601 4TH ST STOP 8312 79415 #048-15-1982 L1983 **VS GS** *020 †85
CAPPS, Harold Richard. 5427 25TH ST, TEXAS TECH UNIV HLTH SCI C 79407 #048-12-1973 L1973 **FM** *020 †18
CAPT, William Michael. ■ 79424 #048-15-2008 *012
CARR, Robert L. ■ 79413 #048-12-1951 L1951 **PD** *071 †55
CARR, Robert Vincent. 602 INDIANA AVE 79415 #048-15-1977 L1977 **ORS** *020 †40
CARRILLO, Jaime Orlando. 3601 4TH ST 79430 #319-01-1993 **IM** *012
CARTER, John Becton. 3601 4TH ST 79430 #048-02-1980 L1980 **AN** *020 †05
CARTER-SNODGRASS, P. 3801 50TH ST 79413 #048-15-1988 L1989 **GE** *020 †20
CASANOVA, Roberto. 3601 4TH ST, STOP 8340 79430 #048-12-1983 L1983 **OBG** *020 †30
CASLER, Travis Lebeau. ■ 79416 #048-02-1965 L1965 **ORS** *071 †40
CEBALLOS, Laura Narvaez. ■ 79413 #048-13-2005 L2008 **OBG** *012
CECALUPO, Anthony John. TEXAS TECH UNIV, DEPT OF PEDIATRICS 79430 #041-14-1974 L1979 **PHO** *020 †55
CERVENAK, Martha Ann. 3506 21ST ST STE 400 79410 #021-01-2003 **FSM** *020
CEVIK, Cihan. 3601 4TH ST 79430 #902-07-1999 **IM** *012
CHAMALES, Michael S. 3615 19TH ST 79410 #048-15-1995 L1996 **EM** *020 †16
CHAMBERS, Clint Edwin. 3506 21ST ST, STE 601 79410 #039-01-1959 L1976 **GS CRS** *071 †85,10
CHAN, Kwan-Ho. ■ 79416 #065-01-1978 L1994 **ORS** *062 †40
CHANDLER, Rachel Elizabet. ■ 79413 #048-15-2007 **IM** *012
CHAVEZ, Jennifer Ruth. ■ 79407 #048-12-2004 L2004 **IM** *100 †20
CHAVEZ, Marina. 6104 AVENUE Q, DEPT. OF MANAGED HLTH CARE 79412 #048-15-1987 L1988 **CHP** *020 †75
CHAVEZ, Pedro Nelson. 3606 21ST ST 79410 #264-01-1991 L2003 **CCP** *020 †55
CHAVEZ, Victor Sostenes. 5015 UNIV AVE UNIT B-1 79413 #034-01-1977 L1978 **UCM FM** *020
CHAYA, Craig John. 3601 4TH ST, DEPT OF OPHTHALMOLOGY/VISU 79430 #005-12-2002 L2004 **OPH** *012 †20
CHEKURU, Naidu Kothandra. 3621 22ND ST STE 400 79410 #495-70-1973 L1979 **IM** *020 †20
CHEKURU, Syamala. 3621 22ND ST STE 400 79410 #495-50-1974 L1979 **PM** *020 †60
CHEN, Hua. ■ 79416 #048-15-2008 *012
CHEN, Shen Siung. 3801 50TH ST STE 5 79413 #244-05-1968 L1978 **GP** *020 ‡
CHENGSON, Richard Anthony. 25 BRIERCROFT OFFICE PARK, 54TH & AVENUE Q 79412 #030-06-1978 L1979 **OM GP** *020
CHIARA, John Spencer. ■ 79415 #048-15-2008 *012
CHING, Ernesto Chan. 3501 22ND ST 79410 #011-02-1967 L1974 **TS** *020 †85,90
CHOKESUWATTANASKUL, Warang. ■ 79413 #891-04-1997 **CD** *012
CHOU, Jui-Lien. 4002 21ST ST, STE A 79410 #244-02-1980 L1986 **RO** *020 †80
CHUAHIRUN, Temduang. TEX TEC U HLTH SCI CTR, DEPT OF INT MED 79430 #891-02-1991 L1998 **NEP** *020 †20
CHUA-TUAN, James Antin. 3615 19TH ST 79410 #748-01-1973 L1977 **EM** *020 †16
CHUNG, Joanne Youn-Bok. 3601 4TH ST, 2B-112 79430 #048-02-1995 L2000 **DR** *020 †80
CHUNGCHANSAT, Kriengkrai. TX TECH SCHL MED STU HLTH 79430 #891-01-1972 L1976 **FM** *020 †18
CHUNGCHANSAT, Porntip. 427 SLIDE RD 79416 #891-01-1972 L1976 **FM** *020 †18
CINDRICH, Patrick Jos. 3502 9TH ST STE 240 79415 #019-02-1977 L1993 **NS** *020 †25
CLARK, James Ollie. ■ 79416 #048-15-2007 **ORS** *012
CLARK, Justin Wayne. 602 INDIANA AVE 79415 #048-02-1996 L1998 **D** *020 †15
CLEMMONS, Thomas J, Jr. 3615 19TH ST 79410 #021-01-1963 L1964 **FM PHP** *020
CLINTON, Stacy Janette. ■ 79416 #048-15-2008 *012
CLOSE, David Robt. 4101 22ND PL 79410 #007-02-1972 L1980 **GPM HEM** *020 †20
COBB, Elizabeth Anne. 3601 4TH ST, DEPARTMENT OF INTERNAL MED 79430 #048-15-2003 L2005 **NEP** *012 †20
COBB, John Michael. 6502 SLIDE RD, STE 311 79424 #048-15-2001 L2003 **P** *020 †75
COBOS, Everardo. 3601 4TH ST 79430 #048-13-1981 L1988 **HEM ON** *020 †20
COCHRAN, Beth Ann. HEALTH SCIENCE, TEXAS TECH UNIV 79430 #048-14-2005 **FP** *012
COCHRANE, Rochelle Deanne. ■ 79416 #005-12-2004 L2004 **OPH** *012
COCKINGS, Curt W. 3606 21ST ST STE 209 79410 #048-04-1989 L1990 **OPH PO** *020 †35
COGSWELL, Steven Chas. 4434 S LOOP 289 79414 #045-01-1985 L1986 **PTH** *020 †50
COLE, Jeanetta L. 3601 4TH ST STOP 8143, DEPARTMENT OF FAMILY MEDIC 79430 #048-15-1994 L1995 **FM** *020 †18
COLEMAN, Robyn G. 3420 22ND PL 79410 #048-13-1995 L1999 **AN** *020 †05
COLLS, Noel Reginald. ■ 79401 #048-15-2008 *012
COLON-LEDEE, Athos G. 3701 20TH ST STE B, DEPARTMENT OF PEDIATRICS 79410 #308-07-1983 L1996 **PDC** *020 †55
COLVIN, Jeffrey Norman. 3420 22ND PL 79410 #048-15-1986 L1987 **AN PME** *020 †05
COMBS, Steven H. 3506 21ST ST 79410 #048-15-1997 L2001 **IM** *020
CONE, Douglas Leigh. 2301 QUAKER AVE, SAINT MARY SURGI CENTER 79410 #048-02-1969 L1969 **AN** *020
CONNOR, Angie. ■ 79424 #041-07-1937 L1946 **PD PHP** *071 †55
CONTRERAS, Edwing Aldo. 3615 19TH ST 79410 #737-01-1969 L1979 **NPM PD** *020 †55
COOK, Ronald Lynn. 3601 4TH ST STOP 8143, TTU HEALTH SCIENCES CENTER 79430 #048-78-1993, ▲ L1994 **FM** *020 †18

■ = Address Information Privacy Protected

COOK, Seth Wayne. 3802 22ND PL 79410 #048-02-1995 L2000 **PTH** *020 †50
CORD, Stephen Archie. 4110 22ND PL 79410 #048-02-1977 L1977 **ORS** *020 †40
CORDERO, Joehassin. 3502 9TH ST, STE 410 79415 #051-07-1994 L2003 **OTO** *020 †45
CORONA, Rita E. ■ 79416 #048-13-2003 *100
COUCH, Matthew Harold. DEPARTMENT OF SURGERY, TEXAS TECH UNIV HEALTH SCI 79430 #143-11-2002 L2008 **GS** *012
COUCH, Robert Earl. 7501 QUAKER AVE 79424 #048-12-1989 L1990 **PD** *020 †55
COX, Cody Allen. 4005 24TH ST 79410 #048-15-1992 L1996 **DR** *020 †80
CRAIG, Donald Ray. 3502 9TH ST STE 130 79415 #048-02-1957 L1957 **PD** *020 †55
CRAWFORD, Kevin. 4110 22ND PL, LUBBOCK SPORTS MEDICINE 79410 #048-12-1992 L1993 **OSM** *020 †40
CREWS, Jonathan Daniel. ■ 79414 #048-15-2008 *012
CROOM, William Sterling. 3801 19TH ST STE 401 79410 #039-01-1948 L1953 **IM** *071 †20
CROSSNOE, Chetlen Ray. 4515 MARSHA SHARP FWY, GRACE CLINIC OF LUBBOCK 79407 #048-04-2003 L2005 **FM** *020 †18
CROW, Steven M. 7601 QUAKER AVE 79424 #048-15-1995 L1996 **FM** *020 †18
CRUCE, John Bill. ■ 79413 #048-15-1976 L1980 **OBG** *071
CRUZ, Janet Talusan. 1126 SLIDE RD UNIT 4B, KIDNEY CLNC OF LUBBOCK 79416 #748-02-1989 L1996 **NEP IM** *020 †20
CRUZ, Jose Carlos. 3601 4TH ST, DEPT OF INTERNAL MEDICINE 79430 #649-52-1989 L1995 **HO IM** *020 †20
CU, Irma Chua. ■ 79416 #748-10-1992 L2007 **P** *100
CULP, Lewis Wayne. 3420 22ND PL 79410 #048-12-1962 L1962 **FM** *071 †18
CUMMING-HOOD, Patricia A. 3601 4TH ST, MS 8143 79430 #048-15-1996 L1997 **FM** *020 †18
CUMMINGS, David A. 4101 22ND PL 79410 #048-15-1998 L1999 **ON** *020 †20
CURTIS, Brigitte. ■ 79416 #007-02-1987 L1993 **P** *020 †75
CUSHMAN, Walter H. 4005 24TH ST 79410 #048-13-1994 L1996 **DR** *020 †80
DABEZIES, Eugene Jean. 3601 4TH ST, STE 4A-097 79430 #021-01-1960 L1991 **ORS HS** *020 †40
DAFNIS, Eugenios K. LUBBOCK GEN HOSP 79409 #418-01-1978 **NEP** *020
DAHLBECK, Scott Weston. 4202 78TH ST, # 7 79423 #048-14-1992 L1997 **RO** *020 †18,80
D'ALISE, Mark D. 3601 21ST ST, NEUROSURGICAL ASSOC. L.L.P 79410 #034-01-1990 L1995 **NS** *020 †25
DANCHAK, Raymond Michael. 4601 5TH ST STE 11 79416 #010-02-1983 L1993 **AN CCM** *020 †05 ‡
DANIEL, Kimrey Janiece. ■ 79413 #048-02-2008 *012
DAVIDSON, Elizabeth Jane. 1602 10TH ST, LUBBOCK REGIONAL MHMR 79401 #034-01-1982 L1993 **P** *020 †75
DAVIS, D Richard, II. 3601 4TH ST 79430 #021-01-1961 L1961 **AN** *071 †05
DAVIS, Susan Rebecca. 2716 82ND ST 79423 #048-15-1984 L1985 **IM IMG** *020
DAVIS, William Jewell. 3508 22ND PL 79410 #048-15-1982 L1983 **AN** *020 †05
DAY, Miles R. 4430 S LOOP 289, INTERNATIONAL PLAIN INSTIT 79414 #048-16-1993 L1994 **APM AN** *020 †05
D'CRUZ, A Alex Z. 5120 29TH DR STE D, LUBBOCK NEUROLOGY PLLC 79407 #495-01-1972 L2000 **N NRN** *020 †75
D'CUNNA, Nicholas Cyril. 3601 4TH ST STOP 9410, TX TECH UNIV HLTH SCIENCES 79430 #495-17-1981 L2003 **HEM** *020 †20
DEANDA, Anita Cave. 3601 4TH ST STOP 7208, DR OF CHAMP & FLINT AVE 79430 #028-02-1986 L1992 **P** *020 †75
DEAVER, Jennifer D. ■ 79424 #048-15-2004 **D** *012
DEBOWSKI, Tomasz E. ■ 79430 #759-10-1981 L1997 **HMP PTH** *020 †50
DE BRITO, Dirk. 4811 2ND DR 79416 #035-01-1997 L2004 **P** *100 †16
DEEB, Emily A. 4501 50TH ST, STE 100 79414 #048-15-1995 L1996 **FM** *020 †18
DEEB, Sammy Anthony. 3509 22ND ST 79410 #048-15-1992 L1993 **GS** *072 †85
DEL GIUDICE, Jose A. 5220 80TH ST 79424 #308-01-1975 L1997 **RHU** *020 †20
DEMIRALP, Gozde. 3601 4TH ST 79430 #902-03-2002 **AN** *012
DENNIS, Allen Lee. ■ 79416 #048-02-2005 L2007 **AN** *012
DENTINO, Andrew Neal. 3601 4TH ST, MAIL STOP 8143 79430 #035-47-1989 L2002 **IMG PLM** *020 †20,75 ‡
DENTINO, Carole Marie. 4604 18TH ST 79416 #035-47-1990 L2002 **DR** *020 †80
DE RIESE, Cornelia. 3601 4TH ST, MS 8340 DEPT OBG 79430 #409-38-1979 L2003 **OBG** *040 †30
DE RIESE, Werner Tamme W. 3502 9TH ST STE 260 79415 #409-38-1979 L2002 *020 †95
DE SHAN, Preston W, Jr. ■ 79407 #039-01-1961 L1965 **OBG** *071 †30
DEVINE, Susan Robertson. 4403 6TH ST 79416 #048-15-1990 L1991 **OBG** *020 †30 ‡
DHIENSIRI, Chanin. ■ 79430 #891-04-1988 L1994 **END IM** *020 †20
DHILLON, Gurpreet Singh. 3601 4TH ST 79430 #917-08-1990 **GS** *012
DICKERSON, Sandra Dee. 4102 24TH ST 79410 #025-01-1983 L1995 **GS** *020 †85
DICKEY, John Coke. 3420 22ND PL 79410 #048-12-1959 L1959 **GYN** *020 †30
DIHENIA, Bhupesh Hasmukh. 3815 23RD ST 79410 #016-11-1992 L1997 **N SME** *020 †75
DIVINSKY, Ianir. 3601 4TH ST 79430 #132-01-1999 **IM** *012
DJAJADI, We-Min. ■ 79423 #048-15-2008 *012
DOCKRAY, Karl Thord. 1810 19TH ST 79401 #048-12-1961 L1961 **R NM** *020 †80,28
DOMINGUEZ, Leonardo Norbe. 3601 4TH ST, STOP 7217 79430 #132-01-1990 *100
DONALDSON, David Lance. 4005 24TH ST 79410 #048-12-1996 L1998 **RNR** *020 †80
DONALDSON, Matthew R. ■ 79401 #049-01-2006 **D** *012
DORSETT, Michael Mark. 3502 9TH ST STE 350 79415 #048-15-1979 L1979 **OBG** *020 †30
DORSETT, Mikal Janelle. 3405 22ND ST STE 30 79410 #048-13-1981 L1981 **OBG** *020 †30
DU BOSE, Clifton Edwin. ■ 79423 #048-12-1980 L1980 **AN** *020 †05
DU BOSE, Jack Edward. 7601 QUAKER AVE, COVENANT HEALTH PLUS 79424 #047-06-1970 L2004 **FM** *020 †18
DUMAIS, Jules Arthur. ■ 79416 #048-15-2004 **ORS** *012
DUNN, Cynthia G. 3614 23RD ST 79410 #048-15-1990 L1991 **OBG** *020 †30
DUNN, Dale Michael. 3601 4TH ST STOP 8115 79430 #065-06-1979 L1983 **PTH** *020 †50
DURIEX, Dennis E. 4404 19TH ST STE C 79407 #042-02-1984 L1990 **ID IM** *020 †20
DUVALL, Philip Erle. ■ 79413 #048-12-1962 L1962 **R OS** *071 †80
DWOSKIN, Joseph Y. 3601 4TH ST 79430 #041-02-1965 L2000 **U UP** *071 †95
DYER, Jack W. 3601 4TH ST, TEXAS TECH UNIVERSITY 79415 #048-13-1989 L1990 **FM** *020 †18
EASTMAN, Dennis Patrick. 4408 6TH ST, LUBBOCK HEART SURGERY 79416 #023-12-1986 L2007 **TS VS** *020 †85,90
EBERLE, Mary Elizabeth. 3615 19TH ST 79410 #048-13-1979 L1979 **PTH PCP** *020 †50
EDWARDS, Andrew Seth. ■ 79416 #005-12-2006 **OPH** *012
EDWARDS, Virginia S. ■ 79416 #016-11-1951 L1952 **P OS** *071
EEZZUDUEMHOI, Deborah R. 3601 4TH ST, TTU SCHO 79430 #418-02-1979 L2002 **OPH** *020 †55
ELAZREG, Malik Omer Ali. 3601 4TH ST, DEPT OF FAMILY MED 79430 #875-02-1995 **FP** *012
ELLIS, Noel A. 1909 RALEIGH AVE OFC 79407 #048-12-1950 L1950 **PD PDA** *071 †55
ELLSASSER, Michael Gordon. ■ 79403 #017-20-1958 L1964 **OPH** *071 †35
EPPRIGHT, Brian Charles. ■ 79423 #048-15-2004 L2005 **AN** *012
EPSTEIN, Anne Carol. 3411 20TH ST 79410 #048-04-1981 L1981 **IM** *040 †20
ERDMANN, Ralph Rodney. ■ 79413 #649-01-1952 L1959 **FOP PTH** *071
ESCUDIER, Suzanne. 805 IRONTON DR 79416 #429-02-1994 L2000 **AN** *020 †05
ESTEP, Rita Merje. 1318 BROADWAY, LUBBOCK 79401 #869-07-1979 L1996 **PD** *020 †55
EVANS, William Garner. 2402 52ND ST, STE 10 79412 #023-07-1947 L1949 **NS** *071 †25
FANG, Suat Cheng Go. 3804 21ST ST STE C 79410 #748-08-1964 L1977 **PD PHO** *020 †55
FARGASON, William E. 3615 19TH ST 79410 #048-15-2000 L2002 **EM** *020
FARMER, Alfred Ray. 3606 21ST ST, STE 207 79410 #048-15-1984 L1985 **PD NPM** *020 †55
FAROOQI, Naghma Aftab. 3601 4TH ST, TEXAS TECH UNIVERSITY HSC 79430 #704-06-1993 L2007 **OBG** *020
FARRELL, Tommie Wade. 3601 4TH ST, STOP 8143 79430 #048-12-2000 L2001 **FM** *020 †18
FARTHING, Vernon C, Jr. 3502 9TH ST 79415 #048-15-1987 L1988 **IM** *020 †20
FASHINA, Modupe Arike. ■ 79424 #048-15-2005 L2007 **IM** *012
FAUST, Robert Jos. 524 N FULTON AVE 79416 #048-02-1964 L1964 **IM CD** *071 †20
FEIST, Mark A. 3506 21ST ST 79410 #048-15-2000 L2006 **PG** *020 †55
FELTON, Carol K. 3601 4TH ST, TTUHSC DEPT OF-GYN 79430 #041-07-1970 L1985 **OBG** *040 †30
FENTON, Boyd S. 3610 24TH ST 79410 #048-15-1998 L1999 **GE** *020 †20
FEOLA, Mario. ■ 79416 #561-10-1950 L1977 **TS GS** *071 †85,90
FERNANDES, Alex R O. 3812 24TH ST 79410 #803-05-1970 L1978 **ORS** *020 †40
FERNANDEZ, Emily Suzanne. ■ 79424 #048-15-2007 **FP** *012
FERRER, Nathaniel G. 1311 BROADWAY 79401 #748-02-1952 L1975 **GP EM** *071
FIGUEROA, Jose A. 4101 22ND PL, JOE ARRINGTON CANCER CTR 79410 #042-01-1987 L1994 **ON** *020 †20
FILIPPONE, John M, Jr. 3420 22ND PL 79410 #021-01-1967 L1970 **OBG** *020 †30
FISHER, Charles Emil. 602 INDIANA AVE 79415 #048-12-1973 L1976 **OPH GP** *071
FITZWATER, John Welton. ■ 79416 #048-12-2005 **GS** *100
FLINN, Don E. 4000 24TH ST 79410 #024-01-1946 L1961 **P** *040 †75
FLIPPIN, Mindee J. 4206 96TH ST 79423 #048-13-1993 L1995 **PDC** *020 †55
FLOOD-SHAFFER, Kellie. 3601 4TH ST STOP 8340, TTUHSC-DEPT OF OB/GYN 79430 #048-15-1987 L1989 **OBG** *040 †30 ‡
FORD, Ronny W. ■ 79423 #048-15-2004 **GS** *012
FORSYTHE, Ted H. ■ 79424 #048-02-1953 L1953 **GYN** *071 †30
FOWLER, Burt N. 3710 21ST ST 79410 #039-01-1976 L1992 **TS** *020 †85,90
FRANKFATHER, Jay Scott. ■ 79413 #048-15-2005 **OBG** *012
FRANKLIN, Jeremy Alan. ■ 79424 #001-02-1998 L2005 **PDI** *020 †55
FRANKLIN, Rodney Thos. 3106 50TH ST STE 400 79413 #048-13-1985 L1986 **FM** *020 †18
FRANKS, Darrell J. 3506 21ST ST STE 20 79410 #048-15-1988 L1989 **ORS** *020
FRASIER, Kelly James. ■ 79424 #048-13-2002 L2006 **OPH** *100
FREEDMAN, Judith A. ■ 79416 #048-15-1989 L1991 **PD** *020
FREEDMAN, Kenn Alan. 4505 82ND ST, STE 5 79424 #048-15-1989 L1990 **OPH** *020 †35
FREZZA, Ermenegildo E. 3502 9TH ST, STE 380 79415 #561-11-1989 L2005 **GS** *020 †85
FRIGYESI, Tamas L. ■ 79416 #473-01-1951 **OS P** *075
FUNK, Kevin Andre. 602 INDIANA AVE 79415 #039-01-1985 L1993 **EM** *020 †18 ‡
GADA, Kumud Premchand. 3601 4TH ST, TX TECH UNIV HLTH SCI CTR 79430 #496-21-1998 **P** *012
GADA, Premchand Bhurabhai. 4000 24TH ST 79410 #495-96-1970 L1977 **GP** *020
GAGE, James Terry. 4102 24TH ST STE 404 79410 #048-14-1979 L1979 **FM** *020 †18
GANDHI, Sandhya S. 2703 50TH ST # 183 79413 #495-83-1982 L1996 **OBG** *020 †30
GANDHI, Sham S. 3602 23RD ST 79410 #028-34-1977 L1978 **OPH** *020 †35
GANGA, Usha R. 3610 24TH ST, LUBBOCK DIGESTIVE DISEASE 79410 #495-50-1985 L1998 **GE** *020 †20
GARCIA, Melinda D. 4102 24TH ST 79410 #048-13-1993 L1994 **HS ORS** *020 †40
GARLAND, Lloyd Marshall. 3506 21ST ST 79410 #048-12-1961 L1961 **NS** *071 †25
GARRETT, Harold Kelley. 2412 50TH ST 79412 #048-02-1954 L1954 **GP** *071
GARZA, George L, II. 3420 22ND PL 79410 #048-14-2001 L2005 **AN** *020 †05
GATES, Stephen Ivie. 3604 4TH ST, DEPT OF ANESTHESIOLOGY 79430 #048-12-1980 L1980 **AN** *040 †05
GEMBLER, Carrie Leane. ■ 79415 #048-14-2004 L2006 **FSM** *012 †18
GEORGE, Richard E. 3601 21ST ST, NEUROSURGICAL ASSOCIATES, 79410 #048-12-1982 L1983 **NS PD** *020 †25
GHANDOUR, Elias. 3814 22ND PL 79410 #264-05-1982 L1988 **GE IM** *020 †20
GILL, Gurdev Singh. 3601 22ND PL 79410 #495-03-1966 L1975 **ORS** *020 †40
GILL, James Brian. 3601 4TH ST STOP 9436, DEPARTMENT OF ORTHOPEDICS 79430 #048-15-2003 L2006 **ORS** *012
GIOCONDO CESAR, Luis G. 5896A 7TH ST 79416 #187-18-1971 L1998 **NS N** *020 †25
GOLDEN, Alana Christina. 1950 ASPEN AVE, SUNRISE CANYON HOSPITAL 79404 #034-01-1994 L2004 **P** *020
GOLDEN, Melvin Avram. 3601 4TH ST 79430 #050-02-1964 L1973 **DR NM** *020 †80,28
GOLDTHORN, Jane Franklin. 3506 21ST ST STE 30 79410 #023-01-1973 L1983 **PDS** *020 †85
GOLDWATER, Carole Elisabe. ■ 79424 #048-15-2005 **PD** *012
GOLIGHTLY, Chester Gene. ■ 79416 #048-12-1955 L1955 **FM** *071 †18
GOLOVKO, Dmitry. 6306 IOLA AVE, STE 300 79424 #028-34-1997 L2001 **IM OM** *020 †20
GONZALES, Arnulfo. 3601 4TH ST STOP 7208, STUDENT HEALTH 79430 #005-14-1987 L1990 **PD** *020 †55
GONZALEZ, Nancy B D. 160 SLATON RD 79404 #748-10-1964 L1984 **IM CD** *020
GORDON, William Hyatt, Jr. 3802 21ST ST STE A 79410 #048-04-1963 L1963 **N** *071 †75
GORE, Thomas O. 3302 34TH ST, REAR 79410 #649-14-1973 L1980 **P GP** *020 †75
GRAGOWSKI, Lindsay A. 3601 4TH ST, DEPARTMENT OF PEDIATRICS 79430 #048-15-2004 L2007 **PD** *100 †55
GRAHAM, Franklin Thomas, III. ■ 79424 #048-14-1995 L1996 **DR** *020 †80
GRAHAM, Suzanne Carol. 3601 4TH ST 79430 #036-07-1975 L1987 **ATP** *020 †50
GRAHAM, Wade A. 602 INDIANA AVE, UNIVERSITY MEDICAL CENTER 79415 #048-15-1995 L1997 **OPH** *020 †35
GRANBERRY, Darla Jo. 3801 24TH ST 79410 #048-15-1975 L1975 **A** *020 †18
GRATTAN, James Gardiner. 3710 21ST ST 79410 #035-09-1975 L1997 **CD IM** *020 †20
GRAVES, Richard M. ■ 79423 #048-15-2004 L2005 **ORS** *012
GRAY, Andy John. 3719 22ND ST STE B 79410 #048-15-1985 L1987 **FM** *020 †18
GRAY, Elizabeth Anne. ■ 79410 #048-15-2008 *012
GREEN, Hal Leslie. 4102 24TH ST, STE 302 79410 #048-02-1960 L1960 **IM** *020 †20
GREGG, Clint W. 4505 82ND ST, STE 5 79424 #048-02-1992 L1993 **OPH** *020 †35

GREWAL, Ratna. 3601 4TH ST 79430 #495-41-1979 **P** *100
GRIGOR, Laura Miriam. 3601 4TH ST 79430 #781-03-1995 L2007 **IM** *012
GRIMES, Jerry Speight. 3601 4TH ST STOP 9436, DEPARTMENT OF ORTHOPEDIC S 79430 #048-02-1999 L2005 **ORS OFA** *020
GRISWOLD, John A, Jr. 3601 4TH ST, TTUHSC - SURGERY 79430 #030-06-1981 L1982 **GS** *020 †85
GROMOV, Sergey A. 3420 22ND PL 79410 #913-50-1983 L2003 **AN** *020
GUERRA, Diana Mireya. 3601 4TH ST 79430 #264-19-1995 **IM** *012
GUETERSLOH, Amanda M. 5215 96TH ST, WEST TEXAS PEDIATRICS, LLP 79424 #048-15-1999 L2001 **PD** *020 †55
GUHA, Sumit. 3615 19TH ST, EMERGENCY DEPARTMENT 79410 #048-15-1992 L1996 **EM** *020 †16
GURURAJ, V J. 3601 4TH ST 79430 #495-09-1959 L1979 **PD OS** *072 †55
GUTHEIL, James Paul. 3601 4TH ST, MS 9436 79430 #038-40-2000 L2003 **OP ORS** *020
HACKL, Theodore E. ■ 79424 #048-15-2008 *012
HADZIC, Daniel Boris. 3601 4TH ST, TEXAS TECH UNIVERSITY HSC 79415 #048-15-2005 L2006 **FP** *012
HAEFNER, Susan Moore. 3615 19TH ST STE 103, COVENANT CHILDREN'S HOSPIT 79410 #004-01-1995 L2002 **CCP** *020 †55
HAGGARD, Corey J. 3615 19TH ST 79410 #048-15-1989 L1990 **AN PME** *020 †05
HAGGARD, Derick Ray. 3611 22ND PL 79410 #048-15-1994 L1995 **GS** *020 †85
HAGSTROM, David Keith. 4316 23RD ST 79410 #039-01-1983 L1987 **PME PMM** *020
HALE, Samuel Andrew, Jr. 6809 SLIDE RD 79424 #048-13-1980 L1980 **FM** *020 †18
HALES, Kurt A. 4102 24TH ST 79410 #049-01-1987 L1996 **OBG** *020 †30
HALL, David Stroman. 2424 50TH ST, RM 304 79412 #048-13-1976 L1976 **OS NTR** *020 †85
HALL, Harry Eugene. 3506 21ST ST STE 202 79410 #048-15-1979 L1979 **ORS** *020 †40
HALL, John Kevin. 3601 4TH ST, DEPARTMENT OF ANESTHESIA 79430 #038-41-1985 L1994 **IM** *020 †05
HALL, Monte David. ■ 79415 #048-15-2008 *012
HALL, Walker M. MS9406, 3601 4TH ST, TTUHSC DEPT OF PEDIATRICS 79430 #048-15-1991 L1994 **PD** *020 †55
HALLDORSSON, Ari Omar. 3601 4TH ST STOP 8312, TEXA TECH UNIV HLTH SCI CT 79430 #484-01-1982 L2001 **TS TRS** *040 †90,85
HALLIER, Stephen John. 3508 22ND PL 79410 #003-01-1992 L1996 **AN** *020 †05
HAMDHEYDARI, Ladan. 3601 4TH ST 79430 #517-01-1998 L2008 **P** *012
HANCOCK, Joseph Edward. 3502 9TH ST, STE 320 79415 #041-09-1977 L1990 **GE EM** *020 †20
HANING, Holly Susan. 602 INDIANA AVE, DEPT OF EMERGENCY MEDICINE 79415 #048-15-1991 L1992 **IM EM** *020 †20
HANNEL, Jeffrey Wayne. 4515 MARSHA SHARP FWY 79407 #030-05-1996 L1997 **FM** *020 †18
HANRETTA, Allan Thomas. 8602 PEACH AVE, MONTFORD PSYCH UNIT 79404 #048-15-1989 L1990 **P** *020 †75
HANSON, Nathan William. ■ 79416 #049-01-2004 L2008 **D** *012
HARATI, Arundhati. 3506 21ST ST STE 60 79410 #495-65-1985 L2003 **IM** *020 †20
HARDWICKE, Fred Lawrence. 3601 4TH ST 79430 #048-13-1985 L1986 **ON HEM** *020 †20
HARPH, Paul Joseph. 1617 27TH ST, STE 140 79411 #330-02-1957 L1969 **GS TS** *071 †85,90
HARRELL, James Earl, Jr. 3514 21ST ST 79410 #048-04-1978 L1978 **TS GS** *020 †90,85
HARRIS, Bryan D. 3715 21ST ST, LEHMAN DERMATOLOGY CLINIC 79410 #048-15-1995 L1999 **D** *020 †15
HARTMAN, James T. ■ 79416 #016-06-1952 L1971 **ORS** *071 †40
HATTON, Amanda B. ■ 79416 #048-13-2006 **OBG** *012
HAVEL, Jamaiya Nicole. ■ 79416 #048-15-2008 *012
HAYES, Christopher Barton. ■ 79416 #048-14-2005 L2006 **AN** *012
HAYNES, Allan L, Jr. 3502 9TH ST, STE 260 79415 #034-01-1973 L2007 **U AM** *020 †95 ‡
HAYS, Johnnie Wayne. 3904 85TH PL 79423 #048-12-1956 L1956 **GS GP** *020
HEADRICK, Jeff Dodson. 4642 N LOOP 289, STE 101 79416 #048-15-1990 L1992 **ORS** *020 †40
HEGAZY, Khaled Rashad. 3601 4TH ST STOP 9410, TEXAS TECH UNIVERSITY HSC 79430 #915-04-1998 L2007 **IM** *100 †20
HEGDE, Narayan Laxman. 3420 22ND PL 79410 #495-35-1969 L1979 **AN PME** *020 †05
HEINEN, Bridget Gayle. 2424 50TH ST, RM 303 79412 #048-15-1983 L1983 **PTH** *020 †50
HEINRICH, Ronald Geo. 3601 4TH ST, DEPARTMENT OF ANESTHESIOLO 79430 #068-01-1962 L1978 **AN OS** *020 †05
HELFRICH, George Baird. 3606 21ST ST STE 104, TRANSPLANT SURG ASSOC 79410 #016-11-1965 L1988 **GS TTS** *020 †85
HEMPSTEAD, James Edward. 4000 24TH ST 79410 #048-12-1958 L1958 **GS** *071 †85
HENDERSHOT, Kerry L. 7601 QUAKER AVE 79424 #048-15-1996 L1997 **FM** *020 †18
HENDERSON, Richard A. 3516 22ND PL 79410 #048-15-1995 L1998 **IM** *020 †20
HENDON, Robert G, Jr. 3805 22ND ST 79410 #021-01-1946 L1956 **U** *072
HENRY, Jack Hopkins. 3601 4TH ST, STE 4A-097 79430 #048-02-1964 L1964 **ORS** *020 †40
HENRY, Melissa K. 5130 82ND STREET, LAKERIDGE PRIMARY HEALTH C 79430 #048-15-1999 L2000 **FM** *020 †18
HENSAL, Frederick John. 3506 21ST ST STE 201 79410 #041-02-1977 L2001 **ORS** *072 †40
HERMAN, James Jay. 3502 22ND ST, ALLERGY & ASTHMA CLN 79410 #048-02-1973 L1973 **AI PDA** *020 †55,03
HERRERA, Samuel B. 3610 21ST ST 79410 #048-15-2001 L2004 **PD** *020
HESS, Wallace Ivan. ■ 79416 #048-12-1946 L1946 **FM** *071 †18
HEWITT, A Lee. ■ 79416 #028-02-1943 L1949 **U** *071
HICKLE, Randall S. 2804 N LOOP 289 79415 #024-01-1983 L1988 **AN** *020 †05
HIGGINS, James V. 3506 21ST ST, STE 101 79410 #048-15-1988 L1989 **PD PG** *020 †55
HILL, Damon Herbie, Jr. 4102 24TH ST, STE 401 79410 #048-15-1979 L1980 **FM** *020
HILL, Gerald Lennon. 3802 21ST ST STE A 79410 #048-12-1966 L1966 **OM** *020 †18
HINES, Kathryn. 3502 9TH ST, STE 170 79415 #048-15-1997 L1999 **IM** *020 †20
HINSHAW, Luke Ruch. 3502 9TH ST, STE 210 79415 #034-01-2001 L2004 **IM** *020
HIRSCH, Benjamin Aaron. ■ 79410 #048-15-2008 *012
HIRSCH, Guy. 3707 21ST ST 79410 #048-15-1975 L1975 **R** *020 †80
HISEL, Christopher G. 3601 4TH ST 79430 #048-13-1998 L1999 **FM** *020 †18
HNATEK, Joe D. 3420 22ND PL 79410 #048-13-1987 L1988 **AN** *020 †05
HNATEK, Joyce Pentecost. 7601 QUAKER AVE 79424 #048-13-1987 L1988 **FM** *020 †18
HO, Ming-Tao. 3702 34TH ST 79410 #244-02-1980 L1993 **OPH** *020 †35
HODGES, David Scott. 3601 4TH ST STOP 9410, DEPT OF INT MED 79430 #048-15-1983 L1983 **GE IM** *020 †20
HOLDEN, Katherine L. ■ 79416 #048-02-2008 *012
HOLMES, Stephen Russell. 3420 22ND PL 79410 #048-12-1976 L1978 **AN** *020 †05
HOLMES, T H, Jr. ■ 79416 #047-06-1946 L1947 **PD** *071 †55
HOOD, Dwight Douglas. 5520 4TH ST 79416 #048-15-1988 L1989 **FM** *020 †18
HOOD, Raleigh Maurice. ■ 79424 #048-12-1946 L1946 **TS VS** *071 †85,90
HOOK, Shelly Yvonne. ■ 79413 #048-15-2007 **OBG** *012
HOPE, Richard H. 4000 24TH ST 79410 #048-13-1991 L1992 **D** *020 †15
HORSLEY, Heidi Charlotte. ■ 79416 #005-12-1978 L1979 **FM EM** *075
HOUSER, Edward Franklin. 3615 19TH ST 79410 #048-12-1957 L1957 **U** *071 †95
HOWARD, Arthur Richard. 3602 SLIDE RD STE 24B 79414 #048-02-1961 L1961 **FM EM** *020
HOWE, Thomas Lee. 3509 22ND ST 79410 #048-15-1999 L2003 **GS** *020 †85
HOWELL, Alan C. 4404 19TH ST STE C, CONSULTANTS IN INFECTIOUS 79407 #048-14-2001 L2007 **ID** *020 †20
HOWELL, David Shannon. ■ 79424 #021-05-2008 *012
HRNACK, Scott Allan. 3601 4TH ST STOP 9436, TX TECH UNIV HSC 79430 #048-14-2004 L2007 **ORS** *012
HU, Chia-Yuan Michael. ■ 79424 #048-15-2008 *012
HUBBARD, Donald Glen. 5130 82ND ST 79424 #305-01-2002 L2005 **FM** *020 †18
HUBBARD, Vicki Lynn. 406 MARTIN LUTHER KNG BLVD 79403 #048-02-2000 L2003 **FM** *020 †18 ‡
HUDGINS, Amanda Sue. HEALTH SCIENCE, TEXAS TECH UNIV 79430 #048-15-2005 L2008 **PD** *012
HUFFMAN, Shane Lance. ■ 79423 #048-15-2008 *012
HUGHES, Benj Franklin, Jr. 3601 4TH ST 79430 #048-12-1965 L1965 **DR GP** *020 †80
HUGHES, Michele Leigh. ■ 79416 #048-13-2006 **D** *012
HUGO, Joan R. ■ 79407 #917-29-1969 L1979 *074
HULL, Orville Brandon. ■ 79410 #035-19-1942 L1947 **CD** *071 †20
HULME, Kyle Layne. 3601 4TH ST 1C143, TEXAS TECH UNIVERSITY HSC 79430 #048-15-2005 L2006 **FP** *012
HUNTER, Danny Odell. 3615 19TH ST 79410 #048-15-1983 L1984 **AN** *020
HURD, Howard Perrin, Jr. 4802 N LOOP 289 79416 #048-13-1973 L1973 **CD IC** *020 †20 ‡
HURST, Daniel Lee. 3601 4TH ST, MEDICAL & SURGICAL NEUROLO 79430 #038-40-1977 L1986 **CHN** *020 †55,75
HUYNH, Barbara. ■ 79416 #005-76-2005, ▲ **P** *012
HWANG, Mary Minghuey. ■ 79424 #033-05-1996 L1999 **PD** *020
HYACINTHE, Micheline. 4102 24TH ST, STE 406 79410 #035-06-1987 L2002 **GS** *020 †85
HYDE, Walter Vaughan, Jr. 4515 MARSHA SHARP FWY, GRACE CLINIC OF LUBBOCK 79407 #048-13-1983 L1983 **FM** *020 †18
IMOISI, Aroboyi Veronica. ■ 79415 #690-06-1992 L2007 **FM** *100
ISLAM, Rafiul Sameer. ■ 79416 #048-15-2008 *012
IVY, David Lee. 3420 22ND PL 79410 #048-12-1972 L1972 **GYN** *020
IZNAOLA ESQUIVEL, Oscar A. 3601 4TH ST, DEPT MED 79430 #649-19-2000 L2006 **NEP** *012 †20
JABARA, Sami Issam. 3502 9TH ST STE 150, FERTILITY & REPRODUCTIVE S 79415 #605-01-1995 L2006 **OBG REN** *020 †30
JABOR, Miled A. 3610 24TH ST, LUBBOCK DIGESTIVE DISEASE 79410 #048-02-1987 L1988 **GE** *020 †20
JAUERNEK, Reinhard Roy. ■ 79415 #060-02-1974 L1982 **DR** *020 †80
JENKINS, Leigh Ann. 3601 4TH ST STOP 9410 79430 #048-15-1983 L1983 **CD** *040 †20
JENKINS, Mark Douglas. ■ 79424 #048-15-2001 L2007 **ORS** *100
JENSEN, Glenn A. ■ 79411 #048-15-2003 **FM** *100
JENSEN, Robert Walter. 3601 4TH ST STOP 8321, TEXAS TECH UNIVERSITY HSC 79430 #005-02-1989 L1991 **N** *030 †75
JENSON, Mark Layne. ■ 79416 #048-15-2005 **ORS** *012
JINICH, David. 3514 21ST ST 79410 #048-04-1983 L1985 **CD IM** *020 †20
JOHNSON, Carson L. 4005 24TH ST 79410 #048-15-1988 L1989 **DR** *020 †80
JOHNSON, Clark Alexander. ■ 79424 #048-02-1948 L1948 **FM** *071 †18
JOHNSON, Jerry Keith. 1318 BROADWAY 79401 #048-02-1973 L1976 **PD PDA** *020 †55
JOHNSON, Lara Wiggins. ■ 79412 #048-04-2002 L2005 **PD** *100
JOHNSON, Lowell Saml. 7601 QUAKER AVE, HEALTH PLUS MEDICAL GROUP 79424 #048-12-1956 L1956 **FM FPG** *020 †18
JOHNSON, Lynne Alice. 3620 INTERSTATE 27 79404 #048-02-1988 L1994 **FM OS** *020 †18
JOHNSON, Mark Wm. 3621 22ND ST STE 400 79410 #026-04-1978 L1981 **PUD IM** *020 †20
JOHNSON, Robert L. 4213 85TH ST, STE B 79423 #048-15-1990 L1991 **IM** *020 †20
JOHNSTON, Glen T. 3601 4TH ST, DEPARTMENT OF ANESTHESIOLO 79430 #048-15-2004 L2006 **AN** *012
JOHNSTON, Robt Victor, Jr. 3601 4TH ST, RM 1C282 79430 #048-04-1977 L1978 **AN CCM** *020 †05 ‡
JONES, Glenn M. 4005 24TH ST 79410 #048-04-1951 L1951 **R** *071 †80
JONES, Kristie E. ■ 79410 #048-15-2006 **IM** *012
JOSHI, Atulkumar B. 3506 21ST ST 79410 #495-17-1978 L2000 **ORS** *020 †40
JOSHI, Raman Chandulal. ■ 79424 #495-37-1959 L1977 **FM GP** *071
JUM, Mehdiabadi Rustam. ■ 79416 #704-09-1966 L1973 **OTO A** *071 †45
JUMPER, Cynthia Ann. 3601 4TH ST, DEPT OF INTERNAL MEDICINE 79415 #048-15-1988 L1989 **PUD** *020 †20
JUSTIZ, Alina Carmen. 3601 4TH ST 79415 #056-06-2001 L2005 **AN** *100 †05
JUSTIZ, Rafael, III. 3601 4TH ST 79415 #056-06-2001 L2007 **AN** *100 †05
KADIYALA, Srinivas P. 3621 22ND ST, STE 400 79410 #495-50-1990 L1999 **PUD CCM** *020 †20
KALLEPALLI, Bhupala Raju. 3301 101ST ST 79423 #495-50-1981 L1996 **CHP P** *020
KARKOUTLY, Ayman. 4001 21ST ST 79410 #875-01-1973 L1980 **CD IM** *020 †20
KASEMSRI, Thivakorn. 3606 21ST ST, STE 103 79410 #045-01-1990 L2000 **CCP PD** *020 †55
KAYASSEH, Hakam A. 3615 19TH ST 79410 #875-01-1980 L1982 **FM** *020 †18
KAYE, Kim Bowden Sutker. 3601 4TH ST, DEPT OF PATHOLOGY 79430 #021-01-1988 L2000 **PTH** *020 †50
KEARSE, Wm Oliver, Jr. 6401 INDIANA AVE 79413 #036-01-1968 L1986 **IM GP** *020 †20
KELLEY, Douglas M. 3420 22ND PL 79410 #048-02-1993 L1994 **AN** *020 †05
KENNEDY, Amantia. ■ 79490 #048-15-2008 *012
KENSING, Kelly Paul. 3610 24TH ST, LUBBOCK DIGESTIVE DISEASE 79410 #048-15-1986 L1987 **GE IM** *020 †20
KERR, Clark Mc Laughlin. 3615 19TH ST 79410 #065-09-1978 L1989 **IM ID** *071 †20
KERR, Kevin Andrew. ■ 79416 #048-12-2007 L2007 **IM** *012
KEY, Mark Richard. ■ 79407 #048-15-2007 **FP** *012
KHAN, Abdul Basith. 5520 4TH ST 79416 #496-27-1996 L2006 **FM** *020 †18 ‡
KHAN, Ashraf Mohammed. 2424 50TH ST, RM 303 79412 #917-13-1980 L1999 **PTH** *020 †50
KHAN, Rubina Jamal. HLTH SCIENCES, TEXAS TECH UNIV 79430 #704-24-2000 **FP** *012
KHANANI, Arshad Mohammad. 3601 4TH ST MS 7217, HEALTH SCIENCE CENTER 79415 #048-15-2004 L2007 **OPH** *012
KHANDHERIA, Manoj P. 2424 50TH ST, RM 301 79412 #495-38-1972 L1983 **U FM** *020 †95

■ = Address Information Privacy Protected

KHANDHERIA, Priyamvada. 2424 50TH ST 79412 #495-75-1978 L1983 **P** *020
KHATER, Timothy Tamim. 5109 80TH ST 79424 #016-06-1992 L1997 **OPH** *020 †35
KHU, James My. 3601 4TH ST STOP 7217, TEXAS TECH UNIVERSITY HSC 79430 #005-14-2005 L2007 **OPH** *012
KILLION, Kristin Leigh. ■ 79413 #048-15-2008 *012
KIM, John Jin. 3601 4TH ST, DEPT OF OPHTHALMOLOGY/VISU 79430 #035-47-2006 **OPH** *012
KIMBROUGH, Robert Cooke. 3601 4TH ST, DEPT IM DIV INFECT DISEASE 79430 #019-02-1969 L1971 **ID IM** *040 †20 ‡
KINCAID, Billy Paul. 3615 19TH ST 79410 #048-12-1959 L1959 **IM** *071
KING, Robert Randolph. 4110 22ND PL 79410 #048-02-1975 L1975 **ORS** *020 †40
KING, Samuel Miles. 5303 21ST ST 79407 #048-02-1956 L1956 **CD** *071 †20
KING, Travis Glen. ■ 79424 #048-15-2006 L2007 **FP** *012
KINI, Chandrakanth M. 4511 UNIVERSITY AVE 79413 #495-34-1961 L1982 **OTO EM** *071
KIRK, James Fredrick. 3612 23RD ST, ADULT AND PEDIATRIC UROLOG 79410 #048-13-1976 L1976 **U** *020 †95
KIRKMAN, Matthew Grant. 3601 4TH ST, TX TECH UNIV 79430 #041-15-2004 L2004 **OPH** *012
KIRKPATRICK, Richard Emer. ■ 79424 #048-15-2008 *012
KLEPPER, Douglas R. GRADUATE MED EDUC MED 79430 #048-15-1989 L1990 **IM PD** *040 †55
KNEER-ARONOFF, Christine. 3612 22ND PL 79410 #011-04-1991 L2002 **OBG** *020 †30
KOLIPAKA, Srinivas. ■ 79416 #495-21-2001 **P** *012
KONOPLEVA, Marina Yurievn. 3601 4TH ST 79430 #913-01-1990 **IM** *012
KOOS, Mariana. 4906 84TH ST 79424 #781-04-1970 L1992 **PD** *020
KOWALESKI, Kevin Robt. 3610 21ST ST, COVENANT CHILDREN'S HOSPIT 79410 #028-02-1980 L1993 **PEM PD** *020 †55
KRIM, Selim Ramzi. 3601 4TH ST STOP 9410, TEXAS TECH UNIVERSITY HSC 79430 #125-01-2000 L2007 **IM** *100 †20
KUMAR, Ashwani. GRADUATE MED EDUC, TX TECH UNIV HLTH SCI CTR 79430 #495-85-1988 L2005 **CD** *012
KUPERSMITH, Joel. 3601 4TH ST, TTU HEALTH SCIENCES CENTER 79430 #035-09-1964 L1999 **CD IM** *030 †20
KURDI, Juan. 3620 INTERSTATE 27 79404 #875-01-1996 L2002 **CD** *020 †20
KURTZMAN, Neil Arnold. 3601 4TH ST, DEPT OF INTERNAL MEDICINE 79430 #035-09-1961 L1986 **IM NEP** *020
KURZ, Michael Wayne. HLTH SCIENCES, TEXAS TECH UNIV 79430 #048-15-2007 **FP** *012
LABIB, Safaa Sanad. ■ 79424 #915-04-1985 L2004 **HMP** *100 †50
LACHMANSINGH, Jinesh Step. ■ 79406 #048-15-2008 *012
LAJARA, Carlos Miguel. ■ 79416 #308-01-1953 L1963 **IM PTH** *071 †50
LAMBERTS, David Winton. 4003 22ND ST 79410 #025-07-1970 L1978 **OPH** *020 †35
LAMPE, Craig Anthony. 3420 22ND PL 79410 #048-12-2001 L2002 **AN** *020 †05
LAMPE, Richard Michael. 3601 4TH ST DEPT PD, TTU HLTH SCI CTR 79430 #056-06-1968 L1992 **PD PDI** *040 †55
LAMPKIN, Douglas Andrew. 3825 22ND PL 79410 #056-06-1992 L1995 **OBG** *020 †30
LANDRY, Cheryl Caffee. 5215 96TH ST 79424 #048-15-1993 L1994 **PD** *020 †55
LANDRY, Joel B. 5915 82ND ST 79424 #048-15-1997 L1998 **FM** *020 †18
LASKI, Melvin Edward. 3601 4TH ST STOP 9410, HEALTH SCIENCES CENTER 79430 #016-11-1976 L1985 **NEP IM** *050 †20
LATHAM, Christian Andrew. ■ 79416 #004-01-2003 L2007 **GS** *012
LATOUR, Jonathan Gilbert. 4601 5TH ST STE 11 79416 #027-01-1990 L1998 **AN** *020 †05
LAURENTZ, David Arlen. 6809 SLIDE RD 79424 #048-14-1979 L1979 **FM** *020 †18
LAUTSCH, Elizabeth V. ■ 79424 #067-03-1944 L1978 **PTH** *040 †50
LAWRENCE, Larry B. 2102 OXFORD AVE, STE B 79410 #048-15-1993 L1998 **OBG** *020 †30
LEAR, Kye Burton. 4515 MARSHA SHARP FWY 79407 #048-02-1979 L1979 **FM** *020 †18 ‡
LEE, Tim Hsin-An. ■ 79416 #048-15-2008 *012
LEHMAN, Joseph Mann. 3715 21ST ST 79410 #048-12-1948 L1948 **D** *020 †15
LEHMAN, Michael Gary. 3715 21ST ST 79410 #048-15-1986 L1987 **D** *020 †15
LEHMAN, Robert. 3715 21ST ST 79410 #048-02-1961 L1961 **D** *071
LEHMAN, Stanley Richard. 3601 4TH ST, MS 9436 79430 #034-01-1971 L1978 **HS ORS** *020 †40
LEICHT, Margaret Ulrike. 2301 QUAKER AVE, COVENANT SURGICENTER 79410 #048-15-1985 L1986 **AN** *020 †05
LEMON, William Lee. 4810 N LOOP 289 79416 #048-02-1963 L1963 **R** *020 †80
LEO, Jin-Shone. 4005 24TH ST 79410 #244-02-1969 L1978 **R** *020 †80
LEOCADIO, Dean Edward. HLTH SCI, TEXAS TECH UNIVERSITY 79430 #005-12-2005 **U** *012
LEVINE, Marc Jos. 3514 21ST ST 79410 #038-06-1983 L1991 **CD IM** *020 †20
LEWIS, David Alan. ■ 79416 #039-01-2006 L2006 **OPH** *012
LEWIS, Ryan Leighton. 3601 4TH ST 79430 #104-01-2007 **GS** *012
LI, Lei. ■ 79415 #243-16-1991 L2006 **FM** *020 †18
LI, Shelley Qingli. ■ 79415 #048-15-2006 **FP** *012
LILJEBLAD, Eileen Aye. 602 INDIANA AVE, UNIV MED CTR DEPT OF RAD 79415 #209-01-1968 L1979 **R** *020 †80
LINCOLN, Annie. 2310 INDIANA AVE 79410 #495-44-1970 L1983 **N P** *020
LINK, G Joanne. 3601 4TH ST 79415 #418-02-1983 L1984 **N OS** *040
LINTON, Kitten Sue. 3601 4TH ST STOP 8143 79430 #048-12-1981 L1981 **FM** *020 †18
LIPTON, Michael Reid. ■ 79424 #048-15-2008 *012
LITTLE, Donald Dale. 3801 50TH ST 79413 #048-15-1981 L1981 **IM** *020 †20
LITTLE, Ellen B. 3601 4TH ST 79430 #048-15-1997 L1998 **PD** *020 †55
LOGVINOFF, Marie Martine. 3601 4TH ST 79430 #396-06-1969 L1980 **PD PUD** *040 †55
LONG, David Randolph. 5130 82ND ST, LAKERIDGE PRIMARY HEALTH C 79424 #048-15-2003 L2004 **FM** *020 †18
LONG, Michael David. 3715 21ST ST 79410 #048-15-1993 L1994 **D DS** *020 †15
LONG, Stephen G. ■ 79416 #048-15-1997 **IM** *100
LONGHOFER, Lisa Kay. ■ 79424 #048-15-2008 *012
LOVELESS, Alita Kay. HLTH SCIENCES, TEXAS TECH UNIV 79430 #048-15-2005 **OBG** *012
LUCKSTEAD, Eugene Freddie. 6104 AVENUE Q, VA OUTPATIENT CLINIC 79412 #018-03-1991 L1994 **IM** *020 †20
LUM, Nelson Wah Kun. 3801 50TH ST 79413 #014-01-1978 L1993 **END IM** *020 †20
LUTHERER, Lorenz Otto. TEX TECH U SCH MED PHYSIOL 79409 #048-15-1977 L1977 *075
MAC ADAMS, Michael R. 3506 21ST ST STE 301, LUBBOCK DIAGNOSTIC CLINIC 79410 #025-01-1976 L1994 **END** *020 †20
MAC DOUGALL, Rebecca M. ■ 79424 #048-14-2004 **PTH** *012
MAC KENZIE, John Malcolm. 3302 67TH ST 79413 #035-01-1966 L1973 **OBG** *020 †30
MAC NAIR, Donald S. ■ 79413 #035-19-1953 L1974 **CLP** *071 †50
MADRID, Shea Tiffany. ■ 79407 #048-15-2006 **PD** *012
MAHAL, Kanwaljit Singh. 4515 MARSHA SHARP FWY, GRACE CLINIC OF LUBBOCK 79407 #048-02-2000 L2006 **U** *020 †95
MAILMAN, Douglas Raymond. 34 BRENTWOOD CIR 79407 #048-12-1992 L1995 **PD** *020 †55
MAJORS, Caroline Tam. 3606 21ST ST 79410 #748-01-1993 L2005 **PD NPM** *020 †55
MALDIA, Ernesto Mendoza. 2412 50TH ST 79412 #748-01-1963 L1974 **GP GS** *020
MALEK-AHMADI, Parviz. 3601 4TH ST, DEPARTMENT OF PSYCHIATRY 79430 #517-01-1968 L1981 **P CHP** *020 †75
MALKI, Qahtan. 3710 21ST ST, TEXAS CARDIAC CENTER 79410 #875-01-1994 L2000 **CD** *020 †20
MAMLOK, Robert Jerry. 3606 21ST ST, STE 311 79410 #165-06-1983 L1986 **AI PD** *020 †55,03
MAMLOK, Viviane. 3601 4TH ST, STE 1A-115 DEPT PATH 79430 #165-06-1983 L1986 **PP** *020 †50
MAMMARAPPALLIL, Marisa C. ■ 79424 #048-13-2004 L2008 **PTH** *012
MANGOLD, David Eugene. 3611 22ND PL 79410 #048-15-1974 L1974 **GS** *020 †85
MANNING, Stephen Matthew. 8602 PEACH AVE, JOHN MONTFORD PSYCHIATRIC 79404 #048-15-1984 L1985 **P FM** *020 †18,75
MANNY, Theodore Bergen. 3420 22ND PL 79410 #048-13-1980 L1981 **AN** *020 †05
MARCHBANKS, John Riddley. 3601 4TH ST, STOP 8312 79430 #048-02-1975 L1975 **OTO** *020 †45
MARK, Lloyd K. 3601 4TH ST 79430 #038-40-1950 L1977 **R NM** *020 †80,28
MARK, Rufus J. 4302 22ND PL 79410 #005-14-1986 L2001 **RO** *020 †80
MARKARIAN, Mark Khajag. ■ 79414 #012-01-2004 L2005 **GS** *012
MARKS, Robert Steven. ■ 79424 #048-02-2006 **GS** *012
MARTIN, Devona Nicole. ■ 79423 #048-15-2007 **PD** *012
MARTIN, Jason Michael. ■ 79416 #048-15-2008 *012
MARTIN, Raymond Andrew. ■ 79414 #539-05-1970 L1979 **P** *020
MARTINCHECK, David J. 3601 4TH ST RM 1C282, HLTH SCIENCES 79430 #048-14-2006 **AN** *012
MARTINELLI, Lawrence P. 4404 19TH ST STE C 79407 #056-06-1985 L1993 **ID IM** *020 †20
MARTINEZ, Rodolfo E. 4002 21ST ST STE B 79410 #054-04-1979 L1984 **ON HEM** *020 †20
MARTINEZ, Waldo M, Jr. 4005 24TH ST 79410 #048-12-1984 L1985 **DR** *020 †80
MASSEY, Evelyn L. 2412 50TH ST 79412 #047-06-1995 L2000 **OPH** *071
MATTHEWS, James Robt. 3903 77TH ST 79423 #048-12-1957 L1957 **FM** *071 †18
MATTISON, Michael Trae. 3802 22ND PL 79410 #048-02-1996 L1998 **PTH** *020 †50
MATTISON, Myron Duane. ■ 79407 #047-06-1944 L1948 **IM** *071 †20
MATTISON, Thomas Randolph. 4000 24TH ST 79410 #048-13-1976 L1977 **PTH** *062 †50
MAY, Donald Robt Lee. 3601 4TH ST 79430 #016-11-1972 L1990 **OPH OS** *071 †35
MAY, Patti N. 4515 MARSHA SHARP FWY 79407 #048-15-2003 L2004 **FM** *020 †18
MAYHEW, James Franckle. 3601 4TH ST RM 1C282, DEPARTMENT OF ANESTHESIOLO 79430 #033-05-1969 L1982 **AN PD** *020 †05,55 ‡
MC CABE, Howard J. 3508 22ND PL 79410 #048-15-1988 L1989 **AN** *020 †05
MC CARRON, Sara H. ■ 79423 #048-12-1989 L1993 **BBK** *020
MC CARTNEY, David Lloyd. 4505 82ND ST, STE 5 79424 #048-13-1982 L1983 **OPH** *020 †35
MC CARTNEY, Susan Marie. ■ 79416 #041-02-1983 L1987 **IM** *074 †20
MCCLAIN, Chase Wagner. ■ 79416 #048-15-2006 L2006 **GS** *100
MCCLINTOCK, Jacob Nelson. ■ 79424 #004-01-2007 **FP** *012
MC DONALD, James Eugene. 3601 4TH ST STOP 7208, TEXAS TECH UNIVERSITY HSC 79430 #048-02-2002 L2005 **FM** *020 †18
MC DONALD, Joshua Michael. 4005 24TH ST, LUBBOCK DIAGNOSTIC RADIOLO 79410 #018-03-2001 L2005 **DR** *020 †80
MCDONALD, Lauren Doughty. ■ 79416 #018-03-2004 L2004 **D** *012
MCDONALD, Rebecca N. ■ 79412 #048-15-2005 **IM** *012
MC DOUGAL, Barbara A. ■ 79416 #034-01-1972 L1975 **IM** *071
MC GILL, Thomas Wayne. 3506 21ST ST STE 302 79410 #051-07-1982 L2004 **GS** *020 †85
MC GUNEGLE, Daniel Edward. 3601 4TH ST, STE E 79430 #025-01-1968 L1988 **OBG** *072 †30
MC INTIRE, Diane L. 6630 QUAKER AVE STE H 79413 #048-15-1994 L1995 **PD** *020 †55
MCLAUGHLIN, Jennifer Ashl. ■ 79424 #004-01-2006 **D** *012
MCLAUGHLIN, Nathan John. 3601 4TH ST 79430 #004-01-2006 L2008 **IM** *012
MC MAHON, Terry Calvin. 3601 4TH ST, TX TECH UNIV HEALTH SCI CT 79430 #005-14-1976 L1978 **P** *040 †75
MC NAIR, Christie Chantal. ■ 79424 #048-13-1995 L1997 **FM** *020 †18
MC NEIL, Buck Wayne. 4010 21ST ST 79410 #048-15-1977 L1977 **AN** *020
MCNEIL, Kristin Wildner. 3601 4TH ST STOP 8182, DEPARTMENT OF ANESTHESIOLO 79430 #048-04-2005 L2007 **AN** *012
MCNUTT, Steven S. 1318 BROADWAY, COMMUNITY HEALTH CTR OF LU 79401 #048-15-1997 L2000 **PD** *020
MC PHERSON, Michael G. 5601 84TH ST 79424 #048-15-1996 L1997 **IM** *020 †20
MEDINA, Erik Conrad. ■ 79413 #048-14-2000 **AN** *100
MENARD, Ralph G, Jr. 4642 N LOOP 289 STE 209 79416 #012-01-1982 L1989 **AN PMM** *020 †05
METZLER, Charles Jos. ■ 79416 #007-02-1953 L1993 **IM CD** *020 †20
METZLER, Jonathan Paul. 2518 23RD ST 79410 #034-01-1990 L1991 **DR** *020 †80
MEYERROSE, Gary Eugene. 3502 9TH ST 79415 #047-06-1975 L1993 **CD NM** *040 †20,28
MILLER, Alan Marc. 602 INDIANA AVE, DEPARTMENT OF RADIOLOGY 79415 #048-13-1976 L1976 **DR** *020
MILLER, Gregory S. 4810 N LOOP 289 79416 #048-15-1990 L1991 **AN** *020 †05
MILNER, Jennifer Nicole. ■ 79423 #048-15-2008 *012
MISRA, Bhagwat Swaroop. 2424 50TH ST, RM 105 79412 #495-34-1959 L1976 **GS AS** *020
MITCHELL, Jennifer Johnso. 3601 4TH ST, STOP 8143 79430 #048-15-1993 L1994 **FM FSM** *100 †18
MITCHELL, Kelly Thrush. 4505 82ND ST, STE 5 79424 #038-41-1990 L2001 **OPH** *020 †35
MITRA, Aloke Kumar. ■ 79423 #495-02-1965 **EM GS** *020
MITTAL, Neha. 3601 4TH ST STOP 9410, TTUHSC - INTERNAL MEDICINE 79430 #495-30-1999 L2004 **IM** *020 †20
MITTAL, Piyush. 3801 50TH ST, STE 5 79413 #495-30-1999 L2003 **IM** *020 †20
MITTEMEYER, Bernhard T. 3502 9TH ST, STE 260 79415 #041-13-1956 L1980 **U** *030 †95
MOELLER, John F. 3601 4TH ST STE 3A13 79430 #021-06-1994 L1995 **OS** *020
MOFFITT, Suzelle Larocque. 416 FRANKFORD AVE, COVENANT MEDICAL GROUP 79416 #067-02-1986 L1989 **FM** *020 †18
MOLLIGAN, Patrick Frank. 3801 21ST ST, STE F 79410 #021-05-1986 L1993 **ORS** *020 †40
MONK, Norman Alison. ■ 79413 #048-02-1948 L1967 **GP** *071 †18
MONTE, Melville R. 3615 19TH ST 79410 #041-13-1949 L1953 **AN** *071
MONTGOMERY, Clifford L. 4TH STREET AND INDIANA, TT UNIVERISTY HEALTH SCI C 79430 #048-02-1954 L1954 **FM** *071 †18
MOORE, Karin Nicole. ■ 79413 #048-15-2008 *012
MORALES, Jose. 3601 4TH ST 79430 #649-01-1978 L1990 **OPH** *020
MORCOS, Ashraf Isaac Lotf. 3601 4TH ST 79430 #915-02-1986 **FM** *100

■ = Address Information Privacy Protected

MORRIS, James Garnett. 1500 BROADWAY STE 1101 79401 #048-04-1946 L1946 **GYN** *071
MORROW, Brenda. 3506 21ST ST STE 602 79410 #048-15-1982 L1983 **IM** *020 †20
MOSKOS, Bill Nick. 4005 24TH ST 79410 #018-03-1992 L1998 **DR** *020 †80
MOSS, Charles B. 4000 24TH ST 79410 #039-01-1949 L1952 **FM** *020 †18
MOSS, Clint Cameron. ■ 79416 #048-15-2008 *012
MOSS, Ennis Edward, Jr. ■ 79416 #047-06-1945 L1946 **OPH** *071 †35
MOSS, James B, III. 3514 21ST ST 79410 #021-01-1985 L1991 **CD IM** *020 †20
MOTHERAL, Lesley Dyan. ■ 79423 #048-15-2005 L2008 **PD** *012
MOUZOUN, Said. 3601 4TH ST, DEPT OF FAMILY MED 79430 #655-03-1998 **FP** *012
MOYES, James Robt. 3516 22ND PL 79410 #035-15-1963 L1970 **AN** *071 †05
MUEHE, Natali Garcia. ■ 79401 #048-15-2008 *012
MUFF, David S. 4005 24TH ST 79410 #048-13-1983 L1987 **DR** *020 †80
MULKEY, Zachary P. 3601 4TH ST STOP 9410, TEXAS TECH UNIVERSITY HSC 79430 #048-15-2004 L2007 **IM** *100 †20
MUNSON, Alex Kerr. 4612 5TH ST 79416 #048-02-1958 L1958 **CHP P** *071
MYERS, W Duke. 1607 W LOOP 289 79416 #020-02-1968 L1978 **NEP IM** *020 †20 ‡
NALL, Brent Boye. 4515 MARSHA SHARP FWY 79407 #048-12-1976 L1978 **OBG** *020 †30
NARENDRAN, Kumara-Pillai. 3712 22ND ST 79410 #495-42-1970 L1979 **GE IM** *020 †20
NARENDRAN, Saradadevi. ■ 79424 #495-31-1977 L1980 **PD** *020 †55
NARRA, Koteswaramma. 3420 22ND PL 79410 #495-50-1977 L1996 **AN** *020 †05
NARRA, Nagarjun. 3615 19TH ST 79410 #495-21-1977 L1996 **EM** *020 †16
NASTOUPIL, Loretta Jo. ■ 79416 #048-12-2007 L2007 **IM** *012
NATARAJAN, Sridhar. 3601 4TH ST STOP 8122, TEXAS TECH UNIV HEALTH SCI 79430 #045-01-1992 L1994 **FOP PTH** *020 †50
NATH, Tapan Kumar. 3506 21ST ST 79410 #160-02-1988 L2003 **IM** *020 †20
NATHAN, Thusha. HEALTH SCIENCE, TEXAS TECH UNIV 79430 #305-01-1998 L2004 **GE** *020 †20
NEAL, Thomas Frederick. 3621 22ND ST 79410 #040-02-1971 L1977 **OTO** *020 †45
NEBLOCK, Michele L. 2716 82ND ST 79423 #048-15-1996 L2002 **FM** *020 †18
NEILSON, Robert W. DEPT OF MED, TEXAS TECH UNIV HEALTH SCI 79430 #048-15-1999 L2002 **IM** *020 †20
NELDNER, Kenneth Herbert. 3601 4TH ST, TX TECH UNIV HSC-DERM 79430 #026-04-1955 L1983 **D DMP** *071 †15
NELIUS, Thomas. 3601 4TH ST, DEPT OF UROLOGY 79430 #408-09-1996 **U** *100
NEUMANN, Thomas Robt. 4302 22ND PL 79410 #048-02-1980 L1980 **RO** *020 †80
NEWTON, Marion L. 9704 AVENUE V 79423 #018-03-1984 L1992 **PD** *020
NGO, Bich-Thy Nguyen. ■ 79407 #048-16-2006 **IM** *012
NGUYEN, Hoa X. 3819 24TH ST 79410 #048-15-1995 L1997 **IC** *020 †20
NGUYEN, Jesse Tyler. ■ 79410 #048-15-2008 *012
NGUYEN, Tam Quang. 3601 4TH ST, DEPARTMENT OF SURGERY 79430 #025-07-1998 L2005 **OTO** *100 †45
NICHOLSON, Brian Emison. 3612 23RD ST 79410 #016-42-1994 L2004 **U** *020 †95
NICKELS, Melinda Beth. 3509 22ND ST 79410 #048-15-1989 L1990 **GS** *020 †85
NICOLAU, Dan Adrian. ■ 79416 #048-15-2008 *012
NIGAM, Mool Perkash. 3506 21ST ST STE 400 79410 #495-05-1958 L1980 **N OS** *020 †75
NORKIEWICZ, Brian J. 3711 22ND ST, STE C 79410 #048-12-1992 L1993 **GS** *020 †85
NORTH, Joshua David. ■ 79413 #048-15-2006 **ORS** *012
NORTH, Ronald Johann. 4404 6TH ST 79416 #039-01-1967 L1978 **PS GS** *020 †85,65
NOVAK, Ronald Anthony. 136 N UTICA AVE 79416 #165-04-1984 L1993 **PM** *020 †60
NUGENT, Kenneth Michael. 3601 4TH ST, DEPARTMENT OF INTERNAL MED 79430 #028-02-1971 L1985 **PUD CCM** *040 †20
OBLENDER, Melanie Gayle. 3606 21ST ST STE 304 79410 #048-02-1982 L1983 **PHO PD** *020 †55
O'BRIEN, Larry Joe. 3801 19TH ST STE 401, MEDICAL PROFESSIONAL BLDG 79410 #012-01-1972 L1973 **IM PUD** *071
O'DONNELL, James Jos. ■ 79407 #035-08-1946 L1947 **ORS** *071 †40
OLIVA, Claude Michel. 2301 QUAKER AVE 79410 #048-15-1989 L1990 **AN PME** *020
OLIVER, Jeffrey W. 3601 4TH ST, 2B-112 79430 #048-15-1995 L1996 **PTH** *020 †50
OMIDVAR, Kamran. ■ 79413 #048-15-2008 *012
O'NEILL, Michael Shea. 3610 21ST ST 79410 #048-15-1990 L1991 **D PD** *020 †55
ORDONEZ, Robert Lee. 2412 50TH ST 79412 #034-01-1977 L1978 **FM** *020 †18
OSBORN, Charles David. 4920 S LOOP 289 STE 101 79414 #039-01-1986 L1987 **PTH** *020 †50
OTAHBACHI, Mohammad. 3601 4TH ST, TX TECH UNIV HLTH SCI CTR 79430 #875-01-1998 L2007 **CD** *012 †20
OVERLIE, Paul Albert. 3710 21ST ST 79410 #007-02-1973 L1989 **CD IM** *020 †20
OWEN, Jeffrey Michael. ■ 79424 #048-15-2005 L2005 **FP** *012
OWEN, Jennifer Michelle. 2215 NASHVILLE AVE 79410 #048-15-2001 L2004 **OBG** *020 †30
OWEN, Michael Fred. 2102 OXFORD AVE 79410 #048-15-1977 L1977 **OBG** *020 †30
OWENS, Danny Paul. 3601 4TH ST 79430 #305-01-2004 **GS** *012
OWNBEY, James Linus. 2424 50TH ST, RM 303 79412 #048-13-1974 L1974 **PTH PCP** *020 †50
OZUNA, Eduardo. ■ 79423 #048-15-2006 **AN** *012
PADILLA VAZQUEZ, Arnoldo. 3601 4TH ST 79430 #649-52-2000 **IM** *012
PAGE, Lola Darlene. 4102 24TH ST 79410 #048-12-1971 L1973 **OBG** *020 †30
PAIK, Hugh H. 2412 50TH ST 79412 #583-02-1965 L1976 **PTH PCH** *020 †50
PAJARES, Richard Luis. 4640 N LOOP 289 79416 #048-12-1977 L1977 **DR PDR** *020 †80
PAL, Dilip Kumar. 3601 22ND PL 79410 #495-15-1957 L1976 **ORS** *020 †40
PALACIO OCHOA, Carlos And. 3601 4TH ST 79430 #264-03-1999 **IM** *012
PANDYA, Yogeshkumar J. 4102 24TH ST, STE 505 79410 #495-23-1974 L1982 **PD** *020 †55
PANKRATZ, Karl George. ■ 79413 #048-15-2003 **ORS** *012
PAONE, Ralph Francis. 3710 21ST ST 79410 #048-02-1986 L1987 **TS** *020 †85,90
PAPPAS, Patrick H. 4206 19TH ST REAR 79407 #048-02-1952 L1952 **IM** *020
PARAGAS, Magdalena G. ■ 79424 #748-01-1964 L1985 **P OS** *020 †55
PARAGAS, Pablo Dulay. 3610 24TH ST 79410 #748-02-1963 L1974 **GE** *071
PARHIZGAR, Robert. ■ 79499 #048-15-2008 *012
PARIKH, Nitin Pranlal. 3420 22ND PL 79410 #496-38-1975 L1985 **AN** *020 †05
PARK, Joon-Myung. 3502 9TH ST 79415 #583-01-1959 L1977 **PDC** *020 †55
PARMAR, Ashok Kumar R. 5201 INDIANA AVE, STE 101N 79413 #496-38-1960 L1976 **GP GS** *020
PARSONS, Thomas Richard. ■ 79424 #034-01-1989 L1992 **PTH** *020 †50
PARUPUDI, Sreeram Venkata. 3601 4TH ST, STOP 9410 79430 #495-11-1987 **IM** *100
PASCUA-LIM, Elvira G. 3223 S LOOP 289 79423 #748-02-1978 L1988 **P** *020 †75
PATEL, Arun Dagarambhai. 6309 INDIANA AVE, STE D 79413 #495-89-1981 L1993 **P** *020 †75
PATEL, Bharatkumar M. 4410 50TH ST 79414 #495-89-1980 L1993 **IM** *020 †20
PATEL, Nilesh Devabhai. 6502 SLIDE RD, COVENENT FAMILY HEALTH CTR 79424 #495-89-1989 L1996 **IM** *020 †20
PATEL, Sanjay Harshadbhai. ■ 79423 #495-89-1979 *100
PATEL, Satish U. 3615 19TH ST 79410 #048-15-1988 L1989 **EM FM** *020 †16 ‡
PATTERSON, Patti Jan. 3601 4TH ST STOP 6232, 2B-440 79430 #048-02-1982 L1983 **PD PHP** *030 †55
PATTISON, Monta Kay. ■ 79416 #048-14-2006 **EM** *012
PAULGER, Brent R. 2202 ITHACA AVE STE C, PAULGER DERMATOLOGY 79410 #048-15-1993 L1994 **D** *020 †15
PAXTON, Jeff Willard. 3601 4TH ST, TEXAS TECH UNIVERSITY 79415 #048-13-1984 L1985 **FM** *020 †18
PECK, Elizabeth K. 3601 4TH ST, MS 8143 79430 #048-15-1990 L1991 **FM** *040 †18
PECK, Ricky C. 4501 50TH ST, STE 100 79414 #048-15-1992 L1993 **FM** *020 †18
PEDDADA, Chitra Chauhan. 4102 24TH ST, STE 200 79410 #305-01-1991 L1998 **IM** *020 †20
PEMBER, Merritt Arthur. 4903 6TH ST 79416 #055-01-1999 L2002 **ORS** *020 †40
PENA, Mario, Jr. 5130 82ND ST 79424 #048-15-1977 L1977 **GP** *020 †16
PENDERGRASS, Desiree B. ■ 79413 #048-14-1987 L1988 **PD PHP** *030 †55,70
PENDERGRASS, Peter W. 1109 KEMPER ST 79403 #048-14-1986 L1988 **GPM IM** *020 †70
PERALES, Marsha R. ■ 79424 #048-15-2004 **OBG** *012
PEREIRA, Clifford Thomas. 3601 4TH ST, TX TECH UNIV HLTH SCI CTR 79430 #495-23-1995 L2007 **GS** *100
PEREZ-BENAVIDES, F. 602 INDIANA AVE, UNIV MED CTR NICU 79415 #649-14-1979 L1990 **NPM PD** *020 †55
PERSHALL, Kim Eugene. 3811 24TH ST 79410 #034-01-1981 L1993 **OTO A** *020 †45 ‡
PETTY, Joseph L. 3601 4TH ST, DEPT OBG 79430 #048-14-2006 **OBG** *012
PFEIFFER, Richard Jon. 3502 9TH ST, STE 450 79415 #007-02-1990 L2005 **ORS** *020 †40
PHAN, Doanh Thi Kim. 4000 24TH ST, COVENANT HLTH SYSTEM 79410 #941-01-1969 L1984 **NPM** *020 †55
PHELPS, Brian Steven. ■ 79424 #048-14-2007 **IM** *012
PHILLIPS, Benny Pothen. 3621 22ND ST STE 100 79410 #495-63-1971 L1978 **GO GYN** *020 †30
PHILLIPS, Dana Speer. 3601 4TH ST, MAIL STOP 8300 79430 #048-02-1987 L1988 **OBG** *020 †30
PHIPPS, Ted Lynn. 3610 24TH ST, LUBBOCK DIGESTIVE DISEASE 79410 #048-04-1982 L1983 **GE** *020 †20
PHISITKUL, Kantima. 3601 4TH ST 79430 #891-01-1997 **IM** *012
PHISITKUL, Sorot. 3601 4TH ST, TEXAS TECH UNIV HSC 79415 #891-04-1998 L2007 **NEP** *020 †20
PIEL, Christopher P. 602 INDIANA AVE, UNIV MED CTR EM CTR 79415 #048-15-1997 L1998 **EM** *020 †16
PIERCE, Stephen Arthur. 4102 24TH ST STE 506 79410 #016-42-1974 L1990 **CD IM** *020 †20
PINNAMANENI, Pavan. 3601 4TH ST 79430 #422-01-2002 L2002 **GS** *100
PINTO, Jose Edson Z. 3615 19TH ST, PATHOLOGY 79410 #187-86-1985 L2003 **PTH** *020 †50
PINTO-KINI, Premilla D. PO BOX 93287 79493 #495-09-1966 L1977 **FM EM** *020
PIRTLE, Floyd E. 3502 9TH ST STE 210 79415 #048-15-1997 L1998 **IM** *020 †20
POE, Gregory Scott. 4005 24TH ST 79410 #039-01-2002 L2007 **DR** *020 †80
POLLOCK, Garry R. 4642 N LOOP 289, STE 105 79416 #048-15-1990 L1991 **HS** *020 †40
PORTER, Scott Cranston. 4005 24TH ST 79410 #048-02-1976 L1976 **DR** *020 †80
PORTO, Boris J. 4412 74TH ST, STE E102 79424 #048-02-1986 L1988 **CHP P** *020 †75
POSTERARO, Robert Hugh. 4005 24TH ST 79410 #008-01-1973 L1980 **DR** *020 †80
POTEET, Melissa S. HEALTH SCIENCE, TEXAS TECH UNIV 79430 #048-15-2005 L2007 **PD** *012
POTOCKI, Stanley E. 3621 22ND ST STE 300 79410 #048-15-1994 L1995 **OTO** *020 †45
PRABHAKAR, Sharma S. 3601 4TH ST RM 4C-178, DEPARTMENT OF MEDICINE 79430 #495-65-1976 L1999 **NEP IM** *020 †20
PRABHU, Fiona R. 3601 4TH ST, TEXAS TECH UNIVERSITY 79415 #048-16-1995 L1996 **FM** *040 †18 ‡
PRADERIO, Carolina. ■ 79416 #048-15-2006 **OBG** *012
PRAHARAJ, Meera. PO BOX 402 79408 #495-13-1992 *100
PRASANNAN, Latha. 3606 21ST ST 79410 #495-53-1982 L2003 **PHO** *020 †55
PRATT, Dustin R. 3601 4TH ST, TEXAS TECH UNIVERSITY HSC 79430 #048-15-2005 L2007 **FP** *012
PREVO, Patrick Timothy. ■ 79415 #422-01-2004 L2007 **FSM** *012 †18
PRIDMORE, Ted Thos. 3506 21ST ST 79410 #048-12-1965 L1965 **IM** *071 †20
QADDOUR, Ahmad. ■ 79401 #875-01-1991 L2002 **CD** *020 †20
QUATTROMANI, Frank Louis. 602 INDIANA AVE, PNS/RADIOLOGY DEPARTMENT 79415 #561-01-1967 L1982 **PDR** *020 †80
QUBTY, Johnny. 3601 21ST ST STE 3A 79410 #048-15-1986 L1987 **PME AN** *020 †05
QUICK, Donald Paul. 4101 22ND PL 79410 #048-04-1982 L1983 **HEM ON** *020 †20
QUIGLEY, Lajohn Bradford. ■ 79407 #048-15-2007 **GS** *012
RABENHORST, Brien Michael. HEALTH SCIENCE, TEXAS TECH UNIV 79430 #021-05-2007 **ORS** *012
RACZ, Gabor Bela. 4430 S LOOP 289, INTL PAIN INST 79414 #352-06-1962 L1977 **PMM** *040 †05
RADHI, Saba Hasan. 3601 4TH ST 79430 #695-01-2000 **IM** *012
RAEDEKE, Rebecca. 3506 21ST ST STE 601 79410 #048-15-1987 L1988 **IM** *020 †20
RAGAIN, Roger M. 3601 4TH ST STE 1C143, TTUHSC DEPT FP 79430 #048-12-1992 L1993 **FM** *040 †18
RAJ, Rishi. 3601 4TH ST STOP 9410 79430 #495-27-1995 L2001 **CCM** *020 †20
RAKVIT, Ariwan. GRADUATE MED EDUC, TX TECH UNIV HLTH SCI CTR 79430 #891-01-1998 L2006 **GE** *100 †20 ‡
RAMSEY, Wayne R. 5009 UNIVERSITY AVE 79413 #060-01-1988 **PTH** *020 †50
RAO, Turlapati Ramamohan. 3809 22ND ST STE C 79410 #495-62-1966 L1979 **GS CRS** *020 †85,10
RATNOFF, William Davis. TEXAS TECH UNIV HEALTH SCI 79430 #023-07-1978 L2001 **RHU IM** *020 †20
RAUTH, Virginia Lynn. PO BOX 53233 79453 #048-15-1977 L1977 **OBG RO** *020 †80,30 ‡
RAVI, Hima Bindu. 4102 24TH ST, STE 401 79410 #495-50-1995 L1999 **CHP** *020 †75
RAY, James Robt. 3420 22ND PL 79410 #048-04-1966 L1966 **GP** *040
REDDY, Madhava G. ■ 79416 #495-70-1973 L1980 **IM PD** *062 †55,20
REDDY, Yasodhara M. 3606 21ST ST 79410 #495-70-1974 L1980 **PD** *020 †55
REED, Jimmie Lee. 6400 QUAKER AVE, STE B 79413 #039-01-1965 L1971 **D DR** *020 †80,28
REEVES, Patrick Darren. 4315 28TH ST 79410 #017-20-1994 L1998 **OPH** *020 †35
REID, James J. 3420 22ND PL 79410 #048-15-2003 L2006 **AN** *100
REYNOLDS, Charles A. 4515 MARSHA SHARP FWY 79407 #048-13-1972 L1972 **FM** *020 †18
REYNOLDS, Jana M. ■ 79410 #048-15-2008 *012
REYNOLDS, Rex Hugh. 3612 23RD ST 79410 #048-13-1980 L1980 **U UP** *020 †95
RHYNE, Craig Desmond. 3509 22ND ST 79410 #048-12-1979 L1979 **GS TRS** *020 †85

■ = Address Information Privacy Protected

RICALDI, Carlos A. 3420 22ND PL 79410 #649-33-1980 L2001 **AN** *020
RICE, Kenneth M. 3502 9TH ST STE 170 79415 #048-15-1994 L1995 **IM** *020
RICHARDS, William E. 3621 22ND ST, STE 100 79410 #048-15-1992 L1993 **OBG** *020 †30
RIDELLA, Maricel Lilian. 3601 4TH ST 79430 #132-01-1992 **IM** *012
RIDENS, Dondi D. 3601 4TH ST 79430 #048-15-2000 L2002 **FM** *020 †18 ‡
RIDGE, Charles Houston. ■ 79424 #048-12-1960 L1960 **FM** *020 †18
RISKO, Timothy M. 3601 4TH ST 79430 #048-14-2001 L2004 **ORS** *100
RIVAS, Sammy D. 3611 22ND PL 79410 #048-15-1994 L1995 **GS** *020 †85
RIVAS, Shannon E. 3621 22ND ST STE 400, PULMONARY ASSOCIATES OF LU 79410 #048-15-1997 L1998 **CCM PCC** *020 †20
RIVERA, Diego. 111 N UNIVERSITY AVE 79415 #042-01-1973 L1982 **GP** *020
RIZZO, Joseph Anthony. 4802 N LOOP 289 79416 #035-09-1982 L1995 **CD IM** *020 †20
RJEPAJ, Piro. DEPT OF NEUROPSY-SCH OF ME, TEXAS TECH UNIV 79430 #120-01-1986 L2000 **P** *020 †75 ‡
ROBERTS, James G. 3420 22ND PL 79410 #048-15-2000 L2004 **AN** *020
ROBERTS, Julie Ann. ■ 79407 #048-15-2007 **AN** *012
ROBERTS, Stephen Jan. ■ 79416 #048-15-2005 **ORS** *012
ROBERTSON, Donald Jack. 3710 21ST ST 79410 #048-15-1980 L1980 **TS VS** *020 †85,90
ROBERTSON, Michael David. 3801 50TH ST 79413 #048-15-1982 L1983 **IM** *020 †20
ROBINS, Linda Aryain. 3610 21ST ST 79410 #048-15-1984 L1985 **PD** *020 †55
ROBINS, Nathan Scott. 3615 19TH ST 79410 #048-02-1978 L1979 **IM** *020 †20
ROBINSON, Andrew. 3606 21ST ST 79410 #919-01-1990 L2003 **PDC** *020 †55
ROBINSON, Eldon S. 2602 50TH ST, STE 300 79413 #048-15-1994 L1996 **FM** *020 †18 ‡
ROBINSON, Matthew C. 3601 4TH ST STOP 9410, TT UNIV HEALTH SCIENCES C 79430 #048-15-2001 L2006 **ID** *100
RODRIGUEZ, Enrique, Jr. 2424 5TH ST STE 20 79401 #042-02-1990 L1993 **IM GP** *020
RODRIGUEZ, Ricardo Mateo. 3401 N UNIVERSITY AVE, MENTAL RETARDATION FACILIT 79415 #748-08-1973 L1977 **GP** *020
RODRIGUEZ SALINAS, Sandra. DEPT OF MED, TEXAS TECH UNIV HEALTH SCI 79430 #264-11-1996 L2007 **IM** *100 †20
ROGERS, Brooks. 5215 96TH ST 79424 #048-15-1996 L1997 **PD** *020 †55
ROGERS, Gregory Ben. ■ 79410 #048-15-2008 *012
ROGERS, Karen Leann. 7501 QUAKER AVE, PEDIATRIC ASSOCIATES 79424 #048-15-1997 L1998 **PD** *020 †55
ROGERS, Paul Lynn. 3601 4TH ST, PEDIATRICS DEPARTMENT 79430 #048-02-1969 L1969 **PD** *040 †55
ROHRA, Lakhu Janimal. 4102 24TH ST STE 410 79410 #495-23-1974 L1979 **IM** *020 †20
ROMANO, Michael Jos. 3601 4TH ST 79430 #048-14-1984 L1993 **CCP PD** *020 †55
RONAGHAN, Catherine Ann. 4102 24TH ST, STE 406 79410 #048-15-1986 L1988 **GS SO** *020 †85
ROSE, Christopher R. 3709 22ND PL, UNIT A 79410 #048-15-1998 L1999 **FM** *020 †18
ROSE, James Todd. 1607 W LOOP 289 79416 #048-15-1999 L2004 **NEP** *020 †20
ROSEN, Richard Andrew. 3611 22ND PL, LUBBOCK SURGICAL ASSOCIATE 79410 #048-15-1984 L1985 **GS** *020 †85
ROSENFIELD, Laura Elizabe. ■ 79424 #048-15-2008 *012
ROSENKRANZ, Kristina Mari. ■ 79423 #048-15-2006 **EM** *100
ROSENSTEIN, Alexander D. 3601 4TH ST STOP 9436, DEPARTMENT OF ORTHOPAEDICS 79430 #026-04-1982 L2004 **ORS** *020 †40
ROW, Alan Dockery. 3813 22ND ST STE 5 79410 #048-15-1979 L1979 **OPH** *020 †35
ROWLETT, Carl D. 3620 INTERSTATE 27 79404 #048-15-1987 L1990 **OM PHP** *030 †70
ROWLEY, Jane Marie. 3519 22ND PL 79410 #030-06-1989 L1997 **PS** *020 †85,65
ROWLEY, Milton Martin. 4404 6TH ST 79416 #030-06-1964 L1974 **PS** *020 †85,65
ROY, Itikana D. 3606 21ST ST 79410 #160-02-1987 L2001 **PD** *020 †55
ROZEAN, Randolph Kyle. 5915 82ND ST 79424 #048-15-1985 L1987 **FM** *020 †18
RUDD, Alexandria E. ■ 79430 #048-14-2004 L2008 **AN** *012
RUDINE, Anthony Clark. ■ 79416 #048-15-2008 *012
RUIZ, Arturo. ■ 79499 #034-01-1996 L2000 **FM** *100
RUSH, Sloan W. ■ 79424 #048-13-2005 **OPH** *012
RUTLEDGE, Michael Roberds. ■ 79424 #048-15-2007 **IM** *012
RUZICKA, William Michael. ■ 79410 #048-15-1998 **FM** *100
RYBURN, Frank M, Jr. ■ 79413 #051-01-1948 L1950 **IM** *071 †20
RYBURN, Frank M, III. 3420 23RD ST 79410 #048-13-1976 L1981 **OPH** *020 †35
SABAR, Rajinder. 3601 4TH ST 79430 #495-03-1990 L2005 **AN** *020 †05
SABATINI, Sandra. 3601 4TH ST, DEPT PHYSIOLOGY 79430 #048-13-1974 L1985 **NEP IM** *050
SABOUNI, Ahmad. ■ 79424 #875-02-1999 L2006 **N** *020 †75
SADHU, Ashish Avinash. 3601 4TH ST, DEPT OF INTERNAL MEDICIN 79430 #496-30-2000 L2005 **ICE** *012
SAHINLER, Bolkar Erol. 3501 22ND ST, STE A 79410 #902-03-1993 L2001 **APM** *020 †05
SAHINLER, Michelle D. 3614 23RD ST 79410 #048-15-1999 L2002 **OBG** *020
SALEM, Robert Joe. 3615 19TH ST 79410 #048-12-1955 L1955 **GS** *030 †85
SALLER, Jeremy Matthew. ■ 79401 #048-15-2008 *012
SAMAD, Zahida. 6104 AVENUE Q, VA OUTPATIENT CLINIC 79412 #495-21-1981 L1990 **P CHP** *020
SAMATHANAM, Christina Ann. ■ 79403 #035-46-1997 L2000 **PTH** *020
SAMUEL, Mark C. ■ 79416 #048-15-2005 *100
SANTANA, Dixon. 3601 4TH ST, RM 3A124 79430 #042-01-1990 L2008 **GS VS** *020 †85
SARDELLA, Paul Anthony. 4601 5TH ST STE 11 79416 #010-02-1988 L1996 **AN** *020 †05
SASIN, Edwin Joe, II. 5211 BROWNFIELD HWY, STE 35 79407 #048-15-1988 L1992 **EM** *020 †16
SCHAUB, Lowry P. 3508 22ND PL 79410 #048-14-1987 L1988 **AN** *020 †05
SCHERR, Jay M. 4005 24TH ST 79410 #048-12-1981 L1985 **DR** *020 †80
SCHIFFER, Randolph B. 3601 4TH ST 79415 #025-01-1976 L1999 **N P** *020 †75
SCHMID, Robert Preston. 4102 24TH ST, STE 305 79410 #048-02-1997 L2000 **PS** *020 †65
SCHMIDT, Rita Elizabeth. 3601 4TH ST, 2B-112 79430 #039-01-1996 L2002 **FM** *020 †18
SCHOETTLE, Byron Wayne. 6923 INDIANA AVE, STE 353 79413 #028-79-1984, ▲ L1993 **VIR** *020
SCHOLZ, Kenneth Chas. 1500 BROADWAY, STE 1238 79401 #047-06-1959 L1962 **ORS** *071 †40
SCHRONK, Kenneth D. ■ 79416 #048-13-2006 **AN** *012
SCHUP, Kimberly A. 3303 UNIVERSITY AVE 79410 #048-15-1993 L1994 **GP** *020
SCHUTT, Robert Clark, Jr. 3601 4TH ST STOP 9436, TT UNIV. HEALTH SCIENCES C 79430 #048-15-1977 L1994 **ORS** *020 †40
SCIOLI, Mark Wm. 4642 N LOOP 289 79416 #048-15-1982 L1983 **ORS OFA** *020 †40
SCOLARO, Philip Alan. 3702 21ST ST STE 103 79410 #048-13-1985 L1986 **OTO** *020 †45
SCOTT, Robert W. 3502 9TH ST, STE G10 79415 #048-15-2000 L2003 **PD** *020 †55
SEARS, Kathleen Kay. 3615 19TH ST 79410 #039-01-1976 L1982 **GYN** *020 †30
SEAY, Gaylon Bill. 602 INDIANA AVE 79415 #048-02-1977 L1977 **ORS** *020 †40
SEDLER, Ross Richard. 3601 21ST ST 79410 #005-15-1972 L1977 **NS** *020 †25
SEGER, Michael A. 3621 22ND ST 79410 #048-15-1974 L1978 **IM** *020
SEHLI, Sharmila. DEPT OF MED, TEXAS TECH UNIV HEALTH SCI 79430 #891-03-2000 **IM** *012
SELBY, John Horace. 1500 BROADWAY 79401 #024-05-1944 L1952 **TS GS** *071 †85,90
SETHI-DIHENIA, Chanda S. 3619 22ND PL 79410 #016-11-1992 L1997 **IM** *020 †20
SHALABY, Ibrahim Adly I. 4101 22ND PL 79410 #915-04-1985 L2002 **IM** *020 †20
SHAMI, Michel. 4517 98TH ST, TEXAS RETINA ASSOCIATES 79424 #605-01-1985 L1990 **OPH** *020
SHANNON, Jacky D. 3601 4TH ST, MS 8182 79430 #048-15-2002 L2004 **AN** *100 †05
SHARIF, M Alan. 4802 N LOOP 289 79416 #875-02-1990 L2003 **CD** *020 †20
SHARMA, Sunil H. TX TECH UNIV HLTH SCI CTR 79409 #065-06-1996 **OPH** *100
SHATERY, Morteza. 5204 86TH ST 79424 #010-03-1990 L2000 **TS** *020 †85,90
SHAVER, William Anderson. 2405 BROADWAY 79401 #048-12-1981 L1981 **GE PLM** *020 †20
SHAW, Ralph Preston. 3515 22ND ST 79410 #048-02-1956 L1957 **P** *020 †75
SHEPHARD, David Michael. 3506 21ST ST 79410 #048-13-2002 L2004 **ORS** *020
SHEPPARD, Joseph Earl. 3601 4TH ST 79430 #011-03-1979 L1998 **ORS HS** *020 †40
SHIELDS, Charles Edward. 3601 4TH ST 79430 #035-01-1957 L1976 **FM IM** *071 †18
SHIHAB, Zuhair. 4003 22ND ST 79410 #605-01-1974 L1982 **OPH** *020 †35
SHOME, Goutam Pada. 6502 SLIDE RD 79424 #160-02-1984 L2002 **AI** *020 †03,20
SHOUKFEH, Fawwaz. 3710 21ST ST 79410 #875-01-1970 L1977 **CD IM** *020 †20
SHOWKIER-ZEITOUNI, Nawal. 7501 QUAKER AVE 79424 #048-15-1996 L1997 **PD** *020 †55
SHRESTHA, Shraddha. 3601 4TH ST 79430 #672-07-2002 **PD** *012
SIEFF, Barry Charles. 3601 4TH ST 79430 #836-01-1965 L1980 **R** *071
SIMEK, Robert Zachary. ■ 79423 #048-15-2008 *012
SIMFUKWE, Maybin. 6923 INDIANA AVE, APT 321 79413 #048-02-1999 L2003 **NEP** *100
SIMMONS, Gary Edward. 4005 24TH ST 79410 #012-01-1987 L2001 **DR** *020 †80
SIMONDS, John Francis. ■ 79416 #010-02-1959 L1980 **CHP P** *020 †75
SINGHATIRAJ, Ekachai. 3601 4TH ST 79430 #891-07-1993 **IM** *012
SISSON, Joseph Andrew. ■ 79499 #028-02-1960 L1960 **PTH** *030 †50
SKELTON, Jonathan D. 3615 19TH ST 79410 #048-15-2002 L2003 **EM** *020 †16
SKINNER, Derek I. 4102 24TH ST, STE 101 79410 #048-15-2002 L2004 **GS** *020 †18
SMITH, Gary Dean. 3621 22ND ST 79410 #034-01-1979 L1990 **PUD CCM** *020 †20
SMITH, Harold Karrlin. 3601 21ST ST, NEUROSURGICAL ASSOCIATES, 79410 #004-01-1988 L1995 **NS** *020 †25
SMITH, Jack C, III. 3514 21ST ST 79410 #048-15-2000 L2001 **CD** *020 †20
SMITH, Jeffrey D. 5601 19TH ST, LCU MEDICAL CLINIC 79407 #048-15-1999 L2000 **FM** *020 †18
SMITH, Jeffrey Dean. 5601 19TH ST, LUBBOCK CHRISTIAN UNIVERSI 79407 #020-02-1991 L1992 **CHP P** *020 †75
SMITH, Jennifer Lynn. 3601 4TH ST, STOP 9400 79430 #003-01-1999 L2003 **D** *020 †15
SMITH, Richard Draper. ■ 79416 #030-05-1944 L1958 **ORS** *071 †40
SMITH, Stephen Reilly. 4517 98TH ST 79424 #021-01-2001 L2006 **OPH** *100 †35
SMITHERMAN, Tony Bryan. 4642 N LOOP 289, STE 101 79416 #048-02-1992 L1993 **ORS** *020 †40
SMYER, John R. 4004 82ND ST 79423 #048-15-1995 L1996 **IM** *020 †20
SNEED, Alvin L. 4515 MARSHA SHARP FWY 79407 #048-02-1975 L1975 **FM** *020 †18
SNODGRASS, W T. ■ 79413 #048-02-1955 L1955 **U** *071 †95
SNODGRASS, Wm Bradley. 3801 50TH ST 79413 #048-15-1988 L1989 **IM** *020 †20
SOLIMAN, Magdi Geo. 3419 21ST ST 79410 #915-02-1966 L1977 **AN** *020 †05
SOLIS, Roberto Enrique. 4802 N LOOP 289 79416 #429-02-1987 L1994 **CD IM** *020 †20
SOOD, Vineeta. HEALTH SCIENCE, TEXAS TECH UNIV 79430 #495-90-1993 **NEP** *012 †20
SORIAL, Usama Moris J. TX TECH UNIV HLTH SCI CTR, DEPT-INT MED 79408 #915-03-1987 **IM** *100
SORIANO, Mark Anthony H. 4004 82ND ST, HEALTH POINT 79423 #748-02-1989 L1996 **IM** *020 †20
SOUTH, Mary Ann. ■ 79430 #048-04-1959 L1959 **IG ID** *050 †55
SPARKS, John E. ■ 79416 #048-15-2005 **PD** *012
SPENCE, Kelly Ann. 3615 19TH ST 79410 #048-13-1985 L1988 **PD** *020 †55
SPICER, Melvin Jos. 3601 4TH ST 79430 #010-03-1963 L1987 **NM CD** *030 †20,28
SPIKES, Samuel Compton. 4000 24TH ST 79410 #048-13-1979 L1979 **DR** *020 †80
SPORE, Scott S. 3502 82ND ST, CORNERSTONE UROLOGY 79423 #048-13-1995 L1997 **U** *020 †95
SPRINGER, William Eugene. 3506 21ST ST, STE 507 79410 #017-20-1992 L2000 **TS** *020 †85,90
SRIDAROMONT, Somkid. 3702 20TH ST STE B 79410 #891-03-1967 L1975 **PDC PD** *020 †55
STACHOWIAK, Janice Ann. 3601 4TH ST 79430 #048-02-1994 L1997 **IM** *020 †20
STAFFORD, Bobby Loyd. 3601 4TH ST 79430 #048-12-1965 L1965 **ORS** *071 †40
STALCUP, Obie Lee. 4515 MARSHA SHARP FWY 79407 #048-02-1963 L1963 **U** *020 †95
STALNAKER, Noel Eugene. ■ 79424 #039-01-1976 L1977 **GP EM** *020
STANBAUGH, Glen Harry, Jr. ■ 79407 #048-02-1967 L1967 **NEP IM** *071 †20
STANLEY, Kathleen. 8003 COUNTY ROAD 6920 79407 #056-05-1975 L1978 **P IM** *020 †20,75
STARNES, Joel Dow, III. 3506 21ST ST 79410 #048-15-2002 L2004 **NEP** *020
STEPHENSON, Kenneth A. 4642 N LOOP 289, STE 101 79416 #048-13-1990 L1992 **ORS** *020 †40
STETSON, Cloyce L. 3601 4TH ST # 4A-100, DEPARTMENT DERMATOLOGY 79430 #048-02-1994 L1996 **D DMP** *020 †15
STEVENS, Faustin Riley. ■ 79424 #048-04-2006 **ORS** *012
STEVENSON, James David. ■ 79430 #024-07-1973 L1985 **AM** *030 †70
STEWART, Holly S. 3502 9TH ST, STE 360 79415 #048-15-1994 L1995 **IM** *020
STEWART, Howard Russell. ■ 79423 #048-04-1954 L1954 **R** *020 †80
STOLLENWERCK, John W. ■ 79414 #048-15-1994 **GS** *100
STRAHAN, Wesley Randell. 4102 24TH ST 79410 #048-02-1957 L1957 **FM** *071 †18
STRANGE, David Lowrie. 6104 AVENUE Q SOUTH DR, DEPARTMENT OF VETERANS AFF 79412 #048-13-1975 L1977 **IM** *020 †20
STREIT, John Edward. 4014 22ND PL, STE 4 79410 #048-15-1984 L1985 **OPH** *020
STRICKLAND, Michael Lynn. 602 INDIANA AVE 79415 #048-15-1983 L1983 **AN** *020 †05
STRINGER, Kimberlly Lashu. TTUHSC, DEPT OF PEDIATRICS 79430 #047-06-2005 **PD** *012
STRIPLING, Robert Lee, Jr. 4102 24TH ST, STE 505 79410 #019-02-1966 L1972 **PD** *020
STRIPLING, Stephen W. 3606 21ST ST STE 20 79410 #048-15-1996 L2000 **PD** *020 †55
SUAREZ, Jose Alejandro. 3601 4TH ST STOP 9410 79430 #341-01-1996 L2003 **IC** *020 †20
SUIT, Carol T. 3502 9TH ST STE 150 79415 #048-15-1999 L2000 **OBG** *012 †18
SUTTER, Thelma W K. 3615 19TH ST 79410 #748-01-1972 L1979 **NPM PD** *020 †55
SUTTHIWAN, Piraon. 3601 4TH ST STOP 9410 79430 #891-02-1997 L2004 **CD** *100 †20
SWENSON, J E. 3420 22ND PL 79410 #048-12-1999 L2003 **AN** *020 †05
SWIM, Holly Lynn. 3606 21ST ST 79410 #048-15-2002 L2005 **PD** *020

SYN, David. 2424 50TH ST STE 30, THE ADVANCED BARIATRIC SUR 79412 #035-08-1996 L2002 **GS** *020

TAFUR, Isaac. 4101 22ND PL, AND TREATMENT CENTER 79410 #737-01-1989 L1999 **ON** *020 †20

TALUSAN, Antonio Dizon. 1126 SLIDE RD UNIT 4B 79416 #748-02-1956 L2001 **IM NEP** *020

TALUSAN-GARCIA, Eileen. 7501 QUAKER AVE, KINGSPARK HEALTHCARE CTR 79424 #748-02-1998 L1998 **AI PD** *020 †55,03

TALUSAN-SORIANO, Karen S. 6502 SLIDE RD 79424 #748-02-1989 L1996 **PG** *020 †55

TARAFDAR, Kaiser Rahman R. 3506 21ST ST, STE 605 79416 #690-01-1988 L2003 **IM** *020 †20

TAYLOR, Victor Marcus. ■ 79413 #048-15-2005 L2007 **AN** *012

TELFEIAN, Albert Edward. 3601 21ST ST 79410 #043-01-1993 L2003 **NS** *020

TELLO, Wael. 3601 4TH ST STOP 9410, DEPT OF INTERNAL MEDICINE 79430 #875-01-1985 L1997 **PCC** *020 †20

TER KEURST, Barbara J. ■ 79416 #048-15-1989 *100

TERRELL, Jason Bradley. DEPT OF PATHOLOGY, TEXAS TECH UNIV HEALTH SCI 79430 #048-14-2006 **PTH** *012

THAMES, Elbert Austin, Jr. 3509 22ND ST 79410 #048-12-1975 L1975 **GS** *020 †85

THEO, John Paul. 4102 24TH ST STE 300, THE CENTER OF ORTH SURG 79410 #836-01-1962 L1981 **ORS OS** *071 †40

THIRUMALA, Seshadri. 3615 19TH ST, DEPARTMENT OF PATHOLOGY 79410 #495-57-1987 L2000 **PCP** *012

THOMAS, David Bryan. ■ 79423 #048-15-2008 *012

THOMAS, Ira Lee. 3601 4TH ST, DEPT OF INTERNAL MEDICINE 79430 #048-15-2005 L2008 **IM** *012

THOMAS, John P. 3502 9TH ST STE 160, SOUTH PLAINS SURGICAL ASSO 79415 #048-13-1993 L1993 **GS** *020 †85

THOMAS, Malcolm James, Jr. 3615 19TH ST, CASE MANAGEMENT DEPARTMENT 79410 #021-01-1956 L1960 **TS GS** *030 †85,90

THOMAS, Stephen C. ■ 79424 #048-13-1987 L1993 **DR** *075 †80

THOMPSON, Amy Nel. ■ 79424 #048-15-2004 L2007 **PD** *100 †55

THORNTON, Stanley Frank. 3420 22ND PL 79410 #048-15-1985 L1986 **AN** *020 †05

THURMON, Kelly A. ■ 79423 #048-78-2006, ▲ **IM** *012

TIDWELL, Justin Neil. 5515 27TH ST 79407 #019-02-2001 L2003 **FM** *020 †18

TITUS, Rebin Thomas. 3601 4TH ST, STOP 8413 79430 #496-31-2004 L2006 **IM** *012

TJIA, Stephanus Richard. 3420 22ND PL 79410 #506-02-1964 L1971 **AN PME** *020

TORI, Carlos Rizo-Patron. 3711 22ND ST, STE A 79410 #737-06-1983 L1995 **ICE CD** *020 †20

TORIO, Rolando Nagar. 5811 11TH PL, SIXTEEN OAKS, # 8 79416 #748-10-1972 L1977 **IM EM** *020

TORRES, Carlos Pangan. 8409 COUNTY ROAD 6940, SWCTRC 79407 #748-02-1979 L1999 **RO** *020 †80

TRAN, Hoa Huu. 3601 4TH ST STE 1C1, TEXAS TECH UNIVERISTY HSC 79430 #048-15-2004 L2007 **FP** *012

TRAN, Manh Ruc. 3601 4TH ST, PATH 79430 #941-01-1970 L1979 **PTH** *020 †50

TROTTER, Rodney H. ■ 79424 #048-15-1993 L1995 **PD** *020 †55

TURNBOW, John Meredith. 3315 81ST ST, STE A 79423 #005-12-1973 L1986 **PD OS** *020 †55

TYLER, Cheryl Marie. 3626 50TH ST, STE B 79413 #048-02-1982 L1983 **FM** *030 †18

UKEGBU, Ibidunni Omolayo. 3506 21ST ST 79410 #690-05-1990 L2002 **IM** *020 †20

UMEZURIKE, Ikechukwu Cyra. 3506 21ST ST 79410 #690-04-1994 L2007 **IM** *020 †20

UONG, Vuong Minh. ■ 79401 #048-12-2006 L2008 **IM** *012

UY, Roberto Nicolas. TX TECH HLTH SCI CTR, DEPT OPTHAL 79430 #748-01-1987 **OPH** *020

VAHORA, Shiraj. 3709 19TH ST, PMB 486 79410 #495-01-1976 L1987 **P** *020 †75

VALDEZ, Nancy. 3601 4TH ST, DEPARTMENT OF PEDIATRICS 79430 #048-15-1999 L2002 **PD** *020 †55

VALLABHAN, Girish C. 4009 19TH ST STE D 79410 #048-13-1988 L1989 **U** *020 †95

VAN BUREN, David Howard. 3601 4TH ST STOP 7260, TTUHSC DEPT OF UROLOGY 79430 #038-44-1981 L1983 **GS OS** *020 †85

VARGAS, Salvador. ■ 79416 #649-14-1976 **P** *100

VARIYAM, Easwaran P. 602 INDIANA AVE 79415 #495-44-1970 L2003 **GE IM** *020 †20

VARMA, Kamlesh. 2424 50TH ST, RM 302 79412 #495-05-1960 L1973 **OBG FM** *020

VARMA, Surendra Kumar. SCHOOL OF MED, TEXAS TECH UNIV HELTH SCIE 79430 #495-05-1962 L1974 **PDE PD** *020 †55

VASANDANI, Jitendra I. 5220 80TH ST 79424 #035-15-1995 L2000 **RHU IM** *020 †55

VAZQUEZ, Hugo Serafin. 3420 22ND PL 79410 #649-30-2001 L2007 **AN** *100

VEAZEY, Bradley B. 3601 4TH ST STOP 9436, TEXAS TECH UNIVERSITY HSC 79430 #048-14-2001 L2005 **ORS** *100

VERMILLION, David L. 3106 50TH ST STE 40 79413 #048-15-2003 L2004 **FM** *020 †18

VILLA, Ruben Dario. 1607 W LOOP 289 79416 #264-12-1988 L2005 **NEP** *100 †20

VILLARREAL, Aliver. ■ 79416 #649-14-1976 **FM** *012

VILLARREAL, Miguel R. 3601 4TH ST 1C143 79430 #048-15-1999 L2002 **FM** *020 †18

VISWANATHAN, Baluswamy. 3601 4TH ST, DEPT OF PEDIATRICS 79430 #495-66-1979 L1992 **PD CCP** *020 †55

VITALI, Ariel Antonio, Jr. ■ 79416 #032-01-1994 **P** *012

VIVO, Rey Percival Duarte. 3601 4TH ST STOP 9410, TX TECH UNIV HEALTH SCIENC 79430 #748-02-2002 L2007 **IM** *100 †20

VOGT-HARENKAMP, Christiane. 3601 4TH ST, DEPT OF ANESTHEISOLOGY 79430 #409-38-1980 L2007 **AN** *100

VORDERMARK, Jonathan S. 3502 9TH ST STE 260, UNIVERSITY UROLOGY ASSOCIA 79415 #051-04-1974 L1979 **UP U** *020 †95

VU, Bao Huu. ■ 79424 #941-01-1963 L1981 **FM** *020 †18

VUGRIN, Davor. 3702 21ST ST, STE 104 79410 #957-01-1968 L1986 **ON HEM** *020 †20

VUSIREDDY, Chowdeswari. 79424 #495-70-1997 **OBG** *100

WAAGNER, David Craig. 3601 4TH ST, 2B-112 79430 #048-15-1984 L1985 **ID PD** *020 †55

WACHTEL, Mitchell Steven. 3601 4TH ST STOP 8115, DEPT PATH 79430 #011-02-1985 L2000 **PTH PCP** *020 †50,19

WAITS, Bryan Scott. DEPARTMENT OF SURGERY, TEXAS TECH UNIV HEALTH SCI 79430 #305-01-2006 **GS** *012

WALTER, Paul David. 3514 21ST ST 79410 #024-01-1971 L1979 **CD IM** *020 †20

WALTERS, George Ronald. 4920 S LOOP 289 STE 101 79414 #048-02-1975 L1975 **OPH** *020 †35

WARMOTH, Larry A. 3801 21ST ST, STE A 79410 #048-15-1992 L1993 **IM NEP** *020 †20

WARREN, Cheryl L. 7501 QUAKER AVE 79424 #048-16-1994 L1995 **FM** *020 †18

WARREN, Donald John. ■ 79423 #035-15-1947 L1948 **GS EM** *071 †85

WARREN, Sabrina M. 3601 4TH ST, MS 8130 79420 #048-15-2000 **P** *100

WARREN, Thomas R. 3601 4TH ST STOP 8312, TEXAS TECH UNIVERSITY HSC 79430 #048-16-1994 L1995 **GS** *020 †85

WATKINS, Jon Robin. ■ 79407 #048-15-2006 L2007 **FP** *012

WEATHERS, Luther B, III. 3514 21ST ST, CARDIOLOGY ASSOCIATES OF L 79410 #048-15-1991 L1992 **CD IM** *020 †20

WEBB, James Butts. ■ 79408 #047-06-1947 L1967 **P N** *071

WEBER, Cheryl Ferguson. 2424 50TH ST RM 104 79412 #034-01-1983 L1986 **PM R** *020 †60

WEDDIGE, Richard La Vern. 3401 N UNIVERSITY AVE, BOX 5396 79415 #048-01-1965 L1965 **P** *020 †75

WEITLAUF, Harry Monroe. TEXAS TECH UNIV HEALTH S, DEPT ANATOMY 79430 #054-04-1963 L1972 **OBG OS** *050

WELLS, Guy Alan. 3819 24TH ST 79410 #048-02-1977 L1977 **CD IM** *020 †20

WELLS, Michael Johnathan. 602 INDIANA AVE 79415 #004-01-1997 L2001 **D** *020 †15

WELT, Selman Irvin. 3601 4TH ST STOP 8340, TEXAS TECH UNIV DEPT OB-GY 79430 #036-01-1972 L1991 **MFM OBS** *020 †30

WERTZ, Rodney Arthur. 3621 22ND ST STE 400 79410 #005-12-1976 L1989 **PUD** *020 †20

WEST, Tim L. 4102 24TH ST, STE 101 79410 #048-12-1979 L1979 **GS** *020 †85

WEY, Robert Jerome. 4802 N LOOP 289 79416 #007-02-1968 L1975 **CD** *020 †20

WHEELER, Clarence Jos, III. 1126 SLIDE RD UNIT 4B 79416 #048-13-1980 L1980 **NEP IM** *020 †20

WHEELER, Ernest Jay. ■ 79424 #048-04-1966 L1966 **OS PTH** *071

WHEELER, Jane E. ■ 79424 #048-15-1984 L1985 **PD** *074 †55

WHITE, Cecil Eugene. 6104 AVENUE Q, VA OUTPATIENT CLINIC 79412 #048-04-1959 L1959 **OBG** *020 †30

WHITE, Kenneth K. 4005 24TH ST 79410 #048-02-1999 L2003 **DR** *020 †80

WHITE, Steven Clark. 4005 24TH ST 79410 #039-01-1998 L2003 **DR** *020 †80

WHITE, Travis Albert. 3601 4TH ST 1BC113, TEXAS TECH UNIV HLTH SCI C 79430 #048-04-1960 L1960 **R** *020

WHITESIDE, Clarence King. 6811 PEORIA AVE 79413 #048-12-1959 L1959 **PD AM** *071 †55

WHITT, Winston A. 5201 INDIANA AVE, STE 103 79413 #048-15-1992 L1993 **CD IM** *020

WILLIAMS, Benjamin J. 3601 4TH ST 79415 #048-02-1987 L1988 **N** *020 †75

WILLIAMS, Brianne Nicole. 3601 4TH ST, DEPT OF FAMILY MEDICINE 79430 #048-15-2006 L2007 **FP** *012

WILLIAMS, Jason A. 3601 4TH ST MS 7415 79430 #048-15-2003 L2005 **AN** *012

WILLIAMS, Julia Kristina. ■ 79423 #048-15-2008 *012

WILLIAMS, Marion Ophelia. 8602 PEACH AVE, TEXAS TECH UNIVERSITY HSC 79404 #004-01-1990 L1995 **IM P** *020 †20,75

WILLIAMS, Thomas Barry. 3707 21ST ST 79410 #048-02-1956 L1956 **R** *071 †80

WILLIAMS, William Clyde. 3610 24TH ST, LUBBOCK DIGESTIVE DISEASE 79410 #048-02-1979 L1980 **GE IM** *020 †20

WILLIS, Harlan L. ■ 79424 #048-04-1953 L1953 **GP GS** *071 †85

WILSON, Billy Herbert. 4315 28TH ST 79410 #048-12-1965 L1969 **OPH** *020 †35

WILSON, Edward Allen. ■ 79416 #017-20-1962 L1975 **AN** *071 †18,05

WILSON, Gerald Leslie. ■ 79416 #062-01-1953 L1976 **OBG** *071 †30

WILSON, Hugh Holmes, Jr. 8602 PEACH AVE 79404 #048-12-1969 L1969 **FM** *020 †18

WILSON, Joseph Nathan. 4642 N LOOP 289, STE 101-201 79416 #034-01-1982 L1990 **ORS** *020 †40

WILSON, Lawrence Ray, Jr. 4601 50TH ST, STE 112 79414 #048-12-1960 L1960 **AN** *071 †05

WILSON, Selma Pierce. 4642 N LOOP 289, STE 211 79416 #034-01-1985 L1990 **PMM AN** *020 †15

WINDISCH, Lola Bennett. 2424 50TH ST, RM 303 79412 #048-16-1990 L1991 **HMP** *020 †50

WINDISCH, Thomas Richard. 4005 24TH ST 79410 #048-16-1991 L1992 **R RNR** *020 †80

WINTER, Mark Lee. 4432 S LOOP 289 79414 #028-03-1976 L1977 **OTO NO** *020 †45

WISHNEW, Jenna Layne. ■ 79416 #048-02-2006 *012

WISNIEWSKI, Keith Wayne. ■ 79416 #048-15-2003 L2006 **D** *100 †15

WOLBOLDT, Clinton G. 7601 QUAKER AVE 79424 #038-43-1990 L1997 **FM** *020 †18

WOLCOTT, Joseph John. ■ 79416 #048-15-2006 L2007 **IM** *012

WOLCOTT, Randall Dennis. 2002 OXFORD AVE 79410 #039-01-1981 L1984 **PM** *020 †18,60

WOLCOTT, Roger J. 4321 BROWNFIELD RD 79407 #048-15-1992 L1993 **PM** *020 †60

WOLFE, James Townsend. 4005 24TH ST 79410 #048-02-1984 L1989 **DR** *020 †80

WOOLAM, Gerald Lynn. 4000 24TH ST 79410 #048-04-1962 L1962 **GS** *071 †85

WORD, Joe Max. 3801 50TH ST 79413 #048-12-1960 L1960 **DR NM** *071 †80

WRIGHT, Douglas H. 4005 24TH ST 79410 #048-14-1990 L1991 **DR** *020 †80

WRIGHT, Tropha A. ■ 79410 #034-01-2007 **GS** *012

WURTS, Lynne Courtney. 4102 24TH ST 79410 #048-15-1979 L1979 **D** *020 †15

WYATT, Jonathan David. ■ 79416 #004-01-2006 **ORS** *012

YANDELL, Roger Bryan. 3601 4TH ST, MAIL STOP 8340-DEPT OB/GYN 79430 #048-02-1980 L1980 **OBG** *020 †30

YANG, William Wenlong. 3601 4TH ST, HEALTH SCIENCE CENTER 79430 #056-05-2004 L2007 **OPH** *012

YAQUB, Yasir. 3601 4TH ST, DEPT OF FAMILY MED 79430 #704-01-2002 **IM** *012

YATES, Marissa R Fout. 3601 4TH ST 1C143 79430 #048-15-2005 L2006 **FP** *012

YEH, I-Tien. 6610 QUAKER AVE 79413 #004-01-1982 L1999 **PTH** *040 †50

YOUNG, Luke Yuanfeng. ■ 79410 #048-15-2003 L2006 **AN** *012

ZALLOUM, Sameeh M J. ■ 79424 #575-01-1989 L1999 **PD EM** *020 †55

ZEPEDA, Maria Cristina. ■ 79416 #048-04-1972 L1972 **OM** *020 †70

ZIAS, John. 4010 22ND ST 79410 #035-08-1983 L1988 **CD IM** *020 †20

ZUBE, Robert L. 3615 19TH ST 79410 #048-12-2002 L2004 **EM** *020 †16

ZUMAYA, Marbella. ■ 79416 #048-15-2006 L2007 **FP** *012

ZUMWALT, Mimi Anh. 3502 9TH ST, STE 450 79415 #004-01-1989 L1999 **ORS OSM** *020 †40

LUFKIN – ANGELINA

ALEXANDER, Johnny B. 190 HICKORY HOLLOW RD 75904 #048-02-1969 L1969 **OTO AM** *071 †45

ALLEN, Cedric Augustus. PO BOX 1648, LUFKIN STATE SCHOOL 75902 #005-12-1955 L1959 **FM** *071 †18

ARNOLD, Hiram Pinckney. ■ 75901 #048-02-1940 L1940 **GYN** *071 †30

ARNOLD, Michael Laverne. 401 GASLIGHT BLVD 75904 #048-02-1978 L1978 **OBG** *020 †30

ATKINSON, Basil Eric. 1608 W FRANK AVE 75904 #048-12-1956 L1956 **OS GP** *020

AYALA, Cynthia Marie. 10 MEDICAL CENTER BLVD 75904 #035-46-1995 L1999 **FM** *100 †14

BACHIREDDY, Ravinder. 310 GASLIGHT BLVD 75904 #495-21-1973 L1980 **IC IM** *020 †20

BAILEY, David John. 1111 W FRANK AVE STE 301 75904 #021-05-1987 L1994 **OTO GS** *020 †45

BARRETT, John G. 1201 W FRANK AVE 75904 #048-04-1952 L1952 **AN** *020

BENITEZ, Marcos Antonio. 511 GASLIGHT BLVD 75904 #270-02-1995 L2004 **N** *020

BLAKESTAD, Blaine Randall. 121 GASLIGHT MEDICAL PKWY, STE 102 75904 #039-01-1977 L1977 **TS** *020 †85,90
BOLNICK, Harold L. 505 S JOHN REDDITT DR, SUGERY DEPT-ANESTHESIA 75904 #035-08-1979 L1981 **AN U** *020 †05
BORTOT, Andrea Teixeira. ■ 75901 #305-01-1998 L2003 **ADL** *020 †55
BRASHEAR, Doyle Hubbard. 1226 ELLIS AVE 75904 #048-02-1955 L1955 **P GP** *020
BROOKS, John Roger. 1306 W FRANK AVE 75904 #035-01-1964 L1983 **OPH** *020 †35
BROOKS, Vivian Earl H. 915 ELLIS AVE 75904 #067-01-1954 L1978 **GS** *071 †85
BRUCE, James Roy. 700 GASLIGHT BLVD 75904 #021-01-1978 L1978 **PTH** *030 †50
BRYANT, William W. ■ 75904 #038-40-1948 L1965 **R** *071 †80
BUSTAMANTE, Hanzy Ferrer. 505 S JOHN REDDITT DR 75904 #748-01-1998 L2005 **IM** *020 †20
CAMPBELL, Brent Barton. 1111 W FRANK AVE, STE 201 75904 #047-06-1989 L1997 **U GS** *020 †95
CAPELLAN-CUEVAS, Jose A. 3 MEDICAL CENTER BLVD 75904 #308-02-1978 L1996 **PCC** *020 †20
CARLIN, Brian Timothy. HWY 69 NORTH, LUFIN STATE SCHOOL 75902 #649-14-1973 L1976 **FM** *020 †18
CARTER, John Danl. 409 GASLIGHT BLVD, STE 2 75904 #048-04-1974 L1974 **ORS** *020 †40
CARTER, Kaywin Mahoney. 503 S JOHN REDDITT DR 75904 #039-01-1983 L1988 **OBG** *020 †30
CASKEY, James Michael. 206 GENE SAMFORD DR, STE B 75904 #048-02-1977 L1977 **FM** *020 †18 ‡
CHANDRASEKAR, Jeevaratnam. 310 GASLIGHT BLVD 75904 #495-59-1974 L1983 **CD IM** *020 †20
CHANG, Nai Kwei. PO BOX 1648, U. S. HIGHWAY 69N 75902 #244-03-1962 L1978 **IM** *020
CHERIYAN, Abraham Fenn. 206 GASLIGHT BLVD 75904 #495-27-1978 L1996 **PUD CCM** *020 †20
CHERIYAN, Sarah. 206 GASLIGHT BLVD 75904 #495-27-1977 L1996 **AI** *020 †20,03
CHERRY, Lila Varghese. 107 MEDICAL PARK DR 75904 #495-31-1974 L1982 **PM** *075 †60
CLARK, Darwin Keith. 1413 BENDING BROOK CIR, 2306 WEST FRANK STREET 75904 #011-02-1991 L1993 **DR** *020 †80
COLE, Melvin Stephenson. 1111 W FRANK AVE STE 301 75904 #048-02-1982 L1983 **GS** *020 †85
COLEMAN, Troy T. 2306 W FRANK AVE STE C 75904 #048-02-1994 L1996 **RNR** *020 †80
CONNELL, Anna B. ■ 75904 #048-04-1949 L1950 **FM** *071 †18
CORLEY, Ronald Gene. 409 GASLIGHT BLVD 75904 #021-05-1964 L1971 **ORS** *020 †40
DAVIS, Glenn Monroe. 1405 BENDING BROOK CIR 75904 #048-12-1976 L1976 **DR** *020 †80
DEAN, Odell Jos, Jr. 302 MEDICAL PARK DR, STE 104 75904 #021-05-1983 L1996 **U TTS** *020 †95
DESHPANDE, Pratibha Amol. 505 S JOHN REDDITT DR, HOSPITALIST OFFICE 75904 #495-56-1986 L1999 **IM** *020 †20
DE VORE, Michael Scott. 357 HICKORY HOLLOW RD 75904 #048-13-1975 L1975 **IM** *020 †20
DOMINGUE, Edward Louis. 409 GASLIGHT BLVD, STE 4 75904 #021-05-1966 L1973 **ORS** *020 †40
DUNCAN, Thomas Everett. 1306 W FRANK AVE 75904 #021-01-1968 L1969 **OPH** *020 †35 ‡
DUVALL, Cody B. 505 S JOHN REDDITT DR, WOODLANDS HEIGHTS MEDICAL 75904 #048-02-1993 L1994 **DR** *020 †80
EDDINS, Frank Meredith. 1301 W FRANK AVE 75904 #048-02-1963 L1963 **GP OS** *020
FERCOWICZ, Andrew. 202 S JOHN REDDITT DR 75904 #759-10-1976 L1996 **FM OBG** *020 †18
FIDONE, George S. 205 GENE SAMFORD DR 75904 #048-16-1987 L1988 **PD** *020 †55
FOGEROUSSE, Chas Louis. 401 GASLIGHT BLVD 75904 #048-02-1978 L1978 **OBG** *020 †30
GARRETT, Robert I. ■ 75904 #048-04-1949 L1949 **GS** *071 †85
GEORGE, Sushil. 206 GASLIGHT BLVD 75904 #495-53-1986 L1997 **IM PCC** *020 †20
GLASS, Jeffrey Lee. 205 GENE SAMFORD DR 75904 #048-02-1995 L1999 **PD** *020 †55
GLENN, David Wren. 1111 W FRANK AVE, STE 100 75904 #021-06-1983 L1986 **IM** *020 †20
GOFF, Melui Hamilton. 505 GASLIGHT BLVD 75904 #020-02-1981 L1984 **FM** *071 †18
GONZALEZ, Waldo. 302 MEDICAL PARK DR # 101 75904 #649-01-1958 L1966 **GS** *020 †85
GRAVES, Cristina M. 205 GENE SAMFORD DR 75904 #048-13-2003 L2006 **PD** *020 †55
GRAY, John P. 1201 W FRANK AVE, MMCET DEPT OF ANESTHESLGY 75904 #048-12-1994 L1999 **AN** *020 †05
GRIFFIN, James Richard. ■ 75904 #048-12-1961 L1961 **DR** *071
GUSE, Roy J, Jr. 208 GASLIGHT BLVD 75904 #056-06-1983 L1985 **ORS OAR** *020 †40
GUTIERREZ, Raul Mario. PO BOX 567, 821 W FRANK ST 75902 #649-02-1961 L1970 **PTH** *071 †50
HALLETT, Robert Victor. 1111 W FRANK AVE, STE 202 75904 #035-08-1972 L2004 **CD CCM** *020 †20
HALTER, Jack Chandler. 402 GASLIGHT BLVD 75904 #048-04-1971 L1971 **IM** *020 †20
HAMBRIC, Bryan W. 302 MEDICAL PARK DR 75904 #048-04-1996 L1998 **GS** *020 †85
HANDLEY, David L. 505 S JOHN REDDITT DR, WOODLANDS HEIGHTS MEDICAL 75904 #048-02-1992 L1993 **DR** *020 †80
HANDLEY, Melissa N. 205 GENE SAMFORD DR, THE CHILD CLC 75904 #048-02-1992 L1993 **PD** *020 †55
HARRIS, Stephen Dale. 1201 W FRANK AVE 75904 #048-12-1982 L1990 **AN** *020 †05
HAYNES, C Doyle. 1201 W FRANK AVE, OF EAST TEXAS 75904 #048-14-1974 L1975 **EM** *020 †16
HUBER, Michael Hunt. 1111 W FRANK AVE, STE 100 75904 #048-14-1996 L1997 **IM** *020
HUMPHREYS, Brian Francis. 121 GASLIGHT MEDICAL PKWY, STE 100 75904 #005-14-1979 L1987 **HNS OTO** *020 †45
IVERSEN, Michael G. 525 N BRENTWOOD 75904 #048-13-1989 L1991 **FM EM** *020 †18
JANES, J Mark. 4101 S MEDFORD DR, BURKE CENTER 75901 #039-01-1989 L1991 **CHP P** *020 †75
JENKINS, Jerry H. 1105 W FRANK AVE, STE 290 75904 #048-12-1994 L1995 **FM OBS** *020 †18 ‡
JOHNSON, Jerry Lee. 503 S JOHN REDDITT DR 75904 #048-12-1991 L1992 **OBG** *020 †30
JONES, Corinne Cofer Monk. ■ 75904 #048-02-1942 L1943 **PD** *071
KARNATI, Sudheer Reddy. 5 MEDICAL CENTER BLVD 75904 #495-21-1988 L1998 **IM** *020 †20
KENT, William R. 505 S JOHN REDDITT DR, WOODLANDS HEIGHTS MEDICAL 75904 #048-04-1977 L1977 **DR** *020 †80
KHALIL, Sondra Louise. ■ 75901 #048-14-1978 L1978 **IM** *020 †20
KHAN, Ghazala B. 205 GENE SAMFORD DR, THE CHLDREN'S CLINIC OF LU 75904 #704-25-1988 L1996 **PD** *020 †55
KHAN, Mohammed Musa. 310 GASLIGHT BLVD 75904 #704-02-1985 L1997 **CD IM** *020 †20
KHAN, Wasim M. 505 S JOHN REDDITT DR, EMERGENCY ROOM 75904 #065-09-1991 L1996 **GP** *020
KHOSHNEVIS-ASL, Gholamreza. 310 GASLIGHT BLVD 75904 #517-08-1989 L1997 **IM ICE** *020 †20
KISTLER, Annaliese E. ■ 75904 #048-02-2008 *012
KISTLER, Billy Gene. 2304 COPELAND ST 75904 #004-01-1962 L1963 **R** *020 †80
KISTLER, Robert David. 3804 S MEDFORD DR 75901 #048-02-1984 L1985 **FM** *020 †18
KOVVALI, Venkata. 310 GASLIGHT BLVD 75904 #495-11-1975 L1994 **CD** *020 †20
KROHN, Karl L. 10 MEDICAL CENTER BLVD, STE E 75904 #048-12-1989 L1990 **IM** *020 †20
KROHN, Kyle Gregory. 10 MEDICAL CENTER BLVD, STE E 75904 #048-12-1989 L1990 **IM** *020 †20
KUMAR, Prashant. 1111 W FRANK AVE, STE 303 75904 #495-45-1998 L2006 **NEP** *020
KYGER, Edgar Ross, III. 2143 FM 819 75901 #041-01-1967 L1969 **TS GS** *071 †85,90
LARNED, David L. 4101 S MEDFORD DR, THE BURKE CENTER 75901 #048-02-1989 L1990 **P** *020
LINDSEY, Robert M. 208 GASLIGHT BLVD 75904 #048-02-1989 L1990 **PM** *020 †60
LUGO-GONZALEZ, Agricel. 3 MEDICAL CENTER BLVD 75904 #308-02-1979 L1996 **RHU IM** *020 †20
MALLADI, Bhagvan Reddy. 319 GASLIGHT BLVD 75904 #495-65-1973 L1981 **IM GE** *020 †20
MALLADI, Suhasini. 319 GASLIGHT BLVD 75904 #495-21-1974 L1982 **PD** *020 †55
MALLADI, Vikram Reddy. 319 GASLIGHT BLVD 75904 #495-13-2000 L2003 **GE** *020 †20
MANGLA, Vivek. 310 GASLIGHT BLVD 75904 #496-09-1990 L1997 **CD IM** *020 †20
MATHEW, Cherry. 107 MEDICAL PARK DR 75904 #495-08-1973 L1981 **N P** *020 †75
MC CLAIN, John B. 232 N JOHN REDDITT DR, STE B 75904 #048-12-1994 L1995 **FM OBS** *020 †18
MC CLURE, Clarence Harold. 300 N JOHN REDDITT DR 75904 #048-02-1972 L1972 **FM** *020 †18 ‡
MC LAURIN, Thomas Banks. 2306 W FRANK AVE, STE C 75904 #048-04-1989 L1991 **DR** *020 †80
MICKELSON, Morris Len. 1111 W FRANK AVE, STE 100 75904 #025-07-1981 L2005 **IM** *020 †20
MORAN, Sean. 1111 W FRANK AVE, STE 100 75904 #048-02-1990 L1992 **IM** *020 †20
MUNIR, Ahmad. 1202 W FRANK AVE, EAST TEXAS HEMOTOLOGY/ONCO 75904 #704-15-1983 L1995 **ON PP** *020 †20
NAZEER, Imran. 1111 W FRANK AVE, STE 303 75904 #704-01-1985 L1996 **NEP** *020 †20
NEWTON, George W. 704 GASLIGHT BLVD 75904 #038-44-1988 L1997 **PS GS** *020 †85,65 ‡
ODERO, Dickson Dancus O. 10 MEDICAL CENTER BLVD, STE B 75904 #905-01-1970 L1979 **IM** *020 †20
ORMAN, Forrest C. 1011 SHERWOOD RD 75904 #048-02-1942 L1942 **GS** *071 †85
PARKER, Owen Stanley. 2807 DANIEL MCCALL DR, APT 214 75904 #422-01-1983 L1988 **EM IM** *020 †20
PATEL, Parul. 1105 W FRANK AVE STE 250 75904 #048-13-1991 L1992 **FM** *020 †18
PEDDU, Koteswara Prasad. 515 GASLIGHT BLVD 75904 #495-37-1973 L1995 **IM** *020
PEITERSEN, Stig Enggaard. 1111 W FRANK AVE, STE 302 75904 #039-01-1990 L1996 **NS** *020 †25
PICKETT, Brian R. 1111 W FRANK AVE STE 203 75904 #048-04-1977 L1977 **CD** *020 †20
PINNAMANENI, Kavitha. 1202 W FRANK AVE 75904 #495-11-1974 L1980 **ON HO** *020 †20
PINNAMANENI, Lenin. ■ 75904 #495-50-1972 L1981 **IM** *020 †20
PLYLER, Charles G. 1411 TURTLE CREEK DR 75904 #048-02-1960 L1960 **P** *020
RAMNATH, Priya. ■ 75901 #495-01-1992 L2004 **AN** *020 †05
READ, Royce Edwin. 1201 W FRANK AVE, MMCET 75904 #048-02-1958 L1958 **UM** *071 †18
REDDY, Bramham A. 1202 W FRANK AVE 75904 #654-01-1996 L2003 **HO** *020 †20
REDDY, Moolamalla R. 319 GASLIGHT BLVD 75904 #495-57-1973 L1984 **GE IM** *020 †20
REID, Walter Jamar. 915 ELLIS AVE RM 219 75904 #048-02-1957 L1957 **GYN** *071
ROBERTS, Sidney C. 1201 W FRANK AVE 75904 #048-04-1987 L1988 **RO** *020 †80
RODGERS, Roger Wm. 1201 W FRANK AVE # D5 75904 #016-06-1972 L1977 **ON HEM** *020 †20
ROWLEY, Matthew J. 107 CHRISTIE DR 75904 #048-12-1990 L1991 **D** *020 †15
RUCKMAN, Richard John. 2 MEDICAL CENTER BLVD, THE CENTER FOR SIGHT 75904 #048-04-1974 L1974 **OPH** *020 †35
RUDIS, John Anthony. 206 GENE SAMFORD DR STE A 75904 #048-02-1986 L1987 **FM OBS** *020 †18
RUNYAN, Bratcher L. 302 MEDICAL PARK DR, STE 101 75904 #048-14-2002 L2007 **GS** *020 †85
SAMUEL, Varughese P. 1113 ELLIS AVE 75904 #495-27-1973 L1989 **IM** *020
SANTIAGO, Josefa. 202 S BYNUM ST, STE 202 75904 #748-01-1987 L2001 **IM** *020 †20
SANTIAGO, Samuel Sengco. 202 S BYNUM ST 75904 #748-01-1987 L2001 **IM** *020 †20
SAXTON, James Earl. 300 N JOHN REDDITT DR # 7 75904 #048-02-1968 L1968 **IM GS** *020 †18
SCHLAUDT, William R, Jr. 1301 W FRANK AVE 75904 #048-04-1981 L1982 **FM** *020 †18
SLOAN, Lance Alan. 10 MEDICAL CENTER BLVD, STE A 75904 #048-14-1985 L1986 **NEP IM** *020 †20
SPINKS, Jerry Lee. 410 GASLIGHT BLVD 75904 #048-02-1973 L1973 **FM** *020 †18
SPIVEY, Dan. ■ 75904 #048-04-1947 L1947 **FM** *071 †18
STRINDEN, William Dean. 116 CHRISTIE DR 75904 #005-06-1981 L1988 **PS** *020 †65,85
SUITER, Cheryl R. 1105 W FRANK AVE STE 200 75904 #048-13-1993 L1995 **OBG** *020 †30
THAMES, Wm Dennis, Jr. 818 W FRANK AVE 75904 #021-01-1947 L1948 **FM** *071 †18
THANNISCH, George E. 1218 ELLIS AVE, GEORGE THANNISCH MD 75904 #048-04-1953 L1953 **PD** *071 †55
THOMAS, Jacob Mannoor. 818 W FRANK AVE 75904 #495-28-1963 L1983 **IM PUD** *020 †20
TIMMONS, Teresa Ann. 1514 ELLIS AVE, DEPT OF VA CHARLES WILSON 75904 #026-08-1984 L1985 **P** *020 †75 ‡
TODD, David Lee. ■ 75901 #047-06-1991 L1996 **SP** *020 †50
TODD, Teresa D. ■ 75901 #038-41-1991 L1996 **PTH** *020 †50
URQUIA, Karina Janeth. 121 GASLIGHT MEDICAL PKWY, STE 101 75904 #451-01-1996 L2002 **FM** *020 †18
VASQUEZ, Mariela. 1201 W FRANK AVE, DEPT PATHOLOGY 75904 #187-08-1989 L1994 **PTH DMP** *020 †50
VEGIRAJU, Krishn Am Raju. ■ 75904 #495-11-1993 L2003 **AN** *100
VENKATAYAN, Natarajan. 505 S JOHN REDDITT DR 75904 #495-61-1988 L2006 **FM** *020 †18
WAGNON, Jackson Dan. 208 GASLIGHT BLVD 75904 #048-02-1984 L1985 **ORS** *020 †40
WAGNON, William E, Jr. ■ 75901 #048-02-1953 L1953 **ORS** *020 †40
WAGNON, William Wright. 2801 S JOHN REDDITT DR, STE B 75904 #048-02-1978 L1978 **OPH** *020 †35
WELLS, Terry Lynn. 1015 ELLIS AVE 75904 #048-02-1991 L1992 **FM** *020 †18
WILLIAMS, Julio Enrique. 121 GASLIGHT MEDICAL PKWY, # 102 75904 #308-04-1985 L1998 **TS** *020 †85,90
WILLIS, Thomas Lester. 402 GASLIGHT BLVD 75904 #047-06-1970 L1973 **IM** *020 †20
ZOLLO, Anthony Jos. 1301 W FRANK AVE 75904 #048-04-1980 L1980 **IM** *030 †20

LULING – CALDWELL

BROWNE, Larry Eugene. 200 MEMORIAL DR 78648 #004-01-1971 L1973 **PM** *020 †60

■ = Address Information Privacy Protected

COURTRIGHT, Jay Gordon. 130 HAYS ST 78648 #039-01-1996 L2003 **HO** *020 †20
JESUDASS, Samson Wilfred. 721 S HACKBERRY AVE 78648 #495-27-1991 L1997 **IM** *020 †20
TEBCHERANY, Dina Joseph. 130 HAYS ST 78648 #649-33-1993 L2001 **HO IM** *020 †20
TOKAZ, Laurence Kevin. 130 HAYS ST 78648 #048-12-1979 L1984 **ON IM** *020 †20
WEINER, Martin Eric. 130 HAYS ST 78648 #048-13-1979 L1979 **FM** *020
WU, Catherine Suchia. 130 HAYS ST 78648 #048-14-2001 L2006 **RO** *020

LUMBERTON – HARDIN

ARANTE, Prospero V. 344 S MAIN ST 77657 #748-07-1981 L1995 **FM** *020 †18 ‡
HAMMETT, Chad Wayne. ■ 77657 #048-02-2004 L2007 **FM** *020
HURTADO, Dennis Manuel. 4614 KEITH RD 77657 #010-03-1998 L2003 **FM** *020 †18
LEE, Jong Joon. 110 W CANDLESTICK DR 77657 #583-02-1971 L1980 **IM** *020 †20
REDDY, Shanthi G. 1233 S MAIN ST 77657 #495-16-1978 L1993 **FM** *020 †18
RISTON, Dennis Dekoven. 768 S MAIN ST 77657 #016-06-1975 L1984 **OBG GP** *020

LYTLE – ATASCOSA

FERNANDEZ, Ernesto. ■ 78052 #649-01-1950 L1964 **P** *071 †75
MASK, Van Steven. ■ 78052 #048-14-1978 L1979 **EM AM** *020 †18

MADISONVILLE – MADISON

HEATON, Daniel Paul. 100 W CROSS ST 77864 #048-02-1959 L1959 **GP** *020
HUBLEY, Grover C, Jr. 1427 OLD MILL LN, LANE (MAILING) 77864 #048-14-1975 L1975 **FM** *020 †18
JONES, Bob Clarence. 100 W CROSS ST 77864 #048-02-1963 L1963 **FM IMG** *020 †18
REED, James E, Jr. 100 W CROSS ST 77864 #048-02-1950 L1950 **GP** *071 †18
ZARDKOOHI, Maria Segreda. 600 BACON ST, MADISONVILLE MEDICAL CENTE 77864 #270-01-1980 L2006 **FM** *020 †18

MAGNOLIA – MONTGOMERY

ALLAM, Belu. 6318 FM 1488 RD, STE 110 77354 #495-83-1975 L1989 **OPH** *020 †35
BAILEY, Paula Kaye. ■ 77355 #010-03-1993 L1997 **AN** *020 †05
CHIN, Ashley Minjung. 6318 FM 1488 RD, STE 100 77354 #048-02-2001 L2003 **FM** *020 †18
DAMMON, James W. ■ 77354 #048-12-1982 L1983 **TS VS** *020 †90,85
DOLLAR, Hunaid. 18535 FM 1488 RD STE 230 77354 #704-08-1988 L1998 **IM** *020 †20 ‡
DOW, Edward Walker. 6315 FM 1488 RD STE B 77354 #065-05-1964 L1976 **FM EM** *071
EARNEST, Brett Thomas. ■ 77354 #048-12-2008 L2008 *012
EDWARDS, Elizabeth D Mair. ■ 77354 #021-05-2003 L2005 **EM** *100 †16
ELHAJJ, Feras Nazih. 6875 FM 1488 RD STE 1500 77354 #422-01-1998 L2002 **FM** *020 †18
FRIDAY, Albert D, Jr. 6875 FM 1488 RD, TOMBALL REG MED CTR 77354 #045-01-1974 L1976 **EM GP** *020 †16
GATEWOOD, Ollie Mae. ■ 77354 #654-01-1981 L1989 **FM** *020 †18
HAMMOND, Pamela A. ■ 77354 #048-13-1993 L1994 **EM** *020 †16
HOSONO, Tsugimori. ■ 77354 #572-20-1952 L1974 **AN** *071 †05
HUTSON, Rodney Kent. ■ 77354 #045-01-1964 L1970 **OPH** *071 †35
MILLET, Rainey. ■ 77355 #048-16-2008 *012
OSTEEN, Paul Kent. ■ 77354 #039-05-1982 L2000 **GS** *071 †85
PALEOLOGO, Fred Peter. ■ 77354 #048-14-1977 L1977 **RO IM** *020 †20,80
PATIENCE, Ian Mark. ■ 77354 #067-01-1970 L1986 **FM** *020
REIMER, Gregory Lee. 7226 BLACK FOREST DR 77354 #030-05-1980 L1981 **FM** *020 †50,18
SCHUERMANN, Mary Patricia. ■ 77355 #048-02-1979 L1979 **EM** *020 †18
SREBRO, Richard. 5022 RANCH HILL DR, UT SOUTHWESTERN MEDICAL CE 77354 #028-02-1959 L1977 **OPH** *050
SUNDARRAJ, Sabari Lakshmi. 33300 EGYPT LN STE A40 77354 #495-94-1997 L2005 **FM** *020 †18
TERRASSON, Edward L. 18602 FM 1488 RD, STE 700 77354 #048-04-1998 L2001 **FM** *020 †18
WALKER, Randall Dean. 827 MAGNOLIA BLVD STE 6 77355 #048-16-1983 L1983 **FM** *020 †18
WILSON, Keith Oliver. ■ 77354 #039-01-1971 L1999 **PD PDP** *071 †55
YOUNG, James L. 12018 LIVE OAK DR 77354 #048-14-1992 L1993 **EM** *020 †16

MALAKOFF – HENDERSON

SANNER, David Paul. 815 E ROYALL BLVD STE 3, HIGHWAY 31 75148 #048-04-1976 L1976 **FM EM** *020 †18

MANCHACA – TRAVIS

HERNDON, Paul T. ■ 78652 #048-13-1999 L2003 **CHP** *020
NORWOOD, Gordon Keith. ■ 78652 #023-07-1958 L1970 **AM** *071 †70
ZIMMERMAN, Wayne Wylie. ■ 78652 #016-06-1944 L1953 **ORS** *071 †40

MANOR – TRAVIS

LINDFORS, Erik G. 8915 BURLESON MANOR RD 78653 #048-02-1994 L1998 **P** *020
SCHWARTZ, Joan F Langford. ■ 78653 #352-07-1951 L1977 **PHP** *075

MANSFIELD – TARRANT

ABBOTT, Lisa Ann. 3601 HIGHWAY 157 N, FAMILY HEALTH CARE 76063 #048-02-1996 L1997 **FM** *020 †18
ABOU-QAMAR, Maamoun Youse. ■ 76063 #473-02-2000 L2005 **IM** *100 †20
ADEYI, Oyedele Adewale. ■ 76063 #690-01-1987 L2002 **SP** *100 †50
ASERON, Cristina R. 1788 HIGHWAY 157 N 76063 #048-14-1997 L1997 **CCM** *020 †20
BARD, Jonathan Benjamin. 710 HUNTERS ROW CT, OUTPATIENT DIAGNOSTIC CTR 76063 #016-42-1993 L1999 **DR** *020 †80

BATRICE, Marwan P. 1802 HIGHWAY 157 N 76063 #048-15-1995 L1997 **IM** *020 †20
BHATI, Deo Kalyan. ■ 76063 #495-20-1962 L1972 **GS ORS** *071
BRADLEY, William T. 2800 E BROAD ST, STE 504 76063 #048-02-1993 L1994 **N CN** *020 †75
CAMPOS, Eckardt William. ■ 76063 #048-12-2006 **PM** *012
CHANCELLOR, Vella V. 2800 E BROAD ST STE 400 76063 #048-12-1978 L1978 **OBG** *020 †30
CHARLES, Darin Lee. 2800 E BROAD ST, STE 318 76063 #039-01-2003 L2005 **FM** *020 †18
COLLINI, Michael P. 309 REGENCY PKWY, STE 103 76063 #048-04-1992 L1994 **U** *020 †95
COLLINI, Wendy Moss. 309 REGENCY PKWY, STE 107 76063 #048-14-1988 L1989 **IM** *020 †20
COOK, Percy L. 315 S MAIN ST 76063 #048-04-1951 L1951 **FM GS** *071
DANIELS, Clive Graham. 2851 MATLOCK RD STE 600, COOK CHILDREN'S PEDIATRICS 76063 #012-05-1988 L2004 **PD** *020 †55
DAUM, Paul Walter. 2800 E BROAD ST, STE 412 76063 #048-12-1980 L1980 **OBG** *020 †30
DE LA TORRE, Francisco J. 3601 HIGHWAY 157 N, FAMILY HEALTH CARE 76063 #048-15-1989 L1990 **FM EM** *020 †18
DIGGIKAR, Shrinivas. 2800 E BROAD ST, STE 218 76063 #495-65-1994 L2003 **HO** *020 †20
DIGGS, Roderick P, III. 2800 E BROAD ST, STE 214 76063 #048-12-1997 L1999 **OBG** *020 †30
DRKULEC, John Antun. 2800 E BROAD ST, STE 124 76063 #065-09-1994 L2002 **ORS OSM** *020 †40
DYSLIN, David Cole. 2800 E BROAD ST, ARLINGTON SURGICAL 76063 #021-01-1990 L1996 **GS** *020 †85
FERGUSON, Donald W, II. ■ 76063 #748-11-1992 L2003 **IM FM** *040 †20
FISHER, Jeffrey J. 1811 HIGHWAY 287 N, STE 150 76063 #048-14-2001 L2004 **FM** *100 †18
FLOYD, Columbus Williams. 2800 E BROAD ST, STE 500 76063 #048-12-1980 L1980 **GS** *020 †85
FOSTER, Leroy Paul, Jr. 900 N WALNUT CREEK DR, STE 100 PMB 255 76063 #035-01-1974 L1982 **EM OM** *020 †70,20,16
GAYAO, Laurence T. ■ 76063 #748-10-1971 L1974 **EM** *020 †18
GORDON, Kevin Ray. 1200 HIGHWAY 287 N, OMEGA OB-GYN ASSOC 76063 #048-12-1997 L2001 **OBG** *020 †30
GREGORY, Mark Shelby. 1705 FOUNTAINVIEW DR, STE 103 76063 #048-12-2001 L2004 **GS** *100
GREVE, Robert Andrew. 1670 E BROAD ST, STE 101 76063 #048-02-1996 L2000 **OBG** *020 †30
HAIDER, Riaz. 1290 HIGHWAY 157 N 76063 #654-01-1989 L1994 **FM** *020 †18
JENNINGS, Jerry Don. 3601 HIGHWAY 157 N, FAMILY HEALTH CARE 76063 #048-12-1974 L1974 **FM EM** *020 †18
LANSFORD, Doyle Keith. 2720 E SEETON RD 76063 #021-01-1955 L1958 **FM** *071 †18
LIAO, Lixin. 2800 E BROAD ST, STE 218 76063 #243-45-1992 L2004 **HO** *020 †20
LIMPERT, Scott Forrest. ■ 76063 #036-05-1984 L1995 **OM PME** *030 †70
LUCK, Mindy B. 1200 HIGHWAY 287 N, OMEGA OB-GYN ASSOC 76063 #048-15-2000 L2004 **OBG** *020 ‡
LYONS, Augustus Eugene. 2800 E BROAD ST, ARLINGTON SURGICAL 76063 #048-13-1999 L2004 **GS** *020 †85
MANN, Robert Wm. 2851 MATLOCK RD, STE 600 76063 #050-02-1964 L1968 **PD** *020 †55
MC DANIEL, Harley R. ■ 76063 #048-12-1962 L1962 **PTH** *071 †50
MC MICHAEL, Robert Edwin. 2800 E BROAD ST, STE 504 76063 #021-05-1978 L1983 **N CN** *020 †75
MIDDLETON, Angela J. ■ 76063 #048-14-1997 L2000 **FM** *020 †18
MITCHELL, Camelia. ■ 76063 #047-06-2004 L2008 **PM** *012
MORGAN, Jeffery Lavere. 1200 HIGHWAY 287 N, OMEGA OB-GYN ASSOC 76063 #051-07-1995 L1997 **OBG** *020 †30
NEWSOME, Donna E. 900 N WALNUT CREEK DR, STE 100 # 211 76063 #051-04-1997 L2002 **N** *020 †75
OLIVE, Trevelyn Janese. 1670 E BROAD ST, STE 101 76063 #021-05-2001 L2005 **OBG** *020 †30
ORR, John D. 2800 E BROAD ST, STE 504 76063 #048-78-1994, ▲ L1999 **CN** *020 †75
PHAN, Khuong D. 920 HIGHWAY 287 N, STE 308 76063 #048-78-2002, ▲ L2003 **IM** *020
PICKEL, John Alvin, Jr. 1200 HIGHWAY 287 N, OMEGA OB-GYN ASSOC 76063 #017-20-1975 L1976 **OBG** *020 †30
PODGURECKI, David Nick. 1670 E BROAD ST STE 102 76063 #649-14-1977 L1979 **FM** *020 †18
PORRES, Felipe G. 1806 FAIRFAX DR, FELIPE PORRES MD 76063 #654-01-1987 L1994 **NEP IM** *020 †20
PRATER, Gretchen. 2800 E BROAD ST SU 76063 #048-16-1987 L1988 **PD** *020 †55
SELIGMAN, Steven Jos. 1200 HIGHWAY 287 N, OMEGA OB-GYN ASSOC 76063 #048-02-1979 L1979 **OBG** *020 †30
SKIE, Gregory. 700 HUNTERS ROW CT 76063 #048-14-1983 L1983 **PME OM** *020
SMITH, Roy L. ■ 76063 #048-12-1946 L1946 **GS** *071 †85
SOLBY, Steve T. ■ 76063 #048-78-2003, ▲ L2007 **AN** *100
STORTS, Keith R. 1200 HIGHWAY 287 N, OMEGA OB-GYN ASSOC 76063 #048-13-1990 L1991 **OBG** *020 †30
TAN, Filemon B. 1788 HIGHWAY 157 N 76063 #748-01-1957 L1977 **GS GP** *072
TOMBERLIN, Julie Ann. 706 HUNTERS ROW CT 76063 #048-12-1999 L2002 **PD** *020 †55
TRIVEDI, Ketan Mayer. ■ 76063 #016-42-2003 L2007 **EM** *020
WAGHORN, Ashley R. ■ 76063 #048-14-2008 *012
WALKER, Angela C. 1670 E BROAD ST, STE 101 76063 #010-02-1997 L2001 **OBG** *020 †30
WALLAR, Philip Harold. ■ 76063 #005-12-1969 L1970 **OPH** *071 †35
WAYNE, Mark A. 706 HUNTERS ROW CT 76063 #048-12-1989 L1990 **PD** *020 †55
WELCH, David Eugene. 920 HIGHWAY 287 N, STE 308 76063 #011-03-1986 L1998 **FM** *020 †18

MANVEL – BRAZORIA

AHMED, Yassar Iftikhar. ■ 77578 #704-25-2001 L2007 **IM** *100 †20
BAUGH, Andrew Clawson. ■ 77578 #049-01-2006 **DR** *012
BROWN, Rodger Hamilton. ■ 77578 #048-04-2006 **PS** *012
BUENDIA, Mary Elaine. ■ 77578 #748-20-2000 L2008 **SP** *100
CORLEY, Adam R. ■ 77578 #048-14-2001 L2004 **EM** *020 †16
GHISOLI BERNAZZANI, Mauriz. ■ 77578 #935-01-1998 **PHO** *012 †55
GOLDSMITH, Corey Rayne. ■ 77578 #048-12-2003 L2007 **IM** *100
HOLMES, Maurice Alvett. ■ 77578 #016-42-2000 L2004 **EM** *020 †16
JANECEK, Stephen C. 7523 RUSSELL ST 77578 #048-14-1987 L1988 **FM** *020 †18
JOHNSON, Sonya Alexis. ■ 77578 #047-07-1996 **AN** *100
KRAUSE, Kurt Lamont. 2818 SHALLOW SPRINGS CT, C/O BRENDA K STANFIELD, ES 77578 #048-04-1980 L1980 **ID IM** *050 †20
LUNDRY, Jessica N. ■ 77578 #048-13-2005 **OBG** *012
PASTORE, Gabienne G. ■ 77578 #869-04-1992 **AI** *100

PEREZ, Cristina Elisa. ■ 77578 #048-12-2007 **OBG** *012
PETTWAY, Darnell Dewan. ■ 77578 #038-40-1998 L2002 **EM** *020 †16
SCOTT, Rahel Selassie. ■ 77578 #048-04-2008 *012
SILBERFEIN, Eric Jay. ■ 77578 #021-01-2003 **GS** *012
SNEED, Stephanie Florence. ■ 77578 #048-14-2000 L2004 **PM** *020
STROH, John J, Jr. ■ 77578 #048-13-1995 L1996 **EM** *020 †16
TRAN, Michelle B. ■ 77578 #048-15-2007 **PD** *012
WADLEY, Terrence Cameron. ■ 77578 #038-06-1997 L2002 **EM** *020 †16
WILLIS, Theresa Castoro. ■ 77578 #048-04-2008 *012
WOLF, Charles Joseph. ■ 77578 #016-11-1999 **MDM** *030
WOLFFE, Eduardo Antonio. 3210 BRONCO CT 77578 #042-03-2000 L2004 **GS** *020 †85
YENNURAJALINGAM, Sriram. ■ 77578 #495-21-1995 L2003 **IM** *020 †20

MARATHON – BREWSTER

JOHNSON, Douglas Elliott. AVENUE G AND 3RD STREET 79842 #048-02-1960 L1960
  U *020 †95

MARBLE FALLS – BURNET

ADELMAN, Harold Frank. 500 AVENUE G 78654 #039-01-1986 L1988 **P** *020 †75
BEVINS, Michael Bryan. 700 HIGHWAY 281 78654 #048-02-2004 L2007 **FM** *020 †18
BISHOP, William Eugene. 802 AVENUE J 78654 #048-02-1977 L1977 **DR** *020 †80
BROWN, Laura Frances. 1123 HWY 1431 78654 #048-14-2002 L2005 **PD** *020
CARSTENS, Paul Andrew. 703 US HIGHWAY 281 78654 #048-13-1986 L1988 **PD** *020 †55
CONE, Howell Anson. 802 AVENUE J 78654 #048-02-1966 L1970 **DR R** *020 †80
CRAIG, Clark Wallace. 703 US HIGHWAY 281 78654 #005-19-1990 L1995 **FM** *020 †18
CRAVEY, Bruce Michael. 703 US HIGHWAY 281 78654 #048-02-1991 L1992 **FM** *020 †18
DICKEY, Michael W. 1701 N HWY 281 78654 #048-02-1989 L1990 **UCM EM** *020 †18
DUNNAGAN, William A. ■ 78654 #023-01-1951 L1960 **R OS** *071 †20
FISHER, Thomas D. 1100 MISSION HILLS DR, STE 200 78654 #048-02-1987 L1989 **ON** *020 †20
GAGE, Jennifer Lynn. ■ 78654 #017-20-1994 **FM GP** *020
GARDELLA, Joseph Edward. 1800 MORMON MILL RD, BLDG B # 2 78654 #035-15-1996 L2006
  CD *020 †20
GEORGE, David Wesley. 703 N HWY 281, STE 201 78654 #048-12-1996 L2002 **HO** *020 †20
GORDON, William Hendon. 802 AVENUE J 78654 #048-02-1983 L1983 **DR GP** *020 †80
GOSSELINK, Peter Gerard. 2503 N HWY 281, LIVE OAK MEDICINE STE 200 78654
  #048-02-1999 L2002 **FM** *020 †18
GREENWELL, David P. 2503 N HWY 281 STE 400 78654 #048-02-1994 L1996 **U** *020 †95
GROVE, Vernon Eugene, Jr. 5900 CIRCLE J RD, # 1 78654 #048-02-1965 L1965 **P** *071 †75
JOHNS, Ronald W. 2300 N HWY 281 78654 #048-13-1993 L1994 **IM** *020 †20
KIRBY, Edward Eugene. 204 GATEWAY N, STE A 78654 #020-12-1977 L1979 **OPH** *020 †35
LIGGETT, Scott Patterson. 703 US HIGHWAY 281 78654 #041-02-1977 L1980 **FM** *020 †18
LINDLEY, James Dawson. 802 STEVE HAWKINS PKWY 78654 #048-02-1966 L1966
  NEP *020 †20
MADRIGAL-DERSCH, Juliette. 715 FM 1431, INTERNAL MEDICINE/PEDIATRI 78654
  #048-16-1997 L2001 **MPD EM** *020 †55,20
MC CURDY, James Phillip. 2503 N HWY 281 STE 300 78654 #048-12-1979 L1979 **FM** *020 †18
MULLER, Stephen Phelan. 101 HIGHWAY 281 S, STE 305 78654 #041-02-1973 L1983
  OTO UM *020 †45
MURRAY, Robert Roos. 802 AVENUE J 78654 #048-12-1980 L1980 **DR** *020 †80
NORWOOD, John Morrah. 609 4TH ST 78654 #021-01-1988 L1988 **IM ID** *020 †20
OFFUTT, Amy L. 707 3RD ST 78654 #048-13-1997 L1998 **FM** *020 †18
OFFUTT, Kelly A. 703 US HIGHWAY 281 78654 #048-15-1995 L2001 **PD** *020 †55
PALMER, Edward Carleton. ■ 78654 #035-20-1971 L2005 **AN** *020 †05
PHILLIPS, Robert Eugene. 2004 N HWY 281 # 757-194 78654 #041-09-1991 L1997
  EM FM *020 †18
PRESTON, Glenn Geoffrey. 1100 MISSION HILLS, STE 200 78654 #028-03-1995 L2005
  HO *020 †20
SHEPPERD, Wilfred I. 118 MAIN ST 78654 #048-02-1947 L1947 **FM** *020
SHINKAWA, Sidney Mariko. 703 US HIGHWAY 281 78654 #048-13-1982 L1992 **IM** *020
SMITH, Barlow. 500 AVENUE G 78654 #026-04-1963 L1981 **NP GS** *020 †75,50
STEDMAN, Horis Tilton. 2300 N HWY 281 78654 #025-07-1991 L1992 **GP** *020
SWETT, David D, Jr. 1107 FM 1431, # 120 78654 #561-01-1976 L1997 **CD** *020 †20
SWIFT, Edward V. ■ 78654 #048-02-1933 L1933 **IM** *071 †20
THOMAS, John Hall. PO BOX 1375 78654 #048-13-1970 L1972 **GP** *074
THOMAS, Sandra Seideman. 1123 FM 1431 78654 #048-16-1986 L1987 **PD** *020
TJIA, Vincent Maurice. 802 STEVE HAWKINS PKWY 78654 #048-13-1999 L2002 **NEP** *020
VAN DORFY, Amy. 2503 N HWY 281 STE 200, LIVE OAK MEDICINE 78654 #048-13-1999 L2002
  FM *020 †18 ‡
WHITAKER, John Jos. 703 N HWY 281, STE 201 78654 #030-06-1958 L1965 **ON HEM** *020 †20
WILLIAMS, Robert Gayle. 802 AVENUE J 78654 #048-02-1975 L1975 **R** *020 †80
YOUMAN, Joseph Dudley, III. 703 US HIGHWAY 281, STE 201 78654 #021-01-1964 L1971
  HO IM *020 †20

MARFA – PRESIDIO

SEEGERS, Steven Paul. PO BOX 1116 79843 #048-12-1986 L1987 **FM** *020 †18

MARION – GUADALUPE

RACKLEY, Tanya M. ■ 78124 #048-13-2005 L2007 **PD** *012

MARLIN – FALLS

AYCOCK, Thomas Marvin. 322 COLEMAN ST 76661 #048-04-1966 L1966 **GS** *020 †18,85
BHATELEY, Dileep. 307 LIVE OAK ST 76661 #048-14-1990 L1992 **FM** *020
CONSTANTINOU, Eugene. 1016 WARD ST 76661 #418-01-1957 L1974 **PTH** *020
DOWNING, Karlan June. 307 LIVE OAK ST 76661 #048-02-1973 L1973 **GP** *020
DUH, Samuel Victor. ■ 76661 #036-01-1984 L1987 **GPM IM** *020

MEHTA, Vinodini Vijay. VET ADMIN HOSP, DEPT SURG 76661 #496-38-1971 L1981 **PTH** *020
OBALDO, Bing Orallo. 322 COLEMAN ST 76661 #748-08-1967 L1979 **R** *020 †80
ROSE, Melanie Y. 322 COLEMAN ST 76661 #048-16-1988 L1989 **GPM** *020
SALZER, Thomas A. 322 COLEMAN ST 76661 #048-04-1989 L1994 **OTO** *020 †45
SMITH, Howard Lee. ■ 76661 #023-07-1952 L1952 **GS U** *020 †85

MARSHALL – HARRISON

ADAMS, John G. 711 E END BLVD S 75670 #001-02-1966 L1976 **FM** *020 †18
ALBANA, Zuhair Ali Abdull. 811 S WASHINGTON AVE 75670 #848-03-1985 L2007 **IM** *100 †20
ALCOX, Gordon Keith. 304 UNIVERSITY AVE STE 201 75670 #039-01-1987 L1995 **GS** *020 †85
ALLMAN, Valarie Lee. 815 S WASHINGTON AVE, STE 100 75670 #048-12-1990 L1991
  IM *020 †20
ARZE, Steven E. 811 S WASHINGTON AVE, EMERGENCY DEPARTMENT 75670
  #048-15-2000 L2003 **EM** *020 †20
BALBUENA, Katharine J. 811 S WASHINGTON AVE, MARSHALL REGIONAL MEDICAL 75670
  #048-13-1992 L1996 **PM** *020 †60
BALBUENA, Luis, Jr. 811 S WASHINGTON AVE, MARSHALL REGIONAL MEDICAL 75670
  #048-13-1991 L1994 **OTO** *020 †45
BALDWIN, Jack Payte. 304 UNIVERSITY AVE STE 203 75670 #004-01-1964 L1976 **D** *020 †15
BELKNAP, Mark L. 815 S WASHINGTON AVE, STE 304 75670 #048-16-1992 L1993 **GS** *020 †85
BENNETT, George E. 811 S WASHINGTON AVE 75670 #021-01-1951 L1951 **FM** *071
BERRY, Richard Lafayette. ■ 75672 #047-06-1957 L1960 **R NM** *071
CARTER, Napoleon. 501 UNIVERSITY AVE 75670 #018-03-1977 L1983 **OPH** *020
CRAYTON, Steven Carlos. 304 UNIVERSITY AVE STE 108 75670 #048-12-1979 L1979
  IM *020 †20
DUNCAN, Douglas Emmett. 304 UNIVERSITY AVE STE 212 75670 #048-12-1980 L1980
  ORS *020 †40
ELLIS, Michael. 304 UNIVERSITY AVE, STE 214 75670 #021-01-1960 L1963 **PTH** *071
EVERING-SIMMS, Diane A. 707 S GROVE ST 75670 #566-01-1979 L1994 **OBG** *020
GASKIN, Charles D. 815 S WASHINGTON AVE, STE 203 75670 #047-07-1981 L1991
  OBG *020 †30
GEARY, David Matthew. 402 S BOLIVAR ST 75670 #030-06-1985 L1996 **FM** *020 †18
GRAVES, Johnson P. ■ 75670 #004-01-1950 L1953 **GS** *071 †85
GREEN, Gordon Franklin. 815 S WASHINGTON AVE # 303, MARSHALL UROLOGY
  ASSOCIATE 75670 #048-13-1988 L2002 **U** *020 †85
GULLION, Jerry Campbell. 815 S WASHINGTON AVE 75670 #048-12-1961 L1961 **IM** *071 †20
HALL, M Kenny, III. 405 E PINECREST DR UNIT A 75670 #048-12-1985 L1986 **OPH** *020 †35
HANUMANTHAIAH, Ravikumar. 107 ARGYLE ST 75670 #496-20-1995 L2007 **IM** *100 †18
HARMON, Roger Q, Jr. 5103 KARNACK HWY 75672 #048-02-1951 L1951 **OS GP** *020
HARRIS, James Harrell, Jr. 75672 #048-12-1968 L1968 **FM** *071 †20
HARRIS, Rush Crews. ■ 75672 #048-13-1970 L1970 **PD** *020 †55
HERRIN, Bob Jo. PO BOX 1526 75671 #039-01-1955 L1956 **GS ORS** *071
HOUCHEN, Norman Darryl. 618 S GROVE ST, STE 100 75670 #039-01-1987 L1993 **PD** *020 †55
KELEHAN, Shaun Bobbi. 300 N ALAMO BLVD 75670 #048-14-2000 L2003 **FM** *020
KEMP, Susan Elizabeth. 620 S GROVE ST STE 105, MARSHALL REGIONAL MEDICAL 75670
  #021-06-1990 L2002 **IM** *020 †20
KILPATRICK, Charles Henry. 815 S WASHINGTON AVE, STE 302 75670 #048-15-1985 L1990
  GS *020 †85
LAMOTHE, Isidore Jos, Jr. ■ 75670 #010-03-1947 L1949 **GP** *071
LITTLEJOHN, Lake, Jr. 304 UNIVERSITY AVE STE 211 75670 #048-02-1959 L1960 **FM P** *071
LITTLEJOHN, Robert Orin. ■ 75672 #048-12-1960 L1960 **GP** *071 †18
LOGAN, James S. 402 S BOLIVAR ST 75670 #048-14-1993 L1996 **FM** *020 †18
MC ASKILL, Glenn R. ■ 75672 #048-02-1992 L1993 **AN** *020 †05
MC CATHRAN, Charles Eric. 815 S WASHINGTON AVE # 301 75670 #021-06-1984 L1988
  OBG *020 †30
MOHAMED, Odette. 402 S BOLIVAR ST 75670 #056-05-1986 L1997 **FM** *020 †18
NEFF, Eileen Mei. 618 S GROVE ST 75670 #021-06-1999 L2002 **PD** *020 †55
PALMER, Robert Wm. 304 UNIVERSITY AVE STE 2 75670 #021-05-1967 L1974
  PTH CLP *020 †50
PAUL, Ricky Allen. 815 S WASHINGTON AVE # 301, MARSHALL WOMEN'S CLINIC 75670
  #021-06-1996 L2003 **OBG** *020 †30
PHAM, Y N. 815 S WASHINGTON AVE, STE 100 75670 #038-40-1999 L2002 **IM** *020 †20
SALAS, Amber Lea. 815 S WASHINGTON AVE 75670 #021-06-2003 L2007 **OBG** *020
SIMPSON, William Gibson. 815 S WASHINGTON AVE, STE 201 75670 #020-12-1988 L1993
  GE *020 †20
SUDHIVORASETH, Niphon. 705 S GROVE ST 75670 #891-01-1966 L1978 **AI PD** *020 †55,03 ‡
TURNER, Carl Robt. 811 S WASHINGTON AVE 75670 #048-14-1975 L1975 **PD** *020 †55
VANDERBURG, James Ralph. 815 S WASHINGTON AVE, STE 301 75670 #021-06-1996 L2000
  OBG *020
WALDMAN, Douglas Alan. 304 UNIVERSITY AVE, STE 212 75670 #048-12-1976 L1976
  ORS *020 †40
WHELCHEL, Dawn Renee. 401 E PINECREST DR 75670 #048-13-1996 L2000 **FM** *020 †20,18

MART – MCLENNAN

BARTONICO, Antonio Sablad. 116 W BURLESON RD 76664 #748-08-1976 L1981 **P GP** *020

MARTINDALE – CALDWELL

KEITH, Thomas A. ■ 572 SPRING RIVER DR 78655 #422-01-2001 L2005 **FM** *020
VARGAS, Alfredo. 15506 SAN MARCOS HWY 78655 #048-13-1979 L1979 **EM** *020 †16

MASON – MASON

CAMPOS, Javier Moises. 216 W COLLEGE AVE 76856 #048-16-2002 L2004 **FM** *020 †18
FRANKLIN, Jack P, Jr. 216 W COLLEGE AVE 76856 #048-12-1995 L1997 **FM** *020 †18
HOERSTER, Dan David. 216 W COLLEGE AVE 76856 #048-12-1978 L1978 **FM** *020 †18

MC ALLEN – HIDALGO

ABREU, Ruben. 100 E RIDGE RD, STE A 78503 #308-04-1987 L1998 **CD** *020 †20

AINSLIE, John Durham. 2000 S MCCOLL RD, STE B 78503 #005-02-1946 L1983 **P** *030 †75
AL-AKASH, Samhar I. 1120 E RIDGE RD 78503 #575-01-1991 L2006 **PN** *020 †55
ALAM, S M Golam Kibriau. 301 LINDBERG AVE, STE D 78501 #160-02-1986 L2004 **CD** *100 †20 ‡
ALEMAN, Ruben. 4408 N MCCOLL RD 78504 #048-02-1982 L1983 **FM** *020 †18 ‡
ALFONSO, Ariston Bendana. 837 E ESPERANZA AVE, STE A 78501 #748-01-1972 L1983 **DR** *020 †80
ALHALEL, Ralph. 1200 E RIDGE RD, STE 5 78503 #737-01-1988 L1992 **IM GE** *020 †20
ALIDINA, Reza Amir. 715 SAVANNAH AVE 78503 #055-01-1986 L1999 **D** *020 †15
ALISEDA, Jose Luis. 301 W EXPRESSWAY 83 78503 #649-01-1957 L1970 **AN** *071 †05
ALLEYN, Robert Eugene. 620 S 12TH ST 78501 #048-14-1985 L1989 **GS** *020 †85
ALMAGUER, Carlos. 222 E RIDGE RD, STE 106 78503 #048-14-1989 L1991 **OBG** *020 †30
ALMANZA, Othon. ■ 78501 #649-02-1990 L1998 **PCP** *020 †50
ALMEIDA, Hilary Francis. 222 E RIDGE RD, STE 115 78503 #495-17-1982 L1995 **ICE IM** *020 †20
ALONSO, Ramiro P. 1401 S 6TH ST 78501 #649-02-1961 L1968 **GS OM** *020
ALVA, Brick Eduardo. 1200 E RIDGE RD, STE 5 78503 #737-06-1997 L2006 **GE** *100 †20
ALVAREZ, Brunhilda. 4121 N 10TH ST, # 279 78504 #005-12-1974 L1999 **DR** *020 †80
ALVAREZ, Vicente Henggele. ■ 78501 #649-19-1964 *071
ANG, Renato O. 101 E RIDGE RD 78503 #748-02-1989 L2001 **PD** *020 †55
AQUI, Ernesto A. 501 N WARE RD, FAMILY PRACTICE CENTER 78501 #748-08-1961 L1977 **PTH GP** *020 †50
AQUINO, Eduardo. 3001 N 23RD ST, STE 1 78501 #275-01-1990 L2005 **IM** *020 †20
ARAFAT, Numan A. 500 E RIDGE RD, STE 202 78503 #575-01-1987 L1996 **PCC CCM** *020 †20
ARECHIGA, Armando. 110 E SAVANNAH AVE, STE A2 78503 #649-02-1962 L1971 **IM** *020 †20
ARGENAL-BEBOUT, Rodrigo. 801 E NOLANA AVE, STE 11 78504 #270-02-1997 L2004 **PD** *100
ARGUELLO, Roberto A. 1910 S 1ST ST STE 100 78503 #726-01-1976 L1984 **OPH** *020 †35
ARIZMENDI, Alejandro. ■ 78504 #649-02-1995 L2007 **IMG** *100 †20
ARRAZOLA, Pedro Mauricio. 5114 N 10TH ST 78504 #341-01-1980 L1990 **IM** *020 †20
ASTACIO, Julio Ernesto. ■ 78503 #341-01-1960 L1982 **DR PDR** *071 †80
ASUAJE, Juan David. 801 E FERN AVE STE 148, 1315 W. POLK, SUITE 12 78501 #935-07-1995 L2003 **FM** *020 †18
ATENCIO, Renato Catanes. ■ 78501 #748-08-1977 L2000 **AN** *020
AURIGNAC, Fabian. 705 N WARE RD 78501 #035-45-1990 L1997 **CD** *020
AYRES, Roberto Alfonso. 1900 S JACKSON RD, STE 7 78503 #737-01-1985 L2006 **PDP** *020 †55
BAGEPALLI, Amar V. 711 W NOLANA ST, STE 204 78504 #495-52-1980 L1996 **IM** *072 †20
BARRERA, Cayetano E. 606 S BROADWAY ST 78501 #048-12-1963 L1963 **FM** *030 †18
BAY, Luis Pablo. 2519 W PECAN BLVD 78501 #308-03-1980 L1994 **IM** *020
BECK, Mohamed Y I. 1801 S 5TH ST, STE 207 78503 #875-01-1967 L1978 **NS N** *020 †25
BEHARA, Ratnam Venkata. 300 LINDBERG AVE 78501 #495-13-1975 L1981 **FM** *020 †18
BELL, Phillip H, II. ■ 78504 #048-14-1982 L1990 **FM** *020 †18
BENAVIDES, Maribel. 2101 S COL ROWE BLVD, MCALLEN OUTPATIENT CLINIC 78503 #048-02-2000 L2002 **FM** *020 †18
BERNAL, Jaime E. 801 E NOLANA ST, STE 11 78504 #264-01-1986 L1997 **PD** *020 †55
BIDDLE, James Laing. 222 E RIDGE RD STE 216 78503 #048-12-1976 L1976 **OBG** *020 †30
BOEK, Marcelo Moreira. 522 E DOVE AVE 78504 #187-02-1988 L2005 **HO** *020 †20
BOHART, William Alton. 801 E NOLANA AVE, STE 6 78504 #021-01-1965 L1986 **OPH** *020 †35
BORLAND, Fredricka M. 110 E SAVANNAH AVE # 202 78503 #048-04-1976 L1976 **GS VS** *020 †85
BOSE, Sarojini Gurusamy. 801 E NOLANA AVE, STE 13A 78504 #305-01-1996 L2002 **PD** *020
BRACAMONTES, Francisco I. 1200 E SAVANNAH AVE STE 20 78503 #649-19-1976 L1994 **CD** *020
BRACAMONTES, Yvonne. 301 N MAIN ST, STE 3 78501 #409-42-1994 L2001 **FM** *020 †18
BRADLEY, Victor Enrique. 101 E RIDGE RD, MED DIR QUALITY DEPT 78503 #649-20-1963 L1968 **IM CD** *030 †20
BROECKEL, Philip G. 301 W EXPRESSWAY 83 78503 #005-12-1950 L1983 **OBG GP** *075 †18
BROWN, Daniel Charles. 2101 S COL ROWE BLVD, MCALLEN VA OUTPATIENT CLIN 78503 #649-38-1989 L2000 **FM** *020 †18
BROWN, Esteban Ortega. 1801 S 5TH ST STE 105, PEPRODUCTIVE INSTITUTE OF 78503 #048-04-1983 L1987 **REN OBG** *020 †30
BROWNE, Charmaine F. 3330 N MCCOLL RD, STE 102 78501 #566-01-1986 L2000 **D** *020
BUJANDA, Benjamin. 1801 S 5TH ST STE 119 78503 #649-01-1968 L1976 **FM** *020
CABALLERO, Ramiro. 2000 S MCCOLL RD, STE B PMB 203 78503 #048-02-1981 L1981 **NPM** *020 †55
CACERES, Enrique. 3016 N MCCOLL RD STE C 78501 #737-06-1989 L1996 **PDI PD** *020 †55
CAMACHO, Diego Rafael. 416 LINDBERG AVE 78501 #429-02-1998 L2005 **GS** *100 †85
CAMPOS, Juan Manuel. 804 S MAIN ST 78501 #048-04-1974 L1974 **FM** *020 †18
CANALES, Edmundo Cantu. 304 LINDBERG AVE, MC ALLEN ANES CONSULTANTS 78501 #048-12-1983 L1983 **AN** *020
CANALES, Erasto T. 101 E RIDGE RD 78503 #649-02-1977 L1993 **FM OBS** *020 †18
CANALES, Layra Zoee. 2101 S COL ROWE BLVD, C/O DEPT OF VETERANS AFFRS 78503 #649-30-1992 L2003 **FM** *020
CANALES, Ricardo. 334 LINDBERG AVE 78501 #649-02-1984 L1998 **FM** *020 †18
CANTU, Fernando. 4328 N MCCOLL RD 78504 #649-02-1988 **APM** *100
CARDENAS, Salvador J. 100 E RIDGE RD, STE B 78503 #048-12-1996 L1998 **OBG** *020 †30
CARTER, Rebecca Ann. ■ 78504 #048-15-1989 L1990 **FM** *020
CASEY, Kathleen Zahn. 316 UVALDE AVE 78503 #048-13-1990 L1991 **IM NEP** *020 †20
CASSO, Ramiro Raul. 3400 PECAN BLVD 78501 #048-12-1956 L1956 **FM** *072 †18
CASTELLVI, Mirtha M. ■ 78504 #308-03-1983 **PD** *020
CASTILLO LUNA, Silvia K. 1200 E RIDGE RD, STE 5 78503 #737-01-1995 L2005 **GE** *100 †20
CASTRO, Victor J. 500 E RIDGE RD, VALLEY CARDIOLOGY PA 78503 #737-06-1990 L2002 **CD** *020 †20
CHANG, Elsa. 1200 E RIDGE RD, STE 5 78503 #737-06-1998 L2006 **ID** *100 †20
CHESTER, Daniel Allenby. 222 E RIDGE RD, STE 116 78503 #048-02-1956 L1956 **GYN OBG** *071 †30
CHHABRA, Ajoy. 2010 S CYNTHIA ST, STE 107 78503 #965-01-1990 L2001 **RHU** *020 †20
CHIRIBOGA, Augusto. 300 W JACKSON AVE 78501 #319-03-1976 L1985 **AN CCM** *020 ‡
COCKINS, Kim Alden. 500 S BICENTENNIAL BLVD 78501 #038-40-1981 L1987 **CD** *020 †20
COON, Margaret L. 1200 E SAVANNAH AVE, STE 10 78503 #048-04-2003 L2005 **PM** *020
COOPER, Viraf Rustom. 1801 S 5TH ST, STE 207 78503 #496-38-1973 L1983 **NS** *020 †25
COOPER-DOCKERY, Dona E. 801 E NOLANA ST STE 12, COOPER INTERNAL MEDICINE 78504 #649-38-1991 L1997 **IM** *020 †20
CORONADO, Cesar. 222 E RIDGE RD, STE 216 78503 #649-02-1982 L1995 **OBG** *020 †30
CORTES, Maria Rosanna M. 711 W NOLANA ST, STE 204 78504 #748-02-1990 L1996 **PN** *020 †55
CORTINAS, Diana C. 4121 N 10TH ST, # 257 78504 #649-02-1983 L1999 **FM** *020 †18
CORTINAS, Guillermo A. 709 S BROADWAY ST 78501 #649-02-1980 L1998 **FM** *020 †18
CORTINAS, Javier Elias. 205 E TORONTO AVE 78503 #649-02-1983 L1993 **IM** *020 †18
CROSLEY, Archer David. 412 LINDBERG AVE 78501 #019-02-1982 L1983 **PD** *071 †55
DALEY, Hearther Asneth. 1200 E RIDGE RD, STE 3 78503 #010-01-1986 L2000 **OBG** *020 †30
DALTON, Dallas Henry, Jr. 1801 S 5TH ST STE 215 78503 #004-01-1955 L1969 **TS CD** *071 †85,90
DAVIS, Brian Neil. ■ 78504 #048-02-2006 L2007 **PTH** *012
DEDIOS, Angelito O. 1301 E RIDGE RD STE A 78503 #748-24-1989 L1998 **NEP** *020 †20
DELAGARZA, Jorge Luis. 224 LINDBERG AVE 78501 #048-14-1982 L1983 **CD VIR** *020 †85,90
DE LA GARZA, Philip A. 205 E TORONTO AVE, FAMILY MED CTR-UT 78503 #048-13-1982 L1983 **FM** *020 †18
DELGADO, Luis B. 5128 N 10TH ST 78504 #048-13-1987 L1988 **FM** *020 †18
DEL PINO, Dino Mario. 110 E SAVANNAH AVE, BLDG A 78503 #737-06-1996 L2004 **GS OS** *020 †85
DESAI, Parul Satish. 244 LINDBERG AVE 78501 #495-89-1986 L2004 **OPH IM** *020 †35
DESAI, Satish D. 522 E DOVE AVE 78504 #495-48-1979 L1996 **ON IM** *020 †20
DEVANESON, Paul Prabhakar. ■ 78504 #495-37-1968 L1980 **FM** *020
DIAZ MARTINEZ, Gabriel. 316 LINDBERG AVE 78501 #649-01-1979 L1997 **N SME** *020
DIENER, Darrel Devon. 5201 N 10TH ST 78504 #042-01-1970 L1994 **FM FPG** *020 †18 ‡
DIMAYUGA, Edwin Enrile. ■ 78504 #748-02-1987 L1996 **OBG** *100
DOVALE, Joad Medeiros. ■ 78504 #187-21-1957 L1976 **FM GS** *072
DYKE, Lester Maris, III. 1801 S 5TH ST STE 215 78503 #048-02-1980 L1980 **TS** *020 †85,90
EANES, David Fulton. 301 W EXPRESSWAY 83 78503 #048-02-1970 L1970 **PTH** *071
ECHAVARRIA, Mario Alberto. 3001 N 23RD ST, STE 3 78501 #649-19-1984 L2002 **FM** *020 †18
ENSLEIN, Jeremey G. 500 E RIDGE RD, STE 300 78503 #011-75-1999, ▲ L2000 **CD** *020
ESCOBAR, Jorge Javier, Jr. 205 E TORONTO AVE, MCALLEN FAMILY MED PGM 78503 #305-01-2005 **FP** *012
ESHWAR, K P. 1901 S 1ST ST STE 600 78503 #495-09-1965 L1995 **IM NEP** *020 †20
FALCON, Maria E. 6900 N 10TH ST STE 11 78504 #048-13-1983 L1983 **AI PD** *020 †55,03
FANO, Benjamin Juarez. 501 N WARE RD 78501 #649-38-1990 L2000 **IM** *020
FARIAS, Jose. 500 E RIDGE RD, STE 201 78503 #649-52-1987 L2004 **GS** *020 †85
FAUST, Arland Kenneth. 1801 S 5TH ST, STE 117 78503 #010-01-1959 L1966 **OPH** *071 †35
FEHR, Gregory Brian. 301 W EXPRESSWAY 83 78503 #060-01-1976 L1997 **EM** *020 †16
FELICI, Alberto Pio A. 6900 N 10TH ST STE 1 78504 #649-01-1961 L1967 **PD** *020 †55
FERNANDEZ, Alonso. 1817 S D ST 78503 #737-09-1996 L2005 **CD** *020
FITCH, James F. 205 E TORONTO AVE, FAMILY MEDICAL CENTER-UT 78503 #048-04-1949 L1949 **FM** *071 †18
FOXX, Ann Cheri. 4121 N 10TH ST, # 307 78504 #045-01-2000 L2006 **AN** *020 †05
FRANCIS, Alberto. 1400 E RIDGE RD, STE 4 78503 #649-01-1971 L1980 **OBG** *020 †30
FULP, Ray R Trey, III. 1801 S 5TH ST, STE 103 78503 #039-79-1989, ▲ L1995 *020
GARCIA, Elvin Rafael. 2108 S M ST, STE 3 78503 #308-04-1987 L2000 **RHU** *020 †20
GARCIA, Leonardo. 110 E SAVANNAH AVE, BLDG C201 78503 #935-03-1968 L1996 **CHN CN** *020 †55,75
GARCIA, Potenciano R, Jr. PO BOX 4876, 4903 MCCOLL RD 78502 #748-02-1973 L1984 **PUD IM** *020 †20
GARCIA, Ricardo F. 1200 E RIDGE RD STE 8 78503 #737-06-1989 L1995 **ID** *020 †20
GARCIA, Samuel T. 3401 N 23RD ST 78501 #649-02-1984 L1989 **FM** *020 †18 ‡
GARCIA DEL VILLAR, R. 110 E SAVANNAH AVE BLDG C, STE 101 78503 #649-01-1965 L1966 **U N** *020 †95
GARRIGOS-ESPARZA, S. 5401 N 10TH ST STE 219, P O BOX 4572 78504 #649-04-1988 L1997 **IM** *020 †20
GARZA, Ernesto, Jr. 416 LINDBERG AVE 78501 #048-02-2002 L2005 **GS** *020
GARZA, Rafael. 1801 S 5TH ST, GARZA ALEMAN & ASSOCIATES 78503 #649-02-1950 L1956 **GP** *071
GARZA TAMEZ, Jesus Miguel. 205 E TORONTO AVE 78503 #649-02-1979 L1999 **FM** *040 †18
GILL, Darshan S. 1120 GALVESTON AVE 78501 #917-25-1962 L1978 **GS U** *020
GILLETT, Richard La Mar. 521 S 10TH ST 78501 #005-14-1979 L1990 **OPH** *020 †35
GIRALDO, Alvaro M. 1200 E SAVANNAH AVE, STE 13 78503 #264-18-1986 L1994 **IM** *020 †20
GLATZ, Frank Robert, III. 2101 S CYNTHIA ST, JHOC 78503 #036-05-1997 L2004 **OTO** *020 †45
GOGIA, Manoj Kumar. 2101 S COL ROWE BLVD 78503 #496-09-1989 L1995 **IM** *020 †20
GOLDSMITH, Gregory S. 110 E SAVANNAH AVE, # 101 78503 #048-13-1981 L1981 **ORS** *020 †40
GOMEZ, Carmen Maureen. 301 W EXPRESSWAY 83 78503 #048-12-1981 L1982 **FM OBG** *020 †18
GOMEZ, Juan Pablo. 1200 E SAVANNAH AVE, STE 16 78503 #264-04-1995 L2004 **PCC** *100 †20
GOMEZ, Julian, III. 1801 S 5TH ST STE 124 78503 #048-04-1973 L1973 **VS GS** *020 †85
GONZALEZ, Esteban A. 236 LINDBERG AVE 78501 #649-02-1983 L1988 **P** *020
GONZALEZ, Jessica. ■ 78503 #048-02-2002 **FM** *100
GONZALEZ, Kate Marie. ■ 78504 #038-44-2003 L2007 **EM** *100
GONZALEZ, Mark Stewert. 100 E RIDGE RD, STE A 78503 #048-14-1985 L1986 **CD IM** *020 †20
GONZALEZ, Robert. 816 S 12TH ST 78501 #025-12-1977 L1978 **FM** *020 †18
GONZALEZ, Roberto. ■ 78503 #649-01-1965 L1975 **P** *071
GONZALEZ, Vicente. 101 E RIDGE RD 78503 #264-06-1983 L1999 **IM EM** *020
GONZALEZ, Victor Hugo. 1309 E RIDGE RD STE 1 78503 #024-01-1988 L1994 **OPH** *020 †35
GORNEY, Stewart Robt. 4121 N 10TH ST, PMB 358 78504 #003-01-1974 L1993 **AN** *020 †05
GRIEGO, Enrique Juan. 1900 S JACKSON RD, STE 9 & 10 78503 #649-02-1988 L1997 **FM** *020 †18
GUAJARDO, Maria Ruby. 1200 E SAVANNAH AVE, STE 14 78503 #649-30-1997 L2002 **FM** *020 †18
GUARDIA, Juan Aquiles. 1901 S 1ST ST STE 600 78503 #715-01-1990 L2000 **NEP IM** *020 †20
GUERRA, Daniel Jos. 606 S BROADWAY ST 78501 #048-13-1980 L1980 **FM** *020 †18
GUERRA, Mario Cesar. 2101 S COL ROWE BLVD 78503 #048-13-1979 L1979 **FM** *020 †18
GULZAR, Zain. 301 LINDBERG AVE, STE D 78501 #704-02-1990 L2000 **IM END** *020 †20
GUNADI, Irwan Kristanto. 101 E RIDGE RD, DEPARTMENT OF RADIOLOGY 78503 #048-02-1979 L1979 **DR** *062 †80
GUTIERREZ, Miguel Angel. 2108 S M ST, STE 4 78503 #649-01-1979 L1999 **N** *020
GUY, Glenford. 721 SAVANNAH AVE 78503 #035-48-1982 L1988 **OBG** *020 †30
GUZMAN, Anna Maria. 301 W EXPRESSWAY 83 78503 #048-14-1986 L1987 **PD** *020 †55
GUZMAN, Eduardo. 101 E RIDGE RD 78503 #048-13-2002 L2005 **FM** *100
GUZMAN, Eugenio. 1001 S 10TH ST, STE E 78501 #649-30-1982 L1985 **TS** *020
GUZMAN HERNANDEZ, Rosa C. 2500 BUDDY OWENS AVE 78504 #308-04-1981 L1995 **PD** *020 †55
HANSEN, James L. ■ 78504 #036-07-1944 **PTH** *071 †50
HAUSLE, Thomas Wm. 301 N MAIN ST STE 7 78501 #649-30-1987 L1990 **FM** *020 †18

8804

■ = Address Information Privacy Protected

HEAD, William Justus. 605 E VIOLET AVE STE 2 78504 #011-04-1979 L1980 **OPH** *020 †35
HERNANDEZ, Cristela. 205 E TORONTO AVE 78503 #024-01-1985 L1986 **MFM OBG** *020 †30
HERNANDEZ, Miguel A. 1421 N COL ROWE BLVD STE A 78501 #341-01-1970 L1993 **ORS** *020 †40
HERSZAGE, Jorge. 222 E RIDGE RD 78503 #649-14-1977 L1983 **AN** *020
HINES, Charles Jefferson. 1200 E SAVANNAH AVE STE 8 78503 #048-02-1974 L1974 **IM** *020 †20
HINOJOSA, Jose Luis. 2222 NOLANA AVE 78504 #038-41-1985 L1986 **FM** *020 †18
HOFFMAN-GUARDIA, Maria E. 1200 E RIDGE RD, STE 12 78503 #715-01-1990 L2000 **PD** *020 †55
HOHENSTEIN, Jacobo Q. 800 E DOVE AVE, STE L 78504 #649-01-1972 L1983 **OBG** *020 †30
HONRUBIA, Vincent Fabre. 301 N MAIN ST STE 2 78501 #005-14-1990 L1995 **OTO AI** *020 †45
HOPKINS, Kevin Sarsfield. 1120 E RIDGE RD 78503 #024-05-1984 L1992 **CFS** *020 †65
HOVORKA, John William. 1018 BEECH AVE, STE 310 78501 #019-02-1994 L1996 **GS** *020 †85
HUBLI, Eric Heinz. 1120 E RIDGE RD 78503 #024-07-1987 L1993 **CFS PS** *020 †65
IBARRA, Aurelio. ■ 78503 #048-12-2003 **FP** *012
IGOA, Jose Esteban. 3600 N 23RD ST, STE 103 78501 #649-14-1978 L1983 **P PYG** *020 †75 ‡
ILIZAROV, Anatoliy M. 222 E RIDGE RD, STE 202C 78503 #913-15-1988 L2004 **NPM** *020 †55
JARAMILLO, Diego F. 2010 S CYNTHIA ST, STE 101 78503 #649-02-1989 L1996 **AN** *020 †05
JAVED, Saeed Uz Zafer. 222 E RIDGE RD, STE 202C 78503 #704-02-1987 L2005 **NPM** *100 †55
JOHNSON, Christina P. 222 E RIDGE RD STE 110, THURMOND EYE ASSOC 78503 #048-04-1988 L1989 **PO** *020 †35
JOHNSON, Gerard Scot. 5110 N 10TH ST STE E 78504 #649-19-1982 L1988 **PD** *020
JOULE, Donnagail. 301 N MAIN ST, STE 3 78501 #039-01-1988 L1989 **FM** *020 †18
KALLUMADANDA, Sunand Monn. 205 E TORONTO AVE 78503 #496-22-2000 L2007 **FM** *020
KANNAN, Ramamurthy. 1200 E RIDGE RD STE 7 78503 #495-04-1976 L1993 **IM** *020 †20
KAPILIVSKY, Allan. 301 W EXPRESSWAY 83 78503 #737-01-1985 L1995 **DR** *020 †28,80
KHABBAZEH, Zuka Arabi. 5517 N MCCOLL RD 78504 #605-01-1984 L1992 **N** *020 †75
KHAN, Muhammad Amar. ■ 78504 #704-04-1996 L2007 **PDC** *100 †55
KILLELEA, Donald Jos. ■ 78504 #016-43-1953 L1954 **R** *072 †80
KINTANAR, Maria Bituin F. 2010 S CYNTHIA ST, STE 107 78503 #748-02-1993 L2004 **CCM** *020 †20
KLENZ, Mary Elizabeth. 4324 N MCCOLL RD 78504 #036-07-1995 L1999 **OBG** *020 †30
KOO, Felix C. 1401 YUCCA AVE 78504 #048-13-1990 L1991 **PD** *020
KOOLWAL, Harish Kumar. 1301 E RIDGE RD, STE B 78503 #495-20-1980 L1990 **CD IM** *020 †20
KOOLWAL, Savita. 220 LINDBERG AVE 78501 #495-20-1983 L1990 **NEP IM** *020 †20
KOWALYSZYN, Pedro Juan. ■ 78504 #132-02-1956 L1970 **GYN OBS** *071 †30
KUDISCH, Alejandro D. 110 E SAVANNAH AVE # B201 78503 #649-02-1986 L1995 **CHP P** *020 †75
LACAR, Edanili S. 400 S BICENTENNIAL BLVD 78501 #748-02-1990 L1996 **PD** *020 †55
LAHIJI, Hossein. 801 E NOLANA ST, STE 20 78504 #033-05-1989 L1995 **U** *020 †95
LANDRUM, Charles Kenneth. ■ 78501 #048-04-1954 L1954 **OBG** *071 †30
LAZO-DIAZ, Guillermo. 1901 S COL ROWE BLVD 78503 #649-02-1995 L2000 **ON** *020 †20
LEAL, Ramiro. 1900 S JACKSON RD, STE 4 78503 #649-02-1990 L2001 **OBG** *020 †30
LEDESMA, Raul Francis P. 801 E FERN AVE, STE 133 78501 #748-02-1993 L2002 **IM** *020 †20
LEE, Chevy Chu. 1913 S 1ST ST STE 100 78503 #048-02-1975 L1975 **OPH** *020 †35
LEMA, Rodrigo. 1200 E SAVANNAH AVE, STE 16 78503 #264-13-1990 L2003 **PCC** *020 †20
LEONARD, Michael Martin. 404 LINDBERG AVE, TEXAS MED REHAB 78501 #048-02-1981 L1981 **PM FM** *020 †60,18
LEWIS, Jonathan Alan. 1005 E NOLANA LOOP 78504 #010-01-1966 L1984 **ORS HS** *020 †40
LICEA, Gustavo Caridad. 2010 S CYNTHIA ST STE 101 78503 #011-02-1984 L1992 **AN** *020 †05
LIM, Antonio S, Jr. ■ 78504 #748-10-1968 L1974 **FM** *071 †18
LINSANGAN, Linette C. 1200 E SAVANNAH AVE, STE 5 78503 #748-02-1990 L1996 **PDI** *020 †55
LITAM, Dolly Dy. ■ 78504 #748-01-1972 L1982 **AN** *071
LITAM, Joseph Pon. 522 E DOVE AVE 78504 #748-01-1973 L1979 **ON** *020
LOJA, Wilmer E. 1200 E SAVANNAH AVE, STE 5 78503 #737-06-1989 L1995 **PD PDI** *020 †55
LOPEZ, Alfredo, Jr. 2010 S CYNTHIA ST, STE 110 78503 #048-13-1994 L1998 **FM** *020 †18
LOPEZ, Jose Alfonso. 205 E TORONTO AVE 78503 #429-01-1991 L2004 **FM** *020
LOPEZ, Noel. 5140 N 10TH ST 78504 #048-14-1988 L1989 **FM** *020 †18
LOZANO, Rodolfo Manuel. 1400 E RIDGE RD, STE 4 78503 #042-03-1996 L2001 **OBG** *020 †30
MACIAS, Maria Antonieta. 1801 S 5TH ST, STE 211 78503 #649-02-1987 L2002 **AI** *020 †55,03
MACIAS, Vicente Richard. 833 E ESPERANZA AVE, STE A 78501 #649-14-1979 L1986 **CG** *020 †19,55
MADALA, Bindu. ■ 78504 #496-22-1999 L2003 **IM** *020 †20
MADRID, Maria Christina. 101 E RIDGE RD 78503 #048-02-2002 L2004 **FM** *020
MAGANA, Ignacio. 2407 N 10TH ST 78501 #649-01-1956 L1961 **P N** *072
MAHURKAR, Priti Laxmanrao. ■ 78501 #496-38-1993 L2005 **CHN** *100 †55
MALUF-RUSSO, Christian F. 1200 S 2ND ST STE A4 78501 #308-01-1990 L2002 **PUD** *020 †20
MANGI, Salil. 1901 S 1ST ST STE 600 78503 #495-36-1976 L1982 **NEP IM** *020 †20
MANGOO-KARIM, Roberto. 1901 S 1ST ST STE 600, S TEXAS KIDNEY SPECIALISTS 78503 #649-30-1989 L1992 **NEP IM** *020 †20
MANOHARAN, Paulrajan. 500 E RIDGE RD, VALLEY CARDIOLOGY PA 78503 #495-33-1972 L1982 **CD** *020 †20
MAREK, Billie Joe. 1901 S COL ROWE BLVD 78503 #048-13-1983 L1988 **ON IM** *020 †20
MARIEL, Eduardo J. ■ 78502 #048-02-1999 L2002 **IM** *020
MARQUEZ, Guillermo D. 620 S 12TH ST 78501 #649-04-1988 L1996 **GS** *020 †85
MARTIN, William Rulon. 905 E ESPERANZA AVE 78501 #049-01-1976 L1986 **DR** *020 †80
MARTINEZ, Angel, III. 222 E RIDGE RD, STE 114 78503 #048-16-1993 L1994 **AN PME** *020 †05
MARTINEZ, Cesar Agusto. 1901 S 1ST ST STE 600 78503 #035-09-1993 L2004 **NEP** *020 †20
MARTINEZ, Robert David. 1200 E SAVANNAH AVE STE 8, # 8 78503 #048-02-1999 L2002 **IM** *020
MARTINEZ GONZALEZ, Jose D. 301 W EXPRESSWAY 83 78503 #649-41-1999 L2006 **IM** *020
MASSANI, Kashmira Kabirud. 5711 N 3RD LN, KASHMIRA MASSANI 78504 #495-48-1997 L2005 **IM** *020 †20
MAYNARD, Curtis Duane. 3415 N 23RD ST 78501 #048-14-1981 L1981 **FM** *020 †18 ‡
MC DONALD, Joseph Damian. 1801 S 5TH ST STE 114 78503 #028-34-1970 L1973 **PD** *020 †55
MEDINA, Marelyn. 412 E DOVE AVE 78504 #035-08-1980 L1996 **U** *020
MEGO, Carlos D. 1200 E SAVANNAH AVE STE 7 78503 #737-01-1986 L1998 **CD** *020 †20
MEGO, Pedro Antonio. 1200 E SAVANNAH AVE STE 7 78503 #737-01-1996 L2005 **IC CD** *020 †20
MELENDEZ, Ivan Gilberto. 1018 BEECH AVE 78501 #042-01-1987 L1989 **EM FM** *020 †18
MENDEZ, Oscar E. 2625 BLUEBIRD AVE 78504 #429-01-1987 L2002 **IM** *020 †20
MENDEZ, Salvador J. 110 E SAVANNAH AVE, BLDG B101 78503 #649-04-1973 L1980 **ORS** *020 †40
MENDIOLA, Joe, Jr. 2000 S MCCOLL RD, STE B PBM 203 78503 #048-13-1980 L1980 **PD** *020 †55
MILLER, Vanessa Lynne. 1200 E RIDGE RD, STE 3 78503 #005-12-1996 L2004 **OBG** *020
MOHME, Ruben Gustavo. 101 E RIDGE RD 78503 #737-06-1993 L2000 **IM** *020 †20
MOHUN, Michael Thos. 101 E RIDGE RD 78503 #048-04-1979 L1979 **EM IM** *020 †20,16
MOLINA, Orestes. ■ 78504 #011-02-2002 L2006 **OBG** *020
MONCADA, Armando. 1421 N 2ND ST STE B 78501 #649-01-1975 L1985 **PS HS** *020
MONTANEZ, Guillermo. 1801 S 5TH ST, STE 206 78503 #042-02-1983 L1988 **OBG** *020 †30
MONTANO, Pedro Spiro. 1801 S 5TH ST STE 107 78503 #649-02-1973 L1980 **OTO** *020
MONTES WALTERS, Miguel. ■ 78504 #737-06-1992 L2004 **ID** *020 †20
MOORE, Mercy R Bayot. 2101 S CYNTHIA ST STE D1, ENDOCRINE CLINIC, PA 78503 #748-02-1989 L1996 **END** *020 †20
MOORE, Richard B, Jr. 101 E RIDGE RD 78503 #048-12-1992 L1993 **IM** *020 †20
MORALES, Carlos E. 1801 S 5TH ST, STE 130 78503 #341-01-1976 L1990 **CD** *020 †20
MORENO, Leonel G. 606 S BROADWAY ST 78501 #649-02-1990 L1995 **FM** *020 †18 ‡
MORGAN, Bill Carroll. 110 E SAVANNAH AVE, BLDG A202 78503 #048-12-1956 L1956 **GP** *071
MOSQUEDA, Robert Arthur. 2113 S BENTSEN RD, THE MOSQUEDA CLINIC 78503 #048-02-1990 L1991 **CHP** *020
MUNOZ, Wilfredo Alfonso. 205 E TORONTO AVE, PRACTICE RESIDE 78503 #737-01-1996 L2006 **FM** *100
NAGARAJ, Namitha. 1400 E RIDGE RD STE 4 78503 #495-37-1995 L2004 **OBG** *020
NARANJO, Jesus Javier. 205 E TORONTO AVE 78503 #048-15-1986 L1988 **FM** *020 †18
NARANJO, Katia Veronica. 500 LINDBERG AVE 78501 #319-04-1997 L2004 **ID** *020 †20
NAYLOR, Lauren B. 1200 E RIDGE RD, STE 12 78503 #048-13-2001 L2004 **PD** *020
NEWTON, Richard C. 216 LINDBERG AVE 78501 #048-02-1982 L1983 **D** *020 †15
NIAMATALI, Gordon Ramzan. 1000 E VERMONT AVE # 52 78503 #539-06-1974 L1988 **AN** *020 †05
NORBERG, William John, Jr. 510 LINDBERG AVE 78501 #026-04-1967 L1993 **PDC CCP** *020 †55
NUBANI, Hasan M. 1120 E RIDGE RD 78503 #605-01-1985 L2003 **PD** *020 †55
NUNEZ URIBURU, Humberto F. 205 E TORONTO AVE 78503 #737-01-1996 **FP** *012
O'CALLAGHAN, Wm Gerard. 100 E RIDGE RD, STE A 78503 #539-04-1977 L2001 **CD ICE** *020 †20
OCHOA, Ricardo Antonio. 205 E TORONTO AVE 78503 #048-14-1997 L2001 **FM** *020 †18
O CONNOR, John A, IV. 222 E RIDGE RD, STE 216 78503 #048-02-1988 L1989 **OBG** *020 †30
OFFIONG, Dominic Asuquo. 1711 SAVANNAH AVE, MCALLEN HOSPITALIST GROUP 78503 #690-06-1986 L2005 **IM** *020 †20
OJEAGA, Macaulay Aigbe. 508 W EXPRESSWAY 83 78501 #041-09-1987 L1993 **OBG** *020
OLIVAREZ, Olga M. 222 E RIDGE RD STE 101, PROV MED & GER ASSOC PA 78503 #649-52-1993 L2005 **FPG PLM** *020 †18
OLIVEIRA, Noel E. 5111 N 10TH ST 78504 #048-02-1988 L1989 **UM FM** *020 †18
ORDONEZ, Jorge Mario. 222 E RIDGE RD, STE 202C 78503 #451-01-1996 L2006 **NPM** *020 †55
ORFANOS, John G. 1801 S 5TH ST STE 120 78503 #649-14-1976 L1986 **GS CD** *020 †85
OSIO, Armando. 1301 E FERN AVE, STE B3 78501 #048-15-1979 L1980 **FM** *020 †18
OVERFIELD, D Michael. 222 E RIDGE RD STE 202C, 200 S. MCCOLL STE B 203 78503 #016-01-1990 L2002 **NPM PD** *020 †55
OWEN, Kaye K. 4865 N MCCOLL RD 78504 #048-16-1988 L1989 **ORS OSM** *020 †40
OZCELEBI, Fatih. 1200 E SAVANNAH AVE STE 19 78503 #902-05-1985 L1996 **GE** *020 †20
PALIMAR, Prakash. 1801 S 5TH ST STE 210 78503 #495-35-1974 L1980 **PUD CCM** *020 †20
PANDAY, Khaim. 3330 N MCCOLL RD, STE 101 78501 #566-01-1982 L1998 **ORS HS** *020
PARRA-MEDELLIN, Rosario. 101 E RIDGE RD 78503 #649-02-1990 L1996 **AN** *020 †05
PASI, Asheesh. 205 E TORONTO AVE, PRACTICE RESIDE 78503 #654-01-2001 L2006 **FM** *020
PECHERO, Guillermo Ruben. 1005 E NOLANA LOOP 78504 #035-03-1992 L1994 **GS** *020 †40
PECHERO, Ruben Daniel. 1005 E NOLANA LOOP 78504 #132-01-1958 L1968 **ORS** *020 †40
PENA, Francisco Inocente. 801 E NOLANA AVE STE 15 78504 #048-02-1962 L1962 **FM LM** *062 †18
PENA, Raul Adrian. 1400 E RIDGE RD 78503 #649-30-1985 L2000 **OPH** *020
PEREIRA, Nicholas. 101 E RIDGE RD 78503 #495-52-1986 L1997 **PD** *020 †55
PEREZ, Florencia. 205 E TORONTO AVE, MCALLEN MED CTR 78503 #048-02-1999 L2001 **FM** *020 †18
PEREZ YOUNG, Irene V. 801 E NOLANA ST, STE 215 78504 #715-01-1990 L2002 **VIR** *020 †80
PINTO, Raul. 2101 S COL ROWE BLVD, VETS ADMINISTRATION OPC 78503 #176-01-1969 L1981 **END IM** *020 †20 ‡
PIZZOLATO, Philip. ■ 78503 #021-05-1940 L1941 **PTH CLP** *071 †50
POPEK, Monique. 520 S 15TH ST 78501 #165-01-1969 L1972 **FM** *020
POSADA DIAZ, Ana Cecilia. 101 E RIDGE RD 78503 #264-16-1989 L2002 **P** *020
POSLUSZNY, Terrence Louis. 1801 S 5TH ST, STE 102 78503 #023-01-1977 L1983 **CD IM** *020 †20
PRASAD, K. A.. 1200 E SAVANNAH AVE, STE 10 78503 #496-39-1993 L2007 **PM** *100
PRIETO HARRIS, Roberto. ■ 78504 #649-13-2001 L2007 **OBG** *020
QUINTANILLA, Ruy Mireles. 1910 S 1ST ST # 20 78503 #649-02-1977 L1987 **P** *020 †75
QUINTEROS, Francisco E. ■ 78501 #341-01-1974 L1997 **P** *020
QUINTEROS, Maria E. 6900 N 10TH ST, STE 1 78504 #341-01-1982 L1996 **PD** *020 †55
RAMIREZ, Ernesto Herman. 6900 N 10TH ST, STE 1 78504 #737-01-1982 L1995 **PD PDE** *020 †55
RAMIREZ, Javier. 413 LINDBERG AVE 78501 #649-01-1972 L1980 **PD NPM** *020 †55
RAMIREZ, Mario Efren. 1801 S MCCOLL RD STE 301 78503 #047-06-1948 L1949 **FM** *071 †18
RAMIREZ, Norman Michael. 100 E RIDGE RD, STE A 78503 #005-11-1981 L1982 **CD IM** *020 †20
RAMIREZ, Samuel A, Jr. 5201 N 10TH ST 78504 #048-13-1997 L2001 **FM** *020 †18
RAMOS, Gustavo V. 1200 E SAVANNAH AVE, STE 2 78503 #649-02-1970 L1983 **NS** *020 †25
RASHID, Shahid. 801 E NOLANA ST, STE 7 78504 #704-02-1984 L1994 **AN** *020 †05
RATNAM, Suresh. 1901 S 2ND ST STE 78503 #495-37-1989 L1996 **ON HEM** *020 †20
RAZDAN, Maharaj Krishan. 222 E RIDGE RD STE 116 78503 #495-49-1962 L1978 **NEP IM** *020 †20
REDDY, Vangala Janardhan. 801 E NOLANA ST, STE 215 78504 #495-57-1971 L1988 **DR IM** *020 †80
REINOSO, Manuel A. 1400 E RIDGE RD STE 7 78503 #737-06-1988 L1997 **PG** *020 †55
RESTREPO, Alvaro. 1901 S COL ROWE BLVD 78503 #264-16-1987 L2001 **HO** *020 †20
RESTREPO, William. 409 LINDBERG AVE 78501 #264-02-1980 L1990 **IM NEP** *020 †20
REYES, Anna R. 717 SAVANNAH AVE 78503 #048-13-1998 L2001 **FM** *020 †18 ‡
REYES, Luis M. 416 LINDBERG AVE 78501 #649-31-1983 L1994 **GS** *020 †85
RIOS, Ana Maria. ■ 78501 #264-04-1995 L2004 **PDI** *020 †55

■ = Address Information Privacy Protected

RIVAS, Homero. 606 S BROADWAY ST 78501 #048-02-1967 L1967 **FM GP** *020 †18 ‡

RIVERA, Juan Carlos. 222 E RIDGE RD, STE 106 78503 #048-02-2002 L2006 **OBG** *020

ROBALINO, Benjamin David. 500 E RIDGE RD, STE 101 78503 #737-06-1982 L1991 **CD IM** *020 †20

ROBLES, Eduardo Estheban. 1717 N WARE RD 78501 #042-01-1997 L2001 **OBG** *020

ROCKWELL, Anthony A. ■ 78502 #649-02-1963 L1979 **PHP NTR** *071

RODRIGUEZ, Diego. 801 E NOLANA ST, STE 9 78504 #264-03-1962 L1984 **CHP P** *020 †75

RODRIGUEZ, Encarnacion. 4324 N MCCOLL RD 78504 #042-01-1988 L1995 **IM RHU** *020

RODRIGUEZ, Ofelia. 3001 N 23RD ST, STE 6 78501 #275-01-1990 L2004 **IM** *020 †20

RODRIGUEZ, Ramon I. 1200 E SAVANNAH AVE, STE 16 78503 #308-04-1989 L1997 **PUD IM** *020 †20

RODRIGUEZ, Richard David. ■ 78501 #024-01-1989 **P** *100

RODRIGUEZ-AGUERO, Jesus. 620 S 12TH ST 78501 #649-01-1953 L1965 **GS TS** *020 †85,90

RODRIGUEZ-AYALA, Heriberto. 1900 S JACKSON RD STE 4, VALLEY WOMENS CARE 78503 #042-03-2000 L2004 **OBG** *020 †30

RODRIGUEZ-SALINAS, F. 500 E RIDGE RD, STE 201 78503 #649-02-1972 L1983 **OS VS** *020 †85,90

RODRIQUEZ-MEDINA, Bertha. 721 SAVANNAH AVE 78503 #048-13-1983 L1984 **OBS FM** *020 †18

ROSSI, Paula J. ■ 78504 #048-78-2004, ▲ L2006 **EM** *020

ROSTENBERG, David. 1801 S 5TH ST STE 114 78503 #649-01-1973 L1976 **PD** *020 †55

RUEDA-ROJAS, Jaime. 5201 N 10TH ST 78504 #264-09-1976 L1980 **FM** *020 †18

RUIZ, Henry Evangelista. 110 E SAVANNAH AVE, BLDG C 78503 #035-47-1989 L2002 **U** *020 †95

SAENZ, Javier Andres. 101 E RIDGE RD 78503 #048-13-1982 L1983 **FM** *020 †18

SAENZ, Juan Jorge. 1200 E RIDGE RD STE 12 78503 #048-04-1976 L1976 **PD** *020 †55

SALAZAR, Juan Jose. 801 E NOLANA ST, STE 2 78504 #030-06-1981 L1984 **IM** *020 †20

SALCEDO, Leonardo Ernesto. 100 E RIDGE RD STE A, RIO GRANDE HEART SPECIALIS 78503 #308-03-1985 L1996 **CD** *020 †20

SALINAS, Guillermo. 500 E RIDGE RD, STE 300 78503 #649-52-1999 L2005 **IC** *100 †20

SALINAS, Hildebrando. 1910 S 1ST ST STE 300 78503 #649-30-1994 L2001 **P** *020

SALINAS, Ricardo F, Jr. 222 E RIDGE RD, STE 204 78503 #024-01-1995 L1996 **AN PME** *020 †05

SALINAS-GARCIA, Ruben F. 5513 N MCCOLL RD 78504 #649-02-1970 L1973 **OPH N** *020 †35 ‡

SALINAS-GARZA, Mariano. 1720 PECAN BLVD 78501 #649-02-1984 L1991 **FM GYN** *020 †18

SALINAS MORALES, Rogelio. 1901 S 2ND ST, SO TEXAS CANCER CENTER-MCA 78503 #649-02-1971 L1985 **RO** *020 †80

SALINAS PEREZ, Homero. 1309 E NOLANA AVE STE A 78504 #649-31-1978 L1997 **IM** *020 †20

SANCHEZ, Manuel Josue. 501 N WARE RD 78501 #649-14-1975 L1978 **FM** *020 ‡

SARIOL, Oscar, Jr. 1801 S 5TH ST 78503 #649-02-1986 L1991 **PD** *020 †55

SAUCEDA, Gerardo Mario. 709 S BROADWAY ST 78501 #649-02-1955 L1972 **FM OM** *071

SEAS, Manuel A. 301 W EXPRESSWAY 83 78503 #737-01-1986 L1996 **IM** *020 †20

SEIBA, Michael Y. 412 E DOVE AVE 78504 #539-06-1990 L1999 **U** *020 †95

SEIF, Ali Abdul-Ilah. 220 LINDBERG AVE 78501 #005-11-1961 L1970 **PS HS** *020 †85,65

SHAH, Ramesh Chimanlal. 612 NOLANA AVE STE 330 78504 #495-22-1961 L1984 **R** *020 †80

SHAREEF, Riaz Ahmed. 222 E RIDGE RD STE 202C 78503 #496-27-2000 L2005 **PD** *020

SHEKAR, Nirupama G. 1901 S COL ROWE BLVD 78503 #495-33-1991 L2006 **HO** *020 †20

SHYN, Han Young. 1804 S 10TH ST 78503 #583-01-1953 L1962 **OPH** *071

SIDHARTHAN, Kusuman. 2000 S MCCOLL RD, STE B PMB 203 78503 #495-44-1975 L1986 **PD PDC** *020 †55

SILVA, Enrique Nordman. 801 E FERN AVE, STE 148 78501 #737-06-1992 L2005 **IM** *020 †20

SINGH, Narendra Chetram. 301 W EXPRESSWAY 83, MCALLEN MEDICAL CENTER 78503 #496-15-1982 L1999 **IM** *020 †55

SNYDER, William David. 400 E DOVE AVE 78504 #018-03-1984 L1988 **ORS** *020 †40

SOLIS, Joel Lee. 5201 N 10TH ST 78504 #033-06-1999 L2001 **FM** *020 †18

SOTELO, Oscar. 6900 N 10TH ST, STE 3 78504 #048-02-1968 L1968 **D** *020 †15

SOTO, Hector Luis. 100 E RIDGE RD, STE A 78503 #308-05-1987 L1997 **CD** *020 †20

SPINETTI, Nelson J. 1400 E RIDGE RD STE 7, GASTROENTEROLOGY PA 78503 #935-01-1994 L2004 **PG** *020 †55

STEWART, James Ramsay. 110 E SAVANNAH AVE, BLDG A 78503 #048-12-1984 L1995 **IM** *020 †20

STINSON, Darryl Lee. 709 S BROADWAY ST 78501 #649-02-1988 L1994 **FM OBS** *020 †18

STOLTZ, Steven Michael. 205 E TORONTO AVE, MCALLEN FAMILY PRACTICE RE 78503 #654-01-2003 L2007 **FM** *100

STURDIVANT, Ted Shawn. 1007 SYCAMORE AVE 78501 #048-02-1990 L1991 **IM** *020 †20 ‡

SU, Yutang J. 1309 E RIDGE RD STE 1, VALLEY RETINA INSTITUTE 78503 #048-14-1993 L1994 **OPH** *020 †35

SWEENEY, Francis Michael. PO BOX 2436 78502 #048-12-1987 L1988 **ORS** *020 †40

SY, Wilson. 110 E SAVANNAH AVE, BLDG C # 202 78503 #748-01-1988 L1996 **CHN** *020 †55,75

TAN, Edward Hauwsien. 612 NOLANA AVE STE 330, P O BOX 720010 78504 #021-01-1986 L1993 **DR** *020 †80

TAVAREZ, Hiram. 801 S MAIN ST, STE C 78501 #649-02-1958 L1963 **IM** *020

TAVAREZ, Marvin. 801 S MAIN ST STE C, TAVAREZ MED CTR 78501 #649-02-1955 L1962 **IM** *020

TESORO, Leonard Jordan. 2101 S CYNTHIA ST, # PLEX 78503 #048-02-1969 L1969 **OTO** *020 †45

TEY, Alejandro Abalos. 801 E NOLANA ST STE 18 78504 #011-02-1991 L1995 **OBG** *020 †30

TIJERINA, Humberto. 1200 S 2ND ST, STE A5 78501 #649-02-1973 L1984 **NS** *020 †25

TIJERINA, Oscar. 6316 N 10TH ST, BLDG C 78504 #649-02-1984 L1992 **EM FM** *020 †18

TIJMES, Jorge E. 320 N MCCOLL RD, STE A 78501 #231-01-1968 L1975 **ORS** *020 †40

TJOA, Giok Twan. 101 E RIDGE RD 78503 #506-02-1965 L1971 **R NM** *071 †80,28

TORRES, Fadi Mogharbel. 6900 N 10TH ST, STE 8 78504 #847-18-1992 L2001 **PD** *020

TREVINO, Ernesto. 4208 N 23RD ST 78504 #649-02-1975 L1976 **FM** *020 †18

TREVINO, Jorge Humberto. 110 E SAVANNAH AVE # A204 78503 #649-02-1948 L1955 **FM** *020

TRUJILLO, Oscar Luis. ■ 78504 #649-07-1975 L1988 **EM** *020 †16

TRUJILLO-VALENCIA, Monica. 413 LINDBERG AVE 78501 #264-16-1987 L1999 **PDI** *020 †55

TUCKER, Donald Tommy. PO BOX 5562 78502 #025-07-1979 L1983 **FM** *020 †16,18

URIBE, Lourdes Arely. 801 E NOLANA AVE STE 18 78504 #048-02-2003 L2007 **OBG** *100

URREGO, Sandra Patricia. 5201 N 10TH ST 78504 #264-11-1988 L2004 **FM** *020 †18 ‡

URRUTIA, Hector. 1801 S 5TH ST STE 130 78503 #341-01-1970 L1979 **CD IM** *020 †20

USEDA, Domingo. 222 E RIDGE RD 78503 #682-01-1952 L1957 **PTH** *071 †50

VAISMAN, Dan. 500 E RIDGE RD STE 1 78503 #132-09-1993 L2005 **CD IC** *020

VALDEZ, Marcos Javier. 1200 E RIDGE RD, STE 2 78503 #649-02-1989 L2001 **CN** *020 †75

VALENCIA, Jose Luis. 101 E RIDGE RD 78503 #649-14-1971 L1975 **PTH HMP** *020 †50

VALENCIA, Mauricio. 2010 S CYNTHIA ST STE 101 78503 #264-16-1986 L1996 **AN** *020

VAZQUEZ, Elizabet. ■ 78504 #042-01-2004 L2007 **EM** *100

VELA, Efraim, Jr. ■ 78503 #047-07-1980 L1981 **OBG FM** *020 †18,30

VELA-FERNANDEZ, Horacio. ■ 78501 #649-02-1986 **IM** *100

VERDOOREN, Ramiro. 801 E NOLANA ST STE 1 78504 #264-02-1969 L1978 **OTO** *020 †45

VERGEL DE DIOS, Roderick. 5105 N MCCOLL RD, VERGEL DE DIOS FAM CLNC 78504 #748-01-1991 L1996 **FM** *020 †18

VILLALOBOS-NIETO, Rafael. 2201 S 23RD ST 78503 #649-04-1988 L2000 **PD** *020 †55,75

VILLANUEVA, Rita. 801 E NOLANA AVE STE 4 78504 #649-30-1997 L2005 **FM** *020

VILLARREAL, Daniel F. 1200 S COL ROWE BLVD # A3 78501 #649-02-1982 L1987 **FM** *020

VILLARREAL, Victor Romeo. 101 E RIDGE RD 78503 #025-01-1977 L1978 **GP** *020

VISWAMITRA, Saroja. 1200 E SAVANNAH AVE STE 10 78503 #495-09-1973 L1995 **PM** *020

WAHID, Nurul Abul. 1901 S COL ROWE BLVD 78503 #160-02-1978 L1995 **ON IM** *020 †20

WALL, Lester Evans. ■ 78501 #028-34-1956 L1978 **A PDA** *020 †55,03

WASEEM, Mohiuddin. 801 E NOLANA AVE STE 7 78504 #704-02-1989 L1997 **IM** *020 †20

WEBB, Christiaan A. 801 E NOLANA ST STE 18 78504 #048-14-2001 L2005 **OBG** *020

WELLS, Oralia Trevino. 5024 N 10TH ST 78504 #048-13-1983 L1983 **PD** *020 †55

WEST, Benjamin Wm. 1901 S COL ROWE BLVD, S TX CANCER CENTER 78503 #001-02-1989 L1995 **RO** *020 †80

WILSON, Ermelinda Antonia. ■ 78501 #048-15-2005 **FM** *100

WILSON, Kevin David. ■ 78501 #048-15-2005 L2008 **FP** *012

WILSON, Wayne Burleson. 222 E RIDGE RD STE 216 78503 #048-12-1980 L1980 **OBG** *020 †30 ‡

WISEMAN, Jeremy D. 900 E VERMONT AVE, APT 17201 78503 #048-02-2006 L2008 **FP** *012

WORRELL, John Douglas. 5201 N 10TH ST 78504 #048-13-1977 L1977 **FM** *020 †18

WRIGHT, John Lawton, III. 101 E RIDGE RD 78503 #012-05-1989 L1998 **DR** *020 †80

WYTTENBACH, William Hayes. 2000 S MCCOLL RD, B173 78503 #036-05-1981 L1991 **AN** *020

YEE, Tommy. 1913 S 1ST ST STE 200 78503 #021-05-1975 L1978 **N** *020 †75

YSSA, Maria D. 205 E TORONTO AVE, MEDICINE PGM 78503 #264-11-1997 **FP** *012

ZAIN, Moeena. 1200 E RIDGE RD, STE 8 78503 #704-02-1990 L2001 **ID** *020 †20

ZAMBRANO, Jacinto. ■ 78501 #048-04-1978 L1978 **PS** *020 †65

ZAMIR, Asif. 301 LINDBERG AVE STE A, VALLEY GASTROENTEROLOGY CL 78501 #704-02-1990 L1997 **GE** *020 †20

ZAMUCO, May Hazel D. 3001 N 23RD ST STE 4 78501 #748-02-1991 L1997 **PD** *020 †55

ZAPATA, Hugo. 501 SAVANNAH AVE 78503 #649-14-1982 L1987 **OBG** *020 †30

ZAPATA-RESTREPO, Patricia. 409 LINDBERG AVE 78501 #264-02-1979 L1990 **PD** *020 †55

ZAVALETA, Jesus A, Jr. 204 W NOLANA ST 78504 #025-01-1978 L1978 **FM** *020 †18

ZAWISLAK, Walter. 3601 N BICENTENNIAL BLVD A 78501 #305-01-1981 L1999 **PUD CCM** *020 †20

MC GREGOR – MCLENNAN

BATHURST, Gregory J. ■ 76657 #048-02-2001 L2007 **DR** *100 †80

BATTLE, Soo Cho. ■ 76657 #048-02-2000 L2003 **PD** *020 †55

DU LANEY, Charles H. ■ 76657 #048-04-1953 L1953 **GP** *020

MANITZAS, Nick Demetrios. 105 LARIAT TRL 76657 #048-15-1994 L2001 **AN** *020 †05

MARTINEZ, Jacob Salomon. ■ 76657 #041-12-2008 *012

MYERS, David Stephen. ■ 76657 #004-01-2004 L2006 **FM** *020

PEREZ, Javier Eduardo. ■ 76657 #005-15-2000 L2005 **EM** *100 †16

REDDY, Vemula Shanth. ■ 76657 #495-57-1970 L1998 **IM** *020 †20

REYNOLDS, Kelley M. 500 JOHNSON DR, MCGREGOR COMMUNITY CLINIC 76657 #048-13-1995 L1996 **FM** *020 †18

ROBERTSON, Wm Carroll. 500 JOHNSON DR 76657 #048-12-1960 L1960 **FM** *071 †18

SCHLABACH, John Carlyle. ■ 76657 #017-20-1987 L2006 **FM IM** *020 †18

SOLENBERGER, Robert I. PO BOX 336 76657 #023-01-1974 L1980 **PDS GS** *020 †85

THALLER, Katherine E. ■ 76657 #048-16-2000 L2002 **PD** *020 †55

WATSON, Josephine E. ■ 76657 #048-02-2006 **FP** *012

MC KINNEY - COLLIN

AJAGBE, Olamide Ayotola. ■ 75069 #690-05-1998 **PD** *100

ALLEN, Jennifer Elliott. 4541 MEDICAL CENTER DR 75069 #036-01-1997 L2002 **OBG** *020 †30

ALVIS, Jeffrey Joel. 175 RIDGE RD STE 200 75070 #048-15-1998 L1999 **PD** *020 †55

ANDERSON, John Randall. ■ 75070 #035-06-1967 L1968 **FPG EM** *071 †16,18

ARMSTRONG, Brent A. ■ 75070 #048-12-1993 L1994 **EM** *020 †16

ASGHAR, Syed Ali. 4510 MEDICAL CENTER DR, STE 305B 75069 #704-02-1991 L1995 **IM** *020

BAILEY, Julia Garza. ■ 75071 #048-12-1999 L2003 **P** *100 †75

BANGERTER, Kurt Duane. 4510 MEDICAL CENTER DR, STE 300 75069 #011-02-1991 L1998 **NS** *020 †25

BANKS, Tracey Ann. 4500 MEDICAL CENTER DR 75069 #005-02-1992 L1999 **OBG** *020 †30

BARNETT, Robert M. 4500 MEDICAL CENTER DR 75069 #048-12-1987 L1988 **IM ISM** *020 †20

BAUTISTA-VAUGHN, Amelita. ■ 75070 #005-14-1990 L1994 **PD** *020 †55

BEAVERSON, Anthony Bret. 4500 MEDICAL CENTER DR, EMERGENCY DEPARTMENT 75069 #004-01-1989 L1996 **EM** *020 †16

BENBOW, Sam Hollan. ■ 75070 #048-12-1959 L1959 **P** *071

BOATMAN, Logan H. ■ 75070 #048-16-2008 *012

BOATMAN, Richard Martin. 1441 N REDBUD BLVD STE 211 75069 #048-12-1977 L1977 **IM** *020 †20

BONDY, Robert C, Jr. ■ 75070 #048-12-1953 L1953 **PD** *020 †55

BORING, Billy Ray. 1441 REDBUD BLVD STE 111 75069 #048-02-1954 L1954 **FM** *020 †18

BORING, Billy Ray, Jr. ■ 75070 #048-14-1985 L1986 **FM** *020 †18

BRINKMAN, Timothy J. 4510 MEDICAL CENTER DR, STE 104 75069 #048-04-1993 L1994 **FM** *020 †18

BROCK, Lee A. 1444 N CENTRAL EXPY 75070 #048-15-1987 L1988 **AN PMM** *020 †05

BROWN, Richard N. 1441 REDBUD BLVD, STE 261 75069 #048-12-1999 L2002 **PM** *020 †60

BULLAJIAN, Jason Douglas. 2709 VIRGINIA PKWY, STE 200 75071 #048-15-2000 L2004 **OPH** *020 †35

BURTON, Todd Michael. 2217 W ELDORADO PKWY 75070 #048-14-1996 L1998 **PD** *020

BUSTILLO, Mayra. 2251 W ELDORADO PKWY, STE 100 75070 #451-01-1986 L2003 **PDP PD** *020 †55

CAIN, Jeffrey Scott. ■ 75070 #023-12-1998 L2007 **EM** *020

CAMPAGNA, Lauri Brozo. 4500 MEDICAL CENTER DR 75069 #007-02-1991 L1996 **PTH PCP** *020 †50

■ = Address Information Privacy Protected

CANAVAN, Lynn D. 4510 MEDICAL CENTER DR, STE 108 75069 #030-05-1990 L1993 **GS** *020 †85

CARDENAS, Alfonso. 7004 OLD YORK RD 75070 #005-02-1986 L1988 **AN** *020 †05

CHAMBLEE, Socorro Alcalen. 8080 STATE HIGHWAY 121 #120 75070 #048-14-1992 L2003 **OTO** *020 †45

CHAN, Renee Louise. 4510 MEDICAL CENTER DR, STE 315 75069 #028-34-2003 L2007 **OBG** *020

CHANDRA, Suruchi. ■ 75070 #008-01-1999 L2002 **CHP** *020

CHEATHAM, Judith C. 1970 N CENTRAL EXPY, STE 170 75070 #048-15-1992 L1994 **GP** *020

CHILDRESS, George Wilson. 120 S CENTRAL EXPY, STE 105 75070 #048-12-1986 L1987 **FM EM** *020 †18

CHIN, Anita Jar-Yu. 4541 MEDICAL CENTER DR 75069 #048-02-2002 L2006 **OBG** *020

CHITTAJALLU, Ravi S. 4521 MEDICAL CENTER DR, STE 500 75069 #495-11-1981 L2001 **IM GE** *020 †20

CHURNER, Rudolf. 1501 REDBUD BLVD 75069 #048-12-1978 L1978 **OPH** *020 †35

CRAIG, Mark Alan. 5971 VIRGINIA PKWY 75071 #021-05-1993 L2003 **OS** *020

CRAST, Frank Wm. ■ 75069 #021-01-1970 L1993 **OM PHP** *030 †55,70

DANIEL, Reena. 4501 MEDICAL CENTER DR, STE 200 75069 #422-01-1995 L2005 **IM** *020 †20

DAVIS, O Robert. 1800 N GRAVES ST 75069 #048-12-1989 L1994 **AN** *020 †05

DEVI, Gita Rani. 3102 VOLTAIRE BLVD 75070 #496-05-1968 L1993 **R** *020 †80,28

DEVILLENEUVE, Scott A. 4510 MEDICAL CENTER DR, STE 108 75069 #048-12-1999 L2004 **GS** *020 †85

DICKSCHAT, Diana Victoria. ■ 75070 #048-12-2007 **PD** *012

DONALDSON, Scott Gregory. 4510 MEDICAL CENTER DR, STE 206 75069 #039-01-1984 L1987 **PUD CCM** *020 †20

DUGOPOLSKI, Suzanne Marie. 2720 VIRGINIA PKWY, STE 200 75071 #028-03-1995 L1997 **PD** *020 †55

DUVAL, Nicole A. 4500 MEDICAL CENTER DR, MEDICAL CENTER 75069 #048-04-1995 L1998 **EM** *020 †16

ELEY, Cheryl D. 4510 MEDICAL CENTR DR #211, CHILDRENS CHOICE PEDS 75069 #025-07-1995 L1997 **PD** *020 †55

EVANS, Sheridan Scott. 5605 VIRGINIA PKWY 75071 #048-12-1997 L2000 **FM** *020 †18

FARRELL, James Michael. 910 W UNIVERSITY DR 75069 #048-12-1978 L1978 **FM** *020 †18

FLAVILL, Eric Christopher. ■ 75070 #048-12-2006 *012

FLAVILL, Paul. 1441 REDBUD BLVD, STE 231 75069 #034-01-1987 L1993 **N** *020 †75

FOSTER, Gregory Harrison. 4510 MEDICAL CENTER DR, STE 206 75069 #025-07-1979 L1984 **PUD SME** *020 †20

FOSTER, Lakeitha Rena. ■ 75071 #047-07-2003 L2006 **NPM** *012 †55

FRANK, Catherine M. 4500 MEDICAL CENTER DR 75069 #048-02-1998 L2001 **PD** *020 †55

GAHAN, Jeffrey Chad. ■ 75070 #048-04-2007 *012

GAMMON, Robert B. 4510 MEDICAL CENTER DR, STE 206 75069 #048-12-1984 L1985 **PUD CCM** *020 †20

GANGASANI, Surekha. 2414 W UNIVERSITY DR, STE 112 75071 #495-21-1987 L1996 **RHU** *020 †20

GEORGE, Jeffrey Allen. 4510 MEDICAL CENTER DR, STE 210 75069 #048-02-2000 L2001 **FM** *020 †18

GIBSON, Gary Max. 1441 N REDBUD BLVD STE 211 75069 #048-12-1977 L1977 **IM** *020 †20

HALDERMAN, Lori Daughters. 4541 MEDICAL CENTER DR 75069 #005-06-1996 L2000 **OBG** *020 †30

HARGETT, John M. 1720 N MCDONALD ST 75071 #048-02-1982 L1983 **FM** *075 †18

HENDERSON, Mark S. 4510 MEDICAL CENTER DR, STE 108 75069 #048-12-1992 L1993 **GS** *020 †85

HILL, Mack Moran, Jr. ■ 75070 #048-04-1946 L1946 **PD PHP** *072

HINES, Larry Jack. 1600 1ST AVE BOX 1 75069 #021-05-1948 L1954 **GS FM** *071 †85

HOPKINS, Rhonda D. 4561 MEDICAL CENTER DR 75069 #048-15-1997 L1999 **FM** *020 †18 ‡

IBAZEBO, Ehireme Anthony. PO BOX 389 75070 #690-07-1991 L2000 **P** *020 †75

ICAZA, Edward Earl. 4201 MEDICAL CENTER DR, STE 260 75069 #039-01-1996 L2000 **N** *020 †75

IFTIKHAR, Faizan. 4510 MEDICAL CENTER DR, STE 316 75069 #704-25-1990 L2004 **CD IC** *020 †20

JAMES, Terry Lawson. 500 W UNIVERSITY DR # 102, P.O BOX 822 75069 #003-01-1975 L1976 **AN PME** *020

JARRAH, Taysir Fawzi. 1601 W UNIVERSITY DR 75069 #605-01-1973 L1976 **CD IM** *020

JOE, Rita K. 4510 MEDICAL CENTER DR, STE 207 75069 #048-02-2001 L2004 **PD** *020 †55

JOHNSON, Kerry Ray. ■ 75069 #049-01-1985 L1994 **EM** *020 †55,16

JONES, Monte Frederick. 4510 MEDICAL CENTER DR, STE 206 75069 #048-04-1990 L1994 **HO** *020 †20

JOYNER, Margaret Smith. 4510 MEDICAL CENTER DR, STE #30 75069 #048-13-1999 L2003 **OBG** *020

KELLNER, Thomas Chas. ■ 75071 #034-01-1991 L1992 **PTH** *020

KERCHNER, Ralph R, Jr. ■ 75070 #005-06-1954 L1955 **GP** *071

KESSINGER, William Andrew. 3701 W ELDORADO PKWY STE A 75070 #048-16-1985 L1987 **PD** *020 †55

KHALEEL, Mohammed Adeeluz. ■ 75070 #035-03-2007 **ORS** *012

KHAN, Amanullah. 4201 MEDICAL CENTER DR, STE 180 75069 #704-01-1963 L1972 **ON HO** *020 †03

KHAN, Muhammad. 4201 MEDICAL CENTER DR 75069 #704-02-1989 L1993 **CD IM** *020 †20

KIM, Richard Wonmo. 1500 W ELDORADO PKWY # 92 75069 #005-18-1988 L1994 **DR** *020 †80

KIOUS, Thomas Roger. 4500 MEDICAL CENTER DR, EMERGENCY DEPARTMENT 75069 #034-01-1997 L2000 **EM** *020 †16

KNIGHT, Pollyanne N. 4500 MEDICAL CENTER DR 75069 #048-12-1998 L1999 **FM** *020 †18

KUREISHY, Shahrukh Ahmad. 4201 MEDICAL CENTR DR #360 75069 #704-02-1988 L2003 **PCC SME** *020 †20

LAM, David Trueson. ■ 75070 #004-01-2003 **NPM** *012 †55

LAMBERT, David M. 4510 MEDICAL CTR DR, STE 214 75069 #048-02-1995 L2003 **GS** *020 †85

LAWRENCE, Neal C. 4510 MEDICAL CENTER DR, STE 210 75069 #048-13-1995 L1999 **FM** *020 †18

LEBOVIC, Gail Shirley. 7850 COLLIN MCKINNEY PKWY, THE COOPER CLINIC 75070 #010-01-1986 L2004 **GS** *020 †85

LEE, Doohi. 120 S CENTRAL EXPY, TEXAS HEMATOLOGY ONCOLOGY 75070 #038-06-1989 L2001 **RNR** *020 †80

LEE, June Jieun. 7850 COLLIN MCKINNEY PKWY 75070 #033-05-2001 L2008 **GS** *020 †85

LESKO, Alexander Wesley. 4510 MEDICAL CENTER DR 75069 #035-01-1997 L2006 **GS** *020 †85

LIDDICOAT, John Ellery. ■ 75070 #025-01-1966 L1973 **TS** *071 †85,90

LINSTRUM, Tom Elton. 1800 N GRAVES ST 75069 #048-02-1954 L1954 **FM** *071

LONGLEY, Michael Preston. ■ 75071 #048-02-1967 L1967 **P CHP** *020 †75

LUCIANI, Gerald D. 4510 MEDICAL CENTER DR 75069 #048-12-1996 L1999 **OBG** *020 †30

MADDALA, Yamini Kavitha. 4521 MEDICAL CENTER DR, STE 500 75069 #495-65-1997 L2006 **GE** *020 †20

MAO, Shifeng. 4601 MEDICAL CENTER DR, CENTER 75069 #243-47-1987 L2004 **ON** *020 †20

MARSHALL, Muriel A. 825 N MCDONALD ST, STE 130 75069 #025-76-1977, ▲ L1993 **FM PHP** *020 †70

MARTENS, Kevin Jasonlee. ■ 75070 #005-12-2003 L2006 **EM** *100

MARTIN, Christopher Troy. ■ 75070 #422-01-2004 L2008 **IM** *020 †20

MC DONALD, Claudia Jean. 4510 MEDICAL CENTER DR, STE 300 75069 #048-02-1985 L1986 **NS PMM** *020 †25

MENCHACA, Virginia. 3701 W ELDORADO PKWY STE A 75070 #048-14-1998 L2001 **PD** *020 †55

MEYER, Darren E. 321 N CENTRAL EXPY, STE 340 75070 #048-12-1988 L1989 **P** *020 †75

MILLER, Brian Richard. ■ 75070 #048-12-2001 L2005 **DR** *020 †80

MILLWEE, Robert H, IV. ■ 75070 #048-12-1992 L1994 **AN** *020 †05

MIR, Ferzana. 4201 MEDICAL CENTER DR, STE 200-A 75069 #704-25-1990 L1997 **PCC** *020 †20

MITCHELL, Billy Don. 1413 N CENTRAL EXPY 75069 #048-12-1964 L1964 **FM** *071

MITCHELL, William Clark. 4501 MEDICAL CENTER DR, STE 100 75069 #048-02-1981 L1981 **U** *071 †95

MOBLEY, Mary H. ■ 75070 #048-13-1987 L1992 **PD** *020 †55

MOOLAMALLA, Kavitha. 1441 REDBUD BLVD, STE 111 75069 #496-24-1989 L1996 **FM** *020 †18

MORGAN, Matt. 4510 MEDICAL CENTER DR, STE 204 75069 #048-04-1999 L2002 **AI PDA** *020 †20,03

NANDEESHWAR, Pallavi. 2414 W UNIVERSITY DR, STE 112 75071 #495-33-1992 L1999 **RHU** *020 †20

NAWAZ, Mohammad Zaim. 4201 MEDICAL CENTER DR, STE 380 75069 #704-21-1997 L2001 **CD** *100 †20

NAYEEM, Qasim. ■ 75070 #704-09-1995 L2008 **IM** *020 †20

NEAL, Robert Chas. 4510 MEDICAL CENTER DR, STE 207 75069 #005-14-1978 L1982 **PD** *020 †55

NGUYEN, Andy Truong. ■ 75070 #038-44-1999 L2006 **IM** *020 †20

NORBURY, James W, Jr. 1501 N REDBUD BLVD, HERITAGE EYE CENTER 75069 #023-12-1984 L1995 **OPH GP** *020 †35

PALMER, Graham Sanford. ■ 75069 #051-04-1961 L1972 **ORS HS** *071

PANG, Yung Soo. ■ 75070 #583-01-1967 L1993 **IM GP** *020 †20

PATEL, Kanubhai A. 1441 REDBUD BLVD, STE 101 75069 #495-23-1976 L1983 **IM** *020 †20

PATEL, Sanjay K. 1501 N REDBUD BLVD 75069 #048-12-1994 L1999 **OPH** *020 †20

PETERSON, E Ragnar. 4510 MEDICAL CENTER DR 75069 #019-02-2000 L2007 **TS** *100 †85

PHO, Luan Quoc. 4300 COMMUNITY BLVD, COLLIN COUNTY DETENTION FA 75071 #048-14-1995 L1996 **IM** *020 †20

PICKENS, Myron Ashley, Jr. ■ 75070 #011-02-1960 L1963 **DR NR** *071

PIGA, Jonathan Cambare. 4500 MEDICAL CENTER DR, MEDICAL CENTER OF MCKINNEY 75069 #748-10-2003 L2007 **IM** *100 †20

PROCTER, Brian C. 7692 W ELDORADO PKWY 75070 #048-15-1997 L1999 **FM** *020 †18

PRUDICH, John F. 1441 REDBUD BLVD STE 121 75069 #048-14-1982 L1983 **ORS** *020 †40

PUTCHA, Rajesh V. 4510 MEDICAL CENTER DR, STE 318 75069 #011-02-1996 L1997 **GE** *020 †20

QUINN, Marcum O. 4510 MEDICAL CENTER DR, STE 206 75069 #048-12-1994 L1995 **PCC** *020 †20

RAFIE, Jean-Jacques. 2720 VIRGINIA PKWY 75071 #605-01-1988 L1993 **OTO NO** *020 †45 ‡

RAHMAN, Rashid. 4510 MEDICAL CENTER DR, STE 206 75069 #704-02-1988 L2004 **PCC** *020 †20

RAJALA, Teresa D. 1800 N GRAVES ST 75069 #048-13-1984 L1985 **IM** *020 †20

RAO, Ramakrishna P. 1600 REDBUD BLVD, STE 207 75069 #048-04-1987 L1989 **IM** *020 †20,75

REEVES, Homer Lee. 825 N MCDONALD ST 75069 #048-02-1960 L1960 **FM AM** *020 †18

REYES, Paul Howard. 4510 MEDICAL CENTER DR, STE 209 75069 #048-13-2001 L2004 **PD** *100 †55

RINKER, Susan K Morris. 3215 VALLEY FRG 75070 #038-40-1973 L1974 **AN** *020 †05

RIZVI, Akbar. 4201 MEDICAL CENTER DR, STE 180 75069 #704-02-1990 L2005 **HO** *020 †20

ROBERT, Sara Ann. 7900 HENNEMAN WAY STE 1 75070 #005-18-2001 L2005 **OBG** *020 †30

ROGERS, Amy E. ■ 75070 #048-13-1998 **FM** *100

ROGERS, David Edward. 7850 COLLIN MCKINNEY PKWY 75070 #048-12-1977 L1977 **GYN** *020 †30

ROHR, William Bruce. 700B WILMETH RD, MEDICAL EXAMINER 75069 #021-05-1979 L1984 **FOP** *020 †50

SADLER, Sean Allison. 4510 MEDICAL CENTER DR, STE 309 75069 #039-79-1999, ▲ L2004 **OBG** *020

SAJJA, Ratna. 4201 MEDICAL CENTER DR, STE 180 75069 #038-06-2000 L2005 **RO** *020 †80 ‡

SARTOR, George Madison. ■ 75070 #021-05-1956 L1956 **GS** *071

SCALFANO, Gary Victor. 4500 MEDICAL CENTER DR 75069 #001-06-1993 L2001 **AN** *020 †05

SCHROEDER, Frank A. ■ 75070 #048-02-2002 L2007 **ORS** *100

SETZENFAND, Roy Alan. 4510 MEDICAL CENTER DR, STE 311 75069 #041-09-1994 L2004 **IM** *020 †20

SHAH, Jagdish Amratlal. 4500 MEDICAL CENTER DR 75069 #495-19-1980 L1992 **IM** *020 †20

SHIMER, Andrew Thomas. 7900 HENNEMAN WAY, STE 100 75070 #048-04-1993 L1994 **OBG** *020 †30

SHIRLEY, Richard Alfred. ■ 75069 #025-01-1959 L1966 **ORS** *071 †40

SHIRODKAR, Sandeepa Amrut. ■ 75070 #023-01-2002 L2005 **PD** *100

SIDDIQI, Fazila. 2300 W WHITE AVE, STE 101 75069 #704-16-1982 L1997 **P** *020 †75

SIDDIQUE, Reziuddin. 4201 MEDICAL CENTER DR, STE 300 75069 #495-98-1978 L2001 **IMG IM** *020 †20

SIDDIQUI, Nadeem Ahmad. 4510 MEDICAL CENTER DR, STE 305B 75069 #704-02-1993 L2003 **NEP IM** *020 †20

SIMMONS, Nelson X. 2770 VIRGINIA PKWY, STE 301 75071 #048-16-1997 L1999 **FM** *020 †18

SIMS, Jerry Lee. 1800 N GRAVES ST 75069 #048-12-1957 L1957 **GS** *020 †85

SINGH, Gayatri J. 1600 REDBUD BLVD STE 207 75069 #496-02-1985 L2002 **PYG** *020

SLABISAK, Vudhi V. 4510 MEDICAL CENTER DR, STE 312 75069 #048-13-1998 L1999 **ORS** *020

SLOMOWITZ, Alan A. 4601 MEDICAL CENTER DR, MCKINNEY REGIONAL CANCER C 75069 #011-02-1971 L1976 **RO** *020 †80

SMITH, Kelley D. 2217 W ELDORADO PKWY, ALL ABOUT CHILDREN PEDIATR 75070 #048-16-2002 L2005 **PD** *100

SNYDER, Ann Hayat. 4561 MEDICAL CENTER DR 75069 #039-01-1996 L1999 **FM** *020 †18 ‡

SPEERS, Cynthia Ann. ■ 75070 #048-12-2004 L2008 **AN** *012

■ = Address Information Privacy Protected

SRINIVASAN, Srilatha. 1920 W ELDORADO PKWY, STE 100 75069 #495-09-1995 L2005 IMG *100 †18 ‡

STEVENSON, Brent E. 130 S CENTRAL EXPY, GREEN OAKS CNS MED CTR 75070 #003-75-2001, ▲ L2005 **SME OS** *020 †75

STRINGER, Jared Danell. 4501 MEDICAL CENTER DR, STE 100 75069 #048-14-2000 L2005 U *020 †95

SUNDARAM, Shankar M. 4510 MEDICAL CENTER DR, STE 112 75069 #048-02-1994 L2003 **TS VS** *020 †85,90

SUTTON, Nicole M. 3701 W ELDORADO PKWY 75070 #048-02-2001 L2004 **PD** *020 †55

TARAZI, Antoine Elie. ■ 75071 #605-01-1985 L1990 **OTO** *020 †45

THRASHER, Richard Devere. 4510 MEDICAL CENTER DR, STE 100 75069 #008-02-1999 L2007 **OTO** *020 †45

THUMASATHIT, Bhoonsri. ■ 75069 #891-02-1957 L1971 **GP HEM** *071

THUMASATHIT, Chote. ■ 75069 #891-02-1954 L1971 **FM DR** *071

TSENG, Jenny. 6850 TPC DR, STE 102 75070 #429-01-1980 L1985 **GE IM** *020 †20

VALLURUPALLI, Nirmala P. 1441 REDBUD BLVD STE 201 75069 #495-58-1977 L1984 **OBG** *020 †30

VALLURUPALLI, Prasad. 4521 MEDICAL CENTER DR, STE 500 75069 #495-58-1975 L1984 **GE IM** *020 †20

VASSA, Rajendra C. 120 S CENTRAL EXPY STE 103 75070 #539-03-1975 L1984 **PD** *020 †55

VERMA, Neelam. 1920 W ELDORADO PKWY, STE 100 75069 #495-66-1994 L2000 **FM** *020 †18

VERNER, Jimmy L. ■ 75070 #047-06-1952 L1952 **PTH** *071 †50

VERNIER, Daniel T. 4510 MEDICAL CENTER DR, STE 207 75069 #048-15-1994 L1997 **PD** *020 †55

WADE, George Robt. ■ 75070 #041-01-1943 L1944 **PD** *071 †55

WADE, Randall Wm. 120 S CENTRAL EXPY STE 124 75070 #048-13-1983 L1984 **FM** *020 †18

WAHID, Faisal. 4510 MEDICAL CENTER DR, STE 208 75069 #704-08-1989 L2000 **IC CD** *020 †20

WENDT-SHIMER, Tricia Ann. 4510 MEDICAL CTR DR # 304 75069 #048-04-1997 L2001 **OBG** *020 †20

WHETSTONE, Charles Lloyd. ■ 75070 #041-12-1957 L1980 **OM PTX** *071 †18

WILLIS, Sheryl Gauntt. 4500 MEDICAL CENTER DR 75069 #027-01-1989 L1994 **PTH** *020 †50

WILSON, James Thompson. 1800 N GRAVES ST 75069 #048-12-1959 L1959 **FM P** *020 †18

WILSON, Rick Ken. 7850 COLLIN MCKINNEY PKWY 75070 #048-13-1976 L1978 **D FPS** *020 †15

WOOD, Virenda Dareles. 4510 MEDICAL CENTER DR, STE 211 75069 #047-06-2000 L2003 **PD** *020 †55

WYSONG, Charles Bradford. 130 S CENTRAL EXPY 75070 #048-13-1973 L1973 **DR** *020 †80 ‡

ZAFAR, Zahid Nadeem. 4201 MEDICAL CENTER DR, STE 300 75069 #704-02-1988 L2000 **IM** *020 †20

MCDADE – BASTROP

HENSLEE, Christopher S. ■ 78650 #048-13-2006 **AN** *012

MEADOWLAKES – BURNET

CARSTENS, Kristin Lois. ■ 78654 #048-15-1989 L1991 **PTH** *020 †50

MANTHEIY, Linda King. ■ 78654 #048-15-1981 L1981 **PD** *020 †55

MEDINA – BANDERA

CHAMBLEE, William Caris. ■ 78055 #021-01-1958 L1961 **AN** *071

WILSON, Donald Dale. ■ 78055 #048-04-1961 L1961 **PM** *071 †60

MEMPHIS – HALL

BERRY, Ronald Ellsworth. 1318 W NOEL ST, RR 1 BOX 1A 79245 #065-06-1957 L1978 **FM** *071

CLARK, Robert Ernest. 305 S 6TH ST 79245 #048-02-1980 L1980 **GP GS** *020

MERCEDES – HIDALGO

CABALLERO, Eduardo. 520 W 3RD ST 78570 #649-30-1985 L1988 **FOP FM** *020

CABALLERO, Gonzalo. 520 W 3RD ST 78570 #649-02-1951 L1962 **GS GP** *071

LIM, Sung Eun. 330 N OHIO AVE 78570 #132-01-1994 L2004 **IM** *020

MARTINEZ, Jorge. 1500 W 1ST ST 78570 #048-14-1989 L1990 **FM** *020 †18

MCDOUGAL, Pedro Emmanuel. 330 N OHIO AVE 78570 #308-04-1989 L1995 **IMG** *020 †20

SALINAS, Benjamin Adrian. 801 W 2ND ST 78570 #649-02-1983 L1988 **FM** *020 †18

SANTISTEVAN, Patricia Lau. ■ 78570 #048-13-2005 **IM** *012

TANNER, Gordon Worth. ■ 78570 #007-02-1943 L1944 **GP** *071

MERIDIAN – BOSQUE

HILDERBRAND, Harold E. PO BOX 467 76665 #039-01-1943 L1947 **GP** *071

SPITZER, Richard Gene. 1110 N MAIN BOX 528 76665 #048-02-1972 L1972 **GP** *020

MERKEL – TAYLOR

TORRES, Salvador. 1508 N 1ST ST 79536 #649-14-1968 L1979 **FM** *020

TRAN, Thuy Dinh. 604 ASH ST 79536 #941-01-1969 L1978 **FM FPG** *020

MESQUITE – DALLAS

ABDO, Ibrahim Samaan. 2698 N GALLOWAY AVE, STE 105 75150 #605-01-1976 L1981 **ORS** *020.

ABOU-KAYYAS, Yousef. 2698 N GALLOWAY AVE # 104 75150 #875-01-1988 L1999 **PCC** *020 †20

ADEYEMI, Anu. 901 N GALLOWAY AVE, STE 107 75149 #016-11-1996 L2000 **OBG** *020

AHMAD, Ahmad Bedair. 929 N GALLOWAY AVE STE 121 75149 #915-02-1982 L2000 **PD** *020 †55

ALDRIDGE, Richard L, Jr. 1011 N GALLOWAY AVE 75149 #018-03-1982 L1983 **EM** *020 †16

ALLADI, Uma D. 5308 N GALLOWAY AVE, STE 200 75150 #495-42-1970 L1981 **NEP IM** *020 †20

ALLAM, Fatma Elzahra. 929 N GALLOWAY AVE, STE 121 75149 #915-02-1982 L2000 **PD** *020 †55

ASHFAQ, Ahmed Rasheed. 2698 N GALLOWAY AVE, STE 101 75150 #495-33-1970 L1977 **IM** *020 †20

ASKINS, Dennis Randall. 929 N GALLOWAY AVE STE 202 75150 #048-12-1983 L1983 **PTH** *020 †50

AWAD, Rebhi Ahmad. 3500 INTERSTATE 30, DEPT RADIOLOGY 75150 #575-01-1982 L1991 **DR** *020 †80

BABUJI, Robert James. 1050 N BELT LINE RD # 101 75149 #495-16-1986 L2006 **CD** *020 †20

BACULI, Randy Herbolario. 1050 N BELT LINE RD, STE 103 75149 #748-10-1988 L2001 **N** *020

BALA, Padma. 1650 REPUBLIC PKWY, STE 100 75150 #495-04-1972 L1985 **PD** *020 †55

BANJO, Chaim. 4725 GUS THOMASSON RD 75150 #065-10-1979 L1983 **IM CD** *020 †20

BASATNEH, Lufti S. 1012 N GALLOWAY AVE, STE 104 75149 #875-02-1982 L1997 **N** *020 †75

BEGLEY, Lew Merrel. PO BOX 850246 75185 #048-04-1960 L1960 **FM** *020

BENJAMIN, Jense. 2704 N GALLOWAY AVE, STE 104 75150 #495-80-1981 L2001 **FM** *020 †18

BERLANDO, Richard Allan. 2540 N GALLOWAY AVE, STE 203 75150 #060-01-1979 L1981 **FM EM** *020 †18 ‡

BIERMAN, Solomon Martin. 3500 INTERSTATE 30, AT MOTLEY 75150 #035-45-1986 L1991 **DR** *020 †80

BIGGERS, Jeffrey Blair. 1050 N BELT LINE RD # 104 75149 #048-12-1981 L1981 **GS CRS** *020 †85

BLAKELY, James Philip. 1425 GROSS RD, WHITE ROCK RADIOLOGY 75149 #017-20-1973 L1977 **DR OS** *020 †80

BODDU, Aruna. 1280 N TOWN EAST BLVD 75150 #495-50-1996 L2004 **FPG** *020 †18

BUENTIPO, Benigno V, Jr. 3916 IH-30/67 75150 #748-02-1956 L1979 **GP GS** *020

BURNEY, Mohammad Umar. 1106 N GALLOWAY AVE 75149 #422-01-2001 L2006 **ORS OSM** *020

CAPPS, Raymond Luis. 1050 N BELT LINE RD, STE 104 75149 #048-12-1987 L1988 **GS** *020 †85

CARUSO, Michela. 4700 N GALLOWAY AVE 75150 #561-17-1980 L1999 **RO IM** *020 †80

CELAN, Anca. ■ 75150 #781-01-1982 *100

CHEATHAM, Bruce Alan. 309 N GALLOWAY AVE STE 107 75149 #048-15-1977 L1977 **DR** *020 †80

CHITHAMBO, Godfrey S. 820 E CARTWRIGHT RD # 10 75149 #047-07-1987 L1996 **IM** *020 †20

CHITTOOR, Sreenivas R. 4700 N GALLOWAY AVE 75150 #495-50-1979 L1994 **ON HO** *020 †20

CHOWDHARY, Sultan Aleem. 2692 N GALLOWAY AVE, STE 103 75150 #704-01-1981 L1995 **HO HMP** *020 †50,20

COHEN, Steven David. 2694 N GALLOWAY AVE, STE 502 75150 #060-02-1983 L1996 **FM PME** *020 †18 ‡

COHEN, Steven Ralph. 4725 GUS THOMASSON RD, STE 8 75150 #550-01-1975 L1979 **OTO** *020 †45

CONSTANTINE, Sami Elias. 901 N GALLOWAY AVE, STE 107 75149 #605-01-1975 L1978 **OBG** *020 †30

CORNELL, Thomas Joseph. 1425 GROSS RD, WHITE ROCK RADIOLOGY 75149 #021-01-1977 L1981 **DR** *020 †80

CRAMER, Andrea Ellen. 1600 REPUBLIC PKWY, STE 140 75150 #041-12-1979 L1987 **PD MG** *020 †19,55

CYNAR, Robert Garret. 1650 REPUBLIC PKWY, STE 100 75150 #017-20-1998 L2001 **FM** *020 †18

DARBY, Castilla A, Jr. ■ 75149 #047-07-1978 L1981 **GP** *020

DAVES, Elizabeth A Alf. ■ 75150 #038-41-1949 L1951 **AN** *071

DAVIDSON, Thomas Scott. 820 E CARTWRIGHT RD, STE 126 75149 #048-12-1975 L1975 **CD IM** *071 †20

DILLAHUNTY, Donald F. 1280 N TOWN EAST BLVD, PRIMACARE MED CTR 75150 #028-78-1989, ▲ L1990 **FM OM** *020

DOCKINS, Cynthia May. 1012 N GALLOWAY AVE, STE 103 75149 #039-01-1990 L2006 **PD** *020 †55

DOYAL, Jessie Dean. 1102 N GALLOWAY AVE 75149 #048-12-1981 L1981 **GP** *020

DUCKWORTH, Azucena S. ■ 75181 #748-09-1969 L1988 **IM** *020

EDWARDS, Lewis Todd. 1650 REPUBLIC PKWY, STE 150 75149 #048-13-1996 L1997 **IM** *020 †20

EGBOH, Nenna K. ■ 75150 #048-12-2008 *012

EGGERT, Bryan Geo. 4700 N GALLOWAY AVE, TEXAS CANCER CENTER-MESQUI 75150 #028-02-1983 L1985 **RO IM** *020 †80

ELASHRAM, Nayer Badawi E. 929 N GALLOWAY AVE, STE 108 75149 #915-09-1977 L1991 **CCM IM** *020 †20

ELLMAN, Michael Gary. 2692 N GALLOWAY AVE, STE 402 75150 #021-01-1991 L1993 **PM** *020 †60

ELSEHETY, Ahmed Elsawy. 929 N GALLOWAY AVE, STE 102 75149 #915-06-1977 L1993 **N PME** *020

FELICIANO, Maria Lourdes. 1010 N BELT LINE RD, STE 105 75149 #748-07-1962 L1975 **AN** *071

FERRIS, Stephanie Holman. 1425 GROSS RD, WHITE ROCK RADIOLOGY 75149 #039-01-1988 L1994 **R VIR** *020 †80

FINO, Sameer Andoni. 1050 N BELT LINE RD 75149 #048-12-1991 L1992 **PM** *020 †60

FOWLER, Donald Benten, Jr. 820 E CARTWRIGHT RD, STE 100 75149 #021-06-1993 L2000 **FM** *020 †18

FRYE, Laura Lynn. 1650 REPUBLIC PKWY, STE 100 75150 #048-12-1995 L1999 **FM** *020 †18

FUNK, Geoffrey A. ■ 75149 #048-16-2004 **GS** *012

GAN, Luisa Yao. 5308 N GALLOWAY AVE 75150 #748-08-1972 L1976 **CD** *020

GANGI, Sumana. 3500 IH 30 BLDG D, SUITE 203 75150 #495-70-1997 L2006 **END** *100 †20 ‡

GARRETT, Gary D. 1650 REPUBLIC PKWY, STE 100 75150 #048-12-1995 L1996 **FM** *020 †18

GOYAL, Satish Kumar. 2540 N GALLOWAY AVE, STE 205 75150 #495-29-1973 L1980 **IM GP** *020 †20

GRANT, J Kirkland. 3500 INTERSTATE 30, STE B120 75150 #048-14-1979 L1979 **OBG** *020 †30

GRAVES, Max Kevin. 1675 REPUBLIC PKWY, STE 100 75150 #021-05-1989 L2001 **CD** *020 †20

GUNUKULA, Srinivas R. 5308 N GALLOWAY AVE 75150 #496-24-1993 L2003 **CD** *020 †20

GUSTAFSON, Tracy Lee. ■ 75181 #005-02-1977 L1982 **PHP PD** *050 †55

HA, Chenxiang. 5115 N GALLOWAY AVE 75150 #243-16-1991 L2004 **FM** *020

HADDAD, Marun Suleiman. 5308 N GALLOWAY AVE, STE 6100 75150 #605-01-1972 L1976 **CD IM** *020 †20

HAFFAR, Shiela. 4700 N GALLOWAY AVE, PARKLAND MEMORIAL HOSPITAL 75150 #048-15-2002 L2005 **HO** *100 †20

HAKERT, James Damian. 1050 N BELT LINE RD, STE 105 75149 #048-14-1986 L1987 **GE** *020 †20

HARIZ, George M. 3500 INTERSTATE 30 # F103, BLDG F 75150 #605-01-1979 L1989 **GS VS** *020 †85 ‡

HERDING, Pierre. 3500 INTERSTATE 30, STE C103 75150 #035-01-1964 L1990 **N FM** *071 †75

HOLTZ, Melissa Nichole. ■ 75150 #056-06-2007 **OBG** *012

HORADAM, Victor Wm. 4700 N GALLOWAY AVE, TEXAS CANCER CTR MESQUITE 75150 #048-12-1976 L1976 **ON HEM** *020 †20

HOUSTON, James Duane. 2944 MOTLEY DR, STE 203 75149 #048-12-1971 L1971 **IM IMG** *020

HUNTE, Michael Steven. ■ 75181 #048-02-2007 **EM** *012

IQBAL, Zahida. 929 N GALLOWAY AVE 75149 #704-21-1982 L1998 **PD** *020 †55

JAKUBOWSKI, Piotr. 2379 GUS THOMASSON RD 75150 #759-03-1988 L1995 **IM** *020 †20

JAY, John Laurence. 929 N GALLOWAY AVE, STE 108 75149 #048-04-1984 L1986 **TS** *020 †85,90

JISHI, Basim Mahmoud. 5308 N GALLOWAY AVE 75150 #605-01-1972 L1996 **IM** *020 †20

KABOLI, Daryoush. 1050 N BELT LINE RD, STE 103 75149 #517-01-1970 L1977 **N AN** *020 †75

KAGAL, Prakash P. SUITE 100, 3500 I-30 BLD C 75150 #495-37-1975 L1996 **IM** *020 †20

KANANI, Harini Pradip. 2698 N GALLOWAY AVE, STE 106 75150 #495-83-1981 L1987 **FM PTH** *020 †18

KENEBREW, Katherine S. 1100 AMUR ST 75150 #048-02-1989 L1990 **M** *030 †20

KENNEY, Alan F. 1645 N TOWN EAST BLVD, STE 174 75150 #063-01-1975 L1986 **FM** *020

KETTER, Gary Warren. 2540 N GALLOWAY AVE, STE 202 75150 #016-11-1978 L1983 **OTO A** *020 †45

KHAN, Khurshid. 2540 N GALLOWAY AVE, STE 102 75150 #704-09-1976 L1993 **IM** *020

KIBLAWI, Isam S. 2540 N GALLOWAY AVE, STE 204 75150 #605-01-1961 L1980 **PD D** *020

KIKKERI, Nagaraj S. 3500 I-30 STE B240 75149 #495-72-1988 L2000 **AN PME** *020 †05

KIRVEN, Sharon Denett. 120 W MAIN ST 75149 #019-02-1994 L1997 **FM** *020 †18

KOLUKULA, Anitha. 1645 N TOWN EAST BLVD 75150 #495-11-1999 L2005 **IM** *020 †20

KOTAMARTI, Aparna R. 1650 REPUBLIC PKWY, STE 150 75150 #495-49-1988 L1995 **IMG** *012 ‡

KREISLER, Aaron Leo. 3500 IH 30 STE B130 75150 #048-02-1966 L1966 **PD NPM** *020 †55

KRONENBERGER, Crystal B. 1650 REPUBLIC PKWY, STE 150 75150 #048-04-1990 L1999 **IM GPM** *071 †20,70

KURILECZ, Michael. 4737 GUS THOMASSON RD # B 75150 #048-02-1949 L1950 **OBG** *020 †30

LACEY, Julian Keith. 1650 REPUBLIC PKWY, STE 100 75150 #012-05-2000 L2003 **PD** *020 †55 ‡

LAZARUS, Stephen Michael. 1011 N GALLOWAY AVE 75149 #036-07-1964 L1993 **U** *020 †95

LEMESHEV, Jodi Gould. 1012 N GALLOWAY AVE # 103 75149 #048-13-2001 L2004 **PD** *020 †55

LEMESHEV, Yuri. 3500 INTERSTATE 30 75150 #913-21-1968 L1984 **PTH** *020 †50 ‡

LEVINE, Arthur H. BLDG BSUITE 260, 3500 -I-30 75150 #067-01-1948 L1978 **GS** *072 †85

LISTON, David Evan. 4053 TOWNE CROSSING BLVD, APT 2704 75150 #048-04-1999 L2006 **APM** *012 ‡

LOWELL, James D. 4928 SAMUELL BLVD, CONCENTRA MEDICAL CENTER 75149 #051-04-1977 L1994 **FM** *040 †18

LUNA, Cynthia. ■ 75181 #048-12-2004 **NEP** *012 †20,18

MAKARY, Michael M. ■ 75150 #048-15-2006 L2008 **IM** *012

MALLICK, Saleem Hayat. 2704 N GALLOWAY AVE, STE 103 75150 #704-04-1971 L1977 **CD IM** *020 †20

MARGASSERY, Suresh Kumar. 2698 N GALLOWAY AVE, STE 107 75150 #495-66-1986 L2004 **NEP IM** *020 †20

MARSHALL, Janice J. 4700 N GALLOWAY AVE 75150 #001-02-1989 L1994 **HO IM** *020 †20

MATHEWKUTTY, Shiny. ■ 75149 #048-14-2007 **IM** *012

MAWLA, Neghae. 2698 N GALLOWAY AVE 75150 #048-14-2001 L2006 **NEP** *012

MERKIN, Andrew David. 2692 N GALLOWAY AVE # 403 75150 #048-02-1979 L1979 **IM EM** *020 †20

MILLER, Robert More. 2694 N GALLOWAY AVE, STE 501 75150 #051-01-1979 L1987 **GE IM** *020 †20

MITCHELL, Charles Dale. 3500 INTERSTATE 30 # C101 75150 #010-03-1966 L1973 **ORS** *020

MUNDLURU, Anuradha L. 1011 N GALLOWAY AVE 75149 #495-62-1988 L1997 **IM** *020 †20

MURAT, Jean Louis. 929 N GALLOWAY AVE 75149 #440-01-1963 L1981 **PD OM** *072

NAMA, Vijaya. 300 W KEARNEY ST 75149 #495-65-1987 L2003 **FM** *020 †18

NELSON, Robert Jerome. 820 E CARTWRIGHT RD, STE 126 75149 #028-02-1972 L1975 **PD** *020

NUNEZ-MUNIZ, Ernesto A. 3230 INTERSTATE 30 STE 100 75150 #308-05-1988 L1997 **PD** *020 †55

NYLUND, Jack Louis. 1011 N GALLOWAY AVE 75149 #036-05-1966 L1971 **R** *071 †80

OGBOGU, Henry U. 3500 INTERSTATE 30 75150 #690-04-1986 L1995 **IM** *020 †20

OLIVER, German Antonio. 2694 N GALLOWAY AVE, STE 501 75150 #042-01-1980 L1988 **GE IM** *020 †20

OTOKITI, Victor Lawani. ■ 75150 #748-20-1989 **ADP** *100

PANG, John J. 200 W KEARNEY ST, PANG FAMILY CLINIC 75149 #654-01-1983 **FM** *020

PAREKH, Sohail. 1010 N BELT LINE RD #704-02-1986 L1998 **IMG** *020 †20

PASCOE, Rana Seils. 1650 REPUBLIC PKWY, STE 100 75150 #005-06-1987 L1993 **FM ADL** *020 †18

PETERSON, Valerie Ann. 1650 REPUBLIC PKWY, AT MESQUITE 75150 #048-02-2004 **FM** *020 †18

PILLAY, Premachandran S. 2704 N GALLOWAY AVE, STE 103 75150 #913-92-1979 L2005 **CD IM** *020 †20

PIRRUNG, James Stuart. 200 W KEARNEY ST 75149 #048-04-1959 L1960 **FM OM** *071 †18

PORT, Teig. 1106 N GALLOWAY AVE 75149 #005-11-1983 L2000 **ORS OSM** *020 †40

POTASZNIK, Joel. 4355 I-30 75150 #048-13-1973 L1973 **OPH** *020 ‡

QAVI, Abdul. 1012 N GALLOWAY AVE STE 102 75149 #704-02-1991 L2003 **ID IM** *020 †20

RAMAN, Indrani Badanna. 2698 N GALLOWAY AVE # 107 75150 #495-62-1997 L2006 **NEP IM** *020

RAMSAY, Sarah J. 3500 INTERSTATE 30 75150 #047-06-1977 L1986 **AN IM** *020 †20,05

RANA, Pushpa Ramnik. 3500 INTERSTATE 30 75150 #495-01-1971 L1976 **PD** *020

RANA, Rajesh S. 3500 INTERSTATE 30, STE C203 75150 #495-17-1984 L1993 **IM** *020 †20

RAO, Mallapur Shashikant. 1645 N TOWN EAST BLVD #174, MESQUITE CLINIC 75150 #495-02-1964 L1978 **FM GS** *020 ‡

REAGANS, Kimberly Nicole. 4200 N GALLOWAY AVE 75149 #048-12-2004 L2007 **EM** *020

RICHARD, Franchell. ■ 75150 #048-13-2007 L2007 **GS** *012

ROBERTS, Gary Frey. 2692 N GALLOWAY AVE, STE 402 75150 #021-05-1977 L1992 **FM** *020 †18

RODRIGUEZ, Alfredo D M. 2540 N GALLOWY AVE #NO-301 75149 #748-01-1969 L1979 **PS** *020 †65

RODRIGUEZ, Rafael A. 929 N GALLOWAY AVE 75149 #308-05-1987 L1996 **IM PLM** *020 †20

ROME, Richard Steven. 1011 N GALLOWAY AVE 75149 #024-05-1977 L1983 **DR NR** *020 †80

RUDNICKI, Richard N. 2856 N GALLOWAY AVE, MESQUITE DERMATOLOGY 75150 #041-77-1986, ▲ L1992 **D DS** *020

SAFAR, James Antoine. 6500 NORTHWEST DR, STE 350 75150 #048-13-1994 L1995 **OPH** *020 †35

SARWAR, Mohammad. 2704 N GALLOWAY AVE, STE 100 75150 #704-01-1967 L1974 **R RNR** *020 †80

SEEGMILLER, Adam Clark. ■ 75181 #048-12-2004 L2007 **HMP** *012 †50

SHOWING, Lidia M. 208 W KEARNEY ST, STE 107 75149 #737-01-1986 L1998 **PTH** *020 †50

SIDDIQ, Zakaria. 1050 N BELT LINE RD, STE 103 75149 #704-02-1986 L1998 **N** *020 †75

SINGHAL, Atul Kumar. 18601 LYNDON B JOHNSON FWY, STE 615 75150 #495-36-1987 L1995 **RHU IMG** *020

SOBEY, Terry Marshall. 1010 N BELT LINE RD # 101 75149 #048-12-1978 L1978 **ORS** *020 †40

SONNEN, Gregory M. 1650 REPUBLIC PKWY, STE 100 75150 #048-16-1995 L1998 **PD** *020 †55

STEPHAN, Michel Khamis. 2540 N GALLOWAY AVE, STE 101 75150 #605-01-1974 L1980 **GS VS** *020 †85

STEWART, Bobby R. 5308 N GALLOWAY AVE, STE 100 75150 #048-04-1981 L1982 **CD IM** *020 †20

STUART, Kyle David. ■ 75149 #048-12-2006 **ORS** *012

SUBRAMANIAN, Geetha. 5308 N GALLOWAY AVE SU, DETROIT RECEIVING HOSPITAL 75150 #028-03-2001 L2007 **OTO** *020

SUMMA, James Angelo. 529 N GALLOWAY AVE 75149 #038-06-1991 L1995 **VIR** *020 †80

SWANSON, Lisa L. 3220 GUS THOMASSON RD, STE 350 75150 #048-13-1985 L1986 **PD** *020 †55

SWEENEY, Patrick Terrence. 120 W MAIN ST, STE 211 75149 #030-05-1994 L1996 **OPH** *020 †35

SYED, Nabeel H. 2540 N GALLOWAY AVE, STE 103 75150 #048-13-1989 L1990 **U** *020 †95

TALATI, Shraddha. 3500 INTERSTATE 30 # BE-10 75150 #496-38-1971 L1979 **OBG** *020

TANAMACHI, Cary Takeo. 1010 N BELT LINE RD, STE 101 75149 #048-13-1972 L1972 **ORS** *020 †40

THUMASATHIT, Suthee. 1645 N TOWN EAST BLVD, STE 174 75150 #048-03-1991 L1994 **IM** *020 †20

TOBIAS, David. ■ 75150 #048-12-2007 **FP** *012

TRIPP, Larry E. 75187 #007-02-1960 L1967 **P PYM** *071 †75 ‡

TRUONG, Tiep Buu. ■ 75149 #048-02-2005 **AN** *012

TUCKER, Sharon E. 1650 REPUBLIC PKWY, STE 100 75150 #048-12-1993 L1994 **FM** *020 †18

UKOHA, Chijioke David. 1800 N GALLOWAY AVE # 100 75149 #690-07-1985 L1995 **IM** *020 †20

USUGA, Luis De Leon. 3500 I-30 BLDG D 75150 #264-03-1986 L1998 **OBG** *020 †30

VEERARAGHAVAN, Krishna A. 5308 N GALLOWAY AVE, STE 200 75150 #495-04-1969 L1982 **U** *020 †20

WALENDA, Beata. 2379 GUS THOMASSON RD 75150 #759-03-1988 L1995 **IM** *020 †20

WILLIAMS, Kynan D. ■ 75149 #048-12-2006 **FP** *012

WILSON, Damalia Teresa. 1011 N GALLOWAY AVE, MEDICAL CENTER OF MESQUITE 75149 #048-02-1999 L2004 **EM** *020 †16

WITTEN, James Fair. 1650 REPUBLIC PKWY STE 150 75150 #048-12-1955 L1955 **IM** *071 †20

WONG, Po Hing. 208 W KEARNEY ST, STE 104 75149 #671-01-1960 L1978 **N** *020

WYATT, John Creedmore, III. 1425 GROSS RD, WHITE ROCK RADIOLOGY 75149 #048-12-1976 L1978 **DR NM** *020 †80

YANG, Michael C. 901 N GALLOWAY AVE STE 107 75149 #048-12-1995 L1996 **OBG** *020 †30

YEAKLEY, Mark. 3500 INTERSTATE 30 75150 #048-02-1976 L1977 **P** *020 †75

YEN, Pedro R-M. 1900 OATES DR STE 1 75150 #187-19-1982 L1997 **FM** *020 †18

YOUNAS, Ahmer. 18601 LBJ FWY STE 315, OF TEXAS, LLP 75150 #305-01-2000 L2006 **HO** *020 †20

ZAKHOUR, Bassam Jamil. 3500 I-30, STE F103 75150 #875-01-1978 L1985 **GS** *020 †85

ZEVALLOS, Pedro T. 18601 LYNDON B JOHNSON FWY, STE 315 75150 #737-01-1971 L1976 **PUD IM** *020 †20

MEXIA – LIMESTONE

CHIN, Yong Uk. 514 S BONHAM ST STE G 76667 #040-02-1992 L1997 **IM** *020

CURTI, Anthony John. 999 N HIGHWAY 171, MEXIA STATE SCHOOL 76667 #035-09-1979 L1988 **PTH** *020 †50

JENSEN, Rima Zita. 201 N MCKINNEY ST 76667 #026-04-1986 L1994 **FM OBG** *020 †18

MADRID CERVANO, Alberto. 515 S BONHAM ST 76667 #649-01-1970 L1981 **GS** *075 †85

RUSSELL, Kenneth L. 514 S BONHAM ST STE H 76667 #048-13-1988 L1989 **IM GE** *020 †20

SIMMONS, Jerry Wayne. 514 S BONHAM ST, STE H 76667 #039-01-1975 L1979 **FM** *020

STOCKBURGER, Robert L. 408 E TYLER ST 76667 #048-78-1977, ▲ L1983 **OBG** *020 †30

WILLIFORD, Carl E. 408 E TYLER ST 76667 #048-12-1952 L1952 **GP GS** *071

WOOD, James Ray. 514 S BONHAM ST, STE C 76667 #048-13-1977 L1982 **GS** *020

MIDLAND – MIDLAND

ADAMS, John Truett. ■ 79701 #048-12-1957 L1957 **GP** *071

ADCOCK, Lori Sherman. 709 W LOUISIANA AVE 79701 #035-46-1983 L1989 **PDE PD** *020 †55

AFINIWALA, Mitul Pradeep. ■ 79707 #496-41-2002 **IM** *012

AGRAWAL, Sudhi. ■ 79707 #495-41-1970 L1983 **PD** *030 †55

ALLEN, Thomas Gordon. ■ 79707 #040-02-1993 L1995 **EM** *020 †16

AWOSEMO, Segun Basiru. ■ 79705 #690-05-1988 L2003 **IM** *020 †20

AZAROV, Nikolay Andreyevi. ■ 79707 #913-04-1994 L2007 **CCM** *100 †20

BALASAKARAN, Bhuvana. 2102 W TENNESSEE AVE 79701 #495-04-1991 L2001 **FM** *020 †18

BALLESTEROS, Wellington F. 2500 DELANO AVE 79701 #748-01-1982 L1989 **PD NPM** *020 †55

BARNETT, James H. 400 N GARFIELD ST STE 240, PERMIAN CARDIOLOGY ASSOCIA 79701 #054-04-1988 L1990 **CD IM** *020 †20

BARTHA, Gregory Woodson. 2203 W TENNESSEE AVE 79701 #008-01-1971 L1977 **IM** *020 †20

BARTOLD, Stephen Peter. 4907 POLO PKWY, 4907 POLO PARKWAY 79705 #025-01-1977 L1990 **IM PTH** *020 †50,20,28

BATCH, Kenneth Herman. 4200 ANDREWS HWY 79703 #047-07-1974 L1982 **AN** *040

BECK, Terry L. ■ 79707 #048-13-1990 L1991 **EM** *020

BELIZAIRE, Roger. 2004 W OHIO AVE 79701 #649-01-1971 L1978 **VS GS** *020 †85

BEST, Paul Wesley. 805 W WADLEY AVE, STE A 79705 #021-01-1972 L1973 **EM ORS** *020 †75,16

BHIMJI, S. 25 VILLAGE CIR 79701 #065-01-1990 L2002 **TS** *020 †85,90

BLONKVIST, Brent Garland. 2200 W ILLINOIS AVE 79701 #048-12-1954 L1954 **PD** *071

BOREN, Ronald Preston. 4214 ANDREWS HWY, STE 306 79703 #021-01-1962 L1969 PD *020 †55

BOZZELL, James Donald. 2200 W ILLINOIS AVE 79701 #048-04-1946 L1946 U *071 †95

BRACHETTA, Guillermo E. 2300 W MICHIGAN AVE, STE 1 79701 #132-02-1973 L1979 GS CRS *020 †10,85

BRAY, John David. 606 KENT ST, STE B 79701 #011-02-1977 L1983 A PUD *020 †55,03

BROCK, Brad Madsen. ■ 79701 #004-01-1991 L1992 AN *020 †05

BROOKS, Joseph Garnett. 2200 W ILLINOIS AVE, MIDLAND MEMORIAL HOSPITAL 79701 #023-12-1994 L2002 AN *020 †05

BROWN, Steven Lewis. 400 N GARFIELD ST, STE 240 79701 #035-01-1990 L1996 CD *020 †20

BURNS, Elvira Canales. 2405 W MISSOURI AVE 79701 #048-04-1985 L1986 FM *020 †18

BURNS, Terry Robt. 2008 W OHIO AVE 79701 #048-13-1979 L1979 ATP *020 †20

CALA, Ruben G. 801 E FLORIDA AVE 79701 #748-01-1965 L1982 IM PUD *020 †20

CALA, Sylvia M Obillo. 2500 DELANO AVE 79701 #748-01-1964 L1981 PD *020 †55

CALLO, Guillermo Antonio. 2407 W LOUISIANA AVE, STE 103B 79701 #737-01-1972 L1978 OBG *020 †30

CAMPBELL, John D. ■ 79705 #048-14-1987 *100

CARMODY, Seamus E. 4405 DALTON DR 79701 #035-06-1964 L1977 GS *020 †85

CARTER, Edward Lee. 2706 W CUTHBERT AVE, BULDG B STE 100 79701 #048-02-1982 L1983 AN *020

CASE, Roberta M Salvini. 2010 W OHIO AVE 79701 #056-06-1973 L1979 OTO *020 †45

CATALASAN, Gerardo M. 2200 W ILLINOIS AVE, MIDLAND MEMORIAL HOSPITAL 79701 #748-01-1996 L2006 PCC *020 †20

CHOLIA, Anand Paritosh. 400 N GARFIELD ST STE 140, MICHIGAN STATE UNIVERSITY 79701 #495-01-1994 L1998 CD *100 †20

COCHRAN, Jerry Lee. 10 DESTA DR STE 100E 79705 #039-01-1973 L1980 OSM *020 †40

CONLIN, Phillip A. 2008 W OHIO AVE 79701 #048-15-1997 L2001 PTH *020 †50

COOPER, Wm Butler Dawkins. ■ 79702 #047-07-1944 L1946 GP *075

CORWIN, James Albert. 400 N GARFIELD ST 79701 #048-04-1972 L1975 RO *020 †80 ‡

CROCKETT, Donald Edwin, Jr. 2706 W CUTHBERT AVE STE C 79701 #048-13-1976 L1976 VS GS *020 †85

CROPPER, Charles Austin. ■ 79702 #048-02-2004 L2006 OM GPM *012

DAS, Samiran Kumar. 25 VILLAGE CIR, WEST TEXAS MEDICAL CENTER 79701 #160-02-1988 L2006 IM *020

DAVIS, Randall K. 4214 ANDREWS HWY, STE 101 79703 #034-01-1983 L1993 OBG FM *020 †18,30

DEAN, John Cannon. 10 DESTA DR, STE 100E 79705 #048-16-1986 L1987 ORS *020 †40

DELGADO, Jose Guillermo. ■ 79705 #264-07-1986 L2004 FM *020 †18

DEME, Srikanth Reddy. 2000 W OHIO AVE 79701 #495-65-1988 L2001 NS *020 †25

DESHAN, David Michael. 4214 ANDREWS HWY STE 200 79703 #048-12-1986 L1987 OBG *020 †20

DE SOCARRAZ, Christine T. 4519 N GARFIELD ST, PRIMARY MEDICAL CLINIC 79705 #021-06-1979 L1980 GP *072

DHINDSA, Sandeep. 10 DESTA DR, STE 190 79705 #495-36-1997 L2005 END *020 †20

DOCTOR, Dolly Prerak. 2817 W LOOP 250 N, STE A 79705 #495-23-1988 L1991 IM *020 †20

DOCTOR, Prerak Manibhai. 2817 W LOOP 250 N, STE A 79705 #495-23-1984 L1991 CHP P *020 †75

DOKE, Ben W. 4214 ANDREWS HWY, STE 200 79703 #048-12-2001 L2005 OBG *020 †30

DOMINGO, Ramon Ko. ■ 79707 #748-01-1970 L1977 FM *020

DRAGUN, Michael John. 122 N N ST 79701 #005-14-1989 L1994 U *020 †95

DYER, Joel Edward. 2706 W CUTHBERT AVE, BLDG B 79701 #048-12-1981 L1981 AN *020 †05

DYER, Morgan Coit Day. 2008 W OHIO AVE 79701 #048-13-1977 L1979 PTH *020

EMENEY, Pamela Louise. ■ 79705 #422-01-1999 L2004 OBG *100

ENGHARDT, Michaele H. 2008 W OHIO AVE 79701 #021-05-1975 L1996 PTH *020 †20

EUGENIO, Marco Tulio. 2000 W OHIO AVE 79701 #935-01-1951 L1961 NS PM *071 †25

FAIZULLAH, Abulbasher. 1816 N MIDLAND DR 79707 #160-01-1973 L1982 IM PD *020

FEIERABEND, Lee Roger. 4904 HILLSBORO CT 79705 #048-04-1974 L1974 EM PS *020

FLORER, Christine M. ■ 79707 #048-15-2000 L2003 OB *020 †55

FLOYD, Donald Wray. 4304 ANDREWS HWY 79703 #048-12-1974 L1978 ORS OSM *020 †40

FOSTER, John Wood. 2409 W ILLINOIS AVE STE D 79701 #048-04-1954 L1954 PD *071 †55

FOSTER, John Wood, Jr. 400 N GARFIELD ST STE 261 79701 #048-04-1979 L1979 N *020 †75

FREDRICKSON, Mark Allan. 1800 HERITAGE BLVD, MIDLAND-ODESSA 79707 #048-12-1988 L1990 PM *020 †60

FRY, Norman De Witt. 4214 ANDREWS HWY STE 200 79703 #021-01-1960 L1964 GYN *071 †30

GANTA, Shylesh Reddy. 2008 W WALL 79701 #496-24-1993 L1999 IM *020 †20

GARCIA, Joseph. 2405 W MISSOURI AVE, PERMIAN CARDIOLOGY 79701 #042-01-1982 L1983 CD *030 †20

GARCIA, Juan. 1802 W WALL ST 79701 #847-04-1957 L1979 ADP *071 †75

GILLHAM, Sherri L. 2008 W OHIO AVE 79701 #048-15-1976 L1980 PTH *020 †50

GOPALAN, Mini. 801 E FLORIDA AVE, MIDLAND COMM HLTH SRVCS 79701 #495-44-1997 L2004 IM *020 †20 ‡

GORANIA, Himatlal K. 3400 ANDREWS HWY, MIDLAND, PA 79703 #539-01-1964 L1976 FM OM *020 †18 ‡

GROSS, Mario Miguel, Jr. 4400 N MIDLAND DR, STE 506A 79707 #025-07-1985 L1998 OBG *020 †30

GROTTI, Lydia H. 2301 W WALL ST, HEART PLACE HOSPITAL 79701 #048-14-1984 L1994 IM CCM *062 †20

GUPTA, Charu. ■ 79705 #048-12-2008 *012

GUPTA, Prem Parkash. 302 SECOR ST 79701 #495-36-1973 L1980 PD *020 †55

GUPTA, Urmila. 302 SECOR ST 79701 #495-36-1976 L1981 PD *020 †55

GURRU, Manoher Lal. 122 N N ST 79701 #704-08-1987 L2001 N CCN *020 †75

HANKINS, Alton B. 10 DESTA DR STE 220 79705 #048-02-1973 L1973 P *020 †75 ‡

HART, Merry Beth. 2409 W ILLINOIS AVE STE D 79701 #048-15-2001 L2004 PD *020 †55

HIBBITTS, Wm Mc Cartney. 2200 W ILLINOIS AVE 79701 #047-05-1948 L1955 IM GE *071

HIGHTOWER, Cheryl White. 4214 ANDREWS HWY, ASSOCIATES 79703 #048-15-1980 L1980 R *020 †80

HINTON, Thomas R. 4214 ANDREWS HWY, ASSOCIATES 79701 #034-01-1980 L1988 DR *020 †80

HORNE, Merrill Callis. 4214 ANDREWS HWY STE 306 79703 #048-02-1971 L1971 PD GP *020 †55

HOWLETT, John Richard, Jr. 1002 W WALL ST 79701 #048-02-1976 L1976 P *020

HTAY, Thwe Thwe. 10 DESTA DR STE 190 79705 #209-01-1994 L2000 IM *020 †20 ‡

HUDDLESTON, James E, Jr. 401 E ILLINOIS AVE, PERMIAN BASIN CENTERS FOR 79701 #048-12-1964 L1964 P *020 †75

HUGHES, Marlon David. 2200 W ILLINOIS AVE 79701 #024-01-1985 L1995 DR *020 †80

HUGHES, Patricia Linn. 4214 ANDREWS HWY, ASSOCIATES 79703 #024-01-1985 L1995 DR *020 †80

HUMPHREYS, James Mack, Jr. 2200 W ILLINOIS AVE, MIDLAND MEMORIAL HOSP 79701 #048-12-1969 L1969 UM OS *030 †30

HUSTON, James William. 314 SECOR ST 79701 #047-06-1994 L1998 IM *020 †20

ILANG-ILANG, Federico, Jr. 2500 DELANO AVE 79701 #748-08-1977 L1981 IM PD *020 †20

INGRAM, Ronald W. 2200 W CUTHBERT AVE # A 79701 #048-04-1986 L1987 OPH *020 †35

JOHNSON, Mark Lynn. 3001 W ILLINOIS AVE 79701 #048-13-1983 L1983 AN *020 †05

JONES, Michael Frederick. 2501 W ILLINOIS AVE STE C 79701 #054-04-1993 L2003 AN *020 †05

KECK, Gregory Mark. 4812 RICHMOND DR 79705 #048-04-1985 L2003 DR VIR *020 †80

KHANDELWAL, Bal Krishna. 2301 W MICHIGAN AVE 79701 #495-34-1969 L1977 RHU IM *020 †20

KHANDELWAL, Niraj. ■ 79707 #048-02-2005 IM *012

KHOURI, Daniel. 1200 W WALL 79701 #067-06-1990 L1999 U *020 †95

KINZIE, Daniel H, IV. 3400 ANDREWS HWY 79703 #005-14-1961 L1985 EM *020 †20

KLEMPNAUER, Richard G. 1403 W ILLINOIS AVE, FAMILY MEDCENTER 79701 #019-02-1955 L1958 GP *020

KLUNICK, Chester H, Jr. 2200 W ILLINOIS AVE 79701 #048-13-1981 L1981 AN EM *020 †16,05

KUTZ, Susan. 1811 W WALL ST 79701 #048-15-1995 L1998 IM *020 †20

LANCASTER, Scott H. ■ 79705 #048-14-1992 L1994 AN *020 †05

LEAK, Morgan Grant. ■ 79706 #048-15-2008 *012

LEUNG, Patrick Yiu Sai. 2102 W MICHIGAN AVE 79701 #060-01-1968 L1978 FM OBS *020 †18

LINEBACK, Wilbur Geo. 2104 W MICHIGAN AVE 79701 #034-01-1991 L1996 CHP *020 †75

LOCKE, Edwin B. 4214 ANDREWS HWY, STE 200 79703 #048-15-1997 L2008 OBG *020 †30

LOEWENSTEIN, Jos Edward. ■ 79705 #048-02-1963 L1965 END DIA *020 †20

LOHMANN, George Young. 6 DESTA DR STE 6300 79705 #035-06-1972 L1994 NS *020 †25

MAC FERRAN, Samuel N, Jr. 2409 W ILLINOIS AVE STE D 79701 #004-01-1983 L1986 PD *020 †25

MADDEN, Gary Dean. 4214 ANDREWS HWY, STE 200 79703 #048-15-1982 L1983 OBG *020 †30

MALLAMS, David John. 2000 W CUTHBERT AVE 79701 #041-13-1975 L1980 ORS HS *020 †40

MANSOUR, Mourad Labib. 1802 W WALL ST 79701 #330-03-1961 L1978 IM *020

MATHEW, Roy Jacob. 600 N MARIENFELD ST # 308 79701 #495-31-1971 L1976 P ADP *020 †75

MAYRON, Bart Richard. 2405 W MISSOURI AVE, PERMIAN CARDIOLOGY 79701 #016-11-1963 L1967 CD IM *020 †20

MC GAVRAN, Wm Lesley, III. 2000 W OHIO AVE 79701 #048-12-1970 L1970 NS *020 †25

MC GEHEE, Frank O, IV. 509 N GARFIELD ST 79701 #048-13-2002 L2006 PMM *012 †05

MC KENNA, John Monroe. 400 N GARFIELD ST, STE 271 79701 #048-12-1975 L1975 PUD IM *020 †20

MC LAREY, Don C, II. 901 W MISSOURI AVE 79701 #048-13-1987 L1988 IM A *020 †20

MEDINA, Alma Nydia. 2500 DELANO AVE 79701 #042-01-1978 L1992 PD *020 †55

MENDEZ, J Ernesto. 3107 N BIG SPRING 79705 #048-15-1975 L1979 GYN GO *020 †30

MICKLE, Edwin Rogers. ■ 79701 #048-02-1952 L1952 *071

MILLER, Michael Sterling. 400 N GARFIELD ST, STE 400 79701 #048-13-1979 L1979 CD IM *020 †20

MOLINERO, Kenneth G, Jr. 400 N GARFIELD ST, STE 281 79701 #041-78-2001, ▲ L2007 ORS *020

MORRISON, Debra Lynn. ■ 79705 #028-03-1977 L1978 AN *020 †05

MUNNELL, Marlys Olivia. ■ 79705 #048-13-1990 L1991 AN *020 †05

MURTHY, Gollapudi G K. 10 DESTA DR, STE 190 79705 #495-11-1962 L1977 END IM *020 †28,20

NABULSI, Nefous Kamal. 5801 W WADLEY AVE, PEDI MED CENTER 79707 #575-02-1993 L1999 PD *020 †55

NABULSI, Sari Ali. 5801 W WADLEY AVE 79707 #575-02-1992 L1998 PD *020 †55

NATH, Manju. 1800 HERITAGE BLVD 79707 #016-02-1989 L1993 PM PMM *020 †60

NELSON, Daniel Geo. 2501 W ILLINOIS AVE, STE D 79701 #048-13-1982 L1983 ORS *020 †40

NEWSOM, Gary D. 4200 W ILLINOIS AVE 79703 #048-02-1983 L1983 NEP IM *020 †20

NUNEZ, Oscar L. ■ 79707 #048-16-2000 L2001 AN *020 †05

ODUKWU, Lyden Chike. 1405 W ILLINOIS AVE 79701 #690-04-1994 L2003 FM *020 †18 ‡

OEI, Joseph. 2300 W MICHIGAN AVE 79701 #506-02-1967 L1976 PME *020 †05

OHLMAN, Julie Reichenbach. 3001 W ILLINOIS AVE, STE 1B2 79701 #001-02-1990 L1996 AN *020 †05

OLIVER, Larry Dale. 4200 W ILLINOIS AVE # 140 79703 #048-02-1978 L1978 NEP IM *020 †20

OLSON, Eric L. 3000 N GARFIELD ST, STE 105 79705 #048-14-1987 L1988 P PYG *020 †75

PALACHECK, Lisa Marie. PO BOX 1746 79702 #048-02-2005 L2006 GS *012

PANDYA, Rajanikant P. 1200 ANDREWS HWY 79701 #495-89-1979 L1995 IM *020 †20

PANUSKA, James Roy. 2407 W LOUISIANA AVE STE 1 79701 #038-06-1980 L1982 AI IM *020 †20

PAPICA, Romeo Padua, II. 2501 W ILLINOIS AVE, STE E 79701 #748-01-1990 L2004 FM *020 †18

PARK, Douglas S. 705 W WADLEY AVE 79705 #583-10-1970 L1980 NEP IM *020 †20

PATEL, Dipakkumar D. 3402 N BIG SPRING ST 79705 #495-23-1981 L1986 IM *020

PATEL, Govind Bhogilal. 4214 ANDREWS HWY 79703 #495-83-1984 L1997 GE IM *020 †20

PATEL, Kirit Narottam. 3001 W ILLINOIS AVE STE 1A 79701 #035-15-1993 L2000 TS VS *020 †85,90

PATEL, Mrunal Champakbhai. 4214 ANDREWS HWY STE 20 79703 #495-80-1991 L1997 IM *020 †20

PATEL, Padmaja Mrunal. 3001 W ILLINOIS AVE # 2B2, FAMILY MEDCENTER 79701 #495-23-1990 L1998 IM *020 †20

PATEL, Pankaj J. 4214 ANDREWS HWY, STE 108 79703 #495-22-1983 L1996 PUD IM *020 †20

PATEL, Pankajkumar V. 4214 ANDREWS HWY STE 100A 79703 #495-23-1984 L1993 CD *020 †20

PATEL, Rajshekhar R. 4214 ANDREWS HWY STE 40, WESTWOOD MED BLDG STE 100B 79703 #495-01-1973 L1980 IM *020 †20

PATEL, Rikesh. ■ 79707 #048-04-2007 IM *012

PATEL, Vikram Narottam. 2407 W LOUISIANA AVE, STE 104 79701 #035-06-1993 L2005 OTO *020 †45

PHAM, Khoa Nguyen. 4301 RALEIGH CT 79707 #942-01-1997 L2007 IM *100 †18,20 ‡

PHILIPPS, James Bartlett. 4214 ANDREWS HWY, ASSOCIATES 79703 #024-05-1994 L2000 DR *020 †80

PITTS, Harold Wendell. 4214 ANDREWS HWY, STE 105 79703 #012-01-1973 L1982 GYN *020 †30

POWER, David James. 4304 ANDREWS HWY 79703 #063-01-1976 L1992 ORS *020

PRUE, Edmund. ■ 79706 #041-77-1960, ▲ L1961 FM *071 †18

RAGHUPRASAD, Puthalath K. 3001 W ILLINOIS AVE, STE 1A 79701 #495-44-1967 L1981 AI IM *040 †20,03
RAMIREZ-VALLE, Francisco. 1001 W PINE AVE 79705 #035-19-2008 *012
RAMOS, Almudena. 1706 W TEXAS AVE 79701 #847-10-1982 L1993 GE IM *020 †20
RANI, Swaroop. 2501 W ILLINOIS AVE STE C 79701 #495-21-1972 L1997 AN PD *020 †05
RAO, Bhairavarasu Kalpana. ■ 79707 #495-65-1998 IM *020
RASTOGI, Ashutosh. 400 N GARFIELD ST STE 100 79701 #496-10-1985 L1999 HO HEM *020 †20
REA, Steven D. 4110 NCR 1243 79707 #048-02-1988 L1989 EM *020 †16
REDDY, Kuraparti Nirmala. 3310 W WADLEY AVE 79707 #495-50-1968 L1981 AN *020
REDDY, Praveen K. 3310 W WADLEY AVE 79707 #048-13-1988 L1989 ORS *020 †40
REDDY, Rajasekhara K. 3310 W WADLEY AVE 79707 #495-50-1967 L1991 ORS *020
REDDY, Tekulapalli Ananth. 2105 W LOUISIANA AVE 79701 #495-65-1967 L1980 IM *020 †20
REESE, Debbie Parchman. 307 N M ST 79701 #048-12-1979 L1979 PD *020 †55
REESE, Richard Glenn. 709 W LOUISIANA AVE 79701 #048-12-1979 L1979 IM IMG *020 †20
RHODE, Carolyn C. 3620 N BIG SPRING ST 79705 #025-01-1972 L1982 FM *020 †18
RHODE, Joseph Geo. 3620 N BIG SPRING ST 79705 #051-01-1960 L1982 FM AM *020 †18
RHODES, Ernesto Philip. 2300 W MICHIGAN AVE, STE 9 79701 #041-13-1989 L1993 OBG *020
ROSINSKA, Anna M. 3316 ANDREWS HWY 79703 #759-03-1991 L1998 IM *020 †20
RUDA, Frank Joseph. ■ 79707 #048-15-2007 *012
RUDNICK, Abraham Herman. ■ 79705 #041-13-1958 L1961 CD IM *020
SAWYER, Russell Wayne. 2706 W CUTHBERT AVE, BLD C 79701 #016-43-1988 L2003 GS VS *020 †85
SHAH, Harshad Girdharlal. 200 ANDREWS HWY 79701 #748-01-1975 L1985 OPH TRS *020 †35
SHAUGHNESSY, Dennis M. 3001 N BIG SPRING ST, STE 103 79705 #030-06-1969 L1980 PME ADM *020
SHAYEB, Joseph. 2501 W ILLINOIS AVE, STE E 79701 #396-24-1986 L1993 IM *020 †20
SHEWARD, Scott Eugene. ■ 79705 #034-01-1983 L1986 DR *020 †80
SHIPKEY, Gregory Michael. ■ 79707 #035-06-1999 L2004 EM *020 †16
SHROFF, Leena N. 2008 W OHIO AVE 79701 #495-17-1969 L1977 PTH *020 †50
SHROFF, Nick Nipank. ■ 79707 #495-27-1970 L1977 U OS *071 †95
SIKES, James Lane. 4214 ANDREWS HWY 79703 #048-15-1996 L1998 GS *020
SINGH, Premila Lakshmi. 3620 N BIG SPRING ST 79705 #048-04-2002 L2006 MPD *020 †20,55
SINGH, Tulsi Dyal. 2300 W MICHIGAN AVE 79701 #566-01-1972 L1978 FM OM *020
SMALL, Stuart David. 9930 W HIGHWAY 80 STE A 79706 #048-12-1973 L1976 AN *020 †05 ‡
SMITH, Alan Danl. 4410 N MIDKIFF RD, STE D1E 79705 #021-05-1982 L1992 OPH *020 †35
SMITH, Jerome A. ■ 79705 #048-02-1950 L1951 N P *071 †75
SPANGHER, Guido G. ■ 79707 #033-05-1977 L1992 P *020
SRINIVAS, Varadachary. 122 N N ST 79701 #495-08-1972 L1993 U *020 †95
STAFFORD, Robert Leroy. ■ 79705 #005-15-1966 L1977 EM OS *020
STAUB, John Barry. 122 N N ST 79701 #039-01-1983 L1988 U OS *020 †95
SUBBARAMAN, Ramnath. ■ 79707 #008-01-2007 *012
SUCKARIEH, Joseph Gabriel. 2200 W ILLINOIS AVE 79701 #875-01-1969 L1979 TS GS *020 †85,90
SYED, Mohsin M. 4506 BRIARWOOD AVE 79707 #704-02-1989 L1997 IM *020 †20
TALWALKAR, Nirupama G. 3001 W ILLINOIS AVE, STE B1 79701 #495-01-1976 L2002 TS VS *020
TILTON, Josiah Batchelder. 2200 W ILLINOIS AVE, MIDLAND MEMORIAL HOSPITAL 79701 #025-07-1994 L1998 AN *020 †05
TOFIELD, Andros. ■ 79705 #917-26-1965 L1978 GP GS *020 †16
TRAXEL, Roger Martin. 2012 W OHIO AVE 79701 #016-43-1970 L1977 OTO *020 †45
TUBB, Terry Douglas. 1304 W TEXAS AVE 79701 #048-02-1968 L1969 PS *020 †65
TUCK, Melissa Sue. ■ 79707 #016-11-2005 L2008 FM *100
UKACHI, Chima Azubike Aus. ■ 79707 #690-07-1996 L2003 GS *020
VALLE, Edgardo. 2200 W ILLINOIS AVE 79701 #042-01-1982 L1987 EM *020 †16
VAN DE WATER, Susan Dean. 2407 W LOUISIANA AVE, STE 103 79701 #048-13-1986 L1987 PM OS *020 †60
VAN HUSEN, Kelly N. ■ 79705 #048-15-2001 L2003 FM *100 †18
VENEGAS, Eric Javier. 5007 PORTICO WAY 79707 #048-02-1997 L1999 OBG *020 †30
VINEY, Robert Shelton. 2706 W CUTHBERT AVE STE C 79701 #048-15-1977 L1977 GS VS *020 †85
VOGEL, Robert Allen. 1407 W ILLINOIS AVE 79701 #048-04-1980 L1980 IM *020 †20
WATKINS, David Lynn. 400 N GARFIELD ST STE 10 79701 #028-02-1978 L1981 ON *020 †20
WATSON, Willie Clyde, III. 2409 W ILLINOIS AVE STE D 79703 #048-14-1974 L1974 PD *020 †55
WELSH, James Barrett. 4214 ANDREWS HWY, STE 303 79703 #048-12-1978 L1978 OBG *020 †18
WEMPE, Noah Alexander. 4 LAKES DR, ODESSA, TX 79761 79705 #048-15-1999 L2004 DR *020 †80
WIESENFELD, Stephen Lee. 2407 W LOUISIANA AVE, STE 108 79701 #005-02-1970 L1977 AI PUD *020
WILLINGHAM, David Barry. 4400 N MIDLAND DR, STE 506A 79707 #048-13-1985 L1986 FM *020 †18
WILSON, Lawrence A. 2200 W ILLINOIS AVE, DEPT OF EMERGENCY MEDICINE 79701 #023-12-1987 L1998 EM *020 †16
WORRELL, John Mays. 1908 W WALL ST, STE 00 PO BX 79701 #048-02-1957 L1957 OS *030
YOUNG, John Winerich, Jr. 3001 W ILLINOIS AVE, STE 7A 79701 #048-12-1970 L1970 OBG *020 †30
YOUNGER, Charles Merrill. 2000 W CUTHBERT AVE 79701 #048-12-1968 L1968 ORS *020 †40

MIDLOTHIAN — ELLIS

ASTBURY, Jeffrey Albert. 1441 S MIDLOTHIAN PKWY 76065 #048-12-1992 L1993 IM *020 †20
BENNETT, John Richard. ■ 76065 #048-12-1964 L1964 AN *020
CHARNOCK, Jane Bryant. ■ 76065 #048-02-1983 L1983 P *074
COLEMAN, Chad E. 1441 S MIDLOTHIAN PKWY 76065 #048-04-1998 L1999 FM *020 †18 ‡
COX, Donald Clifton. ■ 76065 #021-01-1965 L1965 IM CD *071
FULLER, Eileen Elisabeth. ■ 76065 #048-14-2006 L2007 IM *012
GRIMSLEY, Brad Ray. 1441 MIDLOTHIAN PKWY, STE 110 76065 #012-05-1993 L1999 VS *020 †85
JOSLIN, Shirley Courim. 1441 MIDLOTHIAN PKWY, ELLIS CO DIAGNOSTIC CLINIC 76065 #048-12-1990 L1991 PD *020 †55
NEEF, Jason Wayne. 76065 #048-14-2004 L2006 OBG *012
NORDSTROM, Leigh E. 1441 S MIDLOTHIAN PKWY 76065 #048-15-2001 L2004 IM *020
NOTEBOOM, Gerard. ■ 76065 #660-03-1953 L1957 PTH *071 †50

PEARL, Gregory John. 1441 MIDLOTHIAN PKWY, STE 110 76065 #021-01-1980 L1986 VS GS *020 †85
PONDER, Gale Wilson. 4440 E HIGHWAY 287 76065 #045-01-1997 L1998 FM *020 †18
TIRMENSTEIN, Martine G. ■ 76065 #047-06-1953 L1959 AN *071 †05
YEH, Karen Phyllis. 1441 S MIDLOTHIAN PKWY 76065 #048-14-1996 L1997 IM *020 †18 ‡

MINEOLA — WOOD

BANKHEAD, Diana Carol. 1220 N PACIFIC ST, STE 2 75773 #048-02-1986 L1987 GP EM *072
CARGILL, Calvin L. 1302 N PACIFIC ST 75773 #048-13-1988 L1989 FM *020 †18
DUPLECHAIN, Holly Katrina. 5875 S ST HWY 37 75773 #048-14-2003 L2006 IM *020 †20
ELLIOTT, Robert Michael. 415 W KILPATRICK ST 75773 #649-33-1980 L2001 IM *020 †16
GULLY, Kyle L. 1302 N PACIFIC ST 75773 #048-14-1992 L1993 FM *020 †18
HARVEY, Meldrum Johnston. ■ 75773 #039-01-1964 L1981 TS *020 †85
RABORN, Samuel. 5875 S STATE HIGHWAY 37 75773 #048-13-1992 L1994 FM *020 †18

MINERAL WELLS — PALO PINTO

ADAMS, Mathis T. 214 SW 26TH AVE 76067 #048-15-1999 L2002 GS *020 †85
ALLENSWORTH, Robert C. 218 SW 26TH AVE, STE D 76067 #048-12-1984 L1985 IM *020 †20
BAKER, Roger Allan. 1 LONGHORN RD 76067 #048-02-1967 L1968 R NM *020 †80
BERG, James Franklin. ■ 76067 #056-06-1957 L1969 GS *071 †85
BHANDARI, Anantha R. 102 HOLLY HILL RD 76067 #495-09-1976 L1986 PD A *020 †55
BRAUN, Gustav Milan. 107 SW 7TH AVE 76067 #025-01-1965 L1979 OTO FPS *071 †45
DAVE, Kiran Jayrendra. 214 SW 26TH AVE 76067 #495-23-1967 L1978 ORS GS *020 †40
GORE, Ty Lee. 214 SW 26TH AVE, STE B 76067 #048-14-1978 L1978 FM *020 †18
HISEL, Patrick W. 101 HOLLY HILL RD STE B 76067 #048-12-1976 L1980 FM *020 †18 ‡
HOEFELMANN, Richard W. 100 E HUBBARD ST STE 103, LYNCH PLZ 76067 #048-12-1976 L1980 OBG *020 †30
JONES, John E. 400 SW 25TH AVE 76067 #048-16-1994 L1995 FM *020 †18
JONES, Kevin Bruce. 214 SW 26TH AVE, STE C 76067 #048-02-1983 L1983 FM *020 †18
KENNER, Joanne. ■ 76068 #048-12-1947 L1947 GYN *072 †30
KIM, Gun Eung. 400 SW 25TH AVE 76067 #583-03-1962 L1970 DR *071
LASTIMOSA, Augusto Cezar. 400 SW 25TH AVE 76067 #748-08-1972 L1978 N *020 †75
LOCKETT, Edgar Allen. 400 SW 25TH AVE 76067 #005-12-1977 L1988 AN *020 †05
NGUYEN, My Thanh. ■ 76067 #021-01-2001 L2003 FM *020 †18
RAMSEY, Alice L. 214 SW 26TH AVE STE D 76067 #048-14-1996 L1997 FM *020 †18
RAMSEY, David Bruce. 214 SW 26TH AVE STE E 76067 #048-02-1973 L1973 FM FPG *020 †18 ‡
REDDY, Boyareddigari S. 218 SW 26TH AVE STE C 76067 #495-58-1973 L1984 IM GE *020 †20
REDDY, Guduru Jyothirmaya. 108 SW 6TH AVE, MEDICAL AND HEART CENTER 76067 #495-21-1971 L1983 IM PD *020 †20,55
REDDY, Janardhana P. 108 SW 6TH AVE 76067 #495-50-1964 L1972 TS VS *020 †85,90
TARKENTON, Tim Robt. 220 SW 26TH AVE 76067 #048-15-1986 L1987 OBG *020 †20
UPHAM, Mary Kathleen. 2839 FM 3027 76068 #048-02-1981 L1981 OPH FM *020 †18

MISSION — HIDALGO

ABREU, Charity V. 910 S BRYAN RD STE 105 78572 #308-04-1986 L1995 IM *020 †20
AGARWALA, Sanjay Kumar. 4202 SANTA MARINA 78572 #047-07-1993 L2004 DR *020
AKHTAR, Samina. 210 S BRYAN RD STE 5A 78572 #704-16-1990 L1998 PD *020 †55
AMADOR, Alcides N. 1109 PAMELA DR 78572 #649-14-1981 L1995 IM *020 †20
ANZALDUA, Mario R. 1109 PAMELA DR 78572 #048-13-1981 L1981 FM *020 †18
ARANGO, Luis Fernando. 104 S BRYAN RD 78572 #264-03-1974 L1982 PUD *020 †20
AUSTIN, Charles I. 1109 PAMELA DR 78572 #048-13-1979 L1979 FM *020 †18
AVILA, Rafael Antonio. 1022 E GRIFFIN PKWY, STE 110 78572 #048-13-1989 L1998 PS HS *020 †85,65 ‡
AYALA, Mario. 1810 E GRIFFIN PKWY, STE A-4 78572 #016-11-1998 L2006 MPD *020 †20,55
BORJON, Eduardo Fausto. 2118 E GRIFFIN PKWY 78572 #649-30-1975 L1977 FM *020
BRANN, Christopher Scott. 2407 E GRIFFIN PKWY 78572 #048-04-2007 IM *012
BROWN, Jeff John. ■ 78572 #005-12-1999 L2002 IM *020 †20
CANALS, Desi Jr. 210 S BRYAN RD, STE 2 78572 #048-03-1997 L2001 FM *020 †18
CARLSON, Don J. ■ 78572 #048-02-1994 L1995 RO *020
CARRASCO, Enrique. 900 S BRYAN RD, MISSION HOSPITAL ER 78572 #649-18-1954 L1973 FM *071
CARRILLO, Eduardo. 305 E EXPRESSWAY 83 78572 #048-13-2000 L2001 FM *020 †18 ‡
CASSO, Chris. 305 E EXPRESSWAY 83 78572 #048-02-2004 L2006 FM *020 †18
CASTILLO, Juan. 201 S LOS EBANOS RD 78573 #649-54-2000 L2005 FM *020 †18
CASTRILLON, Augusto A. 1300 S BRYAN RD, STE 100 78572 #264-17-1986 L1997 FM *020 †18
CHANG-BROWN, Marlene C. 2013 E GRIFFIN PKWY 78572 #566-01-1987 L1996 IM *020 †20
CHUY QUAN, Juan Oscar. ■ 78574 #429-01-1992 L2003 PD *020 †55
CLAUDIO, Angel L. 2121 E GRIFFIN PKWY, STE 11 78572 #042-03-1981 L1987 IM PUD *020
COIMBRA, Maria De Lourdes. ■ 78572 #187-21-1993 FM *100
DAHLBERG, Jason David. 1920 E GRIFFIN PKWY, FAMILY HEALTH CENTER OF MI 78572 #026-04-1998 L2006 FM *020 †18
DESAI, Mina Chhaganbhai. 900 S BRYAN RD, DEPT ANESTHESIA 78572 #495-76-1974 L1991 AN PD *020 †55,05
DIAZ, Carlos Elvin. 910 S BRYAN RD, THURMOND EYE ASSOC 78572 #016-06-1996 L2002 OPH *020 †35
DIAZ DE LEON, Emma. ■ 78572 #649-04-1989 L1999 PTH *020 †50
D'SA, Anita Maria. 202 E EXPRESSWAY 83 78572 #495-35-1972 L1980 PD *020
DURAN, Alberto D. PO BOX 609, 1211 N RAUL LONGORIA-C 78573 #048-13-1996 L1999 OBG *020
ESCALONA, Cristel. ■ 78572 #048-02-2004 L2007 PD *100
FERNANDEZ, Mario. 900 S BRYAN RD 78572 #429-01-1970 L1995 OTO A *020 †45
FILOSA, Patricia L. 1240 E BUSINESS 83 STE B, FILOSA CHILDRENS CLINIC 78572 #132-04-1980 L1998 PD *020 †18
FLEMING, Richard Anthony. 1605 E EXPRESSWAY 83, STE D 78572 #047-06-1990 L1998 FM EM *020 †18
FUENTES, Jose Armando. 900 S BRYAN RD 78572 #048-13-1978 L1978 AN *020
GARZA, Amanda. ■ 78572 #048-04-2006 GS *012
GEORGE, Sathiyaraj. 2121 E GRIFFIN PKWY, STE 10 78572 #495-42-1987 L1998 IM *020 †20

GILLUM, William Neville. 910 S BRYAN RD, THURMOND EYE ASSOC 78572 #024-07-1972 L1979 **OPH** *020 †35
GIMOTEA, Antonieta A. 1022 E GRIFFIN PKWY 78572 #748-20-1992 L1998 **PD** *020 †55
GODIL, Mushtaq Ahmed. 2310 E EXPRESSWAY 83, STE 7 78572 #704-02-1990 L2001 **PDE** *020 †55
GOMEZ, Ana Laura. ■ 78572 #308-01-1988 L2003 **PD** *020 †55
GOMEZ-ESCANDON, Felipe D. 1605 E EXPRESSWAY 83, STE D 78572 #649-01-1975 L1993 **FM EM** *020 †18
GONZALEZ, Ernesto A. 305 E EXPRESSWAY 83 78572 #048-13-2000 L2002 **FM** *100 †18 ‡
GONZALEZ-VAZQUEZ, Jesus J. ■ 78572 #042-03-1995 L2005 **EM** *020
HAVENER, Steven John. 1920 E GRIFFIN PKWY 78572 #018-03-1984 L1995 **FM** *020 †18
HERNANDEZ, David Peres. 910 S BRYAN RD STE 101, PLAZA WEST 78572 #025-07-1991 L2002 **OBG** *020 †30
HOOK, Stephen Ray. 910 S BRYAN RD, THURMOND EYE ASSOC 78572 #048-04-1982 L1983 **OPH** *020 †35
HURLBUT, Peter Richard. ■ 78572 #024-16-2001 L2005 **OPH** *100 †35
IRIGOYEN-RASCON, F. 2116 E GRIFFIN PKWY, STE A 78572 #649-27-1974 L1982 **P** *020 †75 ‡
JAGADEESAN, Subramaniam. 2121 E GRIFFIN PKWY, STE 10 78572 #495-16-1989 L2003 **IM** *020
JAIN, Dinesh Kumar. 2121 E GRIFFIN PKWY, STE 10 78572 #495-20-1980 L1997 **IM** *020 †20
JIMENEZ, Danielle J. ■ 78572 #048-14-2000 L2004 **OBG** *020
JOHNSON, Jere M. 1920 E GRIFFIN PKWY 78572 #048-04-1988 L1990 **FM FPG** *020 †18 ‡
JOHNSTON, Donald Keith. ■ 78572 #065-06-1952 L1965 **AN** *071 †05
KALAF, Nelson Rafael. 2023 E GRIFFIN PKWY 78572 #308-05-1989 L2000 **IM** *020 †20
KALLUMADANDA, Vinnie Deva. ■ 78572 #496-37-2002 L2008 **FP** *012
KIM, Seong-Cheol. 3404 EL JARDIN 78572 #429-02-1994 L2000 **ID** *020 †20
KOTAKI, Mohammad Hossein. 900 PLAZA DR STE 5 78572 #517-05-1982 L1996 **NEP** *020 †20
LINAN, Enrique Wilder. 1317 ST CLAIRE BLVD, STE A-4 78572 #737-06-1988 L2002 **PM PME** *020 †60
LOPEZ, Linda E. 900 PLAZA DR STE 2, SUITE 2 78572 #042-01-1987 L1992 **PD** *020 †55
MARINA, Jose Mario. 1022 E GRIFFIN PKWY, STE 108 78572 #011-75-1993, ▲ L1998 **ORS** *020
MATHEWS, Jeselle Ann. 2134 E GRIFFIN PKWY 78572 #010-03-1987 L1989 **OBG** *020 †30
MATTIOLI, Carlos A. 900 S BRYAN RD 78572 #132-01-1961 L1975 **PTH IG** *020 †50
MAYHUA, Primo Abel. ■ 78572 #737-06-1991 L2005 **IM** *020 †20
MAYORGA, David A. ■ 78572 #737-06-1990 L2004 **CCM** *020 †20
MBOUDOU, Simon P. ■ 78572 #217-01-1986 L1998 **AN** *020 †20
MEDINA, Javier. 3601 OAKWOOD LN 78573 #649-25-1988 L1994 **FM** *020 †18
MEGO, Agustin Bernabe. 611 N BRYAN RD 78572 #649-38-1998 L2004 **FM** *020
MEYER, Charles Frederick. ■ 78572 #018-03-1949 L1950 **GP IMG** *071
MILLER, Jana Rachelle. ■ 78572 #024-16-2001 L2003 **FM** *020 †18
MIRANDA, Jorge Enrique. 1022 E GRIFFIN PKWY, STE 101 78572 #042-01-1988 L1992 **OBG** *020 †30
MURILLO, Javier. 1500 S BRYAN RD 78572 #005-11-1984 L1985 **FM** *020 †18
MURPHY, Gerard Jos. 900 S BRYAN RD, MISSION HOSPITAL RADIOLOGY 78572 #035-15-1983 L1999 **DR IM** *020 †20,80
NAHHAS, Fayez Nabih. 1011 CONCHO CT, EDINBURG REGIONAL MEDICAL 78572 #039-01-1990 L1998 **FM** *020 †18
NIKICICZ, Henry J. ■ 78572 #759-04-1984 L1997 **AN** *020 †05
OGUNLANA, Bosede Nihinlol. 900 S BRYAN RD 78572 #690-01-1987 L2003 **PD** *020 †55
ORTIZ, Arturo Abraham. 1104 E KIKA DE LA GARZA ST 78572 #649-02-1975 L1978 **FM** *020 †18
PAGAN-HEMER, Teresita. 1500 S BRYAN RD 78572 #649-18-1985 L1999 **PD** *020 †55
PALMIERI, Pier-Paolo R. 808 S SHARY RD, STE 5/321 78572 #016-43-1991 L1998 **PD** *020 †55
PATE, Robert Joyce. 205 E 9TH ST 78572 #649-02-1968 L1969 **GS** *072
PATEL, Ketan P. 611 N BRYAN RD 78572 #495-22-1998 L2003 **IMG** *020 †20
PEAN, Harold Jacques. 909 BUSINESS PARK DR STE 6 78572 #649-47-1984 L1993 **IM** *020 †20
PEREZ, Rodolfo Nestor, Jr. 910 S BRYAN RD, THURMOND EYE ASSOC 78572 #028-02-1968 L1978 **OPH** *020 †35
PERIS, Christopher R. 900 S BRYAN RD 78572 #495-73-1969 L1977 **AN** *020
PIERRE-LOUIS, Michael Max. 2310 E EXPRESSWAY 83 STE 3 78572 #649-14-1976 L1999 **FM** *020 †18
QUAICOE, Sannichie A. 1406 S BRYAN RD 78572 #781-03-1984 L1997 **AN** *020 †05
QUEVEDO, Maria Eugenia. ■ 78572 #649-04-1993 L2007 **FM** *020 †18
RAMIREZ, Carlos Armando. ■ 78572 #264-11-1995 L2005 **EM FM** *020 †18
RAMIREZ, Sergio. 210 S BRYAN RD, STE 5A 78572 #649-35-1980 L1987 **PD** *020
RAMOS, Keith Anthony. 1300 S BRYAN RD, STE 106 78572 #042-03-1994 L2003 **NEP** *020 †20
REGALADO, Carlos Alberto. 2121 E GRIFFIN PKWY STE 1 78572 #737-06-1985 L1995 **PD** *020 †55
REQUENEZ, Daniel. ■ 78572 #048-14-2000 L2003 **AN** *020 †05
REYES-SALINAS, Brenda L. 2521 E GRIFFIN PKWY STE A 78572 #048-02-1998 L1999 **FM** *020 †18
RIVERA, Juan. 1922 E GRIFFIN PKWY, STE E 78572 #649-35-1984 L1996 **PUD IM** *020 †20
RODRIGUEZ, Jose. 2518 E GRIFFIN PKWY, STE B 78572 #042-02-1986 L1987 **GE IM** *020 †20
RODRIGUEZ-REY, Roberto M. ■ 78574 #132-05-1993 L2000 **PD** *020 †55
RUGAMA, Francisco. 2121 E GRIFFIN PKWY, STE 4 78572 #649-14-1981 L1993 **IM** *020
SAENZ, Linda Jo. ■ 78573 #048-13-2006 **FP** *012
SALAZAR, Rodrigo. ■ 78574 #649-02-1972 **GS** *020
SANTA-ANA, Raul Balli. 1928 N CONWAY AVE 78572 #305-01-1981 L1986 **FM** *020 †18
SANTIAGO-BAROUHAS, I. 900 S BRYAN RD 78572 #042-01-1982 L1985 **PD** *020 †55
SHAH, Pankajkumar G. 2025 E GRIFFIN PKWY 78572 #033-06-1989 L1995 **OPH** *020 †35
SHUAIB, Mihaela. 909 BUSINESS PARK, STE 6 78572 #781-01-1985 L1997 **IM** *020 †20
SHUAIB, Tawid Ali. 909 BUSINESS PARK DR, VALLEY CARDIOLOGY PA 78572 #781-01-1985 L1995 **CD** *020 †20
SPIRO, Jean Francois. 900 S BRYAN RD, RADIOLOGY DEPT. 78572 #396-05-1972 L1990 **DR NM** *020 †80
SZETO, Douglas B. ■ 78572 #048-13-2005 **FP** *012
TWAHIRWA, Marcel. 2121 E GRIFFIN PKWY, STE 14 78572 #649-38-1990 L1997 **IM** *020 †20
VALDEZ, Fernando. 2301 E 25 1/2 ST 78572 #048-14-2002 L2003 **FM** *020 †18
VELA, Carlos Cristobal. ■ 78572 #132-03-1981 L1998 **IM** *020
VELASCO, Gretchen Marie. 910 S BRYAN RD STE 204, WEST DOCTORS MED PLZ 78572 #042-02-1994 L2001 **OBG** *020
VELAZQUEZ, Juan Pena. ■ 78572 #649-14-2002 L2007 **FP** *012
VILLANUEVA, Raul. 1001 MILLER AVE 78572 #649-02-1955 L1961 **PM** *020 †60
ZARZAR-SAFIE, Francisco J. 1616 N CONWAY AVE, MISSION CHILDREN'S CLINIC 78572 #270-02-1995 L2001 **PD** *020

MISSOURI CITY - FORT BEND

ADESOBA, Samuel A. ■ 77459 #690-05-1987 L1999 **IM** *020 †20
ADUSEI, Andy B. ■ 77459 #048-12-2006 **GS** *012
AGRAWALA, Sangeeta. 3634 GLENN LAKES LN, STE 195 77459 #495-39-1985 L1992 **PD** *020 †55
AI, Kristy Yu. ■ 77459 #048-14-2001 **FM** *020
AMADOR-SAAVEDRA, Mariano. 4646 RIVERSTONE BLVD 77459 #649-18-1986 L1996 **PD** *020 †55
ARKO, Joseph Chas. 6014 NINE MILE LN 77459 #026-04-1967 L1980 **RO** *020 †80
ARZE, Ernesto J. 3518 MARION CT 77459 #176-03-1956 L1976 **FM** *071
ATLAS, Elissa. 5819 HIGHWAY 6 STE 330 77459 #048-02-1983 L1983 **PD** *020 †55
AZEVEDO, Fernando W. ■ 77459 #187-12-1955 L1972 **AN** *020
BATES, Karmen Nicole. ■ 77459 #048-02-2007 **AN** *012
BISMUTH, Jean. ■ 77459 #297-01-1998 L2007 **VS** *012
BOLTON, Kevin M. ■ 77459 #048-12-2006 **AN** *012
BRAUNREITER, David A. 5819 HIGHWAY 6, STE 380 77459 #056-06-1992 L1999 **FM FSM** *020 †18
BRISCOE, Shelia D. 6727 SUTTERS CREEK TRL 77459 #048-13-1981 L1985 **FM** *020
BROTHERTON, Dana Michele. 5819 HIGHWAY 6, STE 350 77459 #048-14-1998 L1999 **GS** *020
BROWN, Jeremy L. ■ 77459 #048-14-2005 **MPD** *012
BULLEN, Agnes V. 3803 FM 1092 RD # 6 77459 #035-08-1977 L1981 **IM** *020
BUSH, Mickey Vernell. 3424 FM 1092 RD STE 220 77459 #048-02-1979 L1979 **FM EM** *020 †18
CAZARES, Jaime G. 3807 FM 1092 RD, STE 312 77459 #016-11-1980 L2002 **FM** *020 †18
CHANDY, Sivi Mary. ■ 77459 #306-01-1996 L2004 **IMG** *100 †20
CHAO, Dyann Michele. ■ 77459 #021-05-1999 L2001 **PD** *020 †55
DABBASI, Nidal Ismail. ■ 77459 #056-06-1995 L2001 **DR** *020 †80
DAO, Harry, Jr. ■ 77459 #023-07-2008 *012
DESAI, Krishnakant H. ■ 77459 #495-01-1950 L1972 **PD** *071 †55
DIAZ, Liliana. 26 SULLIVANS LN 77459 #042-01-1992 L1999 **PCC** *020 †20
DICKASON, Timothy James. ■ 77459 #030-06-1998 L2007 **GS** *020
DUNEGAN, Gerald Wayne. 5201 HIGHWAY 6, STE 575 77459 #048-04-1963 L1963 **GP** *020
DUNEGAN, Mark A. 3807 FM 1092 RD, STE 316 77459 #048-14-1989 L1990 **GS** *075
DURAND, Darnel Michael. 9011 SIX RIVERS LN 77459 #033-05-1994 L2005 **AN** *020 †20
FINK, Sandra Lynn Clough. 3807 FM 1092 RD, STE 100 77459 #048-04-1993 L2001 **GS** *020 †85
FOURNIER, Keith Francis. ■ 77459 #032-01-2000 L2006 **GS** *020
FOWLER, Aja Jenelle. ■ 77489 #048-14-2006 **FP** *012
FUERST, Donald Edward. ■ 77459 #011-02-1965 L1971 **U** *020 †95
GLAZE, Daniel Gordon. 4010 BRIGHTWOOD ST 77459 #048-04-1974 L1974 **CHN N** *020 †55,75
GMOSER, Dean Jeffrey. 5819 HIGHWAY 6, STE 330 77459 #056-06-1980 L1983 **PD** *020 †55
GOLD, Willard Seymour. ■ 77459 #016-06-1958 L1982 **P PHP** *071
GONZALEZ, Maria Guadalupe. ■ 77459 #048-14-1998 L2001 **FM** *020 †18
GOULD, Alfred Raymond. ■ 77459 #021-01-1954 L1954 **FM FPG** *020 †18
GUERRERO TIBBS, Rita Fe. ■ 77459 #748-16-1994 L2004 **PTH** *020
HENDRICKSON, Glenn G. ■ 77459 #047-05-1940 L1977 **GS OM** *071 †85
HIGGINS, Johanna A. ■ 77459 #016-02-2002 L2007 **AN** *100 †05
HINZE, Karla S. ■ 77489 #048-14-2006 **FP** *012
HUDDLESTON, David Brian. ■ 77459 #048-02-2007 *012
HUSSAIN, Ghazala. ■ 77459 #704-01-1976 L1981 **P** *020 †75
JHINGREE, Isaac. ■ 77459 #048-13-1993 L1997 **EM** *020 †16
JIWANI, Nazlin. ■ 77489 #704-02-1981 *100
KAHN, Raymond A. 5819 HIGHWAY 6, STE 330 77459 #067-01-1973 L1979 **PD** *020 †55
KAPADIA, Mitul Ranjan. ■ 77459 #048-02-2006 L2006 **PPM** *012
KIM, Sejoon. ■ 77459 #048-14-2005 **GS** *100
KOHLI, Asha. 6218 HIGHWAY 6 STE B 77459 #496-07-1978 L1992 **FM** *020 †18
LAM, Pin Kwee. 5819 HIGHWAY 6 STE 360 77459 #825-01-1973 L1977 **EM** *020 †16
LAM, Wilson Wei-Sen. 2935 GLENN LAKES LN 77459 #048-04-2003 L2007 **MPD** *012 †20,55
LAPUS, Angelo Giuseppe. ■ 77459 #048-14-2006 **PTH** *012
LE, Dai Bui. 6202 HIGHWAY 6 STE A, LE PEDITRICS 77459 #048-14-1996 L1999 **PD** *020 †55
LEWIS, Dawn Michelle. 2715 CYPRESS POINT DR 77459 #035-46-1995 L2000 **PD** *020
LYONS, Travis Douglas. ■ 77489 #048-04-2008 *012
MACKAY, Joy R. ■ 77459 #061-01-1966 L1969 **DIA IM** *074 †20
MCGEE, Lindy Upton. 5819 HIGHWAY 6 77459 #048-04-2000 L2004 **PD** *020 †55
MC MULLEN, Deirdre C. 3424 FM 1092 RD, STE 220 77459 #048-14-1996 L1998 **FM** *020 †18
MOONNUMAKAL, Siby Pothen. ■ 77459 #048-04-2003 L2007 **PDP** *012 †55
MUHAMMAD, Stacey Chanel. 6026 TWIN CRK, SOUTHWEST DOCTORS, PA 77459 #048-14-1999 L2002 **FM** *020 †18
NELSON, James A. ■ 77459 #048-14-2005 L2008 **P** *012
PANE, Hillary Elise. ■ 77459 #048-15-2008 L2008 *012
PATEL, Rupert. ■ 77459 #048-13-2000 L2003 **NEP IM** *020 †20 ‡
PATEL, Yagnesh Ranchhod. ■ 77459 #021-06-1999 L2004 **CD** *020 †20
PERIS, Mariette Florence. ■ 77459 #495-52-1974 L1980 **PTH** *020 †50
PHAN, Jack. ■ 77459 #005-14-2006 **RO** *012
PRATER, Samuel Josiah. ■ 77459 #048-04-2007 **EM** *012
RAHIM, Sania. ■ 77459 #048-04-2008 *012
REED, Brent Devin. ■ 77459 #048-14-2007 *012
SCHATTE, Dawnelle June. 3214 OAKLAND LAKE CIR 77459 #048-04-2000 L2005 **CHP** *100 †75
SCOTT, Wesley E, Jr. ■ 77459 #047-07-1950 L1988 **ORS** *071 †40
SHAH, Indu. ■ 77459 #496-38-1968 L1993 **AN** *020
SHANKAR GIRI, Praharaju G. ■ 77459 #495-52-1973 L1980 **RO ON** *020
SHIMPI, Amita Vasant. 8906 DAKOTA CT 77459 #496-38-1998 L2006 **N** *100 †75
SLAUGHTER, Lillie S. 2411 FM 1092 RD, FAMILY MED OF MO CITY INC 77459 #048-14-1991 L1992 **FM** *020 †18
SMIRNAKIS, Karen Vossen. ■ 77459 #041-14-1997 L1999 **IM NEP** *020 †20
SMITH, Don Willard. ■ 77459 #065-01-1959 L1978 **AN** *071
SMITH, Justin R. ■ 77459 #048-12-2006 **PD** *012
SNOW, Judson Horace, Jr. 3803 FM 1092 RD # 6 77459 #048-04-1974 L1974 **DR** *020 †80
SURESH, Ramapriya. ■ 77459 #495-66-1995 L2004 **IM** *020
SUSARLA, Hari Krishna. 4646 RIVERSTONE BLVD, 16659 SOUTHWEST FREEWAY #4 77459 #048-12-1999 L2003 **MPD** *020 †55,20
TAN, Dongfeng. ■ 77459 #243-52-1983 L2006 **PTH** *020 †50
TAN, Maria G. 5819 HIGHWAY 6 STE 360 77459 #748-02-1973 L1979 **GP** *020
TAWFIK, Justin Andrew. 4203 CLEARWATER CT 77459 #048-15-2008 *012
THIDA, Aye. 5201 HIGHWAY 6, STE A 77459 #209-03-1990 L2000 **PD** *020

■ = Address Information Privacy Protected

TRAN, Phuong Huynh. ■ 77459 #048-12-2006 **IM** *012
URBANI, Karen Elizabeth. 5819 HIGHWAY 6 STE 330 77459 #005-11-1985 L1998 **PD** *020 †55
VAUGHAN, Lucretia Lynne. ■ 77459 #048-14-2006 L2008 **P** *012
WANG, Laura Kaiwei. 6202 HIGHWAY 6, STE A 77459 #048-16-2001 L2004 **PD** *020 †55
WEIRICK, Troy Aaron. ■ 77459 #016-45-2003 L2007 **CD** *012 †20
ZAHER, Mona C. ■ 77459 #048-14-1995 L1997 **D DS** *020 †15

MONAHANS – WARD

DAVISON, David William. 405 S MAIN AVE, STE 10 79756 #064-01-1977 L1978 **FM** *020 †18
GONZALEZ, Alfonso Ivan. 405 S MAIN AVE, STE 10 79756 #649-33-2001 L2006 **FM EM** *020
LE, Trang Thi Minh. 405 S MAIN AVE, STE 10 79756 #942-01-1997 L2006 **IM** *020 †20
PRASAD, Suresh. 405 S MAIN ST STE 100, FAMILY MEDICAL CENTER 79756 #495-15-1994 L1999 **IM** *020 †20

MONTGOMERY – MONTGOMERY

ASCARRUNZ, Rolando C. 13438 NORTHSHORE DR, STE 1A 77356 #847-08-1974 L1985 **CD IM** *020 †20
BEERS, Alissa Mccasland. ■ 77356 #048-14-2005 **AN** *012
BUCHANAN, Jorge. ■ 77356 #649-01-1956 L1970 **GE IM** *071
CHILEK, Jennifer Lynn. 19782 HIGHWAY 105 W, STE 111 77356 #048-16-2001 L2004 **FM** *020 †18
CONTE, Robert Salvador. 199 LAKE VIEW CIR 77356 #021-05-1969 L1975 **OM PUD** *030 †20,70
DAVIS, Andrew John. 123 BLUE HERON DR, STE 101 77316 #048-15-1985 L1986 **FM** *020 †18
FAGAN, Vernon C, Jr. ■ 77356 #021-05-1945 L1945 **OM** *071 †05
FLOTTMANN, Jay Thomas. 821C EVA ST 77356 #048-02-1997 L1998 **PD** *020
GELMAN, Irene. 18059 FREEWAY 105 W 77356 #913-06-1989 L2005 **IM** *100 †20 ‡
HARLAND, John Morgan. ■ 77356 #048-02-1947 L1947 **GP** *020
HEBERT, Ray Thos. ■ 77356 #048-02-1964 L1964 **R NM** *071 †80,28
JENKINS, Felix W, Jr. ■ 77356 #047-07-1963 L1964 **NS** *020 †25
JEZIERSKI, Melinda K. ■ 77356 #048-16-2004 L2008 **FP** *012
KAPLAN, Michael Alan. 18057 HIGHWAY 105 W, STE 230 77356 #051-07-2002 L2003 **FM** *020 †18
KIMBALL, Milton Scott. 18445 HIGHWAY 105 W, UNIT 102 PMB 288 77356 #048-02-1988 L1991 **PD** *020 †55
KUFFNER, Marie G. ■ 77356 #048-14-1976 L1976 **AN** *020 †05
LEITCH, William H. ■ 77356 #023-01-1939 L1952 **PTH** *071 †50
METAXAS, Dennis C. 566 FRENCH KINGSTON CT 77356 #048-14-1989 L1990 **AN** *020 †05
MIGUELINO, Oliver Molina. ■ 77356 #748-01-1957 L1970 **CLP ATP** *071 †50
NICHOLS, Mark Edward. 18059 HIGHWAY 105 W # 115 77356 #045-04-1993 L2000 **OBG** *020 †30
O'NEAL, James P. 18059 HIGHWAY 105 W, STE 120 77356 #048-04-2000 L2005 **OTO** *020 †45
ROBINSON, Jack Stephen. 18057 HIGHWAY 105 W, STE 220 77356 #005-14-1975 L2002 **PD PHP** *040 †55
ROSENTHAL, Avram Elyea. ■ 77356 #019-02-1958 L1958 **RO** *071 †80
SHELDON, Edward Alvan. ■ 77356 #025-01-1954 L1962 **R RO** *071 †80
SIMPSON, Matthew S. 19560 HIGHWAY 105 W 77356 #048-13-2000 L2002 **FM** *020 †18
STOWERS, Steven P. 19560 HIGHWAY 105 77356 #048-13-2000 L2001 **FM** *020 †18
TOMLINSON, Micah D. 873B EVA ST 77356 #048-13-1987 L1988 **FM** *020 †18

MOODY – MCLENNAN

RACHUT, Eric Robt. ■ 76557 #018-03-1974 L1976 **PTH** *020 †50
VIA, Lara. PO BOX 252 76557 #048-12-1995 L1998 **FM** *020 †18

MORGANS POINT – BELL

MCNEIL, Jessie M. ■ 76513 #048-16-2006 **FP** *012

MORTON – COCHRAN

GENRAICH, Melvyn Howard. 201 E GRANT AVE 79346 #065-01-1969 L1976 **FM** *020
SCHERER, Alfred Ludwig. 201 E GRANT AVE 79346 #019-02-1957 L1982 **FM** *030 †18

MOUNT PLEASANT – TITUS

ADAMS, Larry E. ■ 75455 #048-12-1991 L1992 **GS** *020 †85
AGUAM, Abul S. 1114 N JEFFERSON AVE 75455 #748-08-1962 L1978 **GS TS** *020 †85
ALLEN, Scott Dennis. 2001 N JEFFERSON AVE # 100, EAST TEXAS ORTHOPAEDICS, P 75455 #024-05-1998 L2005 **HS** *020 †40
BRADSHAW, J Colton. 2001 N JEFFERSON AVE, STE 300 75455 #021-06-1979 L1981 **PD EM** *020 †55
BROWN, Cynthia Danette. 2001 N JEFFERSON AVE, STE 211 75455 #035-08-1994 L2007 **PCC** *020 †20
BROWNSTONE, John. 2001 N JEFFERSON AVE 75455 #836-02-1963 L1981 **AN P** *020
BURLING, Christopher M. 618 N JEFFERSON AVE, # 1 75455 #048-15-1998 L1999 **FM** *020 †18 ‡
CHAPMAN, Joel Don. 2001 N JEFFERSON AVE, STE 300 75455 #021-06-1979 L1982 **PD** *020 †55
COLE, Gary B. 1397 CR 1350 75455 #004-01-1972 L1974 **EM** *020
CUENCA, Rosa Elena. 301 W 18TH ST STE 110 75455 #036-08-1986 L2007 **SO** *020 †85
DAVIS, Milas Eldon. 2001 N JEFFERSON AVE, TITUS CO. MEM HOSP 75455 #004-01-1959 L1991 **DR** *020 †80
DOWNIE, Gordon Hunter. ■ 75455 #016-06-1986 L2007 **PUD** *020 †20
DRIESSNER, Jerry Shan. PO BOX 909, 2001 N JEFFERSON 75456 #048-13-1973 L1973 **DR** *020 †80
EVETTS, Curtis Alan. 2001 N JEFFERSON AVE 75455 #048-12-1979 L1979 **DR** *020 †80
HALIPOTO, M H. 1901 MULBERRY AVE 75455 #704-08-1961 L1964 **OBG** *071 †30
HERNDON, Terri L. 2001 N JEFFERSON AVE, STE 300 75455 #048-15-2000 L2003 **PD** *020 †55

HESTER, David Alan. 2001 N JEFFERSON AVE, STE 100 75455 #024-05-1998 L2002 **OFA** *020 †40
JACOB, Abraham. 2001 MULBERRY AVE, STE B 75455 #654-01-1994 L2002 **FM** *020 †20
KENT, Glen Rayburn. ■ 75455 #021-05-1954 L1956 **FM** *071 †18
KERLEY, J Michael. 2001 N JEFFERSON AVE 75455 #048-04-1982 L1983 **RO ON** *020 †20,80
KUMAR, Jai. 301 W 18TH ST 75455 #495-43-1978 L2008 **N** *020 †75
MACTAL, Josefina A. 108 W 3RD ST 75455 #748-08-1968 L1983 **AN** *020
MACTAL, Josefino A. 108 W 3RD ST 75455 #748-08-1968 L1983 **AN** *071 †05
MAESE, Federico. 203 E 16TH ST 75455 #649-30-1989 L1993 **CD IM** *072 †20
MASON, Christopher N. 2001 N JEFFERSON AVE, STE 220 75455 #048-16-1999 L2000 **OBG** *020 †30
MC KELLAR, Joseph Morris. 304 W 20TH ST 75455 #048-02-1977 L1977 **OBG** *020 †30
MC KELLAR, Lee Dennis. 2001 MULBERRY AVE, MCKELLAR CLINIC 75455 #048-02-1956 L1956 **GP** *020
MERIWETHER, Paul Ollie. 203 W 20TH ST 75455 #048-02-1981 L1981 **FM** *020 †18
MOORE, Carter Jay. 304 W 20TH ST 75455 #048-02-1988 L1989 **OBG** *020 †30
NIX, Thomas Donald, Jr. 108 W 3RD ST 75455 #048-14-1977 L1977 **AN EM** *020
OSBORNE, Isaac John T. ■ 75455 #005-06-1974 L2002 **IM CD** *020
PAYNE, Robert Milton. 2001 N JEFFERSON AVE 75455 #048-12-1966 L1968 **CD** *020 †20
PRAKASH, Sucharu. 2001 N JEFFERSON AVE, STE 210 75455 #495-43-1992 L2000 **HEM** *020 †20
REYES, Antonio Padua. 2005 N JEFFERSON AVE 75455 #264-01-1965 L1978 **OBG GO** *020
RIEPE, Dale Burdette. 2001 N JEFFERSON AVE 75455 #030-05-1963 L1979 **DR** *020
SARMIENTO, Reynaldo D. 2001 N JEFFERSON AVE, STE 120 75455 #748-08-1962 L1974 **GS** *020
SEKULIC, Milan. 2001 N JEFFERSON AVE, STE 212 75455 #005-12-1999 L2005 **CD IM** *020 †20
SINGAPERUMAL, Manavalan. 1702 MULBERRY AVE 75455 #495-04-1979 L1995 **IM** *020 †20
SINGAPERUMAL, Sheela. ■ 75455 #495-04-1978 L2003 **P** *020
SLOVAK-TUCKER, Melissa Sh. 2001 N JEFFERSON AVE, STE 220 75455 #048-15-2000 L2003 **OBG** *020
STAGG, Gerald Alvin. 2001 N JEFFERSON AVE, STE 300 75455 #021-06-1978 L1981 **PD** *020 †55
STUART, Roger Graham, Jr. 2001 N JEFFERSON AVE, STE 202 75455 #027-01-1977 L1978 **U** *020 †95
TWADDELL, Clinton W. 2001 N JEFFERSON AVE, STE 200 75455 #048-12-1988 L1989 **GS** *020 †85
VAN BUSKIRK, Ronald. 2320 HARTS BLUFF RD 75455 #016-06-1970 L1980 **IM** *020 †20
WALKER, Rhey, II. 2001 MULBERRY AVE 75455 #048-04-1947 L1947 **IM PUD** *071
WILLIAMS, Troyce F. 203 W 20TH ST 75455 #048-02-1971 L1971 **GP** *020
WOJCIK, Barbara. 203 E 16TH ST 75455 #759-08-1982 L1996 **N PM** *020
WOJCIK, John Jos. 203 E 16TH ST 75455 #759-01-1985 L1995 **PM** *020
YANG, Ellen C Y. 2001 N JEFFERSON AVE 75455 #583-08-1959 L1970 **PTH PHP** *020 †50
YANG, Ovid. 2001 N JEFFERSON AVE 75455 #583-01-1950 L1969 **PTH** *020 †50

MOUNT VERNON – FRANKLIN

ARRONDO, Louis Lawrence. 920 HWY 37 S 75457 #649-14-1976 L1981 **FM** *020 †18
LATORTUE, Jean Woel. ■ 75457 #440-01-1998 L2007 **FM** *020
MAZHAR, Salma. ■ 75457 #704-02-1998 L2007 **IM** *020

MUENSTER – COOKE

ADVINCULA, Edgardo Galpo. 509 N MAPLE ST, MUENSTER MEMORIAL HOSPITAL 76252 #748-01-1963 L1979 **IM** *071 †20

MULESHOE – BAILEY

JOHNSON, Robert Gustav. 708 S 1ST ST, C/O MAMC 79347 #033-05-1969 L1978 **GS** *020 †85
NITZEL, Grant Eugene. 610 S 1ST ST 79347 #030-05-1996 L2006 **FM** *020 †18
PURDY, Bruce Dale. 701 S 1ST ST 79347 #048-02-1976 L1976 **FM OBS** *020
PURDY, Tyson C. ■ 79347 #048-02-2008 *012
SHEETS, Harry Kyle. 610 S 1ST ST 79347 #048-02-1997 L1999 **FM** *020 †18 ‡
SMITH, Thomas E. 708 S 1ST ST 79347 #048-02-1998 L1999 **FM** *020 †18

MULLIN – MILLS

FRUEH, David Milton. ■ 76864 #048-02-1972 L1972 **OBG** *020 †30

MURPHY – COLLIN

JABBAR, Samad A. ■ 75094 #048-02-2003 L2008 **NEP** *012
LEETE, Tyler G. ■ 75094 #048-12-2005 **DR** *012
NAGPAL, Satwant Kaur. ■ 75094 #495-30-1976 L1982 **FM** *071
PASPULA, Raja Ravi P P. ■ 75094 #495-21-1990 L2007 **IMG** *020 †18
REZVANI, Afshin. ■ 75094 #035-08-2002 L2006 *100
WAKEFIELD, Ylicia Richard. 120 E FM 544 STE 72, PMB 225 75094 #048-12-1991 L1992 **PD** *020 †55
WEST, Jason L. 352 PARKSIDE CT 75094 #048-12-2002 L2007 **GS** *020

NACOGDOCHES – NACOGDOCHES

ALLUMS, James Anderson. ■ 75965 #048-02-1962 L1973 **TS GS** *071 †85,90
ARCHIE, David Stephen. 4920 NE STALLINGS DR, RADIOLOGY DEPT 75965 #047-06-1974 L2001 **DR** *071 †80 ‡
BAKER, Richard Lynn. 1303 RAGUET ST 75961 #048-12-1976 L1980 **IM** *020 †20
BALL, Flamen, Jr. 1018 N MOUND ST STE 10 75961 #048-04-1966 L1966 **PD GP** *020 †55
BALLINGER, Steven Geo. 1023 N MOUND ST, STE E 75961 #005-15-1989 L2002 **ORS** *020 †40
BARNETTE, Mary Frances. 1018 N MOUND ST, STE 201 75961 #027-01-1995 L2002 **PD** *020 †55
BARRON, Stewart S. ■ 75963 #048-12-1953 L1953 **OPH** *071 †35

BERNEY, Joseph P. 4920 NE STALLINGS DR, NACOGDOCHES MEDICAL CENTER 75965 #048-13-1983 L1983 **IM** *020 †20
BOLINGER, Clarence W. 5124 NORTH ST 75965 #021-05-1973 L1976 **EM IM** *020
BOMMANNA, Vasudeva M. 607 RUSSELL BLVD STE B 75965 #495-98-1983 L1997 **AI** *020 †55,03
BOYNTON, James Lester. 4635 NE STALLINGS DR, STE 106 75965 #048-02-1962 L1962 **CHP P** *020
BUCKINGHAM, James Allan. 3516 NE STALLINGS DR 75965 #048-04-1975 L1975 **P** *020 †75
CAGLE, Donald Eugene. 320 RUSSELL BLVD 75965 #039-01-1972 L1980 **GS** *020 †85
CALME, Mary B. 1204 N MOUND ST 75961 #048-13-1992 L1994 **DR** *020 †80
CARROLL, Robt Patrick, Jr. 4920 NE STALLINGS DR 75965 #051-01-1966 L1971 **FM** *020 †18
CASTER, Jon Curtis. 5300 NORTH ST 75965 #046-01-1991 L1992 **OPH AM** *020 †35
CHUA, Josephine D. 3226 N UNIVERSITY DR, STE 200 75965 #748-01-1989 L2000 **NEP** *020 †20
CLINE, Mark A. 4604 NE STALLINGS DR 75965 #048-13-1994 L1995 **FM PD** *020 †18
COATS-RAMEY, Cathy Lane. ■ 75961 #048-14-1984 L1985 **FM** *020 †18
COFFMAN, Dennis Wayne. 4800 NE STALLINGS DR 75965 #039-01-1969 L1973 **GP A** *020 †18
DAVIS, Bryan W. 1320 N UNIVERSITY DR, STE B 75961 #048-13-1998 L2002 **FM** *020 †18
DAVIS, Carl A. 212 RUSSELL BLVD 75965 #048-14-2001 L2004 **FM** *020
DAVIS, James D. 3312 N UNIVERSITY DR STE J 75965 #048-16-1991 L1995 **AN PD** *020 †05
DAVIS, Joseph Earl. 1326 N UNIVERSITY DR 75961 #048-12-1972 L1978 **IM** *020 †20
DELEON, Maria Luisa. 1023 N MOUND ST, STE I 75961 #041-09-1994 L1996 **N** *020 †75
DICKHAUT, Steven Chas. 4800 NE STALLINGS DR, STE 110 75965 #048-04-1977 L1977 **ORS** *020 †40
DOWLING, James Knox. STEPHEN AUSTIN STATE UNIV, POB 13058 SFA STATION 75962 #048-12-1960 L1960 **PD** *020 †55
DRAKE, Willard M, Jr. ■ 75965 #041-02-1941 L1980 **PHP** *071 †95
DUKE, David L, III. 1216 RAGUET ST 75961 #048-04-1982 L1983 **IM GP** *020
ELAMIR, Sherif Taha. 1018 N MOUND ST STE 101 75961 #915-07-1977 L1989 **PM GP** *020 †60
ERWIN, Jack Roy. 4740 NE STALLINGS DR 75965 #048-04-1967 L1967 **OTO** *020 †45
FEARING, Olin K. 1002 N MOUND ST 75961 #048-13-1987 L1988 **FM OBS** *020 †18
FERRARACCIO, Blaise E. 4800 NE STALLINGS DR, STE 1400 75965 #010-01-1979 L2004 **N** *020 †75 ‡
FERREN, Edwin Louis. 1023 N MOUND ST 75961 #036-07-1982 L1983 **ORS** *020 †40
FLECKENSTEIN, Loren Duke. 4920 NE STALLINGS DR 75965 #019-02-1965 L1984 **NS N** *020 †25
FURNISS, Wilburn E, II. 4800 NE STALLINGS DR # 109 75965 #004-01-1970 L1970 **FM** *020 †18
GRAHAM, J Malcolm. ■ 75965 #038-40-1954 L1981 **GP PD** *071
GREGORY, Carroll Dean. ■ 75961 #048-12-1956 L1956 **OBG** *071 †30
GRISSON, Allen Tracy. 1204 N MOUND ST 75961 #036-07-1995 L1997 **RNR** *020 †80
GROHMAN, Tyrrel C. 4920 NE STALLINGS DR 75965 #048-02-1985 L1989 **DR IM** *020 †80
HAIDINYAK, John Gene. ■ 75964 #056-05-1975 L1979 **AN PME** *020
HANID-AWAN, Chaudri S A. 4920 NE STALLINGS DR, MEDICAL CENTER HOSPITAL 75965 #919-03-1972 L1981 **EM IM** *020 †20,16
HASKINS, Tony. 4710 NE STALLINGS DR # A 75965 #048-02-1979 L1979 **OBG** *020 †30
HEARNE, Ronald Homer. ■ 75961 #048-12-1971 L1971 **PTH** *020 †50
HENDERSON, Billy Wayne. 1023 N MOUND ST 75961 #048-12-1958 L1958 **IM GP** *020 †50
HIBBARD, Arlis Wayne. 4920 NE STALLINGS DR 75965 #048-02-1980 L1980 **OTO** *020
HILL, Sheila Lynn. 1018 N MOUND ST, STE 205 75961 #038-43-1988 L2004 **OBG** *020 †30
HOLDER, Stacey Lynn Solis. 4920 NE STALLINGS DR 75965 #048-02-1997 L1998 **IM** *020 †20
HUGMAN, George R, III. 4920 NE STALLINGS DR 75965 #048-04-1981 L1982 **FM FSM** *020 †18
HURST, James A. ■ 75965 #048-02-2008 *012
JACKSON, Morris Kent. 4920 NE STALLINGS DR 75965 #021-06-1982 L1985 **DR NM** *020 †80
JESSIE, Adrian Craig. 409 RUSSELL BLVD, STE A 75965 #048-13-1989 L1994 **FM** *020 †18
JOHNSTON, Russell James. 4800A NE STALLINGS DR, STE 1400 75965 #017-20-1963 L1969 **IM** *071 †20
JONES, William Albert. 4800 NE STALLINGS DR 75965 #028-34-1965 L1972 **R** *071 †80
JORGENSON, Anthony Wayne. 1023 N MOUND ST STE E 75961 #048-02-1969 L1969 **ORS** *020 †40
JORGENSON, Millie F A. 422 E MAIN ST # 214 75961 #048-02-1970 L1970 **DR** *020 †80
KALVAKUNTLA, Laxman Rao. 607 RUSSELL BLVD, STE A 75965 #495-57-1985 L1992 **IM** *020 †20
KHATRI, Abdul Majeed. 1209 N MOUND ST 75961 #704-02-1971 L1981 **N** *020 †75
LA BARBERA, Philip T. 4944 NE STALLINGS DR 75965 #048-02-1971 L1971 **FM** *020 †18
LEDET, Janice Patrick. BOX 13058 SFA STATION 75962 #020-02-1983 L1985 **GP** *020
LEDET, Ted Willis. 4848 NE STALLINGS DR, STE 106 75965 #021-06-1982 L1985 **IM** *020 †20
LEHMANN, Robert Paul. 5300 NORTH ST 75965 #056-06-1973 L1975 **OPH** *020 †35
LEWIS, Kathryn M. 4920 NE STALLINGS DR, LOMA LAIRD CANCER CENTER 75965 #048-14-1985 L1986 **RO** *020 †80
LOWE, William Matt, II. 206 MIMMS AVE 75961 #021-05-1971 L1978 **OBG GP** *020 †30
MANIS, Mary Elizabeth. ■ 75965 #048-02-1991 L1992 **FM** *020 †18
MATHIAS, Bill J. 4800A NE STALLINGS DR, STE 1100 75965 #010-01-1987 L1995 **PM** *020 †60
MAU, Richard Dehlbert. 1004 N MOUND ST 75961 #023-07-1959 L1997 **CD** *020 †20
MAZER, Jennifer Beth. 1401 S UNIVERSITY DR, EAST TEXAS COMMUNITY HEALT 75961 #048-13-1998 L2002 **PD** *020 †55
MC CARTHY, Justin Harold. 1018 N MOUND ST, STE 105 75961 #143-07-1975 L1990 **IM** *020 †20
MC GOWN, Gavin Duncan. ■ 75965 #836-03-1965 L1967 **GP OS** *020
MC LEAN, Michael Roy. 1300 N MOUND ST 75961 #048-02-1974 L1974 **ORS OSM** *020 †40
MC MORRIES, Kim Elliot. 4710 NE STALLINGS DR 75965 #048-02-1977 L1977 **OBG** *020 †30
MIDDLEBROOK, Tom A. 3516 NE STALLINGS DR 75965 #048-12-1983 L1983 **CHP P** *020 †75
MILLER, John Hampton. STEPHEN F AUSTIN 6212 75962 #027-01-1962 L1968 **OBG** *020 †30
MOLLOT, Michael Edward. 1018 N MOUND ST, STE 105 75961 #005-15-1968 L1993 **GE IM** *020 †20
MOON, Kelley Eileen. 1320 N UNIVERSITY DR 75961 #048-13-1998 L2002 **FM** *020 †18
MOREIRA, Sergio G, Jr. 1320 N UNIVERSITY DR, STE A 75961 #187-26-1995 L2007 **U** *020 †95
MURPHY, Alicia Guajardo. 1204 N MOUND ST, 1204 N MOUND 75961 #048-04-1984 L1991 **PTH** *020 †50
NEFF, Louis Eaton. ■ 75964 #048-02-1958 L1958 **GS** *071 †85
NIELSEN, Mark Andrew. 522 RUSSELL BLVD 75965 #048-12-1980 L1980 **U GP** *020 †95
PACK, John Richard. 302 S MOUND ST 75961 #048-02-1963 L1963 **P GP** *071
PAGE, Charles W. 1303 RAGUET ST 75961 #048-04-1994 L1999 **GS** *020 †85
POKALA, Vijaya R. 1023 N MOUND ST STE K 75961 #495-58-1977 L1989 **CD IM** *020 †20
POLK, Aaron Cornelius. 212 RUSSELL BLVD 75965 #021-06-1974 L1976 **FM** *020 †18
PROCELL, Kimberly A. 615 RUSSELL BLVD 75965 #048-16-2002 L2005 **PD** *100
RANDEL, Mark A. 3440 NE STALLINGS DR 75965 #048-02-1988 L1989 **VS GS** *020 †85
RAVINDRAN, Dyanesh G. 1225 N MOUND ST 75961 #495-36-1990 L1997 **HO IM** *020 †20
REDFIELD, James E. 322 RUSSELL BLVD 75965 #048-02-1986 L1987 **GS** *020 †85
RIGGS, Brenda J. 1204 N MOUND ST, NACOGDOCHES MEMORIAL HOSPI 75961 #048-02-1988 L1989 **FM** *020 †18
ROBERTS, Frederick Barry. 4800 NE STALLINGS DR 75965 #065-01-1956 L1978 **PD** *071
ROBINSON, Lawrence Quinn. 422 E MAIN ST # 134 75961 #048-02-1978 L1978 **FM** *020 †18
RUDE, Franklin Joe. 1204 N MOUND ST 75961 #048-02-1965 L1975 **PTH** *020 †50
SANDERSON, David Dunning. 4800 NE STALLINGS DR, STE 108 75965 #021-01-1972 L1977 **ORS** *020 †40
SATIR, Cengiz Paul. 4800 NE STALLINGS DR, STE 115 75965 #048-13-1994 L1995 **FM** *020 †18
SATIR, Vicki Hearne. 4800 NE STALLINGS DR, MAILING: P.O. BOX 631940 75965 #048-14-1997 L1998 **FM** *020 †18
SAVAGE, Robert Thornton. 4800 NE STALLINGS DR, STE 1500 75965 #024-01-1973 L1994 **PUD IM** *020 †20
SCHAFF, David Callahan. 1023 N MOUND ST STE F 75961 #027-01-1978 L1981 **DR** *020 †80
SCHAUS, Kim M. 1018 N MOUND ST, STE 206 75961 #056-06-1990 L2002 **OBG** *020 †30
SCHOFIELD, Gerald Wilmont. 4920 NE STALLINGS DR 75965 #048-12-1963 L1963 **ORS** *020 †40
SLOANE, Janelle Alexander. ■ 75961 #048-02-1961 L1961 **PTH** *071 †50
SMITH, Jeremy Scott. 1002 N MOUND ST 75961 #048-02-2003 L2005 **FM** *020 †18
SMITH, Shannon L. 4920 NE STALLINGS DR 75965 #048-02-1986 L1987 **OPH** *020 †35
SOKUNBI, Dolamu Olumide B. 626 RUSSELL BLVD STE B 75965 #690-01-1981 L1994 **IM NEP** *020 †20
SOKUNBI, Modupe. 626 RUSSELL BLVD, # A 75965 #690-01-1982 L1994 **PD** *020 †55
SPALDING, Marsha. 4635 NE STALLINGS DR, STE 106 75965 #035-03-1986 L1991 **P** *020
SPECK, Arthur Leo. 4800 NE STALLINGS DR # 114 75965 #048-02-1963 L1963 **U** *020 †95
TANHUI, Eduardo Sy. 3226 N UNIVERSITY DR, STE 200 75965 #748-01-1986 L1996 **AN** *020 †05
TATE, Gregory Scott. 508 RUSSELL BLVD 75965 #048-12-1996 L1998 **GS** *020
THOMAS, Clifton Erwin. 3460 NE STALLINGS DR 75965 #048-02-1984 L1990 **GS** *020 †85
THOMPSON, Charles Anthony. 4800 NE STALLINGS DR, STE 106 75965 #021-06-1982 L1986 **OBG** *020 †30
THORSTENSON, Lyle Sheldon. 3302 NE STALLINGS DR 75965 #048-04-1978 L1978 **OPH** *020 †35
TRACY, Richard E. 1401 S UNIVERSITY DR, EAST TX COMMUNITY HEALTH 75961 #037-01-1987 L2000 **FM** *020 †18
VANDROVEC, Anthony Robt. 1204 N MOUND ST 75961 #048-13-1971 L1971 **R** *020
VENTURA, Gerard Joseph. 4848 NE STALLINGS DR # 207 75965 #422-01-1981 L1986 **ON HEM** *020 †20
VESTAL, Kirk Reagan. ■ 75961 #048-15-1985 L1986 **BBK ATP** *075 †50
VINEYARD, David D. 4710A NE STALLINGS DR 75965 #048-12-1997 L1998 **OBG** *020 †30
VINTHER, Randal Neil. 409 RUSSELL BLVD, STE D 75965 #034-01-1986 L1990 **IM** *020
VYAS, Kavita. 607A RUSSELL BLVD 75965 #495-76-1994 L2000 **IM** *020 †20
VYAS, Shyam Arvind. 3516 NE STALLINGS DR 75965 #495-76-1994 L2002 **CHP** *020 †75
WALKER, Larry Leon. 1018 N MOUND ST 75961 #048-04-1966 L1966 **GS** *020 †85
WARTHAN, Mandy Lynn. ■ 75965 #048-02-2001 L2003 **DMP** *020 †15
WARTHAN, Travis Lynn. 4730 NE STALLINGS DR 75965 #048-02-1971 L1971 **D** *020 †15
WATSON, Arthur C, Jr. ■ 75964 #016-06-1950 L1951 **OBG** *071 †30
WILBER, Martin C. 3205 N UNIVERSITY DR, STE D PMB 548 75965 #035-03-1949 L1971 **ORS** *071 †40
WILSON, Walter Brad. 1602 E STARR AVE, STE 100 75961 #039-01-1985 L1988 **IM** *020
WITTPENN, Gregory. 627 RUSSELL BLVD 75965 #011-04-1980 L1990 **PS HS** *020 †85,65
YOUNG, James Robt. 1407 N UNIVERSITY DR STE C 75961 #038-40-1989 L1998 **TS** *020 †85,90
ZIEGLER, Anthony. ■ 75965 #021-01-1958 L1958 **AM GP** *062

NAPLES – MORRIS

GRIFFIN, James Patrick. 101 WILLIS AVE, EAST TEXAS CLINIC ASSOCIAT 75568 #048-15-1981 L1981 **FM** *020 †18 ‡
JOHNSON, Richard A. RR 3 BOX 12 75568 #061-01-1977 L1981 **FM** *020
LEEVES, James Stewart. 101 WILLIS AVE, EAST TEX CLINIC 75568 #048-02-1947 L1947 **GP** *071

NATALIA – MEDINA

BESHLIAN, Vicki Christine. ■ 78059 #048-13-1976 L1977 **PS OS** *020

NAVASOTA – GRIMES

BENTON, Jaime Christine. 501 E WASHINGTON AVE 77868 #021-06-2002 L2005 **FM** *020 †18
CANNEY, Donna Hill. 222 E WASHINGTON AVE 77868 #048-16-1998 L1999 **FM** *020 †18 ‡
COLEMAN, Leonard Outlar. ■ 77868 #048-04-1954 L1954 **GP** *071 †85
GAJEWSKI, David Wayne. 210 S JUDSON ST 77868 #048-15-1990 L1992 **FM EM** *020 †18
GARZA, Roland Robert. 1905 DOVE CROSSING LN # C, GRIMES COUNTY COMM. HEALTH 77868 #048-14-1995 L1997 **FM** *020 †18
HERMANN, Lonnie Gene. 204 BROSIG AVE 77868 #048-02-1979 L1979 **FM** *020 †18
JELINEK, Gregory N. ■ 77868 #035-08-1967 L1981 **R OS** *020 †80
MABRY, F June S. 210 S JUDSON ST 77868 #048-14-1981 L1981 **EM FM** *020
ORMBERG, Audrey. 1905 DOVE CROSSING LN # C, HEALTH CENTER 77868 #016-42-1995 L1998 **FM** *020 †18
PRIHODA, Clarence H, Jr. 501 E WASHINGTON AVE 77868 #021-06-1980 L1983 **FM** *020 †18
SCAMARDO, Luke Pete. 501 E WASHINGTON AVE 77868 #048-04-1976 L1977 **IM** *020 †20
SELVAKUMARRAJ, Pollachi P. 501 E WASHINGTON AVE 77868 #495-04-1991 L2000 **IM** *020 †20 ‡
VOTA, William Ha. 210 S JUDSON ST, GRIMES ST. JOSEPH HOSPITAL 77868 #016-42-1993 L1997 **IM** *020
WALKER, John Ingram. 1225 LEAKE ST 77868 #048-02-1970 L1970 **P** *020 †75 ‡
YILMAZ, Salih M. 1225 LEAKE ST 77868 #902-10-1959 L1977 **IM PHP** *071

NEDERLAND – JEFFERSON

ALAMPUR, Sudhir Kumar. 2400 HIGHWAY 365, STE 203 77627 #495-65-1982 L1993 **GE** *020 †20

AMIN, Murlidhar A. 2300 HIGHWAY 365, STE 150 77627 #495-23-1986 L1995 **CD IM** *020 †20
BADLISSI, Joseph. 2400 HIGHWAY 365, STE 112 77627 #605-02-1968 L1977 **IM END** *020 †20
BATTY, Carol Ann. 2300 HIGHWAY 365, STE 590 77627 #048-12-1978 L1978 **GE IM** *020
BLAIR, A Hatton. 2509 EDGEMONT LN, MIDCOUNTY FAMILY PRACTICE 77627 #048-14-1982 L1983 **FM FPG** *020 †18
CHICA, Gerardo Antonio. 1120 NEDERLAND AVE 77627 #715-01-1971 L1977 **U ON** *020 †95
CRAIG, Lance Anthony. 2100 HIGHWAY 365 77627 #048-02-1974 L1975 **P** *020
DELORD, Craig A. 1323 S 27TH ST STE 700, P O BOX 1444 77627 #048-13-1987 L1988 **DR** *020 †80
EMEJULU, Herbert Mc Iver. 1323 S 27TH ST, STE 300 77627 #010-03-1973 L1975 **FM GS** *020
FERMO, Victor Mendoza, Jr. 405 S MEMORIAL FWY 77627 #748-07-1971 L1978 **P GP** *020
FIELDS, Rita Carriker. ■ 77627 #048-13-1980 L1980 **FM** *062 †18
GARCIA, Ramon Julio. 1323 S 27TH ST STE 700, SOUTHEAST TEXAS IMAGING LL 77627 #011-02-1979 L1979 **DR** *020 †80
HUBER, Tighe. 1409 S HIGHWAY 69, MSCH HEALTH CENTER 77627 #048-13-1991 L1992 **FM** *020 †18
KAISSI, Kahtan A. 1300 FRANKLIN AVE 77627 #528-01-1985 L1996 **IM** *020 †20
KAISSI, Lubna M. 1300 FRANKLIN AVE 77627 #528-01-1985 L2001 **FM** *020 †18
KARIA, Nina Ramesh. PO BOX 73 77627 #495-01-1974 L1978 **FM** *020
KING, Michael Wm. 2300 HIGHWAY 365, STE 200 77627 #048-02-1978 L1978 **FM** *075
KOTZUR, Francis J. 1509 S HIGHWAY 69 77627 #048-13-1990 L1992 **FM** *020 †18
KRULL, Frank Andrew. 2100 HIGHWAY 365 77627 #048-02-1979 L1979 **PTH** *020 †50
KURTIS, Baylor. 2300 HIGHWAY 365, STE 670 77627 #024-07-1966 L1975 **D** *020 †15
MANSKE, Arnold Oscar, Jr. 1323 S 27TH ST, STE 700 77627 #048-02-1964 L1964 **R** *020 †80
MARRERO, Christopher Earl. 2400 HIGHWAY 365, STE 207 77627 #010-03-1991 L2006 **ORS** *020 †40
MC CRAW, Ronald Kent. 2300 HIGHWAY 365 STE 610 77627 #048-78-1990, ▲ L1991 **OBG GP** *020
MC LENDON, William Berry. 1323 S 27TH ST STE 700, P O BOX 1444 77627 #027-01-1980 L1986 **DR NR** *020 †80
NGO, Nancy Ting. 2400 HIGHWAY 365, STE 112 77627 #748-20-1986 L1997 **PD** *020 †55
NIGHTINGALE, Joseph A. 1323 S 27TH ST, STE 700 77627 #048-04-1993 L1994 **DR** *020 †80
ONG, David C. 2630 HIGHWAY 365, MID JEFFERSON HOSPITAL 77627 #209-01-1971 *020
PATEL, Chandrakant G. 1411 S HIGHWAY 69 77627 #495-48-1986 L1993 **IM** *020 †20
PHELPS, Robert Gregory. 415 AVENUE D 77627 #048-04-1990 L1998 **GS** *020 †85
POLVOROSA, Cristeto. 1120 S 27TH ST 77627 #748-01-1967 L1979 **U** *020
RAMSEY, Joe Wesley. 2400 HIGHWAY 365 STE 107 77627 #047-07-1965 L1971 **OBG** *020 †30
RANDOLPH, Harvey H, Jr. 2400 HIGHWAY 365, STE 101 77627 #028-79-1968, ▲ L1969 **FM FPG** *020
RAVAL, Nikhilkumar C. 2630 HIGHWAY 365 77627 #495-48-1979 L1999 **NPM PD** *020 †55
ROSE, Dennis Eric. 3224 AVENUE H 77627 #016-43-1984 L1985 **OTO** *020 †45
SHEFFIELD, Hugh C, Jr. ■ 77627 #048-02-1962 L1962 **R** *071 †80
ST ROMAIN, Chester Jos. HWY 365 & 27TH ST 77627 #048-02-1955 L1955 **FM** *071
VELUSWAMY, Rama Devi. 1323 S 27TH ST, STE 800 77627 #495-21-1974 L1984 **IM** *020
WILLIAMS, Anthony Kirk. 2130 HIGHWAY 365 77627 #048-04-1987 L1988 **GS** *020
WOODRUFF, James Joseph. 2300 HIGHWAY 365 77627 #005-17-1962 L1975 **OBG AM** *071 †30
ZABAD, Feras. 1323 S 27TH ST STE 600 77627 #875-01-1980 L1988 **GE IM** *020 †20

NEEDVILLE – FORT BEND

DEL ROSARIO, Levi Bondoc. ■ 77461 #748-01-1962 L1972 **OBG** *020 †30
KLAWITTER, Art Lee. 3006 SCHOOL ST 77461 #048-12-1978 L1978 **FM** *020 †18 ‡

NEW BOSTON – BOWIE

BACHERS, Gary Edward. 520 HOSPITAL DR 75570 #062-01-1975 L1977 **FM** *075
FLORES, Dennis Ray. 500 HOSPITAL DR 75570 #048-13-1978 L1979 **FM GYN** *020
FREEMAN, L Gerry. ■ 75570 #049-01-1966 L1974 **DR** *071
GURAV, Arati R. 504 HOSPITAL DR 75570 #495-39-1972 L1983 **PD** *020
GURAV, Ramchandra Shankar. 520 HOSPITAL DR 75570 #495-23-1967 L1976 **OBG** *020 †30
SINGH, Balbir. 212 N CENTER ST # 906 75570 #495-03-1959 L1975 **FM IM** *020 †18
TYSON, William S. ■ 75570 #048-02-1953 L1953 **OM GP** *071

NEW BRAUNFELS – COMAL

ALBRECHT, Warren A. 774 LANDA ST, HILL COUNTRY MEDICAL 78130 #048-12-1986 L1987 **FM** *020 †18
ANDERSON, Walter C. 901 LOOP 337 78130 #051-04-1973 L1978 **D IM** *020 †20,15
BAHR, Douglas Frederick. 600 N UNION AVE 78130 #048-02-1985 L1986 **IM** *020 †20
BAILEY, Charles Edward. 1626 E COMMON ST 78130 #036-01-1996 L2005 **IC** *020 †20
BALLI, Edward A. 1644 SUNFIRE CIR 78130 #048-13-1987 L1989 **FM** *020
BARKER, Kevin W. ■ 78132 #048-13-2000 L2003 **DR** *020 †80
BARTAY, James Ray. 876 LOOP 337, STE 101 78130 #048-14-1981 L1981 **FPG** *020 †18
BATENBURG, Caroline C. 189 E AUSTIN ST STE 105 78130 #660-06-1989 L1995 **P CHP** *020 †75
BAZAN, Fernando. 600 N UNION AVE 78130 #048-12-1979 L1979 **DR** *020 †80
BIRD, Gary Wm. 774 LANDA ST, HILL COUNTRY MEDICAL 78130 #048-02-1973 L1973 **FM** *020 †18
BLAIR, Kevin D. 571 N UNION AVE 78130 #048-02-1987 L1989 **OBG** *020 †30
BOECKER, Anna Marie. 1004 MISSION DR 78130 #048-14-1995 L1996 **MPD** *020 †20,55
BOWER, Laurence Robt. 19 GRUENE PARK DR, # B 78130 #039-01-1992 L1995 **N** *020 †75
BURNS, Mark A. 189 E AUSTIN ST, STE 105 78130 #048-12-1987 L1988 **P** *020 †75
CAMPOS, Carlos. 189 E AUSTIN ST STE 102 78130 #048-04-1981 L1981 **FM** *020 †18 ‡
CAREY, Stephen Colwell. 1583 COMMON ST, STE 105 78130 #005-06-1987 L1996 **IM** *020 †20
CARTER-TORRES, Richard E. 555 IH 35 S, STE 400 78130 #042-01-1988 L1996 **CHP** *020 †75
CARVER, Deborah Lynne. 19B GRUENE PARK DR 78130 #019-02-1994 L1995 **N** *020 †75 ‡
CASEY, Christopher W. 1583 COMMON ST, STE 105 78130 #035-03-1984 L1994 **CD IM** *020 †20
CIOLA, Juan Manuel. 1000 N WALNUT AVE, STE B 78130 #132-04-1959 L1964 **OS** *071 †55
COHLE, Ronald Richard. 774 LANDA ST, HILL COUNTRY MEDICAL 78130 #048-04-1973 L1973 **FM** *020 †18
COLES, Edward Francis. 226 N UNION AVE 78130 #010-02-1984 L1992 **GE IM** *020 †20
CROWNOVER, Roy Michael, Jr. ■ 78132 #048-02-2003 L2006 **EM** *020 †16
CULVER, William Ray. 881 ROCK ST 78130 #048-02-1982 L1983 **PM** *020 †60
DAVIS, Bill D. 19 GRUENE PARK DR, # B 78130 #048-14-1988 L1990 **N** *020 †75
DAVIS, Robert J. 600 N UNION AVE, MCKENNA MEMORIAL HOSPITAL 78130 #048-02-2000 L2003 **EM** *020
DE HOYOS, Jose Cristobal. 1626 E COMMON ST 78130 #042-01-1992 L2006 **CD** *020 †20
DE HOYOS, Leopoldo Cesar. ■ 78132 #649-02-1957 L1964 **GS AS** *071
DESCHNER, William Kern. 226 N UNION AVE 78130 #048-04-1983 L1983 **GE IM** *020 †20
DOSS, Sarah B. 774 LANDA ST, HILL COUNTRY MEDICAL 78130 #048-13-2001 L2004 **FM** *100 †18
DUFF, Kenneth Robt. ■ 78130 #048-04-1939 L1939 **ORS PD** *071 †40
ELBEL, Warren Ray. 189 E AUSTIN ST STE 103 78130 #048-04-1978 L1979 **PS** *020 †65
ELLINGTON, Alvin Wm, Jr. ■ 78133 #048-12-1958 L1958 **NS** *071 †25
FILETTI, Christopher L. 1535 E COMMON ST 78130 #016-42-1996 L1999 **PD** *020
FLANAGAN, John Richard. 600 N UNION AVE, MCKENNA MEM HOSP/ER 78130 #048-13-1982 L1983 **EM** *020 †16
FORNEY, John Peter. 113 HILL HAVEN DR 78132 #048-02-1969 L1969 **OBG GYN** *020 †30
FRANKLIN, Gerald M. 598 N UNION AVE STE 230 78130 #048-13-1997 L1998 **OTO** *020 †45
FREIHA, Ghassan S. 876 LOOP 337, BLDG C 78130 #048-04-1993 L1994 **U** *020 †95
FRIESENHAHN, Gerlyn M. 19 GRUENE PARK DR, # B 78130 #048-13-1986 L1987 **N IM** *020 †75
FRUEHOLZ, Frederick, Jr. ■ 78130 #048-02-1953 L1953 **OS** *071
GARZA, Peter A, Jr. ■ 78132 #048-13-1998 L2006 **GS** *020 †85
GELDERNICK, Mary E. 505 N UNION AVE 78130 #048-15-1990 L1991 **OBG** *020 †30
GERMAN, Roy Edward. 600 N UNION AVE 78130 #048-02-1956 L1956 **GYN GP** *071
GITTERLE, Marcus L. 600 N UNION AVE 78130 #048-13-1988 L1989 **EM** *020
GONZALEZ, Filomeno P, Jr. 705 LANDA ST STE F 78130 #048-02-2001 L2005 **FM** *020 †18
GROTE, Curtis Ryan. ■ 78132 #048-12-1983 L1983 **EM** *020 †20
GRUHLKEY, Jay Loyd. 301 MAIN PLZ, # 342 78130 #048-14-1998 L1999 **FM** *020 †18
GWOSDZ-GILMAN, Elaine M. 774 LANDA ST, HILL COUNTRY MEDICAL 78130 #048-14-1995 L1997 **FM** *020 †18
HAMPEL, Frank C, Jr. 705 LANDA ST STE A 78130 #048-13-1976 L1976 **AI PD** *020 †55,03
HARRIS, James M. 876 LOOP 337 STE 302 78130 #048-13-1986 L1994 **U** *050 †95
HENSLEY, Richard G. 600 N UNION AVE, MCKENNA MEMORIAL HOSPITAL 78130 #048-13-1992 L1993 **PTH** *020 †50
HICKMAN, Mark S. 598 N UNION AVE STE 200 78130 #048-02-1982 L1983 **GS TS** *020 †85
HINDMAN, Michael G. 774 LANDA ST, HILL COUNTRY MEDICAL 78130 #048-13-1998 L1999 **FM** *020 †18
HOLTMAN, Harold Anthony. 630 ENCINO DR 78130 #048-02-1956 L1956 **GP GS** *071
HORAN, Terri Tiemann. 901 LOOP 337 B 78130 #048-04-1987 L1989 **RHU** *020 †20
ISBELL, K Melissa Ray. 1561 N IH 35, NEW BRAUNFELS KIDNEY DISEA 78130 #048-02-1990 L1991 **NEP IM** *020 †20
JACKS, Randal Keith. 774 LANDA ST, HILL COUNTRY MEDICAL 78130 #048-02-1984 L1985 **FM** *020 †18
JAMES, Vernon Lester. ■ 78130 #036-01-1955 L1985 **PD OS** *071 †55
JOHNSON, Lin Z. 1528 E COMMON ST 78130 #243-47-1987 L1997 **NEP IM** *020 †20
JOYCE, Roby Paul. ■ 78132 #021-05-1973 L1978 **PTH N** *020 †75,50
KAHLER, Kendrick Nelson. ■ 78130 #048-02-1993 L1995 **FM** *020 †18
KARBACH, Hylmar Emil, Jr. 611 N WALNUT AVE 78130 #048-02-1955 L1955 **GS** *071 †85
KENNADY, Donald Scott. 600 N UNION AVE 78130 #048-02-1954 L1954 **FM GS** *071
KEPCZYK, Thomas. 226 N UNION AVE 78130 #003-01-1986 L1995 **IM GE** *020 †20
KLOSS, William Henry. 600 N UNION AVE 78130 #048-15-1980 L1980 **PTH HMP** *062 †50
KNEUPER, Mark F. 652 N HOUSTON AVE, STE 3 78130 #048-02-1986 L1987 **GS** *020 †85
LANO, Charles F, Jr. 42 GRUENE PARK DR 78130 #048-04-1993 L1996 **OTO** *020 †45
LEVERETT, Cary L. 1619 E COMMON ST, BLDG B 78130 #039-01-1963 L1971 **U** *072 †95
LEVETT, Laurence M. 600 N UNION AVE, MARTIN LEVETT, MD, PA 78130 #308-05-1990 L1997 **IM** *020 †20
LINARES, Silvia Teresa. ■ 78132 #264-10-1993 L2007 **OBG** *100
LOMBA, Maria Del Rosario. 1004 MISSION DR 78130 #042-03-1991 L1994 **PM** *020 †60
LOWE, Richard Emery. 600 N UNION AVE, MCKENNA MEMORIAL HOSPITAL 78130 #017-20-1981 L1996 **DR** *020 †80
LOWRY, Madison D. 1282 E COMMON ST 78130 #048-13-1997 L1999 **FM** *020 †18
MABRY, Robert Leon. ■ 78130 #023-12-1999 L2007 **EM** *020
MALAKOFF, Aaron Francis. 611 N WALNUT AVE, HOPE HOSPICE 78130 #048-02-1968 L1968 **U** *071 †95
MC KEMIE, Jack Furman. ■ 78132 #028-02-1943 L1944 **PD** *072 †55
MELENDEZ, Deborah Lynn. ■ 78130 #048-04-2004 L2006 **FM** *020
MILBOURN, John Mark. 600 N UNION AVE, MCKENNA MEMORIAL HOSPITAL 78130 #023-12-1982 L1995 **DR** *020 †80
MILLER, Eric James. 598 N UNION AVE, STE 320 78130 #048-04-1999 L2004 **AN PME** *020
MOORE, Garry Scott. 958 N IH 35 78130 #048-13-1984 L1985 **OM** *020 †70
MUNOZ, Jeffrey John. 958 N IH 35 78130 #048-13-1995 L1998 **FM OM** *020 †18 ‡
NEGHME, Carlos Amador. 226 N UNION AVE 78130 #016-11-1991 L1996 **GE** *020 †20
NELSON, Jason Arthur. 774 LANDA ST, HILL COUNTRY MEDICAL 78130 #048-13-2000 L2002 **FM** *020 †18
NUCKOLS, Beverly B. 226 N UNION AVE, NEW BRAUNFELS MINOR EMERG 78130 #048-13-1990 L1992 **FM** *020 †18
OUSLEY, Stephen Harris. 955 LOOP 337 78130 #048-02-1976 L1976 **FM** *020 †18
OVERMAN, Dorothy Nell. 774 LANDA ST, HILL COUNTRY MEDICAL 78130 #048-12-1982 L1983 **FM** *020 †18
OWENS, Timothy Wayne. 1535 COMMON ST 78130 #048-04-1978 L1978 **PD** *020 †55
PANNILL, Fitzhugh C, Jr. ■ 78130 #008-01-1945 L1947 **IM** *071 †20
PEACE, Dewey W, Jr. ■ 78131 #048-02-1951 L1951 **IMG** *071
PEDERSON, William Marion. 15 AMBER ARC 78130 #048-12-1966 L1966 **CHP PYA** *020 †75
PEROSSA, Sergio Giovanni. ■ 78130 #048-02-2004 L2008 **IM** *100
POST, Richard J. 705 LANDA ST STE C 78130 #048-12-1998 L2000 **HS ORS** *020 †40
QUINTERO, Vicente. 226 N UNION AVE, BOX 310698 78130 #048-13-1997 L2001 **D** *020 †15
RAMIREZ LEMUS, Oscar G. 226 N UNION AVE 78130 #429-02-1985 L1995 **GE IM** *020 †20
RAMOS, Awilda I. 1535 E COMMON ST 78130 #042-03-1983 L1986 **PD** *020 †55
RATH, Albert Ernest, Jr. 274 E GARZA ST 78130 #048-02-1970 L1970 **OBG** *020 †30
RAY, Dennis Ruel. 705 LANDA ST 78130 #048-02-1970 L1970 **ORS AM** *020 †40
RAY, Robert B. 1583 E COMMON ST STE 100, TX HILL COUNTRY ORTHOPAEDI 78130 #048-04-1998 L2002 **ORS** *100
REDDY, Nagakrishna. 712 N HOUSTON AVE, STE A 78130 #026-04-2000 L2004 **OBG** *020
REEVES, William Edward. 774 LANDA ST, HILL COUNTRY MEDICAL 78130 #048-12-1978 L1978 **FM FPG** *020 †18

■ = Address Information Privacy Protected

RIEGER, Sarah Ellen. 1535 COMMON ST 78130 #048-14-1996 L1999 **PD** *020 †55

RITCHEY, Elizabeth E. 1423 N WALNUT AVE, STE 103 78130 #021-01-1980 L1984 **IM** *020 †20

ROBERTS, Newell Orville. ■ 78133 #352-06-1955 L1958 **P** *071

ROCKWOOD, Kathleen B. 598 N UNION AVE STE 350 78130 #021-05-1983 L1995 **IM** *020 †20

ROEDER, Loddie F, Jr. 189 E AUSTIN ST STE 101 78130 #048-13-1976 L1976 **ORS** *020 †40

ROGER, Nestor Lionel. 731 N WALNUT AVE, STE 101 78130 #042-01-1957 L1977 **IM RHU** *020

ROSSBACH, Mario M. 191 N UNION AVE 78130 #429-02-1991 L2001 **VS GS** *020 †85

RUBALCAVA, Frank John. 1626 COMMON ST 78130 #049-01-1988 L1991 **CD IM** *020 †20

SCALZI, Angela R. 958 N IH 35 78130 #048-13-2002 L2005 **FM** *020 †18

SCHROEDER, Tyrus. 368 N UNION AVE 78130 #048-02-1989 L1990 **PUD IM** *020 †20

SIDDIQI, Ather A. 1448 COMMON ST 78130 #048-13-1997 L2000 **RO** *020 †20,80

SLAGLE, Steven James. 600 N UNION AVE 78130 #048-12-1981 L1981 **IM HEM** *020 †20

SMITH, Stanley Grant. 1527 E COMMON ST 78130 #030-06-1987 L1988 **OPH** *020 †35

SNYDER, Gerald Ray. 730 N HOUSTON AVE 78130 #004-01-1984 L1998 **FM EM** *020 †18

STARCH, David W. 705 LANDA ST STE C 78130 #048-15-1995 L1996 **OSM ORS** *020 †40

STATLER, Mark D. 1535 COMMON ST 78130 #048-02-1982 L1983 **PD** *020 †55

STIGALL, Brian W. 264 W MILL ST 78130 #048-13-1993 L1994 **FM FSM** *020 †18

STILL, Oscar Wilcox. ■ 78130 #048-04-1939 L1939 **GP GS** *071

STRANG, Mary Sofia. 474 W SAN ANTONIO ST 78130 #041-07-1956 L1979 **R NM** *072 †80,28

STRATEMANN, Stacy Ann. 18 MISSION TRCE 78130 #048-12-2001 L2003 **PDC** *012 †55

STUMBO, Keeli L. 598 N UNION AVE, STE 300 78130 #048-15-1999 L2001 **OBG** *020

TEMPLIN, David Brian. 652 N HOUSTON AVE, STE 2 78130 #038-43-2001 L2006 **ORS** *020

TEUFEL, Kenneth Wayne. ■ 78130 #048-02-1970 L1970 **FM PD** *071 †18

THOMPSON, Judith Lynn. 921 LAKEVIEW BLVD STE 300 78130 #048-13-1990 L1996 **GS** *020 †85

THOMPSON, Lynn Elliott. 955 LOOP 337 78130 #048-02-1979 L1979 **FM** *020 †18

THOMPSON, Mary Ruth. ■ 78132 #048-02-1979 L1979 **FM** *020 †18

TIEMAN, John Michael. 1584 COMMON ST 78130 #048-13-1986 L1988 **D** *020 †15

TILLY, Michael Lawrence. 191 N UNION AVE 78130 #048-02-1971 L1971 **GS VS** *020 †85

TRUSEVICH, Theodor, Jr. 1626 COMMON ST 78130 #048-04-1987 L1988 **CD** *020 †20

TSCHOEPE, Michael David. 218 E AUSTIN ST 78130 #048-13-1976 L1976 **OPH OS** *020 †35

UNGER, Loring L. ■ 78130 #017-20-1943 L1943 **U** *071 †95

WAY, David Mott. 457 LANDA ST STE A 78130 #048-04-1967 L1967 **OPH** *020 †35

WEERATUNGE, Chamalee N. 600 N UNION AVE, MCKENNA MEMORIAL HOSPITAL 78130 #220-03-1995 L2006 **ID** *020 †20

WEINBERG, Jay Stuart. 1535 COMMON ST 78130 #048-16-1995 L1996 **PD** *020 †55

WILLIAMS, Gregory James. ■ 78130 #023-12-2005 **P** *012

WILLIAMS, Patrick A. 876 LOOP 337 STE 302 78130 #048-02-1998 L2003 **U** *020 †95

YU, Haoran. 43 YU DR 78130 #243-16-1987 L1998 **IM** *020 †20

ZARBOCK, Floyd M. ■ 78132 #048-12-1963 L1963 **FM GP** *071 †18

ZHANG, Xin. 43 YU DR 78130 #243-16-1988 L1998 **GP PM** *020

ZWEIBACH, Alexander. 1448 COMMON ST 78130 #913-01-1972 L1999 **HO** *020 †20

NEW CANEY – MONTGOMERY

WILLENS, Barry Glenn. 20185 US HIGHWAY 59 STE 72 77357 #016-42-1983 L1986 **FM** *020

NEW WAVERLY – WALKER

MC NATT, James Kenneth. ■ 77358 #048-12-1956 L1956 **GP FM** *020

NEWARK – WISE

BEAM, Codi Dawn. PO BOX 86 76071 #048-13-2007 **OBG** *012

NEWTON – NEWTON

BROWN, Larry Donniel. 207 E COURT ST 75966 #048-13-1982 L1983 **GP** *020 †18

BUSSEY, Jimmie Dale. 802 RUSK ST 75966 #004-01-1962 L1967 **FM EM** *020

POTVIN, Jean-Guy. 207 E COURT ST, STE E 75966 #067-02-1965 L1984 **OS** *071

SAMUEL, Donald Ray. 207 E COURT ST 75966 #038-43-1984 L1989 **OBG** *020

NOCONA – MONTAGUE

CASEY, Shannon Lee. 90 PARK RD 76255 #048-15-1992 L1993 **FM OBG** *020 †18

NOLANVILLE – BELL

CHO, Sunghun. ■ 76559 #023-12-2003 L2005 **D** *100 †15

COZZINI, Christine B. ■ 76559 #023-12-2002 L2004 **OBG** *020 †30

NORMANGEE – LEON

BILSING, William Albert. ■ 77871 #048-02-1952 L1952 **GP P** *072

NORTH RICHLAND HILLS – TARRANT

ABRAHAM, Cherian. 4375 BOOTH CALLOWAY RD, STE 201 76180 #495-37-1994 L2003 **GE** *020 †20 ‡

AGHDAM, Lida. 4401 BOOTH CALLOWAY RD 76180 #047-20-1998 L2002 **IM** *020 †20

ALCALEN, Evelina Vidanes. 4375 BOOTH CALLOWAY RD, STE 207 76180 #048-14-1999 L2003 **OBG** *020 †30

ALLEN, Patrick Lee. 4351 BOOTH CALLOWAY RD, STE 301 76180 #048-13-1995 L1999 **OBG** *071 †30

AMONETTE, Shannon L. 9155 BOULEVARD 26, STE 210 76180 #047-20-1999 L2005 **DR** *020 †80

ANDERSON, Thomas Burton. 4351 BOOTH CALLOWAY RD, STE 308 76180 #065-09-1963 L1978 **OPH** *020

APPEL, Noah Bennett. 9155 BOULEVARD 26, STE 210 76180 #028-02-1997 L2003 **VIR** *020 †80

BAKER, Douglas R. 9155 BOULEVARD 26, STE 210 76180 #048-13-1995 L2001 **DR** *020 †80

BARR, Patrick W. 9155 BOULEVARD 26, STE 210 76180 #048-13-1983 L1983 **NM DR** *020 †28

BARTOS, Justin V. 4351 BOOTH CALLOWAY RD, STE 101 76180 #048-02-1982 L1983 **FM FPG** *020 †18 ‡

BASS, David Raj. 4375 BOOTH CALLOWAY RD, STE 201 76180 #495-09-1974 L1984 **GE IM** *020 †20

BASS, Sally Hayward. 9155 BOULEVARD 26, STE 210 76180 #048-12-1988 L1989 **DR** *020 †80

BOWMAN, Rodney Russell. 9155 BOULEVARD 26, STE 210 76180 #048-13-1996 L1998 **DR** *100 †20,80,28

BUNDY, Scott Alan. 9155 BOULEVARD 26, STE 210 76180 #030-06-1996 L1997 **RNR** *020 †80

CARELOCK, Ted Lee. 9155 BOULEVARD 26, STE 210 76180 #012-01-1966 L1967 **R** *020 †80

CASOLO, Bradley James. 9155 BOULEVARD 26, STE 210 76180 #035-45-1998 L2004 **DR** *020 †80

CHANDRA, Balu. 4375 BOOTH CALLOWAY RD, STE 201 76180 #495-33-1988 L1999 **GE IM** *020 †20

CHAVDA, Deepak V. 8251 BEDFORD EULESS RD, STE 210 76180 #495-48-1981 L1994 **ORS** *020 †20

CHUANG, Alex Tzu-Yueh. 9155 BOULEVARD 26, STE 210 76180 #016-06-1994 L2001 **DR** *100 †80

COHN, Evan Lawrence. 9155 BOULEVARD 26, STE 210 76180 #010-01-1992 L1998 **DR** *020 †80

COKER, Richard Lee. 9155 BOULEVARD 26, STE 210 76180 #039-01-1982 L1988 **VIR** *020 †80

DAVIS, Randy Thos. 4351 BOOTH CALLOWAY RD, STE 308 76180 #018-03-1982 L1991 **HEM ON** *020 †20

DITTMAN, William Ira. 9155 BOULEVARD 26, STE 210 76180 #048-13-1972 L1972 **VIR DR** *020 †80

ELLENBOGEN, Paul Harris. 9155 BOULEVARD 26, STE 210 76180 #035-08-1973 L1978 **DR** *020 †80

FOSTER, Travis Arno. 4375 BOOTH CALLOWAY RD, STE 515 76180 #048-12-1982 L1983 **GS** *020 †85

GAROUTTE, Keila M. 9155 BOULEVARD 26, STE 210 76180 #048-02-1993 L1997 **RNR** *020 †80

GENCO, Frank R. 8245 PRECINCT LINE RD #100, EMERG MED CTR 76180 #028-34-1988 L1993 **EM** *020 †20 ‡

GIFFORD, David L. 7620 NE LOOP 820, DIGESTIVE HEALTH ASSOCIATE 76180 #028-03-1977 L1992 **GE** *020 †20

HAIGOOD, Jody. 4401 BOOTH CALLOWAY RD, NORTH HILLS HOSPITAL 76180 #048-15-2003 L2006 **EM** *020 †16

HALL, Katherine Shelley. 9155 BOULEVARD 26, STE 210 76180 #048-12-1980 L1980 **DR NR** *020 †80

HAMILTON, Clint D. 9155 BOULEVARD 26, STE 210 76180 #048-13-1997 L2003 **DR** *020 †80

HARVEY, William Cushman. 9155 BOULEVARD 26, STE 210 76180 #035-20-1962 L1974 **NM IM** *020 †20,28

HENDERSON, Pamela Martin. 4401 BOOTH CALLOWAY RD 76180 #036-07-1987 L2004 **FM** *020 †18

HEROD, Misty Dawn. ■ 76180 #048-13-2005 L2007 **OBG** *012

HERRMANN, David Read. 4375 BOOTH CALLOWAY RD, STE 210 76180 #048-02-1984 L1994 **IM** *020 †20

HICKS, Carla Rachelle. 4375 BOOTH CALLOWAY RD, STE 506 76180 #004-01-1996 L2000 **OBG** *020 †30

HOFFMANN, John H. ■ 76180 #020-02-1964 L1965 **OBG** *071 †30

HOUSTON, Eli Nelson. 4351 BOOTH CALLOWAY RD, STE 101 76180 #047-06-1962 L1964 **FM** *071 †18

HOWELL-STAMPLEY, Temple S. 9003 AIRPORT FWY, STE 300 76180 #036-08-1993 L1995 **IM** *020 †20

JAMES, Jennifer Sonia. 4351 BOOTH CALLOWAY RD, STE 414 76180 #048-14-2003 L2005 **IMG** *020 †20

KIM, David Daesung. 4375 BOOTH CALLOWAY RD, STE 404 76180 #038-44-1986 L2003 **GS OS** *020 †85

KOLLIPARA, Madhu Sudhan. 4375 BOOTH CALLOWAY RD # 2 76180 #495-99-1999 L2007 **PCC** *100 †20

LAMBERT, Joseph O. 4351 BOOTH CALLOWAY RD, STE 101 76180 #048-14-1995 L1996 **FM** *020 †18

LEE, Augustine Junseog. 4375 BOOTH CALLOWAY RD, STE 404 76180 #048-12-1998 L2003 **CRS** *020 †85,10

LOGAN, Ben Merl. ■ 76180 #048-04-1954 L1954 **R** *071 †80

MARQUINO, Rey C. 4351 BOOTH CALLOWAY RD 76180 #748-01-1993 L2005 **IM** *020 †20

MAUST, Joel R. 9003 AIRPORT FWY, STE 300 76180 #048-14-1993 L1994 **FM** *020 †18

MC GINLEY, W Curtis. 9139 BOULEVARD 26, STE 540 76180 #048-04-1960 L1960 **FM GP** *020 †18

MILLICAN, Geoffrey Means. 4375 BOOTH CALLOWAY RD, STE 410 76180 #048-13-2000 L2006 **ORS** *020

MILLWEE, Robt Hughes, III. ■ 76180 #025-01-1965 L1966 **U EM** *020 †95

MOFFETT, Jeffrey Dean. 4351 BOOTH CALLOWAY RD, STE 208 76180 #039-01-1995 L2001 **ORS** *020 †40

MOODY, Everett Albert. 4401 BOOTH CALLOWAY RD 76180 #048-12-1963 L1963 **PO** *020 †35

OMEY, Monica Lynn. 4351 BOOTH CALLOWAY RD 76180 #021-01-1993 L1995 **ORS** *020 †40

PAK, James P. 9155 BOULEVARD 26, STE 210 76180 #048-13-1992 L1997 **DR** *020 †80

PARIHAR, Pradeep Singh. 8251 BEDFORD EULESS RD, STE 210 76180 #495-93-1990 L2006 **FM** *100 †18

PHAM, Viet Hoai. ■ 76180 #048-02-2008 *012

PHELPS, Jeffrey Bradford. 4375 BOOTH CALLOWAY RD, STE 410 76180 #048-13-1999 L2002 **ORS** *020 †40

RAMAMURTHY, Geethanjali. 4351 BOOTH CALLOWAY RD, STE 303 76180 #496-20-1993 L2003 **NEP** *020 †20

ROBINSON BROWN, Latonjia. 4375 BOOTH CALLOWAY RD, STE 207 76180 #047-07-1997 L2001 **OBG** *020

RUHNKE, Thomas J, Jr. 9155 BOULEVARD 26, STE 210 76180 #048-13-1989 L1990 **DR** *020 †80

RUSSELL, David Dee. 9003 AIRPORT FWY 30 76180 #048-02-1966 L1966 **GYN** *030 †30

SAFELY, Charles A. 4351 BOOTH CALLOWAY RD, STE 206 76180 #048-02-1990 L1991 **OBG** *020 †30

SCRIVEN, Richard Ralph. 4375 BOOTH CALLOWAY RD, ROAD #510 76180 #005-12-1978 L2000 **U** *020 †95

SELF, Angela Donna. 5409 DAVIS BLVD 76180 #422-01-1998 L2003 **IM** *020 †20

SHERRY, Cynthia Stark. 9155 BOULEVARD 26, STE 210 76180 #048-12-1983 L1983 **R** *020 †80

SMITH, Elmer G, Jr. 4351 BOOTH CALLOWAY RD, STE 311 76180 #010-03-1983 L2000
IM *020 †20
SYLER, James Matthew, Jr. 9155 BOULEVARD 26, STE 210 76180 #048-02-1962 L1962
R *071 †80
TALBOTT, Neal Bevan. ■ 76180 #001-06-1989 L1992 FM *020 †18
TAN, Ricardo Barrera. 5152 RUFE SNOW DR, STE 314 76180 #748-07-1972 L1977 GP *020
THORNE, David Lee. 8320 THORNWAY CT 76180 #028-02-1971 L1973 EM *020 †16
THURMOND, John Ira. 9003 AIRPORT FWY, STE 300 76180 #305-01-1997 L2000 IM *020 †20
THWIN, Sandy. 9155 BOULEVARD 26, STE 210 76180 #048-02-1995 L2000 DR *020 †80
TURNER, James Malcolm. 4351 BOOTH CALLOWAY RD, STE 308 76180 #025-01-1982 L1989
HEM ON *020 †20
TYSON, Joe Ellis, Jr. 4109 CAGLE DR, STE B 76180 #047-06-1962 L1964 FM *071
WACASEY, Kevin L. 7801 MID CITIES BLVD, STE 100 76180 #048-02-1994 L1997 EM *020 †16
WILLS, Martha Pauline. 4375 BOOTH CALLOWAY RD, STE 208 76180 #048-13-1990 L1991
GS *020 †85

NOVICE – COLEMAN

DUKE, Jean Douglas. ■ 79538 #048-04-1956 L1956 FM *071

ODESSA – ECTOR

ABIJAY, Joseph Albert L. 601 E 2ND ST STE E 79761 #748-10-1994 L2006 CN *020 †75
ABU-AL-FOUL, Ahmed Mustaf. 800 W 4TH ST, TX TECH UNIV HLTH SCI CTR 79763
#575-02-2001 IM *012
ABU ALI, Al-Muntaser Bill. 800 W 4TH ST 79763 #575-01-2003 IM *100
ACREMAN, Anne Elizabeth. 4222 WENDOVER AVE STE 400 79762 #048-02-1982 L1983
FM *020 †18
ADAMS, Joel Lea. 500 N WASHINGTON AVE, STE 100 79761 #048-12-1963 L1964
PUD IM *020 †20
AGUSALA, Surekha. 318 N ALLEGHANEY AVE STE 2 79761 #495-65-1981 L1998 END *020 †20
AGUSALA, Vasantha. 318 N ALLEGHANEY AVE, STE 402 79761 #495-21-1989 L1997
FM *020 †18
AHMAD, Tanvir. 800 W 4TH ST, TX TECH UNIV HLTH SCI CTR 79763 #496-11-1991 L2004
IM *100
AHMED, Yasir. 800 W 4TH ST 79763 #704-08-2000 IM *012
AKBAR, Salma Khatoon. 800 W 4TH ST 79763 #704-06-2001 FP *012
ALHOURANI, Hazem Mah'D Sa. 800 W 4TH ST 79763 #575-02-2003 IM *012
ALI, Shabnam Asgher. 800 W 4TH ST 79763 #704-02-2003 IM *012
ALROUMOH, Manaf Abedalwha. 108 LAHAINA 79762 #875-01-1998 IM *020 †20
AMARAM, Sudhir. 720 GOLDER AVE 79761 #495-21-1973 L1980 CD IM *020 †20
ANDERSON, Errol Claude. 500 W 4TH ST 79761 #048-12-1981 L1981 VIR R *020 †80
ANGIREKULA, Manohar. 720 GOLDER AVE 79761 #495-50-1993 L2001 CD *020 †20
ANSARI, Mohammed Zafer. 800 W 4TH ST 79763 #495-21-2001 IM *012
ARORA, Suthep. 800 W 4TH ST, TX TECH UNIV HLTH SCI CTR 79763 #495-14-2003 IM *012
AZAD, Mohammad Abul Kalam. 800 W 4TH ST 79763 #160-01-1991 L2007 FP *012
BALASEKARAN, Saroja. ■ 79765 #495-16-1963 L1985 AN *105
BALLA, Purnima Sobha. 800 W 4TH ST 79763 #495-11-2005 IM *012
BANDA, Kanakalingeswara C. 800 W 4TH ST 79763 #495-21-2004 IM *012
BARNARD, Life. 421 GOLDER AVE 79761 #048-12-1966 L1966 FM GPM *020 †18
BARTLETT, Richard Paul. 1940 E 42ND ST 79762 #048-15-1991 L1992 GS *020
BARTLETT, Sylvan. 540 W 5TH ST, STE 340 79761 #028-03-1967 L1977 PS OTO *020 †45,65 ‡
BECKER, Bruce Carl. 500 W 4TH ST 79761 #016-42-1978 L2002 FM FPG *030 †18
BELLO, Sandra M. 703 N HANCOCK AVE 79761 #025-12-1992 L1998 OBG *020 †30
BELLO, Violeta S. 303 E 7TH AVE, PERMIAN PEDIATRICS 79761 #308-01-1983 L1998 PD *020 †55
BENIGNO, Jose Bato, Jr. 115 W 42ND ST 79764 #748-08-1984 L1999 MPD PD *020 †20,55
BENNETT, Robert Earl, Jr. 701 W 5TH ST, DEPT OF PEDIATRICS 79763 #003-01-1977 L1978
NPM *020 †55
BERGQUIST, Carol Adele. 701 W 5TH ST STE 3212, TEXAS TECH HEALTH SCIENCES 79763
#060-01-1967 L1976 OBG REN *020 ‡
BHATIA, Ashwani. 701 W 5TH ST, DEPT OF INTERNAL MEDICINE 79763 #495-45-2002 L2007
IM *020 †20
BHONGIR, Rahul. 701 W 5TH ST, TEXAS TECH UNIV HSC 79763 #495-50-1999 FP *012
BILKIS, Sayeeda. 800 W 4TH ST 79763 #243-16-1997 L2007 IM *012
BLANCO, Jorge D. PO BOX 4859, 520 E SIXTH ST 79760 #047-05-1975 L1979
MFM OBS *020 †30
BLEVINS, Niska A. 2432 S MARKET ST 79766 #048-78-1999, ▲ L2007 DR *020 †80
BOCCALANDRO, Fernando. 720 GOLDER AVE 79761 #935-01-1994 L2003 IC CD *020 †20
BORRA, Renuka. 301 N WASHINGTON AVE 79761 #495-21-1979 L2002 ON HEM *020 †20
BROWN, Elisa Lois. 701 W 5TH ST, OBSTETRICS & GYNECOLOGY 79763 #051-07-1994 L1995
OBG *020 †30
BRYAN, Jos Franklin, Jr. 500 W 4TH ST, MEDICAL CENTER HOSPITAL 79761
#048-15-1983 L1983 AN EM *020 †05
BUENO, Jose Domil. 808 TOWER DR, STE 1 79761 #748-13-1983 L1996 PD *020 †55
BURKS, James Kenneth. 701 W 5TH ST 79763 #048-12-1971 L1971 DIA END *040 †20
BUTLER, Weldon Fred. 700 DOTSY AVE 79763 #034-01-1985 L1986 GP FSM *020 ‡
CAMPAGNA, Gina Brasco. 500 W 4TH ST 79761 #033-05-1992 L2004 DR *020 †80
CAPOCYAN, Lorelei Cabrera. 800 W 4TH ST 79763 #748-01-1995 OBG *012
CAPOCYAN, Owen Calapano. 800 W 4TH ST, TX TECH UNIV HLTH SCI CTR 79763 #748-01-1995
FM *100
CARSON, Willis Thos. ■ 79768 #048-12-1947 L1947 OPH *071 †35
CARTER, Ramona Lea. 701 W 5TH ST STE 3142 79763 #039-01-1994 L1997 FM *020 †18
CARTWRIGHT, Rudolph. 835 TOWER DR, STE 15 79761 #048-04-1974 L1978 NS *020
CASANOVA, Diana. 4241 TANGLEWOOD LN, STE 102 79762 #048-13-1984 L1985 FM *020 †18
CATALASAN, Rosanna Yabut. 800 W 4TH ST 79763 #417-01-1996 FP *012
CEPERO, Ralph. 540 W 5TH ST, STE 410 79761 #048-04-1983 L1983 OTO *020 †45
CHALLAPALLI, John Jangayy. 500 ADAMS AVE STE 400 79761 #495-50-1963 L1975
GS *020 †20
CHALLAPALLI, Kris L. 500 ADAMS AVE, STE 600 79761 #495-50-1962 L1975 PTH *075 †50
CHAPPELL, Robert Lane, Jr. 2487 E 11TH ST 79761 #048-04-1974 L1974 D IM *020 †15
CHEMITIGANTI, Ramachandra. 701 W 5TH ST, DEPT IM 79763 #495-65-1998 L2008
IM *020 †20
CHILKA, Sapna. 701 W 5TH ST, TEXAS TECH UNIV HEALTH SCI 79763 #496-34-2000 L2007
IM *100 †20

CHOUMAROV, George. 414 E 8TH ST 79761 #198-01-1968 L1997 IM PD *020
CHOUMAROV, Kyril. ■ 79765 #048-13-1999 L2002 TS *100 †85,90
CONE, Jesse Donald, Jr. 318 N ALLEGHANEY AVE 79761 #039-01-1947 L1949 FM *071
COX, Jefferson Dee. 500 W 4TH ST, MEDICAL CTR HOSP 79761 #028-02-1980 L1981
DR *020 †80
CULBERT, Richard Bruce. 840 CENTRAL DR 79761 #039-01-1993 L1998 OPH OS *020 †35
CUNNINGHAM, Benjamin John. 318 N ALLEGHANEY AVE, STE 303 79761 #016-02-1995 L2002
ORS *020 †40
CUNNINGHAM, Pamela Shenou. 318 N ALLEGHANEY AVE, STE 303 79761 #025-12-2000 L2005
AN *100 †05
DAGOSTINO, Carl Jos. 500 W 4TH ST 79761 #034-01-1989 L1995 PME PD *020
DANIEL, Craig O. 750 W 5TH ST 79763 #048-13-1986 L1987 GS *020 †85
DAR, Khavar J. 500 N WASHINGTON AVE, STE 200 79761 #704-20-1984 L1999 PCC *020 †20
DAVIS, William Richard. 701 W 5TH ST, TX TECH PERMIAN BASIN 79763 #048-04-1976 L1976
IM *040 †20
DE BOER, Louise Nathalie. ■ 79762 #048-12-1983 L1983 IM *071
DELCAMBRE, John Bruce. 701 W 5TH ST, TTUHSC 79763 #048-15-1977 L1977 GS *020 †85
DESAI, Manisha Mahadev. 808 TOWER DR STE 10 79761 #495-01-1994 L1998 PD *020 †55
DIMRI, Manish. 701 W 5TH ST, TEXAS TECH HSCU 79763 #495-45-1992 L2006 NEP *020 †20
DIXIT, Arati Prabahakar. 800 W 4TH ST 79763 #495-28-1993 L2006 IMG *012 †20
DOHERTY, Mark Gerard. 301 N WASHINGTON AVE 79761 #050-02-1982 L1988
GO GYN *020 †30
DORAN, John Hilton. 500 W 4TH ST 79761 #048-13-1973 L1973 IM CD *020 †20
DORMAN, John K. 221 N LINCOLN AVE 79761 #048-02-1994 L2002 NS *020 †25
DRISCOLL, Nabiha Y Khoury. 415 N SAM HOUSTON AVE 79761 #048-02-1969 L1969
AI PD *071
DRISCOLL, Stephen Edward. 425 N SAM HOUSTON AVE 79761 #048-15-1976 L1978 ORS *071
DUKE, Richard Lawrence. 1340 E 7TH ST 79761 #048-02-1980 L1980 ORS *020 †40
DZIDA, Franklin J. 500 W 4TH ST 79761 #041-09-1978 L1987 ORS *020 †40
EDWARDS, Larry Dewayne. 800 E 7TH ST, PERMIAN BASIN RADIOLOGY 79761
#048-02-1997 L1998 DR *020 †80
ELAM, Gary Wayne. 520 N WASHINGTON AVE 79761 #039-01-1967 L1974 OTO HNS *020 †45
ELLSWORTH, Steven Robt. 5000 E UNIVERSITY BLVD, STE 6 79762 #048-12-1983 L1983
OM FM *020 †70
ELMAAROUF, Abdelaziz. 800 W 4TH ST 79763 #655-01-1986 FM *100
ERIKSEN, Nancy Louise. 421 N TOM GREEN AVE 79761 #038-45-1985 L1989
OBG MFM *020 †30
FAHIM, Tallat. 800 W 4TH ST 79763 #704-01-2003 IM *012
FANOUS, Ghassan N. 540 W 5TH ST, STE 420 79761 #048-14-1991 L1993 OBG *020 †30
FINCH, Albert Benton, Jr. 1509 N TEXAS AVE 79761 #047-05-1946 L1952 GYN *020
FREEMAN, Jenatta. ■ 79762 #047-06-2000 L2005 OBG *020 †30
FURST, Matthew B. 318 N ALLEGHANEY AVE, STE 400 79761 #048-15-1987 L1988
PS *020 †85,65
GADASALLI, Suresh N. 21 SANTA FE PL 79765 #495-98-1986 L1994 CD IM *020 †20
GALLOWAY, Nathan Costillo. 506 N ALLEGHANEY AVE 79761 #021-01-1957 L1968
IM NEP *071 †20
GARCIA, John Thaddeus. 701 W 5TH ST 79763 #048-13-1993 L1994 FM *020 †18
GARCIA, Jose Ramon, Sr. ■ 79760 #018-03-1997 FM *020
GARZA, O T. 4220 WENDOVER AVE STE B 79762 #048-02-1972 L1972 ORS OTR *020
GEITZ, Marten. 2626 JOHN BEN SHEPPRD PKWY, STE C131 79761 #660-04-1956 L1968
ORS *071 †40
GEORGE, Timothy Kilian. 301 N WASHINGTON AVE, WEST TEXAS CANCER CENTER 79761
#034-01-1979 L1990 IM ON *050 †20
GHANTA, Amaranath. 600 N WASHINGTON AVE 79761 #495-62-1980 L1990
PUD CCM *020 †20
GHAZAL, Bahij Georges. 800 W 4TH ST 79763 #875-02-2002 IM *012
GIBBONS, Ronald Oscar. 701 W 5TH ST, DEPT IM 79763 #566-01-1996 L2006 NEP *100 ‡
GIBSON, Allen Elvin. 701 W 5TH ST, HEALTH SCIENCE 79763 #048-13-1994 L2007 IM *100
GIL OLAYA, Juan Carlos. 500 W 4TH ST, MEDICAL CENTER HOSPITAL 79761
#264-01-1991 L2007 IM *020 †20
GODEY, Sreedevi. 800 W 4TH ST 79763 #495-21-2004 IM *012
GOTARDO, Felito. 840 W CLEMENTS ST 79763 #748-09-1961 L1995 FM *020 †18
GUTIERREZ CAMPOS, Gary. 800 W 4TH ST 79763 #737-10-2003 IM *012
HALCOMB, John Darrell. 850 TOWER DR, STE 110 79761 #017-20-1984 L1990
ORS OSS *020 †40
HALPERT, Michael. 701 W 5TH ST, TEXAS TECH SCHOOL OF MED 79763 #048-13-1981 L2007
GS *040 †85
HAMILTON, Delmos Earl. 3051 E UNIVERSITY BLVD 79762 #048-02-1964 L1965 GP GS *071
HAMPTON, Raymond Moss. 701 W 5TH ST, DEPT OB 79763 #048-15-1980 L1980
OBG *040 †30
HARRIS, Norman. 617 N TOM GREEN AVE 79761 #023-01-1977 L1978 OBG *020 †30
HARVEY, Lori G. ■ 79762 #048-78-2002, ▲ OBG *012
HO, Mat Hoang. 701 W 5TH ST 79763 #001-06-1996 OBG *020
HOLLINGSWORTH, Cheryl A. 1111 W 12TH ST, PERMIAN BASIN MHMR 79763
#047-07-1984 L2000 P *020 †20
HOWARD, Kris Lynn. 8141 DORADO DR 79765 #048-15-1985 L1986 D *020 †15
HOWELL, James Weldon. 520 E 6TH ST 79761 #048-12-1962 L1962 ATP CLP *020 †50
HUSSAIN, Iqbal. 701 W 5TH ST, DEPT. OF INTERNAL MEDICINE 79763 #704-16-1994 L1996
CCM *020 †20
INBAR, Shmuel. 318 N ALLEGHANEY AVE, STE 302 79761 #550-03-1979 L1997
ICE CD *020 †20
ISLAM, Jamal. 701 W 5TH ST, TTUHSC AT THE PERMIAN BASI 79763 #160-03-1979 L1998
FM *020 †18
ISLAM, Sajjadul. 320 N MUSKINGUM AVE 79761 #160-02-1973 L1984 DR NR *020
JABUR, Razzak. 509 N ALLEGHANEY AVE 79761 #528-01-1964 L1974 U *020 †95
JAFRI, Aqeel Akhtar. ■ 79762 #704-26-2002 L2005 FP *012
JAIDEV, Ratakonda S. ■ 79762 #495-70-1983 L1998 FM *100
JENNINGS, John C. 800 W 4TH ST, TEXAS TECH UNVIERSITY HEAL 79763 #047-06-1970 L1972
OBG *040 †30
JOHNSON, Arthur Geo. 515 ADAMS AVE, BOX 689 79761 #060-01-1976 L1981 EM *020 †16
KACZOR, Joseph Gerard. 301 N WASHINGTON AVE 79761 #025-07-1983 L1993
RO EM *020 †80,16
KADIR, Abdul. 519 GOLDER AVE 79761 #704-16-1988 L1996 N *020
KANTOR, Harvey Sherwin. 701 W 5TH ST, TEXAS TECH UNIVERSITY 79763 #028-02-1962 L1993
ID MM *071 †20
KARICKHOFF, Alfred Norman. 800 W 4TH ST 79763 #055-01-1963 L1985 NPM *071 †55

KATIKANENI, Shalini. 701 W 5TH ST, TEXAS TECH UNIV HEALTH SCI 79763 #496-34-1999 **IM** *012
KELLY, Randall Tiffany. 701 W 5TH ST, STE 3212 79763 #003-01-1975 L1982 **MFM OBG** *020 †30 ‡
KHAN, Fahim Zaman. ■ 79761 #704-22-1992 L2001 **PCC** *100 †20
KHAN, Muhammad Azeem. 800 W 4TH ST 79763 #704-01-2004 **IM** *012
KHANDELWAL, Pankaj. 301 N WASHINGTON AVE 79761 #005-06-1987 L1993 **HEM** *020 †20
KHARABSHEH, Luma Abed. 800 W 4TH ST 79763 #575-01-2003 **IM** *012
KHATCHADOURIAN, Joseph. 700 N GRANT AVE STE 726 79761 #875-02-1984 L2002 **IM** *020 †20
KHURSHID, Arif. 800 W 4TH ST, TX TECH UNIV HLTH SCI CTR 79763 #704-04-1998 *100
KIM, Hye Tae. 1157 E 42ND ST 79762 #033-06-1989 L1997 **FM GS** *020 †18
KIM, Nam H. 501 GOLDER AVE, STE 203-A 79761 #048-13-1988 L1989 **CD IM** *020 †20
KNAUT, Donald Eugene. ■ 79762 #048-02-1959 L1959 **OBG** *071 †30
KODITYAL, Anjaiah. 315 GOLDER AVE, STE A 79761 #495-65-1970 L1990 **IM** *020 †20
KODITYAL, Meera. ■ 79765 #495-65-1973 L1991 *020
KOLLURU, Ramachandra Rao. 621 N WASHINGTON AVE 79761 #495-50-1974 L1991 **CD** *020 †20
KOLLURU, Samrajyam. 621 N WASHINGTON AVE 79761 #495-50-1972 L1991 **IM** *020 †20
KURRA, Usha Rani. 405 N TOM GREEN AVE 79761 #495-50-1990 L1997 **IM** *020 †20
LE, Chau Minh. 701 W 5TH ST 79763 #942-01-1990 L2000 **FPG** *020 †18
LESHNOWER, Alan Chas. 750 W 5TH ST 79763 #047-06-1969 L1981 **TS CD** *020 †85,90
LEVISON, Lionel. 4692 E UNIVERSTY BLVD #104 79762 #803-01-1964 L1980 **P N** *020 †75
LEWIS, Caroline F. ■ 79762 #048-04-1951 L1951 **OS** *071
LEYCEGUI GARDOQUI, Iker. 800 W 4TH ST 79763 #649-13-2001 L2006 **IM** *020
LI, Eileen. 318 N ALLEGHANEY AVE # 200 79761 #048-14-2001 L2005 **PD** *020 †55
LI, James Yihsing. 318 N ALLEGHANEY AVE, STE 200 79761 #024-05-1994 L2001 **VS GS** *020 †85
LI, Ronald Alan Tung. 800 W 4TH ST 79763 #748-01-2003 **IM** *012
LIBSON, David Solomon. 421 E 7TH ST 79761 #048-12-1985 L1986 **OBG** *020 †30
LITTLE, Vijayavalli. 800 W 4TH ST, TX TECH UNIV HLTH SCI CTR 79763 #495-65-1992 L2008 **IM** *100 †20
LIU, Shai-Yuan. 318 N ALLEGHANEY AVE # 30 79761 #385-04-1966 L1974 **GS CRS** *020 †10,85
LIVELY, Charles Auborn. 608 N MUSKINGUM AVE 79761 #048-15-1988 L1989 **OBG** *020 †30
LIZARRIBAR, Jose Luis. 520 E 6TH ST 79761 #042-01-1980 L1996 **GP** *020 †16
LOVEMAN, Donald Michael. 701 W 5TH ST, INTERNAL MEDICINE CLINIC 79763 #038-06-1973 L1996 **IM** *020 †20
MADHAVA, Agusala. 318 N ALLEGHANEY AVE # 402 79761 #495-21-1978 L1992 **IM** *020 †20
MAGSINO, Nancy Aguilar. 800 W 4TH ST 79763 #748-01-1995 **OBG** *012
MARTIN, Nelida A Noviello. ■ 79762 #132-03-1960 L1974 **GP GYN** *071
MARTINEZ, Raymond. 540 W 5TH ST, STE 420 79761 #048-12-1983 L1983 **OBG** *020 †30
MATTHEWS, Carolyn M. 301 N WASHINGTON AVE 79761 #051-04-1985 L1990 **GO** *020 †30
MAYANS, Jose Alberto. 907 W 2ND ST 79763 #649-01-1972 L1979 **OPH** *020 †35
MC HATTIE, Thomas John. 701 W 5TH ST 79763 #068-01-1969 L2005 **OBG** *040
MC QUILLIN, Pamela A. 1330 E 8TH ST STE 420 79761 #048-15-1998 L2001 **OBG** *020 ‡
MEDI, Ravi. 2626 JBS PKWY, STE C129 79761 #495-50-1984 L1996 **P PYG** *020 †75
MEEK, Thomas Dale. 523 N ALLEGHANEY AVE 79761 #038-40-1961 L1966 **NS** *020 †25
MIRANDA, Leonidas Santos. 701 W 5TH ST, SURGERY CENTER 79763 #319-03-1990 L2001 **GS** *020 †85
MITIS, Charles Z K. ■ 79761 #759-01-1939 L1971 **P N** *071 †75
MOCHERLA, Satish Murthy. 850 TOWER DR, STE 109 79761 #495-65-1988 L1999 **ID** *020 †20
MOHAMED, Amr Ahmed Elhuss. 800 W 4TH ST 79763 #915-06-1992 **IM** *012
MOLLAND, John Robt. 601 N TOM GREEN AVE 79761 #037-01-1991 L1995 **OBG** *020 †30
MONZON, Migdalia. 850 TOWER DR STE 106, 850 TOWER DRIVE ST 106 79761 #042-03-1985 L1999 **PD** *020
MORALES, Andres Rafael. ■ 79762 #649-02-1954 L1964 **TS VS** *071 †85,90
MUJAHID, Ambreen. 701 W 5TH ST, TEXAS TECH UNIV HSC 79763 #704-02-2001 **FP** *012
MURRELL, Brian Scott. 835 TOWER DR, STE 7 79761 #025-07-1983 L1989 **PME IM** *020 †20,05
NAIDU, Bavikati Jayaram. 515 ADAMS AVE 79761 #495-50-1967 L1976 **IM CD** *020
NAIDU, Raja B. 515 ADAMS AVE 79761 #048-12-1995 L1996 **CD** *020 †20
NAITHANI, Vandana. 800 W 4TH ST 79763 #496-10-1995 **FP** *012
NAJJAR, Alia Annette. 3730 FAIRMONT DR 79762 #048-12-2003 L2005 **GS** *100
NALLURI, Venkata Ramana K. 701 W 5TH ST, DEPT OF FAMILY MED 79763 #495-50-1998 **FP** *012
NARAM, Srinivas. 2561 KERMIT HWY 79763 #495-11-1991 L2004 **IM** *020 †20
NAYLOR, Donald Oscar. ■ 79761 #048-02-1957 L1957 **D** *071 †15
NEERUKONDA, Shanti Kiran. 501 GOLDER AVE, STE 202-A 79761 #495-57-1979 L1996 **IM** *020 †20
NEWCOTT, Eric Kristin. ■ 79762 #051-07-2006 L2006 **GS** *100
NGUYEN, Vinh Huu. 4241 TANGLEWOOD LN, STE 101 79762 #038-45-1992 L2002 **IM PD** *020 †20,55
NICOLETTE, Charles Carey. 500 W 4TH ST 79761 #038-40-1964 L1974 **R** *020 †80
NIETO, Carlos, Jr. 701 W 5TH ST, STE 3174 79763 #048-13-1975 L1975 **PD** *020 †55
NUR, Adriana Elizabeth. 500 W 4TH ST, MEDICAL CENTER HOSPITAL 79761 #264-09-1992 L2007 **IM** *020 †20
OGOGOR, Nkechi S. ■ 79763 #019-02-2007 **OBG** *012
OH, Jonathan Chun. 301 N WASHINGTON AVE 79761 #048-12-1997 L1998 **OBG** *020 †30
O'HEARN, Daniel John. 315 GOLDER AVE 79761 #005-14-1976 L1980 **IM** *020 †20
OLANO, Arrel Silva, Jr. 701 W 5TH ST 79763 #748-08-1994 L2005 **IM** *020 †20
ONG, Marichi Oracion. 800 W 4TH ST 79763 #748-01-1995 **FP** *012
ORACION, Renato Marquez. 808 TOWER DR, STE 3 79761 #748-10-1981 L2002 **D** *020 †15
OUD, Lavi. 800 W 4TH ST, TEXAS TECH HSC 79763 #550-03-1989 L1999 **CCM** *020 †20
PAMGANAMAMULA, M. 515 ADAMS AVE 79761 #495-21-1990 L2000 **IM** *020 †20
PANDA, Vandana. 800 W 4TH ST 79763 #495-29-2002 **FP** *012
PAREKH, Manaharlal C. 601 GOLDER AVE 79761 #495-19-1960 L1972 **GS OS** *020 †85
PARK, Jung Won. 701 W 5TH ST STE 3174 79763 #583-01-1971 L1986 **PD PN** *040 †55
PARK, Seung Hoi. 701 W 5TH ST, TX TECH UNIV HLTH SCI CTR 79763 #583-03-1987 L2000 **IM** *020 †20
PATEL, Kaushal Ishverbhai. 800 W 4TH ST, TX TECH UNIV HLTH SCI CTR 79763 #495-22-2000 L2005 **FM** *020 †18
PATEL, Nayankumar Amrutbh. 500 W 4TH ST, MEDICAL CENTER HOSPITAL 79761 #496-41-1997 L2007 **IM** *020 †20
PATEL, Rajesh Janakray. 601 GOLDER AVE # B 79761 #495-23-1976 L1986 **IM IMG** *020 †20
PATEL, Sanjaykumar P. 520 E 6TH ST, ODESSA REGIONAL HOSPITAL 79761 #495-23-1991 L2004 **NPM** *020 †55
PERLMAN, Jeffrey Howard. 318 N ALLEGHANEY AVE, STE 300 79761 #041-12-1982 L1998 **END IM** *020 †20
PHILLIPS, Dewayne Kenneth. ■ 79768 #048-02-1957 L1957 **P** *020 †75
PIETILA, Richard John. 410 N HANCOCK AVE 79761 #046-01-1978 L1979 **OBG** *020 †30
PIRZADA, Faisal Amir. 500 W 4TH ST, MEDICAL CENTER HOSPITAL 79761 #704-25-1994 L1999 **IM** *020 †20
PIRZADA, Noreen Faisal. 701 W 5TH ST, TEXAS TECH UNIV HSC 79763 #704-20-1999 **FP** *012
PORAT, Shimshon. 701 W 5TH ST 79763 #550-02-1984 L1994 **PD ID** *020 †55
PORTER, Kevin Eric. 2453 E 11TH ST 79761 #020-02-1995 L1998 **OS** *020
PRASAD, Kalpana Kumari. 601 E 2ND ST, STE A 79761 #495-15-1997 L2002 **IM** *020 †20
RAJA, Pillarisetty Guru. 405 N TOM GREEN AVE 79761 #495-62-1984 L1997 **OBG** *020 †30
RAJOLI, Naveen. 701 W 5TH ST, DEPT OF FAMILY MED 79763 #495-58-1998 **FP** *012
RAMANATHAN, Chittur V. 500 ADAMS AVE, STE 800 79761 #495-16-1974 L1977 **FM FPG** *020 †18
RAMIREZ, Henry. 800 W 4TH ST 79763 #308-13-2004 **OBG** *012
RAMOS, Victor. 540 W 5TH ST, STE 330 79761 #737-01-1978 L1997 **PD** *072 †55
RAMSEY, Michael L. 221 N LINCOLN AVE, WEST TEXAS SPINE 79761 #048-04-1994 L1995 **OSS** *020 †40
RAO, U Prabhakar. 500 ADAMS AVE STE 700 79761 #495-04-1969 L1980 **GE IM** *020 †20
RAO, Vivek U. 500 ADAMS AVE STE 300, STE 300 79761 #048-12-2001 L2003 **AI** *020 †20,03
RASTOGI, Anjana. ■ 79765 #496-10-1985 L1999 **IM** *020 †20
RATHBUN, Edwin David. 3051 E UNIVERSITY BLVD 79762 #019-02-1962 L1987 **FM** *020 †18
REDDI, Sanjay Puttam. 2453 E 11TH ST, PBOMS 79761 #011-02-2001 L2007 *020
REDDY, Rajani. 611 GOLDER AVE 79761 #495-70-1974 L1979 **PD** *020 †55
REDDY, Varadareddy T. 613 GOLDER AVE 79761 #495-04-1971 L1978 **R** *020 †80
REILLY, William Geo, Jr. 1340 E 7TH ST 79761 #010-02-1985 L1992 **ORS OSM** *020 †40
REINER, Irvin Judeah. 701 W 5TH ST 79763 #021-05-1954 L1960 **OBG** *040 †30 ‡
RHIM, Hae Ran. 1157 E 42ND ST 79762 #583-01-1986 L1997 **RHU** *020 †20
RIJHWANI, Tanuja Surendra. 800 W 4TH ST 79763 #496-47-1996 L2008 **IM** *012
RILEY, Steven Clayton. 1340 E 7TH ST 79761 #048-02-1985 L1986 **ORS** *020 †40
RIVERA, Eliseo. 701 W 5TH ST, TEXAS TECH UNIVERSITY HSC 79763 #042-02-1997 L2002 **OBG** *020 †30
RODENKO, George Nader. 500 W 4TH ST 79761 #048-02-1990 L1991 **DR** *020 †80
RODRIGUEZ, Ana Marina. 800 W 4TH ST 79763 #341-03-2000 **OBG** *012
RUSSOL, Frederick Jos. ■ 79761 #048-02-1977 L1977 **IM** *020
SABA, John Louis. 601 N TOM GREEN AVE, STE B 79761 #028-34-1971 L1978 **U GS** *020 †95
SAFIYEH, Majed Fathi. 800 W 4TH ST 79763 #605-04-2005 **IM** *012
SALAHUDDIN, None. 800 W 4TH ST 79763 #704-27-2000 **IM** *012
SALCEDO, Eduardo. 800 W 4TH ST 79763 #264-18-1988 L2007 **FM** *100 †18
SALCIDO, Francisco J. 710 E 6TH ST 79761 #048-15-1998 L2001 **FM** *020 †18
SANFORD, Scott. 318 N ALLEGHANEY AVE, STE 100 79761 #048-04-1972 L1972 **IM** *020 †20
SAXENA, Shilpa Manoj. 701 W 5TH ST 79763 #496-55-1999 **FP** *012
SAYEED, Asfia Aariz. 800 W 4TH ST 79763 #496-27-2003 **FP** *012
SHAKIL, Jawairia. 800 W 4TH ST 79763 #704-02-2004 **IM** *012
SHARIFI, Mohsen. 701 W 5TH ST # 3106, HLTH SCIENCE 79763 #305-01-1990 L1990 **IC CD** *020 †20
SHEEHAN, James Alfred. ■ 79762 #067-01-1971 L1980 **DR** *020 †80
SHEIKH, Samia Sajid. 701 W 5TH ST, TEXAS TECH UNIV HEALTH SCI 79763 #704-06-1993 **IM** *012
SHELTON, Michael Vise. 4222 WENDOVER AVE, STE 600 79762 #048-02-1977 L1977 **EM FM** *020 †18
SHERIDAN-SHAYEB, Eileen L. 840 W CLEMENTS ST 79763 #649-02-1990 L1994 **PD** *020 †55
SIDDIQUI, Atif Saleem. 800 W 4TH ST 79763 #704-02-2004 **IM** *012
SIMMONS, Michael Duane. 500 W 4TH ST 79761 #028-03-1964 L1970 **EM GP** *020 †16
SKILLERN, Amanda Annemari. ■ 79762 #048-15-2006 **OBG** *012
SLOOP, Gregory Dean. 520 E 6TH ST 79761 #021-05-1989 L2006 **PTH** *020 †50
SOLIS, Wanda I. 613 N TOM GREEN AVE 79761 #042-03-1980 L2001 **PD** *020 †55
SPEAR, David Scott. 500 W 4TH ST 79761 #025-07-1985 L1991 **EM IM** *020 †16
STEPHENS, Charles Anthon. ■ 79762 #048-02-1954 L1954 **OBG** *071 †30
SUBRAMANIAM, Venkatesh. 701 W 5TH ST, HEALTH SCIENCE 79763 #495-59-1987 **IM** *100
TALBERT, Anthony Lyle. 701 W 5TH ST, STE 3174 79763 #033-05-1969 L1986 **NPM PD** *020 †55
TAMAR, Kyron C. 701 W 5TH ST, STE 3212 79763 #035-08-1975 L1981 **GS VS** *020 †85
TANG, Sujie. 800 W 4TH ST 79763 #243-46-1994 **IM** *012
TATE, Harold Austin. 500 W 4TH ST, DEPT OF RADIOLOGY 79761 #010-03-1990 L2003 **DR** *020 †80
THANGAM, Shanthi. 511 N ALLEGHANEY AVE 79761 #496-22-1991 L1999 **P CHP** *020 †75
THEODORE, Gregory Geo. 3308 LANCEWOOD LN 79762 #033-06-1986 L1990 **AN** *020 †05
TIERNEY, Ralph Chas. ■ 79761 #038-41-1956 L1967 **PDC** *071 †55
TOLIA, Kamal Nalin. 6005 EASTRIDGE RD, STE 110 79762 #495-23-1966 L1983 **GYN FM** *020
TOLIA, Nalin Harilal. 6005 EASTRIDGE RD STE 100 79762 #495-23-1966 L1974 **OPH** *020 †35
TURNER, Jack Lee. ■ 79765 #048-04-1946 L1946 **OTO** *075 †45
TURNER, Thomas Chas. 848 CENTRAL DR 79761 #048-12-1976 L1976 **OPH** *020 †35
UDDIN, Mohd. Rakib. 800 W 4TH ST 79763 #160-02-1996 **FP** *012
UMESH, Harsha Sira. 800 W 4TH ST 79763 #495-99-2003 **IM** *012
UNRUH, Terry Max. 4222 WENDOVER AVE STE 800 79762 #021-01-1983 L1985 **GS** *020 †85
USHER, Elenita Loreni. 800 W 4TH ST 79763 #429-01-1996 **FP** *012
USMAN, Umara. 701 W 5TH ST, DEPT OF FAMILY MED 79763 #704-24-1999 **FP** *012
UY, Sing Dy. 2461 E 11TH ST STE A 79761 #748-01-1973 L1981 **PD IM** *020 †20,55
VADDIREDDY, Vijayalakshmi. 800 W 4TH ST 79763 #495-27-1996 L2007 **FP** *012
VALENZUELA, Peter M. 701 W 5TH ST, TEXAS TECH UNIVERSITY HSC- 79763 #048-12-1998 L1999 **FM** *020 †18
VANDERLEE, Margaret Gail. 701 W 5TH ST 79763 #048-04-1980 L1980 **GYN OBS** *020 †30
VELASCO, Andres Felipe. 701 W 5TH ST 79763 #264-12-2000 L2005 **FM** *020 †18
VEMURU, Ravikumar P. 315 E 5TH ST 79761 #495-50-1980 L1993 **GE IM** *020 †20
VENATI, Girikumar. 800 W 4TH ST, TX TECH UNIV HLTH SCI CTR 79763 #495-11-1999 L2007 **IM** *020 †20
VILLANUEVA, Noel F. 850 TOWER DR, STE 111 79761 #748-10-1971 L1995 **GS** *020 †85
VILLAROMAN, Leo De La Paz. 800 W 4TH ST 79763 #748-01-1998 L2008 **FP** *012
VINDHYA, Prem Kumar Chand. 155 SE LOOP 338 STE 500 79762 #495-50-1972 L1983 **AN PME** *020 †05
VINDHYA, Prema Latha. 2479 E 11TH ST 79761 #495-50-1971 L1985 **D** *020
VIZCARRA, Rosa I.. 701 W 5TH ST, TEXAS TECH FAMILY MEDICINE 79763 #649-23-1996 L2008 **FPG** *100 †18
VUELVAS, Johnny Joe. ■ 79764 #048-12-2007 **PD** *012

■ = Address Information Privacy Protected

WALLACE, Joe Long. 3001 W UNIVERSITY BLVD 79764 #048-12-1976 L1978 **AN** *020 †05
WAN, Christine. 4222 WENDOVER AVE, STE 600 79762 #048-02-1997 L1999 **FM** *020 †18 ‡
WEBB, Robert Terrell. 500 W 4TH ST 79761 #048-12-1976 L1990 **EM** *020 †16
WEBER, Samuel Coleman. 500 W 4TH ST 79761 #047-06-1965 L1970 **OTO** *020 †45
WEINTHAL, Joel Adam. 301 N WASHINGTON AVE 79761 #035-01-1985 L1995
  PHO PD *020 †55
WHITTEN, John Wesley, Jr. 315 GOLDER AVE 79761 #048-02-1976 L1976 **IM IMG** *020 †20
WIEHLE, Steven P. 225 N LINCOLN AVE 79761 #039-01-1976 L1977 **U** *020 †95
WILLIAMS, Tamrasha. 500 W 4TH ST, MEDICAL CENTER HOSPITAL 79761 #048-13-1988 L1989
  AN *020 †05
WILLOUGHBY, Marta Gay. 500 W 4TH ST, MEDICAL CENTER HOSPITAL 79761
  #032-01-2002 L2005 **EM** *020 †16
WONG, Kendall H. 318 N ALLEGHANEY AVE, STE 300 79761 #016-43-1994 L1997 **IM** *020 †20
YALAVARTHI, Ranganayaki. 540 W 5TH ST # 460, STE 460 79761 #495-70-1978 L1982
  PD *020 †55
YALAVARTHI, Surendra Babu. 419 W 4TH ST # 200 79761 #495-50-1972 L1985 **IM** *020 †20
ZEECK, Phillip Robt. 500 N WASHINGTON AVE # 400 79761 #048-04-1963 L1963 **ORS** *020 †40

OLMITO – CAMERON

LENZ, Paul Albert. 7100 OLD ALICE RD 78575 #065-10-1985 L1995 **GP OM** *020

OLMOS PARK – BEXAR

GONZALES, Monica V. ■ 78212 #010-01-2005 L2007 *020
HACKER, Hope Schuyler. ■ 78212 #035-20-1984 L1999 **PM PD** *020 †60
WILLIAMSON, John Albert. ■ 78212 #048-04-1954 L1954 **ORS** *071 †40

OLNEY – YOUNG

FAZEL, Mohammed Reza. 107 S AVENUE M 76374 #517-03-1971 L1981 **TS GS** *020
MANKINS, Mark Lester. 306 W MAIN ST 76374 #048-15-1985 L1986 **FM EM** *020 †18
MOORE, David Swaney. ■ 76374 #016-06-1963 L1967 **FM** *071
SORLEY, Carolyn Green. 306 W MAIN ST 76374 #048-13-1989 L1990 **FM** *020 †18

ORANGE – ORANGE

ALLEN, Rollie Edward. ■ 77630 #039-01-1953 L1955 **GP GS** *071
BRANSFORD, Paris Patrick. 610 STRICKLAND DR, STE 130 77630 #048-12-1987 L1989
  CD IM *020 †20
BYERLY, Robert R. 610 STRICKLAND DR, STE 200 77630 #048-14-1998 L2003 **PD** *020 †55
CANTU, Philip Martinez. 2 PUTNAM AVE 77630 #048-12-1993 L1997 **APM** *020 †05
CASTELLANOS, Miguel E. 610 STRICKLAND DR, STE 130 77630 #649-14-1981 L1991
  CD IM *062 †20
CHEN, Frank K. 608 STRICKLAND DR 77630 #048-14-1990 L1991 **AN** *020
CHEN-HAH, Marian M. 610 STRICKLAND DR STE 290 77630 #048-13-1991 L1995 **IM** *020 †20
CHUKWUEKE, Theophilus O. 2801 MACARTHUR DR, STE B 77630 #041-13-1990 L1998
  OPH *020
CLOUD, James P. 1309 W PARK AVE 77630 #017-20-1950 L1956 **ORS** *071 †40
COX, Robert D. 610 STRICKLAND DR, STE 170 77630 #048-14-1990 L1991 **FM** *020 †18
DAY, Charles Steven. 608 STRICKLAND DR 77630 #048-02-1977 L1977 **DR NM** *020 †80
EASTMAN, George L. 1001 W ELM ST 77630 #021-05-1951 L1953 **GP GS** *020
EBEAD, Samir S. 3009 MACARTHUR DR 77630 #915-02-1965 L1986 **OAR** *020
FISETTE, Roderick John. 608 STRICKLAND DR 77630 #021-05-1969 L1970 **FM** *020
GORDON, Victoria Juda. 610 STRICKLAND DR STE 340 77630 #048-13-1994 L1996
  FM *020 †18
HABABAG, Manuel Bercasio. 3321 RIDGEMONT DR 77630 #748-08-1977 L1994 **FM** *020 †18
HAH, Wilbur W. 610 STRICKLAND DR, STE 290 77630 #048-13-1990 L1992 **OTO FPS** *020 †45
HSU, Michael K. 3212 CONCORD ST, STE G 77630 #048-02-1985 L1986 **GS TRS** *020 †85
INGRAM, Robert A. ■ 77630 #048-02-1951 L1951 **FM OS** *071 †18
JONES, David R. 610 STRICKLAND DR 77630 #048-15-1992 L1993 **PM** *020 †60
JONES, James Burton. 2607 WESTERN AVE 77630 #048-02-1965 L1965 **FM ADM** *020 †18
JONES, Roland Ward, III. ■ 77630 #048-07-1975 L1977 **FM** *075
KUSNOOR, Vijay Shriniwas. 610 STRICKLAND DR, STE 130 77630 #496-38-1969 L1979
  PDC CD *020 †55
LE BLANC, Nolan Jos. 505 LANSING ST 77630 #048-02-1958 L1958 **PD** *071
MAZZOLA, Steven David. 610 STRICKLAND DR, STE 260 77630 #048-02-1983 L1983
  IM CCM *020 †20
MC INTIRE, Louis V, Jr. 610 STRICKLAND DR, STE 200 77630 #048-14-1985 L1986 **FM** *020 †18
MEDRANO, Leonides Ponce. 3321 RIDGEMONT DR 77630 #748-08-1977 L1994 **PD** *020 †55
MOHEB, Ramin. 610 STRICKLAND DR, STE 380 77630 #028-34-1996 L2000 **OBG** *020 †30
NGUYEN, Dang Dinh. 18638 HIGHWAY 62 S 77630 #654-01-2003 L2006 **FM** *020 †18
OKPEKI, Annette O. 1301 W PARK AVE, STE C 77630 #690-06-1991 L2003 **PD** *020 †55
OLIVER, Dionne Davidia. 610 STRICKLAND DR, STE 280 77630 #048-04-2001 L2005 **OBG** *020
PARKER, Anne B. 77632 #048-14-1990 L1991 **FM** *100
PARKER, Calvin Rawles. 610 STRICKLAND DR, STE 340 77630 #048-13-1995 L1996
  FM *020 †18
PRETZ, Earnest C. ■ 77631 #048-02-1950 L1950 **GP** *071
RUTLEDGE, Wm Martin, Jr. 610 STRICKLAND DR, STE 200 77630 #048-14-1979 L1979
  FM *020 †18
SARDA, Felipe Antonio. 909 12TH ST 77630 #429-01-1974 L2001 **PD** *030 †20
SOTOLONGO, Rodolfo Pablo. 610 STRICKLAND DR, STE 130 77630 #847-05-1975 L1983
  IM HS *020 †20
STUNTZ, Billie J Williams. 608 STRICKLAND DR 77630 #048-12-1953 L1953 **PD** *071
STUNTZ, Homer C. ■ 77630 #048-12-1952 L1952 **GP** *071
TALATI, Bimalkumar A. ■ 77632 #495-23-1987 L2004 **IM** *020 †20
TOWNSEND, Amy Michelle. 610 STRICKLAND DR STE 1 77630 #048-02-2003 L2006
WALDREP, Jamie Marie. 250 STRICKLAND DR 77630 #048-04-2002 L2006 **PD** *020 †55
WEINTRAUB, Ronald Alan. 608 STRICKLAND DR 77630 #048-13-1991 L1993 **AN** *020
WILLIAMS, Howard C. 1301 W PARK AVE, PARK AVE MEDICAL CENTER 77630
  #048-04-1952 L1952 **FM** *020

ORE CITY – UPSHUR

BAGHERIAN KHARRATY, Vahid. 720 US HIGHWAY 259 S 75683 #517-03-1971 L1982
  GP NP *020 †50
WHITMAN, Rodger Austin. RR 1 BOX 214B 75683 #065-06-1948 L1979 **FM** *020

OVERTON – RUSK

HAMILTON, James M. 304 N MOTLEY DR 75684 #021-05-1952 L1956 **GP** *020 †18
HOLM, Leo M, Jr. 116 E SOUTH ST, OVERTON FAMILY PRACTICE CE 75684 #048-14-1997 L1998
  FM *020 †18

OVILLA – ELLIS

PENDERY, Harry Hugh. ■ 75154 #047-06-1966 L1967 **GP AM** *020
WALKER, Randolph T. 103 SLIPPERY ROCK CT 75154 #048-13-1988 L1989 **AN PME** *020 †05

PALACIOS – MATAGORDA

EMANUEL, Raphael John D. 1519 4TH ST 77465 #539-04-1968 L1977 **FM P** *020

PALESTINE – ANDERSON

AHRENDT, Deborah Kay. 750 N US HIGHWAY 287 75803 #048-02-1979 L1979
  DR PDR *020 †80
AMOS, Joseph Edward. ■ 75803 #048-02-2008 *012
BATES, Stephen Jos. 115 MEDICAL DR 75801 #048-12-1979 L1979 **OBG** *020 †30
BENNETT, Chas Virgil, Jr. 126 MEDICAL DR, STE A 75801 #047-06-1975 L1983
  GYN OBG *020 †30
BENTLEY, George Newell. 127 MEDICAL DR, GLEN GOLDSMITH 75801 #048-02-1980 L1980
  GS *020 †85
BLACKWELL, Robert Gene. 115 MEDICAL DR 75801 #048-15-1982 L1983 **OBG** *020 †30
BORSTAD, Gregory Clark. 2217 S SYCAMORE ST 75801 #037-01-1998 L2006 **RHU** *020 †20
BOWEN, Johnny Lee. 2900 S LOOP 256, PALESTINE REGIONAL MED CTR 75801
  #048-15-1983 L1983 **ATP** *075 †50
BRAZEAL, Brad Alan. 4002 S LOOP 256, STE R 75801 #048-02-1991 L1993 **P** *020 †75
BROWN, Tarsha Michele. 2217 S SYCAMORE ST, STE 101 75801 #024-05-1996 L2000
  IM *020 †20
BUTLER, Roger Gary. 4002 S LOOP 256, STE R 75801 #039-01-1984 L1986 **P** *020 †75
CAROTHERS, Curtis Jay. 3215 W OAK ST, STE 120 75801 #048-15-2001 L2003 **CD** *012 †20
CHICK, Thomas Wesley. 3201 S LOOP 256, STE 120 75801 #004-01-1965 L1967
  IM PUD *020 †20
CLOPTON, Christopher D. 3415 S LOOP 256, PALESTINE CANCER CENTER 75801
  #020-12-1981 L2001 **RO** *020 †80
COE, Relvert Jewell, Jr. 2217 S SYCAMORE ST, STE 101 75801 #021-05-1989 L1991
DUNDAS, Charles G, Jr. 4201 S LOOP 256 75801 #048-04-1988 L1989 **FM** *020 †18
FALCONER, Robert James. 123 MEDICAL DR, STE A 75801 #539-06-1995 L2002
  GS VS *020 †85
FRENCH, Delaney D. 4201 S LOOP 256 75801 #048-13-1988 L1989 **FM** *020 †18
GARCIA, Michael P. 111 MEDICAL DR # 1663 75801 #048-02-1999 L2002 **PD** *020 †55
GOLDSMITH, Glen Ray. 127 MEDICAL DR 75801 #048-12-1979 L1979 **U** *020 †95
GORBY, Michael Sydnor. 126 MEDICAL DR STE B 75801 #048-12-1982 L1983 **IM CCM** *020 †20
HANLEY, Michael Jos. 2900 S LOOP 256 75801 #035-46-1972 L1975 **ORS** *020 †20,40
ISOM, Matthew J. 115 MEDICAL DR, OB/GYN ASSOC OF E TEXAS 75801 #018-75-1999,
  ▲ L2006 **OBG** *020 †30
JACKSON, James Don. ■ 75801 #010-03-1951 L1956 **U GP** *071
JOHNSON, Shelby Eugene. 1920 S LOOP 256 75801 #048-02-1972 L1972 **PME FM** *020
JORDAN, Curtis Rudolph. 2010 CROCKETT RD # A 75801 #048-02-1955 L1955 **GP GS** *071
KANCHARLA, Asha. 4002 S LOOP 256 75801 #495-50-1993 L2002 **APM** *020
KING, Cynthia Anne. 2900 S LOOP 256 75801 #048-02-1993 L1995 **DR** *020 †80
KLEIN, John M, III. 4201 S LOOP 256 75801 #048-12-2001 L2003 **FM** *020 †18
KNOWLES, Heidi C. 2900 S LOOP 256, PALESTINE REGIONAL MEDICAL 75801
  #048-14-2003 L2006 **EM** *020 †16
KORMAN, David Joel. 3320 S LOOP 256 75801 #048-12-1983 L1983 **P** *020 †75
KUYKENDALL, Ken Ellison. ■ 75803 #048-12-1963 L1963 **OS GS** *020 †85
LAW, Alec B. 3201 S LOOP 256, STE 130 75801 #048-02-1980 L1980 **IM** *020 †20
LOVE, Kenneth Carroll. 214 SHADOW WOOD DR, TDCJ BOYD FACILITY 75801
  #048-14-1974 L1974 **GP** *020
LUCE, Patricia Harper. 111 MEDICAL DR, PEDIATRIC ASSOCIATION 75801 #021-06-1991 L1995
  PD *020 †55
MATHIS, Lee R, Jr. 919 S MAGNOLIA ST 75801 #048-02-1953 L1953 **GP GS** *071 †85
MATHIS, Lucy Edenborough. 4000 S LOOP 256 75801 #041-07-1954 L1959 **ATP PTH** *071
MATLAGE, William Theodore. ■ 75801 #048-02-1942 L1942 **PUD** *071
MC COLLOUGH, Martha Lynn. 3215 W OAK ST, STE 105 75801 #041-13-1979 L1994
  D DMP *020 †15
MC FARLANE, Robert Finley. 3201 S LOOP 256, STE 110 75801 #024-01-1978 L1984
  CD IM *020 †20
MEYERS, Jamie Foster. 1721 S SYCAMORE ST 75801 #028-46-1991 L1993 **OS** *020
MILLIGAN, Edward Jos. 321 E SPRING ST, STE 121 75801 #021-05-1983 L1994 **OTO** *020 †45
MILLS, Allen Forbes. 4201 S LOOP 256 75801 #048-12-1985 L1987 **FM** *020 †18
MORRIS, Elizabeth S. 3215 W OAK ST, STE 105 75801 #048-02-1999 L2003 **D** *020 †15 ‡
NEWTON, Jerry Albrecht. 127 MEDICAL DR 75801 #048-12-1973 L1973 **U** *020 †95
O'DONNELL, John Gary. 3201 S LOOP 256, STE 170 75801 #048-12-1977 L1977 **IM** *020 †20
PACKARD, Russell Calvert. 3201 S LOOP 256, STE 140 75801 #005-15-1971 L2002
  N P *020 †75 ‡
PARKHURST, Gary M. 404 N MAGNOLIA ST 75801 #048-02-1988 L1989 **FM** *020 †18
PHONSOMBAT, Supranee. 2031 CROCKETT RD 75801 #891-02-1970 L1978 **OBG** *020
PUVVADA, Lakshmi M. 4002 S LOOP 256 75801 #495-58-1980 L2006 **AI PD** *020 †55,03
PUVVADA, Nandan Kumar. 4002 S LOOP 256 75801 #495-50-1977 L2006 **GS VS** *020 †85
PYLE, Robert Glen. 2217 S SYCAMORE ST 75801 #048-12-1985 L1986 **END IM** *020 †20

RICHARDS, Donald A. 3415 S LOOP 256 75801 #048-13-1983 L1985 **HEM ON** *020 †20
ROSS, John Marvin. 111 MEDICAL DR 75801 #041-13-1982 L1994 **PD** *020 †55
SALTER, Carolyn Frances. 126 MEDICAL DR 75801 #048-12-1981 L1981 **GP AN** *074 †05
SHELMAN, Keith Benj. ■ 75801 #041-02-1983 L1987 **IM** *020 †20
SHILLER, Alan D. 3323 S LOOP 256 75801 #048-02-1989 L1990 **OPH** *020 †35
SKREPNEK, Stan Victor. 2010 CROCKETT RD, STE A 75801 #060-01-1957 L1978 **GP** *020
SMITH, Alan D. 3201 S LOOP 256 75801 #048-78-1982, ▲ L1983 **FM** *075
SOLIS, Tanya Michelle. 4002 S LOOP 256, STE K 75801 #033-05-1997 L2002 **APM PM** *020 †60
THOMPSON, David Lee. 4002 S LOOP 256, STE A 75801 #048-12-1981 L1981 **IM** *020 †20
WARDELL, Davida Jones. 111 MEDICAL DR, PEDIATRIC ASSOC 75801 #047-07-2000 L2003 **PD** *020 †55 ‡
WEST, Kendall Aulton. 712 W PALESTINE AVE 75801 #021-05-1958 L1962 **R** *072
WILDER, James F, Jr. 3415 S LOOP 256 75801 #036-05-1988 L1996 **RO** *020 †18
WILKERSON, James Edward. 3201 S LOOP 256, STE 160 75801 #011-02-1987 L1993 **CD IM** *020
WILKINSON, Lloyd Michael. 2217 S SYCAMORE ST 75801 #048-12-1982 L1983 **GE IM** *020 †20
WILLIAMS, Michael Lee. 321 E SPRING ST STE 129 75801 #010-03-1985 L1989 **IM** *020

PALMVIEW – HIDALGO

ALEGRIA, Aldo H. 2003 PALMVIEW DR, STE B 78572 #737-06-1968 L1977 **PD A** *020
BAZAN, Johnny Martin. 1337 W PALMA VISTA DR, STE A 78572 #737-06-1988 L1996 **IM PD** *020 †20,55
HERNANDEZ, Belinda B. ■ 78572 #048-13-2007 **IM** *012
LAKSHMI, Kondapavuluru. 7410 W EXPWY 83 78572 #495-50-1976 L1984 **IM** *020
VILLALTA, Carlos Roberto. 204 N PALMVIEW DR, STE A 78572 #649-14-1976 L1993 **PD** *020

PAMPA – GRAY

BECK, Wilhelmina Paula. ■ 79065 #660-04-1952 L1970 **GP OS** *071
BHATIA, Laxman. 100 W 30TH AVE, STE 106 79065 #495-30-1975 L1977 **IMG IM** *020 †20
GRABATO, Rene Pelaez. 2931 PERRYTON PKWY 79065 #748-01-1970 L1978 **U** *020
GRABATO, Teresita Q. ■ 79065 #748-01-1970 L1978 **PD** *020
HAMPTON, David Michael. 2931 PERRYTON PKWY 79065 #048-15-1983 L1983 **ORS** *020 †40
HAMPTON, Raymond M. 1 MEDICAL PLAZA 79065 #048-02-1947 L1947 **FM GS** *071 †18
HARROW, Bruce Ira. 408 W KINGSMILL AVE, STE 100 79065 #048-12-1980 L1980 **FM FPG** *020 †18
HISCOCK, Melinda J. 3023 PERRYTON PKWY, STE 202 79065 #048-04-1990 L1993 **OBG** *020 †30
HOFFER, Earl Carol. 112 WALNUT DR 79065 #001-02-1968 L1976 **FM EM** *020 †18
HOUGH, Rebecca Linn. 3023 PERRYTON PKWY, STE 206 79065 #048-15-2002 L2005 **PD** *020 †55
HOUGH, Robert Darrell. 3023 PERRYTON PKWY, STE 206 79065 #048-15-2003 L2007 **PD** *020
JULIAN, Robert Dale. 3023 PERRYTON PKWY, STE 101 79065 #048-14-1985 L1986 **FM PD** *020 †18
KAMNANI, Laxmichand. 104 E 30TH AVE 79065 #495-30-1975 L1977 **CD** *020 †20
KAMNANI, Nirmala. 104 E 30TH AVE, MED SURG DIAGNOSTIC CLINIC 79065 #495-30-1974 L1989 **IM** *020
LAYCOCK, Raymond W. ■ 79065 #047-06-1949 L1950 **FM OM** *071
LEE, Nam-Kyu. 3023 PERRYTON PKWY, STE 101 79065 #583-02-1972 L1976 **FM** *020 †18
MOHAN, Vijaya K. 104 E 30TH AVE 79065 #495-53-1964 L1978 **GS OS** *020 †85
MONTINOLA, Gloria T. 2416 DOGWOOD LN, P O BOX 1618 79065 #748-01-1970 L1977 **AN** *020
NGUYEN, Giang Tuong. 100 W 30TH AVE, STE 101 79065 #021-05-1998 L2002 **MPD** *020 †20,55
PAY, Adrian Philip. 3023 PERRYTON PKWY STE 201 79065 #019-02-1995 L2007 **IM** *020 †20
POWELL, Dan Clayton. 3023 PERRYTON PKWY, STE 101 79065 #048-13-1991 L1993 **FM** *020 †20
RINGEL, Stephen J. 107 W 30TH AVE 79065 #561-01-1970 L1993 **ORS EM** *020 †40
SIECK, Kevin D. 3023 PERRYTON PKWY, STE 101 79065 #048-15-1999 L2002 **IM** *020 †20
SILVER, Steven Leslie. 3023 PERRYTON PKWY 79065 #016-11-1974 L2003 **IM CD** *020 †20
SMITH, George J. 100 W 30TH AVE, STE 108 79065 #048-02-1992 L1994 **GS** *020
THAVARADHARA, Pathom. 100 W 30TH AVE 79065 #891-01-1972 L2004 **PUD IM** *020 †20

PANTEGO – TARRANT

CHAO, Chun-Huai. ■ 76013 #048-15-2000 L2004 **AN** *100 †05
HARDY, Sarah L. ■ 76013 #048-78-2007, ▲ **P** *012
MC CONNELL, Richard F, Jr. 3008 W PARK ROW DR STE B 76013 #048-02-1971 L1971 **AI PUD** *020 †55,03
SHAH, Syed Akhtar Ali. 2102 ROOSEVELT DR 76013 #704-01-1954 L1977 **IM N** *020
STONE, Frederic Albert. ■ 76013 #035-45-1952 L1954 **GS PHP** *071 †85

PARIS – LAMAR

ALVAREZ-MENDOZA, Antonio. PO BOX 100 75461 #649-26-1977 L1996 **PP** *020 †50
ANAND, Rajiv. 575 DESHONG DR, STE B 75460 #496-09-1978 L1989 **OPH** *020 †35
BAGWELL, Jerry Glyn. RR 6 BOX 210 75462 #048-21-1956 L1963 **GP** *071 †30
BALL, Linda J. 3150 CLARKSVILLE ST SU 75460 #048-78-1993, ▲ L1995 **FM** *020 †18
BANDEL, Phillip Bowes. 820 CLARKSVILLE ST 75460 #021-05-1971 L1978 **D DS** *020 ‡
BEDEKAR, Ajay Ranjan. 1055 CLARKSVILLE ST STE 11 75460 #026-04-2000 L2006 **PCC** *020 †20
BELLAMY, Earl De Laine. ■ 75460 #048-02-1957 L1957 **OPH** *071 †35
BERCHER, Paul Richard. 1055 CLARKSVILLE ST # 200 75460 #004-01-1966 L1970 **GP** *020
BOATNER, John Stevens. 3015 NE LOOP 286 75460 #048-02-1967 L1967 **R** *020 †80
BROCK, David Carl. 2870 LEWIS LN 75460 #028-02-1967 L1973 **PD** *071 †55
BROWN, Martha Gash. 820 CLARKSVILLE ST 75460 #039-01-1983 L1997 **PD** *020 †55
BRYANT, Thomas Floyd, Jr. 2850 LEWIS LN 75460 #048-02-1963 L1963 **AN PUD** *071 †05
BURNS, Stephen James. 3737 LAMAR AVE, STE 300 75460 #048-12-1983 L1983 **FM** *072 †18
CALLANAN, David Gordon. 575 DESHONG DR, STE B 75460 #018-03-1983 L1984 **OPH** *020 †35
CAMPBELL, Mark Robt. 420 N COLLEGIATE DR, STE 300 75460 #048-14-1979 L1979 **GS** *020 †85

CARPENTER, David Allen. 2850 LEWIS LN 75460 #048-02-1972 L1972 **OBG** *020 †30
CHADWICK, Tuesday Lea. 2870 LEWIS LN, STE 218 75460 #048-02-1997 L2001 **OBG** *020 †30
CLARK, George Edward, III. 3150 CLARKSVILLE ST, STE 100 75460 #048-04-1976 L1976 **PD** *020 †55
CLIFFORD, James Lee. ■ 75462 #048-12-1950 L1950 **RO** *071 †80
CLIFFORD, Philip Ward. 3015 NE LOOP 286 75460 #048-04-1975 L1975 **R** *020 †80
CLIFFORD, Steven J. 3015 NE LOOP 286 75460 #048-04-1981 L1981 **DR** *020 †80
CLIFFORD, Yvette B. 801 CLARKSVILLE ST STE C 75460 #048-12-1993 L1994 **PD** *020 †50
COCHRAN, E Winston, Jr. 3550 NE LOOP 286, PARIS REGIONAL CANCER CENT 75460 #048-02-1978 L1978 **ON IM** *020 †20
COORS, Lori Ellen. 575 DESHONG DR, STE B 75460 #034-01-1999 L2005 **OPH** *020 †35
CRUMPLER, Toby Don. 170 8TH ST SE, STE C 75460 #004-01-1973 L1978 **GS** *020 †85
CRUZ, Manuel Wilfrido. 1025 DESHONG DR 75460 #024-05-1991 L1999 **CD IM** *020 †20
CUTRELL, Martin Thos, III. 3150 CLARKSVILLE ST, STE 100 75460 #048-12-1977 L1977 **PD** *020 †55
DE LA GARZA, David J. 1000 CLARKSVILLE ST 75460 #048-12-1995 L1999 **ORS** *020 †40
DICKEY, William Daryl. 2870 LEWIS LN, STE 230 75460 #048-02-1985 L1992 **GE IM** *050 †20
DUNNINGTON, Glenn Walter. 820 CLARKSVILLE ST 75460 #039-01-1966 L1979 **U** *020 †95 ‡
DURHAM, John D. 1128 CLARKSVILLE ST, STE 100 75460 #048-15-1995 L1997 **FM** *020 †18
ELIZ, Julian S. 1055 CLARKSVILLE ST, STE 165 75460 #847-09-1968 L2006 **CD IM** *020 †20
EMMITE, Joseph Phillip. 3065 ASPEN 75462 #028-34-1962 L1964 **IM** *071 †20
ERICKSON, Rick E. 1001 E AUSTIN ST 75460 #048-14-1994 L1999 **OTO HNS** *020 †45
FISH, Gary Edd. 575 DESHONG DR, STE B 75460 #048-12-1972 L1978 **OPH** *020 †35
FULLER, Dwain Gordon. 575 DESHONG DR, STE B 75460 #048-04-1966 L1966 **OPH OS** *020 †35
GIBBS, Marvin Kelsey. 2870 LEWIS LN 75460 #048-04-1971 L1971 **GS** *020 †85
GRAVES, Mark Steven. 1235 NE LOOP 286 75460 #039-01-1985 L1989 **OPH EM** *020 †35
GREEN, Amanda Davis. 635 STONE AVE 75460 #048-04-1998 L2003 **IM** *020 †20
GREEN, Gregory Vance. 3435 NE LOOP 286 75460 #048-04-1998 L2003 **ORS** *020 †40
GROSSNICKLE, Richard Dean. 2615 NE LOOP 286 75460 #048-12-1976 L1976 **OPH** *020 †35
GRUBB, Geoffrey Thos. 2880 BONHAM ST, PARIS NEUROSCIENCE CLINIC 75460 #048-02-1971 L1971 **P FM** *020
GULDE, James E. 635 STONE AVE 75460 #048-15-1996 L1997 **IM** *020 †20
GUNDER, Adam L. 820 CLARKSVILLE ST 75460 #048-15-2001 L2002 **IM** *020
HASHMI, Arjunand Farid. 1128 CLARKSVILLE ST, STE 200 75460 #704-02-1986 L2006 **CD IM** *020 †20
HATLEY, Richard B. 865 DESHONG DR, MCCUISTION MEDICAL CENTER 75460 #048-13-1987 L1989 **AN** *020 †20
HAYDEN, Wm De Graffenried. 707 LAMAR AVE STE D 75460 #021-01-1953 L1957 **GS** *020
HOLLINGSWORTH, Harris B. 820 CLARKSVILLE ST 75460 #047-06-1970 L1975 **GS** *020 †85
HUNT, Harold Eugene. 150 8TH ST SE 75460 #048-12-1947 L1947 **OPH** *071 †35
JACKSON, Paul Thomas, Jr. 4550 LAMAR AVE STE 200 75462 #035-09-1994 L1997 **IM CD** *020 †20
JONES, Kyle E. 1055 CLARKSVILLE ST, STE 160 75460 #048-15-1996 L1999 **OM FM** *020 †18
JONES, Monica Denese. 3150 CLARKSVILLE ST, STE 100 75460 #048-15-1994 L1995 **PD** *074
JOST, Bradley Foster. 575 DESHONG DR, STE B 75460 #007-02-1979 L1980 **OPH** *020 †35
KILGORE, Terry Lynn. 2850 LEWIS LN, STE 10 75460 #027-01-1975 L1981 **IM PUD** *020 †20
LEDDY, Michael Dennis. 3150 CLARKSVILLE ST STE 10 75460 #048-13-1980 L1980 **IM AMI** *020
LE DERER, J Frederick. 865 DESHONG DR 75460 #048-12-1960 L1960 **U** *020 †95
LEE, Paul M. 2131 CLARKSVILLE ST 75460 #048-14-1988 L1992 **P** *020 †75
LEWIS, H Michael. 707 LAMAR AVE, STE C2 75460 #048-40-1975 L1992 **TS VS** *020 †85,90 ‡
LINN, David Kenneth. 1235 NE LOOP 286 75460 #010-01-1980 L1991 **OPH** *020 †35
LOQMAN, Nuveed. 1055 CLARKSVILLE ST, STE 110 75460 #160-02-1983 L2007 **PCC IM** *020 †20
LOVE, Lawrence Leslie. 1235 NE LOOP 286 75460 #011-02-1971 L1978 **OPH** *020 †35
LUI, Raphael Chun-Sing. 1055 CLARKSVILLE ST, STE 155 75460 #030-05-1980 L1999 **TS** *020 †90,85
MANN, Lawrence Earl. 3110 DOGWOOD LN 75460 #039-01-1954 L1958 **GYN** *071
MARRERO, Rafael Jorge. 1001 E AUSTIN ST 75460 #048-04-1991 L1993 **OTO HNS** *020 †45
MASSAR, Janna. 3150 CLARKSVILLE ST, STE 100 75460 #048-04-1996 L1998 **IM** *020 †20
MC LEMORE, Theodore L. 1055 CLARKSVILLE ST # 110, PARIS PULMONARY CLNC 75460 #048-04-1981 L1981 **PCC SME** *040 †20
MIESCH, David C. ■ 75460 #048-02-1951 L1951 **IM CD** *071 †20
MIESCH, Mary G. 945 S COLLEGIATE DR 75460 #048-02-1988 L1990 **OBG** *020 †30
NARDONE, Mark Christopher. 3435 NE LOOP 286, PARIS ORTHOPEDIC CLINIC 75460 #041-09-1967 L1969 **ORS PD** *071 †55,40 ‡
NEILSON, Jeffrey Chas. 1000 CLARKSVILLE ST 75460 #039-01-1984 L1985 **ORS** *020 †40
OWENS, Sherry L. ■ 75460 #048-13-1993 L1995 **PD** *020 †55
PARKHILL, Billy J, Jr. 3015 NE LOOP 286 75460 #048-12-1978 L1978 **DR NM** *020 †80
PHILLIPS, William Robt. 865 DESHONG DR 75460 #048-12-1963 L1963 **GS** *071 †85
PLUMMER, Jon Kirk. 1128 CLARKSVILLE ST 75460 #005-12-1967 L1994 **FM** *020 †18
PRESTON, Joseph K. 3435 NE LOOP 286, ALAMO NEUROSURGICAL INST. 75460 #048-12-1995 L2003 **NS** *020 †25
PROCTOR, Richard Owen. ■ 75462 #048-04-1964 L1964 **GPM PD** *040 †55,70
ROWE, Jerry Randal. 480 CLARKSVILLE ST, EMERGENCY ROOM 75460 #048-02-1999 L2000 **FM EM** *020 †18
ROWLAN, Steven Doyle. 820 CLARKSVILLE ST 75460 #039-01-1978 L1983 **ORS** *020 †40
RUNKE, Lawrence Carl. 1055 CLARKSVILLE ST, STE 155 75460 #007-02-1969 L1994 **GS** *020 †85
RUSSELL, Lorna Elizabeth. 1701 CR 33620 75460 #048-13-1983 L1983 **AN** *020 †05
SAADE, Michel. 24 RUE DE CIRY, C/O GEORGE MOKBAT 75460 #605-02-1970 L1976 **HEM** *020
SALAS, David Salvador. 1655 NE LOOP 286 75460 #039-01-1986 L1989 **FM** *020 †18
SALAS-DOMINGUEZ, Rafael. 1055 CLARKSVILLE ST, STE 165 75460 #649-01-1965 L2006 **TS GS** *020 †85,90
SALZMAN, Eric Eugene. 3150 CLARKSVILLE ST, STE 100 75460 #028-34-1978 L1985 **PD** *020 †55
SCHNEIDER, Robert Wm. 1055 CLARKSVILLE ST 75460 #048-12-1976 L1976 **ORS** *020 †40
SCOTT, Clifford T. 3150 CLARKSVILLE ST, STE 100 75460 #048-15-1990 L1991 **PD** *020 †55
SHAFIQ, Khalid. 1055 CLARKSVILLE ST, STE 130 75460 #704-09-1984 L1997 **CD** *020 †20
SNYDER, William Bradford. 575 DESHONG DR, STE B 75460 #047-05-1957 L1966 **OPH** *020 †35
SOLLEY, Wayne Allen. 575 DESHONG DR, STE B 75460 #018-03-1993 L1999 **OPH** *020 †35
SPENCER, William Bertrand. 575 DESHONG DR, STE B 75460 #021-01-1974 L1979 **OPH** *020 †35

■ = Address Information Privacy Protected

STEPHENS, John Craig. 865 DESHONG DR 75460 #048-12-1961 L1961 **R** *071 †80
STEWART, David Lawrence. 2870 LEWIS LN STE 230 75460 #041-14-1975 L1979 **GE IM** *020 †20
STROM, Gordon Bertram, Jr. 2850 LEWIS LN, STE 105 75460 #027-01-1975 L1977 **A IM** *020 †03,20
SURBER, William Edmund. 2850 LEWIS LN, STE 101 75460 #048-12-1978 L1984 **IM** *020
SUTTON, William Claude. ■ 75462 #048-12-1955 L1955 **NM IM** *020 †28
SWINT, Richard Bennett. 2510 STILLHOUSE RD 75462 #048-04-1963 L1963 **AM D** *020
SYED, Ifteqar M. 150 8TH ST SE 75460 #919-02-1989 L1997 **APM** *020
TAYLOR, David Howarth. 707 LAMAR AVE, STE K 75460 #004-01-1981 L1998 **GE IM** *020 †20
THOMAS, Jerry Lynn. 865 DESHONG DR 75460 #048-15-1982 L1984 **AN FM** *020 †05
TIJERINA, Arthur. 811 E AUSTIN ST 75460 #048-02-1969 L1969 **U** *020 †95
TOBIN, Morris. 1055 CLARKSVILLE ST, STE 140 75460 #041-01-1971 L1979 **NEP** *020
TRAMMELL, Chad D. 1128 CLARKSVILLE ST, STE 100 75460 #048-13-1996 L1997 **FM** *020 †18
TROUTT, Thomas Ralph. 927 S COLLEGIATE DR, VILLAGE SHOPPING CENTER 75460 #039-01-1984 L1990 **IM** *020 †20
VAISER, Albert. 575 DESHONG DR, STE B 75460 #737-01-1959 L1966 **OPH** *020 †35
VAUGHN, Mark David. 2850 LEWIS LN STE 107 75460 #039-01-1995 L1999 **OBG** *020 †30
WANG, Robert Chih. 575 DESHONG DR, STE B 75460 #038-40-1996 L2002 **OPH** *020 †35
WHITE, Ernest Sidney. 3150 CLARKSVILLE ST, STE 100 75460 #027-01-1965 L1971 **IM CD** *020 †20
WIKOFF, Donald Lee. 2915 N MAIN ST 75460 #030-05-1975 L1989 **U** *020 †95
WILCOX, Celeste Ann. 3550 NE LOOP 286 75460 #005-18-1995 L1996 **HO** *020 †20
WILKERSON, Clifton E. 2870 LEWIS LN, STE 220 75460 #048-13-1996 L1997 **OBG** *071 †30
WILLIAMS, Benjamin Joel. 2850 LEWIS LN 75460 #048-12-1983 L1983 **PTH** *020 †50
WILLIAMS, Fred A. 1900 FM 195 75462 #048-14-1986 L1987 **GYN** *020 †30
WIN, Zaw Tun. 820 CLARKSVILLE ST 75460 #209-01-1988 L2001 **AN** *020
XAVIER, Agnes Bertha. 875 S COLLEGIATE DR, STE D 75460 #495-52-1973 L1987 **IM** *075 †20
XAVIER, Joseph R. 1055 CLARKSVILLE ST, STE 155 75460 #495-52-1975 L1986 **PM** *020 †60
YOUNG, Robert Michael. 2870 LEWIS LN, STE 228 75460 #048-13-1986 L1987 **GS** *020 †85
ZANCHI, Michael A. ■ 75462 #048-14-1991 L1993 **AN** *020 †05
ZANCHI, Myra. ■ 75462 #561-17-1953 L1961 **GYN FM** *071
ZIMMERMAN, Robert Owin. 170 8TH ST SE, STE B 75460 #048-14-1991 L1992 **PUD CCM** *020 †20

PASADENA – HARRIS

ABU-NASSAR, Hanna J. 3315 BURKE RD STE 206 77504 #605-01-1958 L1975 **IM ID** *071 †20
ADAME, Barbara Lamar. 927 SHAW AVE 77506 #048-02-1995 L1999 **FM** *074 †18
AGUILAR, Carlos Enrique. 3216A SPENCER HWY 77504 #319-02-1985 L1997 **IM** *020 †20
AKUCHIE, Maurice Ekechi. 6319 FAIRMONT PKWY, STE 201 77505 #690-04-1992 L2005 **ID** *020 †20
ALEXANDER, Larry Pearlman. 5125 FAIRMONT PKWY 77505 #048-02-1978 L1978 **OPH** *020 †35
ALMAGUER, Ruben. 6002 FAIRMONT PKWY, STE 100 - P.O. BOX 1090 77505 #649-02-1985 L1990 **FM** *020 †18
ALTUG, Sezen Ayten. 3315 BURKE RD STE 202 77504 #016-42-1991 L1993 **GE** *020 †20
ANDERSON, Eric Edward. 3323 BURKE RD 77504 #028-02-1996 L1999 **PD** *020 †55
AQUINO, Marcos Aurelio. 3331 FAIRVIEW ST 77504 #726-01-1965 L1971 **IM END** *020 †20
AQUINO, Pedro Jose. ■ 77504 #649-14-2005 **IM** *012
ARORA, Ravindra S. 3808 WOODLAWN AVE 77504 #495-30-1960 L1969 **IM HEM** *020 †20
ARREDONDO, Valerie F. 3508 PASADENA FWY 77503 #048-04-1988 L1990 **PD** *020 †55
ATTIA, Engi Farouk. ■ 77502 #048-12-2007 **IM** *012
AWITAN, Ariston P, Jr. 4011 WOODLAWN AVE 77504 #748-02-1959 L1972 **ORS** *071 †40
BAKER, Jack L. 3692 E SAM HOUSTON PKWY S 77505 #048-02-1987 L1992 **DR** *020 †80
BALAKRISHNAN, Palur. 4102 WOODLAWN AVE STE 110 77504 #495-59-1969 L1979 **CD IM** *020 †20
BANSAL, Amit K. 4102 WOODLAWN AVE, STE 260 77504 #048-12-1986 L1987 **OBG** *020 †30
BARRIOS, Octavio E. 7106 SPENCER HWY 77505 #715-01-1985 L1993 **FM OM** *020 †18
BEESON, Robert Ernest. 3315 BURKE RD, STE 300 77504 #048-02-1991 L1993 **AN** *020 †05
BEJARANO, Aldo F. 3801 VISTA RD, STE 350B 77504 #737-06-1988 L1996 **PD** *020 †55
BELENA-BRUCE, Rosa. 4000 SPENCER HWY, COMPANY CARE 77504 #935-07-1987 L2005 **PD** *020 †70
BERGERON, Denis Eugene. 3325 PLAINVIEW ST STE 1 77504 #048-02-1974 L1974 **IM** *020 †20
BESSIRE, Charles Dewart. 3801 VISTA RD, STE 300 77504 #048-02-1962 L1962 **FM AM** *020 †18
BEST, Erin. 3508 PASADENA FWY 77503 #011-04-1999 L2003 **OBG** *020 †30 ‡
BLUMENTHAL, Bernard Jay. 4102 WOODLAWN AVE, STE 150B 77504 #016-06-1955 L1960 **IM GE** *020 †20
BOCCARDO-SABATINI, Silvia. 6243 FAIRMONT PKWY 77505 #924-01-1990 L1997 **IM** *020 †20
BOONE, Hal Browning. 6243 FAIRMONT PKWY, STE 100 77505 #048-12-1972 L1972 **FM** *020 †18
BOONE, Paul Judson. 6243 FAIRMONT PKWY, STE 100 77505 #048-02-1977 L1977 **FM** *020 †18
BRADLEY, Bernard Leo. 4003 WOODLAWN AVE 77504 #918-01-1969 L1975 **IM PUD** *020 †20,70
BRANNAN, Herbert Lee. 4000 SPENCER HWY 77504 #048-02-1957 L1957 **ORS** *071 †40
BROWN, Gerald Andrew. 3325 PLAINVIEW ST # C8 77504 #919-05-1963 L1972 **PS** *020
BRUNNEMANN, Robin R. 4000 SPENCER HWY, DEPARTMENT OF PATHOLOGY 77504 #048-14-1991 L1992 **PTH** *020 †50
BUDDHARAJU, Sushma. 4024 BROOKHAVEN AVE 77504 #496-01-2001 L2006 **PD** *020 †55
BURKE, Robert Lloyd. 4001 PRESTON AVE STE 150, FONDREN ORTHOPEDIC GROUP L 77505 #051-01-1987 L1993 **ORS** *020 †40
CALLIS, Tamara R. 908 SOUTHMORE AVE, STE 100 77502 #048-12-2004 L2008 **PD** *100
CARLSON, Richard F, III. 3315 BURKE RD, STE 300 77504 #048-14-2001 L2005 **AN** *020 †05
CARRIGAN, Ernest Wm, Jr. 1907 E SOUTHMORE AVE 77502 #021-01-1944 L1947 **GP OM** *071
CAYENNE, Sathish. 4000 SPENCER HWY 77504 #495-33-1990 L2002 **CD** *020 †20
CHAVARRIA, Jaime. 4102 WOODLAWN AVE, STE 220 77504 #649-02-1980 L1988 **IM** *020 †20
CHEDID, Silwan. ■ 77505 #048-13-1999 L2002 **ON** *020 †20
CHEN, Ray H. 3351 PLAINVIEW ST, STE 2 77504 #244-02-1969 L1976 **TS** *020 †85,90
CHI, Jia-Yen. 1020 PASADENA BLVD, PASADENA DERMATOLOGY CLIN 77506 #035-15-1975 L1979 **D** *020 †15
CHIU, Alice C. 3333 BAYSHORE BLVD, STE 240 77504 #748-02-1987 L1995 **END** *020 †20
CHOI, Shaena Hyunchu. 3320 PLAINVIEW ST 77504 #048-04-1995 L1999 **OFA** *072 †35
CHRISTEN-HUHN, Amy R. 3323 BURKE RD 77504 #048-02-2001 L2004 **PD** *020 †55
CHUA, Arlene Christine P. 3315 BURKE RD, STE 205 77504 #748-10-1993 L2001 **ID** *020 †20
CLARIDAY, Gregory T. 4102 WOODLAWN AVE, STE 200 77504 #048-02-1981 L1983 **OPH** *020 †35
CLARKE, Lawrence Ross. 3801 VISTA RD, STE 400 77504 #048-12-1983 L1983 **OTO A** *020 †45
COHEN, David K. 3301 PLAINVIEW ST, STE6 77504 #048-12-1986 L1987 **OBG** *020 †30
DARBY, Frank J, Jr. 917 CURTIS AVE, STE 3 77502 #048-04-1966 L1966 **FM** *071
DAVID, Fouad R Dawoud. 3316 PLAINVIEW ST 77504 #330-02-1959 L1972 **U** *020 †95
DAVILA, Manuel, Jr. 3925 FAIRMONT PKWY, STE 100C 77504 #018-03-2000 L2003 **D** *020
DAVIS, Rufus C, Jr. 4000 SPENCER HWY 77504 #048-02-1950 L1950 **GP** *071
DOAN, Jimmy Dung. PO BOX 7692 77508 #422-01-1999 L2003 **MPD** *020 †20
DOW, Douglas Samuel. 3333 BAYSHORE BLVD, STE 340 77504 #048-02-1994 L2000 **U** *020 †95
DUONG, Mai Duyen. 4024 BROOKHAVEN AVE 77504 #048-12-2000 L2002 **PD** *020 †55
DWAIRY, Adeeb Jay. ■ 77505 #048-14-2008 *012
EBEID, Amin Makram. 3333 BAYSHORE BLVD, STE 200 77504 #915-02-1963 L1982 **GS** *071 †85
EVANGELISTA, Benilda P. 524 TATAR ST 8 77506 #748-01-1954 L1980 **GP** *020
EVANGELISTA, Prisco Tinio. 524 PASADENA BLVD 77506 #748-01-1953 L1980 **GS GP** *020
FAIRCHILD, Robert J. 3222 BURKE RD, STE 104 77504 #021-01-1951 L1955 **AN** *071 †05
FEIN, Steven Alan. 3315 BURKE RD STE 202 77504 #011-03-1976 L1979 **GE IM** *020 †20
FERNANDEZ-VILA, Wilfredo. 1714 S HOUSTON RD 77502 #275-01-1943 L1967 **GP GS** *072
FERRON, Francois. 3801 VISTA RD, STE 300 77504 #067-06-1989 L1998 *020 †18
GANNON, Marion E J. 6002 FAIRMONT PKWY, STE B200 77505 #065-06-1969 L1978 **FM** *020
GARCIA, Abiel. 520 SHAVER ST 77506 #649-02-1982 L1990 **FM** *020 †18
GARCIA, Raul Ramon. 3351 PLAINVIEW ST, BLDG A 77504 #308-03-1979 L1985 **U** *020 †95
GARCIA, Severo Clemente. 3333 BAYSHORE BLVD, STE 340 77504 #275-01-1947 L1975 **U** *071
GARMAN, Mary E. 3925 FAIRMONT PKWY 77504 #048-04-2002 L2006 **D** *020 †15
GARNER, Glen Brian. 4000 SPENCER HWY 77504 #039-01-1996 L1998 **GS** *020 †85
GARZA, Luis. ■ 77502 #649-02-1949 L1957 **OS GP** *071
GARZA, Maria Del Rosario. 1105 HARRIS AVE, CO-LOCATION PROGRAM 77506 #649-02-1992 L2001 **CHP** *020 †75
GELBER, David Wm. 3333 BAYSHORE BLVD STE 200 77504 #035-45-1984 L1991 **GS** *020 †85
GENDI, Wagih Adieb S. 908 E SOUTHMORE AVE, STE 340 77502 #915-05-1980 L1996 **PD** *020 †55
GEORGE, Eugenia. 3350 FAIRVIEW ST, MEDICAL SCREENING CLINIC 77504 #016-01-1975 L1988 **OM IM** *020 †20,70
GHORBANI, Ashkan J. 3925 FAIRMONT PKWY # 100C 77504 #035-03-1993 L1997 **D** *020 †15
GIBSON, Jerry D. 3315 BURKE RD, STE 300 77504 #048-14-1982 L1983 **AN** *020 †05
GOLDMAN, Daniel Isser. 4102 WOODLAWN AVE, STE 200 77504 #028-02-1976 L1981 **OPH** *020 †35
GONZALEZ, Arturo. 3325 PLAINVIEW ST STE 9C 77504 #847-04-1962 L1975 **FM IM** *071
GOULDING, Joseph Carroll. ■ 77502 #048-02-1958 L1958 **GP OS** *020
GRANT, Paul Craig. 908 E SOUTHMORE AVE, STE 110 77502 #048-02-1970 L1971 **OPH** *020
GREEN, Jedd Harris. 3923 WOODLAWN AVE 77504 #048-02-1958 L1958 **P** *071
GREEN, Ronald Alan. 3350 FAIRVIEW ST, MEDICAL SCREENING CLINIC 77504 #025-12-1994 L2003 **GPM** *100 †70
GRIFFITHS, Ceri Morgan. ■ 77505 #917-24-1967 L1973 **OTO HNS** *020 †45
HADDAD, Maurice Sadik. 6243 FAIRMONT PKWY STE 202 77505 #308-03-1981 L1987 **GE IM** *020 †20
HADDAD, Souheil Sadik. 6243 FAIRMONT PKWY, STE 100 77505 #308-03-1980 L1985 **IM EM** *020 †20
HADEN, Robert Francis. 908 SOUTHMORE AVE STE 280 77502 #051-04-1957 L1965 **IM NM** *020 †20
HALBERT, Horace Burnard. 1907 E SOUTHMORE AVE 77502 #048-12-1958 L1958 **FM GS** *071 †18
HAMAD, Jamille D. ■ 77505 #048-04-2004 L2008 **PD** *012
HAMER, David Scott. 4004 WOODLAWN AVE 77504 #035-19-1988 L1994 **CD IM** *020 †20
HAMER, Louis Marc. 4004 WOODLAWN AVE 77504 #041-01-1988 L1993 **IM PCC** *020 †20
HAMPEL, Ori. 908 E SOUTHMORE AVE, STE 380 77502 #038-06-1992 L1994 **U** *020 †95
HAQ, Mohamed Maqbool-Ul. 3301 PLAINVIEW ST, # D1 77504 #495-21-1974 L1979 **ON IM** *020 †20
HASHMY, Tariq. 4000 SPENCER HWY 77504 #048-14-1992 L1993 **DR** *020 †80
HEARN, R E. 3222 BURKE RD 77504 #048-04-1953 L1953 **AN OS** *071
HEISEY, Ronald Bruce. 3305 FAIRVIEW ST, ORTHOPEDIC SURGERY 77504 #041-09-1969 L1978 **ORS AM** *062 †40
HENKEL, Cecil Leotis. 901 CURTIS AVE 77502 #048-02-1958 L1958 **GP** *071
HERMANN, Heinz. 3801 VISTA RD STE 420 77504 #869-04-1967 L1974 **CD** *020 †20
HERNANDEZ, Carlos A. 4001 SPENCER HWY, STE C 77504 #042-01-1989 L1994 **OBG** *020
HERNON, James P. ■ 77505 #649-01-1971 L1973 **OBG OS** *020
HICKS, Paul Johnson. 3351 PLAINVIEW ST 77504 #039-01-1956 L1963 **U** *040
HIGGINS, Angelica Yonette. 3508 PASADENA FWY 77503 #047-07-1999 L2002 **PD** *020 †55
HILARIO, Monina C. 6243 FAIRMONT PKWY, STE 102 77505 #748-01-1987 L1995 **PD** *020
HOGGATT, Matthew David. 3333 BAYSHORE BLVD STE 340 77504 #048-14-2001 L2006 **U** *020 †95
HORTON, Courtney Rachelle. ■ 77505 #048-02-2008 *012
HURR, Jennifer Leanne. ■ 77504 #048-14-2004 L2007 **AN** *012
HURWITZ, Gary Stephen. 3333 BAYSHORE BLVD, STE 340 77504 #048-12-1984 L1990 **U GS** *020 †95
HUYNH, Triet Q. 3333 BAYSHORE BLVD, STE 330 77504 #048-04-1990 L1991 **PM GP** *020 †60
ISAAC, Gerald W, Jr. 3508 PASADENA FWY 77503 #048-12-1987 L1989 **IM DIA** *020 †20
IZEN, Joe Alfred. 3301 PLAINVIEW ST, STE 8 77504 #021-05-1943 L1949 **OTO A** *071 †45
JEANG, Ming Kuan. 3337 PLAINVIEW ST STE 8 77504 #023-07-1980 L1980 **CD IM** *020 †20
JEROUDI, Mohamed Oussama. 4102 WOODLAWN AVE, STE 220 77504 #875-02-1980 L1992 **CD** *040 †20
JOHN, Abraham S. 4102 WOODLAWN AVE, STE 150 77504 #495-37-1996 L2003 **FM** *020 †18 ‡
JOSEPH, Aaron Kriss. 4600 FAIRMONT PKWY, STE 104 77504 #048-04-1993 L1994 **D DS** *020 †15 ‡
JOSEPH, Lawrence Maurice. 3925 FAIRMONT PKWY, STE 100C 77504 #048-02-1965 L1965 **D** *020 †15
KIEFFER, Otto H. 3351 PLAINVIEW ST STE A-8, BAYSHORE AREA PED CLNC PA 77504 #737-01-1989 L1996 **PD** *020 †55
KILLINGSWORTH, Chas Price. 3910 FAIRMONT PKWY, STE 228 77504 #048-02-1969 L1969 **FM OM** *020 †18 ‡
KING, Lindsey N. ■ 77503 #048-14-2008 *012

KIRKWOOD, John D. 4001 PRESTON AVE, STE 105 77505 #039-79-1993, ▲ L1995 FM *020 †18
KIRKWOOD, Ronald. 4001 PRESTON AVE, STE 105 77505 #048-78-1987, ▲ L1988 FM *020 †18
KNIGHT, Kyler S. 3801 VISTA RD STE 250 77504 #048-14-1993 L1994 IM *020 †20
KOPPERSMITH, Danl Leonce. 825 FAIRMONT PKWY 77504 #001-02-1977 L1988 P PYA *020 †50,75
LALIBERTE, Josee. 3801 VISTA RD, STE 300 77504 #067-06-1990 L1998 FM *020 †18
LEIS, Paula Faye. 3925 FAIRMONT PKWY # 103 77504 #048-04-1994 L1996 D *020 †15
LEYVA, Jose. 4301 VISTA RD BLDG A, 7505 FANNIN, SUITE 510 77504 #264-01-1960 L1967 P N *020 †75
LI, Xiao Hong. 4301 VISTA RD 77504 #048-02-1976 L1998 IM *020 †20
LINDSEY, Annie Earle. ■ 77504 #001-02-1960 L1962 AN *071
LINKOUS, Danny Michael. 120 CARL ST 77506 #055-01-1973 L1975 IM *020 †20
LIPSKY, William. 4102 WOODLAWN AVE, STE 200 77504 #035-09-1970 L1977 OPH EM *020 †35
LIU, Cheng-Hurd. 4627 NATIONS DR 77505 #244-01-1976 L1984 NPM *020 †55
LOUBSER, Paul Gerhard. 3315 BURKE RD, STE 300 77504 #836-02-1977 L1984 AN *020 †05
LUNG, Sophie Kim. ■ 77505 #048-12-2006 PD *012
MALICK, Alnoor Abdul. 4600 FAIRMONT PKWY, STE 107 77504 #041-09-1991 L1995 A AI *020 †20,03
MANNING, Wiley M. 820 RICHEY ST # 53 77506 #004-01-1951 L1952 AN OS *020
MARKIDES, Danna Michelle. 4000 SPENCER HWY 77504 #048-02-1999 L2002 EM *020 †16
MASCIANGELO, Thomas N. 927 SHAW AVE, STRAWBERRY HEALTH CENTER 77506 #561-11-1984 L1995 IM PCC *020 †20
MATHEW, Nibu. 629 E SOUTHMORE AVE 77502 #495-63-2000 L2000 IM *020 †20
MC DONALD, David Kenneth. 3325 PLAINVIEW ST STE 10 77504 #065-05-1970 L1977 FM *020 †18
MC INROE, Michael C. 3222 BURKE RD STE 104 77504 #048-14-1990 L1991 AN *020 †05
MC MULLEN, William W. 4102 WOODLAWN AVE, STE 200 77504 #048-14-1986 L1987 OPH *020 †35
MEDINA, Karla Ann. 3315 BURKE RD, STE 300 77504 #005-14-1993 L1993 AN *020 †05
MELENDEZ, Carlos A. 908 E SOUTHMORE AVE, STE 200 77502 #042-01-1991 L1994 PD *020 †55
MELILLO, Dixie. 3343 FAIRVIEW ST 77504 #048-02-1978 L1978 GS *020 †85
MILNER, Larry Kenneth. 3333 BAYSHORE BLVD, STE 300 77504 #048-02-1972 L1972 OBG *020
MOLANO-MANRIQUE, Enrique. 908 E SOUTHMORE AVE # 140 77502 #264-04-1961 L1973 GP OM *020
MOMIN, Mustak Mansurali. 1430 PASADENA BLVD, STE A 77502 #048-02-1996 L1999 PD *020 †55
MONDAY, Kimberly E. 4141 VISTA RD 77504 #048-04-1992 L1993 N *020 †75
MONTOYA, Juan S. 3919 WOODLAWN AVE 77504 #451-01-1967 L1974 OBG GYN *020 †30
MULLINS, Jackie Allen. 3337 PLAINVIEW ST STE 8 77504 #039-01-1982 L1983 IC IM *020 †20
MUNIZ, Alexis Santa. 3326 WATTERS RD, BLDG C 77504 #649-14-1976 L1983 PD *020 †55
MUSHTAHA, Akram Adel. 3801 VISTA RD STE 360 77504 #915-04-1979 L1992 AI PD *020
NURUDEEN, Taofeeq Adeola. 3315 BURKE RD STE 300, BAYSHORE ANESTHESIOLOGY GR 77504 #012-21-1992 L1997 AN *020 †05
OCON, Fernando J. 3333 BURKE RD 77504 #270-02-1987 L1995 OBG *020 †30
O'CONNOR, Kristine Anne. 3323 BURKE RD 77504 #042-03-2000 L2003 PD *020 †55
ORAHOOD, Monte Edward. 6243 FAIRMONT PKWY, STE 100 77505 #048-14-1997 L1998 IM PMM *020 ‡
ORELLANA, Hugo V. 4014 WOODLAWN AVE 77504 #319-03-1966 L1976 N *020
OWENS, Terryl Wynn. 3325 PLAINVIEW ST # C8 77504 #007-02-1979 L1984 OTO *020 †45
OWNBY, John Hadden. 4141 VISTA RD, HOUSTON NEUROLOGICAL 77504 #047-06-1986 L1999 CCM N *020 †20,75
PAKZABAN, Peyman. 3801 VISTA RD STE 440 77504 #048-04-1989 L1990 NS *020 †25
PALAMOUNTAIN, Shea E. 3323 BURKE RD 77504 #048-12-1998 L2001 PD *020 †55
PARDUE, Joyce Ann. ■ 77502 #048-02-1976 L1976 P N *020 †75
PARDUE, Larry Henry. ■ 77502 #048-02-1970 L1970 P *020 †75
PARKINSON, Dan West. 3801 VISTA RD, STE 450 77504 #023-12-1982 L1994 ORS *075 †40
PATEL, Ramesh G. 4102 WOODLAWN AVE STE 250 77504 #048-23-1971 L1981 CD IM *020 †20
PATEL, Vipul Manubhai. 629 E SOUTHMORE AVE 77502 #495-23-1993 L1998 IM *020 †20
PATTANAIK, Deepak. 4102 WOODLAWN AVE, STE 150 77504 #495-13-1972 L1983 FM *020 †18
PAYAN, Boris Leon. 4301 VISTA RD, BLDG A 77504 #275-01-1957 L1960 AN *020
PINEDA, Ramon Antonio. 2418 SOUTHMORE AVE 77502 #649-14-1979 L1990 IM *020
PUIG, Louis Frank. 3692 E SAM HOUSTON PKWY S 77505 #048-13-1978 L1978 GP OM *020
PULIDO, Stella Paraguya. 901 CURTIS AVE 77502 #748-01-1974 L1989 PD *071 †55
QUEJA, Eleanor P. 908 E SOUTHMORE AVE, STE 350 77502 #748-01-1973 L1984 PD *020 †55
QURAISHI, Mohammed Ali. 3326 WATTERS RD, BLDG A 77504 #495-21-1972 L1979 ON IM *020 †20
RAMIREZ G, Hugo Antonio. 906 E SOUTHMORE AVE 77502 #264-01-1964 L1972 OBG *075
RAMSAY, Tara Suzanne. 3508 PASADENA FWY 77503 #021-01-1997 L2000 PD *020 †55
RAPP, Ira Hammes. 3222 BURKE RD, STE 104 77504 #048-02-1992 L1996 AN *020 †05
RATH, Keri Lynn. 3333 BURKE RD 77504 #034-01-2002 L2006 OBG *020
RATOOSH, Sheri L. 3925 FAIRMONT PKWY, STE 100-C 77504 #048-04-1991 L1991 D *020 †15
REYES, Jose Ramon. 4301 VISTA RD, BLDG A 77504 #649-30-1990 L1995 AN PME *020
REYES-VEGA, Irene C. 927 SHAW AVE 77506 #748-02-1977 L1995 IM IMG *020 †20
RINTZ, Kathleen Gayle. 4001 PRESTON AVE, STE 150 77505 #016-11-1985 L1993 ORS *020 †40
RIVERA, Raul Antonio. 3808 WOODLAWN AVE 77504 #308-01-1987 L1995 IM *020
ROBERTS, Louie Sanford. 3333 BAYSHORE BLVD, STE 300 77504 #051-04-1994 L1998 OBG *020 †30
RODRIGUEZ, Hector H. 906 E SOUTHMORE AVE 77502 #649-02-1956 GS OS *075
RODRIGUEZ, Jorge Luis. 908 E SOUTHMORE AVE, STE 270 77502 #649-14-1980 L1988 GS *020 †85
RODRIGUEZ, Porfirio J. 908 E SOUTHMORE AVE # 270 77502 #649-33-1981 L1994 GS *020 †85
ROGERS, Doyle Nolan. 4000 SPENCER HWY 77504 #048-12-1963 L1963 PTH LM *072 †50
ROMERO, Alberto Jose. 4343 FAIRMONT PKWY 77504 #264-02-1987 L1997 FM *020 †18
ROMMAN, Karim H. 4024 BROOKHAVEN AVE 77504 #915-03-1971 L1976 PD *020 †55
ROMMAN, Nabeel Hab El. 3325 PLAINVIEW ST 77504 #330-02-1968 L1975 OTO A *020 †45
ROSEN, Gary Howard. 4142 PASADENA BLVD 77503 #065-01-1971 L1977 GP *020
RUBIO, Jose Antonio. ■ 77502 #048-14-2007 GS *012
SABATINI, Luis Alberto. 6243 FAIRMONT PKWY, STE 100 77505 #924-01-1990 L1995 IM *020
SACK, Gordon. 3339 FAIRVIEW ST 77504 #836-02-1960 L1978 FM *020 ‡

SAHEBKAR, Firoozeh. 3508 PASADENA FWY 77503 #048-02-1993 L1997 IM *020 †20
SARRIA, Hugo Antonio. 3919 WOODLAWN AVE 77504 #270-02-1988 L1995 OBG *020 †30
SCHATTE, Edward Curtis. 908 E SOUTHMORE AVE # 380 77502 #036-07-1995 L1999 U *020 †95
SCHMIEGE, Gustav Richard. 3351 PLAINVIEW ST, STE 6 77504 #041-13-1958 L1979 P *020 †75
SCHNELL, Kent David. 4102 WOODLAWN AVE, STE 150 77504 #048-02-1995 L1999 IM *020 †20
SCHWEYER, Carmen G. 908 E SOUTHMORE AVE, STE 340 77502 #847-04-1967 L1997 PD *020
SEGAL, Scott E. 4450 E SAM HOUSTON PKWY S, STE E 77505 #048-02-1994 L1998 OPH *020 †35
SEGURA, Eduardo. 3323 BURKE RD 77504 #264-01-1964 L1974 PD *020 †55
SHABAREK, Faten Mohamed. 4102 WOODLAWN AVE STE 220 77504 #875-02-1980 L1992 NPM PD *020 †55
SHAPIRO, Edward M. 1020 PASADENA BLVD, PASADENA DERMATOLOGY CLNC 77506 #048-02-1952 L1952 D *020 †15 ‡
SHEBIB, Zaher. 6319 FAIRMONT PKWY, STE 201 77505 #875-01-1986 L1996 ID IM *020 †20
SIMMS, Victor A. 3508 PASADENA FWY 77503 #048-04-1996 L1998 IM *020 †20
SMITH, Sidney Andrew. 3222 BURKE RD STE 104 77504 #048-02-1972 L1972 AN *071 †05
SMITH, William Howard. ■ 77502 #039-01-1947 L1962 FM *020 †18
SOFFAR, Saul Wm. 3325 PLAINVIEW ST STE 10 77504 #407-10-1956 L1962 OBG ON *071 †30
SOMERS, Philip Roland, Jr. 3801 VISTA RD, STE 300 77504 #048-02-1966 L1966 GS *071 †85
STEIN, David Alan. 4003 WOODLAWN AVE 77504 #035-09-1975 L1978 PUD IM *020 †20
STREUSAND, Susan B. 4000 SPENCER HWY 77504 #048-04-1979 L1979 PTH *020 †50
SULEMAN, Kausar. 3301 VISTA RD STE # D-1 77504 #704-02-1989 L1999 ON *020 †20
SUNKARA, Durga Prasad. 2702 E SOUTHMORE AVE, PARAMOUNT MED ASSOC 77502 #495-11-1977 L1995 IM *020 †20
TAUSEND, Paul L. 2201 FENWOOD DR 77502 #048-02-1950 L1950 GP *071
TAUSEND, Robert Stephen. 3901 WOODLAWN AVE 77504 #048-13-1979 L1979 D IM *020 †15 ‡
TAWADROS, Victor Anis. 1002 SEYMOUR ST 77506 #915-04-1957 L1976 OTO *071
TAWADROUS, Bassem S. 6243 FAIRMONT PKWY 77505 #048-15-2000 L2002 OBG *020
THERIOT, Vu Doan. 3333 BAYSHORE BLVD, STE 330 77504 #048-04-1986 L1987 FM *020 †18
THRASHER, Ken Lee. 3222 BURKE RD STE 104 77504 #048-02-1993 L1995 AN *020 †05
TRABULSI, Adnan. 4024 BROOKHAVEN AVE, BAYSHORE PEDIATRICS 77504 #875-01-1983 L2001 PD PDI *020 †55
TRAN, James Le Thanh. 3333 BAYSHORE BLVD, STE 250 77504 #422-01-1999 L2002 IM *020 †20
TURNER, Edward Don. 3801 VISTA RD, STE 250 77504 #048-04-1959 L1959 FM GS *071
VARGAS, Enrique. 3337 PLAINVIEW ST STE 1 77504 #264-01-1954 L1976 OBG *020
VICENCIO, Joan Anselmita. 927 SHAW AVE, HARRIS COUNTY HOSPITAL 77506 #748-02-1972 L1978 IM *020 †20
VIDYASAGARAN, Jilly K. 6243 FAIRMONT PKWY STE 102 77505 #495-02-1981 L1992 PD *020 †55
VLAHAKOS, Antonio B. ■ 77506 #048-02-1947 L1947 GP *071
WALLACE, Sharon Doxey. 4301A VISTA RD 77504 #048-02-1994 L1996 FM *020 †18
WALLER, Philip Alan. 4102 WOODLAWN AVE, STE 230 77504 #016-43-1988 L1993 RHU *020
WEBSTER, Alfred Ross. 3333 BAYSHORE BLVD STE 200 77504 #064-01-1967 L1978 GS *020
WEISSFISCH, George. 3911 WOODLAWN AVE 77504 #319-03-1963 L1967 GS CRS *020 †85
WELLMAN, John Michael. 3801 VISTA RD, STE 320 77504 #064-01-1964 L1978 PS *071
WELLS, Buford Avril. 3222 BURKE RD, STE 104 77504 #048-02-1955 L1955 AN *071 †05
WHITE, John Harold. 3222 BURKE RD, STE 104 77504 #004-01-1954 L1959 AN *071 †05
WILBOURN, George R. ■ 77502 #048-04-1951 L1951 OBG *071 †30
WILLIS, Dorothy Mary. 4000 SPENCER HWY, BAYSHORE MEDICAL CENTER 77504 #048-14-1985 L1986 PTH *020 †50
YAWORSKI, Dennis Saml. 3315 BURKE RD STE 306 77504 #062-01-1976 L1979 GP *020
YEN, Albert Andrew. 3801 VISTA RD, STE 430 77504 #048-04-1994 L1995 CN *020 †75
YU, John Chun-Liang. 3337 PLAINVIEW ST, STE 8 77504 #065-01-1987 L1995 CD ICE *020 †20
ZAID, Riad R. ■ 77504 #308-03-1981 PD *020
ZARE-MEHRJERDI, Mohammad. 3611 RED BLUFF RD 77503 #048-14-1994 L1997 FM *020 †18
ZOGRAFOS, James Leonidas. 901 CURTIS AVE STE 27 77502 #048-02-1959 L1959 GP OS *020

PATTISON — WALLER

JOHNSON, Alaina Joelle. ■ 77466 #048-14-2008 *012

PEARLAND – BRAZORIA

ABBASSI, Omid. 2225 COUNTY ROAD 90 # 123, PEARLAND ENT 77584 #048-04-1993 L1994 OTO *020 †45
ADAMS, Gareth John. ■ 77584 #048-04-2004 NS *012
ADIGUN, Yetunde Elizabeth. ■ 77584 #025-07-2004 L2008 OBG *012
ADKINS, Angela Paige. 2225 COUNTY ROAD 90 # 123 77584 #048-04-1997 L2002 OTO *020 †45
ADKISSON, Kendall B. ■ 77584 #048-14-2006 L2008 OBG *012
ADRIEN, Xavier Gavin. ■ 77584 #038-45-2004 AN *012
AGHA, Aamer. ■ 77584 #048-04-2001 L2003 GE *012
AHMED, Hany Hagag. 2518 SUNFISH DR 77584 #915-04-1996 L2005 OBG *020
AHMED, Mohammed Ashfaq. ■ 77584 #496-27-1999 L2005 NEP *012 †20
ALIM, Naureen. ■ 77584 #056-05-2003 L2007 RHU *012 †20
ALLENCHERRIL, Paul J. 8902 SUNGATE DR 77584 #495-52-1987 L2004 IM *020 †20
ALLISON, Nathan Daniel. ■ 77584 #011-03-2005 GS *012
ALP, Hande. 10905 MEMORIAL HERMANN DR 77584 #902-03-1986 L2005 AI *020 †03,55
AMJAD, Nuzha Adnan. 6831 BROADWAY ST STE C, PMB 168 77581 #704-25-1995 L2000 IM *020 †20
AMOR, Courtney Joseph. ■ 77584 #028-02-2007 ORS *012
AMOR, Karrie Marie. ■ 77584 #028-02-2007 IM *012
ANDERSON, Laura L. 9330 BROADWAY ST STE 312 77584 #048-04-1997 L2000 PD *020 †55
ANDRADE ALTUVE, Liliana C. ■ 77581 #935-01-1998 L2008 IMG *012
ANDREI, Andreea. ■ 77584 #781-01-2000 L2007 P *100
ANGELO, Joseph Robert, II. ■ 77584 #016-43-2003 PN *012 †55
ASGARI, Sheida. ■ 77584 #048-04-2004 L2007 PD *100 †55

■ = Address Information Privacy Protected

ASHARIA, Shireen A. ■ 77581 #704-25-1997 **P** *100

ATLURI, Prasad V. ■ 77584 #495-50-1986 L1997 **AN** *020 †05

AZIM, Fouad. 10970 SHADOW CREEK PKWY 77584 #748-20-1987 L1993 **PD** *020 †55

BADGWELL, Wendy Brooks. 1816 BROADWAY ST STE 110 77581 #048-16-1999 L2005 **MPD** *020 †20,55 ‡

BAFFUNNO, Annmarie V. ■ 77584 #005-02-2002 L2007 **OTO** *020

BANGLAWALA, Khursheed. ■ 77584 #035-15-2000 L2004 **FM** *020 †18

BARCZYS, Colette Kiddie. ■ 77581 #005-15-2006 **PD** *012

BARRIENTOS, Ryan R. ■ 77584 #048-14-2006 **IM** *012

BASSIL, Christopher Emile. ■ 77584 #011-02-2004 L2006 **OBG** *012

BATEMAN, Janette K. 3203 BROADWAY ST STE 100 77581 #048-02-1994 L1995 **FM** *020 †18

BATES, Janeen Marisa. ■ 77584 #034-01-2000 L2001 **FM** *100 †18

BELSHA, Jerissa A. ■ 77584 #048-14-2006 **PD** *012

BHARAKTIYA, Shikha. ■ 77584 #496-34-1997 L2005 **END** *012 †20

BITUIN, Lilibeth O. ■ 77584 #048-13-2002 L2006 **AN** *100

BLANCHETTE, Adam R. ■ 77584 #048-13-2004 L2008 **N** *012

BOSE, Debashish. ■ 77584 #023-01-2002 L2008 **GS** *012

BOSQUEZ, Elizabeth L. ■ 77584 #048-04-2006 **PD** *012

BOYLSTON, Yun Lee. ■ 77584 #048-04-2005 **PD** *012

BRIONES, Fermin. ■ 77584 #048-14-2004 L2006 **P** *012

BROADDUS, Brian Mark. ■ 77584 #048-04-2006 **AN** *012

BROWN, Aaron Reed. ■ 77584 #016-42-2007 **EM** *012

BROWN, Lewis Alan. 1901 KIRBY ST, STE 101 77584 #047-05-1976 L1980 **AI PD** *020 †55,03

BROWN, Monica Lashone. ■ 77584 #048-13-2002 L2003 **EM** *100 †16

BRUCE, Tara Lynn. ■ 77584 #008-01-1998 L2006 **OBG** *020 †30

BRYANT, Lori Dionnejames. ■ 77584 #038-06-2006 **PD** *012

BUCK, Valerie Ross. ■ 77584 #023-07-1988 L1998 **FM** *020 †18

BUI, Dien Q. 1801 COUNTRY PLACE PKWY #1 77584 #048-15-1993 L1995 **EM** *020 †16

BUI, Peter Q. ■ 77584 #048-14-2006 *012

BUI, Quang Dang. 10905 MEMORIAL HERMANN DR, STE 200 77584 #048-02-2001 L2004 **FM** *020 †18

BUTKEVICH, Alexander. 1801 COUNTRY PLACE PKWY, STE 114 77584 #550-01-1999 L2004 **CD** *100 †20

BUTLER, Michelle Renee. ■ 77584 #048-04-2008 *012

BUTTS, Ryan James. ■ 77584 #045-01-2005 **PD** *012

CACCIATORE, Anh. 9430 BROADWAY ST STE 120 77584 #011-03-1988 L1991 **IM** *020 †20

CALLIES, Bennie Leon. ■ 77584 #047-07-1961 L1966 **P** *071

CALVIN, Shawn Allen. ■ 77584 #039-01-2005 **AN** *012

CANTU, Samson. ■ 77584 #048-04-2005 L2008 **PD** *012

CARLOCK, Joseph Benjamin. ■ 77584 #048-15-2005 **PM** *012

CASSIDY, Karon Patrick. ■ 77584 #048-04-2006 **PD** *012

CASTILLO, Brian S. ■ 77584 #048-14-2008 *012

CHANG, Emmanuel Yihherng. ■ 77584 #048-04-2007 **TY** *012

CHANG, Shiliang. ■ 77584 #048-12-2003 L2006 **GS** *012

CHAPMAN, Kristin Suzanne. ■ 77584 #021-05-2006 **OBG** *012

CHARAFEDDINE, Nizar C. 2813 SMITH RANCH RD #605-01-1989 L1998 **GE IM** *020 †20

CHEN, Chen. ■ 77584 #243-70-1993 L2002 **PTH** *020 †50

CHEN, Yongxin. 1901 KIRBY ST, STE 101 77584 #243-67-1982 L1999 **AI** *020 †20,03

CHENG, Charlie Chenghsi. ■ 77584 #051-07-2001 L2001 **VS** *012

CHIEM, Binh Diep. ■ 77584 #005-18-2007 **AN** *012

CHOW, Michael Ipo. 11303 SUNLIT BAY DR, UCI MEDICAL CENTER 77584 #014-01-2002 L2003 **TS** *012 †85

CHUMPITAZI, Bruno Pedro. ■ 77584 #024-07-2001 L2007 **PG** *100 †55

CHUNG, Linda Hyun. 3203 BROADWAY ST 77581 #005-02-1998 L2003 **OBG** *020 †30

CIOLETTI, Anne C. ■ 77581 #048-13-2008 *012

COLEMAN, Neil Matthew. ■ 77584 #019-02-2003 L2007 **DMP** *012 †50

COLON, Nilda L. 8501 EDGEWATER BEND LN 77584 #042-01-1986 L1991 **RHU IM** *020 †20

CONKLIN, Lori Dionne. 1122 SAINT JOHN DR 77584 #048-14-1998 L2000 **AN** *100

CONLEY, Anthony Paul. ■ 77581 #048-02-2004 L2007 **HO** *012 †20

COOK, Christopher. ■ 77584 #039-79-2004, ▲ L2008 **AN** *012

COOKE, Kathryn E. 10970 SHADOW CREEK PKWY 77584 #048-12-1983 L1983 **FM** *020 †18

CORNETT, Joseph Edward. ■ 77584 #048-02-2001 L2002 **EM** *012

COTTAM, Jared R. ■ 77584 #021-05-2006 **PD** *012

COVINGTON, Bill Ray. ■ 77584 #048-14-2008 *012

COWART, Jennifer Brooke. ■ 77581 #048-14-2008 *012

CROSS, Mary Ann. 10905 MEMORIAL HERMANN DR, STE 200 77584 #028-03-1976 L1980 **FM** *020 ‡

DANG, Mimi Minh-Ngoc. ■ 77584 #004-01-1996 L2002 **N** *020

DANG, Thai Duc. ■ 77581 #048-14-2007 **IM** *012

DANG, Theresa Phuongloan. ■ 77584 #048-14-2007 **AN** *012

DARJEAN, Melissa Lynnette. ■ 77584 #048-12-2008 *012

DEBERRY CARLISLE, Adair F. ■ 77584 #048-78-2003, ▲ L2004 *100

DECKER, Jason E. 2017 BROADWAY ST, STE A 77581 #048-16-1998 L2001 **PD** *020 †55

DELEON, George Wayne. 2734 SUNRISE BLVD, STE 402 77584 #048-04-1981 L1982 **AN** *020 †05

DENHARTOG, Holli White. ■ 77584 #048-14-2006 **OBG** *012

DHAR, Shweta Utpal. ■ 77584 #495-76-1997 L2008 **MG** *012 †20

DIAZ, Rafael Roberto. ■ 77584 #451-01-1971 L1989 **AN** *020

DINOVO, Anthony A. 3220 AUTUMN CT 77584 #048-02-1994 L1997 **FM** *020 †18

DIVAKARAN, Vijay Ganesh. ■ 77584 #495-04-2001 L2004 **CD** *012 †20

DRAGAN, Elizabeth Rechtin. ■ 77584 #020-12-2007 **IM** *012

DRAKE, Yvette Suzanne. ■ 77584 #010-01-2003 L2008 **CHP** *012

DUDLEY, Holly N. ■ 77584 #048-13-2002 L2007 **CHN** *100

EADDY, Natasha K. ■ 77584 #048-03-2007 L2007 **PM** *100

EHLERT, Bryan A. ■ 77584 #048-14-2008 *012

ELLIS, Wendell Kennell. ■ 77584 #047-07-2002 L2006 **CD** *012 †20

ELLISON, Keith T. ■ 77584 #048-14-2008 *012

ELLSWORTH, Erik Garyson. ■ 77584 #026-08-2003 L2003 **PDC** *012 †55

EL-SAYED, Hosam Farouk. ■ 77584 #915-02-1990 L2000 **VS** *100

ENGLER, David B. ■ 77584 #048-04-1985 L1986 **AI IM** *020 †20,03

ENGLER, Joseph I. 10223 BROADWAY ST, STE L 77584 #048-21-1950 L1950 **A** *071

ESCRIVA, Charles. ■ 77584 #847-08-1949 L1967 **P** *071

FADUL, Nada Abdellatif. ■ 77584 #848-01-2000 L2007 **IM** *020 †20

FAROOQ, Etiya Manzur. ■ 77584 #704-02-1993 L2004 **FM** *020

FASANELLA, Anthony Rocco. 3115 DIXIE FARM RD, STE 107 77581 #016-76-2001, ▲ L2004 **EM** *020 †16 ‡

FEANNY, Mark A. ■ 77584 #048-14-2002 L2006 **GS** *100

FENSTERMACHER, James M. ■ 77584 #041-01-1953 L1965 **AN** *071 †05

FEW, Jennifer Joanne. ■ 77584 #036-01-2005 **PD** *012

FIGUEROA, Salvador, III. 1901 KIRBY ST, STE 101 77584 #649-19-1986 L1996 **AI** *020 †55,03

FLORES, Anthony Richard. ■ 77584 #035-45-2006 **PD** *012

FLORES, Jaime Antonio. ■ 77584 #042-03-2006 **PD** *012

FONG, Stephanie Cheesan. ■ 77584 #048-12-2003 L2007 **MPD** *100 †20,55

FOO, Chieu-Yeun. 10905 MEMORIAL HERMANN DR, STE 200 77584 #919-03-2000 L2006 **FM** *020 †18

FORD, Mary Ann Campbell. ■ 77581 #048-02-1966 L1967 **P CHP** *072

FOX, Benjamin Davis. ■ 77584 #048-04-2005 **NS** *012

FRANCK, Leah Marie. ■ 77584 #018-03-2008 *012

FRIMPONG-BADU, Yaw Boamah. ■ 77584 #412-01-1998 L2008 **IM** *020 †20

GALLAGHER, Sean Michael. ■ 77581 #048-13-2006 **ORS** *012

GALLEGOS, Thomas Edward. ■ 77584 #048-14-2003 **PD** *012

GANNON, Francis Hugh. ■ 77584 #041-02-1991 L2006 **PTH** *020 †50

GANT, Deborah L. 2017 BROADWAY ST # A 77581 #048-02-1989 L1990 **PD** *020 †55

GARBARINO, Celeste M. 9330 BROADWAY ST, STE 312 77584 #048-04-1986 L1988 **PD** *020 †55

GARCIA, Juan A. ■ 77584 #429-02-1990 L1999 **PCC** *020 †20

GARCIA, Mary C. ■ 77581 #048-04-2005 *100

GASTON, Kris Eugene. ■ 77584 #016-06-1999 L2006 **U** *100

GERTEISEN, Martha Frances. 8619 BROADWAY ST STE 100, PEARLAND PRIMARY CARE 77584 #017-20-1994 L1998 **MPD PD** *020 †20,55

GIUGLIANO, Robert Samuel. ■ 77584 #561-10-1962 L1966 **IM IMG** *071 †20

GIVEN, Bruce Daggett. ■ 77584 #016-02-1980 L1983 **IM END** *040 †20

GOGOL, Lynette M. ■ 77581 #055-75-1995, ▲ L2001 **CN N** *071 †75

GONG, Yun. ■ 77584 #243-43-1984 L2008 **PTH** *020 †50

GONZALEZ, Ernest Andrew. 3410 LAWSON DR 77584 #048-15-1997 L2002 **CCS** *020 †85

GORDON, Nancy Beatriz. ■ 77584 #935-01-1993 L2004 **PHO** *100

GOVINDAN, Malavika. ■ 77584 #026-08-2005 **RO** *100

GRAY, Jennifer D. 2017 BROADWAY ST 77581 #048-14-2003 L2006 **PD** *020 †55

GREYTOK, Francis Jos. ■ 77584 #048-02-1964 L1964 **GP** *071

GROUT, Annemarie. ■ 77584 #048-04-2006 **PD** *012

GUIDRY-WHITE, Leah E. 10905 MEMORIAL HERMANN DR, STE 113 77584 #048-14-1998 L1999 **FM** *020 †18

GUILLERMO, Benj Vinluan. 10970 SHADOW CREEK PKWY 77584 #748-02-1972 L1994 **FM** *020 †18

GUNAWAN, Adelina. 2210 ELM FOREST DR 77584 #048-15-2008 *012

GUPTA, Deepali. ■ 77584 #495-45-1992 L2002 **PCP** *100 †50

GUTHIKONDA, Sasidhar. ■ 77584 #495-21-1997 L2004 **IC** *020 †20

GUZMAN ROSARIO, Sara. ■ 77584 #308-05-2000 L2007 **AN** *100

HABIB, Omar. ■ 77584 #016-11-1999 L2007 **TS** *100

HALL, David Austin. 12318 BEND CREEK LN, UTHSC AT HOUSTON 77584 #030-05-2003 L2005 **EM** *100 †18

HAMZEH, Nabeel Yousef. ■ 77584 #575-01-1997 L2005 **IM PCC** *100 †20

HANKINS, Samuel Justin. ■ 77584 #048-04-2008 *012

HARRIS, Adam William. ■ 77584 #021-05-2002 L2003 **DR** *020 †80

HASSAN, Amy Aida. ■ 77584 #048-04-2001 L2005 **IM** *100

HAYEK, Brent Richard. ■ 77584 #048-04-2002 **OPH** *100

HAYNES, Philip Anthony. 3115 DIXIE FARM RD STE 107, TX EMERG CARE SPECIALISTS 77581 #048-02-1995 L1999 **EM** *020 †16

HERRERA, Stephanie Jo. ■ 77584 #048-13-2005 **OTO** *012

HERRINGTON, Amya Jani. ■ 77584 #048-12-2003 L2006 **PD** *020 †55

HOANG, Nam N. 2425 COUNTY ROAD 90 77584 #048-15-1991 L1993 **MPD PD** *020 †20,55

HOANG, Thang Dinh. 1816 BROADWAY ST STE 110 77581 #048-14-1997 L1999 **MPD PD** *020 †20,55

HOFFMAN, Leonard Seymour. 1901 KIRBY ST, STE 101 77584 #048-02-1965 L1965 **A PDA** *072 †55,03

HOLMES, Bradley David. ■ 77584 #048-14-2008 *012

HOPKINS, Paul Wesley. ■ 77584 #048-02-2005 **AN** *012

HURTADO, Carmen Llosa. 1801 COUNTRY PLACE PKWY, STE 109 77584 #010-01-2001 L2005 **IM** *020 †20

HYSLER, Thomas Wayne. ■ 77584 #305-01-2007 **FP** *012

ITAM, Samuelpaul Orok. ■ 77584 #041-14-2005 **OBG** *012

JACKSON, Edward Robert. ■ 77584 #045-04-2004 **ORS** *012

JAIN, Mahendra G. 8619 BROADWAY ST, STE 100 77584 #048-04-1994 L1998 **IM** *040 †20

JAMES, Matthew David. ■ 77584 #010-02-2006 **AN** *012

JERNIGAN, Nicholas Allen. ■ 77584 #036-08-2006 **MPD** *012

JIANG, Nan. 2505 PARK AVE STE B 77581 #243-46-1992 L2003 **FPG** *020 †18

JIMENEZ, Margarita. ■ 77584 #039-01-2004 L2007 **PD** *012 †55

JOHNSON, Shawn Renee. 10905 MEMORIAL HERMANN DR, STE 113 77584 #047-06-1998 L1999 **FM** *020 †18

JONES, Stephen Lloyd. ■ 77584 #048-14-1995 L1997 **IM** *020

JOSEPH, John Kuzhikkompi. ■ 77584 #048-14-2003 **PTH** *100

KABAN, Kerim. ■ 77584 #902-05-1991 **ON** *100 †20

KAGAN, Arnold Gerald. 10905 MEMORIAL HRMN DR #109 77584 #836-01-1974 L1978 **PD** *020 †55

KALEEMULLAH, Anwar J. ■ 77581 #495-21-1968 L1986 **PTH** *071 †50

KAMAL, Junaid. ■ 77584 #704-22-1994 L2004 **APM** *100 ‡

KAMANA, Mallika. ■ 77584 #495-57-1995 L2005 **ID** *100 †20

KARAM, Daoud Boutros. ■ 77581 #605-02-1962 L1970 **PM** *071 †60

KENESON, Bradley James. ■ 77584 #704-25-2004, ▲ **AN** *012

KENNEDY, Erin Marie. 2425 COUNTY ROAD 90 77584 #048-14-1996 L1997 **MPD** *020 †20,55

KESAVAN, Ramesh Babu. ■ 77584 #495-42-1993 L2007 **CCM** *020 †20 ‡

KHAN, Kiran Nawaz. ■ 77584 #704-25-2004 **IM** *012

KHANDUJA, Sanjay. ■ 77584 #048-14-1991 L1998 **IM** *020 †20

KIDAWA, Miroslaw. ■ 77584 #759-12-1979 *100

KIM, Matthew Jae. 2360 COUNTY ROAD 94, STE 108 77584 #025-01-1997 L1999 **PD** *020 †55

KITAGAWA, Ryan Seiji. ■ 77584 #048-04-2006 **NS** *012

KLINE, Glenn Brown. 1901 KIRBY ST, STE 101 77584 #048-02-1983 L1988 **AI PD** *020 †55,03

KLINE, Kris Fallon. ■ 77584 #048-14-2008 L2008 **ACA** *012

KNAUSS, Mary A. 2800 BROADWAY ST STE H 77581 #048-14-1987 L1989 **FM** *020 †18

KOON, Jen L. ■ 77584 #005-18-2002 L2008 **NEP** *020

KOUGIAS, Panagiotis. ■ 77584 #418-01-1993 L2006 **VS** *100 †85

LACOUR, Frene Deshawn. ■ 77584 #048-04-2004 **MPD** *012
LAI, Syeling. ■ 77584 #243-21-1986 L2007 **SP** *100 †50
LANDEN, Charles Nicholson. ■ 77584 #036-01-1998 L2005 **OBG** *020 †30
LANDEN, Donna Akane. ■ 77584 #045-01-2003 **FP** *012
LA PUERTA, Leopoldo. ■ 77584 #847-08-1959 L1965 **PUD IM** *071
LE, Thong Dinh. ■ 77584 #025-07-2006 **AN** *012
LEBLANC, Joy P. 3203 BROADWAY ST 77581 #048-14-1998 L1999 **OBG** *020 †30
LEE, Ben. PO BOX 84818 77584 #038-43-2001 L2006 **DR** *020
LENTZSCH, Carolyn Margare. 2017 BROADWAY ST # A, PEARLAND PEDIATRICS 77581
   #048-04-2005 L2008 **PD** *012
LEONARD, Patricia A. 1901 KIRBY ST, STE 101 77584 #539-05-1996 L2002 **AI** *020 †20,03
LEVENT, Fatma. ■ 77584 #902-09-1999 **PDI** *012 †55
LI, Jing. ■ 77584 #056-05-2006 **RO** *012
LI, Junyi. ■ 77584 #243-05-1984 L2002 **CCA** *100 †05
LI, Yong Fang. 9430 BROADWAY ST, STE 120 77584 #243-16-1968 L1999 **FM** *020 †18
LILES, Nathan Daniel. ■ 77584 #048-02-2005 **PTH** *012
LIM, Jeffrey W. ■ 77584 #048-15-2001 L2005 **AN** *100 †05
LINGAMFELTER, Jennifer Ma. ■ 77584 #048-13-2004 **GS** *012
LIVINGSTON, Andrew Dale. ■ 77584 #030-05-2007 **GS** *012
LOCKETT, Samuel Eugene. ■ 77584 #030-06-1995 **P** *100
LONGORIA, Abel Rene. 10970 SHADOW CREEK PKWY, PEARLAND EMERGENCY
   CENTER 77584 #048-02-1995 L1998 **EM** *020 †16
MADIGAN, Sheila R. ■ 77584 #048-04-2002 **NS** *012
MAGNAN, Elizabeth Mariann. ■ 77584 #056-05-2007 **GS** *012
MAMMEN, Manoj Jacob. ■ 77584 #033-05-2004 L2007 **PCC** *012 †20
MANJUNATH, Suma. 9430 BROADWAY ST STE 120, KELSEY-SEYBOLD CLINIC 77584
   #495-72-1995 L1999 **PD** *020 †55
MANK, Gerald Wayne, III. ■ 77584 #048-14-2006 **IM** *012
MAPOSA, Douglas. ■ 77584 #775-01-1989 *100
MARCIEL, Annmarie. ■ 77584 #048-04-2003 L2005 **DR** *012
MARCOUX, Jean G. 1901 KIRBY ST, STE 101 77584 #067-03-1965 L1977 **AI PDA** *071 †55,03
MARSHBURN, Ann Michelle. ■ 77584 #048-04-2008 *012
MARX, Douglas Pete. ■ 77584 #010-02-2005 **IM** *100
MATHEW, Reeba. ■ 77584 #495-72-2000 L2007 **MPD** *100
MATSUSAKI, Ronald. ■ 77581 #065-01-1973 L1984 **GP OS** *020
MAUIYYEDI, Shamila M. ■ 77584 #704-25-1991 L2002 **PTH** *020 †50
MCCRARY, Amber Ann. ■ 77584 #048-14-2008 *012
MC DONALD, Kathleen Rose. 10905 MEMORIAL HERMANN DR, STE 111 77584
   #030-05-1991 L1996 **OTO** *020 †45
MCDONALD, Ryan Oneill. ■ 77584 #048-04-2004 L2008 **N** *012
MERRITT, Deborah Suzanne. 2017 BROADWAY ST, STE A 77581 #048-13-2002 L2005
   PD *012 †55
MINIYAR, Shilpa Ramnivas. ■ 77584 #048-12-2006 **OBG** *100
MITTAL, Amit. ■ 77584 #048-04-2006 **DR** *012
MONDUY, Migvis. ■ 77584 #011-04-2005 **NDN** *012
MORA, Adan, Jr. ■ 77584 #048-14-2001 L2005 **PCC** *012 †20
MORALES-AMAYA, Ana L. 3203 BROADWAY ST 77581 #048-12-1995 L1999 **OBG** *020 †30
MOTOSUE, Alison Makiko. 11303 SUNLIT BAY DR, SOUTH COAST PEDIATRICS 77584
   #014-01-2002 L2003 **AI** *012 †55
MURCH, Scott Remo. ■ 77584 #056-06-2006 **ORS** *012
MURPHY, Robert Eugene. ■ 77584 #020-12-1990 L1993 **EM PE** *030 †16
NAIK, Aanand Dinkar. ■ 77584 #048-12-1998 L1999 **IMG** *020
NAIR, Lekshmi. 9223 BROADWAY ST, STE 107 77584 #495-84-1996 L2003 **FM** *020 †18 ‡
NAMBI, Vijay. ■ 77584 #495-04-1998 L2005 **CD** *100 †20
NEATHERLIN, Callie Anne. ■ 77584 #048-13-2006 **PD** *012
NEWBROUGH, Scott Alan. ■ 77584 #039-01-2002 L2008 **PS** *012
NGUYEN, David D. 2121 LIMRICK DR 77581 #048-15-2002 L2004 **EM** *020 †16
NGUYEN, Kim Minh. ■ 77584 #048-14-2004 L2007 **IM** *012
NGUYEN, Kimphuong Thi. 1022 ANDOVER DR 77584 #021-01-2001 L2005 **AN** *100 †05
NGUYEN, Michael Phuc. ■ 77584 #048-02-2005 L2007 **DR** *012
NISBET, John J. 10223 BROADWAY ST, STE J 77584 #048-04-1995 L1997 **RNR** *020 †80
NIU, Jiaxin. ■ 77584 #243-72-1995 L2004 **HO** *012 †20
OBUDULU, Rosemary O. ■ 77584 #690-04-1988 L2006 **IM** *012 †20
ODWYER, Anthony. 2505 PARK AVE, STE B 77581 #539-04-1976 L1978 **FM** *020
OLIVARES, Michael Joseph. ■ 77584 #024-01-1995 **IM** *100
ORSAK, Glenn Thomas. 3223 BROADWAY ST 77581 #048-02-1993 L1995 **FM** *020 †18
PALASI, Maria M. 8619 BROADWAY ST, STE 100 77584 #748-17-1984 L1995 **FM** *020 †18
PARIKH, Vaibhave Y. ■ 77584 #017-20-2005 L2005 **AN** *012
PATEL, Hitesh Raman. PO BOX 2569, 11800 ASTORIA BLVD 77588 #001-02-2000 L2002
   EM *020 ‡
PATEL, Jayendrakumar K. 6516 BROADWAY ST STE 108 77581 #495-22-1991 L2003
   IM *020 †20
PATEL, Setul Girishchand. ■ 77584 #051-01-2003 L2006 **EM** *100 †16
PATEL, Vandana Kudva. 1901 KIRBY ST, STE 101 77584 #020-02-1996 L2003 **PD** *020 †55,03
PATTON, Eddie Lee. ■ 77584 #025-07-2005 L2005 **N** *012
PEREZ, Mike. ■ 77584 #048-04-2004 **PTH** *012
PETERS, Kurt Ralph. 10905 MEMORIAL HERMANN DR 77584 #039-05-1985 L1990
   AI PD *020 †55,03
PETERS, Lecresha A. 9430 BROADWAY ST, STE 120 77584 #048-14-1999 L2002 **FM** *020 †18
PODDER, Hemangshu. ■ 77584 #473-01-1986 L2004 *020
PORTER-TUCCI, Linda C. 8619 BROADWAY ST, STE 100 77584 #048-04-1996 L1997
   FM *020 †18
POTTER, Andrew William. ■ 77584 #017-20-2005 L2008 **DR** *012
POWELL, Candace Leigh. ■ 77581 #048-04-2008 *012
PRANGE, Bryan Thomas. ■ 77584 #025-07-2004 L2007 **DR** *012
PUN, Kristoffer John. ■ 77584 #048-04-2003 **DR** *012
RADCLIFF, Kristen E. ■ 77584 #036-07-2004 **ORS** *012
RAJAKARUNA, Mohan. ■ 77584 #422-01-1990 **CD** *012
RAJAN, Raj Tiruch. 10970 SHADOW CREEK PKWY 77584 #495-65-1980 L1990 **CD** *020 †20
RAMANATHAN, Venkataraman. ■ 77584 #495-59-1991 L2004 **NEP** *020 †20
RAMOS, Monica. ■ 77584 #048-13-2004 L2008 **PD** *012
RAO, Radha. ■ 77584 #495-89-1989 L2000 **IM** *020 †20
RENDON, Gabriel. ■ 77584 #048-12-2004 L2008 **GE** *012 †20
REYES, Cesar Augusto. ■ 77584 #308-11-1999 **P** *100
REYES, Manuel M. ■ 77584 #048-14-2005 **IM** *012

REYES, Meredith. ■ 77584 #048-14-2005 L2008 **PTH** *012
RICHEY, Tamara M. ■ 77581 #051-04-1981 L1988 **IM** *020
RIZZOLO, Edward Anthony. ■ 77581 #048-04-1956 L1956 **GYN** *071 †30
ROETHLE, Scott Taggart. ■ 77584 #026-04-2005 L2007 **AN** *012
ROOSTH, Joseph Howard. 3322 E WALNUT ST STE 106 77581 #048-02-1986 L1990
   IM PLM *020 †20
ROSILLO, Patricia Lizette. ■ 77584 #048-14-2007 **MPD** *012
ROSS, Christina Marie. ■ 77584 #048-14-2000 **CHP** *012
SAEED, Mohammad. ■ 77584 #704-25-1991 L2002 **ICE CD** *020 †20
SAENZ, Jesus A. 8325 BROADWAY ST, STE 202 # 51 77581 #048-14-2000 L2004 **DR** *020 †80
SALVATORI, Lorena Ines. ■ 77581 #132-01-2002 **FP** *012
SAMPATH, Karthik. ■ 77584 #048-02-2001 L2002 **PM** *100
SANCHEZ, Amarilis. ■ 77584 #042-01-2005 L2008 **PD** *012
SANDERS, Michael Blake. 12311 BEND CREEK LN 77584 #048-12-2000 L2003 **ORS** *012
SARWAR, Aliya I. 2811 PINEBEND DR, PEARLAND 77584 #704-02-1991 L2000 **N** *020 †75
SAYEGH, Gilbert George. ■ 77584 #308-13-2002 *100
SCHIESSER, Rachel Lynn. ■ 77581 #048-04-2006 **IM** *012
SCHMIDT, Sheila E. 2506 WESTMINSTER ST 77581 #048-14-1993 L1994 **GP** *020
SETTLE, Stephen Holloway. ■ 77584 #047-05-2005 **RO** *012
SHARPLES, Scott Brydson. 3203 BROADWAY ST, STE 100 77581 #048-04-2001 L2003
   FM *020 †30
SHIRLEY, Lawrence Reed. 1901 KIRBY ST, STE 101 77584 #047-05-1976 L1991
   PDA IG *020 †55,03
SMITH, Chad R. ■ 77584 #048-14-2006 **PD** *012
SMITH, Roger Allen. ■ 77581 #048-04-2007 **GS** *012
SNELL, Jackie L. 3203 BROADWAY ST, STE 100 77581 #048-14-1997 L1999 **FM** *020 †18
SOLDANO, Anthony Charles. ■ 77584 #048-13-2001 L2005 **DMP** *100 †50
SOUMAN, Asem. ■ 77581 #875-01-1990 L1996 **IM** *020 †20
SRIVATHS, Poyyapakkam R. ■ 77584 #495-59-1991 L2001 **PN** *012 †55
STAMPEHL, Mark Ryan. ■ 77584 #028-34-2004 L2006 **CD** *012 †20
STANLEY, Kenneth Jermaine. 10100 BROADWAY ST STE 110 77584 #048-04-1998 L2001
   FM *020 †18
STELLING, Carol I Boyer. ■ 77581 #016-06-1972 L1994 **DR** *071 †80
SUBRAMANIAM, Mahesh. ■ 77584 #048-04-1998 L2008 **TS** *100
SUN, Regina Lo. 10970 SHADOW CREEK PKWY, STE 370 77584 #016-06-2002 L2007 **OPH** *100
SWEENEY-GOTSCH, Bridget M. ■ 77584 #048-04-2006 **PD** *012
TALBOT, Brian Joseph. 9330 BROADWAY ST, STE 312 77584 #048-04-1994 L1997 **PD** *020 †55
TAN, Johannes Tjwan Bing. ■ 77584 #506-02-1963 L1977 **DR AM** *071
THOMPSON, Brandon S. ■ 77581 #048-13-2006 **AN** *012
TIMM, Josie S. 10223 BROADWAY ST, STE J 77584 #056-06-1984 L1986 **DR RNR** *020 †80
TJENG, Susan Siufen. 2710 NEWBURY CT 77584 #027-01-1995 L1998 **PD** *020 †55
TORRES, Laura. 8603 BROADWAY ST, STE 101 77584 #048-14-1997 L2003 **ORS** *020 †40
TORRES, Saul Na, Jr. ■ 77584 #048-14-2007 **FP** *012
TREVINO, Eric Jude. ■ 77584 #048-04-2006 L2008 **DR** *012
TRUITT, M Everett. 9330 BROADWAY ST, STE 312 77584 #048-04-1960 L1960 **PD** *071 †55
TUAN, Wei-Ming. 9430 BROADWAY ST STE 120 77584 #048-02-1991 L1992 **IM EM** *020 †20
TYNER, Sarah Christine. ■ 77584 #048-15-2008 *012
TYPPO, Katri Vanamo. ■ 77584 #028-34-2004 L2004 **CCP** *012 †55
UBOGU, Eroboghene E. ■ 77584 #917-33-1998 L2000 **N CN** *050 †75
UNG, Chay Bun. 10970 SHADOW CREEK PKWY, STE 250 77584 #048-15-2002 L2004
   FM *100 †18
VAILAS, George Nikita. 2006 MISTWOOD CT, ASSOC. PROFESSOR OF PEDIAT 77584
   #418-01-1978 L1998 **PD NPM** *020 †55
VASSER, Heather Marie. ■ 77584 #048-15-2005 **GS** *012
VASUDEVAN, Sanjeev A. ■ 77584 #012-05-2001 **GS** *012
VELAMURI, Suryakanta. ■ 77584 #495-23-1996 L2005 **PCC** *020 †20
VU, Henry Hanh. 9303 SUNBONNET DR 77584 #047-06-1989 L1993 **AN PME** *020 †05
VU, Mary Theresa. ■ 77584 #048-14-2005 L2007 **IM** *012
VU, Tri Tien. ■ 77584 #005-18-2002 L2005 **HO** *012 †20
WELCH, Roland Langston. 8325 BROADWAY ST STE 202 77581 #047-07-1956 **P** *071
WELLS, David Clayton. 10223 BROADWAY ST, STE J 77584 #041-01-1994 L1995 **DR** *020 †80
WESLEY, Sherin Elizabeth. ■ 77584 #048-14-2003 L2005 **PD** *020 †55
WIEDERHOLD, Lee Roy. ■ 77581 #048-02-2005 L2007 **RO** *012
WILBER, Matthew Albert. 9330 BROADWAY ST, STE 312 77584 #005-12-2000 L2004
   PD *020 †55
WILDIN, Susan Rose. ■ 77584 #048-04-1984 L1985 **PD** *020 †55
WILLIAMS, Janelle Naomi. ■ 77584 #048-14-2005 L2007 **MPD** *012
WRIGHT, Russell Walter. ■ 77584 #048-04-2007 *012
WU, Yun. ■ 77584 #243-16-1991 L2003 **SP** *100 †50
XIE, Min. ■ 77584 #243-46-1995 **IM** *012
YAREMKO, Brian Patrick. ■ 77584 #060-01-2000 *100
YIN, Cheng. ■ 77584 #243-47-1990 L2004 **PTH** *100 †50
YIP, Beth Yan Yan. 9430 BROADWAY ST, STE 127 77584 #048-04-1991 L1992 **PD** *020 †55
YORDY, John Stuart. ■ 77584 #045-01-2006 **RO** *012
ZAINAB, Asma. ■ 77584 #704-06-1993 L2006 **CCM** *020 †20
ZAMBRANO, Juan Carlos. 1901 KIRBY ST, STE 101 77584 #319-04-1991 L2002 **AI** *020 †55,03
ZHORNE, Derek James. ■ 77584 #018-03-2008 *012
ZHUGE, Wu. ■ 77584 #019-02-2003 L2008 **ORS** *012
ZULFIQAR, Amber Mohsin. ■ 77584 #704-02-1996 **FP** *012

PEARSALL – FRIO

ESCOBAR, Mauricio Antonio. 105 E HACKBERRY ST, STE B 78061 #847-09-1966 L1979
   GP GS *020
GARFIELD, Herbert I. 325 N CHERRY ST 78061 #011-02-1963 L1967 **PD** *075 †55
GARZA, Oscar. 151 MEDICAL DR 78061 #056-06-1985 L1986 **FM OBS** *020 †18
JOHNSON, Erik Lihn. ■ 78061 #030-05-1978 L1980 **FM EM** *020 †18
MC FARLANE, Joe Robt, Jr. 315 E COLORADO ST 78061 #048-04-1961 L1961
   OPH LM *072 †35
SOSA, Jose I. 151 MEDICAL DR 78061 #649-02-1991 L1998 **FM** *020 ‡
ZAMORA, Pedro A, Jr. ■ 78061 #429-01-1970 L1979 **DR R** *020 †80

PECOS – REEVES

ABDO, Ziad Antoine. 880 W DAGGETT ST STE 2 79772 #605-03-1994 L2004 **GS** *020

BANG, Won Joo. 2338 TEXAS ST, MEDICAL ARTS BLDG #1 79772 #583-06-1962 L1972 **GS EM** *072 †16

CERNA, Orville Diaz. 925 W DAGGETT ST 79772 #748-07-1980 L1992 **IM** *020 †20

DARPOLOR, Joseph K. 2348 TEXAS ST 79772 #610-01-1985 L1994 **FM OBG** *020 †18 ‡

KOVAC, Alexander. 2323 TEXAS ST, REEVES COUNTY HOSPITAL 79772 #550-01-1960 L1975 **DR NM** *020 †80 ‡

THOMAS, Fitzgerald M. 2323 TEXAS ST 79772 #048-15-1986 L1988 **HEM IM** *020

PERRIN – JACK

WALTERS, Philip Greenwood. ■ 76486 #039-01-1957 L1957 **OBG** *071

PERRYTON – OCHILTREE

BETTY, Claude Wm. 3020 GARRETT DR 79070 #048-12-1964 L1964 **GP** *020

BROUSSARD, Robt Henry, Jr. ■ 79070 #021-05-1960 L1974 **AN** *071

CHILDERS, Manon Eli, III. 3006 GARRETT DR 79070 #048-15-1983 L1983 **FM EM** *020 †18

MANN, Rex Leland. 3019 S MAIN ST 79070 #048-15-1982 L1983 **FM** *020 †18

PFLUGERVILLE – TRAVIS

ADU-GYAN, Harriet Evelyn. ■ 78660 #016-11-2004 L2006 **FM** *100 †18

AZUMA, Lynn Mildred. 1501 PECAN ST W, STE 101 78660 #016-06-2001 L2007 **PD** *020 †55

BOYD, John Reagan. 200 HEATHERWILDE BLVD 78660 #048-02-1972 L1972 **GP** *020 †18

CAVANAGH, Andrew T. 200 HEATHERWILDE BLVD, STE A 78660 #048-16-2002 L2005 **PD** *020 †55

DRAEGER, Margaret Rose. 103 12TH ST, STE 206 78660 #056-05-1974 L1996 **GYN** *020 †30

ENDERS, Judith Whitmire. 15803 WINDERMERE DR # 103 78660 #025-12-1993 L1997 **PD** *020 †55

GOLDEN, Alma L. 1501 PECAN ST W, STE 101 78660 #048-02-1975 L1976 **PD** *020 †55

GUMASTE, Meghana Anand. 15822 FOOTHILL FARMS LOOP, PFLUGERVILLE CHC - NORTH R 78660 #495-28-1999 L2003 **FM** *020 †18

HAVEMANN, Cathleen Mcinto. 1501 PECAN ST W, STE 101 78660 #048-04-1998 L2001 **PD** *020 †55

HERNANDEZ, Mark Steven. 1501 PECAN ST W, STE 101 78660 #048-04-2003 L2006 **IM** *100 †20

HOLLIMAN, Anna E. 15803 WINDERMERE DR, STE 103 78660 #001-06-1998 L2001 **PD** *020 †55

HOWARD, Daniel Eaton. ■ 78660 #026-08-2006 **PD** *012

KELLER, Shane E. 1615 GRAND AVENU PKWY #112 78660 #048-02-2001 L2004 **FM** *020 †18

LEE, Brenna K. 200 HEATHERWILDE BLVD, STE A 78660 #048-02-2001 L2004 **FM** *100 †18

LICHAA, Vivian. ■ 78660 #048-16-2008 *012

LIN, Wei-Ann. 1420 WELLS BRANCH PKWY, STE 450 78660 #048-13-1990 L1991 **FM** *020 †18 ‡

LORENTZEN, Wayne L. ■ 78660 #048-02-1951 L1951 **IM** *071

MAMBAPOOR, Viswa Jyothi. 200 HEATHERWILDE BLVD, STE B 78660 #495-57-1992 L2000 **IM** *020 †20

MANGOSING, Nieves M. ■ 78660 #748-01-1965 L1983 **P** *071

MILLER, Gwendolyn B. 1615 GRAND AVENUE PKWY, STE 112 78660 #048-02-1988 L1989 **IM** *020 †20

MOLINA, Pablo. 15803 WINDERMERE DR # 300, NORTH RURAL HEALTH CENTER 78660 #048-15-1980 L1982 **FM** *020 †18

PERERA, Chrishanthi M S. 1501 PECAN ST W, STE 101 78660 #422-01-1994 L2007 **MPD PD** *020 †20,55

POWELL, Steven Zachary. 200 HEATHERWILDE BLVD, STE A 78660 #016-01-1997 L1998 **FM** *020 †18 ‡

RAMOS, Alina M. 15822 FOOTHILL FARMS LOOP 78660 #048-14-1987 L1988 **IM** *020 †20

RUSSO, Anthony Ross. 2401 W PECAN ST, STE 103 78660 #048-02-1981 L1981 **GP** *020

SWEET, Charles Thomas. ■ 78660 #016-11-2004 **CHP** *012

WHITED, Everest Austin. 103 12TH ST, STE 101 78660 #048-13-1976 L1976 **FM** *020 †18

PHARR – HIDALGO

AGUILERA RODRIGUEZ, Juan. 807 N CAGE BLVD, DR JUAN AGUILERA & ASSOC 78577 #649-02-1968 L1974 **PD** *020 †55

ARIAS VIAUD, Julio Enriqu. 900 W SAM HOUSTON ST STE 1 78577 #341-03-2002 L2006 **PD** *020 †55

BABINEAUX, Daria. 807 N CAGE BLVD, AQUILLERA PEDIATRICS 78577 #021-05-2000 L2003 **PD** *020

BERMUDEZ, Yuri Oleg. 1100 W SAM HOUSTON ST 78577 #682-01-1991 L1997 **FM** *020 †18

BLUMER, Arlo Roslyn. 78577 #041-13-1954 L1958 **GP OBG** *071 †18

CANTU, Carlos Leal. ■ 78577 #649-02-1953 L1957 **IM CD** *071

DY, Peter L. 806 S CAGE BLVD STE B 78577 #748-01-1984 L1999 **PD** *020 †55

FERNANDEZ, Jose A. 1203 E FERGUSON ST, PHARR FAMILY HEALTH CENTER 78577 #308-01-1954 L1971 **GP PUD** *071

FERNANDEZ-BRITO, Jose R. 420 W SAM HOUSTON ST, STE A 78577 #308-03-1981 L1995 **OBS OBG** *020 †30

FLOREZ, Marco T. 306 W PARK ST 78577 #264-02-1969 L1978 **GP EM** *020

GARCIA, Hiram L. 1002 W SAM HOUSTON ST, STE 4 78577 #048-14-1999 L2001 **FM** *020 †18

GARZA SANCHEZ, Elisa. 905 S JACKSON RD 78577 #048-02-1980 L1986 **P** *020 †75

GOMEZ, Omar A. 524 S CAGE BLVD, STE F 78577 #308-02-1993 L2001 **IM** *020 †20

GONZALEZ, Alfredo V. 420 W SAM HOUSTON ST, STE B 78577 #649-02-1989 L1999 **FM** *020

GONZALEZ, Raul. 78577 #649-02-1960 L1967 **OBG** *071

GONZALEZ PENIZA, Luis M. 78577 #042-04-1986 L1994 **IM** *020

GORDON, Verley. 926 W SAM HOUSTON ST, STE 1 78577 #649-38-1991 L1995 **PD** *020 †55

GREUNER, Carl Eugene. ■ 78577 #407-23-1955 L1963 **OBG** *071 †30

GUZMAN, Christopher Zipag. ■ 78577 #748-01-1979 **PD** *012

HERNANDEZ, Ambrosio, III. ■ 78577 #025-01-1995 L2004 **PDS** *020 †85

HERNANDEZ, Jaime. 524 S CAGE BLVD STE F 78577 #308-04-1981 L1995 **IM** *020 †20

HERNANDEZ, Maximiliano. 502 S CAGE BLVD 78577 #308-04-1989 L1996 **IM** *020 †20

IGLESIAS, Norma. 712 S CAGE BLVD 78577 #048-14-1985 L1986 **FM GYN** *020 †18

LOPEZ, Jose Francisco. 1106 W SAM HOUSTON ST, OCCUPATIONAL & INDUSTRIAL 78577 #048-13-1981 L1983 **FM** *020 †18

MATA, Israel G. 105 E POLK AVE 78577 #649-02-1977 L1992 **PD** *020 †55

MERCADO, Manuel Jose. 502 S CAGE BLVD 78577 #308-04-1991 L2000 **IM** *020 †20

MORENO, Alvaro, II. ■ 78577 #048-02-2007 **P** *012

ORTIZ, Oziel. ■ 78577 #048-02-2008 *012

VALLADARES, Theresa L. 923 E FERGUSON ST, STE C 78577 #048-13-1996 L1998 **FM** *020 †18

PILOT POINT – DENTON

ESPINOZA, Froilan Patrick. ■ 76258 #005-15-1987 L2006 **PTH** *020 †50

PIKE, Barbara Hankinson. 10279 FM 455 E STE 400 76258 #048-12-1993 L1994 **PD** *020

PINEHURST – MONTGOMERY

RISTROPH, Robert Michael. ■ 77362 #048-04-1975 L1975 **TS** *020 †85,90

PINELAND – SABINE

CHUN, Dukja. 501 N TEMPLE AVE 75968 #422-01-1998 L2005 **IM ID** *020 †20

PIPE CREEK – BANDERA

DAVIS, Joseph Robt. 426 DEER OAKS DRIVE 78063 #020-02-1955 L1977 **OM** *071

FREMLAND, Alan David. ■ 78063 #026-04-1962 L1963 **R** *020 †80

JERNIGAN, Clarence A. 3585 BUMP GATE RD 78063 #048-04-1960 L1960 **FM AM** *071 †70,18

KAISER, Charlene Beth. ■ 78063 #035-46-1972 L1974 **OM GPM** *071 †15,70

PITTSBURG – CAMP

BURROW, Rodney Dale. 408 QUITMAN ST 75686 #026-04-1999 L2002 **FM** *020 †18

CREME, Stephen Richard. 414 QUITMAN ST 75686 #008-02-2000 L2003 **FM** *020 †18

DANG, Bao Ngoc. 414 QUITMAN ST 75686 #004-01-2000 L2003 **FM** *020 †18

DE LISI, Craig Martin. 408 QUITMAN ST 75686 #001-02-2000 L2003 **FM** *020 †18

FENG, Zhanbin. 414 QUITMAN ST 75686 #243-46-1987 L2003 **IM** *020 †20

GUERRA, Manuel. 502 QUITMAN ST 75686 #649-01-1948 L1963 **GP** *020 ‡

LAJDA, Dusan Jan. 414 QUITMAN ST 75686 #308-04-1980 L1980 **NEP IM** *020

MACBEATH, Blair Reid. 410 QUITMAN ST 75686 #064-01-1979 L1981 **GP** *020

MICHAUD, Carl Jacques. ■ 75686 #440-01-1966 L1977 **OBG** *075

RENSHAW, Larry Alan. ■ 75686 #048-02-1962 L1962 **R** *071 †80

TRIMBLE, Ted Dawson. 408 QUITMAN ST 75686 #039-05-1982 L1983 **FM** *020 †18

PLAINVIEW – HALE

BALZER, Larry Dale. 2506 XENIA ST, STE 104A 79072 #039-01-1971 L1973 **FM A** *020 †18

BERNHARDT, Herbert Jos. 201 W 6TH ST 79072 #035-19-1941 L1951 **D IM** *075 †15

BRANCH, T Coe. 2222 W 24TH ST 79072 #048-02-1961 L1961 **FM OS** *020 †18

BUSBY, Carroll Lee. 2404 YONKERS ST 79072 #047-06-1947 L1965 **IM PUD** *071

CUMMINS, Douglas Glynn. 2512 XENIA ST, STE 105 79072 #048-15-1994 L1999 **GS** *020 †85

GARVISH, John Franklin. 2404 YONKERS ST 79072 #016-11-1965 L1984 **R NM** *020 †80,28

GRAVES, Michael Thurston. 2404 YONKERS ST 79072 #005-14-1977 L1985 **U** *020 †95

GUEL, Mario Humberto. 2404 YONKERS ST 79072 #649-02-1984 L1988 **FM** *020

GUTIERREZ, Victor Asaldo. 2601 DIMMITT RD 79072 #748-01-1975 L1982 **P** *020

HOLT, Jeffrey Randall. ■ 79072 #048-14-2005 L2007 **FP** *012

HORN, Joseph Jack. 970 COUNTY ROAD AA, MEDICAL DEPT 79072 #048-12-1954 L1954 **IM** *020

HUANG, Yao Jing. 2801 W 8TH ST 79072 #243-77-1983 L2005 **FM** *020 †18

KOPP, Douglas E. 2222 W 24TH ST, UNIT 10 79072 #048-13-1982 L1983 **OPH** *020 †35

LANDERS, Wilson Harry, Jr. 2506 XENIA ST 79072 #048-02-1978 L1978 **ORS** *020

LARA, Sergio Andres. 2508 XENIA ST STE 101 79072 #649-52-1996 L2002 **IM** *020 †20

LOGGINS, Tony Ray. 2222 W 24TH ST, UNIT 3 79072 #048-15-1986 L1987 **FM** *020 †18

MOORE, Donald Milner. 2404 YONKERS ST 79072 #048-12-1956 L1956 **GS** *071 †85

MURCIA, Jaime D. 2202 EDGEMERE DR 79072 #649-38-1987 L1993 **PD** *020

NGUYEN, Tuan Gregory. 1118 HOLLIDAY ST 79072 #048-02-1988 L1989 **DR** *020

ONTAI, Sidney Chas. 2606 YONKERS ST 79072 #014-01-1985 L1999 **FM FPG** *020 †18

OTIENO, Harun Argwings. 2516 XENIA ST, STE 102 79072 #577-01-1995 L2006 **IC** *020 †20

PEELER, Bryan D. 2508 XENIA ST 79072 #048-15-1989 L1990 **IM EM** *030 †20

ROBERTS, Roy H. 730 COUNTY ROAD G 79072 #308-06-1944 L1952 **U** *071 †95

SEIGLER, Gail. ■ 79072 #028-78-1945, ▲ L1945 **GP** *071

TURKOWSKI, Walter Jos. 2601 DIMMITT RD 79072 #019-02-1991 L1996 **IM** *020 †20

TURNER, Stephen Lynn. 2404 YONKERS ST STE 1 79072 #048-15-1983 L1983 **PD ADL** *020

WOLF, Bernhard. 2222 W 24TH ST, UNIT 3 79072 #409-16-1987 L1992 **PD** *020 †55

WOOLLENDS, Michael John. 621 FM 179 # A 79072 #061-01-1968 L1978 *020

YILDIZ, Ilhan. 2404 YONKERS ST 79072 #902-07-1980 L1992 **GS** *020 †85

YODER, Grady D. ■ 79072 #048-13-2000 L2006 **VIR** *100 †80

PLANO – COLLIN

ABDELNABY, Abier A. ■ 75093 #010-03-2001 L2007 **CRS** *100 †85

ABRAHAM, Sindhu Anna. 1600 COIT RD, STE 301 75075 #024-05-1994 L1997 **GE** *020 †20 ‡

ABROL, Rajjit. 1640 COIT RD 75075 #012-05-1998 L2001 **ICE** *100 †20

ACHTMAN, Daniel Seth. 4010 W PARK BLVD 75093 #065-10-1983 L1986 **D** *020 †15

ACKERMAN, Baer Max. 1700 ALMA DR, STE 480 75075 #048-04-1979 L1979 **CHP P** *020 †75

ADAMS, Kenneth Kei. 3901 W 15TH ST 75075 #048-12-1997 L1998 **PM** *020 †60

ADMIRE, Phillip Lee, III. 4700 ALLIANCE BLVD, DEPT. OF EMERGENCY MEDICIN 75093 #016-06-2001 L2003 **EM** *020 †16

AGARWAL, Poonam. 1600 COIT RD STE 105 75075 #495-98-1987 L1999 **CD** *020 †20

AHLUWALIA, Micky S. 3900 W 15TH ST, STE 205A 75075 #065-09-1981 L1991 **AN** *020 †05

AHMAD, Syeda Sultana. 1007 20TH ST 75074 #704-06-1977 L2003 **PD PTH** *020

AHMAD, Yehuda Syed. 2709 W 15TH ST, MEDICAL CARE CTR 75075 #160-02-1972 L1983 **PD** *020
AKUAGWU, Alex Ikem. Benja. ■ 75074 #690-06-1993 L2007 **FM** *020 †18
ALBERT, Thomas Jos, Jr. 6200 W PARKER RD, STE 308 75093 #021-05-1988 L1990 **OBG** *020 †30
ALDRED, Keith Allen. 3901 W 15TH ST 75075 #017-20-1987 L1990 **PTH** *020 †50
ALLEN, Michael Scott. 3901 W 15TH ST 75075 #048-12-1982 L1983 **DR** *020 †80
ANAND, Aditi. 3901 W 15TH ST 75075 #496-07-1979 L1992 **PTH** *020 †50
ANDERSON, Judith Deane. 6305 WOLF RIDGE DR 75024 #048-12-1997 L2000 **NPM** *020 †55
ANNAVAJJHALA, Durga. 3504 CEDAR FALLS LN 75093 #495-79-1980 L2000 **NPM PD** *020 †55
APONTE, Philip Jason. ■ 75093 #048-04-1999 L1999 **FM D** *020
ARAB, Fathima Awnigar. ■ 75023 #496-27-1993 L2007 **IM** *020 †20
ARAKAL, Rajesh George I. 6020 W PARKER RD, STE 200 75093 #033-05-1999 L2004 **OSS** *020 †40
ARAUZO, Art C. 5172 VILLAGE CREEK DR, STE 101 75093 #005-12-1982 L1983 **P** *020 †75
ARNOLD, Ann Carol. 3900 W 15TH ST STE 404 75075 #004-01-1971 L1972 **IM HEM** *020 †20
ASBURY, Karen S. 5805 COIT RD, STE 202 75093 #056-06-1994 L1996 **IM** *020
ASHWORTH, Carolyn J D. 3721 W 15TH ST STE 603 75075 #048-12-1973 L1973 **PD** *020 †55
ATTMORE, Jennifer Teresa. 3900 W 15TH ST, MED CTR OF PLANO SENIOR HE 75075 #048-14-1999 L2003 **IMG** *100
AXMANN, Brenda Lyn. 6124 W PARKER RD, STE 332 75093 #048-12-1987 L1989 **OBG** *020 †30
AZIZI, Ali. ■ 75025 #048-16-2007 L2007 **FP** *012
AZNAVORIAN-BENTLEY, Gail. 6200 PARK MEADOW LN, TEXAS RADIOLOGY 75093 #048-12-1994 L1995 **DR** *020 †80
BABAIAN, Naira Spartak. 5928 W PARKER RD, STE 1200 75093 #913-38-1985 L1998 **FM** *020 †18
BADHIWALA, Shamji P. 6404 INTERNATIONAL PKWY, STE 2100 75093 #495-22-1981 L1988 **P** *020 †75
BADR, Adnan Suleiman. 6200 W PARKER RD, STE 106 75093 #875-03-1988 L1995 **GE** *020 †20
BAIG, Nazia. ■ 75093 #048-15-2007 **PD** *012
BAILEY, Wallace. ■ 75093 #016-11-1953 L1959 **CRS** *071 †10
BAIRD, Kenneth Ewell. 2120 W SPRING CREEK PKWY, STE A 75023 #039-05-1986 L1989 **FM** *020 †18
BAIYERI, Mary Oladunni. 1708 COIT RD, TEXAS CHILD NEUROLOGY 75075 #690-01-1983 L2001 **PD N** *020 †55,75
BAKER, John H. 6300 W PARKER RD, STE 428 75093 #048-15-1987 L1988 **PG PD** *020 †55
BAKHTARI, Ladan. 5941 DALLAS PKWY 75093 #048-13-1994 L1995 **IM** *020 †20
BAKLEH, Mohanad. ■ 75023 #875-01-1994 L2007 **ID IM** *020 †20
BAKSHI, Tracy Ruff. 6200 PARK MEADOW LN, TEXAS RADIOLOGY 75093 #048-04-2000 L2005 **DR** *020 †80
BALACHANDAR, Gowri. 4101 W SPRING CREEK PKWY, STE 400 75024 #495-53-1988 L1998 **GE** *020 †20
BALIREDDY, Narayana Reddy. ■ 75025 #495-62-1994 L2000 **IM** *020 †20
BALL, James Wm, Jr. ■ 75093 #027-01-1992 L1995 **EM** *020 †16
BANKHEAD, Jack Bridges. 4708 ALLIANCE BLVD 75093 #048-02-1970 L1970 **IM GP** *020 †20
BANKSTON-TROIANI, Dawn C. 4001 W 15TH ST, STE 245 75093 #048-12-1994 L1995 **OBG** *020 †30
BARBER, Frank Alan. 5228 W PLANO PKWY 75093 #048-04-1973 L1973 **ORS** *020 †40
BARNETT, Brian David. 6124 W PARKER RD, STE 334 75093 #033-05-1990 L1997 **REN OBG** *020 †30
BARRINGTON, John Wesley. 5940 W PARKER RD 75093 #005-19-2000 L2006 **ORS** *020 ‡
BASEMAN, Adam Glen. 4001 W 15TH ST, UROLOGY CLINIC OF NORTH 75093 #048-04-1997 L1999 **U** *020 †95
BASS, Annie Laura. 1600 COIT RD STE 108 75075 #027-01-1982 L1985 **OBG PD** *020 †55,30
BATES, Rosemary A. 6300 STONEWOOD DR, STE 302 75024 #048-12-1996 L1998 **IM** *020 †20
BAVIKATI, Neeta. 1640 COIT RD 75075 #048-16-1994 L2001 **CD** *020 †20
BEARD, Candis Lesley. 101 E PARK BLVD, STE 911 75074 #048-12-1997 L1998 **EM** *020 †16
BEAVIS, Robert Coleson. 5228 W PLANO PKWY 75093 #068-01-2000 L2007 *100
BECKER, David L. 6124 W PARKER RD, STE 436 75093 #048-15-1993 L1995 **FM** *020 †18
BELL, Paul Ray. 2700 W PLANO PKWY 75075 #024-07-1980 L1983 **IM** *020 †20
BENAIM, Elie. 4708 ALLIANCE BLVD, DALLAS UROLOGY ASSOCIATES 75093 #935-07-1984 L2002 **U** *020 †95
BENDER, Robert Michael. 1600 COIT RD STE 207 75075 #056-06-1970 L1981 **OBG** *020 †30
BENSON, Eric H. 6200 PARK MEADOW LN, TEXAS RADIOLOGY 75093 #048-12-1991 L1992 **VIR** *020 †80
BERGER, Laurie F. 6300 W PARKER RD 75093 #048-12-1992 L1994 **PD** *020 †55
BERK, Jordana Beth. ■ 75093 #048-12-1992 L1993 **PTH** *020
BERKOWITZ, Jeffrey B. 3405 MIDWAY RD, STE 650 75093 #012-05-1996 L1998 **PD** *020 †55
BERRY, Marcy L. 6200 W PARKER RD 75093 #048-15-1996 L1999 **PD** *020 †55
BETZ, Timothy. 1630 COIT RD, PULMONARY DIAGNOSTICS 75075 #048-12-1987 L1988 **PUD** *020 †20
BHATNAGAR, Sarika. ■ 75024 #025-07-2003 L2003 **END** *012 †20
BIEDERMANN, Scott Anthony. 4708 ALLIANCE BLVD STE 770 75093 #048-14-1999 L2002 **PN** *100 †20
BIERIG, Paul Chas. 6124 W PARKER RD, MOB 3, STE 232 75093 #039-01-1990 L1991 **AN** *020 †05
BLACKMON, Michael Bendele. 6124 W PARKER RD, STE 131 75093 #048-02-1995 L1996 **PCC** *020 †20
BLANCHETTE, Katherine L. ■ 75025 #048-14-1985 L1986 **PM** *020 †60
BLOCH, Brandon Lee. 3105 W 15TH ST STE B 75075 #048-12-1978 L1978 **GE** *020 †20
BLOMQUIST, Gregory. 2401 PRESTON RD STE D 75093 #016-42-1991 L1994 **IM EM** *020 †20
BLOMQUIST, Mary Dobias. 3600 COMMUNICATIONS PKWY, STE 675 75093 #048-04-1985 L1986 **AI PD** *020 †03,55
BLUMENTHAL, Scott L. 6020 W PARKER RD, STE 200 75093 #016-06-1982 L1983 **ORS** *020 †40
BODEMER, William Steven. 6020 W PARKER RD 75093 #056-05-2001 L2007 **ORS** *020
BONGALE, Rajshree Namdeor. 6404 INTERNATIONAL PKWY, STE 2100 75093 #496-38-1998 L2005 **CHP** *100 †75
BOOTHBY, Michael Hayden. 4031 W PLANO PKWY, STE 100 75093 #035-01-2000 L2005 **ORS** *020
BOOTHE, William Albert. 3900 W 15TH ST STE 102 75075 #048-12-1981 L1981 **OPH** *020 †35
BORDEN, Richard Dean. 6200 PARK MEADOW LN, TEXAS RADIOLOGY 75093 #048-12-1974 L1974 **R OS** *020 †80
BOREN, Edwin Lawrence, Jr. 3901 W 15TH ST 75075 #004-01-1993 L2000 **NM R** *020 †80,28
BOSITA, Renato Victor, Jr. 6020 W PARKER RD, STE 200 75093 #016-02-1996 L2002 **OSS** *020 †40
BOWMAN, Richard Thomson. 4001 W 15TH ST, STE 180 75093 #005-14-1982 L1989 **TS VS** *020 †85,90
BOYER, Deborah Sue. 101 E PARK BLVD, STE 911 75074 #039-01-1984 L1989 **FM** *020 †18
BOYKO, Trent Russell. 101 E PARK BLVD, STE 911 75074 #005-12-1997 L2000 **EM** *020 †16 ‡
BRANSKY, Aaron Stuart. 6309 PRESTON RD, STE 1200 75024 #016-01-2000 L2005 **CCS** *020
BRATCHER, Christina R. 1708 COIT RD STE 100, TULANE UNIVERSITY HSC 75075 #021-05-1991 L2007 **END** *020 †20
BROCHNER, Michelle L. 4708 ALLIANCE BLVD, STE 825 75093 #048-15-1995 L2003 **OPH** *100
BRODERICK-THOMAS, Jenifer. 6300 W PARKER RD 75093 #012-05-1993 L1997 **OBG** *020 †30
BROOKS, Mitchell D. 5072 W PLANO PKWY 75093 #065-01-1974 L1984 **ORS** *020 †40
BROWN, Chandra Lynn. 6105 WINDCOM CT, STE 100 75093 #047-06-1995 L1999 **FM** *020 †18
BROWN, David Lee. 4708 ALLIANCE BLVD, STE 710 75093 #010-01-1977 L1981 **CD IM** *020 †20
BROWN, Joel Martin. 3801 W 15TH ST, STE 320 75075 #041-02-1974 L1975 **IM** *020 †20
BROWN, Kecia Ledet. ■ 75024 #047-07-1999 L2007 **OBG** *020
BROWN, Kenneth Joseph, Jr. 1600 COIT RD STE 301 75075 #030-05-1998 L1999 **GE IM** *020 †20
BROWN, Robert Dale. 101 E PARK BLVD, STE 911 75074 #017-20-1976 L1979 **EM** *020 †16
BRUEN, Charles Alan. ■ 75093 #048-12-2008 *012
BRYAN, Gary Lee. ■ 75023 #048-14-2002 L2004 **PD** *100
BUERSMEYER, Todd Michael. ■ 75093 #010-02-2006 L2008 **DR** *012
BUNPIAN, Prayoon. ■ 75074 #891-02-1965 L1975 **OBG** *020
BURKET, Phillip Edward. 6957 W PLANO PKWY STE 10 75093 #030-05-1983 L2007 **CD IM** *020 †20
BURT, Randall J. 6124 W PARKER RD, STE 134 75093 #048-12-1998 L2002 **OBG** *020 †30
BURTON, William Comer. 3901 W 15TH ST 75075 #048-12-1975 L1975 **PTH** *020 †50
BUTCHER, Lawrence Ian. ■ 75023 #005-14-1982 L1997 **IM PUD** *020
BUTTLES, Jason Robert. ■ 75024 #005-12-2003 L2007 **PD** *100 †55
BYUN, Susan Kay. ■ 75025 #048-13-2000 **PD** *012
CABLE, James Douglas. 6020 W PARKER RD, STE 200 75093 #016-45-1981 L1982 **FM OM** *020 †18
CALLE-RODRIGUE, Rocio P. 6124 W PARKER RD STE G36, PRESBYTERIAN HOSP 75093 #021-05-1989 L1997 **PTH PCP** *020 †50
CALLEY, William A. 6124 W PARKER RD, BLDG III 75093 #048-12-1987 L1988 **FM PD** *020 †18 ‡
CAMBARE-PIGA, Nena Flor S. 3105 W 15TH ST STE D 75075 #748-10-1974 L1978 **PD ADL** *020 †55
CAMPBELL, Jennifer Dunham. 6124 W PARKER RD, NORTHLAKE OB & GYN P A 75093 #048-13-1996 L2000 **OBG** *020 †30
CANOSE, Jeffrey Lynn. ■ 75093 #041-07-1983 L1986 **AN** *030 †05
CAPOTE, Versallie Riparip. 3105 W 15TH ST 75075 #748-02-2001 L2006 **PD** *100 †55
CARMODY, Cameron Noble. 5228 W PLANO PKWY 75093 #005-15-1989 L2001 **OSS ORS** *020 †40
CARUTH, Jeffrey C. 3108 MIDWAY RD, # 102B 75093 #048-02-1988 L1989 **OBG** *020 †30
CASPER, Wayne Michael. 1600 W PLANO PKWY 75075 #048-16-1986 L1987 **IM** *020 †20
CASTANEDA, Evangelina. 4100 W 15TH ST, STE 118 75093 #649-01-1969 L1982 **END** *020
CATHRINER, Janet R T. ■ 75093 #048-13-1996 L1997 **FM** *020
CATTORINI, Jeffrey F. 4001 W 15TH ST, STE 455 75093 #032-01-1991 L1997 **NS** *020
CAVENEE, Michele Walters. 6200 W PARKER RD, STE 306 75093 #048-12-1988 L1989 **OBG** *071 †30
CHAGANTI, Sridevi. ■ 75074 #495-99-2000 L2006 **IM** *100 †20
CHAIM, Solomon Herman. 5228 W PLANO PKWY 75093 #056-05-1996 L2001 **ORS** *020 †40
CHANDLER, Patricia Ann. 3304 ALMA DR 75023 #048-12-1979 L1979 **FM ADM** *020 †18
CHANDLER, Richard Daryl. ■ 75075 #048-12-1977 **PD GP** *020
CHANDRA, Nagaleela M. ■ 75025 #495-99-1989 L1999 **IM** *020 †20
CHANEY, Christopher Paul. ■ 75023 #048-12-2008 *012
CHANG, Charles Shih-Cheng. 6160 WINDHAVEN PKWY, STE 200 75093 #023-07-1972 L1987 **NS CHN** *020 †55,75,25
CHANG-TUNG, Eric Gerard. 6200 W PARKER RD 75093 #038-41-1979 L1983 **TS VS** *020 †90,85
CHAPMAN, James Brian. 4708 ALLIANCE BLVD 75093 #048-13-1983 L1983 **IM** *020 †20
CHAPPELL, Timothy Rae. 1630 COIT RD STE 104 75075 #030-05-1975 L1976 **PUD IM** *020 †20
CHAVDA, Suresh N. 6957 W PLANO PKWY, STE 1400 75093 #495-17-1982 L1992 **EM** *020 †16
CHEKURI, Laxmi. ■ 75025 #495-21-1994 L2004 **IM** *020
CHEN, Hua Cecilier. 6300 ROUNDROCK TRL UNIT 1 75023 #243-16-1982 L2002 **MPD PD** *020 †20,55
CHEN, Philip Kuan Wen. 1600 COIT RD STE 308 75075 #048-16-1996 L1998 **FM** *020 †18
CHEN, Richard C. 4708 ALLIANCE BLVD 75093 #048-13-1996 L1998 **IM** *020 †20
CHEN, Weina. ■ 75024 #243-16-1985 L2002 **HMP** *020
CHESTER, Donald Wm. 3713 W 15TH ST, STE 401 75075 #048-12-1976 L1976 **OBG** *020 †30
CHICOSKIE, Christopher J. 6200 PARK MEADOW LN, TEXAS RADIOLOGY 75093 #048-12-1998 L2004 **DR** *020 †80
CHIN, Paul Carl. 4004 HALIFAX DR 75023 #048-12-2008 *012
CHINTAPALLI, Uma. ■ 75093 #495-58-1988 L2006 **IM** *100 †20
CHIRUVOLU, Arpitha. ■ 75025 #495-21-1998 L2008 **NPM** *012 †55
CHIU, Kwok-Wai. 1220 COIT RD STE 105 75075 #244-03-1977 L1994 **OM** *020
CHOKSHI, Nancy Gaurang. ■ 75093 #048-15-2007 L2007 *012
CHOWDHARY, Humera Arif. ■ 75093 #704-06-1988 L2007 **CHP** *100
CHOY, Eric Wingkai. ■ 75024 #048-12-2008 *012
CHU, Vincent Wunsan. ■ 75025 #024-07-2006 L2006 **DR** *012
CHURCH, Don Adrian. ■ 75023 #048-16-2002 L2008 **EM** *020 †16
CIBOROWSKI, Carl Eugene. 4700 ALLIANCE BLVD 75093 #048-14-1999 L2002 **IM** *020 †20
CIONE, Dean A. 4708 ALLIANCE BLVD 4240 75093 #048-12-1992 L1993 **GS** *020 †85
CLARK, Jason Andrew. ■ 75093 #017-20-2008 *012
CLARK, Joshua M. ■ 75024 #048-12-2002 L2004 **FM** *020 †18
CLEAVER, Joseph Paul. ■ 75093 #561-17-1984 L1992 **RHU IM** *020 †20
CLEMENT, Loretta Ann. 3704 INTERLAKEN DR 75075 #018-03-1982 L1992 **EM** *075 †16
COBB, William Bethel. 3809 W 15TH ST # 700 75075 #039-01-1966 L1974 **OTO** *020 †45
COEN, John Jeremiah. 5228 W PLANO PKWY, POSMC 75093 #016-06-1989 L2006 **ORS** *020 †40
COLBERG, Eitel Jose. 6100 WINDCOM CT, STE 101 75093 #042-01-1978 L1984 **PD** *020 †55
COLON, Omar Alberto. 2800 W 15TH ST 75075 #042-02-2000 L2002 **PM** *020 †60
COLSON, Jeanette Lee. 2701 W 15TH ST, SOUTHWEST REHABILITATION 75075 #012-01-1984 L1992 **PM** *020 †60
CONE, John Alan. 3540 SAILMAKER LN 75023 #039-01-1964 L1989 **OPH** *071
CONEY, Donald Josephus. 4708 ALLIANCE BLVD, STE 830 75093 #048-02-1964 L1964 **OBG** *020 †30

CONNOR, Charles K. 4708 ALLIANCE BLVD, STE 150 75093 #048-02-1994 L1996 **ON** *020 †20
COOK, Robert Alan. 6124 W PARKER RD STE 138 75093 #048-12-1986 L1987 **FM** *020 †18
COOLEY, Brian Kenneth. 1600 COIT RD, STE 401 75075 #023-01-1982 L1983 **GE IM** *020 †20
CORBETT, Edward R. 5941 DALLAS PKWY 75093 #048-13-1996 L1997 **IM** *020 †20
CORPUZ, Dolores A. ■ 75025 #748-10-1965 L1979 **IM GP** *071 †20
COURTNEY, Stephen Paul. 5228 W PLANO PKWY 75093 #021-06-1989 L1992 **ORS** *020 †40
CRARY, Kyler Gordon. 6200 W PARKER RD, EMERGENCY DEPARTMENT/PEDIA 75093 #021-01-2000 L2003 **PD** *020 †55
CRATES, John Mark. 5228 W PLANO PKWY 75093 #047-06-1992 L1998 **ORS OFA** *020 †40
CRAWFORD, Kimberly A. 3901 W 15TH ST 75075 #048-12-1986 L1987 **AN** *020 †05
CRIBBINS, Allan Joseph. 6020 W PARKER RD, STE 430 75093 #041-12-1995 L2000 **GS** *020 †85
CROW, Christopher C. 5425 W SPRING CREEK PKWY, STE 200 75024 #048-13-1997 L1998 **FM** *020 †18
CURRY, Matthew W. ■ 75023 #048-12-2002 L2004 **PCC** *012 †20
CURUBO, Mario. ■ 75023 #649-38-1989 L2004 **FM** *020 †18
DARROW, Jennifer Lynn. 3801 W 15TH ST, BLDG D 75075 #039-01-1996 L1999 **PD** *020 †55
DAUBER, Kenneth Stuart. 5228 W PLANO PKWY 75093 #035-15-1996 L1997 **PM** *020 †60
DAVE, Manisha Harpavat. 6300 W PARKER RD, STE 428 75093 #041-07-1998 L2006 **PG** *020 †55
DAVILA, Fidel. 6957 W PLANO PKWY STE 100, THE LUNG CLINIC AT HEART F 75093 #024-01-1976 L1978 **OS IM** *030 †20
DAVIS, Hong Wang. 6300 STONEWOOD DR, STE 202 75024 #243-30-1986 L1999 **FM OM** *020 †18
DAVIS, Sarah Ellen. 4205 KAREN CT 75074 #048-12-2008 *012
DAVOLIO, Julie Ann. 1600 COIT RD, PLANO WOMENS HEALTH CARE 75075 #021-01-1993 L1997 **OBG** *020 †30
DECK, Michael Arthur. 6124 W PARKER RD, STE G36 75093 #048-12-1983 L1983 **PTH** *020 †50
DEEB, Kenneth Wayne. 1524 HARRINGTON DR 75075 #020-02-1982 L1990 **GP** *020 †16
DE FINA, Laura Fink. 4708 ALLIANCE BLVD, PAVILION 1 75093 #010-01-1987 L1996 **IM** *020 †20
DEJECACION, Jodie E. 6501 LEGACY DR 75024 #048-15-2002 L2004 **FM** *020 †18
DELANEY, Susan Delphine. 2313 COIT RD STE E 75075 #056-05-1977 L1986 **P** *020 †75
DENG, Changchun. ■ 75094 #243-78-1990 **HO** *012 †20
DENNING, Jennifer Ann. 6124 W PARKER RD, NORTHLAKE OB & GYN P A 75093 #048-02-1999 L2003 **OBG** *020 †30
DENNING, Jeremy Wayne. 4708 ALLIANCE BLVD, STE 620 75093 #048-14-1999 L2006 **NS** *100
DEVILLE, James Brian. 1820 PRESTON PARK BLVD SU 75093 #021-06-1988 L1992 **ICE** *020 †20
DHUDSHIA, Neha V. 3060 COMMUNICATIONS PKWY, STE 101 75093 #048-04-1992 L1993 **IM** *020 †20
DIAZ, Marlene. 1600 COIT RD, PLANO WOMENS HEALTH CARE 75075 #048-12-1991 L1992 **OBG** *020 †30
DICKERMAN, Robby D. 6200 W PARKER RD, STE 1-503 75093 #048-78-1998, ▲ L2004 **NS** *020
DIEBNER, Debra K. 6200 PARK MEADOW LN, TEXAS RADIOLOGY 75093 #028-46-1991 L1996 **DR PDR** *020 †80
DIEBNER, Jeffrey D. 6200 PARK MEADOW LN, TEXAS RADIOLOGY 75093 #048-02-1992 L1993 **DR RNR** *020 †80
DO, Son Tuong. 6124 W PARKER RD, STE 230 75093 #019-02-1986 L1992 **GE IM** *020 †20
DOAN, John Tien. ■ 75024 #039-01-2007 *012
DONLEY, Joan Paula. 4708 ALLIANCE BLVD 75093 #055-01-1974 L1977 **IM** *020 †20
DONOHOE, Amanda C. 6200 PARK MEADOW LN, TEXAS RADIOLOGY 75093 #048-12-1995 L1996 **DR** *020 †80
DORFMAN, Steven George. 1820 PRESTON PARK BLVD, STE 1850 75093 #016-43-1970 L1978 **END IM** *071 †20
DOUGLAS, James Wilbur. 4001 W 15TH ST, STE 425 75093 #047-20-1984 L1990 **REN GO** *072 †30
DOUYON, Erwin. ■ 75024 #010-02-1999 L2002 **GS** *100
DOWNEY, Charles R, Jr. 3901 W 15TH ST 75075 #048-16-1994 L1995 **OBG** *020 †30
DRAKE, Timothy Evan. 6833 COIT RD STE 102 75024 #048-13-1974 L1975 **FM LM** *020
DUEWALL, Jennifer Lynne. ■ 75075 #048-12-2008 *012
DULIN, William Alan. 5316 W PLANO PKWY 75093 #004-01-1997 L2002 **PS** *020 †65
DUNCAN, Gary Woodrow. 3801 W 15TH ST STE 110 75075 #048-14-1981 L1981 **OBG** *020 †30
DUNCAN, John Weinandt. 1640 COIT RD 75075 #030-05-1978 L1993 **CD IM** *020 †20
DUNLAP, Charles S. 5800 COMMUNICATIONS PKWY 75093 #048-12-1993 L1994 **PD** *020 †55
DUNN, Toby Jerome. 4708 ALLIANCE BLVD, STE 240 75093 #036-07-1997 L2005 **GS** *020 †85
DUONG, Danh T. 3304 ALMA DR 75023 #305-01-1998 L2002 **FM** *020 †18
EADES, Brian. 4708 ALLIANCE BLVD, STE 710 75093 #048-15-1998 L2002 **IC** *020
EASTMAN, Geo Leonard, III. 4001 W 15TH ST, STE 350 75093 #048-12-1970 L1970 **PD** *020 †55
EDGERTON, James R. 4708 ALLIANCE BLVD, STE 710 75093 #016-11-1978 L1998 **CD TS** *020 †90,85
EDUPUGANTI, Hima Bindhu. 4708 ALLIANCE BLVD 75093 #012-21-1995 L1998 **IM** *020 †20
EHMER, Dale R, Jr. ■ 75025 #048-12-2003 L2005 **OTO** *012
EICHHORN, Eric Joel. 4708 ALLIANCE BLVD, STE 710 75093 #048-04-1979 L1980 **CD IM** *020 †20
EIDEM, Matthew Wade. 1600 COIT RD, STE 301 75075 #026-04-2000 L2002 **GE** *020 †20
EISENBERG, Dennis C. 3809 W 15TH ST, STE A 75075 #048-15-1992 L1993 **OBG** *020 †30
ELDER, James Everett. 6404 INTERNATIONAL PKWY, STE 2100 75093 #048-12-1996 L1998 **CHP** *020
EL-HAG, Aly Abdelmeguid M. 8941 COIT RD STE 100 75024 #915-02-1977 L1996 **AI** *020 †20,03
ELLER, Thomas Orville. 2200 W SPRING CREEK PKWY, STE B 75023 #048-04-1954 L1954 **FM** *071
ELLIOTT, Paul Timothy. 2701 W 15TH ST, # 112 75075 #048-02-1969 L1969 **FM GP** *075 †18
ELLIS, David Wm. 5800 GRANITE PKWY, STE 900 75024 #065-01-1979 L1982 **FM** *020 †18
EMERSON, Roger Hill, Jr. 5940 W PARKER RD 75093 #008-01-1974 L1986 **OAR** *020 †40
ENGLEMAN, Mark A. 4708 ALLIANCE BLVD, STE 150 75093 #024-07-1995 L1997 **RO** *020 †80
ENKE, Russell Austin. 6601 PRESTON RD, LEGACY HEART CENTER PA 75024 #051-01-1959 L1970 **CD** *071 †20
EPPICH, Keith Ryan. 5501 INDEPENDENCE PKWY, STE 203 75023 #016-43-1998 L2002 **FM** *020 †18
ERWIN, Gary Edward, Jr. 4708 ALLIANCE BLVD 75093 #048-02-2000 L2002 **PCC** *020 †20
ESHELBRENNER, Carrie Lee. ■ 75074 #048-04-2008 *012
ETHERIDGE, Cecilia Moss. 2400 WINONA DR 75074 #048-13-1977 L1977 **PD** *020 †55
EVERSULL, Ashley E. 1600 COIT RD STE 103 75075 #021-05-2000 L2002 **PM** *020 †60
EWALT, David Harris. 4001 W 15TH ST, UROLOGY CLINIC OF NORTH 75093 #048-12-1984 L1986 **UP** *020 †95
EXSTRUM, Terry Dale. 4708 ALLIANCE BLVD 75093 #019-02-1980 L1999 **IM** *020 †20
FADAHUNSI, Shade Eniola. 1600 COIT RD STE 308 75075 #047-07-1998 L2001 **FM** *020
FAJARDO, Osvaldo Clemente. 6601 PRESTON RD, TEXAS REGIONAL HEART CTR 75024 #042-01-1987 L1990 **GE** *020 †20 ‡
FALKNOR, Clayton L. ■ 75093 #048-12-2005 **OPH** *012
FAMILUSI, Folake Omoiara. 3304 ALMA DR 75023 #690-01-1990 L2001 **FM** *020 †18
FARMAR, Jill Renee. 6300 W PARKER RD, STE 221 75093 #048-12-1993 L1994 **OBG** *020 †30
FAROOQI, Muhammad M. 1212 COIT RD, STE 112 75075 #704-02-1988 L1997 **IM AM** *020 †20 ‡
FARROW, Julie Ann. 6200 W PARKER RD, MOB 1, STE 306 75093 #012-22-1996 L1998 **OBG** *020 †30
FARUQUI, Humaira. 2460 CIMMARON DR 75025 #704-02-1995 L2005 **IM** *100 †20
FELD, Stanley. 1600 COIT RD, ENDOCRINE ASSOCS DALLAS P 75075 #035-08-1963 L1969 **END DIA** *071 †20
FERRARA, Jean Murray. 4001 W 15TH ST STE 245, ASSOCIATED WOMEN'S HEALTHC 75093 #024-05-1989 L1998 **OBG** *020 †30
FETNER, Lucy Faye. ■ 75025 #048-02-1985 L1986 **FM** *020 †18
FICKENSCHER, Kevin M. 2300 W PLANO PKWY, PEROT SYSTEMS 75075 #037-01-1978 L1980 **MDM FM** *030 †18
FINKELMAN, Ross Leland. 5800 COMMUNICATIONS PKWY 75093 #038-40-1965 L1969 **PD** *020 †55
FINKELSTEIN, Jason Scott. 4708 ALLIANCE BLVD, STE 650 75093 #422-01-1999 L2006 **IC IM** *020 †20
FITZGERALD, Leo Leslie. ■ 75075 #016-11-1959 L1960 **GP** *020
FLAMING, Daniel Timothy. 6300 W PARKER RD 75093 #005-12-1999 L2000 **FM** *020 †18
FLEMING, Berry A. 3108 MIDWAY RD, STE 201 75093 #048-12-1988 L1992 **OBG** *020 †30
FLETCHER, Sophie G. ■ 75075 #041-12-2002 L2007 **GS** *100
FLIEDNER, Dane Richard. 7000 W PLANO PKWY, STE 110 75093 #035-09-2000 L2006 **PD** *020 †55
FLIPPO, Korie Leigh. 4700 ALLIANCE BLVD STE 4 75093 #048-04-1999 L2003 **IM** *020 †20
FONG, David W I. 3801 W 15TH ST, STE 110 75075 #005-06-1995 L1996 **OBG** *020 †30
FOX, Murray Edward. 3809 W 15TH ST STE A 75075 #048-13-1971 L1971 **GYN** *020 †30
FRAIM, Clifford Jack. 4708 ALLIANCE BLVD 75093 #048-02-1975 L1975 **N** *020 †75
FRANK, Michael Jos. 5940 COMMUNICATIONS PKWY 75093 #028-34-1981 L1994 **PD** *020 †55
FRAZEE, Lewis Jacob. 4100 W 15TH ST, STE 210 75093 #020-02-1977 L1982 **OPH** *020 †35
FREEMAN, Alan Lee. 1220 COIT RD STE 106 75075 #005-02-1967 L1971 **U** *020 †95
FREER, Timothy Wayne. 3801 W 15TH ST, STE C 75075 #048-12-1978 L1978 **DR** *020 †80
FRIEDMAN, Daniel Aaron. 6405 W PARKER RD 75093 #021-05-2000 L2003 **GE** *020 †20
FRIEDMAN, Ronald Michael. 6124 W PARKER RD, BLDG 3 - STE 232 75093 #016-06-1989 L1991 **PS HS** *020 †65
GABLE, Dennis R. 4708 ALLIANCE BLVD, STE 240 75093 #048-04-1992 L1993 **VS GS** *020 †85
GAMARNIK, Shari Carolyn. ■ 75093 #665-02-2007 **FP** *012
GARB, Leslie Julian. 3705 W 15TH ST 75075 #836-01-1963 L1977 **FM FPG** *020 †18
GARCIA-MORALES, Francisco. ■ 75024 #649-02-1980 L2008 **NM** *020 †28,80
GARDUNO, Abel. 5425 W SPRING CREEK PKWY, STE 200 75024 #048-13-1994 L1998 **FM** *020 †18
GARNER, Garrett H. 6124 W PARKER RD, NORTHLAKE OB & GYN P A 75093 #048-12-1996 L1998 **OBG** *020 †30
GARTENBERG, David Saml. 4100 W 15TH ST # NO-114 75093 #062-01-1972 L1977 **FM** *020 †18
GARZA, David Eduardo. 3801 W 15TH ST STE 360, DOCTOR'S OF INTERNAL MEDIC 75075 #048-13-1993 L1995 **IM** *020
GATES, William B. 3108 MIDWAY RD STE 105 75093 #048-12-1995 L1998 **FM** *020 †18
GAUTAM, Micky K. 6404 INTERNATIONAL PKWY, STE 2100 75093 #048-78-1998, ▲ L2001 **P** *020 †75
GEBERT, Alvin Ray. 6200 W PARKER RD 75093 #048-02-1976 L1976 **OBG** *020 †30
GEE, Phyllis Janice. 4601 OLD SHEPARD PL, STE 201 75093 #025-07-1980 L1987 **OBG** *020 †30
GENATO, Jeffrey James. 6009 W PARKER RD STE 149, PMB 140 75093 #016-43-1995 L2002 **IM** *020 †20
GENENDER, Lawrence J. 4001 W 15TH ST, STE 180 75093 #067-01-1959 L1977 **GS** *071 †85
GHAFFAR, Seema Abdul. 5076 W PLANO PKWY 75093 #704-02-1995 L2006 **FM** *020 †18
GIBSON, Georgiana. 1600 COIT RD STE 307 75075 #048-12-1982 L1983 **R** *020 †80
GIEP, Son Nguyen. 6300 W PARKER RD STE 220 75093 #045-01-1997 L2000 **IM** *020 †20
GLADDEN, Jeffrey Robt. 4708 ALLIANCE BLVD, STE 650 75093 #041-13-1982 L1988 **CD IC** *020 †20
GLIDDEN, Geoffrey Glynn. 3700 W 15TH ST STE 100C 75075 #048-04-1978 L1979 **ORS** *020 †40
GLOWACKI, Lori Shannon. 4708 ALLIANCE BLVD, STE 835 75093 #065-06-1983 L1993 **NEP** *020 †20
GODSEY, Kenneth Basil. 4708 ALLIANCE BLVD 75093 #018-03-1978 L1987 **IM** *020 †20
GOLDBERG, Sarah Anne. ■ 75023 #048-12-2007 **DR** *012
GOLDEN, Michael Paul. 4100 W 15TH ST # NO-212 75093 #041-02-1972 L1980 **D IM** *020 †20,15
GOLDSCHMIEDT, Markus. 1600 COIT RD STE 301 75075 #737-01-1982 L1988 **GE** *020 †20
GOMEZ, Anna Maria. 6200 W PARKER RD STE 400 75093 #048-12-1979 L1979 **PD** *020 †55
GONDOL, Sara Lynn. 4001 W 15TH ST STE 3 75093 #048-04-2004 L2007 **PD** *020 †55
GONZALEZ, Justo Jesus. 2220 COIT RD STE 480 75075 #649-02-1972 L1974 **AN PME** *020
GONZALEZ, Pablo I. ■ 75023 #048-12-2008 *012
GOOD, Roger Russell. 5960 W PARKER RD, STE 278 PMB 166 75093 #030-05-1980 L2000 **RO** *020 †80
GOPALAKRISHNAN, Deepika. 4708 ALLIANCE BLVD, STE 710 75093 #495-59-1988 L2001 **CD** *020 †20
GORE, David Christopher. 6200 W PARKER RD, STE 302 75093 #048-15-1993 L1994 **OBG** *020 †30
GOTHARD, Sander Jay. 5425 W SPRING CREEK PKWY, STE 200 75024 #021-05-1995 L1996 **FM** *020 †18
GRAHAM, Chester F. 6124 W PARKER RD, UROLOGY CLINICS OF NORTH 75093 #048-12-1989 L1991 **U** *020 †95
GRAHAM, Robert Lynn, Jr. 4108 W 15TH ST, STE 200 75093 #027-01-1974 L1975 **IM** *020 †20
GRAY, Barry Ken. 3104 CROOKED STICK DR 75093 #019-02-1965 L1990 **EM** *020 †16
GREEBON, Daryl Trent. 3809 W 15TH ST, STE A 75075 #048-12-1975 L1986 **OBG** *020 †30
GRISHAM, Charles K. 6200 W PARKER RD, STE 306 75093 #048-02-1996 L2000 **OBG** *020 †30
GROSS, Michael Brian. 6124 W PARKER RD, UROLOGY CLINICS OF NORTH 75093 #005-14-1989 L1990 **U** *020 †95

GUINN, Todd Bradley. 6200 PARK MEADOW LN, TEXAS RADIOLOGY 75093 #021-06-1991 L1993 DR *020 †80

GUM, Patricia. ■ 75075 #028-46-1995 L2003 CD *020 †20

GUNASEKERA, Irani. ■ 75024 #422-01-1993 L1997 AN *020

GUPTA, Manish. 4708 ALLIANCE BLVD, STE 150 75093 #654-01-1995 L2002 HO *020 †20

GUPTA, Naresh. 4712 DEXTER DR, STE 200 75093 #496-09-1976 L1997 HO *020 †20

GURPINAR, Ediz Ibrahim. 4420 ORCHARD GATE DR 75024 #048-02-1995 L2000 R RNR *020 †80

GURRAPU, Yamuna. ■ 75025 #495-50-2002 IM *012

GUYER, Richard Don. 6020 W PARKER RD STE 200, TEXAS BACK INSTITUTE 75093 #041-01-1975 L1980 ORS *020 †40

HAIDER, Munawar. 3304 ALMA DR 75023 #704-16-1986 L2002 FM *020 †18

HAMN, Stephen V. 6020 W PARKER RD STE 430 75093 #048-13-1982 L1987 GS AM *020 †85

HAMPE, David W. 5920 W PARKER RD, STE 100 75093 #048-15-1988 L1990 GS *020

HAN, Lily Cheng. 6300 W PARKER RD STE 324, WINDHAVEN PEDIATRICS 75093 #035-20-1996 L1999 PD *020 †55

HANDLEY, George Jos. 2209 SCENIC DR 75025 #033-05-1963 L1971 PUD IM *071 †20

HANLEY, John S. 101 E PARK BLVD, STE 911 75074 #048-12-1986 L1987 FM *020 †18

HARANDI, Safoora. 3060 COMMUNICATIONS PKWY, STE 204 75093 #517-12-1994 L2000 IM *020 †20

HARDEN, Robert James. 2222 W SPRING CREEK PKWY, STE 202 75023 #047-07-1979 L1981 CHP P *020 †75

HARMS, Heidi Jo. 4708 ALLIANCE BLVD 75093 #034-01-2001 L2005 OBG *020 †30

HARPER, Stephen Alan. ■ 75075 #023-12-2006 L2007 EM *012

HARRIS, Carolyn. 4100 W 15TH ST, STE 202 75093 #038-44-1993 L2004 IM *020 †20

HARRIS, Scott Wm. 3801 W 15TH ST 75075 #048-12-1983 L1985 PS GS *020 †85,65

HART, John, Jr. ■ 75024 #023-01-1983 L1994 N *020

HARTLEY, Cindy M. 4001 W 15TH ST STE 245 75093 #048-12-1996 L1997 OBG *020 †30

HASHEMI, Mohammad Taghi. 1408 MOCKINGBIRD DR 75093 #422-01-1998 L2003 ORS *012 †20

HASHEMIPOUR, Said. 1705 OHIO DR, STE 100 75093 #060-01-1986 L1993 CRS GS *020 †85,10

HATCHETT, Robert Kevin. ■ 75023 #021-06-1987 L1991 OBG REN *071

HAYDEN, Shawn Andrew. 3108 MIDWAY RD STE 104 75093 #024-16-1985 L2003 ORS OSS *020 †40

HEAD, William Cassidy. 6300 W PARKER RD, STE 220 75093 #004-01-1960 L1964 OAR *020 †40

HEBBUR, Malini. 3801 W 15TH ST, BLDG D 75075 #496-20-1991 L1996 PD *020 †55

HEDAYAT, Marjaneh. 6305 PRESTON RD STE 1000 75024 #028-34-1994 L2001 FM *020 †18

HEFFERNAN, Jill Prince. ■ 75074 #048-16-2005 L2006 RO *012

HELLEMN, Michael E. ■ 75023 #048-12-2006 FP *012

HENDERSON, Eugene B. 3901 W 15TH ST 75075 #048-12-1982 L1983 CD *020 †20

HENRY, Terrence Floyd. 4100 W 15TH ST STE 112 75093 #048-02-1973 L1973 FM *020 †18

HERMANN, Darrell Wm. 7000 W PLANO PKWY, STE 200 75093 #017-20-1977 L1984 PDS *020 †85

HERRERA, Monica. 6300 W PARKER RD, STE 324 75093 #048-04-1992 L1993 PD *020 †55

HERZOG, Briant Gray. 6200 W PARKER RD, STE 310 75093 #049-01-1977 L1986 OBG *020 †30

HEWELL, George Mc Creight. 1300 MEDICAL AVE STE 102 75075 #048-13-1972 L1972 IM *020

HIDALGO, Hector Luis. 6100 WINDCOM CT, STE 101 75093 #042-01-1978 L1983 PD *020 †55

HILL, Francis Gordon. 4708 ALLIANCE BLVD 75093 #016-11-1976 L1988 IM CCM *020 †20

HILLIARD, Stuart Mehl. ■ 75093 #048-15-2001 L2005 HS *100 †85

HILLYARD, John Mansell. 5940 W PARKER RD 75093 #028-34-1981 L1991 ORS *020 †40

HINOJOSA, Enrique E. 100 S RIGSBEE DR 75093 #649-02-1958 L1968 EM OS *071

HINSON, Stacy Alison. ■ 75093 #041-14-2008 *012

HINTON, James Henry, III. 2120 W SPRING CREEK PKWY 75023 #041-13-1977 L1994 FM *020 †18

HO, Linda Marie. ■ 75093 #014-01-1982 L2007 OBG *020 †30

HOCHMAN, Jesse Neil. 6200 PARK MEADOW LN, TEXAS RADIOLOGY 75093 #035-19-1999 L2005 RNR R *020 †80

HOCHSCHULER, Stephen H. 6200 W PARKER RD 75093 #024-01-1968 L1972 OSS *020 †40

HODGE, Nicole C. ■ 75093 #028-34-2003 L2007 AN *020

HOHMANN, Stephen Edward. 4708 ALLIANCE BLVD, STE 240 75093 #005-18-2001 L2004 VS *020 †85

HOLLABAUGH, Eric S. 6100 WINDHAVEN PKWY 75093 #048-02-1988 L1989 D *020 †15

HOLLOWELL, John Scott. 6601 PRESTON RD, LEGACY HEART CENTER PA 75024 #021-06-1985 L1992 CD IC *020 †20

HONAKER, Richard S. ■ 75093 #048-02-1988 L1990 EM *020 †16

HOOPER, Lisa Diane. 5920 W PARKER RD 75093 #011-03-1994 L1996 DR *020 †80

HOPSON, Daniel James. 2800 N DALLAS PKWY, STE 210 75093 #018-03-1980 L1984 N *020 †75

HORRILLENO, Alma. 555 REPUBLIC DR, STE 418 75074 #748-01-1972 L1982 FM *074

HOSTIN, Richard Alan, Jr. 4708 ALLIANCE BLVD, STE 810 75093 #039-01-2000 L2006 OSS *020

HOUSE, Stephanie Lynne. 6537 PRESTON RD 75024 #048-13-2002 L2005 FM *020 †18

HOYLE, Robert Mark. ■ 75093 #036-01-1988 L1991 VS *020 †85

HSU, Judith Wynechi. 3709 W 15TH ST, STE 300 75075 #016-43-1996 L2002 OBG *020 †30

HSU, Kenneth Suway. 4001 W 15TH ST STE 335 75093 #048-12-2000 L2005 OTO *020 †45

HU, Mei. 2800 W 15TH ST 75075 #243-47-1989 L2004 IM *100 †60

HUANG, Alvin Eric. 4708 ALLIANCE BLVD 75093 #047-06-1998 L2004 END *020 †20

HUDGINS, James Judson. 4001 W 15TH ST, STE 180 75093 #027-01-1968 L1984 GS OS *020 †85

HUFFMAN, Henry Thurman. 3901 W 15TH ST 75075 #027-01-1990 L1998 PTH *020 †50

HUGHES, John David. 6124 W PARKER RD, STE 131 75093 #048-12-1978 L1978 CCM PUD *020 †20

HUI, Dawn Szufei. ■ 75093 #048-12-2005 GS *012

HULL, Paul G. 1220 COIT RD STE 104 75075 #039-01-1972 L1976 FM *020 †18

HUMENIUK, William Barry. 4001 W 15TH ST, STE 200 75093 #065-01-1990 L1998 OP *020 †40

HURD, Paul Windham. 2800 N DALLAS PKWY, STE 210 75093 #048-12-1978 L1978 N IM *020,75

HUSAIN, Naveen. 3721 W 15TH ST STE 601, PEDIATRIC ASSOC OF N TX 75075 #704-25-1995 PD *020 †55

HUSSAIN, Ruqaiya. 2419 COIT RD STE B 75075 #495-77-1970 L1982 *020

IVEY, Jack Lyndon. 1900 PRESTON RD, STE 267-234 75093 #048-02-1970 L1970 OBG *020 †30

JABBOUR, Salim Halim. 1705 OHIO DR, STE 100 75093 #048-02-1995 L1998 CRS *020 †85

JACKSON, Tania Alyssa Whi. 6300 W PARKER RD, STE 325 75093 #021-05-1991 L1995 OBG *020 †30

JACOBS, Arlene Jean. 1600 COIT RD, PLANO WOMENS HEALTH CARE 75075 #021-01-1985 L1986 OBG *020 †30

JACOBY, Eric Brian. 3108 MIDWAY RD, STE 201 75093 #021-01-1993 L1997 OBG *020 †30

JAFFEE, Fawzia N. 5940 W PARKER RD, STE 200 75093 #016-42-1991 L1996 OBG *020 †30

JAIN, Alok. 3901 W 15TH ST, MEDICAL CENTER OF PLANO 75075 #919-01-1992 L2004 NPM CCP *020 †55

JAIN, Nisha. 3900 PEBBLE CREEK CT, STE 102 75023 #496-07-1995 L2005 PM *020 †60

JEANG, Jieh Ren. ■ 75093 #385-03-1952 L1980 IM *071

JENKINS, R Doug. 5509 PLEASANT VALLEY DR, STE 20 75023 #048-02-1994 L1997 FM *020 †18

JENKINS, Tammie D. 305 W SPRING CREEK PKWY D 75023 #020-12-1993 L1998 FM *020 †18

JONES, Blaise Warren. 6200 PARK MEADOW LN, TEXAS RADIOLOGY 75093 #048-12-1980 L1980 DR RNR *020 †80

JONES, Gregory Allen. 1600 COIT RD STE 307, BAYLOR UNIVERSITY MEDICAL 75075 #012-01-1994 L1999 VIR *020 †80

JONES, Jeffrey David. ■ 75024 #048-15-2008 *012

JONES, Katherine Kendrick. ■ 75023 #048-04-2008 *012

JONES, Keli Shannon. 6200 W PARKER RD, STE 200 75093 #048-12-1990 L1991 GYN *020 †30

JORDAN, Allison Elizabeth. 7216 HIGH PLAINS DR 75024 #048-12-2008 *012

JOSEPH, George Emil. 4108 W 15TH ST STE 100, EYE SURGERY OF TEXAS 75093 #010-02-1992 L1998 OPH *020

JOSEPH, Rajiv. 7920 PRESTON RD STE 100 75024 #495-52-1980 N SME *020 †75

JOSEPHS, John. 6124 W PARKER RD STE 330 75093 #048-12-1990 L1991 CCS *020 †85

JULIEN, Tya-Mae Yvette. 4708 ALLIANCE BLVD 75093 #041-02-1994 L2002 GE *020 †20

JUNEAU, Leo James, Jr. 2200 W SPRING CREEK PKWY, STE B 75023 #048-02-1968 L1968 FM *020 †20

KADESKY, Keith T. 6124 W PARKER RD, UROLOGY CLINICS OF NORTH 75093 #048-12-1988 L1989 U *020 †95

KADESKY, Kevin M. 7000 W PLANO PKWY, STE 200 75093 #048-12-1988 L1989 PDS *020 †85

KAKAR, Rajdeep Singh. 6313 PRESTON RD STE 400 75024 #021-01-2000 L2004 IM *020 †20

KAMPHAUS, John Nichalos. 1700 ALMA DR STE 480 75075 #039-01-1985 L1987 P *020 †75

KANDALAFT, Nicolas N. 3901 W 15TH ST 75075 #605-01-1974 L1981 NS *020 †25

KANTIPONG, Manit. 3105 W 15TH ST STE C 75075 #891-03-1968 L1976 GS *020 †85

KANTIPONG, Varaporn. 3105 W 15TH ST STE C 75075 #891-03-1968 L1976 PD *020 †55,03

KAPADIA, Darshan K. 3060 COMMUNICATIONS PKWY, STE 101 75093 #048-02-1988 L1989 IM *020 †20

KAPLAN, Adam Jonathan. 4001 W 15TH ST 75093 #048-12-1998 L2001 FM *020 †18

KAPLAN, Eric Richard. 6200 W PARKER RD STE 112 75093 #038-06-1979 L1980 CRS GS *020

KAPLAN, Ernest. ■ 75093 #917-18-1936 L1971 OTO *071

KAPOOR, Vipul. 1600 COIT RD STE 307 75075 #016-06-2001 L2007 RNR *100 †80

KARAS, Barry. 6957 W PLANO PKWY, STE 1000 75093 #035-09-1988 L2008 CD *020 †20

KATKURI, Shobha Rani. 8205 SUTHERLAND LN 75025 #495-21-1987 L2005 FM *020 †18

KATZ, Scott L. 4001 W 15TH ST, STE 350 75093 #048-12-1995 L1996 PD *020 †55

KAVI, Nagesh G. ■ 75093 #495-09-1958 L1974 IM *020 †20

KAYE, Richard Chas. 6200 W PARKER RD BLDG 1, STE 310 75093 #048-12-1990 L1991 OBG *020 †30

KEENE, Richard R. 3415 CUSTER RD, STE 124 75023 #041-02-1971 L1977 PTH *020 †50

KELLAM, Michael P. 4708 ALLIANCE BLVD 75093 #048-13-1999 L2003 N *020 †75

KENNARD, Warrett. 5300 W PLANO PKWY, STE 300 75093 #028-46-1986 L1991 GS *020 †85

KHAN, Ahmed Iqbal. 5930 W PARKER RD 75093 #160-01-1972 L1986 GP *020 †85

KHAN, Ahtaram M. 4002 W PARK BLVD 75093 #704-02-1988 L2001 FM *020 †18

KHAN, Hafiza H. 1600 COIT RD, STE 104 75075 #005-14-1992 L2001 CD *020 †20

KHAN, Jari Ullah. ■ 75093 #704-01-1997 L2004 IM *071

KHAN, Mahmood Raza. 3900 W 15TH ST STE 507 75075 #016-42-1990 L1997 IM *020 †20

KHAN, Mohammed Imran. ■ 75074 #048-15-2007 TY *012

KHAN, Najma Sardar. ■ 75025 #704-01-1970 PD *100

KHAN, Palwasha Nosheen Su. ■ 75074 #704-09-2002 FP *012

KHESHGI, Talat J. 1200 MEDICAL AVE 75075 #704-20-1983 L1999 RHU *020 †20

KHODAPARAST, Omeed. ■ 75024 #048-12-2003 L2007 AN *020

KHOURY, Rima S. 5501 INDEPENDENCE PKWY 75023 #575-01-1985 L1996 FM *020 †18

KIER, Carlos Mc Clellan. 4708 ALLIANCE BLVD 75093 #048-02-1970 L1970 RHU IM *020 †20

KILGORE, Jale Duvenci. 3900 W 15TH ST STE 507 75075 #902-01-1954 L1969 IM PUD *071

KIM, Daniel Wonsuk. 5425 W SPRING CREEK PKWY, STE 100 75024 #048-12-1999 L2006 PM *100 †60

KIM, Danny Y. 6300 W PARKER RD, STE 324 75093 #048-02-1994 L1997 PD *020 †55

KIM, David Hyon. 6200 PARK MEADOW LN, TEXAS RADIOLOGY 75093 #048-04-1994 L1999 VIR *020 †80

KIM, John Yong Ho. 1600 COIT RD STE 307, MASSACHUSETTS GENERAL HOSP 75075 #041-01-1993 L2002 PHO *020 †55

KING, Joseph David. ■ 75024 #041-09-1998 L2003 PAN *020 †05

KINRA, Agnes K. 3900 W 15TH ST STE 404 75075 #048-12-1991 L1992 IM *020 †20

KINSELLA, Virginia M. 6124 W PARKER RD, MOB3, STE 534 75093 #187-80-1987 L2004 HO *020 †20

KIOUS, Jeanelle O. 5501 INDEPENDENCE PKWY, STE 304 75023 #034-01-1997 L2000 FM *020 †18

KIRBY, Janet. 6200 PARK MEADOW LN, TEXAS RADIOLOGY 75093 #048-02-1977 L1977 DR OS *020 †80

KIRBY, Robert Lewis. 6200 W PARKER RD 75093 #028-03-1976 L1982 ON HEM *020 †20

KLAMER, David Lawrence. 1600 COIT RD STE 307, TEXAS RADIOLOGY 75075 #048-12-1985 L1986 DR IM *020 †20,80

KOENIGSBERG, Alan David. 1700 COIT RD STE 210 75075 #396-24-1979 L1985 P PPN *020 †75

KOHOUT, Jan J. ■ 75093 #068-01-1979 L1987 FM EM *020 †16

KOMENDA, Jeffrey Craig. 5944 W PARKER RD, STE 100 75093 #028-34-1988 L1989 *020

KORENMAN, Philip David. 4975 PRESTON PARK BLVD 75093 #048-02-1982 L1983 P *020 †75

KOROGLU, Tolga F. ■ 75025 #902-19-1993 CCP *100

KORT, Henry Warren. 4005 KENOSHA RD 75024 #495-12-1996 L2004 PDC *020 †55

KRAKOS, Patricia A. 6200 PARK MEADOW LN, TEXAS RADIOLOGY 75093 #048-15-1988 L1989 DR *020 †80

KRAUSE, Robert B. ■ 75093 #048-02-1952 L1952 AN *071 †05

KRISHNASWAMI, Janani. ■ 75024 #025-01-2008 *012

KRISIK, Linda Suzanne. 6020 W PARKER RD, STE 420 75093 #041-13-1992 L2004 IM *020 †20

KRUSEN, Donna M. 3941 LEGACY DR #024-194A 75023 #048-12-1987 L1988 CHP P *075

KUAN, Phillip Jung-Wei. ■ 75023 #048-12-2008 *012

KUANG, Tang Yong. ■ 75093 #243-62-1988 L2003 PCC *020 †20

KUFORIJI, Theresa. 3901 W 15TH ST, SHERIDAN NEONATOLOGY 75075 #690-02-1985 L2001 NPM *020 †55

KUHN, John Frederick, III. 4708 ALLIANCE BLVD, STE 650 75093 #039-01-1996 L2004 TS *020 †85,90

KUMAR, Ansuya Sunanda. 2120 W SPRING CREEK PKWY, INOVA FAM PHYS 75023 #495-35-1988 L1997 FM *020 †18

KUMAR, Pradeep. 3900 W 15TH ST, STE 305 75075 #496-14-1992 L2004 CHP *020 †20

KURADA, Mangala Sidram. ■ 75025 #495-37-1985 L2006 PTH *100 †50

KUSCH, Stanford L. 4708 ALLIANCE BLVD 75093 #039-01-1976 L2004 D DMP *020 †15

KUSSMAN, Howard. 3801 W 15TH ST, A340 75075 #836-01-1990 L1997 ID IM *020 †20

KUTSEN, Michael C. 6501 PRESTON RD 75024 #048-12-2001 L2004 EM *100 †16

LAKHIAN, Shamsher Kaur. 1820 PRESTON PARK BLVD, STE 1850 75093 #495-03-1984 L1996 END *020 †20

LAM, Hong. 2808 BROWNING DR, 2808 BROWNING DRIVE 75093 #048-13-1998 L2002 AN *020

LAM, Samuel Mokiu, Jr. 6101 CHAPEL HILL BLVD, STE 101 75075 #048-04-1995 L2002 OTO *020 †45

LANDIS, Gilbert. ■ 75093 #017-20-1949 L1955 OBG *071 †30

LANGFORD, Ginga Ann. 3304 ALMA DR 75023 #048-13-1984 L1986 FM *020 †18

LANKIPALLI, Ramarao Subba. 3900 W 15TH ST STE 503, COLLIN COUNTY CARDIOLOGY 75075 #495-70-1994 L2005 CD *100 †20

LA NOUE, John L, Jr. 7000 W PLANO PKWY, STE 200 75093 #048-16-1992 L1993 PDS *020 †85

LA PORTA, Eleise Beth. 7212 INDEPENDENCE PKWY # A, CHILDRENS MEDICAL CENTER O 75025 #010-01-2001 L2004 PD *020 †55

LAZARESCU, Alice. ■ 75093 #001-02-1999 L2002 IM *020 †20

LE, Dennis Trang. ■ 75075 #048-04-2002 L2004 P *100 †75

LE, Kelly Anh. 6800 ALMA DR, PREMIER MEDICAL 75023 #048-14-1999 L2001 FM PD *020 †18

LE, Thuy Bich. 6300 W PARKER RD, STE 421 75093 #048-12-1999 L2002 HO *020 †20

LE, Tuong Huu. 4100 W 15TH ST, TEXAS DIAGNOSTIC IMAGING, 75093 #026-04-1998 L2005 RNR *100 †80

LEE, Katrina Lafaye. 6124 W PARKER RD, STE 430 75093 #028-02-1998 L2002 OBG *020 †30

LEFFLER, Joel Norman. 4112 W 15TH ST, STE 201 75093 #035-08-1980 L1985 OPH *074 †35

LENSING, William Gregory. 5501 INDEPENDENCE PKWY # 2 75023 #021-05-1979 L1980 FM *020 †18

LEON, Elizabeth Y. 6300 W PARKER RD 75093 #016-02-1992 L1995 PD *020 †55 ‡

LEONARD, Bradley Michael. 4708 ALLIANCE BLVD, STE 650 75093 #048-12-1982 L1983 CD *020 †20

LEONG, Dorothy Ann. PO BOX 262569 75026 #048-15-1985 L1988 PM *020

LEVENO, Joseph K. 1600 COIT RD, STE 102 75075 #048-02-1995 L1996 OBG *020 †30

LEVERTON, Julie Kwa. 1705 OHIO DR STE 100 75024 #028-02-1992 L1998 AS CRS *020 †10,85

LEW, Michael Tom. 101 E PARK BLVD, STE 911 75074 #016-42-1995 L1998 EM *020 †16

LEWIS, Samuel Edgar. 1630 COIT RD, STE 145 75075 #048-12-1975 L1977 NR CD *020 †28

LI, Yan. 4040 MCDERMOTT RD 75024 #243-69-1986 L1997 FM *020 †18

LIE, Hauw Swan. 6200 W PARKER RD 75093 #048-15-2001 L2007 PDP *020

LIEU, Frank Chin-Fan. 3100 MIDWAY RD 75093 #244-02-1979 L1987 PD *020 †55

LIGHTFOOT, Meredith L. 6124 W PARKER RD, UROLOGY CLINICS OF NORTH 75093 #048-02-1998 L2001 U *020 †95 ‡

LILLY, Jeffrey C. 6800 PRESTON RD, MEDICAL STAFF SERVICES 75024 #048-12-2004 L2006 PCC *012 †20

LIN, Joann Hsiao-Chuang. 6101 WINDCOM CT, UCLA MED CTR 75093 #048-12-2000 L2006 PD *100 †55,03

LITTEN, Jason Blair. 7000 W PLANO PKWY, A-CUTE KIDS URGENT CARE 75093 #012-05-2002 L2007 PHO *012 †20

LITTLE, Joseph Hugh. 1600 COIT RD STE 205 75075 #005-14-1972 L1980 PS HS *020 †65

LITTRELL, John Nelson. 4708 ALLIANCE BLVD STE 270 75093 #048-02-1999 L2004 GS *020 †85

LIU, Jianyi. ■ 75025 #243-43-1989 PTH *100

LO, Lowell Jenq. ■ 75093 #048-12-2004 L2007 IM *100 †20

LOCKHART, Susanne G. 5805 COIT RD, STE 203 75093 #048-02-1996 L1997 D *020 †15

LONG, Carl Thos, III. 4708 ALLIANCE BLVD 75093 #048-02-1974 L1974 IM *020 †20

LONG, Tayler H. 6124 W PARKER RD, STE 131 75093 #005-18-1998 L1999 PCC *020 †20

LOWNEY, Jennifer Killeen. 4001 W 15TH ST, STE 280 75093 #024-05-1995 L2007 GS *020 †85,10

LOWRY, Andrew Bryan. 2200 W SPRING CREEK PKWY, STE B 75023 #017-20-1973 L1976 GP *020

LOYOLA, Walter Xavier. 3060 COMMUNICATIONS PKWY, STE 100 75093 #042-03-1980 L1987 NS *020

LU, David Chi. 1201 N CENTRAL EXPY 75075 #048-15-1992 L2004 OPH *020 †35

LUEHRS, James Gerhardt. 4101 E PARK BLVD STE 100 75074 #054-04-1960 L1983 GS OS *071 †85

LUMPKIN, Forrest E. ■ 75074 #041-02-1946 L1950 GS *071 †85

LUNBERRY, Julia J. 1630 COIT RD STE 100, COLLIN CNTY INPT SERV 75075 #019-02-1985 L1999 IM *020 ‡

LUND, Earl R. 5228 W PLANO PKWY, MEDICINE CENTER, INC. 75093 #048-02-1984 L1985 ORS *020 †40

LUND, Karen A. 6100 WINDHAVEN PKWY 75093 #048-02-1985 L1986 D *020 †15

LUNDE, Kevin C. 4708 ALLIANCE BLVD STE 780, BAYLOR MED PAVILLION I 75093 #035-03-1986 L1995 FPS OTO *020 †45

LY, Linda T. ■ 75093 #048-12-2008 *012

LYONS, James Joseph. ■ 75024 #017-20-1994 L1995 DMP *012 †18

MA, Jason Jaeha. 1600 COIT RD STE 307, TEXAS RADIOLOGY ASSOCIATES 75075 #016-11-2001 L2007 NM *020 †80,28

MAALE, Kim Kirchgessner. 6300 W PARKER RD STE 425 75093 #048-15-1986 L1987 OPH IM *020 †35

MACDONALD, Fiona Lesley. 1708 COIT RD STE 220 75075 #065-05-1992 L1994 FM *020 †18

MAC DONALD, Steven Robert. 6124 W PARKER RD, STE 134 75093 #016-06-1993 L1999 OBG *020 †30

MACKENZIE, Donald. 3700 W 15TH ST STE 100C 75075 #060-02-1977 L1986 OSS *020

MAGEE, Mitchell Jay. 4708 ALLIANCE BLVD, STE 710 75093 #048-14-1984 L1985 TS CD *020 †85,90

MAJEED, Muhammad Obaid. 6853 COIT RD STE 100 75024 #704-02-1990 L1999 PD *020 †55

MALLEMALA, Sirisha Reddy. 3600 COMMUNICATIONS PKWY, STE 601 75093 #496-28-1993 L2007 CD *020 †20

MALONE, Sharon A Goodner. 101 E PARK BLVD, STE 911 75074 #048-02-1995 L1998 EM *020 †16

MANJUNATH, Shikaripur D. 5960 W PARKER RD, STE 278 75093 #495-99-1974 L1997 PM *020

MARCUCCI, John F. 4700 ALLIANCE BLVD, EMERGENCY DEPARTMENT 75093 #048-12-1999 L2002 EM *020 †16

MARIN, Gustavo. 2701 W 15TH ST STE 522 75075 #264-06-1960 L1973 FM GP *071 ‡

MAROLY, Poonam Vaman. 6200 W PARKER RD 75093 #495-37-1997 L2003 IM *020 †20

MARSHALL, John Blaine. 101 E PARK BLVD, STE 911 75074 #048-15-2002 L2004 EM *020 †16

MARTZ, Steven Eric. 2401 PRESTON RD STE D 75093 #005-02-1990 L2000 EM *020 †16

MASAND, Amit Hari. ■ 75024 #048-12-2008 *012

MASUD, Maryam. ■ 75093 #704-01-1996 L2005 IM *100 †20

MATHENY, Keith E. 3809 W 15TH ST STE 700-B 75075 #048-14-1998 L2003 OTO *020 †45

MATHEWS, Jeff K. 6200 W PARKER RD, STE 306 75093 #048-13-1988 L1989 OBG *020 †30

MATHEWS, Shirley Rebecca. ■ 75094 #495-37-2005 FP *012

MATTER, Christie Elkins. 5805 COIT RD, STE 203 75093 #048-13-1995 L1996 D *020 †15

MAY, David C. 3600 COMMUNICATIONS PKWY, STE 601 75093 #020-02-1980 L1982 CD CCM *020 †20

MAYNARD, Erik W. 5076 W PLANO PKWY 75093 #048-02-1993 L1994 FM *020 †18

MAZZARULLI, Anthony A. ■ 75024 #033-05-2004 L2007 P *100

MC CONNELL, Carmine Gayle. 2301 COIT RD STE D 75075 #065-10-1983 L1986 FM *020 †18

MCCULLOUGH, Heath Keay. ■ 75024 #048-12-2007 GS *012

MC DONALD, Russell Robt. 4001 W 15TH ST, STE 350 75093 #048-12-1978 L1978 PD *020 †55 ‡

MC GARRY, John Eamon. 5425 W SPRING CREEK PKWY 75024 #048-14-2001 L2006 ORS *100

MC GINNIS, Leslie A. 6200 PARK MEADOW LN, TEXAS RADIOLOGY 75093 #048-12-1998 L1999 DR *020 †80

MC GLOTHIN, Terre Q. 6124 W PARKER RD, STE 532 75093 #047-07-1988 L1995 GS *020 †85

MC GUINESS, Michael A. 6100 WINDHAVEN PKWY 75093 #048-14-1989 L1996 D *020 †20,15

MC KAY, Deborah Marcia. 4708 ALLIANCE BLVD 75093 #038-06-1994 L1998 IMG *020 †20

MC KAY, Donald L, Jr. 4708 ALLIANCE BLVD, DALLAS UROLOGY ASSOCIATES 75093 #020-02-1967 L1970 U *020 †95

MC KENZIE, Aine Patricia. 4031 W PLANO PKWY STE 100 75093 #048-02-1998 L2007 PM *020

MC KENZIE, Marcus E. 6601 PRESTON RD, TEXAS REG HEART CTR 75024 #048-02-1998 L2006 CD *020 †20

MECH, Arnold Walter. 7500 SAN JACINTO PL 75024 #016-43-1977 L1986 P CHP *020 †75 ‡

MEDA, Harinineeraja. 4040 MCDERMOTT RD, OMNI MED CTR STE 100 75024 #495-37-1997 L2005 PD *020 †55

MEDWEDEFF, Lisa E. 5425 W SPRING CREEK PKWY 75024 #048-12-1994 L1996 IM *020 †20

MEHENDALE, Kimberly F. 5940 COMMUNICATIONS PKWY 75093 #021-05-1998 L2000 PD *020 †20

MEHTA, Sejal Saumil. 6404 INTERNATIONAL PKWY, STE 2100 75093 #495-22-1990 L2004 CHP P *020 †75

MELER, James D, II. 1600 COIT RD, STE 307 75075 #048-12-1993 L1995 VIR *020 †80

MELIOTES, Harry Steven. 6124 W PARKER RD, STE 436 75093 #038-45-1984 L1991 FM *020 †18

MELTON, Jack Forrest. 4708 ALLIANCE BLVD 75093 #048-02-1974 L1974 IM *020 †20

MENG, Jianhuan. 400 MAPLELAWN CT, STE 101 75075 #243-45-1985 L1998 IM PD *020 †20,55

MERCHANT, Rhonda Jean. 4512 LEGACY DR, STE 200 75024 #004-01-1996 L1999 PD *020 †20

MERRILL, Robert C. ■ 75025 #008-01-1951 L1953 OM IM *071

MESSAMORE, Andrew Karl. 5604 LINDSEY DR, 2 75093 #048-02-1985 L1986 IM NTR *020 †05

METZ, David Lawrence. 2909 CROOKED STICK DR, 2909 CROOKED STICK DR 75093 #039-01-1984 L1985 AN *020 †05

MICHAELS, Shobha. 5940 COMMUNICATIONS PKWY 75093 #495-27-1990 L2006 PD *020 †55

MIGNUCCI, Luis A. 6160 WINDHAVEN PKWY, NEUROSPINE CONSULTANTS 75093 #042-01-1983 L1990 NS *020 †25

MILES, Michele R. 5920 W PARKER RD 75093 #017-20-1993 L1994 DR OS *020 †80

MILLER, Joseph Norbert. 3900 W 15TH ST STE 304 75075 #048-12-1980 L1980 IM *020 †20

MILLER, Waenard L, Jr. 6601 PRESTON RD, LEGACY HEART CENTER PA 75024 #045-01-1978 L1979 CD IM *020 †20

MILVENAN, James Scot. 3901 W 15TH ST 75075 #048-12-1977 L1977 PTH *020 †50

MINGEA, George Danl. 1600 W PLANO PKWY 75075 #012-01-1971 L1985 FM PD *020 †55

MINSKY, Norman M. 3804 W 15TH ST STE 205 75075 #010-02-1970 L1980 PD *020 †55

MIRMESDAGH, Haideh. 7500 PRESTON RD STE 1 75024 #154-07-1991 L2007 P *020

MIRON, Morton Arthur. ■ 75075 #048-12-1965 L1965 IM PTH *075 †50

MISSIMO, David R. 5824 W PLANO PKWY STE 104 75093 #048-14-1990 L1991 CHP *020 †75

MITLYNG, James A. 4708 ALLIANCE BLVD 75093 #048-12-1986 L1987 IM *020 †20

MOBLEY, David C. 6200 W PARKER RD STE 410 75093 #048-13-1988 L1989 PD *020 †55

MOGER, Adrian Carlos. 1600 COIT RD STE 307, TEXAS RADIOLOGY ASSOCIATES 75075 #011-02-1984 L2008 VIR DR *020 †80

MOHIUDDIN, Syed Ovais. 7212 INDEPENDENCE PKWY 75025 #048-02-2004 L2007 PD *020 †55

MOLAI, Sam. ■ 75075 #048-02-2007 EM *012

MOLAKALAPALLI, Sudhamayi. ■ 75024 #496-24-1995 L2005 IM *020 †20

MOLEN, Kyle D. 4708 ALLIANCE BLVD 75093 #048-13-1995 L1998 IM *020 †20

MONIER, Jules Chas. 3809 W 15TH ST STE A 75075 #048-12-1981 L1981 OBG *020 †30 ‡

MONTGOMERY, William K. 5228 W PLANO PKWY 75093 #048-14-1988 L1989 ORS *020 †40

MOON, John, III. 5425 W SPRING CREEK PKWY, STE 200 75024 #048-12-1998 L2001 FM *020 †20

MOORE, David Owen. 4708 ALLIANCE BLVD, STE 710 75093 #021-05-1981 L1989 TS VS *020 †85,90

MOORE, Gerald Clinton. 3721 W 15TH ST STE 602 75075 #048-13-1972 L1972 AI PDP *020 †55,03

MOORE, John Marshall. 1600 COIT RD STE 103 75075 #048-02-1983 L1984 OTO HNS *020 †45

MOORE, Larry Clyde. 4708 ALLIANCE BLVD, SOUTH WEST CARDIAC 75093 #048-02-1980 L1980 CD IM *020 †20

MOORE, Pamela Dione. 6300 STONEWOOD DR, STE 200 75024 #028-46-1992 L1998 IM *020 †20

MORALES, Philip Andrew. 6601 PRESTON RD, LEGACY HEART CENTER PA 75024 #035-20-1994 L1996 CD *020 †20

MORGAN, James H. ■ 75074 #048-15-2003 L2006 FM *020 †18

MORRIS, Bruce J. 6200 PARK MEADOW LN, TEXAS RADIOLOGY 75093 #031-01-1992 L1994 VIR *020 †80

MOZAFFARI, Brian Bezorgme. ■ 75023 #048-14-2007 IM *012

MUCKATIRA, Bopanna. 400 MAPLELAWN CT, STE 101 75075 #496-20-1989 L2002 IM *020 †20

MULCHIN, William Lloyd. 3900 W 15TH ST, STE 408 75075 #041-13-1971 L1978 U *020 †95

MULLOY, John P. 6200 PARK MEADOW LN, TEXAS RADIOLOGY 75093 #048-04-1993 L1999 DR *020 †80

MULUPURI, Rama Prasad. ■ 75025 #495-83-1992 L2000 **IM** *071 †20
MUTYALA, Sireesha. 4512 LEGACY DR, STE 200 75024 #048-02-1997 L2000 **PD** *020 †55
MYERS, Marian K Solowy. 3901 W 15TH ST 75075 #011-03-1966 L1989 **NPM PD** *020 †55
NAINI, Gnana Sumathi. 1301 CUSTER RD, STE 830 75075 #495-21-1977 L1989
  IM IMG *020 †20
NAIR, Radhakrishnan G. 6601 PRESTON RD, LEGACY HEART CENTER 75024
  #495-31-1988 L2001 **CD** *020 †20
NAJAFI, Parvaneh D.. ■ 75024 #517-06-1983 L2005 **IM** *012
NALLA, Kavitha. ■ 75074 #495-57-2001 L2008 **FM** *020 †18
NAMBURI, Swati. 4708 ALLIANCE BLVD STE 540, BAYLOR MEDICAL PAVILION I 75093
  #024-05-1995 L1998 **IM** *020 †20
NAPIER, Amie L. 4708 ALLIANCE BLVD 75093 #048-13-1996 L1997 **OBG** *020 †30
NARLA, Rama Sulochana. ■ 75093 #495-37-1999 L2004 **IM** *100
NASIR, Mehmooda. ■ 75093 #704-02-1984 L2001 **P** *020 †75
NATALIZIO, Charles F. 4001 W 15TH ST, STE 480 75093 #035-06-1975 L1994 **IM** *020 †20
NAZ, Farah. 6200 W PARKER RD 75093 #704-25-1992 L2000 **PD** *020 †55
NAZEER, Shameem R. 3901 W 15TH ST, MEDICAL CENTER OF PLANO 75075
  #048-14-1997 L2000 **EM** *020 †16
NELESON, Craig S. 6020 W PARKER RD, STE 300 75093 #550-02-1997 L2005
  PMM PRS *020 †60
NELSON, Darren L. 101 E PARK BLVD, STE 911 75074 #048-16-1996 L1999 **EM** *020 †16
NELSON, David Bradford. 101 E PARK BLVD, STE 921 75074 #048-13-1984 L1991 **FM** *020 †18
NEWSOM, Terry Danl. 2701 W 15TH ST 75075 #048-04-1971 L1971 **AN** *020
NGUYEN, Adrian Ha. 3900 W 15TH ST STE 205 75075 #048-12-1998 L1999 **IM** *020 †20
NGUYEN, Anh Q. 2701 W 15TH ST, SOUTHWEST REHABILITATION 75075 #005-15-1990 L1994
  PM *020 †60
NGUYEN, Hanhdieu Thi. 6100 AVENUE K, STE 108 75074 #011-03-1998 L2004 **FM** *020 †18
NGUYEN, Khanh Lebao. 1600 COIT RD STE 306 75075 #039-01-2002 L2006 **CN** *020 †75
NGUYEN, Leigh Echols. 4700 ALLIANCE BLVD, STE 400 75093 #048-12-2001 L2005
  IM *020 †20
NGUYEN, Minh Nhu. 5920 W PARKER RD 75093 #048-02-1991 L1992 **DR** *020 †80
NGUYEN, Nam Thuy Duc. 6200 PARK MEADOW LN, TEXAS RADIOLOGY 75093
  #051-01-1994 L1999 **DR** *020 †80
NGUYEN, William Toan. 3721 W 15TH ST STE 602 75075 #048-14-1997 L2003
  AI IM *020 †20,03
NIEMI, Heli Maarit. 2105 W SPRING CREEK PKWY, STE A300 75023 #374-05-1991 L2005
  FM *020 †18
NIEWIAROWSKA, Ewa K. 6300 W PARKER RD STE 422, MOB #2 75093 #759-03-1984 L1998
  FM *020 †18
NIVENS, Traci Lyn. 6124 W PARKER RD STE 530, MOB 3 75093 #048-13-1997 L1999
  OBG *020 †30
NORRIS, Mark Alan. 4708 ALLIANCE BLVD STE 685, BAYLOR MED PAV I 75093
  #048-02-1978 L1978 **U** *020 †95
NOSNIK, Pedro. 4100 W 15TH ST STE 206 75093 #649-01-1975 L1979 **N PME** *020 †75
NWOYE, Mmiliaku Adaobi. ■ 75023 #016-06-2004 L2006 **OBG** *012
OAKES, Phillip Lee. 6200 PARK MEADOW LN, TEXAS RADIOLOGY 75093 #048-04-1968 L1968
  DR NM *020 †80,28
OBEY, Shawanda R. 6300 W PARKER RD, STE G22 75093 #048-15-2000 L2004 **OBG** *020 †30
ODOM, Todd A. 1705 OHIO DR, STE 100 75093 #048-12-1992 L1993 **CRS EM** *020 †10,85
OH, Frederick Seiwoong. ■ 75023 #051-04-2007 *012
OH, Soo Yeon. ■ 75024 #048-12-2007 **IM** *012
OKAMMOR, Ihunnaya C. 3801 W 15TH ST, STE 120 75075 #019-02-1998 L2000 **PD** *020 †55 ‡
OKECHUKWU, Vivian A. ■ 75093 #025-07-2003 L2003 **FM** *100
OLDHAM, David Graham. ■ 75025 #007-02-1975 L1977 **P** *020 †75
OLUKOGA, Christopher O. ■ 75093 #690-06-1994 L2008 **GS** *020 †85
OOMMEN, Shibu Geevarghese. 4708 ALLIANCE BLVD 75093 #035-15-1999 L2007 **GE** *020 †20
OTTO, Laurie Ann. 3308 PRESTON RD STE 3 75093 #056-06-1988 L1992 **EM** *062 †16
OWREY, Norman D. ■ 75093 #048-12-1953 L1960 **GS** *071 †85
PAMPHILE, Serge Michel. 811 E PLANO PKWY, STE 104 75074 #682-01-1967 L1977
  GP AS *020 ‡
PARK, David II. 6405 W PARKER RD 75093 #048-12-1996 L1997 **GE** *020 †20
PARKER, Darvin C, Jr. 5960 W PARKER RD, STE 278 # 150 75093 #048-12-1996 L1997
  AN IM *020
PARKER, John Matt. 3713 W 15TH ST STE 402 75075 #048-12-1970 L1970 **OBG** *020
PARKER, Richard Geo. 101 E PARK BLVD STE 921 75074 #008-01-1985 L1994 **EM** *020 †16
PARKINSON, Andrew B. 6020 W PARKER RD, TEXAS BACK INSTITUTE 75093
  #005-06-2002 L2007 **ORS** *100
PARR, Norvin G, III. 4708 ALLIANCE BLVD, SOUTH WEST CARDIAC 75093 #048-04-1969 L1969
  CD IM *020
PARRY, Edward Lansing. 6100 WINDHAVEN PKWY 75093 #021-01-1977 L2006 **D GP** *020 †15
PATEL, Ami R. 4700 ALLIANCE BLVD, STE 400 75093 #048-02-2001 L2008 **AR** *020 †80
PATEL, Amitkumar Rasik. 4700 ALLIANCE BLVD, STE 400 75093 #048-12-2002 L2005
  IM *020 †20,80
PATEL, Daksha Mangubhai. ■ 75093 #495-01-1971 L1986 **PD NPM** *020 †55
PATEL, Mitesh J. ■ 75024 #048-02-2000 L2003 **AN** *020 †05 ‡
PATEL, Nayan Raman. 6020 W PARKER RD STE 200 75093 #056-06-1996 L1997 **PM** *020 †60
PATEL, Shivani Yogendra. ■ 75093 #048-13-2001 L2005 **PME** *100 †05
PATEL, Tapan Jayantilal. ■ 75094 #496-41-2003 **IM** *012
PATEL, Vishal Jitendra. ■ 75094 #048-02-2008 *012
PAVELKA, Robert Jason. 5800 COIT RD, STE 400 75023 #048-15-2001 L2004 **OMF** *020
PAYBERAH, Sarah Nastaran. 6300 W PARKER RD, STE 225 75093 #561-27-1988 L1995
  FM *020 †18
PAYBERAH, Susan. 6300 W PARKER RD, STE 225 75093 #561-25-1989 L1995 **FM** *020 †18
PEIKARI, Darius. 4001 W 15TH ST, STE 435 75093 #048-12-1998 L1999 **IM** *020 †20
PERRY, Landon S. 6300 W PARKER RD, STE 427 75093 #048-12-1995 L2003 **GS** *020 †85,65
PERRYMAN, Ray Worth. 1600 COIT RD STE 307 75093 #048-12-1956 L1956 **DR** *071 †18,80
PESKIND, Steven Phillip. 5957 DALLAS PKWY, STE 100 75093 #048-12-1988 L1990
  OTO *020 †45
PETROFF, Patricia A. 1407 14TH ST 75074 #008-01-1998 L2001 **PD** *020 †55
PETZOLD, Carol. 4100 W 15TH ST STE 110 75093 #033-05-1976 L1981 **FM** *020 †18
PEVETO, Rodney Vaughn. 6632 WINGED FOOT WAY 75093 #048-02-1974 L1974 **DR** *020 †80
PEYTON, Sandra E. 3821 W SPRING CREEK PKWY 75023 #048-14-1994 L1997 **FM** *020 †18
PICO, Richard Michael. 2300 W PLANO PKWY 75075 #005-15-1991 L1994 **P** *020 †75
PIEPER, Andrew Allen. ■ 75093 #023-07-2001 L2006 **P** *100
PIERCE, Brock Lawson. ■ 75025 #048-13-2003 **OBG** *100

PIGA, Naomi Cambare. 3105 W 15TH ST STE D 75075 #048-04-2002 L2005 **PD** *020 †55
PIGA, Samuel Afenir. 3105 W 15TH ST, STE E 75075 #748-10-1973 L1978 **IM EM** *020
PILATOVSKY, Jose Leon. 5076 W PLANO PKWY 75093 #649-01-1972 L1975
  FM UCM *020 †18 ‡
PILLARD, Shelley E Walton. 3901 W 15TH ST 75075 #018-03-1979 L1983 **IM FM** *020 †20
PISHKO, Stephen Darryl. ■ 75075 #048-12-2005 **PD** *012
POLIAK, Jorge. 6200 W PARKER RD STE 406 75093 #048-02-1980 L1981 **OBG** *020 †30
POLIAK, Susana C. 6300 W PARKER RD, STE 224 75093 #035-46-1978 L1986 **D** *020 †15
POLLARD, Karana Renee. 6105 WINDCOM CT STE 100 75093 #038-06-1997 L2000
  FM *020 †18
POMARANTZ, Stanley Dean. 1600 W PLANO PKWY 75075 #048-12-1974 L1974
  MDM EM *030 †16
PONG, Edward Michael. 6200 PARK MEADOW LN, TEXAS RADIOLOGY 75093
  #010-01-1993 L2001 **DR** *020 †80
POTLURI, Srinivasa P. 6601 PRESTON RD, LEGACY HEART CENTER PA 75024
  #495-21-1994 L2006 **IC** *020 †20
POWELL, Gregory David. 4031 W PLANO PKWY STE 100, SPORTS MEDICINE 75093
  #056-06-1989 L1993 **PM** *020 †60
POWERS, James Wilson. 6124 W PARKER RD, NORTHLAKE OB & GYN P A 75093
  #048-02-1975 L1975 **OBG** *020 †30
PRETORIUS, Mark Edward. 4100 W 15TH ST, STE 208 75093 #048-14-1979 L1979
  N CN *020 †75
PREWITT, David W. 6601 PRESTON RD, LEGACY HEART CENTER PA 75024
  #048-14-1988 L1989 **CD IM** *020 †20
PREWITT, Maryann M. 4601 OLD SHEPARD PL, STE 209 75093 #048-14-1989 L1990
  OBG *020 †30 ‡
PUTTAGUNTA, Divijani. ■ 75093 #048-12-2005 L2008 **IM** *012
QUARLES, Bryan S. 1600 COIT RD STE 307, TEXAS RADIOLOGY 75075
  #048-12-2001 L2004 **DR** *020 †80
QUENZER, Benjamin Dale. 1000 18TH ST, DALLAS ANESTHESIOLOGY ASSO 75074
  #048-04-2002 L2006 **AN** *020
QUINBY, Rachel Heather V. 3901 W 15TH ST 75075 #048-12-1998 L2006 **D** *020 †15
QUINONES, Hector Luis. 5701 YEARY RD 75093 #042-01-1988 L1993 **AN HNS** *020
QUINTANS, Amadeo S. 4708 ALLIANCE BLVD 75093 #048-01-1964 L1975 **TS** *020
QUIROZ, Benjamin Ricardo. 1200 MEDICAL AVE, STE 104 75075 #048-13-1983 L1985
  PD *020 †55
RACANELLI, John Anthony. 6020 W PARKER RD, STE 240 75093 #048-12-1987 L1989
  ORS OSM *020 †40
RAFIQ, Shahida. 6300 W PARKER RD, STE 128 75093 #704-16-1990 L2000 **FM** *020 †18
RAJAGOPALAN, Ram E. ■ 75075 #495-04-1983 L1986 **CCM IM** *020 †20
RAJAN, Geeta. 4100 W 15TH ST, PLANO NEUROLGY PA #204 75093 #495-20-1986 L1998
  N CN *020 †75
RAJENDRAN, Rosula R. ■ 75025 #495-27-1958 L2004 **IM PCC** *071 †20
RAKKAR, Steven Sudeep S. 2105 W SPRING CREEK PKWY, STE A300 75023
  #917-24-1980 L1983 **FM** *020 †18
RAMESH, Vani. 6853 COIT RD STE 300 75024 #495-42-1988 L1997 **IM** *020 †20
RAMIREZ, Daniel Angel. 6200 W PARKER RD STE 400 75093 #048-12-1979 L1979 **PD** *020 †55
RAMIREZ, Miranda Oler. 3608 PRESTON RD STE 125 75093 #048-14-1994 L1997 **PD** *020 †55
RAMSEY, Duncan Clyde, III. 4100 W 15TH ST 75093 #048-02-1979 L1979 **ORS** *020 †40
RAMSEY, Kenneth Lee. 6124 W PARKER RD STE 5 75093 #048-04-1980 L1980 **GS VS** *020 †85
RAO, Nandita G. 4708 ALLIANCE BLVD, STE 150 75093 #495-58-1995 L2002 **HO** *020 †20
RAO, Seshagiri Aravapalli. 3608 PRESTON RD, STE 120 75093 #495-72-1974 L1981
  PDA PD *020 †55,03
RAPHAEL, Peter. 3801 W 15TH ST, STE 150 75075 #048-12-1984 L1985 **PS** *020 †65
RAPPA, Peter John. 2301 MARSH LN 75093 #048-15-1989 L1990 **PM GP** *020 †60
RASHBAUM, Ralph Franklin. 6020 W PARKER RD, STE 200 75093 #016-42-1968 L1971
  ORS *020 †40
RATLIFF, Hubert W, Jr. 4133 HIDEAWAY LN, ORTHORPEDICS & SPORTS MEDI 75093
  #047-06-1966 L1970 **ORS** *020 †40
RAVI, Sukanya. ■ 75024 #495-16-1992 L2005 **FM** *020 †18
RAWITSCHER, David Alexis. 6601 PRESTON RD, LEGACY HEART CENTER PA 75024
  #048-14-1991 L1997 **CD** *020 †20
RAWITSCHER, Robert Edward. 2812 FENWICK LN 75093 #024-01-1963 L1976 **TS** *020 †85,90
REAGOR, Lee Chappell. 101 E PARK BLVD STE 911, DEPARTMENT OF EMERGENCY 75074
  #048-02-2002 L2005 **EM** *020 †16
REDFERN, Stephen Andrew. 6300 W PARKER RD, FAMILY HEALTH CARE 75093
  #065-01-1968 L1977 **GP** *020 †18
REID, Starling Corbett. 4708 ALLIANCE BLVD 75093 #048-12-1993 L1994 **IM** *020 †20
REIMAN, Lionel Moishe. 3709 W 15TH ST 75075 #067-01-1968 L1974 **OBG** *020 †30
REISLER, Keith James. 3108 MIDWAY RD, STE 205 75093 #035-08-1984 L1985
  OBG OS *020 †30
REITMAN, Richard David. 5940 W PARKER RD 75093 #025-07-1993 L2000 **ORS** *020 †40
RELLAS, James Stephen. 6957 W PLANO PKWY, STE 1000 75093 #030-06-1977 L1981
  CD *020 †20
REMER, Steven Lewis. 6020 W PARKER RD 75093 #025-07-1989 L1993 **AN** *020 †05 ‡
RENARD, Thomas Harold. 7000 W PLANO PKWY STE 200, PEDIATRIC SURGICAL
  ASSOCS 75093 #048-12-1986 L1987 **PDS** *020 †85
RIAN, Roger Leland. 6200 PARK MEADOW LN, TEXAS RADIOLOGY 75093 #038-40-1958 L1973
  DR NR *072 †80
RICKS, Jon T. 3809 W 15TH ST, BLDG 700 75075 #048-13-1992 L1993 **OBG** *020 †30
RIEGEL, Christopher Jos. 3108 MIDWAY RD STE 10 75093 #048-13-1987 L1988 **OBG** *020 †30
RING, David Lynn. 6124 W PARKER RD, STE G36 75093 #048-15-1981 L1981 **PTH** *020 †50
RIVERA, Rodulfo Lee. 910 W PARKER RD, BARIATRIC MEDICAL ASSOCIAT 75075
  #030-05-1975 L1976 **OS AN** *020
RIZVI, Hina. ■ 75093 #704-02-2001 L2004 **FP** *012
ROBERTS, Gregory D. 3001 N DALLAS PKWY, STE E 75093 #048-13-1992 L1994
  OTO FPS *020 †45
ROBERTS, John Paul. 6124 W PARKER RD, STE 134 75093 #039-01-1991 L1995 **OBG** *020 †30
ROBINS, Darrell E. 6124 W PARKER RD, STE 134 75093 #048-02-1988 L1989 **OBG** *020 †30
RODEN, Jay Scott. 7000 W PLANO PKWY, STE 200 75093 #048-02-1981 L1981
  PDS GS *020 †85
RODRIGUEZ, Alfred Jos. 6200 W PARKER RD, STE 215 75093 #048-12-1976 L1976
  OS OBG *020 †30 ‡
ROHN, Gregory Neal. 6300 W PARKER RD, STE 326 75093 #048-12-1989 L1990
  OTO HNS *020 †45
ROMAN, Jorge Luis, III. 1600 COIT RD STE 307 75075 #051-01-1997 L1999 **VIR** *020 †20,80

ROSEMORE, Evelyn Spira. ■ 75093 #001-02-1982 L1985 **P CHP** *020

ROSEN-SCHMIDT, Shari L. 2800 N DALLAS PKWY, STE 210 75093 #048-04-1998 L1999 **N CN** *020 †75

ROSENTHAL, J Edward. 4708 ALLIANCE BLVD, STE 710 75093 #048-12-1967 L1967 **CD** *020 †20

ROTHSCHILLER, James Leo. ■ 75093 #005-14-1991 L1998 **AN** *020 †05

ROVNER, Ivan David. 3709 W 15TH ST, STE 300 75075 #018-03-1973 L1974 **OBG** *020 †30

ROWLAND, Timothy Michael. ■ 75023 #048-04-2003 L2004 **DR** *012

ROWNTREE, Robt James, II. 5800 TENNYSON PKWY 75024 #048-02-1974 L1974 **IM** *020 †20

RUBENSTEIN, David Matthew. 1220 COIT RD STE 104 75075 #010-01-1969 L1976 **OTO** *071 †45

RUDE, Brenda L. 6300 STONEWOOD DR STE 200 75024 #048-02-1992 L1993 **IM** *020 †20

RUMSEY, Bruce Gene. 6200 W PARKER RD, STE 320 75093 #028-03-1982 L1983 **OBG** *020 †30

RYAN, William H, III. 4708 ALLIANCE BLVD 75093 #036-01-1977 L1978 **TS** *020 †85,90

SAAD, John Mikhail M. 3901 W 15TH ST, EMERGENCY DEPARTMENT 75075 #065-06-1993 L1997 **FM** *020 †18

SACHS, Barton Lewis. 6020 W PARKER RD, STE 200 75093 #035-15-1977 L1985 **ORS GS** *020 †40

SACHSON, Richard A. 1820 PRESTON PARK BLVD, STE 1850 75093 #035-08-1968 L1974 **END IM** *020 †20

SACKRISON, Gary Michael. 6300 W PARKER RD 75093 #005-12-1991 L1996 **FM** *020 †18

SAFFRAN, Jill Marcia. 3405 MIDWAY RD, STE 75075 #048-02-1992 L1995 **PD** *020 †55

SAJJAD, Zeba. ■ 75094 #704-06-1990 L2000 **IM** *100 †20

SALAM, Maqbool Ahmed. 3429 LEIGHTON RIDGE DR 75025 #495-04-1979 L1991 **DR NM** *020 †28,80

SALAMON, George. 2101 TEAKWOOD LN 75075 #473-01-1966 L1980 **PD** *020 †55

SALAZAR, Alvaro. 6200 W PARKER RD 75093 #649-14-1982 L1984 **FM** *020

SAMAAN, Sarah Ann. 6601 PRESTON RD, LEGACY HEART CENTER PA 75024 #047-05-1988 L1995 **CD** *020 †20

SAMARA, David Edward. 3801 W 15TH ST, STE D-120 75075 #033-05-1980 L1983 **PD** *020 †55

SAMPLE, Joseph H, Jr. 4708 ALLIANCE BLVD 75093 #048-12-1967 L1967 **IM** *020 †20

SAMSULA, Aaron Lee. 4708 ALLIANCE BLVD 75093 #048-02-2002 L2004 **IM** *020 †20

SANKARAN, Muthiah. 1600 COIT RD, STE 309 75075 #495-42-1961 L1988 **TS** *075

SANTILLI, Gregg Matthew. 3600 COMMUNICATIONS PKWY, STE 675 75093 #038-40-1989 L1997 **AI** *020 †20

SASTRY, Malladi Rama K. 4100 W 15TH ST STE 216 75093 #495-73-1968 L1975 **PUD IM** *020

SAYED, Raza Hasan. 6404 INTERNATIONAL PKWY, STE 2100 75093 #495-99-1997 L2002 **P** *020

SCHACHERER, Timothy G. 6020 W PARKER RD, STE 240 75093 #051-04-1979 L1994 **ORS HS** *020 †40

SCHAFFER, Jeffrey A. 101 E PARK BLVD, STE 911 75074 #048-02-1988 L1989 **EM** *020 †16

SCHAFFER, Lilly Helene. 3604 PRESTON RD STE 200 75093 #041-14-1993 L1998 **D DS** *020 †15

SCHALLER, Laird Faber. ■ 75093 #016-11-1961 L1979 **OM AM** *071 †70

SCHARF, Robert Mendel. 1645 DORCHESTER DR 75075 #005-02-1968 L1976 **OPH** *020 †35

SCHLICHTEMEIER, Alvin Lee. 5320 INVERRARY DR 75093 #030-05-1969 L1979 **RO ON** *020 †80

SCHNEEWEISS-ADLER, Samuel. 3901 W 15TH ST 75075 #649-01-1962 L1967 **PD** *020 †20,03

SCHOCHET, Peter Norman. 6200 W PARKER RD, STE 505 75093 #041-13-1990 L1996 **PDP** *020 †55

SCHRADER, Michael Keith. 6020 W PARKER RD, STE 420 75093 #048-12-1998 L2001 **IM** *020 †20

SCHWARTZ, David Allen. 6601 PRESTON RD, LEGACY HEART CENTER PA 75024 #048-13-1976 L1976 **CD** *020 †20

SCOTT, Ronald Gerard. 6300 W PARKER RD, STE 128 75093 #017-20-1979 L1983 **OS UM** *020 †16 ‡

SEABERG, Elizabeth A. 6200 PARK MEADOW LN, TEXAS RADIOLOGY 75093 #048-14-1999 L2002 **DR** *020 †80

SEGAL, Aaron Philip. 6537 PRESTON RD, SEGAL FAMILY MEDICINE CENT 75024 #048-13-2002 L2004 **FM** *020 †18

SEGAL, Irwin Michael. 6537 PRESTON RD 75024 #067-01-1972 L1977 **FM** *020 †18

SELKIN, Bryan Adam. 5509 PLEASANT VALLY DR #60, DERMATOLOGY CTR OF PLANO 75023 #035-03-1996 L2002 **D** *020 †15

SELKIN, Gilbert Tremayne. ■ 75093 #048-15-2006 **GS** *012

SELKIN, Robert Peter. 3604 PRESTON RD STE 1 75093 #035-03-1993 L1998 **OPH** *020 †35

SESSIONS, Cynthia. 5425 W SPRING CREEK PKWY, STE 200 75024 #045-01-1983 L1991 **FM** *020 †18 ‡

SETO, Keith Edward. 6124 W PARKER RD, STE 330 75093 #056-06-2001 L2006 **GS** *020 †85

SHADLE, Jeffrey Morris. 1708 COIT RD, STE 220 75075 #039-01-1999 L2004 **FM** *020 †18

SHAH, Mrugesh Kantilal. 4100 W 15TH ST 75093 #495-76-1972 L1982 **ORS** *071 †40

SHAHAB, Shamsa Z. ■ 75093 #704-06-1987 **PTH** *100

SHALEK, Marc Scott. 6601 PRESTON RD, LEGACY HEART CENTER PA 75024 #035-09-1986 L1998 **CD** *020 †20

SHALEN, Philip Roger. 3060 COMMUNICATIONS PKWY, STE 103 75093 #035-09-1968 L1979 **DR** *020 †80

SHAMS, Ali A. 3900 W 15TH ST STE 107 75075 #517-01-1961 L1982 **PD PDC** *020 †55

SHAPIRO, Ronald Howard. ■ 75075 #048-13-2007 **IM** *012

SHARAN, Leena. 6124 W PARKER RD, STE 432 75093 #496-41-1993 L2005 **CD** *020 †20

SHARMA, Jivesh. 6300 W PARKER RD, STE 421 75093 #048-02-1987 L1989 **ON HEM** *020 †20

SHARMA, Kavita. ■ 75093 #048-13-2006 **PD** *012

SHARMA, Vagisha. 1600 COIT RD STE 402, WOMEN'S CARE - OB/GYN 75075 #495-74-1992 L2004 **OBG** *020

SHELDON, William Robt, Jr. 5930 W PARKER RD, STE 700 75093 #048-12-1978 L1978 **END DIA** *020 †20

SHELOKOV, Alexis Paul. 4708 ALLIANCE BLVD, STE 810 75093 #048-12-1982 L1983 **ORS** *020 †40

SHELTON, Jack Chas. 4708 ALLIANCE BLVD 75093 #048-02-1968 L1968 **IM** *020 †20

SHERROD, Peter Stewart. 3721 W 15TH ST STE 601 75075 #048-12-1969 L1969 **PD** *020 †55

SHERRY, Steven D. 5824 W PLANO PKWY STE 101, WILLOW BEND COSMETIC SURG 75093 #048-12-2003 L2007 **FPS OMF** *020

SHETH, Aruna Nitinkumar. ■ 75093 #495-96-1970 L1976 **PTH** *020 †50

SHETH, Maushmi Nilay. ■ 75024 #495-76-1996 L2006 **N** *100 †75

SHETH, Nitinkumar H. ■ 75093 #495-01-1970 L1975 **AN PME** *020 †05

SHI, Wenliang. 3100 MIDWAY RD STE 169 75093 #243-49-1985 L2002 **OBG** *020 †30

SHIN, Edward Taejoon. 4100 W 15TH ST, STE 200 75093 #041-13-1991 L2003 **AN** *020 †05

SHIN, Sang Seok. 3100 INDEPENDNC PKWY #103A 75075 #583-01-1972 L1981 **PTH** *020 †50

SHORE, Kenneth Alan. 5501 INDEPENDENCE PKWY, STE 110 75023 #051-07-1980 L1984 **IM** *020 †20

SHORT, Michael C. 6300 W PARKER RD, FAMILY HEALTH CARE 75093 #036-05-2002 L2003 **FM** *020 †18

SHOUSE, Theresa A. 6200 W PARKER RD, STE 410 75093 #048-13-1989 L1990 **PD** *020 †55

SICKLER, Susan Jeanne. 5940 COMMUNICATIONS PKWY 75093 #026-04-1997 L1999 **PD** *020 †55

SIDDIKI, Lubna. 3920 ALMA DR, JOHN PETERS SMITH HOSPITAL 75023 #704-02-1996 L2005 **P** *100

SIEGEL, Jeffrey Brian. 4401 TRADITION TRL 75093 #005-18-1984 L1994 **DR GS** *020 †80

SIGMAN, Amy Gail. 4708 ALLIANCE BLVD 75093 #048-12-1995 L1997 **OBG** *020 †30

SIKKA, Dipali. ■ 75024 #021-01-2001 L2007 **IM** *100

SINGHAL, Anupam Kishore. 6200 PARK MEADOW LN, TEXAS RADIOLOGY 75093 #067-01-1984 L1989 **DR** *020 †80

SKIPPER, Kent K. 6124 W PARKER RD, STE 330 75093 #048-15-1993 L1994 **GS** *020 †85

SKRAINKA, Brian S. 6200 W PARKER RD, PEDIATRIC DEPARTMENT - 4B 75093 #028-03-1985 L2006 **PD PE** *020 †55

SLEDGE, Charles Lee. 4708 ALLIANCE BLVD 75093 #048-12-1967 L1967 **IM** *020 †20

SMALE, John Stanley. ■ 75075 #048-04-1954 L1954 **FM** *071 †18

SMALL, Andrew B. 6200 PARK MEADOW LN, TEXAS RADIOLOGY 75093 #048-12-1998 L2000 **DR** *020 †80

SMALL, Andrew B, III. 1600 COIT RD STE 307 75075 #048-12-1969 L1969 **PME GP** *030 †85

SMITH, Douglas Craig. 6200 W PARKER RD, STE 506 75093 #048-14-1984 L1985 **FM** *020 †18

SMITH, Jeanette L. 6200 W PARKER RD, STE 410 75093 #048-13-1993 L1994 **PD** *020 †55

SMITH, Purcell, III. 5228 W PLANO PKWY, PLANO ORTHO & SPORTS MED 75093 #004-01-1981 L1987 **HS ORS** *020 †40

SMITH, Robert Eugene, II. 2108 DALLAS PKWY, STE 206 75093 #025-01-1986 L2006 **OPH AM** *020 †35

SMITH, Russell Raymond. 5068 W PLANO PKWY, STE 224 75093 #048-14-1985 L1986 **FM** *020 †20

SMREKAR, James Douglas. 3709 W 15TH ST 75075 #048-13-1980 L1980 **OBG** *020 †30

SOLANKI, Kirit Vithaldas. 4801 W PARK BLVD, STE 425 75093 #495-22-1967 L1978 **GP CLP** *020 †50

SOLANKI, Varsha Kirit. 4801 W PARK BLVD STE 425 75093 #495-01-1976 L1982 **IM** *020

SOLOMON, Mark R. 4429 BURNHILL DR 75093 #048-12-1996 L1997 **PD** *020 †55

SOLOMON, Paul Alan. 5800 GRANITE PKWY, UNITED HLTHCR STE 900 75024 #048-02-1980 L1980 **FM FPG** *020 †18 ‡

SOSA, Rodney Wayne. 6009 W PARKER RD, PMB 310 75093 #011-02-1995 L1998 **IM** *020 †20

SPARENBERG, Chas Russell. 3900 W 15TH ST STE 106 75093 #048-02-1972 L1972 **PS** *020 †65

SPENCER, Rowena. ■ 75023 #023-07-1947 L1947 **PDS** *071 †85

SPIVEY, Mark A. 6200 PARK MEADOW LN, TEXAS RADIOLOGY 75093 #048-14-1976 L1976 **DR NR** *020 †80

SPOONER, Melinda Deselle. 1600 COIT RD STE 102 75075 #039-01-1994 L1997 **OBG** *020 †30

STACHNIAK, Joseph B. 3060 COMMUNICATIONS PKWY, STE 201 75093 #048-13-1989 L1998 **NS** *020 †25

STACK, Peter S. 4708 ALLIANCE BLVD 75093 #035-19-1981 L1982 **IM** *020 †20

STAGER, David, Jr. 3900 W 15TH ST STE 406, PEDIATRIC OPHTHALMOLOGY, P 75075 #048-12-1991 L1992 **PO** *020 †35

STANTON, William Alan. 3801 W 15TH ST, STE 120 75075 #048-02-1975 L1975 **PD** *020 †55

STARR, Alicia Leigh. 6200 PARK MEADOW LN, TEXAS RADIOLOGY 75093 #005-14-1992 L1993 **DR** *020 †80

STATMAN, Jerome Maurice. ■ 75024 #048-12-1955 L1955 **P ADP** *071 †75 ‡

STEPHENS, Gregory Knox. 4708 ALLIANCE BLVD, STE 835 75093 #305-01-2002 L2007 **NEP** *100 †20

STEPHENS, Stacy Randolph. 6200 W PARKER RD, STE 502 75093 #023-07-1958 L1968 **OBG** *072 †30

STEWART, Carlyle A. 4708 ALLIANCE BLVD 75093 #033-05-1977 L1983 **IM** *020 †20

STOKES, Deborah F. ■ 75093 #048-13-1984 L1985 **IM CD** *020 †20

STOKOE, Christopher T. 4708 ALLIANCE BLVD, STE 150 75093 #048-02-1996 L1997 **ON** *020 †20

STONE, Phyllis A. 6200 W PARKER RD, STE 410 75093 #048-12-1987 L1989 **PD** *020 †55

STONE, Scott Andrew. 3705 W 15TH ST, NORTH TX REGIONAL CANCER C 75075 #048-15-1994 L1995 **ON** *020 †20

STRAND, William Richard. 4001 W 15TH ST, UROLOGY CLINIC OF NORTH 75093 #026-08-1983 L1994 **U** *020 †95

STRATMANN, Stacy Lynn. 4708 ALLIANCE BLVD, STE 270 75093 #016-45-1997 L1998 **GS** *020 †85

STRAWMAN, David Andrew. 3901 W 15TH ST 75075 #048-12-1996 L1998 **IM** *020 †20

SUBONG, Sylvia Abigail. 6300 W PARKER RD, STE 325 75093 #010-03-1993 L2004 **OBG** *020 †30

SUBRAMANIAN, Sujatha Hari. 6853 COIT RD STE 300, PRIMARY CARE CENTER 75024 #495-96-1991 L2004 **FM** *100 †18

SULLIVAN, John Perry. 6200 PARK MEADOW LN, TEXAS RADIOLOGY 75093 #048-02-1998 L2000 **DR** *020 †80

SUN, Michelle V. 6300 W PARKER RD, STE 404 75075 #048-12-1999 L2002 **IM** *020 †20

SUNGA, Leopoldo Ganaden. ■ 75023 #748-10-1970 **IM** *100

SUREDDI, Suresh. 3920 ALMA DR 75023 #495-99-1991 L1997 **P** *020

SURESH, Keshava G N. 3901 W 15TH ST 75075 #495-33-1979 L1994 **AN** *020 †05

SUTKER, Allan. 5228 W PLANO PKWY 75093 #016-42-1975 L1980 **ORS OSM** *020 †40

SWAMY, Muthuswamy S. ■ 75023 #495-53-1987 **N** *100

SWAROOP, Prabhakar P. ■ 75093 #495-36-1993 L2007 **IM** *020 †20

TABATABAI, Mehra Reza. 1212 COIT RD, STE 105 75075 #043-01-1993 L1994 **ORS** *020 †40

TAO, Rongrong. ■ 75093 #243-16-1981 L2005 **CHP** *020

TARKI, Farhad. ■ 75093 #048-15-1992 L1996 **FM** *020 †18

TATEN, Allison C. 6200 PARK MEADOW LN, TEXAS RADIOLOGY 75093 #048-12-1997 L1998 **DR** *020 †80

TAYLOR, Dennis Ritch, Jr. 1200 COIT RD, STE 109 75075 #004-01-1981 L1984 **AN** *020 †05

TAYLOR, Jeff Earl. 4708 ALLIANCE BLVD 75093 #048-14-1996 L1997 **PCC** *020 †20

TAYLOR, Roger Z. 3901 W 15TH ST 75075 #759-07-1955 L1972 **ORS** *020 †40

TENG, Lilian. ■ 75093 #048-12-2004 L2005 **NPM** *012 †55

TERRILL, Robert Clark. 1220 COIT RD STE 101 75075 #048-12-1970 L1970 **D** *020 †15

THAKOR, Kunjan P. 5930 W PARKER RD, STE 600 75093 #495-17-1985 L1995 **IM** *020 †20

THIEBERG, Mark David. 4708 ALLIANCE BLVD 75093 #035-47-1990 L1994 **D** *020 †15

THOMAS, Karen Sue. 3900 W 15TH ST, SJ MONTGOMERY MD 75075 #048-13-1979 L1979 **AN** *020

THOMAS, Robert Bryan. 6200 W PARKER RD, STE 200 75093 #048-12-1980 L1980 **OBG MFM** *020 †30

THOMPSON, Buddy Glenn. 6200 PARK MEADOW LN, TEXAS RADIOLOGY 75093 #021-06-1991 L2002 **DR** *020 †80

THOMPSON, Christina Lynn. 6300 W PARKER RD 75093 #041-07-1988 L1997 **FM** *020 †18

TIGGES, Gary Alan. 6300 W PARKER RD STE 220 75093 #018-03-1992 L1993 **IM** *020 †20.

TIRANDAZ, Arash. 6124 W 15TH ST 75093 #048-02-1993 L1994 **IM** *020 †20

TOBOLOWSKY, Paul Arthur. 4708 ALLIANCE BLVD 75093 #048-12-1973 L1979 **IM** *020 †20

TODD, Eugene Ray. 3821 LAKEDALE DR 75093 #048-12-1958 L1958 **U** *020 †95

TOLOTTA, Maria A. 6020 W PARKER RD, STE 240 75093 #048-14-1990 L1991 **PM** *020 †60

TOMPKINS, John Robt. 4708 ALLIANCE BLVD, STE 475 75093 #008-01-1990 L1999 **NS** *020 †25

TONG, John T. 3900 W 15TH ST, STE 406 75075 #041-02-1993 L2007 **PSH PO** *020 †35

TON-THAT, Quoc Tuan. ■ 75024 #067-02-1987 **NM** *020 †28

TORRES, Louis A. 5501 INDEPENDENCE PKWY, STE 110 75023 #048-02-1986 L1987 **IM** *020 †20

TORTEN, Dina Naomi. ■ 75025 #550-04-1988 L2007 **IM ID** *020 †20

TORTI, Robert Eugene, II. 4708 ALLIANCE BLVD STE 785 75093 #047-06-1985 L1987 **OPH** *020 †35

TOWNSEND, Henry Bernard. 4708 ALLIANCE BLVD 75093 #001-02-1995 L1996 **RHU** *020 †20

TRAN, Khang Nguyen. 4108 W 15TH ST, STE 200 75093 #048-12-1997 L1998 **IM** *020 †20

TRESE, Susan. 5068 W PLANO PKWY 75093 #048-12-1994 L1996 **CHP P** *020 †75

TRIANA, Lorenzo. 5824 W PLANO PKWY STE 104 75093 #048-14-1991 L1992 **P ADM** *020 †75

TRIMMER, Kenneth Joe. 6200 W PARKER RD, MOB #1, SUITE 302 75093 #019-02-1985 L1990 **OBG MFM** *020 †30

TROOP, Randal Lee. 5228 W PLANO PKWY 75093 #034-01-1984 L1989 **ORS** *020 †40

TROSCLAIR, B Gerard. ■ 75075 #021-05-1957 L1957 **FM** *071 †18

TRYLOVICH, Courtney G. 6124 W PARKER RD, MOB 3 STE 530 75093 #048-13-1993 L1994 **OBG** *020 †30

TSCHOEPE, Ernest J. 1600 COIT RD STE 307, TEXAS RADIOLOGY 75075 #048-12-1993 L1995 **PDR** *020 †80

TSENG, Ewen Y. 3809 W 15TH ST, BLDG 700 75075 #048-04-1992 L1997 **OTO** *020 †45

TUCKER, Mark Oliver. 6124 W PARKER RD, STE 330 75093 #048-02-1997 L1999 **GS** *020 †85

TUCKER, Walter Frank. 1301 CUSTER RD STE 822 75075 #021-05-1964 L1965 **A OTO** *071 †45

TURNER, Ralph James. 6200 W PARKER RD, STE 502 75093 #048-12-1978 L1978 **OBG** *020 †30

UDOH, Emmanuel Malachy. ■ 75074 #041-12-2004 L2004 **FM** *100

UMHOLTZ, Lisa M. 9 15TH ST 75075 #048-12-1985 L1986 **OBG** *020 †30

UNDERWOOD, Ronald Howell. 4708 ALLIANCE BLVD, STE 710 75093 #048-12-1967 L1967 **CD** *020 †20

UNGER, Lily Acupinpin. ■ 75075 #748-07-1964 *100

URECH, Lizabeth Outlaw. 6300 W PARKER RD STE 426 75093 #048-12-1992 L1993 **PD** *071 †55

USMAN, Farhat. ■ 75024 #704-02-2001 L2006 **FM** *020 †18

VAN WAGONER, John Allen. 6101 WINDCOM CT STE 400 75093 #048-12-1996 L1999 **AI PDA** *020 †55,03

VARADI, Kathleen Frances. 6124 W PARKER RD, STE 134 75093 #050-02-1983 L1989 **OBG GYN** *020 †30

VENKATESAN, Jayanti. 4708 ALLIANCE BLVD STE 835 75093 #495-36-1980 L1995 **NEP IM** *020 †20

VERRET, Daniel Joseph. 6545 PRESTON RD, STE 200 75024 #048-12-2001 L2004 **FPS** *100 †45

VINE, Jack Bernstein. 1200 MEDICAL AVE 75075 #048-13-1983 L1983 **RHU IM** *020 †20

VOGT, Arthur C, Jr. ■ 75093 #035-06-1946 L1947 **OM GP** *071

VU, Stephen Lee. ■ 75025 #039-01-2002 L2005 **IM** *020 †20

VU, Them Le. 6300 STONEWOOD DR STE 304 75024 #019-02-1999 L2003 **OPH** *020 †35

VYAS, Shilpa Vijay. ■ 75025 #001-02-1999 L2007 **NPM** *100 †55

WALDO, Rick Talley. 4708 ALLIANCE BLVD 75093 #048-02-1974 L1974 **IM CCM** *020 †20

WALIA, Harjeet Rosie. 1200 COIT RD STE 105 75075 #065-09-1977 L1982 **FM EM** *020 †18

WALKER, Jonathan Alan. 101 E PARK BLVD, STE 911 75074 #048-15-1997 L1998 **EM** *020 †16

WALKER, Mc Donald Hugo. ■ 75093 #062-01-1967 L1980 *020

WALKER, Shannon Jaunita. 6200 PARK MEADOW LN, TEXAS RADIOLOGY 75093 #004-01-1993 L1999 **DR** *020 †20,80

WALLER, Thomas A. 6124 W PARKER RD, STE 234 75093 #048-12-1991 L1992 **CD** *020 †20

WALSH, Katrina H. 1600 COIT RD STE 402 75075 #047-06-1987 L1992 **OBG** *020 †30

WALTER, Frederick Harold. ■ 75025 #026-04-1945 **GP** *071

WALTER, James Cleo, II. 6020 W PARKER RD, STE 240 75093 #028-02-1995 L1996 **OSM ORS** *020 †40

WARD, James Thos, Jr. 3901 W 15TH ST 75075 #048-12-1979 L1979 **EM** *020 †16

WARREN, Beth Goodgion. 6124 W PARKER RD STE 436 75093 #048-13-2002 L2005 **FM** *020 †18

WARREN, G Emory. 701 E PLANO PKWY, STE 103 75074 #004-01-1986 L1991 **FM** *020 †18

WASH, Karen Melissa. PO BOX 866878 75086 #048-12-2001 L2003 **DR** *100 †80

WATKINS, Kelli V. 6200 W PARKER RD, STE 306, MOB 1 75093 #048-12-1996 L2000 **OBG** *020 †30

WATSON, Stephen Wayne. 5824 W PLANO PKWY, STE 101 75093 #048-12-1982 L1984 **CS OMF** *020

WATTS, Jenelle Simon. 3801 W 15TH ST STE 270 75075 #021-01-1991 L1998 **OBG** *020 †30

WAY, Megan K. ■ 75093 #048-13-2004 L2006 **AN** *012

WEBB, Gary Leroy. 6200 PARK MEADOW LN, TEXAS RADIOLOGY 75093 #027-01-1979 L1981 **DR** *020 †80

WEBSTER, Gwen Carol. 5940 W PARKER RD STE 200 75093 #048-12-1997 L1998 **OBG** *020 †30

WEISBERG, Leslie Ann. 6300 W PARKER RD STE 220 75093 #011-02-1991 L1993 **AI** *020 †20,03

WEISBERG, Michael F. 1600 COIT RD STE 301 75075 #048-04-1985 L1986 **GE IM** *020 †20

WELLS, Chet Edward. 6124 W PARKER RD, STE 134 75093 #048-02-1976 L1976 **OBG** *020 †30

WEN, Ted S. 6200 PARK MEADOW LN, TEXAS RADIOLOGY 75093 #048-12-1989 L1990 **PDR** *020 †80

WEST, Thomas Alonzo. 6124 W PARKER RD, STE 330 75093 #048-12-1992 L1995 **GS** *020 †85

WEST, William Todd. 3901 W 15TH ST 75075 #028-03-1999 L2005 **NPM** *020 †55

WEYENBERG, Matthew Gerrit. 5425 W SPRING CREEK PKWY, STE 200 75024 #004-01-2001 L2002 **FM** *020 †18

WHISENANT, Stanley Wayne. 6505 W PARK BLVD, STE 306 # 285 75093 #034-01-1992 L1995 **APM** *020 †05

WHITAKER, Mary Theresa. 6200 W PARKER RD 75093 #048-12-1985 L1986 **GYN** *020 †30

WHITE, Johnny Lee, Jr. 6020 W PARKER RD STE 30 75093 #036-07-1979 L1982 **PME PMM** *020 †05

WHITE, Kathryn E. 4001 W 15TH ST STE 245, ASSOCIATED WOMEN'S HEALTHC 75093 #048-14-1988 L1989 **OBG** *020 †30

WHITWORTH, Melissa Ann. 6200 PARK MEADOW LN, TEXAS RADIOLOGY 75093 #021-01-1996 L2003 **DR** *020 †80

WIEDERMAN, Francis J. 101 E PARK BLVD, STE 911 75074 #748-09-1977 L1994 **EM** *020 †16

WIEN, Todd Mitchell. 5501 INDEPENDENCE PKWY, STE 203 75023 #051-01-1984 L1991 **FM** *020 †18

WIENER, Sharon Lee. 6529 W PLANO PKWY, # B 75093 #048-13-1984 L1985 **PD** *020

WILCOX, Robert D. 5316 W PLANO PKWY 75093 #048-12-1984 L1985 **PS HS** *020 †85,65

WILLIAMS, Barry John. 1708 COIT RD, STE 220A 75075 #061-01-1967 L1977 **FM** *020 †18

WILLIAMSON, Robert G. 6404 INTERNATIONAL PKWY #2 75093 #048-13-1997 L1998 **P** *020 †75

WILNER, Matthew Leonard. 6124 W PARKER RD, UROLOGY CLINICS OF NORTH 75093 #035-19-1984 L1990 **U** *020 †95

WINANS, Robert Gibson. 6601 W PLANO PKWY 75093 #038-40-1961 L1974 **ORS** *062 †40

WITTENBERG, John F. 4108 W 15TH ST, STE 200 75093 #056-05-1976 L1978 **IM** *020 †20

WONG, Jenelle Chen. 3405 MIDWAY RD STE 650 75093 #016-43-1996 L1998 **PD** *020 †55

WOODS, Michael S. 5936 W PARKER RD STE 1100 75093 #048-16-1997 L1998 **CHP** *020 †75

WOODWARD, Robert Alan. 101 E PARK BLVD STE 600 75074 #048-02-1984 L1985 **P EM** *020 †75

WOOLBERT, Samuel Carlin. 6601 PRESTON RD, LEGACY HEART CENTER PA 75024 #021-06-1983 L1990 **CD IC** *020 †20

WOOLRIDGE, Vanessa Elaine. 3801 W 15TH ST, STE 270 75075 #010-03-1991 L1995 **OBG** *020 †30

YAGNIK, Hitesh B. 5930 W PARKER RD STE 90 75093 #495-48-1989 L1998 **IM** *020 †20

YAKER, Natan. 4100 W 15TH ST 75093 #264-03-1970 L1978 **PS HS** *020 †65

YAMFANG, Wanwisa D. ■ 75093 #048-13-2001 L2003 **FM** *020

YASMIN, Khalida. 6200 W PARKER RD 75093 #704-20-1990 L1999 **FM** *020 †18

YATES, Scott William. 6020 W PARKER RD, STE 420 75093 #048-12-1993 L1994 **IM MDM** *020 †20

YEDULAPURAM, Manohar. 3901 W 15TH ST 75075 #495-21-1996 L2005 **IM** *020

YEH, En-Lin. ■ 75025 #385-02-1959 L1967 **NM OS** *020 †28

YIN, Su. ■ 75023 #048-12-2004 L2007 **RHU** *012 †20

YOKUBAITIS, Nathaniel T. 3801 W 15TH ST, STE 320 75075 #048-14-1998 L2001 **IM** *020 †20

YOUNG, Patty Kay. 4104 W 15TH ST, STE 200 75093 #048-12-1987 L1989 **HS GS** *072 †65 ‡

YOUNG, Robert Campbell. 3721 W 15TH ST, P O BOX 940445 75075 #048-02-1956 L1956 **PD** *020 †20

YOUNG, Vincent Depaul. 6501 TIMBER WOLF TRL 75093 #016-06-1993 L2000 **AN** *020 †05

ZAHABI-UNWALA, Fehmida. 6300 STONEWOOD DR, STE 412 75024 #704-02-1987 L1996 **RHU** *020 †20

ZAJICEK, Sara Mc Nally. 6200 PARK MEADOW LN, TEXAS RADIOLOGY 75093 #048-12-1998 L1999 **DR** *020 †80

ZANE, Robert Brian. ■ 75024 #048-12-1993 **AN** *075

ZAVODNY, Catheryne Mccall. 3900 W 15TH ST, STE 404 75075 #047-06-1998 L1999 **IM** *020 †20

ZHANG, Shaoping. 2807 W 15TH ST 75075 #243-21-1970 L1999 **PD** *020 †55

ZIGLER, Jack Elliot. 6020 W PARKER RD, STE 200 75093 #035-15-1977 L1996 **ORS** *020 †40

ZIMMER, Jennifer Knaak. 4708 ALLIANCE BLVD 75093 #018-03-1997 L2004 **IM** *020 †20

ZODROW, James Melvin. 3900 AMERICAN DR, STE 203 75075 #039-01-1985 L1993 **FM** *020 †18

ZOGG, Morna. 6200 PARK MEADOW LN, TEXAS RADIOLOGY 75093 #048-12-1990 L1992 **DR** *020 †80

PLANTERSVILLE – GRIMES

ROWLAND, E Trasel. PO BOX 389 77363 #011-02-1973 L1976 **P** *074

PLEASANTON – ATASCOSA

BADDOUR, Violeta Tamara. 1746 W GOODWIN ST 78064 #935-01-1993 L1999 **RHU IM** *020 †20

BANJO, Abimbola M. ■ 78064 #690-01-1986 L1996 **ID** *020

BLAIR, Lisa Jill. 111 N SMITH ST 78064 #041-13-1996 L1998 **FM** *020 †18

DARLING, David H. 1102 CARDINAL ST 78064 #035-09-1953 L1961 **EM GS** *071 †18

ELMER, Edward Burns. 1102 N MAIN ST 78064 #024-01-1983 L1992 **ORS** *020 †40

ELMER, Laura Marie. 1102 N MAIN ST 78064 #024-01-1992 L1999 **PD** *020 †55

GARCIA, Jaime. 809 N BRYANT ST 78064 #035-46-1984 L1990 **FM** *020 †18

GARCIA ALVAREZ, Enrique. 130 S WATER ST, TEXAS MEDICAL BUILDING, IN 78064 #176-03-1969 L1978 **GP PD** *020

KELLEY, Danny Lynn. ■ 78064 #048-13-1973 L1973 **FM** *020 †18

PALAFOX, Mariade L. 1540 W GOODWIN ST 78064 #048-13-1997 L2005 **GS CCS** *020 †18

PHILLIPS, Gerald Bruce. 111 N SMITH ST 78064 #048-12-1959 L1959 **FM GP** *020 †18

POLIT, Adrian M. 119 S SMITH ST 78064 #836-02-1961 L1981 **AN** *020

RAMIREZ, Robert R. 703 W OAKLAWN RD 78064 #048-04-1997 L2000 **IM** *020 †20

SALVADOR, Eugene Quion. ■ 78064 #005-12-1993 L1997 **AN** *020

SANTOS, Erick Manuel. 1240 W OAKLAWN RD, STE 101B 78064 #041-01-1996 L1997 **ORS** *020

VAZQUEZ, Ines E. 310 W OAKLAWN RD 78064 #042-03-1986 L1992 **IM** *020

VILLARREAL, Armando S. 1540 W GOODWIN ST 78064 #048-14-1983 L1983 **FM** *020 †18

VILLARREAL, Patricio T. ■ 78064 #035-20-1990 L1991 **EM** *020

ZERTUCHE, Scott. 310 W OAKLAWN RD 78064 #048-13-1997 L2001 **FM** *020 †18

POOLVILLE – PARKER

ZAIDLE, Crystal Gayle. ■ 76487 #048-12-2004 *100

PORT ACRES – JEFFERSON

ARCALA, Avila E. 2501 JIMMY JHNSN BLVD #401 77640 #748-08-1969 L1979 **FM** *030 †18 ‡

DUPLAN, Don Auffurth. 2501 JIMMY JOHNSON BLVD, STE 305 77640 #048-02-1982 L1983 **OTO A** *020 †45

PORT ARANSAS – NUECES

CARLSON, Robert Gerald. PO BOX 448 78373 #026-04-1954 L1954 **CD TS** *020 †85,90
CENNI, Louis J. PO BOX 706 78373 #041-13-1943 L1947 **GS** *071 †85
DIAZ, Oscar. ■ 78373 #649-02-1951 L1957 **FM** *071
KLEAGER, Clyde Louis. ■ 78373 #030-05-1943 L1944 **EM** *071 †85
MATISONS, Andris. 631 CHANNEL VIEW DR 78373 #030-05-1963 L1963 **ORS** *020 †40
RUSSELL, Bruce L. 600 CUT OFF RD, STE 14 78373 #048-14-1984 L1985 **FM** *020 †18 ‡
SOMERS, John Edward. ■ 78373 #025-01-1957 L1958 **N** *071 †75

PORT ARTHUR – JEFFERSON

ABDULLAH, Nabeel. 3921 N TWIN CITY HWY 77642 #875-02-1988 L2000 **CD** *020 †20
ABOCHAMH, Dia. 3921 N TWIN CITY HWY 77642 #875-01-1987 L1997 **CD** *020 †20
ADAMS, Barnette E J, Jr. ■ 77640 #021-01-1947 L1954 **GS TS** *071 †85
AGUSTIN, Gilberto. 3780 MEMORIAL BLVD 77640 #748-01-1978 L1986 **N** *020
ALLY, Saeed Abedin. 3787 DOCTORS DR STE 105 77642 #305-01-1995 L2002 **TS** *020 †85,90
ANABTAWI, Isam Nazmi. 4500 GULFWAY DR 77642 #605-01-1956 L1969 **TS GS** *020 †85,90
ANDERSON, Charles William. 3648 PROFESSIONAL DR 77642 #041-02-1962 L1976 **CD** *020
ARCALA, Federico A, Jr. 2501 JIMMY JOHNSON BLVD #4 77640 #748-08-1968 L1979 **GS FM** *020 †18 ‡
ARCHER, Stanley Bruce. 3600 GATES BLVD 77642 #047-06-1969 L1981 **PTH AM** *020 †50
BARLOW, Dick. 2935 PARK PLAZA LN 77642 #048-02-1968 L1968 **OTO** *020 †45
BEAUDRY, Carl Jos. 2501 JIMMY JOHNSON BLVD, STE 202 77640 #065-09-1966 L1977 **ORS** *020 †40
BEAUDRY, Roland Henry. 3787 DOCTORS DR STE 106 77642 #065-09-1957 L1978 **GS OS** *075
BENSKI, Raymond. 3535 GATES BLVD STE 100 77642 #048-02-1962 L1962 **FM IMG** *071 †18
BINUR, Nir Shamai. 8640 CENTRAL MALL DR 77642 #550-03-1983 L1992 **PS HS** *020 †65,85
BOURGEOIS, Richard Jos. ■ 77642 #048-02-1954 L1954 **GP** *071
BRAYE, Edward T, Jr. 8765 9TH AVE 77642 #001-02-1982 L1985 **PD** *055
BUHEIS, Nidal Ismail. 2501 JIMMY JOHNSON BLVD, STE 500 77640 #575-02-1997 L2005 **IC CD** *020 †20
CARABELLE, R Wm. ■ 77642 #048-04-1948 L1948 **OPH** *071 †55,35
CASTILLO, Sonia Martinez. 2001 9TH AVE, STE 300 77642 #748-02-1965 L1979 **GYN** *071 †30
CHAUDHURY, Triptesh Kumar. 4600 9TH AVE 77642 #039-01-1984 L1987 **RO** *020
CHEE MENG, David Ong. ■ 77642 #422-01-1992 L1998 **AN** *020 †05
COLLETTI, Ben Matthew. ■ 77642 #048-02-1945 L1945 **RO** *071 †55
COOMBS, Jacquin Ann. 3705 9TH AVE 77642 #033-06-1999 L2003 **OBG** *020
CORDOVEZ-TAN, Marian. 3220 CENTRAL MALL DR 77642 #748-11-1979 L1995 **PD** *020 †55
DANG, Hau Phung. 525 9TH AVE 77642 #941-01-1969 L1982 **FM GP** *020
ELEFANO-ESPIRITU, Ceres P. 2548 MEMORIAL BLVD, GULF COAST HEALTH CENTER 77640 #748-02-1964 L1975 **PD** *020 †55
ENRIQUEZ, Oscar Olfindo. 8333 9TH AVE, STE A 77642 #748-08-1984 L1996 **IM** *020
EWING, Carol Tillotson. 3310 MEDICAL TRIANGLE ST, STE 3 77642 #007-02-1961 L1974 **PTH** *071 †50
FANASCH-RECKHAUS, Hilal M. 5957 9TH AVE 77642 #528-02-1979 L1996 **HEM ON** *020 †20
FORSYTHE, John Leonard. 3820 HIGHWAY 365, STE 300 77642 #065-05-1971 L1977 **GP P** *020
GAMBRAH-SAMPANEY, Anthony. 7980 ANCHOR DR, STE 400 77642 #412-02-1988 L1996 **IM** *020 †20
GEORGE, Wm De Witt, Jr. 2001 9TH AVE, STE 301 77642 #048-02-1960 L1960 **IM IMG** *020 †20
GORDON, Fallon Turley. 3820 HIGHWAY 365 77642 #048-02-1963 L1963 **TS** *020 †85,90
GOSSETT, Odis W. 4640 9TH AVE, STE 100 77642 #649-45-1992 L1997 **FM** *020 †18
HAHN, Stanley. 2555 JIMMY JOHNSON BLVD 77640 #018-03-1987 L1997 **GS** *020 †85
HAIG, Martin R. 2925 PARK PLAZA LN 77642 #024-07-1950 L1957 **ORS** *020 †40
HALES, Colin L. 3758 PARK PLAZA CIR 77642 #919-05-1967 L1977 **FM A** *020 †18
HARMOUSH, Issam Mohamad. 2001 9TH AVE, STE 100 77642 #915-02-1970 L1983 **OS GS** *020 †85
HEALEY, Gordon Bruce. 3180 CENTRAL MALL DR 77642 #021-01-1974 L1974 **U** *020 †95
HEALEY, Gordon Sean. 3180 CENTRAL MALL DR 77642 #021-01-1993 L1999 **U** *020 †95
HINER, Hervy Harrison. 1750 9TH AVE STE 201 77642 #048-04-1979 L1980 **NEP IM** *020 †20
HYMEL, Ernest C. 8333 9TH AVE, STE G 77642 #048-02-2000 L2005 **RO** *020
ICETON, John A. 2927 PARK PLAZA LN STE 8 77642 #064-01-1976 L1989 **ORS** *020 †40
ISLAM, Mohammed Amirul. 3921 N TWIN CITY HWY 77642 #160-03-1990 L2002 **CD IM** *020 †20
JOHNSON, Marisa Turner. 1750 9TH AVE, STE 201 77642 #004-01-1997 L2003 **NEP** *020 †20
KARIA, Ramesh Ramchand. 2001 9TH AVE, STE 204 77642 #495-96-1996 L1978 **ON HEM** *020 †20
KOTHAPALLI, Srinivasa R. 2501 JIMMY JOHNSON BLVD, STE 500 77640 #495-11-1983 L1992 **CD IM** *020 †20
KULKARNI, Sharad B. 3400 HIGHWAY 365 STE 303 77642 #496-01-1978 L1983 **P CHP** *020
LANG, Margaret May. 2501 JIMMY JOHNSON BLVD SU, REGIONAL PROFESSIONAL BUIL 77640 #024-07-1984 L1987 **IM** *020 †20
LANUZA, Marisa Rivera. 3820 HIGHWAY 365 77642 #748-10-1978 L1983 **ATP CLP** *020 †50
LE BLANC, Cherryll A. 3600 GATES BLVD 77642 #021-05-1975 L1998 **EM** *020 †16
LEMIRE, Jean G. 3787 DOCTORS DR STE 312 77642 #065-09-1966 L1983 **CD** *071
LESTER, Essene Cavetta. 3000 39TH ST, STE 102 77642 #035-45-1997 L2006 **OPH** *020 †35
LINGAM, Vijaya Bhaskar R. 2525 JIMMY JOHNSON BLVD, THE MEDICAL CTR OF SE TX 77640 #495-62-1976 L1998 **AN PME** *020 †05
LONG, Donald Paul. 4640 9TH AVE, STE 101 77642 #649-14-1972 L1977 **OBG** *020
LUHAR, Harashada K. 3050 39TH ST 77642 #495-22-1969 L1986 **NPM PD** *020 †55
LYNCH, Wilson Locke. 3300 MEDICAL TRIANGLE ST 77642 #045-01-1968 L1969 **FM EM** *020 †16
MARTIN, Arsenio Respicio. 2001 9TH AVE STE 102 77642 #748-08-1967 L1979 **PUD IM** *020 †20
MC CAFFREE, David Lee. 3787 DOCTORS DR, STE 206 77642 #041-13-1963 L1966 **ADL** *071 †15
MC DONALD, Sandy Ian R. 2927 PARK PLAZA LN 77642 #065-05-1977 L1993 **GS** *020 †85
MC MAHON, Michael L, II. 2501 JIMMY JOHNSON BLVD, STE 405 77640 #048-02-1991 L1996 **IM PD** *020 †20,55 ‡
MEDINA, Luis Alberto. 3800 HIGHWAY 365, STE 119 77642 #737-01-1980 L1989 **AN** *020 †05
MENNIE, Gary Roy. 2770 AERO DR STE 1 77640 #305-01-1995 L1999 **OBG FM** *020 †18 ‡
MERCADO-MARTIN, Fe. 2001 9TH AVE STE 102 77642 #748-08-1967 L1979 **PD GP** *020 †55
MEZA, Alfonso. 3705 9TH AVE 77642 #319-01-1967 L1977 **OBG** *071 †30
MILES, Richard Wesley. 3600 GATES BLVD 77642 #021-01-1985 L1989 **AN** *020 †05

MILLER, Barry Ray. 3820 HIGHWAY 365, STE 200 77642 #019-02-1983 L1989 **GS GE** *020
MILLER, Otto La Wayne, Jr. 3600 GATES BLVD 77642 #048-13-1979 L1979 **TS VS** *020 †85,90
MOLINA, James Thomas. 3820 HIGHWAY 365 77642 #048-02-1999 L2004 **PTH** *020 †50
MOLINA ESCOBAR, T Jaime. 3820 HIGHWAY 365 77642 #649-02-1972 L1976 **PTH** *020 †50
MORBIA, Pradip Kumar J. 3921 N TWIN CITY HWY, 3921 TWIN CITY HIGHWAY 77642 #495-17-1981 L1989 **IC CD** *020 †20
MOSES, Charles Robt. 7980 ANCHOR DR, STE 1100 77642 #048-12-1974 L1982 **OBG** *020 †30
MYRICK, Terry Wade. 2501 JIMMY JOHNSON BLVD 77640 #048-04-1978 L1979 **TS** *020 †85
NALLURI, Prasada Rao. 2501 JIMMY JOHNSON BLVD, STE 301 77640 #495-58-1991 L1999 **IM** *020 †20
NASSER, Mariano S, Jr. 2555 JIMMY JOHNSON BLVD, RADIOLOGY DEPARTMENT 77640 #748-10-1968 L1978 **DR** *020
NOORI, Nazar Abdullatif. 2501 JIMMY JOHNSON BLVD, STE 501 77640 #528-01-1980 L1999 **IM FM** *020
PADRON, Gustavo Manuel. 3600 GATES BLVD 77642 #308-04-1981 L1992 **DR** *020
PEPLINSKI, Scott Michael. 3600 GATES BLVD 77642 #041-13-1999 L2004 **DR** *020 †80
PICKARD, William Dell. 4640 9TH AVE, STE 100 77642 #048-02-1982 L1983 **FM** *020 †18
POLAVARAPU, Sreedhar. 2501 JIMMY JOHNSON BLVD, STE 207 77640 #495-58-1990 L2004 **IM** *020 †20
PUNSALAN, Erlinda R. 1946 9TH AVE 77642 #748-01-1968 L1979 **PD GP** *020 †55
RAJA, Sekhar N. 2555 JIMMY JOHNSON BLVD, THE MEDICAL CENTER OF SOUT 77640 #495-50-1979 L1992 **AN PME** *020
RAMOS VALDEZ, Ricardo. 3820 HIGHWAY 365 77642 #649-02-1968 L1980 **PTH** *020
REYES, Rizalino Lomotan. 3787 DOCTORS DR, STE 105 77642 #748-01-1984 L1997 **IM** *020
SAWISKY, David Lee. 4640 9TH AVE 77642 #048-02-1996 L1997 **FM** *020 †18
SCHMIDT, John Allen. 3820 HIGHWAY 365 STE 200 77642 #048-02-1978 L1978 **GS EM** *020 †85 ‡
SERRANO, Christopher W. 8599 9TH AVE 77642 #048-13-1990 L1994 **OBG** *020 †30
SHEPHERD, James Thos. 2501 JIMMY JOHNSON BLVD, STE 501 77640 #919-05-1971 L1976 **CD DIA** *020
SHOBASSY, Nezar. 2001 9TH AVE STE 305 77642 #875-01-1966 L1976 **GE IM** *020 †20
SINGLA, Raj Kumar. 3000 39TH ST STE 102 77642 #495-03-1968 L1980 **NPM** *020 †35
SMITH, Arthur Lee. 3600 GATES BLVD 77642 #039-01-1977 L1986 **DR** *020 †80
SMITH, Michael Leigh. 3535 GATES BLVD, STE 100 77642 #048-02-1980 L1980 **CD CCM** *020 †20
STEWARD, Clyde A. ■ 77642 #004-01-1951 L1959 **OM** *072
STEWARD, Robert H. ■ 77642 #048-02-1987 L1988 **AN** *075
STOECKEL, James Allan. 3600 GATES BLVD 77642 #034-01-1978 L1983 **OPH EM** *020 †35
STUBEE, Barbara M. 2770 AERO DR, STE 3 77640 #048-14-1986 L1987 **OBG** *020 †30
SUKHAVASI, Sambasivarao. 2501 JIMMY JOHNSON BLVD, STE 301 77640 #495-50-1979 L1993 **IM** *020 †20
SUKHAVASI, Umadevi. 2501 JIMMY JOHNSON BLVD, STE 301 77640 #495-50-1983 L1998 **FM** *020 †18
THIGPEN, Marsha Evette. 2548 MEMORIAL BLVD, GULF COAST HEALTH, CENTER 77640 #041-13-1983 L1986 **IM EM** *020
THOME, Leonard Michael. 3535 GATES BLVD, STE 100 77642 #048-14-1989 L1990 **CD IC** *020 †20
TOLEDO, Minda Lao. 8333 9TH AVE STE B 77642 #748-22-1984 L2005 **PD** *020 †55
TRINH, Hong Catherine. 3615 PROFESSIONAL DR STE B 77642 #056-05-1983 L1986 **FM** *020 †18
UDONTA, Emem D. 3780 MEMORIAL BLVD 77640 #005-12-1988 L2001 **N CN** *020 †75
UPDIKE, Tracie D. 2933 PARK PLAZA LN 77642 #048-15-1992 L1993 **FM** *020 †18
VADVA, Mohamed Dawood. 2001 9TH AVE STE 305 77642 #965-01-1980 L1993 **GE IM** *020 †20
WALKES, Austin C. 246 DALLAS AVE 77640 #064-01-1967 L1978 **FM PHP** *020
WEATHERFORD, Stephen Char. 2501 JIMMY JOHNSON BLVD 77640 #048-04-1978 L1978 **TS** *020 †85,90
ZAPPIA, Gloria Angelina M. 3648 PROFESSIONAL DR 77642 #748-02-1967 L1977 **IM HEM** *020 †20

PORT LAVACA – CALHOUN

APOSTOL, Cayetano F. 113 PECANWOOD PL, 113 PECANWOOD PL 77979 #748-10-1964 L1979 **IM FM** *020
ARROYO, Richard. 1200 N VIRGINIA ST, PORT LAVACA CLINIC ASSOC P 77979 #042-02-1986 L1993 **IM** *020 †20
BUNNELL, Don Paul. 1200 N VIRGINIA ST 77979 #048-14-1982 L1983 **IM** *020 †20
CROWLEY, William J. 701 N VIRGINIA ST, COASTAL MEDICAL CLINIC 77979 #028-78-1993, ▲ L1999 **FM** *020 †18
CUMMINS, Michelle. 1300 N VIRGINIA ST, STE 112 77979 #065-01-1987 L2000 **OTO** *020
GRIFFIN, Jeannine Louise. 1200 N VIRGINIA ST 77979 #048-14-1983 L1983 **PD** *020 †55
GRIFFIN, John Wallace. 810 N ANN ST 77979 #048-04-1954 L1954 **FM OM** *071 †18
LE, Nhi P. 307 CALHOUN PLZ 77979 #422-01-1996 L1999 **IM** *020 †20
LEE, John Young. 1200 N VIRGINIA ST, PORT LAVACA CLINIC ASSOC, 77979 #023-01-1996 L1999 **FM** *020 †18
LIN, Mau-Shong. 1706 N VIRGINIA ST 77979 #244-04-1971 L1979 **IM** *020 ‡
MARGARIT, Emilio R. 605 N VIRGINIA ST 77979 #132-01-1953 **GP** *100
MC FARLAND, Timothy Ray. 701 N VIRGINIA ST, COASTAL MEDICAL CLINIC 77979 #048-02-1983 L1983 **FM** *020 †18
NIRATSUWAN, Naphaporn. 1200 N VIRGINIA ST 77979 #005-12-1998 L2003 **FM** *020 †18
PENTECOST, Lewis Verne. 17232 FM 1593 77979 #048-04-1956 L1956 **FM** *071 †18
RUPLEY, Marcelina P. 1300 N VIRGINIA ST, STE 111 77979 #048-02-1982 L1982 **PD** *020 †55
SCHROEDER, Russell D. ■ 77979 #048-15-1993 L1994 **VIR DR** *020 †80
SHAFFER, Craig Robt. 1200 N VIRGINIA ST 77979 #016-11-1980 L1981 **FM** *020 †18
SMITH, James Kirby, Jr. 1200 N VIRGINIA ST 77979 #048-12-1969 L1969 **GP GS** *020
SU, Annie Ray. ■ 77979 #048-04-2007 **IM** *012
WILLIAM, George Antone. 1211 W AUSTIN ST STE A, MATERNITY CARE CENTER 77979 #915-03-1976 L1984 **OBG** *020 †30
WRIGHT, John B. 1200 N VIRGINIA ST 77979 #048-14-2003 L2006 **FM** *020 †18

PORT NECHES – JEFFERSON

ALLEN, Joe Danl. 3120 SABA LN 77651 #048-02-1961 L1961 **P CHP** *020
BISHOP, Leslie M. 882 SIERRA DR 77651 #048-04-1992 L1993 **PM PRS** *020 †60

CASTILLO, Vicente T, Jr. 2530 NALL ST 77651 #748-02-1965 L1978 **AN** *020
DRAWHORN, Chester Walter. ■ 77651 #048-04-1956 L1956 **GP** *071
ECHOLS, Obie Laverne. ■ 77651 #004-01-1952 L1955 **GP OM** *071
FORD, Walter Alan. 2237 NEDERLAND AVE 77651 #004-01-1961 L1966 **OPH** *020
HAMBY, Houston Gayle. 2645 NALL ST 77651 #048-02-1962 L1962 **FM OM** *020
JONES, Gene Edward. 3141 SABA LN 77651 #048-02-1964 L1964 **GYN** *020 †30
LOPES, Nicholas Anthony. 2530 NALL ST 77651 #048-02-1956 L1956 **AN** *020
ORGERON, Eugene B. ■ 77651 #016-06-1952 L1952 **PD** *071 †55
PATEL, Vijesh Kanchanlal. 876 MAGNOLIA AVE 77651 #036-08-1990 L1996 **IM** *020 †20
SANDERS, Lawrence Walter. 2645 NALL ST 77651 #048-02-1983 L1983 **FM** *020
SHOOK, Jan Jos. 3186 MERRIMAN ST 77651 #048-02-1969 L1969 **GP** *020
TSAI, Ting-Ing. 2530 NALL ST 77651 #244-02-1974 L1982 **AN** *020 †05

PORT O CONNOR – CALHOUN

KONZEN, Walter Ray. ■ 77982 #048-02-1964 L1964 **OM** *071

PORTER – MONTGOMERY

BERIOS, Angelis. 24540 FM 1314 RD 77365 #418-02-1979 L1986 **FM** *020
BILLAH, Shahreen. ■ 77365 #048-02-2005 **PTH** *012
BROWN, Matthew Austin. ■ 77365 #048-04-2008 *012
CHITRA, Ravichandran. ■ 77365 #495-94-1977 L1983 **IM** *020
COLIGADO, Eduardo Ylanan. ■ 77365 #748-02-1962 L1976 **IM IMG** *071
MARTIN, Christopher R. ■ 77365 #021-06-2004 L2008 **PM** *012
NIKOLAIDIS, Maria Danuta. 24375 FM 1314 RD 77365 #759-07-1962 L1975 **PD GP** *020
PENDLETON, Solomon Alonzo. ■ 77365 #048-02-2007 L2007 **FP** *012
RAVICHANDRAN, Veerabadran. ■ 77365 #495-94-1974 L1977 **GS** *020 †85
SCHNEIDER, Larry Gene. 24420 FM 1314 RD 77365 #048-02-1974 L1974 **FM** *071 †18
SCOBERCEA, Sebastian I. ■ 77365 #016-43-1996 L2007 **FM** *020
STEWART, Diana Ebere. ■ 77365 #048-04-2008 *012

PORTLAND – SAN PATRICIO

ADAMS, Larry Hugh. 1776 BILLY G WEBB 78374 #021-01-1964 L1971 **R** *020 †80
ANDELMAN, Robert Paul. ■ 78374 #050-02-1971 L1997 **EM OM** *020 †16
ANDERSON, Lori Reese. ■ 78374 #025-01-1981 L1985 **PD** *020 †55
ATAMANTYK, David Geo. ■ 78374 #033-05-1979 L1983 **OM** *020 †16
CHARLES, Marissa Garza. ■ 78374 #048-78-2005, ▲ L2007 **FP** *012
CHEPEY, Richard Philip. 1776 BILLY G WEBB 78374 #028-34-1972 L1976 **NR DR** *020 †80
COLLINS, Darryl D. 213 CEDAR DR STE A 78374 #048-16-1989 L1990 **FM** *020 †18
COOK, Kenneth Ray. 1776 BILLY G WEBB 78374 #019-02-1983 L1987 **DR** *020 †80
DEVOLLD, Larry Eugene. 1776 BILLY G WEBB 78374 #048-13-1976 L1978 **DR** *020 †80
ELVIN, Patrick Kelly. 1776 BILLY G WEBB 78374 #005-12-1990 L1996 **VIR** *020 †80
EPUR, Vishnu Vardhanreddy. 311 BUDDY GANEM, STE A 78374 #496-01-1998 L2006 **IM** *020
FAN, Karl Taungkea. 1776 BILLY G WEBB 78374 #005-02-1991 L1999 **VIR** *020 †80
GAYLE, Everett L. 1776 BILLY G WEBB 78374 #048-13-1985 L1986 **DR PTH** *020 †50,80,28
GILMORE, Robert Marshall. 701 WILDCAT DR 78374 #048-02-1956 L1956 **GP** *071
GOVER, Charles Baker, III. 1776 BILLY G WEBB 78374 #042-01-1986 L1996 **RNR** *020 †80
HARRINGTON, Catherine I. ■ 78374 #047-07-2006 L2007 **FP** *012
HEREDIA, David L. 1500 WILDCAT DR, STE H 78374 #566-01-1987 L2004 **IM** *020 †20
HUANG, Ning. 1776 BILLY G WEBB 78374 #039-01-1999 L2006 **DR** *100 †80
IVES, Karen Michele. ■ 78374 #048-15-1996 L2000 **PD** *020 †55
KOZLOWSKI, Mark Ambrose. 1776 BILLY G WEBB 78374 #005-06-1991 L1997 **VIR** *020 †80
LEE SANG, Jerome A. 107 CEDAR DR 78374 #048-13-1995 L1996 **IM** *020 †20
MATEJKA, Kenneth D. 1776 BILLY G WEBB 78374 #011-02-1997 L2003 **DR** *020 †80
MC BURNEY, James Hugh. 1776 BILLY G WEBB 78374 #021-05-1963 L1970 **R** *020 †80
MOBLEY, James Arnold. 2413 MEMORIAL PKWY 78374 #048-13-1973 L1973 **FM** *020 †18
NUDELMAN, James Albert. 1776 BILLY G WEBB 78374 #041-09-1976 L1997 **DR OBG** *020 †30,80
SIMMONS, Michael R. ■ 78374 #048-15-1996 L2000 **EM** *020
STARKEY, John Harrell. 1776 BILLY G WEBB 78374 #048-04-1957 L1957 **R** *071 †80
STOBIE, Paul Edwin. 109 LOST CREEK DR, PEDIATRIX MED GROUP OF TEX 78374 #010-02-1979 L2004 **NPM PD** *020 †55
STRONG, David Burk. 1776 BILLY G WEBB 78374 #048-02-1967 L1967 **DR GP** *020 †80
VIOLANTE, Vanessa. ■ 78374 #048-78-2005, ▲ L2006 **FP** *012
WILSON, David Dean. 1776 BILLY G WEBB 78374 #048-12-1980 L1980 **DR** *020 †80
YIN, Yuming. 1776 BILLY G WEBB 78374 #243-47-1992 L2005 **DR** *020 †80 ‡

POST – GARZA

EDWARDS, William B. 608 W 6TH ST 79356 #048-14-2002 L2003 **FM** *020 †18

POTEET – ATASCOSA

PEREZ, Mario. 8555 N STATE HWY 16 78065 #048-78-1996, ▲ L1998 **FM** *020

POTTSBORO – GRAYSON

FLOHR, Leonard James, Jr. PO BOX 508, 1 VISTA DR 75076 #051-04-1945 L1949 **IM CD** *071 †20
MOORE, Robert Wm. ■ 75076 #048-02-1948 L1948 **IM CD** *071
RAMBO, Catherine Ann. ■ 75076 #021-05-1986 L1988 **EM UCM** *020
WILLIAMSON, Kenneth, III. ■ 75076 #048-13-1989 L2004 **FM** *020 †18

POTTSVILLE – HAMILTON

CORMAN, Samuel Jay. ■ 76565 #048-04-1962 L1962 **PTH** *020 †50

POWDERLY – LAMAR

DIAZ, Rebecca A. ■ 75473 #748-01-1968 L1979 **DR** *020
MYERS, Charles Moran. 571 COUNTY ROAD 44360 75473 #048-02-1966 L1966 **OBG** *020 †30
RESNICK, Peter David. 775 BEAVER CREEK RD, POWDERLY 75473 #165-01-1982 L1985 **AN** *020 †05

PRAIRIE VIEW – WALLER

BERRY, Glenn Edward. BAKER AT EVONS 77446 #048-13-1984 L1987 **GP IM** *020
CLARK, William Michael. ■ 77446 #048-13-1980 L1982 **OBG** *075
OWENS, Emery Roswell. ■ 77446 #024-06-1943 L1965 **GP** *071

PRESIDIO – PRESIDIO

SANTIAGO-PAYAN, Hector. ■ 79845 #649-01-1964 **PTH OS** *020 †50

PRINCETON – COLLIN

CLYNCH, Michael Richard. ■ 75407 #048-12-1978 L1978 **P** *075 †75
DUNCAN, John Van R. ■ 75407 #012-01-1974 L1976 **FM** *075
JANECEK, Thomas R. ■ 75407 #048-14-2001 L2003 **EM** *020 †16
KHAN, Rizwana. ■ 75407 #160-11-2000 L2006 **PD** *012 †18
SHAW, John Orton. ■ 75407 #051-01-1957 L1960 **FM** *071

PROSPER – COLLIN

BUTLER, Erin L. ■ 75078 #048-12-1996 L1997 **OBG** *020 †30
COCKE, Elizabeth Joan M. ■ 75078 #021-05-1965 L1965 **R NM** *071 †80
COCKE, Thomas Bosley. ■ 75078 #021-05-1963 L1963 **IM NEP** *020 †20
DANBY, John Herbert. ■ 75078 #917-05-1956 L1974 **FM** *071 †18
ODOM, Charles Brown, Jr. ■ 75078 #021-01-1962 L1990 **FOP OBG** *020 †30,50

PROVIDENCE VILLAGE – DENTON

MYRE, Christopher Dale. 10117 LAKEVIEW DR 76227 #048-04-1984 L1985 **GP** *020

QUANAH – HARDEMAN

JONES, James Stephen. ■ 79252 #048-15-2003 L2005 **AN** *100
KOCH, Fred. ■ 79252 #048-15-1975 L1975 **AN** *020 †05
MAKKENA, Ramachandra Rao. 200 W 5TH ST 79252 #495-50-1974 L1986 **IM GP** *020 †20
SAYAGO, Francisco Jose. ■ 79252 #132-02-1964 L1969 **GS** *071

QUINLAN – HUNT

TEURMAN, Sarah Anastasia. 734 E QUINLAN PKWY 75474 #054-04-1998 L1999 **FM** *020 †18

QUITMAN – WOOD

CATHEY, George V, Jr. 117 N WINNSBORO ST 75783 #048-14-1982 L1983 **FM EM** *020 †18
CHIMANJI, Mahanprakash D. 117 N WINNSBORO ST 75783 #495-01-1979 L1995 **IM** *020
DOPSON, James D. 117 N WINNSBORO ST 75783 #048-14-2001 L2004 **FM** *020 †18
HICKS, Norman Paul. 117 N WINNSBORO ST, P O BOX 919 75783 #048-12-1982 L1983 **FM** *020 †18
HOWELL, John Scott. 117 N WINNSBORO ST 75783 #048-02-1980 L1980 **EM IM** *020 †20,16
JEROME, Johnnie Jeff. ■ 75783 #048-12-1956 L1956 **AI FM** *071 †03,18
KIM, Sung-Chul. 117 N WINNSBORO ST 75783 #583-02-1967 L1975 **AN** *020
MARTINEZ, Jose Ricardo. 117 N WINNSBORO ST 75783 #019-02-1991 L1994 **IM** *020
MARVEL, James Ebbert. 108 PARKER ST STE 400 75783 #039-01-1968 L1992 **ORS** *020 †40
NIEMANN, Jeffrey Michael. 711 E GOODE ST 75783 #017-20-1968 L1999 **D** *020 †15
OLSON, Scott J. 108 PARKER ST STE 10 75783 #048-15-1999 L2002 **FM** *020 †18
SWINFORD, Melody M. 606 E GOODE ST, STE 100 75783 #028-46-1999 L2002 **FM** *020 †18

RANCHO VIEJO – CAMERON

BURGESS, Michael Andrew. ■ 78575 #143-02-1962 L1973 **ON ID** *020
CHANEY, Ernie Joe. ■ 78575 #019-02-1956 L1956 **FM FPG** *072 †18
GOEL, Shashi Bala. 604 ZAPATA AVE, RANCHO VIEJO 78575 #496-07-1954 L1978 **AN** *020 †05
GOMEZ, Juan Jose. ■ 78575 #649-01-1976 *100
GOMEZ, Micheal. 809 ESCANDON AVE 78575 #308-10-1987 L1993 **AN** *020 †05
LOJI HUI, Flora Monique. 3709 CARMEN AVE 78575 #649-02-1986 L1996 **PD** *020 †55
LOJI-HUI, Ramon A C. 3709 CARMEN AVE 78575 #649-02-1985 L1991 **IM** *020 †20
MARTINEZ, Juan Diego. ■ 78575 #048-02-2005 **IM** *012
NOYOLA, Daniel Ernesto. ■ 78575 #649-04-1993 **PDI** *100 †55
VILLARREAL, Rafael S. ■ 78575 #649-02-1947 L1990 **FM** *071 ‡

RANDOLPH AIR FORCE BASE – BEXAR

BALDWIN, Thos Edward, Jr. 221 3RD ST W, 12TH MEDICAL GROUP 78150 #047-06-1970 L1971 **FM** *030 †18
BECKSTRAND, Devin Paul. 221 3RD ST W, 12TH MEDICAL GROUP 78150 #016-42-1996 L1997 **FM** *020 †70
CAPPS, James Austin, Jr. 1985 1ST ST W UNIT 2908 78150 #004-01-1965 L1965 **AM GP** *030 †18

CARRIZALES, Alesia C. 221 3RD ST W, 12 MEDICAL GROUP 78150 #023-12-1996 L1998 FM †18

CHU, William Yunzhou. 221 3RD ST W, 12TH MEDICAL GROUP 78150 #048-15-2003 L2003 PD *020 †55

CLARKE, Thomas Frederick. 221 3RD ST W, 12TH MEDICAL GROUP 78150 #023-12-1992 L1994 OS *020 †70

COONEY, James Robert. 221 3RD ST W, 12TH MEDICAL GROUP 78150 #023-12-2005 L2006 GS *020

ELDREDGE, Louis Dan. 221 3RD ST W, 12 MEDICAL GROUP 78150 #748-09-1979 L1980 GP *020 †70

FARRELL, Michael Lynn. 221 3RD ST W, 12TH MEDICAL GROUP 78150 #026-04-1979 L1982 AM *020 †70

FOSS, David Robt. 221 3RD ST W, 12TH MEDICAL GROUP 78150 #023-12-1991 L1993 EM *020 †16

HOYUMPA, Danilo Howland. 221 3RD ST W, 12TH MEDICAL GROUP 78150 #048-12-1991 L1992 AM FM *020 †18

HUNSAKER, Keith William. 221 3RD ST W, 12TH MEDICAL GROUP 78150 #049-01-1994 L1997 DR *012 †18

JOHNSON, Esther Yvonne. 221 3RD ST W BLDG 1040, 12TH MEDICAL GROUP 78150 #041-14-1984 L1986 PD *020 †55

JOHNSON, Kimberly Susan. 221 3RD ST W, 12 ADS/SGGAF 78150 #023-12-1998 L1999 PD *020 †55

KINNE, Stephen Mc Neilly. 221 3RD ST W, 12TH MEDICAL GROUP 78150 #035-15-1982 L1987 FM *020 †70,18

KNIGHT, Derek Andrew. 221 3RD ST W, 12TH MEDICAL GROUP 78150 #005-19-1998 L2000 EM *020 †16

LEHMAN, Robert Eugene. 221 3RD ST W, 12 MEDICAL GROUP 78150 #005-19-1977 L1978 OBG FM *020 †30

LOWRY, Patrick David. 221 3RD ST W, 12TH MEDICAL GROUP 78150 #023-12-1998 L2000 GPM *012 †70

MANCHESTER, Stephen F. 550 C ST W STE 6, AFPC/DPPD 78150 #051-01-1982 L1988 PD *030 †55

MONROE, Scott Warren. 221 3RD ST W, 12TH MEDICAL GROUP 78150 #048-04-1977 L1977 FM EM *020 †18

NOLAND, Robert Eldridge. 221 3RD ST W BLDG 1040, 12TH MEDICAL GROUP 78150 #027-01-1996 L2007 FM *020 †18

POWELL, Alton W, III. 221 3RD ST W, 12TH MEDICAL GROUP 78150 #023-12-1982 L1988 AM OM *030 †70

RUSSELL, Tod Shelby. 221 3RD ST W, 12 MEDICAL GROUP 78150 #023-12-1990 L1992 PD PDI *020 †55

SIMONE, Susannah Lillie. 221 3RD ST W, 12TH MEDICAL GROUP 78150 #011-04-2002 L2004 PD *020 †55

STAHLMAN, Richard L. 550 C ST W, STE 6 78150 #007-02-1980 L1981 FM *030 †18

TRAN, Bao Quoc. 221 3RD ST W BLDG 1040, 12TH MEDICAL GROUP 78150 #306-01-1997 L2006 OBG GP *020

TRANT, David Bruce. 221 3RD ST W, 12TH MEDICAL GROUP 78150 #048-02-1984 L1985 IM *020 †20

TROUT, Leonard E, III. 221 3RD ST W, 12TH MEDICAL GROUP 78150 #023-01-1986 L1988 FM *020 †18

WESTFALL, Lorna Ann. 63 MAIN CIR STE 3 78150 #036-01-1989 L1990 FM *030 †18

WILLIAMS, Maureen Noel. 221 3RD ST W, 12TH MEDICAL GROUP 78150 #023-12-1999 L2000 FM *020 †18

WILLIAMS, Peter Maag. 221 3RD ST W BLDG 1040, 12TH MEDICAL GROUP 78150 #023-12-2004 L2005 IM *020

RANGER — EASTLAND

GOHLKE, Luther Ray. ■ 76470 #048-02-1959 L1959 FM *071 †18

WEBB, Philip Rex. 200 WALNUT ST 76470 #048-12-1979 L1979 FM *020 †18

RANKIN — UPTON

KIRKPATRICK, James L. PO BOX 267, 1010 ELIZABETH ST 79778 #143-03-1963 L1974 *071

MC LEAN, Paul E. PO BOX 47 79778 #048-02-1974 L1974 FM *020

RANSOM CANYON — LUBBOCK

LEIGHTON, Kimberly Ann. ■ 79366 #038-43-1991 L1997 FM *100

SCHMITZ, Bettina Ulrike. ■ 79366 #409-25-1987 L2007 *100

RAYMONDVILLE — WILLACY

CANTU, George. 182 E KIMBALL AVE 78580 #305-01-1985 L1994 IM IMG *020 †20

DESAI, Janak Sumanlal. 1601 BUFFALO DR 78580 #495-17-1965 L1977 GP GS *020

KRISTENSEN, John Wm. 165 S 6TH ST 78580 #065-01-1973 L1982 FM *020

MARTINEZ-VELA, Miguel A. 131 FM 3168 78580 #341-01-1979 L1999 PD *020 †55

MIERISCH, Erwin Buitrago. 336 S 8TH ST 78580 #649-14-1971 L1983 OBG *075 †30

ROBINSON, Stephen A. 165 S 6TH ST 78580 #041-03-2001 L2007 FM *100 †18

SINHA, Rajiv R. 637 E HIDALGO AVE 78580 #065-09-1991 L1995 FM *020 †18

SMITH, Albert Lee. 165 S 6TH ST 78580 #048-12-1981 L1981 FM *020 †18

SREENIVAS, Nanjappa. 482 W HIDALGO AVE 78580 #495-33-1967 L1979 P GP *020

RED OAK — ELLIS

CASH, Tiyonnoh Monje. ■ 75154 #048-02-2004 L2007 IM *020

ELKINS, Terri Lynn. 75154 #048-04-1988 L1989 OBG *030

HITT, Edwin Earl. ■ 75154 #021-01-1965 L1968 GP *020 †18

HOLLUB, Alexander J. 273 E OVILLA RD, STE 4 75154 #048-12-1990 L1991 FM *020 †18

MARSHALL, Harold Dwayne. 420 CENTURY WAY, STE 300 75154 #048-02-1992 L1997 PM *020 †60

NEWSOM, Stephanie Beatric. ■ 75154 #048-12-2006 GS *012

NORDSTROM, Jason R. 273 E OVILLA RD, ELLIS COUNTY DIAGNOSTIC CL 75154 #048-15-2001 L2004 IM *020

RUDDER, Lorraine M. 307 E OVILLA RD, STE 600 75154 #048-13-1992 L1993 PM *020 †60

SIMS, Edward Garnel. ■ 75154 #010-01-1975 L1977 IM ON *020 †20

THOMISON, James L, II. 273 E OVILLA RD, STE 4 75154 #048-14-1998 L1999 FM *020 †18

REFUGIO — REFUGIO

COLDWELL, Peter Arthur. 107 1/2 SWIFT ST 78377 #038-43-1994 L2000 FM *020 †18

MASCARENHAS, Russell J. 107 1/2 SWIFT ST 78377 #495-52-1988 L1996 IM *020 †20

WALKER, James S. 107 SWIFT ST 78377 #048-13-2002 L2005 FM *020 †18

REKLAW — CHEROKEE

ROGERS, Jerry Eugene. 1750 N MAIN ST 75784 #021-05-1973 L1974 U GS *020 †95

RENO — LAMAR

BAEZA, Carlos R. ■ 75462 #042-01-1965 OM PHP *075

COMBEST-AVALOS, Sally S. 4230 LAKESHORE DR 75462 #048-13-1992 L1993 AN *020 †05

RHOME — WISE

HOOVER, Andrew W. PO BOX 770, 600 S MAIN 76078 #048-15-1992 L1993 FM *020 †18 ‡

RICHARDSON — DALLAS

ABDULRAHMAN, Ramzi E. ■ 75082 #042-02-1993 L2006 RO *100 †18,80

ACKERMAN, Neel Burnett. 2350 CAMPBELL CREEK BLVD, STE 100 75082 #012-01-1978 L1984 AM NPM *071 †55

ACOSTA, Asuncion A. 375 MUNICIPAL DR STE 134 75080 #748-10-1970 L1978 IM GP *020

ACOSTA, Eduardo Galang. 375 MUNICIPAL DR STE 134 75080 #748-10-1970 L1976 PM *020 †60

ADAMS, Crystal Lynn. ■ 75080 #048-13-2006 OBG *012

AFZAL, Ahmed Zaeem. ■ 75081 #048-02-1988 *075

AHMAD, Baseer U. ■ 75081 #048-12-2008 *012

AHMAD, Shahab. 620 N COIT RD, STE 2175 75080 #704-02-1988 L2000 IM *020 †20

AHMED, Anisa. 3409 SPECTRUM BLVD, # 300 75082 #704-02-1985 L1993 PD *020 †55

AHMED, Shakil. 820 W ARAPAHO RD, RICHARDSON REG SR HLTH CTR 75080 #704-02-1986 L2000 IM *020 †20

ALDRICH, Jennifer Elaine. 300 N COIT RD 75080 #048-02-1996 L1997 FM *020 †18

ALEXANDER, Thomas K. 399 W CAMPBELL RD, STE 212 75080 #495-44-1980 L1996 IM *020 †20

AMIR, Mohammad. 2821 E PRESDNT GRG BSH HWY, STE 301 75082 #704-16-1990 L1996 IM *020 †20

ANDREWS, Robert Stanley. 925 WARREN WAY, NIGHT RAYS PA 75080 #023-12-1999 L2007 DR *020 †80

APONTE, Carole C. 403 W CAMPBELL RD, STE 404 75080 #048-04-1999 L2003 D *020 †15

ARCHER, William Paul, Jr. 3001 GEORGE BUSH HWY, STE 250 75082 #021-01-1996 L2003 PD *020 †55

ARUMUGHAM, Bagyalakshmi. 401 W CAMPBELL RD 75080 #495-16-1970 L1977 P *020 †75

ARUMUGHAM, Palaniappan. 1600 N PLANO RD, STE 1200 75081 #495-42-1965 L1975 FM PD *020 †55,18

ASFEEN, Ummul Zohra. ■ 75081 #496-27-2000 *100

ASHFAQUE, Ambreen. ■ 75081 #704-02-2002 FP *012

AUGUST, Anna Maria. 3001 GEORGE BUSH HWY, STE 250 75082 #001-02-1986 L2005 PD NPM *020 †55

BAMBERGER-PERKINS, A. 208 W SPRING VALLEY RD 75081 #550-02-1983 L1993 PME *020

BANNISTER, Denise Cantu. 403 W CAMPBELL RD, STE 410 75080 #048-02-1993 L1995 IM *020 †20

BASKIND, Allen Frank. 620 N COIT RD STE 2170 75080 #836-01-1965 L1978 GS *071

BATHURST, Gina Rose. ■ 75080 #048-02-2005 GS *012

BEAUJON, William James. ■ 75081 #039-01-2006 IM *012

BELL, Richard Collins. 399 W CAMPBELL RD, STE 102 75080 #048-02-1990 L1993 IM *020 †20

BELL, Ronald J. 401 W CAMPBELL RD 75080 #048-12-1993 L1995 N *020 †75

BELVIN, Brent B. 3201 E PRESDNT GRG BSH HWY, STE 107 75082 #048-15-1999 L2001 PM PRS *020 ‡

BENAVIDES, John Paul. 3201 E PRESDNT GRG BSH HWY, STE 107 75082 #048-78-2001, ▲ L2003 PM *020 †60

BENIGAR, Robert Wesley, Jr. 1755 N COLLINS BLVD # 525 75080 #027-01-2001 L2005 P *100 †20

BHAT, Shubha Prakash. ■ 75082 #495-09-2000 FP *012

BIBAWI, Samer Ernest. 401 W CAMPBELL RD, PIEDMONT HEMATOLOGY-ONCOLO 75080 #915-02-1988 L1999 HO *012

BINDRA, Amby Jeet. 2520 N CENTRAL EXPY, STE 100 75080 #048-15-2001 L2004 PD *020 †18

BINGHAM, Nathan Christian. ■ 75082 #048-12-2008 *012

BLONDEL, Monique Angele. ■ 75080 #048-12-1986 L1988 PD *020 †55

BONNET, David Gregory. 403 W CAMPBELL RD, STE 103 75080 #048-02-1978 L1978 FM *020 †18

BOPPANA, Sita M. 2100 N COLLINS BLVD, STE 204 75080 #495-50-1989 L1997 IM *020 †20 ‡

BORME, Antonio Elio. 970 N COIT RD # 2403A 75080 #561-17-1960 L1974 GP GS *071

BOSHART, Kimberly Wynne. ■ 75081 #048-15-2008 *012

BRADFORD, Katrina Posta. 2520 N CENTRAL EXPY, STE 100 75080 #005-14-1995 L2001 FM *020 †18 ‡

BRIDGES, Vancy Howard. 101 S COIT RD, PO BOX 381327 75080 #005-11-1974 L1985 OBG *020 †30

BURGESS, Gary Howard. 3001 GEORGE BUSH HWY, STE 250 75082 #048-02-1979 L1979 NPM PD *062 †55

CALDWELL, Troy Arthur, Jr. 2089 N COLLINS BLVD, STE 103 75080 #048-12-1977 L1977 P *020

CARRASCO, Jeremy Scott. 399 W CAMPBELL RD STE 2 75080 #048-15-2001 L2005 GS *020

CHADALAVADA, Rakesh. 3518 NEWHAVEN DR 75082 #495-50-1996 L2003 CHP *020 †75

CHANDLER, Preston J, Jr. 330 MUNICIPAL DR STE 104 75080 #051-04-1965 L1973 PS GS *071 †65

CHANG, Shao-Chun R. ■ 75080 #048-12-2006 L2008 OBG *012

CHAPMAN, Sara Lynn. 1221 W CAMPBELL RD STE 221 75080 #048-12-1979 L1979 D *020 †15

CHEN, Barbara Kuoyu. ■ 75082 #048-13-2005 OBG *012

CHEN, Daniel Shu-Eng. 375 MUNICIPAL DR, STE 240 75080 #244-04-1973 L1977 AN *020

CHERNOV, Allan Joel. 901 S CENTRAL EXPY, NORTH BLDG MAIL STOP E 75080 #061-01-1964 L2002 IM *030 †20

CHOUDHRY, Amir Iqbal. 399 W CAMPBELL RD STE 206 75080 #033-05-1999 L2005 CD IM *020

CLARK, Chris A. 399 W CAMPBELL RD, STE 101 75080 #048-16-1994 L1996 FM *020 †18

CLOTHIER, Norman F, Jr. 2821 E PRESDNT GRG BSH HWY, FAMILY HEALTH CARE 75082 #048-12-1991 L1992 FM *020 †18

CO, Jacqueline Bachvan. 403 W CAMPBELL RD STE 310 75080 #048-02-1994 L1996 OPH *020 †35

COLEMAN, Anne Graesser. 375 MUNICIPAL DR, STE 128 75080 #048-12-1989 L1990 IM *020 †20

COLEMAN, Rogers King. 901 S CENTRAL EXPY 75080 #048-04-1956 L1956 GP *071

COTNER, Jerry Bob. 770 N COIT RD STE 2486 75080 #039-01-1959 L1968 OPH *020 †35

COULTHARD, Mark G. 75081 #143-05-1981 CCP *020

COUVILLON, Craig Michael. ■ 75080 #048-13-2008 L2008 *012

COWAN, Sheryl Ann. 403 W CAMPBELL RD, STE 103 75080 #047-06-1988 L1992 FM *020 †18

COWDEN, William Lee. 1333 W CAMPBELL RD # 113 75080 #048-14-1978 L1978 CD OS *020 †20

CROW, Steven Davis. 1112 N FLOYD RD, STE 6 75080 #021-01-1969 L1972 PD *020 †55

DANIEL, Richard Hartman. 3601 N STAR RD 75082 #021-05-1980 L1983 PD *020 †55

DAO, Trung Nguyen. 399 W CAMPBELL RD STE 21 75080 #039-01-1991 L1996 IM *020 †20

DAUGHETY, Jewel Simpson. ■ 75082 #048-12-1955 L1955 PM PLM *020 †60

DEULOFEUT, Richard A. 3001 GEORGE BUSH HWY, STE 250 75082 #264-12-1992 L2006 NPM *020 †55

DIAMOND, Gregg H. 3201 E PRESDNT GRG BSH HWY, STE 107 75082 #048-02-1987 L1988 PM *020 †60

DISRAELI, Allan S. 1701 N COLLINS BLVD, STE 327 75080 #035-06-1961 L1967 OBG *020 †30

DONTHINENI, Manoj Kumar. 2100 N COLLINS BLVD 75080 #495-21-1994 L2007 MPD *020 †20,55

DUTTA, Paritosh Chandra. 275 W CAMPBELL RD, STE 650 75080 #495-15-1959 L1977 AI *020 †03

DUVUURI, Vani. 399 W CAMPBELL RD SU, MEDICAL PLAZA II 75080 #496-35-1996 L2002 END *020 †20

DYO, Robert Kent. 2821 E PRESDNT GRG BSH HWY, STE 510 75082 #048-02-1982 L1983 FM *020 †18

ENGKATANAKORN, Naruchon. ■ 75080 #891-08-1996 L2003 IM *100 †20

ESENWINE, Allison Joy. 401 W CAMPBELL RD, DEPT OF EMERG MEDICINE 75080 #041-12-1999 L2006 EM *020 †16

EZEKIEL, Kalavalli. 375 MUNICIPAL DR STE 102 75080 #495-04-1981 L1994 PD *020 †55

FACKLER, William Rush. 375 MUNICIPAL DR STE 102 75080 #035-20-1956 L1960 PD *072 †55

FAGAN, Elizabeth Louise. 401 W CAMPBELL RD 75080 #039-01-1992 L1998 EM *020 †16

FAVROTH, Daphne Louise. 551 N PLANO RD, FAMILY HEALTH AND WELLNESS 75081 #030-06-1986 L1991 MPD *020 †55,20

FERNANDEZ, Eduardo. 399 W CAMPBELL RD, STE 206 75080 #041-13-1986 L1993 IM CD *020 †20

FISCHER, Laurice Kay. ■ 75082 #028-34-2004 L2006 GS *012

FITUCH-BEAUDOIN, Camellia. 3001 GEORGE BUSH HWY, STE 250 75082 #025-01-1996 L2001 NPM *020 †55

FOSHEE, Soume Daulat. ■ 75082 #035-03-1998 L2004 DR *020 †80

FRANK, Robert Jos. 399 W CAMPBELL RD STE 104 75080 #016-06-1963 L1966 OTO A *020 †45

FRANK, Thomas Christopher. 399 W CAMPBELL RD, STE 104 75080 #048-12-1994 L1999 OTO *020 †45

FRIEDMAN, Lawrie Hilton. 670 N COIT RD, 2355 PROMENADE CENTER 75080 #836-01-1972 L1981 FM EM *020 ‡

FRIEDMAN, Shlomo. 702 W ARAPAHO RD STE 104 75080 #550-01-1967 L1981 PD PHO *020 ‡

FRYER, Andrew D. 648 W CAMPBELL RD, STE B 75080 #005-14-1975 L1990 PDC *020 †55

GADOL, Steven M. 399 W CAMPBELL RD, STE 202 75080 #048-12-1987 L1993 IM *020 †20

GALLAGHER, Christopher Mi. ■ 75080 #048-15-2005 L2006 IM *012

GAUTIER, Damaris. 2400 LAKESIDE BLVD, BLUE CROSS/BLUE SHIELD OF 75082 #042-01-1992 L1993 IM *020 †20

GREBENNIKOV, Vladimir A. 870 N COIT RD, STE 2660 75080 #913-21-1987 L2000 IM *020 †20

GREEN, David Warner. 3001 GEORGE BUSH HWY, STE 250 75082 #018-03-1984 L1990 NPM PD *020 †55

GREENBERG, George Everett. ■ 75082 #004-01-1968 L1968 R *062 †80,28 ‡

GREENFIELD, Keller P. ■ 75082 #048-04-1953 L1953 GPM *072

GRESSLER, Volker Heinrich. 399 MELROSE DR, STE B 75080 #409-10-1981 L1994 ON HEM *020 †20

GRUGLE, Thomas A. 275 W CAMPBELL RD STE 121 75080 #048-12-1984 L1985 P *020 †75 ‡

HALBROOK, Linda Sheldon. 2520 N CENTRAL EXPY, STE 100 75080 #048-12-1984 L1986 FM *020 †18

HAMM, Jeffrey Thos. 399 W CAMPBELL RD, STE 404 75080 #021-06-1984 L1990 ORS *020 †40

HANSSEN, Christopher John. 330 MUNICIPAL DR, STE 102 75080 #048-02-1999 L2004 ORS *020 †40

HARNEY, John Harold. 375 MUNICIPAL DR STE 222 75080 #649-14-1978 L1982 N *020 †75

HARPER, Thomas Edwin. 3001 GEORGE BUSH HWY, STE 250 75082 #023-07-1978 L1987 NPM PD *071 †55

HARRISON, William Jerry. 970 N COIT RD STE 3040 75080 #048-02-1976 L1976 FM *020 †18

HASSAN, Mohamed Saeed. ■ 75080 #495-04-1951 L1980 GP *020

HAYNSWORTH, Robert F, Jr. 2520 N CENTRAL EXPY, STE 400 75080 #048-14-1981 L1981 PME PMM *020 †05 ‡

HELLING, Thomas Sacher, Jr. ■ 75080 #019-02-2002 L2008 DR *100 †80

HENDERSON, Allison Halley. 1112 N FLOYD RD, STE 6A 75080 #039-01-1997 L2000 PD *020 †55

HO, Binh Dac. 4011 E RENNER RD 75082 #021-01-1994 L1997 EM *020 †16

HOGGE, Mark Wayne. 400 W CAMPBELL RD 75080 #051-07-1990 L1992 DR *020 †80

HONG, Seung Kook. 205 E MAIN ST 75081 #583-01-1968 L1979 GS GP *020

HSIAO, Marvin Lee. ■ 75082 #048-12-2004 L2004 OPH *012

HSU, Chung-Sen. 375 MUNICIPAL DR STE 122 75080 #385-01-1964 L1973 OTO *020 †45

HUI, Peter Kim-Ming. 401 W CAMPBELL RD 75080 #065-01-1973 L1978 EM *020 †16

HUYNH, Bobby P. 375 MUNICIPAL DR STE 144 75080 #048-14-1992 L1993 PM *020 †60

IWASKO, Nicholas G. 1920 N COLLINS BLVD 75080 #011-02-1995 L2002 DR *020 †80

JEFFREY, Thomas Eugene. 399 W CAMPBELL RD STE 101 75080 #048-02-1972 L1972 FM *020 †18

JEKOT, Elizabeth A. 3301 E RENNER RD, STE 100 75082 #048-12-1989 L1990 DR *020 †80

JIANG, Chu-Ling. 375 MUNICIPAL DR, STE 244 75080 #244-04-1978 L1987 A PD *020 †55,03

JOHNSON, Thomas Gary. 401 W CAMPBELL RD STE 205, R CTR FOR BREAST HLTH 75080 #045-01-1974 L1978 R GP *020 †80

JONES, George Franklin. 401 W CAMPBELL RD 75080 #048-12-1980 L1980 AN *020

JONES, Wayne Chas. 375 MUNICIPAL DR STE 224 75080 #048-12-1968 L1969 P *020 †75

JUAREZ, Juan, Jr. 5410 WELLINGTON DR 75082 #048-13-1999 L2002 PEM PD *020 †55

KAMPAS, Jennifer Lynne. ■ 75082 #048-14-1993 L1994 FM *020 †18

KARE, Rex Brimbvela. ■ 75082 #748-01-1967 L1985 U *020 †75

KASBARIAN, Charles M. 670 W ARAPAHO RD, STE 6 75080 #048-02-1986 L1987 FM D *020 †18

KETHU, Sripathi Reddy. ■ 75082 #495-62-1995 L2007 GE *020 †20

KHAN, Arif Basir. 375 MUNICIPAL DR, STE 242 75080 #495-77-1987 L2003 APM *020 †05

KHAN, Farha. 3001 GEORGE BUSH HWY, STE 250 75082 #495-77-1994 NPM *020 †55

KHAN, Minhaj Muhammad. ■ 75081 #033-06-1996 L2003 GS *020

KHAN, Yasmin Basir. 403 W CAMPBELL RD, STE 305 75080 #495-98-1989 L2000 OBG *020 †30

KHEMANE, Iqbal Bilal. ■ 75081 #308-11-1987 PM *100 ‡

KIM, John Yah-Sung. 401 W CAMPBELL RD 75080 #005-11-1997 L2002 GS *020 †65

KING, Alice. 3001 GEORGE BUSH HWY, STE 250 75082 #048-15-2001 L2004 PD *020 †55

KUHNE, Robert M. 375 MUNICIPAL DR, STE 108 75080 #048-12-1960 L1960 GYN *071 †30

KULKARNI, Usha R. 1810 N PLANO RD 75081 #495-35-1974 L1993 IM *020 †05

KUNDAWALA, Isufali M. ■ 75082 #495-01-1966 L1976 FM AN *020 †05

KURILSKY, Emil Gregory. ■ 75082 #913-07-1967 L1983 GP *071

KUTSEN, Gregory. ■ 75082 #048-12-2003 L2005 EM *100 †16

KWAN, Louise Ann. 970 N COIT RD, STE 3040 75080 #495-01-1974 L1986 FM *020 †55

LANGE, Rose Lynn Carloto. 1701 N COLLINS BLVD, STE 300 75080 #748-11-1986 L1998 PD *020 †55

LAUDERDALE, Robert Altman. ■ 75080 #048-02-1954 L1954 GS *071

LE, Kenneth Lam. 4076 KYNDRA CIR 75082 #021-01-2005 L2006 DR *012

LEE, Napoleon. 2175 BUCKINGHAM RD 75081 #048-02-1984 L1986 AI PD *020 †55

LEMESHEV, Yan H. ■ 75082 #048-13-2001 L2005 PTH *100 †50

LEMMON, Joshua Alexis. 3201 GEORGE BUSH HWY, STE 101 75082 #038-06-2001 L2007 HS *020

LEWIS, Felicia Lenora. 399 W CAMPBELL RD, MEDICAL PLAZA 2, STE 102 75080 #047-06-1999 L2007 IM *020 †20

LIMANNI, Alex. 2929 N CENTRAL EXPY 75080 #033-05-1979 L1995 RHU *020 †20

LIN, Jonathan. 403 W CAMPBELL RD, STE 103 75080 #048-04-1997 L1998 FM *020 †18

LIN, William Tinghsien. 2821 E PRESDNT GRG BSH HWY, STE 101 75082 #016-42-1996 L2001 PD *020 †55

LITKE, Diane Sue. 403 W CAMPBELL RD, STE 320 75080 #036-01-1991 L1997 ORS *020 †40

LIU, Chong Hui. 1120 N CAMPBELL RD 75080 #243-92-1985 L2000 FM *020 †18

LOCKHART, Albert Belville. 375 MUNICIPAL DR STE 14 75080 #950-01-1962 L1979 OPH *075

LONGORIA, Jason Arturo. ■ 75081 #048-12-2005 P *012

LUMMUS, Gina Page. 3001 GEORGE BUSH HWY, STE 250 75082 #048-15-1999 L2002 PD *020 †55

LUU, Hoa Ngoc. ■ 75082 #010-02-2007 L2007 *012

MADSEN, Terry D. 2821 E PRESDNT GRG BSH HWY, STE 500 75082 #048-13-1999 L2004 ORS *020 †40

MAJOR, Terri Lynn. 3001 GEORGE BUSH HWY, STE 250 75082 #005-14-1994 L2000 NPM *020 †55

MANIA, William Michael. 375 MUNICIPAL DR, STE 110 75080 #048-15-1981 L1981 IM GPM *020 †20

MARCOU, Rosebeth R. 1303 COLUMBIA DR, STE 217 75081 #041-01-1982 L1991 PD *020 †55

MARKS, Richard Alan. 399 W CAMPBELL RD, STE 408 75080 #056-06-1974 L1975 OSS ORS *020 †40

MARKUS, George Michael. 2175 PROMENADE CENTER 75080 #048-12-1980 L1980 IM *020

MARTIN, Dorothy Victoria. 1219 ABRAMS RD STE 240 75081 #048-13-1986 L1987 CHP *020 †75

MASSEY, Lenita Claire. 401 W CAMPBELL RD 75080 #047-06-1964 L1972 GYN *071 †30

MAUPIN, Warren Bryan, II. 403 W CAMPBELL RD 75080 #048-16-1985 L1986 DR *020 †80

MAY, James Lambuth. ■ 75080 #048-12-1948 L1948 OBS OBG *012

MAZAHERI, Mehrdad. 648 W CAMPBELL RD, THE LASIK CENTER 75080 #051-07-1993 L1997 OPH *020 †35

MC CARTHY, Roderick P. 401 W CAMPBELL RD, RICHARDSON REG MED CTR 75080 #063-01-1983 L1992 EM *020

MC GEEHAN, Maureen. 275 W CAMPBELL RD STE 650 75080 #048-13-1997 L2003 AI IM *020 †20,03

MC KINNEY, James R. 714 W ARAPAHO RD 75080 #038-40-1951 L1952 AN PME *062 †05

MC KINNEY, Peter Young. 508 STILLMEADOW DR 75081 #048-02-1975 L1975 OBG *062 †30

MC LEAN, James Patrick. ■ 75082 #033-05-2002 L2005 PM *012 †60

MEHTA, Michelle M. PO BOX 833715 75083 #048-04-2004 L2007 P *012

MEHTA, Sacheen H. 1120 W CAMPBELL RD STE 109 75080 #028-46-1994 L2001 ORS OSM *020 †40

MEIER, Joshua William. ■ 75081 #056-06-2002 L2007 OP *012

MEIER, Paul Danl. 2099 N COLLINS BLVD, STE 100 75080 #004-01-1972 L1976 P *020

MEYER, Adrian. 200 S COTTONWOOD DR # A, STE A 75080 #836-02-1969 L1978 IM OS *020 †20

MILLER, Amy Beth. 2821 E PRESDNT GRG BSH HWY, FAMILY HEALTH CARE 75082 #048-78-2000, ▲ L2002 FM *020 †18 ‡

MILVENAN, Eileen Sullivan. 3001 GEORGE BUSH HWY, STE 250 75082 #048-12-1977 L1977 NPM *020 †55

MINER, Adam S. 620 N COIT RD, STE 2150 75080 #048-13-1989 L1992 FM *020 †18 ‡

MINIRTH, Franklin Brent. 1200 E COLLINS BLVD STE 30 75081 #004-01-1972 L1975 P *020 †75

MINNAL, Deepika. 3301 N STAR RD # 41 75082 #496-07-1998 L2004 PD *020 †55

MOGHADDAS, Yekta Victoria. ■ 75082 #104-01-2003 GP *100

MOOTHA, Ravi Kanth. 2821 E PRESDNT GRG BSH HWY, STE 305 75082 #048-04-1997 L2003 U *020 †95

MORCHOWER, Gary Clay. 1112 N FLOYD RD STE 6A, GARY C MORCHOWER MD 75080 #021-01-1962 L1966 PD GE *020 †55

MORGAN, Brent C. 399 W CAMPBELL RD, STE 400 75080 #048-02-1989 L1990 NS *020 †25

MURO, Rene Ernesto. ■ 75081 #048-02-2003 L2007 AN *100

MURRAY, Jenny Marie. 701 N CENTRAL EXPY 75080 #012-01-1992 L1994 **P** *020 †75

MUSSER, Bradley James. 2821 E PRESDNT GRG BSH HWY, STE 306 75082 #018-03-1995 L1997 **FM** *020 †18

MYINT, Daniel Thet. 2097 N COLLINS BLVD, STE 198 75080 #209-01-1977 L1990 **PD** *020 †55

MYSOREKAR, Nagaraj R. ■ 75082 #495-28-1961 L1977 **IM** *071

NADEEM, Mahe Talat. 208 W SPRING VALLEY RD 75081 #704-16-1993 L2001 **PM** *020 †60

NEAVES, Noe. 1200 E COLLINS BLVD, STE 300 75081 #649-02-1952 L1958 **P** *020

NEWBERRY, Jonathan Warren. ■ 75080 #039-01-2006 **PTH** *012

NEWTON, Jennifer D. ■ 75082 #048-16-2007 **OBG** *012

NGUYEN, Diana K. 401 W CAMPBELL RD 75080 #048-12-1998 L2000 **D** *020 †15

NGUYEN, Nhan Phuc. 399 W CAMPBELL RD, STE 300 75080 #021-06-1997 L2004 **IC CD** *020 †20

NJAMFA, Lydia Oluwatoyin. 101 S COIT RD, STE 399 75080 #690-01-1990 L2000 **FM** *020 †18

NORTON, Carol Beth. 399 W CAMPBELL RD, STE 410 75080 #036-07-1995 L1998 **OBG** *020 †30

NOVAK, Jayshree Jos. 100 N COTTONWOOD DR 75080 #495-17-1981 L1997 **PD** *020 †55

NUSSGEN-FOWLER, Martha. ■ 75080 #649-01-1958 L1981 **PD** *020

NYSTROM, Gerald Alan. 3001 GEORGE BUSH HWY, STE 250 75082 #005-12-1980 L1998 **NPM PD** *020 †55

OCHANI, Poonam. ■ 75082 #704-18-2000 **FP** *012

OISHI, Scott Noboru. 3201 GEORGE BUSH HWY # 101 75082 #024-07-1987 L1989 **PS HS** *020 †65

OLFSON, James Ryder. 2821 E PRESDNT GRG BSH HWY, FAMILY HEALTH CARE 75082 #016-42-1994 L1998 **FM** *020 †18

ORIG, Tito Mansueto. 1206 APOLLO RD 75081 #748-11-1972 L1980 **AN** *020

PACE, Betty Sue. PO BOX 830688, 2601 FLOYD RD 75083 #056-06-1981 L2003 **PHO** *020 †55

PATTERSON, Jennifer G. 403 W CAMPBELL RD STE 410 75080 #048-12-1997 L1998 **IM** *020 †20

PECK, Ramona K. 1112 N FLOYD RD, STE 6 75080 #048-12-1987 L1988 **PD** *020 †55

PEREZ, Eduardo M. 3001 E PRESDNT GRG BSH HWY, STE 250 75082 #737-06-1988 L1998 **NPM PD** *020 †55 ‡

PERRY, Adam Carlton. 1701 N GREENVILLE AVE, CORRECT CARE INC 75081 #041-12-2000 L2000 **FM** *020 †20

PETERS, Elizabeth Ann. 3001 GEORGE BUSH HWY, STE 250 75082 #028-03-1984 L1990 **NPM** *020 †55

PHAN, Bao Long. 330 MUNICIPAL DR, STE 104 75080 #048-12-1995 L2002 **PS** *020 †65

PHUNG, Hang T. 1332 S PLANO RD STE 702 75081 #048-13-1987 L1988 **IM** *020 †20

PHUNG, Tri Minh. ■ 75082 #048-15-2007 **AN** *012

PHUNG, Vu Anh. ■ 75082 #048-15-2005 L2005 **FP** *012

PILLSBURY, Curtis B. 401 W CAMPBELL RD 75080 #030-05-1950 L1952 **GP AN** *072

POLE, Rekha Prithviraj. 1755 N COLLINS BLVD, STE 525 75080 #495-35-1978 L1983 **P CHP** *020 †75

PORTER, John Richard. 1112 N FLOYD RD, STE 10 75080 #048-14-1987 L1988 **PD** *020 †55

POWELL, Cynthia Kay. 3001 GEORGE BUSH HWY, STE 250 75082 #039-01-1984 L2001 **NPM** *020 †55

PROFFITT, Trent. 2904 GLENWOOD SPRINGS CT 75082 #016-11-1996 L2002 **GS** *020 †85

PULLANO, Thomas Paul. 3001 E PRESDNT GRG BSH HWY, STE 250 75082 #035-06-1980 L1986 **NPM** *020 †55

PUPPALA, Anjaneya R. 399 W CAMPBELL RD, MEDICAL PLAZE BLDG, SUITE 75080 #495-70-1966 L1977 **GE IM** *020 †20

QUEVEDO, Maria Eugenia. 3001 GEORGE BUSH HWY, STE 250 75082 #429-02-1991 L1998 **PD NPM** *020 †55

RABINOWITZ, Chad Brian. 101 S COIT RD, MASS GENERAL HOSPITAL 75080 #033-06-2001 L2007 **DR** *020 †80

RAD, Manzar Jabbari. 375 MUNICIPAL DR 75080 #517-01-1956 L1976 **GYN** *071 †30

RANDLES, Norah Kathleen. 1112 N FLOYD RD, STE 6 75080 #039-01-2003 L2005 **PD** *020 †55

RAO, Anand Velliyurnot. 101 S COIT RD STE 36-324, NIGHTRAYS, PA 75080 #041-13-2002 L2007 **DR** *020 †80

RATNER, Ian M. 3001 GEORGE BUSH HWY, STE 250 75082 #032-01-1976 L1984 **NPM** *020 †55

RILEY, Shawn Robert. ■ 75080 #649-02-2003 **FP** *012

ROBERTSON, Jack Cecil. ■ 75081 #016-02-1955 L1961 **PHP FM** *071 †70

ROBLES, Luis Rafael. 401 W CAMPBELL RD 75080 #042-01-1980 L1984 **AN GP** *020

RODRIGUEZ, Lora Brigid. ■ 75082 #048-14-1990 L1999 **PD** *020 †55

ROGERS, Susan B. 399 W CAMPBELL RD, DUIR 101 75080 #004-01-1980 L1983 **FM** *020 †18 ‡

ROSS, Colin Andrew. 1701 GATEWAY BLVD STE 349 75080 #060-01-1981 L1991 *020

ROUNTREE, John R. ■ 75080 #048-12-1952 L1952 **GP** *071

RUIZ, Beatriz. 2821 E PRESDNT GRG BSH HWY, STE 308 75082 #048-02-1996 L1998 **PD** *020 †55

RUKKANNAGARI, Sireesha. ■ 75082 #495-70-1995 L2007 **IM** *020 †20

SAJJAD, Naeem. 3409 SPECTRUM BLVD, STE 100 75082 #704-02-1991 L2004 **PD** *020 †20

SALHAB, Walid A. 3001 GEORGE BUSH HWY 75082 #605-01-1992 L1998 **NPM PD** *020 †55

SANTIAGO, Aralis. 1701 N COLLINS BLVD, STE 300 75080 #042-01-1997 L2002 **PD** *020 †55

SANTIAGO-ACEVEDO, Antonio. 3001 GEORGE BUSH HWY, STE 250 75082 #042-02-1985 L1990 **PD NPM** *020 †55

SCHWARTZ, Robert Jos. 375 MUNICIPAL DR STE 232 75080 #005-14-1988 L1997 **PS** *020 †85,65

SCHWENDEMAN, Clair Alan. 3001 GEORGE BUSH HWY, STE 250 75082 #038-44-1985 L1995 **NPM PD** *020 †55

SEKHAVAT, Abbass. 399 W CAMPBELL RD, STE 406 75080 #517-01-1968 L1982 **ORS GP** *020 †40

SHAH, Ashokkumar C. ■ 75082 #495-22-1974 **IM PTH** *020 †50

SHIN, Soo Nam. ■ 75083 #039-01-2001 *010

SILVERSTEIN, Alanna M. 820 W ARAPAHO RD, STE 200 75080 #048-02-1978 L1978 **IM** *020 †20

SIMON, Anne Christina. 2226 SHADY CREEK DR 75080 #028-79-2005, ▲ L2007 **FP** *012

SLOAN, Crawford Jacobs. ■ 75082 #048-12-1978 L1978 **AN** *020

SMITH, Mark Christopher. 399 W CAMPBELL RD, STE 200 75080 #027-01-1994 L1999 **GS** *020 †85

SNOW, Susan Ruth. 5607 STONEHENGE DR 75082 #032-01-1981 L1993 **EM IM** *020 †20,16

STACY, Doyle Samuell. 212 S COTTONWOOD DR 75080 #048-12-1958 L1958 **OBG** *071

STANLEY, Michael Dale. 3001 E PRESDNT GRG BSH HWY, STE 250 75082 #039-01-1973 L1980 **PD NPM** *030 †55

STANLEY, Rufus Floyd, Jr. 1201 S SHERMAN ST STE 202 75081 #048-04-1960 L1960 **ORS** *071 †40

STEINER, Craig K. 3001 GEORGE BUSH HWY, STE 250 75082 #048-14-1993 L1994 **NPM** *020 †55

STRONG, James Doyce, Jr. 1701 N COLLINS BLVD, STE 327 75080 #048-04-1962 L1962 **OBG** *020 †30

SWISHER, Maureen Lacour. 1221 W CAMPBELL RD, STE 209 75080 #021-06-1987 L1995 **MPD PD** *020 †20,55

TAUFIQUE, Kashif Hussain. ■ 75081 #001-06-2007 **EM** *012

TAYLOR, Tad William. 403 W CAMPBELL RD, STE 300 75080 #008-01-1994 L1997 **IM** *020 †20

TESKA, Lyle Ray. 2095 N COLLINS BLVD, STE 201 75080 #025-07-1989 L1998 **OPH** *020 †35

TOLLE, Michael A. 399 W CAMPBELL RD, STE 204 75080 #048-12-1995 L1998 **FM** *040 †18

TORRES, Ilianai. 2099 N COLLINS BLVD, MEIER CLINICS RICHARDSON 75080 #042-01-2002 L2004 **CHP** *100

TOUCHSTONE, Joy Lynn. 2821 GEORGE BUSH HWY, STE 501 75082 #048-02-1996 L2002 **MPD** *020 †20,55

TOVBIN, David. ■ 75080 #550-01-1981 **NEP** *020

TOWNSEND, Richard P. 1001 BUCKINGHAM RD STE 110 75081 #065-01-1971 L1978 **FM** *020

TRAN, Lamyen. 399 W CAMPBELL RD, STE 101 75080 #048-12-1998 L2002 **FM** *020 †18

TRAN, Michael Son. 300 N COIT RD, STE 255 75080 #041-02-1985 L1988 **IM** *020 †20

TRAN, Oanh Ngoc. 399 W CAMPBELL RD STE 200 75080 #025-07-1984 L1991 **GS** *020 †85

TRAN-NGUYEN, Ha Thi. 3603 ELMSTED DR 75082 #048-14-1997 L2002 **MPD** *020 †20,55

TRULSON, Tamella J. 2099 N COLLINS BLVD # 100 75080 #048-04-1991 L1992 **P** *020 †75

TUAN, Phan Dinh. ■ 75082 #938-01-1949 L1977 **FM NEP** *071

VANDIVER, Kathleen E. ■ 75080 #048-12-2006 **PD** *012

VARGAS, Norberto Caro. 3201 E PRESDNT GRG BSH HWY, STE 107 75082 #042-02-2000 L2003 **PM** *020

VAUGHN, Philip Russell. 3001 GEORGE BUSH HWY, STE 250 75082 #005-14-1988 L2004 **NPM** *020 †55

VEMULA, Venkata N Rao. 399 W CAMPBELL RD, STE 304 75080 #495-50-1974 L1981 **GE IM** *020 †20

VOELKER, Robert M, Jr. 3001 GEORGE BUSH HWY, STE 250 75082 #048-02-1980 L1980 **NPM PD** *020 †55

VOGT, Rachel A. 3001 GEORGE BUSH HWY, STE 250 75082 #048-13-1999 L2005 **NPM PD** *020 †55

VOTH, Gayle Vernon. 399 W CAMPBELL RD, STE 402 75080 #004-01-1967 L1976 **ORS** *020 †40

WAKEFIELD, Sarah Elizabet. ■ 75081 #048-02-2008 *012

WALGREN, Kenneth Lee. ■ 75080 #016-02-1961 L1970 **IM** *071

WALTER, Henry A, Jr. 375 MUNICIPAL DR 75080 #048-02-07-1965 L1980 **GS EM** *071 †85

WANG, Eddie Ling-Tse. ■ 75081 #305-01-2002 L2007 **FM** *012

WANG, Scott Shih-Po. ■ 75082 #048-15-2006 **FP** *012

WARD, Alisa K. 399 W CAMPBELL RD STE 410, MEDICAL PLAZA II 75080 #048-15-1997 L2001 **OBG** *020 †30

WATUMULL, Denton. 3201 E PRESDNT GRG BSH HWY, STE 101 75082 #014-01-1982 L1984 **PS HS** *020 †85,65

WHITE, Gary Warren. 399 W CAMPBELL RD, STE 200 75080 #048-12-1977 L1977 **GS** *020 †85

WHITTLESEY, Daveen B. 901 S CENTRAL EXPY, NORTH BLDG SECTION C 75080 #021-01-1963 L1964 **GYN** *030

WILKINSON, Eduardo M. 375 MUNICIPAL DR STE 140 75080 #132-01-1986 L1993 **IM** *020 †20

WILLIAMS, Embry W, III. 375 MUNICIPAL DR STE 236 75080 #048-15-1979 L1979 **OBG REN** *020 †30

WILLIAMSON, Jamie Lynn. 2821 GEORGE BUSH HWY 75082 #048-14-1997 L1999 **FM** *020 †18

WILLIS, John Joseph. 2929 N CENTRAL EXPY 75080 #048-02-1983 L1983 **RHU IM** *020 †20

WIN, Josephine Than. 2097 N COLLINS BLVD, STE 198 75080 #209-01-1977 L1993 **IM** *020 †20

WINKLER, Thomas P. 401 W CAMPBELL RD 75080 #048-12-1987 L1988 **FM** *020 †18

WITT, Amanda Leigh. ■ 75081 #048-12-2006 **FM** *012

WOOD, John Kenneth. 970 N COIT RD STE 3040 75080 #065-01-1974 L1977 **FM** *020 †18

WOODBRIDGE, Ann Robin. 1701 N COLLINS BLVD, STE 327 75080 #027-01-1985 L1991 **OBG** *020 †30

WRIGHT, Aimee L. 2100 N COLLINS BLVD, STE 206 75080 #048-78-1999, ▲ L2001 **FM** *020 †18

WYLL, Gene Erwin. 610 N COIT RD, STE 2115 75080 #048-04-1972 L1972 **OPH** *020 †35

YALE, Rebecca Jane. 403 W CAMPBELL RD, STE 400 75080 #028-03-1993 L2004 **OBG** *020 †30

YANG, Eden Thomas. 4011 E RENNER RD, STE 110 75082 #048-02-1997 L2000 **EM** *020 †16

YEDWAB, Alan Jeffrey. 2821 E PRESDNT GRG BSH HWY, STE 308 75082 #048-02-1996 L1998 **PD** *020 †55

YEN, Julie J. ■ 75082 #048-13-1999 L2002 **FM** *020 †18

YU, Paul Hengpei. 403 W CAMPBELL RD, STE 103 75080 #048-14-1998 L1999 **FM** *020 †18

RICHLAND HILLS – TARRANT

ATTEBERRY, James L. 7601 GLENVIEW DR 76180 #034-01-1979 L1980 **FM** *020 †18

BAKER, Jonathan A. ■ 76180 #048-12-2004 L2008 **PTH** *012

BELL, James Ardis. 7601 GLENVIEW DR 76180 #048-02-1955 L1955 **FM** *071

CHU, Toni H. 7290 GLENVIEW DR 76180 #048-12-2004 L2007 **PD** *020 †55

DONOHOO, Albert C. ■ 76118 #035-08-1949 L1960 **OPH PHP** *071 †45,70

ERWIN, Ronnie Lee. 7601 GLENVIEW DR, FAMILY HEALTH CARE 76180 #004-01-1972 L1973 **FM** *020 †18

GULLINESE, Robert M. 4604 REDONDO ST 76180 #048-14-2001 L2002 **EM** *020 †16

KARIMI, Shams. 6862 GRAPEVINE HWY 76180 #704-16-1985 L1993 **PD** *020 †55

KIM, Paul Kangsok. 4351 BOOTH CALLOWAY RD, STE 414 76180 #048-44-1991 L1994 **IM** *020 †20

NAIR, Kesavapillai R. 7505 GLENVIEW DR, STE G 76180 #495-63-1968 L1978 **CD** *020 †20

OHMAN, Allan Bratt, Jr. 7601 GLENVIEW DR, FAMILY HEALTH CARE 76180 #048-12-1994 L1998 **MPD PD** *020 †20,55

PAFFORD, Dick Alden. 7601 GLENVIEW DR, FAMILY HEALTH CARE 76180 #048-02-1971 L1971 **FM** *020 †18

RAMIREZ, Pedro Heberto. 7505 GLENVIEW DR STE H 76180 #737-01-1969 L1978 **OBG** *020 †30

REIMER, Mark Dickason. 7601 GLENVIEW DR 76180 #019-02-1982 L1983 **FM** *020 †18

SAKSENA, Prem Narayan. 6862 GRAPEVINE HWY 76180 #495-05-1972 L1981 **PD** *020 †55

SMITH, Karen Vanmatre. 7601 GLENVIEW DR, FAMILY HEALTH CARE 76180 #048-12-2003 L2005 **FM** *020 †18

SUBRAMANIAN, Kalaimani. 7290 GLENVIEW DR 76180 #495-16-1995 L2000 **PD** *020 †55

VU, Hieu Trung. 7601 GLENVIEW DR, FAMILY HEALTH CARE 76180 #048-12-1997 L1998 **FM** *020 †18

WIGHTMAN, Ernest Thos. 7601 GLENVIEW DR, FAMILY HEALTH CARE 76180 #020-12-1976 L1986 **FM AM** *020 †18

WILLIAMS, Marion Fralin. ■ 76118 #048-02-1950 L1950 **GP** *071
ZAMBRANO, Gerardo. 3623 RUTH RD # D 76118 #048-12-1996 L2003 **AN** *020

RICHMOND – FORT BEND

AHMAD, Asma Aftab. 400 AUSTIN ST 77469 #704-02-1991 L2002 **IMG** *020 †18
ALLISON, Rocio Del Pilar. ■ 77469 #264-10-2003 **FP** *012
ALVAREZ-CRUZ, Anita A.. 400 AUSTIN ST 77469 #319-04-1994 L2005 **FM** *100 †18
AMIN, Prafulchandra H. 1705 JACKSON ST 77469 #495-01-1965 L1979 **DR OS** *020 †80
ARZU, Isidora Y. 1603 MAIN ST, DEPT RADIATION ONCOLOGY 77469 #048-02-1998 L2000 **RO** *020 †80
BAICHOO, Shawn Aurelio. ■ 77469 #010-03-2001 L2005 **EM** *020 †16
BORNSTEIN, Michael Eliot. 1300 MAIN ST 77469 #024-05-1990 L1993 **PD** *020 †55 ‡
BREEZE, Scott Walter. 1517 THOMPSON RD 77469 #048-04-1991 L1993 **ORS** *020 †40
CANNON, Richard Arlin. 1705 JACKSON ST 77469 #048-04-1957 L1957 **PD** *071 †55
CHAO, David Chihyo. 1601 MAIN ST, STE 202 77469 #014-01-1988 L2004 **IM PUD** *020 †20
CHAPMAN, Thos Herbert, Jr. 1705 JACKSON ST 77469 #048-02-1965 L1965 **PD GP** *071 †55
CHENNAULT, James R, Jr. ■ 77469 #048-14-1977 L1977 **AN** *071
CHIRANAND, Nanthaphonge. 2100 PRESTON ST 77469 #891-01-1970 L1979 **GP** *020
CHIRANAND, Wena. 2100 PRESTON ST, RICHMOND STATE SCHOOL 77469 #891-01-1970 L1979 **GP** *020 †55
DANDONA, Suklesh. 1601 MAIN ST STE 306 77469 #495-45-1971 L1975 **FM PTH** *020 †50,18 ‡
DESAI, Sejal A.. ■ 77469 #654-01-2000 L2006 **FM** *100 †18
ETMINAN, Mohammad. 1517 THOMPSON RD 77469 #048-04-1995 L2001 **OSS** *020 †40
FAGBOHUN, C Funsho. 1601 MAIN ST STE 206, RICHMOND PROF BLDG 77469 #690-02-1982 L1997 **OBG** *020 †30
FARHEEN, Kiran. ■ 77469 #048-02-2005 L2008 **IM** *012
GALE, Letosha Evette. 1601 MAIN ST, STE 502 77469 #048-13-1997 L1999 **FM** *020 †18
HALL, James K, Jr. ■ 77469 #048-13-2003 L2006 **IM** *020
HALL, William L. 1705 JACKSON ST 77469 #048-02-1953 L1953 **R** *071 †80
HOBSON, David Wilbur. 1601 MAIN ST, STE 302 77469 #016-06-1980 L1981 **OBG FM** *020 †30
JADHAV, Jaisingh Vishnu. ■ 77469 #495-20-1956 L1977 **R GP** *100
KING, Billy D. ■ 77469 #004-01-1949 L1959 **R** *071 †80
KNOEBEL, Kathleen Sue. 1300 MAIN ST 77469 #041-02-1995 L1997 **PD** *020 †55
KRUSLESKI, David W. 400 AUSTIN ST 77469 #048-14-1990 L1991 **FM** *020 †18 ‡
LE, Hong M. 1601 MAIN ST STE 104 77469 #048-13-1991 L1992 **IM** *020 †20
LEIGH, Kecia R. ■ 77469 #048-14-2001 L2004 **FM** *020 †20
LIANG, Jeffrey E. 1517 THOMPSON RD 77469 #028-02-1997 L2002 **FSM** *020 †18
MALIAKKAL, Dominic Jos. JESTER IV HOSP 77469 #495-09-1982 L1992 **P** *020 †75
MEFFORD, Ivan Newton. 1601 MAIN ST, STE 500 77469 #036-07-1995 L1996 **FM** *020 †18
MENDES-NETO, Odorindo. 400 AUSTIN ST 77469 #187-09-1960 L1967 **OBG** *020
MILLER, Stephen Paul. 2027 SPREADING BOUGH LN 77469 #016-42-1964 L1986 **FM EM** *071 †55,18
MOLINA-PINEDA, Julio C. 1601 MAIN ST STE 301 77469 #682-01-1979 L1988 **FM** *020 ‡
MONTALVO, Jose, III. 1705 JACKSON ST 77469 #038-06-1980 L1982 **EM** *020
MUNOZ, Carlos Enrique. 1601 MAIN ST STE 108 77469 #048-14-1995 L1997 **FM** *020 †18
NAIK, Kokila Dilip. J3 TDCJ UNIT 77469 #495-22-1972 L1982 **FM** *020 †60
NIES, Alan Sheffer. 2818 DECROS PT 77469 #024-01-1963 L1964 **PA IM** *050 †20
OKUWOBI, Olukayode O. 1601 MAIN ST STE 307 77469 #308-03-1987 L2003 **IM** *075 †20
OLADUT, Wolley K. 1601 MAIN ST, STE 407 77469 #048-13-1990 L1991 **AN** *020 †05
PARIKH, Kiran R. 2100 PRESTON ST, RICHMOND STATE SCHOOL 77469 #495-23-1977 L1983 **PD** *020 †55
PARIKH, Mayank Kanchanlal. 1601 MAIN ST STE 400 77469 #495-23-1988 L1995 **CD IM** *020 †20
PARKAR, Mehjabin Ismail. 400 AUSTIN ST 77469 #496-36-2002 L2007 **FM** *020
PARTRIDGE, David B. 2100 PRESTON ST 77469 #048-02-1991 **FM** *020 †18
PECCORA, Orlando P. 2710 THOMPSON CROSSING DR 77469 #132-02-1967 L1978 **P** *020
PEDDAMATHAM, Kumara Swamy. 1601 MAIN ST, STE 401 77469 #495-70-1975 L1983 **GE IM** *020 †20
POPATIA, Amirali S. 1603 MAIN ST, # 200 77469 #704-02-1985 L1992 **ON IM** *020 †20 ‡
RAJU, Vijayalakshmi. 1300 MAIN ST 77469 #496-39-1983 L2000 **PD** *020 †55
ROBERTSON, Jimmy Dale. 400 AUSTIN ST 77469 #048-02-1979 L1979 **FM** *020 †18
SHUKLA, Amitabh Yashvant. 1601 MAIN ST, STE 201 77469 #495-22-1980 L1989 **N CN** *020 †75 ‡
SMITH-COOK, Karen E. 1300 MAIN ST 77469 #048-04-2002 L2005 **PD** *020
SPENCE, Susanna Claire. ■ 77469 #048-13-2005 L2008 **DR** *012
SULE, Harsh Prakash. ■ 77469 #016-11-1999 L2002 **EM** *020
SUN, Shih Chien. 2100 PRESTON ST 77469 #385-03-1954 L1975 **GP PTH** *020
THIBODEAUX, Douglas Abner. 1601 MAIN ST, STE 500 77469 #048-02-1958 L1958 **OBG** *020 †30
THOMPSON, Stanley E. 1108 MORTON ST 77469 #005-12-1952 L1952 **GP GS** *071
UTHMAN, Edward Otto. 1705 JACKSON ST, OAK BEND MEDICAL CENTER 77469 #047-06-1977 L1986 **PTH** *020 †50
VU, Jenny Giang. ■ 77469 #048-14-2005 L2006 **IM** *012
YATES, Charles Wilbur, Jr. 1709 HAWTHORN DR 77469 #048-12-1969 L1969 **R** *020 †80

RIESEL – MCLENNAN

BODE, Sonia Kathleen. ■ 76682 #048-02-1996 L1997 **FM** *020 †18

RIO GRANDE CITY – STARR

ABDEEN, Ziad Mahmoud. 2768 PHARMACY RD, FAMILY HEALTH CENTER 78582 #528-01-1998 L2004 **IMG** *100 †20
AHSAN, Khizar. 2768 PHARMACY RD, FAMILY HEALTH CENTER 78582 #704-21-1989 L1998 **GE** *020 †20
ALAM, Khursheed. 2768 PHARMACY RD 78582 #704-09-1995 L2004 **IM** *100 †20
FALCON, Antonio. 2768 PHARMACY RD 78582 #048-14-1977 L1977 **FM** *020 †20
GARCIA, Pedro E, Jr. 2795 PHARMACY RD 78582 #048-12-1975 L1975 **ORS GP** *020
GONZALEZ, Roberto M. 2790 PHARMACY RD 78582 #649-02-1962 L1973 **GP GS** *020
GREGORY, Walter Donald. 600 N GARZA ST, BLDG C 78582 #048-02-1964 L1964 **P** *020
GUERRERO, Rolando A. ■ 78582 #048-13-1997 L1999 **FM** *020 †18

HERNANDEZ, Raul Gerardo. 2544 PALM CIR, STARR COUNTY MEMORIAL HOSP 78582 #048-02-2002 L2006 **AN** *020 †05
KANHERE, Gauri Gopal. 2768 PHARMACY RD 78582 #495-28-1997 L2001 **IM** *020 †20
MARGO, Javier David, Jr. 604 N GARZA ST 78582 #048-16-2001 L2003 **FM** *020 †18
MONTES, Javier G. ■ 78582 #048-12-2005 L2007 **FP** *012
MUDIGOUDAR, Basanagoud Do. 201 E 2ND ST, PEDIATRIC PRACTICE 78582 #495-35-1997 L2004 **PD** *020
RODRIGUEZ, Mario Aristeo. 2768 PHARMACY RD 78582 #048-02-1996 L1997 **FM** *020 †18
RODRIGUEZ, Porfirio S. 2768 PHARMACY RD 78582 #025-12-1977 L1978 **FM** *030 †18
UZOIGWE, Stanislaus N. 201 E 2ND ST, PEDIATRIC PRACTICE ASSOC 78582 #649-45-1994 L2002 **PD** *020
VALENCIA, Luis. 2790 PHARMACY RD 78582 #649-02-1992 L2001 **PD** *020 †55
VAZQUEZ, Jose Andres. 2790 PHARMACY RD 78582 #935-01-1994 L2000 **IM** *020 †20
WINFUL-ACQUAYE, Elizabeth. 2768 PHARMACY RD 78582 #412-02-1992 L2004 **PDI** *020 †55

RIVER OAKS – TARRANT

BANGALE, Anil Tukarampant. 5201 RIVER OAKS BLVD 76114 #495-28-1974 L1977 **GP** *020
CHAUDHRY, Mohammad Akram. 4819 RIVER OAKS BLVD 76114 #704-04-1963 L1974 **FM IM** *020 †18
QASIM, Shabnam Kanwal. 4819 RIVER OAKS BLVD, MC 3098 76114 #704-21-1993 L2000 **IM** *020 †20

RIVIERA – KLEBERG

LEMMONS, Ronald Eugene. ■ 78379 #021-01-1958 L1966 **MDM** *071 †85
NEUBAUER, Dorothea E. ■ 78379 #048-02-1947 L1947 **OS** *071

ROANOKE – DENTON

ADAMS, John William. 2800 E HIGHWAY 114, ARLINGTON CANCER CENTER 76262 #028-79-1975, ▲ L1978 **ON HEM** *020
AMOSSON, Chad Martin. 2800 E HIGHWAY 114, ARLINGTON CANCER CENTER 76262 #048-14-1998 L2002 **RO** *020 †80
ANDERSON, Robert Glenn. 2850 E HIGHWAY 114 76262 #048-12-1974 L1975 **PS** *020 †45,65
ANDREWS, Catherine Jean. ■ 76262 #048-78-2004, ▲ L2006 **OBG** *012
AWAN, Amjad N. 2850 E HIGHWAY 114 76262 #704-04-1986 L1999 **GE** *020 †20
BLEDSOE, Robert C, Jr. 2850 E HIGHWAY 114 76262 #048-14-1983 L1983 **PS** *020 †65
COLYER, Richard A. ■ 76262 #048-12-1995 L1998 **EM** *020 †16
DE PRISCO, John. ■ 76262 #041-77-1954, ▲ L1960 **PM PMM** *071 †60,18
FIRSTENBERG, Barry Alan. 2800 E HIGHWAY 114, ARLINGTON CANCER CENTER 76262 #028-79-1978, ▲ L1984 *020
GHAZALI, Basith Mohammed. 2850 E HIGHWAY 114 76262 #704-25-1988 L1997 **PS** *020 †85,65
GRAYS, Peter Edward. 2850 E HIGHWAY 114 76262 #048-12-1988 L1989 **GS** *020 †85
HAENKE, Richard F. 2850 E HIGHWAY 114 76262 #048-78-1982, ▲ L1983 **ORS** *020
HISEY, Michael Scott. 2850 E HIGHWAY 114 76262 #005-18-1992 L1998 **ORS OSS** *020 †40
KANER, David Barry. ■ 76262 #025-07-1972 L1988 **GS** *100
KHAN, Amir Manzoor. 2850 E HIGHWAY 114 76262 #024-07-1994 L2000 **ORS** *020 †40
KHUBCHANDANI, Zubin Gian. 2850 E HIGHWAY 114 76262 #003-01-1996 L2002 **ORS** *020 †40
KJELDGAARD, Larry M. 2850 E HIGHWAY 114 76262 #041-77-1986, ▲ L1988 **ORS** *020
LEVY, Lawrence Harry. ■ 76262 #016-11-1973 L1985 **IM NEP** *020 †20
PACKWOOD, Jennifer Gracie. 1232 ROBIN DR 76262 #048-04-1996 L2001 **PD** *020 †55
PAGE, Carey Pryor. ■ 76262 #048-04-1968 L1968 **GS ON** *030 †85
PHILLIPS, Suzanne. RR 4 BOX 228C 76262 #048-14-1982 L1983 **EM** *020
SPINGOLA, Dean Bernard. 2850 E HIGHWAY 114 76262 #041-07-1995 L2000 *020
TURNER, Michelle. 1209 CASTLE COVE LN 76262 #019-02-1999 L2002 **EM** *020 †16
WALLACE, Charles A. 2850 E HIGHWAY 114 76262 #048-12-1982 L1983 **PS HS** *075 †65

ROBINSON – MCLENNAN

ROSILES, Joseph R. 635 N ROBINSON DR 76706 #048-02-1980 L1983 **FM** *020 †18
SAMPLES, Roxann Migl. 545 SAFFLE RD 76706 #048-14-1986 L1987 **IM** *020 †20 ‡
STONES, Michael Edward. 701 S ROBINSON DR 76706 #048-13-1982 L1983 **FM** *020 †18

ROBSTOWN – NUECES

ELIZONDO, Marco A. 403 E MAIN AVE 78380 #048-13-1997 L2001 **IM** *020 †20
OZKARAGOZ, Fatih. 101 W AVENUE E, CHILDREN & YOUTH PROJECT 78380 #902-05-1982 L1985 **PD AI** *020 †55,03
ROPER, Amy Dawn. ■ 78380 #048-04-1983 L1983 **OBG** *020 †30

ROCKDALE – MILAM

CRADEUR, Ryan David. 1700 BRAZOS AVE 76567 #021-06-2003 L2004 **FM** *020 †18
DITZLER, John Wm, Jr. 1701 PECOS AVE 76567 #025-01-1970 L1974 **ORS EM** *020 †40
FIELDER, Randal Lee. 707 W CAMERON AVE 76567 #649-30-1983 L1999 **FM IMG** *020 †18
JACKSON, Lawrence Lee. ■ 76567 #016-11-1966 L1968 **U** *071 †95
KAYE, Sterling Schubert. 1700 BRAZOS AVE 76567 #035-08-1966 L1985 **DR NM** *020 †80,28
THOMPSON, Peyton Lee. 1701 PECOS AVE 76567 #048-04-1972 L1972 **P** *020 †75
WASHAM, William Thos. PO BOX 472 76567 #038-40-1945 L1982 **OM FM** *030
WEED, John M, III. 602 N MAIN ST 76567 #048-02-1972 L1972 **FM** *020 †18

ROCKPORT – ARANSAS

ALSOP, Ernest Carson. ■ 78382 #048-02-1993 L1994 **FM** *020 †18
APOSTOL, Melecio Fortuno. ■ 78382 #048-02-1998 L2001 **PD** *020 †55
BEAN, Richard Joseph. PO BOX 2168 78381 #030-05-1995 L1998 **FM** *020

BRACKIN, Jack Howell. 1209 HIGHWAY 35 N, GULF SIDE MEDICAL CLINIC 78382 #004-01-1983 L1991 **FM FPG** *020 †18
BUTT, John A. ■ 78382 #065-01-1948 L1977 **OBG** *071
CAMERON, William Brooks. ■ 78382 #047-06-1952 L1953 **GYN OBG** *071 †30
CERZA, Robert Francis. 2207 HIGHWAY 35 N, STE C 78382 #016-06-1970 L1978 **AN CD** *020 †05
CHASE, Constance Elise. ■ 78381 #048-02-1957 L1957 **OBG** *071 †30
DE SOCARRAZ, Miguel Lino. ■ 78382 #275-01-1941 L1963 **P CHP** *071
GHISELLI, Robert Guido. ■ 78382 #048-02-1963 L1963 **IM** *020 †20
GONZALEZ, Anneliese Odila. 2600 LAKEVIEW DR 78382 #935-07-1996 L2004 **HO** *020 †20
HAMILTON, Doyne B. ■ 78382 #048-04-1951 L1951 **GP** *071
HOPPER, John Jackson. 101 N MAGNOLIA ST 78382 #048-02-1967 L1967 **P** *020 †75
JOHNSON, John William. ■ 78382 #028-78-1962, ▲ L1962 **FM** *071
JOHNSON, Marilyn. ■ 78382 #048-04-1950 L1950 **GYN** *072
LUCCI, Dawn Tumlinson. 106 MARION DR 78382 #048-14-1994 L1997 **OBG** *020 †30
MARONEY, Kimberly S. 400 ENTERPRISE BLVD, STE 2 78382 #048-13-1999 L2001 **FM** *020 †18 ‡
MC CAUGHEY, Everett V, Jr. PO BOX 880 78381 #024-07-1952 L1954 **OBG** *071 †30
MC KINLEY, Thomas R. 2871 HIGHWAY 35 N 78382 #048-04-1951 L1951 **GP PHP** *071
MC KITRICK, Myles Emerson. 1601 8TH ST, HC 4 BOX 134 78382 #030-05-1956 L1962 **AN** *072 †05
MUELLER, William Peter. 1325 BROADWAY ST, SOUTHWEST MEDICAL ASSOCIAT 78382 #023-12-1998 L2001 **FP** *012
NAISMITH, Robert A. 2600 LAKEVIEW DR 78382 #048-12-1993 L1994 **U** *020 †95
NASH, Michael Edward. 2600 LAKEVIEW DR 78382 #048-14-1984 L1985 **HEM ON** *020 †20
NEWELL, Daniel Paul. PO BOX 1723 78381 #048-12-1957 L1957 **GS** *020
PICKETT, John Mitchell. 78381 #047-05-1943 *043-1947 **FP PDA** *071 †55
ROME, Clifford Jos. 12 CATALINA DR, KEY ALLEGRO ISL. 78382 #048-02-1959 L1959 **ORS** *075 †40
ROREX, Eugene Allen. ■ 78382 #048-02-1958 L1958 **IM** *071
TESAR, Janilyn E. ■ 78382 #048-02-1964 L1964 **IM** *071
VEATCH, Charles Alvin. ■ 78382 #016-11-1942 L1971 **OM** *071 †70
WARREN, Fred Dixon. 700 E MIMOSA ST 78382 #047-06-1972 L1975 **FM** *020 ‡
WASAY, Mohammad. PO BOX 2168, 1325 BROADWAY 78381 #704-02-1989 L1997 **N** *020 †75

ROCKSPRINGS – EDWARDS

HERRMANN, George H C, IV. PO BOX 545 78880 #048-02-1950 L1950 **OM GP** *030
TODD, Chester Lee. PO BOX 918 78880 #021-05-1962 L1964 **GP** *020

ROCKWALL – ROCKWALL

ABRAHAM, Cini. 2237 RIDGE RD, STE 101 75087 #496-20-2000 L2005 **CHP P** *100 †75
ACKER, Wesley G. 6435 S FM 549, STE 201 75032 #048-15-2002 L2003 **FM** *020 †18
ALDRICH, Daniel James. 6617 HERITAGE PKWY, STE 110 75087 #016-42-1991 L1997 **ORS** *020 †40
BALLEM, Charles Miller. 2504 RIDGE RD, STE 202 75087 #064-01-1942 L1978 **GE IM** *020
BANG, Richard Cho. 1005 W RALPH M HALL PKWY, STE 201 75032 #038-41-2000 L2003 **FM** *020 †18
BEHNIA, Faranak. 901 ROCKWALL PKWY, THE OB/GYN PLACE 75032 #031-01-1999 L2003 **OBG** *020
BELLINGER, Richard K. 6435 S FM 549 STE 201, FAMILY MEDICAL CENTER AT R 75032 #048-02-1987 L1988 **FM** *020 †18
BERK, Martin Russel. 1005 W RALPH M HALL PKWY, INTERVENTIONAL VASCULAR 75032 #836-01-1977 L1992 **CD IM** *020 †20
BONACQUISTI, Gary Andrew. 1005 W RALPH M HALL PKWY, STE 101 75032 #033-06-1991 L1994 **FM** *020 †18
BOSWANK, Stephen E. 1005 W RALPH M HALL PKWY, STE 211 75032 #048-13-1989 L1990 **ON** *020 †20
BOSWELL, Roger Ward. ■ 75032 #017-20-1978 L1992 **IM EM** *020 †20,16
BROOKS, Richard Lynn. 103 N 1ST ST, LAKE POINTE MEDICAL GROUP 75087 #048-13-1974 L1974 **IM OBG** *020 †20
BRYCE, Kenneth Lynn. 1005 W RALPH M HALL PKWY, STE 221 75032 #048-13-1988 L1989 **GS CRS** *020 †85
BURCHFIEL, Rebecca Lynn. 1005 W RALPH M HALL PKWY, STE 101 75032 #036-01-2003 L2006 **FM** *020 †18
BYRNE, Bruce Andrew. 2504 RIDGE RD STE 202 75087 #038-40-1993 L2000 **PS HS** *020 †65
CHAVIRA, Ricardo, Jr. 75087 #054-04-1990 L1995 **EM** *020
CHINN, Elena N. 2504 RIDGE RD, STE 102 75087 #048-12-2002 L2005 **PD** *020 †55
CHREST, Jonathan Leonard. 302 WOODED TRL 75087 #020-12-1975 L1976 **AN** *020 †05
CRUTCHFIELD, Mary Watts. 2237 RIDGE RD STE 101 75087 #048-12-1984 L1985 **P** *020 †75
DAS, Tony S. 1005 W RALPH M HALL PKWY, INTERVENTIONAL VASCULAR 75032 #048-04-1990 L1991 **CD** *020 †20
DOW, Daniel M. 909 ROCKWALL PKWY 75032 #048-13-1999 L2000 **DR** *020 †80
DUHON, Craig R. 6617 HERITAGE PKWY, STE 110 75087 #048-16-1982 L1983 **OAR OSM** *020 †40
ELLIS, Robert Gardner. ■ 75087 #012-01-1953 L1986 **FM FPG** *071 †85,18
FIELDS, Gwen Ann. 1005 W RALPH HALL PKWY, STE 101 75032 #048-14-1985 L1986 **PM** *020 †60
FIELDSMITH, William J. ■ 75032 #048-12-2006 L2008 **FP** *012
FRAZIER, Jenny M. 2504 RIDGE RD STE 104 75087 #048-13-2001 L2004 **FM** *020
GEHRING, Wayne Robt. 519 E INTERSTATE 30 # 106 75087 #048-12-1972 L1973 **OBG** *100
GRAFF, Jonathan Michael. ■ 75087 #036-07-1990 **IM** *100 †20
HARN, Jason Brooks. ■ 75087 #048-12-2006 **OBG** *012
HARTMAN, Michael Stephen. 909 ROCKWALL PKWY 75032 #038-40-1998 L2000 **DR** *020 †80
HAZEL, Robert Mark. 6701 HERITAGE PKWY 75087 #021-05-1991 L1992 **ORS OSM** *020 †40
HILLMAN, Donald W. ■ 75032 #035-15-1954 L1980 **OM** *071 †70
HOARD, Robert Eugene. ■ 75032 #056-05-1969 L1974 **EM** *020 †16
HOLDER, Douglas Aaron. 909 ROCKWALL PKWY 75032 #048-12-1997 L1998 **DR** *020 †80
HUERTAS, Otoniel, Jr. PO BOX 806 75087 #042-02-1994 L2000 **OBG** *020 †20
JENNINGS, Jerry Bob. 909 ROCKWALL PKWY 75032 #048-02-1967 L1967 **DR** *020 †80
KINSELLA, James Jeremy. ■ 75032 #056-06-2006 **TY** *012
LEVIN, Charles Brooks. 1005 W RALPH HALL PKWY, INTERVENTIONAL VASCULAR 75032 #038-40-1974 L1975 **CD IM** *020 †20

LUNDELL, Andrea L. 105 LIBERTY LN 75032 #008-01-1994 L2000 **DR** *020 †80
MAGRUDER, Robert Lawrence. 6800 HERITAGE PKWY 75087 #048-02-1983 L1983 **FM** *040 †18
MAKOHON, Katherine Rose. 1005 W RALPH M HALL PKWY, STE 221 75032 #016-06-1997 L1998 **GS** *020 †85
MC CREIGHT, Audra L. 1163 SKYLAR DR 75032 #048-12-2001 L2003 **PEM** *100 †55
MIKE-MAYER, Henrik. 75087 #033-05-1986 L1991 **OSS** *020 †40
MILLER, Seth Thomas. 2504 RIDGE RD STE 101, ROCKWALL FAMILY MEDICINE 75087 #048-13-2001 L2004 **FM** *100
ORJI, Mariam U. ■ 75087 #048-12-2008 *012
PALLONE, Joseph D. ■ 75087 #048-13-2005 L2007 **OBG** *012
PFLIEGER, Kurt Loring. 2504 RIDGE RD, STE 102 75087 #422-01-1987 L1994 **PDC PD** *020 †55
POEI, Tiong Sie. ■ 75032 #506-02-1978 L1982 **P** *071
RACZ, Tibor A. 6435 S FM 549 STE 102 75032 #048-02-1992 L1993 **AN** *020 †05
RASHEED, Haroon Ilyas. ■ 75032 #305-01-2000 L2007 **AN** *020 †05
RITTER, David Wm. 1005 W RALPH HALL PKWY 75032 #028-02-1992 L1993 **GS** *020 †85
ROMERO, Cesar P. ■ 75032 #748-08-1966 L1977 **GP GS** *020
ROY, Jacques A. ■ 75087 #067-03-1980 L1984 **EM** *020 †16
SALAND, Kenneth Edward. 1005 W RALPH M HALL PKWY, INTERVENTIONAL VASCULAR 75032 #034-01-1993 L1995 **IC** *020 †20
SCHIFFMANN, Raphael. ■ 75087 #165-03-1980 L1992 **CHN** *020 †75
SCHMIDT, Dennis W. 909 ROCKWALL PKWY 75032 #048-02-1979 L1979 **DR** *020 †80
SEIF, Fayez G. 1005 W RALPH M HALL PKWY, STE 125 75032 #915-02-1985 L1996 **GE** *020 †20
SHEIKHA, Sabri Hassan. 601 WHITE HILLS DR STE 100 75087 #561-14-1979 L1991 **P CHP** *020
SHINDER, Thomas Wayne. PO BOX 965 75087 #016-11-1989 L1993 **IM N** *075
SMITHERS, Victoria E. 6435 S FM 549 STE 201 75032 #048-14-1996 L2001 **FM** *020 †18
SPARKS, Robert D. 103 N FIRST ST, SPARKS CLINIC 75087 #048-78-1977, ▲ L1978 **FM** *020
SPITZBERG, Jack Wolf. 1005 W RALPH M HALL PKWY, INTERVENTIONAL VASCULAR 75032 #035-01-1968 L1975 **CD IM** *020 †20 ‡
STARK, Robert Neil, Jr. 6435 S FM 549, STE 201 75032 #021-05-2003 L2004 **FM** *020 †18
STEPHENS, Jeffrey S. 1005 W RALPH M HALL PKWY, STE 221 75032 #048-12-1991 L1993 **GS** *020 †85
TAN, Connie Wielie. 607 STONEBRIDGE DR 75087 #048-14-1991 L1992 **IM** *020 †20
TAYLOR, Walter Leonard. 6701 HERITAGE PKWY, STE 110 75087 #005-12-1990 L1995 **N** *020 †75
TEERDHALA, Sudha. 1005 W RALPH HALL PKWY, STE 211 75032 #495-11-1987 L1997 **HO** *020 †20
TORRES, Richard Roy. 1560 CHAMPIONS CT 75087 #429-02-1993 L1998 **IM** *020
WALLACE, Jeffrey Scott. 1005 W RALPH M HALL PKWY, STE 233 75032 #021-06-1991 L1993 **OSM** *020 †40
WEBB, Heather Roth. ■ 75087 #039-01-2005 **DR** *012
WEST, Jeffrey Alan. 1005 W RALPH M HALL PKWY 75032 #039-01-1994 L2000 **OTO** *020 †45
WEY, John Tsuyuan. 2504 RIDGE RD STE 203 75087 #038-06-1992 L1997 **ORS OFA** *020 †40
WILCOX, Joanne Paula. ■ 75087 #048-12-1961 L1961 **PM** *074
WILEY, Cherese Hardaway. ■ 75087 #047-07-2005 **IM** *012
WITHERSPOON, Chris A. 1005 W RALPH M HALL PKWY 75032 #048-13-1996 L1997 **FSM** *020 †18
WOLF, Leon. 6701 HERITAGE PKWY, STE 160 75087 #041-01-1972 L1978 **GE IM** *020 †20
WRIGHT, Paul Harry. 1005 W RALPH M HALL PKWY, STE 125 75032 #048-12-1983 L1984 **GE IM** *020
WRIGHT, Weldon Wayne. 301 N FANNIN ST 75087 #048-12-1974 L1975 **OPH** *020 †35
YOUNG, Gregory Alan. 1005 W RALPH M HALL PKWY, STE 107 75032 #048-02-1993 L1995 **OTO** *020 †45

ROMA – STARR

BHONDI, Satnam Singh Sain. 2271 E GRANT ST 78584 #495-01-1997 L2006 **FM** *020 †18
MUSSETT, Raymond Philip. 640 E BRAVO BLVD 78584 #048-14-1977 L1977 **FM** *020 †18
NARRO, Ramiro. 1861 N HIGHWAY 83 78584 #048-12-1963 L1963 **FM** *071

ROSANKY – BASTROP

BELL, Charles Douglas. ■ 78953 #048-12-1956 L1956 **FM PTH** *071 †18
STONE, Susan A. ■ 78953 #048-14-1990 L1992 **P** *020 †75

ROSENBERG – FORT BEND

AUNG, Khin Hla. 2520 B F TERRY BLVD 77471 #209-01-1979 L1994 **FM** *020 †18
BECK, Linda Y. ■ 77471 #047-05-1983 **PA** *100
CHAUDHARY, Khalid Mahmood. 1217 1ST ST 77471 #704-08-1968 L1975 **FM** *020
DAVIS, Byrolyn Guybrette. 4910 AIRPORT AVE 77471 #047-07-1995 L1997 **P** *020
DOWELL, Keith Eugene. 2520 B F TERRY BLVD 77471 #019-02-1969 L1973 **GS GP** *020 †85
GALLOWAY, Jean Nelson. 4520 READING RD STE A, FT BEND COUNTY HLTH SVCS 77471 #038-06-1977 L1979 **PHP GP** *030
GATELY, Kathleen M. 4910 AIRPORT AVE 77471 #048-02-1988 L1990 **P** *020 †20
GONZALEZ, Javier Antonio. 2307 4TH ST 77471 #682-01-1982 L1996 **PD** *020 †55
JOHNSON-MINTER, Jacquelyn. 4520 READING RD, STE A 77471 #001-02-1993 L1995 **GPM** *020 †70
MASHA, Hakeem Olajide. 4910 AIRPORT AVE STE B, TEXANA MHMR CENTER 77471 #690-02-1980 L2007 **CHP** *020
MORA, Yezid Fernando. 4114 AVENUE H 77471 #264-15-1986 L2001 **IM** *020 †20
ORDONEZ, Conrado J. 5633 AVENUE I 77471 #451-01-1984 L1994 **IM** *020 †20
OSAGIE, Owen O. 4910 AIRPORT AVE 77471 #690-06-1985 L1996 **P** *020 †75
PRIETO, Damaris. 4910 AIRPORT AVE, TEXANA 77471 #042-03-2001 L2006 **CHP** *100 †75
REDDY, Vaishnavi Nookala. 2520 B F TERRY BLVD 77471 #496-31-1994 L1998 **FM PD** *020 †18
SATTERFIELD, Robt Beeler. 2520 B F TERRY BLVD 77471 #048-02-1981 L1981 **IM** *030 †20
VAUGHNS, Sylvester Grant. 1229 CORPORATE DR 77471 #048-14-1978 L1981 **FM** *020
YANKOWSKY, Wm Clenney. 2520 B F TERRY BLVD 77471 #047-05-1968 L1975 **GS** *020 †85

ROSHARON – BRAZORIA

DOMINGUEZ, Manuel. ■ 77583 #048-14-2008 *012

FIELDS, Brandon Leigh. ■ 77583 #048-14-2006 L2008 **AN** *012
GARZA, Tomas. ■ 77583 #048-14-2008 *012
HULIPAS, Edgar. 1300 FM 655 RD, C.T. TERRELL UNIT (RAMSEY 77583 #748-01-1989 L2000
  FM *020 †18
OWUSU, Kwabena. 1300 FM 655 RD, UNIV TX MED BRANCH 77583 #048-13-1996 L2001
  FM *020 †18
PEREZ, Jose Jesus, III. ■ 77583 #048-14-2008 *012
ROGNLIE, Carli Deann. ■ 77583 #054-04-2004 **AN** *012
WARD, Julia Renee. 1100 FM 655 RD, UTMB/CORRECTIONAL MANAGED 77583
  #005-06-1994 L2006 **AN** *020

ROTAN – FISHER

CALLAN, Chester Maurice. 774 STATE HIGHWAY 70 N 79546 #048-02-1956 L1956
  FM PYG *050
CARREON, Brian K. 774 STATE HIGHWAY 70 N 79546 #048-15-2003 L2004 **FM** *020 †18
EDISON, Flora. 774 STATE HIGHWAY 70 N 79546 #495-99-1992 L2002 **IM** *020 †20

ROUND ROCK – WILLIAMSON

ADDY, Debaroti M. ■ 78681 #048-04-1998 L2002 **PD** *020 †55
AHMED, Sohail. ■ 78665 #704-02-1991 L2006 **ON** *020 †20
ALAM, Shanawar Ansari. 7200 WYOMING SPGS, DR 1000 78681 #041-02-1993 L1997
  P *020 †75
ANDERSON, Norma Elizabeth. 1000 HESTERS CROSSING RD, STE 100 78681
  #047-06-1992 L1999 **FM** *020 †18
ANTONINI, Tomas Gontijo. 2051 GATTIS SCHOOL RD, STE 250 78664 #187-06-1996 L2002
  OBG *020 †30
ARMSTRONG, Kenneth Lee. 2300 ROUND ROCK AVE, STE 105 78681 #048-12-1980 L1980
  FM *020 †18
AUGUSTIN-WHEELER, Rosie. ■ 78681 #305-01-1999 L2000 **FM** *020 †18
AVILA, Freddy. ■ 78664 #308-01-1969 L1976 **GYN** *020 †30
BAKER, Dana Ray. 2300 ROUND ROCK AVE, STE 109 78681 #048-14-1979 L1979 **FM** *020 †18
BAKER, Dudley Paul. 300 UNIVERSITY BLVD, UNIVERSITY CAMPUS MEDICAL 78665
  #021-05-1962 L1971 **OBG GO** *020 †30
BALARBAR, James B. 2400 ROUND ROCK AVE 78681 #048-02-1994 L1997 **EM** *020 †16
BALASUBRAMANIAN, Lakshmi. 2410 ROUND ROCK AVE, STE 150 78681 #495-59-1997 L2006
  HO *020
BASSARI, Minoo Naimi. ■ 78681 #858-04-1994 L2004 **FM** *020 †18
BAYLOR, Ann Y. 2410 ROUND ROCK AVE # 200 78681 #033-05-1987 L1995 **OBG** *020 †30
BEAUCHAMP, Brandy Lashay. ■ 78681 #048-02-2004 **PD** *012
BECKER, Janet. 900 ROUND ROCK AVE, STE 206 78681 #048-04-1988 L1989 **D** *020 †15
BHUTA, Jagdeep Vamanrai. ■ 78664 #496-38-1980 L1985 **N** *075
BOOKMYER, Stephen Bradley. 2100 ROUND ROCK AVE 78681 #011-03-1999 L2002 **OMF** *020
BOONE, Arthur Richard. 2400 ROUND ROCK AVE 78681 #048-04-1984 L1985 **EM IM** *020 †20
BORICK, Jay Mitchell. 16020 PARK VALLEY DR 78681 #016-42-2000 L2006 **OSM** *100
BORSES, Mary Jean. 300 UNIVERSITY BLVD 78665 #023-12-1992 L2006 **CD** *020 †20
BOSQUEZ, Marco E. 16020 PARK VALLEY DR, ORTHO ASSOC OF ROUND ROCK 78681
  #048-13-1997 L2001 **FSM** *020 †18
BOWLING, Jason E. 2400 ROUND ROCK AVE, # 309 78681 #048-16-2000 L2003 **IM** *020 †20
BOYD, James A. 7200 WYOMING SPGS STE 600 78681 #048-13-1988 L1991 **EM FM** *020 †18
BRODER, Lawrence David. 2400 IH 35 S STE 135 78681 #048-34-1995 L2001 **FM** *100 †18
BROOME, Ruth Anne. 1701 S MAYS ST, STE J-204 78664 #048-02-1974 L1974 **P** *020
BROUSSARD, Erica Monique. ■ 78665 #047-07-2001 L2005 **DR** *020 †80
BROWN, Bernadette M. 894 SUMMIT ST, STE 108 78664 #409-22-1979 L1980 **PD** *020 †55
BROWN, Ingrid. 1000 HESTERS CROSSING RD, STE 400 78681 #048-02-1997 L2007
  OBG *020 †30 ‡
BROWN, Kevin Harris. 1000 HESTERS CROSSING RD, STE 400 78681 #012-01-1998 L2007
  OBG *020 †30
BRUCE, Erik Jude. 2410 ROUND ROCK AVE, STE 170 78681 #021-01-1999 L2007
  ORS *020 †40 ‡
BRUCE, Robert Grady. 511 OAKWOOD BLVD STE 200 78681 #048-13-1993 L1994
  U GYN *020 †95
BUETHE, Erin Nicole. ■ 78681 #048-12-2008 *012
BURNELL, Elizabeth Ellen. 2400 ROUND ROCK AVE 78681 #041-02-1995 L1997 **FM** *020 †18
BURR, Mark Christopher. 2400 ROUND ROCK AVE 78681 #039-01-1982 L1987 **EM** *020 †16
CALDER, John W. 940 HESTERS CROSSING RD, AUSTIN REGIONAL CLINIC 78681
  #048-12-1999 L2001 **FM** *020 †18
CAMERON, Jennifer Dawn. 2400 ROUND ROCK AVE 78681 #003-01-1994 L2007 **FM** *020 †18
CHAMBLESS, Terry Craig. 7200 WYOMING SPGS, STE 1600 78681 #048-16-1982 L1983
  IM *020 †20
CHANG, Kuangyu Marvin. ■ 78664 #048-13-2006 L2008 **AN** *012
CHAPMAN, Amy Mc Lerran. ■ 78665 #048-02-2003 L2007 **OBG** *020
CHARBENEAU, Ryan Patrick. 1499 E OLD SETTLERS BLVD, STE B 78664 #048-02-1998 L2007
  PCC *020
CHAVEZ, Valerie Maxine. 7200 WYOMING SPGS, STE 1600 78681 #048-13-2003 L2006
  IM *020 †20
CHEN, Spenser. 7200 WYOMING SPGS, STE 1600 78681 #048-13-1995 L1997 **IM** *020 †20
CHMELIK, Elizabeth Lynn. 300 UNIVERSITY BLVD 78665 #011-03-1998 L2007 **FM** *020 †18
CHOE, Jessica Wonme. ■ 78681 #048-15-2005 L2008 **PD** *012
CHYLE, Valerian, Jr. 2410 ROUND ROCK AVE, STE 150 78681 #005-14-1990 L1991 **RO** *020 †80
COATES, Kimberly Willis. 511 OAKWOOD BLVD, STE 200 78681 #048-16-1991 L1992
  OBG *020 †30
COUCH, Craig H. 16010 PARK VALLEY DR, STE 100B 78681 #048-04-1990 L1992 **N** *020 †75
CRANE, Stuart D. 212 COMMERCE BLVD, BLUE BONNET TRAILS CMHMRC 78664
  #048-16-1989 L1990 **P** *020 †75
CRETELLA, Richard James. 2400 ROUND ROCK AVE 78681 #038-40-1997 L2001 **EM** *020 †16
CRIGHTON, Carolyn. 511 OAKWOOD BLVD, STE 202 78681 #028-03-1963 L1965 **AN** *020 †05
DANG, Quan Tran. 2400 ROUND ROCK AVE 78681 #048-01-1995 L1998 **IM** *020 †20
DARNELL, Andrew. PO BOX 2142, 2250 ROUND ROCK AVE 78680 #048-13-1974 L1975 **AN** *020
DAVID, Elbert Robt. 7200 WYOMING SPGS, STE 600 78681 #048-13-1982 L1983 **FM** *020 †18
DAVIS, Jad L. 511 OAKWOOD BLVD, STE 202 78681 #048-16-1996 L1997 **AN** *020 †05
DAYAL, Vivek. 2300 ROUND ROCK AVE, STE 207 78681 #048-14-1995 L1998
  MPD PD *020 †20,55

DE HARO, Rafael Alfredo. 7200 WYOMING SPGS, STE 200 78681 #048-12-1986 L1994
  PD *020 †55
DEHART, Marc Mccord. 2410 ROUND ROCK AVE, STE 170 78681 #051-04-1988 L1997
  ORS OAR *020 †40
DELHAGEN, John E, IV. 1304 GLENFIELD CT 78665 #043-01-1992 L2003 **AN** *020 †05
DENNY, Ben Wayne. 511 OAKWOOD BLVD STE 202, BALCONES ANESTHESIOLOGISTS 78681
  #048-12-1982 L1983 **AN** *020 †05
DESAI, Ansuya D. ■ 78681 #495-22-1972 L1983 **P** *072
DESHAZO, Flint K. 7200 WYOMING SPGS, STE 600 78681 #048-14-1985 L1986 **FM** *020 †18
DHIR, Harinder Kumar. 1 CHISHOLM TRL, STE 200 78681 #917-25-1984 L2000
  OM FM *020 †70,18
DIAZ, David Alan. 15930 S GREAT OAKS DR, STE A200 78681 #048-12-1990 L1992 **FM** *020 †18
DICKINSON, Robert B. 300 UNIVERSITY BLVD 78665 #048-02-1999 L2004 **U** *020 †95
DIETERICH, Samantha E. ■ 78665 #048-16-2004 L2007 **PD** *020 †55
DITTMAR, Susan Jane. 1 CHISHOLM TRL STE 200, OPTHALMOLOGY 78681
  #048-13-1981 L1981 **OPH** *020 †35
DLUZNIEWSKI, Holly D. 7200 WYOMING SPGS, STE 1500 78681 #048-14-1999 L2003
  MPD *020 †55,20
DOHERTY, Amber Rae. ■ 78664 #048-15-2003 L2007 **AN** *100
DORSETT, Rebecca Lynn. 2300 ROUND ROCK AVE, STE 205 78681 #048-04-1986 L1987
  OBG *020 †30
EAKIN, Daryl Lee. 2410 ROUND ROCK AVE, STE 150 78681 #048-02-1976 L1976
  ON HEM *020 †20
ECKFORD, John Featherston. 300 UNIVERSITY BLVD 78665 #039-01-2002 L2003 **GS** *020 ‡
EDDINGS, Joseph David. 511 OAKWOOD BLVD STE 202, BALCONES
  ANESTHESIOLOGISTS 78681 #016-11-1997 L1999 **AN** *020 †05
EILERS, William A, III. 511 OAKWOOD BLVD, STE 202 78681 #048-02-1991 L1997
  AN *020 †05 ‡
ELLIS, Kenneth K. 7200 WYOMING SPGS, STE 1300 78681 #048-04-1989 L1991 **GE** *020 †20
ESPARZA, Ramon. 1750 RED BUD LN 78664 #048-02-1998 L2001 **PD** *020
ESPARZA, Sandra Ann. 1750 RED BUD LN 78664 #048-02-2000 L2003 **FM** *020 †18 ‡
ETHEREDGE, Wade B. 2400 ROUND ROCK AVE 78681 #048-13-1991 L1992 **EM** *020 †16
ETHERIDGE, Wade Hollan. 2400 ROUND ROCK AVE 78681 #004-01-1943 L1966
  GS OS *071 †85
EZEKOYE, Olufunke Ewedemi. 1 CHISHOLM TRL STE 4100 78681 #041-12-1996 L1997
  FM *020 †18 ‡
FALLON, Kathleen M. ■ 78681 #048-02-1978 L1978 **IM** *020 †20
FERNANDEZ, Joseph Isaac. 302 UNIVERSITY BLVD, STE 190 78665 #048-12-1989 L1989
  OBG *020 †30
FISHER, John David. 2103 CLEAR LAKE PL 78665 #048-13-1977 L1977 **OPH EM** *020 †35 ‡
FITZGERALD, Patrick D. ■ 78681 #039-01-1971 L1972 **OPH** *071 †35
FITZPATRICK, Michael T. 511 OAKWOOD BLVD, STE 301 78681 #048-02-1983 L1983
  OBG *020 †20
FLETCHER, David D. 2400 ROUND ROCK AVE, ROUND ROCK HOSPITAL 78681 #016-76-1999,
  ▲ L2000 **EM** *020 †16
FORT, Diana Kathleen. ■ 78681 #065-05-1998 L2000 **EM** *020 †16
FOSTER, Robert A. 2410 ROUND ROCK AVE, STE 170 78681 #048-02-1990 L1996
  ORS HS *020 †40
FOX, Edward Jos. 16010 PARK VALLEY DR, STE 100B 78681 #048-04-1988 L1990 **N** *020 †75
FRANK, Carl D. 7200 WYOMING SPGS STE 1300 78681 #048-14-1999 L2001 **GE** *020 †20
FREDERICK, Daniel A. 940 HESTERS CROSSING RD 78681 #048-02-1999 L2003 **APM** *020 †05
FREIDBERG, David W. 7200 WYOMING SPGS, STE 700 78681 #048-02-1987 L1989 **U** *020 †95
GANESH, Meena. ■ 78681 #495-01-1996 L2005 **PD** *100
GEORGE, Vimal T. 1499 E OLD SETTLERS BLVD, STE B 78664 #048-14-2002 L2005 **FM** *020 †18
GILBERT, Jerry Heath. 511 OAKWOOD BLVD, STE 100 78681 #016-06-1995 L1997
  IC CD *020 †20
GILDERSLEEVE, Roger W. ■ 78665 #048-14-2002 L2007 **FM** *020 †18
GILLORY, David Oliver, II. 16020 PARK VALLEY DR, ORTHOPAEDIC ASSOCIATES OF 78681
  #048-02-1978 L1978 **ORS** *020 †40
GOERTZ, Frederick N. 2400 ROUND ROCK AVE 78681 #048-02-2003 L2006 **EM** *020 †16
GOODE, Joel D. 7200 WYOMING SPGS, STE 1500 78681 #048-14-1994 L1995 **FM** *020 †18
GRAY, Nadeen Wyndham. 940 HESTERS CROSSING RD 78681 #048-12-1993 L1998
  FM *020 †18
GRINOVICH, Sean Conrad. 302 UNIVERSITY BLVD, SCOTT & WHITE CLINIC 78665
  #039-01-1995 L1996 **OPH** *020 †35
GRITZKA, Boris Alexander. 940 HESTERS CROSSING RD, AUSTIN REGIONAL CLINIC 78681
  #409-33-1996 L2001 **PD** *020 †55
GUJJA, Usha. ■ 78664 #495-57-2000 L2008 **IM** *100 †20
HALL, John Cooper. 7200 WYOMING SPGS, STE 1600 78681 #016-06-1990 L2000 **IM** *020 †20
HALLETT, Jeffrey Stewart. 16000 PARK VALLEY DR, STE 130 78681 #055-01-1978 L1987
  AI PD *020 †55,03
HARDY, Julie Carol. 940 HESTERS CROSSING RD 78681 #048-04-1999 L2001 **FM** *020 †18
HARRELL, Melinda Denise. 2400 ROUND ROCK AVE 78681 #048-14-2001 L2005
  MPD *020 †55,20
HARVEY, Kristie Kinney. 940 HESTERS CROSSING RD 78681 #048-14-1986 L1991
  PD ADL *020 †55
HARVEY, Ralph Chandler. 511 OAKWOOD BLVD, STE 202 78681 #665-01-2003 L2007 **AN** *100
HAWTHORNE, Andy Leston. 7200 WYOMING SPGS, STE 500 78681 #048-14-2002 L2005
  GS *020 †85
HENDRIX, Thomas Lawrence. 2120 ROUND ROCK AVE 78681 #048-04-1973 L1973
  OPH GS *020 †35
HERNANDEZ, John Jeremy. ■ 78681 #048-15-2003 L2007 **AN** *020
HEYLIGER, Tara Ayodelle. 2410 ROUND ROCK AVE, STE 230 78681 #035-75-2000, ▲ L2005
  OBG *020
HIEGER, Le Roy Roman. ■ 78681 #019-02-1957 L1977 **PTH** *071 †50
HIX-HERNANDEZ, Staci J. ■ 78681 #048-15-2003 **GS** *012
HOLMES, Michael Christoph. ■ 78681 #021-05-2006 **PD** *012
HORVIT, Adam D. 16010 PARK VALLEY DR, STE 100B 78681 #048-04-1992 L1993 **N** *020 †75
HUNT, Kenneth Eugene. 7200 WYOMING SPGS, STE 500 78681 #048-12-1969 L1969
  GS *020 †85
IRONS, Daniel Anthony. 1000 HERITAGE CENTER CIR, PATHOLOGY RESOURCE
  CONSULT 78664 #020-12-1989 L1995 **PCP PTH** *020 †50
IRVIN, Bryan T. 940 HESTERS CROSSING RD, AUSTIN REGIONAL CLINIC 78681
  #048-14-1986 L1987 **FM** *020 †18
IRVIN, Michelle Ann. 2410 ROUND ROCK AVE, STE 200 78681 #048-15-1988 L1990
  OBG *020 †30

■ = Address Information Privacy Protected

IRWIN, Debra Sue. 940 HESTERS CROSSING RD 78681 #048-02-1982 L1983 **FM** *020 †18

ISAAC, Dominique Julie. 940 HESTERS CROSSING RD, AUSTIN REGIONAL CLINIC 78681 #035-03-1998 L2006 **FM** *020 †18

JACOBSON, Jack Merlin. 511 OAKWOOD BLVD, STE 103 78681 #048-02-1957 L1957 **U** *020 †95

JACOMIDES, Lucas. 300 UNIVERSITY BLVD 78665 #048-12-1998 L2000 **U** *020 †95

JADHAV, Swati Prashant. 940 HESTERS CROSSING RD 78681 #495-01-1989 L2000 **FM** *020 †18

JAEGGLI, Nelson S. 2400 ROUND ROCK AVE 78681 #035-01-2004 L2007 **EM** *020

JAHADI, Kambiz. 1402 CHISHOLM TRAIL RD, STE C 78681 #048-13-1990 L1998 **GS** *020 †85,10

JEHANGIR, Saima K. 2051 GATTIS SCHOOL RD, STE 250 78664 #048-13-2001 L2006 **OBG** *100 †30

JENNINGS, Steven Andrew. 2400 ROUND ROCK AVE 78681 #048-12-2003 L2006 **EM** *020 †16

JERE, Sujata Hemant. 1499 E OLD SETTLERS BLVD, STE B 78664 #495-83-1992 L2002 **FM** *020 †18

JOHNSON, Jesse B, III. 2300 ROUND ROCK AVE, STE 107 78681 #048-02-1976 L1976 **OBG** *020 †30

KATALENAS, Marta M. 2300 ROUND ROCK AVE, STE 102 78681 #847-15-1983 L1996 **PD** *020 †55

KITTLEMAN, William Thos. 2120 ROUND ROCK AVE 78681 #048-14-1981 L1981 **OPH** *020 †35

KOCS, Darren Michael. 2410 ROUND ROCK AVE, STE 150 78681 #035-20-1997 L2003 **HO** *020 †20

KODURU, Sunaina. ■ 78664 #496-24-2003 L2007 **IM** *012

KRAMER, Kevin Earl. ■ 78681 #041-14-1987 L1990 **AN PD** *020 †55

KUHL, Walter Brice. 940 HESTERS CROSSING RD, AUSTIN REGIONAL CLINIC 78681 #048-02-1980 L1980 **PD** *020 †55

LABBE, Thad Anthony. 2120 ROUND ROCK AVE 78681 #021-05-2002 L2007 **OPH** *100

LEATH, Brooke Gurkin. 300 UNIVERSITY BLVD, SCOTT AND WHITE UNIVERSITY 78665 #048-02-2000 L2006 **OBG** *020

LEWIS, Christopher Andrew. 3750 GATTIS SCHOOL RD, STE 400 78664 #048-02-2003 L2004 **FM** *020 †18

LEWIS, Rodney Duane. 7200 WYOMING SPGS, STE 500 78681 #048-12-1984 L1985 **GS** *020 †20

LONG, Chad J. 7200 WYOMING SPGS, STE 1300 78681 #016-02-2001 L2007 **GE** *020

LORD, Jennifer Noel. 16020 PARK VALLEY DR 78681 #041-15-2000 L2007 **HS** *020

LUCID, Henry Stanferd. 16010 PARK VALLEY DR, STE 200 78681 #048-04-1995 L1997 **CD** *020 †20

LUX, Louis Joseph. 2400 ROUND ROCK AVE 78681 #048-12-1985 L1990 **IM** *020 †20

MACKAY, Daniel Alexander. 2400 ROUND ROCK AVE 78681 #001-06-1982 L1995 **EM IM** *020 †20

MALONEY, Shaun Angus. 511 OAKWOOD BLVD, STE 200 78681 #048-14-1985 L1987 **U** *020 †95

MARKS, Lianne. 300 UNIVERSITY BLVD, UNIVERSITY MEDICAL CAMPUS 78665 #011-02-2004 L2007 **IM** *020 †20

MARTINEZ, Irene Lucy. ■ 78681 #034-01-1982 L1993 **IM** *020

MARTINEZ, Violeta Vanessa. ■ 78681 #048-14-2004 L2007 **PD** *020 †55

MATSUBARA, Atsushi. 1000 HESTERS CROSSING RD, STE 100 78681 #572-20-1992 L1999 **FM** *020 †18

MAUNDER, Mark E. 511 OAKWOOD BLVD STE 301, OAKWOOD WOMEN'S CENTRE, PA 78681 #048-14-1989 L1990 **OBG** *020 †30

MCCUSKEY, Charles F. 2400 ROUND ROCK AVE 78681 #005-06-1990 L2000 **EM** *020 †16

MC GEE, Timothy Mark. 7200 WYOMING SPGS, STE 300 78681 #048-14-1990 L1991 **PS GS** *020 †65,85

MC KENNON, Stuart C. 2400 ROUND ROCK AVE 78681 #048-12-1980 L1980 **IM** *020 †20

MICHEL, Stephanie Smolen. 2410 ROUND ROCK AVE, STE 200 78681 #021-01-2002 L2006 **OBG** *100

MILLAR, Jose G. 2300 ROUND ROCK AVE, STE 102 78681 #048-02-1990 L2000 **PD** *020 †55

MILLER, Alicia Lynn. 300 UNIVERSITY BLVD, SCOTT AND WHITE UMC 78665 #048-04-2003 L2007 **D** *020 †15

MILLER, Brian Terry. 1201 SAM BASS RD 78681 #048-78-1979, ▲ L1979 **AI IM** *020 †20,03

MILLER, George Martin. 511 OAKWOOD BLVD, STE 202 78681 #473-01-1998 L2003 **AN** *020 †05

MILLER, Larry James. 921 MONADALE TRL, FIRST MEDICAL RESPONSE OF 78664 #025-01-1965 L1973 **EM FM** *030 †16

MILMAN, Robert M. 2120 N MAYS ST, STE 220 78664 #048-16-1986 L1987 **DR** *020 †80

MISTRY, Sandeep Gopinath. 1000 HESTERS CROSSING RD, STE 300 78681 #048-04-2001 L2004 **U** *020

MORRISON, Bryan K. 7200 WYOMING SPGS, STE 600 78681 #048-13-1990 L1991 **FM** *020 †20

MUNIR, Mubashar. 2300 ROUND ROCK AVE # 201 78681 #704-01-1988 L1996 **GE IM** *020 †20

MURPHREE, Paul B, Jr. 511 OAKWOOD BLVD, STE 301 78681 #027-01-1981 L1982 **OBG** *020 †30

MUSGROVE, Michael Andrew. 1201 SAM BASS RD, SETON SHOAL CREEK HOSPITAL 78681 #042-01-2004 L2006 **P** *012

NAEEM, Naheed Haq. 1009 N GEORGETOWN ST 78664 #704-20-1988 L2005 **P** *100

NAJEM, Ahmad Zia. ■ 78664 #118-01-1962 L1973 **GS TRS** *071 †85

NANDA, Nellie. ■ 78681 #016-11-1997 L2001 **IM** *020

NGUYEN, Vu Nhu. 302 UNIVERSITY BLVD 78665 #050-02-2000 L2007 **GE** *100 †20

NOLAN, Kirkland Caves. 300 UNIVERSITY BLVD, COOPER CLINIC, PA 78665 #039-01-1989 L2007 **PCC IM** *020 †20

OLIVER, Paul Benjamin. 2000 S IH 35, STE E1 78681 #048-14-1993 L1994 **FM** *020 †18

OLOBATUYI, Felix Ademola. ■ 78665 #033-06-2001 L2008 **PTH HMP** *100 †50

O'MEARA, Clifton Barbe. 2400 ROUND ROCK AVE 78681 #042-02-1986 L1994 **ORS** *020 †40

ONAN, Marsha Hillary B. 2120 ROUND ROCK AVE 78681 #048-04-1995 L1997 **OPH PO** *020 †35

O'NEILL, Larissa Kaye. 7200 WYOMING SPGS, STE 1500 78681 #048-14-1995 L1996 **FM** *020 †18

ORTH, Susan Elizabeth. 511 OAKWOOD BLVD STE 301 78681 #028-03-1993 L1997 **OBG** *020 †30

OSTADIAN, Mahta. ■ 78681 #048-16-2005 **P** *012

OVERSTREET, Wm Dennis. 2250 ROUND ROCK AVE, OAKWOOD SURGERY CTR 78681 #048-12-1975 L1975 **AN** *020 †05

OWEN, Graves Thorne. 7200 WYOMING SPGS, STE 400 78681 #048-14-1990 L1991 **APM** *020 †05

OWENS, Nancy Elizabeth. 940 HESTERS CROSSING RD, AUSTIN REGIONAL CLINIC 78681 #012-05-1990 L2001 **PD** *020 †55

PAGETTE, Melanie H. 7200 WYOMING SPGS, STE 1100 78681 #048-15-1988 L1989 **OBG** *020 †30

PANDYA, Charuben C. 894 SUMMIT ST, STE 108 78664 #495-23-1989 L1999 **PD** *020 †55

PARGAONKAR, Anjali S. 8003 HERBS CAVE CV 78681 #495-83-1994 L2002 **PCP** *020 †50

PARKER, Ehrin E. 405 OLD WEST DR 78681 #048-78-1996, ▲ L1998 *020

PARR, Catherine. 2410 ROUND ROCK AVE 78681 #019-02-1977 L1998 **OBG** *071 †30

PATEL, Biral T. 300 UNIVERSITY BLVD, SCOTT & WHITE UNIVERSITY M 78665 #654-01-2000 L2005 **AN PME** *020 †20

PATEL, Maitreyee D. 1009 N GEORGETOWN ST 78664 #495-76-1987 L2004 **P** *020 †75

PIKE, Susan Mary. 302 UNIVERSITY BLVD, PLASTIC SURGERY 78665 #016-43-1997 L2003 **PS** *020 †65

PLIEGO, Janet Elizabeth. ■ 78665 #048-02-1981 L1982 **DR** *020

PORCHER, William Jos. 555 ROUND ROCK WEST DR, BLUEBONNET TRAILS MHMR CTR 78681 #016-02-1967 L1975 **CHP P** *020 †75

PUTNEY, Christopher G. 7200 WYOMING SPGS, STE 600 78681 #048-13-1993 L1995 **FM** *020 †18

PUTNEY, Michael E. 16020 PARK VALLEY DR, ORTHOPAEDIC ASSOCIATES OF 78681 #048-02-1985 L1986 **ORS** *020 †40

RAJULAPALLI, Madhavi R. 2300 ROUND ROCK AVE, STE 202 78681 #495-62-1994 L2001 **IM** *020 †20

RANGARAJAN, Anuradha R. 1240 E PALM VALLEY BLVD 78664 #495-17-1989 L2007 **FM UCM** *020 †18

RHODES, Meena V. 300 UNIVERSITY BLVD, ATTN: KATHERINE MCBRADD 78665 #048-02-2004 L2007 **IM** *020 †20

ROANE, Catherine E. 1 CHISHOLM TRL, STE 5100 78681 #048-14-1983 L1983 **OBG** *020 †30

ROBERTS, Elizabeth Ann. 300 UNIVERSITY BLVD 78665 #048-16-2003 L2007 **OPH** *020

ROBERTS, Sam Swinford, III. ■ 78664 #048-02-1978 L1978 **FM** *020 †18,16

ROBIN, Brett N. ■ 78681 #048-13-2008 *012

ROBINS, Timothy Paul. 7200 WYOMING SPGS, STE 1600 78681 #048-15-1986 L1987 **IM** *020 †20

RODRIGUEZ, Alison Ann. 511 OAKWOOD BLVD, STE 301 78681 #021-05-1999 L2003 **OBG** *020 †30

ROEHM, Eric Frison. 2400 ROUND ROCK AVE 78681 #048-04-1979 L1979 **CD IM** *020 †20

ROMBERG, Matthew T. ■ 78665 #048-15-2002 L2006 **OBG** *020

RUGGERO, Roque P. 2400 ROUND ROCK AVE 78681 #048-13-1997 L2000 **EM** *020 †16

RUMI, Mustasim N. 16020 PARK VALLEY DR, ORTHOPAEDIC ASSOCIATES OF 78681 #035-45-1995 L2005 **ORS** *020 †40

RUSSELL, Scott A. 7200 WYOMING SPGS STE 500 78681 #048-12-1987 L1988 **GS VS** *020 †85

RUTLEDGE, Elizabeth W. 511 OAKWOOD BLVD STE 103, UROLOGY ASSOC OF WILLIAMSO 78681 #048-15-1979 L1979 **U GP** *020 †95

SAADEH, Elia. 1499 E OLD SETTLERS BLVD, STE B 78664 #048-02-1992 L1994 **NEP** *020 †20

SARTOR, Charles Don. 402 W TAYLOR AVE # A-377 78664 #649-14-1976 L1982 **PD** *075

SCHULTZ, Richard Benton. 300 UNIVERSITY BLVD 78665 #048-04-1991 L1992 **ORS OSM** *020 †40

SCRANTON, Maria Carmella. 940 HESTERS CROSSING RD 78681 #048-12-1991 L1995 **PD** *020 †55

SHASHOUA, George Leor. 511 OAKWOOD BLVD, STE 301 78681 #048-12-1991 L1993 **OBG** *020 †30

SHELLY, Kevin R. 511 OAKWOOD BLVD, STE 202 78681 #048-12-1997 L1998 **AN** *020 †05

SIDDIQUI, Junaid. 2300 ROUND ROCK AVE, STE 201 78681 #704-20-1990 L2008 **IM** *020 †20

SIEGEL, Craig Owen. 7200 WYOMING SPGS, STE 1400 78681 #048-04-1984 L1985 **CD IM** *020 †20

SIMPKINS, Robert Chas. 2400 ROUND ROCK AVE 78681 #048-04-1989 L1990 **FM** *020 †18

SINT, Thaw. ■ 78681 #017-20-2000 L2007 **PCC** *020

SMALLING, Susan B. 511 OAKWOOD BLVD, STE 202 78681 #048-13-1980 L1980 **AN** *020 †05 ‡

SMITH, Scott A. 2410 ROUND ROCK AVE, STE 170 78681 #048-15-1991 L1996 **ORS** *020 †40

SMITH, Thomas Fugate. 1499 E OLD SETTLERS BLVD, STE B 78664 #051-01-1974 L1998 **AI PUD** *020 †55,03

SOLODKY, Inna Valerie. 1240 E PALM VALLEY BLVD 78664 #913-07-1991 L2004 **FM** *020 †18

SOTELO, Joanne. 300 UNIVERSITY BLVD 78665 #042-01-2000 L2003 **P** *100 †75

SOUTHMAYD, Karen Lea. 511 OAKWOOD BLVD STE 301, OAKWOOD WOMENS CENTRE 78681 #051-07-1984 L1993 **OBG** *020 ‡

SPELLINGS, Veronica A. 7200 WYOMING SPGS, STE 1500 78681 #048-14-1998 L2005 **IM PD** *020 †20,55

STASSEN, Wm Nicholas Leo. 7200 WYOMING SPGS, STE 1300 78681 #539-03-1975 L1985 **GE HEP** *020 †20

STRAWSER, Richard T. 7200 WYOMING SPGS, STE 1500 78681 #030-05-1984 L1989 **FM** *020 †18

STRELNIEKS, Erik Jon. 2400 ROUND ROCK AVE 78681 #047-06-1993 L1998 **EM** *020 †16

SWENSON, Maureen M. 1 CHISHOLM TRL STE 4100 78681 #048-12-1990 L1991 **FM** *020 †18

SZCZYTOWSKI, Joseph M. 511 OAKWOOD BLVD, STE 201 78681 #048-78-2001, ▲ L2003 **CD** *020

SZKRYBALO, Michael. 2400 ROUND ROCK AVE, DEPT OF EMERGENCY MEDICINE 78681 #038-43-1987 L1994 **EM** *020 †16

TABARROK, Mark Dariush. ■ 78681 #001-02-2004 **PD** *012

TABUCO, Arnold Abutanmo. ■ 78664 #748-27-1994 *100

TAMEZ, Oscar A. 2300 ROUND ROCK AVE, STE 203 78681 #048-02-1993 L1995 **OTO FPS** *020 †45

TAY, Chhay Hy. 1499 E OLD SETTLERS BLVD, STE B 78664 #056-06-1999 L2002 **END** *020 †20

TAYLOR, Harold W, Jr. ■ 78665 #039-01-1951 L1952 **GP** *071

TAYLOR MC DANIEL, Lu Anne. 1009 N GEORGETOWN ST, BLUE BONNET TRAILS MENTAL 78664 #056-05-1978 L1979 **P** *020

TEW, Monty B. 1499 E OLD SETTLERS BLVD, STE B 78664 #048-04-1996 L1997 **IM** *020 †20

THAMPOE, Basti Julian. ■ 78665 #422-01-2000 L2004 **IM** *071 †20

THOMAS, Darryl Brian. 300 UNIVERSITY BLVD 78665 #023-07-1995 L2005 **OSM** *020 †40

THOMPSON, Tanna Michelle. 3513 ROCK SHELF LN 78681 #048-02-1997 L2000 **MPD** *020 †55

THOMPSON, Troy D. 2300 ROUND ROCK AVE 78681 #048-13-1998 L2005 **PS** *020 †85,65

TIPTON, Geo Washington, Jr. 2000 S MAYS ST, STE 305 78664 #048-02-1977 L1977 **ORS** *020 †40

TRAMONTE, Jeffrey Jasper. 300 UNIVERSITY BLVD, DEPARTMENT OF NEUROLOGY 78665 #048-16-2000 L2008 **N** *020 †75

TREADWELL, Leah June. 940 HESTERS CROSSING RD 78681 #018-03-1996 L2006 **FM** *020 †18

TURNER, Trevor H. 7200 WYOMING SPGS, STE 1500 78681 #048-14-1991 L1992 **MPD PD** *020 †55,20

TYER, Richard Darnell. 16010 PARK VALLEY DR, STE 100B 78681 #048-02-1993 L1994 **N** *020 †75

UNITE, Anselmo G, III. 15930 S GREAT OAKS DR # B, TREEHOUSE PEDIATRICS 78681 #048-04-1996 L1998 **PD** *020 †55

URIEGAS, Rodolfo. 940 HESTERS CROSSING RD 78681 #005-11-1984 L1985 **FM** *020 †18
URIEGAS, Sabrina Bueno. ■ 78681 #005-11-1984 L1985 **FM** *074 †18
VALASTRO, Michael S. 16020 PARK VALLEY DR, ORTHOPAEDIC ASSOCIATES OF 78681 #048-02-1991 L1992 **ORS** *020 †40
VAN WISSE, Willebrordus S. 117 LOUIS HENNA BLVD # B-2 78664 #660-03-1958 L1969 **GS** *071 †85
VEGA, Benjamin Rodriguez. ■ 78681 #275-01-1940 L1960 **GP P** *071
VICTORICA, Carlos Miguel. 1099 E MAIN ST, STE 200 78664 #011-03-2004 L2007 **FM** *100 †18
VINSON, Thomas Childress. 16010 PARK VALLEY DR, STE 200 78681 #047-06-1988 L2001 **CD** *020 †20
VORACHARD, Jared Amnard. ■ 78665 #048-02-2004 L2007 **EM** *020
WACKER, Nikki Ann Ullrich. ■ 78681 #048-04-1998 L2000 **PD** *020 †55
WALZEL, Jack Lee. 7200 WYOMING SPGS STE 500 78681 #048-13-1984 L1985 **GS** *020 †85
WANG, Emily Sueyin. 2400 ROUND ROCK AVE, # 309 78681 #048-13-2000 L2003 **IM** *020 †20
WATSON, Robin W. 302 UNIVERSITY BLVD 78665 #048-13-1998 L2006 **GS** *020 †85
WAUGH, Michelle D. ■ 78681 #048-13-2002 L2006 **PFP** *100 †75
WELSH, Jenifer Hall. 302 UNIVERSITY BLVD, SCOTT & WHITE UMC 78665 #048-04-1998 L1999 **IM** *020 †20
WEST, Deborah Parsons. 2000 N MAYS ST STE 109, CAROUSEL PEDIATRICS 78664 #041-01-1984 L1994 **PD** *020 †55
WEST, Joseph Everett, III. 511 OAKWOOD BLVD STE 103 78681 #048-04-1974 L1974 **U** *020 †95 ‡
WHITE, Alan Barton. 940 HESTERS CROSSING RD 78681 #048-14-1984 L1985 **PD** *020 †55
WHITE, Kyle Wesley. 300 UNIVERSITY BLVD 78665 #048-04-2003 L2007 **AN** *020
WILSON, Larry Darnell. 117B LOUIS HENNA BLVD, STE 200 78664 #039-01-1985 L1987 **OM** *020 †18
WILSON, Steve Cranford. 16020 PARK VALLEY DR, ORTHOPAEDIC ASSOCIATES OF 78681 #048-15-1980 L1980 **ORS** *020 †40
YORK, Jay L. 300 UNIVERSITY BLVD, ANESTHESIA ASSOCIATES 78665 #048-12-2000 L2004 **AN** *020 †05
ZIEBERT, John Jos. 7200 WYOMING SPGS, STE 1300 78681 #056-05-1990 L1994 **GE** *020 †20
ZOOK, Marc Edward. 940 HESTERS CROSSING RD, AUSTIN REGIONAL CLINIC 78681 #017-20-1995 L2004 **FM** *020 †18

ROWLETT — DALLAS

ABADESCO, Leo. ■ 75088 #748-08-1964 L1975 **PTH EM** *071 †50
ACAR, Ferit. 3528 LAKEVIEW PKWY, STE 101 75088 #902-03-1970 L1981 **IM** *020 ‡
ALLEN, Gary Ralph. 5501 GORDON SMITH DR, STE 500 75089 #048-12-1974 L1974 **FM** *020 †18
ANTONY, Sam O, Jr. 7801 LAKEVIEW PKWY 75088 #021-06-1982 L1987 **OTO** *020 †45
AUNG, Min. 9400 LAKEVIEW PKWY, STE 113 75088 #209-01-1961 L1977 **FM** *020
BAILEY, Donna Marie. 5702 ROWLETT RD STE 200 75089 #048-12-1996 L1997 **FM** *020 †18
BERGGREN, Andrew T. 7801 LAKEVIEW PKWY, TEXAS CARDIAL ASSOC 75088 #048-12-1995 L1997 **CD** *100 †20
BURTON, Lukas E. 6800 SCENIC DR, LAKE POINTE MEDICAL CENTER 75088 #048-02-2001 L2004 **DR** *100 †80
CARP, Joel Harris. 6800 SCENIC DR 75088 #021-05-1984 L1989 **DR** *020 †80
CHAPMAN, Robert Eugene. 6701 HERITAGE PARKWAY 75088 #048-02-1954 L1954 **GP GS** *071
CHOI, Kyungho S. 10006 WATERVIEW PKWY 75089 #033-06-1999 L2002 **EM** *020 †16
CURANOVIC, John. 6900 SCENIC DR, STE 102 75088 #305-01-1998 L2001 **IM** *020 †20
DAVILA, Holanda Lizette. ■ 75088 #935-02-1993 L2002 **PDI** *020 †55
EDUPUGANTI, Ravindra. 7801 LAKEVIEW PKWY, STE 100 75088 #048-02-1992 L1993 **CD** *020 †20
ETEZADI-AMOLI, Shahin. 4106 LAKESIDE DR, GARLAND HEALTH CENTER 75088 #517-01-1966 L1978 **PD MFM** *020
FISHER, Ted Yoshio. 8301 LAKEVIEW PKWY, STE 200 75088 #023-12-1990 L1996 **EM** *020
GILLEAN, Julia R. 6900 SCENIC DR, LAKE POINTE WOMENS CTR 75088 #048-12-1998 L2002 **OBG** *020 †30
GOMEZ-LOZANO, Cesar A. 9706 CASTLEROY LN 75089 #264-17-1986 L1994 **IM** *020 †20
GONINO, V John. 5700 ROWLETT RD, STE 120 75089 #048-78-1991, ▲ L1992 **FM** *020
GRANGER, David Philip. 9100 LAKEVIEW PKWY 75088 #050-02-1977 L1985 **PD GP** *020 †55
HOLLINGSWORTH, Nataki Ave. 7600 LAKEVIEW PKWY, STE 200 75088 #038-41-1997 L2000 **FM** *020 †18
HOLLINGSWORTH, Terry Adam. 7600 LAKEVIEW PKWY, # 200 75088 #047-20-1996 L2000 **FM** *020
HOWARD, James Marshall. 3508 LAKEVIEW PKWY 75088 #048-13-1983 L1983 **FM PD** *075
IANNELLI, Vincent Robert. 9100 LAKEVIEW PKWY 75088 #048-12-1994 L1996 **PD** *020 †55
JANTZ, Candice P. ■ 75089 #048-12-2004 L2007 **IM** *100 †20
JOHNSON, Denise Angelette. 7501 LAKEVIEW PKWY, HIGHWAY 66 75088 #028-03-1988 L1995 **FM OBG** *020 †18
LESLIE, William K. 7801 LAKEVIEW PKWY, STE 130 75088 #048-02-1980 L1980 **PUD IM** *020 †20
LONDON, Dynal Marie. 6900 SCENIC DR STE 103 75088 #048-12-1995 L1997 **PD** *020 †55
MACKEY, Eva Maria. 5702 ROWLETT RD, STE 200 75089 #048-02-2001 L2004 **FM** *020 †18
MILLER, Jennifer M. 6800 SCENIC DR 75088 #001-02-1996 L1999 **FM** *020 †18
MIXON, Michael Dwayne. 8602 LAKEVIEW PKWY, STE E 75088 #004-01-1986 L1992 **IM** *020 †20
MOODY, Gloria Jean. 6800 SCENIC DR 75088 #010-01-1992 L1998 **NPM** *020 †55
MORENO, Susan C. 5700 ROWLETT RD STE 1 75089 #048-78-1999, ▲ L2004 **FP** *012
MORGAN, Jarelle Jamie. ■ 75089 #021-01-2004 **FM** *020
MRNUSTIK, Benny Ralph. 5501 GORDON SMITH DR, STE 500 75089 #048-13-1984 L1985 **FM** *020 †18
MYERS, Jeffrey Paul. 9500 LAKEVIEW PKWY, STE 200 75088 #048-12-1983 L1983 **OBG** *020 †30
NELSON, Jeffery Taylor. 6900 SCENIC DR STE 101 75088 #048-13-2004 L2007 **OBG** *020
OKORO, Chibuike Uzoma. ■ 75088 #048-12-2007 **IM** *012
PARKER, Sean Glenn. 5501 GORDON SMITH DR, STE 500 75089 #049-01-1997 L1997 **FM** *020 †18
PATEL, Ravi Bharat. 9500 LAKEVIEW PKWY, STE 100 75088 #305-01-2000 L2006 **IMG** *020 †20
PECSON, Edilgrace Angeles. 6800 SCENIC DR, CHILDREN'S MEDICAL CENTER 75088 #048-16-2002 L2005 **PD** *100
PERRITT, Dirk Alan. ■ 75089 #038-43-2003 L2005 **EM** *100 †16
PHILLIPS, Nancy Lyn. 9100 LAKEVIEW PKWY, LAKE RAY HUBBARD PEDIATRIC 75088 #035-03-2002 L2006 **PD** *020 †55 ‡

POTTER, Cheryl Ann. 5700 ROWLETT RD, LAKE POINTE WOMENS CTR 75089 #019-02-1992 L1993 **OBG** *020 †30
RAMIREZ, Kenda Leigh. ■ 75088 #018-03-2001 L2002 **IM** *020
REREDDY, Jyothi Reddy. 5702 ROWLETT RD, STE 210-A 75089 #495-65-1991 L1998 **IM** *020 †20
RESTER, Michelle M. 5702 ROWLETT RD STE 200, FMC ROWLETT 75089 #048-14-1993 L1994 **IM IMG** *020 †20
SCHWEERS, Carl Amos, Jr. ■ 75088 #028-02-1963 L1967 **PTH** *020 †50
SHAH, Jaini. ■ 75089 #048-16-2008 *012
SHARP, James Stephenson. 6800 SCENIC DR 75088 #048-02-1981 L1982 **CD IM** *020 †20
SHEN, Yuenan. ■ 75089 #243-45-1985 L2002 **PTH** *020 †50
SMART, Susan Michaelle. 9100 LAKEVIEW PKWY 75088 #039-01-1999 L2001 **PD** *020 †55
STEPHENSON, Scott K. 6800 SCENIC DR 75088 #048-12-1988 L1989 **CD** *020 †20
SUDELA, Thomas Stephen. 6900 SCENIC DR, LAKE POINTE WOMENS CTR 75088 #048-14-1976 L1976 **OBG** *020 †30
WIELAND, Pamela M. 6900 SCENIC DR, STE 103 75088 #030-05-1985 L1988 **PD** *020 †55
YANG, Huan. 7600 LAKEVIEW PKWY 75088 #243-47-1988 L2002 **IM** *020 †20

ROYSE CITY — ROCKWALL

ANDERSON, Susan Garza. 125 W INTERSTATE 30 STE L, PRIMARY CARE ASSOCIATES - 75189 #036-05-1996 L1998 **FM** *020 †18
JONES, Ronald Wayne. 200 N ARCH ST 75189 #018-75-1974, ▲ L1975 **FM APM** *020
RESTER, J Trever. 1101 W 1-30, STE #101 75189 #048-14-1993 L1995 **MPD** *020 †55,20

RUNAWAY BAY — WISE

BREWSTER, Clarence B. ■ 76426 #021-01-1929 L1930 **OPH** *071

RUSK — CHEROKEE

BASHOUR, Samuel B. RR 1 75785 #605-01-1945 L1953 **GS GP** *071 †85
BOLCH, Alfred Price. JACKSONVILLE HWY NORTH 75785 #048-02-1955 L1955 **P GP** *071 †75
BOWERMAN, W Maurice. PO BOX 318 75785 #040-02-1953 L1982 **P** *020
BROWN, Dan Marcus. RR 5, 700 E JOHNSON 75785 #048-12-1946 L1946 **OS FM** *071
CHAMNESS, Daniel Ernest. JACKSONVILLE HWY NORTH 75785 #048-02-1952 L1952 **P N** *071
CRAWFORD, Loyce L. ■ 75785 #021-01-1948 L1953 **P** *074
CUELLAR, Caton B. PO BOX 917 75785 #649-01-1960 L1994 **P PYM** *020 †75
GOODMAN, John Willis. 474 E 5TH ST, 700 E FIFTH ST 75785 #048-02-1965 L1965 **P N** *075
HAWKINS, Larry Rex. 286 W 5TH ST 75785 #048-02-1982 L1983 **P** *020 †75
JOHNSON, Douglas Neil. PO BOX 318, HIGHWAY 69 NORTH MC0318 75785 #048-04-1962 L1962 **AM P** *020 †70
KEMPTON, Brian J. 1801 N DICKINSON DR, EAST TEXAS MEDICAL CENTER 75785 #048-02-1989 L1990 **EM** *030 †16
LAHIRI, Satyajeet. PO BOX 533 75785 #495-73-1973 L1992 **P** *020 †75
LUCAS, James Richard. 501 N BARRON ST 75785 #039-01-1966 L1993 **AN** *071
MORRIS, James Mark. 1325 N DICKINSON DR 75785 #048-15-1985 L1987 **GP** *020
PEYTON, John Chas. 605 W 6TH ST 75785 #048-02-1968 L1968 **IM FM** *071 †20
RAMIREZ, Phyllis Andrea. PO BOX 999, SKYVIEW UNIT, HWY 69 FM 29 75785 #048-02-1994 L2001 **P** *020 †75
RODRIGUEZ, Rodolfo H. ■ 75785 #048-02-1969 L1970 **P** *030 †75
SRINIVASAN, Sethurama. ■ 75785 #495-04-1964 L1976 **P IM** *020 †75
YOUN, Young Mee. PO BOX 318 75785 #583-08-1970 L1977 **GP ADM** *020

SACHSE — DALLAS

DE LA FUENTE GUARDIA, E. ■ 75048 #176-03-1959 L1979 **CHP P** *071
KING, Scottie L. 5915 MURPHY RD 75048 #048-12-1997 L1999 **FM** *020 †18
KOHN, James S. 5250 HIGHWAY 78, STE 750 75048 #024-07-1989 L1997 **GS** *020 †85
MONCEAUX, Darryl Jos. 6106 FIELDCREST LN 75048 #021-06-1985 L1985 **ADP** *020 †75
ZENAVOSA, Nestor Rhett. 5250 HIGHWAY 78, STE 750-411 75048 #016-11-1991 L1992 **EM** *020 †20,16

SAGINAW — TARRANT

BAKER, Shannon Cooke. 833 TOWNE CT 76179 #036-01-2003 L2007 **FM** *020 †18
GILLUM, Ronald Lee. ■ 76131 #016-11-1964 L1972 **CLP PTH** *071 †50
LEWIS, Hayden Lee. 608 E BAILEY BOSWELL RD, STE 140 76131 #048-13-1993 L1999 **FM** *020 †18

SAINT HEDWIG — BEXAR

BANKS, Heather E. ■ 78152 #048-13-2004 L2007 **NEP** *012 †20
HOLT, Clinton L. ■ 78152 #038-06-1953 L1953 **OM** *071 †70

SALADO — BELL

ASHE, William M. ■ 76571 #035-45-1943 L1950 **TS** *071
BARRIER, Chas Wesley, Jr. ■ 76571 #048-02-1954 L1954 **N** *020
FONDA, Beth Ann. ■ 76571 #048-15-1981 L1981 **PD** *020 †55
GROSSMANN, Alicia Maureen. ■ 76571 #048-16-2007 **IM** *012
JARVIS, Jeffrey Lance. ■ 76571 #048-02-2005 L2006 **EM** *012
KUYKENDALL, Samuel James. ■ 76571 #047-06-2006 **GS** *100
MC LAUGHLIN, Allan Evert. ■ 76571 #035-45-1966 L1969 **P CHP** *075 †75
PENA, Ramiro Abraham. 213 MILL CREEK DR, STE 180 76571 #048-02-1963 L1963 **FM GS** *020 †85
SANDERA, Marisa. ■ 76571 #048-13-2002 L2005 **ON** *012 †20
WINN, Richard Earl. 8433 RITA BEND DR 76571 #003-01-1975 L1981 **PUD ID** *020 †16,20

■ = Address Information Privacy Protected

SALT FLAT – HUDSPETH

TRUJILLO, Ralph Eusebio. ■ 79847 #649-33-1985 L1987 **FM** *020 †18

SAN ANGELO – TOM GREEN

ACTON, Hector Flores. 2141 HAMILTON WAY STE 100 76904 #017-20-2000 L2003 **PD** *020 †55
ADAMS, Laura Hill. 225 E BEAUREGARD AVE 76903 #048-13-1993 L2002 **OBG** *020 †30
ALEXANDER, Eugene P. 2021 W BEAUREGARD AVE 76901 #048-04-1941 L1941 **D** *071
ALEXANDER, John Edward. 3308 FOSTER ST 76903 #048-02-1982 L1983 **DR** *020 †80
ALEXANDER, Robert Warren. 3605 EXECUTIVE DR 76904 #048-02-1985 L1986 **ORS OSS** *020 †40
ALEXANDER, Ross Alfred. 120 E BEAUREGARD AVE 76903 #048-02-1979 L1979 **D** *071 †15
ANDERSON, Allen. 3605 EXECUTIVE DR 76904 #048-12-1966 L1966 **OTO A** *020 †45
ANDERTON, Carl Don. 120 E BEAUREGARD AVE 76903 #048-12-1987 L1990 **IM** *020 †20
ARTNAK, Edward Jos. 4450 SUNSET DR 76901 #012-05-1974 L1984 **GE** *020 †20
AWTREY, Staton Langston. 120 E HARRIS AVE 76903 #048-12-1988 L1989 **TS** *020 †85,90
AYASS, Mohamad Ammar F. 3016 VISTA DEL ARROYO DR 76904 #875-01-1988 L2001 **NEP** *020 †20
BAILEY, Julie A. 120 E HARRIS AVE, SHANNON MEDICAL CENTER 76903 #048-04-1995 L1996 **AN** *020 †05
BAKER, Brad R. 1610 S CHADBOURNE ST 76903 #048-14-1986 L1987 **FM** *020 †18 ‡
BAKER, Gaeron Glenn. ■ 76901 #048-02-1988 L1991 **EM** *020 †16
BALLARD, John Sidney, III. 3605 EXECUTIVE DR 76904 #048-12-1969 L1969 **U** *020 †95
BANKSTON, David Paul. 120 E BEAUREGARD AVE, SHANNON CLINIC 76903 #051-01-1975 L1998 **AN PME** *020 †05
BARNES, John Littleton. 319 W HARRIS AVE 76903 #048-04-1965 L1965 **OPH** *020 †35
BARNETT, James C. 120 E BEAUREGARD AVE 76903 #048-12-1995 L1996 **IM** *020 †20
BASKIN, Leland Burleson. ■ 76904 #048-13-1986 L1988 **BBK PCH** *020 †50
BENDER, Thomas Bruce. 2239 N BRYANT BLVD 76903 #048-13-1981 L1981 **FM** *020
BENHAM, Charles D. 7263 S RATLIFF RD 76904 #048-02-1987 L1988 **EM** *020 †16
BETHA, Meena Padmapriya. PO BOX 22000 76902 #495-11-2000 L2005 **IM** *100 †20
BIEDERMANN, Herbert A, III. 120 E BEAUREGARD AVE 76903 #048-02-1984 L1987 **AN** *020 †05
BLANC, Michael Scott. 2141 HAMILTON WAY, STE 108 76904 #038-44-1985 L2002 **CD** *020 †20
BLUDWORTH, Charles Estill. ■ 76904 #048-12-1959 L1959 **CHP P** *071 †75
BOLEN, John G. ■ 76904 #038-40-1949 L1953 **R NM** *071 †80
BOSTER, Stephen Ray. 120 E HARRIS AVE 76903 #048-13-1977 L1977 **EM** *020 †16
BRADLEY, Brian A. 3555 KNICKERBOCKER RD 76904 #048-02-1999 L2006 **U** *020 †95
BREEDLOVE, Kenneth E. 120 E BEAUREGARD AVE 76903 #048-15-1998 L2000 **DR** *020 †80
BREWER, Kirk S. 3501 KNICKERBOCKER RD 76904 #048-12-1991 L1992 **IM** *020 †20
BRYAN, Grady Wilson. 3012 GREEN MEADOW DR 76904 #048-13-1990 L1991 **FPS** *020
BURDINE, Arthur Price. 3605 EXECUTIVE DR 76904 #027-01-1965 L1970 **ORS GP** *020 †40
CAINELLI, Stephen Rudolph. 225 E BEAUREGARD AVE 76903 #033-05-1979 L1981 **GYN** *020
CAMBRE, Penni Davies. 3555 KNICKERBOCKER RD 76904 #048-13-1988 L1989 **PD** *020 †55
CAMPBELL, Peter M. ■ 76901 #021-01-1962 L1962 **U** *071 †95
CARGILE, John Stark, III. 102 N MAGDALEN ST STE 270 76903 #048-12-1981 L1981 **GS VS** *020 †85
CARLETON, Thomas Blair. 3401 LOOP 306, STE A 76904 #048-12-1965 L1965 **GP** *020
CARMICHAEL, Ross M. 3555 KNICKERBOCKER RD 76904 #048-02-1977 L1977 **IM** *071 †20
CARROLL, M Walter. 3501 KNICKERBOCKER RD 76904 #048-13-1997 L1999 **IM** *020 †20
CARSNER, Robert Lee. 120 E BEAUREGARD AVE 76903 #048-02-1961 L1961 **IM** *020 †20
CHANG, Peter P. 120 E HARRIS AVE 76903 #048-02-1984 L1985 **FM** *020 †18
CHARLESWORTH, Ernest Neal. 120 E BEAUREGARD AVE 76903 #048-02-1971 L1971 **D A** *020 †15,20,03
CHASE, Ralph R, Jr. 3555 KNICKERBOCKER RD 76904 #016-06-1951 L1953 **PD** *071 †55
CHILUKURI, Rangarao R. ■ 76904 #495-58-1978 L1996 **IM** *020
CHINN, Cornelius W. 120 E BEAUREGARD AVE 76903 #048-02-1991 L1992 **FM** *020 †18
CHRISTENSEN, Edward W. 102 N MAGDALEN ST, STE 240 76903 #035-01-1961 L1973 **OBG** *071 †30
CHUN, Jacob. 4450 SUNSET DR 76901 #005-06-1997 L2004 **ORS** *020 †40
COATES, Stephen W, Jr. 4450 SUNSET DR 76901 #048-12-1998 L1999 **GE** *020 †20
COBB, John Littleton. ■ 76901 #048-04-1943 L1943 **FM** *071 †18
COCUZZI, John Michael. 1610 S CHADBOURNE ST 76903 #031-01-1986 L2001 **FM OM** *020 †18
COLE, James Christopher. 120 E BEAUREGARD AVE 76903 #021-06-1996 L1997 **DR** *020 †80
CONWAY, Warren L. 3555 KNICKERBOCKER RD 76904 #048-16-1995 L1997 **FM** *020 †18
COOK, Donald Wayne. 3605 EXECUTIVE DR 76904 #035-47-1983 L1990 **U** *020 †95
CORNELL, Jess Michael. 102 N MAGDALEN ST 76903 #048-12-1969 L1969 **GS VS** *020 †85
CORONADO, Elizabeth Neuga. 3501 KNICKERBOCKER RD 76904 #048-16-2001 L2006 **OBG** *020 †30
COUGHLIN, John Patrick. 120 E HARRIS AVE 76903 #016-43-1961 L1968 **PDS** *020 †95
CRAVY, William Danl. 3555 KNICKERBOCKER RD 76904 #048-02-1970 L1970 **OBG** *020 †30
CRENSHAW, Rebecca Sue. 3501 KNICKERBOCKER RD 76904 #048-02-1985 L1990 **N** *020
CROWLEY, John Dale. 1636 HUNTERS GLEN RD 76901 #048-04-1987 L1990 **CHP** *020 †75
DARBY, John Preston. 3555 KNICKERBOCKER RD 76904 #045-01-1954 L1964 **IMG IM** *071 †20
DAVIS, Mark Owen. 3501 KNICKERBOCKER RD 76904 #048-04-1981 L1981 **EM** *020 †16,18
DAY, Walter Gordy. 3001 S JACKSON ST 76904 #048-12-1982 L1983 **FM EM** *020 †18
DEE, James Michael. PO BOX 22000, 120 E BEAUREGARD 76902 #649-14-1976 L1983 **IM** *020 †20
DEFEE, Jason M. 210 E HARRIS AVE 76903 #048-14-1999 L2003 **ORS** *020
DEWAN, Stephen James. 120 E HARRIS AVE 76903 #048-04-1979 L1980 **TS PCS** *020 †85,90
DICKENS, Joel R. 3501 KNICKERBOCKER RD 76904 #048-15-1989 L1992 **OBG** *020 †55,30
DOBSON, Carl Leroy. 3501 KNICKERBOCKER RD 76904 #039-01-1975 L1986 **DR** *020 †80
DODSON, Dwain Freeman. 120 E HARRIS AVE 76903 #048-04-1955 L1955 **PD** *071 †55
DODSON, Jerry Wayne. 1636 HUNTERS GLEN RD 76901 #048-02-1971 L1971 **CHP P** *020 †75
DOWNING, Lloyd Londrosh. 2018 PULLIAM ST 76905 #030-05-1947 L1948 **P IMG** *071
DRIVER, M Coleman, Jr. 3005 GREEN MEADOW DR 76904 #004-01-1973 L1977 **OPH** *020 †35
DUARTE, Luis Eduardo. 102 N MAGDALEN ST 76903 #041-02-1987 L1997 **NS GS** *020 †25
DUNHAM, Gregory Mark. 225 E BEAUREGARD AVE 76903 #048-12-1983 L1983 **OBG** *020 †30 ‡
DURHAM, Dennis L. 3501 KNICKERBOCKER RD 76904 #048-02-1988 L1989 **IM** *020 †20
ECKHARDT, Gus Fuess. 120 E BEAUREGARD AVE 76903 #047-06-1938 L1941 **GS** *071 †85
EMERSON, Timothy Joe. ■ 76904 #048-02-1984 L1985 **GP** *075
EMMETT, Trent Ernest. 120 E HARRIS AVE 76903 #048-02-1979 L1979 **AN** *020 †05
ESCOBAR, Carlos Enrique. 2141 OFFICE PARK DR 76904 #429-01-1976 L1990 **P** *020
FELGER, Jason Edward. 133 W CONCHO AVE, STE 106 76903 #048-13-1994 L1995 **TS** *020 †85,90
FELGER, Mark Chas. 120 E HARRIS AVE 76903 #048-04-1989 L1991 **TS GS** *020 †85,90
FENTON, Ronnie Myron. 2645 VISTA DEL ARROYO DR 76904 #048-12-1970 L1970 **R** *020 †80
FISCHER, Duncan Kinnear. 3515 EXECUTIVE DR 76904 #008-01-1986 L1987 **NS** *020 †25
FISH, Kenton Henry. 4450 SUNSET DR 76901 #048-12-1977 L1977 **OPH** *020 †35
FLOOD, Riefford Gail. 120 E BEAUREGARD AVE 76903 #048-04-1971 L1971 **U** *020 †95
FLORES, Virgilio V. 120 E BEAUREGARD AVE 76903 #014-01-1977 L2000 **AN PME** *020 †05
FLYNN, Emmette T. 120 E BEAUREGARD AVE 76903 #048-15-1991 L1993 **GS** *020 †85
FORLANO, Viki Anna. 4450 SUNSET DR 76901 #048-15-1988 L1989 **FM** *020 †18
FOXCROFT, Paul Jeremy. 4450 SUNSET DR 76901 #836-02-1965 L1978 **ORS** *020
FRENCH, Johnny Boone. ■ 76904 #039-01-1966 L1971 **PUD IM** *071 †20
FRY, Lee Paul. 3605 EXECUTIVE DR 76904 #048-02-1964 L1964 **OTO AI** *020 †45
GIBSON, Patrick Ervin. 3605 EXECUTIVE DR 76904 #048-12-1980 L1980 **GS VS** *020 †85
GIDEON, Jerry K. 120 E HARRIS AVE 76903 #048-02-1988 L1989 **PTH** *020 †50
GILLIS, O Sterling. 3501 KNICKERBOCKER RD 76904 #027-01-1959 L1961 **OBG** *071 †30
GIPSON, Jonathan Scott. 120 E BEAUREGARD AVE, SHANNON CLINIC 76903 #027-01-1998 L2000 **AN IM** *020 †20,05
GOLDMAN, Matthew A. 4450 SUNSET DR 76901 #048-15-1997 L1998 **OPH** *020 †35
GOODPASTURE, John Edgar. 120 E BEAUREGARD AVE 76903 #048-02-1974 L1974 **AN** *020 †05
GRANAGHAN, J Thos. 2142 SUNSET DR 76904 #048-02-1977 L1977 **IM** *020 †20
GRANT, Robert Neil. 120 E BEAUREGARD AVE 76903 #036-07-1962 L1970 **GS CD** *020 †85
GROSS, Robert Hadley. 417 MONTECITO DR 76903 #048-02-1983 L1983 **CHP P** *020
HAJOVSKY, Deborah Best. 3555 KNICKERBOCKER RD, WEST TEXAS MEDICAL ASSOCIA 76904 #048-02-1990 L1991 **OBG** *020 †30 ‡
HAMBLEN, Robert Allen. 2018 PULLIAM ST 76905 #048-12-1965 L1965 **AN** *020 †05
HARDWICKE, Alan C. 2142 SUNSET DR 76904 #048-13-1987 L1988 **IM** *020 †20
HARVEY, David Bennett. 3501 KNICKERBOCKER RD 76904 #005-15-1967 L1996 **CD IM** *020 †20
HARVEY, John Chas. 120 E BEAUREGARD AVE, INTERNAL MEDICINE 76903 #055-01-1989 L2006 **IM** *020 †20
HARZKE, Charles D. 3555 KNICKERBOCKER RD 76904 #048-15-1991 L1992 **OBG** *020 †30
HASSAN, Ahmed Mohamed. 2142 SUNSET DR, CMA WEST 76904 #915-03-1989 L2005 **IM** *020 †20
HEARE, Bruce R. 3605 EXECUTIVE DR 76904 #048-02-1985 L1986 **GE** *020 †20
HEIMBECKER, Daniel A. 3555 KNICKERBOCKER RD 76904 #016-11-1980 L1981 **FM EM** *020 †16
HENDERSON, Henry Glen. 4450 SUNSET DR 76901 #021-01-1954 L1954 **ORS** *071 †40
HENKE, Clyde Alex. 3501 KNICKERBOCKER RD 76904 #048-02-1975 L1975 **OBG** *020 †30
HERBERT, David C. 5301 KNICKERBOCKER RD, STE 100 76904 #048-15-1975 L1976 **MDM GP** *030 †16
HERBERT, James Waldo. 314 E TWOHIG AVE 76903 #048-04-1972 L1972 **PD NPM** *020 †55
HERSHBERGER, Lloyd R. 823 W AVENUE N # D 76903 #018-03-1938 L1946 **PTH** *071 †50
HEWELL, Walter Robt. 2142 SUNSET DR 76904 #048-15-1977 L1977 **IM** *020 †20
HINSHAW, Roberta Kay. 120 E BEAUREGARD AVE 76903 #048-15-1989 L1990 **IM** *020 †20
HOFFMAN, Jeanne Therese. 3555 KNICKERBOCKER RD 76904 #012-05-1989 L2004 **AN** *020 †05
HOPKINS, Timothy Edward. 120 E BEAUREGARD AVE, P O BOX 22000 76903 #027-01-1998 L2003 **NS** *020 †25
HUCHTON, David Morgan. 4450 SUNSET DR 76901 #005-02-1993 L2001 **OTO HNS** *020 †45
HUGHES, Don Warren. 3605 EXECUTIVE DR 76904 #048-02-1970 L1971 **ORS OSM** *020 †40
HUGHSTON, Ty M. 120 E BEAUREGARD AVE 76903 #048-15-1987 L1988 **IM** *020 †20
HUNT, John Dominic. 2141 HAMILTON WAY, STE 110 76904 #008-02-1977 L1983 **ON HEM** *020 †20
IGLER, Eric J. 120 E BEAUREGARD AVE 76903 #048-13-1992 L1993 **AN** *020 †05
INGALA, Rose A. 424 S OAKES ST 76903 #019-02-1984 L1989 **CHP P** *020 †75
IVANS, David Lee. 3555 KNICKERBOCKER RD 76904 #005-14-1979 L1992 **CD IM** *020 †20
JACKSON, Shelton Ray. 2239 N BRYANT BLVD 76903 #027-01-1978 L1979 **EM FM** *020
JETER, Thomas Spradley. 303 W HARRIS AVE 76903 #048-13-1978 L1978 **FPS CS** *020
JOHNSTON, Kay Arbegast. 3123 GREEN MEADOW DR, BEL AMI DERMATOLOGY 76904 #030-05-1991 L1999 **D** *020 †15
JONES, Charles Michael. 3555 KNICKERBOCKER RD 76904 #048-02-1977 L1977 **IM IMG** *020 †20
JURADO, Jesse Lozada. 3501 EXECUTIVE DR 76904 #748-02-1971 L1984 **NEP IM** *020 †20
KAPPELMANN, Douglas James. 3605 EXECUTIVE DR 76904 #056-05-1978 L1983 **OPH** *020 †35
KASBERG, Samuel J. 3535 KNICKERBOCKER RD 76904 #048-15-1990 L1993 **EM** *020 †16
KESSLER, William F. 120 E HARRIS AVE 76903 #048-04-1991 L1992 **GS** *020 †85,90
KING, Wesley Llewellyn. 4208 COLLEGE HILLS BLVD, SHAMROCK CLINIC SOUTH 76904 #007-02-1969 L1997 **GP** *020 †18
KULIG, Martin Jos. 3501 KNICKERBOCKER RD 76904 #048-02-1978 L1978 **PTH** *020 †50
LASATER, Loren S. 3555 KNICKERBOCKER RD, SHANNON CLINIE 76904 #048-02-1986 L2006 **FM** *020 †18
LE GRAND, Robert H, Jr. 211 E COLLEGE AVE 76903 #036-05-1968 L1976 **NS** *020 †25
LEON, Miltiadis N. 3555 KNICKERBOCKER RD 76904 #418-03-1990 L1996 **IC IM** *075 †20
LEWIS, Don Michael. 320 W CONCHO AVE 76903 #048-12-1983 L1983 **PS** *020 †85,65
LIBELL, Sarah K. 244 N MAGDALEN ST 76903 #048-04-1998 L1999 **P** *020 †75
LIND, Gregory Chas. 120 E BEAUREGARD AVE 76903 #048-16-1984 L1985 **FM** *020
LINDEMANN, Timothy L. 3555 KNICKERBOCKER RD 76904 #048-15-2001 L2006 **OTO** *100
LOWE, Thomas Fulton. 8282 GRAPE CREEK RD 76901 #048-02-1966 L1966 **GS GP** *075 †85
LUI, Daniel Shun Hang. 4450 SUNSET DR 76901 #021-01-1994 L1999 **OPH** *020
MARSH, Charles Allen. 120 E HARRIS AVE 76903 #048-02-1971 L1971 **CD IM** *020 †20
MARSH, Denver Curtis, Jr. 102 N MAGDALEN ST 76903 #048-12-1969 L1969 **CD IM** *020 †20
MAYS, Raymond C. 3555 KNICKERBOCKER RD 76904 #048-02-1987 L1989 **P** *020 †75
MC CARTY, Robt Harris, Jr. 3808 SHERWOOD WAY, 3808 SHERWOOD 76901 #048-04-1960 L1964 **IM** *020 †20
MC CLELLAN, Kristi Anne. 107 N MAIN ST 76903 #048-04-1985 *074
MC CLELLAN, Ross Keith. 3555 KNICKERBOCKER RD 76904 #048-14-1984 L1985 **AN** *020 †05
MC CLOY, Steven Thane. 120 E BEAUREGARD AVE 76903 #048-12-1980 L1980 **IM** *020 †20
MC CRARY, John Hughes. 3555 KNICKERBOCKER RD 76904 #048-12-1964 L1964 **DR NM** *071 †80
MC FERREN, Glen Michael. 133 W CONCHO AVE, STE 101 76903 #048-04-1979 L1979 **P PYG** *020 †75

■ = Address Information Privacy Protected

MC IVER, Bradley D. 120 E BEAUREGARD AVE 76903 #048-13-1992 L1994 **U** *020 †95
MELOTT, James E. 3016 VISTA DEL ARROYO DR 76904 #048-15-1992 L1993 **FM** *020 †18
MENDOZA, Pascual. 619 W 29TH ST 76903 #649-04-1979 L1990 **FM OM** *020
MEYER, John Robt. 225 E BEAUREGARD AVE 76903 #048-12-1986 L1987 **OBG** *020 †30
MIMS, Joe A. 102 N MAGDALEN ST STE 270 76903 #034-01-1981 L1982 **CLP ATP** *020 †50
MONAGHAN, Orloff. 225 E BEAUREGARD AVE 76903 #047-06-1974 L1978 **GYN GO** *020 †30
MONTAGUE, Barbara. 3555 KNICKERBOCKER RD 76904 #010-01-1986 L2004 **FM** *020 †18
MONTOYA, Steve Frank, Jr. 136 E CONCHO AVE, WEST TEXAX NEPHROLOGY 76903 #048-12-1974 L1976 **NEP IM** *020
MOORE, Patrick Lynn. 1323 ALGERITA DR 76901 #048-15-1983 L1983 **AN** *020 †05
MORENO, Killeen Thea. 120 E BEAUREGARD AVE 76903 #048-02-1985 L1986 **FM** *020 †18
MORTON, Robert Arthur. 2142 SUNSET DR 76904 #019-02-1978 L1992 **IM IMG** *020 †20
MUELLER, Leslie Jeanne. 3501 KNICKERBOCKER RD 76904 #048-14-1986 L1987 **OBG** *020 †30
MUELLER, Michael Carl. 120 E HARRIS AVE 76903 #050-02-1987 L1995 **TS** *020 †85,90
MULL, James Randall. 120 E BEAUREGARD AVE 76903 #003-01-1989 L1992 **ORS** *020 †40
MURILLO ALFARO, Alekcey. ■ 76902 #270-03-1999 L2002 **FM** *100 †18
MURNANE, Thomas G, Jr. 120 E BEAUREGARD AVE 76903 #048-16-1992 L1993 **DR** *020 †80
MURPHY, Mark Hylton. 120 E HARRIS AVE, SHANNON MEDICAL CENTER 76903 #048-04-1984 L1986 **EM** *020 †16
NANCE, Stefanie Melissa. ■ 76904 #010-03-2003 L2005 **PD** *100
NEILL, James Elmer. 3555 KNICKERBOCKER RD 76904 #021-05-1977 L1983 **CD** *020 †20
NIEMANN, Bobby Brice. 2142 SUNSET DR 76904 #048-02-1975 L1975 **N IM** *020 †75
NILE, Brett Jason. 2141 HAMILTON WAY, STE 105 76904 #040-02-1999 L2001 **FM** *020 †18
NIXON, Peter Alexander. 319 W HARRIS AVE 76903 #001-02-2000 L2006 **OPH** *020 †35
NOACK, Tamara B. 3555 KNICKERBOCKER RD # WT 76904 #048-02-1988 L1989 **IM** *020 †20
NOELKE, Elisabeth L. 2029 W BEAUREGARD AVE 76901 #048-14-1990 L1991 **FM** *020 †18
NOVAK, Yvonne Biedermann. 225 E BEAUREGARD AVE 76903 #048-02-1987 L1988 **OBG** *020 †30
NUSSEY, Gary A. 3016 VISTA DEL ARROYO DR, SHANNON SENIOR HEALTH CENT 76904 #048-14-1983 L1983 **FM** *020 †18
OROPEZA, Ruben M. ■ 76901 #649-01-1955 L2008 **ON GS** *071
OSWALT, John Dawson. 120 E HARRIS AVE 76903 #048-02-1971 L1971 **TS** *020 †85,90
PARKER, James A. 120 E BEAUREGARD AVE 76903 #048-16-1992 L1993 **AN** *020 †05
PATYRAK, Michael Edward. ■ 76904 #048-13-2006 **DR** *012
PATYRAK, Robert S. 3019 GREEN MEADOW DR 76904 #021-01-1974 L1980 **PD** *020 †55
PHAM, Vivien Doan. ■ 76904 #011-03-2004 L2007 **PD** *100 †55
PHILLIPS, Gary P. 120 E BEAUREGARD AVE 76903 #048-02-1988 L1989 **FM** *020 †18
POWELL, Melissa Dianne. ■ 76901 #045-01-2000 L2003 **IM** *020 †20
PRESTON, Jackie L. PO BOX 22000, 120 E BEAUREGARD 76902 #048-12-1987 L1988 **IM HOS** *020 †20
RAHMAN, Fazlur. 3555 KNICKERBOCKER RD 76904 #704-03-1968 L1974 **ON HO** *020 †20
RALSTON, James P. 120 E BEAUREGARD AVE, SHANNON CLINIC 76903 #048-14-2001 L2008 **D** *020
RAMER, Yvonne. ANGELO STATE UNIV, UNIVERSITY CLINIC 76909 #020-02-1974 L1977 **FM** *075 †18
REID, Thomas Ross. 4450 SUNSET DR 76901 #048-02-1966 L1966 **ORS** *020 †40
RICE, Jack Sigmar, Jr. 3605 EXECUTIVE DR 76904 #008-01-1964 L1970 **U** *020 †95
RIDER, Jane C. 2141 HAMILTON WAY 76904 #048-02-1971 L1971 **PD** *020 †55
ROBINSON, Joe D. 3501 KNICKERBOCKER RD 76904 #048-13-1987 L1988 **AN** *020 †05
RODRIGUEZ, Raul G. 1636 HUNTERS GLEN RD 76901 #264-01-1968 L1983 **P** *074 †75
ROUNTREE, Randolph W. 3501 KNICKERBOCKER RD 76904 #048-13-1980 L1980 **OBG** *020 †18,30
ROWLAND, Robert Chas. ■ 76904 #048-12-1963 L1963 **OPH** *071 †35
RUSSWURM, Harvey Dale. 120 E HARRIS AVE 76903 #027-01-1973 L2003 **IM** *020 †20
RYAN, Vernon Loid, II. 303 W HARRIS AVE, STE 1 76903 #048-12-1965 L1965 **ORS** *020 †40
SABORIO, David Vicente. 2142 SUNSET DR 76904 #649-03-1988 L2004 **GS** *020 †85,90
SALAMA, Moustafa M I. 225 E BEAUREGARD AVE 76903 #915-04-1985 L1997 **OBG** *020 †30
SAWYER, Stephen Paul. 225 E BEAUREGARD AVE 76903 #007-02-1997 L2003 **PD** *020 †55
SCHULTZ, Robert Douglas. 225 E BEAUREGARD AVE 76903 #048-04-1977 L1977 **PD** *020 †55 ‡
SCHULZE, Jerry Holt. 4208 COLLEGE HILLS BLVD 76904 #048-04-1970 L1970 **FM** *020 †18
SCHULZE, Victor E, III. 120 E BEAUREGARD AVE 76903 #048-15-1982 L1983 **DR** *020 †80
SEGER, Mary Teresa. 120 E BEAUREGARD AVE 76903 #048-13-1979 L1979 **EM** *020 †16
SEIFERT, Saundra E. 120 E HARRIS AVE 76903 #048-14-1988 L1990 **PD** *020 †55
SEIFERT, Stephen Geo. 2 CITY HALL PLZ 76903 #048-14-1988 L1989 **EM** *020 †16
SELVARAJ, Senthilnathan. 2018 PULLIAM ST, VETERANS ADMIN CBOC 76905 #495-59-1981 L1998 **IM IMG** *020 †20 ‡
SHAFFER, Lauren Cary, II. ■ 76904 #005-14-1969 L1992 **EM OBS** *020 †18,16
SHELL, Eddie G, II. 3501 KNICKERBOCKER RD 76904 #048-13-1997 L2000 **RNR** *020 †80
SHERROD, Gene Allen. 102 N MAGDALEN ST 76903 #048-02-1966 L1966 **CD** *020 †20
SICKELS, Michael Glen. PO BOX 22000, 120 E BEAUREGARD 76902 #018-03-1991 L2000 **DR** *020 †20,80
SIKES, James Clarence. ■ 76904 #012-01-1971 L1993 **P** *020 †75
SMITH, Stephen H. 2531 LOOP 306 76904 #048-02-1990 L1991 **IM** *020 †20
SNUGGS, John H. 3115 LOOP 306, STE 100A 76904 #048-16-1994 L1995 **P** *020 †75
SNUGGS, Michelle Grogan. ■ 76904 #048-16-1995 L1996 **DR** *020 †80
SNYDER, Edward Henry. 3501 KNICKERBOCKER RD 76904 #048-12-1972 L1977 **DR** *020 †80
SNYDER, Jerome Worth. ■ 76904 #045-01-1970 L1979 **P** *075
SOORI, Nilanthi. ■ 76904 #422-01-2000 L2001 **FM** *020 †18
STANLEY, Stephen M. 120 E HARRIS AVE 76903 #048-02-1988 L1992 **PTH** *020 †50
STANLEY, Vayden Foy. 120 E HARRIS AVE 76903 #048-12-1963 L1963 **AN PME** *020 †05
STOEBNER, Richard Coleman. 120 E BEAUREGARD AVE 76903 #048-02-1966 L1966 **GE** *071
STOKES, Eugene Wm. 4450 SUNSET DR 76901 #048-15-1980 L1980 **GE** *020 †20
STRAYER, Michael Patrick. 3501 KNICKERBOCKER RD, EMERGENCY DEPARTMENT 76904 #038-40-2003 L2007 **EM** *020
STUART, Derrill A, Jr. 120 E BEAUREGARD AVE 76903 #001-06-1984 L2004 **GPM** *020 †18,70
STUDT, James Leonard. 102 N MAGDALEN ST STE 120 76903 #048-12-1983 L1983 **RO** *020 †80
SUTLIFF, Lourell Eugene. 225 E BEAUREGARD AVE 76903 #047-06-1974 L1982 **OBG** *020 †30
SYKES, Edwin M, Jr. ■ 76903 #048-02-1941 L1941 **GS** *071 †85
TAYLOR, Jason Grant. 120 E BEAUREGARD AVE, SHANNON CLINIC 76903 #048-16-1996 L1997 **RHU** *020 †20 ‡
THOENE, James John, Jr. PO BOX 22000, 120 E BEAUREGARD 76902 #038-41-1990 L1995 **AN** *020 †05
THOMAS, Bobbie Gene. 3555 KNICKERBOCKER RD 76904 #048-02-1973 L1973 **AN** *020 †05
THOMPSON, Ronald Edward. 120 E HARRIS AVE 76903 #038-40-1974 L1975 **EM** *020 †16
THORPE, Richard Young. 3535 KNICKERBOCKER RD 76904 #048-15-1984 L1985 **EM** *020
THURMAN, Benjamin Hill. 610 S ABE ST STE A 76903 #048-12-1979 L1979 **AN** *020 †05
TRAN, Mark. 120 E HARRIS AVE, SHANNON CLINIC MED CTR 76903 #011-02-2000 L2003 **AN** *020 †05
UNTALAN, Raymund. 3555 KNICKERBOCKER RD 76904 #748-11-1990 L1998 **IM GP** *020 †20
VANDERZANT, Chris Wm. 120 E BEAUREGARD AVE 76903 #048-78-1979, ▲ L1979 **N** *072 †75
VENKATESAN, Kalpathy V. 120 E BEAUREGARD AVE, SHANNON CLINCI 76903 #495-53-1975 L1982 **ON HEM** *020 †20
WADE, Carlos. ■ 76904 #649-38-2001 L2006 **IM** *020 †20
WAGNER, Noel D. 120 E HARRIS AVE, EMERGENCY DEPT. 76903 #048-02-1995 L1998 **EM** *020 †16
WALTHER, Steven Milton. 3501 KNICKERBOCKER RD 76904 #048-12-1978 L1978 **DR** *020 †80
WALVOORD, Keith David. 3605 EXECUTIVE DR 76904 #048-12-1982 L1983 **OTO** *020 †45
WEATHERBY, Theron Karman. 3605 EXECUTIVE DR 76904 #048-12-1966 L1966 **GS VS** *020 †85
WEHNER, Karl K. 225 E BEAUREGARD AVE 76903 #048-04-1979 L1979 **PD** *020 †55
WHITE, James Royal. ■ 76904 #041-14-1994 L2006 **FM** *020 †18
WHITEHEAD, William F, III. ■ 76901 #048-04-1999 L2005 **VS** *020 †85
WILKINSON, Joe Brent. 3605 EXECUTIVE DR 76904 #048-02-1977 L1977 **ORS HS** *020 †40
WILLIAMS, Harvey M, Jr. 3555 KNICKERBOCKER RD, WEST TEXAS MEDICAL ASSOCIA 76904 #048-02-1962 L1962 **D** *071 †15
WILLIAMS, Oliver Alfred. 3535 KNICKERBOCKER RD 76904 #021-05-1967 L1971 **EM** *072 †16
WILLIAMSON, Leslie Kay. 4450 SUNSET DR 76901 #048-04-1975 L1975 **OTO FPS** *020 †45
WILSON, Daniel Morgan. 120 E BEAUREGARD AVE 76903 #048-02-1981 L1981 **OPH** *020 †35
WILSON, Kelly W. 225 E BEAUREGARD AVE, SHANNON CLINIC 76903 #048-15-1990 L1991 **OBG** *020 †30
WILSON, Roy Edward. ■ 76903 #048-02-1952 L1952 **P** *071
WIMPEE, Marc Warner. 2531 LOOP 306 76904 #048-15-1983 L1983 **ORS** *071
WOMACK, James Clifford. 2102 PECOS ST STE 7 76901 #048-02-1959 L1959 **FM GP** *020
WOMACK, William Thos. 319 W HARRIS AVE 76903 #048-02-1954 L1954 **OPH** *071 †35
WOODS, Henry Allen, Jr. 3520 KNICKERBOCKER RD, # 129 76904 #023-12-2003 L2004 **DR** *012
YOST, James Wm. 2142 SUNSET DR, COMMUNITY MEDICAL ASSOCIAT 76904 #019-02-1974 L1979 **RHU IM** *020 †20
YOUNG, Elizabeth Lee. 225 E BEAUREGARD AVE 76903 #048-13-1994 L1995 **PD** *020 †55
ZUBAK, Joseph John. 4450 SUNSET DR 76901 #010-02-1994 L2001 **ORS** *020 †40

SAN ANTONIO – BEXAR

AARONS, Z Alexander. ■ 78209 #016-42-1945 L1946 **PYA P** *020
ABADIE, Wesley Matthew. ■ 78230 #047-05-2003 L2004 **OTO** *012
ABBATE, Steven Michael. 8038 WURZBACH RD, STE 210 78229 #026-08-1996 L2005 **GS** *020 †85
ABBOTT, Julie Beth. 255 E SONTERRA BLVD, STE 100 78258 #048-12-1987 L1999 **IM** *020 †20
ABBOTT, Oscar Douglas. 301 N FRIO ST 78207 #048-02-1973 L1973 **PTH** *071 †50
ABBOUD, Hanna E. 7703 FLOYD CURL DR, U TX HSC DEPT NEPH 78229 #915-03-1971 L1992 **NEP IM** *050 †20
ABBOUD, Nadia Hannah. ■ 78249 #048-13-2008 *012
ABBOUD, Sherry Werner. 4502 MEDICAL DR 78229 #023-01-1976 L1999 **PTH** *020 †50
ABDEL-KARIM, Isam Ali. ■ 78249 #575-01-1998 L2007 **HO** *012
ABELLO, Fortunato Banzon. 3015 SAN PEDRO AVE, STE 102 78212 #748-02-1968 L1984 **PM** *020 †60
ABOU-ZAHR, Fadi. ■ 78258 #396-21-1996 L2000 **NEP** *020 †20
ABRAHAM-COX, Gloria B. 311 CAMDEN ST STE 412 78215 #748-01-1964 L1974 **PD** *020
ABRAMS, David Barry. 14807 SAN PEDRO AVE 78232 #041-02-1987 L2006 **OPH** *020 †35
ABRAMS, Jerri L. 7007 BANDERA RD, STE 19 78238 #048-13-1991 L1992 **PD** *020 †55
ABRAMS, Salvador James. 2827 PALO ALTO RD STE 105, SOUTHWEST MED CLINIC 78211 #649-01-1977 L2001 **EM FM** *020 †18,16
ABREGO, Olivia Ann. 343 W HOUSTON ST, STE 601 78205 #048-12-1984 L1985 **PYG** *072
ABREGO, Victor Allan. 7460 N IH 35 78218 #048-12-1984 L1985 **PTH** *020
ABUABARA, Fuad. 700 S ZARZAMORA ST, STE LL3 78207 #264-01-1962 L1985 **IM** *020 †20
ABUABARA, Sabas Fatule. 730 N MAIN AVE STE 704 78205 #264-01-1970 L1982 **GS GE** *020 †85
ABUEME, Jeremias M. 5282 MEDICAL DR, STE 130 78229 #748-08-1983 L1995 **IM** *020 †20
ABUSOGLU, Canan. 7703 FLOYD CURL DEPT SURG 78229 #902-03-1989 **GS** *100
ACEVEDO, Julio Eduardo. ■ 78230 #264-01-1957 L1968 **CLP AM** *071 †50
ACHARYA, Vinita Jayant. 7703 FLOYD CURL DR #MC7883, UNIV OF TEXAS HEALTH SCIEN 78229 #495-17-1986 L2004 **N** *012
ACHINGER, Steven Gerard. 4502 MEDICAL DR, UNIVERSITY HOSPITAL 78229 #011-02-2000 L2002 **NEP** *020 †20
ACKLEY, Christopher D. 8026 FLOYD CURL DR, SOUTH TEXAS PATHOLOGY 78229 #001-06-1995 L2000 **PTH PCP** *020 †50
ACKLEY, Jacqueline H. 301 N FRIO ST 78207 #034-01-1978 L1985 **PTH HMP** *020 †50
ACOSTA, Luis Jose. 7703 FLOYD CURL DR # 7878, UTHSCSA DEPT OF MEDICARE 78229 #048-13-2001 L2005 **GE** *012
ACOSTA, Ometeotl M. 7703 FLOYD CURL DR, DEPT OBG 78229 #048-13-2007 **OBG** *012
ACOSTA, Peter P. 7703 FLOYD CURL DR 78229 #649-14-1978 L1988 **FM** *020 †18
ADAME, Noemi Edith. 7703 FLOYD CURL DR, DEPT OF PEDIATRICS,DIV. CR 78229 #048-02-2002 L2005 **PD** *020 †55
ADAMS, Donald Fayron. 7810 LOUIS PASTEUR DR, STE 100 78229 #048-13-1981 L1981 **OPH** *020 †35
ADAMS, Fawn Sun. ■ 78251 #021-01-2002 L2004 **GS** *012
ADAMS, Nourdjihe. ■ 78248 #895-01-1996 L2007 **IM** *020 †20
ADAMS, Sandra G. 7703 FLOYD CURL DR, PULMUNARY DISEASE MSC 7885 78229 #048-13-1994 L1995 **PCC** *020 †20
ADAMS, Thomas Allan, Jr. ■ 78258 #023-12-2006 L2007 **PTH** *012
ADAMSON, Van Wesley. ■ 78245 #038-06-2005 L2007 **IM** *012
ADCOX, Brent M. ■ 78240 #048-14-2003 **ORS** *012
ADDINGTON, Shari L. 301 N FRIO ST 78207 #048-14-1989 L1991 **PTH** *062 †50
ADDIS, Hunter Marsden, Jr. 4411 MEDICAL DR, STE 300 78229 #041-14-1991 L2002 **CD** *020 †20
ADDIS, Kimberly Ann. 4400 PIEDRAS DR S, STE 200 78228 #041-14-1999 L2005 **DR** *100 †80

ADEDEJI, Adekunle Adedayo. 7703 FLOYD CURL DR 78229 #690-01-1997 **FP** *012
ADELMAN, Jack A. ■ 78209 #038-40-1940 L1943 **IM CD** *071
ADELMAN, Samuel. 8534 VILLAGE DR STE C 78217 #005-14-1974 L1975 **D PD** *020 †55,15
ADEN, Joy T. 4212 E SOUTHCROSS BLVD 78222 #048-13-2000 L2004 **OBG** *020 †30
ADETONA, Olutola Olugbeng. 7703 FLOYD CURL DR 78229 #690-01-1995 **PD** *012
ADRIAN, Ann Blythe. ■ 78210 #048-13-2000 L2000 **FM** *020
AERTS, Melissa Anne. 5414 FREDERICKSBURG RD, STE 200 78229 #048-13-1991 L1993 **OBG** *020 †30
AGARWAL, Animesh. 4647 MEDICAL DR 78229 #048-13-1992 L1993 **OTR** *020 †40
AGHA, Irfan Ali. 7142 SAN PEDRO, STE 120 78216 #704-22-1991 L2005 **NEP** *020 †20
AGRAWAL, Remedios C. 5414 FREDERICKSBRG RD #100 78229 #748-10-1969 L1975 **NPM** *020 †55
AGUADO, Alma Ludivina. 600 DIVISION AVE, STE G 78214 #649-02-1986 L1998 **IM** *020 †20
AGUILAR, Jaime Estrada. 4499 MEDICAL DR, STE 340 78229 #649-07-1973 L1982 **PHO HEM** *050 †55
AGUILAR, Jesus Javier. 2911 S NEW BRAUNFELS AVE 78210 #649-45-1993 L2005 **IM** *020 †20
AGUILAR, Leticia B. 302 W RECTOR ST, UNIV FAMILY HEALTH CTR NOR 78216 #048-13-1989 L1991 **FM** *020 †18
AGUILAR, Nick S. 10515 STATE HIGHWAY 151, STE 250 78251 #048-13-1995 L1998 **FM** *020 †18
AGUILAR, Ricardo C, Jr. 3066 E COMMERCE ST 78220 #048-02-1998 L1999 **FM** *020 †18
AGUIRRE, Felix. 3453 IH 35 N, STE 207B 78219 #048-13-1991 L1993 **FM** *020
AGUIRRE, Fernando. 9969 FREDERICKSBURG RD 78240 #048-13-1994 L1995 **IM** *020 †20
AGUIRRE, Gilberto. 7400 MERTON MNTR ST #112-E, AUDIE L MURPHY VET HOSP 78229 #048-02-1972 L1972 **OPH** *040 †35
AGUIRRE, Maria D. 1927 CERALVO ST 78237 #041-01-1981 L1982 **PD** *020 †55
AHMAD, Mohammad Mitwalli. 7703 FLOYD CURL # 7836, UTHSCSA DEPT OF OB/GYN 78229 #915-03-1954 L1974 **OBG PHP** *040
AHMAD SALMAN, Umber A. 4647 MEDICAL DR 78229 #704-18-1989 L1998 **DR** *012 †28
AHSAN, Syed Kamran. 7703 FLOYD CURL DR 78229 #704-02-1998 **FP** *012
AHUJA, Seema Singh. 7703 FLOYD CURL DR, AMVAH/DEPARTMENT OF MEDICI 78229 #495-73-1985 L1998 **IM** *020 †20
AHUJA, Sunil Kumar. 7703 FLOYD CURL DR 78229 #495-73-1984 L1997 **ID** *020 †20
AKHRASS, Firas. 5107 MEDICAL DR 78229 #875-02-1993 L2006 **END IM** *020 †20
AKINYI-JOSEPH, Grace M. ■ 78269 #048-13-2008 *012
AKONYE, Angela C. ■ 78249 #048-13-2002 L2006 **OBG** *020
AKRAM, Muhammad. ■ 78240 #704-21-1997 **FP** *012
AKRIGHT, Bruce Donald. 502 MADISON OAK DR, STE 240 78258 #028-02-1980 L1981 **OBG** *020 †30
AKRIGHT, Laura Elizabeth. 8715 VILLAGE DR STE 508 78217 #028-02-1980 L1981 **END** *020 †20
AL-ABDELY, Hail Mater. ■ 78240 #797-01-1990 L1999 **ID** *100
ALBANESE, Helen Garshanin. 4502 MEDICAL DR 78229 #035-01-1967 L1971 **P IM** *020 †75
ALBANESE, Richard Alan. ■ 78217 #035-01-1967 L1981 **OS** *050
ALBERTI, Gustave Nose. ■ 78251 #024-07-2006 L2007 **OPH** *012
ALBRECHT, Michael C. 3851 ROGER BROOKE DR # 36, BROOKE ARMY MEDICAL CENTER 78234 #011-02-1997 L1998 **GS** *020 †85
ALBRITTON, La Mar J. 7922 EWING HALSELL DR #430 78229 #004-01-1981 L1986 **OBG** *020 †30
ALDAPE, Anyssa M. ■ 78229 #048-13-2008 *012
ALDER, Lawrence A. 19260 STONE OAK PKWY, STE 105 78258 #048-12-1995 L1999 **HO** *020 †20
ALDERSON, Gerald Lee. 22554 SCENIC LOOP RD, SAN ANTONIO 78255 #005-12-1967 L1976 **PTH** *030 †50
ALDRIDGE, Milissa S. 4400 PIEDRAS DR S # 200, RADIOLOGY ASSOC OF SAN ANT 78228 #048-02-1995 L1996 **PDR** *020 †80
ALECOZAY, Abraham Anwar. 7430 BARLITE BLVD, STE 105 78224 #048-15-1991 L1992 **OBG** *020 †30
ALEMAN, Marta L. ■ 78251 #048-02-2000 L2002 **FM** *020 †18 ‡
ALEXANDER, Deborah W. 1100 N MAIN AVE 78212 #038-41-1981 L1987 **OPH** *020 †35
ALEXANDER, James Dales. 7703 FLOYD CURL DR 78229 #018-03-1987 L1999 **FM** *030 †18
ALFORD, Stephanie H. 7703 FLOYD CURL DR MC7774 78229 #048-13-2002 L2008 **ORS** *012
AL-HAZMI, Al-Bader Mohd. ■ 78229 #797-02-1991 **DR** *100
ALI, Noor. 1055 ADA ST 78223 #704-17-1980 L1995 **IM** *020 †20
ALI, Rafeeq Adnan. ■ 78229 #797-02-1999 L2008 **END** *012 †20
ALINGOD-APOSTOL, Alma A. 730 N MAIN AVE STE 221 78205 #748-01-1961 L1976 **P** *020
ALLAWALA, Yousuf Jan. 4242 MEDICAL DR, STE 6300 78229 #704-02-1982 L1996 **P FM** *020
ALLEN, Everett H. 4319 MEDICAL DR, STE 210A 78229 #048-13-1996 L2001 **RHU** *020 †20
ALLEN, Kathryn Ruth. ■ 78260 #048-13-2008 *012
ALLEN, Stacey L. 7979 WURZBACH RD 78229 #048-13-1993 L1995 **AN** *020 †05
ALLENBRAND, Brian Todd. ■ 78245 #028-03-2003 L2003 **END** *012 †20
ALLENDE, Hector Domingo. 111 DALLAS ST 78205 #132-02-1974 L1983 **GE IM** *020 †20
ALLIBHAI, Taslim Firoz. ■ 78256 #035-20-2003 L2005 **PD** *100 †55
ALLRED-CROUCH, Andrea L. 8401 DATAPOINT DR STE 6000 78229 #048-13-1984 L1985 **DR** *020 †80
ALLSUP, Karen E. 315 N SAN SABA, STE 1068 78207 #048-13-2002 L2006 **OBG** *020
ALLTON, David Richard. ■ 78245 #025-12-2003 L2004 **ID** *012 †20
ALMAGUER, Enrique Cecilio. 88 BRIGGS ST, STE 220 78224 #048-12-1975 L1975 **PS HS** *020 †65
ALMONTE, Jennifer Melissa. ■ 78249 #048-13-2004 **OBG** *012
ALPERS, Joshua Peter. ■ 78254 #028-03-2004 L2006 **N** *012
ALSABROOK, Grady Dee. 8715 VILLAGE DR, STE 518 78217 #048-13-2001 L2007 **VS** *020 †85
AL-SHAHROURI, Hania Ziad. 7703 FLOYD CURL DR, UTHSCSA-MED-NEPHROLOGY 78229 #575-01-1998 L2007 **NEP** *100 †20
ALSHALCHI, Najah Muhamad. PO BOX 692047, 7712 ECKHERT RD 78269 #528-01-1974 L1982 **IM IG** *020 ‡
ALSIP, Bryan James. 332 W COMMERCE ST, STE 307 78205 #010-02-1994 L2005 **PHP GPM** *030 †70
ALTMAN, David Joseph. 14607 SAN PEDRO, STE 220 78232 #008-02-1996 L2002 **CN** *020 †75
ALUKAL, John Kunjipaulo. 215 N SAN SABA STE 106 78207 #495-44-1980 L1985 **IM** *020
ALVARADO, Hilario, III. 1111 SE MILITARY DR 78214 #048-04-2001 L2003 **FM** *020 †18
ALVARADO, Ricardo Antonio. ■ 78240 #048-13-2005 **GS** *012
ALVARADO, Sergio J. 8042 WURZBACH RD, STE 525 78229 #048-13-2000 L2003 **APM** *100 †05
ALVAREZ, Jorge A. 9439 MAVERICK PASS 78240 #048-13-2000 L2002 **IC** *020 †20
ALVAREZ, Rudy. ■ 78229 #048-13-2008 *012
ALVAREZ ESLAVA, Andrea. 7703 FLOYD CURL DR 78229 #264-16-2002 **IMG** *012 †20
ALVAREZ-MERAZ, Carlos E. 7940 FLOYD CURL DR, STE 600 78229 #649-02-1990 L2001 **IM** *020
ALVIAR, Hector. ■ 78213 #264-04-1967 L1974 **AN** *020
ALVIS, Milton Edwin, Jr. 2833 BABCOCK RD STE 445 78229 #048-13-1980 L1980 **CD IM** *020 †20
AMAYA, Iliana. 11823 MILL ROCK RD 78230 #048-14-2000 L2003 **IMG** *100
AMAYA CHINCHILLA, Hector. 7703 FLOYD CURL DR, DEPT MED 78229 #341-03-2002 **IM** *012
AMEDURI, Ardow R, Jr. 7979 WURZBACH RD, STE 353 78229 #035-09-1968 L1974 **RO P** *020 †80
AMRUNG, Suchakorn Achava. 6711 S NEW BRAUNFELS AVE, SAN ANTONIO STATE HOSPITAL 78223 #891-02-1969 L1981 **CHP P** *020 †75
ANDERSEN, Garrett Karl. 8401 DATAPOINT DR, STE 600 78229 #048-12-1997 L1998 **DR** *020 †80
ANDERSON, Annette Nicole. 7703 FLOYD CURL DR, DEPT PSYCH 78229 #004-01-2004 **P** *012
ANDERSON, Cody N. ■ 78249 #048-14-2003 **ORS** *012
ANDERSON, David Earl. 7703 FLOYD CURL DR, DEPT OF PYSCH 78229 #004-01-2004 L2008 **P** *012
ANDERSON, Edward L. 3201 S GEVERS ST 78210 #048-12-1958 L1958 **FM GS** *071
ANDERSON, Edwin M. ■ 78213 #021-01-1967 L1977 **DR** *075 †80
ANDERSON, Franklin Lee. 7703 FLOYD CURL DR, MC 7838 78229 #048-14-1984 L1985 **AN EM** *020 †05
ANDERSON, Jamie N. 7703 FLOYD CURL DR, MED SCH SAN ANTONIO 78229 #048-13-2007 **IM** *012
ANDERSON, Kyle P. 7703 FLOYD CURL DR, U TX MED SCH 78229 #048-13-2007 **GS** *012
ANDERSON, Nathan S. ■ 78253 #023-12-2007 **IM** *012
ANDERST, James David. 7703 FLOYD CURL DR, MAIL CODE 7829 78229 #056-06-2000 L2004 **PD** *020 †55
ANDRADE, Jose Rene. ■ 78213 #649-04-1992 L1998 **PG** *100
ANDRE, Christine A. 7703 FLOYD CURL DR, MEDICINE OEP 78229 #048-13-2000 L2003 **IM** *020 †20
ANDREWS, Charles Porter. 4410 MEDICAL DR, STE 440 78229 #048-12-1975 L1975 **PUD IM** *020 †20
ANDRY, James M. 2727 BABCOCK RD, STE A 78229 #048-13-1982 L1983 **CCM PUD** *020 †20
ANES, John Crest. 1303 MCCULLOUGH AVE 78212 #008-01-1973 L1978 **IM** *020 †20
ANGEL, Luis Fernando. 7703 FLOYD CURL DR, STE 7841 78229 #264-13-1992 L1998 **PCC** *020 †20
ANGRITT, Peter. ■ 78218 #264-01-1965 L1973 **PTH** *071 †50
ANGUEIRA, Wanda D. 7940 FLOYD CURL DR STE 215 78229 #042-03-1982 L1991 **FM** *020 †18
ANGUIANO, Aaron A. 1715 MCCULLOUGH AVE 78212 #048-16-1994 L2001 **FM** *020 †18
ANGULO PERNETT, Freddy. ■ 78240 #264-12-1990 L2007 **IM** *100 †20
ANSON, Byron Harris, III. 45 NE LOOP 410, STE 900 78216 #048-13-2003 L2007 **AN** *020
ANSON, Michelle G. 3619 PAESANOS PKWY STE 206, AESTHETICS PA 78231 #048-13-2001 L2004 **FM** *020 †18
ANSTEAD, Gregory Michael. 7703 FLOYD CURL DR, MEDICINE ID UTHSC-SA 78229 #016-11-1993 L2000 **ID PD** *020 †20
ANZUETO, Antonio Ramirez. 7400 MERTON MINTER ST, 111E 78229 #429-01-1979 L1991 **PUD CCM** *020 †20
APOSTOL, Emilio Baniqued. 730 N MAIN STE 221 78205 #748-01-1962 L1976 **FM PTH** *020 †50
APPEL, David Alan. ■ 78249 #005-12-2004 L2006 **CD** *012 †20
APPELT, Eric A. ■ 78254 #048-02-1999 L2001 **DR** *012
APPIAH-DWAMENA, Lydia. 102 PALO ALTO RD, STE 230 78211 #412-02-1992 L2004 **OBG** *020 †30
APPLEBY, Jane L. 7703 FLOYD CURL DR 78229 #048-13-1987 L1989 **IM** *020 †20
ARAMBULA, Michael R. 14800 N US HIGHWAY 281, STE 110 78232 #048-13-1987 L1988 **PFP P** *020 †75
ARAMBURU, Socrates B. 927 MCCULLOUGH 78215 #308-01-1963 L1971 **CD** *020 †20
ARANIBAR, Roberto Jose. 18626 HARDY OAK BLVD, STE 240 78258 #737-06-1973 L1980 **NS** *020 †25
ARAR, Mazen Y. 7703 FLOYD CURL DR, MSC 7813 78229 #575-01-1980 L1993 **PD PN** *020 †55
ARBONA, Jose. 540 OAK CENTRE DR, STE 100 78258 #042-02-1982 L1984 **R NP** *020 †80
ARCHER, Cullen John. 2121 SW 36TH ST 78237 #048-13-1999 L2003 **OBG** *020 †30
ARCHER, Sandra V. 4499 MEDICAL DR, STE 119 78229 #056-06-1997 L2001 **OBG** *020 †30
ARCHER, Thomas L. 7703 FLOYD CURL DR, MC 7838 78229 #005-18-1975 L2005 **AN** *020 †05
ARENAS, Javier Lorenzo. ■ 78240 #048-02-2002 L2004 **U** *012
AREVALO, Theodore V. 7703 FLOYD CURL DR, DEPARTMENT OF MEDICINE 78229 #048-04-1992 L1993 **IM AM** *020 †20
ARGUMEDO, Steven. ■ 78228 #048-13-2006 **IM** *012
ARHELGER, Roger Boyd. 750 E MULBERRY AVE, STE 325 78212 #026-04-1958 L1966 **ATP PCP** *071 †50
ARISCO, Amy M. ■ 78229 #048-14-2000 L2006 **U** *012
ARISHITA, Gary I. 21 SPURS LN STE 120 78240 #023-12-1987 L2008 **PS** *020 †85,65
ARIZPE, Nicholas Morgan. ■ 78252 #048-12-2007 **GS** *012
ARKANGEL, Carmelito, Jr. 4502 MEDICAL DR 78229 #033-06-1977 L1979 **EM** *020 †16
ARKHIPOV, Alexei. ■ 78259 #913-01-1982 L2008 **HO** *100
ARMSTRONG, Anna C. ■ 78213 #048-13-1985 L1987 **AN** *020
ARMSTRONG, Felicia A. 7703 FLOYD CURL DR, U TX MED SCH SAN ANTONIO 78229 #048-13-2006 **IM** *012
ARMSTRONG, James Robt. 516 LEXINGTON AVE 78215 #048-04-1963 L1963 **GS** *020 †85
ARMSTRONG, Jeffrey Alan. 4242 MEDICAL DR, STE 3100 78229 #019-02-1979 L1988 **AN** *020 †05
ARMSTRONG, Lee Marshall. 7 SABLE CLF 78258 #048-14-1985 L1986 **PD** *020 †55
ARMSTRONG, Raymond Gordon. 4330 MEDICAL DR, STE 325 78229 #026-04-1958 L1969 **TS** *071 †85,90
ARNO, Mary Hannah H. 224 W EVERGREEN ST 78212 #048-13-1974 L1974 **OS** *020 †35
ARNOLD, Charles Sylvin. 519 W HOUSTON ST 78207 #048-02-1966 L1966 **P** *020 †75
ARNOLD, Christopher W. 7622 LOUIS PASTEUR 78229 #048-14-2001 L2002 **FM** *020
ARNOLD, Hays Lavashious. 3851 ROGER BROOKE DR # 36, BROOKE ARMY MEDICAL CENTER 78234 #011-04-1999 L2001 **GE** *020 †20 ‡
ARNOLD, Joan. 19238 STONEHUE 78258 #048-13-1991 L1994 **PD** *020 †55
ARORA, Mayank. 7703 FLOYD CURL DR 78229 #495-45-2005 **IM** *012
ARORA, Umesh Kumar. ■ 78258 #495-36-1992 L2004 **CD** *020 †20
ARREDONDO, Cordelia L. 7703 FLOYD CURL DR, STE 610L 78229 #048-14-1997 L1998 **FM** *020 †18
ARREDONDO, Eradio Landa. 730 N MAIN AVE, STE 110 78205 #649-02-1962 L1971 **ORS** *020 †40

■ = Address Information Privacy Protected

ARREDONDO, Francisco. 19296 OLD STONE PKWY 78258 #649-52-1990 L1995 **OBG** *020 †30
ARREDONDO CERDA, Leticia. 1202 W BITTERS RD, BLDG 4 78216 #649-02-1986 L1996 **FM** *020 †18
ARRIOLA, Homero. 3700 FREDERICKSBURG RD, STE 233 78201 #048-04-1978 L1979 **IM** *020 †20
ARROYO-OTERO, Carmen N. 4330 MEDICAL DR, STE 275 78229 #042-01-1981 L1987 **PD** *072 †55
ARTHAUD, John Bradley. ■ 78258 #028-03-1965 L1972 **PTH** *071 †50
ARTIS, Danielle Lynette. ■ 78251 #048-02-2003 L2006 **PD** *100
ARVAY, Cynthia Anne. 4242 MEDICAL DR, STE 3100 78229 #041-15-2000 L2006 **AN** *020 †05
ARZOLA, Jennifer Marie. 78230 #048-13-2003 L2007 **OBG** *020
ASAR, Firdous Hasanali. ■ 78245 #704-16-1986 **FP** *012
ASHOK KUMAR, Kaparaboyna. 7703 FLOYD CURL DR, DPT FAMILY MEDICINE MC7794 78229 #495-21-1979 L1999 **FM GS** *020 †18
ASTILLA, Thaddeus. 45 NE LOOP 410, STE 900 78216 #048-13-1990 L1991 **AN** *020 †05
ATHALE, Sanjeev D. ■ 78250 #495-20-1981 L2004 **RNR** *020
ATHREYA, Bakthavathsalam. 215 E QUINCY ST, STE 430 78215 #495-61-1972 L1983 **CD IM** *020 †20
ATIEE, George J. 2108 NW MILITARY HWY, CASTLE HILLS FAMILY PRACTI 78213 #048-13-1985 L1986 **FM** *050 †18
ATILES, Gloria M. 5788 ECKHERT RD, FRANK TEJEDA VA OUTPATIENT 78240 #042-01-1989 L1992 **FM** *018 †18
ATKINS, Donald P. 18626 HARDY OAK BLVD, STE 200 78258 #010-02-1993 L2000 **NS** *020 †25
ATKINS, Jane Troendle. 7922 EWING HALSELL DR, STE 270 78229 #021-05-1987 L1993 **PD** *020 †55
ATLAS, William A. 255 E SONTERRA BLVD, STE 100 78258 #048-13-1989 L1991 **IM** *020 †20
ATLURI, Hema. 7703 FLOYD CURL DR, UNIV TX MED SCH-SAN ANTONI 78229 #495-58-2001 L2007 **IM** *100 †20
ATTIA, Ahmed S. 7940 FLOYD CURL DR, STE 1030 78229 #915-02-1987 L1995 **AN** *020 †05
AUBER, Andrew Eric. 4400 S PIEDRAS DR, STE 200 78228 #010-02-1985 L2000 **RNR** *020 †80
AUNG, Ko Ko. 7703 FLOYD CURL DR, MC 7879 78229 #209-01-1990 L1998 **IM PHP** *020 †20
AURICHT, Bernadette M. 5788 ECKHERT RD, STXVA FRANK TEJEDA VA OPC 78240 #409-20-1983 L1999 **FM** *020 †18
AUST, J Bradley. 7703 FLOYD CURL DR, UT HEALTH SCIENCES CENTER 78229 #035-06-1949 L1966 **GS SO** *040 †90,85
AUSTAD, Gregory Thomas. ■ 78254 #038-41-2003 L2005 **RHU** *012 †20
AUSTIN, Shannon Michelle. 7703 FLOYD CURL DR, U TX MED SCH SAN ANTONIO 78229 #048-13-2006 **PD** *012
AVANT, Wilbur S, Jr. 7711 LOUIS PASTEUR DR #810 78229 #036-05-1967 L1974 **N** *020 †75
AVERYT, John M. 8026 FLOYD CURL DR, SOUTH TEXAS PATHOLOGY 78229 #048-02-1996 L2001 **PTH** *020 †50
AVILA, Fernando T. 700 S SAINT MARYS 78205 #048-12-1982 L1983 **AN PME** *020 †05
AYALA, Francisco. 302 W RECTOR ST, UNIV HEALTH NORTHSIDE 78216 #048-12-1993 L1994 **FM** *020 †18
AYALA, John A. 4499 MEDICAL DR, STE 301 78229 #048-04-1991 L1992 **PS** *020 †65
AYALA, Loida. 7950 FLOYD CURL DR 78229 #042-01-1997 L1999 **PM** *020 †60
AYALA, Miguel. 740 S ALAMO 78205 #042-02-1996 L1998 **IM** *020 †20
AYDELOTT, Zed, Jr. 603 CORINNE DR # 56 78218 #047-06-1961 L1968 **P** *075
AYOUB, Hanan Hussein. ■ 78250 #915-02-1988 L2002 **PP** *020 †50
AYUBI-MOAK, Ineke M. 78232 #005-18-1999 L2001 **FM** *020 †18
AYUS, Carlos Juan. 701 S ZARZAMORA ST 78207 #132-01-1967 L1977 **NEP** *020 †20
AZIZ, Salar Akhtar. 6111 S ZARZAMORA ST, NUSRAT MEDICAL CENTER 78211 #704-01-1950 L1978 **OBG U** *071
BABCOCK, Michael James. ■ 78254 #048-13-2005 **D** *012
BABCOCK, William Sanford. 2829 BABCOCK RD STE 145 78229 #016-06-1966 L1972 **D DMP** *020 †15
BABINSKI, Maciej F. 45 NE LOOP 410, STE 900 78216 #759-03-1964 L1978 **AN** *020 †05
BACA, Wendy. 14807 SAN PEDRO 78232 #016-11-1993 L1998 **OPH** *020 †35
BACHIER, Carlos R. 7711 LOUIS PASTEUR, STE 708 78229 #048-12-1992 L1992 **ON** *020 †20
BACHMANN, Richard E, Jr. ■ 78247 #025-01-1985 L1986 **FM AM** *020 †70
BACHMANN, Stefano. ■ 78238 #869-07-1991 **ID** *100
BACKUS, Scott Russell. ■ 78249 #051-04-2005 **PTH** *012
BACON, Donald David. 403 TREELINE PARK, CONSULTANTS IN PAIN 78209 #048-13-1974 L1974 **AN PMM** *020 †20
BADANI, Ketan Manharlal. 7614 LOUIS PASTEUR STE 310 78229 #496-38-1987 *020
BADEN, Eric Yang. 3851 ROGER BROOKE DR, ATTN: CREDENTIAL OFFICE 78234 #038-06-2001 L2007 **EM** *020 †16
BADEN, Melvin. 5414 FREDERICKSBURG RD, STE 100 78229 #869-04-1960 L1975 **NPM** *020 †55
BADGETT, Robert Gwathmey. 527 N LEONA ST 78207 #036-01-1984 L1992 **GP** *020 †20
BAEZ CABRERA, Luis Manuel. 7703 FLOYD CURL DR, UNIV TX MED SCH 78229 #042-02-2007 **P** *012
BAGG, Mark Raymond. 8800 VILLAGE DR, STE 106 78217 #023-12-1985 L2000 **ORS** *020 †40
BAGGA, Harprabhjot. 2935 THOUSAND OKS DR 6-237 78247 #028-34-1994 L2005 **DR** *020 †80
BAGGETT, James B. ■ 78247 #048-13-1999 L2001 **FM** *020 †20
BAGWELL, Dara Daniela. ■ 78209 #011-02-2003 L2005 **PCC** *012 †20
BAIG, Muhammad Rais. 7703 FLOYD CURL DR 78229 #704-26-2000 **P** *012
BAILEY, Brigitte Yvette. 7703 FLOYD CURL DR # MC779 78229 #034-01-1991 L1993 **CHP** *020 †75
BAILEY, Steven Roderick. 4647 MEDICAL DR 78229 #040-02-1978 L1989 **CD IM** *020 †20
BAILLARGEON, Jacques Guy. 8245 FREDERICKSBURG RD 78229 #028-34-1965 L1970 **P** *020 †75
BAIN, Charles Edward. ■ 78248 #065-05-1983 L2004 *020
BAIN, Walter Mathis. 1303 MC CULLOUGH STE 242 78212 #048-13-1975 L1975 **OTO** *020 †45
BAISDEN, Clinton Eugene. 7703 FLOYD CURL DR, MAIL CODE 7841 78229 #039-01-1975 L1978 **TS** *020 †85,90
BAKA, Michelle Ingeborg. 9895 IH 10 W 78230 #048-13-1982 L1983 **FM** *020 †18
BAKER, Floyd Wilmer. ■ 78209 #019-02-1953 L1953 **GS** *071 †85
BAKER, Todd A. 13722 EMBASSY ROW 78216 #048-13-1996 L1998 **FM FSM** *020 †18
BALA, R. 343 W HOUSTON ST STE 1002 78205 #495-16-1960 L1973 **PS** *020 †85,65 ‡
BALACHANDRAN, Malini. 7703 FLOYD CURL DR, UNIV OF TX MED SCH AT SAN 78229 #048-13-2006 **GS** *012
BALDERAS, Manuel. 7400 MERTON MINTER ST, VA HOSPITAL 78229 #649-02-1980 L2000 **ADP** *020 †75
BALDERAS, Teresita Guzman. 84 NE LOOP 410, STE 140 78216 #649-02-1980 L2000 **P** *020 †75

BALDWIN, Charles Eugene. 18866 STONE OAK PKWY, STE 103-21 78258 #016-11-1974 L2006 **PDS UP** *020 †85
BALE, Scott W. 7703 FLOYD CURL DR, DEPT OF ANESTHESIOLOGY 78229 #048-13-2005 L2007 **AN** *012
BALES, James Roberttoorn. ■ 78251 #010-02-2005 L2007 **ORS** *012
BALIC, Ivana. 7703 FLOYD CURL DR, # 338 78229 #957-01-2000 **P** *012
BALL, Thomas Prioleau. 7703 FLOYD CURL DR 78229 #012-05-1958 L1974 **U** *071 †95
BALLARD, Rachel R. 332 W COMMERCE ST, STE 303 78205 #048-13-1997 L2000 **CHP** *012 †55
BALLESTER-FIALLO, Ana M. 730 N MAIN STE 622, M & S TOWER 78205 #042-01-1982 L1988 **RHU IM** *020 †20
BALLESTEROS, Maria D. 2829 BABCOCK RD, STE 236C 78229 #048-12-1992 L1993 **FM** *020 †18
BALLS, Adam Grant. ■ 78254 #010-02-2004 L2006 **EM** *020
BALL-SCOVEL, Leslee. ■ 78247 #028-46-1998 L2007 **RO** *020
BALSAVER, Azreena A. 7711 LOUIS PASTEUR DR, STE 914 78229 #048-14-1988 L1989 **N** *020 †75
BANKES, Lindy K. 7703 FLOYD CURL DR, HEALTH SCIEN 78229 #048-13-2005 L2007 **CHP** *012
BANKS, Kevin Patrick. 7703 FLOYD CURL DR, DEPT RAD 78229 #023-12-2001 L2006 **NM** *012 †80
BANKS, Robert D. 5711 UNIVERSITY HTS, # 100 78249 #065-01-1987 L2000 **AM** *020
BANNAYAN, George Abcar. 8026 FLOYD CURL DR, SOUTH TEXAS PATHOLOGY 78229 #605-01-1957 L1972 **PTH** *020 †50
BANO, Ameena. 7703 FLOYD CURL DR 78229 #496-27-1997 L2002 **FM** *100
BARBER, Douglas B. 7703 FLOYD CURL DR, DEPT OF REHABILITATION MED 78229 #048-14-1987 L1988 **PM** *020 †60
BARBOSA, Jane Bardawil. 7703 FLOYD CURL DR 78229 #187-13-2002 L2007 **IM** *100 †20
BARBOUR, Alan Geo. 7703 FLOYD CURL DR, DEPT. OF PEDIATRICS 78229 #024-07-1972 L1987 **P IM** *020 †20
BARGE, Jaideep Uday. ■ 78249 #048-13-2007 **IM** *012
BARIBEAU, Alan David. 7830 LOUIS PASTEUR 78229 #048-13-1973 L1973 **OPH** *020 †35
BARKER, Michael Paul. 9643 HUEBNER RD, # 103 78240 #048-02-1989 L1993 **PM** *020 †60
BARNES, Lorraine Theresa. 4212 E SOUTHCROSS BLVD, STE 150 78222 #028-34-1978 L1983 **PD** *020 †55
BARNES, Michelle Margaret. 7711 LOUIS PASTEUR, VANDERBILT UNIVERSITY DEPT 78229 #012-01-1997 L2008 *020
BARNES, Veronique L. ■ 78240 #048-13-1996 *100
BARNETT, Melissa Ann. 4502 MEDICAL DR, UNIVERSITY HOSPITAL 78229 #056-05-2003 L2006 **IM** *020 †20
BARNHILL, Jennifer F. ■ 78248 #048-02-2008 *012
BARONE, Constance Marie. 2829 BABCOCK RD, STE 615 78229 #035-47-1982 L2004 **CS PS** *020 †85,65
BAROS, James Albert, Jr. 540 MADISON OAK DR, STE 220 78258 #048-15-1983 L1983 **FM** *020
BAROS, Larry Wayne. 540 MADISON OAK DR, STE 220 78258 #048-15-1983 L1983 **FM** *020 †18
BARRELLA, Amanda L. 45 NE LOOP 410, STE 900 78216 #048-16-1995 L1999 **AN** *020 †05
BARRENECHE, Rodrigo. ■ 78259 #264-01-1954 L1967 **DR** *020 †80
BARRERA, Abigail Rios. 919 SW MILITARY DR STE 102 78221 #048-13-1990 L1991 **FM** *020 †18 ‡
BARRERA, Alejandro David. 7703 FLOYD CURL DR 78229 #649-38-2003 **IM** *012
BARRERA, Francisco. 8223 FREDERICKSBURG RD 78229 #048-13-1988 L1989 **FM** *020 †18
BARRY, Jessica Leigh. ■ 78253 #036-05-2008 *012
BARTANUSZ, Viktor. ■ 78258 #286-03-1989 *100
BARTHOLOMEW, Thos Howard. 4499 MEDICAL DR STE 347 78229 #048-04-1970 L1970 **UP** *020 †95
BARUCH-BIENEN, Deborah L. 527 N LEONA ST 78207 #035-45-1995 L2001 **IM** *020 †20
BASALDU, Isabel M. 5414 FREDERICKSBURG RD, RD # 100 78229 #048-13-1993 L1994 **NPM** *020 †55
BASEMAN, Daniel Gary. ■ 78230 #048-12-2006 **RO** *012
BASEY, Mary Suzanne. 19238 STONEHUE, ABCD PEDIATRICS, PA 78258 #048-14-1995 L1996 **PD** *020 †55
BASLER, Joseph Wm. 7979 WURZBACH RD 78229 #028-03-1984 L1999 **U GS** *040 †95
BASS, Ann Doan-Do. 1314 E SONTERRA BLVD # 601, NEUROLOGY CTR OF SAN ANTON 78258 #048-13-1993 L1995 **N** *020 †75
BASS, Robert Gene, Jr. 1202 E SONTERRA BLVD, STE 701 78258 #048-13-1993 L1995 **IM** *020 †20
BASSETT, Kathlene E. 8401 DATAPOINT DR, STE 500 78229 #048-13-1990 L1991 **PD** *020 †55
BASTOS, Renata Bonn. 7400 MERTON MINTER ST, VA HOSPITAL SAN ANTONIO 78229 #187-14-1994 L2007 **TS** *100 †85,90
BATES, Le Roy Evans. 519 W HOUSTON ST 78207 #048-02-1928 L1928 **FM** *071 †18
BATTISTA, Michael Arthur. 5414 FREDERICKSBURG RD, STE 100 78229 #041-09-1986 L1997 **NPM** *020 †55
BAUCH, Terry David. 6127 SAN PEDRO, CARDIOSCAN CORP. 78216 #035-08-1988 L1998 **CD IM** *020 †20
BAUER, Charles Rudolph. 7703 FLOYD CURL DR, DEPT SURG. U OF TX HLTH SC 78229 #056-06-1958 L1982 **EM GS** *030 †85,16
BAUER, Jimmie Owen. 7930 FLOYD CURL DR 78229 #038-41-1962 L1974 **GE IM** *071
BAUER, Miriam Cantu. 14855 BLANCO RD STE 400 78216 #048-12-1994 L1997 **PD** *020 †55
BAUER, Richard Lee. 7703 FLOYD CURL DR 78229 #048-40-1974 L1977 **IM** *074 †20
BAUER, Steven M. 14855 BLANCO RD, STE 220 78216 #048-12-1994 L1997 **IM** *020 †20
BAUM, Richard A. 4411 MEDICAL DR, STE 300 78229 #048-02-1987 L1988 **CD IM** *020 †20
BAUST, Joanne. 7703 FLOYD CURL, DEPT ANESTH 78229 #010-02-1989 L1996 **AN** *020 †05
BAXTER, Nicholas Herbert. 720 PLEASANTON RD 78214 #047-06-1972 L1974 **GP OM** *020
BAY, Michael Hsiaoku. 8214 WURZBACH RD 78229 #048-01-1985 L1986 **GE** *020 †20
BAY, Weiann. ■ 78230 #048-13-1992 L1993 **IM** *020 †20
BAYLAN, Salvador Pintado. 4202 SAN PEDRO AVE, SAN PEDRO HEALTH CENTER 78212 #748-01-1970 L1977 **PM** *020 †60
BAYNE, Melvin Arthur. ■ 78248 #023-01-1980 L2004 **P** *020
BAYNTON, Barr L. 8401 DATAPOINT DR STE 500 78229 #039-01-1978 L1981 **EM** *020 †16
BAZAN, Carlos, III. 8627 CINNAMON CREEK DR, BLDG 2 78240 #023-07-1976 L1978 **DR** *020 †80
BEADLE, Sarah S. 7703 FLOYD CURL DR, U TX MED SCH SAN ANTONIO 78229 #048-13-2007 *012
BEAL, Wassel Holland. ■ 78240 #649-02-1963 L1976 **R** *020 †28
BEAMER, Cynthia. 7703 FLOYD CURL DR, DEPT OF PEDIATRICS 78229 #048-13-1992 L1994 **PD** *020 †55
BEARD, Joseph Ranalder, IV. 7703 FLOYD CURL DR, SCIENCE C 78229 #023-12-2000 L2001 **DR** *012

BEARDMORE, Anthony Adam. ■ 78234 #023-12-1995 L1997 **OSM** *020 †40

BEATO, Ubaldo Pajadan, Jr. ■ 78230 #748-01-1972 L1989 **AM OM** *050

BEATTY, Carrie Stephanie. 14855 BLANCO RD, STE 400 78216 #048-13-1994 L1996 **PD** *020 †55

BEAUCHAMP, John Robt. 7959 BROADWAY ST STE 604 78209 #048-12-1964 L1964 **PD** *020 †55

BEBARTA, Vikhyat Sugyani. ■ 78260 #010-01-1998 L2005 **ETX** *020 †16

BEBOUT, Beth Ann. 14855 BLANCO RD, STE 204 78216 #048-13-1996 L1997 **FM** *020 †18

BECEIRO, Anna B. 7950 FLOYD CURL DR 78229 #048-15-1997 L2001 **OBG** *020 †30

BECK, Robert Lee. 4118 MCCULLOUGH AVE STE 14 78212 #036-07-1967 **PS** *020

BECK, William Reynolds. 7700 FLOYD CURL DR 78229 #030-05-1975 L1978 **PD PDI** *020 †55

BECKER, Donald Leo. ■ 78258 #007-02-1946 L1946 **PTH FOP** *071 †50

BECKER, Heidi Ilse. 7703 FLOYD CURL DR MS 6230, DEPARTMENT OF OPHTHALMOLOG 78229 #032-01-2003 L2007 **OPH** *012

BECKER, Larry Eugene. 701 S ZARZAMORA ST 78207 #018-03-1969 L1975 **D DMP** *020 †15 ‡

BECKER, Quinn Henderson. ■ 78239 #021-05-1956 L1956 **OS ORS** *071 †40

BECKER, Richard Arthur. 1303 MCCULLOUGH AVE, STE 374 78212 #048-13-1971 L1971 **END IM** *020 †20

BECKER, Sara Jessica. ■ 78232 #011-04-2004 L2006 **ID** *012 †20

BECKMANN, Brad Bruce. ■ 78218 #010-02-2006 L2007 **EM** *012

BECKMANN, Charles Henry. 124 DALLAS ST, SKINNER CLC 78205 #035-20-1956 L1975 **CD IM** *020 †20

BEDARD, Theodore W. 8601 VILLAGE DR, STE 212 78217 #048-12-1985 L1987 **RHU** *020 †20

BEDDARD, Rachel-Louis. ■ 78258 #016-07-1999 L2006 **BBK** *100

BEDDINGFIELD, Geo Walter. ■ 78209 #021-01-1956 L1956 **TS CD** *071 †85,90

BEER, William Harold. 7400 MERTON MINTER ST 78229 #143-03-1973 L1999 **NTR** *040

BEERAM, Muralidhar. 7703 FLOYD CURL DR MC78, UNIV OF TX HEALTH SCIENCE 78229 #495-21-1994 L2005 **HO** *020 †20

BEGIA, Bruce C. 408 NAVARRO ST 78205 #048-13-1992 L1993 **FM** *020 †18

BEIGHTLER, Eloise Lizzie. 18540 SIGMA RD 78258 #048-02-1986 L1987 **D** *020 †15

BEIGHTLER, William J. 11643 ELM RIDGE RD 78230 #048-02-1984 L1985 **AN** *020 †05

BEINE, Melba Jean. 624 W SUNSET RD, HEALTH TEXAS MEDICAL GROUP 78216 #023-01-1986 L1995 **IM** *020 †20

BELASCO, Marvin Sam. 1303 MCCULLOUGH AVE, STE 125 78212 #048-13-1977 L1977 **DR** *071 †80

BELAYEV, Andrey. ■ 78229 #011-02-2007 **GS** *012

BELCHER, Barbara Louise. 203 E EVERGREEN ST 78212 #050-02-1978 L1981 **PD** *020 †55

BELITSOS, Theodore Geo. 4242 MEDICAL DR, STE 3100 78229 #011-02-1990 L2007 **AN** *020 †05

BELL, David Graham. ■ 78216 #051-01-1999 L2001 **IM** *020 †20

BELL, George Carter. ■ 78232 #047-05-1968 L1975 **AN GP** *020 †05

BELL, Lisa A. ■ 78209 #048-13-2002 L2005 **DR** *100 †80

BELL, Randall Clarence. 4410 MEDICAL DR, STE 440 78229 #019-02-1978 L1981 **PUD IM** *020 †20

BELL, Roy Patrick. 8527 VILLAGE DR # NO-207 78217 #021-05-1970 L1971 **GE IM** *020 †20

BELLER, Barry M. ■ 78257 #035-01-1960 L1968 **CD** *071 †20

BELLINGER, Adam S. ■ 78240 #048-13-2008 *012

BELTRAN, Michael John. ■ 78258 #035-03-2007 **ORS** *012

BELVIS, Erlinda Edralin. 343 W HOUSTON ST, STE 710 78205 #748-07-1965 L1975 **P** *020 †75

BENAVENTE, Oscar. 4647 MEDICAL DR 78229 #132-02-1979 L1999 **N** *020 †75

BENAVIDES, German. 7333 BARLITE BLVD STE 310 78224 #264-01-1965 L1978 **ORS** *020

BENAVIDES, Idalia I. 161 TOMMINS AVE 78214 #048-14-2000 L2003 **NPM** *020 †55

BENAVIDES, Jerome Michael. ■ 78209 #048-13-2003 L2005 **ORS** *012

BENAVIDES, Jose Manuel. 4502 MEDICAL DR, DEPT OF MEDICINE 78229 #649-02-1955 L1957 **IM** *072

BENAVIDES, Lorenzo J. 45 NE LOOP 410, STE 900 78216 #048-13-1995 L1998 **AN** *020 †05

BENAVIDES, Monica Marie. ■ 78209 #048-13-2008 *012

BENBOW, Marshall James. 5282 MEDICAL DR, SOUTHWEST CHILDRENS 78229 #048-02-1978 L1978 **PD** *020 †55

BENCA, Michael John. ■ 78260 #023-12-2002 L2002 **CD** *012 †20

BENEDICT, James Vernon. 5711 UNIVERSITY HTS, STE 100 78249 #048-13-1976 L1976 **FM** *062 ‡

BENEDIKT, Amy Castelbaum. 4242 MEDICAL DR, STE 3100 78229 #036-05-1989 L1993 **AN** *020 †05

BENEDIKT, Richard A. 8401 DATAPOINT DR STE 600, SOUTH TEXAS RADIOLOGY GROU 78229 #035-03-1987 L1993 **R** *020 †80

BENING, Thomas Guy. ■ 78230 #048-13-2002 L2006 **GS** *012

BENNACK-WULFE, Laura J. 5231 BROADWAY ST STE 121 78209 #048-13-1994 L1996 **GP** *020

BENNETT, Dale Edward. ■ 78218 #021-05-1958 L1967 **PTH** *071 †50

BENNETT, Jason Matthew. 7940 FLOYD CURL, STE 1030 78229 #047-06-1992 L1996 **AN** *020 †05

BENNETT, Jason Winslow. ■ 78216 #038-43-2003 L2005 **ID** *012 †20

BENNETT, Raymond S, Jr. 12902 FLAGSHIP 78247 #010-03-1960 L1981 **PTH** *020 †50

BENSON, Amy Elizabeth. 540 MADISON OAK DR, STE 160 78258 #047-20-1987 L1999 **VIR DR** *020 †80

BENSON, Vernon Roger. 255 E SONTERRA BLVD, STE 100 78258 #026-04-1962 L1971 **IM** *020 †20

BENTON, Christine E. 7703 FLOYD CURL DR 78229 #048-04-2000 L2002 **DR** *100 †80

BENZAQUEN, Mathews. 111 DALLAS ST 78205 #649-01-1961 L1966 **GP** *075

BENZICK, Jeffrey Michael. 14800 US 281 N, STE 110 78232 #048-04-1996 L2003 **P** *020 †75

BERARDO, Melora Danielle. 750 E MULBERRY AVE, STE 325 78212 #048-13-1989 L1990 **PCP** *020 †50

BERARDO, Peter Vincent. 2829 BABCOCK RD STE 215, A M I MEDICAL CENTER 78229 #048-13-1990 L1991 **DR** *020 †80

BERENDSON, Robert A. 343 W HOUSTON ST, STE 807 78205 #737-06-1975 L1980 **GE IM** *020 †20

BERG, Michael Walter. 7979 WURZBACH RD 78229 #048-13-1976 L1976 **GE IM** *020 †20

BERGER, Jamie Michelle. ■ 78229 #048-13-2008 *012

BERGMAN, Stuart A, Jr. 7950 FLOYD CURL DR, STE 805 78229 #048-12-1969 L1969 **IM CD** *071

BERKENKAMP, Marie Bisett. 7700 FLOYD CURL DR 78229 #048-04-1985 L1987 **PD** *020 †55

BERKOWITZ, Carl Michael. 343 W HOUSTON ST, STE 808 78205 #024-16-1983 L1986 **ID** *020 †20

BERKUS, Michael David. 5414 FREDERICKSBURG RD, STE 200 78229 #038-06-1976 L1980 **NPM OBG** *020 †30

BERLER, James Melvin. ■ 78218 #048-02-1954 L1954 **OBG** *071 †30

BERLINER, Daniel Saml. 3851 ROGER BROOKE DR, BROOKE ARMY MEDICAL CENTER 78234 #016-11-1969 L1973 **EM AM** *030 †70 ‡

BERMAN, Paul Murray. 12222 VANCE JCKSN RD #1322 78230 #016-42-1990 L2001 **PD PEM** *020

BERMEJO, Carlos Enrique. 7979 WURZBACH RD 78229 #429-02-1994 L2002 **U** *020 †95

BERNHARD, Ernest Rubin. 4242 E SOUTHCROSS BLVD 78222 #048-12-1956 L1956 **FM** *020 †18

BERNSTEIN, Eric. 10515 STATE HIGHWAY 151, STE 370 78251 #016-42-1996 L2007 **FM** *020 †18

BERRY, Alison Joan. 19016 STONE OAK PKWY # 140 78258 #048-02-1979 L1979 **IM ID** *020 †20

BERRY, Jon Mark. 3331 WURZBACH RD, ALAMO CITY EYE PHYSICIANS 78238 #048-12-1990 L1991 **OPH** *020 †35

BERRY, Lloyd Easum, Jr. 7333 BARLITE BLVD 78224 #025-01-1952 L1953 **FM** *020 †35

BERRY, Susan Moore. 19026 STONE OAK PKWY, ALAMO CITY EYE PHYSICIANS 78258 #048-12-1986 L1987 **OPH PD** *020 †35

BERRYHILL, Blake Allen. ■ 78240 #048-15-2007 **OBG** *012

BERRYMAN, Kathryn Elizabe. ■ 78251 #023-01-2006 L2008 **OBG** *012

BERTINO, Michael Harry. 4775 HAMILTON WOLFE RD 78229 #048-12-1968 L1968 **OTO** *020 †45

BERTOLDO, Robert Nelson. 525 OAK CENTRE DR, STE 140 78258 #028-78-1982, ▲ L1999 **AM UM** *020 †70,18

BESHAY, Ami Long. ■ 78229 #048-13-2005 L2008 **FP** *012

BEST, George Stephen. 8601 VILLAGE DR STE 206 78217 #048-13-1977 L1977 **U** *020 †95

BEYER, Ginine Marie. ■ 78216 #038-43-2003 **PTH** *100

BEYER, Jerry Alan. 7703 FLOYD CURL DR, DEPT OF ORTHOPEDICS 78229 #026-04-1997 L1998 **AN** *020 †20

BEZZANT, Shane Michael. ■ 78259 #010-01-2002 L2007 *100 †80

BHAKTA, Samir N. 7703 FLOYD CURL DR 78229 #048-16-2000 **PCC** *100 †20

BHANDARI, Hanul. ■ 78240 #048-02-2008 *012

BHATIA, Neera. 1303 MCCULLOUGH AVE, STE 237 78212 #495-45-1973 L1976 **OBG** *020 †30

BHOGTE, Marc Sriram. ■ 78258 #048-04-2002 L2007 **EM** *020

BIDINGER, Jeffrey J. ■ 78255 #038-41-1998 L1999 **D** *012

BIEDIGER, Charles P. 19026 STONE OAK PKWY, STE 110 78258 #048-13-1992 L1993 **OTO** *020 †45

BIEDIGER, William D. ■ 78209 #048-02-1984 L1988 **PD** *020 †55

BIELER, Luis F. 88 BRIGGS ST, STE 170 78224 #264-07-1988 L1996 **IM PMM** *020 †20

BIENEN, Thomas. 7703 FLOYD CURL DR, U TX MED SCH SAN ANTONIO 78229 #048-13-2006 **IM** *012

BIGGERS, Jackson A. 8711 VILLAGE DR 78217 #048-02-1972 L1974 **GS** *071 †85

BILDERBACK, Robt Douglas. ■ 78232 #028-03-1963 L1967 **ORS** *075 †40

BINGAMAN, Adam Whittier. 7711 LOUIS PASTEUR DR, STE 707 78229 #024-05-1993 L2007 **GS** *020 †85

BINGAMAN, Kimberly T. 315 N SAN SABA, STE 1210 78207 #012-05-1994 L2006 **NS** *020 †25

BINGHAM, Julie Anne. 1 LONE STAR PASS STE 46, TOYOTA FAMILY HEALTH CENTE 78264 #048-15-1998 L1999 **FM** *020 †18

BIRD, David M. ■ 78258 #048-15-1992 L1997 **IM** *020

BIRDSONG, Bailey Arnold. ■ 78209 #048-02-1976 L1976 **PTH BBK** *100 †50

BISCHOFF, Bette Jo. ■ 78230 #019-02-2006 **IM** *012

BISHOP, Jonathan Michael. ■ 78253 #038-40-2002 L2004 **PCC** *012 †20

BITAR, Jamil Nasim. 4502 MEDICAL DR 78229 #605-01-1986 L1992 **CD IM** *020 †20

BITNER, Daniel Martin. 900 NE LOOP 410, STE D207 78209 #034-01-1997 L2003 **AN** *020 †05

BIZZELL, James E, II. 7703 FLOYD CURL DR, DEPT RADIOLOGY 78229 #036-01-1984 L1994 **RO** *012

BLACKBURN, John Dennis. 2235 THOUSAND OAKS DR, RM 115-17 78232 #048-02-1959 L1959 **FM OM** *071 †18

BLACKER, Faye Adina. ■ 78240 #050-02-2004 L2005 **U** *012

BLACKWELL, Charles Rufus. ■ 78258 #047-07-1965 L1965 **AN** *071 †05

BLAIR, James Alan, Jr. ■ 78261 #041-15-2008 *012

BLAKE, Winston Herbert. 8123 DATAPOINT DR 78229 #010-03-1972 L2005 **OBG** *030 †30

BLAKELY, James Frank. ■ 78239 #010-03-1965 L1968 **ORS** *071 †40

BLALACK, Penelope M. ■ 78212 #048-13-1997 L1998 **FM** *020 †18 ‡

BLANCHETT, Dennis Geo. ■ 78209 #048-13-1977 L1977 **PD** *020 †20

BLANCHETT, Michael Gerard. 3066 E COMMERCE ST 78220 #048-13-1978 L1978 **FM** *020 †18

BLANCO, Cynthia Liudmilla. 7703 FLOYD CURL, DEPARTMENT OF PEDIATRICS 78229 #649-02-1997 L2001 **NPM** *100 †55

BLANCO, Ernesto. 4400 S PIEDRAS DR, STE 200 78228 #264-01-1972 L1975 **DR** *020 †80

BLANCO, Gumersindo. ■ 78209 #035-01-1945 L1950 **TS** *071 †85

BLAYLOCK, Heather Dell. ■ 78248 #048-04-2007 **FP** *012

BLECHER, Christa Brady. ■ 78216 #048-13-2004 L2006 *100

BLOCK, William Jos, Jr. 1111 NIX BLDG 78205 #048-02-1945 L1945 **CD** *071 †20

BLODGETT, Janet Louise. 4647 MEDICAL DR 78229 #048-13-1982 L1983 **END IM** *030

BLOND, Carl Jos. 1008 BROOKLYN AVE 78215 #048-13-1976 L1980 **IM NEP** *020 †13

BLOND, Liesa G. 6338 N NEW BRNELS AVE #223 78209 #048-13-1992 L1994 **FM** *020 †18

BLONSKY, Jeffrey James. ■ 78254 #039-01-2003 L2005 **GE** *012 †20

BLOOM, Kenneth Roland. 4499 MEDICAL DR STE 289 78229 #836-01-1965 L1979 **PDC CD** *020

BLOOMER, Ginger A. 4502 MEDICAL DR 78229 #048-13-1990 L1993 **FM** *020 †18

BLUESTEIN, Jean Alice. 7950 FLOYD CURL DR, STE 1009 78229 #030-05-1984 L1985 **D** *020 †15

BLUHM, Joey M. 7703 FLOYD CURL DR, DEPT OF SURGERY MC 7737 78229 #048-14-2004 **GS** *012

BLUM, Gary Takashiro. 21 SPURS LN STE 310, SAN ANTONIO 78240 #014-01-2001 L2007 **HSO** *012

BLUM, Jared Julius. 3851 ROGER BROOKE DR 78234 #025-01-2005 L2006 **AN** *012

BLUM, Maria Elisabeth. 7703 FLOYD CURL DR, DEPT MED 78229 #409-39-1984 L1993 **PD NM** *020 †28

BLUMER, Robert Brunson. 2303 SE MILITARY DR 78223 #047-06-1963 L1974 **PUD IM** *020 †20

BLUMHARDT, Ralph. 7703 FLOYD CURL DR, UTHSCSA RADIOLOGY DEPT 78229 #041-09-1963 L1983 **NM R** *040 †20,28,80

BLUMOFF, Ronald Lee. 111 DALLAS ST 78205 #028-34-1972 L1980 **VS** *020 †85

BOCANEGRA, Javier C. 1616 CALLAGHAN RD 78228 #048-13-1986 L1987 **FM** *020 †18

BODE, Kenneth Spencer. ■ 78253 #023-12-2003 L2005 **ORS** *012

BODE, William Ernest. 7950 FLOYD CURL DR STE 101 78229 #048-15-1977 L1977 **CRS** *020 †10,85

BOEHME, Donna M. 203 W ELMVIEW PL 78209 #048-02-1984 L1985 **ORS** *020 †40
BOGAEV, Christopher A. 4410 MEDICAL DR STE 610 78229 #051-01-1992 L1999 **NS** *020 †25
BOHIL, Gorav. 2827 BABCOCK RD, DEPT OF EMER MED 78229 #001-02-2002 L2006 **EM** *100 †16
BOHNENBLUST, Mary Elizabe. ■ 78229 #048-13-2004 **GS** *012
BOLDT, David Henry. 7979 WURZBACH RD 78229 #024-07-1969 L1981 **IM HEM** *050 †20
BOLDT, John Wesley. 527 N LEONA ST 78207 #047-05-1954 L1959 **GYN GO** *020 †30
BOLLING, David R, Jr. 78229 #048-02-1967 L1967 **OBG U** *075 †30
BONDAREVSKY, Ernesto. 730 N MAIN STE 409 78205 #132-01-1963 L1979 **PUD IM** *020
BONILLA, Carolina. 7703 FLOYD CURL DR, UNIV TX MED SCH 78229 #264-04-1999 L2007 **P** *100
BONILLA, Jorge A. 45 NE LOOP 410, STE 900 78216 #048-02-1995 L2000 **AN** *020 †05
BONILLA, Jose Arturo. 16723 HUEBNER RD 78248 #048-14-1989 L1990 **PDO** *020 †45
BONILLA, Jose V. 343 W HOUSTON ST STE 105 78205 #649-02-1962 L1966 **OBG OS** *020 †30
BONILLA, Juan Alfredo. 16723 HUEBNER RD 78248 #048-13-1983 L1993 **PDO** *020 †45
BONVICINO, Amanda Michell. 78248 #048-16-2006 L2008 **PTH** *012
BOOK, Scott George. ■ 78248 #021-06-2002 L2003 **DR** *100 †80
BOONE VALDEZ, Heliodoro. 343 W HOUSTON ST STE 512 78205 #649-02-1966 L1972 **GS** *020
BORDMAN, Bernard Stanley. ■ 78258 #011-02-1962 L1993 **GS** *071 †85
BORENSTEIN, Jose. 3111 SAN PEDRO AVE 78212 #649-01-1958 L1969 **PD** *020
BOROWSKI, John Talbot. 4400 S PIEDRAS DR, STE 200 78228 #011-02-1968 L1980 **DR IM** *020 †20,80
BORRA, Raja Sekhar. 7330 SAN PEDRO STE 405, IPC HOSPITALIST COMPANY 78216 #496-01-2000 L2005 **IM** *020 †20
BORREGO, Robert A, III. 359 E HILDEBRAND AVE, STE 200 78212 #024-07-1984 L1991 **IM** *020
BORRERO, Norma. 5788 ECKHERT RD, VA OUTPATIENT CLINIC 78240 #042-01-1982 L1985 **FM** *020 †18 ‡
BORRON, Stephen Wayne. 1777 NE LOOP 250, STE 600 78217 #048-02-1984 L1985 **EM OM** *020 †70,16
BOSTANDZHYAN, Yepraksiya. ■ 78250 #913-38-1984 **GS** *012
BOSTICK, Adam Whitnel. ■ 78258 #051-04-2006 L2008 **IM** *012
BOSWELL, Leta J Norvell. ■ 78216 #048-12-1944 L1944 **GP** *071
BOSWELL, Steven Harris. 8038 WURZBACH RD, STE 150 78229 #048-04-1969 L1969 **DR** *071 †80
BOTKIN, Rolan Raymond. 3326 SOUTHCROSS BLVD 78223 #017-20-1955 L1956 **FM GS** *075
BOTLA, Ravi. 621 CAMDEN ST 78215 #495-11-1983 L1995 **GE IM** *020 †20
BOURLAND, Sarah Dunning. 540 OAK CENTRE DR, STE 200 78258 #048-13-2002 L2005 **PD** *020 †55
BOWDEN, Charles Lee. 7703 FLOYD CURL DR 7792, DEPT OF PSYCHIATRY UTHSCSA 78229 #048-04-1964 L1964 **P** *050 †75 ‡
BOWE, Lisa Marie. ■ 78249 #038-40-2006 **AN** *012
BOWEN, Stephanie. 7700 FLOYD CURL DR 78229 #048-13-1991 L1993 **AN** *020 †05
BOWERS, Joe D. 7703 FLOYD CURL DR, U TX MED SCH SAN ANTONIO 78229 #048-13-2006 **N** *012
BOWERS, Krista Wagner. 6126 WURZBACH RD 78238 #048-13-2003 L2006 **IM** *100 †20
BOWES, Anita King. 3646 HUNTERS CLFS 78230 #016-11-1982 L1989 **OTO** *020 †45
BOWES, Harrison N, Jr. 730 N MAIN AVE, STE 721 78205 #016-11-1983 L1989 **OPH OS** *020 †35
BOWIE, Neil John Bernard. DALLAS ST, BAPTIST MEMORIAL HOSPITAL 78215 #803-05-1949 L1964 **RO** *071 †80,28
BOWLAND, Mark Brandon. 4242 MEDICAL DR, STE 3100 78229 #048-13-1999 L2003 **AN** *020 †05
BOWLES, Alfred P, II. 5711 UNIVERSITY HTS, # 100 78249 #017-20-1990 L1996 **GS EM** *050 †85
BOWLES, Amy E. 7703 FLOYD CURL DR, 78229 #048-04-1999 L2003 **PM** *020 †60
BOWLING, Gregory D. 7703 FLOYD CURL DR, INTERNAL MED, MC 7871 78229 #048-04-2002 L2005 **IM** *100 †20
BOX-HUTCHINSON, Louise A. ■ 78229 #018-03-1943 L1972 **A IM** *072 †20,03 ‡
BOYD, Daniel R. 45 NE LOOP 410, STE 900 78216 #048-13-1986 L1987 **AN** *020 †05
BOYD, Sheri Yvonne M. 3851 ROGER BROOKE DR, BROOKE ARMY MED CTR, BLDG 78234 #030-06-1988 L2005 **CD** *020 †20
BOYER, Kara M. ■ 78209 #048-16-2001 L2004 **GP** *020
BOYER, Molly Kathleen. ■ 78212 #048-04-2004 L2008 **IM** *100 †20
BOYLSTON, Tina Havel. 5282 MEDICAL DR, SOUTHWEST CHILDRENS 78229 #048-02-2000 L2003 **PD** *020 †55
BOYS, Gregory Jason. ■ 78248 #056-06-1999 L2003 **RNR** *020 †80
BOZZINI, Miguel Alberto. 8038 WURZBACH RD, STE 270 78229 #132-04-1947 L1976 **RO OS** *071 †80
BRACKEN, Christopher A. 7703 FLOYD CURL DR, UT HEALTH SCIENCE CENTER 78229 #048-13-1984 L1986 **AN CCA** *020 †05
BRADLEY, Yong Chol. 3851 ROGER BROOKE DR, BROOKE AMC, BLDG 3600 78234 #012-01-1990 L2001 **NM DR** *020 †80,28
BRADSHAW, Linda Unmi. ■ 78223 #048-13-2007 **PD** *012
BRADSHAW, William Hollis. 8534 VILLAGE DR STE B 78217 #048-14-1985 L1986 **GS** *020 †85
BRADY, Charles Elmer, III. 4647 MEDICAL DR 78229 #051-04-1971 L1978 **GE IM** *040 †20 ‡
BRADY, Daniel Edward. ■ 78253 #028-34-2003 L2005 **GE** *012 †20
BRAID, Alan Richard. 4499 MEDICAL DR STE 230 78229 #048-13-1972 L1975 **OBG** *020 †30
BRANCH, Charles L. ■ 78217 #047-05-1953 L1968 **NS GS** *071 †25
BRAND, Michelle E. ■ 78240 #048-13-2005 **PM** *012
BRANDON, Heather B. 315 N SAN SABA, STE 1060A 78207 #048-13-2003 L2006 **PD** *100 †55
BRANNAN, Harold Moulden. 1502 NIX BLDG 78205 #048-02-1957 L1957 **R NM** *020 †80,28
BRANSTETTER, Devin James. 7703 FLOYD CURL DR, DEPT OF ANESTHESIOLOGY 78229 #048-13-2006 **AN** *012
BRANTIGAN, John Wilder. 9150 HUEBNER RD, STE 350 78240 #023-07-1970 L1997 **ORS** *071 †40
BRANTLEY, Elisa Knox. ■ 78240 #048-13-2005 **U** *012
BRATCHER, Everett Poole. 7700 FLOYD CURL DR 78229 #038-40-1956 L1963 **GS** *020 †85
BRAULT, Barbara Anne. 5825 NORTHGAP ST 78239 #048-13-1971 L1972 **IM CD** *020 †20
BRAVERMAN, Sheldon Philip. 1100 N MAIN AVE 78212 #035-15-1959 L1967 **OPH** *020 †35
BRAZEAL, Justin Ryan. ■ 78229 #048-12-2006 **ORS** *012
BREADY, Lois Lester. 7703 FLOYDCURL 7790, UTHSCSA 78229 #048-13-1977 L1977 **AN** *040 †05
BREARLEY, Charles Brice. 8711 VILLAGE DR, STE 303 78217 #048-02-1971 L1971 **PUD** *020 †20
BREDT, Robert Jay. ■ 78248 #028-02-1987 L1989 **PTH IM** *020 †50

BREECE, Grady Lee. ■ 78216 #021-05-1954 L1954 **AM GPM** *071 †70
BRENNER, Andrew J. 7979 WURZBACH RD, CTRC, IDD CLINIC 78229 #048-15-2003 L2005 **HO** *012 †20
BRENNER, John. ■ 78240 #055-75-2005, ▲ **AN** *012
BREWER, Dorothy. ■ 78209 #035-01-1943 L1949 **IM** *075 †20
BREWER, Raymond L. 45 NE LOOP 410 STE 900 78216 #023-12-1985 L1996 **PMM FM** *020 †05
BREY, Robin. 4647 MEDICAL DR 78229 #003-01-1981 L1989 **N** *075 †75
BRIEN, Amy Lynn. ■ 78254 #035-06-2004 **OBG** *012
BRIGGS, Arthur Harold. 7703 FLOYD CURL DR, UNIV OF TEX MED SCH AT S A 78229 #023-07-1956 L1969 **PA IM** *040 †20
BRIGGS, Edward Dickon. 45 NE LOOP 410, STE 900 78216 #917-08-1995 L2004 **AN** *100 †05
BRIGGS, Emily Dickinson. ■ 78240 #048-14-2006 **FP** *012
BRIONES, Segundo A. 16614 SAN PEDRO 78232 #737-01-1982 L1995 **FM** *020 †18
BRISENO, Charles George. 414 NAVARRO ST STE 703 78205 #048-12-1966 L1966 **IM** *020 †20
BRISENO, David Leonard. 927 MCCULLOUGH 78215 #048-13-1987 L1988 **CD** *020 †20
BRISENO, Lara Anne. ■ 78209 #028-46-2004 L2005 **IM** *020 †20
BRISTOW, Kelly Patricia. ■ 78251 #012-05-2008 *012
BRITT, Carey Lynn. 2829 BABCOCK RD, STE 129 78229 #027-01-1978 L1981 **OBG** *020 †30
BRITTON, Bloyce Hill, Jr. ■ 78260 #039-01-1960 L1960 **OTO NO** *071 †45
BRITTON, Howard Arthur. 333 N SANTA ROSA AVE 78207 #035-09-1948 L1954 **PHO PD** *072 †55
BROCK, Irvin Pete, III. 12915 JONES MALTSBERGER RD, STE 600 78247 #023-12-1988 L2005 **P PYG** *030 †75
BROCKWAY, Bruce Albert. 3939 MEDICAL DR STE 110 78229 #026-04-1974 L1978 **NEP CCM** *020 †20
BRODRICK, Charles D. 303 E QUINCY ST STE 100 78215 #048-14-1999 L2003 **OPH** *020
BRODY, Jennifer Diane. ■ 78231 #048-13-2002 L2005 **PCC** *012 †20
BROMLEY, James Monty. 3202 SAN PEDRO AVE 78212 #308-03-1986 L1991 **FM** *020 †18
BROOKS, Clifford Wright, III. ■ 78245 #017-20-2006 L2008 **OPH** *012
BROUGHER, Patricia K. 4499 MEDICAL DR STE 191 78229 #048-13-1986 L1987 **OBG** *020 †30
BROUGHTON, George, II. ■ 78229 #030-06-1992 L2001 **PS** *020 †85
BROUGHTON, Kimberly Kay. ■ 78230 #023-12-2007 **ORS** *012
BROUMAND, Behrooz. ■ 78257 #517-01-1965 L1973 **NEP IM** *071 †20
BROUMAND, Varshasb. 343 W HOUSTON ST, STE 609 78205 #011-02-1995 L2008 **NEP** *020 †20
BROWN, Alison. ■ 78240 #048-13-1987 **OBG** *071
BROWN, Candice Lynn. ■ 78245 #023-12-2007 **GS** *012
BROWN, Daniel James. ■ 78231 #023-12-2005 L2006 **EM** *012
BROWN, David Lex. ■ 78260 #048-15-1984 L1985 **FM** *020 †18
BROWN, Elaine Lucille. 540 MADISON OAK DR, STE 160 78258 #047-07-1983 L1984 **DR** *020 †80
BROWN, Erin Leigh. ■ 78248 #048-13-2008 *012
BROWN, Frederick B. 333 N SANTA ROSA AVE, FL 4 78207 #010-02-1971 L2004 **OBG GYN** *020 †30
BROWN, Frederick Wm, III. 6711 S NEW BRAUNFELS AVE 78223 #025-07-1969 L1975 **P** *020 †75
BROWN, Herbert Paul. 7 BROMWICH CT 78218 #024-07-1959 L1972 **OBG** *040 †30
BROWN, James Kenneth. 7703 FLOYD CURL DR 78229 #027-01-2000 L2002 **P** *100 †75
BROWN, James Phillip. 1814 CAVERSHAM PASS LN 78253 #023-12-1987 L1988 **P** *020
BROWN, Jamie R. ■ 78233 #048-13-2008 *012
BROWN, Jeremiah, Jr. 414 NAVARRO ST STE 400 78205 #005-02-1991 L2000 **OPH** *020 †35
BROWN, Marvin Russell. 150 E SONTERRA BLVD, SAN ANTONIO ORTHOPAEDIC 78258 #048-14-1983 L1983 **ORS OFA** *020 †40
BROWN, Mary Louise M. ■ 78232 #039-01-1964 L1972 **IM** *071
BROWN, Patrick Nelson. 4025 E SOUTHCROSS BLVD, STE 24 78222 #048-02-1991 L1992 **OTO** *020 †45
BROWN, Stephen John. ■ 78260 #016-42-1995 L1998 **RNR** *020 †80
BROWN, Thomas Jos. 18626 HARDY OAK BLVD, STE 230 78258 #039-01-1987 L1994 **N** *020 †75
BROWN, Thomas Markham. 7400 MERTON MINTER ST, AUDIE L MURPHY VAMC 78229 #036-07-1989 L2000 **P CCM** *020 †75
BROWN, William Edward. ■ 78251 #051-04-2005 **IM** *012
BROWN, Willis E, Jr. 7703 FLOYD CURL DR, UTHSCSA DIV NS MC 7843 78229 #047-05-1963 L1974 **NS** *071 †25
BROWNE, Frank Stuart, Jr. 8500 VILLAGE DR, STE 101 78217 #048-12-1979 L1979 **R** *020 †80
BROWNE, Kevin Brian. 4499 MEDICAL DR, STE 330 78229 #048-15-1983 L1983 **OTO HNS** *020 †45
BROWNLEE, John Roger. 4499 MEDICAL DR, STE 272 78229 #038-45-1980 L1994 **PDC OS** *020 †55
BRUDER, Jan Marie. 7703 FLOYD CURL DR, ENDOCRINE 78229 #021-05-1986 L1997 **END IM** *020 †20
BRUGGEMAN, Adam John. ■ 78213 #048-13-2007 **ORS** *012
BRUNO, Todd Anthony. ■ 78251 #051-04-2003 L2005 **NEP** *012 †20
BRUSENHAN, Robert Lee. ■ 78209 #048-04-1955 L1955 **U FM** *072 †95
BRUTON, Robert Hugh. 540 MADISON OAK DR, STE 160 78258 #048-02-2000 L2006 **DR** *020 †80
BRYAN, Eugenia Cliburn. 7703 FLOYD CURL DR, DEPT. OF PEDIATRICS 78229 #027-01-1978 L1991 **BBK** *020 †50
BRYANT, Leslie Ray. ■ 78259 #021-05-1988 L1989 **DR** *012 †20
BRYANT, Nancy Dru. 333 N SANTA ROSA AVE, FL 4 78207 #048-02-1977 L1995 **OBG** *040 †30 ‡
BRYSON, Laurance Mathews. ■ 78209 #004-01-1965 L1970 **EM GP** *020 †16
BRZANKALSKI, Gabriela E. 7330 SAN PEDRO STE 405, IPC HOSPITALIST COMPANY 78216 #008-02-2001 L2006 **ID** *020
BRZYSKI, Robert Gerard. 7703 FLOYD CURL DR, DEPT OB 78229 #028-34-2003 L1993 **REN** *050 †30
BUCAY, Moises. 4411 MEDICAL DR, STE 300 78229 #649-03-1982 L1987 **IM CD** *020 †20
BUCCI, Jay Robert. ■ 78209 #008-02-2000 L2002 **NEP** *100 †20
BUCK, Kathryn Dian. 333 N SANTA ROSA 78207 #048-02-1986 L1988 **PD PEM** *020 †55
BUCK, Lauren Ashley. ■ 78240 #048-13-2006 L2008 **GS** *012
BUCKLEN, Kathryn Ann. 7703 FLOYD CURL DR, DEPT. OF PEDIATRICS 78229 #036-05-2001 L2005 **PD** *100 †55
BUCKLEY, Steve B. 4499 MEDICAL DR, STE 190 78229 #048-13-1988 L1988 **OS** *020
BUCKMAN, James F. 8452 FREDERICKSBURG RD, # 278 78229 #054-04-1966 L1997 **OS GE** *071 †20

BUCKNER, Carlos. ■ 78249 #056-06-2007 **PM** *012

BUELL, James Conrad. 255 E SONTERRA BLVD, STE 150 78258 #030-05-1966 L1986
CD IM *020

BUELL, Walter Flynn. 8042 WURZBACH RD, STE 640 78229 #048-02-1965 L1965 **N** *071 †75

BUENTELLO, Sergio. 45 NE LOOP 410 STE 900 78216 #649-02-1970 L1974 **AN** *020 †05

BUFFIN, Taniesha Lasha. ■ 78217 #021-05-2006 **OBG** *012

BUGG, James L, III. 333 N SANTA ROSA AVE 78207 #048-13-1983 L1983 **FM OM** *020 †18

BULLOCK, Allen Culpeper. ■ 78255 #023-01-1954 L1963 **IM PUD** *071

BULLOCK, Delia E. 527 N LEONA ST, UHS DOWNTOWN FFACTS CLINIC 78207
#048-13-1992 L1993 **IM** *020 †18

BULLOCK, Jeffrey S. 520 E EUCLID AVE 78212 #048-15-1997 L1999 **GE** *020 †20

BUNTON, Paulette Salena. 45 NE LOOP 410, STE 900 78216 #048-13-1978 L1978 **AN** *020 †05

BURCH, Charles J. 4410 MEDICAL DR, STE 440 78229 #048-13-1996 L1997 **PCC** *100 †20

BURCH, Francis Xavier. 8527 VILLAGE DR STE 207 78217 #049-01-1972 L1979
RHU IM *071 †20

BURDEN, Alfred Lionel. 414 NAVARRO ST, STE 1034 78205 #048-04-1958 L1959 **OPH** *071 †35

BURDEN, Patricia Anne. 109 GALLERY CIR STE 135 78258 #035-03-1980 L1999
D OBG *020 †15

BURES, Gretchen Marie. ■ 78229 #042-03-2007 **IM** *012

BURGARDT, Ann J. 4201 MEDICAL DR STE 250 78229 #034-01-1977 L1980 **FM UCM** *020

BURGE, Billy Carlton. 13722 EMBASSY ROW 78216 #048-04-1993 L1995 **FM** *020 †18

BURGOS, Alejandro D. 45 NE LOOP 410, STE 900 78216 #048-14-2000 L2004 **AN** *020 †05

BURGOS, Victor Luis. 8401 DATAPOINT DR STE 500, EMANON 78229 #042-01-1973 L1982
EM FM *020 †18,16

BURGUETE, Sergio R. ■ 78240 #048-14-2005 L2007 **IM** *012

BURKE, Vernon P. ■ 78248 #048-13-2008 **PM** *012

BURKETT, Samuel Edward. ■ 78248 #018-03-2004 L2005 **PCC** *012 †20

BURKHARDT, Gabriel Eugene. ■ 78258 #023-12-2006 **GS** *012

BURKHART, Stephen Shelby. 150 E SONTERRA BLVD, SAN ANTONIO ORTHOPAEDIC 78258
#048-02-1976 L1976 **ORS** *020 †40

BURKHEAD, Steven Kendall. ■ 78251 #041-14-2004 L2006 **OTO** *012

BURKHOLDER, George V. 7979 WURZBACH RD, URSCHEL TOWERS #233 78229
#035-20-1960 L1970 **U** *071 †95

BURNETT-JAMES, Jennifer R. ■ 78240 #048-13-2004 †100

BURNS, Dianna Mosley. 1954 E HOUSTON ST, RM 104 78202 #020-02-1980 L1984 **PD** *012

BURNSIDE, John Chas. 13535 JONES MALTSBERGER RD 78247 #048-02-1978 L1978
CHP P *071 †75

BURR, Naomi Lynnea. 7808 VISTA MONTAN 78256 #056-05-1988 L1989 **FM EP** *020 †18

BURR, Shane Jordan. ■ 78249 #030-05-2006 **PM** *012

BURRELL, Jason Ray. ■ 78258 #048-13-2007 L2007 **PD** *012

BURSAW, Andrew Woodrow. ■ 78250 #003-75-2007, ▲ **IM** *012

BURTEA, Iulian M. 7703 FLOYD CURL, MAIL STOP 7800 78229 #048-12-2003 L2008
DR *012

BURTON, Francis C, Jr. ■ 78258 #010-01-1965 L1974 **PS GS** *071 †85,65

BURZLAFF, Thilo Egbert. 8530 VILLAGE DR 78217 #409-04-1990 L1997 **FM** *020 †18

BUSER, Gregory Alan. 21 SPURS LN, STE 330 78240 #023-07-1986 L1996 **CD IM** *020 †20

BUSSEY-SMITH, Kristin L. ■ 78255 #048-13-2001 L2006 **AI** *100 †20,03

BUSTAMANTE, Mario Alberto. 343 W HOUSTON ST, STE 406 78205 #649-02-1980 L1985
ORS PTH *020

BUTLER, Milton C, Jr. 9150 HUEBNER RD STE 250 78240 #048-02-1953 L1953 **ORS** *071 †40

BUTTERY, Harold Donop. 414 NAVARRO ST 78205 #048-02-1945 L1945 **GP GS** *071 †18

BUYANOV, Dmitriy. 2425 BABCOCK RD STE 108 78229 #913-05-1992 L2004 **APM** *100 †05

BYERLY, Doug William. ■ 78245 #038-40-2006 L2008 **GS** *012

BYNUM, David William. 8401 DATAPOINT DR, STE 600 78229 #048-13-1995 L2000 **DR** *020 †80

BYSANI, Sailaja. 7703 FLOYD CURL DR 78229 #496-01-2001 **IM** *012

CABALLERO, Patricia A. 45 NE LOOP 410, STE 900 78216 #048-13-1987 L1993 **AN** *020 †05

CABELLO, Maria M. 7330 SAN PEDRO, STE 405 78216 #048-04-1983 L1985 **FM** *020 †18

CABRERA, Juan Andres. ■ 78245 #001-06-2005 **PM** *012

CABRERA, Lisa O. 4242 E SOUTHCROSS BLVD, STE 16 78222 #048-13-1997 L2000
NEP *020 †20

CABRERA, Timoteo. 303 N FRIO ST 78207 #048-13-1998 L2000 **NEP** *020 †20

CACERES, Douglas. 45 NE LOOP 410, STE 900 78216 #264-01-1963 L1975 **AN** *020 †05

CADAVID, Gilberto. 4400 S PIEDRAS DR, STE 200 78228 #264-03-1970 L1984 **VIR R** *020 †80

CADENA, Ramiro Campos. ■ 78240 #048-02-1956 L1965 **AN** *071 †05

CADENA BONFANTI, Andres A. 7703 FLOYD CURL DR, UNIV TX MED SCH-SAN ANTONI 78229
#264-16-2002 **IM** *012

CADENA ZULUAGA, Jose Anto. 7703 FLOYD CURL DR 78229 #264-16-2001 **ID** *012

CAJAS, George Washington. 315 N SAN SABA STE 1068 78207 #048-02-2002 L2006 **OBG** *020

CAJAS, Olga M. 315 N SAN SABA STE 1075 78207 #048-13-2003 L2006 **PD** *020 †55

CALDAROLA, Vincent August. 4499 MEDICAL DR, STE 250 78229 #649-02-1980 L1982
GS CRS *020 †85

CALDAROLA, Vincent Thos. 4499 MEDICAL DR STE 250 78229 #030-06-1955 L1963 **GS** *020

CALDERON, Daniel Antonio. 540 MADISON OAK DR, STE 450 78258 #042-01-1973 L1986
OBG *020 †30

CALHOON, James Hal. 4647 MEDICAL DR 78229 #039-01-1956 L1963 **TS CRS** *071 †85,90

CALHOON, John H. 7703 FLOYD CURL, STE 7841 78229 #048-04-1981 L1983
TS *020 †85,90

CALHOUN, Wesley B. 8042 WURZBACH RD STE 500 78229 #048-02-2000 L2005 **NEP** *020 †20

CALLANAN, Deborah L. 333 N SANTA ROSA, CHILDRENS EMERGENCY DEPT 78207
#048-04-1977 L1997 **PEM EM** *020 †55

CALLAWAY, Lacie S. ■ 78254 #048-13-2004 L2008 **P** *012

CALMBACH, Walter Louis. 7703 FLOYD CURL DR, DEPT FAM COMMUNITY MEDICIN 78229
#048-13-1979 L1979 **FM** *020 †18

CALZADA, Pedro A. ■ 78240 #048-13-2004 **FM** *100

CAMERO, Eduardo Jesus. 1712 BUENA VISTA ST, BUENA VISTA FAMILY CLINIC 78207
#649-02-1971 L1973 **FM** *020 †18

CAMERON, Jeanne Hart. ■ 78251 #023-12-2008 *012

CAMERON, Kris Allyn. 16414 SAN PEDRO, STE 710 78232 #050-02-2003 L2006 **EM** *020 †16

CAMFIELD, Angela Suzette. 4242 MEDICAL DR, BLDG \3 78229 #654-01-2000 L2006
AN PAN *020

CAMOSY, Pamela Ann. 7622 LOUIS PASTEUR STE 201 78229 #048-13-1980 L1980 **FM** *020 †18

CAMPA, John Ascencion, III. ■ 78230 #649-02-1981 L1983 **N PMM** *075

CAMPAGNA, John Anthony. 1804 NE LOOP 410, STE 270 78217 #041-12-1988 L1997
OPH *020 †35 ‡

CAMPBELL, Anthony J M. 7703 FLOYD CURL DR, DEPT. OF PEDIATRICS 78229
#919-05-1974 L1992 **RO** *071 †80

CAMPBELL, Carlos Boyd G. ■ 78248 #016-11-1963 L1974 **OS** *050

CAMPBELL, Carol Elise. 7703 FLOYD CURL DR, MAIL COD 78229 #021-05-1986 L1998
AN *020 †05

CAMPBELL, Corey Le. 7700 FLOYD CURL DR 78229 #048-13-1996 L2002 **PD** *020

CAMPBELL, Fred C, Jr. 527 N LEONA ST, ASSOCIATES 78207 #048-04-1976 L1977 **IM** *020 †20

CAMPBELL, James E. 45 NE LOOP 410, STE 900 78216 #048-16-1988 L1989 **AN** *020 †05

CAMPBELL, James Robert. 45 NE LOOP 410 STE 900 78216 #047-06-1959 L1960 **R** *071 †80

CAMPBELL, Richard G. 7460 N IH 35 78218 #654-01-1987 L1991 **FM** *020 †18

CAMPBELL, Robert Murray, Jr. 4647 MEDICAL DR, DEPT OF ORTHOPAEDICS 78229
#010-02-1977 L1987 **OP** *020 †40

CAMPBELL, Scot Elliot. ■ 78258 #023-12-1999 L2008 **DR** *100 †80

CAMPBELL, William H. ■ 78229 #016-43-1982 L2006 **P PFP** *020 †05,75,16

CAMPOS, Candace V. 7711 LOUIS PASTEUR, STE 707 78229 #048-13-1997 L1998
CCP *020 †55 ‡

CAMPOS, Juan Ignacio. 8535 WURZBACH RD, STE 106 78240 #715-01-1983 L1999 **CHP** *020

CAMPOS, Rebecca L. ■ 78247 #048-02-2008 *012

CAMPOSVALLE, Jose S. ■ 78240 #341-01-1967 L1976 **R IM** *100

CANALES, Luis. ■ 78255 #042-01-1958 L1976 **PD PHO** *071 †55,80

CANALES, Mark Lawrence. 7434 LOUIS PASTEUR STE 209 78229 #048-13-1986 L1987
CD IM *020 †20

CANBY, John Price. 2304 SE MILITARY DR, TEXAS DEPT OF HEALTH 78223 #047-05-1954 L1985
PD *020 †55

CANTRILL, Christopher H. ■ 78240 #048-13-2005 **U** *012

CANTU, Beatrice Martinez. ■ 78229 #649-02-1950 L1974 **AN** *071

CANTU, John R. 13722 EMBASSY ROW 78216 #048-13-2003 L2005 **FM** *020 †18

CANTU, Julian R. 600 DIVISION AVE STE C 78214 #649-02-1970 L1972 **GP** *020 †18

CANTU, Luis G. 730 N MAIN AVE STE 702 78205 #649-02-1958 L1963 **FM** *020 †18

CANTU, Maria Elena L. 3000 IH 10 W, IH-10 FAMILY CLINIC 78201 #649-02-1967 L1971
FM *020 †18

CANTU, Norma Sanchez. ■ 78228 #422-01-1995 **FM** *100

CANTU, Rodrigo D. 2121 SW 36TH ST, UNIVERSITY HEALTH SYSTEM 78237
#048-16-1998 L1999 **FM** *020 †18

CAPERTON, Charles Lee, II. 7703 FLOYD CURL DR, DEPT OB/GYN MSC 7838 78229
#048-13-1997 L2001 **OBG** *020 †20

CAPERTON, Kelly Lane. 7950 FLOYD CURL, STE 300 78229 #054-04-1997 L2000 **OBG** *020 †30

CAPLAN, Marian Amy. 17118 EAGLE STAR 78248 #041-09-1981 L1997 **P** *020 †75

CAPOTE, Patricia O. ■ 78240 #649-02-1982 L1997 **PD** *020

CAPRA, Jason. ■ 78227 #023-12-2006 L2008 **AN** *012

CARABALLO, Hector Luis. 8401 DATAPOINT DR, STE 500 78229 #041-15-2001 L2005
EM *020 †16

CARABIN, Francis Jos. 4440 S PIEDRAS DR, STE 100 78228 #048-02-1964 L1969 **R** *071 †80

CARBONELL, Carlos D. 510 CUPPLES RD 78237 #275-01-1949 L1971 **IM DIA** *020 ‡

CARCAMO, Gerardo Enrique. 414 NAVARRO ST, STE 810 78205 #005-02-1992 L1997
GS *020 †85

CARCAMO, Karen Maria. 7940 FLOYD CURL STE 900 78229 #005-02-1992 L1996
OBG *020 †30

CARDELL, Debbie L. 527 N LEONA ST 78207 #048-02-1995 L1998 **IM** *020 †20

CARDENAS, Carlos Alberto. 540 MADISON OAK DR, STE 450 78258 #726-01-1968 L1977
OBG *020 †30

CARDENAS, Jose Angel. 2020 BABCOCK RD, STE 19 78229 #048-13-1977 L1977 **PD** *020 †55,

CARDENAS, Michael Anthony. 8042 WURZBACH RD, STE 310 78229 #048-12-1983 L1983
GS *020 †85

CARIS, Timothy Nick. ■ 78213 #038-40-1947 L1970 **IM CD** *071 †20

CARLIN, Vivian Vail. 333 N SANTA ROSA AVE, PEDIATRIC CENTER OF FREDER 78207
#023-07-1999 L2002 **PD** *020 †55

CARLISLE, Daniel W. 7703 FLOYD CURL, UTHSCSA 78229 #048-13-1991 L1992 **ORS** *020 †40

CARLISLE, Lee Anne Stella. 7703 FLOYD CURL, MC 7838 78229 #048-13-1992 L2002
AN *020 †05

CARLSON, Lynn Suzanne. 540 MADISON OAK DR, STE 160 78258 #048-02-2000 L2006
DR *020 †80

CARNOVALE, Richard Louis. 8026 FLOYD CURL, SPECIALTY MRI 78229 #048-13-1972 L1974
DR *071 †80

CARNS, Matthew Reinhard. ■ 78260 #056-06-2005 **IM** *012

CAROLIN, Merrill Kanter. 7703 FLOYD CURL DR, DEPT OF NEUROLOGY MSC:788 78229
#048-13-1984 L1988 **N** *020 †75

CARON, Jean-Louis. 7703 FLOYD CURL DR, CENTER FOR NEUROSURG SCIEN 78229
#065-09-1979 L2004 **NS OS** *020

CARPENTER, Andrea Jean. 7703 FLOYD CURL DR, STE 7841 78229 #010-01-1989 L1997
TS *020 †85,90

CARPENTER, Shannon Lee. 333 N SANTA ROSA AVE 78207 #051-04-1998 L2004
PHO *020 †55

CARRANZA, Alberto Samuel. 333 N SANTA ROSA AVE, CHILDREN'S HOSP EMERG DEPT 78207
#042-02-2001 L2004 **PD** *020 †55

CARRASCO, Arnulfo T. 4763 HAMILTON WOLFE RD, STE 200 78229 #048-15-1987 L1988
PME *020

CARRION, George. 400 E QUINCY ST 78215 #048-14-1984 L1987 *020

CARROLL, Elisa. 540 MADISON OAK DR, STE 450 78258 #561-23-1992 L1999 **OBG** *020 †30

CARRY, Rodney Lynn. 7701 BROADWAY ST STE 5 78209 #048-12-1980 L1980
MFM IMG *020 †20

CARSWELL, Aimee Kreger. ■ 78250 #048-13-2004 L2007 **DR** *012

CARTER, Bonny L. 7703 FLOYD CURL DR, MCS 7838 78229 #048-15-1987 L1988 **AN** *020 †05

CARTER, Jacquelyn Yvonne. 5804 BABCOCK RD # 243, PMB 78240 #047-06-1982 L1986
IM *020 †20

CARTER, John E. ■ 78229 #048-02-1953 L1953 **PS** *071 †85,65

CARTER, John Erskine. 7703 FLOYD CURL 78229 #004-01-1969 L1969 **N OPH** *020 †75

CARTER, Stephen Anthony. 1 LONE STAR PASS, BLDG NO46 78264 #016-11-1989 L1995
FM *020 †18 ‡

CARTER, Victoria Anne. 4647 MEDICAL DR 78229 #048-13-1999 L2003 **N** *020 †75

CARTER-RUBENSTEIN, V. 4242 MEDICAL DR, STE 3100 78229 #048-13-1977 L1977
AN *020 †05

CARVAJAL ULLOA, Hugo F. 525 OAK CENTRE DR, STE 400 78258 #649-01-1964 L1971
CCP NEP *020 †55

CASADA, John H. 1707 BLANCO RD 78212 #048-14-1992 L1998 **P** *020 †75

CASE, George D. 8711 VILLAGE DR STE 312 78217 #016-06-1969 L1974 **U** *020 †95

CASE, John Bronson. 8711 VILLAGE DR STE 312 78217 #016-06-1939 L1946 **U** *071 †95

CASE, John Robert. 8711 VILLAGE DR, STE 312 78217 #021-01-1998 L2005 **U** *020 †95

CASIANO, Victor L. 540 MADISON OAK DR, STE 450 78258 #048-02-1974 L1974 **OBG** *020 †30
CASIANO SUAREZ, Felix Ang. ■ 78269 #042-03-2005 **P** *012
CASILLAS, Mark. 2829 BABCOCK RD, SAN ANTONIO ORTHOPAEDIC 78229 #048-13-1991 L1992 **ORS** *020 †40
CASTANEDA, Hugo. 343 W HOUSTON ST STE 310 78205 #649-01-1959 L1979 **IM** *020 †20
CASTANEDA, Irene. ■ 78240 #048-14-2004 **PTH** *012
CASTANEDA, Tristan A. 414 NAVARRO ST STE 1200, NIX PROFESSIONAL BLDG 78205 #048-02-1965 L1965 **OBG GP** *071 †30
CASTELLANOS, Luis Lugo. 8715 VILLAGE DR, STE 418 78217 #048-02-1969 L1969 **OBG** *020 †20
CASTILLO, Efrem Lone. 5018 SAN PEDRO AVE 78212 #048-13-1992 L1993 **FM IM** *020 †18
CASTILLO, Laudino Manuel. ■ 78258 #042-02-2004 **IM** *100 †20
CASTILLO, Majin M. 803 CASTROVILLE RD STE 120 78237 #048-14-2001 L2004 **IM** *020
CASTILLO, Violetta A Del. 343 W HOUSTON ST STE 807 78205 #275-01-1948 L1973 **P** *071
CASTORENO, Rosemary G. 7330 SAN PEDRO, STE 405 78216 #048-12-2003 L2006 **IM** *100 †20
CASTRO, David M. 7355 BARLITE BLVD, STE 201 78224 #048-14-1999 L2002 **PD** *020 †55
CASTRO, Robert. 7703 FLOYD CURL DR, MSC 7812 78229 #005-02-1983 L1991 **PD NPM** *020 †55
CASTRO, Wilfred. 1202 E SONTERRA BLVD, STE 302 78258 #042-01-1980 L1982 **CHN** *020 †55,75
CATHEY, Steven W. 6711 S NEW BRAUNFELS AVE 78223 #048-13-1993 L1994 **P** *020 †75
CAVANAUGH, Laura James. 7703 FLOYD CURL DR 78229 #048-15-2000 L2003 **PD** *020 †55
CAVAZOS, Anna T. ■ 78209 #048-04-1991 L1993 **ID** *020 †20
CAVAZOS, Antonio, Jr. 2829 BABCOCK RD STE 226 78229 #649-02-1962 L1965 **OBG** *020 †30
CAVAZOS, Antonio, III. 7950 FLOYD CURL, STE 800 78229 #048-04-1983 L1984 **OBG** *020 †30
CAVAZOS, Bernard R, Jr. 9639 HUEBNER RD 78240 #048-13-1978 L1978 **OBG N** *020 †30
CAVAZOS, Carolyn Lewallen. 9639 HUEBNER RD 78240 #048-13-1978 L1978 **OBG** *020 †30
CAVAZOS, Jane E. 7703 FLOYD CURL DR, UNIVERSITY OF TEXAS HEALTH 78229 #649-52-1987 L2004 **N CN** *020 †75
CAVAZOS, Jose F. 1303 MCCULLOUGH AVE, STE 533 78212 #649-01-1963 L1966 **GP IM** *020
CAVAZOS, Mario Armando. ■ 78230 #649-33-1983 **PTH** *075
CAVAZOS, Ramiro David, II. 8811 VILLAGE DR, STE 300 78217 #048-14-1999 L2005 **OS GS** *020 †85
CAVAZOS, Rebecca Claire. 8715 VILLAGE DR, STE 418 78217 #048-15-1986 L1987 **OBG** *020 †30
CAWLEY, Carmen. 701 S ZARZAMORA ST 78207 #048-13-1990 L1992 **IM** *020 †20
CAWTHORN, Tracey Chantell. ■ 78229 #048-13-2008 *012
CAYCE, Jessica R. 7703 FLOYD CURL DR, U TX MED SCH SAN ANTONIO 78229 #048-13-2008 *012
CAZAN-LONDON, Kevin Micha. 14714 BLUEMIST PASS 78247 #010-03-2000 L2006 **OBG** *020
CECCIONI, Patricia Parker. 7909 FREDERICKSBRG RD #110, UROLOGY SAN ANTONIO 78229 #048-13-2000 L2006 **U** *020
CELIO, Paul Vincent. 4411 MEDICAL DR, STE 300 78229 #011-02-1977 L1994 **CD OS** *020 †20
CENTENO, Arthur S. 7979 WURZBACH RD, URSCHEL TOWERS #233 78229 #048-13-1979 L1979 **U** *020 †95
CENTENO, Michael Anthony. 8711 VILLAGE DR, STE 310 78217 #048-15-1988 L1989 **FM** *020 †18 ‡
CEPEDA, Claudio. 8535 TOM SLICK 78229 #264-01-1968 L1984 **CHP P** *020 †75
CERDA, Oscar J. 4522 FREDERICKSBURG RD, STE A14 78201 #649-02-1986 L1996 **FM** *020 †18 ‡
CERDAY, Eddie Leon. ■ 78249 #048-12-1980 L1981 **AN** *020
CERESTE, Heather Xylina. ■ 78251 #050-02-2001 L2003 **IMG** *100
CERNY-LEECOCK, Michele A. 7950 FLOYD CURL DR 78229 #048-14-1999 L2003 **OBG** *020
CERSOSIMO, Eugenio. 701 S ZARZAMORA ST MS10-5 78207 #187-13-1974 L2002 **END NTR** *050 †20
CERVANTES, Charles R, Jr. 2827 BABCOCK RD 78229 #048-04-1979 L1979 **IM IMG** *020 †20
CERVANTES, Margo Flores. 540 MADISON OAK DR, STE 160 78258 #048-13-2000 L2006 **DR** *100 †80
CERVANTES, Ronald Felipe. 7703 FLOYD CURL 78229 #748-01-1985 **RNR** *100
CERVERA URRUTIA, Aurelio. ■ 78249 #649-02-1998 L2007 **ICE** *020 †20
CESPEDES, Richard Duane. 4647 MEDICAL DR 78229 #023-12-1989 L1995 **U GYN** *020 †95
CHACKO, Annie. 7703 FLOYD CURL DR, MAILCODE 7870 78229 #495-08-1976 L1993 **IM** *020 †20
CHACKO, Benjamin. 3851 ROGER BROOKE DR, BROOKE ARMY MED CTR, BLDG 78234 #023-12-1980 L1985 **OPH** *020 †35
CHACKO, Rosemary. 11 MYRTLEWOOD, HEARTLAND HOSPICE 78218 #047-05-1987 L1994 **IM PLM** *020 †20
CHALABY, Marc A. 7400 MERTON MINTER ST, STE 111E 78229 #048-13-1995 L1997 **PCC** *020 †20
CHALFIN, Steven. 7703 FLOYD CURL DR, OPH DEPT 78229 #041-09-1980 L1994 **OPH AM** *040 †35
CHALLAPALLI, Madhu Babu. 255 E SONTERRA BLVD, STE 150 78258 #048-15-1997 L2000 **CD** *020 †20
CHAMBERS, Aubrey Pat. ■ 78209 #028-02-1970 L1976 **P PYG** *020 †75
CHAN, Ka Wah. 4410 MEDICAL DR, STE 410 78229 #462-01-1973 L1992 **PHO HO** *020 †55
CHANDLER, Heather Kay. 7703 FLOYD CURL DR 78229 #048-04-2003 L2006 **PD** *012 †55
CHANDLER, Robert Clayton. ■ 78240 #048-02-2003 L2005 **DR** *012
CHANDRAHASAN, Gopinath C. 7330 SAN PEDRO STE 405 78216 #048-13-1992 L1993 **IM** *020 †20
CHANG, Jonathan Chunhsian. ■ 78230 #048-13-2004 L2006 **P** *012
CHANG, Xiaoying. ■ 78250 #243-01-1982 **P** *012
CHAPA, Jose Martin. 4242 MEDICAL DR, STE 3100 78229 #048-12-1982 L1983 **AN** *020 †05
CHAPA, Maria Dolores. 7330 SAN PEDRO, STE 405 78216 #048-13-2001 L2006 **MPD** *100 †20,55
CHAPMAN, Clyde Edward. ■ 78213 #048-02-1960 L1960 **OBG** *071 †30
CHARI, Asha Renga. 7703 FLOYD CURL DR, DEPT OF ANESTHESIOLOGY 78229 #496-39-1993 L2006 **AN** *040 †20,05
CHASE, Connor Corl. 11467 HUEBNER RD, STE 200 78230 #020-12-1995 L1998 **FM OBS** *020 †18
CHAUDHURI, Jayanta K. 4400 PIEDRAS DR S, STE 200 78228 #048-13-1998 L1999 **DR** *100 †80
CHAUDHURI, Tuhin Kumar. 7400 MERTON MINTER ST 78229 #495-02-1964 L1975 **NM** *012 †28
CHAVANA, Anna Lisa. 8715 VILLAGE DR STE 410 78217 #048-13-1996 L1999 **OBG** *020
CHAVEZ, Amanda B. 2121 SW 36TH ST 78237 #048-13-1998 L2001 **FM** *020 †18

CHAVEZ, Justin C. 7703 FLOYD CURL DR, DEPT OF REHAB MED-MSC 7798 78229
CHAVEZ TEJADA, Jorge A. 7430 BARLITE BLVD, STE 109 78224 #737-01-1966 L1973 **OBG** *020 †30
CHEN, Amy Enhui. ■ 78240 #048-13-2008 *012
CHEN, Christine. ■ 78209 #048-12-2006 **PD** *012
CHEN, Henry. 343 W HOUSTON ST STE 204 78205 #016-11-1991 L1997 **OBG** *020
CHEN, Naili. ■ 78223 #011-75-1995, ▲ L1995 **IM UCM** *012
CHEN, Steve Ifan. ■ 78254 #005-06-2003 L2003 **GS** *012
CHENAULT, C Brandon. 7711 LOUIS PASTEUR DR 78229 #067-01-1956 L1957 **GYN** *072 †30
CHENSAM, Clifford Rodolfo. 1202 E SONTERRA BLVD, STE 401 78258 #649-14-1965 L1978 **OBG** *020 †30
CHERUKU, Kiran Kumar. 7703 FLOYD CURL DR, MC 7872 78229 #495-57-1996 L2008 **CD** *100 †20
CHESLER, Elliot. ■ 78212 #836-01-1955 L1978 **CD** *020 †20
CHESLER, Rosy Thora. 923 CAMBRIDGE OVAL 78229 #836-01-1957 L1980 *020
CHESNEY, Murphy A, Jr. ■ 78245 #047-06-1950 L1951 **IM AM** *071 †20
CHIANG, Ted K. 900 NE LOOP 410 STE D207 78209 #048-14-1992 L1997 **AN** *020 †05
CHICA, Moises Alexander. 9480 HUEBNER RD STE 310 78240 #048-02-2000 L2004 **OPH** *020 †35 ‡
CHILDRESS, Joe R. 8715 VILLAGE DR STE 418 78217 #048-13-1974 L1974 **OBG** *020
CHILDRESS, Roger W. ■ 78251 #048-13-1998 L2000 **GS** *020
CHILDS, Craig Caustin. 8026 FLOYD CURL DR, SOUTH TEXAS PATHOLOGY 78229 #048-15-1976 L1986 **PTH HMP** *020 †12
CHILES, John Adair. 7703 FLOYD CURL DR, DEPT. OF PEDIATRICS 78229 #041-01-1966 L1992 **P** *062 †75
CHIN, Karen De Leon. ■ 78251 #051-01-2002 L2005 **EM** *100 †16
CHINEA, Eugenio Roberto. 2833 BABCOCK RD 78229 #023-01-1986 L1988 **IM IMG** *020 †20
CHING, Robert T. 4243 E STHCROSS BLVD # 201 78222 #016-76-1992, ▲ L1996 **IM** *020
CHINTAPALLI, Kedar Nath. 7703 FLOYD CURL DR, U T HEALTH SCIENCE CENTER 78229 #495-50-1975 L1989 **DR OS** *020 †80
CHINTAPALLI, Meenakshi. 3722 HUNTERS PT 78230 #495-65-1974 L1989 **PD** *020 †55
CHIODO, Laura Katherine. 7703 FLOYD CURL DR 78229 #048-04-1982 L1983 **IMG IM** *020 †20
CHISCANO, Alfonso. 519 W HOUSTON ST 78207 #847-01-1962 L1972 **TS** *020 †85,90
CHISCANO, Kristie Ann. 519 N SAN SABA, STE 1240 78207 #048-15-1998 L2004 **CRS** *020 †85
CHISM WENDLAND, Claire E. 16414 SAN PEDRO AVE # 710 78232 #048-13-1996 L1997 **EM** *020 †16
CHOE, John Hyok. 624 W SUNSET RD 78216 #056-05-1995 L2007 **FM** *020 †18
CHOI, Henry. 7940 FLOYD CURL DR, STE 120 78229 #035-08-2001 L2005 **OPH** *100 †35
CHOU, Jenny. ■ 78254 #005-14-2004 L2005 **OPH** *012 †55
CHOWDHURY, Mahvash. ■ 78248 #517-01-1970 L1986 **PTH PD** *020 †50
CHRISTAL, Jeffrey Lyman. ■ 78256 #048-13-2003 L2008 **PCP** *012
CHRISTIAN, Charles B, Jr. 4499 MEDICAL DR, STE 225 78229 #001-02-1973 L1984 **TS GS** *020 †85,90
CHRISTMAN, Donald Sinclai. ■ 78250 #010-02-2004 L2006 **P** *012
CHRISTOPHER, Marcus. 16414 SAN PEDRO AVE, STE 710 78232 #003-01-1996 L2000 **EM** *020 †16
CHRYSOPOULO, Minas T. 9635 HUEBNER RD 78240 #917-26-1996 L2006 **PS** *020 †65
CHU, Siu-Chung. 7979 WURZBACH RD, 4TH FLOOR, ZELLER BUILDING 78229 #065-01-1997 L2002 *020
CHUANG, Richard Sc. 8401 DATAPOINT DR, STE 500 78229 #011-02-1996 L1999 **EM** *020 †16
CHUMLEY, Delbert Lee. 8214 WURZBACH RD 78229 #048-02-1971 L1971 **GE** *020 †20
CHUNG, Patricia Shing. 78258 #005-14-1996 L2003 **FM** *020 †18
CHURCH, Daniel G. ■ 78249 #048-12-1999 L2004 **DR** *020 †80
CHURCH-HAJDUK, Robin Lynn. 4242 MEDICAL DR, STE 3100 78229 #048-12-1999 L2004 **AN** *020 †05
CIESLAK, Theodore John. 3851 ROGER BROOKE DR, BROOKE ARMY MED CTR 78234 #038-40-1982 L1985 **PD ID** *030 †55
CIGARROA, Francisco G. 7703 FLOYD CURL DR, UTHSCSA OFF OF PRESIDENT 78229 #048-12-1983 L1983 **PDS TTS** *030 †85
CIOLLI, Kenneth. 8637 FREDERICKSBRG RD, STE 250 78240 #048-13-1985 L1989 **FM OSM** *020 †18
CIPRIANI, M Yolanda. 7940 FLOYD CURL DR, STE 1030 78229 #737-06-1997 L2001 **IM** *074
CISNEROS, Luis A. 343 W HOUSTON ST, STE 808 78205 #737-06-1975 L1982 **ID IM** *020 †20
CLARE, Charlotte N M. 7703 FLOYD CURL DR 78229 #048-13-1975 L1976 **PTH** *020 †50
CLARK, Anthony E. 45 NE LOOP 410, STE 900 78216 #048-13-1983 L1983 **AN** *020 †05
CLARK, Brychan M. ■ 78254 #011-02-1999 L2001 **ID** *100 †20
CLARK, Clarence Edward. ■ 78259 #041-14-2004 **GS** *012
CLARK, Dustin Michael. ■ 78251 #020-12-2006 L2006 **AN** *012
CLARK, Kristi G. 2829 BABCOCK RD, STE 110 78229 #048-15-1998 L2001 **IM** *020 †20
CLARK, Richard Andrew. ■ 78253 #023-12-2007 **IM** *012
CLARK, Robert Amos. 7703 FLOYD CURL DR 78229 #035-01-1967 L1996 **ID IM** *050 †20
CLARK, Shane Alan. ■ 78240 #048-13-2005 L2006 **AN** *012
CLARK, William Donald. 333 N SANTA ROSA AVE 78207 #048-02-1970 L1970 **PDO OTO** *040 †45
CLARKE, Ewell Albert, III. 7979 WURZBACH RD, URSCHEL TOWERS #233 78229 #048-13-1976 L1977 **DR** *020 †80
CLAYFLORES, Jose David. 10350 BANDERA RD, STE 210 78250 #033-05-1999 L2002 **PD** *020
CLAYTON, Robert James. ■ 78230 #035-06-1959 L1976 **PD CG** *062 †55,19
CLAYTON, Trevor Lee. ■ 78247 #048-13-2006 L2007 **TY** *012
CLEGG, Michael Jon. ■ 78240 #030-06-2005 L2006 **DR** *012
CLEMENT, John Pinckney, IV. 21 SPURS LN, STE SL-140 78240 #048-04-1999 L2000 **DR** *020 †80
CLEMENT, Nathan Floyd. ■ 78232 #023-12-2005 L2007 **PTH** *012
CLEMONS, Richard. 8401 DATAPOINT DR STE 401 78229 #048-12-1979 L1979 **IM** *020 †20
CLIBON, Unamarie. ■ 78223 #048-02-1984 L1985 **ON HEM** *020 †20
CLIFTON, Guy Travis. ■ 78209 #047-05-2006 L2008 **GS** *012
CLIFTON, J C. ■ 78230 #048-13-2008 **AN** *012
CLINCHARD, William Robt. 2701 BABCOCK RD, PROMPT CARE CLINIC 78229 #042-01-1976 L1977 **DR PD** *075 †55
CLINTON, Charles D. ■ 78248 #048-02-1993 L1995 **GPM** *012 †70
CLINTON, Chelsea Inez. 7703 FLOYD CURL DR, MAIL CODE 7868 78229 #048-14-2004 L2008 **RHU** *012 †20
CLORAN, Francis Joseph. ■ 78251 #028-02-2002 L2004 *020
CLOUSE, Doug Steven. ■ 78240 #021-01-2002 L2004 **OSM** *012

■ = Address Information Privacy Protected

CODY, Kathleen E Murphy. ■ 78230 #048-13-1970 L1973 ADP CHP *100 †75

CODY, Stephen W. 7703 FLOYD CURL DR, UNIVERISTY OF TEXAS HCS 78229 #048-13-1995 L1996 PD *020 †55

COFER, Barry R. 4499 MEDICAL DR, STE 347 78229 #048-04-1987 L1988 PDS PD *020 †85

COFER, Rose C Fritz. 5282 MEDICAL DR, SOUTHWEST CHILDRENS 78229 #048-04-1987 L1988 PD *020 †55 ‡

COFFEY, Linda Royall. 19222 STONEHUE, STE 103 78258 #048-13-1982 L1983 D *020 †15

COGDILL, Rachel Kathleen. ■ 78249 #018-03-2004 L2008 AN *012

COGGS, Granville C. 4219 LAURELTRAIL 78240 #024-01-1953 L1974 R *020 †80

COHEN, David John. 525 OAK CENTRE DR, STE 270 78258 #028-02-1972 L1987 TS GS *020 †85,90

COHEN, Gary R. 45 NE LOOP 410 STE 900 78216 #048-15-1990 L1991 AN *020 †05

COHEN, Jeffrey Harold. 315 N SAN SABA, MEDICAL CENTER 78207 #041-09-1977 L2003 OPH *020 †35

COHEN, Lawrence Allen. 11602 SANDMAN ST 78216 #021-01-1965 L1973 GS *071 †85

COHEN, Lawrence Michael. 7300 BLANCO RD STE 503 78216 #048-12-1975 L1978 EM *020

COHEN, Melvin Lee. 14800 SAN PEDRO AVE, STE 110 78232 #051-01-1977 L1977 CHP PD *020 †55,75

COHEN, Robert Jay. 7940 FLOYD CURL STE 1030, ANETHESIA SCHEDULING INC. 78229 #048-13-1976 L1977 AN *020

COHEN, Stephen Carl. 2130 SE LOOP 410, STE 100 78220 #039-01-1969 L1975 ON HEM *020 †20

COHN, Stephen Martin. 7703 FLOYD CURL DR, DEPT OF SURGERY 78229 #048-04-1980 L1981 GS *020 †85

COLE, Joe L. 5323 BROADWAY ST 78209 #048-12-1978 L1978 RHU IM *020 †20

COLE, John Sherman, IV. ■ 78216 #020-12-2000 L2001 NS *100

COLEMAN, Sadie Anita. 11811 BLANCO RD 78240 #010-01-1982 L1988 GP *020

COLEMAN, Woodward Leslie. 8715 VILLAGE DR, STE 504 78217 #027-01-1980 L1991 HS PS *020 †55

COLEN, Ramon. 803 CASTROVILLE RD STE 120 78237 #048-02-2001 L2004 IM *020

COLLAMER, Angelique Nicol. ■ 78209 #023-12-2004 L2004 IM *100 †20

COLLETTE, David James. 14427 BROOK HOLLOW BLVD, # 311 78232 #048-12-1983 AN ORS *020

COLLIE, Lamar P, III. 7400 MERTON MINTER ST 78229 #012-01-1979 L1984 ORS *020 †40

COLLIE, Lamar Pitcher. 5788 ECKHERT RD 78240 #012-01-1955 L1964 ORS *071 †40

COLLIER, Raymond H. 2827 BABCOCK RD, 4TH FL 78229 #048-13-1993 L1994 FM *020 †18

COLLINS, Shakaala R. ■ 78249 #048-04-2006 AN *012

COLLINS, Terry Leigh. 8601 VILLAGE DR, STE 111 78217 #039-01-1971 L1975 DR NR *020 †80 ‡

COLTMAN, Chas Arthur, Jr. 7979 WURZBACH RD 78229 #041-12-1956 L1977 ON HEM *030 †20

COMER, Ralph Dudley. ■ 78245 #045-01-1957 L1979 OS GPM *071 †70

COMFORT, Kevin Patrick. 8715 VILLAGE DR, STE 510 78217 #054-04-1980 L1982 FM *020 †18

CONDE, Michelle V. 7400 MERTON MINTER ST, AUDIE MURPHY VA (11C) 78229 #048-12-1992 L1993 IM *020 †20

CONE, Robert O, III. 7979 WURZBACH RD, URSCHEL TOWERS #233 78229 #048-13-1978 L1978 DR *020 †80

CONLIN, Giselle Marie. 4242 MEDICAL DR STE 310 78229 #048-16-1994 L1995 AN *020 †05

CONNAUGHTON, James C. 7703 FLOYD CURL DR 78229 #051-04-1998 L2001 GS *020 †85,10

CONNER, William Chance. ■ 78209 #048-12-1992 L2005 TS *020 †85,90

CONNOR, Dallas Allan. 7703 FLOYD CURL DR 78229 #005-02-2000 L2003 PD *020 †55

CONNOR, Ronald W. 150 E SONTERRA BLVD, SAN ANTONIO ORTHOPAEDIC 78258 #048-15-1992 L1993 ORS *020 †40

CONRAD, Dennis Allen. 7703 FLOYD CURL DR, DPEARTMENT OF PEDIATRICS 78229 #038-40-1978 L1981 PDI PD *020 †75

CONTRERAS, Carolina. 502 MADISON OAK, STE 340 78258 #048-02-2004 L2007 PD *020 †55

CONTRERAS, Dolores. 2406 COMMERCIAL AVE, STE E 78221 #048-13-1987 L1988 PM *020 †60

CONTRERAS, Salvador A. 7703 FLOYD CURL, UTHSCSA 78229 #341-01-1973 L1981 P *020 †75

CONWAY, Bruce E. 8042 WURZBACH RD STE 31 78229 #048-13-1993 L1994 GS *020 †85

CONWAY, Deborah. 7703 FLOYD CURL DR, DEPT OF OB/GYN 78229 #048-14-1991 L1992 OBG *020 †30

COOK, John M. 7959 BROADWAY ST, STE 600 78209 #048-13-1991 L1992 PD *020 †55

COOK, Joseph Aaron. 78230 #051-04-1997 L1997 GE *012 †20

COOK, Linda Sarles. 7959 BROADWAY ST, STE 600 78209 #048-13-1990 L1992 PD *020 †55

COOPER, Carrie L. 8301 BROADWAY ST, STE 211 78209 #048-13-1990 L1992 IM *020 †20

COOPER, David Morris. ■ 78249 #048-02-2007 PM *012

COOPER, Harold N. ■ 78209 #048-12-1954 L1954 OM IM *071

COOPER, Rani Michelle. 7434 LOUIS PASTEUR, STE 220 78229 #048-13-2003 L2007 D *020 †15 ‡

COOPWOOD, Joseph B. ■ 78258 #048-12-1993 L1994 GS *020 †85

CORBET, Anthony John S. 5414 FREDERICKSBURG RD, STE 100 78229 #143-01-1962 L1975 NPM *020 †55

CORDERO, David. 1954 E HOUSTON ST, RM 201 78202 #046-11-1996 L1998 FM *020 †18

CORDES, Jeffrey Alan. 7400 MERTON MINTER ST 78229 #048-02-1991 L1992 P PYG *020 †75

CORLEY, Fred Goodwin, Jr. 7703 FLOYD CURL DR, DEPT OF ORTHOPAEDICS 78229 #027-01-1971 L1974 ORS HS *020 †40

CORNEILLE, Michael Gerard. 7703 FLOYD CURL DR, UTHSCSA DEPT OF SURGERY 78229 #051-07-1998 L2003 CCS *020 †85

CORNELIUS, Jonathan P. 400 CONCORD PLAZA DR, STE 130 78216 #017-20-2003 L2008 ORS *012

CORNELIUS, Melani Patrice. ■ 78240 #047-07-2006 OBG *012

CORONADO, Jose Armando. 4214 E SOUTHCROSS BLVD 78222 #649-02-1961 L1965 FM *071

CORONADO, Tomas. 730 N MAIN AVE, STE 719 78205 #048-13-1980 L1980 OPH *020 †35

CORTADA, Xavier Ramon. 13750 SAN PEDRO AVE, STE 850 78232 #132-01-1971 L1988 PD CG *020 †55,19

CORTES, Carlos Leonel. 527 N LEONA ST, ASSOCIATES 78207 #649-02-1990 L1997 FM *020 †18

CORTEZ, Arthur D. 1026 MALTESE GDN 78260 #048-15-2000 L2002 RNR *100 †80

CORTEZ, Cristina. 740 S ALAMO ST 78205 #048-14-2000 L2003 FM *020 †18

CORTEZ, Maria Dolores. 7703 FLOYD CURL DR, DEPT CARDIOLOGY, ROOM 5.65 78229 #048-04-1985 L1986 CD IM *020 †20

CORTEZ, Ofelia Miciano. 1954 E HOUSTON ST RM 104 78202 #748-01-1990 L2006 PD *020 †55

CORTEZ, Ray Valadez. 16410 BLANCO RD, STE 5 78232 #048-02-1992 L1993 PD *020

CORTEZ, Ricardo. 78260 #048-02-1999 L2006 NS *020

COSMELLI, Aristides J. 426 CASTROVILLE RD 78207 #132-01-1948 L1965 FM IM *071

COTRELL, Aaron Joseph. ■ 78212 #048-13-2007 PTH *012

COTTINGHAM, Andrew J, Jr. 2424 BABCOCK RD, STE 101 78229 #036-07-1964 L1985 OPH GP *020 †35

COTTLE, Charles Edwin. 9643 HUEBNER RD, # 103 78240 #039-01-1980 L1981 PM *020 †60

COURAND, Jon A. 7703 FLOYD CURL DR, DEPT OF PEDIATRIC CRIT/CAR 78229 #048-04-1990 L1993 CCP *020 †20

COVEY, Brenda Kay. 45 NE LOOP 410 78216 #048-13-1983 L1983 AN GS *020 †05

COVIN, Chere S. 13750 SAN PEDRO, STE 140 78232 #048-13-1988 L1989 FM *020 †18

COWAN, Kelly G. 8535 WURZBACH RD STE 106 78240 #048-13-1993 L1994 P N *020 †15

COX, Alan Douglas. 333 N SANTA ROSA AVE 78207 #048-12-1972 L1981 PD *040 †55 ‡

COX, Bryan Matthew. 7711 LOUIS PASTEUR DR, STE 200 78229 #048-12-1983 L1983 OBG *020 †30

COX, Robert W, Jr. 2833 BABCOCK RD, STE 300 78229 #048-02-1992 L1993 PD *020 †55

CRAGUN, William Chad. 78251 #051-01-2005 L2006 D *012

CRAIG, William Edward. 4330 MEDICAL DR, STE 140 78229 #019-02-1975 L1986 CD IM *050 †20

CRANDALL, Paul Stuart. 5788 ECKHERT RD, VA OUTPATIENT CLINIC 78240 #048-04-1983 L1983 FM *020 †18

CRAVEN, Phillip R. 9150 HUEBNER RD STE 390 78240 #048-02-1972 L1972 ORS OSM *020 †40

CRAWFORD, George Everett. 4647 MEDICAL DR 78229 #016-06-1972 L1997 IM ID *040 †20

CRAWFORD, Howard Wayne. 4330 MEDICAL DR, STE 325 78229 #048-04-1960 L1960 TS GS *020 †85,90

CRAWFORD, Paula L. 730 N MAIN AVE, STE 418 78205 #041-01-1984 L1985 OPH *020 †35

CRAWFORD, Stanley Everett. 78218 #048-02-1948 L1948 PD *071 †55

CRAWLEY, Peter Gerard. ■ 78209 #018-03-2000 L2002 PCC *012 †20

CREAMER, Dick O. ■ 78209 #048-04-1950 L1950 IM *071

CREUS, Antonio B. 927 MCCULLOUGH 78215 #308-01-1963 L1973 CD *020

CRISCUOLO, Christine D. 333 N SANTA ROSA AVE, FL 4 78207 #034-01-2002 L2005 FM *020 †18

CRITCHLEY, Eric Paul. 7703 FLOYD CURL DR, SCIENCE C 78229 #023-12-2001 L2002 DR *012

CRITTENDEN, Kimberly N. 1730 SW MILITARY DR, CENTRAL WOMENS HEALTH 78221 #048-12-2002 L2006 OBG *020

CROCKETT, Dale Ray. 7700 FLOYD CURL DR, DEPT OF EMERGENCY MEDICINE 78229 #048-16-1991 L1992 EM *020 †16

CROCKETT, Richard W. 45 NE LOOP 410 78216 #048-14-1993 L1995 AN *020 †05

CROFT, Harry Allen. 8038 WURZBACH RD STE 570 78229 #048-02-1968 L1968 P ADM *050 †75

CROMACK, Douglas Ted. 7703 FLOYD CURL DR, MSC 7774 78229 #050-02-1983 L1996 HS PS *020 †65

CROMAR, Jason West. ■ 78254 #023-12-2007 TY *012

CROSS, Criss C. 2827 BABCOCK RD 78229 #048-13-1987 L1990 IM *020

CROSS, Jessica Dale. ■ 78244 #047-06-2007 ORS *012

CROUCH, David Malcolm. 8038 WURZBACH RD, STE 420 78229 #048-02-1961 L1961 GS *020 †85

CROUCH, Thomas H. 78245 #021-01-1939 L1972 ORS AM *072 †40,70

CROW, Keith A. 8026 FLOYD CURL DR, SPECIALTY MRI 78229 #048-02-1996 L1997 DR *020 †80

CROWNOVER, Richard Lynn. ■ 78238 #036-07-1991 L1993 RO *020 †80

CROWTHER, Alan Paul. 999 E BASSE RD, STE 180-402 78209 #048-04-1984 L1986 PHL FM *020 ‡

CRUISE, Mary O. ■ 78244 #010-01-1943 L1956 PD *071 †55

CRUM, Mark E. 4242 MEDICAL DR, STE 3100 78229 #048-12-1985 L1986 AN *020 †05

CRUSER, Mary Bridgid. ■ 78234 #023-12-1993 L1995 P *020 †75

CRUZ, Anatolio B, Jr. 7979 WURZBACH RD 78229 #748-02-1957 L1967 GS OS *071 †85

CRUZ, Jaime Oscar. 215 E QUINCY ST STE 319, DIABETES ENDOCRIN CONS 78215 #024-07-1985 L1989 END *020 †20

CRUZ-JIMENEZ, Pedro R. 527 N LEONA ST 78207 #847-10-1962 L1986 OBG *020 †30

CUBRIEL, Andres. 4402 VANCE JACKSON RD #220, UTHSC SAN ANTONIO 78230 #024-05-2002 L2006 AN *020 †05

CUDA, Suzanne Turco. 3851 ROGER BROOKE DR, BROOKE ARMY MED CTR, BLDG 78234 #023-12-1986 L1988 PD *020 †55

CUELLAR, Juan F. 7922 EWING HALSELL DR 78229 #042-01-1966 L1971 OBG *071 †30

CUELLAR, Natalie Biediger. ■ 78240 #048-13-2004 L2006 FM *020 †18

CUELLAR, Ricardo Luis. ■ 78260 #649-02-1997 L2003 PD *020 †55

CUELLO MAINARDI, Leo. 215 E QUINCY ST STE 310 78215 #396-06-1955 L1967 TS *020 †85,90

CUEVAS, Rita Esther. 215 E QUINCY ST STE 417 78215 #042-01-1985 L1987 RHU IM *020 †20

CULOTTA, Stanley Leo. 590 N GENERAL MCMULLEN DR, STE 1 78228 #048-13-1978 L1980 FM *062 †18

CUMING, George Scott, IV. 8647 WURZBACH RD STE 0 78240 #048-13-1975 L1975 PD GP *020 †55

CUNARRO, Julia A. 12717 HUNTERS CHASE 78230 #132-01-1966 L1975 P IM *071 †75

CUNNINGHAM, Stephen Lewis. 7700 FLOYD CURL DR 78229 #048-04-1985 L1986 PTH *020 †20

CURA, Marco Antonio. 7703 FLOYD CURL DR, MC7800 78229 #132-09-1995 L2004 DR *100 †80 ‡

CURIEL, Tyler Jay. 7979 WURZBACH RD 78229 #036-07-1982 L2000 ON *020 †20

CURRIE, Donald Morgan. 7703 FLOYD CURL DR, UTHSC DEPT REHAB MED 78229 #048-12-1972 L1977 PM *020 †60 ‡

CURRY, Lysa L. 12650 NACOGDOCHES RD 78217 #042-01-1992 L1995 IM *020 †20

CURRY, Mitchell. 414 NAVARRO ST, STE 1034 78205 #042-02-1993 L1996 IM *020 †20

CURTIS, Brian Dwayne. 7490 CULEBRA RD, # 313 78251 #004-01-1999 P *100

CURTIS, Margaret S. ■ 78209 #048-12-1950 L1950 OBG PD *071

CURTIS, Ralph John, Jr. 21 SPURS LN, STE 300 78240 #048-13-1980 L1980 ORS OSM *020 †40

CURTIS, Spencer Joseph. ■ 78256 #023-12-2005 L2007 AN *012

CUSI, Kenneth. 7703 FLOYD CURL DR, RM 3380S 78229 #132-01-1984 L1994 END DIA *050 †50

CUTAIA, Frank J. 1633 BABCOCK RD, PMB 382 78229 #048-13-1980 L1981 *020

CYR, Steven Jeffrey. 21 SPURS LN, STE 245 78240 #048-13-1996 L1997 OSS *100 †40

CZEKAJ, Philip Stephen. ■ 78260 #010-02-1982 L1983 EM *020 †16

DABABO, Mohammad A. ■ 78278 #875-02-1989 L1996 NP *020 †50

DABBOUS, Ash M. 4499 MEDICAL DR, STE 140 78229 #048-13-1994 L1997 OBG *020 †30

DAEHLER, Robert Wm. 540 MADISON OAK, STE 160 78258 #016-11-1988 L1989 DR *020 †80

DAESCHNER, George L. ■ 78230 #048-04-1953 L1953 **PD** *071 †55

DAFTARIAN, Ali. ■ 78250 #048-13-2008 *012

DAGGETT, Benjamin D. ■ 78213 #048-13-2008 *012

DAHIYA, Marium Z. 18850 REDLAND RD 78259 #028-46-1995 L1998 **IM** *020

DAHIYA, Marta Caceres. 8215 EWING HALSELL DR 78229 #264-13-1993 L2004 **RO** *020 †80

DAHIYA, Rajiv S. 8215 EWING HALSELL DR 78229 #028-46-1994 L1995 **RO IM** *020 †20,80

DALESANDRO, Hector H. 26 INWOOD HEIGHTS DR N 78248 #021-05-1981 L2006 **AN** *020 †05

DALKOWITZ, Marcus B. 730 N MAIN AVE, STE 801 78205 #048-12-1953 L1953 **GS** *071

DALRYMPLE, Neal C. 7703 FLOYD CURL DR, DEPARTMENT OF RADIOLOGY 78229 #024-07-1992 L1999 **DR** *020 †80

DALTON, Mark Daniel. ■ 78201 #018-75-2000, ▲ L2002 **IM** *020 †20

DANCE-KWAN, Deanna Louise. 7700 FLOYD CURL DR 78229 #048-13-1996 L2002 **PD** *020 †55 ‡

DANCUART, Frank Traverso. 8215 EWING HALSELL DR 78229 #737-06-1975 L1986 **RO** *020 †80

DANIEL, Kathleen Darleen. 14615 SAN PEDRO AVE, STE 235 78232 #048-02-1969 L1969 **FM GP** *071

DANIELS, Gus Theodore. 17720 CORPORATE WOODS DR 78259 #051-01-2002 L2006 **P** *020

DANIELS, Steven Eugene. 7726 LOUIS PASTEUR 78229 #051-04-1981 L1982 **CD IM** *020 †20

DANIELSON, Daren Sherman. 7703 FLOYD CURL DR, MAIL CODE 7740 78229 #026-04-1997 L2003 **TS** *012 †85

DANNEY, Mark Maxwell. 5107 MEDICAL DR 78229 #023-07-1972 L1981 **PDE PD** *020 †55

DANSBY, Thomas Julius. 11146 VANCE JACKSON RD # 3 78230 #048-02-1976 L1976 **OTO** *020

DAR, Seema A. 19284 STONE OAK PKWY, STE 102 78258 #495-51-1986 L1995 **GE** *020 †20

DAR, Urfan. 19226 STONEHUE STE 101 78258 #495-51-1988 L1994 **AN** *020 †05

DAS, Lloyd Virgil. 4502 MEDICAL DR 2ND FL, EXPRESS MED CLINIC 78229 #016-45-1989 L2005 **FM** *020 †18

DASSORI, Albana Maria. 7703 FLOYD CURL DR 78229 #132-01-1982 L1993 **P** *040 †75

DATTA, Paromita. 7703 FLOYD CURL DR 78229 #495-02-2001 L2008 **HO** *012 †20

DAUM, Allison. ■ 78229 #048-13-2008 *012

DAVENPORT, Daniel Floyd. ■ 78251 #030-06-2005 L2006 **AN** *012

DAVENPORT, Eddie Dean. ■ 78251 #034-01-2003 L2005 **CD** *012 †20

DAVENPORT, James Albert. 4242 MEDICAL DR, STE 3100 78229 #048-02-1973 L1973 **AN** *020 †05

DAVID, Cecily Mary. ■ 78240 #495-04-1971 L1974 **PD** *030 †55

DAVIDSON, James M. 16414 SAN PEDRO AVE, STE 710 78232 #048-04-1998 L2001 **EM** *020 †16

DAVIES, Brett William. ■ 78253 #023-12-2007 **TY** *012

D'AVIGNON, Laurie. ■ 78255 #003-01-2000 L2006 **ID** *100 †20

DAVIGNON, Louis Michael. 7400 MERTON MINTER ST, DIVISION OF PULMONARY & CR 78229 #011-04-1999 L2006 **PCC** *012 †20

DAVILA, Inocencio A. 19958 PARK RNCH, ALAMO AREA ANESTHESIA 78259 #048-12-1983 L1983 **AN** *020

DAVIS, Brian Marvin. 1842 LOCKHILL SELMA RD, STE 101 78213 #018-03-1973 L1981 **D DDL** *020 †15

DAVIS, Brian Michael. 1842 LOCKHILL SELMA RD, STE 101 78213 #023-12-2007 *012

DAVIS, Charles P. 4502 MEDICAL DR 78229 #048-02-1986 **EM IM** *020 ‡

DAVIS, David Frank. 4242 MEDICAL DR, STE 3100 78229 #048-15-1984 L1985 **AN** *020 †05

DAVIS, Jeff H. ■ 78217 #048-12-1952 L1952 **FM** *071 †18

DAVIS, Jessica Michelle. ■ 78229 #048-13-2005 L2007 **PD** *012

DAVIS, Kenneth Mc Kay. 7700 FLOYD CURL DR, DEPT MED 78229 #027-01-1983 L1983 **IMG IM** *020 †20

DAVIS, Larry Robt. 8042 WURZBACH RD STE 500 78229 #048-13-1979 L1979 **NEP IM** *020 †20

DAVIS, Laura F. 4499 MEDICAL DR STE 280 78229 #048-15-1996 L1997 **PD** *020 †55

DAVIS, Lisa A. 414 NAVARRO ST, STE 1023 78205 #048-02-1986 L1987 **IM** *020 †20

DAVIS, Patrick Edward. ■ 78247 #023-12-2005 L2006 **DR** *012

DAVIS, Steven Andrew. 7810 LOUIS PASTEUR DR, STE 200 78229 #048-12-1973 L1983 **D OS** *020 †15

DAVIS, Thomas Clifford. 4775 HAMILTON WOLFE RD, STE 1 78229 #030-06-1999 L2005 **OTO** *020 †45

DAVIS, Thomas Luke. 1122 AUSTIN HWY 78209 #048-13-1983 L1983 **DMP D** *020 †15

DAVIS, William Michael. 4330 MEDICAL DR STE 325, VASCULAR SURGICAL ASSOC., 78229 #048-04-1984 L1985 **TS GS** *020 †90,85

DAVISS, William Burleson. 7703 FLOYD CURL DR, UNIV OF TEXAS SAN ANTONIO 78229 #048-04-1988 L1989 **CHP** *020 †75

DAWES, Michael Anthony. 7703 FLOYD CURL DR, DEPT OF PSYCHIATRY & BEHAV 78229 #036-01-1986 L2001 **ADP** *100 †75

DAY, Calvin Lee, Jr. 7711 LOUIS PASTEUR DR, OAK HILLS MEDICAL BLDG STE 78229 #048-12-1976 L1982 **DMP D** *020 †15

DAY, Randall Wayne. 4242 MEDICAL DR, STE 3100 78229 #034-01-1990 L1992 **AN** *020 †55,05

DEAN, David Franklin. 4410 MEDICAL DR STE 500 78229 #054-04-1965 L1983 **NS** *020 †25

DEAN, James Skylar. 7400 BARLITE BLVD, SOUTHWEST GENERAL HOSPITAL 78224 #004-01-2002 L2005 **EM** *020 †16

DEARMOND, Daniel Thomas. 7703 FLOYD CURL DR, STE 7841 78229 #041-07-1996 L2003 **GS** *100

DE BENEDICTIS, Dean. ■ 78230 #048-13-1982 L1986 **PD** *020 †55

DEBERRY, Brittany Town. 8042 WURZBACH RD, STE 310 78229 #048-02-2001 L2006 **GS** *020 †85

DECHERD, Michael E. 540 MADISON OAK DR STE 6 78258 #048-12-1997 L1998 **PS OTO** *020 †45,65

DEEGEAR, Gary S. ■ 78240 #048-13-1988 L1989 **FM** *050 †18

DEEN, Rhonda. ■ 78232 #023-12-1997 L1999 **IM** *020 †20

DEEP, Anthony Michael. 1002 BECKETT, TRINITY HEALTH PARTNERS 78213 #051-04-1991 L2000 **FM** *020

DEEVES, Shawna Mohney. 1202 E SONTERRA BLVD # 202 78258 #048-13-2000 L2004 **P** *020 †75

DEFFER, Philip A. ■ 78209 #030-05-1945 L1977 **ORS PM** *071 †40

DE FILIPPIS, Elena Anna O. 7703 FLOYD CURL DR 78229 #561-25-1999 **IM** *012

DE FORSTER, Estrella D C. ■ 78217 #649-01-1954 L1983 **P GP** *072

DE FRONZO, Ralph A. 701 S ZARZAMORA ST 78207 #024-01-1969 L1990 **END NEP** *050 †20

DE GASPERI, Joseph Armond. ■ 78209 #048-04-1945 L1945 **OPH** *071

DE GIBBS, I R Gonzalez. 8111 MAINLAND DR, STE 104 78240 #048-14-1996 L2000 **PD** *020 †55

DE HART, Rufus Marion. 2303 SE MILITARY DR 78223 #051-04-1965 L1980 **PHP GPM** *071 †70

DE JESUS, Alex. 5282 MEDICAL DR, STE 200 78229 #042-01-1984 L1989 **RHU IM** *020 †20

DE JESUS, Jose Emilio. 7614 CULEBRA RD, STE 103 78251 #024-01-1981 L1986 **FM EM** *020 †18

DE JESUS, Lilia Granados. 540 MADISON OAK DR, C P V DEJESUS 78258 #748-01-1962 L1978 **IM GP** *071

DELAGARZA, Christine M. 7711 LOUIS PASTEUR DR, STE 200 78229 #048-13-1988 L1989 **OBG** *020 †30

DELANEY, B Peyton. 4499 MEDICAL DR STE 122 78229 #048-02-1973 L1973 **N IM** *020 †75 ‡

DELANEY, Kevin Thomas. ■ 78230 #048-02-2003 L2007 **AN** *020

DELANEY, Todd A. 4242 MEDICAL DR, STE 3100 78229 #048-02-1995 L1999 **AN** *020 †05

DELARIO, Melissa R. 7703 FLOYD CURL DR 78229 #048-13-2004 L2007 **PD** *100 †55

DE LA TORRE, Javier Eduar. ■ 78251 #042-03-2005 L2006 **OPH** *012

DE LA TORRE, Renee Irene. ■ 78258 #005-02-2005 L2007 **PD** *012

DEL CASTILLO, Melissa. ■ 78229 #048-02-2008 *012

DELCID, Mario Rodrigo, Jr. ■ 78229 #021-01-2006 **OPH** *012

DE LEE, Jesse Clyde. 2829 BABCOCK RD, SAN ANTONIO ORTHOPAEDIC 78229 #048-02-1970 L1970 **ORS** *020 †40

DE LEON, Arnold. ■ 78240 #048-13-2007 **GS** *012

DE LEON, Elizeth. ■ 78209 #048-13-2007 **FP** *012

DE LEON, John Jos, Jr. 1303 MCCULLOUGH AVE # 166 78212 #649-02-1971 L1980 **U** *020 †95

DE LEON, Pedro Abraham. 7430 BARLITE BLVD, STE 108 78224 #048-02-1959 L1959 **FM** *020

DELGADO, Celyna Donna. 7940 FLOYD CURL, STE 900 78229 #048-13-1987 L1988 **OBG** *020 †30

DELGADO, Pedro L. 7703 FLOYD CURL DR, UTHSCSA 78229 #048-02-1983 L1983 **P** *020 †75

DELMER, Merle Wade. 301 N FRIO ST 78207 #048-12-1957 L1957 **PTH** *071 †50

DE LOS SANTOS, Laura Ann. 7950 FLOYD CURL DR 78229 #048-13-1994 L1995 **OBG** *020 †30

DEL PRIORE, Joseph A. ■ 78226 #561-01-1960 **FM GP** *020 †18

DEL RINCON, Inmaculada. 7703 FLOYD CURL DR, MC 7874 78229 #847-13-1990 L2005 **RHU** *050

DEL VALLE, Antonio F. 421 FRIO CITY RD 78207 #021-01-1932 L1954 **GP** *020

DEL VECCHIO, Leonard M. ■ 78240 #041-02-1950 L1951 **FM** *071

DEMANDANTE, Carlo Niepes. ■ 78240 #048-13-2001 L2003 **RO** *012

DE MARTELAERE, Sheri Lynn. 3851 ROGER BROOKE DR, BROOKE ARMY MEDICAL CENTER 78234 #026-04-1993 L2004 **OPH** *020 †35

DEMOOR, Thomas Murray. 8207 CALLAGHAN RD, STE 425 78230 #048-13-1986 L1987 **CHP P** *020 †75

DE NAPOLI, Thomas Scott. 9600 DATAPOINT DR 78229 #016-02-1983 L1992 **PTH PP** *020 †50

DENNETT, M Harley. ■ 78232 #067-01-1955 L1959 **R NM** *071 †80,28

DENNIS, Le Baron Wm. 111 DALLAS ST 78205 #024-01-1956 L1980 **PS GS** *020 †85,65

DENNIS, Michael David. 5282 MEDICAL DR, STE 200 78229 #048-04-1975 L1975 **OSS** *020 †40

DENNIS, Rochelle Eileen. 7400 MERTON MINTER ST 78229 #048-13-1974 L1975 **P** *020 †75

DENNIS, Steven Timothy. ■ 78248 #048-02-2004 L2006 **FP** *012 †18

DENNO, Jerjis Jamil. 5282 MEDICAL DR STE 200 78229 #025-01-1981 L1986 **ORS OSS** *020 †40

DE NOIA, Emanuel Philip. 8109 FREDERICKSBURG RD, STE 300 78229 #033-05-1975 L1979 **IM** *020

DENT, Daniel Lawrence. 7703 FLOYD CURL DR 78229 #011-04-1990 L1999 **GS** *020 †85

DENTON, Gwendolyn April. ■ 78240 #048-13-2008 *012

DEPAUL, Scott Andrew. ■ 78254 #041-12-2006 L2008 **IM** *012

DESAI, Devang Pravin. 150 E SONTERRA BLVD # 200 78258 #016-11-1993 L1998 **OTO** *020 †45

DESAI, Manish Anilkumar. ■ 78245 #048-16-2005 L2008 **PD** *012

DESAI, Niraj Nayan. ■ 78216 #012-01-2005 L2005 **OPH** *012

DESCHNER, Paul B. 7940 FLOYD CURL DR, STE 630 78229 #048-04-1988 L1989 **FM** *020 †18

DE SILVA, Thushan N. 18540 SIGMA RD 78258 #041-12-1996 L2000 **D** *020 †15

DES ROSIER, Kenneth F. 8527 VILLAGE DR STE 104 78217 #011-02-1980 L2007 **IM AM** *030 †20

DE TREVILLE, Robt T Paine. 2303 SE MILITARY DR 78223 #045-01-1948 L1986 **ID FM** *071 †70

DEUTER, Brian E. 7703 FLOYD CURL DR 78229 #004-01-2000 L2003 **PD** *020 †55

DEUTER, Melissa Stennett. 1202 E SONTERRA BLVD, STE 202 78258 #004-01-2000 L2003 **P** *020 †75

DEVENEAU, Nicolette E. ■ 78240 #048-13-2008 *012

DE VILLEZ, Richard Louis. 7703 FLOYD CURL DR 78229 #017-20-1966 L1973 **D IM** *071 †15

DEWALT, Adrianne C. 104 GALLERY CIR, STE 126 78258 #048-13-1991 L1992 **AI** *020

DE WITT, Caroline. 136 HARRISON AVE 78209 #048-13-1994 L1997 **ID** *020 †20

DEWITT, Robert Michael. ■ 78251 #051-04-2006 L2008 **IM** *020

DHAM, Anu. 1200 BROOKLYN AVE, STE 115 78212 #495-03-1991 L2007 **HO** *100 †20 ‡

DHANARAJ, Dinesh. ■ 78229 #048-13-2008 *012

DHIR, Meeney. 540 OAK CENTRE DR STE 210 78258 #495-36-1993 L2002 **CD** *100 †20

DIAMOND, Susan Adele. 116 GALLERY CIR, STE 102 78258 #034-01-1985 L1997 **NEP IM** *020 †20

DIAMOND, Susan Michele. 8042 WURZBACH RD, STE 405 78229 #041-01-1980 L1982 **NEP IM** *020 †20

DIANA, Mario. 19234 STONEHUE, STE 101 78258 #561-11-1991 L1999 **PS** *020 †85,65

DIAZ, Aidnag Zaid. 7979 WURZBACH RD 78229 #035-01-1988 L2007 **RO** *020 †80

DIAZ, Aurelio. 4499 MEDICAL DR STE 250 78229 #048-02-1955 L1956 **GYN** *071 †30

DIAZ, Daniel L. ■ 78228 #048-13-2006 **P** *012

DIAZ, Jaime Alberto. ■ 78229 #649-40-1994 L2008 **IM** *012 †20

DIAZ, Jess J. ■ 78230 #028-78-1961, ▲ L1961 **GP** *072

DIAZ, Jose Andres. 1200 BROOKLYN AVE STE 200 78212 #429-02-1995 L1999 **CD** *020 †20

DIAZ, Jose Ignacio. 7979 WURZBACH RD 78229 #847-13-1982 L2006 **PTH** *020 †50

DIAZ, Joseph David. 2414 BABCOCK RD STE 109 78229 #048-02-1983 L1983 **A IG** *020 †20,03

DIAZ, Karen Camille. 7703 FLOYD CURL DR, TEXAS HEALTH SCIENCE CENTE 78229 #048-12-1983 L1983 **GYN** *020 †30

DICE, John Patrick. 2414 BABCOCK RD, STE 109 78229 #051-01-1994 L2003 **AI** *020 †20,03

DICK, Edward Lewis. 1406 FITCH ST, WESLEY PRIMARY CARE CLINIC 78211 #048-15-1993 L2002 **FM OS** *020 †18

DICKSON, James Edward, Jr. 7703 FLOYD CURL DR, UTHSCSA 78229 #048-13-1992 L1994 **P** *075 †75

DICKSON, John E. 325 E SONTERRA BLVD, STE 200 78258 #048-02-1988 L1995 **IM** *020 †20

DIEDRICH, Stefani Lorane. ■ 78251 #023-12-2004 L2006 **AN** *012

DIEHL, Andrew Kemper. 7703 FLOYD CURL DR, UNIV. TEXAS HEALTH SCIENCE 78229 #024-01-1972 L1977 **IM** *040 †20

DIETRICH, Jeffrey James. ■ 78256 #028-34-2000 L2000 **AI** *012 †55 ‡

DIETZ, Duane A. 414 NAVARRO ST, STE 502 78205 #048-14-1990 L1991 **FM EM** *020 †18

DIFURIO, Megan Justine. 3851 ROGER BROOKE DR, DEPT OF PATHOLOGY, RM 427 78234 #033-06-1999 L2007 **PCP PTH** *020 †50

DIGERONIMO, Robert John. 5414 FREDERICKSBURG RD, STE 100 78229 #023-12-1989 L2000 **NPM PD** *020 †55

■ = Address Information Privacy Protected

DILLEY, Dennis E. 7711 LOUIS PASTEUR STE 407 78229 #048-13-1995 L1998 **AI** *020 †55,03
DILWORTH, Donald David. 8715 VILLAGE DR STE 608 78217 #048-15-1996 L1997
   GS CCS *020 †85
DI MAIO, Vincent Jos M. 7337 LOUIS PASTEUR DR 78229 #035-08-1965 L1972 **FOP** *062 †50
DIMETMAN, Carl L. ■ 78230 #132-01-1970 L1974 **AN** *020
DIMETMAN, Daniel Eduardo. 540 MADISON OAK DR, STE 370 78258 #132-01-1965 L1974
   AN *071
DINAMANI, Savitha. 4242 MEDICAL DR, STE 3100 78229 #496-35-1990 L2004 **AN** *100 †05
DINESMAN, Alan Hirsch. 7909 FREDERICKSBURG RD, STE 100 78229 #048-13-1984 L1985
   OTO *020 †45
DINH, Anh T. 7703 FLOYD CURL DR, UNIV OF TX HEALTH SCIENCE 78229 #048-13-1998 L2004
   CCP *100 †55
DIONNE, Douglas Paul. 3851 ROGER BROOKE DR, ATTN MCHE-BM BEHAV MED DEP 78234
   #041-13-1982 L1989 **P** *020 †75
DIRKSON, Kenzer J. 18160 HWY 281 N STE 108, PMB 402 78232 #047-06-1976 L1999
   PS GS *020 †85
DIX, James Earl. 8401 DATAPOINT DR 78229 #012-05-1989 L2000 **RNR** *020 †80
DO, Dat. ■ 78229 #048-13-2000 L2005 **IC** *012 ‡
DO, Khanh Gia. 1439 SW MILITARY DR 78221 #048-14-1993 L1994 **IM** *020 †20
DO, Minh G. 1439 SW MILITARY DR 78221 #048-12-2000 L2004 **IM** *100 †20
DO, Thuy-Danh. 1214 AS NEW BRAUNFELS AVE 78210 #941-01-1966 L1976 **FM FPG** *020 †18 ‡
DOAN, Chuck Quocchinh. 45 NE LOOP 410, STE 900 78216 #048-14-2000 L2004 **AN** *020 ‡
DOBSON, Mickey Brandon. 4242 MEDICAL DR, STE 3100 78229 #048-14-2001 L2003
   AN *020 †05
DOCCA, Rama Krishna V. 7880 FREDERICKSBURG RD, # 3097 78229 #495-21-2001 L2006
   IM *020 †20
DODD, Gerald D, III. 7703 FLOYD CURL DR, HEALTH SCIENCE CTR SAN ANT 78229
   #048-14-1983 L1983 **DR** *040 †80
DOEUNG, Sokchea Yim. ■ 78240 #048-13-2005 L2007 **AN** *012
DOLEN, Jale Goktan. 1933 NE LOOP 410 78217 #902-03-1969 L1981 **AI** *020 †55,03
DOLLINGER, Toni Rae. 11124 WURZBACH RD STE 206 78230 #019-02-1988 L1994 **P** *020 †75
DOMINGUEZ, Emilio J. 1115 W MARTIN ST, CENTER FOR HEALTH CARE SER 78207
   #847-04-1961 L1982 **P CHP** *030 †75 ‡
DOMINGUEZ, Francisco, Jr. ■ 78259 #041-01-2002 L2004 **CD** *012 †20
DOMINGUEZ, Francisco J. 1102 BARCLAY, FAMILY HEALTH CENTER, 78207
   #042-03-1980 L1988 **FM** *020 †18
DOMINGUEZ, Maria Guadalup. 3031 W IH 10 78201 #045-14-1980 L1981 **CHP** *020 †18
DOMINGUEZ, Michael Joseph. 527 N LEONA ST, ASSOCIATES 78207 #048-13-1994 L1995
   FM *020 †18
DOMINGUEZ, Tamara Jeanne. 1954 E HOUSTON ST, RM 201 78202 #048-13-1994 L1995
   FM *020 †18
DOMRES, Harold C, Jr. 711 E JOSEPHINE ST, CENTER HEALTH CARE SERVICE 78208
   #035-06-1962 L1972 **P IM** *071
DONALDSON, Richard. ■ 78253 #055-75-2007, ▲ **IM** *012
DONATO, Mary Louise S. ■ 78209 #048-13-1974 L1974 **AN** *020
DONNEL, James A, Jr. 10350 BANDERA RD, STE 210 78250 #048-13-1999 L2002 **PD** *020
DONOVAN, Daniel J. 4411 MEDICAL DR, STE 300 78229 #023-12-1987 L1996 **CD** *020 †20
DONOVAN, William Blondell. ■ 78230 #056-06-1962 L1971 **P PMM** *071 †55 ‡
DONOWHO, Everett Martin. 7700 FLOYD CURL DR, SOUTHW TX METHODIST HOSP 78229
   #048-02-1966 L1966 **PTH CLP** *071 †50
DONS, Robert Frederick. 1303 MCCULLOUGH AVE # 374, ENDOCRINOLOGY NUCLR
   MED 78212 #016-11-1973 L1997 **END IM** *020 †20
DOOLEY, Byron Neal. 111 DALLAS ST 78205 #048-04-1954 L1954 **TS VS** *071 †85,90
DOOLEY, Byron S. 525 OAK CENTRE DR, STE 350 78258 #048-15-1987 L1989 **PD** *020 †55
DOOLEY, David Patrick. 7400 MERTON MINTER ST, AUDIE MURPHY VA HOSP 14A 78229
   #028-02-1979 L2005 **ID IM** *020 †20
DOOLEY, David R. 7930 FLOYD CURL DR 78229 #048-13-1983 L1983 **OBG** *020 †30
DOOLEY, Elizabeth Brooks. 7703 FLOYD CURL DR, DEPARTMENT OF PEDIATRICS 78229
   #047-20-2001 L2004 **PD** *020 †55
DOOLEY, Melissa Jaok. ■ 78245 #023-12-2005 L2006 **EM** *012
DOPERAK, Martin. ■ 78259 #041-77-1998, ▲ L2000 **FM** *020 †18
DORAN, Terence I. 7703 FLOYD CURL DR, UTHSCSA/DEPT OF PEDIATRICS 78229
   #048-13-1984 L1987 **ID PD** *020 †55
DORNBLUTH, Nella Carol. 7703 FLOYD CURL DR, DEPT. RADIOLOGY, MSC 7800 78229
   #048-13-1975 L1975 **DR OS** *020 †80
DORSA, Michael John. 3201 CHERRY RIDGE ST, STE B200 78230 #048-13-1986 L1988
   FM *020 †18
DORSEY, Kathryn Denise. 45 NE LOOP 410, STE 900 78216 #047-07-1984 L1986 **AN** *020
DOSH, Austin Bradley. ■ 78251 #056-06-2006 L2008 **P** *012
DOSKI, John Jos. 4499 MEDICAL DR STE 347 78229 #035-19-1988 L1994 **GS PDS** *020 †85
DOSSMANN, William Frank. 4410 MEDICAL DR, STE 450 78229 #048-02-1957 L1957
   NS *020 †25
DOSUNMU, Hameed Adedeji. 7400 MERTON MINTER ST, AUCHE MURPHY MEMORIAL
   V.A. 78229 #690-01-1987 L2002 **IM** *020 †20
DOTSON, Avered Dearl. 19016 STONE OAK PKWY, STE 180 78258 #048-02-1976 L1978
   D *030 †15
DOTY, Sue. 4647 MEDICAL DR 78229 #048-02-1985 L1986 **FM** *020 †18
DOUGLASS, Albert Hugo, Jr. 74251 MCCULLOUGH AVE 78212 #048-02-1975 L1975 **GP** *020
DOUGLASS, Clifton Ford. ■ 78229 #048-02-1955 L1955 **R** *071 †80
DOVE, Amanda Mary. 7922 EWING HALSELL DR, STE 355 78229 #048-13-1984 L1985
   PDP *020 †55
DOW, Dorothy E. ■ 78204 #048-13-2006 **PD** *012
DOW, Tristan Joseph. ■ 78250 #003-01-2003 L2006 **CD** *012 †20
DOWD, Donna Catherine. 7700 FLOYD CURL DR 78229 #048-13-1979 L1979 **NP ATP** *020 †50
DOWD, Thomas Charles. ■ 78209 #023-12-2005 L2007 **ORS** *012
DOWDY, James Randolph. ■ 78239 #048-12-1963 L1963 **D FM** *071
DOWNS, John Richard. 7703 FLOYD CURL DR, DEPT OF MEDICINE MC7870 78229
   #023-01-1984 L2007 **IM** *040 †20
DOYLE, Rocio M. 730 N MAIN AVE, STE 224 78205 #649-01-1972 L1994 **PD** *020 †55
DRAEGER, Hilda. 78213 #048-14-2001 L2005 **RHU** *020 †20
DRAGOJEVIC, Steve Milos. ■ 78216 #957-02-1966 L1979 **GE IM** *020 †20
DRAKE, John Michael, Jr. ■ 78249 #048-41-2006 **GS** *012
DRENGLER, Ronald L. 7979 WURZBACH RD, STE 353 78229 #726-01-1988 L1993 **ON** *020 †20
DREVER, Nathan S. 7703 FLOYD CURL DR, DEPT OF OB/GYN MC 7836 78229 #048-13-2005
   OBG *012
DROGIN, Mark. 23445 N HWY 281, UNIT 2 78258 #024-01-1978 L1981 **FM P** *020 †75,18,16 ‡

DROGIN, Tere Lynne. 540 MADISON OAK, STE 240 78258 #004-01-1985 L1991
   IM EM *020 †20,16
DRUKKER, Stephen Craig. 2829 BABCOCK RD, SAN ANTONIO ORTHOPAEDIC 78229
   #048-12-1985 L1986 **HS PS** *020 †85,65
DRUMMOND, Alonzo John. 540 MADISON OAK DR STE 520 78258 #034-01-1972 L1974
   GE IM *071 †20
DU, Liem C. 527 N LEONA ST, UNIVERSITY HEALTH SYSTEM 78207 #048-12-1989 L1991
   IM *020 †20
DUAN, Michael. 45 NE LOOP 410, STE 900 78216 #243-65-1985 L2003 **AN** *020
DUBAL, Deepali Jitendra. 502 MADISON OAK STE 340, NIGHT AND DAY PEDIATRICS 78258
   #048-13-2004 L2007 **PD** *020
DUDEK, Lara Thornton. ■ 78258 #040-02-2004 L2004 **OPH** *012
DUDLEY, Donald Joe. 7703 FLOYD CURL DR, U OF TX HSC SAN ANTONIO 78229
   #048-13-1984 L1999 **MFM OBG** *050 †30
DUFFY, Michael Mann. ■ 78232 #010-01-1957 L1978 **PS GS** *020 †85,65
DUFFY, Steve Laurier. ■ 78245 #048-02-2005 L2007 **GS** *012
DUGO, Michael S. 7390 BARLITE BLVD STE 100 78224 #649-30-1982 L1995 **FM** *020 †18
DUHL, Frederick J. ■ 78212 #035-01-1953 L1981 **P** *071
DUKE, Eleanora Ellen. 4243 E SOUTHCROSS BLVD, STE 205 78222 #048-13-1991 L1992
   IM *020 †20
DUKE, James Reginald. 4499 MEDICAL DR STE 100 78229 #048-02-1958 L1958 **PD** *071 †55
DUKE, Marquinn Dewan. ■ 78240 #048-13-2008 *012
DUKES, Carl E. 2011 E HOUSTON ST, STE 101A 78202 #035-45-1976 L1980 **NEP IM** *020 †20
DULANY, Richard Brooks. ■ 78256 #039-01-1960 L1963 **U** *030 †95
DULLEA, Michael Day. 3851 ROGER BROOKE DR, RADIATION ONCOLOGY SERVICE 78234
   #023-12-1994 L2004 **RO** *020 †20
DUMITRASCU, George A. 7703 FLOYD CURL DR, CODE 7838 78229 #067-01-1998 L2003
   GS *020 †05
DUMITRU, Daniel. 7703 FLOYD CURL DR, REHAB MED-7798 78229 #038-41-1980 L1986
   PM *020 †60
DUNCAN, Charles Alman. 7950 FLOYD CURL DR, STE 620 78229 #012-01-1977 L1987
   CCM PUD *030 †20
DUNCAN, Christopher W. 4242 MEDICAL DR, STE 3100 78229 #048-13-1982 L1983 **AN GP** *020
DUNCAN, Ellen B. 520 MADISON OAK DR 78258 #048-13-1991 L1992 **APM AN** *020 †05
DUNCAN, James Malcolm. ■ 78230 #021-01-1966 L1973 **GE** *074 †20
DUNCAN, Scott Cullers. 999 E BASSE RD, LINCOLN HGTS CTR STE 105 78209
   #048-13-1972 L1972 **OPH** *020 †35
DUNHAM, Timithy Macal. 9150 HUEBNER RD, STE 280 78240 #026-04-1981 L1982
   OPH *020 †35
DUNLAP, Joel Adrian. 8401 DATAPOINT DR STE 600, 7950 FLOYD CURL SL1-20 78229
   #045-01-1987 L1989 **DR** *020 †80
DUNN, Dell Petersen. ■ 78258 #056-06-2007 **TY** *012
DUNN, Joeming Wolfe. 7272 WURZBACH RD, STE 203 78240 #048-02-1992 L1994 **GP** *020
DUNN, John Noel. ■ 78239 #030-06-1954 L1979 **FM GP** *071 †18
DUNN, Neil Marshall. 111 DALLAS ST 78205 #036-07-1969 L1975 **CLP PTH** *071 †50
DUNNE, Morgan Geo. 540 MADISON OAK DR, STE 160 78258 #539-03-1973 L1987
   DR *020 †80
DUPAQUIER, Dale Anthony. 2833 BABCOCK RD STE 300 78229 #048-13-1998 L2000
   PD *020 †55
DUPERIER, Frank Dauterive. 9150 HUEBNER RD, STE 250 78240 #038-41-1996 L2002
   GS *020 †85
DUPRE, Joseph R. ■ 78231 #021-05-1952 L1953 **FM** *071
DURAIRAJ, Govindasamy. 4203 GARDENDALE ST STE 202 78229 #495-16-1960 L1977
   ORS GS *020 †40
DURAIRAJ, Prema. ■ 78257 #495-16-1963 L1977 **AN** *020 †05
DURAIRAJ, Sridevi Christi. 13722 EMBASSY ROW, TEXAS MEDCLINIC 78216
   #496-23-2001 L2004 **FM** *020 †18
DURAN, Leonard. 520 E EUCLID AVE 78212 #049-01-1977 L1986 **GE HEP** *020 †20
DURAN, Teresa Angel. ■ 78240 #048-12-2007 **PTH** *012
DURHAM, Joshua Lee. ■ 78254 #051-01-2006 L2008 **IM** *012
DUTRA, Donald F. 811 E MISTLETOE AVE 78212 #048-13-1987 L1992 **PM** *020 †60
DUTTA, Anil Kumar. 4647 MEDICAL DR 78229 #039-01-1995 L1998 **ORS** *020 †40
DUTTA, Suresh Venkayya. 9102 FLOYD CURL DR 78240 #039-01-1994 L2000 **RO** *020 †80
DUVAL, David John. ■ 78260 #038-43-1996 L1999 **IM** *020
DYER, John Thos. ■ 78209 #048-04-1958 L1958 **P** *020 †75
DZIUK, Melissa A. ■ 78249 #048-13-2007 *012
EADES, Thomas Wm. 1200 BROOKLYN AVE, STE 200 78212 #047-06-1969 L1975 **CD** *020 †20
EARLE, Michael Anthony. 8715 VILLAGE DR STE 600 78217 #048-02-1978 L1978 **ORS** *020 †40
EARLE, Stephen Edward. 8800 VILLAGE DR STE 106 78217 #048-02-1979 L1979
   OSS ORS *020
EARP, Dean Alan. 150 E SONTERRA BLVD, STE 220 78258 #048-15-1999 L2007 **FM** *020 †18
EARTHMAN, Brian S. 7703 FLOYD CURL DR 78229 #048-15-2001 L2002 **P** *020
EASTWOOD, Herbert K. OAK HILLS MEDICAL BUILDING 78229 #048-04-1950 L1950
   OTO AM *071 †45
EATON, Carolyn. 2121 SW 36TH ST, CARE LEVEL MANAGEMENT 78237 #051-04-1996 L1999
   FM *020 †18 ‡
EBERLIN, Eugene W. ■ 78230 #028-02-1950 L1970 **N** *072
ECCLES, Sarah Elizabeth. ■ 78251 #035-09-2008 *012
ECKHOUSE, Shaina Rose. ■ 78229 #048-13-2008 *012
ECKMANN, Maxim Savillion. 7703 FLOYD CURL DR, MAIL CODE 7838 78229
   #048-04-2003 L2007 **AN** *100
ECLARINAL, Zenaida B. 8109 FREDERICKSBURG RD 78229 #748-10-1973 L1975 **P** *020 †75
EDBERG, Michelle Marin. 7703 FLOYD CURL DR, DEPT OPH 78229 #048-13-2006 L2006
   OPH *012
EDEEN, John. 4499 MEDICAL DR, STE 235 78229 #035-01-1985 L1997 **OP** *020 †40
EDWARDS, John Duncan. 8715 VILLAGE DR, STE 618 78217 #048-12-2000 L2005
   OTO *020 †45
EDWARDS, Juanita Pollard. 7703 FLOYD CURL DR 78229 #036-01-2003 L2007 **AN** *020
EDWARDS, Leo King, Jr. 2011 E HOUSTON ST STE 104C 78202 #048-02-1978 L1978 **IM** *020
EDWARDS, Robt Lee Patrick. 7700 FLOYD CURL DR 78229 #048-04-1954 L1954 **OBG** *020 †30
EDWARDS, William Henry. ■ 78209 #048-12-1973 L1977 **ORS** *020 †40
EGGERS, James M. 2424 BABCOCK RD STE 101 78229 #048-02-1974 L1974 **OPH** *020
EGLOFF, Jorge J. 333 N SANTA ROSA AVE 78207 #649-02-1957 L1966 **OBG PHP** *020
EHLERS, Sandra Jo. 333 N SANTA ROSA AVE 78207 #048-02-1991 L1994 **PD** *020 †55
EHRESMAN, Joe Britt. 7711 LOUIS PASTEUR DR #908 78229 #048-04-1963 L1963
   GYN *020 †30

EHSAN, Aamir. 7703 FLOYD CURL DR, DEPT PATHOLOGY 78229 #704-02-1990 L1998 HMP *020 †50

EICKHOFF, Robin Marie. 7622 LOUIS PASTEUR DR, STE 100 78229 #021-01-1994 L1995 FM *020 †18

EID, Issam Naim. ■ 78240 #021-01-2007 OTO *012

EIDEM, Jami Marie. ■ 78229 #048-13-2008 *012

EISELE, Monica T. ■ 78229 #048-13-2004 L2007 IM *020 †20

ELENES, Rafael. ■ 78240 #048-13-2004 L2008 AN *012

ELIZONDO, Ben Joseph. 4499 MEDICAL DR, STE 360 78229 #048-12-1993 L1995 PG *020 †55

ELIZONDO, Emma Margot. 2718 PLEASANTON RD 78221 #048-12-1977 L1977 FM *020

ELIZONDO, Joseph Stephen. ■ 78228 #024-05-2003 L2007 PD *100

ELIZONDO, Roy J, Jr. 4499 MEDICAL DR STE 355 78229 #048-04-1975 L1975 OBG GS *020 †30

ELIZONDO-VEGA, Heather Le. ■ 78250 #021-01-2002 L2002 ADL *012 †55

EL-KHALINY, Adel N. ■ 78260 #915-03-1983 L1999 FM *020 †18

ELLIOTT, Boyce, III. 5364 FREDERICKSBURG RD 78229 #048-02-1966 L1966 P ADM *020 †75

ELLIS, James Brant. 7711 LOUIS PASTEUR, STE 504 78229 #048-13-1975 L1975 ON IM *020 †20

ELLIS, Jay S, Jr. 4242 MEDICAL DR, STE 3100 78229 #023-12-1982 L1984 AN PME *020 †05

ELLIS, Jonathan Edward. ■ 78251 #001-06-2005 L2007 OPH *012

ELLIS, Richard Earl. 78248 #038-06-1959 L1973 FM GPM *072 †70,18

ELLIS, Troy Christopher. ■ 78209 #035-01-2006 L2008 D *012

ELLSWORTH, Linda Rae. 4499 MEDICAL DR, STE 380 78229 #062-01-1977 L1983 OBG REN *020 †30

EL-MERHI, Fadi Mustapha. 7703 FLOYD CURL DR, MS 7800 78229 #605-01-1996 L2004 DR *020 †80

ELSAID, Anas Mohamed. 7703 FLOYD CURL DR 78229 #915-04-1988 P *100

ELTON, John Paul Selmer. ■ 78249 #007-02-2004 ORS *012

EMADI, Homeira. 7355 BARLITE BLVD, STE 201 78224 #517-10-1991 L2004 PD *020 †55

EMERY, Richard E. 4242 MEDICAL DR, STE 3100 78229 #048-02-1982 L1983 AN *020 †05

EMKO, Nida. 4647 MEDICAL DR 78229 #011-02-2001 L2003 FM *020 †18

EMMETT, Alisha Christine. 7703 FLOYD CURL DR, HEALTH SCIEN 78229 #048-02-2005 L2006 P *012

EMMONS, Ethan Errol. 3851 ROGER BROOKE DR, BROOKE AMC, BLDG 3600 78234 #023-12-1992 L2007 PCC *012

EMMONS, Marisa Elaine. ■ 78251 #048-13-2007 FP *012

EMSLIE, Sara J. ■ 78240 #048-13-2008 *012

ENG, Tony Y. 7979 WURZBACH RD 78229 #023-12-1986 L1999 DR *020 †80

ENGELSGJERD, Lillian Beth. 4499 MEDICAL DR STE 275 78229 #048-12-1978 L1978 OBG *020 †30

ENGLAND, Joey A. ■ 78229 #048-13-2008 *012

ENGLEMAN, Howard Dodge. ■ 78248 #019-02-1970 L1997 FM *071 †18

ENGLES, Lily Lore. 6711 S NEW BRAUNFELS AVE, SAN ANTONIO STATE HOSPITAL 78223 #048-02-1988 L1989 P *020 †75

ENGLISH, William Paul. 111 DALLAS ST, STE 210A 78205 #027-01-1997 L2004 VS *020 †85

ENRIQUEZ, John Nila. 343 W HOUSTON ST STE 702, ROSA VERDE TOWERS 78205 #649-14-1974 L1990 P OS *020 †75

ENRIQUEZ, Omar. 7330 SAN PEDRO AVE, STE 405 78216 #048-13-1999 L2002 IM *020 †20

EPNER, Susan Portnoy. 8042 WURZBACH RD STE 640 78229 #048-13-1995 L1998 N *020 †75

EPPERSON, Alice Ann. 7254 BLANCO RD, STE 201 78216 #048-13-1996 L1997 FM *020 †18

EPSTEIN, Franklin M. 7400 MERTON MINTER ST, SURGERY 112-D 78229 #035-19-1973 L1976 NS N *020 †20,75,25

ERIAN, Ralph Fernand. 45 NE LOOP 410, STE 900 78216 #067-06-1980 L1987 AN *020 †05

ERICKSON, Carl Frederick. 6387 BABCOCK RD STE 1B 78240 #048-13-1986 L1987 FM AN *020

ERIKSON, John Michael. 4647 MEDICAL DR 78229 #048-12-1989 L1990 CD *020 †20

ESCALANTE, Agustin. 527 N LEONA ST 78207 #649-01-1983 L1992 RHU IM *020 †20

ESCALANTE, Bethune. 527 N LEONA ST 78207 #048-02-2002 L2005 DR *012 †20

ESCALANTE, Dante Penson. 4364 THOUSAND OAKS DR 78217 #748-02-1960 L1993 IM *020 †20

ESCAMILLA, Hector Antonio. 343 W HOUSTON ST, STE 201 78205 #649-01-1959 L1962 CD TS *020 †85,90

ESCAMILLA, Michael A. 7703 FLOYD CURL DR 78229 #048-12-1989 L2001 P *020 †75

ESCAMILLA, Ricardo. ■ 78240 #048-13-2004 L2008 FM *020

ESCOBAR, Beatriz Elena. 4400 S PIEDRAS DR, STE 200 78228 #264-13-1992 L2000 VIR *020 †80

ESPARZA, Gina Marie. 902 BANDERA RD 78228 #048-02-1998 L2001 FM *020 †18

ESPINO, David Virgil. 7703 FLOYD CURL DR, MC 7795 78229 #048-02-1983 L1983 FPG FM *040 †18

ESPINOZA, Alfredo Agustin. 7703 FLOYD CURL DR 78229 #048-13-2000 L2003 GE *012 †20

ESPINOZA, Jude Vincent. 6800 W IH 10, STE 100 78201 #048-13-1992 L1993 CD *020 †20

ESPINOZA, Sara Elyse. ■ 78256 #051-01-2000 L2006 IMG *100 †20

ESQUIVEL, Carlos Roberto. 21 SPURS LN, STE 100 78240 #048-02-1991 L1992 OTO *020 †45

ESQUIVEL, Linda I. ■ 78238 #048-13-2005 L2006 FP *012

ESQUIVEL, Louis Hector. 7460 N IH 35 78218 #048-12-1986 L1987 FM *020 †18

ESSEX, David Walter. 7979 WURZBACH RD 78229 #033-06-1984 L2003 HEM IM *020 †20

ESTERL, Robt Michael, Jr. 7703 FLOYD CURL DR, UNIV TX HLTH SCI DEPT SURG 78229 #028-34-1986 L1994 GS TTS *020 †80

ESTRADA, Victor Armando. 14615 SAN PEDRO AVE, STE 250 78232 #048-13-1984 L1985 AI *020 †03,55

ETHERIDGE, Jeff D. ■ 78258 #048-14-2001 L2003 FM *100

ETLINGER, John E. 1303 MCCULLOUGH AVE, STE 235 78212 #048-15-1975 L1975 GS *020 †85

EUANS, Heidi Danielle. ■ 78240 #048-13-2005 OBG *012

EVANS, Carl Robt. 333 N SANTA ROSA AVE, PATHOLOGY ASSOCIATES OF 78207 #048-15-1981 L1983 PTH *020 †50

EVANS, John Allan. 150 E SONTERRA BLVD, SAN ANTONIO ORTHOPAEDIC 78258 #065-06-1970 L1976 ORS *020 †40

EVANS, John Rucker. ■ 78238 #048-02-1955 L1955 P *020

EVANS, Richard Milner. 11900 CROWNPOINT DR, MEDICAL CENTER 78233 #048-02-1971 L1971 OPH *020 †35

EVEARITT, Kristin E. ■ 78249 #025-07-2003 L2005 U *012

EWESUEDO, Reginald Bowie. ■ 78229 #690-01-1983 L1995 PHO *020 †55

EXCONDE, Fidel V, Jr. 414 NAVARRO ST, STE 933 78205 #748-08-1962 L1990 N *020 †75

EYRE, Elizabeth A. 7979 WURZBACH RD, STE U242 78229 #048-15-1985 L1986 AN *020 †05

EYRE, Keith E. 7979 WURZBACH RD, URSCHEL TOWERS #233 78229 #048-15-1987 L1988 RO *020 †20,80

EZEKIEL, Walter John. 333 N SANTA ROSA AVE 78207 #495-04-1965 L1974 AI PD *020 †55,03

FABER, Raymond Andrew. 7400 MERTON MINTER ST, 116-A 78229 #035-09-1972 L1980 P N *020 †75

FABRICANT, Lisa Michele. ■ 78216 #036-01-1999 *100

FAIZ, Mohammadullah. 527 N LEONA ST, ASSOCIATES 78207 #118-01-1985 L2002 FM *020 †18

FAJARDO, Ryan Stephen. ■ 78256 #051-01-2000 L2001 DR *100 †80

FALKENHEIMER, Sharon Ann. ■ 78249 #035-15-1978 L1979 AM *030 †70

FANNING, Robert Knox. 613 PASEO CANADA ST 78232 #047-06-1973 L1975 GS *020 †85

FANTI, Paolo. 7703 FLOYD CURL DR, DIV NEPHRLGY MC 7882 78229 #561-01-1979 L2007 IM NEP *020 †20

FARHART, Scott Allen. 502 MADISON OAK DR, STE 240 78258 #048-13-1985 L1989 OBG *020 †30

FARINA, Jose Manuel. 1200 BROOKLYN AVE, CENTRAL WOMENS HEALTH 78212 #649-33-1983 L1989 OBG *020 †30

FARINA, Manuel. 343 W HOUSTON ST STE 807 78205 #275-01-1948 L1973 P *020

FARIVAR MOHSENI, M. 311 CAMDEN ST STE 102 78215 #517-07-1982 L1993 CD *020 †20

FARLEY, Darren Michael. ■ 78245 #019-02-2003 L2007 OBG *100

FARNES, Stephen W. 2313 LOCKHILL SELM RD #138 78230 #048-15-1988 L1989 FM *020 †18

FARRELL, Elnora A. 111 DALLAS ST 78205 #048-02-1953 L1953 GP *020

FARRELL, Franklyn F. ■ 78216 #035-20-2000 L2006 OM *020

FARRELL, Margaret Ruth. 333 N SANTA ROSA AVE 78207 #034-01-1988 L1993 CHP *020 †75

FARRIMOND, Kenneth Lester. 16845 BLANCO RD, STE 110E 78232 #048-12-1967 L1967 GS *020 †85

FASTLE, Rebecca Kay. 8401 DATAPOINT DR, STE 130 78229 #034-01-1995 L2001 PD *020 †55

FATHI, Nastaran. 215 E QUINCY ST STE 420 78215 #517-05-1977 L1982 NEP IM *020 †20

FAULK, Dean M. 2711 PALO ALTO RD, THE CENTER FOR HEALTH CARE 78211 #048-02-1985 L1987 P *020 †75

FAY, Matt Douglas. ■ 78240 #048-13-2008 IM *012

FEATHERS, Todd William. ■ 78244 #041-02-2006 L2007 ORS *012

FEFERMAN, Kery L. ■ 78209 #048-13-2003 L2007 AN *100

FEIN, Eric Andrew. 7703 FLOYD CURL DR, U OF TX HSC SA 78229 #048-13-1995 L1998 IM *020 †20

FEINSTEIN, Jeffrey A. 8527 VILLAGE DR STE 104 78217 #005-14-1998 L2005 RHU *020 †20

FEINSTEIN, Karen Hasty. 7711 LOUIS PASTEUR DR 78229 #048-13-1997 L1998 OBG *020 †20

FELDMAN, Marc David. 4647 MEDICAL DR 78229 #041-01-1981 L1998 CD IM *020 †20

FELDT, Brent Alan. ■ 78253 #023-12-2000 L2006 OM *020

FELTER, Harold Geo, Jr. 1303 MCCULLOUGH AVE, STE 300 78212 #017-20-1970 L1978 CD IM *020 †20

FELTS, Cora Lou Carter. 621 N ALAMO ST 78215 #048-12-1964 L1964 AN *020

FENTON, Alexis M. 2455 NE LOOP 410, STE 242 78217 #048-02-1990 L2001 CD IM *020 †20

FERENCE, Michael, III. 4775 HAMILTON WOLFE RD 78229 #023-07-1972 L1984 OPH *020 †35

FERENCZI, Iudit Margareta. 11811 BLANCO RD 78216 #781-03-1995 L2008 FM *020 †18

FERGUSON, Richard Burks. 8530 VILLAGE DR 78217 #048-13-1975 L1975 IM PLM *020 †20

FERMIN ARIAS, Eileen. ■ 78258 #308-04-1996 L2005 IMG *020 †20

FERNANDEZ, Alberto Thos. 343 W HOUSTON ST STE 409 78205 #048-02-1973 L1974 OTO *020

FERNANDEZ, Andrea Tiffany. ■ 78229 #048-13-2008 *012

FERNANDEZ, Anna R. ■ 78201 #048-13-1991 L1994 PD *020

FERNANDEZ, Benigno Jorge. 17720 CORPORATE WOODS DR 78259 #042-02-1990 L1992 CHP P *020 †75

FERNANDEZ, Emilio Ossadey. 7703 FLOYD CURL DR 78229 #231-01-1970 L1978 OBG *100

FERNANDEZ, Jose Luis. ■ 78258 #649-01-1952 L1960 GP *071

FERNANDEZ, Miguel C. 7703 FLOYD CURL DR, MSC 7849 78229 #056-06-1985 L1996 EM ETX *020 †16

FERNANDEZ, Orlando. 7703 FLOYD CURL DR, DEPT MED 78229 #275-01-1997 IM *012

FERNANDEZ, Patricia M. 7703 FLOYD CURL DR, MAIL CODE 7843 78229 #132-01-1984 L2007 RNR *100 †80

FERNANDEZ, Sharon R. 3066 E COMMERCE ST 78220 #048-13-1993 L1995 FM *020 †18

FERNANDEZ GRISALES, Juan. 7703 FLOYD CURL DR 78229 #264-16-2001 IM *012

FERRAND, Denis C. ■ 78258 #649-41-1986 FM *020

FERRARO, David Michael. ■ 78209 #019-02-2007 IM *012

FERRELL, Shelly Crawford. ■ 78251 #020-02-2005 L2006 AN *012

FERRER, Aracely Isabel. 740 S ALAMO ST, SOUTH ALAMO MEDICAL GROUP 78205 #048-16-2000 L2003 PD *020 †55

FERRER, Robert Louis. 527 N LEONA ST 78207 #041-09-1986 L2000 FM *040 †18

FERRERIS, Juan Jose. 8627 CINNAMON CREEK DR, STE 1 78240 #048-13-1994 L1996 PD *020 †55

FERRUZZI, Giancarlo R. 7950 FLOYD CURL STE 501 78229 #048-13-1990 L1991 CHP P *020 †75

FERRY, Robert J, Jr. 701 S ZARZAMORA ST, CHILDRENS CTR AT TDI 78207 #048-13-1994 L1995 PDE PHP *020 †55 ‡

FETCHICK, Dianne Marie. 8715 VILLAGE DR, STE 508 78217 #011-02-1980 L1983 END *020 †20

FETCHICK, Richard Jos. 343 W HOUSTON ST, STE 808 78205 #011-02-1980 L1982 ID *020 †20

FEUILLET, Pablo Martin. 525 OAK CENTRE DR STE 220 78258 #264-18-1985 L1998 ID IM *020 †20

FIALA, Lois Ann. 102 PALO ALTO RD, STE 140 78211 #023-12-1988 L2001 VS *020 †85

FIALLO, Alfredo Jesus. 1008 BROOKLYN AVE 78215 #042-01-1982 L1989 NEP IM *020 †20

FICHTEL, Frank Manuel. 4410 MEDICAL DR, STE 600 78229 #048-12-1993 L1994 NS *020 †25

FICHTEL, Lisa Meyer. 7979 WURZBACH RD, URSCHEL TOWERS #233 78229 #048-12-1991 L1992 ON *020 †20

FICKE, Roberta F. 3851 ROGER BROOKE DR, BROOKE ARMY MED CTR 78234 #023-12-1988 L1990 IM *020 †20

FIDELLOW, Rebecca E. 4241 WOODCOCK DR STE A, CHRISTUS VNA HOSPICE 78228 #048-13-1997 L2001 FM PLM *030 †18

FIEBELKORN, Kristin Renee. 4502 MEDICAL DR 78229 #023-07-1996 L2002 PTH *020 †50

FIELDS, Karen Keyse. 520 CANTERBURY HILL ST, CANCER THERAPY & RESEARCH 78209 #038-40-1981 L1984 IM HEM *030 †20

FIERRO, Mario Alberto. 5414 FREDERICKSBURG RD, STE 250 78229 #024-01-1997 L2003 PD *020 †55

FIGUEROA, Michael Scott. 7703 FLOYD CURL DR, MAIL CODE 7871 78229 #048-02-2000 L2003 PCC *020 †20

FIGUEROA, Ramon Luis, Jr. 1715 MCCULLOUGH AVE 78212 #042-02-1989 L1994 FM *020 †18

FINCH, Christopher Haynes. ■ 78258 #023-12-2005 L2007 AN *012

FINCKE, Christopher Allen. ■ 78258 #010-01-1996 L2007 GE *020 †20

FINDER, Kimberly A. 14855 BLANCO RD, STE 100 78216 #048-14-1984 L1986 **D** *020 †15
FINDER, Steven Fernand. ■ 78258 #048-14-1982 L1983 **OS** *020 †70
FINLEY, Margaret Rosina. 4647 MEDICAL DR 78229 #034-01-1994 L2006 **IMG** *020 †18
FINNIE, Mitchell F. 12000 HUEBNER RD, STE 104 78230 #048-04-1991 L1992 **FM** *020 †18
FISCHBACH, Michael. 4647 MEDICAL DR 78229 #007-02-1970 L1982 **RHU IM** *050 †20
FISCHER, Jerome S. 5107 MEDICAL DR, DISEASE CLINIC 78229 #041-02-1977 L1983 **END IM** *020 †20
FISCHER, Steven R. 19238 STONEHUE 78258 #048-12-1997 L1999 **PD** *020 †55
FISHER, David Jacob. 7950 FLOYD CURL, STE 904 78229 #836-01-1974 L1979 **HS PS** *020 †65
FISHER, Keith Allan. 11124 WURZBACH RD STE 206, OAK RIDGE SQUARE 78230 #041-15-2001 L2005 **P** *100 †75
FISHER, Peter. 7950 FLOYD CURL DR, STE 904 78229 #836-01-1981 L1990 **PS HS** *020 †65
FISHER, Rowan Elliott. ■ 78212 #048-04-1939 L1939 **IM** *071
FISHER, Roy Scott. 9207 N LOOP 1604 W 78249 #004-01-1997 L2000 **FM** *020 †18
FISHER, Steven J. 315 N SAN SABA, MEDICAL CENTER 78207 #048-13-1982 L1983 **OPH EM** *020 †35
FISHMAN, Barbara Michele. 7703 FLOYD CURL, DEPT SURG/DIV EMERG MED 78229 #041-01-1979 L1982 **IM EM** *040 †20
FITCH, John Thomas, Jr. ■ 78209 #047-05-1995 L1999 **PD** *020 †55
FITCH, John Thos. 7959 BROADWAY ST 78209 #021-01-1963 L1964 **PD** *020 †55
FITCH, Wm Pilcher, III. 7909 FREDERICKSBURG RD 78229 #021-01-1968 L1969 **U** *020 †95
FLAHERTY, Erin M. ■ 78240 #017-20-2007 **GS** *012
FLATLEY, Mary Ann. 7744 BROADWAY ST, STE 105 78209 #048-13-1979 L1981 **P FM** *020 †75,18
FLEMING, Christine B. 4242 MEDICAL DR, STE 3100 78229 #007-02-1993 L1994 **EM** *020 †16
FLEMING, Daniel John. 315 N SAN SABA, STE 1195 78207 #025-01-1993 L2002 **OTO** *020 †45
FLEMING, Keith Allen. 4242 MEDICAL DR, STE 3100 78229 #048-04-1983 L1984 **AN GS** *020 †05
FLETCHER, Daniel Truman. 21 SPURS LN STE 310, SAN ANTONIO 78240 #047-06-2002 L2007 **HSO** *012
FLORES, Antonio P. 45 NE LOOP 410, STE 900 78216 #649-01-1954 L1977 **AN GP** *020 †05
FLORES, Belinda C. 4242 MEDICAL DR, STE 3100 78229 #048-12-1984 L1986 **AN** *020 †05
FLORES, Eddie. 520 E EUCLID AVE 78212 #048-12-1989 L1990 **GE** *020 †20
FLORES, Edna Iris. ■ 78213 #048-13-2007 **IM** *012
FLORES, Hector A. ■ 78240 #048-13-2003 **GS** *012
FLORES, Jorge Alfonso. 343 W HOUSTON ST, STE 405 78205 #048-13-1977 L1979 **PHP** *030 †70
FLORES, Maria A. 7703 FLOYD CURL DR, U TX MED SCH SAN ANTONIO 78229 #048-13-2006 **IM** *020
FLORES, Martin Gonzalez. 621 N ALAMO ST 78215 #026-04-1980 L1990 **AN IM** *020
FLORES, Ramiro, Jr. 88 BRIGGS ST 78 140 78224 #048-13-1981 L1981 **FM** *020 †18
FLORES, Roland A. ■ 78231 #048-04-2004 L2008 **AN** *012
FLORES, Silvia Emilia. ■ 78213 #649-02-1968 L1999 **IM PUD** *020
FLOYD, Hilliard Derek. 4223 KATRINA LN 78222 #048-12-1979 L1979 **GS VS** *020 †85
FLYNN, Dorothy Flood. ■ 78209 #035-09-1952 L1976 **IMG** *071
FLYNN, William John. 5430 FREDERICKSBURG RD, STE 100 78229 #023-12-1990 L2005 **OPH** *020 †35 ‡
FLYNN, William Robt. ■ 78260 #037-01-1989 L2006 **P** *020 †75
FLYNT, Frederick Lee. ■ 78254 #012-22-2005 L2007 **IM** *012
FOGEL, Guy Rutledge. 9150 HUEBNER RD, STE 350 78240 #034-01-1977 L1994 **ORS** *020 †40
FOLEY, Delton Wayne. ■ 78209 #039-01-1980 L1984 **EM** *020 †16
FOLLETT, Wm Wallace, III. 339 ELIZABETH RD, 661 MESA HILLS DRIVE 78209 #048-02-1967 L1967 **CHP P** *020 †75
FOLSON, Cheryl Lynn. ■ 78205 #023-12-1997 L1999 **GPM** *020 †18,70
FONSECA, Vincent Paul. 107 W ASHBY RD 78212 #024-05-1987 L2007 **PHP** *030 †70
FONT, Eugenio. 8627 CINNAMON CREEK DR, BLDG 1 78240 #042-01-1962 L1990 **PD** *020 †55
FONT-CORDOBA, Jose. ■ 78209 #649-52-1992 L1997 **CD** *020 †20
FOOTE, Michelle Joy. 1303 MCCULLOUGH AVE, STE GL70 78212 #021-05-2000 L2004 **OBG** *020 †30
FORBIS, Orie L, Jr. 1201 AUSTIN HWY STE 116, CAMINO-REAL-COMM SVCS-DIV 78209 #048-02-1953 L1953 **CHP P** *071 †75
FORD, Aven Walker. ■ 78250 #023-12-2007 **IM** *012
FORD, George Almond, III. 255 E SONTERRA BLVD, STE 100 78258 #051-01-1976 L1977 **IM** *012
FORERO, Nicolas Augusto. 2391 NE LOOP 410, STE 405 78217 #264-19-1987 L1997 **NEP** *020 †20
FORLAND, Marvin. ■ 78209 #035-01-1958 L1969 **IM NEP** *071 †20
FORNARIS, Rafael J. 333 N SANTA ROSA, CCF, 4TH FLOOR 78207 #048-12-2004 L2006 **FM** *020 †18
FORNOS, Peter Secundino. 311 CAMDEN ST, STE 504 78215 #649-02-1983 L1987 **PCC CCM** *020 †20
FORSTHUBER, Thomas Gunter. ■ 78255 #409-19-1987 L1996 **PTH** *020 †50
FORTENBERRY, Phillip L. 540 MADISON OAK DR, STE 160 78258 #001-06-2000 L2002 **DR** *020 †80
FOSTER, Lynanne Jane. ■ 78229 #048-02-1998 L2004 **ORS** *100 †40
FOSTER, Preston Furn. 7711 LOUIS PASTEUR, STE 707 78229 #048-14-1981 L1981 **GS** *020 †85
FOULDS, David Michael. 7703 FLOYD CURL DR, THE UNIV OF TEXAS HEALTH S 78229 #060-01-1968 L1981 **PD NEP** *040 †55
FOURNIER, Jacqueline F. 525 OAK CENTRE DR, STE 400 78258 #048-15-1996 L1997 **PD** *020 †55 ‡
FOWLER, Amy Riann. ■ 78229 #048-15-2005 L2008 **PD** *012
FOWLER, Larry John. 7703 FLOYD CURL DR, UNIV OF TX HEALTH SCIENCE 78229 #025-07-1976 L1993 **PCP PTH** *020 †20,50
FOX, David Lester. 9230 MARYMONT PARK 78217 #039-01-1984 L1989 **ORS** *020 †40
FOX, Fredrick Lonald. 12050 VANCE JACKSN RD #201 78230 #016-11-1992 L2000 **P** *020
FOX, Peter Thornton. 7703 FLOYD CURL DR, HEALTH SCIENCE CTR/SAN ANT 78229 #010-02-1979 L1991 **N** *050 †75
FRAME, Donald Clarke. 315 N SAN SABA, STE 107 78207 #039-01-1987 L2000 **UM** *020 †20
FRANCO, Albert. ■ 78258 #649-01-1960 L1965 **GP** *071
FRANCO, Dionne A. ■ 78244 #048-13-2007 **PD** *012
FRANCO, James E. 525 OAK CENTRE DR, STE 210 78258 #048-13-1992 L1993 **OS** *020
FRANCO, Zachary Martin. ■ 78229 #041-12-2008 *012
FRANKA, John C. 1055 ADA ST 78223 #048-13-1998 L2002 **OBG** *020 †30

FRANKLIN, Morris E, Jr. 4242 E SOUTHCROSS BLVD, STE 1 78222 #048-12-1967 L1967 **GS GP** *020 †85
FRATER-WILLIAMS, Heather. 525 OAK CENTRE DR 78258 #035-19-1977 L1979 **PD** *020 †55
FRAZIER, Leah Gwendolyn. 7703 FLOYD CURL DR, UNIV TX HLTH SCI CTR 78229 #048-04-2007 **P** *020
FRED-MIRANDA, Iliana. 7434 LOUIS PASTEUR, STE 109 78229 #042-01-1994 L1995 **NEP** *020 †20
FREDRICKSON, Mark David. 7703 FLOYD CURL DR, UNIV OF TEXAS HLTH SCIENCE 78229 #056-05-1994 L2000 **PM** *020 †60
FREEMAN, Gregory Lane. 4411 MEDICAL DR, STE 350 78229 #016-43-1976 L1983 **CD** *020 †20
FREEMAN, Robert J. 2455 NE LOOP 410, STE 100 78217 #048-15-1988 L1990 **FM** *020 †18
FREEMAN, Theodore M. 8285 FREDERICKSBURG RD 78229 #011-04-1980 L1990 **AI IM** *020 †20,03
FREEMYER, Byron C. 16414 SAN PEDRO AVE, STE 355 78232 #048-04-1986 L1987 **EM** *020 †16
FREEMYER, H Paul. 16414 SAN PEDRO AVE, STE 355 78232 #018-03-1964 L1969 **EM** *020 †16
FREIBERG, Joseph Michael. 4499 MEDICAL DR, STE 240 78229 #020-12-1967 L1987 **IM END** *020 †20
FRENCH, Shawn K. ■ 78254 #039-79-2005, ▲ L2007 **IM** *012
FREY, Joseph Boone. 7049 SAN PEDRO 78216 #039-01-1966 L1969 **OPH** *020 †35
FREY, William Christopher. 3851 ROGER BROOKE DR, BROOKE AMC, BLDG 3600 78234 #023-12-1994 L2002 **PCC** *020 †20
FREYTES, Cesar Ovidio. 7400 MERTON MINTER ST 78229 #042-01-1979 L1992 **HEM** *040 †20
FRIED, Jane Du Rant. 7007 BANDERA RD, STE 19 78238 #051-04-1977 L1979 **PD** *020 †55
FRIED, Terrance A. 1008 BROOKLYN AVE 78215 #051-04-1977 L1979 **NEP IM** *050 †20
FRIEDBERG, Michael Albert. 9600 DATAPOINT DR 78229 #048-13-1981 L1998 **PTH** *020 †50
FRIEDBERG, Samuel J. 7703 FLOYD CURL DR, UNIV OF TEXAS MED SCHOOL 78229 #041-01-1952 L1968 **END IM** *072 †20
FRIEDMAN, Miriam J. 300 W BITTERS, STE 130 78216 #048-12-1999 L2003 **OPH** *020 †35
FRIERSON, John H. 1303 MCCULLOUGH AVE, STE 300 78212 #048-13-1982 L1983 **CD** *020 †20
FROEHLICH, Curtis Donald. ■ 78260 #019-02-2001 L2008 **CCP** *020 †55
FROLICHSTEIN, Robert A. 8401 DATAPOINT, STE 500 78229 #028-03-1992 L2002 **EM** *020 †16
FROST, Randall Eugene. ■ 78229 #048-15-1983 L1983 **FOP PTH** *062 †50
FRY, Constance Louise. 7703 FLOYD CURL DR, MC6230 78229 #021-01-1988 L1992 **OPH PS** *020 †35
FUEHRER, Neil Elliot. ■ 78249 #030-05-2006 **PTH** *012
FUENTES, Leonel. 7400 MERTON MINTER ST 78229 #649-02-1955 L1974 **PM** *071 †60
FUENTES, Leonel M. 45 NE LOOP 410, S 900 78216 #048-15-1988 L1989 **AN** *020 †05
FUENTES, Rosaber Amneris. 2040 BABCOCK RD STE 300 78229 #008-02-1982 L1997 **FM** *020 †18
FUJIMOTO, Scott Alan. ■ 78218 #005-19-2000 L2001 **IM** *020 †70
FUKUDA, Raine Gay. ■ 78240 #010-02-2003 **U** *012
FULLER, Clifton David. ■ 78258 #048-13-2006 **RO** *012
FULLER, David Story. 7703 FLOYD CURL DR, DEPT. OF PEDIATRICS 78229 #048-12-1956 L1956 **P** *071
FULTON, Rebecca Lynn. ■ 78249 #005-12-2006 **PTH** *012
FUNDERBURG, Linda G. 8109 FREDERICKSBURG RD 78229 #048-13-1982 L1983 **P** *020 †75
FUNG, Po-Ming. 8303 MILITARY DR W, WESTLAKES PRIMARY CARE 78227 #048-13-1987 L1988 **IM** *020 †20
FUNK, Mark Stephen. 7703 FLOYD CURL DR, DEPT OB 78229 #048-13-1995 L1996 **OBG** *020 †30
FURGERSON, James L, Jr. 3851 ROGER BROOKE DR, BROOKE AMC, BLDG 3600 78234 #048-04-1992 L1993 **CD** *020 †20
FURMAGA, Wieslaw Bogdan. 7703 FLOYD CURL DR, MAIL CODE 78229 #759-01-1984 L2005 **PTH** *020 †50
FURMAN, Joseph Rochman. 8201 EWING HALSELL DR, STE 280 78229 #048-13-1980 L1980 **AN** *020 †55,05
FURNER, Bonnie J Baird. 8122 DATAPOINT DR, STE 1110 78229 #048-13-1983 L1983 **D** *020 †15
FURST, William R D. ■ 78209 #036-07-1949 L1954 **PD** *071 †55
FURUKAWA, Brian Shigenobu. ■ 78249 #005-12-2006 L2008 **IM** *012
GABATIN, Angelita Ramos. ■ 78230 #748-01-1964 L1975 **NM END** *020 †20,28
GABEL, Andrea Lynn. ■ 78258 #011-02-1996 L2007 **FM** *020 †18
GABRIEL, Hoda Riad Wahby. 6750 TEZEL RD STE 103 78250 #915-02-1970 L1983 **PD** *020 †55
GABRIEL, Joseph Stanley. 2425 BABCOCK RD, STE 108 78229 #495-52-1993 L2006 **AN** *020 †05
GABRIEL, Mary T. 6750 TEZEL RD, STE 103 78250 #048-04-1999 L2003 **PD** *020
GAGLIANO, Angelo V. 45 NE LOOP 410, STE 900 78216 #036-07-1969 L1989 **AN GS** *020 †05
GAGLIANO, Donald Angelo. 131 CARDINAL AVE 78209 #016-42-1981 L1981 **OPH MDM** *030 †35
GALAN, John P. 7210 LOUIS PASTEUR DR, PASTEUR MEDICAL 78229 #048-13-1995 L1996 **IM** *020 †20
GALBRAITH, Gervis Foy. 4775 HAMILTON WOLFE RD, STE 1 78229 #021-01-1967 L1972 **GS** *020
GALBREATH, Autumn Dawn. 7711 LOUIS PASTEUR STE 707 78229 #048-13-1996 L1997 **IM** *030 †20
GALINDO, Mayo Jaime, Jr. 150 E SONTERRA BLVD, SAN ANTONIO ORTHOPAEDIC 78258 #048-04-1980 L1980 **ORS** *020 †40
GALINDO, Rene Lawrence. ■ 78228 #048-12-2000 L2007 **PTH** *100
GALL, Norman Grover. 7703 FLOYD CURL DR, UNIV OF TX HEALTH SCIENCE 78229 #025-07-1968 L1973 **PM** *020 †60
GALLAGHER, Mary Shannon. 7711 LOUIS PASTEUR, STE 200 78229 #019-02-1994 L1995 **OBG** *020 †30
GALLEGOS, Francisco A. 111 DALLAS ST 78205 #649-01-1966 L1973 **PS** *020
GALLEGOS, Jesus S. 7210 LOUIS PASTEUR DR, PASTEUR MEDICAL 78229 #048-13-2003 L2006 **IM** *020 †20
GALLUP, Theresa Marie. ■ 78254 #048-12-2006 **GS** *100
GALVAN, Edgar. 6111 S ZARZAMORA ST 78211 #649-01-1969 L1976 **FM** *020
GALVAN, George Marcus. ■ 78249 #017-20-2001 L2001 **NS** *012
GAMPALA, Ranjitha. ■ 78258 #495-57-1989 **FP** *012
GANESHAPPA, K P. 621 CAMDEN ST 78215 #495-52-1964 L1983 **GE IM** *020 †20
GANESHAPPA, Ravi L. 621 CAMDEN ST 78215 #048-13-1997 L1998 **GE** *020 †20
GANGADHARAN, Meera. 2833 BABCOCK RD STE 3, SOUTH TEXAS CENTER FOR PED 78229 #495-53-1993 L2000 **AN** *012 †55

GAONA, Raul Efrain. 98 BRIGGS ST STE 900B 78224 #649-01-1961 L1967 **IM DIA** *020
GAONA, Raul Efrain, Jr. 343 W HOUSTON ST, STE 804 78205 #649-14-1987 L1996 **IM** *020 †20
GARAY, Virginia. ■ 78240 #011-02-2004 **P** *012
GARCIA, Alejandro. 4315 MOONLIGHT WAY, STE 102 78230 #649-02-1998 L2003 **FM** *020 †18
GARCIA, Alejandro Jesus. ■ 78213 #042-02-2006 **GS** *012
GARCIA, Alexandra. 2211 NW MILITARY HWY, STE 201 78213 #048-14-1998 L2001 **FM** *020 †18
GARCIA, Allen Rather. 730 N MAIN AVE STE 815 78205 #649-02-1957 L1965 **CD IM** *072
GARCIA, Cuitlahuac P. 4503 PECAN GRV 78222 #649-01-1963 L1972 **FM** *020
GARCIA, David Augustin. 540 MADISON OAK, STONE OAK MEDICAL BLDG, SU 78258 #048-13-1995 L1997 **GE IM** *020 †20
GARCIA, Eddie Alonzo. 7950 FLOYD CURL STE 709 78229 #048-12-1988 L1989 **OSM** *020 †40
GARCIA, Edmundo O. 9673 MARBACH RD 78245 #048-13-1981 L1982 **FM** *020 †18
GARCIA, Frank Javier. 150 E SONTERRA BLVD, SAN ANTONIO ORTHOPAEDIC 78258 #048-12-1984 L1985 **GS** *020 †40
GARCIA, Glenn Martin. 7703 FLOYD CURL DR, MAIL CODE 7800 7703 FLOYD 78229 #048-13-1996 L1998 **DR** *020 †80
GARCIA, Gordon David. 7323 MARBACH RD STE 104, KELLUM MEDICAL GROUP 78227 #048-02-2000 L2004 **FM** *020
GARCIA, J Roen. ■ 78258 #649-02-1993 L2002 **AN** *100
GARCIA, Jesus Gerardo. 343 W HOUSTON ST STE 606 78205 #649-02-1970 L1976 **CD IM** *020 †20
GARCIA, John Steven. 730 N MAIN AVE, STE 814 78205 #005-18-1976 L1993 **FM** *020 †18
GARCIA, Jose Alberto. 525 OAK CENTRE DR, STE 320 78258 #038-43-1998 L2003 **OBG** *020
GARCIA, Luis A. 2115 PLEASANTON RD, STE 202 78221 #649-02-1965 L1972 **OBG** *020 †30
GARCIA, Luis Ricardo. 123 SAN PEDRO AVE # A 78205 #649-02-1960 L1965 **OBG** *020 †30
GARCIA, Luz-Estefana. 2121 SW 36TH ST 78237 #048-14-1998 L2005 **IM** *074 †20
GARCIA, Manuel Michael. 1303 MCCULLOUGH AVE, STE 270 78212 #048-15-1988 L1989 **CD** *020 †20
GARCIA, Marco V. 7703 FLOYD CURL DR, SCIENCE C 78229 #429-01-1979 L1991 **DR** *100 †55
GARCIA, Marco Xavier. 2991 GARDEN AVE, BLDG 1279 78234 #048-13-1991 L1995 **IM** *020 †20
GARCIA, Michael D. 1715 MCCULLOUGH AVE 78212 #048-12-1981 L1982 **OBG** *020 †30
GARCIA, Paul D. 6218 NW LOOP 410 78238 #048-14-1987 L1988 **IMG** *020 †20
GARCIA, Ronald K. 2829 BABCOCK RD, STE 636 78229 #048-12-1986 L1987 **IM** *020 †20
GARCIA, Sean Erik. 7703 FLOYD CURL DR 78229 #003-01-1999 L2001 **IM** *020 †20
GARCIA, Sergio Andres. 4402 VANCE JACKSON RD #220 78230 #048-02-1997 L1999 **AN** *020 †05
GARCIA CHAPA, Cesar A. 680 STONEWALL ST, 680 STONE WALL 78214 #649-30-1980 L1982 **P** *020
GARCIA DEL VILLAR, Angel. 4115 MEDICAL DR, STE 305 78229 #649-01-1965 L1977 **PD** *020 †55
GARCIA GARCIA, Francisco. 343 W HOUSTON ST, STE 211 78205 #649-02-1967 L1974 **CD IM** *020 †20
GARCIA-GHINIS, Felipe A. 4212 E SOUTHCROSS BLVD, STE 220 78222 #649-52-1996 L2003 **OBG** *020 †30
GARCIA GUTIERREZ, Raul. 88 BRIGGS ST STE 195 78224 #649-02-1969 L1975 **OBG** *020 †30
GARCIA-HODGE, Marisol A. 6315 S ZARZAMORA ST 78211 #048-02-1998 L2002 **OBG** *020 †30
GARCIA-HOLGUIN, Mary H. 12050 VANCE JACKSN RD #101 78230 #048-14-1991 L1993 **CHP** *020 †75
GARCIA-ROJAS, Xavier. 7703 FLOYD CURL DR, MAIL STOP 7800 78229 #048-04-2005 L2007 **DR** *012
GARDEA, Anthony G. 5253 WALZEM RD, UTHSCSA 78218 #048-13-1987 L1989 **PD** *020 †55
GARDNER, James Francis. ■ 78232 #048-14-1982 L1983 **FM EM** *020 †18 ‡
GARDNER, James Harris. 2829 BABCOCK RD STE 540 78229 #048-02-1955 L1955 **FM IM** *071 †18
GARGUENA-BACUTA, Leah R. 24165 IH 10 W STE 114, LEON SPRINGS PEDIATRICS 78257 #748-02-1991 L1999 **PD** *020 †55
GARNER, Allison. 155 E SONTERRA BLVD, STE 200 78258 #048-13-1988 L1990 **ON** *020 †20
GARNER, William Brandt. ■ 78212 #048-04-2005 **PD** *012
GAROUTTE, M Gerald. 8715 VILLAGE DR STE 519 78217 #028-03-1985 L1991 **CD IM** *020 †20
GARRETT, David, Jr. 3018 SWANDALE ST 78230 #048-12-1987 L1988 **NS GS** *020 †25
GARRIDO, Jose Ramon. 8811 VILLAGE DR 78217 #275-01-1952 L1968 **FM IM** *071
GARRISON, James Edward, III. 5430 FREDERICKSBURG RD, STE 400 78229 #045-01-1977 L1988 **N** *020 †75
GARRISON, James R, Jr. 4330 MEDICAL DR, STE 325 78229 #048-15-1990 L1991 **TS VS** *020 †90,85
GARRISON, Stephen F. 1485 N ELLISON DR 78251 #048-02-1979 L1979 **PD** *020 †55
GARTON, Sheryl Ann. 255 E SONTERRA BLVD, STE 201 78258 #041-13-1987 L1996 **PS** *020 †65
GARZA, Armando David. 21195 IH 10 W, STE 2101 78257 #048-14-2002 L2005 **PD** *020 †55
GARZA, Carmen T. 2020 BABCOCK RD, STE 19 78229 #048-15-1985 L1986 **PD** *020 †55
GARZA, David Ernest. 4499 MEDICAL DR STE 151 78229 #048-13-1983 L1983 **END OBG** *020 †30
GARZA, Erika Alvarez. ■ 78214 #048-02-2006 **FP** *012
GARZA, Ernesto. 700 S ZARZAMORA ST STE 308 78207 #649-02-1971 L1976 **IM** *020 †20
GARZA, Heberto, Jr. 5307 BROADWAY ST 78209 #048-02-1997 L2000 **IM** *020 †20
GARZA, Henry, III. 1303 MCCULLOUGH AVE 70 78212 #048-04-1996 L1997 **OBG** *020 †30
GARZA, Homero Remedios. 7950 FLOYD CURL DR STE 801 78229 #024-01-1976 L1978 **GE IM** *020 †20
GARZA, Jaime. 14811 SAN PEDRO 78232 #649-30-1979 L1985 **PD** *020 †55
GARZA, Jaime Ruperto. 21 SPURS LN, STE 120 78240 #021-05-1987 L1988 **PS OTO** *020 †45,65
GARZA, Jorge A. 343 W HOUSTON ST, STE 511 78205 #048-04-1987 L1989 **PD** *020 †55
GARZA, Jose A. 13423 BLANCO RD, # 306 78216 #649-02-1968 L1974 **AN GP** *020 †05
GARZA, Joseph Robt. 502 MADISON OAK DR, STE 230 78258 #048-12-1977 L1977 **OBG REN** *020 †30
GARZA, Juan Carlos. 1616 CALLAGHAN RD 78228 #649-02-1998 L2003 **FM** *020 †18 ‡
GARZA, Juan Luis. 21 SPURS LN, STE 330 78240 #048-12-1981 L1981 **CD IM** *020 †20
GARZA, Lisa Diane. ■ 78223 #028-03-1996 L1999 **FM** *020
GARZA, Magdalene Diana. 7703 FLOYD CURL DR, MAIL CODE 7792 78229 #048-02-2004 **P** *012
GARZA, Mario A. 8214 WURZBACH RD 78229 #048-02-1997 L1999 **GE** *020 †20
GARZA, Martha. 4499 MEDICAL DR STE 151 78229 #048-13-1982 L1983 **GYN REN** *020 †30
GARZA, Nora O. 7614 CULEBRA RD, STE 103 78251 #048-14-1988 L1989 **FM** *020 †18
GARZA, Ramon. 155 E SONTERRA BLVD # 105, DIAB & ENDO CONS 78258 #308-03-1986 L1997 **END IM** *020 †20
GARZA, Remberto Elizondo. 4499 MEDICAL DR, METHODIST PLAZA SUITE 151 78229 #649-02-1947 L1957 **GYN** *072
GARZA, Rodolfo O. 116 GALLERY CIR, STE 101 78258 #048-13-1997 L1998 **NEP** *020 †20
GARZA, Suzanna Pickett. 3066 E COMMERCE ST, SOUTH TEXAS CENTER 78220 #048-13-1981 L1981 **PD** *020 †55
GARZA-COX, Sanjuanita. 5414 FREDERICKSBURG RD, STE 100 78229 #048-13-1997 L2000 **NPM** *020 †55 ‡
GARZA-TREVINO, Enrique S. 730 N MAIN, STE 615 78205 #649-02-1972 L1976 **P** *020
GARZA VALDES, Leoncio A. 343 W HOUSTON ST 78205 #649-02-1964 L1966 **CD PD** *050 †55
GARZA-VALE, Arnulfo R. 9480 HUEBNER RD, STE 320 78240 #048-13-1973 L1973 **NS** *020 †25
GASIC, Gardana. 4647 MEDICAL DR 78229 #957-02-1991 L2002 **AI** *020 †20,03
GASKILL, Harold V, III. 540 MADISON OAK DR, STE 370 78258 #048-13-1977 L1977 **GS MDM** *020 †85
GASPARD, James Joseph, Jr. 2102 E HOUSTON ST, STE E 78202 #021-05-1975 L1976 **FM** *020 †18
GATES, Jeremy Daniel. ■ 78234 #030-06-2005 L2006 **GS** *012
GAUDET, Tracy. 7703 FLOYD CURL DR, DEPT. OF PEDIATRICS 78229 #036-07-1991 L1992 **OBG OS** *072 †30
GAY, Charles T. 4499 MEDICAL DR, STE 396 78229 #048-12-1984 L1985 **N PD** *020 †75
GAZDA, Suzanne Klaus. 4242 MEDICAL DR, STE 6100 78229 #048-13-1985 L1986 **N** *020 †75
GEAR, Christine L. 7703 FLOYD CURL DR, DEPT OF INTERNAL MEDICINE 78229 #048-13-2006 **IM** *012
GEDALA, Murthy Venkata Ra. 7330 SAN PEDRO, STE 405 78216 #495-70-1995 L2005 **IM** *100 †20
GEE, Rebecca Joe. 343 W HOUSTON ST, STE 204 78205 #001-06-1991 L1997 **OBG** *020
GEIGER, Karen L. 6738 SPRING HURST 78249 #048-13-1993 L1994 **DR** *020
GEISER, Clementina Funaro. ■ 78240 #561-13-1949 L1979 **PHO PD** *071 †55
GELFOND, Jonathan Adam. ■ 78258 #048-13-2000 **OS** *050
GELFOND, Joyce J Lemmons. ■ 78232 #039-01-1966 L1972 **P** *075
GELFOND, Stephen David. 2727 BABCOCK RD STE B 78229 #041-02-1968 L1977 **P** *020 †75 ‡
GENNUSO, Rosemaria. 4499 MEDICAL DR, STE 340 78229 #035-47-1984 L2005 **NS** *020 †25
GEORGE, Benjamin Jacob. ■ 78232 #041-02-2002 L2003 **HO** *012 †20
GEORGE, Dawn Marie. 315 HOWARD ST 78212 #021-01-1989 L1998 **OBG** *020 †30
GEORGE, Dinah S. 1055 ADA ST 78223 #048-13-2001 L2005 **FM** *100 †18
GEORGE, Jacob. 7400 MERTON MINTER ST, AUDIE MURPHY VA HOSP 78229 #495-31-1974 L1987 **P** *020 †75
GEORGE, Maged M. 4340 THOUSAND OAKS DR 78217 #915-03-1979 L1998 **PD** *020 †55
GEORGE, Mary Kusum. 9179 GRISSOM RD STE 135 78251 #495-01-1967 L1975 **PD** *020 †55
GEORGE, Saira Jacob. 18540 SIGMA RD 78258 #048-04-2002 L2006 **D** *020 †15
GERGES, Anwar Soliman S. 303 N FRIO ST, RENAL ASSOCIATES PA 78207 #915-04-1977 L1994 **NEP ATP** *020 †20
GERLINGER, Tad Loren. 3851 ROGER BROOKE DR, DEPT. OF ORTHOPAEDICS AND 78234 #023-12-1994 L2006 **ORS** *020 †40
GERMAN, Victor Frederick. 7703 FLOYD CURL DR, UT HSC SA DEPT OF PEDIATRI 78229 #016-02-1975 L1982 **PDP PDA** *020 †55
GERSTENKORN, Craig Bruce. 7700 FLOYD CURL DR, DEPT. OF EMERGENCY MEDICIN 78229 #026-04-1987 L1993 **EM** *020 †16
GERZA, Carol Beth. 7703 FLOYD CURL DR, DEPT. OF PEDIATRICS 78229 #048-13-1976 L1976 **DR** *020 †80
GHEBREMICHAEL, Semhar Jos. ■ 78240 #048-13-2008 *012
GHIATAS, Abraham Antony. 7703 FLOYD CURL DR, DEPT RAD 78229 #418-01-1972 L1987 **R** *020 †80
GHIDONI, John Jos. 8026 FLOYD CURL DR 78229 #035-08-1957 L1967 **PTH** *071 †50
GHIDONI, Patricia Davis. 7703 FLOYD CURL DR 78229 #048-14-1988 L1989 **PD GPM** *020 †55
GHITIS, Leon. 45 NE LOOP 410 STE 900 78216 #264-05-1976 L1979 **AN** *020
GIBBONS, Caroline M. ■ 78240 #048-13-2007 **IM** *012
GIBBONS, Karen Lynn. 7922 EWING HALSELL DR, STE 440 78229 #023-01-1991 L1994 **PD** *020 †55
GIBBS, Matthew P. 8111 MAINLAND DR, STE 104-604 78240 #048-14-1997 L2000 **FM** *020 †18
GIBSON, Brooke Elizabeth. ■ 78229 #048-13-2003 L2007 **AN** *100
GIBSON, James Bruce. 333 N SANTA ROSA AVE 78207 #036-07-1988 L2007 **OS PD** *020 †55,19
GIDDALURI, Prakash. 7703 FLOYD CURL DR 78229 #495-65-2002 L2008 **FP** *012
GIDVANI-DIAZ, Vinod Kumar. 7711 LOUIS PASTEUR DR, STE 705 78229 #023-12-1996 L2007 **PD** *020 †55
GIFFEN, Martin Brener. 7703 FLOYD CURL DR 78229 #041-12-1945 L1964 **P** *040 †75
GIFFIN, Edward L. ■ 78257 #019-02-1965 L1975 **OTO HNS** *071 †45
GIFFORD, Shaun Michael. ■ 78254 #035-06-2005 L2007 **GS** *012
GIL, Jose Dolores. 5126 FREDERICKSBURG RD 78229 #308-01-1963 L1976 **GS** *072
GILES, Francis Joseph. 7979 WURZBACH RD 78229 #539-05-1982 L1998 *020
GILL, Zeba. 7616 CULEBRA RD, STE 130 78251 #704-02-1989 L1996 **IM** *020
GILLARD, Marijan D. 7703 FLOYD CURL DR, UTHSC DEPT OF FAMILY MED 78229 #048-14-1999 L2002 **FM** *020 †18
GILLASPIE, Cassidy Anne. 7703 FLOYD CURL DR, DEPT OF PSYCHIATRY 78229 #048-13-2006 **P** *012
GILLEAN, W Otho, Jr. ■ 78229 #048-02-1961 L1961 **P** *020
GILLEY, James Stanley. 1200 BROOKLYN AVE, STE 100 78212 #051-01-1977 L1991 **DR R** *020 †80
GILLIAM, Christine Lanee. 502 MADISON OAK DR, STE 140 78258 #048-13-2001 L2006 **OTO** *020 †45
GILSTAD, Dennis Wm. ■ 78230 #048-13-1978 L1978 **AN** *020 †05
GIRALDO ECHEVERRI, Abel. 343 W HOUSTON ST STE 1010 78205 #264-06-1963 L1973 **CD IM** *020
GIRGIS, Soheir Halim. 6315 S ZARZAMORA ST 78211 #915-02-1973 L1984 **PD** *020 †55
GISLER, Christopher Alan. 4502 MEDICAL DR 78229 #051-01-2006 L2008 **IM** *012
GISSELL, Michael B. 6501 BLANCO RD 78216 #048-15-2003 L2006 **GS** *100
GIVENS-MOYER, Laura E. 3338 OAKWELL CT 78218 #048-02-1999 L2000 **FM** *020
GLASOW, Patrick Francis. 1901 BABCOCK RD, STE 301 78229 #045-01-1978 L1987 **PDC PD** *020 †55
GLASS, Jeffrey L. 4242 E SOUTHCROSS BLVD, STE 1 78222 #048-13-1990 L1991 **GS** *020 †85
GLASS, Sheldon Michael. ■ 78240 #048-12-1976 L2007 **IM** *020
GLASSER, David W. 4242 MEDICAL DR, STE 3100 78229 #048-13-1999 L2002 **AN** *020 †05
GLAZIER, Elizabeth Joy. 7703 FLOYD CURL DR, MC 7875 78229 #024-07-1999 L2007 **IMG** *020 †20
GLEASON, Paul Douglas, II. 9150 HUEBNER RD, STE 290 78240 #023-12-1996 L2003 **ORS HS** *020 †40

■ = Address Information Privacy Protected

GLEDHILL, Robert B. 8255 FREDERICKSBURG RD 78229 #065-06-1960 L1993 **ORS OSS** *020

GLENDENING, David Logan. 4502 MEDICAL DR 78229 #019-02-1972 L1979 **EM PUD** *020

GLENN, Theodore James. ■ 78258 #048-12-1955 L1955 **P CHP** *071 †75,18

GLODT, Brian Bennettnew. ■ 78251 #023-12-2004 L2006 **PD** *100

GODINO, John. 3851 ROGER BROOKE DR # 36, BROOKE ARMY MEDICAL CENTER 78234 #035-09-1998 L1999 **GE** *020 †20

GODWIN, Gregory C. 614 SW MILITARY DR, SENDERO IMAGING & TREATMEN 78221 #048-16-1983 L1983 **DR** *020 †80

GOEBEL, Phillip John. ■ 78253 #040-02-2005 L2006 **EM** *012

GOEI, Anthony Dhiantie. 3851 ROGER BROOKE DR # 36, BROOKE ARMY MEDICAL CENTER 78234 #035-46-1985 L1988 **VIR GS** *020 †85,80

GOEI, Gwat Lie. ■ 78209 #506-02-1961 L1971 **R** *071 †80

GOEI, Khing Kwie. 426 CASTROVILLE RD 78207 #506-02-1961 L1969 **FM** *071

GOETZ, Joseph Theodor. 519 W HOUSTON ST, HOSP EMERGENCY ROOM 78207 #539-05-1972 L1976 **PD** *020 †55

GOKMEN, Erhan. 7703 FLOYD CURL DR, UTHSCSA MEDICINE-HEMATOLOG 78229 #902-04-1991 L1994 **ON** *020 †20

GOLDBERG, Helen Laura. 4410 MEDICAL DR, STE 150 78229 #041-07-1988 L1995 **HEM** *020 †20

GOLDEN, David A. 4410 MEDICAL DR, STE 200 78229 #043-01-1976 L1983 **DR IM** *020 †20,80

GOLDMAN, Joshua W. 1303 MCCULLOUGH AVE, STE 532 78212 #016-01-1975 L1999 **N IM** *020 †20,75

GOLDNER, Fred Henry. 8214 WURZBACH RD 78229 #056-05-1970 L1983 **GE IM** *030 †20

GOLDSTEIN, Alasdair M. 9643 HUEBNER RD, STE 103 78240 #048-13-1993 L1998 **PM** *020 †60

GOLDSTEIN, Brian Seth. ■ 78209 #048-13-2005 **PD** *012

GOLDSTEIN, Harvey Martin. 7979 WURZBACH RD, URSCHEL TOWERS #233 78229 #016-06-1966 L1973 **DR** *020 †80

GOLDSTEIN, Jeffrey R. 4400 S PIEDRAS DR, STE 200 78228 #048-04-1992 L1994 **VIR** *020 †80

GOLDZIEHER, Joseph Wm. 14635 BLANCO RD 78216 #035-19-1943 L1953 **END REN** *020

GOLETZ, Ty Henry. 7940 FLOYD CURL DR, STE 560 78229 #056-05-1977 L1982 **ORS OSM** *020 †40

GOMEZ, Dalys F. 24165 IH 10 W STE 126 78257 #048-02-1995 L1997 **AI IM** *020 †20,03

GOMEZ, Faustino. 111 DALLAS ST 78205 #847-10-1965 L1970 **D DMP** *071 †15

GOMEZ, Gianina. ■ 78240 #048-02-2004 **P** *012

GOMEZ, Jorge Emilio. 7703 FLOYD CURL DR, UT HEALTH SCI CENTER 78229 #048-13-1987 L1989 **PD PSM** *020 †55

GOMEZ, Lizette U. 333 N SANTA ROSA AVE 78207 #048-13-1992 L1993 **PD** *020 †55

GOMEZ-CARRION, Patricia J. 1115 W MARTIN ST, (WEST ANNEX) 78207 #048-14-1984 L1988 **P** *020 †75

GOMEZ-MARTINEZ, Marissa I. 11811 BLANCO RD 78216 #048-04-2002 L2005 **FM** *020 †18

GONG, Alice Kim. 7703 FLOYD CURL DR 78229 #027-01-1980 L1985 **NPM PD** *020 †55

GONG, Richard John. 2455 NE LOOP 410 STE 245 78217 #027-01-1980 L1985 **GS** *020 †85

GONIMA, Camilo A. 7950 FLOYD CURL DR, STE 600 78229 #048-14-1998 L2002 **OBG** *020 †30

GONZABA, Vincent Gregory. 7616 CULEBRA RD, STE 130 78251 #048-02-1996 L2000 **IM** *020

GONZABA, William. 720 PLEASANTON RD 78214 #048-02-1959 L1959 **FM GS** *030 †20

GONZABA, William Thos. 16414 SAN PEDRO AVE, STE 355 78232 #048-13-1988 L2000 **IM** *020 †16

GONZALES, Arthur. ■ 78230 #048-13-2006 **AN** *012

GONZALES, Donald Albert. 3463 MAGIC DR STE 320 78229 #035-20-2000 L2002 **OTO** *020

GONZALES, Joe Gene. 2833 BABCOCK RD, STE 110 78229 #048-15-1984 L1985 **PM PMM** *020 †60

GONZALES, Michael Ray. 6800 W IH 10 STE 200, OF SAN ANTONIO 78201 #048-02-2000 L2006 **CD** *020 †20

GONZALEZ, Abelardo G. 45 NE LOOP 410, STE 900 78216 #048-13-1997 L1998 **AN** *020 †05

GONZALEZ, Adan. ■ 78201 #048-15-2007 **IM** *012

GONZALEZ, Adelnery. 14855 BLANCO RD, STE 400 78216 #649-02-1987 L1996 **PD** *020 †55

GONZALEZ, Alejandro B. 5414 FREDERICKSBURG RD, STE 100 78229 #048-13-1978 L1978 **NPM** *020 †55

GONZALEZ, Annika Marie. ■ 78217 #048-14-2004 L2007 **FM** *020 †18

GONZALEZ, Bernice. 225 E SONTERRA BLVD, STE 100 78258 #048-13-1993 L1994 **FM** *020 †18

GONZALEZ, David Moses. 400 CONCORD PLZ, STE 300 78216 #048-13-1980 L1980 **OSM ORS** *020 †40

GONZALEZ, Dora Lilia. 3066 E COMMERCE ST 78220 #048-13-1981 L1981 **FM** *020 †18

GONZALEZ, Enrique. 7703 FLOYD CURL DR, UNIV TX MED SCH-SAN ANTONI 78229 #264-01-1986 L1987 **IM** *012

GONZALEZ, Isela. ■ 78249 #048-02-2001 L2004 **IM** *020

GONZALEZ, Javier G. 226 W BITTERS RD STE 100 78216 #649-02-1984 L1993 **FM** *020 †18

GONZALEZ, Jessica M. 19238 STONEHUE 78258 #048-13-1998 L2001 **PD** *020 †55

GONZALEZ, Jocelyn. ■ 78240 #041-07-1978 L1983 **IM END** *020

GONZALEZ, John J. 333 N SANTA ROSA AVE 78207 #048-13-1976 L1976 **D PD** *020 †15

GONZALEZ, John Joseph, Jr. ■ 78258 #035-01-1998 L2001 **GS** *020 †85

GONZALEZ, Joseph D. 6218 NW LOOP 410 78238 #048-14-2001 L2003 **FM** *020 †18

GONZALEZ, Juan Andres. 1920 SW MILITARY DR, STE 2 78221 #010-02-1984 L1987 **IM** *020 †20

GONZALEZ, Juan Carlos. 7330 SAN PEDRO, STE 405 78216 #264-10-1996 L2003 **IM** *020 †20 ‡

GONZALEZ, M Antonieta. 315 N SAN SABA, STE 1075 78207 #649-01-1976 L1992 **PD** *020 †55

GONZALEZ, Marissa R. ■ 78240 #048-13-2008 **012**

GONZALEZ, Moises C. 1303 BASSE RD #275-01-1956 L1975 **FM** *020 †18

GONZALEZ, Narciso. 7703 FLOYD CURL DR, U TX MED SCH SAN ANTONIO 78229 #048-13-2006 **AN** *012

GONZALEZ, Pastor Mel. ■ 78257 #275-01-1954 L1977 **IM** *062

GONZALEZ, Ramon, Jr. 4242 MEDICAL DR, STE 3100 78229 #048-02-1970 L1970 **AN** *020 †05

GONZALEZ, Robert Medell. 16414 SAN PEDRO AVE, STE 355 78232 #016-11-1993 L1997 **EM** *020 †16

GONZALEZ, Rogelio I. 730 N MAIN STE 408 78205 #649-02-1971 L1979 **U ON** *050 †95

GONZALEZ VELA, Armando M. ■ 78229 #649-02-1966 L1969 **PTH** *072 †50

GOODMAN, Eugenia C. ■ 78265 #045-01-1973 L1984 **OS PHP** *030

GOOTEE, Hubert Geo. 414 NAVARRO ST 78205 #048-02-1954 L1954 **AN** *072 †05

GORAL, James Ernest. 7930 FLOYD CURL DR 78229 #048-13-1976 L1977 **IM** *020 †20

GORDON, David Hugh. 7979 WURZBACH RD, URSCHEL TOWERS #233 78229 #038-06-1971 L1977 **ON HEM** *020 †20

GORDON, Donald J. 4201 MEDICAL DR STE 120, DEPT OF EHS UTHSC-SA 78229 #023-01-1977 L1979 **EM OS** *040

GORDON, Gregory D, Jr. 7940 FLOYD CURL, STE 560 78229 #048-14-2001 L2004 **ORS** *020

GORDON, Mathew Charles. 235 E HILDEBRAND AVE 78212 #030-05-1995 L1998 **GS** *020

GORDON, Wayne Houston. 14607 SAN PEDRO AVE, STE 220 78232 #048-04-1981 L1982 **N** *020 †75

GORDON, William Wade. 7940 FLOYD CURL STE 400 78229 #048-04-1970 L1970 **OTO** *020 †45

GORIGOITIA, Raul. 333 N SANTA ROSA AVE 78207 #231-01-1949 L1972 **P** *020

GORLEY, Jesse David. ■ 78249 #048-15-2006 L2008 **P** *012

GORMAN, James Aubrey. ■ 78249 #048-12-1954 L1954 **TS GS** *071 †85

GORSUCH, Paul L. 7979 WURZBACH RD, URSCHEL TOWERS #233 78229 #041-02-1944 L1947 **GS** *071 †85

GOSSEN, Gary Scott. 4499 MEDICAL DR, STE 126 78229 #048-13-1979 L1979 **GE** *020 †20

GOTANCO, Lucille Marie. 8535 TOM SLICK 78229 #024-07-2002 L2007 **CHP** *100 †75

GOTANCO, Ronald Ernest. 1303 MCCULLOUGH AVE # 229 78212 #016-45-2000 L2004 **AN** *020 †05

GOTIMUKULA, Anupama. 7711 LOUIS PASTEUR, STE 707 78229 #495-57-1990 L2007 **PAN** *020

GOUGE, Steven Fielding. 2391 NE LOOP 410 STE 405 78217 #048-02-1979 L1979 **NEP IM** *020 †20

GOWAN, Thomas J. 525 OAK CENTRE DR STE 400 78258 #048-13-1988 L1989 **PEM** *020 †55

GOYTIA, Virginia Rosalind. ■ 78240 #024-01-2003 **RO** *012

GOYTIA-LEOS, Dina Ximene. 414 NAVARRO ST, STE 703 78205 #010-03-1997 L2000 **IM** *020 †20

GRABOW, Maria Therese. 45 NE LOOP 410, STE 900 78216 #041-14-1992 L2002 **AN** *020 †05

GRAFF, Adam Theodore. 7703 FLOYD CURL DR, HEALTH SCI 78229 #019-02-2004 **OTO** *100

GRAFF, Jennifer Lynn. ■ 78249 #019-02-2004 **OBG** *012

GRAHAM, Jess Allen. 3851 ROGER BROOKE DR, NUCLEAR MEDICINE SVC-BAMC 78234 #023-12-1990 L2006 **NM R** *020 †80,28

GRAHAM, Jimmie Richard. ■ 78232 #049-01-1967 L1982 **PTH** *071 †50

GRANADOS, Rodolfo V. ■ 78230 #048-15-1981 L1981 **AN GP** *020 †05

GRANATO, Michael Paul. ■ 78260 #048-14-1997 L2002 **DR** *020 †80

GRANGER, Jeremy Julian. ■ 78251 #048-15-2006 L2008 **PD** *012

GRANGER, Steven Richard. ■ 78231 #049-01-2001 L2007 **CCS** *012 †85

GRANT, Andrine Karen. 1055 ADA ST 78223 #566-01-1997 L2004 **FM** *020 †18

GRANT, David. 602 W FRENCH PL 78212 #008-01-1974 L1976 **CD IM** *020 †20

GRANT, Nicole N. 11 COURT CIR 78209 #005-11-1995 L2003 **IM** *020 †20

GRANT, Ronald L. ■ 78238 #048-13-1994 **IM** *020

GRANT, Wilson Wayne. 5282 MEDICAL DR, SOUTHWEST CHILDRENS 78229 #048-02-1966 L1966 **PD** *020 †55

GRATHWOHL, Kurt Wm. 3851 ROGER BROOKE DR # 36, BROOKE ARMY MEDICAL CENTER 78234 #023-12-1991 L2003 **AN** *020 †05,20

GRATRIX, Max Logan. ■ 78209 #023-12-2006 L2007 **D** *012

GRAVEL, Paul Barringer. ■ 78240 #048-13-2008 *012

GRAY, Gina A. 19016 STONE OAK PKWY, STE 220 78258 #028-46-1983 L1996 **GS** *020 †85

GRAY, Neal Hadley. 4242 MEDICAL DR, STE 3100 78229 #028-03-1966 L1974 **AN ADM** *071 †05

GRAY, Thomas E, Jr. 16414 SAN PEDRO AVE, STE 355 78232 #048-02-1984 L1992 **FM** *075 †18

GRAY, Von Preston. ■ 78209 #048-15-2008 *012

GRAYBILL, John Richard. 7703 FLOYD CURL DR, UNIVER OF TEX HLTH SCIENCE 78229 #035-20-1966 L1975 **ID IM** *050 †20

GRAYSON, Joanne Marie. ■ 78240 #028-03-2005 **IM** *012

GREEN, David Peeler. 8800 VILLAGE DR, STE 106 78217 #048-04-1962 L1962 **HS ORS** *020 †40

GREEN, Gerald Ira. 540 MADISON OAK DR STE 520 78258 #023-01-1968 L1971 **GE IM** *020 †20

GREEN, John Edward, III. 1007 NE LOOP 410 78209 #048-14-1979 L1979 **FM EM** *020 †18

GREEN, Mary Kelly. ■ 78230 #048-13-2005 **OPH** *012

GREEN, Robert Pershing, Jr. 1303 MCCULLOUGH AVE # 561 78212 #048-12-1978 L1978 **OPH AM** *020 †35

GREEN, Ryan Quint. ■ 78240 #048-13-2007 **GS** *012

GREEN, Travis Cochran. 333 N SANTA ROSA AVE, PATHOLOGY ASSOCIATES OF 78207 #048-13-1974 L1974 **PTH** *020 †50

GREEN, William Thornton. 8407 BANDERA RD, STE 133-152 78250 #048-12-1957 L1957 **FM** *020 †18

GREENBERG, Elliot Irving. ■ 78230 #035-19-1953 L1978 **R** *071 †80

GREENBERG, Laurie E. 12672 SILICON DR STE 100, MEDCO HEALTH SOLUTIONS 78249 #048-04-1981 L1981 **FM** *030 †18

GREENBERG, Lewis. 7703 FLOYD CURL DR, MEDICAL DEANS OFFICE 78229 #048-13-1981 L1981 **IM** *030 †20

GREENE, Elizabeth Anne. ■ 78216 #051-01-2002 L2003 *020 †18

GREENE, Mark Wm. 525 OAK CENTRE DR, STE 110 78258 #048-13-1991 L1992 **PS** *020 †65

GREENFIELD, Gerald Q, Jr. 2829 BABCOCK RD, SAN ANTONIO ORTHOPAEDIC 78229 #023-07-1978 L1990 **ORS** *020 †40

GREER, Sam Jones, Jr. 414 NAVARRO ST 78205 #048-02-1943 L1943 **TS** *071 †85,90

GREGORY, Ernest J, Jr. 2707 CASTANET ST, PHYSICIAN'S PLAZA I 78230 #048-04-1951 L1951 **GS ADM** *050 †85

GRESHAM, John Kennedy. 1303 MCCULLOUGH AVE, STE 300 78212 #051-07-1999 L2007 **IC** *100 †20

GRESORES, Adrian. 7930 FLOYD CURL DR 78229 #048-12-1989 L1990 **NPM PD** *020 †55

GREWAL, Ranjit Singh. ■ 78253 #495-03-1976 L1979 **IM** *020

GRIFFIN, Robert W. 6711 S NEW BRAUNFELS AVE 78223 #038-06-1949 L1955 **IM** *071 †20

GRIFFITH, Adam Michael. ■ 78229 #048-13-2008 *012

GRIFFITH, Jason Spencer. 7703 FLOYD CURL DR, OB-GYN DEPARTMENT 78229 #048-13-2002 L2006 **OBG** *100 †30

GRIFFITH, Matthew Edwin. ■ 78258 #023-12-2001 L2002 **ID** *020

GRIFFITH, Stephen Emery. 7703 FLOYD CURL DR, DEPT OF NEUROSURGERY 78229 #028-34-2004 **NS** *012

GRIMES, Jamie Broome. 3851 ROGER BROOKE DR, BROOKE ARMY MEDICAL CENTER 78234 #023-12-1990 L1992 **N P** *020 †75

GRIMES, Steven Roy. 15719 KNOLLRUN 78247 #023-12-1986 L1987 **OPH** *020 †35

GRIMLEY, Michael Sean. 7711 LOUIS PASTEUR, STE 708 78229 #012-05-1992 L2002 **PHO** *020 †55

GROOS, William Penniman. 8606 VILLAGE DR # A 78217 #048-02-1978 L1978 **PD** *020 †55

GROSS, Glenn W W. 7703 FLOYD CURL DR, CENTER AT SAN ANTONIO 78229 #048-04-1987 L1988 **GE IM** *020 †20

GROSS, Leah E. ■ 78249 #048-13-2007 **AN** *012

GROSS, Sheldon G. 4499 MEDICAL DR STE 396 78229 #048-13-1977 L1977 **CHN N** *020 †55,75

GROSZ, Jorge. 315 N SAN SABA, STE 1075 78207 #649-01-1968 L1977 **PD** *020 †55

■ = Address Information Privacy Protected

GROVE, Kathy D. 1200 BROOKLYN AVE, STE 120 78212 #038-45-1998 L2003 **GS** *020 †85

GROWCOCK, Gerald Wayne. 4400 S PIEDRAS DR, STE 200 78228 #048-02-1974 L1974 **R NM** *075 †80,28

GRUESBECK, Clay. 5245 WALZEM RD 78218 #649-45-1986 L1990 **FM** *020 †18

GRYSEN, Lisa R. ■ 78240 #048-13-2005 L2008 **PD** *012

GUAJARDO, Pablo, Jr. 2406 COMMERCIAL AVE STE E 78221 #649-30-1974 L1978 **ORS PM** *020

GUAJARDO SALINAS, Gustavo. 7703 FLOYD CURL DR, DIV OF GENERAL SURGERY 78229 #649-52-2005 **GS** *012

GUAN, Difu. 8038 WURZBACH RD STE 340 78229 #243-47-1968 L1999 **IMG** *020 †20

GUDE, David Lawrence. 9895 IH 10 W 78230 #048-13-1982 L1983 **FM** *020 †18

GUERRA, Antonio Federico. 7330 SAN PEDRO AVE, STE 405 78216 #048-13-1981 L1981 **FM** *020 †18

GUERRA, Ernesto, Jr. 520 E EUCLID AVE 78212 #048-18-1976 L1977 **IM GE** *020 †20

GUERRA, Fernando Amado. 332 W COMMERCE ST RM 307 78205 #048-02-1964 1964 **PD PHP** *030 †55

GUERRA, Thomas Henry. 735 CLEARVIEW DR, THOMAS HENRY GUERRA MD 78228 #048-13-1972 L1973 **IM** *020

GUERRA-CANTU, Sandra. 332 W COMMERCE ST 78205 #048-16-1998 L2000 **FM GPM** *020 †18,70

GUERRERO, David Anthony. 590 N GEN MCMULLEN 78228 #048-13-1982 L1983 **FM** *020 †18

GUERRERO, Jorge Abel. 7711 LOUIS PASTEUR STE 707 78229 #649-14-1993 L2001 **AN** *020

GUERRERO, Juan Alvaro. 4647 MEDICAL DR 78229 #056-06-1999 L2002 **GE** *020 †20

GUERRERO, Sandra. 4243 E SOUTHCROS BLVD #205 78222 #048-14-1994 L1996 **FM** *020 †18

GUILLAUME, Andamo Anthony. 7909 FREDERICKSBURG RD, STE 100 78229 #005-14-1989 L1999 **OTO** *040 †45

GUILLORY, Derek W. 1802 NACOGDOCHES RD 78209 #048-12-2001 L2003 **EM** *020 †16

GUIMBARDA, Luis Adolfo. 7323 MARBACH RD, STE 104 78227 #649-02-1961 L1966 **GP** *020

GUIRL, Michael J. 8214 WURZBACH RD 78229 #048-04-1997 L1998 **GE** *020 †20

GULDE, Christopher G. 8627 CINNAMON CREEK DR, BLD 101 78240 #048-13-1992 L1994 **PD** *020 †55

GULLICK, Richard Anderson. 3851 ROGER BROOKE DR, NEUROGURGY CLC 78234 #023-12-1994 L1995 **NS** *020 †25

GUMMERSON, Matthew Charle. ■ 78251 #010-01-2005 L2006 **AN** *012

GUNKEL, John Harry. 5807 BABCOCK RD, # 231 78240 #048-13-1974 L1974 **PD** *020 †55

GUNN, John Christian R. ■ 78240 #048-01-1997 L2004 **TS** *020

GUNSBORE, B Annette. 540 OAK CENTRE DR STE 200, STONE OAK PHYSICIAN PLAZA 78258 #048-13-1991 L1993 **PD** *020 †55

GUNUGANTI, Manjusha. 20770 N HWY 281, STE 108-492 78258 #496-24-1999 L2006 **PM** *100

GUNUGANTI, Vijay K. 540 MADISON OAK DR, STE 200 78258 #496-27-1995 L2005 **ON HEM** *020 †20

GUPTA, Ajay. 7703 FLOYD CURL DR, DEPT OF SURGERY MC 7841 78229 #025-07-2000 L2004 **TS** *012

GUPTA, Sambit Kumar. 117 LABURNUM DR 78209 #495-54-1989 L2006 **IM EM** *020 †20

GURIAN, John H. 8401 DATAPOINT DR, STE 600 78229 #035-45-1987 L1995 **RNR** *020 †80

GURKOWSKI, Mary Ann. 7703 FLOYD CURL DR, UNIV OF TEXAS HEALTH SCI C 78229 #048-13-1984 L1985 **AN** *020 †05 ‡

GURWITZ, Brad W. 8042 WURZBACH RD STE 310 78229 #048-02-1990 L1992 **GS** *020 †85

GURWITZ, Lisa Blumenthal. 4499 MEDICAL DR, STE 119 78229 #019-02-1990 L1995 **OBG** *020 †30

GUSME, Concepcion C. 525 OAK CENTRE DR, STE 320 78258 #048-13-2001 L2005 **OBG** *020

GUTIERREZ, Amy J. 9355 BANDERA RD STE 136 78250 #048-13-2000 L2003 **FM** *020 †18

GUTIERREZ, Christina E. 1730 SW MILITARY DR, CENTRAL WOMENS HEALTH 78221 #048-12-1998 L2002 **OBG** *020 †30

GUTIERREZ, Constanza J. 7703 FLOYD CURL 78229 #048-14-1996 L2002 **DR** *020 †80

GUTIERREZ, Olivia Aguilar. ■ 78230 #048-15-1985 L1986 **AN** *020 †05

GUTZMAN, Dennis Raymond. 2424 BABCOCK RD, STE 201 78229 #030-05-1975 L1976 **ORS** *020 †40

GUZ, Evan Craig. 16414 SAN PEDRO AVE, STE 355 78232 #025-01-1991 L1994 **EM** *020 †16

GUZLEY, Gregory Jos. 7979 WURZBACH RD, URSCHEL TOWERS #233 78229 #048-04-1978 L1978 **HEM ON** *020 †20

GUZMAN, Alonzo. 2108 NW MILITARY HWY, CASTLE HILLS FAMILY PRACTI 78213 #048-13-1987 L1988 **FM** *020 †18

GUZMAN, Herbert. 6315 S ZARZAMORA ST 78211 #042-02-1994 L1998 **OBG** *020 †30

HA, Chul S. 7703 FLOYD CURL DR, MAIL CODE 7889 78229 #024-01-1987 L1992 **RO** *020 †80

HAASE, Louis Karl, III. ■ 78250 #023-12-2008 *012

HACK, Glendon S. 111 DALLAS ST 78205 #048-14-1998 L1999 **FM** *020 †18

HADDOCK, Neil Forrest. 325 E SONTERRA BLVD # 110 78258 #048-14-1981 L1981 **D** *020 †15

HADLEY, Celene Rosanne. ■ 78249 #021-01-2004 L2007 **DR** *012

HADNOTT, James Leonard. 7950 FLOYD CURL DR 78229 #048-02-1962 L1962 **OBG** *020 †30

HADNOTT, William Hicks. 414 NAVARRO ST 78205 #048-02-1957 L1957 **AN** *071 †05

HAFF, Roderick Canavan. 15060 CADILLAC DR 78248 #008-01-1962 L1977 **GS** *020 †85

HAFFNER, Steven Mark. UNIV TX HLTH SCI CTR EPID 78284 #035-46-1975 L1982 **END** *050 †20

HAGEDORN, Scott Iler. ■ 78254 #016-42-2005 L2007 **IM** *012

HAGINO, Nobuyoshi. 7703 FLOYD CURL DR 78229 #572-37-1957 **OS** *050

HAGINO, Ryan Teruo. 7703 FLOYD CURL DR, MC 7741 78229 #016-06-1990 L1996 **VS** *020 †85

HAHN-NAVAS, Sora Helena. 7703 FLOYD CURL DR, MSC 62 78229 #264-10-1993 **OPH** *012

HAILE, David Johannes. 7703 FLOYD CURL DR, UNIVERSITY OF TEXAS HSC 78229 #023-07-1985 L1995 **HO** *100 †20

HAILPARN, Troy Robbin. 255 E SONTERRA BLVD, STE 210 78258 #035-46-1989 L1994 **OBG** *020 †30 ‡

HAIN, April D. 1055 ADA ST, COMMUNITY MEDICINE ASSOC 78223 #048-04-1999 L2002 **FM** *020 †18

HALE, Albert Spencer. ■ 78229 #036-05-1958 L1965 **DR R** *071 †80,28

HALE, Daniel Esten. 333 N SANTA ROSA AVE 78207 #048-14-1977 L1977 **PDE** *050 †55

HALEY, Timothy Francis. ■ 78248 #050-02-1996 L1998 **NPM** *020 †10

HALFF, Glenn Alexander. 7703 FLOYD CURL DR, UTHSCSA DEPT SUR 78229 #048-14-1983 L1983 **GS** *020 †85

HALKA, Kathleen Grace. 8001 MIDCROWN DR, STE 100-102 78218 #030-06-1980 L1993 **HO HEM** *020 †20

HALL, Brad Bailey. 7400 MERTON MINTER ST 78229 #048-15-1977 L1977 **OSS ORS** *020 †40

HALL, Caitlin Anne. ■ 78216 #024-16-1995 L1998 **PD** *020 †55

HALL, David Allen. ■ 78242 #056-05-1990 **P** *100

HALL, Gordy Saml. 7407 BROADWAY ST, WELLMED NORTHERN HILLS 78209 #048-13-1983 L1983 **FM** *020 †18

HALL, Graham T. 7959 BROADWAY ST STE 600 78209 #048-13-1987 L1988 **PD** *020 †55

HALL, Jordan Manuel. ■ 78259 #023-12-2004 L2006 **PTH** *012

HALL, Kevin Louis. 7979 WURZBACH RD 78229 #023-12-1983 L2003 **OBG GO** *020 †30

HALL, Richard Allen. 3851 ROGER BROOKE DR, BROOKE ARMY MEDICAL CENTER 78234 #021-01-1971 L1972 **GS** *071 †85

HALLMARK, Alaina D. 4318 WOODCOCK DR, STE 120 78228 #048-13-1999 L2002 **FM** *020 †18

HAMDAN, Zakaria Ibrahim. ■ 78249 #042-02-2002 L2005 **NEP** *100 †20

HAMELIN, Stefan Christoph. ■ 78249 #023-12-2008 *012

HAMILTON, Brandon Gregory. ■ 78244 #023-12-2004 L2005 **IM** *020 †20

HAMILTON, Kathryn R. 4242 MEDICAL DR, STE 3100 78229 #048-13-1991 L1993 **APM** *020 †05

HAMLIN, Denise Renee. ■ 78258 #048-13-2002 L2007 **AN** *100 †05

HAMMET, George C. 8401 DATAPOINT DR STE 600, SOUTH TX RADIOLOGY GRP 78229 #036-05-1986 L1998 **DR NM** *020 †80,28

HAMMOND, Lisa A. 7979 WURZBACH RD 78229 #048-13-1991 L1996 **ON** *020 †20

HAMNER, Lawrence R, III. 4330 MEDICAL DR, STE 325 78229 #048-12-1981 L1981 **TS** *020 †85,90

HAMON, Gregory A. 3903 WISEMAN BLVD, STE 304 78251 #048-12-1989 L1990 **GS** *020 †85

HAMPTON, Michael Stewart. ■ 78218 #023-01-2005 L2007 **EM** *012

HAMPTON, Robert W, Jr. 16414 SAN PEDRO AVE, STE 710 78232 #048-02-1988 L1989 **EM** *020 †16

HANCOCK, Heather May. ■ 78253 #023-12-2007 **GS** *012

HANDLER, Tristan Elliot. ■ 78256 #024-05-2005 L2007 **IM** *012

HANN, Matthew Christopher. ■ 78258 #010-02-2003 L2005 **CD** *012 †20

HANNIGAN, Richard Edward. 3851 ROGER BROOKE DR, IMC MCHE-MD2-M 78234 #048-13-1983 L1983 **IM** *020 †20

HANNIGAN, Vicki Ann. 7400 MERTON MINTER ST, AUDIE MURPHY VA HOSPITAL 78229 #048-13-1983 L1983 **IM** *020 †20

HANSELKA-JACOBSON, Leah M. 527 N LEONA ST 78207 #048-13-1994 L1999 **PD** *020

HANSEN, Jason Lindsay. ■ 78250 #048-15-2008 *012

HANSEN, Polly Boren. 540 MADISON OAK DR, STE 160 78258 #048-12-1987 L1988 **DR** *020 †80

HANSEN, Shana Lee. ■ 78216 #023-12-2003 L2005 **ADL** *012 †55

HANYSAK, Bryan John. ■ 78249 #048-13-2002 L2005 **GE** *012 †20

HAQ, Suhaib Waqarul. 527 N LEONA ST MS 49-2, COMMUNITY MEDICINE ASSOCIA 78207 #704-16-1999 L2005 **FM** *020 †20

HARDAWAY, Thomas Gray, II. 3030 NACOGDOCHES RD # 101 78217 #048-13-1979 L1988 **CHP P** *020 †75

HARDEN, Michelle Ann. 7711 LOUIS PASTEUR DR, STE 200 78229 #048-13-1988 L1989 **OBG** *020 †30

HARDIN, Carl Wayne. 7930 FLOYD CURL DR, SOUTH TEXAS MRI, LTD 78229 #048-12-1981 L1988 **DR RNR** *020 †80

HARDIN, Mark Orman. ■ 78258 #004-01-2007 **GS** *012

HARDMAN, Rulon Lawrance. ■ 78254 #032-01-2007 **DR** *012

HARE, Henry P, Jr. 414 NAVARRO ST, 1122 NIX MEDICAL CENTER 78205 #048-02-1947 L1947 **P** *020 †75

HAREA, Mihaela Cristina. 45 NE LOOP 410, STE 900 78216 #781-01-1988 L2003 **AN** *020

HARLAN, Brent Smail. ■ 78251 #038-06-2005 L2007 **P** *012

HARLE, Brian Waid. 7711 LOUIS PASTEUR DR, STE 200 78229 #048-15-1988 L1989 **OBG** *020 †20

HARLE, Harold Lewis. ■ 78232 #048-12-1954 L1954 **PHP** *071 †50

HARLE, Mark Allan. 4242 MEDICAL DR, STE 3100 78229 #048-15-1986 L1987 **AN** *020 †05

HARLE, Raymond Paul. 8042 WURZBACH RD STE 240 78229 #048-12-1956 L1956 **GP** *020 †20

HARMON, William James. 7909 FREDERICKSBURG RD, STE 110 78229 #016-02-1991 L2000 **U** *020 †95

HARNISCH, Michael Chapman. ■ 78209 #016-11-1995 L1996 **GS** *020 †85

HARPER, John Kirk. 6711 S NEW BRAUNFELS AVE, 6711 SOUTH NEW BRAUNFELS 78223 #048-02-1991 L1992 **P CHP** *020 †75

HARPER, John Yerkes, Jr. 311 CAMDEN ST STE 601 78215 #048-02-1954 L1954 **OPH** *020 †35

HARPER, Randall Carrol. ■ 78230 #020-02-1963 L1969 **PTH** *071 †50

HARR, Mary Beth. 7940 FLOYD CURL DR STE 630 78229 #048-13-1994 L1995 **FM** *020 †18

HARREL, Nicholas David, III. ■ 78240 #048-13-2008 *012

HARRELSON, Steven Layne. ■ 78258 #048-13-1986 **FM EM** *020 †18

HARRINGTON, Brian Boru. 45 NE LOOP 410, STE 900 78216 #048-02-1982 L1983 **AN** *020 †05

HARRINGTON, Gerald R, Jr. 8038 FREDERICKSBURG RD, SETTERS MEDICAL GROUP PA 78229 #028-34-1980 L1995 **IM CCM** *020 †20

HARRINGTON, Kathy Louise. ■ 78210 #012-05-1987 L1988 **CD** *020 †20

HARRIS, Adam Isaac. 7950 FLOYD CURL STE 709 78229 #005-18-1985 L1997 **OAR ORS** *020 †40

HARRIS, Bernard Sheldon. 1007 NE LOOP 410 78209 #047-07-1983 L1986 **IM** *020

HARRIS, Dudley Harwell. 14807 SAN PEDRO AVE 78232 #048-12-1969 L1969 **OPH** *020 †35

HARRIS, Elizabeth Spinuzz. 540 MADISON OAK, STE 560 78258 #016-06-1986 L1994 **GS** *020 †65

HARRIS, Judith Lee Knapp. 4212 E SOUTHCROSS BLVD #14 78222 #030-05-1967 L1971 **FM** *020 †18

HARRIS, Robert Eldred. 7922 EWING HALSELL DR, STE 210 78229 #051-01-1961 L1974 **OBG ID** *071 †30

HARRIS, Robert Lee. 14100 SAN PEDRO AVE 78232 #048-12-1958 L1958 **FM** *020 †18

HARRIS, Sabrina Denise. 4502 MEDICAL DR 78229 #048-02-1991 L1992 **IM** *020

HARRIS, Stanley Chester. ■ 78239 #035-08-1955 L1977 **IM NM** *071

HARRIS, William Robt. 6711 S NEW BRAUNFELS AVE, SAN ANTONIO STATE HOSPITAL 78223 #048-13-1976 L1981 **CHP** *020

HARRISON, Chantal Ricaud. UHTSC SA, DEPT PATH 78284 #011-03-1971 L1978 **PTH** *020 †50

HARROFF, Allyson Lynn. 540 MADISON OAK DR, STE 200 78258 #038-43-1998 L2006 **HO** *020 †20

HARSEWAK, Dashartha. ■ 78229 #011-02-2005 L2007 **DR** *012

HARSTON, Chad Winter. ■ 78259 #048-04-2001 L2006 **DR** *100 †80

HART, Kenneth R. 94 BRIGGS ST, STE 600 78224 #048-78-1965, ▲ L1980 **OS** *071 †70

HART, Noal Isaac. ■ 78253 #035-20-2005 L2007 **DR** *012

HART, Polly Denise. 714 E QUINCY ST, ALAMO KIDNEY HEALTH 78215 #028-03-1981 L1987 **NEP IM** *020 †20

HART, Robert Glen. 7703 FLOYD CURL DR, DEPARTMENT OF MED NEUROLOG 78229 #028-03-1977 L1983 **N** *050 †75

HARTMAN, Janna L. 4242 MEDICAL DR, STE 3100 78229 #048-13-1998 L2002 **AN** *020 †05

HARTRONFT, Scotte Ray. 7400 MERTON MINTER ST, ATTN: GRECC/182 78229 #039-01-1998 L2003 **IMG IM** *020 †20 ‡

HARTSELL, Floyd Wright. 8401 DATAPOINT DR, STE 500 78229 #036-05-1984 L1992 **EM AM** *020 †16

HARTSELL, Patrick Allen. 4330 MEDICAL DR, STE 100 78229 #048-15-1992 L1993 **VS** *020 †85
HARTSON, Reid C. 200 CONCORD PLZ, STE 510 78216 #048-14-1989 L1990 **ON** *020 †20
HARTZLER, Anthony Wayne. 7719 LOUIS PASTEUR CT 78229 #038-06-2004 L2007 **ID** *012 †20
HARVEY, Dalila Dawn. 7703 FLOYD CURL DR, DEPT OF OB/GYN MC 7836 78229 #047-07-2004 **OBG** *012
HASSELL, Howard Jay. 8255 FREDERICKSBURG RD 78229 #036-05-1974 L1980 **ORS** *020
HASSELL, Loma H, II. ■ 78210 #051-04-1978 L2006 **NEP IM** *020 †20
HATCH, Mark Wm. 7909 FREDERICKSBURG RD, STE 100 78229 #048-02-1984 L1985 **OTO** *020 †45
HAU, Ann Thien. ■ 78229 #048-13-2008 *012
HAUG, Jendi Lyn. ■ 78247 #048-13-2006 **PD** *012
HAUSENFLUKE, Linda G. 301 N FRIO ST 78207 #048-13-1991 L1992 **PTH** *020 †50
HAUSHEER, Frederick H. 8122 DATAPOINT DR, STE 1250 78229 #028-03-1982 L1992 **ON IM** *030 †20
HAVEL, Richard Dale. ■ 78220 #048-13-1979 L1979 **OM** *030 †70
HAWKINS, Linda Louise. 111 DALLAS ST 78205 #047-05-1980 L1991 **P** *020 †75
HAY, Joshua C. ■ 78254 #048-02-2006 **PM** *012
HAYDA, Roman Artym. 3851 ROGER BROOKE DR, BROOKE ARMY MEDICAL CENTER 78234 #023-12-1988 L1991 **ORS OTO** *020 †40
HAYEE, Abdul-Ahad. 7703 FLOYD CURL DR, DEPT OF ANESTHESIOLOGY 78229 #048-15-2004 L2008 **AN** *012
HAYES, David Keith. 3851 ROGER BROOKE DR, BROOKE ARMY MEDICAL CENTER 78234 #045-01-1983 L1995 **OTO GS** *030 †45
HAYES, Jackie Allen. 3857 ROGER BROOKE DR, BROOKE ARMY MEDICAL CENTER 78234 #027-01-1988 L1989 **PUD CCM** *020 †20
HAYES, Teresa Chu. 8026 FLOYD CURL DR, SOUTH TEXAS PATHOLOGY 78229 #048-13-1982 L1983 **PTH** *020 †50
HAYS, Barrett K. 723 MESA RDG 78258 #047-07-1981 L1981 **FM** *020 †18
HAYS, Janet Virginia. 7703 FLOYD CURL DR, UTHSCSA CARDIO DIVISION 78229 #048-13-1984 L1986 **CD IM** *020 †20
HAZLETT, David Richard. 6711 S NEW BRAUNFELS AVE, SAN ANTONIO STATE SCHOOL 78223 #041-12-1958 L1980 **PUD AM** *020 †20
HEAD, Hayden W, III. 7703 FLOYD CURL DR, UNIV TX MED SCH 78229 #048-04-2002 L2008 **DR** *012
HEALEY, William Vincent. ■ 78240 #035-01-1956 L1976 **GS HNS** *071 †85
HEALY, Betty Jon. 45 NE LOOP 410 STE 900, STAR ANESTH PA 78216 #048-13-1974 L1974 **AN** *020 †05
HEALY, Jane Anne. ■ 78232 #036-07-2008 *012
HEALY, Jean E. ■ 78232 #048-13-2006 **FP** *012
HEALY, Jennifer Marie. ■ 78253 #003-75-2007, ▲ **IM** *012
HEALY, John Patrick. 45 NE LOOP 410, STE 900 78216 #048-13-1974 L1974 **AN** *020 †05
HEALY, Mark Edward. 8401 DATAPOINT DR, STE 600 78229 #021-01-1982 L1989 **DR RNR** *020 †80
HEARNE, Linda Susan. 1102 BARCLAY 78207 #048-02-1986 L1987 **IM** *020 †20
HEARNE, Steven Eric. 1804 NE LOOP 410 STE 101 78217 #048-04-1984 L1985 **GE** *020 †20
HEBERT, Emmy Laine. ■ 78230 #048-15-2007 **PTH** *012
HEBERT, Thomas. 1911 PLEASANTON RD 78221 #021-05-1952 L1953 **FM** *071 †18
HECK, Heidi R. 7711 LOUIS PASTEUR DR, STE 200 78229 #048-13-1985 L1986 **OBG** *020 †30
HECKMAN, Michael Merl. 9150 HUEBNER RD, STE 330 78240 #048-13-1983 L1983 **ORS OSM** *020 †40
HEDGES, Parke J. 7711 LOUIS PASTEUR DR, STE 200 78229 #048-13-1982 L1983 **OBG** *020 †30
HEIMBACH, R Dean. ■ 78213 #016-02-1960 L1979 **AM UM** *071 †70
HEIM-HALL, Josefine Maria. 7703 FLOYD CURL DR, DEPT OF PATH 78229 #561-19-1986 L1996 **PTH PP** *020 †50
HEINRICH, Curtis Seth. 519 W HOUSTON ST 78207 #048-02-1966 L1966 **EM** *020
HEINRICH, Ward D, Jr. 4025 SOUTHCROSS BLVD, STE 30 78222 #041-09-1971 L1976 **OPH FM** *071 †35
HEISSER, Anna Henry. 5788 ECKHERT RD 78240 #021-01-1989 L1998 **AI** *020 †55,03
HEISTAND, Michael. 8042 WURZBACH RD STE 350 78229 #048-04-1971 L1971 **GP** *020
HELD, Edward Conger. 233 TUXEDO AVE 78209 #038-06-1948 L1997 **GP AM** *071
HELD, Kristin Story. 325 E SONTERRA BLVD, STE 100 78258 #048-13-1985 L1986 **OPH** *020 †35
HELD, Steven Dieter. ■ 78249 #045-04-2001 L2003 **IM** *100
HELLER, Kimberly Koester. 4318 WOODCOCK DR, STE 120 78228 #048-13-1985 L1987 **FM** *020 †18
HELLER, Scott Adam. ■ 78229 #035-09-2006 L2008 **IM** *020
HELLING, Eric Robt. 3851 ROGER BROOKE DR, BROOKE ARMY MED CTR. 78234 #023-12-1991 L1993 **PS** *020 †45
HELM, Kristen Elizabeth. 8715 VILLAGE DR STE 300 78217 #048-14-2001 L2005 **OBG** *020 †30
HEMPEL, Karl Hans. 414 NAVARRO ST STE 703 78205 #038-41-1964 L1968 **RHU IM** *020 †20
HEMPHILL, James E. ■ 78239 #019-02-1941 L1941 **PS** *071 †65,85
HEMPHILL, John Carter. ■ 78249 #045-04-2001 L2005 **CD** *012 †20
HENAO MARTINEZ, Andres Fe. 7703 FLOYD CURL DR 78229 #264-05-2003 **IM** *012
HENDELES, Frieda R. ■ 78216 #352-11-1942 L1975 **P N** *071
HENDERSON, Chance J. ■ 78253 #048-12-2006 L2008 **ORS** *012
HENDERSON, Cody Lance. 5414 FREDERICKSBURG RD, STE 100 78229 #001-02-1994 L2004 **NPM** *020 †55
HENDERSON, Deborah Barbar. ■ 78253 #048-12-2006 **D** *012
HENDERSON, Diana K Hood. 4775 HAMILTON WOLFE RD, STE 1 78229 #048-13-1988 L1989 **OTO** *050 †45
HENDERSON, Harry M, Jr. ■ 78209 #010-02-1946 L1946 **GS OM** *072 †85
HENDERSON, Jeffrey M. 6311 BLUEBIRD DR 78240 #048-14-2002 L2004 **PD** *020 †55
HENDRICK, Eric P. 8401 DATAPOINT DR, STE 600 78229 #048-02-1994 L1996 **DR PDR** *020 †80
HENIGAN, Renee. ■ 78240 #048-16-2007 **PD** *012
HENKES, Norman David. 333 N SANTA ROSA AVE, PATHOLOGY ASSOCIATES OF 78207 #048-02-1979 L1979 **PTH PCP** *020 †50
HENRICH, William Lloyd. 7703 FLOYD CURL DR, MCS 7790 78229 #048-04-1972 L1972 **NEP IM** *020 †20
HENRY, James Merrill. 7703 FLOYD CURL DR, UTHSCSA MAIL CODE 7750 78229 #407-20-1964 L2006 **NP N** *040 †50
HENRY, Steven Leonard. 21 SPURS LN STE 310, SAN ANTONIO 78240 #007-02-2001 L2007 **HSO** *012
HENSLEE, Scott M. 7950 FLOYD CURL DR, STE 909 78229 #048-13-1998 L2002 **D** *020 †15
HENWOOD, Beverley L. 9240 GUILBEAU RD, STE 128 78250 #065-09-1972 L1978 **FM** *020 †18 ‡

HENY, Joseph Samara. 903 SW 24TH ST 78207 #048-02-1958 L1958 **FM GS** *020
HERATH, Padmini Dhammika. 7703 FLOYD CURL DR, DEPT FM 78229 #220-05-2000 **FP** *012
HERDMAN, Chase R. ■ 78249 #048-13-2002 L2005 **GE** *012 †20
HERFF, Augustus F, Jr. 7 GARDEN SQ 78209 #041-02-1953 L1953 **GS** *074 †85
HERMANN, Robert Chas, Jr. 4647 MEDICAL DR 78229 #048-02-1969 L1969 **N** *020 †75
HERMSTAD, Erik Lars. 650 GRANITE CLF, EMREGENCY MEDICINE 78251 #019-02-2004 L2007 **EM** *020
HERN, Russell Steven. 4242 MEDICAL DR, STE 3100 78229 #048-12-1980 L1980 **AN** *020
HERNANDEZ, Andres. 1310 MCCULLOUGH AVE 78212 #048-13-1992 L1996 **EM** *020 †16
HERNANDEZ, Antonio. 7703 FLOYD CURL DR, SCIENCE CENTER AT SAN ANTO 78229 #048-02-1999 L2003 **AN CCA** *100 †05
HERNANDEZ, Antonio Jose. ■ 78256 #048-13-2004 L2006 **NPM** *012 †55
HERNANDEZ, Ariel. 1423 GUADALUPE ST STE 105 78207 #048-06-1975 L1980 **FM** *020 †18
HERNANDEZ, Arthur. 7355 BARLITE BLVD STE 405, SOUTHWEST TEXAS PAIN CLINI 78224 #005-06-1971 L1982 **AN PME** *020
HERNANDEZ, Brian N. ■ 78230 #048-15-2005 **P** *012
HERNANDEZ, Carlos O. 4600 NW LOOP 410, STE 110 78229 #048-02-1996 L1998 **IM** *050 †20
HERNANDEZ, Caroline. 1739 SW LOOP 410, STE 402 78227 #048-13-1989 L2003 **IM** *020 †20
HERNANDEZ, Deborah M. ■ 78240 #048-13-2003 L2007 **AN** *100
HERNANDEZ, Edgar Duarte. 7703 FLOYD CURL DR 78229 #649-14-1996 L2006 **OBG** *100
HERNANDEZ, Ernesto. 111 DALLAS ST 78205 #264-04-1966 L1977 **OBG** *020
HERNANDEZ, Harry. 12650 NACOGDOCHES RD 78217 #025-76-1981, ▲ L1983 **FM OMM** *020
HERNANDEZ, Hugo Rafael. 343 W HOUSTON ST, STE 807 78205 #308-01-1962 L1981 **P PFP** *020
HERNANDEZ, Javier. ■ 78259 #036-07-1991 L1992 **U** *020 †95
HERNANDEZ, Jesse, Jr. 45 NE LOOP 410, STE 900 78216 #048-14-1986 L1987 **AN** *020 †05
HERNANDEZ, John D. 2235 THOUSAND OAKS DR, STE 102B 78232 #048-02-1983 L1983 **EM** *020 †20,16
HERNANDEZ, Jorge Alberto. 315 N SAN SABA, STE 1075 78207 #264-10-1983 L1989 **PD** *020 †55
HERNANDEZ, Jose Manuel. 12103 WINDEMERE 78230 #847-02-1974 L1978 **CHP P** *020 †75
HERNANDEZ, Joseph M. 17720 CORPORATE WOODS DR 78259 #048-13-1996 L1999 **P** *020 †75
HERNANDEZ, Juan Carlos. 1200 BROOKLYN AVE, STE 115 78212 #649-31-1982 L1995 **RO** *020 †80
HERNANDEZ, Juan Izabal. ■ 78249 #649-01-1953 L1967 **IM** *020
HERNANDEZ, Mario. 303 E QUINCY ST, STE 104 78215 #649-01-1954 L1971 **IM** *020 †20
HERNANDEZ, Miguel Angel. 45 NE LOOP 410 STE 900 78216 #048-15-1992 L1996 **AN** *071
HERNANDEZ, Raymond H, III. 7810 LOUIS PASTEUR DR, STE 100 78229 #005-11-1991 L1992 **OPH** *020 †35
HERNANDEZ, Raymond Henry. 7810 LOUIS PASTEUR DR, STE 100 78229 #021-01-1963 L1964 **FM** *020 †18
HERNANDEZ, Ricardo A. 343 W HOUSTON ST, STE 1006 78205 #005-19-1981 L1982 **GE** *020 †20
HERNANDEZ, Richard. 12650 NACOGDOCHES RD 78217 #048-02-1958 L1958 **FM GP** *020 †18
HERNANDEZ, Roger. ■ 78257 #021-01-1965 L1970 **OPH** *071 †35
HERNANDEZ, Tania Fernande. 78251 #048-13-2004 **NPM** *012
HERNANDEZ, Timothy A. 7940 FLOYD CURL STE 520 78229 #048-13-1995 L1996 **IM** *020 †20
HERNANDEZ, Valerie. ■ 78201 #048-02-2004 L2007 **FM** *100 †10
HERR, Timothy Mark. 7909 FREDERICKSBURG RD, STE 100 78229 #028-03-1991 L2007 **OTO** *020 †45
HERRERA, Gloria R. 311 CAMDEN ST, STE 403 78215 #048-13-1980 L1980 **OBG** *020 †30
HERRERA, Henry Harrison. 8127 N NEW BRNFLS AVE #201 78209 #048-13-1976 L1976 **AN** *020
HERRERA, Rodolfo B. 78217 #649-01-1962 L1977 **GS** *071 †85
HERRING, John M. ■ 78213 #047-06-1953 L1968 **PM OS** *071 †60
HERRINGTON, Charles Clark. ■ 78209 #025-07-1954 L1955 **GS** *071 †85
HERSH, Daren H. 16414 SAN PEDRO, STE 710 78232 #048-14-1991 L1992 **EM** *020 †16
HERTEL, Susan Marie. 621 N ALAMO ST 78215 #035-06-1991 L1994 **AN** *020 †05
HERZEN, Alexander Taylor. ■ 78232 #048-34-1970 L1971 **OPH** *012
HESITA, Edsel Lumbis. 1200 BROOKLYN AVE, STE 115 78212 #748-21-1999 L2006 **ON** *020
HESS, Floyd Miller, II. ■ 78258 #041-01-1944 L1945 **GP** *071
HETH, Maryam Yazdi. ■ 78256 #018-03-1996 **FM** *020
HETHERLY, Vroni. 5788 ECKHERT RD, FTOPC 78240 #409-06-1971 L1980 **P** *020 †75 ‡
HIBBERD, Alan Eric. 4243 E SOUTHCROSS BLVD, SAN ANTONIO ORTHOPAEDIC 78222 #048-02-1973 L1973 **ORS** *012
HIBRI, Nadi Salah. 4400 S PIEDRAS DR, STE 200A 78228 #605-01-1973 L1980 **DR** *020 †80
HICKEY, Rosemary. 7703 FLOYD CURL DR 78229 #004-01-1981 L1983 **AN** *020 †05
HICKMAN, Alfredo F. 5315 FREDERICKSBRG RD #213 78229 #649-02-1962 L1972 **GS VS** *020 †30
HIGBY, Kenneth. 7909 FREDERICKSBURG RD, STE 227 78229 #025-12-1987 L1991 **MFM OBG** *020 †30
HIGGINS, Lawrence Shepard. 5805 CALLAGHAN RD, STE 100 78228 #024-07-1958 L1967 **IM CD** *020 †20
HIGGINS, Russell Aaron. ■ 78254 #034-01-2002 L2006 **HMP** *100 †50
HIGGS, Jay Brent. 215 ROSEMARY AVE 78209 #018-03-1980 L1982 **RHU IM** *020 †20
HIGHSMITH, Jerome Carl. 1730 SW MILITARY DR, CENTRAL WOMENS HEALTH 78221 #011-03-1979 L1980 **OBG** *020 †20
HIGUCHI, Junji Henry. 1303 MCCULLOUGH AVE, STE 441 78212 #019-02-1973 L1976 **PUD IM** *020 †20
HILBURN, Steven. ■ 78211 #017-20-2005 L2008 **IM** *012
HILDEBRAND, Bernard Augus. ■ 78230 #048-14-2004 L2006 **IM** *020 †20
HILGER, Angela Arrambide. 315 N SAN SABA, STE 1060A 78207 #048-13-2003 L2006 **PD** *020 †55
HILL, Eric James. ■ 78245 #021-05-2006 L2007 **EM** *012
HILL, Gordon Travis, Jr. 3338 OAKWELL CT, STE 107 78218 #048-13-1975 L1975 **FM** *020 †18
HILL, Monica Renee. 408 NAVARRO ST 78205 #048-13-2001 L2005 **FM** *020 †18
HILL, Timothy J. ■ 78229 #048-13-2008 *012
HILL, Vanessa Lynn. 7703 FLOYD CURL DR, DEPT. OF PEDIATRICS MC 781 78229 #048-02-2003 L2006 **PD** *100 †55
HILL, William Deal. 7703 FLOYD CURL DR, DEPT PATH 78229 #007-02-1959 L1990 **PTH** *071 †50
HILLER, Kenneth N. 402 EVANS AVE 78209 #048-12-1993 L1994 **AN** *020 †05
HILLIARD, Donald Morris. 203 E EVERGREEN ST 78212 #048-12-1967 L1967 **PD** *020 †55
HILLIARD, George Darby. 7922 EWING HALSELL DR, STE 170 78229 #047-07-1972 L1979 **OBG PTH** *020 †30

HILLIARD, James Leonard. 5414 FREDERICKSBURG RD, STE 100 78229 #048-04-1975 L1976 NPM PD *020 †55

HILLIARD, Michael Wayne. ■ 78258 #048-14-1996 L1998 EM *020 †16

HILLIARD, Robt Lee Moore. 710 AUGUSTA ST 78215 #048-02-1956 L1956 OBG *020 †30 ‡

HILLIARD, Rudyard Lance. ■ 78229 #048-02-2003 L2005 FM *020 †18

HILLIARD, Tricia Selena. ■ 78258 #048-02-2003 L2006 PD *020 †55

HILLIARD, Yolanda Whittak. 8042 WURZBACH RD, STE 410 78229 #048-13-1980 L1980 OBG *020 †30

HILLMAN, Jack Brittian. 414 NORTHSTAR DR 78216 #048-02-1960 L1970 P *020 †75

HILLS, William J. ■ 78232 #007-02-1946 L1954 GS *071 †85

HILTON, Donald L, Jr. 4410 MEDICAL DR, STE 610 78229 #048-02-1988 L1990 NS *020 †25

HILTON, William Martin. ■ 78258 #023-12-2008 GS *012

HINCHEY, John William. ■ 78240 #048-13-2007 ORS *012

HINCHEY, William Woolford. 301 N FRIO ST 78207 #048-13-1978 L1978 PTH *020 †50

HINITT, Nancy Katherine. 2826 THOUSAND OAKS DR 78232 #048-13-1984 L1985 FM *020 †18

HINOJOSA BUENO, Rolando A. ■ 78212 #649-01-1951 *071

HIPOLITO, Abel. 4822 BUCKNELL ST 78249 #649-01-1965 L1975 P CHP *020 †75 ‡

HIRD, Linda Christine. ■ 78209 #048-02-2005 L2007 GS *012

HLAVINKA, Timothy Chas. 7979 WURZBACH RD, URSCHEL TOWERS #233 78229 #048-02-1984 L1985 U *020 †95

HNATOW, Cynthia Rodriguez. 777 NE LOOP 410, TEXAS MEDICAL CLINIC 78209 #048-04-1995 L1997 FM *020 †18

HNATOW, David Anthony. 4502 MEDICAL DR 78229 #010-02-1985 L1991 EM *030 †16 ‡

HO, Nam Phan. 7703 FLOYD CURL DR, UNIV TX MED SCH-SAN ANTONI 78229 #654-01-2002 FM *100

HO, Tony Tran. ■ 78250 #048-15-2007 IM *012

HOBBS, Edmund Rhodes. 5282 MEDICAL DR, STE 518 78229 #034-01-1975 L1977 D DS *020 †15 ‡

HOBBS, George Paul. ■ 78240 #048-04-2003 L2006 DR *012

HOBERMAN, Lawrence Joel. ■ 78230 #048-05-1967 L1975 IM GE *071 †20 ‡

HOBERNICHT, Susan L. ■ 78251 #023-12-2006 L2008 PD *012

HOCOTT, Joseph Floyd. ■ 78209 #048-04-1943 L1943 GP *071

HOEFLE, Jeffrey David. 16414 SAN PEDRO, STE 710 78232 #021-05-1996 L2005 EM *020 †16

HOEFLE, Stephanie F. 225 E SONTERRA BLVD # 3100, STONE OAK FAMILY DOCTORS 78258 #021-05-1996 L1997 FM *020 †18

HOELSCHER, Jay Michael. 414 NAVARRO ST, STE 1034 78205 #030-05-1999 L2002 IM *020 †20

HOERR, Amy Lynn. ■ 78209 #016-43-1999 L2006 IM *020 †20

HOFFMAN, Ladd Craig. 7703 FLOYD CURL DR, UTHSCSA - DEPARTMENT OF SU 78229 #021-06-2003 L2007 GS *012

HOFFMAN, Michael Robt. 45 NE LOOP 410, STE 900 78216 #048-02-1975 L1975 AN PD *020 †55,05

HOFFMAN, Stephen Francis. 4410 MEDICAL DR, STE 350 78229 #041-01-1966 L1972 N *050 †75

HOGAN, Marguerite Inez. 8535 TOM SLICK 78229 #036-08-1998 L2003 OS *020 †75

HOKE, George Hamlin. ■ 78217 #038-06-1947 L1947 NS *071 †25

HOLAHAN, Joseph Richard. 7979 WURZBACH RD, CTRC ZELLER BLDG Z325 78229 #011-03-1973 L1977 HEM IM *020 †20

HOLCOMB, John Robt. 4410 MEDICAL DR, STE 440 78229 #048-12-1971 L1975 PUD CCM *020 †20

HOLCOMB, Richard Allen. 7703 FLOYD CURL DR 78229 #048-14-2000 L2003 PD PSM *020 †55

HOLDEN, Patrick. 7703 FLOYD CURL DR 78229 #048-14-1973 L1974 CHP P *020 †75,55

HOLDER, Amy Dawn. 7703 FLOYD CURL DR, SCIENCE C 78229 #035-06-2002 L2006 CCP *012 †12

HOLDER, Kenneth Norbert. ■ 78229 #048-15-2007 PTH *012

HOLGUIN, Alfonso Hudson. TEX U SCH PUB HLTH HSC SA 78284 #048-02-1957 L1957 GPM PHP *040

HOLLAN, Otto Roger. 414 NAVARRO 78205 #008-01-1945 L1946 IM GE *071 †20

HOLLANDER, Rachel Fisher. ■ 78240 #048-13-2008 *012

HOLLEY, Linda Janet. 1954 E HOUSTON ST RM 104 78202 #048-13-1981 L1982 PD *020 †55

HOLLIMON, Peter Wilson. 8534 VILLAGE DR, STE E 78217 #048-13-1976 L1976 GS *020 †85

HOLLSTEN, Donald Arthur. 7950 FLOYDCURL, STE 505 78229 #026-04-1977 L1982 OPH *020 †35

HOLMES, Peter Forrest. 9150 HUEBNER RD, STE 200 78240 #048-14-1981 L1981 ORS *020 †40

HOLMES, William D. 1380 PANTHEON WAY, STE 310 78232 #048-02-1987 L1988 CHP P *020 †75

HOLMGREEN, Kimberly Rovan. 7703 FLOYD CURL DR, MS 7838 78229 #048-14-2004 L2007 AN *012

HOLMGREEN, Wm Corbett. 7703 FLOYD CURL DR, DEPT OF ANESTHESIOLOGY 78229 #048-13-1983 L1984 AN *020

HOLSHOUSER, Charles A. 4499 MEDICAL DR STE 183 78229 #048-12-1972 L1979 OBG *020 †30

HOLSHOUSER, Claire Kline. 45 NE LOOP 410, STE 900 78216 #048-13-1981 L1981 AN *020

HOLST, Louis Dan. 999 E BASSE RD, STE 112 78209 #048-02-1965 L1965 GP *020

HOLT, Jean Edwards. 325 E SONTERRA BLVD, STE 100 78258 #028-03-1972 L1978 OPH *020 †35

HOLT, Nasha L. 400 N LOOP 1604 E, STE 345 78232 #065-10-1984 L1997 FM *020 †18

HOLUB, Robert A. 215 E QUINCY ST, STE 610 78215 #048-13-2001 L2005 NEP *100

HOMAN, Susan Elizabeth. 7703 FLOYD CURL DR 78229 #016-43-1980 L1988 NPM PD *020 †55

HOMEYER, Diane Carole. ■ 78251 #041-02-2005 L2007 IM *012

HOMMA, Arturo. 7979 WURZBACH RD, URSCHEL TOWERS #233 78229 #649-02-1991 L2001 PCC *020 †20

HONORE, Charles Rudolph. 7711 LOUIS PASTEUR DR, STE 200 78229 #048-13-1975 L1975 OBG *020 †30

HONORE, Gerard Marcel. 502 MADISON OAK STE 210 78258 #036-05-1992 L1996 REN GYN *020 †30

HOOD, Charles Hardin. 78259 #020-02-1959 L1963 FM *020 †18

HOOPER, Dennis Glenn. 301 N FRIO ST 78207 #031-01-1983 L2002 PTH *020 †50

HOOVER, Lance Randal. 2050 WORTH RD, MEDCOM, USAMEDCOM,MCHO-Q 78234 #017-20-1998 L2007 AN *020 †05

HOOVER, Michael J. ■ 78217 #040-02-1989 PD *020

HOOVER, Nancy Garrett. 3851 ROGER BROOKE DR, BROOKE ARMY MED CTR 78234 #021-01-1996 L1998 AN *012 †55

HOPKINS, Matthew Christop. ■ 78257 #038-41-2003 L2008 PYG *012

HORAN, Jennifer L. ■ 78247 #048-13-2004 L2006 IM *100 †20

HORN, Curtis Scott. 303 W SUNSET RD STE 101 78209 #048-13-1979 L1979 FM *020 †18

HORNER, Bernard G. ■ 78212 #048-12-1953 L1953 GP *071

HORTON, Granville Eugene. 10200 BROADWAY ST STE 200 78217 #048-02-1954 L1954 OM AM *020

HORTON, Kevin Bruce. 255 E SONTERRA BLVD, STE 100 78258 #048-15-1982 L1983 IM *020 †20

HORTON, Monica S. ■ 78258 #048-16-1999 L2003 IMG *020 †20

HORWITZ, David Alexander. 8038 WURZBACH RD 78229 #836-03-1965 L1971 GYN *071 †30

HOSPENTHAL, Maria Angela. 4647 MEDICAL DR 78229 #014-01-1997 L2004 PCC *020 †20

HOSPERS, Teresa A. 4499 MEDICAL DR 78229 #048-13-1989 L1990 PDC PD *020 †55

HOSTETTER, Robin Elno. 10615 PERRIN BEITEL RD 78217 #038-43-1976 L1996 P OS *020 †75

HOUGH, Corey Michael. ■ 78240 #048-15-2006 P *012

HOWARD, Robert, Jr. 45 NE LOOP 410, STE 900 78216 #028-03-1976 L1977 AN *020 †05

HOWARD, Wm Harrison, III. ■ 78213 #051-04-1976 L1983 NM DR *075 †80,28

HOWE, Don Duvall. 1635 NE LOOP 410, STE 501 78209 #039-01-1972 L1974 CHP P *020 †75

HOWELTON, Linda Fay. 525 OAK CENTRE DR, STE 350 78258 #048-02-1982 L1983 PD *020 †55

HOWLE, Susan L. 111 DALLAS ST 78205 #048-13-1985 L1989 EM *020 †16

HOYLER, Cynthia Louise. 8004 WEST AVE, STE 1 78213 #048-13-1994 L1995 P *020 †75

HOYUMPA, Anastacio M. 7703 FLOYD CURL DR, UNIV OF TEXAS HEALTH CENTE 78229 #748-01-1961 L1984 GE IM *040

HSU, James Tienti. ■ 78249 #048-13-2005 L2006 DR *012

HSU, Tzyy-Wen. ■ 78230 #244-04-1966 L1975 GP IM *020

HUANG, Justin C. ■ 78229 #041-15-2005 L2005 PD *012

HUCHUN, Teresa. ■ 78234 #030-06-1994 L2004 DR *020 †80

HUDNALL, Clayton H. 7979 WURZBACH RD, URSCHEL TOWERS #233 78229 #048-12-1984 L1990 U *020 †95

HUDSON, Jos Aloysius, Jr. PO BOX 15825 78212 #048-13-1976 L1976 OPH *020 †35

HUDSON, Josie Uribe. 78209 #048-15-1977 L1978 CHP *020 †75

HUERTAS, Juanita. 4318 WOODCOCK DR, STE 120 78228 #025-01-1994 L1995 FM *020 †18

HUETE, Laura Kathleen. 5018 SAN PEDRO AVE 78212 #048-14-2004 L2005 FM *020 †18

HUEY, Dicky. 540 MADISON OAK DR, STE 340 78258 #048-02-1967 L1967 N GP *020

HUFF, John Paul. 14615 SAN PEDRO, STE 105 78232 #016-43-1983 L1992 RHU IM *020 †20

HUFF, Robert Whitley. 7703 FLOYD CURL DR, UT HEALTH SCIENCE CENTER-S 78229 #048-04-1966 L1966 OBG MFM *020 †30,19

HUFFMAN, Jason Lee. 7703 FLOYD CURL DR, MEDICINE OEP MC 7871 78229 #048-15-2005 L2007 IM *012

HUGEL, Robert Wilhelm. ■ 78229 #407-10-1960 P *071

HUGHES, Jane Lindell. 21 SPURS LN STE 220, TEXAS CTR FOR ATHLETES 78240 #048-13-1980 L1980 OPH *020 †35

HUGHES, Patricia Rosario. 1102 BARCLAY, BARRIO COMPREHENSIVE 78207 #051-01-1999 L2006 PD *020 †55

HUGHES, Philip Stuart H. 7940 FLOYD CURL DR, STE 1010 78229 #018-03-1969 L1973 D DS *020 †15

HUMPHREYS, James Lloyd. 301 N FRIO ST 78207 #048-13-1994 L1995 FOP PTH *020 †50

HUNT, Debra Kay. 7703 FLOYD CURL DR, UNIV OF TX HEALTH SCIENCE 78229 #036-01-1986 L1991 IM *071 †20

HUNTE, Olivia Thea. ■ 78232 #042-03-2007 *012

HUNTER, Curtis James. 3851 ROGER BROOKE DR, BROOKE ARMY MEDICAL CENTER 78234 #023-12-1989 L1990 EM *020 †16

HUNTSINGER, John Dewey. 45 NE LOOP 410, STE 900 78216 #422-01-1996 L2001 AN *020 †05

HUOTT, Michael Arthur. 8401 DATAPOINT DR, STE 130 78229 #023-12-1989 L1997 EM *020 †16

HURA, Claudia. 8042 WURZBACH RD STE 50 78229 #038-40-1979 L1986 NEP IM *050 †20

HURD, Mark Alan. 2121 SW 36TH ST 78237 #048-13-1994 L1995 FM *020 †18

HURD, Thelma Constance. 7703 FLOYD CURL DR, DEPARTMENT OF SURGERY 78229 #033-05-1983 L1992 GS ON *050 †85

HURLEY, Robert James. ■ 78251 #035-09-1968 L1972 OS *071

HUSAIN, Farkhanda Jabin. ■ 78230 #704-02-1954 L1978 AN *020 †05

HUSSAIN, Akhtar. 7330 SAN PEDRO, STE 405 78216 #704-02-1986 L1998 IM *020 †20

HUSSAIN, Rahat. 7703 FLOYD CURL DR, DEPT MED 78229 #704-02-2002 IM *012

HUSSEY, David Holbert. 7703 FLOYD CURL DR, MS 7889 78229 #028-02-1964 L1970 RO R *020 †80

HUSTON, Rebecca Lea. 7703 FLOYD CURL DR, UNIV OF TX HEALTH SCIENCE 78229 #056-05-1984 L1985 PD OS *020 †55

HUTCHINSON, Robert H. ■ 78229 #016-06-1939 L1972 ORS *040 †40 ‡

HUYNH, Thu-Tam Thi. 7703 FLOYD CURL DR 78229 #305-01-2000 L2003 HO *012

HYSLOP, James Anthony. 19238 STONEHUE, PEDIATRIC MEDICINE, P.A. 78258 #038-41-1997 L2006 PD *020 †55

HYUN, Daniel Dong Wook. 315 N SAN SABA STE 1110 78207 #132-01-1989 L2002 N *020 †75

IBARGUEN-SECCHIA, Eduardo. 4499 MEDICAL DR STE 360 78229 #649-28-1982 L1989 PG PD *020 †55 ‡

IBRAHIM, Badreldin A. 7711 LOUIS PASTEUR, STE 605 78229 #915-03-1981 L2005 N CN *020 †75

IBRAHIM, Mounir Labib. ■ 78254 #915-02-1972 L2002 P PYG *020 †75 ‡

ICENOGLE, Diane Marie. 4400 S PIEDRAS DR, STE 200 78228 #048-13-1994 L1995 DR *020 †80

ICONOMOPULOS, Byton Elias. ■ 78230 #649-01-1972 L1975 CD IM *030

IGUN, Olawale A. 7703 FLOYD CURL DR, U TX MED SCH SAN ANTONIO 78229 #048-13-2007 *012

IKEN, Andrea K. 2711 PALO ALTO RD, CHCS PALO ALTO CLINIC 78211 #048-13-1996 L1998 P *020 †75

IM, Stephen Seonbin. 7400 MERTON MINTER ST, BLVD, 111E 78229 #048-12-1992 L1993 PCC *020 †20

INFANTE, Anthony Jos. 7703 FLOYD CURL DR, UNIVERSITY OF TEXAS HEALTH 78229 #017-20-1978 L1984 IG PD *050 †20

INGARI, John V. 8800 VILLAGE DR, STE 106 78217 #023-12-1986 L1995 HS *020 †40

INGLE, Jennifer Ann. 527 N LEONA ST 78207 #048-15-2002 L2005 NEP *012 †20

INGRAM, George Steven. 408 NAVARRO ST 78205 #048-13-1981 L1981 IM *020

INGRAM, Kristyn Becker. 7703 FLOYD CURL DR, UNIV OF TX MED SCH 78229 #048-13-2007 AN *012

INSCORE, Stephen Curtis. 7703 FLOYD CURL MC3900, UNIV OF TEXAS HSC 78229 #039-01-1979 L2001 PDP CCM *020 †55

IRVIN, Lindsay Rockwood. 5921 BROADWAY ST 78209 #048-14-1994 L1996 PD *020 †55

IRWIN, Kimberly Carol. 4499 MEDICAL DR STE 261 78229 #055-01-1986 L1998 **PN N** *020 †55
ISAEFF, Mark Andrew. 1303 MCCULLOUGH AVE, STE 600 78212 #010-01-1998 L1999 **IM** *020 †20
ISBELL, Charles Patrick. 7700 FLOYD CURL DR 78229 #048-02-1990 L1991 **EM IM** *020 †20
ISKANDER, Nader G. 19202 STONE OAK PKWY, STE 103 78258 #915-03-1989 L2002 **OPH** *020 †35
ISLAS OHLMAYER, Miguel An. 7703 FLOYD CURL DR, UNIV TX MED SCH-SAN ANTONI 78229 #649-30-2001 **HO** *012
ISTAFANOUS, Ihab Monir. 7703 FLOYD CURL DR, MAIL CODE 7792 78229 #915-03-1988 L2004 **CHP** *020 †75
IVANOV, Stanislav Petrov. 2142 COUGAR PASS DR 78230 #198-01-1991 L2004 **IM** *020
IVY, Linda Maria. 527 N LEONA ST 78207 #048-13-1985 L1986 **FM** *040 †18
JACELDO, Teodorico H. 8703 WURZBACH RD, LA PAZ COMM HEALTH CTR 78240 #748-01-1952 L1976 **FM P** *071 †18
JACKSON, Carlayne Mertens. 4647 MEDICAL DR 78229 #048-13-1987 L1988 **N** *030 †75
JACKSON, Gregory Mann. 5307 BROADWAY ST 78209 #649-19-1977 L1980 **FM EM** *020 †18
JACKSON, Jack Edward. ■ 78230 #016-06-1965 L1969 **CLP** *100 †50
JACKSON, James Fauntleroy. 855 PROTON RD, GASTROENTEROLOGY CONSULTAN 78258 #048-13-2000 L2007 **GE** *100 †20
JACKSON, Lance Elliot. 18518 HARDY OAK BLVD, STE 300 78258 #028-02-1995 L2003 **NO OTO** *020 †45
JACKSON, Lindsey Nicole. 5804 BABCOCK RD, PMB 183 78240 #048-12-2003 **GS** *012
JACKSON, Michael Eugene. 301 N FRIO ST 78207 #028-03-1978 L1981 **PTH** *020 †50
JACKSON, Nicholas Maxwell. 7418 JOHN SMITH 78229 #048-04-1974 L1974 **DR** *020 †80 ‡
JACKSON, R Blair. 7950 FLOYD CURL DR, STE 101 78229 #048-12-1985 L1986 **CRS** *020 †85,10
JACKSON, Vadean Lafye. 1055 ADA ST 78223 #566-01-1997 L2006 **FM** *020 †18
JACOB, Mark Alan. 2829 BABCOCK RD STE 600 78229 #048-02-1979 L1979 **CD** *020 †20
JACOB, Norman Henry, Jr. ■ 78212 #048-02-1945 L1945 **PTH** *071 †50
JACOBS, Jennifer D'Ann. 7950 FLOYD CURL DR 78229 #048-13-1994 L1997 **OBG** *020 †30
JACOBS, Milton S. 107 E AGARITA AVE 78212 #048-02-1950 L1950 **IM END** *071 †20
JACOBS, Philip Michael. 2829 BABCOCK RD, SAN ANTONIO ORTHOPAEDIC 78229 #030-05-1992 L1995 **OSM** *020 †40
JACOBS, Robert Lee. 8285 FREDERICKSBURG RD 78229 #001-02-1968 L1973 **A IG** *020 †20,03
JACOBSON, Mikael J. 4242 MEDICAL DR STE 1150 78229 #048-13-2000 L2002 **P** *020
JACOBSON, Norman Labe. 8026 FLOYD CURL DR 78229 #016-06-1963 L1967 **IM IMG** *071 †20
JAEN, Carlos Roberto. 7703 FLOYD CURL DR, UNIV OF TX HEALTH SCIENCE 78229 #035-06-1989 L2002 **FM PHP** *030 †18
JAFFAR, Zulfaqqar M. 8038 WURZBACH RD, STE 360 78229 #704-02-1990 L2002 **HO** *020 †20
JAGIRDAR, Jaishree Sudhir. 4502 MEDICAL DR 78229 #495-02-1976 L2003 **PTH** *020 †50
JAHANGIR, Kourosh. 7703 FLOYD CURL DR 78229 #704-16-2002 L2007 **FP** *012
JAHANGIRI, Mohamad F. 7703 FLOYD CURL DR, U TX MED SCH SAN ANTONIO 78229 #048-13-2007 *012
JAIN, Avanindra. 2455 NE LOOP 410, STE 235 78217 #035-06-1980 L1991 **CD IM** *020 †20
JALOMO, Rosalio. 1730 SW MILITARY DR # 105 78221 #048-13-1980 L1983 **PD** *020
JAMES, Joshua Clark. ■ 78240 #048-13-2003 L2008 **OTO** *012
JAMES, Kevin Frank. 1933 NE LOOP 410 78217 #048-04-1978 L1978 **CD IM** *020 †20
JAMESON, David Kittrell. 8811 VILLAGE DR 78217 #048-12-1962 L1962 **FM GP** *071
JAMIESON, Michael James. 7703 FLOYD CURL, DEPT PHARMACOLOGY UTHSCSA 78229 #919-01-1980 L1992 **IM PA** *050
JAMSHIDI, Abol Ghasem. ■ 78258 #517-05-1962 L1971 **ORS OS** *020
JANECEK, Torri M. 7703 FLOYD CURL DR 78229 #018-75-2007, ▲ **OBG** *012
JANES, William Warren. 5101 MEDICAL DR, SOUTH TEXAS PHYSICAL 78229 #035-09-1988 L1992 **PM** *020 †60
JANSEN, Richard Keith. 3851 ROGER BROOKE DR # 36, BROOKE ARMY MEDICAL CENTER 78234 #048-15-1997 L1999 **AN** *020 †05
JANSSEN, Dana R. 1901 BABCOCK RD, STE 301 78229 #048-13-1996 L1998 **PDC** *020 †55
JARDAN, Freeman Cornell. 5407 WALZEM RD 78218 #016-43-1977 L1983 **PD** *020 †55
JASO, Rene Gilbert. 1303 MCCULLOUGH AVE, STE 538 78212 #025-12-1973 L1978 **GS IM** *020 †20,85
JAVIER, Eduardo Santos. 7400 MERTON MINTER ST 78229 #748-01-1956 L1993 **FM** *020 †18
JAYARAM, Kiran N. 255 E SONTERRA BLVD, STE 150 78258 #048-12-1992 L1994 **ICE** *020 †20
JAYES DE GRACIA, Julio Ce. 7703 FLOYD CURL DR 78229 #649-38-2000 **EM** *012
JEAN-PIERRE, Jean Sonny. 7940 FLOYD CURL DR, STE 1030 78229 #048-02-1984 L1985 **AN** *020
JEDLICKOVA, Eva. 4502 MEDICAL DR DEPT NM 78229 #028-02-1972 **NM** *100
JEFFERSON, Virgil Sinatra. ■ 78253 #025-07-1976 L1982 **GS OS** *020
JEFFREYS, Chas Alva, Jr. 1200 BROOKLYN AVE, STE 245 78212 #021-06-1979 L1988 **OBG** *020 †30
JEFFREYS, Matthew D. 7703 FLOYD CURL DR, UTHSCSA - DEPT OF PSYCHIAT 78229 #048-13-1985 L1986 **P** *020 †75 ‡
JEFFREYS, Patricia Marie. 111 DALLAS ST 78205 #021-06-1980 L1982 **PTH** *030 †50
JENDRZEY, Diane Elaine. 7007 BANDERA RD, STE 19 78238 #048-14-1984 L1985 **PD** *020 †18,55
JENEBY, Thomas Tayf. 7272 WURZBACH RD, STE 801 78240 #051-04-1996 L2004 **PS** *020 †65
JENKINS, Douglas Wm, Jr. 8601 VILLAGE DR, SKINNER CLINIC 78217 #025-01-1967 L1973 **PUD IM** *020 †20
JENKINSON, Stephen Geo. 7703 FLOYD CURL DR, PULMONARY DISEASE DIVISION 78229 #021-06-1973 L1983 **PUD** *040 †20
JENNINGS, Hal B, Jr. ■ 78239 #025-01-1941 L1942 **OS PS** *071 †65
JENNINGS, James Floyd. ■ 78213 #020-02-1959 L1978 **P PTH** *020 †50,75
JENNINGS, James Greg. 24165 IH 10 W, STE 118 78257 #048-13-1998 L2001 **FM** *020 †18
JENNINGS, William Patrick. 8122 DATAPOINT DR STE 1010 78229 #017-20-1979 L1983 **IM OM** *020 †20,70
JENSEN, Jani Renae. 7703 FLOYD CURL DR, MAIL CODE 3900, OB/GYN 78229 #056-05-2001 L2005 **OBG** *020
JERABEK, Julie Christine. ■ 78209 #023-12-2005 L2007 **IM** *012
JERNIGAN, John Gavin. ■ 78232 #039-01-1974 L1988 **AM** *030 †70
JETTER, Gina E. ■ 78251 #048-13-2006 **N** *012
JIMENEZ, Alejandro. 7703 FLOYD CURL DR 78229 #264-16-1997 **CD** *012 †20
JIMENEZ, Angel R. 343 W HOUSTON ST, STE 806 78205 #649-02-1966 L1967 **GS** *072 †85
JIMENEZ, David F. 7703 FLOYD CURL DR, UT HEALTH SCIENCE CENTER M 78229 #041-13-1985 L2005 **NS** *020 †25
JIMENEZ, John Lawrence. 4402 VANCE JACKSON RD, STE 220 78230 #054-04-1991 L1996 **AN** *020 †05
JIMENEZ, Robert Leo. 134 E MISTLETOE AVE 78212 #048-02-1966 L1966 **P** *020 †75
JIMMA, Brukey. 343 W HOUSTON ST, STE 402 78205 #048-13-1990 L1993 **IM** *020 †20
JIRKA, Anton J, Jr. 5979 BABCOCK RD 78240 #048-13-1991 L1992 **FM** *020 †18
JIRKA, Anton Jos. ■ 78255 #016-11-1964 L1986 **AN PMM** *062 †05
JIRKA, Maria Hernaiz. 5979 BABCOCK RD 78240 #048-13-1992 L1993 **IM** *020 †20
JOHANSEN, Kristina Alliso. ■ 78251 #021-01-2007 **OBG** *012
JOHNSON, Anthony James. ■ 78259 #023-12-1991 L1992 **OPH** *020 †35
JOHNSON, Colleen Nicole. ■ 78250 #021-01-2005 L2007 **OTO** *012
JOHNSON, Daniel Arthur. 7703 FLOYD CURL DR, MSC 6230 DEPT OF OPTHML 78229 #035-01-1991 L2002 **OPH** *020 †35
JOHNSON, David Gary. ■ 78212 #048-12-1966 L1979 **PYG P** *020 †75
JOHNSON, David Wright. 3111 SAN PEDRO AVE 78212 #048-13-1977 L1979 **PD** *020 †55
JOHNSON, Durkee Paul. 45 NE LOOP 410, STE 900 78216 #048-12-1982 L1983 **AN** *020 †05
JOHNSON, J E B. 1 LONE STAR PASS, STE 46 78264 #048-14-1987 L1988 **FM OM** *020 †18 ‡
JOHNSON, James Frederick. 3851 ROGER BROOKE DR, MED CENT, DEPT OF RADIOLOG 78234 #036-07-1969 L1972 **PDR PD** *020 †80,55
JOHNSON, Joseph E, IV. 520 E EUCLID AVE 78212 #048-12-1983 L1983 **GE IM** *020 †20
JOHNSON, Keith. 1904 GRANDSTAND DR 78238 #048-13-1982 L1983 **EM OM** *020 †16
JOHNSON, Louis F, Jr. ■ 78239 #024-01-1949 L1976 **OM AM** *072 †70
JOHNSON, Michael Edward. ■ 78229 #048-13-2006 **ORS** *012
JOHNSON, Michael M. ■ 78249 #048-13-2002 L2004 **IM** *100
JOHNSON, Oliver H. 520 MADISON OAK DR 78258 #048-13-1985 L1986 **AN** *020 †05
JOHNSON, Patrice Jeanine. 13300 OLD BLANCO RD, STE 223 78216 #048-02-1978 L1993 **CHP P** *020 †75
JOHNSON, Patricia Plauche. 701 S ZARZAMORA ST 78207 #048-13-1978 L1978 **PD OS** *040 †55
JOHNSON, Robert G. 4410 MEDICAL DR, STE 610 78229 #065-01-1976 L1984 **OSS** *020 †40
JOHNSON, Robt Milton Lee. 5788 ECKHERT RD, ATTN: CREDENTIAL OFFICE 78240 #025-76-1978, ▲ L1980 **FM MDM** *020 †18
JOHNSON, Ryan Patrick. ■ 78249 #038-40-2006 L2007 **D** *012
JOHNSON, Scott Bostow. 7703 FLOYD CURL DR, STE 7841 78229 #034-01-1987 L1993 **TS** *020 †85,90
JOHNSON, Tracy Renee. 7703 FLOYD CURL DR, UTHSCSA REHAB MED 78229 #025-12-1994 L1996 **PM** *020 †60
JOHNSON, Wendy L. 7703 FLOYD CURL DR, DEPT OF MED ONCOLOGY 78229 #048-13-1997 L1999 **HO** *012 †20
JOHNSTON, Cindy Louise. 4600 NW LOOP 410, STE 110 78229 #048-13-1994 L1995 **FM** *020 †18
JOHNSTON, James C. ■ 78238 #048-13-1984 L1985 **N** *075 †75 ‡
JOHNSTON, Joe Eric. 8042 WURZBACH RD, STE 310 78229 #048-13-1997 L2005 **CCS** *020 †85
JONES, Amie Elizabeth. ■ 78260 #036-05-2000 L2000 **PD** *020 †55
JONES, Caroline M. 7703 FLOYD CURL 78229 #048-13-2002 L2007 **CCP** *012 †55
JONES, Christopher Brian. 3851 ROGER BROOKE DR, BROOKE ARMY MEDICAL CENTER 78234 #011-02-1997 L1999 **HO** *020 †20
JONES, Daniel Todd. ■ 78229 #017-20-2007 **AN** *012
JONES, David Randolph. 4204 GARDENDALE ST, STE 203 78229 #036-07-1958 L1973 **AM P** *071 †70,75
JONES, Evan Matthew. ■ 78212 #023-12-2007 **ORS** *012
JONES, Harold Wm. ■ 78232 #048-02-1956 L1956 **P** *071
JONES, Herbert. ■ 78260 #047-06-1959 L1959 **IM** *071 †20
JONES, Jennifer Angela. ■ 78258 #016-45-2002 **CD** *012 †20
JONES, Karen Johnston. 8800 VILLAGE DR, STE 106 78217 #047-05-1987 L1995 **HS OS** *020 †40
JONES, Lanning Derryl. 5282 MEDICAL DR, SOUTHWEST CHILDRENS 78229 #036-07-1974 L1975 **PD** *020 †55
JONES, Leroy A, Jr. 7909 FREDERICKSBURG RD, STE 110115 78229 #028-02-1988 L1998 **U** *020 †95
JONES, Lillian Martin. 7922 EWING HALSELL DR 78229 #011-03-1978 L1979 **OBG** *020 †30
JONES, Michael L. 8550 DATAPOINT DR, STE 110 78229 #048-12-1982 L1983 **HS PS** *020 †85,65
JONES, Michael Lloyd. 414 NAVARRO ST STE 1200 78205 #048-04-1990 L1991 **OBG** *020 †30
JONES, Rachel Ellis. 7703 FLOYD CURL DR, DEPT OF PEDS 78229 #045-01-2007 **PD** *012
JONES, Relief, III. 14807 SAN PEDRO AVE 78232 #036-07-2000 L2006 **OPH** *020 †35
JONES, Robert Lewis, Jr. 516 LEXINGTON AVE 78215 #021-01-1963 L1968 **ORS** *020 †40
JONES, Robert Mabry. 4242 MEDICAL DR, STE 3100 78229 #048-12-1980 L1980 **AN** *020
JONES, Robert Norman. 311 CAMDEN ST STE 206 78215 #025-07-1963 L1967 **OPH ADM** *020 †35
JONES, Roberta J. 2040 BABCOCK RD, STE 300 78229 #048-13-1996 L1997 **P** *020 †75
JONES, Ronald Lyman. ■ 78251 #023-12-2006 L2008 **IM** *012
JONES, Stephanie S. 403 TREELINE PARK, CONSULTANTS IN PAIN 78209 #048-13-1992 L1993 **APM** *020 †05
JONES, William Elton, III. ■ 78256 #048-13-2005 **RO** *012
JONES, Wilmer Tracey, III. 7703 FLOYD CURL DR, UNIVERSITY HOSTPITAL 78229 #021-01-1999 L2007 **VS** *020 †85
JORDAN, Hilliard E, Jr. ■ 78240 #047-05-1970 L1976 **IM** *020
JORDAN, Judy S. ■ 78256 #036-01-1979 L1988 **D** *020 †15
JORGENSEN, Tyler S. ■ 78249 #048-13-2008 *012
JOSEPH, Bertram Enoch. 7400 MERTON MINTER ST 78229 #035-08-1967 L1973 **CD IM** *020 †20
JOSHI, Ajeya Padmakar. 4243 E SOUTHCROSS BLVD, SAN ANTONIO ORTHOPAEDIC 78222 #024-01-1997 L2003 **OSS ORS** *020 †40
JOUKOVSKI, Olga. 7330 SAN PEDRO STE 405, IPC 78216 #913-01-1991 L2002 **IM** *020 †20
JOYNER, Melissa M. ■ 78209 #048-13-2002 **RO** *012
JOYNER, Robert Wood. 9150 HUEBNER RD, STE 350 78240 #025-07-1977 L1979 **PME** *020 †05
JUAREZ, Daniel. 1303 MCCULLOUGH AVE, STE 248 78212 #030-06-1978 L1981 **IM** *020 †20
JUAREZ, Mario Regino. 4151 CALLAGHAN RD STE 102 78228 #048-12-1976 L1978 **FM** *020
JUEL, Roger Allen. ■ 78209 #016-11-1945 **ORS** *071
JULES, Avril Cherylann. 302 W RECTOR ST, NORTH 78216 #056-05-1994 L1997 **FM** *020 †18
JUMAO-AS, Ramil C. 7330 SAN PEDRO, STE 405 78216 #748-19-1989 L2001 **IM** *020 †20
JUNDT, Jason Paul. ■ 78230 #048-13-2008 *012
JUNG, Juyoung Adam. 7703 FLOYD CURL DR, SCIENCE C 78229 #048-16-2003 **DR** *012
JURO, David H. 4242 MEDICAL DR, STE 3100 78229 #048-14-2002 L2006 **AN** *020 †05
KAAR, Thomas Kenneth. ■ 78249 #539-02-1986 **OAR** *100

■ = Address Information Privacy Protected

KABO, Robert David. 6711 S NEW BRAUNFELS AVE, SAN ANTONIO STATE HOSPITAL 78223 #041-13-1966 L1971 **IM AM** *020 ‡

KACHRU, Ruchita. ■ 78209 #496-17-1997 L2006 **PD** *020 †55

KADAKIA, Ami Shailesh. 7400 MERTON MINTER ST, AUDIE L MURPHY VA MED CTR 78229 #495-76-1972 L1995 **IM IMG** *020 †20

KADAKIA, Shailesh C. 225 E SONTERRA BLVD, STE 215 78258 #495-23-1973 L1991 **GE IM** *020 †20

KADRI, Abdu. 3338 OAKWELL CT, STE 104 78218 #041-01-1982 L1991 **IM** *020 †20

KAEHLER, Cameron Louise. ■ 78232 #010-02-2007 **EM** *012

KAHL, Bryan M. 1303 MCCULLOUGH AVE # 374, ENDOCRINOLOGY/NUCLEAR MEDI 78212 #048-13-1993 L1994 **END** *020 †20

KAHLENBERG, Morton S. 8711 VILLAGE DR, UNIV OF TEXAS HSC AT SA 78217 #067-01-1990 L1986 **GS SO** *020 †85

KAHN, David Young. 7703 FLOYD CURL DR, UNIV TX HLTH SCI CTR 78229 #003-01-2004 L2006 **HO** *012 †20

KAIHLANEN, Paul Michael. 8026 FLOYD CURL DR 78229 #038-06-1963 L1968 **IM** *050 †20

KAISCH, Kenneth R. ■ 78209 #025-01-1946 L1974 **IM OS** *020

KAISER, Bryan W. 2829 BABCOCK RD STE 700, SAN ANTONIO ORTHOPAEDIC 78229 #048-12-1996 L1997 **OSM** *020 †20

KAISER, Daniel Joseph. 2829 BABCOCK RD, STE 236C TOWER 1 78229 #056-05-2002 L2004 **FM** *020 †18

KAITNER, Mark Alan. ■ 78260 #305-01-2002 L2007 **AN** *020

KALANDIAK, Steven Peter. 4647 MEDICAL DR 78229 #005-14-1994 L2000 **ORS** *020 †40

KALANTRI, Ananthlal. 7703 FLOYD CURL DR, UNIV OF TEXAS HLTH SCIENCE 78229 #495-65-1965 L1983 **PM** *071 †60

KALDAS, Emad Youssef. 502 MADISON OAK DR, STE 245 78258 #915-04-1982 L1999 **PD** *020 †55

KALMIN, Norman David. 6211 I H 10 W 78201 #836-01-1971 L1983 **BBK CLP** *030 †50

KALTER, Robert Lawrence. 12042 BLANCO RD, STE 308 78216 #048-13-1975 L1977 **P CHP** *020 †75

KALTER, Steven Paul. 7979 WURZBACH RD, STE Z373 78229 #048-04-1978 L1978 **ON HEM** *020 †20

KALWERISKY, Kevin. ■ 78231 #035-20-2005 L2007 **OPH** *012

KAMADA, Mika Margaret. 5323 BROADWAY ST 78209 #028-46-1982 L1990 **AI IM** *020 †20,03

KAMATH, Vidya. 88 BRIGGS ST STE 110 78224 #496-38-1973 L1977 **DR** *020 †80

KAMBLE, Swarna. 7930 FLOYD CURL DR 78229 #495-83-1991 L2006 **END** *020 †20

KAMMERL, Jessica L. ■ 78209 #048-13-2001 L2003 **IM** *020

KAMP, John Bentley. 8601 VILLAGE DR, STE 111 78217 #039-01-1971 L1979 **DR** *020 †80 ‡

KANAKIA, Rushit Ranjit. 7703 FLOYD CURL DR 78229 #496-46-2006 **IM** *012

KANESHIRO, Kristina Keiko. 5807 BABCOCK RD 78240 #005-06-2003 L2006 **IM** *020

KANG, Wendy Bay. 7703 FLOYD CURL DR, MC 7838 78229 #048-12-1980 L1980 **AN PME** *020 †05 ‡

KAPASI, Mosin. 7127 SOMERSET RD STE 101 78211 #045-01-1990 L1996 **OBG** *020 †30

KAPILA, Abi Z. 3031 IH 1O W, DEPT P 78201 #495-45-1975 L1982 **P** *020

KAPILA, Ashwani. 4400 S PIEDRAS DR, STE 200 78228 #495-36-1975 L1981 **OS DR** *020 †80

KAPOOR, Rohit. 7979 WURZBACH RD, URSCHEL TOWERS #233 78229 #496-38-1982 L1994 **HEM ON** *020 †20

KAPTURCZAK, Matthias H. 8042 WURZBACH RD, SAN ANTONIO KIDNEY DISEASE 78229 #409-33-1995 L2007 **NEP IM** *050 †20 ‡

KAPUR, Monika. 302 W RECTOR ST 78216 #913-18-1998 L2005 **FM** *020 †18

KARAM, Jose. 315 N SAN SABA, STE 1075 78207 #649-02-1962 L1967 **PD** *020 †55

KARASEK, Dennis Edward. 8042 WURZBACH RD, STE 525 78229 #039-01-1979 L2000 **AN PMM** *020 †05

KARDOS, Thomas Frank. 301 N FRIO ST 78207 #048-05-1978 L1987 **ATP** *075 †50

KARIA, Ravi Arvind. ■ 78229 #048-12-2004 L2008 **ORS** *012

KARNAD, Anand Bhasker. 7979 WURZBACH RD 78229 #495-04-1981 L2004 **IM HEM** *020 †20

KARNEY, David Henry. 2040 BABCOCK RD STE 200 78229 #048-12-1964 L1964 **P FM** *020

KARRH, Larry Rayburn. 333 N SANTA ROSA AVE, FL 4 78207 #048-02-1972 L1972 **FM** *020 †18

KARST, Fernando Enrique. 21815 BARTON WOODS, FAMILY PRACTICE DT ACUTE C 78259 #030-05-1995 L1997 **FM** *020 †20

KASHYAP, Sangeeta. 7703 FLOYD CURL DR 78229 #005-15-1994 L1998 **END IM** *020 †20

KASINATH, Balakuntalam S. 7703 FLOYD CURL DR 78229 #495-33-1974 L1991 **NEP IM** *050 †20

KASINATH, Uma. 5788 ECKHERT RD, VA OUTPATIENT CLC 78240 #495-33-1977 L1991 **ADP** *020 †75

KASPERKHAN, Jibrail Kamil. 540 MADISON OAK DR, STE 320 78258 #528-01-1976 L2005 **IMG** *020 †20 ‡

KATARIYA, Nitin Nath. ■ 78249 #016-06-2003 **GS** *012

KATERNDAHL, David Arthur. 7703 FLOYD CURL DR, UNIV. OF TX HEALTH SCIENCE 78229 #016-11-1977 L1987 **FM** *030 †18

KATIPALLY, Bhoja Reddy. 7703 FLOYD CURL DR 78229 #495-57-2003 **FP** *012

KATZ, Mark Andrew. 8800 VILLAGE DR, STE 106 78217 #041-01-1995 L2004 **HS** *020 †40

KAUFMAN, Christine E. ■ 78253 #038-40-2002 **NPM** *012

KAUFMAN, Holly. ■ 78249 #034-01-2000 L2002 **FM** *020 †18

KAUFMANN, Jeannine Stout. 7007 BANDERA RD 78238 #048-13-1975 L1975 **PD** *020 †55

KAUFMANN, Kathryn Elizabe. ■ 78258 #026-08-2007 **PD** *012

KAUL, Poornima. 7703 FLOYD CURL DR 78229 #671-02-2003 **OBG** *012

KAUVAR, David Seth. ■ 78251 #023-12-2002 L2004 **GS** *012

KAWALIT, Issa Afif. ■ 78240 #575-02-1994 **NEP** *100 †20

KAWASAKI, Michelle Marie. ■ 78255 #048-02-2004 **AN** *012

KAYAMORI, Ryoji. ■ 78229 #572-15-1976 L1980 *100

KAYE, Celia Ilene. 7703 FLOYD CURL DR, UNIV OF TEXAS HEALTH SCI C 78229 #025-07-1969 L1989 **PD CG** *030 †55,19

KAYRUZ, J Naji. 1303 MCCULLOUGH AVE, STE 362 78212 #605-02-1984 L1991 **GS CD** *020 †85

KAYSER, Bradley Basch. 7210 LOUIS PASTEUR DR, PASTEUR MEDICAL 78229 #021-01-1981 L1984 **IM** *020 †20

KAZANDJIAN, Dickran Garo. ■ 78230 #024-05-2003 L2004 **IM** *020 †20

KAZHDAN, Irene. 7979 WURZBACH RD 78229 #913-01-1981 L2005 **IM** *100 †20

KEELER-BOYSEN, Diane E. 4502 MEDICAL DR 78229 #048-13-1983 L1983 **AN PD** *020 †05

KEENER, Gary Norman. 45 NE LOOP 410, STE 900 78216 #048-12-1976 L1979 **AN** *020 †05

KEENEY, James Allen. ■ 78256 #028-02-1993 L2007 **ORS** *020 †40

KEIDEL, Werner Ned. 5414 FREDERICKSBURG RD, STE 100 78229 #021-01-1967 L1969 **NPM PUD** *020 †55

KEIGER, Richard Lester J. 1310 MCCULLOUGH AVE, EMERGENCY DEPARTMENT 78212 #649-38-1987 L1996 **EM** *020 †16

KELLA, Naveen. 7909 FREDERICKSBURG RD, STE 110 78229 #048-12-1998 L2003 **U** *020 †95

KELLER, Charles, III. 7703 FLOYD CURL DR, MC-7784 78229 #048-04-1995 L1998 **PHO** *020 †55

KELLER, Sheryl R. 8039 CALLAGHAN RD # 211 78230 #048-13-1996 **FM** *072

KELLEY, Harmon Watson. 4115 E SOUTHCROSS BLVD, STE 102 78222 #048-02-1971 L1971 **OBG** *020 †30

KELLEY, Jerry Robt. 8715 VILLAGE DR, STE 616 78217 #048-13-1976 L1976 **TS** *020 †85,90

KELLEY, Margaret A. 4115 E SOUTHCROSS BLVD, STE 102 78222 #043-01-1998 L2000 **OBG** *020 †30

KELLEY, Stephanie Lynn. 7703 FLOYD CURL DR, UNIV TX MED SCH 78229 #048-13-2006 L2008 **DR** *012

KELLOGG, Dean L, Jr. 7703 FLOYD CURL DR, DEPT MED UTHSC-S A 78229 #048-13-1978 L1981 **OS IMG** *020 †20

KELLOGG, Nancy Sue Denny. 7703 FLOYD CURL DR, UTHSC - SA 78229 #048-13-1985 L1986 **PD** *020 †55

KELLUM, Daniel H, Jr. 7323 MARBACH RD, STE 104 78227 #048-13-1991 L1992 **FM** *020 †18

KELLUM, John H. 7323 MARBACH RD, STE 104 78227 #048-13-1990 L1992 **OBG** *020 †30

KELLY, Ted Martin. ■ 78248 #005-12-1985 L1991 **EM** *020 †16

KEMMERER, William Taylor. ■ 78245 #021-01-1954 L1975 **GS AM** *071 †85

KEMP, Kenneth Ray. 3851 ROGER BROOKE DR, BROOKE, BLDG 3600 78234 #004-01-1988 L2002 **PUD CCM** *020 †20

KEMPENICH, Jason William. ■ 78249 #056-06-2007 **GS** *012

KEMPF, Kevin James. 4319 MEDICAL DR, STE 210A 78229 #048-04-1991 L1994 **RHU IM** *020 †20

KEMPF, Melissa M. 3338 OAKWELL CT, STE 107 78218 #048-15-1997 L1998 **FM** *020 †18

KENDRICK, Robert Rollins. 5711 UNIVERSITY HTS, # 100 78249 #045-01-1976 L2004 **GS EM** *071 †85

KENNEDY, Bruce D. 45 NE LOOP 410, STE 900 78216 #048-15-1995 L1997 **AN** *020 †05

KENNEDY, Colleen M. 6401 EL VERDE RD 78238 #048-13-1988 L1990 **IMG** *020 †20

KENNEY, John Wesley. 7700 FLOYD CURL DR 78229 #495-12-1955 **GP** *071

KENNY, Julia Porras. 333 N SANTA ROSA AVE, PATHOLOGY ASSOCIATES OF 78207 #847-08-1982 L1997 **PTH** *020 †50

KENTON, Alexander B. 5414 FREDERICKSBURG RD, STE 100 78229 #048-02-1997 L2001 **NPM** *020 †20,55

KEPPLER, John Paul. ■ 78229 #038-41-1978 L1981 **OS PM** *075

KERBY, Paul Glen. 45 NE LOOP 410, STE 900 78216 #048-14-1995 L1996 **AN** *020 †05

KERCHEVILLE, Scott Eugene. 7703 FLOYD CURL DR, MAIL CODE 7838 78229 #048-02-1983 L1983 **AN** *020 †05

KERGOSIEN, Matthew Cole. ■ 78229 #048-13-2007 **GS** *012

KERN, Travis Wade. ■ 78229 #048-13-2007 **GS** *012

KERNEK, William Geo. ■ 78258 #048-12-1965 L1965 **DR** *020 †80

KESAVULU, Shantha. 4242 E SOUTHCROSS BLVD # 6 78222 #495-21-1963 L1981 **PD** *020

KESZLER, Berney Ray. 8637 FREDERICKSBURG RD, STE 160 78240 #048-15-1975 L1975 **AN** *020

KETHIREDDY, Vanaja Rani. 7950 FLOYD CURL DR 78229 #495-21-2000 L2007 **OBG** *020

KEY, Cassandra C. 7703 FLOYD CURL DR, U TX MED SCH SAN ANTONIO 78229 #048-13-2006 **IM** *012

KEY, John Caleb. 218 S LAREDO ST, WACKENHUT CORRECTIONS-CTPV 78207 #048-02-1976 L1978 **GP** *030 †85

KEYSER, Herbert H. ■ 78209 #041-09-1958 L1978 **OBG OS** *071 †30

KHAN, Shakil Ahmed. 302 W RECTOR ST 78216 #704-08-1985 L2006 **FM** *020 †18

KHO, Sie Thong. ■ 78238 #506-01-1956 L1977 **GP** *071

KHODR, Gabriel Shukri. 7614 LOUIS PASTEUR DR #310 78229 #605-01-1967 L1976 **MG OBS** *020 †30,19

KIDD, Joseph Neil, Jr. 4499 MEDICAL DR, STE 347 78229 #048-04-1996 L2003 **PDS** *020 †85

KIESZ, Radoslaw Stefan. 343 W HOUSTON ST, STE 1005 78205 #759-03-1977 L1990 **CD** *020 †20

KIKER, Dustin G. ■ 78229 #048-13-2006 **IM** *012

KILPADI, Krista Lyn. ■ 78249 #001-02-2004 **ORS** *100

KIM, Andrew Myong. ■ 78253 #010-01-1993 L2007 **FM** *020 †18

KIM, Danny Song. ■ 78249 #021-01-2005 L2007 **GS** *012

KIM, David Yuhyon. ■ 78231 #048-04-2005 L2007 **OPH** *012

KIM, Kyu Young. 333 N SANTA ROSA AVE, EMERGENCY DEPT. 78207 #041-13-2000 L2003 **EM** *020

KIM, Seung Hwan. ■ 78233 #583-03-1966 L1979 **PTH** *020 †50

KIMBRELL, Patrick N. 5101 MEDICAL DR 78229 #048-13-1985 L1987 **FM UM** *020 †18

KIMMEL, Robert Butler. ■ 78209 #048-02-1976 L1976 **ORS** *020

KING, Aaron A. 225 E SONTERRA BLVD, STE 100 78258 #048-16-2001 L2005 **FM** *100

KING, Andrea Lynn. 7703 FLOYD CURL DR, MSC 7838 78229 #048-13-2003 L2005 **AN** *100

KING, Carter Anthony. 7703 FLOYD CURL DR, MAIL CODE 7871 78229 #048-13-2003 L2006 **CD** *012 †20

KING, Cheryl Jean. 6547 BANDERA RD 78238 #016-06-1988 L1998 **IM** *020 †20

KING, Clarence Gordon. 7703 FLOYD CURL DR, DEPT OF MED/DEP 78229 #048-04-1973 L1974 **IM NEP** *040

KING, Elizabeth A. 502 MADISON OAK DR, STE 240 78258 #048-16-2001 L2005 **OBG** *020

KING, Elizabeth Edrington. 7703 FLOYD CURL DR, MAIL CODE 7871 78229 #048-13-2003 L2006 **END** *012

KING, Halifax Chas. ■ 78260 #047-07-1974 L1981 **TS** *030

KING, John Barre. ■ 78218 #048-02-1954 L1954 **P PYG** *020 †75

KING, John Chandler. 7703 FLOYD CURL DR, UTHSC DEPT OF REHAB MED 78229 #039-05-1983 L1984 **PM** *020 †60

KING, Justin Michael. ■ 78240 #038-44-2003 **OTO** *012

KING, Lawrence Marion, Jr. ■ 78218 #021-05-1953 L1980 **OPH OS** *071 †35

KING, Melissa Mc Guinn. ■ 78255 #023-12-2003 L2005 **HO** *012 †20

KING, Randall B. ■ 78229 #030-05-1978 L1999 **N** *020 †75

KING, Susan Marenda. 21 SPURS LN, STE 100 78240 #030-06-1989 L1990 **OTO** *020 †45

KINGMAN, Thomas A. 4410 MEDICAL DR, STE 600 78229 #048-12-1980 L1980 **NS** *020 †25

KINNAIRD, Alexander Nabil. ■ 78232 #012-01-2006 **IM** *012

KINNAIRD, Kate E H. ■ 78232 #012-05-2006 L2007 **IM** *012

KINNEY, Marsha Chattin. 7703 FLOYD CURL DR, MAIL CODE 7750 DEPT OF PAT 78229 #048-12-1981 L2002 **PTH HMP** *020 †50

KINZY, Bruce Glenn. 1100 NW LOOP 410, STE 546 78213 #028-03-1971 L1971 **FM PM** *020 †60,18

KIPLIN, Lydell Craig. 9150 HUEBNER RD, STE 280 78240 #030-05-1958 L1965 **OPH** *071 †35

KIPNES, Mark Steven. 5107 MEDICAL DR, DISEASE CLINIC 78229 #041-09-1979 L1985 **END IM** *020 †20

■ = Address Information Privacy Protected

KIRCHNER, Alyson J. ■ 78249 #048-13-2006 **OBG** *012
KIRCHNER, Lee. 4499 MEDICAL DR, STE 370 78229 #030-05-1989 L1995 **PDP** *020
KIRK, William O. 8715 VILLAGE DR, STE 518 78217 #048-12-1987 L1989 **VS** *020 †85
KIRKENDALL, Mary Margaret. 7700 FLOYD CURL DR 78229 #048-14-1985 L1987 **PD** *020 †55
KIRSCH, Susan E. 1405 N MAIN AVE, BIRTHRIGHT INC 78212 #041-13-1981 **PD OS** *020 †55
KISH, Julie Ann. 7979 WURZBACH RD 78229 #025-07-1977 L1984 **ON IM** *020 †20
KIST, Kenneth Alfred. ■ 78213 #041-09-1992 L1993 **DR** *020 †80
KITTRELL, Dave Weldon. 4499 MEDICAL DR STE 156 78229 #048-02-1975 L1975 **OBG** *020 †30
KLAHN, John C. 8601 VILLAGE DR 78217 #035-45-1960 L1976 **IM CD** *020 †20
KLAUS, Duane. 4242 MEDICAL DR, STE 4250 78229 #048-13-1985 L1986 **AN** *020 †05
KLECK, Henry Geo. ■ 78229 #048-02-1958 L1958 **P N** *020
KLEINGUENTHER, Romana S. 2515 BABCOCK RD 78229 #048-13-1990 L1992 **N** *020 †75
KLEM, Samuel A, Jr. ■ 78255 #048-13-2000 L2003 **AN** *020 †05
KLEWENO, Elizabeth Ann. ■ 78251 #048-13-2006 L2007 **PD** *012
KLIEWER, John R. ■ 78209 #048-13-2001 *100
KLINE, Philip S, Jr. ■ 78209 #010-01-1971 L1972 **DR** *020,28
KLOTZ, Jeffrey Kenny. 3151 SCOTT RD, BLDG 2841 78234 #023-12-1997 L2007 **IM** *020 †20
KNAPP, Robert Vaughan. 8038 WURZBACH RD STE 150 78229 #035-01-1967 L1973 **DR** *071 †80
KNIGHT, Jackie N. 6570 INGRAM RD, TEXAS MEDICAL CLINIC 78238 #048-13-1986 L1987 **FM** *020 †18
KNIGHT, James Arthur. 519 E QUINCY ST STE B 78215 #048-15-1986 L1992 **TS** *020 †85,90
KNIKER, William T. 2414 BABCOCK RD, STE 109 78229 #048-02-1953 L1953 **AI PD** *020 †55,03
KNOX, John Stephen. 1310 MCCULLOUGH AVE 78212 #035-09-1955 L1962 **PS** *071 †65
KOBES, Christy Grant. 4499 MEDICAL DR, STE 178 78229 #047-06-1996 L1998 **OBG** *020 †30
KOCH, Joseph A. ■ 78230 #048-13-2008 *012
KOCUREK, Kristen A. 1007 NE LOOP 410 78209 #048-14-1998 L2001 **FSM** *020 †18
KOFOS, Danny Michael. 7711 LOUIS PASTEUR, STE 707 78229 #041-13-1992 L1999 **CCP** *020 †55
KOGAN, Yelenaleonidovna. 7703 FLOYD CURL DR, UNIV TX HLTH SCI CTR 78229 #036-07-2004 L2004 **CD** *012 †20
KOHL, Edward Alan. 4499 MEDICAL DR STE 245 78229 #048-12-1973 L1975 **END IM** *020 †20
KOHLER, Colette Maxine. ■ 78209 #048-02-1955 L1955 **PDC** *074 †55
KOHLMEIER, R E. 7703 FLOYD CURL DR # 7750 78229 #035-15-1991 L2006 **PTH** *020 †50
KOHN, Benjamin. 14350 NORTHBROOK DR, STE 220 78232 #018-03-1979 L1980 **D** *020 †15
KOLI, Malathi Vijay. 14350 NORTHBROOK DR STE 23 78232 #913-92-1971 L1981 **P** *020 †75
KOLI, Vijay Narayanrao. 660 SW MILITARY DR, STE E 78221 #913-92-1971 L1979 **GP IM** *020
KONERU, Suresh. 423 TREELINE PARK, # 300 78209 #048-13-1989 L1996 **PS** *020 †85,65
KONWE, Bielose Chukwunwik. 7703 FLOYD CURL DR, DEPT MED 78229 #690-01-1995 **IM** *012
KOOPS, Maureen Kay. 3851 ROGER BROOKE DR, BROOKE AMC, BLDG 3600 78234 #007-02-1990 L1992 **IM END** *040 †18
KOPECKY, Christopher Leon. 7922 EWING HALSELL DR, STE 200 78229 #048-13-1976 L1979 **CD IM** *020 †20
KOPECKY, Craig Tindall. ■ 78213 #023-12-1997 L1999 **IM** *020
KOPP, James B. ■ 78261 #048-13-1998 L2001 **FM** *020 †18
KOPPES, Gerald Max. 1314 GREYSTONE RDG 78258 #019-02-1972 L1974 **CD IM** *020 †20
KORDY, Kattayoun. ■ 78260 #048-13-2008 *012
KORETSKY, Stella. ■ 78254 #913-50-1990 L2007 **FM** *020
KORP, Susan Alison. 540 MADISON OAK DR, STE 140 78258 #048-14-1983 L1983 **OBG** *020 †30
KOSMATKA, Timothy Jon. ■ 78258 #023-12-1993 L1996 **FM** *020 †18
KOSTER, Kim Richard. 7711 LOUIS PASTEUR STE 707 78229 #019-02-1991 L1996 **PAN AN** *020 †05
KOSUB, Kristy Yvonne. 7703 FLOYD CURL DR, S.A. DEPT OF MEDICINE 78229 #048-13-1986 L1987 **IM** *020 †20
KOTTMAN, William D. 2121 SW 36TH ST, SOUTHWEST UNIVERSITY HEALT 78237 #048-16-1995 L1998 **FM** *020 †18
KOUSHIK, Rahul Shankar. 2391 NE LOOP 410, STE 405 78217 #496-38-1992 L2005 **NEP** *020
KOZLOVSKY, John F. 7810 LOUIS PASTEUR DR, STE 100 78229 #048-04-1990 L1991 **OPH** *020 †35
KRAGH, John Frederick, Jr. ■ 78210 #023-12-1989 L1991 **ORS** *020 †40
KRALJEVIC, Tina Kathy. 7703 FLOYD CURL DR, MAIL CODE 7883 78229 #051-01-2002 L2007 **N** *100
KRAMER, David H. 4330 MEDICAL DR, STE 400 78229 #024-05-1960 L1972 **CD IM** *020 †20
KRAMER, Edward F, Jr. ■ 78230 #021-05-1963 L1977 **OM AM** *030 †70,18
KRAULAND, Kevin John. ■ 78251 #041-13-2008 *012
KRAUS, Eric Werner. 7703 FLOYD CURL DR, UTHSCSA-DERMATOLOGY 78229 #048-13-1974 L1976 **D** *020 †15 ‡
KRAUS, Stephen D. 7979 WURZBACH RD 78229 #033-06-1991 L2002 **U** *020 †95
KRAUSE, Donald Edward. 207 W OAK RD 78227 #048-02-1959 L1959 **GYN** *071 †30
KRENRICH, Scott Wilson. ■ 78249 #005-12-1989 L1991 **PTH** *020
KRIETE, Brian Robert. ■ 78258 #028-34-2005 L2007 **OTO** *012
KROMA, Ghazwan Mhammad Fa. 7703 FLOYD CURL DR 78229 #875-01-1994 L2007 **VIR** *100
KRUCZEK, Michael Edward. 8637 FREDERICKSBURG RD, STE 160 78240 #048-14-1979 L1979 **AN PME** *020 †05
KRUEGER, Otto Allan. 8038 WURZBACH RD 78229 #048-12-1963 L1963 **FM OBG** *071 †18
KRUEGER, Roberta Lynn. 7922 EWING HALSELL DR, STE 310 78229 #021-01-1983 L1983 **OBG** *020 †30 ‡
KRUEGER, Wesley Wm Otto. 2632 BROADWAY ST, S BLDG #201 78215 #048-14-1975 L1976 **NO OTO** *020 †45
KRUSE, Jerry Elliott. 1303 MCCULLOUGH AVE, STE 561 78212 #048-13-1974 L1975 **U GS** *020 †95
KRYZAK, Thomas John. ■ 78256 #024-07-2005 L2005 **GS** *100
KUAN, Anne Sun Wah. 8303 W MILITARY DR 78227 #035-46-1975 L1989 **IM** *020 †20
KUBENA, Kassia L. 5255 PRUE RD, STE 105 78240 #048-13-1995 L1998 **PD** *020 †55
KUEBKER, Craig Wm. 9480 HUEBNER RD, STE 100 78240 #048-13-1981 L1981 **FM** *020 †18
KUEBKER, Joseph Maurice. ■ 78230 #048-04-2006 L2006 **GS** *012
KUESTERMANN, Sven Andre. 9901 IH 10 W, STE 400 78230 #429-02-1995 L2001 **VIR** *020 †80
KUHL, Peter Van Doren. 7950 FLOYD CURL DR 78229 #048-15-1976 L1976 **OBG** *020 †30
KUMAR, Arvind. 1031 ALPINE DR 78260 #495-55-1968 L1976 **IM** *020 †20
KUMAR, Sanjay. 7323 MARBACH RD, STE 104 78227 #495-15-1993 L2001 **IM P** *020 †20
KUMAR, Sudha R. 1202 E SONTERRA BLVD, STE 303 78258 #024-05-1994 L1996 **P** *020 †75
KUMARA, Halekote Nanjegow. 102 PALO ALTO RD, STE 133 78211 #495-09-1970 L1977 **PM** *020 †60

KUNASZ, Markian George. 3851 ROGER BROOKE DR, MCHE-SDP PLASTIC SURG BAMC 78234 #010-02-1994 L1995 **PS GS** *020 †85,65
KUNAU, Robert T, Jr. 7703 FLOYD CURL DR, MED/DIV OF NEPHROLOGY, MC7 78229 #018-03-1962 L1968 **IM** *050
KUO, Li-Mei. 4330 MEDICAL DR STE 325 78229 #244-02-1971 L1980 **GP OS** *075
KUPFERSCHMID, John Paul. 8201 EWING HALSELL DR, STE 280 78229 #017-20-1982 L2000 **TS** *020 †85,90
KURIAN, Elizabeth Marie. ■ 78248 #048-14-2004 L2008 **PTH** *012
KUSIAK, Michael Thos. 1214 STONEWALL ST 78211 #649-14-1980 L1992 **FM** *020 †18
KUSMIERZ, Zbigniew. ■ 78249 #759-11-1986 L2000 **AN** *020 †05
KUSTOFF, Ralph. ■ 78230 #047-06-1950 L1964 **OPH OTO** *071
KUTTNER, Jessica Lynn. ■ 78209 #023-12-2008 *012
KUWAMURA, Frank Kakuzo. 150 E SONTERRA BLVD, SAN ANTONIO ORTHOPAEDIC 78258 #024-05-1989 L1999 **ORS** *020 †40
KVALE, James Noel. 7703 FLOYD CURL DR, UTHSC-SAN ANTONIO 78229 #010-03-1963 L1995 **IMG FPG** *040 †18
KWAN, Michael Douggai. 8201 EWING HALSELL DR 78229 #016-43-1992 L2002 **CD TRS** *020 †20
KWEE, Jason W. 45 NE LOOP 410, STE 900 78216 #506-02-1975 L1987 **AN** *020 †05
KYPUROS, Orlando. 7330 SAN PEDRO STE 405 78216 #048-02-2003 L2006 **IM** *020 †20
LABORDE, Alfredo L, Jr. 4330 MEDICAL DR, STE 100 78229 #048-15-1985 L1992 **GS** *020 †85
LACIVITA, Kathy Ann. 701 S ZARZAMORA ST 78207 #023-12-1985 L1996 **END IM** *020 †20
LACKEY, James M. 10350 BANDERA RD, STE 300 78250 #048-12-2000 L2002 **FM** *020 †18
LACKRITZ, Richard Mark. 4499 MEDICAL DR STE 230 78229 #048-13-1972 L1978 **OBG REN** *020 †30
LACY, Benjamin Watkins. 7703 FLOYD CURL DR, UNIV TX MED SCH 78229 #023-12-2002 **P** *100 †75
LAHAM, Michel Nicolas. 1303 MCCULLOUGH AVE # 161 78212 #011-03-1971 L1981 **AI IM** *020 †20,03
LAI, Tristan Toll. ■ 78259 #023-12-2006 L2007 **AN** *012
LAI, Yvonne Y. 19223 STONEHUE 78258 #048-13-1997 L1999 **FM** *020 †18
LAING, Aurelio, III. ■ 78205 #048-15-2006 **FP** *020
LALANI, Neil. ■ 78232 #048-13-1994 *100
LAM, Khim Kirsten. 7703 FLOYD CURL DR, DEPT. OF OB/GYN 78229 #004-01-1999 L2004 **OBG** *020
LAM, Victor. 111 DALLAS ST 78205 #041-01-1971 L1978 **SME OS** *020 †20
LAMAIE, Nagwa Nabil. 7703 FLOYD CURL DR 78229 #915-02-1997 L2008 **FP** *020
LAMAR, Daniel Lawrence. ■ 78253 #023-12-2004 L2005 **IM** *012
LAMB, Lawrence E. ■ 78232 #019-02-1949 L1955 **CD AM** *040 †20
LAMEY, Veronica Claire. ■ 78232 #023-12-2007 **PD** *012
LAMIELL, James Michael. 3851 ROGER BROOKE DR, BROOKE ARMY MED CTR 78234 #007-02-1976 L2008 **CCM IM** *040 †20
LAMPE, John Henry. 540 MADISON OAK DR, STE 160 78258 #041-13-1993 L1998 **DR** *020 †80
LAMPERT, Morris H. 9502 COMPUTER DR, STE 233 78229 #048-12-1953 L1953 **N OS** *020 †75
LANCASTER, Howard E, Jr. ■ 78209 #048-02-1955 L1955 **P N** *071
LANCASTER, Malcolm C. ■ 78213 #048-12-1956 L1956 **CD IM** *071 †20
LANCASTER-WEISS, Kristen. 8026 FLOYD CURL DR, SOUTH TEXAS PATHOLOGY 78229 #001-02-1991 L1996 **PP** *020 †50,55
LANDEEN, James Monroe. 4499 MEDICAL DR STE 325 78229 #028-03-1965 L1978 **PS HS** *020 †45,65
LANDGREBE, Bernhard H. 7254 BLANCO RD STE 205 78216 #407-07-1947 L1966 **N P** *020
LANE, Daniel Mc Neel. 7619 KIM ST 78209 #048-12-1961 L1961 **PD VM** *050 †55
LANE, Elizabeth Waldman. 4647 MEDICAL DR 78229 #030-05-1992 L1999 **IM** *020 †20
LANE, Frank Childress. 17720 CORPORATE WOODS DR 78259 #048-04-1964 L1964 **CHP P** *020
LANE, Michael Jos. 8401 DATAPOINT DR, STE 600 78229 #030-05-1992 L1999 **DR** *020 †80
LANE, Richard Gary, Jr. 8 COBHAM WAY, 859MSGS/MCST 78218 #011-03-1993 L2005 **OPH** *020
LANG, Amy Solomon. 7979 WURZBACH RD, STE U335 78229 #048-13-1991 L1992 **ON HO** *020 †20
LANGE, Jory Doyle. 8215 EWING HALSELL DR 78229 #048-02-1976 L1976 **RO** *030 †18,80
LANGEVIN, Anne-Marie. 7979 WURZBACH RD 78229 #067-02-1980 L1992 **HEM IM** *020 †55
LANTRY, Bruce Richard. 2020 BABCOCK RD, STE 28 78229 #048-13-1994 L1997 **PD** *072 †55
LAPEY, Sarah Elisabeth. 7400 MERTON MINTER ST, VETERANS HOSP, MAILBOX 11C 78229 #024-01-2000 L2003 **IM** *100 †20
LARA-IMERY, Domingo A. 45 CHAMPION TRL 78258 #341-01-1976 L1984 **N** *020 †75
LARGENT, Matthew. 7703 FLOYD CURL DR, UNIV OF TX MED SCH AT SAN 78229 #048-13-2006 **GS** *012
LARGOZA, Marissa N. 4499 MEDICAL DR, STE 191 78229 #041-02-1994 L2000 **OBG** *020 †30
LARIOS, Patricia. ■ 78240 #042-02-2001 L2004 **IM** *020
LAROE, Michele Clarke. 7703 FLOYD CURL DR, UNIV OF TEXAS HLTH SCI CTR 78229 #048-12-1993 L1994 **PYG** *012 †18
LARRUMBIDE, Margaret F. 1954 E HOUSTON ST, RM 104 78202 #048-12-1988 L1989 **PD** *020 †55
LARSON, Paula R. 8026 FLOYD CURL DR, SOUTH TEXAS PATHOLOGY 78229 #056-05-1978 L1991 **PTH PCP** *020 †50
LASSETER, Adam Barton. ■ 78240 #048-14-2008 *012
LASSITER, Paulette Denise. ■ 78229 #023-12-1999 L2000 **P** *012
LASTER, Dan Wayne. 7703 FLOYD CURL DR 78229 #048-02-1966 L1966 **R** *020 †80
LATCH, Kerry C. 45 NE LOOP 410, STE 900 78216 #048-15-1999 L2006 **AN** *020 †05 ‡
LATHROP, Kate I. 7703 FLOYD CURL DR, U TX MED SCH SAN ANTONIO 78229 #048-13-2007 **IM** *012
LATONI, Dimitri Ernest. 7400 MERTON MINTER ST, NUCLEAR MEDICINE SERVICE (78229 #035-03-1986 L1994 **NM** *020
LATSHAW, James Charles. ■ 78231 #038-40-2002 L2007 **ORS** *020
LAU, Jimmy Junsing. ■ 78259 #023-12-2001 L2006 **AN** *020 †05
LAUFMAN, Joan E. 2211 NW MILITARY HWY, STE 201 78213 #048-13-1991 L1992 **FM** *020 †18
LAUGHY, Jamie Leigh. ■ 78247 #039-01-2007 **PD** *012
LAUGHY, Timothy Neil. ■ 78247 #039-01-2007 **PD** *012
LAURSEN, Gerald Paul. 4025 E SOUTHCROSS BLVD, STE 24 78222 #039-01-1977 L1978 **OTO FPS** *020 †45
LAUTNER, Meeghan Ann. ■ 78229 #025-07-2006 **GS** *012
LAVROVSKAYA, Elena. ■ 78229 #913-72-1989 L2008 **PCP** *100 †50
LAWITZ, Eric Joel. 621 CAMDEN ST, STE 202 78215 #016-01-1993 L2003 **GE** *020 †20
LAWLER, Caroline ■. ■ 78249 #008-02-2008 *012

LAWLER, William Ross. 527 N LEONA ST 78207 #048-02-1968 L1968 **FM** *040 †18
LAWLOR, Colleen. ■ 78209 #048-13-2001 **FM** *100
LAWRENCE, Courtney. 4212 E SOUTHCROSS BLVD, STE 150 78222 #048-13-1990 L1991 **PD** *020 †55
LAWRENCE, Leonard Eugene. ■ 78259 #017-20-1962 L1971 **CHP P** *071 †75
LAWRENCE, Leonard Michael. 45 NE LOOP 410, STE 900 78216 #048-13-1991 L1993 **AN** *020 †05
LAWRENCE, Leslie Jacob. ■ 78209 #038-40-1962 L1970 **R NM** *071 †80,28
LAWRENCE, Valerie Ann. 7400 MERTON MINTER ST 78229 #039-01-1981 L1984 **IM** *020 †20
LAWSON, Rebecca Lynn. ■ 78229 #012-01-2004 L2008 **AN** *012
LAWSON, William J. ■ 78213 #051-04-1956 L1957 **PD AM** *071 †55
LAWTON, Gary Paul. 525 OAK CENTRE DR STE 260 78258 #024-16-1990 L2000 **PS** *020 †65
LAZAGA, Edward J. 1222 MCCULLOUGH AVE 78212 #308-03-1985 L2004 **NEP** *020 †20
LAZARUS, Kenneth Hillard. 4499 MEDICAL DR, STE 260 78229 #021-01-1977 L1984 **PHO** *020 †55
LAZZARA, Attilio I. ■ 78216 #561-17-1958 **GP** *020
LEACH, Charles Thos. 7703 FLOYD CURL DR, UTHSC 78229 #049-01-1982 L1989 **PD ID** *050 †55
LEAL, Sylvia. 333 N SANTA ROSA AVE 78207 #048-13-1992 L1994 **PD** *020 †55
LEATHERMAN, Martha E. 5807 BABCOCK RD, # 195 78240 #048-14-1988 L1990 **P** *020 †75
LE BLANC, Mary M. 8181 TEZEL RD, STE 102 78250 #048-13-1987 L1988 **FM** *020 †18
LEDBETTER, Edgar Otis. ■ 78248 #039-01-1956 L1967 **PD ID** *071 †55
LEDESMA, Elihu J. 7400 MERTON MINTER ST, MURPHY VETERANS HOSPITAL 78229 #042-01-1973 L1982 **GS SO** *020 †85
LEDFORD, Frank Finley. ■ 78230 #038-41-1959 L1959 **ORS MDM** *071 †40
LEDOUX, Peter Robert. 9635 HUEBNER RD 78240 #025-07-1987 L1994 **PS GS** *020 †85,65 ‡
LEE, Da Hae. 525 OAK CENTRE DR, STE 400 78258 #583-03-1967 L1987 **PDC PD** *020 †55
LEE, Dennis Rodney. 7434 LOUIS PASTEUR DR, STE 203 78229 #051-04-1970 L1980 **ORS GP** *020 †40
LEE, Ernest Castro. ■ 78209 #048-14-1994 L1995 **FM OM** *020 †70,18
LEE, Mark Stewart. 4499 MEDICAL DR, STE 120 78229 #010-01-1987 L1995 **D** *020 †15
LEE, Monica I. 4502 MEDICAL DR 78229 #048-13-1999 L2002 **IM** *020 †20
LEE, Nancy Ann. ■ 78258 #008-01-1987 L1991 **IM** *020 †20
LEE, Regina K. 10515 SH 151, STE 240 78251 #048-13-2005 L2008 **FP** *012
LEE, Robert Q. 13903 BLUFFOAK 78216 #048-13-1979 L1979 **AN PME** *020 †05
LEE, Roderick D, Jr. 7355 BARLITE BLVD 78224 #025-12-1975 **PDA** *030
LEE, Samuel Austin. 7703 FLOYD CURL DR, MAIL CODE 7881 78229 #024-05-1993 L2006 **IM ID** *020 †20 ‡
LEE, Shelly Tina. 7703 FLOYD CURL DR, MSC 62 78229 #036-07-2003 L2005 **OPH** *012
LEE, Susan Annette. 7622 LOUIS PASTEUR, STE 100 78229 #048-13-1984 L1985 **FM** *020 †18
LEE, Theresia Lisa. 4499 MEDICAL DR, STE 120 78229 #010-01-1987 L1991 **AN** *020 †05
LEE, Thomas Jacob, Jr. ■ 78253 #001-06-2008 *012
LEE, Washington Tom. 1730 SW MILITARY DR 78221 #048-15-1976 L1976 **OPH** *020 †35
LEES, Toby Fischer. ■ 78253 #023-12-2007 **GS** *012
LEE SANG, Ivan A. ■ 78260 #566-01-1963 L1978 **GP** *071
LEFEBER, Edward James. 4647 MEDICAL DR, DIAGNOSTIC PAVILION 78229 #048-02-1966 L1966 **IM IMG** *020 †20
LEGAY, Douglas Andrew. 8042 WURZBACH RD STE 540 78229 #064-01-1984 L1990 *020
LEGLER, James Danl. 527 N LEONA ST 78207 #048-02-1979 L1979 **PD** *020 †18,55
LEHMANN, James David, Jr. ■ 78209 #048-13-2001 L2004 **OPH** *100 †35
LEIBOLD, David Geo. 7703 FLOYD CURL DR 78229 #048-13-1975 L1975 **OS** *020
LEIBOLD, Robert Waltner. ■ 78212 #041-12-1941 L1942 **GYN** *071 †30
LEICHT, Craig Howard. 4242 MEDICAL DR, STE 3100 78229 #005-12-1982 L2003 **AN PME** *020 †05
LEIDNER, Richard Neil. 4499 MEDICAL DR STE 396 78229 #011-02-1979 L1981 **N** *071 †75
LEILOGLOU, Demetrios G. 2235 THOUSAND OAKS DR, STE 119 78232 #048-04-1998 L2001 **PD** *020 †55
LEININGER, James Richard. 8122 DATAPOINT DR STE 900 78229 #017-20-1969 L1973 **EM** *020
LEININGER, Peter Arthur. 12000 HUEBNER RD STE 103 78230 #017-20-1968 L1978 **U** *071 †95
LEIST, Doris Marie. 7700 FLOYD CURL DR 78229 #048-13-1984 L1985 **GS** *020 †85
LE MAISTRE, Charles F. 7711 LOUIS PASTEUR, STE 707 78229 #048-12-1979 L1979 **ON IM** *050 †20
LE MAISTRE, Chas Aubrey. ■ 78209 #035-20-1947 L1960 **PUD** *071
LE MAISTRE, Joyce Anne. ■ 78230 #048-14-1983 L1983 **CLP HMP** *040 †50
LEMKE, Robert R. 14500 SAN PEDRO AVE, STE 102 78232 #048-13-1991 L1992 **OS** *020
LENDERMAN, Lawrence Lee. 2424 BABCOCK RD STE 200 78229 #036-05-1976 L1980 **ORS** *020 †40
LENOIR, Keri P. ■ 78218 #048-13-1980 L1980 **RO** *074 †80
LENOX, John Bowden. 435 ISOM RD, STE 224 78216 #041-01-1968 L1969 **OS** *050
LEON, Robert Leonard. 7703 FLOYD CURL DR 78229 #007-02-1948 L1958 **P** *071 †75
LEONARD, Ellen Imber. 5101 MEDICAL DR, SOUTH TEXAS PHYSICAL 78229 #048-13-1985 L1986 **PM PDP** *020 †60
LEONARD, Michael Albert. 8715 VILLAGE DR, STE 610 78217 #035-19-1994 L2002 **NS** *020 †25
LEONE, Chas Russell, Jr. 7950 FLOYD CURL DR, DONALD A HOLLSTEN MD 78229 #041-13-1960 L1967 **OPH PS** *071 †35
LE PERE, Robert H. 7930 FLOYD CURL DR 78229 #048-04-1951 L1951 **TS** *071 †85,90
LEPESKA, Michael John. ■ 78258 #016-11-2002 L2008 **DR** *020 †80
LERNER, Charles Jay. 12721 HUNTERS CHASE 78230 #028-34-1966 L1970 **ID IM** *020 †20
LEROUX, Edmond Jos, Jr. 1933 NE LOOP 410 78217 #021-05-1970 L1977 **CD IM** *020 †20
LESLIE, Jeffrey A. 5343 COLTON CRK 78251 #048-13-1998 L2000 **UP** *100
LETT, Willie James. 2011 E HOUSTON ST, STE 101A 78202 #047-07-1971 L1973 **OBG** *071 †30
LETZ, Adrian G. ■ 78251 #048-12-2002 L2004 **AI** *012 †20
LEUSCHEN, Calvin Thomas. 7703 FLOYD CURL DR, UNIV OF TX HLTH SCI CNTR 78229 #030-05-1993 L2003 **DR** *020 †80
LEVCOVITZ, Henrique. 8303 MILITARY DR W 78227 #187-03-1979 L1992 **PD GP** *020 †55
LEVEY, David Stanley. 8627 CINNAMON CREEK DR, BLDG 2 78240 #038-06-1987 L1993 **DR** *020 †80
LEVINE, Deborah Jo. 7703 FLOYD CURL DR, STE 7841 78229 #003-01-1996 L2005 **PCC** *020 †20
LEVINE, Matthew Edward. 1920 BURNET ST, CENTER OR HEALTHCARE SVCS 78202 #024-07-1962 L2002 **P IM** *020 †75
LEVINE, Richard Allen. 4499 MEDICAL DR, STE 316 78229 #035-06-1975 L1981 **PS FPS** *020 †65 ‡
LEVINE, Stephanie Michel. 7703 FLOYD CURL, PULMONARY U TX HEALTH SCI 78229 #010-01-1984 L1989 **CCM PUD** *020 †20
LEVY, Louis Allen. ■ 78258 #036-05-1975 L1994 **PTH** *071 †50
LEWI, Jack E. 2 CHISWICK CT, BROOKE ARMY MEDICAL CENTER 78218 #048-02-1995 L1996 **IM END** *020 †20
LEWIS, Jeffrey David. ■ 78251 #051-07-2005 L2006 **IM** *020
LEWIS, Stephanie A. ■ 78240 #048-13-2008 *012
LEWIS, Wade H. ■ 78216 #048-04-1953 L1953 **P** *071 †75
LEWIS, William Cannon. 26 WORTHSHAM DR 78257 #048-04-1998 L1999 **CRS** *100 †85,10
LEYKUM, Luci Katherine. 929 CAMBRIDGE OVAL, DEPT OF MEDICINE 78209 #035-01-1999 L2004 **IM** *020 †20
LEYTHAM, Thomas Jos. 3453 N IH 35 STE 207B 78219 #001-06-1991 L1995 **FM** *020 †18
LI, Emily. ■ 78229 #035-06-2003 L2004 **IM** *100
LIAO, Lillian F. ■ 78240 #048-13-2004 **GS** *012
LIBOW, Lester Fred. 1122 AUSTIN HWY, S TX DERMPATHLY LAB PA 78209 #010-01-1980 L2003 **DMP D** *062 †15
LICHTENSTEIN, Michael Jos. 4647 MEDICAL DR 78229 #048-04-1978 L1978 **IM** *020 †20
LICON, Carlos Enrique. 2300 W COMMERCE ST, STE 300 78207 #007-02-2003 L2006 **FM** *100 †18
LILES, Deena Ray. ■ 78216 #048-13-2000 L2002 **AN** *100
LILLY, Gregory L. 621 N ALAMO ST 78215 #048-13-1991 L1992 **AN** *020 †05
LIMAYE, Shamkant Daji. ■ 78216 #495-28-1965 L1974 **P** *020
LIMMER, Bobby Lee. 14615 SAN PEDRO AVE, STE 210 78232 #048-02-1968 L1968 **DS D** *020 †15
LIMMER, Bradley L. 14615 SAN PEDRO AVE, STE 210 78232 #048-12-1992 L1994 **D** *020 †15
LIMMER, Byron L. 14615 SAN PEDRO AVE, STE 210 78232 #048-12-1989 L1990 **D** *020 †15
LIMMER, Rachel Lynn. 14615 SAN PEDRO AVE, STE 210 78232 #020-02-1989 L1993 **D** *020 †15
LIMON, David Thomas. 4242 MEDICAL DR, STE 3100 78229 #026-04-1984 L1988 **AN** *020 †05
LIN, Bryan Chih-Chang. 7979 WURZBACH RD 78229 #048-13-1996 L1999 **IM** *020
LIN, Edward Lee. ■ 78250 #048-13-2006 **FP** *012
LIN, Fang-Ying. ■ 78249 #048-02-2002 L2007 **NEP** *100 †20
LIN, Felicity Winifred. ■ 78258 #018-03-1998 L2001 **IM** *020 †20
LIN, Hsiang Chi Cha. ■ 78218 #048-13-2006 L2007 **GS** *012
LIN, James Weishi. ■ 78261 #035-08-2001 L2006 **NEP** *020
LIN, Janet I. 2140 BABCOCK RD STE 200 78229 #048-13-1999 L2003 **IM** *020 †20
LIN, Peichun. ■ 78254 #035-19-2005 L2007 **IM** *012
LIN, Wantin. ■ 78283 #048-13-2001 L2004 **PMM** *020 †60
LINCE, Leonardo. 4330 MEDICAL DR, STE 325 78229 #264-04-1956 L1969 **CD TS** *020
LINDER, Laura L. ■ 78209 #048-13-2006 **PD** *012
LINDHORST-O'NEILL, Grace. ■ 78260 #048-13-2003 L2007 **OPH** *020
LINDNER, Michael Scott. 8800 VILLAGE DR, STE 207 78217 #048-12-1989 L1990 **GE** *020 †20
LINDNER, Patrick W. ■ 78209 #048-13-2006 **IM** *012
LING, Doris D. 8715 VILLAGE DR, STE 510 78217 #048-13-1996 L1997 **FM** *020 †18
LIPSITT, Henry J. 3111 SAN PEDRO AVE 78212 #048-13-1975 L1975 **PD ADL** *020 †55
LISKE, Edward Anthony. 7700 FLOYD CURL DR 78229 #010-02-1955 L1964 **N OS** *071 †75
LITTLE, Michael B. 7703 FLOYD CURL DR 78229 #048-13-2003 L2007 **AN** *100
LITTLEFIELD, Christine A. 7930 FLOYD CURL DR 78229 #048-13-1978 L1978 **PD** *020 †55
LIU, Christine Minnan. 4242 MEDICAL DR, STE 3100 78229 #025-07-1991 L1996 **AN** *020 †05
LIU, Henry Chahen. ■ 78212 #023-12-2003 L2005 **AN** *020
LIU, Jean Hon. 255 E SONTERRA BLVD, STE 150 78258 #187-04-1982 L1988 **CD IM** *020 †20
LIVENGOOD, Tim Warren. ■ 78229 #038-40-2007 **EM** *012
LIVESAY, George B. 4410 MEDICAL DR, STE 610 78229 #048-04-1953 L1953 **NS** *071 †25
LIVINGSTON, Joshua C. 45 NE LOOP 410, STE 900 78216 #048-12-2001 L2005 **AN** *020 †05
LIVINGSTON, Lyudmila Vasi. 7703 FLOYD CURL DR, UNIV TX MED SCH-SAN ANTONI 78229 #913-73-1991 **CHP** *012
LLOYD, Timothy Hamilton. 4242 MEDICAL DR, STE 3100 78229 #264-04-1978 L1980 **AN** *020
LO, Ian K Y. 540 MADISON OAK DR, STONE OAK MEDICAL BLDG 78258 #065-06-1994 L2001 **ORS** *050
LO, Nancy Wingsze. ■ 78250 #023-12-2008 *012
LOCHTE, Erwin Richard, III. 525 OAK CENTRE DR, STE 150 78258 #048-13-1978 L1978 **FM** *020 †18
LOECKER, Thomas Henry. ■ 78227 #030-05-1966 L1975 **R** *071 †80
LOFFREDO, Alexandra Sasha. 527 N LEONA ST 78207 #050-02-2001 L2004 **FM** *020 †18
LOFTIN, Keisma L. 7922 EWING HALSELL DR, STE 170 78229 #048-13-1999 L2003 **OBG** *020 †30
LOLLIS, Blake David. ■ 78223 #039-01-1991 L1993 **FM** *020 †18
LOMBARDO, Lisa Rebecca. ■ 78209 #023-12-2005 *020
LOMOTAN, Emily R. 5414 FREDERICKSBURG RD, STE 150 78229 #748-01-1992 L2005 **IM RHU** *020 †20
LONG, Dorothy Amy. ■ 78230 #048-14-2007 **FP** *012
LONGFIELD, Jenice L Noble. 3851 ROGER BROOKE DR, ATTN: MCHE-CI 78234 #007-02-1973 L1987 **GPM PHP** *030 †70
LONGFIELD, Robert North. 2303 SE MILITARY DR 78223 #007-02-1973 L1988 **ID IM** *020 †20
LOONEY, Timothy Jan. 111 DALLAS ST 78205 #055-01-1971 L1977 **END IM** *020 †20
LOPERA BONILLA, Jorge Enr. ■ 78248 #264-16-1989 L2000 *020 †80
LOPEZ, Adriana M. 7711 LOUIS PASTEUR, STE 707 78229 #048-02-1998 L2004 **CCP** *020 †55
LOPEZ, Alfonso Nicolas. 7700 FLOYD CURL DR 78229 #649-01-1956 L1964 **GP PTH** *020
LOPEZ, Arturo. 4410 MEDICAL DR, STE 440 78229 #048-13-1999 L2006 **PCC** *100 †20
LOPEZ, Cesar Antonio. ■ 78239 #308-01-1948 L1968 **GP U** *071 †95
LOPEZ, David Naranjo. 5282 MEDICAL DR STE 540 78229 #005-11-1988 L1990 **FM** *020 †18
LOPEZ, Esteban Rodriguez. 333 N SANTA ROSA 78207 #025-12-1999 L2000 **MPD** *020 †20,55
LOPEZ, Eva Jeanette. 24165 W IH 10, # 217-615 78257 #048-13-1987 L1988 **IM** *020 †20
LOPEZ, Jesus Antonio. 2406 COMMERCIAL AVE, STE A 78221 #649-02-1985 L2001 **FM** *020 †18
LOPEZ, Joseph A. 333 N SANTA ROSA AVE, FL 4 78207 #048-16-1991 L1992 **FM** *020 †18
LOPEZ, Korina M. ■ 78240 #048-13-2004 L2006 **PD** *020
LOPEZ, Luis A. 13032 NACOGDOCHES RD, STE 211 78217 #737-09-1988 L1996 **PD** *020 †55
LOPEZ, Lydia Ruiz. 12915 JONES MALTSBERGER RD, STE 603 78247 #048-04-1987 L1989 **CHP** *020 †75
LOPEZ, Manuel Antonio. 4775 HAMILTON WOLFE RD, STE 1 78229 #020-02-1998 L2005 **OTO** *020
LOPEZ, Marco Antonio, Jr. 4499 MEDICAL DR, STE 306 78229 #048-13-1971 L1974 **OBG** *020 †30
LOPEZ, Peter Putters. 7703 FLOYD CURL DR, MC 7740 78229 #016-11-1990 L2007 **CCS TRS** *020 †85,18
LOPEZ, Rene Bogarin. 18117 LISCUM HL 78258 #016-11-1993 L1997 **EM** *020 †16

■ = Address Information Privacy Protected

LOPEZ, Shannon Rebecca. 4600 NW LOOP 410, STE 110 78229 #036-08-2000 L2003 FM *020 †18

LOPEZ CARDOZA, Carlos A. ■ 78218 #847-04-1963 L1978 PHP EM *062

LOPEZ-RODRIGUEZ, Abraham. ■ 78230 #649-31-1976 L1981 D GP *020

LOREDO, Rebecca A. 7703 FLOYD CURL DR, DEPT. OF RADIOLOGY 78229 #048-13-1988 L1989 DR *020 †80

LORENZANA, Elias Jurado. 1201 AUSTIN HWY, STE 133 78209 #748-09-1972 L1976 FM PM *020

LORENZO, Carlos. 7703 FLOYD CURL DR, UTHSCSA 78229 #847-01-1980 L2000 RHU IM *050 †20

LOTAY, Harpreet Kaur. 4647 MEDICAL DR 78229 #060-01-1993 L2003 FM *020 †18

LOTHRINGER, Larry Leon. 303 E QUINCY ST 78215 #048-04-1978 L1978 OPH *020

LOUDERMILK, Gary Gwynn. 4242 MEDICAL DR, STE 3100 78229 #048-12-1972 L1973 AN *020 †05

LOUDON, Elizabeth Ann. 7434 LOUIS PASTEUR, STE 220 78229 #007-02-1992 L1994 D *020 †15

LOVELL, James Lloyd. 7700 FLOYD CURL DR 78229 #048-13-1973 L1973 OBS GYN *020 †30

LOVELL, Michael O. 301 N FRIO ST 78207 #048-13-1997 L1999 PCP *020 †50

LOVERIDGE, Benjamin Richa. ■ 78251 #023-12-2007 IM *012

LOVETT, Jeanne Michelle. 2235 THOUSAND OAKS DR, STE 119 78232 #048-04-1997 L2000 PD *020

LOWRY, James K. 519 W HOUSTON ST 78207 #028-34-1951 L1959 PTH *071 †50

LOWRY, Lynnell Chere. 18720 STONE OAK PKWY, STE 119A 78258 #010-01-1993 L1998 OPH *020 †35

LOWRY, Robert Charles. 2425 BABCOCK RD, STE 111 78229 #010-01-1993 L1995 GS *020

LOYA, Amador. 7703 FLOYD CURL DR, SCIENCE C 78229 #048-15-2006 PD *012

LOYD, Amy Marie. ■ 78258 #016-76-2007, ▲ TY *012

LOYOLA, David. 8038 WURZBACH RD STE 340, PHYSICIANS PLAZA ONE 78229 #042-03-1983 L1993 IM *020 †20

LOZADA PLAZAS, Pablo Andr. ■ 78258 #649-14-2001 L2006 IM *100 †20

LOZANO, Carlos Andres. 525 RICHMOND 78215 #048-13-1977 L1977 FM *020 †18

LOZANO, Michael E. 21 SPURS LN, STE 230 78240 #048-13-1994 L1996 IM *020 †20

LOZANO, Rolando A. 315 N SAN SABA STE 1100, DEPT OF PEDIATRICS 78207 #341-01-1982 L2001 PDE PD *020 †55

LU, Deedee H. 6427 WURZBACH RD, APT 44 78240 #048-13-1999 L2006 PTH *062 †50

LU, Tingwei. ■ 78229 #048-02-2003 L2006 HO *012 †20

LUCAS, Jennifer Joy. ■ 78229 #019-02-2002 U *012

LUCAS, Laura Kathryne. ■ 78209 #023-12-2003 GS *012

LUCAS, Leslie Ruth. 6711 S NEW BRAUNFELS AVE 78223 #039-01-1987 L1989 CHP P *020 †75

LUCAS, Thomas Arthur. ■ 78229 #019-02-1965 L1973 U *020 †95

LUCIDI, Richard Scott. ■ 78229 #028-34-1998 L2002 OBG *020

LUDVIGSDOTTIR, Gudbjore K. 7703 FLOYD CURL DR 78229 #484-01-1997 PM *100

LUEDECKE, Robert Alan. 7940 FLOYD CURL, STE 1030 78229 #048-16-1981 L1981 AN *020 †05

LUIS, Cesar B. ■ 78247 #847-04-1956 L1973 NS *072

LUMBRERAS, Christina B. ■ 78250 #048-13-2008 *012

LUNA, Joseph Humberto. 94 BRIGGS ST, STE 300 78224 #048-13-1976 L1979 FM *020 †18

LUNA, Joseph R. 8038 WURZBACH RD STE 120 78229 #048-13-1992 L1996 FM *020 †18

LUNA, Maria G. ■ 78229 #048-04-2004 L2007 NEP *012 †20

LUNA, Martha. 301 N FRIO ST 78207 #048-13-1993 L1995 PTH *020 †50

LUNDBLADE, Deborah Diane. 45 NE LOOP 410 STE 900, 45 N.E. LOOP 410, #900 78216 #048-13-1982 L1983 AN *020 †05

LUNDGREN, Rupert Walter. 4499 MEDICAL DR, STE 140 78229 #048-12-1964 L1964 GYN *020 †30

LUNKE, Roger James. 540 MADISON OAK, STE 350 78258 #056-05-1974 L1979 ORS *020 †40

LUO, Yehung. 301 N FRIO ST 78207 #243-16-1989 L2001 PTH *020 †50

LUTHER, John Scott. UNIV OF TX, DEPT MEDI-NEUR 78284 #036-01-1974 1986 N IM *020 †20,75

LUTHIN, William Nolan. ■ 78251 #036-01-2005 L2007 EM *012

LUTZ, James Douglas. 4400 PIEDRAS DR S, STE 200 78228 #048-12-1987 L1991 VIR R *020 †80

LY, Justin Quoc. 4400 PIEDRAS DR S, STE 200 78228 #023-12-2000 L2005 DR *100 †80

LY, Truc Trung. ■ 78229 #422-01-2002 L2007 TS *012 †85

LYDA, Timothy Stuart. 4330 MEDICAL DR STE 325, VASCULAR SURGICAL ASSOC, P 78229 #048-13-1986 L1990 TS *020 †85,90

LYDAY, Victor Ivan, Jr. 1303 MCCULLOUGH AVE # 361 78212 #048-02-1972 L1972 ORS *020 †40

LYNCH, James Henry. ■ 78247 #043-01-2003 FM *100

LYNCH, Jane Lockwood. 7703 FLOYD CURL DR, MSC 7806 78229 #038-45-1984 L1987 PD PDE *020 †55

LYNCH, Kelly Elizabeth. 7703 FLOYD CURL DR, DEPT OF ANESTHESIOLOGY 78229 #048-13-2006 AN *012

LYNCHARD, Garrett Shawn. ■ 78217 #028-03-2001 L2003 CD *020

LYONS, Paula Marie. 11811 BLANCO RD 78216 #048-13-1981 L1981 FM *020 †18

LYONS, Robert Devlin. 4242 MEDICAL DR, STE 3100 78229 #649-33-1983 L1989 AN *020 †05

LYONS, Roger Michael. 4411 MEDICAL DR STE 100 78229 #062-01-1967 L1975 HEM IM *020

LYONS-BOUDREAUX, V K. 333 N SANTA ROSA AVE, PATHOLOGY ASSOCIATES OF 78207 #010-03-2000 L2006 PCP *100

LYSSY, Kathleen J. 6100 BANDERA RD, STE 403 78238 #917-25-1987 L1995 RHU IM *020 †20

LYSSY, Kenneth M. 6100 BANDERA RD, STE 403 78238 #654-01-1987 L1993 FM *020 †18

LYTVAK, Iryna Mykolaivna. 7703 FLOYD CURL DR 78229 #913-07-1999 PTH *012

MABRY, Leah Raye. 333 N SANTA ROSA AVE, FL 4 78207 #048-13-1982 L1983 FM *040 †18

MAC DONALD, James C. 7703 FLOYD CURL DR, UTHSCSA-DEPT OPHTHALMOLOGY 78229 #033-05-1992 L2000 OPH *020 †35

MACEDO, Carlos Alberto. 8535 TOM SLICK 78229 #187-08-1966 L1979 CHP P *020

MACFADYEN, Andrew John. 7703 FLOYD CURL DR, SCIENCES CENTER IN SAN ANT 78229 #001-02-1990 L1998 CCP *020 †55

MAC GILLIVRAY, Brian K. 20658 STONE OAK PKWY, UNIT 108 78258 #019-02-1996 L2006 FM *020 †18

MACHEN, Kelly I. 7703 FLOYD CURL DR, UNIV OF TX MED SCH 78229 #048-14-2006 PD *012

MACIAS, Norma L. 5788 ECKHERT RD, FRANK TEJEDA OUTPATIENT CL 78240 #048-14-2000 L2002 FM *020

MACKEY, Ray Walton. 7703 FLOYD CURL DR, DEPT. OF PEDIATRICS 78229 #035-45-1954 L1968 CHN *074 †75

MAC RAE, Malcolm M. ■ 78232 #010-01-1944 L1955 GYN *071 †30

MACRIS, Demetrios N. 111 DALLAS ST, STE 210A 78205 #012-05-1986 L1992 VS GS *030 †85

MADDUX, James Frederic. 7703 FLOYD CURL DR 78229 #012-01-1941 1964 P OS *071 †75

MADLA, Frank L, III. 7400 MERTON MINTER ST, AUDIE MURPHY VETERANS HOSP 78229 #048-13-1992 L1993 IM *020 †20

MAENPAA, Juhani Untamo. ■ 78230 #374-02-1978 P *100

MAGEE, Michael M. 8452 FREDERICKSBRG RD #225 78229 #048-13-1996 *100

MAGGIO, Frederick Jos. ■ 78231 #065-10-1981 OM *100

MAGLOIRE, Lissa Kathleen. 5414 FREDERICKSBURG RD, STE 200 78229 #051-01-2000 L2007 OBG *020

MAGNABOSCO, Elizabeth D. 4499 MEDICAL DR, STE 235 78229 #016-42-1994 L1999 OP *020

MAGOON, Michael Raynard. 16414 SAN PEDRO, STE 710 78232 #025-07-1989 L1993 EM LM *020 †16

MAGRANER, Gabriel Arturo. 225 E SONTERRA BLVD, STE 215 78258 #042-01-1987 L1993 GE P *020

MAHANEY, Joe Temple. 7400 MERTON MINTER ST 78229 #048-12-1975 L1975 P *020 †75

MAHLER, Susan Jane. 7810 LOUIS PASTEUR DR, STE 200 78229 #048-13-1989 L1990 D *020 †15

MAJID, Aneesa Shahnaz. 4400 PIEDRAS DR S 200, RADIOLOGY ASSOCS OF SAN AN 78228 #422-01-1996 L2003 R VIR *020 †80

MAKILAN, Ireneo A. S EDGE DR 78240 #748-07-1977 *074

MALAMUG, Lou Rose Machado. ■ 78251 #023-12-2007 IM *012

MALAVE, David. 525 OAK CENTRE DR STE 270 78258 #042-01-1984 L2001 TS GS *020 †85,90

MALAVE-ROSARIO, Hector J. ■ 78231 #847-04-1961 L1965 OBG *020 †30

MALCHOW, Randall John. 3851 ROGER BROOKE DR, BROOKE AMC, BLDG 3600 78234 #056-05-1987 L1994 AN *020 †05

MALDONADO, Elaine Marie. 1901 BABCOCK RD, STE 301 78229 #016-43-1998 L1999 PDC *020 †20

MALDONADO, Jorge L. 4242 MEDICAL DR, ALAMO MENTAL HEALTH GROUP 78229 #429-02-1986 L1997 P *020 †75

MALEK, Farbod. 7703 FLOYD CURL DR, SCIENCE C 78229 #517-01-2004 ORS *012

MALIK, Aamir S. 730 N MAIN STE 321 78205 #704-25-1989 L1997 PCC *020 †20

MALIK, Preeti. ■ 78249 #048-13-2003 L2005 IM *020 †18

MALIK, Shazli N. 333 N SANTA ROSA AVE, PATHOLOGY ASSOCIATES OF 78207 #704-25-1989 L2000 PCP *020 †50

MALKOWSKI, Richard S. 7703 FLOYD CURL DR, UNIV TX MED SCH 78229 #048-14-2002 L2003 AN *012

MALLOTT, William E. 7703 FLOYD CURL DR, OEP RM 5 5554 78229 #048-15-2001 L2004 IM *020 †20

MAMUN, Sumit. 7330 SAN PEDRO AVE, STE 405 78216 #160-03-1990 L2000 IM EM *020 †20

MANCERA, Antonio Emanuel. ■ 78230 #048-13-2007 IM *012

MANCINI, John Gregory. ■ 78209 #047-06-2007 GS *012

MANCUSO, James J. ■ 78240 #048-13-2005 IM *012

MANCUSO, Patricia Ann. 315 N SAN SABA STE 1210, LONE STAR NEUROSURGERY 78207 #035-08-1986 L1997 NS GS *020 †25

MANFREDI, Philip Danl. 8042 WURZBACH RD, STE 480 78229 #008-01-1965 L1972 GS *020 †85

MANGAN, William Timothy. ■ 78201 #048-13-1976 L1976 PD *020

MANGAT, Navneet Mann. ■ 78232 #048-13-2008 *012

MANGOS, John A. 7703 FLOYD CURL DR, UNIV TX HEALTH SCI CENTER 78229 #418-02-1956 L1983 PD PUD *040 †55

MANI, George C. 343 W HOUSTON ST 78205 #035-01-1951 L1958 PTH *071 †50

MANN, Margaret Marie. 7703 FLOYD CURL DR, MAIL CODE 7794 78229 #048-15-2000 L2003 FM *020 †18

MANNING, Elizabeth Blair. ■ 78229 #048-04-2007 PM *012

MANOCHA, Lovelesh Kumar. 124 DALLAS ST, SKINNER CLINIC 78205 #021-06-1996 L1999 IM *020 †20

MANSFIELD, Liem Thanh. 3851 ROGER BROOKE DR, # BAMC 78234 #023-12-1990 L2003 DR *020 †80

MANTRAVADI, Krishana M. 45 NE LOOP 410, STE 900 78216 #495-29-1985 L2003 AN *020 †05

MANUEL, Caroline E. ■ 78240 #495-98-1990 L1998 P *020 †75

MARCINIAK, Robert Anthony. 7703 FLOYD CURL DR, MSC 7884 78229 #024-01-1992 L2001 HO *012 †20

MARCINISZYN, Sara Lynn. ■ 78248 #038-45-2001 L2007 GS *100 †85

MARCOS, Yolanda. 510 MED CT, STE 210 78258 #048-13-1996 L1997 IM *020 †20

MARCOS DACCARETT, Javier. 155 E SONTERRA BLVD, STE 201 78258 #649-02-1966 L1967 TS GS *020 †85,90

MARCOS-FRAIGE, Guillermo. 111 DALLAS ST 78205 #649-02-1966 L1969 GP OS *020

MARCOVICH, Robert. 7703 FLOYD CURL DR, MC7845 78229 #043-01-1995 L2003 GS U *020 †95

MARCUM, John William. 1150 N LOOP 1604 W, STE 108474 78248 #005-06-1999 L2006 PD *020 †55

MARIN, Luisa Fernanda. 3201 CHERRY RIDGE ST, STE B200 78230 #264-10-1996 L2005 IM *020 †20

MARINO, Michelle. ■ 78251 #048-14-2004 L2006 AN *012

MARK, James E. 7922 EWING HALSELL DR, STE 220 78229 #023-01-1976 L1986 GYN GO *020 †30

MARKEY, Keith Lee. 540 MADISON OAK DR, STE 690 78258 #017-20-1974 L1978 ORS OS *020 †40

MARKIEWICZ, Ann. 7922 EWING HALSELL DR, ST 360 78229 #048-13-1993 L1999 PD *020 †55

MARKS, David Alan. 540 MADISON OAK DR, STE 560 78258 #048-13-2001 L2003 PCC *020

MARLAR, Suzanne M. 131 W LYNWOOD 78212 #048-13-1994 L1997 RNR *020 †80

MARMEL, Richard. 8042 WURZBACH RD, STE 260 78229 #048-13-1978 L1993 AN PME *020 †05

MARMESH, Paul John. 816 NIX BLDG 78205 #048-02-1956 L1956 OTO NO *071

MARMOL-VELEZ, Juan Alejan. 7703 FLOYD CURL DR 78229 #264-13-2001 IM *012

MARNATTI, Carl Thos. ■ 78209 #041-12-1961 L1962 FM *071

MAROTTA, Joseph Andrew. 414 NAVARRO ST STE 1001 78205 #048-14-1992 L1995 IM *020 †20

MARRON, Joaquin. 718 CUPPLES RD 78237 #048-02-1961 L1962 FM *020

MARROQUIN, Arturo. 7333 BARLITE BLVD STE 310 78224 #649-02-1962 L1970 GS OS *020 †85

MARSHALL, Douglas Warren. 400 CONCORD PLAZA DR 78216 #025-07-1977 L1984 N *020 †75

MARSHALL, John A, III. 4502 MEDICAL DR MS 32-1, COMMUNITY MEDICINE ASSOCIA 78229 #649-14-1976 L1978 FM GPM *020 †18

MARSHALL, Mary Lou. ■ 78239 #025-01-1960 L1961 PTH *071 †50

MARTEN, Lisa. 4334 APPLE TREE WOODS 78249 #021-01-2001 L2002 OPH *100

MARTIN, Andrew H. 9150 HUEBNER RD, STE 255 78240 #048-13-2002 L2006 **CHP** *020

MARTIN, Bruce G. 7711 LOUIS PASTEUR DR #901 78229 #018-75-1975, ▲ L1985 **AI PD** *020 †55,03

MARTIN, Hal Arthur. ■ 78230 #034-01-1969 L1977 **CD IM** *071 †20

MARTIN, Heidi Blauvelt. 7703 FLOYD CURL DR DEPT R 78229 #051-04-1985 L1991 **DR** *020 †80

MARTIN, James Charles. 333 N SANTA ROSA AVE, FL 4 78207 #048-13-1973 L1973 **FM** *040 †18

MARTIN, Joseph Edward. 4499 MEDICAL DR, STE 200 78229 #048-02-1963 L1963 **OBG** *020 †30

MARTIN, Linda Jones. 6315 S ZARZAMORA ST 78211 #048-14-1979 L1979 **PD ADL** *020 †55

MARTIN, Matthew A. ■ 78231 #048-13-2005 **PTH** *012

MARTIN, Thomas Allen, III. 8535 TOM SLICK 78249 #048-13-1978 L1980 **CHP P** *020 †75

MARTINEZ, Anthony M. 16414 SAN PEDRO, STE 710 78232 #048-04-2004 L2007 **EM** *020

MARTINEZ, Carlos R J. 45 NE LOOP 410, STE 900 78216 #132-01-1961 L1970 **AN OS** *020 †05

MARTINEZ, Cervando, Jr. 7703 FLOYD CURL DR, CTR AT SAN ANTONIO/DEPT OF 78229 #048-12-1966 L1972 **P** *020 †75

MARTINEZ, Daniel James. ■ 78230 #048-15-1977 L1977 **FM** *075 †18

MARTINEZ, Diane Lawson. ■ 78209 #016-11-1975 L1984 **P PYA** *020 †75 ‡

MARTINEZ, Ernesto. 215 N SAN SABA STE 2 78207 #649-01-1948 L1967 **PD** *020 †55

MARTINEZ, Fernando. 2011 E HOUSTON ST, STE E 78202 #048-13-1997 L1998 **FM** *020 †18

MARTINEZ, Jeffrey M. 111 DALLAS ST, STE 210A 78205 #048-13-1988 L1989 **GS** *020 †85

MARTINEZ, Joaquin, III. 45 NE LOOP 410, STE 900 78216 #048-12-1986 L1987 **AN** *020 †05

MARTINEZ, Jose Luis. ■ 78223 #042-01-1977 L1980 **PD** *075

MARTINEZ, Manuel. 720 PLEASANTON ST 78214 #649-52-1994 L2004 **IM** *020

MARTINEZ, Miguel J. 2829 BABCOCK RD STE 4 78229 #042-01-1983 L1993 **AI IM** *020 †20,03

MARTINEZ, Rafael H. 6315 S ZARZAMORA ST, SOUTH PARK MEDICAL CARE CE 78211 #048-04-1988 L1989 **FM** *020 †18 ‡

MARTINEZ, Rebeca Beatriz. 7703 FLOYD CURL DR 78229 #042-03-1993 **PD** *020

MARTINEZ, Renato. 621 CAMDEN ST 78215 #649-02-1963 L1966 **GE** *071 †20

MARTINEZ, Rutilo. 1055 ADA ST 78223 #048-13-1998 L1999 **FM** *020 †18

MARTINEZ, Vicente. ■ 78213 #649-02-1952 **OS GP** *071

MARTINEZ-GARZA, Oscar. 45 NE LOOP 410, STE 900 78216 #649-02-1971 L1974 **AN PME** *071

MARTINEZ-O'FERRALL, Jose. ■ 78232 #042-01-1959 L1990 **AM** *030

MARTINEZ PASTOOR, Sara. 3851 ROGER BROOKE DR, BROOKE AMC, BLDG 3600 78234 #016-42-1995 L2003 **FM** *020 †18

MARTINEZ-PRIETO, Jorge N. 215 E QUINCY ST, STE 315 78215 #649-01-1976 L1985 **N** *020

MARTINEZ-SORIA, Victor M. 803 CASTROVILLE RD, STE 401 78237 #649-02-1988 L1998 **IM** *020 †20

MARTINEZ UGARTE, Maria Lu. 7703 FLOYD CURL DR 78229 #682-01-2004 L2005 **GS** *012

MARTINI, Sharon Rae. 1919 OAKWELL FARMS PKWY 78218 #048-14-1996 L1997 **CHP** *020 †75

MARUSICH, Juan Pablo. 45 NE LOOP 410, STE 900 78216 #048-12-2002 L2006 **AN** *100 †05

MARX, Alvin Jay. 4035 NACO PERRIN BLVD, RURAL & URBAN PATH ASSOCS 78217 #035-46-1963 L1993 **PTH** *071 †50

MARX, Nola Rosanoff. 8042 WURZBACH RD 78229 #035-20-1964 L1993 **OS** *071 †55

MASCARENHAS, Carmen Maria. 6711 S NEW BRAUNFELS AVE, STE 500 78223 #495-65-1977 L1983 **IM IMG** *020 †20

MASILUNGAN, Edgar Aguila. ■ 78227 #748-01-1971 *020

MASON, Aaron Corde. 2833 BABCOCK RD, STE 400 78229 #041-12-1994 L2006 **PS** *020 †55

MASON, Eva Jo. 311 CAMDEN ST, STE 311 78215 #048-13-1989 L1990 **FM** *020 †18

MASON, Mark Lee. 3453 N PANAM EXPY STE 110 78219 #048-13-1977 L1977 **EM** *020 †16

MASON, Richard Patrick. ■ 78209 #048-02-1936 **OS** *071 †70

MASSARI, Rudolph Jos. 414 NAVARRO ST, STE 1030 78205 #048-02-1958 L1958 **U** *020 †95

MASSEY, Freddy Maynord. 7922 EWING HALSELL DR, STE 220 78229 #047-06-1962 L1979 **GO GYN** *020 †30

MASTERS, Patrick Allen. 8214 WURZBACH RD 78229 #048-14-1982 L1983 **GE IM** *020 †20

MASTROVICH, John D. 20650 STONE OAK PKWY, STE 106 78258 #048-15-1996 L2001 **AI** *020 †20,03

MASZAK, Gary Joseph. 927 MCCULLOUGH, CENTRAL CARDIOVASCULAR INS 78215 #016-43-1999 L2006 **IC** *020 †20

MATA, Carlos H. ■ 78248 #048-02-1960 L1960 **U** *071 †95

MATA, Richard Jos. ■ 78218 #048-12-1985 L1985 **IM MDM** *030

MATALON, Ralph Gabriel. 4242 MEDICAL DR, STE 3100 78229 #025-07-1984 L1993 **AN** *020 †05

MATHAI, Sheeba Rachel. 7703 FLOYD CURL DR 78229 #473-04-2003 **FP** *012

MATLOCK, John Sidney. 8401 DATAPOINT DR STE 401 78229 #048-04-1979 L1980 **IM** *020 †20

MATOS, Balduino. 215 N SAN SABA, STE 108 78207 #308-01-1959 L1981 **OPH** *020

MATTHEWS, Kenneth Lee. 7703 FLOYD CURL DR, UTH SCSA 78229 #005-12-1969 L1971 **CHP** *071 †75

MATTHEWS, Mark Ray. 9600 DATAPOINT DR, PATHOLOGY REFERENCE LABORA 78229 #012-01-1994 L2000 **DMP NP** *020 †50

MATTHEWS, Thomas L. 7703 FLOYD CURL, DRIVE, MC-7792 78229 #048-13-1997 L2002 **CHP** *020 †75

MATTHEWS, William H. 701 S ZARZAMORA ST 78207 #021-05-1969 L1970 **ORS** *020 †40

MATTINGLY, Christine M. 24315 ALAMOSA FLS 78255 #028-34-1997 L2003 **DR** *020

MATTSON, Larry Duane. ■ 78254 #048-02-1968 L1969 **FM** *071 †18

MAUK, Bryant Douglas. ■ 78239 #012-05-1960 L1960 **AM GS** *071 †85,70

MAURER, Robert Mize. ■ 78232 #021-05-1962 L1969 **R** *071 †80

MAVERICK, Kenneth Joseph. 7355 BARLITE BLVD, STE 104 78224 #048-14-2000 L2005 **OPH** *020 †35

MAXWELL, Stephen Allan. 3111 SAN PEDRO AVE 78212 #048-13-1975 L1977 **PD** *020 †55

MAYER, Gerald Thos. 525 OAK CENTRE DR, STE 400 78258 #021-05-1965 L1993 **PD PEM** *020 †55

MAYER, Paul T. ■ 78234 #023-12-1994 L2006 **EM** *020 †16

MAYES, Bruce N. 4647 MEDICAL DR 78229 #047-05-1988 L1998 **N** *020

MAYES, Thomas Cullee. 7703 FLOYD CURL DR, MAILCODE 7802 78229 #010-02-1984 L1987 **CCP PD** *020 †20

MAYFIELD, Demmie Gammon. 7400 MERTON MINTER ST 78229 #048-02-1958 L1958 **P ADP** *050 †75

MAYNARD, Duane W. 45 NE LOOP 410, STE 900 78216 #048-13-1988 L1989 **AN** *020

MAYORAL, Jaime Lopez. 7979 WURZBACH RD 78229 #026-04-1985 L1995 **CRS GS** *020 †85,10

MAZLOUM, Bassem. 9502 HUEBNER RD, STE 101 78240 #605-01-1987 L1993 **GE** *020 †20

MAZUMDAR, Bhaskar. 45 NE LOOP 410, STE 900 78216 #495-45-1981 L1998 **AN** *020 †05

MC ALLISTER, Christopher. ■ 78229 #045-01-2003 L2008 **PM** *100

MC BURNEY, Terrance Alan. 7400 BARLITE BLVD 78224 #025-01-1970 L1977 **PTH** *020 †50

MCCAIN, Casey Elizabeth. ■ 78240 #048-13-2008 *012

MC CALL, David. 4647 MEDICAL DR 78229 #919-05-1964 L1984 **CD** *050

MC CAMISH, Sara Dewitt. 4125 MCCULLOUGH AVE 78212 #048-14-1998 L2003 **IM** *020 †20

MC CAMY, Curtis Benj. 2211 NW MILITARY HWY, STE 201 78213 #026-04-1975 L1999 **FM** *020 †18

MC CANN, Shannan E. ■ 78251 #047-20-2002 L2003 **ADL** *012 †55

MC CANN, Thane Daley. ■ 78258 #041-02-2003 L2005 **PM** *020

MC CARROLL, Gregory D. 5430 FREDERICKSBURG RD, STE 400 78229 #048-02-1983 L1983 **IM** *020 †20

MC CARROLL, Karis M. 8431 FREDERICKSBURG RD, STE 100 78229 #048-02-1983 L1983 **D** *020 †15

MC CARTHY, Michael James. 7979 WURZBACH RD, URSCHEL TOWERS #233 78229 #010-02-1975 L1992 **DR EM** *040 †80

MC CASH, Charles S. 85 NE LOOP 410, STE 112 78216 #048-13-1992 L1993 **PO** *020 †35

MCCLAIN, William D. ■ 78229 #048-14-2007 **PTH** *012

MC CLELLAND, Tamre Brooks. 1804 NE LOOP 410 STE 100 78217 #048-13-1988 L1989 **FM** *020 †18

MC COLLEY, Joseph Roland. 7950 FLOYD CURL, STE 200 78229 #017-20-1979 L1991 **DR EM** *020 †80

MC CONNELL, Whitman E. ■ 78255 #011-02-1966 L1972 **AM GPM** *040 †70

MC CORD, Michael Wylie. 4242 MEDICAL DR, STE 3100 78229 #048-12-1983 L1983 **AN** *020 †05

MC CORVEY, B Michelle. 7703 FLOYD CURL DR, UT HEALTH SCIENCE CENTER 78229 #041-02-1997 L2004 **DR** *020 †80

MC CRACKEN, Joseph Dean. 414 NAVARRO ST, STE 1422 78205 #036-07-1965 L1983 **ON IM** *020 †20

MC CRAY, Brandy Lynn. 15316 HUEBNER RD, STE 102 78248 #048-04-1999 L2002 **PD** *020 †55

MC CRELESS, Glen Darrell. 4037 E SOUTHCROSS BLVD 78222 #048-13-1981 L1981 **IM** *020 †20

MCCRISKIN, Brendan James. ■ 78261 #016-43-2007 **ORS** *012

MC CRORY, Dixie Penelope. 740 S ALAMO 78205 #048-02-1999 L2002 **FM** *020 †18

MC CURDY, Elizabeth Anne. ■ 78249 #036-05-2002 L2007 **OTO** *012

MC CURNIN, Donald Chas. 7703 FLOYD CURL DR, UNIVERSITY OF TEX HSC 78229 #048-13-1980 L1982 **NPM PD** *020 †55

MC DANIEL, Edward Lamar. ■ 78259 #023-01-1995 L1999 **IM** *020

MCDONOUGH, Marie Ann. ■ 78209 #050-02-2005 L2007 **EM** *012

MC ELVANY, Kimberly K. 4242 MEDICAL DR, STE 3100 78229 #048-13-1986 L1987 **AN PME** *020 †05

MC FADDEN, Robert Stetson. 2829 BABCOCK RD, STE 300 78229 #048-02-1977 L1977 **HEP GE** *020 †20

MCFARLAND, Melinda B. 502 MADISON OAK STE 210, PERINATAL & FERTILITY SPEC 78258 #048-13-1989 L1990 **MFM CG** *020 †19,30

MC FEE, Arthur Storer. 7703 FLOYD CURL DR, DPT OF SURGERY 78229 #024-01-1957 L1968 **GS PDS** *020 †85

MC GANITY, Peter Louis J. 8601 VILLAGE DR STE 210 78217 #048-13-1975 L1975 **ORS** *020 †40

MC GEHEE, Jarrett Todd. 7434 LOUIS PASTEUR, STE 209 78229 #048-02-1998 L2002 **IC** *020 †20

MCGILL, Henry C, Jr. PO BOX 760549, SW FOUNDATION BIO RESEARCH 78245 #047-05-1946 L1966 **ATP** *071 †50

MCGILL, Robert John. ■ 78245 #023-12-2006 L2008 **ORS** *012

MC GLOTHLIN, Matthew S. 415 EMBASSY OAKS, STE 200 78216 #028-03-1995 L2005 **FM** *020 †18 ‡

MC GOVERN, James Bruce. ■ 78232 #035-20-1959 L1970 **PDS TS** *071 †85,90

MCGRATH, Briana. ■ 78229 #048-13-2008 *012

MC GRATH, Mark Thos. 806 S ZARZAMORA ST 78207 #056-06-1982 L1983 **P** *020

MCGREGOR, Bradley Alexand. ■ 78251 #024-07-2004 L2006 **IM** *020 †20

MC GUIRE, Katherine R. 45 NE LOOP 410, STE 900 78216 #030-06-2001 L2005 **AN** *100 †05

MC GUIRE, Stephen A. 7703 FLOYD CURL DR, DEPT. OF NEUROLOGY 78229 #035-01-1976 L1979 **N** *020 †20,75

MC INNIS, William David. 5 HIGHGATE DR 78257 #039-01-1969 L1971 **GS** *020 †85,65

MC KAY, Patrick Hugh. 7700 FLOYD CURL DR 78229 #048-02-1952 L1952 **GP** *072

MCKEE, Michael S. 225 E SONTERRA BLVD 78258 #649-04-1989 L2002 **AN** *020 †05

MC KENZIE, Heather A. 150 E SONTERRA BLVD, SAN ANTONIO ORTHOPAEDIC 78258 #048-13-2001 L2003 **PM** *020 †60

MCKINLAY, Alex John. ■ 78258 #023-12-2004 L2006 **OTO** *012

MC KINNEY, Jason Matthew. 7703 FLOYD CURL DR, MAIL CODE 7871 78229 #019-02-2004 L2006 **IM** *100

MC LAIN, Landon Douglas. 7703 FLOYD CURL DR, UNIV OF TX MED SCH AT SAN 78229 #048-13-2005 *100

MCLAUGHLIN, Daniel Franci. ■ 78218 #035-03-2004 L2006 **GS** *012

MC MAHON, Brenda Gayle. 302 W RECTOR ST, UFHC-NORTH 78216 #048-14-1996 L1998 **FM** *020 †18

MC MAINS, Diane A Andrews. 14811 SAN PEDRO AVE 78232 #047-05-1967 L1975 **PD** *020 †55

MC MAINS, Kevin C. 7703 FLOYD CURL DR, MC-7777 78229 #048-12-1999 L2005 **OTO** *020 †45

MC MANIS, Susan Elizabeth. 16719 HUEBNER RD, BLDG 2 78248 #028-02-1987 L1996 **P** *020 †75

MC MANUS, John Gerard, Jr. ■ 78258 #012-01-1992 L1999 **EM** *020 †16

MC MANUS, Keiko. 7909 FREDERICKSBURG RD, STE 100 78229 #048-13-1981 L1981 **OTO HNS** *020 †45

MC MASTER, John Browning. ■ 78229 #048-02-1956 L1956 **OS D** *071 †15

MC MASTERS, Joel Wayne. 3851 ROGER BROOKE DR # 36, BROOKE ARMY MEDICAL CENTER 78234 #004-01-1998 L1999 **AN** *020 †05

MCMILLAN, Laurence Derich. ■ 78240 #047-07-2006 **FM** *100

MC MINN, Monty Ruey. 8600 WURZBACH RD 78240 #048-02-1970 L1974 **P** *071

MC MURRAY, Thomas Jay. 11666 WHITE CROSS 78253 #048-12-1987 L1988 **GP** *050

MCMURTRIE, Elzbieta. 1200 BROOKLYN AVE STE 300, SAN ANTONIO KIDNEY DISEASE 78212 #759-04-1991 L2001 **NEP** *020 †20

MC MYLER, Donna Marie. ■ 78249 #048-14-2002 L2005 **GE** *012 †20

MC NABB, Cynthia G. 321 W CRAIG PL 78212 #048-13-1989 L1990 **P** *020 †75

MC NABB, Deborah Lyn. 4499 MEDICAL DR STE 289 #048-04-1984 L1985 **OBG** *020 †30

MC NAIR, Shelly Mewes. 5282 MEDICAL DR, SOUTHWEST CHILDRENS 78229 #048-04-1991 L1993 **PD** *020 †55

■ = Address Information Privacy Protected

MC NEIL, Christopher Ryan. ■ 78247 #030-05-2002 L2008 **EM** *020 †16
MC NEIL, Jeffrey Don. 7703 FLOYD CURL DR, STE 7841 78229 #048-13-1996 L1998
  GS *020 †85,90
MCNEILL, Bryant Rand. ■ 78245 #048-15-2007 **IM** *012
MC NEILL, Scott Shaw. 408 NAVARRO ST, ALAMO CITY MEDICAL GROUP 78205
  #048-13-1991 L1999 **FM** *020 †18
MC NISH, Thomas Mitchell. 5711 UNIVERSITY HTS, BIODYNAMIC RESEARCH CORP 78249
  #012-05-1978 L1979 **AM FM** *030 †70,18
MC QUEEN, William John. 7909 FREDERICKSBURG RD, STE 100 78229 #038-40-1975 L1996
  OTO AM *020 †45
MC REYNOLDS, Rex. 7700 FLOYD CURL DR 78229 #047-05-1954 L1961 **PD A** *020 †55
MC WILLIAMS, Gary Mark. 4502 MEDICAL DR, MS #27-2 78229 #048-13-1974 L1975
  FM *020 †18
MEADOR, Gregory Brant. 2111 SAWGRASS RDG 78260 #048-14-1987 L1988 **EM** *020 †16
MEADOWS, Gilbert Rice. 18626 HARDY OAK BLVD, STE 300 78258 #021-01-1975 L1975
  ORS *020 †40
MEADOWS, Milton W. ■ 78240 #048-13-2005 **PD** *012
MEANEY, Joan T. 7909 FREDERICKSBRG RD #110, UROLOGY SAN ANTONIO 78229
  #048-04-1987 L1988 **U** *020 †95
MEANEY, John Thos. 4242 MEDICAL DR, STE 3100 78229 #048-13-1975 L1978 **AN** *020 †05
MEANEY-DUDLEY, Helen K. ■ 78248 #048-13-1984 L1988 **PD** *074
MEDELL, Robert Jos. 4402 VANCE JACKSON RD, STE 220 78230 #051-01-1986 L1994
  AN *020 †05
MEDELLIN, Christopher D. ■ 78209 #048-14-1997 L1998 **GPM** *020 †70
MEDELLIN, Glen A. 7703 FLOYD CURL DR, MSC-7808 78229 #048-02-1994 L1997 **PD** *020 †55
MEDELLIN, Gustavo J. 8038 WURZBACH, STE 340 78229 #048-13-1984 L1996
  PD IM *020 †20
MEDELLIN, Jesse Earl. 1200 BROOKLYN AVE, STE 115 78212 #048-02-1989 L1990
  HO *020 †20
MEDELLIN, Michelle V. ■ 78230 #048-02-1994 L2000 **IM** *020 †20
MEDENDORP, Andrew Robert. ■ 78249 #016-06-2005 L2006 **U** *012
MEDINA, Edward Antonio. ■ 78209 #048-05-19-2005 **PTH** *012
MEDINA, Gilberto Arturo. 45 NE LOOP 410, STE 900 78216 #048-13-1994 L1996 **AN** *020 †05
MEDINA, Jacinto Renatto. ■ 78209 #341-01-1964 L1972 **D IM** *020
MEDINA, Rolando Antonio. 7703 FLOYD CURL DR, UNIV OF TX HLTH SCI CTR 78229
  #649-01-1969 L2000 **P** *020
MEDLEY, Christopher C. 6710 N NEW BRAUNFELS AVE 78209 #048-13-1995 L1997 **OS** *020
MEDRANO, Martha Alicia. 7703 FLOYD CURL, DEPARTMENT OF PSYCHIATRY 78229
  #048-13-1981 L1983 **CHP PD** *020 †75
MEDRANOVALLE, Gabriel Ado. 7703 FLOYD CURL DR, DEPT OF OB/GYN MC 7836 78229
  #042-02-2004 L2008 **OBG** *012
MEFFERT, Jeffrey John. 1007 NE LOOP 410 78209 #048-13-1981 L1981 **D FM** *020 †18,15
MEGAHED, Hatem Salah. 7711 LOUIS PASTEUR STE 70 78229 #048-04-1981 L1981
  NS NSP *020 †25
MEHTA, Amit. 8401 DATAPOINT DR 78229 #065-01-1997 L2005 **DR** *100 †80
MEHTA, Praful Ravishanker. 5101 MEDICAL DR 78229 #495-22-1961 L1980 **IM** *020 †20
MEHTA, Vidyut Praful. ■ 78249 #495-48-1966 *100
MEIER, Carl Richard. 7979 WURZBACH RD 78229 #409-21-1969 L2005 **HEM IM** *100 †20
MEIER, Patricia Ann. ■ 78209 #019-02-1988 L1993 **HMP** *020 †20,50
MEIER, Primrose Chaudhuri. 5414 FREDERICKSBURG RD, STE 100 78229 #209-01-1968 L1975
  PD NPM *020 †55
MEIN, Calvin Einar. 4499 MEDICAL DR STE 166 78229 #016-11-1975 L1980 **OPH OS** *020 †35
MEISSNER, Kurt Garred. 7909 FREDERICKSBURG RD 78229 #048-02-1995 L2000 **U** *020 †95
MEJIA, Juan Camilo. 7703 FLOYD CURL DR, UNIV TX MED SCH-SAN ANTONI 78229
  #649-14-2004 **GS** *012
MELBY, Peter Clay. 7703 FLOYD CURL DR, DEPARTMENT OF MEDICINE 78229
  #007-02-1983 L1991 **ID IM** *020 †20
MELENDEZ, Gilberto. 4603 BLANCO RD 78212 #042-01-1983 L1985 *020
MELENDEZ, Marla Rae. ■ 78251 #037-01-1994 L2006 **CHP** *020 †75
MELISH, Mark Alan. 525 OAK CENTRE DR, STE 260 78258 #048-12-1984 L1985 **AN** *020 †05
MELO, Frank. 7703 FLOYD CURL DR, DEPT FP 78229 #072-02-2002 **FP** *020
MELO, Jairo A. 7979 WURZBACH RD 78229 #264-13-1991 L1996 **PCC** *020 †20
MEMBRENO-GUZMAN, Fernando. 7711 LOUIS PASTEUR STE 707 78229 #270-02-1995 L2006
  GE *020 †20
MENDELSON, Janice A. ■ 78217 #041-12-1947 L1982 **OS GS** *075 †85
MENDELSSOHN, Richard B. 8401 DATAPOINT DR STE 500 78229 #550-02-1998 L2001
  EM *020 †16
MENDEZ, Marisel Cancel. 14100 NACOGDOCHES RD, HEALTH 78247 #042-03-1996 L2001
  IM *020 †20
MENDICINO, Anthony T, Jr. 615 SOLEDAD ST 78205 #028-79-1959, ▲ L1960 **GP** *071
MENDOZA, Carisse Anne. 7703 FLOYD CURL DR, SCIENCE C 78229 #041-15-2004
  PDE *012 †55
MENDOZA, William Eugene. 7940 FLOYD CURL DR, STE 1030 78229 #025-01-1980 L1983
  AN *020
MENENDEZ, Carlos Eugenio. 4499 MEDICAL DR STE 226 78229 #035-01-1969 L1974
  END IM *020 †20
MENENDEZ, Jorge Luis. 7744 BROADWAY ST, STE 210 78209 #048-12-1984 L1985
  PS FPS *020 †65 ‡
MENETREZ, Jennifer S. 3851 ROGER BROOKE DR, BROOKE AMC, BLDG 3600 78234
  #023-12-1990 L1991 **PM** *020 †60
MENICK, Barry Jay. 7979 WURZBACH RD, URSCHEL TOWERS #233 78229 #036-07-1985 L1991
  DR IM *020 †80
MERCHANT, Tamara Janene. 7950 FLOYD CURL DR, STE 101 78229 #033-05-1999 L2006
  CRS *100
MERIN, Alan Jacob. 1211 E COMMERCE ST 78205 #051-04-1976 L1979 **NEP EM** *020 †20
MERITZ, Neal Stuart. 525 OAK CENTRE DR, STE 150 78258 #048-13-1972 L1972 **FM** *020 †18
MERIWETHER, William A. ■ 78209 #047-06-1946 L1975 **PTH DMP** *071 †50
MERNIN, George Patrick. 2161 NW MILITARY HWY STE 2 78213 #016-11-1960 L1966
  CHP P *020
MERRELL, Jason David. ■ 78245 #023-12-2007 **IM** *012
MERREN, Michael David. 9119 CINNAMON HL 78240 #012-01-1967 L1973 **N** *020 †75
MERRITT, Christina E. ■ 78240 #048-13-2006 **PD** *012
MERRITT, Shirley G. 4242 MEDICAL DR, ALAMO MENTAL HEALTH GROUP 78229
  #048-14-1987 L1988 **P** *020 †75
MERRYMAN, Sally Peyton. ■ 78230 #048-04-2006 **OTO** *012
MESA, Gonzalo. 6711 S NEW BRAUNFELS AVE, SAN ANTONIO STATE HOSPITAL 78223
  #264-03-1965 L1992 **P** *071 †75

MESSENGER, Dennis Dwight. 326 W OAK ESTATES DR, SAN ANTONIO PRIMARY CARE 78260
  #048-12-1979 L1979 **FM** *020 †18
MESSERSCHMIDT, Gerald L. ■ 78209 #040-02-1976 L1984 **ON IM** *050 †20
METERSKY, John B. 7950 FLOYD CURL DR, STE 810 78229 #048-13-1996 L2002 **GS** *020
METTER, Darlene F. 7703 FLOYD CURL DR, UTHSCSA DEPARTMENT OF RADI 78229
  #014-01-1978 L1981 **DR NM** *020 †18,80,28
METTER, John Dean. 8026 FLOYD CURL DR, SOUTH TEXAS PATHOLOGY 78229
  #048-12-1977 L1977 **PTH** *050 †50
METZNER, Wesley R T. ■ 78223 #025-01-1944 L1950 **GP IMG** *071
MEWBORNE, Edward Bruce. 14027 MINT TRAIL DR, RADIOLOGY ASSOC. OF SAN AN 78232
  #051-01-1963 L1971 **PDR R** *020 †80
MEYER, Christopher James. ■ 78258 #038-45-2006 **PD** *012
MEYER, Emily Sullivan. 333 N SANTA ROSA 78207 #048-13-2004 L2006 **FM** *020 †18
MEYER, George Gotthold. 4499 MEDICAL DR STE 267 78229 #016-02-1955 L1970
  P PYG *071 †75
MEYER, Gerhard Arthur. ■ 78213 #035-08-1947 L1955 **IM** *071 †20
MEYER, Tyson K. ■ 78254 #048-14-2005 L2008 **IM** *012
MEZA, Dominic Mark. 18850 REDLAND RD 78259 #048-15-1997 L2000 **IM** *020 †20
MEZA, Mario Alberto. 45 NE LOOP 410, STE 900 78216 #016-11-1984 L1988 **AN IM** *020 †05
MICHELS, Luke Reynolds. 7703 FLOYD CURL DR, HEALTH SCIEN 78229 #023-12-2006 L2008
  P *012
MICHELS, Max I. ■ 78258 #038-41-1953 L1971 **PD ALI** *071 †55,03
MICHELSEN, Soad Loren. 8535 TOM SLICK 78229 #264-04-1992 L2002 **CHP** *020 †75 ‡
MIDDLEBROOK, Michael R. 9150 HUEBNER RD, STE 130 78240 #048-12-1988 L1989
  DR *020 †80
MIDIDODDI, Nataraju Ravin. 4502 MEDICAL DR, UNIVERSITY HOSPITAL 78229
  #495-58-1998 L2006 **NEP** *012 †20
MIEL, Emmanuel Tuyac, Jr. 7703 FLOYD CURL DR 78229 #748-11-2000 **FP** *012
MIERAS, Thomas W. 8401 DATAPOINT DR, DIAGNOSTIC MED, SUITE 401 78229
  #048-13-1987 L1988 **IM** *020 †20
MIESEN, Douglas Alan. 16414 SAN PEDRO STE 710 78232 #005-18-2002 L2005 **EM** *020 †16
MILAM, A Camis. 6609 BLANCO RD STE 247 78216 #048-02-1985 L1986 **P PFP** *020 †75
MILBOURN, Catherine T. 255 E SONTERRA BLVD, STE 201 78258 #023-12-1982 L1997
  PS GS *020 †85,65
MILHOAN, Kimberly Dawn. 333 N SANTA ROSA 78207 #005-19-1998 L2005 **AN PAN** *020 †05
MILLAR, Benjamin Roger. 8715 VILLAGE DR STE 500, RIVER CITY NEUROLOGY, PA 78217
  #049-01-1995 L2007 **N** *020 †75
MILLER, Alexander Lewis. 7703 FLOYD CURL DR 78229 #028-02-1970 L1980 **P** *050 †75
MILLER, Alexander R. 9102 FLOYD CURL DR, CTRC/CANCER HEALTHCARE ASS 78240
  #026-08-1989 L1996 **SO GS** *020 †85
MILLER, Alfred. 7711 LOUIS PASTEUR DR, STE 906 78229 #048-02-1962 L1962 **IM RHU** *020
MILLER, Charles E. 2323 OAKLINE DR 78232 #048-14-1984 L1985 **FM FPG** *020 †18
MILLER, Claudia S. 7703 FLOYD CURL DR, DEPT OF FAMILY PRACTICE 78229
  #048-13-1985 L1986 **AI IM** *020 †20,03
MILLER, Frank R. 7703 FLOYD CURL DR, WHMC/CMC 78229 #043-01-1989 L2001
  OTO HNS *020 †45
MILLER, Gea Malpaga. 3851 ROGER BROOKE DR, BROOKE ARMY MED CTR 78234
  #561-16-1969 L1977 **DR** *020 †55 ‡
MILLER, Heather Lynn. 302 W RECTOR ST 78216 #048-02-1996 L1997 **PD** *020 †55
MILLER, Joseph Paul. 4243 E SOUTHCROSS BLVD, SOUTHEAST IMAGING CENTER 78222
  #036-07-1970 L1976 **DR** *020 †80
MILLER, Joshua Paul. ■ 78244 #030-06-2006 L2008 **EM** *012
MILLER, Lisa A. 414 NAVARRO ST STE 1023 78205 #048-04-1990 L1991 **P** *100 †75
MILLER, Michael S. 7400 MERTON MINTER ST, PSYCHIATRY 116A 78229 #035-06-1986 L1992
  P ADP *020 †75
MILLER, Naomi S. ■ 78249 #048-13-2008 *012
MILLER, Patience B. 7922 EWING HALSELL DR 78229 #048-02-2002 L2006 **OBG** *020
MILLER, Roseann Ulmer. 527 N LEONA ST 78207 #048-13-2001 L2004 **IM** *020
MILLER, Sam S. 7711 LOUIS PASTEUR STE 300 78229 #035-20-1971 L1977 **END** *020 †20
MILLER, Stephen. 8431 FREDERICKSBURG RD, STE 100 78246 #065-01-1974 L1995
  D *020 †15
MILLIGAN, Daun J. ■ 78251 #048-02-2006 L2007 **AN** *012
MIMARI, Damon Andrew. 7703 FLOYD CURL DR, DEPT OF SURGERY MC 7737 78229
  #048-02-2004 **GS** *012
MIMARI, George Edward. 8042 WURZBACH RD STE 630 78229 #048-02-1973 L1973
  GS *020 †85
MIMS, James Luther, III. 311 CAMDEN ST STE 511 78215 #021-01-1968 L1970 **PO PD** *020 †35
MINA, Eman Gamil-Fahim. ■ 78260 #915-03-2002 **FP** *012
MINA, Maged Magdy. 18626 HARDY OAK BLVD, STE 220 78258 #915-04-1991 L1999
  AN *020 †05
MINGS, Thomas Erwin, Jr. 6711 S NEW BRAUNFELS AVE, ATTN:GRACE VILLAREAL 78223
  #048-13-1976 L1976 **P** *020 †75
MINIEL, Pedro N. ■ 78232 #048-04-1950 L1950 **OS GP** *071
MIRA, Joaquin G. 7979 WURZBACH RD, STE 353 78229 #847-04-1966 L1974 **RO** *020 †80
MIRAMONTES, Loretta May. 215 E QUINCY ST, STE 505 78215 #005-02-1979 L1981
  OPH *020 †35
MIRANDA, Estela S. 5405 HURLEY DR 78238 #748-08-1967 L1983 **CHP P** *020
MIRANDA, Jennifer J. ■ 78249 #048-13-2006 **IM** *012
MIRANDA, Yvonne S. 3903 WISEMAN BLVD STE 3 78251 #048-13-1997 L1999 **PD** *020 †55
MIRELES, Veronica Lynn. 333 N SANTA ROSA AVE 78207 #048-13-2002 L2005 **CCP** *012 †55
MIRKOVIC, Nena. 7979 WURZBACH RD, SO. TEXAS ONCOLOGY AND HEM 78229
  #957-01-1990 L2005 **RO** *020 †80
MIRZA, Farooq. 7703 FLOYD CURL DR 78229 #704-01-1973 L1980 **PD** *020 †55
MISRA, Sanjay. 315 N SAN SABA 78207 #048-12-1991 L1992 **ORS** *020 †40
MITA, Catalin. 7979 WURZBACH RD 78229 #781-01-1992 L2006 *100
MITA, Monica Mirela. 7979 WURZBACH RD 78229 #781-01-1992 L2006 **HO** *020
MITCHELL, Baker Adams. ■ 78240 #048-13-2004 **AN** *012
MITCHELL, David Earl. 540 MADISON OAK DR, STE 160 78258 #005-14-1993 L2003
  RNR *020 †80
MITCHELL, David Paul. ■ 78218 #047-06-1960 L1987 **FM** *071 †18
MITCHELL, Elizabeth L. 11124 WURZBACH RD STE 300 78230 #048-13-1976 L1976
  CHP P *020 †75
MITCHELL, George W, Jr. 7703 FLOYD CURL DR 78229 #023-07-1942 L1982 **OBG** *071 †30
MITCHELL, Kristie Denise. ■ 78260 #051-04-2001 L2003 **P** *020 †75
MITCHELL, Melanie C. 525 OAK CENTRE DR, STE 350 78258 #034-01-1989 L1997 **PD** *020 †55
MITCHELL, Romy Lauren. ■ 78230 #048-02-2003 L2007 **AN** *020

MITCHELL, Whitney S. ■ 78212 #048-13-2004 **P** *012
MITCHELL-DRAWERT, Casey. ■ 78249 #048-13-2006 **AN** *012
MITTLER, Brant Steven. 4319 MEDICAL DR, STE 131 PMB 363 78229 #036-07-1972 L1973 **CD IM** *020
MIZANI, Mohammad Reza. 343 W HOUSTON ST, STE 609 78205 #308-05-1996 L2001 **NEP** *020 †20
MOCZYGEMBA, Roger M. 3453 IH 35 N STE 207B 78219 #048-16-1991 L1992 **GP OM** *020
MODY-BAILEY, Priti. 1055 ADA ST, CENTER-SOUTHEAST 78223 #048-04-1990 L1991 **FM** *020 †18
MOE, Roderick Donald, Jr. 8122 DATAPOINT DR, STE 1050 78229 #048-12-1981 L1981 **OTO** *020 †45
MOHAN, Chandra B. ■ 78254 #495-44-1968 L1978 **IM** *020 †20
MOHR, George Carl. ■ 78245 #024-01-1957 **AM** *071 †70
MOISE, Harold Edwin. ■ 78232 #045-01-1976 L1977 **P** *075
MOLINA, Arturo. 626 MERIDA ST, STE 78207 #132-01-1966 L1977 **NEP IM** *020
MOLINA, Blanca C. 5414 FREDERICKSBURG RD, STE 100 78229 #048-04-1976 L1976 **NPM PD** *020 †55
MOLINA, Josue. 3066 E COMMERCE ST 78220 #649-02-1990 L1998 **PD** *020
MOLINA, Marco Tulio, Jr. ■ 78238 #039-01-2006 **FP** *012
MOLINA, Migdalia. 730 N MAIN, STE 515 78205 #042-01-1984 L1987 **IM** *020
MOLINA, Rodolfo. 4511 HORIZON HILL BLVD, STE 150 78229 #048-04-1976 L1976 **RHU** *020
MOLINA, Shanna Marie. ■ 78238 #039-01-2005 L2007 **P** *012
MONCAYO MINNIG, Alejandro. 7703 FLOYD CURL DR 78229 #264-08-1992 *100
MONTALVO, Miguel A. ■ 78253 #042-01-1975 L1981 **OS OPH** *030
MONTANO, Ricardo G. 1624 BUENA VISTA ST 78207 #649-01-1949 L1953 **IMG FM** *071 †18
MONTELONGO, Saul. 720 PLEASANTON RD, GONZABA MEDICAL GROUP 78214 #021-01-1999 L2002 **FM** *020 †18
MONTEMAYOR, David Frank. 7703 FLOYD CURL DR, DEPT OF INTERNAL MEDICINE 78229 #048-12-1980 L1980 **IM** *020 †20
MONTEMAYOR, Francisco J. 7254 BLANCO RD, STE 104 78216 #048-14-1992 L1993 **PD IM** *020 †20,55
MONTEMAYOR, Raul Martin. 2833 BABCOCK RD, STE 435 78229 #021-01-1968 L1980 **IM** *020 †20
MONTEMAYOR, Ricardo A. 525 OAK CENTRE DR, STE 150 78258 #048-13-1990 L1991 **MPD PD** *020 †55,20
MONTENEGRO DE BARRETO, Mar. 7330 SAN PEDRO, STE 405 78216 #682-01-1989 L2005 **FM** *020 †18
MONTES, Erica Amanda. ■ 78240 #048-13-2008 *012
MONTES, Marisol. 5414 FREDERICKSBURG RD, STE 100 78229 #042-01-1980 L1984 **PD** *020 †55
MONTGOMERY, Mary Jo C. ■ 78209 #048-04-1941 L1941 **D** *071
MONTGOMERY, Richard S. ■ 78217 #048-13-2006 **DR** *012
MONTIEL, Milka Mukhlova. 7703 FLOYD CURL DR, UNIV OF TEXAS MED SCHOOL 78229 #198-01-1953 L1971 **PTH OS** *071 †50
MONTOYA, Amy S. ■ 78240 #048-13-2007 **PD** *012
MOODY, Joe Marshall, Jr. 7703 FLOYD CURL DR, CARDIOLOGY DIV 78229 #048-13-1974 L1974 **CD IM** *040 †20
MOON, Susan Miriam. 527 N LEONA ST, FAMILY & COMMUNITY MEDICIN 78207 #024-05-2003 L2006 **FM** *020 †18
MOONEY, Elizabeth Ann. ■ 78233 #055-01-1979 L1999 **DR NM** *020 †80
MOORAD, Philip Jacob, Jr. 8038 WURZBACH RD, STE 234 78229 #035-45-1969 L1977 **P** *020 †75
MOORE, Ben Harold, Jr. 13722 EMBASSY ROW 78216 #048-02-1964 L1964 **EM GP** *020
MOORE, Edward A. ■ 78209 #048-02-1999 **AN** *100
MOORE, James O. 7400 MERTON MINTER ST, AMBULATORY CARE 11C 78229 #048-14-1988 L1989 **IM** *020 †20
MOORE, Jennifer A. ■ 78240 #048-13-2002 L2005 **PD** *100
MOORE, Jolene Christie. 8231 FREDERICKSBURG RD 78229 #019-02-2003 L2007 **P** *012
MOORE, Reginald Hollis. 333 N SANTA ROSA AVE 78207 #023-12-1982 L1988 **PD** *020 †55
MOORHEAD, Frank Albert. 23615 OAKLAND CV 78258 #011-02-1959 L1990 **IM FM** *071 †18,20
MORA, Alexander. 207 SW MILITARY DR 78221 #011-02-1980 L1983 **IM GP** *020
MORA, Rafael Vidal. ■ 78218 #847-06-1975 L1976 **U** *020 †95
MORA, Robert Alexander. 4502 MEDICAL DR, DIV EMERGENCY MEDICINE DSL 78229 #021-01-1996 L2000 **EM** *020 †16
MORALE, Samuel Gregory. 4502 MEDICAL DR 78229 #048-13-1990 L1991 **EM** *020 †16
MORALES, Carlos Augusto. ■ 78248 #048-14-2001 L2007 **RNR** *020 †80
MORALES, Carlos Francisco. 7940K FLOYD CURL DR, STE 860 78229 #042-01-1984 L1993 **PUD CCM** *020 †20
MORALES, Luis. 3066 E COMMERCE ST 78220 #042-01-1989 L1996 **OBG** *020 †30
MORALES, Robert P. 2829 BABCOCK RD STE 250 78229 #048-13-1975 L1975 **VS** *020 †85
MORALEZ, Steven Anthony. 810 SE MILITARY DR 78214 #056-05-1980 L1982 **IM** *020 †20
MORAN, Mark Alan. 403 TREELINE PARK, STE 200 78209 #048-13-2002 L2006 **APM** *020 †05
MORENO, Francisco. ■ 78254 #048-31-1989 **ID** *020
MORENO, Graciela. 14100 N US HIGHWAY 281, STE 450 78232 #048-13-1999 L2002 **FM** *020 †18
MORENO, Jaime. ■ 78256 #025-12-1984 L1985 **IM** *020 †20
MORENO, Linda B. ■ 78256 #042-01-1991 L1995 **IM** *020
MORENO, Luz Amparo. 1335 SE MILITARY DR 78214 #264-04-1985 L1997 **NEP** *020 †20
MORGAN, Ana Elizabeth. ■ 78229 #051-04-2006 L2008 **IM** *012
MORGAN, Christopher D. ■ 78240 #048-13-2005 L2008 **AN** *012
MORGAN, Douglas Preston. 1100 NE LOOP 410 STE 72 78209 #048-12-1972 L1972 **P** *020 †75,05
MORGAN, Lola Claire. 7703 FLOYD CURL DR 78229 #016-43-2000 L2007 **IM** *020 †75
MORGAN, Sybil C Roberts. 8038 WURZBACH RD, STE 280 78229 #048-12-1971 L1971 **FM** *020 †18
MORIN, Robert Philip. 2211 NW MILITARY HWY, STE 201 78213 #305-01-2000 L2006 **FM** *020 †18
MORRISON, James B. 4499 MEDICAL DR STE 300 78229 #048-02-1949 L1950 **IM** *020 †20
MORRISON, Jennifer Clair. ■ 78229 #001-06-2008 *012
MORSE, Martha Ruth. 4499 MEDICAL DR STE 255 78229 #039-01-1980 L1984 **PDP CCP** *020 †55
MORTENSEN, Eric Michael. 7400 MERTON MINTER ST, # 11C6 78229 #041-07-1996 L2002 **IM EP** *020
MORTON, Paul Emery. 7711 LOUIS PASTEUR, PAUL MORTON OB/GYN 78229 #028-03-1981 L2003 **OBG AM** *050 †30
MOSBACKER, Matthew E. 4511 HORIZON HILL BLVD, STE 150 78229 #048-14-1989 L1991 **IM** *020 †20

MOSEBAR, Robert Howard. ■ 78239 #054-04-1957 **OS GS** *071
MOSQUEDA, Albert. 8401 DATAPOINT DR, STE 401 78229 #028-46-1990 L2003 **IM** *020 †20
MOSQUEDA, Kimberly Ann. ■ 78209 #028-46-1990 L1991 **IM** *020 †20
MOUNT, Charles Edward, III. ■ 78251 #055-01-2007 **TY** *012
MOUSSA, Hannah G. ■ 78251 #048-13-2005 **P** *012
MOYERS, Julie Ann. ■ 78230 #005-12-2005 L2007 **IM** *100
MOZERSKY, David Jay. 4330 MEDICAL DR STE 225 78229 #062-01-1964 L1974 **GS VS** *071 †85
MUDD, Jason Eli. ■ 78240 #024-01-2006 **OTO** *012
MUDDASANI, Srirangam. 7703 FLOYD CURL DR, UNIV TX MED SCH-SAN ANTONI 78229 #495-57-1991 **P** *100
MUELLER, Cheryl Lynn. 9480 HUEBNER RD, STE 100 78240 #048-15-1983 L1983 **FM** *020 †18
MUELLER, Edward James. 4499 MEDICAL DR, METHODIST PLZ STE 251 78229 #038-06-1977 L1992 **U** *020 †95
MUELLER, Edwin L, Jr. ■ 78216 #028-34-1951 L1951 **FM** *071 †18
MUELLER, Eric Robert. ■ 78247 #030-06-1996 L2006 **P** *020 †75
MUELLER, Francis Wm. 9480 HUEBNER RD, STE 100 78240 #048-15-1983 L1983 **FM** *020 †18
MUHAMMAD SHARIF ASAR, Bato. 7703 FLOYD CURL DR 78229 #704-27-2002 L2008 **FP** *012
MUIR, Mark Thomas. ■ 78254 #048-12-2006 **GS** *012
MULGREW, Paraic Jos. 10134 HUEBNER RD, CLINIC 78240 #539-04-1969 L1980 **NEP IM** *020 †20
MULLEN, John Patrick. ■ 78231 #539-04-1967 L1968 **ORS** *020 †40
MULLER, Jean Marie. 5282 MEDICAL DR, STE 450 78229 #048-04-1983 L1983 **CD IM** *020 †20
MULLINS, David C. 7950 FLOYD CURL DR, STE 700 78229 #048-12-1988 L1989 **GS** *020 †85
MULLINS, David Clay. 5414 FREDERICKSBURG RD, STE 100 78229 #048-12-1964 L1964 **NPM PD** *020 †55
MULLINS, Rhonda Meier. 4242 MEDICAL DR, STE 3100 78229 #048-12-1988 L1989 **AN** *020 †05
MULROW, Cynthia Diane. 7703 FLOYD CURL DR 78229 #048-04-1978 L1978 **IM** *050 †20
MULROW, John Patrick. 4411 MEDICAL DR, STE 300 78229 #035-09-1978 L1986 **CD** *020 †20
MULROY, Amy Edmondson. 7940 FLOYD CURL DR, STE 1020 78229 #048-13-1993 L1994 **P** *020 †75
MULROY, Patrick Wm. 311 CAMDEN ST, STE 404 78215 #051-07-1991 L1995 **PM** *020 †60
MUMBOWER, Amy L. 4440 S PIEDRAS DR, STE 100 78228 #048-13-1995 L1997 **DR** *020 †80
MUMMA, John Vincent. ■ 78230 #038-06-1964 L1970 **PO OPH** *071 †35
MUMTAZ, Mehnaz. 7703 FLOYD CURL DR 78229 #704-09-2002 **FP** *012
MUNANTE LOPEZ, Mariana. 7703 FLOYD CURL DR 78229 #737-06-2001 L2006 **FM** *020 †18
MUNIR, Muhammed. 19016 STONE OAK PKWY, # 100 78258 #704-02-1965 L1990 **PD** *020 †55
MUNIZ, Christopher J. 540 MADISON OAK DR, STE 160 78258 #048-02-1998 L2004 **VIR** *020 †80
MUNOZ, Jorge. 2515 BABCOCK RD 78229 #649-52-1988 L1995 **GE** *020 †20
MUNOZ, Mark David. 45 NE LOOP 410, STE 900 78216 #048-02-1996 L1998 **AN** *020
MUNOZ, Ricardo, Jr. 525 OAK CENTRE DR 78258 #047-07-1979 L1982 **OBG** *020 †30
MUNSHI, Hamid Khan. 7703 FLOYD CURL DR 78229 #836-01-1969 *100
MURDOCK, Tammy Joy. 502 MADISON OAK DR, STE 240 78258 #041-12-1998 L2002 **OBG** *020
MURGO, Joseph Paul. 927 MCCULLOUGH AVE 78215 #041-01-1966 L1997 **CD IM** *030 †20
MURILLO, Horacio. ■ 78260 #026-08-2004 **DR** *012
MURPHREE, Dennis Haaga. 13750 SAN PEDRO, STE 140 78232 #027-01-1968 L1975 **IM** *020 †20
MURPHREE, Jean Thorne. 5282 MEDICAL DR STE 500 78229 #012-05-1975 L1976 **AI** *020 †55 ‡
MURPHY, Kim David. 7400 BARLITE BLVD 78224 #047-06-1981 L1992 **PTH BBK** *020 †50
MURPHY, Michael L. 225 E SONTERRA BLVD, STE 217 78258 #048-12-1983 L1983 **AN PMM** *020 †05
MURPHY, Sharon Boehm. 8403 FLOYD CURL DR, CHILDRENS CANCER RES INST 78229 #024-01-1969 L2005 **PHO PD** *030 †55
MURPHY, Wayne Thomas. ■ 78218 #048-14-2003 L2004 *100
MURRAY, Clinton Kenneth. 3851 ROGER BROOKE DR, BROOKE AMC, BLDG 3600 78234 #023-12-1996 L1998 **ID** *020 †20
MURRAY, Matthew C. ■ 78249 #048-13-2005 **ORS** *012
MUSE, Roger Kenneth. 1933 NE LOOP 410 78217 #019-02-1990 L1997 **CD ICE** *020 †20
MUSHARAF, Gulam Hussain. ■ 78240 #495-57-1997 L2008 **PN** *100
MUSI, Nicolas. 701 S ZARZAMORA ST 78207 #649-13-1995 L2005 **IM** *020 †20
MUSTELIER, Efigenio Raul. ■ 78248 #275-01-1950 **GP** *071
MUZZA, Hugo Elmo. 7333 BARLITE BLVD STE 120 78224 #649-02-1966 L1967 **FM GS** *020 †18
MUZZA CAVAZOS, Luis. 111 DALLAS ST 78205 #649-02-1965 L1970 **OBG** *020 †30
MYATT, James Phillip. ■ 78240 #048-15-2006 **IM** *012
MYERS, John G. 7703 FLOYD CURL DR, MAIL CODE 7740 78229 #048-13-1992 L1993 **CCS** *020 †85
MYERS, Paul Walter. 8222 WURZBACH RD 78229 #035-03-1946 L1987 **OS NS** *072 †25
MYKKANEN, Leena A. 7703 FLOYD CURL DR 78229 #374-04-1984 *100
NADEAU, Mark Thos. 7703 FLOYD CURL DR, MAIL CODE 7795 78229 #051-01-1982 L1983 **FM** *020 †18
NADELA, Siegfredo Montes. 6811 BRAVE WAY 78256 #748-02-1968 L1978 **AN** *020 †05
NAEEM, Lubna. 19272 STONE OAK PKWY, STE 105 78258 #704-21-1984 L1999 **IM** *020 †20
NAEEM, Muhammad. 225 E SONTERRA BLVD, STE 215 78258 #704-21-1984 L1999 **GE** *020 †20
NAGEL, Thomas Robt. 8401 DATAPOINT DR, STE 130 78229 #014-01-1983 L1995 **PD** *020 †55
NAGORI, Lokesh. 7703 FLOYD CURL DR 78229 #495-74-2000 L2005 **HO** *100
NAIDU, Sharmila. 414 NAVARRO ST STE 1405, NIX MEDICAL CENTER 78205 #495-70-1996 L2006 **IM** *020 †20
NAIK, Amar Anantrao. 17 NOPALITO 78261 #495-28-1966 L1982 **AN** *020
NAIK, Padmaja Abhang. 7703 FLOYD CURL DR 78229 #496-26-2002 L2007 **FM** *020
NAIR, Shalini. 7703 FLOYD CURL DR 78229 #495-52-2005 **IM** *100
NAISER, Shelley Leanne. ■ 78240 #048-13-2008 *012
NAJERA, Jose Eugenio. 7703 FLOYD CURL DR 78229 #649-30-2007 **IM** *012
NAKISSA, Nasser. 700 S ZARZAMORA ST STE LL3 78207 #517-08-1973 L1984 **FM RO** *020 †80
NANCHERLA, Prakash Rao. 343 W HOUSTON ST, STE 906 78205 #495-21-1974 L1985 **NEP IM** *020 †20
NANCHERLA, Swarnalatha. 45 NE LOOP 410, STE 900 78216 #495-21-1979 L1985 **AN** *020 †05
NANDAKUMAR, Bhanumathi. 215 N SANSABA STE 207 78207 #495-09-1965 L1982 **PD OS** *020 †55
NANDYALA, Ramavathi. 414 NAVARRO ST 78205 #495-21-1997 L2004 **CD** *012 †20
NAPIER, Dacia Janel. 540 MADISON OAK DR, STE 160 78258 #048-14-1997 L1998 **DR** *020 †80
NAPIER, Joshua Turner. ■ 78259 #023-12-2003 L2007 **IM** *020 †20

NARDI, Domenick Paul, Jr. ■ 78253 #039-01-2007 **PD** *012

NARLA, Amita Rao. ■ 78216 #495-04-2001 L2007 **IM** *020

NARON, Manuel S. 150 E SONTERRA BLVD # 220, NORTH HILLS FAMILY MEDICIN 78258 #048-13-2001 L2004 **FM** *020

NASKI, Michael Chester. 7703 FLOYD CURL DR, MSC 7750 DEPT PATHOLOGY 78229 #025-01-1991 L2001 **PTH** *020 †50

NASSAR, Eddie Richard. 2235 THOUSAND OAKS DR, STE 119 78232 #048-14-2000 L2002 **PD** *020 †55

NASTA, Armando. 8038 WURZBACH RD 78229 #649-01-1953 L1956 **GYN** *071

NASTALA, Chet Lawrence. 9635 HUEBNER RD 78240 #036-07-1989 L1998 **PS** *020 †85,65 ‡

NATALINO, Michael Robt. 8715 VILLAGE DR STE 320, RESPIRATORY & INTNSVE CARE 78217 #007-02-1975 L1978 **PUD CCM** *020 †20

NATHAN, Habib. 9480 HUEBNER RD, STE 210 78240 #517-01-1961 L1970 **P OS** *020 †75

NATHAN, Marshall David. 7950 FLOYD CURL STE 1002 78229 #025-01-1968 L1980 **OTO GP** *020 †45

NATIONS, Frankie N. ■ 78230 #048-04-1950 L1950 **AN** *071 †05

NAU, Cornelius Hugo. ■ 78209 #048-02-1945 L1945 **PD** *071 †55

NAU, Cornelius Hugo, Jr. 4204 GARDENDALE ST, STE 203 78229 #048-13-1978 L1982 **P** *020 †75

NAU, Thomas Wm. 7940 FLOYD CURL DR, MED CTR TOWER II STE 400 78229 #048-13-1982 L1983 **OTO** *020 †45

NAUS, John P. ■ 78240 #048-13-2005 **P** *012

NAVA, John Jos. ■ 78283 #048-04-1985 L1988 **FM** *020

NAVARRO, Rodolfo M. 7703 FLOYD CURL DR, U TX MED SCH SAN ANTONIO 78229 #048-13-2006 L2008 **FP** *012

NAVARRO-ROMAN, Lydia. 7940 FLOYD CURL DR, STE 215 78229 #264-01-1971 L1983 **PTH CLP** *020

NAVAS, Felipe Alfonso. 18850 REDLAND RD 78259 #264-18-1994 L2006 **OPH** *012

NEAL, Gregory S. 4499 MEDICAL DR, STE 200 78229 #016-16-1988 L1989 **REN OBG** *020 †30

NEAL, Richard Chas. ■ 78258 #040-02-1982 L1986 **TS** *020 †85,90

NEEL, Richard L. 6800 PARK TEN BLVD, STE 266S 78213 #048-13-1982 L1983 **AM** *020 †70

NEELEY, Samuel Robt. 4410 MEDICAL DR, STE 520 78229 #030-05-1976 L1977 **N IM** *020 †20,75

NEELEY, Wendell Wayne. ■ 78258 #048-13-2004 *100

NEELY, Warren F. 4410 MEDICAL DR, STE 600 78229 #020-02-1972 L1975 **NS** *020 †25

NEESVIG, Burton Oswald. ■ 78230 #056-05-1964 L1967 **GP** *071 †18

NEGRON, Roberto Angel. 4410 MEDICAL DR, STE 610 78229 #041-13-1960 L1975 **NS** *020 †25

NEIDRE, Arvo. 7700 FLOYD CURL DR 78229 #065-01-1970 L1976 **ORS** *020 †40

NEIFERT, Paige Lynn. ■ 78248 #007-02-1995 L1997 **D** *012 †18

NEIGUT, Deborah Ann. 7703 FLOYD CURL DR, PEDI GASTROENTEROLOGY 78229 #048-14-1983 L1983 **GE PD** *020 †55

NEIGUT, Joseph Stephen. M & S TWR 78205 #048-02-1957 L1957 **OPH** *020

NEIHEISEL, Margaret D. 4499 MEDICAL DR, STE 347 78229 #038-45-1986 L1991 **PD** *020 †55

NEINER, James Richard. ■ 78258 #023-12-2006 L2007 **D** *012

NELSON, Austin Tyler. ■ 78251 #023-12-2006 L2008 **IM** *012

NELSON, David R. 6570 INGRAM RD 78238 #005-06-1995 L1998 **FM** *020 †18

NELSON, Joseph W. ■ 78229 #003-75-2007, ▲ **PM** *012

NELSON, Mark Wm. 3338 OAKWELL CT STE 114 78218 #012-01-1976 L1985 **RHU IM** *020 †20

NEMARUGOMMULA, Nanda Kish. 7703 FLOYD CURL DR 78229 #496-59-2002 L2008 **FP** *012

NEPOMUCENO, Alex J. ■ 78229 #048-12-2001 **IM** *100

NEPOMUCENO, Concepcion A. ■ 78222 #748-09-1962 L1972 **PD OS** *020 †55

NETT, Robert Burton, Jr. 19026 STONE OAK PKWY, STE 210A 78258 #023-12-1985 L1986 **APM FM** *020

NEUBAUER, Brian Edward. ■ 78254 #035-06-2006 L2007 **IM** *012

NEUFFER, Marcus Christian. ■ 78251 #023-12-2006 L2008 **OPH** *012

NEVAREZ, Hector L. 730 N MAIN AVE, STE 418 78205 #308-02-1977 L1986 **OPH** *020 †35

NEVITT, Kevin Christopher. 540 MADISON OAK DR, STE 160 78258 #048-02-1996 L2001 **DR VIR** *020 †80

NEWBY, Marvin G. 9150 HUEBNER RD STE 250B 78240 #048-04-1953 L1953 **ORS** *071 †40

NEWMAN, Forest Pike, III. 3851 ROGER BROOKE DR, BROOKE ARMY MED CTR, BLDG 78234 #036-01-1974 L1983 **END IM** *020 †20

NEWMAN, Larissa Margriet. ■ 78251 #051-01-2006 L2007 **PD** *012

NEWMAN, Richard Kurt. 4775 HAMILTON WOLFE RD, STE 1 78229 #048-13-1972 L1972 **HNS** *020 †45

NEWTON, Jerry. ■ 78213 #048-02-1944 L1945 **PD PHP** *071 †55

NEWTON, Luke A. ■ 78216 #048-12-2003 L2007 **OBG** *100

NG, Federico R. 7922 EWING HALSELL DR, STE 270 78229 #048-12-1993 L1994 **MPD** *020

NGO, Lan-Anh Le. 19016 STONE OAK PKWY, STE 140 78258 #048-15-1992 L1993 **FM** *020 †18

NGUYEN, Dominic Dung. 7703 FLOYD CURL DR, UNIV OF TEXAS HLTH SCI CTR 78229 #048-15-2005 **RO** *012

NGUYEN, Huy Manh. ■ 78259 #048-13-2008 *012

NGUYEN, Jimmy Diep. ■ 78240 #034-01-2003 L2003 **AN** *020

NGUYEN, John T. 3066 E COMMERCE ST 78220 #048-15-1998 L2002 **OBG** *020

NGUYEN, Nam-Vinh. 45 NE LOOP 410, STE 900 78216 #048-12-1988 L1989 **AN** *020 †05

NGUYEN, Patrick. ■ 78240 #048-13-2004 **GS** *012

NGUYEN, Ruth Thi. ■ 78229 #019-02-2005 **GS** *012

NGUYEN, Thanh Thuy Thi. ■ 78216 #019-02-1991 L1996 **FM** *020

NGUYEN, Vung Duy. 7703 FLOYD CURL DR, THE U OF THSE AT SA 78229 #941-01-1964 L1976 **DR** *040 †20

NGUYEN, Wendy T. 225 E SONTERRA BLVD, STE 100 78258 #048-13-1991 L1994 **FM** *020 †18

NGUYEN-POOLE, Mary S. 7930 FLOYD CURL DR 78229 #048-14-1997 L1998 **FM** *020 †18

NICHOLSON, Karin Mc Elroy. ■ 78260 #023-12-2000 L2002 **PCC** *012 †20

NICHOLSON, Lisa Marie. ■ 78254 #038-45-2008 *012

NICHOLSON, Susannah Eliza. ■ 78254 #038-13-2005 **GS** *012

NIELSON, David H. 1202 E SONTERRA BLVD, # 101 78258 #041-13-1989 L1996 **TS** *020 †85,90

NIELSON, Katherine Joan. ■ 78258 #041-09-1996 L1997 **P** *062

NIERENBERG, Natalie Eliza. ■ 78240 #021-01-2006 **IM** *012

NIETO, Juan Manuel. 4502 MEDICAL DR 78229 #007-02-1974 L1984 **EM GP** *020 †16

NIEVES, Luis Escalante. ■ 78247 #048-12-1998 L2007 **FP** *012

NIKAS, Aris. 1200 BROOKLYN AVE, STE 240 78212 #038-41-1986 L1995 **IM PLM** *020 †20

NIKAS, Vasilis. ■ 78247 #781-03-1961 L1979 **PM** *074 †60

NITSCHKE, Richard Elwood. ■ 78209 #036-07-1937 L1946 **IM** *071 †20

NIXON, Pat Ireland, Jr. ■ 78229 #036-07-1939 L1939 **GP OS** *071

NOBLES, Patrick Allen. 7460 N IH 35 78218 #047-20-1983 L1995 **FM OM** *020 †18

NOBLES, Robert G, III. 5979 BABCOCK RD 78240 #048-13-1982 L1983 **IM** *020 †20

NOEL, Robert Adam. 7703 FLOYD CURL DR, UNIV OF TX HLTH SCIENCE CT 78229 #012-05-1985 L1987 **IM** *020 †55

NOLAN, Charles Raymond. 7703 FLOYD CURL DR, UNIV OF TX HLTH SCI CTR 78229 #007-02-1980 L1993 **NEP IM** *020 †20

NOLAN, Robert Jos, Jr. 7703 FLOYD CURL DR, DEPT OF PEDIATRICS 78229 #011-03-1979 L1984 **PD** *040 †55

NOLL, Janet Monier. 7007 BANDERA RD, STE 19 78238 #048-02-1976 L1976 **PD** *020 †55

NOORILY, Allen David. 7909 FREDERICKSBURG RD, STE 100 78229 #025-01-1985 L1991 **OTO** *020 †45

NOORILY, Susan Chudnow. 7703 FLOYD CURL, UNIV OF TX HEALTH SCIENCE 78229 #025-01-1986 L1991 **AN** *020 †05

NORGARD, Michael John. 226 ROSEHEART 78259 #056-05-1969 L2003 **ON IM** *020 †20

NORMAN, Ruskin Curry. 7979 BROADWAY ST, STE 101 78209 #016-06-1945 L1951 **R** *071 †80

NORRIS, Simone L. 333 N SANTA ROSA AVE, FL 4 78207 #048-13-1992 L1993 **FM** *040 †18

NORTELL, Joseph Harry. 111 DALLAS ST 78205 #748-08-1965 L1970 **GS** *075

NOUNOU, Joseph Michael. ■ 78245 #038-41-2004 L2004 **AN** *012

NOVAK, Joseph David. ■ 78205 #016-02-2008 **EM** *012

NOVAK, Joseph John. 3851 ROGER BROOKE DR, BROOK ARMY MEDICAL CENTER 78234 #030-05-1941 L1943 **OS GP** *071

NOVICK, Donald Nathan. 7950 FLOYD CURL DR, STE 904 78229 #021-01-1971 L1973 **PS** *020 †85,65

NTSOANE, Elias Manhlane. 7703 FLOYD CURL DR #MC7883, SCIENCE C 78229 #305-01-2003 **N** *012

NUGENT, Paul Terrence. 8637 FREDERICKSBURG RD, STE 105 78240 #067-01-1975 L1985 **FM** *020 †18

NUNEZ, Manuel Alejandro. 7703 FLOYD CURL DR 78229 #023-12-2005 **P** *012

NUTT, Terri Jo. ■ 78261 #038-44-1995 L2007 **D** *020 †15

OAKES, Sandra Liliana. 7703 FLOYD CURL DR, STE 610L 78229 #264-01-1995 L2003 **IMG** *020 †18

OBREGON, Maria Luisa. 7703 FLOYD CURL DR 78229 #264-16-2000 **P** *012

O'BRIEN, Eugene Thos. 21 SPURS LN, STE 310 78240 #026-04-1958 L1970 **ORS** *020 †40

O'BRIEN, John Richard. 78209 #041-02-1941 L1951 **GYN OS** *071

OCAMPO, Gloria Lucia. 7703 FLOYD CURL DR, DEPT OF MEDICINE, MC 7870 78229 #264-13-1991 L2003 **END** *020 †20

OCAZIONEZ TRUJILLO, Daniel. 7703 FLOYD CURL DR 78229 #264-16-2003 **IM** *012

OCHOA, Eloy, Jr. ■ 78216 #048-12-1996 L2006 **ORS** *020 †40

OCHS, Robert L. 14855 BLANCO RD, STE 214 78216 #048-13-1990 L1991 **D** *020 †55,15

ODLE, Micheal Allen. ■ 78259 #055-02-2001 L2003 **CD** *012

ODOM, Michael Wilson. 7703 FLOYD CURL DR 78229 #048-12-1983 L1983 **NPM PD** *020 †55

ODU, Justice Uzodinma. ■ 78258 #690-02-2001 L2006 **IM** *020

OEI, Heng Hoei. 11107 WURZBACH RD STE 201 78230 #506-02-1956 L1969 **AN** *020 †05

OEI, Kiem Hoa. 111 DALLAS ST 78205 #506-02-1956 L1971 **PM** *020

OEI, Thomas Omar. 1100 N MAIN AVE 78212 #048-13-1988 L1990 **OPH** *020 †35

OFOBIKE, Blake Ann. 7703 FLOYD CURL DR, DEPT OF OB/GYN 78229 #038-44-2002 L2006 **OBG** *100

OFOBIKE, Emeka Okey, Jr. ■ 78249 #038-06-2003 L2008 **ORS** *012

OGDEN, William Davidson. 6800 W IH 10, STE 300 78201 #048-02-1979 L1979 **GS VS** *020 †85,90

OGLESBY, Paul C. ■ 78213 #048-12-1945 **GP** *074

OGLETREE, James Watson. 11 GROGANS MILL DR 78248 #048-13-1982 L1983 **FM FSM** *020 †18

OGNIBENE, Andre John. ■ 78261 #035-19-1956 L1975 **IM CD** *040 †20

O'GORMAN, Gerald V. 4402 VANCE JACKSON RD 78230 #048-12-1978 L1978 **AN EM** *020

OH, Soo Gi. 45 NE LOOP 410, STE 900 78216 #583-02-1973 L1978 **AN** *020

OISHI, Noboru. 7979 WURZBACH RD 78229 #028-02-1953 L1991 **HEM ON** *071 †20

OJEDA, Herminio F. 4647 MEDICAL DR 78229 #737-06-1995 L2002 **GS** *020 †85

OJINGWA, Joseph. ■ 78240 #016-11-2000 **FP** *012

O'KEEFE, Kevin J. ■ 78240 #048-13-2008 *012

OKOLI, Okechukwu. 4212 E SOUTHCROSS BLVD, STE 215 78222 #690-04-1982 L2001 **OBG** *020 †30

OKORO, Stanley Aham. 7703 FLOYD CURL DR RM 227L, SCIENCE CTR 78229 #047-07-1996 L2006 **PS** *012 †85

OLAISEN, Arlene. 3201 CHERRY RIDGE ST, STE B200 78230 #035-08-1974 L1985 **IMG DIA** *020 †20

OLEA, Efren Saucedo. 343 W HOUSTON ST, STE 408 78205 #649-01-1958 L1971 **P PYA** *071

O'LEARY, Kathleen Maria. ■ 78249 #016-06-2004 L2006 **OBG** *012

OLIN, Fred Harry. 7930 FLOYD CURL DR 78229 #048-13-1973 L1973 **ORS** *020 †40

OLIPHANT, Nekesha. ■ 78229 #048-13-2008 *012

OLIVA, Damaso A. ■ 78258 #847-04-1966 L1969 **P** *071

OLIVA, Damaso Andres, Jr. 343 W HOUSTON ST, STE 301 78205 #649-14-1987 L1996 **P** *020

OLIVARES, Patricia M. 11811 BLANCO RD 78216 #048-12-1987 L1988 **FM** *020 †18

OLIVARES, Rebecca A. 1423 GUADALUPE ST, STE 101 78207 #048-12-1983 L1983 **FM GP** *020 †18

OLIVER, Boyce Boyd, Jr. 1303 MCCULLOUGH AVE, STE 235 78212 #048-02-1970 L1970 **GS** *020 †85

OLIVER, Dennis Carey. 9969 FREDERICKSBURG RD 78240 #035-01-1980 L1991 **IM** *020 †20 ‡

OLIVEROS DONOHUE, Rene A. 7703 FLOYD CURL DR, UN OF TEXAS HEALTH SCIENC 78229 #737-01-1966 L1978 **CD IM** *040 †20

OLIVERSON, Forrest W. 2410 STANLEY RD, BLDG 1029 78234 #049-01-1978 L1998 **PHP OM** *020 †70

OLOMU, Patrick N. 7711 LOUIS PASTEUR, STE 708 78229 #690-01-1985 L2000 **AN PAN** *020 †05

OLSEN, Jerry Geo. 7703 FLOYD CURL DR, MAILSTOP 6220 78229 #054-04-1989 L1994 **IMG** *020

OLSEN, John Richard. 3851 ROGER BROOKE DR, BROOKE AMC, BLDG 3600 78234 #023-12-1983 L1988 **DR VIR** *020 †80

OLSEN, Tandy Garth. ■ 78254 #023-12-1997 L1999 **OBG** *020 †30

OLSON, John David. 7703 FLOYD CURL DR, DEPT OF PATHOLOGY UTHSCSA 78229 #010-02-1970 L1977 **CLP PTH** *030 †50

OLSON, Robert Melvin. ■ 78218 #035-45-1957 L1961 **OS** *050

OLSTA, Susan A. 333 N SANTA ROSA AVE, STE 4703 78207 #048-16-1991 L1995 **OBG** *020 †30

OLVERA, Rene Luis. 333 N SANTA ROSA AVE 78207 #048-12-1990 L1991 **CHP** *020 †75

O'MARA, David Jos. ■ 78218 #018-75-1963, ▲ L1964 **GP** *075 †18

O'NEAL, Lauren Claire. 4214 E SOUTHCROSS BLVD 78222 #048-02-1981 L1982 **LM FM** *075

O'NEILL, Francis Edward. ■ 78209 #019-02-1939 L1940 **R** *071

O'NEILL, James Richard. 4499 MEDICAL DR, STE 220 78229 #019-02-1942 L1946 **CD IM** *020

O'NEILL, Thomas Kevin. 255 E SONTERRA BLVD, STE 203 78258 #017-20-1979 L1985 U *020 †95

ONG, Kathrina Araullo. 7703 FLOYD CURL DR, UNIV TX MED SCH-SAN ANTONI 78229 #748-02-2001 L2008 CCP *012 †55

ONG-HAI, Philip G. 9119 CINNAMON HL 78240 #748-01-1986 L1996 N *020 †75

ONTIVEROS, Margarita M. 311 CAMDEN ST, STE 102 78215 #005-15-1987 L1989 CD *020 †20

OPPELTZ KAZAL, Richard Fr. 7703 FLOYD CURL DR 78229 #935-01-2000 GS *012

OPRY, Jon J. ■ 78254 #048-13-2001 L2003 CHP *020 †75

OQUINN, Ryan Patrick. 7940 FLOYD CURL DR, STE 750 78229 #048-02-1997 L2002 D *020 †15

ORD, John W. ■ 78249 #030-06-1952 CD AM *071 †20

OREJUDOS, Michael Paul. ■ 78255 #023-12-2004 L2005 PTH *012

ORIA, Naser M.. 5788 ECKHERT RD, FRANK M TEJED VA OUT PT CL 78240 #118-01-1988 L2000 FM *100 †18

ORIHEL, Timothy Stewart. 4499 MEDICAL DR STE 393 78229 #021-01-1980 L1983 PM AN *020 †05

ORMAZABAL, Miguel Angel. 5414 FREDERICKSBURG RD, STE 100 78229 #847-09-1970 L1983 PD NPM *020 †55

ORNES, Rene Michael. 8606 VILLAGE DR, STE A 78217 #048-12-1976 L1979 PD *020 †55

O'RORKE, Jane E. 527 N LEONA ST 78207 #035-08-1995 L1996 IM *020 †20

O'ROURKE, Robert Anthony. 7703 FLOYD CURL DR 78229 #030-06-1961 1976 CD PDC *040 †20

OROZCO, Carlos Raul. 221 LEXINGTON AVE, NO. 319 78215 #048-02-1974 L1974 PUD IM *020 †20

ORR, Malcolm David. 7703 FLOYD CURL DR - ANES 78229 #143-05-1964 L1978 AN *020 †05

ORSI, Michael Dana. ■ 78249 #041-15-2004 L2007 DR *012

ORTEGA, Andrew Paul. 902 BANDERA RD 78228 #048-02-1990 L1992 FM *020 †18

ORTEGA, Gerardo. 111 DALLAS ST, STE 210A 78205 #649-02-1974 L1991 OS *020 †85

ORTEGA, Hernando Jose, Jr. 78209 #047-06-1986 L1987 AM OM *030 †70

ORTEGON, Delio P, III. 2829 BABCOCK RD STE 429, SAN ANTONIO COSMETIC SURGE 78229 #048-13-1997 L1999 PS *020 †85

ORTH, Andrea Lynne. ■ 78209 #048-13-2004 L2008 OBG *012

ORTIZ, David Dionisio. 333 N SANTA ROSA AVE, STE F4703 78207 #004-01-1999 L2003 FM *020 †18

ORTIZ, Gabriel. 7254 BLANCO RD STE 201 78216 #048-14-1998 L2000 FM *020 †18

ORTIZ, John Paul. ■ 78210 #649-45-1997 *100

ORTIZ, Jorge Alberto. 7711 LOUIS PASTEUR, STE 707 78229 #035-03-1990 L2004 GS *020 †85

ORTIZ, Jose Clemente. 1303 MCCULLOUGH AVE, STE 600 78212 #048-12-2002 L2005 IM *020 †20

ORTIZ, Julio Enrique. 1303 MCCULLOUGH AVE, STE 226 78212 #042-01-1973 L1975 PS GS *020 †85,65

ORTIZ, Mauro. 4411 MEDICAL DR, STE 300 78229 #048-02-1995 L2000 CD *020 †20 ‡

ORTIZ UBINAS, Amil. 5414 FREDERICKSBURG RD, STE 100 78229 #042-01-1972 L1980 PD *020 †20

OSBORNE, John Randolph. ■ 78231 #023-12-1983 L2001 DR GS *020 †80

OSBOURN, Raymond V. ■ 78258 #422-01-1984 L2008 OM GP *072 †70

OSCOS-SANCHEZ, Manuel A. 7703 FLOYD CURL DR, FAMILY PRACTICE 78229 #005-11-1993 L2000 FM *020 †18

O'SHEA, John Wm. ■ 78213 #016-43-1956 L1967 A *071 †55,03

OSONMA, Timothy I. 7330 SAN PEDRO, STE 405 78216 #690-04-1988 L1995 IM *020 †20

OSTROM, Karen K. ■ 78258 #048-13-1995 L1996 PD *020 †55

OSTROWER, Valerie Ger. 4499 MEDICAL DR, STE 280 78229 #035-09-1968 L1974 PD *020 †55

OTAZO, Julio C. 900 ISOM RD, STE 210 78216 #048-02-1982 L1984 DR *020 †80

OTERO, Carmelo. ■ 78258 #042-01-1981 L1985 TS GS *020 †85,90

OTERO, Pedro Jaime. ■ 78213 #047-06-1948 L1951 GS *071 †85

OTERO, Richard Luis. 8800 VILLAGE DR, STE 207 78217 #048-12-1978 L1978 IM GE *020 †20

OTTO, Nancy Ruth. 8715 VILLAGE DR, STE 504 78217 #035-01-1977 L1988 ORS HS *020 †40

OTTO, Pamela Marie. 7703 FLOYD CURL DR, UTHSCSA DEPT RADIO 78229 #028-03-1988 L1993 DR *020 †80

OTTO, Randal Allen. 7703 FLOYD CURL DR, DEPT OF OTOLARYNGOLOGY 78229 #028-03-1981 L1989 OTO HNS *040 †45 ‡

OUGHATIYAN, Bijan. 7330 SAN PEDRO, STE 405 78216 #409-38-1994 L2001 IM *020 †20

OVERLEY, Scott H. 45 NE LOOP 410, STE 900 78216 #048-16-1991 L1992 AN *020 †05

OWEN, Meisa Jeanette. ■ 78240 #048-13-2007 PD *012

OWENS, Aaron D. 4502 MEDICAL DR 78229 #048-02-1999 L2002 ID *020 †20

OWENS, Nicole Marie. ■ 78232 #023-12-1992 L1994 D IM *020 †20,15

OWINGS, Kathleen Kemp. 414 NAVARRO ST, STE 1111 78205 #048-04-1996 L1998 IMG *100 †18

OXFORD, Diana Lynn. 4242 MEDICAL DR, STE 3100 78229 #048-04-1988 L1990 AN *020 †05

OYARZABAL, Hector A. 1911 PLEASANTON RD 78221 #649-43-1981 L1991 IM *020 †20 ‡

OZER, Michael Allen. 7922 EWING HALSELL DR, STE 440 78229 #048-02-1971 L1971 PD OS *020

OZIGBO, Obinna Henry. ■ 78258 #690-12-1996 L2007 IM *100 †20

PACE, Paul David. 400 CONCORD PLAZA DR, STE 130 78216 #021-01-1974 L1979 HS GS *020 †85

PACHECO, Cecilia. 7333 BARLITE BLVD, STE 400 78224 #026-04-1985 L1988 FM *020 †18

PACHECO, Monica R. 2140 BABCOCK RD, STE 200 78229 #048-16-2000 L2003 PD *020 †55

PACHIPALA, Krishna Kishor. 7703 FLOYD CURL DR, MC-7884 78229 #495-62-1989 L2007 HO *012 †20 ‡

PACHULSKI, Roman Thomas. 19016 STONE OAK PKWY, PKWY,STE 150 78258 #065-09-1983 L2004 CD *020 †20

PACKER, Louan Windham. ■ 78257 #027-01-1985 L1985 P CHP *062 †75

PACL, Dennis S. 8026 FLOYD CURL DR 78229 #048-02-1988 L1989 PLM IM *020 †55,20 ‡

PADILLA, Belinda. 13909 NACOGDOCHES RD, STE 107 78217 #048-13-1977 L1980 FM *020 †18

PADILLA, David Emeterio. 720 PLEASANTON RD 78214 #003-01-1981 L1984 FM *020 †18

PADILLA, Domingo, Jr. 311 CAMDEN ST STE 409, MADISON SQUARE BLDG 78215 #649-02-1972 L1981 OBG *020 †30

PADRON, Sebastian T. ■ 78240 #035-01-1976 L1978 EM IM *020 †20,16

PADUA, Frederico P. 1630 SW MIL DR MEDI RX CLN 78221 #748-09-1972 L1979 FM IM *020

PAEZ, Ana Maria. 7703 FLOYD CURL DR, SCIENCE C 78229 #042-02-2007 PD *012

PAGE, Gregory Alan. 7254 BLANCO RD, STE 201 78216 #048-13-1986 L1987 IM *020 †20

PAGE, John Mann, Sr. ■ 78260 #051-04-2002 L2006 GE *012 †20

PAINE, James Mark. 7703 FLOYD CURL DR, MSC 7836 78229 #048-04-1971 L1972 OBG *030

PALACIO, Santiago. 7703 FLOYD CURL DR #MC7883, SCIENCE C 78229 #132-02-1994 L2003 N *100

PALACIO BEDOYA, Federico. 7703 FLOYD CURL DR 78229 #264-16-2003 IM *012

PALASOTA, Joseph Anthony. 45 NE LOOP 410, STE 900 78216 #048-13-1982 L1983 AN *020 †05

PALEY, Solomon Isaac. 434 N LOOP 1604 W, STE 1204 78232 #048-13-1993 L1994 FM *020 †18

PALLARES, Frank. 4127 E SOUTHCROSS BLVD, STE 2 78222 #065-01-1973 L1978 CD *020 †20

PALMAZ, Julio Cesar. 7400 MERTON MINTER ST, DEPARTMENT OF RADIOLOGY 11 78229 #132-03-1971 L1984 DR *012

PALMER, Bernard Wayne. ■ 78213 #048-12-1960 L1960 OTO *071 †45

PALMER, Patrick Michael. 540 MADISON OAK DR, STE 500 78258 #048-13-1973 1973 ORS *020 †40

PALMER, Richard Duane. 4600 NW LOOP 410, STE 110 78229 #048-12-1982 L1983 FM *020

PALOMERA, Timothy S. 21 SPURS LN, STE 300 78240 #048-13-1997 L2000 FM *020 †18

PALOMINO, George. 4330 MEDICAL DR, STE 140 78229 #048-13-1997 L2003 CD *020 †20

PALUMBO, Michelle Nicole. ■ 78252 #007-02-2005 L2007 OBG *012

PAMAR, Vijayveer Singh. ■ 78240 #495-18-1993 L2008 END *020 †20

PANDAY, Manoj Madhukar. 7703 FLOYD CURL DR, MAIL CODE 7872 78229 #041-02-1998 L2006 ICE IM *100 †20

PANDYA, Devesh Mahesh. ■ 78249 #048-13-2005 IM *012

PANDYA, Kavitha. 7703 FLOYD CURL DR, DEPT RAD 78229 #045-01-2006 DR *012

PANKOWSKY, Helen Orit. 14855 BLANCO RD 78216 #048-13-1981 L1983 P *020

PANKOWSKY, Jaime. ■ 78229 #649-01-1952 L1960 GS *071 †85

PANTHER, Randy Lee. ■ 78256 #036-05-1998 L2008 IM *020 †20

PANTUSA, Anna Marie. ■ 78212 #048-13-1987 L1988 PM *020

PAPADOPOULOS, Kyriakos P. 4319 MEDICAL DR STE 205 78229 #836-01-1985 L2004 IM *020 †20

PAPERMASTER, David Saml. 7703 FLOYD CURL DR 78229 #024-01-1963 L1987 PTH *050 †50

PAPPERT, Eric John. 4647 MEDICAL DR 78229 #028-46-1989 L1998 N *020 †75

PAQUE, Judith T Newman. 999 E BASSE RD STE 128B 78209 #016-11-1974 L1977 OPH *020 †35

PAQUETTE, R Joseph. 7460 N IH 35 78218 #048-14-1994 L1995 FM *020 †18

PARCHMAN, Michael L. 7703 FLOYD CURL DR, UNIV OF TEXAS HSC 78229 #048-12-1982 L1983 FM *040 †18

PAREKH, Dipen Jaysukhlal. 7979 WURZBACH RD 78229 #496-25-1993 L2006 U *020 †95

PARISIEN, Christine J. ■ 78230 #035-46-1998 L2003 CRS *020

PARIZI, Mahdieh. ■ 78229 #048-13-2008 *012

PARK, Eil Bok. ■ 78258 #583-03-1973 L1989 DR R *020

PARK, In Seok. 7330 SAN PEDRO STE 405 78216 #583-10-1980 L2001 IM *020 †20

PARK, William E. ■ 78258 #047-06-1949 L1949 DR *071 †80

PARKER, Jeffrey Taylor. ■ 78258 #030-06-2002 L2003 FM *020 †18

PARKER, Jeremy David. ■ 78253 #023-12-2007 PD *012

PARKER, Michelle Wingmun. 715 STADIUM DR # 1439, TRINITY UNIVERSITY 78212 #048-04-2007 PD *012

PARKER, Robert Warren. 414 NAVARRO ST 78205 #019-02-1971 L1998 FM FPG *040 †18

PARKER, Warren M, Jr. ■ 78231 #004-01-1962 L1979 GP OM *071

PARODI, Aldo Ambrosio. 19016 STONE OAK PKWY STE 2 78258 #682-01-1988 L1996 PCC *020 †20

PARRA, Augusto. ■ 78256 #264-18-1988 L2000 IM N *020 †75

PARRA, Ernesto Ortiz. 6315 S ZARZAMORA ST 78211 #024-01-1982 L1983 FM *020 †18

PARRA, Juan M. 7703 FLOYD CURL DR, DEPT OF PEDIATRICS 78229 #048-13-1985 L1986 PD *050 †15

PARRA, Norma Gomez. 6315 S ZARZAMORA ST 78211 #048-15-1985 L1991 FM *020 †18

PARRA, Rafael. 1303 MCCULLOUGH AVE, STE 440 78212 #264-04-1965 1975 NS *020 †25

PARRY, William Hart. 78218 #017-20-1967 L1984 PD PUD *071 †55

PARSI, Linda Yolanda. 9150 HUEBNER RD STE 260 78240 #048-04-1994 L1997 PD *020 †55

PARSONS, Michael Frank. ■ 78238 #035-06-2007 TY *012

PARTAIN, Robert Abner. 4410 MEDICAL DR, STE 610 78229 #047-05-1959 L1967 NS *071 †25

PARUPATI, Sreedevi. 7330 SAN PEDRO, STE 405 78216 #495-57-1996 L2003 IM *020 †20

PASCUAL, Jose F. ■ 78255 #042-01-1963 L1967 PN PD *072 †55 ‡

PASKO, Carol Linda. ■ 78240 #308-12-1987 L1994 FM PHP *050

PATEL, Aatish Yogesh. 6674 PRUE RD, STE 7208 78240 #021-05-2008 *012

PATEL, Amish Vinubhai. 7703 FLOYD CURL DR 78229 #495-37-2004 FP *012

PATEL, Ankitkumar H. 7703 FLOYD CURL DR, U TX MED SCH SAN ANTONIO 78229 #048-13-2006 L2007 DR *012

PATEL, Bhavini Hasmukh. ■ 78260 #056-06-2005 L2007 PTH *012

PATEL, Devang N. 4647 MEDICAL DR 78229 #917-08-1990 L2002 CD IC *020 †20

PATEL, Dipan Loken. ■ 78258 #654-01-1997 L2003 DR *020 †80

PATEL, Mahendra C. 7711 LOUIS PASTEUR, STE 502 78229 #965-01-1981 L1996 PHO *020 †55

PATEL, Neela Kumari. 7703 FLOYD CURL DR 78229 #496-22-1996 L2008 FP *012

PATEL, Rajnikant C. 3851 ROGER BROOKE DR, CREDENTIALS OFFICE 78234 #495-23-1973 L1977 AN CCA *020 †05

PATEL, Tarak Hasmukh. ■ 78216 #023-12-1997 L1998 PS *012 †85

PATEL, Tarak J. 525 OAK CENTRE DR, STE 400 78258 #048-15-1997 L1998 PDP SME *020 †20

PATEL, Tejas Purushottamb. 7703 FLOYD CURL DR 78229 #495-23-2005 IM *012

PATINO, Gilberto. ■ 78231 #023-12-2002 L2003 CD *012 †20

PATLOVANY, Matthew Louis. ■ 78257 #048-02-2004 L2006 EM *020

PATNAIK, Amita. 4319 MEDICAL DR, STE 205 78229 #065-01-1992 L2000 ON *020 †20

PATRICK, Madison Wm. ■ 78258 #040-02-1974 L1981 EM PD *020 †20

PATTERSON, Jan Evans. 7704 FLOYD CURL DR 78229 #048-14-1982 L1983 ID IM *030 †20

PATTERSON, Thomas Frost. 7703 FLOYD CURL DR, UNIV OF TX HEALTH SCIENCE 78229 #048-14-1983 L1983 ID IM *050 †20

PATTESON, Pat K. ■ 78240 #048-13-2005 L2008 FP *012

PATTILLO, Matt T. ■ 78254 #048-13-2008 *012

PAUL, David Leo. PO BOX 6683 78209 #048-13-1984 L1987 PDE *020 †55

PAUL, Jeffrey Victor. 5414 FREDERICKSBURG RD, STE 100 78229 #021-06-1987 L1988 NPM *020 †20

PAULI, Isham Walker, Jr. 525 OAK CENTRE DR, STE 350 78258 #048-13-1994 L1997 PD *020 †55 ‡

PAYNE, James Everett, Jr. 6207 RUE SOPHIE 78238 #021-01-1961 L1978 GS *030 †85

PAYNE, Rose Zapora. 9901 IH 10 W, STE 400 78230 #041-01-1981 L1992 PD PN *020 †55

PAZ RODRIGUEZ, Jorge A. 2455 NE LOOP 410 78217 #715-01-1988 L1994 IM *020 †20

PEACHER, Jorge Fernando. 311 CAMDEN ST, STE 309 78215 #048-13-1982 L1983 OBG GYN *020 †30

PEAKE, John Lewis. 14800 SAN PEDRO AVE, STE 110 78232 #039-01-1982 L1985 P *020 †75

PEARCE, Jane V. 7700 FLOYD CURL DR 78229 #040-02-1976 L1983 **FM** *020 †18

PEAROSE, Nahim. 1055 ADA ST, CENTER-SOUTHEAST 78223 #118-01-1983 L1995 **FM** *020 †18

PECHA, Marc Daniel. 2701 BABCOCK RD, STE A 78229 #047-06-1995 L1997 **PM** *020 †60

PECHE, William J. 205 E EVERGREEN ST, STE 3 78212 #649-02-1966 L1969 **OBG** *020

PEDERSON, David Norman. 4411 MEDICAL DR STE 3 78229 #010-02-1984 L1993 **ICE CD** *020 †20

PEDERSON, William C. 8800 VILLAGE DR, STE 106 78217 #048-12-1978 L1978 **PS GS** *020 †85,65

PEDROZA, Gregorio E, III. 13750 SAN PEDRO AVE, STE 140 78232 #035-06-1989 L1997 **IM** *072 †20

PEEL, Garrett Keith. ■ 78223 #010-01-2003 L2007 **GS** *012

PEINE, Steven Dean. ■ 78258 #049-01-1997 L1999 **D** *012 †18

PELAEZ, Raul A. ■ 78257 #132-02-1968 L1986 **R EM** *020 †80

PENA, Fernando Jose. 4402 VANCE JACKSON RD, STE 220 78230 #048-12-1986 L1987 **AN CCA** *020 †05

PENA, Horacio. ■ 78213 #649-14-1969 L1975 **GP** *071

PENA, Joel, Jr. 1303 MCCULLOUGH AVE, STE 600 78212 #048-13-1995 L1996 **IM** *020 †20

PENDON, Joseph David. 333 N SANTA ROSA 78207 #010-02-1994 L2005 **EM** *020 †16

PENKAVA, Jeri Lei. 15600 SAN PEDRO, STE 101 78232 #021-05-1977 L1983 **PD** *020 †55

PENNY, Gary L. 7711 LOUIS PASTEUR, STE 812 78229 #048-13-1992 L1993 **P** *020

PEOPLES, George E, Jr. ■ 78209 #023-07-1988 L1996 **GS SO** *020 †85

PEPPAS, Dennis Sotirios. 2833 BABCOCK RD, STE 200 78229 #023-12-1983 L2005 **UP U** *040 †95

PERCHES, Carlos. 7622 LOUIS PASTEUR DR, STE 100 78229 #048-13-1988 L1989 **FM** *020 †18

PERCHES, David. 45 NE LOOP 410 78216 #048-13-1994 L1997 **AN** *020 †05

PERCHES, Laura. 3780 NW LOOP 410, STOP SA 78229 #649-33-1988 L1998 **P** *020 †75

PERCHES, Mario J. 4242 MEDICAL DR, STE 3100 78229 #649-02-1961 L1966 **AN** *075

PEREZ, Aixa. ■ 78247 #042-02-2007 **IM** *012

PEREZ, Ana Y. 311 CAMDEN ST, STE 602 78215 #016-42-1979 L1980 **IM** *020 †20

PEREZ, Carmen. 810 SE MILITARY DR, HEALTHTEXAS MEDICAL GROUP 78214 #048-14-1990 L1991 **IM** *020 †20

PEREZ, Donald H. ■ 78291 #737-01-1957 L1974 **END IM** *075

PEREZ, Enrique Rafael. ■ 78240 #048-13-1993 L1997 **IM** *020

PEREZ, Gabriel Moses. 9793 CULEBRA RD, STE 105 78251 #048-02-2003 L2007 **MPD** *100

PEREZ, Jose L. 730 N MAIN AVE STE 424, MAS TOWER 78205 #042-02-1984 L1988 **OPH AM** *020 †35

PEREZ, Laura Miramontes. 4243 E SOUTHCROSS BLVD, STE 205 78222 #048-02-1999 L2002 **FM** *020 †18

PEREZ, Mary Helen. 8627 CINNAMON CREEK DR, BLDG 1 78240 #048-02-1981 L1981 **PD** *020 †55

PEREZ, Rene. 3903 WISEMAN BLVD STE 3, ALAMO WOMEN'S HEALTH 78251 #048-13-2003 L2007 **OBG** *020

PEREZ-NIEVES, Roberto. 7703 FLOYD CURL DR, PLASTIC SURGERY 227L 78229 #042-02-1992 L1995 **PS** *020 †65

PEREZROMAN-LEON, Lourdes. 2121 SW 36TH ST, UNIVERSITY HEALTH SYSTEM 78237 #048-13-1994 L1996 **FM** *020 †18

PERGOLA, Pablo Ezequiel. 215 E QUINCY ST STE 610 78215 #132-07-1988 L1998 **NEP IM** *020 †20

PERKINS, Henry Stratton. 7703 FLOYD CURL DR, UNIV OF TEXAS HLTH SCIENCE 78229 #025-01-1975 L1984 **IM** *020 †20

PERKINS, Herbert Albert. 7400 MERTON MINTER ST, AUDIE L MURPHY MEM VA HOSP 78229 #048-13-1979 **P CHP** *020 †75 ‡

PERKINS, Matilda. 9895 IH 10 W 78230 #048-13-1977 L1981 **GS** *020 †85

PERKINS, Sebrina D. 7700 FLOYD CURL DR, PEDIATRIC EMERGENCY DEPT 78229 #048-12-1996 L1999 **PEM** *020 †55

PERKINS, Wiley Damon. 7703 FLOYD CURL DR, DEPT OF MEDICINE MC 7871 78229 #048-12-1995 L1996 **IM** *020 †20

PERRETTA, Peter T. 45 NE LOOP 410, STE 900 78216 #048-13-1979 L1979 **AN** *020

PERRITANO, Diane M. 1715 MCCULLOUGH AVE 78212 #048-13-1997 L1998 **FM** *020 †18

PERRY, Adam Thomas. 150 E SONTERRA BLVD, STE 300 78258 #021-06-2002 L2007 **OSM** *012

PERRY, Brian Philip. 21 SPURS LN, STE 100 78240 #030-05-1992 L1999 **OTO NO** *020 †45

PERRY, Van Emmet. 2455 NE LOOP 410 78217 #017-20-1981 L1999 **D PD** *020 †55,15

PERSELLIN, Robert Harold. 1310 MCCULLOUGH AVE 78212 #016-06-1956 L1968 **RHU IM** *020 †20

PERSON, David Wesley. 8800 VILLAGE DR, STE 106 78217 #048-12-1994 L1996 **HS** *020 †85

PERUSEK, Marie Cecelia. 4502 MEDICAL DR 78229 #048-02-1981 L1981 **DR** *020 †80

PESTANA, Carlos. 7703 FLOYD CURL DR, UNIV OF TEXAS MED SCHOOL 78229 #649-01-1959 L1968 **GS** *071 †85

PETERS, Jay Irwin. 4647 MEDICAL DR 78229 #048-04-1977 L1977 **PUD IM** *040 †20

PETERS, Margaret Ann B. 8026 FLOYD CURL DR, SOUTH TEXAS PATHOLOGY 78229 #048-13-1975 L1975 **PTH** *020 †50

PETERS, Patrick Henry, Jr. 6557 BANDERA RD, STE C 78238 #048-13-1975 L1977 **IM** *020 †20

PETERS, Rebecca Christine. 5101 MEDICAL DR 78229 #048-13-1992 L1993 **IM** *020

PETERSHACK, Jean O'Brien. 7703 FLOYD CURL DR, DEPT OF PEDIATRICS SC 7812 78229 #048-13-1991 L1993 **NPM** *020 †55

PETERSON, Richard Matthew. 78251 #654-01-2001 L2003 **GS** *100 †85

PETERSON, Robt Kenneth D. 540 MADISON OAK RD, STE 160 78258 #048-02-1969 L1969 **DR GP** *020 †80

PETR, Frank C. 2391 NE LOOP 410 STE 101 78217 #048-13-1986 L1987 **D** *020 †15

PETROFF, Peter Alex, Jr. 2833 BABCOCK RD STE 435 78229 #016-11-1968 L1975 **PUD IM** *020 †20

PETTIGREW, Howard David. ■ 78240 #050-02-2004 L2008 **IM** *100

PFEIFER, Carl Michael. ■ 78229 #025-01-1961 L1969 **CHP P** *062 †75

PFLUKE, Jason Michael. ■ 78230 #048-15-2004 L2006 **GS** *012

PHAM, Hai Van. 8014 FERNDALE OAKS 78249 #007-02-1987 L1996 **IM** *020 †20

PHILBERT, Richard Nelson. ■ 78257 #017-20-1956 L1961 **AN** *071 †05

PHILLIPS, John Norman. 2455 NE LOOP 410 78217 #048-13-1977 L1978 **FM** *020 †20

PHILLIPS, Michele Ann. 2140 BABCOCK RD STE 200, UFHC NORTHWEST 78229 #038-06-2000 L2007 **FM** *020 †18

PHILLIPS, Paula J. 525 OAK CENTRE DR, STE 320 78258 #048-15-1993 L1994 **END** *020 †20

PHILLIPS, Serena Louise. 102 BABCOCK RD STE 102, CLINICA DEL NORTE PEDIATRI 78201 #048-13-1978 L1978 **PD** *020 †55

PHILLIPS, Thaddeus H. 7703 FLOYD CURL DR, U TX MED SCH SAN ANTONIO 78229 #048-13-2002 *100

PHILLIPS, William Thos. 7703 FLOYD CURL DR, UNIV OF TX HEALTH SCIENCE 78229 #048-02-1980 L1980 **NM** *050 †18,28

PHO, Hoan Q. 7210 LOUIS PASTEUR DR, PASTEUR MEDICAL 78229 #048-13-1993 L1995 **IM** *020 †20

PICHOT, John Thos. 7400 MERTON MINTER ST, AUDIE MURPHY VAMC (116A) 78229 #048-12-1985 L1986 **P** *020 †75

PICK, Terry Eugene. 8407 BANDERA RD, STE 137 78250 #051-04-1973 L1981 **PHO PD** *020 †55

PICKENS, Jeffrey Scott. 24165 W IH 10 78257 #048-02-1981 L1981 **FM** *020 †18

PIDCOKE, Heather Faith. ■ 78212 #005-06-2002 **GS** *012

PIERCE, Alexander W, Jr. 333 N SANTA ROSA AVE 78207 #047-05-1956 L1969 **PD** *071 †55

PIERCE, Jessica L. 7434 LOUIS PASTEUR, STE 109 78229 #048-13-2001 L2005 **NEP** *100

PIERCE, Jos Alphonso, Jr. 1700 FLOYD CURL DR 78229 #047-07-1961 L1970 **AN** *020

PIERCE, Kristine Kathryn. ■ 78259 #023-12-2005 L2006 **OPH** *012

PIERCE, Robert Langford. 343 W HOUSTON ST, STE 704 78205 #048-13-1985 L1997 **PDC PD** *020 †55

PIERCE, Samuel J. 414 NAVARRO ST, STE 400 78205 #048-02-1989 L1991 **OPH** *020 †35

PIERONI, Kevin Paul. ■ 78251 #023-12-2006 L2008 **PD** *012

PIESMAN, Michael. ■ 78248 #024-07-1998 L2008 **GE** *020 †20

PIETZ, Clinton A. 7703 FLOYD CURL DR, PEDIATRIC CRITICAL CARE 78229 #048-13-1992 L1997 **CCP** *020 †55

PILCHER, John Alsop, Jr. 9150 HUEBNER RD, STE 250 78240 #051-01-1990 L1998 **GS** *020 †85

PINERO, Ricardo Felipe. 8600 WURZBACH RD, STE 1000 78240 #132-02-1972 L1980 **PUD PD** *020 †55

PINKLEY, William Harve. 5230 DEZAVALA RD, STE 212 78249 #048-13-1985 L1986 **GP** *020

PINKSTON, Marianne J. 4499 MEDICAL DR, PO 49425 # 170 78229 #048-13-1997 L2000 **FM** *020 †18

PIPER, Jeanna Marie. 7703 FLOYD CURL DR, DEPT OF OB/GYN 78229 #021-01-1986 L1990 **OBG MFM** *040 †30

PIPES, William Farrar. ■ 78209 #048-02-1957 L1957 **FM** *071

PISANO, Steven Michael. 9635 HUEBNER RD 78240 #048-12-1985 L1986 **PS** *020 †85,65

PITOTTI, Christopher Jose. ■ 78250 #051-01-2008 *012

PITTARD, Darren Scott. ■ 78254 #012-01-2005 L2007 **OBG** *012

PITTARD, Joe Tom. 8207 CALLAGHAN RD, STE 425 78230 #048-02-1971 L1971 **P** *020 †75

PITTS, Suzanne. 4242 MEDICAL DR, STE 3100 78229 #048-16-1983 L1983 **AN IM** *020 †05

PIWINSKI, Stephen Edward. 7703 FLOYD CURL DR, DEPT OF MEDICINE 78229 #016-42-1978 L1986 **IM AM** *040 †70,20

PIXLEY, Charles Calvin. ■ 78209 #040-02-1947 L1968 **OS GPM** *071 †85

PLASTINO, Kristen Alison. 3002 NORTHRIDGE DR 78209 #011-04-1999 L2003 **OBG** *020 †30

PLAYER, David Mark. 7434 LOUIS PASTEUR DR, STE 120 78229 #016-11-1970 L1976 **NEP IM** *020 †20

PLISZKA, Steven Ray. 7703 FLOYD CURL DR, U T H S C S A MC 7792 78229 #048-13-1981 L1981 **CHP P** *020 †75

PODBERESKY, Daniel Jay. ■ 78256 #023-01-1998 L2004 **PDR** *020 †80

POE, Richard Orla. 3857 ROGER BROOKE DR, BROOKE ARMY MEDICAL CENTER 78234 #024-01-1961 L1978 **P** *020 †75

POGOSIAN, Elena Grigorevn. ■ 78240 #913-38-1977 **FP** *012

POLHAMUS, Clinton Dustin. 1804 NE LOOP 410, STE 101 78217 #048-02-1977 L1977 **IM** *020 †20

POLK, Henry Lysell. 7703 FLOYD CURL DR 78229 #048-15-2000 L2007 **P** *020 †75

POLLARD, Trevor Gordon. 4242 MEDICAL DR, STE 3100 78229 #048-02-1980 L1980 **AN PD** *020 †05

POLNASZEK, Nathaniel Mich. 7703 FLOYD CURL DR, DEPT OF SURGERY 78229 #056-06-2006 **GS** *012

PONCE DE SOUZA, Yolanda A. ■ 78249 #048-13-2006 **PD** *012

PONSDOMENECH, Saul Eladio. 519 W HOUSTON ST 78207 #275-01-1946 L1969 **P** *071

PONTIUS, Uwe Rainer. 7940 FLOYD CURL DR, STE 560 78229 #021-01-1976 L1977 **ORS OAR** *020 †40

POOVATHOOR, Manju Thomas. 7330 SAN PEDRO, STE 405 78216 #495-31-1998 L2004 **IM** *020 †20 ‡

POPP, David Wayne. 24165 W I H 10, STE 114 78257 #048-04-1984 L1985 **PD PEM** *020 †55

PORET, Leticia Ann. 4522 FREDERICKSBURG RD, STE A14 78201 #021-06-1988 L1991 **IM** *020 †20

PORISCH, Mary Grimm. 3851 ROGER BROOKE DR, BROOKE AMC, BLDG 3600 78234 #023-12-1992 L2000 **PDC** *020 †55

PORR, Darrel Robt. ■ 78212 #038-41-1979 L1981 **FM EM** *030 †18

PORRATA, Edward Albert. 7700 FLOYD CURL DR, METH CHILDS HOSP ER 78229 #048-02-1981 L1982 **PD** *020 †55

PORTER, Carlos Rios. 5804 BABCOCK RD 78240 #048-13-1993 L1994 **FM** *020 †18

PORTER, Clarence Milton. 14100 NACOGDOCHES RD, HEALTH 78247 #048-02-1977 L1979 **FM** *020

PORTILLO, Angelica. ■ 78229 #048-13-2007 **P** *012

PORTNOY, Barry Allan. ■ 78230 #012-05-1966 L1972 **HEM IM** *071 †20

POSS, Geri E. 5430 FREDERICKSBURG RD, STE 400 78229 #048-02-1982 L1983 **FM** *020 †18

POSTOAK, Darren Wayne. 4502 MEDICAL DR 78229 #025-01-1991 L2001 **VIR** *071 †80

POTEET, Robyn Elaine. 7703 FLOYD CURL DR, UTHSCSA 78229 #016-42-1999 L2002 **IM** *020 †20

POTH, Theresa A. ■ 78229 #048-78-2006, ▲ **IM** *012

POTTER, Allen Roger. 7700 FLOYD CURL DR, METHODIST CHILDREN'S HOSP 78229 #003-01-1974 L1989 **PEM** *020 †55

POTTER, Danny Jay. 6338 N NEW BRAUNFELS AVE 78209 #048-12-1970 L1970 **IM** *020 †20

POTTER, Janet Landis. 7703 FLOYD CURL DR, DEPT. OF PEDIATRICS 78229 #048-13-1976 L1976 **DR** *020 †80

POTTERF, Raymond Dewayne. 7410 JOHN SMITH, STE 208 78229 #048-13-1977 L1977 **P** *020 †20

POTYKA, James Smullin. 16414 SAN PEDRO AVE, STE 355 78232 #023-01-1969 L1973 **EM MDM** *030 †16

POURSANI, Ramin Shokati. 527 N LEONA ST, U OF TX HSC SAN ANTONIO 78207 #902-07-1991 L2006 **FM** *020 †18

POWELL, William Cameron. 8715 VILLAGE DR 78217 #048-02-1999 L2002 **OBG** *020 †30

POWERS, George Charles. 5414 FREDERICKSBURG RD, STE 100 78229 #028-02-1989 L1998 **NPM** *020 †55

POWERS, Jessica Faith. ■ 78251 #051-04-2003 L2004 **HO** *012 †20

PRADO, Stephanie M. 7300 BLANCO RD STE 40 78216 #048-04-1989 L1999 **PM** *020 †60

PRANGE, Mark Alan. 7418 MILITARY DR W, TEJAS RECOVERY AND COUNSEL 78227 #048-13-1986 L1987 **IMG PLM** *020 †20

PRASAD, K S A. 4411 MEDICAL DR, STE 300 78229 #495-72-1988 L2002 **CD** *020 †20

PRASAD, Srinivasa Rajanna. 7703 FLOYD CURL, DEPT OF RAD 78229 #496-39-1995 L2007 **AR** *020

PRATER, William Warren. 7342 LAZY TRL 78250 #048-02-1979 L1979 **ADM** *020

PRATT, Taylor Clifton. 7703 FLOYD CURL DR, UNIV OF TX MED SCH AT SAN 78229 #048-13-2005 L2007 *100

PRAUNER, Ronald David. ■ 78209 #030-05-1989 L1991 **PD PHO** *020 †55

PREISSIG, Randall Stephen. 540 MADISON OAK DR, STE 160 78258 #047-06-1971 L1976 **DR OS** *020 †80,28

PRENTICE, Fred David. 78257 #048-14-1975 L1975 **EM** *020 †16

PRESCOTT, Catherine E. 2829 BABCOCK RD, STE 425 SANTA ROS NW TWR 1 78229 #048-15-1995 L1996 **N** *020

PRESSON, Jessica Hamilton. ■ 78251 #048-13-2005 **IM** *012

PRESTIDGE, Bradley R. 7979 WURZBACH RD, URSCHEL TOWERS #233 78229 #023-12-1985 L1990 **RO** *020 †80

PREZAS, Richard. 4600 NW LOOP 410, STE 110 78229 #048-14-1999 L2001 **FM** *020 †18

PRICE, Terrill Eyre, Jr. #78217 #039-01-1961 L1977 **GP OM** *071

PRIDE, Denise L. 7400 MERTON MINTER ST, DEPARTMENT OF PSYCHIATRY 78229 #048-13-1997 L2001 **OS** *020

PRIDGEN, James Edward. 7922 EWING HALSELL DR, STE 105 78229 #021-01-1943 L1947 **GS** *062 †85

PRIETO, Elias Mateo. 730 N MAIN AVE STE 219 78205 #048-02-1958 L1958 **GYN** *020 †30

PRIETO, Luis G. 730 NORTH MAIN, STE 219 78205 #048-13-1990 L1991 **OBG** *020

PRIMOMO, Marion. ■ 78213 #016-43-1947 L1949 **PLM OS** *071

PRIOR, Chad Allen. ■ 78240 #028-34-2004 **GS** *020

PRISACARU, Genoveva Nicol. 7703 FLOYD CURL DR 78229 #781-02-1992 L2006 **OBG** *100

PROPPER, Brandon William. ■ 78231 #023-12-2005 L2007 **GS** *012

PRUETT, Chester Eugene. 4242 MEDICAL DR, 4499 MEDICAL DR STE 393 78229 #021-05-1975 L1982 **AN** *020 †05

PRUITT, Alejandro. 8214 WURZBACH RD 78229 #023-12-1993 L2001 **GE** *020 †20

PRUITT, Basil A, Jr. 7703 FLOYD CURL DR, DEPT OF SURGERY 78229 #024-07-1957 L1977 **GS CCS** *040 †85

PUCKETT, Janet Diane. 4242 MEDICAL DR, STE 3100 78229 #048-02-1975 L1975 **AN** *020 †05

PUGH, Jacqueline Ann. 7400 MERTON MINTER ST 78229 #048-13-1981 L1981 **IM** *050 †20

PULICICCHIO, Louis Umile. 6418 AMBER OAK, TRI CITY MEDICAL HOSPITALI 78249 #045-01-1986 L1995 **FM** *020 †18

PULLEN, Renee Webbink. 4406 SHAVANO WOODS, PULLEN INSURANCE SERVICES 78249 #010-02-1996 L1998 **IM** *020 †20

PULLIN, Clayton Louis. 7913 BANDERA RD 78250 #048-13-1994 L1995 **FSM** *020 †18

PURNELL, Lewis M. 5282 MEDICAL DR, SOUTHWEST CHILDRENS 78229 #048-12-1982 L1983 **PD** *020 †55

PURSWANI, Shyam S. 2455 NE LOOP 410, STE 101 78217 #654-01-1990 L1996 **AN PMM** *020 †05

QUASHNOCK, Joseph M. ■ 78230 #041-12-1937 L1970 **AM** *071 †70

QUESADA, Paul Z. 740 S ALAMO, SOUTH ALAMO MEDICAL GROUP 78205 #048-13-1998 L2001 **PD** *020

QUIJANO CANTU, Victor Ruy. 7703 FLOYD CURL DR 78229 #649-02-1998 **PD** *100

QUINONES, Armando Edgardo. 408 NAVARRO ST 78205 #042-02-1987 L2002 **GP** *020

QUINONES, Manuel M, Jr. 6428 BANDERA RD 78238 #048-04-1982 L1983 **FM** *020 †18

QUIROGA, Pedro. ■ 78229 #649-02-1954 L1966 **ORS** *071 †40

QUIROZ, Rebecca A. 155 E SONTERRA BLVD # 111, QUIROZ ADULT MED CLINIC 78258 #048-13-1989 L1991 **IM** *020 †20

QUNIBI, Wajeh Yam. 4502 MEDICAL DR, UNIVERSITY HOSP 78229 #915-03-1971 L1978 **IM** *050 †20

RABKE, Henry Brandon. ■ 78213 #048-02-1954 L1954 **AN** *071 †05

RABKE, Stephen F. 4242 MEDICAL DR, STE 3100 78229 #048-02-1984 L1987 **AN** *020 †05

RADFORD, Alison Lindsay. 7703 FLOYD CURL DR, SCIENCE C 78229 #048-13-2007 **ORS** *012

RADWIN, Howard Martin. 8038 WURZBACH RD, STE 430 78229 #035-01-1956 L1968 **U** *071 †95

RAEZ, Eduardo Rodolfo. 8715 VILLAGE DR STE 418 78217 #048-13-1984 L1986 **OBG AN** *040 †30

RAHAL, Andres. 7703 FLOYD CURL DR 78229 #264-16-1995 L2007 **DR** *100 †80

RAHM, Ashley L. ■ 78216 #048-16-1991 L1992 **PD** *020 †55

RAIMONDO, Brian Richard. 1111 SE MILITARY DR 78214 #048-13-1999 L2001 **FM** *020 †18

RAINER, Courtney S. 7703 FLOYD CURL DR, U TX MED SCH SAN ANTONIO 78229 #048-13-2007 **IM** *012

RAINOSEK, Delbert Earl. 301 N FRIO ST 78207 #048-13-1983 L1983 **PTH** *020 †50

RAIRDON, Thomas Lee, II. 45 NE LOOP 410, STE 900 78216 #048-14-2003 L2004 **AN** *020

RAJAJOSHIWALA, Paresh K. 7500 BARLITE BLVD, STE 311 78224 #016-06-1994 L2004 **GS** *020 †85

RAMAKRISHNARAO, Kamala. 45 NE LOOP 410 STE 900 78216 #495-53-1972 L1980 **AN** *020 †55

RAMAKRISHNARAO, V R. 234 SAN PEDRO AVE 78205 #495-53-1970 L1980 **OBG GS** *020 †30

RAMAMURTHY, Rajam S. 7703 FLOYD CURL DR, UNIV TX HLTH SCI CTR PEDS 78229 #495-33-1964 L1977 **PD NPM** *040 †55

RAMAMURTHY, Somayaji. 7703 FLOYD CURL DR 78229 #495-37-1964 L1977 **PME PMM** *040 †05

RAMANATH, Bellur Subbanna. 8303 W MILITARY DR 78227 #495-37-1975 L1980 **PD** *020 †55

RAMIREZ, Adriana Michelle. 7703 FLOYD CURL DR 78229 #005-14-2006 **OPH** *012

RAMIREZ, Belinda. 548 E EUCLID AVE 78212 #048-14-1985 L1987 **GE IM** *020 †20

RAMIREZ, Carlos Augusto. ■ 78249 #264-07-1967 L1980 **OBG** *020 †30

RAMIREZ, Daniel Alberto. 8285 FREDERICKSBURG RD 78229 #042-01-1973 L1981 **AI IM** *020 †20,03

RAMIREZ, Dina C. ■ 78229 #048-13-2006 **IM** *012

RAMIREZ, Gracia G. 16414 SAN PEDRO, STE 710 78232 #048-13-1990 L1994 **EM** *020 †16

RAMIREZ, Horacio Rafael. 9179 GRISSOM RD STE 101 78251 #005-18-1976 L1978 **FM** *020 †18 ‡

RAMIREZ, J Arnaldo. 134 CAMINO DE ORO 78224 #056-06-1980 L1981 **NEP IM** *020 †20

RAMIREZ, Jairo. 927 MCCULLOUGH 78215 #264-01-1965 L1979 **IC IM** *020

RAMIREZ, Kacy A. 7703 FLOYD CURL DR, MED SCH SAN ANTONIO 78229 #048-13-2007 **PD** *012 †20

RAMIREZ, Mercedes Ellis. 7703 FLOYD CURL DR, MAIL STOP CODE 7789 78229 #649-33-1987 **P CHP** *050

RAMIREZ, Miguel Angel. 527 N LEONA ST 78207 #042-01-1981 L1989 **FM OM** *020 †70,18

RAMIREZ, Oscar Eduardo. 6 CENTURY GLN, ANESTHESIA SCHEDULING, INC 78257 #132-01-1967 L1974 **IM** *020 †05

RAMIREZ, Peter B. ■ 78251 #048-13-2004 L2007 **NEP** *012 †20

RAMIREZ, Peter E. 301 N FRIO ST 78207 #048-13-1990 L1991 **PTH PCP** *020 †50

RAMIREZ, Ramiro. 8026 FLOYD CURL DR 78229 #048-02-1978 L1978 **GS** *020

RAMIREZ, Ricardo. 45 NE LOOP 410, STE 900 78216 #048-04-1984 L1985 **AN** *020 †05

RAMIREZ, Robert Michael. 4502 MEDICAL DR, UNIVERSITY HEALTH SYSTEM 78229 #042-01-2003 L2005 **AI** *012 †20

RAMIREZ, Stephen F. 109 GALLERY CIR, STE 131 78258 #048-14-1995 L1997 **FM OS** *020 †18

RAMIREZ, Sylvester Garcia. 3851 ROGER BROOKE DR, BROOKE ARMY MED CTR, BLDG 78234 #048-12-1981 L1982 **OTO HNS** *020 †45

RAMON, Sergio. 6315 S ZARZAMORA ST 78211 #048-13-1995 L1996 **PD** *020 †55

RAMOS, David Anthony. ■ 78249 #305-01-2007 **FP** *012

RAMOS, Gerardo J. 1831 S GENERAL MCMULLEN 78226 #048-14-2001 L2003 **FM** *020 †18

RAMOS, Lino Pascual. 7330 SAN PEDRO AVE 78216 #038-06-1990 L2006 **IM** *020 †20

RAMOS, Luis R. 111 DALLAS ST 78205 #042-03-1983 L1988 **AN IM** *020 †05

RAMOS, Raul. 7950 FLOYD CURL, STE 508 78229 #649-02-1966 L1973 **CRS** *020 †10,85

RAMOS, Steven Ray. 8800 VILLAGE DR, STE 207 78217 #048-04-1980 L1980 **GE IM** *020 †20

RAMOS-GONZALES, Evangeline. 540 MADISON OAK DR, STE 450 78258 #048-12-1994 L1995 **OBG** *020 †30

RAMOS-SEIJO, Edwin David. ■ 78239 #042-01-1958 L1965 **AM GPM** *071

RAMSEY, Bryan Christopher. ■ 78250 #023-12-2008 *012

RANA, Chaula J. 2701 BABCOCK RD STE A 78229 #048-04-1985 L1987 **PM** *020 †60

RANA, Jayant Bhulabhai. ■ 78261 #495-23-1957 L1971 **EM OS** *071

RANA-MANOCHA, Jahnavi. 2701 BABCOCK RD, STE A 78229 #016-42-1999 L2002 **PM** *020 †60

RANS, Tonya Sue. ■ 78248 #017-20-1998 L1999 **AI** *012 †55

RANSOM, Richard Wible. ■ 78251 #047-06-1964 L1965 **PTH** *020 †50

RANSONE, James W. ■ 78239 #051-01-1952 L1952 **IM** *071 †20

RAO, Jayashree Nagaraja. 116 GALLERY CIR STE 101, LONE STAR CANCER & BLOOD D 78258 #495-16-1991 L2005 **HO** *100 †20

RAO, Madhavarao Harinadha. 5788 ECKHERT RD 78240 #495-11-1966 L1980 **FM** *020 †18

RAO, Madhurima. ■ 78258 #048-13-1993 L1994 **FM** *020 †18

RAO, Raj. ■ 78245 #306-01-1996 L2004 **IM** *100

RAO, Shyamala. 19707 LA SIERRA BLVD 78256 #495-04-1972 L1976 **P** *020 †75

RAPIER, Geo Mc Carroll, III. 8637 FREDERICKSBURG RD, STE 105 78240 #011-03-1977 L1979 **IM** *071 †20

RASCH, Deborah Kay. 7703 FLOYD CURL DR 78229 #048-02-1978 L1978 **AN PD** *020 †55,05

RASCH, John Wm. 6711 S NEW BRAUNFELS AVE 78223 #048-02-1978 L1979 **FM EM** *020 †18

RASHID, Edward Raymond. 5430 FREDERICKSBURG RD, STE 100 78229 #016-06-1976 L1977 **OPH AM** *020 †35

RASHID, Khusro. ■ 78278 #704-02-1986 L1997 **IM** *020 †20

RASTOGI, Harsh. 7703 FLOYD CURL DR, DEPT RAD 78229 #495-05-1987 **RNR** *100

RASTRELLI, Lawrence E. 4242 MEDICAL DR, STE 3100 78229 #048-12-1979 L1979 **AN** *020 †05

RASTRELLI, Leonard Marlin. 4242 MEDICAL DR, STE 3100 78229 #048-02-1974 L1974 **AN** *071 †05

RATNER, Adam V. 4400 S PIEDRAS DR STE 200A 78228 #048-12-1985 L1986 **DR** *020 †80

RATNER, Evan Seth. 8026 FLOYD CURL 78229 #021-01-1988 L1989 **EM** *020

RATNER, Paul Howard. 7711 LOUIS PASTEUR DR, STE 406 78229 #035-03-1975 L1980 **PDA PD** *020 †55

RAUCH, Robert Raymond. 78251 #035-46-1984 L1985 **P** *020

RAVDIN, Peter Marcus. 7979 WURZBACH RD 78229 #011-02-1981 L1988 **ON** *020 †20

RAVIN, Courtney — see RAINER, Courtney

READING, Jared Tate. ■ 78231 #003-01-2005 L2007 **ON** *012

REALINI, Janet Pamela. 332 W COMMERCE ST, STE 303 78205 #005-02-1975 L1977 **FM** *030 †18

REARDON, Ronald J. 540 MADISON OAK DR, STE 440 78258 #048-13-1983 L1983 **FM** *020 †18

REASNER, Charles A, II. 701 S ZARZAMORA ST 78207 #005-12-1979 L1988 **END** *020 †20

REBECCA, Rachel A. ■ 78229 #048-13-2008 *012

REBOLLEDO, Jose R. 343 W HOUSTON ST 78205 #264-07-1961 L1967 **PDC** *020 †55

RECTOR-FINNEY, Nancy Ann. 7711 LOUIS PASTEUR DR, STE 105 78229 #048-14-1996 L1998 **OBG** *020 †20

REDDICK, Robert Lee. 7703 FLOYD CURL DR, PATHOLOGY MSC7750 78229 #036-01-1973 L1999 **PTH** *020 †50

REDDIX, Mason Chas. ■ 78229 #047-07-1954 L1968 **GS** *071 †85

REDDY, Bal Tummeti. 111 DALLAS ST 78205 #495-21-1975 L1984 **CD IM** *020 †20

REDDY, Lokendra. ■ 78255 #495-57-1968 **P** *071

REDDY, Suraj Gopal. 7703 FLOYD CURL DR, MAIL CODE 7876 78229 #034-01-2004 L2004 **D** *012

REDDY, V Sreenath. 7703 FLOYD CURL DR, STE 7841 78229 #001-02-1995 L2006 **TS** *020 †85,90

REDMOND, Franklin Chas. 7703 FLOYD CURL DR, MAIL CODE 7792 78229 #048-12-1968 L1968 **P** *020 †75 ‡

REDMOND, James R. 8245 FREDERICKSBURG RD 78229 #048-13-1996 L1997 **P** *020 †75

REED, Beverly Grayce. ■ 78254 #048-16-2006 L2008 **OBG** *012

REED, Brian Hadley. 78209 #048-12-1981 L1981 **AM PD** *020 †55

REED, Edward Maxwell. 2455 NE LOOP 410 78217 #048-04-1983 L1983 **FM** *020 †18

REED, Jordan Kory. ■ 78255 #034-01-1978 L1986 **GS** *071 †85

REESE, Erin A. ■ 78240 #048-13-2008 *012

REESE, Susan Lynn. ■ 78254 #040-02-2004 L2004 **FM** *020 †18

REESE, Valerie Fair. 6200 NORTHWEST PKWY, MS TX70-100 78249 #004-01-1990 L2003 **FM** *020 †18

REEVES, Aaron A. 7703 FLOYD CURL DR, DEPT OF PEDIATRICS 78229 #048-13-2005 L2007 **PD** *012

REHMAN, Aamer. 7703 FLOYD CURL DR, DEPT MED 78229 #704-09-1999 **IM** *012

REICHEL, George Weyland. 333 N SANTA ROSA AVE, PATHOLOGY ASSOCIATES OF 78207 #048-13-1974 L1975 **PTH** *020 †50

REID, James F, Jr. 45 NE LOOP 410, STE 900 78216 #048-15-1993 L1994 **AN** *020 †05

REID, William Howard. 4502 MEDICAL DR 78229 #026-04-1970 L1986 **P PFP** *062 †75

REILLEY, Arthur Edward. ■ 78232 #154-02-1964 L1974 **IM PTH** *071

REINECK, Henry John. 8042 WURZBACH RD, STE 405 78229 #038-40-1970 L1976 **NEP IM** *020 †20

REINKER, Kent Alan. 4647 MEDICAL DR 78229 #038-06-1970 L2003 **OP** *020 †40

REIS, Abilio Antunes. ■ 78229 #042-02-2004 **ORS** *012

REISS, Dana Lynne. 9150 HUEBNER RD, STE 250 78240 #012-01-1994 L2000 **GS** *020 †85

REMSING, Tiffany K. ■ 78229 #048-14-2008 *012

RENNIE, Thomas Andrew, Jr. 4319 MEDICAL DR, STE 210A 78229 #023-12-1994 L2005 **RHU** *020 †20

RENSHAW, John Scott. ■ 78251 #048-02-2002 L2004 **HO** *012 †20

RENTHAL, Ann R. 400 N LOOP 1604 E STE 270 78232 #048-13-1980 L1980 **P** *020 †75

RENZ, Evan Michael. ■ 78234 #046-01-1997 L1999 **GS** *100 †85
RESES, Joseph David. ■ 78240 #051-04-2006 **AN** *012
RESSMANN, Ronald Jay. 8601 VILLAGE DR STE 104 78217 #048-02-1971 L1971 **D DS** *020 †15
RESTREPO, Marcos Ignacio. ■ 78258 #264-16-1991 L2004 **PCC** *020 †20
RESTREPO, Santiago. 255 E SONTERRA BLVD # 211 78258 #264-16-1996 L2005 **N** *020 †75
RETTIG, Shaylon Dwayne. 3111 SAN PEDRO AVE 78212 #048-14-2000 L2004 **PSM** *020 †55
RETZLOFF, Jennifer S. ■ 78230 #048-13-1995 L1997 **IM** *020 †20
REUTER, Stewart Ralston. ■ 78230 #038-06-1959 L1980 **R** *040
REVERON, Edmundo. 12730 IH 10 W, STE 306 78230 #042-01-1974 L1978 **AM GP** *020
REYES, Adriana Olivares. 7909 FREDERICKSBURG RD, STE 150 78229 #649-30-1990 L1998 **PTH** *020 †50
REYES, Cesar Augusto. 7616 CULEBRA RD, STE 124 78251 #048-12-2001 L2005 **OBG** *020
REYES, Guillermo Antonio. 2833 BABCOCK RD, STE 210 78229 #048-04-1991 L1992 **CD** *020 †20
REYES, Guy Edmund. ■ 78249 #016-11-2006 **ORS** *012
REYES, Homer C. 14855 BLANCO RD STE 204 78216 #048-13-1986 L1987 **FM** *020 †18
REYES, Javier Guadalupe. 811 N MAIN AVE 78205 #649-02-1965 L1977 **NS** *020
REYES, Jose. 12730 IH 10 W, STE 306 78230 #048-13-1988 L1989 **PHL FM** *020 †18
REYES, Leonel, Jr. 311 CAMDEN ST, STE 104 78215 #048-13-1984 L1985 **FM** *020
REYES, Marcos. ■ 78250 #048-15-2005 **OPH** *012
REYES, Ramon G. 527 N LEONA ST 78207 #042-02-1985 L1992 **FM** *020 †18
REYNA, George S. 215 E QUINCY ST STE 505 78215 #005-11-1988 L1989 **OPH** *020 †35
REYNA, Juan Arnulfo. 315 N SAN SABA, STE 1295 78207 #048-13-1975 L1975 **U** *020 †95
REYNA, Richard S. 215 E QUINCY ST, STE 500 78215 #005-11-1984 L1985 **IM** *020 †20
REYNA, Robert Sanchez. 6315 S ZARZAMORA ST 78211 #005-11-1977 L1979 **IM** *020 †20
REYNA, Rowland Sanchez. 215 E QUINCY ST STE 500 78215 #005-11-1982 L1983 **IMG** *020 †20
REYNARD, Jennifer N. ■ 78259 #048-13-1996 L2005 **PD** *020 †55
REYNOLDS, Thomas Curtis. 3706 S W W WHITE RD 78222 #005-11-1988 **U** *100
RHAME, Frederick Taylor. 8606 VILLAGE DR, STE A 78217 #048-13-1974 L1977 **PD** *020 †55
RHEINER, John P. 9895 IH 10 W 78230 #048-13-1985 L1988 **GS** *020
RHODES, Jonathan Wm. 4242 MEDICAL DR, STE 3100 78229 #048-13-1979 L1979 **AN** *020 †05
RHODES, Linda Jane. 7703 FLOYD CURL DR 78229 #048-02-1975 L1975 **CHP P** *020 †55,75
RHODES, Melvin Auther. ■ 78222 #047-07-1987 **PM** *100
RIBEIRO, Monique Vieira. 7703 FLOYD CURL DR 78229 #187-10-2004 **P** *012
RICE, David Herbert. ■ 78250 #035-06-2000 L2000 **IM** *100 †20
RICE, Maurice Michael. ■ 78240 #016-01-1937 L1938 **PTH** *071 †50
RICE, Nedra Leigh. ■ 78240 #048-13-2006 **OBG** *012
RICE, Robert Alan. 5430 FREDERICKSBURG RD 78229 #021-01-1976 L1985 **OPH AM** *020 †35
RICHARD, Michael L. ■ 78240 #048-15-1987 L1988 **EM** *020 †16
RICHARD, Thomas Joseph. 3851 ROGER BROOKE DR, BROOKE ARMY MED CTR 78234 #041-12-2000 L2002 **HO** *020 †20
RICHARDS, Fred Vick. ■ 78248 #048-04-1943 L1943 **GP** *072
RICHARDS, Jason Paul. ■ 78250 #038-40-2007 **ORS** *012
RICHARDSON, Arthur Welch. 7810 LOUIS PASTEUR DR, STE 200 78229 #007-02-1954 L1962 **D** *020 †15
RICHARDSON, John S. 4242 MEDICAL DR, STE 3100 78229 #048-02-1975 L1975 **AN** *020 †05
RICHMOND, Cliff Morgan. 9600 DATAPOINT DR 78229 #048-13-1982 L1983 **PTH** *020 †50
RICHMOND, George M, Jr. 1303 MC CULLOUGH AVE, STE GL-60 78212 #048-13-1984 L1985 **FM** *020 †18
RICHMOND, James Templeton. ■ 78213 #048-12-1956 L1956 **GP** *071
RICHMOND, Lewis Hilliard. 8103 BROADWAY ST STE 106 78209 #023-01-1958 L1966 **P** *071 †75
RICHTER, James Kelly. 4242 E SOUTHCROSS BLVD 78222 #048-02-1954 L1954 **GP** *071
RICKERSON, Averess Dean. 8601 VILLAGE DR STE 100 78217 #005-18-1981 L1985 **IM** *020 †20
RIDDOCH, Mark David. 8401 DATAPOINT DR STE 401 78229 #048-14-1985 L1986 **IM** *020 †20
RIDDOCK, Ian C. ■ 78251 #023-12-2002 L2004 **CD** *012 †20
RIESZ, David A. 540 MADISON OAK DR, STE 160 78258 #048-12-1996 L1998 **DR** *020 †80
RILEY, Daniel Jos. 4502 MEDICAL DR 78229 #035-15-1987 L1995 **NEP** *020 †20
RILEY, Fred Whitcomb, Jr. 7950 FLOYD CURL DR 78229 #048-04-1957 L1957 **R NM** *071 †80,28
RINCON, Jorge Luis. 730 N MAIN AVE STE 601 78205 #935-07-1992 L2004 **GS** *020 †85
RINN, Odville Alton. 4402 VANCE JACKSON RD #250 78230 #039-01-1957 L1958 **GP** *020
RIOJAS, David C. 21006 WILD SPGS 78258 #048-15-1987 L1989 **PEM IM** *020 †20,55
RIOJAS, Richard Alfred. 4115 MEDICAL DR, STE 305 78229 #649-01-1964 L1968 **PD** *020 †55
RIOS, Cristela D. ■ 78258 #048-13-1987 L1988 **PD** *020 †55
RIOS, Marivel N. ■ 78256 #048-13-2005 **AN** *012
RIOS, Ruben. 111 DALLAS ST 78205 #048-13-1987 L1988 **AN** *020 †05
RIOS DE GIL, Antonia S. ■ 78229 #935-04-1964 L1978 **PD** *062 †55
RITCHIE, Elizabeth L. 4499 MEDICAL DR STE 399 78229 #048-13-1982 L1983 **U PD** *020 †95
RITCHIE, Eric Raymond. 4499 MEDICAL DR, STE 235 78229 #023-12-1992 L2004 **ORS** *020 †40
RITTENHOUSE, Mark Chas. 7940 FLOYD CURL DR, STE 840 78229 #039-01-1970 L1973 **GS** *020 †85
RITTER, Richard Russell. ■ 78232 #041-12-1958 L1980 **AN** *071 †05
RITTER, Tibor. 45 NE LOOP 410, STE 900 78216 #048-13-1972 L1973 **AN** *020
RITTICHIER, Kristine Kay. 8401 DATAPOINT DR, STE 500 78229 #038-41-1990 L2004 **PEM PD** *020 †55
RIVAS, Pedro Agustin. 7434 LOUIS PASTEUR, STE 209 78229 #005-11-1993 L2000 **CD** *020 †20
RIVERA, Jorge Luis. 7390 BARLITE BLVD STE 300 78224 #847-05-1974 L1981 **PUD IM** *020 †20
RIVERA, Kevin Manuel. 7703 FLOYD CURL DR, UNIV TX MED SCH 78229 #038-41-2007 **AN** *012
RIVERA, Luis Roberto. 7909 FREDERICKSBRG RD #110, UROLOGY SAN ANTONIO 78229 #042-01-1973 L1981 **U** *020 †95
RIVERA, Nayda. ■ 78249 #682-01-1974 *100
RIVERA CARTAGENA, Ral A. ■ 78261 #042-01-2003 L2005 **IM** *020
RIZO, Rebecca. 3111 SAN PEDRO AVE, PEDIATRICS & ADOLESCENTS 78212 #016-76-2003, ▲ L2006 **PD** *020 †55
RIZVI, Beenish. 7703 FLOYD CURL DR 78229 #704-02-2003 **IM** *012
ROA, Paul John G. ■ 78230 #748-01-1988 L1997 **PTH** *100 †50
ROACH, Barbara Lynn. ■ 78249 #019-02-1987 L1988 **IM** *030 †20
ROACH, Julie A. ■ 78216 #048-04-2004 L2006 **IM** *100 †20
ROADMAN, Chas Harvey, II. ■ 78259 #012-05-1973 L1974 **OBG AM** *030 †30
ROARTY, Joseph. ■ 78247 #035-09-2005 L2007 **EM** *012
ROBBINS, Justin. ■ 78247 #021-01-2003 L2005 **ORS** *012
ROBBINS, William Warren. 4410 MEDICAL DR, STE 390 78229 #018-75-1978, ▲ L1981 **PME AN** *020 †05
ROBERTS, Bertram W. 701 S ZARZAMORA ST 78207 #004-01-1969 L1977 **NEP IM** *020 †20
ROBERTS, David A. 5282 MEDICAL DR STE 200 78229 #048-12-1982 L1983 **OSS** *020 †40
ROBERTS, David Alan. 16414 SAN PEDRO AVE, STE 710 78232 #007-02-1974 L1989 **EM FM** *020 †16,18
ROBERTS, Stephen Patrick. ■ 78258 #010-03-1992 L2002 **TS** *020
ROBERTSON, Carol Spratt. 19238 STONEHUE, ABCD PEDIATRICS, PA 78258 #041-02-1985 L1992 **PD** *020 †55
ROBERTSON, Frank Michael. 4499 MEDICAL DR, STE 347 78229 #041-02-1985 L1995 **PDS** *020 †85
ROBERTSON, Jeffrey Lyn. ■ 78239 #023-12-2002 L2004 **FM** *020 †18
ROBERTSON, Mark C. 45 NE LOOP 410, STE 900 78216 #048-15-1990 L1991 **AN** *020 †05
ROBETORYE, Ryan Scott. ■ 78258 #048-04-1997 L2003 **HMP** *020 †50
ROBINSON, Charles Wilson, Jr. 414 NAVARRO ST 78205 #036-01-1960 L1967 **PTH IM** *071 †50
ROBINSON, Douglas W. 8042 WURZBACH RD STE 3 78229 #048-02-1973 L1973 **GS** *020 †85
ROBINSON, Guilford R. 5150 BROADWAY ST 610 78209 #001-02-1981 L1985 **IM** *020 †20
ROBINSON, Herbert Joel. 414 VINE ST 78210 #649-02-1966 L1969 **GP PD** *075
ROBINSON, James Parker. 7700 FLOYD CURL DR 78229 #026-04-1957 L1977 **PTH GS** *040 †85,50
ROBINSON, Jocelyn Anne. ■ 78209 #024-07-2007 **EM** *012
ROBINSON, Randal Dean. 3851 ROGER BROOKE DR, BROOKE ARMY MED CTR, BLDG 78234 #028-03-1988 L2006 **REN OBG** *020 †30
ROBLEDO, Bridget. 7333 BARLITE BLVD, STE 400 78224 #048-14-1988 L1989 **FM** *020 †18 ‡
ROBLES-ACEVEDO, Fernando. 3851 ROGER BROOKE DR # 36, BROOKE ARMY MEDICAL CENTER 78234 #042-02-1996 L1998 **DR** *100
ROBSON, Craig Hampton. 7703 FLOYD CURL DR, UNIV TX MED SCH 78229 #005-12-2005 L2006 **U** *012
ROCHA-DAVIS, Rebecca A. 7922 EWING HALSELL DR, STE 440 78229 #048-13-2000 L2003 **PD** *020 †55
ROCKETT, Carl. ■ 78230 #016-45-1992 L1999 **APM** *020
ROCKWOOD, Charles A, Jr. 7703 FLOYD CURL DR, UNIV OF TEX HEALTH SCIENCE 78229 #039-01-1956 L1966 **ORS** *040 †40
RODELA, Charles. 1111 SE MILITARY DR 78214 #048-13-1989 L1991 **FM** *020 †18
RODGERS, Allison Kay. ■ 78240 #025-01-2004 L2004 **OBG** *012
RODGERS, Katherine Lynn. 203 E EVERGREEN ST 78212 #048-12-1959 L1959 **PD** *071 †55
RODGERS, Lee Patrick. ■ 78231 #021-01-1976 L1978 **PD** *020 †55
RODRIGUEZ, Abelardo. 8527 VILLAGE DR STE 200 78217 #048-02-1971 L1971 **FM** *020 †18 ‡
RODRIGUEZ, Ana Iris. 9969 FREDERICKSBURG RD 78240 #025-12-1991 L1993 **IM** *020 †20
RODRIGUEZ, Anna Maria. 5788 ECKHERT RD, FRANK TEJEDA OUTPATIENT CL 78240 #035-47-2002 L2006 **IM** *020 †20
RODRIGUEZ, Armand Robert. 7979 WURZBACH RD, URSCHEL TOWERS #233 78229 #030-06-1980 L1981 **FM** *020 †05
RODRIGUEZ, Carlos L. ■ 78216 #048-04-2004 **AN** *012
RODRIGUEZ, Cesar N. 400 CONCORD PLAZA DR, STE 300 78216 #935-01-1953 **OTO PS** *020
RODRIGUEZ, Daniel. 8038 WURZBACH RD, STE 510 78229 #048-02-1972 L1972 **FM** *020 †18
RODRIGUEZ, David A. ■ 78201 #048-13-2007 **GS** *012
RODRIGUEZ, Francisco J. 311 CAMDEN ST, SUITE 211 MADISON SQUARE M 78215 #308-01-1958 L1966 **P** *020 †75
RODRIGUEZ, Homero. 8534 VILLAGE DR STE A 78217 #649-01-1962 L1971 **FM PTH** *020 †50,18
RODRIGUEZ, J Guillermo. 7355 BARLITE BLVD, STE 402 78224 #649-02-1983 L1993 **PM ORS** *020 †60
RODRIGUEZ, Jeronimo R. ■ 78245 #649-02-1971 **N** *050
RODRIGUEZ, Jesus A. 8606 VILLAGE DR 78217 #048-13-2005 L2008 **FP** *012
RODRIGUEZ, John David. 540 OAK CENTRE DR, STE 280 78258 #048-13-1993 L1994 **IM** *020 †20
RODRIGUEZ, Joy Anne. ■ 78261 #003-01-1996 L1997 **FM** *020 †18
RODRIGUEZ, Luis A. 315 N SAN SABA, STE 1075 78207 #737-06-1980 L1994 **PD** *020 †55
RODRIGUEZ, Luis Antonio. 215 N SANSABA, STE 101 78207 #649-02-1987 L1993 **PD PHO** *020 †55
RODRIGUEZ, Luis C. 315 N SAN SABA, STE 1160 78207 #048-13-1997 L2003 **HO IM** *020 †20
RODRIGUEZ, Manuel J. 7930 FLOYD CURL DR 78229 #042-02-1991 L1994 **IM** *020 †20
RODRIGUEZ, Maria Pilar. 5414 FREDERICKSBURG RD, PEDIATRIX MEDICAL GROUP 78229 #025-01-1986 L1997 **NPM PD** *020 †55
RODRIGUEZ, Marisol L. ■ 78240 #048-13-2008 *012
RODRIGUEZ, Mark Anthony. 13909 NACOGDOCHES RD # 107 78217 #048-14-1987 L1988 **FM** *020 †18
RODRIGUEZ, Moises Gonzalo. 8535 WURZBACH RD, STE 108 78240 #649-02-1980 L1989 **CHP P** *020
RODRIGUEZ, Patsy Ramos. ■ 78260 #048-02-2002 L2005 **PD** *020
RODRIGUEZ, Richard Aaron. 102 PALO ALTO RD STE 450 78211 #048-13-1978 L1978 **OPH** *020 †35
RODRIGUEZ, Roberto. 3851 ROGER BROOKE DR, BROOKE AMC, BLDG 3600 78234 #042-02-1983 L1987 **AI PD** *020 †55,03
RODRIGUEZ, Rolando Xavier. ■ 78212 #649-13-1983 L1992 **P PD** *020
RODRIGUEZ, Rosario. 527 N LEONA ST 78207 #048-13-1992 L1997 **P** *075 †75
RODRIGUEZ, Rosemarie. ■ 78258 #042-02-2003 **PTH** *012
RODRIGUEZ, Victorio. 343 W HOUSTON ST STE 601 78205 #264-01-1963 L1971 **ON HO** *071
RODRIGUEZ, Viola Marquez. ■ 78249 #275-01-1944 L1968 **IM** *071
RODRIGUEZ-BLANCO, Rafael. ■ 78232 #649-14-1980 L1988 **IM PUD** *020 †20
RODRIGUEZ-CANTU, F. 1730 SW MILITARY DR, STE 201 78221 #649-02-1963 L1969 **IM NEP** *020
RODRIGUEZ-FLORES, Javier. ■ 78212 #649-02-1983 L1990 **IM** *020 †20
RODRIGUEZ MERCADO, Gladys. 7979 WURZBACH RD, STE 353 78229 #042-01-1984 L1992 **ON** *020 †20
ROEDER, Elizabeth Rose. 333 N SANTA ROSA AVE 78207 #048-16-1989 L2004 **MG PD** *020 †55,19
ROETH, Charles Louis. 4330 MEDICAL DR, STE 125 78229 #016-11-1967 L1973 **CD IM** *020 †20
ROGENESS, Graham Arthur. 8535 TOM SLICK 78229 #016-11-1964 L1975 **CHP P** *050 †75
ROGERS, Albert Mitchell. 1303 MCCULLOUGH AVE, STE 265 78212 #048-04-1940 L1940 **GP GS** *072
ROGERS, Dora D. 315 N SAN SABA, STE 1180 78207 #048-14-1992 L1993 **OBG** *020 †30
ROGERS, James Henry, Jr. 1901 BABCOCK RD, STE 301 78229 #012-01-1971 L1978 **PDC PD** *020 †55

■ = Address Information Privacy Protected

ROGERS, James Norman. 4502 MEDICAL DR, RM A0301J 78229 #003-01-1987 L1989 **AN PME** *020 †05
ROGERS, Paula J. 301 N FRIO ST 78207 #048-13-1989 L1991 **PTH** *020 †50
ROGERS, Randall David. 1303 MC CULLOUGH AVE, STE 265 78212 #048-13-1977 L1977 **CRS GS** *020 †10,85
ROGERS, Tamrya Lee. 1202 E SONTERRA BLVD, STE 601 78258 #048-13-1995 L2001 **IM** *020 †20
ROGERS, Waid. 7703 FLOYD CURL DR RM 219E 78229 #035-20-1957 L1968 **GS** *071 †85
ROGERS, William M. 333 N SANTA ROSA AVE 78207 #023-01-1980 L1992 **PDE PD** *020 †55
ROHWEDER, Kent Wm. 540 MADISON OAK DR, STE 160 78258 #007-02-1990 L1992 **VIR** *020 †80
ROIG, Chester Austin, III. 7700 FLOYD CURL DR 78229 #021-05-1972 L1975 **PTH** *020 †50
ROJAS, Hugo Alonzo. 333 N SANTA ROSA AVE 78207 #649-30-1985 L1991 **IM FM** *020 †20
ROJAS, Maria Ruiz. PO BOX 592120 78259 #264-01-1983 L2001 **P PFP** *020 †75
ROKA, Alexander S. 19222 STONEHUE, STE 101 78258 #473-01-1989 L1998 **FM** *020 †18
ROLDAN, Carlos Mario. 9969 FREDERICKSBURG RD 78240 #264-03-1991 L1998 **FM PLM** *020 †18
ROLDAN, Jose Fernando. 7703 FLOYD CURL DR, UNIV OF TX HEALTH SCIENCE 78229 #264-16-1992 L2004 **RHU** *020 †20
ROLFINI, Roberto G. 343 W HOUSTON ST STE 102 78205 #935-02-1965 L1970 **PM** *020 †60
ROMAN, Angel Manuel, Jr. 2833 BABCOCK RD, STE 110 78229 #048-13-1978 L1978 **PM PMM** *020 †60
ROMAN, Carlos Alberto. 4411 MEDICAL DR, STE 300 78229 #319-04-1982 L1992 **ICE IM** *020 †20
ROMAN, Gustavo. 7703 FLOYD CURL DR, DEPT OF NEUROLOGY 78229 #264-01-1971 L1983 **N** *020 †75
ROMANI, William Randolph. 10451 HORN BLVD 78240 #038-43-1996 L2002 **DR** *020 †80
ROMERO, Emilio F. 7400 MERTON MINTER ST 78229 #847-06-1972 L1974 **P** *020 †75
ROMERO, Leigh Anne. ■ 78249 #048-13-2006 **FP** *012
ROMERO, Rebecca Suzanne. ■ 78240 #048-13-2004 **N** *012
ROMINGER, J Whitney. 4499 MEDICAL DR STE 190 78229 #048-13-1991 L1992 **OS** *020
ROMO, Thomas, Jr. 400 BALTIMORE AVE 78215 #048-02-1958 L1958 **GP GS** *020
ROMO, Victor M Cosio. 6609 BLANCO RD STE 140 78216 #649-01-1957 L1973 **FM** *020 †18
RONE, Valerie Rene. 301 N FRIO ST 78207 #028-03-1978 L1980 **PTH PCP** *020 †50
ROOF, Willie R. 311 CAMDEN ST STE 602 78215 #048-04-1952 L1952 **TS GS** *071 †85,90
ROOKARD, Paul Allyn. ■ 78230 #048-15-2006 **AN** *012
ROOT, Harlan D. 7703 FLOYD CURL DR 78229 #035-20-1953 L1966 **GS TS** *040 †85
ROSALES, Anna Marie. 3202 SAN PEDRO AVE 78212 #048-02-1988 L1990 **FM** *020 †18
ROSARIO-ROMAN, Domingo. ■ 78218 #042-02-2003 **PTH** *020 †50
ROSAS, Humberto. 1445 SOMERSET RD 78211 #649-03-1955 L1968 **GP OS** *071
ROSCHMANN, Alfred C. 7703 FLOYD CURL DR, UNIV OF TX HEALTH SCIENCE 78229 #048-12-1992 L1995 **DR** *012 †16
ROSCHMANN, Simone Marie. ■ 78260 #048-13-2004 **DR** *012
ROSE, Lewis Craig. 7703 FLOYD CURL DR, UNIV OF TX HEALTH SCIENCE 78229 #917-30-1954 L1985 **FM** *040 †18
ROSE, Mark R. 1303 MCCULLOUGH AVE, STE 460 78212 #048-02-1988 L1995 **IM** *020 †20
ROSE, Stephen Dean. 3851 ROGER BROOKE DR # 36, BROOKE ARMY MEDICAL CENTER 78234 #025-07-1994 L2007 **ORS** *020 †40
ROSEN, Laurence. 431 ISOM RD, STE 123 78216 #048-13-1977 L1977 **AN PME** *020
ROSENBERG, Donald M. ■ 78240 #869-05-1965 L1985 **PHP OM** *071 †70
ROSENBERG, Ethan. ■ 78255 #011-02-2002 L2007 **AN** *020
ROSENBERG, Gerald T. 4511 HORIZON HILL BLVD, STE 150 78229 #028-34-1978 L1979 **RHU IM** *020 †20
ROSENBLATT, Steven Gerald. 8042 WURZBACH RD, STE 500 78229 #035-20-1971 L1975 **NEP IM** *020 †20
ROSENBLOOM, Jeffrey S. 19026 STONE OAK PKWY, STE 110 78258 #048-12-1992 L1993 **OTO** *020 †45
ROSENDE, Carlos Alberto. 7703 FLOYD CURL DR, OPHTHALMOLOGY DEPT UTHSCSA 78229 #011-02-1981 L2001 **OPH** *020 †35 ‡
ROSENKRANZ, Laura M. 6839 LESLIE RD 78254 #781-01-1995 L2004 **GE** *020 †20
ROSENTHAL, Arthur. 8042 WURZBACH RD 78229 #041-09-1969 L1975 **GS** *020 †85
ROSENTHAL, Daniel. 7950 FLOYD CURL DR, STE 101 78229 #605-02-1960 L1975 **CRS GS** *040 †10,85
ROSENTHAL, Saul Haskell. OAK HILLS MEDICAL BLDG 78229 #024-01-1962 L1968 **P** *071 †75
ROSENTHAL, Sharon Kay. 12902 FLAGSHIP 78247 #048-13-1973 L1973 **PTH PCP** *020 †50 ‡
ROSS, David M, Jr. 7922 EWING HALSELL DR, STE 440 78229 #048-13-1999 L2002 **PD** *020 †55
ROSS, James Earl, Jr. 3453 N IH 35 STE 207B, 16 ANCIENT BEND 78219 #012-01-1979 L1989 **EM PD** *020 †16
ROSS, Marnie La Shae. 255 E SONTERRA BLVD, STE 100 78258 #048-13-1992 L1994 **IM** *020 †20
ROSS, Rise P. 540 MADISON OAK DR, STE 160 78258 #011-04-1980 L1984 **DR** *020 †80
ROSS, Roberto David. 7355 BARLITE BLVD, STE 301 78224 #649-14-1981 L1989 **FM IMG** *020 †18
ROSS, Scott K. 1007 NE LOOP 410 78209 #048-04-1986 L1987 **FM** *020 †18
ROSS, Steven Aaron. ■ 78258 #048-12-2004 **DR** *012
ROTH, Gregory Scott. ■ 78230 #041-14-1992 L1997 **EM** *020 †16
ROTHE, Courand N. ■ 78209 #028-34-1939 L1939 **PHP GPM** *071 †70
ROTTER, David Henry. 111 DALLAS ST 78205 #048-02-2000 L2006 **DR** *020 †80
ROTTO, Debra K. 234 COUNTRY LN 78209 #048-13-1988 L1990 **AN** *020 †05
ROUSE, Richard Geo. 4330 MEDICAL DR, STE 325 78229 #016-43-1973 L1980 **TS** *020 †90,85
ROW, James Michael. 8401 DATAPOINT DR, STE 130 78229 #001-02-1978 L1982 **EM** *020 †16
ROWBERRY, Justin Paul. ■ 78250 #035-46-2005 L2007 **PD** *012
ROWE, Janet Hague. ■ 78261 #010-03-1970 L1973 **PD PN** *020 †55
ROWINSKY, Eric Keith. 17110 SPOTTED EAGLE 78248 #047-05-1981 L1996 **ON IM** *020 †20
ROWLAND, Alexander S. 150 E SONTERRA BLVD, SAN ANTONIO ORTHOPAEDIC 78258 #021-01-1997 L1999 **ORS** *020
ROWLAND, Spencer Andrews. 1310 MCCULLOUGH AVE 78212 #041-13-1954 L1961 **HS GS** *071 †40
ROYALL, Don R. 7703 FLOYD CURL DR 78229 #048-14-1984 L1986 **P IM** *020 †20,75
ROYER, Cassandre Laurette. 523 BERWICK TOWN, PEDIATRIX MEDICAL GROUP 78249 #048-02-1996 L1997 **NPM** *020 †55
ROYSTER, Greene Donald. ■ 78251 #023-12-2006 L2008 **OBG** *012
ROZANSKI, Thomas Alan. 7703 FLOYD CURL DR, DEPT. OF UROLOGY, MC 7845 78229 #041-09-1983 L2004 **U** *020 †95
RUBIN, James M O. 100 NE LOOP 410, STE 830 78216 #048-12-1989 L1990 **AN** *020 †05
RUBIN, Jay Michel. 999 E BASSE RD, STE 128B 78209 #048-04-1985 L1986 **OPH** *020 †35
RUBIO, Richard Maurice. 7400 MERTON MINTER ST, AUDIE MURPHY VA HOSP 78229 #016-42-1973 L1977 **IM** *020 †20
RUDA, Richard Jos. ■ 78249 #016-06-1966 L1967 **OP ORS** *071 †40
RUDD, Dawn Marie. 5282 MEDICAL DR 78229 #041-14-1999 L2006 **IM** *020 †20
RUDOLPH, John Dennis. ■ 78259 #033-05-1963 L1970 **GYN** *020 †30
RUEL, Kelly Sean. 2121 SW 36TH ST 78237 #048-04-1999 L2002 **FM** *020 †18
RUENES, Raymond. 2020 BABCOCK RD STE 19 78229 #847-01-1973 L1977 **PD** *020 †55
RUFF, Dennis Anthony. 7700 FLOYD CURL DR 78229 #035-03-1982 L1986 **IM** *050 †20
RUFF, Gregory Ashton. ■ 78260 #041-14-1999 L2001 **IM** *020 †20
RUGGERO, Pedro Alberto. 3031 IH 10 W, SERVICES 78201 #132-02-1969 L1978 **P CHP** *020 †75
RUGH, Kenneth Scott. 4400 S PIEDRAS DR, STE 200 78228 #028-02-1976 L1980 **DR** *020 †80
RUIZ, Antonio Luis. 5282 MEDICAL DR 78229 #005-11-1976 L1978 **IM** *020
RUIZ, Dilma C. 155 E SONTERRA BLVD # 201 78258 #042-01-1991 L1997 **GS** *020 †85
RUIZ, Gilbert Manuel. 4775 HAMILTON WOLFE RD 78229 #048-13-1979 L1979 **OTO** *020 †45
RUIZ, Jose Manuel, III. 7940 FLOYD CURL, STE 900 78229 #021-05-1986 L1998 **OBG** *020 †30
RUIZ, Mario E. 4440 S PIEDRAS DR, STE 100 78228 #429-02-1984 L1997 **PDR DR** *020 †80
RUIZ, Roberto Javier. 590 N GENERAL MCMULLEN DR, STE 1 78228 #048-04-1979 L1979 **FM** *020
RUIZ, Teresa M. 1055 ADA ST, UFHC SE 78223 #048-13-1992 L1997 **PD** *020 †55
RUIZ-HEALY, Josephine H. 519 W HOUSTON ST 78207 #649-28-1982 L1989 **PD** *020 †55
RULON, Jennifer Jean. 7337 LOUIS PASTEUR, BEXAR COUNTY MEDICAL EXAMI 78229 #054-04-1991 L1998 **FOP** *020 †50
RUNNELS, Alexandra. 7711 LOUIS PASTEUR DR, STE 200 78229 #048-14-1999 L2003 **OBG** *020 †30
RUPP, R Nevin. 7711 LOUIS PASTEUR DR #412 78229 #041-01-1958 L1970 **OTO AM** *072 †45
RUSH, Jeremy K. ■ 78260 #048-16-2006 L2007 **ORS** *012
RUSINKO, Andrew. 111 DALLAS ST 78205 #010-02-1957 L1979 **GS GP** *071 †85
RUSINKO, Rachel. 701 S ZARZAMORA ST 78207 #048-13-1987 L1992 **END** *020 †20
RUSSEL, John Robt. 301 N FRIO ST 78207 #067-01-1967 L1976 **PTH PHP** *020 †50
RUSSELL, Daniel A, Jr. 999 E BASSE RD 78209 #021-01-1951 L1953 **OPH AM** *071 †35
RUSSELL, Irwin Jon. 7703 FLOYD CURL DR, DEPARTMENT OF MED DIV OF R 78229 #005-12-1973 L1978 **RHU IM** *050
RUSSELL, John Carroll. 7700 FLOYD CURL DR 78229 #048-04-1962 L1962 **CD** *020 †85,90
RUSSELL, Lewis F, Jr. 8711 VILLAGE DR STE 312 78217 #048-02-1971 L1971 **U** *020 †95
RUSSELL, Michael J. ■ 78253 #048-02-2001 L2002 **PTH** *012
RUST, Stace S. 8800 VILLAGE DR, STE 106 78217 #048-13-1999 L2003 **HS** *020 †40
RUTMAN, Joel Y. 8042 WURZBACH RD, STE 640 78229 #024-01-1963 L1971 **CHN** *071 †55,75
RUTSTEIN, Joel Edward. ■ 78257 #041-01-1971 L1974 **RHU IM** *071 †20
RUTZ, Timothy J. 4242 MEDICAL DR, STE 3100 78229 #030-05-1967 L1973 **AN** *020 †05 ‡
RYDER, Curtis Jude. 13750 US 281 N STE 240 78232 #021-06-1979 L1980 **FM** *071 †18
SAAD, Adham Raja. ■ 78229 #048-13-2005 **GS** *012
SAAD, Robert Martin. 4411 MEDICAL DR, STE 300 78229 #023-12-1985 L1990 **CD IM** *020 †20
SABELLA, Vincenzo. 7950 FLOYD CURL DR, STE 600 78229 #649-30-1981 L1991 **OBG** *020 †30 ‡
SAENGER, Dorothea Rene. 4499 MEDICAL DR, STE 191 78229 #048-15-1993 L1994 **OBG** *020 †30
SAENZ, Rolando H. 343 W HOUSTON ST STE 705 78205 #048-13-1986 L1996 **CRS GS** *020 †85,10
SAFFORD, Kathryn Lynne. 4499 MEDICAL DR STE 252 78229 #056-06-1975 L1983 **GS** *020 †85
SAHA, Arup Kumar. 7703 FLOYD CURL DR MC, UTHSC SAN ANTONIO 78229 #495-39-1990 L2007 **GS** *100 †85
SAHAR, David Edris. ■ 78255 #026-04-1999 L2003 **PS** *012
SAHL, Nicole S. 7703 FLOYD CURL DR, MC 7792 78229 #048-13-2007 **P** *012
SAIDI, Mo H. ■ 78257 #517-01-1967 L1973 **OBG** *071 †30
SAINZ, Irma M. ■ 78229 #649-03-1985 L1996 **PTH** *071
SAINZ-GONZALEZ, Felipe J. ■ 78230 #649-14-1976 L1984 **IMG FPG** *030
SAKO, Edward Yoshiaki. 7703 FLOYD CURL DR, STE 7841 78229 #026-04-1982 L1992 **TS** *020 †85,90
SALAMAT SABERI, Amin. 7703 FLOYD CURL DR, UNIV TX MED SCH-SAN ANTONI 78229 #517-08-1998 **FM** *100
SALAZAR, David. 225 E SONTERRA BLVD, STE 217 78258 #264-16-1995 L2003 **PCC SME** *020 †20 ‡
SALAZAR, Gilbert R. 2911 S NEW BRAUNFELS AVE 78210 #048-04-1985 L1986 **FM** *020 †18
SALAZAR, Ricardo. ■ 78258 #264-13-1991 L2005 **PYG** *020 ‡
SALCHER, Valentin Geo. 2455 NE LOOP 410 STE 100 78217 #048-13-1982 L1983 **FM** *020 †18
SALDANA, Jose A. 900 ISOM RD, STE 210 78216 #649-02-1974 L1975 **DR** *062 †80
SALDANA, Miguel J. 7355 BARLITE BLVD STE 504 78224 #016-43-1968 L1989 **HS** *020 †85
SALDIVAR, Victor A. 333 N SANTA ROSA AVE, PATHOLOGY ASSOCIATES OF 78207 #649-01-1965 L1977 **PP HMP** *020 †50
SALEEM, Shamsa. 14100 NACOGDOCHES RD, HEALTH 78247 #048-04-1990 L1991 **FM** *020 †18
SALGADO, Lauren L. ■ 78216 #048-13-2005 **AN** *012
SALHIN, Amna A. 5107 MEDICAL DR, DISEASE CLINIC 78229 #613-02-1989 L1998 **END** *020 †20
SALINA, Richard James. ■ 78244 #041-12-1954 L1979 **AM GP** *020 †70
SALINAS, Dora Sylvia. 414 NAVARRO ST STE 809 78205 #048-02-2002 L2005 **FM** *020 †18
SALINAS, Grace M. 8535 WURZBACH RD STE 106 78240 #048-13-1996 L2000 **CHP** *020 †75
SALINAS, Jose Alejandro. 2455 NE LOOP 410 78217 #048-02-1981 L1981 **FM** *020 †18
SALINAS, Jose E. 540 MADISON OAK DR STE 260, STONE OAK MED OFC BLDG 78258 #048-04-1987 L1989 **FM GYN** *020
SALINAS, Molly A. 525 OAK CENTRE DR, STE 100 78258 #038-43-1993 L1996 **PD** *020 †55
SALINAS, Nathan Lee. ■ 78253 #041-01-2007 **OTO** *012
SALINAS SALINAS, Rufino. 205 E EVERGREEN ST, STE 1 78212 #649-02-1965 L1972 **U** *020 †95
SALMAN, Najmul Hasnain. 8201 EWING HALSELL DR, STE 280 78229 #305-01-1984 L1995 **PD** *020 †55
SALMON, Cristina Eugenia. 11467 HUEBNER RD, STE 340 78230 #010-02-1999 L2005 **EM** *100
SALTZSTEIN, Daniel Robin. 7979 WURZBACH RD, URSCHEL TOWERS #233 78229 #048-13-1986 L1987 **U** *020 †95
SALVATO, Kalee M. ■ 78216 #048-13-2007 **AN** *012
SAMANIEGO, Hector X, Jr. 4257 NW LOOP 410 78229 #308-11-1984 L1990 **P FM** *020
SAMARRIPA, Candance Andre. ■ 78229 #048-02-2007 **P** *012
SAMMIS, William L. ■ 78209 #028-34-1951 L1951 **GS** *075 †85

SAMPLE, Stephen Curry. ■ 78254 #020-02-2005 L2007 **EM** *012

SAMREEN, Sarah. 7703 FLOYD CURL DR 78229 #704-27-1999 L2008 **FP** *012

SAMUEL, Linda. 2810 THOUSAND OAKS DR, # 233 78232 #048-13-1973 L1973 **LM IMG** *020

SANCHEZ, Armando Antonio. 519 W HOUSTON ST 78207 #048-13-1983 L1985 **FM** *020 †18

SANCHEZ, Jose Antonio. 9969 FREDERICKSBURG RD 78240 #042-03-1991 L1992 **IM** *020 †20

SANCHEZ, Juan Fernando. 4212 MEDICAL DR 78229 #264-16-1997 L2005 **PCC** *012 †20

SANCHEZ, Marlene Lazara. 2455 NE LOOP 410, STE 100 78217 #048-13-1992 L1993 **IM** *020 †20

SANCHEZ, Michael Jos. 16414 SAN PEDRO AVE, STE 355 78232 #034-01-1990 L1999 **EM** *020 †20

SANCHEZ, Moises Eugenio. 11107 WOODRIDGE BLF 78249 #649-01-1986 **SO GP** *050

SANCHEZ, Ninza A. 4203 E SOUTHCROSS BLVD, STE C 78222 #048-13-1995 L1996 **IM** *020 †20

SANCHEZ, Ramon Victor. 343 W HOUSTON ST, STE 203 78205 #048-02-1998 L2004 **ADP** *020 †18

SANCHEZ, Teofilo Resendiz. 505 HOWARD ST 78212 #048-14-2000 L2006 **FM** *100

SANCHEZ GARCIA, Diana Emi. 7703 FLOYD CURL DR, DEPT MED 78229 #649-45-1988 **IM** *012

SANCHEZ-REILLY, Sandra E. 7979 WURZBACH RD 78229 #264-10-1996 L2004 **IMG** *020 †20

SANDER, Patrick Wesley. ■ 78249 #048-14-2004 **ORS** *012

SANDERCOCK, Sharon Kay. 516 LEXINGTON AVE 78215 #048-14-1995 L1998 **PD** *020 †55

SANDERS, Albert Earnest. 7703 FLOYD CURL DR, MAIL CODE 7774 78229 #048-02-1959 L1959 **ORS** *020 †40

SANDERS, James Gerald. ■ 78258 #048-04-1957 L1957 **MDM OBG** *071 †30

SANDERS, Joe Lucien. 60 CAMPDEN CIR 78218 #048-12-1964 L1964 **DR** *020

SANDERS, Robert Pearson. ■ 78232 #051-01-1998 L1998 **PHO** *100 †55

SANDERSON, Jeremy Drew. ■ 78255 #048-13-2005 **GS** *012

SANDIDGE, Ernie Lamar. ■ 78249 #047-06-1968 L1971 **FM OM** *071 †18

SANDOVAL, Kenneth Alan. 4400 PIEDRAS DR S 200, STE 200 78228 #048-02-1996 L1997 **DR** *020 †80

SANDOVAL, Sal S. 1303 MCCULLOUGH AVE # 229 78212 #048-14-1999 L2004 **AN** *020 †05

SANFORD, Donald Keith. 6406 N NEW BRAUNFELS AVE 78209 #047-06-1990 L1999 **OPH** *020 †35

SANGUINETTI-COLO, Yirielis. ■ 78240 #041-13-2006 **PD** *012

SANJANA, Hormuzd Bamansha. 7323 MARBACH RD, STE 104 78227 #496-49-1998 L2004 **FM** *020

SANKAR, Sudheer Kurup. 7703 FLOYD CURL DR, UNIV TX MED SCH-SAN ANTONI 78229 #495-99-1995 L2006 **NEP** *012 †20

SAN MARTIN, Antonio A. 7355 BARLITE BLVD, STE 304 78224 #048-13-1978 L1978 **OPH** *020 †35

SAN MARTIN, Roberto. 315 N SAN SABA, STE 100 78207 #005-14-1974 L1977 **OPH FM** *020 †35

SANTAMARIA, Daniel Luigi. ■ 78230 #019-02-2003 L2007 **FP** *012

SANTIAGO, Rafael Manuel. 225 E SONTERRA BLVD, STE 217 78258 #042-01-1978 L1989 **PUD SME** *020 †20

SANTIAGO-SHINGLE, Pura. ■ 78248 #748-01-1937 L1937 **PD** *075 †55

SANTILLAN, Rebecca Anna. 4242 MEDICAL DR, STE 3100 78229 #048-13-2002 L2007 **AN** *100 †05

SANTINI, Mario A. ■ 78254 #048-14-2007 **AN** *012

SANTOS, Claudia Y. ■ 78240 #048-13-2006 **IM** *012

SANTOS, Jose A. 2701 BABCOCK RD STE A 78229 #048-04-1983 L1985 **PM N** *020 †60

SANTOSCOY, Jesus Rodolfo. ■ 78228 #649-02-1959 L1967 **GYN** *071 ‡

SARABIA, Fermin. 343 W HOUSTON ST STE 412 78205 #275-01-1959 L1966 **P** *072 †75

SARANTOPOULOS, John. 7979 WURZBACH RD 78229 #062-01-1997 L2004 *020

SARAVIA, Jorge Antonio. 2829 BABCOCK RD, STE 436 78229 #649-01-1967 L1979 **N** *020 †75

SAREEN, Rajeev. ■ 78248 #495-47-1978 L1992 **EM IM** *020 †20

SARGENT, Charles Hunt. 2824 NACOGDOCHES RD 78217 #048-14-1984 L1988 **CHP P** *020

SARGENT, Edward Reed. 8401 DATAPOINT DR, STE 401 78229 #028-03-1980 L1981 **IM** *020 †20

SARHILL, Nabeel. 7703 FLOYD CURL DR, UTHSCSA, HEM/ONC & GERI/ON 78229 #875-03-1990 L2006 **HO** *100

SARKAR, Debjeet. ■ 78217 #035-09-2005 L2006 **IM** *020

SARNACKI, Clifford Teofil. 4499 MEDICAL DR, STE 222 78229 #038-40-1963 L1981 **U** *020 †95

SARNOSKI, Elizabeth Gretc. 7703 FLOYD CURL DR, UNIV TX HLTH SCI CTR 78229 #051-04-2007 **P** *012

SAROSDY, Michael Francis. 7979 WURZBACH RD, URSCHEL TOWERS #233 78229 #048-13-1977 L1979 **U** *020 †95

SARREAL, Renato Guerrero. 45 NE LOOP 410, STE 900 78216 #048-02-2001 L2005 **AN** *020 †05

SARTORI, Roberto Jose. ■ 78209 #042-01-1999 L2000 **N** *012

SARVIS, Jamey Alan. 7703 FLOYD CURL DR, MAIL CODE 7845 78229 #011-03-1998 L2007 **U** *012

SATHIANPITAYAKUL, E. ■ 78254 #891-04-1988 L1996 **PCC IM** *020 †20

SATTERFIELD, Tiffany M. 7703 FLOYD CURL DR, DEPT OF OB/GYN MC 7836 78229 #003-75-2005, ▲ **OBG** *012

SAUCEDA, Rito M. ■ 78240 #048-13-2004 L2007 **IM** *020

SAUCEDO, Cynthia Sue. 525 OAK CENTRE DR, STE 150 78258 #649-02-1988 L1991 **FM** *020 †18

SAUERWEIN, Tom Jos. ■ 78251 #023-12-1991 L1994 **END** *020 †20

SAUNDERS, John Frederick. 7711 LOUIS PASTEUR DR #603 78229 #040-02-1968 L1974 **OPH** *020 †35 ‡

SAUNDERS, Thomas Ervin. 45 NE LOOP 410, STE 900 78216 #048-13-1979 L1979 **AN** *020

SAUTTER, Tamar Elise. ■ 78227 #048-14-2004 L2006 **IM** *012

SAVAGE, Jeffrey Allen. ■ 78249 #048-04-01-2005 L2007 **PD** *012

SAVAGE, Jennifer Gentry. 7703 FLOYD CURL DR, DEPT OF NEUROSURGERY 78229 #048-13-2006 **NS** *012

SAVAGE, Stephanie Anne. ■ 78260 #056-05-1999 L2001 **CCS** *020 †85

SAVINOV, Oleg. ■ 78217 #913-55-1986 **AN** *100

SAYEGH, Samir. 17000 SAN PEDRO AVE 78232 #067-02-1972 L1982 **GP** *020

SBAYI, Samer. ■ 78258 #308-11-1998 L2006 **GS** *020

SCALES, David Kenneth. 2829 BABCOCK RD, STE 407 78229 #023-12-1982 L1997 **OPH IG** *020 †35

SCANLAN, Michelle Carol. 7210 LOUIS PASTEUR DR, PASTEUR MEDICAL 78229 #048-14-1995 L1997 **IM** *020 †20

SCARPINO, Steven C. 540 MADISON OAK DR, STE 160 78258 #048-02-1998 L2003 **DR** *020 †80

SCAVONE, Edmond. ■ 78217 #023-01-1944 L1975 **GP** *071 †85

SCAVONE, Michael James. ■ 78232 #048-13-1976 L1976 **P** *020

SCHAFER, George Ezra. ■ 78245 #038-41-1946 L1971 **AM OM** *071 †70

SCHAFFER, Eric S. 1303 MCCULLOUGH AVE # 363 78212 #035-19-1978 L1988 **PS GS** *020 †65,85

SCHANER, Emelia B. ■ 78231 #054-04-1983 L1988 **FM** *074 †18

SCHANER, Patrick John. 7703 FLOYD CURL DR RM 227L, SCIENCE CTR 78229 #041-02-1998 L2000 **PS** *012

SCHATZ, Martha Peterson. 527 N LEONA ST 78207 #025-07-1988 L2002 **OPH** *020 †35

SCHEINER, Christopher A. ■ 78251 #028-34-2003 L2005 **N** *100

SCHEINER, Stuart Leslie. ■ 78229 #010-03-1954 L1979 **TS GS** *071 †85,90

SCHENK, David Anthony. 7979 WURZBACH RD, URSCHEL TOWERS #233 78229 #021-01-1977 L1980 **PUD IM** *020 †20

SCHENKEN, Robert Spencer. 8122 DATAPOINT DR, STE 300 78229 #048-04-1977 L1977 **OBG** *020 †30

SCHENKER, Steven. 7703 FLOYD CURL DR, DEPARTMENT OF MEDICINE MSC 78229 #035-20-1955 L1965 **HEP IM** *050

SCHIEFELBEIN, William H. ■ 78237 #048-02-1958 L1958 **GP** *074

SCHIFFER, Brent Sigmund. 2391 NE LOOP 410, STE 309 78217 #048-13-1981 L1981 **PTH PCP** *020 †50

SCHIFFER, Sydney. 8026 FLOYD CURL DR 78229 #065-01-1938 L1946 **IM DIA** *071 †20

SCHILLERSTROM, Jason E. 7703 FLOYD CURL DR 78229 #048-13-2000 L2004 **PYG** *020 †75

SCHILLERSTROM, Tracy L. 7222 TIMBERLEAF ST 78238 #048-13-2001 L2006 **P** *100 †75

SCHILLING, Harry Edward. 4775 HAMILTON WOLFE RD 78229 #048-12-1980 L1980 **OTO** *020 †45

SCHINDLER, Kevin C. ■ 78254 #048-13-2005 L2008 **IM** *012

SCHINKER, Stephen Michael. ■ 78251 #030-05-2005 L2008 **IM** *012

SCHLATTNER, Wm Hayes, Jr. ■ 78212 #028-34-1948 L1963 **PS** *020 †65

SCHLESINGER, David Scott. ■ 78240 #035-06-2003 L2008 **DR** *012

SCHLOSBERG, Kelly Slayton. 11 CHAMPION TRL 78258 #016-42-1993 L1997 **EM** *020 †16

SCHLOSBERG, Richard T. 19238 STONEHUE, ABCD PEDIATRICS, PA 78258 #016-42-1993 L1998 **PD** *020 †55

SCHMIDT, David Richard. 1 SBC CENTER PKWY, SBC 78219 #048-13-1980 L1980 **ORS** *020 †40

SCHMIDT, Micah Drew. ■ 78258 #023-12-2003 L2004 **EM** *012

SCHMIDT, Stacey Ann. 333 N SANTA ROSA 78207 #030-05-1995 L1997 **PD EM** *020 †55

SCHMIDT, Steven Walter. 45 NE LOOP 410, STE 900 78216 #056-05-1993 L1997 **AN** *020 †05

SCHMIT, David Roger. ■ 78240 #048-13-2008 *012

SCHNEIDER, F David. 4647 MEDICAL DR, UT MED LEONARD G PAUL 78229 #024-05-1987 L1992 **FM** *040 †18

SCHNEIDER, Geo Benj, II. 14100 SAN PEDRO AVE, STE 400 78232 #048-02-1976 L1976 **IM** *020 †20

SCHNITZLER, Robert N. 4330 MEDICAL DR, STE 400 78229 #035-06-1965 L1972 **CD ICE** *020 †20

SCHOLMA, Randal Scott. ■ 78258 #028-34-2005 L2007 **P** *012

SCHORLEMER, Robert. 4499 MEDICAL DR STE 119 78229 #048-12-1964 L1965 **OBG** *020 †30

SCHORLEMER, Wendell C. 4499 MEDICAL DR STE 125 78229 #048-12-1957 L1957 **OBG** *020 †30

SCHOTT, Mysti D W. 4647 MEDICAL DR 78229 #048-12-1997 L1998 **IM** *040 †20

SCHRANK, Amber Elise. ■ 78209 #048-13-2004 L2006 **GS** *012

SCHRAUDENBACH, Penner T. 7703 FLOYD CURL DR, DEPT OF UROLOGY MC 784 78229 #048-13-2004 **U** *012

SCHREIBER, Otto Joachim. ■ 78209 #005-06-1956 L1975 **P CHP** *071

SCHROEDER, Barbara Jeanne. ■ 78240 #048-13-2004 **IM** *100

SCHUENEMEYER, Aneta A. 9480 HUEBNER RD STE 21 78240 #759-06-1992 L1999 **P** *020 †75

SCHUESSLER, William W. 4203 E SOUTHCROSS BLVD 78222 #048-02-1967 L1967 **U** *020 †95

SCHULEMAN, Steven Glen. 7700 FLOYD CURL DR 78229 #048-13-1984 L1985 **AN GS** *020 †05

SCHULTE, Guus Victor. ■ 78212 #660-04-1971 L1991 **GS** *020

SCHULTZ, Donald A. ■ 78251 #048-13-2008 *012

SCHUSTER, Randall H. 16414 SAN PEDRO AVE, STE 710 78232 #048-13-1991 L1992 **EM** *020 †16

SCHWAKE, Jonathon Wayne. ■ 78218 #018-03-2007 **IM** *012

SCHWALIER, Erik Russell. ■ 78251 #023-12-2006 L2007 **IM** *012

SCHWARTING, Bland H. 1100 N MAIN AVE 78212 #048-04-1950 L1950 **OPH** *020 †35

SCHWARTZ, Bernard Stephen. 7400 MERTON MINTER ST, OF PSYCHIATRY 78229 #035-15-1968 L1977 **P** *020 †75

SCHWARTZ, Colin John. 5928 BROADWAY ST # 129 78209 #143-01-1954 L1979 **PTH** *050

SCHWARTZ, Joyce Gensberg. 44 VINEYARD DR 78257 #048-13-1980 L1980 **PTH** *020 †50

SCHWARTZ, Roger Jay. 2827 BABCOCK RD 78229 #649-14-1972 L1976 **AN GP** *071

SCHWARTZ, Sherwyn Leon. 5107 MEDICAL DR, DISEASE CLINIC 78229 #016-11-1972 L1977 **END IM** *020 †20

SCHWESINGER, Wayne Homer. 7703 FLOYD CURL DR 78229 #054-04-1965 L1974 **GS GF** *040 †85

SCOTT, Brian Gregory. 3851 ROGER BROOKE DR, BROOKE ARMY MED CTR, BLDG 78234 #048-12-1986 L1987 **OM PHP** *020 †70

SCOTT, Carla Renee. 7703 FLOYD CURL DR 78229 #004-01-1991 L1998 **PDE PD** *020 †55

SCOTT, Carolyn Knolle. 8725 MARBACH RD, STE 275 78227 #048-04-1954 L1954 **OM GP** *020

SCOTT, John Robert. 4502 MEDICAL DR, DEPT OF EMERGENCY 78229 #048-02-2000 L2003 **EM** *020 †16

SCOTT, Riley Perrin. 7703 FLOYD CURL DR 78229 #028-03-1995 L1998 **DR** *020 †80

SCOTT, Suzanne D. ■ 78240 #048-13-1982 L1985 **IM** *020

SCRIBBICK, Frank Walter. 414 NAVARRO ST, STE 400 78205 #023-12-1987 L2004 **OPH** *020 †35 ‡

SCROGGINS, Daniel James. 5372 FREDERICKSBURG RD, STE 101 78229 #048-16-1981 L1981 **AN** *020 †05

SEALS, John Raymond. 4410 MEDICAL DR, STE 400 78229 #048-04-1966 L1966 **CHN PD** *020 †55,75

SEARS, Alan K. ■ 78253 #035-45-2008 *012

SEASTRUNK, Brian Keith. 45 NE LOOP 410 STE 900 78216 #048-13-1993 L1995 **AN** *020 †05

SEAWELL, Michael Robert. ■ 78240 #048-13-2007 **IM** *012

SEAWORTH, Barbara Joyce. 2303 SE MILITARY DR 78223 #028-02-1977 L1987 **ID IM** *020 †20

SEDILLO, Daniel J. 19816 FIESTA GRANDE, TEXAS TRANSPLANT INSTITUTE 78256 #048-13-1988 L1989 **CCP** *020 †55

SEDLAK, Michael Francis. 540 MADISON OAK, STE 400 78258 #028-34-1991 L2007 **U** *020 †95

SEES, David W. 3851 ROGER BROOKE DR, CARDIOTHORACIC SRVC 78234 #048-16-1990 L1991 **TS GS** *020 †85,90

SEGAL, Graham V. 7703 FLOYD CURL DR, U TX MED SCH SAN ANTONIO 78229 #048-13-2006 IM *100

SEGER, Jennifer Cobb. 6338 N NEW BRAUNFELS AVE, # 224 78209 #048-13-1999 L2000 FM *020 †18

SEGER, Michael V. 2833 BABCOCK RD, STE 415 78229 #048-13-1998 L2000 GS *100 †85

SEIDENFELD, John Jos. ■ 78209 #038-41-1972 L1984 IM PUD *030 †20

SEIDNER, Steven Richard. 7703 FLOYD CURL DR, DEPT OF PEDIATRICS MSC7812 78229 #003-01-1982 L1989 PD NPM *040 †55

SEIFERT, Brandon Michael. ■ 78251 #030-05-2006 ORS *012

SELCK, Wolfgang Wilhelm. PO BOX 17772 78217 #407-21-1952 L1955 P OS *075

SELDEN, Lawrence Edward. 6315 S ZARZAMORA ST 78211 #048-02-1955 L1956 GP *071

SELINKOFF, Paul Matthew. 2833 BABCOCK RD STE 415 78229 #041-02-1970 L1982 GS OS *062 †85

SELLERS, Randall Van. 11122 WURZBACH RD STE 201 78230 #048-02-1980 L1985 P PFP *020 †75

SELVA, Michael A. 7909 FREDERICKSBURG RD, STE 110 78229 #048-13-1993 L1996 RO *020 †80

SELVARAJ, Carrie Lynn. 7703 FLOYD CURL DR, DEPT.OF CARDIOLOGY, MAIL C 78229 #025-07-2000 L2008 CD IM *020 †20

SENELICK, Richard Chas. 9119 CINNAMON HL 78240 #016-11-1970 L1975 N PM *020 †75

SENGER, Brian Paul. 9969 FREDERICKSBURG RD 78240 #028-34-1995 L1996 IM *020 †20

SEPULVEDA, Gladys S. 8401 DATAPOINT DR, STE 600O 78229 #042-01-1974 L1984 R DR *020 †80

SEPULVEDA, Pedro. 910 SAN PEDRO AVE 78212 #649-02-1986 L1994 CCM *020 †20

SEPULVEDA, Rene. 7909 FREDERICKSBURG RD #110 78229 #042-01-1974 L1981 U *020 †95

SERGOT, Paulina Barbara. ■ 78239 #035-01-2006 EM *012

SERNA, Carlos F. ■ 78232 #649-02-1954 L1963 GYN *071

SERRANO, Alberto Carlos. 400 N LOOP 1604 E, AFTON OAKS 11 STE 270 78232 #132-01-1956 L1964 CHP P *071 †75

SERTICH, Anthony P, Jr. 7930 FLOYD CURL DR 78229 #048-12-1981 L1981 OTO FPS *020 †45

SERTICH, Christopher M. 45 NE LOOP 410, STE 900 78216 #048-13-1987 L1988 AN *020 †05

SESSIONS, Daniel John. ■ 78250 #021-05-2008 *012

SEWARD, Jeffrey S. 7500 BARLITE BLVD, STE 313 78224 #048-15-1991 L1992 P *020

SEZGINIS, Aral Muhsin. ■ 78229 #038-40-2006 PM *012

SHABOON, May. ■ 78229 #056-06-1992 L1993 IM *075

SHAFFER, Brett Michael. ■ 78260 #023-12-2006 L2008 EM *012

SHAFFER, Richard Thos. 855 PROTON RD 78258 #010-01-1984 L1993 IM GE *020 †20

SHAH, Amita R. ■ 78230 #048-13-2005 GS *012

SHAH, Anand Devendra. ■ 78248 #035-03-2003 L2005 CD *012 †20

SHAH, Anup Ajit. ■ 78240 #473-01-2003 L2007 ORS *012

SHAH, Jaydeep Shantilal. 45 NE LOOP 410, STE 900 78216 #051-04-1993 L2000 AN PAN *020 †05

SHAH, Jayesh B. 7500 BARLITE BLVD STE 107, SW CTR FOR WOUND CARE 78224 #495-23-1992 L1995 UM IM *020 †20

SHAH, Neil S. 7703 FLOYD CURL DR, U TX MED SCH SAN ANTONIO 78229 #048-13-2007 TY *012

SHAH, Shafqat. 7703 FLOYD CURL DR, MC 7810 78229 #036-07-1991 L1995 PHO *020 †55

SHAIKH, Jawad Zar. 343 W HOUSTON ST STE 109, JAWAD ZAR SHAIKH MD 78205 #704-22-1986 L1997 CD *020 †20

SHAIKH, Suhail Ahmed. 7703 FLOYD CURL DR 78229 #704-16-2001 FP *012

SHALTZ, Abigail Therese. ■ 78209 #026-04-2007 OBG *012

SHANFIELD, Stephen B. ■ 78209 #005-06-1965 L1986 P *071 †75

SHANKLIN, Kenneth Dale. ■ 78245 #049-01-1967 L1969 PS GS *071 †85,65

SHANNON, Nick Harold. 3326 E SOUTHCROSS BLVD 78223 #017-20-1965 L1965 GP GYN *020

SHAPIRO, Jonathan B. ■ 78230 #024-05-2005 L2007 PD *012

SHARAF, Rashid. 8038 WURZBACH RD, STE 480 78229 #704-22-1991 L2003 NEP *020 †20

SHARKEY, Francis Edward. 7703 FLOYD CURL DR, UNIV OF TEXAS HEALTH SCI C 78229 #035-20-1970 L1988 ATP *020 †50 ‡

SHARP, William T. 4242 MEDICAL DR, STE 3100 78229 #048-02-1986 L1987 AN *020 †05

SHARY, Thomas M. ■ 78232 #048-14-2008 *012

SHAUGHNESSY, Paul Jos. 7711 LOUIS PASTEUR, STE 708 78229 #017-20-1991 L1998 HO IM *020 †20

SHAVER, Benjamin Borroum. ■ 78258 #048-02-1939 L1939 PD *071 †55

SHAW, Bryan Ingram. ■ 78240 #028-34-2006 PTH *012

SHAW, Burton G. 1303 MCCULLOUGH AVE, STE 135 78212 #048-13-1982 L1983 FM *020 †16

SHAW, Jerod Kaleb. 7703 FLOYD CURL DR, DEPT OF REAHB MED MSC 7798 78229 #048-02-2005 PM *012

SHAW, Leonora O W. ■ 78256 #023-12-1983 L2004 OBG *020 †30

SHAYNE, John P. 343 W HOUSTON ST, STE 705 78205 #035-06-1980 L2003 GS *020 †85

SHEA, William James. 148 SCHREINER PL, 148 SCHREINER PLACE 78212 #024-16-1980 L1993 DR *020 †80

SHEARING, Robert Lawrence. 3 LA PENINSULA 78248 #005-06-1988 L2005 NS *012

SHEDD, Andrew Douglas. ■ 78229 #048-13-2008 *012

SHEEHAN, Maureen Kelly. ■ 78209 #016-43-1998 L2006 VS *020 †85

SHEIKH, Shahzad A. 14351 BLANCO RD, KID-DOC PEDIATRICS 78216 #704-02-1982 L1998 PD *020 †55

SHEPHERD, Alexander M M. 7703 FLOYD CURL DR, DEPARTMENT OF MEDICINE 78229 #919-02-1969 L1979 PA IM *050

SHEPHERD, John Milton, II. 4242 MEDICAL DR, STE 3100 78229 #023-12-1987 L1998 AN FM *020 †05

SHEPHERD, Matthew Ellis. 4242 E SOUTHCROSS BLVD # 1 78222 #038-43-2001 L2006 GS *020 †85

SHERBURNE, Kelsey Kendall. ■ 78245 #007-02-2006 PD *012

SHERMAN, David Gordon. 7703 FLOYD CURL DR, UNIV HEALTH SCIENCE CENTER 78229 #039-01-1967 L1983 N *040 †75

SHETTY, Ashwinkumar. 7400 BARLITE BLVD, SOUTHEWEST GENERAL HOSPITA 78224 #495-04-1979 L1987 DR NM *020 †80

SHEYPUK, Laureen Helen. ■ 78204 #023-12-2007 GS *012

SHIH, Edwin Chuck. 900 NE LOOP 410, STE D207 78209 #048-13-2000 L2004 AN *020 †05 ‡

SHIH, Roger Yiwei. ■ 78245 #051-04-2007 IM *012

SHIH, Weiwen Vivian. ■ 78245 #048-13-2008 *012

SHIMOTSU, Karen S. 14855 BLANCO RD STE 204 78216 #048-12-1986 L1987 FM *020 †18

SHINGLE, Robert Chas. 7950 FLOYD CURL DR, STE 510 TOWER 1 78229 #048-02-1954 L1954 GP FM *071

SHIPMAN, Bradley N. 5307 BROADWAY ST 78209 #048-13-1995 L1997 IM *020 †20

SHIREMAN, Paula Kay. 7703 FLOYD CURL DR, MC 7741 78229 #017-20-1990 L1999 VS *020 †85

SHIVA, Mallaiah. 14094 OCONNOR RD 78247 #495-33-1969 L1982 GP EM *020

SHIVER, Emily Brooks. ■ 78249 #041-15-2007 PD *012

SHOUMAKER, Robert Dennis. ■ 78230 #049-01-1968 L1978 N *071 †75,20

SHOWS, Jane A. 8715 VILLAGE DR, STE 300 78217 #048-15-1999 L2003 OBG *020 †30

SHRINER, David Lee. 18540 SIGMA RD 78258 #021-01-1990 L1996 DS D *020 †15

SHRINER, Sandra Dean. 13 GRANTS LAKE DR, SANDRA SHRINER MD 78248 #048-02-1992 L1993 PM *020 †60

SHROYER, Steven Roy. 8401 DATAPOINT DR, STE 500 78229 #048-13-1984 L1987 EM *020 †16

SHULMAN, David Geo. 999 E BASSE RD STE 127 78209 #030-06-1973 L1973 OPH *020 †35

SHURE, Lesley. 9150 HUEBNER RD, STE 350 78240 #051-04-1995 L1995 ORS OSS *020

SIBAI, Rana Candice. ■ 78249 #038-41-2006 P *012

SIDDIQUI, Huma Atique. ■ 78256 #704-01-1990 L2005 PP *020 †50

SIDDIQUI, Saima. 527 N LEONA ST 78207 #704-06-1988 L2005 FM *020 †18

SIEGEL, Lawrence Jon. 7400 MERTON MINTER ST, MEDICAL SERVICE 111 78229 #048-04-1980 L1980 GE IM *020 †20

SILASI, Dan-Arin. ■ 78240 #781-04-1993 L2005 OBG *100

SILBER, Gail Frances. 8915 DATAPOINT DR RM A51C 78229 #165-01-1981 L1992 PD *020

SILENAS, Rasa Sylvia. 7700 FLOYD CURL DR 78229 #041-07-1978 L1991 PS GS *030 †85,65

SILL, Joshua Michael. ■ 78209 #048-02-2002 PCC *012 †20

SILVA, Anna L. 9011 POTEET JOURDANTON FWY 78224 #048-13-1990 L1992 PD *020 †55

SILVA, Ezequiel, III. 8401 DATAPOINT DR, STE 600 78229 #048-04-1996 L1997 DR OS *020 †80

SILVA, Jeanette. 7400 MERTON MINTER ST, MC 00E 78229 #264-13-1999 L2005 FPG *020 †18

SILVA, Luis Ysmael. 8038 WURZBACH RD, STE 340 78229 #048-13-2003 L2006 IM *020 †20

SILVA, Roberto Alexius. 5655 S IH 35 78211 #048-12-1978 L1979 N *020

SILVERMAN, Morey Jay. 333 N SANTA ROSA 78207 #004-01-1979 L1980 PEM *020 †55

SILVEY, Michael Sean. ■ 78240 #016-76-2007, ▲ PD *012

SIMCIC, Kenneth Jos. 701 S ZARZAMORA ST 78229 #041-13-1982 L2003 END *020 †20

SIMMONS, Deondra Patrice. ■ 78229 #010-02-2007 IM *012

SIMMONS, James Walter, Jr. 12770 CIMARRON PATH, STE 132 78249 #027-01-1962 L1967 OSS *020 †40

SIMON, Matthias. 7703 FLOYD CURL DR, UNIV TX MED SCH-SAN ANTONI 78229 #409-07-1993 L2006 NEP *100 †20

SIMPSON, Carl Geo. ■ 78232 #025-07-1983 L1989 P *020 †70

SIMPSON, Charles. 7703 FLOYD CURL MS7777, UTHSCSA 78229 #048-02-1990 L1991 OTO *020 †45

SIMPSON, Cristina Paloma. 525 OAK CENTRE DR 78258 #039-01-1996 L1997 OBG *020 †30

SIMPSON, Joseph Anthony. 4242 MEDICAL DR, STE 6300 78229 #019-02-1974 L1976 P *020 †75

SIMPSON, Tamara Smith. 7703 FLOYD CURL DR 78229 #048-14-2001 L2004 PCC *012

SIMS, James Kendall. 4242 MEDICAL DR, STE 310 78229 #048-12-1971 L1971 AN *020 †05

SIMS, Robert Peter. 7330 SAN PEDRO STE 405 78216 #011-03-1980 L1983 EM IM *020 †20

SINE, Christy Ross. ■ 78251 #045-01-2007 IM *012

SINGER, Michael Andrew. 315 N SAN SABA, MEDICAL CENTER STE 970 78207 #024-05-1986 L1995 OPH *020 †35

SINGH, Kamal Deep. ■ 78260 #023-12-2001 L2003 NM *020 †80,28

SINGH, Meera. 1954 E HOUSTON ST, RM 104 78202 #422-01-2002 L2005 PD *020

SINGH, Prafulla Chandra. 1200 BROOKLYN AVE, STE 140 78212 #495-51-1987 L1995 AN PMM *020 †05

SINGH, Shaman Kumar. ■ 78251 #016-11-2005 L2008 IM *012

SINGH, Vivek. 7703 FLOYD CURL DR, UNIV OF TEXAS 78229 #495-65-1994 L2002 P *020 †75

SINGLETON, Charles M. 1303 MCCULLOUGH AVE, STE 600 78212 #012-05-1964 L1977 IM RHU *020 †20

SINGLETON, Randall Parris. 7909 FREDERICKSBURG RD, STE 110 78229 #039-01-1968 L1969 U *020 †95

SINGSTAD, Charles Paul. ■ 78218 #041-01-1995 L1997 EM *020 †16

SINISI, Nuala Jane. 4242 MEDICAL DR, STE 3100 78229 #017-20-1981 L1983 AN EM *020 †05

SIOCO, Geraldo M. 8026 FLOYD CURL DR, FL 2 78229 #048-13-1991 L1992 CD *020 †20

SIOJO-TAPAWAN, Lisabette. ■ 78247 #748-10-1981 RHU *100

SIRINEK, Kenneth Robt. 4647 MEDICAL DR, UT MEDICINE 78229 #056-06-1969 L1979 GS AS *020 †85

SISSON, James H. ■ 78232 #004-01-1948 L1956 PTH *071 †50

SIT, Michelle Tsing. ■ 78218 #023-12-2003 L2005 RHU *012 †20 ‡

SITEK, Roman. 315 N SAN SABA STE 1075 78207 #286-03-1992 L2000 PD *020 †55

SIU, Lillian L. 8122 DATAPOINT DR, STE 700 78229 #065-01-1991 L1997 ON *020 †20

SJUVE, Rolf Ragnar. ■ 78258 #858-01-1996 PTH *100

SKANDIS, Richard James. 7400 MERTON MINTER ST 78229 #016-11-1978 L1980 IM FM *020

SKEETE, Larry Johann. ■ 78251 #043-01-1997 L2004 EM *020 †16

SKERHUT, Holger Ernst I. 1935 NE LOOP 410, STE 164 78217 #048-13-1976 L1976 NS GS *020 †25

SKINNER, Clay Royal. 124 DALLAS ST, SKINNER CLINIC 78205 #021-01-1974 L1980 GS VS *020 †85

SKOP, Brian Perry. 14815 SAN PEDRO AVE 78232 #028-02-1992 L1998 P PFP *020 †75

SLAHETKA-KARABITO, Mary. BEXAR COUNTY HOSP DISTRICT 78284 #048-13-1990 L1992 GE *075 †20

SLAUSON, James Wallace. 16414 SAN PEDRO STE 710 78232 #023-12-1989 L1993 EM IM *020 †20

SLAVINA, Anna. 7703 FLOYD CURL DR, UNIV TX MED SCH-SAN ANTONI 78229 #913-09-1991 L2007 FM *100 †18

SLESARENKO, Yury Anatoly. ■ 78209 #913-17-1991 L2007 ORS *100

SMITH, Anthony F. 540 MADISON OAK DR, STE 160 78258 #048-02-1982 L1983 DR *020 †80

SMITH, Benjamin Lightfoot. 7007 BANDERA RD, STE 19 78238 #422-01-2004 L2008 PD *100 †55

SMITH, Carl Kirk. 45 NE LOOP 410, STE 900 78216 #048-13-1994 L1995 AN *020 †05

SMITH, Cherie L. 7703 FLOYD CURL DR MS 7, HEALTH SCI 78229 #048-13-2005 OTO *012

SMITH, Daniel Douglas. 16414 SAN PEDRO AVE, STE 355 78232 #017-20-1995 L1998 EM *020 †16

SMITH, Douglas Kevin. 7950 FLOYD CURL SL1-21 78229 #036-05-1984 L1998 DR ORS *020 †80

SMITH, Earl Edgar, III. 1150 N LOOP 1604 W 78248 #039-01-1971 L1977 EM *020 †16

SMITH, Eileen A. 8601 VILLAGE DR, STE 118 78217 #048-13-1990 L1992 P *020 †75

SMITH, George Franklin. 8431 FREDERICKSBURG RD, STE 450 78229 #048-02-1977 L1977 FM MDM *030 †18

SMITH, Grace Li. ■ 78209 #008-01-2005 IM *100

SMITH, Harry Lincoln. 5711 UNIVERSITY HTS, STE 100 78249 #048-13-1978 L1978 DR NM *062 †28,80 ‡
SMITH, J Marvin, III. 6800 W IH 10, STE 300 78201 #021-01-1972 L1972 TS GS *020 †85,90 ‡
SMITH, James Howard. ■ 78239 #047-06-1938 L1940 OBG *071 †30
SMITH, James Martin. 4499 MEDICAL DR, STE 327 78229 #039-01-1971 L1974 PS AM *020 †85,65 ‡
SMITH, Jason David. ■ 78247 #021-01-2006 L2007 EM *012
SMITH, John Flint, Jr. 16414 SAN PEDRO AVE, STE 355 78232 #011-02-2000 L2002 EM *020 †16
SMITH, John Michael. ■ 78250 #021-05-2005 L2006 IM *012
SMITH, Ken Rogers. 4241 WOODSTOCK DR, STE A-100 78228 #048-02-1971 1971 IM *020 †20
SMITH, Kirsten L. 4499 MEDICAL DR, METHODIST WOUND CARE CENTE 78229 #048-13-2002 L2007 GS *100 †85
SMITH, Larry Allen. ■ 78209 #016-06-1933 L1971 IM AM *020 †70
SMITH, Lon Shelby. 155 E SONTERRA BLVD, STE 200 78258 #021-06-1979 L1981 ON IM *020 †20
SMITH, Mark Keith. 9969 FREDERICKSBURG RD 78240 #048-13-1984 L1985 FM *020 †18
SMITH, Melvin Douglas. 333 N SANTA ROSA 78207 #010-03-1965 L1981 PDS GS *020 †85
SMITH, Michael Ray. 4214 E SOUTHCROSS BLVD 78222 #048-02-1984 L1985 FM *020 †18
SMITH, Nathan Michael. ■ 78218 #048-14-2007 IM *012
SMITH, Paul H, Jr. 5307 BROADWAY ST 78209 #047-05-1981 L1984 IM *020 †20
SMITH, Paxton Jordan. 540 MADISON OAK DR, STE 320 78258 #048-13-1979 1979 GS *020 †85
SMITH, Reginald B F. 78209 #352-07-1955 L1978 AN *071 †05
SMITH, Sally Tow. ■ 78213 #048-02-1960 L1960 OBG *071 †30
SMITH, Tobie Lynn. 78212 #035-48-2005 L2008 FP *012
SMITH, William Carl. 8715 VILLAGE DR, STE 618 78217 #048-04-1984 L1985 OTO HNS *020 †45
SMOLENS, Peter. 2391 NE LOOP 410, STE 405 78217 #041-13-1975 L1978 NEP IM *020 †20
SMOLIK, Jeremy S. 7703 FLOYD CURL DR, DEPT OF RADIO MS 78 78229 #048-13-2005 L2008 DR *012
SNEAD, Eva Lee. 7400 BARLITE BLVD 78224 #132-01-1965 L1967 FM *075
SNEDDON, Nathan Eldredge. ■ 78238 #030-05-2007 GS *012
SNEED, Letisha Annette. 4212 E SOUTHCROSS BLVD, STE 150 78222 #048-14-1996 L1998 PD *020 †55
SNELL, Erin Kathleen. ■ 78257 #048-04-2006 IM *012
SNIDER, Theodore Earnest. 7700 FLOYD CURL DR, SW TEXAS METHODIST HOSPITA 78229 #048-14-1989 L1990 PCP *020 †50
SNIDER, Thomas Harry. 220 IVY LN 78209 #035-20-1962 L1971 PTH *071 †50
SNIP, Robert Chas. 4775 HAMILTON WOLFE RD, STE 2 78229 #023-07-1974 L1979 OPH *020 †35
SNIP, Russell Thorn. ■ 78240 #023-07-1943 L1950 OPH *071 †35
SNOGA, Patricia A. 2211 NW MILITARY HWY, STE 201 78213 #048-13-1984 L1985 FM *020 †18
SOECHTING, Henry W. 45 NE LOOP 410 78216 #048-02-1982 L1983 AN *020 †05
SOKOLOVA, Elena Anatoliev. 7703 FLOYD CURL DR #MC7883, SCIENCE C 78229 #913-99-1997 L2005 N *012
SOLER, James E. ■ 78230 #010-03-1973 L1985 FM *020 †18
SOLOMON, Brett David. ■ 78240 #048-13-2007 GS *012
SOLOMON, Dale Edward. 4242 MEDICAL DR, STE 3100 78229 #048-13-1984 L1985 AN *020 †05
SOLOMON, Diane H. 7703 FLOYD CURL DR, UT HEALTH SCIENCE CENTER 78229 #048-13-1986 L1987 N *020 †75
SOLOMON, Sabrina Ann. 333 N SANTA ROSA AVE, STE B 78207 #051-04-2008 *012
SOMNER, John Philip. ■ 78229 #305-01-2001 L2006 FP *012
SON, Minnette T. 7703 FLOYD CURL DR, DEPT OF PEDIATRICS 78229 #048-13-1990 L1991 CCP *020 †55
SONETTI, David Andrew. ■ 78249 #056-05-2004 PCC *012 †20
SONGCO, Gary Max. 1200 BROOKLYN AVE STE 250 78212 #016-42-1982 L1987 PUD *020 †20
SOPO, Christine Agnes. ■ 78258 #011-02-1997 L2004 MPD *020 †20,55
SORIANO, Elizabeth J. 311 CAMDEN ST, STE 214 78215 #748-10-1981 L1987 PD NPM *020 †55
SORRELL, Jeff W. ■ 78254 #048-13-2007 IM *012
SOSA, Mario. 2121 SW 36TH ST, UNIV FAMILY HLTH CTR SW UH 78237 #649-07-1978 L1993 PD *020 †55
SOSTRE, Cesar Francisco. 4647 MEDICAL DR 78229 #042-01-1979 L1984 IM GE *020 †20
SOULAS, Moises M, Jr. 343 W HOUSTON ST STE 705 78205 #048-13-1989 L1995 GS *020 †85
SOUNDARRAJ, Dwarakraj. ■ 78216 #495-94-1995 L2005 CD *100
SOWDEN, David. 7703 FLOYD CURL DR, DEPT OF ORAL & MAXILLOFAC 78229 #048-13-2001 GS *100
SOWELL, John Michael. 6711 S NEW BRAUNFELS AVE 78223 #045-01-1957 L1974 PHP *020 †70
SOWIN, Timothy Wm. ■ 78218 #035-09-1982 L1985 P *020 †75,70
SPADACCINI, Cathy J. 301 N FRIO ST 78207 #026-04-1974 L1980 PTH *020 †50
SPAIN, Michael Douglas. ■ 78269 #048-12-1980 L1980 PTH *075 †50
SPARKMAN, Mark K. 4502 MEDICAL DR, UNIVERSITY HOSPITAL 78229 #048-12-1996 L2000 EM *020 †16
SPARKS, John Carston. 24855 BREEZE OAK 78255 #016-11-1953 L1971 P PFP *030 †75
SPARKS, Vicki Jean. 5101 SAN PEDRO AVE # 2 78212 #048-13-1976 L1976 GP EM *020 †16
SPAULDING, Thomas M. ■ 78209 #025-07-1943 L1944 OS OM *071
SPEARS, Robert Paul. 7500 BARLITE BLVD, STE 211 78224 #021-06-1990 L1995 OTO *020 †45
SPEBAR, Michael John. 730 N MAIN, STE 724 78205 #017-20-1973 L1978 TS GS *075 †85
SPECTOR, Morris. 128 LA MANDA BLVD, MAIL ADD: P.O.BOX 15273 78212 #016-06-1957 L1958 GP *071
SPEEDLIN, Richard Arthur. 1200 BROOKLYN AVE, STE 130 78212 #048-13-1980 L1981 FM *020
SPEEG, Kermit Vincent, Jr. 7703 FLOYD CURL DR DEPT IM 78229 #048-12-1972 L1983 IM *050 †20
SPEICHER, Peter Jos. 730 N MAIN AVE, STE 418 78205 #010-02-1982 L1990 OPH *020 †35
SPEIGHTS, James Wm. 7940 FLOYD CURL DR STE 820 78229 #048-04-1968 L1968 OPH *020 †35
SPENCE, C Ritchie. 7909 FREDERICKSBURG RD, STE 125 78229 #048-02-1964 L1964 U *020 †20
SPENCE, Lawrence Roleke. 3453 N IH 35 STE 110, CONCENTRA MEDICAL CENTER 78219 #048-13-1977 L1977 FM *020 †70,18
SPEZIA, Catherine A. 624 E EL PRADO DR 78212 #048-12-1989 L1991 OBG *020 †30
SPIGEL, Matthew Eric. ■ 78254 #003-75-2007, ▲ GS *012

SPILLANE, Anne Patricia. ■ 78218 #023-01-2007 TY *012
SPITZ, Richard Jonathon. 7703 FLOYD CURL DR, UTHSCSA / SURGERY / MC7736 78229 #016-42-1998 L2001 EM *020 †16
SPONSEL, William Eric. 311 CAMDEN ST STE 306, UTHSCSA-DEPT OPHTHALMOLOGY 78215 #917-02-1983 L1994 OPH *020 †35
SPOON, Donald Ray. ■ 78248 #028-02-1977 L1988 FM AM *071 †18
SPRAGUE, Steven D. 14100 NACOGDOCHES RD, HEALTH 78247 #048-13-1991 L1992 FM *020 †18
SPRATLEY, Kristeen R. 13535 JONES MALTSBERGER RD 78247 #048-13-1992 L1994 CHP *020 †75
SRA, Sharon Kaur. 414 NAVARRO ST, STE 400 78205 #048-02-2000 L2006 OPH *020
SREERAMOJU, Pranavi Veera. 7703 FLOYD CURL DR, MC 7881 78229 #495-53-1995 L2005 ID EP *100 †20
SRINIVASAN, Venkatasubrama. 660 SW MILITARY DR, STE E 78221 #495-16-1991 L2002 IM *020 †20
SRINIVASAN, Venkatesan. 4330 MEDICAL DR, STE 325 78229 #495-21-1970 L1983 PCS *020 †85,90
SRIPADA, Prasad Girija. 7703 FLOYD CURL DR 78229 #495-11-1971 L1982 P ADP *020 †75
STAFFORD, Gordon Oceola. ■ 78230 #048-02-1959 L1959 AN OS *071 †05
STAGGS, Rebecca Nonalee. ■ 78240 #048-13-2008 *012
STALKER, Matthew Jay. 540 MADISON OAK DR, STE 160 78258 #030-06-2000 L2006 DR *020 †80
STALLMAN, Kenneth J. 7909 FREDERICKSBURG RD, STE 110 78229 #048-02-1999 L2005 U *020 †95
STALLWORTH, Christian L. ■ 78231 #048-13-2004 OTO *012
STALLWORTH, Terresa L. 6711 S NEW BRAUNFELS AVE, STE 100 78223 #047-06-1963 L1974 P N *030 †75
STANEK, Robert Gunderson. ■ 78209 #005-02-1955 L1956 GS *071 †85
STANLEY, Colleen Noelle. ■ 78251 #016-11-2004 L2006 IM *020 †20
STANLEY, David Micheal. ■ 78238 #021-05-2007 GS *012
STANLEY, Earl Austin. 4499 MEDICAL DR, STE 235 78229 #001-02-1974 L1981 ORS *020 †40
STANLEY, Jay M. 7703 FLOYD CURL DR, U TX MED SCH SAN ANTONIO 78229 #048-13-2007 ORS *012
STARCK, Luz Consuelo. 12050 VANCE JACKSON RD, BLDG 2 78230 #264-05-1982 L1995 P *020 †75
STARCK, Tomy. 8200 IH 10 W, STE 730 78230 #264-05-1982 L1994 OPH *020 †35
STARLING, Garrett Daniel. ■ 78229 #048-13-2008 *012
STARLING, Kelley Marie. ■ 78209 #048-02-2000 L2005 CHP *100
STARR, Thomas Pierce. 215 N SAN SABA, STE 201 #607-20-12-1975 L1984 FM *075
STAWOWY, Lala Maria. 4499 MEDICAL DR STE 226 78229 #035-20-1981 L1987 D *020 †15
STEDMAN, Deborah. ■ 78230 #048-13-2007 IM *012
STEFFEN, Richard Todd. 9150 HUEBNER RD, STE 155 78240 #011-02-1991 L2000 ORS *020 †40
STEFKO, Raymond Matthew. 4499 MEDICAL DR, STE 235 78229 #047-20-1988 L2007 OP OTR *020 †40
STEGEMANN, Lloyd H. 9150 HUEBNER RD, STE 250 78240 #048-14-1998 L2003 GS *020 †85
STEHLY, Eric Matthew. 7703 FLOYD CURL DR, MC-7774 78229 #048-13-2002 L2006 ORS *012
STEIGELMAN, Daniel Anthon. ■ 78251 #023-12-2004 L2006 PD *100 †55
STEIGELMAN, Megan Burgess. ■ 78251 #023-12-2003 L2005 GS *012
STEINHISER, David Lynn, II. ■ 78249 #017-20-1998 L1999 AN *020
STEINKE, Kristopher Scott. 3031 IH 10 W, THE CENTER FOR HEALTH CARE 78201 #048-14-2002 L2006 P *020
STEINMANN, Aric Dennis. ■ 78253 #023-12-2007 IM *012
STENGER, Earl Martin. 123 ASCOT AVE, CENTRO DEL BARRIO 78224 #048-13-1970 L1971 P PMM *020
STEPHENS, Harry Hart, Jr. ■ 78240 #016-11-1959 L1961 FM GS *071 †18
STEPHENS, Peter Jos. ■ 78218 #048-13-1981 L1981 AM *020
STEPHENSON, Jackie Dean. 8601 VILLAGE DR, SKINNER CLINIC 78217 #048-12-1962 L1962 U *020 †95
STEPHENSON, Stacy M. 7703 FLOYD CURL DR RM 227L, SCIENCE CTR 78229 #038-40-2001 PS *012
STERLING, Laura Marie. 5107 MEDICAL DR 78229 #024-05-1994 L2005 FM *020 †70,18
STERN, George Irwin. 7922 EWING HALSELL DR #260 78229 #035-09-1974 L1977 OBG *020 †30
STERN, Michael Paul. UNIV TEX HLTH SCI CTR 78284 #041-01-1963 L1976 DIA CD *050 †20
STERN, Stephen Lewis. 7400 MERTON MINTER ST 78229 #035-19-1971 L2000 P *020 †75
STEVENS, Charles Saml. 5430 FREDERICKSBURG RD, STE 604 78229 #048-13-1977 L1977 DMP D *020 †15
STEVENS, Robert Edward. 414 NAVARRO ST 78205 #018-03-1957 L1963 IM NEP *071 †20
STEWART, Ian James. ■ 78253 #005-06-2006 IM *012
STEWART, James Kenneth. ■ 78216 #004-01-1946 L1950 OM *071
STEWART, James Richard. 7950 FLOYD CURL DR, STE 201 78229 #018-03-1957 L1967 R *071 †80
STEWART, Ronald Mack. 7703 FLOYD CURL DR, UTHSCSA DEPT OF SURGERY 78229 #048-13-1985 L1987 CCS *020 †85
STEWART, Theresa Lynn. 8122 DATAPOINT DR, STE 1300 78229 #025-07-1991 L2003 OBG MFM *020 †19,30
STINSON, Zachary Sullivan. 7703 FLOYD CURL DR, SCIENCE C 78229 #048-02-2007 ORS *012
STOCKER, Allison Jones. ■ 78215 #048-13-1993 L1994 D DS *020 †15
STOCKER, Eric H. 4411 MEDICAL DR, STE 300 78229 #048-15-1993 L1994 CD IM *020 †20
STOGRYN, Ronald S. ■ 78260 #062-01-1974 L1979 PD GP *020
STOKES, James Wm. 2050 WORTH RD STE 10, USA MED COMMAND MCHO CL H 78234 #041-01-1966 L1967 P OM *062 †75
STOKES, John Franklin. 7711 LOUIS PASTEUR DR, STE 212 78229 #048-12-1957 L1957 GYN *071 †20
STOKES, John Pittard. 7703 FLOYD CURL DR, MSC 6230 78229 #048-12-2000 L2004 OPH *020 †35
STOLL, Peggy Anne. 111 DALLAS ST 78205 #048-12-1982 L1983 PTH *020 †50
STOLLER, Jerry Joe. ■ 78258 #018-03-1962 L1973 P N *020
STOLLER, Richard Harris. ■ 78216 #028-03-1970 L1992 OM AM *071 †70
STOLOW, Joshua Bruce. 8527 VILLAGE DR, STE 103 78217 #041-12-1984 L1985 RHU IM *020 †20
STONE, Cynthia L. ■ 78209 #048-16-1993 L1994 FM *020 †18
STONE, Gregory I. ■ 78209 #023-12-1986 L1988 EM *020 †16
STOOL, Claudia R Simon. ■ 78213 #038-41-1949 L1961 D *071 †15
STORANDT, Michelle Lynn. 14855 BLANCO RD STE 400, TEJAS PEDIATRICS 78216 #048-13-2001 L2005 CHN *020 †55

■ = Address Information Privacy Protected

STORY, Jim Lewis. 414 NAVARRO ST 78205 #047-05-1955 L1962 NS *071 †25
STOTHOFF, Alice F. 8401 DATAPOINT DR, STE 500 78229 #048-14-2001 L2004 EM *020 †16
STOWE, Robert Homan. 5802 S PRESA ST 78223 #048-14-1986 L1987 P ADM *020 †75
STRAHAN, Arthur L. ■ 78250 #048-13-2005 ORS *012
STRANSKY, Gregor. 2303 SE MILITARY DR, WOMEN S HEALTH LABORATORIE 78223 #154-07-1984 L1997 PTH *020 †30
STRATTON, Cary Edward. 1310 MCCULLOUGH AVE 78212 #048-02-1967 L1967 OTO *020 †45
STRATTON, Robt Frank, Jr. 7703 FLOYD CURL DR, MAIL CODE 7809 78229 #041-12-1975 L1978 MG *020 †55,19
STREEPER, Necole Marie. ■ 78216 #018-03-2007 GS *012
STREHLOW, Robert. 4242 MEDICAL DR, STE 3100 78229 #048-12-1993 L1997 AN *020 †05
STREITMAN, David C. 5414 FREDERICKSBURG RD, STE 200 78229 #048-04-1994 L1997 OBG *020 †30
STRIBLEY, Richard F. 7703 FLOYD CURL DR, DEPT OF PEDIATRICS MC7812 78229 #025-12-1983 L1983 NPM PD *040 †05
STRICKLAND-SMITH, A. 701 S ZARZAMORA ST 78207 #028-02-1985 L1996 EM IM *020 †16
STRODE, Christofer Aaron. ■ 78244 #023-12-2000 L2007 EM *020 †16
STRUS, Deborah A. ■ 78227 #048-13-1994 GS *012
STUART, Joseph Jay. ■ 78251 #023-12-2003 L2005 ORS *012
STUART, Norton A. ■ 78209 #048-12-1987 L1989 IM *020 †05
STUCKEY, John Hamlin. 7700 FLOYD CURL DR, PATH DEPT 78229 #021-01-1983 L1983 PTH IM *020 †50
STUEMPFIG, Scott Donald. ■ 78230 #056-05-2004 PM *012
STUTTS, Baldwin S, III. 4330 MEDICAL DR STE 400 78229 #021-01-1969 L1978 CD IM *020 †20
STYSLINGER, Edward W. 45 NE LOOP 410 78216 #056-06-1989 L2003 CCA *020 †05
SUAREZ, Laura A. 155 E SONTERRA BLVD # 211 78258 #048-02-1986 L1987 RHU *100
SUDARSHAN, Sunil. 7703 FLOYD CURL DR, MAIL CODE 7845 78229 #036-07-1999 L2007 U *100
SUESCUM, Alfredo Timoteo. PO BOX 240609 78224 #010-01-1962 L1992 PYA *071 †75
SUESCUN, Elkin. 2620 MCCULLOUGH AVE 78212 #264-05-1964 L1973 IM HEM *020
SULISTIO, Melanie Sue. 13815 BENT RIDGE DR, 7703 FLOYD CURL DR, SA, T 78249 #048-13-2002 L2005 CD *012 †20
SULLIVAN, Barbara Mendell. 4400 S PIEDRAS DR, STE 200 78228 #048-04-1979 L1979 DR *020 †80
SULLIVAN, Helen Ludeweka. 6711 S NEW BRAUNFELS AVE, STE 100 78223 #021-05-1975 L1990 GP LM *020
SULLIVAN, William Thrall. 4400 PIEDRAS DR S # 2, RADIOLOGY ASSOC OF SAN ANT 78228 #048-04-1979 L1979 DR *020 †80
SUMERLIN, Linda Ramona. 14427 BROOK HOLLOW, # 278 78232 #048-13-1986 L1987 FM *020 †18
SUMMERS, Ashley V. ■ 78209 #048-13-2007 FP *012
SUMMERS, Shane Michael. ■ 78215 #048-23-2005 L2006 EM *012
SUMNER, Gardner. 750 E MULBERRY AVE STE 325, SEVERANCE AND ASSOCIATES 78212 #048-13-1980 L1980 PTH EM *071 †50
SUMNER, Keith Neal. 45 NE LOOP 410, STE 900 78216 #048-13-1988 L1989 AN *020 †05
SUMNER, Nathan Shane. ■ 78245 #001-06-2006 L2008 IM *020
SUMNER, Todd. 7703 FLOYD CURL DR, U TX MED SCH SAN ANTONIO 78229 #048-13-2001 GS *100
SURENDRANATH, Chittamuru. 315 N SAN SABA STE 1180, SUITE 1240 78207 #495-16-1987 L1997 GS *020 †85
SURIS, Orlando Javier. 540 MADISON OAK DR, STE 450 78258 #048-13-1985 L1986 OBG *020 †30
SURYA, Gundlapalli. 8038 WURZBACH RD STE 680 78229 #495-50-1968 L1988 P CHP *020 †75 ‡
SUTHERLAND, Ellen Wood. ■ 78248 #020-12-1983 L1999 PD *020 †55
SUTTON, Averell Hubbard. 1730 SW MILITARY DR, CENTRAL WOMENS HEALTH 78221 #047-07-1981 L1990 OBG *020 †30
SUTTON, Jennifer C. 1111 SE MILITARY DR 78214 #048-13-2001 L2005 FM *020 †18
SUTTON, Shelby E. ■ 78229 #048-13-2008 *012
SWABY, Michael Garrett. ■ 78228 #048-14-2007 PTH *012
SWAMY, Anita Narayan. ■ 78216 #041-15-2002 L2002 PDE *012 †55
SWAN, John Thos. 8214 WURZBACH RD 78229 #048-02-1980 L1980 GE IM *020 †20
SWANEY, Glenn Paul. 45 NE LOOP 410 STE 900 78216 #038-43-1996 L1998 AN *020 †05
SWANN, Cynthia Ann. 4499 MEDICAL DR, STE 171 78229 #025-01-1981 L1997 DR *020 †80
SWANN, Karl Winston. 4410 MEDICAL DR 78229 #025-01-1979 L1986 NS *020 †25
SWANSON, Gregory Peter. 7979 WURZBACH RD, UTHSCA AT SAN ANTONIO 78229 #048-14-1985 L1986 RO U *020 †80
SWARTZ, Barry Edward. 2829 BABCOCK RD, STE 429 78229 #041-13-1971 L1974 PS *020 †65
SWARTZMAN, Sheila. 4242 MEDICAL DR, STE 3100 78229 #836-01-1966 L1979 AN *040 †05
SWEDEAN, Sandra Kay. ■ 78254 #030-06-2008 *012
SWEET, Melanie. 4502 MEDICAL DR 78229 #035-47-1980 L1987 PN PD *020 †55
SWENSON, Peter Clifton. 45 NE LOOP 410 STE 900 78216 #048-13-1977 L1977 AN *020 †20
SWIFT, Robert Cameron. ■ 78250 #023-12-2005 L2007 AN *012
SWITZER, Richard M, Jr. 4212 E SOUTHCROSS BLVD, STE 150 78222 #035-03-1989 L2005 PD *020 †55
SYED, Nazim Ali. 7400 BARLITE BLVD, ADMINISTRATIVE SUITE 78224 #704-16-1996 L2006 IM *020 †20
SYKES, John Herndon James. ■ 78209 #048-04-1954 L1954 OPH *071 †35
SYKES, Mellick Tweedy. 7950 FLOYD CURL DR STE 109 78229 #048-02-1976 L1976 VS GS *020 †85
SYMONS, John Gideon. ■ 78247 #016-42-2006 L2007 IM *012
SYMS, Charles Augustine. 21 SPURS LN, STE 100 78240 #041-02-1985 L1998 OTO *020 †45
SZABO, Charles Akos. 7703 FLOYD CURL DR, UTSHC AT SAN ANTONIO 78229 #154-07-1989 L1996 N *020 †75
SZETO, Tedmond Chiwai. ■ 78253 #023-12-2007 IM *012
SZEWC, Robert Grzegorz. 315 N SAN SABA, STE 102 78207 #759-06-1991 L2001 NEP IM *020 †20
TABAN, Noela Liyong. 7703 FLOYD CURL DR, DEPT OF ANESTHESIOLOGY 78229 #010-02-2006 AN *012
TABET, Adelaida S. 730 N MAIN AVE STE 520 78205 #682-01-1959 L1965 PD *020
TAEED, Roozbeh. 333 N SANTA ROSA AVE 78207 #048-02-1992 L1993 PD PDC *020 †55
TAIMOURI, Rosaria Abrigo. 3066 COMMERCE ST 78220 #048-02-1995 L1998 IM *020
TAKIMOTO, Chris Hidemi. 4319 MEDICAL DR, STE 205 78229 #008-01-1986 L2000 ON IM *050 †20
TALAL, Norman. 7703 FLOYD CURL DR, DEPT. OF PEDIATRICS 78229 #035-01-1958 L1983 RHU IM *050 †20

TALAYERO, Beatriz Garate. 7703 FLOYD CURL DR, UNIV TX MED SCH-SAN ANTONI 78229 #649-13-2001 L2006 IM *100 †20
TALLEY, Brenda Jean. 333 N SANTA ROSA AVE 78207 #048-13-1984 L1985 P *020 †75
TALLEY, David R. 7979 WURZBACH RD, URSCHEL TOWERS #233 78229 #048-04-1989 L1994 U *020 †95
TALLEY, Elizabeth Dimick. ■ 78232 #048-02-1945 L1945 P *071
TALLEY, Stephen J. 150 E SONTERRA BLVD, STE 200 78258 #048-04-1982 L1983 OTO FPS *020 †45
TALUKDAR, Subrata K. 1200 BROOKLYN AVE STE 200 78212 #495-32-1985 L2004 CD ON *100 †20
TAMAYO, Hector E. 11600 BANDERA RD STE 10, PMB 50 78250 #048-13-1998 L1999 IM *020 †20
TAMEZ, Daniel David. 111 DALLAS ST, STE 200-A 78205 #048-13-1976 L1976 VS *020 †85
TAMEZ, Richard Joseph. 323 NW 24TH ST, COMPLEX 78207 #028-78-1954, ▲ L1955 FM FPG *071
TAN, Chun Wang Y. 1200 BROOKLYN AVE, STE 200 78212 #748-08-1988 L1997 CD *020 †20
TAN, Weihan. ■ 78254 #048-13-2007 L2007 IM *012
TANJAVUR, Abirami Ravikum. 7703 FLOYD CURL DR 78229 #496-28-2000 FM *100
TANJUATCO, Augusto Jose P. 7400 MERTON MINTER ST 78229 #748-02-1987 L1991 END IM *100 †20
TANO, Leonel. 711 KIRK PL 78226 #847-10-1974 L1977 GP *020
TANTON, Damon Danny. ■ 78253 #011-02-1999 L1999 IM *020 †20
TAPIA FLORES, Ricardo Efr. 7703 FLOYD CURL DR 78229 #319-01-1997 L2008 FM *020
TAPIA GOMEZ, Mario Alejan. 7703 FLOYD CURL DR, UNIV TX MED SCH-SAN ANTONI 78229 #231-01-2000 L2008 IM *100
TAPP, David Clarence. ■ 78251 #028-34-1978 L1986 NEP IM *071 †20
TARBOX, Lauren Eleanor. 78229 #048-13-2008 *012
TARBOX, Peter Alan. 2425 BABCOCK RD, STE 111 78229 #056-06-1993 L1998 N *020 †75
TASKER, David Ian. 16500 SAN PEDRO, STE 235 78232 #041-13-1969 L1973 OPH *020 †35
TATUM, Lawrence Glenn. 16414 SAN PEDRO, STE 355 78232 #048-14-1985 L1986 IM *020 †20
TAVAREZ, Roman Erik. 7703 FLOYD CURL DR 78229 #649-02-2005 FP *012
TAVERA, Roberto Antonio. 1200 BROOKLYN AVE, STE 240 78212 #048-12-1980 L1980 IM *020 †20
TAYLOR, G Robt. 1303 MCCULLOUGH AVE 78212 #035-15-1973 L1977 IM *020 †20
TAYLOR, Joel Zachary. 7434 LOUIS PASTEUR DR, ATRIUM #1 78229 #048-13-1975 L1975 OPH *020 †35
TAYLOR, Josiah Byford. ■ 78240 #048-12-1967 L1967 PTH *020 †50
TAYLOR, Kenneth A. ■ 78240 #048-02-1999 L2002 DR *020 †80
TAYLOR, Richard Philip. 7703 FLOYD CURL DR, DIVISION OF CRITICAL CARE 78229 #048-02-1984 L1995 CCP MPD *020 †20,55
TAYLOR, Sally Edith. 7703 FLOYD CURL DR 78229 #048-13-1985 L1986 P *030 †75
TAYLOR, Tim. 16414 SAN PEDRO AVE, STE 710 78232 #048-15-1998 L1999 EM *020 †16
TAYLOR, Travis Jay. ■ 78250 #048-04-2008 *012
TCHOU, Howard Pao-Hui. ■ 78238 #011-02-1964 L1973 PTH *071 †50
TECUANHUEY, Leopold A. 718 CUPPLES RD, STE 102 78237 #048-12-1990 L1993 NEP *020 †20
TECUANHUEY, Yolanda Elvia. 4242 MEDICAL DR, STE 3100 78229 #048-02-1998 L2005 PAN *100 †05
TECUANHUEY-RANGEL, L. 111 DALLAS ST, STE 801 78205 #649-18-1962 L1972 U NEP *072 †95
TEDESCO-EVANS, Katherine. ■ 78209 #021-06-2004 PM *012
TEDJA, Indriati. ■ 78248 #409-16-1982 L1984 PD *100
TENNER, Patricia A. 7711 LOUIS PASTEUR, STE 707 78229 #048-13-1992 L1994 CCP *020 †55
TENNISON, John Tilmon. 7418 MILITARY DR W 78227 #005-11-1998 L1999 P *020 †75
TERMULO, Cesar Santa Cruz. 3859 E SOUTHCROSS BLVD 78222 #748-01-1965 L1971 IM PUD *020
TERPOLILLI, Ralph N. 4502 MEDICAL DR 78229 #038-41-1982 L1986 EM *020 †16
TERRELL, Clark D. 11124 WURZBACH RD STE 206 78230 #048-02-1984 L1985 P *020 †75
TERRERI, Anthony Andrew. ■ 78259 #023-12-1995 L1996 NM *012 †18,80
TERRY, Arlo Clair. 1804 NE LOOP 410, STE 270 78217 #048-12-1979 L1979 OPH *020 †35
TERRY, Patricia Wise. 7909 FREDERICKSBURG RD, STE 110 78229 #048-13-1990 L1991 U *020 †95
TERRY, Stuart Alan. 315 N SAN SABA, STE 990 78207 #016-11-1968 L1973 OPH *020 †35
TESSIER, Darin Douglas. ■ 78249 #048-13-2007 ORS *012
TEZEL, Alicia Valerius. 2827 BABCOCK RD 78229 #048-13-1990 L1991 PD PEM *020 †55
THAGGARD, Alvin, III. 104 CROSS LN, NORTHWEST IMAGING CENTER 78209 #048-12-1972 L1972 DR GP *020 †80
THAKUR, Nishi. 7323 MARBACH RD, STE 104 78227 #496-14-1996 L2004 IM *020
THAMES, Todd A. 333 N SANTA ROSA AVE, FL 4 78207 #048-02-1995 L1998 FM *020 †18
THANGADA, Mrudula Rao. 525 OAK CENTRE DR, STE 400 78258 #001-06-1995 L1997 CHP *020 †75
THARAKAN, David K. 1202 E SONTERRA BLVD, STE 301 78258 #016-42-1997 L2000 FM *020 †20
THARIN, Baxter Dixon. ■ 78251 #023-12-2008 *012
THAYIL, Joseph John. ■ 78248 #495-80-1997 L2005 IMG *020 †20
THEAGENE, Samuel M. 6100 BANDERA RD, STE 710 78238 #649-02-1990 L1995 PM *020 †60
THEARD, Joycelyn Marie. 3338 OAKWELL CT, STE 205 78218 #024-01-1977 L1979 GE *020 †20
THEIS, Vernon David, Jr. 502 MADISON OAK DR, STE 240 78258 #048-14-1981 L1981 OBG *020 †30
THIET, Michele Dieu. 8550 DATAPOINT DR STE 250 78229 #048-02-1978 L1985 PS GS *020 †85,65
THILTGEN, Robert Douglas. 311 CAMDEN ST, STE 303 78215 #048-02-1963 L1963 OTO *071 †45
THODE, Kirstin Isobel. ■ 78249 #032-01-2006 L2008 P *012
THOMAS, Amy L. 2829 BABCOCK RD, TOWER 1, SUITE 236C 78229 #048-13-2002 L2005 FM *020 †18
THOMAS, James Wm. 6926 WASHITA WAY 78256 #048-02-1979 L1979 NTR IM *020 †20
THOMAS, John W. ■ 78232 #048-14-1988 L1989 DR *020 †20
THOMAS, Paul Jan. 333 N SANTA ROSA, PEDS HEM/ONC, 8TH FLOOR 78207 #010-01-1970 L1989 PHO PD *020 †55
THOMAS, Robert Powell. 4499 MEDICAL DR 78229 #048-02-1997 L2003 PDS *100 †85
THOMAS, Ryan Blaine. ■ 78254 #048-02-2005 ORS *012
THOMAS, Scott Andrew. 9157 HUEBNER RD 78240 #038-41-2003 L2007 OPH *020
THOMAS, Scott M. 2211 NW MILITARY HWY 78213 #048-13-2004 L2005 FM *020 †18
THOMASON, Albert Monroe. 6711 S NEW BRAUNFELS AVE 78223 #007-02-1963 L1977 END IMG *020 †20

■ = Address Information Privacy Protected

THOMPSON, Andrew Joseph. ■ 78254 #041-14-2007 **EM** *012
THOMPSON, Bruce Harvard. 8715 VILLAGE DR STE 410 78217 #012-05-1967 L1975 **GYN** *020
THOMPSON, Christopher M. 1 BURNWOOD 78254 #010-02-1991 L1999 **CD** *020 †20
THOMPSON, Elizabeth Jane. 15321 SAN PEDRO, STE 103 78232 #012-01-1953 L1968 **IM** *071
THOMPSON, George Richard. 7703 FLOYD CURL DR, DEPT OF INTERNAL MEDICINE, 78229 #028-03-2003 L2006 **ID** *012 †20
THOMPSON, Gregory Wilkins. 14615 SAN PEDRO, STE 200 78232 #048-02-1971 L1971 **D EM** *020 †15
THOMPSON, Ian Murchie, Jr. 7979 WURZBACH RD 78229 #021-01-1980 L1987 **U** *020 †95
THOMPSON, Jon Wesley. ■ 78249 #048-13-2001 **GS** *100
THOMPSON, Kadee Elizabeth. ■ 78249 #028-03-2003 L2005 **U** *012
THOMPSON, Mark Ernest. 502 MADISON OAK DR, STE 240 78258 #048-13-1994 L1998 **OBG** *020 †30
THOMPSON, Peter Melgaard. 7703 FLOYD CURL DR, MAIL CODE 7792 78229 #024-07-1988 L2000 **P** *020 †75
THOMPSON, Robert Gary. ■ 78258 #018-03-1965 L1966 **END PD** *071 †55
THOMPSON, Robert Knox. 8715 VILLAGE DR, STE 518 78217 #047-06-1983 L1985 **VS GS** *020 †85
THOMPSON, Robert Ladd. 4440 S PIEDRAS, STE 100 78228 #048-14-1981 L1981 **DR** *020 †80
THOMURE, Tiffany Nicole. ■ 78229 #048-13-2008 *012
THORNER, Richard Eric. 343 W HOUSTON ST, STE 808 78205 #024-01-1971 L1978 **ID IM** *020 †20
THORNTON, Cynthia J. 519 W HOUSTON ST, SANTA ROSA CHLDRNS HOSP ER 78207 #048-13-1982 L1985 **PD** *020 †55
THORNTON, Mark Lee. 7720 JONES MALTSBERGER RD 78216 #048-02-1980 L1980 **IM** *020 †20
THORNTON, William Davis, Jr. 45 NE LOOP 410, STE 900 78216 #048-15-1999 L2002 **AN** *020 †05
THUKRAL, Nandish Kumar. ■ 78229 #048-13-2003 L2006 **CD** *012 †20
THURLBY, Sage Vermont. 11519 SPYGLASS HLS 78253 #004-01-1998 L2003 **FM** *020 †18
THURMAN, Andrea Ries. 7703 FLOYD CURL DR, DEPT OF OB/GYN MAIL CODE 7 78229 #016-02-1994 L2006 **OBG** *020 †30
THURMAN, Cameron Mitchell. ■ 78258 #045-01-2006 L2008 **EM** *012
THURSTON, Charles Sparks. 909 ROSA VERDE TOWERS #909 78205 #047-07-1958 L1976 **D** *020 †15
TIAMSON-BEATO, Maria M. 78230 #748-01-1970 L1978 **PD AM** *020 †55
TIBBETTS, Todd Austin. ■ 78248 #048-04-2000 L2003 **DR** *100 †80
TICHY, Elizabeth Hughes. 7940 FLOYD CURL DR, STE 1010 78229 #048-13-2001 L2005 **D** *020 †15
TICKNOR, Christopher B. 1202 E SONTERRA BLVD, STE 202 78258 #048-13-1982 L1983 **P PFP** *020 †75
TIERNEY, John Gregory, II. 1202 E SONTERRA BLVD # 202 78258 #048-13-1988 L1989 **P PYG** *020 †75
TILLES, Jerome. ■ 78213 #023-01-1958 L1972 **P FM** *020 †75,18
TILLEY, Molly Ann. ■ 78245 #035-19-2003 L2005 **NEP** *012 †20
TILLMAN, Barbara Susan. 336 GENESEO RD 78209 #048-13-1984 L1986 **ID** *020 †20
TIMMER, Richard F. 14100 SAN PEDRO AVE, MACGREGOR MEDICAL ASSOCIAT 78232 #048-02-1960 L1960 **FM** *071
TIMMERMAN, Iva M. 7400 MERTON MINTER ST, AUDIE MURPHY VA HOSPITAL 78229 #048-13-1983 L1983 **P** *020 †75
TINER, Billy Don. 4499 MEDICAL DR, STE 190 78229 #048-13-1987 L1987 **OS** *020
TINGLE, Linda J. 4242 MEDICAL DR STE 3100 78229 #048-12-1987 L1989 **AN PME** *020 †05
TINITIGAN, Michelle Ann. ■ 78229 #748-01-2004 **FP** *012
TINKLER, Brandon A. ■ 78240 #048-13-2004 **ORS** *012
TIO, Audrey Oen. 7703 FLOYD CURL DR, DEPT OF INTERNAL MED 78229 #048-13-1999 L2002 **IM** *020 †20
TIO, Fermin. 4502 MEDICAL DR 78229 #748-11-1964 L1974 **ATP CLP** *050 †50
TIPPETT, Joe Wayne. 4203 E SOUTHCROSS BLVD, STE A 78222 #036-01-1967 L1972 **ORS** *020 †40
TISDALL, William Alec. 2425 BABCOCK RD, STE 108 78229 #054-04-2002 L2006 **APM** *020 †05
TJAHJA, Imam Eko. 1200 BROOKLYN AVE, STE 200 78212 #409-16-1981 L1995 **CD IM** *020 †20
TOBIN, Hugh Edward. 333 N SANTA ROSA AVE, PATHOLOGY ASSOCIATES OF 78207 #048-04-1983 L1983 **PTH HMP** *020 †50
TOBIS, John. 7703 FLOYD CURL DR, HEALTH SCIEN 78229 #048-02-2004 **CHP** *012
TOBON, Andrew A. 7909 FREDERICKSBURG RD, STE 110 78229 #048-04-1991 L1993 **U** *020 †95
TOLAR, Patrick Mitchell. 4499 MEDICAL DR STE 178, OB/GYN METHODIST PLZ BLDG 78229 #048-02-1961 L1966 **OBG OS** *020 †30
TOLAYMAT, Shadi Mohammad. 7434 LOUIS PASTEUR, STE 209 78229 #011-02-2001 L2005 **CD** *020
TOLCHER, Anthony William. 4319 MEDICAL DR, STE 205 78229 #061-01-1986 L1998 **ON** *020 †20
TOLEDO, Tony Milton. 1303 MCCULLOUGH AVE # 600 78212 #021-01-1965 L1971 **IM** *071 †20
TOLIN, Brad Steven. 150 E SONTERRA BLVD, SAN ANTONIO ORTHOPAEDIC 78258 #038-43-1986 L1992 **ORS OSM** *020 †40
TOMAN, Jeffrey Robert. 315 N SAN SABA STE 1240 78207 #030-06-1997 L2004 **CRS** *020 †85,10
TOMASOVIC, Jerry Jack. 525 OAK CENTRE DR, STE 400 78258 #016-02-1965 L1985 **N SME** *020 †55,75
TOMLINSON, Gail Elizabeth. 333 N SANTA ROSA 7810, PEDIATRICS-HEM/ONC 78207 #010-01-1984 L1989 **PHO** *040 †55
TONG, Lijuan. 343 W HOUSTON ST, STE 402 78205 #243-71-1987 L2004 **NEP** *020
TOOHEY, John Stephen. 701 S ZARZAMORA ST 78207 #056-05-1977 L1996 **ORS EM** *020 †40
TOOLE, Theron Colomb, II. 4411 MEDICAL DR, STE 300 78229 #047-07-1987 L1991 **AM** *100 †20,70
TORRES, Ernesto. 3851 ROGER BROOKE DR, DEPT. RADIOLOGY 78234 #042-02-1994 L2005 **DR** *020 †80
TORRES, Francis Manguera. ■ 78251 #748-24-2001 **GP** *100
TORRES, Luis Navarrete. 1920 SW MILITARY DR, STE 2 78221 #005-19-1988 L1995 **FM** *020 †18
TORRES, Monica. ■ 78229 #048-13-2005 **PM** *012
TORRES, Moyeda. ■ 78224 #649-02-1940 L1960 **GP** *020
TORRINGTON, Kenneth G. 35 BRISTOL GRN 78209 #030-05-1972 L1979 **PUD IM** *030 †20
TOTEN, Tracey L. 6570 INGRAM RD 78238 #048-02-1986 L1989 **FM** *020 †18

TOTH, Christine Mary. 7434 LOUIS PASTEUR DR, STE 109 78229 #041-09-1990 L1998 **NEP** *020 †20
TOTH, David Neil. 7400 MERTON MINTER ST 78229 #016-02-1972 L1983 **GP AM** *020 †70
TOU, Kevin Mu. ■ 78247 #023-12-2006 L2007 **AN** *012
TOURSARKISSIAN, Boulos A. 7703 FLOYD CURL DR, DEPT OF SURGERY 78229 #020-12-1989 L1998 **VS GS** *020 †85 ‡
TOWELL, Brian Dennis. 333 N SANTA ROSA AVE, PATHOLOGY ASSOCIATES OF 78207 #048-13-1983 L1983 **PTH** *020 †50
TOWNLEY, James Richard. ■ 78251 #023-12-2005 L2005 **OPH** *012
TOWNSEND, Marilu. 3819 HARRY WURZBACH RD, STE 6-3 78209 #056-06-1970 L1997 **EM** *020 †16
TOY, Jana Maria. 6711 S NEW BRAUNFELS AVE, TEXAS MHMR/SASH 78223 #048-13-1982 L1983 **P** *020
TRABAL, Jose F. 8122 DATAPOINT DR, STE 1300 78229 #042-01-1966 L1984 **OBG PHP** *020 †70,30 ‡
TRAKHTENBROIT, Anatole D. 4411 MEDICAL DR, STE 300 78229 #035-46-1984 L1985 **CD IM** *020 †20
TRAKHTENBROIT, David N. 78230 #913-86-1951 L1983 **FM** *020
TRAMER, Jonathan O. 8042 WURZBACH RD, STE 310 78229 #038-06-1969 L1975 **GS** *020 †85
TRAMPOTA, Sarah E. ■ 78229 #048-13-2005 **AN** *012
TRAN, Alyssa H. ■ 78247 #038-75-2007, ▲ **FP** *012
TRAN, Nhung T. 7703 FLYD CRL DR 78229 #048-13-1999 L2005 **PD** *020 †55
TRAUPMAN, Frank William. ■ 78240 #048-13-2008 *012
TRAUTMAN, Paul Andrew. 2020 BABCOCK RD STE 12 78229 #048-02-1983 L1983 **OBG** *020 †30
TREASURE, Robert Lee. 2303 SE MILITARY DR 78223 #007-02-1958 L1974 **TS GS** *071 †85,90
TRESSLER, Samuel D, III. 19238 STONEHUE 78258 #048-12-1977 L1977 **PD** *020 †55
TREVINO, Abram. ■ 78232 #048-13-2003 L2006 **HO** *012
TREVINO, Ana P. 7703 FLOYD CURL, DERMA MSC 7876 78229 #048-13-2002 L2005 **D** *012
TREVINO, Daniel Gerard. 1954 E HOUSTON ST, RM 104 78202 #649-02-1990 L1995 **PD** *020
TREVINO, Hector. 527 N LEONA ST 78207 #649-02-1960 L1984 **GE IM** *020
TREVINO, Hilario. 2827 BABCOCK RD 78229 #649-02-1955 L1966 **ORS** *020 †40
TREVINO, Jaime. ■ 78232 #649-02-1982 L1990 **FM** *020
TREVINO, James Greg. 8038 WURZBACH RD, STE 250 78229 #048-15-1992 L1995 **FM** *020 †18
TREVINO, Katherine E. ■ 78283 #048-13-2004 L2007 **FP** *012
TREVINO, Lucina B. 626 S ZARZAMORA ST 78207 #048-13-1992 L1995 **FM** *020 †18
TREVINO, Robert Pena. 740 S ALAMO ST 78205 #649-01-1980 L1986 **OS IM** *020
TREVINO, Roberto, Jr. 1303 MCCULLOUGH AVE # 428, METROPOLITAN PROFESSIONAL 78212 #649-30-1986 L1992 **IM ID** *020
TREVINO ZEPEDA, Jose A. 622 CAMDEN ST 78215 #649-02-1967 L1975 **OBG** *020 †30
TREXLER, Cheryl Ann. 540 OAK CENTRE DR, STE 200 78258 #048-02-1997 L2000 **PD** *020 †55
TRIANA, Gisela Pubchara. 2040 BABCOCK RD STE 403 78229 #048-13-1980 L1980 **P** *020 †75
TRIANA, Jose Fernando. 4411 MEDICAL DR, STE 300 78229 #264-04-1983 L1990 **CD** *020 †20
TRIANA, Maria Isabel. ■ 78230 #264-04-1992 **IM** *012
TRICHOPOULOS, Nikolaos. ■ 78257 #418-02-1998 L2000 **OPH** *100
TRICK, Lorence Wain. 7703 FLOYD CURL DR, UTHSCSA MSC774 78229 #010-01-1967 L1974 **ORS** *020 †40
TRICKETT, Lesia Malko. 7703 FLOYD CURL DR 78229 #913-99-1994 **P** *012
TRICKETT, Victoria C. 700 S ZARZAMORA ST STE 207 78207 #005-11-2001 L2005 **PFP** *100 †75
TRIGOSO, William F. 5107 MEDICAL DR 78229 #737-06-1987 L1996 **END IM** *020 †20
TRINIDAD, Elizabeth M. 4502 MEDICAL DR, UNIVERSITY NEUROSURGERY CL 78229 #048-13-1994 L2003 **NS GP** *020
TRIPATHY, Chandana. 701 S ZARZAMORA ST 78207 #495-13-1994 L2005 **IM** *100
TRIPATHY, Devjit. ■ 78260 #495-13-1987 L2005 **IM** *100 †20
TRIPP, George Allen. ■ 78251 #030-06-2006 L2008 **PD** *012
TROESTER, Otto Saeger. ■ 78248 #030-05-1954 L1954 **RO R** *071 †80
TROIANO, Robert Michael. ■ 78254 #031-01-2007 **P** *012
TROWBRIDGE, David Brian. ■ 78258 #048-13-2003 L2005 **CD** *012 †20
TROWBRIDGE, Michelle Eliz. 3031 IH 10 W, THE CENTER FOR HEALTH CARE 78201 #048-13-2002 L2006 **P** *100
TROXLER, R George. 527 N LEONA ST 78207 #021-05-1964 L1976 **GP IM** *020 †50
TROY, Janice M. ■ 78258 #048-14-1993 *075
TROY, Michael J. 540 MADISON OAK DR, STE 450 78258 #048-14-1991 L1993 **OBG** *020 †30
TRUAX, Allan Lincoln. 540 MADISON OAK DR, STE 160 78258 #028-34-1991 L2001 **DR** *020 †80
TRUE, Mark Windell. ■ 78258 #023-12-2000 L2006 **END** *020 †20
TRUITT, Christine L. 8042 WURZBACH RD, STE 640 78229 #048-13-1989 L1992 **N** *020 †75
TRUJILLO, Fernando. 999 E BASSE RD STE 127 78209 #264-16-1992 L2003 **OPH** *020 †35
TRUONG, Mayha. ■ 78249 #048-12-2002 L2005 **IM** *100
TRUSS, Hubert Nelson. ■ 78253 #048-12-1987 L2005 **NEP IM** *050
TSAI, Julie C. 343 W HOUSTON ST, STE 903 78205 #011-03-1988 L1995 **OPH IM** *020 †35
TSENG, Clevert Hugo. 315 N SAN SABA, STE 1075 78207 #737-06-1974 L1981 **PN PD** *020 †55
TSUKIFUJI, Neal H. 730 N MAIN AVE, STE 609 78205 #572-16-1948 L1963 **AN** *071
TUBBESING, Daniel Jos. 16414 SAN PEDRO AVE, STE 710 78232 #016-06-1992 L1997 **EM** *020 †16
TUCKER, Christopher J. ■ 78209 #023-12-2004 L2006 **ORS** *012
TUCKER, Myrna B. 6711 S NEW BRAUNFELS AVE 3 78223 #048-16-1988 L1989 **P** *020 †75
TUCKER, Thomas Andrew. 6800 PARK TEN BLVD # 299W 78213 #048-02-1964 L1964 **P N** *071
TUDER, Dmitry. ■ 78209 #023-12-2000 L2005 **HS** *012
TULLOUS, Micam Wade. 2827 BABCOCK RD 78229 #048-13-1984 L1985 **NSP** *020 †25
TULLY, John R. 16414 SAN PEDRO, STE 710 78232 #048-13-2001 L2004 **EM** *020 †16
TURKI, Hussein Wafik. ■ 78249 #012-05-2005 **ORS** *012
TURNER, Kirby Van Cleve. ■ 78270 #048-13-1974 L1974 **P** *020 †75
TURNER, Russell Akin. ■ 78232 #001-02-1984 L1988 **FM** *100 †18
TURULLOLS, Jesus. 5282 MEDICAL DR 78229 #649-01-1943 L1958 **PTH** *072 †50
TYLER, Joshua Andrew. ■ 78253 #023-12-2007 **GS** *012
TYLER, Michael Earl. 14615 SAN PEDRO AVE STE 235 78232 #048-14-1976 L1977 **FM** *020
TYNER, Ryan Patrick. ■ 78229 #035-09-2003 L2005 **GS** *012
UECKER, Jill B. ■ 78258 #048-13-2000 L2005 **PCP** *020 †50
UENO, Cristiane Mayumi. 7703 FLOYD CURL DR, UNIV TX MED SCH-SAN ANTONI 78229 #187-04-1998 **GS** *012
UHLER, Martha Kutashy. 8401 DATAPOINT DR STE 600 78229 #016-43-1989 L1996 **DR** *020 †80

ULMER, Scott Christopher. 155 E SONTERRA BLVD, STE 200 78258 #040-02-1996 L2003 HO *020 †20

ULRICH, Juliette Louise. ■ 78233 #048-13-1991 AN *100

UNGER, Howard R. ■ 78239 #010-01-1952 L1953 AM *071 †70

UNGER, Howard Robt, Jr. 540 MADISON OAK DR, STE 160 78258 #048-13-1982 L1983 DR *020 †80

UNSELL, Bryan Jason. ■ 78258 #023-12-2004 L2005 *100

UNZUETA, Mary R. 7703 FLOYD CURL DR, HEALTH SCIEN 78229 #048-13-2004 CHP *012

UPPAL, Nazli Masud. 8601 VILLAGE DR STE 100 78217 #704-06-1989 L2003 IM *020 †20

URBY, Rodolfo M. 527 N LEONA ST, MAIL STOP 49-2 78207 #048-14-1979 L1979 FM *020 †18

URIBE, Eduardo J. 18850 REDLAND RD 78259 #649-30-1987 L1998 FM *020 †18

URIEGAS, Rosalie C. 4502 MEDICAL DR 78229 #048-13-1999 L2002 FM *020 †18

URRUTIA, Aureliano Adolfo. 414 NAVARRO ST, STE 810 78205 #021-01-1959 L1966 GS *020 †85

USATINE, Richard Philip. 7703 FLOYD CURL DR 78229 #035-01-1982 L2004 FM D *020 †18

UY, Harry Lim. 1303 MCCULLOUGH AVE, STE 374 78212 #748-02-1986 L1994 END IM *020 †20

UY, Jimmy Y. 4242 E SOUTHCROSS BLVD, STE 15 78222 #748-01-1987 L1997 CCM *020 †20

UZQUIANO, Nelson G. ■ 78251 #048-15-1996 L2008 DR *020 †80

VADAKEKALAM, Jacob. 5107 MEDICAL DR 78229 #495-52-1981 L2000 END *020 †20

VAKEY, David Kirk. ■ 78249 #048-13-2008 *012

VALDES, Jesus Angel. 4402 VANCE JACKSON RD, STE 248 78230 #649-14-1980 L1984 IM *020 †20

VALDES, Nora Isabel. 5282 MEDICAL DR, STE 600 78229 #649-30-1986 L2000 FM *020 †18

VALDEZ, Alicia V. 98 BRIGGS ST, STE 800 78224 #016-11-1997 L2001 FM *020 †18

VALDEZ, Daniel C. 150 E SONTERRA BLVD, SAN ANTONIO ORTHOPAEDIC 78258 #048-13-1986 L1987 ORS *020 †40

VALDEZ, David A. 19208 TIERRA CV 78258 #048-13-1991 L1992 FM *020 †18

VALDEZ, Pedro. 3066 E COMMERCE ST 78220 #048-14-1998 FM *100

VALENTE, Philip Thos. 7703 FLOYD CURL DR, PATH DEPT 78229 #035-01-1977 L1988 ATP PCP *040 †50

VALENTIN, Frank Edgar. ■ 78260 #042-02-1998 L2006 OPH *020 †35

VALLE, Calixto Cedric, III. ■ 78212 #048-02-1967 L1967 P LM *062 †75

VALLE, Jose Julian. 4402 VANCE JACKSON RD, STE 220 78230 #036-05-2000 L2006 AN *020 †05

VALLES, Norma Milagros. ■ 78248 #042-01-1993 L2000 IM *020 †20

VAN, Thanh Thi. 9901 IH 10 W, STE 400A 78230 #048-04-1992 L2001 NM *020 †80,28

VAN BIBBER, Cecilia Avina. 3066 E COMMERCE ST 78220 #048-12-1987 L1990 PD *020 †55

VAN CLEAVE, Stephen Jan. 24165 IH 10 W, # 217-508 78257 #048-13-1974 L1974 IM EM *020 †20,16

VAN DELDEN, Ellen Swann. ■ 78257 #048-13-2004 N *012

VANDENBOS, Kermit Quentin. ■ 78213 #054-04-1953 L1980 AM GS *030 †85

VANDERBEEK, Rodger Duane. ■ 78247 #018-03-1982 L1983 GP AM *020 †70

VANDER PLOEG, Darl E. U TEX MED SCH, DEPT DERM 78284 #018-03-1949 L1968 D *071 †15

VANDERPOOL, Beverly Jo. ■ 78209 #048-02-1974 L1974 P CHP *071

VANDERPOOL, John Paul. ■ 78209 #047-06-1965 L1968 P *071 †75

VAN EIMEREN, William. 3066 E COMMERCE ST 78220 #048-02-1990 L1993 FM *020 †18

VAN HORN, Christina Gawry. 7703 FLOYD CURL DR, DEPT OF ANESTHESIOLOGY 78229 #030-06-2005 AN *012

VANN, Elliott Richard. 250 TREELINE PARK, APT 1212 78209 #048-14-2003 L2005 ORS *012

VANOVER, Marilyn Jean. 8715 VILLAGE DR STE 300 78217 #025-07-1981 L1982 OBG *020 †30

VAN ROYEN, Alice Ruth. 7922 EWING HALSELL DR, STE 170 78229 #045-04-1993 L2002 OBG *020 †30

VANSCHAACK, Leslie Ann. ■ 78253 #051-04-2004 L2006 PD *100 †55

VAN SICKLE, Kent R. 7703 FLOYD CURL DR, MAIL CODE 7842 78229 #047-06-1994 L2007 GS *020 †85

VAN WINGERDEN, Gail Dons. 525 OAK CENTRE DR 78258 #016-11-1974 L1989 OBG *020 †30

VARDIMAN, Arnold B. 18626 HARDY OAK BLVD, STE 240 78258 #048-12-1989 L1991 NS *020 †25

VARELA, Ernesto. 700 S ZARZAMORA ST STE 313 78207 #649-33-1981 L1990 PD *020 †55

VARELA, Javier. ■ 78230 #308-03-1982 PD *100

VARGAS, Daniel Mauricio. 7703 FLOYD CURL DR, DEPT OF SUR MC 7742 78229 #048-14-2003 GS *012

VARGAS, Leticia. 527 N LEONA ST 78207 #048-13-2000 L2004 OBG *020 †30

VARGAS BLANCO, Daniel. 7703 FLOYD CURL DR, UNIV TX MED SCH-SAN ANTONI 78229 #264-04-2003 DR *012

VARNER, Louis Matthew. ■ 78213 #027-01-2002 L2004 HO *012 †20

VASAN, Rajiv. ■ 78258 #048-13-2002 L2006 VIR *012 †80

VASIREDDY, Sridhar. 19284 STONE OAK PKWY, STE 101 78258 #496-35-1993 L2006 AN PME *020 †05

VASQUEZ, Adriana M. 2303 SE MILITARY DR, TX CENTER INFECTIOUS DISEA 78223 #264-13-1987 L1995 ID *020 †20

VASQUEZ, Debra Ann. 740 S ALAMO 78205 #048-02-2002 L2005 IM *020 †20

VASQUEZ, Lena Allyson. ■ 78240 #048-13-2006 FP *012

VASQUEZ, Margarita Maria. 7703 FLOYD CURL DR 78229 #028-46-2000 L2003 NPM *100 †55

VASQUEZ, Robert Eloy. 7979 WURZBACH RD, URSCHEL TOWERS #233 78229 #048-02-1983 L1983 DR *020 †80

VASQUEZ, Sandra Murillo. 1 CAMINO SANTA MARIA ST, STUDENT HEALTH CENTER 78228 #048-13-1989 L1990 FM *020 †18

VASSAR, George John. 8711 VILLAGE DR STE 312 78217 #048-13-1994 L1995 U *020 †95

VAUGHAN, Richard Steves. 78209 #048-02-1987 L1988 FM EM *020 †18

VAUGHN, Michael Patrick. 104 GALLERY CIR, STE 126 78258 #051-04-1987 L1990 AI *020 †20,03

VAZQUEZ, Gerardo. 6430 BANDERA RD 78238 #649-14-1971 L1983 GS EM *020

VAZQUEZ, Marilu. 78269 #048-15-1997 FM *100

VAZQUEZ, Miguel Arizpe. 1831 S GENERAL MCMULLEN 78226 #048-04-1980 L1981 FM *020 †18

VAZQUEZ, Salvador C. 3066 E COMMERCE ST 78220 #048-13-1988 L1990 FM *020 †18

VAZQUEZ-SEOANE, Pablo. 2829 BABCOCK RD, SAN ANTONIO ORTHOPAEDIC 78229 #008-01-1985 L1991 OSS GS *020 †40

VECIL, Giacomo. 4502 MEDICAL DR 78229 #065-01-1995 L2008 *100

VEGA, Efren Gilbert. ■ 78257 #048-02-1966 L1966 GS *071 †85

VEGA FERNANDEZ, Patricia. 7703 FLOYD CURL DR 78229 #264-07-2004 PD *012

VELA, Raul. 78216 #649-01-1954 L1964 GS *071 †85

VELA, Raul, Jr. 7950 FLOYD CURL DR, STE 909 78229 #048-04-1984 L1985 D IM *020 †15

VELA, Vanessa Lynn. 711 E JOSEPHINE ST, STE 101 78208 #048-02-2000 L2002 CHP *020 †75

VELASQUEZ, Theresa S. 1920 BURNET ST, ELLA AUSTIN HEALTH CENTER 78202 #048-13-1996 L1996 PD *020

VELEZ, Angela Maria. 7703 FLOYD CURL DR, UTHSCSA 78229 #264-16-1994 L2005 CN *100 †75

VELEZ, Jorge. 4400 S PIEDRAS DR, STE 200 78228 #264-06-1962 L1978 DR *020 †80

VELEZ, Jorge A. 7979 WURZBACH RD, URSCHEL TOWERS #233 78229 #048-14-1994 L1995 VIR *020 †80

VELEZ, Luis Eduardo. 4502 MEDICAL DR 78229 #264-16-1999 L2004 NEP *012

VELEZ MUNERA, Jose Antoni. 7703 FLOYD CURL DR 78229 #264-16-2003 IM *012

VELEZ-VASQUEZ, Enrique. 706 SW 24TH ST 78207 #264-03-1960 L1972 PD PDC *020

VEMULAPALLI, Lakshmi P. 1200 BROOKLYN AVE, STE 200 78212 #495-50-1981 L1994 CD IM *020 †20

VENKATACHALAM, Hasi M. 7703 FLOYD CURL DR, DEPT MED 78229 #495-02-1964 L1979 PTH *050 †70

VENKATACHALAM, Manjeri A. 7703 FLOYD CURL, UNIV OF TEXAS HEALTH SCIEN 78229 #495-39-1962 L1981 PTH *020 †50

VENKATESH, Aruna. 7703 FLOYD CURL DR, SAN ANTONIO, DEPT. MED. 78229 #495-21-1986 L1997 END *020 †20

VERELLEN, Rebecca Marie. ■ 78229 #048-13-2007 IM *012

VERMA, Karuna. 4502 MEDICAL DR 78229 #495-19-1972 DR *020

VERNIER, James Harold. 1303 MCCULLOUGH AVE, STE 229 78212 #048-12-1992 L2000 AN *020 †05

VIBHUTE, Prasanna Ganesh. 7703 FLOYD CURL DR, # MC-7800 78229 #496-26-1991 L2007 RNR *020 †80 ‡

VICK, Sammy C. 8038 WURZBACH RD STE 430, UROLOGY CONSULTANTS, PA 78229 #048-13-1989 L1990 U *020 †95

VICKREY, Jacquelyn Fish. 111 DALLAS ST 78205 #030-06-1993 L2000 PTH HMP *050 †50

VICUNA, Nelson J. 9719 POWHATAN DR # 2 78230 #935-02-1967 IM *100

VILLACORTE, Guillermo V. ■ 78254 #748-01-1957 L1984 AI IG *071 †03

VILLAFANA, Aurora P. 519 W HOUSTON ST 78207 #649-02-1956 L1964 PD PUD *071

VILLAFANA, Richard D. 2455 NE LOOP 410 78217 #048-13-1983 L1983 FM *020 †18

VILLALOBOS, Eliseo M. 7711 LOUIS PASTEUR STE 901 78229 #048-13-1996 L2001 AI *020 †20,03

VILLALOBOS, Roxanne. ■ 78240 #048-13-2007 IM *012

VILLANUEVA, Gil. 8715 VILLAGE DR, STE 410 78217 #048-13-1990 L1991 OBG *020 †30

VILLANUEVA, Rayleen. 720 PLEASANTON RD 78214 #048-13-1996 L1997 IM *020 †20

VILLA-OLVERA, Michelle M. 8715 VILLAGE DR STE 300 78217 #048-12-1993 L1995 OBG *020 †30

VILLAREAL, Cynthia Anne. 7430 BARLITE BLVD, STE 104 78224 #048-13-1985 L1991 IM PD *075 †20,55

VILLARREAL, Deborah Molin. ■ 78240 #048-02-2003 L2007 IMG *100 †20

VILLARREAL, Herman. 7434 LOUIS PASTEUR DR, STE 109 78229 #649-01-1970 L1986 NEP IG *020 †20

VILLARREAL, Laura Alicia. 525 OAK CENTRE DR, STE 150 78258 #048-12-1993 L1994 FM *020 †18

VILLARREAL, Marcelo. 6119 BORDER TRAIL DR 78240 #048-16-1988 L1996 P *020

VILLARREAL, Santiago. 4151 CALLAGHAN RD STE 103 78228 #048-12-1977 L1977 NEP *020 †20

VILLARREAL-RIOS, Alfredo. 8038 WURZBACH RD, STE 211 78229 #649-02-1965 L1977 GS *020 †85,65

VILLASENOR, Hector Raul. 401 N SAN SABA 78207 #048-13-1978 L1979 CD *020 †20

VILLEGAS, Maria Delaluz. ■ 78258 #048-13-2007 IM *012

VINEYARD, Joseph C. ■ 78249 #048-13-2005 ORS *012

VINYARD, Patrick Geo. 4360 GRECO DR 78222 #048-12-1980 L1980 GP PD *020 †60

VIRLAR-CADENA, Jesus A. 7330 SAN PEDRO STE 405, IPC 78216 #048-02-2000 L2003 IM *020 †20

VIROSLAV, Alice Barnes. 8401 DATAPOINT DR, STE 600 78229 #048-12-1989 L1991 RNR *020 †80

VIROSLAV, Sergio. 4243 E SOUTHCROSS BLVD, SAN ANTONIO ORTHOPAEDIC 78222 #048-12-1989 L1997 ORS *020 †40

VISWANATHAN, B. 19260 STONE OAK PKWY, STE 102 78258 #495-16-1976 L1985 GS *020 †85

VOGEL, Paula Sue. 19016 STONE OAK PKWY, STE 180 78258 #023-12-1986 L2000 D *020 †20,15

VOGT, Cristoph. 1430 VANCE JACKSON RD, #1203 78201 #409-25-1994 END *100

VOGTSBERGER, Kenneth N. ■ 78240 #048-13-1975 L1975 ADM P *050 †75

VOJTA, Christopher Norman. ■ 78251 #023-12-2006 L2007 *012

VOLTZ, Phillip Wm. 8038 WURZBACH RD STE 270 78229 #047-06-1952 L1957 RO GPM *071 †80

VON GLASS, Kristen Sonnie. ■ 78250 #030-06-2004 L2006 IM *020

VOS, Jeffrey Albin. 3851 ROGER BROOKE DR, BROOKE ARMY MED CTR 78234 #026-04-1997 L1998 PTH *020 †50

VOSBERG, James L. 5282 MEDICAL DR, STE 610 78229 #048-14-1990 L1991 IM *020 †20

VOSS, Gene Allen. 4227 CENTERGATE ST 78217 #048-13-1980 L1980 AN *071 †05

VU, Thao. 7400 MERTON MINTER ST, AMBULATORY CARE 78229 #048-13-1991 L1997 RHU *020 †20

VU, Vu Nguyen. 7330 SAN PEDRO, STE 405 78216 #019-02-2001 L2004 IM *020

WAGNER, Brent. 7703 FLOYD CURL DR, DIVISION OF NEPHROLOGY 78229 #034-01-1999 L2001 NEP *100 †20

WAGNER, Clyde Walter, Jr. 1303 MCCULLOUGH AVE # 600, INTERNAL MED ASSOC 78212 #021-05-1961 L1969 IM END *071 †20

WAGNER, John Otto. 1950 STANLEY RD 78234 #005-12-1965 L1966 CD IM *020

WAGNER, Kathryn Ann. 414 NAVARRO ST, STE 1407 78205 #048-02-1990 L1992 GS *020 †85

WAGNER, Timothy Downey. 78218 #024-07-2002 L2003 *020

WAKEFIELD, Toni Anne. 7703 FLOYD CURL DR, PEDIATRIC CRITICAL CARE 78229 #048-13-2002 L2005 PD *100 †55

WALD, Peter Harold. 9800 FREDERICKSBURG RD, USAA, UNIT 03579 78288 #024-07-1981 L2004 OM IM *020 †20,70

WALICK, David Joseph. ■ 78209 #021-01-2002 L2004 CHP *012 †75

WALKER, John A. ■ 78247 #048-13-2007 *012

WALKER, Lisa Christine. 18540 SIGMA RD 78258 #048-13-1998 L2000 D *020 †15

WALKER, Nora Lee. 4410 MEDICAL DR, STE 440 78229 #048-02-1992 L1993 PCC SME *012

WALL, Donna Ann. 7711 LOUIS PASTEUR, STE 708 78229 #062-01-1981 L2001 PHO *020 †55

WALL, Shawna Renee. ■ 78240 #048-13-2008 OBG *012

WALLACE, Christopher L. 7703 FLOYD CURL DR, DEPT OF PSYCHIATRY 78229 #048-13-1996 L2000 P *020 †75

WALLACE, Jennifer L. 1303 MCCULLOUGH AVE 78212 #048-13-1989 L1991 IM *020 †20

WALLACE, Mark Kowalski. 3851 ROGER BROOKE DR, BROOKE ARMY MEDICAL CENTER 78234 #016-45-1999 L2001 END *020 †20

WALLACE, Philip Coleman. ■ 78209 #047-07-2005 **PM** *012
WALLER, Jester Johnson. ■ 78258 #048-04-1955 L1955 **EM GP** *071 †18
WALLER, Lynsay L. ■ 78229 #048-13-2005 **IM** *012
WALLING, Ann Dorothy. ■ 78229 #067-03-1984 **CD** *020 †20
WALSH, Andrew L, III. 1200 BROOKLYN AVE STE 250 78212 #048-13-1987 L1988 **PUD CCM** *020 †20
WALSH, Nicolas Eugene. 7703 FLOYD CURL DR, REHABILITATION MEDICINE - 78229 #007-02-1979 L1981 **PM PMM** *040 †60
WALSH, Rhonda Marie. 7703 FLOYD CURL DR, DIV OF URO MAILCODE 7845 78229 #028-03-2002 L2008 **U** *012
WALTER, Elizabeth Anne. 527 N LEONA ST 78207 #038-41-1989 L2001 **ID** *020 †20
WALTERS, Michael James. 3602 HUNTERS BAY 78230 #051-04-1971 L1975 **GS OS** *020 †85
WALTHALL, Walter, IV. 3338 OAKWELL CT, STE 107 78218 #048-14-1997 L2000 **FM** *020 †18
WALTON, Richard Wade. ■ 78209 #048-13-2003 L2007 **DR** *012
WALTON, William Thos. 3331 WURZBACH RD, ALAMO CITY EYE PHYSICIANS 78238 #021-01-1986 L1988 **OPH** *020 †35 ‡
WANG, Howard Tzho. 2833 BABCOCK RD, STE 400 78229 #023-07-1995 L2005 **PS** *020 †85,65
WANG, Peter T H. 4499 MEDICAL DR, STE 347 78229 #035-01-1992 L2000 **PS CFS** *040 †65
WANG, Yuanhong. ■ 78240 #243-47-1992 L2004 **PTH** *020 †50
WARD, Mildred E. 246 DANVILLE AVE 78201 #021-05-1940 L1943 **FM GPM** *071
WARE, Ray Wilsford. ■ 78230 #048-02-1955 L1955 **NM AM** *020 †28
WARMAN, Jeffrey Robt. 18626 HARDY OAK BLVD, STE 320 78258 #035-08-1986 L1992 **OP** *020 †40
WARREN, Bruce Huntington. ■ 78238 #026-04-1958 L1972 **P AM** *071 †70,75
WARREN, Lezlie Rene. ■ 78249 #048-16-2003 L2004 **GS** *020
WASCHER, Thomas Chas. 2221 BUENA VISTA ST 78207 #048-02-1970 L1970 **GP** *020
WASETIS, Jeffery John. 9895 IH 10 W, TEXAS MED CLINIC 78230 #048-13-1986 L1988 **GP** *020
WASHBURN, William Kenneth. 7703 FLOYD CURL DR, ORGAN TRANSPLANTATION 78229 #041-12-1988 L1997 **TTS GS** *020 †85
WASHINGTON, Jerome Torme. 7922 EWING HALSELL DR 78229 #048-02-1981 L1982 **OBG** *020 †30
WASSERTEIL, Vivian. 326 W CRAIG PL 78212 #048-04-1987 L1988 **D** *020 †15
WATERMAN, Scott Mcginnis. ■ 78239 #030-05-2002 L2004 **ORS** *020
WATERS, Brian Michael. ■ 78250 #030-06-2004 L2006 **P** *012
WATHEN, Patricia Irene. 7703 FLOYD CURL DR, UTHSCSA GENERAL MEDICINE-7 78229 #010-02-1987 L1992 **IM** *040 †18,20
WATTS, Clark. 4410 MEDICAL DR, STE 610 78229 #048-12-1962 L1962 **NS LM** *071 †25 ‡
WATTS, James Anthony. ■ 78259 #011-02-2002 L2004 **CD** *012 †20
WAXMAN, Steve Walter. 3851 ROGER BROOKE DR, BROOKE ARMY MED CTR 78234 #019-02-1986 L1987 **U** *071 †95
WAYNE, Richard Saml. ■ 78209 #001-02-1967 L1969 **PD PEM** *030 †55
WEARDEN, Mary Elizabeth. 5414 FREDERICKSBURG RD, STE 100 78229 #048-04-1983 L1983 **NPM PD** *050 †55
WEAVER, Jeffrey Allen. 9207 N LOOP 1604 W 78249 #010-03-1991 L2006 **FM** *020 †18
WEBB, Amy C. 7703 FLOYD CURL, DIV OF GASTROENTEROLOGY 78229 #048-16-1999 L2002 **IM** *020 †20
WEBB, Benjamin D. 7940 FLOYD CURL DR, STE 400 78229 #048-14-2002 L2007 **OTO** *020
WEBBER, Patrick J. 8811 VILLAGE DR 78217 #048-14-1991 L1992 **AN** *020 †05
WEGERT, Paula Weber. 7400 MERTON MINTER ST, SCI UNIT 78229 #038-43-1987 L1997 **PM** *020 †60
WEGERT, Steven John. 8401 DATAPOINT DR, STE 600 78229 #038-43-1987 L1994 **DR** *020 †80
WEHNER, Margaret S. 333 N SANTA ROSA AVE, PATHOLOGY ASSOCIATES OF 78207 #048-16-1996 L2002 **PCP** *020 †50
WEINBERG, Thomas Jakle. ■ 78261 #036-05-1968 L1968 **OBG GS** *020 †30
WEINER, Bernard Karl. 929 MANOR DR, STE 7 78228 #017-20-1953 L1955 **FM** *020 †18
WEINER, Marc H. 7400 MERTON MINTER ST, VAMC, DEPT OF MEDICINE (11 78229 #035-19-1970 L1970 **IM ID** *020 †20
WEINSTEIN, Mark Berton. 7950 FLOYD CURL DR, STE 909 78229 #048-13-1973 L1973 **D** *020 †15
WEIR, Larissa Fern. ■ 78209 #018-03-2005 L2007 **OBG** *012
WEISBROD, Howard Garfield. 3851 ROGER BROOKE DR, BROOKE AMC, BLDG 3600 78234 #041-09-1974 L2002 **PTH AM** *071 †18,50
WEISE, William Christian. 2833 BABCOCK RD STE 300 78229 #048-02-1979 L1981 **PD** *020
WEISS, Geoffrey Roger. 7703 FLOYD CURL DR, ANTONIO, DEPT OF MEDICINE 78229 #028-34-1974 L1992 **ON IM** *020
WEISS, Robert Arthur. 111 DALLAS ST 78205 #041-02-1960 L1967 **IM CD** *020
WEISS, Thomas Roderick. 8122 DATAPOINT DR, STE 1010 78229 #048-13-1981 L1981 **P PYG** *020 †75
WEISSFLOG, Thilo Rudolf. 4243 E SOUTHCROSS BLVD, SAN ANTONIO ORTHOPAEDIC 78222 #048-04-1996 L2002 **HS** *020 †40
WEITMAN, Steven Dale. 7979 WURZBACH RD, URSCHEL TOWERS #233 78229 #056-06-1987 L1992 **PD** *020 †55
WEITZ-MARSHALL, Amanda D. 7703 FLOYD CURL DR, DEPT. OF ORTHO 78229 #048-14-1999 L2006 **ORS** *020
WELCH, Gary Wm. 7703 FLOYD CURL DR, DEPT ANESIOLOGY MSC 7838 78229 #051-01-1970 L1970 **AN** *020 †05
WELCH, Linda Lou. 11312 PERRIN BEITEL RD 78217 #024-05-1967 L1968 **R GS** *071
WELCH, Michelle Dawn. 540 MADISON OAK, STE 400 78258 #035-03-1997 L1999 **END** *020 †20
WELLFORD, Armistead L, IV. 1933 NE LOOP 410, HEART & VASCULAR INT OF TX 78217 #036-01-1984 L2004 **CD IM** *020 †20
WELLFORD, Louanne P. ■ 78209 #041-12-1989 L1993 **EM** *020 †16
WELLS, Dolph T. ■ 78217 #004-01-1951 L1954 **GP** *071
WELLS, Howard Thos. 16414 SAN PEDRO AVE, STE 355 78232 #046-01-1977 L1978 **EM EM** *020 †20
WELLS, Jason Terrance. ■ 78240 #025-01-2007 **GS** *012
WELLS, Ralph Frederick. 414 NAVARRO ST, 703 NIX PROFESSIONAL BUILD 78205 #026-04-1957 L1970 **GE IM** *071 †20
WELTON, Christopher Ronal. ■ 78240 #023-12-2007 **EM** *012
WENCKUS, Dalia Jeanette. ■ 78259 #048-16-43-2005 L2007 **OBG** *012
WENGROVITZ, Mark. 4330 MEDICAL DR, STE 100 78229 #041-12-1986 L1994 **VS GS** *020 †85
WENNER, Kimberly Anne. ■ 78216 #023-12-1997 L1998 **D** *012 †18
WENZEL, David Walter. 1314 E SONTERRA BLVD # 601, NEUROLOGY CTR OF SAN ANTON 78258 #048-04-1990 L1991 **N** *020 †75 ‡
WENZEL, Michael Price. 4242 MEDICAL DR, STE 3100 78229 #048-14-2002 L2006 **AN** *100 †05
WESER, Elliot. 4647 MEDICAL DR 78229 #035-01-1957 L1967 **GE IM** *050 †20

WESS, Michael Miles. 4545 HORIZON HILL BLVD 78229 #016-02-1989 L1991 **CD** *020 †20
WEST, Andrew Jos. 21 SPURS LN, STE 330 78240 #017-20-1990 L2001 **IC CD** *020 †20
WEST, Donald Ray. ■ 78209 #048-02-1961 L1961 **OBG** *071 †30
WEST, Fay B. ■ 78249 #048-13-2004 **PTH** *012
WEST, Gary Wayne. 8215 EWING HALSELL DR 78229 #007-02-1967 L1981 **RO GP** *020 †80
WEST, Robt Van Osdell, III. 789 BURR RD 78209 #048-13-1977 L1978 **EM** *020 †16
WESTBROOK, Robert A, Jr. 419 SAN PEDRO AVE 78212 #048-13-1975 L1975 **OBG EM** *020
WESTERMAN, Donna L. 7400 MERTON MINTER ST 78229 #048-13-1989 L1991 **IM** *020 †20
WESTFIELD, Terry L. 540 MADISON OAK DR, STE 540 78258 #025-07-1971 L1981 **PS OTO** *020 †45,65
WHALEY, Andrew L. 414 NAVARRO ST STE 909 78205 #048-13-1997 L2002 **ORS OSM** *020 †40
WHEAT, Joy Elizabeth. ■ 78251 #048-13-2008 *012
WHEELER, Alan Scott. 7703 FLOYD CURL DR, DEPT OF ANESTHESIOLOGY 78229 #040-02-1970 L2002 **AN** *020 †05
WHEELER, Mary Elizabeth. 7703 FLOYD CURL DR, MC 7838 78229 #048-04-1994 L2000 **AN** *020 †05
WHIDBEE, Janel L. 8535 WURZBACH RD, STE 106 78240 #048-14-1997 L1998 **P** *020 †75
WHISENANT, Justin Tyler. 7703 FLOYD CURL DR, UNIV TX MED SCH 78229 #422-01-2006 **DR** *012
WHITE, Allan James. 7979 WURZBACH RD, STE U 78229 #035-08-1964 L1973 **GO GYN** *020 †30
WHITE, Christopher Eric. 3851 ROGER BROOKE DR # 36, BROOKE ARMY MEDICAL CENTER 78234 #048-13-1997 L1998 **CCS** *020 †85
WHITE, Hugh D. 7703 FLOYD CURL DR, DEPT IM 78229 #048-13-2007 **IM** *012
WHITE, Karola Falke. 7940 FLOYD CURL DR, STE 1040 78229 #409-15-1996 L2004 **CHP P** *020 †30
WHITE, Lindsay Herbert. 1954 E HOUSTON ST RM 103 78202 #008-01-1981 L1995 **IM** *020 †20
WHITE, Randal Warren. 4411 MEDICAL DR, STE 300 78229 #048-12-1979 L1979 **CD** *020 †20
WHITE, William M. 8527 VILLAGE DR, STE 103 78217 #422-01-1997 L2002 **RHU** *020 †20
WHITESELL, Rebecca C. ■ 78249 #048-13-2008 *012
WHITNEY, Edwin James. 1933 NE LOOP 410 78217 #010-02-1978 L1986 **IM CD** *020 †20
WHITNEY, Maria Teresa. ■ 78240 #048-04-2005 **OPH** *012
WHITTAKER, Richard James. 6218 NW LOOP 410 78238 #048-13-1994 L1995 **FM** *020 †18
WHITTEN, Glenn Edward. ■ 78254 #048-02-1977 L1979 **FM** *020 †18
WHOLEY, Michael Henry. 6800 IH 10 W, STE 200 78201 #047-05-1989 L1999 **VIR R** *020 †80
WICHMAN, Beth Ann. 6900 N LOOP 1604 W, STUDENT HEALTH SERVICES 78249 #033-06-1978 L1990 **FM** *020 †18
WICKERSHAM, Pendleton B. 4511 HORIZON HILL BLVD, STE 150 78229 #048-04-2000 L2006 **RHU** *020 †20 ‡
WICKLEY, Aaron Brandon. ■ 78233 #023-12-2008 *012
WICOFF, James Sterling. 11124 WURZBACH RD STE 300 78230 #048-13-1973 L1973 **CHP P** *020 †75
WIDMAN, Lawrence Edward. 7950 FLOYD CURL DR, STE 803 78229 #035-01-1981 L1988 **ICE CD** *020 †20
WIEDEMAN, Geoffrey P. ■ 78245 #050-02-1941 L1974 **GP AM** *071 †70
WIERSIG, Jeremy N. 18802 MEISNER DR, CONCORD IMAGING 78258 #048-12-1987 L1989 **DR** *020 †80
WIESENTHAL, Martin Jerome. 8038 WURZBACH RD STE 320 78229 #048-13-1975 L1975 **IM** *020 †20
WIESNER, Jerome J. 533 OLMOS ORE 78212 #048-02-1945 L1945 **R** *071 †80
WIGGINS, Robert Allan. 333 N SANTA ROSA, CH SANTA ROSA HOSP ER DEPT 78207 #033-06-1976 L1978 **EM** *020 †20
WILBER, Stewart A. ■ 78209 #035-03-1946 L1957 **AN** *072 †05
WILD, James Heiser. 14615 SAN PEDRO, STE 105 78232 #038-40-1967 L1975 **RHU IM** *020
WILDER, James Lowell. 540 MADISON OAK, STE 570 78258 #048-13-1995 L2001 **GO** *020 †30
WILDER, Janna. 1 TRINITY PL, STE 80 78212 #048-13-1978 L1980 **FM** *020 †18
WILE, Frederic Daniel. 45 NE LOOP 410, STE 900 78216 #005-11-2001 L2005 **AN** *020
WILEN, Saul Benj. 3010 WHISPER LARK 78230 #035-08-1970 L1974 **IM PUD** *071 †20
WILKE, Kristin M. 19238 STONEHUE, ABCD PEDIATRICS 78258 #048-14-1998 L2001 **PD** *020 †55
WILKINS, Kaye Evan. 7703 FLOYD CURL DR, UTHSCSA-DEPT OF ORTHOPAEDI 78229 #048-12-1966 L1966 **ORS** *020 †40
WILKINSON, John M. ■ 78212 #048-02-1945 L1945 **IM** *071 †20
WILKINSON, Tolbert Siener. 109 GALLERY CIR 78258 #036-07-1962 L1971 **PS** *020 †85,65
WILKS, Richard Frederick. 1933 NE LOOP 410, HEART & VASCULAR INST OF T 78217 #035-06-1986 L1994 **CD IM** *020 †20
WILKS, Sharon Thomas. 2130 NE LOOP 410, STE 100 78217 #023-12-1986 L1998 **HO HMP** *020 †20
WILLERSON, Wm Darrell, Jr. 2404 COMMERCIAL AVE 78221 #048-12-1967 L1967 **OPH IM** *075 †20,35
WILLEY, Gordon Denis. 4499 MEDICAL DR STE 105 78229 #055-01-1974 L1979 **IM** *020
WILLEY-COURAND, Donna B. 333 N SANTA ROSA AVE 78207 #023-01-1992 L1998 **PDP** *020 †55
WILLHOITE, David Roy. ■ 78229 #039-01-1963 L1972 **ORS** *020 †40
WILLIAMS, Alfred Vaughn. ■ 78229 #048-02-1967 L1967 **P** *075
WILLIAMS, Angeline H. 7711 LOUIS PASTEUR STE 910 78229 #048-13-1977 L1977 **OBG** *020 †30
WILLIAMS, Annette Lynn. ■ 78261 #021-01-2002 L2002 **EM** *100 †16
WILLIAMS, Bradford J. ■ 78254 #048-16-1991 L1992 **FM** *020 †18
WILLIAMS, Charlene Ann. ■ 78258 #023-12-2004 L2007 **AN** *100
WILLIAMS, Christopher D. ■ 78245 #030-06-2001 L2001 **GE** *012 ‡
WILLIAMS, Coyle W, Jr. ■ 78209 #048-02-1950 L1950 **ORS** *071 †40
WILLIAMS, Debra J. 8715 VILLAGE DR STE 300 78217 #048-02-1988 L1995 **OBG** *020 †30
WILLIAMS, Dwight Morgan. U TEX HLTH SCI CTR INF DIS 78284 #023-07-1968 L1976 **ID IM** *040 †20
WILLIAMS, Edmund P, IV. 1380 PANTHEON WAY, STE 310 78232 #048-14-1982 L1983 **P CHP** *072 †18,75
WILLIAMS, Gary Bond. 2827 BABCOCK RD, 4TH FL 78229 #049-01-1972 L1989 **FM** *020 †18
WILLIAMS, Heather Renee. 525 OAK CENTRE DR STE 300, RIVERWALK OB/GYN 78258 #011-02-1994 L2006 **OBG** *020 †30
WILLIAMS, Herman Jos. ■ 78258 #024-05-1988 L1989 **ORS** *030
WILLIAMS, J F. 7703 FLOYD CURL DR, DEPT OF PEDIATRICS 78229 #016-45-1979 L1986 **PD** *050 †20
WILLIAMS, James M. 8026 FLOYD CURL DR 78229 #041-77-1991, ▲ L1993 **EM** *020 ‡
WILLIAMS, Joseph B. 414 NAVARRO ST, STE 1502 78205 #048-02-1993 L1994 **DR** *020 †80

WILLIAMS, Justin Barrett. ■ 78261 #021-01-2002 L2006 **EM** *100 †16

WILLIAMS, Oscar B, Jr. ■ 78258 #048-04-1950 L1950 **AN OS** *071 †05

WILLIAMS, Reginald David. ■ 78230 #056-05-1964 L1971 **ORS** *071 †40

WILLIAMS, Ronald Paul. 7703 FLOYD CURL DR, MC-7774 DEPP OF ORTH 78229 #048-13-1984 L1989 **ORS** *020 †40

WILLIAMS, Theresa Howell. ■ 78259 #048-13-2003 L2007 **P** *100

WILLIAMS, Thomas Eugene. 7703 FLOYD CURL DR, DEPT. OF PEDIATRICS 78229 #048-12-1962 L1962 **ON HEM** *071 †55

WILLIAMS, Thos Harold, Jr. 6611 S NEW BRAUNFELS AVE, SAN ANTONIO STATE HOSPITAL 78223 #048-02-1960 L1961 **P N** *020

WILLIAMS, Vernon F. 1310 MCCULLOUGH AVE 78212 #035-46-1983 L1991 **EM GS** *020

WILLIAMS, Vick Franklin. UNIV TX HEALTH SCIENCE CTR 78284 #048-02-1964 L1964 **OS** *040

WILLIAMSON, Patrick Lane. 7950 FLOYD CURL DR 78229 #048-02-1980 L1980 **OBG** *030

WILLIS, Roger Steven. 2827 BABCOCK RD, EMERG DEPT CHRISTUS SANTA 78229 #012-01-1989 L2000 **EM FM** *020 †18

WILSON, Anthony. ■ 78216 #048-12-1953 L1953 **OTO** *071 †45

WILSON, Charles Louis. ■ 78245 #038-06-1955 L1972 **CD IM** *071 †70,20

WILSON, Christopher J. 3851 ROGER BROOKE DR, BROOKE AMC DEPT ORTHO-REHB 78234 #048-04-1995 L1997 **HS OTR** *020 †40

WILSON, Gary Kyle. 3030 NACOGDOCHES RD # 101 78217 #048-13-1977 L1979 **P CHP** *020 †75

WILSON, Kristopher Charle. ■ 78218 #023-12-2008 *012

WILSON, Margaret Ann. 4242 MEDICAL DR, STE 3100 78229 #003-01-1973 L1976 **AN** *020 †05

WILSON, Martha C. 14615 SAN PEDRO, STE 120 78232 #020-02-1986 L1991 **PS** *020 †35

WILSON, Patrick Henry. 6200 UTSA BLVD, STE 100 78249 #010-03-1970 L1978 **ORS** *020 †40

WILSON, Richard Porter. 6200 UTSA BLVD, STE 100 78249 #021-01-1967 L1968 **ORS** *020 †40

WILSON, Travis David. ■ 78259 #038-43-2002 L2004 **AN** *020 †05

WINAKUR, Jerald. 7210 LOUIS PASTEUR DR, PASTEUR MEDICAL 78229 #041-01-1973 L1976 **IM** *020 †20

WINAKUR, Leslie S Gelfer. 7700 FLOYD CURL DR 78229 #041-01-1973 L1976 **PD** *020 †55

WINKLER, Kenneth William. ■ 78254 #030-06-2002 L2002 **DR** *020 †80

WINN, Brian E. 1303 MCCULLOUGH AVE, STE 600 78212 #048-12-1987 L1989 **RHU** *020 †20

WINNEM, Bjorn Magne. 4502 MEDICAL DR DEPT EANES 78229 #693-02-1976 **AN** *020

WINSTON, John H, III. 315 N SAN SABA, STE 1240 78207 #001-02-1994 L2003 **CRS** *020 †85,10

WINTER, Bruce Lutcher. 2929 MOSSROCK, STE 104 78230 #048-04-1988 L1990 **OPH** *020 †35

WINTER, Cornelia Patricia. 400 CONCORD PLZ, STE 300 78216 #048-15-1986 L1987 **FM** *018

WIRFEL, Kelly L. 701 S ZARZAMORA ST 78207 #034-01-1994 L1997 **END** *020 †20

WIRTH, Michael Alan. 4647 MEDICAL DR 78229 #040-02-1985 L1986 **ORS** *020 †40

WISE, David Stuart. 2455 NE LOOP 410 STE 235 78217 #011-02-1987 L1991 **ICE CD** *020 †20

WISSA, Michael Fawzy. 7940 FLOYD CURL DR, STE 1030 78229 #915-03-1989 L2000 **AN** *020

WISSINGER, John Paul. 4410 MEDICAL DR, STE 610 78229 #010-02-1962 L1970 **NS** *020 †25

WITZ, Craig Arthur. 7703 FLOYD CURL, DEPT OB 78229 #048-04-1988 L1990 **REN OBG** *020 †30

WOHLTMANN, Wendi Elaine. ■ 78256 #041-15-2003 L2004 **D** *012 ‡

WOJCIK, Lilia. 301 N FRIO ST 78207 #759-03-1981 L1990 **PTH** *020 †50

WOJCIK, Wojciech Grzegorz. 540 MADISON OAK, STE 160 78258 #759-03-1981 L1987 **DR** *020 †80

WOLCOTT, Katharine E. ■ 78244 #011-02-2002 L2004 **GS** *020 †85

WOLF, Earl George, Jr. 94 BRIGGS ST, STE 600 78224 #001-02-1978 L2000 **AM UM** *020 †70

WOLF, Edward Anthony, Jr. 4330 MEDICAL DR, STE 100 78229 #030-06-1967 L1977 **VS GS** *020 †85

WOLFF, Hugh Lipman. 7510 FORRESTGLEN DR 78209 #018-03-1955 L1962 **U** *071 †95

WOLFF, Richard C. 8 CHISWICK CT 78218 #050-02-1953 L1972 **AN** *071 †05

WOLNER, Kathleen Marie. 9502 COMPUTER DR, OUTPATIENT CLINIC 78229 #038-41-1984 L1985 **IM IMG** *020 †20

WOLSEY, Gilman Timothy. ■ 78254 #056-06-2002 L2008 **DR** *012

WOMACK, James Stclair. 45 NE LOOP 410, STE 900 78216 #034-01-2003 L2007 **AN** *020

WOMACK, Robin Lidiak. 502 MADISON OAK DR, STE 240 78258 #048-14-1999 L2004 **OBG** *020 †30

WONG, Eric Yan Chee. 7703 FLOYD CURL DR, UNIV OF TX MED SCH 78229 #014-01-2007 **AN** *012

WONG, Peter Y. 730 N MAIN AVE, 609 M S TOWER 78205 #048-02-1953 L1953 **AN** *020 *05

WONG, Vanessa Waijuen. ■ 78229 #023-12-2004 L2006 **P** *012

WOO, Junda Chichi. ■ 78201 #035-06-2002 L2004 **OBG** *100

WOOD, Bruce Andrew. 8800 VILLAGE DR, STE 201 78217 #048-04-1979 L1980 **ID** *020 †20

WOOD, Dale Allen. 341 E HILDEBRAND AVE 78212 #048-12-1969 L1969 **AI PD** *020 †55

WOOD, John Chas. 1406 FITCH ST, WESLEY PRIMARY CARE CLINIC 78211 #036-07-1978 L1983 **FM** *020 †18

WOOD, Leisha Eileen. ■ 78254 #048-13-2003 L2007 **PTH** *100 †50

WOOD, Mary Jean. ■ 78201 #028-03-1963 L1975 **PHP** *071

WOOD, Megan Manser. 21 SPURS LN, STE 310 78240 #048-12-2002 L2006 **HSO** *012

WOOD, Pamela. 9 N SANTA ROSA AVE 78207 #036-07-1977 L1983 **PD** *040 †55

WOODARD, George S, Jr. ■ 78239 #028-02-1949 L1949 **ORS** *071 †40

WOODARD, Noelle Claudine. ■ 78238 #021-05-2007 **IM** *012

WOODARD, Russell Lynn. 8042 WURZBACH RD, STE 310 78229 #047-06-1988 L1993 **GS** *020 †85

WOODBURN, Richard. ■ 78257 #025-07-1966 L1975 **AN** *075

WOODBURY, Anna. ■ 78240 #028-02-2008 *012

WOODHAM, Ryan M. ■ 78249 #048-15-2003 L2007 **CD** *012 †20

WOODMAN, Jean Gale. 5414 FREDERICKSBURG RD, STE 100 78229 #041-02-1978 L1998 **PD** *020 †55

WOODROW, Charles Leroy. 13714 LOOKOUT RD 78233 #047-05-1978 L1988 **GS** *020 †85

WOODWARD, Lee M. 7703 FLOYD CURL DR, MSC 62 78229 #048-13-2004 L2004 **OPH** *012

WOODY, Joshua T. ■ 78258 #048-04-2005 L2007 **ORS** *012

WOODY-GROSS, Denise Ann. 7711 LOUIS PASTEUR STE 410 78229 #048-13-1994 L1995 **GYN** *020 †30

WOOLEY, Michael Wayne. 7950 FLOYD CURL DR STE 620 78229 #048-12-1974 L1974 **PUD CCM** *020 †20

WOOSLEY, Clinton Ross. 7703 FLOYD CURL DR, DEPARTMENT OF PEDIATRICS 78229 #048-13-2000 L2003 **CCP** *100 †55

WOOTEN, Dennis Craig. ■ 78242 #048-14-2000 **PTH** *100

WORRICH, Scott P. 403 TREELINE PARK, STE 200 78209 #048-13-2002 L2006 **AN** *100 †05

WORTHAM, Barry Glen. 4242 MEDICAL DR, STE 3100 78229 #048-02-1978 L1978 **AN** *020 *05

WORTHAM, William Geo. 2391 NE LOOP 410, STE 405 78217 #007-02-1980 L1992 **NEP IM** *020 †20

WRATTEN, Carol Elizabeth. 8715 VILLAGE DR STE 300 78217 #036-01-1975 L1977 **OBG** *020 †30

WRIGHT, Amanda M. ■ 78229 #048-13-2008 *012

WRIGHT, Francis H, Jr. 7711 LOUIS PASTEUR, STE 707 78229 #048-13-1978 L1979 **TTS VS** *020 †85

WRIGHT, James Albert. ■ 78230 #012-01-1975 L1997 **GPM OM** *030

WRIGHT, James Hudell, Jr. 4242 MEDICAL DR, STE 4250 78229 #048-02-1981 L1981 **AN** *020 *05

WRIGHT, Jennifer Lynn. 6711 S NEW BRAUNFELS AVE, STE 100 78223 #048-14-1997 L2006 **P PFP** *020

WRIGHT, Joseph Keith. 414 NAVARRO ST STE 810 78205 #048-02-1994 L1997 **GS** *020

WRIGHT, Randy Peter. 527 N LEONA ST, HEPATOLOGY CLINIC 78207 #048-13-2004 L2007 **IM** *100 †20

WRIGHT, Rebekah Helen. ■ 78248 #048-13-2008 *012

WU, Qingxuan. ■ 78249 #048-16-2004 **N** *012

WU, William Chien Lin. 6800 W IH 10 STE 200 78201 #244-01-1982 L1990 **CD IM** *020 †20

WULFSOHN, Norman Leonard. 45 NE LOOP 410, STE 900 78216 #836-01-1948 L1968 **AN** *020

WYATT, Jamison Neil. 4502 MEDICAL DR 78229 #048-13-2005 L2008 **IM** *012

WYDER, Holly J. ■ 78232 #048-16-2004 L2007 **IM** *020

WYMER, Robert Allen. ■ 78258 #048-02-1966 L1966 **PD EM** *020

WYNN, James Albert. 8038 WURZBACH RD, # 490 78229 #048-12-1958 L1958 **AN** *071 †05

WYNN, James M. 4402 VANCE JACKSON RD 78230 #048-14-1989 L1990 **AN** *020 †05

WYNNE, Susan Kay. 7950 FLOYD CURL DR STE 100 78229 #011-02-1987 L1996 **P CHP** *020 †75

WYSOKI, Joseph. 9969 FREDERICKSBURG RD 78240 #048-78-1984, ▲ L1985 *020

XENAKIS, E Marie-Jeanne. 7703 FLOYD CURL DR, UTHSCSA OBGYN DEPARTMENT 78229 #561-14-1983 L1990 **OBG** *020 †30

XU, Duojia. ■ 78209 #023-12-2005 L2007 **U** *012

YALTHO, Toby C.. 7703 FLOYD CURL DR #MC7883, SCIENCE C 78229 #305-01-2002 L2007 **N** *100

YAMINI, Maryam. ■ 78230 #409-38-1998 **FP** *012

YANG, Ronald S. ■ 78229 #048-13-2008. *012

YANG, Shiwen Zhu. 333 N SANTA ROSA AVE, PATHOLOGY ASSOCIATES OF 78207 #243-46-1982 L2001 **PTH PCP** *020 †50

YANG, Yi. 7400 MERTON MINTER ST 78229 #243-46-1982 L1992 **FM** *020 †18

YANKOV, Yanko Athanassov. 540 MADISON OAK DR, STE 620 78258 #198-01-1974 L2001 **N SME** *020 †20

YATES, Ashley John. ■ 78254 #917-10-1980 L1990 **END IM** *075

YAZDANI, Shahbaz Ahmed. 19178 BLANCO RD, STE 106 78258 #021-06-2000 L2002 **FM** *100 †18 ‡

YBARRA, Doris Ann. 78216 #048-14-2001 L2004 **P** *100 †75

YERRAM, Prashanthi. 4214 E SOUTHCROSS BLVD 78222 #495-21-1997 L2003 **IM** *020 †20

YERRAMILLI, Venkata Rao. 7330 SAN PEDRO STE 405 78216 #496-05-1977 L2001 **FM** *020 †18

YERRINGTON, Robert Foster. 8318 JONES MALTSBERGER RD, STE 118 78216 #048-12-1978 L1978 **FM FSM** *020 †20

YOHE, Sophia Louise. ■ 78248 #026-04-1995 L1997 **HMP** *012 †20,50

YOO, Harrison Wonhee. 255 E SONTERRA BLVD, STE 100 78258 #048-12-1990 L1991 **IM** *020 †20

YOO, Jae Hong. 111 DALLAS ST 78205 #583-02-1972 L1978 **PTH PCP** *020 †50

YOUNG, Derick W. 1715 MCCULLOUGH AVE, RMG HEALTH CENTER 78212 #048-13-1998 L2001 **FM** *020 †18

YOUNG, Eliot J. 2829 BABCOCK RD, STE 236C 78229 #048-13-1993 L1994 **FM** *020 †18

YOUNG, Patricia. ■ 78218 #033-05-1995 L2000 **PM** *020 †60

YOUNG, Robert Michael. 7922 EWING HALSELL DR, STE 470 78229 #048-13-1975 L1975 **OBG** *020 †30

YOUNG, Robert Neal. 525 OAK CENTRE DR, STE 260 78258 #021-01-1975 L1977 **PS GS** *020 †85,65

YOUNGBLOOD, John Wade, Jr. 7703 FLOYD CURL DR, UTHSC SA DEPT OTALRYN 78229 #021-01-1963 L1969 **OTO NO** *071 †45

YOUNGBLOOD, Lloyd Angus. 4410 MEDICAL DR STE 610, NEUROSURGICAL ASSOC OF S.A 78229 #048-04-1973 L1973 **NS** *020 †25

YOUNT, Ira Minter. 27 DONORE SQ 78229 #040-02-1962 L1978 **OP ORS** *020 †40

YU-KABIGTING, Stella V B. 2829 BABCOCK RD STE 110 78229 #748-15-1987 L1999 **IM** *020 †20

YUN, Heather Lynn. ■ 78209 #008-01-2001 L2003 **ID** *100

YUNES, Andrea Christine. ■ 78249 #048-02-2005 **PTH** *012

ZACCARIA, Attilio. 7254 BLANCO RD, STE 200 78216 #048-02-1956 L1956 **GP** *020

ZACHARY, Vance Edward. 2425 BABCOCK RD, STE 111 78229 #038-41-1981 L1985 **FM** *020 †18

ZAER-RAFIE, Abraham Danie. ■ 78258 #048-02-2004 L2005 **DR** *012

ZAFAR, Naushad. 7940 FLOYD CURL DR, STE 260 78229 #704-16-1986 L1997 **CCM NEP** *020 †20

ZAGORIN, Lazaro Hass. 94 BRIGGS ST STE 300 78224 #649-01-1975 L1983 **GS FM** *020

ZAGUNIS, Darius. 2424 BABCOCK RD, STE 202 78229 #305-01-1999 L2006 **AN** *100 †05

ZAHAROFF, Annette Marie. 8122 DATAPOINT DR STE 1100 78229 #025-07-1983 L1985 **PM** *020 †60

ZAHEER, Ayesha Nawaz. 7703 FLOYD CURL DR 78229 #704-05-1998 **FP** *012

ZAJAC, Robert Alan. 150 E SONTERRA BLVD, STE 170 78258 #021-05-1981 L1988 **ID** *040 †20

ZAKULA, Mark. 16414 SAN PEDRO AVE, STE 355 78232 #017-20-1984 L1987 **EM** *020 †16

ZALDIVAR, Mary Ann. 1111 SE MILITARY DR 78214 #048-13-1984 L1985 **FM EM** *020 †18

ZAMORA, Cynthia A. 1603 BABCOCK RD, STE 101 78229 #048-12-1983 L1983 **PUD CCM** *020

ZAMORA-CAMPOS, Veronica. 7430 BARLITE BLVD 78224 #048-13-1995 L1996 **PD** *020 †55

ZAMORA-SALINAS, Rolando. 4499 MEDICAL DR STE 289 78229 #649-30-1984 L1991 **PDC PD** *020 †20

ZANTUA, Omar A. 7330 SAN PEDRO, STE 405 78216 #748-01-1991 L2005 **IM** *020

ZAPATA, Mari-Ethel. ■ 78238 #048-13-2006 **P** *012

ZARATE, Jocelyn V. 414 NAVARRO ST, STE 1422 78205 #305-01-1998 L2006 **IM** *020 †20

ZARATE, Rudy P, Jr. 414 NAVARRO ST, STE 1422 78205 #305-01-1997 L2005 **IM** *020 †20

ZASLOW, Kenneth Howard. 7703 FLOYD CURL DR 78229 #035-03-1973 L2002 **OPH** *020 †35

ZAVALA, Gerardo. 4423 NW LOOP 410, STE 100 78229 #649-02-1971 L1978 **NS** *020 †25

ZAVALA, Juan Manuel. ■ 78213 #048-14-2001 **P** *100

ZAVALETA, Beverly Aist. 2827 BABCOCK RD 78229 #024-01-2000 L2003 **FM** *020 †18 ‡

■ = Address Information Privacy Protected

ZAYAC, Emily A. ■ 78258 #048-14-2008 *012
ZAYAS MIRANDA, Mildred J. ■ 78278 #042-01-1987 L1990 **PD** *074
ZEBALLOS, Claudio F. 4502 MEDICAL DR, EMERGENCY CENTER-UHS 78229
  #048-15-2000 L2003 **EM** *020 †16
ZEIGLER, Michael Grant. 8042 WURZBACH RD, STE 310 78229 #035-20-1962 L1977
  GS *071 †85
ZEITLIN, Michael P. 8038 WURZBACH RD, STE 650 78229 #649-02-1982 L1990
  FM FPG *020
ZEITLIN, Simon P. 111 DALLAS ST 78205 #396-04-1942 L1949 **GP GS** *071
ZELFOND, Anna. ■ 78251 #024-07-2007 **IM** *012
ZERN, Andrea L. ■ 78240 #048-13-2007 **PD** *012
ZHANG, Jin. 301 N FRIO ST 78207 #243-43-1983 L2002 **ATP HMP** *020 †50
ZHANG, Lei. 1222 N MAIN AVE, QTC MED SVCS STE 115 78212 #243-69-1985 L2000
  PM *020 †60
ZHAO, Ming. 14807 SAN PEDRO AVE 78232 #243-76-1982 L2001 **OPH** *020
ZILVETI, Carlos B. ■ 78250 #176-02-1954 L1960 **GPM OM** *071 †55
ZINK, Pearl Louise. ■ 78213 #047-05-1937 L1939 **IMG** *071
ZINN, Philip D. 4411 MEDICAL DR, STE 300 78229 #048-12-1982 L1983 **CD IM** *020 †20
ZIU, Mateo. 7703 FLOYD CURL DR, DEPT OF NEUROSURGERY 78229 #561-21-2001 **NS** *012
ZORINSKY, David Aaron. ■ 78240 #048-04-2008 *012
ZORRILLA-RIOS, Leopoldo. 4330 MEDICAL DR, STE 325 78229 #649-01-1965 L1973
  TS *020 †85,90
ZUAZU, Marcos A. 7703 FLOYD CURL DR, MC 7838 78229 #847-06-1970 L1978
  AN PME *040 †05
ZUBYK, Sylvia. 9102 FLOYD CURL DR, TEXAS CANCER CLINIC 78240 #048-02-1997 L2002
  RO *020 †80
ZUCKER, Michael Norman. ■ 78258 #550-02-1997 L1997 **FM** *100
ZUELZER, Mary E. 14800 N US HIGHWAY 281, STE 110 78232 #048-13-1987 L1988 **P** *020 †75
ZUFLACHT, Michael. 2833 BABCOCK RD STE 435 78229 #869-02-1964 L1970 **N** *020
ZUNIGA, Higinio. 242 E SUNSHINE DR, SAN ANTONIO TEXAS 78228 78228 #649-01-1957 L1963
  P *020 †75
ZUNIGA-MONTES, Luis Ricar. 7703 FLOYD CURL DR, MC 7868 78229 #264-06-1988 L2004
  RHU *020 †20
ZUROVEC, Jennifer C. 4242 MEDICAL DR, STE 3100 78229 #048-13-2000 L2002 **AN** *020 †05
ZUSCHLAG, Ella. 7700 FLOYD CURL DR 78229 #048-02-1939 L1939 **PD OS** *071 †55
ZWAAN, Johan T. 8038 WURZBACH RD STE 520 78229 #660-01-1963 L1990
  PO OPH *020 †35 ‡
ZWART, Benton Phillips. 2833 BABCOCK RD STE 105, WOUND & HYPERBARIC MED 78229
  #008-02-1982 L1999 **UM OM** *020 †70

SAN ANTONIO – COMAL

BRESTLE, Joseline G. ■ 78266 #396-04-1964 L1995 **AN** *071
INGLIS, Robert Mc Gowan. ■ 78266 #803-05-1946 L1960 **PUD** *030
LAWRENCE, Don. 21923 DEER CANYON DR 78266 #028-79-1977, ▲ L2000 **FM** *020 †18
MARRERO, Gualberto. ■ 78266 #042-01-1968 L1978 **CHN N** *020
ORR, Scott Christopher. ■ 78266 #048-13-2004 L2006 **EM** *020
PATRICK, Vijayalakshmy. ■ 78266 #220-01-1964 L1975 **P** *020 †75
WILLIAMS, Raymond Lee M. ■ 78266 #048-15-1980 L1980 **OTO** *020 †16

SAN AUGUSTINE – SAN AUGUSTINE

HALEY, Curtis R. 511 E HOSPITAL ST 75972 #048-04-1951 L1951 **GP GS** *020
OGLESBEE, John Henry, III. 504 E HOSPITAL ST 75972 #048-12-1983 L1983 **FM** *020 †18 ‡
VEGIRAJU, Srihari Raju. 600 E HOSPITAL ST, EL CAMINO REAL INTERNAL ME 75972
  #495-11-1997 L2005 **IMG** *020 †20

SAN BENITO – CAMERON

ATKINSON, Eduardo. 351 N SAM HOUSTON BLVD 78586 #048-04-1985 L1986 **FM** *020 †18 ‡
CANO, Christina Elizabeth. 351 N SAM HOUSTON BLVD 78586 #048-14-1999 L2003
  FM *020 †18 ‡
CARSTENSEN, Harold Geo. ■ 78586 #016-02-1947 L1956 **OBG** *071 †30
DOWNEY, Gale Thos. 1867 N SHORE DR 78586 #068-01-1969 L1973 **N** *020 †75
DURAN, Harry Leo. ■ 78586 #043-01-1989 L1991 **NS** *020
FONSECA, Vanessa. ■ 78586 #048-12-2007 **PD** *012
HARRISON, Mark L. 1401 W EXPRESSWAY 83 78586 #038-41-1982 L1983 **RO** *020 †80 ‡
HEINS, William Howard. 351 N SAM HOUSTON BLVD 78586 #048-02-1972 L1972
  FM *020 †18 ‡
HOSSAIN, Muhammad Itrat. 400 E US HIGHWAY 77 78586 #160-03-1982 L2002 **OBG** *020 †20
KANAAN, Ann Claire. 351 N SAM HOUSTON BLVD, SAN BENITO MEDICAL ASSOC, 78586
  #025-76-1992, ▲ L1995 **GP** *071
LOPEZ, Rafael, Jr. 351 N SAM HOUSTON BLVD 78586 #649-02-1984 L1991 **P** *020 †18 ‡
MUNOZ, Maria De Jesus. 351 N SAM HOUSTON BLVD 78586 #048-02-2002 L2005 **FM** *020 †18
REDFEARN, Donald Stewart. 400 E US HIGHWAY 77 78586 #065-05-1956 L1977 **GP** *071
SALINAS, Jamie M. 295 W HWY 77, STE B 78586 #048-02-2001 L2004 **FM** *020 †18
SIMMONS, Cecil Randall. 351 N SAM HOUSTON BLVD 78586 #048-12-1961 L1961 **FM** *072 †18
STANTON, Lonnie Dean. 351 N SAM HOUSTON BLVD 78586 #048-15-1984 L1989 **GS** *020
TAPANGAN, Roselier Ballos. 1653 W HWY 77, SUNSHINE STRIP 78586 #748-01-1988 L1999
  PD *020 †55 ‡
TUCKER, John Robt. ■ 78586 #048-02-1959 L1959 **GP** *071 †18
VEGA, Marco A. ■ 78586 #048-13-2008 *012

SAN DIEGO – DUVAL

BUTLER, Gregory P. 34520 BOB WILSON DR, STE 100 DEPT OF PD 78384 #048-13-1998 L2001
  *020 †55
ELIZONDO, Andres. 215 S DR E E DUNLAP ST 78384 #048-13-1979 L1979 **IM EM** *020 †20
PUYOL, Franz Ivan. 103 W GRAVIS ST, SAN DEIGO PEDIATRIC CLINIC 78384
  #319-04-1991 L1997 **PD** *020 †55

SAN JUAN – HIDALGO

ALQUIZA, Anna Lyn. 801 W 1ST ST 78589 #748-11-1993 L2004 **IM** *020 †20
BACA, Americo Miguel. 722 S NEBRASKA AVE 78589 #649-02-1980 L1991 **FM** *020 †18
CANTU, Roel E. 2900 N RAUL LONGORIA RD 78589 #649-35-1983 L2002 **PD** *020
DAVIS, Kevin Bruce. 801 W 1ST ST 78589 #048-11-1981 L1981 **OBG** *020 †30
DESHMUKH, Pravin Madhukar. 801 W 1ST ST 78589 #495-01-1991 L2004 **ID** *020 †20
GUERRA, Lauro Genaro. 200 W EXPRESSWAY 83, STE M 78589 #048-12-1954 L1954 **GP** *071
MALMBERG, Gertrud C. 700 RIDGE RD, CARE ATC CLINIC 78589 #858-02-1980 L1994 **N** *020
MATA, Nelson A. 603 S NEBRASKA AVE 78589 #308-01-1989 L1994 **IM** *020 †20
RODRIGUEZ, Edgar Armando. 1211 N RAUL LONGORIA RD 78589 #048-13-2003 L2007
  OBG *020
SHAWN, Michael Douglas. 1201 S SAN ANTONIO AVE 78589 #040-02-1999 L2001 **FM** *020 †18
SIMON, Richard Allen. 801 W 1ST ST 78589 #042-01-1976 L1982 **OBG** *020
VANGUELOV, Ventzislav D. 801 W 1ST ST 78589 #198-01-1984 L2004 **OBG** *020
WICKWIRE, Brian Macy. 801 W 1ST ST 78589 #047-05-1989 L2002 **IM** *020 †20

SAN MARCOS – HAYS

AHMED, Nuzhat Fatima. 115 WARDEN LN 78666 #704-02-1991 L1997 **IM** *020 †20
ALLEN, Terry Stephen. 1301 WONDER WORLD DR 78666 #027-01-1977 L1987
  PTH FM *020 †50
ALPAR, Andrew. 1330 WONDER WORLD DR, STE 101 78666 #061-01-1984 L1995
  NEP IM *020 †20
ANDERSON, Charles Peter. 1400 HIGHWAY 123 78666 #048-04-1973 L1974 **FM** *020 †18
BECKER, Patricia A. 1605 REDWOOD RD STE A 78666 #048-14-1982 L1983 **PD** *020 †55
BERMUDEZ, Jairo L. 1305 WONDER WORLD DR, STE 201 78666 #048-16-1995 L1997
  IM *020 †20
BURDEN, James Harold, Jr. 1300 WONDER WORLD DR 78666 #045-01-1991 L2005
  OPH *020 †35
CAIRUS, Alcides. 1999 MEDICAL PKWY STE C 78666 #132-01-1967 L1982 **GS GP** *020
CALDERON, Guido Jose. 1301 WONDER WORLD DR 78666 #737-06-1992 L1997 **IM** *020 †20
CARRANCO, Emilio. 601 UNIVERSITY DR, TEXAS STATE UNIVERSITY 78666 #048-12-1983 L1983
  IM *030
CASTILLO, Rene Alberto. 1308 WONDER WORLD DR 78666 #649-31-1987 L2006 **HO** *020 †20
CAVERLY, Ola Gail. 1346 THORPE LN STE C 78666 #056-05-1980 L1981 **OBG** *020 †30
CHRISTOPHER, Charles A. 601 UNIVERSITY DR, STUDENT HEALTH CENTER 78666
  #047-07-1974 L1975 **EM FM** *020
CLOGSTON, Curtis Paul. 1348 HIGHWAY 123, STE A 78666 #048-13-1978 L1978
  OM FM *020 †70
COBB, Albert Haaron. 1301 WONDER WORLD DR 78666 #048-13-1972 L1972 **A OTO** *020 †45
COLE, Rex Walton. 1300 WONDER WORLD DR, CENTRAL TEXAS EYE CTR 78666
  #048-12-1965 L1965 **OPH** *020 †35
COLLIER, Terry Morris. 115 WARDEN LN 78666 #048-04-1957 L1957 **END IM** *071 †20
DAKE, Theodore, Jr. 310 STAGECOACH TRL, STE 300 78666 #035-08-1962 L1977
  P AM *020 †75
DANNA, Samuel Colby. ■ 78666 #021-05-2006 **IM** *012
DE LA IGLESIA, Gregory C. 1301 WONDER WORLD DR, SAN MARCOS MEDICAL 78666
  #048-12-1989 L1990 **DR** *020 †80
DELANEY, Beth Galloway. 1305 WONDER WORLD DR, STE 209 78666 #048-13-1999 L2001
  OBG *020 †30
DESAI, Tushar M. 120 BERT BROWN ST 78666 #495-76-1985 L1992 **P CHP** *020 †75
DESCHNER, Rhonda Wirth. 1605 REDWOOD RD STE A 78666 #048-04-1986 L1988
  PD *071 †55
DI CLEMENTE, Michael J. 1305 WONDER WORLD DR, STE 300 78666 #010-02-1998 L2003
  OBG *020 †30
DOLAN, Donna Jean. 1305 WONDER WORLD DR, STE 206 78666 #056-06-1980 L1981
  IM *020 †20
DOMSTEAD, Delbert Anthony. 1301 WONDER WORLD DR 78666 #048-02-1973 L1973
  GYN *071
DRISKELL, Jennifer Lee. 1301 WONDER WORLD DR, ATTN: EMERGENCY DEPARTMENT 78666
  #048-15-1987 L1988 **FM** *020 †18
DURAN, Robert. 1305 WONDER WORLD DR # 300 78666 #048-12-1982 L1983 **GS VS** *020
ELLIOTT, Benge. ■ 78666 #048-02-1945 L1945 **GP GS** *071
FUNG, Frederick H. 115 WARDEN LN 78666 #035-19-1977 L1983 **IM** *020 †20
GALAVIZ, Abel Antonio. 1305 WONDER WORLD DR, STE 206 78666 #056-06-1980 L1981
  GS *020
GODLEWSKI, Boguslaw. 1301 WONDER WORLD DR 78666 #759-03-1967 L1975
  CD IM *020 †20
GRIMM, Ellen M. 1330 WONDER WORLD DR, STE 101 78666 #048-14-1992 L1993
  PN PD *020 †55,20
HALL, Ronald Raybern. 1330 WONDER WORLD DR, STE B108 78666 #048-02-1971 L1971
  CD IM *020 †20
HEALY, William Henry. ■ 78666 #048-04-1973 L1974 **DR** *071 †80
HELLER, Leanne. 100B N EDWARD GARY ST, STE 115 78666 #056-06-1994 L1996 **P** *020
HONLES, Grace Lorena. 601 UNIVERSITY DR, STUDENT HEALTH CENTER 78666
  #005-14-1994 L2000 **FM** *020 †18
HOTZ, Roy Joe, Jr. 1999 MEDICAL PKWY STE C 78666 #048-02-1962 L1962 **FM** *020 †18
HUDSON, Rosalie Pierce. 1301 WONDER WORLD DR, PHYSICIAN'S INPATIENT CARE 78666
  #038-41-1997 L2004 **IM** *020 †20
HUDSPETH, Kenneth Bush. 1301 WONDER WORLD DR 78666 #048-13-1972 L1972
  FM *020 †20
HUNTER, Wallace Cannon. ■ 78666 #048-04-1962 L1962 **P** *071 †75
INGRAM, Janette Louise. 1700 RANCH RD 12, # A 78666 #048-12-1987 L1989 **OBG** *020 †30
IRWIN, Teresita Lynn. 1305 WONDER WORLD DR, STE 209 78666 #048-14-1996 L1997
  OBG *020 †30
JACOBSON, Arthur Ray. 1305 WONDER WORLD DR, STE 209 78666 #048-02-1968 L1968
  OBG *020 †20
JOHNSON, Wayne Alden. SW TEXAS STATE UNIVERSITY, STUDENT HEALTH CLINIC 78666
  #036-05-1963 L1984 **GP OM** *072 †70,18
JONES, David C, Jr. 1304 WONDER WORLD DR 78666 #012-01-1983 L1987 **RO** *020 †80
JONES, John Wm, Jr. 1320 WONDER WORLD DR # 100 78666 #005-06-1989 L1998
  OTO *020 †45

KEMPEMA, James Michael. 1999 MEDICAL PKWY STE D, AIR EVAC EMS INC 78666 #003-01-1996 L1999 **EM** *020 †16

KUNDA, Koteswara Rao. 2001 MEDICAL PKWY STE C 78666 #028-03-1991 L2002 **OBG** *020 †30

LAUE, Richard Reardon. 1999 MEDICAL PKWY STE A, SAN MARCOS FAMILY MED 78666 #026-08-1996 L1998 **FM** *020 †18

LAURENCE, Charles Edwin. 1301 WONDER WORLD DR 78666 #048-02-1979 L1982 **FM** *020 †18

LAWSON, Richard S. 1304 WONDER WORLD DR 78666 #048-13-1999 L2004 **RO** *020 †80

LE DOUX, Lance Lee. 2001 MEDICAL PKWY STE C 78666 #048-02-1975 L1975 **OBG** *020

LEE, Alan Lane. 1999 MEDICAL PKWY STE A 78666 #048-02-1996 L1999 **FM** *020 †18

LEE SANG, John E. 1301 WONDER WORLD DR 78666 #048-13-1995 L1996 **PTH** *020 †50

LOCK, John Michael. 601 UNIVERSITY DR, SOUTHWEST TEXAS STATE UNIV 78666 #048-13-1987 L1988 **FM** *020

LOCKETT, Wm Cleveland. 115 WARDEN LN 78666 #048-04-1977 L1977 **IM** *020 †20

LONG, Kenneth Lee. 1301 WONDER WORLD DR 78666 #048-02-1971 L1971 **IM CD** *020

LYON, Lee Arden. ■ 78666 #048-12-1968 L1968 **FM EM** *071

MATHIS, Charles R. 1305 WONDER WORLD DR, STE 300 78666 #048-14-1991 L1993 **GS** *020 †85

MINOR, Steven Thos. 1330 WONDER WORLD DR, STE B108 78666 #048-04-1979 L1979 **CD IM** *020 †20

MOORE, Gregory Keith. 1305 WONDER WORLD DR, STE 305 78666 #048-04-1983 L1983 **IM** *020 †20

MOSSBURG, Patricia Teresa. 1999 MEDICAL PKWY STE A, SAN MARCOS FAM MED 78666 #048-14-2000 L2003 **FM** *020 ‡

NICHOLS, Cody A. 1305 WONDER WORLD DR, STE 306 78666 #048-15-2000 L2005 **IM** *100 †20

OCCHIALINI, Annette L. 1305 WONDER WORLD DR # 203 78666 #048-13-1985 L1986 **PS GS** *020 †85,65

OUGHOURLIAN, Aurore Marie. ■ 78666 #035-46-2000 L2007 **IM** *100

PARKS, Alan Lee. 1301 WONDER WORLD DR 78666 #048-13-1983 L1983 **OBG** *020 †30

PARSONS, Donald Alva. 1301 WONDER WORLD DR 78666 #017-20-1967 L1974 **PTH** *071 †50

PICKETT, James E, III. 1301 WONDER WORLD DR 78666 #048-14-1982 L1983 **OPH** *020 †35

PORTER, Charles Thos, Jr. 1301 WONDER WORLD DR, SAN MARCOS ANES LLP 78666 #045-01-1978 L1989 **AN GS** *020 †05

RANDOLPH, Mark B. ■ 78666 #048-14-2002 L2004 **FM** *020 †18

REA, Van Earle. 123 QUAIL CREEK DR, BOX 1345 78666 #048-02-1965 L1965 **R** *020 †80

RODRIGUEZ, Ana Luisa. 1340 WONDER WORLD DR, STE 2301 78666 #005-15-1978 L1987 **D** *020 †15

ROMAIN, Michael Anthony. 115 WARDEN LN 78666 #035-48-1993 L1996 **IM** *020 †20

ROSS, Clay Whitten. 1200 NORTH BISHOP STE 2 78666 #048-02-1973 L1974 **P** *020 †75

RUST, John Boyd. 120 BERT BROWN ST 78666 #048-02-1973 L1973 **P CHP** *020

SALMAN, Ghassan Fouad. 115 WARDEN LN 78666 #605-01-1994 L2002 **IM** *020 †20

SCHLOTTER, James Wallace. 1347 THORPE LN 78666 #048-02-1981 L1981 **GS TRS** *020 †18,85

SCHNEIDER, David Lynn. ■ 78666 #048-16-1989 L1990 **FM** *020 †18

SEATON, Stanley Lawrence. 1301 WONDER WORLD DR 78666 #048-12-1960 L1960 **P** *071

SEYBOLD, Randolph C. 1301 WONDER WORLD DR, CENTRAL TEXAS MEDICAL CENT 78666 #021-01-1971 L1996 **IM** *020 †16

SIMPSON, Joseph Walker. 120 BERT BROWN ST, SAN MARCOS TREATMENT CENTE 78666 #048-02-1973 L1974 **CHP P** *020

SMITH, Douglas S. 1301 WONDER WORLD DR, SAN MARCOS MEDICAL 78666 #048-02-1994 L1995 **DR** *020 †80

SMITH, John Christopher. 1101D THORPE LN, STE 629 78666 #048-14-1987 L1988 **AN** *020 †05

SOWELL, Rugel F, Jr. ■ 78666 #048-04-1954 **PHP GP** *071 †70

STANLEY, James H. 1340 WONDER WORLD DR, BLD. 4 STE 4301 78666 #048-12-1996 L2002 **ORS** *020

SWEARINGEN, Stephen D. 1301 WONDER WORLD DR, SAN MARCOS MEDICAL 78666 #048-13-1996 L1997 **DR** *020 †80

SYMON, Julia Beth. 1601 REDWOOD RD STE C 78666 #048-02-1981 L1981 **IM** *020 †20

THOMPSON, James D. ■ 78666 #048-02-1950 L1950 **GP** *071

TOMANENG, Edward U. 2000 MEDICAL PKWY STE C 78666 #748-10-1975 L1985 **OTO** *020

TWEEDY, Dennis Alan. 1308 WONDER WORLD DR 78666 #051-04-1979 L1990 **IM HO** *020 †20

VILLARICO, Joy E. 1301 WONDER WORLD DR, C/O CTMC 78666 #048-14-1992 L1993 **AN** *020

VON HENNER, Charles Mason. 2003 MEDICAL PKWY, STE 1388 78666 #005-12-1951 L1951 **PS LM** *071 †18 ‡

VU, Toan Quoc. 1341 THORPE LN 78666 #942-03-1991 L2005 **CN** *100 †75 ‡

WALLIS, Jack Wesley. 2108 HUNTER RD, STE 116 78666 #048-13-1984 L1985 **FM FSM** *020 †18

WHISENANT, John Dewey. 1301 WONDER WORLD DR 78666 #048-12-1983 L1983 **EM IM** *020 †20

WHISENANT, Margaret G. 601 UNIVERSITY DR, TSU STUDENT HLTH CTR 78666 #048-12-1982 L1983 **IM** *020 †20

WILLIAMS, Grant David. 1301 WONDER WORLD DR, MEDICAL STAFF OFFICE 78666 #048-12-2003 L2006 **EM** *020 †20

WILLIS, Donald Lee. 1601 REDWOOD RD STE A 78666 #048-02-1983 L1983 **U** *020 †95

WILSON, James David. ■ 78666 #028-02-1976 L1978 **OTO** *020 †45

YOUNG, Margaret C. 1301 WONDER WORLD DR, LABORATORY CTMC 78666 #048-02-1983 L1983 **PTH BBK** *020 †50

ZAMORA, Carlos Enrique. 900 BUGG LN, STE 101 78666 #649-04-1970 L1978 **IM** *020 †20

SAN SABA – SAN SABA

FORRISTER, Skylar Stuart. 2005 W WALLACE ST 76877 #048-14-1987 L1988 **FM** *020 †18

SANDIA – JIM WELLS

BLAJER, Stanislav. RR 1 BOX 2478 78383 #286-02-1949 L1977 **OBG** *071 †30

SANGER – DENTON

AGHA, Tasneem K. 105 N STEMMONS ST 76266 #704-16-1980 L1998 **AN PME** *020

SANTA FE – GALVESTON

BARNUM, Patrice Duhon. 12426 HIGHWAY 6 77510 #021-05-2001 L2004 **IM** *020

BURLISON, Scott A. ■ 77510 #021-06-2004 L2007 **AN** *012

CAJIGAS GONZALEZ, Yohmarie. 4225 FM 646 RD N, STE 100 77510 #042-02-2001 L2007 **FM** *020

FREEMAN, Lance M. ■ 77510 #048-02-2008 *012

RICHMOND, Jack Gilbert. ■ 77510 #047-06-1961 L1961 **PTH** *071 †50

STAFFORD, John Sullivan. 4226 WARPATH AVE 77510 #048-02-1983 L1983 **FM** *020

SAVANNAH – DENTON

CHAMBLESS, Wm Stephen. ■ 76227 #039-01-1959 L1965 **OPH** *071 †35

SCHERTZ – GUADALUPE

ACEL, Timothy Carl. 78154 #023-12-2003 L2005 **IM** *020 †20

BERG, Jolene Kay. 3401 FM 3009 78154 #026-04-1979 L1996 **FM** *050 †18

CAPE, Richard Fredrick. 78154 #038-40-1957 L1975 **ORS OS** *072 †40

HARBISON, Richard Wm. ■ 78154 #043-01-1975 L1977 **PD ID** *020 †55

HILL, Barry Trent. ■ 78154 #048-02-2003 **PM** *012

HOFFMAN, Jennifer Marie. ■ 78154 #023-12-2005 L2007 **OBG** *012

INGRAM, William L. ■ 78154 #007-02-1951 L1953 **P** *071 †75

KENNEL, Christopher C. 105 COMMERCIAL PL 78154 #048-15-1998 L2002 **FM** *020 †18

KHAROD, Upendra J. ■ 78154 #495-22-1961 L1969 **OS** *030 †75

LUBIN, Arnold N. ■ 78154 #035-06-1962 L1963 **PHP PD** *071 †55

MASINI, Brendan David. ■ 78154 #038-06-2005 L2007 **ORS** *012

ORR, Justin. ■ 78154 #016-02-2003 L2005 **ORS** *012

PINO, Salustiano Ababon. ■ 78154 #748-01-1961 L1978 **FM FPG** *071 †18

ROWEN, Burt. ■ 78154 #035-19-1945 **GPM PHP** *030 †70

SHIRLEY, Lorraine Lee. 5000 BAPTIST HEALTH DR, STE 102 78154 #045-01-1991 L1992 **IM** *020 †20

WEST, Casey S. 813 MARILYN DR 78154 #048-14-1999 L2002 **EM** *020 †16

SCHULENBURG – FAYETTE

JAMES, Michele Lero. 511 SUMMIT ST, SCHULENBURG COMMUNITY 78956 #048-14-1991 L1992 **PD** *020 †55

KOCUREK, Donald James. 511 SUMMIT ST, SCHULENBURG COMMUNITY CLIN 78956 #048-12-1977 L1977 **GP** *020

KRAEMER, Susan L. 511 SUMMIT ST, SCHULENBURG COMMUNITY 78956 #030-05-1987 L1989 **FM** *020 †18

ROGERS, Anna M. ■ 78956 #048-15-2004 **AN** *012

WALL, Harold James. 511 SUMMIT ST, SCHULENBURG COMMUNITY 78956 #016-42-1970 L1979 **OTO** *020

SCROGGINS – FRANKLIN

MULLEN, John Bernard. 129 KING KENT CT 75480 #016-45-1975 L1981 **NS** *020 †25

SEABROOK – HARRIS

AJALA, Yolanda Bolanle. ■ 77586 #048-02-2004 L2007 **IM** *020 †20

ANGEL, Federico. ■ 77586 #264-01-1952 L1968 **NS** *071

ANTON, Arthur David. 2622 NASA ROAD 1, MSCH HEALTH CENTERS 77586 #028-03-1969 L1969 **GP** *071

BANERJEE, Swapan Kumar. 2622 NASA ROAD 1, SEABROOK MEDICAL CLINIC 77586 #495-32-1967 L1981 **FM IM** *020

CARR, Vicki Lakwanda. ■ 77586 #048-02-2003 L2007 **PDM** *012

CHAMBERLAIN, Blake Von. ■ 77586 #023-12-1991 L1995 **AM EM** *020 †16,70

GARG, Jyotika. ■ 77586 #495-78-2004 L2007 **PD** *012

GUINTO, Faustino Cano. 3129 SEA CHANNEL DR 77586 #748-01-1962 L1978 **RNR R** *040 †80

HAMILTON, Douglas Ross. ■ 77586 #060-02-1991 L1998 **OS** *074 †20

HANDLEY, John Dunlop. 4632 NASA PKWY, LAKESIDE FAMILY PRACTICE 77586 #649-14-1979 L1986 **FM** *020

INGRAM, Felicia Monique. ■ 77586 #048-14-2005 L2008 **P** *012

KUMAR-MISIR, Victor. ■ 77586 #566-01-1970 L1979 *020

LAM, David Nguyen. 710 SHOREWOOD DR 77586 #048-02-1986 L1999 **GS** *020 †85

LEUCK, Jo Crowley. ■ 77586 #048-12-2005 L2008 **EM** *012

LORDON, Robert Edward. ■ 77586 #010-02-1962 L1985 **NEP IM** *071 †20

LYON, Joyce Marie. ■ 77586 #566-01-1970 L1979 *072

MEEHAN, Michelle Ann. ■ 77586 #048-02-1983 L1983 **PN PD** *020 †55

MOZA, Reena. ■ 77586 #048-04-2005 **PD** *012

PATTEN, Ethel Doudine. ■ 77586 #033-05-1967 L1973 **BBK HEM** *071 †20

ROBBINS, Horace T. ■ 77586 #048-04-1951 L1951 **GS** *071 †85

RUMPH, Gregory Evan. ■ 77586 #020-12-2003 L2004 **MEM** *012

SCOTT, Angela Rachelle Le. ■ 77586 #048-02-2008 *012

SEAGOVILLE – DALLAS

MARTIN, Rebekah Leigh. ■ 75159 #048-15-2005 **PM** *012

SEALY – AUSTIN

KRISHNASWAMY, Kannappan. 526 5TH ST 77474 #495-94-1981 L1997 **IM** *020 †20

SEGUIN – GUADALUPE

ACOSTA, Sharron. 128 S MOSS ST, STE 300 78155 #005-14-1994 L1997 **OPH** *020 †35

ALAGOZ, Aysun. 1109 N AUSTIN ST 78155 #041-09-1991 L2002 **OBG** *020
ALLEN, Stanley Llewellyn. 1215 E COURT ST 78155 #036-01-2003 L2006 **EM** *020
ALTER, Bruce R. 519 N KING ST, STE 106 78155 #649-27-1982 L1993 **FM GE** *020 †18 ‡
ANDERSON, John Henry. ■ 78155 #048-14-2008 *012
BACHMAN, George Parfet. 205 N KING ST 78155 #048-02-1947 L1947 **GP** *071
BOULLIOUN, Susan Lorton. 113 E CEDAR ST 78155 #048-15-1994 L1997 **FM** *020 †18
BOWMAN, Steven P. 1215 E COURT ST 78155 #048-13-1999 L2004 **DR** *020 †80
CAMPOS, Daniel, III. 1215 E COURT ST, ANESTHESIA ASSOCIATES OF S 78155 #048-13-1982 L1983 **AN PME** *020 †05
CARREON, Ivonne Sahagun. 1500 E COURT ST STE 300 78155 #649-52-1997 L2003 **PD** *020 †55
CARREON, Melanie G. 1199 E COLLEGE ST 78155 #748-08-1993 L2000 **FM** *020 †18
CASTILLEJA, Jerry F. 1354 E WALNUT ST 78155 #048-13-1989 L1991 **FM** *020 †18
CASTRO, Rebecca. ■ 78155 #048-13-1989 L1991 **P** *020 †75
CHAN, Yeung Hoi. 205 N KING ST 78155 #244-03-1972 L1977 **FM** *020 †18
CODY, Thomas Jos. 1215 E COURT ST 78155 #048-13-1970 L1972 **DR OS** *071 †80
COLLINS, Cleve Brantley. 128 S MOSS ST, STE 500 78155 #012-01-1971 L1978 **NEP IM** *020 †20
COLVIN, James Thos, Jr. 519 N KING ST, STE 101 78155 #048-02-1974 L1974 **OBG FM** *020 †30 ‡
DAGGUBATI, Sreedevi. 1025 N AUSTIN ST 78155 #495-50-1993 L2001 **HO** *020 †20
DEETJEN, Jack Lowell. 515 N KING ST STE 106 78155 #048-04-1983 L1983 **ORS** *020 †40
DWYER, Michael J. 1255 ASHBY ST 78155 #039-01-1969 L1977 **GS EM** *020 †16,85
ETHRIDGE, Kathleen E. 1215 E COURT ST 78155 #048-13-1987 L1988 **PD** *020 †55
FADAL, Robert E, II. ■ 78155 #048-13-1990 L1992 **FM** *020
FATH, Steven Wade. 1346 E WALNUT ST, GUADALUPE VLY SURG ASSOC 78155 #048-13-1993 L1999 **GS** *020 †85
FISHER, James Forrest. 1215 E COURT ST 78155 #048-02-1976 L1976 **PD** *020 †55
FLEMING, Richard Edwin. 1255 ASHBY ST 78155 #048-12-1971 L1971 **OPH** *020 †35
FLORES, Antonio A. 1352 E WALNUT ST 78155 #048-04-2000 L2002 **FM** *100 †18
FLOURNOY, James G. 1215 E COURT ST, GUADALUPE VALLEY HOSPITAL 78155 #048-14-1976 L1976 **DR** *020 †80
FRETS, Robert Lynn. 1255 ASHBY STE B 78155 #048-13-1977 L1977 **IM** *020 †20
GRIEDER, Kevin Thomas. 979 GLENEWINKEL RD 78155 #048-78-1980, ▲ L1980 **PTH HEM** *020 †50
HARPER, Jennifer K. 1215 E COURT ST 78155 #048-12-1994 L1996 **DR** *020 †80
HARTFIEL, Arlynn Henry. 519 N KING ST, STE 103 78155 #048-14-1977 L1977 **FM** *020 †18
HENNESSEE, Jennifer Gaye. 1339 E COURT ST, STE 220 78155 #048-13-2000 L2005 **OTO** *020 †45
HILL, Robert Douglass. ■ 78155 #021-01-1954 L1957 **PD ID** *071 †55
KASPAR, Thomas. 1344 E WALNUT ST 78155 #048-02-1990 L1991 **ID MM** *020 †20 ‡
KOLLAUS, Kennard Lee. 1344 E WALNUT ST 78155 #048-13-1984 L1985 **FM** *020 †18
KUO, Yu-Jie J. 1356 E WALNUT ST 78155 #048-12-1994 L1996 **IM** *020 †20
LEE, Jim. 519 N KING ST, STE 102 78155 #048-13-1974 L1974 **FM** *020 †18
LOPEZ-GLYNN, Michele M. 1005 E COURT ST, STE 300 78155 #048-14-2000 L2003 **PD** *020
MAGNON, Robert Jay. 1342 E WALNUT ST 78155 #048-02-1976 L1976 **D EM** *020 †15
MAJOR, Dolores S. 1215 E COURT ST 78155 #048-13-1984 L1994 **AN PME** *020 †05
MANNEL, George Sterling. 1255 ASHBY ST STE G 78155 #048-02-1980 L1980 **OBG** *020 †30
MAYHORN, Ronald Elliott. ■ 78155 #048-13-1984 L1985 **AN** *020 †05
MONROE, Cynthia Lynn. 128 S MOSS ST, STE 100 78155 #048-16-1997 L2002 **NEP IM** *020 †20
MOORE, Henry H, Jr. 1355 E COURT ST 78155 #048-02-1958 L1958 **FM** *020
MULLEN, Brooks Michael. 908 E COURT ST, STE 2 78155 #048-13-1981 L1981 **OTO FPS** *020 †45
NOVAK, Suzanne. 1215 E COURT ST 78155 #048-13-1981 L1981 **AN PME** *030 †05
OBENG, Pete Kwabena. ■ 78155 #010-03-2008 *012
PEREZ, Juan Garcia. 1025 N AUSTIN ST 78155 #649-02-1956 L1966 **GP GS** *071
PINA, Daniel Angelnarcis. 1215 E COURT ST 78155 #048-13-2000 L2003 **AN** *020 †05
RAETZSCH, Thomas Hayes. 1025 N AUSTIN ST 78155 #048-15-1983 L1983 **FM** *020 †18
RENAGHAN, Thomas. 507 E COURT ST 78155 #048-13-1991 L1992 **P IM** *020 †75
RINN, Phillip Clay. 519 N KING ST, CEDARVIEW MEDICAL CLINIC S 78155 #048-13-1981 L1981 **FM** *020 †18
ROSS, Kim Marie. 1342 E WALNUT ST 78155 #038-43-1994 L1998 **D** *020 †15
RYAN, Robert Thomas, III. 1255 ASHBY ST, HOWARD D. SOLOMON, MD 78155 #048-13-1998 L2004 **U** *020 †95
SAHNI, Irvin K. 1339 E COURT ST 78155 #048-04-1996 L1997 **ORS** *020
SHACKLETT, David Edwards. 1473 E COURT ST 78155 #012-05-1961 L1976 **OPH** *071 †35
SOLOMON, Howard David. 1255 ASHBY ST 78155 #050-02-1971 L1977 **U** *020 †95
SPEZIA, Barbara J. 1215 E COURT ST 78155 #048-13-1996 L1998 **DR** *020 †80
TAMTAM, Sankararao. 205 N KING ST, STE 5 78155 #495-58-1988 L1999 **IM** *020 †20
TERRELL, Woodrow L. ■ 78155 #016-42-1943 L1943 **FM OM** *071
THANGADA, Praveen. 634 E COURT ST 78155 #495-57-1980 L1994 **N P** *020
THARP, William Webster. 147 LONE OAK ST 78155 #048-02-1961 L1962 **GP** *020
TSEN, Tony Nanrung. 219 S LEONARD LN 78155 #048-13-1990 L1995 **GE IM** *020 †20
VELA, Angela. 1215 E COURT ST 78155 #048-02-1978 L1978 **OPH** *020 †35
WHITE, George Steven. 280 S KING ST 78155 #021-06-1979 L1980 **ORS** *020 †40
ZINCONE, Dino Lawrence. 1355 E COURT ST 78155 #065-01-1984 L1994 **FM** *020

SELMA – GUADALUPE

EDENS, Jason Wesley. ■ 78154 #039-01-2005 L2006 **GS** *012
LINCOLN, Katherine Ann. ■ 78154 #022-75-2005, ▲ L2008 **FP** *012
MURRAY, James Paul, Jr. 8341 AGORA PKWY, TEXAS MED CLINIC 78154 #035-06-1997 L2000 **MPD** *020 †55,20
OTTMERS, Jeffrey N. 8341 AGORA PKWY 78154 #048-13-1997 L1998 **FM** *020 †18

SEMINOLE – GAINES

LAYMAN, Mark B. 208 NW 8TH ST, STE 1 79360 #048-15-1996 L1999 **IM** *020
LETELLIER, Jean-Pierre. 1004 HOBBS HWY 79360 #034-01-2004 L2006 **FM** *020
WATSON, Michael Quealy. 208 NW 8TH ST 79360 #021-01-1983 L1984 **FM** *020

SEVEN POINTS – HENDERSON

VANDIVER, William R. 606 S SEVEN POINTS DR, STE 9 75143 #025-12-1993 L1999 **OSM** *020 †40

SEYMOUR – BAYLOR

BUFFINGTON, Ryan Andrew. 201 STADIUM DR 76380 #048-02-2004 L2007 **FM** *020
MARTIN, Kory Lann. 200 STADIUM DR 76380 #048-12-2004 L2007 **FM** *100
NILES, Richard K. 201 STADIUM DR 76380 #048-15-1999 L2001 **FM** *020 †18

SHALLOWATER – LUBBOCK

GRAY, Chad E. 600 8TH ST 79363 #048-13-2001 L2002 **FM** *020 †18
MC LEES, Charles Thos. ■ 79363 #036-01-1965 L1965 **PTH CLP** *071 †50

SHAMROCK – WHEELER

BLACKKETTER, Donald E. ■ 79079 #039-01-1952 L1953 **FM** *071
JUSON, Manuel Jong. 1010 S MAIN ST, FAMILY CARE CLINIC 79079 #748-11-1972 L1994 **PD** *020
LESTER, Joseph K. 301 E INTERSTATE 40 79079 #039-01-1952 L1953 **ORS** *071 †40

SHAVANO PARK – BEXAR

BARROW, Barbi E. ■ 78231 #048-13-2002 L2006 **AN** *100 †05
BHASIN, Vibha. ■ 78231 #495-45-1992 L2004 **PTH** *020 †50
BRENNER, Pryor S. ■ 78231 #023-12-2003 L2004 **OTO** *012
CATHEY, Robert Heaton. ■ 78231 #019-02-1968 L1974 **D** *071 †15
COLLINS, George James, Jr. ■ 78231 #048-02-1966 L1966 **TS VS** *020 †85,90
DRENGLER, Coral Elizabeth. ■ 78231 #726-01-1989 L2000 **IMG** *020
EILERS, Emily A. ■ 78230 #048-14-1993 L1997 **AN** *020
ELMENDORF, Hugo F, Jr. ■ 78231 #048-02-1946 L1946 **R** *071 †80
FISHER, Daniella. ■ 78230 #048-13-2003 L2007 **AN** *020
GONZALEZ, David C. 14439 NW MILITARY HWY, STE 108 PMB 619 78231 #048-02-1994 L1998 **P** *020
GREGERMAN, Robert Isaac. ■ 78231 #024-07-1955 L1969 **END IM** *050 †20
GREIF, William Lawrence. ■ 78230 #024-01-1981 L1994 **DR** *020 †80
GRIFFIN, Charles Jeffrey. ■ 78230 #048-14-1985 L1987 **IM** *040 †20
HARKINS, Patricia M. 4093 DE ZAVALA RD, BLDG 2 78249 #048-13-1990 L2002 **PD** *020 †55
HILLIS, Leslie David. ■ 78230 #035-01-1972 L1974 **CD IM** *020 †20
MIMS, Charles Henderson. ■ 78231 #048-02-1967 L1967 **ON** *020 †20
NANNINI, Louis. ■ 78230 #132-01-1963 L1963 **PTH HEM** *071 †50
NARBONI, Gino Roger. ■ 78231 #396-06-1961 L1975 **ON OS** *071
NEWELL, Michael Eugene. 315 HAPPY TRL, UROLOGY SAN ANTONIO 78231 #035-01-1969 L1970 **U** *020 †95
O'CONNOR, Patrick St John. ■ 78231 #028-34-1970 L1978 **OPH EM** *020 †35 ‡
RAMIREZ, Rosa Enid. ■ 78231 #042-01-1973 L1981 **DR PD** *020 †55,80
SAYLOR, Jack Lloyd. ■ 78231 #016-11-1964 L1997 **GE IM** *071
SLAGLE, James Patton. ■ 78231 #048-02-1965 L1965 **AN** *071
SURI, Rajeev. ■ 78231 #495-08-1992 L2001 **DR** *100 †80 ‡
YOO, Esther Sook Cha. ■ 78231 #583-03-1967 L1972 **PD** *071 †55
YOO, John Sun. ■ 78230 #048-12-2005 **DR** *012

SHELBYVILLE – SHELBY

LIFSHUTZ, David Martin. ■ 75973 #048-12-1972 L1972 **GS EM** *020 †85

SHENANDOAH – MONTGOMERY

AL-KHADOUR, Hussamaddin. 920 MEDICAL PLAZA DR 77380 #875-01-1993 L2001 **IM** *020 †20
ARTHUR, Jeff M. 9201 PINECROFT DR 77380 #048-15-1987 L1988 **AN** *020 †05
ASI, Wael. 920 MEDICAL PLAZA DR 77380 #605-01-1986 L1994 **PCC** *020 †20
BALETTE, Jason Matthew. 9200 PINECROFT DR, STE 250 77380 #048-14-2001 L2005 **GS** *020
BEHNE, Bryan Keith. 8850 SIX PINES DR, AFFILIATES 77380 #048-13-2001 L2005 **OBG** *020
BERKELEY, Ralph Gordon. 9191 PINECROFT DR 77380 #048-04-1954 L1954 **OPH** *020 †35
BHURIWALA, Murtaza N. 920 MEDICAL PLAZA DR, STE 140 77380 #704-02-1991 L2003 **ON** *020 †20
BILLAL, Shazia. 920 MEDICAL PLAZA DR # 550 77380 #704-02-1992 L2005 **FM** *020 †18
BOYD, Alfred Andrew, III. 9201 PINECROFT DR 77380 #048-15-2001 L2007 **FM** *020 †18
CAGLE, Carrol Dean. 9201 PINECROFT DR 77380 #048-04-1972 L1972 **IM HEM** *020 †20
CAPLAN, Michael B. 9191 PINECROFT DR 77380 #048-04-1985 L1986 **OPH** *020 †35
CARWILE, John M. 9201 PINECROFT DR 77380 #048-16-1995 L1996 **HEM** *020 †20
CHAN, Pachie Sabuga. 19073 I H 45 S, STE 115 77385 #048-11-1986 L1998 **FM** *020 †18
CHANDLER, Preston J, III. 920 MEDICAL PLAZA DR # 380 77380 #048-12-1992 L1994 **GS** *020 †85
CHAPMAN, Jack A. 9200 PINECROFT DR STE 280, WOODLANDS PAIN MANAGEMENT 77380 #048-04-1987 L1988 **AN** *020 †05 ‡
CHAUDHARI, Jeffrey Ashraf. ■ 77381 #008-02-2003 **GS** *012
CHERRY, Don Eldon. 9250 PINECROFT DR 77380 #048-13-1985 L1987 **AN** *020 †05
CHOKSI, Ulupi Asit. 9200 PINECROFT DR STE 470 77380 #496-38-1980 L1986 **END IM** *020 †20
COHEN, Scott Alan. 920 MEDICAL PLAZA DR, STE 490 77380 #048-12-1987 L1988 **OTO FPS** *020 †45
COREY, Clyde Leland. 135 VISION PARK BLVD 77384 #048-12-1987 L1988 **U** *020 †95
COS, David S. 1120 MEDICAL PLAZA DR, STE 250 77380 #048-12-1992 L1993 **IM** *020 †20
CROWDER, Wm Edward, Jr. 8850 SIX PINES DR, AFFILIATES 77380 #048-04-1975 L1975 **OBG** *020 †30

DESAI, Ashesh D. 9201 PINECROFT DR 77380 #495-23-1996 L2005 **PCC** *012 †20
DOE, Erin Andrew. 9191 PINECROFT DR 77380 #036-07-1991 L1992 **OPH** *020 †35 ‡
DYLEWSKI, Drew Aric. 135 VISION PARK BLVD, NORTHWOODS UROLOGY ASSOC 77384 #048-04-2001 L2007 **U** *020
EADS, Gregory Lee. 1120 MEDICAL PLAZA DR, STE 200 77380 #055-01-1978 L2006 **OBG EM** *020 †30
ELLENT, David Peter. 920 MEDICAL PLAZA DR, STE 140 77380 #033-05-2000 L2003 **HEM** *020 †20
EL-WALI, Rami Said. 920 MEDICAL PLAZA DR 77380 #605-01-1999 L2006 **PCC** *100 †20
EVERSON, Jennifer Ann. 9200 PINECROFT DR, STE 300 77380 #010-02-1996 L2003 **OBG** *020 †30
FAHEY, Brian K. 9250 PINECROFT DR 77380 #048-02-1989 L1990 **AN** *020 †05
FEIT, Rachel Ann. 9201 PINECROFT DR 77380 #005-06-2001 L2007 **OPH** *020
FELIX, Brian Ross. 9250 PINECROFT DR 77380 #048-04-1987 L1988 **AN** *020 †05
FIELD, James A. 9200 PINECROFT DR, STE 280 77380 #048-13-1995 L2002 **GS** *020 †85
FISHER, Clay J. 9201 PINECROFT DR, SADLER CLINIC 77380 #048-13-1989 L1994 **ORS** *020 †40
FRANCIS, Marra S. 920 MEDICAL PLAZA DR # 560 77380 #008-02-1999 L2003 **OBG** *020
FRANKLIN, Peter David. 18550 I H 45 S, STE 1019 77384 #005-19-1987 L1993 **PM IM** *020 †20
GIANNAKIS, John George. 135 VISION PARK BLVD 77384 #040-02-1985 L1987 **U** *020 †95
GIANNOTTI, Marco A. 8850 SIX PINES DR, AFFILIATES 77380 #048-14-1993 L1995 **OBG** *020 †30
GILL, Inderbir Singh. 9250 PINECROFT DR 77380 #048-02-1992 L1995 **REN OBG** *020 †30
GOMEZ, Sandra Patricia. 9250 PINECROFT DR 77380 #054-04-1997 L2001 **FM** *020 †18
GONZALES, Anna Magda. 111 VISION PARK BLVD, DIGESTIVE SPECIALISTS OF 77384 #048-12-1996 L2002 **GE** *020 †20
GRAHAM, James M. 9200 PINECROFT DR, STE 280 77380 #048-14-1984 L1985 **ORS** *020 †40
GRAHAM, James Michael. 9200 PINECROFT DR, STE 280 77380 #020-02-1979 L1981 **OBG** *020 †30
GRAHAM, Michael F, Jr. 135 VISION PARK BLVD, NORTHWOODS UROLOGY ASSOCIA 77384 #048-04-1990 L1991 **U** *020 †95
GREGER, Jennifer. 9250 PINECROFT DR 77380 #048-14-1993 L1995 **AN** *020 †05
GREGER, Philip Henry, Jr. 920 MEDICAL PLAZA DR, STE 410 77380 #011-02-1991 L1997 **TRS CCS** *020 †85
GROGAN, Alice M. 9201 PINECROFT DR 77380 #539-03-1993 L2004 **FM** *020 †18
GUO, James S. 9250 PINECROFT DR 77380 #048-13-1991 L1992 **AN** *020 †05
HAM, Angelito Andres. 9250 PINECROFT DR 77380 #011-02-1989 L1993 **AN** *020 †05
HAMPTON, Shelby Lee. 9200 PINECROFT DR STE 350 77380 #048-02-2001 L2005 **OBG** *020 †30
HANES, Michelle Aileen. 1120 MEDICAL PLAZA DR, STE 150 77380 #039-01-2001 L2005 **OBG** *100 †30
HARIHARAN, Ramesh. 920 MEDICAL PLAZA DR, STE 495 77380 #495-59-1984 L1997 **ICE** *020 †20
HEDE, Vidyadhar S. 920 MEDICAL PLAZA DR, STE 350 77380 #496-38-1982 L1997 **AN** *020 †05
HENRY, Ronald Glover. 135 VISION PARK BLVD 77384 #048-04-1973 L1974 **U** *020 †95
HESTER, Gregory Daniel. 9201 PINECROFT DR 77380 #048-13-1999 L2003 **U** *020 †95
HOGAN, Matthew M. 135 VISION PARK BLVD 77384 #048-14-1998 L2003 **U** *020 †95
HORRIGAN, Mary Elizabeth. 9250 PINECROFT DR 77380 #048-12-1997 L2000 **EM** *020 †16
HUBBARD, Alan Lee. 9200 PINECROFT DR, STE 220 77380 #048-14-1981 L1981 **GS** *020 †85
HUNTER, Marque Andrew. 9250 PINECROFT DR 77380 #048-15-1984 L1985 **PUD SME** *020 †20
IYER, Vaidyanath L. 9191 PINECROFT DR STE 250 77380 #495-23-1979 L1996 **P** *020 †75
IZADIFAR, Noushin. 920 MEDICAL PLAZA DR, STE 100 77380 #517-05-1986 L2002 **RO** *020 †80
JACKSON, James Stuart. 9250 PINECROFT DR 77380 #039-01-1987 L1990 **AN** *020 †05
JENKINS, Mark Schering. 9250 PINECROFT DR 77380 #028-02-1973 L1973 **OPH** *020 †35
JOHNSON, Beena M. 9200 PINECROFT DR, STE 530 77380 #048-14-1993 L1994 **OBG** *020
JOHNSON, Randall W. 9201 PINECROFT DR 77380 #048-14-1996 L1998 **IM** *020 †20
KALLINA, Charles F. 9201 PINECROFT DR 77380 #048-16-2000 L2005 **HS** *020
KARIM, Altaf. 9201 PINECROFT DR, SADLER CLINIC 77380 #704-02-1984 L1995 **IM** *020
KERSCHENBAUM, Joel. 9201 PINECROFT DR 77380 #065-01-1974 L1978 **FM** *020
KHAN, Farhan Yusuf. 9250 PINECROFT DR, DEPT. OF EMERGENCY MEDICIN 77380 #033-05-2001 L2007 **EM** *020 †16
KHAN, Maryam Ijaz. 920 MEDICAL PLAZA DR, STE 450 77380 #704-01-2001 L2007 **IM** *100 †20
KIM, Soo H. 218 HICKORY RIDGE DR 77381 #048-02-2008 *012
KODITYAL, Sandeep. 9201 PINECROFT DR 77380 #048-15-2001 L2003 **HMP** *020
LAHIRI, Sabrina Ann. 9200 PINECROFT DR, STE 450 77380 #004-01-1994 L1996 **PS GS** *020 †85,65
LE, Thang Ngoc. 9201 PINECROFT DR, SADLER CLINIC 77380 #048-04-1997 L1999 **GE** *020 †20
LEE, Christine Mihee. 920 MEDICAL PLAZA DR, STE 300 77380 #025-07-1997 L2000 **GO OBG** *020
MAGGART, James Ryan. 9201 PINECROFT DR 77380 #048-15-1999 L2004 **GS** *020 †85
MANKARIOUS, Ramy. 9250 PINECROFT DR 77380 #048-14-1994 L1998 **AN** *020 †05
MATHEW, Jefy M. 920 MEDICAL PLAZA DR 77380 #048-04-1996 L2003 **PCC SME** *020 †20
MC KILLIP, Laurel. 1120 MEDICAL PLAZA DR, STE 250 77380 #048-14-1984 L1985 **PD** *020 †55
MC QUEEN, Brent R. 9191 PINECROFT DR 77380 #048-12-1993 L1994 **OPH** *020 †35
MEADA, Riad. 920 MEDICAL PLAZA DR 77380 #875-01-1982 L2005 **TS** *020 †85
MILES, Stephen Edward. 9191 PINECROFT DR STE 290, ALL SEASONS ALLERGY CTR 77380 #048-15-1991 L1993 **AI** *020 †55
MOCK, Robert Duane. 1120 MEDICAL PLAZA DR #380 77380 #005-12-1976 L1977 **FM** *020 †18
MOORE, Alan Greenwood. 1120 MEDICAL PLAZA DR, STE 340 77380 #048-04-1977 L1977 **OBG** *020 †18,30
MULDER, Michelle L. 1120 MEDICAL PLAZA DR, STE 150 77380 #048-13-2000 L2004 **OBG** *020
NAQVI, Shahzeb Raza. 920 MEDICAL PLAZA DR, STE 495 77380 #704-02-1991 L2005 **NEP IM** *020 †20
NGU, Bonaventure Bimambu. 9201 PINECROFT DR 77380 #023-01-2000 L2006 **ORS** *020
PARKE, Frank A. 9201 PINECROFT DR 77380 #048-14-1998 L2001 **RHU** *020 †20
PARKS, William Barto. 9250 PINECROFT DR 77380 #011-04-1979 L1982 **PD** *071 †55
PASCHALIS, Thimos G. 1120 MEDICAL PLAZA DR, STE 250 77380 #048-14-1994 L1996 **IM** *020 †20
PRUS, Robert S. 9250 PINECROFT DR 77380 #759-03-1977 L1985 **AN** *020 †05
RAHMAN, Mohammad Atiar. 9201 PINECROFT DR 77380 #160-02-1985 L2002 **CD** *020 †20
RAMINENI, Naveen. 9201 PINECROFT DR 77380 #041-09-1997 L2001 **PM** *020 †60
RAZA, Syed A. 920 MEDICAL PLAZA DR 77380 #048-04-1996 L1999 **IM** *020 †20
REED, Jane Carol. 9200 PINECROFT DR STE 350 77380 #048-14-1981 L1981 **OBG** *020 †30

REEVES, Robert David. 8850 SIX PINES DR, AFFILIATES 77380 #048-04-1975 L1975 **OBG** *020 †30
RICHTER-WERNING, Andrea L. 9200 PINECROFT DR, STE 400 77380 #048-14-2002 L2005 **OBG** *020 †30
RIDDLE, Jefferson Eugene. 9250 PINECROFT DR 77380 #048-02-1983 L1983 **AN** *020 †05
RITTER, Jack Lendon. 8850 SIX PINES DR, AFFILIATES 77380 #048-04-1975 L1975 **OBG** *020 †30
RIVELA, Lucian Jos. 9191 PINECROFT DR 77380 #048-12-1990 L1998 **PS** *020 †85,65
ROBERTS, Janet L. 9201 PINECROFT DR 77380 #060-02-1989 L1996 **FM** *020 †18
ROBERTSON, Christopher K. 9201 PINECROFT DR 77380 #048-13-1999 L2003 **FM** *020
ROJAS, Raul. 920 MEDICAL PLAZA DR 77380 #016-11-1994 L1997 **OBG** *020
ROOHEY, Tabasam. 9250 PINECROFT DR 77380 #704-01-1981 L2004 **PD NPM** *020 †55
ROSENBLATT, Steven. 9250 PINECROFT DR 77380 #011-02-1973 L1975 **P PYG** *020 †75
SARAF, Sunil Kumar. 9191 PINECROFT DR STE 245, ADVANCED ALLERGY CARE 77380 #495-14-1993 L2005 **AI** *020 †55
SCHAFERLING, Julie Evans. 9250 PINECROFT DR 77380 #048-12-2003 L2005 **EM** *020 †16
SEYMOUR, Gregory Todd. 920 MEDICAL PLAZA DR, STE 140 77380 #025-07-1996 L2000 **ON** *100 †20
SHEFFIELD, James Craver. ■ 77381 #048-02-1973 L1973 **EM FM** *020 †16
SHOOK, Brent Andrew. 8850 SIX PINES DR, STE 290 77380 #048-15-2000 L2002 **D** *020 †15
SIDDIQI, Ather J. 920 MEDICAL PLAZA DR 77380 #704-01-1984 L1999 **PCC SME** *020 †20
SIMMONS, Jerald Howard. 9201 PINECROFT DR 77380 #038-40-1986 L1999 **N IM** *020 †75
SIMS, Emma J. 9200 PINECROFT DR, STE 400 77380 #048-14-1998 L2002 **OBG** *020 †30
SMITH, Mona Abdulmajid. 920 MEDICAL PLAZA DR, STE 200 77380 #797-03-1984 L2001 **PD** *020 †55
SWEENEY, Jeff C. 9201 PINECROFT DR 77380 #005-06-1996 L2001 **FM** *020 †18
SYAL, Rajender K. 920 MEDICAL PLAZA DR # 300, RAJENDER SYAL 77380 #048-02-1988 L1989 **OBG** *020 †20
THOMAS, Celeste M. 920 MEDICAL PLAZA DR, STE 340 77380 #048-13-1989 L1994 **RHU** *020 †20
THOMAS, Daniele Dascy. 9250 PINECROFT DR 77380 #035-08-1980 L1982 **IM** *020 †20
TOMASZEK, David Edward. 111 VISION PARK BLVD, STE 250 77384 #008-02-1981 L1999 **NS** *030
TRUONG, Kevin Anh. 9250 PINECROFT DR, MEMORIAL HERMAN THE WOODLA 77380 #041-13-2000 L2003 **EM** *020 †16
TURCINOVIC, Petar. 9200 PINECROFT DR, STE 250 77380 #048-04-1993 L1998 **GS** *020 †85
TURNER, Tracy Louise. 9200 PINECROFT DR, STE 350 77380 #048-04-2001 L2005 **OBG** *020 ‡
VARNER, William T. 9250 PINECROFT DR 77380 #048-02-1988 L1990 **AN CD** *020 †05
VAZQUEZ, Enrique V. 9201 PINECROFT DR, SADLER CLINIC 77380 #042-01-1982 L1993 **RHU IM** *020 †20
VILLARREAL, Terry Joseph. 9250 PINECROFT DR 77380 #048-02-1997 L2001 **AN** *020 †05
WANG, Benny Shangpin. 9201 PINECROFT DR 77380 #048-12-1998 L2003 **N** *020 †75
WESTMORELAND, Holly M. 920 MEDICAL PLAZA DR, STE 595 77380 #048-02-1999 L2004 **OBG** *020
WETZEL, Stuart P. 920 MEDICAL PLAZA DR, STE 260 77380 #048-02-1990 L1992 **ORS** *020 †40
WILKERSON, Mark H. 9201 PINECROFT DR 77380 #048-12-1985 L1986 **OPH** *020 †35
WOO, Liliana. 135 VISION PARK BLVD 77384 #024-01-1999 L2002 **U** *020 †95
YOUNG, Jerome C. 920 MEDICAL PLAZA DR, STE 560 77380 #048-16-1994 L1995 **OBG** *020 †30

SHEPPARD AIR FORCE BASE – WICHITA

ABELLO, Victor Banzon. 149 HART ST, ATTN: CREDENTIAL OFFICE 76311 #748-02-1965 L1973 **PD** *020 †55
BECK, Patrick J. ■ 76311 #035-09-1973 **P** *020
BRAJER, Allen Raymond. 149 HART ST, INTERNAL MEDICINE 76311 #048-15-1982 L1983 **IM** *020 †20
CLEMENT, Martin Okeny. ■ 76311 #649-38-2002 L2006 **IM** *020 †20
COGAR, Allison Anne. 149 HART ST, 82 MEDICAL GROUP/SGH 76311 #034-01-1999 L1999 **PD** *020 †55
COX, Stephen Brooke. 149 HART ST, ATTN: CREDENTIAL OFFICE 76311 #051-01-1989 L1994 **EM** *020
DORVAL, Jean Baptiste. 149 HART ST, 82 MEDICAL GROUP/SGH 76311 #440-01-1973 L1988 **GS** *020 †85
ESPINOSA, Alvaro Jose. ■ 76311 #264-02-1955 **OTO FPS** *020 †45
GORE, Russell Kahn. ■ 76311 #051-02-2001 L2002 *020
HORVATH, Eva. 149 HART ST, 82ND MEDICAL GROUP 76311 #473-03-1994 L2000 **FM** *020 †18
JOHNSON, Richard Lee. 149 HART ST, 82 MEDICAL GROUP 76311 #048-13-1999 L2001 **GS** *020
KHOURY, Ludwig Edward. 149 HART ST, ATTN: CREDENTIAL OFFICE 76311 #065-06-1989 L1998 **AI IM** *020 †20,03
LAWSON, Jeffrey Alan. 149 HART ST RM 3 76311 #055-01-1993 L1996 **OM** *100 †18,70
MAXEY, Robert Adrian. 149 HART ST, 82 MEDICAL GROUP/SGH 76311 #023-12-1999 L2006 **DR** *100 †80
MUSHLIN, Gennady. 149 HART ST, 82 MEDICAL GROUP/SGH 76311 #913-10-1984 L2002 **FM** *020 †18
NGUYEN, Linh Cao. 149 HART ST 76311 #654-01-2000 L2005 **FM** *100 †18 ‡
PURCELL, Blaine Smith. 149 HART ST, INTERNAL MEDICINE CLINIC 76311 #004-01-1985 L2006 **IM** *020 †20
SAN DIEGO, Armando Gonda. 149 HART ST RM 1 76311 #748-01-1959 L1969 **PTH** *020 †50
SODERGREN, Jeffrey Arnold. 149 HART ST, ATTN: CREDENTIAL OFFICE 76311 #041-12-2000 L2006 **DR** *012
STEPHAN, Phillip John. 149 HART ST, ATTN: CREDENTIAL OFFICE 76311 #048-12-1998 L2001 **PS** *012 †20
SWAFFORD, Erich Lofton. 149 HART ST, ATTN: CREDENTIAL OFFICE 76311 #045-01-2001 L2005 **P** *020
WHITE, Marylin Helen. 149 HART ST RM 1 76311 #003-01-1981 L1990 **OPH** *020 †35
WYATT, Christopher Kevin. ■ 76311 #016-45-1999 L2001 **P** *100

SHERMAN – GRAYSON

ABRANTES, Anthony Clark. 3401 N CALAIS ST 75090 #048-13-1980 L1980 **OBG** *020 †20
AHMED, Ghufran. 425 N HIGHLAND AVE STE 230, SHERMAN INTERNAL MEDICINE 75092 #704-02-1990 L1996 **IM** *020 †20

ALFORD, Stanley Paul. 1800 TEAGUE DR, STE 107 75090 #016-11-1962 L1968 DR NM *071 †80

AL-RIFAI, Mohamad S. 321 N HIGHLAND AVE STE 200, TEXOMA NEUROLOGY ASSOCIATE 75092 #875-01-1986 L2001 CHN PD *020

AMHAN, Muhamad-Emad M. 2605 N MASTERS DR 75090 #875-02-1991 L1998 APM AN *020 †05

ARIFUDDIN, Razi Mohammed. 425 N HIGHLAND AVE, TEXOMA GASTROENTEROLOGY 75092 #422-01-1999 L2006 GE *100 †20

ARZOLA, Fernando Luis. 425 N HIGHLAND AVE, STE 100 75092 #042-01-1997 L2003 IM *020

BARKER, Larry James. 2800 N SAM RAYBURN FWY 75090 #048-02-1976 L1976 ON *020 †20

BARKLEY, Ronald Myers. 425 N HIGHLAND AVE, TEXOMA GASTROENTEROLOGY 75092 #048-13-1972 L1972 GE IM *020 †20

BAUR, Ogden Thos. ■ 75092 #047-06-1965 L1973 GS TS *071 †85

BELL, Wayne Larry. 500 N HIGHLAND AVE 75092 #048-02-1977 L1977 EM *020

BENDER, Jay Stuart. 321 N HIGHLAND AVE, STE 125 75092 #048-12-1993 L1993 ORS *020 †40

BENNETT, Jerry David. 500 N HIGHLAND AVE, EMERGENCY DEPT 75092 #048-02-1981 L1981 FM *020 †16,18

BENSON, J Michael. 300 N BRYANT AVE 75092 #048-12-1976 L1976 IM *020 †20

BERNATH, Alexander Sandor. 1117 GALLAGHER DR 75090 #561-01-1976 L1983 U *020

BERRY, James Eason Butler. 1117 GALLAGHER DR STE 450 75090 #039-01-1959 L1962 IM *020

BHARGAVA, Deepika. 1800 TEAGUE DR, STE 212 75090 #495-73-1985 L2005 PYG *020

BOOTHE, Thomas Earl. 300 N HIGHLAND AVE, STE 415 75092 #048-04-1975 L1975 OBG *020 †30

BOSSEN, Andrew D. 1303 N TRAVIS ST, RGB EYE ASSOCIATES 75092 #048-16-2004 L2008 OPH *020

BOST, J Edgar, Jr. 300 N HIGHLAND AVE, STE 545 75092 #048-04-1981 L1982 OBG *020 †30

BOUDREAU, Donald J. 500 N HIGHLAND AVE 75092 #065-09-1953 L1978 GP IMG *071

BRENNAN, John Herbert. 2203 N HIGHWAY 1417 75092 #048-02-1967 L1968 OPH *071 †35

BRITTON, Morris Lee. ■ 75092 #048-12-1947 L1947 OPH OS *071

BRONOWITZ, Philip F. 619 E HOUSTON ST, SHERMAN INTERNAL MEDICINE 75090 #033-06-1977 L1997 EM IM *020 †20

BROWN, Lyle Lloyd. 425 N HIGHLAND AVE STE 220 75092 #028-03-1974 L1975 TS *020 †85,90

BROWN, Patrick Michael. 500 N HIGHLAND AVE 75092 #028-34-1982 L1995 EM *020 †16

BUCKINGHAM, Charles Glenn. 600 N HIGHLAND AVE, STE 102 75092 #048-02-1963 L1963 GS *020 †85

BUCKNER, Mark B. 332 KLAS RD 75092 #048-15-1991 L1992 EM *020 †16

BURLINGAME, Robert Geo. 1303 N TRAVIS ST 75092 #048-12-1983 L1983 OPH *020 †35

CARDENAS, Alfonso. 119 W HOUSTON ST 75090 #005-14-1982 L1993 EM *020

CASTLEBERRY, Drew Conlan. 500 N HIGHLAND AVE, SHERMAN RADIOLOGY 75092 #048-04-1985 L1986 DR *020 †80

CASTLEBERRY, Lawrence M. PO BOX 340 75091 #048-12-1952 L1952 R *071 †80

CERNERO, Aaron. 300 N HIGHLAND AVE, STE 430 75092 #048-78-2001, ▲ L2002 GS *020

CHAM, Max. ■ 75092 #062-01-1945 L1976 AN *071

COBLE, David Edward. 1000 S FM 1417, HEALTHCENTER ON 1417 75092 #048-04-1966 L1966 PD *020 †55

COGSWELL, Max E, Jr. 500 N HIGHLAND AVE 75092 #048-14-1992 L1993 AN *020 †05

COOK, Judith Hamann. 115 W LAMBERTH RD STE A 75092 #048-13-1973 L1973 P PTH *020 †50

COOPER, Christian A. 809 GALLAGHER DR 75090 #048-14-1989 L1990 FM *020 †18

CRAIG, Grant A. 425 N HIGHLAND AVE, STE 120 75092 #048-14-1985 L1986 FM OS *020 †18

DAVIES, Dale Curtis. 300 N HIGHLAND AVE, STE 54D 75092 #033-06-1992 L1996 IM *020 †20

DAVIS, David Floyd. 305 N HIGHLAND AVE 75092 #048-14-1976 L1976 CD *020 †20

DAWLAH, Zubaer M. 4600 N HIGHLAND AVE 75092 #048-12-1988 L2006 IM *020 †20

DIPPEL, Lennis Kyle. 2008 BOIS D ARC DR 75092 #048-12-1988 L1989 EM FM *020 †18

DONAHUE, Patrice M. 2900 N SAM RAYBURN FWY 75090 #048-13-1989 L1990 P *020 †75

DOSHI, Dipauni Sandeep. 600 N HIGHLAND AVE 75092 #495-22-1995 L2005 IM *020 †20

EHSAN, Alex Ali. ■ 75092 #308-03-2000 L2007 ON *012 †20

ENNIS, Ronnie Lee. 500 N HIGHLAND AVE 75092 #021-06-1991 L1996 PTH *020 †50

ESSIN, Emmett M, Jr. 600 N HIGHLAND AVE 75092 #048-02-1943 L1943 GYN *072

FARIDI, Amir Ali. 2800 N SAM RAYBURN FWY 75090 #704-02-1993 L1998 HO *020 †20

FARRELL, Martin Gregory. 425 N HIGHLAND AVE, TEXOMA GASTROENTEROLOGY 75092 #048-02-1983 L1983 GE IM *020 †20

FERGUSON, John Saml. ■ 75092 #004-01-1954 L1962 D *071

FINCHER, Donald Franklin. ■ 75092 #048-02-1963 L1963 D *071 †15

FLETCHER, John Thomas. 425 N HIGHLAND AVE, TEXOMA GASTROENTEROLOGY 75092 #048-13-1974 L1974 GE IM *020 †20

FRAZIER, Richard Lee. 362 WOODLAND HILLS DR 75092 #025-07-1983 L1987 AN *072

FREY, William Brooks. 500 N HIGHLAND AVE, SHERMAN RADIOLOGY 75092 #017-20-1975 L1994 DR *020 †80

GAJDA, Malgorzata T. 425 N HIGHLAND AVE, STE 542 75092 #759-07-1987 L1998 PD *020 †55

GARCIA-VALDES, Carlos J. ■ 75092 #649-02-1976 GS CD *020

GAY, James Stephen. 1111 GALLAGHER DR 75090 #021-01-1964 L1976 OTO *020 †45

GLEASON, Ronald Patrick. 140 W LAMBERTH RD, STE A 75092 #019-02-1980 L1997 P PTH *020 †75

GOOD, Rudolf H. 2800 S HIGHWAY 75, TEXAS CANCER CENTER 75090 #869-07-1967 L1974 ON IM *020 †20

GOSHEN, Eli. ■ 75092 #781-03-1951 L1978 P *071

GRAFA, Gary Wilbur. 300 N HIGHLAND AVE, STE 545 75092 #048-13-1984 L1985 OBG *020 †30

GRIFFIN, Kaylene Sue Dunn. 809 GALLAGHER DR, DRIVE,STE B 75090 #048-02-1997 L2000 PD *020 †55

GROSS, Guy Herman. 260 E EVERGREEN ST 75090 #048-12-1969 L1973 OBG *020

HABAL, Oussama H. 600 N HIGHLAND AVE, STE 108 75092 #875-01-1973 L1977 PUD IM *020

HANEY, Jasyn H. 809 GALLAGHER DR 75090 #048-15-1997 L1998 FM *020 †18

HARNEY, Gina Gay. 815 PECAN GROVE RD E 75090 #039-01-1994 L1996 D *020 †15

HARRELL, Jimmy Joel. 1117 GALLAGHER DR, STE 420 75090 #048-02-1964 L1964 OBG *071 †30

HEBERT, Mary Elizabeth. 2800 N SAM RAYBURN FWY 75090 #036-01-1989 L1996 RO *020 †80

HERNANDEZ, Robert Jacob. 2108 POST OAK XING 75092 #039-01-1989 L1992 EM IM *020 †20

HILZ, Michael Edward. 300 N HIGHLAND AVE, STE 365 75092 #048-02-1982 L1983 U *020 †95

HODGE, Bradley G. 1906 W US HIGHWAY 82 75092 #048-14-1991 L1992 FM *020 †18

HOLBROOK, Curtis R. 500 N HIGHLAND AVE 75092 #037-01-1985 L2004 AN GS *020 †05

HOSEK, Herve Desire. 913 COTTONWOOD DR, ONE MEDICAL 75090 #396-30-1984 L1988 EM FM *020 †18

ISAAC, Michael G. 310 N BRYANT AVE 75092 #048-12-1992 L1993 CD *020 †20

JELSMA, Richard Dejongh. 425 N HIGHLAND AVE, STE 110 75092 #035-01-1988 L1995 OSM *020 †40 ‡

JOHNSON, Vernon Chas. 302 E BROCKETT ST 75090 #048-02-1990 L1992 CHP *020

JOHNSTONE, Robert Wm. 220 SUNSET BLVD STE C7, PMB 123 75092 #048-02-1968 L1975 OTO AM *020 †45

KALIL, Bryan. 140 W LAMBERTH RD, TEXOMACARE SHERMAN 75092 #836-02-1970 L1996 PD NPM *020 †55

KARIM, Mohammed Asad. 300 N HIGHLAND AVE STE 455 75092 #704-02-1985 L1995 CD IM *020 †20

KHAN, Anwar H. 1800 TEAGUE DR STE 3 75090 #704-04-1969 L1976 AN *071 †05

KHAN, Saleem. 600 N HIGHLAND AVE STE 102, SHERMAN SURGICAL ASSOCIATE 75092 #704-01-1970 L1977 GS TS *020 †85

KILARU, Nagamma. 2600 N HIGHWAY 75 75090 #495-50-1972 L1977 AN *020 †05

KOONE, Mark D. 815 PECAN GROVE RD E 75090 #048-04-1986 L1987 D *020 †15

LAING, Jennifer. 812 PECAN GROVE RD E 75090 #025-07-1991 L1997 PD *020 †18 ‡

LAING, Vern Odean. 1117 GALLAGHER DR, STE 440 75090 #011-03-1964 L1991 A PDA *020 †03,20

LEUNG, Danielle Max. 900 N GRAND AVE, STE 60940 75090 #048-12-2007 L2007 PD *012

LEWIS, Theodore C, Jr. ■ 75090 #048-02-1954 L1954 ORS *071 †40

LOGAN, Neal J. ■ 75092 #019-02-1963 L1984 OPH *071 †35

LONG, Clinton Arvin. 2203 HERITAGE PKWY 75092 #048-14-1997 L1998 OPH *020 †35

LOPEZ, Jerome Earl. 321 N HIGHLAND AVE STE 210, TEXOMA NEUROLOGY ASSOCIATE 75092 #023-01-1992 L2000 IM *020 †75

MAC DONALD, Shawn Bryden. 140 W LAMBERTH RD STE C, SHERMAN MEDICAL 75092 #064-01-1982 L1984 FM EM *020

MALIK, Zafar Iqbal. 3902 TEXOMA PKWY 75090 #704-04-1966 L1981 PUD IM *020

MARLOW, Gary J. 500 N HIGHLAND AVE 75092 #048-12-1992 L1993 AN *020 †05

MARLOW, John E. ■ 75092 #041-12-1953 L1954 FM *072

MARSHALL, Winston S. 310 N BRYANT AVE 75092 #048-12-1993 L1994 CD *020 †20

MATUS, Jose Antonio. 321 N HIGHLAND AVE STE 200, TEXOMA NEUROLOGY ASSOCIATE 75092 #429-01-1982 L1995 N IM *020 †75

MC BRIDE, Alan J. 600 N HIGHLAND AVE 75092 #048-02-1985 L1986 IM IMG *020 †20

MC CARTHY, Paul. 500 N HIGHLAND AVE 75092 #048-12-1990 L1994 AN *020 †05

MC GEE, Thomas E. 500 N HIGHLAND AVE, SHERMAN RADIOLOGY 75092 #048-12-1996 L1998 DR *020 †80

MC KEE, Edgar Geer. 500 N HIGHLAND AVE 75092 #021-01-1968 L1976 ATP CLP *020 †50

MELLEM, Maneeb. 600 N HIGHLAND AVE, STE 101 75092 #025-07-1979 L1982 IM *020 †20

MILLER, Larry Robt. 500 N HIGHLAND AVE 75092 #048-04-1983 L2004 PTH *020 †50

MILLMANN, Paul Robt. ■ 75090 #035-08-1981 L1986 FM *020 †18

MOONEY, Charles Frederick. 425 N HIGHLAND AVE, STE 240 75092 #048-15-1984 L1985 GS *020 †85

MUYSHONDT, Enrique. 1913 STONEBROOK LN 75092 #341-01-1960 L1981 FM GP *071 †85

NIEBERG, Franklin Geo. 425 N HIGHLAND AVE # 2600 75092 #048-04-1967 L1967 GP *020

NIEHUS, Joe L. 500 N HIGHLAND AVE, SHERMAN RADIOLOGY 75092 #048-13-1993 L1994 DR *020 †80

NOOMAN, Abdul Galil. 500 N HIGHLAND AVE 75092 #605-01-1974 L1978 CD IM *075

OSTERMAN, David Wm. 403 N HIGHLAND AVE 75092 #028-34-1979 L1981 ORS *020 †40

PAPAILA, John G. 1419 N TRAVIS ST 75092 #048-12-1984 L1991 PS *020 †85,65 ‡

PHELPS, Charles Ray, II. 500 N HIGHLAND AVE, SHERMAN RADIOLOGY 75092 #048-02-1976 L1980 DR NM *020 †80

PITTS, Philip W. 425 N HIGHLAND AVE 75092 #048-13-1991 L1993 IM *020 †20

PLAUCHE, William Bradley. 1303 N TRAVIS ST, RGB EYE ASSOCIATES 75092 #021-06-2002 L2006 OPH *020

PSUTKA, John Francis. 500 N HIGHLAND AVE 75092 #065-06-1967 L1977 PM *020

PULLIAM, John Hughes, Jr. 300 N HIGHLAND AVE, STE 3 75092 #048-13-1985 L1986 NS *020 †25

RAMSEY, D Bruce. 300 N HIGHLAND AVE, STE 315 75092 #048-15-1988 L1989 NS *020 †25

RATHOD, Kamalsingh M. 321 N HIGHLAND AVE STE 100 75092 #495-76-1975 L1983 CD IM *020 †20

RATHOD, Minaxi K. 321 N HIGHLAND AVE, STE 100 75092 #495-76-1975 L1984 ID IM *020 †20

REDDY, Pratap Tummala. 1107 SARA SWAMY DR 75090 #495-21-1991 L2001 RHU *020 †20

REID, O Creighton. ■ 75092 #039-01-1945 L1950 PD PHP *071

REYNOLDS, David G. 321 N HIGHLAND AVE, STE 105 75092 #048-02-1988 L1989 NEP IM *020 †20

ROQUE, Tammy Elizabeth. 2800 N SAM RAYBURN FWY 75090 #021-06-1984 L1990 ON HEM *020 †20

RUE, Bradley C. 600 N HIGHLAND AVE 75092 #048-14-1998 L2001 IM *020 †20

RUE, Rebecca Renee. 300 N HIGHLAND AVE STE 550 75092 #048-14-1999 L2002 PD *020 †55

RUSSELL, James Tedford. 1906 W US HIGHWAY 82 # 500 75092 #004-01-1974 L1988 FM *020 †18 ‡

SAHERWALA, Fatima Shabbir. 315 W MCLAIN DR, TEXOMA MHMR 75092 #704-02-1988 L2004 P *020

SANDMANN, Timothy Lee. 260 E EVERGREEN ST 75090 #039-01-1987 L1992 OBG *020 †30

SARMAST, Syed Abdul. ■ 75092 #048-15-2008 *012

SARRIS, Ibrahim Hussein. 3515 LOY LAKE RD 75090 #915-08-1970 L1976 CD IM *020

SCHRANK, Kenton Parke. 300 N HIGHLAND AVE, STE 430 75092 #048-02-1976 L1976 GS *020 †85

SCHULZE, Helen Ann. 1906 W US HIGHWAY 82 75092 #065-01-1986 L1994 FM *020 †18

SHARKEY, Patricia K. ■ 75090 #048-13-1983 L1986 IM ID *020 †20

SHARMA-MELLEM, Rita. 600 N HIGHLAND AVE 75092 #025-07-1979 L1982 PM *020 †60

SHAW, Clyde Edward. 300 N HIGHLAND AVE, STE 550 75092 #048-02-1974 L1974 PD *020 †55

SHEA, Thomas Robt. 501 N HIGHLAND AVE STE 102 75092 #008-01-1958 L1960 OPH PS *071 †35

SIDDIQI, Imran. 500 N HIGHLAND AVE 75092 #704-16-1982 L1996 ON *020 †20

SIMPSON, Charles Bob. 500 N HIGHLAND AVE 75092 #004-01-1964 L1966 PTH OS *020 †50

SLOAN, Ralph Russell, Jr. 501 N HIGHLAND AVE 75092 #048-12-1964 L1964 PUD IM *020 †20

SNIPES, Freddie Lee. 2100 MONTE CRISTO DR STE A 75092 #048-12-1956 L1956 PM *071 †20,60

SPENCER, Roy Edward. 815 PECAN GROVE RD E 75090 #048-12-1965 L1965 D *071 †15

STACKS, Kevin D. 500 N HIGHLAND AVE, STE 104 75092 #048-12-1997 L1999 EM *020 †16

STEPHENS, George Raymond. 500 N HIGHLAND AVE 75092 #048-02-1954 L1954 GYN OBG *071 †30

STEWART, J Creed. 815 PECAN GROVE RD E 75090 #039-01-1996 L2002 D *020 †15

STOOLFIRE, Arthur Waldo. ■ 75092 #051-04-1946 L1952 OTO *071 †45

STROBEL, Gennell De An. 230 E EVERGREEN ST 75090 #021-06-1995 L1997 **OBG** *020 †30
SUNDARAM, Bharathy Easwar. 321 N HIGHLAND AVE STE 200, TEXOMA NEUROLOGY ASSOCIATE 75092 #495-04-1985 L1994 **N** *020 †75
SUNDARAM, Easwar M, Jr. 321 N HIGHLAND AVE STE 200, TEXOMA NEUROLOGY ASSOCIATE 75092 #495-61-1984 L1989 **N** *020 †75
SWAMY, Nithya Uthami. ■ 75090 #016-02-2008 *012
SWAMY, Ponnuswamy T. 1111 HERITAGE PARK CIR 75090 #495-16-1967 L1974 **PS GS** *020 †85,65
THOMAS, Jesse Raymond, III. 815 PECAN GROVE RD E 75090 #048-12-1978 L1978 **D** *020 †15 ‡
THORNTON, Stacey L. 300 N HIGHLAND AVE, STE 415 75092 #048-13-1992 L1993 **OBG** *020 †30
TOCATJIAN, Alain Zareh. 300 N HIGHLAND AVE, STE 455 75092 #605-02-1972 L1976 **CD IM** *020 †20
TONELLI, Mary J O'Dell. ■ 75092 #048-04-1950 L1950 **GPM PHP** *071 †70
TRIPLETT, Myrick Neal. 500 N HIGHLAND AVE 75092 #048-12-1947 L1947 **IM PUD** *071 †20
VINCENT, Dale Christopher. 1103 SARA SWAMY DR, VISIONARY MEDICAL IMAGING 75090 #042-01-1989 L1995 **DR** *020 †80
WADE, Andrew Lamont. 809 GALLAGHER DR, STE A 75090 #056-05-1989 L1991 **PS** *020
WATKINS, W Mackey. 500 N HIGHLAND AVE 75092 #048-02-1972 L1972 **NEP IM** *020 †20
WATSON, Nathan A, Jr. 600 N HIGHLAND AVE, STE 104 75092 #048-12-1991 L1993 **IM** *020 †20
WILLS, Susan Elaine. 425 N HIGHLAND AVE, STE 200 75092 #028-03-1994 L2001 **FM** *020 †18
WOODS, Ronald A, Jr. 809 GALLAGHER DR 75090 #048-15-1987 L1988 **FM** *020 †18
YOUNG, Glenn Thomas. 425 N HIGHLAND AVE STE 13 75092 #048-12-1971 L1971 **GE IM** *020
ZEIKUS, Eric Andrew. 500 N HIGHLAND AVE, WILSON N JONES HOSPITAL 75092 #016-02-2001 L2007 **AR** *020 †80
ZEIKUS, Priya Swamy. 1111 SARA SWAMY DR 75090 #016-02-2002 L2007 **D** *100 †15
ZURIQAT, Muqdad Abdalla. 300 N HIGHLAND AVE STE 53 75092 #575-01-1993 L2007 **PCC** *020 †20

SHINER – LAVACA

WAGNER, John Dennis. 822 N AVENUE B, WAGNER & WAGNER DRS PA 77984 #048-02-1958 L1958 **FM** *071 †18
WAGNER, Ralph A. 822 N AVENUE B, WAGNER & WAGNER DRS PA 77984 #048-02-1987 L1988 **FM** *020 †18
WAGNER, Timothy J. 822 N AVENUE B, WAGNER & WAGNER DRS PA 77984 #048-04-1990 L1991 **FM** *020 †18

SILSBEE – HARDIN

AWAR, Ghaleb Salim. 1185 N 11TH ST B 77656 #605-01-1968 L1987 **PD** *020 †55
CARTRETT, Doyce Lee, Jr. 280 HIGHWAY 418 E 77656 #048-02-1996 L1999 **FM FSM** *020 †18
PASTOR, Mary Grace. 755 N 4TH ST 77656 #748-11-1988 L1998 **FM** *020 †18
PATIL, Rajaram Mathu. 1185 N 11TH ST 77656 #495-34-1954 L1977 **FM GS** *072 †18
TENNISON, Douglas Keith. 445 ROOSEVELT DR, 445 ROOSEVELT DR 77656 #021-05-1973 L1974 **FM** *020 †18
TENNISON, George D. 445 ROOSEVELT DR 77656 #021-05-1944 L1946 **GP** *072

SINTON – SAN PATRICIO

GARRETT-ROE, Ronald Duane. 621 E SINTON ST 78387 #048-13-1977 L1977 **FM GP** *020
PINKSTON, Joe Dan. RR 1 BOX 302B, HILL ROAD 78387 #048-02-1965 L1965 **FM GP** *072
SIMPSON, Charles H. 621 E SINTON ST 78387 #048-04-1949 L1949 **GP** *071

SLATON – LUBBOCK

EDWARDS, Patrick James. 130 N 7TH ST 79364 #048-12-1983 L1983 **FM** *020 †18
EUBANKS, Kathy Elaine. ■ 79364 #048-15-2007 **OBG** *012
HAYNES, Aubrey Hugh. 36 & 73, PO BOX 749, ONE MILE N OF LUBBOCK CO 79364 #048-12-1960 L1960 **GYN OBG** *071 †30

SMITHVILLE – BASTROP

CISNEROZ, Arnulfo. 800 E HIGHWAY 71 78957 #048-15-1991 L1992 **FM** *020 †18
JOKIC, Branislav. 800 HIGHWAY 71 E 78957 #957-08-1983 L2003 **IM** *020
NETAJI, Balijepalli. 1501 DOROTHY NICHOLS LN, UNIT A 78957 #495-57-1978 L1988 **ON HEM** *020 †20 ‡
PARCHURI, Ravindra. 605 NE 9TH ST, BOX 665 78957 #495-58-1970 L1982 **IM GP** *020 †20
PASSMANN, Frederick K. 800 E HIGHWAY 71 78957 #048-15-1993 L1994 **AN** *020
SANCHEZ, Guillermo F. 605 NE 9TH ST 78957 #649-01-1969 L1977 **FM** *020 †18

SNYDER – SCURRY

BRICE, Nelson. 5206 TRINITY BLVD, SNYDER MEDICAL CLINIC 79549 #231-01-1968 L1977 **GP** *020
BURLESON, James Ray. 5009 COLLEGE AVE 79549 #048-02-1977 L1977 **FM** *020 †18
COOPER, Bid Allen. 5009 COLLEGE AVE, COVENANT FMLY HLTHCRE CTR 79549 #048-12-1978 L1978 **FM** *020 †18
DUNN, Dale Clauder. 5206 TRINITY BLVD 79549 #048-15-2000 L2005 **FM** *020 †18
KERR, David C. 5009 COLLEGE AVE 79549 #048-12-2004 L2007 **FM** *020 †18
KERR, Thomas Archibald. ■ 79549 #048-12-2004 L2006 **GE** *012 †20
KERR, Thomas L. 5009 COLLEGE AVE 79549 #065-09-1975 L1994 **IM** *020 †20
ODAL, Marcia Jo. 6307 MOUNTAIN VIEW DR 79549 #048-02-1979 L1979 **PD EM** *020 †16
RAKOV, Robert Danl. 5301 TRINITY BLVD, STE F 79549 #035-15-1986 L1998 **FM** *020 †18
THOMPSON, Paul A. 5009 COLLEGE AVE 79549 #048-12-1976 L1976 **FM** *020 †20
WARDLAW, Gail T. 5206 TRINITY BLVD, COGDELL FAMILY CLINIC 79549 #048-02-1976 L1977 **FM** *020 †18

SOCORRO – EL PASO

UGARTE, Adrian. 9963A ALAMEDA AVE 79927 #048-02-1993 L1994 **IM** *020

SONORA – SUTTON

EDWARDS, Kristy L. ■ 76950 #048-15-1997 L1998 **FM** *020 †18
EDWARDS, Mark S. ■ 76950 #048-15-1996 L1997 **FM** *020 †18
PAJESTKA, Charles R. 301 HUDSPETH ST STE A 76950 #048-13-1984 L1985 **FM** *020 †18
WILSON, William R. 301 HUDSPETH ST STE B 76950 #048-15-1992 L1994 **FM** *020 †18

SOUR LAKE – HARDIN

PRUETT, Jack Ridings. 400 HIGHWAY 105 W 77659 #048-13-1971 L1971 **OBG** *020
SHARY, John Harry, III. ■ 77659 #048-12-1977 L1977 **OTO FPS** *020 †45
WELDON, J Eric. ■ 77659 #048-04-1984 L1986 **GS** *020 †85
WESOLOW, Paul David. 517 HIGHWAY 326 N 77659 #759-10-1984 L1992 **FM GS** *020 †18

SOUTH HOUSTON – HARRIS

GARAY, Saturnino Ramon. 1714 HOUSTON BLVD 77587 #275-01-1944 L1977 **GS** *075

SOUTH PADRE ISLAND – CAMERON

EIDE, O Arvid. PO BOX 3290 78597 #026-04-1946 L1946 **FM** *071 †18
EWALT, Donald Hodil. 6608 PADRE BLVD 78597 #041-12-1946 L1953 **PS** *071 †65
GALLAGHER, Michael W. 500 PADRE BLVD # 4801 78597 #038-40-1968 L1969 **TS VS** *020 †85,90
LANCASTER, John Frederick. 110 PADRE BLVD # 420 78597 #024-07-1957 L1965 **CD IM** *071 †20
MACHADO, Gaston. ■ 78597 #275-01-1951 L1955 **PHP** *072
MC COOK, William Frank. ■ 78597 #048-02-1973 L1975 **P** *075
MEISEL, Richard L, Jr. ■ 78597 #019-02-1983 L1984 **MFM OBG** *020 †30
ROGLER-BROWN, Timothy Lee. 6400 PADRE BLVD, # 5 78597 #037-01-1993 L1998 **AN** *020
SHER, Gerald. PO BOX 3229, 222 W HUISACHE ST 78597 #836-03-1955 L1978 **AN** *020
SIMPSON, Bernard Roy. 110 PADRE BLVD 78597 #917-25-1950 L1977 **AN** *071

SOUTHLAKE – TARRANT

AHMED, Azmat Parveen. ■ 76092 #704-02-1987 L2002 **IM** *020 †20
ALEXANDER, Toni Eileen. 2140 E SOUTHLAKE BLVD, STE L # 703 76092 #010-03-1991 L2000 **PM** *020 †60
ANSARI, Mohammed Q. ■ 76092 #704-02-1983 L1988 **CLP PTH** *020 †50
BACHOO, Manjit Robert. ■ 76092 #065-01-1996 L2007 **N** *100
BARRET, Walter Watkins. ■ 76092 #047-06-1958 L1963 **PD** *071 †55
BARTOLOMEI, Juan Carlos. 1545 E SOUTHLAKE BLVD, STE 100 76092 #008-01-1994 L2003 **NS** *020 †25
BENZICK, Arthur E. 731 E SOUTHLAKE BLVD, STE 100 76092 #048-04-1995 L1996 **PD** *020 †55
BLACKBURN, Heather Anne. 1545 E SOUTHLAKE BLVD, STE 100 76092 #048-02-2002 L2006 **PM** *020 †60
BOGDAN, Michael Andrew. 900 E SOUTHLAKE BLVD, STE 100 76092 #005-11-1998 L2007 **PS** *100 †65 ‡
BOWERS, Angela G. 1170 N CARROLL AVE 76092 #048-12-1995 L1996 **D** *020 †15
BRYAN, Michael Dennis. 660 W SOUTHLAKE BLVD, STE 100 76092 #048-02-1991 L1992 **OTO FPS** *020 †45
CHAVEZ, Cindy. ■ 76092 #048-12-2008 *012
CLARKE, Christopher Alan. 660 N CARROLL AVE, STE 120 76092 #005-06-1991 L1999 **AN PAN** *020 †05
COATES, Travis E. ■ 76092 #048-13-1996 L1999 **EM** *020 †16
COGBURN, Angela Claire. ■ 76092 #048-15-2008 *012
CRARY, Shelley Elaine. ■ 76092 #021-01-2000 L2006 **PHO** *100
DERR, Kristen Elizabeth. ■ 76092 #048-12-2007 **ORS** *012
DUSEK, David Armstrong. ■ 76092 #048-12-1986 L1988 **FM** *062 †18
DUVAL, Clinton Edward. ■ 76092 #048-14-1981 L1982 **EM** *020 †18,16
FAWCETT, Deborah Dee. 900 E SOUTHLAKE BLVD, STE 300 76092 #004-01-1977 L1985 **AI** *020 †55,03
FOLEFACK DONGMO, Alain. ■ 76092 #217-01-1998 L2006 **IM** *020 †20
FONTE, Hiyas Dungo. 731 E SOUTHLAKE BLVD, STE 100 76092 #010-01-1998 L2007 **IM** *020 †20
GARCIA, Michael D. 1545 E SOUTHLAKE BLVD, STE 100 76092 #048-12-2000 L2005 **PM** *020 †60
GENZEL, Robert Bruce. 1305 BENT CREEK DR, LIVE NATION MOTORSPORTS 76092 #035-06-1992 L1995 **EM** *020 †16
GIST, Taylor Lee. ■ 76092 #048-12-2008 *012
GOGIA, Rajesh. ■ 76092 #495-47-1990 L2007 **DR** *100 †80
GOLDMAN, William Todd. 2445 E SOUTHLAKE BLVD, STE 100 76092 #048-12-1994 L1996 **P CHP** *020 †75
GUZMAN, Robert Banez. 2435 E SOUTHLAKE BLVD, STE 140 76092 #030-06-1983 L1991 **P IM** *020
HAHN, Michael Kingyau. ■ 76092 #024-07-1991 L2007 **ORS** *020 †40
HARDER, Gerald John. 731 E SOUTHLAKE BLVD, STE 100 76092 #019-02-1992 L1999 **IM** *020 †20
HART, Stephen Marcus. 501 SAINT LAURENT CT 76092 #048-12-1987 L1988 **AN** *020 †05
HATCHER, Stacey. 731 E SOUTHLAKE BLVD, STE 100 76092 #048-14-1994 L1997 **IM** *020 †20
HERLIHY, Chas Edward, Jr. 530 SILICON DR STE 103 76092 #001-06-1976 L2005 **P EM** *075
HOROWITZ, Leon. ■ 76092 #035-19-1952 L1955 **PDA GYN** *071 †55,03
HUNT, Agatha Alexander. 731 E SOUTHLAKE BLVD, STE 100 76092 #048-02-2005 L2008 **PD** *012
IQBAL, Ahmed. ■ 76092 #704-02-1987 L1995 **IM** *020 †20

JACKSON, Richard Alan. 505 REGENCY XING, 505 REGENCY CROSSING 76092 #017-20-1974 L1999 **EM CCM** *020 †16

JOHNSON, David Oran. 731 E SOUTHLAKE BLVD, STE 100 76092 #048-12-1975 L1975 **PD** *020 †55

JORDAN, Heidi A Highley. 1545 E SOUTHLAKE BLVD, STE 280 76092 #048-02-1996 L1997 **ON HEM** *020 †20

KANG, Sunjun. 910 SUFFOLK CT 76092 #038-40-1989 L1990 **NPM** *020 †55

KASDEN, Scott Edward. 1422 MAIN ST STE 27 76092 #010-02-1986 L1993 **PS HS** *020 †65

KASTNER, Galit. ■ 76092 #035-09-1994 L2003 **AN** *020 †05

KING, Christopher M. 200 PECAN CRK 76092 #048-02-1992 L1993 **FM** *020 †18

KING, Lori. 200 PECAN CRK 76092 #048-02-1992 L1993 **FM** *020 †18

KINNEY, Janet Shepard. 1602 DEVON CT, BAYLOR UNIVERSITY MED CTR 76092 #036-07-1980 L1997 **NPM PD** *020 †55

KNAPP, Roger Seaman. 480 W SOUTHLAKE BLVD, STE 133 76092 #048-12-1973 L1973 **PD** *020 †55

KOUROSH, Atoosa. ■ 76092 #048-12-1997 L1999 **PD** *020 †55

KOZEL, Frank Andrew. ■ 76092 #051-01-1993 L2005 **P** *020 †75

LASH, Richard Hyman. ■ 76092 #025-01-1983 L2005 **PTH** *020 †75

LEE, Jessica Doyle. ■ 76092 #027-01-2000 L2007 **VN** *012 †75

LEE, Sang Eui. ■ 76092 #583-01-1966 L1972 **FM** *071 †18

LIEVING, Loree J. 731 E SOUTHLAKE BLVD, STE 100 76092 #048-02-1992 L1999 **IM** *020 †20

LORENZI, Nahla Ibrahim. ■ 76092 #915-02-1981 L1995 **IM** *020 †20

MACKEY, James D. 1545 E SOUTHLAKE BLVD, STE 280 76092 #048-13-2000 L2001 **ON IM** *020 †20

MALIK, Naila S. 175 MIRON DR 76092 #704-06-1987 L2002 **FM** *020 †18

MASON, Mark Edward. 900 E SOUTHLAKE BLVD # 100, SOUTHLAKE PLASTIC SURG 76092 #048-13-1992 L1993 **PS** *020 †65

MIHILLS, Cody Lyn. 1125 DAVIS BLVD, STE 100 76092 #048-04-2001 L2002 **FM** *020 †18 ‡

MITTAL, Shilpi. ■ 76092 #495-77-1998 L2007 **FM** *020 †18

MORRISON, Steven Mark. 731 E SOUTHLAKE BLVD, STE 100 76092 #048-02-1998 L2001 **FM** *020 †18 ‡

MYDUR, Ravi Swamy. ■ 76092 #048-15-2007 *012

NICHOLS, David W. 480 W SOUTHLAKE BLVD, STE 133 76092 #048-12-1993 L1994 **PD** *020 †55

O'BRIEN-SU, Eileen M. 731 E SOUTHLAKE BLVD, STE 100 76092 #048-14-1991 L1993 **MPD** *020 †55,20

PRAGER, Bruce I. 1317 SAINT ALBANS PATH 76092 #035-09-1979 L1985 **ORS OSM** *020

PRENTISS, Donald P, Jr. 2140 E SOUTHLAKE BLVD 76092 #016-43-1994 L1999 **GS** *020 †85

REDDY, Tanuja. ■ 76092 #004-01-2006 **DR** *012

REDDY, Vijayabhasker K. ■ 76092 #495-57-1988 L2006 **FM** *020 †05,18

REEVES, Ryan Scott. 1545 E SOUTHLAKE BLVD, STE 100 76092 #025-07-1999 L2004 **PM** *020 †20

REINKE, Martin Hellmuth. 1422 MAIN ST STE 208 76092 #048-12-1990 L1991 **OPH OS** *020 †35

RICHARDSON, Jared Cee. 1359 CROSS TIMBER DR 76092 #048-02-2000 L2003 **EM** *020 †16 ‡

ROCKEY, Don Chase. ■ 76092 #051-04-1984 L2006 **IM GE** *050 †20

ROH, Daeyoung Dave. ■ 76092 #039-05-1986 L2006 **NEP IM** *040 †20

ROTHBART, David. 1545 E SOUTHLAKE BLVD, STE 100 76092 #016-11-1988 L2002 **NS** *020

RUSSEY, Charles B. 480 W SOUTHLAKE BLVD, STE 115 76092 #048-12-1995 L1997 **FM** *020 †18

SAID, Rana R. ■ 76092 #575-01-1995 L2001 **CHN** *020 †75,55

SCHORN, Keith Alan. 731 E SOUTHLAKE BLVD, STE 100 76092 #048-12-1980 L1980 **IM** *020 †20

SEWELL, Robert Walter. 1545 E SOUTHLAKE BLVD #140 76092 #048-02-1974 L1974 **GS** *020 †85

SMITHSON, Kenneth Wm. ■ 76092 #036-01-1970 L1970 **IM** *020 †20

TAYLOR, Gregory David. 1422 MAIN ST, STE 240 76092 #028-46-2001 L2002 *020

TSENG, Chun Han. ■ 76092 #242-07-1948 L1959 **RO NM** *071

TSENG, Ellen Ai-Pi. ■ 76092 #385-03-1952 L1967 **NM** *071

VAN HAL, Mary Phyllis. 280 E BOB JONES RD 76092 #056-05-1980 L1991 **IM EM** *020 †20

VELASCO, Ferdinand T. ■ 76092 #046-14-1989 L1990 **TS** *030 †85,90

VENUGOPAL, Priya Ravi. 1545 E SOUTHLAKE BLVD, STE 200 76092 #496-39-1992 L2002 **DR** *020 †80

WALKER, Brent Wayne. 731 E SOUTHLAKE BLVD 76092 #048-78-1991, ▲ L1992 **FM** *020 †18

WALTON, Lloyd P. 731 E SOUTHLAKE BLVD, STE 100 76092 #048-12-2003 L2005 **FM** *020 †18

WARD, Kimberly A. 1125 DAVIS BLVD STE 100 76092 #048-15-2000 L2003 **IM** *020

WESTKAEMPER, Jill M. 1405 EAGLE BND 76092 #048-15-1998 L2004 **FM** *020

WYANT, Glen Ray. 660 N CARROLL AVE 76092 #021-05-1983 L1990 **AN** *020 †05

ZWERNEMANN, Erica Johnson. 731 E SOUTHLAKE BLVD, STE 100 76092 #048-02-1997 L2006 **PD** *020 †55

SPICEWOOD – TRAVIS

BLISS, Donald Lee. ■ 78669 #021-05-1973 L1973 **IM** *100 †20

COLLINS, Wyatt Eugene. 4284 BEE CREEK RD 78669 #001-02-1959 L1972 **DR** *020 †80

DONAHUE, Richard Thos. ■ 78669 #048-13-1984 L1985 **AN** *020 †05

EVANS, Dana Glynn. ■ 78669 #048-14-1983 L1983 **FM MDM** *030 †18

FRIEDEWALD, Vincent E. ■ 78669 #048-12-1966 L1983 **CD** *020 †20

HERNDON, Patrick Hurley. PO BOX 397, 121 OAKS RD 78669 #048-78-1982, ▲ L1985 **HO IG** *062

JOHNSON, Glenn Garrett. ■ 78669 #051-04-1981 L1982 **FM** *030 †18

LE SAGE, Robert Louis. ■ 78669 #048-11-1967 L1990 **EM FM** *071 †16,18

SHAW, James Millard. 2520 S PACE BEND RD 78669 #048-13-1973 L1973 **GP** *020

TONNESEN, Alan Stanley. ■ 78669 #035-45-1969 L1977 **CCA AN** *071 †05

WIGGER, Hans-Joachim. ■ 78669 #047-21-1954 L1960 **PTH** *050 †20

ZISKA, James Harold. ■ 78669 #018-03-1967 L1968 **PD** *020 †55

SPRING – HARRIS

ALAPAT, Deepa Francis. 8111 CYPRESSWOOD DR, STE 104 77379 #060-02-2001 L2004 **PD** *020 †55

APPLETON, Gregory Olson. 16000 STUEBNER AIRLINE RD, STE 210 77379 #005-02-1989 L2003 **CD** *020 †20

ASCENCIOS-CORDOVA, A. ■ 77389 #737-01-1962 L1965 **IM** *071

BAUMGARTNER, Edward Willi, Jr. ■ 77373 #048-14-2007 **GS** *012

BAUSANO, Brian John. ■ 77379 #048-04-2004 L2004 **EM** *012

BELLEY, Daniel. 4290 CYPRESS HILL DR, KELSEY-SEYBOLD CLINIC P A 77388 #067-06-1976 L1985 **FM** *020 †18

BENGE, Jim Patrick. 4290 CYPRESS HILL DR 77388 #020-12-1992 L2000 **OBG** *020 †30

BERG, Sven Thomas. ■ 77389 #035-20-1987 L1989 **PHO PD** *020 †55

BETHEA, Henry Lawrence. 17207 KUYKENDAHL RD # 200 77379 #027-01-1974 L1980 **AN** *020 †05

BOLFING, Brandon L. ■ 77373 #048-02-2008 *012

BUSKIRK, Kathryn. ■ 77373 #048-13-1991 L1992 **FPG PLM** *030

CABRERA, Rafael A. ■ 77388 #042-01-1990 L2007 **OBG REN** *020 †30

CALHOUN, Thomas Reynolds. ■ 77389 #021-01-1968 L1969 **TS** *020 †85,90

CHACKO, Reeba Elizabeth. 17207 KUYKENDAHL RD # 100 77379 #496-38-1982 L1992 **CHP P** *020 †75

CHANG, Stephanie Yeeming. ■ 77379 #048-12-2007 **OBG** *012

CHATMAN, Moncenya Ladonna. 6225 FM 2920 RD STE 201, HOUSTON CENTER FOR MATERNA 77379 #001-02-2000 L2007 **OBG** *020 †30

CHEN, Albert I-Kai. ■ 77373 #048-04-1997 L2004 **PTH** *100

CHILDS, Michael Adam. ■ 77373 #048-14-2007 L2007 **GS** *012

CHILUKURI, S V. 17207 KUYKENDAHL RD # 200 77379 #495-58-1967 L1985 **AN** *020 †05

CHU, Lei. ■ 77388 #048-04-2006 L2006 **GS** *012

COLEMAN, Fay Katherine. ■ 77379 #030-06-1986 L1986 **RO** *020 †80

CRENSHAW, Libby Allison. ■ 77379 #048-13-2001 L2005 **EM** *020 †16

DE VALDENEBRO, Enrique. 26 STONEGATE PARK CT 77379 #264-07-1974 L1982 **GS VS** *020

DIANALAN, Sittie Rainni. ■ 77379 #748-10-1990 L2004 **PD** *020 †55 ‡

DIAZ, Rolando G. ■ 77388 #048-14-1998 L1999 **FM** *020 †18

DOLINO, Woodrow Villarosa. ■ 77379 #748-11-1976 L1983 **EM GS** *020 †16

EL HENNAWY, Adel Aly A S. 17418 WILTON PARK CT 77379 #915-02-1982 L1999 **NPM PD** *020 †55

ESTRADA, Christopher Ray. ■ 77379 #024-05-2005 **AN** *012

FISCHER, Stephen Carl. 9005 LOUETTA RD 77379 #048-16-1981 L1981 **GP EM** *020 †16

GARG, Amit Kumar. ■ 77379 #048-04-2004 **RO** *012

GARG, Rajeev Kumar. ■ 77379 #016-11-2004 L2004 **N** *012

GEDDIE, Steven Gwynn. 8006 HIDDEN TRAIL LN 77379 #048-13-1987 L1988 **NPM** *020 †55

GLEASON, Michael William. 17119 SEVEN PINES DR 77379 #048-15-2008 *012

GODIN, Nelly Arielle. ■ 77379 #024-16-2003 L2007 **OBG** *020

GONZALEZ, Sylvia. ■ 77379 #035-01-2002 L2007 **P** *012

GORRELA, Sushma Veera. 6225 FM 2920 RD, STE 100 77379 #495-21-1995 L2003 **FM** *020 †18

GOSNELL, Billye Ruth. 17207 KUYKENDAHL RD, STE 200 77379 #039-01-2002 L2006 **AN** *020

GREEN, Larry Kenneth. ■ 77379 #001-02-1971 L1980 **OBG MDM** *030 †30

GUERRERO, Rafael D. 17207 KUYKENDAHL RD, STE 100 77379 #264-02-1987 L1992 **CHP** *020 †75

HEATON, Gary Lee. 8111 CYPRESSWOOD DR # 104, CENTER 77379 #048-14-1973 L1974 **PD** *071 †55

HENDERSON, Quang Hai. ■ 77379 #048-02-1996 L1997 **EM** *020 †16

HICKS CARMICHAEL, Wanda M. ■ 77379 #048-02-1989 L1990 **DR** *075

HOLLEY, Michele Monique. 17207 KUYKENDAHL RD, STE 200 77379 #047-07-1999 L2002 **AN** *020

HOULTON, Jeffrey John. ■ 77379 #048-02-1996 L1997 **EM** *020 †16

HURTADO-MUNOZ, Jaime. ■ 77388 #264-16-1989 **FP** *012

IDRIS, Naqi. ■ 77379 #704-02-1995 L2007 **NEP** *020 †20

IZADDOOST, Shahed. ■ 77373 #048-02-1968 *012

JAMEEL, Shahid. ■ 77388 #704-02-1986 L2006 **IM** *020 †20

JILANI, Seema Maliha. ■ 77379 #048-04-2006 **PD** *012

JOCSON, Miguel Lasa. 16115 CHAMPION DR 77379 #748-10-1965 L1976 **ORS** *020

KENT, Jennifer Michelle. 17207 KUYKENDAHL RD, STE 200 77379 #048-02-2002 L2005 **AN** *020 †05

KIRKLAND, Arthur A. ■ 77373 #048-04-1951 L1951 **GP** *020

KOVOOR, Timmy A. ■ 77388 #048-12-2005 **OPH** *012

KUEHN, Louis F. ■ 77379 #048-02-1947 L1947 **PDA PD** *071 †55,03

LAKES, Rita Bostick. ■ 77379 #048-04-1976 L1976 **PD** *020 †55 ‡

LOFTIS, Lauren Nicole. ■ 77379 #048-12-2007 **FP** *012

LORENTZ, Rick. ■ 77379 #048-12-1991 L1992 **GS VS** *012

MAGEE, Vallery Mechell. 18707 SPRING HEATHER CT, KELSSEY SEYBOLD WILLOWBROO 77379 #017-20-2001 L2005 **MPD** *020

MAHMOODUDDIN, Faiz. ■ 77379 #048-02-2008 *012

MARKOWSKI, Janusz. 1223 HEATH HOLLOW DR 77379 #759-09-1963 L1980 **PM** *020 †60

MARQUEZ, Luz Marina. 4002 LOUETTA RD 77388 #264-03-1971 L1982 **OBG** *020 †30

MC CLINTOCK, Bettie. 8101 CYPRESSWOOD DR 77379 #048-04-1955 L1955 **PD OS** *071 †55

NGUYEN, Dy Tien. 17207 KUYKENDAHL RD, STE 200 77379 #941-01-1968 L1974 **AN** *020 †05

NGUYEN, Hong Hac H. 16740 CHAMPION FOREST DR 77379 #048-14-1994 L1995 **FM** *020 †18

NGUYEN, Lawrence H. 16116 STUEBNER AIRLINE RD, STE 5 77379 #048-12-2001 L2005 **PM** *100 †60

NGUYEN, Phac D. ■ 77388 #941-01-1961 L1978 **GP** *071

NOH, In Kyu. 4015 ALSHIRE DR 77373 #583-02-1963 L1973 **OBG** *071 †30

ODERINDE, Victor Ayodele. 17207 KUYKENDAHL RD # 100 77379 #690-05-1988 L2000 **CHP** *020 †75

OKEKE, Jos Okonkwo Synday. ■ 77379 #917-02-1962 L1978 **GS GP** *020

O'NEILL, Beth Abram. 8111 CYPRESSWOOD DR, STE 104 77379 #016-45-1985 L1988 **PD** *020 †55

PARKER, Stephanie N. ■ 77379 #048-14-1996 **P** *100

PARUNGAO, Vladimir M. ■ 77379 #748-01-1969 L1978 **FOP GP** *020 †50

PEARSON, Carol Elizabeth. 17207 KUYKENDAHL RD, STE 200 77379 #048-13-1991 L1992 **AN** *020 †05

PECKHAM, Frances Shalek. ■ 77379 #048-14-1986 L1987 **IM IMG** *020 †20

PEER, Adnan Syed. ■ 77379 #048-02-2007 **IM** *012

PERLMAN, Joseph M. 6319 CYPRESSWOOD DR 77379 #043-01-1976 L1979 **PS HS** *020 †85,65

PHAM, Peter Angia. ■ 77379 #028-02-1998 L2002 **OPH** *020 †35

PHAM, Thieu Gia. ■ 77379 #942-01-1967 L1983 *071

PIROK, Edward Warren. ■ 77379 #048-02-2005 **P** *100

PLACENCIA, Carolina Duran. 8111 CYPRESSWOOD DR, STE 104 77379 #048-14-2002 L2005 **PD** *020 †55

POPE, Michael Louis. 8111 CYPRESSWOOD DR STE 10, FM 1960 PEDIATRIC CENTER 77379 #048-14-1982 L1983 **PD** *020 †55

PUREWAL, Dalbir Singh. 16740 CHAMPION FOREST DR 77379 #495-03-1981 L1997 FM *020 †18

QUINTOS, Teodoro Esquevo. ■ 77379 #748-01-1965 L1976 GS *020

ROMANO, Nicola P. ■ 77373 #561-10-1950 L1964 OS GP *020

RUIZ NAZARIO, Javier. 17207 KUYKENDAHL RD, STE 100 77379 #042-01-1988 L1990 CHP P *020 †75

SANDIFER, Sherri Denise. 8111 CYPRESSWOOD DR, STE 104 77379 #008-01-1999 L2002 PD *020 †55

SAPSOWITZ, Steven Howard. 16835 DEER CREEK DR, STE 190 77379 #048-13-1990 L1992 FM IM *020 †18 ‡

SHEN, Michael Chuyueh. ■ 77388 #048-12-2004 L2007 IM *020 †20

SHIRLEY, Tad M. 8714 SPRING CYPRESS RD, STE 200 77379 #048-14-1999 L2001 PD *020 †55

SINGH, Lall. ■ 77389 #495-39-1958 L1973 GP EM *071

SMITH, Donald Willard. 17907 KUYKENDAHL RD # 101 77379 #035-08-1964 L1970 GP *020

SMITH, H Chas. 25106 ARCANE CT 77389 #018-03-1966 L1967 PD OS *071 †55

SPARROW, Alj F. ■ 77379 #047-07-1987 L1994 AN *020

STAMBOULIEH, Geo Gabriel. ■ 77388 #605-01-1938 P N *020

STEFFEK, John Chas. 9611 LOUETTA RD 77379 #048-02-1969 L1969 CHP P *020 †75

STEVENS, Maria Patricia. 8111 CYPRESSWOOD DR, STE 104 77379 #048-15-1995 L2002 PD *020 †55

SUDHAKARAN, Bindu. 21301 KUYKENDAHL RD STE H, SPRING PRIMARY CARE PA 77379 #495-44-1992 L1999 IM *020 †20

TABAH, Bih Nwi. ■ 77379 #036-01-2007 OBG *012

TANDOC, Jose R. ■ 77379 #748-10-1965 L1976 PM *071 †60

THANDI, Amrit. 9910 OXTED LN 77379 #495-43-1997 L2004 FM *020 †18

THANDI, Inqlabi. ■ 77379 #495-29-1967 L1979 GP *020 ‡

TONG, Kai Ming. 16116 STUEBNER AIRLINE RD, STE 9 77379 #385-03-1962 L1977 GP GS *020 †85

TSAI-WEINBERG, Chuwey Lin. 8111 CYPRESSWOOD DR, STE 104 77379 #048-02-1990 L1991 PD *020 †55

VARELA, Louis Eugene. 17207 KUYKENDAHL RD, STE 250 77379 #030-06-1980 L1981 GP EM *020

VILLAFLOR, Rady I. 25235 ARCANE CT 77389 #748-02-1959 L1976 AN *020 †05

VINH, Nguyen Van. ■ 77379 #941-01-1960 L1980 GP PHP *071

VIVEKANANTHAN, Nireshkumar. ■ 77379 #495-59-1990 L2007 IM *020 †20

WANG, Gin Ru. ■ 77379 #036-07-2002 L2006 DR *100 †80

WARE, Kristin Chenille. ■ 77388 #048-02-2008 *012

WATSON, Patricia Kay. 9005 LOUETTA RD 77379 #048-16-1981 L1981 P *020 †75

WOO, Rebecca Jo. ■ 77373 #012-01-2003 L2007 IMG *020

YAN, Pei Sha. ■ 77379 #243-94-1981 L2003 PTH PCP *020 †50

YEAGER, Shana Lea. 20102 REDWICK CT 77388 #048-15-2000 L2002 OBG *020 ‡

ZALAVARRIA, Jonard Herbia. ■ 77388 #048-14-2007 IM *012

ZARZOUR, Andre Youssef. 6526 LOUETTA RD STE A1, ANDRE ZARZOUR MD 77379 #330-04-1962 L1969 PD *020 †55

SPRING – MONTGOMERY

ALEXANDER, Chacko. 1011 MEDICAL PLAZA DR, STE 100 77380 #495-16-1987 L1999 CD *020 †20

AQUINO, Vincent. 1011 MEDICAL PLAZA DR, STE 100 77380 #011-03-1980 L1981 CD IM *020 †20

AZIZ, Joseph Y. ■ 77382 #915-04-1955 L1979 GS PDS *071

BASINGER, Joseph Brewer. 1201 LAKE ROBBINS DR 77380 #039-01-1993 L2003 OM GP *020 †70

BOCTOR, Gamil Abdalla. ■ 77381 #915-02-1956 L1985 IM *100

BOSQUEZ, Lourdes R. 9006 FOREST XING, STE C 77381 #649-02-1984 L1997 CHP P *020

BURKE, Brian Joseph. ■ 77380 #007-02-1994 L2003 VIR *020 †80

CAMPBELL, Andrew Wm. 25010 OAKHURST DR, STE 200 77386 #649-14-1974 L1985 FM PTX *020 †18 ‡

CANNON, Carl Lenne. 1441 WOODSTEAD CT, WOODLANDS SPORTS MEDICINE 77380 #048-15-1980 L1981 ORS OSM *020 †40

CHANDLER, Kristie R. 1595 LAKE FRONT CIR 77380 #048-12-1992 L1994 PD *020 †55

CHARRON, Maria Del Carmen. 25410 INTERSTATE 45 N 77386 #042-01-1975 L1980 GP OS *020

CLARK, Charles Edward. ■ 77382 #021-01-1958 L1969 IM PUD *071

CLARK, Holly Hazlett. 6767 LAKE WOODLANDS DR, WOODLANDS DERMATOLOGY 77382 #048-14-1994 L1995 D *020 †15

CLIFTON, John Bryan. ■ 77382 #048-02-2002 L2005 AN *100

COLEMAN, Gary M. 1011 MEDICAL PLAZA DR, STE 100 77380 #048-14-1984 L1985 CD IM *020 †20

COLEMAN, Kristin M. ■ 77381 #048-14-1999 L2005 DR *020 †80

CRYER, Tommy Michael. 8000 RESEARCH FOREST DR, STE 115 77382 #048-02-1974 L1974 FM *030 †18

CUMMINGS, Robt Mansfield. 7 CRABTREE CT, NORTH KERN STATE PRISON 77382 #005-15-1967 L1973 P GP *020 †75

DELAGUARDIA, Bernardo. 1011 MEDICAL PLAZA DR, STE 100 77380 #649-52-1991 L1997 CD *020 †20

DELASALAS, Harold C. ■ 77386 #048-02-2008 *012

DESJARDINS, Raoul. ■ 77381 #067-02-1958 IMG IM *050

DOENGES, Josef F. 9100 FOREST XING, STE A 77381 #048-15-1997 L1998 D DS *020 †15

FITE, Diana Lynn. 25802 LAKE LAWN DR, NEPTUNE EMERGENCY SERVICES 77380 #048-14-1978 L1978 EM GYN *020 †16

FORTIN, Jorge Alberto. ■ 77393 #649-01-1972 L1977 OBG *071

GARLITOS, Daniel R. 26410 INTERSTATE 45 N 77386 #048-02-1994 L1999 RO *020 †80

GENTON, Edward. ■ 77382 #038-41-1957 L1957 CD IM *071 †20

GIBBS, John Patrick. 1201 LAKE ROBBINS DR 77380 #048-02-1976 L1976 OM EM *074 †70

GREIG, Christina Lauren. ■ 77381 #048-13-2004 L2008 OBG *012

ISLAM, Shahzad. 25214 BOROUGH PARK DR 77380 #704-02-1990 L1996 PD *020

IVERSON, Dale Arthur. ■ 77380 #048-04-1962 L1962 GP OS *071

JORDAN, Richard Ray. 25200 GROGANS PARK DR, TEXAS PAIN & MEDICAL MANAG 77380 #048-04-1982 L1983 AN *020 †05

JUE, Wilson Q. 1441 WOODSTEAD CT STE 300, WOODLANDS SPORTS MED CTR 77380 #048-13-1992 L1993 PMM AN *020 †05

KANADY, Kirk Edward. 26410 INTERSTATE 45 N 77386 #016-06-1992 L1997 RO *020 †80

KASS, Albert. ■ 77381 #035-19-1940 L1946 IM *071

KEENE, Elizabeth M. ■ 77382 #026-08-1988 L1992 P *020 †75

KIRBY, Homer D. 25710 OAKRIDGE FOREST LN 77386 #048-15-2000 L2002 EM *020 †16

LAVENDER, Hilary Anne. 25440 INTERSTATE 45, STE 100 77386 #917-01-1969 L1977 FM *020

LAVERGNE, Christopher H. 1011 MEDICAL PLAZA DR, STE 100 77380 #048-14-1992 L1993 CD *020 †20

LEDBETTER, Leslie Shook. 6767 LAKE WOODLANDS DR, WOODLANDS DERMATOLOGY 77382 #048-14-1997 L1998 D *020 †15

LIAW, Henry Lizen. ■ 77382 #035-20-1999 L2003 EM *020

LUNDY, Julie Cutright. ■ 77382 #048-02-2005 L2008 FP *012

MAHMOOD, Syed Faisal. ■ 77382 #704-25-1997 ID *020 †20

MARTIN, Dana H. ■ 77380 #048-02-1998 L2001 PCC *020 †20

MAYO, James Richard. ■ 77380 #048-02-1976 L1977 P *020 †75

NADLER, James Lawrence. ■ 77382 #025-01-1980 L1999 GPM *030 †70

NAQVI, Jabeen Fatima. ■ 77382 #704-02-1991 L2005 PTH PD *020 †50

NELSON, Todd Eric. 62 SILVERMONT DR 77382 #048-02-1997 L2001 AN *020 †05

NEMETH, Margit A. 1011 MEDICAL PLAZA DR, STE 100 77380 #048-13-1999 L2004 CD *020 †20

ODELOWO, Mobolaji M. ■ 77380 #690-08-1995 L2004 VIR *100 †80

OROCOFSKY, Morris Lee. ■ 77381 #041-02-1968 L1980 IM *020 †20

PARKER, Amanda L. 4415 TROPPER CT 77386 #048-12-2002 L2005 EM *020 †16

PEABODY, Brenda K. 1011 MEDICAL PLAZA DR, STE 100 77380 #048-16-1989 L1990 CD IM *020 †20

PHAN, Cuong Quoc. 26410 INTERSTATE 45 N, GREATER HOUSTON RADIATION 77386 #048-14-2000 L2006 RO *020 †80

PHAN, Thinh Phu. 26410 INTERSTATE 45 N 77386 #048-04-2000 L2006 RO *100 †80

PINNAPUREDDY, Nikhila Red. ■ 77381 #048-12-2008 *012

POLLACK, Lee Stuart. 25440 I H 45, STE 100 77386 #041-02-1987 L1989 N *020 †75

POLO CUETO, Jose Gregorio. ■ 77382 #264-12-2002 *100

PORTER, Daniel M. ■ 77382 #048-13-2006 FP *012

POWELL, Frank Curtis. 210 SPRING HILLS DR STE 15 77386 #016-11-1994 L1995 DR *020 †80

PRENTICE, Mary E. 8000 RESEARCH FOREST DR, STE 115 77382 #048-12-1996 L1997 OBG *020 †30

PROETT, Jesse Morrow. ■ 77380 #048-14-2008 *012

RAY, Amber L. ■ 77386 #048-14-2005 L2007 FP *012

RICHARDSON, Larry Alan. 25000 PITKIN RD, STE 120 77386 #048-13-1979 L1979 GP EM *020 †16

ROBERTS, Suzanne Grondin. 1001 MEDICAL PLAZA DR, STE 200 77380 #021-01-1989 L1992 IM *020 †20

ROSSI, John David, Jr. ■ 77382 #035-20-1989 L1997 N OS *072 †75

ROUNSAVILLE, Robt Teague. ■ 77381 #021-05-1953 L1960 ORS *071

SALERNO, Sal Jos. ■ 77386 #048-02-1967 L1994 EM FM *071 †16

SANSBURY, Julia C. 6767 LAKE WOODLANDS DR, WOODLANDS DERMATOLOGY 77382 #028-03-2000 L2004 D *020 †15

SHAH, Munir Ahmad. 1441 WOODSTEAD CT, WOODLANDS SPORTS MEDICINE 77380 #017-20-1994 L1999 ORS *020 †40

SIDDIQI, Mohammad I. 25211 GROGANS MILL RD 77380 #028-03-1995 L1999 IM *020 †20

SIMMONS, Sarah Vanarsdale. 6704 STERLING RIDGE DR, STE A 77382 #048-15-2002 L2004 FM *020 †18

SOSA, Maria Alejandra. 26410 INTERSTATE 45 N 77386 #048-02-2000 L2005 RO *020 †80

STRAUSSER, David W. 1441 WOODSTEAD CT, WOODLANDS SPORTS MEDICINE 77380 #048-04-1992 L1993 ORS OSS *020 †16

TANKLEFF, Bert Norman. ■ 77393 #056-06-1960 L1973 GP OS *071

TRUONG, Hans Hoffman. 210 SPRING HILLS DR, HORIZON RADIOLOGY LTD LLP 77386 #016-02-1992 L1994 DR *020 †80

URRUTIBEHEITY, Gisele. ■ 77382 #048-14-1990 L1992 P *020 †75

VAN DE WATER, Anne R. ■ 77393 #005-14-1977 L1978 OBG *074

WARKEN, Kristyn A. 6767 LAKE WOODLANDS DR, WOODLANDS DERMATOLOGY 77382 #048-14-2002 L2005 D *020 †15

WILLMAN, Philip J A. ■ 77382 #020-02-1976 L1981 NS *020 †25

WOODS, Patrick G. ■ 77380 #048-02-1998 L2001 EM *020 †16

YUT, Clifford Winston. 4775 W PANTHER CREEK DR, STE 345 77381 #048-04-1996 L1997 MPD *020 †20,55

SPRING BRANCH – COMAL

FOWLER, Brian L. 19750 HWY 46 W UNIT 104 78070 #048-13-1985 L1986 EM OBG *020 †16

NANCE, William Bonham. ■ 78070 #039-01-1973 L1974 EM *020 †16

NICOLA, Matthew Wayne. 6098 FM 311 78070 #048-02-1996 L1998 FM *020 †18

OTTERSON, Warren Nels. ■ 78070 #056-01-1954 L1977 OBG *071 †30

VREEKE, Stephen James. 6098 FM 311 78070 #048-02-1995 L1997 FM *020 †18

SPRINGTOWN – PARKER

CUMMINGS, Ferne Nilsa. 499 E HIGHWAY 199 76082 #048-02-1999 L2002 FM *020 †18

GANZON, Mauro Salandanan. 628 N AVENUE D 76082 #048-12-2000 L2002 FM *020 †18

GILES, Forrest Duane. ■ 76082 #005-17-1962 GP AM *072

STAFFORD – FORT BEND

ABRAHAM, Anitha Thomas. ■ 77477 #496-21-1998 VN *012

BACANI, Alfredo C. ■ 77477 #748-01-1953 L1971 PM *071 †60

BARLAS, Zeba. 210 ANNES WAY 77477 #704-06-1996 L2004 FM *020 †18

BENNETT, Mark Carlon. MED, ORAL ROBERTS UNIV SCH OF 77477 #039-05-1992 *100

BEREZOSKI, Robt Nicholas. 435 B1 FM 1092 STE 256 77477 #051-04-1972 L1973 PS OTO *20 †45,65

BISCHOFF, Scott B. 10521 CORPORATE DR 77477 #048-14-1988 L1989 IM *020 †20

BORKAR, Neil Balkrishna. ■ 77477 #028-46-2006 L2006 *012

CLOUGH, Debra Sue. 11104 W AIRPORT BLVD, STE 135 77477 #048-14-1995 L1996 CHP *020

CORREDOR, Daniel Gustavo. 11929 W AIRPORT BLVD, STE 600 77477 #264-01-1963 L1977 END IM *020

DELA CRUZ, Maureen Ochoa. ■ 77477 #748-01-2003 **FP** *012
DRUMMOND, Derek Stuart. ■ 77477 #060-01-1992 L1997 **PDO OTO** *100
DU, Khoi Huy. ■ 77477 #048-16-2005 **GS** *012
FERGUSON, James P. ■ 77477 #021-05-1951 L1957 **PTH** *075 †50
GAZAWAY, La'Cindy Vashun. 10435 GREENBOUGH DR, STE 300 77477 #048-14-2000 L2003 **PD** *020 †55 ‡
HYMAN, Harvey Ira. 4915 S MAIN ST, STE 103 77477 #561-01-1970 L1975 **RHU IM** *020 †20
JONADOSS, Amirah Keethu. ■ 77477 #016-43-2007 **FP** *012
JUMALON, Virgilio Gongob. ■ 77477 #748-09-1966 **GP** *071
KENDRICK, Ernest A. 4915 S MAIN ST STE 108 77477 #047-07-1978 L1982 **CHP P** *020 †75
LAWSON, Michael S. 10435 GREENBOUGH DR, STE 300 77477 #048-12-1993 L1997 **PD** *020 †55
LIANG, Pamela B. 10435 GREENBOUGH DR, STE 300 77477 #028-02-1997 L2001 **PD** *020 †55
MARRACK, David. 2303 S MAIN ST 77477 #917-25-1947 L1964 **PTH IM** *071 †50
MOSLEY, Angela Nicole. ■ 77477 #038-06-2006 **FM**
NAHM, Wesley K. 12221 S KIRKWOOD RD, STE 100 77477 #048-13-1997 L2002 **EM** *020
READING, William H. 12603 SOUTHWEST FWY, STE 510 77477 #048-13-1984 L1985 **P** *020 †75
SIM, Stephanie Chingyi. 10701 CORPORATE DR, STE 205 77477 #048-02-2001 L2005 **P** *020 †75
SOLANKI, Prabha H. ■ 77477 #495-19-1971 L1979 **PTH** *020 †50
STEEL, Ewing Tisdol. 12701 EXECUTIVE DR, STE 604 77477 #048-02-1960 L1960 **P** *071
SZETO, Ling Kin. 4915 S MAIN ST, STE 112 77477 #048-13-1975 L1975 **PD** *020 †55
VICTORIA, Ricardo S. ■ 77477 #748-08-1973 L1981 **GP EM** *020
VUTPAKDI, Patchari. 12126 GREEN TRAILS DR 77477 #891-02-1963 L1973 **PD ON** *071 †55
WITKOWSKI, Wojciech. 3832 GREENBRIAR DR 77477 #759-06-1963 L2002 **FM OM** *020

STAMFORD — JONES

HART, Michael William. 1303 MABEE ST 79553 #048-13-1993 L1995 **IM** *020
SELMON, Tony Billie. ■ 79553 #048-02-1944 L1944 **GP** *071

STANTON — MARTIN

MILLER, Thomas Cecil. 610 N ST PETER ST 79782 #005-17-1962 L1975 **GP** *020
TEVENI, Pablo C. 207 N LA MESA HIGHWAY 79782 #048-13-1986 L1987 **FM** *020 †18 ‡

STAPLES — GUADALUPE

DANA, Suzanna Elva. ■ 78670 #048-12-1979 L1979 **FOP** *030 †50

STEPHENVILLE — ERATH

BASHAW, Robert James. 140 RIVER NORTH BLVD 76401 #048-02-1983 L1983 **AN OPH** *020 †35,05
BEALKA, Neil M, Jr. 150 RIVER NORTH BLVD 76401 #026-04-1983 L1993 **OPH** *020 †35
BOUCHER, David Chas. 150 RIVER NORTH BLVD, STEPHENVLE MED & SURG CLNC 76401 #048-16-1983 L1983 **IM** *020 †20
BOUCHER, Miranda Alyn. ■ 76401 #048-15-2008 *012
BRAGG, Larry Mark. 561 N GRAHAM ST 76401 #048-13-1976 L1976 **GS** *020 †85
BURROUGHS, Karen. 150 RIVER NORTH BLVD 76401 #048-14-1991 L1992 **FM** *020 †18
CEDARS, Nathan. 1617 E WASHINGTON ST, HOPE CLINIC 76401 #035-45-1947 L1952 **GP ORS** *071 †85
DAYTON, Billy Chas. 411 N BELKNAP ST 76401 #048-02-1959 L1959 **FM** *020 †18
DESHMUKH, Avinash T. 150 RIVER NORTH BLVD 76401 #495-01-1976 L1986 **U GS** *020 †95 ‡
DOGGETT, Kelly S. 2216 W WASHINGTON ST 76401 #048-15-1993 L1994 **FM** *020 †18
DONOHUE, Bobby E, Jr. 251 E HIGHWAY 8 76401 #048-12-1982 L1983 **FM** *020 †18 ‡
EDWARDS, Jeffrey Karl. 150 RIVER NORTH BLVD 76401 #054-04-1991 L2005 **FM** *020 †18
ERCK, Charles S. 150 RIVER NORTH BLVD, SURGICAL CLINIC 76401 #048-15-1990 L1991 **GS** *020 †85
EVANS, Nanette V. 150 RIVER NORTH BLVD 76401 #048-12-1992 L1993 **DR** *020 †80
EVANS, William R. 561 N GRAHAM ST 76401 #048-12-1992 L1993 **ORS** *020 †40
FOWLER, James J. 150 RIVER NORTH BLVD 76401 #048-13-1992 L1994 **OTO** *020 †45
FRAZIER, Charles R. 150 RIVER NORTH BLVD, STEPHENVILLE MEDICAL & SUR 76401 #048-16-1986 L1987 **GS** *020 †85
GILLIAM, Leslie Shane. 630 N GRAHAM ST 76401 #048-14-2002 L2003 **FM** *020 †18
GOKUL, Bhagwandas D. 150 RIVER NORTH BLVD, STEPHENVILLE MED/SURG 76401 #539-04-1966 L1977 **IM CD** *020
HALL, Alan Ray. 411 N BELKNAP ST 76401 #048-14-1982 L1983 **FM** *020 †18
HEFLIN, Jearald Duane, Jr. 725 N GRAHAM ST STE 700 76401 #048-14-1990 L1991 **FM** *020 †18
HEFLIN, Linda L. 725 N GRAHAM ST STE 70 76401 #048-14-1988 L1989 **FM** *020 †18
HERBERTSON, Floyd James. 150 RIVER NORTH BLVD 76401 #025-01-1963 L1987 **ORS** *020 †40
HODGES, John Wm. ■ 76401 #048-02-1975 L1975 **AN IM** *020 †20,05
IP, Kam Woon. 150 RIVER NORTH BLVD, MEDICAL AND SURGICAL CLINI 76401 #060-01-1973 L1977 **FM EM** *020 ‡
LEWIS, John Edward. ■ 76401 #003-01-1978 L1980 **GS** *020 †85
MC MILLION, Janie Sue. 150 RIVER NORTH BLVD 76401 #048-16-1986 L1987 **OBG** *020 †30
MIERTSCHIN, Melvin Albert. ■ 76401 #048-02-1959 L1959 **OBG** *071 †30
MILLER, Kelly A. 2989 COUNTY ROAD 253 76401 #048-78-1997, ▲ L1998 **PD** *020 †55
MILLER, Kelly Sullivan. 103 E FREY ST 76401 #017-20-1990 L1991 **FM** *020 †18
MOORE, Jeffrey Danl. 150 RIVER NORTH BLVD, SURGICAL CLINIC, INTERNAL 76401 #048-12-1986 L1987 **IM** *020 †20
ONG, Helen Chua. 150 RIVER NORTH BLVD 76401 #748-01-1988 L2001 **PD** *020 †55
ONG, Lester Co. 150 RIVER NORTH BLVD 76401 #748-01-1988 L1996 **IM** *020 †20
PAICURICH, Jean E. 150 RIVER NORTH BLVD 76401 #048-12-1994 L1996 **OBG** *020 †30
PATE, Joe Robt. 160 RIVER NORTH BLVD 76401 #048-02-1970 L1970 **GP** *072
PATENAUDE, Lisa Renshaw. 411 N BELKNAP ST 76401 #048-14-1988 L1990 **EM** *020
PERNOKAS, Louis N. ■ 76401 #024-01-1950 L1954 **GS** *071 †85
RAMACHANDRAN, Poongodhai. 2291 NW LOOP 76401 #495-04-1990 L2004 **CD** *020 †20
RATAJCZAK, Kenneth James. 150 RIVER NORTH BLVD 76401 #017-20-1977 L1987 **R** *020 †80

SAUNDERS, Frank Noel. 150 RIVER NORTH BLVD, STEPHENVILLE MED & SURGICA 76401 #048-13-1982 L1984 **FM** *020 †18
SHAFER, Curtis Dwayne. ■ 76401 #048-14-1986 L1987 **FM** *020 †18
SHAH, Neena Yatin. 150 RIVER NORTH BLVD 76401 #495-96-1989 L1998 **PD** *020 †55
SHAH, Yatin Vipin. 150 RIVER NORTH BLVD 76401 #495-96-1989 L1996 **PD** *020 †55
TAHSUDA-SNOW, Christie. PO BOX 973, 650 GREEN ST 76401 #048-01-1989 L1992 **P** *020 †75
TERRELL, Frank Vance. 150 RIVER NORTH BLVD, STEPHENVILLE MED SURG 76401 #048-12-1964 L1964 **OPH** *020 †35
TERRELL, James Clark, Jr. 411 N BELKNAP ST 76401 #048-02-1960 L1960 **GS** *071 †85
WILSON, Robert Storey. 1100 N MCCART ST 76401 #048-78-1975, ▲ L1975 **FM ADM** *020
ZBORIL, Timothy Titus. 411 N BELKNAP ST 76401 #048-14-1983 L1983 **AN** *020 †05
ZIEGLSCHMID, John F. ■ 76401 #016-43-1958 **AM** *071

STOCKDALE — WILSON

SUTTON, Lewis Richard. ■ 78160 #020-02-1957 L1958 **P** *071

STRAWN — EASTLAND

GILLESPIE, John Jackson. ■ 76475 #030-06-1974 L1976 **ATP PCP** *020 †50

SUGAR LAND — FORT BEND

ABDALLA, Sherif Mohamed A. ■ 77479 #915-02-1991 L2001 **PM** *100 ‡
ADAMS, Charles Danl. 2 CIRCLE DR, UTMB SOUTHERN DIVISION 77478 #048-02-1976 L1976 *020
ADEJUMO, Khadijah O. 11810 HUECO TANKS DR 77478 #024-05-2004 L2005 **FM** *020 †18
ADENWALA, Jayshree N. 15200 SOUTHWEST FWY # 260 77478 #495-17-1972 L1980 **APM** *020 †05
AFZALPURKAR, Rekha. ■ 77479 #495-56-1985 L1997 **IM** *020 †20
AH-LIM, Josie Yvonne. ■ 77479 #917-29-1975 **FM** *071
AHMADI, Ahmad Haji. 14140 SOUTHWEST FWY, STE 180 77478 #048-04-1995 L2001 **PS** *020 †85,65
AHMED, Aliya Sehar. 16103 LEXINGTON BLVD STE K, SUGAR LAND PEDIATRICS 77479 #704-25-2000 L2005 **PD** *020 †55
AHMED, Moiz. ■ 77478 #704-16-1999 **FP** *012
AHMED, Rehan. ■ 77479 #047-05-2008 *012
AKHTAR, Farah. ■ 77478 #048-15-2008 *012
AKPAFFIONG, Ekpedeme Ubon. 2808 GRANTS LAKE BLVD, UNIT 204 77479 #028-03-2005 L2007 **FP** *012
AL-ADLI, Naim Mahmoud. 15200 SOUTHWEST FWY, STE 130 77478 #575-01-1979 L1997 **CD IM** *020 †20
ALBRITTON, Tiffany Lynn. 14823 SOUTHWEST FWY 77478 #048-14-2003 L2005 **FM** *020 †18
ALEJO TORRES, Juan Miguel. ■ 77479 #649-51-1988 *100
ALEXANDER, Charlotte Cook. 1201 BROOKS ST, HOUSTON ORTHOPAEDIC 77478 #012-01-1977 L1978 **ORS HS** *020 †40
ALFORD, Jeffery T. 16651 SOUTHWEST FWY, SWEETWATER MEDICAL 77479 #048-14-1992 L1993 **FM** *020 †18
ALI, Amir. 2225 WILLIAMS TRACE BLVD, STE 109 77478 #704-02-1987 L1998 **IM** *020 †20
ALI, Shanaz Karam. 1111 HIGHWAY 6, STE 100 77478 #048-14-2000 L2004 **MPD** *020
ALI, Zahir Noor. ■ 77479 #704-16-1989 L2008 **IM** *020 †20
AMARO, Michael Anthony. 1111 HIGHWAY 6, STE 200 77478 #048-04-1982 L1984 **OBG** *020 †20
AMRAN, David. 4820 SWEETWATER BLVD, ASTHMA & IMMUNOLOGY CENTER 77479 #550-02-1987 L1997 **AI** *020 †55,03
ANANTHAKRISHNAN, Chittur. ■ 77479 #495-08-1967 L1976 **ORS PM** *071 †40
ANDERSON, Cathlyn Ann. 14823 SOUTHWEST FWY 77478 #048-02-1996 L2000 **IM** *020 †20
ANDERSON-PEREZ, Mabel. 16655 SOUTHWEST FWY 77479 #056-06-1984 L1987 **GP FM** *020
ANDREI, Madalina Mariana. 14851 SOUTHWEST FWY, FORT BEND SURGERY CTR 77478 #781-01-1987 L2002 **AN** *020 †05
ANWAR, Faizunnisa. 1111 HIGHWAY 6, STE 250 77478 #495-09-1997 L2004 **FM** *020 †18
ANZALDUA, Jose A. 6350 HIGHWAY 90A STE 600 77478 #048-13-1982 L1983 **FM** *020 †20
ARAMBURO, Charles Joseph. 16651 SOUTHWEST FWY, STE 360 77479 #047-07-1993 L2000 **GS** *020 †85
ARCHIBOLD, Latha. ■ 77478 #035-15-2004 **IMG** *012 †20
ARORA, Anisha. ■ 77479 #048-16-2007 **IM** *012
ASAWA, Ashish. ■ 77479 #048-02-2007 **IM** *012
ASHARY, Nishan A. ■ 77478 #704-02-1993 **CCA** *100
ATAI, Faith Data. ■ 77479 #690-12-1991 **FP** *012
ATUN, Victor J. 17510 W GRAND PKWY, STE 500 77479 #737-06-1990 L1999 **PS GS** *020 †85,65
AXELRAD, Samuel Donald. 16659 SOUTHWEST FWY 77479 #048-02-1964 L1964 **U** *020 †95
AYACHIT, Jyotsna Avinash. 1111 HIGHWAY 6, STE 150 77478 #495-22-1970 L1975 **FM** *020 †18
AZIOS, Blanca Stella. 707 SUGAR CREEK BLVD, SOUTHWEST PEDIATRICS 77478 #048-02-1965 L1965 **PD** *071 †55
BALACHANDRAN, Nalini. 1111 HIGHWAY 6 STE 240 77478 #495-94-1988 L1996 **FM** *020 †18
BALAKRISHNAN, Maya. ■ 77479 #495-37-1998 L1999 **P** *100
BALTAZAR-LOPEZ, Ulises. 4660 SWEETWATER BLVD, STE 130 77479 #649-31-1986 L2005 **VS** *020 †85
BANNAN, Olivia Martinez. 1429 HIGHWAY 6 77478 #048-04-1976 L1976 **IM ID** *020 †20
BARRICK, Richard Herbert. ■ 77478 #047-06-1952 L1972 **A** *072 †20,03
BATRES, Cecilio Enrique. 11555 UNIVERSITY BLVD 77478 #429-01-1972 L1976 **D DMP** *020 †15
BATTU, Surya Kumari. 17510 W GRAND PKWY, STE 340 77479 #495-50-1972 L1977 **PD** *020 †55
BAUER, David Wm. 14023 SOUTHWEST FWY 77478 #033-06-1988 L1997 **FM OBG** *040 †18
BAVARE, Arusha A. 5022 HIGHWAY 90A, STE G113 77478 #496-42-1997 L2004 **FPG** *020 †20
BELL, Monte K. ■ 77478 #048-15-1999 L2001 **N** *100
BERRIOS-RIVERA, Javier P. 2711 SCARLET SUNSET CT, UT MD ANDERSON CANCER CENT 77478 #024-16-1993 L1996 **RHU** *100 †20
BERTHELSEN, Spencer Robt. 11555 UNIVERSITY BLVD 77478 #048-12-1977 L1977 **IM** *030 †20

BHAI, Aziz Wali. ■ 77479 #704-08-1990 L1999 **IM** *020 †20
BHALA, Rachna. 4902 LAUREL HILL CT 77478 #495-74-1997 L2004 **OBG** *020
BHANDARI, Arvind. 1350 FIRST COLONY BLVD 77479 #495-36-1972 L1978 **ON IM** *020 †20
BHANDARI, Meghana S. 1350 FIRST COLONY BLVD 77479 #035-09-2001 L2007 **HO** *020
BHUCHAR, Subodh K. 3533 TOWN CNTR BLVD S #100 77479 #496-38-1980 L1990 **FM PD** *020 †55,18
BINDAL, Rajesh Kumar. 20403 UNIVERSITY BLVD, STE 800 77478 #016-06-1995 L2000 **NS** *020 †25
BISHOP, Michael Jos. 5610 W RIVER PARK DR, STE A 77479 #016-11-1986 L1991 **PD** *020 †55
BLACK, William Houston, Jr. 2225 WILLIAMS TRACE BLVD, STE 108 77478 #048-02-2001 L2004 **PD** *020 †55
BLICHARSKI, Danuta. 14023 SOUTHWEST FWY, MEM FAMILY MEDICINE 77478 #143-05-1972 L1978 **PD PHO** *040 †55
BONAPARTE, Bernadette. ■ 77479 #412-02-1992 L2005 **IM** *020 †20
BOREN, James Stuart. ■ 77478 #021-01-1947 L1954 **U** *071 †95
BOWMAN-HOWARD, Michelle. ■ 77479 #048-14-1990 L1991 **AN** *020 †05
BOYD, Bobby Joe. ■ 77478 #048-02-1965 L1965 **OBG** *071 †30
BRADBURY, Emily K. ■ 77479 #048-02-2008 *012
BRADY, Jessica A. ■ 77478 #048-14-2008 *012
BREEZE, Juliet Stacy. 4911 SANDHILL DR, POLLY RYON MED GRP 77479 #048-04-1995 L1997 **FM** *020 †18
BROOKS, Dominique Walton. ■ 77479 #047-05-1993 L2004 **OPH** *062
BROWN, Frederick Anthony. 16651 SOUTHWEST FWY, STE 450 77479 #031-01-1999 L2000 **FSM** *020 †18
BRYANT, Jean Walker. 5610 W RIVER PARK DR, STE A 77479 #048-14-1993 L1995 **PD** *020 †55
BURKE, Edward Jerome. 16655 SOUTHWEST FWY 77479 #048-14-1990 L1991 **AN** *020 †05
BUTLER, John M. 4911 SANDHILL DR 77479 #048-14-1993 L1994 **ID IM** *020 †20
BUTT, Moien Rafiq. ■ 77478 #704-02-1968 L1978 **PTH** *020 †50
BUTTRAM, Veasy C Bill, Jr. ■ 77478 #048-02-1960 L1960 **GYN** *071 †30
BYERS, Robert Maxwell. ■ 77479 #023-01-1963 L1971 **HNS** *071 †85
BYRD, Richard Lee. 11555 UNIVERSITY BLVD, FT. BEND MEDICAL AND DIAGN 77478 #048-16-1981 L1981 **PD** *020 †55
CANON, Javier Ricardo. 14825 SOUTHWEST FWY 77478 #264-04-1990 L2004 **ADP** *020
CANTU, Nora L. 17510 W GRAND PKWY S, STE 210 77479 #048-16-1993 L1994 **FM** *020 †18
CARDENAS, Victor J. ■ 77478 #649-06-1953 L1973 **P ADM** *020
CARR, Pamela Margaret. 1111 HIGHWAY 6 STE 160 77478 #001-02-1978 L1978 **D** *020 †15
CERDA, Ricardo Alanis. ■ 77479 #649-04-1979 **CD** *020
CHACKO, Abraham. ■ 77478 #048-02-2005 **EM** *012
CHAMPION, Paolo C. 16659 SOUTHWEST FWY 77479 #048-04-1994 L1995 **U** *020 †95
CHANG, Nam-Hsung. ■ 77479 #244-03-1964 L1979 **DR** *020
CHANG, Wen Li. 4911 SANDHILL DR 77479 #048-14-1986 L1988 **IM** *020 †20
CHAUDHURI, Chandra R. 14023 SOUTHWEST FWY 77478 #048-13-2001 L2003 **FM** *020
CHAUDHURI, Debasish. 17510 W GRAND PKWY S, STE 520 77479 #495-45-1985 L2007 **CD IC** *020 †20
CHAUHAN, Subodhsingh R. 4724 SWEETWATER BLVD, STE 105 77479 #495-22-1988 L2005 **OBG REN** *020 †20
CHEN, Rueywen Pi. 16659 SOUTHWEST FWY # 401, STE 401 77479 #048-12-2002 L2005 **FM** *020 †18
CHEN, Xiaoguang. 3047 SAM HOUSTON DR 77479 #243-76-1985 L2004 **CD** *020 †20
CHENTHITTA, Anil Mathew. ■ 77478 #048-12-2002 L2006 **AN** *100
CHENTHITTA, Sheena Ann. ■ 77478 #048-14-2004 **P** *012
CHOW, Clement. 14833 SOUTHWEST FWY, SUGAR LAND MEDICAL PAVILLI 77478 #048-14-1975 L1975 **OTO** *020 †45
CHOW, Penny. 4545 SWEETWATER BLVD 77479 #048-02-1991 L1993 **P** *020 †75
CHUNG, Yulin. ■ 77479 #048-12-2008 *012
COLEMAN, Albert. ■ 77478 #781-01-1980 **CHP** *100
COLLINS, Diana M. 1 SUGAR CREEK CENTER BLVD, STE 955 77478 #048-14-1992 **CHP** *020 †75
COLLINS, N Perryman, Jr. 14023 SOUTHWEST FWY, PHYSICIAN'S AT SUGAR CREEK 77478 #048-14-1985 L1986 **IM** *020 †20
CONDIT, Margaret L. 16655 SOUTHWEST FWY 77479 #048-13-1982 L1983 **OBG** *020 †30
CORTEZ, Gregorio. 5410 BROOK BEND DR 77479 #048-12-1979 L1979 **IM OS** *030 †20
CRAWFORD, Ernest Monroe. ■ 77479 #010-03-1962 L1970 **GS OS** *071
CRESS, Kimberly Buchanan. 4545 SWEETWATER BLVD 77479 #048-13-1994 L1998 **P** *020 †75
CROSS, Warren Davis, Jr. 14815 SOUTHWEST FWY, STE B 77478 #048-04-1969 L1969 **OPH GP** *020
CROWE, Shannon Marie. 4911 SANDHILL DR 77479 #020-12-1996 L1999 **OBG** *020 †20
CUMING, Reid Macinnes. 15200 SOUTHWEST FWY, STE 294 77478 #048-14-1989 L1990 **IM** *020 †20
DAILY, Harold I. 17510 W GRAND PKWY S, SOUTHWEST OB GYN 77479 #048-04-1950 L1950 **GYN** *020 †30
DANZIGER, Susan Kramer. 15400 SOUTHWEST FWY, STE 300 77478 #016-06-1995 L1997 **PD** *020 †55
DAVE, Deepa Chetan. 38 BRIDGETON CT 77479 #495-17-1991 L2005 **IM** *020 †20
DAVINO, Nelson Anthony. 14825 SOUTHWEST FWY 77478 #048-13-1984 L1985 **ORS OP** *040
DAVIS, Eric Barrington. 4760 SWEETWATER BLVD # 104 77479 #048-14-1983 L1983 **CD IM** *020 †20
DAVIS, Robert Errol. 16655 SOUTHWEST FWY 77479 #045-01-1969 L1974 **GE IM** *020 †20
DEMPSEY, Kelly Seymour. 16651 SOUTHWEST FWY, STE 360 77479 #021-05-1999 L2001 **GS** *040 †85
DESAI, Sandip Ranjitrai. 4780 SWEETWATER BLVD 77479 #495-89-1994 L2005 **PCC** *100 †20
DHINDSA CASTANEDA, Luzamar. ■ 77478 #024-05-2007 **IM** *012
DHINGRA, Anjana Satija. 11555 UNIVERSITY BLVD 77478 #495-36-1974 L1979 **PD** *020 †55
DIAMOND, Jennifer Baudat. 4911 SANDHILL DR 77479 #048-14-1997 L1998 **FM** *020 †18
DIASE, Katherine. 17510 W GRAND PKWY S, STE 310 77479 #048-12-1997 L2000 **OBG** *020 †30
DICKERSON, Cassandra A. 4760 SWEETWATER BLVD, STE 102 77479 #048-02-1996 L1999 **PD** *020 †55
DO, Anh My. ■ 77479 #941-01-1970 L1979 **FM** *020
DO, California H. ■ 77479 #048-16-2002 L2005 **EM** *020 †16
DO, Phu M. 15200 SOUTHWEST FWY, STE 292 77478 #043-01-1995 L2001 **GS** *020 †85
DO, Quynh T. ■ 77478 #048-16-2001 L2004 **FM** *020 †18
DO, Victoria Tu Quynh. 14023 SOUTHWEST FWY 77479 #422-01-1999 L2003 **FM** *020 †18 ‡
DOCRAT, Hafiza M. 11555 UNIVERSITY BLVD, FT. BEND MEDICAL AND DIAGN 77478 #704-16-1985 L1994 **IM** *020

EDWARDS, Michael Charles. 7523 OLD BRIDGE CT 77479 #048-04-1999 L2001 **PS** *020
EJEDEPANGKOGE, Irene M. 4911 SANDHILL DR 77479 #010-03-1998 L2003 **ID** *020 †20
ENGINEER, Diana Rustom. ■ 77479 #048-13-2007 **IM** *012
ENGINEER, Yasmin Rustom. 11555 UNIVERSITY BLVD, FT. BEND MEDICAL AND DIAGN 77478 #495-17-1975 L1990 **OBG** *020 †30
ESPEY, Donna Gail. 11555 UNIVERSITY BLVD, FT. BEND MEDICAL & DIAGNOS 77478 #048-04-1981 L1981 **FM** *020 †18
FAN, Lawrence L. 11555 UNIVERSITY BLVD, KELSEY SEYBOLD CLINIC 77478 #048-04-1984 L1985 **PD** *020 †55
FARHAT, Fahim. 11555 UNIVERSITY BLVD, FT. BEND MEDICAL & DIAGNOS 77478 #605-01-1987 L1993 **FM** *020 †18
FARLEY, Philip Lynn. ■ 77479 #048-13-1984 L1985 **CHP P** *020 †60,75
FAROOQ, Omer. 14815 SOUTHWEST FWY 77478 #704-02-1990 L2002 **IM** *020 †20
FAULKNER, Dale Allen. 1111 HIGHWAY 6, STE 275 77478 #038-41-1970 L1971 **CD IM** *020 †20
FERNANDEZ, Carlos H. ■ 77478 #275-01-1947 L1973 **GP OTO** *071 †80
FIELDS, Melanie Erin. ■ 77479 #048-02-2008 *012
FIMAN, Keith H. 16659 SOUTHWEST FWY # 151 77479 #024-05-1986 L1987 **GE IM** *020 †20
FINKELSHTEYN, Yana. 17510 W GRAND PKWY S, STE 210 77479 #048-04-1997 L2000 **FM** *020 †18
FOOTE, Lawrence E. 1350 FIRST COLONY BLVD 77479 #048-04-1983 L1984 **HEM ON** *020 †20
FORD, C Donald, Jr. 4660 SWEETWATER BLVD, STE 190 77479 #048-14-1981 L1981 **IM** *020 †20
FREEMAN, John Paul. ■ 77479 #047-05-1997 L2000 **GS** *020
GAJULA, Leka. 16651 SOUTHWEST FWY 77479 #495-33-1990 L2000 **GE** *020 †20
GALLOWAY, Brent Wesley, Jr. ■ 77479 #048-13-2007 **FP** *012
GALVAN, David Gutierrez. 17510 W GRAND PKWY S, SOUTHWEST OB GYN 77479 #048-02-1974 L1974 **OBG** *020 †20
GANDHI, Anand Ashok. ■ 77479 #030-06-2004 L2008 **PM** *012
GANDHI, Bharatkumar R. ■ 77479 #495-89-1980 L1993 **IM** *020 †20
GANDHI, Deena Manish. 4660 SWEETWATER BLVD, STE 250 77479 #048-14-1992 L1993 **P** *020 †75
GANDHI, Manish M. 11555 UNIVERSITY BLVD 77478 #048-14-1991 L1992 **FM** *020 †18
GANGOPADHYAY, Subroto. 17510 W GRAND PKWY S, STE 520 77479 #495-32-1989 L1993 **CD** *020 †20
GELFER, Polina. ■ 77479 #913-95-1991 L2006 **PD** *020 †55
GENTLES, Anastasia L. 15551 SOUTHWEST FWY 77478 #005-18-1997 L2001 **PD** *020 †55
GEORGE, Lekha Kurudamanni. ■ 77479 #496-23-1993 L2008 **NEP** *012 †20
GIAMMARCO, Dennis John. 4911 SANDHILL DR 77479 #396-16-1980 L1984 **OBG AM** *020 †30
GIDVANI, Molina G. ■ 77479 #495-04-1963 *075
GIDWANI, Girish. ■ 77478 #016-42-2008 *012
GILREATH, Lora Lofties. 3521 TOWN CENTER BLVD S, STE A 77479 #047-06-1994 L1996 **PD** *020 †55
GINSBURG, Burt Allan. 14815 SOUTHWEST FWY, STE B 77478 #047-06-1976 L1987 **OPH** *020
GOSSARD, Geraldine C. 1111 HIGHWAY 6, STE 260 77478 #539-05-1982 L1996 **FM** *020 †18
GREEN, David Mark. 16655 SOUTHWEST FWY 77479 #035-08-1989 L1997 **AN IM** *020 †05
GREENE, Victoria Rader. ■ 77479 #048-14-1984 L1985 **PTH** *062 †50
GUERRA-PAZ, Jose Luis. 14835 SOUTHWEST FWY, FT BEND IMAGING 77478 #649-14-1967 L1973 **DR** *020 †80
GUTTUSO, Paul Andrew. 14023 SOUTHWEST FWY 77478 #035-06-1997 L1998 **FM** *020 †18
HABIB, Naushaba. 64 WATERFORD POINTE CIR 77479 #704-06-1970 L1995 **AN** *020 †05
HALBRIDGE, Bruce Leonard. 17510 W GRAND PKWY 77479 #030-05-1972 L1978 **OBG** *020 †30
HAMILTON, Toby Ray. 16000 SOUTHWEST FWY, 24 HR EMERGENCY ROOM 77479 #048-15-2000 L2002 **EM** *020 †16
HAND, Alan Howard. 1211 HIGHWAY 6 STE 1 77478 #048-04-1987 L1988 **GS** *020
HAQUE, Moona. 16651 SOUTHWEST FWY, SOUTHWEST OB GYN 77479 #048-02-1996 L2000 **OBG** *020 †30
HARRIS, Donyale Kioko. 11555 UNIVERSITY BLVD 77478 #010-03-1994 L2000 **FM** *020 †18
HASSAN, Saira. ■ 77479 #704-01-1992 L2004 **HO** *012 †20
HASSAN, Yusuf. ■ 77479 #704-01-1987 L2006 **CD** *012 †20
HAYNIE, Aisha Cecilia. 14023 SOUTHWEST FWY, PHYSICIANS AT SUGAR CREEK 77478 #048-04-2006 L2008 **FP** *012
HEIKKINEN, Annmarie Rueff. 14823 SOUTHWEST FWY 77478 #021-05-2002 L2007 **FM** *020 †18
HERBERT, Earle A. ■ 77479 #035-20-1949 L1950 **R** *071 †80
HERNANDEZ, Jesus E. 2225 WILLIAMS TRACE BLVD, STE 110 77478 #048-15-1996 L1999 **RHU IM** *040 †20
HERPIN, Anne-Marie. 15400 SOUTHWEST FWY, STE 208 77478 #048-04-1998 L2001 **FM** *020 †18 ‡
HERRERA, Carmen Marbella. ■ 77478 #048-14-2007 **FP** *012
HERRERA REYES, Carlos A. 3525 TOWN CENTER BLVD S 77479 #048-14-1994 L1995 **OBG** *020
HICKS, Carl Andrew. 1201 BROOKS ST 77478 #048-02-1986 L1988 **ORS GS** *020 †40
HICKS, Kelly Anne. ■ 77479 #048-15-2007 **PD** *012
HICKS, Nancy Karen. ■ 77479 #048-04-1978 L1978 **PD** *062 †55 ‡
HILDEBRAND, Michael E. 16107 KENSINGTON DR, # 104 77479 #047-06-1976 L1983 **AN PME** *072 †05
HILL, Jennifer Plisga. 14141 SOUTHWEST FWY 77478 #048-14-1995 *100
HILLERY, Robert Morgan. 16651 SOUTHWEST FWY, STE 360 77479 #048-12-1980 L1980 **GS VS** *020 †85
HIRANI, Saira Sadrudin. 15200 SOUTHWEST FWY, STE 210 77478 #704-25-1991 L1997 **IM** *020 †20
HO, Hubert Yute. 15400 SOUTHWEST FWY # 300 77478 #048-04-1993 L1995 **PD** *020 †55
HOANG, Son Bao. 11555 UNIVERSITY BLVD, KELSEY-SEYBOLD/FT BEND MED 77478 #048-02-1998 L2002 **FM** *020 †18
HOGARTH, Laurie Anne. 3521 TOWN CENTER BLVD S, STE A 77479 #048-02-1997 L2000 **PD** *020 †55
HOLSTER, Terry A. 4660 SWEETWATER BLVD, STE 190 77479 #048-13-2003 L2006 **IM** *020 †20
HOLT-WHITE, Cheryl Diane. 4660 SWEETWATER BLVD # 210 77479 #048-02-1990 L1992 **APM** *020 †05
HOOVER, Gregory Keith. 17510 W GRAND PKWY, STE 450 77479 #047-06-1987 L1988 **ORS** *020 †40
HORNDESKI, Gary Michael. 14887 SOUTHWEST FWY 77478 #038-06-1976 L1982 **PS HS** *020 †85,65
HORSLEY, William Kenneth. ■ 77479 #048-12-1964 L1964 **GP** *072
HOU, Tien Kuei. ■ 77479 #385-03-1954 L1985 **P** *071

HOWARD, Jed Lee. 15309 SOUTHWEST FWY 77478 #024-01-1959 L1965 **OPH** *071 †35

HOWARD, Percy, III. 14023 SOUTHWEST FWY 77478 #048-02-1991 L1992 **FM** *020 †18

HU, Melissa Shan. ■ 77478 #048-13-2008 *012

HUANG, Ming Sheng. ■ 77479 #244-02-1960 L1975 **AN** *071

HUEBNER, Gene Everett. 17510 W GRAND PKWY S, SOUTHWEST OB GYN 77479 #048-02-1976 L1976 **OBG** *020 †30

HUNG, Julie L. 17510 W GRAND PKWY S, STE 210 77479 #048-14-1994 L1996 **MPD PD** *020 †20,55

HUYNH, Qui Dien. ■ 77478 #941-01-1965 L1979 **IM GP** *020

IBRAHIM, Ibrahim Fuad. ■ 77479 #048-12-2007 **IM** *012

IMDAD, Sultan Mahmood. ■ 77479 #704-04-1967 L1973 **OBG** *020 ‡

INALA, Lakshmi. ■ 77479 #495-11-1965 L1979 **GP** *020

IQBAL, Mohammed Javed. ■ 77478 #704-16-1979 *074

IWELU, Emake Alice. ■ 77479 #690-12-2001 **FP** *012

JACKSON, Jeffrey Allen. 16659 SOUTHWEST FWY # 131, SUGAR LAND NEUROLOGY 77479 #048-04-1979 L1980 **N** *020 †75

JADAV, Dip. ■ 77479 #048-16-2008 *012

JADAV, Paresh R. 16659 SOUTHWEST FWY # 201 77479 #496-25-1997 L2004 **NEP** *020 †20

JADAV, Priti S. 3507 TOWN CENTER BLVD S 77479 #495-23-1984 L1994 **IM** *020 †20

JAFAR, Aman. 3531 TOWN CENTER BLVD S, STE 101 77479 #704-25-1992 L1996 **IM** *020 †20

JAIN, Ashok. ■ 77479 #495-45-1987 L1996 **P PFP** *020 †75

JANSSEN, Namieta Mody. 2225 WILLIAMS TRACE BLVD, STE 110 77478 #048-04-1989 L1990 **IM** *020 †20

JIMENEZ, Jorge Eliecer. ■ 77478 #264-03-1965 L1971 **GP** *020

JONES, Andrew Perkins. 4771 SWEETWATER BLVD # 155 77479 #048-14-1986 L1987 **OM IM** *020 †20

JONES, Monique Mc Conduit. 3521 TOWN CENTER BLVD S, STE A 77479 #048-02-2003 L2007 **PD** *020 †55

KALAVAR, Jagadeesh S. ■ 77479 #495-04-1979 L1985 **IM** *020 †20

KALE, Asha Balkrishna. 3123 MONET DR 77479 #495-01-1968 L1976 **AN** *020 †05 ‡

KARIM, Nioti Ryana. ■ 77478 #160-08-1992 L2000 **IM** *020 †20

KAUSHIK, Vinod Prakash. 4780 SWEETWATER BLVD, STE 100 77479 #495-20-1983 L2006 **IMG** *020 †20

KAVADI, Vivek Sharad. 1350 FIRST COLONY BLVD 77478 #024-01-1988 L1989 **RO** *020 †80

KAZIMI, Iram Fatima. ■ 77478 #048-02-2002 **CHP** *012

KELLY, Lisa Maria. 11555 UNIVERSITY BLVD, KELSEY-SEYBOLD CLINIC 77478 #539-01-1982 L2001 **FM** *020 †18

KENT, Michael D. 14825 SOUTHWEST FWY 77478 #048-14-2000 L2002 **ORS** *020 †40

KHAN, Ahsan Mohammad. ■ 77479 #495-37-1998 L2007 **IM** *100

KHAN, Farhana. ■ 77479 #704-08-1993 L2003 **IM** *020

KHANDWALA, Hasnain M. ■ 77478 #704-02-1993 **IM** *100 †20

KHOKHAR, Amjad Parvez. 3531 TOWN CENTER BLVD S, STE 102 77479 #048-04-2000 L2002 **OPH** *020 †35 ‡

KIENTCHA, Rachel Chundenu. ■ 77478 #048-02-2003 L2008 **FM** *100 †18

KIM, Chong Hyo. ■ 77479 #583-01-1966 L1972 **R** *020 †80

KING, Karl. 15500 SOUTHWEST FWY 77478 #028-02-1985 L1997 **RO IM** *020 †20,80

KISER, Keith Wayne. 2205 WILLIAMS TRACE BLVD, STE 105 77478 #048-14-1982 L1983 **FM** *020 †20

KODALI, Rajeswari. ■ 77478 #495-58-1973 L1973 **PM PD** *020

KONIGSBERG, Max Selig. ■ 77478 #407-21-1936 L1937 **IM GE** *071

KOONCE, Lacy Allen. 3515 TOWN CENTER BLVD S, LONE STAR EYE CARE, P.A. 77479 #048-12-1960 L1960 **OPH PD** *020

KRISHNA, Vamsi. ■ 77479 #048-02-2007 *012

KULKARNI, Sundara P. 17510 W GRAND PKWY S, SOUTHWEST OB GYN 77479 #495-45-1968 L1979 **OBG** *020 †30

KWAN, Peter Chi Kit. 14023 SOUTHWEST FWY 77478 #048-14-1983 L1983 **FM** *020 †18

KYAW, Thein. ■ 77478 #035-03-1963 L1994 **IM END** *020

LAI, James Zanhwar. 1111 HIGHWAY 6, STE 120 77478 #028-02-1992 L1999 **OPH PO** *020 †35

LALANI, Farhan Farooq. ■ 77478 #048-12-2008 *012

LALANI, Suleman. 3531 TOWN CENTER BLVD S, STE 101 77479 #704-16-1990 L1998 **IMG** *020 †20

LALJI, Shelena Charania. 16659 SOUTHWEST FWY 77479 #012-05-1993 L1997 **OBG** *020 †30

LAMPKIN, Jon Michael. 16062 SOUTHWEST FWY, STE ONE 77479 #012-05-2001 L2007 **OPH** *020

LE, Duc Bui. 3525 TOWN CENTER BLVD S 77479 #048-14-1996 L1999 **OBG** *020

LE, Long Nguyen. 14023 SOUTHWEST FWY 77478 #005-18-2005 L2006 **FP** *012

LEAL, Liza Jo. 4655 SWEETWATER BLVD, STE 500 77479 #048-14-1996 L1997 **FM** *020

LEE, Bailey Lock. 1111 HIGHWAY 6, STE 120 77478 #025-01-1988 L1994 **OPH** *020 †35

LEE, Bo-Rong. ■ 77478 #244-01-1973 **BBK** *100

LEE, Kirk Reese. 4660 SWEETWATER BLVD, STE 170 77479 #048-02-1990 L1991 **FM** *020 †18

LEE, Sung. ■ 77479 #583-01-1974 L1977 *020

LEECH, Ana L. 14023 SOUTHWEST FWY 77478 #048-14-2005 L2008 **FP** *012

LEIBMAN, Maurice Norman. 17510 W GRAND PKWY S, SOUTHWEST OB GYN 77479 #836-03-1974 L1979 **OBG** *020 †30

LEWIS, Deanne Zezula. 11555 UNIVERSITY BLVD, FT. BEND MEDICAL AND DIAGN 77479 #048-04-1976 L1979 **PD** *020 †55

LEWIS, James Craig. 11555 UNIVERSITY BLVD, FT. BEND MEDICAL AND DIAGN 77479 #048-14-1973 L1973 **IM** *020 †20

LINCOLN, Patricia Q. 1429 HIGHWAY 6 77478 #048-14-1998 L1999 **FM** *020 †18

LITTLE, Perry. 17510 W GRAND PKWY S, STE 210 77479 #048-02-1994 L1997 **FM** *020 †18

LIU, Bei Fang. 1350 FIRST COLONY BLVD 77479 #025-07-2000 L2006 **ON** *100 †20

LIU, Frank J F. ■ 77479 #244-01-1964 L1981 **PTH** *071 †50

LIU, Kuo Tai. ■ 77479 #244-03-1962 L1974 **GP OBS** *075

LOWDER, Cecilia Irene. 11555 UNIVERSITY BLVD, FT. BEND MEDICAL AND DIAGN 77479 #649-02-1981 L1987 **IM** *020 †20

LYOU, Chihyu. ■ 77479 #048-02-2008 *012

MAHANKALI, Archana Murty. ■ 77479 #495-92-1992 L2007 **IM** *020 †20

MAHONEY, Ronald Paul. 4660 SWEETWATER BLVD 77479 #016-43-1963 L1970 **CD IM** *020 †20

MAIER, Michael C. 15200 SOUTHWEST FWY, STE 290 77478 #048-12-2001 L2006 **ORS** *020

MAKHLOUF, Grace A. 1429 HIGHWAY 6, HILLCROFT MEDICAL CENTER 77478 #605-01-1992 L1996 **RHU** *020 †20

MANGIN, Earl Lewis, Jr. 4660 SWEETWATER BLVD 77479 #021-05-1985 L1986 **CD IM** *020 †20

MANJI, Nasrullah. 4760 SWEETWATER BLVD, STE 101 77479 #704-02-1980 L1992 **GE IM** *020

MAO, Robert C. 16651 SOUTHWEST FWY # 180 77479 #429-01-1978 L1981 **PD** *020 †55

MARTIN, James C, Jr. 15200 SOUTHWEST FWY, STE 100 77478 #021-05-1982 L1993 **OTO** *020 †45

MASOOD, Mujaddid. ■ 77478 #704-02-1985 L2000 **IM** *100 †20

MATA, Henry Albert. ■ 77478 #048-14-1995 L1997 **FM** *020 †18

MATSU, Eddie Tatsuo. 1201 BROOKS ST 77478 #062-01-1969 L1974 **ORS** *020 †40

MATZELLE, Wayne John. 16651 SOUTHWEST FWY, STE 360 77479 #041-02-1966 L1969 **GS** *020 †85

MAZZA, Frank S. 4660 SWEETWATER BLVD, STE 170 77479 #048-14-1992 L1993 **FM** *020 †18

MC CAIN, Angela. 16659 SOUTHWEST FWY, STE 235 77479 #048-14-1984 L1985 **RHU IM** *020 †20

MC CLAMROCH, James R. 1111 HIGHWAY 6, STE 275 77478 #021-05-1976 L1981 **CD IM** *020 †20

MC CLENDON, Robert Louis. 14823 SOUTHWEST FWY 77478 #048-14-1975 L1975 **FM** *020 †18

MC DONALD, Deanna D. 3525 TOWN CENTER BLVD S 77479 #048-14-1994 L1995 **OBG** *020 †30

MC GREGOR, Jon B. 4660 SWEETWATER BLVD 77479 #048-02-1993 L1995 **CD** *020 †20

MC KAY, Mary Carolyn. 3521 TOWN CENTER BLVD S, # A 77479 #023-01-1979 L1979 **PD** *071 †55

MC KELVEY, Jessica B. 4911 SANDHILL DR 77479 #048-14-1997 L1999 **FM** *020 †18

MC MENEMY, Matthew G. 16659 SOUTHWEST FWY, STE 201 77479 #048-14-1982 L1983 **OPH** *020 †35

MC MENEMY, Scott D. 3425 HIGHWAY 6 STE 105 77479 #048-14-1984 L1985 **D** *020 †15

MEISNER, Carl Roger. 2225 WILLIAMS TRACE BLVD, STE 102 77478 #025-07-1977 L1978 **FPG FM** *020 †18 ‡

MERCADO-ARGAO, Maria S. 11555 UNIVERSITY BLVD, FORT BEND MEDICAL AND DIAG 77478 #748-02-1981 L1996 **FM** *020 †18

MICHAS, Maria Garifalia. 14023 SOUTHWEST FWY 77478 #048-14-1994 L1995 **GPM** *020 †70 ‡

MICHELS, John Spiegel, Jr. ■ 77479 #005-06-2008 *012

MILLER, George Givens. 2205 WILLIAMS TRACE BLVD 77478 #048-14-1984 L1985 **CD IC** *020 †20

MITCHELL, Patricia Shupp. 17510 W GRAND PKWY S, SOUTHWEST OB GYN 77479 #048-04-1985 L1989 **OBG** *020

MOIN, Zaki. 15200 SOUTHWEST FWY, STE 240 77478 #704-02-1986 L1998 **P** *020 †75

MOLINA, Laurie Dempsey. 16659 SOUTHWEST FWY, STE 301 77479 #048-14-1991 L1992 **PD** *020 †55

MOMIN, Tajuddin Qasimali. 4911 SANDHILL DR 77479 #704-08-1980 L1999 **IM** *020 †20

MONCAYO SUAREZ, Sonia Pat. ■ 77479 #264-09-1999 L2004 **FM** *020 †18

MOORE, Barbara A. ■ 77479 #048-02-1992 L1993 **P** *020 †75

MOORE, Thomas W, III. 16651 SOUTHWEST FWY, STE 360 77479 #048-02-1992 L1993 **GS** *020 †85

MORENO, Luis Jesus. ■ 77478 #275-01-1952 L1957 **AN** *071

MORGAN, Kathi J. 3521 TOWN CENTER BLVD S, STE A 77479 #048-14-1999 L2002 **PD** *020 †55

MORI, Shahram. ■ 77479 #422-01-2007 **IM** *012

MOSCOSO-DONOSO, Wilson R. 14023 SOUTHWEST FWY, MEMORIAL FAMILY PRACTICE C 77478 #319-06-1981 L1994 **FM** *020 †18

MOSTERT, Jacqueline F. 14833 SOUTHWEST FWY 77478 #048-12-1989 L1990 **OTO** *020 †45

MUHAMMAD, Mehdi. 2655 CORDES DR, STE 120 77479 #704-16-1988 L1999 **IM** *020 †20

MUKHTAR, Kunwer Naveed. ■ 77479 #704-16-1991 L1996 **NEP** *100 †20

MULLANGI, Chandra Prab. ■ 77479 #495-50-1966 L1977 **TS** *020

MURPHY, James Francis. 17500 W GRAND PKWY 77478 #048-04-1974 L1974 **DR VIR** *020 †80

MUTYALA, Indira Devi. ■ 77479 #495-58-1969 L1983 **PM** *020 †60

MUTYALA, Murthy. ■ 77479 #495-58-1973 L1983 **FM OS** *020 †18

NAGARKAR, Devdutt. ■ 77479 #495-33-1973 L1980 **AN** *020 †05

NEILSON, Charles Jos. 322 OYSTER CREEK DR 77478 #035-03-1975 L1977 **EM** *020

NGO, Nathaniel Brandon. ■ 77478 #048-12-2008 *012

NGO, Tuan Dang. ■ 77479 #941-01-1975 L1980 **AN** *020

NGUYEN, Cuong. 14090 SOUTHWEST FWY, STE 101 77478 #048-14-1991 L1992 **OBG** *020 †30

NGUYEN, Dawn Phuong. 15200 SOUTHWEST FWY # 301 77478 #048-15-1993 L1994 **IM** *020

NGUYEN, Hanh Thi. 17510 W GRAND PKWY 77478 #048-14-1997 L1999 **PD** *020 †55

NGUYEN, Nhan Trong. ■ 77479 #941-01-1963 L1982 **GP** *071

NGUYEN, Rosalyn Thuyhong. ■ 77478 #005-11-2005 L2006 **PM** *012

NHU, Bui Thi. ■ 77479 #941-01-1963 L1978 **PD GP** *020

NICKELL, Kevin G. 16659 SOUTHWEST FWY 77479 #048-14-1989 L1992 **U** *020 †95

NIKAM, Srinivas Rao. 16659 SOUTHWEST FWY # 361 77479 #495-09-1971 L1980 **CD IM** *020 †20

NIRAVATH, Polly Ann. ■ 77479 #005-15-2005 L2007 **IM** *012

NOLAN, Steven Edgar. 14861 SOUTHWEST FWY, STE C 77478 #048-02-1977 L1977 **ORS** *020 †40

NOWLAKHA, Prem Kumar. 3511 TOWN CENTER BLVD S 77479 #495-98-1981 L1997 **IM** *020 †20

OBI, Gregory Chinedum. 11126 RAMP CREEK LN, CENTER FOR THE WELL WOMAN 77478 #010-03-1994 L1999 **OBG** *020 †30

OBIJIOFOR, Obiageli C. 4911 SANDHILL DR, OAK BEND MED GRP 77479 #690-04-1992 L2001 **ID IM** *020 †20

OGLETREE, Carl Wesley. 15200 SOUTHWEST FWY, STE 380 77478 #038-41-1986 L1988 **U GS** *020 †95

OLIVOS, Barbara J. ■ 77479 #737-01-1966 L1974 **PD** *100

OMESSI, Terri Ruder. 1211 HIGHWAY 6 STE 50, SUGARLAND MRI AND DIAGNOST 77478 #005-11-1989 L1994 **DR** *020 †80

ONUOHA, Bernadette Ukachi. 12808 W AIRPORT BLVD STE 2 77478 #690-05-1983 L1999 **P CHP** *075

ORIA, Alcides A. ■ 77479 #275-01-1945 L1971 **GP** *071

ORSAK, Shannon Michael. 16062 SOUTHWEST FWY, STE 2 77479 #048-14-1995 L1997 **EM** *020 †16

OTAH, Eseroghene. 17510 W GRAND PKWY, STE 590 77479 #035-08-1996 L2003 **GS** *020 †85

OTAH, Kenneth Ese. 17510 W GRAND PKWY S, STE 590 77479 #690-09-1989 L2003 **CD** *020 †20

OTNESS, Erin Floyd. 2225 WILLIAMS TRACE BLVD, STE 108 77478 #048-04-2003 L2006 **PD** *100 †55

OVIEDO, Rodolfo Jose. ■ 77479 #048-13-2007 **GS** *012

PALLARES GOMEZ, Victor A. ■ 77496 #319-03-1961 L1969 **GS** *071 †85

PAPAGEORGE, Seva. 4911 SANDHILL DR 77479 #048-14-1997 L1999 **FM** *020 †18

PARGHI, Sharvari Rakshit. 5307 WEATHERSTONE CIR 77479 #028-03-2001 L2005 **MPD** *100 †20,55

PARIKH, Kokila Prakash. 1214 CARDINAL AVE, ONE MEMORIAL SOUTHWEST 77478 #495-22-1968 L1978 **OBG** *020

PARIKH, Sanket Suresh. ■ 77478 #496-42-2002 L2007 **FM** *020

PARR, Thomas Jackson. 14090 SOUTHWEST FWY, STE 130 77478 #048-12-1975 1975 **ORS OSM** *020 †40

PASSMORE, John Murrah, Jr. 4660 SWEETWATER BLVD 77479 #047-05-1973 L1986 **CD CCM** *020 †20,16

PATEL, Aniruddha P. ■ 77478 #048-02-2007 **IM** *012

PATEL, Bhagwat. 1111 HIGHWAY 6 STE 125 77478 #305-01-1999 L2004 **IM** *020 †20

PATEL, Devki Mahendra. ■ 77479 #048-12-2008 *012

PATEL, Ghanshyam M. 1111 HIGHWAY 6, STE 190 77478 #495-22-1983 L2003 **OPH** *020

PATEL, Jyotsna Navalrai. ■ 77479 #495-22-1960 L1983 **OBG** *071

PATEL, Maya R. 16651 SOUTHWEST FWY, STE 300 77479 #048-13-1994 L1999 **IM PD** *020 †20

PATEL, Nimesh N. 823 LAKESHORE DR 77478 #048-12-1999 L2001 **FM** *020 †18

PATEL, Niraj C. 3525 TOWN CENTER BLVD S 77479 #048-13-1995 L1998 **OBG** *020 †30

PATNI, Shamim Banu. 2202 UPLAND PARK DR 77479 #495-37-1979 L1994 **GPM** *100 †18

PAWLOWSKI, Michael A. 3902 WOODHOLLOW CT 77479 #011-02-1982 L1983 **EM** *020

PEARCE, James S. 6350 HIGHWAY 90A, STE 600 77478 #048-15-2000 L2003 **FM** *020 †18 ‡

PEARSALL, Joel Patrick. ■ 77479 #005-14-1993 L2002 **EM** *020 †16

PEDDAMATHAM, Usha. ■ 77478 #495-33-1977 L1983 **PTH** *074 †50

PEHR, Charles Edward. 17510 W GRAND PKWY S, SOUTHWEST OB GYN 77479 #048-02-1972 L1972 **OBG** *020 †30

PEPPER, Gregory Scott. 4610 SWEETWATER BLVD, STE 220 77479 #056-06-1996 L1999 **CD ICE** *020 †20

PEREZ, Joseph Cudilla. 14090 SOUTHWEST FWY, STE 101 77478 #048-14-1997 L1999 **AI** *020 †20,03

PERVEZ, Bobby Asad. 15200 SOUTHWEST FWY, STE 285 77478 #704-02-1987 L1996 **AN** *020 †05

PETERSON, Eric Wayne. 11555 UNIVERSITY BLVD 77478 #048-12-1991 L1993 **OBG** *020 †30

PHAM, Bao Quoc. ■ 77478 #048-15-2008 *012

PHAM, Yen Hoang. ■ 77478 #048-14-2007 **PD** *012

PHAN, Charles Gia. 14090 SOUTHWEST FWY, STE 306 77479 #056-06-1992 L2003 **GE** *020 †20

PINKERTON, Jody Lyn. 17510 W GRAND PKWY S, SOUTHWEST OB GYN 77479 #039-01-1993 L1995 **OBG** *020 †30

PLUMMER, Catherine Sapp. 4645 SWEETWATER BLVD, STE 500 77479 #021-01-2001 2005 **CHP** *020

POINDEXTER, Yvette M. 14897 SOUTHWEST FWY, STE A106 77478 #048-02-1993 L1996 **OBG** *020 †30

POLASEK, Jerry W. ■ 77478 #048-04-2004 L2007 **DR** *012

POLINGER, Iris S. 1415 HIGHWAY 6, C400 77478 #035-08-1975 L1977 **D** *071 †15

PONCE DE LEON, Anne M. 17510 W GRAND PKWY S, STE 210 77479 #048-14-1999 L2002 **FM** *020 †18

PONCE DE LEON, Guillermo. 16651 SOUTHWEST FWY, STE 360 77479 #048-14-1992 L1993 **GS EM** *020 †85

PORTER, John Warren. ■ 77479 #039-01-2004 L2004 **AN** *012

PORTER, Veronica Curtin. 16655 SOUTHWEST FWY 77479 #036-08-1989 L1993 **AN** *020 †05

POTTKOTTER, Louis Edward. 3425 HIGHWAY 6, STE 109 77478 #048-02-1975 L1975 **PD** *020 †55

POWELL, Audrey Mitchell. 1111 HIGHWAY 6, STE 250 77478 #048-02-1996 L2001 **MPD** *020,55

POZZI, John. 15400 SOUTHWEST FWY, STE 205 77478 #048-14-1990 L1991 **FM OM** *020 †18

PUCILLO, Ronald Michael. 16659 SOUTHWEST FWY, STE 461 77479 #035-09-1980 L1982 **FM** *020 †18

PURANIK, Niranjan Subhash. ■ 77479 #422-01-2005 L2005 **MPD** *100

QUIRCH, Jorge G. 2503 WIND FALL LN 77479 #275-01-1957 L1970 **FM GPM** *071 †18

RAHMAN, Hassan Toufiqur. ■ 77479 #048-04-2006 **IM** *012

RAM, Vyju. 5610 W RIVER PARK DR STE A 77479 #038-44-1995 L2004 **ADL** *020 †55

RAMIREZ, Olga. 14857 SOUTHWEST FWY, SW SPTS MEDCN & TRAIN CTR 77478 #275-01-1949 L1965 **P** *071

RANGALA, Nalinakshi S. 15500 SOUTHWEST FWY 77478 #495-27-1965 L1982 **RO** *020 †80

RASHID, Anis. ■ 77479 #704-02-1977 L2005 **P** *020 †75 ‡

RAUF, Abdur. 1310 TAHOE VALLEY LN 77479 #704-09-1979 L2001 **IM** *020 †20

REICHMAN, Alan John. 14815 SOUTHWEST FWY 77478 #836-01-1966 L1978 **FM GP** *020

REINOSO, Mauricio A. 3521 TOWN CENTER BLVD S, STE B 77479 #319-03-1984 L1994 **PUD CCM** *020 †20

RICHEY, L E. 14835 SOUTHWEST FWY 77478 #048-02-1954 L1954 **R GS** *071 †80

RILEY, William Barker, Jr. 4665 SWEETWATER BLVD, STE 110 77479 #036-01-1967 L1977 **PS HS** *020 †65

RIPEPI, Antoinette C. ■ 77478 #041-07-1961 L1968 **GS CD** *071 †85,90

RIVENES, Scott Richardson. ■ 77478 #016-42-1992 L1996 **EM** *020 †16

RIVERS, Thomas Burk. 14825 SOUTHWEST FWY 77478 #048-16-1996 L1997 **ORS** *020 †40

RO, Kenneth Gene. 3350 HIGHWAY 6 STE A # 139 77478 #048-14-1988 L1990 **IM** *020 †20

RODRIGUEZ, Patricia A. 3521 TOWN CENTER BLVD S 77479 #048-14-2003 L2006 **PD** *020 †55

ROSEN, Bernard. ■ 77479 #048-02-1947 L1947 **R NM** *071 †80

ROTH, Dover. ■ 77479 #024-01-1951 L1951 **P** *020 †75

ROTHSCHILD, David E. 1429 HIGHWAY 6 77478 #048-04-1977 L1977 **IM** *020 †20

RUDRA, Sonali. 4230 GREYSTONE WAY 77479 #023-07-2008 *012

SAEED, Mohammad Ali. ■ 77479 #704-24-1999 L2006 **VIR** *100 †80

SAHARIA, Ashish. ■ 77479 #495-77-1996 *100

SAIKIA, Sangeeta. 16651 SOUTHWEST FWY, STE 310 77479 #495-78-1990 L1997 **CD IM** *020 †20

SAMPANG, Benjamin Paul. ■ 77479 #028-34-2004 L2008 **AN** *012

SANDERS, Mark Odell. 17510 W GRAND PKWY S, STE 210 77479 #048-14-1979 L1979 **FM** *020 †18

SANDERS, Pamela Jean. 11555 UNIVERSITY BLVD 77478 #018-03-1982 L1986 **PD** *020 †55

SARANATHAN, Singan Anand. ■ 77479 #422-01-2003 L2007 **NEP** *012 †20

SARNA, Manpreet Kaur. 4655 SWEETWATER BLVD # 450 77479 #495-45-1997 L2004 **PD** *020 †55 ‡

SATISH, Shivarudrappa. 15200 SOUTHWEST FWY, STE 180 77479 #495-09-1984 L1994 **IM** *062 †20

SCHIFFMAN, Zvi Jacob. 16659 SOUTHWEST FWY 77479 #550-01-1974 L1984 **U** *020 †95

SCHOLIN, Harold Gilbert. 17510 W GRAND PKWY S, SOUTHWEST OB GYN 77479 #025-12-1997 L1997 **OBG** *020 †30

SCHULZE, Keith E. 15400 SOUTHWEST FWY, STE 150 77478 #048-14-1989 L1990 **D DS** *020 †15

SEHGAL, Puja Anil. ■ 77479 #496-17-1997 L2007 **FM** *100 †18

SETHI, Sanjay. 1350 FIRST COLONY BLVD 77479 #496-09-1992 L2005 **HO** *020 †20

SETHI, Sonal. ■ 77479 #496-41-1995 L2005 **IM** *020

SHAH, Alap Pravin. ■ 77479 #028-46-2004 L2006 **IM** *100

SHAH, Bhadresh. 4780 SWEETWATER BLVD, STE 150 77479 #495-22-1986 L1997 **CCM** *020 †20

SHAH, Biren R. 11211 S HIGHWAY 6, STE B 77478 #495-17-1991 L2005 **DR** *020 †80

SHAH, Pragnesh Rajnikant. ■ 77479 #016-42-2003 L2007 **IM** *100 †20

SHAH, Ulka Kishor-Niraj. ■ 77479 #048-02-2007 **PD** *012

SHAH, Viren Navinchandra. 15200 SOUTHWEST FWY # 265 77478 #495-23-1990 L2001 **IM** *020 †20

SHANNON, Gregory Lance. 17510 W GRAND PKWY, STE 220 77479 #016-06-1996 L1999 **GE** *020 †20

SHETH, Mona Niraj. 4911 SANDHILL DR 77479 #048-13-2001 L2004 **FM** *020 †18

SHETTY, Padmaja. ■ 77479 #048-40-1998 L2003 **IM** *020

SHOSS, Stanford Marvin. 15200 SOUTHWEST FWY, STE 100 77478 #048-04-1981 L1981 **OTO HNS** *020 †45

SHPATS, Inna. 16659 SOUTHWEST FWY # 301 77479 #913-09-1973 L1988 **FM** *020 †18

SIDDIQUI, Sohailur-Rab. 15200 SOUTHWEST FWY, STE 200 77478 #704-02-1987 L1994 **IM** *020 †20

SIDHWA, Yazdi Jal. ■ 77479 #704-02-1969 L1982 **OBG** *020

SINGH, Sapna. 3533 TOWN CENTER BLVD S 77479 #048-16-2003 L2006 **PD** *100 †55

SITTER, Timothy Christian. 1201 BROOKS ST 77478 #048-14-1987 L1988 **OSM** *020 †40

SKINNER, Ryan Todd. ■ 77478 #039-01-2005 L2007 **DR** *012

SMITH, Carlton Edward. 3506 HIGHWAY 6, # 334 77478 #005-18-1985 L1992 **FM LM** *020 †18

SMITH, Clifton Wayne. ■ 77478 #048-02-1968 **IG** *050

SMITH, Melvyn Lee. 1111 HIGHWAY 6 STE 150 77478 #027-01-1969 L1971 **FM OS** *020 †18

SMITH, Toussaint. 3527 TOWN CENTER BLVD S 77479 #024-05-1993 L1999 **CD IM** *020 †20

SONWALKAR, Subodh. 1602 PARKWAY BLVD, SUGAR CREEK MED CTR PA 77478 #495-47-1981 L1996 **IM** *020 †20

SRIDHAR, Srikanth. ■ 77478 #048-12-2007 **GS** *012

STAPENHORST, David P. 4665 SWEETWATER BLVD, STE 110 77479 #048-15-2001 L2006 **PS** *012 †85

STARR, Gregory A. 4415 HIGHWAY 6 77478 #048-15-1992 L1993 **EM FM** *020

STARR, Jane Atkins. 17510 W GRAND PKWY S, SOUTHWEST OB GYN 77479 #035-03-1981 L2004 **OBG** *020 †30 ‡

STASICHA, Thomas R, Jr. 11555 UNIVERSITY BLVD 77478 #001-02-2003 L2006 **IM** *020 †20

STEIN, Stanley Howard. 17510 W GRAND PKWY S, STE 350 77479 #004-01-1977 L1979 **GE IM** *020

STEPHENSON, Charles T. ■ 77478 #048-04-1953 L1953 **ORS** *071 †40

STOERNER, Joan Whitaker. 16103 LEXINGTON BLVD STE K 77479 #051-04-1973 L1976 **PD NPM** *020 †55

SUAREZ, Edwin. 15200 SOUTHWEST FWY 77479 #176-03-1969 L1978 **AN** *020

SUAREZ, Jessica Maria. ■ 77478 #048-12-2004 **GS** *012

SUN, Derrick Yuan. ■ 77478 #048-02-2008 L2008 *012

SUNG, Bin Sheng. 4780 SWEETWATER BLVD, STE 100 77479 #244-02-1987 L1992 **PD** *020 †55

SUR, Sudha. ■ 77479 #495-32-1958 L1971 **OBG** *071 †30

SUSTACHE, Gilberto. 20403 UNIVERSITY BLVD, STE 200 77478 #024-16-2001 L2004 **FM** *020 †18

SYED, Ruhi Fatima. ■ 77479 #005-14-2004 **FP** *012

TALLURI, Sita Devi. ■ 77478 #495-11-1959 L1988 **OBG** *071 †30

TAM, John K. 11555 UNIVERSITY BLVD, FT. BEND MEDICAL AND DIAGN 77478 #048-14-1993 L1994 **IM** *020

TAMIRISA, Aparna. 3519 TOWN CENTER BLVD S, STE B 77479 #016-42-2005 **IM** *012

TAMIRISA, Renu. 3519 TOWN CENTER BLVD S, STE B 77479 #495-65-1976 L1982 **IM** *020 †20

TAMIRISA, Srinivasachary. 3519 TOWN CENTER BLVD S #B 77479 #495-50-1972 L1981 **OBG GS** *030 †30

TANG, Sherman Y. 3527 TOWN CENTER BLVD S 77479 #244-05-1982 L1994 **CD IM** *020 †20

TETZLAFF, Mary Elizabeth. ■ 77479 #021-05-2004 L2007 **PD** *020

THAKUR, Nivedita. ■ 77479 #048-14-2008 *012

THECCANAT, Gigi M. ■ 77479 #495-13-1984 L1991 **PTH PCP** *020 †50

THOMAS, Dimitri Michael. ■ 77479 #048-12-2008 *012

TODD, Emily Rebecca. 3521 TOWN CENTER BLVD S, STE A 77479 #048-04-1998 L2005 **PD** *020 †55

TOLOSA, Bernabe Cambare. ■ 77478 #748-07-1970 *100

TORRES, Elizabeth. 15200 SOUTHWEST FWY, STE 301 77478 #048-04-1981 L1981 **IM** *020 †20

TRAN, Khoan Van. ■ 77478 #941-01-1960 L1977 **GP PTH** *072

TRAN, Nhut Minh. ■ 77479 #941-01-1967 L1981 **GP** *020

TRANG, Tony. ■ 77478 #048-02-2008 *012

TRIPPETT, James M. 17510 W GRAND PKWY S, STE 210 77479 #048-14-1988 L1989 **FM** *020 †18

TRUONG, Hanh H. 16651 SOUTHWEST FWY, STE 340 77478 #048-04-1994 L1996 **IM** *020 †20

TSAI, Lisa Rayin. 4655 SWEETWATER BLVD # 225 77479 #055-01-1992 L2002 **OBG** *020 †30

UMER, Arshad. 11211 S HIGHWAY 6 STE A 77478 #704-02-1998 L1998 **IM** *020 †20

URSO, Richard Geo. 1111 HIGHWAY 6, STE 120 77478 #048-14-1988 L1989 **OPH** *020 †35

VALDEZ, Ray R. 1201 BROOKS ST 77478 #048-02-1983 L1985 **ORS** *020 †40

VANDERZYL, John R. 15400 SOUTHWEST FWY, STE 205 77478 #048-14-1990 L1991 **FM** *020 †20

VIANCOS, Jaime Gumucio. ■ 77479 #231-01-1958 L1971 **AN** *071

VIJ, Deepak. ■ 77479 #495-41-1971 L1983 **GS EM** *020 †85

VIRANI, Asha Jamal. 15200 SOUTHWEST FWY, STE 301 77478 #048-04-1993 L1994 **IM** *020 †20

VU, Lisa. ■ 77478 #048-02-2008 *012

VU, Loc Tien. ■ 77479 #941-01-1971 L1979 **EM FM** *020 †18 ‡

VU, Phong Viet. ■ 77478 #048-12-2007 **PD** *012

VU, Tuan A. 1451 HIGHWAY 6 77478 #048-02-1989 L1995 **PS** *020 †65

WAHID, Rubina. 15200 SOUTHWEST FWY, STE 200 77478 #704-02-1987 L1996 **AI** *020 †20,03

WANG, Samuel C. 1111 HIGHWAY 6, STE 260 77478 #048-14-1991 L1992 **FM** *040 †18

WANG, Vincent Yatchung. ■ 77479 #048-04-2004 L2006 **NS** *012

WAXALI, Anisha Vakil. 4780 SWEETWATER BLVD, STE 100 77478 #048-14-1995 L1997 **IM** *020 †20

WEBB, Melissa Kay. ■ 77479 #048-13-2008 *012

WEBER, Tayma S. 4911 SANDHILL DR 77479 #048-13-1999 L2001 **FM** *020 †18

WELLER, James Patrick, Jr. 1211 HIGHWAY 6 STE 1 77478 #031-01-2001 L2004 **EM** *020 †16 ‡

WEXLER, Alvin S. 16659 SOUTHWEST FWY, # 300 77479 #021-05-1947 L1951 **GYN** *071 †30

WHITE, Dina B. 16651 SOUTHWEST FWY, SWEETWATER MEDICAL 77479 #048-14-1995 L1998 FM *020 †18

WHITE, Stephen Vincent. 1111 HIGHWAY 6 # 7 77478 #017-20-1964 L1970 OPH *020 †35

WIBLE, Judith Laine. ■ 77479 #048-02-1965 L1965 P *071

WIETING, Robert Wm. 15400 SOUTHWEST FWY, STE 300 77478 #048-14-1985 L1986 PD *020 †55

WILLIAMS, Dwayne O. 17510 W GRAND PKWY, STE 180 77479 #048-14-1987 L1988 FM *020 †18

WILLIAMS, Rachele Martine. 20403 UNIVERSITY BLVD, STE 400 77478 #021-01-2000 L2005 PM *100

WOLINSKY, Joel Scott. 20403 UNIVERSITY BLVD, STE 600 77478 #024-05-1984 L1996 N *020 †75

WONG, Alexander Lai Sing. 16651 SOUTHWEST FWY, STE 331 77479 #748-01-1983 L1995 ON IM *020 †20

WONG, Chong Shun. ■ 77479 #065-01-1980 RO *020 †80

WOOD, Jeffrey Ben. 1201 BROOKS ST 77478 #048-04-1993 L1994 ORS GS *020 †40

WOOD, Michael Todd. 16651 SOUTHWEST FWY, STE 360 77479 #048-14-1996 L1997 GS *020 †85

WOODRUFF, Christy A. 15200 SOUTHWEST FWY, STE 370 77479 #048-14-1999 L2001 D *020 †15

YAGHMAI, Beryl Hsiokwen. ■ 77479 #048-12-2007 L2007 PD *012

YAMAUCHI, Toshio. 16651 SOUTHWEST FWY # 150 77479 #048-14-1979 L1979 PD *020 †55

YANG, Eddy Ping. 15200 SOUTHWEST FWY, STE 230 77478 #048-14-2002 L2004 GS *100

YANG, Lan. ■ 77479 #243-76-1988 *100

YEE, Gary Newman. 4803 MENLO PARK DR 77479 #048-13-1977 L1977 EM *020 †16

YELIN, Julie Beth. 17510 W GRAND PKWY, STE 500 77479 #036-07-1994 L1998 OPH *020 †35

YU, Quntao. 4427 HIGHWAY 6 STE J 77478 #243-98-1983 L2000 PD *020 †55 ‡

ZAIDI, Mona Javed. ■ 77478 #048-16-2006 L2006 MPD *012

ZAIDI, Sarah Moid. 15200 SOUTHWEST FWY # 170 77478 #704-02-1990 L2000 IM *020 †20

ZAIDI, Syed Moid Hussain. 15200 SOUTHWEST FWY # 170 77478 #704-16-1990 L2000 IM *020 †20

ZAKI, Ateka. 15200 SOUTHWEST FWY, STE 240 77478 #704-16-1990 L2003 CHP *020 †75

ZAYDMAN, Irina S. 16659 SOUTHWEST FWY, STE 301 77479 #913-32-1957 L1987 PD *020 †55

ZEVE, Philip Stanford. 5610 W RIVER PARK DR, STE A 77479 #028-34-1969 L1970 PD *020 †55

ZHANG, Mei. 4645 HIGHWAY 6, STE J 77478 #243-47-1984 L2004 FM *020 †18

ZHAO, Xun. 16651 SOUTHWEST FWY # 330 77479 #243-47-1982 L2001 IM *020 †20

ZOBAIRI, Sumaiya Ellam. 16659 SOUTHWEST FWY, STE 461 77479 #704-25-1998 L2005 FM *100 †18

SULPHUR SPRINGS – HOPKINS

ARNECKE, Darren J. 115 MEDICAL CIR 75482 #048-15-1993 L1995 IM *020 †20

BALKCOM, Ichabod L, IV. 105 MEDICAL PLZ 75482 #305-01-1984 L1993 FM EM *020 †18

CAMERON, Ricky Leon. 115 AIRPORT RD 75482 #048-02-1996 L1999 FM *020 †18

CONNER, Tod S. 113 AIRPORT RD, STE 200 75482 #048-14-1999 L2002 PD *020

CUTRELL, Curtis Watson. 105 MEDICAL PLZ 75482 #048-12-1978 L1978 FM *020 †18

DIETZE, William Edward. 101 MEDICAL PLZ 75482 #048-02-1967 L1967 OTO *020 †45

DOUGHTIE, James D. 113 AIRPORT RD STE 300, MEMORIAL MEDICAL PLAZA 75482 #048-14-1987 L1988 OBG *020 †30

DRAYER, Sherri Stone. 1317 N HILLCREST DR, JORDAN'S PLACE PEDIATRICS, 75482 #048-14-1996 L1999 PD *020 †18

GLAESS, Alfred Waldemar. ■ 75483 #016-43-1942 L1968 R *071

HINES, Paul Michael. 107 MEDICAL CIR, SURGICAL ASSOCIATES 75482 #048-12-1979 L1979 GS VS *020 †85

HUFFMAN, Jeffry Lee. 113 AIRPORT RD STE 302 75482 #016-43-1978 L2007 U *020 †95

JONES, Charles Bruce. 105 MEDICAL PLZ 75482 #048-12-1974 L1974 FM FPG *020 †18

KOSUB, Laura K. 113 AIRPORT RD, STE 300 75482 #048-13-1991 L1992 FM *020 †18

LONGINO, James Boyd. 530 DAVIS ST N 75482 #048-13-1983 L1983 PD *020 †55

LONGINO, Joseph B. ■ 75482 #047-05-1943 L1947 GP *071

MILLER, William Mark. 105 MEDICAL PLZ 75482 #048-12-1965 L1965 FM *020 †18

MITCHELL, Terry Lynn. 101 SHERRY LN 75482 #048-14-1982 L1983 EM FM *020

MOREHOUSE, Don Michael. 115 AIRPORT RD 75482 #054-04-1993 L1999 AN *020 †05

O'NEAL, Don Martin. 105 MEDICAL PLZ 75482 #048-12-1973 L1974 FM *020 †18

PATTERSON, David Kennith. 115 AIRPORT RD, HOPKINS COUNTY HOSPITAL 75482 #048-12-1982 L1983 FM *020 †18

PIERCE, Darrel Glenn. 113 AIRPORT RD, STE 200 75482 #048-13-1998 L2004 FM *020 †18

POWELL, Scott J. 105 MEDICAL PLZ 75482 #048-02-1998 L2004 GS *020 †85

RAM, Dhawal. 1619 RAINTREE CIR 75482 #891-01-1966 L1975 OBG *020 †30

RANDALL, Randy Craig. 106 MEDICAL CIR 75482 #048-02-1981 L1981 IM *020 †20

REYNOLDS, Claude Earl. 105 MEDICAL PLZ 75482 #048-12-1958 L1958 FM *071 †18

SHACKELFORD, Robert Paul. 113 MEDICAL CIR, SULPHUR SPRINGS ORTHOPEDIC 75482 #039-01-1981 L1981 ORS *020 †40

SRIRATANA KORN, T. 104 MEDICAL CIR 75482 #891-01-1968 L1976 PD *020 †55

STYPKO, Andrzej Piotr. 115 AIRPORT RD, ADVANCED WOUND THERAPY 75482 #759-15-1978 L2006 FM *020 †18 ‡

TEMPLE, Samuel D. 115 AIRPORT RD 75482 #048-16-1987 L1988 ORS *020 †40 ‡

TRISARNSRI, Somjai. 117 MEDICAL CIR 75482 #891-01-1967 L1980 OBG *020 †30

VALDEZ, Joe Gilbert, Jr. 105 MEDICAL PLZ 75482 #048-02-2001 L2005 FM *020

WASSON, Brian David. 105 MEDICAL PLZ 75482 #048-12-2003 L2006 FM *020 †18

SUNDOWN – HOCKLEY

DALTON, Jeremy R. ■ 79372 #048-14-2005 L2008 PD *012

SUNNYVALE – DALLAS

CAIN, Charles Raymond. ■ 75182 #048-12-1956 L1956 IM CD *071

CAPPS, Joseph Robt. 214 MANSFIELD BLVD 75182 #048-12-1976 L1978 IM *020 †20

SUNRISE BEACH – LLANO

BURTON, Kenneth G. 101 SANDY MOUNTAIN DR 78643 #021-05-1951 L1952 GP GS *020

SUNSET VALLEY – TRAVIS

KING, John David. ■ 78745 #019-02-1954 PTH *020 †50

SWEENY – BRAZORIA

BARR, David Thurston. 303 N MCKINNEY STE 3 77480 #048-13-1982 L1983 FM *020 †18

LEAL, Enrique A. 303 N MCKINNEY ST, STE E 77480 #048-02-1982 L1985 FM *020 †50,18

MENDLER, Thomas Michael. ■ 77480 #048-14-2008 *012

MILIAN, Alexander Stephen. 303 N MCKINNEY ST 77480 #048-02-1984 L1985 FM EM *020 †18

MILIAN, Teofilo Jose. ■ 77480 #275-01-1948 L1969 GP PD *071 †18

RAMANATHAN, Subramaniam V. 303 N MCKINNEY ST 77480 #495-16-1984 L2005 IM *020 †20

SWEETWATER – NOLAN

DORMAN, James Paul. 301 JENNY GEORGE LN 79556 #048-12-1969 L1969 GS SO *020 †85

EAKER, Robert G. 301 JENNY GEORGE LN 79556 #048-13-2002 L2003 FM *020 †18

FERGUSON, Sarah Braaten. 201 E ARIZONA AVE 79556 #048-14-2001 L2005 IM *020 †20

FISH, Daniel Brian. 1400 SAM HOUSTON ST 79556 #010-01-1987 L1994 NM *020 †80,28

JOHNSON, Jennifer Leigh. ■ 79556 #048-15-2008 *012

KASSIS, Frederick John. 201 E ARIZONA AVE 79556 #016-43-1970 L1988 IM *020 †20

LINDSEY, George Crockett. 201 E ARIZONA AVE 79556 #048-78-1977, ▲ L1977 FM *020 †18 ‡

LOWTHIAN, John Thos. 301 JENNY GEORGE LN, (LOCUM TENENS MD ONLY) 79556 #021-05-1975 L1984 OBG *020 †30

MC EACHERN, Larry Edward. 201 E ARIZONA AVE 79556 #003-01-1974 L1975 GP *020

MURRAY, Michael. 1401 HAILEY ST 79556 #048-14-1991 L1992 CHP *020 †75

PRITCHARD, Stephen Lee. 200 E ARIZONA AVE 79556 #048-02-1972 L1972 EM *020 †18

ROWLEY, Raymond Douglas. 301 JENNY GEORGE LN 79556 #048-12-1973 L1999 OBG *020 †30

TAFT – SAN PATRICIO

BENAMU PINO, Jose Eduardo. 1155 GREGORY ST 78390 #737-06-1988 L1996 IM *020 †20

BOOSTROM, Ardys Grosjean. 309 RETAMA AVE 78390 #048-12-1978 L1978 PHP *074 †18

TAHOKA – LYNN

CHAMBLER, Kenneth. ■ 79373 #803-03-1951 L1961 GS ORS *020

FREITAG, Donald C. BROWNFIELD HWY 79373 #048-15-1989 L1990 FM *020 †18

POWELL, Paul H, Jr. ■ 79373 #041-13-1946 L1946 GP GS *072

TARPLEY – BANDERA

DORANG, Louis Albert. 343 INDIAN MOUND RD 78883 #041-13-1962 L1986 GS AM *020 †85

TATUM – RUSK

KNOERR, Albert Copeland. 240 N HILL ST, ETMC-TATUM CLINIC 75691 #048-02-1966 L1966 GP *071

TAYLOR – WILLIAMSON

BENNETT, Samuel Coles. 305 MALLARD LN 76574 #649-14-1978 L1985 IM EM *020

DANIEL, Crawford A. 403 MALLARD LN 76574 #048-02-1951 L1951 FM R *072 †18

DEARMAN, Patricia Barker. 603 MALLARD LN 76574 #048-14-1974 L1974 OPH *020 †35

FARQUHARSON, Scott Andrew. 305 MALLARD LN, JOHNS COMMUNITY HOSPITAL 76574 #063-01-1995 L1997 FM *020 †18

GAUDREAULT, Pascal Edward. 305 MALLARD LN 76574 #021-06-1997 L2000 FM *020 †18

HAVALDA, James Tibor. 305 MALLARD LN 76574 #286-02-1964 L1981 GS *020 †85

HAWKINS, Hal Kenneth. 305 MALLARD LN 76574 #036-07-1972 L1984 PTH PD *020 †50

HAYS, John T. 305 MALLARD LN 76574 #048-14-1982 L1983 CD NM *020 †20

HUCKABY, William Ben. ■ 76574 #048-02-1960 L1960 FM OS *020

LEHMBERG, Seth Ward. 403 MALLARD LN 76574 #048-12-1944 L1944 GP *071

LESHIKAR, Marvin J. ■ 76574 #048-02-1951 L2003 FM OS *071 †18

MAXWELL, Michael W. 305 MALLARD LN 76574 #048-15-1994 L1995 FM EM *020

MEYER, Joseph L. 603 MALLARD LN 76574 #048-04-1993 L1994 OPH *020 †35

MISRA, Meen. 305 MALLARD LN, JOHNS COMMUNITY HOSPITAL 76574 #495-41-1997 L2003 IM *020 †20

PULLEN, Thomas Francis. 305 MALLARD LN 76574 #048-02-1974 L1974 FM *020 †18

RANDALL, Albert G. ■ 76574 #047-06-1951 L1958 PHP ID *071

SCOTT, Lauren Allen. ■ 76574 #048-02-2008 *012

SMALLEY, Franklin John. 403 MALLARD LN 76574 #048-16-2005 L2007 FP *012

SMITH, Clyde Dietrich. 305 MALLARD LN, JOHNS COMM HOSP HLTH CLN 76574 #028-34-1969 L1974 GS *020 †85

VARGHESE, Koshy K. 305 MALLARD LN 76574 #495-13-1989 L1998 IM GE *020 †20

TEAGUE – FREESTONE

HALBERT, Bill Lee. 315 MAIN ST 75860 #048-04-1956 L1956 GP *071

TEMPLE – BELL

ABBASI, Seema. 2401 S 31ST ST 76508 #704-16-2000 L2008 IM *100 †20

ABE, Clayton Takami. 190A S 1ST ST, CNTRL TX VET HLTH CARE SYS 76501 #014-01-1987 L1989 AN IM *020

ABERCROMBIE, Barbara Anne. 2401 S 31ST ST 76508 #024-01-1975 L2000 RHU IM *020 †20

ABLARD, Leslie Ann. ■ 76502 #019-02-2006 **OBG** *012
ACOSTA, Lori. ■ 76502 #048-16-2008 *012
ADAMS, Louis Wm. 2401 S 31ST ST 76504 #048-04-1968 L1968 **PO** *020 †35
AGLIE, Bradley. ■ 76504 #048-16-2008 *012
AGUIRRE, Roberto Ignacio. 2401 S 31ST ST, SCOTT AND WHITE CLINIC 76508 #048-02-1983 L1983 **IM** *020 †20
AIRHART, Jim B. 2401 S 31ST ST 76504 #048-16-1996 L1997 **PYG** *020 †75
AKINS, John Parrish. 2401 S 31ST ST, WHITE HOSP 76508 #004-01-2004 **ORS** *012
ALBERS, James H. 2401 S 31ST ST 76504 #048-02-1988 L1989 **PM** *020 †60
ALEXANDER, David William. 2401 S 31ST ST 76508 #048-14-2003 L2005 **GS** *012
ALI, Hameed Qutub. 2401 S 31ST ST 76504 #048-78-2003, ▲ L2006 **IM** *100 †20
ALLEN, Scott Michael. ■ 76504 #048-02-2006 **DR** *012
ALLEN, Steven Robt. 2401 S 31ST ST 76504 #028-02-1984 L1994 **MFM OBG** *020 †30
ALLERKAMP, Eric A. ■ 76502 #048-12-2004 L2008 **OBG** *012
ALLRED, Jared J. ■ 76504 #048-16-2008 *012
ALVARADO, Gladys. ■ 76502 #042-01-1988 L1994 **FM** *020
AMARAL, Barbara Watson. 2401 S 31ST ST 76508 #019-02-1960 L1964 **ON HEM** *020
ANDERSON, Christopher Tod. 2401 S 31ST ST 76504 #048-13-2005 L2007 **P** *012
ANDERSON, Douglas Michael. 2401 S 31ST ST 76504 #021-01-1978 L1999 **AN IM** *020 †20,05
ANDERSON, Kristy Ellen. ■ 76502 #048-13-2004 L2007 **FM** *020
ANDREASEN, Russell George. 1901 VETERANS MEMORIAL DR, VA MED CTR DEPT 116A 76504 #048-12-2000 L2004 **P ADP** *020 ‡
ANDROES, Le Roy. 1901 S 1ST ST UNIT 18A 76504 #019-02-1958 L1966 **P** *071 †75
ANTUNES, Phillip W. 2401 S 31ST ST 76504 #048-14-1993 L1994 **P** *020 †75
APPEL, Kristine Wilkinson. 2401 S 31ST ST 76508 #048-12-1994 L2001 **PHO PD** *020 †55
ARBOUR, Pierre. 1809 SW H K DODGEN LOOP, EAR NOSE & THROAT CENTER 76502 #067-02-1958 L1979 **OTO FPS** *071
ARELLANO, Mercedes E. ■ 76502 #682-01-1989 L2007 **AI** *020 †03,55
ARMSTRONG, Christopher St. ■ 76502 #048-15-2005 **AN** *012
ARROLIGA, Alejandro C. 2401 S 31ST ST 76504 #649-20-1984 L2007 **PUD CCM** *020 †20
ASBURY, John Robt, Jr. 2401 S 31ST ST 76504 #048-04-1969 L1969 **PD** *030 †55
ASTARITA, Robert Wm. 1901 S 1ST ST # V113, CENTRAL TX VA HLTH CARE SY 76504 #035-45-1967 L1971 **PTH HMP** *020 †50
ATKINS, Marvin D, Jr. 2401 S 31ST ST 76504 #048-14-2000 L2003 **VS** *100 †85
ATLAS, Holly E. 1402 W AVENUE H, MEDICINE CLINIC 76504 #048-12-1993 L1994 **FM** *071 †18
AULAKH, Kanwaljit Singh. 2401 S 31ST ST 76508 #422-01-2007 **PTH** *012
AVOTS-AVOTINS, Andrejs E. 2401 S 31ST ST 76504 #048-02-1984 L1985 **GE IM** *020 †20
AVOTS-AVOTINS, Karlis V. 1901 S 1ST ST 76504 #594-01-1942 L1966 **GS** *071
AYUB, Muhammad. 2401 S 31ST ST 76508 #495-98-1994 L2005 **FM** *020 †18
BADEN, Wayne Franklin. ■ 76504 #018-03-1943 L1945 **GYN** *071 †30
BAGGETT, Charlie Brandon. TEXAS A&M SCOTT & WHITE, GRAD MED EDU 76508 #021-05-2004 L2008 **CD** *012
BAINS, Louis W. ■ 76502 #048-02-1953 L1953 **P** *071
BAKER, Kenneth Melvin. 1901 S 1ST ST BLDG 162, DIR DIV MOLECULAR CARDIO 76504 #041-13-1974 L2000 **CD IM** *050 †20 ‡
BALCELLS, Sharon P. 2401 S 31ST ST, SCOTT & WHITE COMM INT MED 76508 #051-01-1993 L1998 **IM** *020 †20
BALL, Timothy R. ■ 76502 #048-16-2006 **AN** *012
BALMAN, John Bernard. ■ 76502 #023-12-2005 L2007 **FP** *012
BALTRUN, Joseph R. 2401 S 31ST ST 76504 #011-02-1980 L1994 **PD** *020 †55
BANKS, Crystal. ■ 76504 #048-16-2008 *012
BANSAL, Mohit. 2401 S 31ST ST 76508 #495-30-2004 L2008 **IM** *012
BARBER, Richard Brian. ■ 76502 #048-02-2005 **ORS** *012
BARBER, Sharon Louise. 1402 W AVENUE H 76504 #039-01-1993 L1996 **FM** *020 †18
BARENHOLTZ, Lawrence. 1605 S 31ST ST, SCOTT & WHITE CLINIC 76508 #025-01-1969 L1992 **IM** *020 †20
BARKER, Luke Anthony. ■ 76502 #047-20-2005 **OPH** *012
BARNES, Robert Nelson. 1901 S 1ST ST 76504 #039-01-1954 L1982 **CD IM** *071 †20
BARNES, Zachariah James. TEXAS A&M-SCOTT AND WHITE, GRAD MED ED 76508 #005-06-2006 **GS** *012
BARNETT, Clint D. ■ 76502 #048-16-2004 L2006 **ORS** *012
BARNIDGE, Michael, Jr. ■ 76502 #021-06-2007 **DR** *012
BARRETTO, Luciana Avellar. 2401 S 31ST ST 76508 #187-21-1999 L2007 **NEP** *100 †20
BASSEL, Maria Elena Salem. 1901 S 1ST ST 76504 #649-02-1955 L1965 **IM** *071
BAST, Peter Henry. ■ 76502 #025-01-2006 L2006 **OPH** *012
BATHURST, Christopher C. ■ 76502 #048-16-2004 L2007 **DR** *012
BAUGH, Reginald Franz. 2401 S 31ST ST 76504 #025-01-1981 L1987 **OTO OS** *020 †45
BEAN, William John. ■ 76502 #048-12-1962 L1962 **IM PLM** *020 †20
BEAN-LIJEWSKI, Jolene D. 2401 S 31ST ST 76508 #407-02-1979 L1982 **AN PD** *020 †55,05
BECKENDORF, Richard C. 2401 S 31ST ST 76504 #048-02-1995 L2003 **PCC** *020 †20
BECKER, Kenneth G. 1901 VETERANS MEMORIAL DR, MS 111 76504 #048-02-1988 L1989 **IM** *020 †20
BEERAM, Madhava Reddy. 2401 S 31ST ST 76504 #495-70-1979 L1994 **PD NPM** *020 †55
BEISSNER, Robert Steven. 2401 S 31ST ST 76504 #048-13-1984 L1985 **PTH** *020 †50
BELLENS, Edward Edmond. 2401 S 31ST ST, SCOTT & WHITE 76508 #165-04-1959 L1971 **OTO** *071 †45
BENEVIDES, Rui Carlos. ■ 76502 #010-03-2005 L2008 **IM** *012
BENNETT, Daniel David. 409 W ADAMS AVE, SCOTT & WHITE DERM 76501 #026-08-1999 L2002 **D** *020 †15
BENNETT, Rachel Cashdolla. 409 W ADAMS AVE 76501 #026-08-2000 L2003 **FM** *020
BENTON, Edward Garrison, Jr. ■ 76502 #048-15-2007 **ORS** *012
BERRY, Nathan E. 2401 S 31ST ST 76508 #048-15-1999 L2002 **OPH** *020 †35
BERRY, Paul Anthony. ■ 76502 #028-02-2004 **PS** *012
BEYER, Erik Arnold Karl. 2401 S 31ST ST, SCOTT & WHITE CLINIC 76508 #047-06-1994 L1995 **TS** *020 †85,90
BHAT, Sanjay Vasudev. 1901 S 1ST ST, DEPT OF RADIOLOGY 76504 #495-01-1992 L1998 **DR** *071 †80
BHATT, Bankim D. 1901 S 1ST ST, VA MED CTR 76504 #495-22-1982 L1990 **IM GE** *020 †20
BIGGS, Kelly William. ■ 76502 #048-04-2005 **DR** *012
BILHARTZ, Rocky D. ■ 76502 #048-15-2004 L2007 **CD** *012 †20
BIRCHEM, Jessica Anne. ■ 76501 #018-75-2003, ▲ L2004 **CD** *012 †20
BIRD, Erin T. 2401 S 31ST ST 76504 #048-04-1993 L1995 **U** *020 †95
BIRKEMEIER, Krista Nartke. ■ 76502 #038-41-2005 **DR** *012
BITTENBINDER, Timothy M. 2401 S 31ST ST 76504 #048-12-1985 L1986 **AN** *020 †05
BLACK, Dorris B. 2401 S 31ST ST 76504 #048-13-1986 L1988 **PD** *074 †55
BLACK, James Nelson. 2401 S 31ST ST 76504 #048-12-1981 L1982 **CD OS** *020 †20
BLACKWELL, Jeffry Scott. ■ 76502 #004-01-2007 **IM** *012
BLANTON, Karen H. ■ 76502 #048-13-2004 L2007 **IM** *100 †20
BLEVINS, John Kollen. 2401 S 31ST ST 76504 #048-14-1973 L1974 **PD** *020 †55
BLEVINS, John Ray. ■ 76502 #048-02-2007 **IM** *012
BOBBITT, Rodney Dale. 518 N 5TH ST 76501 #048-02-1964 L1964 **EM** *030
BOETHEL, Carl David. 2401 S 31ST ST 76504 #021-06-1997 L2004 **PCC** *020 †20 ‡
BOHANNON, William T. 2401 S 31ST ST 76504 #048-16-1994 L1995 **VS** *020 †85
BOLIN, Andrew C. TEXAS A&M SCOTT AND WHITE, DIV OF GASTROENTEROLOGY 76508 #048-14-2004 L2006 **GE** *012 †20
BOLLINGER, Bruce Chas. 2401 S 31ST ST 76504 #010-01-1973 L1982 **EM** *020 †16
BOLLINGER, Robert A. ■ 76502 #048-78-2007, ▲ *012
BOLTON, Paul Dewey, Jr. 1901 S 1ST ST, OLIN E TEAGUE VETERANS CEN 76504 #048-02-1975 L1975 **IM IMG** *020 †20
BONNER, Aleta B. 2401 S 31ST ST, DEPT OF EMERG MED 76508 #048-16-1994 L1995 **PEM** *020 †55
BONNER, Richard B. 2401 S 31ST ST 76504 #048-14-1994 L1995 **CCP** *020 †55
BONNET, John D. 1909 CURTIS B ELLIOTT DR, TEMPLE COMMUNITY FREE CLNC 76501 #023-07-1952 L1958 **ON HEM** *071 †20
BORAH, Adam Michael. 3010 SCOTT BLVD STE 103 76504 #035-09-2001 L2006 **P** *020 †75
BOSSEN, Adam Carl. ■ 76502 #048-16-2007 **AN** *012
BOUR, Robert Kenneth. ■ 76502 #048-16-2008 *012
BOWLING, John Riley. 2401 S 31ST ST 76508 #039-01-1975 L1980 **IM** *020 †20
BOYLE, Mark R. 2401 S 31ST ST 76508 #048-14-2005 L2006 **EM** *012
BOYLE-DOYLE, Teresa. 2401 S 31ST ST 76504 #016-43-1982 L1999 **RO** *020 †20,80
BRABHAM, David G.. 2401 S 31ST ST 76508 #048-78-2004, ▲ L2007 **CD** *012 †20
BRADFORD, Jason Clark. 2401 S 31ST ST 76508 #048-16-2005 **OBG** *012
BRAKEMEIER, Robert Henry. 2401 S 31ST ST 76504 #035-03-1969 L1976 **OBG** *020 †30 ‡
BRAKOVEC, Jenny Lee. ■ 76502 #030-06-2007 **OBG** *012
BRAMMEIER, Thomas Glen. 2401 S 31ST ST 76504 #051-07-1990 L1998 **GS** *020 †45
BRANNEN, Jason L. ■ 76502 #048-02-2006 **ORS** *012
BRASHER, George W. 2401 S 31ST ST 76508 #047-06-1961 L1966 **AI PD** *071 †55,03
BREWER, Luther M. 2401 S 31ST ST, SCOTT & WHITE HEALTH PLAN 76508 #048-12-1961 L1961 **IM PUD** *071 †20
BRINDLEY, Glen Owens. 2401 S 31ST ST 76504 #048-02-1975 L1975 **OPH** *020 †35
BRINDLEY, Hanes Hanby, Jr. 2401 S 31ST ST 76504 #048-02-1972 L1973 **ORS OP** *020 †40
BRINKLEY, Laura Lynn. 2401 S 31ST ST 76504 #048-14-1995 L1996 **AN** *020 †05
BROCKER, Jason Anthony. ■ 76502 #048-13-2006 **GS** *012
BRODERS, Charles Wm. 2401 S 31ST ST 76508 #030-05-1947 L1957 **GS** *071 †85
BROOKS, Charles D. ■ 76502 #048-15-2004 L2007 **DR** *012
BROWN, Aubrey Kenna, Jr. ■ 76502 #047-06-1945 L1946 **OTO** *071 †45
BROWN, Ellis Neal. 1905 SW H K DODGEN LOOP 76502 #030-05-1965 L1972 **AN** *071 †05
BROWN, Jacob Wayne. ■ 76502 #021-06-2007 **EM** *012
BROWNE, Brandon Alban. TEXAS A&M-SCOTT AND WHITE, DEPT OF EMERGENCY MED 76508 #048-04-2006 L2007 **EM** *012
BRUNER, Wayne Morgan. 2401 S 31ST ST, S&W HOSP-DEPT EMERGENCY M 76508 #011-04-2004 L2006 **EM** *020
BRYAN, Edward R. ■ 76502 #048-13-2005 L2008 **AN** *012
BRYAN, John N. VETERANS CTR 76504 #048-04-1944 L1944 **GP** *020
BUCHANAN, Robert Joseph. 2401 S 31ST ST 76504 #028-34-1993 L1996 **NS** *020 †75
BUCKLEY, Clifford James. 2401 S 31ST ST 76504 #041-09-1962 L1976 **VS GS** *040 †85
BURCH, Micah Matthew. ■ 76502 #039-01-2006 **IM** *012
BURKE, Robert E. 2401 S 31ST ST 76504 #048-13-1982 L1983 **PD** *020 †20,75,55 ‡
BURNS, Paul A. ■ 76502 #048-16-2007 **EM** *012
BUSH, Ruth Lee. 2401 S 31ST ST 76504 #036-01-1992 L2003 **VS** *020 †85
BUSICK, Thomas L. 409 W ADAMS AVE 76501 #048-12-2004 L2007 **D** *012
BUSWELL, Arthur Lee. 1901 VETERANS MEMORIAL DR, CTRL TX VETERANS HLTH CARE 76504 #039-01-1987 L2005 **P** *020 †75
BUTLER, David Ford. 2401 S 31ST ST, DIVISION OF DERMATOLOGY 76508 #048-02-1980 L1980 **D** *040 †15
BYRD, Timothy M. ■ 76502 #048-02-2008 *012
CABALLERO, Joshua. ■ 76502 #048-16-2008 *012
CABLE, Christian Thomas. 2401 S 31ST ST 76504 #048-16-1999 L2001 **ON** *020 †20
CADE, Aaron Micah. 2401 S 31ST ST, DEPARTMENT OF ANESTHESIOLO 76508 #048-15-2006 **AN** *012
CAIN, Jennifer L. 2401 S 31ST ST, MEMORIAL HOSPI 76508 #048-16-2004 L2007 **OBG** *012
CAIN, Phillip T. 2401 S 31ST ST 76508 #048-02-1974 L1974 **IM** *020 †20
CALDERWOOD, Gordon Wright. 2401 S 31ST ST 76504 #039-01-1983 L1988 **RNR DR** *020 †80
CALERO, Shanna. ■ 76504 #048-16-2008 *012
CAMARILLO, Luis Cortez. 2401 S 31ST ST 76504 #048-02-1999 L2002 **IM** *020 †20
CAMPBELL, Joel Mark. 2401 S 31ST ST 76508 #048-16-1990 L1991 **IM** *020 †20
CANTRELL, Nicholas Cade. ■ 76504 #016-11-2003 L2008 **DR** *012
CAPEN, Charles Vernon. 2401 S 31ST ST 76504 #047-06-1973 L1983 **GO OBG** *020 †30
CARABASI, Robert John. ■ 76502 #041-02-1948 L1950 **PUD IM** *071 †20
CARAVEO, Juan. 2401 S 31ST ST 76504 #649-27-1971 L1978 **IM HEM** *020 †20
CARGILE, John C. ■ 76502 #048-16-2007 **AN** *012
CARPENTER, John Loder. 2401 S 31ST ST 76504 #048-04-1970 L1974 **IM** *020 †20
CARPENTIER, Wm Raymond. 2401 S 31ST ST 76508 #061-01-1961 L1971 **NM AM** *020 †70,28
CARRELL, Thomas Malcolm. 2401 S 31ST ST 76504 #048-12-1984 L1985 **ORS OSM** *020 †40
CARTER, Glenn Allen. 600 S 25TH ST 76504 #021-05-1956 L1963 **PD** *020 †55
CARTER, Jason Daniel. TEXAS A&M-SCOTT AND WHITE, ORTHOPAEDICS 76508 #048-14-2004 **ORS** *012
CASE, Robert S. 2401 S 31ST ST 76508 #048-16-2001 L2004 **RNR** *020 †80
CASH, Cassandra Lane. ■ 76502 #030-05-2008 *012
CASSO GOMEZ, L.S.. ■ 76502 #048-16-2008 *012
CASTLEBERRY, Stephen Brya. ■ 76502 #021-05-2004 L2006 **GS** *012
CASTRO, Manuel Alberto. 2401 S 31ST ST, MEMORIAL HOSPI 76508 #270-02-2000 L2007 **CHP** *020
CASTRO, Tim, III. ■ 76502 #048-02-2006 **IM** *012
CASTRO BARNETT, Ysabella. ■ 76502 #048-16-2004 L2006 **GS** *100
CAUTHEN, Don Baker. 2401 S 31ST ST, DEPT FP 76508 #048-12-1970 L1970 **FM** *030 †18
CEARLEY, David M. 2401 S 31ST ST 76504 #048-16-1999 L2007 **OP** *100
CESANI, Jose A. 1605 S 31ST ST 76508 #048-14-1994 L1996 **IM** *020 †20
CHANDLER, James B, Jr. 2401 S 31ST ST 76504 #012-01-1960 L1960 **GE IM** *020
CHANEY, Phillip Lee. 2401 S 31ST ST 76504 #048-02-1981 L1981 **GE** *071 †20

■ = Address Information Privacy Protected

CHANG, Annie Y. 4610 WATERBURY DR 76502 #048-78-2001, ▲ L2003 **MPD** *020
CHAPUT, Christopher D. 2401 S 31ST ST 76504 #048-04-1997 L1998 **ORS** *020 †40
CHAUHAN, Manish Sagarmal. 1905 SW H K DODGEN LOOP 76502 #496-38-1991 L2004 **CD** *020 †20
CHAVEZ, Anthony Hugo. TEXAS A&M-SCOTT AND WHITE, DIV OF UROLOGY 76508 #003-01-2006 **U** *012
CHEN, Stanley V. 2401 S 31ST ST, SCOTT & WHITE HOSPITAL 76508 #048-13-1998 L2001 **IM** *020
CHEUNG, Alan Yung-Cheong. 2401 S 31ST ST 76504 #462-01-1970 L1977 **RO** *020 †80
CHEUNG, Peter Yuk. 2401 S 31ST ST 76504 #035-19-1997 L2005 **ICE** *020 †20
CHILDS, Ed W. 2401 S 31ST ST 76504 #048-16-1989 L1990 **CCS** *020 †85
CHILES, Christopher D. 2401 S 31ST ST 76504 #048-02-1997 L2001 **CD** *020 †20
CHILES, Lenore Renee. 409 W ADAMS AVE 76501 #048-02-1997 L1999 **D** *020 †15
CHINTAPALLI, Girija S. 1901 S 1ST ST, VA HOSPITAL 76504 #495-50-1965 L1977 **P** *020 †75
CHISHOLM, Cary Daniel. ■ 76502 #048-12-2008 *012
CHLAPEK, Ben Hejl. 2401 S 31ST ST 76504 #028-78-1975, ▲ L1977 **EM** *020 †16
CHOU, Ching Juliet. MEMORIAL HOSP, SCOTT & WHITE 76508 #025-76-2003, ▲ L2003 **P** *012
CHRISTOFF, Nicholas. 2401 S 31ST ST 76508 #016-02-1953 L1978 **N** *072 †75
CHUNE, Gary Wing. 2401 S 31ST ST, SCOTT 76508 #025-07-1980 L1996 **END IM** *020 †20
CICERI, David Paul. 2401 S 31ST ST 76504 #033-05-1984 L1999 **AN IM** *020 †20,05
CIPRIANI, Cheryl Ann. 2401 S 31ST ST 76504 #048-02-1979 L1979 **NPM PD** *020 †55
CISNEROS, Alfredo Augusto. 1901 S 1ST ST, CENTRAL TX HEALTH CARE SYS 76504 #682-01-1966 L1975 **FM** *020 †18
CLANTON, Craig W. 2401 S 31ST ST 76504 #048-16-1982 L1983 **FM** *020 †18
CLARK, Eilis Kisis. 1901 VETERANS MEMORIAL DR, 116 MHC 76504 #036-01-1995 L1996 **P FM** *100 †18
CLARK, Elmer L. 600 S 25TH ST 76504 #048-04-1945 L1945 **IM** *071
CLARK, Jeffrey W. 2401 S 31ST ST 76504 #048-78-1989, ▲ L1990 **N** *020 †75
CLARK, Jessica L. ■ 76502 #048-16-2008 *012
CLARK, Marilyn K. 2401 S 31ST ST 76508 #048-04-1991 L1992 **RHU** *020 †20
CLARY, Matthew Todd. ■ 76502 #045-04-2004 L2004 **OPH** *012
COBBS, Lauren Stephanie. 2401 S 31ST ST 76508 #023-01-1995 L2003 **IM** *020 †20
COCHRAN, Jeffrey Dwight, Jr. ■ 76502 #031-01-2007 **EM** *012
COFFIELD, King Scott. 2401 S 31ST ST 76504 #027-01-1971 L1972 **U** *020 †95
COLATO ZAVALETA, Fernando. ■ 76502 #341-03-2005 **IM** *012
COLBY, Ethan A. ■ 76502 #048-12-2003 L2008 **DR** *012
COLVIN, Christopher S. 2401 S 31ST ST 76504 #048-14-2003 L2005 **EM** *100 †16
CONCEPCION, Luis. 2401 S 31ST ST 76504 #737-06-1986 L2000 **NEP IM** *020 †20
CONGER, Leo A, Jr. 1809 SW H K DODGEN LOOP 76502 #048-15-1984 L1985 **D AM** *020 †70,15
CONLEY, Joseph A. ■ 76502 #048-02-2006 **DR** *012
COOK, John R. ■ 76504 #048-02-1953 L1953 **GP** *071
COONEY, Donald Robt. 2401 S 31ST ST 76504 #038-40-1970 L1998 **PDS** *050 †85
CORNELIUS, Lisa Dawn. 2401 S 31ST ST 76504 #048-04-1997 L2003 **ID** *020 †20
CORPREW, Robert Normanlee, Jr. TEXAS A&M-SCOTT AND WHITE, GRAD MED ED 76508 #036-08-2007 **GS** *012
CORRELL, Bodie James. ■ 76504 #048-16-2008 *012
CORTES, Robert. 600 S 25TH ST 76504 #048-04-1979 L1979 **FM GS** *020 †18
COSTA, Steven M. 2401 S 31ST ST 76504 #048-02-2000 L2002 **CD** *100 †20
COUCH, Courtney Aarant. ■ 76502 #048-02-2003 L2006 **PD** *100
COUCHMAN, Glen Renaldo. 1402 W AVENUE H 76504 #018-03-1979 L1981 **FM** *020 †18
COUNCILMAN-GONZALES, Lisa. 2401 S 31ST ST 76504 #011-02-1997 L1998 **AN** *020 †05
COWAN, Craig. ■ 76502 #003-75-2007, ▲ **EM** *012
COX, Charles H, Jr. ■ 76501 #048-02-1944 L1944 **GP** *071
CRAUN, Michael Len. 2401 S 31ST ST 76504 #048-12-1974 L1980 **TRS CCS** *020 †85
CRCHOVA, Melissa. 2401 S 31ST ST 76504 #067-01-1993 L1998 **PTH** *100 †75
CRISP, Edwin Darrell. 2401 S 31ST ST 76504 #048-14-1975 L1975 **CHN PD** *020 †55,75
CRISP, Matthew Brandon. 2401 S 31ST ST 76504 #048-04-2001 L2005 **PDR** *100 †80
CROSS, David Alan. 2401 S 31ST ST 76504 #039-01-1968 L1994 **AN CCA** *020 †05 ‡
CROSSNO, Ronald Jay. 2626 S 37TH ST B 76504 #048-13-1981 L1981 **PLM FPG** *020 †16,18
CUERVO, Luis J. 2401 S 31ST ST 76508 #048-02-2006 **IM** *012
CULP, Laura R. 2401 S 31ST ST 76504 #048-02-2000 L2004 **RO** *100 †80
CULP, William Combs, Jr. 2401 S 31ST ST 76504 #048-02-1998 L2001 **AN** *020 †05
CUNNINGHAM, Richard D. 600 S 25TH ST 76504 #026-04-1957 L1964 **OPH** *071 †35
CURRY, Kelly Ann. ■ 76502 #055-01-2005 **IM** *012
CURTIS, John Cecil. ■ 76502 #021-05-1955 L1963 **PD** *071 †55
CUSTER, Monford Danl, III. 2401 S 31ST ST 76504 #051-04-1981 L1990 **GS PDS** *020 †85
DANIEL, Michael Evan. ■ 76502 #048-15-2006 **DR** *012
DANIELS, Don Jose. 2401 S 31ST ST 76504 #023-12-1982 L1987 **AN PMM** *030 †05
DAVE, Rupesh Kiritkumar. ■ 76502 #495-48-2002 L2007 **PCC** *012 †20
DAVIS, John Thos. 1901 S 1ST ST 76504 #048-02-1954 L1954 **DR** *020 †80
DAVIS, Robert Douglas. 2401 S 31ST ST 76504 #048-14-1982 L1983 **OPH** *020 †35
DAVIS, Samuel H. 2401 S 31ST ST 76504 #048-12-2001 L2007 **PD** *100 †55
DE BORD, Bert Alvin, Jr. ■ 76501 #048-04-1939 L1939 **OTO** *071 †45
DEHMER, Gregory Jos. 2401 S 31ST ST 76504 #056-05-1975 L1977 **IC CD** *030 †20
DEKERATRY, Dominic R. 2401 S 31ST ST 76504 #048-02-1993 L2000 **PCC** *020 †20 ‡
DEMPSEY, James P. ■ 76502 #035-06-1964 L1993 **GP** *020 †18,16
DENSON, Thomas Chas. ■ 76502 #048-12-1960 L1960 **PD FM** *071
DESAI, Ansuya N. 1901 S 1ST ST 76504 #495-22-1978 L1981 **IM** *020 †20
DESALVO, Daniel. ■ 76502 #048-16-2008 *012
DESHAZER, Katherine Irene. ■ 76502 #048-14-2003 L2007 **PD** *100
DESHAZER, Mitchell Edward. ■ 76502 #048-04-2007 **IM** *012
DIAS, Ronald Percival F. 1901 S 1ST ST 76504 #495-52-1975 L1980 **AN** *020 †05
DICHOSO, Daryl Demetri. 2401 S 31ST ST 76508 #748-01-2000 L2008 **MPD** *012
DIECKERT, J Paul. 2401 S 31ST ST 76504 #048-12-1977 L1977 **OPH** *020 †35
DILLON, Paul Lee. 2401 S 31ST ST 76504 #039-01-2003 L2007 **AN** *020
DO, Michael K. ■ 76502 #048-16-2004 **DR** *012
DOLIN, Elizabeth Kay. 2401 S 31ST ST, SCOTT & WHITE MEM HOSP 76508 #039-79-2002, ▲ L2004 **PCC** *012
DOLLAR, Bradley T. 2401 S 31ST ST 76504 #048-12-2001 L2004 **VIR** *100 †80
DOMINGUEZ, David Emilio. 2401 S 31ST ST, WHITE HOSP 76508 #036-07-2006 **ORS** *012
DONNER, Ludvik Rafael. 2401 S 31ST ST 76504 #286-11-1965 L1986 **PTH** *020 †50
DOUTY, Truman Benj, Jr. 2401 S 31ST ST 76508 #048-14-1974 L1974 **PD** *020 †55
DRAKE, Glen B. 2401 S 31ST ST 76504 #048-12-1975 L1975 **CD** *020 †20
DREHER, Gerald Francis. 1901 S 1ST ST, VAMC TEMPLE 76504 #035-01-1977 L1978 **ORS** *020 †40
DRIGALLA, Dorian F. 2401 S 31ST ST 76504 #048-13-2002 L2006 **EM** *020 †16
DRISCOLL, Matthew David. ■ 76502 #048-04-2008 *012
DROEMER, Danl Reinhold, Jr. 1901 S 1ST ST, OLIN TEAGUE VA CENTER 76504 #048-02-1976 L1976 **IM** *020 †20
DUGGAN, Raymond G. 2401 S 31ST ST 76508 #048-78-2002, ▲ L2004 **GE** *012 †20
DUKE, Mark Stanfield. 2401 S 31ST ST 76504 #028-34-1978 L1994 **NEP IM** *020 †20
DVORACEK, John Earl. 2401 S 31ST ST 76508 #026-04-1974 L1979 **IM AI** *020 †20,03
DYCK, Walter Pete. ■ 76502 #019-02-1961 L1968 **GE IM** *071 †20
DYSART, Donald Norman. 600 S 25TH ST 76504 #018-03-1947 L1952 **DR** *071 †80
EANES, David F S, Jr. 518 N 5TH ST 76501 #004-01-1943 L1944 **FM IM** *071
EASLEY, David J. 2401 S 31ST ST 76504 #048-13-1989 L1990 **PD** *020 †55
EASTON, Wiley Ben. ■ 76502 #045-04-2005 L2006 **EM** *012
EBERTS, John Paul. 2401 S 31ST ST 76508 #048-12-1961 L1961 **R** *071 †80
ECKHART, Erin Alice. ■ 76502 #048-16-2008 *012
EIDSON, Jack Leigh, III. ■ 76502 #048-02-2006 **GS** *012
EISENHAUER, Gail Lynn. 2401 S 31ST ST 76504 #004-01-1979 L1987 **CHP P** *020 †75
ELIESON, Marc S. ■ 76502 #048-15-2005 **IM** *012
ELIJOVICH, Fernando. 1605 SOUTH 31ST STREET 76508 #132-01-1967 L1998 **IM CD** *050 †20
ELLIOTT, Kent Franklin. 2401 S 31ST ST 76504 #039-01-1981 L1984 **AN PD** *020 †05
ELLIS, Brian Thomas. ■ 76502 #039-01-2006 **PD** *012
ELLIS, Donald Lynn. 1901 S 1ST ST 76504 #040-02-1956 L1961 **GS** *071 †85
ENCARNACION, Elmyra V. 2401 S 31ST ST 76504 #422-01-1995 L1996 **N IM** *020 †75
EPURU, Deepika Reddy. ■ 76504 #008-02-1997 L2001 **END** *012 †20
ERICKSON, Richard Arnold. 2401 S 31ST ST 76504 #005-18-1978 L1995 **GE IM** *020 †20
ERWIN, John P, III. 2401 S 31ST ST 76504 #048-16-1992 L1994 **CD** *020 †20
ESHBAUGH, Calvin Goodrich. 2401 S 31ST ST 76504 #011-02-1995 L1996 **OPH** *020 †35
EVANS, Tanya N. ■ 76502 #048-12-2005 L2008 **IM** *012
FAIZ, Shazia. 2401 S 31ST ST 76504 #704-05-2000 L2007 **END** *020 †20
FARRIS, Amanda Cathren Ha. 2401 S 31ST ST 76504 #048-78-2004, ▲ L2007 **PD** *100
FELDTMAN, Robert Warren. 2401 S 31ST ST 76504 #048-02-1972 L1972 **TS VS** *020 †85,90
FIALA, Katherine Hutka. 409 W ADAMS AVE 76501 #048-16-2003 L2007 **D** *020 †15
FILLMORE, Geoffrey Alan. 2401 S 31ST ST 76508 #039-79-2004, ▲ L2006 **IM** *100 †20
FILLMORE, Summer A. ■ 76502 #039-79-2005, ▲ L2008 **FP** *012
FINCH, Daniel Chester. 1901 VETERANS MEMORIAL DR 76504 #048-02-1973 L1973 **IM** *020 †20
FINCH, James Robt. ■ 76504 #048-02-1963 L1963 **D** *020 †15
FINKLEA, James Davidson. ■ 76504 #048-02-2004 **IM** *012
FIOCCO, Guy P. 2401 S 31ST ST 76504 #035-46-1978 L1987 **RHU IM** *020 †20
FLIPPIN, Nicholas William. ■ 76502 #048-16-2005 L2008 **DR** *012
FLORES, Virginia M. 2401 S 31ST ST 76504 #048-16-2001 L2006 **P** *020
FLORY, Jennifer M. 1402 W AVENUE H 76504 #048-16-1998 L1999 **FM** *020 †18
FOLLENDER, Alan Bruce. 2401 S 31ST ST, SCOTT AND WHITE CLINIC 76508 #011-02-1967 L1973 **N** *071 †75
FOREST, Patricia Lauren. 1901 S 1ST ST 76504 #036-08-1984 L1985 **IM** *020 †20
FORNFEIST, Douglas S. 2401 S 31ST ST 76504 #048-15-1993 L1994 **HS** *020 †40
FOSTER, Delbert Ray. 3605 WOLVERINE TRAIL 76508 #048-04-1971 L1971 **D** *020 †15
FOTHERGILL, Russell E. 2401 S 31ST ST 76504 #048-02-2000 L2001 **OBG** *020
FRANCIS, Scott A. ■ 76501 #048-15-2004 L2007 **P** *012
FRANKE, Craig Brandon. 2401 S 31ST ST, MEMORIAL HOSPI 76508 #048-02-2004 L2007 **P** *012
FRANKEL, Arthur Edward. 2401 S 31ST ST 76504 #024-01-1973 L2005 **ON IG** *050 †20
FRIEDMAN, Paul A. 2401 S 31ST ST 76504 #048-13-1987 L1994 **PM** *020 †60
FRITCHER, Seth Harlon. 4114 CRIPPLE CREEK DR 76502 #048-16-1999 L2001 **VS** *020 †85
FRITZ, David A. 2401 S 31ST ST 76504 #048-12-1995 L2001 **EM** *020 †16
FULCHER, Samuel Fisher A. 2401 S 31ST ST 76504 #048-14-1983 L1983 **OPH** *020 †35
FULLER, Allie Marie. ■ 76502 #048-16-2007 **PD** *012
FULLER, Monica Marc. 2401 S 31ST ST, SCOTT & WHITE MEM HOSP 76508 #028-03-2006 **D** *012
FULLERTON, John Carr, III. 1901 VETERANS MEMORIAL DR, GEN SURGERY SERVICE-112 76504 #051-01-1977 L1982 **GS** *020 †85
FURMAN, Alisa A. 1713 SW H K DODGEN LOOP 76502 #030-06-1995 L1996 **OBG** *020 †30
FURMAN, Matthew Jason. 1905 SW H K DODGEN LOOP 76502 #030-06-1994 L1996 **FM** *020 †18
GAGLANI, Manjusha. 2401 S 31ST ST 76504 #496-38-1982 L1996 **PD ID** *050 †55
GAINES, Richard Keith. ■ 76502 #048-04-1959 L1959 **P** *071 †75
GAMMON, Jane Ellen. 2401 S 31ST ST 76508 #048-16-1986 L1987 **IM** *071 †20
GANTT, David Scott. 2401 S 31ST ST 76504 #018-75-1976, ▲ L1982 **CD IC** *020 †20
GARCIA, Anthony Fabro. ■ 76504 #048-14-2007 **AN** *012
GARMON, Emily H Haas. ■ 76502 #048-02-2006 **AN** *012
GARZA-GONGORA, Ricardo Da. ■ 76502 #048-02-2004 L2008 **DR** *012
GAYLORD, Robert Waymon. ■ 76504 #407-10-1964 L1973 **IM PTH** *071
GAYTON, Melissa Sue. TEXAS A&M-SCOTT AND WHITE, PEDIATRIC PGM 76508 #048-02-2007 **PD** *012
GHAI, Veena. 304 S 22ND ST 76501 #495-90-1975 L2000 **P** *020 †75
GIBSON, Jeff Ray, Jr. 2401 S 31ST ST 76504 #048-12-1972 L1978 **AN OS** *020 †05
GIBSON, Jeremy Lewis. 2401 S 31ST ST 76504 #048-02-1998 L2000 **PD** *020 †55
GIBSON, Sara Beth. ■ 76502 #048-15-2006 L2008 **OBG** *012
GIEBEL, Dan W. 2401 S 31ST ST 76504 #048-16-1987 L1994 **CD** *020 †20
GIEBEL, Shelley Cole. 3010 SCOTT BLVD, STE 104 76504 #048-16-1987 L1994 **OBG** *020 †30
GILBERTSON, Jodi L. 2401 S 31ST ST 76504 #048-13-2002 L2004 **EM** *020 †16
GILLESPIE, Charles Harvey. ■ 76504 #048-02-1940 L1940 **OS AN** *071 †05
GILLILAND, Paul Francis. ■ 76502 #048-02-1956 L1956 **END IM** *071 †20
GIST, Ashley K. 2401 S 31ST ST 76504 #048-14-2002 L2007 **DR** *100 †80
GLOYNA, David Frederick. 2401 S 31ST ST 76504 #048-02-1978 L1978 **AN OS** *020 †05
GO, Lisa Jennifer. 2401 S 31ST ST, SCOTT & WHITE CLINIC 76508 #048-13-1996 L1997 **IM** *020 †20
GO, Mitzi Donabel Ang. 2401 S 31ST ST 76508 #748-01-2002 **PD** *012
GOEN, Patricia Anne. 2401 S 31ST ST 76508 #048-13-1986 L1987 **CCP PD** *020 †55
GOEN, Paul S. 2401 S 31ST ST 76508 #048-13-2004 L2005 **EM** *020
GOMEZ, John G. 2401 S 31ST ST, DEPT OF EMERGENCY MEDICINE 76504 #048-13-1999 L2000 **IM** *020 †16
GONZALEZ, Damary. 2401 S 31ST ST, SCOTT & WHITE MEM HOSP 76508 #016-11-2002 L2006 **IM** *020
GOOD, Joshua Alan. TEXAS A&M SCOTT AND WHITE, DEPT OF ANESTHESIOLOGY 76508 #021-06-2007 **AN** *012

GOPAL, Shanthi. ■ 76504 #495-72-1985 L2000 **HMP** *020 †50
GORDEN, Todd Bradley. 1618 CANYON CREEK DR, STE 120 76502 #048-12-1978 L1978 **OPH** *020 †35
GOROMBEY, Steve Josef. ■ 76502 #473-04-1993 L1999 **PCP** *020 †50
GOUNER, Christopher Shaw. 2401 S 31ST ST 76504 #048-02-2002 L2006 **DR** *020 †80
GOWAN, Eugene, III. 2401 S 31ST ST 76504 #048-13-1976 L1976 **IM** *020 †20
GREEN, Jacob Benj, III. SCOTT & WHITE, ROOM 407J EDUCATION CTR 76508 #048-02-1965 L1965 **ON HEM** *071 †20
GREENBERG, Robert Danl. 2401 S 31ST ST 76504 #021-06-1988 L1992 **EM** *040 †20
GREENE, John Frank. 2401 S 31ST ST 76504 #005-12-1969 L1976 **PTH DMP** *020 †50
GREENE, Pamela Perry. 2401 S 31ST ST 76504 #048-16-1982 L1983 **OBG** *040 †30
GREENE, Thomas James. 2401 S 31ST ST, SCOTT & WHITE 76508 #048-13-1981 L1981 **EM GP** *020 †85,16
GREGG, Adam Thomas. ■ 76504 #019-02-2007 **DR** *012
GRIMWOOD, Ronald Eugene. ■ 76502 #048-40-1974 L1989 **D** *020 †15
GRODSKY, Pauline. 600 S 25TH ST 76504 #047-06-1950 L1977 **AN** *071 †05
GROTHAUS, Peter Christian. 2401 S 31ST ST 76508 #836-02-1974 L1987 **PS** *020 †65
GROVES, Charles Edward. ■ 76502 #039-01-2007 **DR** *012
GUO, Jie. 2401 S 31ST ST 76504 #243-69-1988 L2006 **NPM** *020 †55
GUPTA, Krishan L. ■ 76502 #495-36-1965 L1969 **FM FPG** *020 †18
GUPTA, Namita Krishan. ■ 76502 #048-15-2008 *012
GUPTA, Rajiv. ■ 76503 #495-39-1993 L2006 **IC** *100 †20
GUTIERREZ, Ricardo. 2401 S 31ST ST 76508 #048-02-1997 L1999 **IC** *020 †20
GUTTIKONDA, Gopal Rao. 1713 SW H K DODGEN LOOP 76502 #495-50-1972 L1981 **N P** *020 †75
GUTTIKONDA, Lakshmi Vani. 1901 S 1ST ST, TEMPLE VETERANS ADMINISTRA 76504 #495-50-1975 L1982 **PM** *030 †60
GUY, Ronald Edwin. 1905 SW H K DODGEN LOOP, KINGS DAUGHTENS CLINIC 76502 #021-05-1977 L1985 **IM** *020 †20
GUZIK, Patrycya B. ■ 76504 #048-13-2007 **IM** *012
HACKETHORN, David Lyon. 409 W ADAMS AVE 76501 #048-02-1975 L1975 **IM** *020 †20
HAGEN, Barbara A Taylor. 2401 S 31ST ST 76508 #048-14-1984 L1985 **PD** *020 †55
HAGER, Casey Shaun. ■ 76502 #055-01-2004 L2005 **CD** *012 †20
HAHN, H Herbert. 2401 S 31ST ST 76508 #048-02-1958 L1958 **IM ID** *071 †20
HAJDIK, Rodney L. 2401 S 31ST ST 76504 #048-02-1994 L1998 **DR** *020 †80
HAJRA, Bhrigu Ram. ■ 76502 #495-38-1958 L1972 **CD IM** *020
HALL, Beatriz Maria. 2401 S 31ST ST, DEPT OF GENERAL MEDICINE 76508 #048-14-1987 L1989 **IM** *020 †20
HALL, Jeffrey Allen. 409 W ADAMS AVE 76501 #048-78-1988, ▲ L1989 **FM** *020 †18
HALL, Jerry A. 2401 S 31ST ST 76504 #048-15-1991 L1992 **PD** *020 †55
HALL, Regan D. 1905 SW H K DODGEN LOOP 76502 #048-14-1990 L1991 **IM** *020 †20
HALL, Robert Eben. 2401 S 31ST ST 76504 #024-01-1977 L2004 **IM ON** *020 †20
HALL, Sheila G. 2401 S 31ST ST 76508 #048-14-1987 L1988 **OBG** *020 †30
HAMILTON, Wesley H. ■ 76502 #048-14-2005 L2006 **EM** *012
HAMILTON, William Paul. 2401 S 31ST ST 76504 #048-02-1981 L1981 **ORS** *020 †40
HANCE, Joseph W. ■ 76502 #038-41-1949 L1971 **FM AN** *072 †05
HANDCOCK, Tyler Donald. 2401 S 31ST ST, DEPT. OF OB/GYN 76508 #046-01-2004 L2006 **OBG** *012
HANNA, Homer H. ■ 76502 #048-12-1952 L1952 **OTO** *071 †45
HANNA, Jacqueline Rose. ■ 76504 #048-16-2008 *012
HANSEN, Darci Janell. ■ 76504 #048-16-2008 *012
HAQ, Muhammad Z. 1901 VETERANS MEMORIAL DR, CENTRAL TX VET HLTH CARE S 76504 #704-02-1989 L1998 **IM NEP** *020 †20
HARDIN, Carlton E, II. 1905 SW H K DODGEN LOOP, KING'S DAUGHTERS CLINIC 76502 #004-01-1982 L1983 **PTH** *020 †50
HARDIN, William Joel. 1713 SW H K DODGEN LOOP, DIV KINGS DAUGHTERS CLNC 76502 #048-04-1962 L1962 **GS** *071 †85
HARDING, Deborah Rae. 2401 S 31ST ST 76504 #048-02-1978 L1978 **PD** *020 †55
HARDY, David Ray. 2401 S 31ST ST 76508 #048-02-1979 L1979 **CCP PD** *020 †55
HARRELL, Robert B. 2401 S 31ST ST 76504 #048-16-2004 **GS** *012
HARRIS, Charles Lloyd. 1901 S 1ST ST, CENTRAL TEXAS VA HOSPITAL 76504 #048-12-1966 L1966 **CD IMG** *020 †20
HARRIS, Frank Stephen. 2401 S 31ST ST 76504 #017-20-1973 L1994 **NS** *020 †25
HART, Bradley J. 2401 S 31ST ST 76508 #048-13-2004 L2006 **GS** *012
HARTMAN, Randy Joe. ■ 76502 #048-04-2007 **EM** *012
HAVEMANN, Benjamin D. 2401 S 31ST ST 76504 #048-04-1999 L2004 **GE** *100 †20
HAVEMANN, David Fred. 2401 S 31ST ST 76504 #048-13-1973 L1973 **IM GPM** *020 †20
HAYNES, Juliet G. ■ 76502 #036-05-2003 **GS** *012
HAYWARD, Ronald Hamilton. ■ 76502 #671-01-1951 L1963 **TS** *071 †85,90
HEARDMON, Samuel Javar. ■ 76504 #048-16-2008 *012
HEIDENREICH, Joseph Wilfr. 2401 S 31ST ST 76504 #003-01-2004 L2005 **EM** *100
HELPERT, Christopher A. 191 S 1ST ST, VA MEDICAL CENTER 76501 #048-16-1997 L2004 **OPH** *020 †35
HEMPHILL, Gregory Lynn. 2205 WINDSONG LN 76502 #028-02-1975 L1975 **OPH** *020 †35 ‡
HENDERSON, John Wesley. 1901 SW H K DODGEN LOOP 76502 #048-02-1978 L1978 **GP** *020 †16
HENDERSON, Jonathan Lewis. ■ 76504 #048-16-2008 *012
HENDERSON, Marcia Heather. ■ 76502 #048-16-2005 L2007 **IM** *012
HENDRICKS, John Chas. 2401 S 31ST ST 76504 #018-03-1972 L1982 **GS** *020 †85
HENRY, Alicia Anne. ■ 76502 #048-14-2007 **OBG** *012
HENRY, Robert Allen, Jr. 1402 W AVENUE H, SANTA FE FAMILY MEDICINE C 76504 #025-76-1977, ▲ L1986 **FM** *020 †18
HENSON, Jody Kathleen. ■ 76502 #034-01-2004 L2006 **EM** *020
HENSON, Nathanael Mark. GRADUATE MED EDUCATION, TEXAS A&M UNIV/SCOTT & WHI 76508 #012-01-2006 **OPH** *012
HERMANS, Michael Rowe. 2401 S 31ST ST 76504 #050-02-1978 L1980 **U** *020 †95
HERVAS, Eliseo Jayme, Jr. 2401 S 31ST ST 76504 #748-08-1962 L1974 **HO** *020
HICKS, Russell J. ■ 76502 #048-13-2007 **AN** *012
HILL, Morris Reagan. 2610 EXCHANGE PL 76504 #048-02-1959 L1959 **GP** *020
HILL, Paul S. ■ 76504 #048-02-1959 L1959 **P PYG** *020 †70,75
HITT, Kirby Dee. 2401 S 31ST ST 76504 #048-15-1986 L1987 **ORS** *020 †40
HOBBS, Gregory Dew. 2401 S 31ST ST, SCOTT WHITE CLINIC 76508 #048-13-1985 L1988 **EM** *020 †16
HODGES, John Carlton. 2401 S 31ST ST, SCOTT & WHITE HOSPITAL 76508 #048-16-1981 L1981 **IM** *020 †20

HOFFER, John Lee. 2401 S 31ST ST 76504 #036-01-1976 L1978 **AN GP** *020 †05
HOGG, Benjamin Reaves. 2401 S 31ST ST, SCOTT & WHITE MEMORIAL HOS 76508 #021-06-2002 L2007 **DR** *012
HOGG, Ronald James. 2401 S 31ST ST 76504 #917-06-1970 L1975 **NEP PD** *050 †55
HOLBERT, Brenda L. 2401 S 31ST ST 76504 #055-01-1982 L1983 **DR** *020 †80
HOLBERT, John Michael. 2401 S 31ST ST 76504 #055-01-1980 L1982 **DR** *020 †80
HOLGUIN, Mark H. 2401 S 31ST ST, HEMATOLOGY ONCOLOGY 76508 #048-16-1982 L1983 **HEM ON** *020 †20
HOLLEMAN, Vernon Daughty. 600 S 25TH ST 76504 #048-04-1958 L1958 **IM** *020
HOLLINGSWORTH, Mark F. 2401 S 31ST ST 76504 #048-14-1983 L1983 **OPH** *020 †20
HOLMES, Gary Paul. 2401 S 31ST ST, SCOTT AND WHITE CLINIC 76508 #048-13-1980 L1980 **ID IM** *040 †20
HOLTHUS, Emily Jean. 2401 S 31ST ST, MEMORIAL HOSP 76508 #019-02-2007 **OBG** *012
HOLY, Sarah Elizabeth. 2401 S 31ST ST 76504 #021-06-2001 L2005 **OPH** *100 †35
HOPENS, Theodore. 1901 S 1ST ST 76504 #035-06-1968 L1978 **DR GE** *020 †20,80
HOUCK, Philip David. 2401 S 31ST ST 76504 #016-06-1979 L1990 **CD IM** *020 †20
HOUSEWRIGHT, Chad D. ■ 76502 #048-16-2007 **IM** *012
HUANG, Shoei-Kuen. 2401 S 31ST ST 76504 #244-04-1972 L2003 **CD IM** *020 †20
HUDDLESTON, Kevin P. 2401 S 31ST ST 76504 #048-16-1988 L1989 **OBG** *020 †30
HUFFAKER, Roland Keith. 2401 S 31ST ST 76508 #047-20-2002 L2006 **OBG** *100
HULIN, James Brett. 2401 S 31ST ST 76504 #039-79-2005, ▲ **AN** *012
HULL, Joshua Michael. ■ 76504 #048-15-2007 **IM** *012
HUNG, Lynne. 2401 S 31ST ST 76504 #005-06-1998 L2006 **CD** *020 †20
HURD, Howard Perrin, III. 2401 S 31ST ST, DEPT OF RADIOLOGY 76508 #048-15-1996 L1997 **GS DR** *100
HURLEY, Douglas Lee. 2401 S 31ST ST 76504 #023-07-1970 L1975 **ID IM** *020 †20
HUTCHINSON, Lewis Ray. 2401 S 31ST ST 76504 #048-16-1983 L1983 **PD OTO** *020 †45
HUTKA, Johnnie Gene. ■ 76502 #048-02-1968 L1968 **R** *071 †80
HYMAN, Benjamin. 2401 S 31ST ST, SCOTT & WHITE MEMORIAL HOS 76508 #048-04-2003 L2006 **DR** *012
IBARRA, Jesse D, Jr. 2401 S 31ST ST 76508 #649-01-1945 L1950 **IM END** *071
ILSE, Jordan R. ■ 76504 #048-16-2007 **IM** *012
IMES, Sandra K. 2401 S 31ST ST 76508 #048-02-1993 L1996 **FM** *020 †18
INGRAHAM, John Michael. ■ 76502 #041-14-2003 **PS** *012
ISBELL, Travis Scott. TEXAS A&M-SCOTT AND WHITE, GRAD MED ED 76508 #048-16-2005 **GS** *012
JADHAV, Yashodeep P. 1901 VETERANS MEMORIAL DR, IMAGING DIV O E TEAGUE VET 76504 #496-38-1992 L2002 **DR** *020 †80
JAFFE, Jon Edward. 2401 S 31ST ST 76504 #041-13-1975 L1987 **EM PD** *020 †55,16
JAFFERS, Gregory John. 2401 S 31ST ST 76504 #051-07-1976 L1980 **TTS GS** *020 †85
JALIAWALA, Saher. TEXAS A&M-SCOTT AND WHITE, GRAD MED EDUC 76508 #039-01-2002 L2006 **MPD** *100
JAMES, Anthony H. ■ 76501 #048-16-2007 *012
JAMROZ, Casimir. VET ADMIN HOSP 76504 #407-10-1961 L1962 **PTH** *020 †50
JEFFRIES, Mark A. 2401 S 31ST ST 76504 #028-78-1985, ▲ L2000 **GE** *020 †20
JEMELKA, Brooke. ■ 76504 #048-16-2008 *012
JENKINS, Eric Richard. ■ 76502 #048-16-2007 *012
JESSE, Mary Kristen. ■ 76502 #048-02-2007 **TY** *012
JESSE, Richard Henry. 1605 S 31ST ST 76508 #048-02-1976 L1976 **IM** *020 †20
JEW, Andrew. 1905 SW H K DODGEN LOOP 76502 #048-13-1980 L1980 **GS VS** *020 †85
JEW, Katherine M. 2401 S 31ST ST 76504 #048-13-1980 L1980 **IM IMG** *020 †20
JEWELL, Coty W. ■ 76501 #048-15-2000 L2003 **CD** *012
JINADATHA, Chetan. 2401 S 31ST ST, SCOTT & WHITE MEM HOSP 76508 #495-99-2002 **IM** *012
JOHNSON, Alan James. 2401 S 31ST ST 76504 #018-03-1986 L1987 **NO OTO** *020 †45
JOHNSON, Chas Frank, III. 1901 S 1ST ST 76504 #048-02-1966 L1966 **U GP** *075
JOHNSON, Edwin Will. 1901 S 1ST ST 76504 #001-02-1977 L1980 **PTH** *020 †50
JOHNSTON, William Elliott. 2401 S 31ST ST 76504 #036-07-1975 L1992 **AN GS** *050 †05
JONES, Alan Clifford. 1817 SW H K DODGEN LOOP 76502 #025-01-1971 L1978 **OPH** *071 †85
JONES, Eldo M. ■ 76502 #028-02-1952 L1959 **GS** *071 †85
JONES, Kathleen A. 2401 S 31ST ST 76504 #048-16-1994 L1995 **ATP** *062 †50
JONES, Richard O'Neal. 2401 S 31ST ST 76504 #039-01-1973 L1980 **MFM OBG** *020 †30
JONES, Shirley Fong. 2401 S 31ST ST 76504 #004-01-2000 L2006 **PCC** *100 †20
JONES, Thomas Russell. 2401 S 31ST ST 76504 #048-14-1989 L1990 **EM** *020 †16
JONES, Tiffany Carol. 1402 W AVENUE H 76504 #027-01-2004 **FM** *020 †18
JORDAN, Charles M. ■ 76504 #048-14-2008 *012
JORDAN, Sarah. ■ 76502 #048-16-2008 *012
JOSEPH, Thomas Kenneth. 2401 S 31ST ST 76504 #050-02-1996 L2002 **PM** *020 †60
JOSHI, Meghna. 2401 S 31ST ST, SCOTT & WHITE DEPT OF PSY 76508 #048-13-2002 L2004 **CHP** *012
JOSHI, Nikhil Shashikant. 2401 S 31ST ST, DEPT OF CARDIOLOGY 76508 #025-07-2001 L2004 **IC** *012 †20
JOULES, Nasheel. ■ 76504 #048-02-2007 **IM** *012
KADHIM, Thikra Jawdet. ■ 76502 #528-04-1986 L2005 **FM** *020 †18
KANNAN, Seethalakshmi. 1901 S 1ST ST, CENTRAL TEXAS VETERANS HE 76504 #495-42-1984 L2000 **IM** *020 †20
KASTNER, Randy R. 2401 S 31ST ST 76504 #048-16-1993 L1994 **PD** *020 †55
KAVOUSSI, Parviz K. ■ 76502 #048-02-2002 L2008 **U** *012
KAY, Marguerite Murray. 76503 #005-02-1975 L1978 **IG IM** *071
KAYANI, Saima Naeem. 2401 S 31ST ST 76504 #704-01-2002 **PD** *012
KEBERT, Cory Brit. ■ 76502 #039-01-2006 L2007 **EM** *012
KERIC, Natasha. TEXAS A&M-SCOTT AND WHITE, GRAD MED ED 76508 #016-11-2007 **GS** *012
KERR, Len Dan. ■ 76502 #048-02-1962 L1962 **P FM** *071 †75
KEYSER, Daniel L. 2401 S 31ST ST 76504 #048-02-1986 L1993 **N** *020 †75
KHAN, Gul Mohammed. ■ 76502 #496-27-2001 L2006 **PCC** *012 †20
KHODE, Renu Ramesh. GRAD MED ED, TEXAS A&M-SCOTT AND WHITE 76508 #496-38-1996 **PTH** *012
KIM, Boo-Ho. 1901 S 1ST ST, SURGICAL SERVICE (112-D) 76504 #583-03-1966 L1980 **AN** *040 †05
KIM, Tae Kyu. ■ 76502 #654-01-2003 **FP** *012
KIMMEY, Kathy Ann. 2401 S 31ST ST, SCOTT WHITE CLINIC 76508 #048-15-1985 L1986 **IM** *020 †20
KIRBY-KEYSER, Linda J. 2401 S 31ST ST, SCOTT & WHITE MEM HOSP 76508 #048-02-1986 L1988 **PN** *020 †55
KIRKWOOD, Toby C. ■ 76502 #018-75-2007, ▲ **FP** *012

KIRMANI, Batool Fuad. 2401 S 31ST ST 76504 #704-20-1995 L2002 **CN** *100
KIRSCHNER, Ronald Irwin. 2401 S 31ST ST 76504 #035-46-1986 L2008 **ETX EM** *040 †20,16
KITCHINGS, Olen E, III. 2401 S 31ST ST 76504 #012-01-1966 L1976 **AN** *020 †05
KLIEWER, James A. 1901 VETERANS MEMORIAL DR 76504 #048-02-1974 L1974 **FM EM** *020 †18
KLUGO, Richard C. 2401 S 31ST ST 76508 #035-03-1962 L1984 **U** *071 †95
KNIGHT, Alfred Bishop. 2401 S 31ST ST 76504 #038-06-1972 L1986 **MFM OBG** *030 †30
KNIGHT, Wade Leon. 2401 S 31ST ST 76504 #048-04-1970 L1970 **TS** *020 †85,90
KO, Harry H. ■ 76502 #583-02-1962 L1971 **DR NM** *020 †80
KOEHLER, Bruce David. 2401 S 31ST ST 76508 #023-01-1979 L1986 **IM** *020 †20
KOEN, Sophia A. ■ 76502 #048-02-2002 L2006 **FP** *012
KOHL-THOMAS, Belinda M. 2401 S 31ST ST 76504 #048-16-1998 L1999 **OBG** *020 †30
KONVICKA, James J. 2401 S 31ST ST 76504 #048-14-1998 L1999 **AN PMM** *020
KOO, Tin Wai Judy. 2401 S 31ST ST, SCOTT AND WHITE 76508 #462-01-2002 **CHP** *012
KOROMPAI, Ferenc Laszlo. 2715 MICHAELS DR 76502 #048-04-1963 L1963 **TS VS** *020 †85,90
KOSS, William. 2401 S 31ST ST 76504 #132-01-1976 L1988 **PTH HMP** *020 †50
KOTRLA, Kathryn Jo. 2401 S 31ST ST 76504 #048-16-1988 L1989 **P** *020 †75
KOVACS, Dezsoe T. ■ 76502 #473-02-1953 L1960 **IM** *071
KRAUSS, David Roy. 2401 S 31ST ST 76504 #028-02-1969 L1976 **NPM PD** *020 †55
KREUTZ, Daniel Edward. ■ 76502 #030-06-2008 *012
KROLL, Jeffery Dale. 1905 SW H K DODGEN LOOP 76502 #048-12-1985 L1986 **U** *020 †95
KUHNHEIN, Robert Francis. 2401 S 31ST ST 76504 #048-02-1971 L1971 **R** *020 †80
KWAN, Nathan A. ■ 76502 #048-14-2007 **OBG** *012
KYLBERG, Roger Wm. 1905 SW H K DODGEN LOOP, KINGS DAUGHTERS CLINIC P.A 76502 #048-14-1988 L1990 **FM** *020 †18
LADD, Daniel Jos. 2401 S 31ST ST 76508 #023-01-1969 L1979 **CLP BBK** *030 †50
LAFFER, Cheryl Leora. 2401 S 31ST ST 76504 #011-02-1985 L1995 **IM** *050 †20
LAIRMORE, Terry Curtis. 2401 S 31ST ST 76504 #047-05-1988 L2005 **GS** *020 †85
LANE, Bryan L. 2401 S 31ST ST 76504 #048-78-1993, ▲ L1994 **GP** *020
LAO, Kenneth Chichih. ■ 76502 #001-02-2002 L2003 **OPH** *012 †18
LARKIN, William Robert. ■ 76502 #048-14-2006 **DR** *012
LARSEN, Douglas Alan. ■ 76502 #048-14-2007 **PTH** *012
LARSEN, Eric Jon. TEXAS A&M SCOTT AND WHITE, DEPT OF ANESTHESIOLOGY 76508 #048-14-2007 **AN** *012
LARSEN, Reagan A. ■ 76502 #048-14-2007 **PD** *012
LARSON, Claire Ruth. ■ 76502 #021-05-2007 **GS** *012
LAUVER, Linda Lininger. 1901 S 1ST ST, CENTRAL TX VET HLTHCARE SY 76504 #039-01-1988 L1998 **NM** *020
LAWLIS, Richard S. 2401 S 31ST ST 76508 #048-15-1992 L1993 **IM** *020 †20
LAWN, Beryl Bruckart. 2401 S 31ST ST, SCOTT & WHITE CLINIC 76508 #041-13-1972 L1994 **P IM** *020 †20,75
LAWRENCE, Lorry Ann. 409 W ADAMS AVE 76501 #048-78-1989, ▲ L1990 **FM** *020 †18
LAWRENCE, Mark Elliott. 2401 S 31ST ST 76504 #048-78-1989, ▲ L1990 **CD** *020 †20
LAZARUS, Kimberly Darlene. ■ 76502 #048-04-2002 L2005 **PD** *020 †55
LAZENBY, Shirley Jones. 2401 S 31ST ST, DESK 5C 76508 #048-04-1986 L1987 **EM GS** *020 †85
LAZOTT, Laurie W. ■ 76502 #048-16-2004 L2008 **AN** *012
LEADBEATER, John C, Jr. ■ 76502 #007-02-1961 L1976 **IM PHP** *071 †20
LEAHY, Michael J. 2401 S 31ST ST 76504 #048-02-1999 L2003 **ORS** *020 †40
LEAK, David. 2401 S 31ST ST, SCOTT & WHITE CLINIC, 76508 #919-03-1956 L1994 **CD IM** *071
LEATH, Thomas Michael. 2401 S 31ST ST 76504 #048-02-2000 L2006 **AI** *020 †55,03
LEAVELLE, Lurry Floyd. 2401 S 31ST ST 76504 #004-01-1967 L1974 **OBG** *030 †30
LEE, Shang Hoon. 1901 VETERANS MEMORIAL DR, CENTRAL TX VET HLTH CARE 76504 #583-02-1968 L1976 **PM** *020 †60
LEMPER, Paul David. 2401 S 31ST ST 76508 #041-01-1965 L1983 **PM IM** *020 †20,60
LENEHAN, Richard P. 2401 S 31ST ST 76504 #048-02-1972 L1972 **N IM** *020 †20,75
LENIS, Armando. 409 W ADAMS AVE 76501 #264-05-1968 L1981 **OTO DS** *020 †45
LESLEY, Walter S. 2401 S 31ST ST 76504 #020-12-1987 L2004 **ESN RNR** *020 †80
LETSINGER, Terry James. ■ 76504 #048-12-2006 L2006 **EM** *012
LEWIS, Carlton Todd. 2401 S 31ST ST 76508 #422-01-2005 **PD** *100
LICHOTA, Derek Kent. 2401 S 31ST ST 76504 #048-16-1987 L1988 **ORS OSM** *020 †40
LIM, Dominic. ■ 76504 #748-01-1933 L1933 **P AN** *071
LIM, Freddy G. ■ 76504 #748-02-1964 L1976 **IM** *071 †20
LIND, Jeffrey Gilbert. ■ 76502 #045-04-2007 **GS** *012
LINDZEY, David Lewis. 2401 S 31ST ST, SCOTT & WHITE 76508 #048-15-1984 L1985 **IM** *020 †20
LINZ, Walter Jos. 2401 S 31ST ST 76504 #036-05-1991 L2005 **BBK PTH** *020 †50
LIPSETT, Marie Frankel. 1901 S 1ST ST 76504 #561-01-1939 L1961 **IM PUD** *020
LIU, Timothy. ■ 76502 #048-16-2006 **AN** *012
LIVERS, Nathan Duane. ■ 76502 #004-01-2006 **OBG** *012
LODHIA, Ishwarlal V. 19015 1ST STREET, DEPT OF CARDIOLOGY 76504 #496-38-1972 L1983 **CD IM** *020 †20
LOESCH, William R. ■ 76502 #048-02-2006 L2008 **IM** *012
LONG, William Farrow. 1717 SW H K DODGEN LOOP, STE 119 76502 #048-15-1976 L1976 **AI IM** *020
LOPEZ, Lisa Mari'. 2401 S 31ST ST 76504 #048-16-1996 L1997 **ATP** *020 †50
LOTAN, Dan. 1905 SW H K DODGEN LOOP 76502 #048-02-2000 L2002 **IM** *020 †20
LOWE, Christopher H. ■ 76504 #048-13-2004 L2007 **AN** *012
LOWE, Darla G. 2401 S 31ST ST 76508 #048-16-1990 L1992 **IM** *020 †20
LOWRY, Patrick Shepherd. 2401 S 31ST ST 76504 #048-02-1996 L1998 **U** *020 †95
LOWRY, Wallace Edwin. 2401 S 31ST ST 76508 #048-04-1965 L1965 **ORS HS** *030 †40
LOWTHER, Ervin, II. ■ 76502 #048-16-2008 *012
LUCIA, Dominic J. ■ 76501 #048-16-2006 L2007 **EM** *012
LUDWIG, Aaron Theodore. ■ 76502 #018-03-2003 **U** *012
LYNCH, Dennis James. 2401 S 31ST ST 76508 #010-02-1965 L1974 **PS** *020 †85,65
MACIP, Stacey Ann. ■ 76502 #021-05-2007 **DR** *012
MACKEY, Don Alan. 2401 S 31ST ST 76504 #048-13-1973 L1973 **IM EM** *020 †20
MADLER, Jerome James. VET ADMIN MED CTR 76504 #016-11-1976 L1977 **IMG IM** *020 †20
MADSEN, James Earl. 2401 S 31ST ST 76504 #030-05-1974 L1984 **FM** *020 †18
MAHABIR, Raman Chaos. 2401 S 31ST ST 76504 #061-01-2000 L2007 *100
MAHAJAN, Ashutosh Kumar. 2401 S 31ST ST, MEMORIAL HOSP 76508 #495-90-1997 L2007 **NEP** *012 †20
MAHER, Janae Lynn. ■ 76502 #019-02-2008 *012
MAHJOOBI, Maziar. ■ 76502 #035-75-2004, ▲ L2007 **CD** *012 †20
MAILLARD GONZALEZ, Katya. ■ 76502 #649-52-2003 **FP** *012
MALABONGA, Vic Malabunga. 1901 S 1ST ST, OLIN E TEAGUE VETS MED CTR 76504 #748-02-1981 L1994 **PUD IM** *020 †20
MANGE, Natalie Leila. ■ 76504 #039-01-2004 **DR** *012
MANIPULA, Ethel. 2401 S 31ST ST 76508 #748-10-1975 **PD** *100
MANNING, Larry Gene. 2401 S 31ST ST 76508 #019-02-1967 L1975 **VS** *020 †85
MANSOUR, Paul George. ■ 76504 #048-14-2004 L2007 **IM** *012
MANYAM, Bala V. 2401 S 31ST ST, SCOTT & WHITE CLINIC 76508 #495-33-1968 L1999 **N IM** *020 †75
MARBACH, James Christian. 2401 S 31ST ST 76508 #048-04-1983 L1987 **RO FM** *071 †80,18
MARTIN, Bryan Eric. 2401 S 31ST ST, MEMORIAL HOSP 76508 #054-04-1996 L1998 **ON** *012 †20
MARTIN, Michael Philip. 1605 S 31ST ST 76508 #026-04-1980 L1981 **IM IMG** *020 †20
MARTINEZ, George. 1901 S 1ST ST 76504 #048-12-1987 L1988 **IM** *020 †20
MARTINEZ, Javier F. 2401 S 31ST ST, MEMORIAL HOSPI 76508 #048-02-2003 L2007 **P** *020
MARTT, Jack Mac Pherson. 600 S 25TH ST 76504 #028-02-1946 L1969 **CD IM** *071 †20
MASCORRO, Samuel A, III. 2401 S 31ST ST 76504 #048-13-1988 L1989 **AN** *020 †05
MATHEW, Nancy Ann. 1901 S 1ST ST, GREEN TEAM O11AC 76504 #048-78-2002, ▲ L2004 **IM** *020 †20
MATHEWS, Pamela A. 2401 S 31ST ST, DEPT OF PSYCHIATRY 76508 #048-16-1991 L1992 **P** *020 †75
MATLOFF, Luke E. 2401 S 31ST ST, SCOTT & WHITE MEM HOSP 76508 #039-79-2006, ▲ L2008 **EM** *012
MATTHEWS, Thos Keller, III. 2401 S 31ST ST 76504 #048-16-1981 L1981 **AN PMM** *020 †05
MATTSON, Elizabeth R. 1905 SW H K DODGEN LOOP 76502 #048-12-1994 L1995 **FM** *020 †18
MAY, Jon Lyle. 2401 S 31ST ST 76508 #048-12-1972 L1972 **IM** *020 †20
MAY, Warne Saml, Jr. 2401 S 31ST ST 76508 #018-03-1969 L1984 **AN** *020 †05
MC ALLISTER, Russell K. 2401 S 31ST ST 76504 #048-02-1995 L1996 **AN PMM** *040 †05
MC CLENDON, James Eugene. 1901 S 1ST ST 76504 #021-01-1955 L1957 **IM** *020 †20
MC CONNELL, Betty Golter. 2401 S 31ST ST 76508 #038-41-1946 L1969 **NM** *071 †28
MC DAVID, Andrew Johnson. 2401 S 31ST ST 76504 #048-02-1984 L1985 **AN** *020 †05
MC DONALD, Douglas Kyle. 2401 S 31ST ST 76504 #034-01-2000 L2003 **DR VIR** *020 †80
MCDONALD, J. Walker. ■ 76502 #021-06-2004 L2005 **GE** *012
MC DONALD, Shelley R. ■ 76501 #048-78-2004, ▲ L2007 **IM** *020 †20
MC GOWAN, Jill Marie. 2401 S 31ST ST 76504 #048-13-1994 L1998 **PM** *020 †60
MC KENNEY, John F, Jr. 2400 S 31ST ST 76504 #021-01-1941 L1941 **GS** *071 †85
MC KENZIE, Gregory Allen. ■ 76502 #004-01-1999 L2000 **HMP** *012
MCKERNAN, Nicholas Paul. ■ 76502 #003-01-2007 **AN** *012
MC LAUGHLIN, Brenda S. 2401 S 31ST ST 76504 #048-16-2002 L2005 **OBG** *100
MC LESKEY, Chas Hamilton. 2401 S 31ST ST, SCOTT & WHITE CLINIC 76508 #036-05-1972 L1985 **AN** *030 †05
MC MAHAN, Sandra Ann. 2401 S 31ST ST 76508 #048-02-1972 L1972 **AI** *020 †55,03
MC MANUS, James P A. 2401 S 31ST ST 76508 #803-03-1956 L1979 **GE** *071
MCMORRIES, Kyle P. ■ 76504 #048-02-2006 **OBG** *012
MC NEAL, Catherine J. 2401 S 31ST ST 76504 #048-16-1996 L1998 **MPD** *020 †55,20
MC NEAL, Tresa Muir. ■ 76501 #048-16-2002 L2005 **MPD** *100 †20,55
MEEK, William James. 2401 S 31ST ST 76504 #004-01-1979 L1987 **IMG P** *020 †75
MEHTA, Nand Lal. ■ 76502 #495-74-1978 L1989 **IM** *020 †20
MEHTA, Vijaykumar A. VET ADMIN HOSP, DEPT SURG 76504 #495-48-1970 L1979 **GS** *020 †85
MENDENHALL, Max K. ■ 76502 #028-02-1951 L1973 **AN** *071 †05
MENEFEE, Kiplan Trey. ■ 76502 #048-16-2005 **AN** *012
MESA, Gregory Lee. ■ 76504 #048-16-2005 **FP** *012
METZGER, Paul, III. 2401 S 31ST ST 76504 #048-13-1988 L1989 **DR GP** *020 †80
MIDDLETON, Michael Lance. 2401 S 31ST ST 76504 #048-16-1989 L1990 **NM** *020 †28
MILLER, Jon Matthew. ■ 76502 #048-02-2004 L2007 **DR** *012
MILLER, Laura S. 1901 S 1ST ST, SYSTEM, OLIN TEAGUE VETERA 76504 #024-16-1992 L2007 **IM** *020 †20
MILLER, Timothy David. ■ 76502 #048-15-2005 L2007 **IM** *012
MILTENBURG, Darlene M. 2401 S 31ST ST 76504 #065-10-1989 L1998 **GS** *020
MINGS, Jamie Rae. ■ 76502 #048-14-2004 L2008 **PTH** *012
MIRKES, Curtis Ray. SCOTT & WHITE MEM HOSP, DEPT MED/PED 76508 #039-79-2002, ▲ L2004 **MPD** *100 †20,55
MITCHELL, Louis Adair. ■ 76502 #012-01-1972 L1974 **AN** *020 †05
MITCHELL, Michael Joseph. ■ 76508 #048-16-1998 L1999 **AN** *012 †18
MIXON, Timothy Alan. 2401 S 31ST ST 76504 #048-13-1996 L1997 **IC CD** *020 †20
MOBBS, Karl. ■ 76502 #048-16-2008 *012
MOFFITT, Michael J. 2401 S 31ST ST, DEPT HOSP MED 76508 #048-16-1998 L1999 **IM** *020 †20
MOLDOVAN, Amir. 1905 SW H K DODGEN LOOP 76502 #035-09-2001 L2006 **RHU IM** *020
MONG, Dennis Paul. ■ 76502 #041-13-1970 L1973 **END IM** *040 †20
MONTEMAYOR, Enrique A. ■ 76502 #048-14-2006 **AN** *012
MONTGOMERY, Johnny Lester. 2401 S 31ST ST 76508 #048-02-1958 L1958 **R** *020 †80
MONTGOMERY, Mark L. 2401 S 31ST ST 76504 #048-16-1993 L1994 **DR VIR** *020 †80
MONTICCIOLO, Debra L. 2401 S 31ST ST 76504 #025-07-1983 L2002 **DR** *020 †80
MOORE, Randall Franklin. 2401 S 31ST ST 76504 #021-06-1985 L1998 **P PFP** *020 †75
MORALES-CABRANES, Manuel. 1901 S 1ST ST, TEMPLE VA MEDICAL CENTER 76504 #042-01-1962 L1970 **OBG GS** *020 †30
MORGAN, David L. 2401 S 31ST ST 76504 #011-02-1982 L1983 **EM** *020 †16
MORGAN, James Keith. 2408 S 37TH ST, PUBLIC HEALTH REGION 7 76504 #048-04-1985 L1986 **FM** *020 †70
MORGAN, Mark A. 1901 VETERANS MEMORIAL DR, TEMPE VAMC 76504 #048-15-1997 L1998 **OPH** *020 †35
MORGAN, Victoria Barrera. 304 S 22ND ST, CENTRAL COUNTIES CNTR FOR 76501 #048-16-1995 L1996 **P** *020 †75
MORRIS, James E. 2401 S 31ST ST 76504 #048-15-2003 L2005 **EM** *100 †16
MORRISON, Rebecca Lynn. ■ 76502 #048-13-2008 *012
MORROW, Kyle Eric. ■ 76502 #048-02-2004 L2008 **CHP** *012
MORTON, Gary Howard. 2401 S 31ST ST 76504 #065-01-1968 L1982 **AN** *020 †05
MOTT, Frank E. 2401 S 31ST ST 76504 #048-16-1988 L1989 **HEM** *020 †20
MOY, Edward Theodore. ■ 76502 #048-16-2005 **FP** *012
MUIR, Tristi Wood. 2401 S 31ST ST 76504 #026-08-1993 L2005 **OBG** *020 †30
MUKHOPADHYAY, Phalguni. OLINE TEAGUE VET CTR HEM 76504 #495-02-1965 L1980 **ON IM** *020 †20
MUKHOPADHYAY, Shantasri. ■ 76502 #495-02-1979 L1998 **FM** *020 †18
MULNE, Arlynn Faye. 2401 S 31ST ST 76504 #038-40-1973 L1987 **PHO PD** *020 †55
MUNROE, Scott M. 2401 S 31ST ST 76504 #048-13-1997 L1999 **ORS** *020 †40
MUNSHI, Nidhi Mattoo. 2401 S 31ST ST, MEMORIAL HOSP 76508 #495-55-1999 L2007 **NEP** *012 †20

MURTHI, M S T. ■ 76505 #495-04-1962 **GE** *020
MYERS, Dennis Lee. 2401 S 31ST ST 76504 #048-14-1976 L1976 **IM PUD** *030 †20
MYERS, John David. 2401 S 31ST ST, SCOTT AND WHITE HOSPITAL 76508 #048-16-1997 L2001 **IM** *020 †20
MYERS, Robert Emmett. SCOTT & WHITE CLINIC 76501 #004-01-1955 L1962 **PD** *071 †55
NAGAPRASADRAO, Pokala V J. 3006 STRATFORD DR, CENTRAL TEXAS VETERANS HOS 76502 #495-21-1975 L1994 **CD IM** *050 †20
NAIK, Parimal C. 2401 S 31ST ST 76504 #048-02-1993 L1995 **DR** *020 †80
NAIK, Sunil S. ■ 76502 #048-13-2007 **IM** *012
NAMARSA, Somjira. 2401 S 31ST ST 76508 #005-77-2005, ▲ **FP** *012
NAMPOOTHIRI, Madhaven Mar. ■ 76502 #495-63-1982 L2001 **PCC** *020 †20
NATHU, Prakash. 2401 S 31ST ST 76504 #654-01-2000 L2005 **CHP** *020
NAUL, Lea Gill. 2401 S 31ST ST 76504 #048-16-1981 L1981 **DR** *020 †80
NAUS, Peter Joseph. 2401 S 31ST ST, DEPT OF MEDICINE - DIV OF 76508 #048-13-2000 L2002 **GE** *020 †20
NECESSARY, Sharon Dianne. ■ 76502 #048-13-1994 L1995 **P** *020 †75
NEESE, Paul Alan. 2401 S 31ST ST 76504 #048-04-1978 L1978 **VIR DR** *020 †30,80
NEWMAN, Joseph Matthew. ■ 76504 #048-16-2005 **OPH** *012
NEWMAN, Nick Jay. ■ 76504 #048-15-1987 L1990 **IM** *075
NEWMAN, Trichelle Angelen. ■ 76504 #048-16-2005 L2008 **PD** *012
NGUYEN, Katherine Kim. 2401 S 31ST ST 76508 #048-02-2001 L2004 **GE** *012
NGUYEN, Tuan Van. 2401 S 31ST ST 76508 #048-16-2003 L2003 **NS** *012
NICE, Tate Richard. ■ 76504 #048-16-2008 *012
NICHOLSON, Samuel Austin. 2401 S 31ST ST 76508 #027-01-2004 L2006 **EM** *020
NICKEL, Allan Eugene. 2401 S 31ST ST 76504 #038-40-1975 L1977 **NEP IM** *030 †20
NICKEL, Susan Pohlman. 2401 S 31ST ST 76504 #038-40-1975 L1978 **PD ADL** *020 †55
NIMERICK, Jennifer R. 2401 S 31ST ST 76508 #048-13-2001 L2006 **EM** *100 †16
NIPPER, Michael Lee. 2401 S 31ST ST 76504 #048-12-1985 L1986 **DR** *030 †80
NORMAN, Stafford L. 1901 S 1ST ST 76504 #048-02-1945 L1945 **IM** *071 †20
NSIEN, Ephraim E. 2401 S 31ST ST, SCOTT & WHITE 76508 #024-07-1983 L2007 **GE IM** *020 †20
O'BRIEN, Jeana D. 2401 S 31ST ST 76504 #048-16-1989 L1991 **PCC IM** *020 †20
ODTOHAN, Shawn Mojica. 2401 S 31ST ST 76508 #748-03-2001 **P** *012
OGDEN, Paul Edward. 2401 S 31ST ST, SCOTT & WHITE HOSPITAL 76508 #048-16-1981 L1981 **IM** *040 †20
O'KEEFE, Terry. ■ 76502 #046-01-1979 L1984 **R** *020 †80
OKESON, Gyman Clare. 2401 S 31ST ST 76508 #048-04-1962 L1970 **PUD IM** *071 †20
OLTORF, Charles Edward. 2401 S 31ST ST 76504 #048-02-1968 L1968 **NPM PD** *020 †55
OLUFS, Richard Dean. 1905 SW H K DODGEN LOOP, KING'S DAUGHTERS CLINIC 76502 #016-11-1974 L1990 **PD** *020 †55
ONHAIZER, Brad. ■ 76504 #048-16-2008 *012
OSMAN, Mark Robt. 1901 VETERANS MEMORIAL DR, HEMATOLOGY-ONCOLOGY (111H) 76504 #035-46-1968 L1983 **ON HEM** *071 †20
OSTADIAN, Mahan. TEXAS A&M-SCOTT AND WHITE, DEPT OF ANESTHESIOLOGY 76508 #048-78-2004, ▲ L2007 **AN** *012
OWEN, Billy Ray. ■ 76501 #019-02-1969 L1972 **PD** *071 †55
PAAUW, James Donald. ■ 76502 #025-01-2005 **OPH** *012
PADON, Allison Gee. TEXAS A&M-SCOTT AND WHITE, PEDIATRIC RESIDENCY PROGRA 76508 #048-14-2003 L2006 **PD** *100 †55
PAI, Ronica Meera. ■ 76508 #048-16-2005 **OBG** *012
PALM-LEIS, Ants. ■ 76502 #056-05-1995 L2000 **IC** *012 †20
PALTIYEVICH-GIBSON, Sofya. ■ 76501 #913-21-1985 L2005 **IM** *020 †20
PANDYA, Parikshit P. 1901 VETERANS MEMORIAL DR, CENTRAL TX VETERANS HLTH C 76504 #495-01-1972 L1988 **U** *020 †95
PAPACONSTANTINOU, Harry T. 2401 S 31ST ST 76504 #048-04-1995 L2003 **CRS GS** *020 †85,10
PAREKH, Kishorkumar N. ■ 76502 #495-48-1972 L2000 **IM** *020 †20
PAREKH, Nisha Kishorkumar. 1901 S 1ST ST, VA MEDICAL CENTER 76504 #035-08-1998 L2007 **IM** *020 †20
PAREKH, Palak Kishorkumar. 409 W ADAMS AVE 76501 #041-02-2005 **D** *012
PARMAN, Linda Marie. 2401 S 31ST ST 76504 #019-02-1991 L1996 **DR** *020 †80
PATEL, Ashishkumar Kanu. TEXAS A&M-SCOTT AND WHITE, PEDIATRIC RESIDENCY PROGRA 76508 #665-01-2003 L2006 **NPM** *012
PATEL, Belur Janakray. 2401 S 31ST ST 76504 #023-01-1992 L1994 **U** *020 †95
PATEL, Chirag Shashikant. ■ 76502 #048-16-2006 L2007 **ORS** *100
PATEL, Mittun Chandrakant. ■ 76502 #048-16-2006 **DR** *012
PEDRAZA, Ruben. ■ 76502 #048-16-2008 *012
PEREZ, Annalisa B. 2401 S 31ST ST 76504 #010-01-2002 L2007 **NEP** *020 †20
PEREZ-GUERRA, Francisco. 2401 S 31ST ST 76504 #042-01-1960 L1974 **SME PUD** *020 †20
PERURENA, Osvaldo Hector. ■ 76504 #132-01-1971 L2004 **N** *020 †75
PETERSEN, William Gerard. 2401 S 31ST ST 76504 #028-03-1982 L1983 **PUD CCM** *020 †20
PETERSON, Christy Renee. ■ 76502 #048-16-2008 *012
PETTY, Frederick Chas. ■ 76502 #047-06-1954 L1968 **R NM** *071 †80,28
PFANNER, Timothy P. 2401 S 31ST ST 76504 #048-13-1985 L1986 **GE IM** *020 †20
PHAN, Kelly Myanh. ■ 76502 #048-16-2007 **IM** *012
PHILIP, Joyce Anne. ■ 76502 #048-14-2005 L2008 **PD** *100
PHILLIPS, Michael J. 2401 S 31ST ST 76504 #035-03-1990 L1998 **DR** *020 †80
PICKVANCE, William. ■ 76502 #352-07-1960 L1970 **GP OBG** *071
PIKE, Jennifer L. ■ 76504 #048-02-2006 **D** *012
PINKSTON, David R. 2401 S 31ST ST 76504 #048-16-1989 L1990 **OTO** *020 †45
PISAR, Donald Edward. ■ 76502 #030-05-1957 L1963 **ORS** *071 †40
PISCHINGER, Russell James. 3512 WHITE OAK DR, SCOTT & WHITE DEPT OF RAD 76502 #038-40-1972 L1989 **R** *020 †80
PIZIAK, Veronica Kelly. 2401 S 31ST ST 76508 #020-12-1976 L1981 **END DIA** *020 †20
PLIEGO, Jose Francisco. 2401 S 31ST ST 76504 #649-28-1976 L1982 **REN OBG** *020 †30
PLISKA, John Edward. 5314 WINROCK CIR 76502 #040-02-1983 L1989 **PDC PD** *020 †55
POHL, John Frederick. 2401 S 31ST ST 76504 #048-02-1995 L2001 **PG** *020 †55
POHL, Susan. 409 W ADAMS AVE 76501 #048-02-1995 L2001 **FM** *020 †18
POKALA, Suma. 1901 S 1ST ST, 111 GM-T 76504 #495-11-1981 L1998 **IM** *020 †20
POLAVARAPU, V Ratnam. 1901 SW H K DODGEN LOOP 76502 #496-01-1972 L1986 **P** *020 †75
POLLOCK, Barbara Lee. 2401 S 31ST ST 76504 #028-03-1978 L1981 **AN EM** *020 †05
PONZO, John Anthony. 2401 S 31ST ST 76508 #035-47-1991 L1998 **RNR** *020 †80
POOLE, Kimberly M. MEMORIAL HOSP, SCOTT & WHITE 76508 #048-78-2007, ▲ *012
POPEJOY, Andrew Bernard. 2401 S 31ST ST 76508 #048-02-2003 L2005 **EM** *020 †16
POSADA, Juan G, Jr. 2401 S 31ST ST 76504 #847-05-1975 L1984 **ON HEM** *020 †20
POSEY, Delma Powell. 2401 S 31ST ST 76508 #048-04-1963 L1963 **D** *020 †15
POTEET, Herman B, Jr. 1905 SW H K DODGEN LOOP 76502 #048-02-1977 L1977 **IM** *020 †20
POUSSON, Camille Maria. 304 S 22ND ST 76501 #048-14-1978 L1978 **P** *020 †75
PRAYAGA, Sujatha Lakshmi. 2401 S 31ST ST 76508 #495-11-1997 L2008 **CHP** *012
PREJEAN, Ashley Joseph. ■ 76502 #021-06-2003 **DR** *012
PRESTON, Rebecca Ann. 2401 S 31ST ST 76504 #048-16-1983 L1983 **AN PD** *030 †55,05
PRESTON, William Jack. 2401 S 31ST ST, SCOTT & WHITE 76508 #039-01-1963 L1963 **OTO** *020 †45
PRICE, Allan Ernest. 1901 S 1ST ST 76504 #048-02-1965 L1965 **CD IM** *030
PRINCE-FIOCCO, Marilynn A. 2401 S 31ST ST 76504 #036-07-1979 L2008 **PUD** *020 †20
PROBE, Robert Alan. 2401 S 31ST ST 76504 #048-16-1984 L1985 **OTR ORS** *020 †40
PRYOR, James Edward. ■ 76505 #045-01-1976 L1981 **D GP** *020
PRYOR, Robert Wilton. 2401 S 31ST ST 76504 #048-02-1977 L1977 **CCM PD** *020 †55
PUSCHETT, Jules Bernard. 2401 S 31ST ST, RM 407L MEDICAL ED BUILD 76508 #041-01-1959 L1960 **NEP IM** *050
QUITADAMO, Christopher Ma. ■ 76502 #031-01-2006 L2007 **EM** *012
RADDAOUI, Emadeddin M. 701 BRAZOS DR 76504 #875-01-1988 L2002 **PCP** *020
RAHM, Mark D. 2401 S 31ST ST 76504 #048-16-1987 L1988 **ORS OSS** *020 †40
RAJAN, Abraham. 2915 SAULSBURY DR, TEMPLE KIDNEY CENTER 76504 #495-63-1993 L2006 **NEP** *100 †20
RAJAN, Sabitha G. ■ 76504 #038-06-1995 L1996 **PCC** *020 †20
RAJU, Naktavenkata S. 2401 S 31ST ST 76504 #495-21-1984 L2003 **PD** *020 †55
RAMIREZ, Marcela C. ■ 76504 #451-01-1997 **GS** *100
RAMPISELA, Debby. TEXAS A&M-SCOTT AND WHITE, GRAD MED EDUC 76508 #506-01-1995 L2007 **PTH** *100 †50
RANEY, Lewis Adron. 1901 VETERANS MEMORIAL DR, CENTRAL TEX VET HOSPITAL 76504 #021-01-1958 L1961 **OTO** *020 †45
RAO, Arundhati. 2401 S 31ST ST 76508 #495-09-1982 L1996 **PTH** *020 †50
RAO, Uma Pillarisetti. 3006 STRATFORD DR 76502 #495-11-1981 L1990 **IM** *020 †20
RAPPAPORT, Edward Steven. 2401 S 31ST ST 76504 #016-43-1969 L1974 **HEM BBK** *020 †50
RASCOE, Terry Glenn. 409 W ADAMS AVE, CLINIC 76501 #048-16-1985 L1986 **FM** *020 †18
RAY, Suzanne. 1901 S 1ST ST, CENTRAL TX VETERANS HLTH 76504 #023-01-1976 L1983 **ORS** *020 †40
READY, Duren Michael. 1402 W AVENUE H 76504 #048-15-2000 L2001 **FM** *020 †18 ‡
REDDELL, David Lloyd. 1905 SW H K DODGEN LOOP, KINGS DAUGHTERS CLNC 76502 #048-02-1972 L1972 **PD** *020 †55
REDDY, Santosh Prabhakar. 2401 S 31ST ST, SCOTT & WHITE HOSP 76508 #496-20-1994 L2005 **IM** *020 †20
REEVE, Robert Edward. 2401 S 31ST ST 76504 #048-04-1986 L1987 **ORS OSM** *020 †40
REILLY, Thomas P, Jr. 2401 S 31ST ST 76504 #048-12-1968 L1968 **U** *020 †95
REITER, Charles Geo. 2401 S 31ST ST 76504 #048-12-1979 L1979 **TS GS** *020 †85,90
RESENDES, George J. 2401 S 31ST ST 76508 #048-13-1985 L1986 **IM** *020 †20
REVELEY, Michael August. ■ 76504 #048-12-1970 L1970 **P** *050
REVOTE, Araceli Ocomen. 1901 VETERANS MEMORIAL DR, CARE SYSTEM 76504 #748-07-1990 L1997 **IM** *020 †20
REZNIK, Scott Ira. 2401 S 31ST ST 76504 #028-02-1995 L2005 **TS** *100 †85,90
RICHERSON, Peter John. ■ 76502 #048-14-2007 **EM** *012
RIGGINS, Michele Malene. ■ 76502 #048-16-2007 **IM** *012
RIOS, Charles Michael. 2401 S 31ST ST 76504 #048-12-1978 L1980 **PD** *020 †55
RIPPERGER-SUHLER, Jane A. 2401 S 31ST ST 76504 #048-15-1992 L1994 **CHP P** *020 †75
RISER, Rebecca M. 2401 S 31ST ST, DEPT OF PEDS SCOTT & WHITE 76508 #048-16-1999 L2002 **PD** *020 †55
RIVERA, Jana Lisa. 2401 S 31ST ST 76504 #026-08-1999 L2005 **AN PD** *020 †55,05
ROARK, Kimberly Michelle. ■ 76502 #001-02-2008 *012
ROBERSON, Charles R. 2401 S 31ST ST 76504 #048-02-1986 L1987 **AN PME** *020 †05
ROBERTS, John Wm. 2401 S 31ST ST 76504 #030-05-1967 L1970 **GS** *020 †85
ROBINSON, Eric Joe. ■ 76502 #004-01-2003 L2005 **CD** *012 †20
ROBINSON, James Carlton. ■ 76502 #048-02-1967 L1967 **IM NEP** *020 †20
ROBY, Richard E. 1901 S 1ST ST 76504 #048-16-1993 L1994 **IM** *020 †20
RODRIGUEZ, Joaquin. 2401 S 31ST ST 76504 #048-14-1990 L1991 **GS** *020 †85
ROETH, Nathan Adam. ■ 76502 #031-01-2008 *012
ROHACK, J James. 2401 S 31ST ST 76504 #048-02-1980 L1980 **CD IM** *030 †20
ROSA, Robert H, Jr. 2401 S 31ST ST 76504 #048-16-1990 L1991 **OPH** *040 †35
ROSE, David M. ■ 76502 #048-04-2005 **DR** *012
ROSENBERGER, Randall S. ■ 76502 #048-02-1977 L1977 **ID IM** *020 †20
ROSS, C Andrea. ■ 76502 #033-05-1991 L2007 **P PFP** *020 †75
ROUSH, William H. VET ADMIN CTR, DEPT R 76504 #035-08-1953 L1969 **DR R** *071 †20
RUNGE, Val Murray. 2401 S 31ST ST 76504 #005-11-1981 L2001 **DR** *020 †80
RUNNELS, Clay W. 2401 S 31ST ST, DEPT OF EMERGENCY MEDICINE 76508 #048-12-1997 L1998 **EM** *020 †16
RUSH, James Avery. ■ 76504 #048-15-2005 L2007 **P** *012
RUSH, Stephanie Sparks. 2401 S 31ST ST, SCOTT & WHITE MEM HOSP 76508 #016-76-2006, ▲ **FP** *012
RUUD, Christopher Owen. 2401 S 31ST ST 76504 #048-04-1978 L1980 **ON HEM** *020 †20
RYNEARSON, Robert Repp. ■ 76502 #026-04-1958 L1965 **P** *071 †75
SADOWSKI, Brian Michael. ■ 76502 #030-06-2005 L2007 **GS** *012
SAEED, Madeeha. ■ 76504 #048-16-2008 *012
SAENZ, Anastacio. ■ 76502 #048-16-2008 *012
SAITO, John. 2401 S 31ST ST 76504 #041-13-1999 L2005 **PDP** *100 †55
SAMUEL, Stephen Varghese. ■ 76502 #048-14-2006 **PTH** *012
SANCHEZ, Santiago A. 600 S 25TH ST 76504 #016-06-1952 L1954 **IM** *071 †20
SANDERS, Charles Walter. 1600 UNIVERSTY E DR 76508 #048-13-1981 L1981 **OBG** *020 †30
SANDOVAL, Maria D. ■ 76502 #048-14-2006 **PD** *012
SANTEMA, Sharyl J. 2401 S 31ST ST 76504 #046-01-1987 L1994 **PD** *020 †55
SANTIAGO, Jose M. 2401 S 31ST ST 76504 #042-01-1988 L1992 **DR PDR** *020 †80
SAYAGE, Lubna Hanna. 2401 S 31ST ST 76504 #584-01-1986 L1995 **PTH PCP** *020 †50
SCHIERLING, Steven J. ■ 76502 #048-16-2004 L2006 **GS** *012
SCHMITZ, James Martin. 2401 S 31ST ST 76504 #056-05-1980 L1981 **CD** *020 †20
SCHNITKER, James B. 2401 S 31ST ST 76504 #048-12-1989 L1990 **DR** *020 †80
SCHOOLAR, Earl Jerome, Jr. SCOTT AND WHITE CLINIC 76508 #039-01-1964 L1966 **DR VIR** *020 †80
SCHREMMER, Melissa Lynn. TEXAS A&M SCOTT AND WHITE, DEPT OF ANESTHESIOLOGY 76508 #039-01-2006 **AN** *012
SCHUCHMANN, John Alan. 2401 S 31ST ST 76504 #038-40-1971 L1980 **PM OM** *020 †60
SCHUHMACHER, Darren A. 2401 S 31ST ST 76504 #048-13-2002 L2004 **APM** *020 †05

8900

■ = Address Information Privacy Protected

SCHULZE, Victor Ewald, Jr. 1901 S 1ST ST 76504 #048-02-1954 L1954 **IM CD** *040 †70,20
SCHYDLOWER, Lisa. ■ 76504 #048-15-2005 L2008 **PD** *012
SCOTT, George Richard. 409 W ADAMS AVE, NORTHSIDE FAMILY CENTER 76501 #023-12-1995 L2005 **FM** *020 †18
SCOTT, Robert Churchill, III. 2401 S 31ST ST 76508 #048-14-1992 L1993 **CD IM** *020 †20
SEARS, Dawn Marie. 2401 S 31ST ST 76504 #048-16-1998 L1999 **GE HEP** *020 †20
SETTLE, Phillip K. 2401 S 31ST ST, SCOTT AND WHITE CLINIC 76508 #028-34-1999 L2002 **FM** *020 †18
SEVERSON, Judson M. 2401 S 31ST ST, DEPT NEPH 76504 #048-78-2003, ▲ L2006 **NEP** *012 †20
SEVERSON, Sarah K. ■ 76502 #048-78-2005, ▲ L2008 **FP** *012
SHABAHANG, M Mohsen. 2401 S 31ST ST 76504 #010-02-1990 L2002 **GS SO** *020 †85
SHAH, Rajnikant Sunderlal. VET ADMIN MED CTR 76504 #495-23-1973 L1978 **DR** *020 †80
SHARMA, Meenu. ■ 76504 #495-41-1995 *100
SHEFFIELD, Heather K. ■ 76502 #048-78-2005, ▲ **FP** *012
SHEPHERD, James Robt. 2401 S 31ST ST 76504 #048-13-1977 L1977 **DR** *020 †80
SHERWOOD, Edward J. 1901 VETERANS MEMORIAL DR 76504 #024-05-1975 L1979 **OS IM** *030 †20
SHINKAWA, Shigeo. PO BOX 3051 76505 #041-09-1942 L1943 **OPH** *071 †35
SHMOCK, Carlton L, Jr. ■ 76502 #038-41-1949 L1981 **IM CD** *071 †20
SHOOK, Ilaina S. 2401 S 31ST ST 76504 #048-78-1997, ▲ L1998 **P** *020 †75
SHOWALTER, Thomas Ammen, III. 2401 S 31ST ST 76508 #039-79-2005, ▲ L2007 **IM** *012
SHULL, Bobby Lewis. 2401 S 31ST ST 76504 #021-01-1968 L1973 **OBG** *020 †30
SIBBITT, Stephen J. 2401 S 31ST ST, TEXAS A&M UNIV HLTH SCI CT 76508 #654-01-1994 L2001 **IM** *020 †20
SIDDIQUI, Imran Alam. 2401 S 31ST ST, SCOTT AND WHITE CLINIC 76508 #704-02-1998 L2004 **IM** *020 †20
SIKKA, Pawan. 1901 S 1ST ST, CTVHCS DEPT OF MED PULM 76504 #495-45-1994 L2001 **PCC SME** *020 †20
SIMMONS, Doyle Lee. 2401 S 31ST ST, DEPT RADIATION ONCOLOGY 76508 #048-12-1960 L1960 **RO R** *071 †80
SINCLEAIR, Spencer T. 2401 S 31ST ST 76504 #048-16-1999 L2002 **DR** *020 †80
SING, James T, Jr. 2401 S 31ST ST 76504 #048-78-1997, ▲ L1998 **GE IM** *020 †20
SINGH, Hitesh B. ■ 76502 #048-13-2007 **IM** *012
SINGH, Pankaj. ■ 76504 #496-10-1991 L2002 **GE** *020 †20
SINGPURWALA, Perin Erach. ■ 76502 #495-28-1971 L1983 **IM OPH** *020 †20,35
SKINNER, Odis Duane. 2401 S 31ST ST 76508 #048-04-1958 L1958 **RO R** *020 †80
SLAVCHEVA, Elena G. 2401 S 31ST ST 76508 #198-01-1992 L1996 **NEP** *020 †20
SMAISTRLA, Jeffrey. ■ 76502 #048-16-2008 *012
SMITH, Daniel A. 2401 S 31ST ST 76508 #005-76-2007, ▲ **PTH** *012
SMITH, Daniel Jay. 2401 S 31ST ST 76508 #048-02-1976 L1976 **IM** *020 †20
SMITH, David Allen. 2401 S 31ST ST 76504 #034-01-1982 L1986 **EM** *040 †16
SMITH, Glen A. 1901 VETERANS MEMORIAL DR, CENTRAL TEXAS VETERANS HEA 76504 #048-02-1985 L1986 **IM** *020
SMITH, Jeffrey Kevin. 2401 S 31ST ST 76504 #048-16-2001 L2007 **HS** *100
SMITH, Kyle Hunter. 2401 S 31ST ST 76504 #048-13-1986 L1987 **OPH** *020 †35
SMITH, Kyle James. ■ 76502 #048-13-2002 L2005 **CD** *012 †20
SMITH, Michael Chas. 2401 S 31ST ST 76504 #048-12-1979 L1979 **PD** *020 †55
SMITH, Randall Walter. 2401 S 31ST ST 76504 #025-07-1981 L1986 **GS** *020 †85
SMYTHE, William Roy. 2401 S 31ST ST 76504 #048-16-1989 L1998 **TS SO** *020 †85,90
SNYDER, Samuel Kevin. 2401 S 31ST ST 76504 #016-43-1974 L1980 **GS** *020 †85
SOCOTEANU, Matei P. ■ 76502 #021-06-2004 L2008 **ON** *012 †20
SOORYA, Neeta Dushyant. TEXAS A&M SCOTT AND WHITE, DEPT OF EMERGENCY MED 76508 #028-46-2007 **EM** *012
SOUDER, Christopher Dwigh. ■ 76502 #048-15-2007 **ORS** *012
SOUDER, Nicholas Paul. ■ 76502 #048-15-2005 **ORS** *012
SPEARS, Michelle Miller. 2401 S 31ST ST 76504 #051-04-1999 L2003 **OBG** *020
SPEIGHTS, V O, Jr. 2401 S 31ST ST 76504 #048-78-1980, ▲ L1981 **PTH** *020 †50
SPELMAN, Dawn Brittany. ■ 76502 #048-14-2006 **FP** *012
SPOHN, Micheal Joseph. ■ 76502 #047-06-1999 L2006 **EM** *012
SPRADLEY, Christopher D. 2401 S 31ST ST 76504 #048-16-2000 L2002 **PCC** *100 †20
STAHL, Daniel L. 2401 S 31ST ST, WHITE HOSP 76508 #048-02-2006 **ORS** *012
STALLARD, Timothy C. 2401 S 31ST ST 76504 #048-16-1993 L1994 **EM** *020 †16
STANLEY, William G. 2401 S 31ST ST 76504 #028-78-1977, ▲ L1985 **PM** *020 †60
STARR, John Caleb. 24015 31ST STREET, SCOTT-WHITE CLINIC 76508 #051-01-1965 L1973 **A IM** *020 †20,03
STEELE, A Dean. 600 S 25TH ST 76504 #041-01-1960 L1968 **RHU IM** *071 †20
STENGL, Lorraine Idell. ■ 76502 #041-07-1947 L1948 **FM** *071
STEVANOVIC, Radomir D. 2401 S 31ST ST, DEPT OF MEDICINE 76504 #396-18-1983 L1988 **IM** *020 †20
STEWART, Adam Keith. ■ 76502 #048-15-2007 **IM** *012
STEWART, David A, II. 808 N 5TH ST 76501 #048-13-1993 L1994 **CD** *012 †20
STEWART, Karen Joyce. 1901 S 1ST ST, OLIN E TEAQUE VETERANS CEN 76504 #048-02-1977 L1977 **DR** *020 †80
STEWART-FOULKS, Patricia. 2401 S 31ST ST 76504 #048-13-1984 L1985 **PD** *020 †55
STOEBNER, John Martin. ■ 76502 #048-02-1959 L1959 **DR** *071 †80
STONE, Charles Keith. 2401 S 31ST ST 76504 #038-43-1987 L2003 **EM** *020 †16
STRANGE, Chad D. ■ 76502 #048-16-1998 L1999 **DR** *012 †18
STRECKER-MC GRAW, M. 2401 S 31ST ST 76504 #031-01-1998 L2000 **EM** *100
STROBER, Mark David. 2401 S 31ST ST 76504 #035-46-1988 L2002 **NM** *020 †28
STROHMEYER, William A. 2401 S 31ST ST 76504 #048-78-1993, ▲ L1994 **AN** *020 †05
STUART, Stephanie Faye. TEXAS A&M SCOTT AND WHITE, DEPT OF EMERGENCY MED 76508 #023-07-2007 **EM** *012
SUH, Dick Young. 2401 S 31ST ST, SCOTT & WHITE HOSPITAL 76508 #048-04-1991 L2003 **PHO** *020 †55
SULAK, Patricia Jane. 2401 S 31ST ST 76504 #048-13-1980 L1980 **OBG** *020 †30
SULLIVAN, Jaron Paul. ■ 76504 #048-16-2008 *012
SULLIVAN, Joachim A. ■ 76504 #048-15-2004 L2007 **P** *012
SWOFFORD, Timothy Ryan. ■ 76502 #048-16-2008 *012
SYMMONDS, Richard E, Jr. 2401 S 31ST ST 76504 #012-05-1974 L1979 **GS** *020 †85
SZYMANSKI, Jared L. 2401 S 31ST ST, PATHOLOGY DEPARTMENT 76504 #003-75-2003, ▲ L2006 **PCP** *012 †50
TADROS, Eiriny Magdy. ■ 76504 #048-16-2008 *012
TATE, Claude B, Jr. ■ 76502 #048-02-1960 L1960 **OPH** *071 †35
TAY, Richard. 1905 SW H K DODGEN LOOP 76502 #056-06-1986 L1992 **GE IM** *020 †20
TAYLOR, Jason Max. 2401 S 31ST ST 76508 #039-79-2003, ▲ **FP** *012
TAYLOR, Louis Roberts. 2401 S 31ST ST 76508 #048-78-2005, ▲ **P** *012
TEAFORD, Alan Kent. 2401 S 31ST ST 76508 #016-06-1966 L1973 **DR** *020 †80
TERRY, Edwin Eugene. 2401 S 31ST ST 76504 #048-04-1970 L1970 **CD IM** *020 †20
TESSMER, Carl F. VET ADMIN CTR DPT LAB SERV 76504 #041-12-1935 L1963 **PTH** *020 †50
THALLAPUREDDY, Anantha. 1901 S 1ST ST 76504 #495-62-1995 L2006 **NEP IM** *020 †20
THIRUMURTHI, Manjankarani. ■ 76505 #495-16-1962 L1982 **IM OS** *020 †20
THOMAS, Jimmy S. 2401 S 31ST ST 76504 #048-16-1998 L1999 **CRS** *020 †85,10
THOMPSON, John Quincy. 2401 S 31ST ST 76508 #048-04-1947 L1947 **END IM** *071 †20
THOMPSON, John Quincy, Jr. 2401 S 31ST ST 76504 #048-78-1975, ▲ L1976 **PD** *020 †55
TIBBETTS, Ryan Michael. ■ 76502 #048-14-2004 **ORS** *012
TIDWELL, James Elliott. ■ 76504 #048-04-2005 L2007 **PS** *100
TOBLEMAN, William Ross. 2401 S 31ST ST, SCOTT AND WHITE EMERGENCY 76508 #048-14-2003 L2004 **EM** *100 †16
TOOFANFARD, Marc Philip. TEXAS A&M SCOTT AND WHITE, DEPT OF EMERGENCY MED 76508 #016-11-2007 **EM** *012
TROTTER, Bradley R. 2401 S 31ST ST 76504 #048-13-1992 L1993 **DR** *020 †80,28
TROWBRIDGE, Arthur A, Jr. 2401 S 31ST ST 76508 #055-01-1966 L1969 **HEM ON** *071 †20
TRUITT, Timmy D. 2401 S 31ST ST 76504 #048-16-1987 L1989 **DR** *020 †80
TRUMBLY, Alan Ray. 2401 S 31ST ST 76508 #039-79-2005, ▲ L2007 **IM** *012
TSAI, Jonathan Hongsoo. 2401 S 31ST ST 76504 #045-04-1998 L2007 **OPH** *020 †35
TUSA, Mark Grogan. 409 W ADAMS AVE, S & W DERMATOLOGY 76501 #016-42-2004 L2007 **D** *012
TUTT, Carrie Danae. ■ 76502 #048-02-2007 **AN** *012
UFEMA, John Wm. 2401 S 31ST ST 76508 #012-05-1971 L1994 **DR** *020 †80
ULLOA, Erin Michelle. ■ 76504 #048-16-2008 *012
VACULA, Benjamin B. 2401 S 31ST ST, DEPT OF ANESTHESIOLOGY 76504 #048-13-2004 L2004 **AN** *012
VADHER, Bharat Narshinh. 1905 SW H K DODGEN LOOP 76502 #495-48-1978 L1995 **AN CCM** *020 †05
VALLE, Ramsis Omar. ■ 76504 #042-02-2004 L2007 **NEP** *012 †20
VAN CLEAVE, Holly A. 2401 S 31ST ST 76508 #048-16-1997 L1998 **IM** *020 †20
VANDEVER, Misty A. ■ 76502 #048-15-2004 L2008 **OBG** *012
VAN WORMER, Valerie H. 1901 VETERANS MEMORIAL DR, CEN TX VETERANS HLTHCARE 76504 #056-05-1984 L1987 **PM** *030 †60
VARALLO, Timothy Michael. 1916 STRATFORD DR 76502 #007-02-2004 L2006 **EM** *020
VARGHEES, Seema Susan. ■ 76504 #048-16-2008 *012
VARGHEES, Sunita Elizabet. ■ 76504 #048-16-2005 **IM** *012
VARGHESE, Flora P. ■ 76504 #048-12-2005 L2007 **GS** *012
VARUGHESE, Roy. ■ 76504 #048-16-2008 *012
VASEK, James Vencil, Jr. ■ 76502 #048-02-2005 **DR** *012
VELASQUEZ, Juvencio, Jr. 1605 S 31ST ST, SANTA FE EMERG CLINIC 76508 #030-05-1992 L1998 **IM** *020 †20
VENABLE, John R. ■ 76502 #048-02-1953 L1953 **OM** *071 †70
VERDONK, Carlos Amedee. 2401 S 31ST ST, DEPT OF ENDOCRINOLOGY 76508 #165-02-1973 L1981 **IM END** *020 †20
VERHEYDEN, Charles Nash. 2117 S 61ST ST 76504 #048-02-1973 L1973 **PS GS** *020 †85,65
VIA, Robert M. 600 S 25TH ST 76504 #048-12-1995 L1997 **FM** *020 †18
VIETH, Kelly Matlock. TEXAS A&M SCOTT AND WHITE, DEPT OF ANESTHESIOLOGY 76508 #048-16-2003 **AN** *012
VILLAMARIA, Frank Jos. 2401 S 31ST ST 76504 #019-02-1980 L1989 **AN** *020 †05
VILLARREAL, Roque. 2401 S 31ST ST 76508 #048-13-1988 L1989 **FM** *020 †18
VINCENT, Jennifer Lynn. 2401 S 31ST ST 76508 #039-79-2003, ▲ L2005 **GE** *012 †20
VO, Phat Tan. 1901 VETERANS MEMORIAL DR 76504 #941-01-1972 L1986 **PM** *020 †60
VOURGANTI, Bhaskar. ■ 76502 #495-21-1969 L1975 **END IM** *020 †20
VU, Duc H. 2401 S 31ST ST 76508 #048-15-2001 L2003 **GE** *012
WAGHELA, Sarju S. 2401 S 31ST ST 76508 #048-78-2004, ▲ L2008 **ON** *012 †20
WAGNER, Kristofer Ross. 2401 S 31ST ST 76504 #039-01-2000 L2002 **U** *020 ‡
WAJIMA, Takeshi. ■ 76502 #572-06-1960 L1979 **HEM ON** *071 †20
WALKER, Kim L. 2401 S 31ST ST 76504 #048-16-1990 L1991 **AN** *020 †05
WALKER, Sondra. ■ 76502 #048-16-2008 *012
WALKER, Stephen C. 2401 S 31ST ST 76508 #048-14-1983 L1983 **IM** *020 †20
WALKER, Thos Alwyn Windle. ■ 76501 #039-01-1956 L1963 **GYN** *071 †30
WALLACE, Henry Caston. ■ 76502 #004-01-2005 **ORS** *012
WALLACE, Ralph Elois. 1905 SW H K DODGEN LOOP 76502 #048-02-1956 L1956 **OBG** *020
WALSH, Ronald Edward. ■ 76502 #038-40-1961 L1968 **PUD IM** *071 †20
WARREN, Lisa. 2401 S 31ST ST 76504 #005-76-2001, ▲ L2003 **PD** *020 †55
WARWICK, Kelley Mia. ■ 76502 #048-16-2005 L2007 **EM** *012
WATKINS, David Matthew. ■ 76502 #048-15-2003 L2007 **DR** *012
WATKINS, James William. 2401 S 31ST ST, DEPT OF PEDIATRICS 76508 #305-01-2003 L2007 **PD** *100 †55
WATSON, Linley Everett. 2401 S 31ST ST 76504 #019-02-1966 L1979 **CD IM** *020 †20
WATSON, Michael Lance. ■ 76502 #039-01-2006 L2008 **EM** *012
WAUGH, David Eugene. V A CENTER CHIEF SURG SERV 76504 #038-40-1955 L1980 **GS** *071 †85
WAXMAN, Jeffrey Alan. 2401 S 31ST ST 76504 #048-13-1980 L1980 **U** *020 †95
WEBER, Robert Alan, Jr. 2401 S 31ST ST 76504 #048-16-1988 L1989 **HS PS** *040 †65
WEIL, Thomas Smith. 2027 S 61ST ST 76504 #048-13-1995 L1996 **FPS** *020
WEINBLATT, Jack S. PO BOX 1027 76503 #048-04-1951 L1951 **FM** *020 †18
WEINBLATT, James Sayre. 2401 S 31ST ST 76508 #048-13-1979 L1979 **IM** *020 †20
WEINFELD, Adam Bryce. 2401 S 31ST ST 76504 #048-04-1999 L2007 **PS** *100
WEISS, Barbara A. 2401 S 31ST ST 76508 #048-16-1986 L1987 **IM** *020 †20
WELCH, C Charles. 2401 S 31ST ST, SCOTT & WHITE CLINIC 76508 #016-06-1955 L1974 **CD IM** *071 †20
WESSON, Donald Everett. 2401 S 31ST ST 76504 #048-04-1978 L1978 **NEP IM** *020 †20
WESTBLOM, Tore Ulf Goran. 1901 S 1ST ST, OLIN E TEAGUE VETERANS CTR 76504 #858-02-1978 L1983 **ID IM** *030 †20
WESTWICK, Thomas James. 2401 S 31ST ST, SCOTT & WHITE CTR FOR DIAG 76508 #011-03-1985 L1986 **IM** *020 †20
WHALEY, John Gregory. ■ 76502 #048-16-2005 L2007 **GS** *012
WHITE, Andrew John. ■ 76502 #019-02-2008 *012
WHITE, Heath D. ■ 76502 #048-78-2005, ▲ L2007 **IM** *012
WHITE, Joseph Gregory. 2401 S 31ST ST 76504 #048-16-1982 L1983 **GE IM** *020 †20
WHITE, Raleigh R, IV. 2117 S 61ST ST 76504 #041-01-1967 L1976 **PS** *020 †85,65
WHITE, William Arlington. 1901 VETERANS MEMORIAL DR, VA MED CTR # 112-NS 76504 #048-02-1961 L1961 **NS** *020 †25

■ = Address Information Privacy Protected

WIATREK, Rebecca Lynn. ■ 76502 #048-16-2005 L2007 **GS** *012

WICK, Lori L. 2401 S 31ST ST 76504 #048-16-1987 L1988 **CCP PD** *020 †55

WIEBELHAUS, Hubert A. 1905 SW H K DODGEN LOOP, KINGS DAUGHTERS CLINIC 76502 #030-06-1959 L1966 **GS** *072 †85

WIETERS, Jerald S. 2401 S 31ST ST 76508 #048-13-2001 L2003 **EM** *020 †16

WILKINSON, James Terry. 2401 S 31ST ST 76504 #048-02-1976 L1976 **N** *020 †75

WILKINSON, John Benjamin. ■ 76504 #048-16-2008 *012

WILLIAMS, Charlie Dee. 2401 S 31ST ST 76504 #048-16-1984 L1987 **PD** *020 †55

WILLIAMS, Johnathan D. ■ 76502 #036-01-1986 L1987 **MPD PD** *020 †20,55 ‡

WILLIAMS, Jonathan Martin. ■ 76502 #048-16-2008 *012

WILLIAMS, Julie Carter. ■ 76504 #048-02-2006 L2008 **EM** *012

WILLIAMS, Kenneth Dean. 2401 S 31ST ST 76504 #036-07-1978 L1987 **RNR** *020 †80

WILLIAMS, Troy Howard. 2401 S 31ST ST 76508 #051-04-1964 L1983 **CD** *071 †20

WILSON, Donnie Parks. 2401 S 31ST ST 76504 #027-01-1974 L1976 **PDE PD** *020 †55

WIN, Sonny. 2401 S 31ST ST 76508 #048-16-1992 L1995 **IM** *020 †20

WINCEK, Thomas John. 2401 S 31ST ST 76504 #028-02-1977 L1985 **OBG** *020 †30

WONG, Lucas. 2401 S 31ST ST 76504 #048-13-1988 L1994 **HO IM** *020 †20

WOOD, Adam S. 2401 S 31ST ST 76504 #048-16-2008 *012

WOOD, David Gardner. 1901 VETERANS MEMORIAL DR, CENTRAL TX VA HLTH CARE SY 76504 #045-01-1980 L1980 **AN** *020 †05

WOOD, Nathan Timothy. 1905 SW H K DODGEN LOOP 76502 #039-01-1996 L2002 **FM** *020 †18

WOODS, Bryan Tighe. 1901 S 1ST ST, VAMC 76504 #051-01-1967 L1968 **N** *020 †75

WRIGHT, Coy A. ■ 76504 #048-16-2007 **ORS** *012

WRIGHT, Ethan Joseph. ■ 76502 #028-03-2004 L2008 **OPH** *012

WU, Angie. ■ 76502 #048-16-2008 *012

WU, Hou-Sheng. 1901 VETERANS MEMORIAL DR 76504 #244-02-1970 L1985 **FM** *020 †18

WURSTER, John Chas. 1901 S 1ST ST 76504 #016-06-1964 L1973 **U** *020 †95

XINDARIS, Julie Eva. ■ 76502 #048-16-2005 **AN** *012

YANDELL, Paul Michael. 2401 S 31ST ST 76504 #034-01-1984 L1985 **GYN** *020 †30

YANG, Diana. ■ 76504 #048-16-2007 **TY** *012

YAU, Peter. 2401 S 31ST ST 76508 #654-01-2002 L2005 **PCC** *012 †20

YELETI, Venkata Rao. 1901 S 1ST ST, SURGICAL SVC 112D 76504 #495-58-1967 L1994 **AN CCA** *020 †05

YOUSUFI, Abdullah. 1901 VETERANS MEMORIAL DR, BLDG 163 76504 #649-28-1981 L1995 **FM** *020 †18

YUEN, Yue Lucille. ■ 76502 #243-21-1942 L1970 **PTH** *071 †50

ZAPHIRIS, Helen Alexandra. 2401 S 31ST ST 76504 #048-16-1986 L1987 **CHP P** *020 †75

ZERRIS, Vasilios A. 2401 S 31ST ST 76504 #043-01-2000 L2007 **NS** *100

ZHOU, Chen. ■ 76502 #243-03-1996 L2007 **IM** *100 †20

ZU, Stella Yuan-Hui Tseng. ■ 76502 #035-46-1984 L1988 **IM** *040 †20

TENAHA — SHELBY

GINN, William V, Jr. 107 ED WALL ST 75974 #047-06-1959 L1977 **GS GP** *071

TERRELL — KAUFMAN

ALLEN, Virginia R D. ■ 75160 #016-06-1942 L1967 **AN OS** *020

ALTSHULER, Steven Lane. 102 E MOORE AVE, STE 214 75160 #035-01-1981 L1983 **DR** *020 †80

BARNES, Tyson H, Jr. 200 N VIRGINIA ST 75160 #048-12-1980 L1980 **FM** *020 †18

BEALL, Bobby Dragoo. ■ 75160 #048-02-1957 L1957 **P N** *071

BIDNER, Sandy. 819 E MOORE AVE, STE A 75160 #065-09-1976 L1992 **ORS** *020

BRASHEAR, Benjamin R. 1551 HIGHWAY 34 S, MEDICAL CENTER AT TERRELL 75160 #048-13-2001 L2002 **FM** *100

CHANG, Chin Juei. 209 N ROCKWALL ST 75160 #244-05-1968 L1975 **OBG** *020 †30

CLAXTON, Anthony Lee. 1200 E BRIN ST 75160 #039-01-1984 L1988 **P** *020 †75

COLLIER, Michael Edward. 102 E MOORE AVE, STE 214 75160 #048-12-1977 L1977 **DR NM** *020 †80

COOK, Chester Edwin. 1200 E BRIN ST 75160 #048-12-1945 L1945 **P OS** *072 †20,75

FIGUEROA, Sergio Victor. 505 W BRIN ST # 100 75160 #649-02-1952 L1962 **FM GS** *020

GOEN, Monte Lee. 1200 E BRIN ST 75160 #048-12-1990 L1991 **PYG** *020 †75

GRUCHACZ, Pamela Ann. 1553 HIGHWAY 34 S, STE 700 75160 #016-43-1996 L2001 **GS** *020 †85

HIMMELHEBER, Christopher. 107 TEJAS DR, STE 103 75160 #005-06-1987 L1996 **OTO** *020 †45

HUGHES, Lark. 400 AIRPORT RD, LAKES REGIONAL MHMR 75160 #048-04-1981 L1982 **P** *020 †75

IRURITA, Luis Alberto. PO BOX 70 75160 #737-01-1955 L1966 **P** *020 †75

JONES, John Shannon. 102 E MOORE AVE STE 214 75160 #039-01-1980 L1985 **DR** *020 †80

KAZA, Somasekharam. ■ 75160 #495-58-1969 L1993 **P ADM** *020

KEMP, Eric Scott. 400 AIRPORT RD, HEALTH SERVICES 75160 #047-06-1987 L1991 **CHP** *020

KHAN, Mohammad Nasrullah. 200 N VIRGINIA ST 75160 #704-05-1983 L1995 **CD** *020 †20

LANCE, Christian Ann. 200 N VIRGINIA ST 75160 #048-14-2003 L2006 **FM** *020 †18

LAWLER, Lanika Lawless. 200 N VIRGINIA ST, BAYLOR FAMILY MEDICINE CEN 75160 #021-05-2004 L2007 **FM** *020 †18

LAYENI, Abimbola Olufemi. 1200 E BRIN ST, TERRELL STATE HOSP 75160 #690-01-1989 L2000 **P** *020 †75

MAKOWSKI, John Jaroslaw. 1200 E BRIN ST 75160 #048-12-1991 L1992 **P** *020 †75

MARTINEZ, Jorge. 606 N ROCKWALL ST 75160 #264-02-1953 L1975 **GP AS** *020

MC GHEE, Orsel S. 617 W MOORE AVE STE B 75160 #010-03-1980 L2000 **OBG** *020

MENENDEZ, Marta Emilia H. BRIN STREET, TERRELL STATE HOSPITAL 75160 #275-01-1950 L1975 **P** *071

MULL, Royce Allan. 1200 E BRIN ST 75160 #048-02-1959 L1959 **GP** *071

MUNOZ, Alejandro. 1200 E BRIN ST 75160 #649-01-1976 L1985 **P CHP** *020

NG, Raymond Hin Wai. 1551 HIGHWAY 34 S 75160 #065-01-1988 L1992 **PD** *020 †45

NGUYEN, Quynh Ngoc. 1200 E BRIN ST 75160 #941-01-1968 L1985 **P** *020

PATEL, Mahendra Natwarlal. 1553 HIGHWAY 34 S STE 600 75160 #495-50-1968 L1981 **OBG** *020 †30

POEI, Kian Nio. 1200 E BRIN ST 75160 #506-02-1957 L1979 **CHP P** *071

PORTER, R Wayne. 303 E COLLEGE ST STE A 75160 #004-01-1984 L1987 **FM** *020

PURIMETLA, Kranti. 1200 E BRIN ST, TERRELL STATE HOSPITAL 75160 #495-21-2001 L2006 **IM** *020 †20

RISINGER, Charles Cobb. 200 N VIRGINIA ST 75160 #048-15-1984 L1985 **FM** *020 †18 ‡

RIVERA, Joel Alumisin. 1200 E BRIN ST, TERRELL STATE HOSPITAL 75160 #748-08-1986 L2000 **P** *020 †75

SATYU, Nuggehalli Neil. 200 N VIRGINIA ST 75160 #495-33-1970 L1979 **FM** *020 †18 ‡

SNEIDER, William David. ■ 75160 #048-04-1978 L1986 **AN GS** *020 †85,05

SOBIN, Paul Bennet. 1200 E BRIN ST, TERRELL STATE HOSPITAL 75160 #005-06-1982 L1994 **P** *020 †75

SUNIO, Fortunato O. 1200 E BRIN ST 75160 #748-02-1957 L1969 **PD OS** *071 †55

VALLABHAN, Ravi C. 200 N VIRGINIA ST 75160 #048-13-1988 L1989 **CD IC** *020 †20

VASANI, Rameshchandra P. 1553 HIGHWAY 34 S, STE 200 75160 #495-23-1972 L1979 **PD GP** *020 †55

VYAS, Priti B. 809 W NASH ST, STE 100 75160 #495-22-1973 L1983 **CD IM** *020 †20

WEIDOW, Margaret A. 1200 E BRIN ST, TERRELL STATE HOSPITAL 75160 #048-15-1993 L1994 **P** *072 †75

WILLIAMS-WHITE, Reba Kaye. 718 W MOORE AVE, STE 103 75160 #038-45-1985 L1987 **OBG** *075

WILSON, Bruce Frank. ■ 75160 #048-12-1955 L1955 **GP** *071

TEXARKANA — BOWIE

ALBIN, Amy Wilson. 5002 COWHORN CREEK RD 75503 #004-01-1996 L1999 **PD** *020 †55

ALKIRE, Carey Christian. 3708 SUMMERHILL RD 75503 #021-06-1980 L1984 **ORS** *020 †40

ALSTON, Thomas Joe. 1400 COLLEGE DR, STE 202 75503 #004-01-1963 L1968 **IM IMG** *020 †20

ANDREWS, Allie E, Jr. ■ 75503 #004-01-1952 L1969 **DR RO** *072 †80

ARIZMENDI, Gil De Hoyos. ■ 75501 #649-01-1985 *100

BAILES, Jerry Ray. 2434 COLLEGE DR 75501 #021-01-1954 L1955 **GP** *071 †70

BAILEY, Christopher A. 1002 TEXAS BLVD STE 300 75501 #039-01-1989 L1996 **PCC** *020 †55,20

BALASEKARAN, Ranga. 1920 MOORES LN, TEXARKANA GASTROENTEROLOGY 75503 #048-12-1994 L1998 **GE** *020 †20

BALMAIN, Laura Gayle. 1920 MOORES LN 75503 #048-12-1991 L1992 **GE IM** *020 †20

BEATY, William Robt. ■ 75503 #004-01-1961 L1964 **R OS** *071 †80

BENBOW, Bryan Douglas. 5508 SUMMERHILL RD 75503 #021-06-1991 L1995 **AN** *020 †05

BINGHAM, D'Andra Darlyn. 5002 COWHORN CREEK RD, COLLOM & CARNEY CLINIC 75503 #004-01-1999 L2001 **OBG** *020 †30

BLACK, Douglas Scott. 5502 MEDICAL PARKWAY DR 75503 #004-01-1994 L2000 **CD** *020 †20

BOHMFALK, George Lee. 1001 MAIN ST 75501 #048-13-1973 L1973 **NS N** *071 †25

BOOKER, James Ovid. 1920 GALLERIA OAKS DR 75503 #011-04-1984 L2003 **GS** *020 †85

BORRELL, Charles A. 5002 COWHORN CREEK RD 75503 #048-16-1989 L1990 **DR** *020 †80

BOWEN, Bryan David. 4701 W 7TH ST 75501 #004-01-1994 L1996 **FM** *020 †18

BOWERS, Robert M. 2801 RICHMOND RD # 278 75503 #048-02-1990 L1991 **EM** *020 †16

BROWN, Stephen Roman. 2006 MOORES LN 75503 #021-06-1980 L1984 **OBG** *020 †30

BROWN, William Randall. 5508 SUMMERHILL RD 75503 #021-06-1978 L1982 **DR EM** *020 †80

BUONO, Lee M. 2600 SAINT MICHAEL DR 75503 #041-02-1997 L2003 **NS** *020 †25

BURLESON, James Dewain. 4100 SUMMERHILL RD 75503 #048-04-1986 L1987 **N** *020

BURNETT, James Robt. 2600 SAINT MICHAEL DR 75503 #021-01-1979 L1984 **AN CCM** *020 †20,05

BURNS, Billy Ray. 4503 TEXAS BLVD 75503 #021-05-1976 L1983 **PD NPM** *020 †55

BUSCEME, Heidi Waldren. 5002 COWHORN CREEK RD, COLLOM & CARNEY CLINIC 75503 #048-14-1996 L1998 **PD** *020 †55

CALHOUN, John G, Jr. 1401 OLIVE ST 75501 #004-01-1951 L1952 **OTO** *071 †45

CAMPANINI, J Scott. 2400 SAINT MICHAEL DR 75503 #041-09-1983 L1993 **DR GS** *020

CANNON, Michael Bruce. 2604 SAINT MICHAEL DR, STE 425 75503 #039-01-1990 L1999 **OS VS** *020 †90,85

CARLISLE, David Lee. 1406 COLLEGE DR STE 4, TEXARKANA, L.L.P. 75503 #048-02-1976 L1976 **AN PME** *020 †05

CARLTON, Rodney Franklin. 803 MAIN ST, ASSOCIATED PATHOLOGISTS 75501 #004-01-1960 L1979 **PTH FOP** *071 †50

CHILDRESS, Jack Richard. 2602 SAINT MICHAEL DR, STE 205 75503 #048-02-1983 L1989 **IM CD** *030 †20

CLARKE, Karen Ann. ■ 75503 #035-09-1996 L1997 **IM** *020 †20 ‡

CLEVENGER, Cheryl Steele. 2931 RICHMOND RD 75503 #039-01-1986 L1995 **GP** *020

CLEVENGER, Michael E. 5002 COWHORN CREEK RD 75503 #039-01-1986 L1995 **N IM** *020 †75

CLINTON, Constance Elaine. 1000 PINE ST, EMERGENCY DEPARTMENT 75501 #047-07-1980 L1996 **EM IM** *020

COHEN, H Gene. ■ 75501 #004-01-1979 L1983 **OBG** *020 †30

COLLEY, Johnny Mack. 1000 PINE ST 75501 #048-02-1979 L1979 **AN** *020 †05

CONTRERAS, Freddie Lee. 33313 N STATELINE AVENUE 75504 #039-01-1981 L1983 **NS** *075 †25

COOK, Lewis Carlton. 2323 KENNEDY LN 75503 #021-01-1967 L1973 **OPH** *020 †35

COZART, John C. 1920 MOORES LN 75503 #048-12-1994 L1998 **GE** *020 †20

CRAYTOR, Bret Fredrick. 5002 COWHORN CREEK RD 75503 #039-01-1988 L1995 **PCC IM** *020 †20

CROUTHER, Marcus Anthony. 2600 SAINT MICHAEL DR 75503 #025-01-1987 L1991 **FM** *020 †18

DANZIGER, Zelik J. ■ 75504 #004-01-1951 L1953 **OS** *071

DAVIS, Terry R. 2602 SAINT MICHAEL DR 75503 #004-01-1963 L1966 **GP** *071

DEAN, Thurston E, III. ■ 75503 #048-16-1982 L1983 **GS** *020 †85

DE CAPRIO, Jeffrey David. 1002 TEXAS BLVD STE 320 75501 #035-19-1993 L1996 **VS** *020 †85

DECAPRIO, Theresa M. ■ 75503 #048-12-1994 L1997 **OBG** *020 †30

DE HAAN, Jeffrey Thomas. 3708 SUMMERHILL RD 75503 #018-03-1981 L1982 **ORS** *020 †40

DENSON, Alyson Land. 5002 COWHORN CREEK RD 75503 #004-01-1998 L2001 **PD** *020 †55

DESKIN, Roy Lynn. 5002 COWHORN CREEK RD 75503 #048-02-1975 L1975 **PD** *020 †55

DIETZE, John B. 1002 TEXAS BLVD, STE 406 75501 #048-12-1994 L1997 **NS** *020

DINGELDEIN, Geo Peter, Jr. 4321 MCKNIGHT RD 75503 #035-01-1970 L1983 **PS** *020 †65

DITSCH, Craig Edward. 5002 COWHORN CREEK RD, COLLOM & CARNEY CLINIC 75503 #007-02-1972 L1988 **FM** *020

DODD, Nathan Leland. ■ 75503 #004-01-1972 L1986 **PTH CLP** *071

DODGE, John Mc Laurin. 1000 PINE ST 75501 #048-04-1957 L1957 **GYN** *071 †30

DOUGLAS, Donald Stratton. 3510 RICHMOND RD, STE 100 75503 #004-01-1996 L2000 **IM** *020 †20

DOUGLAS, Lori Kruse. 1000 PINE ST 75501 #004-01-1996 L2000 **FM** *020

■ = Address Information Privacy Protected

DUNN, Deborah A. 18 HIGH POINT DR 75503 #048-13-1999 L2000 **OM** *030
ECHOLS, Roderick E. 2602 SAINT MICHAEL DR, CHRISTUS ST MICHAEL HEALTH 75503 #028-02-2002 L2006 **IM** *020
EICHLER, Edward A, Jr. 2604 SAINT MICHAEL DR, PHYS OFFICE BLDG STE 210 75503 #048-14-1981 L1981 **ON HEM** *020 †20
ELLISON, Eugene Thos, Jr. 5402 SUMMERHILL RD 75503 #004-01-1973 L1977 **OPH** *020
ENGSTROM, Gary P. 5002 COWHORN CREEK RD 75503 #048-12-1991 L1992 **ON** *020 †20
FINLEY, George Michael. 2600 SAINT MICHAEL DR, CHRISTUS ST MICHAEL ADMINI 75503 #004-01-1981 L1994 **FM OBG** *030 †18
FLOYD, Benjamin J. 1002 TEXAS BLVD, STE 501 75501 #048-02-1953 L1953 **U** *071 †95
FORTENBERRY, Dewitt C. ■ 75503 #023-07-1990 L2004 **EM** *020 †16
FOURNIER, Donald Chas. 1819 MOORES LN 75503 #048-02-1974 L1974 **AI IG** *020 †20,03
FREY, John Lawrence. 2801 RICHMOND RD # 31 75503 #035-03-1992 L2002 **EM** *020 †16
FRY, Robert Bryant, Jr. 1000 PINE ST 75501 #048-02-1975 L1975 **EM** *020 †18
GABBIE, Mark Otis. 2602 SAINT MICHAEL DR, STE 201 75503 #004-01-1986 L1989 **FM OM** *020 †18
GARY, Lloyd Edwin. 1000 PINE ST 75501 #021-01-1955 L1961 **GYN** *071
GLENN, Stephen Bryan. 5002 COWHORN CREEK RD, P O BOX 1490 75503 #021-06-1978 L1979 **IM** *020 †20
GOESL, Andrew Geo. 1000 PINE ST 75501 #056-06-1942 L1952 **IM CD** *071
GRAHAM, John Windsor. 5002 COWHORN CREEK RD 75503 #048-13-1982 L1983 **IM** *020 †20
GRANT, James Sherrod. 1421 PINE ST, STE A 75501 #010-03-1972 L1976 **IM** *020
GRAVES, Blane Alan. 1408 COLLEGE DR 75503 #004-01-1999 L2002 **FM** *020 †18
GREATHOUSE, David Edward. 5002 COWHORN CREEK RD 75503 #004-01-1994 L1998 **OBG** *020 †30
GREEN, Barry Mc Alister. 3716 SUMMERHILL RD 75503 #048-04-1959 L1960 **ORS** *020 †40
GREEN, Robert Clark. 5002 COWHORN CREEK RD 75503 #004-01-1987 L1990 **PD** *020 †55
GREER, Beverly Jeanne. ■ 75503 #024-05-1983 L1987 **IM** *020 †30
GREGORY, John Reeves. 2011 MOORES LN 75503 #021-06-1977 L1982 **ORS** *020 †40
GRIFFIN, Bryan Jeffrey. 2600 SAINT MICHAEL DR, FL 2 75503 #048-15-1982 L1983 **PTH** *020 †50
GRIFFIN, Harold Brooks. ■ 75503 #004-01-1940 L1941 **IM** *071
GRIFFIN, John Stanley. 5002 COWHORN CREEK RD 75503 #004-01-1947 L1955 **CD IM** *071 †20
GRIFFIN, John Stanley, Jr. 5002 COWHORN CREEK RD 75503 #004-01-1987 L1990 **IM** *020 †20
GRIFFIN, Nancy Lynn. 5002 COWHORN CREEK RD, 4800 TEXAS BLVD 75503 #048-13-1982 L1983 **N** *020 †75
HALL, Eric Eugene. 2008 MOORES LN 75503 #048-12-1978 L1978 **OBG OS** *020 †30
HALL, Jon Douglas. 1000 PINE ST 75501 #004-01-1966 L1970 **PD** *020 †55
HAMILTON, Marshall Earl. 1000 PINE ST, WADLEY REG MED CTR 75501 #048-12-1968 L1976 **PTH** *020 †50
HAMLIN, Frank D, Jr. 1002 TEXAS BLVD STE 407 75501 #038-43-1977 L1979 **ORS** *020 †40
HARPER, Don S. 2600 SAINT MICHAEL DR, CHRISTUS ST. MICHAEL HEALT 75503 #048-04-1986 L1987 **FM EM** *020 †18
HAVENER, Allen Vere. 5002 COWHORN CREEK RD, COLLOM & CARNEY CLINIC 75503 #011-02-1981 L2001 **DR** *020 †80
HEGDE, Prakash. 1000 PINE ST 6TH FL 75501 #495-98-1990 L2003 **IM** *020 †20
HEKIER, Ron Joseph. 2717 SUMMERHILL RD 75503 #024-07-1997 L2003 **GS** *020 †85
HEMPHILL, Hayden Nix. 5002 COWHORN CREEK RD, COLLOM CARNEY CLINIC 75503 #048-14-1997 L2002 **NEP** *020 †20
HERNDON, Greta. 2600 SAINT MICHAEL DR 75503 #004-01-1987 L1994 **FM EM** *020 †18
HESTER, Wes Lee. 5002 COWHORN CREEK RD, COLLOM & CARNEY CLINIC ASS 75503 #004-01-1995 L2000 **FM** *020 †18
HILBORN, Richard Major. 2604 SAINT MICHAEL DR, STE 239 75503 #047-05-1979 L1987 **ORS** *020 †40
HILL, Michael L. 5508 SUMMERHILL RD 75503 #048-02-1992 L1996 **DR** *020 †80
HILLER, Durell A, III. 5002 COWHORN CREEK RD 75503 #021-06-1974 L1983 **OBG** *020 †30
HILLIS, Thomas Michael. 5002 COWHORN CREEK RD, COLLOM & CARNEY CLINIC 75503 #004-01-1974 L1979 **GS TS** *020 †85
HOLLAND, Michael Nesbitt. 5002 COWHORN CREEK RD, COLLOM & CARNEY CLINIC 75503 #021-05-1974 L1975 **OBG** *020 †30
HOLLINGSWORTH, Chas E, II. 5420 MEDICAL PARKWAY DR 75503 #048-13-1976 L1976 **PS OTO** *020 †45,65
HOLMAN, Steven W. 5508 SUMMERHILL RD 75503 #048-16-1983 L1983 **DR VIR** *020 †80
HOUSE, Roger Dale. 2401 SUMMERHILL RD, APT A 75501 #004-01-1977 L1992 **CHP P** *020 †18
HUETER, John Edwin, Jr. 5002 COWHORN CREEK RD 75503 #048-12-1976 L1979 **N OS** *020 †75
HUNLEY, Thomas Aicklen. 4500 SUMMERHILL RD 75503 #048-12-1989 L1991 **AN** *020 †05
HUNTER, George Rheamond. 1902 MOORES LN 75503 #004-01-1961 L1969 **U** *071 †95
HUTCHESON, Fred A, Jr. 2602 SAINT MICHAEL DR, SOUTHERN CLINIC, P.A. 75503 #004-01-1969 L1973 **IM** *071 †20
HUTCHESON, James Arthur. 4214 TEXAS BLVD 75503 #004-01-1995 L2001 **OTO** *020 †45
JACKSON, Randy Alan. ■ 75503 #048-14-2005 **IM** *012
JACOBSEN, Erik I. 2600 SAINT MICHAEL DR, EMERENCY DEPARTMENT 75503 #654-01-2001 L2004 **FM** *020
JAYAPRABHU, Sudheer M. 1002 TEXAS BLVD STE 200 75501 #048-16-1997 L2001 **OBG** *020 †30
JEAN, Alan Bradley. 4102 RICHMOND MDWS 75503 #004-01-1980 L1984 **DR** *020 †80
JEAN, James Lewis. 2400 SAINT MICHAEL DR 75503 #004-01-1993 L1999 **VIR** *020 †80
JENIKE, Joseph Shannon. 5002 COWHORN CREEK RD 75503 #038-41-1960 L1965 **N** *020
JOHNSON, Charles Franklin. ■ 75503 #654-01-2006 **FP** *012
JOHNSON, Martin Lewis. 5002 COWHORN CREEK RD, COLLOM & CARNEY CLINIC 75503 #021-06-1986 L2007 **D ILI** *030 †15
JONES, Johnny Wayne. 2801 RICHMOND RD, # 9 75503 #021-06-1976 L1976 **OBG** *020 †30
JONES, Richard Lee. ■ 75503 #021-05-2002 L2007 **DR** *020 †80
JOYCE, Frederick Eugene. 2900 SAINT MICHAEL DR, STE 301 75503 #004-01-1968 L1978 **PTH** *071 †50
KEEVER, James Earl. ■ 75503 #019-02-1969 L1973 **ORS** *020 †40
KEILIN, Rachael Audrey. 2717 SUMMERHILL RD 75503 #048-04-1996 L2002 **GS** *020 †85
KNIGHT, Norris C, Jr. 1002 TEXAS BLVD, STE 407 75501 #027-01-1959 L1965 **ORS** *020 †40
KNOWLES, Stanley C. 1920 MOORES LN 75503 #048-12-1980 L1980 **GE IM** *020 †20
KUNKEL-THOMAS, Jean A. 5002 COWHORN CREEK RD 75503 #004-01-1993 L2001 **N** *020 †75
LACADEN, Victor Edwin, Jr. 4126 MCKNIGHT RD 75503 #748-09-1974 *100
LARSEN, Katharine. 1406 COLLEGE DR, STE 4 75503 #048-02-1985 L1986 **AN** *020 †05
LEE, Jason Z. 5002 COWHORN CREEK RD, COLLOM & CARNEY CLINIC 75503 #243-36-1983 L2005 **NEP** *020 †20
LEONARD, Stacy Laraine. 1730 GALLERIA OAKS DR 75503 #004-01-1995 L1999 **OBG** *020 †30
LOE, Arlis Wayne. 5002 COWHORN CREEK RD, DERMATOLOGY 3RD FL 75503 #004-01-1967 L1975 **D** *020 †15 ‡
LOFTIS, M Dean. 4807 TEXAS BLVD STE 130 75503 #047-06-1973 L1974 **OPH** *075
LOWER, Kristin. 5002 COWHORN CREEK RD 75503 #048-12-1993 L1995 **OTO** *020 †45
MACHAUER, Malcolm David. 30 OAKRIDGE DR 75503 #021-05-1980 L1994 **EM OS** *020 †16
MACK, Robert Lynne. 1000 PINE ST 75501 #004-01-1962 L1972 **R** *071 †80
MALIK, Khalid. 2602 SAINT MICHAEL DR 75503 #704-01-1991 L2003 **N** *020 †75
MARROW, Charles Taylor. 3517 SUMMERHILL RD STE A 75503 #051-01-1948 L1975 **PUD CD** *020
MARTIN, Kathleen R. 5002 COWHORN CREEK RD 75503 #048-12-1978 L1978 **IM** *020 †20
MARTIN, Michael Roy. 5002 COWHORN CREEK RD, COLLOM & CARNEY CLINIC 75503 #048-12-1978 L1978 **IM** *020 †20
MC CASH, Paul Kellam. 2600 SAINT MICHAEL DR 75503 #048-02-1958 L1958 **D** *071 †15
MC CUBBIN, Jack Hamblin. 5002 COWHORN CREEK RD, COLLOM & CARNEY CLINIC 75503 #048-12-1971 L1971 **OBG** *020 †30
MC GOUGH, Benny Joe. ■ 75503 #048-02-1955 L1955 **FM** *071
MC KAY, David Edward. 5002 COWHORN CREEK RD 75503 #048-02-1981 L1981 **FM** *020 †18
MC MILLAN, Christopher E. 5508 SUMMERHILL RD 75503 #048-02-1995 L2002 **DR** *020 †18,80
MELTON, Charles Lewis. 2604 SAINT MICHAEL DR # 34 75503 #048-12-1980 L1980 **CD IM** *020 †20
MENGES, Jack E, Jr. ■ 75503 #048-12-1995 L1998 **FM** *020 †18
MIDDLETON, Donald Gene. 2801 RICHMOND RD, PMB 3 75503 #048-14-1978 L1978 **FM EM** *020 †18
MONTOYA, Gregory Raymond. 1902 GALLERIA OAKS DR 75503 #048-13-1974 L1988 **P** *020 †75
MORICZ, George Frank. 1002 TEXAS BLVD, STE 301 75501 #024-16-1994 L2001 **OBG** *020 †30
MORRIS, Howard Glenn. 2604 SAINT MICHAEL DR, STE 319 75503 #010-01-1978 L1988 **RO EM** *020 †16,80
MULHOLLAN, Jennifer Ann. 2600 SAINT MICHAEL DR, FL 2 75503 #048-13-1984 L1985 **PTH** *020 †50
MYRICK, Jarrell Thos. 5002 COWHORN CREEK RD 75503 #047-06-1975 L1984 **NEP IM** *020 †20
NAGULAPALLI, Chaitanya. 1000 PINE ST 75501 #495-21-1998 L2004 **IM** *100
NASH, David Moulton, III. 13 TIMBERWILDE ST STE 311 75503 #048-12-1978 L1979 **PTH** *020 †50
NICOL, David Andrew. 1000 PINE ST 75501 #048-15-1983 L1984 **DR** *062
NIX, John Edward. 2101 GALLERIA OAKS DR 75503 #004-01-1993 L1999 **FM** *020 †18
NORTHAM, Jon Mark. 6 WOODMONT XING, TEXARKANA GYNCOLOGY & COSM 75503 #048-13-1985 L1986 **OBG** *020 †30
NORTHAM, Wanda M. 5402 SUMMERHILL RD 75503 #048-13-1987 L1991 **OPH** *020 †35
O'BANION, Dennis David. 1920 GALLERIA OAKS DR 75503 #021-06-1979 L1984 **GS** *020 †85
O'BANION, Dennis David. ■ 75503 #048-13-2008 *012
O'BRYAN, Deborah Stewart. 2600 SAINT MICHAEL DR 75503 #004-01-1986 L1994 **FP** *075
O'DONALD, Jacqueline T. 2801 RICHMOND RD 75503 #004-01-1998 L2002 **IM** *020 †20
OJO, Edwin J. 5002 COWHORN CREEK RD 75503 #690-01-1987 L1997 **GE** *020 †20
OSBORN, Harvey J. 7703 NILE AVE, HARVEY OSBORN PA 75503 #048-15-1992 L1993 **AN** *020 †05
OVERLOCK, Timothy Lee. 1002 TEXAS BLVD, STE 201 75501 #305-01-1991 L1997 **IM** *020 †20
PAOLUCCI, Michael John. 5002 COWHORN CREEK RD 75503 #048-14-1991 L1992 **GE IM** *020 †20
PAPPAS, Michael Abraham. 5002 COWHORN CREEK RD, COLLOM & CARNEY CLINIC 75503 #025-07-1991 L1998 **ORS** *020 †40
PAPPAS, Paul Henry. 4110 RICHMOND PL 75503 #004-01-1997 L2000 **FM** *020 †18
PAPPAS, Peter. 4110 RICHMOND PL, PAPPAS MEDICAL CLINIC 75503 #048-02-1954 L1955 **GP** *071
PAPPAS, Pui Fun Wong. 4110 RICHMOND PL 75503 #004-01-1997 L2000 **FM** *020 †18
PARHAM, Kimberly Jo. 3502 RICHMOND RD 75503 #039-01-1993 L1997 **D** *020 †15
PARHAM, Robert G. 1902 MOORES LN 75503 #048-13-1991 L1992 **U** *020 †95
PARISH, Stephen Royce. 5002 COWHORN CREEK RD 75503 #048-12-1977 L1977 **IM PTH** *020 †50,20
PARSONS, Billy Dale. 2604 SAINT MICHAEL DR 75503 #039-01-1989 L1996 **TS GS** *020 †85,90
PATEL, Hiren Dinesh. 5002 COWHORN CREEK RD, DEPT OF INTERNAL MEDICINE 75503 #495-23-1999 L2004 **IM** *020 †20
PATEL, Jayendra D. 5002 COWHORN CREEK RD 75503 #495-23-1971 L1980 **IM HEM** *020 †20
PATEL, Minakshi D. 2604 SAINT MICHAEL DR, STE 345 75503 #496-38-1974 L1982 **CD IM** *020 †20
PAYNE, Alvin Donald. 1002 TEXAS BLVD, STE 201 75501 #048-02-1986 L1987 **IM** *020 †20
PAYNE, Christina Marie. 5002 COWHORN CREEK RD 75503 #048-12-1996 L2001 **PD** *020 †55
PAYNE, Christopher Todd. 1902 MOORES LN, COLLOM & CARNEY UROLOGY 75503 #048-12-1996 L2001 **U** *020 †95
PAYNE, Richard Jackson. 1406 COLLEGE DR, STE 4 75503 #004-01-1992 L1996 **AN** *020 †05
PEEBLES, Larry Mason. 2400 SAINT MICHAEL DR 75503 #004-01-1965 L1966 **R FM** *020 †80
PEREZ, Carlos Luis. 921 TEXAS BLVD, STE D 75501 #042-03-1992 L1999 **PCC** *020
PERRY, Angela Faye. 2323 KENNEDY LN 75503 #016-06-1986 L2003 **OPH** *020 †35
PICKELMAN, Jason Todd. 1902 MOORES LN 75503 #048-02-1997 L2002 **U** *020 †95
PLATT, Henry John. ■ 75503 #004-01-1993 L1996 **EM** *020 †16
PORTER, Cindy R. 5002 COWHORN CREEK RD 75503 #048-14-1993 L1994 **PD** *020 †55
POTEET, Charles L, Jr. 2600 SAINT MICHAEL DR 75503 #004-01-1982 L1994 **FM** *075 †18
POTTER, Troy Dean. 5002 COWHORN CREEK RD 75503 #028-03-1991 L2002 **IM** *020 †20
QUINN, Bayard Paul. 5002 COWHORN CREEK RD 75503 #047-06-1984 L1989 **NEP IM** *020 †20
RADOMSKI, Meko M, Jr. 5002 COWHORN CREEK RD 75503 #048-15-1991 L1992 **GS** *020 †85
REEP, Wilmer Lynn. 2931 RICHMOND RD 75503 #048-02-1973 L1973 **GP** *020
REYNOLDS, Timothy Lyndon. 2801 RICHMOND RD, # 19 75503 #049-01-1993 L1995 **EM** *020 †16
RICHTER, Gregory A. 5002 COWHORN CREEK RD 75503 #048-13-1991 L1994 **FM** *020 †18
RICHTER, Sharon Henning. 5002 COWHORN CREEK RD, COLLOM & CARNEY CLINIC 75503 #048-13-1991 L1993 **AI** *020 †55,03
RIDOUT, Robert Mastin. 2600 SAINT MICHAEL DR, FL 2 75503 #048-12-1980 L1980 **PTH** *020 †50
ROBBINS, Joseph Richard. 2400 SAINT MICHAEL DR 75503 #004-01-1984 L1988 **DR** *020 †80
ROBERTSON, William Jerry. 2604 SAINT MICHAEL DR, STE 410 75503 #004-01-1977 L1981 **OBG** *020 †30
ROBINSON, Brent Wm. 2604 SAINT MICHAEL DR, STE 345 75503 #048-13-1991 L1996 **CD** *020 †20

■ = Address Information Privacy Protected

ROBINSON, William Dewitt. 2602 SAINT MICHAEL DR, MED SELECT 75503 #016-11-1959 L1964 IM *071

RODRIGUEZ, Rey. 5510 COWHORN CREEK RD 75503 #056-05-1987 L1996 **RO** *020 †80

ROUNTREE, Glen Atlee, Jr. 1902 MOORES LN 75503 #048-02-1968 L1968 **U** *020 †95

ROYAL, Jack Lee. ■ 75503 #004-01-1962 L1975 **R GP** *020 †80

ROZENBOOM, Morgen Melinda. 2801 RICHMOND RD STE 1 75503 #048-13-1995 L1997 **EM** *020 †16

RUSH, Ronald D. 5503 N STATELINE AVE 75503 #048-02-1998 L1999 **FM** *020 †18

SANTOS DAY, Jacqueline. ■ 75503 #308-05-1988 L1993 IM *071 †20

SAPORITO, Joseph Justin. 1002 TEXAS BLVD STE 325 75501 #308-03-1986 L2005 CD IM *020 †20

SARNA, Paul Duane. 1408 COLLEGE DR 75503 #004-01-1993 L1996 **FM** *020 †18

SARRETT, James Randall. 2101 GALLERIA OAKS DR 75503 #004-01-1985 L1987 FM EM *020 †18

SCALES, James Anthony. 5002 COWHORN CREEK RD 75503 #048-15-1986 L1987 OBG *020 †30

SCHMIDT, Howard Randall. 1920 GALLERIA OAKS DR 75503 #027-01-1984 L1989 GS VS *020 †85

SCHNEBLE, Richard Jos. ■ 75503 #016-06-1945 L1954 IM *071 †20

SEIBOLD, Wm Richard, Jr. ■ 75503 #004-01-1954 L1962 **R NM** *071 †80,28

SHAFFER, Vernon C, Jr. 2604 SAINT MICHAEL DR, STE 410 75503 #021-06-1980 L1983 OBG *020 †30

SHARMA, Roshan Lal. 520 TEXAS BLVD 75501 #496-14-1980 L1991 **PM** *020 †60

SHARP, Richard Brian. 5002 COWHORN CREEK RD 75503 #004-01-1989 L2003 **PM** *020 †60

SHIELDS, William Ernest. 1000 PINE ST 75501 #036-05-1944 L1958 **OS ON** *071 †85

SKINNER, Robert Alfred. 1323 HAZEL ST 75501 #004-01-1977 L1982 **GE IM** *020 †20

SMITH, Arnett D, Jr. 5002 COWHORN CREEK RD, COLLOM & CARNEY CLINIC 75503 #021-01-1965 L1972 **GS VS** *020 †85,90

SMITH, Cathy S. 3510 RICHMOND RD, STE 100 75503 #021-06-1985 L1995 **FM** *020 †18

SMITH, Charles Jackson. 5002 COWHORN CREEK RD 75503 #047-06-1961 L1969 **NEP IM** *071 †20

SMITH, James Sidney. 5002 COWHORN CREEK RD 75503 #051-01-1967 L1973 **IM** *071 †20

SMITH, Malcolm Andrew. 5002 COWHORN CREEK RD 75503 #004-01-1990 L1996 **PCC IM** *020 †20

SMOLARZ, Gregory Joseph. 3708 SUMMERHILL RD 75503 #048-02-1981 L1981 **ORS** *020 †40

SOLOMON, John Alan. 5002 COWHORN CREEK RD 75503 #004-01-1978 L1983 **GS** *020 †85

SOMERVILLE, Patrick Jon. 1902 MOORES LN 75503 #048-12-1974 L1974 **U** *020 †95

SORENSON, Marney K. 5002 COWHORN CREEK RD, COLLOM & CARNEY CLINIC 75503 #048-13-1991 L1992 **GS** *020 †85

SPRINGMANN, Kurt Emil. 1000 PINE ST, WADLEY ANESTHESIA DEPT 75501 #003-01-1984 L2001 **AN** *020 †05 ‡

STANLEY, Reginaldo Denis. ■ 75503 #726-01-1961 L1970 **GS** *020 †85

STRAYHORN, John Michael. 1002 TEXAS BLVD STE 40 75501 #048-16-1986 L1987 CD IM *020 †20

STRINGFELLOW, Jerry B. 1400 COLLEGE DR 75503 #004-01-1966 L1974 **GP FPG** *020 †18

STUSSY, Shawn Alan. 2101 GALLERIA OAKS DR 75503 #004-01-1984 L1997 FM *020 †18

SUTHERLAND, Mark E. 2717 SUMMERHILL RD 75503 #017-20-1988 L1994 **GS** *020 †85

THETHI, Inderpal Singh. ■ 75503 #104-01-2007 **FP** *012

THOMAS, James Herman. 1001 MAIN ST 75501 #048-02-1959 L1959 **N P** *071

THOMAS, Jeffory Ford. 3510 RICHMOND RD STE 10 75503 #004-01-1994 L1996 **FM** *020 †18

THOMAS, Jonathan Felts. 5002 COWHORN CREEK RD 75503 #004-01-1994 L1999 **RHU** *020 †20

THOMPSON, Douglas Edward. 5002 COWHORN CREEK RD, COLLOM AND CARNEY CLINIC 75503 #048-13-1997 L2002 **ORS** *020 †40

THOMPSON, Jennifer M. 5002 COWHORN CREEK RD 75503 #048-13-1997 L2002 OBG *020 †30

THORNTON, Charles Neil. 1820 GALLERIA OAKS DR 75503 #004-01-1980 L1985 **OPH** *020 †35

TOBEY, Edward Wm. 1902 GALLERIA OAKS DR 75503 #039-01-1984 L1992 **P** *020 †75

TOMPKINS, Wm Chas, Jr. 1920 GALLERIA OAKS DR 75503 #027-01-1968 L1974 **GS** *071 †85

TOUBIA, Elie J. ■ 75503 #422-01-1990 L2007 **IMG FM** *020

TOWNSEND, Gene Morris. 1000 PINE ST 75501 #004-01-1958 L1969 **GS** *071 †85

TRAN, Hai Anthony. 5510 COWHORN CREEK RD 75503 #056-05-1987 L1994 **RO ON** *020 †80

TRIPPE, Douglas A. 5508 SUMMERHILL RD 75503 #048-13-1987 L1988 **DR** *020 †80

URBINA, James Humberto. 2602 SAINT MICHAEL DR, COGENT HEALTHCARE 75503 #048-04-2000 L2003 **IM** *020 †20

VEREEN, Lowell Emery. 921 TEXAS BLVD STE D 75501 #048-02-1980 L1980 **PUD IM** *020 †20

WADE, Billy Kossuth. 2501 COLLEGE DR 75501 #004-01-1973 L1994 **EM GP** *020 †16

WAIT, Creed L. 5002 COWHORN CREEK RD, COLLOM AND CARNEY CLINIC A 75503 #049-01-1989 L2006 **IM** *020 †20

WARR, Robert Boyce. ■ 75503 #047-06-1975 L1989 **DR** *071 †80

WATSON, Thomas Ray. 4500 SUMMERHILL RD 75503 #048-12-1980 L1980 **AN** *020 †05

WEBB, Kathleen E Egner. 2701 PINE ST 75503 #004-01-1951 L1959 **R** *071

WEBER, David Robt. 4500 SUMMERHILL RD 75503 #056-05-1986 L1997 **AN PMM** *020 †05

WEBER, Patrick Lowry. 2602 SAINT MICHAEL DR 75503 #004-01-1980 L1987 **FM** *020 †18

WEEMS, Harold G, Jr. 3708 SUMMERHILL RD 75503 #048-12-1993 L1994 **ORS** *020 †40

WEINSTEIN, Jonathan R. 1730 GALLERIA OAKS DR 75503 #023-01-1993 L2002 OBG *020 †30

WEST, Kenneth Wyatt. 1002 TEXAS BLVD STE 200 75501 #004-01-1996 L2001 OBG *020 †30

WHITT, David Lee. 1000 PINE ST 75501 #048-12-1978 L1978 **OTO EM** *020 †45

WHITT, Paul D. 4214 TEXAS BLVD 75503 #048-16-1994 L1999 **OTO** *020 †45

WILHELM, Frieda. ■ 75503 #004-01-1943 L1946 **IM** *071

WILLIAMS, David Lee. 5002 COWHORN CREEK RD 75503 #048-15-1981 L1981 **FM OM** *020 †18

WILLIAMS, James Patrick. 1406 COLLEGE DR, STE 4 75503 #004-01-2002 L2006 **AN** *100

WILSON, Thomas Laurence. 520 W 12TH ST 75501 #039-01-1982 L1984 OBG *020 †30

WOMACK, Gary Lynn. 5402 SUMMERHILL RD 75503 #048-15-1975 L1977 OPH *020 †35

WOMACK, Joseph S. 5002 COWHORN CREEK RD 75503 #048-12-1992 L1993 **U** *020 †95

WONG, Pui Sum. 2602 SAINT MICHAEL DR, LITTLE ROCK INTERNAL MEDIC 75503 #048-14-1998 L2001 **IM** *020 †20

WREN, Mark Andrews. 3510 RICHMOND RD, STE 400 75503 #021-01-1991 L1995 **PM** *020 †60

WRIGHT, Mark Wayne. 5002 COWHORN CREEK RD 75503 #004-01-1982 L1985 **PD** *020 †55

WRIGHT, Nathan Jones. 2014 GALLERIA OAKS DR 75503 #004-01-1992 L1995 **IM** *020 †20

WRIGHT, Nathan Lee. 921 TEXAS BLVD 75501 #004-01-1960 L1966 **PD PDC** *071 †55

WYRICK, Scott Wayne. 3333 POTOMAC AVE, WYRICK DERMATOLOGY 75503 #048-13-1991 L1992 **FM** *020 †18 ‡

WYRICK, Walter James, Jr. 3333 POTOMAC AVE 75503 #048-12-1965 L1965 **D GS** *020 †85

YOUNG, Jeffrey Paul. 1732 GALLERIA OAKS DR, DERMATOLOGY ASSOCIATES LLP 75503 #004-01-1994 L1998 **D** *020 †15

YOUNG, Matthew Stephen. ■ 75503 #004-01-1996 L1999 **EM** *020 †16

YOUNG, Mitchell M. 1406 COLLEGE DR, MITCHELL YOUNG M D 75503 #004-01-1953 L1958 **GS** *075

YOUNG, Thomas Christopher. 2604 ST MICHAEL DR S239 75503 #048-13-1993 L1999 **ORS** *020 †40

ZAMAN KHAN, Muhammad Aame. 1002 TEXAS BLVD, STE 325 75501 #704-01-1999 L2007 **N** *020

TEXAS CITY – GALVESTON

ACHARYA, Siddhartha A. 6807 EMMETT F LOWRY EXPY, STE 108 77591 #495-23-1981 L1993 CD IM *020 †20

ADHIKARY, Ravi. ■ 77591 #041-13-2004 L2004 **DR** *012

AHMEDUDDIN, Jameela. 6807 EMMETT F LOWRY EXPY, STE 301 77591 #495-65-1970 L1976 **PTH** *050 †50

ALHASSAN, Abdul-Aziz. 2000 TEXAS AVE, STE 200 77590 #649-02-1988 L1998 **FM** *020 †18

ALKARRA, Nehme. 1125 HIGHWAY 3 N STE 190 77591 #875-03-1988 L1995 **IM EM** *020 †20

ANDERSON, Viola Veronica. 6807 EMMETT F LOWRY EXPY, STE 200 77591 #035-08-1974 L1996 **IM** *020 †20

BAETHGE, Bruce Armo. 6807 EMMETT F LOWRY EXPY, STE 200 77591 #048-12-1978 L1978 **RHU IM** *050 †20

BELL-GRAY, Anika Trenelle. 2000 TEXAS AVE, GALVESTON CNTY COORD COMM 77590 #048-02-2002 L2004 **FM** *020 †18

BILLINGSLEY, Travis Allen. ■ 77591 #048-02-2004 **PD** *012

BINDER, Cynthia Alvarado. 6400 MEMORIAL DR, PEDIATRIC ASSOCS TEXAS CIT 77591 #048-02-1998 L2002 **PD** *020 †55

BOSWELL, Jeffrey Mitchell. 2401 5TH AVE S, HEALTH SERVICES DEPARTMENT 77590 #048-04-1981 L1983 **OM FM** *020 †70,18

BROMAN, Charles Raymond. 702 9TH ST N 77590 #019-02-1960 L1966 **OPH** *020 †35

BRUCE, Lena Rochelle. 6518 MEMORIAL DR 77591 #048-02-1988 L1989 **FM** *020 †18

BYERS, William Seal. 6801 EMMETT F LOWRY EXPY 77591 #023-01-1964 L1974 **CD** *020 †20

CANN, Anthony Joseph. 9300 EMMETT F LOWRY EXPY, STE 128 77591 #654-01-1991 **FM** *020

CLINE, Donald M. 6801 EMMETT F LOWRY EXPY, DEPT OF ANESTHESIOLOGY 77591 #048-12-1992 L1999 **AN** *020 †05

COCHRANE, John H, Jr. 818 5TH ST N 77590 #048-02-1956 L1956 **FM** *071

CONRAD, Brandy M. ■ 77591 #048-14-2007 **AN** *012

COX, George William. 6501 MEMORIAL DR 77591 #048-02-1961 L1961 **ORS** *020 †40

COX, Natasha Lanai. ■ 77590 #048-02-2004 **PD** *012

CROWDER, Janice Renee. 1125 HIGHWAY 3 N, STE 160 77591 #010-03-1986 L1991 OBG *020 †30

DANZIGER, Julius. 6801 EMMETT F LOWRY EXPY 77591 #836-01-1964 L1977 **R** *020 †80

DIMAANDAL, Avelina Santos. 609 9TH AVE N 77590 #748-08-1962 L1975 **PD** *020 †55

DIMAS, Vanessa Miranda. ■ 77591 #048-02-2007 **PS** *012

FAIRCHILD, Robert Leo. 6801 EMMETT F LOWRY EXPY 77591 #048-13-1984 L1987 **AN** *030 †05

FALCONE, Adam M. 2801 FM 2004 RD 77591 #048-02-2008 *012

FAUS-ESCRIVA, Salvador. 818 5TH ST N 77590 #847-08-1959 L1968 **AS GS** *071

FOWLER-GULDE, Janis Jean. 6807 EMMETT F LOWRY EXPY, STE 103 77591 #422-01-1990 L1996 **IM** *020 †20

FRADKIN, Allan Hirsch. 6409 MEMORIAL DR, EYE CLINIC OF TEXAS 77591 #048-02-1967 L1967 **OPH** *020 †35

FUCHS, Carl J. 1206 14TH ST N 77590 #048-02-1951 L1951 **GP** *071

GODINICH, Mary Josephine. 8900 EMMETT F LOWRY EXPY, STE 200 77591 #048-15-1986 L1988 **NEP** *020 †20

GRANT, Jim C. 3201 PALMER HWY 77590 #048-02-1994 L1996 **OTO** *020 †45

GRAY, Jon Roger. ■ 77591 #023-12-2006 L2008 *020

HAISCHER, Gayle Denise. ■ 77591 #048-02-2008 *012

HARVEY, Charles Minor. 6607 EMMETT F LOWRY EXPY 77591 #048-13-1975 L1975 **FOP** *050 †50

HAY, Matthew J. 6400 MEMORIAL DR 77591 #048-02-1994 L1995 **PD** *020 †55

HAYES, Gregory Patrick. ■ 77591 #048-12-2006 **IM** *100

HINK, Burton W. 818 5TH ST N 77590 #048-02-1953 L1953 **GS** *071 †85

HUTTON, Lee Aubry. 6807 EMMETT F LOWRY EXPY, STE 106 77591 #048-13-1978 L1979 **U** *020 †20

IYER, Hemalatha R. 6801 EMMETT F LOWRY EXPY 77591 #495-59-1983 L1992 **IM** *020 †20

JAIN, Roshan Lal. 6801 EMMETT F LOWRY EXPY 77591 #495-43-1959 L1966 **FM IM** *075

JOWERS, Dana Dempsey. 9300 EMMETT F LOWRY EXPY, STE 128 77591 #048-02-1992 L1993 **PD** *020 †55

JUDICE, Cynthia Ann. 6400 MEMORIAL DR 77591 #021-05-1974 L1977 **PD** *020 †55

KOCUREK, Alberto T. 1125 HIGHWAY 3 N, STE 100 77591 #048-02-1989 L1992 **UM EM** *020 †20

KONIKOWSKI, Janusz Andrew. 6807 EMMETT F LOWRY EXPY 77591 #048-02-1968 L1968 **FM OM** *020 †18

KORNDORFFER, William Earl. 6607 HIGHWAY 1764 77591 #024-01-1956 L1958 **FOP LM** *071 †50

KOUSSAYER, Tarek. 929 7TH AVE N, RURAL METRO AMBULANCE 77590 #875-02-1983 L1991 **GE** *020 †20

LE, Hung Minh. 6807 EMMETT F LOWRY EXPY, STE 200 77591 #051-01-2002 L2005 **IM** *020 †20

LEWIS, Beverly Guillory. 1228 N LOGAN ST STE 200 77590 #048-04-1979 L1979 **GS** *020 †85

LI, Fan. 6807 EMMETT F LOWRY EXPY, STE 310 77591 #243-47-1982 L2000 **FM** *020 †18

LIN, Chia Chin. 1711 6TH ST N 77590 #422-01-1995 L2001 **FM** *020 †18

LONGMIRE, Warren T, Jr. 6801 EMMETT F LOWRY EXPY 77591 #048-02-1963 L1963 **FM GPM** *020 †18

MAO, Tammy Alexander. 2000 TEXAS AVE 77590 #047-07-1999 L2002 **FM** *020 †18

MC CLURE, Suzanne. 1125 HIGHWAY 3 N, STE 150 77591 #048-02-1980 L1980 **IM ON** *020 †20

MCGRADY, William E. ■ 77590 #048-02-2008 *012

MERCADO, Mary G. 6807 EMMETT F LOWRY EXPY, STE 304 77591 #048-04-1992 L1993 CD IM *020 †20

MERCATANTE, Michelle Anne. 9300 EMMETT F LOWRY EXPY, STE 138 77591 #048-13-1986 L1987 **IM** *020 †20

MERRITT, Dorothy F. 6807 EMMETT F LOWRY EXPY, STE 103 77591 #019-02-1984 L1986 **IM** *020 †20

MIDDLETON, Jaime Jenee. ■ 77591 #023-01-2004 OBG *012

MILSTEIN, Bernard Allen. 6409 MEMORIAL DR, EYE CLINIC OF TEXAS 77591 #048-02-1967 L1967 **OPH** *020 †35

MOORE, John North, Jr. 9300 EMMETT F LOWRY EXPY, STE 138 77591 #045-01-1975 L1978 **FM** *020 †18

MOORE, Uzoma Bertram. ■ 77591 #048-02-2007 *012

NEELY, Linda Denise. 6801 EMMETT F LOWRY EXPY 77591 #039-01-1990 L1994 **PD** *020 †55

NGUYEN, Bich G. 6807 EMMETT F LOWRY EXPY, STE 200 77591 #048-04-1994 L1996 **IM** *020 †20

NICKESON, David C S. 6807 EMMETT F LOWRY EXPY, STE 303 77591 #041-02-1977 L1979 **PUD CCM** *020 †20

NODARSE, Alfredo. 6807 EMMETT F LOWRY EXPY, STE 200 77591 #649-01-1962 L1966 **IM GE** *020

PATEL, Sonia Shantilal. 6401 MEMORIAL DR 77591 #048-15-2003 L2006 **IM** *100 †20

PETERSON, Adri A. 6400 MEMORIAL DR 77591 #048-13-2002 L2005 **PD** *100 †55

PHILIPS, Dudley A, III. 6409 MEMORIAL DR 77591 #021-05-1969 L1978 **OBG** *020 †30

RAC, Martha Wattinefra. ■ 77591 #048-14-2008 *012

REEVES, John Purcell. 9300 EMMETT F LOWRY EXPY 77591 #048-02-1955 L1955 **FM** *071

RISINGER, Carolyn R. 6400 MEMORIAL DR 77591 #048-02-1983 L1983 **PD** *020 †55

ROBINSON, Diane C. 6807 EMMETT F LOWRY EXPY, STE 101 77591 #048-12-1990 L2001 **GS** *020 †85

ROBINSON, Pamela B. 702 9TH ST N 77590 #048-13-1993 L1994 **OPH** *020 †35

RODRIGUEZ, Jennifer J. 6807 EMMETT F LOWRY EXPY, STE 108 77591 #048-13-1999 L2006 **CD** *020 †20

ROTKIEWICZ-PIORUN, Anna M. 6510 MEMORIAL DR 77591 #759-03-1990 L2004 **IMG** *020

SCHMALSTIEG, Elisabeth J. 6417 MEMORIAL DR 77591 #048-02-1973 L1973 **N** *020 †75

SHAH, Kiran H. 926 14TH ST N 77590 #495-22-1971 L1978 **OBG** *072 †30

SILLER, Terry A. 6501 MEMORIAL DR 77591 #048-04-1990 L1992 **ORS** *020 †40

SOLEJA, Nusrat B. 6417 MEMORIAL DR, STE B 77591 #704-02-1977 L1995 **IM** *020 †20

ST CLAIR, Ladale Kacey. 6504 MEMORIAL DR, MAINLAND MEDICINE SPECIALT 77591 #007-02-2001 L2003 **END DIA** *100

SULLIVAN, Robert Emmett. ■ 77591 #048-02-1956 L1956 **FM GS** *071 †18

SYAL, Ashu. 608 BUTTONWOOD DR 77591 #495-03-1991 L2006 **PN** *012 †55

UZOWULU, Obinna Chimezie. 77591 #473-02-2003 **FP** *012

VELOUDAKIS, Theodore C. 616 6TH ST N 77590 #418-01-1961 L1975 **ORS** *020

VUONG, Duc C. 6807 EMMETT F LOWRY EXPY, STE 305 77591 #048-16-2000 L2005 **GS** *020 †85

WARNER, William Scott. 1125 HIGHWAY 3 N STE 180, MAINLAND MEDICAL PAVILION 77591 #048-02-1993 L1996 **ID IM** *020

WENGROFF, Sean Daryl. 6409 MEMORIAL DR 77591 #021-01-1996 L2002 **OBG** *020

WICHELHAUS, Harlan Paul. 1125 HIGHWAY 3 N, STE 130 77591 #036-05-1981 L1991 **GP** *020 †30

WILLIAMS, Marian Yvette. ■ 77591 #021-01-2004 **OBG** *012

WOODSON, Drury Lewis. 6510 MEMORIAL DR 77591 #048-02-1965 L1965 **IM IMG** *020 †20

YANG, Mary Yun-Ping. 6807 EMMETT F LOWRY EXPY, STE 307 77591 #462-01-1981 L1991 **PTH PCP** *020 †50

THE COLONY – DENTON

HIGGS, Robert E. 75056 #021-01-1949 L1954 **U** *020 †95

PARUOLO, William Anthony. 6053 MAIN ST, STE 225 75056 #048-14-1996 L1999 **PD** *020 †55

PICKETT, Jan W. 5000 MAIN ST STE 318 75056 #048-12-1986 L1987 **GP** *020 ‡

RIEHS, Jason M. ■ 75056 #048-14-1998 L2000 **MPD** *020

STELLMAN, Harry M, IV. 6053 MAIN ST, STE 225 75056 #048-15-1999 L2002 **PD** *020 †55

TORRES, Lorinda K. 6053 MAIN ST STE 230, CEDAR NILES INTERNAL MEDIC 75056 #028-46-1997 L1998 **IM** *020 †20

VOLLENWEIDER, Gary M. 6053 MAIN ST STE 130 75056 #048-12-1985 L1986 **FM** *020 †18

ZEITMAN, Henry. 6053 MAIN ST STE 130 75056 #065-01-1974 L1978 **FM** *020

ZUBERI, Shimaila Hashmi. 6053 MAIN ST STE 13 75056 #704-02-1996 L2004 **FM** *020 †18

THE HILLS – TRAVIS

ALEXANDER, Thomas Conrad. ■ 78738 #048-02-1970 L1970 **GS** *020 †85

CROMACK, William Henry. ■ 78738 #048-12-1960 L1960 **P OS** *020 †75

ERICKSON, Brenda Ruth. ■ 78738 #012-05-1990 L1990 **P** *020 †75

HOULE, Dudley B. ■ 78738 #024-07-1953 L1967 **FM AM** *071 †85

JACKSON, Roland Davies. ■ 78738 #021-01-1956 L1963 **ORS** *072 †40

SHETH, Kirtikant V. ■ 78738 #496-38-1965 L1972 **PTH** *062 †50

VANDIVIER, Thomas Gilman. ■ 78738 #023-07-1954 L1958 **END IM** *071 †20

WINTER, Wm Chisholm, Jr. 1 SUNVIEW RD 78738 #051-04-1946 **IM OS** *030

THE WOODLANDS – HARRIS

CHEN, Jennifer Mingfay. ■ 77389 #021-05-2003 **MPD** *100 †20,55

THE WOODLANDS – MONTGOMERY

ABUSHARR, Raja. 6886 WOODLANDS PKWY, STE C 77382 #040-02-2000 L2006 **FM OBS** *020 †18 ‡

ALEXANDER, Sunitha Chacko. ■ 77381 #496-29-1996 L2003 **IM** *020 †20

ALLMON, Brent Michael. 6704 STERLING RIDGE DR, STE A 77382 #048-14-2000 L2004 **FPG** *020 †18

ALVAREZ-DEL REAL, Gonzalo. 6767 LAKE WOODLANDS DR # A 77382 #649-31-1995 L2005 **AI** *020 †20,03

ANDREWS, Lawrence W. 7901 RESEARCH FOREST DR, STE 900 77382 #048-16-1987 L1988 **FM** *040 †18

AQUINO, Honorio Guillermo. ■ 77381 #341-01-1955 L1976 **AN** *071

ARAUJO PREZA, Carlos E. 17350 ST LUKES WAY, STE 350 77384 #341-03-1994 L2001 **PCC** *020 †20

ASLAM, Shamaila Adnan. 17191 ST LUKES WAY 77384 #704-01-1995 L2005 **IM** *020 †20

AWALT, Hazel Leonor. ■ 77381 #048-04-1979 L1979 **PTH** *020 †50

BAKEWELL, Connie Lynn. ■ 77382 #048-15-2008 *012

BANKER, Nitesh A. ■ 77381 #048-02-1993 L1996 **DR** *020 †80

BARKER, Mariellen. 1441 WOODSTEAD CT, STE 300 77380 #048-14-1988 L1989 **PM P** *020 †60

BASHIR, Saadia Feroze. ■ 77380 #704-02-1986 *100

BASS, James Richard. ■ 77382 #021-05-1980 L1994 **OBG** *020 †30

BEERS, Charles J. 3091 COLLEGE PARK DR, STE 240 77384 #048-13-1982 L1983 **FM** *020 †18

BETHEA, Louise Huffman. 17198 ST LUKES WAY STE 240 77384 #027-01-1972 L1980 **AI PDA** *020 †55,03

BHAKTA, Amish Manu. 4545 RESEARCH FOREST DR, STE A 77381 #047-06-1997 L2003 **PD** *020 †55

BIGLER, Peter Christopher. 6704 STERLING RIDGE DR, STE A 77382 #048-04-2001 L2002 **FM** *020 †18

BOLIVAR, Ricardo. 145 N RAINBOW RIDGE CIR, BOX 131224 77381 #935-01-1972 L1977 **ID IM** *020 †20

BONNES-NEUMANN, Marlaina. 8000 RESEARCH FOREST DR, STE 360 77382 #035-45-1993 L2003 **IM** *020 †20

BRONSHTEYN, Igor V. ■ 77381 #035-48-1996 L2005 **CD** *020 †20

BROUSSARD, Crystal Ray. 17191 ST LUKES WAY 77384 #048-14-2002 L2004 **FM** *020 †18

BROWN, Clarence A. ■ 77381 #048-04-1949 L1950 **PTH CLP** *071 †50

BRYARLY, Richard Colwin, Jr. 17191 ST LUKES WAY 77384 #048-02-1975 L1975 **OTO PDO** *020 †45

BUGENHAGEN, Veronica G. 9100 FOREST XING, STE A 77381 #048-14-1997 L1999 **FM** *020 †18

BUMGARDNER, Amy Christine. 9303 PINECROFT DR, STE 150 77380 #048-14-2003 L2006 **D** *020 †15

BURKE, Rosalia C F. 17191 ST LUKES WAY 77384 #028-02-1996 L2003 **OTO** *020 †45

BURRESS, Robert Spencer. 9301 PINECROFT DR, STE 100 77380 #011-04-1981 L1998 **AI PUD** *020 †20,03

CHANG, Eduardo Enrique. 17350 ST LUKES WAY STE 350 77384 #005-12-1995 L2000 **PCC AI** *020 †20 ‡

CHANG, Hsiawluen. 17198 ST LUKES WAY, STE 540 77384 #048-13-1991 L1993 **OBG** *020 †30

CHEN, Frank Yi. 4840 W PANTHER CREEK DR, STE 210 77381 #028-34-1998 L1999 **P** *020

CHENG, Anthony Enrique. ■ 77380 #005-14-1989 L1990 **DR** *040 †80

CHIMENTI, Brian Thomas. 1441 WOODSTEAD CT STE 300, THE WOODLANDS SPORTS MEDIC 77380 #048-04-1994 L1998 **ORS** *020 †40

CHUA, Evelyn Tan. 17200 ST LUKES WAY 77384 #748-01-1989 L2002 **FM** *020 †20

CHUN, Stephen S C. ■ 77381 #583-01-1968 L1982 **GS** *020 †16

CHUNG, Chong Chauw. ■ 77380 #244-02-1965 L1975 **AN** *071 †05

COLLINS, Carol A. 17198 ST LUKES WAY, STE 540 77384 #034-01-1981 L1983 **OBG** *020 †30

COOK, Robert L. 17350 ST LUKES WAY, STE 200 77384 #048-04-1995 L2000 **GS** *020 †85

COUPE, Kevin J. 10333 KUYKENDAHL RD, STE D 77382 #048-14-1990 L1991 **ORS OTR** *020 †40

DALTON, Conrad Ivan. ■ 77382 #048-02-1970 L1971 **AM** *071 †70

DASTOOR IRANI, Natasha. 4545 RESEARCH FOREST DR, STE A 77381 #067-01-1996 L1998 **PD** *020 †55

DAVIS, Sakina Husein. 9595 SIX PINES DR, STE 6250 77380 #012-01-1996 L2000 **FM** *020 †18

DEVOS, Cynthia M. 4840 W PANTHER CREEK DR, STE 210 77381 #048-14-1991 L1992 **CHP** *020 †75

DEW, Edward House. ■ 77382 #048-02-1958 L1958 **PTH** *071 †50

DIAZ, Luis N. ■ 77381 #451-01-1991 L1995 **FM** *020 †18

DRUCKER, Carol Raye Jones. 395 SAWDUST RD, # 2028 77380 #048-04-1976 L1976 **D** *020 †15 ‡

DURHAM, Carlos John. 3115 COLLEGE PARK DR, STE 103C 77384 #048-12-1983 L1983 **AN** *020 †20

DURST, John Wakefield. 1001 MEDICAL PLAZA DR #280 77380 #048-13-1978 L1978 **OBG** *020 †30

ECKHARDT, Donald Kent, Jr. 17191 ST LUKES WAY 77384 #048-02-1991 L1992 **OBG** *020 †30

EDRALIN, Joseph V. 4800 W PANTHER CREEK DR, STEP PEDIATRICS PA SUITE 1 77381 #048-14-1990 L1992 **PD** *020 †55

EGERMAN, Mark John. 1441 WOODSTEAD CT STE 260 77380 #048-04-1983 L1983 **AN ADM** *020 †05

ENI, Ikedinobi Ugochukwu. 17198 ST LUKES WAY, STE 530 77384 #690-01-1982 L1998 **IM** *020 †20

ESPITIA, Leonardo. 17350 ST LUKES WAY STE 200 77384 #264-05-1999 L2005 **FM** *020 †18

FARMER, Amy C. 17191 ST LUKES WAY 77384 #048-14-1998 L2002 **D** *020 †15

FAYAZ, Imran. ■ 77382 #065-01-1990 L2005 **NS** *020 ‡

FINALLE, Cheri Lyn. ■ 77381 #048-13-2007 **EM** *012

FLANAGAN, Roland R. 4545 RESEARCH FOREST DR, STE A 77381 #048-02-1992 L1993 **IM** *020 †20

FOX, Shari Charna. 17191 ST LUKES WAY 77384 #048-13-1999 L2002 **END** *020 †20

FREIMAN, Joel. ■ 77381 #035-09-1981 L1985 **IM** *020 †20

FRIDLEY, William Allen. 9100 FOREST XING, STE A 77381 #021-05-1992 L1995 **IM** *020 †20

GAFFNEY, Kevin Clifford. 9303 PINECROFT DR, STE 270 77380 #024-07-1989 L2002 **N SME** *020 †75

GARZA, Daniel F. 7575 GOSLING RD 77382 #048-04-1985 L1986 **EM GP** *020

GAUDREAULT, Suzanne Marie. ■ 77382 #021-05-2002 L2002 **FM** *100 †18

GEERLING, Sonja. 35 CURRYMEAD PL 77382 #836-01-1964 L1978 **PTH** *040 †50

GHIDE, Solomon. ■ 77384 #366-01-1989 L2000 **ID** *012 †20

GORDLEY, Kyle P. 4850 W PANTHER CREEK DR, STE 105 77381 #048-12-2002 L2007 **PS** *012

HAGGERTY, Bernadette S. 1011 MEDICAL PLAZA DR, STE 220 77380 #038-40-1995 L1998 **PD** *072 †55

HARPER, Robert Douglas. ■ 77381 #048-14-1976 L1976 **ORS OSM** *020 †40

HAYES, William M. 6701 LAKE WOODLANDS DR, STE 101 77382 #048-13-1991 L1992 **ORS** *020 †40

HEIMAN, Eugene L. 1441 WOODSTEAD CT STE 3 77380 #024-05-1975 L1980 **ORS OSM** *020 †40

HERMAN, Christopher M. ■ 77382 #025-07-1996 L2007 **DMP** *020

HILL, Rebecca Beckman. 1595 LAKE FRONT CIR, HOMETOWN PEDIATRICS 77380 #045-01-1976 L1992 **ADL PD** *040 †55

HO, Nhue Anh. ■ 77381 #010-01-1996 L2003 **IM** *020 †20

HUEY, Doyle W. 4840 W PANTHER CREEK DR, STE 108 77381 #048-13-1983 L1983 **FM** *020 †18

HUGHES, George Griffin. 1001 MEDICAL PLAZA DR, STE 220 77380 #048-02-1973 L1973 **D** *020 †15

HUSSAIN BASHIR, Kauser. ■ 77380 #704-02-1986 L1995 **P** *020 †75

HUTTON, Connie Clifford. 17200 ST LUKES WAY 77384 #048-02-1972 L1972 **TS VS** *020 †85,90

ISAAC, George M. 10 COLDSPRINGS CT 77380 #495-31-1969 L1976 **IM** *020 †20

JAMIL, Nadeem. 3115 COLLEGE PARK DR, STE 110 77384 #704-02-1991 L2001 **IM** *020 †20

JIMENEZ-QUINTERO, Laura P. 1011 MEDICAL PLAZA DR #200 77380 #649-02-1985 L1991 PTH *020 †50

JOHN, Tony. 1595 LAKE FRONT CIR, HOMETOWN PEDIATRICS 77380 #048-14-2002 L2004 PD *020 †55

JOHNSON, Keith Waynevahe. 6701 LAKE WOODLANDS DR, STE 101 77382 #024-05-2001 L2007 ORS *020

KAHNEY, Scott A. 8000 RESEARCH FOREST DR, STE 360 77382 #048-04-1994 L1997 FM *†18

KAISER, David George. 4840 W PANTHER CREEK DR, STE 210 77381 #654-01-1997 L2000 CHP P *020 †75

KAMATH, M Vasudeva. ■ 77380 #495-37-1976 L2004 NPM PHP *020 †55

KAPADIA, Mona. 17198 ST LUKES WAY, STE 500 77384 #033-05-2001 L2005 ID *100 †20

KOPINSKI, Joseph C. ■ 77382 #051-04-1960 L1977 R PD *071 †55,80

KOZAK, Mark Ryan. 17350 ST LUKES WAY, STE 200 77384 #048-02-2001 L2004 PD *020 †55

KRETSCHMER, Andrew P. 10333 KUYKENDAHL RD STE B 77382 #048-02-1984 L1985 EM *020

KRUPPSTADT, Paula J. 77384 #048-13-1990 L1992 PD *020 †55

KUCERA, Christine. 6767 LAKE WOODLANDS DR # A 77382 #014-01-1992 L2000 IM AI *020 †20,03

KUSHWAHA, Rajnikant. 17198 ST LUKES WAY, STE 500 77384 #495-41-1992 L1999 IM *020 †20

KVAPIL, Peter Raymond. 3115 COLLEGE PARK DR, STE 107 77384 #017-20-1999 L2002 IM *020 †20

LADEN, Patricia E. 17198 ST LUKES WAY, STE 250 77384 #048-15-1986 L1987 OBG *020 †30

LAPIS, Rose. 4545 RESEARCH FOREST DR, STE A 77381 #473-02-1986 L1993 PD *020 †55

LAXMAN, Rama. 1776 WOODSTEAD CT STE 101 77380 #495-42-1986 L1998 IM *020 †20

LEIBMAN, Neville Saul. 17200 ST LUKES WAY 77384 #550-02-1999 L2003 AN *020 †05

LI, Kwok. 17350 ST LUKES WAY, STE 330 77384 #035-06-1996 L2001 OPH *020 †35

LINDER, Vanessa Kaye. 4840 W PANTHER CREEK DR, STE 207 77381 #020-02-2002 L2004 P *020 †75

LIPSCOMB, Albert B, Jr. 10333 KUYKENDAHL RD, STE D 77382 #047-05-1981 L1987 ORS *020 †40

LOONEY, Paul Alan. 26203 OAK RIDGE DR 77380 #048-02-1981 L1981 P *020 †75

LUCAS, Marshall. 4840 W PANTHER CREEK DR, STE 210 77381 #048-14-1990 L1991 CHP P *020 †75

MA, John Ming-Kay. 3115 COLLEGE PARK DR, SUITE 106 COLLEGE PK MED 77384 #048-02-1997 L1998 FM *020 †18

MABRY, David Randolph. 1055 EVERGREEN CIR 77380 #048-04-1980 L1981 FM *020 †18

MALONEY, Daniel Patrick. 17350 ST LUKES WAY, STE 200 77384 #023-01-1982 L1984 PD *020 †55

MANGAPURAM, Balakrishna R. 9004 FOREST XING # E, STE E 77381 #495-21-1990 L1995 IM *020 †20

MANIAM, Santhi Battumalai. ■ 77382 #048-02-2004 L2008 DR *012

MANNS-RIZZO, Susan M. ■ 77382 #028-34-1984 L1993 IM *020 †20

MARKOS, Ferenc. 17191 ST LUKES WAY 77384 #048-14-1990 L1991 OBG *020 †30

MARUPUDI, Seshasree. ■ 77382 #496-24-2001 L2007 IM *020 †20

MC ADEN, Bret Allen. 17350 ST LUKES WAY, STE 200 77384 #048-14-1990 L1991 IM *020 †20

MC MANUS, Mila Q. ■ 77380 #048-14-2000 L2002 IM *020 †18 ‡

MEDINA, Sheryl. ■ 77385 #048-15-1995 L1998 IM *071 †20

MICHAEL, Doris Abadeer. ■ 77382 #915-02-1964 L1998 FM *100 †18

MOONAT, Joohee N. ■ 77384 #048-12-2005 GS *012

MOORE, James Lee. ■ 77381 #035-20-1960 L1962 PS *062 †65

MUECK, Gary Paul. 1055 EVERGREEN CIR 77380 #048-14-1990 L1991 FM *020 †18

MUI, Dan-Vy Quy. 9595 SIX PINES DR, STE 8210 77380 #028-02-1999 L2007 P *040 †75

MULLER, Adalberto Agustin. 10077 GROGANS MILL RD, STE 280 77380 #715-01-1976 L1981 D *020

MURPHY, John Jos. 1733 WOODSTEAD CT STE 101 77380 #539-02-1975 L1978 FM *020 ‡

NASSER, George Alan. 17198 ST LUKES WAY, STE 440 77384 #017-20-1988 L1995 CD IM *020 †20

NEWLAND, Donald Earl. 1011 MEDICAL PLAZA DR, STE 250 77380 #048-14-1998 L2003 OTO *020 †45

NG, Howard. ■ 77381 #048-04-1980 L1980 EM *020 †16

NGUYEN, Kinh Van. ■ 77381 #941-01-1966 L1987 P *075 †75

NGUYEN, Tony Quang. 17350 ST LUKES WAY 77384 #048-13-2003 L2006 IM *020 †20

NICHOLS, Robert Carroll. ■ 77381 #048-02-2002 L2004 FP *012

NIX, William Lowrie. 6707 STERLING RIDGE DR, STE A 77382 #048-04-1973 L1973 PD PHO *055

NORDMANN, Amy Marie. ■ 77382 #028-02-1999 L2007 DR *020 †80

NORTON, John W. ■ 77380 #010-02-1960 L1980 IM FM *020

O'CONNOR, Pamela C. 6701 LAKE WOODLANDS DR, STE 101 77382 #048-16-1996 L2004 FSM *020 †18

OLIVEIRA, Victor Louis. 17200 ST LUKES WAY 77384 #048-13-1982 L1983 PTH *020 †50

O'NEIL, Susan J Reitz. 6707 STERLING RIDGE DR, STE A 77382 #030-05-1980 L1982 PD *020 †55

OWUSU-AGYEMANG, Pascal O. 39 S AVONLEA CIR 77382 #913-65-1995 L1996 AN *020 †05

PAKANATI, Rajgopal Reddy. 74 N BERRYLINE CIR 77381 #495-21-1988 L1997 AN *020

PALWAI, Rama Reddy. ■ 77381 #495-62-1993 L2005 IM RHU *020 †20

PARKERSON, Susan. 6707 STERLING RIDGE DR, STE A 77382 #035-48-1985 L2000 PD FM *020 †55

PEARCE, Ralph Purcell. 9006 FOREST XING STE B 77381 #021-05-1978 L1983 GE IM *020 †20

PEET, John J. 17200 ST LUKES WAY 77384 #048-16-1996 L1997 OBG *020 †30

PINERO, Susan Smith. 22 N SEASONS TRCE 77382 #048-14-1981 L1981 DR *020 †80

PRICE, Eric William. 17191 ST LUKES WAY 77384 #048-02-1996 L2001 ORS *020 †40

PRICE, Nathan J. ■ 77384 #041-01-1963 L1964 ORS *071 †40

PRIHODA, Christopher D. 4775 W PANTHER CREEK DR, STE 345 77381 #048-14-2003 L2006 FM *020 †18

PURCELL, Joan Saunders. 4800 W PANTHER CREEK DR, STE 100 77381 #048-02-1990 L1991 PD PSM *020 †55

QUINTERO, Enrique T. 9301 PINECROFT DR, STE 100 77380 #649-30-1984 L1987 AI PDP *020 †55,03

RAWSON, Jon M R. 1001 MEDICAL PLAZA DR, STE 280 77380 #048-04-1980 L1980 REN GYN *020 †30

REGER, Gregg A. 9004 FOREST XING, STE D 77381 #048-02-1995 L1999 PHL FM *020 †18 ‡

RICHARDSON, Paul Vernon. ■ 77380 #048-04-1954 L1954 GP GS *020 †16

RIVERS, Franklin M, Sr. 5055 W PANTHER CREEK DR, APT 1101 77380 #021-05-1946 L1953 IM CD *071

ROBLES, Jose Antonio. ■ 77381 #748-01-1970 L1981 DR NR *020

RODSUWAN, Charles Chalerm. ■ 77381 #891-02-1955 L1989 GP *020

ROGERS, John Cecil. 2170 BUCKTHORNE PL, STE 190 77380 #048-02-1976 L1976 FM *020 †18

RUBIO, Pedro Antonio. 10 WATERWAY CT 77380 #649-01-1968 L1975 GS TS *071 †85 ‡

SAGEBIEL, Tara L. ■ 77382 #048-04-2001 L2005 DR *100 †18

SAMANIEGO, Jesus Enrique. 17198 ST LUKES WAY, STE 540 77384 #048-04-1986 L1987 OBG *020 †30

SAMUEL, Paulraj Anandrupk. ■ 77381 #048-04-2006 L2006 IM *012

SCHLEMBACH, Pamela Jean. 17198 ST LUKES WAY, STE 130 77384 #038-43-1997 L2001 RO *020 †80

SCHOONMAKER, John Bullard. 25325 BOROUGH PARK DR, STE 200 77380 #035-03-1961 L1982 P *020 †75

SCOTT, Terri. 17191 ST LUKES WAY 77384 #048-13-1996 L1997 OBG *020 †30

SERIEL, Randal Kenneth. ■ 77381 #048-14-1992 L1994 EM *020 †18,16

SHANNON, Thomas Oswald. 3115 COLLEGE PARK DR, STE 101B 77384 #041-14-1988 L1993 PS GS *020 †85

SHATBY, Meena Wilson. 1441 WOODSTEAD CT, STE 300 77380 #048-04-2001 L2006 OFA *020

SHAW, Ching-Chia. ■ 77380 #048-13-1983 L1983 AN *020

SHEDDEN, Peter Mc Intyre. 9200 NEW TRAILS DR, STE 100 77381 #065-05-1986 L1992 NS *020 †25

SIDDIQUI, Asma N. 17350 ST LUKES WAY, KELSEY SEYBOLD CLC 77384 #704-02-1988 L1995 PD *020

SIDDIQUI, Nihal Urrab. 9004 FOREST XING 77381 #915-03-1983 L1997 FM *020 †18 ‡

SILER-FISHER, Angela. ■ 77382 #048-15-2001 L2006 EM *020 †16

SLOAN, Thomas Mitchell. ■ 77381 #048-15-1981 L1981 IM *020 †20

SMITH, Bruce David. ■ 77381 #010-03-1965 L1976 R *020 †80

SPARKMAN, Chris A. 10807 KUYKENDAHL RD, STE 408 77382 #048-14-2001 L2002 FM *020 †18

STARK, Thomas Wheeler. 17191 ST LUKES WAY 77384 #048-13-1978 L1978 OTO *020 †45

STILLWAGON, Donald Edward. 4775 W PANTHER CREEK DR, STE 345 77381 #035-08-1976 L1984 FM *020 †18

STREHLOW, Stacy L. 17200 ST LUKES WAY, MEDICAL ARTS BUILDING #1, 77384 #048-04-2000 L2007 OBG *100

STRICKLAND, Donald W. 9100 FOREST XING, STE A 77381 #027-01-1987 L1996 IM *020 †20

STRONG, Steven Michael. 1001 MEDICAL PLAZA DR #280 77380 #005-18-1993 L1997 OBG *020 †30

SULTANA, Nighat. 25214 BOROUGH PARK DR 77380 #704-02-1990 L1996 PD *020 †55

TAMM, Audrey K. 4800 W PANTHER CREEK DR, STE 100 77381 #048-14-1990 L1991 PD *020 †55

TAYLOR, William Marks. ■ 77382 #035-09-1964 L2000 OM AM *071 †70

TILL, Larry P, Jr. ■ 77381 #048-13-1990 L1991 FM *020 †18

TORRES, Norman Jose Justo. 9200 NEW TRAILS DR, STE 100 77381 #748-02-1982 L1999 NS *020

UNTERMAN, Brian Michael. 9001 FOREST XING, STE D 77381 #021-06-1997 L1998 GS *020

URANO, Gary Hideo. 52 WATERWAY CT 77380 #062-01-1969 L1977 GYN *020 †30

VADALA, Richard Michael. 1011 MEDICAL PLAZA DR, STE 220 77380 #048-02-1974 L1975 PD *020 †55

VADAS, Joseph Sylvester. 26 S WATERTREE LN 77380 #065-06-1963 L1978 OM PRS *020

VARTABEDIAN, Bryan S. 17198 ST LUKES WAY, TEXAS CHILDREN'S HEALTH CE 77384 #024-16-1991 L1996 PG NTR *020 †55

VIPULANANDAN, Giritha. 25211 GROGANS MILL RD, STE 400 77380 #220-04-1984 L1993 PD *020 †55

WALKER, John E. 8000 RESEARCH FOREST DR, STE 360 77382 #048-02-1986 L1987 FM *020 †18

WALKER, Wesley Robert. 17191 ST LUKES WAY 77384 #048-13-2000 L2004 IM *020

WALL, Lester Aubrey, Jr. ■ 77381 #023-01-1941 L1941 IM PUD *071 †20

WARRINER, Robert A, III. 1610 WOODSTEAD CT STE 460 77380 #047-05-1976 L1980 UM EM *030 †05

WATTS, Thomas Edwin. 17350 ST LUKES WAY, STE 200 77384 #048-04-1972 L1972 FM *020 †18

WHITE, Charles Edward. 17198 ST LUKES WAY STE 200 77384 #048-02-1974 L1974 OBG *020 †30

WONG, Chun-Kwok. 17191 ST LUKES WAY 77384 #048-13-1986 L1989 END IM *020 †20

WRIGHT, Christopher Jay. 38 W MIRROR RIDGE CIR 77382 #001-02-1994 L1996 FM DR *020 †80

WRIGHT, Randall John. 17191 ST LUKES WAY 77384 #012-05-1998 L2003 CN *020 †75

WUEST, Stephanie Nicole. ■ 77380 #048-04-2008 *012

YAU, Philbert T. 1055 EVERGREEN CIR 77380 #048-14-2001 L2005 MPD *020 †20,55

YELIZAROV, Yelena. ■ 77382 #048-16-2001 ON *100

ZEBALLOS, Jorge Mauricio. 17200 ST LUKES WAY 77384 #048-15-1998 L2000 EM *020

THROCKMORTON – THROCKMORTON

BEASLEY, Craig Clark. 1100 N MINTER AVE 76483 #048-14-1995 L1996 FM *020 †18

TIKI ISLAND – GALVESTON

BALBASTRO, Jeeathbell. ■ 77554 #048-02-2004 L2008 IM *012

MIRYALA, Radheshyam. 1441 LOTUS DR 77554 #048-02-1999 L2001 FM EM *020 †18

RADCLIFFE, Brian Patrick. 435 HANA DR 77554 #048-14-1991 L1994 DR *020 †80

TOMBALL – HARRIS

ABDULLA, Amina. 605 HOLDERRIETH BLVD 77375 #495-28-1967 L1983 P *020

ABROL, Rajeshwar P. 425 HOLDERRIETH BLVD, STE 113 77375 #495-03-1982 L1994 GE IM *020 †20

AHMED, Asiya. 455 SCHOOL ST, STE 27 77375 #704-02-1982 L2002 IM *020 †20

ALI, Shaikh. 455 SCHOOL ST, STE 27 77375 #704-02-1984 L1995 RHU IM *020 †20

AMINE, Maged. 13406 MEDICAL COMPLEX DR, STE 110 77375 #915-04-1986 L1996 CD *020 †20

ASLAM, Ahmad Adnan. 425 HOLDERRIETH BLVD, STE 208 77375 #704-21-1990 L2004 CD *020 †20

AZIMUDDIN, Khawaja. 1101 ALMA ST, STE 106 77375 #704-02-1988 L2005 GS CRS *020 †85,10

BACON, Stacy A. 455 SCHOOL ST, STE 24 77375 #048-14-2000 L2005 ORS *100

BALSARA, Viren J. 605 HOLDERRIETH BLVD 77375 #495-01-1975 L1983 DR *020 †80

BEATIE, Susan J. 13414 MEDICAL COMPLEX DR, STE 6 77375 #048-14-1995 L1998 IM *020 †20

BELTRAN, Jesus. 24914 TOMBALL PKWY, STE 180 77375 #649-14-1985 L1994 FM *020 †18

BHURIWALA, Shujauddin. 13406 MEDICAL COMPLEX DR, STE 150 77375 #704-02-1987 L1999 NEP *020 †20

BLACKWELL, Michael Lee. 425 HOLDERRIETH BLVD, STE 110 77375 #048-02-1991 L1993 ORS *020

BLASCHKE, Donald G, II. 605 HOLDERRIETH BLVD 77375 #048-04-1994 L1997 EM UCM *020 †16

BROWN, Richard Sterling. 425 HOLDERRIETH BLVD # 101 77375 #048-02-1973 L1974 GS *020 †85

BRUCE, Stephanie Swafford. 455 SCHOOL ST, STE 29 77375 #048-16-1997 L1998 OBG *020 †30

CASAGRANDE, Michael G. 13406 MEDICAL COMPLEX DR, STE 190 77375 #048-14-1995 L1996 FM *020 †18

CHAHAL, Balbir S. 455 SCHOOL ST, STE 44 77375 #495-29-1970 L1998 IM IMG *020 †20

CHIU, Sara Marie. ■ 77377 #048-04-2001 L2005 CHP *012 †75

CIBOROWSKI, Amy D. 200 N CHERRY ST 77375 #048-04-1983 L1983 IM *020 †20

CORDES, Stephanie K. 455 SCHOOL ST, STE 26 77375 #048-02-1995 L1998 OTO *020 †45

CUBBAGE, Matthew Palmer. 455 SCHOOL ST, STE 24 77375 #048-04-1997 L2003 ORS *020 †40

DAIRYWALA, Ismail T. 13406 MEDICAL COMPLEX DR, STE 110 77375 #704-02-1992 L2000 IC *100 †20

DAO, Jasmine. ■ 77377 #048-13-2007 *012

DE BAKEY, Gary Alan. 455 SCHOOL ST, STE 29 77375 #048-14-1982 L1983 OBG *020 †30

DELGADO, Armando F. 605 HOLDERRIETH BLVD, STE 6 77375 #275-01-1947 L1969 FM *071 †18

DESCANT, E Paul, II. 909 GRAHAM DR 77375 #649-14-1972 L1975 FM *020 ‡

DESPLINTER, Traci. 13414 MEDICAL COMPLEX DR, STE 7 77375 #048-15-1997 L2002 OBG REN *030

DITERESA, Michael Anthony. 425 HOLDERRIETH BLVD # 209, TOMBALL ADULT INTERNAL MED 77375 #048-12-2000 L2002 IM *020 †20

DUXBURY, William John. ■ 77377 #010-01-1960 L1961 EM *071 †18

FARUQI, Sohaib. 425 HOLDERRIETH BLVD # 109, NORTHWEST GASTROENTEROLOGY 77375 #704-01-1987 L2002 GE *020 †20

FERAY, Cotton Danl E. 720 LAWRENCE ST 77375 #048-13-1970 L1970 GP *020 †18

FLOWER, Linda Whidden. 13414 MEDICAL COMPLEX DR 77375 #011-02-1975 L1977 FM *020 †18

GERBER, David Gerard. 28155 TOMBALL PKWY STE 4 77375 #048-13-1984 L1985 EM *020

GILMORE, John F, III. 1101 ALMA ST, STE 104 77375 #048-15-1995 L1996 FM *020 †18

GOHEL, Raka C. 425 HOLDERRIETH BLVD, STE 211 77375 #495-37-1988 L1995 PME AN *020 †05 ‡

GRAHAM, Norman E. 605 HOLDERRIETH BLVD, TOMBALL REG HOSP 77375 #041-13-1947 L1950 OS *020 †18

GRIFFIN, Monica P. 605 HOLDERRIETH BLVD, TOMBALL REG HOSP PATHOLOGY 77375 #048-14-1991 L2003 PTH *020 †50

GURAM, Maninder Singh. 425 HOLDERRIETH BLVD # 113 77375 #495-03-1980 L1991 GE IM *020 †20

HAMMIT, Matthew D. 13635 MICHEL RD, TEXAS ORTHOPAEDIC & SPORTS 77375 #048-16-1998 L2004 ORS *020

HARKINS, Michael Brian. 455 SCHOOL ST, STE 10 77375 #021-05-1989 L1997 GS *020 †85

HARKLESS, Megan Corina. ■ 77377 #007-02-2003 L2003 PD *020 †55

HARMAN, Louis E, III. 28120 TOMBALL PKWY 77375 #023-01-1973 L1981 ORS OSM *072 †40

HENRY, Robert Lee, Jr. 13406 MEDICAL COMPLEX DR 77375 #649-45-1980 L1987 PD *020 †55

HOLDER, Jimmy Lloyd, Jr. ■ 77375 #048-12-2005 PD *012

HOLNESS, Sharon Lynn. PO BOX 823 77377 #016-43-1998 L2008 PD *020

HOUBALEK, Lenke. ■ 77377 #035-08-1957 L1973 FM *071 †55

HUYNH, Hung Cong. 605 HOLDERRIETH BLVD, WOUND CARE DEPARTMENT 77375 #048-02-1996 L1998 FM OS *020 †18

IRFAN, Muhammad. 1205 GRAHAM DR 77375 #704-02-1991 L1996 IM *020 †20

IRFAN, Muhammad. 1205 GRAHAM DR 77375 #704-05-1989 L1992 IM *020

JACOB, Shehnaz. 425 HOLDERRIETH BLVD 77375 #495-08-1975 L1984 PD *020 †20

JACOB, Susan C. 801 ALMA ST 77375 #495-27-1964 L1975 PDA PD *020 †55

JAMALI, Shabbir-Husain. 421 SCHOOL ST, STE 110 77375 #704-02-1987 L1997 GE *020 †20

JOHNSON, Gerald Wayne. 28301 STATE HIGHWAY 249, STE 500 77375 #004-01-1966 L1969 PS *020

JORDAN, Maria L. 27920 TOMBALL PKWY, STE 210 77375 #048-14-1994 L1996 FM *020 †18

KARN, Willard R. ■ 77377 #048-04-1953 L1953 OM GPM *071

KARR, Carl Allan. 13624 MICHEL RD, STE 201 77375 #048-13-1991 L1993 PD *020 †55

KASTHURIRANGAN, Mythili. 13406 MEDICAL COMPLEX DR, STE 200 77375 #495-59-1976 L1981 PD *020 †55

KHAN, Waqar A. 610A LAWRENCE ST, CARDIOVASCULAR CLINIC OF T 77375 #704-01-1986 L1992 CD EM *020 †20

KIRKPATRICK, Kurt J. 425 HOLDERRIETH BLVD, STE 204 77375 #048-14-1988 L1991 OBG *020 †30

KOVAR, Jay L. 605 HOLDERRIETH BLVD 77375 #048-13-1989 L1992 EM *020 †16

KURZYDLO, Grzegorz Piotr. 455 SCHOOL ST, STE 20 77375 #759-01-1992 L2003 N *020

LAM, Yvonne. ■ 77375 #035-45-2005 IM *012

LE, David Thanh. 455 SCHOOL ST, STE 40 77375 #035-03-1995 L1997 IM *020 †20

LE, Mark Dinh. 455 SCHOOL ST, STE 40 77375 #048-09-1995 L1998 IM *020 †20

LE BAUD, Pierre. 605 HOLDERRIETH BLVD 77375 #396-04-1970 L2002 ORS *020 †40

LEDER, Stuart Andrew. 13414 MEDICAL COMPLEX DR, STE 12 77375 #048-04-1989 L1990 N *020 †75

LEHMANN, Shaun Dennison. 425 HOLDERRIETH BLVD # 206 77375 #037-01-1997 L1999 PM *020 †60

LESCH, Jack Wayne. 14011 PARK DR STE 201 77377 #048-04-1971 L1976 FM *020 †18

LESSARD, Larry C. 605 HOLDERRIETH BLVD 77375 #065-05-1979 L1981 AN *020 †05

LIGHT, Rodney A. 13414 MEDICAL COMPLEX DR, STE 6 77375 #048-02-1985 L1987 IM UM *020 †20

MARINO, Barbara Doyle. 425 HOLDERRIETH BLVD, STE 212 77375 #038-43-1985 L1990 CS GYN *020 †30

MARTIN, Earl Francis. 710 LAWRENCE ST 77375 #649-02-1970 L1973 FM *020 †18 ‡

MATHIS, James E, Jr. 13635 MICHEL RD, 13635 MICHEL 77375 #048-15-1997 L2002 ORS *020 †40

MATTI, Steve Joseph. 605 HOLDERRIETH BLVD 77375 #025-01-1996 L2001 EM *020 †16

MC CHESNEY, William David. 455 SCHOOL ST, STE 24 77375 #010-02-1982 L1991 ORS OSM *020 †40

MC NEILL, Roger. 425 HOLDERRIETH BLVD, STE 107 77375 #950-01-1966 L1978 OTO *020 †45

MIDDLEBROOK, John D. 24727 TOMBALL PKWY, STE 120 77375 #048-14-2002 L2005 EM *020 †16

MURILLO, George Jos. 425 HOLDERRIETH BLVD # 112 77375 #048-02-1971 L1973 FM *020 †20

MUTTIANA, Daljit S. 355 SCHOOL ST, STE 101 77375 #495-03-1979 L1993 CD *020 †20

NAMBIAR, Anakha. ■ 77377 #496-29-1992 L2005 FM *100 †18

NASIR, Marwan A. 605 HOLDERRIETH BLVD 77375 #605-01-1984 L1990 PTH *020 †50

NATH, Anil. 605 HOLDERRIETH BLVD, TOMBALL HOSPITAL 77375 #917-09-1980 L1985 AN *020 †05

NATHANI, Imran S. 1205 GRAHAM DR 77375 #704-02-1991 L1996 IM *020 †20

NGUYEN, Anh Van. 455 SCHOOL ST, STE 49 77375 #048-02-1988 L1989 D *020 †15

OGDEN, Brian Anthony. ■ 77377 #021-05-2005 L2007 DR *012

ONORATO, James Jos. 425 HOLDERRIETH BLVD 77375 #038-06-1984 L1997 NEP IM *020 †20

PAI, Arvind Madhav. 425 HOLDERRIETH BLVD # 104 77375 #496-38-1972 L1980 CD IM *020

PALANPURWALA, Khozema. 13406 MEDICAL COMPLEX DR, STE 200 77375 #704-02-1988 L1995 NPM PD *020 †55

PALMEROS, Alejandra. ■ 77375 #048-13-1997 L1999 FM *020 †18

PARUNGAO, Dorothy C. ■ 77375 #048-14-1997 L1997 FM *020 †18

PIRTLE, Philip L. 909 GRAHAM DR STE B 77375 #048-02-1990 L1991 CCM *020 †20

POTHURI, Bharat. 425 HOLDERRIETH BLVD STE 207 77375 #495-22-1998 L2004 GE *020 †20

RAHI, M Atif. 13406 MEDICAL COMPLEX DR, STE 180 77375 #704-01-1988 L1997 IM *020 †20

RAMZY, Sherif R M. 1101 ALMA ST, STE 106 77375 #915-02-1979 L1993 N *020

RAND, Scott Edward. 605 HOLDERRIETH BLVD 77375 #046-01-1989 L2000 FM ESM *020 †18

RODRIGUEZ, Michael Arthur. 929 GRAHAM DR STE B 77375 #056-06-1978 L1979 OBG *020

ROSE, Allinson Macaulay. 13624 MICHEL RD STE 201 77375 #030-05-1992 L1996 PD *020 †55

ROUSE, Jerry Duane. 13414 MEDICAL COMPLEX DR, STE 13 77375 #048-13-1979 L1981 U *020

SAGAR, Bhuvana. 455 SCHOOL ST, STE 27 77375 #495-59-1994 L2000 ON *020 †20

SCHUTZMANN, Katherine M. 605 HOLDERRIETH BLVD 77375 #021-05-1988 L1989 EM *020 †16

SHAHZAD, Arsalan. 610 LAWRENCE ST 77375 #033-06-1997 L2006 CD *020 †20

SHAIKH, Muhammad Aquil. 13406 MEDICAL COMPLEX DR, STE 180 77375 #704-16-1985 L1996 ID *020 †20

SHEFFIELD, Hayne J, Jr. 13414 MEDICAL COMPLX DR #4 77375 #048-02-1969 L1969 OPH *020 †35

SINGH, Balbir. 455 SCHOOL ST, STE 20 77375 #495-29-1977 L1992 N *020 †75,55

SINGH, Harvinderpal. 425 HOLDERRIETH BLVD, STE 205 77375 #048-16-1997 L1998 GS *020 †85

SINGH, Poonam. 455 SCHOOL ST, STE 21 77375 #495-90-1977 L1992 PD *071 †55

SINGHAL, Ashish. 605 HOLDERRIETH BLVD 77375 #048-13-1995 L1997 EM *020

SKRIPKA, Charles F, Jr. ■ 77377 #048-12-1967 L1967 U NM *020

SMITH, Tinsley Gordon. 605 HOLDERRIETH BLVD 77375 #048-04-1966 L1966 OPH *020 †35

SOHNER, Marie Therese. 929 GRAHAM DR, STE B 77375 #048-02-1981 L1981 OBG *020 †30

STATON, Kimberlea Ward. 455 SCHOOL ST, STE 24 77375 #048-02-1996 L2002 HS *020 †40

STERNICK, Cary Steven. 990 VILLAGE SQUARE DR, STE K 77375 #056-05-1975 L1983 N LM *020 †75

SUN, John. 13628 MICHEL RD, STE 200 77375 #033-05-1997 L2000 FM *020 †18

SUN, Tom Hong Chih. 455 SCHOOL ST STE 47 77375 #033-06-1990 L1994 OPH *020 †35

TOMPKINS, William Earl. 13414 MEDICAL COMPLEX DR, STE 6 77375 #016-06-1974 L1977 IM IMG *020 †20 ‡

TULLIDGE, Archer K, Jr. 402 FLORENCE ST 77375 #047-20-1984 L1997 P *020 †75

TURBAY, David. 425 HOLDERRIETH BLVD # 208 77375 #264-04-1991 L2001 CD *020 †20

TYE, Kathleen M. 605 HOLDERRIETH BLVD 77375 #048-14-1993 L1994 FM *020 †18

VALDEZ, George Andrew. 1101 ALMA ST STE 104 77375 #048-02-1999 L2002 FM *020 †18

VANKAWALA, Hemant Hasmukh. 24727 TOMBALL PKWY 77375 #048-13-2001 L2003 EM *020

VEJLANI, Mustansir. 602 LAWRENCE ST, STE B 77375 #704-02-1989 L1996 PCC SME *020 †20

VELASCO, Joseph Eugene. ■ 77377 #035-08-1957 L1973 D *071 †15

WANNER, Elizabeth J. 1101 ALMA ST, STE 102 77375 #048-14-1989 L1990 FM *020 †18

WARREN, Joseph Fielding. ■ 77375 #048-04-1954 L1954 P *071

YANG, Theodore K. 605 HOLDERRIETH BLVD 77375 #048-02-1993 L1994 RO *020 †80

ZAHIRUDDIN, Shaukath Q. 28465 STATE HIGHWAY 249 77375 #495-65-1972 L1981 FM *020

ZIA, Tariq. 455 SCHOOL ST, STE 22 77375 #704-21-1986 L1998 END IM *020 †20

ZIRL, Robert Sabal. 605 HOLDERRIETH BLVD, TOMBALL REGIONAL HOSPITAL 77375 #048-02-1982 L1983 PTH *020 †50

TOW – LLANO

SHEPHERD, Donald Ray. ■ 78672 #048-12-1962 L1962 PTH *071 †50

TRINIDAD – HENDERSON

LOOS, Jason T. ■ 75163 #048-13-2002 L2006 PTH *020 †50

MURPHY, Wilson Darell. ■ 75163 #048-02-1972 L1972 EM *071 †16

TRINITY – TRINITY

DESHPANDE, Amol Sudhakar. 924 ROBB ST, RAJ MEDICAL 75862 #495-17-1985 L1998 PD *020 †55

EL-ASWAD, Naim Bassem. ■ 75862 #605-01-1997 L2002 IM *020 †20 ‡

ROMEZI, Masoud. 900 PROSPECT DR, RURAL HEALTH CL 75862 #517-07-1982 L1995 IM *020 †20

TROPHY CLUB – DENTON

DRYDEN, Charles F, Jr. 2800 E HIGHWAY 114 STE 130 76262 #048-15-1994 L1995 EM *020 †16

GIBBS, Sharon Jill. 2800 E HIGHWAY 114 STE 220 76262 #020-02-1997 L1998 PM *020 †60

MORTON, Ronald G. 2800 E HIGHWAY 114 76262 #048-02-1985 L1986 OTO HNS *020 †45

YI, David Chaeman. 301 TROPHY LAKE DR 76262 #048-12-2001 L2004 **FM** *020 †18

TROUP – SMITH

CALDWELL, Rodney Lynn. 530 COUNTY ROAD 3811 75789 #048-15-1983 L1983 **GP** *020

TROY – BELL

BASKERVILLE, Jerry Ray. 4500 FRANKLIN RD, C/O EMERGENCY DEPT 76579 #060-01-1976 L1982 **EM** *020 †16
CANTU, Cesar Emilio. 606 GOATES RD 76579 #047-07-1981 L1987 **FM** *020 †18

TULIA – SWISHER

CULWELL, Cody Greg. 105 HOSPITAL AVE, STE 846 79088 #048-12-2002 L2003 **FM** *020 †18
FOREMAN, Lee S. ■ 79088 #048-04-1953 L1953 **GP** *071
MARNELL, Tori G. 105 HOSPITAL AVE, STE 846 79088 #048-12-1996 L1997 **FM** *020 †18 ‡
ROSSI, Steven B. 105 HOSPITAL AVE, STE 846 79088 #048-15-2000 L2002 **FM** *020 †18 ‡
SCOTT, Gordon W. ■ 79088 #048-04-1953 L1953 **GP GS** *071 †85

TYLER – SMITH

ABERNATHY, E Maxey. 925 E DAWSON ST 75701 #048-04-1966 L1969 **DR** *071 †80
ABRAHAM, Sujatha. 1100 S BECKHAM AVE 75701 #048-03-1993 L1996 **IM** *020 †20
ABRAMEIT, Ann H. 910 E HOUSTON ST STE 600 75702 #048-16-1991 L1992 **OBG** *071 †30
ABRAMEIT, Warren A. 910 E HOUSTON ST, STE 550 75702 #048-16-1991 L1992 **GS** *020 †85
ADELMAN, Neil H. ■ 75703 #165-04-1978 L1995 **ON** *020 †20
AHMED, Nabeel Kamran. 1133 MEDICAL DR 75701 #704-21-1991 L1999 **NEP IM** *020 †20
AKIN, Kathryn Brooks. 11937 US HWY 271, U.T. HEALTH CENTER AT TYLE 75708 #048-04-1984 L1985 **PD PHP** *020 †55
AKIODE, Oladimeji Samson. 800 E DAWSON ST 75701 #690-01-1989 L2002 **IM** *020 †20
ALBAHRA, Motaz. 755 S BECKHAM AVE 75701 #875-02-1979 L1995 **PTH DMP** *040 †50
ALBRIGHT, Charles D, II. 520 DOUGLAS BLVD 75702 #048-05-1961 L1968 **IM** *071 †20
ALEXANDER, Thomas Howard. 1100 S BECKHAM AVE 75701 #048-02-1955 L1957 **IM** *020 †20
ALLEN, Timothy Craig. 11937 US HWY 271, THE UNIV OF TX HLTH CTR 75708 #048-04-1984 L1985 **PTH PCP** *020 †50
ALLEY, Darrell Eugene. 1020 E IDEL ST 75701 #025-12-2001 L2008 **CCS** *020 †85
ALWAN, Imad. 800 E DAWSON ST 75701 #875-01-1990 L2004 **CD** *020 †20
AMARO-GALVEZ, Rodolfo. 11937 US HIGHWAY 271 75708 #649-26-1980 L1993 **PDP PD** *020 †55
ANDERSON, Lawrence L. 1367 DOMINION PLZ 75703 #023-12-1984 L1996 **D** *020 †15
ANDERSON, Mark Robt. 1701 WOODLANDS DR 75703 #003-01-1985 L1991 **EM** *020 †16
ANDERSON, Richard Allen. 520 DOUGLAS BLVD 75702 #048-12-1974 L1974 **IM** *020 †20
ANDREWS, Duane Neil. 910 E HOUSTON ST, STE 530 75702 #048-04-1963 L1963 **IM** *020 †20
ANDREWS, John Peterson. 2301 S BROADWAY AVE, STE B8 75701 #048-14-1983 L1983 **DR** *062 †80
ANTHONY, James M. 3320 TROUP HWY STE 260, OMEGA & REHAB VOC EVAL CLC 75701 #048-02-1944 L1944 **OTO PME** *020 †45
ARCE, Luis Roberto. 910 E HOUSTON ST, STE 250 75702 #341-03-1996 L2005 **END IM** *020 †20
ARDILL, William David. 6001 RALEIGH DR 75703 #010-01-1980 L1981 **GS** *020 †85
AREGO, Donald Edward. 701 OLYMPIC PLAZA CIR 75701 #048-04-1982 L1983 **PM** *020 †60
ARISCO, Joseph P. 3302 OLD JACKSONVILLE RD 75701 #048-02-1982 L1983 **P** *020 †75
ARMSTRONG, Stephen K. 2301 S BROADWAY AVE, STE B8 75701 #048-13-1986 L1987 **DR GS** *020 †80
ARNOLD, Thomas Jefferson. 2301 S BROADWAY AVE, STE B8 75701 #048-13-1978 L1978 **DR** *020 †80
AUGUSTUS, Lazel B. 520 DOUGLAS BLVD 75702 #048-02-1997 L2000 **IM** *020 †20
AUSTIN, Michael D. 1000 E 5TH ST 75701 #048-13-1995 L1998 **PD** *020
AVENT, James K, Jr. 3502 S BROADWAY AVE, STE H 75701 #021-01-1951 L1959 **GYN** *071
AVERY, Wilbur G. 11937 US HIGHWAY 271 75708 #035-01-1952 L1980 **PUD CD** *071 †20
AZZI, Elie Youssef. 11937 US HWY 271 75708 #605-02-1994 L2008 **PUD** *020 †20
BABER, Daniel. 1000 S BECKHAM AVE 75701 #048-02-1987 L1988 **FM** *020 †18
BABINEAU, Hugh Paul. 1100 E LAKE ST, STE 230 75702 #035-45-1996 L2001 **GS** *020 †85
BAER, Henry Allen. 800 E DAWSON ST 75701 #023-01-1956 L1977 **PS GS** *071 †85,65
BAINES, Johnathan C. ■ 75701 #026-07-2007 **FP** *012
BAINS, Arvinder Kaur. 3414 GOLDEN RD 75701 #495-43-1991 L2003 **IM** *020 †20
BAINS, Harshivinderjit. 1519 E FRONT ST, HARSHI BAINS, MD.,PA 75702 #023-07-1997 L2003 **OPH** *020 †35
BALL, David Warren. 1133 MEDICAL DR 75701 #027-01-1994 L1997 **IM** *020 †20
BANGALORE, Nirmala P. 11937 US HWY 271 75708 #496-35-1994 L2006 **FPG** *100 ‡
BANKHEAD, Molly May. 700 S FLEISHEL AVE 75701 #048-12-1990 L1991 **NEP** *020 †20
BARBARISI, Leonard. ■ 75703 #024-07-1963 L2002 **GS** *071 †85
BARKER, Robert N. 11937 US HWY 271 75708 #048-16-1991 L1991 **AN** *020 †05
BARNES, Peter Francis. 11937 US HWY 271 3154, CTR FOR PULMONARY & INFEC 75708 #005-06-1981 L1998 **ID** *050 †20
BARRET, Mark M. 706 TURTLE CREEK DR, PEDIATRICS 75701 #048-12-1992 L1993 **PD** *020 †55
BARROWS, Susan Alison. 11937 US HIGHWAY 271, TYLER 75708 #005-06-1983 L1998 **PD PDP** *020 †55
BARTON-NIELSEN, Karen M. 645 S BROADWAY AVE 75701 #048-02-1988 L1989 **FM** *020 †18
BASILE, Myrtha Elsie. 721 CLINIC DR, TYLER HEMATOLOGY ONCOLOGY 75701 #041-12-1983 L2003 **ON HEM** *020 †20
BASKIN, Thomas Grady. ■ 75701 #048-02-1947 L1947 **P CHP** *071 †75
BATES, Joe Boyd. 15892 CR 26, AZLEWAY BOYS RANCH 75707 #021-05-1965 L1971 **P PD** *020 †55,75
BAUM, Martin L. 800 E DAWSON ST, TRINITY MOTHER FRANCES HOS 75701 #048-15-1993 L1994 **EM** *020 †16
BEAIRD, David H. 520 DOUGLAS BLVD 75702 #048-12-1984 L1987 **IM** *020 †20
BEALL, Charles V. 910 E HOUSTON ST, STE 550 75702 #048-12-1988 L1989 **GS** *020 †85
BEALS, Ronald David. 800 E DAWSON ST 75701 #030-06-1971 L1987 **EM OM** *062 †16

BECK, Timothy L. 700 OLYMPIC PLAZA CIR #700 75701 #048-13-1990 L1991 **ORS OFA** *020 †40
BECKER, Royal Matthew. 800 E DAWSON ST 75701 #026-04-1993 L1997 **IM** *020 †20
BECKLEY, Dannise. 5791 NEW COPELAND RD 75703 #048-15-1986 L1987 **D** *020 †15
BEDKOWSKA, Urszula A. 3414 GOLDEN RD 75701 #759-07-1978 L1996 **FM** *020 †18
BEDKOWSKI, Stanislaw M. 11937 US HWY 271, UTCH TYLER 75708 #759-07-1978 L1996 **FM** *020 †18
BEENE, Christopher Lee. 11937 US HIGHWAY 271, DEPT FM 75708 #039-01-2007 **FP** *012
BEETS, Michael Thos. 800 E DAWSON ST 75701 #048-02-1979 L1979 **FM** *020 †18
BELCHER, Stacey Rose. 3311 WOODS BLVD, ELLIS EXECUTIVE CENTER 75707 #048-13-1995 L1996 **P** *020 †75
BELT, W Thomas, Jr. 11937 US HIGHWAY 271 75708 #048-12-1981 L1981 **IM IMG** *020 †20
BELUE, Joe Bill. 800 E DAWSON ST 75701 #048-12-1964 L1965 **GYN** *020 †30
BENGTSON, Todd D. 1327 TROUP HWY 75701 #048-12-1992 L1994 **VS** *020 †85
BENNETT, Bobby Gene, Jr. 3200 TROUP HWY, STE 200 75701 #027-01-1988 L1989 **AN** *020 †05
BENTLEY, Andrew Edward. 921 SHILOH RD STE C-1 75703 #048-04-1994 L1995 **FM** *020 †18
BERNE, Evelyn Gonzalez. 700 OLYMPIC PLAZA CIR, STE 406 75701 #024-01-1994 L2000 **GS SO** *020 †85
BERNE, John Denis. 1020 E IDEL ST 75701 #005-06-1991 L1999 **TRS CCS** *020 †85
BESSONETT, Paula A. 4111 UNIVERSITY BLVD 75701 #048-13-1987 L1988 **FM** *020 †18
BETTINGER, Jerry Joe. 935 S BAXTER AVE STE 105 75701 #048-14-1976 L1976 **N** *020 †75
BINGHAM, Nicholas Orville. 11937 US HWY 271, AT TY 75708 #016-11-2004 L2004 **GPM** *012
BLAU, Jonathan. 1814 ROSELAND BLVD, STE 200 75701 #056-06-1989 L1993 **PM** *020 †60
BOCHOW, Thomas Wiley. 2440 E 5TH ST, EYECARE ASSOCIATES OF EAST 75701 #023-07-1988 L1989 **OPH** *020 †35
BOHN, Jeffrey Lee. 1424 E FRONT ST, DEHAVEN EYE CLINIC 75702 #025-07-1985 L1997 **OPH IM** *020 †35
BOONE, Corbett H. 11937 US HIGHWAY 271, FAMILY PRACTICE DEPT 75708 #048-14-2005 L2007 **FP** *012
BOREN, Sunni S. 2017 RICKETY LN 75703 #048-16-2000 L2003 **OBG** *020
BORUCKI, Michael J. 11937 US HIGHWAY 271, UNIVERSITY OF TEXAS HEALTH 75708 #048-02-1983 L1984 **IM ID** *040 †20
BORUCKI, Sally Sandlin. 11937 US HWY 271 75708 #048-02-1985 L1986 **N** *020 †75
BORUM, Stanley Edward. 800 E DAWSON ST 75701 #048-12-1970 L1971 **AN** *020 †05
BOURIANOFF, Gleb Gordon. 605 CHASE DR, STE B 75701 #048-02-1970 L1970 **EM IM** *071
BOWERS, Bruce Thos. ■ 75703 #007-02-1956 L1967 **OPH** *071 †35
BOYD, Gary D. 700 OLYMPIC PLAZA CIR, STE 407 75701 #048-02-1981 L1981 **GE IM** *020 †20
BOYD, Stephen. 1000 S BECKHAM AVE 75701 #065-02-1974 L1978 **GP** *020
BOYLAN, Christopher Scott. 619 S FLEISHEL AVE 75701 #035-09-1990 L1991 **CD** *020 †20
BOYNE, Robert L. 700 OLYMPIC PLAZA CIR, STE 912 75701 #048-16-1997 L2002 **CN** *020 †75
BRADLEY, John Carter. 3200 TROUP HWY, STE 200 75701 #048-04-1997 L2001 **AN** *020 †05
BRANDON, Catherine Jordan. 910 E HOUSTON ST STE 65, ROSS BREAST CENTER 75702 #005-15-1985 L1997 **DR** *020 †80
BRELSFORD, William Geo. 1212 CLINIC DR 75701 #048-02-1981 L1982 **RHU IM** *030 †20
BRIDGES, Ben Ford. 420 DOUGLAS BLVD 75702 #048-12-1947 L1947 **IM** *020 †20
BRIGGS, Darrell Sherman. 3200 TROUP HWY, EAST TX ANESTHESIOLOGY ASS 75701 #048-14-2004 L2008 **AN** *012
BRIGHT, Thomas Clements. 700 OLYMPIC PLAZA CIR, UROLOGY TYLER PA 75701 #047-06-1971 L1974 **U** *020 †95
BROWN, C Edward. 912 S FLEISHEL AVE, S 75701 #048-12-1981 L1981 **IM** *020 †20
BROWN, Carlos Jose. ■ 75703 #021-06-2005 L2008 **EM** *012
BROWN, William E. 910 E HOUSTON ST STE 600 75702 #048-12-1977 L1977 **GYN** *020 †30
BRUNSON, Clinton R. 1030 E AMHERST DR 75701 #048-02-1992 L2000 **DR** *020 †80
BUCHANAN, Patrick H. 719 W FRONT ST STE 100 75702 #048-02-1964 L1964 **P** *020
BURK, Patti L. 11937 HIGHWAY 271 75708 #048-15-2000 L2002 **FM** *020 †18
BURTON, Robert F. 700 OLYMPIC PLAZA CIR, STE 908 75701 #048-04-1985 L1987 **N** *020 †75
BUZBEE, Thomas M, Jr. 1910 ROSELAND BLVD 75701 #048-14-1991 L1992 **IM** *020 †20
BYRD, Marcus A. 800 E DAWSON ST 75701 #048-15-2000 L2003 **IM** *020
CABELL, James Franklin, III. 520 DOUGLAS BLVD 75702 #001-02-1998 L2003 **R** *062 †80
CACCITOLO, James Andrew. 910 E HOUSTON ST, STE 530 75702 #016-43-1994 L2004 **TS GS** *020 †85,90
CALHOUN, Kirk Aquilla. 11937 US HIGHWAY 271, UNIV TX HLTH CTR AT TYLER 75708 #019-02-1978 L1994 **IM NEP** *030 †20
CALLENDER, Troy A. 3413 GOLDEN RD 75701 #048-04-1989 L1990 **OTO GS** *020 †45
CALODNEY, Aaron Kenneth. 1814 ROSELAND BLVD, 2ND FL 75701 #028-03-1984 L1988 **AN PME** *020 †20
CAMERON, Harold Brown. 1020 E LAKE ST 75701 #048-04-1942 L1942 **GYN** *071 †30
CAMP, John T. 700 OLYMPIC PLAZA CIR #700 75701 #048-15-1989 L1990 **ORS HS** *020 †40
CAMPBELL, Melinda Ann. 11937 US HIGHWAY 271, DEPT OF FAMILY MEDICINE 75708 #007-02-2006 **FP** *012
CANTU, Jathan Paul. 1000 E 5TH ST 75701 #048-04-1984 L1985 **FM** *020 †18 ‡
CAPLINGER, Robert A. 1000 S BECKHAM AVE 75701 #025-01-1952 L1957 **IM** *071
CARNEY, David John. 505 S FLEISHEL AVE 75702 #030-06-1981 L1987 **ORS** *020 †40
CARNEY, Robert John. 619 S FLEISHEL AVE, STE 101 75701 #028-03-1978 L1987 **CD IM** *020 †20
CAROE, Carl D. 5414 S BROADWAY AVE 75703 #048-13-1986 L1987 **FM** *020 †18
CARTER, Bruce Carlton. 2301 S BROADWAY AVE, STE B8 75701 #048-13-1984 L1985 **DR** *020 †80
CARTER, Clinton John. 11937 US HIGHWAY 271 75708 #048-14-2004 L2006 **FM** *020 †18
CASAS, Kari Ann. 910 E HOUSTON ST STE 25 75702 #037-01-1998 L2006 **MG** *020 †19,55
CASAS, Luis. 910 E HOUSTON ST, STE 250 75702 #039-01-1998 L2006 **END** *020 †20,55
CECCOLI, Hector Domingo. 115 W 5TH ST 75701 #132-04-1990 L2000 **CD IM** *020 †20
CHALMERS, John Holbrook. 11937 US HWY 271, UT HEALTH CENTER TYLER 75708 #048-04-1970 L1970 **DR NM** *020 †80,28 ‡
CHAMBERS, Angela Nell. 1000 S BECKHAM AVE 75701 #038-45-1996 L1999 **IM** *020
CHAMBERS, William Henry. 910 E HOUSTON ST STE 600 75702 #048-13-1972 L1972 **GYN** *020 †30
CHAMPION, Stanton Pyburn. 700 OLYMPIC PLAZA CIR, UROLOGY TYLER PA 75701 #048-13-1970 L1970 **U** *020 †95
CHERRY, Debbie Carol. 11937 US HWY 271 75708 #048-15-1995 L1998 **OM GPM** *040 †70
CHOU, Chih-Hao G. 1327 TROUP HWY 75701 #244-04-1986 L2003 **RHU** *020 †20
CLARK, Carey Alexander. 3414 GOLDEN RD 75701 #047-06-1990 L1999 **HS ORS** *020 †40
CLARK, James Tillman. 1100 E LAKE ST STE 330 75701 #048-02-1966 L1966 **PS OTO** *020 †45,65

■ = Address Information Privacy Protected

CLARK, P Le Mon, III. ■ 75703 #047-06-1945 L1953 **PUD** *071 †85,90
CLAYPOOL, Sharon L. 11937 HWY 271 75708 #048-14-1985 L1986 **OBG** *020 †30
COATS, David Alexander. 3200 TROUP HWY 75701 #036-05-1964 L1964 **R NM** *020 †80,28
COGDILL, Douglas G. 305 W RUSK ST 75701 #048-13-1995 L2000 **PD** *020 †55
COHEN, Steven Jay. 1327 TROUP HWY 75701 #041-07-1984 L1995 **RHU IM** *020 †20
COLE, Vannoy Stewart. 1417 S SOUTHEAST LOOP 323 75701 #047-07-1972 L1975 **P** *020
COLLINS, Lester B. 700 OLYMPIC PLAZA CIR # 91 75701 #048-14-1975 L1975 **N** *020 †75
COLTMAN, Douglas C. 520 DOUGLAS BLVD 75702 #048-13-1993 L1995 **IM** *020
CONFLITTI, Joseph M. 700 OLYMPIC PLAZA CIR 75701 #048-16-1995 L1996 **OTR ORS** *020 †40
CONNELL, Laura E. 620 S FLEISHEL AVE 75701 #048-16-1999 L2002 **PS** *020
CONNER, William Chace. 912 S FLEISHEL AVE 75701 #048-02-2000 L2007 **FM** *100
CONSTANTE, Benjamin Jesse. 6210 S BROADWAY AVE, EMERGENCY DEPARTMENT 75703 #048-15-1999 L2004 **OBG EM** *020 †18
COOLEY, Joe P, Jr. 3200 TROUP HWY, STE 200 75701 #048-16-1998 L1999 **AN** *020 †05
COOPER, Thomas Watson. 417 S SAUNDERS AVE, ENT 75702 #048-12-1970 L1970 **OTO** *020 †45
COTTON, James Russell, Jr. 1133 MEDICAL DR 75701 #048-02-1969 L1969 **NEP IM** *020 †20
COUCH, Leslie Ann. 11937 US HIGHWAY 271, UNIV TX HLTH CTR 75708 #048-02-1983 L1983 **PUD IM** *020 †20
COULTAS, David Bruce. 11937 US HIGHWAY 271, UNIVERSITY OF TEXAS HEALTH 75708 #011-03-1979 L2005 **PUD CCM** *050 †20
COX, Steven Warren. 11937 US HIGHWAY 271, DEPT OF SURG U OF TX HLTH 75708 #019-02-1992 L1997 **GS** *020 †85
CRAIG, Edouard. 520 DOUGLAS BLVD 75702 #198-01-1995 L2003 **IM** *020 †20 ‡
CREATH, Robert Gerald. 17182 PILOT DR 75707 #025-07-1987 L1991 **EM** *020 †16
CRISP, George O. 751 S BECKHAM AVE 75701 #048-12-1952 L1952 **IM OM** *071 ‡
CROWDER, Marietta. 1517 W FRONT ST 75702 #036-05-1955 L1963 **PHP IM** *030
CRUTCHFIELD, J Stuart. 722 CLINIC DR 75701 #048-04-1988 L1989 **NS GS** *020 †25
CURRY ALEXANDER, Cynthia. 800 E DAWSON ST 75701 #048-02-1985 L1986 **AN** *020 †05
CUSHMAN, Kenneth Donald. 520 DOUGLAS BLVD 75702 #065-01-1969 L1977 **FM** *020
DALTON, David Lee. 214 E HOUSTON ST 75702 #048-13-1971 L1971 **OBG** *020 †30
DANIELS, William D. 800 E DAWSON ST 75701 #048-14-1998 L2002 **AN** *020
DANIELSON, Guy Otis, III. 1814 ROSELAND BLVD, FL2 75701 #039-01-1968 L1976 **NS** *020 †25
DANLY, David Robt. 2323 W FRONT ST 75702 #048-14-1988 L1989 **CHP** *020
DAVIDSON, Barbara Ryno. 1100 E LAKE ST, STE 340 75701 #048-13-1993 L1998 **PM** *020 †60
DAVIS, Brent O. 619 S FLEISHEL AVE, TYLER CARDIOVASCULAR 75701 #048-16-1997 L2004 **IC** *020 †20
DAVIS, Herbert Allen. 2323 W FRONT ST 75702 #048-02-1965 L1965 **P** *020
DAVIS, Kent Matthew. 11937 US HIGHWAY 271, U.T. HEALTH CENTER AT TYLE 75708 #007-02-1982 L1989 **IM** *020 †20
DAVIS, Ronald Stephen. 700 OLYMPIC PLAZA CIR, STE 404 75701 #021-01-1975 L1981 **D PS** *020 †15
DAVIS, Sharon Hall. 11937 US HIGHWAY 271, DEPT OCCUP & ENVIRON MED 75708 #048-13-1989 L1992 **OM** *020 †70
DECARLO, J Leonard. 700 OLYMPIC PLAZA CIR, UROLOGY TYLER PA 75701 #039-01-1986 L1991 **U** *020 †95
DE HAVEN, Charles Roger. 1424 E FRONT ST 75702 #025-01-1957 L1964 **OPH** *071 †35
DE LA GARZA-GRAHM, M. 800 E DAWSON ST 75701 #649-39-1982 L1992 **GS** *020 †85
DEMBERG, James H. PO BOX 133170 75713 #010-01-1978 L1979 **IM UM** *062 †20
DENNIS, Robert W. 3414 GOLDEN RD 75701 #048-14-1987 L1989 **ORS** *020
D'ERAMO, Mark Anthony. 3800 PALUXY DR STE 425 75703 #048-02-1985 L1990 **P** *020
DESTARAC, Luis A. 912 S FLEISHEL AVE 75701 #429-02-1991 L1996 **AI** *020 †20
DETWILER, Paul Wellington. 700 OLYMPIC PLAZA CIR, STE 850 75701 #035-46-1993 L2000 **NS** *020 †25
DE WET, Pieter Juan. 4801 TROUP HWY, STE 800 75703 #836-03-1985 L1991 **FM EM** *040 †18
DHILLON, Amanpreet Singh. ■ 75703 #495-10-1998 L2006 **OM** *020 †18,70
DIAZ, Stefanie Martin. 1133 MEDICAL DR 75701 #187-78-1992 L1999 **NEP** *020 †20
DICK, David Michael. 1000 S BECKHAM AVE 75701 #048-02-1982 L1984 **CD IC** *020 †20
DICKSON, Charles T, Jr. 700 OLYMPIC PLAZA CIR, UROLOGY TYLER PA 75701 #048-15-1988 L1990 **U** *020 †95
DICKSON, Teresa May. 4293 KINSEY DR 75703 #048-15-1987 L1988 **FM** *020 †18
DI PAOLO, David Pat. 11937 US HIGHWAY 271 75708 #041-14-1989 L1995 **DR RNR** *020 †80
DOBROWOLSKI, Robert C. 815 E 1ST ST 75701 #041-02-1994 L1995 **NEP** *020 †20
DODGE, Billy Gene. 1020 E LAKE ST 75701 #048-04-1961 L1961 **D** *071 †15
DOMINGUEZ, Edward Anthony. 3200 TROUP HWY, STE 310 75701 #048-04-1986 L1987 **ID IM** *040 †20
DONALDSON, Ronald Jack. 700 OLYMPIC PLAZA CIR, STE 850 75701 #039-01-1963 L1972 **NS** *071
DOOLABH, Neelan S. 1100 E LAKE ST STE 210 75701 #048-12-1995 L1996 **TS** *020 †85,90
DOSSEY, Adam Patrick. 3415 GOLDEN RD, HEATON EYE ASSOCIATES 75701 #048-02-2000 L2002 **OPH** *020 †35
DRAPEAU, Marc Louis. 911 S BECKHAM AVE 75701 #035-09-1998 L2005 **RO** *100 †80
DREW, Eric C. 910 E HOUSTON ST, STE 270 75702 #048-16-1999 L2002 **N** *020
DUNCAN, Silas Edwin. 1100 S BECKHAM AVE 75701 #048-12-1968 L1968 **VS GS** *020 †85
DUNLOP, Lawrence Clifton. ■ 75703 #048-12-1959 L1959 **GP OM** *071
DURRETT, James Harris. 3131 TROUP HWY 75701 #048-16-2000 L2002 **FM** *020 †18 ‡
DUVALL, George A. 1720 S BECKHAM AVE 75701 #048-04-1990 L1991 **GE** *020 †20
EARL, Gene Markley. 1100 S BECKHAM AVE 75701 #039-01-1966 L1972 **IM** *020 †20
ECKHOUT, Gifford Van, Jr. 800 E DAWSON ST 75701 #028-34-1985 L2006 **AN MDM** *030 †05
EIJSINK, Stephanie K. 1401 E LAKE ST # 217, TYLER JUNIOR COLLEGE 75701 #409-16-1989 L1995 **FM EM** *020 †18
EKANEM, Felix M. 5201 S BROADWAY AVE # 240, C/O ECS OF TEXAS, PA 75703 #033-11-1988 L1997 **FM** *020 †18
ELLIS, Jaishree Riva. 214 E HOUSTON ST 75702 #016-11-1994 L1998 **OBG** *020 †30
ELLIS, Robert Stephen. 612 S FLEISHEL AVE, TRAUMA SURGERY/SURGI CRITI 75701 #041-13-1996 L2005 **CCS** *100
EMIRU, Mingiziem Abebe. 1133 MEDICAL DR, TYLER NEPHROLOGY ASSOCIATE 75701 #366-03-1993 L2004 **NEP** *020 †20
ENGLISH, Grace Ching-Shin. PO BOX 1999, BETHESDA HEALTH CENTER 75710 #048-12-1993 L1994 **IM** *020 †20
ENGLISH, John P. 800 E DAWSON ST 75701 #048-12-1993 L1994 **FM** *020 †18
ESFANDIARY, Neda. 520 DOUGLAS BLVD 75702 #517-08-1991 L2004 *020
EVELAND, Kenneth Ward. 11937 US HIGHWAY 271, U.T. HEALTH CENTER AT TYLE 75708 #048-12-1978 L1978 **GS** *071 †85
EVERETT, Harold U. 706 TURTLE CREEK DR, PEDIATRICS 75701 #048-12-1993 L1994 **PD** *020 †55
FABRE, Robin Dees. 800 E DAWSON ST, MOTHER FRANCES HOSP 75701 #021-06-1992 L1995 **IM** *030
FAGAN, Marian Frances. 11937 US HIGHWAY 271, U/T HEALTH CENTER 75708 #048-02-1982 L1983 **PTH** *020 †50
FANNING, Paul M. 733 S FLEISHEL AVE 75701 #048-14-1993 L1994 **OBG** *020 †30
FANOUS, Elias Issa. 700 OLYMPIC PLAZA CIR # 5 75701 #048-02-1989 L1990 **GE** *020 †20
FELDMAN, Jerry. 11937 US HIGHWAY 271, AT TYLER 75708 #016-11-1987 L1997 **D IM** *020 †15
FENDER, Harris R, Jr. 1015 HOSPITAL DR 75701 #048-02-1972 L1972 **GS SO** *020 †85
FERRELL, Oran L, Jr. 1100 E LAKE ST STE 340 75701 #048-02-1950 L1950 **GYN** *071
FIDONE, Jeffrey W. 912 S FLEISHEL AVE 75701 #048-02-1988 L1989 **PUD CCM** *020 †20
FIELDS, Ronald Kevin. 910 E HOUSTON ST, STE 250 75702 #048-04-1998 L2005 **CN** *100 †75
FIESELER, Catherine Mary. 1327 TROUP HWY 75701 #010-02-1985 L2004 **FSM FM** *020 †18
FINLAY, David E. 11937 US HIGHWAY 271, UNIV TX HLTH CTR 75708 #048-02-1986 L1987 **DR** *020 †80
FLANAGAN, Cole. 700 OLYMPIC PLAZA CIR #602 75701 #048-13-1991 L1998 **OBG** *020 †30
FLETCHER, David King. 816 S FLEISHEL AVE 75701 #048-12-1961 L1961 **RHU** *020
FOOX, Gerald Peter. 1405 S FLEISHEL AVE 75701 #836-01-1971 L1977 **PM** *020
FORD, Steven Roy. 3200 TROUP HWY, STE 200 75701 #039-01-1983 L1988 **AN CCM** *020 †05
FOREHAND, Foy G, II. 1726 S BECKHAM AVE 75701 #048-14-1993 L1994 **SP** *020 †50
FOREMAN, Kim Alan. 3414 GOLDEN RD 75701 #048-15-1981 L1981 **OSM ORS** *020 †40
FRANCISCO, Ma. Aileen Con. 1000 E 5TH ST 75701 #748-02-1998 L2004 **FM** *020 †18
FRAZIER, Joan Marie. 1517 W FRONT ST, PUBLIC HLTH REGION 4&5N 75702 #048-02-1976 L1976 **FM** *020
FRAZIER, Ronald K. 520 DOUGLAS BLVD, TRINITY CLINIC 75702 #048-16-1991 L1992 **MPD** *020 †55,20
FREDERICK, Robert W. 910 E HOUSTON ST, STE 470 75702 #048-16-1997 L1999 **U** *020 †95
FREEMAN, Louie Donell. 733 S FLEISHEL AVE, DIGESTIVE HEALTH SPECIALIS 75701 #021-01-1975 L1983 **GE IM** *020 †20
FULLERTON, Douglas B. 11937 US HIGHWAY 271, MC 3154 75708 #048-12-1988 L1989 **FM** *020 †18
FULMER, R Paul. 417 S SAUNDERS AVE, TYLER EAR, NOSE & THROAT C 75702 #048-02-1989 L1990 **OTO** *020 †45
FULSOM, Donald R. 401 E FRONT ST, STE 134 75702 #048-13-1998 L2003 **CHP P** *020 †75
FULTS, Kenneth Lloyd. 223 E 5TH ST 75701 #028-78-1968, ▲ L1968 **PME PM** *020
GADDY, Howell Robt, Jr. ■ 75707 #048-12-1944 L1944 **GP** *071 †18
GADDY, Howell Robt, III. 2301 S BROADWAY AVE, STE B8 75701 #048-12-1978 L1978 **DR GS** *071 †85,80
GARB, Howard S. 3413 GOLDEN RD 75701 #048-12-1992 L1993 **OTO GS** *020 †45
GARRETT, Jan Hansen. 1905 S DONNYBROOK AVE 75701 #048-04-1966 L1966 **ORS** *072 †40
GARWOOD, Susan K. 912 S FLEISHEL AVE 75701 #048-14-2001 L2007 **PCC** *020
GASS, George David. 912 S FLEISHEL AVE, # 301 75701 #016-45-1981 L1986 **PUD CCM** *020 †20
GERARD, Beverly E. 11937 US HWY 271 75708 #048-15-1987 L1988 **OBG** *020 †30
GERARD, Roy Dupuy, Jr. 1133 MEDICAL DR 75701 #048-13-1985 L1989 **NEP IM** *020 †20
GERDES, Melissa Susan. 800 E DAWSON ST 75701 #016-43-1996 L1997 **FM** *020 †18
GHUGE, Raghavendra. 120 E CHARNWOOD ST, STE B 75701 #496-38-1988 L1996 **IM** *020 †20
GIRALDO, Mauricio. 1100 E LAKE ST STE 180 75701 #264-04-1986 L2004 **GS SO** *020 †85
GIRARD, William Meshew. 11937 US HIGHWAY 271, U.T.HEALTH CENTER AT TYLER 75708 #021-05-1972 L1982 **PUD IM** *020 †20
GOMINAK, Stasha Christina. 700 OLYMPIC PLAZA CIR, STE 904 75701 #048-04-1983 L1983 **N** *020 †75
GONZALEZ, Herbert F. 800 E DAWSON ST, ANESTHESIOLOGY DEPT 75701 #048-15-1988 L1989 **AN** *020 †05
GONZALEZ, Virgilio Viceo. 1000 S BECKHAM AVE 75701 #748-01-1951 L1963 **PTH OS** *071 †50
GOODFRIED, Gary Paul. 1905 S DONNYBROOK AVE 75701 #048-13-1978 L1978 **OAR** *020 †40
GOOGINS, Judy C. 5604 OLD BULLARD RD, 1 75703 #048-16-1988 L1989 **P** *020
GORDON, Charles R. 1000 S BECKHAM AVE 75701 #048-04-1987 L1989 **NS** *020 †25
GORDON, Robert Edward. 2301 S BROADWAY AVE, STE B8 75701 #048-12-1978 L1978 **R** *020 †80
GOSS, Vernon V. ■ 75701 #021-05-1943 L1955 **OPH** *071 †35
GOULD, Theodore Israel. 11937 US HIGHWAY 271, UT HEALTH CENTER TYLER 75708 #065-01-1972 L1985 **EM** *020 †16
GOULDEN, Dudley Decatur. 11937 US HWY 271, UNIVERSITY OF TEXAS HSC AT 75708 #011-03-1967 L1973 **CD IM** *020 †20
GRABSKI, William John. 1720 S BECKHAM AVE, STE 102 75701 #041-13-1979 L1994 **D** *020 †15
GRAHAM, Bradley S. 1720 S BECKHAM AVE, STE 102 75701 #048-02-1990 L2001 **D DMP** *020 †15 ‡
GRAHAM, Helen Marie. 4111 UNIVERSITY BLVD, HOSPICE OF EAST TEXAS 75701 #048-12-1969 L1969 **IM PTH** *020 †50
GRAHM, Thomas W. 700 OLYMPIC PLAZA CIR, STE 850 75701 #048-02-1983 L1990 **NS** *020 †25
GRAVES, Glen S. 4293 KINSEY DR, TEXAS ARTHRITIS & RHEUMATO 75703 #048-12-1991 L1992 **RHU** *020 †20
GRAVES, Lisa Joan. ■ 75706 #038-43-1996 L2003 **IM** *072 †20
GRAY, James Kent. ■ 75707 #048-04-1981 L1982 **FM EM** *020 †18
GREEN, Frank Dudley. 800 E DAWSON ST 75701 #047-06-1944 L1955 **IM** *071
GREEN, Kevin Dwight. 1720 S BECKHAM AVE, DIGESTIVE HEALTH SPECIALIS 75701 #048-12-1983 L1983 **GE IM** *020 †20
GREENBERG, Mark. 700 OLYMPIC PLAZA CIR, UROLOGY TYLER PA 75701 #001-02-1968 L1971 **U** *020 †95
GREGORY, Thomas F. 910 E HOUSTON ST STE 100, TYLER CANCER CTR 75702 #048-02-1993 L1995 **ON** *020 †20
GRIFFITH, David Eugene. 11937 US HIGHWAY 271 75708 #048-04-1977 L1977 **PUD IM** *020 †20
GRIFFITH, Duane Lee. 1814 ROSELAND BLVD 75701 #034-01-2002 L2007 **AN** *100 †05
GROSS, Gary Edward. 825 MEDICAL DR, BLOOD AND CANCER CTR OF ET 75701 #035-01-1976 L1977 **ON HEM** *020 †20 ‡
GUNTER, Craig Alan. 4111 UNIVERSITY BLVD, HOSPICE OF EAST TEXAS 75701 #048-12-1999 L2000 **FM** *020 †18
GUTIERREZ, Ralph Aaron. 2301 S BROADWAY AVE, STE B8 75701 #028-02-1982 L1990 **DR** *020 †80
HAAS, Charles Danl. 825 MEDICAL DR, BLOOD & CANCER CTR OF E TX 75701 #019-02-1968 L1992 **ON IM** *020 †20

HACKBARTH, Mark Aaron. 700 OLYMPIC PLAZA CIR, STE 850 75701 #039-05-1982 L1983 **AN PME** *020 †05
HALLMAN, Jerry Manning. 2806 ROCKBRIDGE RD 75701 #048-02-1971 L1983 **GS FM** *020 †85,18
HAMIC, Clifton Ross. ■ 75703 #021-06-2006 **FP** *012
HAMMETT, Malcolm Reid. 901 TURTLE CREEK DR 75701 #048-12-1960 L1960 **PTH** *071 †50
HAMON, Shane Tillman. 800 E DAWSON ST 75701 #054-04-2002 L2006 **AN** *020 †05
HAMPE, Clark Carl. 800 E DAWSON ST 75701 #018-03-1974 L1975 **IM OS** *020 †20
HAMPTON, Herman L, Jr. 3627 RIVER OAKS CT 75707 #047-06-1961 L1961 **GS VS** *071 †85
HANDLEY, Richard Dwight. 520 DOUGLAS BLVD, RADIOLOGY 75702 #017-20-1973 L1976 **DR** *020 †18,80
HANEY, Michael P. 800 E DAWSON ST 75701 #048-13-2002 L2006 **AN** *020 †05
HANKS, Marel A. 2990 N BROADWAY AVE 75702 #048-02-1988 L1989 **PD ADL** *020 †55
HANSON, Lianne Xanthia. 6709 HOLLYTREE CIR 75703 #021-01-1990 L2001 **OBG** *020 †30
HARGROVE, Thomas A. 706 TURTLE CREEK DR, THE TRINITY CLINIC 75701 #048-12-1988 L1989 **PD** *020 †55
HARRELL, William Bruce. 910 E HOUSTON ST STE 470, UNIVERSITY OF UTAH HOSPITA 75702 #048-04-2000 L2008 **UP** *100 †95
HARRIS, Amanda Baker. 910 E HOUSTON ST STE 600, TYLER OBSTETRICS & GYNECOL 75702 #048-16-1993 L1994 **OBG** *020 †30
HARRIS, Brent Reavley. 1726 S BECKHAM AVE 75701 #048-12-1980 L1980 **PTH** *020 †50
HARRIS, Jack Richard. 1128 MEDICAL DR, ALLERGY CLINIC 75701 #048-13-1981 L1982 **AI** *020 †55,03
HARRIS, James Robt. 3414 GOLDEN RD 75701 #048-02-1979 L1981 **ORS** *020 †40
HARRISON, Craig Edward. 1100 E LAKE ST 75701 #020-02-1983 L1984 **PS GS** *020 †85,65
HARRISON, James B. 700 OLYMPIC PLAZA CIR 75701 #048-16-1987 L1988 **VS GS** *020 †85,10
HARRISON, Preston Ershel. 1301 DOCTORS DR, EAST TEXAS NEUROLOGY 75701 #048-04-1970 L1970 **N** *020 †75
HAYDEN, Margaret R. 800 E DAWSON ST 75701 #048-12-1988 L1989 **IM** *020 †20
HAYES, Thomas Keller. 2301 S BROADWAY AVE, STE B8 75701 #048-04-1978 L1978 **N DR** *020 †80
HAYGOOD, Fred Donald. 1000 S BECKHAM AVE 75701 #048-04-1967 L1967 **GS VS** *020 †85
HAYGOOD, Kenneth D. 1304 DOCTORS DR 75701 #048-04-1995 L1997 **FM** *020 †18
HAYGOOD, Laura Jennifer. 455 RICE RD, STE 104 75703 #048-04-1995 L1997 **D** *020 †15
HEATON, Charles Lawson. 3415 GOLDEN RD, HEATON EYE ASSOCIATES 75701 #048-12-1979 L1979 **OPH GP** *030 †35
HEATON, Steuart Lawrence. 3413 GOLDEN RD 75701 #048-12-1978 L1978 **OTO HNS** *020 †45
HECKER, M Stella. 904 S BECKHAM AVE 75701 #748-20-1993 L2003 **END** *020 †20
HECTOR, David A, Jr. 619 S FLEISHEL AVE, TYLER CARDIOVASCULAR 75701 #038-41-1978 L1982 **CD IM** *020 †20
HENDRICKS, Michael B. 800 E DAWSON ST 75701 #048-04-1991 L1992 **AN** *020 †05
HENDRICKSON, Marjorie L H. 10621 COUNTRY RD, STE 334 75708 #048-02-1958 L1958 **AN** *071 †05
HENRY, Joe Byron, Jr. 11937 US HIGHWAY 271, DEPT FM 75708 #021-06-2007 **FP** *012
HIATT, Mark. 520 DOUGLAS BLVD 75702 #036-05-1999 L2004 **DR** *100 ‡
HICKERSON, Steven L. 3200 TROUP HWY, STE 310 75701 #048-15-1988 L1989 **ID PD** *020 †55,20
HICKMAN, Willett J. 520 DOUGLAS BLVD 75702 #021-05-1972 L1975 **GPM FM** *020 †16
HILLIS, Robert Stephen. 700 OLYMPIC PLAZA CIR, STE 700 75701 #048-12-1969 L1969 **U** *020 †95
HO, Coty H. 11937 US HIGHWAY 271, DEPARTMENT OF HEMATOLOGY/O 75708 #036-01-1992 L2007 **ON** *020 †20
HOBBS, William Robert. 800 E DAWSON ST 75701 #023-07-1993 L2001 **OSM** *020 †40
HOOVER, Andrew Edward. 1000 E 5TH ST 75701 #008-01-1972 L1975 **PD** *020 †55
HORNELL, Allen B. 6210 S BROADWAY AVE 75703 #048-13-1995 L1997 **FM** *020 †18
HORNELL, Lauren L. 6210 S BROADWAY AVE 75703 #048-13-1995 L2001 **FM** *020 †18
HOSCH, Amy Jo. 520 DOUGLAS BLVD 75702 #041-07-1997 L1998 **FM** *020 †18
HOSTETLER, Wayne E, Jr. 1312 DOCTORS DR 75701 #038-41-1974 L1985 **N** *020 †75
HOUSTON, Edna Snell. PROFESSIONAL ASSOCIATES 75711 #047-07-1962 L1972 **AN** *071
HOUSTON, Samuel Deloyd. 800 E DAWSON ST 75701 #047-07-1962 L1971 **GS VS** *071 †85
HOWARD, Robert George, Jr. 700 OLYMPIC PLAZA CIR, STE 600 75701 #024-05-2000 L2006 **ORS** *100
HUBER, Gary Louis. 400 E CHARNWOOD ST, TEXAS NUTRITION INSTITUTE 75701 #054-04-1966 L1987 **NTR PUD** *062 †20
HUDNALL, John Franklin. 3413 GOLDEN RD 75701 #048-12-1961 L1961 **OTO** *020 †45
HUGGINS, Barbara W. 11937 US HIGHWAY 271, UNIV TX HLTH CTR 75708 #048-14-1985 L1986 **PD** *020 †55
HUNTER, Jeffrey S. 3415 GOLDEN RD, HEATON EYE ASSOCIATES 75701 #048-14-1991 L1992 **OPH PO** *020 †35
HUNTER-CARL, Stephanie L. 733 S FLEISHEL AVE 75701 #048-15-1996 L1998 **OBG** *020 †30
HURLEY, Janet L. 800 E DAWSON ST 75701 #048-16-2000 L2001 **FM PD** *020 †18
HURST, Charles Richard. ■ 75703 #048-04-1958 L1958 **FM** *071 †18
HURST, George Anderson. 11937 US HIGHWAY 271 75708 #048-12-1958 L1958 **PUD IM** *071 †20
HURST, Irby J, Jr. PO BOX 2003, AT TYLER 75710 #021-05-1948 L1972 **TS GS** *020
HUTTO, Stephen Allen. 700 OLYMPIC PLAZA CIR, STE 410 75701 #047-05-1987 L1993 **GE** *020 †20
HWANG, Julia Daejin. 520 DOUGLAS BLVD 75702 #019-02-1985 L1987 **FM** *020 †18
HYLAND, Bryan Todd. 6210 S BROADWAY AVE 75703 #048-14-1998 L2000 **FM** *020 †18
HYMAN, William J. 910 E HOUSTON ST STE 100 75702 #048-04-1985 L1986 **ON HEM** *020 †20
IDELL, Steven. 11937 US HIGHWAY 271, U.T. HEALTH CENTER AT TYLE 75708 #041-13-1977 L1985 **PUD IM** *020 †20
ISLAM, David Matthew. 800 E DAWSON ST 75701 #021-01-1990 L2006 **AN** *020 †05
ISLAM, Janine Coles. 223 E 5TH ST, PAIN RECOVERY CTR 75701 #021-01-1990 L2006 **PM OM** *020 †60
JACKMAN, John Daniel. 619 S FLEISHEL AVE, TYLER CARDIOVASCULAR 75701 #021-01-1985 L1986 **IM CD** *020 †20
JAMES, Kyle D. 11937 US HIGHWAY 271, UTHCT DEPT FP 75708 #048-13-1989 L1990 **FM EM** *040 †18
JERNIGAN, Samuel Carlyle. ■ 75707 #048-02-1962 L1962 **OBG** *071 †30
JETHVA, Alpesh Ramesh. 1133 MEDICAL DR 75701 #048-14-1996 L1999 **NEP** *020 †20
JOHNSON, Gregory Paul. 11937 US HWY 271 75708 #048-13-1981 L1981 **EM** *020 †16
JOHNSON, Joel David. 618 S BROADWAY AVE 75701 #045-01-1980 L1985 **PUD CCM** *020 †20
JOHNSON, Walter Lloyd. 3802 MANHATTON DR STE 203 75701 #021-01-1964 L1968 **GP** *020 †18
JONES, David Irwin. 800 E DAWSON ST 75701 #039-01-1982 L1988 **PUD CCM** *020 †20
JONES, Lee Matthew. 3414 GOLDEN RD 75701 #048-15-1984 L1985 **ORS** *020 †40
JONES, Rebecca. 1424 E FRONT ST 75702 #048-02-1990 L1995 **OPH** *020 †35
JONES, Robert F. 214 E HOUSTON ST 75702 #048-14-1987 L1988 **OBG** *020 †30
JORDEN, Armon Jack. 13594 HWY 64 E 75707 #021-06-1983 L1992 **IM** *020 †20
KARAKI, Wayne Susumu. 11937 US HIGHWAY 271, UNIV TX HLTH CTR 75708 #028-34-1984 L1985 **IM** *020 †20
KARIAMPUZHA, George W. 910 E HOUSTON ST, STE 270 75702 #577-01-1992 L2001 **N** *020 †75
KARIAMPUZHA, Sylvia Ann. 910 E HOUSTON ST STE 25 75702 #495-63-1995 L2002 **IM** *020 †20
KEITZER, Walter Ford. UTHCT 75710 #025-01-1956 L1977 **GS** *071 †85
KEMP, Kenneth Ray, Jr. 700 OLYMPIC PLAZA CIR # 5, ETMC FIRST PHYSICIANS 75701 #048-02-1993 L1994 **PM PRS** *020 †60
KERNS, David Brent. 700 OLYMPIC PLZ CIR # 510 75701 #048-12-1987 L1996 **VS GS** *020 †85
KEUER, Steven Paul. 520 DOUGLAS BLVD 75702 #048-04-1975 L1975 **IM** *020 †20
KHAN, Masroor A. 11937 US HWY 271, UNIV OF TX HLTH CT TYLER 75708 #704-02-1990 L2000 **CD** *020 †20
KIM, Jin Koo. 1133 MEDICAL DR 75701 #035-46-2002 L2007 **NEP** *020 †20
KIMMEL, Gary Thos. 910 E HOUSTON ST 75702 #038-41-1968 L1974 **HO IM** *020 †20
KING, Beurett A, Jr. ■ 75703 #048-04-1968 L1968 **R** *071 †80
KING, Bradley Owen. 1000 S BECKHAM AVE, EMERGENCY DEPARTMENT 75701 #039-01-1997 L2000 **EM** *020 †16
KING, Kendra Tay. 6210 S BROADWAY AVE 75703 #039-01-1997 L2000 **FM** *071 †18
KING, T Kevin. 5701 OLD BULLARD RD, STE 119 75703 #048-04-1970 L1970 **AN** *020 †05
KINGRY, Roy Lee, Jr. 11937 US HWY 271, U.T. HEALTH CENTER AT TYLE 75708 #001-02-1969 L1983 **TS GS** *020 †85,90
KIRKPATRICK, Andrew K. 910 E HOUSTON ST, STE 470 75702 #048-13-1993 L1994 **U** *020 †95
KLOUDA, Katharina A. 2017 RICKETY LN 75703 #016-01-1992 L1994 **OBG** *020 †30
KLOUDA, Michael James. 700 OLYMPIC PLAZA CIR, STE 101 75701 #016-01-1992 L1994 **DR** *020 †80
KNARR, Donald Richard. 3802 MANHATTON DR, STE 203 75701 #020-02-1961 L1966 **FM** *020
KNIGHT, Lee Roger. 1420 WSW LOOP 323 75701 #048-04-1955 L1955 **GS** *071
KNOX, James Daniel. 11937 US HWY 271 75708 #041-13-2005 L2006 **FP** *012
KNUTSON, James Blake. 800 E DAWSON ST 75701 #048-14-2002 L2005 **IM** *020 †20
KOCH, Sandra Jean. 701 OLYMPIC PLAZA CIR 75701 #048-04-1982 L1983 **PM** *020 †60
KOHLI, Rajan Singh. 1000 S BECKHAM AVE 75701 #495-28-2001 L2005 **FM** *020 †18
KOLKER, James David. 721 CLINIC DR, DEPT OF RADIATION ONCOLOGY 75701 #041-02-1981 L1996 **RO** *020 †20,80
KOSTER, Leeann. 1100 S BECKHAM AVE, EAST TEXAS MEDICAL CENTER 75701 #001-06-2000 L2003 **EM** *020 †16
KRONENBERG, Richard Saml. ■ 75703 #016-06-1963 L1986 **PUD IM** *030 †20
KULA, Gary Paul. ■ 75703 #039-01-1978 L1979 **P PYG** *020 †75
KUMMERFELD, Kenneth Brent. 619 S FLEISHEL AVE STE 10 75701 #048-02-1979 L1979 **CD IM** *020 †20
KWAKU, Maxwell Prosper. 1000 E 5TH ST 75701 #010-03-2000 L2005 **END** *030 †20 ‡
LAKEY, David Leroy. 11937 US HWY 271, U.T. HEALTH CENTER AT TYLE 75708 #017-20-1990 L1999 **ID IM** *020 †55,20
LAMB, Scott Jos. 700 OLYMPIC PLAZA CIR, STE 850 75701 #038-41-1992 L1996 **PM PMM** *020 †60
LANGSJOEN, Peter Harald. 1107 DOCTORS DR 75701 #048-13-1980 L1980 **CD IM** *030 †20
LAPINSKY, Anthony Stanley. 1327 TROUP HWY, TRINITY CLINIC ORTHOPAEDIC 75701 #035-15-1987 L2005 **ORS PDS** *020 †40
LARA, Fernan F. ■ 75703 #649-01-1961 L1973 **IM** *020 †20
LARRINAGA, John Andrew. 910 E HOUSTON ST STE 650 75702 #005-06-1988 L2002 **DR** *020 †80
LAWRENCE, Kevin Scott. 4707 GRETNA GREEN LN 75703 #048-02-1999 L2000 **FM** *020 †18
LE, Minh Quang. 11937 US HIGHWAY 271, U T HEALTH CENTER AT TYLER 75708 #018-03-1996 L2001 **FM** *020 †18
LEDLIE, Jon Taylor. 700 OLYMPIC PLAZA CIR # 8 75701 #039-01-1977 L1983 **NS** *020 †25
LEE, Arielle Shebay. 721 CLINIC DR # A 75701 #048-04-1981 L1981 **ON HEM** *020 †20
LEE, Charles Harwick. 1000 S BECKHAM AVE, EAST TEXAS MEDICAL CTR 75701 #048-04-1981 L1981 **TS** *020 †85,90
LEE, James Fletcher. 1301 DOCTORS DR, EAST TEXAS NEUROLOGY 75701 #036-07-1960 L1967 **NS** *071 †25
LEEVES, Wayne Neal. 751 S BECKHAM AVE 75701 #048-02-1977 L1977 **GP** *020
LEIHGEBER, Timothy J. 2301 S BROADWAY AVE, STE B8 75701 #048-13-1986 L1987 **DR** *020 †80
LE SAUVAGE, Stephen Chas. 800 E DAWSON ST 75701 #035-08-1970 L1976 **PS** *020 †65
LEVIN, Jeffrey L. 11937 US HIGHWAY 271 75708 #048-13-1983 L1983 **OM IM** *020 †20,70
LEWIS, Michael Ross, Jr. 3413 GOLDEN RD 75701 #048-14-1996 L1998 **OTO** *020 †45
LIEB, Nancy S. 910 E HOUSTON ST STE 600 75702 #028-02-1982 L1986 **OBG** *020 †30
LIM, Paul Joonyeob. 1814 ROSELAND BLVD 75701 #038-40-1993 L1998 **IM** *020 †20
LIN, Sauyu. 910 E HOUSTON ST, STE 330 75702 #047-05-1999 L2005 **GE** *020 †20
LIPTAK, Richard Andrew. 921 SHILOH RD 75703 #021-05-1963 L1975 **A PD** *072 †55,03
LIVELY, James Anthony. 3802 MANHATTON DR, STE 203 75701 #048-14-1997 L1998 **FM** *020 †18
LLOYD, Scott M. 800 E DAWSON ST 75701 #028-03-1984 L1987 **PTH** *020 †50
LOEWENSTEIN, Ingeborg A. 11937 US HIGHWAY 271, UT HEALTH CENTER AT TYLER 75708 #409-21-1975 L1995 **IM NEP** *020 †20
LOVETT, Robert Lawson. ■ 75707 #018-03-1962 L1963 **CLP PTH** *020 †50
LOWERY, Bryan M. 3802 MANHATTON DR, STE 203 75701 #048-12-1991 L2002 **FM** *020 †18
LOWERY, Thomas Andrew. 1133 MEDICAL DR 75701 #048-04-1969 L1969 **NEP IM** *020 †20
LOWRY, Lisa Renee. 1367 DOMINION PLZ 75703 #021-01-1989 L1991 **D** *020 †15
LOWRY, Richard William, Jr. 115 W 5TH ST, CARDIOVASCULAR ASSOCIATES 75701 #039-01-1987 L1990 **CD** *020 †20
LUCKETT, Henry Peyton. 700 OLYMPIC PLAZA CIR, STE 503 75701 #048-02-1976 L1976 **OBG** *020 †30
LUNDY, David Carroll. 700 OLYMPIC PLAZA CIR, STE 407 75701 #039-01-1975 L1976 **GE IM** *020 †20
LUTZ, Brock Dixon. 3200 TROUP HWY, STE 310 75701 #039-01-1996 L2002 **ID** *020 †20
LUZIETTI, Nicholas Paul. 700 OLYMPIC PLAZA CIR, STE 602 75701 #004-01-1996 L1998 **OBG** *020 †30
LYLES, Thomas W. 1038 S FLEISHEL AVE 75701 #048-02-1955 L1955 **D** *071 †15
MACCLEMENTS, Jonathan E. 11937 US HIGHWAY 271, UNIVERSITY OF TEXAS HEALTH 75708 #836-01-1989 L1997 **FM** *020 †18
MACHA, Douglas B. 2301 S BROADWAY AVE, STE B8 75701 #048-02-1999 L2005 **DR** *020 †80

MACHA, Patricia Doughty. 800 E DAWSON ST 75701 #048-02-1999 L2005 **AN** *020 †05
MACK, Leo Wm, Jr. 820 S BAXTER AVE 75701 #016-43-1969 L1975 **OPH** *020 †35 ‡
MADORE, Eric Shane. 800 E DAWSON ST 75701 #021-06-1997 L2004 **IM** *020 †20
MAHAFFEY, Mcdavid Michael. 11937 US HIGHWAY 271, FAMILY MEDICINE DEPT 75708 #048-14-2005 L2008 **FP** *012
MARINO, Colin Alexander. 5525 WESTCHESTER DR 75703 #001-02-1998 L2002 **EM** *020 †16
MARKOWITZ, Jonathan Adam. 618 S BROADWAY AVE 75701 #008-02-1986 L1998 **PUD CCM** *020 †20
MARSHALL, Dustyn Shane. ■ 75701 #048-02-2007 **TY** *012
MARTIN, Thalia Marie. 800 E DAWSON ST, TRINITY CLINIC ANESTHESLGY 75701 #012-05-1984 L2004 **AN PAN** *020 †05 ‡
MARTINEZ, Radames, Jr. 11937 US HWY 271 75708 #048-12-1977 L1977 **R** *020 †80
MAY, Kevin Glen. 800 E DAWSON ST 75701 #048-12-1983 L1983 **IM** *020 †20
MAZZARE, Mark Alan. 800 E DAWSON ST 75701 #048-13-1993 L1997 **MPD PD** *020 †55,20
MC ANDREW, James D. 700 OLYMPIC PLAZA CIR, UROLOGY TYLER PA 75701 #048-12-1987 L1988 **U GS** *020 †95
MC ARTHUR, Michael S. 1020 E LAKE ST, STE B 75701 #048-02-1966 L1966 **TS CD** *071 †85,90
MC CARTHY, Charles T, Jr. 1905 S DONNYBROOK AVE 75701 #021-01-1953 L1955 **ORS** *071 †40
MC CLINTOCK, Roy Alan. 1100 E LAKE ST STE 260, OBSTETRICS & GYNECOLOGY OF 75701 #048-15-1991 L1992 **OBG** *020 †30
MC GEHEE, Clinton Joseph. 910 E HOUSTON ST, STE 550 75702 #021-06-1995 L1997 **GS** *020 †85
MC GOVERN, Thomas M, Jr. 1020 E LAKE ST 75701 #035-15-1984 L1999 **TRS** *020 †85,90
MCINNIS, Justin Michael. 11942 LANEY RD 75708 #048-02-2005 **FP** *012
MCKELLAR, Heidi Louise. 721 CLINIC DR 75701 #048-14-1994 L1995 **RO** *020 †80
MC KINLEY, James Wayne. 11937 US HIGHWAY 271, UNIVERSITY OF TEXAS HLTH C 75708 #048-14-1987 L1988 **FM FSM** *020 †18
MC KINNEY, Robert A. 910 E HOUSTON ST, STE 270 75702 #048-14-1982 L1983 **GS** *020 †85
MC NEEL, Tynus Wm. 1615 OAK CREEK CIR 75703 #048-02-1960 L1960 **PFP** *062 †75
MC NEIL, Chad J. 1905 S DONNYBROOK AVE 75701 #048-12-2003 L2007 **PM** *020
MC RAE-VOGLER, Nancy C. 3414 GOLDEN RD 75701 #048-14-1995 L1997 **PD** *020 †55
MEADS, Shanna Burris. 1367 DOMINION PLZ 75703 #004-01-2000 L2005 **D** *020 †15
MEDLEY, George Everett. 1318 DOCTORS DR 75701 #048-02-1958 L1960 **ORS** *020 †40
MEESE, Roderick Bryan. 619 S FLEISHEL AVE STE 10 75701 #038-41-1981 L1982 **IM CD** *020 †20
MELTON, Andrea M. ■ 75703 #048-12-2008 *012
MELTON, Ellen Redd. 1000 E 5TH ST 75701 #048-04-1979 L1979 **PD** *020 †55
MENARD, James Ryan. ■ 75701 #021-06-2007 **FP** *012
MERCER, Lloyd F. 2301 S BROADWAY AVE, STE B8 75701 #048-13-1982 L1983 **CHN PD** *020
MERIANO-WRIGHT, Mary R. ■ 75703 #048-02-1996 L1999 **PD** *020 †55
MERRITT, Bradley Scott. 3131 TROUP HWY, TYLER REHABILITATION HOSPI 75701 #005-15-1993 L1995 **PM** *020 †60
MEYERS, Peter Kevin. 733 S FLEISHEL AVE, DIGESTIVE HEALTH SPECIALIS 75701 #035-01-1978 L1986 **GE** *020 †20
MICHAELS, James P. 1814 ROSELAND BLVD STE 200, FL 2 75701 #048-15-1992 L1996 **PM PME** *020 †60
MICHAELS, Wanda Jeanne. 122 W 4TH ST 75701 #010-01-1986 L1993 **P** *020
MILAN, Joseph F. ■ 75703 #017-20-1952 L1952 **GS** *071 †85
MILLER, John Martin. ■ 75703 #803-03-1958 L1965 **IM CD** *071 †20
MILLER, William Wade. 733 S FLEISHEL AVE 75701 #048-12-1971 L1971 **OBG** *020 †30
MILLS, Monique R. 11937 US HWY 271, UTHCT DEPARTMENT OF PEDIAT 75708 #048-13-1992 L1994 **PD** *020 †55
MITCHELL, Li Yu Huang. 6210 S BROADWAY AVE 75703 #048-16-1999 L2000 **FM** *020 †18
MOORE, Forrest Odell, III. 1020 E IDEL ST 75701 #056-06-1997 L2004 **CCS** *020 †85
MOORE, J Kathleen. 1306 DOCTORS DR 75701 #034-01-1987 L1991 **PD** *020 †55
MOORE, William Leo. 352 S GLENWOOD BLVD 75702 #048-14-1974 L1974 **EM FM** *030 †18,16
MORANVILLE, Gary Lee. 4101 UNIVERSITY BLVD 75701 #018-03-1970 L1977 **P** *020 †75
MORELAND, Donald Gene. 3802 MANHATTON DR STE 203 75701 #019-02-1963 L1975 **GP** *020 †18
MORRIS, Darrin R. 520 DOUGLAS BLVD 75702 #048-02-1999 L2004 **DR** *020 †80
MORROW, Lynn. 3300 S BROADWAY AVE, STE 101 75701 #035-47-1976 L1987 **P** *020 †75
MORSE, Jack A. 2017 HOLLYSTONE DR 75703 #048-13-1985 L1986 **FM** *020 †18
MOTLAGH, James Rastgar. 700 OLYMPIC PLZ CIR # 420 75701 #033-05-1992 L2002 **PS** *020 †85,65
MULLINS, Ryan D. 520 DOUGLAS BLVD 75702 #048-02-1999 L2000 **FM** *020 †18
MUMTAZ, Humayun Husain. ■ 75701 #704-01-1968 L1973 **PUD IM** *071
MUMTAZ, Sanober Humayun. 820 E FRONT ST, WILLOW WELLNESS CTR 75702 #704-06-1971 L1976 **FM** *020
MURPHY, Simon Wayne, Jr. 800 E DAWSON ST 75701 #021-05-2002 L2006 **AN** *020 †05
MUSE, James Morris. 910 E HOUSTON ST, STE 600 75702 #048-02-1968 L1968 **OBG GP** *020 †30
NADIGA, Gana Rhiann. 1424 E FRONT ST 75702 #035-45-1998 L2004 **OPH** *020 †35
NAVETTA, Frank I. 619 S FLEISHEL AVE, TYLER CARDIOVASCULAR 75701 #035-09-1984 L1990 **CD IM** *020 †20
NEILL, Sherroll Aubrey. 800 E DAWSON ST 75701 #048-02-1958 L1958 **GS** *020 †85
NELSON, Kenwyn Gordon. 11937 US HIGHWAY 271, UT HEALTH CENTER 75708 #051-01-1948 L1974 **TS** *071 †85,90
NGO, Edward Khoa. 11937 US HIGHWAY 271, DEPT OF FAMILY MEDICINE 75708 #048-14-2004 **FP** *012
NORRIS, John Anthony. 612 S FLEISHEL AVE 75701 #048-15-1975 L1975 **VS GS** *020 †85
NORTON, Michael Jos. 910 E HOUSTON ST, STE 550 75702 #048-12-1987 L1988 **GS** *020 †85
NORWOOD, Scott Harold. 1020 E IDEL ST, EAST TEXAS MEDICAL CENTER 75701 #036-01-1977 L1992 **GS CCM** *020 †85 ‡
NWASURUBA, Chiagozie U. 11937 US HIGHWAY 271, U T HEALTH CENTER AT TYLER 75708 #690-04-1987 L1996 **IM** *020 †20
OLIVER, Joe Hicks. ■ 75703 #048-02-1967 L1967 **P OS** *020 †75
OLSEN, Lloyd Martin. 520 DOUGLAS BLVD 75702 #048-02-1975 L1975 **IM** *020 †20
OLSSON-DETWILER, Aleksandr. 912 S FLEISHEL AVE 75701 #759-07-1986 L2001 **IM** *020 †20
OLUSOLA, Bolarinwa F. 11937 US HIGHWAY 271, UNIV OF TX HEALTH CENTER 75708 #690-05-1990 L1998 **GE** *020 †20
ORJI, Charles Obioma. 1133 MEDICAL DR 75701 #048-13-1998 L1999 **NEP IM** *020 †20
ORR, George. 800 E DAWSON ST 75701 #803-03-1958 L1965 **GP** *071
ORTEN, Kenneth Lee. 800 E DAWSON ST 75701 #021-01-1964 L1965 **GP OM** *071
OSTEEN, David C. 706 TURTLE CREEK DR, TRINITY PEDIATRIC CLINIC 75701 #048-12-2005 L2008 **PD** *012
PADINJARAYVEETIL, Joseph. 11939 US HWY 271, UNIV OF TX HLTH CTR-TYLER 75708 #496-38-1988 L1999 **PCC IM** *020 †20
PALMISANO, Peter John. ■ 75701 #050-02-1954 L1974 **R NM** *071 †80,28
PAMATMAT, Marinel Munda. 1000 E 5TH ST 75701 #748-01-1990 L2002 **PD** *020 †55
PAMATMAT, Stephen D. 1133 MEDICAL DR 75701 #748-01-1989 L2002 **NEP** *020 †20
PARAMESWARAN, Perumkulan. 1000 S BECKHAM AVE 75701 #495-16-1961 L1980 **GS TS** *020 †85
PARK, Dana Michael. 1910 ROSELAND BLVD 75701 #048-02-1974 L1974 **IM** *020 †20
PARKS, Willie Joe, Jr. ■ 75707 #048-13-1996 L1998 **GS** *020
PATEL, Suhel. 800 E DAWSON ST 75701 #775-01-1998 L2005 **IM** *020 †20
PAUL, Alan Russell. 520 DOUGLAS BLVD 75702 #065-01-1968 L1978 **FM** *020 †18
PAUL, Kevin Russell. 3131 TROUP HWY 75701 #048-02-1997 L2003 **PM** *020 †60
PAUZA, Kevin Jos. 700 OLYMPIC PLAZA CIR # 8 75701 #041-14-1990 L1994 **PM** *020 †60
PAYNE, Donald E. 2020 MONTROSE DR 75701 #039-01-1952 L1955 **PD** *071 †55
PENNINGTON, Vanis. ■ 75703 #047-06-1953 L1960 **IM OM** *020 †20
PERKINS, Raymond C, II. 912 S FLEISHEL AVE 75701 #048-14-1985 L1986 **PCC CCM** *020 †20
PESNELL, James Henry. ■ 75703 #048-02-1963 L1963 **IM PUD** *071 †20
PETRAKIAN, Alexandre. 115 W 5TH ST 75701 #605-01-1993 L1998 **ICE CD** *020 †20
PFEIFFER, Brian Douglas. 800 E DAWSON ST, SYSTEM 75701 #019-02-1996 L1999 **IM** *020 †20
PHILLIPS, Michal Maranto. 11937 US HIGHWAY 271 75708 #021-06-2004 L2006 **FM** *020 †18
PHILLIPS, Wendell Stephen. 704 S FLEISHEL AVE 75701 #021-01-1966 L1997 **TS** *020 †85,90
PHILLIPS, William F, III. 1327 TROUP HWY 75701 #048-15-1999 L2002 **ORS** *020
PIERCE, Shawn D. 212 GRANDE BLVD STE C-1 75703 #048-14-1992 L1993 **FM** *020 †18
PIERRE, Mariette. 1350 E RICHARDS ST, NORTHEAST TEXAS PUBLIC HEA 75702 #004-01-1995 L2004 **IM** *020 †20,55 ‡
PINKENBURG, Ronald Jos. 2440 E 5TH ST 75701 #048-04-1967 L1967 **OPH** *071 †35
PINSON, Barbara N. 11937 US HIGHWAY 271 75708 #048-13-1989 L1990 **FM** *020 †70
PIRTLE, George W, Jr. ■ 75703 #048-04-1953 L1953 **GP** *071
PITTS, Paul W. 305 W RUSK ST, PEDIATRICS 75701 #047-06-1984 L1988 **PD** *020 †55
PLOTKIN, George Michael. 700 OLYMPIC PLAZA CIR #904 75701 #024-05-1989 L2000 **N CN** *020 †75
POGUE, John G. 4101 UNIVERSITY BLVD 75701 #048-14-1991 L2000 **P** *020 †75
PORTER, Roger Wm. 11937 US HIGHWAY 271, UNIV TX HLTH CTR TYLER 75708 #004-01-1975 L1976 **RHU IM** *020 †20
POWELL, Christine Ann. ■ 75703 #048-13-1994 L1995 **FM** *020 †18
POWELL, William Raymond. 910 E HOUSTON ST, STE 530 75702 #048-04-1977 L1977 **CD** *020
PRADOS, Wilfred O, III. 800 E DAWSON ST 75701 #021-05-1981 L2006 **AN PMM** *020 †05
PRASAD, Ritesh Rajendra. 906 E FRONT ST 75702 #048-02-1995 L1996 **PM** *020 †60
PRASZEK, Karie Catherine. 11937 US HWY 271, UNIV OF TX HLTH CTR 75708 #040-02-2000 L2003 **IM** *020 †20
PRICE, Danny L. 928 N GLENWOOD BLVD, COMMUNITY HEALTH CLINICS 75702 #048-12-1993 L1994 **PD** *020 †55
PRIDDY, John Franklin. 3414 GOLDEN RD 75701 #021-06-1997 L2003 **ORS OFA** *020 †40
PRIMER, Charles Austin. 1000 S BECKHAM AVE 75701 #048-12-1959 L1959 **GYN** *071 †30
PROPST, Charlie Wayne. 1100 S BECKHAM AVE 75701 #048-12-1969 L1969 **IM** *020 †20
PRUD'HOMME, Joseph Lynn. 1015 E IDEL ST 75701 #048-02-1962 L1962 **GS VS** *020 †85
PUTMAN, Jerry Sim. 910 E HOUSTON ST STE 600 75702 #048-02-1979 L1979 **OBG** *020 †18,30
QUEVEDO, Enrique M, II. 800 E DAWSON ST 75701 #048-02-1992 L1995 **AN** *020 †05
RAABE, Todd M. 1905 S DONNYBROOK AVE 75701 #048-16-1991 L1992 **ORS** *020 †40
RAASOCH, John Wm. 6811 HOLLYFREE CIR, UTMB CORRECTIONAL MANAGED 75703 #056-05-1973 L2003 **P** *020 †75 ‡
RADFORD, Craig Michael. 733 S FLEISHEL AVE, DIGESTIVE HEALTH SPECIALIS 75701 #016-11-1982 L1988 **GE** *020 †20
RAGGIO, Michael Joseph. 912 S FLEISHEL AVE 75701 #021-06-1998 L2004 **PCC** *020 †20
RAWLS, Donald Eugene. 910 E HOUSTON ST STE 550 75702 #048-02-1976 L1976 **GE IM** *020 †20
RAY, William Henry. ■ 75701 #048-12-1956 L1956 **ORS** *020 †40
READ, William Tyler. 815 N BROADWAY AVE, TYLER SMITH COUNTY 75702 #048-02-1956 L1956 **PD** *071 †55
REITMEYER, Margaret R. 910 E HOUSTON ST, STE 250 75702 #048-16-1993 L2000 **END PDE** *020 †20
REMMERS, August R, Jr. 3600 W ERWIN ST 75702 #020-02-1955 L1962 **NEP IM** *072 †20
RENFRO, Mark Bennit. 700 OLYMPIC PLAZA CIR, STE 850 75701 #011-03-1990 L1997 **NS** *020 †25
RENTERIA, Henry. 11937 US HIGHWAY 271, DEPT FM 75708 #048-15-2007 **FP** *012
REULAND, Kurt S. 2301 S BROADWAY AVE, STE B8 75701 #048-02-1992 L1993 **RNR** *020 †80
REUTER, Frank Peter, Jr. 712 S BOIS D ARC AVE 75701 #048-02-1975 L1975 **IM IMG** *020 †20
REUTER, Robert Hunter. 2301 S BROADWAY AVE, STE B8 75701 #048-02-1993 L1994 **RNR** *020 †80
REYES, Alan Doyle. 4101 UNIVERSITY BLVD 75701 #048-02-1981 L1981 **P** *020 †75
RIDENOUR, Lee Howard. 520 DOUGLAS BLVD 75702 #048-02-1978 L1978 **IM** *020 †20
RIEPE, David Burdette. 2301 S BROADWAY AVE, STE B8 75701 #048-13-1996 L1997 **DR** *020 †80
RISHEL, William Dela. 1130 DOCTORS DR, PEDIATRIC ASSOCIATES OF TY 75701 #048-15-1986 L1987 **PD** *020 †55
ROACH, Louis C. 1405 S FLEISHEL AVE # 315 75701 #047-07-1978 L1992 **GS** *020 †85
ROBBINS, Mark Richard. 1028 E IDEL ST STE B 75701 #018-03-1995 L2001 **VS** *020 †85
ROBERTS, Andrew C. 1100 E LAKE ST, STE 160 75701 #048-14-1995 L2000 **U** *020 †95
ROBERTS, Mark D. 3200 TROUP HWY, STE 200 75701 #048-02-1994 L1995 **AN** *020 †05
ROBERTS, Paul Baden. 11937 US HIGHWAY 271, U.T. HEALTH CENTER AT TYLE 75708 #836-01-1983 L1994 **EM** *020 †18
ROBERTS, Steven Bruce. 700 OLYMPIC PLAZA CIR, STE 700 75701 #016-06-1961 L1968 **U** *020 †95
ROBERTSON, Bradley D. 1809 CAPITAL DR 75701 #048-02-1989 L1990 **FM** *020 †18
ROGERS, James Richard. 706 TURTLE CREEK DR, PEDIATRICS 75701 #048-12-1980 L1980 **PD** *020 †55
ROGERS, William Blant. 3311 WOODS BLVD 75707 #021-05-1977 L1992 **P** *020 †75
ROOSTH, Wiley. 1025 HOSPITAL DR 75701 #048-02-1946 L1946 **FM** *020 †18
ROSENFIELD, Laurence. 800 E DAWSON ST 75701 #035-47-1983 L1990 **PME AN** *020 †05
ROSS, Sabine. 912 S FLEISHEL AVE 75701 #409-42-1985 L1994 **ID** *020 †20
ROSSMAN, Robert E. 1720 S BECKHAM AVE, STE 102 75701 #048-02-1953 L1953 **D** *020 †15
ROUNDS, Jack Sherman, Jr. 3200 TROUP HWY STE 200 75701 #035-20-1964 L1982 **AN** *020 †05

■ = Address Information Privacy Protected

ROWE, Stephen Adam. 1020 E IDEL ST 75701 #035-03-1996 L2005 **GS** *020 †85
ROWE, William E. ■ 75703 #048-04-1949 L1949 **PD** *071
RUSSELL, Michael E, II. 1905 S DONNYBROOK AVE 75701 #048-12-1991 L1992 **ORS** *020 †40
RYDER, James F. 800 E DAWSON ST 75701 #048-02-1987 L1988 **EM** *020 †18
RYDZAK, Stephen P. 1100 S BECKHAM AVE 75701 #048-13-1989 L1990 **IM** *020 †20
SAAR, James Douglas. 620 S FLEISHEL AVE 75701 #039-01-1992 L2001 **PS** *020 †85,65
SADANA, Amit. 910 E HOUSTON ST, STE 550 75702 #035-03-1997 L2004 **GE** *020 †20
SAIGUSA, Makoto. 805 TURTLE CREEK DR 75701 #048-13-1995 L1996 **OMF** *020
SANCHEZ, Robert Bradley. 2301 S BROADWAY AVE, STE B8 75701 #034-01-1986 L1997 **DR** *020 †80
SANCHEZ, Steven Ray. 1726 S BECKHAM AVE 75701 #039-01-2001 L2006 **PTH HMP** *020 †50
SANDS, Scott Jeffrey. 1424 E FRONT ST 75702 #048-02-1974 L1974 **OPH AM** *020 †35
SANFELIPPO, Peter Michael. 11937 US HIGHWAY 271 75708 #056-06-1965 L1991 **TS OM** *071 †85,90
SANFORD, Clyde Fagg, III. 619 S FLEISHEL AVE STE 101, STE 101 75701 #048-12-1976 L1977 **CD IM** *020 †20
SATTERFIELD, Scott Thomas. 910 E HOUSTON ST STE 55 75702 #016-11-1980 L1981 **GE** *020 †20
SAUNDERS, Mark Wayne. 910 E HOUSTON ST 75702 #004-01-1988 L1994 **RO** *020 †80
SAURETTE, Jennifer Bisnet. 6210 S BROADWAY AVE 75703 #048-02-2004 L2006 **FM** *020 †18
SCARDINA, Ray Gerard. 3300 S BROADWAY AVE, STE 102 75701 #021-06-1979 L1986 **CHP P** *020 †75
SCHMIEGE, Lorenz M, III. 1726 S BECKHAM AVE 75701 #048-16-2001 L2004 **PTH** *020 †50
SCHNEIDER, Heidi E. 1327 TROUP HWY 75701 #048-02-2001 L2005 **RHU** *020
SCHREIBER, Jon Trueheart. 2440 E 5TH ST 75701 #048-14-1973 L1974 **OPH** *020 †35
SCHREIBER, William Edward. 1905 S DONNYBROOK AVE 75701 #048-12-1969 L1969 **ORS OSM** *020 †40
SCHULTZ, Gregory Alan. 2301 S BROADWAY AVE, STE B8 75701 #048-14-1988 L1989 **RNR** *020 †80
SCHWARZBACH, Jerry W. 1905 S DONNYBROOK AVE 75701 #048-04-1987 L1988 **PM** *020 †60
SCROGGINS, John William. 520 DOUGLAS BLVD 75702 #021-05-1973 L1978 **FM** *020 †18 ‡
SEIDEL, Richard H, II. 1720 S BECKHAM AVE 75701 #023-01-1992 L1993 **GE** *020 †20
SELMAN, Joseph. 1020 CLINIC DR, TYLER RADIOLOGY ASSOCIATE 75701 #038-06-1940 L1949 **R** *071 †80
SHAFER, David Richard. 11937 US HIGHWAY 271, U TX HLTH CTR AT TYLER 75708 #048-04-1978 L1978 **IM DIA** *020 †20
SHAFFER, Monica Jane. 417 S SAUNDERS AVE 75702 #048-13-1998 L2003 **OTO** *020 †45
SHARKEY, Paul C, Jr. 5100 OLD BULLARD RD, STE B 75703 #048-02-1989 L1991 **AI** *020 †03,55
SHAW, George W. ■ 75703 #048-12-1953 L1954 **ORS** *071 †40
SHEFA, Barry Z. 912 S FLEISHEL AVE, TYLER INPATIENT MANAGEMENT 75701 #048-02-2004 L2007 **FM** *020 †18
SHEPARD, Martin Jos. 1814 ROSELAND BLVD 75701 #019-02-1968 L1974 **ORS** *020 †40
SHEPHERD, Robert. 520 DOUGLAS BLVD, RADIOLOGY 75702 #067-01-1976 L1985 **OBG** *020
SHEPPARD, David. 4500 S BROADWAY AVE 75703 #060-01-1971 L1985 **EM** *020
SHERMAN, Denise Ione. 3309 UNIVERSITY BLVD, MAGNOLIA INTERNAL MEDICINE 75701 #019-02-1989 L1997 **IM** *020 †20
SHIRODKAR, Alka Pradeep. ■ 75701 #495-17-1973 L2007 **FM** *074 †18
SHIRODKAR, Pradeep S. 11937 US HIGHWAY 271 75708 #495-01-1973 L1997 **FM** *020 †18
SHIRODKAR, Samir Pradeep. ■ 75701 #048-04-2006 **U** *012
SHORT, Herbert David. 910 E HOUSTON ST, STE 530 75702 #048-04-1973 L1974 **TS GS** *040 †85,90
SHORT, Hope Daughtrey. 455 RICE RD STE 111, - 112 75703 #048-13-1996 L1997 **FM** *020 †18
SHORT, Kevin Alan. 2301 S BROADWAY AVE, STE B8 75701 #048-15-1990 L1991 **VIR** *020 †80
SHULL, John Robinson. ■ 75703 #019-02-1962 L1966 **PM** *071 †60
SHUM, John Hinchung. 214 E HOUSTON ST 75702 #048-02-2000 L2002 **OBG** *020 †18
SIBLEY, Warren Oxsheer. 3300 S BROADWAY AVE STE 10 75701 #048-12-1975 L1975 **P** *074
SIGAL, Stephen Lee. 1100 E LAKE ST, STE 370 75701 #008-01-1984 L1991 **CD IM** *020 †20
SIMPSON, Amy Kathryn. 1910 ROSELAND BLVD 75701 #048-12-1989 L1991 **IM OS** *020 †20
SIRIANNI, Peter Anthony. 800 E DAWSON ST 75701 #003-01-1993 L1997 **AN** *020 †05
SLOAN, David James. 1100 E LAKE ST, STE 240 75701 #048-02-1978 L1978 **IM** *020 †20
SMITH, Eric Richard. 3802 MANHATTON DR, STE 203 75701 #048-12-1982 L1983 **FM** *020 †18
SMITH, Evans Swann. 1000 S BECKHAM AVE 75701 #048-02-1997 L2000 **EM** *020 †16
SMITH, Gary Earl. ■ 75703 #028-03-1984 L2000 **FM** *020 †18
SMITH, Homer Don. ■ 75701 #048-12-1963 L1963 **AN** *071 †05
SMITH, Jeffrey P. 3414 GOLDEN RD, P O BOX 13866 75701 #048-14-1990 L1993 **PD** *020 †55
SMITH, Sally L. 520 DOUGLAS BLVD 75702 #048-13-1989 L1990 **FM** *020 †18
SMITH, Todd P. 910 E HOUSTON ST, STE 530 75702 #048-13-1995 L1998 **VS** *020 †85
SMITH, Valerie J. ■ 75703 #048-12-2001 L2004 **PD** *020 †55
SMYTH, William C. 520 DOUGLAS BLVD 75702 #048-02-1953 L1953 **GP IM** *071
SNELL, Brian Elliott. 700 OLYMPIC PLAZA CIR, STE 850 75701 #017-20-1998 L2005 **NS** *020
SNIDER, Walter Herd, Jr. 3200 TROUP HWY, STE 200 75701 #048-12-1963 L1963 **AN** *071 †05
SPAIN, Stephen Craig. 6210 S BROADWAY AVE 75703 #048-14-1981 L1981 **FM** *020
SPARROW, William Thos. 901 TURTLE CREEK DR 75701 #048-12-1963 L1963 **PTH** *071 †50
SPENCE, Julius Hoff. ■ 75701 #048-02-1945 L1954 **AN** *071
SPENCER, Charla Cushing. 733 S FLEISHEL AVE 75701 #027-01-1996 L2000 **OBG** *020 †30
SPIVEY, Charles G, Jr. ■ 75701 #051-04-1951 L1972 **PUD IM** *071 †20
STANFORD, James N. 520 DOUGLAS BLVD 75702 #048-14-1994 L1997 **IM** *020 †20
STAPLES, Marcus E. 214 E HOUSTON ST, FAMILY CARE CENTER 75702 #048-13-1993 L1995 **OBG** *020 †30
STARLING, William Howard. 305 W RUSK ST, CHILDRENS CLINIC 75701 #048-12-1962 L1962 **PD** *020 †55
STARR, Amy M. 706 TURTLE CREEK DR, PEDIATRICS 75701 #048-12-1990 L1991 **PD** *020 †55
ST CLAIR, William Ernest. 3614 ROCK CREEK DR 75707 #048-02-1959 L1959 **FM** *040 †18
STEADMAN, Bevan Ellis. 4101 UNIVERSITY BLVD 75701 #048-02-1971 L1971 **CHP P** *020 †75
STEEGER, Jennifer Ann. 305 W RUSK ST 75701 #004-01-1999 L2002 **PD** *020 †55
STEINBACH, Barbara G C. 721 CLINIC DR 75701 #041-12-1965 L1997 **DR PD** *020 †55,80
STEPH, Donal W. 1015 E IDEL ST 75701 #048-12-1953 L1953 **GS** *020 †85
STEPHEN, Albert Michael P. 520 DOUGLAS BLVD 75702 #566-01-1986 L1997 **FM OTO** *020 †18
STEPHENSON, Kenna. 2702 E 5TH ST 75701 #048-15-1989 L1990 **FM** *020 †18 ‡
STEWART, Mack Dwight. 800 E DAWSON ST 75701 #048-14-1984 L1985 **EM FM** *020 †18
STOCK, Alexander. 520 DOUGLAS BLVD, TRINITY CLNC 75702 #065-01-1974 L1977 **GP** *020 †70
STOCKS, James Martin. 11937 US HIGHWAY 271 75708 #048-12-1979 L1979 **PUD SME** *020 †20
STONE, Brian Henry. ■ 75703 #048-15-2004 L2007 **GS** *100
STOVALL, James Gregory. 520 DOUGLAS BLVD 75702 #048-02-1978 L1978 **IM** *020 †20
STRAUSS, Glenn Howard. 3415 GOLDEN RD, HEATON EYE ASSOCIATES 75701 #048-02-1980 L1980 **OPH** *040 †35
STROUPE, Earnest W. 800 E DAWSON ST 75701 #048-14-1987 L1988 **EM FM** *020 †18
SULSER, Norman Carl, Jr. 800 E DAWSON ST 75701 #048-12-1980 L1980 **AN** *071 †05
SUTHERLAND, Robert Martin. 700 OLYMPIC PLAZA CIR, STE 850 75701 #016-11-1981 L2002 **AN PME** *020 †05
SWARTWORTH, William J. 1327 TROUP HWY, HEALTH WORK 75701 #051-07-1984 L2007 **OM** *020 †70
TANO, Benoit Deki. 11397 US HIGHWAY 271 75708 #038-43-1999 L2006 **AI** *100 †20,03
TASKAR, Varsha S. 11937 US HIGHWAY 271, UNIVERSITY OF TEXAS AT TYL 75708 #496-38-1988 L1999 **PCC SME** *020 †20
TAYLOR, Don Corbett. 214 E HOUSTON ST 75702 #048-14-1992 L1995 **OBG** *020 †30
TAYLOR, Tara Leigh. ■ 75703 #035-08-1998 L2006 **IM** *020 †20
TEEGARDEN, David Kent. 910 E HOUSTON ST, STE 500 75702 #048-02-1971 L1971 **GE IM** *020 †20
TERRES, Jayson J. 805 TURTLE CREEK DR 75701 #048-13-2002 L2006 **OMF** *020
THERIOT, Maxine Arlene. 800 E DAWSON ST, WOUND CARE CENTER 75701 #005-12-1994 L1996 **FM** *020 †18 ‡
THIELE, Stefan Peter. 1100 E LAKE ST, STE 220 75701 #048-02-1997 L2002 **GS** *020
THOMAS, Alan Q. 912 S FLEISHEL AVE 75701 #048-12-1995 L1996 **PCC** *020 †20
THOMAS, Patrick Reese. 611 S FLEISHEL AVE, TMFHS FOUNDATION 75701 #048-02-1959 L1959 **GS VS** *071 †85
THOMPSON, Harry Hyman. 4101 UNIVERSITY BLVD, UNIVERSITY PARK HOSPITAL 75701 #004-01-1965 L1976 **P** *020
THOMPSON, Jack Raymond. 1350 E RICHARDS ST, ST PAUL CLINIC 75702 #004-01-1955 L1958 **GP** *071
THOMPSON, James Edward. ■ 75703 #028-78-1965, ▲ L1965 **GP** *071
TIBILETTI, Claire. 1814 ROSELAND BLVD 75701 #048-02-1982 L1983 **PME** *020
TOBY, Joshua D. 800 E DAWSON ST, ANESTHESIOLOGY DEPT 75701 #048-16-2000 L2004 **AN** *020 †05
TOLER, Robert John. ■ 75701 #028-78-1953, ▲ L1956 **GYN GP** *071
TOMPKINS, Robert B. 11937 US HIGHWAY 271 75708 #048-02-1994 L1995 **FM** *020 †18
TONEY, James Danl. 417 S SAUNDERS AVE, ENT 75702 #048-02-1968 L1968 **OTO PS** *020 †45
TOPHAM, R Todd. 3309 UNIVERSITY BLVD 75701 #019-02-1992 L1997 **IM** *020
TREADWELL, Richard Dale. 800 E DAWSON ST 75701 #048-02-1991 L1992 **AN** *020 †05
TRUONG, Nghia D. 1100 S BECKHAM AVE, REGIONAL HEALTH CARE SYSTE 75701 #048-12-1993 L1994 **IM** *020 †20
TURER, Jana Miller. ■ 75703 #048-15-1987 L1988 **P** *071 †75
TURNER, William Franklin. 1100 E LAKE ST, STE 210 75701 #048-04-1981 L1982 **TS GS** *020 †85,90
TUTT, Richard Ray. 700 OLYMPIC PLAZA CIR #504 75701 #048-12-1979 L1979 **OBG** *020 †30
TYER, Richard Wayne. 11702 HIGHWAY 64 E 75707 #048-02-1966 L1966 **FM** *020
UDUMA, Ndukwe Kalu. ■ 75703 #690-04-1984 L2007 **CHP** *020 †75
ULRICH, Richard Frank. 1301 DOCTORS DR, EAST TEXAS NEUROLOGY 75701 #038-40-1964 L1974 **N IM** *020 †75
VAIL, Theresa M Vrana. 606 S FLEISHEL AVE 75701 #048-02-1995 L2000 **P PFP** *020 †75
VALERO, Gustavo. 5701 OLD BULLARD RD 75703 #649-02-1988 L1991 **ID IM** *020 †20
VALLEJO, Gerard Eaton. ■ 75701 #048-14-1992 L2003 **P CHP** *020 †75
VAN DUSEN, Delbert W. 11980 HIGHWAY 155 N 75708 #649-01-1978 L2000 **FOP PTH** *062 †50
VAN HOY, Tess Blanchard. 1000 S BECKHAM AVE 75701 #021-06-1993 L1995 **EM** *020 †16
VARNAM, Jessica Heather. ■ 75701 #005-12-2008 *012
VASQUEZ, Luis Edmundo. 4293 KINSEY DR, TX ARHTRITIS & RHEUMATOLOG 75703 #341-03-1990 L1996 **RHU IM** *020 †20
VAUGHAN, Joseph K, Jr. 700 OLYMPIC PLAZA CIR # 91 75701 #051-04-1993 L2002 **N CN** *020
VAUGHN, Chester Alexander. 800 E DAWSON ST, TRINITY MOTHER FRANCES HOS 75701 #048-12-1957 L1959 **OPH** *071
VERSHAW, Anna E. ■ 75701 #048-14-2008 *012
VIKEN, Richard Melvin. 11937 US HIGHWAY 271, UNIV OF TX HLTH CTR 75708 #040-02-1974 L1987 **FM FPG** *040 †18
VILLARREAL, David H. 1020 E IDEL ST, ETMC-TYLER TRAUMA 75701 #649-02-1989 L2000 **CCS GS** *020 †85
VILLENA, Ramiro Miguel. 1910 ROSELAND BLVD 75701 #132-01-1998 L2003 **IM** *020 †20
VOLATILE, Thomas Burkart. 1327 TROUP HWY 75701 #023-01-1979 L2007 **ORS OAR** *020 †40
VUKELJA, Svetislava J. 910 E HOUSTON ST, STE 100 75702 #023-12-1983 L1996 **ON IM** *020 †20
WALDRON, Richard Lloyd. ■ 75701 #048-02-1961 L1961 **AN** *071 †05
WALKER, John Fletcher. 1905 S DONNYBROOK AVE 75701 #021-01-1965 L1966 **ORS** *020 †40
WALKER, Kerfoot Pollock. PO BOX 2039 75710 #048-12-1955 L1955 **PHP** *030
WALKER, Roger K. 2301 S BROADWAY AVE, STE B8 75701 #048-13-1988 L1989 **VIR** *020 †80
WALLACE, Richard J, Jr. 11937 US HIGHWAY 271, DEPT MICROBIOLOGY 75708 #048-04-1972 L1972 **ID** *050 †20
WALLACE, William Randolph. 1809 CAPITAL DR 75701 #048-02-1989 L1991 **EM** *020 †18
WALLACH, Perry Chandler. 1100 S BECKHAM AVE 75701 #035-08-1988 L2006 **IM PM** *020 †20,60
WALLING, Stephen Boyd. 800 E DAWSON ST 75701 #048-15-1976 L1976 **IM** *020 †20
WARD, Frank Thos. 910 E HOUSTON ST, STE 100 75702 #024-01-1978 L1999 **HO IM** *020 †20
WATSON, David Gregory. 7113 HOLLY SQUARE CT 75703 #005-15-1993 L1998 **EM** *071
WEBB, Kent P. 1327 TROUP HWY 75701 #017-20-1989 L1993 **VS** *020 †85
WEI, Yunfei. ■ 75703 #243-72-1988 L2007 **IM** *100 †20
WEINER, Stanislav. 619 S FLEISHEL AVE, TYLER CARDIOVASCULAR 75701 #035-46-1996 L2003 **ICE CD** *020 †20
WELLS, Charles Donald, Jr. 11937 US HIGHWAY 271, UT HEALTH CENTER TYLER 75708 #027-01-1979 L1980 **DR** *020 †80
WELLS, Robert Brian. 1726 S BECKHAM AVE 75701 #021-06-1988 L1995 **PTH** *075 †50
WEST, Stephanie Michelle. 5414 S BROADWAY AVE, TMF DIRECT CARE 75703 #048-14-1995 L1996 **FM** *020 †18
WESTBROOK, Carl Urban. 1324 S BECKHAM AVE, STE 207 75701 #047-07-1972 L1973 **OBG** *020 †30
WHARTON, Arnold D. 900 MEDICAL DR 75701 #048-02-1966 L1966 **OBG** *020 †30
WHETSELL, Joe Ed. ■ 75703 #048-02-1956 L1956 **GE IM** *071 †20
WICK, Melanie Power. 706 TURTLE CREEK DR 75701 #048-12-1993 L2003 **PD** *020 †55
WICK, Paul H. 3300 S BROADWAY AVE 75701 #048-02-1961 L1961 **P PYG** *020 †75 ‡
WIERTZ, Larry Martin. 1000 E 5TH ST 75701 #065-05-1968 L1978 **END IM** *020 †20

■ = Address Information Privacy Protected

WIES, Karen. 1100 S BECKHAM AVE 75701 #028-34-1983 L2003 IM *020 †20
WILCOX, Leland G. ■ 75701 #021-05-1942 L1950 ORS *071 †40
WILES, Peter John. 5815 WOODGLEN DR 75703 #048-12-1965 L1974 OBG MDM *020 †30
WILLENS, Mitchell Lee. 910 E HOUSTON ST STE 60 75702 #016-42-1976 L1979 OBG *020 †30
WILLIAMS, Hampton D, III. 800 E DAWSON ST 75701 #027-01-1977 L1978 AN *020 †05
WILLIAMS, Michael C. 1000 S BECKHAM AVE 75701 #048-04-1993 L1994 EM *020 †16
WILLIAMS, Robert C. 700 OLYMPIC PLAZA CIR # 7 75701 #048-78-1999, ▲ L2005 U *020 †95
WILLIAMS, Victor Glenn, II. 910 E HOUSTON ST STE 33 75702 #056-06-2001 L2007 NS *100
WILLIAMSON, Gary Wayne. 800 E DAWSON ST 75701 #048-12-1978 L1978 FM *020 †18
WILLIS, Sherilyn A. 2017 RICKETY LN 75703 #048-16-2001 L2005 OBG *020 †30
WILLIS, Ted S. 520 DOUGLAS BLVD, RADIOLOGY 75702 #048-13-1986 L1987 R DR *072 †80
WILLMS, Richard Kenneth. 1100 E LAKE ST, STE 100 75701 #016-11-1956 L1960 GS TS *020 †85,90
WILSON, Frederic Barlow. 700 OLYMPIC PLAZA CIR #510 75701 #026-04-1988 L2004 ORS OTR *072 †40
WILSON, Oscar Ray. 520 DOUGLAS BLVD, TRINITY CLINIC 75702 #048-12-1983 L1983 FM *020 †18
WINANS, Robert Campbell. 3200 TROUP HWY STE 200, EAST TEXAS ANESTH ASSOCIAT 75701 #048-14-1991 L1993 AN *020 †05
WOODARD, Terry D. 700 S FLEISHEL AVE 75701 #048-15-1989 L1990 NEP *020 †20
WORTHINGTON, Thomas Mason. 1404 COLD WATER DR 75703 #048-02-1983 L1983 FM *020 †18
WRENN, Christopher Jay. 1128 MEDICAL DR 75701 #030-05-1973 L1975 AI PD *020 †55,03
WRIGHT, Bill J. 800 E DAWSON ST 75701 #046-01-1980 L1981 EM *020 †16
WRIGHT, Paul Weyer. 2030 DRESSAGE LN 75703 #020-12-1966 L1967 FM *072 †18
WRIGHT, Scott Alan. 115 W 5TH ST 75701 #048-02-1997 L2000 CD *020 †20
WUPPERMAN, Patrick L. 3414 GOLDEN RD 75701 #048-14-2000 L2006 ORS *100
WYRICK, Drew Hawley. 1100 E LAKE ST, STE 150 75701 #048-14-1996 L1999 IM *020 †20
XIA, Kai. 910 E HOUSTON ST, STE 330 75702 #024-01-1999 L2005 GE *020 †20
YAKLIN, Yvonne M. 700 OLYMPIC PLAZA CIR # 9 75701 #048-15-1993 L1994 IM *020 †20
YATES, Robert R. 3200 TROUP HWY, STE 310 75701 #048-12-1986 L1987 ID *020 †20
YIN, Po-Chin H. 2990 N BROADWAY AVE, PEDIATRIC SERVICES 75702 #385-02-1968 L1977 PD *020 †55
YODER, Steven K. 800 E DAWSON ST, ANEST DEPT 75701 #048-12-1985 L1986 AN *020 †05
YOUNG, David Lawrence. 700 OLYMPIC PLAZA CIR, STE 510 75701 #048-16-1994 L1999 GS *020 †85
ZEORLIN, Anne Marie. 520 DOUGLAS BLVD 75702 #039-01-1984 L1990 FM *020 †18

UNIVERSAL CITY — BEXAR

BARCHIE, Matthew Frederic. ■ 78148 #034-01-2007 GS *012
BAXTER, William Keith. ■ 78148 #004-01-1995 L1995 FM *020 †20,18
BROWN, Priscilla R. ■ 78148 #748-08-1969 FM *020
CRISP, Howard Champion. ■ 78148 #051-07-2006 L2007 IM *012
DAY, Richard Thos. ■ 78148 #018-03-1948 L1980 AM GPM *071 †70
DECLEENE, Nareda W H. ■ 78148 #001-02-1983 L1984 IM *020 †20
HARMAN, Louis E, Jr. ■ 78148 #036-07-1949 L1952 D *071 †15
KOTTMAN, Robert Wm. 300 KITTY HAWK RD, ALAMO PHYSICIANS SERV INC 78148 #038-40-1972 L1975 EM *020 †16
MAYS, Anthony Watkins. ■ 78148 #048-02-1956 L1956 FM *071 †18
MEHTA, Sumeru Ghanshyam. ■ 78148 #010-01-2000 L2005 EM *020 †16
MOLINA, Diane Kimberley. ■ 78148 #048-13-1998 L2000 PTH *020
NAIK, Suneeta. 2009 PAT BOOKER RD 78148 #495-45-1974 L1982 FM *020
PARK, Richard. 2009 PAT BOOKER RD 78148 #056-06-1959 L1978 FM OM *020 †70
POOLE, Ronald Dale. ■ 78148 #649-30-1982 L1984 GPM *012 †75,18
REIFLE, Sheila R. 2318 PAT BOOKER RD, SATMED MEDICAL CLINIC 78148 #048-13-1988 L1995 FM PD *020
SAUNDERS, Andrea J. ■ 78148 #048-02-2008 *012
STEVENS, Victor Louis. ■ 78148 #019-02-1982 L1996 P ADP *020 †75
WALLACE, Frank Liebig. ■ 78148 #048-02-1998 L2002 AN *020 †05
WILEY, John Ross. 14001 OAK MDWS # 2 78148 #007-02-1957 L1981 OS AM *062 †70

UVALDE — UVALDE

AMADI, Fidelis Eze. 1025 GARNER FIELD RD 78801 #048-14-2001 L2004 FM *020 †18
BARRIENTOS, Eusebio Lujan. 1042 GARNER FIELD RD 78801 #048-13-1988 L1989 FM *020 †18
BATKI, Dara. 1025 GARNER FIELD RD 78801 #023-12-1982 L1988 EM *020
BONDOC, Rosario Maramba. 329 S CAMP ST, P O BOX 1816 78801 #748-01-1993 L2002 FM *020 †18
BOX, Gloria H. 1025 GARNER FIELD RD 78801 #048-12-1990 L1991 ORS *020
CARPINTEYRO, Ralph, Jr. 121 W SOUTH ST 78801 #048-02-1981 L1982 IM *020 †20
FLANDERS, Barry Nyal. 1025 GARNER FIELD RD 78801 #005-06-1980 L1985 DR *020 †80
FRIEDMAN, David Julian. 1025 GARNER FIELD RD 78801 #836-01-1971 L1989 PHO IM *020 †20
GAITONDE, Gajanan V. 101 JOLLEY ST 78801 #496-15-1973 L1981 GS GP *020
GARZA, Reynaldo Esteban. 1800 GARNER FIELD RD 78801 #048-02-1985 L1986 FM *020 †18
GRUN, Tanya R. 200 EVANS ST 78801 #048-16-1989 L1990 FM *020 †18
HNATOW, Brenda Jean. 1025 GARNER FIELD RD 78801 #056-06-1983 L1988 DR *020 †80
HUSSAIN, Mohammad. 137 W NOPAL ST 78801 #704-09-1985 L1998 IM RHU *020
KILPATRICK, Hamilton, III. ■ 78801 #048-04-1952 L1952 GP *071
KUMAR, Sanjiv Ramesh. 927 E MAIN ST 78801 #024-01-1991 L1995 OPH *020 †35
LEWIS, Jacques Brandon. 1020 E LEONA RD 78801 #649-33-1983 L1989 FM *020 †18
LOCKETT, Kerry Lane. 1025 GARNER FIELD RD 78801 #048-16-1981 L1981 FM *020 †18
LUTTON, Richard Bruce. 1800 GARNER FIELD RD 78801 #048-14-1983 L1984 FM *020 †18
MEYER, James Richard. 1038A GARNER FIELD RD 78801 #021-01-1974 L1975 OBG *020 †30
NGOFA, Nwosu Osaro. 1025 GARNER FIELD RD, UVALDE SURGICAL CLINIC 78801 #010-03-1991 L2006 FM *020 †85
PARTEN, Elizabeth H. 1025 GARNER FIELD RD 78801 #048-13-1988 L1989 CHP *020
SANTIAGO, Manuel Antonio. 1025 GARNER FIELD RD 78801 #042-01-1986 L1995 ON IM *050 †20
SHUDDE, John Lottman. 1042 GARNER FIELD RD 78801 #048-04-1961 L1961 GP AN *071 †18
STRICKLAND, Martha Burke. ■ 78801 #039-01-1945 L1972 A PD *020 †55

STRICKLAND, Martha J. 1018 E LEONA RD, CENESA HILL MEDICAL CENTER 78801 #654-01-1991 L1994 FM *020 †18
THARIAN, Brenda. ■ 78801 #048-16-2005 U *012
UPTERGROVE, Kevin L. 2100 GARNER FIELD RD 78801 #048-13-1991 L1992 FM EM *020 †18
UTTERBACK, Carlin Danl. 2100 GARNER FIELD RD 78801 #048-15-1984 L1985 FM *020 †18
WATKINS, Harry O'Neal. 1042 GARNER FIELD RD 78801 #048-02-1961 L1961 GS *020

VAN ALSTYNE — GRAYSON

SMITH MILLER, Jeanne Hele. ■ 75495 #035-09-1943 L1954 P PYA *071 †55
WESTMORELAND, Paul A, II. PO BOX 448, VAN ALSTYNE FAMILY PRACTIC 75495 #048-14-1997 L1998 FM *020 †18

VENUS — JOHNSON

CARROLL, Donald Washburn. 1100 HIGHWAY 1807, VENUS CORRECTIONAL CENTER 76084 #048-02-1954 L1954 GP *071
RILEY, Murlefranklin. ■ 76084 #305-01-1991 L1996 *100

VERNON — WILBARGER

BAKER, David Ray. 4730 COLLEGE DR, VERNON CAMPUS 76384 #048-12-1966 L1966 P *020
BARROW, Nancy Eleanor. PO BOX 2231, VERNON CAMPUS - BMTP UNIT 76385 #048-02-1975 L1975 CHP P *020
BASORA, Manuel Hernandez. 4301 COLLEGE DR RM 200 76384 #847-01-1969 L1983 FM GS *020
BLACK, Joseph Lee. 4730 COLLEGE DR, NORTH TEXAS STATE HOSP 76384 #048-02-1966 L1966 P PFP *020 †75
BORCHARDT, Robt Henry, Jr. 1015 HILLCREST DR 76384 #048-02-1970 L1970 FM *020 †18
CARREON, Rosario Cortez. 1000 GARLAND JOHNSTON DR 76384 #748-10-1981 L1987 IM NEP *020
COLLINS, Arthur Cowan. 4730 COLLEGE DR, VERNON STATE HOSPITAL 76384 #048-12-1967 L1992 P N *020 †75
DRAUGHON, Edwin S, Jr. 4730 COLLEGE DR, NORTH TEXAS STATE HOSPITAL 76384 #004-01-1985 L1998 CHP *020 †75
EKSAENGSRI, Pipadh. ■ 76384 #891-02-1970 L1979 OBG *020 †30
FANIRAN, Olayemi Ayodele. 4730 COLLEGE DR, NORTH TEXAS STATE HOSPITAL 76384 #690-01-1990 L2007 PYG *100
FERGUSON, Melissa R. PO BOX 2231, 4730 COLLEGE DR 76385 #048-14-1986 L1987 P *020 †75
HARDIN, John Brown. 1900 PEASE ST, STE 209 76384 #048-02-1954 L1955 GP *071
HASSELTINE, Christopher J. 4730 COLLEGE DR 76384 #048-13-1995 L1997 P *020 †75
MANIAGO, Reynaldo Gabriel. 4301 COLLEGE DR 76384 #748-10-1971 L1980 PD ADL *020
MENDOZA, Joe, Jr. 4301 COLLEGE DR, RM 600 76384 #649-14-1977 L1980 FM EM *020
ODOM, Linda A. 4730 COLLEGE DR RM 78-1998, ▲ L2007 P *020 †75
PATEL, Babubhai M. 4730 COLLEGE DR, VERNON STATE HOSPITAL 76384 #495-01-1955 L1979 IM PD *071 †55 ‡
RAINWATER, Sherry Lynn C. 920 HILLCREST DR 76384 #048-13-1986 L1988 IM *020 †20
SCHAFFNER, Randall L. 4301 COLLEGE DR RM 300 76384 #048-15-1990 L1991 FM *020 †18
THACHIL, John. 1015 HILLCREST DR 76384 #495-31-1983 L1998 HO IM *020 †20
TOLENTINO, Reynaldo T. 4301 COLLEGE DR, RM 500 76384 #748-01-1961 L1971 GS *020 †85
VELAMATI, Vani. 920 HILLCREST DR, RADIOLOGY DEPT 76384 #495-58-1975 L1994 DR *020

VICTORIA — VICTORIA

ABDELGHANI, Wael M. 108 ASHFORD DR 77904 #915-03-1992 L2003 OPH *100 †35 ‡
ADAMS, Robin E. 2710 HOSPITAL DR STE 304 77901 #048-02-1989 L1996 PUD *020 †20
AFRIDI, Shah Nawaz. 2710 HOSPITAL DR, STE 200 77901 #913-12-1990 L1999 IM *020 †20
AIMONE, Roy John. 4402 N LAURENT ST STE A 77904 #048-02-1980 L1980 D EM *020 †15
ALLEN, Patricia Bette. 2701 HOSPITAL DR, CITIZENS MEDICAL CENTER 77901 #035-08-1990 L2007 EM *020 †16
ALLEN, Richard C, Jr. 2701 HOSPITAL DR 77901 #021-01-1950 L1950 FM *071 †18
ALMOND, Patrick Stephen. 4304 N LAURENT ST, STE A 77901 #011-03-1987 L2005 PDS *020 †85
ALVARADO, Lissette. 605 E SAN ANTONIO ST, STE 414E 77901 #042-01-1989 L1995 FM *030 †18
ANDERSON, Conde Nevin. 301 E AIRLINE RD 77901 #048-02-1973 L1973 GP *020
ANDERSON, Kevin Blake. 2700 CITIZENS PLZ, STE 204 77901 #028-78-2000, ▲ L2007 IM *020 †20 ‡
ARABI NEZHAD, Mehran. 2710 HOSPITAL DR 77901 #048-13-1993 L1995 IM *020 †20
ARAFILES, Rolando G. 5001 JOHN STOCKBAUER DR #C, NATURAL BIO HEALTH INTEGRA 77904 #748-10-1977 L1998 FM *020 †18
ARAOZ, Carlos Adolfo. 2710 HOSPITAL DR STE 106 77901 #132-01-1961 L1992 PTH NP *020 †50 ‡
ARQUISOLA, Arnel C. 2705 HOSPITAL DR, STE 204 77901 #748-11-1983 L1998 PD *020 †55
ASHY, Thomas Michael. 1501 E MOCKINGBIRD LN, STE 220 77904 #048-02-1968 L1968 AN OTO *020 †05
BARBER, John Edward. 601 E SAN ANTONIO ST, VICTORIA SURGICAL 77901 #048-14-1984 L1985 GS *020
BAUKNIGHT, Bruce Mingus. 601 E SAN ANTONIO ST # 101 77901 #048-02-1968 L1968 ON IM *020 †20
BELEW, Michael S. 601 E SAN ANTONIO ST, VICTORIA SURGICAL 77901 #048-16-1993 L1994 GS *020 †85
BHATIA, Sanjeev. 4504 N LAURENT ST 77901 #495-36-1994 L2003 IM PCC *020 †20
BICKFORD, Elmer Daryl. 117 MEDICAL DR STE 1 77904 #048-13-1975 L1976 OTO HNS *020 †45
BIGELOW, Eugene Lampson. 6007G COUNTRY CLUB DR 77904 #649-02-1958 L1959 PTH FM *050 †50
BOBELE, Gary Bruce. 4304 N LAURENT ST, STE A 77901 #048-13-1979 L1979 CHN PD *020 †55,75
BOOZALIS, George Theodore. 107 JAMES COLEMAN DR 77904 #023-07-1987 L1988 OPH *020 †35

BORCHERS, Charles Lewis. ■ 77901 #048-02-1955 L1955 **GP** *071
BOURAS, John Michael. 2710 HOSPITAL DR, STE 206 77901 #012-01-1998 L2006 **P** *020
BOUTHILLETTE, Michael. 4804 N NAVARRO ST 77904 #067-03-1965 L1978 **FM** *020
BOWEN, Joy Sharon. 2701 HOSPITAL DR 77901 #048-02-1970 L1970 **GS** *020 †85
BOWERS, Rodney Eugene. 4502 N LAURENT ST 77901 #041-09-1973 L1980 **CD IM** *020 †20
BRANFMAN, Gary Stewart. 110 MEDICAL DR, STE 105 77904 #048-15-1984 L1985 **PS HS** *020 †65
BREECH, Donald Wayne. 605 E SAN ANTONIO ST, STE 410E 77901 #048-13-1973 L1973 **ORS** *020 †40
BRENDEL, William Brian. 506 E SAN ANTONIO ST 77901 #048-02-1978 L1978 **PD NPM** *020 †55
BRIDGES, Doye R. 601 E SAN ANTONIO ST, STE 302 77901 #048-04-1953 L1953 **GYN** *071
BROWNING, Iley Baker, III. 4304 N LAURENT ST, STE A 77901 #036-01-1982 L1983 **PDP PD** *020 †55
BRUGO, Eduardo A. 2501 N NAVARRO ST 77901 #132-02-1968 L1977 **PTH** *020 †50
BURKS, Joseph Emerson. 2806 N NAVARRO ST, STE C 77901 #048-02-1973 L1973 **PUD CCM** *020 †20
BURNS, Brian Fred. 601 E SAN ANTONIO ST, STE 302W 77901 #048-15-1984 L1986 **PS HS** *020 †85,65
CAMPBELL, William T, Jr. 2700 CITIZENS PLZ, STE 300 77901 #048-02-1984 L1985 **IM CD** *040 †20
CANCHOLA, Samuel Victor. 506 E SAN ANTONIO ST 77901 #649-02-1976 L1979 **EM OS** *020 †18
CATE, Bain C. 2805 N NAVARRO ST 77904 #048-14-1985 L1986 **FM** *030 †18
CAVALLO, Francesco Maria. 1607 N MAIN ST 77901 #030-06-1991 L1992 **DR** *020 †80
CHANDNA, Harish. 2104 PATTERSON DR 77901 #496-03-1985 L1998 **CD** *020 †20
CHANG, Craig Gesheng. 2700 CITIZENS PLZ, STE 401 77901 #019-02-1993 L1995 **GS** *020 †85
CHAPUT, Christopher Jos. 2700 CITIZENS PLZ STE 200 77901 #048-04-1968 L1968 **NS** *020 †25
CHEN, Karl Kong-Yuan. 2807 N BEN WILSON ST, STE 201 77901 #011-02-1981 L1982 **RO** *020 †80
CHINEA, Carlos E. 605 E SAN ANTONIO ST, STE 414E 77901 #042-01-1989 L1999 **GE** *020 †20
CLEMMONS, Andrew C. 601 E SAN ANTONIO ST, VICTORIA SURGICAL 77901 #048-78-1987, ▲ L1988 **GS** *020
COPELAND, Oliver Preston. 803 CHAMPIONS ROW 77904 #048-02-1968 L1969 **DR NM** *020 †80
COX, Gary Forrest. 2700 CITIZENS PLZ STE 100 77901 #048-13-1975 L1975 **D** *020 †15
CRABTREE, Jerry Wesley. ■ 77905 #021-05-1955 L1957 **OM GS** *071 †18
CREAGER, Gregory B. 2710 HOSPITAL DR, STE 202 77901 #048-13-1993 L1994 **P** *020 †75
CULPEPPER, Burford W. ■ 77904 #012-01-1965 L1978 **OM GP** *071 †18,70
DANIEL, Charles Paul. 2700 CITIZENS PLZ STE 40 77901 #048-02-1975 L1975 **ORS** *020 †40
DAY, Ralph Ernest. 8410 FM 236, MISSION VALLEY CLINIC 77905 #048-13-1979 L1979 **FM** *020 †18
DE FLORIO, Paul Thomas. 2701 HOSPITAL DR 77901 #047-05-2001 L2006 **EM** *020 †16
DE LEON, Jesse Vianes. 601 E SAN ANTONIO ST 77901 #649-30-1982 L1985 **FM EM** *020 †18
DELGADO, Ana M. 601 E SAN ANTONIO ST # 204 77901 #847-04-1984 L1991 **IM** *020 †20
DENTLER, Stephen M. 2710 HOSPITAL DR, STE 204 77901 #048-78-1992, ▲ L1993 **PD** *020 †55
DEVINE, Guy Alfred. 506 E SAN ANTONIO ST 77901 #012-01-1970 L1971 **OPH GP** *071 †35
DEWEY, Geo Carpenter, Jr. 1607 N MAIN ST 77901 #005-02-1967 L1975 **DR IM** *071 †20,80
DHINGRA, Yogesh Chand. 4304 N LAURENT ST 77901 #495-69-1972 L1977 **PD** *020 †55
DIAZ, Jorge A. 2710 HOSPITAL DR, STE 306 77901 #649-02-1990 L1996 **IM** *020 †20
DONAHOE, Cashell, Jr. 117 MEDICAL DR STE 1 77904 #051-01-1970 L1977 **OTO PS** *020 †45
D'ORSOGNA, Desiree E. 506 E SAN ANTONIO ST 77901 #048-13-1981 L1981 **PTH** *020 †50
DOTTER, James F. 1502 E AIRLINE RD, STE 25 77901 #048-14-1993 L1994 **P** *020 †75
DU, Yong. 605 E SAN ANTONIO ST, STE 430E 77901 #243-40-1984 L2002 **NEP** *020 †20
DUFFY, James Hardeman. 2901 N CAMERON ST 77901 #019-02-1955 L1962 **CHP** *071 †75
ESPINOSA, Fabian Ernesto. 2710 HOSPITAL DR, STE 200 77901 #319-06-1984 L1998 **IM** *020 †20
FAYKUS, Max Henry. ■ 77904 #048-12-1953 L1953 **R** *020 †80
FERRELL, Edward Vincent. 301 E AIRLINE RD 77901 #051-07-1990 L1994 **FM** *020 †18
FISHER, Johnnie Gaylard. 2700 CITIZENS PLZ, STE 300 77901 #048-02-1970 L1970 **P** *020 †75
FLIPPIN, Jill Melody. ■ 77904 #048-16-2005 L2008 **PD** *012
FOLLOWWILL, Jerry Lee. 605 E SAN ANTONIO ST 77901 #018-03-1988 L1992 **ORS** *020 †40
FRY, Frederick Martin. 2701 HOSPITAL DR 77901 #054-04-1966 L1969 **U** *020 †95
FULLER, James Kellum. 2701 HOSPITAL DR 77901 #048-02-1976 L1976 **CD TS** *020 †85,90
GAALLA, Ajay K. 2104 PATTERSON DR 77901 #048-14-1992 L1993 **CD IC** *020 †20
GARRETT, Derrick L. 1 OCONNOR PLZ 77901 #048-02-1995 L1997 **AN** *020 †05
GARZA, Dante Homero. 506 E SAN ANTONIO ST, 4TH FL 77901 #048-02-1999 L2002 **FM** *020 †18
GARZA, Pablo Garza. 2806 N NAVARRO ST 77901 #649-14-1973 L1976 **FM** *020 †18
GBALAZEH, Boniface Saye. 2006 N NAVARRO ST, STE F 77901 #048-04-1976 L1976 **EM FM** *020 †18,16
GIETZ, Leonard. 2710 HOSPITAL DR STE 106 77901 #060-01-1969 L1975 **PTH** *020 †50
GILLIAM, Robert Milton. 102 MEDICAL DR 77904 #048-02-1974 L1974 **OPH** *071 †35
GILNER, Leon Ira. 115 MEDICAL DR, STE 101A 77904 #035-15-1974 L1995 **NS** *020 †25 ‡
GLOVER, George E, Jr. 101 MEDICAL DR 77904 #048-02-1946 L1946 **IM FM** *071 †18
GOBER, Lane Lloyd. 605 E SAN ANTONIO ST, STE 430E 77901 #048-02-1976 L1976 **NEP IM** *020 †20
GOFF, E Wayne. 205 WOODGLENN DR 77904 #048-02-1961 L1961 **P** *071
GONZALEZ, Dana Marie. 2705 HOSPITAL DR, STE 300 77901 #048-02-2002 L2006 **OBG** *020
GREINER, Theodore Herman. 2001 E SABINE ST STE 107 77901 #028-02-1947 L1957 **P** *071 †75
GRUMMAN, James Andrew, Jr. 2403 N LAURENT ST 77901 #019-02-1970 L1992 **IM** *020 †20
GUEL, Veronica. 202 JAMES COLEMAN DR 77904 #048-13-2000 L2002 **FM** *020 †18
GULLAPALLI, Srinivas Bant. ■ 77904 #473-01-2002 **IM** *100
GULLAPALLI, Uma Rani. 4208 RETAMA CIR, # B 77901 #495-58-1975 L1992 **PM** *020
HAGER, Mark Wayne. 110 MEDICAL DR, STE 100 77904 #048-02-1976 L1976 **OBG** *020 †30
HAMILTON, Sean Michael. ■ 77904 #051-04-2000 L2007 **GS** *020 †85
HARVEY, Robert Edgar. 3901 N NAVARRO ST 77901 #048-04-1974 L1974 **AI** *020 †20,03
HASHMI, Shahid Hussain. 601 E SAN ANTONIO ST, VICTORIA SURGICAL 77901 #704-01-1969 L1978 **GS** *020 †85
HAYES, James Robt. 2705 HOSPITAL DR, STE 300 77901 #048-02-1975 L1975 **OBG** *020 †30
HEARD, Richard H. 107 PROFESSIONAL PARK DR 77904 #048-02-1953 L1953 **GP** *020
HEFFERNAN, Linda G. 1502 E AIRLINE RD STE 40 77901 #048-13-1985 L1986 **IM** *020 †20
HENRY, Grant Hardeman. 202 JAMES COLEMAN DR, STE C 77904 #048-02-2002 L2005 **FM** *020 †18
HICKS, Robert Lawrence. 2705 HOSPITAL DR, STE 300 77901 #005-19-1985 L1991 **OBG** *020 †30
HICKS, William Morse, Jr. 2701 HOSPITAL DR 77901 #038-41-1948 L1955 **IM CD** *030 †20
HILBERT, William Loren. 110 MEDICAL DR, STE 103 77904 #021-01-1978 L1985 **PD** *020 †55 ‡
HOANG, Joseph. 117 MEDICAL DR, STE 1 77904 #048-13-1989 L1997 **OTO** *020 †45
HOUGEN, Stephen Thorsheim. 2700 CITIZENS PLZ, STE 401 77901 #048-13-1978 L1978 **VS GS** *020 †85
JAIN, Ashok Kumar. 4304 N LAURENT ST, STE A 77901 #495-03-1978 L1993 **PD** *020 †55
JANECEK, Stephen E. 1501 E MOCKINGBIRD LN, STE 220 77904 #048-16-1988 L1989 **AN** *020 †05
JANSSEN, David L. 2700 CITIZENS PLZ, STE 201 77901 #048-02-1982 L1983 **RO** *020 †80
JANZOW, Matthew Theophil. 601 E SAN ANTONIO ST, VICTORIA SURGICAL 77901 #028-02-1995 L2003 **GS** *020 †85
JAYNES, Charles Ray. 110 MEDICAL DR STE 100 77904 #048-02-1973 L1973 **OBG** *020 †30
JOHN, Elizabeth. ■ 77904 #496-23-1995 L2004 **P** *100 ‡
JOHNSTON, Robert Hugh. 6412 N NAVARRO ST STE B 77904 #048-04-1957 L1957 **TS VS** *020 †85,90
KATHPALIA, Rakesh Kumar. 605 E SAN ANTONIO ST, STE 310 77901 #495-36-1992 L2006 **IM IMG** *020 †20
KATHPALIA, Suruchii. 605 E SAN ANTONIO ST, STE 310 77901 #495-36-1996 L2006 **IMG** *020 †20
KIEL, Frank Wilson. 2701 HOSPITAL DR 77901 #010-01-1954 L1977 **PTH FOP** *020 †50 ‡
KLEIN, Michael Philip. 4804 N NAVARRO ST 77904 #048-02-1988 L1990 *020
KOENIG, Reuben E. 2700 CITIZENS PLZ STE 203 77901 #048-04-1953 L1953 **GS HNS** *020 †85
KOPECKY, Alfred Allen. 2501 N NAVARRO ST 77901 #048-02-1962 L1962 **U** *020 †95
KRUEGER, Kurtis Ray. 2700 CITIZENS PLZ, STE 300 77901 #048-14-1981 L1981 **IC CD** *020 †20
KUMAR, Bangaruswamy V. 601 E SAN ANTONIO ST, STE 403 77901 #495-04-1984 L1998 **N** *020 †75
LE, Tri Minh. 202 JAMES COLEMAN DR, STE C 77904 #305-01-2001 L2007 **FM** *100 †18
LLOMPART-ZENO, Juan A. 2710 HOSPITAL DR, STE 202 77901 #035-19-1979 L1981 **PUD PCC** *020 †20
LONG, Joseph Merl. 2700 CITIZENS PLZ STE 101 77901 #017-20-1970 L1972 **FM** *020 †18
LYKES, Frederick Freeman. 303 E AIRLINE RD STE 1 77901 #048-02-1966 L1966 **D** *020
LYMAN, Robert C. 2710 HOSPITAL DR, STE 202 77901 #048-02-1984 L1985 **P** *020 †75
LYSTER, Alexander Kennedy. 2501 N NAVARRO ST 77901 #041-09-1959 L1966 **PTH** *072 †50
MABRAY, C Richard. 115 MEDICAL DR STE 202 77904 #048-04-1966 L1966 **OBG NTR** *020 †30
MALIK, Azhar Ali. 605 E SAN ANTONIO ST, STE 430E 77901 #704-21-1990 L2005 **NEP** *020 †20
MARROQUIN, Santiago. 403 BERKSHIRE ST 77904 #048-02-1999 L2001 **VIR** *020 †80
MC CAULEY, Ronald Keith. 102 MEDICAL DR 77904 #018-03-1974 L1978 **DR NM** *020 †80
MC DOWELL, Anthony Butler. 2705 HOSPITAL DR, STE 300 77901 #048-02-1989 L1990 **OBG** *020 †30
MC MAHON, Robert Thos. 4406 N LAURENT ST 77901 #030-06-1969 L1978 **OPH** *020 †35
MERIAN, Frederick Louis. 6502 NURSERY DR 77904 #048-02-1967 L1967 **FM AM** *020 †18
MINOCHA, Gulshan Kumar. 2700 CITIZENS PLZ, STE 406 77901 #495-69-1974 L1979 **IM DIA** *020 †20
MONDOLFI, Paul Enrique. 605 E SAN ANTONIO ST, STE 450E 77901 #935-01-1967 L1996 **PS HS** *020 †85,65
MOONEY, Ern Cunningham. 506 E SAN ANTONIO ST 77901 #048-12-1944 L1944 **FM** *071
NELSON, Ginna. 506 E SAN ANTONIO ST 77901 #048-12-1992 L1993 **FM EM** *020 †18
NEUMANN, James Francis. 2710 HOSPITAL DR STE 110 77901 #048-02-1971 L1971 **DR OS** *020 †80
NEW, Aaron Robert. ■ 77904 #048-14-2008 *012
NGUYEN, Luci T. 115 MEDICAL DR, STE 104 77904 #048-15-1993 L1997 **PM** *020 †60
NGUYEN, Peterminh Van. 2710 HOSPITAL DR STE 108, WELLMEDICINEPA 77901 #021-06-1995 L1998 **OM** *020 †70
NIELSEN, Buddy Ray. 1501 E MOCKINGBIRD LN, STE 220 77904 #049-01-1991 L1995 **AN** *020 †05
NORVILL, Keith A. 506 E SAN ANTONIO ST 77901 #028-79-1990, ▲ L1993 **NS** *020 ‡
OAKLEY, Robt Francis, Jr. 2700 CITIZENS PLZ, STE 300 77901 #048-02-1975 L1975 **CD** *020 †20
ORTIZ, Silvestre A. 1607 N MAIN ST 77901 #042-01-1971 L1977 **DR** *020 †80
O'SULLIVAN, Sean Kevin. 1401 VICTORIA STATION DR, STE A 77901 #048-14-1988 L1989 **DR** *020 †80
OWENSBY, Loren Cook. 601 E SAN ANTONIO ST # 305 77901 #001-02-1973 L1977 **GE IM** *020 †20
PAREKH, Minaxi Pradip. 110 MEDICAL DR, STE 104 77904 #495-01-1981 L1987 **PD** *020 †55
PARIKH, Daksheshkumar. 2104 PATTERSON DR 77901 #496-01-1988 L1993 **CD** *020 †20
PARMA, Frank Stephen. 2403 N LAURENT ST 77901 #048-13-1984 L1985 **FM** *020 †18
PATEL, Haroon I. 4304 N LAURENT ST, STE A 77901 #836-01-1988 L2002 **PDS** *020 †85
PATHIKONDA, Maya S. 601 E AIRLINE RD 77901 #495-56-1982 L1995 **PD** *020 †55
PATHIKONDA, Suresh N. 601 E AIRLINE RD 77901 #496-01-1978 L1995 **PD** *020 †55
PEREZ, Edward Roy. 2710 HOSPITAL DR, STE 106 77901 #021-06-1991 L1996 **SP** *020 †50
PERKINSON, Joseph Chas. 2710 HOSPITAL DR, STE 310 77901 #045-04-1992 L1998 **FM** *020 †18
PIGOTT, Shirley Persons. 1412 E RED RIVER ST 77901 #048-02-1980 L1980 **FM EM** *020 †18 ‡
PLOWMAN, Donald Lee. 605 E SAN ANTONIO ST, STE 410E 77901 #048-02-1967 L1967 **ORS** *020 †40
PONDER, Stephen Winfield. 4304 N LAURENT ST, STE A 77901 #048-02-1984 L1985 **PDE PD** *020 †55
PRATKA, Christopher Lynn. ■ 77904 #048-14-1995 L1997 **AN** *020 †05
PYLE, George Gilbert C. 2373 LOWER MISSION VALY RD 77905 #048-04-1956 L1956 **OPH** *071 †35
QADRI, Ahmad Imtiaz. 601 E SAN ANTONIO ST, STE 402W 77901 #704-02-1986 L2001 **HEM** *020 †20
RAMOS, Maria. 2501 N NAVARRO ST 77901 #847-09-1972 L1983 **PTH** *020 †50
RAO, Gullapalli Nageswara. 3901 N NAVARRO ST 77901 #495-50-1969 L1977 **OPH** *020 †35,03,55
RAO, Radha Krishna G. 3901 N NAVARRO ST 77901 #495-98-1973 L1978 **PDA AI** *020
RECORD, James Alfred, Jr. 2710 HOSPITAL DR, STE 306 77901 #048-02-1975 L1975 **OM GS** *020 †85
REGUEIRA, Felix Fermin. 4304 RETAMA CIR 77901 #847-05-1975 L1977 **PD ADL** *020 ‡
RESENDEZ, Adelaida. 110 MEDICAL DR STE 103 77904 #048-02-1999 L2002 **PD** *020
RIEDEL, Larry Otto. 605 E SAN ANTONIO ST, STE 510E 77901 #048-02-1956 L1956 **IM** *020 †20

■ = Address Information Privacy Protected

RIESZ, Peter Benj. 1401A VICTORIA STATION DR 77901 #041-09-1959 L1969 **DR RO** *062 †80

RIKHYE, Rakesh Kumar. 202 JAMES COLEMAN DR, STE C 77904 #065-01-1979 L1981 **FM** *020 †18

ROBINSON, Luke E, III. 605 E SAN ANTONIO ST, STE 310E 77901 #048-02-1975 L1975 **OBG** *020 †30

ROGERS, Richard Earl. 2700 CITIZENS PLZ, STE 403 77901 #048-14-1984 L1985 **GE IM** *020 †20

ROJAS, Peter Paul. 601 E SAN ANTONIO ST, VICTORIA SURGICAL 77901 #048-02-1970 L1970 **GS** *020 †85

ROMERO, Orestes A. 601 E SAN ANTONIO ST, STE 205 77901 #682-01-1983 L1996 **FM** *020 †18

SABBAGH, Mohammad H. 2700 CITIZENS PLZ, STE 203 77901 #875-01-1988 L2001 **HO** *020 †20

SACHDEV, Manju. 6502 NURSERY DR, STE 300 77904 #063-01-1992 L1998 **PD** *020 †55

SAGE, William Patrick. 117 MEDICAL DR STE 1 77904 #048-12-1969 L1969 **OTO FPS** *020 †45

SAIYED, Shabbir Imdad. 1501 E MOCKINGBIRD LN # 2, VICTORIA ANESTHESIOLOGY AS 77904 #704-02-1985 L1994 **AN** *020

SAMBANDAM, Kamalanathan K. ■ 77904 #048-02-2003 L2008 **NEP** *012 †20

SAMPLES, Steve M. 1501 E MOCKINGBIRD LN, STE 220 77904 #048-16-1997 L1998 **AN** *020 †05

SANDIGO, Gustavo Humberto. 6502 NURSERY DR 77904 #270-02-1986 L1992 **FM** *020 †18

SARABOSING, Luciano J, Jr. 1908 N LAURENT ST, STE 100 77901 #748-09-1983 L1994 **PD** *020 †55

SAWYERS, Richard Arthur. 2700 CITIZENS PLZ, STE 303 77901 #048-02-1974 L1974 **N** *020 †75

SCHAPER, Mark S. ■ 77904 #048-13-1991 L1996 **EM** *020

SCHNICKER, Steven Craig. 213 HOSP DR STE 110 77901 #018-03-1974 L1981 **DR** *020 †80

SCHULTHEISS, John F. 601 E SAN ANTONIO ST # 502 77901 #056-05-1970 L1980 **GE IM** *020 †20

SEILER, Tanya Baranowski. 2705 HOSPITAL DR, STE 300 77901 #048-02-1998 L2001 **OBG** *020 †30

SHAY, William Bihshing. 2710 HOSPITAL DR, STE 102 77901 #048-13-1992 L1994 **IM** *020 †20

SHENOUDA, Rouchdy Shehata. 2806 N NAVARRO ST, STE I 77901 #330-04-1959 L1977 **FM GS** *020

SHIELDS, Frederick S T. 2710 HOSPITAL DR, STE 116 77901 #048-02-1959 L1959 **GP** *071

SHOOK, James B. 115 MEDICAL DR STE 101 77904 #018-75-1973, ▲ L1979 **ORS** *020

SIDDIQI, Zakia. 1502 E AIRLINE RD STE 40, VICTORIA VA OUTPATIENT CLI 77901 #704-02-1993 L2000 **IM** *020

SMITH, Cloid Danl. ■ 77904 #048-02-1969 L1969 **EM** *020

SOULE, John Phillip. 2700 CITIZENS PLZ, STE 405 77901 #048-04-1983 L1986 **IM GPM** *020 †20

STARKEY, John T. 4804 N NAVARRO ST 77901 #048-02-1985 L1986 **FM OM** *020 †18

STEINER, Kathleen Naomi. 6502 NURSERY DR STE 100 77904 #017-20-1985 L1991 **FM** *020 †18

STERNE, Thomas L. ■ 77901 #048-02-1952 L1952 **PD** *071 †55

STEVENS, Mark L. 601 E SAN ANTONIO ST, # 102W 77901 #048-13-1990 L1991 **FM EM** *020 †18

STEVENSON, Rufus A, Jr. 2701 HOSPITAL DR 77901 #048-02-1945 L1945 **D** *071 †15

STONE, Ernest L. 1501 E MOCKINGBIRD LN, STE 220 77904 #048-13-1986 L1987 **AN** *020 †05

STOVAL, Richard Geo. 115 MEDICAL DR STE 101 77904 #028-34-1965 L1976 **ORS** *071 †40

STRAUSS, David Dennis. 2001 E SABINE ST, STE 102 77901 #048-02-1971 L1971 **AN** *020 †05

SUAREZ, Philip Thos. 110 MEDICAL DR, STE 100 77904 #028-34-1982 L1990 **OBG** *020 †30

SULLIVAN, Margaret P. ■ 77904 #036-07-1950 L1956 **PD ON** *071 †55

SWAMI, Indrani Dorai. 1501 E MOCKINGBIRD LN, STE 220 77904 #495-59-1971 L1974 **AN** *020 †05 ‡

THAMWIWAT, Prapinporn. 2701 HOSPITAL DR, CITIZEN MED CNTR. EMERGENC 77901 #016-76-2002, ▲ L2005 **FM** *100 †18

THARP, David Bruce. 2710 HOSPITAL DR STE 110, VICTORIA RADIOLOGY ASSOCIA 77901 #048-15-1992 L1996 **DR** *020 †80

TIBBITTS, Stephen William. 2710 HOSPITAL DR STE 110 77901 #021-01-1979 L1981 **DR** *020 †20

TILLMAN, Tywaun Kretrica. 2700 CITIZENS PLZ, STE 300 77901 #012-01-1998 L2007 **IC** *020 †20

TOBIN, Walter Dennis. 2700 CITIZENS PLZ STE 303 77901 #019-02-1972 L1978 **N** *020 †75 ‡

TUPA, Christi Marie. 115 MEDICAL DR, STE 208 77904 #048-14-1997 L2002 **PD** *020 †55

VARONA, Orlando Bilbao. 2710 HOSPITAL DR, STE 906 77901 #748-07-1959 L1973 **PTH OS** *020 †50

VASAVADA, Rasendu J. 601 E SAN ANTONIO ST, STE 100 77901 #495-48-1982 L1997 **IM** *020 †20

VAUGHAN, John Warner. 506 E SAN ANTONIO ST, DETAR HEALTH CARE SYSTEMS 77901 #048-12-1979 L1979 **FM** *020

VELASCO, Cesar Baquiran. 601 E SAN ANTONIO ST, STE 503W 77901 #748-01-1992 L1998 **PM** *020 †60

VELASCO, Maria Christina. 601 E SAN ANTONIO ST, STE 205W 77901 #748-01-1989 L1998 **IM** *020 †20

VERMA, Omesh. 4504 N LAURENT ST 77901 #495-69-1990 L1997 **IM** *020 †20

WAGNER, Donna R. 105 E MOCKINGBIRD LN, STE 220 77904 #048-04-1990 L1991 **AN** *020 †05

WAGNER, Rosalyn Poole. 2701 HOSPITAL DR 77901 #025-12-1975 L1984 **IM NEP** *020 †20

WAGNER, William Jordan. ■ 77901 #048-02-1954 L1954 **D** *071 †15

WAGNER, Wm Jordan, Jr. 601 E SAN ANTONIO ST, VICTORIA SURGICAL 77901 #048-02-1972 L1972 **GS** *020

WALROD, Clyde Barton. 2701 HOSPITAL DR 77901 #027-01-1978 L1979 **EM** *020 †18,16

WALTER, Joseph N. 4304 N LAURENT ST, STE A 77901 #048-14-1999 L2002 **PDP** *020 †55

WESTFORD, Yvette Faye. 110 MEDICAL DR, STE 100 77904 #305-01-2001 L2005 **OBG** *020 †30

WHEELER, Bruce Eldon. 2710 HOSPITAL DR STE 114 77901 #017-20-1975 L1978 **IM** *020 †20

WHITE, John Henry. 2501 N NAVARRO ST 77901 #048-02-1994 L1999 **U** *020 †95

WHITEHOUSE, Henry H. 2705 HOSPITAL DR, STE 300 77901 #048-02-1976 L1976 **OBG** *020 †30

WILSON, Linda Ornelas. 605 E SAN ANTONIO ST, STE 508E 77901 #005-06-1975 L1977 **PME** *020 †05

WILSON, Melissa Luker. 110 MEDICAL DR, STE 100 77904 #048-14-2003 L2007 **OBG** *020

YAHAGI, Yusuke. 1701 E RED RIVER ST, CARDIOTHORACIC AND VASCULA 77901 #572-73-1996 L2005 **TS** *020

YOUSSOUFIAN, Hagop. 601 E SAN ANTONIO ST STE 402 77901 #024-16-1983 L1998 **IM HEM** *020 †20,19

YU, Kevin. ■ 77901 #024-05-2006 **IM** *012

ZUNIGA, Oscar Garza. 2701 HOSPITAL DR 77901 #048-02-1961 L1961 **IM** *071

VIDOR – ORANGE

BOWELL, Duncan Geo Peter. 535 N MAIN ST 77662 #065-05-1968 L1977 **FM** *020

OH, Sei Chang. 515 S ARCHIE ST 77662 #583-01-1971 L1979 **PD GP** *020

VINTON – EL PASO

REDING, Perry Wm. 7920 DONIPHAN DR 79821 #048-02-1982 L1983 **EM OS** *020

WACO – MCLENNAN

AIYER, Bala N. 4800 MEMORIAL DR, CARE SYSTEMS WACO ICF 76711 #495-16-1961 L1977 **CD IM** *020 †20

AKINS, Jack Lewis. ■ 76708 #048-02-1958 L1958 **OS** *071

ALLINSON, Richard Ward. 7700 FISH POND RD 76710 #048-12-1980 L1980 **OPH** *020 †35

ALLISON, Dale Crawford. 2201 MACARTHUR DR, STE 100 76708 #048-02-1974 L1974 **FM** *020 †18

AMAR, Meera. 333 LONDONDERRY DR, STE 200 76712 #495-21-1977 L1982 **END IM** *062 †20

AMAR, Niran Jan. 333 LONDONDERRY DR, STE 100 76712 #495-57-1966 L1982 **AI ID** *071 †55,03

ANCHA, Hari Babu. 364 RICHLAND WEST CIR, STE A 76712 #495-50-1986 L1998 **GE** *020 †20

ANCHA, Lakshmi Vijaya. 3501 N 19TH ST, WACO, TEXAS 76708 76708 #495-50-1996 L2006 **CHP** *020 †75

ANDERSON, Robert Lee. 1700 WEST AVE, STE 6 76707 #040-02-1975 L1982 **HEM IM** *050 †20

ANGUEIRA, Carlos Efrain. 6901 MEDICAL PKWY 76712 #042-03-1984 L1989 **IM** *020 †20

ANNETT, Thomas E. 1600 PROVIDENCE DR 76707 #048-15-2004 L2005 **FM** *020

ARNOLD, Jeffrey Lynn. 301 RICHLAND WEST CIR 76712 #048-02-1990 L1992 **FM** *020 †18

ASHFORD, Shane J. ■ 76708 #048-78-2006, ▲ L2007 **FP** *012

ASHLEY, Ian Marcus. 6901 MEDICAL PKWY 76712 #048-04-1996 L1998 **EM** *020 †16

AUFFANT, Rafael. ■ 76708 #847-10-1971 L1979 **P** *050

BACHOFEN, Claudia Gomez. 7700 FISH POND RD 76710 #048-13-1995 L1996 **OBG** *020 †30

BAGNASCO, John Francis. 601 W HWY 6 STE 101 76710 #045-04-1994 L1998 **OBG** *020 †30

BAHAR, Habib Ullah. 2329 N 39TH ST 76708 #160-02-1983 L1997 **NEP** *020 †20

BANDELA, Srikanth. 4800 MEMORIAL DR, BLDG 4 76711 #495-65-1993 L1995 **IM** *020 †20

BARBIN, Gary Kent. 2800 LYLE AVE 76708 #048-02-1975 L1975 **IM** *020 †20

BARDGETTE, John Jos, Jr. 2329 N 39TH ST 76708 #048-04-1974 L1974 **NEP** *020 †20

BARKER, Timothy Dwain. 6901 MEDICAL PKWY 76712 #048-13-1984 L1985 **FM** *040 †18

BARRETT, Timothy Marcus. 6600 FISH POND RD, STE 202 76710 #048-02-1975 L1975 **U** *071 †95

BARRON, Lauren Gallemore. 1001 HEWITT DR 76712 #048-14-1992 L1993 **FM** *020 †18

BARRY, Floyd Lee. 1600 PROVIDENCE DR, FAMILY PRACTICE CENTER 76707 #034-01-1988 L1997 **PD** *020 †55

BATTLE, Jacob Richard. 6600 FISH POND RD, STE 201 76710 #048-12-2000 L2005 **ORS** *020 †40

BAURER, Martin E. 1414 CHAPEL HILL DR 76712 #035-19-1957 L1979 **FM GP** *071

BAWDUNIAK, John Joseph. ■ 76705 #048-12-2002 L2007 **GS** *020 †85

BAZE, Christy. 1600 PROVIDENCE DR 76707 #048-78-2007, ▲ **FP** *012

BEAIRD, Mark Alan. 405 LONDONDERRY DR, STE 310 76712 #048-04-1991 L1992 **OBG** *020 †30

BEALKA, Neil Michael. ■ 76712 #026-04-1961 L1962 **FM** *071 †18

BEATY, William Robt. 7030 NEW SANGER RD STE 204 76712 #048-02-1973 L1973 **GYN** *020 †20

BECKER, Brian Kelly. 601 W STATE HIGHWAY 6, # 101 76710 #048-02-1991 L1992 **OBG** *020 †30

BECKER, Gary Lloyd. 6600 FISH POND RD, STE 201 76710 #048-02-1973 L1973 **ORS** *020 †40

BELL, Dan Wm. 5906 MOUNT ROCKWOOD CIR 76710 #048-13-1973 L1973 **GE** *020 †20

BENHAM, Jerry Alan. 6600 FISH POND RD, STE 201 76710 #048-13-1985 L1986 **ORS** *020 †40

BERRYHILL, Bill Hall. 7003 WOODWAY DR 76712 #048-12-1977 L1977 **ORS HS** *020 †40

BEYER, David Henry, Jr. 110 S 12TH ST, BOX 860 76701 #048-14-1983 L1983 **P** *020 †75

BISHARA, Rima. 2115 N 34TH ST 76708 #005-12-1986 L1992 **IM** *020 †20

BLACKBURN, Matthew L. ■ 76708 #048-78-2007, ▲ **FP** *012

BLAIR, William Edward. 8300 OLD MCGREGOR RD STE 2 76712 #028-02-1970 L1992 **ORS OSS** *062 †40

BLAISDELL, Greg D. 301 LONDONDERRY DR 76712 #048-13-1989 L1990 **P** *020 †75

BLAND, Anna Nell. ■ 76712 #047-06-1952 L1953 **PTH OS** *020 †50

BLATTMAN, Scott. 7300 BOSQUE BLVD 76710 #048-12-1991 L1992 **FM** *020 †18

BLATTMAN, Todd E. 7300 BOSQUE BLVD 76710 #048-14-1994 L1995 **FM** *020 †18

BOEHM, Henry J, III. 3000 HERRING AVE, DEPT RAD 76708 #048-02-1992 L1994 **DR** *020 †80

BOLES, Keith A. 7700 FISH POND RD 76710 #048-15-1996 L1997 **FM** *020 †18

BOLEY, Jason M. 301 LONDONDERRY DR 76712 #048-15-2001 L2005 **P** *020

BOLTE, Brett J. 2115 N 34TH ST 76708 #048-13-1987 L1991 **PM IM** *020 †60

BOROWSKI, Adam M. 6901 MEDICAL PKWY, WACO RADIOLOGY PA 76712 #048-15-1991 L1992 **RNR** *020 †20

BOSS, James Wesley. 364 RICHLAND WEST CIR, STE A 76712 #048-02-1989 L1990 **GE** *020 †20

BOWDEN, James Alan. 3500 HILLCREST DR, WACO BONE & JOINT CLINIC P 76708 #048-04-1968 L1968 **ORS** *020 †40

BRADSHAW, Ronald Wm. 209 SPEIGHT AVE, ONE BEAR PLACE #97060 76706 #048-02-1988 L1989 **FM** *040 †18

BREWER, Ronda Dianne. ■ 76710 #048-14-1990 L1992 **FM** *020

BRINDLEY, Mace Lain. 3115 PINE AVE, WACO OTOLARYNGOLOGY ASSOCI 76708 #048-02-1973 L1973 **OTO** *020 †45

BRITTON, Thomas Franklin. 1927 COLUMBUS AVE 76701 #048-04-1970 L1970 **FM** *020

BROWDER, Joseph Bond. 7005 WOODWAY DR STE 101 76712 #048-15-1977 L1977 **IM** *020 †20

BROWN, Robert Gordon. 1600 PROVIDENCE DR 76707 #048-04-1976 L1976 **FM** *020 †18

BRYANT, Jason K. 6901 MEDICAL PKWY 76712 #048-14-2000 L2001 **EM** *020

BULL, Brian D. 851 N LOOP 340 76705 #048-14-1989 L1990 **FM** *020 †65

BUNN, Simon Milford, Jr. 3115 PINE AVE, STE 108 76708 #048-02-1965 L1965 **PTH** *020 †50

BURGARD, Steven R. 405 LONDONDERRY DR, STE 105 76712 #048-13-1996 L1997 **AN** *020 †05

BUTLER, Charles Frank, Jr. ■ 76710 #048-14-1974 L1974 IM *071 †20

CALDERON, April M. 1600 PROVIDENCE DR, FAMILY HEALTH CENTER 76707 #048-78-2007, ▲ FP *012

CALLENDER, Kathleen. ■ 76712 #034-01-1991 L1996 CD IM *020 †20

CAMPBELL, James V, Jr. 7030 NEW SANGER RD, STE 102 76712 #021-01-1973 L1973 OPH FM *020 †18,35

CANNING, Lawrence Carroll. 2911 HERRING AVE, STE 209 76708 #048-04-1959 L1963 ON END *020 †20

CARPENTER, Edward Dean. 364 RICHLAND WEST CIR, STE A 76712 #048-02-1979 L1979 GE IM *020 †20

CARTMELL, Larry Wayne, Jr. ■ 76710 #039-01-1987 L1988 PTH *020 †50

CESSNUN, Colby Wayne. 1600 PROVIDENCE DR, FAMILY PRACTICE CENTER 76707 #048-14-2004 L2006 FM *020 †18

CHAKMAKJIAN, Stephen S. 601 W STATE HIGHWAY 6, # 102 76710 #048-15-2000 L2003 PD *020 †55 ‡

CHAMNESS, Jimmy M, II. 405 LONDONDERRY DR, STE 105 76712 #048-14-1984 L1985 AN *020 †05

CHANCELLOR, Jeff David. 601 W STATE HIGHWAY 6, # 101 76710 #048-04-1998 L2002 OBG *020 †30

CHANG, Baochong B. 3420 PINE AVE 76708 #243-78-1989 L2004 ON *020 †20

CHASTAIN, Richard Louis. ■ 76712 #048-14-1947 IM *071

CHEN, Gideon Hsiang. ■ 76712 #748-09-1979 OS *071

CHENG, Clint Chi. 1600 PROVIDENCE DR, FAMILY PRACTICE CTR 76707 #048-12-2005 L2007 FP *012

CHOP, William M, Jr. 1600 PROVIDENCE DR, FAMILY PRACTICE CENTER 76707 #048-14-1982 L1991 FM *020 †18

CHOWNING, Scott. PO BOX 82553 76798 #023-07-2008 *012

CIZDZIEL, Kara. ■ 76712 #048-16-2007 FP *012

COBBS, Kenneth F. 2201 MACARTHUR DR STE 2200 76708 #048-04-1992 L2005 ORS *020 †40

COLE, Russell David. ■ 76712 #012-05-2007 FP *012

COLEMAN, James Arch, Jr. 301 RICHLAND WEST CIR, PROVIDENCE MEDICAL CLINIC 76712 #047-06-1946 L1947 IM *071

COLEMAN, Wm Pierce, Jr. 504 MEADOWLAKE CTR 76712 #004-01-1963 L1970 GP *020 †85

CONLEY, Charles Callaghan. VET ADMIN CTR 113 76711 #026-04-1947 L1948 PTH IM *020 †50

CONTRERAS, Edward D. 364 RICHLAND WEST CIR, STE A 76712 #048-13-1988 L1989 GE *020 †20

COPELAND, James Lloyd, Jr. 2800 LYLE AVE 76708 #048-02-1972 L1972 IM *020 †20

COPELAND, Kathy Lauren. ■ 76708 #048-02-2004 L2008 AN *012

CORBETT, Joseph H. 2201 MACARTHUR DR 76708 #048-02-1952 L1952 GP *072

CORWIN, Robert Francis. ■ 76710 #036-07-1961 L1966 U *071 †95

CORWIN, Stephen Herbert. ■ 76710 #036-05-1965 L1966 U *071 †95

COVINGTON, Ray Wm. 3500 HILLCREST DR, HILLCREST MEDICAL PLAZA 76708 #048-04-1963 L1963 ORS OSM *020 †40

CRIM, Chad D. ■ 76710 #048-02-2006 FP *012

CROWLEY, Daniel Stephen. ■ 76708 #539-02-1970 L1990 AN *100

CROYLE, Philip Henderson. 405 LONDONDERRY DR STE 200, PROVIDENCE MEDICAL PLAZA 76712 #048-04-1973 L1974 TS VS *020 †85,90

CUNNINGHAM, Ariana S V. 6901 MEDICAL PKWY 76712 #048-16-1998 L1999 OPH *020

DAFTARY, Pramila K. 3115 PINE AVE STE 108 76708 #495-19-1970 L1982 AI PD *020 †55,03

DANIELL, Jon Eric. 6901 MEDICAL PKWY, EMERGENCY ROOM 76712 #010-01-1996 L2000 EM *020 †16

DAVIS, Emsley Aclifton. 1616 COLCORD AVE 76707 #047-07-1967 L1977 GP GS *071 †85

DE ARMOND, Lynda Barry. 1600 PROVIDENCE DR 76707 #048-15-1989 L1990 FM *040 †18

DEMUTH, Robert W. 6901 MEDICAL PKWY, PROVIDENCE HEALTH CENTER 76712 #048-15-2000 L2007 IM *020 †20

DE STAFFANY, Nelson Dale. 405 LONDONDERRY DR STE 105 76712 #048-14-1979 L1979 AN *020 †05 ‡

DEWBRE, Jacquelin D. 2201 MACARTHUR DR, STE 103 76708 #048-78-2002, ▲ L2005 PD *020 †55

DHOMA, Bhaskara. ■ 76712 #495-70-1973 L1984 IM *020 †20

DIETRICK, John Daly. 1600 PROVIDENCE DR 76707 #048-14-1979 L1979 FM *040 †18

DUCHAMP, Lisa A. 3000 HERRING AVE 76708 #048-14-1994 L1996 MPD *020 †20

DUNN, Carl A. 405 LONDONDERRY DR STE 310 76712 #048-02-1996 L1999 OBG *020 †30

DUTTON, Kirk Steven. 305 LONDONDERRY DR STE 6 76712 #019-02-1972 L1977 P *020 †75

EASTWOOD, Thomas F. 364 RICHLAND WEST CIR, STE A 76712 #026-04-1984 L1990 GE *020 †20

EBERT, Didi E. ■ 76708 #048-78-2007, ▲ FP *012

EDWARDS, Cecil Gervais. ■ 76705 #021-05-1955 L1970 IM GP *071 †20

ELLIS, Jon Michael. 7030 NEW SANGER RD STE 200 76712 #048-13-1994 L1996 OSM *020 †40

ELWELL, Steven M. 6901 MEDICAL PKWY 76712 #048-12-1991 L1992 IM EM *020 †20

ENCARNACION, Carlos A. 1700 WEST AVE, STE 6 76707 #042-01-1986 L1991 ON *020 †20

ETHRIDGE, John Kendall. 6600 FISH POND RD, STE 201 76710 #047-06-1974 L1978 ORS *020 †40

FADAL, Richard Geo. 2000 N 25TH ST 76708 #048-12-1955 L1955 AI PUD *071 †03

FAILLACE, John J. 2201 MACARTHUR DR STE 2200 76708 #048-14-1992 L1993 HS OTR *020 †40

FALLS, Lisa Lynnette. 1600 PROVIDENCE DR 76707 #047-07-1994 L1999 CHP *020 †75

FERGUSON, Douglas Bismark. ■ 76712 #048-14-1982 L1983 EM *020 †20

FERGUSON, James Wm. 301 RICHLAND WEST CIR 76712 #048-02-1975 L1975 PD OS *020 †55

FINDLEY, Michael Donovan. ■ 76702 #048-15-2003 L2007 P *020

FINDLEY, Michael Stan. 851 N LOOP 340 76705 #048-15-1982 L1987 FM *020 †18

FISCHER, Gary W. 3000 HERRING AVE 76708 #048-12-1984 L1985 AN *020 †05

FLOWERS, Adam David. ■ 76708 #048-14-2005 L2007 FP *012

FOSS, Jessica Kristin. ■ 76712 #048-16-2004 L2006 FM *020 †18

FREITAG, Joel Gary. 340 RICHLAND WEST CIR 76712 #048-04-1988 L1995 N *020 †75

FUNG, Hing Sheung Eugene. 2911 HERRING AVE, STE 306 76708 #244-02-1971 L1992 RHU IM *020 †20

GALEANO, Jose W. 405 LONDONDERRY DR, STE 204 76712 #682-01-1964 L1979 PD *020

GAMBLE, Charles E. 2201 MACARTHUR DR, STE 103 76708 #048-04-1952 L1952 PD *071 †55

GARCES, Dahlia V. 4800 MEMORIAL DR, WACO VA MEDICAL CENTER 76711 #748-11-1966 L1977 P *020

GARDELL, Randy Carl. 340 RICHLAND WEST CIR 76712 #048-02-1986 L1987 N *020 †75

GARDERE, Robert Andre-M. 3115 PINE AVE STE 908 76708 #065-09-1967 L1977 PS HS *020

GARDERE, Sandra Ann. 3115 PINE AVE STE 908 76708 #065-09-1967 L1977 D *020

GARRIDO, Jose Manuel. 3416 HILLCREST DR 76708 #016-11-1985 L1992 CD IM *020 †20

GEIGER, Joseph F. 1600 PROVIDENCE DR 76707 #048-13-1985 L1987 OBG *040 †30

GELDMEIER, Gary F. 3115 PINE AVE STE 108 76708 #048-13-1982 L1983 PTH *020 †50

GEORGES, Rebekah Leigh. ■ 76712 #048-13-2007 FP *012

GERECKE, William Beman. ■ 76710 #649-02-1960 L1966 AN PUD *071

GERIK, Jeffrey C. 3000 HERRING AVE 76708 #048-12-1989 L1990 DR *020 †80

GERMANN, Robert E. ■ 76712 #165-01-1976 L1996 NS *020 †25

GIBBONS, Alfred Earl, Jr. 3115 PINE AVE STE 301 76708 #055-01-1971 L1975 OBG *020

GILCHRIST, James Lee. 3000 HERRING AVE 76708 #048-02-1975 L1975 FM *071 †18

GILL, Craig Allen. 6901 MEDICAL PKWY, PROVIDENCE HOSPITAL 76712 #048-02-1993 L1999 FM *020 †18

GILL, John Howard. 1600 PROVIDENCE DR 76707 #034-01-1989 L1991 FM *040 †18

GILL, Matthew Treston. ■ 76706 #056-06-2006 OTO *012

GO, Robert Joseph S. 2329 N 39TH ST 76708 #748-11-1992 L2007 NEP *020 †20

GOBLE, Katie Marie. ■ 76708 #048-12-2008 *012

GOEBEL, Gregg R. 7700 FISH POND RD 76710 #048-04-1983 L1985 FM *020 †18

GOERTZ, Roland A. 1600 PROVIDENCE DR, FAMILY HEALTH CENTER 76707 #048-13-1981 L1981 FM MDM *030 †18

GOLDBERG, Herbert Stephen. 3115 PINE AVE, NEUROSURGICAL ASSOCIATES 76708 #048-02-1964 L1964 NS OS *071 †25

GOODNIGHT, Jon M. 6600 FISH POND RD, STE 201 76710 #048-13-1991 L1992 ORS *020 †40

GORDON, Carole Lynn. 3500 HILLCREST DR STE 8 76708 #048-12-1982 L1983 U UP *020 †95

GRAHAM, James T, Jr. 1001 HEWITT DR 76712 #048-14-1991 L1992 FM *020 †18 ‡

GRANT, Christopher R. 7700 FISH POND RD 76710 #048-13-1995 L1996 FM *020 †18

GRAVES, Reese Cabot. ■ 76710 #048-12-2006 L2007 FP *012

GRAY, James Edward. 3000 HERRING AVE, HILLCREST HEALTH SYSTEM 76708 #028-03-1971 L1979 GE IM *030 †20

GRAYSON, Robert Wynn, Jr. 7030 NEW SANGER RD, STE 204 76712 #048-12-1974 L1974 OBG *020 †30

GREENER, Christopher D. 405 LONDONDERRY DR STE 105 76712 #048-02-1998 L2002 AN *020 †05

GRIGGS, Jackson Overton. 1600 PROVIDENCE DR 76707 #048-14-2003 L2005 FM *100 †18

GUERRA, Carlos Arnoldo. 2201 MACARTHUR DR 76708 #048-04-1979 L1979 FM *020 †18

GUESS, Rebecca D. 405 LONDONDERRY DR, STE 105 76712 #048-13-1990 L1992 AN *020 †05

GUPTA, Shikta. PO BOX 3276 76707 #495-05-2001 L2005 IMG *100 †18

GUTIERREZ, Miguel A. 1600 PROVIDENCE DR, FAMILY PRACTICE CENTER 76707 #048-12-2000 L2001 FM *020 †18

HAIR, Barbara M. 4205 FRANKLIN AVE, CONCENTRA MEDICAL CENTER 76710 #048-78-1996, ▲ L1997 OM GPM *020

HALUSKA, Glenn Martin. 3000 HERRING AVE 76708 #041-13-1965 L1978 RO NM *020 †80

HAMILTON, John Bryan. 6901 MEDICAL PKWY, EMERGENCY DEPARTMENT 76712 #005-15-1995 L1999 EM *020 †16

HARRIS, Edwin Bryan. 405 LONDONDERRY DR STE 104 76712 #021-05-1945 L1959 R *071 †80

HASKETT, William R, Jr. 601 W STATE HIGHWAY 6, # 101 76710 #048-11-1988 L1989 OBG *020 †30

HATHHORN, Thomas Kelly. ■ 76712 #038-40-1963 L1979 IM HEM *020 †20

HAYNES, Katherine Anne. 405 LONDONDERRY DR, STE 300 76712 #004-01-1999 L2005 OBG *020 †30

HAYS, Robert F. 1600 PROVIDENCE DR, FAMILY PRACTICE CTR 76707 #048-14-2006 L2007 FP *012

HECTOR, Casey D. 405 LONDONDERRY DR, STE 105 76712 #048-13-1986 L1987 AN *020 †18,05

HERMANN, Scotty Roy. 405 LONDONDERRY DR, STE 203 76712 #021-06-1978 L1982 OBG *020 †30

HERSH, Stanley. 321 RICHLAND WEST CIR 76712 #038-06-1957 L1961 OPH *020 †35

HESS, Burritt William. 1600 PROVIDENCE DR 76707 #001-06-1999 L2001 FM *020 †18

HICKS, Paul Brently. 4800 MEMORIAL DR, CENTRAL TX VET HLTH CARE 76711 #048-04-1983 L1983 P *030 †75

HIGGS, Carson P. 1600 PROVIDENCE DR, FAMILY PRACTICE CTR 76707 #048-12-2006 FP *012

HILLIS, William Danl. ■ 76706 #023-07-1957 L1983 GP PHP *050

HILTON, Nathan E. 1700 WEST AVE, STE 6 76707 #048-02-1994 L1995 RO *020 †80

HINDS, William Mark. 7700 FISH POND RD 76710 #048-13-1995 L1996 FM *020 †18 ‡

HINSON, Horace Gibson, III. 1001 HEWITT DR 76712 #048-14-1987 L1988 FM *020 †18

HOFFMAN, David Glenn. 6600 FISH POND RD STE 101 76710 #048-02-1980 L1980 VS GS *020 †85

HOLLAND, Bradford Warren. 3000 HERRING AVE 76708 #048-12-1997 L2002 OTO A *020 †45

HOLMES, Amanda N. 301 LONDONDERRY DR, PROVIDENCE CLINIC DEPAUL 76712 #048-16-1994 L1995 CHP *020 †20

HORNER, Keith Douglas. 7300 BOSQUE BLVD 76710 #016-45-1987 L1988 FM *020 †18

HOTT, Kimberly Anne. 3000 HERRING AVE, EMERGENCY DEPARTMENT 76708 #036-05-1986 L2002 EM *020 †16

HOWLETT, Stephen Gabriel. 3115 PINE AVE STE 901 76708 #539-04-1972 L1979 N *020 †75

HOWTON, Johnny D, Jr. 3115 PINE AVE STE 803 76708 #048-12-1990 L1991 CRS *020 †85,10

HUESTON, Allen Lee. PO BOX 890, 110 S 12TH ST 76703 #018-03-1977 L1984 P ADM *020 †75

HUFFMAN, Charles Engle. 405 LONDONDERRY DR, STE 104 76712 #003-01-1977 L1979 R GP *071 †80

HULL, Ivan Wyllys. ■ 76708 #039-01-1954 L1955 GP GS *071

HURLEY, Richard Kenneth. 2200 N 25TH ST 76708 #048-02-1977 L1977 PME *020 †05

ILLICH, Melanie Bivona. 213A OLD HEWITT RD 76712 #048-16-1991 L1992 P *020 †75

IRONS, Kerry Dean. 701 W LOOP 340 # A 76712 #019-02-1973 L1975 FM OM *020 †18

JACKSON, Thomas Henry, Jr. 1607 LAKE SUCCESS DR 76712 #048-04-1969 L1969 D *071 †15

JAGSI, Rajnikant Lalji. ■ 76712 #495-01-1967 L1981 FM *020 †18

JAHRMARKT, Michael L. 1600 PROVIDENCE DR 76707 #048-15-1990 L1991 FM *020 †18

JANSMA, David Gordon. 3000 HERRING AVE 76708 #018-03-1965 L1972 R NM *020 †80,28

JAYASINGHE, Girly Bennett. 4800 MEMORIAL DR, VETERANS AFFAIRS MEDICAL C 76711 #220-02-1990 L2006 P *020

JENSEN, Randall Dean. 7700 FISH POND RD 76710 #030-05-1978 L1985 FM *020 †18

JERNIGAN, Floyd Edsil. 556 N LOOP 340 76705 #048-16-1990 L1991 FM *020 †18

JOHNSON, Ronald Lee. 405 LONDONDERRY DR, STE 306 76712 #054-04-1958 L1961 OTO *071 †45

JOHNSON, Susan Rose. ■ 76712 #048-14-1981 L1981 P *075 †75

JOSEPHS, Zelig Maurice. ■ 76710 #048-02-1945 L1945 P *071

JULIAN, Danny Sean. 1600 LAKE SHORE DR 76708 #024-16-1997 L1998 FM *020 †18

KANNWISCHER, Lewis R. 3115 PINE AVE, STE 202 76708 #048-04-1968 L1968 OPH *020 †35

KAVANAGH, James Kevin. 405 LONDONDERRY DR STE 105 76712 #041-02-1984 L1986 AN *020 †05

KEMPER, Karen Cervenka. 2201 MACARTHUR DR, STE 103 76708 #048-02-1982 L1983 PD *020 †55 ‡

KESSMANN, Jennifer Ruth. 7700 FISH POND RD 76710 #048-16-1993 L1994 FM *020 †18

KING, Walter B, Jr. ■ 76710 #048-02-1940 L1940 GS *071 †85

KIRALY, Elizabeth Marie. 6600 FISH POND RD, STE 101 76710 #038-40-1988 L2000 GS AS *020 †85

KLASKIN, Howard Norman. 6901 MEDICAL PKWY, WACO RADIOLOGY PA 76712 #048-13-1994 L1996 DR *020 †80

KNIPPER, Joseph E. 601 W STATE HIGHWAY 6, STE 103 76710 #048-13-1990 L1991 D *020 †15 ‡

KOERITZ, Kenneth W. 2124 N 25TH ST 76708 #048-12-1985 L1986 OBG *020 †30

KOESTER, Donald Ray. 1600 PROVIDENCE DR 76707 #048-14-1981 L1981 FM *040 †18

KOLLER, Frances E. 301 LONDONDERRY DR, PROVIDENCE CLINIC-DEPAUL 76712 #048-02-1988 L1993 CHP *020 †75

KOLTER, William Henry. ■ 76710 #048-04-1955 L1955 GS *072 †85

KOSAREK, John David. 201 OLD HEWITT RD 76712 #048-13-1983 L1983 FM *020 †18

KREIS, Siegfried Richard. 405 LONDONDERRY DR STE 106 76712 #048-14-1991 L1992 IM *020 †20

KUNKEL, Weldon Louis. 6901 MEDICAL PKWY 76712 #048-02-1973 L1973 EM *020 †16

LAGRONE, Benjamin Ford. 405 LONDONDERRY DR, STE 105 76712 #048-15-1986 L1987 AN *020 †05

LAUCK, Robert Edwin. ■ 76702 #048-04-1941 L1941 OBG *071 †30

LEA, Walker Alfred, Jr. 3000 HERRING AVE 76708 #048-04-1954 L1954 D *071 †15

LEBEAU, William Emanuel. 305 LONDONDERRY DR STE 5 76712 #041-12-1948 L1976 P *020 †75 ‡

LE BLANC, Christen Jared. 6600 FISH POND RD, STE 101 76710 #021-05-2001 L2005 CRS *100

LEE, Edward Morris. 3115 PINE AVE STE 308 76708 #048-04-1960 L1960 U *020 †95

LEE, Edward Sangjoon. ■ 76706 #048-04-2007 *012

LEE, Soo Paik. ■ 76712 #045-04-2006 FP *012

LEE, Stella Sychia. ■ 76706 #048-04-2007 GS *012

LEHR, Andrew James. 3115 PINE AVE, STE 808 76708 #048-12-1990 L1991 OTO HNS *020 †45 ‡

LEINFELDER, Jeffrey J. 3115 PINE AVE, STE 202 76708 #048-14-1990 L1991 OPH *020 †35

LEONARD, Michael G. ■ 76710 #539-02-1954 L1963 AN *071 †05

LESSMAN, Stacy Lynn. 611 W HIGHWAY 6, STE 108 76710 #048-02-1999 L2000 FM *020 †18 ‡

LEWIN, Marcial G. 342 RICHLAND WEST CIR 76712 #231-03-1966 L1977 NS *020 †25

LEWIS, Donald Kemp. 7030 NEW SANGER RD, STE 204 76712 #048-12-1968 L1968 OBG *020 †30

LIND, Isabel Alvarez. 1600 PROVIDENCE DR 76707 #231-01-1997 L2006 FM *100 †18

LINDSEY, Jene Hall. ■ 76710 #048-12-1956 L1956 GYN *071 †30

LIPPE, Isaac J. 7700 FISH POND RD 76710 #048-12-2000 L2002 FM *020 †18 ‡

LIPPE, Natalie Crump. 7104 NEW SANGER RD 76712 #048-12-2001 L2003 FM *100 †18

LIU, John Frederick. 321 RICHLAND WEST CIR 76712 #048-14-1983 L1988 OPH *020 †35

LOCKHART, David Lloyd. 3301 WESTMINISTER 76708 #004-01-1968 L1976 U *071 †18 ‡

LODEN, Michael A. 2100 LAKE SHORE DR 76708 #048-15-1996 L1997 FM *020 †18 ‡

LONG, James Michael. 914 LAKE AIR DR, STE G 76710 #048-13-1993 L1997 FM *020 †18

LONG, Robert John. 7125 NEW SANGER RD, STE B 76712 #048-02-1977 L1977 PUD CCM *020 †20

LORENZEN, Mark Andrew. 301 RICHLAND WEST CIR, STE B 76712 #048-02-1977 L1977 PD *020 †55

LOVETT, Twiladawn J. 3000 HERRING AVE 76708 #048-15-1991 L1994 IM *020 †20

LOWDER, Webster Shively. 3400 HILLCREST DR 76708 #048-02-1975 L1975 GS VS *020 †85

MADISETTY, Sasi. ■ 76710 #495-62-1972 L1995 P *020 †75

MADISETTY, Sudhir. 1607 LAKE SUCCESS DR 76710 #495-57-1973 L1993 PD *020

MANGAWANG, Pedrito Tualla. 4800 MEMORIAL DR, DEPT OF VETERAN AFFAIRS 76711 #748-08-1966 L1997 IM *020

MANGRUM, John Chas. 4800 MEMORIAL DR, VA MED CTR 76711 #023-07-1967 L1970 P AM *020 †75

MANGUM, Charles Edward. 3115 PINE AVE STE 108 76708 #048-12-1991 L1993 PTH *020 †50

MANNING, Jeffrey T. 405 LONDONDERRY DR, STE 105 76712 #048-14-2001 L2005 AN *020 †05

MANNING, Michelle Trice. 601 W STATE HIGHWAY 6, # 101 76710 #048-14-2001 L2005 OBG *020

MARK, Stephen Leonard. 405 LONDONDERRY DR, STE 202 76712 #048-02-1974 L1974 P *020 †75 ‡

MARROQUIN, Gerard. 7300 BOSQUE BLVD 76710 #048-12-1990 L1991 FM *020 †18

MARSELLUS, Cessley Denise. 7700 FISH POND RD 76710 #010-03-1992 L2004 PD *020 †55

MARTIN, Joseph C. 7700 FISH POND RD 76710 #048-15-1995 L1996 FM *020 †18

MARTIN, Patrick William. ■ 76708 #305-01-2005 FP *012

MARTINDALE, Timothy Dean. 7104 NEW SANGER RD 76712 #048-02-1996 L1997 FM *020 †18 ‡

MASON, James Wilcox. 405 LONDONDERRY DR, # 205 76712 #048-02-1977 L1977 D *020 †15

MATHEW, Annamma Thomas. 4800 MEMORIAL DR 76711 #495-31-1965 L1976 P AM *020 †75

MC BRIDE, Michael Owen. 7125 NEW SANGER RD, STE D 76712 #033-05-1997 L2005 TS *020 †90

MC CALL, David Timmons. 1600 PROVIDENCE DR 76707 #047-06-1975 L1980 FM *020 †18

MC CARTHY, Sean D. 8414 OLD MCGREGOR RD # B 76712 #048-12-1986 L1987 P *020 †75

MC CLARY, Joan Marie. 1616 AUSTIN AVE, # B 76701 #048-02-1985 L1988 FM *020 †18

MC CLELLAN, Russell Lynn. 3000 HERRING AVE BOX 5100, HILLCREST XRAY PHYSICIANS 76708 #048-02-1984 L1985 DR RNR *020 †80

MC COURT, Amy Rachelle. 6901 MEDICAL PKWY, WACO RADIOLOGY PA 76712 #048-02-1996 L2001 DR *020 †80

MC DONALD, Andrew W. 2201 MACARTHUR DR, STE 103 76708 #048-13-1992 L1993 PD *020 †55

MC DONALD, Hemprova G. 1204 SPEIGHT AVE 76706 #495-02-1941 L1962 PTH IM *072 †50

MC DONALD, Hendley A. 1204 SPEIGHT AVE 76706 #048-02-1947 L1947 IM *071

MC TAGGART, David Manly. 3000 HERRING AVE 76708 #030-06-1964 L1971 PTH OS *020 †50

MEDINA, Jason X. ■ 76708 #048-12-2005 L2006 FP *012

MEYER, Micah Stephen. 2329 N 39TH ST 76708 #038-44-1996 L2002 NEP *020 †20

MICHAELS, Douglas B. 6901 MEDICAL PKWY, PROVIDENCE HEALTH CENTER 76712 #048-04-1980 L1980 PTH *020 †50

MICUS, Kimberly L. 405 LONDONDERRY DR STE 310, 405 LONDONDERRY STE 310 76712 #048-13-1995 L1997 OBG *020 †30

MIGNOSA, Aurora Mary. 301 LONDONDERRY DR, PROVIDENCE DEPAUL CLINIC 76712 #748-01-1996 L2006 CHP *100

MILLER, Bret Hunter. 2201 MACARTHUR DR, STE 101 76708 #048-02-1986 L1987 ORS *020 †40

MILLER, S Bradley. 1111 HERRING AVE 76708 #048-12-1959 L1959 CHP OS *020 †75

MILLING, David Carlos. 4800 MEMORIAL DR 76711 #649-02-1952 L1971 P *020

MILLS, George R. 405 LONDONDERRY DR, STE 105 76712 #048-02-1998 L2002 AN *020 ‡

MITCHELL, William Crit. 117 ROYAL CT 76711 #048-02-1994 L1993 FM *020

MOEN, Jonas Owen. 1000 W HIGHWAY 6, STE 100 76712 #048-14-1988 L1989 CHP P *020 †75

MOFFATT, Todd A. 6600 FISH POND RD, STE 101 76710 #048-04-1991 L1993 GS *020 †85

MOORE, Mark K. 601 W HWY 6 STE 101 76710 #048-12-1994 L1996 OBG *020 †30

MORRIS, Brock Allen. 8414 OLD MCGREGOR RD # B 76712 #048-02-1975 L1975 P *072

MORRIS, John E. 4800 MEMORIAL DR 76711 #048-15-1983 L1984 P ADP *020 †75

MORRISON, Edwin Bigger. 3115 PINE AVE STE 108 76708 #048-12-1974 L1974 PTH *020 †50

MORROW, Aaron Stanford. 1600 PROVIDENCE DR 76707 #036-08-2003 L2005 FM *020 †18

MOTAPARTHI, Pushpavathi. 4800 MEMORIAL DR 76711 #495-50-1971 L1981 PM *020 †60

MUNDY, Larry James. 3000 HERRING AVE, FENTRESS CANCER CTR 76708 #038-41-1985 L1987 RO *020 †80

MUNDY, Sheila Denise. 3501 N 19TH ST 76708 #045-01-1996 L2000 P *020 †75

MURFF, Wilbur Gene. 3115 PINE AVE STE 1001 76708 #048-02-1966 L1966 OBG *020 †30

MUTYALA, Satyanarayana. 4800 MEMORIAL DR 76711 #495-58-1970 L1979 IM *020 †20

MYERS, Anna Catherina. 7700 FISH POND RD 76710 #004-01-2002 L2005 PD *020 †55

NAIK, Pankaj Mohanlal. 307 LONDONDERRY DR 76712 #496-38-1974 L1980 CHP *020 †75

NESMITH, William R. 601 W STATE HYWY 6, STE 102 76710 #048-13-2000 L2003 PD *020 †55

NEWMAN, Gregory Stephen. 405 LONDONDERRY DR 76712 #048-15-1995 L1999 AN *020 †05

NI, Karen Yushien. 7700 FISH POND RD 76710 #048-12-2001 L2006 GS *020 †85

NICHOLS, Ashley Cochran. ■ 76706 #048-12-2006 L2008 MPD *012

NICHOLS, Steven Lee. 851 N LOOP 340 76705 #056-05-1981 L2006 FM AM *030 †18

NORMAN, Robert M. 4800 MEMORIAL DR 76711 #048-15-2002 L2007 P *020

NORTHCUTT, Alan D. 3115 PINE AVE STE 108 76708 #048-13-1982 L1983 PTH DMP *020 †50

NORWID, Mark Raymond. 3000 HERRING AVE 76708 #028-34-1988 L1997 EM *020 †16

OBERG, Lance Gordon. 405 LONDONDERRY DR STE 202 76712 #030-05-1972 L1976 P AM *030 †75

OEI, Kian Bing. 6901 MEDICAL PKWY, PROVIDENE WOUND CARE CENTE 76712 #506-02-1961 L1971 FM *017 †18

OISHI, Masaki. 342 RICHLAND WEST CIR 76712 #035-20-1996 L2003 NS *020 †25

OKANI, Ofobuike. 2911 HERRING AVE STE 209 76708 #690-04-1985 L1995 HO IM *020 †20

OLMSTED, James E. 6901 MEDICAL PKWY, WACO RADIOLOGY PA 76712 #048-13-1988 L1993 DR *020 †80

ORR, Samuel Reed. 7700 FISH POND RD 76710 #027-01-1998 L2000 PD *020 †55

OSBORNE, Jonathan Daniel. PO BOX 3276 76707 #048-78-2005, ▲ L2008 FP *012

OSWALT, Barry Fussell. 6600 FISH POND RD STE 101 76710 #048-15-1983 L1983 GS *020 †85

OSWALT, Charles E, III. 3000 HERRING AVE, P O BOX 5100 76708 #048-02-1970 L1970 TRS GS *020 †85

PARKER, Claude L. 4800 MEMORIAL DR, WACO VA HOSP PSYCH 76711 #306-01-1985 L1992 P *020 †75

PARKER-HUDSON, Courtney B. 1600 PROVIDENCE DR 76707 #048-14-1992 L1993 FM *040 †18

PARKS, Dennis Leroy. 6901 MEDICAL PKWY, WACO RADIOLOGY PA 76712 #021-06-1984 L1987 DR *020 †80

PATEL, Vikas Navinchandra. 3000 HERRING AVE, HILLCREST BAPTIST MEDICAL 76708 #422-01-2000 L2005 IM *020

PATTERSON, Karen Mann. 405 LONDONDERRY DR, STE 310 76712 #048-14-1985 L1986 OBG *020 †30

PATTON, James Russell. 3500 HILLCREST DR 76708 #041-01-1954 L1954 OPH *071 †35

PAYNE, Mack Baygent. 4205 FRANKLIN AVE 76710 #048-02-1969 L1970 FM *020 †18

PAYSON, Tony A. 213A OLD HEWITT RD, DE PAUL CENTER 76712 #048-13-1983 L1983 P *020 †75

PEPER, William Arthur. 405 LONDONDERRY DR, STE 303 76712 #048-12-1980 L1980 TS CCS *020 †85,90

PEPPER, Jennifer L. 49 SETTLERS CRK 76712 #048-14-1994 L1995 EM *020 †16

PEREZ, Rafael Jose. 2201 MACARTHUR DR STE 2200 76708 #035-19-1979 L1998 PUD IM *020 †20

PETTIT, James C. 3728 CHIMNEY RIDGE DR 76708 #048-78-1981, ▲ L1981 FM *020 †18

PETTY, Michael K. 7300 BOSQUE BLVD 76710 #048-78-1994, ▲ L1995 FM *020 †18

PHILLIPS, Troy M. ■ 76710 #048-78-2006, ▲ L2007 FP *012

PINKSTAFF, David M. 601 W HWY 6, STE 105 76710 #048-12-1999 L2005 U *020 †95

PITMAN, Gerald G. 4800 MEMORIAL DR 76711 #048-12-1953 L1953 GS FM *020 †85

PLANTE, Dennis Michael. 3000 HERRING AVE, HILLCREST BAPTIST MED CTR 76708 #024-05-1984 L1988 EM *020 †16

PLEMMONS, Robert M. 7030 NEW SANGER RD, STE 202 76712 #048-13-1989 L1990 ID *020 †20

POPEJOY, Vicki Vrana. 2201 MACARTHUR DR, STE 103 76708 #048-02-2002 L2005 PD *020 †55

PORTER, Matthew R. 7125 NEW SANGER RD, STE C 76712 #048-13-1993 L1996 FM *020 †18

PRASAD, Motaparthi A. ■ 76712 #496-01-1970 L1980 CD IM *075 †20

PRYOR, Pat. 7100 OLD MCGREGOR RD 76712 #048-04-1974 L1974 FM EM *020 †18

QUINIUS, Herman John, III. 3115 PINE AVE, STE 202 76708 #048-12-1983 L1983 OPH *020 †35

RAIMONDO, Jeffrey Thomas. 1600 PROVIDENCE DR 76707 #048-13-2003 L2005 FM *020 †18

RAINEY, Robert Craig. 1600 PROVIDENCE DR 76707 #048-14-2004 L2007 FM *020 †18

RALEY, Stephen Paul. 1001 HEWITT DR 76712 #048-14-1977 L1977 FM EM *020 †18

RALSTON, Samuel Warren. 1001 HEWITT DR 76712 #048-02-1981 L1981 FM *030 †18

RAMADAN, Mohamed Hussein. 3000 HERRING AVE 76708 #915-03-1977 L1993 IM NEP *020 †20

RAMAMOORTHY, Kuttai V. ■ 76712 #495-42-1961 L1980 IM *020

READY, Norris Hamilton. ■ 76712 #065-05-1955 L1982 AN *071

REAGAN, Ross Burney. 6600 FISH POND RD STE 101 76710 #048-12-1969 L1969 GS TS *020 †85,90

REDDY, Anugu Bhooma. 4800 MEMORIAL DR 76711 #495-57-1975 L1997 IM *020 †20

REDDY, Kota Dharma. 4800 MEMORIAL DR, DEPT PSYCH 76711 #495-57-1966 L1981 P *020 †75

REDMAN, Paul C, II. 601 W HWY 6 STE 101 76710 #048-13-1997 L2005 OBG *020 †30

REEDER, Phillip Hayward. 364 RICHLAND WEST CIR, STE A 76712 #020-12-1976 L1978 GE IM *020 †20

REESE, Woody J, Jr. 2329 N 39TH ST 76708 #048-02-1984 L1985 NEP IM *020 †20

REIS, Michael David. 7700 FISH POND RD 76710 #048-14-1984 L1995 FM *020 †18

REYES-MIGNOSA, Aurora F. ■ 76712 #748-01-1952 L1979 P *072

RICHIE, Rodney Chas. 7125 NEW SANGER RD, STE B 76712 #048-04-1972 L1972 PUD CCM *020 †20

RIDER, David Michael. ■ 76707 #048-02-2006 L2007 **FP** *012
RISINGER, David O. 3000 HERRING AVE 76708 #048-13-1988 L1990 **DR** *020 †80
RISINGER, Donald Lester. 3000 HERRING AVE 76708 #048-02-1963 L1963 **DR** *020 †80,28
RISTER, Joel Mark. 2124 N 25TH ST 76708 #048-12-1982 L1983 **OBG** *020 †30
ROBINSON, Fred Wm. ■ 76710 #025-01-1943 L1953 **GS OS** *071 †85
ROBINSON, Ty Bennett. 1600 PROVIDENCE DR, WACO FAMILY HEALTH CENTER 76707 #055-75-2001, ▲ L2005 **OBG** *020 †30
RODDY, William Nathan. 6901 MEDICAL PKWY 76712 #048-02-1945 L1945 **CD IM** *071
ROSARIO, Maydee Annette. 7125 NEW SANGER RD, STE B 76712 #042-03-1999 L2004 **PUD** *020 †20
ROSENQUIST, Jason Lance. 1600 PROVIDENCE DR 76707 #048-13-2001 L2004 **FM** *100 †18
ROWE, Mark S. 405 LONDONDERRY DR, STE 311 76712 #048-02-1982 L1983 **OBG** *020 †30
RUDDELL, Timothy John. ■ 76707 #048-12-2008 *012
SALINAS, Gerald. 201 OLD HEWITT RD 76712 #048-02-1988 L1989 **FM** *020 †18
SAMPLES, Daniel Robt. 3115 PINE AVE, STE 108 76708 #048-13-1990 L1991 **PTH** *020 †50
SANCHEZ, Jorge Edward. 1600 PROVIDENCE DR, FAMILY PRACTICE CTR 76707 #048-13-2006 **FP** *012
SANDERS, Jeffrey Scott. 6600 FISH POND RD, STE 202 76710 #048-12-1992 L1993 **U** *020 †95
SANDERS, William Bruce. 4800 MEMORIAL DR, VAMC 112 76711 #047-06-1959 L1962 **GYN** *020 †20
SAWYER, Dianne Waddell. 3115 PINE AVE STE 903 76708 #048-02-1982 L1983 **OBG** *020 †30
SAWYER, J Clay. 305 LONDONDERRY DR STE 6 76712 #048-02-1982 L1983 **P** *020 †75
SAXTON, Robert Hibberd. 3115 PINE AVE, SAXTON & EVANS 76708 #038-06-1955 L1964 **NS** *071 †25
SCHICKNER, David John. 300 RICHLAND WEST CIR 76712 #038-41-1987 L1993 **NS** *020 †25
SCHILLER, Timothy W. 851 N LOOP 340 76705 #048-78-1996, ▲ L1998 **FM** *020 †18
SCHLECTE, Marvin C, III. 321 RICHLAND WEST CIR 76712 #048-02-2003 L2007 **OPH** *020
SCHLECTE, Marvin Charles, Jr. 321 RICHLAND WEST CIR 76712 #048-13-1974 L1974 **OPH** *020 †35
SCHMIDT, Timothy J. 405 LONDONDERRY DR STE 105 76712 #048-16-1989 L1990 **AN** *020 †05
SCHUBERT, Max H. 4800 MEMORIAL DR, # 151-W 76711 #048-15-1998 L2000 **P** *020 †75
SCHWARTZE, George Mark. 342 RICHLAND WEST CIR 76712 #036-05-1978 L1979 **N** *020 †20,75
SCHWARTZE, Jeffrey Mark. ■ 76710 #048-02-2008 *012
SCHWEDOCK, Nicholas. 1600 PROVIDENCE DR 76707 #048-15-1994 L1995 **FM** *040 †18
SCIBIELSKI, Paul M. 333 LONDONDERRY DR, STE 100 76712 #048-15-2002 L2007 **AI** *012 †55
SCOTT, Richard E, Jr. 3115 PINE AVE, STE 403 76708 #048-78-1994, ▲ L1995 **PM PME** *020 †60
SCRUGGS, James Harry, Jr. 3115 PINE AVE, STE 202 76708 #048-02-1945 L1945 **OPH** *071 †35
SEELY, Jeremiah B. ■ 76710 #048-12-2006 L2008 **FP** *012
SEIRAFI, Homayun. 2911 HERRING AVE STE 206 76708 #517-01-1975 L1982 **OBG** *040 †30
SHELLENBERGER, Charles G. ■ 76710 #039-01-1945 L1947 **PD** *071
SHELTON, John Buford. 7300 BOSQUE BLVD 76710 #048-16-1997 L1998 **FM** *020 †18
SHIPP, Ross Franklin. 2800 LYLE AVE 76708 #048-02-1969 L1969 **IM** *020 †20
SHORT, Helen Ann. 3501 N 19TH ST, WACO CENTER FOR YOUTH 76708 #051-07-1987 L1996 **P AN** *020 †18
SHUTT, Bryce C. 321 RICHLAND WEST CIR 76712 #048-04-1991 L1992 **OPH** *020 †35
SIMS, Ann Knight. ■ 76712 #048-02-1975 L1975 **OBG** *071 †30
SIMS, Gayland Lee. 6600 FISH POND RD STE 101 76710 #048-02-1975 L1975 **GS** *020 †85
SKEEN, Shawn J. ■ 76712 #048-16-2006 **IM** *012
SLADE, Harry Warren. ■ 76710 #048-04-1946 L1946 **N PME** *071 †25
SLETTE, Darrell Roger. ■ 76710 #010-01-1958 L1974 **IM OS** *071 †20
SMITH, J William. 3500 HILLCREST DR, STE 2 76708 #048-04-1959 L1960 **OPH** *020 †35
SMITH, Jeff Donald. 1600 PROVIDENCE DR 76707 #048-15-2005 L2006 **FP** *012
SMITH, Nathan M. 1600 PROVIDENCE DR, FAMILY PRACTICE CTR 76707 #048-12-2006 **FP** *012
SMITH, Scott Hatter. 3500 HILLCREST DR, HILLCREST MEDICAL PLAZA 76708 #048-04-1990 L1991 **OPH** *020 †35
SMITH, Ted R. ■ 76708 #048-13-1987 L1989 **GS TRS** *020 †85
SPAIN, Latrisha Faye. 1600 PROVIDENCE DR 76707 #048-12-2005 **FP** *012
SPARK, Harvey. 3115 PINE AVE 76708 #048-02-1963 L1964 **PD OS** *020 †55
SPECKMIEAR, John Wm. 201 OLD HEWITT RD 76712 #048-04-1976 L1976 **FM** *020 †18
SPRINGER, Robert Ralph. 1000 W STATE HIGHWAY 6, STE 150 76712 #016-43-1972 L1975 **SME PUD** *020 †20
STERN, Charles H. 7700 FISH POND RD 76710 #048-13-1986 L1987 **FM** *020 †18 ‡
STERN, Sharon Wright. 209 SPEIGHT AVE, BAYLOR STUDENT HEALTH CENT 76706 #048-13-1987 L1988 **FM** *020 †18
STEVENS, Charles R. 6901 MEDICAL PKWY 76712 #048-02-1960 L1960 **P** *071
STEWART, Donald A. 601 W HWY 6, STE 100 76710 #048-13-1987 L1992 **U** *020 †95
STIDVENT, Thomas Wesley. 3105 N 19TH ST, WACO CENTER FOR YOUTH 76708 #048-13-1974 L1974 **CHP P** *020 †75
STOCKTON, Robert Louis. 76708 #039-01-1959 L1961 **NS AM** *071 †25
STORY, Mark Walter. 601 W HWY 6, STE 105 76710 #048-02-1977 L1977 **U** *020 †95
STOVALL, Geo Alston, Jr. 364 RICHLAND WEST CIR, STE A 76712 #048-12-1985 L1987 **GE IM** *020 †20
SUDAN, Arthur Wayne. 2800 LYLE AVE 76708 #048-04-1980 L1981 **IM** *020 †20
SULLIVAN, Linda J. 1600 PROVIDENCE DR, FAMILY HEALTH CENTER 76707 #048-78-2007, ▲ **FP** *012
SWANN, Russell Eugene. 201 LONDONDERRY DR 76712 #021-01-1975 L1976 **OPH** *020 †35
SWIFT, Ronald Jay. 405 LONDONDERRY DR, STE 105 76712 #039-01-1994 L1996 **AN** *020 †05
TALBERT, Amy Lee. 1600 PROVIDENCE DR 76707 #048-14-2003 L2006 **FM** *020 †18
TANDY, James R. 3115 PINE AVE, STE 808 76708 #048-12-1989 L1993 **OTO HNS** *020 †45
TEICHELMANN, Michael P. 405 LONDONDERRY DR STE 105 76712 #048-13-1998 L2001 **AN** *020 †05
TENERIELLO, Michael Guy. 1700 WEST AVE, STE 6 76707 #035-47-1983 L1996 **GO GYN** *020 †30
THALLER, Ephraim Isaac. 333 LONDONDERRY DR, STE 100 76712 #048-16-2000 L2002 **AI** *100 †55,03
THAMBAN, Immanuel Stephen. ■ 76712 #495-27-1968 L1976 **IM** *020 †20
THEBAULT, R C. ■ 76710 #048-15-2006 L2008 **FP** *012
TRIPPE, Karl Michael. 2100 LAKE SHORE DR 76708 #048-15-1996 L1997 **FM** *020 †18
TSAI, Chien-Li. 4800 MEMORIAL DR, DEPT PSYCHIATRY 76711 #244-05-1967 L1982 **P** *030 †75
TUEL, David Chas. 5900 OLD MCGREGOR RD 76712 #048-16-1984 L1985 **AN PD** *020 †05
TULLOS, Mark A. PO BOX 5100, 2201 MACARTHUR SUITE 2200 76708 #048-04-1994 L2006 **GS** *020 †85

TURNAGE, Elizabeth B. 2201 MACARTHUR DR, STE 100 76708 #048-16-1994 L1995 **FM** *020 †18 ‡
TURNER, Tammie F. 3501 N 19TH ST 76708 #048-15-1986 L1987 **PD** *020
TURNEY, William Henry. 6600 FISH POND RD, STE 101 76710 #048-12-1968 L1968 **GS** *020 †85
UPTERGROVE, Richard W. 6901 MEDICAL PKWY 76712 #048-16-1986 L1987 **EM FM** *020 †18
VAUGHAN, David B. 301 RICHLAND WEST CIR, STE A 76712 #048-13-1990 L1991 **FM** *020 †18
VEAZEY, Randolph Bryant. 340 RICHLAND WEST CIR 76712 #048-02-1985 L1986 **N** *020 †75
VERNER, Edward Farley. 7030 NEW SANGER RD, STE 202 76712 #048-02-1980 L1980 **ID IM** *020 †20
VILLARREAL, Gustavo G, Jr. 6901 MEDICAL PKWY, WACO RADIOLOGY PA 76712 #048-02-1989 L1990 **R** *020 †80
VILLARREAL, Lucy Konop. 405 LONDONDERRY DR STE 300 76712 #048-02-1989 L1994 **OBG** *020 †30
VOIGE, Hayley. ■ 76710 #048-78-2003, ▲ L2006 **OBG** *100
WALKER, Eric P. 6901 MEDICAL PKWY, PROVIDENCE HOSPITAL - IMS 76712 #048-16-2002 L2005 **ID** *100
WALTERS, Fred Allen. 3000 HERRING AVE 76708 #048-12-1979 L1979 **DR** *020 †80
WANG, Chia-Lien. 3115 PINE AVE STE 1001 76708 #048-02-1991 L1993 **OBG** *020 †30
WANG, May Yung-Fun Woo. ■ 76710 #008-01-1960 L1966 **PD PHO** *071 †55
WATSON, Floyd Clinton. 1800 GURLEY LN, WACO FAMILY HLTH CTR 76706 #048-02-2003 L2005 **FM** *020 †18
WATSON, Jose Vernon. ■ 76702 #048-04-1996 L1997 **DR** *020 †80
WATSON, William Lake. ■ 76710 #048-12-1955 L1955 **OTO A** *071
WEAVER, Sally Pyle. 1600 PROVIDENCE DR 76707 #048-02-1996 L1997 **FM** *020 †18
WEEKLEY, Frederick Clay. ■ 76712 #048-04-1937 L1937 **GP GS** *071
WEHMEYER, Van A. 7700 FISH POND RD 76710 #048-14-2004 L2006 **FM** *020 †18
WELTER, Timothy Michael. 3000 HERRING AVE 76708 #056-05-1985 L1989 **EM IM** *020 †20
WEST, James Milton. 1204 SPEIGHT AVE 76706 #048-12-1964 L1964 **FM** *020 †18
WHEELER, Darrell Stafford. 3000 HERRING AVE, WACO NEONATAL GROUP 76708 #048-14-1985 L1986 **NPM PD** *020 †55
WHITE, Thomas Brian. 3000 HERRING AVE, HILLCREST X-RAY PHYSICIANS 76708 #048-02-1996 L2001 **DR** *020 †80
WHITE, Thomas M. 405 LONDONDERRY DR, STE 105 76712 #048-02-1985 L1987 **AN** *020 †05
WILCOX, Patricia A. 6614 SANGER AVE 76710 #048-14-1994 L1995 **FM** *020 †18 ‡
WILCOX, Robert W. 6614 SANGER AVE 76710 #048-14-1993 L1994 **FM** *020 †18
WILLIAMS, Holly A. 405 LONDONDERRY DR, STE 105 76712 #048-13-1997 L1998 **AN** *020 †05
WILLIAMS, Linda Ann. 209 SPEIGHT AVE, BAYLOR UNIVERSITY HEALTH C 76706 #048-02-1978 L1978 **FM** *020 †18
WILLIAMS, Roger Thomas. 405 LONDONDERRY DR, STE 105 76712 #048-02-2004 L2008 **AN** *012
WILLITS, Jamie Lynn. ■ 76708 #048-02-2004 L2006 **FM** *020 †18
WILSON, Ronald L. 2329 N 39TH ST 76708 #048-04-1974 L1974 **NEP IM** *020 †20
WOLF, Robert Earl. 3500 HILLCREST DR 76708 #048-12-1989 L1990 **OMO ORS** *020 †40
WOODS, Terriawkia Aurelia. 1600 PROVIDENCE DR 76707 #020-12-2001 L2005 **OBG** *020
YOST, James Gregory. 7700 FISH POND RD 76710 #048-15-1986 L1987 **GS** *020 †85
ZECCA, Guido E, III. 6901 MEDICAL PKWY 76712 #034-01-1998 L1999 **EM** *020 †16
ZEIGLER, Ray Lacy. 405 LONDONDERRY DR, WACO RADIOLOGICAL CLINIC 76712 #048-12-1956 L1956 **R NM** *071 †80,28
ZIELINSKI, Steven Christo. 342 RICHLAND WEST CIR, NEUROSURGERY & NEUROSCIENC 76712 #067-01-1995 L2007 **NS** *020 †25
ZINN, Brandon Keith. PO BOX 3276, MC LENNAN CO MED ED RES FN 76707 #048-78-2006, ▲ **FP** *012

WAKE VILLAGE – BOWIE

HAYWOOD, Bobbie Jean. ■ 75501 #025-12-1983 L1986 **IM** *071
KAHL, Andrew. ■ 75501 #759-03-1967 L1986 **IM END** *020 †20
KEMPSON, Steven Eugene. 815 N KINGS HWY, WEST SIDE CLINIC 75501 #004-01-1995 L1998 **FM** *020 †18
KJERVIK, Abner R. ■ 75501 #056-05-1940 L1941 **GP** *074
QADRI, Syed Ghouse. ■ 75501 #649-35-1985 *100
SHAW, Michael Allen. ■ 75501 #004-01-1999 L2005 **FM** *020
STEPHENS, Ronald D. 815 N KINGS HWY, COLLOM CARNEY CLINIC 75501 #048-15-1986 L1987 **FM** *020 †18 ‡
TARPLEY, Jon Allen. 815 N KINGS HWY 75501 #039-01-1997 L1999 **FM** *020 †18
WYMAN, Monserrat Sosa. ■ 75501 #748-07-1966 **GP** *020

WALLER – WALLER

ALLAIRE, Bo Jonathan. ■ 77484 #048-04-2008 *012
HASEEB, Abdul Q. 31303 FM 2920 RD STE G 77484 #704-16-1991 L1997 **AI PD** *020 †55,03
REYES, Robert R. 1221 FARR ST 77484 #048-14-1986 L1991 **FM** *020 †18
TAHIR, Saifuddin. 31303 FM 2920 RD STE G 77484 #704-02-1989 L1997 **PD** *020 †55

WASHINGTON – WASHINGTON

HAND, Henry Hagen. ■ 77880 #048-02-1959 L1959 **GP** *020
KIRBY, Edward Jos. ■ 77880 #056-06-1953 L1961 **PS** *071 †65

WATAUGA – TARRANT

ABRAHAM, Akram Rasmy. 6651 WATAUGA RD STE 104, RUFE SNOW CLINIC 76148 #915-03-1990 L2000 **FM** *020 †18
BESTAWROUS, Reda Saber. 6651 WATAUGA RD STE 104 76148 #915-04-1982 L1997 **FM** *020 †18
CHEESMAN, Heather Carol. 5920 WATAUGA RD 76148 #062-01-1976 L1978 **FM** *020
GUJJU, Lakshmi Poorna. 6651 WATAUGA RD, STE 104 76148 #496-40-1992 L2007 **FPG** *020 †18

WAXAHACHIE – ELLIS

ADELL, Ruth A. 505 N HIGHWAY 77, STE 200 75165 #048-78-2001, ▲ L2003 **FM** *020

AGOSTINI, Julia Toxey. 1405 W JEFFERSON ST, AMERICAN RADIOLOGY 75165 #024-01-1988 L1998 **DR IM** *020 †80
ARREDONDO, Adam Gallardo. 128 N HIGHWAY 77 75165 #649-02-1992 L1999 **APM AN** *020
ARREDONDO, Mary J. 1710 W 287 BUSINESS, STE 100 75165 #048-14-1985 L1986 **PD** *020 †55
AUSLOOS, Ken Allen. 1305 W JEFFERSON ST, STE 160 75165 #056-06-1986 L1992 **PUD** *020 †20
BOONE, Benjamin D. 1626 W HIGHWAY 287 BUSINES, STE 108 75165 #020-02-1945 L1945 **GS** *020 †85
BOONE, Benjamin Dance, Jr. 1626 W 287 BUSINESS, STE 108 75165 #020-02-1977 L1981 **ORS** *020
BOUSQUET, John A, III. 505 N HIGHWAY 77 STE 200, ELLIS COUNTY DIAGNOSTIC CL 75165 #048-13-1984 L1985 **IM** *020 †20
BRADY, John Irvin, Jr. 1505 W JEFFERSON ST, STE 170 75165 #048-15-1985 L1986 **OBG** *020 †30
BROWN, Jason P. 1505 W JEFFERSON ST STE 12 75165 #048-12-1998 L2001 **OBG** *020 †30
CARTWRIGHT, Gregory B. 201 FERRIS AVE STE C 75165 #048-15-1989 L1990 **FM** *020 †18
CHAN, Katherine Wong. 1405 W JEFFERSON ST 75165 #748-08-1979 L1984 **PTH** *020 †50
CHARUWORN, Phanomkiate. 201 FERRIS AVE, MEDICAL CTR 75165 #891-01-1967 L1973 **OBG** *020 †30
CHARUWORN, Plernsri. 201 FERRIS AVE 75165 #891-01-1958 **OBG AN** *020
CHATAWANICH, Sukhum. ■ 75165 #891-01-1967 L1975 **OBG** *071 †30
COMPTON, John Graham. 201 FERRIS AVE, STE G 75165 #048-02-1954 L1954 **GP** *020
COWLEY BRADY, Yolanda M. 505 N HIGHWAY 77, STE 200 75165 #048-15-1984 L1985 **IM** *020 †20
DIAMOND, Norman Geo. 1405 W JEFFERSON ST, AMERICAN RADIOLOGY 75165 #035-01-1974 L1982 **VIR** *020 †80
DOMINGUEZ, David. 1405 W JEFFERSON ST 75165 #005-14-1989 L1990 **FM** *020 †18
EASON, Martin D. 800 N HIGHWAY 77, STE 160 75165 #048-14-1998 L2002 **AN** *020 †05
ETINDI, Ransome Njeka. 505 N HIGHWAY 77 STE 200 75165 #017-20-1998 L2001 **IM** *020 †20
FATAHI, Mohamad Ebrahim. 1405 W JEFFERSON ST 75165 #517-01-1964 L1973 **DR** *020 †80
FAYIGA, Yomi O. 1626 W HWY 287 BUS, STE 102 75165 #048-14-1990 L1991 **CRS GS** *020 †85,10
FEARIS, David Porteus, III. ■ 75165 #021-01-1961 L1966 **FM** *020
FEDOR, Robert Dale. ■ 75165 #026-04-1954 L1954 **PTH** *071 †50
FELTY, Bob K. 1405 W JEFFERSON ST 75165 #048-14-1988 L1989 **FM** *020 †18
FELTY, Mary Fogarty. 411 E JEFFERSON ST, HOPE CLINIC 75165 #048-14-1988 L1989 **FM** *020 †18
FORD, Kenneth L, III. 1405 W JEFFERSON ST, AMERICAN RADIOLOGY 75165 #048-04-1991 L1992 **DR** *020 †80
FULMER, James M. 1405 W JEFFERSON ST, AMERICAN RADIOLOGY 75165 #048-12-1984 L1985 **DR R** *020 †80
FUNG, Deborah C. 505 N HIGHWAY 77, STE 200 75165 #048-04-1996 L1998 **PD** *020 †55
GARRISON, Christopher Jay. 507 N HIGHWAY 77, STE 700 75165 #048-02-1992 L1993 **PM** *020 †60
GLASTAD, Karl Andrew. 1405 W JEFFERSON ST, AMERICAN RADIOLOGY 75165 #048-12-1985 L1987 **DR** *020 †80
GORMAN, Valerie Jean. 1305 W JEFFERSON ST, STE 120 75165 #048-12-1999 L2004 **GS** *020 †85
GRAHAM, Andre Dean. 1305 W JEFFERSON ST 75165 #019-02-1998 L2007 **GS** *020 †85
GREENOUGH, William Geo. 1405 W JEFFERSON ST, AMERICAN RADIOLOGY 75165 #019-02-1961 L1967 **DR** *020 †80
GREENWAY, Guerdon. 1405 W JEFFERSON ST, AMERICAN RADIOLOGY 75165 #025-01-1970 L1980 **DR** *020 †80 ‡
GRIFFETH, Landis King. 1405 W JEFFERSON ST, AMERICAN RADIOLOGY 75165 #036-07-1984 L1993 **NM** *020 †28
GROSSMAN, Stanley Jay. 1405 W JEFFERSON ST, AMERICAN RADIOLOGY 75165 #026-08-1980 L1996 **NM IM** *020 †20,28 ‡
HAMILTON, Elizabeth Costa. 1305 W JEFFERSON ST, STE 200 75165 #031-01-1997 L2000 **GS** *020 †85
HAMILTON, William Mark. 1405 W JEFFERSON ST, AMERICAN RADIOLOGY 75165 #048-12-1972 L1972 **OS NM** *020 †80
HENRY, Travis Scott. 505 N HIGHWAY 77, STE 200 75165 #047-06-1997 L2000 **PD** *020 †55
HISE, Joseph Henry. 1405 W JEFFERSON ST, AMERICAN RADIOLOGY 75165 #048-16-1984 L1985 **RNR** *020 †80
HURST, David Christopher. 1405 W JEFFERSON ST, AMERICAN RADIOLOGY 75165 #048-12-1987 L1988 **DR** *020 †80
JOHNS, Theodore Andrew. 1405 W JEFFERSON ST, AMERICAN RADIOLOGY 75165 #048-12-1994 L1995 **DR** *020 †80
JOHNSTON, Stephen Bryce. 1305 W JEFFERSON ST 75165 #048-13-1981 L1981 **CD** *020 †20
JONES, Nelson Wm. ■ 75165 #048-02-1955 L1955 **FM** *071 †18
JORDAN, John Michael. 1305 W JEFFERSON ST, STE 160 75165 #048-12-1982 L1983 **PUD IM** *020 †20
JOSLIN, Eddie R. 505 N HIGHWAY 77, STE 200 75165 #048-12-1990 L1991 **IM** *020 †20
KARE, Ramon Paulo. 1410 W JEFFERSON ST 75165 #048-14-1997 L1999 **FM** *020 †18
KEMP, Richard Galen. 1626 W 287 BUSINESS, STE 105 75165 #048-12-1979 L1979 **OPH** *020 †35
KLATTE, Karen Kaye. 1305 W JEFFERSON ST 75165 #048-12-1996 L1998 **CD** *020 †20
LANSDOWNE, Paul Allan. 1505 W JEFFERSON ST, STE 120 75165 #019-02-1997 L2001 **OBG** *020 †30
LATIFI, Hamid Reza. 1405 W JEFFERSON ST, AMERICAN RADIOLOGY 75165 #028-02-1990 L2001 **NM DR** *020 †80,28
LEDBETTER, Thomas Glenn. 505 N HIGHWAY 77, STE 200 75165 #021-06-1983 L1984 **IM** *020 †20
LINGUIST, Peggy Fenton. 505 N HIGHWAY 77 STE 200, BAYLOR FAM MED CTR WAXAHAC 75165 #048-13-1994 L1997 **PD** *020 †55
LINQUIST, David Lane. 1405 W JEFFERSON ST 75165 #048-13-1994 L1997 **FM** *020 †18
MAJOR, William Chas. 1626 W HWY 287 BUS, STE 101 75165 #048-12-1975 L1975 **GS** *020 †85
MC NALLY, Joseph Francis, Jr. 1404 W JEFFERSON ST 75165 #010-02-1952 L1963 **AI PDA** *071 †80
OBI, Cyril Chidi. ■ 75167 #690-04-1990 L2003 **IMG** *020 †20 ‡
OPATOWSKY, Michael J. 1405 W JEFFERSON ST, AMERICAN RADIOLOGY 75165 #036-05-1987 L2003 **RNR DR** *020 †80
OWENS, D Chase. 1405 W JEFFERSON ST, ELLIS COUNTY EMERGENCY DEP 75165 #045-01-1991 L1999 **FSM** *020 †18
PICKENS, James Wesley. 1410 W JEFFERSON ST 75165 #048-02-1983 L1983 **FM** *020 †18
POWELL, Patti B. 505 N HIGHWAY 77, STE 200 75165 #048-12-1999 L2003 **IM** *020 †20
REDER, Paul A. 1305 W JEFFERSON ST # 115 75165 #048-02-1989 L1994 **OTO HNS** *020 †45
REDINGTON, Richard Dana. 1410 W JEFFERSON ST 75165 #048-02-1972 L1972 **FM** *020 †18
REED, Jennifer Blumoff. 1405 W JEFFERSON ST, AMERICAN RADIOLOGY 75165 #048-12-1997 L1998 **DR** *020 †80
REES, Chet R. 1405 W JEFFERSON ST, AMERICAN RADIOLOGY 75165 #017-20-1982 L1986 **VIR** *020 †80
ROUX, Marcus A. 1404 W JEFFERSON ST 75165 #048-16-2000 L2002 **ORS** *020 †40
ROYE, Robert P. 1324 BROWN ST STE 100 75165 #048-13-1988 L1989 **ORS** *020 †40
ROYE, Watson Payne, Jr. 1305 W JEFFERSON ST, STE 120 75165 #048-15-1983 L1983 **GS OS** *020 †85
RUGWANI, Rajiv. 507 N HIGHWAY 77 STE 704-1 75165 #048-13-1998 L2001 **OPH** *020
SALES, Jack Leroy. 1626 W HIGHWAY 287 BYP, STE 103 75165 #065-06-1955 L1979 **GS** *020
SAMBELL, Andrew C. 1626 W HWY 287 BUS STE 10 75165 #048-12-1991 L1993 **U AM** *020 †95
SCHACK, M Ricardo C. 1302 N HIGHWAY 77 STE 1 75165 #649-14-1976 L1982 **P N** *020 †75
SCHUCANY, William Gregory. 1405 W JEFFERSON ST, AMERICAN RADIOLOGY 75165 #048-02-1992 L1997 **DR** *020 †80
SCHUMACHER, John Ryan. 1305 W JEFFERSON ST 75165 #017-20-1978 L1980 **CD IC** *020 †20
SEGGERMAN, Richard Edward. 1405 W JEFFERSON ST, AMERICAN RADIOLOGY 75165 #048-02-1996 L2001 **DR** *020 †80
SINGH, Jasbir. 1505 W JEFFERSON ST, STE 170 75165 #048-12-1999 L2003 **OBG** *020
SWEET, Kimberly Karla. 505 N HIGHWAY 77, STE 200 75165 #048-12-1998 L2001 **PD** *020 †55
THACKER, Brett Mc Kinney. 201 FERRIS AVE, STE I 75165 #048-02-1981 L1981 **IM** *020 †20
THACKER, Ike Clayton. 1405 W JEFFERSON ST, AMERICAN RADIOLOGY 75165 #048-02-1996 L2003 **RNR** *020 †80
TOKER, Steven Ilterhan. ■ 75167 #048-14-2006 **AN** *012
TOPPINS, Anthony Charles. 1405 W JEFFERSON ST, AMERICAN RADIOLOGY 75165 #039-01-1996 L1997 **DR** *020 †80
WALTON, Rhonda L. 505 N HIGHWAY 77, STE 200 75165 #038-45-1986 L1990 **PD** *020 †55
WEBB, David Lewis. 1505 W JEFFERSON ST, STE 160 75165 #048-12-1969 L1969 **OTO** *020 †18,45
WEISBRUCH, Gregory J. 1405 W JEFFERSON ST, AMERICAN RADIOLOGY 75165 #048-12-1984 L1985 **R DR** *020 †80
WILLIAMS, David Willard. 1410 W JEFFERSON ST 75165 #048-02-1958 L1958 **FM IM** *071 †18
ZEIGLER, Neal Alexander. 1405 W JEFFERSON ST, EMERGENCY DEPARTMENT 75165 #016-42-2002 L2005 **EM** *020
ZIBILICH, Mark Walter. 1405 W JEFFERSON ST, AMERICAN RADIOLOGY 75165 #048-12-1978 L1978 **DR** *020 †80

WEATHERFORD – PARKER

ANDERSON, Merlin G. ■ 76087 #005-12-1963 L1964 **ORS OAR** *040 †40
BACK, Heather D. ■ 76087 #048-78-2005, ▲ L2007 **FP** *012
BARNES, John Whitmill. ■ 76088 #048-12-1957 L1957 **PTH** *071 †50
BARRERA, Tres Aaron. ■ 76087 #048-14-2006 L2006 **IM** *012
BEERY, Paul Dwight, Jr. 713 E ANDERSON ST 76086 #048-12-1967 L1967 **DR GP** *020
BINZER, Thomas Chas. 750 EUREKA ST STE C 76086 #041-13-1990 L1992 **HS** *020 †40
BLAYLOCK, Sheryl L. 1105 SANTA FE DR, STE 102 76086 #048-02-1994 L1995 **IM** *020 †20
BRUHL, Daniel Edward. 804 SANTA FE DR 76086 #154-07-1935 L1935 **GPM GP** *071
CARDENAS, Richard K. 750 EUREKA ST STE A 76086 #048-02-1981 L1982 **OBG** *020 †30
DIAMOND, Kevin Drew. 925 SANTA FE DR, STE 114 76086 #016-42-1996 L2002 **U** *020 †95
DIXON, Richard P. 1814 OLD DICEY RD 76085 #048-13-1987 L1988 **EM FM** *020 †18
D'SPAIN, David M. ■ 76087 #048-78-2003, ▲ L2005 **ON** *012 †20
EIDSON, Jack Leigh. ■ 76086 #048-04-1946 L1946 **FM GP** *071 †18
EIDSON, Mark Carroll. 710 E ANDERSON ST 76086 #048-13-1979 L1979 **FM** *020 †18
FLEISCHER, A Georg. ■ 76087 #048-02-1966 L1966 **PM** *072 †60
FLOYD, Eric Ross. 713 E ANDERSON ST 76086 #048-12-1997 L1998 **FM** *020 †18 ‡
FORD, Ricky Joe. 750 EUREKA ST STE E 76086 #048-02-1981 L1981 **ORS** *020 †40
GHATALIA, Bipin Kantilal. 103 W LEE AVE 76086 #495-17-1957 L1972 **GP GS** *020 †18
GILBERT, Mark. ■ 76085 #011-02-1970 L1972 **PTH** *062 †50
GUNTER, Amelia A. ■ 76086 #048-16-1998 L2000 **GS** *020 †85
GUYNES, Suzanne M. 115 E LEE AVE 76086 #048-14-1990 L1991 **PYG P** *020 †75
HALS, Jessica. 911 FOSTER LN 76086 #041-78-1999, ▲ L2000 **ON** *020
HELDT, Richard C, III. 713 E ANDERSON ST 76086 #048-13-1997 L2001 **AN** *020 †05
HENDRICKS, Geo David, Jr. 804 SANTA FE DR 76086 #048-12-1980 L1980 **OPH** *020 †35
HINZ, Reinhold Hans. ■ 76087 #407-21-1956 L1969 **OBG** *071 †30
HUGGINS, Timothy Lebron. 1212 CLEAR LAKE RD, STE 100 76086 #001-06-1989 L1992 **GE** *020 †20
IRVINE, James, Jr. ■ 76087 #048-12-1953 L1953 **AN** *071 †05
IVEY, Donna Lee. 713 E ANDERSON ST 76086 #048-02-1984 L1985 **EM** *020 †20
KAPILA, Kiran. 925 SANTA FE DR, STE 108 76086 #495-74-1977 L1992 **IM** *020 †20
KAPILA, Rishi Ram. PO BOX 2379 76086 #048-15-2004 L2007 **IM** *100 †20
KAPILA, Yagya Valik. 925 SANTA FE DR, STE 108 76086 #495-29-1970 L1992 **GE IM** *020 †20
KHAN, Nadeem Ahmed. 713 E ANDERSON ST 76086 #704-16-1993 L1999 **FM** *020 †20,18
KHAN, Nadeem Ullah. ■ 76087 #704-25-1994 **IM** *100 †20
KHAN, Nusrat Ali. 2111 FORT WORTH HWY 76086 #036-08-1998 L2006 **MPD DIA** *020 †20,55 ‡
KUMAR, Sumant A. 103 W LEE AVE 76086 #495-37-1968 L1972 **FM EM** *020 †18
LIVINGSTON, Kim. 320 WILSON LN, P O BOX 516 76087 #048-02-1980 L1980 **AN** *020 †05
MARSH, Michael D. 1929 FORT WORTH HWY 76086 #048-15-1995 L1997 **PD** *020 †55
MARTIN, William Clyde. 706 EUREKA ST 76086 #048-04-1967 L1967 **OBG** *071
MC BRIDE, Lindsay M. ■ 76085 #048-78-2005, ▲ L2006 **OBG** *012
MERRICK, John Blake. ■ 76086 #010-01-1942 L1946 **GP** *071 †18
MERRITT, Walter M, III. 713 E ANDERSON ST 76086 #027-01-1968 L1974 **R OS** *020 †80
NEWMAN, Stephen D. 914 FOSTER LN 76086 #048-02-1988 L1990 **CD** *020 †20
NEWTON, James Bailey. 710 E ANDERSON ST 76086 #048-12-1977 L1977 **FM** *020 †18
NGUYEN, Thanh Xuan. 907 FOSTER LN 76086 #048-02-2000 L2005 **RO** *020 †80
PACHIGOLLA, Ravi V. 716 E ANDERSON ST STE 101 76086 #048-02-1995 L1998 **OTO** *020 †45
PARCHUE, John Anthony. 804 SANTA FE DR 76086 #010-01-1986 L1999 **IM** *020 †35
PENCE, Ronald M. 1715 SANTA FE DR, PECAN VALLEY MHMR CLINIC 76086 #048-13-1986 L1987 **CHP P** *020

RAY, Christopher S. PO BOX 1569, 2991 W I20 S FRONTAGE 76086 #048-14-2000 L2004 AN *020

REEVE, David Lee. 710 E ANDERSON ST 76086 #048-14-1975 L1975 FM *020 †18

RHEAMS, Christopher N. 713 E ANDERSON ST, WEATHERFORD INPATIENT PHYS 76086 #021-06-1980 L2004 IM *020 †20

ROLAND, James Keith. 710 E ANDERSON ST 76086 #048-12-1978 L1978 FM *020 †18

ROSE, Donal B. 713 E ANDERSON ST 76086 #031-01-1996 L2001 ORS *020 †40

SANKARAPANDIAN, Ponniah S. 504 SANTA FE DR 76086 #495-42-1966 L1979 NEP IM *020

SCARBOROUGH, Jon Sidney. ■ 76087 #048-02-1986 L1987 FM *020 †18

SCHWARTZ, Gregory Gerald. ■ 76087 #048-02-1991 L1992 ORS *020 †40

SHOLDRA, Eugene Peter. 810 S MAIN ST 76086 #065-01-1965 L1977 OPH *020

SHRESTHA, Jharana. 716 E ANDERSON ST, NWA ARTHRITIS AND OSTEOPOR 76086 #496-07-1991 L1999 RHU *020 †20

SHRESTHA, Sanjeeb. 111 W AKARD ST 76086 #704-02-1989 L2000 GE *020 †20

SINGH, Lakheram. 1020 FORT WORTH HWY, STE 500 76086 #060-02-1975 L1977 FM GPM *020

SMITH, Jeffrey Scott. 907 EUREKA ST, STE B 76086 #005-14-1991 L1997 ORS *020 †40

STAMATIS, Stephen Paul. 706 EUREKA ST 76086 #048-15-2003 L2005 OBG *020

THOMPSON, John Howard. 713 E ANDERSON ST 76086 #048-02-1971 L1971 GS FM *020 †85

WALKER, Andrew Scott. 925 SANTA FE DR, STE 107 76086 #048-13-1997 L1999 GS *020 †85

WALKER, Susan Gauntt. 712 E ANDERSON ST, WEATHERFORD PEDIATRICS PA 76086 #048-15-1987 L1989 PD *020

WESTERFIELD, Lewis. 713 E ANDERSON ST 76086 #048-78-1993, ▲ L1994 EM IM *020

WILSON, Richard Dan. ■ 76087 #048-04-1982 L1983 IM *020 †20

ZAGUIRRE, Jose Yia, Jr. ■ 76086 #748-01-1952 L1960 AN *075

WEBSTER – HARRIS

ABBOTT, James Ronald. 16 PROFESSIONAL PARK DR 77598 #048-02-1969 L1969 PD *020

ABBOTT, Lillian Tanaka. 17 PROFESSIONAL PARK DR 77598 #018-03-1969 L1973 OBG *020 †30

ABREO, Gerard. 530 ORCHARD ST 77598 #495-52-1991 L1996 CD *020 †20

ADAM, Todd Wayne. 1015 MEDICAL CENTER BLVD, STE 1800 77598 #039-01-1990 L1995 PS *020 †65

AHMED, Ahmed Safwat. 450 MEDICAL CENTER BLVD, STE 308 77598 #915-02-1993 L2000 IC *020 †20

ALAPPAT, John Jose. 561 MEDICAL CENTER BLVD, STE E 77598 #038-44-1993 L1997 OPH *020 †35

ALBRIGHT, Teresa L. 711 W BAY AREA BLVD # 500 77598 #048-13-1985 L1986 FM *040 †18

ALI, Mir Nadir. 450 MEDICAL CENTER BLVD, STE 550 77598 #495-65-1984 L1992 CD IM *020 †20

ALLEN, Joseph C. 520 BLOSSOM ST, FONDREN ORTHOPEDIC GROUP 77598 #048-14-1993 L1994 ORS GS *020 †40

AL-SAMMAN, Ghyath M. 450 MEDICAL CENTER BLVD, STE 202 77598 #875-01-1983 L2001 CD *020 †20

AMIN, Sushila M. ■ 77598 #495-23-1974 L1981 AN HMP *020

APISARNTHANARAX, Narin. 450 MEDICAL CENTER BLVD, STE 309 77598 #048-02-1998 L2002 D *020 †15

APISARNTHANARAX, Prapand. 450 MEDICAL CNTR BLVD #309 77598 #891-02-1966 L1973 D DMP *020 †15

ASHFAQUE ARIAN, Mohammad. 250 BLOSSOM ST, STE 300 77598 #704-15-1978 L2003 END *020 †20

BACAL, Kira. ■ 77598 #048-04-1996 L1999 GPM *020 †16,70

BAREGAMIAN, Naira. ■ 77598 #422-01-2003 GS *012

BARNES, Nathaniel. 250 BLOSSOM ST, STE 220 77598 #024-01-1989 L1998 U *020 †95

BERMAN, Joel Michael. 7099 TEXAS AVE 77598 #836-02-1967 L1978 OTO *020 †45

BHAKTA, Pranavkumar H. 17448 HIGHWAY 3 STE 160 77598 #048-14-1995 L1997 IM *020 †20

BHUTANI, Neera. 16 PROFESSIONAL PARK DR 77598 #495-43-1972 L1977 PD *020

BORTOLOTTI, Julie S. 17030 HIGHWAY 3 77598 #048-14-1999 L2002 FM *020 †18

BOWMAN, Freda Joy. 450 MEDICAL CENTER BLVD 77598 #047-07-1989 L1998 OBG *020 †30

BOYER, Edward Gene. 500 MEDICAL CENTER BLVD 77598 #041-09-1968 L1975 OTO *020 †45

BRAEUER, Harry Lee. 200 MEDICAL CENTER BLVD, NO-101 77598 #048-02-1959 L1961 GS *071 †85

BRANNEN, Adelia E Boehm. 250 BLOSSOM ST, STE 300 77598 #048-02-1987 L1988 FM *020 †18

BROWN, Dennis Lloyd. 17448 HIGHWAY 3, STE 200 77598 #048-02-1979 L1979 FM *020 †18

BURRIS, Hugh Benton. 500 MEDICAL CENTER BLVD 77598 #048-02-1972 L1972 EM FM *020

CHANG, Bill Keng. 1560 LIVE OAK ST, STE A 77598 #048-12-2000 L2006 VS *020 †85

CHANG, Charlie Chih Lee. 450 MEDICAL CENTER BLVD, STE 600 77598 #048-12-2000 L2003 END *020

CHANG, Janice Rollefson. 12 PROFESSIONAL PARK DR 77598 #048-04-1994 L1996 D *020 †15

CHINOOKOSWONG, Vradej. 7 PROFESSIONAL PARK DR 77598 #891-03-1965 L1974 PS *020 †85,65

CHONG-RAMASUTE, Maria. 711 W BAY AREA BLVD, STE 500 77598 #048-13-1997 L2001 IMG *020 †20

CHOY, Patricia. 450 MEDICAL CENTER BLVD, STE 400 77598 #016-42-1993 L2002 OBG *020 †30

CHU, Ping Sun. 1015 MEDICAL CENTER BLVD, STE 2800 77598 #011-02-1982 L1988 ON IM *020 †20

CLARKE, Lewis Kilman. 655 E MEDICAL CENTER BLVD, # 310 77598 #048-15-1986 L1987 PM OM *020 †60

DALEY, Phillip Gene. 520 BLOSSOM ST, FONDREN ORTHOPEDIC GROUP L 77598 #028-34-1963 L1964 ORS *020 †40

DAVIS, Alecia M. 17448 HIGHWAY 3 77598 #048-13-1988 L1989 OBG *020 †30

DAVIS, Ronald Mervyn. 500 MEDICAL CENTER BLVD 77598 #005-15-1963 L1964 FM GP *071

DE LA CRUZ, Toni Irene. 265 EL DORADO BLVD 77598 #048-02-2000 L2007 FM *100

DE LOACH-BANTA, Linda J. 12 PROFESSIONAL PARK DR 77598 #023-12-1982 L1993 D *020 †15

DILLARD, Howard Lavon. 6 PROFESSIONAL PARK DR 77598 #048-02-1972 L1972 IM *020 †20

EDEN, Sydney James C. 9 PROFESSIONAL PARK DR 77598 #065-06-1967 L1978 FM *020

EDMONDSON, Steven R. 450 MEDICAL CNTR BLVD #540 77598 #048-02-1984 L1985 OBG *020 †30

EHLERS, Richard Allan, II. 200 MEDICAL CNTR BLVD #101 77598 #048-02-1995 L2001 SO GS *020 †85

EKONG, Mfon. 500 MEDICAL CENTER BLVD 77598 #038-41-2004 L2007 PD *020 †55

EL-SAID, Saleh Saddallah. ■ 77598 #473-02-2003 FP *012

ESWARAN, Meena. 17448 HIGHWAY 3 77598 #919-05-1985 L1995 FM *020 †18

ETHRIDGE, Kristen M. 709 MEDICAL CENTER BLVD, CLEAR LAKE 77598 #048-02-1999 L2000 RNR *100 †80

FALK, Stephen. 17 PROFESSIONAL PARK DR 77598 #035-01-1965 L1972 OBG *020 †30

FARNAM, Jafar. 450 MEDICAL CENTER BLVD, STE 204 77598 #517-03-1972 L1981 AI PD *071 †55,03

FARRELL, Robert Wm. 450 MEDICAL CENTER BLVD, STE G 77598 #038-41-1975 L1982 CD IM *020

FILES, Beth Katherine. 251 MEDICAL CENTER BLVD, STE 300 77598 #016-02-1997 L2001 OBG *020 †30 ‡

FINDLEY-SMITH, Joi M. 450 MEDICAL CENTER BLVD 40 77598 #038-45-1991 L1996 OBG *020 †30

FISCHER, Conrad Alexander. 250 BLOSSOM ST, STE 230 77598 #028-03-1968 L1976 ORS HS *020 †40

GANDHI, Nita S. 500 MEDICAL CENTER BLVD, PEDIATRIC CONSULTANT 77598 #495-22-1987 L1997 PD *020 †55

GARCIA, Eduardo A. 17448 HIGHWAY 3, STE 136 77598 #048-04-1993 L1994 APM PMM *020 †05

GARCIA, Jan. 333 N TEXAS AVE 77598 #042-01-1975 L1981 PS HS *020 †65

GARCIA, Marvin L. 400 MEDICAL CENTER BLVD #2 77598 #048-02-1999 L2004 GS *020

GAUTHIER, Jerry Wayne. 500 MEDICAL CENTER BLVD 77598 #048-13-1990 L1991 PTH *020 †50

GILL, David Paul. 501 MEDICAL CENTER BLVD, DEKE SLAYTON CANCER CENTER 77598 #048-02-1976 L1977 IM HEM *020 †20

GOODRUM, Linda Ann. 251 MEDICAL CENTER BLVD, STE 300A 77598 #021-06-1989 L1993 OBG MFM *020 †30

GORBACK, Michael Scott. 17099 TEXAS AVE, STE 300 77598 #023-01-1979 L1995 PME CCA *020 †05

GORDON, William, Jr. 501 MEDICAL CENTER BLVD 77598 #035-45-1978 L1983 RO *020 †80 ‡

GREEN, George Edward. 9 PROFESSIONAL PARK DR 77598 #065-05-1962 L1978 ORS *071

GRIFFIN, Darrell Alton. 500 MEDICAL CENTER BLVD 77598 #048-02-1966 L1966 P CHP *020 †75

GUNDERSON, Charlise A. 555 E MEDICAL CENTER BLVD, STE 101 77598 #048-16-1991 L1993 OPH *020 †35

GYENING, Isabella K. 17448 HIGHWAY 3 77598 #010-03-1990 L1994 D *020 †15

HANSEN, Kathleen Murphy. 17030 HIGHWAY 3 77598 #048-13-1985 L1990 GP OTO *020

HARTIG, Vivian Ruth. 17030 HIGHWAY 3 77598 #048-04-2000 L2003 FM *020 †18 ‡

HERLONG, William Byron. 711 W BAY AREA BLVD, STE 500 77598 #001-02-1968 L1974 IM *020 †20

HOLLIS, Kenneth Wayne. 450 MEDICAL CENTER BLVD, STE 600 77598 #019-02-1979 L1993 GS EM *020 †85

HOOKER, Mark Allen. 17030 HIGHWAY 3 77598 #048-14-1995 L1996 FM *020 †18

HOUGHTON, Angela Denise. 450 BLOSSOM ST, STE C 77598 #048-02-1990 L1992 OBG *020 †30

HWANG, Li-Min. 17448 HIGHWAY 3 77598 #244-02-1976 L1987 OBG *020 †30

INGHAM, Denise Ann. 14212 HIGHWAY 3 STE F, SUNRISE PSYCHIATRIC CLINIC 77598 #021-06-1985 L1990 CHP P *030 †75

JAFFERY, Hyder S H. 501 ORCHARD ST STE 200, SUITE 200 77598 #495-21-1996 L2004 PCC *020 †20

JAGGARAO, Nattama Sathya. 450 MEDICAL CENTER BLVD 77598 #495-62-1971 L2002 IM *020 †20

JAVANSHIR, Hassan Ali. 250 BLOSSOM ST, STE 230 77598 #517-05-1990 L2002 CN *020 †75

JOHNIGAN, Richard Henry, III. 561 MEDICAL CENTER BLVD, STE A 77598 #048-02-2000 L2004 OTO HNS *020 †45

JOHNSTON, John R. 250 BLOSSOM ST 77598 #048-02-1987 L1989 FM *020 †18

KAKULAVAR, Pallavi. 711 W BAY AREA BLVD # 500, GERIATRIC ASSOC OF AMERICA 77598 #842-27-1995 L2005 IMG *020 †20

KATSIGIANNIS, Christos A. 450 MEDICAL CENTER BLVD, STE 201 77598 #048-15-1990 L1991 TS VS *020 †85,90

KLEIN, Geffrey H. 450 BLOSSOM ST 77598 #048-04-1992 L1993 OBG *020 †30

KLOERIS, Steven Philip. 250 BLOSSOM ST, STE 300 77598 #048-02-1980 L1980 FM *020 †18

KO, Emmie H. 350 N TEXAS AVE, STE A1 77598 #016-43-1993 L1998 ORS *020

KOMETANI, Sydney Maile. 425 HENRIETTA ST 77598 #014-01-1996 L1999 PD *020 †55

KORMAN, Erwin Manfred. 17 PROFESSIONAL PARK DR 77598 #060-01-1975 L1979 OBG *020 †30

KUMAR, Mohan Sankara P. 250 BLOSSOM ST, STE 130 77598 #495-31-1980 L1996 CD *020 †20

LAPORTE, Kristin Jaime. 17448 HIGHWAY 3, KELSEY-SEYBOLD CLEAR LAKE 77598 #016-43-2003 L2007 OBG *020

LE, Di Van. 250 BLOSSOM ST, STE 300 77598 #941-02-1972 L1983 FM DR *020 †18

LE BAS, W Marie. 333 N TEXAS AVE, STE 3200 77598 #048-02-1993 L1996 N *020 †20

LEE, Roberta Tam Sue. 16 PROFESSIONAL PARK DR 77598 #048-14-1976 L1976 PD *020 †55

LUGO-RUIZ, Rafael A. 250 BLOSSOM ST, STE 300 77598 #042-02-1993 L1999 GS *020 †85

MAHMOOD, Khalid. 450 BLOSSOM ST, STE E 77598 #704-01-1981 L2005 IM NEP *020 †20

MAHMOOD, Khalid. 450 BLOSSOM ST, STE E 77598 #704-16-1984 L2003 HO *020 †20 ‡

MAKSOUD, Alfred S. 501 ORCHARD ST STE 200 77598 #605-01-1989 L1994 PCC *020 †20

MARCUM, Stephen Craig. 1015 MEDICAL CENTER BLVD, STE 1400 77598 #041-02-1981 L1986 GE *020 †20

MARIETTA, Richard Alan. 17099 TEXAS AVE STE 100 77598 #048-02-1975 L1975 IM *030 †20

MARTIN, Gordon Hunter. 333 N TEXAS AVE, STE 4200 77598 #036-01-1992 L1994 VS GS *020 †85

MATWIJIW, Igor. 450 MEDICAL CENTER BLVD, STE 600 77598 #065-01-1979 L1993 IM END *020

MAYEN, Jose I. 561 MEDICAL CENTER BLVD, STE C 77598 #429-01-1983 L1993 IM *020

MC CREE, Kathi S. 250 BLOSSOM ST, STE 300 77598 #039-01-1984 L1985 FM *020 †18

MEHTA, Sanjay C. 501 MEDICAL CENTER BLVD 77598 #048-12-1997 L2000 RO *020 †80

MENA, Raquel M. 250 BLOSSOM ST, STE 300 77598 #308-02-1988 L1993 PD *020 †55

MILLER, Deborah Wilson. 561 MEDICAL CENTER BLVD, STE A 77598 #048-02-1994 L1996 OTO *020 †45

MILLER, Warren Calhoun. 450 BLOSSOM ST STE B 77598 #048-12-1966 L1966 PUD IM *020 †20

MITCHELL, Rachel Shelea. PO BOX 57671 77598 #048-02-2008 *012

MOLIVER, Clayton L. 575 E MEDICAL CENTER BLVD 77598 #048-15-1984 L1985 PS HS *020 †65,85

MORNEAU, James Edward. 17099 TEXAS AVE 77598 #021-05-1966 L1973 U *020 †95

NAHAS, Cesar. 450 MEDICAL CENTER BLVD, STE 201 77598 #605-02-1983 L1989 TS *020 †85,90
NATHOO, Mansur I. 200 MEDICAL CENTER BLVD, STE 102 77598 #495-57-1972 L1982 IM P *020 †20
NEUMANN, Everardo. ■ 77598 #649-04-1983 GS *020
NEWMAN, Terry S Stewman. 250 BLOSSOM ST, STE 400 77598 #048-14-1987 L1988 FM *020 †18
NGUYEN, Chan Thien. 16 PROFESSIONAL PARK DR 77598 #021-05-1994 L1998 PD *020 †55
NISBET, Virginia Minyard. 251 MEDICAL CENTER BLVD, STE 300 77598 #048-02-1994 L1996 OBG *020 †30
ONORATO, Michelle. 530 ORCHARD ST 77598 #038-06-1989 L1995 ID *020 †20
ORTIZ-COLBERG, Rafael A. ■ 77598 #008-01-1989 L1997 PS *020
PALMER, Sunita Bilimoria. 16 PROFESSIONAL PARK DR 77598 #048-02-1995 L1998 PD *020 †55
PANG, Sindy Chia. 250 BLOSSOM ST, STE 400 77598 #018-03-1997 L1999 D *020 †15
PATEL, Bharatkumar S. 17448 HIGHWAY 3 STE 175 77598 #495-23-1980 L1989 CD IM *020 †20
PATEL, Jigar Natwar. ■ 77598 #027-01-2005 DR *012
PATEL, Ranjit Kumar P. 102 TRAVIS ST 77598 #495-23-1992 L1997 N *020 †75
PATEL, Sandip Kanchan. 500 MEDICAL CENTER BLVD, NEONATAL CONSULTANTS, LLP 77598 #048-15-1995 L1998 NPM *020 †55
PETITT, Michael Andrew. 17 PROFESSIONAL PARK DR 77598 #048-04-1975 L1975 OBG *020 †30
PETRINI, Bart Edward. ■ 77598 #048-02-2003 L2007 DR *012
PHAM, Hoang Quoc. 200 MEDICAL CENTER BLVD, STE 101 77598 #041-01-1999 L2003 GS *020 †85
PHILLIPS, Cynthia L. 251 MEDICAL CENTER BLVD, STE 300 77598 #048-78-1995, ▲ L2000 OBG *020 †30
POAG, Mary Abbott. 17 PROFESSIONAL PARK DR, # 9511 77598 #021-01-1997 L1998 OBG *020 †30
POCSIK, Stephanie. 16 PROFESSIONAL PARK DR 77598 #051-04-1988 L1992 PD *020 †55
POLSEN, Jeanne A. 500 MEDICAL CENTER BLVD 77598 #035-09-1991 L1993 D *020
PRAKASH, Swayam. 500 MEDICAL CENTER BLVD 77598 #495-15-1965 L1976 CD IM *020 †20
QUILLIN, Robert Louis. 400 MEDICAL CENTER BLVD, STE 207 77598 #048-02-1997 L1999 PD *020 †55
RAINFORD, Tannique N. 17448 HIGHWAY 3 STE 200 77598 #048-04-1999 L2001 FM *020 †18
RAO, Nagamani Chakunta. 26 PROFESSIONAL PARK DR 77598 #495-21-1981 L1990 OBG END *020 †30
RAPP, Keith Lee. 711 W BAY AREA BLVD, STE 500 77598 #026-04-1976 L1982 FPG *020
RAPPAPORT, Martin Paul. 450 MEDICAL CENTER BLVD, STE D 77598 #021-01-1960 L1968 IM NEP *020 †20
REYNOLDS, Ian John. 450 MEDICAL CENTER BLVD, STE 206 77598 #017-20-1974 L1981 ORS *020 †40
RODNEY, Alan Joseph. 501 MEDICAL CENTER BLVD 77598 #021-05-2000 L2003 ON *020 †20
ROSEN, Philip Eugene. 250 BLOSSOM ST, STE 230 77598 #048-12-1969 L1969 ORS *020 †40
ROSENBLATT, Michael Jay. 655 E MEDICAL CENTER BLVD, STE 255 77598 #016-42-1989 L1993 PM *020 †60
ROSENTHAL, Harold Myron. 2 PROFESSIONAL PARK DR 77598 #010-02-1974 L1979 CD IM *020 †20
ROWE, Thomas Floyd. 251 MEDICAL CENTER BLVD, STE 300A 77598 #048-04-1989 L1990 OBG MFM *020 †30
RUDY, Robert Patrick. 450 MEDICAL CNTR BLVD #300 77598 #048-02-1978 L1978 IM ID *020 †20
RUNDELL, Marion Miller. 500 MEDICAL CENTER BLVD, 2ND FLR-PATHOLOGY DEPT 77598 #021-05-1974 L1976 ATP CLP *020 †50
SALIM, Amir. 450 N TEXAS AVE STE C 77598 #048-04-1997 L1999 FM *020 †18
SALVADY, Hema. 250 BLOSSOM ST, STE 400 77598 #495-49-1990 L2003 IM *020 †20
SAPIRE, David Warren. 940 CLEAR LAKE CITY BLVD, STE 200 77598 #836-01-1963 L1981 PDC PD *020 †55
SAWYER, George Scott. 555 E MEDICAL CENTER BLVD, STE 101 77598 #004-01-1983 L1991 OPH *020 †35
SCHNELL, Vicki Lynn. 1015 MEDICAL CENTER BLVD, STE 2100 77598 #048-04-1983 L1983 REN GYN *020 †30
SCHUHMACHER, Chas Allen. 6 PROFESSIONAL PARK DR 77598 #048-02-1967 L1967 IM OM *020 †20,70
SENS, Franklin Everett. 500 MEDICAL CENTER BLVD 77598 #048-02-1959 L1959 GP *071
SHACKELFORD, Linda Carol. ■ 77598 #027-01-1980 L1993 ORS *020 †40
SHAH, Rakesh Kanaiyalal. 450 MEDICAL CENTER BLVD, STE 550 77598 #495-23-1991 L2002 IC *020 †20
SHALABY, Mohamed Lofty. 450 MEDICAL CENTER BLVD, STE 308 77598 #915-02-1995 L2004 CD *020 †20
SHARMA, Arun. 617 COLE ST 77598 #495-47-1978 L1992 EM RHU *020 †20
SHARMA, Kiran. 617 COLE ST 77598 #495-47-1976 L1994 AI *020 †20
SHUMAN, Maxim Erric. 16 PROFESSIONAL PARK DR 77598 #048-04-1996 L1997 PD *020 †55
SIDDIQI, Zohra Farooq. 450 MEDICAL CENTER BLVD, STE 600 77598 #028-78-1996, ▲ L1999 FM *020 †20
SIM, Leila P. 250 BLOSSOM ST, STE 300 77598 #748-01-1981 L1989 PD *020 †20
SIMS, Jerry Austin. 1015 MEDICAL CENTER BLVD, STE 2100 77598 #039-01-1986 L1987 REN OBG *020 †30
SINHA, Randhir Prasad. 525 BLOSSOM ST 77598 #495-15-1966 L1975 NS N *020 †25
SLUSKY, Harvey Edward. 17500 HIGHWAY 3, STE B 77598 #048-12-1983 L1983 CD IM *020 †20
SMITH, Fannie E. ■ 77598 #048-16-1982 L1983 END IM *050 †20
SMITH, Marilyn Stauber. 200 MEDICAL CENTER BLVD 77598 #030-05-1963 L1983 AN *071 †05
SONPAVDE, Guru P. 501 MEDICAL CENTER BLVD, TEXAS ONCOLOGY, P.A. 77598 #495-27-1990 L2003 HO *020 †20
SRIPARAMESWARAN, Anuja. 500 MEDICAL CENTER BLVD, GENERAL PEDIATRICS DEPT. 77598 #048-02-2001 L2004 PD *020 †55
STEPHAN, Elias Michel. 450 MEDICAL CENTER BLVD, STE 600 77598 #605-01-1995 L2002 END *020 †20
STRUNK, Chester Lee, Jr. 561 MEDICAL CENTER BLVD, STE A 77598 #048-13-1974 L1974 OTO PD *020 †55,45
SUBRAMANI, Ravishanker M. 1015 MEDICAL CENTER BLVD, STE 1700 77598 #495-52-1978 L1986 GE IM *020 †20
SUBRAMANYAM, Kalyanam. 1015 MEDICAL CENTER BLVD, STE 1300 77598 #495-04-1975 L1981 GE IM *020 †20
SULEMAN, Mumtaz. 400 MEDICAL CENTER BLVD, STE 108 77598 #704-08-1986 L2003 P *020 †75

TANG, Dennis. 250 BLOSSOM ST, STE 300 77598 #048-14-1993 L1995 IM *020 †20
TAYLOR, Peggy Hejtmancik. 450 MEDICAL CENTER BLVD #4 77598 #048-14-1984 L1985 OBG *020 †30
THARP, Ralph P. 250 BLOSSOM ST, STE 400 77598 #026-04-1966 L1977 FM P *020 †18
THIAGARAJAN, Rajeswari. 250 BLOSSOM ST, STE 300 77598 #495-33-1976 L1981 FM *020 †18 ‡
THOMAS, Beena M. 400 MEDICAL CENTER BLVD, STE 207 77598 #048-12-1997 L2000 PD *020 †55
THOMPSON, Joyce Mai. 711 W BAY AREA BLVD, STE 500 77598 #025-01-1992 L1998 IMG *020 †20
TOBON-RANDALL, Beatriz L. 333 N TEXAS AVE 77598 #048-12-1986 L1988 AN *020 †05
TOOTHAKER-ALVAREZ, Joseph. 17448 HIGHWAY 3 STE 130 77598 #025-12-1982 L1989 AN PME *020 †20
TREMAINE, Annemarie. ■ 77598 #035-15-2006 L2007 *100
TRIPATHY, Ashok. 350 N TEXAS AVE STE D 77598 #495-45-1982 L1990 FM *020 †18
TURAKHIA, Bhupendra T. 250 BLOSSOM ST, STE 130 77598 #495-52-1970 L1978 CD IM *020 †20
TURNER, Rod Jay. 402 BLOSSOM ST 77598 #021-01-1987 L1992 OBG *020 †30
UNGER, Kenneth Michael. 450 BLOSSOM ST STE B 77598 #035-46-1968 L1976 PUD CCM *020 †20
VAN JAARSVELD, Johan. ■ 77598 #422-01-2003 IM *100
VERNON, Kimberly Ann. ■ 77598 #305-01-2005 L2005 MPD *012
VISARIA, Shree Devi. 450 MEDICAL CENTER BLVD, STE 400 77598 #011-03-2001 L2005 OBG *020 †30
VU, Chau Minh. 1567 LIVE OAK ST STE A 77598 #048-14-1996 L1998 NEP IM *020 †20
WAGNER, Henry R, Jr. 8 PROFESSIONAL PARK DR 77598 #048-12-1968 L1968 U *020 †95
WALKER, David Paul. 501 MEDICAL CENTER BLVD, DEKE SLAYTON CANCER CENTER 77598 #007-02-1968 L1985 RO R *020 †80
WARNEKE, Richard M. 1015 MEDICAL CENTER BLVD, STE 1400 77598 #048-15-1999 L2002 GE *100 †20
WASCHEROHL, Franz. ■ 77598 #407-01-1943 L1960 AN *071 †05
WEISS, Gary B. 501 MEDICAL CENTER BLVD, DEKE SLAYTON CANCER CENTER 77598 #035-19-1971 L1977 ON HEM *020 †20
WILLETTE, Roger Chas. 500 MEDICAL CENTER BLVD 77598 #048-04-1983 L1984 IM *020 †20
WILLIAMS, Terry Earl. 12 PROFESSIONAL PARK DR 77598 #038-40-1969 L1974 D IM *020 †15
WIMBERLY, Winnette. 500 MEDICAL CENTER BLVD 77598 #048-02-1970 L1970 PD *020 †55
WOO, Jae-Soon. 17448 HIGHWAY 3 77598 #583-08-1988 L2005 FM *020 †18
YANCY, Verna Jovita. 333 N TEXAS AVE 77598 #005-14-1991 L1995 AN *020 †05
YO, Insoo. 250 BLOSSOM ST, STE 300 77598 #048-16-1994 L2000 GS *020 †85
ZIDEK, Kathryn Ann. 655 E MEDICAL CENTER BLVD 77598 #048-04-1992 L1995 PM PD *020 †60,55

WEIMAR – COLORADO

DUCHICELA, Olga Isabel. 402 YOUENS DR 78962 #319-04-1990 L2000 FM *020 †18 ‡
DUCHICELA SANTACRUZ, J. 402 YOUENS DR 78962 #056-05-1984 L1987 FM *020 †18 ‡
OREY, Kristina Nichole. ■ 78962 #048-15-2008 *012
ORTEGA, Juan Carlos. 402 YOUENS DR 78962 #319-03-1989 L2000 FSM *020 †18 ‡
PETRICK, Constance Arlene. 1648 FM 2144, NEW BEILAH HEALTH ASSOCIAT 78962 #056-05-1979 L1991 IM *020
YOUENS, Robert Allen. 402 YOUENS DR 78962 #048-04-1976 L1976 FM *020 †18 ‡

WESLACO – HIDALGO

ABREU, Ricardo. 1604 E 8TH ST, # A 78596 #308-04-1992 L2001 PCC *020 †20
ACEVEDO, Leonel M, Jr. 1330 E 6TH ST 78596 #048-02-1982 L1985 BBK PTH *020 †50
ACHANTA, Venkatasubbaraya. ■ 78596 #495-58-1997 L2006 IM *020 †20
ALANIS, Heriberto Jose. 1401 E 8TH ST, KNAPP MEDICAL CENTER 78596 #048-02-1992 L1993 EM UM *020 †16
ALTIMUS, Myles E, III. 1401 E 8TH ST 78596 #041-01-1965 L1966 EM *020 †16
ALVAREZ, Julian Fernando. 626 N TEXAS BLVD 78596 #264-06-1990 L2004 PD *020 †55
AVILA, Felipe Miguel. 1408 E 8TH ST 78596 #275-01-1990 L2001 PD *020 †55
AVILES, Wilfredo Aulio. 1313 E 6TH ST 78596 #341-01-1970 L1976 PD CHP *020 †55
BADIGA, S Murthy. 902 S AIRPORT DR STE 6 78596 #495-50-1981 L1994 GE IM *020 †20
BAKER, David Michael. 1401 E 8TH ST 78596 #041-13-1963 L1991 EM FM *020 †16
BELL, Anthony Wm. 2205 WOODLAND DR 78596 #038-41-1976 L1993 AN *020 †20,05
BHAGAT, Francis P. 1401 E 8TH ST 78596 #495-22-1956 L1976 GS *071 †85
BLANCO-QUANT, Ronald E. 1116 E 8TH ST, STE 2 78596 #682-01-1977 L1992 OBG *020 †30
BOYER, Clark Abilio. ■ 78596 #737-06-1995 L2004 PDC *020 †55
BUENTELLO-MERCADO, G. 1220 E 6TH ST 78596 #649-02-1966 L1974 PD *020 †55 ‡
CALVO, Dionisio B, III. 1402 E 8TH ST STE 3 78596 #748-08-1973 L1980 IM ON *020
CANTU, Wilfrido Tijerina. 1401 E 8TH ST 78596 #649-02-1957 L1967 AN FM *040
CAYABYAB-AQUI, Erlinda G. ■ 78596 #748-08-1961 L1979 AN *071
CEPEDA, Alberto T. 1502 E 8TH ST 78596 #264-01-1969 L1977 OBG *020 †30
CHANDRASEKHARAN, R. 1210 E 8TH ST STE I 78596 #495-33-1967 L1976 ORS TRS *020 †40
DOMINGUEZ, John J. 901 E 6TH ST STE 3 78596 #048-02-1984 L1985 IM *020 †20
DZIECIOL, Gordon. 1311 E 6TH ST 78596 #065-06-1984 L1996 GP *020
ESCALANTE, Mario S. 1313 E 6TH ST, MID VALLEY PEDIATRICS, INC 78596 #341-01-1979 L1996 PD *020 †55
ESQUIVEL, Sandra. 1330 E 6TH ST, KNAPP MED PLZ STE 201 78596 #048-12-1991 L1992 GS *020 †85
FARRAY-BERGES, Daniel. 1330 E 6TH ST, STE 204 78596 #308-02-1998 L2005 HO *020 †20
FESLER, Ken Wayne. 2300 S WESTGATE DR 78596 #021-01-1965 L1970 R *071 †80
FINGER, Michael James. 910 E 8TH ST, STE 9 78596 #010-02-1987 L2006 U *020 †95
FUENTES, Alejandro. 1710 E 8TH ST, MID VLY FP ASSOC 78596 #048-13-1985 L1986 FM *020 †18
FUENTES, Melecia. 1315 E 6TH ST, STE 12 78596 #038-40-1996 L1999 FM *020 †18
GARCIA, Tomas. 1412 E 8TH ST STE A 78596 #649-14-1984 L1990 FM *020 †28,80
GARCIA MARTINEZ, Tomas. 1412 E 8TH ST 78596 #649-02-1976 L1978 GP *020
GARZA, Rudolph R. MEDICAL ARTS BLDG 78596 #030-06-1974 L1975 PTH *071 †50
GHADDAR, Habib M H. 1330 E 6TH ST STE 204 78596 #048-06-1989 L1992 HO *020 †20
GHORI, Farah Yasmeen. 1401 E 8TH ST 78596 #704-02-1990 L2000 IM END *020 †20
GONZALEZ, Gabriel Clemens. 1330 E 6TH ST, STE 101 78596 #048-04-1985 L1988 IM *020

GONZALEZ-DICKSON, Juan J. 909 JAMES ST STE A 78596 #264-04-1978 L1991 **OBG** *020 †30
GOPALKRISHNAN, Elizabeth. 1331 E 6TH ST 78596 #495-08-1963 L1973 **OBG END** *020 †30
GOPAL-KRISHNAN, Subram. 1331 E 6TH ST 78596 #495-08-1962 L1973 **ORS** *020 †40
GUERRERO, Rodolfo. 1402 E 8TH ST 78596 #649-18-1973 L1975 **GS** *020 †85
HEREDIA, Roger Raymond. 1710 E 8TH ST 78596 #048-14-1978 L1981 **FM** *020 †18
IJAZ, Mohammad T. 1001 RONE DR, STE 2 78596 #704-09-1993 L2002 **END IM** *020 †20
KAPLAN, Adolfo Enrique. 1604 E 8TH ST STE A 78596 #132-05-1994 L2005 **PCC SME** *020
KUTUGATA, Jorge Luis. 902 S AIRPORT DR, STE 1 78596 #649-02-1980 L1985 **PD** *020 †55
LANGLEY, Olga Yuryevna. 1401 E 8TH ST, KNAPP MEDICAL CENTER 78596 #913-69-1987 L2005 **FM** *020 †18
LEATHERWOOD, Bradley D. 1401 E 8TH ST, KNAPP MEDICAL CENTER 78596 #048-14-2002 L2006 **AN** *020 †05
LIZARDO GUZMAN, Segundo L. ■ 78596 #308-04-1998 L2006 **PD** *020 †55
LOCKE, William Edward. 1501 S AIRPORT DR 78596 #035-15-1954 L1964 **OBG** *071 †30
LOPEZ, Julio A. 1311 E 6TH ST 78596 #649-01-1968 L1975 **GP GS** *020
LYNN-MACRAE, Alastair G. 910 E 8TH ST, VALLEY EAR NOSE & THROAT 78596 #035-20-2000 L2005 **OTO** *020 †45
MADRID, Carlo Eric. ■ 78596 #048-02-2007 L2007 **FP** *012
MC ALLEN, Cullen Ashley. 1114A S WESTGATE DR 78596 #047-05-1987 L1988 **FM AN** *020 †05
MEDRANO, Jaime. 415 S AIRPORT DR, STE E 78596 #649-04-1990 L1997 **PD** *020 †55
MERY, Donna Anne. 1710 E 8TH ST 78596 #048-14-1985 L1986 **FM** *020 †18
MINCK, Rory Noel. 1600 E US HIGHWAY 83 78596 #016-42-1976 L1997 **OBG FM** *020 †30 ‡
NANDIPATY, Sivakumari. 1620 E 8TH ST STE 1 78596 #495-62-1982 L1995 **PD** *020 †55
NARRO, Dario Eden. 1330 E 6TH ST STE 301 78596 #048-13-1993 L1994 **N** *020 †75
NUNEZ, Gregoris Elias. 1604 E 8TH ST, STE B 78596 #308-04-1992 L2000 **OBG** *020 †30
OAKES, Maria Joslyn. 512 S WESTGATE DR, STE F 78596 #748-02-1992 L1997 **PD** *020 †55
OCHOA, Alfonso. 909 S AIRPORT DR 78596 #649-02-1980 L1984 **IM** *020 †18 ‡
ORTIZ, Juan Manuel. 1604A E 8TH ST 78596 #264-18-1985 L2003 **PCC SME** *020 †20
OWENS, Edwin Ellis. ■ 78596 #649-03-1963 L1967 **AN** *020
OWENS, Sarah Audrey. ■ 78596 #048-02-2007 **PD** *012
PARDO, Roberto. 1216 E 6TH ST 78596 #264-01-1967 L1973 **IM** *020
PARKER, Maxwell V. 1501 S AIRPORT DR, LOT 403 78596 #048-02-1960 L1960 **OBG** *020 †30
PATHAK, Umesh Kumar. 1010 S AIRPORT DR, MID VALLEY PED ALLERGY CTR 78596 #495-69-1987 L1998 **PD AI** *020 †55
PEGUERO, Eduardo A. 1315 E 6TH ST STE 1 78596 #048-04-1993 L1999 **IM** *020 †20
PENA, Jose Fernando A. 906 S BRIDGE AVE 78596 #308-01-1986 L1995 **IM** *020 †20
PENALO, Pedro Joel. 906 S BRIDGE AVE 78596 #308-04-1996 L2003 **IM** *020
PFLUGRAD, Chester Lee. RR 2 BOX 175B 78596 #649-14-1973 L1978 **EM FM** *020
PICOU, Keith Andrew. 910 E 8TH ST, VALLEY EAR NOSE & THROAT 78596 #048-04-1974 L1974 **OTO D** *020 †15,45
PIERSON, Claudia C. 1401 E 8TH ST 78596 #308-04-1990 L1998 **IM** *020 †20
POSADA-TOLLAST, Catarina. ■ 78596 #319-01-1986 L1997 **PD** *020 †55
PRECIADO, Sergio G. 1313 E 6TH ST 78596 #649-03-1986 L1995 **PD** *020 †55
RAMIREZ, Maria Teresa. 1330 E 6TH ST, STE 305 78596 #048-02-2000 L2003 **FM** *020 †18
RANGEL, Lionel. 1330 E 6TH ST, STE 305 78596 #048-02-1957 L1958 **U** *020 †95
REDDY, R V. 1010 S AIRPORT DR, ALLERGY CENTER 78596 #495-57-1968 L1980 **PD GP** *020 †55
ROBERTSON, Colette. 6151 N FM 88 78596 #007-02-1994 L1998 **FM** *020 †18
ROBLES, James. 412 E 18TH ST 78596 #056-06-1986 L1994 **AN** *020 †05
SANDER, James Christopher. ■ 78596 #048-04-2006 **U** *012
SANDER, Maynard D. 1330 E 6TH ST, STE 105 78596 #048-04-2000 L2004 **OSM** *020
SAVINON SERRATA, Julio A. 902 S AIRPORT DR STE 3 78596 #308-02-1988 L1996 **IM** *020 †20
SEPULVEDA, Robert R. 901 E 6TH-5 78596 #649-45-1981 L1988 **IM** *020
SHELTON, Thomas Oscar. 1401 E 8TH ST, KNAPP MEDICAL CENTER 78596 #048-12-1968 L1968 **DR** *020 †80
SIDERIS, Stylianos. 1330 E 6TH ST STE 305 78596 #048-04-1998 L2005 **U** *100 †95
SLAVIN, Dennis. 910 E 8TH ST, STE 1 78596 #035-08-1989 L1994 **AN** *020 †05
SMITH, Bruce Douglas. 1401 E 8TH ST, DEPT. OF RADIOLOGY 78596 #046-01-1984 L1986 **OSM ORS** *020 †40
SORCE, James Joseph. 910 E 8TH ST, VALLEY EAR NOSE & THROAT 78596 #035-06-1991 L1996 **OTO** *020 †45
TAYLOR, Sarah Ann. 1604 ORANGE AVE 78596 #032-01-2007 **IM** *012
TORKELSON, Nina Mingfung. ■ 78596 #048-14-2006 **FP** *012
VOLPE, Leticia Marie. 1210 E 8TH ST STE 4 78596 #048-12-1977 L1977 **IM** *020 †20
WEEKS, Ralph Harmon. 500 N TEXAS BLVD 78596 #017-20-1966 L1972 **OPH** *020 †35
WIEGAND, Jeanne Lynn. 1010 S AIRPORT DR, CENTER 78596 #048-02-1990 L1991 **PD** *020 †55

WEST – MCLENNAN

BELL, Theresa A. 301 W PECAN ST, P O BOX 369 76691 #048-16-1989 L1991 **FM** *020 †20
CHUDEJ, Eric John. ■ 76691 #048-15-2007 **FP** *012
EISMA, Jose A. 401 MEADOW DR 76691 #748-01-1963 L1974 **IM FM** *020 †18 ‡
MANAX, Stanley Joseph. 1505 JANE LN 76691 #065-06-1964 L1978 **EM** *020
MANAX, William Geo. ■ 76691 #065-06-1959 L1977 **FM GS** *072 ‡
PIERCE, Billy Don. 501 MEADOW DR 76691 #047-06-1956 L1958 **GP GS** *071
WILSON, Eric John. ■ 76691 #231-01-1963 L1975 **ORS** *071 †40

WEST COLUMBIA – BRAZORIA

BURNS, Jimmy Clay. ■ 77486 #048-04-1960 L1960 **FM P** *020 †18
JARRELL, Susan Somogyi. 503 DANCE DR 77486 #048-04-1995 L1999 **FM** *020 †18
OHLEN, Alfred Carl. 217 S 17TH ST 77486 #004-01-1973 L1974 **FM OM** *020
RICKS, Alfred, Jr. 2142 RIVERSIDE DR, ALFRED RICKS JR 77486 #048-12-1976 L1976 **IM EM** *020

WEST LAKE HILLS – TRAVIS

AOUEILLE, Bernard, III. 1101 S CAPITAL OF TEXS HWY, BLDG A 78746 #048-04-1979 L1979 **P** *020 †75
APOSTOLAKIS, Louis W. 5656 BEE CAVE RD, STE E201 78746 #038-40-1995 L2001 **FPS** *020 †45

BALTHASER, Harvey Jerry. 1250 S CAPITAL OF TEXS HWY, BLDG 1 78746 #041-01-1980 L1983 **PD HOS** *030 †55
BELSHER, Jon Leslie. 515 S CAPITAL OF TEXAS HWY, STE 225 78746 #048-12-1998 L2008 **CCM** *100 †18,20
BLAIR, Stephen D. 912 S CAPITAL OF TEXAS HWY 78746 #048-02-1994 L1995 **FM** *020 †18
BRADER, Trey G. 5656 BEE CAVE RD STE M302 78746 #048-13-1995 L1998 **FM** *020 †18
BRIGGS, Russell Deane. 102 WESTLAKE DR STE 103 78746 #011-03-1998 L2006 **OTO** *020 †45
BUCK, Brian C. 5656 BEE CAVE RD, STE G201 78746 #048-02-1983 L1988 **PM RPM** *020 †60
BUCKINGHAM, Edward Dean. 102 WESTLAKE DR STE 104 78746 #048-02-1997 L1998 **FPS** *020 †45
CANADA, William Hammond. 5656 BEE CAVE RD, STE E201 78746 #051-04-1956 L1962 **PS** *071 †65
CARIDI, Robert Clark. 4407 BEE CAVE RD, STE 303 78746 #048-14-1985 L1996 **PS GS** *020 †65
DE SABRA, Ximena. 515 S CAPITAL OF TEXAS HWY, STE 100 78746 #043-01-1995 L2003 **OPH** *020
DONALDSON, Marlowe Helen. 3736 BEE CAVE RD STE 4, PMB 184 78746 #048-12-1973 L1973 **CHP** *020 †75
DOUGLASS, Cary D. 5656 BEE CAVE RD, STE E200 78746 #048-14-1989 L1993 **FM** *020 †18
DUHON, David Richard. 102 WESTLAKE DR STE 102 78746 #021-05-1986 L1990 **SME N** *020
DUMITRESCU, Mihnea. 4613 BEE CAVE RD STE 1 78746 #048-12-2000 L2006 **PM PME** *100 †60 ‡
EDWARDS, Ted Leroy, Jr. 4201 BEE CAVE RD STE B112 78746 #048-12-1960 L1960 **GE NTR** *020
ELLZEY, Robert Franklin. ■ 78746 #039-01-1954 L1958 **R NM** *071 †80
ERLANDSON, Errol Edward. ■ 78746 #025-01-1971 L1972 **VS GS** *071 †85
EXLINE, Albert L, Jr. 5000 BEE CAVE RD, BEE CAVES ALLERGY CLINIC 78746 #021-01-1947 L1952 **A PD** *071 †55,03
FERRIN, Charles Edwin. ■ 78746 #048-02-1956 L1956 **GP** *071
FESTE, Joseph Rowland. 4407 BEE CAVE RD, BLDG 5 78746 #048-04-1961 L1961 **GYN** *071 †30
FOLEY, Neal Thomas. 5656 BEE CAVE RD STE H201 78746 #016-11-1976 L1978 **TS VS** *020 †85,90
GARCIA, Peter, Jr. 5656 BEE CAVE RD, STE G201 78746 #048-15-1980 L1981 **ORS** *020 †40
GOWDA, Ashwin. 102 WESTLAKE DR, STE 102 78746 #496-22-1995 L2002 **SME P** *020 †75 ‡
GUPTA, Rajat. 4407 BEE CAVE RD, STE 211 78746 #016-11-1990 L1996 **N PMM** *020 †75 ‡
HAMILTON, Elaine Leigh. 5656 BEE CAVE RD, STE C104 78746 #007-02-1986 L1988 **PD** *020 †55
HANLEY, Patricia S. 912 S CAPITAL OF TEXAS HWY 78746 #048-13-1988 L1990 **FM** *020 †18
HENDRICKS, Katherine Ann. 1101 S CAPITAL OF TEXS HWY, MED INST FOR SEX HLTH 78746 #016-11-1983 L1989 **PHP EM** *040 †70
HIBNER, Barbara L. ■ 78746 #649-02-1957 L1964 **P CHP** *050
HOLCOMB, William Louis, Jr. 515 S CAPITAL OF TEXAS HWY, STE 230 78746 #021-01-1994 L1997 **FM VS** *020 †75
HUTCHENS, Lisa W. 4201 BEE CAVE RD, STE C100 78746 #048-12-1984 L1985 **PD** *020 †55
JACOBY, David James. 5656 BEE CAVE RD, STE M302 78746 #048-02-1974 L1974 **EM** *020 †16
KASPAR, Robert Luther. ■ 78746 #048-13-1972 L1972 **IM ID** *020 †20
KNOLLE, Guy Edmund, Jr. 515 S CAPITAL OF TEXAS HWY, STE 100 78746 #021-01-1962 L1963 **OPH** *020 †35
LEBOEUF, Brandi C. 309 EANES SCHOOL RD 78746 #048-02-2001 L2004 **EM** *020 †16
LEWIS, Melba F. 4407 BEE CAVE RD, STE 112 78746 #048-16-1985 L1987 **OTO HNS** *020 †45
LIFSHEN, Michael S. 912 S CAPITAL OF TEXAS HWY 78746 #048-02-1987 L1988 **FM** *020 †18
LIGON, Laurence A. 912 S CAPITAL OF TEXAS HWY, STE 100 78746 #048-02-1986 L1987 **FM** *020 †18
LOCKER, Eric Stuart. ■ 78746 #048-12-1975 L1975 **D** *020 †20,15
LOWN, Ira G. 5656 BEE CAVE RD, STE K200 78746 #048-14-2000 L2006 **HS** *020 †85
LUSK, Samuel Gary. 1001 S CAPITAL OF TEXS HWY, BLDG L - STE 100 78746 #048-14-1986 L1987 **P** *020 †75
MARTINEZ, Mary Ann. 5300 BEE CAVE RD, BLDG 3 78746 #048-13-1993 L1994 **D** *020 †15
MC ILHANEY, Joe S, Jr. 1101 S CAPITAL OF TEXS HWY, STE B100 78746 #048-04-1961 L1961 **OBG** *071 †30
NIEMEYER, R Dean. 3736 BEE CAVE RD STE 4, PMB 184 78746 #048-12-1972 L1973 **PTH** *071 †50
NILAND, Nona Frances. ■ 78746 #025-01-1978 L1983 **OS PD** *050 †55
PATEL, Sadhana S. 912 S CAPITAL OF TEXAS HWY 78746 #654-01-1984 L1993 **FM** *020 †18
PAZDRAL, George. 4407 BEE CAVE RD STE 513 78746 #048-02-1978 L1978 **P** *020 †75
PICKRELL, Michael Bowen. 5656 BEE CAVE RD STE J-20 78746 #039-01-1985 L1990 **IM RHU** *020 †20
PICKRELL, Paul Keith. 5656 BEE CAVE RD, STE J200 78746 #039-01-1990 L1996 **RHU** *020 †20
PLAYFAIR, Paul Anthony. 5656 BEE CAVE RD, BLD J335 78746 #047-20-1992 L1996 **AN** *020 †05
RALPH, David Randall. ■ 78746 #025-12-1977 L1982 **PTH PD** *020 †50
RAMSDELL, Wm Marshall. 102 WESTLAKE DR, STE 100 78746 #048-04-1979 L1979 **D** *020 †15
REID, Randal Ray. 912 S CAPITAL OF TEXAS HWY, STE 100 78746 #048-02-1979 L1979 **FM** *020 †18
RIEKERT, Paul W. 840 ROCK CREEK DR 78746 #048-02-1993 L1997 **EM** *020 †16
ROBISON, James T, IV. 5656 BEE CAVE RD STE M301 78746 #048-15-1991 L1992 **PS** *020 †85,65
ROBY, Russell R. 4407 BEE CAVE RD, STE 122 78746 #048-13-1973 L1974 **A PD** *075
ROSE, Gary Lee. 1101 S CAPITAL OF TEXS HWY, BLDG B 78746 #048-12-1971 L1971 **PUD IM** *071 †20
ROY, Marci Anne. 5656 BEE CAVE RD, STE J202 78746 #048-02-1992 L1994 **N** *020 †75
RUSSELL-HOWARD, Pamela J. 5656 BEE CAVE RD STE J202, AUSTIN NEURO-DIAGNOSTIC CL 78746 #048-14-1992 L1993 **N** *020 †75
SCHOCKET, Sandford M. 5656 BEE CAVE RD, STE L-317 78746 #011-04-2001 L2003 **AN** *100 †05
SCHWARTZ, Michael Alan. 5450 BEE CAVE RD, STE 1E 78746 #035-20-1969 L2006 **P** *020 †75
SIEVERT, William, Jr. ■ 78746 #048-15-1980 L1980 **GE IM** *050 †20
SILVERTOOTH, Erin J. 5656 BEE CAVE RD, STE D202 78746 #048-02-1998 L2005 **OS** *020
SMOOT, J Brannan. 5656 BEE CAVE RD, STE G201 78746 #048-12-1993 L1998 **ORS** *020 †40
SPANN, Scott Weaver. 5656 BEE CAVE RD, STE K200 78746 #045-04-1986 L1996 **ORS OSS** *020 †40
SPILLAR, Lynn Layman. 4407 BEE CAVE RD STE 513 78746 #048-04-2000 L2004 **P** *020 †75 ‡
STIERMAN, Karen Lee. 102 WESTLAKE DR 78746 #048-02-1996 L1997 **OTO** *020 †45
TARRANT, Angelyn Lenell. 5656 BEE CAVE RD, STE C104 78746 #048-02-1999 L2002 **PD** *020

TISDALE, Marie C. ■ 78746 #021-05-1939 L1944 **PD** *071
VENDAL, Zarmeena. 515 S CAPITAL OF TEXAS HWY, STE 100 78746 #048-13-2000 L2005
  OPH *100 †35
WISEMAN, Charles V. 5656 BEE CAVE RD, BLDG H # 100 78746 #048-12-1985 L1987
  DR *020 †80
XIMENES, Rey. 3701 BEE CAVE RD, S-104 78746 #048-14-1983 L1983 **AN PME** *020 †05
YOUNG, Sue Ellen. 515 S CAPITAL OF TEXAS HWY, STE 100 78746 #048-02-1969 L1969
  OPH *020 †35

WHARTON – WHARTON

AHMED, Fayyaz. 2100 REGIONAL MEDICAL DR 77488 #704-02-1990 L2000 **IMG RHU** *020 †20
BRIDGES, Robert A. ■ 77488 #048-02-1953 L1972 **VS PD** *020
CARAWAY, Robert Bruce, Jr. 2100 REGIONAL MEDICAL DR 77488 #048-04-1947 L1947
  GS *071 †85
CULPEPPER, Chantal R. 2100 REGIONAL MEDICAL DR, SO. TEXAS MEDICAL CLINICS, 77488
  #038-40-1998 L2006 **FM** *020 †18
CUMBERBATCH, Karyn Anne B. 2100 REGIONAL MEDICAL DR 77488 #010-03-1988 L1992
  OBG *020 †30
DANIEL, Vivi Susan. 3007 N RICHMOND RD 77488 #495-47-1973 L1983 **P** *020 †75
ELLIS, Neely J. 2100 REGIONAL MEDICAL DR 77488 #048-04-1953 L1953 **AS GP** *071
ELY, James Everett. 2100 REGIONAL MEDICAL DR 77488 #028-03-1979 L1983 **OBG** *020 †30
FERGUSON, Robin L. 2100 REGIONAL MEDICAL DR 77488 #028-46-1993 L1999 **GE** *020 †20
GARDEZI, Syed Ali Raza. 2100 REGIONAL MEDICAL DR 77488 #704-21-1995 L2006
  MPD *020 †20
GINDY, Adel Messak. 10141 US 59 RD 77488 #915-02-1968 L1996 **FM EM** *020 †18
GOELZER, Ronald Eric. 10141 US 59 RD 77488 #048-04-1957 L1957 **GS VS** *071 †85,90
GUBBELS, Jeffery L. 2100 REGIONAL MEDICAL DR 77488 #048-16-1986 L1987 **OBG** *020 †30
GURKIN, Mystan Ashley. 2100 REGIONAL MEDICAL DR, DEPT OF SURGERY 77488
  #048-02-1997 L1999 **GS** *020 †85
HUERTA, Vincent F, Jr. 2100 REGIONAL MEDICAL DR 77488 #048-12-1980 L1980 **FM** *020 †18
HUYNH, Thai Dang. 2100 REGIONAL MEDICAL DR 77488 #011-02-1999 L2002 **IM** *020 †20
IBANEZ, Joe David. 2100 REGIONAL MEDICAL DR 77488 #048-13-1976 L1976
  PTH CLP *020 †50
KEFFER, Greg Lane. 2100 REGIONAL MEDICAL DR 77488 #030-06-1983 L1987 **OBG** *020 †30
LIPSCOMB, Larry Bernard. 1319 HOSPITAL DR, STE 1319 77488 #048-15-1983 L1983
  FM *020 †18
LOPEZ-ROMAN, Henry Javier. 2100 REGIONAL MEDICAL DR 77488 #682-01-1972 L1977
  HO *020 †20
LUKOSE, Biju Mathew. ■ 77488 #496-29-1998 L2007 **GS GP** *012 †85
MADSEN, Dan Frederick. 2100 REGIONAL MEDICAL DR, SOUTH TEXAS MEDICAL CLINIC 77488
  #048-02-1980 L1980 **OTO** *020 †45
MANDAL, Vanessa J. 2100 REGIONAL MEDICAL DR, SOUTH TEXAS MEDICAL CLINIC 77488
  #041-09-1997 L2005 **IMG** *020 †20 ‡
MANG, Huat Za. 423 BOLLING GREEN DR 77488 #209-01-1967 L1998 **FM** *020 †18
MC COY-MOORE, Deborah D. 2100 REGIONAL MEDICAL DR 77488 #016-01-1997 L2007
  IM *020 †20
MILLER, Lowell Stephen. 10141 US 59 RD 77488 #036-07-1945 L1955 **RO** *071 †80
MONTOYA-ZERMENO, Carmen. 2100 REGIONAL MEDICAL DR, SOUTH TEXAS MEDICAL
  CLINIC 77488 #649-30-1979 L1983 **FM** *020 †18
MORRIS, Milinda M. 2100 REGIONAL MEDICAL DR, MILINDA M. MORRIS, M.D.&AS 77488
  #048-12-1984 L1985 **OBG** *020 †30
NORTHINGTON, Harold M. ■ 77488 #048-02-1942 L1943 **IM** *071
NORTMAN, Henri A. 2100 REGIONAL MEDICAL DR 77488 #048-02-1999 L2002 **PD** *020 †55
ORTIZ, Francisco Juan. 1317 HOSPITAL DR, WHARTON FAMILY CLINIC 77488
  #649-02-2002 L2006 **FM** *020 †18
PANKIEWICZ, Irena. 2100 REGIONAL MEDICAL DR 77488 #759-08-1985 L1996 **N** *020
PERCHES, Hector. 109 E MILAM ST 77488 #649-02-1954 L1963 **PTH** *071 †50
QURASHI, Nadeem. 2100 REGIONAL MEDICAL DR 77488 #704-16-1988 L1995 **ON** *020 †20
RANGANATHAN, Venkatesan. 2022 REGIONAL MEDICAL DRIVE, STE 1319 77488
  #495-04-1989 L2000 **GE** *020 †20
RILEY, Gorman Lind. ■ 77488 #048-04-1955 L1955 **GP** *071
SALAZAR, Fernando Antonio. 2100 REGIONAL MEDICAL DR 77488 #649-14-1993 L2002
  GE *020 †20
SAMUELSON, David Winston. 2100 REGIONAL MEDICAL DR 77488 #027-01-1963 L1967
  IM *071 †20
SANGALLI, Marc A. 2100 REGIONAL MEDICAL DR, SOUTH TEXAS MEDICAL CLINIC 77488
  #048-13-1992 L1993 **OBG** *020 †30
SCHAUER, David Philip. 2100 REGIONAL MEDICAL DR 77488 #048-02-1980 L1980 **IM** *020 †20
SEARS, Thomas Maynard. 2100 REGIONAL MEDICAL DR 77488 #048-02-1981 L1981
  FM *020 †55
SECOR, Harold E. ■ 77488 #048-04-1949 L1950 **OBG** *071 †30
SEVILLA, Cesar Augusto. 2100 REGIONAL MEDICAL DR 77488 #682-01-1974 L1982
  ORS TRS *020 †40
SNELLING, Jon Benj. 2100 REGIONAL MEDICAL DR 77488 #021-06-1976 L1977 **OPH** *020 †35
SPEARS, Clark Gordon. 10141 US 59 RD 77488 #028-03-1963 L1965 **OS FM** *071 †05
TORIO, Fredrick Uy. 2100 REGIONAL MEDICAL DR 77488 #748-20-1988 L1995 **IM** *020 †20
TORP, Raymond Turner. 2100 REGIONAL MEDICAL DR 77488 #041-13-1957 L1968 **IM** *071
WILLIAMS, Sandra Alyse. 2100 REGIONAL MEDICAL DR 77488 #048-04-1976 L1976
  PD *020 †55
WINSTON, Thomas Payton. 2100 REGIONAL MEDICAL DR, SOUTH TEXAS MEDICAL
  CLINIC 77488 #048-02-1980 L1980 **FM** *020 †18 ‡
WOLFF, Herman Walter, Jr. 2100 REGIONAL MEDICAL DR 77488 #048-02-1963 L1963
  GS *020 †85
WOODSON, Clinton E. ■ 77488 #048-02-1951 L1951 **FM** *071

WHEELER – WHEELER

EDDENS, Christopher B. ■ 79096 #048-02-1985 L1986 **FM** *020 †18
GALUTIA, Robert Carl. 306 E 9TH 79096 #039-01-1975 L1977 **FM** *020
LAVELLE, John Patrick. ■ 79096 #001-02-1978 L1983 **AN** *020
MENDIOLA, Louie Luciano. 309 E 9TH 79096 #748-01-1961 L1973 **FM** *020 ‡

WHITE OAK – GREGG

MARTIN-HOLM, Sharon. 204A E US HIGHWAY 80 75693 #027-01-1998 L1999 **FM** *020 †18
SEID, Norman Qua. 204 E US HIGHWAY 80 75693 #027-01-1977 L1980 **AN** *075

WHITE SETTLEMENT – TARRANT

YEE, Jordan. ■ 76108 #308-07-1981 L1983 **P PYG** *020

WHITEHOUSE – SMITH

CUNNINGHAM, Joe H. 15632 HWY 110 S 75791 #048-16-1983 L1983 **IM CD** *020 †20
GREEN, Marthalyn Johnson. 107 STACY DR 75791 #048-12-1949 L1949 **PD PHP** *071 †70
HENNINGTON, Rex H. PO BOX 671 75791 #048-12-1953 L1953 **AN** *071 †05
LEACH, Jeffrey Brian. 602 STATE HIGHWAY 110 N 75791 #021-06-2003 L2005 **FM** *030 †18
MULLINS, Amy L. 601 STATE HIGHWAY 110 N, BAY O 75791 #048-02-1999 L2000 **FM** *020 †18
SANDERS, William Pearson. ■ 75791 #021-06-2006 **FP** *012
THOMPSON, Robert B. 1200 STATE HIGHWAY 110 N, STE E 75791 #065-06-1953 L1972
  IMG HEM *071 ‡
YOUNG, Brett Devere. 602 HWY 110 N 75791 #019-02-2002 L2004 **FM** *020 †18

WHITESBORO – GRAYSON

HAAG, Edmund Lee, Jr. ■ 76273 #048-12-1944 L1945 **R** *071 †80

WHITNEY – HILL

BAILEY, Chas Ferguson, Jr. 256 COUNTRY CLUB RD 76692 #048-02-1958 L1958 **GP** *071 †95
BARTON, James Gregory. 101 E JEFFERSON AVE 76692 #048-02-1956 L1956 **FM** *071 †18
BENAVIDES, Luis Rey. 1314 N BRAZOS ST, WHITNEY MEDICAL ASSOCIATES 76692
  #048-02-2003 L2006 **FM** *020
COVENTRY, William Vaden. ■ 76692 #048-02-1942 L1942 **FM** *071
HENDERSON, Randall Dale. 202 E JEFFERSON AVE 76692 #048-78-1999, ▲ L2001 *020
HOFFMAN, James C. ■ 76692 #048-15-1998 L2000 **FM** *020 †12
MANAX, Teresa Smith. 305 S BOSQUE ST 76692 #539-03-1967 L1980 **FM** *020
PICKERING, Clayton L. 202 E JEFFERSON AVE, P O BOX 2171 76692 #048-78-1998, ▲ L1999
  FM *020
SHAH, Syed-Aman Ali. ■ 76692 #704-09-1992 L2005 **FM** *100
SHAW, Guy Graham, Jr. ■ 76692 #048-04-1940 L1940 **AN** *071
SMITH, Regina Mary. 305 S BOSQUE ST 76692 #539-03-1968 L1979 *020

WICHITA FALLS – WICHITA

ABAZID, Ahmad Ghassan. ■ 76308 #875-02-2004 **FP** *012
ABI HANNA, Pierre Hanna. ■ 76308 #605-01-1992 L1999 **ID** *020 †20
AGYEPONG, Michael K A. 4601 OLD JACKSBORO HWY 76302 #412-01-1990 L2000
  PD *020 †55
AHMED, Mohammed Bakhtiar. 1301 3RD ST 76301 #496-27-2001 *012
AHMED, Waseem. 6515 KEMP BLVD 76308 #704-02-1991 L1997 **P** *020
AL SAMMAN, Mhd. Mounaf. ■ 76309 #875-01-2001 L2007 **FP** *012
ANASTASE, Mihaela Estera. 4601 OLD JACKSBORO HWY 76302 #781-01-1979 L1992
  FM *020 †18
ANDERSON, Michael Alan. 1808 BROOK AVE 76301 #045-04-1998 L2003 **P** *020 †75
ANWASI, Francis Chukwudi. 1301 3RD ST STE 200, FAMILY PRACTICE 76301
  #690-04-1988 L2008 **FM** *020 †18
ASHLOCK, Steven J. 4601 OLD JACKSBORO HWY 76302 #048-14-1992 L1993 **DR** *020
ASHRAF, Mussarat. ■ 76310 #704-16-1989 *100
ASKINS, Jack C. 1100 BROOK AVE 76301 #048-15-1974 L1976 **CD** *020
ATIEH, Samir Rafiq. 1301 3RD ST, NORTH CENTRAL TX MED FNDN 76301 #198-03-1983 L2007
  FM *020 †18
ATLURI, Rajesh. 1619 MIDWESTERN PKWY, ENDOCRINOLOGY 76302 #495-62-1986 L1998
  IM END *020 †20
AVERA, Charles Blake. 1704 11TH ST 76301 #048-15-1986 L1987 **OPH** *020 †35
AZEEM, Muhammad. 5509 LONG LEAF DR 76310 #704-01-1978 L2007 **FM** *020 †18
BANNON, Ryan Jeremy. ■ 76308 #048-16-2003 L2007 **OBG** *020
BAREKZAHAI, Waliullah. ■ 76308 #495-56-2002 **FP** *012
BARNHART, Benny L. 4601 OLD JACKSBORO HWY 76302 #048-12-1990 L1991 **P PYG** *020 †75
BARTEL, Danny Ray. 1722 9TH ST 76301 #048-02-1976 L1976 **N** *020 †75
BEBB, Edwin C. ■ 76308 #048-04-1941 L1941 **GS** *071 †85
BEREND, Klonie Lee. 808 BROOK AVE, RADIOLOGY ASSOCIATES 76301 #048-02-1996 L2000
  RNR *020 †80
BIBB, Richard C. 1808 BROOK AVE 76301 #020-12-1967 L1973 **P** *020 †75
BICE, Paul Lankford. 808 BROOK AVE, WICHITA FALLS, P.A. 76301 #048-13-1980 L1980
  R *040 †80
BILAL, Satti Fageri Nasr. 1301 3RD ST 76301 #848-01-1994 L2008 **FP** *012
BOLIN, Daniel Huffman. 1208 BROOK AVE 76301 #048-02-1976 L1976 **OM ADM** *020
BOMER, Donald Louis. 1622 11TH ST 76301 #027-01-1965 L1972 **OTO HNS** *020 †45
BORK, Harry Vanzandt. ■ 76308 #047-06-1960 L1963 **OBG PHP** *071
BRADFIELD, Robert Steven. 5400 KELL BLVD, TEXOMA CANCER CENTER 76310
  #017-20-1976 L1981 **RO OBG** *020 †80
BRAZIL, Clark Wesley. 1508 10TH ST 76301 #039-01-1968 L1973 **VM EM** *020 †85
BUCAG, Feliciano R. 4601 OLD JACKSBORO HWY 76302 #748-01-1979 L1995 **FM** *020 †18
BUCHANAN, Martha B. 1600 8TH ST 76301 #041-12-1944 L1946 **PD** *071
BURROSS, D Clifford. 2414 BRENTWOOD DR 76308 #048-12-1953 L1953 **FM GS** *071 †18
BURTON, Bernard Alison. 804 DENVER ST 76301 #030-05-1974 L1981 **D FM** *020 †15
BUTERA, Adam Stephen. 1722 9TH ST, N TEXAS NEUROLOGY ASSLC 76301
  #011-04-1995 L2003 **N** *020
CARAS, John Anthony. 4601 OLD JACKSBORO HWY 76302 #017-20-1968 L1978
  END IM *020 †20

CARMONEY, Walter J, Jr. 808 BROOK AVE, RADY ASSOCS WICHITA FLS PA 76301 #051-04-1962 L1966 **R** *071 †80
CARPENTER, Ken John. ■ 76309 #040-02-2001 L2007 **ORS** *100
CARR, Roy Lynn. 1301 3RD ST STE 2 76301 #048-12-1987 L1988 **FM** *020 †18 ‡
CASTRO HERRERA, Mauricio. ■ 76308 #270-01-2003 **FP** *012
CERRETA, David Jos. ■ 76310 #018-03-1986 *100
CHAKINALA, Chandramouli. 2200 9TH ST 76301 #495-65-1969 L1978 **PUD IM** *020 †20
CHALLAGALLA, Jagathi Devi. 1600 7TH ST, STE 2 76301 #496-24-1991 L1998 **HEM** *020 †20
CHAPA, Daunne M. 4601 OLD JACKSBORO HWY 76302 #048-12-1996 L1999 **PD** *020
CHAPA, Phillip E. 1615 KEMP BLVD 76309 #048-12-1997 L2000 **EM** *020 †16
CHATURVEDULA, Rajani P. PO BOX 300 76307 #495-19-1963 L1981 **P** *020
CHEN, Betty. ■ 76309 #033-06-1995 L2003 **DR** *020 †80
COLEMAN, Blair P. ■ 76308 #036-07-1951 L1956 **IM CD** *071
COOPER, Dianne Margaret. 1722 9TH ST 76301 #027-01-1998 L2003 **RHU** *020 †20
COULTER, Marina Da Silva. 1301 3RD ST 76301 #187-03-1976 **FP** *012
DANIELS, Felicia Benita. 3313 ROBIN LN, WICHITA ANESTHESIA 76308 #041-13-1991 L1997 **AN** *020 †05
DAVIS, George Stefan. 1600 11TH ST 76301 #039-01-1979 L1987 **IM** *071 †20
DAY, Richard Allen. 4601 OLD JACKSBORO HWY 76302 #048-13-1984 L1985 **PUD CCM** *020 †20
DEAN, Garland Ray. 1600 8TH ST 76301 #048-12-1957 L1957 **FM** *030 †18
DEAN, Joe Arlis. 5500 KELL BLVD, STE 400 76310 #048-12-1971 L1971 **GE IM** *020 †20
DEAN, William Franklin. 912 BURNETT ST 76301 #048-12-1969 L1969 **TS GS** *020 †85,90
DE ASIS, Myrna Catalan. 1819 10TH ST 76301 #748-01-1984 L1998 **IM** *075
DECENA, Hector R. 500 BROAD ST, HELEN FARABEE CENTER 76301 #748-02-1952 L1982 **P** *020 †75
DE LIZIO, Pasquale R. 5400 KELL BLVD, TEXOMA CANCER CTR 76310 #035-08-1968 L1976 **ON IM** *020 †20
DESIRE, Andre Pothel. 1709 10TH ST, STE B 76301 #035-06-1986 L1998 **CD P** *020 †20
DJAFARI, Fardin Steven. 4601 OLD JACKSBORO HWY 76302 #025-07-1993 L2000 **CD** *020 †20
DOWD, Phillip E. 5500 KELL BLVD, STE 200 76310 #048-15-1988 L1989 **U** *020 †95
DRYDEN, Charles Ballard. ■ 76308 #048-12-1945 L1945 **U** *071 †95
DRYDEN, John Stephen. 4601 OLD JACKSBORO HWY 76302 #048-13-1977 L1977 **U** *020 †95
DUHAN, Christopher M. 4412 KELL BLVD, KELL WEST FAMILY PRACTICE 76309 #473-04-2000 L2005 **FM** *020
EBRAHIM, Ellaheh. ■ 76301 #517-06-1994 **FP** *012
EGBUCHUNAM, Christiana Uz. 1301 3RD ST 76301 #690-04-1991 L2005 **FM** *020 †18
ELFARRA, Gehad Adel. 1301 3RD ST 76301 #915-04-1983 **FP** *012
ESSA, Mohsain. ■ 76308 #624-01-1972 L1980 **P** *020 †75
FADOW, Peter Geo. 6515 KEMP BLVD 76308 #025-07-1991 L1995 **P** *020 †75
FANOUS, Ailsa Elizabeth. ■ 76308 #919-01-1975 L1980 **FM** *071
FANOUS, Labib Helmy. ■ 76308 #915-02-1970 L1980 **OBG** *020
FARRELL, Frederic O. 501 MIDWESTERN PKWY E 76302 #016-42-1980 L1981 **DR** *020
FITZSIMMONS, Mc Murry. 2211 MIDWESTERN PKWY, STE 2 76308 #021-06-1974 L1978 **AI** *020
FLACK, David Al. 1600 11TH ST 76301 #048-13-1983 L1983 **PTH** *020 †50
FONTENOT, James Nolan, Jr. 501 MIDWESTERN PKWY E 76302 #021-01-1975 L1984 **ORS EM** *020 †40
FOSMIRE, Jennifer. 1600 8TH ST 76301 #048-12-1989 **FM** *100
FRANDO, Angelita Loida B. 3901 ARMORY RD, ACCUCARE CLINIC OF N TEXAS 76302 #748-02-1982 L1998 **FM** *020 †18
FRANDO, Virgil Grabador. 3901 ARMORY RD 76302 #748-02-1976 L1997 **PM** *020 †60
FRISCHER, Robert. 1817 10TH ST 76301 #038-41-1971 L1980 **OBG GP** *020 †30
GANESHRAM, Vedampattu P. 1709 10TH ST, DR. VEDAMPATTU GANESHRAM 76301 #495-16-1991 L2003 **ICE** *020 †20
GEORGEOS, Majdouleen Mich. ■ 76308 #875-02-2001 **FP** *012
GEYER, Charles M. ■ 76302 #019-02-1951 L1958 **R RO** *071 †80
GHABRIAL, Nabil W. 3808 KEMP BLVD STE B 76308 #915-02-1985 L1996 **AN** *020 †05
GHANBARI, Hossein. 1921 9TH ST, HOSSEIN GHANBARI, MD PA 76301 #517-01-1972 L1984 **OBG** *020
GHAYAS, Arjumand. ■ 76301 #704-02-2000 **FP** *012
GILL, Shivjit Singh. ■ 76309 #496-50-2001 **FP** *012
GLEASON, Patrick Langham. 1722 9TH ST 76301 #024-01-1989 L2003 **NS** *020 †25
GLIDEWELL, Myron Gayle. ■ 76308 #048-12-1962 L1962 **ORS** *071 †40
GODFREY, Cameron Dean. 4601 OLD JACKSBORO HWY 76302 #048-13-1980 L1980 **OTO FPS** *020 †45
GODFREY, Steven Lee. 4601 OLD JACKSBORO HWY 76302 #048-12-1984 L1985 **OBG** *020 †30
GODWIN, James Weimer. 5420 KELL BLVD 76310 #048-02-1976 L1976 **AN PME** *020
GONZALES, Alma Gladys Lim. 501 MIDWESTERN PKWY E, SIU SPRINGFIELD FAMILY PRA 76302 #748-01-1991 L2008 **FP** *012 †18
GONZALEZ, Jose E. 4412 KELL BLVD 76309 #649-06-1985 L2001 **FM** *020 †18
GONZALEZ-LOPEZ, Ruth. 2611 HARRISON ST STE 900 76308 #042-01-1990 L1997 **RHU** *020 †20
GUGENHEIM, Stephen Marc. 4601 OLD JACKSBORO HWY 76302 #007-02-1982 L2003 **OTO FPS** *020 †45
GUILLERMO, Caryl Lizette. ■ 76302 #748-10-2004 **FP** *012
HANES, Lori Lee. 4206 CALL FIELD RD, ASSOCIATES 76308 #048-14-1991 L1994 **FM** *020 †18
HARRINGTON, Jeffrey V. 1508 BROOK AVE 76301 #048-12-1980 L1980 **OPH** *020 †35
HARVEY, Lowell Lloyd. 1508 10TH ST, STE B 76301 #030-05-1970 L1975 **PUD IM** *020 †20
HAW-ABAD, So Kim Florence. 4206 CALL FIELD RD, ASSOCIATES 76308 #748-08-1982 L1997 **FM** *020 †18
HEARN, Yvonne R. 1600 11TH ST 76301 #048-02-1986 L1987 **PTH CLP** *020 †50
HEINIS, Diana Valerie. 4206 CALL FIELD RD, ASSOCIATES 76308 #649-13-1996 L2003 **FM** *020 †18
HELBING, Daniel Howard. 1105 BROOK AVE 76301 #048-12-1975 L1975 **AN** *020 †05
HIJAZI, Bilal Mustapha. ■ 76309 #913-16-1999 **FP** *012
HO, Ricky Yuen Yau. 2303 MIRAMAR ST 76308 #462-01-1970 L1978 **GE IM** *020 †20
HORTH, Flavia Zeri. 1601 9TH ST, STE B 76301 #187-04-1986 L1999 **OBG** *020 †30 ‡
HOSSAIN, Md Akhtar. 1518 10TH ST 76301 #160-02-1983 L1998 **IM** *020 †20
HOYER, John Scott. 4601 OLD JACKSBORO HWY 76302 #048-13-1980 L1980 **IM** *020 †20
HUANG, David S. 1518 10TH ST 76301 #056-06-1975 L1981 **ORS HS** *020 †40
HUDKINS, Philip Geo. 1600 11TH ST 76301 #048-13-1980 L1980 **PTH** *020 †50
HUFF, Mark Emly, Jr. ■ 76309 #048-12-1958 L1958 **ORS** *071 †40
HUMPHREY-FRANCOIS, Cheryl. 200 MLK JR BLVD, NORTH CENTRAL TEXAS 76301 #021-05-1989 L1998 **PD** *020
HURST, Paul Williams. 4601 OLD JACKSBORO HWY 76302 #270-02-1996 L2003 **OBG** *020 †30
JENNINGS, Lynn Ulbrik. 2934 KEMP BLVD, CHAMPIONS CLINIC 76308 #047-06-1985 L1995 **FM** *020 †18
JOHN, Donald Hugh. 4206 CALL FIELD RD, ASSOCIATES 76308 #048-04-1975 L1975 **N IM** *020 †20,75
JOHNSON, Gail Irene. PO BOX 300 76307 #048-02-1980 L1982 **P** *074
JOHNSON, Terry L. 3506 BUCHANAN ST STE B, TERRY JOHNSON MD PA 76308 #040-02-1989 L1994 **PD** *020 †55
JONES, Ronald Carrel. 2200 KELL BLVD, SPORTS MEDICINE CENTER 76309 #024-01-1983 L1995 **ORS** *020 †40
JONES, William Randal. 4601 OLD JACKSBORO HWY 76302 #048-02-1980 L1980 **OBG** *020 †30
KABLE, Warren Tim, Jr. 1600 11TH ST 76301 #041-12-1944 L1953 **OBG** *071 †30
KADIRI, Mohamed. 1301 3RD ST STE 200 76301 #655-03-1997 L2007 **FM** *020 †18
KANG, Yadwinder Singh. 1301 3RD ST 76301 #473-04-2000 *012
KASHANI, Nasser. ■ 76308 #517-01-1981 **FP** *012
KELLY, Jason Alexander. ■ 76310 #048-14-2003 L2005 **FM** *020 †18
KELLY, Phillip Wayne. 1704 11TH ST 76301 #021-01-1973 L1980 **OPH** *020 †35
KIM, Tai Jung. 6515 LAKE RD 76308 #583-08-1975 L1978 **IM** *020 †20
KIM, Yoon Berm. PO BOX 300 76307 #583-02-1958 **IG** *050
KING, Robert Kyle. 4601 OLD JACKSBORO HWY 76302 #048-14-1982 L1983 **U** *020 †95
KING, Sumi Lorrane. 1601 9TH ST, THE WOMEN'S CLINIC 76301 #048-14-1984 L1986 **OBG** *020 †30
KINNARD, Paul George. ■ 76305 #005-12-1962 L1967 **OBG AM** *071 †30
KONG, Rita Khin-Ohnmar. 4601 OLD JACKSBORO HWY 76302 #209-02-1991 L2001 **IM** *020 †20
KONG, Soe-Ni Nicholas. 4601 OLD JACKSBORO HWY 76302 #209-01-1991 L2000 **CD** *020 †20
KOSRAVI-PARVARI, Mohammad. 1518 10TH ST 76301 #517-07-1973 L1990 **IM** *020
KRAMER, Quentin Theodore. 1601 9TH ST STE A 76301 #048-04-1957 L1957 **ORS** *071 †40
KUEMPEL, Russell Henry. 4601 OLD JACKSBORO HWY 76302 #048-02-1980 L1980 **OPH** *020 †35
LAMAR, Michael E. 4601 OLD JACKSBORO HWY 76302 #048-16-1996 L1997 **OBG** *020 †30
LANGNER, Frederick M. 4601 OLD JACKSBORO HWY 76302 #048-02-1984 L1989 **GS** *020 †85
LARSON, David E. ■ 76308 #048-02-1990 **IM** *050
LEASEBURG, Jason Thaddeus. 1 W MEDICAL CT 76310 #048-04-2001 L2007 **ORS** *100
LE BEAU, George L, Jr. 1518 10TH ST 76301 #021-05-1951 L1959 **IM** *071 †20
LEE, Frank J. ■ 76309 #048-02-1950 L1950 **GYN** *071 †30
LEE, Mark Steven. 1600 7TH ST, STE 2 76301 #048-14-1982 L1983 **RO** *020 †80
LEUZINGER, Donn E. 501 MIDWESTERN PKWY E, WICHITA FALLS CLINIC 76302 #026-04-1953 L1963 **U OS** *075 †95
LE VASSEUR, Justin Paul. 1600 7TH ST 76301 #021-05-1961 L1971 **RO** *071 †80
LEWIS, Wassel Andrew. 2621 ELMWOOD AVE 76308 #048-04-1978 L1981 **P** *020 †75
LIM, Jaime. 1722 9TH ST, NORTH TEXAS NEUROLOGY ASSO 76301 #748-10-1980 L1985 **N** *020
LIM, Jose Audie Eduarte. 1518 10TH ST, TMC BLDG 76301 #748-01-1986 L1998 **IM** *020 †20
LOPEZ, Juan Manuel. ■ 76310 #275-01-1954 L1974 **P** *071
LYFORD, Lawrence Duane. 200 MARTIN LUTHER KNG BLVD 76301 #018-03-1975 L1978 **PD** *020 †55
MADDULOORI, W Wm. 2113 9TH ST 76301 #495-11-1939 **CLP PTH** *075
MAGUCHI ALDRETE, Megumi. 1301 3RD ST 76301 #649-14-1998 *012
MANKODI, Rashmi. 6515 LAKE RD 76308 #496-07-1965 L1977 **P** *020
MANKODI, Rashmikant P. 1517 10TH ST 76301 #496-38-1964 L1975 **NEP IM** *020
MANSUR, Harl D, Jr. PO BOX 8106 76307 #039-01-1939 L1940 **OPH** *071 †35
MARETH, Thomas Ray. 6515 LAKE RD, NORTH TEXAS STATE HOSPITAL 76308 #048-02-1974 L1974 **CHP P** *020 †75
MARICHETTY SIDDHAPPAN, Mur. 1301 3RD ST 76301 #495-16-1988 L2008 **FP** *012
MARTIN, Harvey Connett. 1808 ROSE ST 76301 #019-02-1967 L1978 **CHP P** *020 †75
MATTAR, Ahmad Abdelaziz. 1301 3RD ST STE 200 76301 #915-02-1982 L2005 **FM** *020 †18
MAY, Brett H. 2945 SOUTHWEST PKWY 76308 #048-12-1995 L1996 **GS** *020 †85
MC BROOM, Robert Louis. 1601 BROOK AVE 76301 #048-02-1977 L1980 **ID** *020 †20
MC CALL, J Preston. ■ 76308 #048-04-1948 L1948 **IM** *020 †20
MC CLELLAN, Timothy W. 1104 BROOK AVE, WICHITA FALLS GASTROENTERO 76301 #048-13-1997 L1998 **GE** *020 †20
MC MANUS, Jimmy Wayne. 6515 KEMP BLVD EEP4, NORTH TEXAS STATE HOSPITAL 76308 #048-14-1984 L1988 **P** *020 †75
MCMILLAN, Brian R. 4318 BERWICK DR 76309 #048-78-2001, ▲ L2003 **AN** *100 †05
MEHTA, Mrudula Virendra. 1600 8TH ST 76301 #495-23-1973 L1982 **AN** *020
MEHTA, Virendrakumar D. 1815 10TH ST 76301 #495-75-1972 L1982 **OBG** *020 †30
MENCHACA, Rodrigo Xavier. 1600 11TH ST 76301 #649-14-1978 L1986 **EM FM** *020 †18
MENDEZ, Michael Perez. ■ 76301 #048-15-2008 *012
MENOOFLI, Nihad Ahmed. 1301 3RD ST 76301 #848-03-1998 *012
MENZIES, William. 1511 10TH ST 76301 #041-12-1954 L1963 **U** *071 †95
MERCER, Leo Clifford, Jr. 1600 10TH ST 76301 #048-15-1980 L1985 **TRS** *040 †85
MEYER, Stuart Jackson. 1600 11TH ST, UNITED REGIONAL HEALTH CEN 76301 #039-01-1979 L1990 **EM FM** *020 †16
MILLER, Daniel M. 3420 STIRLING ST 76310 #048-02-1993 L1994 **AN** *020 †05
MILLER, Joseph R. 1601 9TH ST 76301 #017-20-1961 L1973 **OBG OS** *071 †30
MILLS, Dana Ray. 501 MIDWESTERN PKWY E, WICHITA FALLS CLINIC 76302 #048-15-1986 L1987 **PD** *020 †55
MINER, Douglas Lee. 4601 OLD JACKSBORO HWY 76302 #049-01-1972 L1985 **DR** *020 †80
MINTER, Glen A. 1301 3RD ST, STE 200 76301 #048-14-1987 L1988 **FM** *040 †18
MIRZA, Fayyaz Ul-Hasan. 808 BROOK AVE 76301 #704-01-1972 L1981 **DR** *020 †80
MITCHELL, Darius Franklin. 2950 S SHEPHERDS GLN, OUHSC 76308 #004-01-1999 L2005 **ORS** *020 †40
MOFFAT, Doug D. 808 BROOK AVE 76301 #048-13-1989 L1990 **DR** *020 †80
MOISANT, Michael A. 4412 KELL BLVD 76309 #048-78-1997, ▲ L1999 **FM** *020 †18
MOLINA, Pablo Esteban. 200 MLK JR BLVD, NORTH CENTRAL TEXAS 76301 #649-52-1997 L2002 **PCC** *020 †20
MONTGOMERY, John Paul. 4601 OLD JACKSBORO HWY 76302 #048-02-1981 L1981 **GYN** *020 †30
MORENO, Armando Taube. 1600 11TH ST 76301 #649-14-1980 L1995 **FM OBG** *020 †18
MOSHTAGHI, Aliakbar A. 1518 10TH ST 76301 #517-01-1973 L1982 **U** *020 †95
MOSS, Robert Lee. 1105 BROOK AVE 76301 #048-12-1973 L1978 **AN** *020 †05 ‡
MURPHY, Barbara Ann. 4909 JOHNSON RD 76310 #048-02-1981 L1981 **IM PLM** *020 †20
MURTHY, Konappa H. 1815 10TH ST 76301 #495-33-1973 L1982 **GE IM** *020 †20
MUSTAFA, Eid Baker H. 1201 BROOK AVE 76301 #915-03-1973 L1982 **PS HS** *020 †85,65

■ = Address Information Privacy Protected

MYERS, Alan S. 601 FILLMORE ST 76301 #048-15-1991 L1992 **FM** *020 †18
MYERS, Jerry K. 5500 KELL BLVD STE 100 76310 #048-02-1974 L1974 **GS CRS** *020 †85
NAIR, Uma C. 1600 11TH ST, IPC THE HOSPITALIST COMPAN 76301 #048-13-1990 L1991 **IM** *020 †20
NAZ, Huma. 1301 3RD ST, DEPT FP 76301 #704-16-1994 **FP** *012
NEIMAN, Richard Braden. 1722 9TH ST 76301 #018-03-1997 L2001 **N** *020 †75
NILASENA, Samuel Shaw. ■ 76308 #891-01-1946 L1960 **D** *071 †15
OGUNLEYE, Sesan Fatuade. 1301 3RD ST 76301 #690-01-1986 L2007 **FP** *012
OGUNWOLE, John Olabode. 1301 3RD ST STE 200, FAMILY PRACTICE 76301 #016-11-2001 **FM** *100
OLAYA, Bernardo. 2211 MIDWESTERN PKWY, STE 3 76308 #264-04-1974 L1985 **OBG** *020 †30 ‡
OLOBIA, Igho Clement. 200 EASTSIDE DR, NORTH CENRTRAL TX COMMHL 76301 #690-08-1990 L1997 **PD** *020 †55
OSORIO, Jaime Quintin. WICH FALLS STATE HOSP 300 76307 #176-02-1953 L1968 **GS PS** *071
OWEN, Raymond Lee. 2945 SOUTHWEST PKWY 76308 #048-02-1981 L1981 **FM EM** *020 †18
OZIER, Gary Pearson. 4601 OLD JACKSBORO HWY 76302 #048-16-1981 L1981 **FM** *020 †20
PACIN, Enrique. WICHITA STATE HOSP B 300 76307 #275-01-1944 L1974 **IM AN** *020
PADAKANDLA, Catherine S. 2100 9TH ST 76301 #495-27-1968 L1995 **ID IM** *020 †20
PALMER, Bruce L. 1100 BROOK AVE 76301 #048-15-1998 L1999 **IC** *020 †20
PALOMO, Sharon Rose Yap. 501 MIDWESTERN PKWY E, CLINICS OF NORTH TEXAS 76302 #748-01-1994 L2007 **FM** *020 †18
PARAMASIVAN, Kanchanadevi. 1301 3RD ST 76301 #495-95-1993 L2008 **FP** *012
PARKEY, Paul James. 809 INDIANA AVE 76301 #048-02-1966 L1966 **FM** *020
PARSONS, Lauren Denise. 6515 KEMP BLVD 76308 #038-44-1983 L1990 **P** *030 †75
PASSI, Jatinder Pal. 1301 3RD ST 76301 #496-51-2000 *012
PATEL, Arti A. 1600 8TH ST 76301 #048-13-1983 L1996 **IM** *020 †20
PATEL, Ashwinkumar N. 5420 KELL BLVD 76310 #495-48-1982 L1996 **NEP IM** *020 †20
PENA, Richard C. 1607 BROOK AVE 76301 #048-02-1978 L1978 **RHU IM** *020 †20
PINO, Guillermo Anton. 501 MIDWESTERN PKWY E 76302 #649-30-1977 L1982 **ORS** *062
PINO, Jonathan William. ■ 76310 #665-01-2006 **FP** *012
POGUE, David Mac Charles. 1600 8TH ST, CARDIO PULMONARY REHAB DPT 76301 #016-11-1964 L1973 **CD** *020
PORTA, Cesar Humberto. 1600 11TH ST 76301 #270-02-1988 L1994 **FM EM** *020 †18
POSTON, James Gordon. 1600 8TH ST 76301 #047-06-1971 L1972 **AN PD** *020 †18
PRESSON, John T. 4206 CALL FIELD RD, ASSOCIATES 76308 #048-15-1995 L2001 **FM** *020 †18
PRESTRIDGE, Barry Barton. 1622 11TH ST 76301 #048-02-1971 L1971 **OTO FPS** *020 †45
QUBTI, Wael Fouad. 1301 3RD ST 76301 #418-02-1989 L2008 **FP** *012
RADKAR, Mrunalini Vinayak. 501 MIDWESTERN PKWY E 76302 #495-56-1993 L2005 **IM** *020 †20
RADKAR, Vinayak J. 4601 OLD JACKSBORO HWY 76302 #654-01-1993 L2002 **N** *020
RAMANNA, Vinutha Mysore. ■ 76308 #496-22-1990 L2004 **FP** *012
RAO, Aruna S. ■ 76309 #496-32-1996 L1999 **CHP** *100 †75
RAO, Gadam Mohan Anand. 1718 10TH ST 76301 #495-57-1980 L1996 **PD** *020 †55
RASHIDI BIRGANI, Parvane. 1301 3RD ST 76301 #517-08-1994 L2007 **FM** *020 †18
REDD, Richard Allan. ■ 76308 #040-02-1976 L1978 **DR** *020 †80
REDDY, Praveen Jada Kumar. 5400 KELL BLVD, TEXOMA CANCER CENTER 76310 #495-62-1994 L2004 **IM** *020 †20
REED, Karen Jeanette H. 4601 OLD JACKSBORO HWY 76302 #048-15-1983 L1983 **PD** *020 †55
REINHARDT, Linda Andrus. 2601 HARRISON ST STE 500 76301 #048-14-1978 L1978 **D** *071 †15
REINKE, Dennis Dean. 1600 11TH ST 76301 #005-12-1979 L1985 **PTH** *020 †50
RENTON, Paul N, Jr. 808 BROOK AVE 76301 #048-12-1984 L1984 **DR** *020 †80
RITCHIE, Joyce Janelle. 808 BROOK AVE 76301 #039-01-1988 L1990 **DR** *020 †80
RIVERA-RIVERA, Rafael. 1508 10TH ST, STE B 76301 #042-01-1993 L1993 **PUD** *020 †20
ROBISON, Wm Whitwell, III. 1600 8TH ST 76301 #048-04-1978 L1979 **IM** *020 †20
RUIZ, Ricardo. 1600 11TH ST, SYSTEM 76301 #341-03-1990 L1996 **FM** *020 †18
RUYLE, Stephen Don. 1 W MEDICAL CT 76310 #048-02-1979 L1979 **ORS** *020 †40
SAIED, Victor Camal. 1600 8TH ST BOX 5184 76301 #048-02-1955 L1955 **AN** *020 †05
SAMUELSON, Bradley Erle. 1004 BROOK AVE 76301 #041-07-1987 L1993 **CD IM** *020 †20
SANCHEZ-LEAL, Henry. 1901 10TH ST, STE 114 76301 #011-04-1980 L1981 **P PA** *072
SANDERS, Wallace Robt. ■ 76309 #039-01-1956 L1963 **OPH** *071 †35
SARTOR, Tammy King. 1600 BROOK AVE 76301 #048-16-1992 L1999 **GS** *020
SCHLOMACH, Richard Don. 501 MIDWESTERN PKWY E, WICHITA FALLS CLINIC 76302 #048-04-1959 L1959 **GP GS** *071
SCHULTZ, Jessica Lynne. 4601 OLD JACKSBORO HWY 76302 #034-01-2000 L2004 **N** *020 †75
SCOTT, John Harold. 1627 11TH ST 76301 #039-01-1973 L1976 **PTH** *020 †50
SEEGERS, Terry R. 808 BROOK AVE 76301 #048-14-1997 L1999 **DR** *020 †80
SELVARAJ, Ramaswamy. 1600 11TH ST, URHCS 76301 #495-59-1981 L1992 **EM** *020 †18
SERRANO, Lesley T. 4601 OLD JACKSBORO HWY 76302 #748-10-1972 L1978 **GP** *020
SHAALAN, Ezzat A R. 501 MIDWESTERN PKWY E 76302 #915-02-1955 L1997 **IM** *071
SHANES, B Adam. 501 MIDWESTERN PKWY E 76302 #654-01-1997 L2005 **FM HOS** *020 †18
SHARP, Larry Eugene. 501 MIDWESTERN PKWY E 76302 #048-14-1983 L1983 **FM** *020 †18
SHAW, Richard Biller. 501 MIDWESTERN PKWY E 76302 #035-08-1967 L1975 **GS** *020 †85
SHAW-FONTENOT, Sherrette. 1419 9TH ST 76301 #021-06-1994 L1998 **IM** *020
SHEEN, Michael R. 501 MIDWESTERN PKWY E, PARKWAY EAST 76302 #010-01-1978 L1984 **ORS** *020 †40
SHEPLEY, Felix Rhodes. 1518 10TH ST 76301 #028-34-1942 L1949 **OTO** *071 †45
SINGLETON, Earl Fain. 5420 KELL BLVD 76310 #048-02-1964 L1964 **OTO FPS** *020 †45
SLEEPER, Julian Chandler. 2524 HIGHWAY 79 S 76310 #028-02-1954 L1962 **CD** *071 †40
SLOWEY, James E. 6391 KOVARIK RD 76310 #919-01-1973 L1986 **AN** *071 †05
SMITH, Art Glenn. 500 BROAD ST 76301 #048-02-1985 L1988 **P** *020 †75
SOBIESK, Emory John. 6515 KEMP BLVD, WICHITA FALLS CAMPUS 76308 #016-11-1961 L1981 **P AM** *071 †70,75
SOLIVEN, Cecile Gapas. 6515 LAKE RD, NORTH TEXAS STATE HOSPITAL 76308 #748-01-1982 L1996 **P** *020 †75
SOODA, Kusumakar. 1301 3RD ST STE 200, FAMILY PRACTICE 76301 #495-98-1994 L2007 **FM** *100
SORLEY, James A. 1301 3RD ST 76301 #048-13-1992 L1993 **FM** *071
SOSOLIK, Randolph C. 1600 11TH ST 76301 #048-13-1991 L2005 **PTH** *020 †50
SPEARS, Jaycile Little. ■ 76301 #048-02-1982 L1983 **OBG** *071 †30
SPEED, James Allen. 1600 11TH ST 76301 #048-15-1998 L1999 **GP EM** *020
SPENCER, David Rae. 808 BROOK AVE 76301 #048-12-1976 L1976 **DR** *020 †80
STEPHENSON, Philip Logan. ■ 76308 #039-01-1958 L1963 **GS** *071

STORSETH, Nicole J. 4206 CALL FIELD RD, ASSOCIATES 76308 #048-14-2000 L2002 **FM** *020 †18
STRATE, Susan Marie. 5420 KELL BLVD, KELL W REGIONAL HOSP 76310 #030-05-1979 L1982 **PTH** *020 †50
SUDARASHAN, Sriram. 2101 9TH ST 76301 #495-65-1969 L1980 **CD IM** *020 †20
SUDARSHAN, Shonalatha J. 2101 9TH ST 76301 #495-65-1968 L1980 **IM** *020 †20
SUGGS, Mark Wesley. 4007 SEABURY DR, SUGGS EYE CENTER 76308 #048-15-1984 L1985 **OPH** *020 †35
SULTEMEIER, Kenneth L. 4601 OLD JACKSBORO HWY 76302 #048-13-1985 L1986 **PD** *020 †55
SUNDARESAN, Sanjoy. 1511 10TH ST 76301 #008-01-1990 L1996 **NS** *020 †25
SUTTON, Beth Howell. 1600 BROOK AVE 76301 #048-04-1976 L1976 **GS** *020 †85 ‡
SUTTON, Richard Neel. 808 BROOK AVE, RADY ASSOCS WICHITA FLS PA 76301 #041-01-1966 L1974 **DR NM** *071 †80
SYED, Zahida. ■ 76308 #704-06-1997 L2007 **P** *020
SZCZERBA, Arthur Jack. 1301 3RD ST 76301 #759-11-1985 L2000 **FM** *020 †18 ‡
TADROS, Magdi M. 4601 OLD JACKSBORO HWY 76302 #915-04-1986 L1996 **FM** *020 †18
TAHIR, Tazeen. ■ 76309 #704-18-1992 **FP** *012
TALBERT, Tom S, Jr. 4601 OLD JACKSBORO HWY 76302 #048-02-1982 L1983 **OM FM** *020 †20
TAN, Lucy. 4601 OLD JACKSBORO HWY 76302 #209-03-1980 L1996 **FM** *020 †18 ‡
TAURIAINEN, Mikko Peter. 912 BURNETT ST 76301 #065-01-1990 L1997 **TS VS** *020 †85,90
TAYLOR, Thomas E. 1500 BROOK AVE 76301 #048-02-1960 L1960 **D** *020
TERRY, Donald Franklin. 5420 KELL BLVD 76310 #028-02-1957 L1961 **CD IM** *071 †20
THANAM, Dedeepya Reddy. ■ 76308 #495-70-1999 L2003 **FP** *012
THOMAS, Timothy Kevin. 2945 SOUTHWEST PKWY 76308 #048-12-1982 L1983 **GS OS** *020 †85
THORNTON, Gail, Jr. ■ 76308 #048-04-1952 L1952 **GP** *071
THOTA, Venkateswarlu. 1518 10TH ST, WICHITA FALLS CARDIAC CARE 76301 #495-50-1986 L1998 **CD IM** *020 †20
THUESON, Charles Ray. 1104 BROOK AVE, WICHITA FALLS GASTROENTERO 76301 #026-04-1976 L1990 **GE IM** *020 †20
TIDMORE, William Lewis. ■ 76309 #004-01-1968 L1969 **DR NM** *020 †80
TOLENTINO, Elvira P. 4601 OLD JACKSBORO HWY 76302 #748-01-1978 L1994 **FM** *020 †18
TOMLINSON, Jack Randolph. 2410 9TH ST 76301 #048-12-1957 L1957 **P** *020
TORRES, Oscar Camerino J. 5420 KELL BLVD 76310 #649-14-1980 L1992 **FM** *020
TOULAN, Michael Walter. 5500 KELL BLVD STE 200, TEXOMA UROLOGY CENTER 76310 #010-02-1992 L2000 **U** *020 †20
TROUTMAN, Gerad Albert. ■ 76305 #048-15-2007 L2007 *012
TRUJILLO, Joel. 4601 OLD JACKSBORO HWY 76302 #034-01-1971 L1995 **FM** *020 †20
UCOL, Jesus D. 1718 10TH ST, STE A 76301 #748-20-1984 L1995 **PD** *020 †55
UGAZ, Jorge Enrique. ■ 76301 #737-01-1963 L1970 **GS** *071 †85
ULRICH, Brian Kent. 5400 KELL BLVD 76310 #019-02-1974 L1984 **ON HEM** *020 †20
VACHHANI, Ashokkumar N. 4328 BERWICK DR 76309 #495-48-1971 L1981 **P IM** *020
VALENCIA, Jorge Ricardo. 5 EUREKA CIR, STE C2 76308 #264-19-1986 L1999 **FM** *020 †18
WAGNER, Grant Hulse. 6515 LAKE RD, BOX 300 76308 #048-12-1964 L1973 **CHP P** *071 †75
WALKER, Olyn Mc Clinton. ■ 76309 #047-07-1963 L1983 **TS VS** *071 †85,90
WARD, Jeremy Lynn. ■ 76308 #048-14-2004 **GS** *012
WARNOCK, Kenneth Mathew R. 6 EUREKA CIR 76301 #007-02-1974 L1976 **GS** *020 †85
WATSON, Earl Franklin. ■ 76301 #016-06-1954 L1959 **FM** *071 †18
WEHRLY, David James. 1208 BROOK AVE, GRACE MED CLNC 76301 #048-12-1975 L1977 **OM IM** *020 †20,70
WHITTIKER, David Michael. 4206 CALL FIELD RD, ASSOCIATES 76308 #048-12-1984 L1985 **FM** *020 †18 ‡
WIECK, Bryan. 1819 8TH ST 76301 #048-02-1990 L1991 **CHP P** *020
WILLIAMS, Russell E, Jr. 501 MIDWESTERN PKWY E, PARKWAY EAST 76302 #036-01-1969 L1979 **IM** *020 †20
WILLIAMSON, Keith H. 200 MLK JR BLVD, NORTH CENTRAL TEXAS 76301 #048-12-1987 L1988 **FM** *020 †18
WILSON, Louis J. 5420 KELL BLVD 76310 #048-12-1989 L1997 **GE IM** *020 †20
WILSON, Steven J. 1 W MEDICAL CT 76310 #048-15-1993 L1994 **GS** *020 †40
WINFREY, Mandy L. 1601 9TH ST, STE B 76301 #048-14-2002 L2006 **OBG** *020
WOOD, Robert Fred. 1105 BROOK AVE 76301 #048-12-1974 L1974 **AN** *020
WORKMAN, Mark Albert. 4301 MAPLEWOOD AVE, STE A 76308 #038-40-1990 L1999 **PME AN** *020 †05
WYATT, Wendell Irving. 501 MIDWESTERN PKWY E 76302 #019-02-1960 L1974 **IM** *071
YAMBOARIAS, Ramon. 76306 #042-01-1998 L2000 **FM** *012
YAP, Francis Eric D. 4601 OLD JACKSBORO HWY 76302 #748-01-1990 L2006 **IM** *020 †20
YAP, Rodney D. 4601 OLD JACKSBORO HWY 76302 #748-01-1988 L1997 **PD** *020 †55
YOAST, Kenneth Lee. 4601 OLD JACKSBORO HWY 76302 #048-13-1982 L1983 **DR** *020 †80
YOUNG, Lawrence Yau Hoon. 1601 9TH ST, WOMEN'S CLINIC 76301 #041-13-1972 L1977 **OBG** *020 †30
ZARDAIN, Victor Manuel. 1600 8TH ST, UNITED REGIONAL HLTH CARE 76301 #649-13-1995 L1999 **FM** *020 †18

WILLIS – MONTGOMERY

ADAMS, Frank. ■ 77318 #065-10-1975 L1980 **OS P** *020
BUTLER, Tracie Lynette. ■ 77318 #028-02-2004 L2004 **PD** *100 †55
GUROL, Unal Kadri. 408 W MONTGOMERY ST, P O BOX 1060 77378 #902-03-1956 L1973 **IM** *020
LACSON, John P. 500 W MONTGOMERY ST 77378 #048-13-1993 L1995 **IM** *020 †20
LANINGHAM, Rodney Jason. 408 W MONTGOMERY ST 77378 #048-02-1996 L1997 **FM** *020 †18
NGUYEN, Trang D. 500 W MONTGOMERY ST 77378 #039-01-2001 L2004 **FM** *020 †18

WILLOW PARK – PARKER

LITTLEJOHN, William Donal. ■ 76087 #048-12-1967 L1967 **GP OS** *071
SPETMAN, Karen Lynn. 132 EL CHICO TRL 76087 #030-05-1977 L1988 **IM EM** *020 †20,16
WILSON, Johnny Mark. 136 EL CHICO TRL STE 1 76087 #021-06-1980 L2002 **FM** *020 †18

WILLS POINT – VAN ZANDT

ATKINSON, William Hudson. 106 N 4TH ST 75169 #048-12-1974 L1974 **GS** *020

MOORE, Kendall H. ■ 75169 #048-12-1952 L1952 **AM GP** *072
REYES-PESCADOR, Carlos. 129 S 4TH ST 75169 #649-31-1975 L1983 **CCS** *020 †85
SAWKA, Jerome Edward. ■ 75169 #038-43-1976 L2002 **FM** *020 †18

WILSON – LYNN

THOMAS, Griffith Wm. 1691 FM 211, 2600 LOCKWOOD AVENUE 79381 #038-43-1985 L1994
   FM *020 †18 ‡

WIMBERLEY – HAYS

ADELSON, Allen Donald. ■ 78676 #021-01-1967 L1969 **GP** *020
ALMOND, Thomas Henry. 102 BROOKHOLLOW DR 78676 #917-23-1958 L1968 **AN OS** *020
BIRCHALL, Janis L. ■ 78676 #028-03-1966 L1971 **NEP IM** *071 †20
COFFEE, Keith Allan. ■ 78676 #045-01-1992 L1999 **PCC** *020 †20
DODDS, Alexander Earl. ■ 78676 #035-45-1948 L1950 **GP** *071
GREER, James Wm. 555 RANCH ROAD 3237, DEER CREEK NURSING CENTER 78676
   #048-04-1946 L1946 **IM FM** *071
HOLMES, Glen I. ■ 78676 #004-01-1940 L1950 **U** *071 †95
KOEPPE, Patsy Ruth P. ■ 78676 #047-06-1957 L1968 **IM IMG** *020
KUHL, Ivan W. ■ 78676 #035-06-1945 L1954 **D ID** *071 †15
MAHOOD, Allan F. 6801 MOUNT SHARP RD, UNIT G 78676 #048-13-1988 L1989
   FM EM *020 †18
MC CREIGHT, W Joe. 440 FISCHER STORE RD 78676 #048-13-1992 L1993 **FM** *020 †18
MINNIGERODE, Lana K Carr. ■ 78676 #028-03-1966 L2006 **OS** *071 †60
MINNIGERODE, Turner Lewis. ■ 78676 #028-03-1964 L1964 **IM** *071 †20
MORALES, Milton David. 125 WATER PARK RD 78676 #048-04-1968 L1968 **AN GP** *072 †05
SCHNAUTZ, Nancy Lee. 230 BLUE HERON RUN, SAN MARCO TREATMENT CENTER 78676
   #048-02-1962 L1967 **CHP P** *020 †55
SEBRING, Lane. 16811 RANCH ROAD 12 78676 #048-02-1991 L1995 **FM** *020 †18
STRICKLAND, Janet L A. ■ 78676 #048-02-1975 L1975 **OM** *020 †20
WOOD, Albert J. ■ 78676 #048-02-1970 L1970 **ON HEM** *071 †20

WINDCREST – BEXAR

FREDERICK, John Howard. ■ 78239 #041-01-1955 L1962 **FM FPG** *071 †18
GRUNWELL, John R, Jr. ■ 78239 #010-01-1939 L1946 **OPH** *071
PLUNKETT, Guy Downs. ■ 78239 #035-20-1955 L1981 **OBG** *071 †30
ROSE, Howard Richard. 710 WINDROCK DR 78239 #021-05-1960 L1962 **FM** *020 †18

WINNIE – CHAMBERS

EL MALLAH, Mai Kamal. 538 BROADWAY, WINNIE COMMUNITY HOSPITAL 77665
   #918-01-2001 L2005 **PD** *020
PACKARD, Marshall B. 538 BROADWAY 77665 #048-13-1999 L2001 **IM** *020

WINNSBORO – WOOD

AVENDANIO, Prudencio C. 719 W COKE RD 75494 #748-02-1962 L1979 **R NM** *020 †80,28
BLACKBURN, John Roberts. 719 W COKE RD, STE 4 75494 #048-12-1975 L1975 **U** *020 †95
BLAIR, Robert Van. 719 W COKE RD, STE 1 75494 #055-01-1984 L1989 **GS** *020
BURLINGHAM, Kim. 719 W COKE RD, STE 1 75494 #649-14-1981 L1989 **PD** *020 †55
CLOTHIER, Mark Allen. 719 W COKE RD STE 2, CLINIC 75494 #048-14-1983 L1983 **IM** *020 †20
DELA CRUZ, Alberto R. 719 W COKE RD # BLDG3-7 75494 #748-08-1970 L1980 **GS** *020
DE LA CRUZ, Rowena B. 719 W COKE RD, STE 7 75494 #748-08-1969 L1980 **PD IM** *020
GOLDEN, Mitchell Keith. 719 W COKE RD 75494 #027-01-1983 L1990 **FM** *020 †18
MAC MASTER, Benzel C. 719 W COKE RD, STE 5 75494 #048-12-1972 L1979 **ORS** *020 †40
MURLEY, David Chadwell. 600 E COKE RD 75494 #047-06-1959 L1960 **GP** *020
MURLEY, Warren Thad. 600 E COKE RD BOX 65 75494 #048-12-1956 L1956 **GP** *071
ROBERTS, Joyce Gammill. 719 W COKE RD 75494 #048-15-1984 L1985 **FM** *020 †18
SHAPIRO, Howard Michael. 719 W COKE RD 75494 #025-01-1970 L1980 **DR** *020 †80
WILSON, Jennifer M. 719 W COKE RD, STE 4 75494 #048-78-2003, ▲ L2006 **FM** *020 †18

WINTERS – RUNNELS

BIDDIX, Jerry Wayne. PO BOX 747 79567 #036-05-1974 L1975 **FM** *020
ENDICOTT, Sarah Beate. 7771 STATE HIGHWAY 153, NRH CLINIC 79567 #409-06-1993 L2002
   FM *020 †18

WOLFFORTH – LUBBOCK

BEAVER, Thomas R. ■ 79382 #422-01-1986 L1988 **FOP PTH** *020 †50
BOGAR, Mark Darrow. PO BOX 1223 79382 #048-14-1998 L2002 **PM** *020 †60
BURNETT, Christopher J. ■ 79382 #039-01-2003 L2007 **AN** *020
COLEMAN, Jody Mae. ■ 79382 #048-14-2005 **DR** *012
JOHNSON, Kimberli N. ■ 79382 #048-12-2000 L2005 **IM** *020
KLAISLE, Deborah Irene. ■ 79382 #007-02-1986 L1987 **FOP** *020 †50,30
MUSICK, Kerry Lynn. ■ 79382 #048-15-2008 *012

WOODVILLE – TYLER

BROWN, James Mc Farley. 104 N BEECH ST 75979 #048-14-1978 L1978 **FM EM** *020 †18
BURTON, Layton Gayle. 1100 W BLUFF ST 75979 #048-04-1947 L1947 **FM** *071 †18
GARNER, Curtis Marion. 181 W FOREST DR 75979 #048-02-1959 L1959 **GP AN** *020 †18
GILCHRIST, John Quincy. ■ 75979 #048-04-1948 L1948 **GP** *071
KANTE, Satyanarayana Pras. 104 N BEECH ST 75979 #495-58-1997 L2005 **IM** *100 †20
SCHULTZ, Paula La Jean. 104 N BEECH ST 75979 #048-02-1980 L1980 **FM** *020 †18

WOODWAY – MCLENNAN

ANGEL, Robert Tate. 7125 NEW SANGER RD 76712 #048-04-1961 L1961 **TS** *020 †85,90
ATTAS, Michael. 7125 NEW SANGER RD 76712 #048-02-1973 L1973 **CD IM** *020 †20
BROWN, Kendall Paul. ■ 76712 #027-01-2000 L2001 **PYG** *020 †75
COWART, Roger Wade. 7005 WOODWAY DR, STE 101 76712 #654-01-1988 L1992 **IM** *020 †20
CROSS, Donald Stanley. 7125 NEW SANGER RD, STE 502 76712 #048-02-1996 L1998
   CD IM *020 †20
DAY, Andrew Kiilani. 7125 NEW SANGER RD, STE 502 76712 #048-13-1998 L1999
   CD IM *020 †20
DOW, David Sontag. ■ 76712 #025-01-1958 L1964 **OPH** *071 †35
FALCONE, Michael Wayne. 7125 NEW SANGER RD, STE 502 76712 #010-02-1966 L1973
   CD IM *020 †20
HAMILTON, Harold Bruce. 205 WOODHEW DR, STE 200 76712 #021-05-1990 L1996
   NS *020 †20
HAPPEL, Christopher Charl. ■ 76712 #048-15-2007 **FP** *012
HAYNES, David Edward. 7030 NEW SANGER RD, STE 200 76712 #004-01-1999 L2005
   ORS *020 †40
HODGES, James Ray. 7005 WOODWAY DR 76712 #422-01-1997 L2000 **IM** *020
KLEIMAN, Richard B. 7005 WOODWAY DR 76712 #048-02-1947 L1947 **IM** *020
LUNDEEN, Thomas Erland. 7125 NEW SANGER RD, STE 502 76712 #037-01-1978 L1980
   CD IM *020 †20
MAHAN, Rebecca Diane. ■ 76712 #048-13-2007 **FP** *012
MARTIN, Steve Nelson, Jr. 8224 MOSSWOOD DR 76712 #048-15-2001 L2003 **FM** *020 †18
O'NEILL, Eric Franklin. 1000 W STATE HIGHWAY 6, STE 500 76712 #048-15-1986 L1987
   PS *020 †85,65
PIETSCH, Darrell R. 7100 OLD MCGREGOR RD 76712 #048-13-1998 L1999 **FM** *020 †18
PITTS, William R. 7125 NEW SANGER RD, STE A 76712 #048-12-1992 L1993 **CD IM** *020 †20
PLEMMONS, Rita Lynn Haws. ■ 76712 #048-13-1989 L1990 **FM** *020 †18
RYAN, Rodney Patrick. 7736 CENTRAL PARK DR 76712 #064-01-1974 L1977 **EM FM** *020 †18
SHEFA, Ahmad Zia. 1009 KNIGHTSBRIDGE 76712 #118-01-1971 L1975 **GP** *020
SHEFA, Bobbie L Flynn. 1009 KNIGHTSBRIDGE 76712 #004-01-1973 L1975 **GP** *020
SHOULTZ, Charles A. 7125 NEW SANGER RD, STE 502 76712 #048-14-1987 L1994
   CD IM *020 †20
SHOULTZ, Chas Arthur, Jr. 7125 NEW SANGER RD, STE 502 76712 #048-02-1963 L1970
   CD IM *020 †20
SMITH, Randall D. ■ 76712 #048-13-1995 L1997 **EM** *020 †16
STANKO, Sue E. 1201 HEWITT DR, STE 204 76712 #048-16-1992 L1993 **PD** *020
STONE, Bryan. ■ 76712 #917-01-1960 L1975 **FM** *071 †18
TYSON, Todd Brown. 5900 OLD MCGREGOR RD 76712 #048-12-1990 L1991 **AN** *020 †05
VALIGURA, Thomas Joe. 5900 OLD MCGREGOR RD 76712 #048-02-1985 L1986
   AN PME *020 †05
WALKER, Jackson Kyle. 7005 WOODWAY DR 76712 #048-02-1957 L1957 **IM OS** *020 †20
WILSON, John Samuel. ■ 76712 #048-12-2007 **IM** *012
WRIGHT, Robert Max. 7003 WOODWAY DR STE 303 76712 #048-04-1978 L1978
   PS HS *020 †65
WRIGHT, Valerie Kim. 7003 WOODWAY DR STE 303 76712 #041-07-1977 L1978
   PS HS *020 †65
YOUNG, Donald J. 7125 NEW SANGER RD STE D, CENTRAL TEXAS CARDIOVASCUL 76712
   #048-15-1988 L1989 **TS** *020 †85,90

WYLIE – COLLIN

BATES, Scott W. ■ 75098 #048-14-2007 **IM** *012
BENNINGTON, Michael J. 613 S HIGHWAY 78 STE 200, FIRST AID FAMILY CARE 75098
   #048-15-2000 L2006 **FM** *100
CAUDILL, Travis Michael. 600 COOPER DR, STE 100 75098 #012-01-2002 L2003 **FM** *020 †18
CHRISTOPHER, Larry Don. ■ 75098 #004-01-1991 L1993 **IM** *020 †20
FUNK, Presley C, III. 406 HILLTOP LN 75098 #048-12-1950 L1950 **FM** *071
GANDHI, Neelay Ramesh. ■ 75098 #422-01-2007 **FP** *012
HUGHES, Eric M. 801A S HIGHWAY 78, STE 207 75098 #023-01-1996 L1998 **FM** *020 †18
KIM, Stephen Alan. 613 S HWY 78 STE 200, FIRST AID FAMILY CARE 75098 #422-01-2003 L2007
LANMAN, Nicole Lowery. ■ 75098 #048-02-2001 L2004 **PD** *020 †55
OSIMIRI, Philomena. ■ 75098 #130-01-2000 L2004 **FM** *100 †20
PATTERSON, Tena. 600 COOPER DR STE 100, FAMILY MEDICAL CENTER WY 75098
   #018-03-1993 L1996 **FM** *020 †18
PILKINGTON, Ronald Saml. 900 W KIRBY ST STE A 75098 #060-02-1973 L1982 **PD PSM** *020
STEWART, De Shawn Kirk. ■ 75098 #019-02-2000 L2000 **FM** *020 †18

YOAKUM – LAVACA

BISHOP, Marshall Clinton. 303 HUBBARD ST 77995 #048-14-1998 L1999 **FM OBS** *020 †18
DROST, James Everett. 210 NELSON ST, STE C 77995 #048-14-1983 L1983 **FM OBS** *020 †18 ‡
LAMBERT, Robert Martin. 402 HUBBARD ST, YOAKUM MEDICAL CLINIC 77995
   #038-45-1984 L1987 **GP FM** *020
MOEHLMAN, William David. 210 NELSON ST STE A 77995 #048-12-1976 L1976 **FM** *020 †18
MORRIS, Craig Jude. 210 NELSON ST, STE C 77995 #048-16-1998 L2000 **FM EM** *020 †18
WATSON, David Henry. 402 HUBBARD ST, YOAKUM MEDICAL CLINIC 77995
   #048-04-1957 L1957 **FM** *020 †18

ZAPATA – ZAPATA

MILOVANOVIC, Zeljko. PO BOX 355 78076 #957-05-1997 L2004 **FM** *020 †18
MONTES, Rosa Guevara. ■ 78076 #048-02-1997 L2002 **FM** *020

ZAVALLA – ANGELINA

CAIN, Donald Neil. 4 ANGELINA ST 75980 #017-20-1947 L1948 **TS GS** *071 †85

ZEPHYR – BROWN

ENSENAT, Jose Rafael. ■ 76890 #023-07-1953 L1978 **OBG** *071 †30

ALPINE – UTAH

AIKEN, J Lee. ■ 84004 #017-20-1963 L1964 **FM GP** *071 †18

EPPICH, Irel Scott. ■ 84004 #023-12-1991 L2003 **NEP** *020 †20

HOFFMAN, Clark Gilchrist. 484 KNIGHT CIR 84004 #054-04-1973 L1988 **FM** *020 †18

HOLLAND, Renae. ■ 84004 #654-01-1987 L1988 **PD** *020 †55

MUIR, Jeffery Johnson. ■ 84004 #049-01-2008 L2008 *012

PACK, Steven Richard. ■ 84004 #049-01-1989 L1992 **EM** *020 †16

PARKER, Virgil Jon. ■ 84004 #049-01-1957 L1958 **IM** *020

ROMNEY, Robert Pratt. ■ 84004 #049-01-1961 L1962 **GYN** *071 †30

AMERICAN FORK – UTAH

AAGARD, Robert Orr. 120 N 1220 E STE 7 84004 #049-01-1990 L1999 **OBG** *020 †30

BABB, Stephen Rex. 120 N 1220 E # 17 84003 #306-01-1985 L1991 **IMG IM** *075

BANKS, Alan Merrill. 1184 E 80 N 84003 #049-01-1977 L1978 **ORS** *020 †40

BARRATT, Justin T. 170 N 1100 E 84003 #041-13-2000 L2005 **IM** *020 †20

BATCHLER, Jack Wm. 170 N 1100 E 84003 #049-01-1968 L1969 **EM** *071

BATEMAN, Adam. ■ 84003 #048-14-2004 L2006 *100

BENTLEY, Bradley John. 170 N 1100 E, AMERICAN FORK HOSPITAL 84003 #049-01-1991 L1994 **EM** *020 †16

BEZZANT, John Lloyd. 170 N 1100 E, AMERICAN FORK HOSP 84003 #049-01-1977 L1978 **D** *020 †15

BOYLES, Cory David. 212 S 1100 E 84003 #005-18-1989 L2005 **EM** *020 †16

BREYER, Wendy Anne. 1152 E 200 N 84003 #036-05-1992 L2000 **HO** *020 †20

BRUNSDALE, Lenard Chas. 170 N 1100 E 84003 #049-01-1991 L1999 **EM** *020 †16

CAHOON, Daniel Vernon. 1159 E 200 N STE 300 84003 #049-01-1993 L2001 **U** *020 †95

CALLAHAN, Michael Earl. 1184 E 80 N 84003 #010-01-1974 L1977 **ORS OS** *020 †40

CLARK, Jay Austin. 1152 E 200 N, AMERICAN FORK CANCER CENTE 84003 #049-01-1993 L2001 **RO** *020 †80

CONNER, Marsena Elaine. 1159 E 200 N, STE 200 84003 #041-09-1997 L1998 **PD** *020 †55

COSGRAVE, Michael L. 226 N 1100 E 84003 #048-15-1975 L1980 **FM** *020 †18

CRAWFORD, Brenda Kristine. 170 N 1100 E, DEPT OF EMERGENCY MEDICINE 84003 #005-14-2000 L2006 **EM** *020

DENYS, Douglas. 1159 E 200 N STE 325 84003 #049-01-1995 L2000 **OTO HNS** *020 †45

EBERTING, Cheryl Lee D. 170 N 1100 E 84003 #049-01-2000 L2006 **D** *020 †15

ENTEZARI-TAHER, Mohammad. 52 N 1100 E 84003 #517-01-1987 L1997 **N CN** *020 †75

FISHER, Kuhia Loren. 170 N 1100 E 84003 #049-01-1997 L2005 **AN** *020 †05

GLADE, Gordon. 1159 E 200 N, STE 200 84003 #035-45-1977 L1980 **PD** *020 †55

GOOCH, Willis Manford, III. 1084 E STATE RD, STE Q 84003 #048-04-1965 L1979 **PTH PD** *020 †55,50

GRANT, Morgan Kia. 170 N 1100 E 84003 #049-01-1997 L2002 **AN** *020 †05

GREEN, Matthew Collin. ■ 84003 #035-46-2006 **ORS** *012

GREENWOOD, Dale Wm. 170 N 1100 E, DEPT OF EMERGENCY 84003 #016-43-1975 L1981 **IM EM** *020 †20

HAFEN, David Kartchner. 226 N 1100 E, STE A 84003 #049-01-1994 L1995 **FM** *020 †18

HANSEN, Marlan Len. 1159 E 200 N, STE 150 84003 #048-02-1978 L1996 **HOS PLM** *020 †20

HARRIS, Dixie Lee. 170 N 1100 E 84003 #048-02-1989 L2005 **PUD CCM** *020 †20

HEMMERT, Wynn Howard. 36 N 1100 E STE A, CENTRAL UTAH CLINIC PC 84003 #035-20-1971 L1978 **GE IM** *020 †20

HERAS, Heidi Ann. 125 E MAIN ST # 611 84003 #049-01-1994 L1999 **OTO** *020 †45

HOGGARD, Timo J. 226 N 1100 E, STE A 84003 #010-01-1990 L1994 **FM** *020 †18

HUNSAKER, Jesse Neville. 12 N 1100 E 84003 #049-01-1978 L1982 **OPH** *020 †35

JOHNSON, Cheryl Anne. 226 N 1100 E 84003 #048-12-1990 L1993 **FM** *020 †18

JOHNSON, George Brent. 226 N 1100 E 84003 #049-01-1974 L1975 **FM** *020 †18 ‡

JONES, Ryan Nelson. 1159 E 200 N STE 250 84003 #056-06-1996 L2000 **OBG** *020 †30

KARNAM, Uma Prasanna. 36 N 1100 E, STE A 84003 #045-16-1993 L2001 **GE** *020 †20

KENDELL, Kurtis Richard. 170 N 1100 E 84003 #023-07-1996 L2003 **DR** *020 †80

LAMOREAUX, James P. 120 N 1220 E, STE 7 84003 #049-01-1983 L1987 **OBG** *020 †30

LAWRENCE, Kari Fulp. 1159 E 200 N STE 250, LEGACY OBSTETRICS & GYNECO 84003 #037-01-1994 L1998 **OBG** *020 †30

LIND, Brent Karl. 120 N 1220 E, STE 7 84003 #049-01-1977 L1981 **OBG** *020 †30

LING, Yun. 1175 E 50 S, STE 241 84003 #243-21-1995 L2006 **IM** *020 †20

MAC ARTHUR, Toran James. 226 N 1100 E STE A, 1100 E PROFESSIONAL CENTER 84003 #049-01-1997 L2002 **FM** *020 †18

MARTIN, Stacy Ann. 170 N 1100 E, AMERICAN FORK EMERGENCY RO 84003 #049-01-1992 L1997 **EM** *020 †16

MC DANIEL, Bruce Clark. ■ 84003 #049-01-1981 **P** *074

MEHR, David Steven. ■ 84003 #016-42-1993 L1994 **PTH** *072 †50

MELENDEZ, Terry Dwain. 120 N 1220 E STE 7 84003 #030-05-1992 L1996 **OBG** *020 †30

MEYERS, Jonathan Taylor. 1175 E 50 S, CENTRAL UTAH CLINIC 84003 #049-01-2001 L2007 **AN** *100

MOWER, Douglas Reed. 226 N 1100 E 84003 #025-07-1985 L1988 **FM** *020 †18

MUMFORD, Scott Harris. 1159 E 200 N, STE 200 84003 #049-01-2002 L2005 **PD** *020 †55

MURDOCK, Kenneth Joe. 226 N 1100 E 84003 #025-07-1971 L1972 **FM** *020 †18

NEELEMAN, Stephen Dale. 1159 E 200 N, STE 350 84003 #049-01-1998 L2005 **GS** *020 †85

NELSON, James Robt. 48 N 1100 E STE A, ALPINE WOMENS CLINIC 84003 #038-45-1984 L1993 **OBG** *020 †30 ‡

NILSON, Jay Todd. 170 N 1100 E 84003 #028-34-1992 L1998 **AN** *020 †05

NUTTALL, David Craig. 120 N 1220 E, STE 1 84003 #005-15-1976 L1982 **PD** *020

PEUGH, William Noel. 1159 E 200 N STE 350 84003 #028-02-1990 L2002 **GS OS** *020 †85

POLLAK, Rebecca Irene. 36 N 1100 E STE D, SUNRISE MEDICAL, INC, REBE 84003 #003-01-1993 L1996 **IM** *020

REYNOLDS, Christopher Jay. 52 N 1100 E 84003 #028-34-1982 L1985 **N** *020 †75

RICHARDS, Guy Adams. ■ 84003 #010-01-1943 L1947 **DMP** *071

RIESSEN, Erik Reinhard. 1159 E 200 N, STE 150 84003 #026-04-1999 L2000 **IM** *020 †20

RITCHIE, Paul Kohler. 1184 E 80 N 84003 #036-05-1998 L2004 **ORS** *020 †40

ROBINSON, Paul Howard. 1159 E 200 N, STE 350 84003 #049-01-1975 L1979 **GS** *020 †85

ROWLEY, Steven Dean. 48 N 1100 E, STE B 84003 #049-01-1974 L1981 **OTO** *020 †45

SANDERSON, Mark C. 1184 E 80 N, NORTH VALLEY SURGICAL ASSO 84003 #048-15-1987 L1992 **GS** *020

SAUNDERS, Ronald Jay. 1159 E 200 N, STE 4 84003 #049-01-1965 L1981 **U** *020 †95

SHEFFIELD, Clark W. 225 N 1100 E, STE C 84003 #049-01-1987 L1997 **GS** *020 †85

SHELTON, Dean W. 170 N 1100 E 84003 #025-07-1980 L1983 **EM** *020 †18,16

SHELTON, Richard Stewart. ■ 84003 #028-34-2007 **IM** *012

SMITH, Andrea N. 1159 E 200 N, STE 250 84003 #007-02-1996 L2005 **OBG** *020 †30

THOMSON, Terrell Alden. 660 E 770 N, TRI CITY MEDICAL 84003 #051-04-1983 L1986 **IM EM** *020 †20

TIMPSON, David Geo. 170 N 1100 E 84003 #049-01-1978 L1980 **AN** *020 †05

WALKER, Jerry Dale, Jr. 48 N 1100 E, STE B 84003 #041-02-1994 L2003 **CD** *020 †20

WATABE, Bryan Masao. 1159 E 200 N STE 250, LEGACY OB/GYN 84003 #033-06-2000 L2004 **OBG** *020 ‡

WEIPERT, John David. 476 W 50 N 84003 #036-08-1986 L1989 **PD** *020 †55

WELCH, Kerry Dean. 120 N 1220 E STE 1 84003 #049-01-1977 L1982 **FM AM** *020

WELCH, Von Fred. 1159 E 200 N, STE 150 84003 #049-01-1988 L1992 **OBG** *020 †20

WELLS, John Tracy. 1184 E 80 N 84003 #020-02-1992 L2000 **ORS** *020

WHITING, Michael Don. 48 N 1100 E STE C 84003 #028-34-1980 L1982 **PD** *020 †55

WILCOX, Ryan Brent. 1159 E 200 N, STE 200 84003 #049-01-1998 L2001 **PD** *020 †55

WOLD, Gary L. 120 N 1220 E, STE 13 84003 #049-01-1979 L1983 **OBG** *020 †30

YOUNG, Michael Scott. 170 N 1100 E 84003 #049-01-1993 L1996 **EM** *020 †16

BEAVER – BEAVER

MELLING, Mitchell Joe. 85 N 400 E 84713 #028-34-1995 L1998 **FM** *020 †18

MURDOCK, C Dale. PO BOX 1136, 170 N 1100 E 84713 #049-01-1964 L1965 **GP OS** *072

NADRI, Quaid J. ■ 84713 #704-02-1989 L1995 **NEP** *100 †20

OAKDEN, Richard Wade. ■ 84713 #654-01-1998 L2001 **FM** *020 †18

ROBINSON, Byron Noal. PO BOX 1690 84713 #049-01-1971 L1972 **FM** *020 †18

SMITH, Roger Hal. PO BOX 1690 84713 #049-01-1980 L1981 **FM** *020 †18

BLANDING – SAN JUAN

BLACK, Curtis Legrand. 804 N 400 W 84511 #056-06-2004 L2005 **FM** *020 †18

FISHER, Mahana Shane. 799 S 200 W, BLANDING FAMILY PRACTICE 84511 #049-01-1997 L2000 **FM** *020 †18

GIBBONS, De Lamar Johnson. ■ 84511 #010-01-1959 L1982 **GP OS** *075

BLUFFDALE – SALT LAKE

JOHANSEN, Richard Bart. 14350 S 2200 W 84065 #049-01-1988 L1991 **EM** *020 †16

BOUNTIFUL – DAVIS

AFFLECK, Gordon William. 1551 RENAISSANCE TOWNE DR, STE 400 84010 #049-01-1966 L1967 **ORS** *071 †40

ALTHAUS, Sandra Jill. 380 N 200 W STE 209, UTAH IMAGING ASSOCIATES 84010 #056-05-1984 L2000 **DR** *020 †80

ANDING, Eric Scott. 520 MEDICAL DR, STE 300 84010 #041-09-1990 L2000 **CD IM** *020 †20

ANGELES, Patrick Rasco. 280 N MAIN ST 84010 #016-11-1994 L1996 **IM** *020 †20

ASHTON, Matthew David. ■ 84010 #038-40-2006 L2008 **IM** *012

BAER, Robert David. ■ 84010 #038-40-1952 L1960 **PM** *020 †60

BAIRES, Enrique Perez. 280 N MAIN 84010 #049-01-2000 L2003 **FM** *020 †18

BALLIF, Mark Gordon. 1551 RENAISSANCE TOWNE DR, STE 340 84010 #049-01-1983 L1987 **OPH** *020 †35

BANKHEAD, Douglas C. 1551 RENAISSANCE TOWNE DR, STE 200 84010 #049-01-1978 L1980 **AN PME** *020 †05

BECK, Stephen Alexander. 415 MEDICAL DR # B 84010 #049-01-1974 L1975 **FM** *020 †18

BETTERIDGE, Benjamin B. 425 MEDICAL DR, SPORTS MEDICINE SPECIALIST 84010 #019-02-2002 L2005 **FSM** *020 †16

BLACK, Craig Dan. 390 N MAIN ST 84010 #049-01-1981 L1985 **PD** *020 †55

BLACKBURN, Celia Webb. 390 N MAIN ST 84010 #049-01-1995 L1996 **FM OBS** *020 †18

BLACKHURST, William David. ■ 84010 #038-40-2007 L2007 **IM** *012

BROWN, Blake James. 630 MEDICAL DR 84010 #049-01-1991 L1992 **AN** *020 †05

BURNETT, Kara Fadel. 620 MEDICAL DR 84010 #049-01-1997 L1998 **PD** *020 †55

BUSTOS, Manuel. 235 LYMAN LN 84010 #132-01-1958 L1968 **GP** *071 †85

CAMPBELL, Elizabeth Garre. ■ 84010 #017-20-2005 L2006 **PD** *012

CAPEL, Winston Timothy. 620 MEDICAL DR, STE 300 84010 #016-42-1991 L2005 **NS** *020 †25

CHEN, Stephanie Wei-Ying. ■ 84010 #049-01-2008 *012

CHENG, Christine Ann. 415 MEDICAL DR, STE D102 84010 #036-07-1990 L1995 **PS OS** *020 †65 ‡

CHRISTIAN, Grant Le Roy. 425 MEDICAL DR STE 118 84010 #008-01-1965 L1968 **IM CD** *020

CHRISTIAN, Mark E. 620 MEDICAL DR, STE 150 84010 #049-01-2002 L2005 **FM** *100 †18

CLARK, Kevin Newell. 425 MEDICAL DR, STE 101 84010 #004-01-1985 L1990 **GS** *020 †85

COOMBS, Douglas Ray. 520 MEDICAL DR STE 301 84010 #036-05-1972 L1978 **PD ID** *020 †55

CROCKETT, Sarah Snyder. 720 S BOUNTIFUL BLVD 84010 #049-01-2005 L2005 **EM** *012

DEA, Christopher John. ■ 84010 #049-01-2007 **IM** *012

DOTY, Donald Benjamin. ■ 84010 #005-11-1962 L1983 **TS GS** *071 †85,90

DOXEY, Brett William. 620 MEDICAL DR, STE 200 84010 #049-01-2001 L2004 **GE** *020

DRUEDING, Regina Walther. 415 MEDICAL DR, STE D201 84010 #021-05-1983 L1992 **IM** *020 †20

EDWARDS, John Covey. 1551 RENAISSANCE TOWNE DR, STE 400 84010 #049-01-1987 L1993 **OSM ORS** *020 †40

ERICKSON, Scott Austin. 440 MEDICAL DR, SCOTT A. ERICKSON MD 84010 #028-34-2002 L2005 **FM** *020 †18

FABER, Anthony C. 1030 WOODMOOR DR 84010 #012-05-1989 L1992 **AN** *020 †05

FOSTER, Carla Sue. 214 W 1500 S, FIRST MED-NORTH 84010 #028-03-1995 L1998 **FM** *020 †18

FREEMAN, Jan S. 425 MEDICAL DR, STE 101 84010 #049-01-1966 L1968 **GS** *020 †85

FREESTONE, Allen Arthur. 620 MEDICAL DR, STE 150 84010 #049-01-2002 L2005 **FM** *020 †18

FRUIN, Claudia Jerit. 620 MEDICAL DR 84010 #016-11-1986 L1989 **PD** *020 †55

GASSER, George Walter. 74 E 500 S STE 200 84010 #016-01-1942 L1956 **GYN** *071 †30

GESTELAND, Per Hans. 280 N MAIN ST 84010 #049-01-1996 L2000 **MPD** *020 †20,55

GIANNINI, Jacqueline Kim. 620 MEDICAL DR 84010 #035-03-1990 L1996 **PD** *020 †55

GROEBS, Allison Mary. 620 MEDICAL DR 84010 #049-01-1995 L2002 **PD** *020 †55

■ = Address Information Privacy Protected

GUYMON, Orson Henry. ■ 84010 #049-01-1954 L1955 **FM** *071 †85
HALL, Robert Hubert. ■ 84010 #028-02-1945 L1969 **AN** *071 †30
HAMMOND, Gregory Dean. 520 MEDICAL DR, STE 200 84010 #010-01-1998 L2004 **PCC** *020 †20
HANDLON, Kenneth Michael. 380 N 200 W STE 209 84010 #011-04-1997 L2002 **DR** *020 †80
HANSEN, Val Reese. 425 MEDICAL DR NO 110 84010 #049-01-1968 L1973 **IM** *020
HARBRECHT, David Jos. 425 MEDICAL DR STE 107 84010 #019-02-1972 L1982 **OTO** *020 †45
HART, James Henry. ■ 84010 #056-06-2004 L2007 **FM** *100 †18
HENDLER, Nedda Beth. 390 N MAIN ST 84010 #021-05-1982 L1997 **IM** *020 †20
HESS, Michael Muir. 1551 RENAISSANCE TOWNE DR, STE 400 84010 #049-01-1982 L1987 **ORS** *020 †40
HICKEN, Lloyd R. ■ 84010 #049-01-1949 L1952 **GP OS** *071
HICKMAN, Joshua Mc Kinnon. 1551 RENAISSANCE TOWNE DR, STE 400 84010 #036-01-1997 L1998 **ORS** *020 †40
HILBIG, Clarke Andrew. 620 MEDICAL DR, STE 200 84010 #041-09-1998 L2004 **GE IM** *020 †20
HILDEBRAND, Pamela Japlit. 620 MEDICAL DR, STE 100 84010 #030-06-2003 L2004 **PD** *020 †55
HORSLEY, David Grant. 390 N MAIN ST 84010 #049-01-1991 L1992 **IM** *020 †20
HUGHES, Matthew Adams. ■ 84010 #049-01-1993 L2000 **OM** *020 †70
HUISH, Steven B. 1551 RENAISSANCE TOWNE DR, STE 400 84010 #035-15-1994 L2000 **HS** *020 †40
JENSEN, Richard Clayne. ■ 84010 #035-45-2008 *012
JOHNS, Richard Elias, Jr. 1284 BEVERLY WAY 84010 #041-13-1972 L1973 **OM PHP** *030 †70
JOHNSON, Matthew Hall. ■ 84010 #049-01-2001 L2005 **AN** *020 †05 ‡
JOHNSTON, Eric C. 1551 RENAISSANCE TOWNE DR, STE 400 84010 #028-34-1991 L1996 **ORS OFA** *071 †40
JONES, Stephen Kent. ■ 84010 #305-01-1999 L2006 **AN** *100 †20 ‡
JORDAN, Robert Wesley. 1551 RENAISSANCE TOWNE DR, STE 400 84010 #040-02-1972 L1981 **ORS** *071 †40
JUDD, Earl Robert. 620 MEDICAL DR 84010 #012-01-2002 L2003 **PD** *020 †55
KASTELER, Douglas Spence. 390 N MAIN ST 84010 #010-01-1991 L1992 **FM** *020 †18
KELLY, Steven M. 1551 RENAISSANCE TOWNE DR, STE 310 84010 #049-01-1989 L1990 **OTO PDO** *020 †45
KIME, Matthew Hudson. ■ 84010 #049-01-2008 *012
KJAR, Joseph Gregory. 469 MEDICAL DR STE 100 84010 #049-01-1978 L1983 **PS** *020 †65
KNOWLTON, Alisa Ann. 390 N MAIN ST 84010 #049-01-1997 L1998 **FM** *020 †18
LE CHEMINANT, Wilford H. ■ 84010 #049-01-1951 L1958 **PTH** *020 †50
LEOPARDI, Enrico A, Jr. ■ 84010 #016-43-1950 L1956 **OM GPM** *071
LEWIS, David Geo. 415 MEDICAL DR 84010 #010-01-1973 L1977 **OBG** *020 †30
LIANG, Bernard Joseph. 280 N MAIN ST 84010 #054-04-1999 L2004 **MPD** *100 †20,55
LIOU, Kathleen Mc Namara. 620 MEDICAL DR 84010 #010-01-1986 L1998 **PD** *020 †55
LORE, Steven Clarence. 630 MEDICAL DR 84010 #049-01-1999 L2003 **FM** *020 †18
LUND, Glen K. ■ 84010 #049-01-1959 L1960 **OTO** *071 †45
LYMAN, John Bingner. 520 MEDICAL DR STE 201 84010 #040-02-1974 L1980 **OPH** *020 †35
MARTYNSKI, Stanislaw. 1714 RIDGE POINT DR 84010 #759-01-1955 L1991 **EM PD** *071 †55,18,16
MASON, Lyle Beyer. 1551 RENAISSANCE TOWNE DR, STE 400 84010 #021-01-1972 L1978 **ORS** *020 †40
MC DONALD, Joseph Ralph. 630 MEDICAL DR 84010 #049-01-1947 L1970 **ORS OS** *071 †40
MEARS, Molly. 1560 RENAISSANCE TOWNE DR, STE 102 84010 #056-06-2000 L2004 **OBG** *020
MEYSENBURG, Clare P. 280 N MAIN ST 84010 #034-01-1994 L1996 **IM** *020 †20
MURRAY, R Pepper. 1551 RENAISSANCE TOWNE DR, STE 400 84010 #024-01-1986 L1991 **ORS** *020 †40
NELSON, J Kent. 425 MEDICAL DR STE 117 84010 #016-06-1966 L1973 **PD IM** *071
NICHOLS, John Wm. ■ 84010 #049-01-1966 L1973 **OPH** *071 †35
NIELSEN, Douglas Brent. 390 N MAIN ST 84010 #049-01-1977 L1980 **PD ADL** *020 †55 ‡
OKA, Jeffery Ray. 425 MEDICAL DR, STE 108B 84010 #049-01-1986 L1987 **PM** *020 †60
OKAWA, Kaname Kay. ■ 84010 #049-01-1961 L1965 **CD IM** *071 †20
OLDROYD, Glen Scott. 973 BOUNTIFUL BLVD 84010 #049-01-1972 L1973 **AN** *020 †05
OTTOWICZ, Jozef. 440 MEDICAL DR, BOUNTIFUL NEUROLOGY, PC 84010 #759-07-1981 L1995 **N IM** *020 †75
PANTZIRIS, Nancy B Narrod. 535 E 500 S STE 6 84010 #035-46-1988 L1992 **P** *020 †75
PEAD, Gene. 390 N MAIN ST 84010 #049-01-1982 L1986 **OBG** *020 †30
PETERSON, David C. 630 MEDICAL DR, LAKEVIEW HOSP 84010 #010-01-2002 L2006 **AN** *100 †20
PETERSON, Dennis Roger. 415 MEDICAL DR STE B200 84010 #049-01-1972 L1975 **FM** *020 †18
PETERSON, John Louis. 520 MEDICAL DR, STE 200 84010 #049-01-1978 L1992 **D** *020 †15
PICKENS, James Elliot. 425 MEDICAL DR, # 110 84010 #012-01-1967 L1969 **PS CRS** *020 †65
PIKE-BOSTRUM, Samantha N. ■ 84010 #011-03-1994 L1996 **PD P** *020 †30
PUTNAM, William Don. 190 S 500 W 84010 #005-12-1954 L2007 **FM** *020 †18
REESE, Randy Scott. 390 N MAIN ST 84010 #049-01-1977 L1980 **PD ADL** *020 †55 ‡
RICHARDS, Wilford Lynn. ■ 84010 #049-01-1955 L1956 **AN** *071 †45
ROBISON, John Elbert. 520 MEDICAL DR, STE 320 84010 #051-04-2002 L2007 **D** *020 †15
ROSS, Gerald Harvey. ■ 84010 #064-01-1974 L1999 **A OM** *030
SADLER, William Taylor. 415 MEDICAL DR STE C202 84010 #024-01-1980 L1981 **PUD IM** *020 †20
SEARE, Jerald Gilbert. 1308 CANYON CREEK DR 84010 #049-01-1984 L1985 **GS** *020
SELLERS, Daniel Shane. 620 MEDICAL DR, STE 310 84010 #040-02-1981 L1987 **PS HS** *020 †65
SHIELDS, Russell Brent. 425 MEDICAL DR STE 108 84010 #049-01-1970 L1973 **IM** *020 †20
SHURTLIFF, Lyman Folkman. 425 MEDICAL DR, STE 201 84010 #049-01-1957 L1958 **PTH** *072 †50
SKEDROS, Demetrios G. 1551 RENAISSANCE TOWNE DR, STE 310 84010 #016-42-1988 L1993 **OTO** *020 †45
SLADE, David Snow. ■ 84010 #003-01-2007 **IM** *012
SMART, Wallace David. 535 MEDICAL DR 84010 #060-01-1988 L1992 **P** *020 †75
SMITH, Rhonda Ellena. 760 E 1050 N 84010 #032-01-1993 L1994 **FM** *020 †18
SMITH, Wallace Dean. 620 MEDICAL DR STE 340 84010 #010-01-1975 L1979 **OBG** *071 †40
SOUTHWORTH, Scott Ernest. 520 MEDICAL DR, STE 200 84010 #049-01-1984 L1986 **IM** *020 †20
STEELY, June Michelle. 390 N MAIN ST 84010 #007-02-1999 L2000 **IM** *020 †20
STEVENS, David Wayne. ■ 84010 #048-12-2000 L2006 **ORS OSS** *020
STEWART, Dawn Lynn. 630 MEDICAL DR STE 438 84010 #046-01-2001 L2003 **P** *020
STOCK, Curt Robt. 1551 RENAISSANCE TOWNE DR, STE 310 84010 #030-06-1981 L1992 **OTO** *020 †45

STOKER, Kelly Esperson. 1551 RENAISSANCE TOWNE DR, STE 310 84010 #049-01-1987 L1988 **OTO GS** *020 †45
STOWERS, Mark A. 390 N MAIN ST 84010 #654-01-1988 L1991 **OBG PMM** *020 †30
SYKES, Scott Owen. 1551 RENAISSANCE TOWNE DR, STE 340 84010 #023-07-1993 L1997 **OPH IM** *035
TAYLOR, Le Roy Cecil. 520 MEDICAL DR STE 210 84010 #049-01-1965 L1966 **FM GYN** *020 †18
TEW, Jonathan Milton. ■ 84010 #305-01-2004 L2007 **PD** *020
THOMASON, Isaac R, III. 620 MEDICAL DR, STE 200 84010 #048-12-1976 L1977 **GE IM** *020 †20
TODD, Russell Haymore. 425 MEDICAL DR STE 101 84010 #049-01-1990 L1995 **GS** *020 †85
TOLTON, Kevin Dean. ■ 84010 #049-01-1987 L1989 **AN GS** *020 †05
TRACH-MOSKUN, Kathleen A. 390 N MAIN ST 84010 #005-18-1994 L1995 **PD** *020 †55
TUCKER, Kenneth R. 79 E CENTER ST, APT 141 84010 #049-01-1951 **OBG** *071 †30
VANDEMERWE, David Allen. 390 N MAIN ST 84010 #049-01-1995 L1998 **FM** *020 †10
VIRANT, Mandy Jo. ■ 84010 #007-02-2003 L2004 **NS** *012
WALLIN, Anthony Richard. 280 N MAIN ST 84010 #028-34-1994 L1995 **IM** *020 †20
WALTERS, Perry Trowbridge. 425 MEDICAL DR STE 112 84010 #056-06-1969 L1972 **U** *020 †95
WARD, Nathan Clark. 620 MEDICAL DR, STE 340 84010 #023-12-1992 L2004 **OBG** *020 †30
WARD, Raymond Paul. 620 MEDICAL DR STE 150 84010 #054-04-1999 L2007 **OBG** *020 †18
WEST, Scott H. 520 MEDICAL DR, STE 300 84010 #049-01-1979 L1982 **CD IM** *020 †20
WESTON, Raul K. ■ 84010 #051-04-2006 L2008 **FM** *100
WHITE, Charles David. 440 MEDICAL DR, STE 3 84010 #056-06-2000 L2003 **FM** *020 †18
WILCOX, Michael Blair. 1551 RENAISSANCE TOWNE DR, STE 340 84010 #045-01-1997 L1998 **OPH EM** *020 †35
WILSON, George Saml. 440 MEDICAL DR 84010 #049-01-1985 L1986 **FM** *020 †18
WING, Robert Wm. 415 MEDICAL DR, STE C201 84010 #049-01-1977 L1981 **OPH** *020 †35
WONNACOTT, Matthew Paul. 870 HIGHLAND OAKS DR 84010 #023-12-1995 L2004 **FM** *020 †18
YANG, Yvonne. 630 MEDICAL DR 84010 #049-01-1983 L1984 **IM** *071 †20
YOUNG, Whitney Blair. ■ 84010 #019-02-1963 L1968 **OPH GP** *071

BRIAN HEAD – IRON

SIMONS, Margaret A. PO BOX 190206, 768 N COLUMBINE CIR 84719 #049-01-1979 L1983 **DR** *071 †80

BRIGHAM CITY – BOX ELDER

ASHDOWN, Jan Michael. 950 S 500 W STE 104 84302 #049-01-1986 L1992 **TS GS** *040
BEARD, Lynn Quinney. 984 MEDICAL DR, STE 1 84302 #049-01-1980 L1983 **IM** *020 †20
BITNER, Matthew Fetzer. 990 MEDICAL DR STE G4 84302 #030-06-1990 L1993 **ORS** *020 †40
BUNDERSON, Dean L. 47 N 1ST E 84302 #016-02-1946 L1951 **FM GS** *071
CHECKETTS, Spencer Craig. ■ 84302 #041-15-2004 L2004 **GS** *020
CURTIS, Robert Burnell. 950 MEDICAL DR, BRIGHAM CITY COMMUNITY HOS 84302 #048-15-1988 L2000 **EM IM** *020 †20
DAWSON, Brian Christopher. 984 MEDICAL DR, STE 1 84302 #028-34-1995 L1998 **FM** *020 †18
DEGENER, David Fenton. 950 MEDICAL DR, ASSOCIATES OF PATHOLOGY 84302 #007-02-1976 L1992 **PTH PCP** *020 †50
DIBBLE, Carlos Morley. 980 MEDICAL DR 84302 #049-01-1980 L1981 **OBG** *020 †30
DUNN, Charles Richard. 950 MEDICAL DR 84302 #049-01-1969 L1982 **R** *020 †80
FERGUSON, Daniel Richard. 984 MEDICAL DR, BRIGHAM CTR FOR WOMENS 84302 #030-06-1998 L2002 **OBG** *020
FONTEYNE, Douglas C. 984 S 500 W, MEDICAL ARTS GROUP 84302 #060-01-1992 L1994 **FM** *100
GILBERT, Arnold B. ■ 84302 #049-01-1958 L1960 **GP** *071
HANNUM, Thomas Loftin. 984 MEDICAL DR 84302 #035-45-1956 L1959 **FM D** *071 †18
HESS, David Glenn. 950 S 500 W, ANESTHESIA DEPT 84302 #019-02-1982 L1985 **AN CCM** *020
HILLAM, Joseph Dale. 990 S 500 W, MEDICAL ARTS CLINIC 84302 #049-01-1970 L1971 **GS GE** *020 †85
IDDLES, Alan. ■ 84302 #035-20-1948 L1950 **GS** *071 †85
JOHNSON, Kent Garth. 950 MEDICAL DR, BRIGHAM CITY COMMUNITY HOS 84302 #049-01-1982 L1984 **AN** *020 †05
KELLER, Bruce Weaver. 600 W HOSPITAL RD 84302 #049-01-1969 L1970 **GP** *020
LEWIS, David Peterson. 990 MEDICAL DR 84302 #049-01-1980 L1984 **OPH** *020 †35
LISH, Jeffrey Ray. 984 MEDICAL DR, STE 1 84302 #049-01-1987 L1988 **FM** *020 †18
LLOYD, Carey Deyoung. 980 MEDICAL DR STE 2, BRIGHAM PEDIATRICS 84302 #049-01-1993 L1995 **PD** *020 †55
LOMBARDO, James Frederick. 950 MEDICAL DR, ASSOCIATES OF PATHOLOGY 84302 #034-01-1989 L1994 **HMP** *020 †50
MAC KAY, Dewey C, III. 950 MEDICAL DR, STE 06 84302 #049-01-1973 L1977 **ORS** *072 †40
MARKESON, John Robt. 600 W HOSPITAL RD 84302 #026-04-1974 L1978 **IM** *020 †20
MATTHEWS, Thomas M. 600 W HOSPITAL RD, P O BOX 719 84302 #049-01-1976 L1977 **FM** *020 †18
MERRILL, M Reed. 111 E FOREST ST 84302 #049-01-1949 L1951 **GP** *071
ORTON, Mark Douglas. 950 MEDICAL DR, ASSOCIATES OF PATHOLOGY 84302 #040-02-1997 L2003 **PTH** *020 †50
ROCK, Jonathan Charles. 950 S 500 W 84302 #030-06-1994 L2004 **DR** *020 †80
SHAW, Michael Clyde. 984 MEDICAL DR, STE 1 84302 #030-06-1996 L2002 **FM** *020 †18
SMITH, Otto Fay. ■ 84302 #035-45-1954 L1956 **FM** *072
STARR, Stephen E. 980 MEDICAL DR, STE 1 84302 #049-01-1983 L1991 **OBG** *020 †30
STEINER, David Scott. 950 MEDICAL DR, ASSOCIATES OF PATHOLOGY 84302 #021-06-1991 L1997 **PTH** *020 †50
TAYLOR, James Robt. 600 W HOSPITAL RD 84302 #049-01-1980 L1986 **FM** *020 †18
TURNER, Scott Darrin. 990 MEDICAL DR, BRIGHAM EYE SPECIALISTS 84302 #028-34-2003 L2007 **OPH** *020
VONK, Harold. 984 MEDICAL DR 84302 #004-01-1972 L1983 **RHU IM** *020 †20
WILDING, David Gregg. 600 W HOSPITAL RD 84302 #049-01-1990 L1991 **IM** *020
WILDING, Gregg Harry. 600 W HOSPITAL RD 84302 #049-01-1969 L1970 **GP** *030

BRIGHTON – SALT LAKE

CAMERON, Robert Wm. ■ 84121 #026-04-1963 L1969 **OPH** *071 †35

■ = Address Information Privacy Protected

OGILVIE, James W. ■ 84121 #008-01-1968 L1969 **ORS** *020 †40

CEDAR CITY – IRON

ANDERSON, Chad Wareing. 1811 W ROYAL HUNTE DR 84720 #005-12-1990 L1995 **OPH** *020 †35

BAKER, Shane Arthur. 1303 N MAIN ST, VALLEY VIEW MEDICAL CENTER 84720 #054-04-1998 L2003 **DR** *020 †80

BLEAZARD, Jeffery Lynn. 595 S 75 W 84720 #016-42-1996 L1999 **EM** *020

BROWN, Scott L. 170 E ALTAMIRA DR, IHC HEALTH CENTER-CEDAR CI 84720 #049-01-1966 L1967 **FM** *071 †18

BURROWS, Brian Neil. 1333 N MAIN ST, COLOR COUNTRY PEDIATRICS 84720 #422-01-2002 L2005 **PD** *020

CASTORINO, Stephen Cheste. 1303 N MAIN ST, STE C 84720 #041-15-2004 L2007 **IM** *020

COLBERT, Rand Lee. 166 W 1325 N, STE 250 84720 #056-06-2003 L2007 **D** *020 †15

CORRY, Robert Decker. 1303 N MAIN ST, STE C 84720 #049-01-1974 L1976 **FM** *020 †18

COX, Richard Colton. 595 S 75 E 84720 #049-01-1984 L1989 **EM** *020

DELCORE, Randy Geo. 1335 N 380 W, STE 200 84720 #041-02-1990 L1995 **ORS** *020 †40

DOWSE, Robert Kenneth. 1251 NORTHFIELD RD, STE 301 84720 #030-06-1990 L1995 **PD** *020 †55

DUNFORD, William S, Jr. ■ 84721 #023-01-1952 L1961 **GS U** *071

ELLSWORTH, Lansing Grant. 166 W 1325 N, STE 250 84720 #054-04-1991 L1999 **D** *020 †15

FIELDING, Steven Lynn. 1303 N MAIN ST, STE E 84720 #049-01-1965 L1967 **OBG** *071 †30 ‡

GARDNER, Ellen. 170 E ALTAMIRA DR 84720 #049-01-1987 L1988 **GP EM** *020 ‡

GARDNER, Jeffrey Glen. 1303 N MAIN ST, EMERGENCY DEPT 84720 #049-01-2002 L2007 **EM** *100

GARRETT, Todd Michael. ■ 84720 #035-03-2007 **IM** *012

GATHERUM, Daren O. 1303 N MAIN ST, STE C 84720 #018-75-2000, ▲ L2003 **OBG** *020 †30

GRAY, Jarid D. 110 W 1325 N, STE 200 84720 #049-01-1999 L2002 **FM** *020 †18

HANSEN, Mark Traveller. 166 W 1325 N, STE 350 84720 #049-01-1993 L1998 **GS** *020 †85

HARDENBURG, Harold C, Jr. ■ 84720 #041-13-1958 **NEP IM** *071

HATCH, Harvey Ray. 1303 N MAIN ST 84720 #049-01-1969 L1974 **DR** *062 †80

HEATH, Terence Alon. 110 W 1325 N, STE 300 84720 #023-12-1996 L2006 **OBG** *020 †30

HENDRIX, Bruce Allen. 1303 N MAIN ST, STE C 84720 #017-20-1980 L2003 **IM** *020 †20

KEY, Wendell Gene. 1072 W 800 S, 1072 W. 800 S. 84720 #308-11-1986 L1991 **FM** *020 †18

MARSHALL, Thomas T. 1303 N MAIN ST, STE C 84720 #049-01-1979 L1982 **FM EM** *020 †18

MCCUNE, Brian Clark. 1333 N MAIN ST, COLOR COUNTY PEDIATRICS 84720 #305-01-2004 L2007 **PD** *020

MC CUNE, Craig Scott. 1303 N MAIN ST 84720 #010-01-1967 L1999 **ON IM** *020 †20

MC NAUGHT, David Ross. 150 E ALTAMIRA DR, STE 200 84720 #060-01-1960 L1977 **ORS OS** *071

MC PEEK, Raymond Roger. 440 N PAIUTE DR, PAIUTE INDIAN TRIBE OF UT 84720 #051-01-1971 L1995 **RHU IM** *020 †20

MILLER, Gia D. 1251 NORTHFIELD RD, STE 301 84720 #003-01-1999 L2006 **PD** *020 †55

MUNFORD, Michael Irving. 166 W 1325 N, STE 350 84720 #049-01-1993 L2001 **GS** *020

NAISBITT, Scott Raymon. ■ 84720 #024-01-2001 *100

NAKKEN, Robert Eugene. 1326 N, STE 350 84720 #028-34-1993 L1998 **ORS** *020 †40

NEWMAN, Steven Richard. 110 W 1325 N, STE 200 84720 #049-01-1999 L2003 **IM** *020 †18

PEARSON, Robert Dean. 1251 NORTHFIELD RD, STE 200 84720 #049-01-1994 L1999 **OTO** *020 †45

PETTY, William Clayton. PO BOX 716 84721 #049-01-1965 L1968 **AN** *071 †05

PHILLIPS, Steven D. 1303 N MAIN ST, VALLEY VIEW MEDICAL CENTER 84720 #016-06-1987 L1992 **DR** *020 †80

PORTER, Julie Lyn. 1303 N MAIN ST, STE C 84720 #049-01-2000 L2003 **IM** *020

SANDERS, Stephen Michael. 1303 N MAIN ST STE A 84720 #048-04-1998 L2002 **OBG** *020 †30

SHABANA, Tawfik A. 1306 W 1070 S 84720 #915-02-1978 L1998 **MPD OBG** *020 †55,20

SMITH, Philip Evan. 1303 N MAIN ST, STE C 84720 #049-01-1991 L1992 **IM** *020

STULTS, Michael Garnett. 166 W 1325 N, STE 350 84720 #024-07-1972 L1983 **GS EM** *020 †16

TE, Joseph Derit. 1870 N MAIN ST 84720 #748-08-1989 L1999 **HEM** *020

THINNES, Charles John, Jr. 1303 N MAIN ST, STE C 84720 #016-11-1973 L1978 **FM** *020 †18

WILSON, Michael Lee. ■ 84720 #005-18-2001 L2004 **EM** *020 †16

WOOLLEY, Galen Snow. ■ 84720 #049-01-1955 L1959 **OBG** *071 †30

CEDAR HILLS – UTAH

JONES, Justin Earl. ■ 84062 #010-01-2004 L2006 **FM** *100 †18

CENTERVILLE – DAVIS

ASHRAFI, Shadi. ■ 84014 #049-01-2008 *012

EDMUNDS, Alyson Elaine. ■ 84014 #049-01-2007 L2007 **PD** *012

HOLT, Howard Lee. ■ 84014 #005-16-1962 L1975 **IM NTR** *071

ISAACSON, Eddie Arnold. ■ 84014 #049-01-1959 L1961 **PHP GPM** *071 †70

KAWA, Chad Barrett. 582 N 340 E 84014 #038-34-2007 **IM** *012

LARSEN, E Wayne. ■ 84014 #056-06-1988 L1992 **AN** *020 †05

MANN, David Benjamin. ■ 84014 #036-05-2008 *012

MC CURRY, Mindy. ■ 84014 #049-01-2007 **FP** *012

MORRILL, Arnold Brett. 26 S MAIN ST 84014 #028-79-2001, ▲ L2004 **FM** *020 †18

PLEACHER, Kristine Mary. ■ 84014 #051-04-2002 L2005 **CCP** *012 †55

SMITH, Cal Leonard. ■ 84014 #056-06-2006 L2006 **EM** *012

TORRES, Anthony Ronald. ■ 84014 #049-01-1974 **CLP** *050

TRUMP, Bryce Eugene. 718 E 850 S 84014 #048-13-1991 L2005 **AN** *020 †05

WEBSTER, Jami Sue. 26 S MAIN ST 84014 #039-01-1997 L1998 **PD** *020 †55

WEEKS, Wm Richard, Jr. 26 S MAIN ST 84014 #025-01-1972 L1977 **PD NPM** *020 †55

CLEARFIELD – DAVIS

BODILY, Kory Ray. ■ 84015 #023-12-2004 **AN** *012

CLINTON – DAVIS

ASTLE, Nelson La Farr. 1792 W 1800 N, WESTSIDE MEDICAL 84015 #049-01-1981 L1984 **FM** *020 †18

COTTONWOOD – SALT LAKE

AFSHAR, Andrew Andisheh. ■ 84121 #005-06-2000 L2008 **GS** *020

AKHTAR, Faheem. ■ 84121 #031-01-2001 L2006 **VS** *012 †85

LIPTON, Ross Eliott. 2133 PINNACLE TERRACE WAY, UNIT 10-302 84121 #041-09-1990 L1999 **N CN** *071 †75 ‡

YUKNIS, Brook Ann. ■ 84121 #030-06-2007 **PD** *012

COTTONWOOD HEIGHTS – SALT LAKE

GRINSELL, Matthew Michael. ■ 84121 #031-01-2000 L2007 **PN** *100 †55

DELTA – MILLARD

HENRIE, David Paul. 130 WHITE SAGE AVE # B 84624 #049-01-1970 L1971 **GP** *020

JACKSON, Easton David. 140 WHITE SAGE AVE 84624 #049-01-2001 L2004 **FM** *020 †18

SHAMO, Steven Wayne. 140 WHITE SAGE AVE 84624 #049-01-1992 L1993 **FM** *020 †18

SMITH, Alan Ross. 140 WHITE SAGE AVE 84624 #049-01-1988 L1989 **FM** *020 †18

DRAPER – SALT LAKE

BALLARD, Robert Henriod. ■ 84020 #049-01-1944 L1948 **ORS** *072 †40

BLANCH, George Marsden. 11506 S STATE ST # 2 84020 #049-01-1974 L1975 **OTO** *074 †45

BRADY, Steven E. ■ 84020 #049-01-1985 L1987 **OPH** *071 †35

CALL, Gary Scott. 12176 S 1000 E 84020 #054-04-1988 L1989 **FM** *020 †18

CARLTON, Alisa. 12176 S 1000 E STE H 84020 #051-07-1997 L2001 **OBG** *020 †30

CLAYTON, Daniel Bennion. 114 E 12450 S, OFC 84020 #035-01-2002 L2005 **PD** *020

COLEMAN, Jeremy Bryce. 1126 DRAPER PKWY 84020 #005-12-2004 L2005 **FM** *020 †18

FEINDT, Karla Ann. 12176 S 1000 E, DRAPER 84020 #056-05-1997 L1998 **PD** *020 †55

GARDEN, Richard Michael. ATTN: MEDICAL, UTAH STATE PRISON 84020 #005-18-1993 L1994 **MDM GP** *030

GIANOULIS, Tony. 14708 DRAPER VIEW CV 84020 #049-01-1990 L1991 **AN** *020

GOOCH, Harold Norman. 12176 S 1000 E 84020 #049-01-1988 L1989 **FM** *020 †18

GROATHOUSE, Anthony R. ■ 84020 #049-01-1991 L1992 **UCM FM** *020 †18

HANSEN, Kimberly. 12176 S 1000 E, DRAPER 84020 #049-01-1994 L1995 **PD** *020 †55

HARRIS, Duane J. 12422 S 450 E, STE C 84020 #049-01-1985 L1987 **AI IM** *020 †20,03

HOLMES, James David. ■ 84020 #422-01-2003 L2005 **IM** *100

HORNYIK, Galina Renata. 12176 S 1000 E, DRAPER 84020 #040-02-1993 L1994 **PD** *020 †55

JOHNSON, Samuel S. ■ 84020 #023-12-1983 L1988 **FM P** *030 †18

LEWIS, Bradley Kay. 1126 E 12300 S 84020 #049-01-1991 L1994 **PS** *020

LOPEZ, Ronald Frank. 12176 S 1000 E 84020 #005-18-1991 L1992 **FM** *020 †18

MARSHALL, Barry J. 12050 LONE PEAK PKWY, TRIMED SPECIALTIES INC 84020 #143-06-1974 L1989 **IM** *050 †20

MINER, Sharlene. 328 BROWN FARM LN, UTAH EMERGENCY PHYSICIANS 84020 #049-01-1994 L2004 **EM** *020 †16

MOSKOWITZ, Peter Kenneth. 12176 S 1000 E, STE G 84020 #035-19-1996 L1997 **PD** *020 †55

NIELSEN, Bradley Peter. ■ 84020 #049-01-1990 L1994 **AN** *020 †05

RODIER, Hugo Encinas. 12433 FORT ST 84020 #049-01-1984 L1989 **FM** *020 †18

RYAN, Jimmy Lynn. ■ 84020 #001-02-1978 L1984 **PD** *020 †55

SLOAN, Carrie Leigh. 12176 S 1000 E, STE H 84020 #035-09-1996 L2004 **OBG** *020 †30

STAMPFL, Daniel Ray. 12176 S 1000 E, DRAPER 84020 #056-05-1994 L1995 **PD** *020 †55

WOODS, Rachel Jordan. 114 E 12450 S, OFC 84020 #049-01-2003 L2004 **PD** *020 †55

DUCHESNE – DUCHESNE

BURKLEY, David Perry. ■ 84021 #030-06-1964 L1969 **PDA PD** *071 †55,03

EDEN – WEBER

COBABE, Alvin Fred. ■ 84310 #049-01-1963 L1964 **GP** *071

STUKAN, Nancy Kathryn. ■ 84310 #005-02-1978 L1981 **GYN** *020 †30

ELK RIDGE – UTAH

GRAHAM, Raymond Leon. ■ 84651 #048-13-1975 L2002 **PTH** *075 †30,50

EPHRAIM – SANPETE

BATEMAN, Kim Alan. 39 E 450 N 84627 #049-01-1974 L1975 **FM** *020 †18

HANSEN, T Randy. 525 N MAIN ST 84627 #049-01-1987 L1988 **GS** *020 †85

JACKSON, Eileen K. 525 N MAIN ST 84627 #049-01-2003 L2004 **FM** *020 †18

NUNN, Tristy Guercio. 525 N MAIN ST 84627 #025-07-1997 L2001 **FM** *020 †18

OLSEN, Darrel Ward. 525 N MAIN ST 84627 #049-01-1989 L1990 **FM** *020 †18

FARMINGTON – DAVIS

BARLOW, Bill Richter. ■ 84025 #056-06-2004 L2005 **OPH** *012

BENNETT, George Martin. PO BOX 98 84025 #049-01-1968 L1969 **AN** *071 †05

BERWALD, Charles John. 800 W STATE ST, MEDICAL UNIT 84025 #025-01-1963 L1973 **FM GP** *020 †18

BOWMAN, Aaron Thomas. ■ 84025 #038-40-2003 L2004 **HO** *012 †20

CAMPBELL, Vance Dewey. ■ 84025 #049-01-1955 L1966 **AN OS** *071 †05

CHILD, Brent Stanley. 1287 WOODLAND CT 84025 #049-01-1976 L1979 **AN** *020 †05

CLARKE, James Harker. 810 SHEPARD LN # 1 84025 #016-11-1948 **GP** *071

EDWARDS, Charles Bryner. ■ 84025 #010-01-1964 L1966 **GS SO** *071 †85

FRITINGER, Thomas. 1466 N HIGHWAY 89, STE 220 84025 #038-45-1994 L2005 **FM** *020 †18

HIBBARD, Julie Cleek. 1401 N HIGHWAY 89 STE 220 84025 #047-05-2000 L2001 **FM** *020 †18

HUNGERFORD, Patrick Ryan. ■ 84025 #051-07-2004 L2005 **END** *012 †20
JACKSON, Richard Landrum. 1587 CHERRY CIR 84025 #036-01-1983 L1987 **P** *020 †75
KENNARD, Richard Franklan. ■ 84025 #056-06-2007 **TY** *012
KIRKHAM, Jason Anthony. ■ 84025 #035-09-1999 L2005 **DR** *100 †80
OLDROYD, John Jay. ■ 84025 #023-01-1966 L1971 **GS HNS** *020 †85
SPENCER, Neil Orrin. 722 SHEPARD LN STE 102 84025 #010-01-1987 L1989 **OBG** *020 †30
TAN, Sally Suklun. 1401 N 1075 W, STE 220 84025 #016-43-1997 L1998 **FM** *020 †18

FILLMORE – MILLARD

BROWN, Wayne Orval. 674 S HIGHWAY 99 84631 #050-02-2000 L2001 **FM** *020 †18
GROSE, Craig Michael. 700 S HIGHWAY 99 84631 #010-01-1995 L1996 **FM** *020 †18
JACKSON, Brent David. 700 S HIGHWAY 99 STE 3 84631 #049-01-1978 L1979 **FM** *020 †18
LIMBURG, David Greaves. ■ 84631 #049-01-1972 L1973 **FM GP** *020 †18

FRUIT HEIGHTS – DAVIS

GARRISON, Garth William. ■ 84037 #049-01-2005 L2005 **IM** *012
MORRIS, Erin A. ■ 84037 #049-01-2008 *012

GARLAND – BOX ELDER

SCHOW, Jan-Erik. 300 W 1400 S, BEAR RIVER MED ARTS 84312 #048-15-1992 L1995 **FM** *020 †18

GUNNISON – SANPETE

BECK, Kimberly Elizabeth. 67 E CENTER 84634 #055-02-1992 L1994 **FM** *020 †18
CHRISTENSEN, Jan F. 64 E 100 N 84634 #026-12-1974 L1977 **FM** *020 †18
INOUYE, Dwight Hideo. 64 E 100 N 84634 #049-01-1977 L1979 **FM** *020 †18
JACKSON, Christine. ■ 84634 #649-33-1988 L1995 **FM** *020 †18
NAY, Richard Bill. 64 E 100 N 84634 #049-01-1982 L1984 **EM** *020 †18
PRATT, Von S. 64 E 100 N 84634 #005-15-1973 L1976 **FM** *020
STEWART, Lamar H. 79 E CENTER ST 84634 #049-01-1954 L1955 **GP OS** *071
WILLDEN, Gerald James. ■ 84634 #049-01-2004 L2005 **FM** *020 †18

HEBER CITY – WASATCH

BERG, Tod L. 1467 S HIGHWAY 40 84032 #049-01-1992 L1993 **FM** *020 †18
BURTON, Neal Jay. 35 S 500 E 84032 #049-01-1974 L1977 **FM** *020
CHAMBERLAIN, Michelle A. 380 E 1500 S, HEBER VALLEY 84032 #047-05-1995 L1996 **PD** *020 †55
CHRISTENSEN, Wendell, Jr. ■ 84032 #049-01-1962 L1963 **U** *020 †95
FASSIO, John B. 1471 S HIGHWAY 40 84032 #020-02-1989 L1993 **OPH OS** *020 †35
GOODRICH, Coriann. ■ 84032 #016-42-1992 L1997 **FM** *075
HADERLIE, Todd Matthew. 1465 S HIGHWAY 40 84032 #049-01-1990 L1992 **FM** *020 †18
HULL, Maggie. 380 E 1500 S, HEBER VALLEY 84032 #049-01-2000 L2003 **PD** *020 †55
LARSON, David Charles. 380 E 1500 S, HEBER VALLEY 84032 #049-01-1995 L1998 **PD** *020 †55
MC DONALD, Stanton B. 35 S 500 E, WASATCH MEDICAL CLINIC 84032 #049-01-1976 L1977 **FM** *020 †18
MILLER, Steven Kay. 1485 S HIGHWAY 40 84032 #049-01-1986 L1990 **OTO** *030 †45
NIELSON, Karl Douglas. 347 GREENER HILLS RD 84032 #049-01-1967 L1988 **NS GS** *071 †25
PITTS, George D. 35 S 500 E 84032 #049-01-1971 L1972 **FM** *020 †18
SCHAFFER, Monica Maria. 380 E 1500 S, HEBER VALLEY 84032 #026-04-1994 L1997 **PD** *020 †55
SHARP, Gary Howard. 1473 S HIGHWAY 40 84032 #023-12-1982 L2004 **OBG** *020 †30
SOUTHWICK, James Philip. ■ 84032 #008-01-1971 L1978 **AN AM** *071 †05
TAYLER, Gregory Paul. 1469 S HIGHWAY 40 84032 #049-01-1995 L1996 **FM** *020 †18 ‡
TOWNSEND, Duane Everett. 1485 S HIGHWAY 40 84032 #005-14-1960 L1992 **GYN GO** *020 †30
WILLIAMS, Richard Bart. 965 N 800 E 84032 #056-06-2007 **GS** *012

HERRIMAN – SALT LAKE

ADAMS, Robert Henry. ■ 84096 #017-20-1963 L1963 **P** *074
DAYNES, Gregory Sharp. 5746 W 13400 S 84096 #049-01-2000 L2003 **FM** *100 †18
PETERSON, Michael James. 5746 W 13400 S 84096 #010-01-2000 L2003 **FM** *020 †18
POOR, David Dewile. 5746 W 13400 S 84096 #005-12-2003 L2004 **FM** *020 †18

HIGHLAND – UTAH

BLACKWELL, Elizabeth K. ■ 84003 #041-02-1974 L1977 **FM EM** *020
CARROLL, Tyler Shawn. 10968 N ALPINE HWY 84003 #051-07-2002 L2003 **FM** *020 †18
SHEFFIELD, Roger Whiteley. 10488 EDINBURGH DR, ROGER W. SHEFFIELD MD 84003 #049-01-1975 L1984 **GS EM** *020 †85,16
SLACK, Robert W.. 10968 N ALPINE HWY 84003 #028-79-2002, ▲ L2003 **FM** *020 †18
TALL, Bruce Asael. ■ 84003 #049-01-1963 L1964 **U** *071
WALTON, Charles Wesley. ■ 84003 #049-01-1970 L1973 **ADM AN** *071 †05 ‡

HILL AIR FORCE BASE – DAVIS

ANDERSON, Dellray Hansen. 7321 11TH ST BLDG 570, 75 MDG 84056 #049-01-1985 L1986 **FM** *020 †18
BENNION, James Roald. ■ 84056 #023-12-1990 L1992 **OM** *030 †70
BISHOP, Scott Russell. 7321 11TH ST BLDG 570, 75TH MEDICAL GROUP 84056 #023-12-2005 L2007 **FM** *020 †18
BURST, Annette Gralia. ■ 84056 #017-20-1971 L1982 **OM PHP** *020 †70

BUSK, Neal Christian. 7321 11TH ST BLDG 570, 75TH MEDICAL GROUP 84056 #056-06-2004 L2006 **FM** *020 †18
COLL, Joseph Kenneth, III. 7321 11TH ST BLDG 570, 75TH MEDICAL GROUP 84056 #033-05-2000 L2002 **P** *020 †75
FULLER, Douglas Conrad. 7238 6TH ST, BLDG 249 84056 #049-01-1982 L1998 **OM** *040 †70,18
KLEIN, Henry J. 7321 11TH ST BLDG 570, 75TH MEDICAL GROUP/ MEDICA 84056 #187-09-1983 L1994 **IM CD** *020
ROBERTS, Debra Ann. 7321 11TH ST BLDG 570, 75TH MEDICAL GROUP 84056 #041-14-2001 L2003 **FM** *020
THACKER, Dave H. 7321 11TH ST, BLDG 570A 84056 #028-34-1989 L1997 **PD** *020 †55
ULISSEY, Laurence A. ■ 84056 #048-13-2001 L2001 **FM** *020
VILLATA, Richard Bruce. 7321 11TH ST BLDG 570, ATTN: CREDENTIAL OFFICE 84056 #033-05-1995 L1998 **AM OM** *020 †70
VON HAZMBURG, Romulus S. AIR FORCE HOSP 84056 #016-43-1961 **PHP AM** *020 †70

HOLLADAY – SALT LAKE

BANKHEAD, Byron Rey. ■ 84117 #028-34-2001 L2002 **AN** *100 †05
FLINT, Robert. 4970 S 900 E STE C, DR ROBERT L FLINT 84117 #020-02-1993 L1996 **OS HNS** *020
JONES, Colin David. ■ 84117 #060-01-2003 L2007 **DR** *012
MC GOUGH, Edwin Clifford. 1055 E 3900 S, ROBERT A PLACE 84124 #021-01-1961 L1972 **TS** *071 †85,90
OLIVER, Brian Samuel. ■ 84124 #010-01-2003 L2006 **EM** *020 †16
PARZYCH, Kevin Kenneth. 1151 E 3900 S, STE B299 84124 #035-03-1995 L1997 **FM** *020 †18
PROBST, Jared Bailey. 4624 HOLLADAY BLVD 84117 #049-01-1996 L1999 **FM** *020 †18
ROSKELLEY, Maurice Kay. 1151 E 3900 S 84124 #016-06-1956 L1964 **D** *071 †16
SHAKA, James Athan. 1580 E 3900 S 84124 #023-07-1952 L1969 **P PTH** *071 †50
SMITH, Stephen Brent. 1624 E 4500 S, IHC HEALTH CENTER 84117 #010-01-1978 L1990 **GS CRS** *020 †10,85
STEVENS, Larry Phillip. ■ 84124 #049-01-1968 L1976 **DR** *020 †80
TOPHAM, Earl Barry. 1775 E 4500 S 84117 #041-01-1968 L1974 **D DMP** *020 †15
WHITEHEAD, Paul L. ■ 84117 #049-01-1960 L1967 **P CHP** *071 †75
WILKERSON, Donald Keith. 1580 E 3900 S 84124 #005-02-1966 L1979 **CHP P** *072 †75
WOOD, James Stewart. 1414 E 4500 S, STE 1 84117 #049-01-1975 L1977 **IMG IM** *020 †20
WOOLSEY, Carl T, Jr. 1151 E 3900 S, STE 299 84124 #023-01-1971 L1974 **OBG** *071
WYATT, Paul Wade. 4878 HIGHLAND DR, UNGRICHT EYE ASSOCIATES 84117 #049-01-1996 L2007 **OPH** *020 †35
ZURCHER, Emily Brooke. ■ 84117 #049-01-2008 *012

HUNTSVILLE – WEBER

BOYCE, Joey Burl. 1057 S 6525 E 84317 #039-01-1983 L1996 **AM** *050 †70
CATANZARO, Ronald John. ■ 84317 #028-02-1958 L1958 **P OS** *030 †75
DAVIS, Jack J. 7478 E FIRST ST 84317 #016-06-1948 L1949 **DR** *071
HEDGES, Ward Horace. ■ 84317 #049-01-1958 L1960 **P CHP** *071
HOPSON, Patricia A Craig. ■ 84317 #025-07-1953 L1954 **P** *071 †75
MOYAL, Aaron Henri R. ■ 84317 #396-06-1964 L2005 **P** *071
VIGH, Sara Sipos. ■ 84317 #473-04-1969 L1985 **PD ADL** *020
WACHTER, Susan Blake. ■ 84317 #049-01-2006 L2007 **IM** *012

HURRICANE – WASHINGTON

CLARK, Robert Wilford. ■ 84737 #049-01-1964 L1965 **END IM** *071 †20,28
GREEN, Peter Carlyle. ■ 84737 #049-01-1947 L1950 **AN** *071 †05
HAWKINS, Anne Marie. 90 S 700 W 84737 #003-01-1978 L2000 **IM** *020 †20
HUBBARD, Jonathan P. 90 S 700 W 84737 #028-79-1997, ▲ L2000 **FM** *020 †18
KOFOED, Kenneth Ralph. 90 S 700 W 84737 #010-01-1975 L1983 **U** *020 †95
LAMBERT, Gary Hardy. 90 S 700 W 84737 #049-01-1970 L1971 **EM** *020 †16
TAYLOR, Bruce L. 90 S 700 W 84737 #016-76-1998, ▲ L1999 **FM** *020 †18
WELSH, Thomas Herbert. 90 S 700 W 84737 #003-01-1978 L2000 **EM IM** *020 †20
WORWOOD, Danny K. 75 N 2260 W, HURRICANE FAMILY PRACTICE 84737 #023-12-1993 L2003 **FM** *020 †18

HYDE PARK – CACHE

GONZALES, Shane Toby. ■ 84318 #056-06-2000 L2002 **AN** *020 †05

HYRUM – CACHE

GRAHAM, Charles James. 10 N 600 E 84319 #049-01-1965 L1966 **GS GP** *020 †85

IVINS – WASHINGTON

APOSTOL, Ferdinand V. 272 E CENTER ST 84738 #748-08-1990 L2001 **IM** *020 †20
ASHTON, Henry Lindsay. ■ 84738 #010-01-1966 L1967 **EM GP** *071 †16
BRIZOLARA, Alberto A. 272 E CENTER ST STE 104 84738 #187-25-1992 L2003 **IC** *020 †20
BUSH, Candida Janet. ■ 84738 #016-02-1980 L1983 **EM** *020 †16
CARY, Robert Franklin, Jr. ■ 84738 #016-02-1962 L1965 **P** *071
DE SAIBRO, Luciana. 272 E CENTER ST STE 201 84738 #187-25-1991 L2003 **CN** *020 †75
HARDIN, Dana. 272 E CENTER ST STE 206 84738 #016-11-1996 L1999 **FM** *020 †18
ISAKSON, Larry Harold. ■ 84738 #049-01-1974 L1977 **FM EM** *071 †18
JACKS, John James. ■ 84738 #005-14-1971 L1972 **OM FM** *071 †18
JONES, Gary Lee. 272 E CENTER ST, STE 210 84738 #049-01-1987 L1988 **N** *020 †75
MANALO, Jane Grace M. 272 E CENTER ST, SNOW CANYON CLINIC 84738 #748-01-1992 L2001 **IM HO** *020 †20
MIDDLETON, Raymond J. 272 E CENTER ST 84738 #065-05-1957 L1978 **FM OS** *071 †18
NIELSEN, Cantril. ■ 84738 #010-01-1966 L1967 **CHP P** *071 †75
PADWICK, Michael John. ■ 84738 #056-05-1967 L1983 **FM PG** *071 †18

ROWE, Lynn Brockbank. 139 PAINTED HILLS DR 84738 #010-01-1961 L1980 **GS** *071
SCHMIDT, John Gerhard. 272 E CENTER ST, SNOW CANYON CLINIC 84738 #026-04-1985 L2006 **N** *020 †75
SOUCY, John Clovis, Jr. ■ 84738 #028-34-1961 L1961 **IM PUD** *020 †20

JOSEPH – SEVIER

WARNER, Jonathan Nicholas. 550 N HIGHWAY 89 84739 #049-01-2007 **GS** *012

KAMAS – SUMMIT

KUMAGAI, John Y. PO BOX 38 84036 #049-01-1946 L1949 **GP** *071

KANAB – KANE

ANDERSON, Michael Burton. 180 W 300 N 84741 #049-01-1983 L1984 **ORS** *020 †40
BENTLEY, Wendell James. ■ 84741 #010-01-1973 L1974 **PS** *072
BOWMAN, Jonathan Craig. 355 N MAIN ST, KANE COUNTY HOSPITAL 84741 #049-01-2000 L2003 **FM** *020 †18
BURST, Stephen Jos. 48 N 200 W 84741 #017-20-1971 L1985 **PD** *020 †55
PANDYA, Avnish Popatlal. 256 W 300 N 84741 #905-01-1972 L1979 **FM P** *020
PARRY, Scott Alvarus. 180 W 300 N 84741 #041-01-1991 L1996 **ORS** *020 †40
PRINCE, Edward John. 180 W 300 N 84741 #056-06-2000 L2005 **ORS** *020
ROBERTS, Howard L, Jr. 220 N 300 N 84741 #049-01-1961 L1971 **FM** *020

KAYSVILLE – DAVIS

BARKLEY, John Chas. ■ 84037 #048-04-1980 L1982 **AN** *071
BASS, Randall Dwight. ■ 84037 #041-07-1993 L2007 **HMP** *020
BELNAP, Wilford Dean. ■ 84037 #049-01-1947 L1948 **CHP** *020 †55
EVANS, Ryan Newell. 380 N 400 W 84037 #049-01-1993 L1996 **PD** *020 †55
GUNTHER, Loretto Ann. ■ 84037 #041-07-1965 L1966 **EM** *020
HOENES, Douglas Radford. ■ 84037 #049-01-1968 **IM OM** *071 †20
HUMPHERYS, Ben R. ■ 84037 #028-78-2002, ▲ L2007 **M** *020 †60
KELLY, V Robt. ■ 84037 #049-01-1951 L1952 **FM** *071 †18
KIRKHAM, Michael Don. 380 N 400 W 84037 #049-01-1989 L1991 **FM** *020 †18
KNOWLTON, Edward Ute. 84037 #049-01-1958 L1959 **R** *071 †80
LEE, Gary David. 380 N 400 W 84037 #049-01-1992 L1993 **FM** *020 †18 ‡
MORRELL, Stephen Lynn. 380 N 400 W 84037 #049-02-1998 L1999 **FM** *020 †18
PHILLIPS, Ross Milton. ■ 84037 #049-01-1959 L1960 **DR** *071
POTTER, Steven Jared. 307 N 300 W, STE 301 84037 #023-01-2003 L2005 **FM** *020 †18
PRICE, Mary Bishop. ■ 84037 #049-01-2006 **EM** *012
RYAN, Michael Edward. ■ 84037 #019-02-1966 L1998 **IM NEP** *020 †20
SCHAELLING, Michael P. 380 N 400 W 84037 #049-01-1989 L1991 **FM** *020 †18
SNELL, George Francis. ■ 84037 #010-01-1958 L1962 **FM** *071 †18
TAYLOR, John Barron. 47 CRESTWOOD RD 84037 #012-05-1974 L1978 **GP** *020
WARDEN, David Royal. 7 CRESTWOOD RD, KAYSVILLE MEDICAL CENTER 84037 #041-01-1964 L1968 **FM AM** *071 †18
WILLIAMS, Ariel L, Jr. ■ 84037 #049-01-1960 L1961 **DR** *071
ZUBELDIA, Pedro. ■ 84037 #847-17-1979 **PTH** *071

KEARNS – SALT LAKE

DEDRICK-ZEHNDER, Jean. 3809 W 6200 S 84118 #025-07-1989 L1990 **PD P** *020 †75,55
FEIST, Laura. ■ 84118 #037-01-2008 *012
GONTRUM, David Martin. 4745 S 3200 W 84118 #040-02-1996 L1997 **FM** *020 †18
SONI, Poonam. 3703 W 6200 S 84118 #047-06-1986 L1987 **CHP P** *020 †75

LAYTON – DAVIS

ALEXANDER, Gary James. 2121 ROBINS DR 84041 #049-01-1987 L1988 **PUD IM** *020 †20
ALLAMEH, Vida. ■ 84040 #056-06-1993 L1994 **PD** *075
ALLRED, Michael Glade. 2121 ROBINS DR 84041 #049-01-2001 L2002 **FM** *020 †18
AL-RAYESS, Khaldoun M. 1492 W ANTELOPE DR, STE 205 84041 #875-01-1997 L2005 **END** *020 †20
AL-SADAT, Ahmad Nadim. 1492 W ANTELOPE DR, STE 205 84041 #875-01-1997 L2002 **N CN** *020 †75
AMIL, Brent Ricardo. 2250 N 1700 W, LAYTON UNIT 84041 #049-01-1987 L1995 **CHP** *020 †75
ANDERSON, Marc Olsen. 2121 ROBINS DR 84041 #028-34-1988 L1995 **FM A** *020
ANDERSON, Mark V. 2102 ROBINS DR, STE 103 84041 #049-01-1978 L1981 **OM EM** *020
ARANGO, James F. 1600 W ANTELOPE DR, INTEGRATED CARE AT DAVIS 84041 #011-02-1968 L1972 **OS** *020
ARCHULETA, Letitia P. 2102 ROBINS DR, STE 103 84041 #049-01-1987 L1989 **GPM OM** *020 †70
ASHBY, Eric Robt. 2121 ROBINS DR 84041 #005-02-1989 L1997 **PS HS** *020 †65 ‡
AU, Charmaine Kawehilani. ■ 84041 #049-01-2008 *012
BALCOMBE, D Joan. 1600 W ANTELOPE DR, INTEGRATED CARE AT DAVIS 84041 #016-02-1980 L1981 **EM GS** *020 †85,65
BARENG, Robin Keoni. ■ 84041 #023-12-2005 L2006 **PD** *100
BARKER, Layne Thomas. 2121 ROBINS DR 84041 #021-01-1996 L2000 **FM IM** *020 †20,18
BARNEY, Douglas Paul. 934 S MAIN ST, KAYSVILLE CLINIC 84041 #049-01-1979 L1980 **FM** *020 †18
BASS, Clayton Allen. 1600 W ANTELOPE DR, INTEGRATED CARE AT DAVIS 84041 #027-01-1991 L2006 **EM** *020 †16
BAXTER, Mark Ephraim. 2121 ROBINS DR 84041 #049-01-1989 L1993 **FM** *020 †18 ‡
BEAN, Charles Parrish. 2121 ROBINS DR 84041 #049-01-1975 L1979 **ORS** *020 †40
BELL, Christopher Conrad. 2075 N 1200 W 84041 #041-02-2004 L2005 **FM** *020 †18
BERNHISEL, Harris Glenn. 2121 ROBINS DR 84041 #049-01-1948 L1964 **DR N** *071
BERRY, Edward Wm. 1600 W ANTELOPE DR 84041 #028-03-1986 L1991 **AN** *020 †05

BEUS, Michael Lynn. 2121 N 1700 W 84041 #049-01-1985 L1989 **FM** *020 †18
BISHOP, Bruce Lyman. 2121 N 1700 W 84041 #049-01-1970 L1971 **D** *071 †15
BITNER, Mark Robert. 2121 N 1700 W 84041 #649-33-1981 L1984 **OBG** *020 †30
BITNER, Robert F. 2121 ROBINS DR, B GRANT BISHOP 84041 #049-01-1951 L1953 **IM CD** *071
BOS, Norman Calvin, II. 2121 N 1700 W 84041 #010-01-1976 L1978 **ORS** *020 †40
BOWMAN, Adam Merlin. 1580 W ANTELOPE DR, STE 175 84041 #021-01-2003 L2007 **OPH FM** *020
BURNINGHAM, Ted Howard. 2121 ROBINS DR 84041 #010-01-1993 L1994 **FM** *020 †18
BURRELL, John Charles. 1580 W ANTELOPE DR, STE 145 84041 #065-05-1975 L1994 **ORS OSS** *020
BURTENSHAW, Bruce Francis. 2121 N 1700 W 84041 #035-01-1975 L1978 **IM** *020 †20
CATASCA, John Vincent. 1600 W ANTELOPE DR, UTAH IMAGING 84041 #034-01-1991 L1994 **DR** *020 †80 ‡
CHECKETTS, Scott Richard. 2121 ROBINS DR 84041 #033-06-1992 L1994 **D** *020 †20,15
CHOWDHURY, Arif A. 2121 ROBINS DR 84041 #160-03-1978 L1997 **N** *020
CHUNG, Hannah Lim. 1600 W ANTELOPE DR, UTAH IMAGING 84041 #038-40-1995 L1996 **DR** *020 †28,80
CODY, Michael Cameron. 1660 W ANTELOPE DR, STE 225 84041 #061-01-1965 L1996 **CD IM** *020 †20
COOK, David Allen. 2121 ROBINS DR 84041 #047-05-1987 L1993 **ORS** *020 †40 ‡
COOK, Johnnie Vance. 2075 N 1200 W, IHC HEALTH CENTER LAYTON 84041 #049-01-1991 L1992 **FM** *020 †18 ‡
COX, Jack Arvil. 1660 W ANTELOPE DR, STE 315 84041 #007-02-1966 L1980 **OTO GS** *071 †45
CROCKETT, Geoffrey M. 1600 W ANTELOPE DR, INTEGRATED CARE AT DAVIS 84041 #025-07-2002 L2005 **EM** *020 †16
DAVENPORT, Arthur Malcolm. 1600 W ANTELOPE DR, INTEGRATED CARE AT DAVIS 84041 #041-01-1962 L1965 **EM** *020
DEDRICKSON, David Ray. 1600 W ANTELOPE DR, UTAH IMAGING 84041 #049-01-1985 L1991 **DR** *020 †80
DEGRAUW, Jeffery Lee. 1492 W ANTELOPE DR, STE 208 84041 #040-02-1990 L1993 **FM** *020 †18
DURBIN, Teresa V K. 1580 W ANTELOPE DR STE 290 84041 #001-02-1978 L1992 **OBG** *020 †30
EARL, Brett Joseph. 1600 W ANTELOPE DR, INTEGRATED CARE AT DAVIS 84041 #031-01-1999 L2002 **EM** *020 †16
EBERHARD, Brent Keith. 2121 ROBINS DR 84041 #010-01-2001 L2003 **PD** *020 †55
FARLEY, Duane Earl. 2121 ROBINS DR 84041 #049-01-1990 L1997 **OBG** *020 †30
FENNELL, James A, II. 1580 W ANTELOPE DR, STE 100 84041 #036-08-1988 L1991 **PD** *020
FILLERUP, Sharon Lee. 2121 ROBINS DR 84041 #049-01-1991 L1996 **OBG** *020 †30
FLANDERS, Edward Dean, Jr. 2121 N 1700 W 84041 #049-01-1979 L1982 **GS** *020 †85
FRANCIS, Joseph Allen, Jr. 2084 N 1700 W, STE 6 84041 #049-01-1997 L2000 **FM** *020 †18 ‡
FREER, John Bryant. 1580 W ANTELOPE DR, STE 100 84041 #020-12-1994 L1995 **PD** *020 †55
GABRIELSEN, Alvin A, Jr. 1580 W ANTELOPE DR, STE 100 84041 #025-12-1984 L1987 **PD** *020 †55
GAHLINGER, Paul M. 934 S MAIN ST, KAYSVILLE CLINIC 84041 #005-19-1993 L1997 **OM GP** *020 †70
GARDNER, Kevin Lee. 1492 W ANTELOPE DR, STE 208 84041 #049-01-1997 L2000 **FM** *020 †18
GILLIS, Mark Robt. 1600 W ANTELOPE DR, NORTH DAVIS 84041 #034-01-1989 L2002 **AN** *020 †05
GILSOUL, Jennifer Marion. 1580 W ANTELOPE DR, STE 100 84041 #048-12-1998 L2006 **PD** *020 †55
GREENWOOD, Leslie Howard. 1600 W ANTELOPE DR, INTEGRATED CARE AT DAVIS 84041 #049-01-1999 L2002 **EM** *020 †16
HAGGART, Marie Elizabeth. 1992 W 2000 N, STE 2B 84041 #003-01-1990 L2002 **FM FSM** *020 †18
HALES, Brian Clint. 1600 W ANTELOPE DR, DAVIS HOSPITAL 84041 #049-01-1985 L1989 **AN** *020 †05
HALL, Charles Chauncey. 2121 ROBINS DR, B GRANT BISHOP 84041 #024-01-1947 L1949 **ORS** *075 †40
HALL, Craig Robt. 2121 N 1700 W 84041 #010-01-1985 L1989 **OBG** *020 †30
HANSEN, Craig Lane. 497 ARTISTS WAY 84040 #049-01-1992 L1993 **AN** *020 †05 ‡
HANSEN, Harold Lewis. 2121 ROBINS DR 84041 #049-01-1964 L1965 **FM** *071 †18
HANSEN, Vincent Lee. 2121 ROBINS DR 84041 #049-01-1972 L1973 **ON IM** *020 †20 ‡
HANSON, Joel Wallace. 1454 N HILL FIELD RD STE 2 84041 #035-45-1990 L1991 **P IM** *075 †75
HARDY, Michael Kent. 2102 ROBINS DR, STE 103 84041 #049-01-1991 L1992 **OM** *020 †70
HARPE, Charles Clifford. 2121 ROBINS DR 84041 #011-02-1993 L1994 **IM** *020 †20
HEALY, Michael John. 1492 W ANTELOPE DR STE 206 84041 #010-01-1976 L1982 **OBG** *020 †30
HENDERSON, David Jay. 2121 ROBINS DR 84041 #049-01-1975 L1976 **U** *020 †95
HESS, Christian Leonard. 1660 W ANTELOPE DR STE 105 84041 #049-01-1995 L1999 **OPH** *035
HOAGLAND, Jason Roy. 2121 N 1700 W, TANNER CLINIC 84041 #049-01-1998 L2000 **PD** *020 †55
HOBBS, Rachel Bird. 2121 ROBINS DR 84041 #049-01-2001 L2002 **FM** *020
HOLBROOK, Bryan G. 1544 W ANTELOPE DR, DAVIS SURGICAL CENTER 84041 #016-11-1985 L1989 **AN** *020 †05
HOLLEY, Shay Whitney. 1600 W ANTELOPE DR, INTEGRATED CARE AT DAVIS 84041 #049-01-1991 L1994 **EM** *020 †16
HORANI, Jamal. 1492 W ANTELOPE DR, STE 205 84041 #875-01-1998 L2005 **ID** *020 †20
HUGHES, William Gregory. 1580 W ANTELOPE DR, STE 290 84041 #030-05-1975 L1979 **OBG** *020 †30
HUMISTON, Daniel J. 1660 W ANTELOPE DR, DRIVE, #225 84041 #035-03-1990 L1994 **CD** *020 †80
HURST, Craig Leroy. 2132 N 1700 W STE 300 84041 #049-01-1977 L1981 **OBG** *020 †30
HUSSEMAN, Michael Patrick. 1580 W ANTELOPE DR, STE 100 84041 #054-04-1993 L1994 **PD** *020 †55
JACOBSEN, Robert A. 2121 N 1700 W 84041 #036-05-1969 L1970 **GS GE** *020 †85
JEE, Kenneth Wesley. 2121 N 1700 W 84041 #049-01-1983 L1984 **ORS GS** *020 †40
JENSEN, Allen Royce. 1600 W ANTELOPE DR, INTEGRATED CARE AT DAVIS 84041 #060-01-1971 L1981 **FM** *020
JENSEN, Paul Russell. 1600 W ANTELOPE DR, UTAH IMAGING 84041 #049-01-1985 L1989 **DR** *020 †80
JOHNSON, Marc Leon. 2075 N 1200 W, LAYTON IHC CLINIC 84041 #049-01-1998 L1999 **FM** *020 †18
JOHNSON, Steven Lowell. 2121 ROBINS DR 84041 #049-01-1982 L1986 **OBG** *020 †30
JOHNSON, Val Budge. ■ 84040 #028-02-1969 L1974 **PTH** *071 †50

JONES, James Neldon. 1600 W ANTELOPE DR, UTAH IMAGING 84041 #020-02-1970 L1971 DR RNR *020 †80

JORGENSEN, C Louis. 1580 W ANTELOPE DR, WEE CARE PEDIATRICS 84041 #023-01-1940 OM OBG *071 †30

JORGENSON, Bruce Donald. 1580 W ANTELOPE DR STE 100 84041 #041-13-1970 L1986 PD *020 †55

JOSEPH, Charles W, IV. 1580 W ANTELOPE DR, STE 290 84041 #045-01-1971 L1972 OBG AM *020 †30

JULIEN, Craig Kenneth. 2084 N 1700 W, STE 6 84041 #001-02-1976 L1982 FM EM *020 †18

KAMALU, Layne K. 934 S MAIN ST, KAYSVILLE CLINIC 84041 #028-34-1993 L1996 FM *020 †18

KELLN, Kenneth Lee. ■ 84040 #005-12-1964 L1971 GE IM *071 †20

KEMP, Kris Reid. 1600 W ANTELOPE DR, INTEGRATED CARE AT DAVIS 84041 #056-06-2002 L2005 EM *020 †16

KIRKHAM, Mark D. 2121 ROBINS DR 84041 #049-01-1989 L1992 FM *020 †18

KIYOMURA, Robert S. 2084 N 1700 W, STE B 84041 #028-02-1976 L1978 GE IM *020 †20

KRAMER, Frank-Dieter. 2121 N 1700 W 84041 #409-15-1972 L1978 PD *020 †55

LARSEN, Wade Bryant. 2121 N 1700 W, TANNER MEMORIAL CLINIC 84041 #035-03-1997 L2003 GS *020 †85

LAZENBY, Dewayne Charles. 2244 E 3500 N 84040 #049-01-2002 L2005 PD *100 †55

LEACH, Robert James. 1580 W ANTELOPE DR 84041 #019-02-1995 L2007 NEP *020 †20

LEBEGUE, Breck Jon. ■ 84040 #017-20-1975 L1976 P *020 †75,70

LEEMAN, Earl Kome. 1544 W ANTELOPE DR 84041 #049-01-1979 L1993 AN *020 †05

LLOYD, Michael Brian. 1580 W ANTELOPE DR, STE 100 84041 #007-02-1991 L1997 CHN *020 †55

LOVERIDGE, Brian Willard. 1600 W ANTELOPE DR, INTEGRATED CARE AT DAVIS 84041 #049-01-1999 L2005 EM *020 †16

LOW, James C. 1600 W ANTELOPE DR #005-11-1953 L1979 FM *071 †18

LUCE, Marcus Christopher. ■ 84040 #030-06-2003 L2006 PD *100 †55

LUCE, Mari Suto. ■ 84040 #030-06-2003 L2006 PD *100 †55

MARTINEAU, Michael Reed. 2121 ROBINS DR 84041 #049-01-1998 L2002 D DS *020 †15

MASOOD, Syed Omar. 2102 N 1700 W, STE 104 84041 #704-02-1997 L2006 IM *020 †20

MATTINGLY, Deborah Spradl. 2102 ROBINS DR, STE 103 84041 #026-04-1989 L1991 OM *020 †70

MCKINLEY, Kristina. 268 N 1350 E 84040 #049-01-2007 PD *012

MEEK, Steven Charles. 2121 ROBINS DR, TANNER MEMORIAL CLINIC 84041 #049-01-1984 L1988 OBG *020 †30

MELLOR, Robert Lynn. 2121 ROBINS DR 84041 #004-01-1983 L1987 OTO HNS *020 †45

MILLIGAN, Mark Kelly. 2075 N 1200 W, IHC HEALTH CENTER-LAYTON 84041 #049-01-1992 L1993 FM OBG *020 †18

MOHR, Robert Russell. 1492 W ANTELOPE DR STE 203 84041 #049-01-1991 L1992 IM *020 †20

MORRELL, David Glen. 2121 N 1700 W 84041 #049-01-1991 L1996 GS *020 †85

MORRELL, Glen Robert. 2121 ROBINS DR 84041 #005-11-1998 L2004 DR *020 †80

MORTENSEN, Joseph Mylan. ■ 84040 #049-01-2008 *012

NELSON, Laurence M. 2121 ROBINS DR 84041 #048-16-1991 L1999 OPH *020 †35

NELSON, Lawrence Meier. 2121 N 1700 W 84041 #030-05-1937 L1940 D DMP *071 †15

NEVILLE, Bruce Taylor. 2084 ROBINS DR, STE 6 84041 #049-01-1962 L1963 FM *071 †18

NEVILLE, Roark Bradford. 2084 ROBINS DR, STE 6 84041 #049-01-1983 L1987 FM *020 †18

NIELSEN, Michael Stanley. 2075 N ANGEL ST 84041 #049-01-1996 L1997 FM *020 †18

NILSON, Bart Rodney. 1600 W ANTELOPE DR, INTEGRATED CARE AT DAVIS 84041 #049-01-1973 L1974 EM FM *020 †18

OGILVIE, Orin Howard. 934 S MAIN ST, DAVIS MENTAL HEALTH CENTER 84041 #035-01-1976 L1981 P *020 †75

OLSEN, Carla. 2102 ROBINS DR, STE 103 84041 #049-01-2002 L2003 GPM *020 †70

OLSEN, Stephanie Laurel. 1660 W ANTELOPE DR, STE 225 84041 #023-01-1985 L1986 CD IM *020 †20

PENG, Wei. 1600 W ANTELOPE DR, HOSPITALIST OFFICE, DAVIS 84041 #243-52-1982 L2003 PCC *100

PHAM, Marian Hong. 1492 W ANTELOPE DR, STE 203 84041 #019-02-1998 L2004 MPD *020 †20

PORTER, Joel G. 2075 N ANGEL ST 84041 #049-01-1990 L1991 FM *020 †18

REES, James H. 2084 N 1700 W STE 6 84041 #049-01-1974 L1982 FM *020 †18

REES, Richard Bryant. 2478 VALLEY VIEW DR, RICHARD B. REES, MD 84040 #005-15-1969 L1971 PD *020 †55

REIS, John Kleber. 1492 W ANTELOPE DR, STE 203 84041 #005-14-1970 L1975 IM ADM *020 †20

REYNOLDS, James Robert. 2121 ROBINS DR 84041 #049-01-1998 L1999 U *020 †95

RICHARDS, Bryan Lee. 2121 ROBINS DR 84041 #049-01-1994 L1999 OTO *020 †45

RICHARDSON, Melvin Kent. 1600 W ANTELOPE DR 84041 #003-01-2002 L2006 AN *020 †05

RIVERA-VELEZ, Abdiel. ■ 84041 #451-01-1977 L1983 GS *075

ROLLINS, Lyman Val. 1600 W ANTELOPE DR, INTEGRATED CARE AT DAVIS 84041 #003-01-1975 L1976 EM FM *020 †18

RUSH, Mark Emory. 1600 W ANTELOPE DR, NORTH DAVIS 84041 #048-02-1983 L1984 AN IM *020 †05

SCHENK, Julana Noel. 2250 N 1700 W 84041 #049-01-2002 L2003 P *020 †75

SHEFFIELD, William K. 1600 W ANTELOPE DR, INTEGRATED CARE AT DAVIS 84041 #049-01-1992 L1996 EM *020 †16

SHELBY, Todd Lenard. 2075 N 1200 W, IHC HEALTH CENTER-LAYTON 84041 #049-01-1992 L1993 FM OBS *020 †18

SIGG, Laurent. 934 S MAIN ST, STE 8 84041 #034-01-1998 L2001 PD *020 †55

SILAS, Peter Edward. 1580 W ANTELOPE DR, STE 100 84041 #047-05-1995 L1996 PD *020 †55

SIMMONS, Robert Reed. 1600 W ANTELOPE DR, INTEGRATED CARE AT DAVIS 84041 #049-01-2001 L2004 EM *020 †16

SMITH, Brian K. 1588 E 525 N 84041 #005-19-1992 L2000 AN *020 †05

SORENSEN, Robert Michael. 1600 W ANTELOPE DR 84041 #049-01-1987 L1990 AN *020 †05

STANLEY, Bruce N. 2075 N ANGEL ST 84041 #028-34-1999 L2000 FM *020 †18

STELTER, Casey Lawrence. 124 S FAIRFIELD RD 84041 #049-01-2002 L2005 FM *020 †18

STEVENS, Michael Cooper. 934 S MAIN ST, DAVIS BEHAVIORAL HEALTH 84041 #036-01-1984 L1985 P CHP *020 †75

STINNETT, Jason Mark. 1492 W ANTELOPE DR, STE 125 84041 #004-01-1998 L1999 HO *100 †20

SUMSION, Kevin Spafford. 2121 N 1700 W 84041 #010-01-1990 L1991 OBG *020 †30

SVAGR, Bohus. 2121 ROBINS DR 84041 #286-13-1993 L2003 OSS *020

TAYLOR, Paul Ray. 124 S FAIRFIELD RD, MOUNTAIN VIEW FAMILY CARE 84041 #010-01-1974 L1975 FM *020 †18

TAYLOR, Roy Robt. 2121 N 1700 W 84041 #051-07-1981 L1982 IM RHU *020 †20

TENSMEYER, David Kent. 2075 N ANGEL ST 84041 #049-01-1981 L1982 FM FSM *020 †18

THOMPSON, Scott Kent. 1660 W ANTELOPE DR, STE 315 84041 #035-45-2000 L2006 FPS OTO *020 †45 ‡

TREFT, Robert L. 1580 W ANTELOPE DR, STE 175 84041 #049-01-1981 L1982 OPH FM *020 †35

VAN LEEUWEN, Richard Neil. 2121 N 1700 W, TANNER MEMORIAL CLINIC 84041 #049-01-1993 L2007 OTO *020 †45

VAN STADEN, Gavin Nichola. 1240 E HIGHWAY 193, STE G1 84040 #836-01-1996 L2005 FM *020

VERCILLO, Darin Michael. 1600 W ANTELOPE DR, DAVIS HOSPITAL AND MEDICAL 84041 #049-01-2000 L2001 IM *020

WALLIN, Richard Keith. 2121 N 1700 W 84041 #049-01-1980 L1983 FM *020 †18

WALLIN, Trevin Richard. 1660 W ANTELOPE DR STE 105 84041 #049-01-2003 L2007 IM *100

WARREN, Steven Edward. 3135 N FAIRFIELD RD, STE A 84041 #010-01-1981 L1982 FPG PLM *071 †15

WASHBURN, Michael D. 1660 W ANTELOPE DR STE 105 84041 #010-01-1970 L1976 OPH *020 †35

WATSON, Brent Thomas. 2132 N 1700 W, STE 230 84041 #023-12-1990 L1992 ORS *020 †40

WEEKS, Jonathan Andrew. 124 S FAIRFIELD RD 84041 #018-03-2000 L2001 FM *020 †18

WILSON, James Michael. ■ 84041 #048-14-2007 EM *012

WILSON, Peter Vincent. 1580 W ANTELOPE DR STE 230 84041 #007-02-1999 L2004 GS *020 †85

YATES, Jay Reese. 2121 N 1700 W 84041 #049-01-1975 L1978 FM *020 †18 ‡

YATES, York Jay. 2121 ROBINS DR 84041 #049-01-1997 L2003 PS *020 †65

YERMAN, Blake Jefferson. 1600 W ANTELOPE DR, INTEGRATED CARE AT DAVIS 84041 #035-45-2000 L2003 EM *020 †16

YURTH, Daniel Allen. 1600 W ANTELOPE DR 84041 #049-01-1975 L1977 AN OS *020 †05

ZELENKOV, Kristine Marya. 1580 W ANTELOPE DR, STE 290 84041 #049-01-1981 L2001 OBG *020 †30

LEHI – UTAH

ABBINANTI, Martin Lambert. 250 E STATE ROAD 73 84043 #049-01-1990 L1992 FM *020 †18

BEARNSON, Rosemary. 2975 EXECUTIVE PKWY, STE 411 84043 #049-01-2004 L2004 R *012

CHRISTENSEN, Robert W. 250 E STATE ROAD 73, SARATOGA SPRINGS CLINIC 84043 #049-01-2003 L2004 FM *020 †18

COOK, William Paul. 2975 EXECUTIVE PKWY, STE 411 84043 #049-01-1982 L1989 AN *020 †05

CRAIG, Yohanna Sachiko. ■ 84043 #056-06-2007 L2007 PD *012

EDWARDS, Robert Philip. 2975 EXECUTIVE PKWY, STE 411 84043 #016-11-1974 L1998 AN *020 †05

EGAN, Daniel Winston. 680 E MAIN ST 84043 #010-01-1996 L1997 FM *020 †18

FARLEY-JONES, Dianne. 3300 RUNNING CREEK WAY, BLDG B 84043 #040-02-1989 L1990 FM *020 †18

GARAYCOCHEA, Christian I. 2975 EXECUTIVE PKWY, STE 411 84043 #040-02-2003 L2007 AN *100

HSIAO, Suzanne Chaowei. 2975 EXECUTIVE PKWY, STE 411 84043 #017-20-1998 L2006 AN *020 †05

JOHNSON, Allen Carl. 2975 EXECUTIVE PKWY, STE 411 84043 #049-01-1975 L1978 AN *020 †05

KUMP, Ronald. ■ 84045 #005-15-1962 L1963 R *071 †80

MANGELSON, Evan Glen. ■ 84043 #049-01-1969 L1970 FM *071 †18

MATTHEWS, George Morris. 2975 EXECUTIVE PKWY, STE 411 84043 #049-01-1977 L1978 AN *020 †05

PATTERSON, Alan Ross. 2975 EXECUTIVE PKWY, STE 411 84043 #049-01-1979 L1986 AN CCM *020 †05 ‡

SEYMOUR, Todd Charles. 2975 EXECUTIVE PKWY, STE 411 84043 #051-01-1998 L1999 AN *020 †05

SHARP, Richard. 3300 RUNNING CREEK WAY, BLDG B 84043 #023-12-1987 L1996 FM *020 †18

SMITH, Bradford Douglas. 2975 EXECUTIVE PKWY, STE 411 84043 #049-01-2000 L2001 AN *020 †05

SMITH, Samuel Joseph. 2975 EXECUTIVE PKWY, STE 200 84043 #049-01-2000 L2004 AN *020 †05

SUNDWALL, Peter V. 680 E MAIN ST 84043 #049-01-1994 L1997 FM *020 †18

TEFTELLER, Glenn G. 250 E STATE ROAD 73 84043 #021-05-1974 L2004 FM *020 †18

THOMAS, Claude Ray. ■ 84043 #049-01-1961 L1962 GP *071

WHITING, David Todd. 3231 N 1120 E, ALPINE PEDIATRICS 84043 #016-11-1997 L2000 PD *020 †55

WILLIAMS, Paul Matley. ■ 84043 #049-01-1957 L1960 AN *020 †05

LEWISTON – CACHE

HIRST, Russell Nelson, Jr. 1565 S 800 E 84320 #028-02-1965 L1971 IM PUD *020

LINDON – UTAH

CROFTS, Kim M. 385 W 600 N 84042 #049-01-1989 L1996 PS HS *020 †65

HARRIS, Michael D. ■ 84042 #048-13-1996 L1998 GS *020

JONES, Mark L. ■ 84042 #049-01-1989 L1990 AN *020 †05

SHEFFIELD, Polly Walker. ■ 84042 #049-01-1989 L1999 PD *020 †55

TROST, Landon Westlund. ■ 84042 #021-01-2007 L2007 GS *012

UNICE, Scott Douglas. 114 DRY CANYON DR 84042 #049-01-1991 L1992 AN *020 †05

LOGAN – CACHE

ADAMS, David Michael, Jr. 1350 N 500 E, BUDGE CLC UROLOGY 84341 #021-01-2002 L2007 GS *100

ANDERSEN, Blaine. 1300 N 500 E, STE 260 84341 #049-01-1981 L1988 PS HS *020 †85,65

ANDERSON, Allan David. 1300 N 500 E, IHC BUDGE CLINIC SURGICAL 84341 #028-02-1986 L2005 GS VS *020 †85

ANDERSON, Timothy M. 1350 N 500 E 84341 #049-01-1975 L1980 PD *020 †55

ARMSTRONG, Craig Wayne. 2380 N 400 E, STE C 84341 #049-01-1977 L1984 PD GP *020 †55

BAILEY, John Chas. 655 E 1300 N 84341 #049-01-1970 L1973 PHP *071 †70

BARRETT, John Weldon. 1400 N 500 E 84341 #035-01-1992 L2003 **FM** *020 †18
BENEDICT, James Patton. 1350 N 500 E 84341 #040-02-1977 L1993 **OBG** *020 †30
BEN-JACOB, Ali. 550 E 1400 N STE W, AND RESEARCH CLINIC 84341 #012-01-1991 L1995 **HO** *020 †20
BISHOP, Theral Michael. 1400 N 500 E 84341 #010-01-1966 L1967 **EM** *071
BOHMAN, Verle Duane. 630 E 1400 N # 100A 84341 #039-01-1976 L1982 **GE IM** *020 †20
BRILLIANT, Lee Steven. ■ 84321 #005-19-1975 L1979 **OBG** *071
BROADBENT, Lee Stokes. 550 E 1400 N STE D 84341 #049-01-1971 L1973 **GS** *020
BROWN, Nordell Tim. 1350 N 500 E 84341 #049-01-1991 L1994 **IM PD** *020 †55,20
BRYNER, Frank Robt. ■ 84321 #049-01-1960 L1964 **ORS** *020 †40
BULLEN, Reed, Jr. 850 E 1200 NORTH 84322 #049-01-1974 L1977 **IM** *020
CALLISTER, Michael Scott. 1350 N 500 E 84341 #049-01-1991 L1997 **U** *072 †95
CANNING, Curtis Ray. 1162 EASTRIDGE DR 84321 #049-01-1973 L1976 **P** *020
CARLISLE, John Willard. ■ 84321 #049-01-1956 L1961 **PD** *071 †55
CASEY, David N. N.. 235 E 400 N 84321 #028-78-2004, ▲ L2007 **FM** *020 †18
CLARK, Thomas Houston. 235 E 400 N, LOGAN INSTACARE 84321 #049-01-1998 L2005 **FM** *020 †18
CLARKE, Derrel Wolter. 1350 N 500 E 84341 #040-02-1979 L1992 **PD PDE** *020 †55
CLEGG, Michael L. 2310 N 400 E, STE A 84341 #049-01-1998 L2002 **PM** *020 †60
CLISSOLD, Matthew Alfred. 274 N MAIN ST 84321 #049-01-1987 L1988 **AN** *020 †05
COPPIN, David Frank. 1350 N 500 E 84341 #049-01-1970 L1971 **OBG** *071 †30
CRAIG, Kristin Flint. 1350 N 500 E, IHC HEALTH CENTER-BUDGE CL 84341 #054-04-1995 L1999 **OBG** *020 †30
DAINES, Jonathan Hill. ■ 84321 #010-01-1964 L1968 **R** *020 †80
DAINES, Merrill Clyde. 1400 N 500 E 84341 #049-01-1945 L1946 **IM CD** *071 †20
DAINES, Newel Geo, Jr. 1400 N 500 E 84341 #010-01-1948 L1957 **AN** *072
DAINES, Paul Hatch, Jr. 550 E 1400 N, EMERGENCY DEPT 84341 #054-04-1983 L1987 **EM** *020 †20
DAINES, Peter Carlson. 280 EASTRIDGE LN, LOGAN REGIONAL HOSPITAL 84321 #049-01-1985 L1989 **AN** *020 †05
DAINES, Samuel R, II. ■ 84321 #010-01-1997 *100
DAVIS, Dirk R. 630 E 1400 N, NORTHERN UTAH GASTO 84341 #047-06-1986 L1988 **GE** *020 †20
DAVIS, James Walter. 850 EAST 1200 NORTH, 9100 OLD MAIN HILL 84322 #018-03-1978 L1979 **EM** *020 †18,16
DAVIS, Ted B. 550 E 1400 N 84341 #305-01-1985 L1991 **FM** *020 †18
DEER, Emily Lynn. ■ 84321 #049-01-2008 *012
DUKE, Earl Lawrence. 1400 N 500 E 84341 #049-01-1968 L1977 **OBG** *020 †30
EMMETT, John W. 1400 N 500 E 84341 #049-01-1952 L1953 **R** *071 †80
ESPLIN, Douglas Neil. 235 E 400 N, LOGAN INSTA CARE 84321 #049-01-2000 L2003 **FM** *020 †18 ‡
EVANS, William Brent. 1400 N 500 E, EMERGENCY DEPARTMENT 84341 #010-01-1992 L1994 **EM** *020 †16
FALK, Jeanne Marie. 1350 N 500 E 84341 #049-01-2001 L2005 **OBG** *020 †30
FINLAYSON, Terry Inkley. 2310 N 400 E, STE A 84341 #049-01-1991 L1998 **ORS OTR** *020 †40
FOWERS, Gary Ken. 1325 N 600 E, STE 102 84341 #049-01-1994 L1998 **OBG** *020 †30
FUNK, Steven Charles. 129 W 1320 S 84321 #049-01-1990 L1997 **AN** *020 †05
GARG, Vikram. 1350 N 500 E 84341 #495-46-1989 L2002 **GE** *020 †20
GIBBONS, Gary Ray. 2380 N 400 E STE D 84341 #010-01-1971 L1979 **OTO HNS** *071 †45
GIBBS, Earl Kent. 550 E 1400 N STE R 84341 #025-01-1964 L1970 **OBG** *071 †30
GOBLE, Deserae Jeannette. 2380 N 400 E, CACHE VALLEY SPECIALTY HOS 84341 #010-01-1997 L2001 **FM** *020 †18
GOBLE, E Marlowe. 2380 N 400 E, STE G 84341 #028-02-1976 L1977 **ORS** *020 †40
GROVER, Scott W. 550 E 1400 N, STE D 84341 #018-75-1995, ▲ L2003 **GS** *020
HARRIS, Matthew Fronk. 1400 N 500 E 84341 #049-01-1996 L1999 **EM** *020 †16
HART, Douglas Blaine. ■ 84341 #049-01-1956 L1957 **OTO** *071 †45
HATCH, Guy Meredith. 1400 N 500 E 84341 #049-01-1975 L1978 **PD** *020 †55
HAWKES, John Robt. 1400 N 500 E 84341 #049-01-1972 L1973 **AN PD** *020 †55,05
HICKEN, Gregory Jon. 2310 N 400 E, STE A 84341 #048-12-1987 L1997 **ORS OSM** *020 †40
HIGGINBOTHAM, Thomas O. 1300 N 500 E, STE 130 84341 #049-01-1999 L2005 **OSM** *020 †40
HLAVATY, Raymond Dean. 1350 N 500 E 84341 #049-01-1961 L1962 **PD** *071 †55
HOLDAWAY, Don Reed. 1173 ASPEN DR 84341 #049-01-1971 L1975 **D** *020 †15
HOLT, Dean Anderson. ■ 84341 #049-01-1957 L1958 **FM** *071 †18
HOOLEY, Eric Wayne. 1300 N 500 E, STE 130 84341 #048-16-2001 L2007 **OSS** *100
HORKLEY, Tyson Stuart. 1350 N 500 E 84341 #051-07-2004 L2005 **PD** *020 †55
HOUSLEY, Michael Clinton. 1400 N 500 E, WORK MED 84341 #049-01-1993 L1994 **OM** *020 †18
HUBBARD, Kelly W. 2380 N 400 E, STE B 84341 #049-01-1996 L2000 **D** *020 †15
HUFFMAN, Jeffrey Mark. 1350 N 500 E 84341 #010-02-1995 L1997 **IM** *020 †20
HYLDAHL, Douglas Richard. 550 E 1400 N, STE Y 84341 #010-01-1976 L1979 **FM** *020 †18
ISAACSON, Bruce Arnold. 550 E 1400 N STE Z 84341 #010-01-1983 L1988 **FM** *020 †18
ISOM, Casey Nathan. 550 E 1400 N, STE S 84341 #054-04-2000 L2006 **PS** *020 †65
JAUSSI, Walter R. 550 E 1400 N 84341 #023-12-1986 L2001 **OPH** *020 †35
JENKINS, James Porter. ■ 84321 #041-13-1947 L1948 **GP OS** *020
JENSEN, Robert Le Roy. 1300 N 500 E, JENSEN & WARREN INC 84341 #049-01-1957 L1960 **OPH** *071 †35
JONES, Gary Ricks. 168 N 100 E 84321 #049-01-1984 L1988 **OPH** *020 †35
JORGENSEN, Nina Gay. 2380 N 400 E, STE C 84341 #032-01-1993 L1994 **PD** *020 †55
KERSHISNIK, Matthew M. 550 E 1400 N, STE H 84341 #030-06-1989 L1990 **BBK** *020 †50
KEYSER, Jeffrey Steven. 1350 N 500 E, IHC HEALTH CENTER-BUDGE CL 84341 #047-06-1987 L1999 **OTO** *020 †45
KING, Bryan Croft. 1300 N 500 E, STE 130 84341 #023-12-1990 L2002 **ORS OSM** *020 †40
KIRBY, James V. 500 E 1400 N, LOGAN REGIONAL HOSPITAL-BH 84341 #049-01-1987 L1996 **P** *020 †75
KIRKMAN, David Alan. 1325 N 600 E, STE 102 84341 #003-01-1987 L2004 **OBG** *020 †30
KRUMLIK, Jerry J. ■ 84341 #065-01-1971 L1987 **PD CHN** *020 †55
LARSEN, Bryan R. 630 E 1400 N # 100A 84341 #010-01-1984 L1986 **GE IM** *020 †20
LARSEN, La Grande C. 1400 N 500 E 84341 #049-01-1947 L1965 **U** *071 †95
LARSEN, Ryan Harold. 550 E 1400 N, STE J 84341 #049-01-1985 L1986 **U GS** *020 †95
LARSON, Shane Ronald. 1400 N 500 E 84341 #049-01-1990 L1997 **AN** *020 †05
LYONS, Trek Daniel. 1300 N 500 E, STE 130 84341 #049-01-1999 L2006 **FSM** *020 †18
MALOUF, James Thos. 2380 N 400 E, STE G 84341 #049-01-1975 L1980 **ORS** *020 †40
MALOUF, Raymond Nasif. ■ 84321 #023-01-1941 **GP** *071
MARTIN-GARG, Prafulla. 1350 N 500 E 84341 #495-01-1994 L2002 **PD** *020 †55
MC CULLOCH, Kimberly Dawn. 1350 N 500 E 84341 #037-01-1999 L2003 **OBG** *020 †30
MILLER, Brent Warburton. 2310 N 400 E, ALPINE ORTHOPAEDIC SPECIAL 84341 #005-06-1976 L2008 **ORS HS** *020 †40
MORTENSEN, Glenn Owens. 550 E 1400 N, STE Y 84341 #049-01-1975 L1977 **FM OBS** *020 †18
MORTENSON, Francis Neal. 550 E 1400 N STE K 84341 #049-01-1960 L1961 **OBG** *071 †30
MURRAY, David Paul. 1300 N 500 E, STE 130 84341 #049-01-1987 L1999 **ORS** *020 †40
NASH, Robert Michael. 1350 N 500 E 84341 #041-14-1984 L1986 **IM** *020 †20
NEELEY, James Patton. 225 E 4TH N 84321 #023-01-1955 L1958 **GS** *071 †85
NELSON, Brian David. 550 E 1400 N 84341 #049-01-1989 L1993 **AN** *020 †05
NELSON, John James. 1350 N 500 E, IHC HEALTH CENTER BUDGE CL 84341 #040-02-1969 L1974 **OBG** *071 †30
NELSON, Joseph Harold. 1400 N 500 E 84341 #049-01-1958 L1968 **ORS** *071 †40
NOORDA, Barry Albert. 1325 N 600 E, STE 102 84341 #031-01-1993 L1997 **OBG** *020
O DELL, John Dennis. 1350 N 500 E 84341 #016-02-1979 L1984 **PD OS** *020 †55
ODELL, Shaun Vernon. 261 N 1570 E 84321 #016-02-2008 *012
ORADY, Mona El-Sayed. ■ 84341 #065-06-2001 L2008 **OBG** *020 †30
OTRUSINIK, Rudolf. 500 E 1300 N, STE 320 84341 #286-03-1988 L1995 **CD** *020 †20
O'VERY, Bruce Alan. 1325 N 600 E, STE 101 84341 #049-01-1995 L1999 **MPD** *020 †20,55
PARKINSON, Leonard S. ■ 84321 #040-02-1949 L1950 **GYN** *071 †30
PAYNE, Ronald J. ■ 84341 #007-02-1966 L1976 **GE IM** *071 †20
PETERSON, Frank E. 500 E 1400 N 84341 #049-01-1976 L1978 **AN** *020
PHILLIPS, Rebecca Copp. 235 E 400 N 84321 #017-20-1993 L2007 **FM** *020 †18
PLOWMAN, Douglas Paul. 1400 N 550 E 84341 #049-01-1990 L1993 **EM** *020 †16
PORTER, Brett Cardon. 76 E 200 N 84321 #049-01-1993 L1994 **IM** *020 †20
RAYMOND, John Scott. 550 E 1400 N STE P 84341 #035-20-1974 L1980 **OPH GP** *020 †35
REDD, Edward Hunter. 655 E 1300 N 84341 #049-01-1986 L1989 **IM** *071 †20
REESE, David Allan. 1400 N 500 E 84341 #034-01-1997 L2000 **EM** *020 †16
SALISBURY, Steven Scott. 1300 N 500 E, STE 370 84341 #049-01-1983 L1988 **IM** *020 †20
SAUL, William Lee. 1300 N 500 E STE 320 84341 #005-02-1977 L1992 **CD IM** *020 †20
SCHNEIDER, Stephen D. 1350 N 500 E 84341 #021-01-1993 L1996 **PD** *020 †55
SILER, Jon Alan. 1300 N 500 E, STE 350 84341 #023-07-1989 L1993 **OPH** *020 †35
SKABELUND, Robert E. ■ 84321 #016-06-1950 L1952 **AN** *071
STONES, Michael John. 1350 N 500 E 84341 #049-01-1976 L1979 **IM** *020 †20
STOWELL, Paul R. ■ 84321 #008-01-1955 L1957 **PD** *071 †55
STREBEL, Robert Paul, Jr. 550 E 1400 N STE I 84341 #654-01-1982 L1984 **OBG** *020 †30
STRONG, Jeffrey Sherwood. 1350 N 500 E 84341 #032-01-1991 L1998 **IM** *020 †20
SUMMERS, Bradley Kent. 1400 N 500 E 84341 #049-01-1986 L1987 **D DS** *020 †15
SWALLOW, Charles Truman. 1350 N 500 E, IHC HEALTH CENTER-BUDGE CL 84341 #049-01-1966 L1968 **U** *071 †95
SZPUNAR, Agnieszka Marta. 1350 N 500 E, INTERNAL MEDICINE/CACHE VA 84341 #759-01-1992 L1999 **IM** *020 †20
VISICK, Michael Keane. 1350 N 500 E 84341 #049-01-1995 L2000 **PD IM** *020 †20,55
WALKER, Corey Wyn. 1350 N 500 E 84341 #028-34-1997 L2006 **RHU IM** *020 †20
WATERMAN, David Glenn. 1300 N 500 E STE 350 84341 #049-01-1994 L1998 **OPH** *020 †35
WEBER, William Farnsworth. 90 E 200 N 84321 #008-01-1962 L1997 **P** *020 †75
WEINER, Robert Gills. 550 E 1400 N, STE M 84341 #008-01-1965 L1985 **ORS FM** *071 †40
WEISS, Bartley Myron. 1350 N 500 E, THE BUDGE CLNC 84341 #011-03-1977 L1979 **GS** *020 †85
WELTER, Lorraine C N. 2310 N 400 E, STE A 84341 #056-06-1999 L2005 **PM** *020 †60
WILLIAMS, Michael Henry. 1350 N 500 E 84341 #048-12-1973 L1974 **N** *020 †75
WOOD, Gordon S, Jr. 2380 N 400 E STE D 84341 #010-01-1983 L1991 **OTO FPS** *020 †45
WORLEY, John C, Jr. 258 E 9TH N 84321 #016-06-1952 L1953 **GS OS** *020
WUTHRICH, Richard Carl. 850 E 1200 NORTH 84322 #040-02-1971 L1979 **D** *020 †15
YOUNG, Robert Paul. 550 E 1400 N, STE Q 84341 #040-02-1985 L1995 **D** *020 †15 ‡
YOUNG, Steven Robt. 1300 N 500 E, STE 220 84341 #049-01-1985 L1986 **OPH** *020 †35
YOUNG-HAWKINS, Danee. 920 N 200 W STE A 84321 #005-19-1981 L1990 **OBG** *020 †30

MAGNA – SALT LAKE

CHRISTENSEN, Jacob Leo. ■ 84044 #048-02-2007 L2007 **AN** *012
HARRIS, Paul Don. PO BOX 6001, 8362 W 10200 S 84044 #049-01-1984 L1985 **OM PHP** *030 †70
JACOBS, Francine Nadeen. 8211 W 3500 S 84044 #035-48-1999 L2007 **PD** *020 †55
MARTINEZ-FERRATE, Rodolfo. 8211 W 3500 S 84044 #270-02-1993 L2006 **FM** *020 †18 ‡
MC BRIDE, Jill Diane. 8211 W 3500 S 84044 #005-12-2000 L2006 **FM** *020 †18 ‡
MC CLOSKEY, Roberta Allan. ■ 84044 #049-01-1995 **PTH** *100
ROJAS, Adriana I. 8211 W 3500 S 84044 #264-09-1995 L2006 **IM** *020 †20
SPENCER, Steven J. 8211 W 3500 S 84044 #049-01-1997 L1998 **FM** *020 †18

MANTI – SANPETE

ARMSTRONG, Robert Dale. 159 N MAIN ST 84642 #049-01-1978 L1984 **FM** *020 †18
BRUGGER, Archie Maynard. ■ 84642 #049-01-1955 L1976 **GS TS** *020 †85,90
FRISCHKNECHT, Michael S. 159 N MAIN ST 84642 #049-01-2000 L2001 **FM** *020 †18 ‡
JACOBSEN, Darren Clark. 308 W UNION ST 84642 #049-01-1990 L1999 **AN** *020 †05

MAPLETON – UTAH

GRIFFIN, Glen Chas. ■ 84664 #048-02-1958 L1959 **FM IMG** *030 †55
STUBBS, Gina Rae. 656 N 1600 E 84664 #016-42-1988 L1998 **P** *020 †75

MIDVALE – SALT LAKE

ALBANO, Nicole Suzanne. ■ 84047 #049-01-2007 *012
BACKMAN, Richard L. 7495 S STATE ST, GREENWOOD HEALTH CENTER 84047 #048-13-1994 L2001 **FM** *020 †18
BANK, Stacey. 6965 S 700 E 84047 #010-02-2002 L2003 **FM** *020 †18
BRINTON, Wayne Robt. 632 W 7250 S 84047 #035-20-1971 L1973 **DR RNR** *020 †80
BROWNSTEIN, Ellie Sue. 7495 S STATE ST 84047 #005-18-1992 L1997 **PD** *020 †55
CARLSON, Katherine Lenore. 7434 S STATE ST, VALLEY MENTAL HLTH 84047 #032-01-1999 L2003 **P** *020 †75

■ = Address Information Privacy Protected

CLINE, Jeffrey Wade. 7495 S STATE ST 84047 #049-01-2001 L2005 **PD PSM** *020 †55
COPELAND, Jim Winston. ■ 84047 #048-12-1972 **EM D** *020
DAVIS, Gerald Wickman. 7495 S STATE ST 84047 #007-02-1956 L1983 **GP** *071
DIETLEIN, John Rogers. 6947 S 900 E 84047 #031-01-1980 L1983 **FM PLM** *020 †18
FAIZI, Sajid. 7309 S 180 W, HIGHLAND RIDGE HOSP 84047 #704-20-1989 L2004 **P** *020
GANT, Charlotte Elaine. 7434 S STATE ST 84047 #047-06-1981 L1983 **P CHP** *020
GARDNER, Noel Cameron. 1225 FORT UNION BLVD, ALTA VIEW CTR FOR 84047 #005-12-1984 L1988 **P** *020 †75
GOODHUE, Angelique D. 7434 S STATE ST, SOUTH VALLEY MENTAL HLTH 84047 #048-13-1995 L1996 **P** *020 †75 ‡
GUPTA, Sumati Virendra. 7495 S STATE ST 84047 #496-38-1997 L2002 **IM** *020 †20
HADJBIAN, Ehsan. 1275 FORT UNION BLVD, STE 118 84047 #305-01-2001 L2003 **FM** *020
HANLON, Michael Murray. 632 W 7250 S 84047 #047-02-1987 **OMO** *100
HASHIMOTO, Roopa S. 7001 S 900 E, STE 400 84047 #049-01-1979 L1986 **PD** *020 †55
HOLT, Richard Blaine. 632 W 7250 S 84047 #010-01-1976 L1977 **DR** *020 †80
JENSEN, Joseph Davis. 7396 UNION PARK AVE, STE 201 84047 #049-01-1977 L1978 **IM CD** *020 †20
JENSEN, Joseph Dean. 7396 UNION PARK AVE, STE 201 84047 #049-01-1990 L1994 **D IM** *020 †15
LAZAR, Gerald Martin. 7309 S 180 W, HIGHLAND RIDGE HOSPITAL 84047 #035-03-1969 L1986 **P** *020
LUIKENAAR, Rixt Anna C. 7495 S STATE ST 84047 #660-02-1997 L2003 **OBG** *020
MAULDEN, Bryan Scot. 1225 FORT UNION BLVD, ALTA VIEW CTR FOR 84047 #047-20-1994 L1995 **P** *020 †75
MEIER, Stephen Jay. 7495 S STATE ST 84047 #021-05-1974 L1991 **GS** *020 †85
MINGIARDI, Anne Marie. 1275 FORT UNION BLVD 84047 #065-10-1992 L1994 **FM** *020
NAATZ, Jonathan Paul. 632 W 7250 S 84047 #005-14-1988 L1994 **DR** *020 †80
OWAN, Patience E. 1225 FORT UNION BLVD, STE 200 84047 #690-06-1988 L2007 **PD** *020 †55
POLLARY, Rodney Anthony. 7001 S 900 E, STE 400 84047 #049-01-1974 L1975 **PD** *020 †55
RUGGLES, Brian Todd. 7495 S STATE ST 84047 #026-08-1985 L1986 **FM** *071 †18
SAMUDRA, Kalyani Anant. 7309 S 180 W, ARTEC SOUTH CAMPUS 84047 #038-40-1991 L2006 **CHP** *020 †75
SEGAL, Richard Avery. 1225 FORT UNION BLVD, ALTA VIEW CTR FOR 84047 #011-02-1973 L1974 **P** *020 †75
SHAKERI, Mehrnoosh. 7495 S STATE ST 84047 #308-10-1990 L1999 **GPM IM** *020 †20
TERRY, Susan A. 7500 S STATE ST 84047 #055-02-1984 L1997 **IM** *020 †20
TEYNOR, Steven Vincent. 1225 FORT UNION BLVD, ALTA VIEW CTR FOR 84047 #026-04-1989 L1990 **P** *020 †75
TOWNSON, Walter Karl. 7495 S STATE ST 84047 #048-12-1989 L1993 **OBG** *020 †30
VORON, Stephen Carl. ■ 84047 #041-02-1970 L1995 **RNR NR** *020 †80
WILLIAMS, Scott Dean. 6985 UNION PARK CTR, STE 500 84047 #049-01-1982 L1983 **PD** *030 †55,70
WILLS, Richard Evans. ■ 84047 #306-01-1987 **EM** *040
YAROSHCHUK, Larisa Boriso. 7495 S STATE ST 84047 #913-72-1987 L2004 **FM** *020 †18

MIDWAY – WASATCH

BLACK, Henry Edward. ■ 84049 #352-01-1958 L1976 **CD IM** *071 †20
ERB, Blair D, Sr. ■ 84049 #047-06-1953 L1953 **IM CD** *020 †20

MILFORD – BEAVER

SPAULDING, Bradley Bruce. ■ 84751 #049-01-1982 L1983 **FM** *020 ‡
SYMOND, David A. #610, 840 SOUTH 500 WEST 84751 #005-06-1953 L1955 **FM** *071 †18

MOAB – GRAND

ANDREW, Ray Allen. 255 WILLIAMS WAY 84532 #028-34-1998 L2002 **FM** *020 †18
BARROWES, Lowell D. 719 W 400 N 84532 #028-34-1975 L1978 **EM** *020 †16
ERICKSON, Flora Macleod. ■ 84532 #803-01-1956 L1961 **PD** *071
FISHBURN, Bruce Robt. 375 S MAIN ST, # 230 84532 #049-01-1963 L1970 **OPH** *071 †35
HAYES, Kris Attwood. 630 W 400 N, STE B 84532 #019-02-1979 L2004 **GS GE** *020
HORNIG-ROHAN, James Ed. 719 W 400 N 84532 #041-07-1988 L2004 **PM** *020
KEMPA, James Steven. 375 S MAIN ST STE 140 84532 #016-11-1978 L1998 **IM IMG** *020 †20
KEYS, Dell A. ■ 84532 #007-02-1982 L1998 **FM** *020 †18
KLOEPPER, Robert George. 719 W 400 N 84532 #005-19-1995 L1996 **ORS** *020 †40
KOPELL, Philip Anthony. 395 WEST 200 SOUTH 84532 #035-08-1985 L1996 **AN** *020 †05
LANDEEN, Jon Lawson. 380 N 500 W # 2, MOAB REG MED CLC 84532 #035-20-1965 L1971 **GYN** *020 †30
LANDMAN-REINER, Alicia. 3566 KERBY LN 84532 #035-46-1982 L2005 **FM** *020 †18
MALAS, Kenneth Lee. 198 E CENTER ST, FOUR CORNERS BEHAVIORAL HE 84532 #028-02-1976 L1989 **P** *020 †75
MARCUS, Robert Steven. ■ 84532 #035-20-1968 L1992 **OBG OS** *020 †30
MARQUARDT, Donald Nilan. 267 N MAIN ST, MOAB IMMEDIATE CARE AND X- 84532 #028-02-1977 L1978 **EM FM** *020
MUNGER, Jonas Seth. 38 W 300 S 84532 #031-01-1999 L2002 **FM** *020 †18
MURRAY, Robert O. 719 W 400 N 84532 #010-01-1963 L1964 **GP** *071
ROUSSO, Judith R. 198 E CENTER ST, FOUR CORNERS MENTAL HEALTH 84532 #035-06-1973 L1981 **P** *071
ROUZER, Steven Victor. 267 N MAIN ST, MOAB MEDICAL CENTER 84532 #051-01-1974 L1981 **FM EM** *020 †18
SMITH, Maxcy Jean. ■ 84532 #030-05-1947 L1947 **PD** *071 †55
VAN VALKENBURGH, Marianne. ■ 84532 #041-07-1968 L1970 **PD FM** *020
WILLIAMS, Katherine K. 38 W 300 S, MOAB MEDICAL CENTER 84532 #049-01-1997 L2000 **FM** *020 †18
WILLIAMS, Kenneth Lewis. 38 W 300 S 84532 #049-01-1997 L2000 **FM** *020 †18

MONROE – SEVIER

JACKSON, John W. 260 E CENTER ST, P O BOX 566 84754 #649-33-1990 L1994 **EM** *020 †18 ‡

MONTEZUMA CREEK – SAN JUAN

JONES, Lloyd Val. MONTEZUMA CREEK HEALTH CTR 84534 #048-04-1981 L1988 **FM** *020 †18

MONTICELLO – SAN JUAN

REDD, James De Mar. 364 WEST 100 NORTH 84535 #049-01-1976 L1977 **FM** *020

MORGAN – MORGAN

HAWS, John Larry. ■ 84050 #023-12-1992 L2003 **AN** *020 †05
HENLEY, Cheryl. ■ 84050 #005-12-1988 L1989 **FM** *020 †18

MOUNT PLEASANT – SANPETE

BURNHAM, Bruce Owen. 1100 S MEDICAL DR 84647 #049-01-1976 L1977 **FM OS** *071 †18
COLE, Gary M, Jr. 1100 S MEDICAL DR 84647 #018-75-1998, ▲ L2001 **FM EM** *020 †18 ‡
DAY, Allen Merrill. 1100 S MEDICAL DR 84647 #049-01-2000 L2001 **FM** *020 †18 ‡
HARLESS, J Bruce. 255 W MAIN ST 84647 #005-11-1960 L1970 **GP** *020
JONES, Bryan Thos. 220 S 400 E, STE 72 84647 #056-06-1989 L1991 **DR** *020 †80
NUNN, Charles Edward. 1100 S MEDICAL DR, MT PLEASANT CLINIC 84647 #025-07-1997 L2001 **FM** *020 †18
SMITH, Michael Lavern. 255 W MAIN ST, DEPT OF PSYCHIATRY 84647 #049-01-1988 L1989 **P** *020 †75
SPEAKMAN, Gene E. 1100 S MEDICAL DR 84647 #049-01-1960 L1961 **GP** *020

MURRAY – SALT LAKE

ALDER, John Bryant. 164 E 5900 S STE A101 84107 #040-02-1991 L1995 **OPH** *020 †35
ANCTIL, Carolyn Lee. 5770 FASHION BLVD 84107 #032-01-1992 L1996 **EM** *020 †16
ANDERS, Suphithay. 5770 S 250 E STE G50, OBSTETRICAL CLINIC 84107 #049-01-1996 L2000 **OBG** *020 †30
ANDERSON, Jeffrey Lance. 5121 COTTONWOOD ST, HEART & LUNG LEV 6 84107 #024-01-1972 L1973 **CD ICE** *020 †20
BANKS, Diana Darr. 5323 WOODROW ST, STE 201 84107 #047-06-1988 L1989 **N** *020 †75
BANKS, Duane Robert. 845 E 4800 S, STE 200 84107 #005-12-1996 L1997 **P** *020 †75
BEALES, George Landon. 5770 S 300 E 84107 #049-01-1960 L1961 **IM** *020
BERGQUIST, Elizabeth Ann. 5770 S 250 E, STE G50 84107 #008-01-1985 L1993 **OBG** *020 †30
BERNTSON, Dale Rampton. 5770 S 300 E 84107 #023-01-1954 L1954 **GP GS** *020
BINDRUP, Jed Reed. 5770 S 250 E, STE 375 84107 #049-01-1990 L1995 **PS** *020 †65
BJORDAHL, Terrence Scott. 5979 FASHION BLVD 84107 #038-40-2001 L2002 **NEP** *100
BLATTER, Duane David. 5444 GREEN ST 84123 #049-01-1983 L1989 **R DR** *020 †80
BOOK, Lisa Suzanne. PO BOX 571117 84157 #016-43-2002 L2006 **EM** *100
BOWEN, Brent James. 5810 S 300 E STE 300 84107 #054-04-1990 L1994 **PM CN** *020 †60
BOYD, William Eyring. 5770 FASHION BLVD 84107 #049-01-1979 L1980 **EM** *020 †18
BRADLEY, Rulon Ralph. 166 E 5900 S STE 111 84107 #049-01-1974 L1978 **D** *020 †15
BRINTON, Gregory S. 5169 COTTONWOOD ST, STE 630 84107 #049-01-1976 L1983 **OPH** *020 †35 ‡
BUTTERFIELD, Russell Jame. ■ 84107 #016-11-2004 L2005 **CHN** *012
CALL, Gregory Kent. 6040 FASHION BLVD STE 201, WASATCH NEUROLOGICAL CLINI 84107 #041-13-1974 L1982 **N PTH** *020 †75
CARRASCO, Charles Ray. 5444 GREEN ST 84123 #028-02-1977 L1978 **DR IM** *071 †20,80
CHAMBERS, May. 5770 S 250 E, STE G50 84107 #049-01-1990 L1992 **OBG** *020 †30
CHUNG, Jeff B. 5250 COMMERCE DR, STE 200 84107 #038-44-1988 L1993 **PM** *020 †60
CHUNG, Michael Byunghak. 5250 COMMERCE DR, STE 200 84107 #038-40-1993 L1997 **PM** *020 †60
CLARK, Philip Hone. 5770 S 250 E 84107 #035-09-1959 L1962 **OBG** *071
CLAWSON, Junius Jackson. 5810 S 300 E STE 300 84107 #056-06-1997 L2003 **ORS** *020 †40
CLAYSON, Stephen Eugene. 5169 COTTONWOOD ST, STE 600 84107 #049-01-1982 L1991 **TS VS** *020 †85,90
CLAYTON, David N. 5770 S 250 E STE 235, CLAYTON PLASTIC SURGERY SP 84107 #049-01-1976 L1977 **PS HS** *020 †65
CLAYTON, John Naylor. 5770 S 250 E STE 235 84107 #049-01-1976 L1978 **PS** *020
CRANE, Alma Peter. ■ 84107 #049-01-1947 L1956 **PTH** *071 †50
CUTLER, Christopher Scott. 5770 S 250 E, STE 445 84107 #025-07-1988 L1995 **GE** *020 †20
CUTLER, Clifford Noble. 5770 S 300 E 84107 #010-01-1957 L1959 **FM GP** *072
DAVIS, Craig Woods. 5810 FASHION BLVD, STE 236 84107 #049-01-1969 L1973 **PS GS** *020 †65
DIENHART, David G. 5980 FASHION BLVD 84107 #028-46-1980 L1994 **CCM ON** *020 †20
EBERHARD, Todd. 5770 S 250 E, STE 170 84107 #049-01-1976 L1982 **FM** *020 †18
EDWARDS, Corwin Quent. 5121 COTTONWOOD ST, # 303 84107 #049-01-1972 L1976 **IM** *050 †20
EGGLESTON, E Leland. 5763 HANSEN CIR 84107 #049-01-1948 L1953 **AN** *071 †05
ELLIOTT, C Gregory. PO BOX 577000, 5121 COTTONWOOD ST 84157 #023-01-1973 L1976 **PUD PCC** *020 †20
FAIRBANKS, Donald John. 5911 FASHION BLVD, FIRST MED URGENT CARE 84107 #049-01-1995 L2003 **FM** *020 †18
FITZPATRICK, Amelia G. 5121 COTTONWOOD ST, RICU T4S 84107 #007-02-1999 L2001 **PCC** *020 †20
FOTHERINGHAM, Bart W. 5250 COMMERCE DR, STE 200 84107 #049-01-1988 L1992 **PM** *020 †60
FUTRELL, Nancy Nielson. 5292 COLLEGE DR STE 204 84123 #049-01-1981 L1990 **N NRN** *020 †75
GARRICK, David Glenn. 5770 S 300 E 84107 #049-01-1984 L1992 **ORS** *075 †40
GLAD, Blaine Wm. 5770 S 300 E 84107 #049-01-1970 L1971 **IM END** *071
GUTIERREZ, Gayle. 5284 COMMERCE DR, STE C294 84107 #048-13-1987 L1988 **P** *020 †75
GUTIERREZ, Luis. 5284 COMMERCE DR, STE C294 84107 #847-04-1970 L1975 **P** *020 †75
HALDEN, William Jos, Jr. 5444 GREEN ST 84123 #048-04-1980 L1980 **DR** *020 †80
HAMMON, Daniel Jay. 5848 FASHION BLVD 84107 #049-01-1988 L1994 **HS ORS** *020 †40
HARDY, David Clayton. 296 E 3900 S 84107 #049-01-1977 L1978 **DR** *020 †80 ‡
HARKER, Colleen Patricia. 5444 GREEN ST 84123 #005-18-1990 L1996 **DR VIR** *020 †80

HARKER, David Lawrence. 296 E 3900 S 84107 #010-01-1990 L2000 **GS** *020 †85
HARNSBERGER, Janet Kuska. 250 E 5770 S STE 330 84107 #005-14-1978 L1981
  GE PD *020 †55 ‡
HARRIS, Dale Peterson. 5770 S 300 E 84107 #049-01-1989 L1994 **DR** *020 †80
HARRIS, David Tab. 5979 FASHION BLVD, HEART & LUNG INSTITUTE OF 84107
  #028-02-1981 L2006 **PUD** *020 †20
HARRIS, John Warton. 5770 S 250 E STE # 84107 #010-01-1954 L1965 **OBG** *071 †30
HAUPT, Russell Scott. 5292 COLLEGE DR STE 302 84123 #028-34-1989 L1994 **PS CS** *020 †65
HEASTON, David L. 5770 S 300 E 84107 #060-02-1973 L1975 **FM** *071
HEBDON, Bruce Rulon. 5444 GREEN ST 84123 #049-01-1987 L1996 **R** *020 †80
HEIDEN, Karen Drews. 5848 FASHION BLVD 84107 #005-11-1994 L2006 **ORS HS** *020 †40
HEINER, Andrew Martin. 5770 S 250 E, STE 445 84107 #048-02-1987 L1989 **GE** *020 †20
HIGHTOWER, Robert Ross. 164 E 5900 S, STE A112 84107 #001-02-1971 L1974 **PD** *020 †55
HOLMSTROM, Michael Carl. 5848 FASHION BLVD, THE ORTHOPEDIC SPEC HOSP 84107
  #049-01-1996 L1997 **OSM ORS** *020 †40
HORSLEY, Rolfe Purdy. 6040 FASHION BLVD, STE 203 84107 #049-01-1974 L1979 **D** *020 †15
HUNT, Steven Thos. 5444 GREEN ST 84123 #028-02-1981 L1982 **DR** *020 †80
HUNTER, Robert Gail. 5169 COTTONWOOD ST, STE 310 84107 #049-01-1987 L1992
  OTO HNS *020 †45
IRION, Richard Alan. 5063 COTTONWOOD ST STE 4 84107 #049-01-1977 L1978 **OBG** *020 †30
JACK, Joseph Erle, Jr. 5770 S 300 E 84107 #049-01-1947 L1958 **GS** *071 †85
JACKSON, Alan Elvon. 201 E 5900 S STE 101 84107 #021-01-1991 L1993 **OPH** *020
JACOBS, John M. 5444 GREEN ST, MOUNTAIN MEDICAL PHYSICIAN 84123 #028-46-1981 L1982
  DR NM *020 †80
JELSING, Elena Jean. ■ 84107 #026-08-2008 *012
JEPSON, Steven Paul. 5323 WOODROW ST, STE 101 84107 #049-01-1993 L1996 **IM** *020 †20
JONES, Christopher Wayne. 5810 S 300 E, STE 205 84107 #049-01-1998 L2001 **IM** *020 †20
JONES, Joseph Clarke. ■ 84107 #049-01-1955 L1957 **OBG** *071
JONES, Randall Kay. 328 ELM ST, RANDALL K. JONES MD 84107 #049-01-1981 L1984
  GS NTR *020 †85
JORGENSEN, Kenneth M. 5770 FASHION BLVD 84107 #045-01-1993 L1997 **EM** *020 †16
KENAL, Katherine Antonia. 201 E 5900 S, IHC WORKMED 84107 #048-15-1990 L1991
  FM FSM *020 †18
KENDELL, Scott David. 5444 GREEN ST, MOUNTAIN MEDICAL PHYS SPEC 84123
  #049-01-1998 L2004 **DR** *100 †80
LABRUM, Jeffrey Miles. 5063 COTTONWOOD ST STE 4 84107 #049-01-1978 L1979
  GYN *020 †30
LAMBERT, Paul Elwin. ■ 84123 #049-01-2008 *012
LARKIN, Ronald Max. 5063 COTTONWOOD ST STE 4 84107 #049-01-1975 L1976
  OBG *020 †30
LEE, Sharon Marie. 5770 S 250 E, STE 170 84107 #035-09-1989 L1990 **FM EM** *020 †18 ‡
LEININGER, Richard Greg. 5770 S 300 E 84107 #049-01-1979 L1988 **DR** *020 †80
LLOYD, Lewis Kimball. 5063 COTTONWOOD ST, STE 400 84107 #049-01-1975 L1976
  OBG *020 †30
LOMBARDI, Anthony Koy. 5770 S 300 E, UTAH EMERGENCY PHYSICIANS 84107
  #038-40-2002 L2005 **EM** *020 †16
LONDON, Margret C. 5770 S 300 E 84107 #005-15-1983 L1986 **AN** *020 †05
LORDON, Stephen Patrick. 5250 S 320 W STE 305, SUMMIT PAIN MNGMNT PC 84107
  #016-42-1984 L1986 **PME AN** *020 †05
LUERS, Patrick Richard. 5444 GREEN ST 84123 #011-02-1977 L1978 **VIR R** *020 †80
MADSEN, Bard Robt. 5980 FASHION BLVD 84107 #010-01-1976 L1982 **CD** *020 †20
MAIR, Margaret G. 5770 S 300 E, COTTONWOOD HOSPITAL MEDICA 84107
  #031-01-1989 L1991 **EM** *020 †16
MANN, Howard. 296 E 3900 S 84107 #836-01-1978 L1985 **DR** *020 †80
MC LAUGHLIN, Michael J. 5770 FASHION BLVD 84107 #035-01-1991 L1996 **HS** *020
MC NALLY, Jeffrey Michael. 5770 S 300 E, COTTONWOOD HOSPITAL 84107
  #054-04-1989 L1993 **IM** *020 †20
MICKLOS, Timothy John. 5801 FASHION BLVD, STE 190 84107 #038-41-1981 L1985
  DR *020 †80
MIDDLETON, George Wm. 181 E 5600 S, STE 130 84107 #035-20-1969 L1975 **U** *020 †95
MILLER, George A. 5770 S 250 E 84107 #060-01-1951 L1953 **FM** *071 †18
MILLIKAN, Clark H. 5292 COLLEGE DR, STE 204 84123 #019-02-1939 L1976 **N** *030 †75
MIZELL, Louis Lee. 250 E 5770 S STE 330 84107 #021-01-1979 L1982 **PG PD** *020 †55 ‡
MORRISON, Kendrick Oliver. 5770 S 250 E # E-475 84107 #049-01-1963 L1969 **OTO** *071 †45
MORRISON, William James. 5444 GREEN ST, MOUNTAIN MEDICAL PHYSICIAN 84123
  #023-07-1971 L1978 **DR** *020 †80
MUHLESTEIN, Joseph Brent. 5121 COTTONWOOD ST, HEART & LUNG LEV 6 84107
  #049-01-1984 L1992 **CD IC** *020 †20
MUSCI, Anthony Gerard. 5121 COTTONWOOD ST, STE 300 84107 #016-43-1987 L1989
  IM *020 †20
NAYLOR, Allen Oblad. 5770 S 300 E 84107 #049-01-1989 L1990 **FM** *020 †18
NELSON, Patricia Landon. 5980 FASHION BLVD 84107 #028-02-1983 L1986 **PUD IM** *020 †20
NELSON, Robert Harvey. 5770 S 300 E 84107 #030-05-1966 L1967 **GP** *071 †18
NEWHALL, Stanley Clark. 5770 S 250 E 84107 #025-01-1977 L1983 **EM** *020 †16
NOLAN, Kelly Diane. 5169 COTTONWOOD ST, STE 410 84107 #041-13-2000 L2001 **GS** *020 †85
NOYES, Michael Brent. 5770 S 300 E 84107 #005-12-1985 L1990 **IM** *020 †20
OLSEN, Phillip Gane. 5770 S 250 E, STE 170 84107 #018-03-1985 L1988 **FM** *020 †18
ONIKI, Dan. 166 E 5900 S, STE B103 84107 #049-01-1947 L1956 **GS AS** *020
ORCHARD, Anna. 164 E 5900 S, STE A112 84107 #913-05-1986 L1997 **PD** *020 †55 ‡
OTT, Mark John. 5169 COTTONWOOD ST, STE 309 84107 #049-01-1989 L2002 **GS** *020 †85
OUTTRIM, Trinh Nguyen. 5911 FASHION BLVD STE 105, NIGHTIME URGENT CARE 84107
  #048-13-1992 L2000 **PD** *020 †55
PANDITA, Sunny. 5980 FASHION BLVD 84107 #495-51-1993 L2002 **PCC SME** *020 †20
PATTON, Larry Kent. 5169 COTTONWOOD ST, STE 410 84107 #049-01-1972 L1974
  PS HS *020 †85,65
PETERSON, Gaylon King. 5770 SOUTH 300 EAST-ANES 84107 #049-01-1971 L1972
  AN *020 †05
PINGREE, James Hazen. 166 E 5900 S STE 10 84107 #005-11-1959 L1964 **GS** *020 †85 ‡
QUINN, Jeffrey D. 5770 S 250 E STE G50 84107 #049-01-1979 L1983 **OBG** *020 †30
RAMPTON, Jack Burton. 5801 FASHION BLVD, STE 190 84107 #049-01-1969 L1970
  DR NM *020 †80
REICHMAN, Mark Vernon. 5169 COTTONWOOD ST, STE 500 84107 #016-43-1984 L1985
  NS *020 †25
ROBERTS, Joseph Allen. 164 E 5900 S STE A1 84107 #049-01-1966 L1969 **PD** *020
ROBINSON, John Gerald. ■ 84107 #041-01-1961 L1963 **AN** *071

ROGERS, Charles Mitchel. 6095 FASHION BLVD STE 100 84107 #056-06-1974 L1978
  A *020 †20,03
ROSS, Mark T. 5770 S 250 E STE 110 84107 #028-34-1975 L1988 **FM** *020
RUFF, Ronald James. 5444 GREEN ST 84123 #049-01-1981 L1982 **R VIR** *020 †80
RYSER, David Kirkham. 5121 COTTONWOOD ST 84107 #049-01-1982 L1984 **PM** *020 †60
RYSER, Randall James. 5770 S 250 E, STE 445 84107 #049-01-1977 L1979 **GE** *020 †20
SANDERS, John Mervyn. 166 E 5900 S 84107 #049-01-1965 L1966 **NS** *071 †25
SCHLICHTER, Gary Warren. 164 E 5900 S, STE A112 84107 #051-04-1998 L2000 **PD** *020 †55
SCHLOESSER, Peter Ernst. 5323 WOODROW ST, MOUNTAIN MEDICAL 84107
  #019-02-1983 L1999 **EM** *020 †16
SEARE, William John, Jr. 5770 S 250 E, STE 235 84107 #049-01-1973 L1975
  ORS HS *020 †40,65
SEARLE, Clark L. 5444 GREEN ST 84123 #049-01-1986 L1987 **DR** *020 †80
SMITH, Lane Fielding. 279 E 5900 S STE 201 84107 #049-01-1988 L1994 **PS OTO** *020 †45,65
SNARR, Gerald Vernon. 5770 S 300 E 84107 #049-01-1955 L1961 **PD** *071 †55
SONNTAG, Paul Lenzi. 5444 GREEN ST 84123 #049-01-1974 L1979 **DR** *020 †80
SOUTER, Steve Roe. 5770 FASHION BLVD 84107 #048-12-1985 L1986 **IM** *020 †20
SOUZA, Steven John. 5444 GREEN ST 84123 #005-02-1985 L1999 **VIR R** *020 †80
SPENCER, David Arthur. 164 E 5900 S STE A101 84107 #049-01-1987 L1991 **OPH** *020 †35
STEVENS, Scott Mckenzie. 5121 COTTONWOOD ST, # 303 84107 #005-12-1995 L1996
  IM *020 †20
SUNDWALL, Peter V. 4815 CENTER ST 84107 #049-01-1965 L1968 **GP** *020
SWARTZ, Mano. 5169 COTTONWOOD ST, STE 630 84107 #023-07-1971 L1979 **OPH** *020 †35
SWEENEY, Patrick Jos. 5770 FASHION BLVD 84107 #049-01-1976 L1979 **EM** *020 †16
SWENSEN, Laird Strickler. 5848 FASHION BLVD 84107 #010-01-1972 L1977 **HS ORS** *020 †40
SYMKOVIAK, Gary Paul. 5980 FASHION BLVD 84107 #021-05-1974 L1976 **CD IM** *020 †20
SZWAJKUN, Konstantyn Y. 5980 FASHION BLVD 84107 #005-07-1982 L1992 **CD** *020 †20
TERRY, Stephen Robt. 5770 S 250 E 84107 #049-01-1977 L1978 **OBG EM** *020 †30
TESTA, Massimo. 5848 FASHION BLVD, THE ORTHOPEDIC SPECIALTY H 84107
  #561-14-1982 L2007 *020
THOMAS, Maya. 5323 WOODROW ST, STE 203 84107 #495-11-1984 L1996 **CN** *020 †75
THOMPSON, Brooks David. 5770 S 300 E 84107 #031-01-1988 L1992 **FM OBS** *020 †18
THOMSEN, George. PO BOX 57700, INTERMOUNTAIN MED CTR 84157 #005-12-1984 L1992
  PUD IM *020 †20
THUESON, John Miller. 5770 FASHION BLVD 84107 #049-01-1969 L1985 **EM GS** *071 †85
TIPPETS, Richard Hayward. 5169 COTTONWOOD ST, STE 500 84107 #049-01-1985 L1986
  NS *020 †25
TROXELL, Robert Todd. 5444 GREEN ST 84123 #032-01-1986 L1987 **R** *020 †80
VARGYAS, George Alan. 5770 FASHION BLVD 84107 #033-06-1994 L1997 **EM** *020 †16
VOORHEES, Hugh David. 4000 S 7TH E STE 9 84107 #049-01-1972 L1973 **GS** *020 †85
WALLACE, Aaron David. ■ 84107 #005-12-2006 L2007 **AN** *012
WALLACE, William Dean. 747 W 4170 S 84123 #049-01-1977 L1982 **PTH** *020
WEED, Thomas Stuart. 5770 S 300 E 84107 #010-01-1978 L1979 **EM FM** *020 †18,16
WELLING, Eric Clark. 5770 S 300 E 84107 #021-01-1984 L1985 **AN** *020 †05
WILLCOX, James Andrew. 5292 COLLEGE DR STE 301 84123 #019-02-1991 L1992 **IM** *020 †20
WILLIAMS, Robert Dean. 5770 S 300 E 84107 #649-33-1985 L1993 **FM** *020 †18
WILMOTH, Jon Darrell. 491 W 5300 S 84123 #030-05-1966 L1991 **FM IMG** *020 †18
WYNE, Carl E. 5801 FASHION BLVD STE 175, IHC SENIOR CLINIV 84107 #016-11-1973 L1995
  IMG *020
YOUNG, Justin M. 5929 FASHION BLVD 84107 #041-02-2004 L2007 **OMF PSH** *100
ZAMAN, Faisel Mohammed. 5250 COMMERCE DR, STE 200 84107 #665-01-2000 L2003
  PM *020 †60

NAPLES – UINTAH

CHEUNG LAU, Antonio Kwok. 822 SOUTH JOSHUA ST 84078 #715-01-2000 **FP** *012

NEPHI – JUAB

ANDERSON, Richard Edward. 48 W 1500 N, CENTRL VLY HOSP 84648 #049-01-1988 L1989
  GS GP *020 †85
BAILEY, Stanton Andersen. 48 W 1500 N 84648 #051-04-1989 L1994 **OBG** *020
BESENDORFER, James M. 48 W 1500 N 84648 #049-01-1981 L1984 **FM** *020 †18
OVESON, Mark Clark. 48 W 1500 N 84648 #049-01-1986 L1987 **FM** *020 †18
PETERSON, Michael Cary. 48 W 1500 N 84648 #049-01-1991 L1992 **IM** *020 †20
RASMUSSEN, Grant J. 48 W 1500 N 84648 #049-01-1990 L1991 **FM** *020 †18
TATTON, James Andrew. PO BOX 267, 1910 W 1900 S 84648 #049-01-1976 L1977
  FM EM *071 †16,18
WALLENTINE, Steven Lee. 48 W 1500 N, CENTRAL UTAH CLINIC PC 84648
  #422-01-2000 L2006 **IM** *100 †20 ‡

NORTH LOGAN – CACHE

ASTLE, Hal G. 2380 N 400 E STE A 84341 #048-15-1988 L2007 **N** *071 †75
BLOTTER, James Wallentine. 2380 N 400 E, STE D 84341 #049-01-1995 L2000
  OTO FPS *020 †45
GARG, Vikas. 2380 N 400 E, CACHE VALLEY SPECIALITY HO 84341 #495-29-1996 L2005
  FM PME *020 †18
HUFF, Glen Forrest. 2380 N 400 E STE C 84341 #049-01-1995 L1999 **PD** *020 †55
LARKIN, April. ■ 84341 #028-46-1998 L2005 **FM** *020 †18
LARSON, Brad Jos. 2310 N 400 E STE A, ALPINE ORTHOPAEDIC SPECIAL 84341
  #049-01-1982 L1987 **ORS** *020 †40
NELSON, Keith Jay. 2310 N 400 E STE A, ALPINE ORTHOPAEDIC SPECIAL 84341
  #049-01-1991 L1996 **ORS** *020 †40
PALFREYMAN, Richard Bruce. ■ 84341 #049-01-1989 L1993 **AN** *020 †05
STEVENS, Lyman Brimhall. ■ 84341 #049-01-1969 L1970 **AN** *020 †05
ST ONGE, Richard Arthur. 2380 N 400 E, ALPINE ORTHOPAEDIC SPECIALI 84341
  #008-01-1970 L1996 **ORS** *071 †40
WELTER, Matthew John. 2380 N 400 E, STE H 84341 #056-06-1999 L2005 **FM** *020 †18

NORTH OGDEN – WEBER

ALLEN, Carl Preston, IV. 2400 N WASHINGTON BLVD, NORTH OGDEN IHC CLINIC 84414
  #049-01-1997 L1998 **FM** *020 †18

ALSUP, Daniel Dennis, Jr. 2400 N WASHINGTON BLVD 84414 #010-01-1994 L1995 **FM** *020 †18 ‡

HALL, Michael Jay. ■ 84414 #025-07-2007 L2007 **TY** *012

HEALEY, Curtis Mack. 2400 N WASHINGTON BLVD, NORTH OGDEN IHC CLINIC 84414 #049-01-1998 L1999 **FM** *020 †18

LARSEN, Bruce Darrell. 2400 N WASHINGTON BLVD 84414 #028-34-2000 L2001 **FM** *020 †18 ‡

MARTENSON, Sven Heiti. 2400 N WASHINGTON BLVD 84414 #654-01-1982 L1997 **FM OM** *020 †18

SCHMITT, Ann M. 2400 N WASHINGTON BLVD, INTERMOUNTAIN NORTH OGDEN 84414 #054-04-1990 L1991 **FM** *020 †18

WYNN, Steven Winder. 2400 N WASHINGTON BLVD 84414 #049-01-1992 L1995 **FM** *020 †18

NORTH SALT LAKE – DAVIS

CHAN, Christy. ■ 84054 #049-01-2006 L2007 **FP** *012

CHRISTENSEN, Clint. ■ 84054 #049-01-2002 L2006 **AN** *100 †05

CHRISTENSEN, Jay Rulon. ■ 84054 #049-01-1994 L1994 **OBG** *075 †30 ‡

EDWARDS, Charles Eugene. ■ 84054 #010-02-1955 L1956 **N** *071 †75

GEE, Ivin Laurence. ■ 84054 #049-01-1962 L1963 **PD** *071 †55

HARKER, Christopher Owen. ■ 84054 #051-01-2005 L2006 **DR** *012

HEBERTSON, Richard M. ■ 84054 #049-01-1958 L1959 **OBS** *071 †30

KELLEY, Todd William. ■ 84054 #038-40-2002 L2007 **PTH** *100 †50

KIRKHAM, Keith Arthur. ■ 84054 #049-01-1972 L1974 **AN** *020

KNAPP, Ralph Wm. 1130 W CENTER ST 84054 #049-01-1972 L1978 **CHP P** *020

LINFORD, Samuel Wray. ■ 84054 #054-04-2007 L2012

MATHEWSON, Cynthia Marie. ■ 84054 #021-01-1995 L2001 **FM** *020 †18

MCQUIVEY, Ross Wayne. ■ 84054 #049-01-2000 **OBG** *100

MIRANDA, George Guinto. ■ 84054 #005-12-2004 L2005 **HO** *012 †20

PHO, Thanhlan Ngoc. ■ 84054 #049-01-2006 **IM** *012

RAEMISCH, Michael Ernest. ■ 84054 #026-08-1997 L2005 **HS** *020 †40

ROACH, Christopher M. ■ 84054 #038-40-2002 L2003 **PDR** *012 †80

TAYLOR, Michael Binns. ■ 84054 #005-15-2007 *012

VICKERMAN, Robert Peteris. ■ 84054 #056-05-1995 L2000 **GS** *020 †85

WRIGHT, Trenton Mcneil. ■ 84054 #028-34-1997 L1998 **DR** *020 †80

OAKLEY – SUMMIT

BODDEN, Vernie D. PO BOX 664, 5224 N 750 W 84055 #048-13-1972 L1972 **OBG** *020 †30

OGDEN – WEBER

ABDULLA, Alan Robt. 4403 HARRISON BLVD, STE 3620 84403 #011-02-1972 L1975 **PUD IM** *020 †20

ABEL, Jeffrey Alan. 4403 HARRISON BLVD, STE 2455 84403 #017-20-1980 L1985 **PUD IM** *020 †20

ADAMS, James Willis. 6112 S 1550 E, STE 202 84405 #048-02-1970 L1975 **OS ORS** *030 †40

ADAMS, Robert Lee. 1355 W 3400 S, IHC WORKMED 84401 #030-06-1981 L1984 **FM OM** *020 †18

AGARWAL, Adhish Kumar. 425 E 5350 S, STE 320 84405 #495-45-1997 L2001 **NEP** *020 †20

AHLSTROM, Jon Walter. 5475 S 500 E 84405 #035-20-1991 L2001 **OBG** *020 †30

ALDER, C Mark. 4650 HARRISON BLVD, RADIOLOGY 84403 #019-01-1995 L2003 **DR** *020 †80

ALDER, Richard Leon. 4403 HARRISON BLVD, STE 1635 84403 #028-03-1972 L1977 **OS** *020 †85

ALLEN, David Edgar. 3860 JACKSON AVE, STE 2 84403 #049-01-1972 L1976 **D DMP** *020 †15

ALLEN, David More. 3860 JACKSON AVE STE 2 84403 #056-06-1999 L2003 **D** *020 †15 ‡

ALLEY, Robert Jones. 4401 HARRISON BLVD 84403 #049-01-1978 L1983 **GS EM** *020 †85

ALMONY, Gregory Thos. 5405 S 500 E STE 204, UTAH CARDIOLOGY 84405 #035-19-1988 L1996 **IM CD** *020 †20

ANDEN, Corey Dawn. 4403 HARRISON BLVD STE D, 84403 #041-12-1984 L1988 **PM LM** *020 †60

ANDERSON, Anne Hotchkiss. 4401 HARRISON BLVD, NEONATOLOGY DEPT 84403 #020-02-1989 L1990 **NPM** *100 †55 ‡

ANDERSON, Christopher K. 4403 HARRISON BLVD, STE 2455 84403 #049-01-1988 L1996 **IM PCC** *020 †20

ANDERSON, Douglas Kent. 425 E 5350 S STE 130 84405 #049-01-1990 L1995 **OTO** *020 †45

ANDERSON, Joseph Robert. 1682 E 5600 S, INTERMOUNTAIN ALLERGY & 84403 #028-34-1977 L1982 **AI** *020 †20,03

ANDRES, Robert L. 4401 HARRISON BLVD, MFM DEPT 84403 #030-05-1984 L1985 **MFM OBG** *050 †30

ARBOGAST, Richard Chas. 4403 HARRISON BLVD, STE 700A 84403 #023-07-1965 L1979 **FM P** *040 †75,18

ARCHIBALD, Lyle H. 4403 HARRISON BLVD, STE 1635 84403 #049-01-1971 L1973 **GS** *020 †85

ARGYLE, Bruce Reed. 4401 HARRISON BLVD 84403 #049-01-1978 L1979 **EM GP** *020 †16

ARMSTRONG, John Dale. 4360 WASHINGTON BLVD, MOUNT OGDEN EYE CENTER 84403 #047-06-1974 L1979 **OPH** *020 †35

ARRINGTON, Jeffrey Todd. 4403 HARRISON BLVD, STE 2645 84403 #056-06-2000 L2005 **OBG** *020

ASHWORTH, William D, Jr. 4650 HARRISON BLVD 84403 #028-02-1982 L1985 **IM** *020 †20

BABCOOK, Catherine Jean. 4403 HARRISON BLVD 84403 #065-10-1987 L1998 **DR** *020 †80

BACHISON, Casey Clifford. ■ 84404 #010-01-2005 L2005 **ORS** *012

BAILEY, Zachary Max. 4403 HARRISON BLVD, STE 700A 84403 #056-06-2006 L2007 **FP** *012

BALKEN, John Bruce. 3939 HARRISON BLVD 84403 #028-02-1943 L1953 **PD** *020 †55

BARANKO, Anne M. 3955 HARRISON BLVD STE L 84403 #003-01-1992 L1998 **PD** *020 †55

BARANKO, Brent Michael. 4350 WASHINGTON BLVD, OGDEN CLINIC - WASHINGTON 84403 #003-01-1992 L1998 **ORS** *020 †40

BARHORST, Donna Marie. 4403 HARRISON BLVD, STE 4875 84403 #048-15-1986 L1996 **PD** *020 †55

BARLOW, Stewart Ellison. 3955 HARRISON BLVD, STE U6 84403 #010-01-1986 L1991 **OTO** *020 †45

BARNETT, Randall Dean. 4403 HARRISON BLVD, STE 3680 84403 #016-43-1987 L1994 **PS HS** *020 †65

BATSON, John Hansell. 5475 S 500 E 84405 #047-06-1958 L1988 **GS** *071 †85

BAUGHMAN, John Lee, Jr. 4401 HARRISON BLVD, MCKAY-DEE HOSPITAL 84403 #021-05-1971 L1979 **CCM IM** *020 †20

BELFRY, Carolyn Anne. 4650 HARRISON BLVD 84403 #062-01-1995 L1998 **FM** *020 †18

BELNAP, Norman Blaine. 5030 HARRISON BLVD, MCKAY-DEE INST BEHAVRL MED 84403 #049-01-1956 L1957 **P** *020

BENSON, Leo Walter. 3930 WASHINGTON BLVD 84403 #021-01-1936 **OM GPM** *075

BENTLEY, Melissa Jean. ■ 84403 #049-01-2006 L2007 **IM** *012

BERGER, James Irwin. 5475 S 500 E, OGDEN REGIONAL MED CENTER 84405 #030-05-1987 L1993 **NPM** *020 †55

BERGMAN, Daniel Albert. 1649 RUTHERFORD RIDGE RD 84403 #018-03-1963 L1965 **OBG** *071 †30

BERRY, Julie Lin. 3955 HARRISON BLVD, STE L1 84403 #028-03-1986 L1991 **PD** *020 †55

BIDDULPH, Glen F. 4403 HARRISON BLVD, STE 3875 84403 #031-01-1996 L1997 **IM** *020 †20

BIERER, David Roy. 1525 E 6000 S 84405 #028-34-1990 L1997 **OBG** *020 †30

BIGGS, Sean D. 2400 N 400 E 84414 #049-01-2000 L2001 **FM** *020 †18

BIKHAZI, Nadim Bechara. 4650 HARRISON BLVD 84403 #005-18-1993 L1999 **OTO** *020 †45

BLACKBURN, Brent Louis. 4650 HARRISON BLVD, OGDEN CLINIC 84403 #049-01-1991 L1996 **IM PD** *075 †55

BLOCKER, Robert Ray. 4401 HARRISON BLVD, DEPT OF ANESTHESIOLOGY 84403 #024-05-2003 L2004 **AN** *020

BOEHM, Mindy Mendenhall. 1159 E 12TH ST 84404 #019-02-1978 L1990 **PD** *020 †55

BOHMAN, Bradford Kirk. 5475 S 500 E 84405 #020-02-1982 L1985 **AN** *020 †05

BOOTH, Jeffrey Edward. 4403 HARRISON BLVD, STE 3650 84403 #049-01-1974 L1977 **RHU IM** *020 †20

BOOTH, Jeremy Todd. 4401 HARRISON BLVD, MCKAY DEE HOSPITAL 84403 #049-01-2002 L2006 **EM** *100 †16

BOOTH, Jodi Creer. 4401 HARRISON BLVD, MCKAY DEE HOSPITAL 84403 #049-01-2003 L2006 **EM** *100 †16

BOSSLER, Karen Ann. 4401 HARRISON BLVD 84403 #054-04-1987 L1988 **FM** *020 †18

BRANDT, William Frederick. 5405 S 500 E, STE 200 84405 #030-06-1983 L1984 **PM** *020 †60

BREWER, Fred French, Jr. 4650 HARRISON BLVD 84403 #056-05-1960 L1967 **ORS** *071

BROADBENT, Mary Catherine. ■ 84403 #049-01-1995 L1996 **PD** *020

BRODIS, Walter Evan. ■ 84403 #041-01-1981 L1992 **IM** *071 †20

BRODSTEIN, David Edwin. 875 COUNTRY HILLS DR 84403 #041-02-1987 L1992 **OPH** *020 †35

BRODSTEIN, Robert Saml. 875 COUNTRY HILLS DR 84403 #041-02-1957 L1965 **OPH** *071 †35

BROWN, Edward Douglass. 4650 HARRISON BLVD 84403 #049-01-1981 L1984 **PD** *020 †55

BROWN, Frank Henry. 2400 N WASHINGTON BLVD 84414 #026-08-1984 L1985 **FM** *020 †18 ‡

BROWN, Martin Delaney. 4364 WASHINGTON BLVD 84403 #051-04-1982 L1986 **AN** *020 †05

BRUCE, Stephen James. 5740 CRESTWOOD DR 84405 #030-05-1982 L1985 **FM** *020 †18

BRYAN, Donald William. 4403 HARRISON BLVD, STE 2600 84403 #023-01-1969 L1977 **ORS OSS** *020 †40

BRZOWSKI, Anita Ellis. ■ 84403 #012-01-1989 L1999 **PD** *020 †55

BRZOWSKI, Brian Keith. 1525 E 6000 S STE C, BRZOWSKI PLASTIC SURGERY 84405 #012-01-1988 L1999 **PS GS** *020 †85,65 ‡

BUCH, Michael Howard. 4403 HARRISON BLVD, STE 3450 84403 #025-01-1978 L1988 **TS** *020 †85,90

BUDGE, Arthur Farr. ■ 84403 #049-01-1958 L1965 **R** *071 †80

BURDETT, Brent Ray. 1682 E 5600 S, INTERMOUNTAIN ALLERGY & 84403 #049-01-1971 L1975 **A PD** *020 †55,03

BURDETT, Laurence S. 4364 WASHINGTON BLVD 84403 #049-01-1993 L1997 **AN** *020 †05

BURDETT, Ray Earl. 3939 HARRISON BLVD 84403 #016-06-1944 L1949 **PD** *071 †55

BYCK, Dann Conrad, III. 4403 HARRISON BLVD, STE 2600 84403 #020-02-1991 L2002 **ORS** *020 †40

CAILLOUET, Gilbert Eugene. 1292 E 5375 S 84403 #021-06-1983 L1986 **IM EM** *020 †20

CAIN, Albert Steven. 4403 HARRISON BLVD # 3450 84403 #001-02-1968 L1970 **TS VS** *020 †85,90

CALL, Jeffrey Holt. 4403 HARRISON BLVD STE 365 84403 #049-01-1983 L1984 **IM** *020

CALLISTER, Neil Barton. 4403 HARRISON BLVD STE 240 84403 #049-01-1993 L1999 **HS** *020 †40

CALTON, Farrell Marlon. ■ 84403 #028-02-1959 L1964 **CD** *071

CALTON, Thomas F. 4403 HARRISON BLVD, STE 2400 84403 #020-02-1990 L1996 **ORS** *020 †40

CAMPBELL, Bryan Joe. 4403 HARRISON BLVD, STE 700A 84403 #054-04-1980 L1981 **FM** *040 †18

CAMPBELL, Curtis M. 4403 HARRISON BLVD, STE 4400 84403 #049-01-1975 L1978 **U** *020 †95

CARABINE, Steven John. 4403 HARRISON BLVD, STE 1635 84403 #049-01-1992 L1993 **GS** *020 †85

CARDON, Louis Scott. 975 CHAMBERS AVE 84403 #049-01-1986 L1989 **FM** *020 †18

CARLIN, Bruce Wayne. 3620 OGDEN AVE 84403 #017-20-1969 L1977 **U IM** *020 †95

CARLQUIST, David Alma. 4401 HARRISON BLVD, MCKAY DEE HOSPITAL ER DEPT 84403 #049-01-1970 L1974 **EM IM** *020 †20,16

CATON, Charles Allen. 698 12TH ST 84404 #048-04-1964 L1966 **EM OM** *020 †16

CATTRON-BLEWETT, Kimberly. 4403 HARRISON BLVD STE A70 84403 #028-79-2006, ▲ L2007 **FP** *012

CHALLBURG, Norman Lee. 5475 S 500 E 84405 #005-15-1966 L1975 **FM** *020 †18

CHAMBERLAIN, Philippa M. 5740 CRESTWOOD DR 84405 #054-04-2003 L2006 **FM** *020 †18

CHARLAT, Richard Arnold. 5030 WASHINGTON BLVD, BEHAVIORAL MEDICINE 84403 #008-01-1970 L1985 **P AM** *020 †75,70

CHILD, Dustin Gary. 975 CHAMBERS ST 84403 #028-34-1998 L1999 **FM** *020 †18

CHILD, Troy Rex. 4401 HARRISON BLVD, MCKAY-DEE HOSPITAL 84403 #049-01-1993 L1997 **AN** *020 †05

CHRISTENSEN, Gary Orson. 6028 S RIDGELINE DR 84405 #049-01-1976 L1977 **IM** *020 †20

CHRISTENSEN, Karen Messer. 3670 QUINCY AVE, STE 101 84403 #034-01-1986 L1992 **P** *020 †75

CHRISTENSEN, Robt Dennis. 4401 HARRISON BLVD 84403 #035-01-1974 L1976 **NPM PD** *050 †55

CHRISTIANSEN, Van G. 4650 HARRISON BLVD 84403 #049-01-1991 L1993 **FM** *020 †18

CLARK, John Michael. 4401 HARRISON BLVD, NEONATOLOGY 84403 #049-01-1973 L1975 **NPM PD** *020 †55

CLAWSON, Charlene Godfrey. 3955 HARRISON BLVD, STE L1 84403 #049-01-1983 L1986 **PD** *020 †55

CLAYSON, Fred Eli. 4403 HARRISON BLVD, STE 3600 84403 #049-01-1973 L1974 **OPH** *020 †35

COLEMAN, Anne Margaret. 4401 HARRISON BLVD 84403 #018-03-1983 L1984 **PTH** *062 †50

COLEMAN, Sherman Michael. 4403 HARRISON BLVD # 3450 84403 #049-01-1976 L1984 **TS VS** *020 †85,90

COLLADO, Sergio Rafael. 4403 HARRISON BLVD, STE 3490 84403 #308-05-1982 L2003 **CD IM** *020 †20

CONRAD, Jos Alexander, Jr. 425 E 5350 S, STE 335 84405 #028-34-1967 L1983 PUD IM *020 †20

COOK, Catherine. 4650 HARRISON BLVD, OGDEN CLINIC 84403 #049-01-1997 L2000 PD *020 †55

COOPERSMITH, Kathie Ellen. 5495 S 500 E, STE 120 84405 #031-01-1981 L1989 PD *020 †55

COTTRELL, Ann Carol. 6112 S 1550 E, STE 202 84405 #010-03-1993 L1994 PM *020 †60

CRAWFORD, Michael Eugene. 5405 S 500 E, STE 204 84405 #045-01-1982 L1996 CD IM *020 †20

CROFTS, Robert D. 4401 HARRISON BLVD 84403 #049-01-1993 L1997 EM *020 †16

CROSLAND, Jack Weatherly. 6112 S 1550 E, STE 202 84405 #048-12-1971 L1976 ORS *020 †40

DAINES, Lowell Raymond. 6136 WOODLAND DR 84403 #010-01-1958 L1959 GS *071 †85

DAMES, Shelby Teru. 4403 HARRISON BLVD, STE 3650 84403 #018-03-2001 L2002 IM *020

DARGAN-MC DONALD, Ann E. 4401 HARRISON BLVD, MCKAY DEE HOSPITAL 84403 #045-04-2000 L2002 HO *100 †20

DAVIDSON, Richard Sherman. 1452 E RIDGELINE DR, STE 151 84405 #010-01-1978 L1979 P FM *020 †75

DAVIS, Toby Ace. 4403 HARRISON BLVD, STE 700A 84403 #028-79-2006, ▲ L2007 FP *012

DEFRIEZ, Curtis Boe. ■ 84405 #049-01-1983 L1984 AN GP *075

DE REMER, Kathleen Rose. 5405 S 500 E STE 101 84405 #033-06-1975 L1996 IM *071 †20

DIEHL, Michael John. 5405 S 500 E, STE 204 84405 #011-03-1986 L1995 CD IC *020 †20

DING, Hu. 5475 S 500 E, ASSOCIATES OF PATHOLOGY 84405 #243-35-1983 L2003 PTH *100 †50

DIXON, Tyler Carnahan. 4403 HARRISON BLVD STE A70 84403 #003-75-2005, ▲ L2006 FP *012

DOGU, Turhan Sitki. 3939 HARRISON BLVD 84403 #902-10-1949 L1977 AN *072 †05

DOWNS, Warren Shelby. 4401 HARRISON BLVD 84403 #005-12-1997 L2000 EM *020 †16

DRURY, David Walter. 4401 HARRISON BLVD 84403 #038-41-1998 L2001 EM *020 †16

DURTSCHI, Amy Camille. 4403 HARRISON BLVD, STE 3650 84403 #049-01-1992 L2002 IM *020 †20

DYE, Joseph Douglas. 5030 HARRISON BLVD, MCKAY-DEE INST. FOR BEH. M 84403 #055-01-1983 L2005 P *020 †75

DYMOTT, Cleo Elaine. 5475 S 500 E, DEPT OF RADIATION THERAPY 84405 #005-12-1969 L1987 RO *071 †80

EGBERT, William Richard. 3939 HARRISON BLVD 84403 #010-01-1956 L1959 OBG *071 †30

EVANS, Evan F. 4403 HARRISON BLVD 84403 #016-06-1950 L1956 GYN *071 †30

FANTLE, David Michael. 425 E 5350 S, STE 315 84405 #056-05-1986 L1997 N CHN *020 †75

FARBER, Jack Lee. ■ 84405 #005-19-1976 L1986 P *071 †75

FARR, Boyd J. 4650 HARRISON BLVD 84403 #010-01-1952 L1956 GYN *071 †30

FARR, Brad R. 4650 HARRISON BLVD, OGDEN CLINIC 84403 #049-01-1985 OS *050

FAUCETT, Clyde J, Jr. 4403 HARRISON BLVD, STE 3875 84403 #034-01-1979 L1989 IM ID *020 †20

FELT, Douglas Patterson. 875 COUNTRY HILLS DR 84403 #049-01-1979 L1982 OPH *020 †35 ‡

FERGUSON, Cory William. 4403 HARRISON BLVD, STE 3650 84403 #049-01-2004 L2007 IM *020 †20

FERGUSON, Gregory Barber. 3903 HARRISON BLVD 84403 #049-01-1981 L1982 AN *020 †05

FERNELIUS, Colby Arthur. ■ 84405 #023-12-2006 L2008 PTH *012

FINNEGAN, Robert Franklin. 270 E 12TH ST, UTAH PAIN AND REHAB 84404 #004-01-1973 L2003 PME AN *071 †05

FLINDERS, Kurt Timothy. 4403 HARRISON BLVD, STE 700A- MCKAY DEE HOSP 84403 #028-79-2007, ▲ FP *012

FOLEY, Craig Ralph. 4403 HARRISON BLVD, STE 2855 84403 #049-01-1988 L1994 CRS *020 †85,10

FOLEY, Ralph Blaine. 6028 S RIDGELINE DR, STE 205 84405 #016-06-1961 L1963 GS *071

FRIDEN, John Stanley. 975 CHAMBERS ST 84403 #005-19-1979 L1980 FM *020 †18

FUENTES, Juan. 4403 HARRISON BLVD 84403 #737-01-1974 L1984 OS DR *062 †80

FUNK, Kevin Chas. 1486 E SKYLINE DR 84405 #049-01-1984 L1998 RNR *020 †80

GABBERT, Clayton Ronald. 5475 S 500 E 84405 #049-01-1958 L1959 ORS *071 †40

GARDNER, Henry Jerry. 975 CHAMBERS ST 84403 #049-01-1968 L1969 FM *071 †18

GARRISON, Thomas Edwin. 4401 HARRISON BLVD, MCKAY-DEE HOSPITAL 84403 #023-12-1982 L1984 EM *020 †16

GARVEY, Sheila Gay. 5475 S 500 E 84405 #049-01-1993 L1994 GS *020 †85

GOCHNOUR, Gregory Lowell. 4403 HARRISON BLVD, A700 84403 #049-01-1992 L1995 FM *020 †18

GODFREY, Merrill Anderson. 3905 HARRISON BLVD 84403 #030-05-1964 L1965 OBG *071 †30

GOFF, David Reed. 4403 HARRISON BLVD, STE 3450 84403 #049-01-1986 L1993 TS *020 †85,90

GONCHAROVA, Elena Lvovna. 5405 S 500 E, STE 101 84405 #913-66-1986 L2003 IM *020 †20

GONZALES, Chad Michael. 4403 HARRISON BLVD, STE 2855 84403 #049-01-1999 L2000 GE *020 †20

GORDON, Ronald Farrell. 3955 HARRISON BLVD STE U5 84403 #049-01-1977 L1978 OTO *020 †45

GOUCHER, Gary Kent. 4403 HARRISON BLVD, STE 2455 84403 #010-02-1974 L1979 PUD IM *020 †20

GOUCHER, Nicholas Roy. 4403 HARRISON BLVD, STE 2400 84403 #038-43-2000 L2006 ORS *020

GRAHAM, Stanley Tanner. 4403 HARRISON BLVD, STE 700A 84403 #048-15-2006 L2007 FP *012

GRAY, Carl Roger. 5405 S 500 E, STE 202 84405 #048-14-1995 L2004 HO *020 †20

GRAY, Robert Nelson. 1715 DARLING ST, APT 1 84403 #016-06-1965 L1976 EM *020 †18,16

GREENBERG, Daniel Jos. 5837 S 2550 E, OGDEN REGIONAL MEDICAL CEN 84403 #023-12-1981 L1992 AN CCM *020 †05

GREENHALGH, Jason Ryan. ■ 84404 #051-04-2005 L2005 U *012

GREGOIRE, Richard Jos. 2240 ADAMS AVE, MIDTOWN COMMUNITY HEALTH C 84401 #035-06-1991 L1992 FM *020 †18

GUENZEL, Elizabeth Violet. 4401 HARRISON BLVD, MCKAY-DEE HOSPITALIST SERV 84403 #025-07-1996 L2004 IM *020 †20

GUYMON, Garth J. 4401 HARRISON BLVD, DEPT ANESTH MCKAY DEE HOSP 84403 #049-01-1984 L1985 AN *020 †05

HACKETT, Deborah Anthony. ■ 84403 #049-01-1999 L2004 END *020 †20

HALE, Phillip Nathan. 875 COUNTRY HILLS DR 84403 #005-14-1963 L1970 OPH *020 †35

HALES, Dean Wilson. ■ 84403 #056-05-1945 L1952 OTO *071 †45

HALL, Christopher Lee. 4401 HARRISON BLVD, MCKAY-DEE HOSPITAL CENTER 84403 #034-01-1978 L2000 PTH *020 †50

HALL, David Lynn. ■ 84404 #040-02-2007 FP *012

HALL, Michael Joel. 4350 WASHINGTON BLVD 84403 #056-06-1999 L2004 ORS *100 †40

HALLIDAY, Michael K. 4401 HARRISON BLVD 84403 #022-75-1995, ▲ L1997 EM *020 †16

HARB, Tareq Shehadeh. 4403 HARRISON BLVD, STE 3490 84403 #035-06-1995 L2006 IC *020 †20

HARLINE, Wesley Grant. 625 25TH ST 84401 #041-13-1945 L1953 GS PS *071

HARRISON, Jeffrey Danl. 4403 HARRISON BLVD, STE 2400 84403 #003-01-1992 L1993 OSM *020 †40

HARTMAN, Albert Ray. 4403 HARRISON BLVD, STE 4625 84403 #010-01-1976 L1980 OBG OS *020 †30

HASLAM, Marlan J. 3905 HARRISON BLVD 84403 #049-01-1957 L1964 ORS *071 †40

HASSRICK, Philip Heyl. 4650 HARRISON BLVD 84403 #030-06-1991 L1993 FM *020 †18

HEATON, Brian Wm. 4403 HARRISON BLVD, STE 4400 84403 #049-01-1988 L1989 U *020 †95

HEGDE, Hemant. 4401 HARRISON BLVD, MCKAY-DEE HOSPITAL / IHC 84403 #495-23-1983 L2004 IM *020 †20

HEMMERSMEIER, John M. 5740 CRESTWOOD DR 84405 #049-01-2001 L2004 FM *020 †18

HERNANDEZ, Alex Yasser. ■ 84401 #049-01-2008 *012

HEROLD, Richard Jos. 6028 S RIDGELINE DR, STE 204 84405 #028-34-1976 L1979 IM *020 †20

HILGER, William Chas. 5030 HARRISON BLVD, MCKAY-DEE INST FOR BEHAV H 84403 #049-01-1971 L1994 CHP P *020 †75

HILL, Lisa J. 425 E 5350 S STE 155 84405 #005-12-1998 L1999 FM *020 †18

HIRSCHI, Wayne La Mar. 5475 S 500 E, ST BENEDICTS HOSPITAL 84405 #049-01-1957 L1959 DR *071 †80

HOFFMAN, Terri Lee. ■ 84415 #028-34-1995 L1998 PCC *020 †20

HOLLAND, Gary Franklin. 1623 HISLOP DR 84404 #051-04-1987 L2000 FM *020 †18

HOLLAND, Grant K. 4403 HARRISON BLVD 84403 #016-45-1975 L1980 CD IM *020 †20 ‡

HOLLINGSWORTH, Helen High. 4401 HARRISON BLVD, MCKAY-DEE HOSPITAL 84403 #012-01-1998 L1999 IM *020 †20

HOM, King Fai. 4403 HARRISON BLVD STE 48, MCKAY DEE IHC / PEDIATRICS 84403 #041-01-1986 L1996 PD *020 †20

HOUDEN, Timothy Scott. 4335 HARRISON BLVD, STE D 84403 #056-06-1988 L1990 PMM PME *020 †05

HOUSEL, Darren Wayne. ■ 84404 #049-01-1990 L2002 OBG *020 †30

HOUSLEY, Mark Delmon. 2240 ADAMS AVE, MIDTOWN COMMUNITY HEALTH C 84401 #049-01-2002 L2003 FM *020 †18

HUNTER, Bruce Clyde. ■ 84403 #010-01-1973 L1979 OBG *020

HUNTER, Daniel Clyde, Jr. ■ 84403 #049-01-1946 L1950 EM OM *071 †85

HUSTAD, Susan C. 425 E 5350 S, STE 335 84405 #037-01-1998 L1999 IM PLM *020 †20

HUTCHINSON, Anne. 4403 HARRISON BLVD, STE 700A 84403 #049-01-1997 L1998 FM *020 †18

HYDE, Oliver Wendell, Jr. 3939 HARRISON BLVD 84403 #049-01-1960 L1961 GP *071

IGO, Robert Paul. ■ 84403 #049-01-1952 L1957 PD *071 †55

IMANI, Jahangir. 6112 S 1550 E, FL 2 84405 #654-01-1986 L1993 N OS *020

INGERSOL, Leslye. 4401 HARRISON BLVD, STE 1755 84403 #049-01-1985 L1989 RO *020 †80

ISKOS, Demosthenes N. 4403 HARRISON BLVD, STE 3400 84403 #418-01-1989 L1991 ICE CD *020 †20

IVESTER, Charles Thomas. 4403 HARRISON BLVD, STE 2455 84403 #045-01-1996 L1997 IM *020 †20

JACOBSON, Michael Thos. ■ 84403 #025-12-1988 L1997 FM PLM *020 †18

JANEWAY, Lawrence Michael. 4350 WASHINGTON BLVD, OGDEN CLINIC 84403 #030-05-1965 L1972 ORS GP *071 †40

JENSEN, Chad Ryan. 4403 HARRISON BLVD, STE 700A 84403 #049-01-2005 L2006 FP *012

JIRICKO, Audrey Anne. 4403 HARRISON BLVD, STE 4440 84403 #017-20-1998 L2004 OBG *020 †30

JOHNSON, Harold Mark. 5405 S 500 E, STE 202 84405 #049-01-1986 L2000 ON IM *020 †20

JOHNSON, Steve Farr. ■ 84403 #049-01-1976 L1980 OBG *071 †30

JOHNSON, Vernal Hyrum. ■ 84403 #016-06-1938 OBG *071 †30

JOHNSON, Wendell Cardwell. 4403 HARRISON BLVD 84403 #049-01-1993 L1994 DR *020 †80,28

JORDAN, Edward Alfonso. 4650 HARRISON BLVD, OGDEN CLINIC 84403 #035-19-1990 L1997 GS *020 †85

JUERGENS, Andrew Louis. 982 CHAMBERS AVE 84403 #028-02-1978 L1979 FM OM *020 †70,18

JUERGENS, Andrew Louis, II. ■ 84414 #048-04-2008 *012

KAMMEYER, Steven Edward. 4403 HARRISON BLVD, STE 2645 84403 #049-01-1972 L1975 OBG *020 †30

KAUSHAL, Sujata. ■ 84403 #017-20-2003 L2007 IM *100 †20

KEETON, Mark Ross. 4403 HARRISON BLVD 84403 #836-02-1983 L1996 DR *020 †80

KELLEY, Susan G. 2981 LINCOLN AVE 84401 #665-01-1999 L1999 IM *020

KELSON, James Ross. 6028 S RIDGELINE DR # 201A 84405 #049-01-1976 L1977 IM *020 †20

KHODAKOV, Yuri V. 4401 HARRISON BLVD, MCKAY-DEE HOSPITAL 84403 #913-81-1991 L2007 IC *020 †20

KIM, Paul Bomin. 4401 HARRISON BLVD, MCKAY-DEE HOSP ICU 84403 #036-07-1987 L2002 CCM IM *020 †20

KING, David R. 4401 HARRISON BLVD, EMERGENCY DEPT 84403 #047-06-1976 L1982 EM *020 †16

KLUTHE, Margaret Ann. 425 E 5350 S, ORMC PROF BLDG #355 84405 #049-01-1994 L1996 PD *020 †55

LAMB, Robert Benere. 4403 HARRISON BLVD 84403 #049-01-1983 L1988 DR *040 †80

LANE, Paul Wilson. 4401 HARRISON BLVD 84403 #056-06-1990 L1993 EM *020 †16

LAWTON, Charles Brian. ■ 84403 #165-01-1981 L1996 OTO AN *020 †05

LEHR, Rhonda. 4403 HARRISON BLVD, BHI 84403 #034-01-1984 L1988 P *020 †75

LESSER, John David, II. 4403 HARRISON BLVD, STE 2645 84403 #023-12-1981 L1998 OBG *040 †30

LESSER, Rosemary T. 4403 HARRISON BLVD, STE 2645 84403 #023-12-1981 L1992 OBG *020 †30

LEUNG, Felix. 4401 HARRISON BLVD, CRITICAL CARE/INTENSIVIST 84403 #035-20-1998 L2002 PCC *100 †20

LEWIS, O Marvin. ■ 84403 #041-01-1952 L1953 IM *071 †20

LEWIS, Seth Rich. 5405 S 500 E, STE 101 84405 #049-01-1991 L1993 IM *020 †20

LISTER, Margit Szabo. 4403 HARRISON BLVD, STE 4440 84403 #038-45-1999 L2006 OBG *020 †30

LOCHNER, Denise M. 4403 HARRISON BLVD, STE 4650 84403 #048-12-1999 L2003 OBG *020 †30

LOFGRAN, Brian Curtis. ■ 84404 #054-04-2007 FP *012

LOW, Eugene Jensen. MC KAY DEE HOSP, DEPT PATH 84402 #049-01-1968 L1971 ATP CLP *071 †50

LOWE, George Henry, Jr. ■ 84401 #016-06-1943 L1947 GS CRS *071 †85

LOWE, John Earl. 6028 S RIDGELINE DR, STE 201 84405 #016-06-1973 L1978 **GE IM** *020 †20
LUND, John Fredrick. 4403 HARRISON BLVD 4403 84403 #049-01-1996 L1998 **CD** *020 †20
LYONS, John Hugh, III. 4650 HARRISON BLVD 84403 #050-02-1984 L1994 **D DMP** *020 †15
LYONS, Vicki Jennifer. 4403 HARRISON BLVD, STE 4640 84403 #021-06-1989 L1994 **AI** *020 †20,03
MABEY, Brent Edward. 3939 HARRISON BLVD 84403 #049-01-1983 L1986 **EM** *020 †16
MAC KENZIE, Garry Wayne. 4403 HARRISON BLVD 84403 #060-01-1969 L1992 **CD** *020
MADLANG, Rodolfo Gregory. 4401 HARRISON BLVD, MCKAY-DEE HOSPITALCENTER 84403 #016-42-1979 L1982 **AN** *020 †05
MAJOR, Heather Michelle. 4403 HARRISON BLVD, STE 2645 84403 #049-01-1996 L2001 **OBG** *020 †30
MALAN, Lee Jeppson. 3955 HARRISON BLVD 84403 #049-01-1967 L1974 **PS** *020 †65 ‡
MANSFIELD, Justin Wade. 4403 HARRISON BLVD, STE 3650 84403 #049-01-1999 L2000 **IM** *020 †20
MARCUM, James Michael. 5030 HARRISON BLVD 84403 #011-02-1982 L2003 **P PPN** *020 †75
MARRIOTT, Rodney Geo. 5495 S 500 E, STE 310 84405 #036-05-1977 L1981 **OBG** *020 †30
MATTSSON, Carl Anthony. 4403 HARRISON BLVD, STE 2600 84403 #023-01-1966 L1973 **ORS** *020 †40
MAUGHAN, Julie Anne. 6028 S RIDGELINE DR, STE 200 84405 #005-14-2000 L2003 **D** *020 †20,15
MAUGHAN, Willard Zinn. 6028 S RIDGELINE DR # 200 84405 #049-01-1972 L1977 **D** *020 †15
MC ENTIRE, Jay W. 978 E 5479 SOUTH 84405 #049-01-1950 L1951 **GP EM** *071
MC GAUGHEY, Hugh Raymond. ■ 84403 #539-01-1956 L1988 **NPM PD** *020 †55
MC QUILKIN, Shawn David. 1128 UNIVERSITY CIR 84408 #016-42-1984 L1987 **IM** *020 †20
MELVILLE, Bradley Rulon. 4403 HARRISON BLVD, STE 1875 84403 #020-02-1984 L1987 **PM** *020 †60
MERRELL, Preston Rees. ■ 84414 #028-02-1955 L1960 **PD** *071 †55
MIAN, Hamid A. 425 E 5350 S 84405 #308-05-1986 L2007 **NEP** *020 †20
MICHAELSON, Chauncey D. 2252 N 400 E 84414 #049-01-1960 L1961 **GP OS** *071
MIJER, John Frits. 4403 HARRISON BLVD, STE 3650 84403 #007-02-1988 L1989 **RHU IM** *020 †20
MILAVETZ, Donna Latari. 3903 HARRISON BLVD, STE E400 84403 #003-01-1992 L2003 **IM** *020 †20
MILAVETZ, James Jared. 5405 S 500 E, STE 204 84405 #026-04-1989 L2002 **CD** *020 †20
MILLER, Mitchell Ray. 4403 HARRISON BLVD STE A 84403 #003-75-2005, ▲ L2006 **FP** *012
MOESINGER, Robert Clark. 4403 HARRISON BLVD, STE 1635 84403 #049-01-1992 L2006 **GS** *020 †85
MOESINGER, Robert Lionel. 3955 HARRISON BLVD, STE U6 84403 #010-01-1965 L1970 **OTO** *020 †55
MOHAN, Chandrakala Gowda. 5475 S 500 E, NEONATOLOGIST 84405 #495-33-1987 L1999 **NPM** *020 †55
MONSON, E Conrad. ■ 84403 #049-01-1945 **OBG** *071 †30
MONTGOMERY, Robert F. ■ 84414 #049-01-1961 L1991 **GS** *071
MOORE, Donald Mahaney. 3939 HARRISON BLVD 84403 #028-02-1942 L1942 **IM** *071 †20
MORGAN, Brian Hayden. 5405 S 500 E 84405 #055-02-1992 L1996 **PM** *020 †60
MORRIS, Jared Abraham. 4403 HARRISON BLVD, STE 700A-MCKAY DEE HOSP 84403 #018-75-2007, ▲ **FP** *012
MORTON, Edward D. ■ 84403 #048-12-1953 L1958 **FM ADM** *072 †18
MOUNDAY, Amber Dawn. 4401 HARRISON BLVD, UTAH EMERGENCY PHYSICIANS 84403 #019-02-2002 L2007 **EM** *100 †16
MUSE, Brett Trenton, Jr. 975 CHAMBERS AVE 84403 #049-01-1994 L1995 **FM** *020 †18
NAISBITT, Byron Hunter. ■ 84405 #049-01-1947 L1948 **OBG** *020 †30
NAISBITT, Jed Paul. 5475 S 500 E 84405 #049-01-1981 L1985 **OBG** *020 †30
NAISBITT, Paul Faddies. ■ 84403 #049-01-1952 L1954 **OBG** *071 †30
NASSIF, Mariam Nabil. 4403 HARRISON BLVD, STE 3490 84403 #915-02-1989 L2006 **IM** *020 †20
NEBEKER, Adam Rich. 2240 ADAMS AVE 84401 #049-01-2000 L2003 **FM** *020 †18
NEBEKER, Conrad Hansen. 3939 HARRISON BLVD 84403 #041-01-1962 L1965 **IM OS** *071
NEILL, Robert Harrison. 5475 S 500 E 84405 #038-40-1967 L1974 **ORS** *071 †40
NEMETZ, David Warren. 1159 E 12TH ST 84404 #030-06-1982 L1986 **FM** *020 †18
NEWMAN, Robert Crouch. 4403 HARRISON BLVD # 4440 84403 #028-02-1969 L1973 **OBG** *071 †30
NEWTON, John D. ■ 84405 #049-01-1952 L1953 **IM OM** *071
NICHOLS, Elwood Mark. 2570 GRANT AVE 84401 #040-02-1972 L1976 **P GPM** *100 †70
NIELSEN, Amie. 4401 HARRISON BLVD 84403 #023-07-2000 L2003 **EM** *020
NOWERS, Kenneth Justin. 4403 HARRISON BLVD 84403 #049-01-1998 L1999 **DR** *020 †80
OATES, Kristine Michelle. ■ 84404 #056-06-2007 **FP** *012
OKAWA, Allisyn. 6112 S 1550 E, STE 202 84405 #049-01-1987 L1995 **HS** *020 †65
OWENS, William I. 3903 HARRISON BLVD, STE E201 84403 #017-20-1966 L1976 **OTO OS** *020 †45
PACKARD, Dean Wilson. ■ 84403 #049-01-1957 L1959 **U** *071 †95
PANUSHKA, Cole Jos. 5475 S 500 E, UTAH IMAGING ASSOCIATES 84405 #049-01-1985 L1990 **DR** *020 †80
PARR, Christopher John. 5475 S 500 E, OGDEN REGIONAL MEDICAL CEN 84405 #049-01-1996 L1997 **DR** *020 †80
PATEL, Mahendra J. ■ 84403 #495-75-1970 L1983 **AN** *020
PEACH, Dolly Louise. 4401 HARRISON BLVD, HOSPITALIST SERVICE 84403 #054-04-2002 L2003 **IM** *020
PENKA, Christopher F. 4403 HARRISON BLVD, STE 1815 84403 #649-14-1977 L1981 **NS** *020 †25
PETERS, Adam Scott. 4403 HARRISON BLVD, STE 700A 84403 #054-04-2004 L2005 **FM** *020 †18
PETERSON, Bryan J. 5475 S 500 E 84405 #049-01-1990 L1996 **AN PME** *020 †05
PITTMAN, Joel Eric. 4401 HARRISON BLVD, MCKAY DEE HOSPITAL 84403 #025-07-2001 L2002 **PCC** *012
PLEACHER, Michael David. 4403 HARRISON BLVD, STE 4875 84403 #051-04-2001 L2005 **FSM** *100 †55
POLLARD, Matt Gary. 4401 HARRISON BLVD 84403 #056-06-2002 L2005 **EM** *020 †16
POOLE, Jeffrey Scott. 6028 S RIDGELINE DR, STE 201 84405 #038-43-1996 L2003 **GE** *100 †20
PORTER, Steven Alexander. 4403 HARRISON BLVD, STE 2855 84403 #021-05-1988 L2000 **GE** *020 †20
QADER, Nameer Tarik. 5495 S 500 E, STE 100 84405 #528-01-1992 L2003 **FM** *020 †18
RANKIN, Ronald Scott. 4403 HARRISON BLVD 84403 #035-20-1968 L1977 **DR** *020 †80
REES, Joseph Richard. ■ 84405 #049-01-1962 L1971 **TS GS** *062 †85,90
REINHART, Douglas James. 4401 HARRISON BLVD 84403 #048-12-1984 L1987 **AN** *020 †05
RICH, Homer Redd. ■ 84403 #047-06-1942 L1948 **PD** *071 †55

RICHARDS, Bradley Wayne. 875 COUNTRY HILLS DR 84403 #049-01-1985 L1990 **OPH** *020 †35
RICHARDS, Scott Courtney. 875 COUNTRY HILLS DR 84403 #049-01-1985 L1986 **OPH** *020 †35
RICH-DENSON, Carolyn. 4401 HARRISON BLVD, MCKAY DEE HOSP-NICU 84403 #049-01-1983 L1986 **NPM PD** *020 †55
RICHTER, Howard Samuel. 4403 HARRISON BLVD, STE 2400 84403 #048-12-1997 L2005 **ORS** *020 †40
RIFLEMAN, Kurt Edward. 2240 ADAMS AVE, MIDTOWN COMMUNITY HEALTH C 84401 #049-01-1995 L1996 **FM** *020 †18
RIGBY, Dwight Avard. 4403 HARRISON BLVD, STE 3400 84403 #049-01-1979 L1980 **CD** *020 †20
ROBERTS, Sidney Gregory. 1355 HINKLEY DR 84401 #035-09-1992 L1993 **IM** *020 †20
ROBERTSON, Brent Farr. 1764 VICTORIA CT 84403 #049-01-1979 L1982 **D IM** *020 †20
ROCCO, Jeffrey Joseph. 4403 HARRISON BLVD, STE 2600 84403 #038-06-1994 L2005 **ORS** *020 †40
ROSE, Allyn Patrick. 5495 S 500 E STE 330 84405 #049-01-1975 L1980 **PD PDC** *020 †55
ROUNDY, Michael Scott. 237 26TH ST, WEBER HUMAN SERVICES 84401 #023-12-1992 L2003 **P** *020 †75
ROUZER, Janeth Ruth. ■ 84414 #051-01-1978 L1981 **N CHN** *030 †55
RUTHERFORD, Philip C. 4401 HARRISON BLVD 84403 #016-76-1998, ▲ L2002 **EM** *020 †16
RYAN, Earl Leo. 5566 S 100 E 84405 #030-06-1955 L1984 **FM** *071 †18
SADIQ, Smitha. 1452 E RIDGELINE DR # 151 84405 #496-35-1997 L2004 **IM MPD** *020 †20
SAFAEE SEMIROMI, Masood. 4401 HARRISON BLVD, MCKAY-DEE HOSPITAL 84403 #517-08-1987 L2000 **IM** *020 †20
SARVER, Edward John. 5395 OLD POST RD 84403 #036-07-1968 L1976 **VIR** *020 †80
SATTERFIELD, Trevor Y. 4403 HARRISON BLVD, STE 700A 84403 #049-01-2006 L2007 **FP** *012
SCHARMANN, Stephen Daryl. 4403 HARRISON BLVD, STE 700A 84403 #005-02-1984 L1987 **FM FSM** *020 †18
SCHEULLER, Michael C. 4403 HARRISON BLVD, STE 2645 84403 #032-01-1998 L2004 **OTO** *020 †45
SCHKUDOR, George Walter. 4403 HARRISON BLVD 84403 #025-07-1981 L1986 **DR** *020 †80
SCHMITZ, J David. 1159 E 12TH ST 84404 #037-01-1982 L1987 **FM** *020 †18
SCHUSSMAN, Lee Carl. 2400 N WASHINGTON BLVD, INTERMOUNTAIN NO. OGDEN CL 84414 #005-15-1972 L1973 **FM OS** *020 †18
SEALE, Fred G, IV. 4403 HARRISON BLVD, STE 2645 84403 #048-13-1996 L2003 **OBG** *020 †30
SENEKJIAN, Harry Oshin. 425 E 5350 S STE 320 84405 #041-09-1972 L1982 **NEP IM** *020 †20
SHEFFIELD, Mark James. 4403 HARRISON BLVD, NEONATOLOGY 84403 #049-01-1998 L2004 **NPM** *020 †55
SHEPHERD, Doug Tracey. 5405 S 500 E STE 200 84405 #048-13-1990 L1994 **PM** *020 †60
SIDDOWAY, John R. 4650 HARRISON BLVD 84403 #049-01-1979 L1991 **OTO FPS** *020 †45
SILVER, Gary Stott. 4401 HARRISON BLVD, LABOR AND DELIVERY ANESTHE 84403 #049-01-1978 L1979 **AN FM** *020 †18,05
SIMMONS, Gary Alfred. 3903 HARRISON BLVD 84403 #049-01-1982 L1983 **AN** *020 †05
SLADE, Travis Derral. 5475 S 500 E, ANESTHESIOLOGY DEPT 84405 #049-01-2001 L2005 **AN** *020 †05
SMITH, Brian Keith. 4401 HARRISON BLVD, EMERGENCY DEPARTMENT 84403 #025-01-1986 L1987 **EM** *020 †18
SMITH, Bryson Swain. 4403 HARRISON BLVD, STE 1815 84403 #049-01-1985 L1993 **NS** *020 †20
SMITH, Dennis Hugh. 5030 HARRISON BLVD #020-12-1991 L1999 **P** *020 †75
SMITH, Lance Clyde. 4403 HARRISON BLVD, STE 700A 84403 #038-43-2005 L2006 **FP** *012
SMITH, Michael Laurence. 1522 CAHOON ST, MICHAEL L SMITH MD. PC 84401 #028-34-2003 L2007 **AN** *020
SMITHING, Larry O. 4650 HARRISON BLVD 84403 #014-01-1985 L1986 **OBG** *020 †30
SNIDER, Louis R. 425 E 5350 S STE 125, DOUGLAS P FELT MD PC 84405 #049-01-1952 L1953 **OPH** *071 †35
SOBOTKA, Dennis Wayne. 6028 S RIDGELINE DR, STE 201 84405 #018-03-1978 L1983 **GE IM** *020 †20
SOLICH, Chara Schryvers. 4403 HARRISON BLVD, STE 3650 84403 #030-06-1997 L2005 **RHU** *020 †20
SORENSEN, Jeffery Todd. 4350 WASHINGTON BLVD, OGDEN CLINIC 84403 #019-02-1993 L1999 **ORS** *020 †40
SOUTHWICK, Jed Craig. 4401 HARRISON BLVD, ER DEPT 84403 #056-06-2004 L2007 **EM** *020
SOUTHWICK, Merlin Paul. 3939 HARRISON BLVD 84403 #049-01-1945 L1946 **IM** *071 †20
SPENCER, La Val Wing. 3939 HARRISON BLVD 84403 #049-01-1963 L1963 **FM** *071 †18
SPENCER, Matthew S. ■ 84403 #049-01-2007 **FP** *012
STAGG, Gordon N. 950 25TH ST 84401 #049-01-1959 L1960 **GP** *071
STAGG, Gordon Niel. 4403 HARRISON BLVD 84403 #049-01-1987 L1988 **FM** *020 †18
STALLINGS, Scott Manley. 698 12TH ST, CARE PLUS PC 84404 #023-12-1994 L1997 **FM** *020 †18
STANLEY, Daniel Scott. 5475 S 500 E 84405 #019-02-1984 L1988 **AN PMM** *020 †05
STARLEY, James Wm. 425 E 5350 S STE 125 84405 #030-06-1972 L1973 **OBG** *020 †30
STAUFFER, Robert Fern. 425 E 5350 S, STE 280 84405 #049-01-1984 L1987 **CHP P** *020
STEINFELDT, Randall Lynn. 2400 N 400 E 84414 #056-06-1991 L1992 **FM** *020 †18
STEVENSON, Kenneth Edward. 5495 S 500 E, STE 120 84405 #028-34-1995 L1999 **PD** *020 †55
STEVENSON, Leo Monte. 555 E 5300 S STE 7 84405 #049-01-1962 L1963 **OBG IM** *020 ‡
STEWART, Connie Chang. 4403 HARRISON BLVD, STE 700A 84403 #048-12-2005 L2006 **FP** *012
STOKES, Catherine Olsen. 4403 HARRISON BLVD, STE 4875 84403 #049-01-1995 L2000 **PD** *020 †55
SUMMERS, Clarke Carney. 237 26TH ST 84401 #038-06-1973 L1978 **P** *020 †75
SUTHERLAND, Travis S. 975 CHAMBERS ST 84403 #049-01-1991 L1999 **FM** *020 †18
SWIFT, Scott D. 4403 HARRISON BLVD 84403 #049-01-1976 L1977 **OBG** *020 †30
SWINDLER, Charles M. ■ 84403 #041-12-1940 L1951 **ORS** *071 †40
SWINYARD, Michael Theron. 5495 S 500 E, STE 120 84405 #049-01-1984 L1995 **END PDE** *020 †55 ‡
TAYLOR, Robert D. 3939 HARRISON BLVD 84403 #049-01-1989 L1993 **AN PME** *020 †05
TAYLOR, Stephen Douglas. 4401 HARRISON BLVD 84403 #049-01-1969 L1973 **EM OM** *020 †16
THOMSON, Stephen Talmage. 6028 S RIDGELINE DR, STE 102 84405 #010-01-1972 L1973 **D** *020 †15
TILARO, Frank E. 4401 HARRISON BLVD, MCKAY DEE HOSPITAL 84403 #561-01-1978 L1988 **IM OS** *020 †20
TRASK, Timothy Michael. 3939 HARRISON BLVD 84403 #028-02-2000 L2001 **IM** *020 †20 ‡

URRY, Larry Edwin. 4403 HARRISON BLVD, STE 2635 84403 #049-01-1979 L1987 **D IM** *020 †20,15

UTTERBACK, Manly. 950 25TH ST 84401 #028-02-1942 L1949 **D** *020 †15

VAN HOOK, Cloyd Dinsmore. ■ 84414 #021-05-1943 L1947 **NS** *071 †25

VARELA, Victor Weitzel. 4403 HARRISON BLVD, STE 1635 84403 #027-01-1998 L2003 **GS** *020 †85

VARGHESE, Jacob A. 4403 HARRISON BLVD, STE 4875 84403 #035-15-1999 L2004 **PD** *020 †55

VARMA, Navin Kumar. 1452 E RIDGELINE DR, STE 151 84405 #024-05-1988 L1997 **N** *020 †75

VEIGEL, Jake Doyle. 4403 HARRISON BLVD, STE 700A 84403 #056-06-2005 L2006 **FP** *012

VON STEIN, Diane Elaine. 1486 E SKYLINE DR, STE 202 84405 #038-41-1981 L2006 **OP** *020 †40

WADSWORTH, Kenneth Harold. 4403 HARRISON BLVD, STE 4400 84403 #049-01-1994 L2000 **U** *020 †95

WAGNON, Alton Harvey, Jr. 4403 HARRISON BLVD, STE 1685 84403 #039-01-1973 L1984 **ON HEM** *020 †20

WAHLEN, Jack D. 4403 HARRISON BLVD # 3630 84403 #049-01-1974 L1979 **END DIA** *020 †20

WAHLSTROM, Norman O, Jr. 5475 S 500 E 84405 #049-01-1979 L1981 **PTH BBK** *062 †50

WALLACE, Jesse Lee. 5475 S 500 E 84405 #048-04-1962 L1969 **EM GS** *071 †16

WARD, Sheldon Don. 1802 QUAIL RUN DR 84403 #049-01-1970 L1971 **AN** *020 †05

WATTS, Donald Fred. 3955 HARRISON BLVD, STE L1 84403 #048-02-1976 L1979 **PD** *020

WEBB, Michael Stephen, Jr. 4403 HARRISON BLVD 84403 #036-07-1989 L1998 **DR VIR** *020 †80

WEEKS, Matthew Gunn. 2400 N WASHINGTON BLVD, INTERMOUNTAIN HEALTH CARE 84414 #031-01-1996 L2003 **FM** *020 †18

WELLING, Blake Gammell. 4403 HARRISON BLVD, STE 1815 84403 #049-01-1987 L1997 **NS GS** *020 †25

WELLMAN, James Emil. 5998 S 2950 E 84403 #048-13-1972 L1979 **GS** *071 †85

WEST, Renee Rochelle. 4650 HARRISON BLVD 84403 #030-05-1992 L1999 **FM** *020 †18

WHIPPLE, Gary Lynn. 4401 HARRISON BLVD, INTERMOUNTAIN MEDICAL GROU 84403 #049-01-1992 L2002 **RO** *020 †80

WHIPPLE, Robert Douglas. 4650 HARRISON BLVD 84403 #025-12-1972 L1987 **GS** *020 †85

WHITE, John Edward. 5740 CRESTWOOD DR 84405 #041-02-1997 L2001 **FM** *020 †18

WHITE, John Emmett. 5740 CRESTWOOD DR 84405 #048-02-1948 L1948 **DR NM** *071 †80,28

WHITE, Justin Shane. 4403 HARRISON BLVD STE A70 84403 #018-75-2006, ▲ L2007 **FP** *012

WHITE, Richard Sanderson. 4403 HARRISON BLVD, STE 3400 84403 #041-13-1962 L1973 **CD IM** *020 †20

WHITFIELD, Sandra M. 698 12TH ST 84404 #048-13-1971 L1978 **PD** *071 †55

WILCOX, Milton Farr. ■ 84405 #049-01-1945 L1949 **AN** *071

WILLIAMS, Carroll Basil. 4650 HARRISON BLVD 84403 #049-01-1956 L1959 **CD IM** *071 †20

WILLIAMS, David Howard. 4401 HARRISON BLVD 84403 #020-12-2001 L2004 **EM** *020 †16

WILLIAMS, Nevin Brent. 975 CHAMBERS ST 84403 #049-01-1979 L1980 **FM** *020 †18

WILSON, Diane Elainehales. 698 12TH ST, CARE PLUS PC 84404 #049-01-1989 L1990 **FM** *020 †18

WINTERS, Dennis Damian. 4403 HARRISON BLVD, STE 1815 84403 #051-07-1993 L2007 **NS GS** *020 †25

WOLSEY, Brandon A. 4401 HARRISON BLVD 84403 #049-01-1995 L2002 **EM** *020 †16

WOLTHUIS, John Scot. 4650 HARRISON BLVD 84403 #049-01-1979 L1986 **U** *020 †95

WOOD, Thomas Jay. 4401 HARRISON BLVD, MC KAY-DEE EMERGENCY DEPT. 84403 #049-01-1996 L1997 **FM** *020 †18

WOODS, Hyrum Darrell. 4403 HARRISON BLVD, STE 4440 84403 #045-01-1964 L1968 **OBG** *020 †30

WOOLMAN, Michael Dennis. 5740 CRESTWOOD DR 84405 #025-01-1976 L1979 **FM** *020 †18

WRAY, Roger William. 698 E 12TH ST 84404 #067-01-1978 L1999 *020

YAWORSKY, Raymond Geo. 3939 HARRISON BLVD 84403 #065-05-1957 L1976 **CLP PTH** *071 †50

ZIEGLER, Robert Henry, Jr. 3939 HARRISON BLVD 84403 #004-01-1991 L2000 **FM GE** *020 †20

ORDERVILLE – KANE

BALLARD, Anthony. ■ 84758 #049-01-1957 L1993 **ORS** *071 †40

OREM – UTAH

ABRAMS, Barbara J. 331 N 400 W 84057 #043-01-1988 L1997 **EM** *020 †16

ABRAMS, Michael Scott. 700 W 800 N STE 160, EXCEL EYE CENTER 84057 #043-01-1988 L1997 **IM** *020 †35

ADAM, Walter Max. 740 W 800 N, STE 440 84057 #019-02-1995 L1998 **FM** *020 †18

ALLEN, Wilmer Collier. ■ 84097 #005-11-1959 L1968 **ORS GP** *071 †40

ANDERSON, Carl David. 1065 E 3005 84097 #049-01-1964 L1965 **FM** *071 †18

ANDERSON, David Kim. ■ 84097 #010-01-1986 L1989 **EM** *020 †16

ANDERSON, James Wm. ■ 84097 #007-02-1954 L1955 **FM** *071 †18

BAILEY, Ernest A. 750 W 800 N 84057 #049-01-2001 L2004 **PD** *020 †55

BANCILA, Alexandru Iulian. ■ 84097 #781-03-1973 L1977 **FPG** *020 †18

BAXTER, Jae Kelly. 505 W 400 N 84057 #035-20-1982 L1989 **OBG** *020 †30

BENCH, Pahl Gerald. 560 S STATE ST, STE B1 84058 #649-01-2001 L2007 **FM** *020 †18

BERG, Joseph Edward. 498 E 800 N 84097 #019-02-1993 L1998 **PS** *020 †65

BERRY, Steven L. 173 N 400 W # C11 84057 #049-01-1996 L1997 **FM** *020 †18

BINGHAM, Joseph Chas. 505 W 400 N 84057 #030-06-1978 L1989 **FM** *020 †18

BISHOP, Jon Bradley. 700 W 800 N STE 442 84057 #049-01-1983 L1998 **GS PS** *020 †85,65

BOLICK, Larry Eugene. ■ 84097 #005-06-1961 L1972 **PTH UM** *071 †50

BRINGHURST, Cory Lynn. 331 N 400 W 84057 #049-01-1993 L1997 **EM** *020 †16

BRINTON, James Ashby. 160 E UNIVERSITY PKWY, STE L 84058 #049-01-1975 L1978 **OBG** *020

BRINTON, Jennifer Geary. 716 W 800 N, # 300 84057 #049-01-1998 L1999 **PD** *071 †55

BROADBENT, Paul W. 331 N 400 W 84057 #049-01-1971 L1995 **EM** *020 †16

BROMLEY, Richard Green. 750 W 800 N 84057 #049-01-1967 L1968 **ORS GP** *071 †40

BROWN, Matthew Albert. 1975 N STATE ST 84057 #049-01-1998 L1999 **FM** *020 †18

BUTLER, Ronald Bay. ■ 84058 #049-01-1957 L1962 **PTH** *071 †50

CALL, Richard Ambrose, II. 560 S STATE ST 84058 #010-01-1975 L1978 **RHU IM** *020 †20

CARN, Thomas R. 575 S STATE ST 84058 #049-01-1982 L1983 **FM** *020 †18

CARTER, Melvin Eric. 700 W 800 N, STE 280 84057 #049-01-1988 L2001 **CD** *020 †20

CHRISTENSEN, Robert Dale. 331 N 400 W 84057 #049-01-1994 L1998 **EM** *020 †16

CHRISTENSON, Vernon Lars. 1975 N STATE ST 84057 #051-01-2002 L2003 **FM** *020 †18

CLARK, Jeffrey Paul. 155 N 400 W STE B6 84057 #025-07-1987 L1988 **FM MDM** *071 †18

CLARK, Paul Kenneth. 155 N 400 W, # B6 84057 #035-09-1958 **U** *020 †95

CORNISH, Matthew Jared. 750 W 800 N 84057 #012-05-2001 L2003 **PD** *020 †55

CRIST, Robert H. 774 S 400 E 84097 #049-01-1962 L1964 **P** *071

CURZON, Sean R. 700 W 800 N, STE 220 84057 #028-79-1999, ▲ L2002 **IM** *020 †20

DUNAWAY, Wm Claude, Jr. 145 W 1300 S, ATTN: CENTER OPERATIONS 84058 #308-07-1981 L1990 **FM** *020 †18

DUROS, Peter. 700 W 800 N, STE 220 84057 #286-03-1987 L1996 **IM** *020 †20

EYRE, Russell Warren. 486 W 800 N, STE 201 84057 #049-01-1981 L1986 **D** *020 †15

EYRE, Steven Paul. 486 W 800 N, PINEHURST PLZ STE 201 84057 #049-01-1986 L1990 **D** *020 †15

EYRE, Warren Gene. 486 W 800 N, STE 201 84057 #049-01-1962 L1969 **D DMP** *072 †15

FAATZ, Jill Bateman. 1975 N STATE ST, INTERMOUNTAIN HLTH CARE 84057 #049-01-2003 L2004 **FM** *020 †18

FAIRBANKS, David Weston. 452 W 1260 N, MOXTEK INC 84057 #051-01-1989 L2006 **FM EM** *071 †18

FONSECA, Walstir H. 700 W 800 N, STE 220 84057 #187-03-1989 L1996 **IM** *020 †20

FRANCK, David Bruce. ■ 84097 #040-02-1954 L1955 **IM** *072

FREESTONE, James Phillip. 171 N 400 W C-12 84057 #003-01-1974 L1977 **PD** *020 †55

GAILUSHAS, Shane Andrew. ■ 84097 #021-01-2008 *012

GAMETTE, Kent R. 700 W 800 N 84057 #035-20-1971 L1977 **OBG** *020 †30

GEORGE, Gordon Petty. 800 N 700 W STE 340-A 84057 #049-01-1978 L1981 **AN GS** *020 †05

GERSTMANN, Dale Richard. 730 W 800 N, STE 340B 84057 #054-04-1977 L1991 **NPM PD** *050 †55

GESSEL, Marie Susan. ■ 84057 #049-01-2007 *012

GROVER, Bruce Barton. ■ 84097 #049-01-1992 L1993 **FM** *020 †18

GRUWELL, Elmo Lowery, Jr. 331 N 400 W 84057 #039-01-1975 L1979 **EM GP** *020 †16

HACKING, Douglas Wayne. 171 N 400 W BLDG C-12 84057 #056-06-1971 L1974 **PD** *020 †55

HALVERSON, Diana Lynelle. ■ 84097 #049-01-2005 **EM** *012

HAMMOND, Samuel Jensen. 423 N OREM BLVD 84057 #040-02-1963 L1970 **GP** *020

HANSEN, Roger Scott. 674 W 800 N, STE B-10 84057 #030-06-1995 L2000 **RO** *020 †80

HARLINE, Donald Neal. 423 N OREM BLVD, TIMPANOGOS FAMILY MEDICINE 84057 #005-12-1993 L2000 **FM** *020 †18

HARRIS, Robert Alan. 674 W 800 N, STE B-10 84057 #023-12-1992 L2004 **RO UM** *020 †80

HARWARD, Kory Alvin. 505 W 400 N 84057 #018-75-2003, ▲ L2007 **OBG** *020

HAYES, John K, Jr. 674 W 800 N, STE B-10 84057 #049-01-1983 L1984 **RO** *020 †80

HILLAM, David Richard. 145 W UNIVERSITY PKWY 84058 #038-41-1998 L2001 **FM** *020 †18

HOOKER, Keith Ronald. 331 N 400 W 84057 #040-02-1965 L1970 **GP** *020 †16

HYER, Brian B. 331 N 400 W 84057 #049-01-1995 L1998 **EM** *020 †16

JACOB, Scott Richard. 700 W 800 N 84057 #049-01-1996 L2005 **OBG** *020 †30

JENSEN, Michael Henrie. 331 N 400 W 84057 #049-01-1987 L1988 **GP OS** *020

JENSON, Kraig Krueger. 1385 E 750 N 84097 #049-01-1974 L1980 **D EM** *020 †15,16

JONES, Trenton Cox. 1375 E 800 N, STE 205 84097 #049-01-1993 L2002 **PS** *020 †65

KENDALL, Melissa Ann. 750 W 800 N 84057 #049-01-1995 L1998 **PD** *020 †55

KENNARD, Lee Gordon. 367 W CARRIAGE CIR 84058 #049-01-1975 L1979 **AN** *020 †05

KENNEDY, Michael Stephen. 145 W UNIVERSITY PKWY 84058 #025-12-1998 L2001 **FM** *020 †18

KING, Stuart Wesley. 839 E 1200 S 84097 #003-01-1986 L1990 **PM** *020 †60

LEAVITT, Matthew Okerlund. ■ 84097 #032-01-2003 L2007 **PTH** *100 †50

LEWIS, Roger Belden. ■ 84097 #049-01-1969 L1975 **FM** *020 †18

LIU-BARTHOLOMEW, Diane. ■ 84097 #049-01-2005 L2008 **PD** *012

LYMAN, William R. 331 N 400 W 84057 #028-34-1992 L1998 **AN** *020 †05

MADSEN, Jeffrey Winn. 750 W 800 N, EMERGENCY DEPT. 84057 #049-01-2004 L2007 **EM** *020

MARSHALL, Kent G. 700 W 800 N, STE 220 84057 #049-01-1989 L1990 **IM** *020 †20

MC CANN, Ulysse George, II. ■ 84097 #048-13-1996 L2007 **TS** *100 †85,90

MC GIRK, Blair Franklin. 750 W 800 N 84057 #031-01-1992 L1993 **PTH** *020 †50

MERRILL, Steven Little. 421 N OREM BLVD 84057 #016-06-1962 L1992 **IM CD** *020

MICHEL, Marlon B. ■ 84097 #060-01-1999 L2004 **AN** *020 †05

MILLWARD, Michael H. 1975 N STATE ST, IHC HLTH CTR 84057 #352-07-1960 L1998 **FM P** *020 †18

MINEER, Wayne Alvin. 575 S STATE ST 84058 #049-01-1958 L1960 **GP** *071 †18

MONROE, Jamie Maria. 175 N 400 W, CATARACT & LASIK CTR 84057 #047-05-1988 L1993 **OPH** *020 †35

MURDOCK, Douglas Calvin. 331 N 400 W 84057 #049-01-1994 L1997 **EM** *020 †16

MYERS, David James. ■ 84057 #056-06-2006 **FM** *100

NELSON, Duane James. 1055 N 300 W 84057 #023-12-1988 L1990 **OPH** *020 †35

NELSON, Henry Stephen. 331 N 400 W, IHC WORKMED 84057 #043-01-1976 L1999 **FM** *020 †18

NELSON, Manfred R. ■ 84097 #010-01-1962 L1976 **GS FM** *071

NIELSEN, Gregory William. 171 N 400 W, STE C12 84057 #035-45-2002 L2005 **PD** *020 †55

OGDEN, Jeffrey Gale. 421 N OREM BLVD 84057 #005-06-1990 L1993 **IM** *020 †20

OLSEN, Allen Kent. 505 W 400 N 84057 #049-01-1980 L1983 **D** *020 †18

OLSEN, Maynard Robt. 575 S STATE ST 84058 #036-05-1974 L1997 **FM** *020 †18

PATTEN, Craig P. 331 N 400 W 84057 #049-01-1992 L1994 **EM** *020 †16

PATTEN, Joy Richelle Cook. 515 S PALISADES DR 84097 #049-01-1992 L1994 **PD** *020 †55

PAULSON, David Louis. 361 E 1200 S, STE 201 84058 #049-01-2000 L2002 **P** *020 †75

PEARSON, Delbert Perry. 1350 E 750 N 84097 #040-02-1967 L1968 **CHP P** *020

PETERSEN, Aaron Holms. ■ 84058 #038-43-2006 L2008 **FP** *012

PETERSON, David Noel. 575 S STATE ST 84058 #010-01-1962 L1964 **FM OBG** *020 †18

PETERSON, Scott David. 575 S STATE ST 84058 #049-01-1993 L1994 **FM** *020 †18

PRESTON, Wm Dollinger. 155 N 400 W 84057 #060-01-1975 L1978 **GP OM** *020

PROWS, Merrill S. ■ 84097 #021-01-1945 L1947 **CD GP** *071

RICHARDS, Spencer Elliott. 29 E 1700 N 84057 #049-01-2002 L2005 **FSM** *020 †18

ROBERTS, Stanley Dwayne. 331 N 400 W 84057 #060-01-1985 L1994 **FM EM** *020 †18

ROGERS, C Leland. 674 W 800 N, STE B-10 84057 #020-12-1986 L1987 **RO** *020 †80

ROGERS, Randy Lee. 505 W 400 N 84057 #046-01-1980 L1983 **FM EM** *020 †18

SCHUMANN, Thomas Lee. 331 N 400 W, IHC WORK MED 84057 #018-03-1975 L1982 **OM FM** *020 †70,18

SIMMONS, Daniel G. 171 N 400 W, STE C12 84057 #049-01-1983 L1986 **PD** *020 †55

SMITH, Jerrold C. ■ 84058 #049-01-1960 L1961 **GP FM** *071

SMITH, Lane Farr. 1350 E 750 N 84097 #049-01-1965 L1969 **P** *030 †75 ‡

SPRINGER, Karyn Ann. 1975 N STATE ST 84057 #049-01-1998 L1999 **FM** *020 †18

STACEY, Darrell Richard. 505 W 400 N 84057 #049-01-1980 L1983 **FM FSM** *020 †18

STODDARD, Ronald Aaron. 331 N 400 W 84057 #010-01-1977 L1978 **NPM PD** *020 †55

■ = Address Information Privacy Protected

TAYLOR, Bruce Thos. 331 N 400 W 84057 #049-01-1972 L1973 **EM** *020 †20
TAYLOR, Heather. ■ 84097 #049-01-2007 **IM** *012
THORPE, Jefferoy R. 700 W 800 N 84057 #028-34-1994 L1998 **OBG** *020 †30
TITTENSOR, Jennifer J. 177 S 240 W 84058 #049-01-1999 L2006 **GS** *100 †85
TUBBS, Kennon Christopher. 331 N 400 W 84057 #010-02-1996 L1997 **FM EM** *020 †18
UDALL, Marc Richard. 505 W 400 N 84057 #054-04-1975 L1978 **FM OS** *020 †18 ‡
VIEHWEG, Wayne R. ■ 84057 #048-04-1949 L1949 **GP OS** *071
WILDE, Jeffrey Virgil. ■ 84058 #051-07-2007 **FP** *012
WYNN, Gregory Scott. 716 W 800 N, STE 300 84057 #048-04-1994 L1997 **PD** *020 †55
WYNN, John Richard. 750 W 800 N 84057 #049-01-1991 L1994 **PD** *020 †55
YEATES, Henry Moyle. 159 N 400 W STE B8 84057 #030-06-1976 L1980 **AI** *020 †55,03
YOUNG, Wayne Robt. 505 N 400 W 84057 #049-01-1991 L1997 **OBG EM** *020 †30
ZIMMERMAN, John Bruce. 472 W 1680 S 84058 #049-01-1989 L1993 **AN** *020 †05

PARK CITY – SUMMIT

AHERN, Matthew Todd. ■ 84098 #038-75-2003, ▲ L2008 **EM** *012
ARMSTRONG, Dale Parry. ■ 84060 #025-01-1958 L1959 **PS** *071 †65
BARNETT, Michael Bruce. ■ 84060 #026-04-1961 L1962 **DR** *071 †80
BARNETT, Robert Willis. 1665 BONANZA DR 84060 #038-40-1978 L1979 **FM** *020 †18
BASERGA, Mariana Claudia. ■ 84098 #132-07-1991 L2004 **PD** *020 †55
BATES, William Oswald. ■ 84060 #016-06-1956 L1957 **AN** *071 †05
BECKER, Robert Edmond. ■ 84060 #067-01-1960 L1962 **P** *071 †75
BERGER, Donna Christine. ■ 84060 #020-02-1997 L2000 **OBG** *100
BERMAN, Joseph Harold. 1743 REDSTONE AVE, STE 115 84098 #023-01-1990 L1991 **FM** *020 †18
BIRKIN, Barry Michael. 1850 SIDEWINDER DR, STE 410 84060 #010-01-1991 L1993 **DR** *020 †18
BOHNN, Cress Roy. 1665 BONANZA DR 84060 #048-02-1985 L1986 **FM** *020 †18
BOWES, Watson Allen, III. ■ 84098 #036-01-1988 L1990 **AN** *020 †05
BRADLEY, Maureen A Kelly. ■ 84068 #040-02-1970 L1972 **IM** *020 †20 ‡
BROUMAND, Cyrus. ■ 84098 #017-20-1966 L1966 **R** *020 †80
BROWDY, Sol. ■ 84098 #036-05-1946 L1946 **PD** *071 †55
CANELAS, Annmarie Cecilia. ■ 84098 #016-11-1995 L2004 **IM** *020 †20
CARVELAS, James Louis. ■ 84060 #038-41-1948 L1993 **IM GE** *071
CHILD, Todd A. 1777 SUN PEAK DR, STE 150 84098 #049-01-1991 L1992 **OTO HNS** *020 †45
CLARK, Terry Kevin. ■ 84060 #019-02-1984 L1985 **GS** *020 †85
COMPTON, William Randall. ■ 84060 #024-01-1971 L1972 **DR IM** *020 †80
CONNORS, Jennifer Gates. PO BOX 3913 84060 #050-02-2003 L2004 **P** *100
COOLEY, Vernon Jackman. 1820 SIDEWINDER DR 84060 #024-01-1991 L1996 **ORS** *020 †40
CRAIG, Richard Mcintyre. 1743 REDSTONE AVE, STE 115 84098 #035-06-1990 L1999 **IM GE** *020 †20
DAVIES, Seabury Landon. ■ 84060 #041-12-1985 L1998 **AN CCM** *020 †05
DE BLANC, Harold J, Jr. ■ 84098 #021-05-1963 L1963 **OS NM** *020 †50,28
DETERS, Robert Lyle. PO BOX 980670 84060 #007-02-1973 L2001 **PTH FOP** *020 †50
DILLON, Douglas Clifford. 7436 WHILEAWAY RD W 84098 #050-02-2004 L2007 **EM** *100
DOLAN, Julia Anne. 1600 SNOW CREEK DR, MOUNTAIN FAMILY HEALTH 84060 #054-04-1993 L1994 **FM** *020 †18
EVERS, Robert Jos. 1665 BONANZA DR 84060 #038-41-1976 L1978 **FM** *020 †18
FANG, John C. 1743 REDSTONE AVE, STE 115 84098 #028-02-1989 L1998 **GE** *020 †20
FERRITER, Joseph Patrick. 1665 BONANZA DR, P O BOX 680670 84060 #050-02-1994 L1995 **FM** *020 †18
FINDEISS, Laura Katherine. ■ 84098 #041-12-1997 L2008 **VIR** *020 †80
FU, Huey Duen. 6300 SAGEWOOD DR STE H-440 84098 #055-01-1994 L1996 **IM** *020 †20
GERSTEIN, Lee S. ■ 84098 #024-05-1985 L1989 **AN** *071 †05
GIBB, Lawrence D. ■ 84098 #049-01-1961 L1962 **PD** *020 †30
GREEN, Cheryl Lynn. ■ 84098 #004-01-1993 L1997 **DR** *072 †80 ‡
HALE, William Bradley. 1850 SIDEWINDER DR, STE 410 84060 #049-01-1999 L2003 **DR** *100 †80
HANRAHAN, John Jos. 510 MAPLE DR 84098 #023-01-1989 L1992 **FM** *020 †18
HARRIS, Susie Nagi. PO BOX 2686 84060 #001-02-1995 L2007 **P** *020 †75
HAYS, Christopher Lee. 1665 BONANZA DR 84060 #018-03-1990 L1995 **FM** *020 †18
HODO, Paul White. ■ 84098 #001-02-1983 L1987 **PTH** *062
HOLVERSON, Jeffrey S. 6300 SAGEWOOD DR, STE H 84098 #041-02-1995 L2001 **IM** *020
HUGHES, Richard Kenneth. ■ 84060 #005-11-1955 L1955 **TS** *071 †85,90
HURWITZ, Beverly. ■ 84060 #305-01-1981 L1990 **PME** *020 †55
JALILI, Rockni. ■ 84098 #517-01-1963 L2006 **FM PTH** *020 †50
JENKINS, Robert Dove. ■ 84060 #016-11-1959 L1995 **OPH** *071 †35
JONES, Jackson Brent. ■ 84098 #010-01-2005 L2006 **ORS** *012
JONES, Jess Emery. ■ 84098 #035-01-2007 †012
KERN, Steven Mark. 2700 HOMESTEAD RD STE 30 84098 #005-06-1985 L1999 **D** *020 †15 ‡
KIERSTEAD, Allison Elizab. ■ 84098 #049-01-2004 L2005 **IM** *020 †20
KIPP, Patricia A. PO BOX 1881 84060 #016-43-1983 L1985 **IM** *074 †20
KIRSCHNER, Jack R. ■ 84098 #038-41-1953 L1993 **IM** *071 †20
KLETTKE, Dwight Ronald. ■ 84098 #025-01-1977 L1980 **FM** *071 †18
LA MERE, Richard Guy. PO BOX 683815, 31 BANCROFT CT 84068 #033-05-1974 L2006 **PD** *020 †55
LASSETTER, James Kipp. ■ 84098 #020-12-1985 L1987 **GP EM** *020
LEACHMAN, Sancy Ann. 1743 REDSTONE AVE, STE 115 84098 #048-12-1993 L1998 **D** *050 †15
LEONARD, Larry Givens. 1795 SIDEWINDER DR, STE 200 84060 #023-07-1971 L1981 **PS** *020 †85,65
LEVITAN, Lynne Ann. ■ 84098 #005-19-2000 L2006 **APM** *020 †05
LUPATKIN, Morde. ■ 84060 #869-07-1957 L1987 **GPM OM** *072 †18
MA, Syaufu. ■ 84098 #025-01-1987 L1997 **OBG** *020 †30
MC GRORY, Kenneth Robt. 2174 FENCHURCH DR 84098 #045-01-1980 L1987 *020
METCALF, Michael Hawkes. 1820 SIDEWINDER DR, CLINIC 84060 #049-01-1995 L2001 **ORS** *020 †40
MILLER, Lisa A. ■ 84098 #049-01-1995 L2000 **EM** *020 †16
MINTZ, Allan Ronald. ■ 84060 #065-09-1973 L1985 **ORS** *100 †40
MORRISON, Charley Reese. 1665 BONANZA DR 84060 #049-01-1998 L2003 **FM** *020 †18
MULVIHILL, Kimberley K. ■ 84098 #005-06-1982 L1983 **OBG** *062 †30
NGUYEN, Vietdung Nang. 1612 UTE BLVD, STE 112 84098 #049-01-1997 L2002 **MPD** *020 †20,55
NICKMAN, Donald Francis. ■ 84098 #030-05-1961 L1961 **R OS** *071 †80

OROSZ, Larry John. 1600 SNOW CREEK DR 84060 #017-20-1971 L1993 **EM** *020 †16
OSTLER, Kathy Marie. 1790 SUN PEAK DR, CITY 84098 #049-01-1998 L2001 **PD** *020 †55
PARSONS, Mary H. 1743 REDSTONE AVE, STE 115 84098 #016-11-1982 L1994 **IM** *020 †20 ‡
PEACOCK, Penny Jean. 1612 UTE BLVD STE 112, PEDIATRICS 84098 #023-01-1998 L1999 **MPD** *020 †20,55
PEARSON, David Arthur. ■ 84060 #016-11-1984 L1993 **AN GS** *020 †05
PELLEGRINE, Robert Eugene. ■ 84098 #561-06-1971 L2000 **IM** *071
PIDWELL, William Bryant. 1665 BONANZA DR 84060 #047-05-2003 L2004 **FM** *020 †18
POLLARD, Emil Edward. ■ 84098 #025-01-1961 L1979 **AN** *071 †05
ROBINSON, Christopher L. ■ 84098 #020-02-2004 **FM** *100
ROSENBERG, Thomas Dee. 1820 SIDEWINDER DR 84060 #049-01-1973 L1974 **ORS** *020 †40
RUSH, Brian Johns. 1600 SNOW CREEK DR, SNOW CREEK EMERGENCY 84060 #035-03-1995 L1996 **FM** *020 †16
RUSKIN, Lisa Joan. 1743 REDSTONE CENTER DR, STE 115 84098 #035-47-1978 L1998 **ORS** *020
SCHIEFER, Mark Anthony. 7771 BUCKBOARD DR 84098 #004-01-1990 L1996 **ETX OM** *020 †70
SCHWARTSMAN, Vladimir. ■ 84060 #913-32-1967 L1992 **ORS** *071 †40
SCOTT, Kim Ellen. 1777 SUN PEAK DR STE 150 84098 #030-05-1979 L1996 **IM** *020 †20
SEDGWICK, Eleanor H. ■ 84060 #005-14-1966 L1967 **AN PD** *071 †55
SILVERSTEIN, Jonathan S. ■ 84068 #036-07-1985 L2008 **DR** *020 †80
SJOQUIST-TERRY, Lena K. 1790 SUN PEAK DR, CITY 84098 #858-01-1986 L1994 **PD** *020 †55
SMITH, Wendy Michelle. ■ 84060 #005-18-2006 L2007 **OTO** *012
SMITH, William Gary. ■ 84060 #065-06-1968 L1978 **ON GYN** *020 †30
SNEAD, John Peyton, IV. ■ 84060 #051-01-1959 L2000 **CHP P** *071 †75
SOBEL LUNDY, Barbara. ■ 84060 #041-01-1964 L1965 **PS HS** *071 †85,65
STRAY-GUNDERSEN, James. PO BOX 681094 84068 #016-43-1977 L2006 **GS** *050 †85
STRUPP, Annie M. ■ 84098 #043-01-1977 L1998 **BBK PTH** *020 †50
TABIN, Jean De Marchis. 1743 REDSTONE AVE, STE 115 84098 #033-05-1987 L2005 **OPH** *020 †35
TAYLOR, Frederic Foote. ■ 84098 #035-15-1953 L1955 **IM** *071 †20
THOMAS, Michael Craig. 3903 VIEW POINTE DR 84098 #038-06-1978 L1996 **EM** *030 †16
VAN LEUVEN, Sandra Lynn. 1665 BONANZA DR 84060 #035-03-1998 L2003 **FM** *020 †18
WEBSTER, June E Opdyke. ■ 84098 #038-40-1961 L1961 *020
WEBSTER, Leslie Worthen. 1790 SUN PEAK DR, CITY 84098 #010-02-1990 L1991 **PD** *020 †55
WIEDMEIER, Susan E. ■ 84098 #049-01-1978 L1984 **NPM PD** *020 †55
WIERZBA, Rachel Katherine. ■ 84098 #056-05-2003 L2003 **GPM** *020 †70
WILLIAMS, Anna M. 1753 SIDEWINDER DR, VALLEY MENTAL HEALTH SUMMI 84060 #034-01-1993 L1994 **P CHP** *020 †75,55
WINDERS, Robert Evans. ■ 84060 #018-03-1965 L1966 **DR** *071 †80
WOLKOFF, Kenneth Alan. ■ 84060 #016-06-1973 L1985 **FM P** *074 †18
WOODRUFF, Michael Masson. ■ 84098 #035-01-1997 L1998 **EM** *100 †16
WOOLSEY, Carl Taliaferro. ■ 84060 #028-02-1943 L1944 **GYN** *071 †30
ZUCKERMAN, Scott Jerome. 7381 BUCKBOARD DR, MEDICAL ACUPUNCTURE OF NY 84098 #035-08-1985 L2001 **PD PEM** *020 †55

PAROWAN – IRON

ROBINSON, Cole Warren. ■ 84761 #049-01-2007 **AN** *012

PAYSON – UTAH

ALSHUQAIRAT, Talaat Adnan. 1120 E 100 N, STE 1 84651 #575-01-1998 L2005 **PCC** *020 †20
ANDERSON, Cameron Dean. 39 PROFESSIONAL WAY 84651 #049-01-1986 L1998 **OBG** *020 †30
BAIR, Mark N. 1000 HIGHWAY 6 84651 #049-01-1991 L1993 **EM** *020 †16
BARLOW, Ronald Perry. 1000 HIGHWAY 6 84651 #054-04-1975 L1991 **EM** *020 †16
BEHRMANN, Gary L. 1172 E 100 N, STE 2 84651 #030-06-1979 L1982 **PD** *020 †55
BENNION, David Fred. 1120 E 100 N 84651 #049-01-1978 L1979 **IM CCM** *020 †20
BRISTOW, Dean Leroy. 50 S MEDICAL DR, STE 5 84651 #005-15-1972 L1976 **U** *072 †95
CANNON, Max Kent. 39 PROFESSIONAL WAY, STE 2 84651 #051-01-1988 L1997 **GS OS** *020 †85
CHIPMAN, Bret. 910 E 100 N, STE 105 84651 #305-01-2000 L2005 **FM** *020 †18 ‡
CHRISTENSEN, Raymond O. 1000 E 100 N 84651 #049-01-1948 **PTH** *020 †50
CLARK, Robert Brent. 97 PROFESSIONAL WAY, STE 2 84651 #049-01-1979 L1980 **FM** *020 †18
COLLINS, William Thos, Jr. 50 S MEDICAL DR, STE 5 84651 #041-13-1981 L2000 **U** *020 †95
DAYTON, Elizabeth Anne. 97 PROFESSIONAL WAY, STE 2 84651 #049-01-1997 L2000 **FM** *020 †18
DEWEY, Steven John. 39 PROFESSIONAL WAY 84651 #049-01-1984 L1987 **OBG** *020 †30
DINKINS, Joseph Alan. 1000 HIGHWAY 6, EMERGENCY DEPARTMENT 84651 #005-12-1991 L1999 **EM** *020 †16
EGBERT, Larre Dean. 1000 HIGHWAY 6 84651 #049-01-1985 L1988 **EM** *020 †16
ENCE, Bradford Kelly. 39 PROFESSIONAL WAY, STE 1 84651 #028-34-1985 L1988 **OTO FPS** *020 †45
FITZGERALD, Jackson R. 1000 HIGHWAY 6 84651 #049-01-1990 L1992 **AN** *020 †05
FRAZIER, Mark Alan. 97 PROFESSIONAL WAY 84651 #305-01-1995 L2000 **FM** *020 †18
GABLER, Glen Richard. ■ 84651 #055-01-1976 L1996 **OBG** *071
GIBB, Randal Boyd. 39 PROFESSIONAL WAY, STE 1 84651 #049-01-1974 L1980 **OTO FPS** *020 †45
GIBBON, Stanley Laverne. 1000 E 100 N 84651 #056-06-1966 L1972 **PTH** *020 †50
GREEN, Adam Stanley. 1000 E 100 N, MOUNTAIN VIEW HOSPITAL 84651 #001-02-2004 L2008 **DR** *012 †20
JACKMAN, Frederick V. 1000 HIGHWAY 6 84651 #049-01-1951 L1952 **GS U** *071 †85
JONES, Brent Elwood. 1000 E 100 N, SALEM AMBULANCE 84651 #049-01-1991 L1995 **EM** *020 †16
JONES, Lowell Maurice. 1000 HIGHWAY 6 84651 #018-03-1969 L1972 **AI IM** *071 †20,03
JUDD, Thomas Robt. 1000 HIGHWAY 6 84651 #020-02-1944 L1969 **GP** *071
KNOCHEL, Miguel Luis. 910 E 1000 N 84651 #049-01-2004 L2005 **PD** *020 †55
KRONMILLER, Patrick Wm. 50 S MEDICAL DR, STE A 84651 #030-06-1971 L1972 **U GS** *020 †95 ‡
LE ROY, Ellis William. 1120 E 100 N 84651 #012-05-1975 L1976 **IM** *020 †20
LINTON, Norman Kent. 1172 E 100 N, STE 4 84651 #038-40-1974 L1983 **OPH** *020 †35
LUNCEFORD, Troy Adam. 1120 E 100 N, STE 1 84651 #422-01-2004 L2007 **IM** *020 †20

MILLER, Garron Eugene. 50 S MEDICAL DR, STE 2 84651 #654-01-1999 L2006 **PD** *020 †55
MONEY, Nolan Boyce. 97 PROFESSIONAL WAY 84651 #049-01-1980 L1981 **FM** *020 †18
PETERSON, Jonathan Paul. 50 S MEDICAL DR, STE 2 84651 #305-01-2004 L2007 **PD** *020 †55
REES, Stephen M. 1120 E 100 N STE 3 84651 #036-05-1974 L1977 **OBG** *020 †30
SIRES, Mazen. 1120 E 100 N, STE 1 84651 #875-02-1997 L2006 **IM** *020 †20
THEURER, James Gary. 1172 E 100 N, STE 4 84651 #049-01-1994 L1998 **OPH** *020 †35
TIPTON, David John. 97 PROFESSIONAL WAY 84651 #023-12-1984 L1986 **FM** *020 †18
TRAN, James T. 1000 E 100 N, MOUNTAIN VIEW HOSPITAL 84651 #016-43-1995 L2001 **NS** *020 †25 ‡
VIZMEG, Karl Karce. 1000 HIGHWAY 6 84651 #038-06-1993 L1996 **EM** *020 †16
WARNER, William Lawrence. 1120 E 100 N, STE 3 84651 #040-02-1974 L1997 **OBG** *020 †30
WATTERS, David Hoffman. 1000 HIGHWAY 6 84651 #039-01-1974 L1981 **DR NR** *020 †80
WILLIAMS, Nathan Dwight. 100 E 100 N 84651 #039-01-1974 L1976 **EM OM** *071 †16

PERRY – BOX ELDER

CHILD, Douglas Dean. 1930 S HIGHWAY 89, AVOCET MEDICAL IMAGING 84302 #049-01-1979 L1983 **DR EM** *020 †80

PLEASANT GROVE – UTAH

ARNOLD, Bradley Clark. 1912 W 930 N 84062 #012-05-1998 L2002 **PD** *020 †55
BILLS, Gary Lynn. ■ 84062 #049-01-1968 L1971 **ORS** *020 †40
CORRY, Elwood Jones, Jr. 830 N 2000 W 84062 #049-01-1985 L1987 **FM** *020 †18
CURTIS, Michael Steven. 487 E 1000 S 84062 #056-06-2002 L2004 **FM** *020 †18
DAVIS, Todd Jeffrey. 84062 #028-34-1997 L2007 **EM** *020 †16
EDWARDS, William Foster. 1912 W 930 N 84062 #049-01-1997 L2004 **PD** *020 †55
FRODSHAM, Aaron Eugene. 84062 #050-02-2005 **DR** *012
FULLER, Glen Robert. 830 N 2000 W, TRI-CITY MEDICAL CLINIC 84062 #039-01-1977 L1982 **FM EM** *020 †18,16
GARNER, Gary Melvin. 4382 W 9200 N 84062 #049-01-1992 L1999 **FM PLM** *020 †18
JOHNSON, David Sterling. 1912 W 930 N, ALPINE PEDIATRICS 84062 #041-12-1974 L1993 **PD NPM** *020 †55
KNORR, Brett Kelsey. 1912 W 930 N 84062 #049-01-1996 L1999 **PD** *020 †55
LIDDLE, Joseph Brent. 830 N 2000 W, TRI CITY MEDICAL CLINIC IN 84062 #028-34-1997 L1999 **FM** *020 †18
MARTIN, Jerry Raty. 1575 W 2600 N 84062 #049-01-1961 L1964 **EM** *071 †18,16
MIDGLEY, Melinda Mc Donal. 830 N 2000 W 84062 #049-01-1997 L2000 **FM** *020 †18
NIMER, Richard Albert. 119 W BATTLECREEK DR 84062 #005-11-1955 **IM** *071
PARKER, E William, Jr. 1886 W 800 N 84062 #049-01-1974 L1977 **OBG** *020 †30
SAUNDERS, Mark Thos. 1886 W 800 N 84062 #056-06-1991 L1995 **OBG** *020 †30 ‡
SHAH, Chirag Aniruddha. ■ 84062 #495-23-1994 L1997 **HO** *020 †20
SMITH, Scott Leroy. 830 N 2000 W 84062 #049-01-1981 L1989 **FM** *020 †16,18
SPENCER, Weston Eugene. 1912 W 930 N, ALPINE PEDIATRICS 84062 #041-14-2003 L2006 **PD** *020 †55
SUNTAY, Robert R. ■ 84062 #010-02-1950 L1952 **IM OM** *071
VARGO, Beverly L. 1912 W 930 N, ALPINE PEDIATRICS 84062 #048-04-1992 L2000 **PD** *020 †55
WILLIS, Marshall F, Jr. 830 N 2000 W 84062 #561-17-1977 L1980 **FM** *020 †18
WISE, Dustin Bryant. 1888 W 800 N 84062 #049-01-2000 L2003 **PD** *020 †55 ‡

PRICE – CARBON

ALLEN, Glori M. 300 N HOSPITAL DR, CASTLEVIEW HOSPITAL 84501 #048-15-1989 L1992 **IM** *020 †20
ASAY, Mark Stanley. 300 N HOSPITAL DR 84501 #049-01-1992 L2005 **VIR DR** *020 †80
BAUERMEISTER, Milton Lee. 300 N HOSPITAL DR 84501 #017-20-1959 L1968 **R** *071 †80
BEUTLER, Barry Charles. ■ 84501 #041-14-2006 L2006 **IM** *012
BLACK, Carl Milton. 300 N HOSPITAL DR 84501 #010-01-1989 L2000 **DR VIR** *020 †80
BOYLE, John Francis. 945 N HOSPITAL DR STE 7 84501 #007-02-1971 L1991 **ORS** *020 †40
BROWN, Gordon D. 300 N HOSPITAL DR 84501 #049-01-1967 L1968 **R** *020 †80
BYERS, Timothy Lee. 200 N FAIRGROUNDS RD, STE 2 84501 #041-14-1996 L1997 **OPH** *020 †35
CHANDLER, Brent Cross. 300 N HOSPITAL DR 84501 #049-01-1963 L1969 **R** *020 †80
COX, Wayne Eldon. 945 N HOSPITAL DR 84501 #049-01-1976 L1980 **GS** *020 †85
CRAWFORD, Tyler Lee. 300 N HOSPITAL DR 84501 #005-14-2000 L2005 **DR** *020 †80
ETZEL, Glenn Thos. 230 N HOSPITAL DR, STE 5 84501 #030-06-1980 L1982 **FM** *020 †18
GAGON, Shane Darel. 377 N FAIRGROUNDS RD, CASTLE COUNTRY FAMILY MEDI 84501 #049-01-1997 L1998 **FM** *020 †18
HANSEN, Jeffrey Earl. 200 N FAIRGROUNDS RD, STE 2 84501 #005-02-1991 L1995 **OPH** *020 †35
HARDY, Leo Wm. 300 N HOSPITAL DR, DEPT LABORATORY 84501 #049-01-1989 L1992 **PTH** *020 †50 ‡
HEINER, David Robt. 945 N HOSPITAL DR STE 8 84501 #049-01-1977 L1982 **ORS** *020 †40
JOHNSON, Todd Wm. 945 W HOSPITAL DR, STE 4 84501 #049-01-1990 L1998 **AN** *020 †05
JUSTESEN, Scott Charles. 377 N FAIRGROUNDS RD, CASTLE COUNTRY ORTHOPAEDIC 84501 #028-34-2001 L2007 **OSM** *020
KING, Kurt Vere. 300 N HOSPITAL DR 84501 #049-01-1986 L1987 **IM EM** *020 †20
LATIMER, Darin Hansen. 300 N HOSPITAL DR, CASTLEVIEW HOSPITAL 84501 #028-79-2000, ▲ L2004 **AN** *020
MADSEN, Edward Keith. 590 E 100 N, STE 4 84501 #049-01-1974 L1977 **PD** *020
MC CLELLAN, Jeffrey Scott. 300 N HOSPITAL DR 84501 #049-01-1987 L1993 **DR** *020 †80
MC IFF, Eldon Bruce. 300 N HOSPITAL DR 84501 #049-01-1968 L1973 **R** *071 †80
MONAHAN, Daniel Chas. 230 N HOSPITAL DR, STE 3 84501 #033-05-1976 L1997 **IM** *020
MONTGOMERY, John Sloan. 575 E 100 S, 4 CORNERS COMM BEHAVIORAL 84501 #048-12-1961 L1990 **P OS** *020 †75
MORGAN, Max Gorishek. 230 N HOSPITAL DR, STE 4 84501 #049-01-1971 L1972 **FM AM** *020 ‡
NICHOLS, David Alan. 284 N HOSPITAL DR STE 2 84501 #028-03-1982 L1991 **IM** *020 †20
NIELSEN, F Rex. 280 N HOSPITAL DR STE 2 84501 #047-05-1990 L1994 **OBG** *020 †30
PETERSEN, Rodney Clair. 300 N HOSPITAL DR 84501 #049-01-1969 L1975 **R** *020 †80
POTTER, Sterling Glade. 945 N HOSPITAL DR STE 2 84501 #049-01-1978 L1981 **FM** *020 †18
RADLEY, Karen Murray. 280 N HOSPITAL DR, STE 4 84501 #049-01-1999 L2000 **FM** *020 †18

SANNELLA, Joseph John. 300 N HOSPITAL DR, PATHOLOGY DEPARTMENT 84501 #035-06-1957 L1958 **PTH AM** *071 †50
SNIHUROWYCH, Walter M. 250 N FAIRGROUNDS RD, STE 2 84501 #060-01-1969 L1979 **U** *020
THAYN, David Mathis. 1989 AIRPORT RD 84501 #665-02-2006 **MPD** *012
VAN VLOTEN, Ada X. 280 N HOSPITAL DR, STE 2 84501 #418-01-1980 L2004 **PD** *062
WENDEL, John David. 300 N HOSPITAL DR 84501 #026-08-2000 L2006 **PDR** *020 †80
WILLIAMS, Cameron S. 300 N HOSPITAL DR 84501 #060-01-1978 L1981 **EM GP** *020

PROVIDENCE – CACHE

BEAN, Kenneth Alan. 336 S 250 W 84332 #049-01-2003 L2006 **EM** *100 †16
BERGESON, Lars. 169 SPRING CREEK PKWY, STE 100 84332 #045-01-1979 L1983 **FM GP** *020 †18
CALL, Nathan Holt. 190 S HIGHWAY 165 84332 #049-01-1993 L1996 **FM** *020 †18
CARLSON, Vera Braiden. 169 SPRINGCREEK PKWY # 170, PEACHTREE FAMILY MED 84332 #913-06-1994 L2005 **FM** *020 †18
DUSHKU, Nicholas. ■ 84332 #024-05-1964 L2006 **OPH** *020 †35
FIRTH, Ronald Mark. 190 S HIGHWAY 165 84332 #054-04-1991 L1994 **FM** *020 †18
GROSSL, Armin M. ■ 84332 #154-02-1955 L1959 **DR NR** *020 †80
JONES, Aaron Wilson. ■ 84332 #010-02-2001 L2002 **FM** *020 †18
STEVENS, Richard Thomas. 169 SPRING CREEK PKWY, STE 100 84332 #056-06-2003 L2006 **FM** *100 †18
STOLWORTHY, Ryan James. 459 HILLSBOROUGH DR, ROCKY MOUNTAIN EMERGENCY S 84332 #056-06-1999 L2002 **EM** *020 †16
TAYLOR, Matthew Gregg. 190 S HIGHWAY 165 84332 #051-01-2001 L2002 **FM** *020 †18
VEDINA, Anna. ■ 84332 #049-01-2007 L2007 **IM** *012

PROVO – UTAH

ABOLNIK, Igor Z. 1055 N 500 W, CENTRAL UTAH MED CLNC 84604 #550-01-1988 L1995 **ID** *020 †20
ALBRECHT, Mitchell D. 1034 N 500 W 84604 #021-01-1990 L1998 **AN** *005
ALLEN, John William. 1055 N 500 W, CARDIOLOGYDEPARTMENT 84604 #005-17-1962 L1998 **CD** *071 †20
ALLEN, Marvin R. 1055 N 500 W, CENTRAL UTAH MULTI-SPECIAL 84604 #010-02-1990 L1997 **CD** *020 †20
ALSOLAIMAN, Mohammad M. 1055 N 500 W, CENTRAL UTAH MULTI-SPECIAL 84604 #875-02-1995 L2004 **GE** *020 †20 ‡
ALTAMIRANO, Hugo G. 745 N 500 W 84601 #132-02-1970 L2001 **PDA AI** *020 †55,03
ALTAMIRANO, Lucy Scott De. 3685 N 100 E, STE A 84604 #132-02-1966 L2001 **N** *020
ALWARD, William T. 1055 N 300 W, STE 84604 #654-01-1986 L1994 **PUD CCM** *020 †20
ANDERSON, Bradley Wayne. 1355 N UNIVERSITY AVE, STE 210 84604 #049-01-2001 L2004 **PD** *020 †55
ANDERSON, Kirk Robt. 1055 N 500 W, STE 212 84604 #049-01-1977 L1978 **IM** *020 †20
APOLLO, Anthony E. 1034 N 500 W 84604 #048-14-1998 L2004 **IM** *020 †20
ARBON, Robert Ashby. 1034 N 500 W 84604 #049-01-1964 L1966 **OTO** *020 †45
ARMSTRONG, Joseph R. 1034 N 500 W 84604 #049-01-1962 L1970 **U** *020 †95
ARORA, Surender Kumar. 1055 N 500 W, CENTRAL UTAH CLINIC 84604 #496-09-1991 L2005 **END** *020
ASAY, Ronald W. 1055 N 500 W 84604 #035-45-1976 L1985 **CD IM** *020 †20
ASHBY, Clark S. 585 N 500 W 84601 #028-34-1993 L1997 **AN** *072 †05
ASHBY, Kenny. 585 N 500 W 84601 #049-01-1963 L1964 **AN** *071 †05
ASTLE, Lawrence Walter. 151 S UNIVERSITY AVE #1400, UT COUNTY SUBSTANCE ABUSE 84601 #049-01-1968 L1969 **FM ADM** *020 †18
BACON, Carl W, II. 1055 N 500 W STE 121, CENTRAL UTAH CLINIC PC 84604 #049-01-1984 L1989 **ORS** *020 †40
BADGER, Rodney Seymour. 1055 N 500 W 84604 #005-18-1980 L1991 **CD IC** *020 †20
BADGER, Troy Jones. ■ 84604 #049-01-2008 *012
BARKER, Lance Fred. 475 W 940 N 84604 #040-02-2006 L2007 **FP** *012
BARLOW, Lynn Burnham. 1355 N UNIVERSITY AVE, STE 210 84604 #049-01-1965 L1966 **PD** *020 †55
BATEMAN, Lynn Lamont, Jr. 777 N 500 W 84601 #049-01-1964 L1965 **IM** *020 †20
BEAL, Benjamin Ryan. ■ 84601 #005-19-2006 **AN** *012
BELLER, Michael J. 1034 N 500 W 84604 #030-06-1983 L1997 **FM** *020 †18
BENNETT WYLIE, Donna. 1355 N UNIVERSITY AVE, STE 110 84604 #048-14-1987 L1992 **FM** *020 †18
BERGESON, Joseph Scott. 1034 N 500 W 84604 #049-01-1972 L1973 **IM** *020 †20
BEVANS, Duane Arlo. 750 N 200 W, WASATCH MENTAL HLTH 84601 #060-01-1971 L1986 **P CHP** *020 †75
BIGLER, Steven Dee. 1034 N 500 W 84604 #021-01-1975 L1979 **OBG** *020 †30
BINGHAM, Scott Eugene. 1055 N 500 W 84604 #047-05-1986 L1992 **CD IM** *020 †20
BISHOP, Clark T. 1055 N 300 W, STE 500 84604 #049-01-1980 L1985 **PUD CCM** *030 †20
BLAIR, Tarlton Jay. 1055 N 500 W, STE A-102 84604 #049-01-1980 L1985 **RO** *020 †80
BODILY, Kurt Olsen. 1055 N 500 W 84604 #054-04-1990 L1996 **GE** *020 †20
BODNAR, Peter R. 3585 N UNIVERSITY AVE, STE 150 84604 #654-01-1993 L2007 **N** *020 †75
BOTT, J Cordell. 1055 N 500 W, STE 202 84604 #049-01-1975 L1979 **ON HEM** *020 †20
BRADSHAW, Brian R. 1055 N 500 W 84604 #049-01-1988 L1994 **D** *020 †15
BRINKERHOFF, Joshua Duain. ■ 84601 #049-01-2008 *012
BROADBENT, David Harrison. 1355 N UNIVERSITY AVE, STE 130 84604 #049-01-1974 L1975 **OBG** *020 †30
BROADBENT, Jay S. 1275 N UNIVERSITY AVE 84604 #049-01-1946 **GYN** *071
BROBERG, Jeffrey Charles. 920 N 500 W 84604 #036-05-1998 L2005 **OBG** *020 †30
BROTHERS, William S. 1034 N 500 W 84604 #007-02-1956 L1972 **D** *072 †15
BROWN, Blaine Whitney. 1034 N 500 W, UTAH VALLEY REGIONAL MEDIC 84604 #031-01-2002 L2006 **AN** *020
BROWN, David Le Roy. ■ 84604 #023-12-1994 L1996 **FM** *020 †18
BROWN, Richard Clifton. 1034 N 500 W 84604 #019-02-1969 L1973 **RO** *020 †80
BROWN, Stephen Douglas. 1034 N 500 W, DEPT OF RADIOLOGY 84604 #049-01-1996 L2005 **VIR** *020
BROWN, Wayne Frederick. 1300 E CENTER ST, UTAH STATE HOSPITAL 84606 #305-01-1982 L1987 **P** *020 †75
BUCUR, Silvana Z. 1055 N 500 W, STE 201 84604 #781-03-1988 L2006 **OM** *020
BUTLER, Kelly V. ■ 84604 #049-01-1982 **OS** *030

CAMERON, Denton Jackson. BRIGHAM YOUNG UNIV, T-112 MHC 84602 #034-01-1974 L1976 IM EM *020

CARTWRIGHT, Kimberly D. ■ 84604 #048-04-1987 L1988 IM *020 †20

CARVER, John A. 1055 N 300 W, STE 210 84604 #005-02-1976 L1980 OPH *020 †35 ‡

CASSAT, David Jason. 475 W 940 N, UTAH VALLEY FAMILY MEDICIN 84604 #048-16-2004 L2005 FSM *012 †18

CHAPMAN, Eugene H. ■ 84604 #016-06-1949 ORS *071 †40

CHEAL, Rodney Alan. 1300 E CENTER ST, UTAH STATE HOSPITAL 84606 #049-01-1992 L1993 P *020

CHEN, Michael Mako. 3585 N UNIVERSITY AVE, STE 150 84604 #005-14-2008 *012

CHRISTENSON, Mark David. 1034 N 500 W, UTAH VALLEY REGIONAL MEDIC 84604 #028-34-2003 L2004 IM HOS *020 †20

CHRISTIANSEN, Chad Kent. ■ 84604 #056-06-2008 *012

CHRISTIANSON, Howard Kael. ■ 84604 #047-05-2005 L2005 DR *012

CHUN, Spencer James. ■ 84604 #014-01-2007 FP *012

CLARK, James L. 3200 N CANYON RD STE D 84604 #048-15-1989 L1990 FM *020 †18

CLARK, Jeffery A. ■ 84604 #048-15-1989 L1993 AN PME *020

CLARK, Nicole Anne. 475 W 940 N 84604 #050-02-1999 L2000 FM *020 †18

CLARK, Riley Garner. ■ 84604 #021-05-1938 PD *071

CLARK, Robert Craig. ■ 84601 #041-02-1948 L1949 GS *071 †85

CLAYTON, James M. 280 RIVER PARK DR, STE 240 84604 #049-01-1970 L1978 PS HS *020 †65 ‡

CLAYTON, Keith Jos. 1675 N 200 W 84604 #049-01-1970 L1971 PD *020 †55

COATES, Sam Joel. 1034 N 500 W, MEDICAL CENTER 84604 #030-05-1987 L1992 P *020 †75

COLLEDGE, Alan Lawrence. 1055 N 500 W STE 121, CENTRAL UTAH CLINIC PC 84604 #045-01-1985 L1988 OM FM *020 †18

COLLINS, John Sauls. 1034 N 500 W 84604 #021-01-1993 L1999 DR VIR *020 †80

COLVER, Kevin Jay. 1034 N 500 W 84604 #049-01-1983 L1986 IM *020 †20

CONLEY, Michael Max. 1034 N 500 W 84604 #049-01-1990 L1997 AN *020 †05

COOK, Craig Sheldon. 3550 N UNIVERSITY AVE, STE 150 84604 #049-01-1998 L2002 GS *020 †85

COOK, Loran Davis. 1055 N 300 W STE 204 84604 #049-01-1970 L1973 OPH *020 †35

COOK, Todd. 1055 N 300 W STE 204, UTAH VALLEY EYE CENTER 84604 #048-13-1997 L2001 OPH EM *020 †35

COREY, Richard Paul. 1055 N 300 W, STE 210 84604 #049-01-1997 L2003 OPH *020 †35

CORNIEA, Robert Edmond, Jr. 1055 N 500 W 84604 #049-01-1993 L1996 IM *020 †20

COTTAM, David Robert. 1034 N 500 W, DEPT OF RADIOLOGY 84604 #056-06-2001 L2007 DR *100 †80

CRAGUN, David Turley. 1055 N 500 W 84604 #049-01-2000 L2006 IC CD *020 †20

CRANE, Peter M. 682 WYMOUNT TER 12C 84604 #049-01-2008 *012

CRANER, Gregory Eugene. 1055 N 500 W, DIV SURGERY 84604 #040-02-1971 L1989 GE IM *020 †20

CRITCHFIELD, Mark Noel. 1034 N 500 W 84604 #031-01-1993 L1994 AN PME *020 †05

CRUMP, Kenneth Lyle. 3200 N CANYON RD, STE E 84604 #054-04-1991 L1994 FM *020 †18

DAHL, Charles Frelen. 1055 N 500 W 84604 #003-01-1975 L1976 CD IM *020 †20

DAMBACH, Linda. 1034 N 500 W 84604 #005-19-1986 L1993 PD *020 †20

DANE, James Thomas. 1055 N 300 W STE 110, PROVO CARDIOVASCULAR & THO 84604 #048-02-1997 L2003 TS *020 †85,90

DAVIS, Duane Ellis. 1055 N 300 W STE 316 84604 #049-01-1959 L1960 U *071 †95

DAY, Robert Walter. 1134 N 500 W, STE 103 84604 #007-02-1981 L1984 IM *020 †20

DAYTON, Leland Kay. ■ 84604 #049-01-1946 L1947 IM *071 †20

DAYTON, Lynn Taylor. 920 N 500 W 84604 #049-01-1968 L1973 OBG GP *020 †30

DEKORSE, Tyson Benjamin. 475 W 940 N, MERRILL GAPPMAYER FAMILY M 84604 #025-12-2005 L2008 FP *012

DELANEY, George Robert. 215 W 100 N, MOUNTAINLANDS COMMUNITY H. 84601 #056-06-1995 L1998 FM *020 †18

DIAL, Brandon Clark. 1034 N 500 W 84604 #010-02-2002 L2003 AN *020 †05

DICKINSON, Thomas Albert. 1055 N 500 W, CENTRAL UTAH CLINIC, PC 84604 #035-45-1976 L1981 GE *020 †20

DICKMAN, Otto Frederick, IV. 977 CEDAR AVE 84604 #011-03-2000 L2001 FM *100 †18

DIZON-TOWNSON, Donna S. 1034 N 500 W, DEPT OF MATERNAL FETAL MED 84604 #048-12-1990 L1994 OBG *020 †30

DONALDSON, Mark L. 1055 N 500 W, STE 111 84604 #049-01-1978 L1982 D IM *020 †15

DONALDSON, Stephen L. 1275 N UNIVERSITY AVE, STE 10 84604 #051-04-1987 L1988 OPH *020 †35

DUERKSEN, Ronald Gary. 1055 N 300 W STE 416 84604 #005-12-1968 L1976 PM OS *020 †60

DUNN, Jared Clauder. 1134 N 500 W, STE 102 84604 #045-01-2001 L2002 FM *020 †18

DUNN, Val Dalton. 1034 N 500 W, UVRMC DEPT OF RADIOLOGY 84604 #049-01-1976 L1977 DR *020 †80

EAMES, Wendell Owen. 1034 N 500 W, UTAH VALLEY HOSPITALIST SE 84604 #054-04-1998 L2004 IM *020 †20

ELLINGSON, William Lyle. ■ 84604 #026-04-1954 L1974 R *071 †80

ELLSWORTH, Randal Nylan. 1735 N STATE ST, EXCEL EYE CENTER 84604 #010-02-1986 L1994 OPH *020 †35

ENGEN, Todd Brian. 1735 N STATE ST, EXCEL COSMETIC SURGERY 84604 #049-01-1992 L1998 OPH FPS *020 †35

FABER, Daniel Rey. 1034 N 500 W 84604 #005-18-1983 L1988 AN PME *020 †05

FARNSWORTH, Richard Young. 1355 N UNIVERSITY AVE, STE 210 84604 #049-01-1978 L1981 PD *020 †55

FAUX, Jonathan Robert. 1055 N 500 W 84604 #010-01-1997 L2003 ORS *020 †40

FERNANDEZ, Salvador. 215 W 100 N 84601 #649-46-1987 L2004 FM *020

FIDELDIA-HELMER, Vilma T. 1300 E CENTER ST, UTAH STATE HOSPITAL 84606 #748-08-1972 L1986 P *020

FISHER, Ethan Kemp. 1034 N 500 W 84604 #049-01-1992 L1996 AN *020 †05

FLINDERS, David Cannon. 475 W 940 N 84604 #049-01-1972 L1975 FM *040 †18

FRANCIS, Howard R. 920 N 500 W 84604 #035-20-1958 L1961 OBG *072

FREESTONE, Steven Wilford. 1034 N 500 WEST DEPT OF PA 84604 #003-01-1973 L1979 PTH *020 †50

FRISCHKNECHT, John Kay. 1055 N 500 W, STE 101 84604 #016-06-1972 L1974 CD IM *020 †20

FULLMER, Mark Allen. 1055 N 300 W STE 304 84604 #049-01-1964 L1971 GS TS *020 †85

GADD, Wendell Simpson. 1034 N 500 W, UVRMC 84604 #038-41-1969 L1972 EM GP *071 †16

GARDANIER, Sutter A, II. ■ 84604 #007-02-1966 L1970 PTH *072 †50

GARDNER, H Rex. ■ 84604 #010-01-1964 L1966 PDR DR *020 †80

GARDNER, Morris David. 1055 N 500 W 84604 #049-01-1957 L1960 GE IM *071

GARDNER, Paul Kenneth. 1055 N 300 W, STE 400 84604 #028-34-1984 L1999 NS *020 †25

GARDNER, Thomas Lloyd. 1034 N 500 W 84604 #049-01-1997 L1998 AN *020 †05

GARRY, David Patrickjohn. 3550 N UNIVERSITY AVE, STE 250 84604 #010-02-1991 L1998 GS *020 †85

GAUFIN, Lynn Miller. 1055 N 300 W, STE 400 84604 #035-20-1966 L1975 NS *020 †25

GEARY, Edward Stewart. ■ 84604 #005-11-1990 1991 U *020

GERDAY, Erick Bernard. 1034 N 500 W, UTAH VALLEY REGIONAL MED C 84604 #396-06-1997 L2006 PD *100 †55

GIBBY, Wendell Arlen. 280 RIVER PARK DR, STE 100 84604 #049-01-1983 L1988 DR *020 †80

GILBERT, Jennifer Sariah. 475 W 940 N, UTAH VALLEY FAMILY MEDICIN 84604 #035-09-2005 L2006 FP *012

GLENN, Clair Jos. 1055 N 300 W STE 305, PHYSICIANS OFFICE PLZ 84604 #049-01-1977 L1985 OBG *020 †30

GOATES, Michael. 3325 N UNIVERSITY AVE, STE 375 84604 #306-01-1988 L1992 P *020 †75

GORDON, Gregory R. 1355 N UNIVERSITY AVE, STE 110 84604 #748-10-1981 L1995 OBG *020 †30

GOVINDJI, Jayanti. 1034 N 500 W 84604 #495-23-1969 L1979 AN *020

GRAHAM, Wayne Richard. 475 W 940 N, UTAH VALLEY FAMILY MEDICIN 84604 #028-79-2004, ▲ L2005 FM *020 †18

GRIFFIN, Brent Lundstrom. 1675 N 200 W STE 12A 84604 #048-14-1974 L1978 CHP P *020 †55,75

GROESBECK, Philip Dickson. 1034 N 500 W, UVRMC ANESTHESIOLOGY DEPT 84604 #005-06-1987 L1992 AN *020 †05

GROVER, Julie Glenn. 1055 N 300 W 84604 #049-01-1998 L1999 OBG *020 †30

GROVES, Jeffrey William. 1055 N 500 W STE 212, CENTRAL UTAH CLINIC 84604 #422-01-2003 L2005 N *020

GUNDLAPALLI, Madhumathy. 1300 E CENTER ST, UTAH STATE HOSPITAL 84606 #495-04-1990 L1998 P PYG *020 †75

GURAU, Izabella. 1055 N 500 W 84604 #781-03-1994 L2004 NEP *020 †20

HADLEY, Scott Robert. ■ 84604 #005-15-2007 ORS *012

HAMMOND, Roy Charles. 1034 N 500 W 84604 #005-02-1995 L1996 DR *020 †80

HAMMOND, Terry C. 1055 N 500 W, STE 222 84604 #048-02-1986 L1995 NEP *020 †20

HARKNESS, Gordon William. 3200 N CANYON RD, STE D 84604 #049-01-2000 L2003 FM *020 †18 ‡

HARKNESS, James Richard. ■ 84604 #023-07-2006 L2006 IM *012

HARLAN, Brian Leon. 1034 N 500 W 84604 #004-01-1999 L2007 P *020

HATCH, C Steven. ■ 84604 #023-07-1943 L1946 U GS *071 †85,95

HATCH, Daniel Joe. 1034 N 500 W, UTAH VALLEY REG. MED. CENT 84604 #049-01-1994 L2000 VIR *020 †80

HATHAWAY, Bruce Neerings. 777 N 500 W STE 104 84601 #049-01-1975 L1978 ID IM *020 †20

HATT, David Lynn. 1055 N 300 W, STE 411 84604 #049-01-1978 L1984 OBG *020 †30

HAYMOND, David Ruel. 1034 N 500 W 84604 #049-01-1961 L1964 P *020

HAYWARD, Gerald Lynn. 585 N 500 W 84601 #049-01-1967 L1968 AN GS *071 †05

HEASTON, Dennis Kay. 1034 N 500 W, DEPT RADIOLOGY UVRMC 84604 #049-01-1975 L1977 R RO *020 †80

HEINER, Douglas C. ■ 84604 #041-01-1950 L1960 AI PD *071 †55,03

HELLEWELL, James Lynn. 475 W 940 N, UTAH VALLEY FAMILY MEDICIN 84604 #056-06-2006 L2007 FP *012

HERRMANN, Keri Bennett. UTAH STATE HOSP 84603 #049-01-1988 L1995 CHP P *030 †75

HESS, Dennis Clark. 2230 N UNIVERSITY PKWY, STE 1A 84604 #049-01-1964 L1965 FM *020 †18

HILL, Bruce Binkley. 3550 N UNIVERSITY AVE, STE 250 84604 #016-11-1991 L1995 GS *020 †85

HILL, Tracy Arnold. 1055 N 300 W, STE 500 84604 #040-02-1978 L1981 PUD IM *020 †20

HILMO, David Scott. 1034 N 500 W, 1034 NORTH 500 WEST 84604 #005-12-1997 L2001 PM *020 †60

HOFFMAN, Lloyd Eugene, Jr. B.Y.U. 84602 #011-03-1964 L1966 PD PDC *020 †55

HOHL, Justin Burnell. ■ 84604 #035-01-2006 L2006 ORS *012

HOLMES, Richard J. 2230 N UNIVERSITY PKWY, STE 1A 84604 #042-02-1986 L2000 FM *020 †18

HOPSON, Curtis T. 1034 N 500 W 84604 #049-01-1989 L1990 AN *020 †05

HWANG, Chun. 1055 N 500 W 84604 #187-33-1982 L1995 CD *020 †20

IONESCU-TAJTI, Claudiu-Gil. 1134 N 500 W, STE 102A 84604 #781-01-1995 L2007 IM *020 †20

JACKSON, Richard Taylor. 1055 N 500 W STE 121, CENTRAL UTAH CLINIC PC 84604 #049-01-1974 L1975 ORS *020 †40

JACKSON, Robert Taylor. 1055 N 500 W STE 121, CENTRAL UTAH CLINIC PC 84604 #049-01-1974 L1975 ORS *020 †40

JACKSON, Scott Taylor. 1055 N 500 W, 700 W 800N SUITE 100 84604 #021-01-1982 L1985 ORS *020

JENSEN, Jeffrey Louis. 1355 N UNIVERSITY AVE, STE 210 84604 #049-01-1999 L2002 PD *020 †55

JOHNSON, Curtis C. 1055 N 500 W, STE 121 84604 #049-01-1989 L1995 ORS *020 †40

JOHNSON, Daniel Adams. ■ 84604 #005-11-1972 L1973 PD *071 †55

JOHNSON, Jeffrey Wilson. 1055 N 500 W 84604 #005-06-1977 L1984 IM AM *020 †20

JOHNSON, Joseph Michael. 1675 N 200 W, STE 9C 84604 #012-05-2002 L2005 PD *020 †55

JOHNSSON, Staffan C G. 1034 N 500 W, ANESTHESIA DEPT 84604 #012-01-1976 L1978 AN AM *020

JONES, Douglas Ramon. 475 W 940 N, UTAH VALLEY FAMILY MEDICIN 84604 #036-05-1994 L1998 FM *020 †18

JONES, Ronald Calvin. 3325 N UNIVERSITY AVE, STE 100 84604 #005-15-1968 L1983 PD *020

JUDD, Thomas Elwyn. 1355 N UNIVERSITY AVE, STE 110 84604 #005-02-1972 L1974 OBG *020

KEPAS, Demetrius Emmanuel. 1034 N 500 W 84604 #418-01-1954 L1972 PTH *020 †50

KEZERIAN, Nephi K. ■ 84604 #020-02-1943 L1945 ORS *071 †40

KIMBALL, Kirt Michael. 1055 N 500 W STE 121, CENTRAL UTAH CLINIC, PC 84604 #005-14-1974 L1996 ORS *020 †40

KOHLER, Dorrel Douglas. 3295 N 650 E 84604 #049-01-1969 L1970 GS *020 †85

KOO, Jason Tungcheng. 1034 N 500 W 84604 #023-01-1992 L2007 PS *100

KREBS, G Cloyd. ■ 84604 #023-07-1947 L1949 IM *071

KROMMENHOEK, Adam Robert. 1034 N 500 W 84604 #048-13-2002 L2005 EM *020 †16

LANDAU, Stewart T. 1055 N 300 W, STE 316 84604 #049-01-1987 L1992 U *020 †95

LANG, Leslie Mark. 1034 N 500 W, CENTER, NICU 84604 #028-02-1986 L1993 NPM *020 †55

LARKIN, Dixon Ferrin. ■ 84604 #049-01-1974 L1975 RO *074 †80

LARSEN, Mitchell Williams. 1055 N 500 W, STE 121 84604 #010-02-1999 L2005 OSM *020 †40

LATER, Richard Wesley. 1055 N 500 W, STE 307 84604 #049-01-1979 L1982 PD *020 †55

LAURET, Michael H. 1355 N UNIVERSITY AVE #210, UTAH VALLEY PEDIATRICS, LL 84604 #014-01-1988 L1991 PD *020 †55

LAYTON, Brent Thos. 1055 N 500 W, STE 112 84604 #028-02-1987 L1999 DR *020 †80

LEE, Martin Mao Ting. 1055 N 500 W, CREDENTIALING 84604 #539-04-2000 L2005 CCM *020 †20

LEMERY, Robert. 1055 N 500 W 84604 #067-06-1979 L2005 CD IM *020 †20

LICHTI, Douglas Jon. 3550 N UNIVERSITY AVE, STE 250 84604 #030-05-1979 L1990 GS *020 †85

LIND, David Gordon. 1034 N 500 W 84604 #030-06-1977 L1978 AN *020 †05

LOHNER, Richard W. 1701 N 1450 E 84604 #049-01-1955 L1966 OBG *071 †30 ‡

LOHNER, William Scott. 1735 N STATE ST, EXCEL EYE CENTER 84604 #049-01-1994 L1998 OPH *020 †35

LOVELL, Robert Geo. 1034 N 500 W 84604 #049-01-1972 L1973 PTH GS *020 †50

MAC ARTHUR, Arthur Creig. 1055 N 300 W, STE 12 84604 #010-01-1967 L1973 ORS OS *020 †40

MAC KAY, Calvin R. ■ 84604 #049-01-1946 L1948 ORS GS *071 †85,40

MATHESON, Evan J. 745 N 500 W, PROVO ALLERGY & ASTHMA CLI 84601 #049-01-1985 L1986 IM AI *020 †20,03 ‡

MATHEWS, Jeffrey Lee. 3650 N UNIVERSITY AVE, STE 150 84604 #049-01-1978 L1981 RHU IM *020 †20,16 ‡

MATURLO, Susan Joy. 1055 N 500 W, STE 212 84604 #041-07-1972 L1998 END IM *020 †20

MC ALLISTER, Bruce Craig. 1055 N 500 W, CENTRAL UTAH CLNC CANCER 84604 #049-01-1993 L1994 RO *020 †80

MCCANDLESS, Jeremy R. 475 W 940 N, UTAH VALLEY FAMILY MED 84604 #049-01-2006 L2008 FP *012

MC ELROY, Betty Howell. 5600 HERITAGE SCHOOL DR 84604 #048-02-1961 L1990 P *020

MC HENRY, Kenneth Wayne. ■ 84604 #028-03-1972 L1974 OBG *020 †30

MCLAY, Michael S. 475 W 940 N, UTAH VALLEY FAMILY MEDICIN 84604 #305-01-2006 L2007 FP *012

MEYER, Julia. 1055 N 300 W, STE 402 84604 #231-01-1958 L1982 CHN SME *020 †55,75

MILITARU, Loredana Cornel. 1034 N 500 W, UVRMC 84604 #781-06-1997 L2004 IM *020

MILLER, Todd James. 475 W 940 N, UTAH VALLEY FAMILY MEDICIN 84604 #049-01-2006 L2007 FP *012

MILLWARD, Christian Scott. 1134 N 500 W, STE 101 84604 #056-06-2004 L2005 FSM *012 †18

MINER, Joseph Kay. 151 S UNIVERSITY AVE, STE 2800 84601 #049-01-1974 L1977 PHP OM *030 †70

MINTON, Stephen Dennis. 1034 N 500 W 84604 #038-41-1971 L1977 NPM PD *020 †55

MITCHELL, John H. 1055 N 300 W, STE 110 84604 #023-12-1987 L2003 TS *020 †90,85

MONNAHAN, James Raymond. PO BOX 531 84604 #026-04-1953 L1957 R NM *071 †80

MOODY, Milo Lyman. 777 N 500 W STE 104 84601 #016-06-1965 L1966 IM *020 †80

MORELLI, Susan H. 1034 N 500 W, UVRMC 84604 #008-02-1994 L1996 NPM *020 †19,55

MORRISON, Craig Wilbur. 1034 N 500 W 84604 #040-02-1970 L1978 GP *020

MORTENSEN, Wayne W. 1134 N 500 W STE 101 84604 #049-01-1980 L1987 ORS *020 †40

MOSS, Richard Lee. 3507 N UNIVERSITY AVE, STE 225 84604 #049-01-1976 L1977 D DMP *020 †15

MURDOCK, Jared Elwin. ■ 84606 #024-07-2005 GS *012

MURRAY, Brad Lynn. 1034 N 500 W, PSYCHIATRY DEPT 84604 #049-01-2000 L2002 P *020

MYERS, Kelly Jay. 1034 N 500 W 84604 #035-01-1993 L1994 AN *020 †05

MYERS, Thomas Dyreng. 280 RIVER PARK DR STE 22 84604 #049-01-1999 L2002 OPH *020 †35

MYERS, Thomas Edwin. 3200 N CANYON RD, STE D 84604 #001-02-1976 L1977 FM *020 ‡

NEAL, Donald E. PO BOX 354 84603 #748-09-1984 *074

NELSON, Devon Ammon. 1055 N 500 W 84604 #049-01-1973 L1974 ORS *050 †40

NELSON, Ivan Wm, II. 556 E 4020 N 84604 #049-01-1970 L1971 FPS *020 †45

NGATUVAI, Tauaina James. 475 W 940 N, UTAH VALLEY FAMILY MEDICIN 84604 #049-01-2005 L2006 FP *012

NGUYEN, Thu Anh. 1055 N 500 W 84604 #026-08-2002 L2007 N *100 †75

NIELSEN, Gregory L. 2230 N UNIVERSITY PKWY, STE 1A 84604 #060-02-1988 L1990 FM *020 †18

NIELSEN, Ryan B. 1034 N 500 W, DEPT OF RADIOLOGY 84604 #030-06-1995 L2001 VIR *020 †18

NOBLE, Larry. 1034 N 500 W 84604 #040-02-1964 L1966 OPH PHP *020 †35

NOBUHARA, Lawrence Ken. 1055 N 500 W, CENTRAL UTAH MULTI-SPECIAL 84604 #005-12-1993 L1994 IM *020

NOKES, Matthew Evan. 1034 N 500 W, DEPARTMENT OF RADIOLOGY 84604 #056-06-2001 L2007 VIR *100 †80

OAKS, Merrill Clayton. 1034 N 500 W 84604 #035-45-1963 L1965 OPH *071 †35

O'BRIEN, Benjamin Wayne. 1300 E CENTER ST 84606 #305-01-2000 L2003 P *100 †75 ‡

OCKEY, Robin R. 3585 N UNIVERSITY AVE 84604 #010-01-1989 L2003 PM *020 †60

OGDEN, Bruce Edward. 1034 N 500 W, UVRMC-NEONATOLOGY 84604 #049-01-1978 L2002 PD NPM *020 †55

OLDROYD, Ronald Irvin. 1055 N 300 W, STE 316 84604 #040-02-1973 L1978 U *020 †95

OLENSLAGER, Brian Kenneth. 3585 N UNIVERSITY AVE, STE 150 84604 #049-01-2000 L2004 PM *020 †60

OLSEN, Alonzo Young, Jr. 2230 N UNIVERSITY PKWY 84604 #005-06-1964 L1992 FM GP *020 †18

OLSEN, Richard Kent. 1055 N 500 W, STE 212 84604 #049-01-1992 L1994 IM *020 †20

OLSON, Paul Ferron. 1055 N 300 W, STE 204 84604 #049-01-1979 L1986 OPH *020

PARK, David Alan. 3610 N UNIVERSITY AVE, STE 150 84604 #020-02-1999 L2002 *020

PARKINSON, Richard White. 5314 N 250 W, STE 220 84604 #021-01-1974 L1975 D DMP *020 †15

PARSONS, Matthew Reed. 1735 N STATE ST 84604 #049-01-1986 L1990 OPH *020 †35

PARSONS, Stephen Paul. 1055 N 300 W, STE 401 84604 #049-01-2001 L2006 OTO *020 †45

PEARCE, Michael John. 1055 N 500 W STE 500 84604 #028-34-1989 L1990 PUD CCM *020 †20

PERRY, Anne. 1034 N 500 W 84604 #049-01-2003 L2006 IM *020 †20

PETERSEN, Robert Juul. ■ 84604 #028-02-1956 L1963 OTO A *071 †45

PETERSON, David Arthur. 148 W 3300 N, DAVID A. PETERSON, MD 84604 #001-02-1976 L1982 DR *020 †40

PETERSON, David Odell. 463 E NORMANDY DR 84604 #056-05-1980 L2004 AN *020 †05

PETERSON, Lee M. 3550 N UNIVERSITY AVE, STE 250 84604 #049-01-1982 L1987 GS *020 †85

PETERSON, Matthew Romell. 280 RIVER PARK DR, STE 200 84604 #037-01-1998 L2004 APM *020 †05

PETERSON, Samuel Ray. 1055 N 500 W, STE 111 84604 #048-14-1998 L2003 D *020 †15

PETERSON, Shaun Nathan. ■ 84604 #048-02-1998 L1999 ORS *100

PETTY, Robert Wm. 930 N 500 W 84604 #028-02-1948 L1954 OPH *071 †35

PHAN, Alex Huanphong Duy. 3585 N UNIVERSITY AVE # 1 84604 #035-09-2001 L2007 IM *100

PLATT, Mckay Lyman. 1055 N 300 W, STE 300 84604 #021-01-1984 L1988 U *020 †95

PLEDGER, Charles Vatcher. 3650 N UNIVERSITY AVE, STE 200 84604 #049-01-1977 L1982 PS *020 †65

PORTER, Barbara. ■ 84604 #049-01-1970 L1971 GP *074

PURSER, Danny Clinton. 2255 N UNIVERSITY PKWY, STE 27-292 84604 #027-01-1985 L1986 FM FPG *071

QUICK, Nichole Amber. ■ 84604 #049-01-2008 *012

RAJHANS, Sachin M. 1300 E CENTER ST U, UTAH STATE HOSPITAL 84606 #496-38-1993 L2003 P *100

RASBAND, James Edwin. ■ 84604 #010-01-1958 L1971 R *071 †80,28

RASBAND, Joseph Daniel. 1034 N 500 W, UTAH VLY RED MED CTR-RAD 84604 #035-45-1999 L2000 DR NR *020 †80,28

RASMUSSEN, Ralph Richard. 3550 N UNIVERSITY AVE, STE 250 84604 #049-01-1998 L2003 GS *085

REICHMAN, Howard Reed. 1055 N 300 W, STE 400 84604 #049-01-1982 L1992 NS *020 †25

REICHMAN, Owen Howard. ■ 84604 #049-01-1956 L1964 NS *020 †25

REMINGTON, Dennis Wayne. 1675 N FREEDOM BLVD, STE 11D 84604 #060-01-1969 L1980 FM *020

RHODES, Michael Lilburn. 475 W 940 N, UTAH VALLEY FAMILY PRACTIC 84604 #012-01-1991 L1994 FM *040 †18

RICH, Brent S E. 1134 N 500 W, STE 101 84604 #054-04-1988 L1991 FM FSM *020 †18

RICH, Nathan Terry. 1034 N 500 W 84604 #038-40-2000 L2006 ON *020 †20

RICHARDS, Ryan A. 1055 N 500 W, STE 121 84604 #035-03-1999 L2005 HS *020

RICKS, Marc. ■ 84604 #005-02-1945 L1983 GP A *071

RIDDLE, Brian Thos. ■ 84604 #030-06-1988 L1995 FM *020 †18

RIDDLE, Seth Allred. 1055 N 300 W, STE 401 84604 #049-01-1993 L1998 OTO *020 †45

RIRIE, Delbert Glen. 930 W 500 N 84601 #035-20-1967 L1971 OPH *071 †35

ROBERTSON, L Eugene. ■ 84604 #049-01-1950 L1953 PS *071 †85,65

ROBINS, Kipp Moreno. 2230 N UNIVERSITY PKWY, STE 9B 84604 #028-34-1988 L1989 OTO *020 †45

ROBINS, Melvin Moreno. 1355 N UNIVERSITY AVE, STE 210 84604 #049-01-1959 L1961 PD *020 †55

ROSE, Kevin Gordon. 320 RIVER PARK DR, STE 245 84604 #047-07-1998 L2004 PS *020

ROSENTHAL, Richard Mark. 3585 N UNIVERSITY AVE, STE 150 84604 #049-01-1985 L1988 PMM ADM *020 †05

ROSS, Douglas Scott. 1055 N 300 W, STE 402 84604 #040-02-1985 L1986 PUD IM *020 †20

RUPPER, John Heber. 1275 N UNIV AVE 84604 #010-02-1943 L1943 IM *071

SAMPSON, Richard B. ■ 84606 #649-14-1974 L2001 FM *020 †18

SATURNINO, Lisa Marie. 1134 N 500 W, STE 102 84604 #025-12-2000 L2001 FM *020 †18

SAVAGE, Shelly Lynne. 1959 N STATE ST 84604 #049-01-1999 L2000 FM *020 †18

SBEI, Ahmed Mouaz. 852 N 500 W, CENTRAL UT CLNC 84604 #875-01-1992 L2001 N *020 †75

SCHEMMER, Glenn Kenneth. 1034 N 500 W, UTAH VALLEY REG MED CTR 84604 #011-04-1986 L2001 OBG MFM *020 †30

SCHOW, Douglas, Jr. 1055 N 300 W STE 203 84604 #049-01-1972 L1973 ORS *020 †40

SCOTT, David Lawrence. 1034 N 500 W 84604 #049-01-1969 L1970 PD *020 †55

SEAGER, Paul Robinson. 1034 N 500 W 84604 #049-01-1978 L1980 AN *020 †05

SELLERS, Terrell Lee. 1034 N 500 W 84604 #028-34-1991 L1995 OBG *020

SHEROD, Earl Glenn. 1034 N 500 W 84604 #049-02-1967 L1970 AN *071

SIPHERD, Ryan Ammon. ■ 84604 #042-02-2004 L2007 EM *020

SLINGERLAND, Stuart Wayne. 1275 N UNIVERSITY AVE, UTAH VALLEY PEDIATRICS 84604 #041-01-1961 L1970 PD OS *071 †55

SMILANICH, Robert Paul. 1055 N 300 W, STE 205 84604 #010-01-1990 L2000 VS GS *020 †85 ‡

SMITH, D Lowry. BYU HEALTH CTR 84602 #049-01-1950 L1953 GYN GP *071

SMITH, Douglas Richard. 1055 N 500 W 84604 #005-15-1979 L1980 CD IM *020 †20

SMITH, Gregory Blake. 1055 N 500 W, CENTRAL UTAH CLINIC 84604 #010-01-1996 L2003 DR *020 †80

SMITH, Jeffrey Randall. 1134 N 500 W 84604 #049-01-1983 L1989 ORS *020 †40

SMITH, Thales Haskell. 1275 N UNIVERSITY AVE, STE 18 84604 #041-13-1947 L1954 PD *071 †55

SMOOT, Harlow Eldredge. ■ 84604 #005-14-1962 L1963 OBG *071 †30

SOMASUNDARAM, Porur E. 1055 N 500 W, CREDENTIALING 84604 #495-04-1988 L2008 ICE *020 †20

SORENSEN, Brian Shaw. ■ 84604 #050-02-2005 DR *100

SPENCER, Herbert Beck. 1055 N 300 W STE 316 84604 #049-01-1958 L1960 U *020 †95

SPENCER, Richard Beck. 1300 E CENTER ST, UTAH STATE HOSPITAL 84606 #028-02-1976 L1977 P *030 †75

STAHELI, John Kent. 1055 N 500 W 84604 #049-01-1994 L1996 IM *020 †20

STEEL, James Merrill. ■ 84604 #049-01-1965 L1967 ORS *020 †40

STEFFEN, Susan. 1034 N 500 W, WOMEN AND CHILDREN'S CLINI 84604 #049-01-1977 L1988 OBG *020 †30

STEFFENSEN, Mark Harvey. 1034 N 500 W 84604 #049-01-1984 L1987 AN *020 †05

STEPHANZ, Gerald Bernard. 1055 N 500 W, STE 222 84604 #019-02-1983 L1994 NEP IM *020 †20

STEWART, Charles H. 3650 N UNIVERSITY AVE, STE 200 84604 #649-14-1979 L1985 PS HS *020

STONE, Richard Lloyd. 1375 N UNIVERSITY AVE 84604 #049-01-1970 L1972 D *020

STRONG, William Edward. 1067 N 500 W 84604 #049-01-1984 L1988 AN PME *020 †05

STURIM, Howard Stuart. ■ 84604 #035-45-1957 L1959 PS *071 †85,65

SUNDAR, Krishna M. 1055 N 300 W, STE 402 84604 #496-09-1990 L1996 PCC *020 †20

TAYLOR, Kimball Blake. 1034 N 500 W 84604 #049-01-1989 L1993 DR *020 †80

TAYLOR, Michael Dean. 1034 N 500 W 84604 #049-01-1981 L1982 AN *020 †05 ‡

TAYLOR, Robert Walter. 3200 N CANYON RD, CANYON MEDICAL PLAZA STE D 84604 #060-01-1969 L1974 FM *020 †18

TEMPLEMAN, John Frederic. ■ 84604 #065-10-1984 L2003 FM *020

THOMAS, Dan Eugene. 1754 COBBLESTONE DR 84604 #023-12-1988 L1990 AN PME *020 †05

THOMAS, Richard Milton. 3550 N UNIVERSITY AVE #250 84604 #021-05-1975 L1978 GS GP *020 †85

THORNE, Willes Max. 1034 N 500 W 84604 #021-01-1980 L1992 PTH HMP *020 †50

THORPE, Brett Leat. 1055 N 500 W, STE 100 84604 #049-01-2000 L2001 GE *020

TRIVEDI, Sara Christensen. ■ 84604 #005-11-1962 L1989 IM PYA *071

TUDOR, Brian Peter. 1055 N 500 W STE 202, CENTRAL UTAH CLINIC, PC 84604 #005-14-1979 L1980 ON HEM *020 †20

URIE, Paul. 1034 N 500 W, UTAH VLY REG MED CTR 84604 #049-01-1979 L1980 PTH *020 †50

VALADEZ, Scott Douglas. 1055 N 500 W, STE 112 84604 #049-01-2000 L2006 DR *100 †80

VINCENT, Pamela Lynne. 280 RIVER PARK DR, DRIVE, #350 84604 #056-05-1986 L1992 N PMM *020

VITALE, Dennis Elwood. 1055 N 300 W STE 30, UTAH VALLEY PHYSICIANS PLA 84604 #023-01-1961 L1969 PDS GS *071 †85

UTAH

VITKO, Cynthia Louise. 1300 E CENTER ST, UTAH STATE HOSPITAL 84606 #032-01-1994 L2005 PFP *020 †75

WALKER, Glen Harris. 3985 QUAIL RUN 84604 #067-01-1956 L1957 TS GS *071

WALLENTINE, Jeffrey Max. 1055 N 500 W, STE 121 84604 #049-01-1992 L1998 ORS OSM *020 †40

WARD, Jon Quayle. 1034 N 500 W 84604 #049-01-1963 L1965 AN *071 †05

WATKINS, Joseph Reed. 1055 N 300 W, STE 400 84604 #048-04-1982 L1983 N *020

WATTS, David Michael. 3550 N UNIVERSITY AVE, STE 250 84604 #023-12-1985 L2007 GS *020 †85

WATTS, Gary Maughan. 280 RIVER PARK DR 84604 #049-01-1968 L1973 DR NM *020 †80,28

WEENIG, Karl Nephi. 1055 N 500 W 84604 #049-01-2002 L2003 FM *020 †18

WEST, Timothy William. ■ 84604 #005-02-2006 IM *012

WESTBROOK, Benjamin James. ■ 84604 #023-12-2007 L2007 GS *012

WHITAKER, Neil Smith. 1034 N 500 W, UVRMC ADMIN 84604 #048-02-1981 L1988 IM *030 †20

WHITE, Vernon. 215 W 100 N 84601 #049-01-1989 L1992 FM *020 †18

WHITEHEAD, Paul David. 1300 E CENTER ST, UTAH STATE HOSPITAL 84606 #049-01-1994 L2000 PFP *020 †75

WILDER, Carol Jean. 1134 N 500 W, STE 101 84604 #056-06-1995 L2006 FM *020 †18

WILSON, Carl Thayne. 1034 N 500 W, UVRMC/DEPT OF ANESTHESIOLO 84604 #028-02-1984 L1988 AN *020 †05

WING, Sherman Douglas. 1034 N 500 W, DEPT OF RADIO 84604 #049-01-1971 L1976 DR RNR *020 †80

WISE, Stuart Roland. ■ 84604 #049-01-1971 L1977 OBG *020 †30

WOCHNIK, Eliza E. 1034 N 500 W, UVRMC 84604 #759-03-1963 L1986 CHP P *020 †75

WOLSEY, Brian La Ray. 890 N 500 W 84604 #060-01-1972 L1976 OBG P *020 †30

WOOD, Christopher Reed. 475 W 940 N 84604 #049-01-1994 L2003 FM *020 †18

WOODMANSEE, James Albert. 2230 N UNIVERSITY PKWY, STE 1A 84604 #422-01-1988 L1989 FM OBS *020

WOODMANSEE, Terrell R. ■ 84604 #041-13-1955 OM AM *071

WORDEN, William Lamont, Jr. ■ 84604 #008-01-2007 *012

WORTH, Eugene Reed. 1034 N 500 W, UVRMC, HYPERBARIC MEDICINE 84604 #028-03-1980 L2006 AN *020 †05

ZARKOU, Mary Ann. ■ 84606 #049-01-2008 *012

ZOLLO, Kenneth Allen. 1055 N 300 W, STE 311 84604 #035-01-1981 L1996 PD AM *020 †55

RICHFIELD — SEVIER

BLOMQUIST, Roger Dale. 1000 N MAIN ST, SEVIER VALLEY MED CTR 84701 #049-01-1963 L1964 R NM *020 †80,28

CHAPPELL, Leland Jeffery. 1100 N MAIN ST 84701 #049-01-1990 L1991 FM *020 †18 ‡

COLLINS, David Vern. 1100 N MAIN ST 84701 #049-01-1977 L1981 PUD IM *020 †20

DAVIE, Daniel Glenn. 1100 N MAIN ST, SEVIER VALLEY HOSPITAL 84701 #042-02-2002 L2003 FM *020 †18

GREENWOOD, Mark Robert. 460 N MAIN ST, RICHFIELD CLINIC 84701 #010-01-2000 L2001 FM *020 †18

GREENWOOD, Mark Wm. 460 N MAIN ST 84701 #010-01-1971 L1972 GP *020 †18

JAUSSI, James Rolland. ■ 84701 #016-06-1968 L1975 OBG *020 †30

POPE, David Michael. 850 N MAIN ST, STE 3 84701 #040-02-1991 L1992 FM *020 †18

POTTS, Robert Earle. ■ 84701 #020-02-1961 L1971 GP EM *020

RICHMOND — CACHE

BELL, Ryan R. ■ 84333 #056-06-2005 L2008 PD *012

RIVERTON — SALT LAKE

ATZET, Jonathan Joseph. 3859 W 12600 S 84065 #010-01-1996 L2005 PD *020 †55

BARBUTO, John Patrick. 1733 W 12600 S 84065 #005-15-1973 L1977 N *020 †75

BARLOW, Carrolee. ■ 84065 #049-01-1989 L1991 END *100 †20

DAVIS, John Tucker. 1288 W 12700 S, P O BOX 1010 84065 #049-01-1996 L2000 PD *020 †55

DUFFY, John Timothy. 3859 W 12600 S 84065 #005-02-1997 L1998 PD *020 †55

ELLIS, Raymond C. ■ 84065 #040-02-1947 L1950 P *071

JESSOP, Katherine Marie. ■ 84065 #049-01-2008 *012

KENDRICK, Ernest Jeremy. ■ 84065 #049-01-2005 L2006 PD *012

KIMBALL, Chad Brigham. ■ 84096 #041-15-2006 L2008 IM *012

LISTER, Katrina Lee. ■ 84065 #049-01-2008 *012

LONGENECKER, Elwood Neil. 3859 W 12600 S, S RIDGE INSTA CARE 84065 #012-01-1996 L2000 UCM FM *020 †18

PAYNE, Brent Richards. ■ 84065 #049-01-1975 L1976 EM *020 †18

SRINIVASAN, Bharani G. 3859 W 12600 S, INTERMOUNTAIN SOUTHRIDGE C 84065 #495-16-1995 L2001 IM *020 †20

THOMPSON, Daniel Owen. 1756 PARK AVE 84065 #049-01-1996 L1999 FM *020 †18

VALENTINE, Marilyn Ashby. 3859 W 12600 S 84065 #030-05-1999 L2003 PD *100 †55

ROOSEVELT — DUCHESNE

ARIF, Saroosh. 250 W 300 N, UINTAH BASIN MEDICAL CENTE 84066 #704-02-1990 L2001 HO *020 †20

BEALES, Jason Scott. 210 W 300 N 75-3 84066 #056-06-2000 L2003 PD *020 †55 ‡

BLAKE, John Steele. 210 W 300 N 75-3 84066 #049-01-1988 L2001 D DS *020 †15

BUXTON, Terry Mackley. 210 W 300 N # 75-3 84066 #010-01-1962 L1963 GP *071

CATTEN, Michael Dennis. 210 W 300 N 84066 #049-01-1996 L2001 OTO *020 †45

DUNCAN, Laura T. 250 W 300 N 84066 #032-01-2001 L2006 IM *100 †20

DUNCAN, Matthew Swain. 250 W 300 N 84066 #032-01-2001 L2006 P *100 †75

EVANS, Keith Hale. 205 W 300 N STE 7512 84066 #040-02-1976 L1977 OBG *020

KRZYMOWSKI, David Kent. 210 W 300 N 75-3 84066 #036-07-1999 L2004 GS *020 †85

LARSON, Jason Jerry. 250 W 300 N, UINTAH BASIN MEDICAL CENTE 84066 #016-43-2000 L2003 EM *100 †16

MASON, Mark William. 250 W 300 N, UINTAH BASIN MEDICAL CLINI 84066 #049-01-1994 L1999 ORS *020 †40

MITCHELL, Mark Edward. 210 W 300 N, UINTAH BASIN MEDICAL CLINI 84066 #039-01-1989 L1993 GP *020

NOLTE, John Dennis. 250 W 300 N 84066 #030-06-1994 L1998 OBG *020 †30

PAULSEN, Sean David. 250 W 300 N, UINTAH BASIN MEDICAL CENTE 84066 #049-01-2000 L2005 DR *100 †30

PEHRSON, Steve E. ■ 84066 #308-11-1984 L1987 EM FM *020 †18

POWELL, Shane Keith. 210 W 300 N, NORTHEASTERN UTAH MEDICAL 84066 #049-01-1994 L1995 OPH *020 †35

RIPPLINGER, Rex Fowler. 210 W 300 N, NORTHEASTERN UTAH MEDICAL 84066 #308-11-1985 L1988 IM *020 †20

ROBERTSON, Glenn Lewis. 210 W 300 N, NORTHEASTERN UTAH MEDICAL 84066 #051-07-1996 L1999 FM *020 †18

SAUNDERS, Kristine Renee. 250 W 300 N 84066 #005-06-1994 L2006 PTH *062 †50

SMITH, Kent E. 210 W 300 N, UINTAH BASIN MEDICAL CENTE 84066 #308-11-1986 L1990 IM *020

SMITH, Russell Norwood, III. 250 W 300 N 75-3 84066 #305-01-2002 L2005 FM *020 †18

STAKER, Gregory Larry. 210 W 300 N, 75-3 84066 #049-01-1997 L2001 MPD *020 †20,55

STAKER, Shannon Rachelle. 210 W 300 N 84066 #049-01-1997 L2001 PD *020 †55

WHITE, Gary Banks. 210 W 300 N 84066 #010-01-1964 L1965 GP *020

WHITE, James Derrick. 210 W 300 N, NORTHEASTERN UTAH MEDICAL 84066 #049-01-1992 L1993 PM PMM *020 †60

ROY — WEBER

ACCOLA, Brian Gene. 1915 W 5950 S, C/O BRANDON G. WINTLE, M.D 84067 #025-07-2002 L2003 FM *020 †18

ALVEY, Justin Charles. 5991 S 3500 W, STE 100 84067 #028-02-1995 L1996 PD *020 †55

CAMPBELL, Zachary Mccoy. 1915 W 5950 S 84067 #035-09-2001 L2004 FM *020 ‡

FERRIN, Tricia L. 1915 W 5950 S 84067 #028-78-2003, ▲ L2004 FM *020 †18

FRIZ, Ralph Eugene. 4695 S 1900 W, STE 2 84067 #06-1953 L1958 AN *020 †05

MERKLEY, Christon Huber. 1915 W 5950 S 84067 #049-01-1979 L1986 FM *020 †18

OBAYASHI, Mikio. 1915 W 5950 S 84067 #049-01-1984 L1986 FM *020 †18

PENNINGTON, Charles L. ■ 84067 #049-01-1952 L1954 EM *071

PRUITT, Anthony Gene. 5991 S 3500 W, STE 100 84067 #019-02-2000 L2004 PD *020 †55

RIGGS, Brannick Barton. 5991 S 3500 W STE 400, ROCK RUN MEDICAL 84067 #003-01-2001 L2002 FM *020 †18

SMITH, Laurence Ray. 1915 W 5950 S 84067 #010-01-1977 L1978 FM *020 †18

WALLACE, Brent E. 1915 W 5950 S 84067 #049-01-1976 L1977 FM *020 †18

WHITE, Leon Howard. 5756 S 2000 W 84067 #049-01-1961 L1962 PD *020

WINTLE, Brandon Gary. 1915 W 5950 S 84067 #049-01-2002 L2003 FM *020 †18

WOOD, John Russell. 1915 W 5950 S 84067 #049-01-1977 L1979 FM *020 †18

WOOLF, Kurtis Alden. 5991 W 5950 S 84067 #048-13-1999 L2000 FM *020 †18

SAINT GEORGE — WASHINGTON

AFFLECK, Paul Jeffrey. 1380 E MEDICAL CENTER DR 84790 #023-12-1993 L2003 AN PMM *020 †05

AHEE, Jason Abraham. 1085 S BLUFF ST 84770 #025-07-1999 L2003 OPH *020 †35

ALLEN, Glenn Lewis. ■ 84790 #020-02-1943 GS GP *071

ANDRUSS, Coleen M B. 1173 S 250 W, STE 110 84770 #026-04-1990 L1998 IM NTR *020 †20

ANDRUSS, Robert John. 1380 E MEDICAL CENTER DR, STE 2100 84790 #026-04-1989 L1998 ORS OSM *020 †40

ARNOLD, Blake Winn. 1380 E MEDICAL CENTER DR 84790 #041-14-1997 L1998 DR *020 †80

ASTLE, Craig Dee. 515 S 300 E, STE 206 84770 #049-01-1983 L1987 OBG *020 †30

BALIAN, Gary Matthew. 2079 W 1600 N 84770 #025-07-1988 L1991 P *020

BARNETT, David Lee. ■ 84770 #016-42-1990 L1994 EM *020 †16

BARNEY, William Wesley. 736 S 900 E, STE 107 84790 #049-01-1991 L1992 IM *020 †20

BART, Gregory Vernon. ■ 84770 #030-05-1974 L2002 PD A *020 †55

BARTON, Scott David. 736 S 900 E STE 203 84790 #049-01-1997 L1998 FM *020 †18

BECKER, Taj N. 736 S 900 E, STE 202 84790 #030-06-1978 L1994 N OS *020 †75

BENHAM, Brady Nolan. 515 S 300 E, STE 206 84770 #019-02-1994 L2005 OBG *020 †30

BENSON, Robert Taft. 1380 E MEDICAL CTR DR, CENTER DRIVE 84790 #010-02-1999 L2003 EM *020 †16

BENSON, Stanford James. 1380 E MEDICAL CENTER DR D, EMERGENCY DEPT DRMC 84790 #049-01-1990 L1993 FM *020 †18

BERGER, Robin Mccleve. 640 E 700 S STE 1 84770 #049-01-1989 L1996 D *020 †15

BIRD, Nicholas Hagen. 544 S 400 E, DEPT OF HYPERBARIC MEDICIN 84790 #539-06-1999 L2006 FM *020 †18

BLACK, William Thos. ■ 84790 #049-01-1961 L1963 GP GS *071

BONOMO, Catherine A. 1380 E MEDICAL CTR DR 84790 #049-01-1996 L1999 EM *020 †16

BOORMAN, David C. 736 S 900 E STE 107 84790 #049-01-1981 L1983 CD CCM *020 †20

BOOTH, Craig Lang. 544 S 400 E 84770 #049-01-1971 L1973 GP *020

BOUDREAU, Robert James. ■ 84770 #060-02-1978 L1983 NM DR *071 †28

BOWLES, Brent Jason. 1380 E MEDICAL CENTER DR, STE 2600 84790 #049-01-1996 L2001 TS *020 †85,90

BOWN, James Wm. 368 E RIVERSIDE DR, STE A 84790 #049-01-1990 L1995 GE *020 †20

BRITO-DELLAN, Norman J. 555 NORTHRIDGE AVE 84770 #935-01-1994 L1999 IM *020 †20

BROWN, David Warren. 146 E SAINT GEORGE BLVD 84770 #049-01-1960 L1961 FM GS *020 †18

CAIN, Larry Arthur. 577 S RIVER RD 84790 #049-01-1997 L2000 FM *020 †18

CALLAHAN, Thomas Dee. 1240 E 100 S, STE 15A 84790 #049-01-1975 L1976 FM *020 †18

CALLISTER, John W. ■ 84790 #049-01-1949 L1950 PTH *072 †50

CAPEL, Neal Conrad. 620 S 400 E STE 7 84770 #023-01-1955 L1956 ORS OSS *071 †40

CARTER, Boyd Allen. 577 S RIVER RD, IHC HEALTH CENTER 84790 #049-01-1976 L2000 FM *020 †18

CARTER, Bruce M. 1490 E FOREMASTER DR, BLDG C 84790 #023-12-1989 L1991 AN *020 †05

CARTER, Gayle M. 515 S 300 E STE 201 84770 #049-01-1980 L1981 OBG *020 †30

CARTER, Grant Lael, Jr. 515 S 300 E, STE 201 84770 #049-01-1978 L1979 OBG *020 †30

CHALMERS, Robert Wallace. 346 E 600 S, INTERMOUNTAIN WOMEN'S HEAL 84770 #041-02-1999 L2007 OBG *020 †30

CHAMBERLAIN, Howard Lee. 736 S 900 E STE 203, MEDICAL ASSOC. OF ST. GEOR 84790 #049-01-1993 L1995 FM *020 †18

CHANDER, Keshav. 1380 E MEDICAL CENTER DR 84790 #495-03-1986 L2001 CD *020 †20

CHANDLER, Michael Warren. 1380 E MEDICAL CENTER DR 84790 #034-01-1983 L1985 AN *020 †05

CHASE, Lawrence Jos. 321 N MALL DR, STE N 84790 #041-02-1971 L1992 **PS HS** *020 †85,65
CHASE, Steven Paul. 1490 E FOREMASTER DR, STE 350 84790 #028-34-2000 L2005 **OTO** *020 †45
CHRISTIAN, Mckay Donald. 736 S 900 E, STE 203 84790 #049-01-1974 L1976 **FM** *020
CHRISTIANSEN, Brett David. 544 S 400 E 84770 #035-01-1997 L2000 **EM** *020 †16
CLARK, John R. ■ 84790 #041-09-1959 L1963 **NS GS** *071 †25
COBB, William B. 1380 E MEDICAL CTR DR, CENTER DRIVE 84790 #010-03-1978 L1989 **ID IM** *020 †20
COHEN, David Bennett. 1791 E 280 N 84790 #049-01-1988 L1992 **OPH** *020 †35
COHEN, Louis Kenneth. ■ 84770 #021-01-1967 L1967 **D A** *020 †15
COLLINS, Edgar Ernest. 1240 E 100 S, STE 18B 84790 #306-01-1984 L1987 **P** *020 †75
CONDIE, Philip Glenn. ■ 84770 #005-15-1971 L1972 **GP** *071
COPE, Robert Merrill. 1490 E FOREMASTER DR, STE 300 84790 #049-01-1986 L1987 **U GS** *020 †95
CROUCH, Ronald Hugh. 391 E 500 S 84770 #049-01-1975 L1980 **U** *020 †95
CURTIS, Lindsay Raine. PO BOX 146, 1021 S VALLEY VIEW DR 84771 #007-02-1942 **OBG** *071 †30
DALY, Kathleen Marie. 301 N 200 E, STE 2A 84770 #031-01-1988 L1992 **IM** *020 †20
DANDOY, Suzanne Eggleston. ■ 84770 #005-14-1960 L1961 **PHP GPM** *071 †70
DAVIS, John Albert. 1380 E MEDICAL CENTER DR, DEPT OF RADIOLOGY IMAGING 84790 #049-01-1984 L1989 **DR EM** *020 †80
DAVIS, Steven Boyd. 1380 E MEDICAL CENTER DR, DEPT OF RADIOLOGY 84790 #049-01-1988 L1995 **RNR** *020 †80
DEBENHAM, David Arthur. 544 S 400 E, DIXIE MEDICAL CENTER 84770 #049-01-1987 L1991 **AN PMM** *020 †05
DONALDSON, Craig William. 544 S 400 E 84770 #049-01-1993 L2005 **RO** *020 †80
DOXEY, G Paul. 736 S 900 E, STE 201 84790 #049-01-1980 L1981 **OTO FPS** *020 †45
DUKE, Dean Woodrow. 383 S 300 E 84770 #049-01-1971 L1980 **D** *020 †15
EGGERT, Joan Vann. 2235 S 1400 E, UNIT 15 84790 #049-01-1984 L1987 **GYN** *020 †30
EGGERT, Larry D. 544 S 400 E, NEONATOLOGY 84770 #036-01-1977 L1978 **NPM PD** *020 †55
ELLSWORTH, John Bryan. 391 E 500 S 84770 #031-01-1991 L1992 **U EM** *020 †95
EVANS, Creed Miles. ■ 84770 #869-05-1955 L1987 **AM OM** *071
EVANS, David Glenn. ■ 84790 #422-01-2004 L2004 **PD** *100
EVANS, Eric Alan. 354 E 600 S, STE 204 84770 #049-01-1994 L1998 **AN** *072 †05
FAGNANT, Robert John. 346 E 600 S 84770 #030-06-1982 L2006 **OBG ID** *020 †30
FAWSON, Norman Hall. 736 S 900 E, STE 203 84790 #049-01-1966 L1968 **FM OS** *020
FOSTER, Christine Kay. 1380 E MEDICAL CENTER DR D 84790 #049-01-1998 L2006 **IM** *020 †20
FOX, La Mar Monson. ■ 84770 #049-01-1961 L1962 **CHP P** *071 †75
FRIEDEN, Derek L. 301 N 200 E, STE 2A 84770 #305-01-1998 L2005 **APM** *020 †05
FRIEDEN, Karen Marlina. 1380 E MEDICAL CTR DR, CENTER DRIVE 84790 #305-01-1998 L2005 **IM** *020 †20
GANDHI, Zahabia Taher. 640 E 700 S, STE 105 84770 #496-30-1997 L2002 **IM** *020 †20
GARDNER, Kent Eric. 1490 E FOREMASTER DR, STE 350 84790 #049-01-1993 L1999 **OTO HNS** *020 †45
GATES, Lawrence Keith. ■ 84790 #049-01-1946 L1947 **OPH** *071 †35
GONZALEZ, Frederick A. 544 S 400 E, OB-GYM DEPT 84770 #035-01-1976 L2007 **MFM OBG** *020 †30
GOODGER, William Pearce. ■ 84770 #021-05-1983 L1995 **FM** *020 †18
GRAFF, Arnold Lamar. 544 S 400 E 84770 #049-01-1985 L1988 **AN** *020 †05
GRAFF, William Tolley. 630 S 400 E STE 101 84770 #049-01-1977 L1978 **FM** *020 †18
GREEN, Michael Richard. 1490 E FOREMASTER DR, STE 260 84790 #054-04-1986 L1995 **ORS OSM** *020 †40
GREENE, Mark Hindley, Jr. 544 S 400 E 84770 #049-01-1948 L1949 **HS ORS** *071 †40
GURR, Gaylen Smith. 1490 E FOREMASTER DR, BLDG C 84790 #049-01-1982 L1986 **AN** *020 †05
GURUNADHAM, Lalitha. PO BOX 2999, 700 S 55 E TOWNHOUSE 4 84771 #495-11-1971 L1998 **ATP PCP** *030 †50
HAESEMEYER, Scott Walter. ■ 84770 #019-02-1996 L2003 **VIR** *020 †80
HAGEN, Jerold. 577 S RIVER RD 84790 #654-01-1985 L1988 **IM** *020
HAMASHIGE, Shinichi. ■ 84790 #038-06-1957 L1957 **PTH** *071 †50
HANSEN, Mette. 1490 E FOREMASTER DR, STE 150 84790 #005-14-1997 L2004 **PM** *020 †60
HASAN, Mosaab A. 368 E RIVERSIDE DR, STE A 84790 #875-01-1992 L2001 **GE** *020 †20
HAYCOCK, Carl Don. 144 W BRIGHAM RD, STE 19 84790 #010-01-1995 L1997 **FM** *020 †18
HENDRIX, Jason Wayne. 676 S BLUFF ST 84770 #010-01-2002 L2006 **OPH** *020
HENRIE, John N. ■ 84791 #049-01-1952 L1953 **ORS GP** *072 †40
HESS, Richard Alfred. ■ 84770 #030-06-1970 L2006 **OPH** *020 †35
HIXSON, Lee J. 368 E RIVERSIDE DR, STE A 84790 #049-01-1980 L1981 **GE IM** *020 †20
HUARD, G Stedman, II. 1490 E FOREMASTER DR # 310 84790 #019-02-1980 L1997 **VS GS** *020 †85
HYDE, Christian Cooper. 544 S 400 E, RADIATION ONCOLOGY 84770 #005-14-2001 L2006 **RO** *020 †80
IVEY, Roger Lee. 1380 E MEDICAL CENTER DR, ANESTH DEPT/ATTN DR IVEY 84790 #031-01-2001 L2005 **AN** *020 †05
JENTZER, John Henry. ■ 84790 #035-47-1975 L2006 **CD IM** *020 †20
JEPPSEN, Malcolm Seth. 805 S RIVER RD, UNIT 47 84790 #048-04-1948 L1949 **GP** *071
JEVSEVAR, David Scott. 1490 E FOREMASTER DR, BLDG C 84790 #010-02-1988 L1996 **ORS OSM** *020 †40
JONES, Thomas Kelly. 577 S RIVER RD 84790 #049-01-1992 L1993 **IM** *020 †20
KADDU, Rajiv J. 1380 E MEDICAL CENTER DR, STE 3100 84790 #495-98-1989 L1999 **PD PG** *020 †55
KEEP, Mark Hawthorne. 736 S 900 E, STE 107 84790 #035-03-1988 L1989 **CD IM** *020 †20
KHOURY, Michael David. 1380 E MEDICAL CENTER DR, STE 2600 84790 #025-07-1982 L2006 **VS** *020 †85
KLINE, Michael Ronald. 1380 E MEDICAL CENTER DR 84790 #654-01-1987 L1999 **PUD IM** *020 †20
KLOMP, Aaron O'Connor. 346 E 600 S 84770 #031-01-2000 L2007 **PS** *020
KRAMER, David Randall. 577 E TABERNACLE ST 84770 #049-01-1981 L1984 **P EM** *020 †16
KVARFORDT, Tracy Dee. 515 S 300 E STE 205 84770 #054-04-1986 L2006 **OBG** *020 †30
LARAWE, Judd Lane. 620 S 400 E, STE 201 84770 #026-04-1988 L1999 **IM** *020 †20
LARSEN, Gordon Lowell. 1380 E MEDICAL CENTER DR 84790 #049-01-1991 L1994 **EM** *020 †16
LARSON, Gordon Kay. ■ 84790 #049-01-1973 L1974 **AN** *020 †05
LAST, George Gregory. 544 S 400 E 84770 #049-01-1982 L1985 **FM** *020 †18
LAUB, Raymond Myron. ■ 84770 #049-01-1969 L1970 **BBK** *071 †50
LEITZE, Zachary Robert. 736 S 900 E, STE 106 84790 #008-01-1999 L2005 **ORS OSM** *020 †40
LEMON, Robert Hugh. 544 S 400 E, CANCER & BLOOD INSTITUTE O 84770 #005-15-1986 L2006 **ON HEM** *020 †20
LEWIS, Mark Meredith. 1791 E 280 N 84790 #005-06-1972 L1976 **OPH** *020 †35
LEWIS, Ryan Daniel. 1490 E FOREMASTER DR, STE 200 84790 #041-09-1998 L2000 **OTO** *100
LIND, Ben Wyland. 2490 SPRINGS DR 84790 #049-01-2000 L2001 **AN** *020 †05
LIVINGSTON, Jennifer Lynn. 736 S 900 E, STE 203 84790 #019-02-1996 L2004 **FM** *020 †18
LUNT, Chad Curtis. 515 S 300 E STE 205 84770 #003-01-1990 L1998 **OBG** *020 †30
MACFARLANE, Howard C. 180 N MAIN ST, BOX 476 84770 #049-01-1957 L1958 **P** *072
MADSEN, Daniel Bailey. 1490 E FOREMASTER DR, STE 210 84790 #049-01-1974 L1975 **IM** *020
MAHAJAN, Renu. 577 S RIVER RD 84790 #495-03-1987 L2002 **IM** *020 †20
MANLEY, Mark Edward. 515 S 300 E STE 109 84770 #003-01-1995 L2003 **CHP P** *020 †75
MARSDEN, Jerry. 1490 E FOREMASTER DR, STE 350 84790 #049-01-1970 L1971 **OTO** *020 †45 ‡
MARTIN, Albert F. ■ 84770 #016-06-1955 L1957 **ORS** *072 †40
MATHESON, James Ronald. ■ 84770 #005-02-1947 L1950 **R** *071 †80
MC DONALD, Kent B. 515 S 300 E STE 105 84770 #028-34-1975 L1980 **IM** *020 †20
MC DONNELL, Mary Ann. 736 S 900 E, STE 107 84790 #049-01-1972 L1975 **CD** *040 †20
MERCADO, Carlos Alberto. 301 N 200 E, STE 1D 84770 #264-12-1999 L2007 **NEP IM** *020 †20
MERRILL, Malcolm D. ■ 84790 #005-02-1953 L1992 **RO** *071 †80
MILLAR, Roger Clive. 1380 E MEDICAL CENTER DR, # 2600 84790 #049-01-1969 L1987 **TS** *020 †85,90
MILLER, John Tuggey. 1490 E FOREMASTER DR, BLDG C 84790 #049-01-1992 L1997 **GS** *020 †85
MINER, John Edwin. 1380 E MEDICAL CENTER DR 84790 #049-01-1999 L2001 **AN** *020 †05
MINER, Lonnie Jefferson. ■ 84790 #028-34-1998 L1999 **NPM** *020 †55
MOESINGER, Scott Gilbert. 1380 E MEDICAL CENTER DR, PATH DEPT 84790 #049-01-1976 L1979 **PTH** *020 †50
MONTAGUE, Terry L. 1380 E MEDICAL CENTER DR, DIXIE MEDICAL CENTER 84790 #049-01-1981 L1986 **DR** *020 †80
MOORE, David Earl. ■ 84770 #049-01-1977 L1982 **ORS** *071 †40
MOORE, Dennis James. 1739 W SUNSET BLVD 84770 #049-01-1974 L1975 **FM** *020 †18
MYERS, Brad A. 1490 E FOREMASTER DR, BLDG C 84790 #049-01-1986 L1991 **GS** *020 †85
MYERS, Susan Marie. 544 S 400 E 84770 #049-01-1989 L1990 **FM** *020 †18
NAUTIYAL, Ashoka. 1380 E MEDICAL CENTER DR, IHC SOUTHWEST CARDIOLOGY 84790 #495-73-1970 L2003 **CD** *020 †20
NAVAR, Paul David. 166 N 300 W STE 3 84770 #048-12-1982 L1984 **GPM GP** *020 †16
NELSON, Erven Jean. ■ 84790 #010-01-1958 L1959 **OPH** *071
NELSON, Tyler Wayne. 201 SHADOW POINT DR 84770 #005-06-2001 L2005 **AN** *100 †05
NILSON, Wendell T. 1490 E FOREMASTER DR # 130 84790 #049-01-1976 L1982 **PD** *020 †55
NIMER, Lynn R. 1380 E MEDICAL CENTER DR, STE 3500 84790 #056-06-1987 L1988 **CD** *020 †20
NOBLE, Vici. 544 S 400 E 84770 #049-01-1977 L1978 **ATP CLP** *020 †50
NYGAARD, Martin J. 352 E RIVERSIDE DR, STE C2 84790 #049-01-1986 L1994 **PD** *020 †55
ORR, Tracy Roger. ■ 84790 #031-01-1996 L2000 **DR** *020 †80
OTT, Richard Wayne. 515 S 300 E STE 206 84770 #028-34-1994 L2002 **OBG** *020 †30
OWEN, John Alun. ■ 84790 #049-01-2000 L2006 **DR** *100 †80
OWEN, Robert D. 544 S 400 E 84770 #049-01-1988 L1991 **EM** *062 †16
PARADELA, Grace Jeanne S. 620 S 400 E, STE 209 84770 #748-11-1996 L2002 **IM** *020 †20
PARKER, Robert Jeffrey. 1791 E 280 N 84790 #028-34-1980 L1996 **OPH** *020 †35
PARRY, Todd Richard. 1490 E FOREMASTER DR, BLDG C 84790 #049-01-1996 L2004 **ORS** *020 †40
PATEL, Bhupendra C. 1791 E 280 N 84790 #917-06-1980 L1992 **OPH** *020
PENDLETON, Gus Curtis. 736 S 900 E STE 203 84790 #049-01-1993 L1994 **FM** *020 †18
PETERSEN, Gary Vern. 736 S 900 E, STE 108 84790 #049-01-1969 L1972 **CD** *020 †20
PETERSON, Robert Warren. 1490 E FOREMASTER DR, STE 350 84790 #005-06-1961 L1993 **OTO FPS** *071 †45
PINNA, Charisma Ong. 515 S 300 E, STE 101 84770 #748-11-1995 L2004 **PM** *020 †60
PINNA, Kenneth Ralph. 515 S 300 E, STE 101 84770 #748-19-1996 L2003 **AI** *020 †20,03
PLUMB, Todd Reynolds. 1380 E MEDICAL CENTER DR, DEPT. OF ANESTHESIOLOGY 84790 #049-01-1991 L1992 **FM** *020 †18,05
PRICE, Gregory Dodson. 736 S 900 E STE 108 84790 #654-01-1986 L1991 **CD** *020 †20
PULSIPHER, Mark Wm. 1380 E MEDICAL CENTER DR, STE 1500 84790 #049-01-1988 L1989 **CD IC** *020 †20
RASMUSSEN, Brian Louis. 545 S VALLEY VIEW DR 84770 #023-01-1963 L1967 **GS** *071 †85
RHODES, J Robt. 676 S BLUFF ST STE 207 84770 #049-01-1971 L1974 **PS** *020 †18,85,65
RICHARDS, Ray Stayner. 544 S 400 E 84770 #049-01-1985 L1989 **RO** *020 †80
RICHENS, Sharon R Metzger. 619 S BLUFF ST, STE 1B 84770 #049-01-1992 L2000 **OPH** *020 †35 ‡
RIGNELL, Robert Paul. 515 S 300 E STE 105 84770 #049-01-1978 L1979 **IM** *020 †20
ROGERS, Jeffrey Gordon. 515 S 300 E, STE 206 84770 #049-01-1984 L1985 **OBG** *020 †30
ROSS, John Alton. ■ 84770 #049-01-1954 L1955 **FM** *072 †18
ROUNDY, Kent Dee. 1240 E 100 S, STE 15A 84790 #049-01-2001 L2005 **P** *100
ROWLAND, Gerald Kim. ■ 84790 #649-14-1984 L1987 **EM** *020 †16
ROY, Abinash Chandra. 720 S RIVER RD, STE D1100 84790 #160-01-1979 L2001 **NEP** *020 †20
ROYER, Jared. 1380 E MEDICAL CTR DR, DIXIE REG MED CTR 84790 #005-18-2001 L2006 **AN** *020 †05
RYSKIN, Alexey A. 676 S BLUFF ST 84770 #913-01-1993 L2004 **APM AN** *020 †05 ‡
SAIFEE, Mustufa Taher. 640 E 700 S, STE 105 84770 #495-73-1991 L2002 **PUD** *020 †20
SHEPHERD, Edward Quin. 1300 E MEDICAL CENTER DR 84790 #049-01-1986 L1991 **DR** *020 †80
SHEPPARD, Glen Milo. ■ 84790 #049-01-1965 L1966 **GP GS** *071
SIDDOWAY, Roger Lewis. 368 E RIVERSIDE DR, STE A 84790 #010-01-1979 L1981 **GE IM** *020 †20
SLEZAK, Roy Menard. 544 S 400 E 84770 #016-11-1955 L1985 **OS** *020 †30
SMITH, Gordon Lowell. 577 S RIVER RD, 577 RIVER ROAD 84790 #049-01-1997 L2000 **IM** *020 †20
SMITH, Scott Mendenhall. 736 S 900 E, STE 106 84790 #054-04-1980 L1997 **ORS** *020 †40
SMITH, Wallace Bret. 383 S 300 E 84770 #056-06-1986 L1988 **D** *020 †15
SNOOK, Gary Don. ■ 84770 #049-01-1971 L2004 **ORS** *020 †40
SNOW, Ronald Lee. 1085 S BLUFF ST, DBA DIXIE EYE CENTER 84770 #036-05-1974 L1979 **OPH** *071 †35
SOWA, Ronald Walter. 784 S RIVER RD, RONALD WALTER SOWA MD 84790 #028-02-1963 L2004 **ORS** *020 †40
SPEAKMAN, James Jared. 1490 E FOREMASTER DR, BLDG C 84790 #049-01-1997 L1998 **GS** *020 †85

■ = Address Information Privacy Protected

STAHELI, Clark John. 736 S 900 E STE 203 84790 #049-01-1961 L1965 FM *020
STEVENS, Michael Henry. 1490 E FOREMASTER DR, STE 350 84790 #049-01-1966 L1967 OTO *020 †45
STOTT, Dale Gerald. 301 N 200 E, STE 2A 84770 #003-01-1987 L1998 FM *020 †05
STRATFORD, C Kerry. 736 S 900 E, STE 203 84790 #049-01-1983 L1986 FM *020 †18
STUART, Franklin R, Jr. 1962 N CASCADE CANYON DR 84770 #023-01-1968 L1975 ORS *071 †40
STUCKI, Warren Jay. 391 E 500 S 84770 #049-01-1974 L1975 U *020 †95
SYMOND, Michael David. 162 E 300 S 84770 #049-01-1978 L1981 EM FM *020 †18
SYPHUS, Merrill Tullis. 676 S BLUFF ST STE 200 84770 #023-01-1960 L1999 GS GP *020
TATARIAN, Horton Edgar. PO BOX 1990 84771 #005-14-1974 NTR OS *071
TAYLOR, Gregory Scott. 1490 E FOREMASTER DR, STE 300 84790 #049-01-2000 L2006 U *020 †95
TAYLOR, Richard A. 354 E 600 S, STE 204 84770 #005-18-1991 L1995 AN *020 †05
TEMPLE, Anthony Robt. ■ 84790 #049-01-1968 L1970 PDT *071 †55
THOMAS, H Clark. 1287 W BLOOMINGTON DR S, UNIT 17 84790 #049-01-1989 L1993 AN *020 †05
TORMEY, Karen Adelle. 515 S 300 E STE 107 84770 #049-01-1990 L1996 GS *020 †85
TREMEA, Michael Oliver. 1380 E MEDICAL CENTER DR 84790 #049-01-1994 L1997 EM *020 †16
TRIMBLE, Karl Kirk. 169 W 2710 SOUTH CIR, STE 101 84790 #055-01-1992 L2004 D DS *020 †15
TWIGGS, Jerry Douglas. 1240 E 100 S STE 14 84790 #054-04-1982 L1988 PD *020 †55
VAN NORMAN, Steven Allan. 1380 E MEDICAL CTR DR, MED STAFF OFF DIXIE REG MD 84790 #025-01-1976 L1983 EM IM *030 †20,16
VAN WAGONER, Jos Dallas. 929 W SUNSET BLVD STE 21, PMB 141 84770 #028-34-1970 L1973 OBG *071 †30
VENGER, Benjamin Herschel. 301 N 200 E, STE 2C 84770 #048-14-1983 L1997 NS GS *020 †25
WALKER, Adrianne Ruth. 1380 E MEDICAL CENTER DR, STE 3100 84790 #049-01-2004 L2005 PD *020 †55
WARNER, Claude Alan. 577 S RIVER RD 84790 #019-02-1988 L1994 IM *020 †20
WATKINS, Kirk Grant. 251 HILTON DR STE 107 84770 #030-05-1995 L1996 FM SME *020 †18
WELKER, Robert. 162 E 300 S, RED CLIFFS FAMILY MEDICINE 84770 #003-01-1980 L1987 FM *020 †18
WELSH, Joy Lynne. 1490 E FOREMASTER DR, STE 310 84790 #019-02-1984 L1997 OBG *020 †30
WERNER, Scott Rulon. ■ 84790 #028-34-1986 L1990 FM GP *020
WETZLER, Harry Parker. 577 S RIVER RD, WORKMED 84790 #049-01-1975 L1977 EP OM *050 †70
WHEELER, Rachel. 770 E SAINT GEORGE BLVD, CINNAMON HILLS 84770 #028-46-1988 L1992 CHP *020
WILKERSON, David Lee. ■ 84790 #049-01-1957 L1958 GP *071 †18
WILLIAMS, Bruce Call. 1490 E FOREMASTER DR, BLDG C 84790 #049-01-1970 L1974 GS TS *020 †85
WINTCH, Richard Wallace. 515 S 300 E STE 102 84770 #035-01-1974 L1981 GS *020 †85
WINWARD, Tracy Watson. 515 S 300 E STE 206 84770 #049-01-1990 L1991 OBG *020 †30
WOODBURY, Kory Urie. 1380 E MEDICAL CENTER DR, STE 1500 84790 #049-01-1996 L2003 TS *020 †85,90
WOOLLEY, Joseph Hunter. 1490 E FOREMASTER DR, STE 210 84790 #039-01-2004 L2008 MPD *012

SALEM – UTAH

GREEN, Stanley W. 55 E 100 S 84653 #001-02-1978 L1979 DR EM *020 †80
WASHBURN, Philip. 251 HIGHWAY 198 # 3 84653 #049-01-1959 L1961 P PYA *020

SALT LAKE CITY – SALT LAKE

AAGAARDTILLERY, Kjersti M. 30 N 1900 E, & CLINICS / ATTN: OB/GYN 84132 #026-04-2000 L2004 OBG *100
ABBOTT, Thomas M. 1200 E 3900 S 84124 #049-01-1973 L1974 PTH FM *020 †50
ABBOTT, Weldon Sylvesta. ■ 84102 #004-01-1947 L1959 IM *071
ABEL, Edwin Jason. 30 N 1900 E, DIV OF UROLOGY 84132 #048-14-2003 L2004 U *012
ABEL, Evan Dale. 15 N 2030 E, BLDG 533 84112 #566-01-1985 L2001 END IM *050 †20
ABELE, Joan Catherine. 8TH AVE & C ST 84143 #025-07-1980 L1983 AN *020 †05
ABILDSKOV, Junior A. 50 N MEDICAL DR BLDG 100 84143 #049-01-1946 L1948 CD *050 †20
ABRAHAM, Devaprabu. 615 ARAPEEN DR STE 100, UTAH DIABETES CENTER 84108 #495-66-1987 L2001 END *020 †20
ABRAHAM, Josephine Devapr. 50 N MEDICAL DR, INTERNAL MEDICINE #4C104 84132 #495-66-1988 L2002 NEP *020 †20
ABUEG, Florentino M. 50 N MED DR, UNIV OF UT DIVISION OF 84132 #748-02-1989 L1997 IM IMG *075 †20
ABU-KHALAF, Susan Mahmoud. 615 ARAPEEN DR, UTAH DIBETES CENTER 84108 #575-01-1998 L2004 END *020 †20
ABU ROMEH, Ibrahim Saleh. ■ 84111 #575-01-2002 L2007 IM *100 †20
ACKERLY, John Arnold. 1954 FORT UNION BLVD, STE 101 84121 #051-01-1980 L2002 AN CCM *020 †05
ADAMS, Danielle Mercedes. 30 N 1900 E, DEPARTMENT OF SURGERY 84132 #032-01-2004 L2005 GS *012
ADAMS, Jeremy Tyler. ■ 84158 #049-01-2007 *012
ADAMS, Richard Paul. ■ 84118 #049-01-02-1944 L1944 GP AN *072
ADAMS, Wayne Dewitt. 5444 GREEN ST, MOUNTAIN MEDICAL PHYSICIAN 84123 #038-41-1989 L1990 NR *020 †80,28
ADAMS, William Roy. 1345 E 3900 S STE 104 84124 #010-01-1966 L1970 GYN *020 †30
ADAMSON, Ann Taylor. 400 C ST 84143 #049-01-1995 L1996 HMP *050
ADASHI, Eli. 30 N 1900 E, STE 2B200 84132 #550-02-1972 L1997 OBG REN *030
ADELGAIS, Kathleen Marie. 127 S 500 E, STE 600 84102 #026-04-1995 L2003 PD *020 †55
ADUSUMALLI, Subba Rao. 1954 FORT UNION BLVD, STE 102 84121 #495-21-1970 L1977 AN *020
AFFLECK, David Gordon. 1140 E 3900 S, STE 340 84124 #049-01-1996 L1997 TS *020 †85,90
AFRA, Pegah. 30 N 1900 E 3R210, DEPT OF NEURO 84132 #473-02-1999 L2007 CN *100
AFZALI-JONES, Neda. 50 N MEDICAL DR 84132 #007-02-2005 L2008 PD *012

AGARWAL, Cori Ann. 30 N 1900 E 3B400 84132 #014-01-1997 L2007 PS *020
AGARWAL, Jayant Prasad. 30 N 1900 E 3B400, UNIVERSITY OF UTAH/DEPT OF 84132 #038-06-2000 L2007 PS *020 ‡
AGARWAL, Neeraj. 2000 CIRCLE OF HOPE DR, STE 2123 84112 #495-18-1995 L2004 ON HEM *020 †20
AGRICOLA, Christian David. 50 N MEDICAL DR, PSYCHIATRIC DEPARTMENT 84132 #038-45-2005 L2006 P *012
AGY, Peter Clark. 1160 E 3900 S, # G-200 84124 #028-34-1980 L1981 IM *020 †20
AHLERS, Gordon Kinsella. 3934 S 2300 E, IHC PHYSICIANS DIVISION 84124 #021-01-1980 L2000 FM *020 †20
AHMED, Ali. 1160 E 3900 S, STE G-300 84124 #495-51-1993 L2002 PCC *020 †20
AHMED, Nusrat. 1020 S MAIN ST, VALLEY MENTAL HEALTH 84101 #704-02-1973 L1988 P FM *020
AHMED, Osman. 30 N 1900 E, RM 4A100 84132 #305-01-2002 L2006 CD *012
AHN, Yong Hui. 24 S 1100 E STE 304, SALT LAKE INTERNAL MEDICIN 84102 #020-12-1988 L1991 IM *020 †20
AHRANO, Judith. 44 N MEDICAL DR 84113 #012-05-1974 L1989 PD *071 †55
AIREY, Kelly Jane. 30 N 1900 E, UNIV OF UTAH MED CTR 84132 #065-01-1990 L2007 ICE *012
AJAX, Ernest T. ■ 84117 #049-01-1951 L1958 N *071 †75
AKERLEY, Wallace L, III. 2000 CIRCLE OF HP DR #2165, HUNTSMAN CANCER INSTITUTE 84112 #043-01-1981 L2002 ON HEM *020 †20
AKOUM, Nazem Walid. 4A100 SOM, 30 NORTH 1900 EAST 84132 #605-01-2001 L2005 CD *012 †20
ALBANO, Joseph John. 1914 LINCOLN ST 84105 #035-15-1989 L1993 FM FSM *020 †18
ALBO, Dominic, Jr. 50 N MEDICAL DR 84132 #028-34-1960 L1966 GS VS *020 †85
ALBRO, James Edward. 400 C ST 84143 #049-01-1988 L1989 BBK *020 †50
ALBU, Dan Sabin. 3195 S MAIN ST, STE 200 84115 #781-01-1974 L1984 IM *020 †20
ALDEN, Meredith. 1020 S MAIN ST, VALLEY MENTAL HEALTH 84101 #036-07-1979 L1980 P *030 †75 ‡
ALDERSON, Mary Kathryn. 1200 E 3900 S 84124 #005-14-1981 L1982 N CN *020 †75
ALDOUS, Edwin Winder. 3725 W 4100 S 84120 #049-01-1968 L1976 OTO *020 †45
ALDOUS, Richard Allen. 65 N MEDICAL DR 84132 #049-01-1956 L1958 OPH *020 †35
ALDRICH, John Talbot. 1160 E 3900 S STE 1000 84124 #038-06-1968 L1972 IM *020 †20
ALHOV, Vladimir. 6360 S 3000 E, STE 360 84121 #913-12-1985 L2005 PM *070
ALLDREDGE, Claron Douglas. 4400 S 700 E, STE 140 84107 #049-01-1996 L2002 OPH *020 †35
ALLDREDGE, Oren C. 4400 S 700 E, STE 140 84107 #049-01-1972 L1973 OPH *020 †35
ALLEN, Bryce C. 1168 SHERMAN AVE 84105 #048-04-2002 L2003 ORS *020
ALLEN, Elizabeth Margaret. 100 N MEDICAL DR, DIV OF PED EMERGENCY MEDIC 84113 #038-06-1993 L1990 CCM PD *020 †55
ALLEN, Jared Whiting. ■ 84105 #005-14-2007 *012
ALLEN, Louis S, Jr. 44 N MEDICAL DR, BOX 144710 84113 #051-01-1967 L1982 PD OS *020 †55
ALLEN, Richard Elliot. 1250 E 3900 S, ST MARKS FAMILY MEDICINE 84124 #049-01-1997 L2002 FM *040 †18
ALLEN, Richard Merle. 1954 FORT UNION BLVD, STE 102 84121 #010-01-1966 L1968 AN PUD *020 †05
ALLEN, Steven Robt. 3730 W 4700 S, U OF U WESTRIDGE HEALTH CT 84118 #056-06-1987 L1995 PD *020 †55
ALLEN, Todd Larsen. 8TH AVE & C ST, DEPT EMERGENCY MEDICINE 84143 #049-01-1995 L1999 EM *020 †16
ALLISON, Mandy Atlee. ■ 84105 #049-01-2001 L2003 PD *020 †55
ALLRED, Gerald Lyle. 2000 S 900 E, MEMORIAL CLINIC 84105 #049-01-1972 L1977 PD *020 †55
ALLRED, Nathan Alma. ■ 84109 #049-01-2008 *012
ALLRED, Sherman Wm. 34 S 500 E 84102 #049-01-1946 L1947 ORS *072 †40
ALONSO, Diane. 50 N MEDICAL DR, SURGICAL DEPT 84132 #005-19-2001 L2003 GS *020 †85
ALVARADO, Julia Feliz. 25 N 1900 EAST, PULMONARY & CRITICAL CARE 84132 #047-05-2001 L2004 PCC *012 †20
AMBER, Ina Judith. 1151 E 3900 S, STE B299 84124 #025-07-1979 L1984 ID IM *020 †20
AMINI, Aminullah. 175 N MEDICAL DRIVE EAST, DEPT OF NEUROSURGERY 84132 #051-04-2002 L2004 NS *012
AMOS, Zoe. ■ 84103 #049-01-2008 *012
AMPOFO, Kwabena Krow. 30 N 1900 E, RM 2A100 84132 #412-01-1991 L2002 PD *020 †55
AMSTUTZ, Paul G. 500 FOOTHILL DR, DEPT OF NEUROSURGERY 84148 #040-02-1983 L2007 NS *020 †25
ANASTASIOU-NANA, Maria. ■ 84108 #418-01-1972 L1984 CD IM *050
ANDEREGG, Christine M. 370 E SOUTH TEMPLE, STE 260 84111 #049-01-2001 L2005 EM *016
ANDERSEN, Curtis Glen. 3845 W 4700 S, CENTER IHC 84118 #021-01-1990 L1996 FM *020 †18
ANDERSEN, Matthew Todd. 1365 W 1000 N 84116 #049-01-2002 L2003 FM *100 †18
ANDERSEN, Sara Jane. 50 N MEDICAL DR, # 2C454 84132 #049-01-1971 L1975 RHU IM *020 †20
ANDERSON, Anthon E, III. 5770 S 250 E, STE G50 & G80 84107 #010-01-1965 L1966 OBG *071 †30
ANDERSON, C Le Roy. ■ 84124 #049-01-1980 L1982 P *020 †75
ANDERSON, Cheronne D. 50 N MED DR, UNIV OF UTAH MED CTR 84132 #005-19-1990 L1991 PD P *020 †75
ANDERSON, Darrell Glenn. 860 E 4500 S, STE 200 84107 #654-01-1981 L1983 P *020
ANDERSON, David Bryan. ■ 84112 #049-01-2006 L2008 *012
ANDERSON, Derek Wade. 1954 FORT UNION BLVD, STE 100 84121 #049-01-1998 L2000 AN *020 †05 ‡
ANDERSON, Deryk L. 2000 S 900 E 84105 #023-12-1984 L1988 FM GP *020 †18
ANDERSON, Eric D. 5169 COTTONWOOD ST, STE 410 84107 #030-06-1976 L1982 GS *020 †85
ANDERSON, Jeffrey Scott. 30 N 1900 E, RADIOLOGY DEPT 84132 #016-06-2001 L2002 RNR *100 †80
ANDERSON, Katherine A. 50 N MEDICAL DR, DEPT OF INTERNAL MEDICINE 84132 #054-04-2005 L2006 IM *012
ANDERSON, Kory T. 30 N 1900 E RM 4C104, UNIV OF UTAH MED CTR 84132 #040-02-2005 L2006 IM *012
ANDERSON, Rachel Elizabet. 100 N MEDICAL DR, PEDIATRIC RESIDENCE OFFICE 84113 #054-04-2005 L2006 PD *012
ANDERSON, Richard Lee. 1002 E SOUTH TEMPLE, STE 308 84103 #018-03-1971 L1984 OPH PS *020 †35
ANDERSON, Steven Jay. 1151 EAST 3900 SOUTH B 275 84124 #049-01-1970 L1974 RHU IM *020 †20

ANDERTON, Barry J. 100 N MEDICAL DR, ANESTHESIA 84113 #054-04-1974 L1981 AN *020 †05

ANDTBACKA, Robert Hans Ig. 30 N 1900 E, DEPARTMENT OF SURGERY 84132 #067-01-1997 L2006 *020 †85

ANGERBAUER, Steven Ralph. 2150 S 1300 E, STE 500 84106 #041-02-2004 L2007 GPM *012

ANKER, Christopher James. 1950 CIRCLE OF HOPE DR, RM 1570 84112 #035-15-2005 L2006 RO *012

ANTOMMARIA, Armand Mathen. 100 N MEDICAL DR, PRIMARY CHILDREN'S MEDICAL 84113 #028-02-2000 L2001 PD *020 †20

ANTONOW, Juli Ann. 50 N MEDICAL DR, 3B420 SOM 84132 #026-04-1975 L1995 PD *030 †55

AOKI, Jon Richard. 3725 W 4100 S 84120 #049-01-1979 L1980 OTO *020 †45

AOKI, Joseph Moss, Jr. 3845 W 4700 S 84118 #049-01-1981 L1987 GS *020 †16

AOKI, Stephen Kenji. 370 9TH AVE, STE 205 84103 #035-47-1999 L2000 OSM *020 †40

APFELBAUM, Jonathan D. 3460 PIONEER PKWY, INTEGRATED CARE AT 84120 #049-01-1994 L2001 EM *020 †20

APFELBAUM, Ronald Ira. 30 N 1900 E STE 3B-409 84132 #041-09-1965 L1986 NS AM *020 †25

ARCHAMBAULT, Maureen K. 4021 S 700 E STE 300, COMPHEALTH 84107 #024-07-1957 L1960 RO *072 †80

ARCHER, Victor E. ■ 84124 #016-06-1949 L1981 OM GPM *050 †70

ARENA, Charles Martin. 5337 COTTONWOOD CLUB DR 84117 #035-06-1983 L1984 IM DIA *020 †20

ARGUELLO, Fares Jos. 448 E 6400 S, STE 200 84107 #049-01-1975 L1976 P OS *050 †75

ARLEDGE, Kimberly Nicole. ■ 84102 #005-12-2005 L2007 GS *012

ARMSTRONG, Crystal Tolley. ■ 84102 #056-06-2005 L2006 FP *012

ARMSTRONG, Dustin Andrew. ■ 84102 #056-06-2005 L2006 IM *012

ARNDER, Lance Lee. 1050 E SOUTH TEMPLE, UTAH IMAGING 84102 #036-07-1994 L2001 DR *020 †80

ARRINGTON, Cammon Bart. 100 N MEDICAL DR, PEDIATRIC CARDIOLOGY DEPT 84113 #018-03-2001 L2002 PDC *100 †55

ASCH, Julie. EAST 8, LDS HOSPITAL 8TH AVE AND C 84143 #033-06-1988 L2001 PHO BBK *020 †55

ASHTON, Arden Lindsay, Jr. 3845 W 4700 S, TAYLORSVILLE INSTACARE 84118 #049-01-1977 L1984 IM EM *020 †20

ASHTON, Daniel Joshua. LDS HOSPITAL, 8TH AVE AND C STREET 84143 #048-13-2007 *012

ASHTON, Reed Dennis. 7138 HIGHLAND DR 84121 #049-01-1974 L1975 PD *020 †55

ASHWOOD, Edward R. 500 CHIPETA WAY 84108 #007-02-1974 L1988 CLP *020 †50

ASHWORTH, James C. 501 CHIPETA WAY 84108 #049-01-1989 L1992 CHP *020 †75

ASHWORTH, William Dean. 500 FOOTHILL DR, 110PB 84148 #008-01-1954 L1959 GE *071 †20

ASIRVATHAM, Rajan. 1275 FAIRFAX RD, SHRINERS HOSP DPT CRPPLD C 84103 #495-59-1980 OP *020

ASMAR, Paul Salim. 1050 E SOUTH TEMPLE, UTAH IMAGING 84102 #038-41-1992 L1993 RNR *020 †80

ASTLE, Kevin Lawrence. 1200 E 3900 S, DEPT OF ANESTHESIOLOGY 84124 #049-01-1991 L1992 AN *020 †05

ASTLE, Marvin Jeremy. 1200 E 3900 S, ST. MARK'S REGIONAL HOSPIT 84124 #008-02-2001 L2005 AN *020 †05

ATHENS, John Wm. ■ 84121 #023-07-1948 L1955 HEM ON *071 †20

AUNE, David L. 3451 S 5600 W, STE F 84120 #049-01-1997 L1999 FM *020 †18

AUSTIN, Philip. ■ 84107 #352-05-1940 L1951 GP *071

AVELAR, Erick Tadeu. 50 N MEDICAL DR, CARDIOLOGY, 4A100 84132 #187-07-1993 L2003 CD *100 †20

AVENT, James Monroe. 400 C ST 84143 #036-07-1978 L1981 PTH PCP *020 †50

AVIZONIS, Vilija Neris. 333 S 900 E 84102 #034-01-1986 L1987 RO *020 †80

AVNER, Dennis Lee. 1220 E 3900 S STE 3C 84124 #016-06-1973 L1974 GE IM *020 †20

AXELROD, Deborah Ann. ■ 84108 #048-04-2005 L2006 AN *012

AYERS, Charles Michael. 324 10TH AVE STE 285 84103 #018-03-1988 L1989 IM *020 †20

BAAR, Rachel Elizabeth. ■ 84103 #049-01-2003 L2005 PD *020 †55

BABITZ, Marc Edward. 375 CHIPETA WAY, STE A 84108 #005-02-1972 L1994 FM PHP *040 †18

BACA, Gregory Karl. 30 N 190 EAST, DEPT RM 5R156 84132 #034-01-2002 L2005 ADP *012

BACKMAN, Sylvie M. 1439 S 1400 E 84105 #048-13-1994 L2001 PD *020 †55

BADER, Cynthia Diane. ■ 84111 #054-04-2007 PD *012

BADER, Feras Mohammad. 30 N 1900 E, 1C41QO 84132 #575-01-1998 L2003 CD *100 †20

BAESE, Philip Luke. 650 KOMAS DR, STE 200 84108 #007-02-1997 L1998 OS *020 †55,75

BAHLER, David Wendell. ■ 84121 #035-45-1987 L2000 PTH *020 †50

BAHR, Albert Lee. 296 E 3900 S, SPECIALISTS 84107 #035-45-1970 L1983 R *020 †80

BAHR, Brooks Albert. ■ 84102 #049-01-2007 *012

BAIDEN, Erica Nancy. ■ 84106 #049-01-2007 OBG *012

BAILEY, Contresia Ladonna. 275 E 200 S 84111 #027-01-2003 L2005 FM *020 †18

BAILEY, Courtney M. 359 8TH AVE 84103 #049-01-1991 L1992 AN *020 †05

BAIR, Byron Dee. 500 FOOTHILL BLVD, GRECC (182) 84148 #049-01-1986 L1992 P IM *020 †20,75

BAJWA, Harjinder Singh. ■ 84116 #495-29-1986 L2006 OP *012

BAKER, Ann Marie. ■ 84105 #048-14-2004 L2005 IM *020 †20

BAKER, Maurice Gordon. 5872 S 900 E, STE 100 84121 #049-01-1958 L1959 FM *020 †18 ‡

BALBIERZ, Janet Marie. 166 E 5900 S, STE B106 84107 #025-01-1984 L1988 PM *020 †60

BALDWIN, George Nicholas. 1050 E SOUTH TEMPLE 84102 #056-06-1967 L1975 RNR *020 †80

BALE, James F, Jr. 30 N 1900 E, STE 3R210 84132 #025-01-1975 L1978 PD CHN *020 †75,55

BALL, Robert Henry. 1140 E 3900 S, STE 390 84124 #049-01-1985 L1997 OBG *020 †30

BALTER, Kevin S. 1250 E 3900 S, STE 30 84124 #038-44-1986 L2006 PME *020 †05

BANCROFT, Timothy David. 2000 S 900 E, IHC MEMORIAL CLINIC 84105 #033-05-1991 L1992 PD *020 †55

BANE, Jesse David. 3725 W 4100 S 84120 #048-12-1970 L1973 IM *020

BANKS, Amy. 4624 HOLLADAY BLVD 84117 #026-04-2003 L2007 FM *020 †18

BARALDI, Carole Annelisa. 24 S 1100 E, STE 209 84102 #023-07-1991 L1997 IM IMG *020 †20

BARDANA, Davide Domenico. 1525 W 2100 S 84119 #060-02-1994 L1999 OSM *100

BARINGER, John Richard. 50 N MEDICAL DR, UNIV OF UTAH MED CTR 84132 #038-06-1959 L1982 N OS *030 †75

BARKER, Allan Howard. 333 S 9TH E 84102 #049-01-1952 L1956 CD IM *071 †20

BARKLOW, Jeff Anthony. 650 E 4500 S STE 210 84107 #038-41-1997 L2002 NEP *020 †20

BARLOW, Lynn Burnham, II. 370 E SOUTH TEMPLE STE 260, EMERGENCY PHYSICIAN INTEGR 84111 #016-42-1997 L2000 EM *020 †55

BARMAN, Thomas Francis. 1160 E 3900 S STE 1000 84124 #005-18-1986 L1987 IM *020 †20

BARNES, A David. ■ 84117 #539-04-1966 L1998 OBG PHP *020 †30 ‡

BARNES, Elizabeth Anne. 1525 W 2100 S 84119 #019-02-1979 L1991 FM *020 †18

BARNETTE, Phillip Evan, Jr. 576 8TH AVE 84103 #040-02-1997 L2000 PHO *020 †55

BARNEY, William West. 3725 W 4100 S 84120 #049-01-1960 L1961 IM CD *071 †20

BARR, Lucy Jane. ■ 84101 #040-02-2002 L2003 OTO *100

BARRERA, Alexandra. 36 S STATE ST, MEDICAL STAFF SERVICES, 16 84111 #409-16-2001 L2006 PD *020 †55

BARRETT, E Le Verl. ■ 84108 #028-02-1943 L1943 IM A *072

BARRETT, Mark Brendan. 5770 S 250 E 84107 #048-02-1989 L1992 PD *020 †55

BARRY, William Harvey. MEDICAL N, UTAH MED CTR 50 N 84132 #024-01-1965 L1983 CD *050 †20

BARTEL, Roxanne Lynette. 501 CHIPETA WAY 84108 #008-01-1987 L1992 P *020 †75

BARTLETT, James Allen. ■ 84106 #049-01-2008 *012

BARTOK, Beatrix. 50 N MEDICAL DR 84132 #473-03-1997 L2007 IM *012

BARTON, Erik David. 30 N 1900 E, RM 3B110 84132 #005-18-1992 L2001 EM *020 †16

BARTON, Jeffrey Hunter. 5770 S 250 E STE 240, COTTONWOOD TOWER 84107 #028-34-1987 L1991 OBG *020 †30

BARTON, Lewis Jerome. 24 S 1100 E 84102 #049-01-1964 L1965 IM NEP *020 †20

BARTON, Ray Hunter, Jr. 6331 HAVEN CHASE LN 84121 #041-13-1943 GP *071

BARTON, Richard Gene. 30 N 1900 E, SCHOOL OF MED 84132 #049-01-1982 L1983 CCS GS *020 †85

BARTON, Scott Roy. 3970 S 700 E, STE 14 84107 #049-01-1988 L1992 OBG *020 †30

BATEMAN, Lucinda. 1002 E SOUTH TEMPLE, STE 408 84102 #023-07-1987 L1988 IM *020 †20

BATES, Cory Scott. 50 N MEDICAL DR, DEPARTMENT OF UROLOGY 84132 #048-04-2006 L2008 U *012

BATISTA HINCAPIE, Oscar A. 6360 S 3000 E, STE 300 84121 #715-01-1993 L2005 GE *020 †20

BATTAGLIA, Deborah F. 777 11TH AVE 84103 #025-01-2001 L2005 EM *100 †16

BATTARTON, Sarah Elizabet. ■ 84106 #017-20-2006 L2007 PD *012

BATTISTONE, Michael J. 50 N MEDICAL DR, UNIV OF UTAH 4B200 SOM 84132 #036-07-1991 L1992 RHU *020 †20

BAUER, August Robt, Jr. PO BOX 17533 84117 #025-01-1954 L1973 GS *050 †85

BAUER, David Michaeljose. ■ 84102 #032-01-2006 L2007 DR *012

BAUMAN, Thomas Dredge. 333 S 900 E 84102 #049-01-1975 L1980 ORS *020 †40

BAUMBACHER, Manya Maclay. ■ 84102 #049-01-1969 L1972 P *020

BAUMGARTNER, Jennifer M. ■ 84111 #016-42-2001 L2001 EM *020 †16

BAUTISTA DAVIS, Edith C. 1954 FORT UNION BLVD, STE 103 84121 #047-07-1992 L1997 AN PME *020 †20

BEACHY, Joanna Christine. ■ 84124 #010-01-1985 L2001 NPM PD *020 †55

BEALL, Scott Nelson. 1560 HANOVER DR 84108 #017-20-1985 L2001 AN *020 †55

BEALS, Timothy Campbell. 590 WAKARA WAY 84108 #040-02-1990 L1996 ORS *020 †40

BEAMS, Kelly David. 1160 E 3900 S, STE 2000 84124 #005-12-1987 L1990 IM *020 †20

BEAN, Barbara Ellen. 5770 S 250 E 84107 #021-01-1988 L1989 PD *020 †55

BEARD, Mary Kathryn. 455 E SOUTH TEMPLE, STE 202 84111 #004-01-1965 L1973 OBG IM *020 †30

BEARNSON, Patricia. 348 E 4500 S, STE 200 84107 #049-01-1984 L1985 OBG *020 †30

BEAUDOIN, Denise Elaine. ■ 84103 #041-07-1988 L1992 PHP *030 †70

BECK, Anna C. 3838 S 700 E STE 100, CENTER SQ/MEDICAL OFFICE B 84106 #048-04-1986 L1987 ON HEM *020 †20

BECK, Michael Marshall. ■ 84103 #049-01-2004 L2008 GS *100

BEDDHU, Srinivasan. 50 N MEDICAL DR, DIV OF NEPHROLOGY 84132 #495-16-1989 L1999 NEP *020 †20

BEHRENS, Charles Donald. ■ 84109 #010-01-1955 L1962 IM *071 †20

BEHRENS, Michael Neal. 30 N 1900 E, SOM, RM 3C444 84132 #010-01-1994 L1995 CCM *020 †05

BEIER, Frances R. 44 W 300 S # 6075 84101 #049-01-1958 L1959 PD *071 †55

BEKANICH, Stephen James. 1525 W 2100 S, 1ST & 2CD FLOOR 84119 #035-06-1998 L2001 IM *020 †20

BELFORT, Michael A. 50 N MEDICAL DR 84132 #836-01-1981 L1997 OBG *020 †30 ‡

BELL, Jennifer Lynn. 555 FOOTHILL DR STE 301, UNIVERSITY FAMILY HEALTH C 84112 #047-05-1986 L1993 FM *020 †18

BELL, John William. 50 N MEDICAL DR, DEPT OF RADIOLOGY 84132 #049-01-2006 L2007 DR *012

BELL, Kenneth G. ■ 84103 #048-12-1989 L1993 AN *020 †05

BELL, Robert Michael. 3970 S 700 E, STE 24 84107 #049-01-1980 L1985 DR *020 †80

BELLE, Ralph Michael. ■ 84108 #065-06-1984 *100

BELNAP, Le Grand Petty. 1250 E 3900 S, STE 220 84124 #049-01-1973 L1974 GS OS *020 †85

BENATOR, Rachel Sharon. 1025 E 3300 S, STE B 84106 #048-12-1986 L1987 OPH *035 †35

BENCH, Clyde Jardine. 333 S 900 E 84102 #049-01-1968 L1970 RHU IM *020 †20

BENDER, Jeffrey Michael. 100 N MEDICAL DR, 4TH FL 84113 #005-18-2003 L2004 PD *100 †55

BENEDICT, Susan Lee. 30 N 1900 E, STE 3R210 84132 #030-06-1997 L2000 CHN *020 †75,55

BENJAMIN, Ivor James. 30 N 1900 E, RM 4A100 84132 #023-07-1982 L2003 CD IM *050 †20

BENNETT, Michele Ann. ■ 84103 #019-02-2006 L2008 OBG *012

BENNETT, Neel Everett. 1599 FEDERAL HEIGHTS DR 84103 #020-02-1972 L1978 DR NM *062 †80

BENNETT, Richard Wayne. 1160 E 3900 S, STE 1200 84124 #026-04-1983 L1984 IM *020 †20

BENNETT, Stephen David. 30 JORTH 1900 EAST, DEPT OF UROLOGY 84132 #026-04-2004 L2005 U *012

BENNETT, Stephen Higgs. 1045 E 3900 S, STE 201 84124 #049-01-1967 L1977 PS *020 †85,65

BENNETT, Sterling T. 8TH AVE & C ST, LDS HOSP DEPT OF PATH 84143 #049-01-1987 L1992 CLP BBK *062 †50

BENNION, Jerald Horne. ■ 84108 #023-01-1956 L1963 OTO *071 †45

BENOWITZ, Barry Alan. 324 10TH AVE STE 250 84103 #024-07-1973 L1976 END IM *020 †20

BENSON, Lowell Scott. 50 N MEDICAL DR, INTERNAL MEDICINE DEPT 84132 #049-01-2006 L2008 IM *012

BENTLEY, Louis Frank. 2000 S 900 E, IHC MEMORIAL PEDIATRICS 84105 #049-01-1974 L1976 PD *020 †55

BENTZ, Brandon Geigle. 30 N 1900 E, RM 3B110 84132 #041-12-1993 L2003 OTO *020 †45

BENTZ, Joel Steven. 50 N MEDICAL DR, ANATAMIC PATH UNIV HOSP 84132 #037-01-1990 L1991 PTH PCP *020 †50

BERENSON, Malcolm Mark. 1525 W 2100 S 84119 #041-12-1963 L1971 GE IM *020 †20

BERESFORD, Zach Martin. ■ 84108 #026-04-2005 L2006 PM *012

BERGERON, Jennifer Ellen. UNIVERSITY OF UTAH, DEPARTMENT OF PEDIATRICS - 84132 #050-02-2003 L2004 PD *100

BERGESON, Adam Gary. 590 WAKARA WAY, U OF U/DEPARTMENT OF ORTHO 84108 #054-04-2006 L2007 ORS *012

BERGQUIST, Barry Dale. 165 ALTA ST 84103 #008-01-1985 L1993 AN IM *020 †20,05

BERK, Howard Sidney. 5770 S 250 E, STE G50 & G80 84107 #016-06-1970 L1973 OBG *020 †30

BERKEBILE, Susan Mary. ■ 84103 #028-02-1989 L1993 **IM** *020 †20
BERLIN, Gary Leonid. 6440 MILLROCK DR, STE 175 84121 #016-02-1998 L2001 **EM MDM** *030 †16
BERMEN, John Francis, Jr. 3465 S 4155 W STE 5 84120 #049-01-1971 L1976 **ORS** *020 †40
BERNARD, Philip Seth. ■ 84105 #049-01-1996 L2001 **PTH** *020 †50
BERNEIKE, John Alan. 1250 E 3900 S, ST MARKS FAMILY MEDICINE 84124 #007-02-1997 L1998 **FM** *040 †18
BERNHISEL, Kurt Ted. 1C026 SOM, 30 NORTH 1900 EAST 84132 #049-01-1980 L1984 **EM IM** *020 †20,16
BERNHISEL, Ted B. ■ 84103 #049-01-1946 L1949 **IM** *071 †20
BERNHISEL-BROADBENT, Jan. 2000 S 900 E 84105 #049-01-1983 L1993 **IG PD** *020 †55,03
BERNSTEIN, Paul Steven. 50 N MEDICAL DR 84132 #024-01-1988 L1995 **OPH** *020 †35
BERRY, Robert Michael. 5810 S 300 E, STE 300 84107 #005-06-1978 L1989 **OSS** *020 †40
BERTIN, Kim Conrad. 5323 WOODROW ST, STE 202 84107 #049-01-1978 L1979 **ORS** *020 †40
BESS, Robert Shay. 590 WAKARA WAY 84108 #023-07-1999 L2005 **OSS** *020 †40
BETTELS, Deborah Annette. 6440 MILLROCK DR, STE 175 84121 #019-02-1985 L1986 **IM** *020 †20
BEUKEMA, Richard John. 375 HAMPTON AVE 84111 #041-13-2002 L2003 **FM** *100 †18
BEVERIDGE, Robert J. ■ 84109 #007-02-1949 L1956 **TS** *071 †85,90
BHATT, Margi Ashutosh. 1200 E 3900 S, CARE MEDICAL, LLC 84124 #496-41-1996 L2007 **IM** *100
BIDWAI, Arun Vasudeo. 617 E 3900 S, LIFETREE MEDICAL INC 84107 #495-20-1963 L1972 **AN** *020 †05
BIDWAI, Vanamala Arun. ■ 84108 #495-20-1969 *100
BIEDERMANN, Eric Roy. ■ 84101 #035-03-1965 L1993 **OBG** *020 †30
BIGELOW, Richard Percival. ■ 84102 #035-20-1954 L1960 **IM GE** *071
BILDER, Deborah Ann. 50 N MEDICAL DR, UNIV OF UTAH HOSPITAL 84132 #047-05-1998 L1999 **CHP PD** *020 †55,75
BINGMAN, Jana Dianne. 650 KOMAS DR STE 208, DEPT OF CHILD & ADOLESCENT 84108 #039-01-2003 L2006 **CHP** *012
BINHAMMER, Paul A. ■ 84108 #065-01-1986 L1993 **HS** *020
BIRGENHEIER, Nathaniel Ma. ■ 84108 #030-06-2007 L2007 **IM** *012
BISHOFF, Jay Todd. 5169 COTTONWOOD ST, STE 420 84107 #023-12-1991 L1995 **U** *020 †95
BISHOP, Frank Seisaku. 30 N 1900 E, # 3B409 84132 #056-06-2004 L2005 **NS** *012
BISSON, Erica Fay. 175 N. MEDICAL DR. EAST, DEPT. OF NEUROSURGERY 84132 #024-07-2000 L2007 **NS** *020
BITNER, Alan Fetzer. 333 S 900 E 84102 #023-12-1982 L1986 **AI PD** *020 †55,03
BJORKMAN, David Jess. 30 N 1900 E, RM 1C109 84132 #049-01-1980 L1985 **GE IM** *030 †20
BLACK, Evan G. 5323 WOODROW ST, STE 201 84107 #049-01-1991 L1992 **N** *020 †75
BLACK, Richard Eugene. 100 N MEDICAL DR STE 2600 84113 #049-01-1974 L1976 **PDS** *020 †85
BLACKBURN, Marcus Kim. ■ 84106 #049-01-2007 **PD** *012
BLACKHAM, Brenda Kay. ■ 84124 #031-01-1989 L1990 **AN** *020 †05
BLAIR, Sarah Anne. ■ 84106 #050-02-2006 L2007 **AN** *012
BLANCH, Jonathan W. 24 S 1100 E, STE 304 84102 #049-01-1999 L2003 **IM** *020 †20
BLASCHKE-BONKOWSKY, Anne. 30 N 1900 E, UNIV OF UTAH PEDIATRIC INF 84132 #005-18-2000 L2001 **PDI** *020 †55
BLASER, Jason L. 400 C ST 84143 #031-01-1994 L2007 **DMP** *100 †50
BLAYLOCK, Robert Chas. 40 N 1900 EAST, UNIV. OF UTAH HLTH. SCIEN. 84132 #049-01-1986 L1987 **PTH** *020 †50
BLEDSOE, Joseph Robert. ■ 84106 #007-02-2005 L2007 **EM** *012
BLEYL, Steven Benjamin. 50 N MEDICAL DR, DIV OF MED GENETICS 84132 #049-01-2000 L2003 **MG** *100 †55,19
BLISS, Eugene L. 50 N MED DR, UNIV OF UTAH MED CTR 84132 #035-09-1943 L1950 **P** *072 †75
BLOLAND, Eric Craig. 5848 FASHION BLVD 84107 #005-19-1982 L1984 **AN** *020 †05
BLOOM, Ronald Saml. 50 N MEDICAL DR, UNIV OF UTAH MEDICAL CENTE 84132 #028-02-1964 L1993 **NPM AS** *030 †55
BLOOMER, Herbert Allan. 1200 E 3900 S 84124 #056-06-1954 L1963 **NEP IM** *071 †20
BLUMENTHAL, Deborah T. 2000 CIRCLE OF HOPE DR, DIV NEURO ONCOLOGY #2152 84112 #012-01-1990 L1998 **N OS** *020 †75
BODNAR, Anna S. 3384 SHADY TREE COURT 84106 #041-07-1967 L1971 **PD IM** *020 †55
BOEBEL, Kristen Kathleen. ■ 84121 #056-05-2003 L2007 **PCC** *012 †20
BOHNSACK, John F. 50 N MEDICAL DR DEPT PD 84132 #051-01-1978 L1987 **RHU PD** *050 †55
BOLTAX, Jonathan Peter. 1163 LAKE ST 84105 #041-13-2002 L2003 **IM** *020 †20
BOLTE, Robert Glenn. 100 N MEDICAL DR, PRIMARY CHILDREN'S MED. CT 84113 #020-12-1977 L1980 **PD EM** *020 †55
BOND, Edward Gerow. ■ 84124 #005-12-1936 L1936 **FM** *071
BOND, Robert Edward. ■ 84124 #005-12-1964 L1965 **NEP IM** *020 †20
BONE, David Earl. 10 W BROADWAY, STE 500 84101 #004-01-1970 L1976 **P** *020
BONFANTE, Carola E. 275 E 200 S 84111 #012-01-1999 L2002 **EM** *020
BONK, Roy Thomas, Jr. 5444 GREEN ST, SPECIALISTS 84123 #005-15-1993 L1999 **DR** *020 †80
BONKOWSKY, Joshua Leitch. 295 CHIPETA WAY 84108 #005-18-2000 L2001 **CHN** *020 †55,75
BOOK, Linda Sue Pipoly. 100 N MEDICAL DR, STE 2650 84113 #038-41-1971 L1974 **GE PD** *020 †55
BORDER, Wayne Allen. 391 CHIPETA WAY STE E, FIBROSIS RESEARCH LAB 84108 #028-02-1968 L1983 **NEP** *050 †20
BORGENICHT, Louis. 850 E 300 S STE 5 84102 #038-06-1970 L1973 **PD** *020 †55
BOSCHERT, Mark E. 6360 S 3000 E, STE 300 84121 #038-44-1984 L1989 **GE IM** *020 †20
BOSSART, Peter Wm. 324 10TH AVE STE 280 84103 #033-05-1983 L1989 **CRS** *020 †85,10
BOSSART, Philip John. 75 N MEDICAL DR, 1150 MORAN BLDG 84132 #035-20-1981 L1982 **EM IM** *040 †20,16
BOTKIN, Jeffrey Robt. 50 N MEDICAL DR # 1C 84132 #041-12-1979 L1992 **PD** *030 †55
BOTT, Steven I. 30 N 1900 E, DEPT OF ANESTHESIOLOGY 3C4 84132 #049-01-1998 L1999 **AN** *020
BOTTO, Lorenzo Davide. 50 N MEDICAL DR 2C412, DIVISION MEDICAL GENETICS 84132 #561-23-1985 L2007 **MG** *100 †19
BOURKE, Karyn Elizabeth. 65 N MEDICAL DR, MORAN EYE CENTER 84132 #012-01-2005 L2006 **OPH** *012
BOURNE, Hal H. ■ 84109 #049-01-1957 L1964 **U** *020 †95
BOURNE, Michael Hal. 1160 E 3900 S, STE 500 84124 #049-01-1984 L1989 **OAR OSM** *020 †40
BOURNE, Robert Bryan. 82 S 1100 E, STE 303 84102 #028-34-1986 L1988 **ISM OS** *020
BOURNE, Talmage Lee. 3725 W 4100 S 84120 #049-01-1971 L1972 **FM** *020 †18
BOVA, Charles Mikell. 1250 E 3900 S, STE 440 84124 #041-13-1974 L1991 **PMM ESM** *020 †16
BOVOS, Mike Elias. 1250 E 3900 S, ST MARKS FAMILY MEDICINE 84124 #049-01-2004 L2007 **FM** *020 †18
BOWEN, Glen Montrose. 30 N 1900 E, ROOM 4B 454 SOM 84132 #049-01-1990 L1999 **D** *020 †15
BOWERS, John Hampton. 6360 S 3000 E, STE 310 84121 #049-01-1970 L1974 **GE IM** *020 †20
BOWLEN, Michelle Dawn. 100 N MEDICAL DR 84113 #017-20-2001 L2002 **AN** *020 †05
BOWLES, Catherine Ann. 1200 E 3900 S, DEPT OF PATH/ST MARKS HOSP 84124 #018-03-2001 L2002 **PTH** *020 †50 ‡
BOWMAN, Glen F. 50 N MEDICAL DR 84132 #041-12-1993 L1996 **AN** *020 †05
BOWMAN, Jane Crittenden. 5770 S 250 E, STE 135 84107 #054-04-1990 L1991 **OBG** *020 †30
BOX, Terry Dean. 6360 S 3000 E, STE 300 84121 #048-12-1977 L1979 **GE IM** *020 †20
BOYD, William Adam. 1200 E 3900 S 84124 #024-05-1958 L1959 **AN** *072 †05
BOYDEN, John Sterling, Jr. ■ 84108 #049-01-1967 L1970 **LM** *062
BOYER, Michael Wayne. 30 N 1900 E, SOM 4C416 84132 #017-20-1987 L2006 **PHO** *020 †55
BOYER, Richard Stuart. 100 N MEDICAL DR, MEDICAL IMAGING 84113 #049-01-1973 L1978 **DR PDR** *020 †20,80
BRADLEY, Joshua David. 333 S 900 E 84102 #049-01-2002 L2007 **OTO** *020
BRADSHAW, Amber Dawn. ■ 84106 #049-01-2005 L2006 **OBG** *012
BRADSTREET, Chester Upton. ■ 84119 #049-01-2008 *012
BRADWAY, Alice. ■ 84103 #046-01-1978 L1981 **PD** *020 †55
BRADWAY, James Arthur, II. 30 N 1900 E, RM 3C444 84132 #039-01-1977 L1980 **AN** *040 †05
BRADY, Bruce Ryan. 333 S 900 E 84102 #049-01-1997 L2000 **END** *020 †20
BRADY, Ellen Mae. ■ 84121 #025-07-1974 L1975 **IM GPM** *020 †20
BRADY, John H. ■ 84108 #049-01-2003 L2005 **ORS** *012
BRANCH, David Ware, Jr. 50 N MEDICAL DR 84132 #051-04-1979 L1983 **NPM OBG** *040 †30
BRANDON, Kathryn. FOOTHILL STATION 84158 #016-01-1941 L1954 **ADL OM** *071 †55
BRANN, William Marcus. 24 S 1100 E, STE 304 84102 #032-01-1980 L1994 **CD IM** *020 †20
BRANT-ZAWADZKI, Peter Bol. ■ 84105 #539-06-2002 L2003 **GS** *012
BRASHER, Craig A. 3725 W 4100 S 84120 #049-01-1979 L1982 **PD** *020 †55
BRATTON, Susan Lee. 295 CHIPETA WAY, DEPT OF PEDIATRICS 84108 #004-01-1987 L1989 **PD CCP** *020 †55
BRAUN, Anne Christine. 30 N 1900 E 1C026, DIV OF EMERGENCY MED 84132 #005-11-2006 L2008 **EM** *012
BRAY, Bruce Earl. 50 N MEDICAL DR # 4A132 84132 #005-12-1977 L1981 **CD IM** *050 †20
BRAY, Patrick Francis. 50 N MEDICAL DR, DEPT PED 84132 #035-45-1947 L1951 **N PD** *040 †55,75
BRETZ, Bradley P. 546 CHIPETA WAY, STE 220 84108 #048-15-1999 L2001 **PMM** *012 †05
BRIESACHER, Mark Richard. 2180 E 4500 S, STE 210 84117 #028-03-1992 L1993 **PD MDM** *020 †55
BRIESKE, Mary Elizabeth. 400 C ST 84143 #056-05-1992 L1993 **PTH BBK** *020 †50
BRIGANTI, Cesar Enrique. UNIV OF UTAH HEALTH CARE, INT MED/PEDIATRIC RES PROG 84132 #035-45-2006 L2008 **MPD** *012
BRINEY, Roy Everett. ■ 84117 #049-01-1955 L1956 **OBG** *071
BRINGHURST, Jade Reed. ■ 84109 #049-01-2008 *012
BRINTON, Eliot Ashby. 420 CHIPETA WAY, STE 1160 84108 #049-01-1978 L2003 **OS IM** *050 †20
BRINTON, Jason Philip. LDS HOSPITAL, 8TH AVE AND C STREET 84143 #024-01-2006 *012
BRINTON, Milton Harvey. PO BOX 30150, RIO DE JANIERO BR MISSSION 84130 #010-01-1977 L1978 **VS GS** *071 †85
BRISCOE, Kathleen Ellen. 6440 MILLROCK DR, STE 175 84121 #005-02-1966 L1967 **ON** *020 †20
BROADBENT, Kenneth R. 1140 E 3900 S, ST MARKS 84124 #036-07-1987 L1993 **PD** *020 †55
BROADBENT, Thomas Ray. ■ 84158 #036-07-1946 L1947 **PS** *071 †85,65
BROCKBANK, David Thomas. 201 E 5900 S, STE 101 84107 #035-03-2003 L2007 **OPH** *020
BROCKMEYER, Douglas Lee. 100 N MEDICAL DR, # 1475 84113 #038-06-1987 L1988 **NS GS** *020 †25
BRODHAG, Laura Ann. ■ 84107 #038-44-1993 L1994 **FM** *020 †18
BRODIE, Lesley Thompson. 650 KOMAS DR, STE 208 84108 #050-02-2003 L2004 **CPP** *012
BRODKE, Darrel Scott. 50 N MEDICAL DR 84132 #005-02-1989 L1997 **ORS OSS** *020 †40
BROGAN, Shane Edward. 546 CHIPETA WAY, STE 220 84108 #539-06-1997 L2001 **APM** *020 †05
BROGLI, Julia C. 5770 S 250 E 84107 #020-02-1989 L1992 **PD** *020 †55
BROMBERG, Mark. 30 N 1900 E, STE 3R210 84132 #025-01-1982 L1994 **N OS** *050 †75
BRONSKY, Edwin Ansell. 150 S 1000 E 84102 #036-05-1958 L1972 **AI** *071 †55,03
BROOKE, Wallace Sands. ■ 84102 #023-07-1942 L1947 **GS CRS** *071 †85
BROWD, Samuel Robert. 30 N 1900 E STE 3B409, NEUROSURGERY 84132 #011-03-2000 L2002 **NS** *100 ‡
BROWN, Bridget Marie. 100 N MEDICAL DR, PEDIATRICS DEPARTMENT 84113 #035-45-2006 L2007 **PD** *012
BROWN, Bryant Jerome. 3970 S 700 E, STE 14 84107 #049-01-1974 L1975 **OBG** *020 †30
BROWN, George Ralph. ■ 84103 #049-01-1960 L1964 **D IM** *071 †20,15
BROWN, Melissa Ann. 333 S 900 E 84102 #049-01-1999 L2001 **OBG** *020 †30
BROWN, Roger A. 4970 S 900 E, BONNEVILLE MEDICAL GROUP 84117 #016-06-1944 L1952 **OS OBG** *071 †30
BROWN, Ronald Earl. 3725 W 4100 S 84120 #049-01-1988 L1997 **CD** *020 †20
BROWN, Russell Thos. ■ 84117 #056-06-1956 L1957 **AS GP** *071
BROWN, Samuel Morris. 26 N 1900 E RM 701, UNIVERSITY OF UTAH MEDICAL 84132 #024-01-2001 L2006 **PCC** *012
BROWN, Terry Allen. 3688 APOLLO DR 84124 #016-11-1975 L1991 **OM GP** *020 †70
BROWNING, Scott Marriner. 3826 S 2300 E 84109 #049-01-1975 L1976 **HEM IM** *020 †20
BRUEN, Erica Ryberg. 30 N 1900 E, INTERNAL MEDICINE ROOM 84132 #049-01-2004 L2005 **IM** *100 †20
BRUEN, Kevin John. 30 N 1900 E, 3B110 84132 #036-01-2002 L2003 **GS** *012
BRUGGERS, Carol Sue. 100 N MEDICAL DR, MEDICAL CENTER 84113 #025-12-1984 L1992 **PHO PD** *020 †55
BRUNETTI, Ross Anthony. 2295 FOOTHILL DR, FOOTHILL FAMILY CLINIC 84109 #028-34-1992 L1998 **FM** *020 †18
BRUNKER, Cherie Pratt. 8TH AVE & C ST, GERIATRICS CLINIC 84143 #049-01-1987 L1988 **IMG** *020 †20
BRYAN, Nathaniel Anthony. 30 N 1900 E, DEPT OF ORTHOPEDICS 84132 #007-02-2000 L2001 **OSM** *020
BRYNER, James Rex. 5770 S 250 E STE G45 84107 #049-01-1969 L1970 **REN GYN** *020 †30
BRYNER, Wallace Franklin. 50 N MEDICAL DR, DEPT OF OB-GYN 84132 #049-01-1973 L1975 **OBG** *020 †30
BRYSON, Philip Lowell. 2890 E COTTONWOOD PKWY, DEPT 38 84121 #049-01-1967 L1973 **IM** *071 †20
BUCHANAN, Marcus Preston. 50 N MEDICAL DR, DEPT OF PEDIATRICS 84132 #049-01-2006 L2008 **PD** *012

BUCHANAN, Thomas Maurice. 30 N 1900 E # 3R210, DEPARTMENT OF NEUROLOGY 84132 #016-42-2006 L2007 **N** *012
BUCHI, Karen Jean. 50 N MEDICAL DR, DEPT OF PEDIATRICS 84132 #049-01-1984 L1985 **PD** *020 †55
BUCKLEY, Fiona Margaret. 30 N 1900 E RM 3C444, ANESTHESIOLOGY DEPARTMENT 84132 #048-04-2001 L2003 **AN** *020
BULAJ, Zaneta Jadwiga. 1160 E 3900 S, STE 1000 84124 #759-10-1994 L2002 **IM** *020 †20
BULL, David Andrew. 30 N 1900 E, UNIV OF UTAH SCHOOL OF MED 84132 #005-02-1985 L1992 **TS** *020 †85,90
BULLOCK, Edward James. 3845 W 4700 S 84118 #028-34-1985 L1986 **IM** *020 †20
BUNNELL, Robert John. 282 F ST 84103 #049-01-2004 L2005 **IM** *020 †20
BURCH, Phillip Todd. 100 N MEDICAL DR, STE 2800 84113 #001-06-1998 L2006 **TS** *020 †85,90
BURDETTE, Allene Salcedo. 50 N MEDICAL DR, RM 1A71 84132 #020-12-1997 L2002 **DR** *020 †80
BURDICK, Dwight Eugene. ■ 84117 #048-02-1968 L1974 **EM** *020 †16
BURELBACH, Ann Elizabeth. 370 E SOUTH TEMPLE STE 260 84111 #049-01-2001 L2005 **EM** *020 †16
BURGESS, Mary Josephine. ■ 84105 #010-01-1960 L1969 **IM OS** *071
BURGETT, Alton Douglas. 3725 W 4100 S 84120 #049-01-1998 L2004 **OBG** *020 †30
BURKE, John Patrick. 370 9TH AVE STE 204 84103 #018-03-1964 L1970 **IM ID** *020 †20
BURKETT, Rox Chas. 5442 S 900 E 84117 #049-01-1973 L1981 **FM** *020
BURKI, Regula Elisabeth. 715 E 3900 S, STE 203 84107 #869-02-1978 L1984 **GYN OBS** *020 †30 ‡
BURKS, Robert Todnem. 590 WAKARA WAY 84108 #028-34-1978 L1988 **ORS** *020 †40
BURNHAM, Evva Jean. 1050 E SOUTH TEMPLE 84102 #036-05-1962 L1964 **AN** *020
BURNS, James B, Jr. 30 N 1900 E, STE 3R210 84132 #016-06-1974 L1986 **N** *050 †75
BURNS, Leland L. 50 N MEDICAL DR 84132 #049-01-1991 L1992 **P** *020 †75
BURR, Robert Eaton. 3725 W 4100 S 84120 #041-09-1973 L2005 **END OM** *020 †20,16,70
BURRIS, Mary Kay. 30 N 1900 E, DEPART OF PSYCHIATRY 84132 #031-01-2004 L2005 **CHP** *012
BURT, Randall Walter. 2000 CIRCLE OF HOPE DR 84112 #049-01-1974 L1977 **GE IM** *050 †20
BURTON, Arthur M. ■ 84103 #041-13-1945 **D** *075 †15
BURTON, Catherine E. 5770 S 1500 W # B 84123 #049-01-1998 L1999 **FM** *020 †18 ‡
BURTON, David A. 36 S STATE ST STE 2100 84111 #035-01-1970 L1972 **OS EM** *030 †16
BURTON, David Scott. 333 S 900 E 84102 #036-05-1991 L1992 **IM** *020 †20
BURTON, Mary Dunson. 2000 S 900 E 84105 #036-05-1990 L1991 **PD** *020 †55
BURTON, Wayne Patrick. ■ 84108 #049-01-2004 *100
BUSER, Anna Favret. ■ 84124 #054-04-2006 L2007 **EM** *012
BUSHNELL, Lowry Avon. 501 CHIPETA WAY 84108 #049-01-1981 L1985 **P** *020
BUTLER, John Edmund. 4000 S 700 E, STE 10 84107 #041-09-1994 L1996 **OTO** *020 †45
BUTLER, Sherri Michelle. 50 N MEDICAL DR, UNIVERSITY OF UTAH HOSPITA 84132 #056-06-1999 L2000 **CCP** *020 †55
BUTTERFIELD, Warren Lewis. 370 9TH AVE, STE 205 84103 #038-40-2001 L2007 **ORS** *020
BUYS, Saundra S. 2000 CIRCLE OF HOPE DR, STE 2100 84112 #024-07-1979 L1981 **HEM ON** *020 †20
BYBEE, Blair La Mar. 50 N MEDICAL DR # 1C26 84132 #049-01-1970 L1971 **PHO PD** *020 †55
BYINGTON, Carrie Lynn. 50 N MEDICAL DR, DEPT PEDIATRICS 84132 #048-04-1989 L1995 **PD ID** *020 †55
BYREDDY, Deepthi Venkat. ■ 84102 #049-01-2008 *012
BYRNE, Janice L B. 50 N MEDICAL DR, DEPT OB/GYN 2B.200 84132 #048-12-1987 L1988 **MFM CG** *020 †19,30
BYRNE, Kathryn Rose. ■ 84103 #048-14-2002 L2003 **GE** *012 †20
CACCIAMANI, Mark Joseph. 50 N MEDICAL DR, DEPT. OF FAMILY PRACTICE 84132 #010-02-1999 L2001 **FM** *020 †18
CAHALAN, Michael Kermit. 30 N 1900 E, RM 3C444 84132 #041-13-1975 L2001 **AN** *020 †05
CAHILL, Barbara Clare. 50 N MEDICAL DR, 701 WINTROBE BUILDING 84132 #016-11-1985 L1996 **PUD CCM** *050 †20
CAINE, Thomas Hugh. 30 N 1900 E RM 4B-120 84132 #049-01-1963 L1964 **IM CD** *020
CALAME, Thomas Robt. 82 S 1100 E, STE 103 84102 #023-01-1973 L1977 **CD IM** *020 †20
CALL, Kevin Donald. 30 N. 1900 E - 3R210 SOM, DEPT OF NEUROLOGY 84132 #038-40-2004 L2005 **N** *012
CALL, Newel Branson. 324 10TH AVE STE 185 84103 #036-07-1974 L1980 **OPH PS** *020 †35
CALL, Steven Elliott. 30 N 1900 E, UNIV OF UTAH HOSPITAL 84132 #038-40-2003 L2004 **RHU** *012 †20
CALLIS, Kristina Patrice. 50 N MEDICAL DR STE 4A330, DEPT DERM 84132 #054-04-1993 L2000 **D** *100 †15,20
CALLIS, Mary Charline. ■ 84117 #049-01-2008 *012
CALLISTER, Paul S. ■ 84109 #049-01-1956 **PTH OS** *074
CAMARGO, Marcelo. ■ 84103 #187-86-1985 **GS** *100
CAMPANA, Chris Frank. 400 C ST 84143 #018-03-1991 L1992 **PCP** *020 †50
CAMPBELL, Christopher M. 1300 E 3900 S, DEPT OF ANESTHESIOLOGY 84124 #048-12-2000 L2001 **AN** *020 †05
CAMPBELL, Edward Jos. 410 CHIPETA WAY STE 108 84108 #028-02-1972 L1989 **PUD EM** *050 †20
CAMPBELL, Kristine Ann. 100 N MEDICAL DR, SAFE AND HEALTHY FAMILIES 84113 #023-07-1996 L2006 **PD** *020 †55
CANALE, Christopher Copp. 50 N MEDICAL DR, INTERNAL MEDICINE DEPT 84132 #047-05-2001 L2002 **GE** *012 †20
CANNING, Peter Devin. ■ 84124 #040-02-2008 *012
CANNON, Cynthia Susan. 455 E SOUTH TEMPLE, STE 202 84111 #005-18-1991 L1992 **OBG** *020 †30
CANNON, Donald Maurice. ■ 84109 #035-20-2008 *012
CANNON, George H. 5121 COTTONWOOD ST 84107 #049-01-1976 L1980 **PTH** *020 †20,50
CANNON, Grant Brain. 4190 HIGHLAND DR STE 112 84124 #001-02-1979 L1980 **FPS** *020
CANNON, Grant Wilson. 30 N 1900 E, DEPT RHEUM 4B200 84132 #049-01-1979 L1980 **IM RHU** *040 †20
CANNON, Richard Bowman. ■ 84109 #010-01-1969 L1972 **END IM** *071 †20
CANNON, Wayne Hales. 525 E 100 S, STE 500 84102 #049-01-1979 L1981 **PD NPM** *020 †55
CAO, Thai Minh. 30 N 1900 EAST, SOM 4C416, DIVISION OF HEMATOLOGY 84132 #019-02-1994 L2004 **IM** *020 †20
CAPRAU, Diana Mihaela. 50 N MEDICAL DR 84132 #781-04-1995 **NPM** *012
CARAVATI, Edwin Martin. 30 N 1900 E, RM 1C26 84132 #051-04-1981 L1985 **EM ETX** *020 †16
CARBONE, Paul Sean. 2A200 SOM, 50 NORTH MEDICAL DRIVE 84132 #016-42-1995 L2006 **PD** *020 †55
CARDENAS-WALLENFELT, P. 4505 WASATCH BLVD, STE 330E 84124 #026-04-1991 L1996 **P** *020 †75 ‡
CAREY, John Clayton. 50 N MEDICAL DR, RM 2C412 84132 #010-02-1972 L1979 **PD MG** *030 †55,19
CARLETON, Scott Szucs. 50 N MEDICAL DR 84132 #473-04-2006 **PD** *012
CARLISLE, James Gerald. 500 FOOTHILL DR 84148 #025-01-1991 L2004 **VIR** *020 †80
CARLSTON, Cory V. ■ 84108 #049-01-2008 *012
CARNEY, Heather Mary. ■ 84105 #050-02-2005 L2006 **PTH** *012
CARNEY, Stephanie Ann. 500 FOOTHILL BLVD, VA MEDICAL CENTER 84148 #049-01-1998 L1999 **IM** *020 †20
CAROL, Susan Betty. 1685 W 2200 S, WORK MED 84119 #028-34-1983 L2002 **EM OM** *020 †16
CARPENTER, Craig Michael. 1050 E SOUTH TEMPLE, UTAH IMAGING 84102 #025-07-1980 L1981 **DR** *020 †80
CARR, Stephen Lamoni. 36 S STATE ST, FL 22 84111 #010-01-1967 L1968 **PD** *020
CARROLL, Kristen Lee. ■ 84108 #035-03-1990 L1991 **OP** *020 †40
CARROLL, Stephen Brent. 1151 E 3900 S, STE B150 84124 #049-01-2001 L2007 **RNR** *020 †80
CARROLL, Travis Rod. 295 CHIPETA WAY 2N100, C/O DEPT OF PEDIATRICS 84108 #422-01-2004 L2007 **NPM** *012 †55
CARSON, Gary Chad. 5848 FASHION BLVD 84107 #049-01-1985 L1988 **AN** *020 †05
CARTWRIGHT, Patrick Carol. 30 N 1900 E, RM 3B110 84132 #048-12-1984 L1985 **UP U** *020 †95
CARVETH, Holly Jean. 26 N 1900 E 84132 #014-01-1982 L1983 **IM PUD** *020 †20
CASE, Shanna Lee. 4C116 SOM, 30 N 1900 E 84132 #049-01-2006 L2008 **IM** *012
CASTLE, C Hilmon. 1160 E 3900 S STE 2000 84124 #036-07-1951 L1957 **CD IM** *071 †18,20
CASULL, Kathryn. 508 E SOUTH TEMPLE, STE 300 84102 #049-01-1994 L1996 **IM** *020 †20
CATE, Thomas R, Jr. 1160 E 3900 S STE 1000 84124 #048-12-1989 L1990 **IM** *020 †20
CATEN, Eric Lee. 5770 S 1500 W 84123 #047-06-1998 L1999 **P** *020 †75
CATHEY, William John. UNIV-UTAH COLL MED 84112 #040-02-1947 **PTH OS** *062
CATINELLA, A Peter. 375 CHIPETA WAY, STE A 84108 #003-01-1981 L1997 **FM** *030 †18
CAUGHRON, Stephen Chappel. ■ 84105 #048-14-2007 **EM** *012
CAWTHON, Richard Moore. ■ 84105 #008-01-1983 L1988 **P** *020
CHACHAS, Angelo Gregory. 24 S 1100 E, STE 201 84102 #049-01-2000 L2005 **GS** *020 †85
CHADWICK, Barbara Elizabe. 30 N 1900 E, 5C124 SOM 84132 #005-12-2004 L2005 **PTH** *012
CHAMBERLAIN, James Joseph. 615 ARAPEEN DR STE 1 84108 #047-05-1995 L1996 **IM** *020 †20
CHAMBERLAIN, Will. ■ 84103 #005-14-1966 L1992 **AN** *020 †05
CHAMBERLIN, Frances Edith. ■ 84109 #049-01-1993 L1996 **PTH** *100
CHAN, Gary Mannerstedt. 3451 EASTWOOD DR 84109 #005-06-1972 L1977 **PD NPM** *020 †55
CHAN, Melissa Marie. 3451 EASTWOOD DR 84109 #049-01-2008 *012
CHAN, Titus T. DEPARTMENT OF PEDIATRICS -, UNIV OF UT MED CTR 84132 #060-01-2003 L2005 **CCP** *012 †55
CHANDLER, Swithin, Jr. 6069 HIGHLAND DR, BEEHIVE MEDICAL BLDG 84121 #041-01-1943 L1973 **GP AM** *020
CHANDLER, Wells Michel. 30 N 1900 E RM 5C124, HEALTH SCIE 84132 #050-02-2006 L2008 **PTH** *012
CHANG, Beverly. 2000 S 900 E, VIRGINIA MASON MEDICAL CEN 84105 #016-06-1999 L2007 **IM** *020 †20
CHANG, Eun Jin. ■ 84117 #049-01-2004 L2004 **GS** *012
CHAPA, Richard William. 2295 FOOTHILL DR 84109 #049-01-1975 L1976 **OBG** *020 †30
CHARDACK, Michael Rene. 370 9TH AVE STE 205 84103 #010-02-1987 L2002 **ORS OTR** *020 †40
CHARLTON, Kevin Hoffman. 4400 S 700 E, STE 100 84107 #049-01-1975 L1980 **OPH** *020 †35
CHATFIELD, Barbara A. SUITE 1450, 100 NORTH MEDICAL DRIVE 84132 #051-04-1985 L1995 **PDP CCM** *020 †55
CHAUDHARI, Angela. 30 N 1900 E, 2B200 84132 #038-44-2000 L2006 **OBG** *020
CHAVEZ, Margarita. 500 FOOTHILL DR, VA HOSPITAL SALT LAKE CITY 84148 #048-02-1997 L2001 **IM** *020 †20
CHEN, Christine. 100 N MEDICAL DR 84113 #038-40-1994 L2001 **AN** *020 †05
CHEN, Jergin. 1950 CIRCLE OF HOPE DR, RM 1570 84112 #049-01-2003 L2004 **RO** *012
CHEN, June Shushing. 7240 HIGHLAND DR, STE 175 84121 #048-02-1995 L2001 **PS** *020 †65
CHEN, Lei L. ■ 84112 #035-46-1983 L2006 **IM ON** *050 †20
CHEN, Priscilla Aye. 5911 FASHION BLVD, FIRSTMED URGENT CARE 84107 #209-01-1980 L1999 **PD** *020
CHEN, Xinjian. ■ 84121 #243-76-1982 L2005 **PTH** *020 †50
CHENG, Clement Chenhung. 30 N 1900 E, UNIVERSITY MEDICAL CENTER 84132 #016-11-2005 L2007 **IM** *012
CHERUKURI, Sudhakar V. 65 N MEDICAL DR 84132 #025-01-2002 L2006 **OPH** *020
CHEUNG, Alfred Kwan-Hon. RENAL SECT VA MED CTR 11H 84148 #035-03-1977 L1983 **NEP IM** *020 †20
CHICHESTER, Danny Lynn. 1140 E 3900 S, STE 300 84124 #030-05-1976 L1980 **GYN** *020 †30
CHICK, Leland R. 24 S 1100 E, STE 201 84102 #020-12-1981 L1989 **PS HS** *020 †85,65
CHIDESTER, Lynn Scott. 5169 COTTONWOOD ST, STE 420 84107 #049-01-1992 L1993 **U** *020 †95
CHILD, Stanley R. ■ 84102 #049-01-1945 L1947 **PD** *071 †55
CHILDS, Donald William. 5169 COTTONWOOD ST, STE 500 84107 #049-01-2003 L2006 **EM** *020 †16
CHILDS, Lane Clifford. 4252 HIGHLAND DR, STE 200 84124 #048-13-1987 L1992 **U** *020 †95
CHIPMAN, Corey Brent. ■ 84124 #038-40-2005 L2006 **IM** *012
CHOUCAIR, Ali Khalil. 324 10TH AVE STE 228 84103 #060-02-1979 L1981 **N OS** *020 †75
CHRASTIL, Jesse Lee. ■ 84105 #030-05-2008 *012
CHRISTENSEN, Bradd K. 1377 E 3900 S STE 104 84124 #049-01-1975 L1980 **PS** *020 †65
CHRISTENSEN, Brent David. 7138 S 20TH E 84121 #016-06-1976 L1979 **PD** *071 †55
CHRISTENSEN, Brent James. 324 10TH AVE STE 224 84103 #049-01-1984 L1989 **GS TRS** *020 †85
CHRISTENSEN, Carl Russell. 50 N MEDICAL DR, RADIOLOGY DEPT 84132 #049-01-1994 L1999 **DR** *020 †80
CHRISTENSEN, Daniel Dee. 501 CHIPETA WAY 84108 #049-01-1972 L1973 **P** *020 †75 ‡
CHRISTENSEN, Danis J. ■ 84121 #049-01-1973 L1975 **IM** *020 †20
CHRISTENSEN, John Curtis. 324 10TH AVE STE 285, HOSPITALIST OFFICE 84103 #035-01-2002 L2003 **IM** *100 †20
CHRISTENSEN, Lorimer T. ■ 84108 #049-01-1961 L1965 **A** *071 †55,03
CHRISTENSEN, Peter Lloyd. 3725 W 4100 S 84120 #049-01-1988 L1991 **FM** *020 †18
CHRISTENSEN, Shane Glade. 6360 S 3000 E, STE 100 84121 #028-34-1991 L1992 **FM** *020 †18
CHRISTENSEN, Thomas James. ■ 84124 #005-06-2007 *012
CHRISTENSEN, Wm Rozelle. ■ 84105 #024-01-1942 L1949 **DR** *071 †80
CHRISTIANSEN, Alicia. ■ 84103 #016-06-2003 L2005 **PD** *100 †55
CHRISTIANSEN, Robert M. 324 10TH AVE STE 155 84103 #049-01-1978 L1982 **OPH OS** *020 †35

■ = Address Information Privacy Protected

CHUN, Young Catherine. 2243 E 6200 S 84121 #028-46-1995 L1996 **AN** *020 †05

CHUNG, Philip Woosung. ■ 84106 #035-46-2001 L2003 **EM** *100 †16

CHURCH, Tyler Glen. ■ 84124 #049-01-2004 L2005 **AN** *012

CLARK, Edward Bowersox. 100 N MEDICAL DR 84113 #035-03-1970 L1996 **PDC PD** *050 †55

CLARK, Erin S. ■ 84108 #026-08-2002 L2003 **OBG** *100 †30

CLARK, Holly B. 1250 E 3900 S, STE 360 84124 #003-01-1997 L2001 **GE** *020 †20

CLARK, Homer Hone. ■ 84109 #010-01-1948 L1953 **PTH** *020 †50

CLARK, Jennifer Hanlon. ■ 84106 #550-04-2003 L2004 **FP** *012 †18

CLARK, Lealand L. ■ 84106 #035-01-1956 L1960 **D** *071 †15

CLARK, Linda Gale. 275 E 200 S 84111 #025-01-1991 L1994 **EM** *020 †16

CLARK, Nicole Christine. 30 N 1900 E, DEPARTMENT OF NEWROLOGY 84132 #028-03-2004 L2005 **N** *012

CLARK, Norman James. 50 N MEDICAL DR 84132 #005-12-1979 L1983 **AN GS** *020 †05

CLARK, Steven Leigh. 1140 E 3900 S, STE 390 84124 #056-05-1979 L1985 **MFM** *020 †30

CLARK, William Matt. 100 N MEDICAL DR 84113 #049-01-1982 L1983 **AN PME** *020 †05

CLARKE, Dana H. 615 ARAPEEN DR, STE 100 84108 #023-01-1966 L1969 **DIA END** *020 †20

CLASSEN, David Carey. 8TH AVENUE & C STREETS, LDS HOSPITAL 84143 #051-01-1982 L1986 **ID IM** *020 †20

CLAWSON, Jeff Johnson. 139 E SOUTH TEMPLE STE 500, MEDICAL PRIORITY CONSULTAN 84111 #049-01-1974 L1975 **FM EM** *020

CLAYTON, Frederic C. UN UT MED CTR, DEPT PATH 84132 #028-02-1977 L1982 **PTH** *020 †50

CLAYTON, John L. 5770 S 250 E, STE 235 84107 #049-01-1950 L1952 **PS** *071 †65

CLEGG, Daniel Orme. 50 N MEDICAL DR 84132 #049-01-1977 L1978 **RHU** *020 †20

CLEMENTS, James Byron. 30 N 1900 E, RM 4C104SOM 84132 #030-05-2006 L2007 **MPD** *012

CLEMMER, Terry Paul. EIGHT AVE AND C ST, LDS HOSPITAL 84143 #010-01-1967 L1976 **CCM IM** *040 †20

CLEVENGER, Todd Aryan. 50 N MEDICAL DR, DEPT OF ORTHOPEDICS 84132 #036-05-2006 L2007 **ORS** *012

CLINE, Richard Clark. 650 E 4500 S, # 201 84107 #048-12-1984 L1985 **NEP IM** *020 †20

CLOTHIER, Brian David. 30 N 1900 E RM 1C026, DEPT OF SURGERY/DIV OF EME 84132 #031-01-2002 L2007 **EMP** *020

CLOWARD, Tom Vernon. 451 BISHOP FEDERAL LN, ST JOSEPH'S VILLA 84115 #049-01-1991 L1994 **PUD** *020 †20

COBELL, William Jay. ■ 84108 #049-01-2008 *012

COCHELLA, Susan E Wohletz. ■ 84108 #031-01-1996 L1997 **FM** *040 †18

COCHRAN, Amalia Lenora. UNIVERSITY OF UTAH, 50 NORTH MED DR SOM 3B313 84132 #048-16-1998 L1999 **OS TRS** *020 †85

CODY, Heather Heim. ■ 84121 #026-08-2002 L2003 **FM** *100

COFFIN, Cheryl Marlene. 100 N MEDICAL DR 84113 #050-02-1980 L1994 **PTH** *020 †50

COLE, Boyd Neil. 1002 E SOUTH TEMPLE # 205 84102 #049-01-1970 L1975 **PS OTO** *020 †45,65

COLE, Chad Douglas. ■ 84116 #049-01-2005 L2007 **NS** *012

COLE, David Frederic. 3460 PIONEER PKWY, INTEGRATED CARE AT 84120 #025-07-1992 L1996 **EM FM** *020 †16

COLE, Harold Stephen, Jr. 2000 S 9TH E 84105 #005-11-1967 L1970 **GE IM** *020 †20

COLEMAN, Donald Aubrey. 590 WAKARA WAY, 3B165 84108 #049-01-1979 L1986 **ORS** *020 †40

COLEMAN, Landon Wayne. 400 C ST 84143 #049-01-1997 L1998 **DMP** *020 †50

COLEMAN, Stephen Dexter. 6360 S 3000 E, STE 100 84121 #049-01-1994 L1998 **FM** *020 †18

COLLETT, Camille. 4745 S 3200 W, OQUIRRH VIEW COMM HLTH CLN 84118 #049-01-1983 L1984 **FM PD** *020 †18

COLLINS, Brian Tyler. 84103 #028-46-1988 L2007 **PTH PCP** *020 †50

COLLINS, Michael Patrick. 324 TENTH AVE STE 205 84103 #034-01-1974 L1978 **TS GS** *020 †85,90

COMBS, George G. ■ 84106 #759-04-1956 L1976 **AN** *071

COMSTOCK, Jessica. ■ 84109 #018-03-2004 L2005 **PTH** *012

CONDIE, Alan Skidmore. UN MED CTR DR 84132 #049-01-1978 L1982 **EM** *071 †16

CONDIE, Lyman Wilson. ■ 84108 #049-01-1945 L1946 **P** *030

CONDON, Virgil Raymond. ■ 84102 #030-05-1955 L1962 **PDR** *071 †80

CONKLIN, Jamie David. 50 N MEDICAL DR 84132 #422-01-2005 L2007 **IM** *012

CONNER, Thomas Kane, Jr. 6360 S 3000 E, STE 100 84121 #041-09-1997 L1998 **FM OBG** *020 †18

CONNOLLY, Michael Scott. 650 KOMAS DR, STE 208 84108 #039-01-2003 L2006 **CHP** *012

CONNORS, Rafe Christian. 30 N 1900 E, DEPT OF SURGERY, RM 3B324 84132 #049-01-2002 L2003 **GS** *012

CONOVER, Thomas Gerard. 501 CHIPETA WAY, UNI 84108 #038-41-2000 L2001 **OS** *100 †55,75

CONSTANTINO, Tawnya M. U. OF UTAH DEPT. OF NEUROL, 3R210 SOM, 30 N 1900 E 84132 #005-12-1994 L1995 **N** *020 †75

CONTRERAS, Yvonne Marie. 575 11TH AVE 84103 #048-12-2004 L2005 **NPM** *012 †20

COOK, Joseph Vernon. ■ 84103 #049-01-1962 L1966 **FM** *020 †18

COOK, Paula Jane. ■ 84102 #049-01-2006 **FP** *012

COON, Valerie Catherine. 175 N MEDICAL DRIVE EAST, DEPT. OF NEUROSURGERY 84132 #005-11-2005 L2006 **NS** *012

COOPER, Andrew D. 82 S 1100 E, STE 303 84102 #045-01-1999 L2005 **ORS** *020 †40

COOPER, Leslie Werder. 2465 PROMONTORY DR 84109 #036-07-1998 L2004 **FM** *020 †18

COOPER, Michelle. ■ 84108 #049-01-2006 L2008 **AN** *012

COOR, Cynthia Lee. 1174 E 2760 S, STE 7 84106 #049-01-1986 L1987 **PD** *020 †55

COPE, David Geo. 8TH AVE & C ST 84143 #031-01-1987 L1988 **FM** *020 †18 ‡

COPELAND, Woodrow W. ■ 84105 #049-01-1954 L1955 **R OS** *071 †80

CORBETT, Marilyn Debra. 1954 FORT UNION BLVD, STE 101 84121 #054-04-1987 L1988 **AN** *020 †05

COREY, Daniel Lyman. 50 N MEDICAL DR, DEPT. OF RADIOLOGY 84132 #049-01-2004 L2005 **DR** *020

CORKERY, John Ripley, III. ■ 84121 #021-01-1970 L1973 **EM** *020 †16

CORNELI, Howard Morgan. 100 N MEDICAL DR 84113 #056-05-1979 L1981 **PD EM** *040 †55

CORWIN, David Lewis. 100 N MEDICAL DR # 3400, PRIMARY CHILDRENS MEDICAL 84113 #025-12-1976 L1999 **CHP PFP** *030 †75

COSGROVE, William Edward. 5770 S 250 E 84107 #049-01-1980 L1981 **PD** *020 †55

COTTER, Murray Adrian, II. ■ 84132 #025-01-2003 L2004 **D** *100 †15

COUDREAUT, Michael F. 8TH AVE AND C ST, LDS HOSPITAL 84143 #035-01-1990 L1994 **P** *020 †75

COULDWELL, William Tupper. 30 N 1900 E, STE 3B409 84132 #067-01-1984 L2002 **NS** *020 †25

COULTER, David Murray. 295 CHIPETA WAY, P O BOX 581289 84108 #035-45-1971 L1981 **NPM** *020 †55

COUPAL, Dustin James. 50 N MEDICAL DR, JOHN MORAN EYE INSTITUTE 84132 #068-01-1999 L2005 *100

COWAN, Leland Burt. ■ 84105 #035-01-1953 L1958 **RO GS** *071 †85,80

COWLEY, Collin Geo. 100 N MEDICAL DR, STE 1500 84113 #049-01-1992 L1993 **PDC** *020 †55

COWLEY, Cris G. 5848 FASHION BLVD 84107 #049-01-1977 L1978 **AN** *020 †05

COX, Chad Martin. 100 N MEDICAL DR 84113 #041-14-2005 L2006 **PD** *012

COX, Gina Marie. 8TH AVE & C ST 84143 #049-01-1998 L2001 **FM** *020 †18

COX, Jennifer Amy. 1060 E 100 S, STE 400 84102 #001-02-1990 L1992 **PD** *020 †55

COX, Shannon Marie. 30 N 1900 E, RM C412 84132 #047-07-2006 L2007 **PD** *012

COYLE, Dustin Eric. 30 N 1900 E, STE 3C444 84132 #049-01-2001 L2002 **AN** *020 †05 ‡

CRAIG, William H. 50 N MEDICAL DR, PHYSICAL MEDICINE REHABILI 84132 #061-01-1999 L2001 **PM** *012

CRAMER, Joseph Grant. 5770 S 250 E 84107 #003-01-1977 L1981 **PD** *020 †55

CRANDALL, Alan Slade. 4400 S 700 E, STE 240 84107 #049-01-1973 L1981 **OPH** *020 †35

CRAPO, Robert Olsen. LDS HOSPITAL, PULMONARY DIV 84103 #035-45-1969 L1973 **PUD IM** *030

CRAVEIRO, Cristina Marie. ■ 84108 #049-01-2004 L2005 **AN** *012

CREAGER, Dick Nash. 3460 PIONEER PKWY, INTEGRATED CARE AT 84120 #049-01-1982 L1983 **EM MDM** *020

CRIM, Julia Ruth. ■ 84103 #035-01-1985 L1997 **DR** *020 †80 ‡

CRIST, Jonathan Clark. 375 CHIPETA WAY, STE A 84108 #031-01-2004 L2007 **FM** *020 †18

CRITCHFIELD, Gregory C. 320 WAKARA WAY, MYRIAD GENETIC LABORATORIE 84108 #049-01-1980 L1987 **PTH** *020 †50

CROSKELL, Sarah Elisabeth. 520 TENTH AVE, 520 TENTH AVE 84103 #019-02-1991 L1992 **PD** *020 †55

CROUCH, Andre Kim. 30 N 1900 E 1C026, DIVSION OF EMERGENCY MEDIC 84132 #005-12-2003 L2004 **EM** *012 †20

CRUZ, Pedro A. 4021 S 700 E STE 300 84107 #264-02-1960 L1970 **PTH** *071 †50

CSONTOS, Eileen Rae. 30 N 1900 E, RM 3C444 84132 #056-06-1985 L1986 **AN** *040 †05

CULBERTSON, Joe C. 370 E SOUTH TEMPLE, STE 550 84111 #047-05-1971 L1977 **P CHP** *020 †75

CUMMINS, Brendan Forrest. 8TH AVE & C ST, LDSH- DEPT OF EMERGENCY ME 84143 #005-06-1997 L2000 **EM** *020 †16

CURRAN, Marilyn Louise. 461 S 400 E 84111 #016-06-1984 L1985 **FM** *020 †18

CURRIER, Nathan Robt. 50 N MEDICAL DR, 3B420 SOM 84132 #017-20-1979 L1985 **P FM** *020 †18,75

CURTIS, Benjamin David. 2177 DOWNINGTON AVE, U OF U/DEPT OF ORTHOPAEDI 84108 #049-01-2006 L2008 **ORS** *012

CURTIS, David Earl. 1250 E 3900 S, STE 440 84124 #049-01-1976 L1981 **ORS OSM** *020 †40

CURTIS, Glade Brian. 6337 HIGHLAND DR, # 2054 84121 #035-45-1979 L1983 **OBG** *020 †30

CURTIS, Mark Kennedy. 5770 S 250 E, STE 135 84107 #003-01-1977 L1981 **OBG** *020 †30

CUTILLO, Antonio. 50 N MEDICAL DR 84132 #561-17-1957 L1977 **PUD IM** *050

CUTLER, Carolee Marie. ■ 84124 #049-01-2006 **GS** *012

CUTLER, Michael Larry. 650 E 4500 S, STE 300 84107 #021-01-1991 L1994 **FM** *020 †18

CUTLIP, Cheryle Lynne. 3725 W 4100 S 84120 #055-01-1995 L1999 **FM** *020 †18

CYRUS, Rachel Marie. 30 N 1900 E RM 4C104, UNIV OF UTAH MED CTR 84132 #016-01-2005 L2006 **IM** *012

DACCARETT, Marcos. 30 N 1900 E, 4A100 84132 #264-04-2000 L2006 **ICE** *012

DAFTARY, Ameet Shirish. 100 N MEDICAL DR, PEDIATRICS PULMONARY 84113 #496-38-1995 L2007 **PDP** *100 †55

DAHL, Douglas Seely. ■ 84108 #016-06-1961 L1969 **U** *071 †95

DAILEY, Andrew Timothy. 175 N. MEDICAL DR. EAST, DEPT OF NEUROSURGERY 84132 #035-01-1989 L1998 **NS** *020 †25

DAINES, Stephen Pinkney. 8TH AVE & C ST 84143 #010-01-1972 L1973 **OBG** *071

DAINES, Steven Marc. UNIV OF UTAH SCH OF MED, OTOLARYNGOLOGY - HEAD AND 84132 #005-15-2006 L2008 **OTO** *012

DAL CANTO, Florence Clare. ■ 84124 #028-34-2002 L2008 **PD** *020 †55

DALCANTO, Richard Andrew. 333 S 900 E, SALT LAKE CLINIC 84102 #005-11-2000 L2005 **ORS** *100

DALL, Joel Tracy. 1160 E 3900 S STE 5000, SALT LAKE ORTHOPAEDIC CLN 84124 #049-01-1990 L1994 **PM** *020 †60

DAMCE, Melanie Ann. ■ 84109 #005-02-2006 **GS** *012

DANCE, Timothy Robert. ■ 84109 #005-02-2008 *012

DANENHAUER, Karen Vesely. 30 N 1900 E, DIVISION OF EMERGENCY MEDI 84132 #016-45-2005 L2006 **EM** *012

DANFORTH, Rebecca Louise. 50 N MEDICAL DR, UNIVERSITY OF UTAH HOSPITA 84132 #054-04-2002 L2004 **IM** *100

DANGERFIELD, Enoch Gibson. 1414 E 4500 S, STE 5 84117 #049-01-1961 L1963 **P N** *072

DANSIE, David Marvin. 100 N MEDICAL DR, MEDICAL IMAGING 84113 #049-01-1999 L2001 **PDR** *020 †55,80

DANSIE, Elbert M. 745 E 300 S, BRYNER CLINIC PEDIATRICS 84102 #049-01-1962 L1964 **PD** *071 †55

DASCOMB, Kristin Kimberly. 30 N 1900 E, RM 4B319 84132 #021-05-2002 L2006 **ID** *012 †20

D'ASTOUS, Jacques L. FAIRFAX RD AT VIRGINIA ST, SHRINERS HOSP 84103 #065-09-1972 L1995 **OP** *020 †40

DATZ, Frederick Lloyd. ■ 84124 #048-12-1975 L1980 **DR** *071 †28

DAUBS, Michael David. 590 WAKARA WAY 84108 #031-01-1989 L2006 **OSS** *020 †40

DAVE, Sonal Bhasker. 65 N MEDICAL DR, DEPT OF OPTHALMOLOGY (ELAI 84132 #018-03-2003 L2007 **OPH** *100

DAVENPORT, Karen Marie. 4021 S 700 E STE 300 84107 #038-43-1993 L1999 **PD** *020 †55

DAVEY, Debra L. 30 N 1900 E RM 1C4, UNIVERSITY OF UTAH, DEPART 84132 #007-02-2006 L2007 **PD** *012

DAVID, Traci Lynn. 501 CHIPETA WAY 84108 #028-46-1987 L1988 **CHP** *020 †75

DAVIDSON, Hans Christian. 50 N MEDICAL DR, UNIV UT DEPT RAD 84132 #049-01-1989 L1996 **DR** *020 †80

DAVIS, Alan Munter. 50 N MEDICAL DR, UNIVERSITY OF UTAH 84132 #422-01-1987 L1997 **PM** *020 †50

DAVIS, Daniel Woods. 525 E 100 S, STE 500 84102 #047-07-1989 L1990 **IM** *020 †20 ‡

DAVIS, Jennifer Jean. 50 N MEDICAL DR, DEPT OF ANESTHESIOLOGY 84132 #040-02-1998 L1999 **AN** *040

DAVIS, Marc Jerome. 5050 S 2100 E 84117 #016-11-1988 L1993 **P** *020

DAVIS, Roger Woods. ■ 84115 #049-01-1968 L1969 **PM** *071 †60

DAVIS, Ronda Payne. 5770 S 550 W 84123 #005-12-1996 L1997 **OS** *020 †75

DAVIS, Roy Kim. 30 N 1900 E, RM 3B110 84132 #049-01-1975 L1983 **OTO** *020 †45

DAVIS, Tyler Scott. ■ 84103 #049-01-2007 *012

DAVIS, Virgil Welch. 30 N 1900 E, ROOM 1C26 DIV OF EM 84132 #028-03-1996 L2007 **EM** *020 †16

DAWSON, Bessann. ■ 84108 #041-02-1986 L1987 **FM** *020 †18
DAWSON, Kristin. ■ 84105 #020-12-2007 **P** *012
DAWSON, Matthew Stewart. ■ 84105 #020-12-2007 **EM** *012
DAY, John David. 5169 COTTONWOOD ST, BLDG B # 510 84107 #023-07-1995 L2001 **CD** *020 †20
DAY, Julie Louise. 1525 W 2100 S 84119 #049-01-1979 L1980 **GP** *020
DAY, Kristen Elizabeth. ■ 84109 #039-01-2007 **PD** *012
DAY, Ronald Wm. 100 N MEDICAL DR, PRIMARY CHILDREN'S MEDICAL 84113 #049-01-1984 L1991 **PDC PD** *050 †55
DAY, Stefani Jane. 461 S 400 E, CENTRAL CITY CHILDREN HOSP 84111 #025-01-1998 L1999 **FM** *020 †18
DAYNES, Randall Price. 3920 S 1100 E STE 220 84124 #010-01-1975 L1980 **FM** *020 †18
DAYNES, Todd Ellsworth. 324 10TH AVE STE 260 84103 #049-01-2001 L2005 **OPH** *020 †35
DAYTON, Jodi Foley. 3C-444 SOM, 30 NORTH 1900 EAST 84132 #049-01-2002 L2003 **AN** *100 †05
DEAN, Alan Porter. ■ 84124 #035-45-1961 L1971 **AN** *020
DEAN, Jonathan Michael. 100 N MEDICAL DR, UNIT2ND FLOOR 84113 #016-06-1977 L1987 **CCM AN** *050 †55
DEAN, Nathan Christopher. 333 S 900 E 84102 #005-11-1977 L1978 **PUD CCM** *020 †20
DEATON, Emily Christina. 275 E 200 S 84111 #020-12-2002 L2003 **IM** *100
DE BRUIN, Clayton Herbert. ■ 84103 #040-02-1960 L1963 **AN** *075
DECHET, Christopher Burr. 1950 CIRCLE OF HOPE DR 84112 #041-01-1995 L2001 **U** *020 †95
DECHET, Pilar Weiss. 2000 S 900 E 84115 #041-01-1995 L2001 **ORS** *020 †40
DECKER, Harold Alvin. ■ 84102 #049-01-1956 L1959 **PD PHP** *071 †55
DECOU, Jennifer Ann. 30 N 1900 E RM 3C444, DEPARTMENT OF ANESTHESIOLO 84132 #049-01-2003 L2004 **AN** *100
DEISS, Elmer Andrew. ■ 84103 #036-07-1956 L1967 **HEM ON** *030 †20
DE JOHN, Terri. 540 ARAPEEN DR STE 110, HYPERBARIC MED CTR 84108 #049-01-1978 L1979 **EM OS** †16
DE LA GARZA, Amy Noel. ■ 84108 #007-02-2005 **OTO** *100
DELAVAN, George W, III. PO BOX 142001, UTAH DEPT OF HLTH CFHS 84114 #048-04-1970 L1977 **PD** *020 †55
DEL CASTILLO, Alexander N. 1200 E 3900 S, ST HARK'S SENIOR HEALTH CE 84124 #748-01-1992 L1999 **IMG** *020 †20
DELGADO, Julio Cesar. 15 MEDICAL DR, STE 1100-F 84112 #264-09-1993 L2006 **PTH** *020 †50
DELLACROCE, John Thomas. 50 N MEDICAL DR, OPTHALMOLOGY DEPT. 84132 #021-06-2002 L2006 **OPH** *100
DEN BLEYKER, Jennifer J. 3725 W 4100 S 84120 #016-06-1996 L1997 **FM** *020 †18
DENNY, Gerald Blalock. ■ 84101 #036-05-2007 **IM** *012
DESJARDINS, Georges. 3C-444 SOM, 30 NORTH 1900 EAST 84132 #067-03-1988 L2006 **AN** *020 †05
DESPAIN, Robert Verne. 315 S 10TH E 84102 #010-01-1957 L1958 **OPH** *071 †35
DEVLIN, Kwanza Nicole. 3336 PIONEER PKWY, STE 201 84120 #030-05-2005 L2008 **FP** *012
DE VRIES, Catherine Rhu. 30 N 1900 E, RM 3B110 84132 #005-11-1984 L2000 **U GS** *020 †95
DE WEERD, Peter James. 1300 E 3900 S, ST MARKS HOSP EMERG RM 84124 #036-05-2001 L2003 **FM** *020 †18
DE WITT, Lucy Dana. 30 N 1900 E, STE 3R210 84132 #021-01-1978 L2004 **N** *020 †75
DIAZ, Jason Anthony. 50 N MEDICAL DR, DIV OF OTOLARYNGOLOGY 3C-1 84132 #012-01-2003 L2004 **OTO** *012
DICKERSON, Ty Triston. 100 N MEDICAL DR, DIVISION OF INPATIENT MEDI 84113 #018-03-1998 L2006 **PD** *020 †55
DICKINSON, Ruth Ann. 500 FOOTHILL BLVD # 116-A 84148 #036-01-1987 L1994 **P** *020 †75
DICKSON, Landon Ellsworth. ■ 84108 #049-01-2008 *012
DIEL, Heath Rulin. 7100 S 2155 E 84121 #049-01-2002 L2003 **AN** *020 †05
DIESSNER, Ardell Wm. ■ 84107 #026-04-1948 L1949 **P** *071 †75
DIGRE, Kathleen Bernice. 65 MARIO CAPECCHI DR, DEPT OF NEUROLOGY 84132 #018-03-1981 L1987 **N OPH** *020 †75
DILDY, Gary Andrew, III. 1140 E 3900 S, STE 390 84124 #021-01-1985 L1991 **OBG MFM** *020 †30
DILLON, Betty J Pintar. ■ 84108 #038-06-1951 L1957 **AN** *071 †05
DIMICK, Roland Page. 2000 S 900 E, DEPARTMENT OF PEDIATRICS 84105 #049-01-1997 L2000 **PD** *020 †55
DINH, Elena T. ■ 84103 #049-01-2008 *012
DI RUSSO, Roseann L. 7788 S 3500 E 84121 #041-02-1991 L1996 **PD** *020 †55
DITLEV-ASTE, Lisa. 2150 S MAIN ST STE 403 84115 #048-13-1986 L1988 **IM** *071 †20
DOANE, John Allen. 50 N MEDICAL DR, DIV GEN INTERNAL MED 84132 #036-05-1987 L1988 **IM** *020 †20
DODDS, Thomas Andrew. 8TH AVE & 'C' ST, LDS HOSPITAL 84143 #032-01-1986 L1998 **PM** *050 †60
DODSON, Mark Kane. 30 N 1900 E, B200 U OF UTAH DPT OB/GYN 84132 #047-20-1988 L1995 **GO OBG** *020 †30
DOLCOURT, John Lawrence. 100 N MEDICAL DR 84113 #007-02-1975 L1980 **NPM PD** *040 †55
DONAHUE, Kevin L. ■ 84106 #048-14-1990 L1991 **P** *020
DONALDSON, David L. 615 ARAPEEN DR STE 100, UTAH DIABETES CTR 84108 #005-14-1976 L1999 **PDE PD** *020 †55
DONNELLY, Ryan Thomas. ■ 84106 #028-34-2007 **PD** *012
DONOHUE, Anne. ■ 84108 #010-02-1999 L2000 **GPM** *012 †18
DORROUGH, Michael Benjami. 30 N 1900 E, ANESTHESIA DEPT, RM 3C444 84132 #056-06-2005 L2006 **AN** *012
DOTY, John Richard. 5169 COTTONWOOD ST, STE 600 84107 #010-02-1994 L2003 **TS** *020 †85,90
DOWLING, Alice. 50 N MEDICAL DR 84132 #286-04-1993 **PD** *012
DOWNEY, Earl Courtney, Jr. 100 N MEDICAL DR STE 2600 84113 #016-06-1978 L2001 **PDS GS** *020 †85
DOYLE, Anthony James. UNIV OF UTAH SCH OF MED/RA, 1A71 MEDICAL CENTER 84132 #671-01-1981 L1989 **DR** *040 †80
DOYLE, Gerard Stephen. 50 N MEDICAL DR, UUHSC EMERGENCY DEPARTMENT 84132 #050-02-1994 L2004 **EM** *020 †16
DRAGE, Brian Gary. 4460 HIGHLAND DR, HIGHLAND FAMILY PRACTICE 84124 #056-06-1996 L1997 **FM** *020 †18
DRAKE, Frederick Thurston. ■ 84103 #049-01-2008 *012
DRAPER, Michael Lynn. 30 N 1900 E RM 2B200, UNIV OF UT OB-GYN DEPT 84132 #049-01-1992 L1993 **MFM OBG** *020 †30
DRIES, David Christopher. 50 N MEDICAL DR, OPHTHALMOLOGY & VISUAL SCI 84132 #056-05-1992 L2002 **OPH** *020 †35

DRINKAUS, Harold John. 77 S 700 E 84102 #025-07-1964 L1969 **PD** *071 †55
DROSTEN, Ralph. 30 N 1900 E RM1A71, RADIOLOGY DEPT 84132 #836-01-1992 L2003 **R NM** *020 †80
DRUZGAL, Colleen. ■ 84105 #041-01-2004 L2005 **PD** *020 †55
DRUZGAL, Thomas Jason. ■ 84105 #041-01-2003 L2004 **DR** *012
DUBE, Bukhosi Boniface. ■ 84108 #049-01-2008 *012
DUDLEY, Nanette Christine. 100 N MEDICAL DR 84113 #041-01-1987 L1992 **PEM** *020 †55
DUDOVA, Nadezda Ludmila. ■ 84124 #286-03-1965 L1975 **AN** *074
DUFFY, Keith Lawrence. UNIV OF UTAH DEPT OF DERM, 4B454 SCHOOL OF MEDICINE 84132 #035-15-2004 L2006 **D** *012
DUFFY, Owen H. 8TH AVE AND 'C' ST, EMERGENCY DEPARTMENT 84143 #049-01-1976 L1978 **EM** *020 †20,16
DUHON, Bradley Stuart. 30 N 1900 E, DEPT. OF NEUROSURGERY 3B40 84132 #048-14-2004 L2005 **NS** *012
DULL, Randal Owen. 30 N 1900 E, ANESTHESIOLOGY, 3C-444, SO 84132 #016-11-1995 L2003 **AN** *020 †05
DUNCAN, David Laurence. 500 FOOTHILL BLVD BLDG 47, VAMC SLC 84148 #019-02-1991 L1992 **P** *020 †75
DUNKERLEY, Christopher Jo. 3C-444 SOM, 30 NORTH 1900 EAST 84132 #049-01-2006 L2008 **AN** *012
DUNN, Harold Kenneth. 590 WAKARA WAY 84108 #048-04-1963 L1969 **ORS** *020 †40
DUNNAVANT, Gregory R. 8TH AVE & C ST 84143 #049-01-1990 L1992 **IM** *020 †20
DUNSON, Wm Albert, Jr. 2000 CIRCLE OF HOPE DR, UNIVERSITY OF UTAH 84112 #036-05-1992 L1993 **IM** *020 †20
DURCAN, Simon Philip. 100 N MEDICAL DR 84113 #049-01-1998 L1999 **AN** *020 †05
DURHAM, George Homer. 525 E 100 S, STE 500 84102 #036-07-1973 L1974 **PD** *020 †55
DUVERNAY, Patrice Ann. 333 S 900 E 84102 #032-01-1989 L1990 **N** *020 †75
EBORN, Shana Kinsey. 2295 FOOTHILL DR 84109 #049-01-2000 L2005 **FM** *020 †18
ECKART, Danielle Erin. LDS HOSPITAL, 8TH AVE AND C STREET 84143 #034-01-2007 *012
EDGLEY, Steven Richard. 30 N 1900 E 84132 #016-43-2001 L2004 **PM** *020 †60
EDSON, D Michael. ■ 84108 #049-01-1966 L1967 **R** *071 †80
EDWARDS, Hannah Eileen. 1525 W 2100 S 84119 #010-02-1999 L2000 **GPM** *020 †18,70
EDWARDS, Meghan Rebecca. UNIV OF UTAH HLTH SCI CTR, 50 N MED DR 84132 #010-02-2006 L2008 **GS** *012
EDWARDS, Susan Lynn. 1050 E SOUTH TEMPLE 84102 #049-01-1982 L1983 **FM** *020 †18
EDWARDS, Thos Stonestreet. 3725 W 4100 S 84120 #039-05-1986 L1987 **IC CD** *020 †20
EFSTRATIADIS, Stilianos. 30 N 1900 E, RM 4A100 84132 #561-24-1998 L2005 **CD** *012 †20
EGAN, Talmage Dan. 30 N 1900 E, RM 3C444 84132 #049-01-1986 L1987 **AN GS** *020 †05
EICHWALD, Ernst J. UNIV OF UTAH MED CENTER 84112 #407-05-1938 L1969 **CLP PTH** *050 †50
EKINS, Jacob Brent. ■ 84108 #049-01-2008 *012
EKSTRAND, Jeffrey John. 100 N MEDICAL DR, PEDIATRICS DEPT 84113 #056-05-2002 L2007 **PD** *020
ELBERT, William Val. PO BOX 713100, COMP HEALTH LOCUM TENENS 84171 #012-01-1991 L1992 **FM** *020 †18
ELDREDGE, Stephen James. ■ 84117 #049-01-1989 L1990 **AN** *075
ELIASON, Mark Joseph. ■ 84105 #005-15-2003 L2006 **D** *012
ELIASON, Richard James. ■ 84103 #049-01-1955 **U** *071 †95
ELKINS, John Glen. ■ 84105 #016-02-1979 L1981 **GP** *020
ELLER, Charles David. 1200 E 3900 S 84124 #036-05-2001 L2005 **EM** *020 †16
ELLINGTON, Stewart Lane. 24 S 1100 E # EAST-103 84102 #036-01-1969 L1974 **GE IM** *020 †20
ELLIOTT, Keith Leonard. ■ 84103 #005-12-2007 *012
ELLIS, Diane Elizabeth. ■ 84105 #033-06-1994 L1998 **OBG** *020 †30
ELLIS, Gregory Wilkins. 2844 PALMA WAY 84121 #049-01-1987 L1988 **P CHP** *020 †75
ELLSWORTH, Homer S. 5770 S 250 E STE G80 84107 #010-01-1945 L1948 **OBG** *071 †30
ELSTAD, Mark Richard. 50 N MEDICAL DR 84132 #026-04-1980 L1983 **PUD CCM** *050 †20
ELY, Joy Wilson. ■ 84105 #049-01-1950 L1951 **P** *072
EMAM, Mansoor S. 415 E 3900 S 84107 #049-01-1990 L1991 **IM** *020 †20
EMERSON, Lyska Leigh. 50 N MEDICAL DR, 3B420 SOM 84132 #048-14-1995 L2000 **PTH** *020 †50
EMERY, Garrett John. 370 E SOUTH TEMPLE, STE 260 84111 #016-42-1995 L1998 **EM** *020 †16
ENGEN, Judy J. 120 N 200 W RM 201, STATE UTAH 84103 #018-03-1980 L1981 **FM** *075 †18
ENGLISH, John Byron. 1954 FORT UNION BLVD, STE 100 84121 #049-01-1973 L1977 **AN** *020 †05
ENGLISH, Patrick H. 1200 E 3900 S 84124 #049-01-1976 L1977 **AN GP** *020 †20
ENNIS, Harry H. ■ 84106 #010-01-1952 L1956 **OBG** *071
ENSIGN, Margaret Frances. 296 E 3900 S, SPECIALISTS 84107 #054-04-1984 L1985 **DR IM** *020 †20
ENSLIN, Kyle Richard. 1954 FORT UNION BLVD # 104, MILLCREEK ANESTHESIA INC 84121 #005-14-1978 L1982 **AN OS** *020 †20,05
ERICK, Antonia Reyes. 617 E 3900 S 84107 #748-11-1965 L1977 **AN** *071 †05
ERICKSEN, Marty L. 100 N MEDICAL DR 84113 #060-01-1996 L1998 **AN** *020
ERICKSON, Jeffrey Gus. 30 N 1900 E 84132 #049-01-2003 L2004 **PD** *100 †55
ERZINGER, Joanna. 1160 E 3900 S, STE 4100 84124 #005-06-1987 L1991 **N** *020
ESHAM, Kristina Eve. 100 N MEDICAL DR, PCMC 84113 #038-40-1997 L2002 **PD** *020 †55
ESKANDARI, Ramin. DEPT OF NEUROSURGERY, UNIV OF UTAH HOSP 84132 #025-07-2006 L2008 **NS** *012
ESPLIN, Michael Sean. 30 N 1900 E RM 2B 84132 #049-01-1993 L1994 **OBG** *020 †30
ETHERIDGE, Susan Payne. 100 N MEDICAL DR STE 1500, PRIMARY CHILD HOSP DPT PDC 84113 #016-01-1987 L1994 **PDC ICE** *020 †55
ETHERINGTON, Linsey. ■ 84108 #049-01-2004 L2006 **GS** *012
EVANS, Bruce Gordon. 1160 E 3900 S STE 5000, SALT LAKE ORTHOPAEDIC CLN 84124 #003-01-1981 L1982 **ORS OAR** *020 †40
EVANS, Daniel Ashby. 100 N MEDICAL DR 84113 #049-01-1996 L2001 **AN PAN** *020 †05
EVANS, Edmund Cannon. 745 E 3RD S 84102 #049-01-1955 L1956 **PD** *020 †55
EVANS, Gordon Robbins. ■ 84108 #049-01-1957 L1958 **IM** *071
EVANS, Matthew Craig. 1138 WILMINGTON AVE 84106 #038-40-2005 L2006 **FP** *012
EVERITT, Melanie D. 100 N MEDICAL DR, PRIMARY CHILDREN'S MEDICAL 84113 #028-02-1999 L2005 **PDC** *020 †55
EVERTON, Kathryn Louise. ■ 84108 #049-01-2007 *012
EYRE, Harmon J. ■ 84106 #049-01-1966 L1971 **IM HEM** *030 †20
EYRING, Edward Joseph, II. 348 E 4500 S STE 200 84107 #047-06-1994 L1995 **CRS GS** *020 †85,10
EYZAGUIRRE, Carlos Edward. 410 CHIPETA WAY 84108 #231-01-1947 **OS** *030

■ = Address Information Privacy Protected

FABBROCINI, Maria F. 100 N MEDICAL DR, PRIM CHLDRNS MED CTR 84113 #056-05-1998 L2005 **PAN** *020 †05
FABER, David Wayne. 4400 S 700 E, STE 200 84107 #005-18-1991 L1997 **OPH** *020 †35
FABER, Dorian Rey. 4638 HUNTERS RIDGE CIR D 84124 #049-01-1961 L1963 **PTH NM** *062 †28,50
FAIRBANKS, Bryce Jay. ■ 84117 #049-01-1946 L1948 **OPH OTO** *071 †35 ‡
FAIRBANKS, Grant Andreas. 1151 E 3900 S STE B110 84124 #051-07-1992 L1994 **PS CS** *020 †65
FAIRBANKS, Grant Ruthven. 1151 E 3900 S STE B110 84124 #049-01-1964 L1966 **PS GS** *020 †85,65
FAISAL, Misbahuddin. ■ 84121 #704-02-1999 L2005 **PCC** *012 †20
FAIX, Roger Gordon. 295 CHIPETA WAY 2N122, NEONATOLOGY DIVISION 84108 #035-20-1975 L2002 **NPM PD** *020 †55
FALAHATI-NINI, Alireza. 1250 E 3900 S, STE 420 84124 #154-07-1994 L2001 **END** *020 †20
FANG, Deanna C. ■ 84102 #028-34-2008 *012
FANG, Oliver Lin. ■ 84103 #049-01-1995 *100
FANG, Wayne Sy. ■ 84106 #016-06-2002 L2007 **RNR** *012 †80
FARNEY, Robert Jacob. 333 S 9TH E 84102 #019-02-1970 L1974 **PUD IM** *020 †20
FARNSWORTH, James Richard. 400 C ST 84143 #049-01-1994 L1995 **PCP** *020 †50
FARNSWORTH, Kent Walker. 1509 FEDERAL HEIGHTS DR 84103 #049-01-1971 L1972 **OBG** *071 †30 ‡
FARNSWORTH, Steven Thad. 5848 FASHION BLVD 84107 #049-01-1990 L1992 **AN** *020 †05
FARRUKH, Hanadi. 555 FOOTHILL DR, STE 203 84112 #605-01-1989 L1992 **IM** *020 †20
FARRUKH, Imad Saad E. 50 N MEDICAL DR, 3B420 SOM 84132 #528-01-1980 L1988 **PUD IM** *050
FASSL, Bernhard. 100 N MEDICAL DR, PCMC 84113 #154-07-1995 L2003 **PD** *020 †55
FAUSETT, M Bardett. 50 N MEDICAL DR, RM 2B200 84132 #023-12-1993 L1997 **MFM OBG** *020 †30
FEINAUER, Lyman R, Jr. 8TH AVE & C ST 84143 #049-01-1971 L1972 **PD NPM** *075
FELEMA, Biftu Gebremichae. ■ 84102 #005-12-2007 **IM** *012
FELIX, Brent Argyle. 1160 E 3900 S, STE 500 84124 #049-01-1991 L1997 **OSS** *020 †40
FELT, Robert S. 48 W BROADWAY APT 2004N 84101 #049-01-1950 L1954 **OPH** *071 †35
FENTON, Peter Craig O. 6360 S 3000 E, STE 300 84121 #566-01-1992 L2001 **GE** *020 †20
FENTON, Stephen Joseph. 30 N 1900 E, DEPT OF SURGERY 84132 #030-06-2002 L2003 **GS** *012
FEOLA, Bonnie Blazar. ■ 84108 #048-04-1990 L1997 **PD** *020 †55
FEOLA, Giosue Peter. 100 N MEDICAL DR 84113 #048-04-1990 L1997 **PDR VIR** *020 †80
FERGERSON, Byron Douglas. 50 N MEDICAL DR, UNIVERSITY OF UTAH/ANESTHE 84132 #016-06-2003 L2004 **AN** *100
FERGUSON, James Mecham. 448 E 6400 S STE 200, PHARMACOLOGY RESEARCH CORP 84107 #005-11-1971 L1986 **P** *050 †75
FERGUSON, Robert Thos. ■ 84124 #049-01-1955 L1958 **OTO** *071 †45
FERNANDEZ, Genaro. ■ 84103 #007-02-2007 **IM** *012
FERRE, Richard Chas. 5770 S 1500 W, WASATCH CANYONS CAMPUS 84123 #049-01-1970 L1974 **CHP P** *020 †75
FERREIRA, Paul J. 2180 E 4500 S STE 210 84117 #030-05-1993 L1994 **PD** *020 †55 ‡
FIELD, Patricia. ■ 84107 #065-01-1950 L1963 **P** *072 †75
FIELDS, Katherine Sibley. 30 N 1900 E, DERMATOLOGY DEPT 84132 #051-04-2002 L2003 **D** *100 †15
FILLOUX, Francis Maurice. 30 N 1900 E, STE 3R210 84132 #005-14-1981 L1982 **N CHN** *050 †55,75
FINE, Perry Gordon. 615 ARAPEEN DR STE 200 84132 #051-04-1981 L1982 **AN PLM** *062 †05
FINLAYSON, Keith Neil. 333 S 900 E 84102 #049-01-1975 L1976 **OTO** *020 †45
FINLAYSON, Troy Wesley. ■ 84106 #049-01-2008 *012
FINN, Mike A. 175 N. MEDICAL DR. EAST, DEPT OF NEURO SURGERY 84132 #005-14-2003 L2004 **NS** *012
FISCHBACH, Ada Jennifer. 333 S 900 E 84102 #049-01-1978 L1980 **RO** *020 †80
FISCHER, Rachel Caryn. ■ 84105 #049-01-2006 L2008 **IM** *012
FISHER, Barbra Mindy. 50 N MEDICAL DR 2B200, UNIV OF UTAH DEPT OF OBGYN 84132 #056-06-2002 L2003 **OBG** *100
FISHER, Harry E, Jr. 1050 E SOUTH TEMPLE 84102 #039-01-1952 L1956 **U GS** *071 †95
FISHER, Kerry Scott. 324 10TH AVE, STE 224 84103 #028-34-1987 L1993 **GS** *020 †85
FISHER, Peter Charles. 4252 HIGHLAND DR, STE 200 84124 #049-01-2001 L2005 **U** *020 †95
FISHLER, Kenneth O. ■ 84108 #049-01-1948 L1949 **PD OS** *071 †55
FITZGERALD, Jason Troy. 30 N 1900 E, UNIV OF UTAH MED CTR 84132 #054-04-1999 L2006 **TS** *012 †85
FITZPATRICK, Wm Knox, Jr. ■ 84108 #012-01-1952 L1958 **MDM OS** *071 †85,90
FLAHERTY, Erin Elizabeth. ■ 84103 #050-02-2008 *012
FLAMMER, Mark Gordon. 3460 PIONEER PKWY, INTEGRATED CARE AT 84120 #049-01-1984 L1990 **EM ESM** *020 †16
FLANIGAN, Kevin Matthew. 30 N 1900 E, STE 3R210 84132 #016-01-1990 L1995 **N** *020 †75
FLEMING, William R. 4021 S 700 E STE 300 84107 #654-01-1989 L1991 **FM** *020 †18
FLINT, Ivan Dean. 1250 E 3900 S STE 450 84124 #049-01-1988 L1996 **D** *020 †15
FLORELL, Scott Robert. SCIENCES CENTER, UNIVERSITY OF UTAH HEALTH 84132 #030-05-1993 L1994 **D DMP** *020 †50,15
FLORENCE, Lauren O. 1250 E 3900 S STE 330 84124 #049-01-1981 L1989 **PS GS** *020 †65
FLUCHEL, Mark Naihaniel. 100 N MEDICAL DR, 4TH FL 84113 #047-05-2000 L2007 **PHO** *100 †55
FLYNN, Jeannette Riddle. 100 N MEDICAL DR, PRIMARY CHILDREN'S MEDICAL 84113 #048-14-2000 L2005 **PD** *100
FLYNN, Michael Clinton. 3730 W 4700 S 84118 #048-14-2000 L2004 **MPD** *020 †20,55
FLYNN, Richard Rowan. 1200 E 3900 S 84124 #023-01-1958 L1963 **R PD** *071 †55,80
FOGG, Reed E. 5810 FASHION BLVD, STE 300 84107 #049-01-1962 L1964 **ORS OSS** *020 †40
FOLEY, John F. 370 9TH AVE STE 106 84103 #056-06-1983 L1984 **N OS** *020 †75
FOLKERS, Milan Elmer, III. ■ 84102 #026-04-2003 L2004 **GE** *012 †20
FOLLAND, David Stoker. 100 N MEDICAL DR 84113 #035-20-1972 L1977 **PD** *020 †55
FOOT, Laura Marie. 1686 DOWNINGTON AVE 84105 #049-01-2004 L2005 **U** *012
FOOTE, Mark Chas. 333 S 900 E 84102 #010-01-1989 L1993 **P** *020 †75
FORD, Clyde De Jong. 8TH AVE & C STREET 84143 #049-01-1971 L1976 **HEM ON** *020 †20
FORD, Clynn R. 333 S 900 E 84102 #016-06-1951 L1960 **TS CD** *020 †85,90
FORD, Rulon Newell. 1200 E 3900 S 84124 #035-20-1956 L1963 **DR** *071 †80
FORSBERG, Farrell G. 333 S 900 E 84102 #030-06-1975 L1978 **R** *020 †80
FOSNOCHT, David Edward. 1150 MORAN BLDG, 175 N. MEDICAL DRIVE EAST 84132 #041-01-1991 L1998 **EM** *020 †16
FOSTER, Carol Ann. 615 ARAPEEN DR STE 100, UTAH DIABETES CENTER 84108 #028-02-1978 L2005 **PDE** *050 †55
FOSTER, Norman Louis. 30 N 1900 E, RM 3R210 84132 #028-02-1977 L1979 **N** *050 †75
FOSTER, William A. 617 E 3900 S 84107 #048-13-1988 L1989 **AN** *020 †05
FOWLER, James Raymond. 1200 E 3900 S 84124 #012-05-1964 L1977 **HS PS** *071 †85,65
FOWLES, Robert Earl. 333 S 900 E 84102 #024-01-1973 L1983 **CD IM** *020 †20
FOX, Jesse Neve. 525 E 100 S, STE 500 84102 #036-05-1974 L1975 **PD** *020 †55
FOX, Julie Ann. PO BOX 9280 84109 #017-20-1988 L1991 **EM** *020 †16
FOX, Rita Glasscock. 77 S 700 E, STE 270 84102 #021-01-1987 L1992 **PD** *074 †55
FRAME, Richard Neil. 82 S 1100 E, STE 403 84102 #025-07-1981 L1985 **IM** *020 †20
FRAMPTON, Robert Allen. 500 FOOTHILL DR, VA SLC HCS (110) 84148 #039-01-1971 L1974 **FM** *020 †18
FRANCHEK-ROA, Kathleen M. 50 N MEDICAL DR, DEPARTMENT OF PEDIATRICS 84132 #048-04-1994 L2006 **PD** *020 †55
FRANCIS, Kurt Fribley. 1220 E 3900 S STE 2C 84124 #039-01-1981 L1987 **PUD EM** *020 †20
FRASIER, Lori Dawn. 100 N MEDICAL DR, PRIMARY CHILDRENS MEDICAL 84113 #049-01-1983 L2001 **PD** *030 †55
FRAZER, John Kimble. 50 N MEDICAL DR, DEPT OF PEDIATRICS 84132 #039-01-2000 L2001 **PHO** *020 †55
FRECH, Edward John. 30 N 1900 E, DEPT OF GASTROENTEROLOGY 84132 #051-07-2001 L2002 **GE** *012 †20
FRECH, Peter Holmberg. 30 N0RTH 1900 E #1A71, DEPARTMENT OF RADIOLOGY 84132 #032-01-2002 L2003 **DR** *020 †80
FRECH, Tracy M. 30 N 1900 E, PEDIATRICS / INTERNAL MEDI 84132 #051-07-2001 L2002 **MPD** *020 †20,55
FREDERICK, Adam Randall. 555 FOOTHILL DR, RM 301 84112 #035-03-2006 L2007 **FP** *012
FREDERICK, Philip Rue. LDS HOSP, DEPT RAD 84143 #016-06-1948 L1949 **DR NM** *071 †28
FREEDMAN, Roger A. 50 N MEDICAL DR, UNIV OF UTAH MEDICAL CENTE 84132 #024-01-1978 L1984 **CD IM** *040 †20
FREEMAN, Andrew Leigh. 30 N 1900 E, INTERNAL MEDICINE 4C104 84132 #007-02-2005 L2006 **IM** *012
FREENY, Ingrid Charyl. ■ 84105 #041-15-2006 L2006 **TY** *012
FRIAS, Antonio Emmanuel. 50 N MEDICAL DR, UNIV HOSPITAL DEPT OB/GYN 84132 #026-08-1998 L1999 **OBG** *020 †30
FRIEDLINE, Nathan Kinneer. 175 N. MEDICAL DR. EAST, UNIVERSITY OF UTAH/NEUROSU 84132 #051-04-2006 L2007 **NS** *012
FRIKKE, Maureen Jane. 48 N MEDICAL DR 84113 #028-02-1986 L1991 **FOP** *020 †50
FROERER, Christian Donald. 5063 COTTONWOOD ST, STE 400 84107 #049-01-1996 L2000 **OBG** *020 †30
FRUIN, Mark Edward. 1050 E SOUTH TEMPLE, SALT LAKE REGINAL MED CTR 84102 #016-11-1984 L1989 **DR RNR** *020 †80 ‡
FUKUSHIMA, Brian Weiling. 5323 WOODROW ST, STE 200 84107 #049-01-1998 L2003 **ORS** *100 †40
FULKS, Brian Christopher. 100 N MEDICAL DR, PEDIATRICS DEPT 84113 #054-04-2006 L2008 **PD** *012
FULLER, Gene Raymond. 3920 S 1100 E STE 220 84124 #039-01-1983 L1988 **FM** *020 †18
FULTON, Ben Edgar. 130 S 400 W 84101 #021-01-1967 L1968 **DR** *020
FULTS, Daniel Webster. 50 N MEDICAL DR 84132 #048-12-1979 L1987 **NS** *050 †25
FUNG, Camille Manyan. ■ 84105 #041-02-1999 L2006 **NPM** *100 †55
FURST, Sheldon Richard. 1954 FORT UNION BLVD, STE 111 84121 #005-18-1989 L1994 **AN CCP** *020 †05
FYANS, Joseph Clark. 2804 GLENMARE ST 84106 #035-09-2004 L2005 **PM** *012
GABOR, Vazul Frank. 5444 GREEN ST, RADIOLOGISTS 84123 #040-02-1989 L1990 **DR** *020 †80,28
GADELIYA, Agnessa Violet. HEALTH CARE, UNIVERSITY OF UTAH 84132 #007-02-2006 **IM** *012
GAFFNEY, David Kassler. 50 N MEDICAL DR, UNIV OF UT SCHOOL OF MEDIC 84132 #056-06-1992 L1993 **RO** *020 †80
GAISFORD, Walter Dan. 324 TENTH AVE STE 142 84103 #005-06-1958 L1969 **GS GE** *071 †85
GALARIA, Irfan Ibrahim. 50 N MEDICAL DR RM 3B205, PLASTIC/RECON SURGERY 84132 #041-02-2001 L2006 **PS** *012
GALAVIZ, Charles Edward. 30 N 1900 E, RM 3C-444 84132 #018-03-2001 L2005 **AN** *100 †05
GALLAGHER, Katherine Marg. 100 N MEDICAL DR, PRIMARY CHILDREN'S MEDICAL 84113 #038-43-2006 L2008 **PD** *012
GALLOP, Christina L. 30 N 1900 E, RM 4C116 84132 #041-13-2003 L2005 **IM** *020 †20
GAMBLE, Christopher James. 4624 HOLLADAY BLVD 84117 #049-01-1982 L1983 **FM** *020 †18
GAMMON, Daniel Stoel. ■ 84103 #040-02-2006 L2007 **AN** *012
GANDOLFI, Roy Jos. 3725 W 4100 S 84120 #025-01-1981 L1982 **IM** *020 †20
GANELLEN, Edward W. 24 S 1100 E, STE 105 84102 #016-11-1985 L1992 **CD IM** *020 †20
GANGE, Steven Norris. 4252 HIGHLAND DR # 2 84124 #005-14-1986 L1996 **U** *020 †95
GARBER, Howard Lee. ■ 84124 #049-01-1980 L1981 **EM** *020 †16
GARDINER, Arthur Young. 525 E 100 S, STE 500 84102 #049-01-1976 L1979 **PD** *020 †55
GARDINER, James Raymond. 370 9TH AVE, STE 205 84103 #049-01-1999 L2007 **OSM ORS** *020 †40
GARDNER, Blake Isaac. ■ 84106 #011-02-2006 L2007 **IM** *012
GAREY, Michael K. 3949 S 700 E STE 180, MEDICAL CENTER 84107 #023-12-1987 L1997 **EM UME** *020
GARRETT-SCHAWALDER, F. ■ 84108 #869-02-1979 L1982 **GP IM** *020 †20
GARRISON, Andrew William. 555 FOOTHILL DR, RM 301 84112 #036-07-2005 L2006 **FP** *012
GARTRELL, Alan Duane. 1954 FORT UNION BLVD, STE 111 84121 #048-12-1981 L1982 **AN** *020 †05
GASPARO, Beth Ann. ■ 84108 #035-06-1982 L1986 **CHP** *020 †75
GAWLICK, Ute. 30 N 1900 E, DEPT OF GENERAL SURGERY 84132 #016-11-2005 L2006 **GS** *012
GAY, Christopher Allan. 555 FOOTHILL DR, STE 301 84112 #021-01-1988 L1989 **FM** *020 †18
GEBHART, Ronald John. 500 FOOTHILL DR, DEPT OF VETERANS AFFAIRS 84148 #051-04-1972 L2000 **IM ID** *030 †20
GELLNER, Cynthia Lynn Ehr. 1200 E 3900 S 84124 #048-13-2003 L2006 **PD** *020 †55
GELMAN, Martin Israel. 30 N 1900 E # 1A71, UNIV OF UTAH HLTH SCI CTR 84132 #041-13-1964 L1971 **DR** *020 †80
GELMAN, Stephanie Sue. 1525 W 2100 S 84119 #041-02-1996 L1997 **ID** *020 †20
GEMMELL, Lois Jeanne. 455 E SOUTH TEMPLE STE 202 84111 #005-12-1980 L1985 **OBG** *020 †30
GENEBACH, Edwin Dennis. 5801 FASHION BLVD STE 175, SENIOR CLINIC 84107 #051-04-1976 L1987 **IM IMG** *020 †20
GEORGE, Stuart Allan. 1525 W 2100 S 84119 #025-01-1971 L1981 **GS** *071 †85
GEORGESCU, Dan. 50 N MEDICAL DR, MORAN EYE CENTER 84132 #781-01-1999 L2006 **OPH** *012
GERBING, Raymond F. SUITE 200, 10W. 100 SOUTH 84101 #308-07-1981 L1994 **IM** *020
GEROSO, Amy Michelle. 54 N 800 W, NORTH TEMPLE CLINIC 84116 #056-05-1991 L1992 **FM** *020 †18

■ = Address Information Privacy Protected

GEZON, John Alden. 1050 E SOUTH TEMPLE, ER DEPARTMENT 84102 #016-06-1968 L1973 EM IM *020 †16

GHAJARNIA, Mmehdi. ■ 84102 #041-12-2003 L2007 *100

GHICADUS, Chris J. ■ 84103 #007-02-1953 L1971 P IM *071

GHIZ, Adam Fredrick. 8TH AVE & C ST 84143 #028-02-2002 L2005 EM *020 †16

GIBBONS, Harry Leon. 8TH AVE & C ST 84143 #049-01-1958 L1971 GPM AM *072 †70

GIBBS TAYLOR, Paula Kaye. 501 CHIPETA WAY, STE 1123 84108 #049-01-1983 L1984 P GPM *020 †18,75

GIBSON, Kathryn Elizabeth. 501 CHIPETA WAY 84108 #049-01-2007 FP *012

GIBSON, Keri Louise. 30 N 1900 E, OB/GYN DEPT 84132 #051-01-2005 L2006 OBG *012

GIBSON, Mark. 30 N MEDICAL DR, RM 2B200, DEPT OF OB/GYN 84132 #038-06-1972 L2003 OS END *020 †30

GIDDINGS, Luther Edwin. ■ 84124 #049-01-1955 L1958 PD *020 †55

GIER, Richard Howard. 500 FOOTHILL BLVD, PSYCHIATRY SERVICE (116A) 84148 #016-02-1958 L1992 P *040 †75

GIESE, Jeffrey Lloyd. 1250 E 3900 S, SURGERY CENTER, #100 84124 #056-05-1979 L1982 AN *020 †05

GIFFORD, Thomas Owen. RM 3C120, DIVISION OF OTOLARYNGOLOGY 84132 #016-43-2004 L2005 OTO *012

GILBERT, Edward Michael. 50 N MEDICAL DR, UNIV OF UTAH 84132 #025-07-1978 L1984 CD IM *020 †20

GILBERT, Eric Hunter. 5404 EMIGRATION CYN 84108 #038-40-1990 L1996 EM *020 †16

GILBERT, Michelle Heather. 2000 CIRCLE OF HOPE DR, DEPARTMENT OF ONCOLOGY 84112 #049-01-2001 L2002 HO *012

GILCHRIST, Milton R. 4021 S 700 E, COMPHEALTH INC 84107 #060-01-1951 L1979 R *071 †80

GILES, Lisa Lloyd. 501 CHIPETA WAY 84108 #049-01-2002 L2007 OS *100 †55

GILFEATHER, Maryellyn. 650 E 4500 S, STE 100 84107 #024-07-1989 L1996 DR *020 †80

GILILLAND, Jeremy Mark. ■ 84106 #005-15-2007 *012

GILL, Troy Donald. 2024 LA TOUR CIR 84121 #010-03-1963 L1972 P CHP *020

GILMORE, Kirk M. 8TH AVE & C ST 84143 #014-01-1975 L1976 IM EM *020 †20,16

GILMORE, Paul Stephen. 1160 E 3900 S, STE 2100 84124 #030-06-1980 L2006 CD IM *020 †85

GLASGOW, Robert Edward. 30 N 1900 E, RM 3B110 84132 #005-02-1992 L2001 GS *020 †85

GLEICH, Gerald Jos. 30 N 1900 E RM 4B454, DEPT OF DERMATOLOGY 84132 #025-01-1956 L2001 AI IM *020 †20,03

GLENN, Consuelo Maria. ■ 84121 #024-16-1987 L1987 PN PD *062

GLENN, Martha Jane. 2000 CIRCLE OF HP DR #2100, HUNTSMAN CANCER INSTITUTE 84112 #035-01-1989 L1997 HO *012

GLISSMEYER, Eric Wallace. ■ 84102 #049-01-2008 *012

GMELCH, Destiny Jennifer. ■ 84103 #040-02-2007 PD *012

GNADINGER, Philip Nichola. 30 N 1900 E, RM 3C444 84132 #007-02-2004 L2006 AN *012

GO, Mae Foung. 500 FOOTHILL BLVD, VA SLC HEALTHCARE SYS 111G 84148 #047-06-1978 L2001 IM GE *050

GODDARD, Mark Kimball. 84103 #054-04-1993 L1995 PCC *020 †20

GOLDBERG, Elliott B. 6440 MILLROCK DR, STE 175 84121 #035-08-1976 L1977 PD *020 †55

GOLDFARB, Deborah Ann. ■ 84111 #035-20-1976 L1982 P CHP *020 †75

GOLDMAN, Alan Jay. 5810 S 300 E STE 300 84107 #025-01-1971 L2001 N IM *062 †75

GOLDSMITH, Jason Aidan. 50 N MEDICAL DR, MORAN EYE CENTER, UNIV OF 84132 #005-11-1997 L2002 OPH *020 †75

GOLDSTEIN, Michael Louis. 1151 E 3900 S 84124 #016-02-1970 L1974 N CHN *020 †75

GOLDSTON, Edgar Clinton. 8TH AVE & C ST 84143 #026-04-1988 L1990 PM PRS *020 †60

GONZALES, Gloria R. 3725 W 4100 S 84120 #748-01-1992 L2001 IM *020 †20

GONZALEZ, Victor Jose. 1950 CIRCLE OF HOPE DR, HUNTSMAN CANCER CENTER 84112 #011-05-2005 L2006 RO *012

GOOCH, Judith Linette. 100 N MEDICAL DR, DEPT OF REHABILITATION 84113 #025-01-1983 L1986 PM *020 †60

GOODART, Roy Allen. 4400 S 700 E # 200 84107 #004-01-1975 L1976 OPH *020 †35

GOODLIN, Sarah Jean. 618 17TH AVE 84103 #032-01-1980 L1998 IMG IM *030 †20

GOODMAN, Gerald Neil. 1160 E 3900 S STE 4100 84124 #049-01-1959 L1970 GS AM *020 †85

GOODMAN, Greg Robt. 5323 WOODROW ST, STE 102 84107 #048-12-1987 L1988 VS *020 †85

GOPEZ, Evelyn V. UNIV OF UTAH, DEPT OF PATHOLOGY 84132 #748-01-1979 L1997 PTH PCP *020 †50

GOPINATH, Shamin. 8TH AVE & C ST, LDS HOSPITAL 84143 #048-04-2003 L2007 P *020

GORDON, Benjamin H. 30 N MEDICAL DR, 1A71 DEPT OF RADIOLOGY 84132 #036-05-2003 L2004 DR *012

GORDON, Jennifer Ann. 13 N 1900 EAST, RM 1C026, EMERGENCY MED RESIDENCY DE 84132 #049-01-2004 L2006 EM *012

GORDON, Launce Giechuan. 4021 S 700 E STE 300 84107 #041-09-1958 L1996 FM *062 †18

GORLIN, Andrew William. 275 E 200 S 84111 #035-01-2001 L2004 EM *100 †16

GORMAN, Darcie Reasoner. ■ 84107 #047-05-2004 L2005 IM *100 †20

GORMAN, Troy Michael. 590 WAKARA WAY, CENTER 84108 #047-05-2004 L2005 ORS *012

GOTTFRIED, Oren Nathan. 50 N MEDICAL DR, NEUROSURGERY DEPT 84132 #003-01-2001 L2003 NS *012

GOTTLIEB, Frederick Lewis. 24 S 1100 E, STE 209 84102 #055-01-1984 L1987 IMG IM *020 †20

GOULSTON, Claudia. 30 N 1900 E, RM 4B319 84132 #050-02-1990 L2008 ID *020 †20

GOURLEY, David Scott. 6065 FASHION BLVD, INTERMOUNTAIN ALLERGY & 84107 #041-13-1981 L1990 AI PD *020 †55,03

GOUW, Jun T. ■ 84109 #049-01-2000 L2001 HO *100

GOWANS, Don F. ■ 84109 #049-01-1962 L1963 DR *071 †80

GRAFF, Shirl Ray. 3449 S 4155 W 84120 #049-01-1952 L1954 GP OS *020

GRANDE SARPA, Hege. 30 N 1900 E, RM 4B454SOM 84132 #005-19-2001 L2005 D *012

GRANGER, Donald Lee. 50 N MEDICAL DR RM 4B322 84132 #049-01-1972 L1995 IM *020 †20

GRANTZ, Matthew Ryan. ■ 84109 #007-02-2007 *012

GRAUL, Elizabeth Sumsion. 5005 S 900 E, STE 100 84117 #049-01-1987 L1994 OBG *020 †30

GRAVELLE, Lisa Marie. 5063 COTTONWOOD ST, STE 120 84107 #054-04-2000 L2004 OBG *020 ‡

GRAVENSTEIN, Dietrich. 50 N MEDICAL DR, 3B420 SOM 84132 #011-03-1989 L1993 AN *020 †05

GRAY, Dean Williams. 50 N MEDICAL DR, 3B420 SOM 84132 #005-11-1956 L1961 OTO *072 †45

GRAY, Robert George. 100 N MEDICAL DR, CARDIOLOGY DEPT 84113 #024-07-1999 L2007 PDC *100 †55

GRAZIANO, Kelli. ■ 84115 #037-01-2007 IM *012

GRAZULIS, Diana. 6360 S 3000 E, STE 100 84121 #913-96-1984 L1998 FM *020 †18

GREAVES, Keith C. ■ 84121 #010-01-1951 L1960 GS *071 †85

GREEN, David Edward. 1163 LAKE ST 84105 #041-13-2004 L2005 IM *020

GREEN, Joel Richard. 1050 E SOUTH TEMPLE 84102 #049-01-1971 L1973 PTH *071 †50

GREEN, Larry S. 30 N 1900 E, # 4A100 84132 #049-01-1973 L1976 CD IM *050 †70

GREEN, Patrick Nelson. 1250 E 3900 S, STE 260 84124 #048-01-2006 L2008 FP *020

GREEN, Richard Raymond. 359 8TH AVE 84103 #049-01-1983 L1984 AN *020 †05

GREENBERG, Richard Alan. 295 CHIPETA WAY, WILLIAMS BLDG 84108 #005-19-1999 L2000 PEM *100 †55

GREENLEE, John Edward. 30 N 1900 E, STE 3R210 84132 #035-45-1969 L1986 N *050 †75

GREENLEE, Patricia R. ■ 84108 #049-01-1984 L1986 GPM *020

GREENLEE, Robert Ross. 8TH AVE & C ST, LDS HOSPITAL 84143 #049-01-1984 L1986 IM *020 †20

GREENWOOD, Jessica Lynn. 555 FOOTHILL DR, STE 301 84112 #005-14-2003 L2004 FM *100 †18

GREENWOOD, Nick C. ■ 84106 #004-01-2006 L2008 FP *012

GREER, Robert Jos. 1046 E 100 S 84102 #054-04-1956 L1961 P *071

GREGER, Susan. 1250 E 3900 S, STE 260 84124 #028-02-1999 L2006 FM *020 †18

GREGG, Xylina T. 3838 S 700 E, STE 100 84106 #048-04-1991 L2005 HO *020 †20

GREIS, Patrick Edward. 590 WAKARA WAY, DEPT OF ORTHOPEDICS 84108 #025-01-1988 L1997 OSM *020 †20

GREY, Todd Cameron. ■ 84108 #032-01-1980 L1986 PTH *020 †50

GRIFFIN, David Corwin. ■ 84105 #030-05-2005 L2006 GS *012

GRIFFIN, Gary Scott. 1160 E 3900 S 84124 #012-05-1992 L1995 IM *020 †20

GRIFFIN, John Anthony. 1220 E 3900 S STE 4D 84124 #005-12-1997 L2003 CRS *020 †85,10

GRIMMER, Johannes Fredrik. 100 N MEDICAL DR, STE 4500 84113 #035-46-1999 L2005 PDO *020 †45

GRISSOM, Colin. 5121 COTTONWOOD ST, CRITICAL CARE 84107 #008-01-1990 L1993 CCM PUD *020 †20

GRISSOM, Janet Wisniewski. 5770 S 1500 W 84123 #049-01-1998 L1999 P *020 †75 ‡

GRIZZLE, Lindsay Jean. 1138 WILMINGTON AVE, FAMILY HEALTH CENTER 84106 #049-01-2005 L2008 FP *012

GROEBS, Allen Reiner. 5323 WOODROW ST, STE 200 84107 #049-01-1995 L2001 HS *020 †40 ‡

GROESBECK, David Welling. 1954 FORT UNION BLVD, STE 102 84121 #049-01-1977 L1979 AN IM *020 †20,05

GROSE, Douglas David. 1200 E 3900 S 84124 #049-01-1969 L1970 GP *020 †70

GROSSELL, Emily Marie. 50 N MEDICAL DR, DIV OF CHILD PSYCHIATRY 84132 #036-08-2005 L2007 CPP *012

GROSSER, Bernard Irving. 30 N 1900 E 5R328 84132 #038-06-1959 L1960 P *040 †75

GROSSMAN, Douglas. 30 ORTH 1900 E 4B454 50M, OF DERMATOLOGY 84132 #048-04-1994 L2000 D *020 †20

GROSSMAN, Allie C. ■ 84109 #040-02-2007 PTH *012

GROSSMANN, Kenneth Freder. ■ 84109 #040-02-2004 L2007 HO *012

GROSVENOR, Alexandra R. 30 N 1900 E, RM 2B200 84132 #036-05-2001 L2005 OBG *100 †30

GROTZKE, Marissa Paige. 615 ARAPEEN DR STE 100, DEPT OF INTERNAL MEDICINE, 84108 #007-02-2002 L2004 END *012 †20

GROUTAGE, Jonathan. ■ 84106 #056-06-2007 PTH *012

GRUA, James Russell. 333 S 900 E 84102 #049-01-1986 L1989 END PDE *020 †20

GUENTHER, Elisabeth Ann. 295 CHIPETA WAY 84108 #040-02-1992 L1997 PD *020 †55

GUERRA, Carlos Alejandro. 461 S 400 E 84111 #048-13-1994 L1995 FM *020 †18

GUERRA, Paula Anne. 4745 S 3200 W, COMMUNITY HEALTH CENTERS, 84118 #048-13-1994 L1995 FM *020 †20

GULLETT, Shannon Lee. 30 N 1900 E, PSYCHIATRY 54110 84132 #045-01-2004 L2005 P *012

GUNDLAPALLI, Adiseshu V. 404 S 400 W, FOURTH STREET CLINIC 84101 #495-04-1990 L1999 ID *020 †20

GUNTHER, Julia Kelsey. ■ 84103 #035-08-2005 L2008 PD *012

GUO, Aili. 30 N 1900 E, SOM 4C104 84132 #243-21-1983 L2006 END *012 †20

GUPTA, Deepa. ■ 84109 #495-08-1981 L1985 IM *020 †20

GUPTA, Indu. 2000 S 900 E, IHC 84105 #047-06-1993 L2005 PD *020 †55

GUPTA, Nandita C. 324 10TH AVE, STE 160 84103 #495-45-1998 L2004 IM *020 †20

GUPTA, Saurabh. 50 N MEDICAL DR, DIVISION OF CARDIOLOGY 84132 #495-45-1995 L2004 IC CD *012 †20

GURTCHEFF, Shawn E. 30 N 1900 E, STE 2B200 84132 #055-01-2000 L2001 OBG *020 †30

GUTHERY, Stephen Leonard. 100 N MEDICAL DR STE 2650, DIV OF PED GASTRLGY-NUTRN 84113 #040-02-1996 L2002 PG *020 †55

GUTHRIE, Ellen Hobson. 2875 DECKER LAKE DR, STE 550 84119 #035-01-1984 L1985 EM IM *020 †20

GUZMAN, Ignacio. ■ 84112 #049-01-2008 *012

HAAKENSON, Caroline. ■ 84105 #026-08-2007 OBG *012

HABERMAN, Paula Louise. 5872 S 900 E STE 100 84121 #054-04-1991 L1992 FM *020 †18

HABIB, Arsalan Naiyer. 30 N MEDICAL DR, DIVISION OF NEPHROLOGY 84132 #049-01-2000 L2001 NEP *100 ‡

HADLEY, David Alan. 30 N 1900 E, RM 3B420 84132 #005-12-2005 L2006 U *012

HADLEY, Jason Charles. 30 N 1900 E, 4B454 84132 #012-05-2006 L2008 D *012

HADLEY, Kevin Shawn. 50 N MEDICAL CENTER DR, RM 3C120 84132 #038-40-2000 L2001 NO *020 †45

HADLEY, Michael Lynn. 30 N 1900 E 4A330 SOM, DEPT OF DERMATOLOGY 84132 #049-01-1998 L2003 D *020 †15

HAIDENBERG, Jaime. 30 N 1900 E, 3B 205, UNIVERSITY OF UTAH 84132 #649-13-1998 L2005 PS *100

HAIGHT, Whitney James. 1050 E SOUTH TEMPLE 84102 #020-02-1943 L1944 OTO *071 †45

HAIZLIP, Julie Ann. 100 N MEDICAL DR, DIV OF PEDIATRIC CRITICAL 84113 #036-01-1996 L2000 CCP PD *020 †55

HALE, De Von C. 30 N 1900 E RM 4B319, DIV OF INFECTIOUS DISEASES 84132 #049-01-1969 L1977 ID OS *030 †20

HALE, Jonathan. ■ 84103 #049-01-1993 L1996 IM *075 †20

HALES, Reid Boyd. 525 E 100 S, STE 500 84102 #003-01-1994 L2001 IM *020 †20

HALL, Clifton Samuel. ■ 84102 #049-01-2007 IM *012

HALL, Joshua Edward. ■ 84106 #049-01-2002 L2003 DR *100 †80

HALL, Nathaniel Lyle Stri. ■ 84105 #037-01-2005 L2006 IM *012

HALLOWS, Rhett Kendall. 590 WAKARA WAY, U OF U ORTHOPAEDIC CENTER 84108 #049-01-2003 L2004 ORS *012

HALVERSEN, Gary Lane. ■ 84121 #049-01-1967 L1978 DR RNR *071 †80

HALVERSEN, Roy Chad. 1160 E 3900 S STE 4100 84124 #049-01-1967 L1968 GS OS *020 †85

HAMDEN, Mohamed Hussain. 30 N 1900 E, DIVISION OF CARDIOLOGY (4A 84132 #605-01-1987 L2005 IM *020 †20

HAMILTON, Blake Douglas. 30 N 1900 E RM 3B-420, UNIV OF UTAH AFFILIATED HO 84132 #005-02-1991 L1992 U *020 †95

HAMILTON, Michael Thomas. ■ 84124 #023-12-2000 OPH *020 †35
HAMILTON, William Lee. 5121 COTTONWOOD ST 84107 #049-01-1981 L1983 AN *030 †05
HAMMOND, M Elizabeth H. 400 C ST 84143 #049-01-1967 L1977 ATP OS *050 †50
HAMMOUD, Ahmad Omar. ■ 84109 #605-02-2000 L2005 OBG *012 †30
HAMULA, Jason Franklin. 333 S 900 E 84102 #049-01-1995 L1998 FM *020 †18
HANDY, Jerry E. 296 E 3900 S, SPECIALISTS 84107 #049-01-1986 L1987 DR NM *020 †28,80
HANFORD, Ruth Jessica. 391 CHIPETA WAY, STE C 84108 #035-03-1978 L2007 GPM *012
HANKINS-CESSNA, Melissa A. 400 C ST 84143 #034-01-1999 L2000 PTH *100
HANKS, Kyle Sutherland. 7862 MAJESTIC RIDGE DR 84121 #049-01-1982 L1987 DR *020 †80
HANLON, Beth Chapman. 1060 E 100 S, STE L10 84102 #048-14-1987 L1988 IM *020 †20
HANNAH, Ralph Ernest. 2168 PRESTON ST 84106 #005-12-1968 L1977 AN *020
HANNON, Emily Aikenhead. ■ 84102 #605-02-2004 L2005 PD *012 †55
HANNON, George Duggan. 100 N MEDICAL DR, DEPT OF ANESTHESIA 84113 #001-02-1986 L1987 AN PD *020 †05,55
HANRAHAN, Christopher J. 50 N MEDICAL DR, RADIOLOGY DEPT 1A71 84132 #008-02-2001 L2003 DR *100 †80
HANSEEN, Ross Byron. 333 S 900 E 84102 #010-01-1980 L1988 ORS OAR *020 †40
HANSEN, Benjamin Jacob. ■ 84106 #049-01-2005 L2005 ORS *012
HANSEN, C David. 30 N 1900 E, 48454 SCHOOL OF MEDICINE 84132 #049-01-1973 L1977 D *020 †15
HANSEN, Christopher B. 50 N MEDICAL DR, DEPARTMENT OF DERMATOLOGY 84132 #049-01-2002 L2006 D *100 †15
HANSEN, Colby Reed. ■ 84108 #018-03-2005 L2006 PM *012
HANSEN, David Alonzo. 515 S 400 E 84111 #049-01-1961 L1983 GYN OBS *071 †30
HANSEN, Karen Kirhofer. 100 N MEDICAL DR 84113 #030-06-1979 L1985 PD *020 †55
HANSEN, Lucy Elizabeth. 30 N 1900 E, 1C412 84132 #051-04-2006 L2007 PD *012
HANSEN, Matthew Christian. 1160 E 3900 S, STE 1000 84124 #028-03-1995 L1996 IM *020 †20
HANSEN, Pamela Ann. 590 WAKARA WAY 84108 #016-06-1999 L2003 PM *020 †60 ‡
HANSEN, Robert Peter, Jr. 1250 E 3900 S, STE 440 84124 #028-34-1980 L1985 ORS *020 †40
HANSON, Jarom Elden. ■ 84109 #049-01-2008 *012
HANSON, Nicholas Gary. ■ 84105 #049-01-2008 *012
HARDMAN, Lara Lynelle. 2000 S 900 E, MEMORIAL HEALTH CENTER 84105 #017-20-1994 L1998 PCC SME *020 †20
HARDY, Edward Leslie G. 50 N MEDICAL DR, UNIV OF UTAH H.S.C. 84132 #068-01-1992 L1998 HO *020
HARDY, Richard Wayne. 50 E NORTH TEMPLE, COCHABAMBA BOLIVIA TEMPLE 84150 #049-01-1956 L1957 GS *071 †85
HARDY, Thomas Coleman. ■ 84124 #054-04-1958 L1959 P *020 †75 ‡
HARE, Bradford D. 50 N MEDICAL DR DEPT ANES 84132 #049-01-1975 L1979 AN PME *040 †05
HARGES, Richard A. 1954 FORT UNION BLVD, STE 102 84121 #024-05-1977 L1979 AN *020 †05
HARGREAVES, Harold P. 1050 E SOUTH TEMPLE 84102 #047-06-1948 L1951 GS OM *071
HARKER, Dustin Brook. 30 N 1900 E # 3R210, UNIVERSITY OF UTAH DEPARTM 84132 #038-43-2006 L2008 N *012
HARLAN, Gregory Adam. 100 N MEDICAL DR, DIVISION OF INPATIENT MEDI 84113 #005-06-2000 L2003 PD HOS *020 †55
HARLAN, Susan Rider. ■ 84108 #005-02-2003 L2005 DR *012
HARMAN, Clifford Gary. 24 S 1100 E STE 103 84102 #049-01-1963 L1965 GE IM *071
HARMON, H Craig. 333 S 900 E, SALT LAKE CLINIC 84102 #010-01-1982 L1984 IM *020 †20
HARMON, Hallard Benj. 1050 E SOUTH TEMPLE 84102 #049-01-1945 L1947 GS *062 †85
HARMSTON, Gordon Eugene. 6360 S 3000 E, STE 300 84121 #049-01-1995 L1998 GE HEP *020 †20
HARNSBERGER, H Ric. 50 N MEDICAL DR, UNIV UTAH MED CTR DPT RAD 84132 #005-14-1978 L1980 DR RNR *020 †80
HAROLD, Emily Jane. 30 N 1900 E, INTERNAL MEDICINE DEP SOM 84132 #038-40-2004 L2005 IM FSM *020
HARPRING, Amanda Eileen. 1250 E 3900 S, MEDICINE RESI 84124 #036-07-2002 L2005 FM *100 †18
HARRIE, Roger Pettit. 333 S 9TH E, SALT LAKE CLINIC 84102 #035-20-1974 L1980 OPH OS *020 †35
HARRIS, David A. 3725 W 4100 S 84120 #049-01-1979 L1984 PD *020 †55
HARRIS, Estelle Susan. 50 N MEDICAL CENTER DRIVE, UNIV OF UTAH HLTH SCIENCE 84132 #007-02-1988 L1996 PUD *020 †20
HARRIS, Mark. 3838 S 700 E, LIFETREE PAIN CLINIC 84106 #305-01-1982 L2005 AN IM *020
HARRIS, Mark John. 50 N MEDICAL DR, ANESTHESIA DEPT 84132 #919-05-1992 L1998 AN *020 †05
HARRIS, Quinton Smith. ■ 84108 #049-01-1955 L1959 IM *071 †20
HARRIS, Robert Hill. 1250 E 3900 S, STE 360 84124 #001-02-1995 L2007 GE *100 †20
HARRIS, Ronald Mark. 30 N 1900 E, 48454 SCHOOL OF MEDICINE 84132 #005-02-1989 L1996 D *020 †50,15
HARRISON, Colby Eugene. UNIV OF UTAH HEALTH CARE, INTERNAL MEDICINE RES PROG 84132 #040-02-2006 L2008 IM *012
HARRISON, Megan Elizabeth. ■ 84103 #051-07-2007 PD *012
HARRISON, Suzanne Maria. 8TH AVE & C STS, LDS HOSP DEPT OF ANES 84143 #049-01-2001 L2005 AN *020 †05 ‡
HART, Allyson. ■ 84117 #005-02-2004 L2006 IM *012
HART, Paul Douglas. 333 S 900 E, WILLIAM M MCCAA MD 84102 #023-07-1964 L1968 IM ID *071 †20
HARTMAN, Guy L. ■ 84108 #035-06-1946 L1952 PD *071 †55
HARTSELL, Stephen Carl. 1150 MORAN BLDG, 75 N MEDICAL DR 84132 #036-01-1982 L1983 EM *020 †16
HARTVIGSEN, Richard Neil. 130 S 400 W 84101 #049-01-1967 L1969 DR RO *020
HARTZ, Arthur J. ■ 84102 #056-06-1982 L2008 FM DR *050
HARWOOD, Mark Douglas. 30 N 1900 E, RM 4C104 84132 #005-06-2004 L2005 CD *012 †20
HASBROUCK, Douglas James. 2890 E COTTONWOOD PKWY 84121 #026-04-1981 L1984 IM *030 †20
HASBY, Peter Jarl. 461 S 400 E 84111 #035-15-1987 L1992 FM *020 †18
HASE, Charles Wm. 275 E 200 S 84111 #016-11-1963 L1964 R *020 †80
HASHIMOTO, Edward Geo. 166 E 5900 S STE B103 84107 #049-01-1981 L1986 GS *020
HASLEM, Derrick Shawn. 30 N 1900 E, INTERNAL MEDICINE DEPT. 84132 #049-01-2004 L2005 HO *012 †20
HASSAN, Hafsa. ■ 84121 #704-02-1999 L2005 MM *012 †20
HASTINGS, Robert William. ■ 84118 #030-06-2004 L2005 DR *012
HATASAKA, Harry H, Jr. RM 2B200, 30 N MEDICAL DRIVE 84132 #051-04-1983 L1991 OBG *020 †30

HATCH, Burke Mark. 30 N 1900 E, EMERGENCY MEDICINE 84132 #038-40-2006 L2008 EM *012
HATCH, Joseph Lloyd. 65 N MEDICAL DR 84132 #041-13-1954 L1956 OPH *020 †35
HATHAWAY, Peter Blaine. 1050 E SOUTH TEMPLE, UTAH IMAGING 84102 #049-01-1993 L1999 DR *020 †18
HATTON, Nathan Daniel. SOM 4C104, DEPT OF INTERNAL MEDICINE 84132 #017-20-2002 L2003 PCC *012 †20
HAU, Vincent Sinh. 65 N MEDICAL DR, JOHN A. MORAN EYE CENTER 84132 #003-01-2005 L2006 OPH *012
HAUG, Peter John. 4646 LAKE PARK BLVD 84120 #056-05-1976 L1977 OS IM *050 †20
HAUGAN, Shelby Lea. 30 N 1900 E, RM 2B200 84132 #040-02-2004 L2005 OBG *012
HAUSAM, Robert Roy. 257 E 200 S, STE 600 84111 #028-03-1984 L1985 FM *020 †18
HAVLIK, Kevin Loras. 2000 S 900 E 84105 #018-03-1980 L1981 PD *020 †55
HAWES, Justin Patrick. 5323 WOODROW ST, STE 200 84107 #049-01-1998 L2004 ORS *020 †40
HAWKINS, John Alan. 100 N MEDICAL DR, STE 2800 84113 #019-02-1980 L1981 TS *020 †85,90
HAYNES, Howard Harry, Jr. ■ 84108 #023-01-1945 L1945 GS *071
HAZARD, Lisa Jennifer. 1950 CIRCLE OF HOPE DR, RADIATION ONCOLOGY 84112 #035-06-1999 L2001 RO *020 †80
HEATH, Steven Wright. 4624 HOLLADAY BLVD 84117 #049-01-1987 L1990 FM *020 †18
HEATON, Kim T. 3845 W 4700 S 84118 #049-01-1982 L1983 FM EM *020
HEBDON, Carl Kent. 2040 MURRAY HOLLADAY RD, STE 209 84117 #049-01-1976 L1977 IM PME *020 †50
HEBERT, Andrea J. 333 S 900 E 84102 #048-16-2001 L2002 OBG *020 †30
HEBREW, John Linke. 3460 PIONEER PKWY, INTEGRATED CARE AT 84120 #049-01-1985 L1986 *020
HECHT, Malgorzata F. 324 10TH AVE STE 285, 324 10TH AVE 84103 #035-08-1975 L1977 IM *020 †20
HECKER, Susan Carnine. ■ 84106 #054-04-2007 IM *012
HEDGES, Dawson Ward. 50 N MEDICAL DR DEPT PSYCH 84132 #049-01-1988 L1989 P *020 †75
HEGMANN, Kurt Timothy. 1525 W 2100 S 84119 #056-06-1987 L1988 OM IM *040 †70,20
HEIDEN, Eric Arthur. 5848 FASHION BLVD, STE 110 84107 #005-11-1991 L2006 ORS *020 †40
HEILBRUN, Marta Elise. 50 N MEDICAL DR 84132 #049-01-2001 L2006 DR AR *100 †80
HEINBECKER, Peter Papin. 967 MURRAY HOLLADAY RD, STE 4F 84117 #028-34-1974 L1984 P LM *020 †75
HEJAZI, Jamal S. ■ 84121 #517-01-1979 L1993 P CHP *020 †75
HELFER, John. 6762 S 1300 E, STE 2 84121 #847-09-1979 L1984 CHP P *020 ‡
HEMOND, Joni Anne. ■ 84106 #035-47-1999 L2000 PD *020 †55
HENDERSHOT, Richard W. 333 S 900 E, NAT'L JEWISH MEDICAL 84102 #007-02-2001 L2007 AI *020 †20,55,03
HENDERSON, Shaw Cartin. 50 N MEDICAL DR, DEPT OF INTERNAL MEDICINE 84132 #050-02-2001 L2003 PCC *012 †20
HENLEY, Courtney Nash. 359 8TH AVE 84103 #011-03-1999 L2000 AN *020 †05
HENNESSEY, Theresa Ann. ■ 84111 #007-02-2000 L2005 OP *100
HENNIG, Holger T. 1954 FORT UNION BLVD, STE 101 84121 #409-20-1992 L2000 APM *020
HENRIE, John Nathanial. 296 E 3900 S, SPECIALISTS 84107 #021-01-1989 L1997 DR *020 †80
HENRIKSEN, Clarence Richa, III. ■ 84142 #035-46-2007 FP *012
HENRY, Anthony Robt. 6065 FASHION BLVD, INTERMOUNTAIN ALLERGY & 84107 #048-04-1977 L1992 AI IM *020 †20,03
HENRY, Dan Craig, Jr. 2295 FOOTHILL DR 84109 #054-04-1974 L1976 FM *020 †18
HENSLEIGH, Darrell Geo. 333 S 9TH E, SALT LAKE CLINIC 84102 #016-43-1969 L1977 IM ON *020 †20
HERBEL, Brent David. 4021 S 700 E, STE 220 84107 #037-01-1994 L1996 VIR *020 †80
HERBENER, Amy M. 30 N 1900 E, RM 2A100 84132 #049-01-1994 L1998 PD *020 †55
HERBST, Melissa Ann. 1140 E 3900 S, STE 390 84124 #021-06-1998 L2005 OBG *100
HERLIHY, Vincent Brendan. 30 N 1900 E # 1A071 84132 #051-01-2003 L2008 DR *012
HERMAN, Bruce Elliott. 100 N MEDICAL DR, EMERGENCY DEPARTMENT 84113 #036-01-1986 L1988 PD *020 †55
HERRERA, Christian Y. 100 N MEDICAL DR 84113 #231-01-1962 L1979 PD ADL *020 †55 ‡
HERROD, Henry Coleman. ■ 84108 #047-06-2002 L2007 RNR *012 †80
HEUSTON, Kary Patricia. ■ 84117 #049-01-2000 P *100
HEWES, Hilary Anne. ■ 84106 #034-01-2004 L2005 PD *012 †55
HEWITT, Lance Oliver. ■ 84103 #048-02-1996 L1998 IM *020
HEYES, Edward Andersen. 1646 MAPLE AVE 84106 #049-01-1968 L1969 ORS *020 †40
HIBBARD, Robert Spencer. 1200 E 3900 S, OR DEPT 84124 #049-01-1992 L1996 AN *020 †05
HIBBS, John Burnham, Jr. 500 FOOTHILL DR, VA MEDICAL CENTER 84148 #041-12-1962 L1976 ID IM *020
HIBBS, Luc Arnaud. ■ 84117 #049-01-2008 *012
HICK, Jeffrey Michael. ■ 84109 #005-30-2008 *012
HICKS, Harry G. 8TH AVE & C ST 84143 #049-01-1951 L1955 PTH *071 †50
HIEMSTRA, Robert C. ■ 84121 #005-14-1973 L1997 EM *074 †16
HIGGINS, Thomas F, II. 590 WAKARA WAY, ORTHOPAEDIC CENTER 84108 #043-01-1994 L2000 OTR *020 †40
HILDEBRAND, William E, III. 8TH AVE & C ST 84143 #049-01-1982 L1985 EM *020 †20
HILL, Britani Rhea. ■ 84105 #054-04-2005 L2006 GS *012
HILL, David Parker. 2000 S 900 E, MEMORIAL HEALTH CENTER 84105 #049-01-1986 L1992 OTO *020 †45
HILL, Douglas Chas. ■ 84106 #049-01-1982 L1983 AN *020 †05
HILL, Harry Raymond. 50 N MEDICAL DR 84132 #048-04-1966 L1974 PD CLP *050 †55
HILL, Robert Chas, Jr. 4624 HOLLADAY BLVD 84117 #056-05-1974 L1976 FM *020 †18
HILLYARD, David R. 50 N MEDICAL DR, 3B420 SOM 84132 #035-01-1977 PTH *020
HILLYARD, Robert Ferris. 370 9TH AVE STE 205 84103 #049-01-1979 L1981 ORS *020 †40
HILYER, Laurie Lynne. 525 E 100 S, STE 500 84102 #001-02-1984 L1987 PD PHP *020 †55
HINCKLEY, George Vivian. 1060 E 100 S 84102 #049-01-1952 L1954 OBG *071
HINDERT, Kristina Falk. 1855 MEDICAL DR 84112 #049-01-1978 L1979 CHP P *020 †75 ‡
HINES, Jerod L. ■ 84102 #049-01-2006 *012
HINES, Wirt Anderson, Jr. 1121 E 3900 S # C125 84124 #011-02-1968 L1969 PS HS *020 †65
HINICH, Erin Elizabeth. 30 N 1900 E, DEPARTMENT OF ANESTHESIOLO 84132 #049-01-2004 L2005 AN *012
HINSON, Douglas Marvin. 30 N 1900 E, RM 3B110 84132 #036-01-1983 L1994 GS *020 †85
HINSON, Joanne Sumpio. 850 E 300 S, STE 1 84102 #036-01-1983 L1994 OBG *020 †30
HINZ, William Allen. 30 N 1900 E, SCHOOL OF MEDICINE 4C104 84132 #049-01-2006 L2007 IM *012
HIRNING, Patrice Ferron. 508 E SOUTH TEMPLE STE 300 84102 #003-01-1985 L1991 IM *020 †20

HIRSHBERG, Eliotte Lynn. PO BOX 581289, 295 CHIPETA WAY 84158 #049-01-1999 L2003 CCP *012 †20,55

HITCHCOCK, Ying Jia. 1950 CIRCL OF HP DR RM1570, DEPT OF RADIATION ONCOLOGY 84112 #243-95-1985 L2003 RO *020 †80

HIXON, Brittany Anne. 26 N 1900 E, RM 701 84132 #012-01-2003 L2007 PCC *012 †20

HO, Albert K. ■ 84124 #028-02-2001 L2006 HMP *100 †50

HOARE, Jane Victoria. ■ 84117 #143-05-1973 L1983 IM *020 †20

HODO, Laura Nell. 1365 W 1000 N, COMMUNITY HEALTH CENTER 84116 #024-01-2003 L2004 FM *020 †18

HOEG, Karin L. 100 N MEDICAL DR, MEDICAL IMAGING DEPARTMENT 84113 #016-43-1998 L2007 PDR *020 †80

HOEHLER, Amanda Elizabeth. 215 I ST, UNIVERSITY OF UTAH/PEDIATR 84103 #005-15-2002 L2006 PEM *012

HOFFMAN, John Malcolm. 2000 CIRCLE OF HOPE DR, STE 2121 84112 #007-02-1980 L2005 NM N *050 †28

HOFFMAN, Robert Orin. 65 N MEDICAL DR, UNIV OF UTAH COLLEGE OF ME 84132 #049-01-1981 L1986 OPH PO *020 †35

HOFMANN, Aaron Adam. 590 WAKARA WAY, ORTHOPEDIC CTR. 84108 #048-12-1976 L1981 ORS TRS *020 †40

HOFMANN, Michelle G. 100 N MEDICAL DR, PEDIATRIC INPATIENT MEDICI 84113 #035-03-2000 L2004 CCP *020 †55

HOGLE, Hugh Hollister. 1050 E SOUTH TEMPLE 84102 #049-01-1967 GS *071 †85

HOIDAL, John Reginald. HLTH SCI CTR 4R 240 84132 #026-04-1969 L1988 IM *020 †20

HOLBROOK, John Hamilton. 50 N MEDICAL DR, UNIV HOSP 4 B 120 84132 #049-01-1967 L1968 IM *071 †20

HOLBROOK, Suzanne Post. 1060 E 100 S, STE 400 84102 #049-01-1990 L1994 IM *020 †55

HOLDEN, Joseph A. 50 N MEDICAL DR, 3B420 SOM 84132 #025-01-1982 L1987 PTH *020 †50

HOLLEY, Eric Abraham. 100 N MEDICAL DR 84113 #056-06-2002 L2007 PAN *020 †05

HOLLINGSED, Timothy C. 3725 W 4100 S 84102 #030-05-1989 L1990 GS *020 †85

HOLM, James Robt. 8TH AVE & C ST, HYPERBARIC DEPT 84143 #010-02-1985 L2007 EM *020 †20,16

HOLMAN, Joel Earl. 590 WAKARA WAY 84108 #041-15-2004 L2005 ORS *012

HOLMBERG, Trent C. 5770 S 1500 W 84123 #049-01-1998 L1999 P PFP *020 †75

HOLMES, Edward Bruce. 1525 W 2100 S 84119 #020-12-1989 L1993 GPM GP *020 †70

HOLMES, Jennifer Lynne. 333 S 900 E, MAIN OFFICE 84102 #049-01-2003 L2007 OBG *020

HOLMES, Kevin Christopher. 50 N MEDICAL DR 84132 #049-01-2000 L2005 P *100

HOLMES, Stephanie Marie. 100 N MEDICAL DR, STE 4550 84113 #023-07-1998 L2003 ORS *020 †40

HOLMGREN, Calla Michelle. 30 N 1900 E, DEPT OF OB/GYN, HEALTH SCI 84132 #056-06-1999 L2004 OBG *100 †30

HOLSTI, Maija. 100 N MEDICAL DR, PEDIATRIC EMERGENCY MEDICI 84113 #036-01-1999 L2002 PEM *100 †55

HOLT, Christopher Austin. 30 N 1900 E 3C444 SOM, ANESTHESIOLOGY DEPT 84132 #047-06-2004 L2005 AN *012

HOLT, Ralph Giselius. 1525 W 2100 S, NETWORK 84119 #041-01-1962 L1976 PD *071 †55

HOLZ, Huckleberry Amnon. 1003 SOUTH 1400 EAST 84132 #005-19-2002 L2006 OPH *100

HOM, Anna. ■ 84105 #035-48-1993 L2000 IM *020 †20

HOMEL, Steven Robt. ■ 84121 #041-02-1961 L1979 PD ADL *020

HOOD, Robert Sidney. 24 S 1100 E, STE 302 84102 #039-01-1970 L1975 NS *020 †25

HOPF, Harriet Williams. 30 N 1900 E, UNIV UTAH RM 3C444 84132 #032-01-1986 L2006 AN UM *020 †05

HOPKIN, John Taggart. 1020 S MAIN ST, NORTH VALLEY MENTAL HEALTH 84101 #049-01-1968 L1994 P IM *020 †75

HOPKINS, Paul Nathan. 420 CHIPETA WAY, STE 1160 84108 #049-01-1984 L1985 CD IM *020 †70

HOPKINS, Scott Alan. 4252 HIGHLAND DR STE 200 84124 #049-01-1994 L2000 U *020 †95

HORN, Rachael Sue. ■ 84103 #030-06-2003 L2004 OPH *100

HORVATH, Susan Toung. 1140 E 3900 S 84124 #016-11-1994 L2001 OBG *020 †30

HORWITZ, Daniel Scott. 590 WAKARA WAY 84108 #028-02-1990 L1995 ORS *040 †40

HORWOOD, Keith Owen. 4745 S 3200 W 84118 #054-04-1984 L1985 FM *020 †18

HOUCHINS, John Chas. 1138 WILMINGTON AVE 84106 #016-01-1983 L1984 FM *020 †18

HOUPT, Darren Clifford. 275 E 200 S 84111 #305-01-2001 L2006 FM *020 †18

HOUSE, Paul A. 30 N 1900 E, STE 3B409 84132 #028-02-1998 L1999 NS *100

HOUSTON, Donald. ■ 84121 #049-01-1960 L1963 GS *020

HOUSTON, Donald Stuart. 710 E 200 S, STE 1B 84102 #068-01-1982 GP *020 †20

HOUTS, Thomas Dixon. 6040 FASHION BLVD STE 201 84107 #005-15-1976 L1979 N IM *020 †20,75

HOWARD, James Gordon. 5169 COTTONWOOD ST, BLDG B 84107 #049-01-2001 L2007 OPH *020 †35

HOWE, David James. 1050 E SOUTH TEMPLE 84102 #049-01-1973 L1976 ORS *020 †40

HOWELL, Elizabeth Fulton. 501 CHIPETA WAY 84108 #045-01-1980 L2004 ADP ADM *020 †75

HOWELL, William Raymond. 50 N MEDICAL DR, RM 4B120 84132 #539-06-1990 L1994 IM *020 †20

HUAN, Mengjing. 30 N 1900 E, ATTN: CREDENTIALLING 84132 #048-12-2004 L2007 N *012

HUDDLESTON, Brent Joshua. 30 N 1900 E, 5C124 SOM 84132 #049-01-2004 L2005 PTH *012

HUERTER, Luke Michael. 50 N MEDICAL DR, INTERNAL MEDICINE 84132 #019-02-2006 L2008 IM *012

HUFF, Stanley Mark. 50 N MEDICAL DR 84132 #049-01-1981 L1982 PTH *020 †50

HUFFMAN, Heather Barrett. ■ 84102 #005-14-2004 L2007 PEM *012

HUGHES, Craig Dale. 1160 E 3900 S, STE 1000 84124 #049-01-2002 L2004 FM *020 †18

HUGHES, Dennis G. 3970 S 700 E STE 14, PROFESSIONAL PLAZA 84107 #049-01-1974 L1975 OBG *020 †30

HUGHES, Joseph Preston. 1250 E 3900 S STE 320 84124 #049-01-1969 L1970 CRS *020 †85,10

HUGHES, Warren M. ■ 84107 #049-01-1947 L1954 IM CD *071

HUHTALA, Timothy Allen. 50 N MEDICAL DR, DEPT OF INTERNAL MEDICINE 84132 #040-02-2001 L2002 IM *020

HULL, Christopher Mackay. 30NORTH 1900EAST, 4B454 SOM UNIVERSITY OF UT 84132 #054-04-2000 L2001 D *020 †15

HULME, Joan. 50 N MEDICAL DR, 3B420 SOM 84132 #049-01-1977 L1979 NPM PD *020 †55

HUMPHREY, Martha Robb. ■ 84121 #020-12-1976 L1979 IM PUD *062 †20

HUNG, Irene Hwang. 50 N MEDICAL DR, 2C412 SOM 84132 #028-02-1998 L2006 MG *012 †55

HUNN, Jessica Rae. UNIV OF UTAH MED CTR, DEPT OF OB/GYN 84132 #049-01-2004 L2005 OBG *012

HUNNINGHAKE, Adam Joseph. HEALTH CARE, UNIVERSITY OF UTAH 84132 #016-06-2007 IM *012

HUNT, Jason Patrick. 3C120 SOM, 50 NORTH MEDICAL DRIVE 84132 #001-02-2000 L2006 OTO *020 †45

HUNT, John Randolph. 525 E 100 S, STE 500 84102 #039-01-1992 L1993 IM *020 †20

HUNT, Kenneth John. 590 WAKARA WAY 84108 #049-01-2003 L2005 ORS *012

HUNT, Stephen Joseph. 1200 E 3900 S, EMERGENCY PHYSICIANS GROUP 84124 #049-01-1994 L1998 EM *020 †16

HUNTER, Gary Reed. 333 S 900 E, SALT LAKE CLINIC 84102 #049-01-1971 L1975 PS *020 †85,65

HUNTER, J Poulson. 2131 E 2100 S 84109 #023-01-1946 L1947 FM *071

HUNTER, Kenneth Duke. 2490 S STATE ST, WOMEN'S CARE CENTER 84115 #049-01-1963 L1965 OBG *050

HUNTER, Rene C. 50 N MEDICAL DR, RM 2A152 84132 #049-01-1999 L2000 PD *020 †55

HUNTSMAN, Kade T. 1160 E 3900 S, STE 500 84124 #051-07-1996 L2002 ORS *020 †40 ‡

HUNZIKER, Jason William. 50 CHIPETA WAY 84132 #049-01-1998 L1999 P *020 †75

HURLEY, David Clinton. 5770 S 250 E 84107 #048-04-1980 L1983 PD *020 †55

HURST, Barbara. 348 E 4500 S, STE 200 84107 #049-01-1986 L1987 OBG *020 †30

HURST, Craig. 684 9TH AVE 84103 #064-01-1998 L2003 CFS *100 †65

HURST, Scott Nathan. 5848 FASHION BLVD 84107 #049-01-1981 L1983 AN *020 †05

HURWITZ, Kenneth Michael. 1245 BRICKYARD RD 84106 #305-01-1981 L1990 PD PME *020 †55

HUTCHINSON, Douglas T. 30 N 1900 E, RM 35165 84132 #041-02-1984 L1990 ORS *020 †40

HUTSON, William R. 30 N 1900 E, RM 4R118 84132 #055-01-1982 L1988 GE IM *020 †20

HYDE, Marc Paul. 1200 E 3900 S 84124 #665-01-2004 L2007 EM *020

HYLAND, Kelli Jo. ■ 84105 #049-01-2006 L2008 P *012

HYLEN, John Carter. 288 N 1460 W 84116 #040-02-1964 L1984 CD IM *020 †20

HYNES, Nicolas Marcus. 50 N MEDICAL DR # 3B165, DEPT ORTHOPEDICS 84132 #065-10-1991 L1998 ORS *100

HYNYNEN, Liina Maaria. ■ 84102 #049-01-2008 *012

ILSTRUP, Sarah J. 400 C ST 84143 #026-04-1988 L1996 PTH BBK *062 †50

IMES, Seward Keith. 84109 #030-05-1948 L1948 OS R *071 †80

INGEBRETSEN, Richard J. 1200 E 3900 S 84124 #049-01-1993 L1994 UCM *020

IRVINE, Bruce Chamberlin. 3725 W 4100 S 84120 #049-01-1968 L1972 GS *020 †85

ISAAC, Jorge Cesar. 400 C ST 84143 #264-04-1983 L1999 PTH *020 †50

ISANI, Alexander Irfan. 5250 S 320 W, ATRIUM BUILDING, STE #305 84107 #305-01-2000 L2005 APM *020

ISENBERG, Philip Nathanae. 30 N 1900 E, RM 1C412 84132 #005-12-2005 L2006 MPD *012

IVAN, Eugen. RM 4A100, 30N 1900 E 84132 #781-01-1993 L2006 IC CD *020 †20

IVERIUS, Per Henrik. 50 N MEDICAL DR, 3B420 SOM 84132 #858-03-1974 L1985 IM END *020 †20

IWAMOTO, Kumiko. PO BOX 520176 84152 #049-01-1967 L1970 AN *062 †05

JAATOUL, Raquel. 1525 W 2100 S 84119 #649-27-1986 L2005 FPG *012

JABEEN, Musaret. 1140 E 3900 S, STE 400 84124 #495-51-1991 L2002 ID *020 †20

JACKMAN, Geoffrey Alan. 127 S 500 E, STE 600 84102 #049-01-1994 L2000 PD PEM *020 †55

JACKSON, Brian Richard. 500 CHIPETA WAY, ARUP LABS 84108 #049-01-1996 L2003 CLP *030 †50

JACKSON, Christopher Geo. 50 N MEDICAL DR 84132 #047-05-1979 L1981 RHU IM *020 †20

JACKSON, George Gee. ■ 84103 #049-01-1945 L1945 IM ID *072 †20

JACKSON, Gilbert M. 8TH AVE & C ST, DEPT MATERNAL FETAL MEDICI 84143 #048-12-1985 L1991 MFM OBG *020 †30 ‡

JACKSON, Heidi Holman. 50 N MEDICAL DR, SCIENCES C 84132 #049-01-2003 L2004 GS *012

JACKSON, Richard Leon. 100 N MEDICAL DR 84113 #017-20-1972 L1975 PD *071 †55

JACKSON, Steven Taylor. 201 E 5900 S STE 101 84107 #049-01-1972 L1973 OPH FPS *020 †35

JACKSON, William Danl. 100 N MEDICAL DR 84113 #023-07-1982 L1989 NTR PG *040 †55

JACOBSEN, Jeffrey Ronald. 5C124 SCH OF MED, 30 NORTH 1900 EAST 84132 #016-11-2004 L2006 PTH *012

JACOBSON, Jay Andrew. EIGHTH AVE AND C ST, LDS HOSPITAL-MEDICAL ETHIC 84143 #011-03-1971 L1978 ID IM *040 †20 ‡

JAEGER, April Rene. 715 LACONIA CT 84111 #050-02-2003 L2004 PD *020 †55

JAFFE, Michael Jonathan. 333 S 900 E 84102 #024-16-1995 L1997 PM *020 †60

JAFFE, Richard Barnett. 100 N MEDICAL DR, PCMC DEPT PED MED IMAGING 84113 #054-04-1966 L1973 PDR *030 †80

JAGER, Janell Lyn. 500 FOOTHILL DR, VA MEDICAL CENTER 84148 #049-01-1998 L1999 IM *020 †20

JAIN, Priyank. 1200 E 3900 S, CARE MEDICAL LLC 84124 #495-36-2002 L2007 IM *100 †20

JAMES, Brent Carl. 36 S STATE ST, FL 21 84111 #049-01-1978 L1979 PHP GP *050

JAMES, Mary Elena. 1002 E SOUTH TEMPLE, STE 207 84102 #048-02-1991 L1996 N *020 †20

JAMES, Michael Lee. 77 S 700 E STE 240 84102 #030-05-1982 L1983 P *020 †75

JANKOWSKI, Dorian Elaine. 50 N MEDICAL DR 84132 #028-02-1985 L1986 PD *020 †55

JANTZEN, Audrey Michelle. 30 N 1900 E # 3R 210, DEPT. OF NEUROLOGY 84132 #056-06-2004 L2007 N *012

JARVIS, Joseph Quinn. ■ 84103 #049-01-1982 L1983 OM PHP *062 †70,18

JAVELLANA, Carmela J. 860 E 4500 S, STE 302 84107 #748-14-1982 L1994 P CHP *020 †75

JEFFERDS, Ann. 324 10TH AVE, STE 160 84103 #026-04-1987 L1989 PUD *020 †20

JEFFREYS, Nicole. LDS HOSPITAL, 8TH AVE AND C STREET 84143 #049-01-2004 AN *012

JENKINS, Edward Gabbott. 1140 E 3900 S, ST MARKS 84124 #010-01-1969 L1971 PD *020 †55

JENKINS, Wallace Vernon. 2000 S 900 E 84105 #049-01-1955 L1958 IM OS *071 †20

JENNINGS, Carter B, Jr. ■ 84124 #036-01-1974 L1981 AN GP *074 †05

JENNINGS, Michael Scott. 3920 S 1100 E STE 220 84124 #047-06-1979 L1993 FM EM *020 †18

JENSEN, Cleleo Lund. 1255 E 3900 S 84124 #049-01-1947 L1954 IMG *020 †05

JENSEN, Craig R. 359 8TH AVE 84103 #049-01-1983 L1984 AN *020 †05

JENSEN, Elizabeth Jane. 500 FOOTHILL BLVD MC113 84148 #049-01-1991 L1997 PTH *020 †50

JENSEN, Gordon Charles. 264 E 6400 S 84107 #056-06-1996 L2000 OPH *020

JENSEN, Jack Monsen. 8TH AVE & C ST 84143 #010-01-1953 L1954 IM *020

JENSEN, James Christian. 1050 E SOUTH TEMPLE 84102 #016-02-1986 L1988 U *020 †95

JENSEN, Niels Fredrik. 2022 CRESTHILL DR 84117 #049-01-1982 L1983 AN *020 †05

JENSEN, Peter Edward. ■ 84103 #047-05-1981 L2004 PTH *050 †50

JENSEN, Randy Lynn. UNIVERSITY OF UTAH, DEPT OF NEUROSURGERY 84132 #049-01-1991 L1997 NS *020 †25

JENSEN, Wade K. ■ 84103 #054-04-2002 L2007 ORS *020

JENSON, Conrad Belnap. 324 10TH AVE STE 160 84103 #049-01-1952 L1958 TS *020 †85,90

JEPPSEN, E Alan. 5005 S 900 E STE 100 84117 #049-01-1966 L1968 P PMM *020 †75

JEPPSON, Taylor Alan. 3920 S 1100 E, STE 220 84124 #010-01-1970 L1973 FM *020 †18

JERMAN, Jonathan David. ■ 84108 #049-01-2007 IM *012

JIJI, Ronny Sara. 50 N MEDICAL DR 84132 #550-04-2004 L2005 CD *012 †20

JIRICKO, Philip. 375 CHIPETA WAY, RMC OCCUPATIONAL MEDICINE 84108 #038-40-2004 L2006 GPM *020 †70

JOHNS, Michael Craig. ■ 84108 #049-01-1974 L1980 PTH *074

JOHNSEN, Justin Rodney. 6440 WASATCH BLVD, STE 390 84121 #012-05-1999 L2006 OPH *020 †35

JOHNSON, Brian Douglas. ■ 84108 #048-14-2003 L2005 ORS *012

JOHNSON, Brian Lacy. ■ 84105 #047-06-2006 L2007 IM *012

JOHNSON, Dale Gedge. 30 N 1900 E, RM 3B110 84132 #049-01-1956 L1963 PDS *071 †85

JOHNSON, Daniel Newel. UNIV OF UTAH SCH OF MED, DEPT OF RADIOLOGY 84132 #036-07-2005 L2007 DR *012

JOHNSON, David Wyatt. 50 N MEDICAL DR DEPT PED 84132 #032-01-1984 PD *020 †55

JOHNSON, G Blake. 1060 E 100 S STE 110, MIDDLETON UROLOGICAL ASSOC 84102 #035-09-1999 L2005 U *020 †95

JOHNSON, Gary Hall. 370 9TH AVE, STE 101 84103 #049-01-1964 L1971 GO ON *071 †30

JOHNSON, Gary Kevin. 8TH AVE & C ST 84143 #049-01-1989 L1993 AN *020 †05

JOHNSON, Glen Eric. 3940 W 4100 S 84120 #056-05-1971 L1972 P *020 †75

JOHNSON, Gordon S. 1020 S MAIN ST, STE 300 84101 #020-02-1944 L1944 P *020

JOHNSON, Jason Lynn. 850 E 300 S, STE 1 84102 #026-04-1994 L1995 OBG *020 †30

JOHNSON, Jay Carter. 30 N 1900 E # 1A071, RADIOLOGY DEPARTMENT 84132 #007-02-2002 L2007 DR *020 †80

JOHNSON, John Philip. 100 N MEDICAL DR 84113 #025-01-1975 L1985 MG PD *020 †55,19

JOHNSON, Joyce Dunn. 1060 E 100 S, STE L10 84102 #049-01-1957 L1958 IM *071

JOHNSON, Kenward Borg. 30 N 1900 E RM 3C444, DEPARTMENT OF ANESTHESIA 84132 #021-01-1991 L1996 AN *020 †05

JOHNSON, Leland Paul. 30 N 1900 E, RM 3C120 84132 #035-20-1968 L1973 OTO *020 †45

JOHNSON, Mark Dale. 6321 S REDWOOD RD, STE 100 84123 #049-01-1989 L1990 FM FSM *020 †18

JOHNSON, Sara Emilieh. 850 E 300 S STE 5 84102 #049-01-2001 L2003 PD *020 †55

JOHNSON, Stacy Aric. ■ 84115 #016-42-2005 L2006 IM *012

JOHNSON, Steven Eric. 2243 E 6200 S 84121 #049-01-1990 L1991 AN *020 †05

JOHNSON, Steven Wesley. ■ 84106 #030-06-2007 TY *012

JOHNSON, Timothy Allen. 5810 FASHION BLVD, STE 205 84107 #049-01-2002 L2006 IM *100 †20

JOHNSSON, Birgitta Hope. 30 N 1900 E, DEPARTMENT OF INTERNAL 84132 #035-48-2002 L2003 HO *012 †20

JOHNSTON, Mark Aaron. 419 WAKARA WAY, STE 200 84108 #049-01-1990 L1991 P *020 †75

JOHNSTON, Sarah Linn. ■ 84105 #030-06-2004 L2006 OBG *012

JOHNSTON, Stephanie Brook. 50 N MEDICAL DR 84132 #012-21-2006 L2007 PD *012

JOHNSTON, W Cory Melrose, III. ■ 84105 #041-12-2006 L2008 GS *012

JOLLES, Christopher Jesse. 508 E SOUTH TEMPLE, STE 205 84102 #008-01-1976 L1982 ON GYN *020 †30

JOLLEY, Scott James. 8TH AVE & C ST 84143 #049-01-1993 L1996 EM *020 †16

JOLMA, Catherine Daria. 50 N MEDICAL DR, DEPARTMENT OF PEDIATRICS 84132 #003-01-1997 L2006 PD *020 †55

JONES, Barbara Ellen. UNIV OF UTAH HEALTH CARE, INTERNAL MEDICINE RES PROG 84132 #054-04-2006 L2008 IM *012

JONES, Christopher Robt. 30 N 1900 E, STE 3R210 84132 #024-01-1981 L1983 N *020 †75

JONES, Cynthia. 560 E 200 S, MEDICAL DIRECTOR 84102 #049-01-1982 L1983 OBG *020 †30

JONES, J S Roger. 100 N MEDICAL DR, ANESTHESIA 84113 #067-01-1965 L1968 AN PD *020 †55,05

JONES, Jodi Danielle. 675 E 2100 S STE 390 84106 #041-13-2001 L2005 EM *020 †16

JONES, Kent Woolley. 5169 COTTONWOOD ST, STE 600 84107 #049-01-1969 L1977 TS *020 †85,90

JONES, Kimberly Anne. 2000 CIRCLE OF HOPE DR, DEPT OF ONCOLOGY, SUITE 21 84112 #003-01-2002 L2005 HO *012 †20

JONES, Kirtly Parker. 50 N MEDICAL DR, DEPT OBG 84132 #007-02-1977 L1983 REN *020 †30

JONES, Makoto Murakami. 50 N MEDICAL DR, DEPT ID 84132 #028-34-2004 L2007 ID *012 †20

JONES, Robert Errol. 615 ARAPEEN DR STE 100, UTAH DIABETES CTR 84108 #049-01-1976 L1996 END IM *062 †20

JONES, Robert Glenn. 5770 S 250 E, STE 445 84107 #036-05-2000 L2001 GE *020 †20

JONES, Spencer Bennion. 2758 CHANCELLOR PL, RADIANT RESEARCH 84108 #049-01-1971 L1972 IM *050 †20

JONES, Thomas Llewellyn, Jr. ■ 84117 #010-01-1965 L1975 OBG GP *072 †30

JOPLING, Ronald J. 7138 HIGHLAND DR 84121 #649-19-1977 L1982 PD *040 †55

JOSEPH, Laurene Gay. ■ 84103 #011-04-1985 L1991 IM *074 †20

JOSEPH, Ronald D. 1250 E 3900 S STE 360 84124 #054-04-1983 L1990 GE *020 †20

JOWERS, Casey Thomas. 30 N 1900 E 1C026, DIV OF EMERGENCY MED 84132 #040-02-2005 L2006 EM *012

JOY, Elizabeth Anne. 555 FOOTHILL DR 84112 #026-04-1988 L1995 FM *020 †18

JOY, Sarah Brewster. ■ 84112 #040-2-2012 *012

JOYCE, Steven Martin. 315 E 200 S, 7TH FLOOR MEDICAL DIVISION 84111 #038-40-1979 L1986 EM *020 †16

JUDD, V E. 555 FOOTHILL BLVD 84132 #049-01-1980 L1982 PD PDC *020 †55

JULIAN, Christie Jo. 50 N MEDICAL DR, DEPT OF PEDIATRICS 84132 #054-04-2006 L2008 PD *012

JUNEJO, Nazia J. 3725 W 4100 S 84120 #704-08-1991 L2002 NEP *020 †20

JUNG, August Larry. 295 CHIPERA WAY, P.O.BOX 581289 84132 #049-01-1961 L1965 NPM PD *020 †55

JUNKINS, Edward Paul, Jr. 100 N MEDICAL DR, THE UNIVERSITY OF UTAH 84113 #023-07-1991 L1997 PD *020 †55

JUNKINS, Scott R. ■ 84103 #048-13-2004 L2005 AN *012

KABLITZ, Carl. 85 MEDICAL DR, DUMKE BUILDING 535 84112 #409-21-1975 L1981 NEP DIA *012

KAELBERER, Daniel Fred. 5063 COTTONWOOD ST, STE 400 84107 #049-01-2001 L2005 OBG *020 †30

KAHN, Bruce Alan. 3944 S 400 E 84107 #038-40-1985 L2005 P IM *020 †75

KALLEPALLI, Aruna Kakarak. 500 FOOTHILL DR, DEPT OF PMAR RM 3B19 84148 #495-21-1995 L2002 PM *020

KALM, Benjamin Aaron. 100 N MEDICAL DR 84113 #038-40-2003 L2006 PD *020 †55

KALM, Michael Alan. 3191 VALLEY ST, STE 152 84109 #035-08-1970 L1975 P CHP *020 †75

KALUVAPALLE, Jayasankar R. 30 N 1900 E, 4R312 DIVISION OF NEPHROLO 84132 #495-62-1993 L2001 NEP *012 †20

KALVA, Girish Kumar. 1200 E 3900 S 84124 #495-65-1996 L2004 IM *020 †20

KAMAE, Kandon. ■ 84124 #014-01-2006 IM *012

KAMAYA, Hiroshi. 500 FOOTHILL DR, ANESTHESIA VA MED CTR 84148 #572-20-1969 L1974 AN *050 †05

KAMBUROWSKI, Marta Anna. 100 N MEDICAL DR, MEDICAL STAFF SERVICES 84113 #038-41-2003 L2007 PD *100 †55

KAMIYA, Toru. 30 N 1900 E, UNIV OF UTAH HOSP INFECTIO 84132 #572-58-1991 L2006 ID *100 †20

KAN, Peter. 50 N MEDICAL DR 84132 #065-01-2001 L2003 NS *012

KANG, Dae Myung. 8TH AVE & C ST 84143 #583-04-1964 L1974 AN OBG *012

KANG, Juneku Brian. 295 CHIPETA WAY 84108 #035-09-2000 L2007 PDP *100 †55

KANNER, Richard Elliot. 26 N 1900 E 84132 #035-08-1962 L1970 PUD OM *050 †20

KAPETANOVIC, Suad. DEPT OF PSYCHIATRY, UNIV OF UTAH HEALTH SCIENC 84132 #957-01-1995 L2001 CHP *075

KAPLAN, David A. ■ 84108 #003-01-2008 *012

KAPLAN, Ron Lawrence. 675 E 2100 S STE 390, VISTA STAFFING SOLUTIONS 84106 #036-01-1992 L1994 PD *020 †20

KAPSA, Richard Leo. ■ 84103 #049-01-1958 OBG *020

KAREUS, Seth Andrew. 30 N 1900 E # 3R210, DEPARTMENT OF NEUROLOGY 84132 #004-01-2006 L2007 N *012

KARGE, Michael John, Jr. 30 N 1900 E, DEPT OF ANESTHESIOLOGY, SU 84132 #021-05-2002 L2007 AN *012

KARTCHNER, Kelly Dean. 359 8TH AVE 84103 #034-01-1984 L1986 AN *020 †16

KARWANDE, Shreekanth V. 30 N 1900 E, UNIV OF UTAH MEDICAL CENTE 84132 #495-65-1974 L1985 TS GS *020 †20

KASTENMEIER, Andrew Sean. ■ 84106 #056-05-2004 L2005 GS *012

KATZ, Bradley Jay. 30 N 1900 E, STE 3R210 84132 #016-11-1993 L1998 OPH OS *020 †35

KATZMAN, Howard A. 1485 E 3900 S, STE 104 84124 #030-06-1976 L1980 OPH *020 †35

KAWAMURA, Ryohei. 617 E 3900 S 84107 #572-40-1963 L1975 AN *071 †05

KAY, Dennis. ■ 84109 #049-01-1981 IM EM *075

KEAN, Bret Thomas. 590 WAKARA WAY 84108 #041-02-2002 L2007 GS *100

KEDDINGTON, Robert Saml. 3460 PIONEER PKWY, INTEGRATED CARE AT 84120 #035-01-1973 L1975 EM *020 †16

KEEN, Angela Margaret. 370 NINTH AVE STE 200 84103 #036-01-1995 L1996 PS CFS *020 †85,65

KEENAN, Heather T. 100 N MEDICAL DR, PEDIATRIC CRITICAL CARE 84113 #067-01-1991 L2003 CCP *050 †55

KEESHIN, Brooks Ryan. 50 N MEDICAL DR, TRIP AWARD 84132 #038-41-2005 L2006 CPP *012

KEITER, John Edward. 6040 FASHION BLVD, STE 101 84107 #036-01-1965 L1974 PS GS *020 †65 ‡

KELLER, Allison Anne. ■ 84109 #007-02-2000 L2003 PEM *012 †20,55

KELLER, Merle Leroy, III. 50 N MEDICAL DR, UNIVERSITY OF UTAH 84132 #049-01-2006 L2008 PD *012

KELLER, Richard Hubbard. ■ 84102 #023-01-1958 L1960 R *071 †80

KELLER, Robert Wesley. 1250 E 3900 S STE 360 84124 #016-02-1966 L1972 GE IM *071 †20

KELLEY, Karen Raye. 3934 S 2300 E 84124 #049-01-1981 L1982 EM FM *020 †18

KELLY, Colin Keith. 1250 E 3900 S STE 250 84124 #049-01-1970 L1971 PD *020 †55

KELLY, Elizabeth Ann. 50 N MEDICAL DR, INTERNAL MEDICINE 84132 #049-01-2006 L2008 IM *012

KEMPER, Dan Daily. 590 WAKARA WAY, ORTHOPAEDIC CENTER 84108 #005-12-2005 L2006 ORS *012

KENLY, Michael Scott. ■ 84124 #017-20-2005 L2006 PM *012

KENNEDY, Anne Maria. 30 N 1900 E # 1A71, UNIVERSITY OF UT SOM/RADIO 84132 #539-03-1982 L1992 DR *020 †80

KENNEDY, Brent Duane. 5929 FASHION BLVD 84107 #041-09-1981 L1982 CS OMF *020

KENNEDY, Thomas Preston. 50 N MEDICAL DR, UNIV UTAH MEDICAL CTR 84132 #047-01-1975 L1995 PUD OM *050 †20

KERR, Lynne Margaret. 30 N 1900 E, STE 3R210 84132 #049-01-1987 L1988 N PD *020 †55,75

KERR-VALENTIC, Mahlon Ald. 2963 S ADAMS GARDEN CV 84106 #040-02-2004 L2006 PS *012

KESTLE, John Richard W. 100 N MEDICAL DR, DIV. OF PEDIATRIC NEUROSUR 84113 #065-06-1984 L1998 NS *020 †25

KEVAL, Aziza Omar. 3336 PIONEER PKWY, STE 2 84120 #366-01-1973 L1978 AM OM *020 ‡

KEYSER DE LA O, Angela F. 50 N MEDICAL DR, DEPT OF PEDIATRICS 84132 #049-01-2006 L2007 PD *012

KFOURY, Abdallah Georges. 8TH AVE & C ST, LDS HOSPITAL 84143 #605-01-1987 L1991 CD *020 †20

KHAN, Ayesha Sultana. 391 CHIPETA WAY STE C, RESIDENCY PROGRAM 84108 #665-01-2001 L2005 OM *020 †20

KHAN, Farman Ullah. 2107 KARIN CT, APT 306 84121 #704-09-1997 L2008 IM *012

KHAN, Muhammad Faisal. SCIENCES CTR, UNIV OF UTAH HLTH 84132 #704-01-1991 L2008 CD *012 †20

KHAN, Sajid. 50 N MEDICAL DR, UNIV UT MED CTR 84132 #704-01-1981 IM *100

KHAN, Umar. 30 N 1900 E RM 4C104, UNIV OF UTAH MED CTR 84132 #704-31-2002 IM *100

KHODAVERDIAN, Reza. ■ 84115 #517-01-2001 L2008 TS *012

KHOR, Lillian Lei Ching. 50 N MEDICAL DR, 4A100 CARDIOLOGY SON MEDIC 84132 #539-06-1997 L2001 CD *100 †20

KHOROVETS, Andrei. 50 N MEDICAL DR, ANESTHESIOLOGY DEPT, RM 3C 84132 #913-06-1988 L1996 AN *020 †05

KILBRIDGE, Thomas Martin. 6440 MILLROCK DR, STE 175 84121 #023-07-1962 L1962 HEM ON *020 †20

KILLEEN, Ita Marguerite. 70 S 900 E, NE FHC 84102 #023-01-1977 L1980 FM *020 †18

KIM, Benjamin. 1220 E 3900 S STE 4F, UTAH CANCER INSTITUTE LLC 84124 #035-01-1978 L1990 GS SO *020 †85

KIM, Dong Hyun. 1954 FORT UNION BLVD, STE 102 84121 #583-01-1962 L1978 AN *071 †05

KIM, Hyong Tae. 30 N 1900 E, DEPT OF SURGERY 84132 #031-01-2002 L2003 CRS *012 †85

KIMBALL, Amy Louise. 36 DARTMOOR PL 84103 #049-01-2000 L2004 NPM *020 †55

KIMBALL, David Ashby. 1200 E 3900 S 84124 #049-01-1962 L1970 U *071 †95

KIMBALL, Edward James. 50 N MEDICAL DR, RM 3B110 84132 #049-01-1994 L1998 EM *020 †16

KIMBALL, James Leroy, III. 8TH AVE & C ST 5 CENT, LDS HOSP 84143 #049-01-1999 L2003 P *020 †75

KIMBALL, Jordan Andrew. 333 S 900 E 84102 #049-01-1992 L1998 R RNR *020 †80

KING, Jerald Dale. 50 N MEDICAL DR, UUMC DEPT NEON/PEDS 84132 #049-01-1977 L1982 NPM PD *020 †55

KING, Larry Edling. ■ 84103 #005-14-1964 L1970 P *020

KING, Wilson Tzuyun. ■ 84124 #048-41-2004 L2007 PDC *012 †55

KINGHORN, Jennifer Carter. 1140 E 3900 S, STE 410 84124 #049-01-2000 L2002 OBG *020

KINIKINI, Daniel Vaiokema. 30 N 1900 E, 3C344 84132 #049-01-1997 L2004 VS *100 †85

KIRALY, Bernadette O. 1138 WILMINGTON AVE 84106 #035-03-1996 L1997 FM *018 †18

KIRK, Amy Tremain. 30 N 1900 E, RM 2A100 84132 #020-12-1998 L1999 NPM *020 †55

KIRK, Donald Angus. 8TH AVE & C ST 84143 #010-01-1944 L1949 **OBG** *071 †30
KISHIMOTO, Mitsumasa. ■ 84121 #572-60-1998 L2001 **RHU** *100
KITAHARA, Mitsuo. ■ 84112 #572-20-1967 L1974 **HEM ON** *040 †20
KITHAS, Philip Adamont. 500 FOOTHILL BLVD, DIV OF GENERAL MEDICINE 84148 #001-06-1990 L1991 **IM** *020 †20
KJELDSBERG, Carl Rasmus. 500 CHIPETA WAY, ARUP LABS 84108 #803-03-1966 L1973 **CLP** *030 †50
KLATT, Joshua W B. 50 N MEDICAL DR, U OF U DEPT OF ORTHOPEDS 84132 #041-14-2001 L2003 **ORS** *020
KLEIN, David. 1220 E 3900 S, STE 2C 84124 #007-02-1993 L1997 **PCC** *020 †20
KLEIN, Richard Chas. 50 N MEDICAL DR, UNIV OF UTAH MEDICAL CTR 84132 #038-40-1973 L1991 **CD IM** *020 †20
KLEIN, Stephanie Zone. 30 N 1900 E, # 4B454 84132 #049-01-2002 L2007 **D** *020 †15
KLEINSCHMIT, Kristi Kay. 30 N 1900 E RM 2A152, DEPT OF PEDIATRICS 84132 #021-01-2002 L2003 **OS** *100 †55
KLIGMAN, Michael Alan. 650 KOMAS DR STE 207E 84108 #005-02-1984 L1996 **P** *020 †75
KNECHT, Thomas Paton. 615 ARAPEEN DR, STE 100 84108 #005-18-1990 L1995 **END** *020 †20
KNIGHT, David Paul. 1200 E 3900 S 84124 #049-01-1978 L1981 **PTH** *020 †50
KNIGHT, Joseph Adams. 30 N 1900 E, UNIV OF UTAH SCH PATH DEPT 84132 #049-01-1963 L1964 **PCH CLP** *040 †50
KNODEL, Daniel Harley. 615 ARAPEEN DR, STE 100 84108 #040-02-1978 L2000 **END IM** *020 †20
KNORPP, Scott Wm. 370 E SOUTH TEMPLE, STE 300 84111 #031-01-1987 L1988 **PM IM** *020 †60
KNOWLES, Conrad Jasper. ■ 84117 #049-01-1962 L1963 **OS GP** *071
KNUDSON, Laura Bryce. ■ 84102 #026-04-2006 **FP** *012
KOCOLAS, Irene. ■ 84109 #049-01-2007 **PD** *012
KOEHLER, P Ruben. 4325 ZARAHEMLA DR 84124 #869-02-1956 L1970 **DR** *020 †80
KOENING, Curry L. ■ 84105 #048-16-2000 L2001 **IM** *100 †20
KOEPKE, Mark Robt. 8TH AVE & C ST 84143 #007-02-1992 L1996 **EM** *020 †16
KOFFORD, Nathaniel David. ■ 84111 #049-01-2008 *012
KOHAN, Donald Elliot. 50 N MEDICAL DR, UNIV OF UTAH MC DIV NEPHR 84132 #011-02-1982 L1990 **IM NEP** *040 †20
KOKENY, Kristine E. 1950 CIRCLE OF HP DR #1570, HUNTSMAN CANCER HOSPITAL 84112 #025-01-1990 L2005 **RO** *020 †80
KOLBER, Sharon Sue. 3460 PIONEER PKWY, INTEGRATED CARE AT 84120 #007-02-1988 L1999 **EM** *020 †16
KOLC, Jana. 1220 E 3900 S, STE 3F 84124 #286-02-1967 L1995 **GS VS** *020
KOLEK, Matthew James. ■ 84109 #049-01-2008 *012
KOLFF, Therus C. 275 E 200 S 84111 #049-01-1974 L1976 **OS** *030
KONDO, Douglas Gavin. 501 CHIPETA WAY, STE 1662 84108 #049-01-1999 L2007 **CHP P** *050 †75
KONOPA, Kelly Lynn. ■ 84102 #056-05-2002 L2003 **IM** *020 †20
KOOP, Jana Jo. ■ 84105 #005-12-2005 L2007 **N** *012
KOSMICKI, Douglas Lee. 50 N MEDICAL DR # 4C104, INTERNAL MEDICINE DEPT 84132 #030-05-2001 L2002 **IC** *012
KOTTARATHIL, Thomas John. 1525 W 2100 S 84119 #495-11-1986 L1996 **IM** *020 †20
KOTTLER, Michael Stephen. 4400 S 700 E 84107 #038-06-1970 L1976 **OPH** *020 †35
KOURETAS, Peter Chris. 100 N MEDICAL DR, STE 2800 84113 #010-02-1992 L2004 **TS** *020 †85,90
KOVALAK, Mary Anne. 30 N 1900 E, SOM 4R118 84132 #025-12-2002 L2006 **GE** *012 †20
KOVNICK, Jeffrey Arnold. 324 10TH AVE, STE 280 84103 #056-06-1990 L1991 **P CHP** *020 †75
KRAFT, Adam Michael. 324 10TH AVE, STE 285 84103 #019-02-2000 L2001 **IM** *020 †20
KRAISS, Larry Wayne. 30 N 1900 E, # 3C344 84132 #048-04-1986 L1995 **VS GS** *020 †85
KRALIOS, Alexandros C. 500 FOOTHILL BLVD, SLC VA HEALTHCARE SYSTEMS 84148 #418-01-1960 L1971 **CD IM** *050
KRALIOS, Fany A. UNIV OF UTAH BLDG 500, NOVA ECCLES HARRISON CVRTI 84112 #418-01-1965 **CD PD** *050
KRAUS, George. 50 N MEDICAL DR, UNIV OF UTAH HOSPITAL 84132 #035-08-1944 L1999 **IM GPM** *020
KREITSCHITZ, Sebastian. 50 N MEDICAL DR 84132 #422-01-2005 L2006 **P** *012
KRETE, Derek Michael. 50 N MEDICAL DR, UNIVERSITY OF UTAH HOSPITA 84132 #661-02-2004 L2005 **PM** *012
KREZOWSKI, Joseph Thomas. ■ 84103 #054-04-2007 **IM** *012
KRIESEL, John D. 500 FOOTHILL DR 84148 #028-02-1988 L1989 **ID IM** *050 †20
KRINGLEN, Mark William. 5444 GREEN ST, MOUNTAIN MEDICAL PHYSICIAN 84123 #051-01-2001 L2007 **VIR** *100 †80
KRISHNA, Panangipalli. 500 FOOTHILL DR, DEPT ANES 84148 #495-62-1966 L1980 **AN** *062
KRIVIAN, Katalin. 110 PR, 500 FOOTHILL DRIVE 84148 #011-03-2000 L2001 **IM** *020 †20
KROLL, Becky S. ■ 84106 #049-01-2008 *012
KRONENBERG, Stephen James. 1729 PRINCETON AVE 84108 #020-02-2003 L2004 **AN** *012
KRUEGER, Gerald Gene. 4A330 SOM, 30 N 1900 E 84132 #005-12-1966 L1972 **D IG** *050 †15
KUBIAK, Erik Noble. ■ 84108 #054-04-2000 L2007 **ORS** *100
KUENTZEL, William Paul. 515 S 700 E STE 3C 84102 #018-03-1973 L1976 **P** *020 †75
KUIDA, Hiroshi. 50 N MEDICAL DR 84132 #049-01-1951 L1958 **CD IM** *030
KULBACKI, Evan Loren. ■ 84108 #049-01-2008 *012
KUNKEL, Gary A. 50 N MEDICAL DR, DIV OF RHEUMATOLOGY 84132 #048-12-1999 L2001 **IM** *020 †20
KUO, Annie Furay. 65 N MEDICAL DR, MORAN EYE CENTER 84132 #016-02-2006 L2007 **OPH** *012
KUO, David. 1160 E 3900 S STE 1200 84124 #019-02-2000 L2001 **IM** *020 †20 ‡
KUO, Geraldine Pelaez. 333 S 900 E, IHC SALT LAKE CLINIC 84102 #041-02-1992 L1998 **PM** *020 †60
KUPPAHALLY, Suman Suresh. SCIENCES CTR, UNIV OF UTAH HLTH 84132 #495-83-1996 L2007 **CD** *012 †20
KUREK, Erin Patrice. 30 N 1900 E, 1C412 UNIVERSITY MEDICAL C 84132 #050-02-2006 L2007 **IM** *012
KURRUS, Jeffrey Anton. 1220 E 3900 S, STE 2C 84124 #049-01-1991 L1994 **PUD** *020 †20
KUSHNER, James Paul. 30 N 1900 E RM 4C416 84132 #041-12-1962 L1970 **HEM ON** *020 †20
KUWADA, Scott Ken. 4R118 MEDICAL CENTER, 50 N MEDICAL DR 84132 #014-01-1988 L1994 **GE IM** *020 †20
KUWAHARA, Lisa Kay Lund. 324 TENTH AVE STE 285 84103 #026-04-1988 L1991 **IM** *020 †20
KUWAHARA, Melvin Den. 333 S 900 E 84102 #026-04-1986 L1991 **GE IM** *020 †20
KWAN-GETT, Clifford S. 1055 E 3900 S 84124 #143-03-1963 L1972 **TS** *071 †85,90
KWUN, Robert Choi. 5169 COTTONWOOD ST, STE 630 84107 #035-01-1993 L2000 **OPH** *020 †35
LABARGE, Donald Vincent. 30 N 1900 E # 1A71, DEPARTMENT OF RADIOLOGY 84132 #025-12-2002 L2007 **RNR** *012 †80
LABRUM, Shirley Oleson. ■ 84121 #049-01-1944 L1970 **GP P** *071
LACIAK, Robert John. UNIV OF UTAH SCHOOL OF MED, DIVISION OF UROLOGY 84132 #016-11-2006 L2008 **U** *012
LACOURSIERE, Daphne Y. 30 N 1900 E STE 2B200 84132 #005-18-1999 L2003 **OBG** *100 †30
LAHEY, Michael James. 8TH AVENUE & 'C' STREET, OUTPATIENT CLINIC/LDS HOSP 84143 #049-01-1978 L1980 **IM** *020 †20
LAINE, Hannele Marie. 455 E SOUTH TEMPLE, STE 202 84111 #020-12-2003 L2004 **OBG** *100
LAINHART, Janet Elizabeth. 650 KOMAS DR, STE 206 84108 #025-07-1979 L1994 **P CHP** *020 †55,75
LAM, Toan Hoang. 1060 E 100 S, STE 400 84102 #014-01-1980 L1985 **PD** *020 †55
LAMB, Harold B, Jr. ■ 84109 #023-12-1981 L1985 **AN** *040 †05
LAMB, Randy Don. ■ 84112 #049-01-2008 *012
LAMB, Sara Mundt. 50 N MEDICAL DR, INTERNAL MEDICINE — PEDS 84132 #025-12-2000 L2001 **MPD** *020
LAMB, Stephen Earl. 1140 E 3900 S, STE 410 84124 #049-01-1981 L1997 **OBG** *020 †30
LAMBERT, Elbert Jay. 2036 S 13TH E 84105 #049-01-1954 L1955 **GS GP** *071
LAMBERT, Joseph Gordon. 3959 W 1820 S 84104 #049-01-1969 L1970 **PD** *020 †55
LAMBERT, Kevin Del. 650 KOMAS DR STE 207 84108 #049-01-1981 L1982 **P** *020
LAMBERT, Richard Gary. 650 E 4500 S 84107 #049-01-1972 L1977 **NEP IM** *020 †20 ‡
LAMBOS, Angelo. 201 E 5900 S, STE 100 84107 #041-02-1992 L1993 **IM** *020 †20
LAMIRAND, Thomas Hugh. ■ 84115 #056-06-2005 L2006 **PD** *012
LAN, Timothy Yeushiuan. ■ 84109 #049-01-2008 *012
LANCE, Jason Noel. 2070 KENSINGTON AVE 84108 #005-06-2003 L2005 **DR** *012
LANE, Robert Henry. 30 N 1900 E, RM 2A100 84132 #016-06-1989 L2003 **NPM** *020 †55
LANG, Christopher M. 1141 E 3900 S, CHILDREN'S OUTPATIENT UNIT 84124 #143-03-1975 L1985 **CHP P** *020 †75
LANG, Robert Francis, Jr. 795 N 400 W 84103 #049-01-1970 L1971 **OPH OS** *071 †35
LANGELAND, Fritjof Fluge. 324 10TH AVE, STE 172 84103 #049-01-1976 L1977 **OBG** *020 †30
LANGELL, John Thomas. 30 N 1900 E, SOM 3B115 84132 #041-15-1999 L2006 **GPM** *020 †85
LANGEN, Robert Francis. 295 CHIPETA WAY RM 2S010, PEDIATRIC ADMINISTRATION 84108 #032-01-2002 L2005 **NPM** *012 †55
LANSPA, Michael John. 30 N 1900 E, DEPT OF INTERNAL MEDICINE 84132 #030-06-2004 L2006 **IM** *100 †20
LANTAGNE, Christiane. 50 N MEDICAL DR 84132 #067-06-1982 *100
LAPINE, Timothy Robt. 100 N MEDICAL DR, PCMC 84113 #049-01-1989 L1993 **NPM** *020 †55 ‡
LARCOM, Peter Gordon. 5323 WOODROW ST 84107 #024-07-1989 L1996 **OAR** *020 †40
LARSEN, Brent L. 2360 SCENIC DR 84109 #016-42-1996 L1999 **EM** *020 †16
LARSEN, David Arnold. ■ 84103 #026-04-2004 L2005 **GS** *012
LARSEN, David Charles. 3920 S 1100 E STE 220 84124 #049-01-1997 L2000 **FM** *020 †18
LARSEN, Gary Fisher. 5911 FASHION BLVD, STE 100 84107 #049-01-1966 L1967 **ORS** *071 †40
LARSEN, Gitte Yvonne. 295 CHIPETA WAY, UNIVERSITY OF UTAH 84108 #054-04-1991 L1992 **CCP** *020 †55
LARSEN, Lawrence Vincent. 2523 CUPECOY DR 84121 #028-34-1983 L1995 **AI IM** *050 †20,03
LARSEN, Lowell Don. ■ 84117 #049-01-1959 L1964 **PTH CLP** *071 †50
LARSON, Adam L. 50 N MEDICAL DR 84132 #048-02-2006 L2007 **AN** *012
LARSON, Scott Alan. 65 N MEDICAL DR 84132 #005-12-1998 L2003 **OPH** *020 †35
LASH, Stephen David. 1060 E 100 S STE 400 84102 #049-01-1986 L1990 **OBG** *020 †30
LAU, Sey Mon. 650 E 4500 S, STE 210 84107 #065-09-2000 L2007 **IM** *100 †20
LAURO, Lawrence Wm. 5872 S 900 E STE 100 84121 #011-02-1980 L1981 **FM** *020 †18
LAUTENSCHLAEGER, Natascha. 1138 WILMINGTON AVE, SUGARHOUSE FAMILY HEALTH C 84106 #045-04-2000 L2003 **FM** *020
LAVENDER, Katherine Rebec. 100 N MEDICAL DR, PRIMARY CHILDREN'S HOSPITA 84113 #048-02-2005 L2006 **PD** *012
LAWLISS, Kathleen Marie. 1200 E 3900 S 84124 #035-15-1995 L1999 **EM** *020 †16
LAWRYNOWICZ, Sandra Barba. 50 N MEDICAL DR, UNIV OF UT MED CTR 84132 #759-01-2006 L2008 **PD** *012
LAYFIELD, Lester James. 1950 CIRCLE OF HOPE DR 84112 #005-14-1979 L1997 **PTH** *020 †50
LAYMAN, Jennifer Brooke. 3900 S 1200 E, MARKS HOSPITAL 84124 #049-01-2002 L2003 **AN** *020 †05
LAZAR, J Brett. ■ 84109 #035-03-1966 L1985 **PHP** *030 †70
LAZARUS, Harrison Miller. 324 10TH AVE STE 254 84103 #023-07-1964 L1971 **GS VS** *020 †85
LEAMAN, Howard Michael. 451 BISHOP FEDERAL LN, ST JOSEPH VILLA 84115 #038-41-1979 L1982 **IM OM** *020 †20,70
LECKMAN, Linda Cordell. 36 S STATE ST STE 2100, INTERMOUNTAIN HLTH CARE 84111 #034-01-1977 L1979 **GS** *030 †85
LECKMAN, Scott Albert. 1220 E 3900 S STE 3G 84124 #049-01-1983 L1985 **GS** *020 †85
LEE, Glenn Richard. 500 FOOTHILL DR 84148 #049-01-1956 L1961 **HEM IM** *030 †20
LEE, Janet. 175 N MEDICAL DRIVE EAST, DEPARTMENT OF NEUROSURGERY 84132 #005-02-2005 L2006 **NS** *012
LEE, Jennifer C. 30 N 1900 E RM 4C104, UNIV OF UTAH MED CTR 84132 #041-15-2005 L2007 **IM** *012
LEE, Karin Louise. 1374 HARRISON AVE, KARIN LEE, MD HEALER, LLC 84105 #051-04-1999 L2000 **FM** *020 †18
LEE, Mark Wm. 5872 S 900 E, STE 100 84121 #023-12-1986 L1996 **FM** *020 †18
LEE, Stephen Byounghyun. 3738 S 900 E, UTAH IMAGING 84106 #048-02-2003 L2007 **DR** *012
LEE, Steven B. 3970 S 700 E, STE 24 84107 #047-06-1996 L1997 **DR** *020 †80
LEE, Timothy Guy. 325 8TH AVE 84143 #016-11-1965 L1978 **R** *071 †80
LEE, Wally Wonwoo. 4507 FORTUNA WAY 84124 #005-15-1988 L1994 **EM** *020 †16
LEECH, Cindi Jo. 500 FOOTHILL DR, PRIMARY CARE DEPT 84148 #036-01-1997 L1998 **IM** *020 †20
LEGANT, Patricia. 164 E 5900 S, A106 84107 #035-01-1977 L1979 **HO** *020 †20
LEHMAN, Christopher Mark. 50 N MEDICAL DR, 3B420 SOM 84132 #049-01-1986 L1996 **BBK** *020 †50
LEHMAN, Wilhelm Thomas. 30 N 1900 E 1C026 84132 #020-02-1999 L2000 **FM** *020 †18
LEIBEL, Sydney Adam. 50 N MEDICAL DR 84132 #143-11-2005 L2007 **PD** *012
LEIFERMAN, Kristin Marie. 30 N 1900 E, 4A330 SCHOOL OF MEDICINE 84132 #026-08-1978 L2001 **D DDL** *050 †15
LEIS, Edward Anthony. ■ 84117 #019-02-1984 L1988 **PTH** *020 †50
LEISER, Jennifer Paul. 1138 WILMINGTON AVE 84106 #026-04-1987 L1998 **FM** *020 †18
LEMOINE, Tara Jackson. 50 N MEDICAL DR 84132 #020-75-2005, ▲ L2006 **PD** *012
LEMONS, Richard Scott. 100 N MEDICAL DR, # 1400 84113 #010-01-1980 L1987 **PHO** *050 †55
LENZ, Peter Swift. 8TH AVE & C ST 84143 #054-04-1984 L1989 **EM IM** *020 †20
LESSNICK, Stephen Lee. 2000 CIRCLE OF HOPE DR, HUNTSMAN CANCER INSTITUTE 84112 #005-14-1996 L2004 **PD** *020 †55

LEVENTAKI, Vasiliki. 50 N MEDICAL DR 84132 #418-01-2004 **PTH** *012

LEVITT, Jodie K. 82 S 1100 E, STE 303 84102 #041-07-1989 L2002 **NS** *020 †25

LEWIN, Susan O. 50 N MEDICAL DR, DIV. OF MEDICAL GENETICS 84132 #836-01-1976 L1998 **MG PD** *020 †19

LEWIS, Edward C, II. 500 FOOTHILL DR, SURGICAL SERVICE 84148 #041-12-1949 L1974 **PS GS** *020 †85,65

LEWIS, Mark Rich. 333 S 900 E 84102 #049-01-1987 L1990 **IM** *020 †20

LEWIS, Matthew David. 4745 S 3200 W 84118 #016-42-1993 L1996 **FM** *020 †18

LEWIS, Nicholas Jay. ■ 84111 #049-01-2007 **MPD** *012

LEWIS, Tamara. 36 S STATE ST, FL 21 84111 #049-01-1989 L1990 **PHP** *030

LEWIS, Wesley James. 6360 S 3000 E, STE 100 84121 #003-01-1991 L1998 **FM FSM** *020 †18

LI, Dean. 15 N 2030 E RM 4490, UNIV OF UTAH MEDICAL CENTE 84112 #028-02-1990 L1998 **CD** *020 †20

LIBRE, Kenneth Paul. 461 S 400 E, CENTRAL CITY CHC 84111 #032-01-1994 L1996 **FM** *020 †18

LIDDLE, David Gordon. ■ 84124 #049-01-2007 **IM** *012

LIDDLE, Harold V. ■ 84124 #035-20-1951 L1964 **TS** *071 †85,90

LIDDLE, Melinda Sue. ■ 84117 #049-01-2007 **PD** *012

LIEN, Ellisiv. DIV OF PHYS MED/REHAB, UNIV OF UTAH MED CTR 84132 #759-01-2000 L2004 **PM** *100

LIEPERT, Amy Erna. 30 N 1900 E, RM 1C412 84132 #056-06-2006 L2007 **GS** *012

LIM, Hwee Yong. 2000 CIRCLE OF HP DR #2100, SCHOOL OF MEDICINE/UNIV OF 84112 #539-04-1998 L2006 **HO** *012 †20

LIM, Tobin. 50 N MEDICAL DR, RESIDENT 84132 #305-01-2006 L2008 **IM** *012

LIN, Anne Ginwei. 650 KOMAS DR STE 208 84108 #049-01-1999 L2004 **CHP** *100 †75

LINARDAKIS, Nikos M. 6465 S 3000 E, STE 105 84121 #016-42-1997 **GP** *062

LINCOLN, Michael Jos. 50 N MEDICAL DR, DEPT OF PEDS 84132 #025-01-1980 L1983 **PUD IM** *020 †20

LINDEM, Martin Carl, Jr. ■ 84109 #024-01-1959 L1965 **GS CD** *071 †85

LINDGREN, Peter Chase. 2000 S 900 E, IHC MEMORIAL CLINIC 84105 #016-01-1996 L1997 **PD** *020 †55

LINDLEY, Eric Melvin. ■ 84121 #010-01-2008 *012

LINDSAY, Alan Norton. 508 E SOUTH TEMPLE, STE 310 84102 #049-01-1975 L1980 **PD PDE** *020 †55

LINES, Robin Elizabeth. ■ 84105 #049-01-2008 *012

LINFORD, Jennifer. 2180 E 4500 S, STE 210 84117 #003-01-1991 L1999 **PD** *020 †55

LINGEMAN, Jenifer Kate. PO BOX 581289, 295 CHIPETA WAY 84158 #016-06-2003 L2007 **PEM** *012

LINSCOTT, M Scott, Jr. 30 N 1900 E, RM 1026 84132 #019-02-1969 L1981 **EM PA** *020 †20,16

LIOU, Theodore Gehlu. 26 N. MEDICAL DRIVE, PULMONARY DIVISION 84132 #010-01-1986 L1990 **PUD CCM** *050 †20

LISIECKI, Ronald Stanley. ■ 84105 #024-05-1995 L1996 **IM** *020 †20

LISTER, Graham Duncan. 50 N MEDICAL DR 84132 #919-05-1960 L1987 **PDP P** *071 †65

LITTON, Gregory James. 333 S 900 E 84102 #054-04-1983 L1987 **ON HEM** *022

LITWIN, Christine Melnyk. 50 N MEDICAL DR, 3B420 SOM 84132 #028-02-1985 L1993 **CLP** *020 †50

LITWIN, Sheldon Ellis. 50 N MEDICAL DR, DEPT CARDIOLOGY 84132 #028-02-1985 L1993 **CD IM** *050 †20

LIU, Ellen Anita. 2752 COMANCHE DR 84108 #041-02-1987 L1996 **NPM** *020 †55

LIU, James Kuanhsin. 30 N 1900 E STE 3B409, DEPT. OF NEUROSURGERY 84132 #035-09-2000 L2003 **NS** *020

LIU, Peter Shungee. 30 N 1900 E RM 3C444, DEPT OF ANESTHESIOLOGY 84132 #038-40-2001 L2007 **GS** *020

LIU, Ting. ■ 84121 #243-14-1983 L2006 **SP** *100

LIVERS, Gregory Lawrence. ■ 84103 #051-01-2003 L2004 **GS** *012

LLOYD, Bennion N. ■ 84124 #049-01-1952 L1973 **OBG** *071

LLOYD, Earl A. 2000 S 900 E 84105 #049-01-1959 L1963 **PD** *071 †55

LLOYD, Erika Christine. 1220 E 3900 S, STE 4A 84124 #024-07-1993 L1994 **GS** *020 †85

LLOYD, Layne Robert. 36 S STATE ST, STE 1650 84111 #759-01-2000 L2006 **FM** *020 †18

LOEWEN, Natalie Kay. 1060 E 100 S, STE 400 84102 #005-12-1998 L1999 **OBG** *020 †30

LOFFLER, Pedro Max. 2780 OQUIRRH DR 84108 #132-01-1965 L2000 **P** *020 †75

LOH, Elizabeth Sitsuda. ■ 84105 #038-41-2005 L2007 **PD** *012

LONG, Deanne. 30 N 1900 E, RM 3B110 84132 #049-01-1997 L2000 **EM** *020 †16

LONG, James W, Jr. 5169 COTTONWOOD ST, STE 600 84107 #028-03-1982 L1990 **GS OS** *020 †85,90

LONG, Tamiko A. 1954 FORT UNION BLVD, STE 111 84121 #024-05-1992 L1998 **AN** *020 †05

LONGE, Jamie. 6360 S 3000 E, STE 100 84121 #036-05-1985 L1986 **FM** *020 †18

LONGO, Nicola. 50 N MEDICAL DR, PEDS/GENETICS 2C412 SOM 84132 #561-13-1982 L2001 **MG CBG** *050 †19

LONT, Menno. 324 10TH AVE STE 285 84103 #660-03-1989 L1993 **IM** *020 †20

LOOSE, Evelyn Charlotte. 30 N 1900 E, DEPT OF ANESTHESIOLOGY 84132 #409-42-1995 L2000 **AN** *020

LOPANSRI, Bert Kamolsit. 30 N 1900 E, RM 43319 84132 #016-43-1997 L2000 **ID** *020 †20

LOUDER, Teri Anne. ■ 84106 #049-01-1996 L1998 **N** *100

LOVELACE, Todd D. 8TH AVE & C ST, RADIOLOGY DEPT 84143 #048-13-1996 L2004 **DR** *020 †80

LOWICHIK, Amy. 100 N MEDICAL DR, DEPT OF PATH/PCMC 84113 #025-01-1983 L1996 **PTH PD** *020 †50,55

LOWRY, Michael Roy. 501 CHIPETA WAY 84108 #018-03-1974 L1980 **P** *030 †75 ‡

LU, Jeffrey Kenneth. 30 N 1900 E RM 3C444, UNIV UTAH DEPT ANESTHESIOL 84132 #026-04-1987 L1988 **AN CD** *020 †05

LUEBKE, Aaron. ■ 84102 #037-01-2007 **IM** *012

LUEDTKE, Patrick Frank. 46 N MEDICAL DR 84113 #056-06-1992 L2001 **IM** *030 †70

LUNARDI DE AMORIM BERNSTEI, . 960 DONNER WAY, UNIT 340 84132 #187-26-1997 L2008 **RO** *012

LUNDSBERG, Kelton Wade. 1955 E 5600 S 84121 #016-11-1979 L1983 **IM** *020 †20

LUNOE, Leif Chesnut. 30 N 1900 E RM 3C444, DEPT. ANESTHESIOLOGY 84132 #054-04-2004 L2005 **AN** *012

LUPASH, Daniel Paul. ■ 84103 #016-43-2005 L2006 **IM** *012

LURAS, John Chris. 24 S 1100 E, STE 209 84102 #005-06-1988 L1991 **IM** *020

LYLE, William Andrew. 755 E 3900 S 84107 #048-04-1967 L1973 **OPH** *020 †35

LYM, Robert Merrill. 3845 W 4700 S 84118 #007-02-1998 L2001 **FM** *020 †18

LYNCH, Robert Emmett. 500 FOOTHILL DR 84148 #024-01-1964 L1971 **PTH OS** *050 †20

LYNCH, Steven Mark. 100 N MEDICAL DR 84113 #024-07-1982 L1988 **PD** *020 †55

LYON, Joseph Lynn. 375 CHIPETA WAY STE A 84108 #049-01-1967 L1968 **PHP FM** *050 †70

MAC DONALD, Joel Douglas. 50 N MEDICAL DR, DEPT NEUROSURGERY 84132 #036-01-1989 L1990 **NS** *020 †25

MACE, Nancy Lynn. ■ 84111 #035-08-1992 L1994 **IM** *020

MACFARLANE, John Richard. 5169 COTTONWOOD ST, STE 500 84107 #049-01-1990 L1991 **NS** *020 †25

MACFARLANE, Thomas Cardon. 370 E SOUTH TEMPLE STE 260, EMERGENCY PHYSICIANS INT C 84111 #028-34-2000 L2004 **EM** *020 †16

MAC GREGOR, Bronwyn Franc. 50 N MEDICAL DR, INTERNAL MEDICINE 84132 #671-02-1997 L1987 **IM** *100 †20

MACKIE, Robert Wm. 24 S 1100 E, STE 105 84102 #035-20-1974 L1976 **CD IM** *020 †20

MACKIN, James Stephen. 1954 FT UNION BLVD 84121 #048-02-1973 L1978 **AN PME** *020 †05

MACLEAN, Courtney. ■ 84102 #036-07-2005 L2006 **OBG** *012

MAC PHERSON, Jane Ellen. 3838 S 700 E, STE 100 84106 #025-12-1988 L1997 **FM** *020 †18

MACY, Vicki Lee. 455 E SOUTH TEMPLE, STE 202 84111 #040-02-1981 L1982 **OBG** *020 †30

MADDOCK, Robert Kent, Jr. 670 E 3900 S, STE 300 84107 #051-01-1962 L1966 **IM NEP** *071 †20

MADSEN, Michael Brent. 1405 W 2200 S, STE 200 84119 #049-01-1975 L1976 **OBG** *071 †30

MADSEN, Troy Edward. 30 N 1900 E #!C26, UNIVERSITY OF UTAH 84132 #023-07-2003 L2006 **EM** *100 †16

MAGILL, Michael Kevin. 375 CHIPETA WAY, STE A 84108 #036-07-1977 L1994 **FM** *030 †18

MAINWARING, Robin G. 1140 E 3900 S, STE 300 84124 #048-15-1989 L1990 **GYN** *020 †30

MAJERSIK, Jennifer Juhl. 50 N MEDICAL DR, NEUROLOGY DEPT 84132 #050-02-2001 L2002 **N** *020 †75

MALASANA, Gangadhar Rao. HEALTH CARE, UNIVERSITY OF UTAH 84132 #495-11-2003 **IM** *012

MALECHEK, Lindsay. 1050 E SOUTH TEMPLE, SALT LAKE REGIONAL MEDICAL 84102 #049-01-2003 L2005 **FM** *100 †18

MALIK, Amer Mohammed. 30 N 1900 E, U OF U/DEPT OF NEUROLOGY 84132 #023-01-2005 L2007 **N** *012

MALLIN, Michael Patrick. ■ 84108 #045-04-2007 **EM** *012

MALONEY, Christopher G. 50 N MEDICAL DR DEPT PED 84132 #028-03-1990 L1991 **CCP** *020 †55

MAMALIS, Nick. 65 N MEDICAL DR, DEPT OF OPHTHALMOLOGY 84132 #049-01-1982 L1987 **OPH** *020 †35

MANASTER, Betty Jean. ■ 84101 #011-03-1978 L1983 **R** *040 †80

MANGELSON, Michael W. 333 S 900 E 84102 #030-06-1989 L1995 **U** *020 †95

MANGELSON, Ned Le Grande. ■ 84102 #049-01-1961 L1962 **U** *071 †95

MANGUM, Todd Adams. 989 E 900 S, A-1 84105 #049-01-1990 L1997 **FM** *020 †20

MANNING, Jared Ray. ■ 84106 #056-06-2005 L2006 **IM** *012

MANOV, Ludmil Kirilov. 100 N MEDICAL DR 84113 #198-01-1987 L2001 **CHP** *020

MANUCK, Tracy Ann. 30 N 1900 E RM 2B200, DEPARTMENT OF OBSTETRICS A 84132 #036-05-2003 L2007 **OBG** *100

MANUEL, F Russell. ■ 84121 #065-01-1957 L1981 **GPM GP** *071

MANULLANG, Jocelyn L. 50 N. MED DR, UNIV. OF UTAH MED CTR 84132 #005-12-1995 L1996 **AN** *071 †05

MANWARING, Jotham Charles. ■ 84106 #049-01-2008 *012

MARCHAND, James A. 508 E SOUTH TEMPLE, STE 205 84102 #021-05-1959 L1963 **OBG** *071 †30

MARCHAND, William Rush. 500 FOOTHILL BLVD, VA SLC HEATLH CARE SYSTEM 84148 #055-01-1986 L1987 **P** *020 †75

MARGETTS, Jeffrey C. 1250 E 3900 S STE 200 84124 #049-01-1981 L1988 **NS** *020 †25

MARIANI, Ernest Marc. 1160 E 3900 S, STE 300 84124 #049-01-1981 L1989 **OAR** *020 †40

MARKEWITZ, Boaz Alexander. 26 N 1900 E, PULMONARY/CRITICAL CARE DI 84132 #035-15-1985 L1990 **PUD** *020 †20

MARKLEY, Laura Allyson. ■ 84108 #038-44-2004 L2006 **CPP** *012

MARROUCHE, Nassir Fadel. 30 N 1900 E, RM 4A100 84132 #409-10-1997 L2005 **ICE** *020

MARSDEN, Craig. 5770 S 300 E, COTTONWOOD HOSPITAL 84107 #049-01-1988 L1994 **EM** *020 †16

MARSHALL, Bruce Cameron. 50 N MEDICAL DR, PULMONARY DIV 701 WINTROBE 84132 #023-01-1979 L1988 **PUD** *020 †20

MARSHALL, Charles Jay. 50 N MEDICAL DR DEPT PATH 84132 #016-45-1985 L1986 **PTH** *020 †50

MARSHALL, Nicole Elise. 30 N 1900 E, DEPT. OF OB/GYN, 84132 #026-08-2004 L2005 **OBG** *012

MART, Christopher Robin. 100 N MEDICAL DR, STE 1500 84113 #004-01-1986 L2004 **PDC GS** *020 †55

MARTIN, Christopher H. 1160 E 3900 S, STE 500 84124 #010-01-1992 L1999 **HS** *020 †40

MARTIN, Debra Sue. 1200 E 3900 S 84124 #051-07-1986 L1995 **EM** *020 †16

MARTIN, Jonathan Edward. 3C-444 SOM, 50 NORTH MEDICLA DRIVE 84132 #049-01-2003 L2004 **AN** *020

MARTIN, Patrick Daniel. 30 N 1900 EAST, 4C116 SOM, DEPARTMENT OF INTERNAL MED 84132 #034-01-2006 L2008 **IM** *012

MARTINEAU, Roger Jared. 500 FOOTHILL BLVD, BLDG 47 84148 #305-01-2000 L2004 **P** *020 †75

MARTINEZ, Betty M. 310 E 4500 S STE 300 84107 #007-02-1980 L1981 **FM** *020 †18

MARTINEZ, Mark Luis. 26 N 1900 E, RM 7001 84132 #049-01-1998 L2002 **PCC** *100 †20

MARTINEZ-OKRASSA, Gustavo. 675 E 2100 S STE 39, VISTA ATTN CLAUDIA 84106 #429-01-1958 L1978 **P** *071

MARTINI, Dominick Richard. 100 N MEDICAL DR, PRIMARY CHILDRENS MED CTR 84113 #030-05-1982 L2008 **CHP** *020 †75

MARTINKUS, Rachel Anne. LDS HOSPITAL, 8TH AVE AND C STREET 84143 #030-06-2007 *012

MASON, Jay Wolf. 50 N MEDICAL DR, UNIV. OF UT HEALTH SCIENCE 84132 #041-01-1972 L1980 **CD** *020 †20

MASTERSON, Timothy Alan. 30 N 1900 E, UROLOGY DEPT 84132 #017-20-2001 L2002 **U** *020

MASTIN, Mary Kay. 500 FOOTHILL BLVD, SURGICAL SERVICE 112 84148 #016-11-1974 L1996 **GS** *020 †85

MASUD, Salman. 50 N MEDICAL DR, 3B420 SOM 84132 #704-01-1980 L1995 **AN** *020 †05

MATHENY, Cali Christine. 100 N MEDICAL DR, RESIDENCY PROGRAM 84113 #028-02-1995 L2006 **PD** *012

MATHESON, Robert D. ■ 84108 #049-01-1951 L1952 **GS GP** *071

MATICH, Andrea Jensen. 555 FOOTHILL DR, RM 301 84112 #028-34-2005 L2006 **FP** *012

MATIS, Wendy L. 710 E 200 S STE 1B 84102 #023-07-1987 L1991 **D** *020 †15

MATLAK, Michael Edward. 100 N MEDICAL DR, STE 2600 84113 #016-43-1968 L1977 **PDS GS** *020 †85

MATSEN, Cindy Brown. UNIV OF UTAH HLTH SCI CTR, 50 N MED DR 84132 #016-02-2006 L2007 **GS** *012

MATSEN, John Martin. 50 N MEDICAL DR, DEPT PATH 84132 #005-14-1963 L1975
CLP MM *030 †55

MATSUMURA, Kyle Shigeru. 6321 S REDWOOD RD STE 102 84123 #049-01-1993 L1995
AN PMM *020 †05

MATSUO, Fumisuke. 30 N 1900 E, STE 3R210 84132 #572-13-1968 L1975 N *020 †75

MATTE, Nancy Jw. 391 CHIPETA WAY STE C, RMCOEH 84108 #049-01-2005 L2007 GPM *012

MATTHEWS, Richard Douglas. ■ 84105 #024-05-2003 L2005 GS *012

MATTOX-EMMERMAN, D. 6440 MILLROCK DR, STE 175 84121 #048-12-1986 L1989
PD *020 †55

MAUCH, Teri Jo. 50 N MEDICAL DR, UTAH UNIV SOM 2B422A 84132 #030-05-1987 L1994
PN *050 †55

MAULDEN, Sarah Annamarie. 30 N 1900 E, STE 3R210 84132 #049-01-1998 L1999
N OS *050 †75

MAURER, Anya Jeanne. 3C444 SOM, 30 NORTH 1900 EAST 84132 #050-02-2006 L2007
AN *012

MAVES, Constance Kiesler. 100 N MEDICAL DR 84113 #017-20-1986 L2002 PDR R *020 †80

MAWHINNEY, Mark Ryan. ■ 84106 #007-02-2008 *012

MAXWELL, Christopher Ian. 30 N 1900 E, RM 84132 #019-02-2005 L2006 IM *012

MAXWELL, Russell Paul. 333 S 900 E 84102 #049-01-1995 L1998 IM *020 †20

MAY, Joe Thos, Jr. 1735 S REDWOOD RD 84104 #016-02-1970 L2003 OM FM *020 †16,18

MAYER, Jeanmarie. 30 N 1900 E RM AC221, UNIVERSITY OF UTAH SOM 84132
#035-45-1985 L1990 ID *020 †20

MAZZOLA, Robert Louis. 26 N 1900 E, DIV OF PULMONARY DISEASES 84132
#021-05-2002 L2005 PCC *012 †20

MC AFFEE, Don B. 3369 HIGHLAND DR 84106 #010-01-1944 L1953 OPH *071 †35

MCALLISTER, Bradley Jay. 8TH AVE & C ST 84143 #049-01-1990 L1991 AN *020 †05

MCALLISTER, Brian Gage. ■ 84106 #050-02-2005 L2006 AN *012

MC ANULTY, Melinda Jean. 650 E 4500 S, STE 210 84107 #051-07-1988 L1992 NEP *020 †20

MCBRIDE, Brayden Thomas. ■ 84112 #049-01-2008 *012

MC CALL, Todd David. ■ 84105 #054-04-2002 L2004 NS *012

MC CANDLESS, Jeremy Bell. 590 WAKARA WAY 84108 #038-06-2004 L2006 GS *100

MCCANDLESS, Rachel Thomps. 100 N MEDICAL DR 84113 #038-06-2004 L2006 PDC *012 †55

MCCANN, David Lewis. 4190 HIGHLAND DR STE 102 84124 #023-01-1971 L1972 P *020 †75

MCCANN, Jeffrey Lee. ■ 84106 #041-14-2007 P *012

MC CANN, John David. 1002 E SOUTH TEMPLE # 308, CENTER FOR FACIAL APPEARAN 84102
#018-03-1991 L1995 OPH *020 †35

MCCARTHEY, Rachele Mary. ■ 84108 #049-01-2004 L2005 CPP *012

MC CLAIN, Donald Allan. 50 N MEDICAL DR, RM 4C116 84132 #035-20-1979 L1999
END IM *020 †20

MC CLELLAN, Bruce C. 275 E 200 S 84111 #010-01-1989 L1992 FM *020 †18

MCCOOL, Ryan Russell. 50 N MEDICAL DR, 3C120 84132 #001-02-2006 L2007 OTO *012

MC COWAN, Christy Lee. 30 N 1900 E, RM 1C26 84132 #049-01-1996 L2002 EM *020 †16

MC DONALD, Duncan Keith. 4400 S 700 E STE 240 84107 #010-01-1960 L1966 OPH *071 †35

MC ELLIGOTT, Kathleen M. 50 N MEDICAL DR, DEPT PEDS 84132 #040-02-1981 L1983
PD *020 †55

MC FADDEN, Gary Jackson. ■ 84105 #041-13-1976 L1988 IM *020 †20

MC GANN, Christopher J. 440 D ST, STE 200 84103 #051-01-1994 L1997 CD *020 †20

MCGAULEY, James Leo. ■ 84121 #025-01-1971 L1974 NS *020 †20

MC GEE, Jill Suzanne. 295 CHIPETA WAY, UNIV OF UTAH 84108 #030-05-2003 L2007 CCP *012

MC GEE, Zell Allison. 50 N MEDICAL DR 84132 #036-01-1961 L1982 ID IM *050 †20

MC GREEVY, James Michael. 30 N 1900 E, RM 3B110 84132 #041-12-1973 L1976 GS *020 †85

MC GREGOR, Duncan Ross. 30 N 1900 E, INTERNAL MEDICINE DEPT 4C1 84132
#026-04-2004 L2006 NEP *012

MC GREGOR, Randall Kerr. 1954 FORT UNION BLVD, STE 116 84121 #025-07-1981 L1982
PME AN *020 †05

MC INTOSH, J Michael. 50 N MEDICAL DR # 5R110 84132 #005-14-1987 L1991 P *040 †75

MCINTOSH, Scott E. 30 N MEDICAL DRIVE, UNIVERSITY OF UTAH 84132 #050-02-2002 L2005
EM *100 †16

MC KAY, Edward R. ■ 84108 #041-13-1943 L1954 CRS *071 †85,10

MCKELLAR, Angela. ■ 84121 #049-01-2008 *012

MC KINLAY, Rodrick D. 1160 E 3900 S STE 4100 84124 #049-01-1997 L2004 GS *020 †85

MC LAUGHLIN, Michael J. 5770 S 300 E, P O BOX 57117 84107 #049-01-1992 L1997
EM *020 †16

MC LAUGHLIN, Nancy Lindem. 508 E SOUTH TEMPLE, STE 300 84102 #049-01-1985 L1986
IM *020 †20

MCLAUGHLIN, Patrick Neal. ■ 84115 #007-02-2005 L2008 IM *100

MC LUCAS, Katherine G. 500 CHIPETA WAY, A R U P LABORATORIES 84108
#007-02-2001 L2007 PTH *020 †20

MC MAHON, William Martin. 30 N 1900 E, STE 206 84132 #019-02-1974 L1976 P CHP *020 †75

MC MILLAN, Sean Eric. 324 10TH AVE, STE 250 84103 #011-03-1999 L2005 RHU IM *020 †20

MCMULLIN, Jaron Hudson. RECON SURGERY, DIV OF PLASTIC 84132 #049-01-2007 PS *012

MC NALLY, Joseph Scott. ■ 84111 #012-05-2006 L2008 DR *012

MC QUARRIE, Howard Gurr. ■ 84108 #010-01-1955 L1958 GYN *071 †30

MC QUEEN, Craig Hugh. 1250 E 3900 S, STE 440 84124 #049-01-1968 L1969 ORS *020 †40

MEAD, Arthur F. 869 E 4500 S # 130 84107 #016-11-1950 L1990 ORS *071 †40

MEARS, Scott Lynn. ■ 84117 #049-01-1985 L1986 AN *020 †05

MEASOM, Michael Owen. 5965 S 900 E # 240 84121 #049-01-1989 L1993 P *020 †75

MEAUX, Scott Gary. 5199 GREEN ST 84143 #054-04-1981 L1988 PTH *050 †50

MEEKER, Nathan. 100 N MEDICAL DR, OF HEMATOLOGY/ONCOLOGY 84113
#016-11-2002 L2005 PHO *012 †55

MEIER, Albert Paul. ■ 84102 #034-01-2005 L2006 DR *012

MEIKLE, Alfred Wayne. 615 ARAPEEN DR, STE 100 84108 #047-05-1965 L1969
END IM *020 †20

MEINECKE, Barbara Jean. ■ 84111 #056-06-2007 GS *012

MELTZER, Nathan Paul. ■ 84117 #036-08-2006 L2008 OBG *012

MEMMOTT, Jim C. 7138 HIGHLAND DR 84121 #028-34-1995 L1998 PD *020 †55

MENDOZA, Christopher John. 333 S 900 E 84102 #005-15-2001 L2002 PM *020 †60

MENNENGA, Deborah Lee. 5770 S 1500 W, FOR COUNSELING 84123 #030-06-1992 L1993
P CHP *020 †75

MEREDITH, Kent Guy. 30 N 1900 E, RM 4A100 84132 #038-43-1999 L2005 IM *020 †20

MERKLEY, Kevin H. 755 E 3900 S, EYE INSTITUTE OF UTAH 84107 #049-01-1987 L1992
OPH *020 †35

MERRELL, Steven Wm. 5323 WOODROW ST, STE 102 84107 #047-05-1983 L1984
VS GS *020 †85

MERRILL, Robert Don. 5770 S 250 E, STE G50 & G80 84107 #003-75-2000, ▲ L2004
OBG *020 ‡

MERVEILLE, Caroline Flore. 50 N MEDICAL DR 84132 #654-01-2004 L2006 P *012

MESSINA, Anthony G. 50 N MEDICAL DR, DEPT OF ANESTHESIOLOGY 84132
#035-08-1981 L2002 AN CD *020 †05

METCALF, Thomas James. 1140 E 3900 S, ST MARKS 84124 #005-11-1970 L1975
PD PHP *020 †55

MEULEMAN, Thomas Richard. 617 E 3900 S, LIFETREE MEDICAL INC 84107
#028-34-1978 L1979 AN *020 †05 ‡

MEYER, Jay Jeffrey. ■ 84112 #049-01-2008 *012

MEYER, Laurence John. 30 N 1900 E, RM 4B454 84132 #011-02-1982 L1983
IMG D *020 †20,19,15

MEYERS, Rebecka Louise. 100 N MEDICAL DR STE 2600, UNIV OF UTAH PEDIATRICS SU 84113
#040-02-1985 L1994 PDS *020 †85

MICHAEL, Clara Thompson. 30 N 1900 E, SOM 5R 110 84132 #049-01-1997 L1998 P *020 †75

MICHAEL, John Russell. 50 N MEDICAL DR, SCHOOL OF MEDICINE 84132 #023-07-1974 L1988
PUD IM *050 †20

MICHAELS, Andrew David. 30 N 1900 E RM 4A100, UNIV UT DEPT CARDIO 84132
#005-02-1994 L2006 CD IC *020 †20

MICKELSEN, Richard Wayne. 5965 S 900 E, # 220 84121 #049-01-1992 L2003 CHP *020 †75

MICKELSON, Travis Scott. 50 N MEDICAL DR, PSYCHIATRY DEPARTMENT 84132
#049-01-2006 L2008 P *012

MIDDLETON, Anthony W, Jr. 8TH AVE & C ST 84143 #035-20-1966 L1969 U *071 †95

MIDDLETON, Elizabeth Anne. ■ 84105 #049-01-2007 IM *012

MIDDLETON, Jon Alan. 3934 S 2300 E 84124 #005-14-1982 L1983 FM *020 †18

MIDDLETON, Richard G. 30 N 1900 E, # 3R210 84132 #035-20-1958 L1967 U *020 †95

MIESCIER, Michael John. 100 N MEDICAL DR, RAPID TREATMENT UNIT 84113
#051-04-1995 L1996 NPM *020 †20,55

MIHALOPOULOS, Nicole L. 50 N MEDICAL DR, 2A200 SOM 84132 #521-01-1999 L2005
ADL *050 †20,70

MILEA, Adrian V. ■ 84124 #781-01-1974 L1994 IM *075

MILLAR, C Kay. 50 N MEDICAL DR, DEPT CARDIO 84132 #035-15-1960 L1968 IM *050 †20

MILLAR, D. Anderson. ■ 84106 #049-01-2007 GS *012

MILLER, Arthur John, II. 1047 S 1000 E 84105 #049-01-1992 L1995 CHP *020

MILLER, Charles Wesley. 1735 S REDWOOD RD STE 115, CONCENTRA MEDICAL
CENTER 84104 #047-20-1983 L2000 FM OM *020 †18

MILLER, Christopher Ray. 100 N MEDICAL DR 84113 #001-02-1998 L1999 AN *020 †05

MILLER, Christopher Wayne. 100 N MEDICAL DR, DEPT OF ANESTH 84113
#049-01-2002 L2003 MPD *100 †20,55

MILLER, Corey Alan. 1485 E 3900 S, STE 103 84124 #049-01-1979 L1984 OPH *020 †35

MILLER, Franklin John, Jr. 50 N MEDICAL DR, UNIVERSITY OF UTAH HOSPITA 84132
#041-13-1966 L1976 DR *020 †80

MILLER, Gregory James. 3838 S 700 E STE 100, UTAH CANCER SPECIALISTS, P 84106
#043-01-1981 L1993 PM PLM *020 †60

MILLER, James Allen. 1208 E 3300 S 84106 #039-01-1989 L1990 P *020

MILLER, James Rex, Jr. ■ 84108 #016-06-1937 IM N *071 †20

MILLER, Karen Louise. 30 N 1900 E, DEPT OB/GYN RM 2B200 SOM 84132 #039-01-1982 L1983
GYN IMG *040 †30

MILLER, Karla Lissette. 30 N 1900 E, RHEUMATOLOGY 84132 #034-01-2003 L2004
RHU *012 †20

MILLER, Robert Frederick. ■ 84103 #036-07-1967 L1972 GE IM *020 †20

MILLER, Ronald James. 1050 E SOUTH TEMPLE, UTAH IMAGING 84102 #030-05-1976 L1991
DR *020 †80

MILLER, Russell Raymond. 8TH AVE &, CRITICAL CARE MEDICINE 84143 #036-01-2001 L2007
PCC *012

MILLER, Stephen L. 5292 COLLEGE DR, STE 201 84123 #049-01-1992 L1998 CD *020 †20

MILLER, Thomas Lee. 50 N MEDICAL DR, STE 5A224 SOM 84112 #010-01-1988 L1989
IM *020 †20

MILLER-DALY, Suzanne. 1250 E 3900 S STE 360 84124 #001-06-1996 L2002 GE *020 †20

MILLET, F Jackson. 745 E 300 S 84102 #049-01-1966 L1967 ORS *071 †40

MILLEY, John Ross. 30 N 1900 E RM 2A134, UNIV OF UTAH SCH OF MED 84132
#016-02-1975 L1988 NPM PD *040 †55

MILLINGTON, Wendy Kay. 2232 FOOTHILL DR, F208 84109 #048-14-2004 L2005 PD *020 †55

MILLION, Lynn. ■ 84103 #011-03-1986 L1991 RO *071 †80

MILNE, Caroline Kay. 50 N MEDICAL DR, INTERNAL MEDICINE 84132 #056-05-1994 L1996
IM *020 †20

MILNER, Tiffany Lee. ■ 84103 #048-13-2008 *012

MINEAU, David Edward. 1050 E SOUTH TEMPLE, UTAH IMAGING 84102 #048-12-1970 L1971
DR VIR *020 †80

MINER, Paul Alan. 5770 S 250 E, STE 415 84107 #049-01-1974 L1976 END IM *020 †20

MINICH, L Lu Annn. 100 N MEDICAL DR, UNIV OF UTAH MEDICAL CENTE 84113
#055-01-1986 L1992 PD *020 †55

MINTZ, Steven Jay. 24 S 1100 E STE 201 84102 #048-12-1976 L1977 GS *020 †85

MIR-KASIMOV, Mir-Mustafa. 26 N 1900 E, DIVISION OF PULMONARY DISE 84132
#913-06-1996 L2006 PCC *012 †18,20 ‡

MIROW, Susan Marilyn. 73 G ST 84103 #041-07-1973 L1976 P CHP *020 †75

MIRSHEKAR, Kamran. ■ 84106 #858-04-2001 GS *100

MISHRA, Archana. 50 N MEDICAL DR, UNIV OF UT MED CTR 84132 #495-18-1995 L2005
HMP *012

MISKA, Robert Miles. 370 9TH AVE STE 106 84103 #056-06-1983 L1991 N *020 †75

MITCHELL, Nicole Renae. ■ 84121 #030-05-2003 L2007 NPM *012

MITCHELL, Rachel A. 333 S 900 E, INTERMOUNTAIN SALT LAKE CL 84102 #035-45-2003 L2006
IM *020 †20

MIXCO, Javier Marcelo. ■ 84106 #036-07-2007 IM *012

MOBLEY, Steven Ross. 50 N MEDICAL DR 84132 #048-14-1995 L2002 OTO *020 †45

MOENCH, Brian John. ■ 84124 #049-01-1977 L1981 AN *020 †05

MOENCH, Louis Alan. 333 S 9TH E 84102 #049-01-1970 L1971 P OS *020 †75

MOENCH, Matthew Louis. 650 KOMAS DR, STE 208 84108 #051-01-2002 L2006 P *020 †75

MOFFAT, Craig Mather. 333 S 900 E, SALT LAKE CLINIC 84102 #049-01-1975 L1982
AI IM *020 †20,03 ‡

MOHR, Michaela Siemes. 1514 EMERSON AVE 1500 84105 #407-21-1966 L1981 P *020 †75 ‡

MOHR, Robert Carl. ■ 84108 #049-01-1959 P N *071

MOINUDDIN, Shiraz. 275 E 200 S 84111 #047-06-2004 L2005 IM *100 †20

MOMBERGER, Glenn Lee. 3336 PIONEER PKWY STE 201 84120 #049-01-1958 L1965
ORS *071 †40

MOMBERGER, Nathan Glenn. 5848 FASHION BLVD 84107 #049-01-1994 L1996 ORS *020 †40

MONIZ, Melinda Carollokel. ■ 84102 #041-15-2005 L2006 ORS *012

MONROY, Franz Medina. ■ 84116 #049-01-2008 *012

MONTEJO, Michael Edward. 1950 CIRCLE OF HP DR #1570, HUNTSMAN CANCER HOSPITAL 84112 #011-04-2006 L2007 **RO** *012

MONTGOMERIE, Bruce Z. 3725 W 4100 S 84120 #005-19-1990 L1991 **PD** *020 †55

MOOERS, Frederick Bruce. 325 8TH AVE, LDS HOSPITAL 84143 #040-02-1981 L1984 **EM** *020 †20,16

MOOERS, Mary Gretchen. 324 TENTH AVE STE 160 84103 #040-02-1984 L1985 **IM ID** *020 †20

MOOERS, Shireen Mulla. 77 S 700 E, STE 220 84102 #040-02-1984 L1985 **PD** *020 †55

MOON, Anne Marguerite. 100 N MEDICAL DR, PRIMARY CHILDREN'S MED CEN 84113 #028-02-1992 L1995 **CCP** *020 †55

MOORE, David A. 1002 E SOUTH TEMPLE, STE 508 84102 #049-01-1976 L1984 **FM** *020 †16,18

MOORE, Hillary Marie. ■ 84108 #054-04-2006 L2008 **OBG** *012

MOORE, Jill Caroline. 30 N 1900 E, SOM 4R118 84132 #049-01-2003 L2005 **GE** *012 †20

MOORE, John Greenwood. VET ADMIN HOSP 84148 #049-01-1961 L1968 **GE IM** *040 †20

MOORE, Kevin Roy. 100 N MEDICAL DR 84113 #024-07-1991 L1994 **RNR** *020 †80

MOORE, Stephanie Vrable. 50 N MEDICAL DR, DIVISION OF CARDIOLOGY 84132 #038-41-1994 L1997 **CD** *020 †20

MORALES, Louis, Jr. 325 8TH AVE 84117 #048-13-1975 L1983 **PS GS** *020 †85,65

MORELAND, Jay Caesar. 8TH AVE & C ST 84143 #005-06-1992 L1993 **FM OS** *020 †18

MORESS, Gerald Roy. 370 E SOUTH TEMPLE STE 300 84111 #035-45-1962 L1966 **N** *030 †75

MORGAN, David Edwin. ■ 84108 #007-02-2005 L2007 **AN** *012

MORGAN, James Michael. 5848 S 300 E, THE ORTHO SPECIALTY HOSP 84107 #049-01-1986 L1987 **ORS** *020 †40

MORGAN, Jessica Angela. 1160 E 3900 S STE 1000, WASATCH INTERNAL & FAMILY 84124 #026-04-2000 L2001 **FM** *020 †18 ‡

MORGAN, Lisa Ann. 1140 E 3900 S STE 410, MILLCREEK WOMENS CENTER 84124 #049-01-1996 L2000 **OBG** *020 †30

MORGAN, Ross Eric. 324 10TH AVE STE 274 84103 #028-02-1978 L1979 **HO IM** *020 †20

MORITA, Denise Catherine. 30 N 1900 E RM 3R210, DEPT OF NEUROLOGY 84132 #054-04-2002 L2003 **CHN** *020

MORLEY, Kimberly Ann. ■ 84105 #049-01-2007 **IM** *012

MORRIS, Alan Howard. 325 8TH AVE, PULMONARY DIVISION 84143 #008-01-1964 L1973 **PUD IM** *050

MORRIS, Dennis Laraine. 1954 FORT UNION BLVD, STE 104 84121 #049-01-1978 L1981 **AN** *020

MORRIS, Donald Robert, Jr. 650 E 4500 S, STE 200 84107 #001-02-1998 L1999 **NEP** *020 †20

MORRIS, Dustin Grev. 1200 E 3900 S, ST MARK'S HOSPITAL 84124 #035-01-2000 L2004 **AN** *020 †05

MORRIS, Maisa Nagi. 4624 HOLLADAY BLVD, OLYMPUS CLINIC 84117 #001-02-1998 L1999 **FM** *020 †18

MORRIS, Stephen Eugene. 30 N 1900 E 84132 #049-01-1982 L1984 **GS CCS** *020 †85

MORRISON, Leland Jed. 3588 HIGHLAND DR 84106 #016-06-1971 L1972 **FM P** *020 ‡

MORROW, Robert Earl. 650 E 4500 S, STE 300 84107 #041-02-1955 L1959 **ORS** *020 †40

MORSHEDZADEH, Jack Hojjat. 30 N 1900 E, RM 4A100 84132 #049-01-2003 L2004 **CD** *012 †20

MORTON, Kathryn Ann. 30 N 1900 E # 1471, DEPT OF RADIOLOGY 84132 #049-01-1982 L1984 **DR NM** *020 †80,28

MOSELEY, Robert Figuers. ■ 84102 #035-03-1967 L1971 **ORS** *020 †40

MOSER, Karen. ■ 84106 #028-34-2007 **PTH** *012

MOSER, Royce, Jr. 391 CHIPETA WAY STE C 84108 #024-01-1961 L1985 **OM AM** *040 †70,18

MOSHIRFAR, Majid. 65 N MEDICAL DR, MORAND EYE CTR 84132 #010-02-1992 L1996 **OPH** *020 †35

MOSS, Emily. ■ 84102 #049-01-2002 *071

MOSS, Scott William. 1954 FORT UNION BLVD, STE 104 84121 #030-05-1994 L1999 **GS** *020 †05

MOTOKI, David S. 3980 S 700 E STE 23 84107 #049-01-1980 L1981 **PS** *020 †85,65

MOUGEY, Adam Michael. 30 N 1900 E RM 4C104, UNIV OF UTAH MED CTR 84132 #040-02-2005 L2006 **IM** *012

MOVSESIAN, Matt Arthur. 50 N MEDICAL DR, DEPT CARIO 84132 #024-01-1978 L1986 **CD IM** *040 †20

MUELLER, Michelle Tower. 30 N 1900 E # 3C344, DIVISION OF VASCULAR SURGE 84132 #007-02-1997 L1998 **GS** *020 †85

MULROY, John Joseph, Jr. 1954 FORT UNION BLVD, STE 111 84121 #028-02-1979 L1992 **AN PD** *020 †55,05

MULVIHILL, Sean Jordan. 50 N MEDICAL DR 3B110, DEPT OF SURGERY 84132 #005-06-1981 L2001 **GS** *030 †85

MUMERT, Michael Lee. ■ 84106 #019-02-2007 *012

MUMFORD, Brian Ronald. 1151 E 3900 S STE B150, WESTERN NEUROLOGICAL ASSOC 84124 #049-01-1995 L2006 **RNR** *020 †80

MUNSON, Robert James. 1200 E 3900 S 84124 #049-01-1989 L1992 **EM** *020 †16

MUNTZ, Harlan Ray. 100 N MEDICAL DR, STE 4500 84113 #028-02-1977 L2000 **PDO HNS** *020 †45

MURDAY, Michelle Elise. 1250 E 3900 S, STE 330 84124 #051-07-1998 L2005 **CRS GS** *020 †85,10

MURNIN, Kelly Patrick. 1525 W 2100 S 84119 #049-01-1983 L1986 **IM** *020 †20

MURPHY, Nancy Alice. 50 N MEDICAL DR, DEPT OF PEDIATRICS 84132 #033-05-1990 L2001 **PM PD** *020 †55,60

MURRAY, Ais Kerrywillia. ■ 84124 #007-02-2007 *012

MURRAY, Kathleen Ann. 50 N MEDICAL DR, UT MEDICAL CENTER 84132 #017-20-1983 L1984 **PDR DR** *040 †80

MURRAY, Mary Ann. 615 ARAPEEN DR STE 100, UTAH DIABETES CTR 84108 #017-20-1985 L2002 **PDE** *020 †55

MUSE, Derek David. 4460 HIGHLAND DR STE 400 84124 #048-12-1986 L1989 **FM EM** *020 †18

MYERS, Garth G. 100 N MEDICAL DR 84113 #005-06-1949 L1951 **CHN PHP** *071 †55

NADAULD, Lincoln Dyreng. ■ 84106 #049-01-2007 **IM** *012

NAGLE, Marisa Johanna. 30 N 1900 E, DEPT OF PEDIATRICS 84132 #049-01-2004 L2005 **PD** *020 †55

NAMBA, Alfred Hideshi. 6360 S 3000 E, STE 100 84121 #049-01-1959 L1960 **IM** *072

NANES, Ioannis N. ■ 84108 #418-01-1971 L1984 **CD** *020

NARUS, Jo Ann Crane. ■ 84103 #049-01-1997 **IM** *100

NATHAN, David Jay. 24 S 1100 E, STE 302 84102 #041-13-1997 L2006 **NS** *020

NAUN, Christopher Allen. ■ 84103 #024-16-2003 L2004 **CCP** *020 †55

NAYLOR, Robert G. 1220 E 3900 S STE 4A 84124 #049-01-1969 L1970 **GS** *020 †85

NEBEKER, Jonathan Rich. 50 N MEDICAL DR, DIV OF GERIATRICS AB1193 84132 #041-01-1994 L1997 **IMG** *020 †20

NEFF, Christian Mclain. ■ 84109 #049-01-2005 L2006 **EM** *012

NEGRETE, Abelardo. 6440 MILLROCK DR, STE 175 84121 #649-01-1957 L1971 **P** *075

NELSON, Bryan Lee. 6360 S 3000 E, STE 100 84121 #049-01-1994 L1995 **MPD** *020 †20,55

NELSON, Cheryl Ann. HEALTH CARE, UNIVERSITY OF UTAH 84132 #031-01-2007 **IM** *012

NELSON, Don Harry. 50 N MEDICAL DR 84132 #049-01-1947 L1957 **END IM** *071 †20

NELSON, Douglas. 100 N MEDICAL DR, DIV OF PED EMERGENCY MED 84113 #008-01-1987 L1992 **PEM** *020 †55

NELSON, Edward Waller. 3B322 SOM, 30 NORTH 1900 EAST 84132 #049-01-1974 L1975 **GS NEP** *020 †85

NELSON, James Alonzo. 50 N MEDICAL DR DEPT R 84132 #024-01-1965 L1986 **DR CD** *020 †80

NELSON, John Clark. 348 E 4500 S, HEALTHSIGHT 84107 #049-01-1969 L1970 **OBG PHP** *062 †30

NELSON, Lawrence Grant. 50 N MEDICAL DR 84132 #104-01-2002 L2005 **FM** *020 †18

NELSON, Raoul Devin. 50 N MEDICAL DR, UNIV OF UT/ DEPT OF PEDIAT 84132 #028-02-1986 L1987 **PN** *020 †55

NELSON, Richard John. ■ 84108 #049-01-1946 L1950 **IM** *071 †20

NELSON, Russell Lee. 5323 WOODROW ST, STE 202 84107 #049-01-1998 L2004 **ORS** *100 †40

NELSON, Russell Marion. 47 E SOUTH TEMPLE 84150 #049-01-1947 L1949 **TS CD** *071 †85,90

NELSON, Ryan William. 2688 S 1500 E 84106 #049-01-2001 L2002 **AN** *020 †05

NELSON, Todd Andrew. ■ 84108 #010-01-2008 *012

NELSON, Todd Robert. 1160 E 3900 S, STE 1000 84124 #038-41-1997 L1998 **FM** *020 †18

NEMETH, Andras Zoltan. 5444 GREEN ST 84123 #049-01-1997 L2007 **DR** *020 †80

NESS, Daniel Anfin. 100 N MEDICAL DR 84113 #039-01-1991 L2004 **AN** *020 †05

NEST, Kelly Jean. ■ 84102 #026-04-2003 L2004 **IM** *100 †20

NESTER, Theresa Ann. 50 N MEDICAL DR, 3B420 SOM 84132 #035-45-1994 L1996 **PTH** *020 †50

NEUMAN, Mark David. 1208 E 3300 S 84106 #270-02-1995 L2000 **P** *020 †75

NEUMAYER, Leigh Anne. 1950 CIRCLE OF HOPE DR, HUNTSMAN MED CENTER 84112 #048-04-1985 L1992 **GS** *020 †85

NEWMAN, Bretton Heather. 2250 S 1300 W 84119 #035-06-1999 L2000 **FM** *020 †18

NEWMAN, Jonathan Andrew. HEALTH CARE, UNIVERSITY OF UTAH 84132 #051-01-2007 **IM** *012

NEWTON, Bruce Young. 1160 E 3900 S, STE 500 84124 #049-01-1989 L1993 **PM** *020 †60

NEWTON, Joseph Raymond. 2000 S 900 E 84105 #049-01-1946 L1948 **PD A** *071 †55

NG, Perry Pak-Nin. 30 N 1900 E, RM 1A71 84132 #143-07-1992 L2005 *100

NGUYEN, Andy. HEALTH CARE, UNIVERSITY OF UTAH 84132 #048-46-2006 **IM** *012

NGUYEN, Anh Tai. 1819 W 3500 S STE 1C 84119 #942-01-1978 L1987 **GP** *020

NGUYEN, Richard Phu Duc. 171 SCHOOL OF MEDICINE, DEPARTMENT OF RADIOLOGY 84132 #051-07-2004 L2005 **DR** *012

NIAZI, Toba Nyra. 30 N 1900 E STE 3B409, DEPARTMENT OF NEUROSURGERY 84132 #023-01-2004 L2005 **NS** *012

NIBLEY, William Eliott. 333 S 900 E 84102 #010-01-1991 L1992 **HO** *020 †20

NICHOL, Peter Frosio. 100 N MEDICAL DR STE 2600, PCMC 84113 #028-02-1997 L2005 **PDS** *020 †85

NICHOLES, Karl Ray Kelly. 3655 S STATE ST, DEPT OF CORRECTIONS 84115 #049-01-1957 L1963 **EM** *020

NICHOLLS, Chad Mc Kay. 3460 PIONEER PKWY, ER DEPT 84120 #054-04-2003 L2006 **EM** *020 †16

NICHOLS, Don Haskell. 130 S 400 W 84101 #025-07-1963 L1971 **R NM** *020 †80,28

NICHOLS, James Monroe. 1008 OMNI CIR 84116 #049-01-2001 L2002 **AN** *020 †05 ‡

NICHOLS, Stephen H. 1160 E 3900 S STE 2000 84124 #016-06-1965 L1973 **CD IM** *020 †20

NIEDERMEIER, David Willia. 1250 E 3900 S, ST MARKS FAMILY MEDICINE 84124 #056-05-2005 L2006 **FP** *012

NIELSEN, Adolph Martin. 3750 HIGHLAND DR, # 166 84106 #016-01-1940 **GS** *071 †85

NIELSEN, James Barry. 5770 S 250 E STE 285 84107 #049-01-1973 L1975 **OTO** *020 †45

NIELSEN, Jamie Rebecca. ■ 84107 #049-01-2004 L2004 **EM** *012

NIELSEN, Joe Roth. 8TH AVE & C ST 84143 #034-01-1984 L1988 **D** *020 †15

NIELSEN, Peter Christian. 324 10TH AVE, STE 100 84103 #010-01-1977 L2001 **GE IM** *020 †20

NIELSEN, Richard Wendell. 220 S 900 E 84102 #030-06-1971 L1974 **OTO** *020 †45

NIELSEN, Robert Orville. 333 S 900 E 84102 #049-01-1971 L1972 **GE IM** *020 †20

NIELSON, Eric Cline. 1220 E 3900 S, STE 3E 84124 #049-01-1990 L1994 **OBG** *020 †30 ‡

NIELSON, Kenneth Geo. 3725 W 4100 S 84120 #049-01-1988 L1990 **CD** *020 †20

NIELSON, Kenneth J. 745 E 300 S 84102 #049-01-1959 L1963 **IM IMG** *071 †20

NIELSON, Robert Yancey. ■ 84108 #028-34-1990 L1992 **P** *020

NIKOPOULOS, George John. 5770 S 1500 W 84123 #048-02-1988 L1994 **P PYG** *020 †75

NILSSON, Gwen. 745 E 300 S 84102 #049-01-1982 L1983 **PD** *020 †55

NIRULA, Raminder. 3B148, 30 N 1900 EAST, DIVISION OF GENERAL SURGER 84132 #062-01-1994 L2007 **CCS** *020 †85

NIXON, C Richard. 8TH AVE & C ST 84143 #010-01-1957 L1966 **R** *072 †20

NIXON, George Wm. 100 N MEDICAL DR, PRIMARY CHILDRENS MEDICAL 84113 #049-01-1965 L1966 **PDR OS** *020 †80

NMEZI, Murphy Chima. 383 E VINE ST, STE 114 84107 #154-07-1982 *071

NOEHREN, Theodore H. ■ 84115 #035-45-1942 L1950 **PUD IM** *071

NOONAN, Erika M. ■ 84108 #028-34-2008 *012

NOONAN, Thomas Donald. 1250 E 3900 S, STE 440 84124 #028-34-1958 L1963 **ORS** *020 †40

NORD, John William, Jr. UNIV OF UTAH HEALTH CARE, INTERNAL MEDICINE RES PROG 84132 #049-01-2006 L2008 **IM** *012

NORD, Nathaniel Martin. 370 E SOUTH TEMPLE, STE 300 84111 #049-01-1965 L1967 **N** *071 †75

NORLIN, Chuck. 50 N MEDICAL DR, DEPR PEDS 84132 #035-09-1976 L1980 **PD** *020 †55

NORRIS, Jennifer Lyn. 1160 E 3900 S, WASATCH INTERNAL MEDICINE, 84124 #016-11-1983 L1996 **IM** *020 †20

NORTON, Peggy Anne. 50 N MEDICAL DR RM 2B20, UNIV UTAH SCHOOL OF MEDICI 84132 #040-02-1982 L1988 **OBG** *020 †30

NOVAK, Kirsten Leah. 500 FOOTHILL BLVD, SALT LAKE VETERANS HOSPITA 84148 #049-01-1997 L1999 **IM** *020 †20

NOVAK, Peter Jerry. 1160 E 3900 S, STE 500 84124 #049-01-1988 L1995 **ORS** *020 †40

NOYES, Robert Dirk. 324 10TH AVE, STE 249 84103 #035-45-1973 L1975 **SO HNS** *020 †85

NUARA, Michael James. OF OTOLARYNGOLOGY, 3C 120 DIVISION 84132 #016-11-2003 L2004 **OTO** *012

NULL, Donald Morley, Jr. 100 N MEDICAL DR, NEONATLA CRITICAL CARE SER 84113 #055-01-1969 L1999 **NPM PD** *040 †55

NUSS, Kara Jean. ■ 84108 #051-07-2003 L2004 **U** *012

NUTTALL, Marc Travis. ■ 84103 #040-02-2006 L2007 **IM** *012

NYGAARD, Ingrid Elisabet. 30 N 1900 E RM 2B200, DEPT OF OB/GYN 84132 #028-03-1985 L2005 **OBG** *020 †30

■ = Address Information Privacy Protected

OBAH, Christian Chidozie. 541 CHIPETA WAY STE 220, PAIN MANAGEMENT CENTER 84108 #690-03-1992 L2005 **APM** *100 †20

O'BRIEN, Elizabeth Ann. 295 CHIPETA WAY, DIVISION OF NEONATOLOGY 84108 #056-06-1994 L1998 **NPM** *020 †55

O'BRIEN, Richard Thos. 100 N MEDICAL DR, PRIMARY CHILDRENS HOSP 84113 #035-01-1965 L1977 **HEM PD** *040 †55

ODELL, David Hardy. 50 N MEDICAL DR, DEPT OF ANESTHESIOLOGY 84132 #056-06-1998 L2000 **AN** *020

O'DELL, Richard Hardy. 1345 E 3900 S 84124 #049-01-1969 L1971 **D GP** *020 †15 ‡

ODELL, Timothy Wm. 555 FOOTHILL DR, STE 203 84112 #005-18-1980 L1991 **IM** *020 †20

ODER, Terrence Frederic. 650 E 4500 S, STE 210 84107 #024-05-1995 L2004 **NEP** *020 †20

ODONOHOE, Jennifer Grace. ■ 84102 #550-04-2006 **CPP** *012

O'DRISCOLL, Jeff. EIGHTH AVE & C ST, LDS HOSPITAL 84143 #049-01-1989 L1990 **EM** *020 †20

OGDEN, L Lazarre, III. 30 N 1900 E 3C444, DEPT OF ANESTHESIOLOGY 84132 #020-02-1993 L1997 **AN** *020 †05

OGILVIE, Orin Edward. ■ 84109 #049-01-1944 **ATP CLP** *071 †50

O GORMAN, Molly Ann. 100 N MEDICAL DR, PRIMARY CHILDRENS MEDICAL 84113 #035-06-1986 L1994 **PD** *020 †55

OH, Andrew Hyunwhan. ■ 84119 #005-12-2004 L2008 **AN** *100

OKI, Allison. ■ 84103 #049-01-2002 L2004 **PM** *012

OLIVARES, Christopher Rom. 30 N 1900 E 1C026, DIV OF EMERGENCY MED 84132 #040-02-2005 L2006 **EM** *012

OLPIN, Jeffrey Dee. 30 N 1900 E 1A71, RADIOLOGY DEPT 84132 #021-01-1995 L2003 **DR** *020 †80

OLSEN, John Leo. 50 N MEDICAL DR, DEPT PSYCHIATRY 84132 #035-48-2006 L2007 **P** *012

OLSON, Randall J. 65 N MEDICAL DR 84132 #049-01-1973 L1979 **OPH** *030 †35

O'MARA, Kathleen Anne. 7138 HIGHLAND DR 84121 #041-13-1989 L1993 **PD AN** *020 †55

O'MELIA, Anne Marie. 501 CHIPETA WAY 84108 #020-12-1995 L1997 **P** *020 †75,55

O'MURA, Terry H. 5770 S 250 E 84107 #028-34-1996 L1997 **PD** *020 †55

O'NEIL, Kathleen Anne. 3970 S 700 E, STE 24 84107 #035-45-1993 L1995 **DR** *020 †80

OOTTAMASATHIEN, Siam. 100 N MEDICAL DR, STE 2200 84113 #007-02-1999 L2007 **UP** *100

OPITZ, John Marius. 50 N MEDICAL DR, # 2C412 SOM 84132 #018-03-1959 L1997 **PD** *050 †55,19

ORD, Russell Jon. 333 S 9TH E, SALT LAKE CLINIC 84102 #049-01-1968 L1975 **OTO A** *071 †45 ‡

OREMLAND, Gordon Thier. ■ 84121 #035-09-1996 L2004 **FM** *020 †18

ORLANDI, Richard R. 50 N MEDICAL DR # 3C 84132 #035-19-1991 L2000 **OTO** *020 †45

ORME, Geoffrey Alvin. 333 S 900 E 84102 #010-01-1976 L1982 **ORS OSS** *020 †40

ORME, Heidi Taylor. 30 N 1900 E, DEPT OF NEUROLOGY 84132 #049-01-2004 L2006 **N** *012

ORME, James Forrest, Jr. 8TH AVENUE C STREET, LDS HOSPITAL CRITICAL CARE 84143 #024-01-1971 L1977 **CCM** *020 †20

ORMSBY, Sarah Ann. 1140 E 3900 S, ST MARKS 84124 #050-02-1989 L1990 **PD** *020 †55

ORSMOND, Garth Stanley. 100 N MEDICAL DR 84113 #836-01-1967 L1976 **PDC** *020 †55

ORTIZ-PACHECO, C. 1525 W 2100 S 84119 #042-03-1993 L2004 **FM** *020 †18

OSBORN, Anne Gregory. 50 N MEDICAL DR, DEPT OF RADIOLOGY 84132 #005-11-1970 L1974 **DR** *020 †80

OSBORN, Carol Ann. 461 E 200 S, STE 100 84111 #038-41-1985 L1986 **FM** *020 †18

OSTERLING, Wendy Lee. ■ 84103 #032-01-2004 L2005 **CHN** *012

OSTERSTOCK, Jan. 1954 FORT UNION BLVD, STE 102 84121 #049-01-1983 L1985 **AN** *020 †05

OTA, Teresa Lee. 1200 E 3900 S, DEPT OF ANESTHE 84124 #049-01-1988 L1995 **AN** *020 †05

OVEN, Sarah Jane. 6440 MILLROCK DR, STE 175 84121 #038-40-1997 L1998 **FM** *020 †18

OVERALL, James Carney, Jr. 50 N MEDICAL DR 84132 #047-05-1963 L1970 **ID CLP** *040 †55

OVERTON, Sean D. 30 N 1900 E RM 3C444, ANESTHESIA DEPT. 84132 #028-34-2004 L2005 **AN** *012

OWAN, Theophilus Ekpong. ■ 84109 #690-10-1987 L2007 **CD** *012 †20

OWENS, Casey Ray. 6678 STONE MILL DR 84121 #051-01-2005 L2006 **IM** *012

OWENS, Crystal Dawn. 1624 E 4500 S 84117 #005-12-2001 L2002 **FM** *020 †18

OWENS, Cynthia Smart. 1140 E 3900 S, ST MARKS 84124 #008-01-1990 L1997 **PD** *020 †55

PACE, Loyal J. 1954 FORT UNION BLVD, STE 102 84121 #049-01-1978 L1981 **AN** *020 †05

PACE, Nathan Leon. 30 N 1900 E, RM 3C444 84132 #005-02-1970 L1976 **AN OS** *071 †05

PACKER, Alissa Ann. 50 N MEDICAL DR, PEDIATRICS 84132 #049-01-2005 L2006 **PD** *012

PAISLEY, Margaret P. 30 N 1900 E 1C026 84132 #032-01-1999 L2000 **FM** *020

PAISLEY, Theodore S. 30 N 1900 E 1C026 84132 #032-01-1999 L2000 **FM** *020 †18

PALMA, Lombardo F. 6095 FASHION BLVD, INC.# 130 84107 #682-01-1976 L1983 **FM GPM** *020 †70,18

PALMER, David Keith. 4000 S 700 E STE 10 84107 #041-07-1986 L1992 **OTO A** *020 †45

PALMER, Shayne Tarrel. 50 N MEDICAL DR, INTERNAL MEDICINE DEPARTME 84132 #049-01-2006 L2008 **IM** *012

PANKO, Jacqueline May. 4B454 SOM, 30 NORTH MEDICAL DRIVE 84132 #050-02-2003 L2005 **D** *012

PARADISE, Mark J. 1200 E 3900 S, ST MARKS HOSP-EMG PHYS GP 84124 #016-06-1993 L1996 **EM OM** *020 †16

PARK, Albert H. 100 N MEDICAL DR, STE 4500 84113 #028-02-1990 L2002 **OTO PDO** *020 †45

PARK, Gordon Sherman. 1525 W 2100 S 84119 #049-01-1975 L1979 **OBG GP** *020 †30

PARK, Gregory C. 1748 ONEIDA ST 84108 #023-12-1992 L2004 **PS** *020 †45,65

PARK, Jun Tae. ■ 84103 #665-01-2002 L2006 **CHN** *012

PARK, Kang Sik. 1774 FORT DOUGLAS CIR, PO BOX 2308 84103 #583-01-1967 L1976 **AN** *071

PARK, Sung Eun. 100 N MEDICAL DR, DEPT OF PEDIATRICS RESIDEN 84113 #016-01-2005 L2006 **PD** *012

PARK, Tammy K. 1200 E 3900 S 84124 #049-01-1998 L2003 **EM** *020 †16

PARKER, Charles Johnson. 500 FOOTHILL BLVD, VA MEDICAL CENTER (111H) 84148 #036-01-1975 L1985 **HEM IM** *020 †20

PARKIN, Gregory Albert. 525 E 100 S, STE 500 84102 #030-06-1993 L1994 **IM** *020 †20

PARKIN, James Lamar. 50 N MEDICAL DR, 3C120 UNIV OF UTAH MED CTR 84132 #049-01-1966 L1972 **OTO HNS** *071 †45

PARKINSON, Brett Thos. 296 E 3900 S, SPECIALISTS 84107 #021-01-1985 L1991 **DR** *020 †80

PARKS, Amanda Leigh. 30 N 1900 E, PHYSICIAN 84132 #422-01-2004 L2008 **ID** *012 †20

PARRISH, Charles Maxfield. ■ 84105 #005-02-1946 L1957 **TS** *071 †85,90

PARRY, Richard Wright. 50 N MEDICAL DR 84132 #054-04-2001 L2002 **PM** *020 †60

PASCUAL, Franchette Tagav. ■ 84102 #014-01-2007 **IM** *012

PASSEY, Mark Miles. 5810 S 300 E STE 300, COTTONWOOD HOSP 84107 #049-01-1980 L1981 **APM** *020 †20

PATCH, Gregory Grant. 130 S 400 W 84101 #049-01-1985 L1989 **DR** *020 †80,28

PATEL, Alpesh A. 590 WAKARA WAY 84108 #016-06-2000 L2006 **ORS** *020

PATEL, Aruna Arvind. 1954 FORT UNION BLVD, STE 102 84121 #495-23-1969 L1977 **AN** *020

PATEL, Jay Laxman. 30 N 1900 E RM 5C124, HEALTH SCIE 84132 #003-01-2006 L2007 **PTH** *012

PATEL, Jeetendra B. 30 N 1900 E RM 4A100, HEALTH SCIENCES CENTER 84132 #495-76-1997 L2005 **CD** *012 †20

PATEL, Jesal Chinubhai. UNIV OF UTAH HEALTH CARE, INTERNAL MEDICINE RES PROG 84132 #017-20-2006 L2008 **IM** *012

PATEL, Rakesh D. 6440 MILLROCK DR, STE 175 84121 #024-05-1990 L1992 **IM PD** *020 †20,55

PATEL, Shrena Niranjan. 295 CHIPETA WAY 84108 #539-02-2003 L2006 **NPM** *012 †55

PATILLO, Dominic Patrick. ■ 84108 #028-02-2004 L2004 **ORS** *012

PATTEN, Richard Mccurry. 50 N MEDICAL DR, INTERNAL MEDICINE 84132 #049-01-2006 L2007 **MPD** *012

PATTERSON, Colleen Lynn. ■ 84109 #019-02-2003 L2004 **OBG** *100

PAVIA, Andrew T. 50 N MEDICAL DR, DEPT OF INFECTIOUS DISEASE 84132 #043-01-1981 L1988 **ID IM** *050 †20

PAWASARAT, Julie Marie. ■ 84103 #056-06-2007 **OBG** *012

PAYNE, Robert Marr. 166 E 5900 S, STE B111 84107 #010-01-1959 L1960 **FM GS** *020 †18

PEACOCK, Derek John. 324 10TH AVE, STE 250 84103 #917-19-1981 L1995 **RHU IM** *020 †20

PEARCE, James Richard. 6095 FASHION BLVD, STE 240 84107 #030-06-1970 L1971 **IM** *020 †20

PEARCE, Maunsel B, Jr. ■ 84117 #021-01-1963 L1972 **TS** *071 †85,90

PEARL, James Everett. 324 10TH AVE STE 170 84103 #011-02-1975 L1976 **PUD CCM** *020 †20

PEARSON, Jonathan David. 50 N MEDICAL DR, UNIVERSITY HOSPITAL PEDS 84132 #026-04-1999 L2001 **PD** *020 †55

PEARSON, Keith Milo. 2121 NOWELL CIR 84115 #020-02-1945 L1952 **IM GP** *071 †20

PEAT, Bruce G. 50 N MEDICAL DR, PLASTIC SUR DIV 3C-127 84132 #671-02-1981 **PS HS** *020

PEAT, Elizabeth Briar. 50 N MEDICAL DR, UNIV UT MED CTR 84132 #671-02-1983 **CLP** *100

PECHE, William Joseph. 324 TENTH AVE, STE 280 84103 #018-03-2001 L2003 **CRS** *020 †85

PEDERSEN, Peder Jens. 1250 E 3900 S, STE 360 84124 #026-04-1993 L1996 **GE** *020 †20

PEETERS, George Anton. 50 N MEDICAL DR, 3B420 SOM 84132 #005-11-1981 L1986 **CD IM** *020 †20

PEIFFER, Andy Philip. 1002 E SOUTH TEMPLE, STE 202 84102 #067-03-1989 L1994 **EM OS** *020

PELEGRIN, Peter Christoph. ■ 84121 #046-01-2006 L2007 **AN** *012

PELO, Jared William. ■ 84109 #049-01-2008 *012

PELT, Christopher Earl. 590 WAKARA WAY, UNIVERSITY ORTHOPAEDIC CEN 84108 #030-06-2005 L2006 **ORS** *012

PELTZER, Wesley Eugene. ■ 84109 #016-11-1939 L1947 **CD** *071 †20

PENDLETON, Robert C. 1525 W 2100 S, 1ST & 2CD FLOOR 84119 #048-04-1997 L1998 **IM** *020 †20

PENDO, Anne Marie. 324 TENTH AVE STE 285 84103 #005-06-1985 L1993 **IM IMG** *020 †20

PENG, Marlene. ■ 84106 #016-06-2002 L2008 **AI** *100 †55,03

PENNINGTON, Mary Jane. 3725 W 4100 S 84120 #028-02-1985 L1986 **PD** *020 †55

PENROD, Michael Jason. 30 N 1900 E, DEPT OF INTERNAL MEDICINE 84132 #056-06-2003 L2004 **IM** *100 †20

PENZ, Janet Frances. 500 FOOTHILL 84184 #030-06-1993 L2002 **GS** *020 †85

PERAGALLO, Raul Alejandro. 50 N MEDICAL DR, BLDG 3C444 84132 #132-07-1994 L1996 **AN** *020 †05

PERIC-GOLIA, Ludvik. ■ 84124 #957-03-1951 L1972 **ATP** *071 †50

PERKINS, Sherrie Lynn. 50 CHIPETA WAY, MEDICAL DIR AREA 84108 #028-02-1985 L1990 **ATP HMP** *020 †50

PERKINS, Waldo Clyde. 333 S 9TH E 84102 #049-01-1956 L1960 **OTO OS** *071 †45

PERRY, Betsy Nell. OF DERMATOLO, UNIV OF UTAH DEPT 84132 #012-22-2003 L2007 **D** *012

PERRY, Roger Scott. 3460 PIONEER PKWY, INTEGRATED CARE AT 84120 #049-01-1973 L1976 **EM** *020 †16

PETERS, Angela Yvonne. ■ 84105 #048-04-2004 L2006 **N** *100

PETERS, Christopher Lee. 590 WAKARA WAY 84108 #005-06-1988 L1989 **ORS** *020 †40

PETERS, Jeffrey Leigh. 1200 E 3900 S 84124 #049-01-1974 L1975 **AN IM** *020 †05

PETERSEN, Barr Jonathan. ■ 84105 #007-02-2006 L2008 **IM** *012

PETERSEN, Darlene Lynnett. 1250 E 3900 S STE 260, ST MARK'S FAMILY MEDICINE 84124 #305-01-2006 L2007 **FP** *012

PETERSEN, David Byrum. 4400 S 700 E, STE 100 84107 #028-02-1998 L2003 **OPH PO** *020 †35

PETERSEN, Drew Mathew. ■ 84115 #028-34-1940 L1946 **IM** *071 †20

PETERSEN, Emily Lara. 30 N 1900 E, UNIV OF UTAH HOSPITAL 84132 #049-01-2004 L2005 **IM** *100 †20

PETERSEN, Finn Bo. 400 CENTER ST, STE E8 84103 #297-01-1978 L1992 **ON HEM** *040

PETERSEN, Gregory Grant. ■ 84117 #049-01-2002 L2003 **AN** *100 †05

PETERSEN, Marta Jean. 30 N 1900 E RM 4A330, DEPT OF DERMATOLOGY 84132 #049-01-1979 L1981 **D IM** *050 †20,15

PETERSEN, Megan Marie. ■ 84105 #007-02-2007 *012

PETERSEN, Peggy Brinkmann. ■ 84109 #049-01-1985 L1986 **AN OBG** *020 †05

PETERSEN, Phil Brent. 5770 S 1500 W 84123 #049-01-1972 L1973 **CHP P** *020 †75

PETERSEN, Russell Scott. 4124 MOUNT OLYMPUS WAY, RUSSELL S. PETERSEN, MDPC 84124 #049-01-1990 L1991 **AN** *020 †05

PETERSEN, Shane Lewis. 2021E HIGHLAND VIEW CIR 84109 #049-01-2001 L2002 **AN** *020 †05 ‡

PETERSEN, Stanley Keith. 2455 PARLEYS WAY 84109 #016-06-1959 L1965 **GE IM** *030 †20

PETERSON, Cameron Glade. 50 N MEDICAL DR 84132 #305-01-2005 L2006 **PM** *012

PETERSON, Charles Matthew. 30 N MEDICAL DR RM 2B-200, DEPT OF OBSTETRICS & GYNEC 84132 #049-01-1981 L1985 **OBG** *020 †30

PETERSON, Chase Nebeker. 375 CHIPETA WAY STE A, SCHL OF MED 84108 #024-01-1956 L1962 **IM** *040 †20

PETERSON, David Scott. 1151 E 3900 S STE B240 84124 #049-01-1997 L1998 **N SME** *020

PETERSON, James Todd. 2295 FOOTHILL DR 84109 #030-05-1997 L2000 **FM** *020 †18

PETERSON, Lyn Claire. 3434 E 7800 S, MAILBOX 105 84121 #014-01-1983 L1985 **NPM PD** *020 †55

PETERSON, Matthew L. 820 SHERMAN AVE, MILLCREEK ANESTHESIA 84105 #005-18-2000 L2002 **AN** *100 †05

PETERSON, Perry A. ■ 84103 #067-01-1966 L1967 **GYN OS** *071 †30

PETERSON, Richard Blaine. 333 S 9TH E 84102 #049-01-1958 L1960 **DR** *071 †80

PETERSON, Robert G, II. 370 9TH AVE STE 111 84103 #049-01-1979 L1988 **NS N** *020 †25

PETERSON, Wallace Curtis. 100 N MEDICAL DR, ANESTHESIOLOGY 84113 #049-01-1981 L1982 **AN PAN** *020 †05

PETILOS, Teresita Daep. ■ 84117 #748-07-1956 L1975 **IM** *071

PETKO, Colin. ■ 84103 #409-12-2000 L2005 **PDC** *012 †55

■ = Address Information Privacy Protected

PETRAVAGE, Jacqueline B. 500 FOOTHILL DR, SALT LAKE CITY HEALTH CARE 84148 #049-01-1980 L1981 **P** *020 †18,75
PETRON, David J. 590 WAKARA WAY, ORTHOPAEDIC CLINIC 84108 #037-01-1986 L1990 **FM** *020 †18
PETTEY, Jeff Hale. ■ 84109 #038-40-2007 **IM** *012
PETTI, Cathy Anne. 500 CHIPETA WAY 84108 #036-07-1996 L2003 **ID MM** *020 †20
PFEIFER, Lauren Joan. 2040 MURRAY HOLLADAY RD 84117 #025-01-1990 L1996 **AN** *020
PFITZNER, Mark Alan. 100 N MEDICAL DR, PCMC, 3RD FLOOR 84113 #028-03-1991 L1995 **PD** *020 †55
PHAM, Kieuanh Thi. 4568 HIGHLAND DR, STE 200 84117 #049-01-1993 L1994 **IM** *020 †20
PHELPS, Amy Nielsen. 100 N MEDICAL DR, DEPT OF ANESTHESIOLOGY 84113 #034-01-1984 L1985 **AN** *020 †05
PHILLIPS, Sandra Arico. 508 E SOUTH TEMPLE, STE 310 84102 #032-01-1992 L1993 **PD** *020 †55
PIEPER, Sara Jane. 333 S 900 E 84102 #047-05-1999 L2001 **OBG** *020 †30
PIERCE, Jennifer Rose. ■ 84105 #007-02-2007 **IM** *012
PINGREE, George Cannon. 8800 KINGS HILL DR 84121 #049-01-1962 L1969 **OPH** *071 †35
PINGREE, James Cameron. 1250 E 3900 S, STE 440 84124 #049-01-1996 L1997 **NS** *020 †25
PINTO, Nelangi Marie. 100 N MEDICAL DR, CARDIOLOGY - CLINIC A 84113 #025-01-2000 L2007 **PDC** *100 †55
PIPPITT, Karly Ann. 1138 WILMINGTON AVE, SUGARHOUSE CLINIC 84106 #049-01-2006 L2008 **FP** *012
PIROZZI, Cheryl Bond. UNIV OF UTAH HEALTH CARE, INTERNAL MEDICINE RES PROG 84132 #043-01-2006 L2008 **IM** *012
PIROZZI, Michael Anthony. ■ 84105 #043-01-2006 L2008 **IM** *012
PISANI, David Eric. 5323 WOODROW ST, STE 101 84107 #005-06-1989 L1990 **RNR DR** *020 †80
PITTMAN, Jessica R. ■ 84105 #017-20-2007 **OBG** *012
PLAGGE, Amy. ■ 84106 #049-01-2007 **IM** *012
PLENK, Henry P. 8TH AVE INC ST 84143 #016-06-1943 L1952 **RO** *071
PLUMB, Jennifer. ■ 84108 #049-01-2000 L2003 **PD** *020 †55
PLUNKETT, Stephanie. 1950 E 7000 S, FIRST MED 84121 #038-44-1997 L2003 **FM** *020 †18
PODOLSKY, Gilbert. 1220 E 3900 S STE 3F 84124 #041-01-1969 L1972 **IM** *020 †20 ‡
POETTER, Vivian Ruth. ■ 84102 #036-05-2007 **IM** *012
POLAGE, Christopher R. 500 CHIPETA WAY, ARUP LABS INC 84108 #034-01-2000 L2002 **PTH MM** *100 †50
POLLACK, Gregory Andrew. 2000 CIRCLE OF HOPE DR, HUNTSMAN CANCER INSTITUTE 84112 #011-03-2002 L2003 **HO** *012 †20
POLLAK, Elizabeth R. ■ 84102 #016-06-1979 L1992 **CLP** *020 †50
POMBO, David Jon. 8TH AVE & C ST, LDS HOSPITAL 84143 #049-01-1988 L1991 **IM ID** *020 †20
PONDER, Corey Eugene. 590 WAKARA WAY, ORTHOPAEDIC CENTER 84108 #039-01-2002 L2007 **ORS** *020
PONDER, Michelle Marie. ■ 84108 #039-01-2002 L2004 **DR** *100 †80
PONDER, Rebecca Louise. 333 S 900 E 84102 #048-16-2001 L2003 **OBG** *020 †30
POOLE, Garrett Reed. HEALTH CARE, UNIVERSITY OF UTAH 84132 #051-01-2007 **IM** *012
POON, Kasey Benson. 50 N MEDICAL DR, AB193 84132 #041-13-1998 L2003 **IM** *020
POPE, Charita Dynese. 6440 MILLROCK DR, STE 175 84121 #047-07-1985 L1986 **CHP IM** *020 †75
POPE, Richard Jack. 130 S 400 W 84101 #017-20-1976 L1980 **DR** *020 †80
POPP, Suzanne Amalie. ■ 84103 #054-04-2005 L2006 **PD** *012
PORBIN, Sean Matthew. 4021 S 700 E STE 300 84107 #033-06-1994 L1996 **FM** *020 †18
PORTER, Troy Flint. 8TH AVE & C ST, PERINATOLOGY LDS HOSPITAL 84143 #054-04-1990 L1994 **OBG MFM** *020 †30
PORTH, Jeffery David. 50 N MEDICAL DR 84132 #021-05-1986 L1998 **AN** *020 †05
PORTOCARRERO, Leonard J. 2000 S 900 E, INTERMOUNTAIN MEMORIAL INS 84105 #035-06-1986 L1987 **IM UCM** *020 †20
POSS, William Bradley. ■ 84108 #019-02-1987 L1992 **CCP PD** *020 †55
POULSEN, Jason John. ■ 84121 #049-01-2004 L2005 **AN** *012
POULSON, Bo Shaun. 370 E SOUTH TEMPLE, STE 260 84111 #051-04-2003 L2006 **EM** *020 †16
POWEL, Robert Seaver. 1160 E 3900 S STE 200 84124 #043-01-1985 L1990 **IMG IM** *020
POWELL, Amy Paulette. 590 WAKARA WAY 84108 #054-04-1999 L2003 **FSM** *020 †20
POWELL, Douglas Lester. 50 N MEDICAL DR, ATTN: TRICIA TIBOLLA 84132 #049-01-1992 L1994 **D** *020 †15
POWERS, Annie Louise. ■ 84103 #049-01-2008 *012
PRAHALAD, Sampath. 30 N 1900 E, PEDIATRICS-U OF UTAH SOM 84132 #495-70-1991 L2001 **PPR** *050 †55
PRATER, Susan. ■ 84124 #035-03-2006 L2006 **GS** *100
PRATHER, Stephen E. 1060 E 100 S STE 400 84102 #019-02-1975 L1978 **OBG** *020 †30
PRCHAL, Josef Thomas. 30 N 1900 E, SCM 4C416 84132 #286-02-1968 L2006 **HEM** *050 †20
PREECE, Kevin. ■ 84108 #049-01-2008 *012
PREECE, Michael John. 333 S 900 E 84102 #049-01-1969 L1973 **CD IM** *071 †20
PRIBBLE, Charles Gene. 1954 FORT UNION BLVD, STE 111 84121 #047-05-1984 L1985 **CCP AN** *020 †05,55
PRICE, Lynn. 1160 E 3900 S, STE 1000 84124 #049-01-1998 L2002 **FM** *020 †18
PRICE, Raymond Richard. 5169 COTTONWOOD ST, STE 410 84107 #024-01-1987 L1992 **GS** *020 †85
PRICE, Richard Raymond. 333 S 900 E 84102 #049-01-1960 L1962 **GS TRS** *030 †85
PRICE, Robert Sheldon. 5169 COTTONWOOD ST, STE 410 84107 #049-01-1989 L1990 **GS** *020 †85
PRIEST, Nicole L. 1160 E 3900 S # 100 84124 #049-01-1998 L1999 **FM** *020 †18
PRIESTER, Tiffany Christi. 30 N 1900 E, RM 4A100 84132 #005-12-2004 L2007 **CD** *012 †20
PRIESTLY, Daniel Howard. 500 FOOTHILL DR 84148 #021-05-1985 L2007 **DR** *040 †80
PRINCE, Jeffrey Scott. 100 N MEDICAL DR, DEPT OF MEDICAL IMAGING P 84113 #005-14-1998 L2003 **PDR** *020 †80
PROSKAUER, Stephen. ■ 84105 #024-01-1966 L2003 **P CHP** *071
PROVOST, John Martin. 1160 E 3900 S STE 5000, SALT LAKE ORTHOPAEDIC CLN 84124 #049-01-1967 L1984 **HS ORS** *071 †40
PROVOST, Scott Lyles. 84 R ST # 3 84103 #004-01-2001 L2002 **AN** *100
PRUITT, Charles William. ■ 84124 #038-40-1993 L2006 **PD** *020 †55
PRYSTAS, Elizabeth Mary. 324 10TH AVE, STE 274 84103 #041-07-1986 L1987 **ON HO** *020 †20
PUCHALSKI, Michael David. 100 N MEDICAL DR 84113 #025-07-1994 L1997 **PDC** *020 †55
PUGLIA, Kathleen Haynes. 50 N MEDICAL DR, RM 1A71 84132 #010-02-1999 L2000 **DR** *100 †80
PULSIPHER, Michael Allen. 100 N MEDICAL DR, DIV OF ONCOLOGY/BMT 84113 #005-11-1990 L1998 **PHO PD** *020 †55
PULVER, Aaron Frank. ■ 84108 #036-07-2002 L2003 **PDC** *012 †55
PULVER, Laurie Self. 2A200 SOM, GENERAL PEDIATRICS, 84132 #036-07-2002 L2003 **PD** *100 †55
PUTMAN, Stanford S. 324 10TH AVE, STE 178 84103 #048-14-2002 L2004 **U** *020
PUTNAM, Cathey Ann. 3460 PIONEER PKWY, INTEGRATED CARE AT 84120 #005-12-1984 L1994 **EM** *020 †16
PYSHER, Theodore James. 100 N MEDICAL DR 84113 #016-02-1973 L1985 **PTH PD** *020 †50,55
QARNI, Muhammad Uwais. 50 N MEDICAL DR, UNIV OF UTAH HOSPITAL 84132 #704-17-1989 L1997 **IM** *020 †20
QUAN, James Young. 1140 E 3900 S, STE 400 84124 #024-07-1984 L1997 **IM** *020 †20
QUARLES, Leto. 4745 S 3200 W, OQUIRRH VIEW CLINIC 84118 #305-01-1998 L2001 **FM** *020 †18
QUICK, Jody Lynne. ■ 84121 #049-01-2008 *012
QUIEL, Edward Lawrence. 359 8TH AVE 84103 #005-18-1982 L1983 **AN** *020 †05
QUIGLEY, Edward Patrick. 50 N MEDICAL DR, RADIOLOGY DEPT 84132 #016-43-2001 L2002 **RNR** *100 †80
QUINLAN, David John. 370 9TH AVE STE 101 84103 #836-01-1983 L1994 **OBG** *020
QUINN, Denise Callister. 1839 HONEYBROOK PL 84106 #028-02-1943 **CHP** *071 †75
RABIN, Mara Lee. 1002 E SOUTH TEMPLE, STE 404 84102 #010-02-1996 L2000 **FM** *020 †18
RACICOT, David Francis. ■ 84111 #024-16-1975 L1984 **FM** *020 †18
RADA, Mark Alan. 1160 E 3900 S, STE 1200 84124 #003-01-1997 L1998 **IM** *020 †20
RADWIN, Martin Ira. 3725 W 4100 S 84120 #050-02-1981 L1997 **GE IM** *020 †20
RAFFIN, Celeste Edeskuty. 1200 E 3900 S 84124 #049-01-1990 L1993 **EM** *020 †16
RAGLE, Nathan John. 30 N 1900 E, SCHOOL OF MEDICINE 4C104 84132 #016-42-2006 L2007 **IM** *012
RAGLE, Ryan Lawrence. 30 N 1900 E, SOM4C104 84132 #030-06-2006 L2007 **IM** *012
RAJAGOPAL, Arun. 1250 E 3900 S STE 30, INTERVENTIONAL SPINE & PAI 84124 #048-12-1992 L2003 **AN** *020 †05
RALLIS, Tena Maria. 50 N MEDICAL DR, UNIV OF UTAH MEDICAL CENTE 84132 #034-01-1988 L1989 **D** *020 †20,15
RALLISON, Mark West. 1200 E 3900 S 84124 #049-01-1988 L1989 **AN** *020 †05
RALLISON, Marvin L. 615 ARAPEEN DR STE 100, UTAH DIABETES CENTER 84108 #049-01-1957 L1958 **PD END** *071 †55
RALLISON, Scott West. 333 S 900 E, # 101 84102 #049-01-1986 L1987 **OBG** *020 †30
RALSTON, Charles Wm, III. 5770 S 250 E, # 210S 84107 #036-01-1975 L1976 **OS PD** *020 †55
RAMPTON, John Wilcox. 100 N MEDICAL DR, MEDICAL IMAGING DEPARTMENT 84113 #049-01-1998 L2007 **PDR** *020 †80
RANDALL, Louisa Harper. 44 N MEDICAL DR 84113 #032-01-1987 L1988 **PD** *020 †55
RANDALL, R Lawrence. 2000 CIRCLE OF HOPE DR, STE 4260 84112 #008-01-1992 L1998 **ORS** *020 †40
RANDLE, Jeffrey Graff. 1160 E 3900 S, STE 500 84124 #049-01-1991 L1995 **PM OS** *020 †60
RANDOLPH, Todd Lenwell. 400 C ST 84143 #017-20-1990 L1996 **PCP** *020 †50
RAPHAEL, Kalani Lukela. 30 N 1900 E 84132 #014-01-2002 L2003 **IM** *100 †20
RAPP, Daniel Clay. 8TH AVE & C ST, LDS HOSPITAL 84143 #016-43-1981 L1990 **P** *020 †75
RAPPLEYE, Alan Tunis. 3970 S 700 E STE 14 84107 #049-01-1974 L1975 **OBG** *020 †30
RASMUSEN, Carl Geo. 501 CHIPETA WAY 84108 #060-01-1986 L1989 **P** *020 †75
RASMUSEN, Lee Albert. 448 E 6400 S, STE 200 84107 #060-02-1988 L1995 **P** *020 †75
RASMUSSEN, Brad Don. 333 S 900 E 84102 #010-01-1995 L2004 **D** *020 †15
RASMUSSEN, Brian Craig. 6191 S STATE ST STE 202 84107 #010-01-1998 L2003 **FM** *020 †18
RASMUSSEN, Clark J. 5169 COTTONWOOD ST, STE 410 84107 #049-01-1992 L1997 **GS** *020 †85
RASMUSSEN, Dee Martin. 333 S 900 E, SALT LAKE CLINIC 84102 #049-01-1960 L1966 **D** *020 †15
RASMUSSEN, Erwin Kent. 333 S 9TH E, SALT LAKE CLINIC 84102 #049-01-1967 L1969 **OBG** *071 †30
RASMUSSEN, Gary Lynn. 5848 S 300 E 84107 #049-01-1978 L1979 **ORS** *020 †40
RASMUSSEN, James Anthony. 3460 PIONEER PKWY 84120 #018-03-1998 L2001 **PCC** *020 †20
RASMUSSEN, Trent Dalley. 3460 PIONEER PKWY, INTEGRATED CARE AT 84120 #054-04-1993 L1994 **OS** *020 †16
RASMUSSON, Brad Y. 324 10TH AVE, STE 104 84103 #026-04-1980 L1981 **PUD** *020 †20
RASSNER, Leslie. 50 N MEDICAL DR, FAMILY/PREVENTATIVE MEDICI 84132 #010-01-1997 L2001 **FSM** *100
RASSNER, Ulrich Andreas. 50 N MEDICAL DR, RM 1A071 84132 #409-19-1998 L2003 **RNR** *100 †80
RATCLIFFE, Stephen D. 1172 HILLVIEW DR 84124 #028-02-1979 L1980 **FM PHP** *040 †18
RAYBURN, Robert Louis. 1954 FORT UNION BLVD, STE 111 84121 #011-03-1972 L1978 **AN PD** *071 †55,05 ‡
READING, Teresa. 324 10TH AVE STE 224 84103 #049-01-1995 L1996 **GS** *020 †85
RECINE, Alexis Christina. ■ 84102 #031-01-2007 **P** *012
REDD, Amasa Mason. ■ 84106 #049-01-1963 L1964 **P** *071 †75
REDDY, Nagendra Prasad. 1200 E 3900 S 84124 #495-21-1997 L2006 **HOS IM** *020
REDELMAN, Ryan Joseph. HEALTH CARE, UNIVERSITY OF UTAH 84132 #017-20-2007 **IM** *012
REED, Kristina Michelle. ■ 84102 #048-13-2000 L2005 **PM** *020
REED, Kurtis Bryon. ■ 84123 #026-08-2008 *012
REES, Robert Lorraine. 4400 S 700 E # EAST-240 84107 #016-06-1945 **OPH** *071 †35
REES, Vincent Le Roy. ■ 84102 #016-02-1938 L1939 **GS** *071 †85
REES, William Vincent. 333 S 900 E 84102 #035-20-1974 L1981 **GS ON** *020 †85
REESE, Don Loren. 1377 E 3900 S STE 200 84124 #049-01-1977 L1979 **D** *020 †15 ‡
REEVES, Maylinda Rose. 794 SCOTT AVE, UNIT B 84106 #005-12-2003 L2004 **IM** *020 †20
REGRUTO, Michelle. ■ 84102 #049-01-2008 *012
REICHERT, Walter Hugo. 1151 E 3900 S, STE B150 84124 #049-01-1972 L1978 **N** *020 †75
REID, Barbara P Snarr. 100 N MEDICAL DR, PCMC DEPT PED MED IMAGING 84113 #041-07-1968 L1983 **PDR NM** *071 †80
REID, Barbara Sue. 100 N MEDICAL DR, PRIMARY CHILDRENS MED CTR 84113 #036-07-1975 L1977 **OS PD** *020 †55
REID, Bruce Bennett. 5169 COTTONWOOD ST, STE 600 84107 #049-01-1993 L1996 **TS** *020 †85,90
REILLY, Wm Francis, Jr. 333 S 900 E 84102 #056-06-1964 L1972 **HO IM** *020 †20
REILY, Melissa R. 50 N MEDICAL DR, UNIVERSITY HOSPITAL 84132 #048-16-2006 L2007 **IM** *012
REIMER, Larry Gene. 30 N 1900 E # 1C100, UNIV OF UTAH SCH OF MED 84132 #007-02-1975 L1984 **MM ID** *030 †20
REIMHERR, Frederick Wm. UNIV UTAH HLTH SCIENCES CT, DEPT PSYCH 84132 #038-06-1972 L1973 **P** *020 †75

■ = Address Information Privacy Protected

REISER, A Hamer, Jr. 8TH AVE & C ST 84143 #049-01-1945 L1947 **IM** *071
REISER, Albert Hamer, III. 324 10TH AVE STE 172 84103 #049-01-1976 L1977 **OBG** *020 †30
REISER, David E. ■ 84108 #049-01-1950 L1951 **CHP P** *020 †75
REISER, Rebecca Haussler. 30 N 1900 E, UNIVERSITY OF UTAH HOSPITA 84132 #049-01-2005 L2006 **N** *012
REISS, G Russell, III. 675 ARAPEEN DR, PARIDINE BLDG 84108 #041-09-1993 L2000 **TS** *020 †85,90
RENLUND, Dale Gunnar. 8TH AVE AND C ST, LDS HOSP DIV CARDIO 84143 #049-01-1980 L1986 **CD IM** *040 †20
RENNER, David Roman. 30 N 1900 E, STE 3R210 84132 #030-05-1997 L2000 **CN** *020
RENOLLET, Harold Le Roy. 4021 S 700 E STE 300 84107 #026-04-1956 L1956 **EM OS** *020 †18,16 ‡
REUBEN, Brian Christopher. 50 N MEDICAL DR, DEPT OF SURGERY 84132 #056-06-2002 L2003 **GS** *012
REVELEY, Christopher G. ■ 84103 #032-01-1989 L1993 **AN** *020 †05
REVELO PENAFIEL, Monica P. 1950 CIRCLE OF HOPE DR, DEPT OF PATHOLOGY 84112 #319-01-1986 L2007 **PTH** *100
REVENAUGH, James Robt. 5169 COTTONWOOD ST, BLDG B 84107 #016-06-1987 L1997 **CD** *020 †20
REZVANI, Maryam. ■ 84108 #017-20-2001 L2007 **DR** *100 †80
RHODE, Michael Gene. 320 WAKARA WAY, MYRIAD GENETIC LAB INC 84108 #019-02-1992 L1994 **PTH MGG** *100 †50
RHODES, David Alan. 590 WAKARA WAY 84108 #030-05-2006 L2007 **ORS** *012
RHONDEAU, Steven Michael. 325 8TH AVE, DEPT ANSTH 84143 #049-01-1988 L1989 **AN PME** *020 †05
RHUDY, Jackson Montgomery. 24 S 1100 E STE 102, OPTIMUM CLINICAL RESEARCH 84102 #005-19-1973 L1974 **EM** *020 †16
RIAZ, Awais. 30 N 1900 E, STE 3R210 84132 #704-01-1985 L2004 **N** *020 †75
RICH, Charles Christian. 5169 COTTONWOOD ST, STE 500 84107 #024-01-1993 L1999 **NS** *020 †25
RICH, Christopher Eric. 30 N 1900 E, RM 4R312 84132 #041-02-2002 L2003 **NEP** *012 †20
RICH, Gregory R. 30 N 1900 E RM 3C444, DEPT OF ANESTHESIOLOGY 84132 #028-78-2004, ▲ L2005 **AN** *012
RICH, Joseph Chas. 370 9TH AVE STE 111 84103 #049-01-1965 L1970 **NS** *071 †25
RICH, Michael Everett. ■ 84108 #049-01-2008 *012
RICHARDS, Ann Withrow. 2000 S 900 E 84105 #005-02-1985 L1988 **IM** *020 †20
RICHARDS, Brett Evan. 590 WAKARA WAY 84108 #305-01-2001 L2007 **HSO** *012
RICHARDS, Charles David. 2000 S 900 E 84105 #035-20-1970 L1971 **GS** *072 †85
RICHARDS, Charles E. 745 E 3RD S 84102 #049-01-1950 L1952 **PD** *020
RICHARDS, Christina Gail. 24 S 1100 E STE 201 84102 #038-40-1993 L1999 **GS** *020 †85
RICHARDS, David W. 2000 S 9TH E 84105 #049-01-1951 L1954 **CD IM** *071 †20
RICHARDS, Kent Farnsworth. 324 10TH AVE, STE 224 84103 #049-01-1972 L1975 **GS OS** *020 †85
RICHARDS, L Stephen, Jr. ■ 84108 #018-03-1952 L1964 **TS GS** *071 †85,90
RICHARDS, Preston Nibley. 1954 FORT UNION BLVD, STE 102 84121 #049-01-1985 L1986 **GS** *020 †05
RICHARDSON, Scott Philip. 30 N 1900 E, UNIV OF UTAH 84132 #048-02-1991 L1992 **AN** *020 †05
RICHARDSON, Stephen F. 4252 HIGHLAND DR STE 200 84124 #016-11-1970 L1980 **U** *020 †95
RICHEY, Gary Dale. 1250 E 3900 S, STE 360 84124 #048-04-1973 L1975 **GE IM** *071 †20
RICKS, Daniel Jay. ■ 84105 #049-01-1991 L1992 **IM ID** *020 †20
RICKS, Jane Hales. 1440 SUNNYSIDE AVE, JANE H RICKS, MEDICAL 84105 #049-01-1990 L1991 **FM** *020 †18
RIDGES, Joseph Douglas. 1160 E 3900 S, STE 2000 84124 #049-01-1964 L1970 **CD IM** *020
RIEKHOF, F Tempel. ■ 84109 #028-03-1963 L1970 **OPH** *071 †35
RIES, Kristen Marianne. ■ 84106 #041-07-1967 L1981 **IM ID** *071 †20
RIET, Eugenia Kirsanow. 617 E 3900 S 84107 #011-03-1962 L1965 **AN PD** *071
RIGBY, Eric Woodbury. 8TH AVE & C ST 84143 #038-40-1998 L1999 **AN** *020 †05
RIGBY, Kim Novak. 525 E 100 S, STE 500 84102 #049-01-1982 L1984 **PD** *020 †55
RIGBY, Odell Franklin. ■ 84108 #049-01-1964 L1969 **U** *071 †95
RIGBY, Rohn Clark. 3460 PIONEER PKWY, HOSPITALIST 84120 #305-01-2002 L2007 **FM** *100 †18
RIGGS, Ryan Keith. 370 E SOUTH TEMPLE, STE 260 84111 #049-01-1998 L2007 **EM** *020 †16
RINDFLESH, Mark Alan. 501 CHIPETA WAY 84108 #049-01-1973 L1974 **P CHP** *020 †75
RING, Shellie Jean. 7138 HIGHLAND DR 84121 #016-01-1997 L1998 **PD** *020 †55
RING, Wallace Harold. ■ 84108 #007-02-1957 L1962 **AN** *071
RITZMAN, John Ray. ■ 84117 #049-01-1971 L2001 **AN** *020 †05
RIVA-CAMBRIN, Jay. 100 N MEDICAL DR # 1475, PRIMARY CHILDS MED CTR 84113 #060-01-1998 L2006 **NSP** *020
RIVAS, Wyatt Harlan. ■ 84108 #049-01-2008 *012
ROACH, Michael Judson. 30 N 1900 E, DEPT OF CARDIOTHORIACIC SU 84132 #047-20-2001 L2006 **TS** *012
ROALSTAD, Christina Louis. ■ 84105 #049-01-2007 *012
ROBB, James Barry. 1220 E 3900 S STE 3F 84124 #049-01-1966 L1967 **GS** *020 †85
ROBERTS, Julie A. 1954 FORT UNION BLVD, STE 101 84121 #048-14-1989 L1990 **AN** *020 †05
ROBERTS, Philip Leonard. 1160 E 3900 S, STE 1200 84124 #048-04-1976 L1977 **IM** *020 †20
ROBERTS, Scott Thomas. 590 WAKARA WAY, UNIVERSITY OF UTAH 84108 #016-06-2003 L2007 **PM** *012
ROBERTS, Theodore Seybold. 50 N MEDICAL DR 84132 #056-05-1955 L1957 **NS** *071 †25
ROBERTS, William Lewis. 500 CHIPETA WAY, ARUP LABORATORIES 84108 #038-06-1990 L1998 **CLP PCH** *050 †50
ROBERTSON, Dale Frances. 100 N MEDICAL DR 84113 #067-01-1987 **PDP** *020 †55
ROBINSON, Clyn A. 1954 FORT UNION BLVD, STE 101 84121 #048-12-2000 L2004 **AN** *020 †05 ‡
ROBINSON, David Edward. 1365 W 1000 N, NORTHWEST COMMUNITY H.C. 84116 #028-02-1979 L1990 **FM** *020 †18
ROBINSON, Jeffrey Louis. 324 10TH AVE STE 285 84103 #045-01-1992 L1993 **IM** *020 †20
ROBINSON, Lucinda J. 455 E SOUTH TEMPLE 84111 #049-01-1988 L1992 **OBG** *020 †30
ROBISON, Jon Richard. 3461 S 3125 E 84109 #028-34-1997 L1998 **AN** *020 †05
ROBISON, Reid Justin. 50 N MEDICAL DR, PSYCHIATRY DEPT 84132 #049-01-2005 L2006 **P** *012
ROCKWELL, Wm Bradford. 30 N 1900 E, # 3B400 84132 #028-02-1984 L1992 **PS HS** *020 †65
RODGERS, Geo Marion, III. 50 N MEDICAL DR 84132 #021-01-1976 L1988 **HEM IM** *050 †20
RODRIGUES, Robert Lynn. 3725 W 4100 S 84120 #007-02-1999 L2006 **PS** *020
ROGERS, Robert Kevin. 30 N 1900 E, RM 4A100 84132 #012-05-2002 L2007 **CD** *012 †20
ROGERS, Steven Craig. 295 CHIPETA WAY, PO BOX 581289 84108 #033-05-2000 L2005 **PEM** *012 †55
ROGIN, Robyn L. 2040 MURRAY HOLLADAY RD 84117 #026-04-1982 L1985 **AN** *020 †05 ‡
ROHR, Louis Ralph. U OF UTAH MED CTR, DEPT PTH 84132 #048-04-1968 L1991 **PTH** *020 †50
ROHRER, Winifred Hobson. 3690 S MAIN ST 84115 #035-20-1995 L1996 **PD** *040 †55
ROKEACH, Steven Alan. 1160 E 3900 S, STE 2000 84124 #011-02-1975 L1998 **CD IM** *020 †20
ROLLER, Dean Edwards. 8TH AVE AND C ST, LDS HOSPITAL 84143 #034-01-1994 L2003 **N CCM** *020 †20,75
ROLLINS, Douglas Earl. 20 S 2030 E, UNIVERSITY OF UTAH, BPRB R 84112 #049-01-1973 L1980 **PA** *020
ROMNEY, Douglas Maurice. 5810 FASHION BLVD, STE 205 84107 #040-02-1990 L1994 **IM** *020 †20
ROMNEY, Joshua Steven. 2000 S 900 E 84105 #035-45-2003 L2004 **IM** *020 †20
ROMNEY, Kent Christian. 2000 S 900 E 84105 #049-01-1990 L1993 **IM** *020 †20
ROMNEY, Ralph B. 500 FOOTHILL DR 84148 #048-04-1948 L1950 **IM CD** *030 †20
RONDINA, Matthew Thomas. 30 N 1900 E, UNIVERSITY OF UTAH HOSP 84132 #049-01-2003 L2004 **IM** *100 †20
ROPE, Alan Frederick. 50 N MEDICAL DR, DIVISION OF MEDICAL GENETI 84132 #038-43-1998 L2003 **MG** *020 †55,19
ROSADO, Harry. 30 N 1900 E RM 4B319, INFECTIOUS DISEASES 84132 #042-01-1983 L1995 **ID IM** *020 †20
ROSE, John Wm. 500 FOOTHILL DR, NEUROVIROLOGY RESEARCH 15B 84148 #023-01-1975 L1985 **N IM** *050 †75
ROSE, Kristi D. ■ 84109 #049-01-2008 *012
ROSE, Nancy Carol. 8TH AVE & C ST, DEPT MATERNAL / FETAL MEDI 84143 #035-09-1984 L2003 **OBG** *020 †19,30
ROSE, Richard Sunkyukwan. 500 FOOTHILL DR, SALT LAKE CITY VAMC 84148 #054-04-2003 L2004 **IM** *100 †20
ROSE, Susan Marie. 30 N 1900 E, DEPT OB/GYN 2B200 84132 #054-04-2003 L2004 **OBG** *100
ROSEN, Mark Allen. 5911 FASHION BLVD STE 100 84107 #048-04-1984 L1989 **ORS** *020 †40
ROSENBLUTH, Evan Michael. 30 N 1900 E, DEPT OF OB/GYN 84132 #021-01-2005 L2007 **OBG** *012
ROSENBLUTH, Jeffrey Paul. 50 N MEDICAL DR 84132 #035-09-1996 L2001 **PM** *020 †60
ROSENTHAL, Regina Ellen. 324 10TH AVE STE 249 84103 #035-46-1982 L1991 **IM GS** *020 †85
ROSS, Rustin Ronald. 333 S 900 E, DERMATOLOGY DEPT 84102 #049-01-2003 L2007 **D** *100 †15
ROSZELL, Douglas King. 1050 E SOUTH TEMPLE 84102 #026-04-1966 L1992 **P** *062 †75
ROTH, James Thos. 3970 S 700 E, STE 14 84107 #049-01-1989 L1993 **OBG** *020 †30
ROTHBERG, David Lynn. ■ 84102 #037-01-2007 *012
ROTHENBERG, Joseph M. 323 S 600 E 84102 #010-02-1976 L1990 **IM** *020 †20
ROTHFEDER, Robert Keith. 175 W 200 S, STE 4009 84101 #026-04-1973 L1975 **EM IM** *020 †16
ROTHSTEIN, Gerald. 50 N MEDICAL DR 84132 #011-03-1962 L1971 **IM** *020 †20
ROUSSEL, Danielle L. 30 N 1900 E, RM 3C444 84132 #019-02-2000 L2001 **AN** *020 †05
ROW, David Jinn. ■ 84117 #005-12-2001 L2007 **GS** *020 †85
ROWLANDS, Lawrence Kirk. 308 E 4500 S, STE 175 84107 #056-06-1995 L1996 **PM** *020 †60
ROWLEY, Shari Lyn. 370 E SOUTH TEMPLE STE 580 84111 #049-01-1996 L2001 **EM** *020 †16
ROY, Nicole Alexis. ■ 84109 #047-06-2003 L2004 **DR** *012
RUBACH, Matthew Palmer. ■ 84106 #003-01-2007 **MPD** *012
RUBIN, Michael Adam. 30 N 1900 E, RM AC-230A 84132 #016-11-1997 L1998 **ID** *020 †20
RUCK, Jane Elizabeth. 50 N MEDICAL DR 84132 #671-02-1984 **PD** *020 †55
RUDRAPATNA, Venkatesh K.. 50 N MEDICAL DR 84132 #496-36-1998 L2006 **IM** *012
RUFFY, Rodolphe. 4228 PARK TERRACE DR, 4228 S PARK TERRACE DRIVE 84124 #869-05-1968 L1989 **CD IM** *050 †20
RUNNELS, Sean Torin. 30 N 1900 E, RM 3C444 84132 #040-02-1997 L1999 **AN** *020 †05
RUPPER, Randall William. 500 FOOTHILL BLVD, GRECC, BLDG 2 84148 #005-11-1998 L2003 **IM** *020 †20
RUSSELL, Dennis Darrell. 333 S 900 E 84102 #049-01-1967 L1968 **D** *020 †15
RUSSELL, John G. ■ 84103 #060-01-1950 L1953 **DR NM** *020 †28
RUST, Harold Mathew. 30 N 1900 E, RM 3C444 84132 #049-01-2003 L2005 **AN** *020
RUTLEDGE, Dale Austin. 1955 E 5600 S 84121 #001-02-1989 L1990 **IM** *020 †20
RYSER, Mark Ralph. 6287 S REDWOOD RD, STE 103 84123 #021-05-2004 L2008 **GS** *100
SAAREL, Elizabeth Vickers. 100 N MEDICAL DR, PEDIATRIC CARDIOLOGY 84113 #005-14-1992 L2005 **PDC** *020 †55
SADLER, Christina Aurell. ■ 84103 #049-01-2008 *012
SADRI-NAINI, Hadi. ■ 84103 #517-01-1954 *100
SAFFLE, Jeffrey R. 30 N 1900 E, U OF U RM 3B-306 84132 #016-02-1976 L1977 **GS** *020 †85
SAGAN-OTTOWICZ, Anna. ■ 84121 #759-09-1977 **IM** *100 ‡
SAKAGUCHI, Farrant Hirosh. ■ 84112 #049-01-2008 L2008 *012
SAKATA, Derek Jo. 30 N 1900 E, RM 3C444 84132 #005-12-1999 L2000 **AN** *020 †05
SAKONJU, Ai. ■ 84105 #049-01-2001 L2007 **CHN** *100
SALAMA, Mohamed Elsayed. ■ 84121 #915-02-1994 L2006 **HMP** *100 †50 ‡
SALARI, Ali. 1138 WILMINGTON AVE, FAMILY & PREVENTIVE MEDICI 84106 #003-75-2005, ▲ L2006 **FP** *012
SALTZ, Marcia B. ■ 84105 #187-31-1982 L1986 **PTH** *020 †50
SALTZ, Renato. 5445 HIGHLAND DR 84117 #187-02-1980 L1994 **PS GS** *020 †85,65
SALTZMAN, Charles Louis. 590 WAKARA WAY 84108 #036-01-1985 L2005 **ORS** *020 †40
SALZMAN, Karen Lisa. 30 N 1900 E # 1A71, DEPT OF RAD 84132 #011-03-1993 L1999 **RNR** *020 †80
SAMBADO, Dorene Kay. 508 E SOUTH TEMPLE STE 300 84102 #005-19-1987 L1988 **IM** *020 †20
SAMOLITIS, Nancy Jo. 30 N 1900 E, 4B454 SCHOOL OF MED 84132 #020-12-2001 L2003 **D** *100 †15
SAMORE, Matthew Howard. 50 N MEDICAL DR, UNIV OF UTAH S.O.M./ RM AC 84132 #056-05-1984 L1998 **ID IM** *020 †20
SAMOWITZ, Wade Stewart. 50 N MEDICAL DR, 3B420 SOM 84132 #035-08-1981 L1987 **PTH** *020 †50
SAMPSON, Jacinda Beth. 30 N 1900 E, STE 3R210 84132 #001-02-2000 L2001 **N** *020 †75
SAMSON-FANG, Lisa Jane. 50 N MEDICAL DR 2A200, GENERAL PEDIATRICS 84132 #023-07-1989 L1998 **PD** *020 †55
SAMUELSON, Cecil O, Jr. 50 N MEDICAL DR 84132 #049-01-1970 L1973 **RHU IM** *071 †20
SAMUELSON, Kent Mitchell. 370 9TH AVE STE 205 84103 #049-01-1971 L1972 **ORS OAR** *020 †40
SAMUELSON, Scott James. 2521 MAYWOOD DR 84109 #049-01-2002 L2005 **HO** *012 †20
SAMUELSON, Wayne M. 50 N MEDICAL DR, PULMONARY DIV U OF UTAH 84132 #049-01-1980 L1995 **PUD IM** *020 †20

■ = Address Information Privacy Protected

SANDERS, Amy L. ■ 84103 #040-02-2004 L2006 **PS** *012
SANDERS, Gill Oldroyd. 2000 S 900 E, SALT LAKE CLINIC-MEMORIAL 84105 #049-01-1972 L1973 **PD** *020 †55
SANDERS, Karl Alan. 500 FOOTHILL DRIVE, VA SLC HEALTH CARE SYSTEM 84132 #019-02-1989 L1993 **PUD CCM** *040 †20
SANDERS, Marc Neil. 2000 S 900 E, MEMORIAL CLNC 84105 #049-01-1982 L1983 **D** *020 †15
SANDERS, Richard K. 50 N MEDICAL DR, # 1A71 84132 #048-13-1992 L2000 **DR** *020 †80
SANDHU, Iqbal Singh. 324 10TH AVE STE 189 84103 #495-45-1985 L1999 **GE** *020 †20
SANDVIG, Jenifer Lynn. 1140 E 3900 S, ST MARKS 84124 #040-02-1993 L1994 **PD** *020 †55
SANDWEISS, David Rubin. ■ 84103 #005-14-1996 L2002 **CCP** *100 †55
SANTORA, Stephen Dennis. 1160 E 3900 S, STE 5000 84124 #049-01-1984 L1985 **OP PD** *020 †40
SANYER, Osman Necmi. 555 FOOTHILL DR, RM 301 84112 #056-05-1983 L1986 **FM** *020 †18
SAPERSTON, Adam Robt. 1050 E SOUTH TEMPLE, INTEGRATED CARE AT SALT 84102 #023-12-1990 L2004 **EM** *020 †16
SARDELLI, Matthew Carl. ■ 84105 #025-07-2004 L2006 **ORS** *012
SARFATI, Mark Russell. 30 N 1900 E, RM 3B110 84132 #041-02-1989 L1998 **GS** *071 †85
SARKER, Ashit Baran. ■ 84124 #160-05-1980 L2004 **PCP** *100 †50
SASAKI-BLACK, Karen. 6360 S 3000 E STE 100, FOOTHILL FAMILY CLINIC 84121 #049-01-1984 L1986 **P CHP** *020 †75
SATOVICK, Nicholas John. ■ 84109 #049-01-2007 **IM** *012
SATOVICK, Robert Mark. 1151 E 3900 S, BLDG B # 150 84124 #049-01-1962 L1970 **N** *071 †75
SATYADEV, Anand Mahendrab. 275 E 200 S 84111 #495-22-1999 L2002 **IM** *020
SAUNDERS, Mary Dang. 2923 S NIBLEY GARDEN PL 84106 #007-02-2001 L2004 **PEM** *100 †55
SAUSE, William Thos. 325 8TH AVE 84143 #056-06-1972 L1973 **RO** *020 †80
SAVIA, Philip V. 3540 S 4000 W, STE 250 84120 #422-01-1984 L1986 **N PD** *020 †55,75
SAWCHUK, Terry C. 5810 S 300 E STE 300 84107 #043-01-1984 L1990 **PM** *020 †60
SAWITZKE, Allen Dale. 30 N 1900 E, SOM 4 B200 84132 #016-02-1985 L1986 **RHU IM** *020 †20
SAYAMA, Christina Mieko. ■ 84105 #049-01-2007 *012
SCAIFE, Courtney Lynne. 50 N MEDICAL DR, DEPT OF SURGERY 84132 #056-05-1995 L1996 **GS** *020 †85
SCAIFE, Eric Richard. 30 N 1900 E, RM 3B110 84132 #056-05-1993 L1996 **PDS GS** *020 †85
SCALES, Erin Mckee. 1250 E 3900 S, STE 260 84132 #011-03-2000 L2001 **FP** *012
SCHABEL, Alexander Brian. UNIV OF UTAH SCH OF MED, DEPT OF RADIOLOGY 84132 #056-05-2006 L2008 **DR** *012
SCHABEL, Kathryn L. ■ 84109 #056-06-2003 L2004 **ORS** *012
SCHAECHER, Kenneth L. 3725 W 4100 S 84120 #046-01-1982 L1983 **IM** *020 †20
SCHAFIR, Michael. ■ 84124 #021-01-1955 L1959 **PD** *071 †55
SCHIFFERN, Alison Nicole. 590 WAKARA WAY 84108 #049-01-2005 L2006 **ORS** *012
SCHLISMAN, Alison K. 163 4TH AVE 84103 #041-07-1997 L2000 **IMG** *020 †20
SCHMELZER, Rodney Evan. 5089 S 900 E STE 100 84117 #038-06-1997 L2005 **PS** *020 †65
SCHMIDT, Charles Du Wayne. ■ 84109 #049-01-1954 L1959 **PUD IM** *071 †20
SCHMIDT, Katherine Mckins. 30 N 1900 E 1C026, DIV OF EMERGENCY MED 84132 #041-12-2005 L2006 **EM** *012
SCHMIDT, Leonard James. 501 CHIPETA WAY 84108 #024-07-1962 L1967 **P** *030 †75 ‡
SCHMIDT, Meic Helmut. 175 N. MEDICAL DR. EAST, DEPT OF NEUROSURGERY 84132 #056-06-1994 L2002 **NS** *020 †25
SCHMIDT, Richard Hall. 50 N MEDICAL DR DEPT NS, UNIV OF UT HLTH SCI CTR 84132 #018-03-1985 L1993 **NS** *020 †25
SCHNYDER, Drew David. 275 E 200 S 84111 #012-01-1992 L2002 **FM** *020 †18
SCHOBER, Michelle. ■ 84117 #264-16-1991 L2004 **CCP PD** *020 †55
SCHOLAND, Marybeth. ■ 84108 #028-02-1990 L2001 **PCC** *020 †20
SCHOLL, Mark David. 82 S 1100 E, STE 303 84102 #016-06-1998 L2003 **OSM** *020 †40
SCHONROCK, Krista Lang. 5810 FASHION BLVD, STE 205 84107 #041-09-1991 L1994 **IM** *020 †20
SCHORLEMMER, Gilbert R. 1160 E 3900 S STE 3500, MOUNTAINSTAR CARDIOVAS SUR 84124 #048-12-1978 L1983 **CD VS** *020 †85,90
SCHREIBER, Nathan T N. ■ 84102 #056-05-2007 **OTO** *012
SCHRIEWER, Sharon Kay. 1060 E 100 S, STE 400 84102 #003-01-1994 L1995 **PD** *020 †55
SCHROEDER, Erika Dee. ■ 84105 #054-04-2007 **EM** *012
SCHULTZ, Edward Richard. 2225 PANORAMA WAY 84124 #003-01-1996 L1997 **FM** *020 †18
SCHUNK, Allison Lara. ■ 84121 #049-01-2005 L2006 **PD** *012
SCHUNK, Jeffrey Edward. 100 N MEDICAL DR, PRIMARY CHILDRENS MEDICAL 84113 #040-02-1983 L1984 **PD PEM** *020 †55
SCHWARTZ, Jason. 30 N 1900 E, DEPT OF SURG SCHL OF MD 84132 #016-11-1996 L2005 **TTS GS** *020 †85
SCHWARTZ, Maria A. 30 N 1900 E, PM&R DIVISION 84132 #049-01-1999 L2001 **PM** *020 †60
SCHWARTZ, Richard H. 1220 E 3900 S, STE 4E 84124 #023-07-1976 L1989 **NS** *020 †25
SCHWEI, Mark Gerard. 5770 S 1500 W, BLDG G 84123 #005-18-1982 L2004 **CHP P** *020 †75
SCOTT, James Raymond. 423 WAKARA WAY STE 201 84108 #018-03-1962 L1977 **OBG IG** *062 †30
SCOTT, Jennifer Lynn. 30 N 900 E RM 4C116, DEPT OF MEDICINE 84132 #020-12-2004 L2005 **IM** *020 †20
SCOTT, Steven Merle. 1160 E 3900 S, STE 500 84124 #007-12-1980 L1981 **ORS OP** *020 †40
SEAMAN, James Peter. 5252 INTERMOUNTAIN DR, INTERMOUNTAIN MEDICAL CENT 84107 #049-01-1975 L1976 **PTH** *020 †50
SEEDAHMED, Elfateh Mohame. ■ 84107 #848-01-1999 L2006 **PCC** *012 †20
SEGAL, Lorissa. ■ 84108 #040-02-2005 L2006 **IM** *012
SEGER, Carl James. 30 N 1900 E, 1C026 84132 #054-04-2006 L2007 **EM** *012
SEGERSON, Karen Elaine. 30 N 1900 E, INTERNAL MEDICINE DEPT 84132 #054-04-2001 L2002 **IM** *020
SEGERSON, Nathan Michael. 30 N 1900 E, INTERNAL MEDICINE DEPT 84132 #054-04-2001 L2002 **ICE** *012
SEHY, Luke Timothy. ■ 84105 #016-11-2004 L2005 **AN** *012
SELF, John Michael. 5292 COLLEGE DR, STE 202 84123 #001-02-1978 L1998 **PS HS** *020
SELLS, Laura Lynn. ■ 84108 #047-05-1994 L2006 **PD** *020 †15
SEVERSON, Erik Paul. ■ 84109 #026-04-2004 L2005 **ORS** *012
SHAABAN, Akram Mohamed. 50 N MEDICAL DR, UNIV OF UTAH MED CTR 84132 #915-03-1989 L2000 **DR** *020 †80
SHADDY, Robert Eugene. 100 N MEDICAL DR, PRIMARY CHILDRENS MED CTR 84113 #030-06-1980 L1986 **PDC** *020 †15
SHADOW, L Kristin. 5770 S 1500 W # G, COUNSELING 84123 #031-01-1995 L1996 **CHP P** *020 †55,75
SHAH, Amrapali Mahendra. 26 N 1900 E, 701 WINTROBE 84132 #039-01-2000 L2001 **PCC** *100 †20

SHAH, Bharat H. PO BOX 95 84110 #495-20-1967 L1976 **AN** *020
SHAH, Lubdha Mahavir. ■ 84108 #020-02-1998 L2008 **RNR** *100 †80
SHAH, Madhuri. 515 S 400 E, 1ST FL 84111 #495-12-1965 L1979 **GYN** *020
SHAH, Mark Bipin. ■ 84121 #056-05-2000 L2006 **EM** *020
SHAH, Shital Rajiv. 650 E 4500 S, STE 210 84107 #495-76-1996 L2003 **NEP** *020 †20
SHAH, Sudha Bharatkumar. 3460 PIONEER PKWY 84120 #495-22-1969 L1976 **AN** *020 †05
SHAMI, Paul J. 50 N MEDICAL DR, 3B420 SOM 84132 #605-01-1988 L1997 **HO** *020 †20
SHANE, Craig Lloyd. 8TH AVE & C ST 84143 #049-01-1992 L1996 **EM** *020 †16
SHANNON, John R. ■ 84106 #035-19-1951 L1973 **GP** *071 †85
SHAPIRO, Mary Goyer. 3730 W 4700 S 84118 #023-01-1998 L2006 **PD** *020 †55
SHARMA, Pawan K. 1160 E 3900 S, STE 2000 84124 #495-45-1980 L1996 **CD IC** *020 †20
SHARMA, Pramod Kumar. 7138 HIGHLAND DR, STE 213A 84121 #035-06-1991 L2001 **OTO HNS** *020 †45
SHARP, Howard Cannon. 50 N MEDICAL DR 84132 #049-01-1947 L1948 **GYN PMM** *071 †30
SHARP, Howard Taylor. 30 N 1900 E, DEPT OF OB/GYNROOM 28200 84132 #021-01-1990 L1991 **OBG** *020 †30
SHARP, Richard Paul. 1200 E 3900 S 84124 #038-40-1958 L1966 **AN** *071 †05
SHARP, Sally Dee. 3725 W 4100 S 84120 #038-06-1984 L1987 **CD IM** *020 †20
SHASKEY, David J. 1160 E 3900 S STE 5000 84124 #011-03-1988 L1989 **FM** *020 †20
SHAW, James Thatcher. ■ 84103 #010-01-1963 L1966 **DR NR** *071 †80
SHE, Rosemary Chiajeng. ■ 84106 #005-18-2003 L2004 **MM** *012
SHEAN, Fredric Carl. 50 N MEDICAL DR, DIV OF CARDIOLOGY 84132 #005-14-1965 L1994 **CD IM** *020 †20
SHEETS, Michael Frederick. 95 S 2000 E, U OF UTAH/CARD/BLDG 500 84112 #018-03-1977 L1997 **IM CD** *050 †20
SHEETZ, Mary Joan. 100 N MEDICAL DR, DIVISION OF INPATIENT MEDI 84113 #007-02-1995 L1996 **PD** *020 †55
SHEHADEH, Nasfat Jameel. 82 S 1100 E, STE 403 84102 #575-02-1992 L2007 **ON HO** *020 †20
SHELGIKAR, Anita Valanju. 8TH AVE & C ST, SLEEP MEDICINE 84143 #025-07-2001 L2007 **N** *100 †75
SHELGIKAR, Chinmaya Suhas. 30 N 1900 E, RM 3C344 84132 #056-06-2001 L2007 **VS** *012
SHELTON, Clough, IV. 50 N MEDICAL DR, 3C120 84132 #048-12-1981 L1993 **NO** *020 †45
SHEN, Katherine Anne. 4745 S 3200 W, OQUIRRH VIEW CHC 84118 #031-01-1995 L1996 **FM** *020 †18
SHEPHERD, Laurel Ann. ■ 84109 #018-03-1988 L1990 **AN** *020 †70
SHEPHERD, Mark Mckean. 8TH AVE & C ST 84143 #049-01-1983 L1988 **IM** *020 †20
SHERBOTIE, Joseph R. 50 N MEDICAL DR, PEDIATRIC NEPHROLOGY 84132 #041-14-1982 L1996 **NEP** *020 †20
SHERRY, Katherine F. 650 KOMAS DR STE 208, CHILD & ADOLESCENT PSYCHIA 84108 #047-05-2001 L2002 **OS** *100 †75
SHETH, Shruti Vikrambhai. 333 S 900 E 84102 #495-48-2000 L2006 **RHU** *020
SHIGEOKA, John Wade. 500 FOOTHILL DR # 111B 84148 #041-02-1969 L1977 **PUD IM** *020 †20
SHIHAB, Fuad Said. 50 N MEDICAL DR - 4R312, UNIV OF UTAH DIV OF NEPHRO 84132 #605-01-1985 L1992 **NEP** *020 †20
SHILLING, Kevin Charles. INTERMOUNTAIN SLEEP CENTER, LDS HOSPITAL 8TH AVE AND C 84143 #010-02-1995 L2001 **PCC SME** *020 †20
SHIOZAWA, Brian Elwood. 1200 E 3900 S, ST MARKS EMERG DEPT 84124 #054-04-1981 L1982 **FM EM** *020 †18,16
SHOARI, Mohammad. ■ 84102 #517-01-2001 L2004 **CN** *012
SHOCKEY, Mark Steven. 1220 E 3900 S STE 2C 84124 #019-02-1976 L1979 **PUD CCM** *020 †20
SHORT, James Gordon. 225 W 2855 S, BREVIS CORP 84115 #005-12-1956 L1965 **CLP PTH** *062 †50
SHORTER, Rose Arabella. 2000 S 900 E, 2000 SOUTH 900 EAST 84105 #035-45-1999 L2002 **IM** *020 †20
SHRIEVE, Dennis Chas. 50 N MEDICAL DR 84132 #011-02-1989 L2000 **RO** *020 †80
SHUMSKY, Ilana Beth. 50 N MED DR, UNIV OF UTAH MED CTR 84132 #005-14-1991 L1992 **IM** *020 †20
SHUPUT, Stephen Randall. 359 8TH AVE 84103 #049-01-1981 L1982 **AN** *020 †05
SIDDIQI, Faizi Ahmad. 30 N 1900 E, SOM 3B400 84132 #035-48-1993 L2002 **PS** *020 †65
SIDDOWAY, John L. 36 S STATE ST, FL 22 84111 #010-01-1946 L1952 **PD** *071 †55
SIEGFRIED, Susan Lynn. 500 FOOTHILL BLVD, MAIL CODE 116 OP 84148 #005-14-1994 L2007 **P** *020 †75 ‡
SIEGLER, Richard Louis. 30 N 1900 E 84132 #030-06-1965 L1970 **NEP PD** *020 †55
SIGGARD, Kipley John. 3465 PIONEER PKWY 84120 #049-01-1984 L1985 **ORS** *020 †40
SIKORA, Magdalena Barbara. 30 N 1900 E, U OF U/DEPT OF INTERNAL ME 84132 #759-10-2002 L2007 **IM** *012
SILAS, Stephanie Diane. 50 N MEDICAL DR, UNIV OF UTAH HLTH SCI CENT 84132 #047-05-1995 L1996 **RHU** *020 †20
SILVER, Robert Mitchell. 30 N 1900 E, RM 2B200 84132 #041-07-1986 L1991 **OBG** *020 †30
SILVERMAN, John A. 1200 E 3900 S, ST. MARK'S HOSPITAL 84124 #050-02-1991 L1994 **EM** *020 †16
SILVERTON, Natalie Anne. ■ 84124 #049-01-2007 **EM** *012
SIMARD, Marie Francine. 615 ARAPEEN DR, STE 100 84108 #067-03-1980 L2002 **END IM** *020 †20
SIMMONS, Matthew Reeves. ■ 84112 #049-01-2008 *012
SIMMONS, Rulon Andrus. 2000 S 900 E 84105 #049-01-1968 L1971 **IM** *020 †20
SIMON, Kirk Anthony. 50 N MEDICAL DR, 3B420 SOM 84132 #056-06-1994 L1996 **OS P** *020 †75,55
SIMON, Tamara Danielle. 100 N MEDICAL DR, INPATIENT MEDICINE 84113 #036-01-2001 L2006 **PD** *020 †55
SIMONE, Joseph V. ■ 84103 #016-43-1960 L1997 **PHO PD** *071 †55,20
SIMONS, Marilee Michelle. ■ 84109 #030-06-2008 *012
SIMPER, Steve Chas. 1160 E 3900 S, STE 4100 84124 #049-01-1982 L1987 **GS TS** *020 †85
SIMPSON, Robert I. 375 CHIPETA WAY, STE A200 84108 #048-12-1997 L2000 **PCC** *020 †20
SINDT, Jeffrey Russell. ■ 84108 #007-02-2008 **IM** *012
SINGH, Gagandeep. 50 N MEDICAL DR, UNIVERSITY HOSPITAL & CLIN 84132 #495-45-1995 L2005 **P** *020 †75
SINGHAL, Arun Kumar. 30 N 1900 E RM 3C127, DIVISION OF CARDIOTHORACIC 84132 #051-01-1994 L2006 **GS** *020 †85,90
SINGLETON, John Robinson. 30 N 1900 E, STE 3R210 84132 #007-02-1990 L1996 **N** *020 †75
SJOSTROM, Christopher Mic. ■ 84108 #049-01-2006 L2007 **PTH** *012
SKALABRIN, Elaine J. 30 N 1900 E, STE 3R210 84132 #056-06-1992 L2000 **N** *020 †75
SKEDROS, John Gregory. 5323 WOODROW ST, STE 202 84107 #049-01-1990 L1997 **ORS OSM** *020 †40

■ = Address Information Privacy Protected

SKLOW, Bradford. 30 N 1900 E 84132 #005-11-1994 L2003 **CRS** *020 †85,10
SKRIPENOVA, Silvia. 30 N 1900 E, 5C124 SOM 84132 #050-02-2005 L2007 **PTH** *012
SKUSTER, Denise L Zmolek. 333 S 900 E, SALT LAKE CLINIC 84102 #018-03-1989 L1990 **N** *020 †75
SLAYTON, William Birdsall. 100 N MEDICAL DR, PCMC 84113 #011-03-1992 L1997 **PHO** *020 †55
SMITH, Albert Gordon. 30 N 1900 E, STE 3R210 84132 #026-08-1992 L1997 **N** *020 †75
SMITH, Benjamin Paul. 30 N 1900 E, DEPT. OF INTERNAL MEDICIN 84132 #035-15-2005 L2006 **IM** *012
SMITH, Brigham Ronald. ■ 84109 #012-05-2005 L2006 **IM** *012
SMITH, Charles Bryan. ■ 84101 #024-01-1962 L1969 **ID IM** *071 †20
SMITH, Colin L. ■ 84117 #671-01-1977 *100
SMITH, Danielle Elise. ■ 84106 #049-01-2008 *012
SMITH, Douglas Lee. 36 S STATE ST, FL 17 84111 #017-20-1981 L1982 **IM** *030 †20
SMITH, George W J. 970 MURRAY HOLLADAY RD, STE 2F 84117 #038-06-1953 L1957 **CHP P** *020
SMITH, Gregory Phillip. 1200 E 3900 S, PATHALOGY ST MARKS HOSP 84124 #012-05-1986 L1991 **PTH** *020 †50
SMITH, Hildegard K. 736 3RD AVE 84103 #409-39-1991 L1994 **PCC** *020 †20
SMITH, Homer Redd. ■ 84109 #049-01-1979 L1981 **AN** *020 †05
SMITH, James Christopher. ■ 84101 #010-02-2002 L2007 **RNR** *012 †80
SMITH, James Frank. RM 3B-420, UROLOGY / DEPT 56 84132 #005-02-2002 L2003 **U** *100
SMITH, John E. 3195 S MAIN ST, STE 200 84115 #049-01-1950 L1951 **GS GP** *030 †85
SMITH, John Taylor. 100 N MEDICAL DR, DEPT ORTHOPAEDIC SURGERY 84113 #011-03-1981 L1982 **ORS** *020 †40
SMITH, Kelly W. 30 N 1900 E, RM 3C444 84132 #049-01-1977 L1978 **AN** *050 †05
SMITH, Kit Dean. 8TH AVE & C ST 84143 #040-01-2972 L1976 **AN** *020 †05
SMITH, Kyle Michael. ■ 84102 #030-06-2007 **CPP** *012
SMITH, Marshall Edmund. 30 N 1900 E, RM 3C-120 84132 #016-11-1984 L1997 **PDO OTO** *020 †45
SMITH, Matthew Cary. ■ 84106 #049-01-2008 *012
SMITH, Norman Lee. 3838 S 700 E, LIFETREE PAIN CLINIC 84106 #049-01-1968 L1972 **IM P** *020 †20
SMITH, Robin S. 1140 E 3900 S 84124 #049-01-1989 L1992 **NPM** *020 †55
SMITH, Ruth Ann. 50 N MEDICAL DR, UNIV OF UTAH MEDICAL CTR 84132 #016-02-1970 L1975 **CD** *020 †20
SMITH, Sherman C. 1160 E 3900 S STE 4100 84124 #049-01-1976 L1983 **GS** *020 †85
SMITH, Stacy Ruth. 50 N MEDICAL DR 84132 #049-01-2003 L2006 **OPH** *012
SMITH, Terry Alan. 1200 E 3900 S 84124 #017-20-1971 L1978 **AN** *020 †05
SMITH, Tiffany Ann. ■ 84108 #033-06-2007 **PD** *012
SMITH-TEUNIS, Candice B. ■ 84108 #012-05-2005 L2007 **ORS** *012
SMOCK, Kristi Johnson. ■ 84102 #049-01-2003 L2004 **HMP** *012 †50
SMOOT, A Owen. 8TH AVE & C ST 84143 #049-01-1961 L1963 **ORS** *072 †40
SMOOT, Richard Mc Kean. 3730 W 4700 S, WESTRIDGE HEALTH CENTER 84118 #049-01-1977 L1980 **FM** *040 †18
SNOW, Brent Walter. 100 N MEDICAL DR 84113 #049-01-1978 L1984 **U** *020 †95
SNOW, Dan Gary. ■ 84109 #031-01-1994 L1997 **EM** *020 †16
SNOW, Robert Groesbeck. ■ 84102 #024-01-1935 L1940 **OTO** *071 †45
SNYDER, Travis Gene. ■ 84105 #017-20-2000 L2006 *020 †80
SOHREVARDI, Mahtab. 5770 S 250 E, STE 310 84107 #517-01-2000 L2003 **END** *020 †20
SOISSON, Andrew P. 30N 1900 E, #2B200 84132 #010-02-1981 L2003 **OBG GO** *020 †30
SOLOMON, Margaret Hope. 1525 W 2100 S 84119 #049-01-2001 L2005 **MPD** *100 †20,55
SOLTANI ARABSHAHI, Razieh. 2641 STRINGHAM AVE # 207C 84109 #517-01-2002 *100
SOLTANZADEH, Payam. 2641 STRINGHAM AVE APT 207 84109 #517-01-2000 **N** *012
SOMMERS, Daniel Norman. ■ 84132 #032-01-2001 L2006 **DR** *020 †80
SONKENS, Jerry Wayne. 4000 S 700 E, STE 10 84107 #010-01-1972 L1976 **OTO** *020 †45
SONKISS, Joshua J. 50 N MEDICAL DR 84132 #067-01-2006 L2008 **P** *012
SOPRANO, Joyce Virginia. 100 N MEDICAL DR, PRIMARY CLDS MED CTR 84113 #024-01-1993 L2000 **PD** *020 †55
SORENSEN, Bruce Farrell. ■ 84108 #041-13-1960 L1961 **NS** *071 †25
SORENSEN, Carissa. ■ 84106 #049-01-2008 *012
SORENSEN, John Burbidge. 30 N 1900 E, SOM 3B110 84132 #041-13-1986 L1993 **GS OS** *020 †85
SORENSEN, Sherman Gordon. 5169 COTTONWOOD ST, STE 610 84107 #035-20-1973 L1982 **NM CD** *020 †20
SORENSON, Chas Wallace, Jr. 36 S STATE ST STE 2200 84111 #035-20-1977 L1979 **U** *030 †95
SORRELL, Matthew J. 50 N MEDICAL DR, SURGERY DEPT, RM 3B110 SOM 84132 #047-05-1995 L2007 **CCS** *012 †85
SOSSENHEIMER, Michael J. 6360 S 3000 E STE 310, MOUNTAIN WEST GASTROENTERO 84121 #409-37-1989 L1998 **GE IM** *020 †20
SOTIRIOU, Leo. 250 E 3RD S STE 3 84111 #012-01-1971 L1973 **D** *020 †15
SOUTHWICK, Andrew William. 50 N MEDICAL DR, RM 3B420 84132 #049-01-1997 L1998 **U GS** *020 †95
SOUTHWICK, Grant H. ■ 84103 #041-13-1951 L1952 **GS** *071 †85
SPANN, Marvin Douglas. 30 N 1900 E, DEPARTMENT OF SURGERY 84132 #047-07-2000 L2007 **PS** *012
SPAULDING, Jason Kenneth. 30 N 1900 E, DEPT. OF INTERNAL, RM SOM 84132 #048-12-2004 L2005 **IM** *020 †20
SPEAKMAN, Mori Samuel. ■ 84102 #049-01-2008 *012
SPEED, John. 30 N 1900 E, DEPT PM & R 84132 #143-03-1981 L1988 **PM PMM** *020 †60
SPENCER, Edward Chipman. 201 E 5900 S STE 201 84107 #010-01-1968 L1973 **ORS** *020 †40
SPENCER, Maitland G. 6069 HIGHLAND DR 84121 #023-01-1957 L1958 **GP GS** *071
SPERRY, Richard Jones. 30 N 1900 E, RM 3C444 84132 #049-01-1983 L1987 **AN** *030 †05
SPIEGEL, Timothy Eric. 100 N MEDICAL DR, RESIDENT PHYSICIAN 84113 #028-34-2006 L2008 **CPP** *012
SPIKER, William Ryan. ■ 84106 #005-06-2007 *012
SPRINGER, Jason Michael. ■ 84118 #020-02-2007 **IM** *012
SPRUANCE, Spotswood Lee. UNIVERSITY HOSP, DEPT IM 84132 #038-06-1966 L1970 **IM OS** *050 †20
SRIVASTAVA, Rajendu. 100 N MEDICAL DR - MARS 84113 #065-01-1994 L2001 **PD** *020 †55
STAABY, Mary Elizabeth. 100 N MEDICAL DR, PEDIATRICS DEPARTMENT 84113 #041-13-2006 L2007 **CPP** *012
STACK, Warren Randolph. 5005 S 900 E, STE 120 84117 #049-01-1979 L1982 **IM** *020
STADLER, E Warren, Jr. 5810 S 300 E, STE 300 84121 #048-02-1983 L1984 **PM** *020 †60
STAHELI, Harvey Kent. 1200 E 3900 S 84124 #049-01-1955 L1987 **GS** *071 †85

STAKER, Larry Victor. 60 E SOUTH TEMPLE, 3RD FL 84111 #049-01-1968 L1969 **IM** *020 †20
STALEY, Tyler Jay. 50 N MEDICAL DR 84132 #422-01-2007 **IM** *012
STANDTEINER, Heidi E. 1060 E 100 S STE L10 84102 #031-01-2003 L2006 **IM** *020 †20
STANFORD, Gary Brewster. 1250 E 3900 S STE 310 84124 #060-01-1961 L1969 **OPH** *020 †35
STANFORD, Joseph Barney. 375 CHIPETA WAY STE A, HEALTH RESEARCH CTRS DFPM 84108 #026-04-1988 L1993 **FM** *050 †18
STANLEY, Theodore Henry. 50 N MEDICAL DR # ANES 84132 #035-01-1965 L1972 **AN** *050 †05
STARR, Jennifer Lynn. 501 CHIPETA WAY, UNIVERSITY NEUROPSYCHIATRI 84108 #030-05-2003 L2004 **P** *100
STASKUS, Gitana. 615 ARAPEEN DR, STE 100 84108 #913-49-1995 L2000 **END** *020 †20
STATLER, Kimberly Dawn. 100 N MEDICAL DR, PCMC 84113 #016-06-1995 L2002 **CCP** *020 †55
STEADMAN, Christopher Joh. ■ 84102 #049-01-2008 *012
STEELE, Max Michael. 370 9TH AVE, STE 101 84103 #049-01-1971 L1975 **OBG** *020 †30
STEENBLIK, Matthew Howe. ■ 84106 #049-01-2007 **IM** *012
STEFANIDES, Paraskevas. ■ 84102 #539-04-2003 L2006 **PM** *012
STEFFENS, John David. 30 N 1900 E, STE 3R210 84132 #054-01-1990 L1994 **N** *020 †75
STEHLIK, Josef. 500 FOOTHILL BLVD, 111 CT 84117 #286-13-1996 L2004 **CD IM** *020 †20
STEHLIKOVA, Zuzana. 50 N MEDICAL DR, UNIV OF UTAH 84148 #286-13-1996 L2004 **AN** *100 †05 ‡
STEPHEN, Robert L. 50 N MEDICAL DR, DIV OF EMER MED 84132 #049-01-1995 L1999 **EM** *020 †16
STEPHENSON, Brent David. 30 N 1900 E # 1A71, DEPARTMENT OF RADIOLOGY 84132 #023-12-1993 L2005 **DR** *020 †80
STEPHENSON, Gary Mills. 1020 S MAIN ST 84101 #056-05-1969 L1972 **P** *020
STEPHENSON, Katherine Ann. ■ 84108 #026-04-2007 **P** *012
STEPHENSON, Robert Anson. 1950 CIRCLE OF HOPE DR, HUNTSMAN CANCER HOSP 84112 #049-01-1978 L1991 **U SO** *020 †95
STERN, Colette Avi. ■ 84105 #012-01-2003 L2005 **PS** *012
STEVENS, Edwin Arthur. 30 N 1900 E 1A71, UNIVERSITY OF UTAH, S.O.M. 84132 #012-01-1971 L1997 **DR** *020 †80
STEVENS, Gregory Paul. 1955 E 5600 S, HOLIDAY HEALTH CLINIC 84121 #049-01-1980 L1981 **IM** *020 †20
STEVENS, Lawrence Elbert. 8TH AVE & C ST 84143 #049-01-1952 L1955 **GS** *071 †85
STEVENS, Mark Edward. 1234 PRINCETON AVE 84105 #049-01-1998 L2002 **EM** *020 †16
STEVENS, Mark Howard. 5169 COTTONWOOD ST, STE 400 84107 #049-01-1981 L1987 **GS** *020 †85
STEVENS, Peter Morris. 100 N MEDICAL DR STE 4400 84113 #035-03-1973 L1974 **ORS** *020 †40
STEVENSON, Adam Thomas. 50 N MEDICAL DR, PEDIATRICS DEPT 84132 #049-01-2001 L2002 **PD** *100 †55
STEVENSON, David Andrew. 50 N MEDICAL DR, PEDIATRICS, GENETIC 2C 412 84132 #049-01-1999 L2002 **MG** *100 †55,19
STEVENSON, Gerald P. 1045 E 1ST S 84102 #049-01-1952 L1955 **DR** *075
STEVENSON, Loren Michael. ■ 84105 #005-19-1996 L1997 **FM** *100
STEWART, Chad Bryan. 100 N MEDICAL DR, PEDIATRIC DEPT 84113 #048-12-2005 L2006 **PD** *012
STEWART, Gayle Marie. 1060 E 100 S, STE 400 84102 #017-20-1992 L1996 **OBG** *020 †30
STEWART, John Richard. 1345 E 3900 S, A ALLERGY CLINIC 84124 #049-01-1968 L1969 **A PD** *075 †03
STEWART, John Robt. 50 N MEDICAL DR DEPT RO 84132 #049-01-1958 L1971 **RO** *071 †80
STIERS, Justin Lambertjam. ■ 84121 #030-05-2008 *012
STIGGE, Kevin Wayne. 1160 E 3900 S, STE 1200 84124 #019-02-1990 L1991 **IM** *020 †20
STILLNER, Erica Tracy. 100 N MEDICAL DR, PRIMARY CHILDREN'S MEDICAL 84113 #054-04-2005 L2006 **PD** *012
STINSON, James Battey. 650 E 4500 S 84107 #048-02-1974 L1978 **IM NEP** *020 †20
STIPELMAN, Carole Hannah. 4745 S 3200 W, OQUIRRH VIEW CLINIC 84118 #040-02-1998 L1999 **PD** *020 †55
STOBBE, Joseph Wm. ■ 84108 #049-01-1949 L1950 **OBG OS** *071
STOCKHAM, Randall Jay. 1200 E 3900 S 84124 #049-01-1980 L1981 **AN** *020 †05
STODDARD, Wm Franklin. 1954 FORT UNION BLVD, STE 116 84121 #032-01-1984 L1988 **AN GS** *020 †05
STOERNER, Scott Alan. ■ 84105 #034-01-2005 L2006 **IM** *012
STOESSER, Kirsten Lee. 1138 WILMINGTON AVE 84106 #025-01-1999 L2000 **FM** *020 †18
STOKES, Wayne Laurence. 1525 W 2100 S 84119 #050-02-1988 L2004 **PM** *020 †60
STONE, Bryan Lee. 100 N MEDICAL DR, PCMC 84113 #049-01-1986 L1991 **PD IM** *020 †20,55
STONEBURNER, Hugh Milam. 1525 W 2100 S, REDWOOD CENTER 84119 #051-04-1988 L1992 **IM** *020 †20
STORHEIM, John E. 1121 E 3900 S # C-115, DBA AVILA CLINICAL RESEARC 84124 #028-78-2000, ▲ L2006 **AN PME** *020 †05
STORZ, Benjamin Neil. ■ 84103 #005-12-2004 L2005 **FM** *020 †18
STOTT, Phillip Kevin. ■ 84109 #049-01-2008 *012
STOTTS, Alan Kendrick. 100 N MEDICAL DR, STE 4550 84113 #048-13-1995 L2000 **OP** *020 †40
STOUT, Lisa. 1060 E 100 S, STE 110 84102 #010-01-1990 L1999 **U** *020 †95
STOUT, Mason Gardner. ■ 84108 #649-33-1977 L1978 **IM OS** *071
STRAITS, Cathy Anne. 6440 MILLROCK DR, STE 175 84121 #036-08-1989 L1995 **ID** *020 †20
STRASSER, Catherine Ann. HEALTH SCIE, UNIVERSITY OF UTAH 84132 #049-01-2003 L2004 **PD** *020 †55
STRAUB, Catherine Marie. ■ 84103 #051-01-2005 L2007 **GS** *012
STREAM, Joshua Owen. HEALTH CARE, UNIVERSITY OF UTAH 84132 #023-07-2007 **IM** *012
STRINGHAM, Jack Dunyon. ■ 84108 #049-01-1948 L1949 **AN** *071
STRINGHAM, James Cannon. 82 S 1100 E, STE 103 84102 #049-01-1987 L1994 **TS** *020 †85,90
STRINGHAM, James Grant. 30 N 1900 E, RM 3B110 84132 #023-01-1957 L1957 **PD** *075
STRINGHAM, Paul G. ■ 84115 #049-01-1949 L1950 **GP** *071
STROMQUIST, Don Leonard. 324 10TH AVE STE 250 84103 #008-01-1982 L1991 **RHU IM** *020 †20
STRONG, Michael Brent. 1525 W 2100 S, 1ST & 2CD FLOOR 84119 #048-04-1993 L1994 **IM** *020 †20
STRONG, Sharon Ann. ■ 84124 #035-20-1981 L1984 **FM** *020 †18
STROUD, Susan Kendrick. 30 N 1900 E 1C026, UNIV OF UT HEALTH SCIENCES 84132 #023-07-1997 L2003 **EM** *020 †16
STROUP, Gregory Michael. 30 N 1900 E, UNIVERSITY OF UTAH HOSPITA 84132 #030-06-2003 L2004 **GS** *012
STUART, Roger Koontz. 1685 W 2200 S 84119 #025-01-1969 L1973 **EM** *020 †16

STUBBS, Rachael. 1200 E 3900 S 84124 #048-02-1989 L1990 **IM** *020 †20
STUCKI, John Francis. ■ 84117 #049-01-1946 L1947 **R NM** *071 †80
STULTS, Barry Mac Neill. INTERNAL MEDICIN, DEPARTMENT OF 84132 #035-45-1975 L1979 **PUD IM** *020 †20
STULTS, Connie Child. ■ 84121 #049-01-1976 L1979 **IM** *074
STURGES, Zachary Scott. 30 N 1900 E 1C026, EMERGENCY MEDICINE 84132 #054-04-2006 L2007 **EM** *012
SUCKOW, Bjoern Dominik. UNIV OF UTAH HLTH SCI CTR, 50 N MED DR 84132 #005-14-2007 *012
SULLIVAN, Amy Elizabeth. 50 N MEDICAL DR, DEPT OB/GYN RM 2B200 84132 #050-02-1996 L2000 **OBG** *020
SULLIVAN, Charles Leon. 590 WAKARA WAY, UNIVERSITY OF UTAH ORTHOPA 84108 #049-01-2001 L2005 **ORS** *100
SULLIVAN, Marc David. 1250 E 3900 S, ST MARKS FAMILY MEDICINE 84124 #003-01-2004 **FP** *012
SULLIVAN, Patrick Morris. 1267 4TH AVE 84103 #035-19-2008 *012
SUMMERFIELD, Robert Arthu. 6040 FASHION BLVD STE 201, WASATCH NEUROLOGICAL CLINI 84107 #065-01-1992 L2002 **N** *020 †75
SUMMERS, Donald Fredrick. U OF UT MED CTR 84132 #016-11-1959 L1965 **OS IM** *050
SUMMERS, Paul Richard. 30 N 1900 E # 2, U OF U HEALTH SCIENCES CEN 84132 #007-02-1973 L1991 **OBG** *020 †30
SUNDERMAN, Elizabeth R. 2000 S 900 E, INTERMOUNTAIN MEMORIAL CLI 84105 #054-04-2000 L2001 **N** *020 †75
SUNDIN, Jon Ransom. 5848 FASHION BLVD 84107 #021-05-1981 L1985 **AN IM** *020 †20,05
SUPIANO, Mark Andrew. ■ 84108 #056-05-1982 L2005 **IMG IM** *075 †20
SUPRUNOWICZ, Karen. 5121 COTTONWOOD ST, ER 84107 #049-01-1980 L1982 **EM IM** *020
SUTHERLAND, Harold P, Jr. DEPT OF ANES, LDS HOSP 84143 #049-01-1975 L1976 **AN** *020
SUTHERLAND, Harold Pratt. ■ 84171 #016-06-1954 L1957 **OBG FM** *071
SUTTON, Richard Bruce. 500 FOOTHILL DR 84148 #049-01-1964 L1966 **CD IM** *071 †20
SVENSSON, Annika B M. 500 CHIPETA WAY, MEDICAL DIRECTORS AREA 84108 #858-03-1988 L2005 **MGP** *012 †50
SWABB, Edward Allen. 320 WAKARA WAY, MYRIAD PHARMACEUTICALS 84108 #041-01-1977 L1981 **IM** *050
SWALLOW, Charles Edward. 3738 S 900 E 84106 #016-02-1991 L1993 **RNR** *020 †80
SWANSON, Eric R. 30 N 1900 E RM 1C026, DIV OF EMGY MED 84132 #049-01-1992 L1995 **EM** *020 †16
SWANSON, John Lee. UNIV UTAH MED CTR, DEPT PTH 84132 #030-05-1962 L1962 **PTH** *020
SWENSEN, Paul Harding. 508 E SOUTH TEMPLE 84102 #049-01-1980 L1981 **PD** *020 †55
SWENSEN, Swen Russel. 324 10TH AVE STE 224 84103 #010-01-1969 L1974 **GS TRS** *020 †85
SWENSON, James Reed. 50 N MEDICAL DR 84132 #049-01-1959 L1960 **PM** *071 †60
SWENSON, Jeffrey Duwayne. 50 N MEDICAL DR, DEPT. OF ANESTHESIOLOGY 84132 #010-01-1985 L1993 **AN** *020 †05
SWENSON, Leanne. 333 S 900 E 84102 #049-01-1996 L1998 **END** *020 †20
SWENSON, Lori Raelynn. 3336 PIONEER PKWY, STE 306 84120 #049-01-2000 L2005 **GS** *020 †85
SWENSON, Randal W. 4000 S 700 E STE 10 84107 #049-01-1979 L1985 **FPS OTO** *020 †45
SWIFT, Robert Minton. 617 E 3900 S 84107 #649-14-1979 L1974 **AN PMM** *020 †15
SWIGERT, Jason Clair. HEALTH CARE, UNIVERSITY OF UTAH 84132 #040-02-2007 **IM** *012
SWINYER, Leonard James. 3920 S 1100 E STE 310 84124 #050-02-1966 L1973 **D DMP** *020 †15
SWITZER, Nikki Dewar. 1160 E 3900 S STE G200, THE SENIOR HEALTH CENTER 84124 #048-12-1992 L2003 **IM** *020 †20
SWOBODA, Kathryn J. 30 N 1900 E, STE 3R210 84132 #016-06-1990 L1998 **CN** *020 †75,19
SWOBODA, Paul Richard. SUITE 408, 1002 EAST TEMPLE 84102 #016-01-1991 L1998 **FM** *020 †18
SZCZESNY, Lorraine B. 508 E SOUTH TEMPLE STE 300 84102 #032-01-1979 L1986 **IM** *020 †20
TABIN, Geoffrey C. 65 N MEDICAL DR, MORAN EYE CENTER 84132 #024-01-1985 L2004 **OPH** *020 †35
TACKE, Amber Dawn. ■ 84106 #007-02-2005 L2007 **AN** *012
TADOM, Tammy Laureene. ■ 84111 #041-12-1991 L1993 **EM** *020
TAGGART, Dennis De Vere. 1050 E SOUTH TEMPLE 84102 #010-01-1963 L1971 **IM NEP** *020 †20
TAGGE, Bryan Curtis. 22 S 900 E 84102 #049-01-1995 L2001 **OTO A** *020 †45
TAIT, Vera Frances. 44 N MEDICAL DR, CARE NEEDS/ P.O.BOX 144610 84113 #020-12-1977 L1981 **CHN PD** *020 †55,75
TALBOT, Vanessa Loreley. ■ 84106 #005-12-2005 L2006 **AN** *012
TALBOT, Verl Henry. ■ 84121 #049-01-1961 L1962 **GYN GP** *071 †30
TALBOTT, Andrew Peyton. 30 N 1900 E # 3C444, ANESTHESIOLOGY DEPT 84132 #020-02-2002 L2006 **APM** *020
TALEBREZA, Shaida. 1250 E 3900 S, ST MARKS FAMILY MEDICINE 84124 #049-01-2002 L2005 **FM** *020 †18
TAM, Jessica Waiying. 537 S 900 E, UNIT BI 84102 #010-02-2005 L2006 **IM** *012
TANAKA, Ryoma. 8TH AVE & C ST, LDS HOSP 84143 #572-01-1997 L2002 **PCC** *100 †20
TANDAR, Anwar. 50 N MEDICAL DR, UNIV UTAH HEALTH SCIENCES 84132 #506-14-1994 L2003 **IC** *020 †20
TANI, Lloyd Yasuo. 100 N MEDICAL DR, PRIMARY CHILDREN'S MEDICAL 84113 #005-14-1982 L1989 **PDC** *020 †55
TANNER, David Lyon. 100 N MEDICAL DR 84113 #049-01-1991 L1992 **AN** *020 †05
TANNER, George Stanley. 1220 E 3900 S STE 4-H 84124 #049-01-1957 L1959 **OPH** *071
TAPPEN, Joy C. 50 N MEDICAL DR, UNIV OF UT SCH OF MED 84132 #049-01-2000 *100
TASHJIAN, Robert Zaray. ■ 84108 #024-07-1999 L2006 **ORS** *012
TAYLOR, Christopher Scott. 1121 E 3900 S, C-130 84124 #048-14-2000 L2006 **AI** *020 †55,20,03
TAYLOR, Cole Robert. ■ 84117 #049-01-2006 L2006 **FP** *012
TAYLOR, George Whitaker. ■ 84108 #016-01-1941 L1970 **FM RO** *072
TAYLOR, Jack Alan. 2295 FOOTHILL DR 84109 #649-11-1973 L1974 **FM** *020 †18
TAYLOR, Joel Richard. 30 N 1900 E, RM 1C026 84132 #049-01-2005 L2006 **EM** *012
TAYLOR, Kim Young. 65 N MEDICAL DR, MORAN EYE CTR 84132 #049-01-1961 L1962 **OPH** *020 †35
TAYLOR, Mark Bowen. 440 W 200 S, STE 250 84101 #049-01-1974 L1975 **D** *020 †15
TAYLOR, Simon Frank. 451 BRANDT CT # 11 84107 #143-03-1989 **OPH** *100
TCACIUC, Isabella Oscar H. 4460 HIGHLAND DR, STE 100/110 84124 #165-06-1989 L2002 **P** *020
TEDROW, Jack Lowry. ■ 84121 #041-12-1942 L1948 **P POP** *072 †75
TEKIPPE, Jenarah Leigh. 30 N 1900 E 1C026, DIV OF EMERGENCY MED 84132 #018-03-2006 L2008 **EM** *012

TEMAN, Carolin Julia. 30 N 1900 E RM 5C124, HEALTH SCIE 84132 #026-08-2006 L2007 **PTH** *012
TEMAN, Paul Thadeo. 30 N 1900 E, SCHOOL OF MEDICINE/SLEEP-W 84132 #026-04-2001 L2004 **P** *100 †75
TEMPLEMAN, Mark Cliffton. 5063 COTTONWOOD ST, STE 160 84107 #018-03-1989 L1990 **PD** *020 †55
TERPSTRA, Jan Ido. 50 N MEDICAL DR, UNIT 5 84132 #003-01-1992 L2000 **P** *020 †75
TESKE, Michael Paul. 50 N MEDICAL DR, DEPT OPH 84132 #005-14-1982 L1983 **OPH** *020 †35
TESSNOW, Kathryn Anne. 30 N 1900 E 4R118 84132 #048-12-1996 L1997 **GE** *020 †20
TEYNOR, Paul David. 2835 E 3300 S, STE 300 84109 #026-04-1987 L1988 **OM** *020 †70
THACKERAY, Elizabeth M. 30 N 1900 E, RM 3C444 84132 #049-01-2003 L2004 **AN** *100
THAKUR, Sonia Sonal. ■ 84111 #759-12-2008 L2005 **IMG** *020 †20
THATCHER, Grant Wm. 500 FOOTHILL DR 84148 #049-01-1970 L1974 **P** *072 †75
THATCHER, John William. SCIENCES C, UNIV OF UTAH HEALTH 84132 #049-01-2003 L2004 **P** *020
THEURER, Dave Edgar. 160 S 1000 E STE 120 84102 #049-01-1959 L1960 **OBG** *020 †30
THEURER, Henry A, Jr. 1050 E SOUTH TEMPLE 84102 #049-01-1945 L1945 **OBG** *071 †30
THOBE, Susanne Christine. 30 N 1900 EAST, 3R210 SOM, DEPT OF NEUROLOGY 84132 #034-01-2002 L2003 **OM** *100 †70
THOEN, Dennis Duane. 1151 E 3900 S 84124 #018-03-1961 L1970 **N OS** *020 †75
THOMAS, Allan Perry. 333 S 9TH E 84102 #016-06-1952 L1953 **PD** *071 †55
THOMAS, Anne Marie. ■ 84103 #035-45-2002 L2007 **P** *100
THOMAS, David Ray. 2180 E 4500 S # 210 84117 #049-01-1963 L1969 **PD** *020 †55
THOMAS, David Snow. 370 9TH AVE STE 200 84103 #049-01-1978 L1985 **PS GS** *020 †85,65
THOMAS, Frank Oliver. EIGHT AVE AND C ST, LDS HOSPITAL 84143 #050-02-1977 L1979 **IM** *020
THOMPSON, Gregory Alan. ■ 84103 #020-02-1989 L1990 **IM** *020 †20
THOMPSON, Joel Adrian. 30 N 1900 E, STE 3R210 84132 #007-02-1969 L1974 **CHN PD** *020 †55,75
THOMPSON, Perry Lyn. 8TH AVE & C ST 84143 #049-01-1967 L1968 **OSM ORS** *071 †40
THOMPSON, Robert G. ■ 84103 #045-01-1938 L1954 **D** *071 †15
THOMPSON, Sally B L. 5241 S STATE ST, LASILC PLUS 84107 #032-01-1984 L1995 **OPH** *020 †20,35
THOMPSON, Sarah Bennett. 5738 S REDWOOD RD STE 530 84123 #023-07-1977 L1978 **P** *100 †16
THOMSON, John Wallace. 400 C ST 84143 #010-01-1974 L1975 **RO** *020 †80
THOMSON-EYRE, Margaret Su. ■ 84108 #012-01-2002 L2002 **P** *012
THOR, Elizabeth Atkin. ■ 84124 #858-02-1968 L1975 **NEP IM** *071
THORELL, Emily Anne. 30 N 1900 E, RM 2A132 84132 #049-01-2000 L2007 **PDI PD** *020 †55
THORKILDSON, Julia Anne. ■ 84102 #035-03-2007 **FP** *012
THORN, Trenten Don. 3460 PIONEER PKWY, INTEGRATED CARE AT 84120 #049-01-2003 L2006 **EM** *020 †20
THORNE, J Kent. 1160 E 3900 S, STE 3500 84124 #049-01-1978 L1979 **TS** *020 †85,90
THORNE, Joseph L. 1160 E 3900 S, STE 2000 84124 #049-01-1961 L1962 **CD IM** *071
THORNTON, Nathan Lee. 414 FOURTH AVE 84103 #048-12-2003 L2004 **NPM** *012 †55
THUESON, John Darrell. ■ 84103 #049-01-1965 L1966 **FM** *071 †18
THUESON, Ross Kelley. ■ 84103 #027-01-1987 L1988 **FM** *020
THULIN, Justin Forth. 1151 E 3900 S, PARKVIEW BLDG # B259 84124 #028-02-1990 L1996 **D** *020 †15
THULIN, Perla Cassayre. 30 N 1900 E, STE 3R210 84132 #005-11-1989 L1996 **N** *020 †75
THURGOOD, Randy Frederick. 1200 E 3900 S 84124 #049-01-1988 L1989 **AN** *020 †05
TIELBORG, Michael C. 30 N 1900 E, RM 3C444 84132 #040-02-1998 L1999 **AN** *020 †05
TIEN, Dave Thang. 650 E 4500 S, STE 210 84107 #048-12-1996 L1999 **NEP** *020 †20
TIETZE, Christopher Chas. 50 N MEDICAL DR, 4R118 MED CTR 84132 #011-02-1984 L1990 **GE IM** *020 †20
TILLY, Shannon Liz. 1200 E 3900 S 84124 #007-02-2002 L2003 **OBG** *020
TIMMINS, Bryan Scott. 8TH AVE & C ST 84143 #049-01-1988 L1989 **AN** *020 †05
TODD, Meri Murphy. 1060 E 100 S, STE 400 84102 #047-05-2001 L2004 **PD** *020 †55
TOLMAN, Keith Grant. 30 N 1900 E, U OF U MEDICAL CTR 84132 #061-01-1966 L1970 **GE PA** *020 †20
TOM, Clifford C. LDS HOSPITAL, 8TH AVE AND C STREET 84143 #007-02-2007 *012
TOMCO, Abraham Robert. 1250 E 3900 S, STE 260 84124 #028-34-2006 L2008 **FP** *012
TONNERRE, Claude Andre. 30 N 1900 E RM 4B319, INVECTIOUS DISEASE DEPT 84132 #869-04-1996 L2002 **ID** *100 †20
TOPHAM, Matthew Kent. 2000 CIRCLE OF HOP DR #536, UNIVERSITY OF UTAH 84112 #049-01-1992 L1994 **PCC** *020 †20
TORGENSON, Marcus Jewell. 30 N 1900 E 3B110, DEPT OF SURGERY 84132 #028-02-2003 L2004 **GS** *012
TOWNER, Steven Richard. 333 S 9TH E 84102 #026-08-1983 L1984 **IM** *020 †20 ‡
TOWNSEND, David Wayne. 8TH AVE & C ST 84143 #038-43-1974 L1977 **AN** *020 †05
TOWNSEND, Jeannette J. 50 N MEDICAL DR, DEPT PTH 84132 #005-02-1969 L1982 **NP** *040 †50
TOYOTA, Toshiko. 1200 E 3900 S 84124 #041-07-1944 **GP** *071
TRACHTENBERG, Joel Daniel. 1160 E 3900 S STE 1200, INTERNAL MEDICINE 84124 #041-02-1998 L2001 **ID IM** *020 †20
TRAN, Nguyen-Toan. 50 N MEDICAL DR, FAMILY PRACTICE 84132 #869-05-1997 L2001 **FM** *020 †18
TRAN, Tao Duyet. 3695 S REDWOOD RD, UNIT 1 84119 #941-02-1973 L1993 **GP** *062
TRAUBA, Thomas Kent. 3838 S 700 E, LIFETREE PAIN CLINIC 84106 #049-01-1985 L1986 **P** *020 †75
TRAUSCHTVANHORN, Jennifer. 50 N MEDICAL DR STE 2B200, UNIVERSITY OF UTAH 84132 #054-04-1992 L1995 **OBG** *020 †30
TRAWICK, Roy Hallum. 5848 S 300 E 84107 #048-13-1993 L1998 **OSM ORS** *020 †40
TREDE, Anna Katharina. 1020 S MAIN ST, N VALLEY MENTAL HLTH 84101 #396-12-1989 L2004 *020
TREDE, Nikolaus Sebastian. 2000 CIRCLE OF HOPE DR, HUNTSMAN CANCER INSTITUTE 84112 #409-05-1987 L2004 **PHO** *020 †55
TREIMAN, Gerald Saul. 500 FOOTHILL DR, SURGICAL SERVICE DEPT 84148 #005-02-1986 L1997 **VS** *020 †85
TRIEU, Belinda. ■ 84103 #049-01-2003 L2006 **IM** *012
TRIMBLE, Gregory Robert. ■ 84103 #051-04-2003 L2005 **MPD** *100 †20
TRISTANI, Martin James. 100 N MEDICAL DR, PRIMARY CHILDREN'S MED CEN 84113 #026-04-1988 L1996 **PDC** *020 †20
TRISTANI-FIROUZI, Payam. 30 N 1900 E, 48454 SCHOOL OF MEDICINE 84132 #026-04-1996 L1998 **D** *020 †15
TROWBRIDGE, David Bradley. 1250 E 3900 S STE 360, GASTRO ASSOC PC 84124 #028-03-1995 L1996 **GE** *020 †20

TSAI, Schickwann. 30 N 1900 E, # 4C416 84132 #244-02-1980 L2001 IM *020 †20

TSCHETTER, Kevin William. 1160 E 3900 S, STE 1200 84124 #026-04-1994 L1995 IM *020 †20

TUBAY, Marc Spencer. ■ 84106 #012-05-2003 L2004 DR *012

TUBAY, Amy Michele. 1798 S WEST TEMPLE, STE 100 84115 #012-05-2003 L2004 FM *020 †18

TUROK, David Keith. 30 N MEDICAL DRIVE, DEPT OF OB/GYN 2B200 84132 #024-07-1995 L1998 OBG *100 †18,30

TUTEJA, Ashok K. 50 N MEDICAL DR, SCHOOL OF MEDICINE 4R118 84132 #495-45-1979 L2001 GE *020 †20

TWARD, Jonathan David. 1950 CIRCLE OF HOPE DR, HUNTSMAN CANCER HOSPITAL 84112 #024-07-2003 L2004 RO *012

TWITCHELL, Jeffrey S. 333 S 900 E 84102 #049-01-1991 L1993 IM OS *020 †20

TYSER, Andrew Robert. 590 WAKARA WAY, UNIVERSITY OF UTAH/DEPT OF 84108 #056-05-2006 L2008 ORS *012

UCHIDA, Derek Akio. 100 N MEDICAL DR, PEDIATRIC PULMONARY 84113 #005-11-1982 L1995 PDP *020 †55

UDALL, King Smith. 1400 FOOTHILL DR STE 101 84108 #049-01-1976 L1977 FM GPM *020 †70,18

UEDA, Issaku. 500 FOOTHILL DR RM 112A 84148 #572-20-1948 L1972 AN *020 †05

UNDERWOOD, Amelia E. 500 FOOTHILL DR, # 110 84148 #036-01-1999 L2001 IM *020 †20

UNGRICHT, Albert Lon. 5770 S 250 E, STE 410 84107 #008-01-1982 L1988 OPH *020 †35 ‡

UPDIKE, Wanda Susanne. 1060 E 100 S, STE L10 84102 #051-04-1982 L1985 ID IM *020 †20

URIE, Bradley A.. 5250 S 320 W, ATRIUM BUILDING STE 305 84107 #305-01-2003 L2008 PMM *012

VAGEFI, M Reza. 1002 E SOUTH TEMPLE, STE 308 84102 #008-01-2002 L2005 OPH *020 †35

VALDEZ, Angelika. ■ 84103 #034-01-2005 L2006 PD *012

VALENTI, David Alan. 5770 S 300 E, EMERGENCY DEPARTMENT 84107 #003-01-1979 L1980 EM *020 †20,16

VALLES, Rene Joseph. 30 N 1900 E, DEPT OF PSYCHIATRY 84132 #049-01-2002 L2004 CHP *020

VAN BLARCOM, Jeffrey R. 100 N MEDICAL DR, DIVISION OF INPATIENT MEDI 84113 #019-02-1996 L2004 PD *020 †55

VAN BOERUM, Don Howard. 324 10TH AVE, STE 112 84103 #049-01-1996 L2006 CCS *020 †85

VAN BOERUM, Drew Howard. 5848 FASHION BLVD 84107 #049-01-1997 L1998 ORS *020 †40

VANDENBERGHE, Jed B. 2160 E 4500 S 84117 #049-01-1985 L1987 PD *020 †55

VANDERHOOFT, Jan Eric. 1160 E 3900 S, STE 500 84124 #049-01-1988 L1994 HS *020 †40

VANDERHOOFT, Sheryll Land. 30 N 1900 E, DEPT OF DERMATOLOGY 84132 #049-01-1988 L1994 D OS *040 †15

VAN DER WERF, Willem Jos. 1250 E 3900 S STE 220 84124 #049-02-1988 L2003 GS TTS *020 †85

VAN GINKEL, Bernard. 100 N MEDICAL DR 84113 #836-03-1992 L2001 PAN *020 †05

VANHALA, Sonja Nadeen. 1138 WILMINGTON AVE 84106 #025-01-1998 L1999 FM *020 †18

VAN KOMEN, George J W. 2000 S 900 E, MEMORIAL HEALTH CENTER 84105 #036-05-1972 L1973 IM *020 †20

VAN ORDEN, Richard T. 1525 W 2100 S, REDWOOD CENTER 84119 #049-01-1955 L1956 OTO *071 †45

VAN ORMAN, Colin B. 100 N MEDICAL DR, PEDIATRICS/NEUROLOGY DEPT 84113 #060-02-1978 L1992 N PD *020 †55,75

VARGAS, Gabriela M. 30 N 1900 E RM 3B324, GENERAL SURGERY DEPARTMENT 84132 #049-01-2006 L2007 GS *012

VARGO, Daniel James. 30 N 1900 E, 3B-202 SOM 84132 #048-04-1992 L2000 TRS CCS *020 †85

VARNER, Michael Walter. 50 N MEDICAL DR, RM 2B200 84132 #026-04-1975 L1987 NPM OBG *020 †30

VASQUEZ, Juan C. 50 N MEDICAL DR, DEPT OF SURGERY 84132 #048-14-2001 L2002 GS *100

VEASY, Lloyd Geo. 50 N MEDICAL DR, STE 2A152 84132 #049-01-1946 L1948 PD PDC *072 †55

VELAZQUEZ, Sonia Michelle. 30 N 1900 E # 1A71, DEPARTMENT OF RADIOLOGY 84132 #042-02-2000 L2006 RNR R *100

VENNER, Linda Marie. 324 TENTH AVE STE 285 84103 #007-02-1996 L1997 IM *020 †20

VENTRE, Kathleen Maria. 100 N MEDICAL DR, CRITICAL CARE 84113 #023-01-1994 L2004 CCP *100 †55

VERNON, Donald Douglas. 100 N MEDICAL DR 84113 #040-02-1979 L1987 CCM *020 †55

VEST, Kevin W. 500 FOOTHILL BLVD 84148 #049-01-1992 L1993 P *020 †75

VEZINA, Daniel Pierre. 30 N 1900 E, RM 3C444 84132 #067-04-1995 L2001 AN *020

VIERA, Loida Mairim. ■ 84103 #021-01-2004 L2007 IM *020 †20

VIERRA, Virginia. 5063 COTTONWOOD ST, STE 160 84107 #049-01-1995 L2002 PD *020 †55

VILLAREAL, James Michael. 790 DONNER HILL CIR 84108 #038-40-1991 L1994 EM *020 †16

VINCENT, G Michael. 8TH AVE AND C ST, LDS HOSPITAL 84143 #049-01-1967 L1971 CD IM *030 †20

VINCENT, William Chas. 2000 S 9TH E 84105 #038-40-1965 L1970 CD IM *071

VINE, Daniel Brennan. 1002 E SOUTH TEMPLE, STE 407 84102 #048-04-1983 L1984 N *020 †75

VINEGRA, Christopher Jose. DEPT OF PSYCHIATRY, UNIV OF UTAH HEALTH SCIENC 84132 #305-01-2001 L2003 P *020

VINEY, James Pritchard. 100 N MEDICAL DR, PRIMARY CHILDREN'S MEDICAL 84113 #005-11-1976 L1983 AN PD *020 †55,05

VINIK, Russell Guy. 1525 W 2100 S, 1ST & 2CD FLOOR 84119 #048-12-1999 L2002 IM *020 †20

VINTON, John Rudisill. 2838 NANILOA CIR 84117 #041-07-1974 L1985 MDM IM *030 †20

VINUEZA, Tirso Lizardo. 500 FOOTHILL BLVD, VASLCHCS 116 84148 #319-01-1952 L1963 P *020 †75

VIRSHUP, David Marc. ■ 84103 #023-07-1981 L1990 PHO PD *050 †55

VISKOCHIL, David Hadley. GENETRICS/50 N MEDICAL DR., 2C412 SOM DIV OF MEDICAL 84132 #036-01-1985 L1986 PD DS *020 †55,19

VITALE, Albert Thos. 50 N MEDICAL DR, JOHN MORAN EYE CTR 84132 #035-09-1987 L2002 OPH IM *020 †35

VITEK, Dagmar. 2001 S STATE ST, # S2400 84190 #286-04-1980 L1987 R IM *030

VOELKERDING, Karl Virgil. ■ 84108 #038-41-1983 L2007 PCH BBK *040 †50

VOGEL, Douglas Clements. 8TH AVE & C ST, EMERGENCY DEPT 84143 #021-01-2002 L2005 EM *020 †20

VOGT, Jennifer Elizabeth. ■ 84103 #018-03-2007 MPD *012

VOITANIK, Simon. 6360 S 3000 E, STE 360 84121 #913-70-1974 L1995 PMM PM *020

VOLKER, Ellen Elizabeth. ■ 84106 #040-02-2007 IM *012

VOLLGER, Helmuth Frank. 310 E 4500 S, STE 300 84108 #036-05-1987 L1988 DR *020 †80

VON RIOTTE, Alisa Blount. 855 S 2000 E 84108 #016-01-1994 L1998 P *020 †75

VOORHIES, Benjamin Newell. ■ 84115 #010-01-2007 IM *012

VOSS, Stephen Cummings. 850 E 3RD S, STE 1 84102 #021-01-1981 L1982 OBG *020 †30

VOSSKUHLER, John Walter. ■ 84117 #008-01-1954 L1981 R AM *072 †80

VUKIN, Matthew Christian. RM 5R110, PSYCHIATRY DEPT 84132 #038-41-2005 L2006 P *012

WADE, Matthew William. ■ 84109 #010-01-2007 IM *012

WADHVANIA, Samir. 1200 E 3900 S, CARE MEDICAL LLC 84124 #496-41-1996 L2007 IM *020 †20

WAGNER, Jeffrey Charles. 30 N 1900 E # 3R210, DEPARTMENT OF NEUROLOGY 84132 #040-02-2002 L2006 CN *100 †75

WALCZAK, Cheryl Ann. 50 N MEDICAL DR, 3B420 SOM 84132 #016-43-1982 L1988 DR *020 †80

WALKER, Crayton Ross. 1060 E 100 S STE 204 84102 #048-13-1981 L1982 FPS *020

WALKER, Kay B. 1121 E 3900 S, STE C130 84124 #005-19-1979 L1987 AI *020 †55,03

WALKER, Kevin Alan. 30 N 1900 E, RM 1C412 84132 #038-40-2006 L2008 N *012

WALKER, Marion Lavelle. 100 N MEDICAL DR 84113 #047-06-1969 L1974 NS *020 †25

WALL, John Brickman. 5770 S 250 E 84107 #005-18-1995 L1996 PD *020 †55

WALL, Jon Thos. 4624 HOLLADAY BLVD 84117 #016-11-1975 L1976 FM *020 †18

WALLACE, Robert Duncan. 2972 DEVONSHIRE CIR 84108 #049-01-1963 L1965 P *020

WALLACE, Seth Browning. 1250 E 3900 S, ST MARKS FAMILY MEDICINE 84124 #021-01-2004 L2006 FM *020 †18

WALLENTINE, Crystal Brenn. ■ 84158 #049-01-2007 IM *012

WALLENTINE, Jeremy Christ. ■ 84158 #049-01-2005 L2007 PTH *012

WALLIN, Richard Dean. 1200 E 3900 S 84124 #049-01-1968 L1969 EM *071 †16

WALLIS, Kenneth Craig. 3434 BENGAL BLVD, # 130 84121 #047-06-1976 L1981 P *020 †75

WALLIS, M Chad. 100 N MEDICAL DR, STE 2200 84113 #038-40-1999 L2006 U *100 †95

WALSH, Jessica Ann. 500 FOOTHILL DR, DEPT OF INTERNAL MEDICINE 84148 #049-01-2003 L2004 RHU *012 †20

WALSH, William Joseph, III. 30 N 1900 E, INTERNAL MEDICINE DEPARTME 84132 #017-20-2004 L2006 PCC *012 †20

WANDER, Theodore Jos. 8TH AVE & C ST, LDS HOSPITAL 84143 #026-08-1987 L1988 P *020 †75

WANG, Angela Amy. 1525 W 2100 S 84119 #035-01-1993 L1999 HS *020 †40

WANG, Roberta Yen. 2000 CIRCLE OF HOPE DR, CLINICAL TRIALS OFFICE (RM 84112 #043-01-1981 L2005 OBG *020 †30

WANNER, Nathan Alan. 30 N 1900 E, INTERNAL MEDICINE DEPT 84132 #017-20-2001 L2002 IM *020 †20

WAPNER, Francis John. 1250 E 3900 S STE 310 84124 #035-01-1989 L1993 OPH *020 †35

WARBURTON, Robert Lyne. ■ 84108 #035-20-1969 L1972 P *075

WARD, John Harris. 2000 CIRCLE OF HOPE DR, HUNTSMAN CANCER INSTITUTE 84112 #049-01-1976 L1979 ON HEM *020 †20

WARD, Katherine Diane. ■ 84105 #049-01-2008 IM *012

WARD, Kenneth Jos. 2749 PARLEYS WAY, STE 210 84109 #011-03-1982 L1983 MFM OS *050 †19,30

WARD, Matthew Stephen. ■ 84106 #049-01-2008 *012

WARD, Robert Marshall. 30 N 1900 E RM 2A122 84132 #023-07-1974 L1985 NPM PA *050 †55

WARD, Ronald Wells. 24 S 1100 E STE 305 84102 #049-01-1963 L1968 IM CD *020 †20

WARDEN, Glenn Donald. 5470 PIONEER FORK RD, WARDEN BIOSCIENCE ASSOCIAT 84108 #049-01-1968 L1970 GS OS *020 †85

WARENSKI, James Carl. 50 N MEDICAL DR 84132 #035-20-1954 L1955 OBG *040 †30

WARNER, Judith. 30 N 1900 E, STE 3R210 84132 #035-01-1989 L1994 N IM *020 †75

WARNER, Stephen John. 440 D ST, STE 206 84103 #054-04-1987 L1994 OSS *020 †40

WARREN, Frank Manley, III. 300 20TH AVE NORTH, THE OTOLOGY GROUP 84132 #040-02-1999 L2006 OTO *100 †45

WARREN, Jennifer Elizabet. 30 N 1900 E, STE 2B-200 84132 #011-03-2002 L2003 OBG *020 †30

WARRIER, Smitha. 30 N 1900 E RM 3, UNIVERSITY OF UTAH/DEPT OF 84132 #021-05-2004 L2008 OTO *100

WASSERSTEIN, Mitzi Lynn. 500 FOOTHILL BLVD 84148 #036-05-1993 L1994 P *020 †75

WATABE, Jeffrey Masahisa. 501 CHIPETA WAY, UNIVERSITY NEUROPSYCHIATRI 84108 #049-01-1999 L2004 P *100 †75

WATANABE, Fumi. ■ 84106 #572-29-1955 L1975 PUD IM *071

WATANABE, Suetaro. ■ 84106 #572-29-1955 L1973 PUD IM *071

WATERMAN, Bradley James. 1060 E 100 S, STE 110 84102 #049-01-2002 L2007 U *100

WATERS, John H. ■ 84109 #021-01-1943 L1946 GP *071

WATSON, Alexander Richard. ■ 84117 #049-01-2008 *012

WATSON, Gordon Andrew. 400 C ST, LDS RADIATION ONCOLOGY 84143 #011-02-1989 L1999 RO *020 †20,80

WATTS, Daren A. 1151 E 3900 S, STE B299 84124 #056-06-1996 L1997 OBG *020 †30

WEAVER, Lindell Ken. ■ 84103 #003-01-1979 L1983 CCM UME *020 †20

WEBER, Quinn Michael. 3460 PIONEER PKWY, INTEGRATED CARE AT 84120 #049-01-2000 L2003 EM *020 †16 ‡

WEBSTER, Joseph Bradley. 50 N MEDICAL DR 84132 #036-01-1991 L2003 PM *020 †60

WEBSTER, Lynn Roy. 3838 S 700 E, LIFETREE PAIN CLINIC 84106 #030-05-1976 L1977 PME AN *071 †05

WEEKS, Howard Raymond, III. 501 CHIPETA WAY, NEUROPSYCHIATRIC INSTITUTE 84108 #036-07-1997 L1999 OS *020 †75

WEEKS, Lionel E. 1060 E 100 S, STE 101 84102 #035-01-1973 L1975 ORS EM *020 †16,40

WEEKS, Wendy Allyson. 675 E 2100 S STE 39 84106 #041-13-2000 L2002 GS *020 †85

WEINSTEIN, Sharon Mae. 30 N 1900 E, RM 3C444 84132 #035-46-1986 L1998 N PMM *020 †75

WEINTRAUB, Arden Loren. 650 KOMAS DR STE 208 84108 #049-01-1981 L1982 CHP P *020 †75

WEIR, Peter Thompson. 555 FOOTHILL BLVD., MADSEN HEALTH CENTER 84132 #056-06-2000 L2001 FM *020 †18

WEIR, Rachel Anne. 845 E 4800 S, STE 200 84107 #056-06-2000 L2001 CHP *020 †75

WEIS, John Rainer. 500 FOOTHILL BLVD, VA MEDICAL CENTER 84148 #026-04-1984 L1985 HO ON *020 †20

WEISS, Kathleen Joy. ■ 84124 #049-01-2008 *012

WEISS, Paul Norman. 3970 S 700 E, STE 24 84107 #049-01-1973 L1986 DR NR *020 †80

WEISS, Ronald Leslie. 50 N MEDICAL DR 84132 #030-06-1980 L1981 PTH *030 †50

WELCH, Dennis Michael. 5444 GREEN ST, MTN MED PHYS SPECIALISTS 84123 #016-06-1971 L1978 DR NM *020 †28,80

WELCH, Michael Barney. 100 N MEDICAL DR 84113 #035-45-1981 L1996 AN *020 †05

WELCH, Shari Jule. 8TH AVE & C ST 84143 #035-45-1982 L1996 EM PD *020 †16

WELLS, Sara Ann. 2131 E 2100 S 84109 #038-41-1994 L1995 FM *020

WELLS, Thomas Johnson. 50 N MEDICAL DR 84132 #051-04-1966 L1976 PD PHP *020 †55

WENNHOLD, Ann Ruhmann. 500 FOOTHILL DR 84108 #038-08-1958 L1960 P *071 †75

WERNER, Theresa Louise. 2000 CIRCLE OF HP DR #2100, HUNTSMAN CANCER INSTITUTE 84112 #017-20-2000 L2001 IM *020

WEST, Gavin Sean. 500 FOOTHILL DR, INTERNAL MEDICINE/PRIMARY 84148 #049-01-2000 L2001 IM *020

WEST, Hugh Sloan, Jr. 5848 FASHION BLVD 84107 #049-01-1985 L1986 **ORS OSM** *020 †40
WESTENFELDER, Christof. 500 FOOTHILL BLVD 84148 #407-36-1968 L1983 **NEP IM** *020 †20
WESTERMANN, Robert B. 2000 S 900 E, INTERMOUNTAIN MEM HLTH CTR 84105 #035-01-1984 L1985 **IM** *020 †20
WETHINGTON, Kevin Lee. 50 N MEDICAL DR, RM 3C444 84132 #048-13-1992 L1996 **AN** *020 †05
WETJEN, Nicholas Michael. 100 N MEDICAL DR 84113 #018-03-2000 L2007 **NS** *100
WETTSTEIN, Daniel Albert. ■ 84105 #005-11-1993 *100
WEVER, Robert C. ■ 84121 #040-02-1952 L1969 **AN** *071 †05
WHEELER, Catherine Jeanne. 1140 E 3900 S, STE 410 84124 #021-01-1987 L1988 **GYN** *020 †30
WHEELER, Lisa Ann. ■ 84106 #056-05-2004 L2005 **P** *012
WHEELER, Michael M. 5444 GREEN ST 84123 #049-01-1994 L2007 **DR** *020 †80
WHEELER, Richard Herbert. ■ 84112 #025-01-1969 L1999 **ON IM** *030 †20
WHEELER, Robert Ross. 2890 E COTTONWOOD PKWY, M/S 38 84121 #005-02-1976 L2008 **IM** *030 †20 ‡
WHITAKER, Kurt Todd. ■ 84103 #035-01-2001 L2006 **EM** *100 †16
WHITE, Autumn Lee. ■ 84105 #049-01-2008 *012
WHITE, Julia Ann. 275 E 200 S 84111 #016-02-1990 L1991 **OBG** *020 †30
WHITE, Keith Stevenson. 100 N MEDICAL DR 84113 #049-01-1985 L1994 **PDR DR** *020 †80
WHITE, Thomas Wm. 5169 COTTONWOOD ST, STE 400 84107 #056-06-1985 L1986 **GS VS** *020 †85
WHITEHEAD, Kevin John. 30 N 1900 E, RM 4A100 84132 #060-01-1995 L1998 **CD** *020 †20
WHITESIDES, Alan N. 55 N REDWOOD RD, INSTACARE 84116 #016-06-1985 L1988 **IM** *020 †20
WHITTAKER, Thomas Carlyle. ■ 84103 #010-02-2004 L2006 **FM** *100 †18
WHITTEN, Matthew Guyon. 50 N MEDICAL DR, DEPARTMENT OF SURGERY 84132 #045-01-2001 L2002 **VS** *012
WHITTINGHAM, Sara Ann. ■ 84103 #021-01-2002 L2006 **AN** *012
WHITTLE, Scott Byler. 5770 S 1500 W BLDG A, PRIMARY CHILDRENS HOSPITAL 84123 #003-01-1997 L1998 **CHP** *020 †75
WICHER, Christopher Georg. 30 N 1900 E, DIVISON OF UROLOGY 84132 #049-01-2005 L2006 **U** *012
WICKER, Karl Seth. 30 N 1900 E, RM 3C444 84132 #035-01-2005 L2006 **AN** *012
WICKERN, Gregory Mathew. 150 S 1000 E, INTERMOUNTAIN ALLERGY & IM 84102 #023-12-1985 L2007 **AI** *020 †55,03
WIDMER, Benjamin James. 590 WAKARA WAY, UNIVERSITY ORTHOPAEDIC CEN 84108 #016-02-2004 L2006 **ORS** *012
WIESE, Julie Ann. 1020 S MAIN ST, STE 100 84101 #028-34-1994 L1995 **P** *020 †75
WIESLEY, Brett Wood. 1200 E 3900 S, DEPARTMENT OF EMERGENCY ME 84124 #038-43-2003 L2006 **EM** *020 †16
WIET, Susan. 501 CHIPETA WAY, DEPARTMENT OF PSYCHIATRY 84108 #016-06-1997 L1999 **CHP** *020 †75
WIGGINS, Richard H, III. 30 N 1900 E, STE 1A71 84132 #048-14-1993 L1999 **DR** *020 †80
WIGHT, Earl Abbott. 1060 E 1ST S 84102 #049-01-1959 L1960 **IM** *071
WILCOX, Lynn Lawrence. 1250 E 3900 S, STE 360 84124 #049-01-1972 L1974 **GE IM** *071 †20
WILCOX, Todd Randall. 2825 E COTTONWOOD PKWY, STE 500 84121 #047-05-1992 L1993 **UCM** *012
WILDE, Clayton S. 1220 E 3900 S STE 3, MT OLYMPUS OB/GYN 84124 #049-01-1979 L1983 **OBG** *020 †30
WILDE, Nicole. ■ 84112 #049-01-2008 *012
WILDER, Michael James. 50 N MEDICAL DR, NEUROLOGY CLINIC 84132 #035-09-2005 L2006 **N** *012
WILDER, Stephanie Kresch. 30 N 1900 E, RM 2B200 84132 #035-09-2005 L2006 **OBG** *012
WILKE, Venus Moe. 30 N 1900 E, DEPT OF PEDIATRICS 84132 #031-01-1999 L2000 **PD** *020 †55
WILKERSON, Julie Ilsun. 3725 W 4100 S 84120 #018-03-2002 L2003 **PD** *020 †55
WILKINSON, Craig West. 1250 E 3900 S STE 301 84124 #049-01-1974 L1979 **GS VS** *020 †85
WILKINSON, Ernest Leigh. 4400 S 700 E 84107 #049-01-1979 L1990 **OPH EM** *020 †35
WILLIAMS, A Thomas. 1200 E 3900 S 84124 #049-01-1971 L1972 **OPH PO** *071 †35
WILLIAMS, Brian Jeffrey. 6065 FASHION BLVD, STE 125 84107 #049-01-1999 L2003 **D** *020 †15
WILLIAMS, Dorothy Louise. 2295 FOOTHILL DR 84109 #017-20-1996 L1997 **N** *020
WILLIAMS, Garett Randall. ■ 84117 #051-04-2006 **FP** *012
WILLIAMS, Howard J, Jr. 30 N 1900 E, RHEUMATOLOGY 84132 #049-01-1969 L1972 **RHU IM** *020 †20
WILLIAMS, Marc Stave. 324 10TH AVE, STE 130 84103 #056-05-1981 L2005 **PD MG** *030 †55,19
WILLIAMS, Richard V. 100 N MEDICAL DR, PRIMARY CHILDRENS MC 84113 #051-04-1991 L1998 **PDC PD** *020 †55
WILLIAMS, Susan. ■ 84105 #047-07-2005 L2007 **MPD** *012
WILLIAMS, Tyler Ray. 30 N 1900 E, SOM4C104 84132 #056-06-2006 L2007 **IM** *012
WILLIAMS, Zachary Rand. ■ 84111 #049-01-2007 **IM** *012
WILLICK, Stuart Eliot. 590 WAKARA WAY 84108 #033-06-1993 L1999 **PM PRS** *020 †60
WILLIS, David. ■ 84103 #028-02-2004 L2005 **AN** *012
WILLIS, Heather Lynn. ■ 84106 #036-08-2007 *012
WILLIS, Mark Warfield. ■ 84105 #007-02-2007 **OTO** *012
WILLS, Jason Corwin. 1250 E 3900 S, STE 360 84124 #030-05-1995 L2000 **GE** *020 †20
WILSON, Amy Lynette. ■ 84103 #049-01-2008 *012
WILSON, Brent Donald. 50 N MEDICAL DR, MEDICINE DEPT 84132 #005-11-2000 L2001 **CD** *100
WILSON, Dana Edwin. 1160 E 3900 S 84124 #038-06-1962 L1971 **IM END** *050 †20
WILSON, John Francis, Jr. ■ 84106 #038-41-1952 L1958 **PTH PD** *071 †55,50
WILSON, Matthew Allen. ■ 84112 #049-01-2007 **OTO** *012
WILSON, Merrill Larsen. 508 E SOUTH TEMPLE 84102 #007-02-1956 L1957 **GS** *071 †85
WILSON, Ryan Robert. ■ 84117 #010-01-2008 *012
WILSON, Vanez Budge. 4252 HIGHLAND DR STE 200 84124 #049-01-1966 L1969 **U** *020 †95
WING, Howard Junior. 1138 WILMINGTON AVE, U FAMILY HEALTH CENTER 84106 #462-01-1977 L1994 **FM** *020 †18 ‡
WINKEL, Vicki Leigh. ■ 84112 #049-01-2007 **P** *012
WINN, Robert Thos. 50 N MEDICAL DR 84132 #041-14-1974 L1975 **PD** *020 †55
WINTCH, Juliann. HEALTH CARE, UNIVERSITY OF UTAH 84132 #049-01-2007 *012
WINTERS, William Dean. 100 N MEDICAL DR 84113 #049-01-1983 L2001 **PDR DR** *020 †80
WINWARD, Kirk Edward. 5169 COTTONWOOD ST, STE 630 84107 #049-01-1986 L1992 **OPH** *020 †35
WIRKUS, Paul Egbert. 5770 S 250 E 84107 #049-01-1989 L1990 **PD PPR** *020 †55
WIRTH, Amanda Jane. 4460 HIGHLAND DR, STE 400 84124 #056-06-1997 L1998 **FM** *020 †18

WIRTHLIN, Alvin Jacob. 324 10TH AVE STE 225 84107 #049-01-1967 L1973 **N** *020
WIRTHLIN, Douglas James. 5323 WOODROW ST 84107 #025-01-1991 L2003 **VS** *020 †85
WIRTHLIN, Le Roy Samuel. 324 10TH AVE STE 142, C/O DOUGLAS WIRTHLIN 84103 #024-01-1962 L2001 **VS** *020 †85
WISNIEWSKI, Mark Lloyd. 122 PAXTON AVE, # 2 84101 #051-07-1991 L1994 **AN** *020 †05
WITBECK, J E Teddy. 6360 S 3000 E STE 10, FOOTHILL FAMILY CLINIC 84121 #060-01-1992 L1994 **FM** *020 †18
WITT, Mark Thomas. 2180 E 4500 S, STE 210 84117 #056-05-1994 L1995 **PD** *020 †55
WITTE, Madolin Kay. 100 N MEDICAL DR, CRITICAL CARE DIVISION 84113 #010-01-1979 L1988 **PD PUD** *050 †55
WITTER, David Michael. 3725 W 4100 S 84120 #038-40-2002 L2006 **PM** *020 †60
WITTWER, Carl Thos. 50 N MEDICAL DR, DEPT OF PATH 84108 #025-01-1984 L1985 **PTH DIA** *020 †50
WOICZIK, Marcella Rae. 100 N MEDICAL DR, PRIMARY CHILDREN'S MEDICAL 84113 #038-43-2002 L2007 **OP** *012
WOLLER, Scott Christopher. ■ 84121 #016-06-2000 L2001 **IM** *020 †20 ‡
WOLSEY, Darcy Kaye. ■ 84106 #034-01-2002 L2003 **OPH** *020
WONG, George Kam Kwong. 5980 FASHION BLVD 84107 #143-03-1971 L2005 **CD IM** *020 †20
WONG, Gilbert Chengyoung. 65 N MEDICAL DR, MORAN EYE CENTER 84132 #025-01-2006 L2007 **OPH** *012
WONG, Harry Chow. ■ 84108 #056-05-1958 L1961 **AN OS** *071 †05
WONNACOTT, Monica Child. 3725 W 4100 S 84120 #422-01-2003 L2007 **PD** *020 †55
WOOD, Diane Jean. ■ 84102 #034-01-2006 L2007 **AN** *012
WOOD, Eric Marshall. 1525 W 2100 S 84119 #049-01-1995 L1998 **FM OM** *020 †70,18
WOOD, Stephen Danl. 6360 S 3000 E, STE 100 84121 #005-12-1978 L1979 **FM OM** *020 †70,18
WOODRUFF, Paul Nicola. ■ 84124 #005-12-1963 L1970 **AN** *030
WOODS, Jackson Jay. 1525 W 2100 S 84119 #055-01-1973 L1975 **FM** *020 †18
WOODS, Jamile Sarah. 2280B PANORAMA WAY 84124 #409-38-1992 L1997 **PCC** *020 †20
WOODS, Marion Lester, II. 50 N MED DR RM 4B322 84132 #049-01-1976 L1983 **ID IM** *020 †20
WOODWARD, Paula Jean. 30 N 1900 E # 1A71, UNIVERSITY OF UTAH 84132 #007-02-1984 L1992 **DR** *020 †80
WOOLSEY, Sarah Lynn. 50 N MEDICAL DR FAM PR 84132 #016-11-1997 L1998 **FM** *020 †18
WORKMAN, David Henry. 1405 W 2200 S, STE 200 84119 #049-01-1987 L1988 **FM** *020 †18
WOSETH, Douglas Marr. 3920 S 1100 E, STE 310 84124 #016-02-2000 L2006 **D** *020 †15
WRAY, Robert Bradley. 50 N MEDICAL DR, 3B420 SOM 84132 #049-01-1967 L1968 **CD** *071 †20
WREN, Michael Victor. 1050 E SOUTH TEMPLE, SALT LAKE REGIONAL MEDICAL 84102 #023-07-1975 L1984 **IM IMG** *020 †20
WRIGHT, Jennifer Anne. 100 N MEDICAL DR, ONCOLOGY DEPT 84113 #017-20-2000 L2007 **PHO** *100 †20,55
WRIGHT, Larry Jan. 370 NINTH AVE STE 204 84103 #049-01-1964 L1971 **IM OS** *020 †20
WRIGHT, Michael Thomas. 400 C ST 84143 #049-01-1993 L1995 **PTH** *020 †50
WRIGHT, Nelson E. 1955 E 5600 S, SALT LAKE CLINIC 84121 #049-01-1960 L1967 **IM CD** *020 †18
WRONA, Robert Chandler. ■ 84105 #040-02-2007 **GS** *012
WU, Albert Yapo. 65 NOLRTH MEDICAL DRIVE, JOHN E MORAN CENTER/U OF U 84132 #054-04-2005 L2006 **OPH** *012
WU, Jianhua. 500 FOOTHILL DR, VA SALT LAKE CITY HEALTH C 84148 #243-73-1983 L2006 **PTH** *100 †50
WYMAN, Dennis Jon. 175 W 200 S 84101 #050-02-1976 L1977 **EM PM** *020 †16
YAISH, Hassan M. 100 N MEDICAL DR, HEMATOLOGY/ONCOLOGY 84113 #875-01-1963 L2003 **HEM PD** *020 †55
YAMASHIRO, Vernon Koyu. 1151 E 3900 S, STE B299 84124 #005-12-1984 L1994 **OBG** *020 †30
YANG, Chiar-Ping. 50 N MEDICAL DR, UNIVERSITY OF UTAH 84132 #005-06-2004 L2005 **OTO** *012
YANG, Paul. ■ 84101 #032-01-2006 L2007 **OPH** *012
YANOWITZ, Frank. 325 8TH AVE 84143 #035-15-1966 L1973 **IMG IM** *040 †20
YARBROUGH, Peter Michael. 30 N 1900 E RM 4C104, UNIV OF UTAH MED CTR 84132 #038-41-2005 L2006 **IM** *012
YARLAGADDA, Sirisha. ■ 84117 #495-50-1998 L2006 **CD** *012
YARRISH, Daniel Walter. 1160 E 3900 S, STE 1000 84124 #048-14-1996 L1999 **IM** *020 †20
YAU, Joseph. 5965 S 900 E # 420 84121 #244-05-1974 L1987 **CHP P** *030 †75
YAUNEY, Kenneth Duff. 100 N MEDICAL DR 84113 #049-01-1999 L2004 **PAN** *020 †05
YEATES, Tyler Marshall. 30 N 1900 E, DEPT OF ANESTHESIOLOGY, 3C 84132 #049-01-2002 L2006 **AN** *100 †05
YEATON, William Lee. 6440 MILLROCK DR, STE 175 84121 #032-01-1985 L1997 **FM** *020 †18
YEO, Tsin Wen. 50 N MEDICAL DR, DEPT OF INFECTIOUS DISEASE 84132 #825-01-1991 L2001 **ID** *020 †12
YETMAN, Angela T. 100 N MEDICAL DR 1500, PRIMARY CHILDREN'S MED CNT 84113 #065-10-1991 L2006 **PD PDC** *020 †55
YI, Johnny. ■ 84105 #056-06-2007 **OBG** *012
YODER, Bradley Allen. 295 CHIPETA WAY RM 2N114, C/O WILLIAMS BLDG 84108 #041-12-1979 L2005 **NPM** *050 †55
YONEMURA, Kenneth Stephen. 30 N 1900 E, STE 3B409 84132 #041-02-1984 L2005 **NS OSS** *020 †25
YOO, Meela. 6440 MILLROCK DR, STE 175 84121 #026-04-1997 L2001 **EM** *020 †16
YORGASON, Joshua G. 50 N MEDICAL DR, STE 3C120 84132 #035-01-2004 L2007 **NS** *012
YOST, Christian Con. 30 N 1900 E # 2A100, UNIV HOSP NEONATOLOGY 84132 #049-01-1997 L2000 **NPM** *020 †55 ‡
YOUNG, Paul Christopher. 50 N MEDICAL DR, DEPT PEDS 84132 #016-06-1967 L1992 **PD** *020 †55
YOUNG, Russell Vernon. 5353 S 960 E, STE 150 84117 #049-01-1978 L1979 **PS** *020 †65
YOUNG, Timothy Paul. ROOM 201, 375 CHIPETA WAY 84132 #422-01-2006 **FP** *012
YOUNGQUIST, Scott Travis. 30 N 1900 E 1C026 84132 #005-14-2002 L2007 **EM** *020 †16
YU, Margaret Kerhui. 320 WAKARA WAY, UNIVERSITY OF UTAH 84108 #056-06-1997 L1998 **HO** *020 †20
YUNUS, Adnan. 4021 S 700 E STE 300, COMPHEALTH 84107 #704-21-1988 L1995 **CCM** *020 †20
ZABRISKIE, Norman Andrew. 4400 S 700 E, STE 240 84107 #049-01-1990 L1995 **OPH** *020 †35
ZABROCKI, Aleksandra Jani. 295 CHIPETA WAY, PEDIATRIC/NEO-NATOLOGY 84108 #051-07-2004 L2007 **PD** *020 †55
ZABROCKI, Luke Anthony. 295 CHIPETA WAY, UNIV OF UTAH 84108 #023-12-2002 L2007 **CCP** *012
ZAFAR, Ubaid. 50 N MEDICAL DR 84132 #704-30-2002 L2008 **P** *012
ZAGOREC-MARKS, Tamara. 3970 S 700 E 84107 #049-01-1984 L1992 **DR** *020 †80
ZAHNISER, John Chas. 7372 COMSTOCK CIR 84121 #041-09-1971 L1978 **NS** *071 †25

ZAMRINI, Edward Youssef. 30 N 1900 E, DEPT OF NEUROLOGY, 3R210 S 84132 #605-01-1984 L2006 **N IMG** *020 †75
ZANGER, Isabelle Marie. ■ 84105 #026-04-1928 **OS** *075
ZANOLLI, Eugene P. ■ 84102 #047-06-1978 L1979 **IM** *020 †16
ZARBOCK, Zachary Robert. 100 N MEDICAL DR, PEDIATRIC RESIDENCE 84113 #038-40-2005 L2006 **PD** *012
ZAREK, Sarah Elaine. 30 N 1900 E RM 2B200 84132 #045-01-2006 L2007 **OBG** *012
ZARKOOB, Mehrnoosh. 30 N 1900 E, UNIV OF UTAH - DEPT OF HEM 84132 #517-06-1992 L2003 **HO** *100 †20
ZAUGG, Misty Brook. ■ 84120 #049-01-2002 *100
ZEBRACK, Celia Michelle. 100 N MEDICAL DR, DEPT OF EMERG MED 84113 #031-01-1996 L1997 **CCP** *100 †20,55
ZEBRACK, James Scott. 24 S 1100 E, STE 105 84102 #031-01-1995 L1996 **CD** *020 †20
ZEFT, Andrew Samuel. 30 N 1900 E, SCHOOL OF MEDICINE ZA152 84132 #056-06-1997 L2005 **PPR** *100 †55
ZEHNDER, Brian Keith. 3336 PIONEER PKWY, STE 2 84120 #025-07-1989 L1990 **FM** *020 †18
ZELUFF, Gary Richard. 1200 E 3900 S 84124 #003-01-1975 L1976 **ORS OSM** *020 †40
ZEMPOLICH, Karen Ann. 1140 E 3900 S, STE 340 84124 #036-07-1993 L1994 **OBG** *020 †30
ZENGER, Mark Robison. 5770 S 250 E, STE 415 84107 #045-01-1984 L1999 **PUD IM** *020 †20
ZGODA, Adam. ■ 84108 #561-01-1951 L1955 **R** *071
ZHANG, Kang. 50 N MEDICAL DR, JOHN A MORAN EYE CENTER 84132 #024-01-1995 L2002 **OPH** *020 †35
ZHOU, Hong. 100 N MEDICAL DR, PCMC 84113 #243-33-1983 L1999 **PP** *020 †50
ZIEGLER, John. 50 N MEDICAL DR, 3B420 SOM 84132 #012-05-1984 L1998 **AN CCA** *020 †05
ZIMMER, Ruth A. 359 8TH AVE 84103 #048-15-1992 L1993 **AN** *020 †05
ZIMMERMAN, Guy Alexander. 15 N 2030 E BLDG 533, PROGRAM IN HUMAN MOLECULAR 84112 #048-04-1973 L1977 **IM PUD** *050 †20
ZIMMERMAN, Joshua Micah. 50 N MEDICAL DR, UNIVERSITY OF UTAH ANESTHE 84132 #017-20-2002 L2003 **AN** *100 †05
ZIMMERMAN, Susan Michelle. 3725 W 4100 S 84120 #017-20-2001 L2002 **N** *020
ZINKHAN, George Martin. HEALTH CARE, UNIVERSITY OF UTAH 84132 #048-12-2007 **IM** *012
ZIPNICK, Richard Ira. 1250 E 3900 S, STE 440 84124 #035-08-1990 L2006 **OSS** *020 †40
ZIRKLE, Toby Allen. 1250 E 3900 S, ST MARKS FAMILY MEDICINE 84124 #017-20-2005 **FP** *012
ZITO, Ruben Alberto. 5169 COTTONWOOD ST, BLDG B 84107 #132-06-1970 L2002 **IM CD** *050 †20
ZOBELL, Dean Harding. ■ 84103 #005-02-1958 L1961 **OTO** *071 †45
ZOLLINGER, Lauren Virgini. ■ 84105 #049-01-2004 L2005 **DR** *012
ZONE, John Jos. 50 N MEDICAL DR, DEPARTMENT OF DERMATOLOGY 84132 #035-15-1971 L1977 **D IM** *030 †20,15
ZUBAIR, Imran. 82 S 1100 E, STE 103 84102 #001-02-1985 L1988 **CD IM** *020 †20
ZURASKY, John Fredrick. 8TH AVE AND C ST., NEUROVASCULAR DEPT 84143 #017-20-1998 L2006 **N** *020 †75
ZURCHER, Daniel Christian. ■ 84117 #028-02-2008 *012
ZWIEBEL, William John. 500 FOOTHILL DR, DEPT RAD 84148 #041-09-1969 L1984 **DR CD** *020 †80
ZYCHOWSKI, Stanley Jos. 275 E 200 S 84111 #028-34-1974 L1975 **PD** *020 †55

SANDY – SALT LAKE

ADAMS, Michael Ryan. 7998 S 1300 E 84094 #049-01-2002 L2003 **FM** *100 †18
ADELMAN, Scott. 10011 CENTENNIAL PKWY, STE 500 84070 #050-02-1991 L1992 **PM** *020 †60
ADJEI-POKU, Yaw Amaning. ■ 84092 #049-01-2008 *012
AHLSTROM, Nancy Gail. 348 CRESCENT VISTA LN 84070 #019-02-1985 L1994 **NEP IM** *020 †20
ALLDREDGE, O Layton. 9720 S 1300 E, STE W110 84094 #049-01-1976 L1978 **GS** *020 †85
ALLEN, Donald Wain. 8074 S 1300 E 84094 #010-01-1977 L1984 **FM APM** *020 †18 ‡
ANDERSON, Craig W. 9690 S 1300 E # EAST-200 84094 #049-01-1977 L1978 **OTO** *020 †45
ANDERSON, David. 7390 CREEK RD, STE 101 84093 #035-06-1996 L1999 **GS** *020
ANDERSON, Frederick Leon. ■ 84092 #049-01-1964 L1967 **CD OS** *071 †20
ASLAMI, Stephen Shane. 10965 S STATE ST, STE 100 84070 #049-01-1993 L1994 **IM** *020 †20
AUSTIN, Van O. ■ 84092 #035-03-1967 L1970 **P OM** *020
BAILEY, Donald K. ■ 84092 #038-06-1945 L1953 **R** *071 †80
BARKER, Bryce Gardner. 9500 S 1300 E 84094 #021-01-1981 L1982 **OPH** *020 †35
BARNES, David Richard. 9660 S 1300 E 84094 #049-01-2001 L2004 **EM** *020 †16
BARNETT, Robert K. 9829 S 1300 E, STE 303 84094 #048-15-1987 L1988 **GE IM** *020 †20
BIGELOW, Barclay Fiske. 880 E 9400 S, STE 105 84094 #049-01-1987 L1990 **IM** *020 †20
BINGHAM, Isaac Joseph. 10971 CINDY CIR, UTAH EMERGENCY PHYSICIANS 84092 #041-14-2004 L2007 **EM** *020
BLACKHAM, Richard Bren. ■ 84092 #049-01-2008 *012
BLAUER, Keith Leon. 10150 PETUNIA WAY 84092 #054-04-1983 L2004 **REN OBG** *020 †30 ‡
BLOOD, Todd Spencer. 8184 HIGHLAND DR 84093 #049-01-1994 L1995 **AN** *020 †05
BOETTGER, David Robt. 9720 S 1300 E, STE W120 84094 #048-12-1983 L1984 **PD** *020 †55
BOLICK, David Reed. 10011 CENTENNIAL PKWY, STE 310 84070 #036-07-1986 L1990 **PCP DMP** *020 †50
BORT, Ermita. ■ 84093 #913-49-1985 L2004 **MPD** *020
BOWERS, Paula Beth. 9720 S 1300 E # 100, MOUNTAIN VIEW KIDSCARE 84094 #056-06-2002 L2003 **PD** *020 †55
BRADLEY, Stephen Kent. 9660 S 1300 E 84094 #028-02-1979 L1984 **AN** *020 †05
BRAND, Elizabeth Demos. 9660 S 1300 E, ALTA VIEW HOSPITAL/ER DEPT 84094 #008-02-2002 L2007 **EM** *100 †16
BRAUER, Hans-Paul. ■ 84093 #409-22-1984 L1993 **CD** *100
BREADY, Randall Jos. 8184 HIGHLAND DR, STE C7 84093 #028-34-1985 L1993 **AN** *020 †05
BREDING, David Joel. 9844 S 1300 E STE 335 84094 #005-02-1988 L1989 **IM** *020 †20
BROOKS, Shawn Michael. ■ 84092 #030-05-1998 L2002 **IM** *020 †20
BROWN, Richard Wallace. 9500 S 1300 E 84094 #049-01-1971 L1978 **IM** *020 †20
BROWN, Wesley Ronald. 385 W 9000 S, CONCENTRA 84070 #047-05-1985 L1986 **OM** *020 †70
BRYANT, Robert John. 9660 S 1300 E 84094 #671-01-1998 L2004 **EM** *020 †16
BUCHANAN, Esther C M. ■ 84093 #041-13-1939 L1951 **AN** *071
BURKE, James Lee. 9844 S 1300 E, STE 350 84094 #048-02-1973 L1976 **CD IM** *020 †20
BURNS, Jonathan David. 10011 CENTENNIAL PKWY, STE 500 84070 #033-05-2003 L2007 **PM** *020
CALDWELL, Steven Bryce. 9660 S 1300 E 84094 #051-04-2001 L2004 **EM** *020 †16
CANFIELD, Charles Olin. 1135 BRONZE LN 84094 #048-04-1987 L1990 **FM** *100
CASTERELLA, Peter John. 9844 S 1300 E, STE 350 84094 #010-02-1988 L2001 **CD IM** *020 †20
CHIN, Steven Sueyming. ■ 84093 #035-19-1991 L2004 **NP ATP** *072 †50
CHOU, Stella Yi. 8789 HIGHLAND DR STE 100 84093 #017-20-1995 L1996 **OPH** *020 †35
CLARK, Stanley Corbin. 9690 S 1300 E STE 100 84094 #049-01-1978 L1984 **U** *020 †95
CLAYTON, Paul N. 9660 S 1300 E 84094 #049-01-1979 L1980 **AN GP** *020 †05
COBBLE, Michael Edward. 9355 S 1300 E, CANYON MEDICAL CENTER 84094 #049-01-1992 L1993 **FM CD** *020
CONOVER, Mitzi Schmidt. 9720 S 1300 E STE E100 84094 #049-01-1999 L2000 **PD** *020 †55
COPPIN, Thomas Don. 10011 CENTENNIAL PKWY, STE 300 84070 #049-01-1967 L1968 **PTH** *071 †50
CORCORAN, Melissa C. 9720 S 1300 E, STE W210 84094 #036-07-1990 L2005 **ON PHO** *020 †20,55
CORSON, Robert. 7998 S 1300 E 84094 #018-03-2002 L2003 **FM** *020 †18
CRANDALL, Brian Gregory. 9844 S 1300 E, STE 350 84094 #054-04-1985 L1986 **CD IM** *020 †20
CURD, Jason Wade. ■ 84094 #048-14-2000 L2002 **P** *020
DAL CANTO, Albert John. 9500 S 1300 E 84094 #028-02-2001 L2007 **OPH** *100
DAVIS, Judy Lynne. 955 E 11400 S 84094 #062-01-1977 L1997 **FM** *020 †18
DAZLEY, Justin Moroni. ■ 84070 #041-15-2006 **ORS** *012
DECKER, Marshall Smith. ■ 84092 #049-01-1946 **OBG** *071
DESAUTELS, Steven Gregg. 9829 S 1300 E, STE 303 84094 #011-03-1990 L1991 **GE** *020 †20
DIAZ, Cesar Fabian. ■ 84090 #049-01-1994 **FM** *100
DICKSON, Dee Miner. ■ 84092 #049-01-1946 L1949 **AN GP** *071 †05
DIEHL, Paul Jacob. ■ 84093 #049-01-1975 L1978 **AN** *020 †05
DIETZ, Thomas Morgan. 9844 S 1300 E STE 200 84094 #049-01-1975 L1976 **IM** *020 †20
DI FIORE, Kent C. 9720 S 1300 E, STE W210 84094 #010-01-1975 L1976 **ON HEM** *020
DRENNAN, Daniel Alan. ■ 84092 #012-01-2003 L2007 **PMM** *012
DUFFIN, Robert Michael. 33 E LONE HOLLOW DR 84092 #023-07-1977 L2007 **OPH** *071 †35
ELLISON, Mary Jane. ■ 84092 #019-02-1982 L1984 **NM DR** *020
ENGSTROM, Fae Louise. 8184 HIGHLAND DR, STE C7 84093 #049-01-1986 L1989 **AN** *020 †05
FARLEY, Michael Owen. 9660 S 1300 E 84094 #049-01-1982 L1983 **AN** *020 †05
FEHLAUER, Charles Steven. 2773 ETIENNE WAY 84093 #049-01-1986 L1987 **IMG IM** *020 †20
FERGUSON, Ryan Patrick. ■ 84094 #049-01-2005 L2006 **AN** *012
FLINNER, Robert Lewis. 9660 S 1300 E 84094 #019-02-1956 L1971 **PTH** *020 †50
FRANK, Deborah Urich. 9720 S 1300 E, STE E100 84094 #051-01-1998 L1999 **CCP** *100 †55
FRYER, Richard Henry. 9829 S 1300 E, STE 200 84094 #049-01-1997 L2002 **PS** *020 †65
GALIAN, John Nicholas. 9720 S 1300 E, STE E100 84094 #032-01-1996 L2000 **PD** *020 †55
GARDNER, Barry Reed. ■ 84092 #049-01-1994 L1996 **FM** *020
GEHLE, Kim Christine. 9720 S 1300 E, STE E100 84094 #038-43-1995 L1997 **PD** *020 †55
GIOVANNIELLO, Michael T. 10011 CENTENNIAL PKWY, STE 500 84070 #035-06-1994 L2001 **PM PRS** *020 †60
GLASGOW, Tiffany Squiers. 9720 S 1300 E, STE E100 84094 #005-02-1994 L2001 **PD** *020 †55
GORANG, Alan David. 9720 S 1300 E, STE 230 84094 #005-19-1982 L1988 **FM** *020 †18
GORDON, Anthony Scott. 9844 S 1300 E STE 100 84094 #007-02-1986 L1993 **ORS** *020 †40
GOURDE, Theresa Dolores. 10011 CENTENNIAL PKWY, STE 150 84070 #005-15-1990 L1993 **IM** *020 †20
GRANT, Lillian. ■ 84070 #049-01-1979 L1981 **GS** *020 †85
GREMILLION, Richard Brian. 11333 S 1000 E, # 100 84094 #010-01-1990 L1992 **IM RHU** *020 †20
GUBLER, David Brent. 10965 S STATE ST, STE 100 84070 #049-01-1997 L1998 **IM** *020 †20
HALLEY, Tullius W. ■ 84070 #030-06-1946 L1947 **GS** *071
HANSEN, Darrin Fred. 9720 S 1300 E, STE W110 84094 #049-01-1994 L1999 **GS** *020 †85
HANSEN, Elden Keith. 9600 S 1300 E STE 305 84094 #041-13-1972 L1973 **OBG IM** *020 †30
HANSEN, Leon W. 9600 S 1300 E # E-300 84094 #054-04-1982 L1984 **OBG EM** *020 †30
HANSEN, Scott F. 9600 S 1300 E, STE 300 84094 #049-01-1976 L1977 **IM EM** *020 †20,16
HANSON, Berkeley Roy. ■ 84093 #010-01-2001 L2007 **DR** *020 †80
HARKER, William Graydon. 9720 S 1300 E, STE W210 84094 #049-01-1975 L1984 **ON** *020 †20
HARRISON, Paul Eugene. 10011 CENTENNIAL PKWY, STE 200 84070 #005-06-1988 L1997 **D** *020 †20,15
HASLETON, David. 9660 S 1300 E 84094 #016-11-1999 L2004 **EM** *020 †16
HAWKINS, Grant E. 9844 S 1300 E STE 200 84094 #049-01-1979 L1982 **IM** *020 †20
HEATH, Joseph M. ■ 84093 #049-01-1958 L1960 **FM** *071 †18
HECK, Robert Walter. 9660 S 1300 E 84094 #016-06-1989 L1993 **EM** *020 †16
HEINER, James Spencer. 10150 PETUNIA WAY 84092 #048-02-1985 L1995 **OBG REN** *020 †30
HIRSH, Elizabeth Rowley. ■ 84070 #016-02-1976 L1982 **CHP P** *020
HOOPER, Rina Melanie. 7998 S 1300 E 84094 #045-01-2001 L2002 **FM** *020 †18
HOOPES, Phillip Carl. 10011 CENTENNIAL PKWY, STE 400 84070 #036-05-1976 L1977 **OPH** *020 †35
HOOPES, Phillip Carl, Jr. 10011 CENTENNIL PKWY #4000, HOOPES ALLDREDGE VISION 84070 #036-05-2000 L2004 **OPH** *020 †35
HORNE, Jonathan Hughes. 9720 S 1300 E STE 130, ALTA VIEW MEDICAL PLAZA 84094 #035-20-1963 L1965 **ORS OSS** *071 †40
HORNE, Robert Hughes. 9844 S 1300 E, STE 300 84094 #035-20-1960 L1966 **ORS HS** *020 †40
HORTON, Steven Curtis. 9844 S 1300 E, STE 350 84094 #048-04-1980 L1981 **CD** *020 †20
HUANG-ASLAMI, Amie Jo. ■ 84093 #049-01-1995 L1996 **P** *020
IORG, Eddie Charles. 9660 S 1300 E 84094 #049-01-1991 L1994 **EM** *020 †16
JACK, David Bruce. 9829 S 1300 E, STE 101 84094 #023-12-1981 L1982 **FM OS** *020 ‡
JACKSON, Tanya Shae. 9500 S 1300 E, IHC SANDY HEALTH CENTER 84094 #021-01-2001 L2002 **PD** *020 †55
JENSEN, Peter Erik. 9690 S 1300 E, STE 224 84094 #049-01-1990 L1992 **TS** *020 †90,85
JOHNSON, Mark Rolfe. 8074 S 1300 E, HEALTHSOUTH REHAB 84094 #049-01-1988 L1991 **IM** *020 †20
JOHNSON, Michael W. 9720 S 1300 E, STE 240 84094 #049-01-1997 L2007 **ORS** *020 †40
KATKURI, Rajani Reddy. ■ 84092 #495-21-1991 L2001 **IM** *020 †20
KEEFER, Frank Jay. 3324 SEVEN SPRINGS DR 84092 #010-01-1961 L1990 **GYN** *020 †30
KILLPACK, Clayton Denning. 9660 S 1300 E 84094 #028-34-2000 L2001 **AN** *020 †05
KILLPACK, Michael Darwin. ■ 84092 #049-01-1987 L2006 **IM** *020 †20
KIMBALL, Gordon Richard. 9844 S 1300 E STE 275 84094 #049-01-1970 L1977 **ORS** *020 †40
KLEIN, Regina. 9720 S 1300 E, STE W210 84094 #187-09-1983 L1994 **ON IM** *020 †20
KRATOCHVIL, Mary Jane. ■ 84092 #049-01-1988 L1989 **FM** *020 †18
KRUEGER, John Bradford. 9500 S 1300 E 84094 #048-13-1988 L1994 **PUD CCM** *020 †20
KURRUS, Thomas Anton. 10965 S STATE ST, STE 100 84070 #016-11-1966 L1972 **IM ID** *020 †20
LABASKY, Richard Francis. 9600 S 1300 E STE 301 84094 #048-02-1983 L1984 **U** *020 †95
LANCASTER, Vere Lloyd. 9500 S 1300 E 84094 #010-01-1975 L1977 **IM** *020 †20
LAPPE, Donald Lewis. 9844 S 1300 E, STE 350 84094 #023-07-1972 L1975 **CD IM** *020 †20

■ = Address Information Privacy Protected

LARSEN, Kenneth S. 9600 S 1300 E, STE 308 84094 #049-01-1986 L1993 **OBG** *020 †30
LATER, Robert Wendell. 9600 S 1300 E STE 302 84094 #049-01-1979 L1983 **OBG** *020 †30
LEE, Bonnie Jean. PO BOX 2106 84091 #005-12-1982 L1984 **IM PM** *020 †20
LEE, Robert Jeffrey. 9720 S 1300 E, STE W210 84094 #012-05-1991 L1992 **RO** *020 †80
LINDLEY, Thomas S. 9500 S 1300 E 84094 #049-01-1976 L1981 **PS HS** *020 †65
LIU, Vernon Kai-Ying. 880 E 9400 S, STE 102 84094 #048-15-1985 L1986 **EM IM** *020
LOESER, Edward Arthur. 8184 HIGHLAND DR, STE C7 84093 #035-15-1969 L1970 **AN** *020 †05
LOFGREN, David Nils. 1434 E 9400 S STE 100 84093 #049-01-1985 L1986 **PD PHP** *020
LUNDBERG, Max S. 11333 S 1000 E, # 100 84094 #049-01-1985 L1985 **RHU IM** *020 †20
LUNDELL, Ryan B. 9660 S 1300 E 84094 #049-01-1999 L2001 **DMP** *020 †50
LUNT, Margaret Sydnie. 10965 S STATE ST, STE 100 84094 #034-01-1995 L1996 **IM** *072 †20
MARBLE, Stephen Paul. 8074 S 1300 E 84094 #012-01-1988 L1992 **PM** *020 †60
MARSHALL, Rosa H P. ■ 84092 #012-05-1999 L2007 **IM** *020 †20
MARTIN, William Patrick. ■ 84092 #049-01-1980 L1981 **EM** *020 †16
MAUSBERG, Lionel N. ■ 84093 #065-01-1963 L1987 **P** *020 †75
MAXWELL, Richard Gerald. 63 E 11400 S, # 305 84070 #049-01-1998 L1999 **AN** *020
MAYER, Dean Arthur. 9844 S 1300 E, STE 350 84094 #049-01-1993 L1995 **IM** *020 †20
MC ALLISTER, Douglas Boyd. 9660 S 1300 E 84094 #049-01-1984 L1985 **AN** *020 †05
MC DERMOTT, Patrick R. 9500 S 1300 E 84094 #010-02-1983 L1994 **IM** *020 †20
MC HENRY, John Andrew. ■ 84092 #005-02-1988 L1989 **CD** *020 †20
MEHR, Daniel Scott. 9500 S 1300 E 84094 #056-05-1994 L2003 **GS** *020 †85
MERENDINO, John Rizzotte. 9844 S 1300 E STE 100 84094 #033-05-1964 L1974
   ORS OSM *071 †40
MERRILL, Anina. 8074 S 1300 E, HLTHSOUTH REHABILITATIONHO 84094 #040-02-1989 L1997
   PM *020 †60
MILLER, David Alan. 10011 CENTENNIAL PKWY, STE 300 84070 #016-01-1979 L2001
   PTH PCP *020 †50
MITCHELL, Marcia Keller. ■ 84092 #054-04-1954 L1967 **IM PUD** *071
MITCHELL, Robert Glen. ■ 84092 #054-04-1958 L1965 **DR** *071 †80
MORGAN, Joseph E. 7530 BROOKBEND LN, HOLY CROSS JORDAN VALLEY H 84093
   #049-01-1983 L1987 **AN** *020 †05
MORSE, Marc Jennings. 955 E 11400 S, ROCKY MOUNTAIN PRIMARY CAR 84094
   #003-01-1991 L2007 **FM** *020 †18
MUGGELBERG, Marcia Louise. 9500 S 1300 E, IHC SANDY HEALTH CENTER 84094
   #051-01-1979 L1999 **AI IM** *020 †20,03
NAISBITT, Mark Snarr. 10150 CENTENNIAL PKWY, STE 400 84070 #049-01-1986 L1991 **AN** *020
NEUBERGER, Kirk Madson. ■ 84093 #049-01-1963 L1984 **GS** *071 †85
NIEDEREE, Laurie Ann. 9660 S 1300 E 84094 #019-02-1988 L1989 **AN** *020 †05
OLIVER, Marquam Riddell. 10965 S STATE ST, STE 100 84070 #010-01-1989 L1990
   ID IM *020 †20
ORASKOVICH, Mark Gerard. 9660 S 1300 E 84094 #026-04-1993 L1997 **EM** *020 †16
ORME, Robert Lynn. 1434 E 9400 S, STE 105 84093 #049-01-1985 L1989 **D** *020 †15
OSBORN, Jeffrey Scott. 9844 S 1300 E, STE 350 84094 #028-46-1981 L1987 **ICE CD** *020 †20
PALMIERI, Lisa Danelle. 9500 S 1300 E 84094 #005-12-1994 L1995 **PD** *020 †55
PARK, Brandon Birg. ■ 84093 #049-01-2007 **GS** *012
PARKIN, Jay David. 9844 S 1300 E, STE 100 84094 #005-11-1988 L1993 **ORS** *020 †40
PELLATT, Morton. 9500 S 1300 E 84094 #065-09-1976 L1983 **IM** *020 †20
PONCE, Sean Anthony. 7370 CREEK RD, STE 101 84093 #040-02-2000 L2001 **FM** *020 †18
POPPEN, R Scott. 10965 S STATE ST, STE 100 84070 #021-01-1982 L1992 **IM IMG** *020 †20
POTTER, Vernon Dewaine. 9829 S 1300 E 84094 #016-11-1989 L1995 **FM** *020 †18
PURVIN, Jonathan Mark. 9557 S 700 E, STE 100 84070 #035-03-1985 L1986 **P** *075
QUTOB, Hisham Fozi. ■ 84093 #049-01-2008 †012
RAMSEY, John Francis. 9720 S 1300 E STE E210 84094 #018-03-1972 L1974 **OPH** *020 †35
REDDY, Sathyavathi. 9500 S 1300 E 84094 #495-33-1977 L1992 **GE** *020 †20
RILEY, Nicola Irene. 10150 PETUNIA WAY 84092 #049-01-2002 L2004 **FM** *020 †18
RITCHIE, Keith Leon. ■ 84093 #049-01-1967 L1968 **CD IM** *074 †20
RIZZARDI, Barbara Eve. 1434 E 9400 S, STE 208 84093 #031-01-1981 L1982 **IM EM** *020 †20
RODDY, Hugh John. 10011 CENTENNIAL PKWY, STE 300 84094 #028-03-1971 L2005
   PTH *020 †50
RODIN, Ernst Anthony. ■ 84092 #154-07-1949 L1988 **N** *020 †75
SAGAN, Andrzej. ■ 84093 #759-09-1982 **PD** *100
SANDHU, Seema. 9844 S 1300 E, STE 125 84094 #495-45-1989 L2000 **N** *020
SANZENBACHER, Eric David. 9355 S 1300 E 84094 #036-08-1993 L1995 **IM** *075
SCHIRACK, John David. ■ 84070 #016-43-1953 L1958 **AN** *072
SCHMIDT, Donald Alfred. 9844 S 1300 E STE 275 84094 #049-01-1975 L1981
   ORS OSM *020 †40
SCHMIDT, Jeffrey Cannon. 9500 S 1300 E 84094 #049-01-1982 L1985 **PD** *020 †55
SCHMIDT, John David. 9829 S 1300 E, STE 300 84094 #041-02-2000 L2008 **GE** *012 †20
SCHWITZER, Gregory Allan. 9660 S 1300 E 84094 #049-01-1975 L1977 **EM IM** *030 †20,16
SHAKESPEAR, Jonathan S. ■ 84070 #056-06-2005 L2006 **DR** *012
SHAKULA, John Robt. 9720 S 1300 E, STE W120 84094 #011-03-1972 L1975 **PD** *020 †55
SHARP, Merrill J. ■ 84093 #049-01-1951 L1952 **GP OBG** *071
SHIELDS, Kenneth Gary. 9660 S 1300 E 84094 #049-01-1965 L1966 **AN** *071
SIMBARI, Bernard Jose. 9442 TURNPIKE LN 84070 #011-03-1967 L1969 **D** *075
SMART, Eric Vincent. 9010 S 150 E 84070 #049-01-1983 L1986 **EM ESM** *020 †16
SMITH, Layne Alan. 9600 S 1300 E, STE 305 84094 #049-01-1996 L1997 **OBG** *020 †30
SMITH, Russell Alan. 9600 S 1300 E, STE 300 84094 #021-01-1994 L2001 **OBG** *020 †30
SNOW, Corinne Mc Laughlin. ■ 84093 #035-03-1950 **FM** *071
SORENSEN, Russell La Mar. 9844 S 1300 E STE 250 84094 #049-01-1977 L1979 **ORS** *020 †40
STANCHFIELD, John Bartley. 10965 S STATE ST, STE 100 84070 #056-06-1967 L1971
   END IM *072 †20
STAPLES, Mark Harold. 10011 CENTENNIAL PKWY, STE 100 84094 #024-07-1993 L1994
   AN *020
STEINVORTH, June Caro. 955 E 11400 S 84094 #021-05-1983 L1996 **FM** *020 †18
STEVENS, Craig Needham. 9690 S 1300 E STE 200, SANDY ENT 84094 #049-01-1975 L1976
   OTO *020 †45
STOLMAN, Karen Rebecca. 9500 S 1300 E, SANDY HEALTH CENTER 84094
   #035-19-1997 L2003 **D** *020 †15
STONE, Steven Arvil. ■ 84093 #049-01-1984 L1985 **IM** *075
STRONG, Richard Kline. 9720 S 1300 E 84094 #049-01-1978 L1981 **PD** *020 †55
SYBROWSKY, Christian Layn. ■ 84092 #049-01-2006 L2006 **ORS** *012
TANNER, Gregory Chas. 9600 S 1300 E 84094 #049-01-1973 L1974 **OBG** *020 †30
TAVAZOIE, Sohail Fakhr. ■ 84093 #024-01-2003 L2003 **HO** *012 †20
TEMPEST, Mathew Richard. 9720 S 1300 E, STE E210 84094 #056-06-1997 L2001
   OPH *020 †35

TORONTO, Russell Alan. 9720 S 1300 E, STE 240 84094 #049-01-1979 L1980 **FM EM** *020
TUCKER, Kathleen Louie. 9493 S 700 E, SANDY INSTACARE 84094 #014-01-1978 L1983
   PS EM *020
TWEDE, Michael Lamar. 10011 CENTENNIAL PKWY, STE 350 84070 #049-01-1988 L1989
   OBG REN *020 †30
VALENTINE, Dale Mark. 9500 S 1300 E 84094 #049-01-1984 L1985 **PD** *020 †55
VICKROY, Jos Walter, Jr. 9660 S 1300 E 84094 #005-18-1982 L1990 **N PM** *020 †75
VOGELER, Douglas Malcolm. 9600 S 1300 E STE 303 84094 #035-20-1975 L1976 **FM** *020 †18
WALKER, Kathryn E. 9600 S 1300 E STE 308, SANDY OB/GYN 84094 #003-01-1989 L1997
   OBG *020 †30
WALL, Michael James. 8074 S 1300 E, HEALTH SOUTH REHAB HOSP 84094
   #011-04-1987 L1988 **IM P** *020 †20
WALSH, Kevin Jos. 9844 S 1300 E, STE 350 84094 #016-11-1980 L1981 **CD IM** *020 †20
WARNOCK, Steven Hansen. 9829 S 1300 E, STE 200 84094 #049-01-1992 L1993 **PS** *020 †65
WATERFALL, Brian Tennant. 9660 S 1300 E 84094 #049-01-1987 L1988 **AN** *020 †05
WEATHERED, Natalie Rae. ■ 84092 #049-01-2008 *012
WEISS, Jonathan Peter. 9844 S 1300 E, STE 350 84094 #051-01-1995 L2004 **CD** *020 †20 ‡
WHISENANT, Brian Keith. 9844 S 1300 E, STE 350 84094 #035-01-1992 L2000 **CD** *020 †20
WHISENANT, Jonathan Reed. 9720 S 1300 E, STE W210 84094 #005-02-1998 L2005
   HO *020 †20
WHITE, Douglas Edward. 955 E 11400 S 84094 #038-06-1992 L1996 **FM FSM** *020 †18 ‡
WHITLOW, Dennis Reed. ■ 84092 #024-01-1963 L1968 **PS** *071 †85,65
WHITTINGTON, Richard A. 9844 S 1300 E, STE 200 84094 #016-45-1994 L1998 **IM** *020 †20 ‡
WILLESEN, Kavita Gangar. 9844 S 1300 E, STE 200 84094 #495-01-1992 L2002 **IM** *020 †20
WILSON, Kathleen Barrett. 10965 S STATE ST, STE 100 84070 #049-02-2001 L2003 **IM** *020 †20
YEE, James Bradley. 8465 GAD WAY 84093 #048-15-1988 L1989 **AN** *020 †05
YOUNGBLOOD, Robert Lee. 880 E 9400 S, STE 111 84094 #012-01-1962 L1970
   PS GS *020 †65

SANTA CLARA — WASHINGTON

MORGAN, Arthur James. ■ 84765 #041-09-1955 L1985 **P LM** *020 †75
SHORE, Norman M. (KAYENTA/IVINS, UT), 1166 W. SHONTO WAY 84765 #016-11-1944 L1948
   GP *071

SANTAQUIN — UTAH

BINGHAM, Jared Lee. 57 W MAIN ST 84655 #049-01-1997 L2000 **FM** *020 †18
NELSON, Clint Reid. ■ 84655 #048-04-2007 **PD** *012
VAIL, Connie Mitchell. ■ 84655 #049-01-1984 L1986 **DR** *020 †80

SARATOGA SPRINGS — UTAH

BELOY-NOVILLA, Maria L L. ■ 84045 #748-29-1990 *062
HUANG, Georgiana L W. ■ 84045 #041-07-1975 L1976 **FM** *020
PAVICH, Greg Matthew. 1307 N COMMERCE DR STE 120 84045 #049-01-1996 L2002
   PD *020 †55
TUCKER, Stephen R. 1305 N COMMERCE DR, STE 120 84045 #748-02-1989 L1994
   MPD PD *020

SMITHFIELD — CACHE

AVERY, Delwin B, Jr. 502 S MAIN ST 84335 #051-04-1982 L1989 **FM** *020 †18
BROWN, Todd A. 291 S MAIN ST, STE C 84335 #054-04-1982 L1989 **FM** *020 †18
BUDGE, Edwin Cole. ■ 84335 #049-01-1945 L1947 **GP GS** *072
CARLSON, Brian William. 291 S MAIN ST, SMITHFIELD MEDICAL DENTAL 84335
   #056-06-2002 L2003 **FM** *020 †18
FIFE, Marlin Albert. ■ 84335 #005-15-1962 L1975 **AN** *071
HARRIS, Gary Lee. 502 S MAIN ST 84335 #054-04-1979 L1985 **FM** *020 †18
THAIN, Wilbur Sutton. ■ 84335 #005-06-1953 L1955 **FM OS** *071 †18

SOUTH JORDAN — SALT LAKE

BARNEY, Brandon Mitchell. ■ 84095 #049-01-2008 *012
BEAN, Robert S. ■ 84095 #049-01-1951 L1955 **GP** *071 †18
BIGGS, Jeremy J. ■ 84095 #049-01-2006 L2007 **PM** *012
COX, Matthew Nelson. 1268 W SOUTH JORDAN PKWY 84095 #028-34-1995 L1998
   PD *020 †18
CRUZ, Victor, Jr. ■ 84095 #035-48-1999 L2006 **GS** *020 †85
DAVIS, Brian Richard. 1325 W SOUTH JORDAN PKWY, STE 103 84095 #028-34-1990 L1994
   OPH CS *020 †35
EGLI, David Lambert. ■ 84095 #049-01-1972 L1976 **P** *020
FILLMORE, Gary Lee. ■ 84095 #056-06-2001 L2005 **OPH** *020 †35
GASECKI, Andrew P. 1325 W SOUTH JORDAN PKWY, STE 101 84095 #759-03-1983 L1998
   N SME *020 †75
GOOD, Brian Pierce. 1268 W SOUTH JORDAN PKWY 84095 #539-06-2000 L2001 **PD** *020 †55
GREER, Fred L. ■ 84095 #049-01-1960 L1961 **DR** *020 †80
HARSTON, Dennis Tucker. 10421 S JORDAN GTWY, STE 400 84095 #048-04-1974 L1977
   MDM FM *030 †18
HOLLINGSWORTH, Martin A. 3556 W 9800 S, COPPERVIEW MEDICAL CENTER 84095
   #012-01-1997 L1998 **MPD** *020 †20,55
JOHNSON, Michael Ray. 1268 W SOUTH JORDAN PKWY 84095 #049-01-1998 L2000
   PD *020 †20
JONES, Michael David. 1325 W SOUTH JORDAN PKWY, PARKWAY 102 84095
   #038-40-1994 L1999 **FM** *020 †18
KATZ, George D. ■ 84095 #869-01-1938 L1940 **P** *071
KORTH, Michelle Lyn. ■ 84095 #049-01-2008 *012
LANTANGE, Christiane. ■ 84095 #067-06-1982 L2004 **GPM** *100
LANTZ, Karen Elisabeth. 1268 W SOUTH JORDAN PKWY, STE 201 84095 #023-07-1996 L2003
   PD *020 †55
LE, Trung Minh. ■ 84095 #049-01-2003 L2006 **PD** *020 †55

LEI, Paul. 3556 W 9800 S, COPPERVIEW MEDICAL CENTER 84095 #049-01-1997 L1998 PD PDP *020 †55

LONNI, Yvonne Gwendolyn W. ■ 84095 #049-01-1967 L1968 **PTH** *020 †50

MACIEVIC, Jeffrey Alexand. ■ 84095 #005-18-2006 L2008 **AN** *012

MARCROFT, Patrick Wm. 11444 S REDWOOD RD 84095 #049-01-1992 L1996 **FM FSM** *020 †18

MC ALLISTER, Sumner Todd. 1325 W SOUTH JORDAN PKWY, STE 102 84095 #056-06-1995 L2001 **FM** *020 †18

NEWMAN, Clinton Bronson. ■ 84095 #021-01-1968 L1971 **AN** *071

OWEN, David Gareth. 1091 W SOUTH JORDAN PKWY 84095 #038-40-1997 L1998 **FM** *020 †18

REICHMANN, Lawrence E. ■ 84095 #049-01-1958 L1959 **AN** *071 †05

RICHARDS, John L, Jr. 11444 S REDWOOD RD 84095 #049-01-1983 L1984 **FM** *020 †18

SANDER, Richard. ■ 84095 #005-06-1961 L1977 **OM FOP** *030 †50

SOJOURNER, Heather Diemer. 1325 W SOUTH JORDAN PKWY, STE 102 84095 #004-01-2002 L2005 **FM** *020 †18

SONNTAG, Bryan Vern. 10437 S JORDAN GTWY 84095 #021-01-1986 L1996 **PS** *020 †65

STREAMER, Charles W. ■ 84095 #007-02-1949 L1983 **PD** *071 †55

TIPTON, Mary Delila. 3556 W 9800 S, STE 101 84095 #049-01-2001 L2005 **MPD** *020 †20,55

TURNER, Bryan W. 10393 S 1300 W, STE 102 84095 #048-15-1992 L1993 **OTO** *020

UNANUE, John Lawrence. 10464 S REDWOOD RD 84095 #049-01-1999 L2000 **FM** *020 †18

VERBRUGGE, Dorothea Joy. 10421 S JORDAN GTWY 84095 #038-06-1996 L1997 **FM** *030 †18

WELCH, John Chas. ■ 84095 #007-02-1965 L1966 **GS GP** *020

YOUNG, Vernon Cole. ■ 84095 #010-01-1955 L1956 **FM AS** *071 †18

SOUTH OGDEN — WEBER

GARDINER, Matthew James. 1452 E RIDGELINE DR, STE 151 84405 #049-01-1996 L2000 **P** *020 †75

HALL, Richard Glade. 975 CHAMBERS ST 84403 #051-07-1997 L2000 **FM** *020 †18

JOHANSSON, Julia Wanetta. 1525 E 6000 S 84405 #041-13-1993 L2003 **OBG** *020 †30

MAJOR, Michael Scott. 5896 S RIDGELINE DR STE B 84405 #049-01-1996 L2001 **OTO AM** *020 †45

NELLIS, Noel. ■ 84405 #049-01-1960 L1961 **GS VS** *071 †85,90 ‡

RALSTON, Stephan Lynn. 1452 E RIDGELINE DR 84405 #049-01-1975 L1980 **PS** *020 †65

SADIQ, Mohamed H. 5974 FASHION POINT DR, STE 200 84403 #495-09-1991 L2001 **CN N** *020

THIESZEN, Sheldon Lester. 1486 E SKYLINE DR, MOUNTAIN MEDICAL PHYSICIAN 84405 #030-05-1997 L1998 **DR** *020 †80

THOMAS, Bruce Edward. 1486 E SKYLINE DR 84405 #012-01-1989 L2002 **GS** *020 †40

VINCENT, Drake Glen. 1710 E 5600 S 84403 #001-02-2001 L2005 **OMF CS** *020

SOUTH WEBER — WEBER

HUMPHERYS, Clint Grant. ■ 84405 #049-01-2008 *012

SPANISH FORK — UTAH

BENNETT, D John Noren. 325 W CENTER ST 84660 #056-06-1991 L1992 **PD** *020 †55

CLARKE, James Pearson. ■ 84660 #041-01-1963 L1965 **U** *020 †95

FRANDSEN, Tracy Mackay. 325 W CENTER ST 84660 #049-01-1983 L1986 **FM** *020 †18

HOGENSON, Eric M. 325 W CENTER ST 84660 #060-02-1993 L1995 **FM** *020 †18

JUCHAU, Jeffrey Jay. 325 W CENTER ST 84660 #048-13-1988 L1994 **FM** *020 †18

KIRK, Stephen Thomas. ■ 84660 #018-03-2008 *012

LUDLOW, David Emil. 325 W CENTER ST 84660 #036-07-1979 L1987 **OBG** *020 †30

LUDLOW, Enoch Andrus. 325 W CENTER ST 84660 #036-07-1954 L1957 **FM AM** *020

LYTLE, Carter Sanders. 325 W CENTER ST, SPANISH FORK CLINIC 84660 #056-06-1994 L1997 **FM** *020 †18

PAXTON, Richard Devon. 325 W CENTER ST 84660 #049-01-1999 L2001 **PD** *020 †55

ROBERTS, David Taylor. 78 E 900 N 84660 #005-19-1985 L1990 **N PMM** *020

ROSE, James Jos, Jr. 325 W CENTER ST 84660 #005-15-1974 L1976 **FM** *020 †18

TAKASAKI, Roman Yasuo. 325 W CENTER ST 84660 #049-01-1987 L1990 **FM OBS** *020 †18

VALDEZ, Orlando Raymond. 325 W CENTER ST 84660 #005-02-1993 L1994 **PD** *020 †55

SPRING CITY — SANPETE

KETCHUM, Robert D. PO BOX 219 84662 #005-11-1950 L1985 **IM OS** *020 †20

SPRINGDALE — WASHINGTON

GALLIA, Leonard C. PO BOX 58 84767 #048-13-1986 L1999 **FM** *072 †18

RUTZ, David Alan. PO BOX 536 84767 #005-02-1968 L2002 **PTH NM** *020 †50,28

SPRINGVILLE — UTAH

BIESINGER, Wilford G. ■ 84663 #016-06-1943 L1946 **GS** *020 †85

BOWCUT, Don Leslie. ■ 84663 #010-01-1989 L1992 **FM** *020 †18

CRAWFORD, Robert Hayes. 385 S 400 E, IHC- INSTACARE 84663 #001-02-2000 L2007 **FM** *020 †18

DESCHWEINITZ, Peter Alan. ■ 84663 #051-01-1998 L1999 **FM** *020 †18

DEVENPORT, David Scott. 269 E 400 S, UTAH COUNTY MEDICAL ASSOCI 84663 #051-07-1993 L1995 **PD** *020 †55

DRAPER, Randall Edwin. 1184 WILLOWBROOK LN 84663 #049-01-1985 L1986 **P IM** *030 †75

GALE, Michael Joseph. 762 W 400 S 84663 #036-05-2000 L2001 **FM** *020 †18

GLEDHILL, Kent Merrill. TERRACE AVE 84663 #049-01-1992 L1997 **RNR** *020 †80

HALL, Michael Brandon. 762 W 400 S 84663 #003-01-2002 L2003 **FM** *020 †18

JACKSON, Edward Wm. ■ 84663 #010-01-1959 L1990 **GP AN** *030 †18

JOHNSON, Sherman B. 1278 N 750 W, STE 100 84663 #049-01-1969 L1979 **PD GP** *020

KELLEY, Paul S. ■ 84663 #016-02-1953 L1955 **A PDA** *020

MC MASTER, Ian Bruce. 269 E 400 S, UTAH COUNTY MEDICAL ASSOCI 84663 #049-01-1997 L2000 **FM** *020 †18

MENDENHALL, John Paul. PO BOX 837 84663 #049-01-1967 **ORS** *020 †40

MICHALEK, Jorge Horacio. 269 E 400 S STE 2 84663 #132-01-1968 L1988 **PD** *020 †55

NANCE, Steven Greg. 285 E 400 S 84663 #049-01-1979 L1980 **OBG** *020 †30

PARKER, Norman L. ■ 84663 #049-01-1950 L1951 **GP** *071

PENROD, Marc Allan. 5 E 400 N 84663 #051-01-1999 L2000 **FM** *020 †18

PRIEST, Jeffrey G. 1456 E PHEASANT RUN DR 84663 #023-12-1987 L1996 **AN** *020 †05

REED, Chris. ■ 84663 #056-06-2005 **DR** *012

SHINKLE, Aaron Timothy. ■ 84663 #026-08-2008 *012

TAYLOR, John Stewart. 5 E 400 N 84663 #049-01-1996 L1999 **FM** *020 †18

TOVEY, Daniel B. 762 W 400 S 84663 #021-01-1998 L1999 **FM** *020 †18

WILLMORE, David Keith. ■ 84663 #049-01-1992 L1993 **FM** *020 †18

WYLIE, Wesley D. 5 E 400 N 84663 #048-14-1989 L1992 **FM** *020 †18

STANSBURY PARK — TOOELE

DINH, An Tuong. 220 MILLPOND, STE 100 84074 #035-09-1999 L2000 **FM** *020 †18 ‡

HEITZ, Bridget Jo. ■ 84074 #016-45-2005 L2006 **PD** *012

MC MILLAN, Heidi Susan Ro. 210 MILLPOND 84074 #041-14-2002 L2005 **PD** *020 †55

SZALKOWSKI, Veronica Mari. ■ 84074 #035-06-2008 *012

VAN DRUNEN, Hendrika A. ■ 84074 #660-01-1951 L1962 **PHP PD** *071 †55

VINCENT, John Paul. ■ 84074 #016-43-2001 L1966 **PHP OS** *074

STOCKTON — TOOELE

BLACK, Brent Dale. 11600 STARK RD 84071 #049-01-1982 L1983 **FM** *071 †18

MATRAVERS, Gary Wayne. 11600 STARK RD, EG&G DEFENSE MATERIALS, IN 84071 #016-11-1975 L1983 **FM** *020

SYRACUSE — DAVIS

BUTLER, Warren Leroy. 2038 S 1900 W 84075 #028-34-1994 L1995 **FM** *020 †18

OWEN, Robert Evan. ■ 84075 #049-01-2004 L2005 **PD** *020 †55

SORENSEN, Teela S. 2038 W 1900 S, TANNER CLINIC 84075 #056-06-1991 L1999 **OBG** *020 †30

STEWART, Ryan Lee. 2038 W 1900 S 84075 #049-01-2003 L2004 **FM** *020 †18

TAYLORSVILLE — SALT LAKE

BROCKBANK, Keven Dean. ■ 84123 #010-01-1980 L1984 **OBG** *020

CROOKSTON, Michael James. 5770 S 1500 W, BLDG C 84123 #049-01-1980 L1981 **ADP CHP** *020 †05,75

GREENWOOD, Stephen Dale. ■ 84118 #005-14-2004 L2005 **AN** *012

HUNTINGTON, Jeremy David. ■ 84118 #049-01-2008 *012

MINER, David Bryant. 3845 W 4700 S, 3845 WEST 4700 SOUTH 84118 #049-01-1997 L2000 **FM** *020 †18

NEWBOLD, Douglas Reed. 3845 W 4700 S 84118 #056-06-1999 L2000 **FM** *020 †18

RAWLING, David Arthur. 6011 S REDWOOD RD 84123 #016-02-1978 L1986 **ICE CD** *020 †20

SCHAAT, Timothy James. ■ 84119 #049-01-2002 L2003 **DR** *100

SHAH, Rajiv Rasik. 6321 S REDWOOD RD STE 102, UTAH PAIN SPECIALISTS 84123 #495-23-1992 L2003 **APM** *020

SMITH, Douglas Roland. 3845 W 4700 S, TAYLORSVILLE HEALTH CENTER 84118 #056-06-2003 L2004 **FM** *020 †18

SPANN, Candace Denise. 3845 W 4700 S 84118 #047-07-2000 L2007 **D** *020

TEASDALE — WAYNE

MORRELL, James Francis. PO BOX 91 84773 #016-06-1968 L1973 **U** *020 †95

OSBORN, Lucy Morin. PO BOX 87, 1475 E 875 S 84773 #016-06-1972 L1974 **PD GPM** *030 †70,55

TOOELE — TOOELE

ABARCA, Sergio. 2055 N MAIN ST 84074 #005-18-2000 L2003 **FM** *020 †18

ANTINORI, James Vincent. 2055 N MAIN ST, INTEGRATED CARE AT 84074 #011-03-1974 L1976 **EM** *020 †16

ATKINSON, Kathy Jo. 2055 N MAIN ST, INTEGRATED CARE AT 84074 #054-04-1977 L1978 **EM FM** *020 †18,16

AUGUSTYN, Melissa. 196 E 2000 N STE 107, MOUNTAIN W OB/GYN CLINIC 84074 #035-06-2000 L2005 **OBG** *020 †30

BEAZER, Blake Richard. 1929 AARON DR, STE 1 84074 #005-18-2000 L2003 **FM** *020 †18

BOWEN, Anneli Ririe. 220 MILLPOND, STE 100 84074 #025-01-1996 L1999 **D** *020 †15

BRADLEY, Russell Stuart. 2055 N MAIN ST, INTEGRATED CARE AT 84074 #050-02-1993 L1998 **EM** *020 †16

BROWN-TRUDEL, Linda. 1959 AARON DR, STE C 84074 #305-01-1998 L2001 **FM** *020 †18 ‡

BUCHANAN, Bennion Douglas. 2055 N MAIN ST, INTEGRATED CARE AT 84074 #049-01-1977 L1978 **EM** *020 †16

CALLISTER, Stanley Johns. 15 N 100 E 84074 #049-01-1971 L1974 **EM OM** *030 †16

CASHMORE, Blaine Johnson. 196 E 2000 N, STE 106 84074 #010-01-1996 L2005 **GS** *020 †85

CHANDRAMOULI, Nitin B. 196 E 2000 N, STE 107 84074 #018-03-1996 L1999 **HO** *020 †20

DOWDALL, Michael David. 2055 N MAIN ST, MOUNTAIN WEST MEDICAL CTR 84074 #048-04-1974 L1977 **EM** *071 †16

DUGGLEBY, Daniel Rowland. 2055 N MAIN ST, INTEGRATED CARE AT 84074 #054-04-1982 L1983 **EM** *020 †16

FINKLEMAN, Arnold. 2055 N MAIN ST, INTEGRATED CARE AT 84074 #021-01-1973 L1995 **EM** *020 †16

FLORENCE, Andrew Gardner. 2055 N MAIN ST, INTEGRATED CARE AT 84074 #010-02-2003 L2006 **EM** *020

FORBES, Carolyn. 1959 AARON DR, STE F 84074 #017-20-1994 L1997 **FM** *020 †18

GANNON, Robert Duhn. 2055 N MAIN ST, INTEGRATED CARE AT 84074 #028-34-1982 L1985 **EM** *020 †16

GOULD, Jim Julian. 196 E 2000 N, STE 104 84074 #054-04-1998 L2001 **PD** *020 †55
GUBLER, Kelly Herman. ■ 84074 #016-06-1945 **GS GP** *071 †85
HAROUTUNIAN, Gagik G. 196 E 2000 N, STE 110 84074 #913-38-1982 L2002 **PD** *020 †55
HEAP, Alan Franklin. 185 N MAIN ST STE 601 84074 #049-01-1977 L1984 **P** *020 †75
HOPKINS, James Lewis. 2055 N MAIN ST 84074 #005-18-1975 L1976 **GS GP** *020 †85
JACKSON, Mark Ransome. 2055 N MAIN ST, MT WEST MEDICAL CTR 84074 #049-01-1995 L2005 **EM IM** *020 †20
JAHN, Kristen Marie. 2055 N MAIN ST, INTEGRATED CARE AT 84074 #056-06-1997 L2000 **EM** *071 †16
LEE, Jeffrey D. 220 MILLPOND STE 100 84074 #056-06-1993 L1994 **FM** *020 †18
MALLENDER, Charles David. 2055 N MAIN ST, INTEGRATED CARE AT 84074 #017-20-1984 L1989 **IM** *020 †20
MASARYK, John Anthony. 2055 N MAIN ST, INTEGRATED CARE AT 84074 #038-43-1984 L1987 **EM** *020 †16
MILLER, Jeffrey V. ■ 84074 #049-01-2008 *012
MOHAMMED, Sirajuddin Hamm. 2055 N MAIN ST, MOUNTAIN WEST MEDICAL CENT 84074 #495-65-1999 L2005 **IM** *020
OWENS, Lance Stuart. 2055 N MAIN ST, INTEGRATED CARE AT 84074 #035-01-1978 L1990 **IM GS** *020 †16
PEASE, David Gordon. 2055 N MAIN ST, INTEGRATED CARE AT 84074 #003-01-1991 L1992 **FM** *020 †18
REID, Thomas Michael. 100 S 1000 W, VALLEY MENTAL HEALTH 84074 #049-01-1992 L1993 **P** *020 †75
SATTER, Paul Anthony. 15 N 100 E, 15 NORTH 100 EAST 84074 #028-34-1993 L1994 **IM** *020 †20
SCALA, Emi Masui. 196 E 2000 N 84074 #572-23-1994 L2001 **PDE** *071 †55
SERRA, Marian Hamilton. 2055 N MAIN ST, INTEGRATED CARE AT 84074 #035-47-1981 L1996 **EM** *020 †20
SHEWELL, David V. 2055 N MAIN ST, INTEGRATED CARE AT 84074 #836-02-1987 L2005 **EM** *020 †20
SMITH, Elizabeth Rowe. 220 MILLPOND, STE 100 84074 #036-01-2001 L2002 **PD** *020 †55
SPECTOR, Jay M. 196 E 2000 N, STE 100 84074 #017-20-1978 L1978 **FM** *020 †18
STEARMAN, Ralph James. ■ 84074 #030-05-1964 L1965 **GP** *020 †18
STRINDBERG, Gail. 196 E 2000 N, STE 106 84074 #035-01-1992 L2002 **TS** *020 †85,90
TAYLOR, Doyle H. 5047 DROUBAY RD, BOX 1272 84074 #049-01-1960 L1961 **AN** *071 †05 ‡
THURMAN, Richard K. 2055 N MAIN ST, INTEGRATED CARE AT 84074 #048-02-1981 L1993 **EM FM** *020 †18,16
TRUDEL, Ronald Raymond. 1959 AARON DR, STE C 84074 #305-01-1996 L2001 **IM IMG** *020
VENTURA, Peter Gibbs. 1244 N MAIN ST, STE 200 84074 #049-01-1984 L2005 **OTO AI** *020 †45
VOKT, Christina Marie. ■ 84074 #031-01-1999 L2004 **OM** *020 †70
WEBBER, James Thomas. ■ 84074 #049-01-1995 L2002 **DR** *020 †80
WILLIAMS, Richard Judd. TOOELE ARMY DEPOT, U.S. ARMY HEALTH CLINIC 84074 #049-01-1970 L1971 **GS EM** *020 †16,85
WORKMAN, Allen Edson. 196 E 2000 N, STE 105 84074 #005-12-1969 L1999 **ORS** *020

TORREY – WAYNE

HEBERTSON, Wayne M. PO BOX 750249 84775 #049-01-1952 L1954 **N** *071

TREMONTON – BOX ELDER

ANDERSON, Mark Daniel. 440 W 600 N 84337 #049-01-1998 L1999 **DR** *020 †80
BITWINSKI, John Gerard. 440 W 600 N 84337 #033-05-1991 L2003 **DR** *020 †80
FICKLIN, George C. 440 W 600 N 84337 #030-06-1938 **GP** *071
HOPKINS, Clair Richard. 440 W 600 N 84337 #005-12-1990 L1994 **DR** *020 †80
JOB, Jeffrey Scott. 440 W 600 N 84337 #010-01-1984 L1992 **DR** *020 †80
KERR, C Duane. 725 W 10TH N 84337 #049-01-1960 L1961 **GP** *071
MERRELL, Chad Lynn. 440 W 600 N 84337 #049-01-1983 L1984 **FM** *020 †18
MERRELL, Rodney Wm. 420 W 600 N 84337 #049-01-1981 L1982 **FM** *020 †18
MOORE, Nichole C. 420 W 600 N 84337 #021-06-2004 L2007 **FM** *020
MORTENSON, Blake C. 440 W 600 N 84337 #049-01-1992 L2000 **VIR** *020 †20
MURPHY, Kevin Alan. 471 W 600 N, INTERMOUNTAIN HEALTH GROUP 84337 #010-01-1994 L1996 **GS** *020 †85
PARKER, Daniel John. 440 W 600 N 84337 #049-01-1998 L2003 **DR** *020 †80

VERNAL – UINTAH

ALLEN, James Franklin. 175 N 100 W, STE 101 84078 #049-01-1969 L1970 **FM** *020 †18
ANDERSON, Rodney S. 379 N 500 W STE 1A 84078 #049-01-1989 L1991 **FM** *020 †18
ARNOLD, Laura Balch. 379 N 500 W, # 1A 84078 #038-41-1984 L1985 **FM** *020 †18
BASTIAN, Bevan Vern. 151 W 200 N 84078 #049-01-1986 L1992 **DR** *020 †80
BREITENBACH, Karl Lee. 379 N 500 W # 1A 84078 #028-46-1984 L1985 **FM** *020 †18 ‡
DANIEL, Bruce Allen Ii. 151 W 200 N 84078 #025-07-1992 L1995 **FM** *020 †18
DURANT, William Preston. 151 W 200 N 84078 #021-05-1974 L1983 **FM** *020 †18
GRIFFITH, John Lloyd. 175 N 100 W STE 103 84078 #028-34-1989 L2006 **OBG** *020
HUGHES, Jon Wm. 175 N 100 W STE 205A 84078 #024-07-1987 L1993 **IM** *020 †20
KARLSSON, Hans Goran. 175 N 100 W STE 202 84078 #858-02-1980 L1984 **VS GS** *020
MADSEN, Ace Arthur. 175 N 100 W STE 205B 84078 #049-01-1981 L1984 **IM** *020 †20
MASSAND, Ghanshyam P. 175 N 100 W, STE 204 84078 #496-38-1964 L2006 **ORS OS** *020 †40
MEMON, Kashif Abubakar. 175 N 100 W, STE 205C 84078 #704-08-1997 L2001 **IM** *020 †20
NIELSON, Norman Sanford. 1957 W 2500 N 84078 #049-01-1980 L1981 **EM GP** *020 †16
OLSEN, Michael Taylor. 379 N 500 W STE 1A 84078 #654-01-2000 L2003 **FM** *020 †18
PERRY, David Morrill. 151 W 200 N, RADIOLOGY DEPARTMENT 84078 #049-01-1991 L1995 **DR NM** *020 †80,28
RICHARDS, David Taylor. 175 N 100 W, STE 202 84078 #056-05-1974 L2004 **GS** *020 †85
THOMAS, Richard V. 175 N 100 W, STE 105 84078 #028-34-1989 L2004 **OBG** *020
WILCKEN, Larry T. 151 W 200 N 84078 #016-01-1974 L1975 **EM FM** *020 †18
WOODWARD, Kirk J. 379 N 500 W STE 1A 84078 #654-01-1999 L2002 **FM** *020 †18
YOUNG, Burk Teal. 175 N 100 W, STE 201 84078 #039-01-1992 L1997 **ORS** *020 †40

WASHINGTON – WASHINGTON

DAVEY, Bruce Winthrop. ■ 84780 #016-06-1972 L1977 **ORS** *071 †40

EARDLEY, Gene Pixton. ■ 84780 #049-01-1946 L1947 **GP** *071
HINTON, Raymond Kay. 195 W CENTER ST 84780 #049-01-1970 L1983 **FM** *020
JOHNSON, Blaine Hart. ■ 84780 #049-01-1979 L1987 **ORS** *020
PETERSON, Marcus L. ■ 84780 #023-12-1986 L1990 **PS** *072 †65,85

WASHINGTON TERRACE – WEBER

SMITH, Wayne Edward. 5333 S 500 E, STE C 84405 #049-01-1970 L1976 **D DMP** *020 †15

WELLSVILLE – CACHE

SHILL, Talmage Webb. ■ 84339 #049-01-1960 L1962 **A FM** *071 †18

WEST JORDAN – SALT LAKE

ADJEI-POKU, Michael. 3584 W 9000 S, STE 209 84088 #412-01-1985 L1995 **CD** *020 †20
AILES, Robert James. 7818 REDWOOD RD 84088 #038-06-1964 L2006 **PM** *020 †18
AIZAD, Tazeem A. 1561 W 7000 S, STE 202 84084 #704-02-1968 L1986 **PD NPM** *020 †55
ALLEN, Brandon Reid. 2751 W 9000 S STE 100 84088 #041-14-1999 L2002 **FM** *020 †18
ANDERSEN, Dana Andrew. 2751 W 9000 S 84088 #049-01-1983 L1984 **FM** *020 †18
BALOG, Kimberly Ann. 9071 S 1300 W, STE 301 84088 #049-01-1997 L2000 **PD** *020 †55
BARNEY, Mitchell Fowles. 3570 W 9000 S STE 210 84088 #049-01-1983 L1984 **OBG** *020 †30
BECK, Charles L, Jr. 3580 W 9000 S 84088 #021-05-1982 L1987 **OSM** *020 †40 ‡
BOAM, W Derek. 2655 W 9000 S 84088 #010-01-1992 L1993 **FM** *020 †18
BOSWORTH, Darin Gary. 9071 S 1300 W, SOUTHPOINT 84088 #036-01-1998 L2001 **PD** *020 †55
BOUD, Thomas Jeremy. 2655 W 9000 S 84088 #019-02-1994 L1997 **FM** *020 †18
BOYNTON, Kathleen K. 3584 W 9000 S, STE 300 84088 #011-03-1984 L1988 **GE IM** *020 †20
BREISCH, Stuart T. 3580 W 9000 S, INTEGRATED CARE AT JORDAN 84088 #041-09-1978 L1979 **EM** *030 †16
BUCHANAN, Brian John. 9071 S 1300 W, SOUTHPOINT 84088 #049-01-1996 L1999 **PD** *020 †55
BUCHI, Kenneth Norman. 3584 W 9000 S STE 300 84088 #049-01-1978 L1979 **GE IM** *020 †20 ‡
BURNHAM, John Philip. ■ 84084 #035-01-1953 L1954 **U** *071 †95
BUZZARD, Travis Lynn. 2655 W 9000 S, INTERMOUNTAIN HEALTH CARE 84088 #004-01-1995 L1997 **FM** *020 †18
CHAMBERLAIN, Bruce Harry. 3580 W 9000 S 84088 #023-07-1988 L1994 **IM** *020 †20
CHRISTENSEN, Chad Dallan. 2655 W 9000 S 84088 #049-01-1994 L1995 **FM** *020 †18
CHRISTENSEN, Scott K. 3580 W 9000 S 84088 #049-01-1975 L1978 **AN PD** *020 †55,05
CHRISTENSEN, Thomas Russe. 3570 W 9000 S, STE 100 84088 #305-01-2002 L2006 **FM** *020
COLBY, Spencer Neil. 3580 W 9000 S, STE 206 84088 #010-01-1989 L2000 **OBG** *020 †30
CROMBIE, Courtney Heather. 3580 W 9000 S 84088 #034-01-1993 L1999 **PS** *020 †65
DAHL, Barbara Diane. 3580 W 9000 S, EMER DEPT 84088 #054-04-1997 L2001 **EM** *020 †16
DARR, Thomas Glenn. 3580 W 9000 S, INTEGRATED CARE AT JORDAN 84088 #028-03-1982 L1983 **EM** *020 †18,16
DEVENPORT, Stephen Brent. 2751 W 9000 S 84088 #010-01-1993 L2006 **FM** *020 †18
FILLMORE, Randall Reid. 2751 W 9000 S 84088 #049-01-1984 L1987 **FM** *020 †18
FILLOUX, Ruth Hegeman. 3580 W 9000 S, INTEGRATED CARE AT JORDAN 84088 #005-14-1981 L1982 **EM** *020 †16
FINE, Stephanie Grace. 3584 W 9000 S, STE 304 84088 #034-01-1989 L1990 **GS** *020 †85
FORSHA, Douglass Wm. 3570 W 9000 S STE 220 84088 #047-05-1985 L1991 **D** *020
FUKUSHIMA, Taira. 1847 W 9000 S 84088 #049-01-1964 L1965 **PHP GPM** *071 †70
GILES, Ryan Grant. 3580 W 9000 S, INTEGRATED CARE AT JORDAN 84088 #035-09-1998 L2001 **EM** *020 †16
GOLDBERG, Kenneth W. 3590 W 9000 S, STE 240 84088 #005-06-1990 L1999 **IM** *020 †20
GOODWIN, Leslie Lash. 9071 S 1300 W, SOUTHPOINT 84088 #049-01-1977 L1978 **PD** *020 †55
HANCEY, Brian Craig. 2655 W 9000 S 84088 #049-01-1998 L2001 **FM** *020 †18
HANRAHAN, Maura Killeen. 3570 W 9000 S STE 100 84088 #023-01-1989 L1992 **FM** *020 †18
HANSEN, Scott Eugene. 3570 W 9000 S STE 210 84088 #005-18-1989 L1993 **OBG** *072 †30
HARRIS, Leslie James. 3584 W 9000 S 84088 #005-14-1970 L1994 **ORS** *020 †40
HAWS, Charles Wesley. 3584 W 9000 S, STE 209 84088 #049-01-1979 L1984 **CD IM** *020 †20
HOUGAARD, Joni. 3570 W 9000 S STE 100, STE 100 84088 #031-01-1994 L1995 **FM** *020 †18
HULL, Dale Brent. 3570 W 9000 S STE 210 84088 #049-01-1985 L1986 **OBG** *020 †30
HURLEY, Amy Leigh. ■ 84084 #046-01-2005 L2006 **PD** *012
JACKSON, Jeffrey Barrett. 1995 W 9000 S 84088 #056-05-1990 L1997 **PD** *020 †55
JARRETT, Arlen Kent. 3570 W 9000 S STE 210 84088 #049-01-1982 L1984 **OBG GP** *020 †30
JOHNSON, Kevin Barrus. 3590 W 9000 S, STE 240 84088 #049-01-1982 L1987 **IM** *020 †20
JULIEN, Katie Ann. 1575 W 7000 S 84084 #305-01-2001 L2004 **FM** *020
KASPER, Joseph Francis. 3855 W 7800 S, STE 100 84088 #060-01-1995 L1998 **FM** *020 †18
KENDRA-SLACK, Caryn Marie. 3570 W 9000 S, STE 100 84088 #026-04-2000 L2004 **FM** *020 †18
KIRSTEIN, Judith Lee. 3590 W 9000 S, STE 300 84088 #005-14-1978 L1979 **FM** *020 †18
LAMBERT, Richard Ernest. 3580 W 9000 S, DEPT. OF ANESTHESIA 84088 #049-01-1993 L1997 **IM** *020 †05
LANE, Roni. ■ 84084 #005-14-1997 L2004 **PEM** *100 †55
LANGER, Kathleen Marie. 3570 W 9000 S, STE 210 84088 #056-01-1995 L1996 **OBG** *020 †30
LASH, Kevin Brook. 9071 S 1300 W, SOUTHPOINT 84088 #049-01-1992 L1995 **PD** *020 †55
LEVINE, Rebecca J. 1575 W 7000 S 84084 #048-02-1993 L1996 **FM** *020 †18
LITZINGER, Marcia Jean. 3590 W 9000 S, STE 135 84088 #001-02-1980 L1985 **CHN OS** *050 †55
MACINTYRE, James Gillis. 3584 W 9000 S, STE 405 84088 #065-06-1978 L1991 **FSM** *020
MARSHALL, Nathan James. 2655 W 9000 S 84088 #049-01-1996 L1999 **FM** *020 †18
MARSHALL, Stuart Charles. 3584 W 9000 S, STE 405 84088 #016-43-2000 L2005 **OSM** *020 †18
MASHKURI, Pari Lynne. 8822 S REDWOOD RD, STE C211 84088 #035-08-1991 L1996 **PD** *020 †55
MAY, Mark Spencer. 3580 W 9000 S, INTEGRATED CARE AT JORDAN 84088 #025-12-1985 L1993 **EM** *020 †16
MC FADDEN, Michael Roy. 3584 W 9000 S 84088 #049-01-1969 L1976 **U** *020 †95
MEADS, Garner B, Jr. 3590 W 9000 S, STE 300 84088 #049-01-1978 L1979 **OTO HNS** *020 †45
MEHR, Douglas Stewart. 3855 W 7800 S, STE 210 84088 #016-42-1999 L2005 **OPH OS** *020 †35 ‡

MENELLO, John Matthew. 1990 W 7800 S 84088 #034-01-1994 L1999 **FM UCM** *020 †18

MIMNAUGH, Steven Robert. 3580 W 9000 S, INTEGRATED CARE AT JORDAN 84088 #049-01-1981 L1982 **EM** *020 †16

MOLBERG, Holly Jean. 8822 S REDWOOD RD, STE C211 84088 #012-05-1979 L1982 **PD** *020 †55

MOORE, M Kirk. 8822 S REDWOOD RD, STE C111 84088 #011-02-1993 L2005 **PS** *020 †65

MORELAND, Kimberly Ann. 3570 W 9000 S, STE 210 84088 #005-06-1992 L1993 **OBG** *020 †30

NWIZU, Chidi Azubike. ■ 84088 #690-06-1988 L2006 **ID** *012 †20

OKUBO, David H. 1995 W 9000 S 84088 #049-01-1979 L1981 **PD DIA** *030 †55

ONEIDA, Maria Antonia. 3570 W 9000 S STE 200 84088 #049-01-1981 L1982 **FM OBG** *020 †18

OUTTRIM, Rex A. 3584 W 9000 S, STE 209 84088 #048-13-1992 L2000 **CD IM** *020 †20

PAGE, Ann Waugh. 3580 W 9000 S, INTEGRATED CARE AT JORDAN 84088 #032-01-1979 L1980 **EM** *020 †16,18

PETERSON, Brian Ray. 3584 W 9000 S, STE 311 84088 #049-01-1990 L1996 **OTO NO** *020 †45

PILGRAM, Paul Edward. 1561 W 7000 S, STE 200 84084 #041-02-1978 L1981 **IM EM** *020 †20,16

PORRETTA, Jane Marie. 3584 W 9000 S STE 304, JORDAN VLLY SURG SPECIALIS 84088 #025-07-1989 L1990 **GS** *020 †85

PRECIADO, Alfonso. 3584 W 9000 S, STE 304 84088 #715-01-1989 L2007 **GS GP** *020 †85

PRINCE, Gerry D. 3570 W 9000 S, KATE DEISS 84088 #060-01-1985 L1995 **FM** *020

PUGH, Brenten Clark. 7478 CAMPUS VIEW DR # 100, STE 100 84084 #049-01-2000 L2002 **FM** *020 †18

RAHANIOTIS, Valerie L. 8822 S REDWOOD RD STE C211 84088 #016-42-1998 L2001 **PD** *020 †55

RASMUS, Renee Elizabeth. 8822 S REDWOOD RD, ST. C-211 84088 #422-01-1999 L2003 **PD** *020 †55

RUSCHKE, Diane Sigrid. 3580 W 9000 S, INTEGRATED CARE AT JORDAN 84088 #016-01-1989 L1993 **EM** *020 †16

SCHEIDELL, Renee Nilsson. 8822 S REDWOOD RD, STE E-122 84088 #049-01-1990 L1992 **IM** *020 †20

SESSIONS, Wade Manning. 3584 W 9000 S, STE 405 84088 #001-02-2001 L2006 **ORS** *020

SLAWSON, Edward D, III. 3584 W 9000 S, STE 304 84088 #049-01-1971 L1973 **GS** *020 †85

SMITH, David John. 3590 W 9000 S, STE 120 84088 #456-05-1983 L1986 **N IM** *020 †75

SOLLEREDER, Gordon John. 2414 W 7800 S, STE 202 84088 #060-01-1977 L1979 **FM** *020

SPENCE, Richard John. 3580 W 9000 S, INTEGRATED CARE AT JORDAN 84088 #005-18-1982 L1984 **EM FM** *020 †18

SPRUNG, Robert Frederick. 3570 W 9000 S, STE 110 84088 #028-34-1990 L1994 **CD** *020 †20

TERASHIMA, Robert S. 8925 S 2700 W 84088 #049-01-1975 L1977 **PD** *020 †55

THACKERAY, Steven Milton. 3584 W 9000 S, STE 206 84088 #049-01-1996 L2000 **OBG** *020 †30

THOMAS, Mark Carl. 3570 W 9000 S, STE 110 84088 #007-02-1971 L1980 **ORS** *020 †40

TURNER, Craig Alan. 3580 W 9000 S, INTEGRATED CARE AT JORDAN 84088 #011-03-1996 L1999 **EM** *020 †16

URBAN, Scott Dieter. 7611 JORDAN LANDING BLVD, STE 102 84084 #026-08-2001 L2003 **FPS** *020

VACHAROTHONE, Rachot K. 7611 JORDAN LANDING BLVD 84084 #001-06-1994 L1996 **IM** *020 †20

WATSON, Randall Lawrence. 1575 W 7000 S 84084 #001-02-1985 L1986 **EM FM** *020 †18

WOLFE, Timothy Robt. 3580 W 9000 S, INTEGRATED CARE AT JORDAN 84088 #049-01-1988 L1992 **EM** *020 †16

WOOD, Kelly Elizabeth. ■ 84084 #018-03-2004 L2007 **PD** *100 †55

ZACKRISON, David Randall. 3590 W 9000 S STE 240 84088 #041-09-1984 L1988 **IM EM** *020 †20

ZIMMERMAN, Patrick Hardin. 2655 W 9000 S 84088 #028-02-1995 L1998 **FM** *020 †18

WEST VALLEY – SALT LAKE

AGRESTA, Matthew David. 3451 S 5600 W 84120 #008-02-2003 L2004 **FM** *020 †18

ALLEN, Kathryn. 3540 S 4000 W, STE 340 84120 #005-12-1984 L1985 **FM FSM** *020 †18

BARLOW, Stephen Loren. 4646 LAKE PARK BLVD 84120 #040-02-1977 L1980 **IM** *071 †20

BOOTH, Edgar John. 3460 PIONEER PKWY, DEPT RADIOLOGY 84120 #005-14-1987 L1988 **DR NM** *020 †80,28

BRASHER, Burton F. 4067 CONTINENTAL DR 84120 #049-01-1951 L1952 **FM** *071

BURROWS, James Douglas. 3336 PIONEER PKWY, STE 102 84120 #065-01-1983 L1994 **HS PS** *020 †65

CHURCH, Jason Victor. 3336 PIONEER PKWY, STE 201 84120 #012-01-2003 L2006 **PD** *020

CLARK, Jayne E. 3460 PIONEER PKWY 84120 #049-01-1979 L1980 **PM LM** *020 †60

DINGER, Steven Chas. 3725 W 4100 S, GRANGER MEDICAL CLINIC 84120 #049-01-1975 L1984 **OBG** *020 †30

DITTRICH, Karen Anne. 3460 PIONEER PKWY, PIONEER VALLEY HOSP 84120 #050-02-1990 L1991 **DR** *062 †80

DOUVILLE, Douglas Richard. 3725 W 4100 S, GRANGER MEDICAL CLINIC 84120 #019-02-1974 L1994 **AM FM** *030 †70,18

DUPONT, Gregory Patrick. 3336 S 4155 W, STE 303 84120 #048-14-1985 L1989 **PUD SME** *020 †20

EMPEY, Ryan Bruce. ■ 84119 #049-01-2008 L2008 *012

EYRE, Alyson. 3725 W 4100 S, GRANGER MEDICAL CLINIC 84120 #049-01-1996 L1999 **PD** *020 †55

GALLEGOS, David A. 3460 PIONEER PKWY 84120 #049-01-1990 L1991 **PTH** *020 †50

GARCIA, Evelyn Marie. 3460 PIONEER PKWY, PIONEER VALLEY HOSPITAL 84120 #034-01-1989 L2000 **DR** *020 †80

GORDON, Dennis Harvey. 3336 PIONEER PKWY, STE 102 84120 #023-01-1966 L1967 **ORS OAR** *020 †40

GRANGE, Timothy Scott. 3336 PIONEER PKWY, STE 202 84120 #049-01-1987 L1989 **PM** *020 †60

HALL, Jennifer Kay. 3239 CALKARY CIR 84120 #054-04-2003 L2005 **PD** *020 †55

HARPER, Sean Scott. 3725 W 4100 S 84120 #040-02-2004 L2005 **FM** *020 †18

HARRINGTON, Keith Edward. 3451 S 5600 W, STE F 84120 #038-40-1988 L1997 **IM** *020 †20

HARRISON, Reid Chambers. 3725 W 4100 S, GRANGER MEDICAL CLINIC 84120 #049-01-1995 L1999 **MPD PD** *020,55

HOTTES, Frederick Allen. 3460 PIONEER PKWY 84120 #049-01-1975 L1976 **ATP CLP** *020 †50

ISAAC, David Bert. 3460 PIONEER PKWY 84120 #010-02-1966 L1970 **OBG GP** *071 †30

JOHNSON, Matthew Brent. 3460 PIONEER PKWY 84120 #038-40-2001 L2004 **FM** *020

KARABSHEH, Shadi Mashhour. 3460 PIONEER PKWY, PIONEER VALLEY HOSPITAL 84120 #575-01-1998 L2007 **IM** *020 †20

LE, Dinhkim. ■ 84119 #049-01-2004 L2005 **GS** *012

LOMBARDI, Dennis Louis. 3460 PIONEER PKWY 84120 #049-01-1969 L1972 **PTH DMP** *020 †50

LYNCH, Beverly Jeanne. 3460 PIONEER PKWY 84120 #031-01-1995 L1996 **PTH** *020 †50

MILES, Jeffrey Grady. ■ 84120 #049-01-1995 L1996 **FM** *020 †18

MORRIS, Ray, III. 3465 S 4155 W STE 2 84120 #048-13-1985 L1993 **FM** *020 †18

OELSNER, David Howard. 3460 PIONEER PKWY 84120 #021-01-1991 L2006 **GE IM** *020 †20

PARKINSON, Justin Paul. 4052 PIONEER PKWY, STE 202 84120 #049-01-2001 L2006 **U** *020 †95

PFEFFER, Kathleen Denise. 3336 S 4155 W STE 303, UTAH SLEEP SPECIALISTS, LL 84120 #005-14-1981 L1989 **PUD PD** *050 †55

POULSEN, Jerry Kay. 2702 S 3600 W, STE E 84119 #049-01-1967 L1968 **GP EM** *020

ROSENFIELD, Micah M. 3725 W 4100 S, GRANGER MED CLNC 84120 #041-01-1994 L2000 **FM** *020 †18

SHAH, Saurabh B. 3725 W 4100 S, GRANGER MEDICAL CLINIC 84120 #005-02-1995 L2000 **OTO** *020 †45

SHERIDAN, Scott. 3725 W 4100 S, GRANGER MEDICAL CLINIC 84120 #049-01-1989 L1992 **FM** *020 †18

SMITH, David Clayton. ■ 84120 #049-01-2007 **IM** *012

SMITH, John Lynn. 3336 PIONEER PKWY, STE 102 84120 #049-01-1965 L1967 **ORS** *020 †40

SMITH, Robert Eric. 3725 W 4100 S 84120 #049-01-1994 L1998 **OPH** *020 †35

TAILLAC, Peter Provosty. 5545 W 3100 S 84120 #021-01-1985 L1993 **EM** *020 †16

TRAN, Tan Duy. 3336 PIONEER PKWY, STE 302 84120 #305-01-2000 L2002 **FM** *020

VALENTINE, Christopher B. 4052 PIONEER PKWY, STE 109 84120 #030-05-2000 L2003 **FM** *100 †18

WALKER, Dean Nichols. 3725 W 4100 S, GRANGER MEDICAL CLINIC, IN 84120 #048-13-1989 L1994 **ORS** *020 †40

WYATT, Michelle Terese. 3725 W 4100 S, GRANGER MEDICAL CLINIC 84120 #016-43-1991 L2006 **IM** *062 †20

YEE, Adrain W Cheong. 3715 W 4100 S, UTAH SURGICAL CENTER 84120 #049-01-1976 L1977 **AN** *020 †05

WEST VALLEY CITY – SALT LAKE

BOUGHTON, Lori. 3730 W 4700 S, WESTRIDGE HEALTH CENTER 84118 #038-40-2002 L2006 **FM** *020 †18

CHAPMAN, Dale L. 3725 W 4100 S 84120 #048-14-1982 L1984 **PD PDP** *020 †55

CIVISH, Frederic Marsh. 3534 S 6000 W 84128 #049-01-1988 L1991 **FM** *020 †18

HUTCHISON, Christopher V. 3725 W 4100 S 84120 #049-01-1995 L1999 **OBG** *020 †30

JORGENSEN, Trisha. ■ 84128 #035-15-2008 *012

PINGREE, Michael F. 3465 S 4155 W, STE 4 84120 #049-01-1998 L2002 **OPH** *020 †35

REUSCH, Clifford Sumner. 3460 S 4155 W 84120 #019-02-1956 L1981 **PTH IM** *062 †20,50 ‡

SKELTON-FORREST, Eloise. 3451 S 5600 W, STE E 84120 #010-03-1977 L2006 **OBG** *020 †30

SOUTHWICK, Edward Glen. 3465 S 4155 W STE 1 84120 #010-01-1967 L1974 **D DMP** *020 †15

WOODLAND HILLS – UTAH

WRIGHT, Dalton Henry. 970 S SETTLEMENT DR 84653 #049-01-1981 L1986 **DR NM** *020 †80

WOODS CROSS – DAVIS

DEATHERAGE, Lindy Sue. ■ 84087 #040-02-2005 L2006 **AN** *012

HALL, Jennifer Louise. ■ 84087 #049-01-2008 *012

MARSHALL, Bret D. 592 W 1350 S, BENCHMARK HOSP 84010 #049-01-1988 L1989 **P CHP** *020

MURPHEY, James Peters. 576 W 900 S, STE 105 84010 #021-01-1974 L1977 **PTH** *020 †50

VANCE, Jerome Erwin. 592 W 1350 S, BENCHMARK BEHAVIORAL HEALT 84010 #049-01-1989 L1990 **P** *020 †75

ALBURGH – GRAND ISLE

SCARLET, Alexander John. ■ 05440 #781-01-1942 L1965 **GP PM** *075

ARLINGTON – BENNINGTON

WADE, John Lauris. ■ 05250 #016-06-1990 L2006 **DR** *020 †80

BARNARD – WINDSOR

ZIMMERMAN, Camille. ■ 05031 #035-47-1991 **PD** *071

BARNET – CALEDONIA

BAKER, Stanley Lawrence. ■ 05821 #025-12-1988 L1993 **FM** *020 †18
HARTMAN, Ted Elsner. ■ 05821 #051-01-1979 L1998 **FM** *075 †18

BARRE – WASHINGTON

ABAJIAN, Michael Wm. ■ 05641 #050-02-1978 L1981 **AN** *020 †05
ANTHONY, Janet. PO BOX 547, BOX 547 BARRE 05641 #023-01-1972 L1977 **FM** *020 †18,16
BARTRUM, Royal Jay, Jr. PO BOX 547 05641 #024-01-1969 L1987 **DR** *071 †80 ‡
BURNS, Le Grand Cannon. ■ 05641 #035-03-1962 L1966 **IM HEM** *020 †20
BUTSCH, David Winfield. 3270 AIRPORT RD - BERLIN 05641 #038-06-1966 L1972 **GS** *020 †85
CARR, Priscilla Wheatley. 225 S MAIN ST, BARRE HLTH CTR 05641 #024-16-2000 L2000 **IM** *020 †20
COELLO, Armando J. 58 E VIEW LN STE 1 05641 #737-06-1967 L1973 **OPH** *020 †35 ‡
CURCHIN, Thomas James. 82 E VIEW LN, STE 3 05641 #050-02-1986 L1989 **FM** *020 †18
EHRET, Rose Szeming. 77 VINE ST 05641 #021-01-1992 L1997 **CHP** *020 †75
GRANAI, Cornelius O, Jr. ■ 05641 #050-02-1952 L1953 **OBG** *071
HOLM, J Lorimer. 1276 EAST RD - BERLIN 05641 #024-01-1960 L1964 **R** *071 †80
KENDALL, Marvin. 225 S MAIN ST, BARRE HEALTH CENTER 05641 #005-12-1973 L1974 **FM GP** *020 †18
KHAN, Arif Ullah. PO BOX 547 05641 #495-51-1968 L1986 **PUD IM** *020
KURESHI, Suraiya Aisha. 225 S MAIN ST, BARRE PEDIATRICS 05641 #539-06-2003 L2006 **PD** *020 †55
LANDVATER, Stephanie J. 82 E VIEW LN, STE 1 05641 #025-12-1987 L1988 **ORS** *020 †40
LINDSAY, Margaret V. 225 S MAIN ST, BARRE PEDIATRICS 05641 #035-08-2003 L2006 **PD** *020 †55
MALEK, Marvin Keith. 225 S MAIN ST, BARRE INTERNAL MEDICINE 05641 #035-15-1978 L2001 **IM** *020 †20
MC GINNIS, John M, Jr. ■ 05641 #050-02-1961 L1969 **OTO HNS** *071 †45
MINDRUM, Michael Reid. 225 S MAIN ST 05641 #020-02-2003 L2004 **IM** *100 †20
PATTI, Lucy. 82 E VIEW LN, STE 3 05641 #032-01-1990 L1991 **FM** *020 †18 ‡
ROBINSON, Robert D, III. 30 KEITH AVE 05641 #017-20-1979 L1984 **IM** *020 †20
SEIDEMAN, Sam. 58 E VIEW LN STE 1, THE EYE CENTER 05641 #035-06-1971 L1976 **OPH** *020 †35 ‡
SIVAK, Louise Elizabeth. 225 S MAIN ST, BARRE PEDIATRICS 05641 #028-02-1989 L2002 **PD** *020 †55
STARR, Bram Stephen. 82 E VIEW LN, STE 3 05641 #024-05-1984 L1991 **FM** *020 †18
TALMADGE, Bruce Alexander. 225 S MAIN ST 05641 #051-01-1957 L1977 **IM CD** *020
THOMASHOW, Peter Martin. PO BOX 547, CENTRAL VERMONT MED CTR 05641 #035-19-1982 L2000 **P N** *030 †75
WELLER, Peter Thos. PO BOX 547, CENTRAL VT HOSPITAL-EMERGE 05641 #021-01-1988 L1993 **IM** *020 †20
YORRA, Mark Nelson. ■ 05641 #035-46-1974 L1977 **IM** *020 †20
ZAGROBA, John Anthony. ■ 05641 #050-02-1953 L1954 **U** *071
ZAHM, Michael Jos. 244 GRANGER RD 05641 #017-20-1975 L1980 **U** *020 †95

BARTON – ORLEANS

WOOD, Brian Moffat. 488 ELM ST 05822 #001-06-2001 L2004 **FM** *020 †18

BELLOWS FALLS – WINDHAM

CARRASQUILLO, Hector A. 184 ROCKINGHAM ST 05101 #035-48-1975 L1978 **OBG** *020 †30
GRASS, William Samuel. 18 OLD TER, WINDHAM CENTER FOR PSYCHIA 05101 #050-02-1994 L1994 **PCC** *020
GRIFFITHS, Walter John. 81 WESTMINSTER TER 05101 #035-15-1973 L1974 **FM FPG** *020 †18 ‡
HALL, Eliot Randall. 1 HOSPITAL CT, BELLOWS FALLS PEDIATRICS 05101 #040-02-1992 L1999 **PD** *020 †55
LEPPMAN, John Armstrong. 18 OLD TER 05101 #050-02-1973 L1976 **IM** *020 †20
LORBATI, Albert Richard. 1 HOSPITAL CT STE 12 05101 #050-02-1967 L1967 **P** *030 †75
PEAKE, Matthew J. 1 HOSPITAL CT 05101 #035-19-1979 L1982 **FM** *020 †18
POST, Ellen Renee. 1 HOSPITAL CT, STE 9 05101 #055-01-2001 L2006 **FM** *020
ROONEY, Valerie Anne. 128 ATKINSON ST 05101 #033-05-1986 L1990 **PD** *020 †55
SBARDELLA, Edward F, Jr. 18 OLD TER, HEALTH CENTER AT BELLOWS F 05101 #027-01-1969 L1987 **P CHP** *071
SLOWINSKI, Susan Sutphen. 128 ATKINSON ST 05101 #041-07-1982 L1998 **PD** *020 †55
VENMAN-CLAY, Gary A. 18 OLD TER 05101 #024-16-1984 L1987 **FM** *020 †18

BENNINGTON – BENNINGTON

ALGUS, Michael. 140 HOSPITAL DR, STE 19 05201 #035-08-1979 L1991 **PUD IM** *030 †20
ANSELMO, Randall Scott. 1 COLLEGE DR 05201 #011-03-1993 L2003 **FM** *020 †18
BAKER, Dudley Moore. 332 DEWEY ST 05201 #050-02-1957 L1964 **ORS** *071 †40
BARSOTTI, Christopher E. 100 HOSPITAL DR, CTR EMERGENCY ROOM 05201 #016-11-1999 L2004 **EM** *020 †16

BENNETT, Roberta. 140 HOSPITAL DR 05201 #017-20-1980 L1986 **P CHN** *020 †75
BEVIN, Christopher. 2 HARWOOD DR, ORAL AND FACIAL SURGERY AS 05201 #026-08-2005 L2007 **OMF** *020
BINNICK, Alan Neal. 140 HOSPITAL DR 05201 #041-02-1973 L1976 **D DMP** *020 †15
BLOCK, Robert Stuart. 332 DEWEY ST, TACONIC ORTHOPAEDICS PC 05201 #035-15-1972 L1978 **ORS OSS** *020 †40
BOLTON, Joanna Grace. ■ 05201 #050-02-2004 L2005 *020
BURTIS, Richard Thos. 339 DEWEY ST, BENNINGTON ASSOCIATES IN 05201 #024-01-1960 L1965 **IM GE** *020 †20
CATAPANO-FRIEDMAN, Lisa K. 357 SHIELDS DR 05201 #024-07-1977 L1991 **P** *020 †75 ‡
CESTONE, Kenneth Joseph. ■ 05201 #035-20-1962 L1965 **AN** *071 †05
CHAPMAN, Timothy D. 100 HOSPITAL DR, DEPT OF PATHLGY SVMC 05201 #005-12-1995 L2001 **PTH** *020 †50
CHERRY, Leo H. 100 HOSPITAL DR 05201 #847-04-1975 L1977 **PD** *075
COFFIELD, Terrell Lee. 100 HOSPITAL DR DEPT RAD 05201 #055-01-1975 L1978 **DR** *020 †80
COHEN, Adam Reid. 100 HOSPITAL DR, EMERGENCY DEPARTMENT 05201 #035-08-1999 L2004 **EM IM** *020,16
COWDER, Andrew John. 140 HOSPITAL DR, STE 110 05201 #035-48-1996 L2002 **U** *020 †95
CUNNINGHAM, Brian Philip. 140 HOSPITAL DR 05201 #041-01-1969 L1978 **IM** *020 †20
DAHL, Sarah Perkins. 345 ELM ST 05201 #050-02-1995 L2000 **OBG** *020 †30
DANFORTH, Nicholas. 100 HOSPITAL DR, SOUTHWESTERN VERMONT MED C 05201 #035-03-1963 L1995 **P** *071 †75
DOBSON, Carl Weathers, III. 100 HOSPITAL DR, SOUTHWESTERN VERMONT MED 05201 #047-06-2002 L2005 **EM** *020 †16
DRANGINIS, Therese E. 655 MAIN ST 05201 #041-14-1982 L1990 **FM** *020 †18
DREW, Simon Paul. 140 HOSPITAL DR, STE 203 05201 #050-02-1991 L2004 **GS** *020 †85
DREYER, Michael Danton. 140 HOSPITAL DR STE 210, NEUROLOGICAL CONSULTANTS P 05201 #836-02-1986 L2000 **N** *020 †75
DU BOFF, Stuart Michael. 322 DEWEY ST 05201 #035-09-1969 L1974 **OPH** *020 †35
DUNDAS, G Richard. 339 DEWEY ST, BENNINGTON ASSOCIATES IN 05201 #024-07-1968 L1974 **IM** *020 †20
EDWARDS, Keith Robt. 140 HOSPITAL DR, STE 210 05201 #036-07-1973 L1974 **N** *050 †75
ELLEM, Kay Adrian Oswald. PO BOX 620 05201 #143-03-1955 **ON OS** *050
FABRICIUS, Richard N. 332 DEWEY ST 05201 #050-02-1953 L1960 **ORS** *072 †40
FAMIANO, Frank Carl. 100 HOSPITAL DR, SOUTHWESTERN VERMONT MED C 05201 #041-13-1974 L1994 **NEP IM** *020 †20
FREYER, Stuart. 100 HOSPITAL DR 05201 #035-01-1964 L1972 **OTO OS** *020 †45
FRISCIA, Marisa. 140 HOSPITAL DR STE 106 05201 #422-01-1987 L2002 **IM PUD** *020 †20
FROST, Eric Scott. 140 HOSPITAL DR 05201 #050-02-1985 L1990 **GS VS** *020 †85
GEORGE, Marie Juliet. 100 HOSPITAL DR 05201 #010-02-1987 L1999 **ID** *020 †20
GERISCH, Robert Albert. ■ 05201 #025-07-1946 L1947 **CD IM** *020 †20
GHOSH, Manindra Nath. 120 HOSPITAL DR 05201 #495-02-1965 L1972 **PD A** *020 †55
GIDDINGS, W Philip. ■ 05201 #024-01-1938 L1950 **GS** *071 †85
GOLDSCHMIDT, Thomas G. 100 HOSPITAL DR 05201 #024-16-1993 L2007 **IM** *020 †20
GORSON, David Marc. 140 HOSPITAL DR, STE 301 05201 #041-14-1981 L1992 **END IM** *020 †20
GRABOWSKI, Eugene Walter. 140 HOSPITAL DR, STE 201 05201 #024-07-1968 L1973 **GS CD** *020 †85
GUERRERO, Richard Luis. ■ 05201 #035-20-1965 L1969 **IM CD** *071 †20
HEARST, John Eric. 100 HOSPITAL DR 05201 #010-01-1983 L1988 **FM** *020 †18
HEMM, Robert Mark. 194 NORTH ST 05201 #035-20-1977 L1994 **IM** *020 †20
HENLEY, Deborah Ann. 332 DEWEY ST, BENNINGTON HANDS & FEET, L 05201 #035-15-1992 L2007 **ORS** *020 †40
HICKEY, Catherine M. 100 LEDGEHILL RD 05201 #048-04-1994 L1998 **P** *020 †75
HOWARD, Orion Maurice. 140 HOSPITAL DR 05201 #035-20-1992 L2007 **ON** *020 †20
INMAN, Jeffrey Eugene. ■ 05201 #036-08-2002 L2006 **AN** *020
JOHNSON, Theodore Lee. 194 NORTH ST, BROOKSIDE PEDIATRICS 05201 #016-11-1978 L1981 **PD** *020 †55
KELLEY, William Harold. 100 HOSPITAL DR, SOUTHWESTERN VT MEDICAL CE 05201 #024-05-1990 L2003 **AN** *020 †05
KETCHAM, Brock Treverton. 100 HOSPITAL DR 05201 #050-02-1973 L1979 **R PHP** *020 †80
KETTERER, William Francis. 332 DEWEY ST, TACONIC ORTHOPAEDICS PC 05201 #038-40-1972 L1980 **ORS** *020 †40
KING, J Gregory. 655 MAIN ST, MT ANTHONY PRM CARE STE 1 05201 #035-06-1980 L1986 **FM** *020 †18
KING, Peter Knight. 325 NORTH ST, VA OUTREACH CLINIC 05201 #050-02-1982 L1989 **FM** *020 †18
KRATZER, Joseph Harold. 140 HOSPITAL DR, STE 309 05201 #056-06-1981 L1991 **N IM** *020 †75
KUMAR, Archana. 100 LEDGEHILL RD 05201 #495-99-1991 L2001 **CHP** *020 †75
LEFEBVRE, Steven David. 100 HOSPITAL DR, CTR EMERGENCY ROOM 05201 #050-02-2004 L2007 **EM** *020
LOY, Frederick Peter. 140 HOSPITAL DR 05201 #035-20-1969 L1976 **GS VS** *020 †85
LYON, Edd Gilbert. 100 HOSPITAL DR 05201 #035-03-1975 L1978 **FM** *020 †18
MACK, Karin Franseen. 100 HOSPITAL DR 05201 #041-13-1970 L1995 **P** *020 †75
MACKENZIE, Glen Carlisle. 160 BENMONT AVE STE 22 05201 #016-43-1991 L1995 **OBG** *020 †30
MARTE, Benjamin Othoniel. 100 LEDGEHILL RD, UNITED COUNSELING SERVICE 05201 #748-02-1986 L1994 **CHP** *020 †75
MARTIN, Bradford John. 100 HOSPITAL DR 05201 #019-02-1978 L1987 **AN** *062
MARTIN, Markus Chaim. 100 HOSP DR, SOUTHWESTERN VT MED CTR 05201 #067-01-1974 L1979 **OBG** *020 †30
MARTINEZ, Philip. 100 HOSPITAL DR 05201 #035-15-1954 L1959 **FM OS** *071
MAURER, Lloyd Herbert. 140 HOSPITAL DR, ONCOLOGY ASSOCIATES 05201 #035-03-1964 L1987 **ON** *071 †20
MC LELLAN, John Matheson. 140 HOSPITAL DR, MEDICAL OFFICE BLDG 05201 #067-01-1968 L1974 **OBG** *020 †30
MENSH, Ronald Stephen. 140 HOSPITAL DR 05201 #041-01-1976 L1981 **GE IM** *020 †20
MILLER, Donna Marie. 2 N TERRACE DR 05201 #016-43-1990 L1995 **CCP** *020 †55
MILLS, Letha Elaine. 140 HOSPITAL DR, STE 116 05201 #032-01-1977 L1979 **ON OS** *020 †20
MISKOVSKY, Emil Peter. 140 HOSPITAL DR STE 211 05201 #035-03-1985 L2001 **GE IM** *020 †20
MOOK, John Milton. PUTNAM MEM HOSP, DEPT OBG 05201 #035-45-1943 L1949 **EM CRS** *071 †85
MOORE, Michele Claire. 100 HOSPITAL DR 05201 #539-06-1974 L1976 **FM GPM** *071
MULDER, Martien Adriaan. 140 HOSPITAL DR 05201 #035-45-1962 L1984 **GS ON** *071 †85

NOFZIGER, Matthew Jacob. 332 DEWEY ST, TACONIC ORTHOPAEDICS PC 05201 #017-20-1997 L2004 **OSM** *020 †40

NOVOTNY, Mark. 100 HOSPITAL DR, BOX 65 05201 #050-02-1977 L1979 **IM MDM** *030 †20

ORTON, Judy Kay. 901 MAIN ST, GREEN MOUNTAIN PEDS PC 05201 #011-04-1986 L1989 **PD** *020 †55 ‡

OSTERLAND, C Kirk. 100 HOSPITAL DR, SW VERMONT HEALTHCARE 05201 #062-01-1957 L1998 **IG RHU** *030 †03

PARO, Roger Ronald. 88 SOUTHSHIRE DR 05201 #028-34-1990 L1995 **AN** *020 †05

PERREGAUX, Daniel Edouard. 100 HOSPITAL DR, CTR EMERGENCY ROOM 05201 #035-06-1999 L2004 **EM** *020 †16

PEZZULICH, Robert Anthony. 100 HOSPITAL DR, BOX 21 05201 #035-20-1965 L1973 **GE** *030 †85

POLINARD, Thomas C. 120 HOSPITAL DR 05201 #048-02-1983 L2000 **IM** *020 †20

POULIN, Denise Frances. 140 HOSPITAL DR, STE 302 05201 #050-02-1984 L1995 **OBG** *020 †30

RASKIN, Barbara Ellen. 100 HOSPITAL DR 05201 #025-07-1979 L1985 **FM** *020 †18

RAZO, Antonio O. 10 GREENVIEW DR 05201 #748-01-1964 L1972 **AN** *020 †05

REYNOLDS, Sara Jean. 339 DEWEY ST, BENNINGTON ASSOCIATES IN 05201 #035-45-1986 L1989 **IM EM** *020 †20

RICHMOND, Henry Gordon. 111 ELM ST, UROLOGY CONSULTANTS PC 05201 #024-07-1963 L1971 **U OS** *071 †95

ROBBINS, Daniel S. 332 DEWEY ST, TACONIC ORTHOPAEDICS PC 05201 #010-03-1982 L1988 **ORS** *020 †40

SABER, Walid Sherif M. 100 HOSPITAL DR, ATTN: MEDICAL STAFF OFFICE 05201 #915-04-1995 L2005 **CD** *012 †20

SALAZAR, Carol Mahon. 325 NORTH ST 05201 #035-06-1981 L2000 **IM NEP** *020 †20

SALEM, Charles Henry. 345 ELM ST 05201 #050-02-1991 L1996 **GS** *020 †85

SAUPE, Richard L. 100 HOSPITAL DR, SOUTHWESTERN VERMONT MED C 05201 #035-45-2000 L2004 **AN** *020 †05

SCATTERGOOD, Nancy Lee. 100 HOSPITAL DR 05201 #035-46-1978 L1982 **FM** *062 †18

SCHUSTER, Nancy Ann. 100 HOSPITAL DR, SOUTHWESTERN VERMONT MED C 05201 #038-45-1999 L1999 **IM** *020 †20

SEYFERTH, Eric Steven. 100 HOSPITAL DR STE 310 05201 #035-03-1983 L1989 **IM** *020 †20

SHEA, James Seward. ■ 05201 #050-02-1954 L1955 **GP IM** *071

SHEDDEN, Andrew Ian. 100 HOSPITAL DR, DEPT OF RADIOLOGY 05201 #017-20-1988 L2001 **RNR DR** *020 †80

SILBERSTEIN, Julie Ellen. 100 HOSPITAL DR, SOUTHWESTERN VT MEDICAL CE 05201 #025-12-1984 L1988 **IM** *020 †20

SISCHY, David Manfred. 100 HOSPITAL DR, STE 300 05201 #035-45-1974 L2008 **IM HEM** *020 †20

STITELMAN, Martha. 4 TEL RD 05201 #035-01-1978 L1993 **FM** *030 †18

SWANN, Ann Marie. 100 HOSPITAL DR, SVMC 05201 #010-02-1998 L2005 **MPD** *020 †20,55

TARAZI, E Michael. 100 HOSPITAL DR, ANESTH ASSOCS OF BENNINGTO 05201 #007-02-1992 L2000 **AN** *020 †05

TIHEN, William Spear. 100 HOSPITAL DR 05201 #024-01-1963 L1970 **PTH CLP** *071 †50

TOOLAN, James Michael. ■ 05201 #035-20-1947 L1960 **P CHP** *020 †75

TURTON, Arthur Frank. 140 HOSPITAL DR 05201 #038-41-1973 L1975 **U** *020 †95

VANDER ELS, Barth. 100 HOSPITAL DR 05201 #035-20-1962 L1969 **PTH** *020 †50

WALLACE, Harold James, Jr. 140 HOSPITAL DR STE 116, SVH ONCOLOGY ASSOCS 05201 #050-02-1958 L1959 **ON HEM** *071 †20

WARNER, Elizabeth Ellen. 140 HOSPITAL DR, STE 203 05201 #035-03-2000 L2007 **GS** *020 †85

WELTHER, Michael John. 100 HOSPITAL DR 05201 #056-05-1979 L1987 **FM** *020 †18

WHITTUM, James Ream. 332 DEWEY ST, TACONIC ORTHOPAEDICS PC 05201 #038-45-1989 L1996 **ORS** *020 †40

WINGATE, Angela L. 209 WASHINGTON AVE 05201 #051-04-1983 L2000 **FM** *020 †18

WINSEMAN, Jeffrey Scott. 100 HOSPITAL DR, SW VERMONT MED CTR 05201 #035-06-1992 L1996 **P** *020 †75

WITHAM, Peter Harold. 140 HOSPITAL DR, STE 302 05201 #010-01-1988 L2000 **IM** *020 †20

WOOD, Avery Schroder. 100 HOSPITAL DR 05201 #010-01-1991 L1997 **FM** *020 †18

YOUNG, Andrew John. 140 HOSPITAL DR, SWVMC CANCER CENTER 05201 #041-15-2001 L2006 **RO** *020

YUCHT, Jeff Allan. 100 HOSPITAL DR, CTR EMERGENCY ROOM 05201 #035-06-1987 L1990 **EM** *020 †16

ZIMPFER, Mark Jos. 100 HOSPITAL DR, CTR EMERGENCY ROOM 05201 #038-40-1989 L1992 **EM** *020 †16

BERLIN — WASHINGTON

ADLER, Kenneth Elliot. 130 FISHER RD, CENTRAL VERMONT HOSPITAL 05602 #035-09-1972 L1999 **P** *020 †75

ASNIS, Eric Lawrence. 195 HOSPITAL LOOP, STE 7 05602 #035-48-1986 L1994 **GE** *020 †20

ASNIS, Jamie T. 130 FISHER RD, STE 1-6 05602 #035-48-1987 L1995 **N** *020 †75

ATKINSON, Debbie Laurie. 130 FISHER RD, STE 3-1 05602 #035-15-1996 L2001 **FM** *020 †18

BEAN, Christian Howard. 130 FISHER RD, BLDG A 05602 #043-01-1989 L1995 **HS** *020 †40

BELANGER, Nicole. 195 HOSPITAL LOOP STE 3, MOUNTAINVIEW MEDICAL 05602 #035-15-2002 L2002 **IM** *020 †20

CALLAN, Felix James M. 195 HOSPITAL LOOP, STE I 05602 #008-01-1956 L1973 **ORS** *071 †40

CARIASO, Jerome Abellana. 266 FISHER RD, STE 1 05602 #748-11-1990 L2006 **PD** *020

CHANDLER, James Russell. 130 FISHER RD, UNIT 1 05602 #067-01-1970 L1973 **DR OS** *020 †80

COATES, John Boyd, III. 195 HOSPITAL LOOP STE 5 05602 #041-01-1967 L1974 **OBG** *020 †30 ‡

CRANDALL, Richard A, III. ■ 05602 #041-13-1979 L1980 **FM** *020 †18

CRANE, Mark Everett. 286 HOSPITAL LOOP 05602 #025-12-1995 L2000 **GS** *020 †85

DALE, Peter Allen. 195 HOSPITAL LOOP STE 3, MOUNTANVIEW MEDICAL 05602 #050-02-1980 L1988 **IM ID** *020 †20

EHRET, Roger Eugene, Jr. 130 FISHER RD, AND OBSTETRICS 05602 #021-01-1992 L1996 **OBG** *020 †30

GILBERT, Andre B. 130 FISHER RD 05602 #032-01-1998 L2002 **IM** *020 †05

GLAESS, Sheila Renee. 130 FISHER RD, STE 1-4 05602 #033-06-1997 L2001 **OBG** *020 †30

HART, Marilyn J. 195 HOSPITAL LOOP STE 3, MOUNTAINVIEW MEDICAL 05602 #041-12-1972 L1975 **IM** *020 †20

HAYES, Michael Gurney. 130 FISHER RD, STE 2-1 05602 #050-02-1996 L1996 **IM** *020 †20

HEITZMAN, Mark Robt. 130 FISHER RD, STE 2-1 05602 #035-15-1978 L1981 **CD IM** *020 †20

HINZMAN, Janet Y. 286 HOSPITAL LOOP, STE 2 05602 #035-19-1976 L1981 **D** *020 †15

IMOBERSTEG, Albert M. 130 FISHER RD BLDG A, STE 2-2 05602 #035-09-1981 L2006 **ORS** *020

JENSEN, Kristopher Lund. 130 FISHER RD, STE 3-1 05602 #012-05-1990 L1995 **FM** *020 †18

JOHNSON, Robert Dale. 130 FISHER RD, UNIT 1 05602 #055-01-1975 L1977 **R** *020 †80 ‡

JORDAN, William Cyrus. CTR VT HOSP MED LIBRARY 05602 #008-02-1977 L1980 **PD** *020 †18,55

KATZMAN, Richard. 286 HOSPITAL LOOP 05602 #008-01-1971 L1974 **FM** *020 †18 ‡

KELLOGG, Roger Bradford. 286 HOSPITAL LOOP STE 5 05602 #024-01-1971 L1973 **IM** *020 †20

KOENIG, Karl Marc. 130 FISHER RD, CENTRAL VERMONT MEDICAL CE 05602 #048-04-2003 L2006 **ORS** *012

KOWALSKI, Lise S. 130 FISHER RD, STE 3-1 05602 #043-01-1986 L1992 **FM** *020 †18

MAC DONALD, Gregory John. 130 FISHER RD, STE 2-1 05602 #050-02-1976 L1978 **CD** *020 †20

MADSEN, Nathaniel John. 130 FISHER RD, CENTRAL VERMONT MEDICAL CE 05602 #016-43-2005 L2005 **IM** *020 †20

MASON, Michael Howard. 286 HOSPITAL LOOP 05602 #035-15-1976 L1978 **GS** *020 †85

MERIAM, Christopher M. 130 FISHER RD, BLDG A 05602 #035-08-1990 L1990 **ORS** *020 †40

MILNE, James Royal. 266 FISHER RD STE 1 05602 #050-02-1969 L1977 **PD** *020 †55

MINKIN, Andrew Bennett. 195 HOSPITAL LOOP STE 7, GREEN MOUNTAIN GASTROENTER 05602 #051-01-1980 L2001 **GE IM** *020

OSPINA, David J. 195 HOSPITAL LOOP 05602 #715-01-1987 L1995 **HO GE** *020

PAPPAS, Charles Nicholas. 130 FISHER RD, UNIT 1 05602 #051-04-1988 L1989 **DR** *020 †80

PEKALA, Joseph Stanley. 130 FISHER RD, DEPARTMENT OF RADIOLOGY 05602 #032-01-1999 L2006 **RNR** *100 †80

ROSE, James Gary. 130 FISHER RD STE 3-1 05602 #050-02-1983 L2002 **OTO** *020 †45

SARVER, Russell Gary. 130 FISHER RD, AND OBSTETRICS 05602 #033-06-1990 L2004 **U** *071 †95

SEGEL, William Dana. 11 WILLARD BEAN RD 05602 #024-01-1967 L1976 **GS** *020 †85

SHEA, Harriott Meyer. 266 FISHER RD STE 1, ASSOCIATES IN PEDIATRICS 05602 #050-02-1984 L1997 **PD PSM** *020 †55

STAFFORD, Dale Donald. 130 FISHER RD, STE 3-1 05602 #050-02-1981 L1983 **FM** *020 †18

STOLL, Andrew Martin. 1021 PAINE TPKE N, POB 1277 05602 #035-15-1986 L1993 **P** *020

VALENTINE, John Wm. 195 HOSPITAL LOOP STE 3 05602 #035-45-1975 L1980 **ON IM** *075 †20

WILLIAMS, Anthony V. 266 FISHER RD, STE 2 05602 #051-01-1985 L1988 **IM** *020 †20

WILLIAMS, Stuart English. 130 FISHER RD, STE 3-1 05602 #035-46-1975 L1979 **FM** *020 †18

WOODRUFF, Stephen John. 130 FISHER RD, AND OBSTETRICS 05602 #050-02-1973 L1977 **OBG** *020 †30

YANOWITCH, Gail Susan. 130 FISHER RD STE 1-4 05602 #016-02-1980 L1990 **OBG** *020 †30

ZIEDINS, Eduards Gunars. 130 FISHER RD, STE 3-1 05602 #023-01-1997 L1997 **GS** *020 †85

BOMOSEEN — RUTLAND

BERRYHILL, Bradley Alan. 275 ROUTE 30 N, CASTLETON FAMILY HEALTH 05732 #035-15-1986 L2001 **FM** *020 †18

CONGDON, David Ralph. 275 ROUTE 30 N, CASTLETON FAMILY HLTH CTR 05732 #050-02-1964 L1964 **GP A** *075

CROSS, Robert Marshall. 275 ROUTE 30 N 05732 #050-02-1964 L1965 **IM FM** *020 †18

DIERCKSEN, Hans Peter. 275 ROUTE 30 N, CASTLETON FAMILY HEALTH 05732 #035-15-1979 L1982 **FM** *020 †18

FOSTER, Julie Anne. 275 ROUTE 30 N, CASTLETON FAMILY HEALTH 05732 #054-04-1999 L2005 **FM** *020 †18

KORNBLUTH, Stephen Simon. 275 ROUTE 30 N, C H C R R 05732 #035-03-1980 L2007 **FM** *020 †18

ROSMUS, Stephan Marion, Jr. 275 ROUTE 30 N, CASTLETON FAMILY HEALTH 05732 #050-02-1975 L1978 **FM** *020 †18

BONDVILLE — BENNINGTON

CASTELBAUM, Martin. ■ 05340 #036-05-1958 L1958 **IM** *020

CATHERMAN, Robert Lewis. ■ 05340 #041-13-1958 L1959 **FOP** *072 †50

BRADFORD — ORANGE

CLARK, Thomas Sutherland. 331 UPPER PLN, UPPER VALLEY PEDIATRICS 05033 #032-01-2001 L2005 **PD** *020

CONNOLLY, Kevin J. PO BOX 318 05033 #043-01-1983 L1995 **ID IM** *020 †20

HARRIS, Mark Steven. 331 UPPER PLN 05033 #010-02-1974 L1977 **PD** *020

KROUT, Robert Melvin. RR 1 BOX 169A 05033 #041-01-1948 L1949 **FM** *020 †60

OSADCHEY, Lance Morris. ■ 05033 #035-15-1963 L1979 **FM** *020 †18

ROGERS, Steven John, Jr. ■ 05033 #050-02-2000 L2005 **OPH** *020 †35

BRANDON — RUTLAND

BARRETT, William Donald. 61 COURT DR 05733 #050-02-1973 L1976 **FM** *020 †18

BROSTEK, Ronald Wm. ■ 05733 #035-09-1957 L1958 **ADL GPM** *071

BURBANK, John. ■ 05733 #024-01-1943 L1944 **R** *071 †80

JORDAN, James Lewis. ■ 05733 #035-01-1978 L1979 **FM** *020

WEINSTEIN, Stephen Wm. ■ 05733 #050-02-1959 L1961 **NEP** *050

WULFMAN, Carrie C. 61 COURT DR, NESHOBE FAM MED 05733 #017-20-1991 L1998 **FM** *020 †18

WULFMAN, Jeffrey Scott. 61 COURT DR 05733 #017-20-1991 L1998 **FM OTO** *020 †18

BRATTLEBORO — WINDHAM

ABNEY, Ray Chandler. 38 PARK PL 05301 #047-05-1973 L1974 **P** *020 †75

AGALLIANOS, Dennis D. 75 LINDEN ST 05301 #781-03-1948 L1969 **P** *020 †75 ‡

AHN, Suzanne. 21 BELMONT AVE 05301 #016-11-1998 L2003 **PD** *020 †55

ALBRIGHT, David John. 21 BELMONT AVE, BRATTLEBORO PRIMARY CARE 05301 #041-09-1969 L1974 **IM ID** *020 †20

ALLDEN, Kathleen Marie. 51 FAIRVIEW ST 05301 #038-41-1980 L1984 **P** *020 †75
BALLANTINE, Percy, Jr. PO BOX 803, THE BRATTLEBORO RETREAT 05302 #038-41-1973 L1976 **P** *020 †75
BLOFSON, Tony. 120 MAPLE ST 05301 #035-48-1990 L2000 **FM** *020 †18
BOOKWALTER, John Robt. 19 BELMONT AVE 05301 #024-01-1964 L1971 **AS CD** *020 †85,90
BREDER, Hilke Thiessen. 21 BELMONT AVE 05301 #018-03-1976 L1981 **IM EM** *020 †20
BRESNAHAN, Harry Dean. 53 FAIRVIEW ST 05301 #016-06-1968 L1972 **FM** *020 †18 ‡
BRODHURST, Cheri A. 387 CANAL ST 05301 #035-08-1975 L1979 **OBG** *020 †30
BUNKER, James Ellsworth. 28 BELMONT AVE, BRATTLEBORO OBSTETRICS & G 05301 #021-01-1990 L1999 **OBG** *020 †30
CARRASQUILLO, Ivan. 387 CANAL ST 05301 #042-01-1961 L1969 **GYN** *071 †30
CHARD, John Turner. 9 BELMONT AVE 05301 #035-20-1958 L1966 **ORS OS** *020 †40
CLARKE, R Keith. 24 NEW ENGLAND DR 05301 #050-02-1955 L1956 **FM** *071 †18
CROWLEY, Frederick Wade. 17 BELMONT AVE, DEPT OF RADIOLOGY 05301 #050-02-1968 L1968 **R NM** *072 †80 ‡
DALY, John Stockton F. 191 CLARK AVE, # 1 05301 #024-05-1970 L1990 **U GS** *020 †95
DALY, Patricia. 51 FAIRVIEW ST 05301 #041-15-2001 L2003 **CHP** *020 †75
DAMASCO, Remeline Corpuz. 21 BELMONT AVE 05301 #005-19-1996 L2003 **IM** *020 †20
DIXON, John Paul. 17 BELMONT AVE STE 2 05301 #024-01-1962 L1968 **GS TS** *020 †85
DONALDSON, Deirdre Hunter. 19 BELMONT AVE, STE 104 05301 #047-05-1986 L1998 **N** *050 †75
DU MONT, Kingsley A. 17 BELMONT AVE 05301 #950-01-1964 L1966 **GP OBG** *020
ELLIOTT, Edward F, Jr. 17 BELMONT AVE, RADIOLOGY DEPARTMENT 05301 #017-20-1979 L1991 **DR** *020 †80 ‡
ENGSTROM, Frederick Wm. PO BOX 803, 75 LINDEN ST 05302 #035-45-1974 L1998 **P** *020 †75
EVANS, Thomas Otto. 21 BELMONT AVE, STE 2 05301 #010-02-1982 L1989 **FM** *020 †18
FAGELSON, David Lavine. 15 FAIRVIEW ST 05301 #016-43-1957 L1975 **OS OTO** *075 †45
FAGELSON, Robert Stephen. 1 FAIRVIEW ST 05301 #016-43-1960 L1975 **OTO** *020 †45
FARRAR, Tasha Michele. ■ 05301 #030-05-2002 L2006 **P** *020 †75
FIELD, Jane Katz. 16 BELMONT AVE 05301 #033-05-1976 L2003 **PD OM** *020 †55
FISHELMAN, Lesley Nan F. 922 PUTNEY RD, UNIT 106 05301 #008-01-1969 L2000 **P** *020 †75
GADOWSKI, Amy Shedd. 19 BELMONT AVE, STE 201 05301 #050-02-1995 L1998 **IM** *020 †20
GADOWSKI, Gregory Raymond. 9 BELMONT AVE STE 201 05301 #016-02-1989 L1989 **GS** *020 †85
GIBBONS, Peter Douglas. 17 BELMONT AVE 05301 #008-01-1966 L1971 **DR** *020 †80
GLICK, John Lawrence. 19 BELMONT AVE 05301 #038-06-1964 L1970 **END IM** *020
HAYDOCK, Anne Heywood. 21 BELMONT AVE 05301 #050-02-1978 L1981 **PD** *020 †55
HERZOG, Lynn. 21 BELMONT AVE 05301 #038-06-1970 L1973 **PD** *020 †55
JONES, Rebecca Marie. 138 ELLIOT ST, STE ONE 05301 #024-16-1992 L2000 **D** *020 †15
KINLEY, Donald Leslie. 71 GSP DR, EXIT 1 PARK 05301 #067-01-1964 L1972 **ORS** *020 †40
KNORR, William Alan. 75 LINDEN ST 05301 #041-13-1974 L1984 **CHP P** *020 †55,75
LANDIS, Loren Anthony. 167 MAIN ST, STE 207B 05301 #038-40-1977 L1980 **P ADP** *020
LANGWEILER, Clifford B. 17 BELMONT AVE 05301 #051-01-1980 L1989 **FM** *020 †18
LEE, Amalia Frieder. 167 MAIN ST, STE 202 05301 #035-47-1979 L2000 **P** *020 †75
LEE, Barbara Kingsberry. PO BOX 1734 05302 #041-13-1985 L1992 **PS** *020
LEWIS, Thomas Walter. 19 BELMONT AVE, STE 105 05301 #016-06-1968 L1971 **IM GP** *020 †20
MARX, Otto M. 14 PARK PL 05301 #005-02-1957 L1985 **P OS** *020
MC BEAN, Judith Howard. 28 BELMONT AVE, BRATTLEBORO OBSTETRICS/GYN 05301 #050-02-1987 L1987 **OBG REN** *020 †30
MC GINN, Dana Francis. 238 WESTERN AVE 05301 #050-02-1980 L1984 **OPH** *020 †35
MCLARNEY, Elizabeth Ann. 17 BELMONT AVE STE 2 05301 #035-03-1992 L2000 **ORS FSM** *020 †40
METSCH, Laura Sharon. 21 BELMONT AVE 05301 #035-19-1991 L1994 **IM** *020 †20
MEYER, Christopher L. 21 BELMONT AVE, BRATTLEBORO PRIMARY CARE 05301 #024-01-1995 L2000 **IM** *020 †20
NASSAU, Robert David. 13 BELMONT AVE 05301 #041-12-1966 L1971 **PD** *020 †55
NEWTON, Clyde Alfred. 19 BELMONT AVE STE 101 05301 #025-01-1962 L1970 **OPH** *020 †35
NEWTON, Margaret. ■ 05303 #050-02-1954 L1994 **IMG FM** *071 †20
PAASCHE, Denise Ellen. 120 MAPLE ST 05301 #050-02-1991 L2000 **FM** *020 †18
POFCHER, Eric Rudolph. 21 BELMONT AVE, STE 3 05301 #050-02-1985 L2001 **IM** *020 †20
POTASH, Jeffry Brian. 63 BELMONT AVE, STE 2 05301 #41-02-1982 L1996 **GE** *020 †20
RESNIK, Michael David. 17 BELMONT AVE, DEPT OF RADIOLOGY 05301 #028-34-1981 L2005 **DR PD** *020 †55,80
RIGHI, Paul Danl. 21 BELMONT AVE, GANNETT MEDICAL BUILDING 05301 #024-01-1986 L1988 **OTO GS** *020 †45
RINDER, Craig Alan. ■ 05301 #067-01-1988 L1993 **U** *020 †95
ROSEN, Joseph Elliot. 21 BELMONT AVE, GANNETT MED BLVD 05301 #048-04-1982 L1994 **GS SO** *020 †85
ROWLAND, Timothy N. 75 LINDEN ST 05301 #050-02-1974 L1975 **P PYG** *020 †75
SALAM, Saba Maheen. 20 TECHNOLOGY DR UNIT 9, SALAM PSYCHIATRIC SERVICE, 05301 #704-21-1995 L2001 **P** *020 †75
SCHMIDT, Christopher J. 541 CANAL ST, RESCUE INC 05301 #024-16-1979 L1982 **FM EM** *020 †18
SCZESNY-ALESHNICK, Martina. 63 BELMONT AVE 05301 #409-38-1990 L1997 **FM** *020 †18
SENIOR, Neil Frederick. 80 LINDEN ST 05301 #143-05-1970 L1978 **OS CHP** *030 †75
SOMMER, Felix. 75 LINDEN ST 05301 #154-01-1954 L1965 **P** *071 †75
TAYLOR-OLSON, Carolyn L. 19 BELMONT AVE, STE 204 05301 #005-06-1979 L1989 **IM** *020
TEPFER, Burton David. 19 BELMONT AVE, STE 106 05301 #024-05-1969 L1983 **CD** *020 †20
THATCHER, Jonathan Chas. 17 BELMONT AVE 05301 #024-05-1982 L1993 **ORS** *020 †40
TORTOLANI, Anthony J. 63 BELMONT AVE 05301 #035-45-1967 L1971 **FM FPG** *020 †18
TRUMPER, John Yewdall. 75 LINDEN ST 05301 #041-01-1958 L1964 **PD** *071 †55
VALDES MURUA, Honorio. 17 BELMONT AVE, DEPARTMENT OF ANESTHESIA 05301 #649-28-1982 L2005 **AN CD** *020 †20
VRANOS, William. 17 BELMONT AVE, STE 2 05301 #012-05-1988 L2005 **ORS** *020 †40
YANDOW, Valery Worth. 9 BELMONT AVE 05301 #050-02-1956 L1983 **P** *071 †75

BRIDGEWATER – WINDSOR

GOFFINET, Sara Beatty. ■ 05034 #023-07-1960 L1965 **AN** *071 †05

BRISTOL – ADDISON

BOUCHARD, Marion. 30 MOUNTAIN ST, MOUNTAIN HEALTH CTR 05443 #067-01-1990 L1992 **FM** *020 †18

BROWN, Dewees Harold. ■ 05443 #050-02-1954 L1955 **FM IM** *071 †18
CARSEN, Marjorie A L. 172 HEWITT RD 05443 #035-08-1969 L1998 **P** *020 †75
CLARK, Charles E, Jr. 30 MOUNTAIN ST 05443 #050-02-1982 L1983 **FM** *020 †18
HENDERSON, David F. 6 SOUTH ST 05443 #041-02-1969 L1975 **GP** *020
JAQUITH, Alison Elizabeth. ■ 05443 #050-02-2006 L2006 **IM** *012
KRAKOFF, Irwin Harold. ■ 05443 #038-40-1947 L1976 **ON** *071 †20

BROOKFIELD – ORANGE

DONNER, Marda Elisa. ■ 05036 #041-01-1980 L2007 **PUD IM** *020 †20
POFFENBERGER, John R. RIDGE ROAD 05036 #035-01-1945 L1975 **R IM** *071

BROOKLINE – WINDHAM

BALLOU, Laurence H. ■ 05345 #050-02-1951 L1953 **OM** *071

BURLINGTON – CHITTENDEN

ABAJIAN, John Christian. MED CTR HOSP OF VERMONT, DEPT OF ANESTHESIA 05401 #050-02-1969 L1969 **AN PAN** *020
ABNET, Kevin R. 111 COLCHESTER AVE 05401 #024-01-1992 L2001 **AN** *020 †85,05
ABRAMSON, Leslie Sue. 111 COLCHESTER AVE, CHILDRENS SPECIALTY CENTER 05401 #041-01-1977 L1982 **PD RHU** *020 †55
ADAMS, David C. 111 COLCHESTER AVE, FAHC DEPT OF ANESTHESIOLOG 05401 #025-12-1988 L2000 **AN** *020 †05
ADAMS, Julie Ellen. 111 COLCHESTER AVE, VASCULAR SURGERY 05401 #038-45-1997 L1997 **VS** *100 †85
ADAMS, Shirley Lorraine. 111 COLCHESTER AVE, FAHCDEPT OF SURGERY 05401 #025-12-1998 L1998 **P** *100
ADES, Philip A. MEDICAL CENTER HOSP VT, MC CLURE 1 CARDIOLOGY 05401 #023-01-1978 L1983 **CD IM** *020 †20
ADES, Steven. 89 BEAUMONT AVE, GIVEN BLDG, E-214 05405 #067-01-1996 L2007 **HO** *100 †20
ADKISON, Talissa Beth. 111 COLCHESTER AVE WP22, INTERNAL MEDICINE 05401 #539-06-2007 L2007 **IM** *012
AJAR, Amir Hossayne. 111 COLCHESTER AVE, FAHC DEPT OF SURGERY 05401 #050-02-2004 L2005 **OTO** *012
ALADJEM, Eva Veda. 111 COLCHESTER AVE 05401 #050-02-1990 L1992 **AN** *020 †05
ALBARO, Cecilia Anne. ■ 05401 #049-01-2005 L2006 *100
ALBERTINI, Richard Jos. 32 N PROSPECT ST, GENETICS LABORATORY 05401 #056-05-1963 L1972 **OS IG** *050
ALFINITO, Rosiane S. ■ 05405 #050-02-2007 *012
ALIZADEH, Kayvon. 111 COLCHESTER AVE, FAHCDEPT OF SURGERY 05401 #007-02-2002 L2002 **GS** *012
ALLEN, Gilman Baker, III. 111 COLCHESTER AVE, PATR 311 MCHV CAMPUS 05401 #011-03-1995 L1999 **PCC** *020 †20
ALOSI, Julie Ann. 111 COLCHESTER AVE, FAHCDEPT OF SURGERY 05401 #050-02-2005 L2005 **GS** *012
ALPERT, Jamie Allison. 1 S PROSPECT ST, UNIVERSITY HEALTH CENTER 05401 #050-02-1990 L1994 **D** *020 †15
ALPERT, Jeffrey Blake. GIVEN BOX 15, UVM COLLEGE OF MEDICINE 05405 #050-02-2004 L2007 **DR** *012
ALSOFROM, Gary Floyd. 111 COLCHESTER AVE 05401 #035-08-1979 L1982 **DR RNR** *020 †80
ALSTON, Wallace Kemper. MED CTR HOSP OF VT, INFECTIOUS DISEASES UNIT 05401 #035-09-1987 L1993 **ID IM** *020 †20
ALTHOFF, Robert Russell. 1 S PROSPECT ST, PSYCHIATRY DEPT 05401 #016-11-1999 L2001 **CHP** *100 †75
AMBAYE, Abiy Berhie. 111 COLCHESTER AVE, FAHC 05401 #286-13-1991 L2003 **PTH PCP** *020 †50
AMSTERLAW, Carole-Anne L. 1 S PROSPECT ST # PATH 05401 #035-46-1973 **PTH** *050
ANAFI, Ron Chaim. 111 COLCHESTER AVE 05401 #026-04-2004 L2004 **IM** *020 †20
ANDERSON, Paul Sidney. ENDV OF VT MED COLL, GIVEN BLDG BOX #4 05405 #050-02-2003 L2007 **AN** *100
ANDERSON, Scott Robert. 111 COLCHESTER AVE, SMITH 2 05401 #005-12-1997 L2003 **PCP** *100 †50
ANDERSSON, Jean Kimball. 111 COLCHESTER AVE, FAMILY PRACTICE 05401 #050-02-2005 L2005 **FP** *012
APPLEBEE, Angela Marie. 111 COLCHESTER AVE, FLETCHER ALLEN HEALTH CARE 05401 #046-01-2002 L2002 **N** *100 †75
APPLEBEE, Garrick Alton. 111 COLCHESTER AVE, MOD B - RM 113 05401 #035-06-2002 L2002 **PD** *100 †55
APPLETON, John Stephen, Jr. 111 COLCHESTER AVE WP2, FAHC DEPT OF SURGERY 05401 #048-13-2006 L2006 **ORS** *012
ARDAO, Alberto D. 111 COLCHESTER AVE 05401 #924-01-1980 L2002 **PM** *020 †60
ARDELL, Stephanie Kendra. ■ 05401 #050-02-2005 L2005 **PD** *012
ARONSON, David Douglas. STAFFORD HALL ROOM 434B 05405 #025-01-1973 L1990 **ORS** *020 †40
ASSAAD, Peter Sherif. ■ 05405 #050-02-2007 *012
ATTARIAN, Hrayr Pierre. 111 COLCHESTER AVE 05401 #605-01-1992 L2003 **N SME** *020 †75
AUSTIN, James Francis. ■ 05408 #050-02-1967 L1967 **IM** *020
AVENI, Maria Christine. 68 MARBLE AVE, P O BOX 441 05401 #050-02-1991 L1992 **AN** *020 †05
BABBOTT, David. ■ 05401 #041-01-1955 L1967 **IM** *071 †20
BAMBACE, Nadia. 111 COLCHESTER AVE, INTERNAL MEDICINE 05401 #067-02-2005 L2005 **IM** *012
BARLOW, Raiel Dawn. ■ 05408 #050-02-2007 L2007 **IM** *012
BARMAN, Subhadeep. 111 COLCHESTER AVE, DEPT OF PSYCHIATRY 05401 #495-02-2002 L2007 **P** *012
BARSS, Mary Brooke. 222 LOOMIS ST 05401 #025-07-1985 L1987 **P** *020 †75
BATES, Adam Clinton. 111 COLCHESTER AVE, FLETCHER ALLEN HEALTH CARE 05401 #050-02-2004 L2007 **IM** *100 †20
BATOR, Marta Zofia. 111 COLCHESTER AVE, FAHC DEPT OF ANESTHESIA 05401 #050-02-2005 L2007 **AN** *100
BEATON, Elizabeth Marie. ■ 05405 #050-02-2007 **OBG** *012

BEATTIE, James Ray. 1 S PROSPECT ST, NEUROLOGY HEALTH CARE 05401 #018-03-1989 L1995 **N** *020 †75

BELL, Roy Watson. ANESTHESIA DEPT, MED CTR HOSP OF VT INC 05401 #803-03-1956 L1968 **AN** *071 †05

BELLOMO, Stephanie Cowan. 789 PINE ST 05401 #050-02-1985 L1985 **FM** *020 †18

BENOIT, Michel Y. 1 S PROSPECT ST 05401 #067-02-1985 L1992 **ORS HS** *020 †40

BENVENUTO, Anna Leigh. ■ 05405 #050-02-2008 *012

BERGER, Claudia Alberta. 1 S PROSPECT ST 05401 #035-46-1991 L1991 **IM** *020 †20

BERGNER, Renee K. 111 COLCHESTER AVE 05401 #024-07-1959 L1965 **A PD** *020 †55,03

BERNER, Keith Martin. 111 COLCHESTER AVE WP2, FAHC DEPT OF PSYCHIATRY 05401 #004-01-2006 L2006 **P** *012

BERNSTEIN, Ira Mark. 111 COLCHESTER AVE, FAHC DEPT OBG 05401 #050-02-1983 L1987 **MFM OBG** *020 †30

BERNSTEIN, Richard Alan. 111 COLCHESTER AVE, PATRICK 4 05401 #024-05-1970 L1973 **P** *020 †75

BERRY, Zail Suzanne. 111 COLCHESTER AVE 05401 #005-02-1986 L1996 **IM IMG** *020 †20

BERTGES, Daniel Joseph. 111 COLCHESTER AVE, UHC 4 VASCULAR SURG 05401 #041-12-1994 L2003 **VS** *020 †85

BETTS, Douglas Hilchie. ■ 05401 #064-01-1961 L1977 **P CHP** *020

BEVAN, John A. 1 S PROSPECT ST, DEPT PHARM 05401 #352-07-1953 **OS** *050

BHADRA, Krishnendu. 111 COLCHESTER AVE, INTERNAL MEDICINE 05401 #011-02-2004 L2004 **PCC** *012 †20

BHAVE, Anant Dattatraya. 111 COLCHESTER AVE, FHAC, DEPT OF RADIOLOGY 05401 #016-11-1995 L2001 **DR** *020 †80

BIELINSKI, Raphael Stanis. 111 COLCHESTER AVE, FLETCHER ALLEN HLTH CARE 05401 #759-01-2005 L2005 **FP** *012

BIENIEK, Eva Barbara. 111 COLCHESTER AVE, FAHC 05401 #050-02-2004 L2004 **RO** *012

BIHLMEYER, Sharon Kay. 111 COLCHESTER AVE, FAHC 05401 #025-12-2002 L2004 **PTH** *012

BINGHAM, Peter Matthias. 89 S WILLIAMS ST 05401 #035-01-1987 L2000 **N PD** *020 †75

BINTER, Nancy Ellen. 94 COLCHESTER AVE 05401 #033-06-1981 L1982 **NS** *020 †25

BISSELL, Benjamin Todd. 111 COLCHESTER AVE, FAHCDEPT OF ORTHOPAEDICS 05401 #030-05-2004 L2004 **ORS** *012

BISSON, John Alfred. 64 COLCHESTER AVE 05401 #050-02-1973 L1975 **U** *020 †95

BLAKE, Kimberly Diane. ■ 05401 #035-06-1990 L1990 **OBG** *020 †30

BLEVINS, Lynn Zanardi. 108 CHERRY ST BX 70, VERMONT HEALTH DEPT 05401 #051-04-1995 L2006 **GPM** *072 †70

BODOR, Cristina Ioana. 111 COLCHESTER AVE, DEPT OF PSYCHIATRY 05401 #781-01-1991 L1995 **P** *100 †75

BOLDUC, Allyson Miller. 1 COLCHESTER AVE, HCFAMILY PRACTI 05401 #050-02-1995 L1995 **FM** *020 †18

BOLTON, Margaret Ann. 300 FLYNN AVE 05401 #050-02-1990 L1990 **PFP** *020 †75

BONNEY, Elizabeth Ann. 111 COLCHESTER AVE 05401 #005-11-1987 L2002 **OBG** *020 †30

BORRAZZO, Edward C. 111 COLCHESTER AVE, FLETCHER 462 05401 #035-48-1994 L2001 **GS** *020 †85

BOUCHARD, Richard E. 1 S PROSPECT ST 05401 #050-02-1949 L1950 **IM CD** *071 †20

BOVILL, Edwin Gladstone. E203 GIVEN BLDG, UNIV OF VT COLLEGE OF MED 05405 #005-02-1974 L1979 **HMP** *050 †50

BOYD, James Thomas. 1 S PROSPECT ST, UHC CAMPUS 4TH FLOOR 05401 #063-01-2000 L2000 **N** *100 †75

BOYMAN, Kym Margaret. 23 MANSFIELD AVE 05401 #050-02-1999 L1999 **GYN** *020 †30

BRAFF, Samuel Benjamin. ■ 05405 #050-02-2007 L2007 **GS** *012

BRAFF, Steven Paul. 111 COLCHESTER AVE, RADIOLOGY 05401 #025-07-1976 L1992 **DR** *020 †80 ‡

BRANDA, Richard Frank. 1 S PROSPECT ST, FLETCHER ALLEN HEALTH CARE 05401 #024-01-1966 L1983 **HEM IM** *050 †20

BRANDES, Melissa Kaye. 1205 NORTH AVE 05408 #035-15-1997 L1997 **IM** *020 †20

BRECKENRIDGE, Matthew L. 111 COLCHESTER AVE, INTERNAL MEDICINE 05401 #050-02-2005 L2005 **AN** *012

BRODY, Charlotte Sue. ■ 05401 #016-01-1980 L1982 **OBG** *100 †30

BROOKLYN, John Ross. 111 COLCHESTER AVE 05401 #043-01-1989 L1989 **FM OS** *050 †18

BROWN, Kenneth Andrew. 1 S PROSPECT ST, DEPT CD 05401 #035-20-1977 L1984 **CD IM** *020 †20

BROWN, Murray Carol. ■ 05401 #063-01-1994 L1998 **FM** *020

BRUMSTED, John Robt. 111 COLCHESTER AVE, DEPT OBG 05401 #032-01-1978 L1984 **OBG** *020 †30

BRUNDAGE, William J. 111 COLCHESTER AVE, WEST PAVILION LEVEL 4 05401 #041-02-1987 L1987 **OTO** *020 †45

BRYAN, Locke Johnson. ■ 05406 #027-01-2008 *012

BRYANT, Ronald John. ■ 05405 #025-01-1979 L1982 **PCP** *020 †50

BUDD, Ralph Chas. 1 S PROSPECT ST # D301 05401 #035-20-1977 L1978 **IG RHU** *050 †20

BURBANK, Heather Nicole. 111 COLCHESTER AVE, DEPARTMENT OF RADIOLOGY 05401 #050-02-2001 L2002 **DR** *100 †80

BURDETTE-RADOUX, Susan. 111 COLCHESTER AVE, HEMATOLOGY/ONCOLOGY 05401 #008-01-1981 L2002 **HEM ON** *050 †20

BURFOOT, Michael Francis. 80 COLCHESTER AVE BOX 2262 05401 #352-09-1958 L1970 **AN** *071

BURGETT, Melissa Marie. 111 COLCHESTER AVE 05401 #038-41-2005 L2005 **PD** *012

BURKE, Leah Weyerts. 112 COLCHESTER AVE 05401 #036-01-1987 L2000 **PD CG** *020 †55,19

BURNS, Stanley Livingston. 1 S PROSPECT ST 05401 #050-02-1955 L1960 **HEM** *071 †20

BUSHNELL, Andrew Charles. 111 COLCHESTER AVE, FLETCHER ALLEN HLTH CARE 05401 #023-01-1994 L2002 **EM** *020 †16

BUTNOR, Kelly Jo. 111 COLCHESTER AVE, MCHV CAMPUS SMITH 246 B 05401 #036-07-1997 L2002 **PTH** *020

CACCAVO, Francis A. ■ 05401 #050-02-1943 L1945 **OM GS** *071 †85

CANAKIS, Anne-Marie. 111 COLCHESTER AVE 05401 #067-01-1995 L2004 **PDP** *020

CAPELESS, Eleanor Jean. 1 S PROSPECT ST 05401 #010-02-1976 L1980 **OBS GYN** *020 †30

CAPELESS, Mark A. 1 S PROSPECT ST, UNIVERSITY PEDIATRICS 05401 #010-02-1976 L1982 **CD IM** *050 †20

CAPOLICCHIO, John Paul. 111 COLCHESTER AVE, # ACC 05401 #067-01-1992 *020 †95

CARNEY, Jan Kirk. 371 PEARL ST 05401 #038-41-1981 L1984 **PHP IM** *062 †20,70

CARRACINO, Maria Giovanna. ■ 05405 #050-02-2007 L2007 **OBG** *012

CASEY, Alicia Hoag. ■ 05401 #050-02-2005 L2005 **PD** *012

CASEY, Angela Sanfilippo. 111 COLCHESTER AVE, FLETCHER ALLEN HLTH CARE 05401 #020-02-2003 L2007 **PRD** *012 †15

CASEY, Colleen Louise. 89 BEAUMONT AVE, GIVEN BUILDING 05405 #026-04-2001 L2005 **OBG** *100 †30

CASSON, Peter R. 1 S PROSPECT ST, FLETCHER ALLEN HEALTH CARE 05401 #065-05-1984 L2000 **OBG** *020 †30

CATALDO, Peter Anthony. 111 COLCHESTER AVE, # ACC 05401 #024-07-1985 L1995 **GS CRS** *020 †85,10

CAULEY, Keith Alan. 111 COLCHESTER AVE, FLETCHER ALLEN HEALTHCARE- 05401 #050-02-2002 L2007 **RNR** *012

CAYER, Makara Elissa. ■ 05401 #024-05-2006 L2007 **AN** *012

CHAPIN, John Carruth. ■ 05405 #050-02-2007 **PD** *012

CHAPMAN, Dean Walter. 111 COLCHESTER AVE, INTERNAL MEDICINE 05401 #011-03-2007 L2007 **IM** *012

CHARASH, William Edward. 111 COLCHESTER AVE, MCHV CAMPUS - FLETCHER 466 05401 #035-20-1984 L2003 **CCS** *020 †85

CHASE, Christopher Russel. 111 COLCHESTER AVE # ANES, MED CTR HOSP OF VT 05401 #050-02-1974 L1979 **AN** *020 †55

CHASE, David Stuart. 183 SAINT PAUL ST, MANSFIELD PROFESSIONAL BLD 05401 #050-02-1962 L1968 **OPH** *071 †35

CHEROUNY, Peter Herbert. 111 COLCHESTER AVE, FAHC SHEPARDSON 331 05401 #422-01-1981 L1992 **MFM OBG** *020 †30

CHHABRIA, Nisha Prakash. 111 COLCHESTER AVE, MCHV MAIL RM-NEUROLOGY 05401 #654-01-2005 L2007 **N** *012

CHKHENKELI, Irina Sozarie. 111 COLCHESTER AVE, FAHC 05401 #913-23-1994 L2004 **N** *100

CHODOSH, Adam Brett. 111 COLCHESTER AVE, INTERNAL MEDICINE 05401 #035-46-2002 L2002 **CD** *012 †20

CHOMA, Joseph David. 111 COLCHESTER AVE, INTERNAL MEDICINE 05401 #050-02-2002 L2005 **GE** *012 †20

CHRISTENSON, Catherine M. 111 COLCHESTER AVE, MCHV CAMPUS, ANESTHESIA 05401 #051-07-1982 L1996 **AN FM** *040 †18,05

CHRISTIAN, Timothy Fowler. 111 COLCHESTER AVE, BAIRD 191, FAHC 05401 #035-03-1982 L2005 **CD IM** *020 †20

CHUNG, Arnold Daniel. 111 COLCHESTER AVE, FAHCDEPT OF SURGERY 05401 #024-05-2002 L2002 **GS** *012

CHURCH, Karalyn Lee. ■ 05401 #050-02-2006 *012

CIAMPA, Armando. 111 COLCHESTER AVE, FAHC DEPT OF PATHOLOGY 05401 #561-26-1995 L2004 **PTH** *100

CIOLINO, Allison Leigh. 111 COLCHESTER AVE, FAHC DEPT OF PATHOLOGY 05401 #050-02-2004 L2005 **PTH** *012

CLARK, Kelley Dawne. 111 COLCHESTER AVE, SMITH 4 05401 #020-12-1990 L2002 **OBG** *020 †30

CLAUSS, David Ward. 111 COLCHESTER AVE, DEPT EM 05401 #012-05-1987 L1987 **EM IM** *020 †20

CLEWLEY, Elizabeth C. 111 COLCHESTER AVE 05401 #050-02-1956 L1957 **PD** *071 †55

CLIFFORD, Patrick Paul. 111 COLCHESTER AVE 05401 #050-02-1984 L1984 **OBG** *020 †30

CLOUGH, Jaina P. 111 COLCHESTER AVE, INTERNAL MEDICINE 05401 #050-02-2005 L2005 **IM** *012

COATES, Matthew D. ■ 05401 #050-02-2007 L2007 **IM** *012

COHEN, Julius Geo. 86 LAKE ST 05401 #050-02-1945 L1947 **P** *071 †75

COLE, Lisa Lynne. 111 COLCHESTER AVE WP2, FAHC DEPT OF PATHOLOGY 05401 #050-02-2005 L2005 **PTH** *012

COLLEN, Allison Beth. ■ 05405 #050-02-2008 *012

COLLETTI, Richard Bernard. 89 BEAUMONT AVE, UNIVERSITY OF VERMONT 05405 #041-12-1968 L1974 **GE NTR** *020 †55

COLLINS, Keith Grady. 111 COLCHESTER AVE 05401 #045-01-1990 L1990 **ID** *020 †20

COLLINS, Linda A. 425 PEARL ST, STUDENT HEALTH CENTER 05401 #050-02-1986 L1993 **ID** *020 †20

COMMICHAU, Christopher S. 111 COLCHESTER AVE, FLETCHER ALLEN HEALTH CARE 05401 #010-02-1993 L2004 **N** *020 †75

CONGDON, Robert Ganje. ■ 05401 #050-02-2005 L2005 **DR** *012

CONNOLLY, Gregory John. ■ 05405 #050-02-2007 L2007 **PD** *012

CONROY, Leslie Mc Coy. 86 LAKE ST 05401 #038-40-1985 L1992 **CHP P** *020 †75

CONTOMPASIS, Stephen H. PEDIATRICS GIVEN A121, FLETCHER ALLEN HEALTH CARE 05405 #024-07-1985 L1991 **PD** *020 †55

COOK, Deborah Lynn. 111 COLCHESTER AVE, FLETCHER ALLEN HEALTH CARE 05401 #050-02-1990 L1990 **DMP** *020 †50

COOPER, Sheldon Mark. 111 COLCHESTER AVE, RHEUMATOLOGY/FAHC 05401 #035-19-1967 L1982 **RHU IG** *020 †20

COSTEDIO, Meagan Marie. 111 COLCHESTER AVE, FAHC 05401 #050-02-2003 L2003 **GS** *012

COSTELLO, Leah Mclane. ■ 05405 #050-02-2007 **PD** *012

CRAINICH, Paul. 111 COLCHESTER AVE, INTERNAL MEDICINE 05401 #050-02-2005 L2005 **IM** *012

CRETE, Ryan Nicholas. ■ 05405 #050-02-2007 L2007 **TY** *012

CROOKES, Bruce Alan. 111 COLCHESTER AVE, FLETCHER 4 MCHV CAMPUS 05401 #035-47-1996 L2003 **TRS CCS** *020 †85

CULLEN, Kimberley Renee. ■ 05405 #050-02-2008 *012

CUMMINS, Andrew Brinker. ■ 05405 #050-02-2006 L2008 **IM** *012

CUSHMAN, Mary. 111 COLCHESTER AVE, FLETCHER ALLEN HLTH CARE 05401 #050-02-1989 L1989 **HEM** *050 †20

D AGOSTINO, Robert. 111 COLCHESTER AVE, FLETCHER ALLEN HEALTH CARE 05401 #035-47-1987 L1996 **DR GS** *020 †80

DANIELSON, Gregory Paul. 111 COLCHESTER AVE, FLETCHER ALLEN HLTH CARE 05401 #050-02-2001 L2001 **OTO** *012

DAUERMAN, Harold Lee. 111 COLCHESTER AVE, UVM, MCCLURE 1, CARDIAC UN 05401 #024-01-1991 L2001 **CD IC** *020 †20

DAUERMAN, Kimberly Pryce. 1 S PROSPECT ST, GIVEN HEALTH CTR 05401 #024-01-1998 L2001 **IM** *020 †20

DAVIS, Gerald Sundt. 1 S PROSPECT ST # C317 05401 #051-01-1970 L1975 **PUD** *050 †20

DAVIS, John Herschel, Jr. ■ 05408 #038-06-1948 L1969 **GS VS** *071 †85

DEAN, Howard B, III. 325 S COVE RD 05401 #035-46-1978 L1979 **IM** *020 †20

DEDAM, Jeanpaul Henri. 111 COLCHESTER AVE, FAHC DEPT OF ORTHOPEDICS 05401 #032-01-2006 L2006 **FP** *012

DE LOZIER, Howard Luther. 1 S PROSPECT ST 05401 #028-02-1973 L1978 **OTO** *075 †45

DESAI, Kajal Ashvin. ■ 05408 #036-01-2006 L2006 **IM** *012

DESJARDINS, Isabelle. 111 COLCHESTER AVE, PATRICK 4 05401 #067-02-1993 L2003 **P** *020 †75

DI CARLO, Antonio. 111 COLCHESTER AVE, FLETCHER 469A, MCHV CAMPUS 05401 #067-01-1996 L2003 **GS** *020 †95

DICKERMAN, Joseph David. DEPT OF PEDIATRICS, UNIVERSITY OF VERMONT 05405 #035-20-1965 L1971 **PD PHO** *020 †55

■ = Address Information Privacy Protected

DIETRICH, Peter Anthony. 111 COLCHESTER AVE 05401 #038-06-1965 L1972 **R** *020 †80
DITTUS, Kim Lynnette. 111 COLCHESTER AVE, OF HEMATOLOGYONCOLOG 05401 #047-20-2003 L2005 **HO** *012 †20
DIXON, Anne E. 111 COLCHESTER AVE, PATRICK 311 05401 #917-09-1990 L2001 **PCC** *020 †20
DIXON, Majorie Elizabeth. 89 BEAUMONT AVE, GIVEN MED BLDG RM C211 05405 #067-01-1997 L2002 *020
DOLACK, George Leo. ■ 05405 #054-04-1981 L1983 **CD IM** *020 †20
DOLGIN, Rebecca Lynn. ■ 05408 #024-07-2007 L2007 **IM** *012
DOMINICK, Timothy Scott. 111 COLCHESTER AVE, DEPT OF ANESTHESIOLOGY 05401 #050-02-2001 L2006 **AN** *020 †05
DOWNS, April Harris. 199 MAIN ST, COURTHOUSE PLAZA 05401 #048-13-2000 **OBG** *020
DRUCKER, Nancy Ann. 111 COLCHESTER AVE, FAHC MCHV PATRICK 581 05401 #023-07-1985 L1992 **PDC** *020 †55
DULANEY, Eugene D. 111 COLCHESTER AVE, MCHV, BROWN 3 05401 #043-01-1991 L2001 **N CN** *020 †75
DULSKY, Lisa Watkins. 108 CHERRY ST STE 30, VERMON DEPARTMENT OF HEALT 05401 #041-01-1985 L1988 **PD** *020 †55
DUMONT, Travis Michael. 111 COLCHESTER AVE WP2, FAHC DEPT OF NEUROSURGERY 05401 #024-07-2005 L2005 **NS** *012
DUNCAN, James Armstrong. PO BOX 1150, VERMONT MANAGED CARE 05402 #005-11-1978 L1984 **IM** *020 †16
DUNCAN, Paula M. 1 S PROSPECT ST, VCHIP ARNOLD 5 UHC 05401 #041-07-1972 L1984 **PD** *030 †55
DUNNING, Susan Patricia. 111 COLCHESTER AVE, PATRICK 311 05401 #035-01-1992 L1995 **IM** *020 †20
DURFEE, Herbert A, Jr. ■ 05401 #050-02-1948 L1957 **OBG** *071 †30
EASTWOOD, Charles B. 111 COLCHESTER AVE 05401 #067-01-2003 L2003 **AN** *012
EBERT, George Meyer. 111 COLCHESTER AVE, FLETCHER ALLEN HEALTH CARE 05401 #016-02-1985 L2002 **R RNR** *020 †80
EDWARDS, John Ray. 118 PINE ST 05401 #045-01-1972 L1973 **P** *020 †75
EHSANI, Hamid. 111 COLCHESTER AVE, FLETCHER ALLEN HEALTHCARE 05401 #028-02-1996 L2001 **EM CCM** *020 †16
EICKER, Joan Nathalie. 1 S PROSPECT ST, GIVEN HEALTH CARE CENTER 05401 #025-01-1983 L1983 **FSM** *020 †20
EISINGER, Maj. 100 COLCHESTER AVE, ER FLETCHER ALLEN HEALTH 05401 #005-02-1986 L1991 **EM IM** *020 †20,16
ELHOSSEINY, Abdelmonem A. 111 COLCHESTER AVE, PATHOLOGY DEPT SMITH 244B 05401 #915-03-1972 L2002 **PCP ATP** *020 †50 ‡
ELLIS, Rusty Todd. 111 COLCHESTER AVE, INTERNAL MEDICINE 05401 #048-15-2006 L2007 **IM** *012
ELMQVIST, Lars-Gunnar. REHABILITAT, MCHVORTHOPAEDICS 05401 #858-05-1971 L1991 *100
EMERY, Edward S, III. 111 COLCHESTER AVE, FLETCHER ALLEN 05401 #035-01-1961 L1969 **CHN N** *020 †55,75
EMMONS, Robert Smyth. 92 ADAMS ST 05401 #018-03-1985 L1985 **P** *020 †75
EMMONS, Steven Patrick. ■ 05405 #003-01-2000 L2006 **HO** *012 †20
EMOTT, Molly Morgan. 1 S PROSPECT ST, UHC CAMPUS 05401 #008-02-2001 L2007 **MPD** *020 †20,55
ENGELKEN, Dustin Thomas. 111 COLCHESTER AVE, SMITH 140 05401 #019-02-2001 L2005 **PCC** *012 †20
ESLIN, Rebekah Darlene. ■ 05405 #050-02-2007 *012
ESTES, Melinda Louise. 111 COLCHESTER AVE, FLETCHER ALLEN HEALTH CARE 05401 #048-02-1978 L1978 **NP N** *030 †75
EUSER, Anna Gerrit. ■ 05408 #050-02-2008 *012
EYLER, A Evan. 106 CARRIGAN DR, 235 ROSWELL BLDG 05405 #025-01-1984 L2002 **FM P** *020 †75,18
FADNESS, Pamela Kay. 2 CHURCH ST, STE 4E 05401 #035-15-1990 L2003 **P** *020
FAHEY, Michael Christian. 111 COLCHESTER AVE, FAHCDEPT OF PEDIATRICS 05401 #035-01-2002 L2002 **PDC** *012 †55
FAIRBANK, Jonathan Thos. 111 COLCHESTER AVE # RAD, MED CTR HOSP OF VT 05401 #038-06-1967 L1969 **DR NM** *020 †80,28
FAMA, Teresa Ann. 111 COLCHESTER AVE, FAHCDEPT OF RHEUMATOLOGY 05401 #050-02-2002 L2002 **RHU** *020 †20
FARRAG, Abeer Bakhiet. 111 COLCHESTER AVE, MCHV MAIL ROOM-NEUROLOGY 05401 #915-05-1994 L2006 **N** *012
FASSLER, David Gary. 86 LAKE ST 05401 #008-01-1982 L1984 **CHP OS** *020 †75
FEDERICO, Andrea Christin. ■ 05401 #035-19-2008 *012
FERNANDEZ, Nathanial. 111 COLCHESTER AVE, DEPARTMENT OF SURGERY 05401 #007-02-2000 L2000 **GS** *020
FERRENTINO, Nicholas. 111 COLCHESTER AVE 05401 #035-15-1989 L1996 **GE** *020 †20
FILIPPI, Christopher G. 111 COLCHESTER AVE 05401 #035-20-1990 L2004 **DR** *020 †80
FINETTE, Barry Alan. DEPARTMENT OF PEDIATRICS, E203 GIVEN MEDICAL BLVD 05405 #048-12-1988 L1989 **PD** *020 †55
FINGAR, Ann Rachel. ■ 05408 #016-11-1977 L2001 **GPM GP** *020 †70 ‡
FINGAR, Elizabeth Lynn. ■ 05408 #032-01-2008 *012
FINGAR, James Raymond. ■ 05408 #016-06-1977 L1978 **GP** *072
FIORENZA, Monica Claire. 111 COLCHESTER AVE 05401 #050-02-2000 L2003 **PD** *020 †55
FIRST, Lewis R. UNIVERSITY OF VERMONT COLL, GIVEN E-203, DEPT. OF PEDI 05405 #024-01-1980 L1994 **PD EM** *030 †55
FISHER, John Matthew. 111 COLCHESTER AVE 05401 #050-02-1985 L1986 **AN GS** *020 †05
FISHER, Patricia Losinske. 617 RIVERSIDE AVE 05401 #048-14-1999 L2003 **FM** *020 †18
FITZGERALD, Joseph Robt. 111 COLCHESTER AVE, FAHC, ANESTHESIOLOGY 05401 #050-02-1992 L1998 **CCA** *020 †05
FLISZAR, Evelyne. PO BOX 1063, 1 S PROSPECT ST 05402 #050-02-1992 L1998 **DR** *020 †80
FLOYD, Wm Carlton, Jr. COLCHESTER AVENUE 05401 #021-01-1967 L1971 **P** *071
FOERG, Florian Ernst. 111 COLCHESTER AVE, BAIRD 196 05401 #050-02-1998 L1998 **IM** *020 †20
FOGARTY, John P. 235 ROWELL 05405 #035-03-1975 L1995 **FM FSM** *030 †18
FOLEY, Joseph C. ■ 05401 #050-02-1949 L1951 **R** *071
FORD, Dorothy Ellen. 1 S PROSPECT ST 05401 #028-02-1954 L1968 **PM** *071 †60
FORGIONE, Patrick Michael. 111 COLCHESTER AVE, DIGESTIVE DIS CTR-MAIN PAV 05401 #050-02-1997 L1998 **GS** *020 †85
FOWLER, Jennifer Lynn. 111 COLCHESTER AVE WP2, FAHC DEPT OF SURGERY 05401 #047-06-2004 L2006 **GS** *100
FRANCKE, Bertold Richard. 1 S PROSPECT ST 05401 #409-16-1967 L1989 **P** *020 †75
FRANKOWSKI, Barbara L. 1 S PROSPECT ST, UNIVERSITY PEDIATRICS 05401 #023-07-1980 L1985 **PD** *020 †55

FREIBURG, Carter Bolton. ■ 05408 #016-43-2003 L2003 **GS** *012
FREMGREN, Heather Eileen. ■ 05405 #050-02-2007 **PD** *012
FRIES, Timothy James. 89 S WILLIAMS ST 05401 #026-04-1981 L1985 **N** *020 †75
FUJIWARA, Mika. ■ 05405 #050-02-2007 **PTH** *012
FUKAGAWA, Naomi Kay. GIVEN BUILDING ROOM C-207, COLLEGE OF MEDICINE 05405 #016-06-1976 L1978 **NTR PG** *050 †55
GAGNE, Havaleh Marie. 111 COLCHESTER AVE, FAHC 05401 #050-02-2003 L2003 **RO** *100
GALBRAITH, Richard A. 111 COLCHESTER AVE, FLETCHER ALLEN HEALTH CARE 05401 #917-19-1974 L1995 **END IM** *050
GALLANT, Janice Mary. 111 COLCHESTER AVE, FAHC RADIOLOGY 05401 #050-02-1989 L1989 **PDR** *020 †80
GANATRA, Kalpesh D. 111 COLCHESTER AVE, FAHC/PULMONARY & CRITICAL 05401 #495-96-1998 L2002 **PCC** *020 †20
GANGULY, Eric Kumar. 111 COLCHESTER AVE, FLETCHER ALLEN HEALTH CAR 05401 #024-16-1999 L1999 **GE** *100 †20
GARCIA-RUBI, Ernesto. 111 COLCHESTER AVE, FAHCINTERNAL MEDICINE 05401 #649-01-1983 L1999 **IM** *100
GARRA, Brian Stephen. 111 COLCHESTER AVE, FLETCHER ALLEN HEALTH CARE 05401 #054-04-1976 L1998 **DR** *050 †80
GATZKE, Angela Marie. 111 COLCHESTER AVE, FAMILY MEDICINE 05401 #056-05-2006 L2006 **FP** *012
GAUTHIER, Eric Andre. 111 COLCHESTER AVE, FLETCHER ALLEN HEALTH CARE 05401 #050-02-2002 L2002 **CD** *012 †20
GEIDER, Jillian Sarah. 111 COLCHESTER AVE, FLETCHER ALLEN HEALTH CARE 05401 #050-02-2004 L2004 **PD** *100 †55
GENNARI, Frank John. 111 COLCHESTER AVE, FAHC-BURGESS 315 05401 #008-01-1963 L1979 **NEP IM** *040 †20
GENTCHOS, George Ernest. 111 COLCHESTER AVE, FLETCHER ALLEN HEALTH CARE 05401 #010-02-1996 L2001 **DR** *100 †80
GENTLER, Marinshine Duffe. ■ 05401 #050-02-2005 L2005 **IM** *012
GERSON, Rachel Faye. 111 COLCHESTER AVE, FAHCDEPT OF RADIOLOGY 05401 #032-01-2001 L2002 **DR** *100 †80
GHOSTINE, Jimmy. 111 COLCHESTER AVE 05401 #067-01-2003 L2004 **DR** *012
GIBBARD, Bruce Alexander. 86 LAKE ST 05401 #065-05-1961 L1977 **PYA P** *071
GIBSON, Cheryl Ann. 23 MANSFIELD AVE 05401 #050-02-1985 L1985 **OBG** *020 †30
GIBSON, Melisa Gail. 111 COLCHESTER AVE, FAHC 05401 #035-45-2004 L2004 **FM** *100
GIBSON, Pamela C. 111 COLCHESTER AVE, DEPT PATH 05401 #050-02-1990 L1990 **PCP ATP** *020 †50
GIBSON, Thomas Chometon. 111 COLCHESTER AVE 05401 #352-03-1946 L1964 **CD IM** *071
GIRGIS, Cherif Ezzat. ■ 05401 #915-02-1996 L2005 **FP** *012
GIROUX, Roger Jos. 111 COLCHESTER AVE 05401 #050-02-1987 L1987 **FM** *020 †18
GOGO, Prospero Barquero. 111 COLCHESTER AVE, FLETCHER ALLEN HEALTH 05401 #010-01-1997 L1997 **IC** *020 †20
GOLDMAN, Glenn David. 1 S PROSPECT ST, FLETCHER ALLEN HEALTH CARE 05401 #035-20-1991 L1996 **D** *020 †15
GOLDOBINE, Olga P. ■ 05405 #050-02-2007 L2007 **AN** *012
GOLDSBOROUGH, Richard H. 60 COLCHESTER AVE 05401 #041-12-1951 L1961 **OTO A** *071 †45
GOMBRICH, Matthew David. ■ 05408 #038-06-2005 *100
GOMEZ, Antonio Johnson. 1 S PROSPECT ST, FLETCHER ALLEN HEALTH CARE 05401 #748-01-1960 L1972 **N** *071
GONZALEZ-MUNOZ, Annmarie. ■ 05406 #132-02-1991 L2001 **APM** *020 †05
GOODWIN, Andrew Jackson. 111 COLCHESTER AVE, FAHC 05401 #050-02-2003 L2003 **PTH** *020
GORMAN, Emily Frances. 111 COLCHESTER AVE, VERMONT-FLETCHER ALLEN 05401 #001-02-2007 L2007 **GS** *012
GORMAN, Eric Benjamin. ■ 05401 #048-12-2001 L2002 **HMP** *020 †50
GORMAN, Mark Jeffrey. C219D GIVEN BLDG., 89 BEAUMONT AVE 05405 #025-07-1985 L2005 **N IM** *020 †20,75
GRACE, Christopher James. SMITH 275, 111 COLCHESTER AVE 05405 #035-09-1979 L1987 **ID** *020 †20
GRAHAM, William Geo Brown. 111 COLCHESTER AVE 05401 #041-01-1956 L1971 **PUD IM** *020 †20
GRANT, Barbara Winslow. 111 COLCHESTER AVE, FLETCHER ALLEN HEALTH CARE 05401 #032-01-1978 L1984 **HEM IM** *050 †20
GRANT, Ruth Kennedy. 1 MILL ST, PKC CORP 05401 #050-02-1977 L1980 **IM** *020 †20
GRANT, Steven Mark. 111 COLCHESTER AVE 05401 #012-05-1993 L1996 **IM** *020 †20
GREEN, Andrea Elizabeth. 1 S PROSPECT ST, UHC PEDIATRICS 05401 #067-01-1991 L2002 **PD** *020 †55
GREEN, Curtis Emery. 111 COLCHESTER AVE, DEPT OF RADIOLOGY 05401 #048-12-1976 L1999 **DR** *020 †80
GREENBLATT, Jeanne Ellyn. 108 CHERRY ST 05401 #050-12-1987 L2000 **CHP P** *020 †75
GREENBLATT, Marc Steven. 89 BEAUMONT AVE, GIVEN E214 05405 #041-02-1983 L1995 **ON IM** *050 †20
GREENE, Christopher M. 111 COLCHESTER AVE, FLETCHER ALLEN HEALTH CARE 05401 #050-02-1986 L1999 **CCA IM** *020 †05
GREENE, Laura Aman. 111 COLCHESTER AVE 05401 #050-02-2000 L2000 **PTH DMP** *020 †50
GREENHOUSE, David Garrett. 111 COLCHESTER AVE, VERMONT-FLETCHER ALLEN 05401 #035-20-2007 L2007 **GS** *012
GRENIER, Allison Jean. ENDV OF VT MED COLL, GIVEN BLDG BOX #133 05405 #050-02-2004 *100
GRIECO, Verena Steiner. DEPARTMENT OF PATHOLOGY, UVM MEDICAL ALUMNI BLD 05405 #054-04-1983 L1985 **PTH PCP** *020 †50
GRONDIN, Lydia Sophie. 111 COLCHESTER AVE, FLETCHER ALLEN HEALTH CARE 05401 #050-02-2001 L2001 **AN** *100 †05
GROSS, Tobias Peter. 111 COLCHESTER AVE, INTERNAL MEDICINE 05401 #409-16-1994 L1997 **IM** *020 †20
GRUENBERG, David Alexande. ■ 05401 #024-07-2005 L2005 **IM** *012
GRUNBERG, Steven Marc. 1 S PROSPECT ST, UHC CAMPUS/ST JOSEPH 3400 05401 #035-20-1975 L1993 **ON IM** *050 †20 ‡
GUILLOT, Ann Packer. 111 COLCHESTER AVE 05401 #041-02-1974 L1975 **PD PN** *020 †55
GUMP, Dieter W. GIVEN BLDG 05401 #023-07-1960 L1966 **ID IM** *020 †20
HAGAN, Joseph F, Jr. 410 SHELBURNE RD 05401 #010-02-1976 L1977 **PD ADL** *020 †55
HAIDER, Maruf. 111 COLCHESTER AVE, INTERNAL MEDICINE 05401 #539-06-2004 L2005 **IM** *012
HAJDU, Stephen. ■ 05401 #473-01-1941 **OS CD** *071

HALL, Allison Yeakel. 86 LAKE ST 05401 #005-02-1984 L1995 **CHP P** *020 †75
HALL, Constance Brownell. ■ 05401 #050-02-1949 **OS** *075
HALLIBURTON, Cory Shea. 60 COLCHESTER AVE 05401 #045-01-2001 L2007 **GE** *020
HALSTED, Harry Cary. ■ 05401 #050-02-1941 L1967 **OM** *071 †70
HAMILL, Robert Wallace. 89 BEAUMONT AVE, UNIV OF VT CLGE OF MED 05405 #036-05-1968 L1993 **N IM** *040 †75
HAMLIN, Mark Pettengill. 111 COLCHESTER AVE, MCHV CAMPUS, PATRICK LEVEL 05401 #050-02-1994 L1999 **CCA** *020 †05
HAMPSON, Christopher Ohar. 111 COLCHESTER AVE WP2, FAHC DEPT OF RADIOLOGY 05401 #035-01-2004 L2006 **DR** *012
HAMRELL, Burton B. GIVEN BLDG 05401 #016-11-1962 L1968 **OS CD** *050
HANSON, Greta Elizabeth. 96 COLCHESTER AVE, C/O AFFILIATES IN OB/GYN 05401 #035-09-2004 L2004 **OBG** *012
HANSON, John Sherwood. MARY FLETCHER HOSP 05401 #035-19-1954 L1955 **CD PUD** *030
HARDIN, Nicholas Jackson. 111 COLCHESTER AVE, FLETCHER ALLEN HEALTHCARE 05401 #035-20-1970 L1977 **ATP** *040 †50
HARLOW, Seth Perry. 111 COLCHESTER AVE, MCCLURE 1207 FLETCHER-ALLE 05401 #024-16-1984 L1994 **GS** *020 †85
HARMON, Maureen Lee. 111 COLCHESTER AVE 05401 #050-02-1988 L1988 **PTH** *020 †50
HARTLEY, Jennifer A. ■ 05405 #050-02-2007 *012
HASELTON, Cynthia Ames. 789 PINE ST 05401 #050-02-1994 L1994 **FM** *020 †18
HASSLER, Carol Reinhardt. 108 CHERRY ST 05401 #041-01-1976 L1985 **PD** *030 †55
HATFIELD, Joanna Wagner. 111 COLCHESTER AVE, FAHC 05401 #005-11-2004 L2004 **OBG** *012
HAY, Jennifer Lynne. ■ 05401 #020-12-2006 L2007 **IM** *012
HAYWARD, Robert Geo. 1 S PROSPECT ST, WOMENS HEALTH CARE SVC 05401 #051-04-1977 L1981 **OBG** *020 †30
HEATH, Jennifer Adele. 1 S PROSPECT ST, ALLEN FLETCHER HEALTH CARE 05401 #035-01-1990 L1993 **PD** *020 †55
HEBERT, Christopher J. 28 S WILLIAMS ST 05401 #050-02-2002 L2002 **IM** *020 †20
HEBERT, James Chas. 111 COLCHESTER AVE, DEPT OF SURG FAHC 05401 #050-02-1977 L1982 **GS** *020 †85
HEESE, Virginia Katherine. 425 PEARL ST, CENTER FOR HEALTH AND WELL 05401 #067-01-1998 L2005 **FM** *020 †18
HEILMAN, Richard S. 111 COLCHESTER AVE, DEPT RAD 05401 #041-01-1959 L1964 **R** *020 †80
HEIMANN, Ruth. 111 COLCHESTER AVE 05401 #033-05-1989 L2003 **RO ON** *020 †80
HERRINGTON, Heather Chamb. ■ 05401 #040-02-2006 L2006 **OTO** *012
HERSCHORN, Sally Deborah. 111 COLCHESTER AVE, FLETCHER ALLEN HEALTH CARE 05401 #067-01-1982 L1987 **DR** *020 †80
HIKEL, Katharine M. GIVEN BLDG 05401 #050-02-1991 *100
HOBBS, Cara Llewellyn. 111 COLCHESTER AVE, FAHC 05401 #050-02-2004 L2004 **PTH** *012
HOCKETT, Mia Fay. ■ 05401 #050-02-2007 L2007 **IM** *012
HOFFMAN, Howard. 111 COLCHESTER AVE, ALLEN HTH CARE, 05401 #018-03-1997 L2002 **DR** *020 †80
HOLDRIDGE, Regan Carrie. 111 COLCHESTER AVE, FLETCHER ALLEN HEALTH CARE 05401 #050-02-2002 L2002 **HO** *012 †20
HOLMES, Todd Edgar. 111 COLCHESTER AVE WP, DIVISION OF DERMATOLOGY 05401 #050-02-2003 L2003 **PRD** *015
HOMANS, Alan Chas. 111 COLCHESTER AVE, MOD B RM 113 05401 #038-40-1979 L1992 **PHO** *050 †55
HONG, Richard. 655 SPEAR ST BLDG C 05405 #016-11-1953 L1992 **PD IG** *050 †55,03
HONORIS, Lily. ■ 05405 #050-02-2008 *012
HOOD, Virginia Louise. 1 S PROSPECT ST, RENAL SERVICES REHAB 2 FAH 05401 #143-03-1970 L1977 **NEP** *040 †20
HOPKINS, Amelia Jeanne. 111 COLCHESTER AVE, PEDIATRIC CRITICAL CARE-SM 05401 #008-02-2001 L2001 **CCP** *100 †55
HOPPES, Tobin James. 111 COLCHESTER AVE, FAHCDEPT OF NEPHROLOGY 05401 #038-40-2001 L2001 **NEP** *100 †20
HORBAR, Jeffrey David. 1 S PROSPECT ST, DEPT PED 05401 #035-08-1977 L1979 **NPM PD** *040 †55
HORGAN, Michael Andrew. 111 COLCHESTER AVE, FAHC 05401 #033-05-1992 L2000 **NS** *020 †25
HOSKIN, Mark Lewis. 111 COLCHESTER AVE, MENTAL HEALTH SERVICE 05401 #050-02-1988 L1989 **P** *020 †75
HOUCK, Robin Courtland. 111 COLCHESTER AVE, MCCLURE 1 05401 #024-07-2000 L2005 **CD IM** *012
HOUSTON, Charles Snead. ■ 05401 #035-01-1939 L1967 **OS IM** *075 †20
HOWE, James Gregory. 1 S PROSPECT ST 05401 #050-02-1973 L1975 **ORS OS** *040 †40
HUBBELL, Richard Nicholas. 111 COLCHESTER AVE, WEST PAVILION LEVEL 4 05401 #050-02-1980 L1981 **OTO** *020 †45
HUDSON, Page, III. 111 COLCHESTER AVE 9D, FLETCHER ALLEN HEALTH CARE 05401 #036-01-1987 L1996 **EM** *020 †16
HUDZIAK, James Jos. MEDICAL ALUMNI 05405 #026-04-1988 L1993 **P CHP** *020 †75
HUGHES, John Russell. OF MED, UNIV OF VERMONT-COLL 05405 #027-01-1975 L1985 **P** *050 †75
HULSEY, Steve Mark. 111 COLCHESTER AVE 05401 #038-43-1986 L1997 **EM** *020 †16
HUNT, Elizabeth Aldenkrei. 111 COLCHESTER AVE, DEPARTMENT OF PEDIATRICS 05401 #050-02-2008 *012
HURWITZ, Craig G. 111 COLCHESTER AVE 05401 #035-08-1996 L1996 **NEP** *020 †20
HUSSAIN, Sarah I. 111 COLCHESTER AVE 05401 #704-25-1988 L2002 **CCM NEP** *020 †20
HUSTON, Christopher D. 111 COLCHESTER AVE, 304 BURGESS-FLETCHER ALLEN 05401 #035-20-1994 L1994 **ID** *020 †20
HWANG, Jiann-Chang. 1 S PROSPECT ST # D346 05401 #244-04-1968 *100
HYAT, Arooj. ■ 05405 #050-02-2007 L2007 *012
HYMAN, Neil Howard. FLETCHER 464, FAHC 05401 #050-02-1984 L1990 **CRS** *020 †85,10
INKER, Rachel Hana. 493 S UNION ST 05401 #024-16-1998 L1998 **FM** *020 †18
IRWIN, Alan Emory. 111 COLCHESTER AVE, OPHTHOLMOLOGY 5-WEST ACC 05401 #050-02-1971 L1977 **OPH** *020 †35
IRWIN, Edward Suter. ■ 05401 #050-02-1955 L1956 **OPH** *071 †35
ITTLEMAN, Frank Paul. C/O UNIV HEALTH CTR 05401 #038-41-1972 L1980 **TS** *020 †85,90
IVES, John Othniel. 1 S PROSPECT ST, DEPT PSY 05401 #035-20-1965 L1972 **P** *071 †75
JACKSON, Thomas Lane. 111 COLCHESTER AVE, EAST PAVILION 5TH FL 05401 #032-01-1984 L1986 **U GS** *020 †95
JACOBI, Nicole. 111 COLCHESTER AVE, FAHCHEMATOLOGYONCOLGOY 05401 #409-32-1993 L1999 **HO** *100 †20

JACOBSON, Erica Rae. 111 COLCHESTER AVE, OF PATHOLOGY 05401 #050-02-1999 L2000 **HMP** *020 †50
JACOBSON, James Lee. 1 S PROSPECT ST, ARNOLD 6 05401 #016-06-1979 L2000 **P PYA** *040 †75
JAMES, Kenneth Andrew. 111 COLCHESTER AVE, FAHC DEPT OF PSYCHIATRY 05401 #054-04-2005 L2005 **P** *100
JAMES, Ted. 111 COLCHESTER AVE, SURGICAL ONCOLOGY/BREAST C 05401 #041-07-1996 L2005 **SO** *020 †85
JAMES, Wendy Ann. 111 COLCHESTER AVE 05401 #024-07-1993 L2001 **EM** *020 †16
JAVED, Shehzad Ahmad. 111 COLCHESTER AVE, FAHCPSYCHIATRY 05401 #704-05-1992 L2001 *100
JEWELL, Ryan Phillip. 111 COLCHESTER AVE, FLETCHER 5 05401 #050-02-1999 L1999 **NS** *100
JOHN, Alex. 60 COLCHESTER AVE 05401 #028-03-1984 L1988 **GE** *020 †20
JOHNSON, David Loren. 111 COLCHESTER AVE, FLETCHER ALLEN HEALTHCARE 05401 #056-06-1976 L1979 **AN** *020 †05
JOHNSON, Julia Virginia. 111 COLCHESTER AVE, FLETCHER ALLEN HEALTHCARE 05401 #012-01-1984 L1990 **REN OBG** *020 †30
JOHNSON, Michael Craig. 111 COLCHESTER AVE, FLETCHER ALLEN HLTH CARE 05401 #408-17-2002 L2002 **FM** *020 †18
JOHNSTON, Anne Maxwell. GIVEN BLDG E203A, UNIVERSITY OF VERMONT 05405 #065-10-1981 L1984 **NPM PD** *020 †55
JONES, Cresta Wedel. 111 COLCHESTER AVE, FLETCHER ALLEN SMITH 4 05401 #056-06-2001 L2001 **OBG MFM** *020
JONES, David Caldwell. 111 COLCHESTER AVE, ACC 4TH FLR E PAVILILLON 05401 #041-14-1987 L2001 **MFM OBG** *020 †30
KACER, Martina. 111 COLCHESTER AVE, DEPT OF PDE 05401 #286-13-1995 L2006 **PD PDE** *100 †55
KALSNER, Louisa Rechama. 111 COLCHESTER AVE, ACC 4E 05401 #035-46-1994 L2003 **CHN** *020 †55,75,19
KAMINSKY, David Alan. 111 COLCHESTER AVE, UNIV OF VERMONT SMITH 133A 05401 #024-16-1987 L1995 **PUD CCM** *050 †20
KANDIL, Dina Hamdy Ibrahi. 111 COLCHESTER AVE, HEALTH CARE-UNI 05401 #915-04-1999 L2005 **PTH** *012
KANE-RAYFIELD, E Holliday. 86 LAKE ST, OTTER CREEK ASSOCIATES 05401 #050-02-1994 L1996 **P** *020 †75
KAO, Patricia Charmin. 111 COLCHESTER AVE, OF GASTROENTEROLOGY 05401 #051-01-2001 L2001 **GE** *020
KARAARSLAN, Mehmet H. 111 COLCHESTER AVE, INTERNAL MEDICINE 05401 #902-07-1989 L1998 **RHU** *100
KAST, Richard Eric. 2 CHURCH ST 05401 #297-01-1978 L1988 **P GP** *020
KASZNICA, Peter. 111 COLCHESTER AVE, FAHCGME OFFICE 05401 #024-05-2004 L2004 **OTO** *012
KEATING, David P. 111 COLCHESTER AVE, DEPT. RADIOLOGY 05401 #035-01-1990 L2001 **DR** *020 †80
KEET, Kevin Robert. ■ 05405 #050-02-2007 **IM** *012
KEHOE, Stephanie Shim. 111 COLCHESTER AVE 05401 #050-02-2004 L2004 **FM** *020
KELLER, Gary Aron. 789 PINE ST 05401 #024-07-1981 L1985 **P** *020 †75
KELLER, Jay Edgar. 1 S PROSPECT ST 05401 #050-02-1940 L1941 **GS** *071 †85
KELLER, Sheryl Peterson. 1 S PROSPECT ST, BREAST CARE CENTER 05401 #050-02-1985 L1992 **GS** *020 †85
KELLEY, Michael Bryant. 111 COLCHESTER AVE, INTERNAL MEDICINE 05401 #050-02-2004 L2004 **IM** *100
KELLY, Erin Kathleen. 111 COLCHESTER AVE, FLETCHER ALLEN HLTH CARE 05401 #539-06-2006 L2006 **P** *012
KENNEDY, Barbara Castle. 1205 NORTH AVE 05408 #056-06-1981 L1994 **PD** *020 †55
KENNEDY, Suzanne Maria. 111 COLCHESTER AVE, PATRICK 4 MCHV CAMPUS FAHC 05401 #063-01-1996 L2001 **PD** *020 †75
KETCHAM, John Patrick. 111 COLCHESTER AVE, FAHC/DEPT OF ANESTHESIOLOG 05401 #007-02-2001 L2002 **AN** *020 †05 ‡
KHAN, Farrah B. UVM - HEME/ONC, GIVEN E-214 05405 #539-06-2003 L2007 **HO** *012 †20
KIDA, Masatoshi. 111 COLCHESTER AVE 05401 #045-01-1986 L2000 **PTH** *020 †50
KIEN, Craig Lawrence. 89 BEAUMONT AVE, UVM DEPARTMENT OF PEDIATRI 05405 #038-41-1972 L2004 **NTR PD** *050 †50
KIKUT, Janusz Karol. 111 COLCHESTER AVE, RADIOLOGY, PATRICK 1 05401 #759-03-1992 L2000 **DR** *020 †80,28
KIRWAN, Janet Maria. 111 COLCHESTER AVE, FAHC-DEPT OF CARDIOLOGY 05401 #539-02-1993 L1998 **IM** *100 †20
KLEIN, Harvey Jay. 267 PEARL ST 05401 #025-07-1969 L1974 **P** *020
KLEIN, Jeffrey Seth. 111 COLCHESTER AVE, RADIOLOGY DEPT MCHV #128 05401 #035-08-1983 L1995 **DR IM** *020 †80
KOKA, Rahul. GIVEN BOX 205, UVM COLLEGE OF MEDICINE 05405 #050-02-2004 L2005 **AN** *012
KOOB, Nadine Claudia. 111 COLCHESTER AVE, FAHC/DEPT OF PEDIATRICS 05401 #054-04-2002 L2002 **NPM** *012
KOPLEWITZ, Martin J. 111 COLCHESTER AVE, # ACC 05401 #050-02-1952 L1960 **GS CRS** *071 †85
KORCZ, Jeffrey Allen. 111 COLCHESTER AVE, FAHC DEPT OF PSYCHIATRY 05401 #048-12-2000 L2000 **P** *020
KORSON, Roy. U.V.M. COLLEGE OF MEDICINE 05405 #041-02-1947 L1952 **ATP** *071 †50
KORZ, Dorian Mark. ■ 05405 #050-02-2008 *012
KOUTRAS, John George. 1 S PROSPECT ST, ARNOLD 6 05401 #035-03-1995 L2004 **CHP** *020 †75
KOVACIC, Jeffrey John. 111 COLCHESTER AVE, FAHC DEPT OF ORTHOPAEDICS 05401 #038-45-1999 L2003 **ORS** *100
KRAG, David Nielsen. 1 S PROSPECT ST 05401 #016-43-1980 L1991 **GS** *020 †85
KRAG, Martin Hans. UNIV OF VT COL MED, DEPT ORTHO & REHAB 05405 #008-01-1975 L1981 **OSS ORS** *020 †40
KRAMER, Jonathan. 111 COLCHESTER AVE 05401 #035-08-1982 L1998 **R RNR** *020 †80
KRAWITT, Edward Len. 111 COLCHESTER AVE 05401 #035-20-1959 L1969 **HEP IM** *020
KREUTZ, Joseph Michael. 111 COLCHESTER AVE, FAHC, ANESTHESIOLOGY 05401 #056-05-1983 L1984 **AN PD** *020 †55,05
KRISTENSEN, Heidi. 111 COLCHESTER AVE, DEPT ANES 05401 #065-10-1976 L1980 **AN** *020 †05
KRUSINSKI, Paul Anthony. 89 BEAUMONT AVE, GIVEN D208 05405 #038-40-1968 L1974 **D** *020 †15

■ = Address Information Privacy Protected

KUPIC, Edward Anthony. 1 S PROSPECT ST 05401 #050-02-1960 L1962 **R** *020 †80
LA CROIX, Dale Jeanne. 96 COLCHESTER AVE 05401 #050-02-1992 L2000 **OBG** *020 †30
LAHIRI, Thomas. 111 COLCHESTER AVE, SMITH 574 05401 #008-02-1995 L1995 **PDP** *020 †55
LAKE, Tiffini Jaye. 111 COLCHESTER AVE, ATTN: ANESTHESIA DEPARTMEN 05401 #019-02-1999 L2004 **APM** *100
LALA, Deepa Shyam. 111 COLCHESTER AVE, FAHC/PULMONARY & CRITICAL 05401 #495-01-1998 L2002 **PCC** *100 †20
LANDRIGAN, Gary Patrick. 1 S PROSPECT ST 05401 #064-01-1986 L1993 **OTO** *020 †45
LANDRY, Francis John. 1205 NORTH AVE STE 6 05408 #024-07-1987 L1989 **IM** *020 †20
LANG, Rainer. ■ 05401 #409-04-1987 L1996 **NEP** *100
LANGEVIN, Helene M. UNIV OF VERMONT, GIVEN B205 DEPT OF NEUROLO 05405 #067-01-1978 L1993 **END IM** *020 †20
LARRABEE, Jerry Gregory. 1 S PROSPECT ST, UHC CAMPUS 05401 #047-05-1992 L2005 **PD** *055
LASALA, Paul Rocco. 111 COLCHESTER AVE, FAHC/SMITH 2 LABORATORY 05401 #012-01-1998 L1999 **MM** *100 †50
LASEK, Joseph Adam. 300 FLYNN AVE 05401 #035-15-2001 L2001 **P** *020 †75
LATHROP, Nancy-Coalter. 3 MAIN ST STE 216 05401 #050-02-1976 L1996 **P** *020 †75
LATIF, Shahid. 111 COLCHESTER AVE, FAHCDEPT OF PSYCHIATRY 05401 #704-01-1984 L1997 **CHP** *100
LAU, Chi Chi. 1 S PROSPECT ST, UHC CAMPUS 05401 #035-20-1982 L1996 **RHU IM** *020 †20
LAUB, Donald Rudolf, Jr. 111 COLCHESTER AVE 05401 #056-06-1990 L1994 **PS HS** *020 †65
LAWLOR, Peter Paul, Jr. 111 COLCHESTER AVE #065-09-1958 L1960 **PO** *071 †35
LAWRENCE, Therese Annette. 86 LAKE ST STE 6 05408 #050-02-1978 L1981 **P** *020 †75
LE, Uyenphuong. ■ 05405 #050-02-2007 L2007 **PTH** *012
LEAHY, John L. UNIVERSITY OF VERMONT, GIVEN C331 05405 #051-04-1977 L1996 **DIA** *062 †20
LEAVITT, Bruce Jason. 1 S PROSPECT ST 05401 #050-02-1981 L1988 **TS GS** *020 †85,90
LEE, Austin Paul Nairn. ■ 05401 #919-03-1951 L1970 **PYA** *071
LEIB, Edward Saml. 111 COLCHESTER AVE, E PAVILION LEVEL 5 05401 #025-01-1971 L1978 **RHU IM** *020 †20
LEIMAN, Gladwyn. 111 COLCHESTER AVE 05401 #836-01-1967 L2000 **ATP PCP** *020
LEITNER, David Welker. 1 S PROSPECT ST 05401 #025-07-1975 L1984 **PS** *020 †85,65
LEMOS, Diego Fernando. 111 COLCHESTER AVE WP2, FAHC DEPT OF RADIOLOGY 05401 #264-08-1998 L2006 **DR** *012
LEMOS FRANCO, Julio Andre. 111 COLCHESTER AVE, DEPT RAD 05401 #264-08-2000 L2006 **DR** *012
LEONARD, Karen Smoller. 1 S PROSPECT ST FA, UNIVERSITY PEDIATRICS 05401 #047-05-2000 L2000 **PD** *020 †55
LEVERENZ, Keith Carl. 111 COLCHESTER AVE, DEPT OF ANESTHESIA 05401 #008-01-1978 L1985 **AN CCM** *020 †05
LEVERS, Lorraine Christin. ■ 05401 #028-34-2008 *012
LEWELLYN, Brett James. ■ 05405 #050-02-2007 *012
LE WINTER, Martin Melvin. 111 COLCHESTER AVE, HEALTH CARE 05401 #035-19-1969 L1985 **CD IM** *020 †20
LEWIS, Judith Lynne. 111 COLCHESTER AVE 05401 #050-02-1989 L2003 **P** *020 †75
LEWIS, Michael Richard. 111 COLCHESTER AVE, FAHC PATHOLOGY ACC EP1 05401 #048-02-1996 L1996 **HMP PTH** *020 †50
LIBMAN, Bonita Sandra. 111 COLCHESTER AVE, ACC LEVEL 5 EAST PAVILION 05401 #065-01-1987 L1993 **RHU IM** *020 †20
LICATA, Anita Louise. 111 COLCHESTER AVE, W PAVILION-5 05401 #008-01-1989 L1993 **D** *020 †15
LICHTENBERGER, Jason C. ■ 05401 #033-06-2003 L2003 **OTO** *012
LIDOFSKY, Steven David. 414 FAHC/MCHV, UVM COLLEGE OF MEDICINE 05405 #035-01-1982 L1997 **HEP GE** *040 †20
LIEB, Julian. ■ 05408 #836-01-1966 L1973 **P** *071 †75
LILLY, Jacob William. ■ 05401 #050-02-2005 *100
LIMANEK, James Stephen. 1 S PROSPECT ST 05401 #050-02-1983 L1984 **AN** *020 †05
LIM CHOW TOM, Nicholas Kh. 111 COLCHESTER AVE, DEPT OF CARDIOLOGY 05401 #539-02-2004 L2007 *100
LINDER, Robert Eric. 1 LAWSON LN 05401 #067-01-1976 L1979 **P PFP** *062 †75
LINDSEY, James Michael. 111 COLCHESTER AVE WP2, FAHC DEPT OF SURGERY 05401 #021-01-2007 L2007 **GS** *012
LINNELL, Grant James. 111 COLCHESTER AVE, DEPT OF RADIOLOGY 05401 #025-76-1997, ▲ L2005 **DR** *020 †80
LITTENBERG, Benjamin. 1 S PROSPECT ST 05401 #038-06-1983 L1999 **IM** *050 †20
LOBEL, Robert Michael. 111 COLCHESTER AVE, FLETCHER ALLEN HEALTH CAR 05401 #024-05-1999 L2006 **ICE** *100 †20
LOHFF, Cortland Jesse. 108 CHERRY ST, VERMONT DEPARTMENT OF HEAL 05401 #056-05-1997 L2004 **GPM** *030 †70
LONDON, Marshall Gene. 6 ORCHARD TER 05401 #050-02-1955 L1957 **IM RHU** *071
LOPEZ, Debra Alice. 118 PINE ST 05401 #011-04-1978 L1981 **P** *020 †75
LOWELL, Jane Anne. 96 COLCHESTER AVE, MAITRI HEALTHCARE/WOMEN 05401 #041-14-2000 L2000 **OBG** *020 †20
LUCEY, Jerold F. 89 BEAUMONT AVE, UNIV VT COLLEGE MED 05405 #035-19-1952 L1955 **NPM** *040 †55
LUNDE, John Henry. 111 COLCHESTER AVE, ACC EAST PAVILION 2 05401 #050-02-1980 L1985 **PTH HMP** *020 †50
LURIA, Scott De Lima. 1 S PROSPECT ST 05401 #010-01-1981 L1987 **IM** *020 †20
LUSTGARTEN, Daniel L. 111 COLCHESTER AVE, MCHV CAMPUS 05401 #035-46-1993 L2002 **ICE** *020 †20
LYON, Caroline Elise. 111 COLCHESTER AVE, FLETCHER ALLEN HEALTH CARE 05401 #050-02-2002 L2002 **IM** *100 †20
MACAULEY, Robert Conover, Jr. 111 COLCHESTER AVE, SMITH 266 05401 #008-01-1995 L2002 **PD** *020 †55
MAC CARTY, Denton Edward. ■ 05408 #050-02-1957 L1958 **R NM** *071 †80
MACDONALD, Kathleen Sara. 111 COLCHESTER AVE, DEPT OF ANESTHESIA 05401 #041-13-2004 L2005 **AN** *012
MAC DONALD, Murdo G. ■ 05401 #050-02-1951 L1952 **OS IM** *071 †20
MAC PHERSON, Bruce Reed. 111 COLCHESTER AVE, DPT PATH 05401 #050-02-1967 L1973 **PTH IG** *040 †50
MADDEN, Michelle. ■ 05401 #050-02-2006 L2006 **PTH** *012
MADSEN, Michael Scott. ■ 05408 #016-02-2006 L2006 **PTH** *012
MAGUIRE, Kathleen J. 199 MAIN ST 05401 #050-02-1974 L1980 **OPH** *071 †35
MAHAJAN, Angela. 111 COLCHESTER AVE, FAHC 05401 #050-02-2003 L2003 **GS** *100
MALSKA-JANCZA, Bozena A. 111 COLCHESTER AVE, HEALTH CAREPSYC 05401 #759-06-1985 L1996 **P** *100

MANDELL, Todd. 108 CHERRY ST, ALCOHOL & DRUG ABUSE PROGR 05401 #024-05-1985 L1989 **P** *020 †75
MANNAL, Patrick William. 111 COLCHESTER AVE WP2, FAHC DEPT OF SURGERY 05401 #035-03-2007 L2007 **GS** *012
MAO-DRAAYER, Yang. 1 S PROSPECT ST, UHC CAMPUS 4TH FLOOR 05401 #243-03-1990 N *100 †75 ‡
MARCY, Theodore Wendell. 111 COLCHESTER AVE, MED CTR CAMPUS E PAVILION 05401 #008-01-1980 L1993 **PUD CCM** *020 †20
MARTIN, Herbert L. ■ 05401 #024-05-1950 L1954 **N** *071 †75
MARTIN, Jacob Anthony. 111 COLCHESTER AVE, FLETCHER ALLEN HEALTH CARE 05401 #050-02-2003 L2003 **AN** *100
MASE, Vincent Joseph, Jr. 111 COLCHESTER AVE WP2, FAHC DEPT OF SURGERY 05401 #050-02-2002 L2006 **GS** *012
MATTHEWS, Ralph Lewis. 111 COLCHESTER AVE, FAHC 05401 #048-14-2004 L2004 **PTH** *012
MAURER, Tracey Sue. 111 COLCHESTER AVE 05401 #045-04-1987 L2001 **OBG** *020 †30
MAYER, Paul Julius. 111 COLCHESTER AVE 05401 #035-45-1969 L1971 **IM GE** *020 †20
MAZUZAN, John Edmund. 111 COLCHESTER AVE, DEPT ANES 05401 #050-02-1954 L1960 **AN** *030 †05
MC CAHILL, Laurence E. BLDG E309, SURGERY DEPT - GIVEN 05405 #036-07-1990 L2002 **GS** *020 †85
MC CUBBIN, Kathleen Rose. 111 COLCHESTER AVE, & LABORA 05401 #056-05-2006 L2006 **PTH** *012
MC FADDEN, David Wayne. 111 COLCHESTER AVE, FAHC FLETCHER HOUSE 301 05401 #051-01-1980 L2007 **GS SO** *012
MCGEE, Mark Robert Joseph. ■ 05401 #050-02-2008 *012
MC KAY, David Montgomery. 425 PEARL ST 05401 #050-02-1982 L1986 **P** *020 †75
MC KAY, Robert James, Jr. 1 S PROSPECT ST 05401 #024-01-1943 L1949 **PD RHU** *071 †55 ‡
MC LAUGHLIN, Thomas Paul. 60 COLCHESTER AVE 05401 #561-17-1980 L1986 **GE** *020 †20
MC SHERRY, Joseph Wall. 111 COLCHESTER AVE, PATRICK 5 05401 #048-04-1971 L1977 **N CN** *020 †75
MC SWEENEY, E Douglas, Jr. 1 S PROSPECT ST 05401 #065-09-1958 L1960 **GS VS** *071 †85
MEAD, Philip Bartlett. 111 COLCHESTER AVE, FLETCHER ALLEN HEALTH CARE 05401 #035-20-1963 L1971 **OS GYN** *030 †30
MELAMED, Trevor Ross. 111 COLCHESTER AVE, FAHCDEPT OF PSYCHIATRY 05401 #665-01-2005 L2005 **P** *012
MELLO, Claude H. 204 N WINOOSKI AVE 05401 #187-04-1954 L1974 **PTH HEM** *020 †50
MERCIER, Charles Eugene. 111 COLCHESTER AVE, VERMONT CHILDREN'S AT FAHC 05401 #008-02-1985 L1992 **NPM** *020 †20
MESSINA, Joseph Anthony. 1 S PROSPECT ST, ST JOSEPH'S THREE 05401 #028-34-1965 L2004 **P** *020 †75
MEYER, Lutz-Michael. ■ 05401 #409-05-1990 L1993 **PD** *100 †55
MEYER, Marjorie Clare. 1 S PROSPECT ST, ALLEN FLETCHER HEALTH CARE 05401 #011-03-1984 L1988 **OBG** *020 †20
MEYER, Markus Franz. 111 COLCHESTER AVE, MCHV - MCCLURE 1 -CARDIOLO 05401 #409-05-1992 L2000 **CD** *100 †20
MICHEL, Donald Angemarie. 111 COLCHESTER AVE, FAHCGME OFFICE 05401 #047-07-2001 L2004 **OBG** *020
MIHALICH, Robert Michael. 111 COLCHESTER AVE, & REHAB 05401 #024-07-2000 L2000 **ORS** *100
MILIARESIS, Christa Linda. 111 COLCHESTER AVE, PEDIATRIC CARDIOLO 05401 #008-02-2000 L2005 **PDC** *020 ‡
MILLAY, Donna Jean. 111 COLCHESTER AVE 05401 #051-04-1981 L1989 **FPS OTO** *020 †45
MILLAY, Robert H. 1 S PROSPECT ST 05401 #051-04-1980 L1989 **OPH** *020 †35
MILLER, Vincent James. 111 COLCHESTER AVE 05401 #654-01-2002 L2005 **AN** *100
MILLS, Sadie Elizabeth. ■ 05401 #050-02-2006 L2006 **IM** *012
MINGIN, Gerald C, Jr. ■ 05401 #033-05-1994 L2007 **UP** *020 †95
MIRO, Santiago Pedro M. 111 COLCHESTER AVE, DEPT OF RADIOLOGY 05401 #067-02-1992 L2000 **DR VIR** *020 †80
MISSELBECK, Wayne J A. 111 COLCHESTER AVE, FLETCHER ALLEN HEALTH CARE 05401 #041-09-1983 L1986 **EM** *040 †16
MOJDEHI, Rosa. 111 COLCHESTER AVE, FAHC DEPT OF OB/GYN 05401 #067-01-2006 L2006 **OBG** *012
MONAHAN, Meredith Davies. 111 COLCHESTER AVE, DEPT OF PEDIATRICS 05401 #003-01-2003 L2003 **PD** *100 †54
MOONEY, Sarah Jillian. 111 COLCHESTER AVE 05401 #539-02-2003 **IM** *012
MOORE, Eugene F. 28 S WILLIAMS ST, STE F 05401 #048-04-1998 L1998 **IM** *020 †20
MOORE, Jesse S. 111 COLCHESTER AVE, FAHCGME OFFICE 05401 #035-08-2004 L2004 **GS** *012
MORRIS, Christopher Scott. 111 COLCHESTER AVE 05401 #038-06-1985 L1991 **DR** *040 †80
MORRIS, Harold H, III. 89 S WILLIAMS ST 05401 #048-04-1968 L2004 **N CN** *020 †75
MORRIS, Julie Olin. 111 COLCHESTER AVE, AMBULATORY CARE CTR FAHC E 05401 #018-03-1985 L1985 **HEM** *020 †20
MORROW, Paul Lowell. 111 COLCHESTER AVE # 1 05401 #050-02-1976 L1981 **FOP LM** *020 †50 ‡
MOSES, Peter L. 111 COLCHESTER AVE MP-5, FAHC DIGESTIVE DISEASES CT 05401 #038-06-1990 L1991 **GE** *020 †20
MOUNT, Sharon Lee. 111 COLCHESTER AVE 05401 #048-12-1988 L1990 **PTH** *020 †50
MOUSSA, Runna Fayez. ■ 05405 #050-02-2007 L2007 **IM** *012
MROSZCZYK MC DONALD, Alex. ■ 05405 #050-02-2008 *012
MUELLER, Joachim Georg. 111 COLCHESTER AVE, INTERNAL MEDICINE 05401 #409-10-1995 L2005 **CD** *012 †20
MUNIZ-GIRON, Joaquin M. 111 COLCHESTER AVE, DEPT PUL DIS 05401 #847-15-1976 L1987 **PUD** *100
MURPHY, Laura L. 111 COLCHESTER AVE 05401 #024-05-1997 L1997 **PD** *020 †55
MURRAY, Christine A. 111 COLCHESTER AVE, FAHC, DEPT OF OB-GYN 05401 #026-08-1987 L1999 **P** *020 †30
MURRAY, John Jos, Jr. 1205 NORTH AVE 05408 #050-02-1963 L1965 **PD PSM** *020 †55 ‡
MURRAY, Sarah Grace. ■ 05401 #035-01-2008 *012
MUSS, Hyman B. 1 S PROSPECT ST 05401 #035-08-1968 L1996 **ON HEM** *020 †20
NAGLE, Keith Jos. 111 COLCHESTER AVE, PATRICK 5 05401 #019-02-1990 L1996 **N** *020 †75
NARASIMHAN, Beth Ann. 111 COLCHESTER AVE WP2, FAHC DEPT OF SURGERY 05401 #025-01-2005 L2005 **NS** *012
NATHAN, Muriel Helene. 1 S PROSPECT ST 05401 #025-12-1984 L1990 **END IM** *020 †20
NELSON, Alisa Lee. 111 COLCHESTER AVE, FAHC 05401 #048-14-2004 L2004 **PTH** *100 †50
NELSON, Robert Scott. 111 COLCHESTER AVE, DEPT OF FAMILY MEDICINE 05401 #035-09-2005 L2005 **FP** *012

NESLER, Sara Marie. 111 COLCHESTER AVE, FLETCHER ALLEN HEALTH CARE 05401 #018-03-2002 L2002 AN *020 †05

NEWHOUSE, Paul Alfred. 1 S PROSPECT ST 05401 #016-43-1977 L1988 P PYG *050 †75

NEY, Douglas Edward. 111 COLCHESTER AVE, FAHC 05401 #035-45-2003 L2003 IM *100

NICKERSON, Joshua Paul. 111 COLCHESTER AVE, FAHCDEPT OF RADIOLOGY 05401 #005-12-2005 L2006 DR *012

NIGRO, Neil John. 111 COLCHESTER AVE 05401 #024-05-1998 L2001 EM *020 †16

NOROTSKY, Mitchell C. 111 COLCHESTER AVE, FLETCHER 454 05401 #050-02-1989 L1989 TS *020 †85,90

OBERG, Kristin Channing. 111 COLCHESTER AVE, FAMILY MEDICINE 05401 #008-02-2003 L2004 FM *100 †18

O'BRIEN, John Patrick. 111 COLCHESTER AVE, DEPT OF RADIOLOGY 05401 #050-02-1989 L2000 DR *020

O'BRIEN, Patricia Jeri. 1 S PROSPECT ST, HEMATOLOGY ONCOLOGY 05401 #050-02-1985 L1989 IM *020

O'DONNELL, Stephen Edward. 111 COLCHESTER AVE, DEPT OF ANESTHESIOLOGY 05401 #050-02-1992 L1996 AN *020 †05

OPPENHEIMER, Robert Gould. 111 COLCHESTER AVE, DEPT OF RAD 05401 #024-16-1974 L1988 DR *020 †05

ORGAIN, Nathan Guthrie. ■ 05401 #050-02-2007 L2007 IM *012

ORR, Robert David. 111 COLCHESTER AVE 05401 #067-01-1966 L1971 FM *071 †18

OSLER, Turner M. 111 COLCHESTER AVE 05401 #051-04-1977 L1995 GS *020 †85

PACKARD, Sara Jane. 111 COLCHESTER AVE 05401 #050-02-1990 L1990 IM *020 †20

PAGANELLI, William C. MED CTR HOSP OF VERMONT, DEPT OF ANESTHESIA 05401 #024-01-1986 L1990 AN *020 †05

PAGE, Harold Gordon. 1 S PROSPECT ST 05401 #050-02-1945 L1948 GS *020 †85

PAGE, Kristin Marie. 111 COLCHESTER AVE, FAHCDEPT OF PEDIATRICS 05401 #050-02-2002 L2002 PHO *012

PALMER, Cathy Joy. 111 COLCHESTER AVE 05401 #017-20-1993 L1997 PTH PCP *020 †50

PANITCH, Hillel Selig. 89 S WILLIAMS ST 05401 #035-19-1967 L2000 N *050 †75

PAPINEAU, Karl. 111 COLCHESTER AVE, FAHC DEPT OF PSYCHIATRY 05401 #067-02-2005 L2006 P *012

PARANYA, Gretchen F. ■ 05408 #067-01-2005 L2005 OBG *012

PARKER, Suzanne Revoir. 118 PINE ST 05401 #050-02-1973 L1974 P *020 †75 ‡

PARSONS, Polly Elsbeth. 111 COLCHESTER AVE, FLETCHER 311 FAHC 05401 #003-01-1978 L2000 PUD IM *050 †20

PASANEN, Mark Eliot. 310 PINE ST 05401 #050-02-1992 L1996 IM *020 †20

PATEL, Charmaine Kamini. ■ 05405 #050-02-2007 L2007 PD *012

PATEL, Kumar Ravjibhai. 111 COLCHESTER AVE, MCHV MAIL ROOM-NEUROLOGY 05401 #496-41-2001 L2006 N *012

PATERSON, Ryan Douglas. ■ 05405 #050-02-2007 L2007 EM *012

PEASE, Richard E. 80 COLCHESTER AVE BOX 2262 05401 #050-02-1949 L1950 AN *071 †05

PECSENYICKI, Stephen M. 111 COLCHESTER AVE, AMBULATORY CARE CENTER 05401 #056-06-1998 L2005 OPH *020 †35

PELLETIER, Corinne Anne. 2 CHURCH ST STE 4E 05401 #054-04-1991 L1992 P *020 †75

PENAR, Paul Louis. 111 COLCHESTER AVE # FAHC, 507 FLEUTUTER MCHV CMPS 05401 #025-01-1981 L1988 NS *020 †25

PENDLEBURY, William Ward. 1 S PROSPECT ST # PATH, UTM COLLEGE OF MEDICINE 05401 #050-02-1976 L1979 NP *020 †75

PENNEY, Robert Alan, Jr. 789 PINE ST 05401 #050-02-1975 L1986 FM *020 †18

PENTSOVA, Olena Ivanovna. 111 COLCHESTER AVE, MCHV MAIL ROOM-NEUROLOGY 05401 #913-04-1992 L2006 N *012

PERRON, Michelle Leigh. 1205 NORTH AVE 05408 #050-02-1995 L1999 PD *020 †55

PERUSSE, Karina. 111 COLCHESTER AVE, FLETCHER ALLEN, RADIOLOGY 05401 #067-03-1997 L2006 *100

PHAN, Son Lam. 111 COLCHESTER AVE, FAHC 05401 #050-02-2003 L2003 DR *012

PHILIPS, George K. 1 S PROSPECT ST, ST JOSEPH 3400 05401 #495-01-1986 L1999 IM HO *020 †20

PHILLIPPE, Mark. 111 COLCHESTER AVE, FLETCHER ALLEN HEALTH CARE 05401 #016-06-1974 L2001 MFM OBG *030 †30

PHILLIPS, Carol Leah F. ■ 05401 #008-01-1958 L1966 ID PD *071 †55

PIERCE, Kristen Kelly. 111 COLCHESTER AVE, INTERNAL MEDICINE 05401 #050-02-2003 L2003 ID *012 †20

PIERSON, Dianne Carol. 168 BATTERY ST 05401 #048-02-1968 L1972 P NTR *020

PILCHER, David Bogart. 111 COLCHESTER AVE 05401 #035-45-1961 L1963 TRS GS *020 †85

PINN, Elke. 111 COLCHESTER AVE, DEPT MED 05401 #050-02-1989 L1989 AN *020 †05

PLANK, Benjamin Girton. ■ 05401 #011-02-2006 L2006 IM *012

PLANTE, Mark Kenneth. 111 COLCHESTER AVE EP5, FAHC / UROLOGY ASSOCIATES 05401 #067-01-1991 L1996 U *020 †95

POLISH, Louis B. 111 COLCHESTER AVE, SMITH 274 05401 #050-02-1981 L2004 PUD IM *020 †20

PORTER, Jon Kevin. 425 PEARL ST 05401 #054-04-1982 L1992 FM FSM *020 †18

POST, Alexander Farber. 111 COLCHESTER AVE, FAHCDEPT OF NEUROSURGERY 05401 #035-47-1999 L1999 NS *012

POTHIAWALA, Gulnar Amin. ■ 05405 #050-02-2008 *012

POWELL, Hannah S. 86 LAKE ST STE 3 05401 #050-02-1988 L1998 P *020 †75

POWELL, Platt Rugar. 111 COLCHESTER AVE 05401 #050-02-1939 L1946 U *072 †95

PRATLEY, Richard Edwin. 40 COLCHESTER AVE, FLETCHER ALLEN HEALTH CARE 05401 #025-07-1983 L2004 DIA IMG *050 †20

PRICE, Frederick Mason. 111 COLCHESTER AVE, FAHCDEPT OF PSYCHIATRY 05401 #025-12-1997 L1999 P *040

PRICE, Nathaniel Owen. 111 COLCHESTER AVE, DEPT OF INTERNAL MED 05401 #539-06-2006 L2006 IM *012

PRIMM, Jane Carol. 111 COLCHESTER AVE, FLETCHER ALLEN HEALTH CARE 05401 #054-04-1985 L2002 DR *020 †80

PRIVETTE, Alicia Renee. ■ 05401 #049-01-2005 L2005 GS *012

QUAYLE, Sara A. 1205 NORTH AVE 05408 #050-02-1983 L1987 PD *020 †55

RABINOWITZ, Terry. 111 COLCHESTER AVE 05401 #038-06-1989 L1996 P PFP *020 †75

RACHA, Lori Beth. 1 S PROSPECT ST, 3RD FL 05401 #024-01-1997 L2004 PD *020 †55

RACZKOWSKA NAYLOR, M. 1 S PROSPECT ST, DEPT PSYCH 05401 #759-03-1976 L1993 P PME *020 †75

RAHIM, Azra. 111 COLCHESTER AVE WP22, FAMILY MEDICINE 05401 #040-02-2005 L2007 GS *100

RAI, Inderjeet Kaur. ■ 05405 #050-02-2007 FP *012

RAMUNDO, Mary Beth. 1 S PROSPECT ST 05401 #033-06-1986 L1995 ID IM *040 †20

RASZKA, William Vincent. GIVEN BLDG, UNIV OF VERMONT COLLEGE OF 05405 #024-05-1985 L1995 PD PDI *020 †55

RATKOVITS, Bela. M FLETCHER UNIT, DEPT RAD 05401 #016-02-1962 L1974 RNR *020 †80

REARDON, Mildred Ann. 89 BEAUMONT AVE, GIVEN E-109 05405 #050-02-1967 L1968 IM ON *071 †20

REEVES, Shane Aaron. 111 COLCHESTER AVE 05401 #035-45-2002 L2005 OBG *100

REHMAN, Tariq. 1 S PROSPECT ST, REHAB 2 , UHC CAMPUS 05401 #704-01-1999 L2006 NEP *012 †20

REPP, Allen Bowman, II. 1 S PROSPECT ST, GIVEN HEALTHCARE, UHC CAMP 05401 #048-12-1999 L2003 IM *020 †20

RETTEW, David Charles. 1 S PROSPECT ST, ARNOLD 6 05401 #050-02-1996 L2002 CHP *020 †75

RICCI, Michael Anthony. 111 COLCHESTER AVE 05401 #035-15-1982 L1988 VS *020 †85

RICE, Sarah Arnott. 111 COLCHESTER AVE 05401 #054-04-2000 L2005 FM *020 †18 ‡

RIDDICK, Daniel Howison. 111 COLCHESTER AVE, WOMEN'S HEALTHCARE SERVICE 05401 #036-07-1967 L1985 OBG REN *020 †30

RIDEOUT, Marianne Everett. 1 S PROSPECT ST, UNIVERSITY PEDIATRICS 05401 #067-01-1994 L1994 PD *020 †55

RIESENFELD, Erik Peter. 111 COLCHESTER AVE, FLETCHER ALLEN HEALTH CARE 05401 #035-45-2001 L2001 PCC *012

RIMMER, Jeffrey Michael. 111 COLCHESTER AVE, MED CTR HOSP OF VT 05401 #008-02-1976 L1979 IM NEP *020 †20

RINEHART, Jill Stuart. 410 SHELBURNE RD 05401 #026-04-1996 L1996 PD *020 †55

RIOUX, Nicole Ann. 111 COLCHESTER AVE, FLETCHER ALLEN HEALTH CARE 05401 #050-02-2001 L2001 RHU *012 †20

RISSACHER, Patty Waterhou. 111 COLCHESTER AVE WP2, FAHC DEPT OF PEDIATRICS 05401 #050-02-2005 L2005 PD *012

ROBERTSON, Peter Alexande. & REHABILITATI, UVMORTHOPAEDICS 05405 #671-01-1982 L1991 *100

ROBINSON, Donald Stetson. ■ 05401 #041-01-1959 L1962 PA IM *071 †20

ROBINSON, Keith Johnson. ■ 05405 #050-02-2007 L2007 PD *012

ROGERS, Frederick Bolles. UNIVERSITY VERMONT, GIVEN D319 05405 #050-02-1981 L1990 GS *020 †85

ROLAND, Thomas Arthur. 111 COLCHESTER AVE 05401 #038-41-1973 L1978 RO *020 †80

ROMANKO, Monica Catheryn. 16 HENRY ST 05401 #050-02-2003 L2003 FM *020 †18

ROMANO, Joann Frances. 111 COLCHESTER AVE, FAHCDEPT OF PEDIATRICS 05401 #050-02-2006 L2006 PD *012

ROOMET, Andres. 89 S WILLIAMS ST 05401 #041-01-1970 L1974 N *020 †75

ROOS, John Robt. 2 CHURCH ST, STE 2B 05401 #026-04-1981 L1986 GPM P *020

ROSENAU, Paul Tenney. 111 COLCHESTER AVE, FLETCHER ALLEN HEALTH CARE 05401 #024-01-2004 L2004 PD *100 †55

RUBIN, Alan Saul. 371 PEARL ST 05401 #035-19-1968 L1973 IM *040 †20

RUBIN, Deborah Zlata. 111 COLCHESTER AVE 05401 #007-02-1984 L1984 RO HEM *020 †80

RUBIN, Richard Lewis. 789 PINE ST 05401 #028-34-1972 L2002 P CHP *050 †75

RUBMAN, Amy Beth. 1205 NORTH AVE 05408 #050-02-1996 L2000 IM *020 †20

RUBMAN, Jeffrey Warren. 1205 NORTH AVE 05408 #050-02-1971 L1973 IM *020 †20 ‡

RUBRIGHT, James Hardman. OF MED, UNIV OF VERMONT COLL 05405 #036-01-2007 L2007 ORS *012

RUCH, Stuart Wm. 111 COLCHESTER AVE, FAHC DEPT OF CARDIOLOGY 05401 #004-01-1991 L2002 CD *020 †20

RUDE, Catherine Suzanne. 1 S PROSPECT ST, 3RD FL 05401 #041-14-1983 L1991 PD *020 †55

RUESS, Johanna M De Rot. 1 S PROSPECT ST 05401 #660-03-1956 L1973 PM *071 †60

RUFA, Erik Paul. 111 COLCHESTER AVE, CHIEF RESIDENT, INTERNAL 05401 #539-06-2003 L2003 IM *100 †20

RUFFLE, Thomas Matthew. ■ 05401 #035-19-1971 L1986 IM *020 †55

RUGHANI, Anand Indulal. 111 COLCHESTER AVE, FAGC DEPT OF SURGERY 05401 #067-01-2006 NS *012

RUNGE, Carl Frederick. 1205 NORTH AVE 05408 #067-01-1962 L1967 IMG IM *030

SALERNO, Richard Anthony. 111 COLCHESTER AVE, MCCLURE 3 PICU 05401 #051-04-1993 L2004 CCP *020 †20,55

SALSALI, Afshin. 1 S PROSPECT ST, ENDOCRINE CLINIC, UHC 5TH 05401 #517-01-1991 L2001 END IM *040 †20

SALTZMAN, Beth Melanie. 111 COLCHESTER AVE, INTERNAL MEDICINE 05401 #034-01-2007 L2007 IM *012

SANDERS, Justin J. ■ 05405 #050-02-2007 *012

SANDHU, Faraz. 111 COLCHESTER AVE, FAHCDEPT OF CARDIOLOGY 05401 #704-25-2000 L2006 CD *012 †20

SANTOS, Arvin Lopez. 111 COLCHESTER AVE, FLETCHER ALLEN HLTH CARE 05401 #748-02-2002 L2007 NEP *012 †20

SARTORELLI, Kennith Hans. 111 COLCHESTER AVE, FLETCHER ALLEN HEALTH CARE 05401 #050-02-1987 L1987 PDS *020 †85

SAULNIER, Giselle Linda. 111 COLCHESTER AVE, FAHC 05401 #035-09-1999 L2005 PHO *100 †55

SAUNDERS, Jessica Ann. ■ 05408 #050-02-2002 L2005 IM *020 †20 ‡

SCHAFFER, William Allen. 111 COLCHESTER AVE, DEPT PSYCH FAHC 05401 #054-04-1975 L2006 P *012 †20 ‡

SCHAPIRO, Howard Marc. 111 COLCHESTER AVE, FLETCHER ALLEN HLTHCARE 05401 #050-02-1980 L1980 AN *020 †05

SCHERMERHORN, Suzanne Hel. ■ 05401 #026-04-2005 L2005 IM *012

SCHMOKER, Joseph D. 111 COLCHESTER AVE, FLETCHER 454 05401 #028-34-1987 L1987 TS *020 †85,90

SCHNEIDER, David John. 111 COLCHESTER AVE, MCCLURE 1 CARDIO FAHC 05401 #038-41-1986 L1994 CD IM *050 †20

SCHNEIDER, John Gregory. 111 COLCHESTER AVE, VERMONT-FLETCHER ALLEN 05401 #056-06-2006 L2006 GS *012

SCHNURE, Joel J. 1 S PROSPECT ST, FIFTH FLOOR 05401 #035-06-1966 L2001 DIA END *020 †20

SCHULTES, Glenn James. ■ 05401 #016-01-1987 L2005 DR *012

SCHULTZ, Joseph Donald. 425 PEARL ST 05401 #041-02-1955 L1956 OS *020 †18

SCHWARZENBERGER, Kathryn. 111 COLCHESTER AVE 05401 #048-02-1987 L2006 D IM *020 †20,15

SCRIVER, Geoffrey Michael. 111 COLCHESTER AVE, FAHC DEPT OF SURGERY 05401 #050-02-2003 L2003 GS *012

SECKER-WALKER, Roger H. 1 S PROSPECT ST 05401 #917-30-1959 L1981 IM NM *050 †28

SEROU, Michael John. 111 COLCHESTER AVE WP2, FAHC DEPT OF RADIOLOGY 05401 #021-05-2002 L2006 DR *100 †80

SEWARD, Elizabeth Anne. 18 PINE ST 05401 #050-02-1985 L1988 IM *020 †20

SHACKFORD, Steven Robt. 1 S PROSPECT ST # SURG, UVM COLLEGE OF MEDICINE 05401 #028-34-1973 L1989 GS *020 †85

SHAFRITZ, Adam Brent. 1 S PROSPECT ST, FLETCHER ALLEN HEALTH CARE 05401 #041-01-1995 L2001 **HS** *020 †40

SHAH, Anuj Kumar. 1 S PROSPECT ST AR, FAHC DEPT OF ORTHOPEDICS 05401 #016-43-2005 L2006 **FP** *012

SHAH, Dishant Girish. 111 COLCHESTER AVE, FAHC DEPT OF RADIOLOGY 05401 #050-02-2004 L2005 **DR** *100

SHAPIRO, Jeryl Robt. 111 COLCHESTER AVE 05401 #041-02-1974 L1977 **AN** *020 †05

SHAPIRO, Robert E. 1 S PROSPECT ST, UHC CAMPUS 6TH FLOOR 05401 #035-01-1987 L1998 **N** *020 †75

SHAPIRO, Steven Lawrence. 111 COLCHESTER AVE, MEDICAL EX 05401 #050-02-1993 L1999 **PTH** *020 †50

SHEESER, Jon Michael, Jr. ■ 05401 #034-01-2002 L2004 **EM** *020 †16

SHERMAN, Jessica F. ■ 05408 #035-15-2003 L2003 **PCP** *012 †50

SHERMAN, William M. 111 COLCHESTER AVE, FAHCMEDICINE 05401 #035-15-2003 L2003 **DR** *012

SHIELDS, Joseph Thomas. 111 COLCHESTER AVE, FLETCHER ALLEN HLTHCARE 05401 #050-02-1998 L1999 **DR** *100 †80

SHOLLER, Peter Frederick. 1 S PROSPECT ST 05401 #035-09-1999 L2005 **IM** *020 †20

SHORT, Cynthia Larrabee. 84 HOWARD ST 05401 #035-03-1986 L2002 **NEP** *020 †20

SHRINER, Wilbur L, III. 37 N PROSPECT ST 05401 #050-02-1980 L1981 **EM** *020 †16

SIEGEL, Andrew. 196 BATTERY ST 05401 #041-01-1968 L1974 **P** *020 †75

SILLICK, Craig Daniel. ■ 05408 #023-01-2007 L2007 **FP** *012

SILVERMAN, Damon Andrew. 111 COLCHESTER AVE, W PAVILION LVL 4 OTOLERTGN 05401 #005-19-1997 L2004 **OTO** *020 †45

SIMPATICO, Thomas Anthony. 111 COLCHESTER AVE, UNIVERITY OF VERMONT/FAHC 05401 #016-01-1984 L2004 **P** *030 †75

SIMS, Ethan Allen H. 1 S PROSPECT ST 05401 #035-01-1942 L1950 **END** *072 †20

SINGARAM, Vanitha. 111 COLCHESTER AVE, HEALTH CAREGME 05401 #495-94-1997 L2005 **END** *020 †20

SINGER, Clifford Milo. 1 S PROSPECT ST, DEPT OF PSYCH 05401 #011-03-1980 L2005 **P PYG** *040 †75

SIROIS, Michael. 617 RIVERSIDE AVE, COMMUNITY HEALTH CTR BURLI 05401 #032-01-1983 L1988 **FM** *020 †20

SKITT, Rochelle Jettahn. ■ 05401 #028-34-2007 L2007 **IM** *012

SLABYJ, Natalka Antonia. 1 MILL ST, BOX C13 05401 #050-02-1990 L2000 **IM** *020 †20

SLAVIK, Paul William. 111 COLCHESTER AVE, INTERNAL MEDICINE 05401 #056-05-2004 L2004 **IM** *100

SLINGERLAND, David Tucker. 111 COLCHESTER AVE, HEALTH CAREGME 05401 #422-01-2005 L2005 **FP** *012

SMAIL, David Frederick. 111 COLCHESTER AVE, DEPARTMENT ANESTHESIOLOGY 05401 #024-07-1970 L1977 **AN** *020 †05

SMILEY, Shannon Laverne. 111 COLCHESTER AVE, FAHCDEPT OF PATHOLOGY 05401 #422-01-1997 L1999 **ON** *100 †20

SMITH, Cynthia Susanne. 1 S PROSPECT ST 05401 #024-07-2000 L2000 **IM** *020 †20

SMITH, Susan Fay. 23 MANSFIELD AVE 05401 #025-01-1976 L1977 **OBG** *020 †30

SOARES, Jennifer Jean. ■ 05405 #050-02-2007 L2007 **PD** *012

SOBEL, Halle Giffin. 1 S PROSPECT ST, 1 SOUTH PROSPECT ST 05401 #050-02-1999 L2002 **IM** *020 †20

SOBOL, Krzysztof. 111 COLCHESTER AVE, INTERNAL MEDICINE 05401 #759-01-2004 L2005 **IM** *100

SOFFERMAN, Robert Alan. 1 S PROSPECT ST 05401 #023-01-1967 L1975 **OTO OS** *020 †45

SOKOL, Karen Elizabeth. ■ 05401 #050-02-2003 L2005 **FM** *100 †18

SOLL, Roger Franklin. 111 COLCHESTER AVE, BURGESS 426 F ALLEN HLTH 05401 #016-42-1978 L1983 **NPM** *050 †55 ‡

SOLOMON, Richard Jay. 1 S PROSPECT ST, UHC 2309 05401 #008-01-1970 L2002 **NEP IM** *020 †20

SOOD, Jaideep. 111 COLCHESTER AVE - PATRI, FLETCHER ALLEN HEALTH CARE 05401 #661-03-2003 L2006 **PCC** *012

SOTO, Julio Cesar, Jr. 111 COLCHESTER AVE WP2, FAHC DEPT OF SURGERY 05401 #305-01-2006 L2006 **GS** *012

SOULTANAKIS, Emmanuel N. 111 COLCHESTER AVE, DEPT OF OB/GYN 05401 #050-02-1996 L1996 **OBG** *020 †30

SPAULDING, Laurie. 111 COLCHESTER AVE, ACO MAIN PAVILION 5TH FLOO 05401 #050-02-1984 L1984 **GS** *020 †85

SPECTOR, Peter Salem. 111 COLCHESTER AVE, MCCLURE 1 - CARDIOLOGY 05401 #035-46-1990 L1990 **CD** *020 †20

SPROUL, Marga Susan. 89 BEAUMONT AVE, UVM E215 05405 #050-02-1976 L1978 **FM** *071 †18

STACKPOLE, James Ward. 1205 NORTH AVE 05408 #050-02-1956 L1958 **PD ADL** *072 †55

STANLEY, Andrew Carl. 1 S PROSPECT ST 05401 #043-01-1991 L1998 **VS** *020 †85

STANLEY, Mary Armstrong. 111 COLCHESTER AVE, WPZ-CANCER CTR-FAHC 05401 #043-01-1990 L1998 **GS** *020 †85

STAPLETON, Renee Doney. 111 COLCHESTER AVE, UNIVERSITY OF VERMONT/FLET 05401 #054-04-1998 L2007 **PCC** †20

STEINBERG, Judith Ellen. 111 COLCHESTER AVE 05401 #035-46-1979 L1982 **IM** *020 †20

STEINGARD, Sandra. 300 FLYNN AVE 05401 #024-07-1981 L1993 **P** *020 †75

STEMMONS, Jessica Bland. 111 COLCHESTER AVE, FAHCDEPT OF ANESTHESIOLOGY 05401 #048-13-2005 L2006 **AN** *012

STEPHENS, Bradford Dougla. 111 COLCHESTER AVE WP22, FAHC DEPT OF PEDIATRICS 05401 #054-04-2005 L2005 **PD** *012

STOPPACHER, Robert. 111 COLCHESTER AVE, FAHC DEPT OF PATHOLOGY 05401 #050-02-1996 L1996 **FOP** *020 †50

STOUCH, William H. ■ 05401 #035-01-1961 L1965 **IM** *071 ‡

STRADER, Doris Bea. 111 COLCHESTER AVE, GASTNLGY DEPT CLGE OF MED 05401 #010-02-1987 L2002 **IM** *020 †20

STRAUSS, John Stuart. 111 COLCHESTER AVE, HEALTH CARE/PSY 05401 #065-01-1992 L1996 **CHP** *100 †75

STRICKLER, William Lee. ■ 05408 #024-01-1956 L1956 **U** *071 †95

STURTEVANT, Norman Vaughn. 111 COLCHESTER AVE # RAD, MED CTR HOSP OF VT 05401 #050-02-1980 L1983 **DR** *020 †80

SUPPAN, Thomas. 111 COLCHESTER AVE 05401 #050-02-1994 L1994 **PTH** *020 †50

SURATT, Benjamin T. 149 BEAUMONT AVE, HSRF 230 05405 #035-01-1993 L2002 **PCC IM** *050 †20

SUSSMAN, Betsy Lee. MED CTR HOSP OF VT, DEPT OF RAD PATRICK 1 05401 #050-02-1981 L1986 **DR** *040 †80

SUTHERLAND, Michael Alan. ■ 05408 #049-01-2004 L2004 **AN** *012

SWARTZ, Donald Reed. 111 COLCHESTER AVE 05401 #055-01-1963 L1967 **PD** *030 †55

SWIFT, Peter De Mott. 111 COLCHESTER AVE 05401 #035-15-1977 L1984 **RO** *020 †80

SZMODIS, Michael Louis. 111 COLCHESTER AVE, INTERNAL MEDICINE 05401 #010-02-2007 L2007 **IM** *012

TABAKIN, Burton S. 111 COLCHESTER AVE 05401 #041-01-1947 L1949 **PDC CD** *071 †20

TADROS, Caroline Ramzi. 111 COLCHESTER AVE, FAHC/UVM 05401 #035-46-2002 L2006 **GE** *012 †20

TAHERI, Paul Abbas. 111 COLCHESTER AVE 05401 #035-19-1988 L2007 **GS** *020 †85

TAM, Judy Kit. 111 COLCHESTER AVE, FLETCHER ALLEN HEALTH CARE 05401 #005-02-1988 L1995 **DR** *020 †80

TAMPAS, John Peter. MED CENTER HOSP OF VERMONT, DEPARTMENT OF RADIOLOGY 05401 #050-02-1954 L1959 **R** *072 †80 ‡

TAMURA, Thomas Kiyoshi. 111 COLCHESTER AVE, OF OTOLARYNGOLOGY 05401 #033-05-2006 L2007 **OTO** *012

TANDAN, Rup. 1 S PROSPECT ST, UNIV HEALTH CENTER 05401 #495-05-1970 L1983 **N OS** *020 †75

TANG, Mary Elizabeth. 111 COLCHESTER AVE, FAHC LABORATORY 05401 #050-02-1984 L1989 **CCG PCH** *020 †50

TAPE, Christopher James. ■ 05401 #034-01-2004 L2004 **PTH** *012

TAPUCU, Nilgun. 1 S PROSPECT ST, 3RD FL 05401 #067-01-1999 L2003 *020 †55

TEHRANI, Taraneh. 111 COLCHESTER AVE, INTERNL MED 05401 #050-02-2004 L2005 **IM** *100 †20

TEKLE, Alemnesh Mesfin. 111 COLCHESTER AVE, INTERNAL MEDICINE 05401 #024-16-2006 L2006 **IM** *012

TEO, Elrond Yi Lang. 111 COLCHESTER AVE, FAHC DEPT OF SURGERY 05401 #917-31-2006 L2007 **GS** *012

TERRIEN, Christopher Marl. 111 COLCHESTER AVE, FAHC 05401 #050-02-2003 L2003 **GS** *012

TERRIEN, Timothy John. 28 S WILLIAMS ST 05401 #050-02-1968 L1969 **IM NEP** *020 †20

THAKKER, Manoj Mangaldas. 111 COLCHESTER AVE, ACC WP5 05401 #035-47-1999 L2005 **OPH** *035

THIBAULT, Amy Beth. 96 COLCHESTER AVE 05401 #024-16-1999 L1999 **OBG** *020 †30

THOMPSON, Margaret V. 111 COLCHESTER AVE, FAHC 05401 #032-01-2004 L2004 **IM** *100

THOMPSON, Nathaniel Clark. ■ 05408 #028-34-2006 L2006 **IM** *012

THORBURN, Charles Webster. 111 COLCHESTER AVE # CARD, MED CTR HOSP OF VT 05401 #917-23-1967 **CD** *020

TILLUCKDHARRY, Lynda Seet. 111 COLCHESTER AVE, INTERNAL MEDICINE 05401 #539-06-2004 L2006 **IM** *012

TINDLE, Barbara Heywood. 1 S PROSPECT ST, DEPT HEM 05401 #041-07-1961 L1977 **HMP PTH** *020 †50

TORBIN, Valery Vasilievic. 111 COLCHESTER AVE, OF ANESTHESIOLOGY 05401 #913-39-1976 L2005 **AN** *100

TORMEY, David Michael. GIVEN BLDG 05401 #035-09-1948 **IM** *030 †20

TRABULSY, Philip Patrick. 1 S PROSPECT ST 05401 #051-07-1985 L1985 **GS** *020 †85,65

TRABUSLY, Mario Elizabeth. 111 COLCHESTER AVE 05401 #050-02-1991 L1996 **EM** *020 †16

TRAINER, Thomas Dermott. 111 COLCHESTER AVE 05401 #024-07-1954 L1960 **PTH** *020 †50

TRAN, Thai Lan Nguyen. ■ 05401 #050-02-2008 †012

TRANMER, Bruce Ian. 111 COLCHESTER AVE, NEUROSURGERY, ACC EP 5 05401 #065-05-1979 L1999 **NS** *020 †25

TRAVIS, Lewis Nathaniel. ■ 05401 #352-07-1960 L1967 **N** *071 †75

TREIAL-KINK, Salme. ■ 05408 #363-01-1939 L1960 **P** *071

TREVISANI, Gino Thos. 111 COLCHESTER AVE, DEPT OF SURGERY, FLETCHER 05401 #050-02-1991 L1991 **GS** *020 †85,10

TRILLIS, Christina Marie. ■ 05405 #050-02-2007 L2007 **IM** *012

TROTTER, Samuel J. 111 COLCHESTER AVE, # ACC 05401 #016-11-1981 L1983 **U** *020 †95

TRUONG, Minh Thinh. 111 COLCHESTER AVE, FAHC 05401 #143-11-2003 L2004 *100

TSAI, Erin Mc Quaide. 111 COLCHESTER AVE, FAHCDEPT OF RADIOLOGY 05401 #050-02-2002 L2002 **DR** *100

TSAI, Mitchell Honbing. 111 COLCHESTER AVE, FLETCHER ALLEN HEALTH CARE 05401 #050-02-2002 L2003 **AN** *100 †05

TUFO, Henry Michael. GIVEN HEALTH CARE CTR, MED CTR HOSP OF VT 05401 #016-11-1964 L1970 **IM** *075 †20

TUTSCHKA, Barbara G. 111 COLCHESTER AVE 05401 #759-03-1962 L1989 **PTH** *020 †50

TZIMAS, Georgios Nicolas. 111 COLCHESTER AVE 05401 #418-01-1992 L2002 **GS** *020

TZOU, Katherine S. ■ 05401 #038-40-2007 L2007 **IM** *012

UKENA, Thomas Eric. ■ 05401 #024-01-1975 L1978 **PTH** *030 †50

UNGER, Byron Paul. 111 COLCHESTER AVE, HEALTH CAREANES 05401 #068-01-1993 L1996 **AN** *020 †05

UPHOLD, Ruth Esther. 111 COLCHESTER AVE 05401 #024-07-1974 L1981 **EM** *040 †16

VALENTON, Kathleen Rochel. ■ 05405 #050-02-2007 *012

VANBUREN, Peter Carmen. 111 COLCHESTER AVE, FLETCHER ALLEN HLTH CTR 05401 #050-02-1987 L1992 **IM** *020 †20

VANE, Dennis Wm. 111 COLCHESTER AVE, FLETCHER ALLEN HLTHCARE 05401 #165-01-1978 L1990 **PDS TRS** *020 †85

VECCHIO, James Anthony. BURGESS 416 MCHR, UNIVERSITY OF VERMONT 05405 #067-01-1980 L1987 **GE IM** *020 †20

VELTKAMP, Jessica Katheri. 111 COLCHESTER AVE WP2, FAHC DEPT OF OBGYN 05401 #011-03-2006 L2006 **OBG** *012

VERLEUR, Denise Anne. 3 S WILLARD ST 05401 #041-07-1984 L1984 **OBG** *020 †30

VIANI, Bruce Allan. 111 COLCHESTER AVE 05401 #016-06-1983 L1987 **AN** *020 †05

VIAPIANO, James. 111 COLCHESTER AVE, FAHL PATRICK 2 DEPT ANBEST 05401 #050-02-1988 L1998 **AN** *020 †05

VISCOMI, Christopher M. ■ 05401 #048-02-1985 L1992 **AN OBS** *020 †05

VON ZUR MUHLEN, F K. 111 COLCHESTER AVE, FAHC-MCHV CAMPUS, CARDIOLO 05401 #409-07-1992 L2001 **IM** *020 †20

VORENKAMP, Kevin Edward. 111 COLCHESTER AVE, OF ANESTHESIOLOGY 05401 #025-01-2002 L2006 **APM** *020 †05

WAGENER, Jessica Heimer. ■ 05408 #035-06-1991 L1992 **EM IM** *020 †20

WAGERS, Scott Stanley. 111 COLCHESTER AVE 05401 #007-02-1995 L1995 **PCC** *020 †20

WALLACE, Harold James, III. 111 COLCHESTER AVE, FLETCHER ALLEN HLTH CARE 05401 #050-02-1988 L2000 **RO** *020 †80

WALSH, Michael Thomas. ■ 05401 #017-20-2001 L2003 **NS** *012

WARING, John Timothy. 111 COLCHESTER AVE, OF ANESTHESIOLOGY 05401 #012-05-2003 L2005 **AN** *012

WARNKEN, Wayne Leslie, II. 617 RIVERSIDE AVE 05401 #007-02-2000 L2004 **FM** *020 †18

WARWICK, Arthur Mark. 111 COLCHESTER AVE, PATRICK 4, PSYCHIATRY 05401 #023-01-1970 L1998 **P PYG** *020 †75

WASSERMAN, Richard Charle. 1 S PROSPECT ST, 3RD FL 05401 #041-02-1976 L1977 PD GPM *071 †55 ‡

WATERMAN, Gerald Scott. 89 BEAUMONT AVE, GIVEN E215 05405 #025-01-1982 L1993 P CHP *040 †75

WATERS, Brenda. 1 PROSPECT AVE 05405 #050-02-1977 L1982 PTH *020 †50

WATSON, Nicholas C. 111 COLCHESTER AVE, OF ANESTHESIOLOGY 05401 #025-01-2003 L2005 AN *012

WEAVER, Curtis Randall. ■ 05408 #038-45-2007 L2007 IM *012

WEAVER, Donald Lee. 111 COLCHESTER AVE, PATHOLOGY ACC 05401 #050-02-1984 L1985 ATP CLP *020 †50

WEED, Lawrence Leonard. 1 MILL ST 05401 #035-01-1947 L1969 OS IM *030

WEGNER, Elisabeth Kirsten. 111 COLCHESTER AVE, SMITH 420, MCHV CAMPUS 05401 #008-02-1992 L1992 OBG *020 †30

WEIMERSHEIMER, Peter E. 111 COLCHESTER AVE, EMERGENCY DEPT-MAIL DROP 2 05401 #050-02-1995 L1995 EM *020 †16

WEIRATHER, Kelly Jean. 111 COLCHESTER AVE, FLETCHER ALLEN HLTH CARE 05401 #050-02-2007 L2007 PD *012

WEISE, Wolfgang Johannes. 1 S PROSPECT ST 05401 #409-19-1980 L1993 IM *020 †20

WEISS, Daniel Jay. 149 BEAUMONT AVE, HLTH SCIE RESEAR FACIL, RM 05405 #035-47-1988 L2001 IM CCM *020 †20

WEISSGOLD, David Jay. 181 SAINT PAUL ST, RETINA CTR OF VERMONT 05401 #035-15-1991 L1997 OPH *020 †35

WESTON, Julia Randall. 111 COLCHESTER AVE 05401 #050-02-1998 L1998 OBG *020

WHITTAKER, Laurie Anne. 111 COLCHESTER AVE, PATRICK 311 05401 #024-07-1996 L2002 IM *020 †20

WICK, Heather Addison. 111 COLCHESTER AVE, FAHC-DEPT OF ANESTHESIOLOG 05401 #035-03-1999 L1999 FM *100

WILD, John James, III. 111 COLCHESTER AVE, FAHC 05401 #021-01-2003 L2003 ORS *012

WILLIAMS, Robert Keith. 111 COLCHESTER AVE, FLETCHER ALLEN HEALTH CARE 05401 #041-14-1982 L1984 PD GP *020 †05,55

WILLIAMSON, Genevieve Ann. ■ 05408 #041-12-2005 L2005 P *012

WILLINGHAM, Jennifer Lynn. 617 RIVERSIDE AVE, OF BURLINGTON 05401 #048-13-1999 L2002 FM *020 †18

WILLIS, Stephen Laird. 111 COLCHESTER AVE MP5 05401 #033-06-1998 L1998 IM *020 †20

WILLMUTH, Lewis Ragon. 1 S PROSPECT ST 05401 #004-01-1963 L1970 P *020 †75

WILSON, Lauren S. 111 COLCHESTER AVE 05401 #067-01-2007 L2007 PD *012

WINN, Washington C, Jr. 1 PROSPECT AVE 05405 #051-01-1967 L1977 PTH MM *075 †50

WINTERS, Ryan Daniel. ■ 05405 #050-02-2008 *012

WOLFSON, Daniel Lawrence. 1 S PROSPECT ST, F A H C 05401 #050-02-2000 L2002 EM *020 †16

WONG, Cheung. 1 S PROSPECT ST, FLETCHER ALLEN HEALTH CARE 05401 #035-19-1992 L1999 GO *020 †30

WOOD, Marie E. 89 BEAUMONT AVE, GIVEN E214 05405 #007-02-1985 L1997 ON HEM *020

WOOD, Michael James. 111 COLCHESTER AVE, FAHC 05401 #024-07-2004 L2004 GS *012

WRIGHT, John Matthew. 1205 NORTH AVE 05408 #050-02-2000 L2000 IM *020

YAMAGUCHI, Jon Steven. 111 COLCHESTER AVE, FLETCHER 469 05401 #041-13-1999 L2007 GS *100 †85

YARNELL, Ralph William. 111 COLCHESTER AVE, FLETCHER ALLEN HEALTH CARE 05401 #065-05-1977 L2004 AN *020 †05

YEAGER, Scott Brand. 111 COLCHESTER AVE, ACC-EP4 05401 #051-01-1975 L1979 PDC *020 †55

YEH, Frank. 111 COLCHESTER AVE, FAHC/UVM 05401 #016-42-2003 L2007 GE *012 †20

YEN, Christopher Andrew. 111 COLCHESTER AVE, FLETCHER ALLEN HLTH CARE 05401 #024-07-2006 L2007 AN *012

YOO, Carolyn Joohyun. ■ 05405 #050-02-2008 *012

YOUNG, Leslie Webster. ■ 05405 #050-02-2007 L2007 PD *012

YOUNG, Michael Peter. 111 COLCHESTER AVE, FAHC 05401 #050-02-1982 L2000 IM CCM *020 †20

YOUNG, Michelle Lynn. 199 MAIN ST, FLETCHER ALLEN HEALTH CARE 05401 #064-01-1996 L2001 *020

YOUNG, Roger Chas. 111 COLCHESTER AVE, FLETCHER ALLEN HEALTH CENT 05401 #036-01-1982 L2006 OBG *020 †20

ZAGROBA, Marie Lynn. ■ 05401 #050-02-1987 L1988 AN *020 †05

ZAKAI, Neil Adrian. 89 BEAUMONT AVE, GIVEN E-214 05405 #051-01-2000 L2000 HO *100 †20

ZEHLE, Christa Maria. 111 COLCHESTER AVE 05401 #050-02-1999 L2003 PD *020 †55

ZIMAKAS, Paul James Alexa. 111 COLCHESTER AVE, FLETCHER ALLEN HLTH CARE 05401 #067-01-1997 L2002 PDE PD *020 †55

ZNOJKIEWICZ, Pierre. 111 COLCHESTER AVE, FAHC DEPT OF INTERNAL MED 05401 #759-01-2005 L2005 IM *012

ZUBARIK, Richard Sanford. 111 COLCHESTER AVE, FLETCHER ALLEN HEALTH CARE 05401 #035-48-1992 L1992 GE IM *020 †20

CABOT — WASHINGTON

BILLINGS, Carl Emery. RT 2 BOX 2814 05647 #016-02-1942 L1956 IM *071 †20

CAMBRIDGE — CHITTENDEN

BERTOCCI, Paul Vincent. 272 N MAIN ST, FAMILY PRACTICE 05444 #024-05-1970 L1975 FM *020

BLAND, John Hardesty. ■ 05444 #041-02-1944 L1948 IM RHU *071 †20

LEADBETTER, Guy W, Jr. ■ 05444 #023-07-1953 L1967 U *071 †95

MILLER, Donald Barker, Jr. 272 N MAIN ST, FAMILY PRACTICE 05444 #050-02-1972 L1974 FM *020

NORMAN, Richard Jos. 236 LOFTFIELD DR 05444 #048-02-1971 L1976 IM EM *020 †20,16

NORRIS, Laura Mary. 272 N MAIN ST, FAMILY PRACTICE 05444 #050-02-1992 L1995 FM *020 †18

RICHTER, Deborah Ann. 272 N MAIN ST, FAMILY PRACTICE 05444 #035-06-1986 L1999 FM *020 †18

CASTLETON — RUTLAND

BAUZO, Luis Alberto. ■ 05735 #024-05-1984 L2007 PD *020 †55

ROGERS, Wallace A. 2194 SOUTH ST, P O BOX 315 05735 #026-04-1965 L1971 PTH *020 †50

CAVENDISH — WINDSOR

LEVEN, Seymour. 244 DENSMORE RD, WHITES HILL 05142 #025-01-1950 L1973 P *071 ‡

CHARLOTTE — CHITTENDEN

ADAMS, Nathan Bradley. ■ 05445 #050-02-2006 L2006 IM *012

BALABAN, Robert J. 2583 GREENBUSH RD 05445 #025-12-1981 L1999 P *020 †75

BERNSTEIN, Richard H. 527 FERRY RD 05445 #038-06-1972 L1973 GP *020

BOWEN, Scott Martin. ■ 05445 #036-01-1999 L2006 OMF *020

CARTELLI, Carina. ■ 05445 #035-15-2001 L2001 IM *100 †20

CLEMMONS, Jackson J W. 2055 GREENBUSH RD 05445 #038-06-1959 L1962 PTH OS *040 †50

D'AMICO, Michael Anthony. ■ 05445 #010-01-1996 L2004 PG *020 †55

DAVIS, Jeffrey Brian. 34 N OLDE CARRIAGE RD 05445 #035-45-1990 L1994 IM *020 †20

GLUCK, Charles M. ■ 05445 #024-05-1957 L2000 IM END *071 †20

GRAHAM, Valerie Ann Leval. ■ 05445 #024-01-1965 L1973 OS *040

HIGGINS, Timothy Joseph. ■ 05445 #041-01-1994 L2002 PDR *100 †18,80

LISLE, David Knight. ■ 05445 #050-02-2000 L2007 FSM *020 †18

VAN BUSKIRK, David. ■ 05445 #024-01-1957 L1990 CHP P *020 †75

WEISMAN, Lee Floyd. 527 FERRY RD 05445 #050-02-1986 L1988 FM *020 †18

CHELSEA — ORANGE

BINDER, Michael Jos. 360 BROOK RD 05038 #041-13-1979 L1982 PTH GP *050

MARTIN, Brewster Davis. PO BOX 128 05038 #050-02-1952 L1953 GP OS *071

PATTISON, David Grange. 356 VERMONT RTE 110, CHELSEA CLINIC 05038 #023-07-1990 L1993 PD IM *020 †20,55

CHESTER — WINDSOR

JACKSON, Robert N. ■ 05143 #035-15-1942 L1943 GP *020 †85

KECK, Charles. ■ 05143 #036-07-1953 L1961 ORS *071 †40

SCHWARTZ, Robert John. 55 VERMONT ROUTE 11 W, CHESTER FAMILY MEDICINE 05143 #050-02-2002 L2005 FM *020 †18

SPINRAD, Walter Ira. PO BOX 427, 662 MAIN ST 05143 #035-19-1941 L1971 IM *071

TIMURA, Brian Michael. 172 GREEN MOUNTAIN TPKE 05143 #024-07-1983 L1988 IM *020 †20

COLCHESTER — CHITTENDEN

ABATE, Joseph A, III. 125 COLLEGE PKWY 05446 #024-07-1988 L1997 OSM ORS *020 †40

ANDERSON, Charles Edwin. 65 CREEK FARM PLZ, STE 7 05446 #561-01-1971 1973 FM A *020 ‡

ANDERSON, Emily Louise. ■ 05446 #050-02-2008 *012

ARCHAMBAULT, Jacques, Jr. ■ 05446 #067-02-1971 L1988 ORS *020 †40

BENJAMIN, Scott Evan. 790 COLLEGE PKWY, FAHC - DEPT OF REHABILITAT 05446 #021-01-1996 L2003 PM *020 †20

BUNKER, Clarence Edward. 790 COLLEGE PKWY 05446 #050-02-1962 L1968 GS *071 †85

COHEN, Jonathan Saml. 162 HEGEMAN AVE, VA OUTPATIENT CLINIC 05446 #016-01-1987 L1987 IM *020 †20

COLLMAN, Rebecca J. 164 MAIN ST, STE 202 05446 #040-02-1984 L1985 PD *020 †55

CONNOR, Ann Marie. ■ 05446 #035-15-1984 L2007 PTH HMP *020 †50

CRAIGHEAD, John Edward. 208 S PARK DR # 2, UNIV OF VT 05446 #049-01-1956 L1968 PTH *050 †50

DANIELSON, Ursel. ■ 05446 #050-02-1967 L1968 CHP P *071 †75

DAVIES, Sarah Lynn. ■ 05446 #010-02-2007 L2007 FP *012

DENTE, Gino Aldo. 101 COLLEGE PKWY 05446 #050-02-1941 L1946 AN *071 †05

DEPPE, Susan Leigh. 1565 COLCHESTER POINT RD 05446 #018-03-1983 L1985 P PYG *020 †75

ESPARZA, Vivian R. 790 COLLEGE PKWY, FANNY ALLEN CAMPUS 05446 #048-13-1995 L1998 FM *020 †18

EZERMAN, Robert Hilger. 101 COLLEGE PKWY 05446 #041-02-1968 L1972 FM IM *075

FISHER, Dorothy Y. 786 COLLEGE PKWY 05446 #050-02-1998 L1998 IM IMG *020 †20

FITZGERALD, John Matthew. 792 COLLEGE PKWY, STE 303 05446 #050-02-1979 L1984 IM CD *020 †20

FLORANCE, Jared Egerton. 789 VERMONT NATIONL GRD RD, STATE MEDICAL COMMAND 05446 #051-04-1982 L1983 PHP MDM *030 †70

GONZALEZ, Kathryn. 162 HEGEMAN AVE STE 100, VA CLINIC AT FORT ETHAN AL 05446 #005-15-1994 L2001 IM *020 †20

GREEN, Peter Alexander. ■ 05446 #035-15-2007 L2007 ORS *012

GUILFORD, Alicia Theris. ■ 05446 #050-02-2006 L2006 FP *012

HEALEY, Brenda Jane. 308 BLAKELY RD, # 100 05446 #065-05-1985 L1999 EM FM *020

HEALEY, Mark Anthony. 308 BLAKELY RD, # 100 05446 #065-05-1986 L1999 CCS *020 †85

HILDEBRAND, Andrea Lynn. 101 COLLEGE PKWY 05446 #011-03-1991 L1998 DR *020 †80

HOLMES, Chris Elaine. 208 S PARK DR, STE 2 05446 #051-01-1997 L1997 HO *020 †20

HOWARD, Phillip Lloyd. ■ 05446 #051-01-1964 L1967 BBK OS *071 †50

JACOBS, Alicia Ann. 883 BLAKELY RD 05446 #008-01-1996 L1996 FM *020 †18

JOHNSON, Alisa Kathleen. ■ 05446 #050-02-2006 L2006 DR *012

JOHNSON, Jason Michael. ■ 05446 #003-01-2006 L2007 DR *012

JOHNSON, Robert Jonathan. 125 COLLEGE PKWY 05446 #018-03-1964 L1971 ORS *020 †40

JOHNSON, Scott Eric. ■ 05446 #035-03-2008 *012

JONES-FRASER, Candace L. 883 BLAKELY RD 05446 #067-01-1985 L1994 FM *020

JOYCE, Rebecca Lynne. ■ 05446 #050-02-2008 *012

KIANKHOOY, Armin. ■ 05446 #026-04-2005 L2005 GS *012

KING, John Frederick. 899 MAIN ST STE ONE, SUITE ONE 05446 #038-40-1976 L1976 P *020 †75

KNAKAL, Roger Chaloner. 790 COLLEGE PKWY, FLETCHER ALLEN REHAB 05446 #035-09-1990 L2000 PM *020 †60

KOUTRAS, Anya S. ■ 05446 #035-03-1995 L2004 **FM** *020 †18

KRISTIANSEN, Thomas Kurt. 792 COLLEGE PKWY, STE 101 05446 #035-15-1978 L1983
ORS *020 †40

KUTLER, Marc Stewart. 790 COLLEGE PKWY 05446 #036-05-1983 L1984 **IM EM** *020 †20

MAC LENNAN, Susan E. 354 MOUNTAIN VIEW DR # 103 05446 #032-01-1994 L2000
PS *020 †65

MILHOUS, Raymond Lee. 790 COLLEGE PKWY 05446 #041-01-1961 L1968 **PM** *071 †60

MORRISON, Richard Dodge. 28 VERMONT AVE 05446 #050-02-1961 L1962 **GP IM** *020

NEPVEU, Karen. 245 S PARK DR, STE 5 05446 #050-02-1987 L1989 **RHU** *020 †20

NESBIT, Robert David. 354 MOUNTAIN VIEW DR, STE 103 05446 #012-01-1995 L2005
PS *020 †65

NEWMAN, Elizabeth R. 790 COLLEGE PKWY 05446 #035-46-1985 L1985 **FM** *020 †18

NICHOLS, Claude Elmer. 125 COLLEGE PKWY 05446 #041-13-1979 L1985 **ORS** *020 †40

NUNNINK, Johannes C. 792 COLLEGE PKWY, STE 207 05446 #050-02-1980 L1981
ON OS *020 †20

PACE, William Anthony. ■ 05446 #035-01-2004 L2004 **DR** *012

PINCKNEY, Richard G. 790 COLLEGE PKWY 05446 #035-06-1994 L1994 **IM** *050 †20 ‡

PRAKELT, Herbert Gerhard. ■ 05446 #050-02-1961 L1961 **GP** *020

RAMSAY, Allan Murray. 883 BLAKELY RD 05446 #012-05-1973 L1980 **FM IM** *020 †20

REBACK, Charlotte A. 790 COLLEGE PKWY 05446 #660-01-1988 L1993 **FM** *020 †18

RENSTROM, Per A. 792 COLLEGE PKWY STE 101 05446 #858-05-1972 L1983 **ORS** *020

RUOFF, Paul Allyn. ■ 05446 #035-45-1972 L1976 **CHP** *020 †75

SANDERS, Dennis Allen. 792 COLLEGE PKWY, STE 207 05446 #005-15-1986 L1995
ON IM *020 †20

SARGENT, Michael Edward. 792 COLLEGE PKWY STE 101 05446 #032-01-1976 L1993
PD PSM *020

SCHMITT, Charles Jos. 790 COLLEGE PKWY, FLETCHER ALLEN HEALTHCARE 05446
#050-02-1989 L2007 **FM** *020 †18

SCHUYLER, Walter Buckleyj, III. ■ 05446 #050-02-2008 *012

SEGAL, Alan Scott. 208 S PARK DR, STE 2 05446 #016-02-1985 L1996 **IM** *020 †20

SEGER, Clint Wade. 883 BLAKELY RD 05446 #054-04-2002 L2002 **FM** *020 †18

SHANG, Yanan. ■ 05446 #038-43-2006 L2006 **N** *012

SLAUTERBECK, James Robt. 125 COLLEGE PKWY 05446 #003-01-1988 L2005 **ORS** *020 †40

SOBEL, Burton E. 208 S PARK DR, UNIV OF VERMONT CRF 05446 #024-01-1962 L1993
CD IM *050 †20

TALLEY, Carol Ann. 790 COLLEGE PKWY 05446 #025-12-1983 L1988 **PM** *020 †60 ‡

TARVER, Jerry Mark. 356 MOUNTAIN VIEW DR, STE 200 05446 #048-13-1985 L1999
PME AN *020 †05

THABAULT, Wilfrid L. 101 COLLEGE PKWY 05446 #050-02-1947 L1950 **OS** *072

THOMAS, Christian A. 792 COLLEGE PKWY, STE 207 05446 #409-23-1986 L1999 **HO** *020 †20

UNGER, Paul Stephen. 792 COLLEGE PKWY, STE 207 05446 #024-01-1986 L1990
ON HEM *020 †20

VINES, Derek Gavin. ■ 05446 #047-20-2003 L2003 **P** *020

WEINSTEIN, Daniel Jay. 790 COLLEGE PKWY 05446 #050-02-2000 L2000 **FM** *020 †18 ‡

WHITMAN, Todd Jay. ■ 05446 #035-45-2002 L2002 **HO** *012 †20

WILKINSON, Lynn Elizabeth. 790 COLLEGE PKWY, WALK-IN CARE CENTER, FA CA 05446
#047-05-1995 L1999 **IM** *020 †20

WOODS, Dennis Dwight. 790 COLLEGE PKWY, REHABILITATION CTR 05446
#019-02-1986 L1995 **IM** *020 †20 ‡

ZWEBER, Thomas Jay. 101 COLLEGE PKWY 05446 #026-04-1984 L1998 **PM** *020 †60

CONCORD – ESSEX

VODRASKA, Sarah Maudeliz. US RT 2 BOX 355 05824 #050-02-1994 L2000 **FM OS** *020 †18

CORNWALL – ADDISON

BURTON, Robert Argo, Jr. ■ 05753 #050-02-1970 L1970 **EM PYA** *071

WRIGHT, James Robt. ■ 05753 #041-01-1972 L1973 **OPH** *071 †35

CRAFTSBURY – ORLEANS

HAGLER, Abigail. ■ 05826 #012-05-1981 L2003 **IM OS** *020 †20

CRAFTSBURY COMMON – ORLEANS

BABBOTT, Joan Griggs. ■ 05827 #035-15-1951 L1963 **GPM PHP** *030

DANVILLE – CALEDONIA

ALBRIGHT, Charles P. ■ 05828 #035-20-1953 L1963 **GP IM** *071

BAILEY, James Thurston. ■ 05828 #050-02-1956 L1958 **OBG** *071

JOHNSON, Jeffrey Jay. ■ 05828 #561-17-1982 L1993 **IM** *020 †20

LONDON, Wayne Paul. ■ 05828 #024-01-1965 L1981 **P** *020 †75

ROUSSE, Michael Raymond. ■ 05828 #050-02-1988 L2004 **FM** *020 †18

TANNER, Timothy Hamil. 26 CEDAR LN, DANVILLE HEALTH CENTER 05828 #008-01-1985 L1993
MPD *020 †20,55

DERBY – ORLEANS

MEREDITH, Mark C. ■ 05829 #017-20-1990 L1995 **GS** *020 †85

TATUM, Brent W. 4267 US RTE 5 05829 #008-01-1988 L1991 **IM** *020 †20

DERBY LINE – ORLEANS

BOUCHARD, Gilles R. 40 MAIN ST 05830 #067-02-1963 L1975 *020

WOOD, Robert W. ■ 05830 #024-16-1980 L1988 **IM GS** *020 †05,20

DORSET – BENNINGTON

BAMFORD, Joseph Chas. ■ 05251 #035-09-1956 L1972 **OBG** *074 †30

HARDING, Lois Schultes. PO BOX 515, 3142 DORSET WEST RD 05251 #033-05-1992 L1993
P *062

DUMMERSTON – WINDHAM

REST, Herbert Frank. ■ 05301 #041-09-1965 L1971 **IM OS** *020 †20

EAST ARLINGTON – BENNINGTON

HONG, Songho. ■ 05252 #407-33-1966 L1974 **GP** *071

EAST BURKE – CALEDONIA

ANDERSON, Francesca Monic. PO BOX 78 05832 #007-02-2006 L2008 **PD** *012

FRANK, Louis Jay. ■ 05832 #649-33-1980 L1982 **P AN** *020 †05

REIDER, Horace Oliver. PO BOX 10 05832 #024-01-1971 L1972 **GP** *020

EAST CORINTH – ORANGE

ERB, John Byron. 720 VILLAGE RD, VALLEY HEALTH CENTER 05040 #065-01-1978 L2004
FM *020 †18

EAST DORSET – BENNINGTON

AHLBORG, Jean Elizabeth. ■ 05253 #005-11-1985 L1989 **OBG** *040

CHARNOCK, David Robt. 51A TENNIS WAY 05253 #035-09-1984 L1992 **OTO FPS** *020 †45

SHATTUCK, Theodore Geo. 51A TENNIS WAY 05253 #067-01-1970 L1978 **OTO HNS** *020 †45

SMITH, Richard Barlow, III. 51A TENNIS WAY 05253 #038-06-1978 L2000 **OTO** *020 †45

EAST DUMMERSTON – WINDHAM

GROSSMAN, I Wm. ■ 05346 #023-01-1960 L1971 **PTH** *020 †50,28

EAST MIDDLEBURY – ADDISON

COEBY, Lynn Marie. ■ 05740 #033-06-1982 L2001 **EM GS** *020 †16

RODDY, Frederick L. 42 LOWER PLAINS ROAD 05740 #660-03-1967 L1976 **GP PTH** *071 †50

EAST MONTPELIER – WASHINGTON

FROST, Kendal. ■ 05651 #005-06-1956 L1964 **ORS** *020

EAST THETFORD – ORANGE

KNAPP, Herbert A. 385 ROUTE 113 05043 #035-19-1951 L1993 **LM OS** *020

ENOSBURG FALLS – FRANKLIN

BABB, Lorne M N. 84 WATER TOWER RD, STE 1 05450 #067-01-1987 L1988 **FM** *020 †18

BALSAM, Maria Geneva. ■ 05450 #561-17-1962 L1977 **P PM** *020

HAAG, Deanne Marie. 44 CENTER ST, MOUSETRAP PEDIATRICS 05450 #050-02-1999 L1999
PD *020 †55

LARROW, Daniel Wilder. 44 CENTER ST, MOUSETRAP PEDIATRICS 05450 #050-02-1983 L1986
PD IM *020 †55

ROSENBERG, Ralph Jay. ■ 05450 #024-05-1972 L1974 **GP** *050

ROSS, Craig Edward. 84 WATER TOWER RD, STE 1 05450 #025-12-1991 L2004 **FM** *020 †18

TUCKER, Elrie Clifford. ■ 05450 #067-01-1961 L1990 *020

ESSEX JUNCTION – CHITTENDEN

ARCHER, Jeremy Michael. ■ 05452 #011-03-2004 L2006 **PD** *012

AYER, Nathan R. 87 MAIN ST 05452 #035-45-2001 L2001 **IM** *020

BADAMI, Arpita Dinesh. ■ 05452 #035-03-2006 L2007 **GS** *012

BERTSCH, Tania Fernandez. 87 MAIN ST 05452 #025-12-1978 L1983 **IM** *020 †20

BROPHEY, Gregory Jason. 16 RAILROAD ST, ESSEX EYE ASSOC 05452 #038-43-2001 L2008
OPH *020 †35

CHANDRA, Birbala Dikshit. ■ 05452 #495-05-1967 L1978 *020

CHANDRA, Girish. ■ 05453 #495-05-1966 L1976 **OPH GP** *075

COSTELLO, Paul Mc Lane. 89 MAIN ST, ESSEX PEDIATRICS 05452 #050-02-1978 L1980
PD *020 †55

COTTRELL, Caroline Marie. 26 LINCOLN ST 05452 #016-02-2008 L2008 *012

DENNETT, Douglas Edward. 8 CARMICHAEL ST UNIT 204 05452 #050-02-1976 L1989
CHP P *020 †75

DION, Cindy Louise. ■ 05452 #050-02-2006 L2006 **IM** *012

DRURY, Tucker Andrew. ■ 05452 #038-43-2004 L2004 **ORS** *012

DUHAN, Praveen. ■ 05452 #496-09-1996 L2005 **N IM** *100

FELDMAN, Nathalie L. 55 MAIN ST, CHAMPLAIN OB/GYN 05452 #067-01-1987 L1992
OBG *020 †30

FLAHERTY, Kara Ann. 55 MAIN ST 05452 #035-03-1999 L1999 **OBG** *020 †30

FOLSOM, Jeffrey Bruce. ■ 05452 #050-02-2001 L2002 **GS** *100

FULLER, Ithiel Lokenames. ■ 05452 #051-04-2005 L2005 **AN** *012

FUNG, Mark Kin. ■ 05452 #001-02-1999 L2003 **PTH** *100 †50

GALLAGHER, John Jos, Jr. 55 MAIN ST, STE 3 05452 #050-02-1980 L1984 **OBG** *020 †30
GIEFER, Matthew Joseph. ■ 05452 #016-43-2006 L2006 **PD** *012
GOODMAN, Rebecca Lynn. ■ 05452 #036-01-2007 L2007 **PD** *012
GRABOWSKI, Gregory. ■ 05452 #023-01-2005 L2005 **ORS** *012
GUILFOY, Edwin Jos. 16 RAILROAD ST 05452 #033-05-1977 L1981 **OPH** *071 †35
HALE, Jerry Steven. 89 MAIN ST, ESSEX PEDIATRICS 05452 #036-01-1991 L1991 **PD** *020 †55
HASAN, Saad Mahmud. ■ 05452 #605-01-1952 L1978 **R** *020 †80
HEATH, Barry Wm. 89 MAIN ST 05452 #050-02-1977 L1980 **PD** *020 †55
HELDT, Mikaila Lynn. ■ 05452 #050-02-2008 *012
JERTSON, Jill Evelyn. 55 MAIN ST, CHAMPLAIN OB/GYN 05452 #024-07-1992 L1992
    OBG *020 †30
JILLSON, Elizabeth Howard. 89 MAIN ST, ESSEX PEDIATRICS 05452 #050-02-1988 L1988
    PD ADL *020 †55
KAPSALIS, Sandra K. 89 MAIN ST, ESSEX PEDIATRICS 05452 #050-02-1996 L1996 **PD** *020 †55
KEENAN, Edward Allen, Jr. ■ 05452 #050-02-1944 L1945 **GP** *071
KING, Patricia Ann. 87 MAIN ST 05452 #050-02-1996 L1996 **IM** *020 †20
LEVINE, Mark Alan. 87 MAIN ST #035-45-1979 L1981 **IM** *020 †20 ‡
MAC LEAN, Charles Duncan. 87 MAIN ST 05452 #067-01-1982 L1983 **IM** *020 †20
MAJERCIK, Donald Anthony. 18 PEARL ST 05452 #050-02-1971 L1972 **GS OS** *020 †85
MASOOD, Yasmin. ■ 05452 #305-01-2000 L2005 **CD** *012
MCLAUGHLIN, Joseph Stephe. ■ 05452 #024-16-2006 L2006 **ORS** *012
MIDDLETON, Nancy Laura. ■ 05452 #025-01-1978 L1981 **P GP** *020 †75
MINADEO, John Paul. ■ 05452 #050-02-1995 L1998 **EM** *020 †16
MINER, Paula Mae. 55 MAIN ST 05452 #035-15-1997 L2002 **OBG** *020 †18,30
MONGEON, Maurice Edward. ■ 05452 #050-02-1959 L1963 **IM GP** *071
O'BRIEN, Roberta Pauline. 87 MAIN ST 05452 #041-09-1988 L1988 **IM** *020 †20
OVERFIELD, Jane Ellen. ■ 05452 #050-02-1996 L1996 **IM** *020 †20
PAULSEN, Malcolm Jack. ■ 05452 #050-02-1948 L1949 **GP** *071
PUGLIANO, Melissa Angela. ■ 05452 #041-15-2004 L2005 **D** *012
RATHMELL, Barbara Anne. 139 WOODS HOLLOW RD 05452 #036-05-1987 L1992
    NPM *020 †55
RAWSON, Burnett Sheldon. ■ 05452 #050-02-1939 **U** *071 †95
REYNOLDS, Bradley Paul. 5 DEER CROSSING LN 05452 #041-02-1984 L2002 **SME** *012 †20
RIPPA, Diane Carol. 8 ESSEX WAY, STE 201 05452 #050-02-1982 L1984 **FM** *020 †18
SALESKY, Joel Saul. ■ 05452 #033-06-2005 L2006 **DR** *012
SCHOLAN, John V. ■ 05452 #033-05-1960 L1961 **GP** *020
SEAH, Adrian Shaohwa. ■ 05452 #025-12-2007 L2007 **GS** *012
STEPHENS, Dean Hugh. ■ 05452 #012-01-2004 L2004 **RHU** *012 †20
STIFLER, David E. 89 MAIN ST, ESSEX PEDIATRICS 05452 #010-02-1976 L1977 **PD** *020 †55
STOCKWELL, Sally Annabell. 55 MAIN ST, STE 3 05452 #050-02-1974 L1976 **OBG IM** *020 †30
TAVERNA, Josephine Amalia. ■ 05452 #035-47-2004 L2007 **IM** *012
TILL, George Wm. 55 MAIN ST STE 3 05452 #041-01-1981 L1988 **OBG** *020 †30
TOBITA, Mari. ■ 05452 #572-52-1987 L2005 **N** *012
UPTON, Michael Dodds. 15 PINECREST DR 05452 #050-02-1994 L1996 **P** *020 †75
VEIT, Alicia Jean. ■ 05452 #041-01-2004 L2004 **PD** *020 †55
VITHALA, Madhuri Venkata. ■ 05452 #496-24-1998 L2007 **HO** *012 †20
WEIR, Douglas Edward. 1000 RIVER ST, MEDICAL DEPT 9651H 05452 #038-06-1980 L1983
    OM IM *030
WULFKUHLE, Kelley Carmeli. ■ 05452 #007-02-2005 L2005 **OBG** *012

FAIRFAX – CHITTENDEN

BOWER, Natasha Ann. ■ 05454 #011-02-2005 L2005 **OBG** *012
MARCO, Teig Dry. 1199 MAIN ST 05454 #422-01-1985 L1989 **IM** *020
ROUSE, Jessica Alice. ■ 05454 #050-02-2006 L2006 **FP** *012
SAFERSTEIN, Susan Laurie. 4178 HIGHBRIDGE RD 05454 #035-48-1979 L1982 **FM** *020 †18
STURGIS, Miriam Stern. 4178 HIGHBRIDGE RD 05454 #008-02-1985 L1985 **FM** *020 †18
THAYER, Carol Leah. 4178 HIGHBRIDGE RD 05454 #050-02-1983 L1990 **FM** *020 †18
VON LEPEL, Audrey E. 1199 MAIN ST 05454 #305-01-1983 L1988 **IM** *020

FAIRFIELD – FRANKLIN

HOWRIGAN, Thomas Gerald. 2 HOWRIGAN RD 05455 #050-02-1961 L1961 **GS OS** *020
WIRTS, Henry Kyle. 537 FAIRFIELD HILL RD 05455 #041-13-1963 L1972 **OBG** *071 †30

FAIRLEE – ORANGE

BLACK, Stephanie Alice. ■ 05045 #032-01-2007 L2007 **PD** *012
HUGHES, James Raymond. 94 PASSUMPSIC PT 05045 #024-01-1960 L1970 **PD** *071 †55
TEALE, Stanley N. ■ 05045 #064-01-1949 L1953 **CD IM** *071 †20

FERRISBURGH – ADDISON

MORRISON, Nan Callaghan. ■ 05456 #051-01-1963 L1963 **OS** *075

GRAND ISLE – GRAND ISLE

KALOF, Alexandra Nava. ■ 05458 #050-02-2000 L2000 **PTH** *020 †50

GREENSBORO – ORLEANS

MC QUILLEN, Eleanor N. ■ 05841 #024-05-1960 L1976 **FOP CLP** *071 †50
SHARP, Gregory Hamilton. PO BOX 189 05841 #036-07-1979 L1982 **PTH** *020 †50

GUILFORD – WINDHAM

GREGG, Michael Barrows. ■ 05301 #038-06-1956 L1961 **PHP IM** *071 †70
LADNER, Christopher J. ■ 05301 #016-43-1999 L2006 **NRN** *100 †80

HARDWICK – CALEDONIA

DENSMORE, Raymond Carl. STAR RT 05843 #050-02-1939 **GP** *071
MORGAN, Sarah Elizabeth. ■ 05843 #005-11-2001 L2004 **FM** *020 †18

HARTFORD – WINDSOR

MANSFIELD, Richard J. ■ 05047 #051-01-1998 L2000 **IM** *020 †20

HARTLAND – WINDSOR

AAKRE, Kimberly Jo. ■ 05048 #056-05-1986 L1996 **PD** *062 †20,55
BRUEN, Marian Anthon. ■ 05048 #035-01-1973 L1975 **IM N** *074 †75
BURKE, Gregory P. ■ 05048 #035-08-1972 L1977 **HO IM** *062 †20
KEITT, Alan Seaver. ■ 05048 #024-01-1961 L1963 **IM HEM** *071
WAKANA, Minoru. ■ 05048 #572-20-1951 L1963 **PTH** *071 †50

HINESBURG – CHITTENDEN

GEORGE, Argilla Rose. 22 COMMERCE ST, POST OFFICE BOX 250 05461 #050-02-1988 L1996
    FM *020 †18
MC CORMICK, Gregory James. ■ 05461 #050-02-2001 L2006 **OPH** *100 †35
MRAVKOV, Borislav Margari. ■ 05461 #198-03-1986 L2005 **N** *012
REYNOLDS, John Weldon. 22 COMMERCE ST 05461 #041-01-1988 L1996 **FM** *020 †18
ULAGER, James Robert. 22 COMMERCE ST, HINESBURG FAMILY HEALTH 05461
    #041-01-2004 L2004 **FM** *020 †18

HUNTINGTON – CHITTENDEN

GOODYEAR, Daniel Millett. ■ 05462 #050-02-2005 L2005 **FP** *012

IRASBURG – ORLEANS

HOLLAND, Robert Ronald. ■ 05845 #050-02-1972 L1973 **IM** *074 †20

ISLE LA MOTTE – GRAND ISLE

HORRIGAN, William Donald. ■ 05463 #035-20-1955 L1965 **R** *071 †80

JACKSONVILLE – WINDHAM

HEIN, Karen R Kramer. PO BOX 607 05342 #035-01-1970 L1973 **ADL PD** *062 †55

JAY PEAK – ORLEANS

SCHIPPER, Hirsh Leo. ■ 05859 #396-06-1956 L1966 **GP GS** *075

JEFFERSONVILLE – LAMOILLE

COSLETT, Martha M Y. ■ 05464 #036-07-1986 L1987 **FM** *074 †18
MANN, Roger Wendell. JEFFERSONVILLE 05464 #050-02-1939 L1940 **FM FOP** *071

JERICHO – CHITTENDEN

ALEXANDER, Stuart Aldrich. ■ 05465 #050-02-1967 L1970 **EM PD** *071
BRADEEN, Heather. ■ 05465 #034-01-2001 L2001 **PD** *100 †55
CALHOUN, Brian Lewis. 129 BROWNS TRACE RD 05465 #051-01-1984 L1989 **AN GS** *020 †05
CHEN, Diane. ■ 05465 #050-02-2003 L2006 **IM** *020
CLEGG, Anne R. ■ 05465 #050-02-2000 L2005 **FM** *100 †18,75
DRUCKER, William Richard. 76 ORR RD 05465 #023-07-1946 L1953 **GS** *040 †85
KNOX, F Melinda. ■ 05465 #035-06-2003 L2004 **DR** *012
RICHARDS, Alisson Leigh. ■ 05465 #004-01-2007 L2007 **P** *012
TAYLOR, Howard C, III. ■ 05465 #035-01-1955 L1960 **P PTH** *071 †50
WOODRUFF, Wm Aloysius A. ■ 05465 #352-07-1952 L1962 **P LM** *071

JOHNSON – LAMOILLE

CUNNINGHAM, Peter R. ■ 05656 #008-01-1949 L1986 **PD** *071 †55
GERIN-LAJOIE, Michele. 224 RAILROAD ST 05656 #050-02-1988 L1989 **FM** *020 †18
ROGERS, Paul M. RR 1 BOX 1335 05656 #035-08-1977 L1978 **GP** *020 †18

LAKE ELMORE – LAMOILLE

HIGGINS-OLSEN, Susan M. PO BOX 115 05657 #030-06-1978 L1981 **EM IM** *020 †20

LINCOLN – ADDISON

MAC DONALD, Alex S, Jr. 1612 W HILL RD, 1612 WEST HILL RD LINCOLN 05443
    #035-20-1941 L1983 **PD** *071 †55
OLIVEAU, Donald Clark. ■ 05443 #035-45-1962 L1964 **P** *020 †75

LONDONDERRY – WINDHAM

MC CABE, Robert E, Jr. PO BOX 399 05148 #035-20-1953 L1954 **GS CD** *071 †85

■ = Address Information Privacy Protected

LUDLOW – WINDSOR

BEEHLER, Cecil Cook, II. 8 MAIN ST 05149 #011-03-1998 L2001 **FM** *020 †18
MILLER, Mitchell Reed. 70 MAIN ST 05149 #056-06-1994 L1997 **FM OS** *020 †18
NEAL, Ronald Howard. 33 LAKESHORE DR 05149 #050-02-1947 L1948 **AN OM** *020 †18
ROSEN, Jeffrey David. PO BOX 558 05149 #033-05-1973 L1975 **OBG** *020 †30
SALERNO, Richard Dante. ■ 05149 #007-02-1962 L1963 **OTO** *075 †45
TOPE, John Wesley, III. ■ 05149 #016-06-1947 L1947 **GS** *071 †85

LYNDONVILLE – CALEDONIA

DOBBERTIN, Joyce Marie. 182 S WHEELOCK RD, BOX 83 05851 #050-02-1998 L1998 **FM** *020 †18
SARGENT, William Alan. 815 N KIRBY RD 05851 #050-02-1974 L1978 **EM** *020
THOMPSON, Lloyd L, III. ■ 05851 #041-01-1971 L1973 **IM** *020 †18

MANCHESTER – BENNINGTON

AYRE, Harvey Brandon. PO BOX 146, 371 VILLAGE GLEN RD 05254 #067-01-1980 L2005 **EM** *020 †16
FREEBERN, Robert Kenneth. PO BOX 495 05254 #035-15-1960 L1965 **IM** *071 †20
HARRIGAN, Frank E, Jr. PO BOX 616 05254 #050-02-1942 L1943 **GP AM** *071
LIEBLING, Mara V. PO BOX 50, 3869 MAIN ST 05254 #050-02-1992 L2000 **FM** *020 †18
SHERMAN, Byron Grant, Jr. ■ 05254 #035-19-1948 L1952 **AN** *071
YEDINSKY, Sylvia Schein. ■ 05254 #041-07-1960 L1988 **P OS** *071

MANCHESTER CENTER – BENNINGTON

JAGER, Natacha Irene. 5957 MAIN ST, NORHTSHIRE MEDICAL CENTER 05255 #024-16-1995 L1998 **FM** *020 †18
KEYSER, John Jacob. ■ 05255 #035-01-1965 L1970 **PS HS** *071 †85,65 ‡
LA PENTA, John Jos. 5222 MAIN ST 05255 #051-04-1980 L1984 **OPH** *020 †35
LAROSA, Timothy Jay. 113 SCHOOL ST 05255 #035-06-1994 L1998 **P** *020
LAYDEN, Maureen Quenya. 5957 MAIN ST, NORTHSHIRE MEDICAL CENTER 05255 #024-16-1997 L2004 **FM** *020 †18
LEWIS, Sidney. ■ 05255 #024-15-1941 **IM** *071
MEADOWS, Edmund Curtis. ■ 05255 #024-01-1944 L1946 **GS** *071 †85
MICHL, Keith Wilson. 5957 MAIN ST 05255 #038-41-1981 L1984 **IM IMG** *020 †20
MOST, James Anthony. 5957 MAIN ST, NORTHSHIRE MEDICAL CENTER 05255 #024-07-1998 L2002 **PD IM** *020 †20
PARMER, Michael Andrew. ■ 05255 #033-05-1964 L1966 **OS GP** *071 †85
POLIFKA, Michael David. 5957 MAIN ST 05255 #050-02-1978 L1980 **IM** *071 †20 ‡
PROVENZANO, Richard J. 5222 MAIN ST 05255 #024-07-1975 L1980 **OPH** *020 †35
SCHWARTZ, Robert Michael. 5957 MAIN ST, NORTHSHIRE MEDICAL CENTER 05255 #016-06-1985 L1992 **FM OM** *020 †18
SITKOWSKI, Suzanne. ■ 05255 #035-08-2004 *040
UVA, Jane Louise. ■ 05255 #038-45-1993 L2001 **EM** *020 †16

MARLBORO – WINDHAM

BARTLETT, Ann Shirley. PO BOX H, 979 SOUTH RD 05344 #050-02-1999 L2003 **AN** *020 †05
DOTZAUER, Bernd. ■ 05344 #409-35-1998 L2008 **AN** *020 †05
FRIEDMAN, Hylar Lewis. ■ 05344 #035-08-1977 L1985 **GP PTH** *020

MARSHFIELD – WASHINGTON

HORVATH, James Jay. ■ 05658 #025-07-1945 L1946 **ORS** *072 †40

MENDON – RUTLAND

ZARA, Harvey David. ■ 05701 #035-09-1973 L1988 **OBG** *071 †30
ZARA, Shelley Ann. ■ 05701 #035-09-1973 L1988 **GP EM** *020

MIDDLEBURY – ADDISON

ALEXANDER, Lisa Pippa. ■ 05753 #035-08-1992 L2007 **OPH IM** *020 †35
ANDERSON, Kristofer Ethan. 115 PORTER DR, PORTER HOSPITAL INC 05753 #038-41-2001 L2006 **OTO** *020 †45
ANDREWS, Bertrand J. ■ 05753 #050-02-1942 L1943 **OBS** *071
APRIDONIDZE, Teimuraz Nod. ■ 05753 #913-23-1994 L2008 IM *012
ARMSTRONG, Bradford W. 116 PORTER DR, PORTER INTRNL MED 05753 #035-45-1988 L1995 **IM** *020 †20
AYER, Alan Dwight. 116 PORTER DR 05753 #050-02-1971 L1971 **OBG** *020 †30
BARNARD, Diana Lynn. 44 COLLINS DR, STE 201 05753 #050-02-1991 L1994 **FM** *020 †18
BENZ, Eric Burritt. 1436 EXCHANGE ST 05753 #024-01-1994 L2002 **ORS** *020 †40
BICKNELL, Timothy Donald. 44 COLLINS DR 05753 #050-02-1992 L1995 **FM** *020 †18
BRAKELEY, Johana Kashiwa. 110 PORTER DR 05753 #035-15-1977 L1978 **PD** *020 †55
BRUCH, Frank Osborne. MEMORIAL FIELD HOUSE, SPORTS MEDICINE DEPT 05753 #038-06-1956 L1977 **ISM** *072 ‡
CALL, Elizabeth Mather. 108 PORTER DR 05753 #024-16-1997 L1999 **OBG** *020 †30
COBB, Carl Wade. 115 PORTER DR, PORTER HOSPITAL 05753 #001-02-1990 L2000 **DR** *020 †80
COLANDER, Patrice P. 44 COLLINS DR 05753 #035-06-1990 L1991 **PD** *020 †55
COLLINS, Ray W, Jr. 15 SOUTH ST 05753 #050-02-1938 L1947 **GS** *071 †85
COPE, Timothy Trevor. 116 PORTER DR, STE 200 05753 #041-09-1969 L1974 **FM EM** *020 †18
COVEY, Alan Dix. SOUTH ST, PORTER HOSPITAL 05753 #050-02-1972 L1975 **IM EM** *020 †20
DALTON, John Jos, Jr. ■ 05753 #050-02-1960 L1965 **U** *071 †95
DALTON, John Jos, II. ■ 05753 #054-04-1961 L1997 **OS GS** *072

DOHERTY-FULLER, Eileen M. 115 PORTER DR, MIDDLEBURY FAMILY HEALTH 05753 #041-02-1982 L1985 **PD FM** *020 †55,18
EARLE, Morris, Jr. 1330 EXCHANGE ST, STE 201 05753 #050-02-1983 L1995 **PD CCP** *020 †55
EICHNER, William John. 1330 EXCHANGE ST, STE 102 05753 #030-05-1968 L1976 **OPH GP** *020 †35
FIFIELD, William Kenneth. 116 PORTER DR, CHAMPLAIN VALLEY FAMILY 05753 #050-02-1971 L1971 **FM** *020 †18
FJELD, George Christian. 115 PORTER DR 05753 #050-02-1981 L1983 **FM EM** *020 †18
FLYNN, Dedra Mary. 1330 EXCHANGE ST, MIDDLEBURY PED. AND ADOL. 05753 #050-02-2000 L2005 **PD** *020 †55
FUKUDA, Christopher S. 107 COLLINS DR, GREEN MOUNTAIN UROLOGY 05753 #050-02-1986 L1992 **U UP** *020 †95
FULLER, Bradbury. 116 PORTER DR 05753 #035-20-1982 L1982 **GS VS** *020 †85
GALANTE, Anne Lorraine. 104 PORTER DR, PORTER HOSPITAL - OB/GYN 05753 #050-02-1998 L2002 **OBG** *020 †30
GILL, Paul Geo, Jr. 15 SPRINGSIDE RD, PAUL G. GILL, JR. 05753 #001-02-1974 L1988 **EM** *020 †16
GORMAN, Stephen Myles. 812 EXCHANGE ST 05753 #038-40-1973 L1980 **PUD IM** *020 †20
HOLM, Anders Gustaf. 1330 EXCHANGE ST STE 202, DBA PORTER ENT 05753 #050-02-1996 L2001 **OTO** *020 †45
HOLM, Peter Jan. PORTER HOSP 05753 #018-03-1968 L1969 **R** *020 †80
HOLMES, Breena Welch. 1330 EXCHANGE ST, STE 201 05753 #024-16-1993 L1997 **PD** *020 †55
HOLMES, Lewis Ball, Jr. 99 COURT ST, CEDAR LEDGE FAMILY PRACTIC 05753 #024-16-1993 L1997 **FM** *020 †18
IANNI, Kevin Louis. 75 S STREET EXT 05753 #050-02-1984 L1985 **AN** *020 †05
JIMERSON, Robert Chas. 89 MAIN ST, ADDISON COUNTY 05753 #008-01-1974 L1978 **P** *020 †75
KEELER, Bonnie Pease. ■ 05753 #035-20-1993 L2007 **GS** *020
KIERNAN, Michael Jos. ■ 05753 #028-34-1990 L1994 **FM** *020 †18
KIERNAN, Tawnya Ann. 44 COLLINS DR STE 202, RAINBOW PEDIATRICS 05753 #050-02-1999 L2002 **PD** *020 †55
KING, Charles Henry. ■ 05753 #010-02-1979 **P** *100
KLITZNER, Dayle. 115 PORTER DR, MIDDLEBURY FAMILY HEALTH 05753 #050-02-1986 L1988 **FM** *020 †18
KNIFFIN, Fred Wigfield. 115 PORTER DR, PORTER HOSPITAL 05753 #047-05-1987 L1987 **IM** *020 †20
KNISELY, Geoffrey Robt. 75 S STREET EXT 05753 #038-41-1979 L1982 **EM IM** *020 †20,05
KOLLER, Stephen Mark. 115 PORTER DR 05753 #050-02-1991 L1991 **DR** *020 †80
LAFIANDRA, Robert P. 116 PORTER DR, PHYSICNS BLDG 05753 #035-20-1965 L1969 **IM** *020 †20
LARSON, Linn Marie. 115 PORTER DR, MIDDLEBURY FAMILY HEALTH 05753 #050-02-1985 L1991 **FM** *020 †18
LAWRENCE, Langdon Swain. 135 CREEK RD 05753 #023-07-1998 L1998 **FM** *020 †18
LESSOFF-PERRY, Robin C. 89 MAIN ST, COUNSELING SERV OF ADDISON 05753 #050-02-1995 L1995 **CHP** *020 †75
LUGINBUHL, Lynn Marie. 1330 EXCHANGE ST, STE 201 05753 #050-02-1983 L1995 **ID** *040 †55
MAHONEY, Andrew Charles. 107 COLLINS DR, GREEN MOUNTAIN UROLOGY 05753 #007-02-1993 L2001 **U** *020 †95
MALCOLM, James Arthur, III. 116 PORTER DR, PORTER MED CTR PHSY BLDG 05753 #051-01-1970 L1971 **OBG** *020 †30
MAYER, Jack Lawrence. 44 COLLINS DR 05753 #035-19-1971 L1972 **PD** *020 †55 ‡
MC INTOSH, Kate H. 44 COLLINS DR 05753 #007-02-1994 L2004 **PD** *020 †55 ‡
MC KEON, Lucy. 115 PORTER DR 05753 #050-02-1988 L1988 **FM** *020 †18
MORRISON, J Scott. ■ 05753 #039-01-1962 L1962 **P** *071 †75
MULHOLLAND, Kevin John. 115 PORTER DR 05753 #038-40-1991 L1991 **IM** *020 †20
PELUSO, W Mark. PARTON HEALTH CTR, MIDDLEBURY COLLEGE 05753 #024-05-1996 L2000 **FM FSM** *020 †18
PETRI, Carl B. 116 PORTER DR 05753 #016-43-1979 L1985 **GS** *020 †85
PIERATTINI, Robert Alan. 47 COURT ST 05753 #008-01-1982 L1982 **P** *020 †75
PISANELLI, Patricia Ann. 119 COLLINS DR 05753 #050-02-1979 L1985 **GS** *020 †85
PORTER, William H. 115 PORTER DR, MIDDLEBURY FAMILY HEALTH 05753 #043-01-1992 L2000 **FM** *020 †18
PROCTER, Elizabeth Doton. ■ 05753 #050-02-1943 L1947 **PHP** *071
PULS, Wendie Margaret. 75 S STREET EXT, PORTER HOSP DEPT EMERG 05753 #050-02-1982 L1985 **IM** *020 †20 ‡
RAABE, Danl Stauffer, Jr. 812 EXCHANGE ST 05753 #035-01-1967 L1975 **CD** *020 †20
RACUSIN, Jessica Sarah. 115 PORTER DR, PORTER HOSPITAL 05753 #024-07-2001 L2004 **EM** *020
ROSENBERG, Benjamin Neal. 1436 EXCHANGE ST, P O BOX 915 05753 #024-16-1986 L1993 **ORS OSM** *040
SCHWARZ, Hans Juergen. ■ 05753 #023-01-1970 L1976 **DR** *071 †80
SMITH, Scott Douglas. 99 COURT ST, CEDAR LEDGE FAMILY PRACTIC 05753 #041-02-1990 L1994 **FM** *020 †18
SPLAIN, James Lawrence. 1330 EXCHANGE ST, STE 201 05753 #038-06-1990 L1995 **PD** *020 †55
STINE, Patrick Hervey. PHYSICN BLD PORTER MED CTR 05753 #025-01-1967 L1980 **OTO** *020 †45
STRUBLE, Joy Elizabeth. ■ 05753 #025-12-2007 L2007 **IM** *012
THOMPSON, John Stephen. ■ 05753 #035-01-1946 L1974 **IM** *071 †20
VENMAN, Robert Lyon. 1 WASHINGTON ST, BOX 562 05753 #067-01-1965 L1972 **GS GP** *020 †85
YURISTA, Thomas Wm. 53 ROAD 18 05753 #026-04-1988 L1988 **IM** *020 †20
ZIMMERMANN, Maja Ruth. 116 PORTER DR, CHAMPLAIN VALLEY FAMILY 05753 #034-01-1977 L1979 **FM EM** *020 †18

MILTON – CHITTENDEN

BERGMANN, James Ray. 28 CENTRE DR 05468 #008-02-1979 L1983 **FM OFA** *020 †20,18
CAREY, Peggy Ann. 28 CENTRE DR 05468 #050-02-1992 L1992 **FM** *020 †18
DI MICHELE, John Mark. 349 ROUTE 7 S, UNIT101 05468 #067-01-1992 L1992 **PPD** *020 †55
FELEMEGOS, Ioannis. 28 CENTRE DR, FAMILY MEDICINE 05468 #661-03-2007 L2007 **FP** *012
FERGUSON, John Crawford. 28 CENTRE DR, MILTON FAMILY PRACTICE 05468 #050-02-1977 L1978 **FM** *020 †18

GEURTS, Maurice Anna J. 28 CENTRE DR 05468 #660-01-1993 L2000 **FM** *020 †18
HAGEMAN, Kimberly Ann. 28 CENTRE DR, MILTON FAMILY PRACTICE 05468 #038-06-1998 L1998 **FM** *020 †18
HULSE, Charles Louis. 28 CENTRE DR 05468 #036-01-1995 L1995 **FM** *020 †18
KING, John Gridley. 28 CENTRE DR 05468 #035-45-1984 L2003 **FM FPG** *020 †18
LIEBER, Deborah Yvonne. ■ 05468 #004-01-2008 *012
LITTLE, David Nelson. 28 CENTRE DR, MILTON FAMILY PRACTICE 05468 #050-02-1975 L1976 **FM** *020 †18
MAC GILVRAY, Phyllis Mc C. 28 CENTRE DR 05468 #045-01-2002 L2002 **FM** *100 †18
PETERSON, Thomas Chas. 28 CENTRE DR 05468 #035-45-1983 L1984 **FM** *020 †18
RODGERS, Kevin Allen. 28 CENTRE DR, MILTON FAMILY PRACTICE 05468 #034-01-1990 L1996 **FM** *020 †18
SAIA, John Jerome. 28 CENTRE DR 05468 #050-02-1966 L1971 **FM IM** *020

MONTPELIER — WASHINGTON

ALLARD, William Edward. RFD #4 BOX 1370 05602 #050-02-1957 L1962 **OS FM** *071 †18
ANGSTREICH, David Elias. RD 4 BOX 1740 05602 #035-01-1966 L1987 **GS** *020 †85
BALLARD, Harlow Geo, III. 9 HEATON ST, POB 647 05602 #032-01-1987 L1988 **P** *020 †75
BURDICK, Timothy Edward. 156 MAIN ST 05602 #032-01-2002 L2005 **FM** *020 †18
CHICKERING, Nancy Wright. ■ 05602 #005-02-1988 L1994 **FM** *020 †18
COLLETT, Nancy Belle. ■ 05601 #056-05-1961 L1972 **P** *075
DALE, Porter Hinman. ■ 05602 #050-02-1947 L1948 **IM** *071 †20
DAVIGNON, Russell Paul. RR 4 05602 #050-02-1973 L1978 **ORS IM** *020 †40
DICKINSON, Christine C. 17A N FRANKLIN ST 05602 #050-02-1995 *100
ECKHAUS, Jeremiah Martin. 156 MAIN ST, MONTPELIER HEALTH CENTER 05602 #041-15-1999 L2007 **FM** *020 †18
ELLERSON, R David. ■ 05602 #035-03-1955 L1962 **PD** *071 †55
FAWBUSH, Shahbaz Vikram L. ■ 05602 #913-23-2002 **FM** *100
FERRY, Ronald M, Jr. ■ 05602 #024-01-1948 L1958 **GS** *071 †85
FRIES, Frederick. 338 RIVER ST 05602 #165-03-1982 L1984 **N** *020
GAIDYS, William. RR 4 BOX 1620 05602 #050-02-1979 L1980 **PD** *020 †55
GRAVES, Stuart Mc Laren. 9 HEATON ST 05602 #050-02-1972 L1973 **P** *020 †75
IVERSON, Mark Richard. 81 RIVER ST 05602 #050-02-1983 L1987 **OPH** *020 †35
JERARD, Deborah. RR 4 BOX 1820 05602 #051-04-1985 L1988 **PD** *020 †55
KALIBAT, Francis Paul. 132 MAIN ST 05602 #035-03-1967 L1993 **P** *020 †75
KLOSTER, Nels Andreas. 9 HEATON ST, WASH CO MENTAL HEALTH SVC 05602 #050-02-2001 L2001 **P** *020 †75
LABARTHE, Susan Schifter. ■ 05602 #050-02-1996 L1999 **IM** *020 †20
LAFFAL, Paul David. 133 ELM ST 05602 #038-41-1970 L1971 **FM GP** *020 †18
LEE, Claudia E. 156 MAIN ST 05602 #050-02-1992 L1999 **IM** *020 †20
LINDBERG, Bruce Alan. NAT'L LIFE INS CO 05602 #023-01-1962 L1966 **PUD CD** *071
MAIER, Beth Ann. RR 4 BOX 1620 05602 #038-06-1975 L1978 **PD** *020 †55
MINDRUM, Christa Raylene. 156 MAIN ST, MONTPELIER HLTH CTR 05602 #063-01-2003 L2005 *020
MOCKAPETRIS, Anne Marie. RD 4 BOX 1370, BERLIN FAMILY HEALTH 05602 #035-47-1986 L1986 **FM** *020 †18
NELSON, Marilyn Adella. 156 STATE ST 05602 #040-02-1959 L1961 **PD** *071 †55
PERKINS, Stephen Eugene. PO BOX 186 05601 #055-01-1979 L1998 **FM** *030 †18
RAPAPORT, Michael Edwin. 156 STATE ST 05602 #050-02-1993 L1996 **FM** *020 †18
RIGGEN, Robert Jay. 1 NATIONAL LIFE DR 05604 #035-03-1969 L1991 **EM** *030 †16
RITVO, Jesse Levine. ■ 05602 #043-01-2006 L2006 **P** *012
ROMEYN, Dirk. RR 4 BOX 1590, ASSOCIATES IN OBGYN 05602 #024-05-1962 L1965 **OBG** *071 †30
SCHILLHAMMER, Wm R, Jr. ■ 05602 #023-07-1948 L1966 **IM PUD** *071 †20
SEIGLE, Eliot Brandon. PO BOX 716 05601 #035-48-1987 L1992 **P** *020 †75
STONE, James S. 73 MAIN ST, RM 28 05602 #037-01-1989 L1993 **P** *020
TOMASI, Ernest Philip. ■ 05602 #050-02-1942 L1946 **OS OBG** *071
VASSAR, Carol Anne. 150 MAIN ST 05602 #051-07-1983 L1988 **IM EM** *020 †20
WATSON, Richard Bradford. ■ 05602 #050-02-1993 L1993 **AN** *020 †05
WEKER, Jonathan Lloyd. 100 STATE ST, STE 245 05602 #023-01-1980 L1990 **P PFP** *020 †75 ‡
WILLIAMS, M Henry, Jr. ■ 05602 #008-01-1947 L1949 **PUD** *040 †20
WRIGHT, Arthur R. ■ 05602 #025-02-1954 L1960 **FM GS** *071 †85
YEE, Richard H, Jr. ■ 05602 #024-05-1977 L1985 **ON** *020
ZAUR, Alan Leonard. 162 ELM ST STE 4 05602 #041-09-1975 L1989 **P PYA** *020 †75

MORETOWN — WASHINGTON

NOWLAN, William James. 116 CARRIGAN RD 05660 #035-46-1978 L1983 **EM FM** *020 †16,18
SMITH, Benjamin Giddings. ■ 05660 #035-01-2002 L2006 **EM** *100 †16
STEWART, Emily Rachael. ■ 05660 #050-02-2004 L2004 **IM** *012 †20
VAN HEUVEN, Wichard A J. ■ 05660 #035-09-1959 L2007 **OPH** *020 †35

MORRISVILLE — LAMOILLE

BALU, Sarayu. 1126 LAPORTE RD, ROUTE 100 05661 #495-16-1975 L1980 **PD** *020 †55
BASKA, Robert Stanley. 530 WASHINGTON HWY, STE 3 05661 #028-34-1983 L1992 **GS** *075 †85
BLOWERS, Lewis Carlton. 528 WASHINGTON HWY, COPLEY HOSPTIAL 05661 #035-09-1957 L1965 **GS** *030 †85
BRUNO, Kimberly Masayo. 607 WASHINGTON HWY, CARE 05661 #050-02-1996 L1996 **FM** *020 †18
BUCKLEY, Brendan N. 528 WASHINGTON HWY 05661 #010-01-1982 L1985 **IM ISM** *020 †20
CODDAIRE, David Miller. 607 WASHINGTON HWY, CARE 05661 #050-02-1972 L1973 **FM** *020 †18
DANDURAND, Louis Paul. 528 WASHINGTON HWY 05661 #050-02-1995 L1999 **EM** *020 †16
DAUM, Richard Michael. 528 WASHINGTON HWY 05661 #035-20-1983 L1998 **CD IM** *020 †20
GANNON, Liam Gerard. 528 WASHINGTON HWY 05661 #028-34-1997 L2000 **FM** *020 †18
GODDARD, Philip Anthony. 528 WASHINGTON HWY 05661 #050-02-1963 L1963 **GP GS** *071 †85
HEAGHNEY, Patrick Edward. 528 WASHINGTON HWY, COPLEY HOSPITAL 05661 #028-34-1982 L1995 **EM** *020 †20,16

HUBER, Bryan Matthew. 555 WASHINGTON HWY, MANSFIELD ORTHOPAEDICS 05661 #050-02-1992 L1992 **ORS** *020 †40
JAMES, Richard. 555 WASHINGTON HWY, MANSFIELD ORTOPAEDICS 05661 #035-48-1992 L2003 **FM** *020 †18
KEYSSAR, Alexander. WASHINGTON HWY 05661 #396-06-1939 L1955 **IM END** *072
KIELY, Philip Geo, Jr. 607 WASHINGTON HWY, CARE 05661 #024-07-1987 L1992 **FM** *020 †18
KOZUB, Robert Eugene. 439 WASHINGTON HWY, STE 3 05661 #038-40-1959 L1996 **CD IM** *020 †20
LICHTENSTEIN, Mark David. 528 WASHINGTON HWY 05661 #041-02-1976 L1979 **FM FPG** *020 †18
MCCORMACK, Mirjam. 528 WASHINGTON HWY, COPLEY HOSPITAL 05661 #049-01-2000 L2001 **AN** *020 †05
MECH, John Jos. 528 WASHINGTON HWY 05661 #041-02-1968 L1973 **PTH** *020 †50
MULLINS, Eric Ronald. 555 WASHINGTON HWY 05661 #020-02-1999 L1999 **HS** *100 †40
NEALE, Stephen Glen. RR 3 BOX 765-8 05661 #050-02-1985 L1987 **ORS GS** *072 †40
NEEL, Hartley Stockton. 528 WASHINGTON HWY 05661 #024-07-1969 L1972 **R** *020 †80,28
NEPVEU, Judith T O'Connor. 528 WASHINGTON HWY 05661 #050-02-1959 L1961 **P** *020
ORTIZ, Candice Enid. 528 WASHINGTON HWY 05661 #033-05-1993 L1993 **DR** *020 †20
PAGE, Russel S. 528 WASHINGTON HWY, COPLEY HOSP 05661 #050-02-1972 L1973 **EM PD** *020 †55,16
PLOCIENNIK, Krzysztof. 530 WASHINGTON HWY, STE 8 05661 #050-02-1995 L1995 **OBG** *020 †30
PRUNTY, Jean M. 530 WASHINGTON HWY 05661 #035-08-1987 L1991 **N** *020 †75
RACETTE, Cathryn Dyeanne. 530 WASHINGTON HWY, STE 3 05661 #019-02-1984 L2002 **GS** *020 †85
ROSSMAN, Fred Joel. 607 WASHINGTON HWY 05661 #041-01-1977 L1982 **OBG** *020 ‡
ROY, David Lucien. 607 WASHINGTON HWY, CARE 05661 #050-02-1982 L1985 **FM** *020 †18
RUSSELL, Victoria. ■ 05661 #038-06-1974 L2000 **P** *020 †20
SILVERSTEIN, Joel Wolfe. 530 WASHINGTON HWY 05661 #035-46-1972 L1974 **IM GE** *020
SMALE, Brian F. 530 WASHINGTON HWY 05661 #041-09-1975 L2002 **GS CRS** *020 †85
SOUTHALL, Henry. 439 WASHINGTON HWY 05661 #041-01-1966 L1973 **IM CD** *020
TAYLOR TASI, Stephanie. 528 WASHINGTON HWY 05661 #024-01-1984 L1991 **FM** *020
TISCHLER, Marc David. 528 WASHINGTON HWY 05661 #024-01-1986 L1991 **CD IM** *020 †20
VITALETTI, Anne. 530 WASHINGTON HWY, STE 1POB 05661 #035-45-1987 L1994 **AN** *020
WARING, Gary Lynn. 530 WASHINGTON HWY 05661 #041-14-1974 L1977 **FM** *020 †18

NEW HAVEN — ADDISON

MUELLER, Enkhtuyaa Lkhasu. ■ 05472 #652-02-2001 L2006 **IM** *012

NEWFANE — WINDHAM

BOUTIN, Paul David. ■ 05345 #054-04-2002 L2007 **CHP** *020

NEWPORT — ORLEANS

ALSOBROOK, Arthur David, Jr. 189 PROUTY DR, NORTH COUNTRY HOSPITAL 05855 #048-04-1974 L1984 **EM** *020 †18
BANNACH, Alexandra. 121 MEDICAL VILLAGE DR 05855 #409-10-1995 L2004 **PD** *071 †55 ‡
BELOIN, Richard Michael. PINE, FAMILY PRACTICE OF NEWPORT 05855 #050-02-1972 L1974 **FM** *071
BOLTON, Edwin Robt, Jr. PROUTY DR 05855 #033-05-1976 L1978 **GP IMG** *075
BONVOULOIR, Armand L. ■ 05855 #067-02-1956 L1956 **GS GP** *071
BOUCHARD, Marc Raymond. 189 PROUTY DR 05855 #067-02-1995 L1997 **FM** *020 †18
BRUNELLI, William James. 189 PROUTY DR 05855 #308-03-1983 L2000 **EM** *020 †20 ‡
DAVIS, Everett Lee. PROUTY DRIVE 05855 #050-02-1943 L1945 **GP OBG** *071 †30
DI SANTO, Rachel B. 189 PROUTY DR, NORTH COUNTRY HEALTH SYSTE 05855 #050-02-2004 L2004 **FM** *020 †18
FATIGATI, Maria Domenica. ■ 05855 #561-26-1993 L2005 **IMG** *020 †20
FELTMARCH, Alan Brian. ■ 05855 #050-02-1972 L1973 **EM** *020
HAAS, Nelson Stuart. 189 PROUTY DR, NORTH COUNTRY HOSP 05855 #034-01-1994 L2001 **GPM** *020 †20,70
HACKETT, Sharon Lee. 189 PROUTY DR, (VISITING PHYSICIANS) 05855 #065-10-1979 L2001 **D** *020
HAQ, Rizwan U. 189 PROUTY DR, MEDICAL ARTS BLDG 05855 #704-20-1985 L1993 **N** *020 †75
HARRIS, Peter Bridge. 41 MEDICAL VILLAGE DR, COMMUNITY MEDICAL ASSOCIAT 05855 #035-45-1985 L1989 **IM PD** *020 †20,55
HOLCOMB, James Newell. 81 MEDICAL VILLAGE DR 05855 #050-02-1974 L1977 **FM** *020 †18
IRWIN, Louis Jordan. 189 PROUTY DR, DEPT OF ANESTHESIA-NCH 05855 #051-04-1982 L1990 **AN FM** *020 †18,05
JEDLOVSZKY, Veronika. 189 PROUTY DR, NORTHERN VT PULMONARY/SLEE 05855 #473-01-1994 L2001 **PUD IM** *020 †20
JULIEN, Paul M. 212 PROUTY DR, STE 4 05855 #067-02-1973 L2004 **OTO** *020 †45
KILEY, Donna Marie. 154 DUCHESS AVE 05855 #050-02-1990 L1999 **P** *020 †75
LA BRIE, Paul Leon. PO BOX 807, MEDICAL ARTS BUILDING 05855 #041-01-1976 L1990 **GS** *020 †85
LA CARRUBBA, Lisa. 81 MEDICAL VILLAGE DR, STE 1 05855 #033-06-1997 L2000 **FM** *020 †18
LADAK, Ferial. 189 PROUTY DR, NORTH COUNTRY HOSP 05855 #061-01-1983 L1986 **FM EM** *020 †18
LADD, Jennifer Kelley. 189 PROUTY DR, DEPT OF ANESTHESIOLOGY 05855 #050-02-2000 L2004 **AN** *020 †05
LAWLOR, David Peter. 212 PROUTY DR, STE 2 05855 #050-02-1994 L1999 **OPH** *020 †35
LINTON, George, III. 189 PROUTY DR 05855 #021-01-1970 L1974 **FM** *020 †18
LIPPMANN, John Andrew. 81 MEDICAL VILLAGE DR, STE 1 05855 #024-16-2000 L2000 **FM** *020 †18
LOCKRIDGE, Leslie Charles. 189 PROUTY DR 05855 #016-42-1996 L2006 **HEM** *020 †20
MAAS, James Calvin. 212 PROUTY DR, BIRCHWOOD MEDICAL BUILDING 05855 #041-02-1971 L1978 **ORS** *020 †40
MC DOWELL, Robert Wm. 189 PROUTY DR, NORTH COUNTRY HOSPITAL 05855 #017-20-1977 L1981 **PTH CLP** *020 †50
MOSELEY, Thomas A E, III. 121 MEDICAL VILLAGE DR 05855 #050-02-1979 L1982 **PD ADL** *020 †55

■ = Address Information Privacy Protected

NEWTON, Paul Mario. 189 PROUTY DR, N CO HOSP-EMER MED 05855 #051-04-1995 L1998 **FM** *020 †18

NIEMIRA, Denise Aileen. 5420 US ROUTE 5 STE D 05855 #033-05-1976 L1977 **GP** *020

PECK, William Bouck. 81 MEDICAL VILLAGE DR 05855 #012-01-1976 L1977 **OBG** *020 †30

PEDERSEN, Pamela Carol. 2559 GLEN RD, NORTHERN STATE C.F. 05855 #035-08-1982 L1998 **IM** *020 †20

PEER, Christopher William. 189 PROUTY DR, ORTHOPAEDIC SURGERY 05855 #010-02-2000 L2005 **OSM** *020

PERLIN, Steven Jeffrey. 189 PROUTY DR 05855 #008-02-1983 L2006 **DR** *020 †80

POUND, Rebecca Lynne. 189 PROUTY DR 05855 #041-14-2000 L2003 **FM** *020 †18

PRIMEAU, Robert Earl. 41 MEDICAL VILLAGE DR 05855 #048-04-1987 L1991 **IM PD** *020 †20,55

PROVATO, Frank Leonard. 41 MEDICAL VILLAGE DR, COMMUNITY MEDICAL ASSOCIAT 05855 #035-15-1974 L2001 **IM OM** *020 †20

RICKMAN, Christopher E. 41 MEDICAL VILLAGE DR, COMMUNITY MEDICAL ASSOCIAT 05855 #041-14-1995 L1997 **IM** *020 †20

SAPAROFF, Gerald Robin. 212 PROUTY DR, STE 2 05855 #024-07-1971 L1976 **OPH** *020 †35 ‡

SHUMWAY, Allegra Lucille. 79 COVENTRY ST 05855 #050-02-1988 L1988 **FM** *020 †18

SISSON, Larry Allen. 184 PROUTY DR, MEDICAL ARTS BLDG 05855 #056-05-1982 L1988 **GS VS** *020 †85

STUART, Peter John. 81 MEDICAL VILLAGE DR, STE 2 05855 #041-01-1995 L1999 **OBG** *020 †30

SULLIVAN, Christopher Mic. 189 PROUTY DR, NORTH COUNTRY HEALTH SYSTE 05855 #016-01-2004 L2004 **OBG** *012

TATUM, Miriam Bodgett. 189 PROUTY DR 05855 #008-01-1986 L1991 **PD** *020 †55

TREMBLEY, Robert A. 41 MEDICAL VILLAGE DR 05855 #010-01-1982 L1985 **IM** *020 †20

WALKER, Gregory Allen. 189 PROUTY DR, NORTH COUNTRY HOSPITAL 05855 #050-02-1991 L1995 **APM** *020 †05

NORTH BENNINGTON – BENNINGTON

FLOOD, William Arthur. 35 BANK ST 05257 #050-02-1947 L1948 **OBG** *020 †30

RHODE, Solon L, III. ■ 05257 #041-02-1964 L1971 **OS** *050

NORTH CLARENDON – RUTLAND

GREGORY, Todd David. ■ 05759 #035-03-2004 L2007 **EM** *020

NORTH HARTLAND – WINDSOR

SMITH, Scott Dillard. ■ 05052 #051-07-2004 L2004 **DR** *012

NORTH HERO – GRAND ISLE

BROWN, Bruce Edward. 5500 US ROUTE 2 05474 #041-01-1963 L1964 **R** *020 †80

DE HART, Geo Kenneth, Jr. PO BOX 126, 1298 SAVAGE PT RD 05474 #035-45-1965 L1966 **DR NM** *020 †80

ENGLAND, Georgia. ■ 05474 #016-11-1991 L1992 **P** *020

PITTAWAY, Kathy Campbell. ■ 05474 #050-02-1988 L1988 **P** *020 †75

RAYMOND, Giles P. PO BOX 131, E SHORE RIDGE LN #182 05474 #067-02-1968 L1978 **D** *020 †15

NORTH SPRINGFIELD – WINDSOR

NEGLIA, Walter. ■ 05150 #561-01-1956 **PTH** *071 †50

NORTH TROY – ORLEANS

PENFIELD, Amos Jefferson. PO BOX 564 05859 #023-07-1953 L1953 **GYN** *072 †30

NORTHFIELD – WASHINGTON

CROWLEY, Kevin Danl. 63 CRESCENT AVE, GREEN MOUNTAIN FAMILY PRAC 05663 #041-02-1974 L1979 **FM** *020 †18

NATVIG, Duane Marlowe. ■ 05663 #018-03-1972 L1974 **EM** *020 †16

SULLIVAN, Craig Deming. 63 CRESCENT AVE 05663 #016-43-1980 L1983 **FM** *020 †18

NORWICH – WINDSOR

ADAMS, Lisa Virginia. ■ 05055 #032-01-1990 L1991 **IM** *040 †20

ANDERSON, Paul Christophe. ■ 05055 #032-01-2008 *012

ARNOLD, Winslow Hayden. ■ 05055 #035-19-1955 L1962 **IM OS** *020 †20

BARTHOLOMEW, Lee E. ■ 05055 #035-01-1950 L1954 **RHU IM** *072 †20

BATEMAN, Brian Thomas. ■ 05055 #035-01-2006 L2006 **IM** *012

BISNO, David Chas. ■ 05055 #028-02-1966 L1988 **OPH** *071 †35

BORSODI, Kathryn Simpson. ■ 05055 #024-16-2004 L2004 **AN** *012

BRADLEY, David John. PO BOX 342 05055 #024-01-1944 **OS** *075

CRUZ, Heidi Marie. ■ 05055 #005-15-2003 L2007 **PM** *020

DAULAIRE, Nils Maarten P. PO BOX 1330 05055 #024-01-1976 L1980 **PHP** *030 †70

DAULAIRE, Siri Liana. ■ 05055 #032-01-2008 *012

DETERS, Levi Aaron. ■ 05055 #054-04-2007 L2007 **GS** *012

DUNN, John Lawrence. ■ 05055 #041-02-1958 L1963 **PTH** *071 †50

FABRICANT, Arnold Steven. ■ 05055 #035-06-1972 L1978 **GS** *040 †85

HALSEY, David Alexander. 17 BRAGG HILL RD 05055 #033-06-1985 L1985 **ORS** *020 †40

JOHNSON, Anne Marjorie. ■ 05055 #024-01-2006 **OBG** *012

KATZ, Arnold Martin. ■ 05055 #024-01-1956 L2002 **CD IM** *071

LAWE, John Edwards. ■ 05055 #352-07-1956 L1964 **CLP BBK** *040 †50

LYONS, John Hugh, Jr. ■ 05055 #024-01-1955 L1962 **GS** *020 †85

MADDOX, Patrick Tate. ■ 05055 #036-08-2006 L2008 **OTO** *012

MAISLEN, Sidney Earl. ■ 05055 #050-02-1938 **OPH OTO** *071 †35

MILLER, Ashley Ann. ■ 05055 #032-01-2006 L2006 **PD** *012

NELSON, Henry B, III. ■ 05055 #054-04-1976 L2007 **P** *075 †75

RACUSIN, Robert J. 76 MCKENNA RD 05055 #010-02-1971 L1975 **CHP P** *020 †75

RATCLIFFE, Nora Rae. ■ 05055 #007-02-1991 L1996 **BBK** *072 †50

REICH, Annmarie Kathryn. ■ 05055 #010-02-2007 *012

SCHNED, Laura Meredith. ■ 05055 #050-02-2006 L2006 **PTH** *012

SEIBERT, Dean John. 386 MAIN ST 05055 #035-03-1958 L1977 **OS PHP** *030 †20,70

WATTS, Bradley Vincent. ■ 05055 #039-01-1992 L1997 **P** *020 †75

ORLEANS – ORLEANS

BOURGEOIS, David. 30 EAST ST 05860 #048-02-1983 L1989 **FM** *020 †18

CROTEAU, Stacy E. ■ 05860 #043-01-2007 L2007 **PD** *012

STURTEVANT, Allison Marie. 30 EAST ST 05860 #005-12-1998 L2001 **FM** *020 †18

ORWELL – ADDISON

DUFFY, John L. ■ 05760 #035-09-1952 **PTH** *071 †50

PAXSON, Edwin M. ■ 05760 #041-02-1954 L1956 **PD** *071 †55

PANTON – ADDISON

LUGINBUHL, Wm Hossfeld. ■ 05491 #016-06-1953 L1960 **OS** *071 †50

PAWLET – RUTLAND

PILLEMER, Eric Anthony. ■ 05761 #005-11-1983 L1988 **ON HEM** *075 †20

PEACHAM – CALEDONIA

MC DONNELL, Sharon Mae. PO BOX 197 05862 #005-18-1985 L2003 **GPM PHP** *020 †70

PARRISH, Roy Gibson. ■ 05862 #005-14-1978 L2003 **PHP OM** *062 †50

PERKINSVILLE – WINDSOR

ELLIS, William Stephen. ■ 05151 #051-04-1982 L1991 **OBG** *020 †30

STOHRER, Anne Elizabeth. ■ 05151 #051-04-1982 L1991 **OBG** *020 †30

PERU – BENNINGTON

WELCH, Edmund T, Jr. ■ 05152 #035-20-1949 L1992 **AN** *071 †05

PITTSFIELD – RUTLAND

KOPALD, Hugh Humphreys. #59 HAWK MTN RD 05762 #024-01-1959 L1970 **IM OS** *071 †20

PLAINFIELD – WASHINGTON

CRAIG, Wm Alexander P. PO BOX 320, 157 TOWNE AVE 05667 #050-02-1992 L1997 **FM** *020 †18

CROSE, Ruth Ann. RR 2 BOX 320, THE HEALTH CTR 05667 #017-20-1976 L1979 **FM** *020 †18

MATTHEW, John Douglas. 157 TOWNE AVE 05667 #047-05-1971 L1980 **IM FM** *020 †20,18

TONN, Elizabeth Charlotte. PO BOX 157 05667 #056-05-1976 L1985 **FM** *020 †18

PLYMOUTH – WINDSOR

TAYLOR, Richard Fiske. ■ 05056 #038-40-1958 L1958 **AN** *071 †05

TONKIN, Russell Joseph. ■ 05056 #047-06-1979 L2001 **IM** *071 †20

POST MILLS – ORANGE

LANDMAN, E D M. PO BOX 117 05058 #847-11-1981 L1983 **IM NEP** *071 †20

PROCTOR – RUTLAND

GRAY, James Alexander. 30 CHATTERTON PARK 05765 #035-15-1959 L1961 **OS PHP** *071

PUTNEY – WINDHAM

BARTLETT, Edward Wayland. ■ 05346 #008-01-1967 L1980 **P** *075

GARBER, Norton Sanford. 227 HICKORY RIDGE RD 05346 #035-19-1963 L1977 **PYA CHP** *020

HOSKINS, Thomas Reeve. 7 SMALL MEADOWS LN 05346 #035-45-1971 L1978 **GP** *020

SATTERFIELD, Sharon L B. ■ 05346 #025-01-1970 L2000 **P CHP** *075

SLOWINSKI, Walter Dayton. 126 MAIN ST 05346 #026-08-1984 L1998 **FM GP** *020

QUECHEE – WINDSOR

GREENWALD, Seymour. ■ 05059 #869-04-1958 L1960 **IM OS** *071

HOLMGREN, Robert Blakeley. ■ 05059 #033-05-1967 L1968 **D** *020

PINDYCK, Frank. PO BOX 1229 05059 #035-08-1966 L2001 **GS VS** *020 †85

■ = Address Information Privacy Protected

YANKIVER, Burt J. ■ 05059 #035-09-1978 L2006 **NEP IM** *071 †20

RANDOLPH – ORANGE

BELDING, Ralph Michael. 44 S MAIN ST 05060 #025-01-1967 L1975 **PTH** *020 †50
BURGEE, Gary Brent. 1 MAPLE ST 05060 #023-01-1977 L1980 **OBG FM** *020 †18,30
CHOBANIAN, Margarethe M. 44 S MAIN ST, GIFFORD MEDICAL CENTER 05060
#041-12-1980 L2005 **PD** *074 †55
COXON, Marcus Howard. 44 S MAIN ST, GIFFORD MEDICAL CENTER 05060
#065-10-1989 L1996 **FM** *020 †18
CURTIS, Michael Rudge. 44 S MAIN ST, GIFFORD MEDICAL CENTER 05060 #038-06-1990 L1992
U *020 †95
DI NICOLA, Louis Anthony. 44 S MAIN ST, GIFFORD MEDICAL CENTER 05060
#041-13-1973 L1976 **PD** *020 †55
ERMOLD, Larry Allen. 44 S MAIN ST 05060 #041-01-1968 L2005 **FM EM** *020
FARLEY, Sara Cajetan. 44 S MAIN ST 05060 #024-07-1996 L2000 **PD** *020 †55
FOULK, Rebecca Ann. 4 MAPLE ST 05060 #050-02-1980 L1982 **PD** *020 †55
FOWLER, Milton Geo. 44 S MAIN ST, GIFFORD MEDICAL CENTER 05060 #017-20-1969 L1973
IM *020 †18
GOULDING, Jonna Coxon. 44 S MAIN ST, GIFFORD MEDICAL CENTER 05060
#065-10-1993 L1996 **FM** *020 †18
HENZIG, Dennis Arthur. 44 S MAIN ST, GIFFORD MEDICAL CENTER 05060 #056-05-1976 L1992
AN *020
JEWETT, Elizabeth H. 44 S MAIN ST, GIFFORD MEDICAL CENTER 05060 #041-09-1973 L1976
PD *020 †55
JOHNS, Martin Christopher. 44 S MAIN ST, GIFFORD MEDICAL CENTER 05060
#654-01-2001 L2006 **MPD** *020
KELLER, Marc Ira. 44 S MAIN ST 05060 #050-02-1973 L1975 **EM** *020 †20,16
KIERNAN, Joseph Robt. ■ 05060 #038-40-1984 L1998 **GS** *020 †85
KNOFF, Jon-Richard. 44 S MAIN ST, GIFFORD MEDICAL CENTER 05060 #019-02-1996 L2007
AN *020 †05
LA PLACA, Thomas Jos. 44 S MAIN ST, GIFFORD MEDICAL CENTER 05060 #050-02-1974 L1977
AN *020 †05
NAYLOR, Robert Michael. 44 S MAIN ST 05060 #048-12-1967 L1970 **R NM** *020 †80,28
NGUYEN-KNOFF, Ngoc-Lan T. 44 S MAIN ST 05060 #019-02-1995 L2000 **FM** *020 †18
PANCHOLY, Navin Chimanlal. 44 S MAIN ST, GIFFORD MEDICAL CENTER 05060
#495-22-1965 L2006 **GS TS** *020 †85 ‡
PELLETIER, Joseph Charles, III. 44 S MAIN ST, GIFFORD MEDICAL CENTER 05060
#056-06-2000 L2003 **PD** *020 †55
PLAVIN, Joshua Avram. 44 S MAIN ST, GIFFORD MEDICAL CENTER 05060 #035-09-1996 L2000
MPD *020 †55
PORTER, John H, III. 44 S MAIN ST, GIFFORD MED CTR 05060 #028-02-1952 L1989 **P** *020 †75
SCHWARTZ, Robin A. 44 S MAIN ST, GIFFORD MEDICAL CENTER 05060 #003-01-2000 L2003
N CN *020 †75
SHARP, Nina Adams. 44 S MAIN ST, GIFFORD MEDICAL CENTER 05060 #050-02-1986 L1986
AN *020 †05
SINGER, Jack A. 45 S MAIN ST 05060 #035-08-1981 L1985 **OPH** *020 †35
SMITH, Maury Drane, Jr. 44 S MAIN ST, GIFFORD MEDICAL CENTER 05060 #024-01-1987 L2001
GS *020 †85
TRAVIS, Brian Taylor. 44 S MAIN ST, GIFFORD MEDICAL CENTER 05060 #021-01-1972 L1978
PTH *020 †50 ‡
TROST, Susanne Ursula. 44 S MAIN ST, GIFFORD MED CTR 05060 #409-05-1995 L2000
END *020 †20
WARD, Jerald Austin. 60 S PLEASANT ST 05060 #023-01-1979 L1982 **IM** *020 †20
WOLLAEGER, Lucy Jane. 3 MAPLE ST, GIFFORD MED OFFICE BLDG 05060
#026-04-1979 L1987 **IM** *020

RICHFORD – FRANKLIN

GRONDIN, Claude. ■ 05476 #067-03-1961 L1983 **CD GS** *071 †85,90
LAVALLEE, Erick J P. 44 MAIN ST, STE 200 05476 #067-01-1991 L2004 **FM** *020 †18 ‡

RICHMOND – CHITTENDEN

LIBBY, Wendy M. ■ 05477 #067-01-1996 L2007 **FM** *020 †18
MITCHELL, Chad Thomas. ■ 05477 #050-02-2007 L2007 **IM** *012
PARKER, Paul Jon. 12 BURNETT CT, & ADOLESCE 05477 #067-01-1993 L1993 **PD** *020 †55

ROCHESTER – WINDSOR

ERGAS, Ralph Edward. ■ 05767 #033-05-1961 L1988 **PD** *020 †55
JEWETT, Mark Douglas. 235 S MAIN ST, GIFFORD MEDICAL CENTER 05767
#041-09-1973 L1976 **IM** *050 †20
THOMAS, Gailyn Brooke. 235 S MAIN ST, GIFFORD MEDICAL CENTER 05767
#041-07-1990 L2000 **OBG** *020 †30
TINLING, David Calvert. ■ 05767 #054-04-1959 L1965 **P OS** *020

RUTLAND – RUTLAND

ABEYTA, Roberto Battram. ■ 05701 #041-01-1990 L1993 **IM** *020 †20
ADAMS, Allison Barbara. 1 GENERAL WING RD 05701 #035-06-2004 L2007 **PD** *020 †55
AHEARN, Jeffrey Alan. 160 ALLEN ST 05701 #038-40-1997 L1997 **IM** *020 †20
AUSTIN, Barry Michael. 69 ALLEN ST, STE 13 05701 #041-01-1977 L1980 **D** *020 †15 ‡
BACKER, Marianne. 160 ALLEN ST, RRMCORTHOPEDICS 05701 #297-01-1984 L1999 *100
BAGLEY, Frederick Hartley. 160 ALLEN ST 05701 #026-04-1970 L1979 **GS OS** *071 †85
BAHNSON, David Hastings. 3 ALBERT CREE DR, VERMONT ORTHOPAEDIC 05701
#041-12-1973 L1984 **ORS** *020 †40
BAKER, Richard Carleton. 160 ALLEN ST 05701 #035-03-1984 L1991 **FM** *020 †18
BAKER, Roger David. 1 GENERAL WING RD 05701 #050-02-1962 L1964 **PD** *071 †55
BARKELL, Laurel Suzanne. 160 ALLEN ST, DEPT OF EMERGENCY MEDICINE 05701
#050-02-2003 L2006 **EM** *100 †16

BATES, Griffin Miller, Jr. 160 ALLEN ST 05701 #035-01-1961 L1971 **OS** *030 †75
BEERWORTH, Mary Elizabeth. 71 ALLEN ST STE 402, INFERTILITY P.C. 05701
#050-02-1983 L1985 **OBG** *020 †30
BERGQUIST, Roy Jeffrey. 33 VICTORIA DR 05701 #050-02-1975 L1977 **OPH** *071 †35
BESSINGER, Victoria J. 160 ALLEN ST, MID-VT PATH 05701 #035-46-1991 L1996 **PTH** *020 †50
BIEBUYCK, Jean-Christo. 17 FIELD AVE 05701 #035-06-1989 L1994 **DR** *020 †80
BLISH, Susan Eloise. 160 ALLEN ST, HOSPITALIST RM 306 05701 #035-15-1994 L2000
FM *020 †18
BONAZINGA, Bartholomew J. 160 ALLEN ST, CENTER DEPARTMENT OF 05701
#035-08-1976 L1979 **CD IM** *020 †20
BOVE, Ernest Michael. 145 ALLEN ST 05701 #050-02-1981 L1985 **U** *020 †95
BOYNTON, Melbourne Duncan. 3 ALBERT CREE DR, VERMONT ORTHOPAEDIC 05701
#016-06-1987 L1997 **OSM ORS** *020 †40 ‡
BRIGGS, Stephanie. 160 ALLEN ST, EMERGENCY DEPARTMENT 05701 #050-02-1991 L1995
EM *020 †16
BRITTAIN, Stephen Memhard. 160 ALLEN ST 05701 #008-02-1976 L1981 **N** *020 †20,75
BUCKSBAUM, Mark Jay. 69 ALLEN ST, STE 9 05701 #422-01-1984 L1989 **PM PMM** *020 †60
BULLOCK, Bruce Duncan. 160 ALLEN ST 05701 #041-13-1986 L1992 **FM** *020 †18
BUTTARAVOLI, Philip Miles. 160 ALLEN ST, MEDICAL STAFF SERVICES 05701
#050-02-1970 L2000 **EM** *020 †16
BUZAS, Peter L. 160 ALLEN ST, RUTLAND REGIONAL MEDICAL C 05701 #473-01-1988 L2002
IM *020 †20
CANCIO-BELLO, Santiago E. 160 ALLEN ST 05701 #011-02-1968 L1974 **OBG GYN** *020 †30
CHEN, Harry. 160 ALLEN ST 05701 #040-02-1979 L1988 **EM** *020 †16
COCO, John Frederick. 71 ALLEN ST, STE 202 05701 #050-02-1984 L1985 **OPH** *020 †35
COGHLAN, Alban Jos. 160 ALLEN ST 05701 #539-06-1964 L1974 **P ADM** *020 †75
COLLINS, Roslinde Mary. ■ 05701 #024-16-1994 L2007 **IM** *020 †20
CONWAY, Matthew Aloysius. 241 STRATTON RD 05701 #050-02-1993 L1993 **GS** *020 †85
COOK, Timothy George. 25 N MAIN ST 05701 #055-02-1994 L1996 **FM** *020 †18 ‡
COOMBS, Seth Gregoire. 12 COMMONS 05701 #056-05-1992 L1996 **IM** *020 †20
CORBETT, Joseph E, Jr. 160 ALLEN ST 05701 #050-02-1982 L1993 **NS** *020 †25
CORNELIUS, Chris Robert. 73 CENTER ST 05701 #050-02-1997 L1999 **FM** *020 †18
CROSS, David Faris. 254 STRATTON RD 05701 #008-01-1963 L1967 **FM** *075 †20
DALY, Margaret Anderson. 8 ALBERT CREE DR 05701 #048-02-1991 L2007 **END IM** *020 †20
DALY, Timothy Alan. 160 ALLEN ST 05701 #048-02-1991 L2007 **AN** *020 †05
DARROW, Robert Person. ■ 05701 #008-01-1947 L1956 **GS TRS** *071 †85
DICK, John Frederick. 160 ALLEN ST 05701 #050-02-1967 L1968 **IM** *020 †20
DIER, Douglas Lee. 160 ALLEN ST 05701 #035-45-1985 L1988 **RHU IM** *020 †20
DRABYN, Gerald Anthony. 160 ALLEN ST 05701 #017-20-1969 L2001 **PS** *071 †65
DUNN, Holly Aruffo. 160 ALLEN ST 05701 #036-01-1993 L2000 **EM** *020 †16
EISEMANN, Allan Danl. 160 ALLEN ST 05701 #019-02-1986 L1992 **ON IM** *020 †20
EMERSON, Luther Lee. 160 ALLEN ST 05701 #008-01-1968 L1974 **IM** *020 †20
FABIAN, Jozsef. 734D US ROUTE 4 E, MID-VERMONT ANESTHESIA PC 05701
#473-03-1983 L2002 **AN** *020 †05
FAGAN, Emmett L, Jr. 160 ALLEN ST 05701 #050-02-1953 L1955 **PD** *071 †55
FAUNT LEROY, Jennifer M. 160 ALLEN ST, DEPT FP 05701 #035-19-1978 L1997 **FM** *020 †75
FEBLES, Anthony John. 160 ALLEN ST, RUTLAND REGIONAL MEDICAL C 05701
#043-01-2002 L2005 **DR** *012
FITTS, James Michael. 160 ALLEN ST, CENTER DEPARTMENT OF 05701 #035-09-2001 L2007
CD *020
FOLEY, Daniel Mahar. 71 ALLEN ST 05701 #050-02-1979 L1983 **OBG** *020 †30
FOSSATI, Andrea Theresa. 160 ALLEN ST 05701 #041-02-1993 L1993 **CD** *020 †20
FULLER, Courtney H. 160 ALLEN ST 05701 #054-04-2004 L2007 **EM** *100
GAMMONS, Matthew R. 160 ALLEN ST 05701 #305-01-1999 L2004 **FM FSM** *020 †18
GARCIA, Michael. 160 ALLEN ST 05701 #008-02-1985 L1992 **FM** *020 †20
GERRETSON, E Susan B. 7 COURT SQ, RUTLAND MNTL HLTH SERVS 05701
#048-14-1988 L1992 **P** *020 †75
GIERING, Robert William. 160 ALLEN ST, RUTLAND REGIONAL MED CENTE 05701
#035-03-1999 L2004 **PM** *100 †60
GUNDEL, Walter Dietrick. 160 ALLEN ST, CENTER DEPARTMENT OF 05701 #067-01-1965 L1971
CD IM *020 †20
HARTMANN, John Christian. 160 ALLEN ST 05701 #036-01-1993 L1997 **EM** *020 †16
HESSION, Mary K Towle. 1 GENERAL WING RD 05701 #024-07-1971 L1974 **PD** *020 †55
HESSION, Robert A. 1 GENERAL WING RD 05701 #024-07-1971 L1974 **PD** *020 †55
HIGGINS, John Christian. 160 ALLEN ST, CENTER DEPARTMENT OF 05701 #033-06-1988 L1988
CD IM *020 †20
HILLEMANN, Steffen. 160 ALLEN ST, CENTER DEPARTMENT OF 05701 #409-42-1994 L1996
IM *020 †20
HOGENKAMP, Lisa Marie. 160 ALLEN ST 05701 #035-15-1994 L1997 **FM** *020 †18
HOGENKAMP, Peter Karl. 160 ALLEN ST 05701 #035-15-1993 L1997 **FM** *020 †18
HOLLAND, Baxter Clay. 160 ALLEN ST, RUTLAND REG MED CTR 05701 #021-01-1974 L1995
MDM *030 †55
HOLMES, Edgar Miller, III. 160 ALLEN ST 05701 #024-05-1965 L1970 **ORS** *071 †40
HOPKINS, William Edward. 160 ALLEN ST, CENTER DEPARTMENT OF 05701
#016-02-1985 L1995 **CD IM** *020 †20
IBARRA, Clemente. 160 ALLEN ST, RUTLAND REGIONAL-ORTHOPAED 05701
#649-01-1991 L1998 **OSM** *100
ITALIA, Peter J. ■ 05701 #308-12-1987 **GS** *100
JAGER, Thomas Edward. 160 ALLEN ST 05701 #024-16-1995 L1998 **EM** *020 †16
JANIK, Dale Stewart. 9 COMMONS 05701 #041-01-1986 L1989 **IM** *020 †20
JENSON, Cynthia L. 160 ALLEN ST 05701 #035-06-1992 L1995 **AN** *020 †05
JIMMO, Brad Lee. 215 STRATTON RD, STE 6 05701 #050-02-1996 L1996 **GS** *020 †85
KEENAN, Patrick Francis. 160 ALLEN ST 05701 #050-02-1973 L1974 **OBG** *020 †30
KELLER, David Jay. 4 DEER RUN 05701 #050-02-1968 L1977 **ORS OSM** *020 †40
KELLEY, Colleen Elisabeth. 160 ALLEN ST 05701 #048-02-1988 L1992 **EM** *020 †16
KELLY, Gordon Randolph. 160 ALLEN ST 05701 #008-01-1966 L1970 **OPH** *020 †35
KENOSH, Michael Jos. 160 ALLEN ST 05701 #038-43-1992 L1997 **PM** *020 †60
KESHAVA, Praveen H. 254 STRATTON RD, CENTRAL VERMONT EYE CARE, 05701
#035-19-2000 L2006 **OPH** *020
KRAUSE, William Lawrence. 160 ALLEN ST, RUTLAND REGIONAL MEDICAL C 05701
#032-01-1992 L1994 **PCC** *020 †20
KRUPNICK, Kurt Andrew. 69 ALLEN ST, STE 10 05701 #422-01-1995 L1998 **IM** *020 †20
LANGO, Richard Patricij. 73 CENTER ST, NEUROLOGY MICROPRACTICE 05701
#035-08-1998 L2007 **N** *020
LAPETINA, Graciana. 160 ALLEN ST, RUTLAND REGIONAL MEDICAL C 05701
#035-19-1999 L2001 **P** *020

■ = Address Information Privacy Protected

LAPP, Philip Ray. 8 ALBERT CREE DR 05701 #050-02-1990 L1995 END *020 †20
LEFFEL, Wendy L. 160 ALLEN ST 05701 #035-06-1994 L1995 FM *020 †18
LEFFLER, Stephen Michael. 160 ALLEN ST 05701 #050-02-1990 L1993 EM *020 †16
LEFKOE, Todd Philip. 160 ALLEN ST 05701 #041-07-1988 L1991 PM *020 †60
LEIGHT, Robin Lorain. 71 ALLEN ST STE 402 05701 #041-13-1988 L1992 OBG *020 †30
LESZNIK, George Richard. 160 ALLEN ST, RUTLAND REGIONAL MEDICAL C 05701 #550-02-1983 L1999 AN *020 †05 ‡
LEVY, Arthur Maurice. 160 ALLEN ST, CENTER DEPARTMENT OF 05701 #035-20-1956 L1958 CD PDC *040 †20
LIGHTHART, William Andrew. 3 ALBERT CREE DR 05701 #035-06-2000 L2007 ORS *020
LILE, Buddy W. 160 ALLEN ST, R R M C 05701 #048-14-1994 L2004 P *020 †75
LOGAN, Mark Edward. 160 ALLEN ST, STE 203 05701 #050-02-1979 L1982 EM *020 †16
LOURAS, John Christopher. 160 ALLEN ST 05701 #050-02-1979 L1984 GS *020 †85
LOVETT, Richard Dana, Jr. 160 ALLEN ST, COMMUNITY CANCER CENTER 05701 #050-02-1985 L1990 RO *020 †80
LOVKO, Indra Ray. 1 GENERAL WING RD, PEDIATRIC ASSOCIATES 05701 #051-01-1995 L1995 PD *020 †55
LOVKO, T R. 160 ALLEN ST 05701 #051-01-1995 L1998 IM *072 †20
LYNCH, Annette Mary. 143 ALLEN ST 05701 #143-03-1961 L1988 P GPM *075
MALETTA, Thomas Jos. ■ 05701 #561-11-1955 L1972 U *071 †95
MAR, Kenneth E. 160 ALLEN ST 05701 #308-11-1986 L1995 PUD *020 †20
MARSH, Eric James. 3 ALBERT CREE DR, VERMONT ORTHOPAEDIC 05701 #038-40-2000 L2006 ORS *020
MASUCK, Tony Michael. 160 ALLEN ST 05701 #056-06-1990 L1995 PTH *020 †50
MC CAULIFFE, Danl Patrick. 3 MAHONEY AVE 05701 #035-03-1981 L2000 D *020 †20,15
MC CORMICK, Thomas Edward. 57 CHESTNUT AVE 05701 #050-02-1975 L1984 IM *020 †20
MCINTYRE, Donald R. ■ 05701 #041-01-1963 L1971 D *071 †15
MCMAHON, Scott Fitzgerald. 160 ALLEN ST, RUTLAND REGIONAL MEDICAL C 05701 #422-01-2001 L2007 P *020
MC NALLY, Walter Ernest. 160 ALLEN ST, MEDICAL STAFF OFFICE 05701 #050-02-2002 L2004 AN *020
MENSCH, Leon Shalom. 160 ALLEN ST, RUTLAND REGIONAL MED CTR 05701 #041-07-1995 L1995 PCP *050 †50
MESSIER, Mark Norman. 160 ALLEN ST 05701 #024-07-1982 L1989 FM *020 †18
MEUB, Daniel Warren. ■ 05701 #005-02-1947 L1998 NS *071 †25
MITCHELL, Daniel Richard. 160 ALLEN ST, RUTLAND REGIONAL MEDICAL C 05701 #047-05-1986 L2000 DR *020 †80
MUELLER, Edward August. 65 N MAIN ST, PMB 263 05701 #048-12-1975 L1986 P *020 †75
NAJARIAN, Kenneth Earl. 160 ALLEN ST 05701 #050-02-1980 L1983 VIR R *020 †80
NELSON, Judy A. 1 GENERAL WING RD, PEDIATRIC ASSOCIATES 05701 #035-19-1984 L1989 PD *020 †55
O'FARRELL, Diarmuid A. 160 ALLEN ST, RUTLAND REGIONAL MEDICAL C 05701 #539-04-1985 L1998 OSM *100
O'ROURKE, Daniel John. 160 ALLEN ST, CENTER DEPARTMENT OF 05701 #035-15-1990 L1996 CD *020
O'ROURKE, William Andrew. 160 ALLEN ST 05701 #050-02-1957 L1958 IM ID *071
PAVINI, Marie T. 160 ALLEN ST 05701 #422-01-1994 L2003 IM CCM *020 †20
PERRY, James Perrin. 160 ALLEN ST 05701 #010-01-1964 L1970 GP GS *071 †18
PIPER, Jeffery Graham. 160 ALLEN ST 05701 #011-02-1989 L1996 OPH *020 †35
PISANELLI, Victor J, Jr. 69 ALLEN ST STE 6 05701 #050-02-1973 L1977 GS *020 †85
PRATT, William Arthur. 254 STRATTON RD 05701 #050-02-1943 L1946 IM OS *071 †20
RADEMACHER, James Norbert. 160 ALLEN ST, RUTLAND HOSPITAL INC 05701 #026-04-1977 L1978 DR *020 †80
RAGAN, Chas Lindbergh, II. 7 COURT SQ, RUTLAND MENTAL HLTH SVCS 05701 #048-12-1980 L2004 CHP PYA *020 †75 ‡
REDDEN, Suzanne. 160 ALLEN ST 05701 #010-02-1996 L1996 PCC *020 †20
REICH, Harvey Steven. 160 ALLEN ST 05701 #033-05-1981 L1994 CCM IM *020 †20
ROBERTELLO, Michael E. 160 ALLEN ST, CENTER DEPARTMENT OF 05701 #305-01-1984 L1996 CD IM *020 †20
ROBERTS, James Wesley. 160 ALLEN ST, RUTLAND REGIONAL MEDICAL C 05701 #038-43-1996 L2000 MPD *020 †20,55
RUSSELL, James Anthony. 160 ALLEN ST, RUTLAND REGIONAL MEDICAL C 05701 #050-02-1980 L1982 EM *020 †16
SCHOENFELD, Charles Deem. 160 ALLEN ST DEPT RAD 05701 #041-01-1956 L1962 R *071 †80
SCHULZ-HEIK, Katherine An. ■ 05701 #035-48-2005 L2008 PTH *100
SCOVNER, Michael Earl. 160 ALLEN ST 05701 #038-40-1984 L1988 IM PD *020
SHAPIRO, Stanley Marc. 160 ALLEN ST, CENTER DEPARTMENT OF 05701 #016-01-1980 L1983 CD IM *020 †20
SHOWN, Thomas Earl. 160 ALLEN ST 05701 #020-02-1961 L2002 U *020 †95
SIVAGNANAM, Nathan. 160 ALLEN ST 05701 #220-01-1977 L1985 R *020 †80
SMITH, Clifford Baxter. 160 ALLEN ST, CENTER DEPARTMENT OF 05701 #050-02-1976 L1982 IM *020 †20
SMITH, George Jay Walker. 160 ALLEN ST 05701 #021-01-1995 L1998 ATP PUD *030 †50
SMITH, Heather M P. 160 ALLEN ST, RUTLAND INPATIENT CARE 05701 #050-02-2001 L2004 IM *020
STANNARD, Edward C. 160 ALLEN ST 05701 #050-02-1942 L1945 GP *072
STEIN, Ann C. 3 ALBERT CREE DR, VERMONT ORTHOPAEDIC 05701 #033-06-1982 L1989 ORS HS *040
STEIN, Steven Hal. 160 ALLEN ST 05701 #008-02-1982 L1984 EM *020 †16
STICKNEY, J Carleton. 160 ALLEN ST 05701 #035-03-1943 L1946 GP *071
STICKNEY, Mark C. 3 COMMONS ST 05701 #035-03-1985 L1988 IM *020
STICKNEY, Peter Chas. 69 ALLEN ST, STE 5 05701 #035-03-1970 L1973 IM *020
STRONCZAK, Christopher R. 160 ALLEN ST 05701 #048-02-1994 L2002 EM *020 †16
SZOSTAK, Lorri Lewis. 69 ALLEN ST, STE 6 05701 #035-09-1989 L1998 P *020 †75
TAGER, David Scott. 11 COMMONS ST 05701 #035-19-1987 L2001 IM GE *020 †20
THOMAS, James Eugene. 54 WOODSTOCK AVE 05701 #038-40-1969 L1974 FM *071 †18
THURMOND, Michell. 69 ALLEN ST, STE 1 05701 #047-05-1994 L2006 OTO *020 †45
UPTON, Peter Dodds. 160 ALLEN ST 05701 #050-02-1963 L1965 NS *020 †25
VALLARIO, Ronald Dominic. 160 ALLEN ST 05701 #033-06-1986 L2003 FM FPG *020 †18
VANDENBERG, Susan Nell. 160 ALLEN ST 05701 #025-07-1978 L1994 EM *020 †85,16
VARGAS, Joseph Henry, III. 160 ALLEN ST 05701 #050-02-1965 L1965 ORS *071 †40
WADDINGTON, Margaret M. ■ 05701 #050-02-1961 L1962 OS *071 †75
WARREN, Renee Beth. 160 ALLEN ST 05701 #056-05-1977 L1988 PTH *020 †50
WATKINS, Matthew Wells. 160 ALLEN ST, CENTER DEPARTMENT OF 05701 #041-01-1985 L1985 CD *020 †20

WEAVER, Howard Alfred. 3 ALBERT CREE DR 05701 #038-41-1965 L1971 GE IM *020 †20
WEIDNER, Mark Howard. 1 PROSPECT ST 05701 #041-02-1992 L1992 NEP *020 †20
WHEELER, Donald Billings. 160 ALLEN ST 05701 #035-03-1967 L1968 DR *020 †80
WHEELER, John Chas. 3 ALBERT CREE DR 05701 #035-03-1969 L1970 PS HS *020 †65 ‡
WILLIAMS, John Rathbone. 160 ALLEN ST 05701 #024-07-1942 L1952 R *020 †80
WINGET, Joseph Frederick. 6 COMMONS ST 05701 #035-03-1985 L1986 IM *020 †20
WOLK, Arthur Dave. 3 MAHONEY AVE 05701 #050-02-1943 L1951 PD *071 †55
WOOD, David Frank. 160 ALLEN ST 05701 #035-20-1966 L1989 ON IM *072 †20
WOOD, Stephen James. 1 GENERAL WING RD, PEDIATRIC ASSOCIATES 05701 #041-14-1998 L2001 PD *020 †55
ZAK, Andrew Paul. RR 2 BOX 8502 05701 #050-02-1959 L1962 IM *020
ZMURKO, Matthew George. 3 ALBERT CREE DR, EXECUTIVE WOODS 05701 #023-01-1997 L2007 OSS *020

SAINT ALBANS – FRANKLIN

ADAMSONS, Roland J, Jr. NORTHWESTERN MED CTR, DEPT OF ANESTHESIA 05478 #035-08-1988 L1993 AN *020 †05
BACKUS, Verne Lemay. 260 CREST RD, STE 101 05478 #032-01-1993 L1999 GPM DR *020 †70
BARBER, Donald S. ■ 05478 #024-07-1953 L1963 OBG GP *071
BEATTIE, Robert N. 3 CREST RD, NORTHWESTERN ORTHOPAEDIC 05478 #065-05-1980 L1991 ORS *020 †40
BELLSTROM, Laura Ann. 10 CREST RD 05478 #050-02-1989 L1996 PD *020 †55
BURKE, Peter Richard. 133 FAIRFIELD ST, MEDICAL CENTER 05478 #032-01-1984 L1988 PTH *020 †50
CALCAGNI, Kristen Wells. 10 CREST RD 05478 #050-02-2000 L2004 PD *020 †55
CARMOLA, John R. ■ 05478 #035-06-1966 L1968 IM *020 †20
CHIAPPINELLI, Emanuele Q. 11 CREST RD, MOUSETRAP PEDIATRICS 05478 #050-02-1975 L1980 PD *020 †55
COCHRANE, Robert Timothy. 133 FAIRFIELD ST 05478 #050-02-2003 L2003 IM *020 †20
DOWHAN, Thomas Peter. 156 N MAIN ST, ST ALBANS EYE CTR 05478 #050-02-1987 L2000 OPH *020 †35
FLIMLIN, Mary T. 260 CREST RD STE 101, OCCUPATIONAL HEAL 05478 #016-42-1985 L2004 PM *030 †60
FONTAINE, Elisabeth. 12 CREST RD, GREEN MOUNTAIN OB/GYN 05478 #067-04-1988 L1994 OBG *020 †20
GELLIS, Janice Elizabeth. 77 FAIRFIELD ST 05478 #050-02-1989 L1989 AN *020 †05
GRUNERT, Richard Thos. 27 FISHER POND RD, GREEN MOUNTAIN UROLOGY 05478 #016-01-1986 L1991 U *020 †95
HARRISON, Thomas Paul. 133 FAIRFIELD ST 05478 #016-01-1994 L2003 AN *020 †05
HATCH, Jeremy. 3 CREST RD, STE 3 05478 #065-01-1979 L2006 ORS *020 †40
HICKEY, Nancy Marilyn. FAIRFIELD ST, NORTHWESTERN MED CTR 05478 #065-09-1979 L1995 R *020 †80
HOLMES, Frederick Carson. 11 CREST RD, MOUSETRAP PEDIATRICS 05478 #020-12-1967 L1968 PD *020 †55
KENNEDY, Michael Timlin. 148 FAIRFIELD ST 05478 #050-02-1995 L1999 GS *020 †85
KEOGH, Kurt William. 133 FAIRFIELD ST, NORTHWESTERN MEDICAL CENTE 05478 #026-04-2001 L2005 EM *020
LAWS, James Eustace. NORTHWESTERN MED CTR, DEPT OF RAD 05478 #065-09-1955 L1990 *071
LUNA, Sergio Horta. 107 FISHER POND RD 05478 #649-02-1982 L1998 P *020 †75
MACHANIC, P Brian. 156 N MAIN ST 05478 #050-02-1966 L1990 OPH *020 †35
MANCHESTER, Stewart P. 9 CREST RD 05478 #065-01-1981 L1994 *071
MANSOORANI, Roya. 11 CREST RD, MOUSETRAP PEDIATRICS 05478 #517-11-1991 L1994 PD *020 †55
MASON, Stephen Bradley. 133 FAIRFIELD ST 05478 #050-02-1991 L1993 AN PAN *020 †05
MODZELEWSKI, Zdzislaw A. 42 S MAIN ST 05478 #759-09-1970 L1994 OTO *020 †45
MOONEY, David R. 107 FISHER POND RD 05478 #654-01-1992 L1993 P *020 †75
NASCA, Joseph Dean. 133 FAIRFIELD ST 05478 #050-02-1988 L1991 PD *020 †55
NEWMAN, William Hadlock. 133 FAIRFIELD ST 05478 #050-02-1990 L1997 IM *020 †20,03
NICHOLSON, John Christie. 2 CREST RD 05478 #036-07-1989 L2001 IM EM *020 †20
NICHOLSON, Pamela Bond. ■ 05478 #036-07-1989 L1989 IM *020 †20
NIELSEN, Terri Thomas. 9 CREST RD, ST ALBANS PRIMARY CARE 05478 #035-15-1996 L2003 FM *020 †18
PAYNE, Stephen Russell. 148 FAIRFIELD ST, NORTH WESTERN MEDICAL SURG 05478 #050-02-1983 L1983 GS TRS *020
PEREZ, Elizabeth Zumwalt. 27 FISHER POND RD, GREEN MOUNTAIN UROLOGY 05478 #050-02-1995 L2000 U *020 †95
PERKINS, David Llewellyn. ■ 05478 #050-02-1965 L1968 AN *071
ROBERTS, Amy Beth. 12 CREST RD, DOCTORS OFFICE COMMONS 05478 #050-02-1990 L1995 IM *020
ROBERTS, William Alan. 133 FAIRFIELD ST 05478 #050-02-1988 L1989 AN *020 †05
ROHATGI, Lavi. 133 FAIRFIELD ST, APOGEE PHYSICIANS 05478 #495-38-1998 L2007 FM *020 †18
ROSE, Quentin Forrest. 133 FAIRFIELD ST 05478 #056-06-1977 L2005 DR *020 †80 ‡
SADKIN, Toby Renee. 9 CREST RD 05478 #016-01-1988 L1988 FM *020 †18
SALOMONE, Joseph Michael. 1 CREST RD 05478 #012-05-1991 L1996 GS *020 †85
SCHNEIDER, Elizabeth Sue. 110 LAKE ST 05478 #035-47-1991 L1991 FM *020 †18
SCHOLTEN, Marietta Carola. 148 FAIRFIELD ST 05478 #008-02-1987 L1987 FM *020 †18
SHEPPARD, John Paul. ■ 05478 #010-02-1967 L1974 GP GS *075 †85
SHULMAN, Ned Irwin. 92 FAIRFIELD ST 05478 #005-06-1967 L1975 IM *020 ‡
SILVERSTEIN, Mark F Levin. 133 FAIRFIELD ST, APOGEE PHYSICIANS 05478 #025-07-1994 L1998 IM *020
SOBEL, Steven Neil. 107 FISHER POND RD 05478 #550-02-1987 L1993 P *020 †75 ‡
SULLIVAN, Lawrence Lowrey. 12 CREST RD 05478 #050-02-1995 L1999 OBG *020 †30
TRAN, Thuy T. ■ 05478 #048-13-1996 L2001 PTH *020 †50
TREMBLAY, Leonard. 12 CREST RD, GREEN MOUNTAIN ASSOC IN OB 05478 #067-03-1979 L1991 OBG *020 †20
VIJUPS, Mara Vija. 10 CREST RD 05478 #050-02-1993 L1994 FM *020 †18
WAGENKNECHT, Walter C. 133 FAIRFIELD ST, NORTHWESTERN MEDICAL CENTE 05478 #024-05-1979 L2000 DR *020 †80
WEBB, Adrian Leslie. 107 FISHER POND RD, NORTHWESTERN COUNSELING & 05478 #917-20-1980 L2007 P *020 †75
WENNAR, Martin Howard. 1 CREST RD 05478 #035-03-1968 L1976 GS *071 †85

WRIGHT, Alice Lee. 107 FISHER POND RD 05478 #038-06-1963 L1966 **P CHP** *071 †75
YATES, Harold Taylor, Jr. 91 S MAIN ST 05478 #051-04-1969 L1976 **PD ADL** *072 †55 ‡
YEATTS-PETERSON, Maryann. 53 FAIRFAX RD, STE 2 05478 #050-02-1991 L1995
  OBG *020 †30
ZSOLDOS, Frank Jos, Jr. 156 N MAIN ST 05478 #055-01-1965 L1977 **IM** *020 †20 ‡
ZVOLENSKY, Heidi Ludwig. 11 CREST RD, MOUSETRAP PEDIATRICS 05478
  #055-01-2001 L2001 **PD** *020 †55

SAINT JOHNSBURY – CALEDONIA

ABADI, Ardeschir. 114 UNDERCLYFFE RD 05819 #407-15-1957 L1966 **IM** *071
AJAMIE, John Michael. 185 SHERMAN DR, STE 1 05819 #017-20-1980 L1984 **FM** *020 †18
BRODY, David Steven. 1290 HOSPITAL DR 05819 #024-07-1987 L1993 **IM** *020 †20
CUSANO, Phillip John. 1315 HOSPITAL DR, DEPT OF ANES 05819 #422-01-2001 L2007
  AN *100 †05
DANIELSON, Kenneth S. 1235 HOSPITAL DR, STE 1 05819 #024-01-1965 L1980
  GS PDS *020 †85
DREISBACH, Craig De Witt. 1315 HOSPITAL DR 05819 #025-01-1979 L1984 **ORS HS** *020 †40
FINE, Sharon Debra. 18 WESTERN AVE 05819 #016-01-1994 L1994 **FM** *020 †18
GAGNON, Richard Normand. 1315 HOSPITAL DR 05819 #043-01-1977 L1982 **ORS** *020
HAMMER, Charles John, III. 1290 HOSPITAL DR, STE 3 05819 #023-01-1987 L1994 **D** *020 †15
HARTONG, John Michael. 1315 HOSPITAL DR 05819 #028-34-1968 L1996 **GS** *020 †85
HERSHEY-SILVERMAN, Alice. 1235 HOSPITAL DR, STE 3 05819 #035-08-1981 L1992
  P *020 †75
HOULE, Ted V J. 1290 HOSPITAL DR, STE 5 05819 #051-01-1968 L1974 **OPH** *020 †35
JAUCH, Robert Jos. 714 BREEZY HILL RD 05819 #038-06-1970 L1978 **OTO AM** *020 †45 ‡
KELLER, Betty Jane. ■ 05819 #050-02-1988 L1992 **FM** *071 †18
KELLOGG, John Hamilton. ■ 05819 #051-07-1990 L1992 **IM** *020 †20
KIM, Shin Hyoung. 1315 HOSPITAL DR 05819 #583-02-1956 L1974 **AN** *071
KRAUS, Dana Charlotte. 222 SUMMER ST 05819 #032-01-1992 L1995 **FM** *020 †18
LONG, William Frank. 1315 HOSPITAL DR 05819 #026-04-1976 L1998 **OBG** *020 †30
MEIERDIERCKS, Charles F. 9 BOYNTON AVE 05819 #035-19-1942 **IM** *071
MEIERDIERCKS, Frank Jos. 185 SHERMAN DR, STE 2 05819 #024-01-1975 L1978 **IM** *020 †20
PATNO, Karyn Marie. 97 SHERMAN DR 05819 #038-43-1983 L1985 **PD** *055
PAUL, Elaine Susan. 1315 HOSPITAL DR, PO BOX 905 05819 #041-09-1987 L2001
  OBG *020 †30
PHIPPS, Stephen Jonathan. 1290 HOSPITAL DR, STE 5 05819 #030-06-1996 L2000
  OPH *020 †35
PRICE, Mark John. 97 SHERMAN DR, ST JOHNSBURY PEDIATRICS 05819 #047-05-1983 L1984
  PD *020 †55
RANKIN, Jerry Dean. 1315 HOSPITAL DR 05819 #035-19-1965 L1968 **GS** *020 †85
READY, Mary Oleary. ■ 05819 #050-02-2002 L2005 **FM** *020 †18
RIPPLE, Gregory Harold. 1080 HOSPITAL DR 05819 #056-05-1991 L2000 **ON** *020 †20
ROBINSON, William Henry. ■ 05819 #023-01-1945 L1951 **R OS** *020 †80
SLOSBERG, Richard Murray. 1394 MAIN ST 05819 #024-07-1964 L1995 **PHP PD** *020 †55
STASNY, Elaine Victoria. 97 SHERMAN DR, ST JOHNSBURY PEDIATRICS 05819
  #055-01-1985 L1985 **PD** *020 †55
THOMAS, Eustace Alfred. 1290 HOSPITAL DR 05819 #011-03-1966 L1970 **OPH** *071
TOLL, David. 1394 MAIN ST 05819 #038-06-1948 L1951 **PD** *020 †55
WALKO, Martin Stephen. 1315 HOSPITAL DR, NORTHEASTERN VT SURGICAL G 05819
  #033-06-1994 L2005 **GS** *020 †85
WHITEHOUSE, David John. ■ 05819 #032-01-1982 L1986 **P** *030 †75
ZIOBROWSKI, Thomas Frank. 185 SHERMAN DR, STE 2 05819 #041-01-1975 L1978
  IM IMG *020 †20

SALISBURY – ADDISON

CARBO, Ralph John, Jr. CAMP 102 RFD #1 05769 #010-02-1947 L1976 **GP OPH** *071

SANDGATE – BENNINGTON

PEFF, Peter Jos. PO BOX 569 05250 #035-19-1972 L1977 **FM** *020 †18

SHAFTSBURY – BENNINGTON

ELLISON, Arthur E. ■ 05262 #024-01-1951 L1954 **ORS OS** *020 †40
FARIS, Arthur Slee. PO BOX 379 05262 #035-03-1953 L1954 **FM** *071 †18
FARIS, Eliz Cunningham. ■ 05262 #035-03-1953 L1954 **FM** *071
KING, David Elmer. 677 VT ROUTE 7A 05262 #041-02-1983 L1986 **FM** *075 †18
MAYER, Barry Saul. PO BOX 6, 743 TOWN LINE RD 05262 #010-02-1964 L2000 **DR** *020 †80
NIEMI, Allison Page. 677 VT ROUTE 7A 05262 #023-01-2000 L2004 **FM** *020 †18
TOCK, William Roger. PO BOX 226, 613 DWYERS CAMP RD 05262 #016-06-1995 L2002
  IM *020 †20

SHARON – WINDSOR

DAKE, Peter Denteh. ■ 05065 #869-05-1962 L1977 **GS** *020
INDENBAUM, David. 2859 FAYBROOK RD 05065 #050-02-1980 L1981 **PD** *020
TYSON, Judith. ■ 05065 #050-02-1970 L1971 **OBG** *071 †30

SHEFFIELD – CALEDONIA

ZIMMERMAN, Veva Hampton. PO BOX 78, 3301 RTE 123 05866 #024-07-1962 L2004
  P *071 †75

SHELBURNE – CHITTENDEN

ALLEN, Sinclair T, Jr. ■ 05482 #024-01-1940 L1942 **PUD IM** *071 †20
AUSTIN, Richard C. ■ 05482 #035-20-1950 L1994 **OM CRS** *072 †85

BABBOTT, Frank L, Jr. ■ 05482 #035-15-1951 L1963 **PHP GPM** *071 †70
BACKUP, Edna F Dole. ■ 05482 #050-02-1946 L1948 **GYN GP** *071
BASHAW, Donald Louis. ■ 05482 #050-02-1942 L1946 **IM** *071
BROWNE, Harry Herbert. ■ 05482 #035-03-1956 L1959 **R** *071 †80
BUNDOCK, Elizabeth Ann. ■ 05482 #016-42-2001 L2007 **FOP** *020 †50
BURKE, Karen Joyce. 100 WAKE ROBIN DR 05482 #050-02-1978 L1988 **FM EM** *020 †16,18
CLEARY, Karen E. 10 MARSETT RD, STE 1 05482 #038-43-1980 L1992 **OPH** *020 †35
CRAIG, Robert H. ■ 05482 #065-01-1944 L1959 **IM** *071 †20
DAVIGNON, Philip Jos. 145 PINE HAVEN SHORES RD, STE 1127 05482 #050-02-1981 L1995
  FM OM *020
FINK, Theodore James. 5138 SHELBURNE RD 05482 #035-08-1970 L1971 **IM** *020 †20
GENTILE, Douglas Alan. ■ 05482 #056-06-1981 L1994 **EM** *020 †20,16
GIBSON, Barbara Wilmer. ■ 05482 #008-01-1955 L1975 **OBG PD** *071 †55
GOLODETZ, Arnold. ■ 05482 #035-45-1953 L1969 **PHP IM** *071 †20
GRANT, Joseph Lewis. ■ 05482 #041-01-1946 L1954 **IM PUD** *071 †20
GROVER, Ralph Wier. ■ 05482 #035-01-1945 L1946 **D DMP** *071 †15
HEDDEN, David Kirke, III. ■ 05482 #038-45-1980 L1983 **CHP P** *020 †75
HUNZIKER, Robert Jacob. 35 SOUTH FORTY ROAD 05482 #050-02-1952 L1953 **DR** *071 †80
JACKSON, Richard Stuart. ■ 05482 #041-02-1975 L1982 **TS** *075 †85,90
JENKINS, Ward Sherman. 100 WAKE ROBIN DR 05482 #008-01-1944 L1958 **A** *071 †03
JONES, Joshua Calvinwayne. 285 OAKHILL RD 05482 #054-04-2002 L2002 **PFP** *100
KELLNER, Jeanne Rodseth. 10 MARSETT RD 05482 #016-11-1982 L1987 **PD** *020 †55
KUNIN, Arthur S. ■ 05482 #050-02-1952 L1957 **NEP** *071
LINTON, Peter Castle. ■ 05482 #035-03-1956 L1964 **PS** *071 †65
LUKENS, Robert W, Jr. ■ 05482 #041-02-1955 L1956 **ORS** *071 †40
MC COOEY, John Henry. ■ 05482 #035-08-1956 L1995 **IM** *071 †20
MOLLOY, Maureen Katherine. ■ 05482 #035-08-1957 L1966 **LM OP** *020 †40
NORTHRUP, Christine Dee. 4070 SHELBURNE RD 05482 #050-02-1993 L1993 **IM** *020 †20 ‡
PAGE, Kristen Lynn. ■ 05482 #050-02-2002 L2006 **OBG REN** *100 †30
PARKER, Colleen Marie. 4047 SPEAR ST, ANESTHESIOLOGIST 05482 #049-01-2003 L2004
  AN *020
PATTERSON, W Bradford. ■ 05482 #024-01-1950 L1989 **ON GS** *071 †85
POMICTER, Edward Tyler. ■ 05482 #050-02-1998 L1998 **AN** *020 †05
RYDER, Richard Alan. ■ 05482 #035-01-1963 L1965 **IM OM** *020 †20,70
SAXE, Neal Alexander. ■ 05482 #050-02-2005 L2005 **AN** *012
SCHUMACHER, George Adam. ■ 05482 #035-20-1936 L1950 **N** *071 †75
SHELDON, Huntington. ■ 05482 #023-07-1956 L1985 **PTH OS** *040
SHULL, Susan. PO BOX 850, THE CREAMERY 05482 #050-02-1997 L1997 **IM** *020 †20
STERN, Peter. 130 HARBOR RD 05482 #050-02-1981 L1983 **AN** *020 †05
VAN BUREN, Henry Carmer. ■ 05482 #050-02-1954 L1960 **IM** *030 †20
WAGNER, Katherine Jane. ■ 05482 #050-02-2006 L2006 **OBG** *012
WHEELER, Edward Martin. ■ 05482 #035-01-1942 L1975 **EM ORS** *071 †40
WILLITTS, Bruce Kirby. ■ 05482 #038-06-1956 L1993 **OBG** *071 †30
YAROW, Natalie. 100 WAKE ROBIN DR 05482 #051-04-1940 L1992 **P CHP** *071 †55,75

SHOREHAM – ADDISON

CURTISS, Allan Pond, Jr. 156 SCHOOL RD 05770 #045-01-1975 L1989 **IM CD** *020

SHREWSBURY – RUTLAND

MARTIN, Gerry David. ■ 05738 #036-05-1967 L1967 **OPH** *071 †35

SOUTH BURLINGTON – CHITTENDEN

ABRAHAMS, Irving. ■ 05403 #035-08-1954 L1955 **D** *071 †15
ADAMS, Ryan Scott. ■ 05407 #031-01-2006 L2007 **AN** *012
AHLUWALIA, Harleen Kaur. 53 TIMBER LN, TIMBER LANE ALLERGY & ASTH 05403
  #038-43-2002 L2007 **AI** *020 †20,03
AITKEN, Phil Allen. 55 TIMBER LN 05403 #048-04-1967 L1974 **OPH N** *075 †35 ‡
AKSELROD, Dmitriy Grigori. ■ 05403 #035-15-2007 **TY** *012
ALDEN, Peter Dunham. 1 TIMBER LN, AESCULAPIUS MEDICAL CTR 05403 #024-01-1958
  IM GE *071 †20
ALLAN, David Scott. ■ 05403 #051-07-2004 L2004 **P** *012
AMBURGEY, Odul Aktan. ■ 05403 #038-41-2003 L2007 **OBG** *100
AMBURGEY, Robert Gutshall. ■ 05403 #038-41-2004 L2007 **EM** *020
ANDERSON, Phillip Richard. ■ 05403 #038-41-2004 L2007 **CD** *012 †20
ANTLEY, Catherine Murer. 50 TIMBER LN, TIMBER LN MEDICAL CENTER 05403
  #036-01-1991 L1998 **PTH DMP** *020 †20
AYER, Jennifer Main. 1 TIMBER LN, AESCULAPIUS MEDICAL CENTER 05403
  #035-45-2001 L2001 **IM** *020
BAAD, Stephen Christopher. 368 DORSET ST, STE 1 05403 #050-02-2001 L2001 **IM** *020
BARNEY, Bernard Benj. ■ 05403 #050-02-1943 L1947 **PS** *071 †45,65
BARTLETT, Craig S. 192 TILLEY DR 05403 #035-03-1991 L1997 **ORS OTR** *020 †40
BATES, Thomas Clinton. 52 TIMBER LN, TIMBER LANE MEDICAL CENTER 05403
  #067-01-1962 L1967 **PD** *071 †55
BEATTY, Dennis Reed. 1 TIMBER LN 05403 #041-02-1994 L1994 **IM** *020 †20
BENNUM, Richard Raymond. 620 HINESBURG RD 05403 #050-02-1980 L1984
  DR NM *020 †80 ‡
BJERREGAARD, Jens. ■ 05403 #028-34-2006 L2007 **AN** *012
BJORNSON, Gerhild F. 70 BARTLETT BAY RD, THE HEALTH PLACE SUITE 1 05403
  #056-05-1975 L1981 **ON HEM** *020
BLACKBURN, Ethan Wade. ■ 05403 #020-02-2007 L2007 **ORS** *012
BORRELLO, Michael T. 62 TILLEY DR, FLETCHER ALLEN HEALTH CARE 05403
  #048-14-1990 L1993 **APM** *020 †05
BRAUN, John Thos. 192 TILLEY DR 05403 #035-20-1989 L2006 **OSS** *020 †40
BURNS, Lisa Denise. ■ 05403 #021-01-1995 L2007 **PD** *020 †55
BUTTLES, Roy Vedder. ■ 05403 #050-02-1940 L1947 **PTH** *071 †50
CAMPBELL, Douglas Murray. 6 SAN REMO DR 05403 #025-12-1981 L1986 **ORS** *020 †40
CAREY, Kevin Thos. 364 DORSET ST, STE 1 05403 #050-02-1985 L1992 **CD** *020 †20
CARLSON, Nancy Ann. 364 DORSET ST 05403 #035-15-1986 L1989 **OBG** *020 †30
CAVIN, Thomas Jeffrey. 54 TIMBER LN 05403 #024-01-1980 L1984 **OPH** *020 †35

■ = Address Information Privacy Protected

CHRISTIAN, Rose Crowley. 3 TIMBER LN, VERMONT REGIONAL DIABETES 05403 #035-03-1985 L2005 **IM** *020 †20
CRESPO, Eric Michael. ■ 05403 #008-02-2000 L2007 **ICE** *012 †20
CUNNINGHAM, Alicia Marier. 1 TIMBER LN 05403 #024-01-2002 L2005 **IM** *100 †20
DAVIS, Wendy Sue. 51 TIMBER LN 05403 #051-01-1981 L1987 **PD** *040 †55
DEE, Tristan Rebecca. ■ 05403 #020-02-2007 L2007 **IM** *012
DENNISON, W Landon, Jr. 368 DORSET ST STE 2, FOUR SEASONS DERMATOLOGY 05403 #041-02-1962 L1970 **D** *071 †15
DI CELLO, Michael Caesar. 53 TIMBER LN, ASTHMA ASSOCIATES, P.C. 05403 #038-40-1994 L1999 **AI** *020 †20,03
FRENZEN, Seth W. 6 SAN REMO DR 05403 #043-01-2001 L2001 **ORS** *012
FRIESEN, Bradley Todd. 52 TIMBER LN 05403 #041-14-1998 L1998 **PD** *020 †55
GEER, Benjamin Lawrence. ■ 05403 #025-07-2005 L2005 **ORS** *012
GENTRY, Stokes. 53 TIMBER LN 05403 #041-13-1955 L1958 **AI PD** *071 †55,03
GERSON, William Thos. 52 TIMBER LN 05403 #023-07-1982 L1988 **PD PDP** *020 †55 ‡
GILWEE, Jennifer. 1 TIMBER LN 05403 #050-02-1997 L2000 **IM** *020 †20
GORDON, Robert David. 364 DORSET ST, STE 204 05403 #050-02-1973 L1986 **D** *020 †15
GRAHAM, Michael Steven. ■ 05403 #035-09-2007 L2007 **FP** *012
GRAMLING, Jason Todd. 1 TIMBER LN 05403 #051-01-1993 L1998 **IM** *020 †20
GUIDULI, Robert Cesare. 55 TIMBER LN 05403 #050-02-1961 L1962 **OPH N** *020 †35
GUNTHER, Peter G S. 368 DORSET ST, STE 1 05403 #035-20-1982 L1985 **IM** *020 †20
HAYDEN, Jonathan Brewster. 1 TIMBER LN 05403 #050-02-1978 L1984 **IM** *020 †20 ‡
HELZER, John Earl. 54 W TWIN OAKS TER STE 14 05403 #049-01-1967 L1989 **P** *050 †75
HUNT, Elizabeth Ann. ■ 05403 #035-08-2005 L2005 **FP** *012
IYER, Anita Subramanian. ■ 05403 #495-01-1994 L2007 **SP** *020 †50
JAFFE, Elizabeth Fern. 53 TIMBER LN, TIMBERLANE ALLERGY/ASTHMA 05403 #054-04-1993 L1994 **AI PDA** *020 †55,03
KAPLAN, Andrew Stone. 6 SAN REMO DR 05403 #035-01-1987 L1992 **ORS** *020 †40
KASPRISIN, Duke Oscar. ■ 05403 #035-47-1972 L1993 **PD PHO** *030 †55
KATZ, James Edward. 110 KIMBALL AVE STE 115 05403 #008-02-1978 L2003 **EM** *020 †16,70
KENT, Edward Francis. 53 TIMBER LN 05403 #041-12-1983 L1989 **PD** *020 †55,03
KERSHEN, Richard Todd. 1775 WILLISTON RD, THE CONTINENCE CENTER 05403 #035-46-1994 L2003 **U** *020 †95
KUHLMANN, Raymond F B. ■ 05403 #028-02-1939 L1948 **ORS** *071 †40
KUNIN, Adam William. 364 DORSET ST, STE 1 05403 #050-02-1993 L1996 **IM** *020 †20
LACOMBE, Julie Ann. 1775 WILLISTON RD, FLETCHER ALLEN HLTH CARE, 05403 #011-04-1999 L2006 **OBG** *100
LAND, Marshall L. 52 TIMBER LN 05403 #038-41-1972 L1974 **PD** *020 †55
LAWLIS, John F, III. 6 SAN REMO DR STE 101, ASSOC IN ORTHOPAEDIC SURGE 05403 #041-02-1982 L1992 **ORS OSM** *020 †40
LAZAROVICH, Mark. 53 TIMBER LN 05403 #165-03-1987 L1993 **AI IM** *020 †20,03
LISLE, Jennifer Webster. 192 TILLEY DR, ORTHOPEDIC SPECIALTY CENTE 05403 #050-02-2000 L2007 **ORS** *100
LOCHHEAD, Roger P. ■ 05403 #035-20-1951 L1953 **IM CD** *071 †20
LONG, John Gerald. 52 TIMBER LN 05403 #050-02-1975 L1978 **PD NPM** *020 †55
LORD, Kelly Lynn. ■ 05403 #050-02-1991 L1995 **PTH** *030
LUEBBERS, Robert Alden. 1775 WILLISTON RD, SOUTH BURLINGTON FP 05403 #032-01-1992 L1992 **FM** *020 †18
MACY, John. 6 SAN REMO DR 05403 #033-05-1992 L1992 **ORS** *020 †40
MADISON, Joan G Hoshauer. 53 TIMBER LN 05403 #041-13-1955 L1965 **A IM** *071 †03
MAHONEY, Patrick Jos. ■ 05403 #050-02-1968 L1970 **ORS** *071 †40
MARTENIS, Thomas Williams. 1 TIMBER LN, AESCULAPIUS MEDICAL CTR 05403 #041-01-1960 L1966 **IM RHU** *071 †20
MARTINO, Jenny Livia. ■ 05403 #001-02-2005 L2005 **IM** *012
MERCIA, William Martin. 110 KIMBALL AVE, STE 115 05403 #050-02-1974 L1978 **FM** *020 †20
MILNE, John Hollister. 1 TIMBER LN 05403 #024-01-1956 L1961 **IM** *020 †20
MOGAN, James Vincent. 43 TIMBER LN 05403 #050-02-1972 L1973 **HS ORS** *020 †40
MORWOOD, Betty Jo. 35 TIMBER LN 05403 #050-02-1974 L1976 **CHP P** *020 †75 ‡
MOUSSA, Amr Naguib. ■ 05403 #915-03-1999 L2007 **IM** *020 †20
NICELY, Christopher Cory. ■ 05403 #055-02-2004 L2004 **DR** *012
NICHOLAS, Edward Palen. ■ 05403 #035-05-2006 L2007 **DR** *012
NOUD, Patrick Henry. ■ 05403 #025-01-2003 L2003 **ORS** *012
PARSONS, Daniel Jacob. ■ 05403 #050-02-2006 L2007 **AN** *012
PARTILO, Steven Robert. 366 DORSET ST STE 2, FOUR SEASONS DERMATOLOGY 05403 #050-02-2000 L2000 **D** *020 †15
PATTON, Chad Matthew. ■ 05403 #020-02-2005 L2005 **ORS** *012
PEREZ-ABELE, Norma E. 192 TILLEY DR 05403 #005-15-1998 L2000 **FM** *020
PINEDA-MASSARI, Christophe. ■ 05403 #050-02-2002 L2006 **DR** *012 †20
PINO, Carlos Ariel. 62 TILLEY DR 05403 #231-01-1996 L2001 **AN** *020 †05
PITCHER, Mark Andrew. 368 DORSET ST, STE 1 05403 #035-45-1987 L1987 **IM** *020 †20
PONTZER, Elizabeth Jane. 366 DORSET ST STE 10, STONE HOUSE ASSOCIATES 05403 #035-48-2002 L2002 **P** *020
PREIS, Karen. 36 TIMBER LN 05403 #050-02-1970 L1971 **CHP P** *020 †75
PREMSAGAR, Bonam Paul. ■ 05403 #495-27-1960 L1972 **EM CD** *071 †55
RAMBALLY, Cherridan. ■ 05403 #041-15-2004 L2006 **N** *012
SANDOVAL, Marie Bona. 1 TIMBER LN, AESCULAPIUS MEDICAL CENTER 05403 #056-05-1995 L1998 **IM** *020 †20
SCHWARTZ, Mitchell Edward. 329 DORSET ST 05403 #041-09-1977 L1997 **D** *020 †15
SCOLLINS, Mary E Duffy. ■ 05403 #024-05-1969 L1974 **CHN PD** *071
SCOLLINS, Michael John. 1 TIMBER LN 05403 #024-05-1969 L1972 **IM PA** *020
SCRIGGINS, Alan Lee. ■ 05403 #067-01-1965 L1968 **PD** *071 †55
SEAGLE, Finley Alexander. 1233 SHELBURNE RD, STE E1 05403 #047-06-1961 L1969 **CD IM** *071
SEAL, Patricia Louise. 30 FARRELL ST, # 200 05403 #007-02-1979 L1989 **D** *020 †20,15
SHINOZAKI, Tamotsu. ■ 05403 #572-09-1958 L1966 **AN** *071 †05
SHUMA-HARTSWICK, Debra. 52 TIMBER LN 05403 #050-02-1990 L1990 **PD** *020 †55
SINCLAIR, Natalie Faye. ■ 05403 #050-02-2006 L2006 **IM** *012
SLIMOVITCH, Caroline L. 1775 WILLISTON RD, SOUTH BURLINGTON FAMILY PR 05403 #067-01-1991 L1991 **FM** *020 †18
SMITH, Robert Michael. 620 HINESBURG RD 05403 #019-02-1997 L2002 **DR** *020 †80
SPRAGUE, Julian Ruffin. ■ 05403 #051-01-2001 L2001 **HO** *100
STARR, Geoffrey Edward. 20 KIMBALL AVE, STE 308 05403 #050-02-1991 L1991 **N** *020 †75
STRENIO, Jonathan Scott. 1233 SHELBURNE RD, EMSA CORRECTIONAL CARE 05403 #041-12-1983 L1986 **FM OS** *071 †18
STRODTBECK, Wyndam M. 62 TILLEY DR 05403 #018-03-2002 L2006 **APM** *020 †05

SUEBLINVONG, Viranuj. ■ 05403 #891-01-1998 L2003 **PCC** *100 †20
SUZUKI, Takeki. ■ 05403 #572-03-2000 L2006 **CD** *012 †20
TENEBACK, Charlotte Catha. ■ 05403 #045-01-2004 L2007 **PCC** *012 †20
TERRIEN, C M, Jr. 62 TILLEY DR 05403 #050-02-1967 L1968 **CD IM** *020
TERRIEN, Edward Francis. 62 TILLEY DR, STE 102 05403 #050-02-1987 L1994 **CD** *020 †20
THABAULT, Noelle C. 368 DORSET ST, STE 1 05403 #050-02-1984 L1992 **OBG** *020 †30
TONINO, Richard Philip. 368 DORSET ST, STE 1 05403 #035-47-1977 L1983 **IM** *020 †20
TOWLE, Mattie Elizabeth. ■ 05403 #050-02-2006 L2006 **FP** *012
VINSON, Robert Karl. ■ 05403 #024-01-1972 L1977 **U MDM** *071 †95
WARD, Norman Stewart. 1775 WILLISTON RD 05403 #043-01-1981 L1987 **FM** *020 †18
WATSON, James Dana. 55 TIMBER LN 05403 #050-02-1967 L1994 **OPH** *020 †35
WEINSTOCK, Joanna Sheldon. 7 FAYETTE DR, CHAMPLAIN VLY URGENT CARE 05403 #050-02-1997 L1997 **FM** *020 †18 ‡
WEISCHEDEL, Garry R. 1775 WILLISTON RD 05403 #036-07-1987 L1999 **FM EM** *020 †18
WELCH, Joshua Aaron. ■ 05403 #025-12-2003 L2003 **FM** *020 †18
WHITE, Elizabeth Sosna. 110 KIMBALL AVE 05403 #050-02-1989 L1992 **FM** *020 †18
WING, Delight A. 52 TIMBER LN 05403 #050-02-1975 L1978 **PD** *020 †55
WINOKUR, Rebecca Chloe. 6 SAN REMO DR 05403 #050-02-2000 L2000 **FSM** *020 †18
WRIGHT, William Clyde, Jr. 53 TIMBER LN 05403 #041-01-1966 L1967 **A PD** *071 †55,03
YOUNG, Lari Leigh. ■ 05403 #050-02-2007 L2007 **P** *012
ZIEGELMAN, David Scott. 1 TIMBER LN 05403 #025-01-1985 L1985 **IM** *020 †20

SOUTH HERO – GRAND ISLE

BANNISTER, Linda Johnston. ■ 05486 #012-05-1979 L1982 **PD** *020 †55
GRAS, Alfred Edward. 341 W SHORE RD 05486 #036-07-1944 L1946 **A DIA** *071
WILDS, Daniel Curtis. ■ 05486 #020-02-1994 L1995 **IM** *020 †20

SOUTH ROYALTON – WINDSOR

SANBORN, Frederick. ■ 05068 #024-01-1937 L1941 **GP** *071

SOUTH RYEGATE – CALEDONIA

EDELMAN, Steven Paul. ■ 05069 #025-07-1972 L1999 **GP** *020

SOUTH STRAFFORD – ORANGE

DAVIS, Paul H. ■ 05070 #028-44-1933 **GP OS** *071

SPRINGFIELD – WINDSOR

BELL, Jeffrey Michael. 368 RIVER ST 05156 #041-09-1969 L1998 **IM** *020 †20
BETTENCOURT, Marieclaud D. 364 RIVER ST, SPRINGFIELD UROLOGY 05156 #023-12-1990 L2004 **U** *020 †95
BRENNAN, Thomas Eugene. 25 RIDGEWOOD RD, SPRINGFIELD HOSPITAL 05156 #024-16-1977 L1989 **RNR** *020 †80
CAHILL, James David. 268 RIVER ST 05156 #050-02-1969 L1969 **OBG** *020 †30 ‡
CIOCCHI, John Steven. 29 RIDGEWOOD RD 05156 #561-20-1983 L1988 **GS** *020 †85
CODY, Thornton S, Jr. 368 RIVER ST, RIDGEWOOD ASSOC INTERNAL M 05156 #023-01-1983 L1986 **IM** *020 †20
CUNNINGHAM, Charles C. 25 RIDGEWOOD RD 05156 #035-45-1951 L1957 **PTH** *071 †50
DALTON, Barbara Justina. 156 WALL ST 05156 #035-09-1979 L1989 **FM** *020 †18
DAVIS, Roger Wolcott, Jr. DUTTON DISTRICT RD 05156 #008-01-1943 L1973 **EM ORS** *071 †40
DONNELLY, Craig Lanier. 390 RIVER ST 05156 #050-02-1989 L1996 **CHP** *020 †75
DURGIN, Gwendolyn Frost. 25 RIDGEWOOD RD, EUREKA DIAGNOSTIC IMAGING 05156 #032-01-1999 L2004 **DR** *020 †80
EGBERT, Charles Cornelius. 25 RIDGEWOOD RD, SPRINGFIELD HOSPITAL 05156 #041-12-1992 L1993 **FM** *020 †18 ‡
FERGUSON-KANTOLA, Amy E. 29 RIDGEWOOD RD 05156 #050-02-1995 L1998 **PD** *020 †55
FIALLOS, Federico E. 29 RIDGEWOOD RD 05156 #847-05-1975 L1989 **GS** *020 †85
FOX, Roger Christopher. 252 RIVER ST 05156 #917-24-1970 L1975 **IM GP** *020 ‡
GUILMETTE, Frederic Jos. 25 RIDGEWOOD RD 05156 #050-02-1943 L1946 **PD** *071
HAMILTON, Mark Congdon. 368 RIVER ST 05156 #035-08-1974 L1977 **IM** *020 †20
HERTFORD, Steve Craig. 59 MAIN ST STE 103 05156 #033-06-1986 L1996 **FM** *020 †18
HUGHES, John Donald. 29 RIDGEWOOD RD, STE 1A 05156 #023-01-1972 L1975 **IM** *020 †20
JAMES, Douglas Harold. 25 RIDGEWOOD RD, SPRINGFIELD HOSPITAL 05156 #024-01-1960 L1990 **CD IM** *020 †20
JOHNS, Robert Reagen. 268 RIVER ST 05156 #021-05-1967 L1992 **OBG OS** *020 †30
JONES, Warner Edrick. 29 RIDGEWOOD RD, RIDGEWOOD PROFESSIONAL BLD 05156 #024-07-1961 L1966 **IM AM** *020 ‡
LANE, Richard Alexander. PO BOX 830, 441 RIVER ST 05156 #035-03-1980 L1987 **OPH** *020 †35
LAWRENCE, Yolanda G. 156 WALL ST 05156 #050-02-1992 L1996 **FM** *020 †18
LEMEI, Susan Lynn. 25 RIDGEWOOD RD 05156 #035-45-1995 L2004 **FM** *020 †18 ‡
LEWIS, Thomas Hugh. 25 RIDGEWOOD RD 05156 #050-02-1981 L1982 **GS CRS** *020 †10,85
LUHRMANN, George Wm. 25 RIDGEWOOD RD 05156 #035-01-1965 L1987 **P ADP** *020 †75
LUSS, Charles H. ■ 05156 #005-12-1945 L1945 **AN GP** *071
MARASA, Richard Anthony. 25 RIDGEWOOD RD, SPRINGFIELD HOSPITAL 05156 #023-01-1980 L1993 **EM IM** *020 †20,16 ‡
MC QUADE, Debra Valori. 107 PARK ST 05156 #008-02-1998 L2002 **CHP** *020 †75
OKELO, Caroline Laker. ■ 05156 #035-48-2002 L2005 **IM** *100 †20
OWEN, Roger Alexander. 29 RIDGEWOOD RD, BOX 2003 05156 #024-07-1972 L1976 **PD PDE** *020 †55
PAGE, Robert Griffith. 25 RIDGEWOOD RD 05156 #041-01-1945 L1976 **IM EM** *071
PRAH, Gregory Nicholas. 25 RIDGEWOOD RD 05156 #041-07-1991 L2000 **AN OS** *020 †05
REVILLE, Roger David. ■ 05156 #024-05-1962 L1970 **GS** *071 †85
REVILLE, Stephen Andrew. 29 RIDGEWOOD RD 05156 #050-02-1999 L2002 **PD** *020 †55
ROBBINS, Theodore Bennett. 390 RIVER ST 05156 #035-01-1964 L1972 **P** *020 †75
RYDER, Christopher John. 364 RIVER ST, CONNECTICUT VALLEY ENT 05156 #038-41-1985 L2004 **OTO** *020 †45

SMITH, Ed Ray. 25 RIDGEWOOD RD 05156 #021-06-1984 L1986 **DR** *020 †80
SOLANO, Simon. 362 RIVER ST 05156 #010-02-1962 L1992 **OBG** *020 †30
TENTINDO, Christine C. 25 RIDGEWOOD RD 05156 #035-19-1978 L1997 **END** *050 †55
WALKER, George Andrew, Jr. 60 FOREST DR 05156 #048-12-1969 L1978 **ORS** *020 †40
WEISS, William P. 25 RIDGEWOOD RD 05156 #035-01-1956 L1971 **IM GYN** *020 †70
WELLENS, Mark Danl. 25 RIDGEWOOD RD, SPRINGFIELD HOSPITAL 05156 #035-46-1975 L1980 **DR** *020 †80
WU, Gene Wenchieh. 25 RIDGEWOOD RD, SPRINGFIELD HOSPITAL 05156 #050-02-1993 L1999 **AN** *020 †05

STOWE — LAMOILLE

BAK, Martin Paul. ■ 05672 #035-46-1984 L2003 **IM GS** *020 †20
BISBEE, David Mark. 1878 MOUNTAIN RD, STOWE FAMILY PRACTICE 05672 #026-04-1983 L1986 **FM** *040 †18
COLLINS, Matthew A. ■ 05672 #032-01-1999 L2003 **EM** *020 †16
CONLEY, Christine Marie. 394 MOUNTAIN RD STE 1 05672 #034-01-1987 L1996 **FM** *020 †18
COPPOLA, Vincent P, Jr. RR 1 BOX 2745 05672 #010-02-1948 L1984 **GS GYN** *071 †85
CRAWFORD, Howard Robt. ■ 05672 #038-41-1945 L1983 **ORS HS** *071 †40
DUNN, Edward. ■ 05672 #035-15-1951 L1992 **GS MDM** *071 †85
ECHENIQUE, Ana Maria. ■ 05672 #011-02-1991 L2005 **DR** *020 †80
FAGAN, William Thos, Jr. PO BOX 1508 05672 #050-02-1948 L1949 **U** *071 †95
GLEINER, J Arthur. ■ 05672 #020-12-1976 L1995 **IM** *071 †20
GRAY, David H. TABER RIDGE RD 05672 #024-01-1953 L1954 **IM PHP** *071
GRINBERG, Francisco. ■ 05672 #649-01-1981 L2006 **AN** *020 †05
HARRIS, Henry Lewis. ■ 05672 #035-08-1962 L2000 **PD ADL** *071 †55
HO, Kenneth Shiu Kee. ■ 05672 #050-02-1956 L1971 **FM IM** *071 †18
HORSLEY, Heide Billes. ■ 05672 #010-01-1969 L1996 **PD CHN** *071 †55
JAMES, Clea. 1878 MOUNTAIN RD, STE 3 05672 #005-02-1996 L2004 **FM** *020 †18
JAQUA, Patricia Irons. ■ 05672 #038-06-1976 L1984 **GS** *020
KEITH, Patrick Norman. 1878 MOUNTAIN RD, STE 3 05672 #050-02-1998 L2001 **FM** *020 †18
LABOW, Samuel Barry. 112 S MAIN ST STE 101 05672 #067-01-1962 L1980 **CRS** *071 †85,10
MC AREE, Christopher P. 161 MOUNTAIN RD 05672 #539-01-1956 L1965 **P** *071 †75
MC GILL, J Bishop. ■ 05672 #050-02-1946 L1951 **GS HS** *071 †85
ROGERS, Sidney Ivan. ■ 05672 #067-01-1945 L1951 **D** *071 †15
SAMPSON, Michael Robt. 1878 MOUNTAIN RD, BOX 3 05672 #026-04-1984 L1991 **FM** *020 †18
SMITH, Joseph Henry. ■ 05672 #021-01-1961 L1965 **IM OM** *072
VOLANSKY, Melissa Carol. 1878 MOUNTAIN RD 05672 #050-02-1996 L1999 **FM** *020 †18

STRATTON MOUNTAIN — WINDHAM

HOMES, Robert S. 128 QUARTER MILE ROAD 05155 #018-03-1949 L1966 **GP EM** *071 †85

SUTTON — CALEDONIA

BROUHA, Anne King. 92 QUEEN ELIZABETH FARM LN 05867 #005-11-2001 L2004 **IM** *020

SWANTON — FRANKLIN

BOUCHER, Bernard Gille. ■ 05488 #050-02-1958 L1965 **OBG** *071 †30
CORRIGAN, Michael John. 12 CHURCH ST 05488 #050-02-1980 L1982 **FM** *020 †18
DANIEL, Gerard Lucian. 25 CANADA ST 05488 #050-02-1954 L1955 **IM** *071
DUGAN, Otley Leland. ■ 05488 #050-02-1942 L1943 **GP** *071
GARDNER, Zechariah Symmes. 3649 LOWER NEWTON RD, NW STAT CORECT FAC HEALTH 05488 #050-02-2005 L2005 **IM** *012
HAKEY, Diane Jean. 3649 LOWER NEWTON RD, NORTHWEST STATE CORRECTION 05488 #050-02-2004 L2004 **IM** *020
STIMETS, Wendell Anthony. ■ 05488 #050-02-1952 L1955 **GP** *071
YOUNG, Charlene Susan. ■ 05488 #065-01-1977 L1997 **OS** *020 †80
ZELAZO, Robert M. 45 CHURCH ST 05488 #024-05-1975 L1978 **IM** *020 †20

THETFORD — ORANGE

HOAGLAND, Mahlon Bush. PO BOX 153 05074 #024-01-1948 **OS** *030

THETFORD CENTER — ORANGE

FROEHLICH, Gregory Walden. ■ 05075 #008-02-1986 L1988 **IM** *020 †20
GERKE, Luke Christopher. ■ 05075 #035-01-2007 **IM** *012
HICKEY, Denise M. ■ 05075 #041-02-1989 L1992 **HO** *020 †20
ROWLES, Andrew Burton. ■ 05075 #054-04-1974 L1978 **FM** *071

TINMOUTH — RUTLAND

DRACHMAN, Robert Henry. ■ 05773 #035-15-1955 L1995 **PD GPM** *071 †55

TOPSHAM — ORANGE

SHERWOOD, Edward S. ■ 05076 #050-02-1949 L1985 **PD** *071 †55

TOWNSHEND — WINDHAM

BACKUS, Robert Wolcott. RT 35 P O BOX 216 05353 #050-02-1976 L1979 **FM** *020 †18
BARSTOW, Alexandra H. 185 GRAFTON RD, GRACE COTTAGE FAM PRAC 05353 #008-02-2001 L2001 **FM** *020 †18
CARROLL, Noel. GRACE COTTAGE HOSPITAL 05353 #539-06-1962 L1970 **DR** *071
LINDER, Elizabeth K. ■ 05353 #050-02-1994 L1997 **PD** *020 †55

LINDER, Moss Jacob. ■ 05353 #050-02-1991 L1997 **FM** *075 †18
MULHERN, Edward Thos. PO BOX 308 05353 #028-03-1974 L1978 **FM** *020
SHAFER, Timothy Philip. RT 35 P O BOX 216 05353 #032-01-1981 L1984 **FM** *020 †18
TIETZ, Judith Hepburn. PO BOX 216 05353 #020-12-1991 L1991 **P** *020 †75

TUNBRIDGE — ORANGE

GUTH, Scott Chas. ■ 05077 #028-34-1961 L1982 **P** *075
SPORN, Michael Benj. ■ 05077 #035-45-1959 L1960 **IM** *050

UNDERHILL — CHITTENDEN

BROWN, Chad Tee. ■ 05489 #048-14-2004 L2004 **P** *012
DANFORTH, Elliot, Jr. ■ 05489 #035-03-1962 L1970 **END** *071 †20
GRAVELINE, Duane Edgar. ■ 05489 #050-02-1955 L1956 **FM GPM** *075 †70

VERGENNES — ADDISON

ADAMS, Rebecca Howcroft. 10 NORTH ST, LITTLE CITY FAMILY PRACTIC 05491 #049-01-2003 L2003 **FM** *020
BICKNELL, Donald Skinner. 10 NORTH ST 05491 #050-02-1961 L1964 **GP** *071
CAPOBIANCO, Joseph J. 10 NORTH ST 05491 #030-06-1979 L1983 **FM OBS** *020 †18
COVEY, Wilton Warner. RR 1 BOX 1644 05491 #050-02-1944 L1948 **P** *071
HOFFMAN, Mark R. 10 NORTH ST 05491 #050-02-1987 L1991 **FM** *020 †18
KEEVER, Edward Dudley. ■ 05491 #067-01-1953 **ORS** *071 †40

VERNON — WINDHAM

DIETRICH, Roger W. ■ 05354 #024-07-1976 L2003 **GS** *020 †85

WAITSFIELD — WASHINGTON

CLARK, Samuel Smith. 1005 STAGECOACH RD 05673 #067-01-1958 L1967 **U** *071 †95
COOK, Francis Wm. III. 859 OLD COUNTY RD 05673 #010-02-1978 L1981 **FM** *020 †18
ELLIOTT, Dawn Elyse. ■ 05673 #050-02-2000 **OBG** *020 †30
ENSALADA, Leon. ■ 05673 #032-01-1979 L2002 **PME OM** *020 †05
KROTZER, Lawrence Stewart. ■ 05673 #035-01-1955 L1963 **R** *062 †80
LANSER, Marc Eric. ■ 05673 #035-03-1977 L1979 **GS** *020 †85
WARGO, Timothy John. 5360 MAIN ST, STE 1 05673 #050-02-1974 L1985 **EM FM** *020 †18
WINHOLD, Otto Ernest. ■ 05673 #407-16-1948 L1966 **AN** *071

WALLINGFORD — RUTLAND

NICKLAS, James N. ■ 05773 #035-08-1953 L1983 **OBG** *071 †30

WARREN — WASHINGTON

GEHLERT, Sidney R, Jr. 395 BURNT MOUNTAIN RD 05674 #023-01-1968 L1999 **IM OM** *020 †20
HAMMEL, John. ■ 05674 #024-07-1982 L2005 **P** *012 †20
MACLEOD, Catherine Mary. 202 BRIDGES CIR, # 61 05674 #062-01-1976 L1976 **PA ID** *050 †20
VAKKUR, George Juri. ■ 05674 #143-03-1960 L1970 **N** *071 †75

WATERBURY — WASHINGTON

BATRA, Jaskanwar Singh. 103 S MAIN ST 05671 #495-08-1997 L1999 **P** *020 †75
BLACK, Deborah Naomi. 103 S MAIN ST, VERMONT STATE HOSP 05671 #067-01-1979 L1998 **N** *062 †75
COTTON, Paul Gerald. 103 S MAIN ST 05676 #024-07-1970 L1994 **P PFP** *020 †75
DAYE, Kathleen. 103 S MAIN ST 05676 #041-14-1975 L1981 **FM P** *020
DUNCAN, Robert Walmsley. 103 S MAIN ST 05671 #050-02-1987 L1987 **P** *020 †75
FREEMAN, Kalev. ■ 05676 #007-02-2003 L2006 **EM** *100
GARCIA, Rafael Erfe. ■ 05676 #748-01-1948 L1975 **P** *071
GELBSTEIN, Jennifer Beth. 130 S MAIN ST, WATERBURY MEDICAL ASSOCIAT 05676 #033-05-1996 L1999 **FM** *020 †18
KERN, Arthur B. ■ 05676 #024-05-1944 L1949 **D** *071 †15
MALLOY, John Robt, Jr. 103 S MAIN ST, VERMONT STATE HOSPITAL 05676 #038-06-1990 L1990 **P** *020 †75
MC MAINS, William Donald. 103 S MAIN ST 05676 #039-01-1971 L1977 **P CHP** *074 †75
MURRAY, Robert Wm. 130 S MAIN ST 05676 #010-01-1969 L1972 **FM** *020 †18
PAYNE, Christine Ellen. 130 S MAIN ST, WATERBURY MEDICAL ASSOCIAT 05676 #032-01-1988 L1998 **FM** *020 †18
SCHMIDT, Maria Laura. 103 S MAIN ST 05676 #132-01-1983 L1996 **P** *020 †75
STARK, John N. 103 S MAIN ST 05676 #035-03-1951 L1959 **PS** *071
TRAVIS, Randall H. ■ 05676 #038-06-1952 L1984 **IM DIA** *071
TURNER, Elizabeth Anne. 103 S MAIN ST 05676 #023-01-1968 L1977 **EM FM** *020 †18,16
VAN TUINEN, Craig Robt. 13 WINOOSKI ST, P O BOX 78 05676 #025-12-1981 L1988 **P** *020 †75
WEHRY, Susan Marie. 103 S MAIN ST, DIV OF MENTAL HEALTH 05671 #020-02-1979 L1994 **P** *020 †75
WENNBERG, Emma F O. RR 1 RUBY RAYMOND ROAD 05676 #067-01-1961 L1970 **OS** *075

WATERBURY CENTER — WASHINGTON

GRIFFIN, Robert Franklin. ■ 05677 #012-05-1974 L1999 **GS AM** *020 †85

WELLS — RUTLAND

KISTLER, Edwin Morley. ■ 05774 #041-13-1945 L1963 **AN** *072 †05

WELLS RIVER – ORANGE

GENEREAUX, Stephen H. 65 MAIN ST N 05081 #032-01-1987 L1987 **FM** *075 †18
HOMAN, Fay Frances. 65 MAIN ST N 05081 #050-02-1990 L1993 **FM OBS** *020 †18
PERRY-HOOKER, John H. ■ 05081 #050-02-1947 L1949 **OS GP** *075
ROWE, Harry Morrison. 65 MAIN ST N 05081 #050-02-1943 L1944 **FM** *071 †18

WEST DANVILLE – CALEDONIA

HEBERT, Albert Jos, Jr. ■ 05873 #050-02-1974 L2005 **FM** *020
POLLACK, Irwin Wm. PO BOX 226, 1499 W SHORE RD 05873 #050-02-1956 L1998 **P** *071 †75

WEST HARTFORD – WINDSOR

ANDERSON, Julius H, Jr. 773 MAIN ST, # 323 05084 #008-01-1968 L1994 **IM** *020 †20

WEST HAVEN – RUTLAND

BRAXTON, Jeffrey Paverman. ■ 05743 #165-04-1971 L1991 **OPH** *071 †35
FELBER, Troy Dean. ■ 05743 #048-12-1965 L1965 **D** *020 †15

WEST PAWLET – RUTLAND

BECKLER, Carl Edward. 278 VT ROUTE 149, METTOWEE VALLEY FAMILY 05775
#051-04-1987 L1990 **FM** *020 †18
KILPATRICK, Brian Nelson. 278 VT ROUTE 149, METTOWEE VALLEY FAMILY 05775
#039-05-1983 L1999 **MPD PD** *020 †20,55
KIRCHNER, Karen Joanna. 278 VT ROUTE 149 05775 #035-03-1992 L1995 **FM** *020 †18
MUELLER, Mark Allen. 278 VT ROUTE 149, METTOWEE VALLEY FAMILY 05775
#038-45-1996 L2000 **FM** *020 †18
WAGENBRENNER, William Jos. ■ 05775 #407-16-1963 L1965 **P** *071

WESTFORD – CHITTENDEN

KIRKPATRICK, Beth D. ■ 05494 #035-03-1992 L1999 **ID** *020 †20

WHITE RIVER JUNCTION – WINDSOR

AARON, Jason Elliot. 215 N MAIN ST, QUALITY SCHOLARS PROGRAM 05009
#048-14-2002 L2002 **GPM** *100 †20
ADAMS, John G, Jr. ■ 05001 #050-02-1954 L1956 **AN** *071 †05
BALAN, Stefan Ion. ■ 05001 #781-01-1993 L2002 **ON** *020 †20
BARNEY, Christine Anne. 2456 CHRISTIAN ST, STE 202 05001 #035-45-1986 L2004 **P** *020 †75
BAUMAN, Andrew Jay. VA HOSPITAL 05001 #024-01-1979 L1980 **END IM** *040 †20
BAUMAN, Toni Goodman. ■ 05001 #032-01-1992 L1998 **N** *100
BELL, James Russell. VET ADMIN HOSP 05001 #035-19-1969 L1982 **CD IM** *020 †20
BERMAN, Stephen Alan. 215 N MAIN ST, WHITE RIVER JUNCTION VA. H 05009
#016-11-1974 L2000 **N OS** *050 †75
CLARK, Susannah Taylor. 215 N MAIN ST, PRIMARY CARE SERVICE, VA M 05009
#032-01-2001 L2003 **IM** *100
COCHRAN, Nancy Ellen. WRJ VA HOSPITAL 05009 #024-01-1981 L1986 **IM** *020 †20
DACEY, Linda Brown. 70 N MAIN ST, GOOD NEIGHBOR HEALTH CLINI 05001
#038-41-1984 L2002 **IM** *020 †20 ‡
DAVIS, Julie Sanders. 331 OLCOTT DR 05001 #032-01-1995 L1998 **FM** *020 †18
DAVIS, Kathryn Lorann. ■ 05001 #030-06-2007 L2007 **GS** *012
DAVISON, William Townsend. N HARTLAND RD 05001 #036-07-1944 L1950 **ORS** *072 †40
D'SOUZA, Sharlene Lillian. ■ 05001 #039-01-2005 L2005 **IM** *012
EMORY, Trevor Burlingame. ■ 05001 #024-07-2007 L2007 **AN** *012
FISHER, Elliott Speer. ■ 05001 #024-01-1981 L1986 **GPM PHP** *050 †20
FORBUSH, Benjamin Wyatt. 215 N MAIN ST, VETERANS AFFAIR MED CENTER 05009
#032-01-1995 L1997 **GS** *020 †85
FOSTER, Tina C. 215 N MAIN ST 05009 #005-02-1984 L1986 **OBG** *020 †30
FRIEDMAN, Matthew J. 215 N MAIN ST, NATL CTR FOR PTSD (116D) 05009
#020-12-1969 L1973 **P PA** *030 †75
GEILING, James Arthur. 215 N MAIN ST, VA MEDICAL CENTER 05009 #023-12-1982 L1985
CCM IM *030 †20
GERETY, Robert P. ■ 05001 #008-01-1952 L1955 **EM GP** *071
GIBSON, Daniel Peter. ■ 05001 #008-01-2005 L2005 **NS** *012
HERRICK, Michael David. ■ 05001 #024-07-2007 L2007 **AN** *012
HUMPHRIES, Robert Hunter. ■ 05001 #035-01-1964 L1996 **P** *071 †75
JACOBS, Scott Rebhun. 215 N MAIN ST, VA MEDICAL CENTER 05001 #051-01-1990 L1991
P *020 †75
KAKOULIDES, George Vasili. ■ 05001 #024-07-2007 L2007 **NS** *012
KASBARI, Samer Saman. ■ 05001 #422-01-2001 L2003 **HO** *012
KELLY, John. 215 N MAIN ST, 2-123 BEN 44 05009 #539-06-1989 L1992 **MDM** *030 †20
KERIN, Kevin Daniel. 215 N MAIN ST, WHITE RIVER JUNCTON VA 05001 #032-01-1993 L2002
RHU *020 †20
KERN, Audrey Margaret. 70 N MAIN ST, GOOD NEIGHBOR HEALTH CLINI 05001
#035-09-1988 L2000 **EM** *020 †16
LACY, Blair Tulloch. ■ 05001 #024-07-2007 L2007 **OBG** *012
LAFFELY, Nicholas Henry. ■ 05001 #056-06-2001 L2001 **CD** *012
LARSON, Robin Joyce. MEDICAL CTR 111B, VA OUTCOMES GRP 05009 #040-02-1998 L1998
IM *020 †20
LE, Lien Hong. ■ 05001 #043-01-2004 L2004 **IM** *100 †20
LEARMONTH, Susanne Judith. VET ADMIN CTR, DEPT ANES 05001 #024-01-1952 L1973
AN *071 †16
LENZ, James Emmett, Jr. NORTH HARTLAND ROAD 05001 #036-01-1980 L1991 **DR** *020 †80
LIU, Jean Y. 215 N MAIN ST, VA HOSPITAL (112) 05009 #035-46-1994 L1999 **GS** *020 †85
LOESCHER, Peter Martin. 331 OLCOTT DR 05001 #024-16-1998 L1999 **FSM** *020 †18

LYNCH, Franklin. ■ 05009 #032-01-1975 L1976 **ORS** *020 †40
LYONS, Michael Leo. 331 OLCOTT DR 05001 #050-02-1990 L1995 **FM** *020 †18
MAYO, Lorna Korinne. 215 N MAIN ST, ATTN: DESK 60 05001 #018-03-1999 L2002 **OS** *050 †20
MIROLO, Hugh Alfred. ■ 05001 #132-09-1983 **N** *100
MOGIELNICKI, Robert Peter. VA MED CTR N HARTLAND RD 05001 #024-01-1966 L1969
IM CD *020 †20
MOYER BROOKS, Suzanne T. ■ 05001 #035-09-1991 L1995 **P** *020 †75
MUMFORD, Joel Hutchings. 215 N MAIN ST 112, WHITE RIVER JUNCTION VAMC 05009
#050-02-1970 L1996 **AN** *020 †05
MYERS, Warren P L. ■ 05001 #035-01-1945 L1946 **ON END** *071 †20
NAGY, Linda Mae. 215 N MAIN ST, PSYCHIATRY SERVICE 116A 05009 #038-06-1983 L1998
P *020 †75
NAPIORKOWSKI, Patricia A. 205 BILLINGS FARM RD, STE 3B 05001 #008-02-1987 L1998
P CHP *020 †75
NUNLIST, Mark Moora. 331 OLCOTT DR 05001 #043-01-1980 L1983 **FM** *020 †18
O'DONNELL, Joseph Francis. 215 N MAIN ST, DEPARTMENT OF MEDICINE 05009
#024-01-1973 L1976 **ON** *020 †20
OGRINC, Gregory Simon. 215 N MAIN ST 11Q 05001 #038-06-1997 L1998 **IM** *020 †20
PARK, David Jin. 331 OLCOTT DR, STE U3 05001 #041-02-2001 L2004 **FM** *020 †18
PARROTT, Thomas Brinkley. 331 OLCOTT DR 05001 #011-02-1969 L1976 **FM** *020 †18
PELTIER, Deborah Ann. 215 N MAIN ST 05009 #012-05-1976 L1982 **IM IMG** *020 †20
PERKINS, Frederick M. 215 N MAIN ST, # 112 05009 #050-02-1974 L1980 **AN PMM** *020 †05
POMERANTZ, Andrew Simon. 215 N MAIN ST 05009 #016-42-1971 L1972 **P** *020 †75
RAUSCHKOLB, Paula Kirkpat. ■ 05001 #003-75-2007, ▲ L2007 **IM** *012
ROSS, John Robt, Jr. 2820 CHRISTIAN ST # 113 05001 #035-01-1938 L1975 **P CHP** *071 †75
RUSSELL, Michelle Ann. ■ 05009 #024-07-1994 L2005 **OBG** *020 †30
SAUVIGNE, Arthur Emile. VA MED CTR N HARTLAND RD 05001 #035-01-1972 L1976
IM *020 †20
SCHWARTZ, Lisa Miriam. 215 N MAIN ST, VA OUTCOMES GROUP 111B 05009
#035-19-1989 L1997 **IM** *050 †20
SHIRLEY, Eric Andrew. 215 N MAIN ST, VA MEDICAL CENTER 05001 #010-01-1977 L1979
IM *020 †20
SINGH, Aneek. 28 FARMVU DR # 1 05001 #035-47-1989 L1994 **P** *020 †75
SIROVICH, Brenda Ellen. 215 N MAIN ST, VA MEDICAL CENTER (111B) 05009
#008-01-1991 L2008 **IM** *020 †20
STENOVITCH, Jude Edward. 215 N MAIN ST, V A MEDICAL CENTER 05001 #001-06-2004 L2006
P *012
STEPHENSON, Jon William. ■ 05001 #026-04-2005 L2006 **AN** *012
STERN, Kathleen E Mc Kee. ■ 05001 #035-09-1958 L1981 **P PD** *072 †55
SUMMERALL, Elmina Lanier. 215 N MAIN ST, VAM & ROC (11Q) 05001 #007-02-2001 L2005
P *050
TAYLOR, Thomas Henry. 215 N MAIN ST, WHITE RIVER JCT VA HOSP 05009
#007-02-1972 L1974 **IM RHU** *020 †20
TOMS, Angela Marie. 331 OLCOTT DR STE U3, WHITE RIVER FAMILY PRACTIC 05001
#032-01-1997 L1998 **FM** *020 †18
VRAKATITSIS, Kerry Linda. 215 N MAIN ST, VA MEDICAL CENTER 05001 #032-01-1997 L2000
IM *020 †20
WELCH, Henry Gilbert. N HARTLAND RD, MED & REG OFFICE 05009 #038-41-1982 L1992
IM *020 †20
WOLOSHIN, Steven Edward. 215 N MAIN ST, VA MEDICAL CENTER 05001 #024-05-1987 L1997
IM *020 †20
ZLOTNICK, David Michael. ■ 05001 #035-15-2005 L2005 **IM** *012

WHITING – ADDISON

SUNDERMAN, F Wm, Jr. 270 BARNES RD 05778 #041-02-1955 L1956 **PTX CLP** *071 †50

WHITINGHAM – WINDHAM

DE PALO, Michael. ■ 05361 #561-01-1957 L1962 **GS** *071

WILDER – WINDSOR

BACHELDER, Sheilla Marie. PO BOX 145 05088 #050-02-2006 L2006 **FP** *012
FREW, Julia Renee. ■ 05088 #043-01-2005 L2007 **P** *012
REINECK, Abby Lynn. ■ 05088 #038-45-2006 L2007 **P** *012

WILLIAMSTOWN – ORANGE

MARTIN, Marsha Sue. ■ 05679 #051-01-1986 L1989 **IM** *020 †20
MC KEE, Marion C. ■ 05679 #041-13-1953 L1955 **CHN** *071 †55
SHANER, Alice Lucille. ■ 05679 #011-02-1964 L1965 **OM** *071 †70

WILLISTON – CHITTENDEN

AMES, Suzanne Elizabeth. 158 HURRICANE LN, SPINE INSTITUTE 05495 #050-02-1996 L1996
OSS *020 †40
BEESLEY, Ronald Duane. ■ 05495 #023-12-2001 L2007 **OBG** *020
BROMAGE, Philip Raikes. ■ 05495 #917-30-1944 L1972 **AN** *071
CAMELO, Ingrid Yolanda. ■ 05495 #264-19-1999 L2006 **PD** *012
CHARLAND, Diane Marie. 71 KNIGHT LN STE 10, UROGYNECOLOGY ASSCIATI 05495
#038-06-1992 L2000 **OBG** *020 †30
COON, Robert W. ■ 05495 #035-45-1944 L1955 **PTH** *071 †50
DAWSON, Pamela Jane. 586 OAK HILL RD, THOMAS CHITTENDEN HLTH 05495
#067-01-1996 L1998 **FM** *020 †18
DILL, Mary Margaret. 586 OAK HILL RD, THOMAS CHITTENDEN HLTH 05495
#050-02-1990 L1990 **FM** *020 †18
DONNELLY, Harley Danl. 586 OAK HILL RD, THOMAS CHITTENDEN HLTH 05495
#050-02-1987 L1988 **FM** *020 †18
DOUGHERTY, James Francis. 28 PARK AVE, EVERGREEN FAMILY HEALTH 05495
#016-11-1995 L1995 **FM** *020 †18

ENGELKEN, Michelle Marie. ■ 05495 #019-02-2004 L2005 **AN** *012

ENGISCH, Robert Richard. ■ 05495 #035-20-1955 L1961 **N** *075

ERICKSON, Brian Anthony. 4185 ST GEORGE RD 05495 #026-04-1987 L1987 **P** *020 †75

FLOYD, Lisa Anne. ■ 05495 #010-02-2002 L2002 **GS** *012

FUJII, Satoshi. ■ 05495 #572-29-1981 L1995 **CD IM** *050

FUKUDA, David M. ■ 05495 #572-12-1946 L1961 **AN PUD** *071

GRZYB, Stanley Edward. 158 HURRICANE LN 05495 #008-02-1973 L1981 **ORS** *020 †40 ‡

HADDOCK, Jeffrey Erik. 586 OAK HILL RD, THOMAS CHITTENDEN HLTH 05495 #050-02-2003 L2006 **FM** *020 †20

HADDOCK, Joseph Hoskin. 586 OAK HILL RD, THOMAS CHITTENDEN HLTH 05495 #016-06-1972 L2007 **FM** *020

HAINES, Carleton R. 16 MOUNTAIN VIEW RD 05495 #050-02-1943 L1946 **GS ON** *071 †85

HARTFORD, Orville Albert. ■ 05495 #032-01-2005 L2006 **D** *012

HASTINGS, Molly Mahon. 33 BLAIR PARK RD 05495 #035-15-1975 L1996 **PO PD** *020 †55,35

JACKSON, Pamela Lee. 353 BLAIR PARK RD 05495 #024-01-1985 L1992 **PD** *020 †55

KELLER, Ray Eugene. ■ 05495 #041-12-1985 L1992 **EM** *020 †16

KIM, Brian Young. ■ 05495 #028-34-2000 L2006 **OPH** *100 †35

KLEH, Thomas Robt. 205 WILLISTON RD, VERMONT EYE ASSOCIATES 05495 #010-01-1953 L1963 **OPH** *071 †35

KLIKUNAS, Marvin Frank. 353 BLAIR PARK RD 05495 #038-43-1981 L1992 **IM IMG** *020 †20

LANTMAN, John C. ■ 05495 #050-02-1951 L1953 **GP IM** *071 †18

LARSON, Juli Ann. 5399 WILLISTON RD, STE 101 05495 #016-11-1989 L1992 **OPH** *020 †35

LEGACY, Susan N. 188 ALLEN BROOK LN 05495 #048-15-1989 L1989 **P** *020 †75

MANN, Stephen Christopher. 586 OAK HILL RD, THOMAS CHITTENDEN HLTH 05495 #050-02-1984 L1984 **FM CLP** *020 †18

MAST, William Edward. ■ 05495 #048-04-1971 L1971 **GE IM** *020 †20

MC DAY, John Bruce. 2907 SOUTH RD 05495 #041-13-1976 L1980 **RO** *020 †80

MILLER, Lucy Hope. 353 BLAIR PARK RD 05495 #035-47-1994 L1994 **IM** *020 †20

MONSEY, Robert Danl. 158 HURRICANE LN 05495 #054-04-1986 L1986 **ORS** *020 †40

MUNSON, Richard Garver. ■ 05495 #035-15-1990 **P** *100 †35

NAUMANN, Terence Dwight. 124 W OAK HILL RD, COMMUNITY HEALTH PLAN 05495 #050-02-1982 L1983 **FM** *020 †18

NELSON, Eliot W. 353 BLAIR PARK RD 05495 #005-11-1979 L1991 **PD** *020 †55

PARK, David Raymond. TCHC-124 OAK HILL RD 05495 #035-45-1963 L1967 **FM PD** *020

PLANTE, Dennis Armand. 353 BLAIR PARK RD 05495 #050-02-1979 L1983 **IM GPM** *020 †20 ‡

PUTNAM, Ryan Michael. ■ 05495 #003-01-2003 L2003 **ORS** *012

RABIN, Susan Hannah. 586 OAK HILL RD, THOMAS CHITTENDEN HLTH 05495 #050-02-1997 L1997 **FM** *020 †18

READ, John Chas. ■ 05495 #035-06-1955 L2002 **PTH FOP** *071 †50

REISS, Paul Julian. 28 PARK AVE, EVERGREEN FAMILY HEALTH 05495 #035-45-1983 L1985 **FM** *020 †18

RINEHART, Warren Thos. 158 HURRICANE LN 05495 #019-02-1968 L2002 **ORS** *020 †40

RYAN, William John. 124 W OAK HILL RD, THOMAS CHITTENDEN HLTH CTR 05495 #035-19-1963 L1966 **FM IM** *071

SCHULTZ, Mark Stuart. 4185 ST GEORGE RD 05495 #038-06-1980 L1984 **P** *020 †75

SHANE, Susan Patricia. 124 W OAK HILL RD, THOMAS CHITTENDEN HLTH CTR 05495 #035-15-1984 L1988 **FM** *020 †18

SIMPSON, James Edwin. ■ 05495 #050-02-1943 L1946 **ORS OS** *071 †40

SINGH, Paramjit. ■ 05495 #045-47-1991 L2005 **N** *012 †20

SMANIA, Lindsay Marie. ■ 05495 #025-07-2006 L2006 **DR** *012

STANILONIS, Paul Byron. THOS CHITTENDEN HLTH CTR 05495 #050-02-1965 L1966 **IM FM** *020 †18

STEIER, Michael Edward. ■ 05495 #016-42-1968 L2003 **TS** *071 †85,90

THERIAULT, Joseph Gilbert. 586 OAK HILL RD, THOMAS CHITTENDEN HLTH 05495 #050-02-1998 L1998 **FM** *020 †18

VISELLI, Anne Louise. 71 KNIGHT LN STE 10 05495 #041-14-1988 L1993 **GYN** *020 †30

WEINBERG, Donald Neal. 586 OAK HILL RD, THOMAS CHITTENDEN HLTH 05495 #050-02-1986 L1990 **IM FM** *020 †20

WERNER, Todd Robert. 75 FORTIER DR 05495 #033-06-1994 L1994 **IM** *075 †20

WHITNEY, Patricia Groden. 586 OAK HILL RD, THOMAS CHITTENDEN HLTH 05495 #050-02-2000 L2000 **FM** *020 †18

WITTPENN, Ann Saylor. 353 BLAIR PARK RD 05495 #051-01-1987 L1995 **PD** *020 †55 ‡

WILMINGTON – WINDHAM

DUNN, Ruth Ann. 1 SCHOOL ST 05363 #048-13-1987 L2005 **PD PM** *020 †55

NICHOLS, Michael. ■ 05363 #396-08-1972 L1975 **IM ON** *020

PARK, Peter Chunghyon. 30 ROUTE 100 S, DEERFIELD VALLEY MEDICAL C 05363 #024-07-1995 L1997 **FM** *020 †18

SHAPIRO, Daniel. PO BOX 845, 41 SHAPIRO RD 05363 #016-11-1945 L1973 **PYA P** *071 †75

SHEA, Donald Francis, Jr. DEERFIELD VALLEY HLTH CTR 05363 #050-02-1977 L1980 **IM** *075

TARNAS, Robert Hommel. 30 ROUTE 100 S, DEERFIELD VALLEY MEDICAL C 05363 #025-07-1979 L1985 **FM** *020 †18

WINDSOR – WINDSOR

BAGLEY, Nancy Ann. 289 COUNTY RD 05089 #026-08-1979 L1982 **PM** *020 †60

BARTON, Gail Melinda. ■ 05089 #041-07-1966 L1982 **P PHP** *072 †75 ‡

BRACK, Virginia Carle. 289 COUNTY RD, MT ASCUTNEY PHYSICIAN PRAC 05089 #005-02-1989 L2000 **PD** *020 †55

CLATTENBURG, Richard N. 289 COUNTY RD, MT ASCUTNEY PHYSICIAN PRAC 05089 #024-01-1976 L1978 **PD FM** *020 †55

COLWELL, Stacie A. 289 COUNTY RD, MT ASCUTNEY PEDIATRICS 05089 #016-11-1998 L2000 **PD** *020

CONGER, Seymour Beach. 289 COUNTY RD, MT ASCUTNEY HOSP 05089 #024-01-1967 L1977 **IM P** *020 †20

DEVINE, Katherine. 289 COUNTY RD, MT. ASCUTNEY PHYSICIAN PRA 05089 #023-07-2002 L2002 **IM** *100 †20

FANCIULLO, Gilbert Jos. 289 COUNTY RD, MT. ASCUTNEY HOSPITAL AND 05089 #035-03-1987 L2002 **AN PME** *020 †05

GEAGAN, Kathleen Ann. 289 COUNTY RD, MT ASCUTNEY PHYSICIAN PRAC 05089 #050-02-1985 L1988 **PD** *020 †55

GEPHART, Dale Seymour. 289 COUNTY RD, MT ASCUTNEY PHYSICIAN PRAC 05089 #005-06-1966 L1972 **IM** *040 †20

HOURDEQUIN, Kathryn Cunni. 289 COUNTY RD, MT ASCUTNEY HOSPITAL 05089 #008-01-2000 L2006 **IM** *020 †20

LIPE, Brea Christine. ■ 05089 #035-03-2005 L2007 **IM** *012

LIPFERT, Jennifer Stockma. 289 COUNTY RD, MOUNT ASCUTNEY HOSPITAL 05089 #035-48-2003 L2006 **PD** *020 †55

LITTLEFIELD, James Allen. 289 COUNTY RD, MT. ASCUTNEY HOSPITAL & HE 05089 #005-12-1957 L1981 **ADM** *020

LORD, C Fredrick. 17 STATE ST 05089 #050-02-1978 L1985 **ADM OS** *020 †40

MEYER, Richard Alan. 289 COUNTY RD, MOUNT ASCUTNEY HOSPITAL 05089 #035-03-1983 L1990 **IM** *020 †20

MORLEY, Kenneth C, Jr. 289 COUNTY RD 05089 #024-05-1960 L1972 **GS VS** *071 †85

NOVELLO, Renee J. 289 COUNTY RD, MT ASCUTNEY HOSPITAL 05089 #033-05-1998 L2006 **OBG** *020 †30

PALMER, William Stanage. 289 COUNTY RD 05089 #035-01-1987 L1994 **IM** *020 †20

PEARSON, Adam Mackay. ■ 05089 #008-01-2004 L2007 **ORS** *012

PILCHMAN, Lawrence Danl. 238 ORCHARD LN, C/O SOHO 05089 #035-09-1959 L1994 **OBG** *020

RATLIFF, Amanda W. 289 COUNTY RD, MT ASCUTNEY PHYSICIAN PRAC 05089 #035-48-1996 L1997 **IM** *020 †20

RILEY, Diane Cooper. 289 COUNTY RD 05089 #032-01-1989 L1998 **HS** *020 †40

RUSSO, David Paul. 289 COUNTY RD 05089 #035-08-1972 L1997 **IM** *020 †20 ‡

SACHS, Marlene Henning. 289 COUNTY RD 05089 #032-01-1979 L1979 **IM** *020 †20

SCOTT, Deborah Jo Long. 289 COUNTY RD, MT ASCUTNEY PHYSICIANS PRA 05089 #010-01-1989 L1992 **IM** *020 †20

STOKES, Erica Elizabeth. ■ 05089 #016-42-2001 **GPM** *100

WHITE, Richard Bruce. 289 COUNTY RD, MT ASCUTNEY PHYSICIAN PRAC 05089 #048-13-1985 L1985 **FM EM** *020 †18

WING, Daniel Cushing. 189 COUNTY RD, MT ASCUTREY HOSP 05089 #032-01-1973 L1976 **PM** *020 †60

ZBEHLIK, Alicia Jane. 289 COUNTY RD 05089 #005-19-1999 L1999 **IM** *020 †20

WINOOSKI – CHITTENDEN

ANSPACH-HANSON, Joshua. ■ 05404 #003-01-2007 L2007 **PTH** *012

BROOKS, Erin Grace. ■ 05404 #056-05-2005 L2005 **PTH** *012

BURKETT, Kelley Erin. ■ 05404 #041-12-2008 *012

CAPERTON, Robin Lois. ■ 05404 #051-07-2008 *012

DICKERSON, Jeremiah E. ■ 05404 #035-15-2005 L2005 **P** *012

GOERING, Ann. 32 MALLETTS BAY AVE 05404 #050-02-1991 L1994 **FM** *020 †18

KAMIN, John Spencer. 20 W CANAL ST, THE WOOLEN MILL OFFICES 05404 #010-01-1994 L2003 **P** *020 †75

KARLITZ-GRODIN, Justin Br. ■ 05404 #035-08-2007 L2007 **FP** *012

KNOTT, Anne Minor. 32 MALLETTS BAY AVE, WINOOSKI FAMILY HEALTH 05404 #035-45-1994 L1998 **FM** *020 †18

KUHN, Nicholas Aloisius. ■ 05404 #050-02-2006 L2006 **IM** *012

LYONS, Richard Chandler. 389 E ALLEN ST 05404 #033-05-1971 L1976 **OTO GS** *020 †45

MYERS, Wendy Anne. ■ 05404 #033-06-2004 L2007 **D** *012

O'BRIEN, James Kevin. 18 MANSION ST 05404 #050-02-1985 L1990 **CD IM** *020 †20

O'BRIEN, Robert E. 18 MANSION ST 05404 #050-02-1945 L1948 **IM CD** *071 †20

PANZER, Sarah E. ■ 05404 #056-05-2007 L2007 **IM** *012

REGAN, Andrea Vanburen. ■ 05404 #050-02-2005 L2005 **FP** *012

SHAFFER, Rebecca Morgan. ■ 05404 #054-04-2007 L2007 **OBG** *012

STAATS, Christine Mary. 32 MALLETTS BAY AVE 05404 #050-02-2002 L2002 **FM** *020 †18

SUCKOW, Joel Michael. ■ 05404 #040-02-2004 L2004 **P** *012

SZILVA, Jean. ■ 05404 #016-06-1975 L1978 **FM EM** *020 †18

WU, Shasha. ■ 05404 #242-69-1994 L2007 **N** *012

WOLCOTT – LAMOILLE

SUBASIC, Joseph Francis. 885 BROWN HILL RD 05680 #041-13-1975 L1976 **EM N** *020 †16

WOODSTOCK – WINDSOR

BIGLOW, John Robinson. ■ 05091 #032-01-1989 L1989 **AN** *020 †05

BUCKLEY, Robert Walker. ■ 05091 #024-05-1943 L1946 **P N** *071 †75

DIETRICH, Anthony Paul. PO BOX 437 05091 #005-14-1977 L1992 **P** *020 †75

FITZ, Reginald Heber. ■ 05091 #024-01-1945 L1951 **IM** *071 †20

HERMANN, Hugh Piesen. 4 THE GRN 05091 #024-01-1954 L1957 **FM** *020 †18

KILCULLEN, Michael John. 32 PLEASANT ST, OTTAUQUECHEE HEALTH CENTER 05091 #041-02-1975 L1979 **PD FM** *020 †55

LALONDE, Maryse Helene. 32 PLEASANT ST, OTTAUQUECHEE HEALTH CENTER 05091 #060-01-1992 L1994 **FM** *020 †18

MC CUTCHEON, John J, Jr. GRASSY LANE 05091 #050-02-1949 L1950 **DR** *071 †80

SMITH, Steven Bradbury. 32 PLEASANT ST 05091 #025-01-1984 L1984 **IM FM** *020 †20

STIMSON, Allan Braddock. ■ 05091 #024-01-1943 L1943 **PD** *071 †55

SULLIVAN, Barbara Mary. ■ 05091 #038-06-1985 L1988 **IM** *020 †20

UITERWYK, Sean. 32 PLEASANT ST, OTTAUQUECHEE HEALTH CENTER 05091 #016-43-2000 L2007 **FM** *020 †18

WILEY, Kate Margaret. 32 PLEASANT ST 05091 #065-05-1990 L1999 **FM** *020

WOLLMAN, Harry. ■ 05091 #024-01-1958 L1959 **AN CCA** *071 †05

WORCESTER – WASHINGTON

KAEDING, John Harry. ■ 05682 #026-04-1973 L1977 **EM** *020 †18,16

ABINGDON – WASHINGTON

ARMSTRONG, Joseph Rogers. 351 COURT ST 24210 #047-06-1978 L1987 **OPH** *020 †35
ARMSTRONG, Kevin C. 351 COURT ST 24210 #021-01-1987 L2004 **AN** *020 †05
ARMSTRONG, Paul Christian. 275 WHITE ST NE, ABINGDON SURGICAL ASSOC, P 24210 #001-01-1984 L1987 **GS** *020 †85
BAKER, William John. 191 JOHNSON ST, INTERNAL MED ASSOC 24210 #038-43-1989 L1994 **IM** *020 †20
BARROW, Guy Jos. 351 COURT ST 24210 #051-04-1948 L1948 **IM GE** *071
BENCH, John Bigler. 390 COMMERCE DR, STE B 24211 #308-11-1987 L1998 **P** *020 †75
BLANKENSHIP, Stephen Broc. ■ 24211 #047-20-2004 L2007 **EM** *020
BOWDEN, James Harris. 191 JOHNSON ST 24210 #012-01-1959 L1961 **IM** *020
BUDDINGTON, Richard S. 351 COURT ST 24210 #023-01-1968 L1973 **PTH** *020 †50
CARRIER, Sarah Selig. 351 COURT ST 24210 #047-20-1994 L1996 **EM** *020 †18
CASTRO, Eduardo. 16501 JEB STUART HWY 24211 #032-01-1978 L1979 **P** *020
CHANG, Warren Andrew. 601 CAMPUS DR, HIGHLANDS INTERNAL MED 24210 #495-37-1993 L2007 **IM** *020 †20
COBURN, Ernest Lee, Jr. 351 COURT ST 24210 #027-01-1971 L1973 **R EM** *020 †80 ‡
COLE, Randolph Robinson. 176 VALLEY ST NW, ASSOCIATION., P.C. 24210 #051-01-1982 L1993 **OTO** *071 †45
COOK, Jolanda I. 617 CAMPUS DR 24210 #660-06-1982 L1996 **FM** *020 †18
COWAN, Bennett Young, Jr. 617 CAMPUS DR 24210 #047-06-1975 L1984 **ON HEM** *020 †20
COX, Larry Herbert. 273 WHITE ST NE, CARDIOVASCULAR ASSOCIATES 24210 #051-04-1974 L1975 **CD IM** *020 †20 ‡
CUMMINS, William Tenhet. 275 WHITE ST NE 24210 #047-20-1998 L2007 **GS** *020 †85
CUNNINGHAM, Dorris Alvin. ■ 24211 #051-01-1947 L1947 **DR** *071
DEBORD, Emily Jane. 322 VALLEY ST NE 24210 #051-04-2001 L2001 **IM** *020
DELAPLANE, David Robert. 104 ABINGDON PL 24211 #047-07-1999 L2004 **IM** *020 †20
DENTON, James Wayne. 275 WHITE ST NE 24210 #051-01-1980 L1986 **GS VS** *020 †85
DUNCAN, Mary Elizabeth. 351 COURT ST, JOHNSTON MEM HOSP ER DEPT 24210 #047-20-1990 L1999 **IM** *020
EMORY, Roger Earl, Jr. 112 ABINGDON PL, PLASTIC SURGERY SPECIALIST 24211 #051-07-1989 L1999 **PS GS** *020 †85,65
FINGLASS, Lacyoni Moraes. 390 COMMERCE DR, STE A 24211 #187-39-1984 L2000 **CD IM** *020 †20
GARDNER, James Lee. 300 E VALLEY ST NO 807 24210 #051-04-1959 L1959 **ORS** *071 †40
GARDNER, James Matthew. 611 CAMPUS DR STE 200 24210 #051-04-1992 L1993 **FM** *020 †18
GILMER, Robert Dickenson. 351 COURT ST 24210 #051-04-1973 L1974 **AN FM** *020 †05,18
GLOVER, Roger Arthur. 110 HILLSIDE DR NE, P O BOX 771 24210 #051-01-1959 L1959 **OBG** *071
GOODMAN, Julius Temple. ■ 24211 #051-04-1954 L1954 **GP** *071
GRANTHAM, Alan W. 351 COURT ST 24210 #06-06-1953 L1961 **GS** *020 †85
GREGORCZYK, Margaret. ■ 24210 #048-13-1989 L1990 **GP** *020
HAASER, Richard Crane. 350 RUSSELL RD NW 24210 #024-07-1984 L1996 **P** *050 †75
HANDY, William Mark. 389 FALLS DR NW 24210 #036-08-1992 L1993 **FM** *020 †18
HAWKINS, Diane Starnes. 24211 #047-06-1991 L1995 **P** *020 †75
HAYS, Rachel Ann. 108 ABINGDON PL, ABINGDON PROFESSIONAL CENT 24211 #047-06-1978 L1995 **GE** *020 †20
HAYTER, Deborah York. ■ 24211 #001-02-1977 L1989 **NEP** *074 †20
HEIMAN, Melvin Leo. 613 CAMPUS DR, STE 200 P.O. BOX 807 24210 #005-06-1970 L1977 **ORS** *020 †40
HENRY, Ernest Noel. 322 VALLEY ST NE 24210 #539-02-1983 L1992 **IM NEP** *020 †20
HIGINBOTHOM, Bruce Carter. 445 PORTERFIELD HWY SW, STE A 24210 #036-05-1993 L1996 **FM** *020 †18
HORSCH, Robert Franklin. ■ 24210 #041-12-1959 L1977 **GS GYN** *071 †18
HUDGENS, David R. 351 COURT ST 24210 #045-01-1989 L1994 **PTH** *020 †50 ‡
HUDGENS, Donna Rice. 191 JOHNSON ST, HIGHLANDS PEDIATRICS, P.C. 24210 #045-01-1990 L1994 **NPM** *020 †55
HUMPHREYS, Susan B. 351 COURT ST 24210 #051-04-1981 L1985 **DR** *020 †80
HURLBURT, Charles Phillip. 445 PORTERFIELD HWY SW # A 24210 #023-01-1989 L1992 **FM** *020 †18
IVINS, Jeffrey Jos. 351 COURT ST 24210 #001-02-1980 L1997 **IM** *020 †20
JOHNSTON, Helen Lee. 191 JOHNSON ST 24210 #028-46-1987 L1994 **PD** *020 †55
JOHNSTON, John Dorrens. 211 W MAIN ST 24210 #919-03-1957 L1975 **U** *071 †95
KEGLEY, Mary Anne. 351 COURT ST, JOHNSTON MEMORIAL HOSP 24210 #051-04-1980 L1992 **GP** *020 ‡
LAVIGNE, Jay Wayne. 277 WHITE ST NE 24210 #030-06-1981 L1989 **OBG** *020 †30
LAWLER, Douglas Reed, II. ■ 24211 #011-02-1985 L1988 **FM** *020 †18
LEIGHT, Melanie Ann. 277 WHITE ST NE, ABINGDON OB/GYN 24210 #047-05-1998 L1998 **OBG** *020 †30
MANN, James Alan. 108 ABINGDON PL 24211 #016-11-1967 L1995 **GE IM** *020 †20
MC CRAW, Jeffrey Allen. 351 COURT ST 24210 #051-01-1994 L1998 **AN** *020 †05
MC GARRY, Timothy Gerard. 300 E VALLEY ST NO 807 24210 #051-01-1987 L1992 **ORS** *020 †40
MC HANEY, Mark Brian. 191 JOHNSON ST 24210 #028-02-1992 L1998 **PD** *020 †55
MC KAIN, Carey Wilson. 300 E VALLEY ST 24210 #036-07-1976 L1993 **ORS** *020 †40
MC REYNOLDS, Casey Dillon. 351 COURT ST 24210 #051-04-1996 L1997 **DR** *020 †80
MELLON, Christine Marie. 277 WHITE ST NE 24210 #033-06-1993 L2007 **OBG** *020 †30
MELLON, Richard Wilson. 277 WHITE ST NE 24210 #033-06-1993 L2007 **OBG** *020 †30
MILLER, Samuel E. ■ 24210 #051-01-1950 L1950 **FM** *071 †18
MONAHAN, Martin Francis. 322 VALLEY ST NE 24210 #025-07-1971 L1972 **IM** *020 †20
MOORE, James Danl. 351 COURT ST 24210 #051-04-1972 L1976 **OBG** *020 †30
MOTLEY, Virgil Atwell. 15489 ELEMENTARY DR 24210 #051-01-1955 L1955 **GP** *071
MULLENS, John Richard, III. 351 COURT ST 24210 #027-01-1979 L1984 **DR** *020 †80
MYERS, Pamela Ann. 191 JOHNSON ST, HIGHLANDS PEDIATRICS PC 24210 #003-01-1993 L1999 **PD** *020 †55
NAIRN, Todd Harris. 227 W MAIN ST 24210 #020-12-1994 L1997 **IM** *020 †20
NEAL, Roger Dale. 176 VALLEY ST NW 24210 #051-04-1968 L1968 **OTO** *020 †45 ‡
PELTZER, Leticia Ibarra. 613 CAMPUS DR, STE 100 24210 #041-01-1993 L2005 **OTO** *020 †45
PENNINGS, Simon Peter. 617 CAMPUS DR 24210 #041-02-1981 L1982 **FM EM** *020 †16
PINKERTON, Herman H, Jr. 466 COURT ST 24210 #023-07-1951 L1957 **PDA PD** *071 †55,03
PRESTOWITZ, William Fred. 351 COURT ST 24210 #010-01-1981 L1989 **OPH** *020 †35
PRILL, Karen Sue Johnson. 617 CAMPUS DR 24210 #048-02-1991 L1997 **ON** *020 †20
RAY, John Harold. ■ 24211 #055-01-1989 L2005 **IM** *020 ‡

REED, Kathryn Lea. 328A CUMMINGS ST, EYE PHYSICIANS OF S.W. VA 24210 #047-06-1999 L2006 **OPH** *020 †35
RHINEHART, Andrew Scott. 601 CAMPUS DR, HIGHLANDS INTERNAL MED 24210 #023-01-1992 L1995 **IM** *020 †20
ROBERTS, Donald Lynn. ■ 24210 #020-02-1974 L1998 **GS EM** *020 †85
ROBINETTE, Emory H, Jr. 322 VALLEY ST NE 24210 #051-07-1978 L1979 **PUD IM** *020 †20
ROSS, Maureen. 104 ABINGDON PL, UNIVERSITY OF VIRGINIA 24211 #011-02-1984 L1997 **HEM** *020 ‡
RUPE, Joe Milton. 351 COURT ST 24210 #051-01-1996 L1999 **IM** *020 †20
SHAFFER, John S. 227 W MAIN ST 24210 #051-04-1943 L1943 **GP** *071
SIMCOX, Mark Wm. 351 COURT ST 24210 #047-06-1989 L1994 **OS** *020 †05
SMALL, F David. 20242 AVONDALE RD 24211 #048-13-1978 L1989 **EM** *071 †16
SMITH, Catherine Richard. ■ 24210 #010-01-1941 L1942 **P GPM** *072
SMITH, David Hunt. 275 WHITE ST NE 24210 #051-04-1981 L1987 **GS** *020 †85
SOOKLAL, Damian Haimdath. 351 COURT ST, JOHNSON MEMORIAL HOSPITAL 24210 #010-03-1998 L2006 **IM** *020 †20
SPIEGEL, Naum. 390 COMMERCE DR 24211 #051-03-1989 L1998 **U** *020 †95
STRACNER, Darcy Lynn. 351 COURT ST 24210 #001-02-2001 L2007 **EM** *020 †16
STRAWBRIDGE, Wendy R. 407 E MAIN ST, P O BOX 2196 24210 #051-04-1981 L1984 **OBG** *020 †30
STUETZEL, Marcus. ■ 24211 #654-01-1986 L1989 **FM** *020
SWANK, Jonathan Trego. 191 JOHNSON ST, ASSOCS PC 24210 #041-07-1993 L2000 **FM** *020 †20
TERRY, Joseph Bradley. 277 WHITE ST NE 24210 #051-04-1991 L1995 **OBG** *020 †30
THOMPSON, Theodore Tellef. 227 W MAIN ST 24210 #036-01-1993 L1997 **IM** *020 †20
TISDALE, Bernard Alvan. 26079 LEE HWY, JOHNSTON MEMORIALCANCER CE 24211 #051-01-1985 L1986 **RO FM** *020 †80,18
TOOTLE, Karen Patricia. 607 CAMPUS DR 24210 #047-20-1987 L1994 **IM EM** *020 †20
TRIPLETT, Laramie Curtis. 611 CAMPUS DR, STE 200 24210 #027-01-1985 L1997 **FM** *020 †18
VAN DYKE, James Luther. 386 WINTERHAM DR 24211 #041-04-1982 L1985 **AN IM** *020 †05
WADE, James Meron. 176 VALLEY ST NW, ABINGDON ENT ASSOC. 24210 #055-01-1970 L1978 **OTO A** *020 †45 ‡
WAITES, Christopher Lamar. 277 WHITE ST NE 24210 #012-01-1996 L2003 **OBG** *071 †30
WALLACE, Patrick Clay. 215 VALLEY ST NE 24210 #001-02-1989 L1992 **IM** *020 †20
WESSELS, Mia Ruth. 351 COURT ST 24210 #051-04-1981 L1987 **D** *020 †15
ZHU, Gaoyong. 351 COURT ST, SOUTH HILL INTERNAL MEDICI 24210 #243-45-1983 L2006 **IM** *020 †20

ACCOMAC – ACCOMACK

MARGOLIUS, Michael Louis. 23191 FRONT ST, EASTERN SHORE DISTRICT 23301 #165-01-1973 L1998 **PTH** *020 †50
SIMPSON, Thomas W. PO BOX 507, 23368 CROSS ST 23301 #023-07-1943 L1983 **ID IM** *071 †20

AFTON – NELSON

EVANS, Richard Patrick. ■ 22920 #026-04-1978 L1979 **EM** *071 †16
GREER, Steven Macon. ■ 22920 #047-20-1987 L1998 **FM** *020
GUERTLER, Andrew Thos. 8410 SIGNAL HL 22920 #051-04-1985 L1987 **EM** *020 †16
HODSON, Andrew Kenneth. ■ 22920 #917-02-1970 L1999 **N PD** *020 †55,75
KALAGHER, Sean Daniel. ■ 22920 #024-05-2006 L2006 **DR** *012
MC COY, Sue. ■ 22920 #051-01-1980 L1981 **GS OS** *071 †85
RAYNOR, Robert Cook. ■ 22920 #051-01-1956 L1956 **FM** *020 †18
SCHMITZ, Stephen Palmer. 7849 ROCKFISH VALLEY HWY, AFTON FAMILY MEDICINE 22920 #051-01-2001 L2001 **FM** *020 †18

ALBERTA – BRUNSWICK

NOWLIN, John Burton. PO BOX 338, FIRST & MAPLE STREETS 23821 #036-07-1959 L1993 **IM** *071

ALDIE – LOUDOUN

HALL-FINNEY, Annette. 42274 HIDDENWOOD LN 20105 #051-04-1988 L1992 **IM** *020 †20

ALEXANDRIA – ALEXANDRIA CITY

ABRAMSON, Edward Gerald. 1707 OSAGE ST, STE 301 22302 #051-01-1967 L1967 **U** *020 †95
ADESON, Robert Lawrence. 4660 KENMORE AVE STE 220 22304 #024-07-1956 L1963 **GS** *071 †85
AGOLINI, Stefano Franco. 4660 KENMORE AVE, STE 419 22304 #051-01-1993 L1998 **GS** *020 †85
AHMADI, Satar Abdul. 50 S PICKETT ST 22304 #118-01-1967 L1988 **FM GP** *020
AHMED, Mehboob. 4600 KING ST STE 4N 22302 #495-45-1966 L1981 **OTO RO** *020 †80,45
AKBARI, Marjaneh. 4660 KENMORE AVE, STE 800 22304 #051-04-1984 L1993 **CD** *020 †20
AKRAMI KHASRAGHI, Fardin. 205 YOAKUM PKWY UNIT 1626 22304 #517-01-1999 L2005 **IM** *020 †20
AKSENTIJEVICH, Ivan. 4660 KENMORE AVE, STE 1018 22304 #957-02-1986 L2003 **HO IM** *020 †40
ALEXANDER, Edward G, Jr. 4801 KENMORE AVE STE 101 22304 #010-01-1966 L1971 **ORS** *020 †40
ALEXANIAN, Herminee O. ■ 22304 #575-01-1980 L1994 **PD** *020 †55
ALHAZMI, Ala Abdullah. ■ 22304 #010-01-2003 L2004 **GS** *012
ALI, Muhammad. 3450 N BEAUREGARD ST, STE 2 22302 #704-21-1985 L1991 **IM CD** *020 †20
ALVARADO, Marcio A E. 5268 DAWES AVE 22311 #451-01-1972 L1995 **PD** *020 †55
ALWAY, David Walter. 4660 KENMORE AVE, NEUROLOGY & HEADACHE 22302 #035-46-1997 L2001 **N** *100 †75
ALZAKI, Talib S. ■ 22304 #797-03-1989 L1995 **EM** *020 †16
AMIN, Surendra Pranjivan. 3450 N BEAUREGARD ST, STE 1 22302 #495-22-1970 L1979 **IM IMG** *020 †20

AMINI, Massoud. 101 S WHITING ST, STE 201 22304 #517-01-1968 L1979 **OTO PS** *040 †45

AMIR, Abdul-Razack A. ■ 22302 #797-02-1989 L1998 **NEP** *020 †20

ANANGUR GANESAN, Chitra D. ■ 22311 #495-59-1998 L2006 **IM** *012

ANDERSON, Warner J. 5113 LEESBURG PIKE, STE 910 SKYLINE 4 22302 #011-03-1980 L1982 **EM IM** *020 †20

ANDRAWIS, Moheb Saleh. 2500 N VAN DORN ST, STE 109 22302 #915-04-1982 L2002 **PD** *020 †55

ANSARI, Zafar A. 2849 DUKE ST, STE 4 22314 #016-42-1995 L1998 **IM** *020 †20

ANSHER, Alan Frederic. 4660 KENMORE AVE, STE 305 22304 #023-01-1982 L1984 **GE IM** *020 †20

ARABIAN, Aram A. ■ 22314 #043-01-1975 L1995 **IM** *020

ARAYA, Henok. 5249 DUKE ST, STE L11 22304 #025-12-1999 L2003 **GS** *020

ARIA, Nancy Nazanine. 2865 DUKE ST 22314 #010-01-1998 L1999 **D** *020 †15

ARTILES, Carlos. 2001 N BEAUREGARD ST, STE 200 22311 #008-02-1982 L1988 **R RNR** *020 †80 ‡

ASESOR, Maria Concepcion. 5249 DUKE ST 22304 #748-02-1989 L1998 **IM END** *020 †20

ASGEIRSSON, Gudmundur. ■ 22302 #484-01-1978 L1985 **PD ID** *020 †55

ASHBY, Richard Bruce. 2500 N VAN DORN ST, STE 106 22302 #010-03-1983 L1985 **FM** *020 †18

ASMAMAW, Abraham. 5249 DUKE ST, STE 309 22304 #473-01-1988 L1999 **PM PMM** *020 †60

ATIYEH, Lyna. 4320 SEMINARY RD, INOVA ALEXANDRIA HOSPITAL 22304 #010-01-1997 L2003 **AN** *020 †05

AYALEW, Kassa. 4921 SEMINARY RD STE 115 22311 #366-01-1989 L2002 **PDI PD** *020 †55

AZER, Nigel Merriett. 417 N WASHINGTON ST 22314 #051-01-1996 L1996 **ORS** *020

AZER, Rida Naguib. 417 N WASHINGTON ST 22314 #330-02-1959 L1972 **ORS** *030 †40 ‡

BAGLA, Sandeep. ■ 22311 #422-01-2002 L2007 **VIR** *012 †80

BALASUBRAMANIAN, Varagur. 4141A DUKE ST 22304 #495-45-1983 L2000 **NEP IM** *020 †20

BALISTRERI, Denise Tunsta. 4660 KENMORE AVE, STE 500 22304 #036-05-1991 L1994 **PD** *020 †55

BALL, John Edward. 4320 SEMINARY RD, 1ST FL 22304 #047-06-1983 L1987 **AN** *020 †05

BANKS, Stephen Joshua M. 4320 SEMINARY RD, INOVA ALEXANDRIA CNCR CTR 22304 #005-11-1993 L1997 **RO** *020 †80

BAPNA, Mitali. 2001 N BEAUREGARD ST, STE 200 22311 #024-01-1999 L2005 **DR** *100 †80 ‡

BARBOT, Henry Claude. 720 N SAINT ASAPH ST, ALEXANDRIA MENTAL HEALTH 22314 #440-01-1977 L1994 **P GP** *020 †75 ‡

BARBU, Richard R. 2001 N BEAUREGARD ST, RADIOLOGISTS, PCSUITE 200 22311 #035-03-1989 L2001 **DR RNR** *020 †80

BARKIN, Ronald Jay. 4660 KENMORE AVE 22304 #035-19-1987 L1992 **GE HEP** *020 †20

BARROS, Monica Mary. ■ 22302 #016-11-2004 L2004 **P** *012

BAUTISTA-QUINT, Edith V. 2823 DUKE ST 22314 #748-17-1982 L2002 **PM** *020 †60

BENNET, Justin David. 4660 KENMORE AVE, STE 810 22304 #019-02-1990 L1999 **GE IM** *020 †20

BERMAN, Harold John. 4660 KENMORE AVE 22304 #035-19-1953 L1959 **D** *020 †15

BERNANKE, Abraham David. 4660 KENMORE AVE, STE 604 22304 #035-19-1957 L1964 **IM END** *020 †20

BHATIA, Maya. 101 S WHITING ST, LANDMARK TOWERS SUITE 212 22304 #495-01-1967 L1978 **CHP P** *020 †55,75

BIGELOW, Llewellyn Barry. 109 S FAIRFAX ST 22314 #024-01-1961 L1968 **P** *020 †75

BLAIR, Deborah Nibley. 5055 SEMINARY RD, STE 104 22311 #008-01-1982 L1987 **R** *020 †80

BLUMENTHAL, Rachael Beth. ■ 22302 #003-75-2006, ▲ L2006 **PD** *012

BOSCH, Ryan Gordon. 3104 OLD DOMINION BLVD 22305 #051-01-1995 L1996 **IM** *020 †20

BOUTROS, Mark Samir. ■ 22304 #305-01-2005 L2005 **IM** *012

BOWERS, Deborah. 4660 KENMORE AVE STE 902, PHYSICIANS AND MIDWIVES 22304 #050-02-1994 L1998 **OBG** *020 †30

BRANDT, Kurt Theodore. 2355A MILL RD, SERVICES 22314 #007-02-1975 L1982 **GP** *020

BREEN, Lenore Adele. ■ 22314 #048-02-1977 L1977 **N OS** *075 †75

BRENNAN, Walter Jos. ■ 22314 #041-02-1944 L1952 **P** *072 †75

BROOKS, Sidney Chas. 127 S FAIRFAX ST, STE 450 22314 #025-01-1971 L1972 **P N** *020 †75

BUENAVENTURA, Susan Kelly. 5425 DUKE ST 22304 #051-04-1988 L1994 **PS** *020 †85,65

BUHAIN, Wilfrido J. 6300 STEVENSON AVE 22304 #748-02-1964 L1974 **PUD IM** *020 †20

BULLARD, Steven R. 2865 DUKE ST 22314 #036-07-1994 L1994 **OPH PO** *020 †35

BURNETT, Michelle Kay. 4320 SEMINARY RD, ALEXANDRIA HOSPITAL 22304 #010-01-1984 L2001 **AN** *020 †05

BURNS, Thomas E, III. 4320 SEMINARY RD, INORA ALEXANDRIA HOSP 22304 #051-04-1995 L1995 **OBG** *020 †30

BURTON, Timothy James. 4320 SEMINARY RD 22304 #023-01-1978 L1999 **PTH PCP** *062 †50

BUTLER, Lilia G. 4320 SEMINARY RD, ALEXANDRIA HOSPITAL 22304 #748-10-1965 L1972 **PD** *020 †55

BUXO, Francisco Jose. 2853 DUKE ST 22314 #042-03-1984 L1993 **OBG** *020

CALVERT, Preston Crockett. 5249 DUKE ST, STE 401 22304 #043-01-1979 L1990 **N OS** *020 †75

CAMPBELL, Robert Douglas. ■ 22311 #048-12-1952 L1952 **IMG** *071

CARPENTER, Barry Lee. ■ 22320 #047-07-1973 **PTH** *075

CHAILLET, Jeremy James. ■ 22314 #056-05-2004 L2007 **PD** *100 †55

CHANDRA, Poornima. 1200 N HOWARD ST, CASEY HEALTH CENTER ATTN M 22304 #010-01-1998 L2006 **PD** *020 †55

CHANG, Samuel Wise. 4320 SEMINARY RD 22304 #583-04-1959 L1975 **FM GP** *071 †18

CHAPMAN, Corry Allen. ■ 22301 #010-02-2006 L2007 **FP** *012

CHARABATY, Samar Michel. ■ 22304 #605-02-2002 L2005 **RHU** *012 †20

CHARBEL, Halim Nabil. ■ 22304 #605-02-2002 L2003 **GE** *012 †20

CHARNEY, David L. 1444 DUKE ST 22314 #035-15-1968 L1974 **P** *020

CHEN, Cheng-Nan. 312 S WASHINGTON ST, STE 6B 22314 #385-01-1965 L1973 **FM** *020 †18

CHINERY, Roger Chas D. 2 E GLEBE RD 22305 #412-02-1982 L1992 **IM** *020 †20

CHOI, Walter Sik. 2001 N BEAUREGARD ST, STE 200 22311 #051-01-1965 L1965 **R** *071 †80

CLARK, Jacob A. 411 N WASHINGTON ST 22314 #042-01-1981 L1987 **OPH OS** *020 †35

CLARK, Thomas Harding. 4320 SEMINARY RD, INOVA ALEXANDRIA HOSPITAL 22304 #010-01-1974 L1986 **EM** *020 †20,16

CLINEDINST, Candace. 3450 N BEAUREGARD ST, STE 1 22302 #041-12-1999 L2002 **IM** *020 †20

CLOYD, Dale Edward. ■ 22314 #038-40-1963 L1963 **GE AM** *020 †18,70,20

COHEN, Howard Jay. 1444 DUKE ST 22314 #035-09-1981 L1987 **P** *020 †75

CONRAD, Elizabeth Tierney. 5249 DUKE ST STE 212 22304 #035-01-1991 L1995 **FM** *020 †18

COO, Albert Wu. 6300 STEVENSON AVE, STE D 22304 #748-10-1983 L1987 **DIA END** *020 †20

COOK, Robert Craig. 4320 SEMINARY RD, 1ST FL 22304 #023-01-1984 L1988 **AN** *020 †05 ‡

COOPER, James Mark. 2001 N BEAUREGARD ST, STE 200 22311 #035-20-1987 L1998 **VIR** *020 †80

CORDTS, Paul Roger. ■ 22304 #023-12-1984 L1987 **VS GS** *030 †85

CORNWELL, Stephen Lester. 4401 FORD AVE STE 250 22302 #010-01-1987 L1989 **FM** *020 †18

COURT, Eleanor Marie. ■ 22314 #035-03-2003 L2003 **GS** *012

COZZENS, Dennis Thos. 1707 OSAGE ST, STE 404 22302 #038-41-1982 L1985 **CHP ADL** *020 †75

CROSS, Gerald Marion. ■ 22314 #005-12-1977 L1982 **FM ADM** *030 †18

CRUZ, Carlos Alberto. 1707 OSAGE ST, STE 303 22302 #682-03-1994 L2001 **PD** *020 †55

CUDDEBACK, John Kitchin. 1422 DUKE ST 22314 #017-20-1979 **OS CLP** *030

CUSHING, Cameron Mark. 4320 SEMINARY RD, DEPT. OF EMERG PHYSICANS 22304 #010-02-1994 L1998 **EM** *020 †16

CUTTING, Mary Elizabeth. 4660 KENMORE AVE, STE 902 22304 #051-01-1980 L1982 **OBG** *020 †30

DABBOUS, Ibrahim A. 5262 DAWES AVE 22311 #605-01-1961 L1987 **PD PHO** *020 †55

DAKIN, Pemmaraju Saleena. 1200 N QUAKER LN 22302 #012-22-1995 L2001 **PD CCP** *020 †55

DALKILIC, Alican. 1000 HARRISON CIR 22304 #902-19-1993 L2001 **P PHP** *020 †75

DALLAS, Akilah Hasanati. ■ 22304 #010-02-2003 **OBG** *012

DALY, Farrah Nicole. ■ 22314 #041-15-2002 L2004 **N** *100

DANCEL, Rosario Gonsalez. 6000 STEVENSON AVE, STE 104 22304 #748-10-1966 L1980 **PD ADL** *020

D'ANDRADE, Annalise Marie. ■ 22314 #010-01-2006 L2006 **PD** *012

DANESHVAR, Hafez. 5001 SEMINARY RD STE 116 22311 #517-01-1980 L1992 **AI IM** *020 †20,03

DANILYANTS, Natalya Eduar. ■ 22302 #021-05-2004 L2004 **OBG** *012

DAVIES, John Benj. ■ 22304 #041-02-1956 L1966 **P** *071 †75

DAVIS, Donald Irvin. 220 S WASHINGTON ST 22314 #041-01-1968 L1972 **P** *020 †75

DAWSON, Eric Geoffrey. 321 SOUTH PATRICK ST 22314 #010-03-1984 L1992 **ORS** *020

DAY, Stephen Mark. 4660 KENMORE AVE, STE 1200 22304 #056-06-1993 L1998 **CD** *020 †20

DE FALCON, Elizabeth. ■ 22314 #023-12-2002 L2004 *020 †55

DE GRAZIA, John Barrett. 2001 N BEAUREGARD ST # 200 22311 #035-19-1974 L1979 **DR** *020 †80

DELANEY, Michael D. 4320 SEMINARY RD, 1ST FL 22304 #010-02-1973 L1978 **AN** *020

DELAUNE, Eugene Francis. 4320 SEMINARY RD, DEPARTMENT OF EMERGENCY ME 22304 #021-01-1991 L1998 **EM** *020 †16

DEMPSEY, Danielle Caroleo. ■ 22305 #026-04-2005 L2005 **OBG** *012

DESAI, Narendra G. 3450 N BEAUREGARD ST, STE 1 22302 #495-23-1969 L1974 **IM CD** *020 †20

DE SANDIES, Kenneth Andre. 4600 DUKE ST STE 332 22304 #047-07-1973 L1978 **OBG** *020 †30

DE SHIELDS, Laurence M, III. ■ 22314 #038-45-1999 L2000 **FM** *020 †18

DIETRICH, Anne Marie. 4660 KENMORE AVE, STE 701 22304 #023-01-1987 L1995 **P** *020 †75

DIEZ-LEE, Marina. ■ 22314 #051-04-1941 L1941 **OS** *071

DI PINTO, Felix Roberto. 4801 KENMORE AVE STE 102 22304 #132-02-1973 L1983 **IM PUD** *020 †20

DISPENZA, Sebastian J, Jr. 4320 SEMINARY RD, SUNLIFE OB/GYN 22304 #051-01-1974 L1976 **OBG** *020 †30

DIXON, Walter Dillard. 4320 SEMINARY RD, ALEXANDRIA HOSPITAL 22304 #023-12-1986 L2002 **EM** *020 †16

DJAMIL, Fertikh. 2001 N BEAUREGARD ST # 200, ASSOC OF ALEXANDRIA RAD 22311 #125-01-1993 L2005 **RNR** *020 †80

DO, Cuong Hoang. 5266 DAWES AVE 22311 #051-07-1991 L1993 **FM** *020 †18

DOBRZYNSKI, Robert F. 5226 DAWES AVE 22311 #010-02-1969 L1971 **HEM ON** *020 †20

DOSSOLA, Jose Maria. 5272 DAWES AVE 22311 #132-01-1966 L1974 **IM PUD** *020 †20

DOUGHERTY, Timothy Russel, Jr. ■ 22304 #023-01-2008 *012

DUBOW, Emanuel. ■ 22313 #021-05-1941 **PD PHP** *071 †55

DUNKWU, Anthony Amechi. 2807 DUKE ST 22314 #011-03-1977 L1983 **OBG** *020 †30

DYER, Cinda Robin. 4320 SEMINARY RD 22304 #065-01-1984 L1986 **EM FM** *020 †75

EBADI-TEHRANI, Mehrdad. 5226 DAWES AVE 22311 #025-07-1991 L1996 **ON IM** *020 †20

EBBERT, Timothy James. ■ 22304 #056-06-2003 L2004 **AN** *012

ELBASH, Mohammed. 2849 DUKE ST, STE 14 22314 #028-02-2001 L2007 **OPH** *020 †35

ELFEKY, Hamed Abdelfatah. 4320 SEMINARY RD 22304 #915-04-1980 L1995 **SP** *020 †50

ELLISON, Craig M. 4660 KENMORE AVE, STE 305 22304 #010-01-1997 L2003 **GE** *020 †20 ‡

ELLYN, Nicholas. 1707 OSAGE ST, STE 205 22302 #010-01-1975 L1976 **OPH GP** *020 †35

EVANS, Amanda Suarez. ■ 22305 #048-02-2004 L2004 **PD** *100

FARAGASSO, Devin John. ■ 22304 #051-01-2003 L2006 **EM** *020 †16

FELLEKE, Tesfaye Akalu. ■ 22304 #366-01-1988 *100

FERNANDO, Judith Sheolie. ■ 22311 #010-01-2008 *012

FERRIER, Cheryl-Ann. 1320 PRINCE ST 22314 #010-03-1993 L1998 **OBG** *020 †30

FILAK, Stefani Jane. 5021 SEMINARY RD, STE 109 22311 #048-04-1982 L1984 **OBG** *062 †30 ‡

FISHER, Gerald John. 5244 DAWES AVE 22311 #035-08-1944 L1953 **IM** *071

FLEMING, Meghan Catherine. ■ 22314 #035-06-2004 L2007 **PD** *020 †55

FLINT, Laurie Ann. ■ 22304 #051-07-1985 L1987 **FM** *062 †18 ‡

FLIS, Joseph F, Jr. 4320 SEMINARY RD 22304 #010-02-1968 L1969 **GE IM** *020

FLORENTINO, Paul F. ■ 22314 #028-34-1981 L1988 **ID** *071 †20

FORNOS, Aurelia C. ■ 22304 #275-01-1945 *100

FOX, Fiona Jane. 720 N SAINT ASAPH ST, ALEXANDRIA MENTAL HEALTH C 22314 #036-01-1998 L1998 **P** *020 †75

FOZDAR, Pratima Singh. 4921 SEMINARY RD STE 117 22311 #495-24-1975 L1985 **IM GP** *020 †20

FRANCE, Margaret Lynne. 4320 SEMINARY RD 22304 #047-05-1981 L1998 **PD NPM** *020 †55

FRANCIS, Peter. 4660 KENMORE AVE, STE 1018 22304 #035-19-1985 L1988 **IM** *020 †20

FRANCO, Edna Valera. 201A E CUSTIS AVE 22301 #748-01-1958 L1980 **EM** *071

FRASURE, Sarah Elisabeth. ■ 22314 #008-01-2008 *012

FREEDMAN, Irwin Stanley. 4660 KENMORE AVE, STE 1210 22304 #010-01-1959 L1960 **GP** *020

FRIEDMAN, Michael Herbert. 5055 SEMINARY RD, STE 104 22311 #035-08-1966 L1972 **R NM** *020 †80,28

GAGLIOTI, Anne Hazen. ■ 22311 #038-06-2005 L2007 **FM** *100 †18

GAGNON, Pierre P. 312 S WASHINGTON ST, STE 4C 22314 #067-03-1950 L1988 **OTO** *020

GAHN, Gina Christine. ■ 22304 #038-43-2003 L2003 **OBG** *020

GAHRES, Edward Elias. 5021 SEMINARY RD, STE 109 22311 #051-01-1958 L1958 **GYN** *071 †30

GALLAGHER, Doris B. ■ 22302 #041-07-1956 L1958 **AN** *071

GARCIA, Maria Mercedes. 4660 KENMORE AVE, STE 805 22304 #042-01-1987 L1992 **END** *020 †20

GARDNER, Charles William. 4401 FORD AVE, STE 250 22302 #055-01-1978 L1981 **FM** *020 †18 ‡

GAUGHAN, Robert Troy. 4320 SEMINARY RD 22304 #010-02-1957 L1964 **ORS** *071 †40
GERTZ, Bennett Eli. ■ 22302 #024-16-2004 L2004 **PD** *100
GHIDINI, Alessandro. 4320 SEMINARY RD, INOVA ALEXANDRIA HOSP 22304 #561-03-1982 L1996 **MFM CG** *020 †19,30
GIAMMITTORIO, David C. 4660 KENMORE AVE, STE 902 22304 #051-04-1974 L1975 **OBG** *020 †30
GILL, Waltus Hughes, III. ■ 22311 #021-01-2007 L2007 **GS** *012
GILLIAN, Monjari C. 5055 SEMINARY RD, STE 104 22311 #028-03-1993 L1999 **DR** *062 †80
GILLINSON, Roy Stuart. 4320 SEMINARY RD 22304 #352-05-1946 L1956 **AN OS** *071
GILMORE, Bruce Leslie. 4660 KENMORE AVE STE 604, ALEXANDRIA HOSP PROF CTR 22304 #024-01-1956 L1963 **IM** *071 †20
GIRMA, Beletshache Rachel. ■ 22304 #041-15-2002 L2005 **EM** *020
GIUNTA, Stephen Xavier. 4216 KING ST 22302 #010-02-1964 L1983 **FPS OS** *020 †45
GLASS, James Douglas. 4320 SEMINARY RD, 1ST FL 22304 #051-01-1997 L1997 **AN** *020 †05
GLASSMAN, Bruce David. 4660 KENMORE AVE 22304 #024-07-1988 L1994 **D** *020 †15
GOALD, Harold Jerome. ■ 22305 #041-13-1954 L1962 **NS** *071 †25
GOHARI, Geeti Parsa. 50 S PICKETT ST 22304 #517-04-1987 L2001 **PM** *020 †60
GOLDBLATT, Seymour Zonald. 4320 SEMINARY RD 22304 #041-02-1956 L1960 **PD** *071
GONDOR, Leslie G. 3541 W BRADDOCK RD STE 101 22302 #010-01-1997 L1999 **FM** *020
GONDOR, Leslie Paul. 3541 W BRADDOCK RD 22302 #473-04-1946 L1957 **GP** *071
GONZALEZ, Miguel Hernando. 5242 DAWES AVE STE 3- 22311 #264-04-1959 L1969 **VS TS** *071 †85,90
GRAPIN, Fern Lorraine. 4660 KENMORE AVE, PHYSICIANS FOR WOMEN 22304 #010-01-1983 L1986 **OBG** *020 †30
GRAYSON, Jane. 4320 SEMINARY RD # PD, ALEXANDRIA HOSPITAL 22304 #024-01-1973 L1989 **RO** *020 †55,80
GRECO, Philip Scot. 5249 DUKE ST STE 307 22304 #035-19-1971 L1978 **P** *020 †75
HABIBULLA, Kolar Syed. ■ 22311 #704-02-1961 L1982 **IM** *020
HAGEN, Ralph Leslie. 333 N FAIRFAX ST, STE 400 22314 #016-11-1970 L1994 **CHP P** *020 †75
HAKIM, Arcadius Hanna. 3541 W BRADDOCK RD 22302 #875-01-1951 L1960 **OTO FM** *071
HALLY, Robert Jeffery. 4660 KENMORE AVE, STE 305 22304 #041-13-1989 L2001 **GE** *020 †20
HAMASAKI, Sharon Ann T. 3905 KELLER AVE 22302 #048-02-1974 L1980 **P** *020 †75
HAMMACK, Phillip Larry. 2847 DUKE ST 22314 #041-12-1969 L1977 **GS CD** *020 †85
HANDLER, Wendy Ellen. 4921 SEMINARY RD 22311 #033-05-1991 L1994 **FM** *020 †18
HANES, Chad Fitzhugh. 4320 SEMINARY RD, 1ST FL 22304 #051-07-1994 L1994 **AN** *020
HARPER, Cortney Elizabeth. ■ 22304 #021-01-2005 L2005 **OBG** *012
HARVELL, Jeffrey Darren. ■ 22314 #051-01-1991 L2004 **PTH** *020 †50
HASELTINE, Florence Pat. ■ 22314 #035-46-1972 L2006 **OBG** *020 †30
HASHEMI, Homayoun A. 4320 SEMINARY RD 22304 #305-01-1985 L2003 **VS** *020 †85
HAUT, Donald David. 5249 DUKE ST, STE 100 22304 #041-13-1958 L1971 **IM** *020 †20
HECKER, Carlos Metsch. 3450 N BEAUREGARD ST 22302 #021-01-1963 L1968 **P GP** *071
HEINEN, Robert J. 4660 KENMORE AVE, STE 604 22304 #023-01-1980 L1983 **IM** *020 †20
HENRY, Debra Anne. 228 S WASHINGTON ST STE 22 22314 #047-07-1990 L1992 **P** *020
HERON, Alicia Gail. 321 S PATRICK ST 22314 #025-01-1974 L1979 **GP GS** *020
HERREROS, Rodrigo. 1685 HUNTING CREEK DR 22314 #231-03-1989 L2003 **AN** *020 †05
HERSCOWITZ, Robert David. 5216 DAWES AVE 22311 #010-02-1990 L1997 **PCC** *020 †20
HERTZBERG, Michael. 803 FRANKLIN ST 22314 #035-15-1971 L1976 **P** *020 †75
HINDLE, Wm Vincent, Jr. 2001 N BEAUREGARD ST, STE 200 22311 #035-20-1967 L1975 **DR** *020 †80
HO, David K. 312 S WASHINGTON ST, STE 6B 22314 #244-04-1980 L1998 **IM** *020 †20
HOART, Barbara J Reddy. 517 WYTHE ST 22314 #010-01-1970 L1976 **P** *020
HODGES, Emory Falcon, Jr. ■ 22311 #051-01-1947 L1947 **P** *071 †75
HOFFMAN, Richard Alan. 6300 STEVENSON AVE, STE B 22304 #035-15-1983 L1984 **PUD IM** *020 †20
HOLLIDAY, Michael Anthony. 4320 SEMINARY RD STE 3000, INOVA ALEXANDRIA HOSPITAL 22304 #047-07-1983 L1994 **PD NPM** *020 †55
HORAN, Anne Regina. 113 N WASHINGTON ST 22314 #010-02-1987 L1998 **OPH** *040
HOUK, Russell Richard. 4320 SEMINARY RD 22304 #025-07-1980 L1986 **PTH** *062 †50
HOYLE, John D. 312 S WASHINGTON ST 22314 #010-01-1943 L1949 **GS OS** *071 †85
HUBERMAN, Richard. 4660 KENMORE AVE 22304 #016-42-1963 L1967 **OPH** *020 †35
HUDSON, Charles A. ■ 22314 #051-01-1943 L1943 **CD IM** *071
HUNT, Kelly Jo. 5249 DUKE ST, STE 5 22304 #045-01-2004 L2004 **PD** *100
HURLEY, Michael Stephen. 4480 KING ST 22302 #010-01-1974 L1982 **FM** *020
HURLOCK, Donna Graves. 205 S WHITING ST STE 303 22304 #023-01-1979 L1985 **GYN** *020 †30
HURTADO, Rodrigo Claudio. 3450 N BEAUREGARD ST, STE 1 22302 #231-01-1964 L1973 **AI GP** *020 †55,03
HUTCHINS, Debra Ann. 4660 KENMORE AVE STE 220 22304 #048-04-1990 L1998 **GS** *020 †85
ILOABACHIE, Nwamaka Obiag. ■ 22311 #038-40-2006 L2006 **OBG** *012
INFANTE, Mary Ruth. 4660 KENMORE AVE, STE 420 22304 #748-08-1987 L1991 **P** *020 †75
IRANYI, Magdolna A. 3541 W BRADDOCK RD 22302 #473-01-1953 L1961 **PD** *071
IRELAND, Robert Roy. 3558 S GEORGE MASON DR 22302 #045-04-1985 L1987 **P AM** *020 †75
ISAACS, Ibukun-Olu Akinye. ■ 22311 #690-08-1998 **P** *012
JACKSON, Christopher D. ■ 22305 #010-01-2004 **AN** *012
JACKSON, Hampton James. 417 N WASHINGTON ST 22314 #010-03-1972 L1977 **ORS GS** *020 †40
JACKSON, Keith Lynn, II. ■ 22304 #010-02-2008 *012
JAHAN, Sheila. 5238 DAWES AVE 22311 #495-33-1985 L1994 **N** *020
JANATI, Abdorasool. ■ 22314 #517-01-1972 L1989 **N OS** *020 †75
JENKINS, Matthew V. ■ 22302 #054-04-2006 **ORS** *012
JOHN, Reverly Michelle. ■ 22311 #566-01-1996 L2000 **CCM** *020 †20
JONES, George Owens. 321 S PATRICK ST 22314 #010-03-1976 L1981 **CD IM** *020 †20
JONES, Wilbert Livingston. ■ 22304 #036-07-2006 **GS** *100
JOSEPH, Alice. 5244 DAWES AVE 22311 #495-63-1978 L1985 **IM NEP** *020 †20
KAM, Laurance Winghong. 4660 KENMORE AVE, STE 800 22304 #041-01-1990 L2002 **CD** *020 †20
KAMBAL, Khalid Ali Elkhid. ■ 22304 #915-02-1994 L2000 **HEM** *020 †20
KAPLIN, Arnold Jay. 5021 SEMINARY RD STE 123 22311 #024-07-1960 L1964 **P** *020
KARPICK, Ronald John. 4320 SEMINARY RD 22304 #008-01-1965 L1973 **PUD IM** *071 †20
KASENETZ, Pamela Hilary. ■ 22304 #010-01-2008 *012
KATZEN, Jay Everett. 4900 SEMINARY RD STE 350 22311 #010-01-1972 L1976 **OPH** *020 †35
KAUFFMAN, Stephen Charles. 3450 N BEAUREGARD ST, STE 1 22302 #041-02-1964 L1965 **GP** *020
KAVJIAN, David Alan. 4801 KENMORE AVE STE 101, NORTHERN VIRGINIA ORTHOPAE 22304 #041-09-1982 L1987 **ORS** *020 †40
KEENAN, Richard Leo. ■ 22314 #030-06-1957 L1977 **AN** *071 †05
KELLY, Kathleen Patricia. 4320 SEMINARY RD 22304 #041-07-1984 L1988 **EM PEM** *020 †16
KELLY, Richard John. 4801 KENMORE AVE 22304 #023-01-1964 L1969 **GS IMG** *071
KEMPF, Phillip Wm. 4320 SEMINARY RD 22304 #418-02-1984 L1992 **RHU IM** *020 †20
KEPHART, Curtis Jeffrey. ■ 22304 #041-14-2007 **ORS** *012
KERNESS, Elisabeth A. 4320 SEMINARY RD, MEDICAL STAFF OFFICE 22304 #041-07-1992 L1996 **EM** *020 †16
KHACHIKIAN-SHAHANI, G. 50 S PICKETT ST STE 210 22304 #517-01-1967 L1978 **OBG** *020
KHAN, Mohammad Aqiq. 4141A DUKE ST 22304 #704-01-1958 L1973 **IM GE** *020
KHOSLA, Jaswinder Shavind. 4660 KENMORE AVE, NEUROLOGY & HEADACHE 22304 #495-56-1992 L2005 **CN** *020 †75
KIM, Jeong Ai. ■ 22304 #583-08-1983 **P** *012
KIM, John Kihun. 6300 STEVENSON AVE, STE B 22304 #051-01-1995 L2000 **IM** *020 †20
KIM, Joon Hyuk. ■ 22311 #035-09-2005 L2005 **IM** *012
KIM, Jung Ok. ■ 22311 #583-10-1978 L1981 **AN IM** *100
KIM, Woo Jae. 4320 SEMINARY RD, INOVA ALEXANDRIA HOSPITAL/ 22304 #010-03-1998 L2002 **EM** *020 †16
KIMLIN, Edward Joseph. ■ 22305 #021-01-2006 L2006 **EM** *012
KIRILENKO, Linda Theresa. 417 N WASHINGTON ST, ORTHOPAEDIC ASSOC 22314 #010-02-1984 L1990 **ORS HS** *020 †40
KIRKMAN, Marian Sue. 1701 N BEAUREGARD ST 22311 #036-01-1982 L1989 **IM END** *020 †20
KOLANSKY, Saul Kalman. 110 N SAINT ASAPH ST, S KALMAN KOLANSKY MD PC 22314 #010-02-1965 L1972 **P CHP** *072 †75
KONGKASUWAN, Kimberly R. 4660 KENMORE AVE, STE 902 22304 #055-01-1998 L1998 **OBG** *020 †30
KONIGSBERG, Charles, Jr. 4480 KING ST, STE 413 22302 #047-06-1965 L1999 **PHP** *030 †70
KOSLOW, Joel Lester. 5001 SEMINARY RD, STE 113 22311 #010-01-1964 L1970 **IM CD** *020 †20
KOWALCZYK, Courtney Anne. ■ 22314 #051-01-2007 L2007 **GS** *012
KUMAR, Seema Pania. 5249 DUKE ST 22304 #016-02-1994 L1995 **IM** *020 †20
KUYKENDALL, Harry Canter. ■ 22304 #051-04-1962 L1962 **FM** *071 †18
LAMB, Tammy Joy. 2001 N BEAUREGARD ST, RADIOLOGISTS, P.C.SUITE 20 22311 #035-19-1993 L2002 **DR** *020 †80
LANDAY, Kimberly. 2001 N BEAUREGARD ST, STE 200 22311 #036-07-1988 L2003 **DR** *020 †80
LARSON, Charlotte G. 4600 KING ST, STE 4J 22302 #021-01-1991 L1996 **OBG** *020 †30
LAYMAN, Kerri Lyn. ■ 22301 #010-02-2006 **EM** *012
LEABHART, John Wm, Jr. ■ 22302 #010-01-1953 L1961 **ORS** *071 †40
LEAVITT, Kathleen Anne. 4320 SEMINARY RD, INOVA ALEXANDRIA HOSPITAL 22304 #035-15-1986 L1995 **AN IM** *020 †05
LE BOLT, Scot A. 2001 N BEAUREGARD ST # 200, RADIOLOGISTS, PC 22311 #012-05-1984 L1985 **DR** *020 †80
LECHAUX, Pierre Aymar. 4320 SEMINARY RD 22304 #396-06-1951 L1954 **PD OS** *071 †55
LEE, Chong Wook. 4901 SEMINARY RD STE 110 22311 #583-01-1963 L1973 **TS CD** *020
LEE, Chong Wook. 4901 SEMINARY RD STE 110 22311 #583-02-1963 L1973 **U** *020 †95
LEE, Kyung Ja. 4320 SEMINARY RD 22304 #583-08-1966 L1976 **OBG GP** *020
LEE, Suong Kyu. 4320 SEMINARY RD 22304 #055-01-2002 L2005 **AN** *100
LEE, Won Ro. 3450 N BEAUREGARD ST, STE 2 22302 #583-02-1962 L1975 **CD IM** *071 †20
LEFRAK, Edward Arthur. 4320 SEMINARY RD 22304 #017-20-1969 L1977 **TS CD** *020 †85,90
LESTER, Nichelle Secorra. ■ 22311 #010-01-2003 **PD** *012
LEVENSON, Deborah Elyse. 4660 KENMORE AVE, STE 200 22304 #041-09-1988 L1992 **GE** *020 †20
LEX, Carolyn Kimberly. ■ 22314 #038-06-2004 L2007 **EM** *100
LI, Si-Ju. ■ 22314 #041-07-1965 L1975 **AN** *071 †05
LICHTER, Allen Sollie. 1900 DUKE ST, STE 200 22314 #025-01-1972 L1973 **RO** *020 †80
LINCE, Ana C. 720 N SAINT ASAPH ST 22314 #264-16-1987 L1996 **P** *020 †75
LITTLE, Cheryl Ann. ■ 22314 #038-43-1985 L1988 **PD** *020 †55
LIU, Yaning. 4320 SEMINARY RD 22304 #243-71-1982 L2000 **CD** *020 †20
LIVINGSTON, Schuyler Davi. ■ 22302 #012-05-2008 *012
LLOYD, Beth A. 5194 DAWES AVE, FAMILY PRACTICE & SPORTS 22311 #654-01-1989 L1995 **FM** *020 †18
LONGO, Antonio Miguel. 4600 KING ST, STE 6K 22302 #010-02-1964 L1971 **IM PUD** *071
LOTFI, Karan. 2001 N BEAUREGARD ST, RADIOLOGISTS, P.C. SUITE 2 22311 #041-01-1992 L2000 **DR** *020 †80,28
LOVELL, Mark Alan. 4501 FORD AVE, - ATTN:CSTE-SU 22302 #018-03-1985 L1986 **OM FM** *030 †70,18
LUGO-ESCHENWALD, Vivian L. 5249 DUKE ST, STE 100 22304 #042-02-1990 L1993 **FM** *020 †18
LUNDGREN, Kathleen P. 4660 KENMORE AVE, STE 500 22304 #035-06-1997 L2000 **PD** *020 †55
LYLES, Robert Lee, Jr. 4520 KING ST, STE 101 22302 #649-33-1981 L1983 **AN PMM** *020 †05
MAC INTOSH, Houston Hood. 218 N LEE ST 22314 #035-45-1961 L1979 **PYA P** *071 †75
MACK, Andrew William. ■ 22311 #041-01-2004 L2006 **ORS** *012
MAHONEY, John Thos. ■ 22314 #041-02-1965 L1969 **P** *020
MALETSKY, Shari Gayle. ■ 22302 #010-01-2007 L2007 **IM** *012
MALHOTRA, Suresh Kumar. 4660 KENMORE AVE STE 810 22304 #495-73-1980 L1986 **GE IM** *020 †20
MANCIAS, Joseph Douglas. 126 QUAY ST 22314 #035-20-2008 *012
MANSFIELD, Patrick David. 4320 SEMINARY RD, 1ST FL 22304 #010-02-1973 L1983 **AN** *071
MARAK, George Edward, Jr. 4320 SEMINARY RD 22304 #041-12-1964 L1971 **OPH** *020 †35
MARFORI, Joseph Belarmin. 4320 SEMINARY RD, MEDICAL STAFF OFFICE 22304 #038-43-2001 L2006 **EM** *020 †16 ‡
MARTIN, Eleanor Anne. ■ 22314 #021-01-2004 L2004 **PD** *012 †55
MARTINELLI, Thomas A. 2805 DUKE ST, COMMONWEALTH ORTHODAEDICS 22314 #010-02-1985 L1989 **ORS** *020 †40
MAZANEC, Mary Beth. ■ 22314 #038-06-1981 L1985 **IM** *050 †20
MC CULLOUGH, Michael F. 2001 N BEAUREGARD ST, STE 200 22311 #010-02-1996 L2003 **VIR** *020 †80
MC KEE, Thistle M. 4320 SEMINARY RD 22304 #035-20-1934 L1942 **PD PHP** *020 †55
MC KENZIE, Paula A. 3327 DUKE ST 22314 #005-11-1983 L1987 **OBG** *020 †30
MCKITTY, Simone Alicia. 4660 KENMORE AVE 22304 #010-02-2002 L2005 **D** *020 †15
MC KNIGHT, Alice M. 4660 KENMORE AVE, PHYSICIANS FOR WOMEN 22304 #041-07-1981 L1987 **OBG** *020 †30
MC PHERSON, Douglas C. 4305 WHEELER AVE 22304 #051-04-1985 L1993 **IM PUD** *020 †20
MEDINA, Salvador. ■ 22311 #649-01-1974 L1978 **GS CRS** *020 †85,10
MEHTA, Shobha N. 5021 SEMINARY RD STE 106 22311 #495-48-1978 L1987 **OBG** *020 †30

■ = Address Information Privacy Protected

MELONI, Charles Robt. 4701 KENMORE AVE 22304 #035-09-1955 L1969 **DIA IM** *071 †20
MENDEZ, Leonardo. 4320 SEMINARY RD 22304 #035-01-1985 L1995 **GE HEP** *020 †20
MENDEZ, Ramon Eduardo. 4141A DUKE ST 22304 #042-01-1982 L1990 **NEP IM** *020 †20
MENSCH, Arthur H. 4320 SEMINARY RD 22304 #035-08-1962 L1976 **PTH** *020 †50
MILLER, George Francis. 4600 KING ST, STE 4C 22302 #010-01-1958 L1967 **PS OTO** *071 †45
MINTON, Stephen Mark. 5249 DUKE ST 22304 #051-01-1988 L1991 **IM** *020 †20
MIRCEA, Mirela Lavinia. 5249 DUKE ST, STE 100 22304 #781-03-1985 L1997 **FM** *020 †18 ‡
MITCHELL, Michael David. 4320 SEMINARY RD, STE 1210 22304 #051-04-1994 L1997 **IM** *020 †20
MOGADAM, Michael. 4660 KENMORE AVE STE 1206 22304 #517-01-1962 L1969 **GE IM** *020 †20
MOHYUDDIN, Farooq. 411 1/2 N WASHINGTON ST 22314 #704-16-1990 L2003 **P** *100 †75
MOLA, Margaret Wong. ■ 22314 #012-01-1946 L1950 **GP** *020
MOLCHON, Andrew B. 4660 KENMORE AVE STE 420 22304 #024-07-1967 L1971 **P PYG** *020 †75
MORROW, Robert Clegg. 4825 MARK CENTER DR, CNA CORPORATION 22311 #048-04-1976 L1992 **PHP FM** *050 †70
MRZLJAK, Vesna. 6300 STEVENSON AVE STE A 22304 #957-01-1974 L1983 **OTO FPS** *020 †45
MUAWWAD, Rafik David. 417 N WASHINGTON ST 22314 #605-01-1974 L1983 **ORS** *020 †40 ‡
MURPHY, Victoria Hecht. 5249 DUKE ST 22304 #010-01-2001 L2004 **IM** *020 †20
NABAVI, Mehdi. 1202 S WASHINGTON ST, APT 324C 22314 #517-01-1960 L1973 **EM PD** *071
NELSON, Margit A David. 4320 SEMINARY RD, ALEXANDRIA HOSP PATHOLOGY 22304 #473-02-1955 L1972 **PTH OS** *071 †50
NEUMANN, Mary Paula. 4320 SEMINARY RD 22304 #026-04-1982 L1987 **ATP CLP** *020 †50
NICHOLSON-ELBAOR, D M. 101 S WHITING ST STE 105 22304 #024-05-1981 L1985 **RHU IM** *020 †20
NIECHNIEDOWICZ, Lynne M. 1250 S WASHINGTON ST, UNIT 514 22314 #010-01-1976 L1981 **OTO A** *071 †45
NIELSEN, David Richards. 1 PRINCE ST, AMERICAN ACAD OF OTO 22314 #049-01-1979 L1980 **OTO NO** *030 †45
NIGRO, Michael F, Jr. 4660 KENMORE AVE, STE 220 22304 #035-20-1970 L1978 **GS SO** *020 †85
NOWAK, Anne Kathryn. 4320 SEMINARY RD, INOVA ALEXANDRIA HOSPITAL 22304 #550-02-1987 L1999 **IM** *020 †20
O'BRIEN, Paul John. 4660 KENMORE AVE, STE 800 22304 #051-01-1986 L1997 **CD IM** *020 †20
O'CONNOR, Robert Eugene. ■ 22314 #041-07-1982 L2007 **EM** *020 †16
OERTEL, James Edward. 2151 JAMIESON AVE # 1410 22314 #021-05-1958 L1958 **PTH** *071 †50
OMEISH, Esam Salem. 2849 DUKE ST, STE 14 22314 #010-02-1993 L1998 **GS** *020 †85
OMIDVAR, Berna Maria. 50 S PICKETT ST, STE 229 22304 #308-13-1998 L2004 *020
OMIDVAR, Jemal. 50 S PICKETT ST, STE 229 22304 #308-13-1998 L2004 **PD** *020
OSBORNE, Daniel Joseph. ■ 22314 #024-05-2003 L2003 **AN** *020
OXENHANDLER, Donald Craig. 4320 SEMINARY RD 22304 #028-02-1969 L1977 **NS** *020 †25
PAPADOURIS, Dimitrios C. 2001 N BEAUREGARD ST, STE 200 22311 #065-06-1998 L2006 **R VIR** *020 †80
PARIKH, Saumil Harshad. ■ 22304 #051-04-2004 L2007 **EM** *100
PARK, Jennifer Hyesong. 2001 N BEAUREGARD ST, SUTIE 200 22311 #023-01-1995 L2001 **DR** *020 †80
PARK, Sue Young. 4660 KENMORE AVE STE 500 22304 #051-01-1995 L1995 **PD** *020 †55
PARK, Theresa Min. 2001 N BEAUREGARD ST, STE 200 22311 #035-19-1997 L2003 **DR** *020 †80
PASTORE, Jay Anthony. 4660 KENMORE AVE, STE 1100 22304 #041-12-1985 L1989 **OBG** *020 †30
PATEL, Nalin Gordhanbhai. 4320 SEMINARY RD 22304 #495-23-1984 L1990 **IM** *020 †20
PEPPER, Franklin Jay. 4600 DUKE ST STE 424 22304 #030-05-1965 L1969 **P** *020 †75
PETERS, Lawrence Stephen. 4660 KENMORE AVE, STE 305 22304 #035-19-1972 L1976 **GE** *020 †20
PETERSON, Tiffany Brooke. ■ 22304 #030-05-2007 L2007 **TY** *012
PFUNDSTEIN, Joann. 6300 STEVENSON AVE, STE D 22304 #033-06-1990 L1995 **ID** *020 †20
PITTMAN, Richard Edward. 5021 SEMINARY RD, SUITE 125 BERKELEY BLDG 22311 #012-05-1967 L1976 **AN** *020 †85,10,05
POGGI, Sarah Hougen. 4320 SEMINARY RD 22304 #008-01-1996 L2001 **MFM OBS** *020 †30
POLLACK, Alan Jay. 4660 KENMORE AVE, STE 416 22304 #035-19-1996 L2000 **OPH** *020
PONQUINETTE, Julie C. 5249 DUKE ST STE 200 22304 #047-07-1963 L1969 **P OS** *020
POPP, Lorena Simona. 2863 DUKE ST 22314 #409-16-2001 L2005 **IM** *100 †20
PRATT-UBANAMA, Monique. ■ 22314 #305-01-2000 L2004 **IM** *100
PREUSS, James Wm. 4660 KENMORE AVE, STE 1018 22304 #035-20-1955 L1968 **NS** *071 †25
PRICE, Kazuko Kukita. 4701 KENMORE AVE, STE 118 SEMINARY TOWERS E 22304 #572-18-1950 L1961 **OBG PD** *071 ‡
PROCACCINO, Frank. 4660 KENMORE AVE, STE 810 22304 #010-01-1987 L1997 **GE** *020 †20
PROPHETE, Guy Emmanuel A. ■ 22304 #132-02-1976 **GPM** *020
PRUETTE, David Franklin. ■ 22302 #045-01-2005 L2005 **PD** *012
PULIZZI, John S, Jr. 3450 N BEAUREGARD ST, STE 1 22302 #041-09-1961 L1963 **GP IM** *020
QUAN, Leslie May. ■ 22305 #050-02-2005 L2005 **PD** *012
QUARLES, Pamela Anne. 5249 DUKE ST STE 200 22304 #041-01-1979 L1982 **P** *075 †75
RADICE, Alicia B. 5021 SEMINARY RD, SUIE 109 22311 #132-01-1960 L1992 **AN** *020 †05
RAHMANIAN SHAHRI, Majid. ■ 22304 #517-04-1990 L2007 **IM** *100
RAINES, Kristen Betsy. ■ 22314 #047-05-1979 L1981 **END IM** *030 †20
RAMADA, Antonio. 6000 STEVENSON AVE, STE 101 22304 #748-08-1985 L2001 **FM** *020 †18
RAMBHALA, Lalitha S. 4660 KENMORE AVE STE 902, RATIVE PRACTICE PC 22304 #495-50-1977 L1990 **OBG** *020 †30
RAO, Ramesh B S. 2001 N BEAUREGARD ST, STE 200 22311 #495-09-1991 L2003 **DR NM** *020 †80,28
RAYMAN, Russell Barry. 320 S HENRY ST 22314 #025-01-1961 L1991 **AM FM** *030 †70,18
REEVES, James D. ■ 22314 #011-03-2002 L2007 **ORS** *100
REICHNER, Cristina Aiken. ■ 22314 #010-02-1999 L1999 **PCC** *100 †20
REID, Lucienne Laraine. ■ 22311 #033-06-2002 L2005 **IM** *100
REID, Sara Y. ■ 22304 #051-07-2001 L2003 *020 †18
REINES, Eric David. 6300 STEVENSON AVE, STE D 22304 #422-01-1982 L1988 **IM ID** *020 †20
RHEE, John Wonyong. 4320 SEMINARY RD 22304 #041-02-1984 L1995 **TS** *020 †85,90
RHODES, Donald R, Jr. ■ 22304 #041-12-1995 L2004 **FM** *020 †18
RHOLL, Kenneth Scott. 2001 N BEAUREGARD ST, STE 200 22311 #026-04-1982 L1986 **VIR CD** *020 †80
RICHARDSON, Constance C. ■ 22313 #010-03-1972 L1978 **EM GS** *062
RICHARDSON, Maurice H, IV. 4320 SEMINARY RD, ALEXANDRIA HOSP 22304 #051-01-1980 L1993 **EM ADM** *020 †16
RIMINGTON, Todd Randall. ■ 22302 #016-02-2005 L2006 **ORS** *012
RIOS, Jorge C. ■ 22311 #132-01-1959 L1968 **IM CD** *030
ROBARGE, Ignace J. ■ 22314 #025-01-1949 L1962 **GP D** *071
ROBBINS, Kenneth Xenophon. 5055 SEMINARY RD 22311 #035-19-1967 L1971 **P GP** *020 †75
ROBINSON-ARRIETA, Paula. 322 GALLATIN ST NW 22305 #010-03-1977 L1979 **PD** *040 †55
RODRIGUEZ, Gloti M. 5278 DAWES AVE 22311 #737-03-1988 L1996 **PD** *020 †55
ROJAS, Guido. 5248 DAWES AVE 22311 #176-03-1975 L2003 **EM** *020
ROLAND, Jason Charles. ■ 22314 #023-01-2001 L2002 **GS** *100 †85
ROMNEY, Rebecca. 2 E GLEBE RD, COLORADO SPRINGS SENIOR ME 22305 #051-01-1981 L1984 **IM** *020 †20
RONGIONE, Anthony John. 4320 SEMINARY RD 22304 #016-01-1992 L2001 **TS** *020 †85,90
ROSE, Henry S. 2001 N BEAUREGARD ST, STE 200 22311 #024-05-1975 L2001 **DR** *020 †80
ROSE, Rosemarie D. ■ 22302 #048-12-1989 L1990 **FM** *062 †18
ROSENFELD, Stephen Philip. 4660 KENMORE AVE, STE 1200 22304 #038-41-1974 L1981 **CD** *020 †20
ROTHMAN, Barry Stephen. 4660 KENMORE AVE, PHYSICIANS FOR WOMEN 22304 #010-01-1975 L1978 **OBG** *020 †30
ROWLEY, William Robt. ■ 22314 #026-04-1970 L1971 **VS GS** *071 †85
RUBIN, Lawrence Richard. 4660 KENMORE AVE, STE 1200 22304 #051-01-1991 L2000 **CD** *020 †20
RUONA, Luanne. ■ 22302 #025-01-1967 L1972 **OS P** *020
RUSSELL, Telly Raschard. ■ 22304 #010-02-2008 *012
RYAN, Enda Kieran. 1200 N HOWARD ST, ALEXANDRIA HEALTH DEPT 22304 #539-03-1963 L1970 **PD** *020
RYAN, Richard Herrick. 4660 KENMORE AVE, STE 500 22304 #056-06-1957 L1964 **PD OS** *071 †55
SABET, Haideh Y. 5130 DUKE ST, STE 9 22304 #026-08-1999 L1999 **N** *020 †75
SAID, Shoukry Habib. 4660 KENMORE AVE STE 400 22304 #330-02-1949 L1974 **GS** *071 †85
SALCEDO, Hernando P. 1707 OSAGE ST STE 301 22302 #264-04-1961 L1970 **U** *071 †95 ‡
SALEM, Yousef Hussien. 4660 KENMORE AVE, ADULT & PEDIATRIC 22304 #035-06-1988 L1991 **U** *020 †95 ‡
SALGADO, Sonia J. 4660 KENMORE AVE, STE 1100 22304 #042-01-1985 L2000 **OBG** *020 †30
SAMPSON, Alan L. 5249 DUKE ST STE 5 22304 #028-03-1975 L1976 **D** *020
SAMUEL, Colleen Rochelle. ■ 22304 #051-04-2005 L2005 **PD** *012
SANG, Evadne. ■ 22314 #010-03-1974 L1978 **P CHP** *020
SAUNDERS, Victoria Angela. ■ 22305 #051-04-2004 L2007 **PD** *020 †55
SAYLES, David Anthony. 1707 OSAGE ST STE 404 22302 #016-43-1993 L1998 **PYG** *020 †75
SCHLEY, Emily Eleanor. ■ 22314 #051-07-2006 **IM** *012
SCHULTZ, Adrienne Joann. 1225 MARTHA CUSTIS DR, STE C1 22302 #019-02-1979 L2000 **FM** *020 †18
SCHWARTZ, David Taylor. 4320 SEMINARY RD 22304 #035-01-1963 L1971 **U** *075 †95
SCHWARTZ, Harvey Albert. 101 S WHITING ST STE 105 22304 #035-06-1967 L1974 **RHU A** *020 †03,20
SCHWARTZ, Richard Alan. 4660 KENMORE AVE STE 800 22304 #035-20-1965 L1971 **CD IM** *020 †20
SCOTT, Pierre Brutsche. 3541 W BRADDOCK RD, PIERRE B SCOTT MD LTD 22302 #051-01-1953 L1953 **OPH** *071 †35
SEBASTIAN, Melinda Maximo. 6000 STEVENSON AVE, STE 101 22304 #748-01-1982 L1992 **PD** *020 †55 ‡
SEDBERRY, Sherry V. ■ 22314 #036-01-2001 L2003 **U** *100
SEKYERE-NYANTAKYI, Paul. ■ 22304 #023-07-1997 **IM** *100
SENDI, Houchang. 5425 DUKE ST 22304 #869-04-1957 L1969 **PD** *071 †85
SETHI, Rajesh Kumar. 4600 KENMORE AVE, STE 408 22304 #495-08-1977 L1989 **N** *020 †75
SHAFFER, Warren Basil. 2867 DUKE ST, BELLE HAVEN FAMILY MED 22314 #047-07-1995 L1998 **FM** *020 †18
SHAHIDPOUR, Hossein. ■ 22304 #517-04-1998 **IM** *100
SHAHIN, Hassan M. 4141A DUKE ST 22304 #575-01-1997 L2004 **IM** *020 †20
SHAMMAS, Sameer Bahjat. 4600 KING ST 22302 #875-01-1974 L1981 **ORS TRS** *075 †40
SHEA, Sofia Marica. ■ 22302 #051-04-2007 L2007 **IM** *012
SHEELY, William Edward. ■ 22302 #041-02-1948 L1955 **R NM** *071 †80,28
SHEIKH, Salwa Shabbir. ■ 22302 #797-02-1989 L1998 **PTH** *020 †50
SHEIKHALI, Saeed A. ■ 22304 #007-02-1995 L2006 **IM** *100
SHEIKH IBRAHIM, Hanan Ibr. ■ 22304 #875-01-1991 L2002 **IMG** *020 †20
SHIH, Teh-Chang. ■ 22304 #385-02-1957 L1968 **IM IMG** *071 †20 ‡
SHOEMAKER, Richard G. ■ 22305 #264-05-1983 L1992 **IM** *020
SIEGEL, Ayn D. ■ 22302 #041-02-1984 L1986 **P GP** *020
SIEGEL, Marc Evan. 4660 KENMORE AVE, PHYSICIANS FOR WOMEN 22304 #010-02-1991 L1995 **OBG** *020 †30
SIMPSON, Joanne Kelly. 5249 DUKE ST, STE LL1 22304 #036-05-2003 L2007 **D** *020 †15
SIMS, Dodd Allison. 4660 KENMORE AVE, STE 604 22304 #016-01-1982 L1985 **IM** *020 †20
SKOLNICK, Marvin Ralph. ■ 22305 #008-01-1963 L1968 **P** *071 †75
SMITH, Thomas Larry. 5249 DUKE ST STE LL1 22304 #027-01-1968 L1995 **D** *020 †15
SPENCER, David Ashley. 4320 SEMINARY RD, 1ST FL 22304 #048-12-1984 L1988 **AN** *020 †05
SPIEGLER, Enrique. ■ 22304 #132-01-1953 **GS** *071 †85
SPURLOCK, David Jason. ■ 22304 #025-01-2006 L2007 **GS** *012
STAGE, William Syms. 424 S WASHINGTON ST 22314 #005-14-1973 L1980 **P** *020 †75
STARK, Stuart Robert. 4660 KENMORE AVE, NEUROLOGY & HEADACHE 22304 #023-01-1978 L1983 **N** *020 †75
STEINMETZ, Marie Frances. 1225 MARTHA CUSTIS DR, STE C1 22302 #041-12-1980 L1983 **FM OS** *020 †18
STERLING, Keith Michael. 2001 N BEAUREGARD ST, STE 200 22311 #035-09-1989 L1995 **R CD** *020 †80
STEWART, Rhonda Renee. 5055 SEMINARY RD, STE 104 22311 #041-14-1984 L1990 **DR** *030 †80
STIER, Fred Manifold. 1707 OSAGE ST STE 301 22302 #010-02-1969 L1977 **U** *020 †95
STOLL, Kantha R K. 5249 DUKE ST STE 100 22304 #010-01-1992 L1998 **IM** *020 †20
STONE, Laura R. 205 S WHITING ST, STE 303 22304 #035-45-1986 L1993 **GYN** *020 †30
STORER, Dean James. 1707 OSAGE ST STE 404 22302 #038-41-1983 L1990 **PYG** *020 †75
STRUDWICK, William J. 4320 SEMINARY RD, ALEXANDRIA HOSPITAL 22304 #010-03-1988 L1995 **EM** *020 †16
SULLIVAN, Brendan Lee. 4660 KENMORE AVE STE 500 22304 #051-04-1997 L2000 **PD** *020 †55
SUVARI, Ando Ivar. 3520 DUKE ST, STE 310 22304 #407-16-1951 L1954 **P** *020
SWEZEY, Maureen Joan. ■ 22314 #023-12-1995 L1997 **OBG** *020 †30
SWITKES, Ross Spencer. 4320 SEMINARY RD, INOVA ALEXANDRIA HOSPITAL 22304 #035-09-1993 L2000 **EM** *020 †16

■ = Address Information Privacy Protected

SWITZER, Robert E. ■ 22313 #017-20-1942 L1986 **CHP** *072 †75
SYED, Amjad Ali. ■ 22311 #704-16-1983 *100
SYME, Robert Haldane. 4320 SEMINARY RD 22304 #010-01-1947 L1953 **GYN** *071 †30
TALIB, Sawsan Attia El S. 5791 WINSTON CT STE 160 22311 #915-02-1976 L1986 **PD** *020 †55
TARANTINO, David Arthur. ■ 22314 #010-02-1992 L1993 **FM** *020 †18
TAWIL, George Wadie. 4660 KENMORE AVE, ADULT & PEDIATRIC 22304 #605-01-1973 L1981 **U GS** *020 †95 ‡
TEAME, Akeza Wasse. ■ 22304 #019-02-2001 L2004 **ID** *100 †20
TEKLEBERHAN, Zewditu. 4320 SEMINARY RD 22304 #366-02-1988 L2000 **IM** *020 †20
TEKLEMARIAM, Elias Alemu. ■ 22314 #366-01-1994 *100
TEMME, Joel Mc Govern. 4660 KENMORE AVE, STE 604A 22304 #051-01-1978 L1985 **IM** *020 †20
TEREK, Megan Elizabeth. ■ 22311 #038-44-2007 L2007 **IM** *012
THIEL, Melissa Joy. 205 S WHITING ST, STE 203 22304 #035-20-1979 L1988 **GYN** *020 †30
THOMAS, Shontell Nakisha. 1200 N QUAKER LN, EPISCOPAL HIGH SCHOOL 22302 #036-01-2007 *012
THOMPSON, Daniel Edward. 2805 DUKE ST 22314 #027-01-2000 L2000 **ORS** *020
TIU, Roshiel Doble. ■ 22314 #422-01-2002 L2006 **OBG** *020
TJENALOOI, Angelique C. ■ 22311 #010-02-2005 L2005 **IM** *012
TOKARZ, John Patrick. 1707 OSAGE ST STE 203 22302 #047-06-1974 L1979 **FM** *020 †18
TOM, Jaimie Shannen. 4320 SEMINARY RD, C/O EMERGENCY DEPT. 22304 #014-01-1998 L2005 **EM** *020 †16
TOMLINSON, H Evangeline. 4921 SEMINARY RD STE 107, TOWERS-ASHLAWN BLDG 22311 #038-40-1971 L1976 **OBG EM** *020
TRAN, Cuong Trong. 312 S WASHINGTON ST, STE 3B 22314 #396-06-1965 L1973 **RO R** *020 †80
TRENT, Peter S. 417 N WASHINGTON ST 22314 #035-48-1982 L1994 **ORS** *020 †40
TRIMBER, Connell James. 3223 DUKE ST, STE G 22314 #041-02-1960 L1968 **OPH** *020 †35
TRIVEDI, Mehul Kirit. 5249 DUKE ST 22304 #016-42-2002 L2005 **IM** *020 †20
TROJANOWSKI, Martin Andre. ■ 22314 #045-01-2006 L2006 **IM** *012
TRUONG, Huy Tin. 1200 N HOWARD ST, DEPT OF HEALTH 22304 #941-01-1969 L1988 **IM GP** *020
TUAZON, Oscar C. 4320 SEMINARY RD 22304 #748-07-1955 L1968 **GS** *020
UENO, Winston Mizuo. 4660 KENMORE AVE, STE 1018 22304 #030-06-1966 L1972 **ON HEM** *020 †20
UPTON, David Leslie. ■ 22314 #008-01-1969 L1974 **P PMM** *071 ‡
VAN, Truong Son. 312 S WASHINGTON ST, STE 2D 22314 #941-01-1970 L1979 **EM IM** *020 †20
VAN BREDA, Arina. 2001 N BEAUREGARD ST, STE 200 22311 #024-05-1976 L1983 **DR CD** *020 †80
VAN DOREN, Isabel B. ■ 22313 #038-06-1961 L1961 **PD** *074
VAN HOEF, Marlies E. ■ 22304 #660-04-1983 **ON** *020
VARELA, A G. ■ 22302 #847-11-1992 L1995 **FM** *020
VELENA, Samson Salazar. 5249 DUKE ST STE 301 22304 #748-01-1961 L1987 **OM FM** *020 †18
VERA, Luis F. 4320 SEMINARY RD DEPT PD 22304 #231-01-1967 L1977 **PD** *020
VERDIN, Peter Jos, Jr. 2805 DUKE ST, ALEXANDRIA ORTHOPAEDIC ASS 22314 #023-01-1981 L1988 **ORS** *020 †40
WADE, Larren. 5194 DAWES AVE 22311 #011-02-1992 L1996 **IM** *020 †20
WALKER, Sheneika Marie. ■ 22304 #036-01-2004 L2004 **OBG** *012
WALTER, Allison Joanne. ■ 22314 #021-06-2008 L2012
WALTERS, Colin Stpatrick. 4320 SEMINARY RD, SUNLIFE OB/GYN-ALEXANDRIA 22304 #010-03-1994 L1998 **OBG** *020 †30
WANG, Richard. 101 S WHITING ST, STE 106 22304 #041-01-2001 L2007 **OMF** *020
WARE, Bradley Richard. 5249 DUKE ST STE 100 22304 #038-41-1977 L1994 **FM** *020 †18
WELCH, James Nicholas. ■ 22311 #010-02-2005 L2005 **FM** *020
WELMAN, Martha. 3804 EXECUTIVE AVE, ADT D-1 22305 #005-02-1987 L1991 **PD** *020 †55
WERNICK, Meredith Hope. ■ 22304 #010-02-2007 L2007 **IM** *012
WERTHEIM, Raymond B. 220 S WASHINGTON ST 22314 #041-13-1969 L1981 **P CHP** *020 †55,75
WHITTAKER, Scott Lincoln. 4660 KENMORE AVE STE 1210 22304 #041-13-1998 L2001 **IM** *020 †20
WIEDERHORN, A Roger. 1707 OSAGE ST STE 301, FAIRLINGTON PROF BLDG 22302 #035-01-1969 L1971 **U** *071 †95 ‡
WIENER, Michael Allen. ■ 22311 #041-09-1969 L1994 **P OS** *020 †75
WIGTON, Roger Bruce. 5216 DAWES AVE 22311 #038-41-1973 L1978 **PUD CCM** *020 †20
WILLIAMS, Patricia Day. ■ 22301 #041-02-1978 L1991 **DR FM** *062 †18
WILLS, Walter Neil. 1101 KING ST, STE 100 22314 #051-01-1994 L2000 **OPH** *020 †35
WILSON, Charles Clinton. 2001 MILL RD 22314 #010-03-1971 L1998 **AN** *020 ‡
WITHERS, Benjamin Guy. 909 N WASHINGTON ST, ARMED FORCES BENEFIT ASSN 22314 #023-12-1985 L1995 **GPM OM** *020 †70
WOLDEABEZGI, Ashebir. 6300 STEVENSON AVE, STE D 22304 #366-01-1990 L2006 **ID IM** *020 †20
WOLDEHER, Getachew Y. 4200 KING ST 22302 #366-01-1991 L2002 **MPD** *020 †20
WOLVERTON, Robert Keith. 3701 W BRADDOCK RD 22302 #028-02-1986 L1991 **AMI IM** *020 †20
WONG, Jeffrey Edward. 1707 OSAGE ST STE 301 22302 #035-09-1994 L2001 **U** *020 †95
WOODWARD, Kelly H. 1200 N HOWARD ST, CASEY HEALTH CENTER 22304 #018-75-1984, ▲ L2007 **GPM FM** *030 †70,18
WU, Wayne Chihwei. 4660 KENMORE AVE, STE 1210 22304 #012-01-1995 L2002 **IM** *020 †20
WYATT, Renee Denise. ■ 22304 #051-04-1998 L1999 **DR FM** *100
WYNNE, Sarah Margaret. ■ 22314 #010-02-1998 L1998 **ID** *020 †20
YAN, Weijia Xia. 4320 SEMINARY RD, INOVA ALEXANDRIA HOSPITAL/ 22304 #243-16-1984 L2001 **AN** *020 †05
YBARRA, Michael Anthony. ■ 22311 #010-02-2008 *012
YOHANNES, Gerbremedhin. 4320 SEMINARY RD, INOVA ALEXANDRIA HOSPITAL 22304 #366-01-1987 L1999 **IM** *020 †20
YOU, Young Joon. 2805 DUKE ST, ALEXANDRIA ORTHOPEDIC ASSO 22314 #583-02-1974 L1982 **ORS** *020 †40
YOUNG, Charles Chen-Siung. 5055 SEMINARY RD STE 109 22311 #244-02-1975 L1988 **PM** *020 †60
YOUNOSSI, Gulam Mustafa. 5212 DAWES AVE, PEDIATRICS INTERNATIONALE 22311 #409-25-1984 L1996 **PD OS** *020 †55
YOUSSEF, Lelia Mikhail. 3450 N BEAUREGARD ST STE 1 22302 #915-02-1986 L2001 **IM** *020 †20
YUHANIAK, Pamela A. 1200 N HOWARD ST, CASEY HEALTH CENTER 22304 #231-04-1984 L1991 **IM** *020 †20

ZEAVIN, Bernard H. 5055 SEMINARY RD, THE EYE CENTER 22311 #062-01-1950 L1957 **OPH** *071 †35
ZEDD, Arnold Jay. ■ 22314 #051-01-1973 L1976 **PD** *050
ZINCKE, Valeria H. 4480 KING ST, DEPARTMENT OF HEALTH 22302 #231-01-1969 L1983 **PD PEM** *020 †55
ZIRAK, Kaiser Simab. ■ 22304 #704-21-1996 *100
ZUBAIR, Muhammad. ■ 22304 #704-01-1974 L1979 **GS PTH** *075
ZUROWSKI, Robert David. 4320 SEMINARY RD, 1ST FL 22304 #051-07-1985 L1987 **AN CCM** *020 †05

ALEXANDRIA – FAIRFAX

ABDUL-AL, Hala Mahmoud. ■ 22309 #915-04-1986 **PTH** *012
ABIDIN, Michael Robt. 6355 WALKER LN STE 308 22310 #051-01-1988 L1996 **OTO HNS** *020 †45
ADAWI, Adnan S. 8101 HINSON FARM RD 22306 #550-02-1988 L1999 **PUD CCM** *020 †20
AGGARWAL, Sanjeev. ■ 22310 #495-45-1985 *020
AHDOOT, Habibollah. 2616 SHERWOOD HALL LN, STE 208 22306 #517-01-1964 L1972 **OBG** *020 †30
AHDOOT, Kenneth Michael. 2616 SHERWOOD HALL LN, STE 208 22306 #010-02-1999 L2003 **OBG** *020 †30
AHDOOT, Samantha Weslee. 6355 WALKER LN 22310 #010-02-1999 L2003 **PD** *020 †55
AHMED, Mahmoud. ■ 22312 #915-03-1980 **IM** *020 †20
ALCASABAS, Nilda Zorrilla. ■ 22309 #748-01-1962 L1994 **CHP PD** *020 †75
ALEXANDERWICZ, Melvin J. 7910 ANDRUS RD, STE 16 22306 #033-05-1961 L1967 **P OS** *020 †75
ALMEIDA, Sandra Ann. ■ 22315 #032-01-1984 L1988 **GPM GP** *050 †70
ALPERSTEIN, Joel Barry. 22303 #023-01-1967 L1972 **U OS** *072 †95
AMINI, Lina. ■ 22312 #051-04-2003 L2008 **OPH** *100
AMZUTA, Ioana Gabriela. ■ 22312 #781-01-1997 L2007 **PCC** *020 †20
ANDERSON, Robert Kay. ■ 22315 #047-07-1959 L1959 **P** *020
ANDERSON, Walter E. 2501 PARKERS LN 22306 #016-06-1949 L1965 **FOP PCP** *071
APPIAH, Yvette Efua. 6355 WALKER LN STE 311 22310 #016-02-1997 L2001 **D** *020 †15
ARAYA, Aster. 6078 FRANCONIA RD STE B, MEDICAL CENTERS 22310 #366-03-1992 L2000 **PD** *020 †55
ARDESHIRPOUR, Zardoshte M. ■ 22310 #517-05-1963 **PD** *100
ARNOLD, Jacqueline. 1451 BELLE HAVEN RD, KIDZ DOCS 22307 #010-01-1987 L1990 **PD** *020 †55
ATALLA, Mohamed Awny. ■ 22315 #915-04-1999 L2003 **GS U** *100
ATHANASIADOU, Panayiota A. ■ 22309 #418-02-1949 L1956 **PTH** *071 †50
ATIQUE, Muhammad. ■ 22312 #704-08-1997 **P** *012
AXELROD, David Zuckerman. 6355 WALKER LN, STE 408 22310 #561-01-1968 L1976 **OBG** *071 †30
AYELE, Petros Assefa. 85 S BRAGG ST, STE 100 22312 #366-02-1991 L2007 **IM** *020
BACKUS, Sikira Chantal. ■ 22312 #033-06-2006 L2006 **PD** *012
BAEZ-PAGE, Socorrito. ■ 22312 #016-43-1980 L1984 **FM** *074
BAJWA, Manjit Rajinder. 6391 LITTLE RIVER TPKE 22312 #495-29-1964 L1973 **PMM GPM** *074 †05
BALCHA, Messay. 8350 RICHMOND HWY, STE 301 22309 #473-03-1992 L1999 **IM** *020 †20
BALLO, Joseph Michael. ■ 22307 #041-06-1977 L1979 **PTH CLP** *020 †50
BANKS, Taylor Allen. ■ 22306 #051-01-2007 *012
BARRETT, Matthew Owen. ■ 22306 #047-06-2002 L2007 **ORS** *020
BASANTI, Nabil Karam. ■ 22312 #848-01-1978 *030
BENDECK, Denise. 2616 SHERWOOD HALL LN, STE 208 22306 #010-02-1995 L1997 **OBG** *020 †30
BESCH, George Andrew. 6355 WALKER LN, STE 406 22310 #010-01-1975 L1978 **CD IM** *020 †20
BIENERT, Susan Elisabeth. 6160 FULLER CT, FRANCONIA FAMILY MEDICINE 22310 #051-01-1995 L1995 **FM** *020 †18
BINZEL, Philip E, Jr. ■ 22310 #028-34-1953 L1953 **GP** *071
BIRCHANSKY, Christine Ann. 8850 RICHMOND HWY STE 202, MT VERNON MENTAL HLTH CTR 22309 #011-02-1986 L1995 **P** *020 †75
BISSELL, Marion C. 6355 WALKER LN, STE 408 22310 #035-09-1984 L1988 **OBG** *020 †30
BOAKYE, Edward. 1451 BELLE HAVEN RD, STE 420 22307 #412-01-1977 L1998 **IM** *020 †20
BOLAD, Aladdin Abbas. 2616 SHERWOOD HALL LN, STE 303 22306 #848-01-1985 L1995 **IM** *020 †20
BONDAREFF, Erwin Allen. 6355 WALKER LN, STE 401 22310 #010-01-1959 L1963 **PD A** *020 †55
BORNEMANN, Paul H. ■ 22306 #033-06-2006 L2008 **FPP** *012
BOUCHER, Henry Robert. 2501 PARKERS LN, STE 200 22306 #024-16-1996 L2001 **ORS** *020 †40
BOULWARE, Wendell C. 5855 GOVERNORS HILL DR, DEPARTMENT OF ANESTHESIOLO 22310 #010-03-1990 L2004 **AN** *020 †05
BRACEY, Victor Alfred. 2616 SHERWOOD HALL LN, SHERWOOD HALL IMAGING CENT 22306 #036-07-1990 L1996 **DR** *020 †80
BRAUN, Christina Isabel. 8101 HINSON FARM RD 22306 #051-01-1985 L1990 **OPH** *020 †35
BREGMAN, Robert L. 5901 MOUNT EAGLE DR # 1018 22303 #010-02-1950 L1955 **PD** *020 †55
BRIDEAU, Donald J, Jr. 6355 WALKER LN STE 310 22310 #010-01-1984 L1991 **FM** *020 †18
BRIDGES, Vestinia. 6355 WALKER LN, GREATER METROPOLITIAN 22310 #010-03-1991 L2002 **ORS** *020 †40
BROOME, Catherine Meyers. 8I01 HINSON FARM RD, SUTIE 211 22306 #021-06-1985 L1993 **ON HO** *020 †20
BROWN, Deborah S. 2501 PARKERS LN, MOUNT VERNON HOSPITAL 22306 #048-02-1977 L1993 **AN** *020 †05
BRUNO, John A, Jr. 5845 RICHMOND HWY, STE 400 22303 #035-08-1966 L1976 **ORS** *020 †40
BRUTSCHE, Robert Legate. ■ 22308 #048-12-1947 L1947 **GE PHP** *071 †20
BYRNE, John Philip. 6355 WALKER LN, GREATER METROPOLITIAN 22310 #010-02-1987 L1990 **ORS** *020 †40
CABAHUG-HEYRANA, Josefina. 7906 ANDRUS RD, STE 8 22306 #748-11-1981 L1994 **FM** *020 †18
CALEJESAN, Amelita Anne. ■ 22303 #041-12-2005 L2007 **FP** *012
CARLINI, Dennis Angelo. 6355 WALKER LN, GREATER METROPOLITIAN 22310 #010-02-1973 L1979 **ORS** *020 †40
CARROLL, Frank A, Jr. ■ 22307 #041-02-1951 L1952 **FM** *072

CARTER, Valarie Lorraine. 1612 COURTLAND RD 22306 #035-19-1985 L1990 **OBG** *020 †30

CARTER-STINSON, Stephanie. 8109 HINSON FARM RD, STE 504 22306 #007-02-1991 L1998 **IM** *020 †20

CARTY, Brian Clifford. 3111 TELEGRAPH CORNER LN, STE 100 22310 #036-05-1990 L1993 **FM** *020 †18

CARUSO, Janis Michele. 8109 TIS WELL DR, STE 511 22306 #047-06-1996 L2003 **FM OBG** *020 †18 ‡

CASTLE, Jason Allan. 2501 PARKERS LN, STE 200 22306 #012-05-1999 L2006 **ORS** *020

CATILO, Maria Cecilia C.. ■ 22312 #035-46-2007 **IM** *012

CAVENDER, William Francis. ■ 22306 #016-11-1959 L1968 **P** *071 †75

CAVROS, Evie Kalli. 7015C MANCHESTER BLVD, THE PEDIATRIC GROUP 22310 #051-07-1991 L1994 **PD** *020 †55

CAVROS, George Nick. ■ 22310 #051-01-1956 L1956 **FM** *020

CAZENAVE, Lorraine A. ■ 22305 #035-08-1981 L1991 **PHO** *020

CHADIVE, Vasanthi. 6078 FRANCONIA RD, SUITES A&B 22310 #496-24-1994 L2000 **PD** *020

CHANDRA, Himani. ■ 22308 #010-02-2002 L2002 **END** *012 †20

CHAO, Yu-Hua. ■ 22307 #242-47-1949 L1960 **IM** *012 †18

CHAPMAN, A Bradley. 2059 HUNTINGTON AVE # 108 22303 #005-11-1966 L1971 **CHP P** *020 †75

CHARALAMBOPOULOS, John. ■ 22303 #041-02-2006 L2006 **IM** *020

CHARY, Bejjenki Srinivasa. 2616 SHERWOOD HALL LN, STE 303 22306 #495-73-1984 L2002 **IM** *020 †20

CHAUDRI, Faisal Asif. 8350 RICHMOND HWY, STE 301 22309 #422-01-1997 L2003 **IM** *020 †20

CHEUNG, K F Danielle. ■ 22312 #396-04-1971 L1986 **GP R** *020

CHOI, David Kwan. 6641 WAKEFIELD DR STE 108 22307 #583-06-1961 L1973 **IM** *020

CHOWLA, Arun. 7598 TELEGRAPH RD 22315 #495-45-1988 L1997 **GS VS** *020 †85

CHUNG, Vickie Kyuran. 22315 #550-02-2002 L2007 **IM** *100 †20

CHUPKOVICH, Victor Stoian. ■ 22307 #957-01-1956 L1960 **IM CD** *071

CLARK, Laurence Jordan. 8101 HINSON FARM RD, STE 119 22306 #010-02-1977 L1979 **IM** *020 †20

CLEARY, Thomas F. ■ 22309 #010-02-1953 L1976 **FM** *071 †18

COLE, Jasmin Kilayko. ■ 22315 #016-06-1996 L2008 **FM** *020 †18

COOPER, Albert Francis. ■ 22309 #041-09-1944 L1958 **GS** *072 †85

COX, Kenneth Lee. ■ 22310 #040-02-1984 L1988 *020 †70

CRIARES, George J. 6607 NETTIES LN, UNIT 1611 22315 #035-09-1952 L1999 **GS** *020 †85

CUIPER, Leslie L. 8101 HINSON FARM RD, STE 306 22306 #025-07-1989 L2003 **PCC** *020 †20

DAING, Renato. 2501 PARKERS LN 22306 #748-08-1986 L1998 **PD** *020

DANIEL, Emmeth Arturo. ■ 22309 #035-06-1975 L1978 **EM IM** *020 †20,16

DAVALOS, Hugo A. 2616 SHERWOOD HALL LN 22306 #726-01-1966 L1975 **ORS PTH** *020 †40

DAVIS-SPAULDING, Tanya R. 7910 ANDRUS RD, STE 6 22306 #010-03-1992 L1998 **GE IM** *020 †20

DEE, James Francis. 7910 ANDRUS RD STE 16 22306 #649-33-1983 L1984 **P OS** *020 †75

DEEGAN, William Francis. 6355 WALKER LN STE 502 22310 #024-07-1988 L1995 **OPH OS** *020 †35

DESIMONE, James Mario. 7015E MANCHESTER BLVD 22310 #051-04-1987 L1990 **IM** *020 †20

DESMAN, Eric. 6355 WALKER LN, STE 510 22310 #041-02-1990 L1997 **PS** *020 †65

DHARIA, Subarna B. 6303 LITTLE RIVER TPKE, STE 300 22312 #035-03-2001 L2005 **PD** *020 †55

DI LALLO, Chester Anthony. 6355 WALKER LN, GREATER METROPOLITIAN 22310 #035-03-1962 L1970 **ORS** *020 †40

DOMSON, Joanne M Froio. 7906 ANDRUS RD, STE 7 22306 #041-07-1969 L1983 **AI PD** *020 †55,03

DOMSON, Kelly Keffler. 2501 PARKERS LN 22306 #051-04-1993 L1994 **PTH** *020 †50

DOUTHARD, Regine A. ■ 22315 #397-01-1985 **GPM** *100

DRISCOLL, Sean Michael. ■ 22306 #023-12-2008 *012

DURSO, Anthony Michael. ■ 22307 #035-19-2000 L2002 **DR** *020 †80

DURSO, Nancy M. 6355 WALKER LN, STE 500 22310 #051-01-1983 L1990 **REN OBG** *020 †30

EDER, Myriam Elizabeth U. 2616 SHERWOOD HALL LN #203 22306 #715-01-1977 L1983 **GE IM** *020 †20

EGLOFF, Brian Patrick. ■ 22315 #023-12-2006 L2006 **FP** *012

EISEN, Veronica Rebecca. ■ 22306 #035-15-2004 L2004 **RO** *012

ELAM, William N, Jr. ■ 22307 #028-02-1953 L1955 **AM FM** *020 †18

EL KASHEF, Ahmed M. 8119 HOLLAND RD, HEALTH, LTH CTR. 22306 #915-02-1977 L1990 **P** *050 †75

EMBREY, Everett Clayton. 2501 PARKERS LN, EMERGENCY DEPT 22306 #030-06-1993 L1996 **EM** *020 †16

ENGH, Charles Anderson. 2501 PARKERS LN, STE 200 22306 #051-01-1963 L1963 **OAR ORS** *020 †40

ENGH, Chas Anderson, Jr. 2501 PARKERS LN, STE 200 22306 #051-01-1985 L1987 **ORS** *020 †40

ENGH, Gerard Anderson. 2501 PARKERS LN, STE 200 22306 #051-01-1966 L1966 **ORS** *020 †40

FAGHFOORY, Amir Pooyan. ■ 22310 #010-01-2008 *012

FENWICK, James Adam. 2501 PARKERS LN, STE 200 22306 #041-12-1997 L2007 **ORS** *020 †40

FERGUSON, Katrina Nicole. ■ 22306 #023-12-2006 L2007 **FP** *012

FERNANDEZ, Fausto Danl. 6020 RICHMOND HWY, STE 100 22303 #847-02-1981 L1986 **GP** *020

FERRER, Gustavo. ■ 22310 #275-02-1994 L2006 **PCC** *012

FIELD, Laraine Terry. 6412 BEULAH ST, STE 100 22310 #035-46-1984 L1989 **IM CD** *020 †20

FIELDS, Eve S. 8119 HOLLAND RD 22306 #023-01-2002 L2007 **P** *020 †75

FISHMAN, Simon. 6355 WALKER LN STE 313, INTEGRATED NEUROLOGY SVCS 22310 #041-02-1995 L2000 **N CN** *020 †75

FOREMAN, Deidra Sheno. ■ 22312 #010-03-2006 L2006 **OBG** *012

FORSTER, David John. 6355 WALKER LN, STE 405 22310 #035-06-1985 L1991 **OPH** *020 †35

FRANCIS, Cleveland, Jr. 6355 WALKER LN, STE 406 22310 #051-04-1973 L1978 **CD IM** *050 †20

FRANCIS, Yvette F. ■ 22303 #008-01-1950 L1953 **IM HEM** *020 †55

FRANKEL, Faith Grietzer. 6303 LITTLE RIVER TPKE, STE 300 22312 #035-06-1991 L1994 **PD** *020 †55

FUENTES, Ana Sophia. ■ 22315 #016-06-2004 L2007 **EM** *020

FUNK, Martin Albert. ■ 22309 #016-43-1956 L1958 **P** *071 ‡

GALLIVAN, Monica V E. 2501 PARKERS LN, MOUNT VERNON HOSPITAL 22306 #539-04-1971 L1988 **PTH BBK** *020 †50

GARBER, Vera. 3111 TELEGRAPH CORNER LN, STE 100 22310 #051-04-1979 L1980 **FM** *020 †18

GARG, Shaila. ■ 22315 #495-29-1990 L2002 **CD** *012 †20

GASPAR, Jonathan Patrick. ■ 22309 #051-04-2007 **IM** *012

GASPAR, Patrick Sunderraj. 2501 PARKERS LN, MOUNT VERNON HOSPITAL 22306 #495-52-1977 L1981 **AN** *020 †05

GEHRING, David Wm. 8109 HINSON FARM RD # 504 22306 #654-01-1982 L1986 **IM** *020 †20

GELTNER, Jane W. 2501 PARKERS LN 22306 #035-08-1968 L1976 **PTH PD** *062 †55,50

GHAEMI, Kamal. PO BOX 11137 22312 #517-01-1955 L1972 **N GP** *074

GHANEI, Arman. 7598 TELEGRAPH RD 22315 #409-25-1987 L1993 **IM** *012 †20

GIANCHANDANI, Deepa P. ■ 22315 #495-47-1967 L1988 **R OS** *020 ‡

GIBBONS, Rebecca Leigh. ■ 22308 #051-04-2008 *012

GIBSON, Robert J. 8101 HINSON FARM RD 22306 #035-06-1969 L1979 **FM** *020

GILES, Columbus J, Jr. 7906 ANDRUS RD, STE 8 22306 #045-01-1985 L1993 **FM** *020 †18

GILL, George M. ■ 22303 #041-01-1958 L1959 **ON PHO** *071 †55

GILLIGAN, John H, Jr. ■ 22310 #010-02-1962 L1965 **OPH** *020 †35

GIORLANDO, Stephanie A. 2501 PARKERS LN, DEPT OF PM AND R 22306 #035-75-1983, ▲ L1987 **PM** *020 †60

GISOLFI, Roger Vincent. 2501 PARKERS LN, MT VERNON REHAB MED ASSOC 22306 #010-02-1966 L1971 **PM SCI** *020 †60

GLIDDEN, David Jonathan. ■ 22315 #035-45-2003 L2003 **PTH** *020 †50

GODFREY, Elissa May. 8119 HOLLAND RD, MT VERNON CTR 22306 #030-06-1979 L1990 **CHP P** *020 †75

GORDON, Ian David. 8109 HINSON FARM RD, STE 501 22306 #067-01-1975 L1989 **ORS** *020 †40

GRAMLICH, Martha Jane P. ■ 22309 #024-05-1973 L1979 **EM IM** *020 †20,16

GRANGER, Martha Sumners. ■ 22306 #010-01-1967 L1971 **PYA P** *020

GRANT, Aaron Daniel. ■ 22303 #010-02-2007 *012

GRAYNOVSKY, Margaret. 2501 PARKERS LN, PM&R DEPT 22306 #913-69-1983 L2000 **PM SCI** *020 †60

GREEN, Robert W. ■ 22309 #041-12-1950 L1984 **IM GE** *071 †20

GREY, Samantha Joy. 7015C MANCHESTER BLVD 22310 #011-02-2004 L2007 **PD** *020 †55

GRIFFITH, Gillian. ■ 22306 #566-01-1996 L2002 **RNR** *020 †80

GRIGORYEVA, Anna. ■ 22303 #028-34-2002 L2007 **OTO** *020

HABIB, Tahira. 6355 WALKER LN, STE 411 22310 #704-02-1967 L1985 **END** *050 †20

HAGER, Ewald Joseph. 2501 PARKERS LN 22306 #154-07-1959 L1980 **OTO** *071 †45

HAGHIGHI, Parham. 6355 WALKER LN STE 30, ADVANCED PULMONARY- CRITIC 22310 #517-01-1996 L2003 **IM** *012 †20

HAMMAD, Walid Mohamed Faw. 5980 RICHMOND HWY, APT 1-207 22303 #915-03-1999 *100

HARK, William Henry. ■ 22309 #051-04-1957 L1960 **AM** *071 †70

HATALA, John Vincent. ■ 22315 #748-10-1979 L1981 **IM** *020 †70

HEID, Laura Klann. 2616 SHERWOOD HALL LN, STE 407 22306 #023-12-1984 L1996 **OBG** *020 †30

HENRY, Rosemarie Walden. ■ 22310 #041-13-1976 L1977 **PD** *020 †55

HERRERA, Alberto Antonio. 8109 HINSON FARM RD, STE 504 22306 #308-02-1986 L1989 **IM** *020 †20

HICKS, Leah. ■ 22309 #025-01-1996 **GS** *100

HILL, Mary H. 2616 SHERWOOD HALL LN, STE 105 22306 #051-04-1989 L2001 **GS** *020 †85

HIMMELSTEIN, Lisa Ruth. ■ 22308 #008-02-1983 L1988 **OBG** *020 †30

HOPPER, Michael James. 6355 WALKER LN, STE 401 22310 #010-02-1997 L2001 **PD** *020 †55

HOU, Damon. 6355 WALKER LN STE 508 22310 #003-01-1995 L1995 **OBG** *020 †30

HUNG, Lien Ai. ■ 22310 #308-07-1983 **P** *020

HUNT, Christopher Wade. 6355 WALKER LN, STE 303 22310 #036-01-1991 L1994 **IM** *020 †20

INGA, Victor Miguel. ■ 22303 #737-01-1980 *071

IRWIN, Matthew. ■ 22308 #010-01-2001 L2003 **FM** *020 †18

ISIDRO, Rose Marie. 8119 HOLLAND RD, HLTH LTH CTR 22306 #748-01-1964 L1973 **P** *020

IWANSKI, Jesse Paul. 2501 PARKERS LN, EMERGENCY DEPARTMENT 22306 #010-01-2003 L2006 **EM** *100 †16

JACHOWSKI, Maile Jean A. ■ 22306 #005-11-1987 L2004 **PD** *020 †55

JACOBS, Edmund Perry. 6917 VICTORIA DR 22310 #016-02-1956 L1973 **GPM AM** *071 †70

JAICKS, Christina F. ■ 22307 #035-09-1968 L1971 **EM AN** *020

JANDER, Ryan Michael. 6355 WALKER LN, GREATER METROPOLITAN 22310 #033-05-2000 L2006 **ORS** *100

JOHNSON, Don Robt. ■ 22307 #010-01-1959 L1966 **OPH** *071 †35

JOHNSON, Karen Evalyn. 6355 WALKER LN, STE 300 22310 #051-01-1992 L1993 **PCC** *020 †20

JOHNSON, Michael Ramont. ■ 22312 #024-01-1981 L1982 **OPH** *075

JONAS, Wayne Boice. 6009 BEECH TREE DR, 6009 BEECH TREE DR 22310 #036-05-1981 L1985 **FM** *020 †18

JORDAN, David Lee. 6355 WALKER LN STE 200, INOVA SURGERY CTR 22310 #055-01-1979 L1983 **AN** *020 †05

JOSE, Nora D. 2616 SHERWOOD HALL LN, SHERWOOD HALL MED CTR 22306 #748-10-1963 L1972 **PD** *020 †55

KABIRI, Hamed. ■ 22303 #517-01-2000 L2005 **EM** *012

KADLEC, Robert Peter. ■ 22306 #023-12-1983 L1988 **PHP AM** *030 †70

KAFKA, Richard Michael. ■ 22310 #021-05-1946 L1951 **R** *071 †80

KAMRAN, Ali. 6355 WALKER LN STE 300 22310 #704-16-1990 L1998 **NEP** *020

KAPLAN, Geoffrey Robt. 6355 WALKER LN, STE 502 22310 #012-05-1980 L1996 **OPH** *020 †20

KARIA, Kunal. ■ 22312 #051-04-2008 *012

KASS, Erik Serge. 6355 WALKER LN, STE 411 22310 #010-01-1991 L2003 **OTO** *020 †45

KATIRA, Reshma C. 6355 WALKER LN, STE 502 22310 #035-06-2000 L2004 **OPH** *020 †35

KEANEY, Terrence Colin. ■ 22308 #051-01-2008 *012

KENNEDY, Carol Elizabeth. ■ 22309 #010-02-1970 L1971 **IM** *071 †55

KERNAN GRUNZKE, Anne B. 6355 WALKER LN, STE 401 22310 #005-06-1996 L2005 **PD** *020 †55

KHARBANDA, Nirmala. 6090 FRANCONIA RD STE A 22310 #495-30-1968 L1982 **PD** *020 †55

KHMURETS, Miraslava Edmun. ■ 22315 #913-32-1986 **P** *012

KHOURI, Samir A. 2501 PARKERS LN 22306 #875-01-1991 L2000 **PCC IM** *020 †20

KHUBCHANDANI, Indra M. ■ 22310 #495-22-1962 **P** *075

KIM, Sea Hun. 2501 PARKERS LN 22306 #041-13-1993 L2001 **PM** *020 †60

KITTREDGE, Ben W, IV. 6355 WALKER LN, STE 202 22310 #051-01-1990 L1997 **ORS OSM** *020 †40

KLIMOWICZ, Maryida. 2501 PARKERS LN, INOVA MOUNT VERNON HOSPITA 22306 #041-02-1984 L1990 **IM EM** *020 †20

KLOUSIA, John Walter. 2616 SHERWOOD HALL LN, ADULT & PEDIATRIC 22306 #051-01-1971 L1974 **U** *020 †95 ‡

KNIGHT, Jaime Lauren. 4427 ROUNDHILL RD 22310 #051-04-2008 *012

KULKARNI, Nikhil Vijay. 2501 PARKERS LN, MOUNT VERNON HOSPITAL 22306 #010-01-2001 L2004 **AN** *020

KUSIC, Michael Brian. 6355 WALKER LN STE 508, NORTHERN VA GYNECOLOGISTS 22310 #041-12-1998 L2002 **OBG** *020 †30

LANDO, Howard Milton. 8101 HINSON FARM RD, STE 219 22306 #051-04-1975 L1979 **END DIA** *020 †20

LARKIN, Sylvia Amanda. 1451 BELLE HAVEN RD, KIDZ DOCS 22307 #010-01-1985 L1987 **PD** *020 †55

LAUTENSCHLAGER, Karl Alan. ■ 22315 #023-12-2007 *012

LEE, Bothwell Graves. 8101 HINSON FARM RD, STE 112 22306 #012-01-1978 L1999 **NS** *020 †25

LEE, James Jay. 6355 WALKER LN STE 308, METROPOLITAN ENT 22310 #035-46-2000 L2005 **OTO** *020 †45

LEE, Jong Kook. 4605 PINECREST OFFC PRK DR, # A 22312 #583-02-1958 L1981 **FM EM** *072 †18

LEE, Thomas Dae. 6355 WALKER LN, STE 411 22310 #011-02-1998 L2005 **OTO** *020 †45

LEONIDOV, Michael Henri. 6206 OLD FRANCONIA RD 22310 #048-13-1986 L1988 **FM** *020 †18

LETKO, Alexander N. ■ 22310 #035-03-1952 L1953 **OPH** *071

LEVINE, Leonard S. 6355 WALKER LN STE 508 22310 #035-08-1955 L1963 **OBG** *020 †30

LEVY, Micheline Sarah. ■ 22307 #396-08-1956 L1963 **PD** *020 †55

LEYKAM, Nancy Jenkins. 7015C MANCHESTER BLVD, THE PEDIATRIC GROUP 22310 #051-01-1989 L1992 **PD** *020 †55

LIEBERMAN, Michael David. 8101 HINSON FARM RD, MOUNT VERNON PRIMARY CARE 22306 #016-42-1966 L1968 **FM** *020 †18

LIM, Adrianus Patrick. ■ 22310 #010-01-2008 *012

LIN, Eugenia Ihsien. 7015C MANCHESTER BLVD, THE PEDIATRIC GROUP 22310 #016-06-2001 L2005 **PD** *020 †55

LOFTUS, Thomas Jos. ■ 22310 #041-02-1977 L1979 **FM OS** *020 †18,70

LOUGHRIDGE, Chalmers A. ■ 22309 #035-01-1954 L1959 **EM IM** *071

LOWEN, Beal Aptheker. 8109 HINSON FARM RD, STE 504 22306 #051-04-1970 L1970 **IM IMG** *020 †20

LUISADA, Paul Victor. 2616 SHERWOOD HALL LN 22306 #016-42-1971 L1974 **P** *020 †75

LUKOWSKY, Maria C. 6412 BEULAH ST, STE 100 22310 #051-01-1991 L1996 **IM** *020 †20

LUTTA, Kevin Charles. ■ 22306 #010-03-2004 **ORS** *012

MAHMOOD, Khalid. 7692 RICHMOND HWY, SOUTH COUNTY HEALTH CENTER 22306 #704-16-1981 L1994 **IM** *020 †20

MALIK, Salman Masood. 6355 WALKER LN, STE 406 22310 #305-01-1999 L2006 **CD** *100 †20

MAPES, Courtney Lynn. ■ 22303 #028-34-2006 L2007 **FP** *012

MARTIN, John Patrick. 6355 WALKER LN, STE 405 22310 #035-01-1995 L1995 **OPH** *020 †35

MARTINO, Janet Teresa. 6307 FORT HUNT RD, MED IT HLTHCARE INTOMTCS 22307 #035-48-1983 L1986 **IM** *020 †20

MATIAS, Esther. 1707 BELLE VIEW BLVD # A2 22307 #748-01-1972 L1975 **IM** *020

MATIN, Terri Aminah. 2501 PARKERS LN 22306 #011-02-1990 L1993 **TS** *020 †85

MATINI, Khosrow. 7910 ANDRUS RD STE 5 22306 #517-04-1966 L1977 **PS HS** *020 †85,65

MATTHEWS, Melissa Anne. ■ 22307 #010-01-2003 L2004 **EM** *020

MAY, Dean Francis. 1451 BELLE HAVEN RD 22307 #028-34-1957 L1966 **PD** *071 †55

MC ALPINE, Marion Kay. ■ 22309 #010-01-1995 L1995 **PM** *020 †60

MC ATEER, Marybeth. 6355 WALKER LN, STE 405 22310 #010-02-1982 L1987 **OPH** *074 †35

MCCLENDON, Nicole Annette. ■ 22315 #010-02-2004 L2004 **OBG** *012

MC CLOSKEY, Carolyn A. 6232 YELLOWSTONE DR 22312 #051-01-1979 L1982 **PD** *030

MC CONE, Jonathan, Jr. 8109 HINSON FARM RD, STE 515 22306 #011-03-1972 L1979 **GE IM** *020 †20

MC CURDY, Paul R. 645L ELMDALE RD 22312 #024-01-1949 L1977 **IM HEM** *071 †20

MC LEAN, Robert Brennan. ■ 22308 #041-01-1961 L1984 **OM GS** *071 †85

MEYER, Louis. 8637 ENGLESIDE OFFICE PARK 22309 #035-46-1968 L1975 **GS** *020 †85

MEYERS, Louis Block. ■ 22308 #010-01-1993 L1996 **IM** *020 †20

MEYERS, Stuart Allan. 1451 BELLE HAVEN RD, STE 210 22307 #165-04-1978 L1980 **CD IM** *020 †20

MICHENER, Frank Ervine. 2059 HUNTINGTON AVE # 108 22303 #041-01-1965 L1973 **CHP P** *020

MIKESKA, Marvin Josef. 6355 WALKER LN, STE 200 22310 #034-01-2002 L2006 **AN** *020 †05

MILLER, Julie Albeg. 2501 PARKERS LN, MOUNT VERNON HOSPITAL 22306 #011-02-1994 L2001 **AN** *020 †05

MIRZA, Khaled Shams. ■ 22306 #305-01-2003 L2005 **P** *012

MOHINDRA, Rachna. 2501 PARKERS LN 22306 #495-45-1993 L2005 **AN** *020 †05

MONDALL, Philip. ■ 22309 #781-01-1952 L1975 **PM** *071 †60

MONTALBANO, Foster R. 6355 WALKER LN, STE 310 22310 #654-01-1981 L1983 **IM UM** *020 †20

MOON, Young Ho. 2501 PARKERS LN 22306 #583-10-1964 L1970 **CD IM** *020 †20

MOORE, Molly Jo. ■ 22310 #024-16-2007 **PD** *012

MORCOS, Claudine Ann. ■ 22312 #024-05-2005 L2005 **PTH** *012

MOSELY, Linda Hays. 6355 WALKER LN, STE 409 22310 #021-05-1967 L1979 **PS HS** *020 †85,65 ‡

MUJAHID, Humera Parveen. 8370 BROCKHAM DR 22309 #496-27-1992 L2000 **PUD** *020 †20

MUNTERS, Manfreds. 8101 HINSON FARM RD, STE 301 22306 #035-08-1962 L1980 **ORS** *020 †40

MURALI-DURAISAMI, P. ■ 22310 #495-59-1990 L2008 **AN** *020

MURPHY, Cornelius Francis. ■ 22303 #010-02-1956 L1972 **R NM** *071 †80,28

NACHAJSKI, Peter John. 6355 WALKER LN STE 401 22310 #010-01-1960 L1967 **PD ADL** *020 †55

NAIDORF, Tobin Scott. 7910 ANDRUS RD STE 6 22306 #051-07-1984 L1989 **GE** *020 †20

NAJI, Mohammed Hisham. 2501 PARKERS LN 22306 #875-01-1972 L2001 **AN PME** *020 †05

NARULA, Jatinder. ■ 22312 #051-04-2002 L2005 **PM** *100 †60

NATHAN, Michael Jay. 2616 SHERWOOD HALL LN, STE 408 22306 #422-01-1982 L1988 **OTO FPS** *020 †45

NAYYAR, Rashid. 6355 WALKER LN, STE 300 22310 #704-02-1989 L2001 **PCC SME** *020 †20

NEDZBALA, Robert Michael. ■ 22309 #010-02-1962 L1973 **IM PUD** *071 †20

NELSON, Jane Ellen. 3111 TELEGRAPH CORNER LN, STE 100 22310 #026-04-1983 L1986 **FM** *020 †18

NEMETH, Richard Desider. 5946 RICHMOND HWY 22303 #051-07-1996 L1998 **FM** *020 †18

NESTERENKO, Tetyana Hryho. ■ 22303 #913-89-1992 L2005 **NPM** *012 †55

NGO, Minh Van. 2501 PARKERS LN 22306 #023-01-1992 L1998 **CD** *020 †20

NGO, Tan Duy. ■ 22310 #010-02-2008 *012

NGUYEN, Trach Ngoc. 2501 PARKERS LN, INOVA MOUNT VERNON HOSPITA 22306 #051-04-1989 L1992 **AN PME** *020 †05

NOTTINGHAM, Stuart C. ■ 22308 #051-04-1955 L1955 **PHP** *071 †70

NUSSBAUM, Robert Alan. 6355 WALKER LN, STE 309 22310 #035-47-1986 L1992 **GE IM** *020 †20 ‡

OCEAN, Ronald Hugh. 2501 PARKERS LN 22306 #035-46-1970 L1975 **GS** *020 †85

OKAIL, Kamal K. 6371 LITTLE RIVER TPKE 22312 #915-02-1957 L1972 **OTO GP** *071

OLIVER, Jessica Elizabeth. 6355 WALKER LN, STE 405 22310 #036-05-1995 L2000 **OPH** *020 †35

ONDRUSH, Joanne Mary. 6355 WALKER LN, STE 300 22310 #305-01-1998 L2001 **CCM** *020 †20

ORDONEZ, Ester Belo. 2501 PARKERS LN 22306 #748-01-1954 L1963 **P IM** *020

ORFALY, Mohammed Tarek. 6355 WALKER LN STE 308, SURGERY 22310 #020-12-1996 L2003 **OTO** *020 †45

OWENS, Tremikae Renee. ■ 22310 #004-01-2002 L2007 **FP** *012

PALACE, William Geo. 2501 PARKERS LN, MOUNT VERNON HOSPITAL 22306 #041-02-1975 L1983 **EM** *020 †16

PALMER, Richard R. 2616 SHERWOOD HALL LN SU 22306 #010-02-1971 L1974 **P** *020 †75

PARENTE, Kathleen O'Neil. 6355 WALKER LN 22310 #010-02-1985 L1989 **PD** *020 †55

PARVIN, Shahinodokht. 6275 FRANCONIA RD 22310 #517-06-1966 L1975 **PD** *020

PATLA, Jayasree. 6303 LITTLE RIVER TPKE, STE 160 22312 #495-65-1982 L2001 **FM** *020 †18

PATTERSON, Kerry B. 4719 HANRAHAN PL 22309 #049-01-1978 L1979 **GPM** *020 †50,70

PEARLMAN, Adam Michael. 2616 SHERWOOD HALL LN, STE 209 22306 #012-05-1999 L2006 **NEP** *100 †20

PECKAR, Paul Joshua. 2616 SHERWOOD HALL LN, STE 305 22306 #038-06-1975 L1981 **P** *020

PEREDO-PINTO, Helkha. ■ 22309 #176-03-1994 **PD** *012

PETTIT, William James. 6160 FULLER CT, FRANCONIA FAMILY MEDICINE 22310 #041-02-1997 L1997 **FM** *020 †18

PHAM, Tina T. 6355 WALKER LN, STE 408 22310 #017-20-1997 L2000 **OBG** *020 †30

PICCIO-AZARCON, Marlene. 2616 SHERWOOD HALL LN, STE 402 22306 #748-01-1978 L1987 **PD** *020 †55

PICKENS, Leslie Rochelle. 6020 RICHMOND HWY, STE 100 22303 #021-01-1984 L1991 **EM GS** *020 †16

POLICELLI, Vincent A. 6355 WALKER LN, STE 508 22310 #010-02-1972 L1974 **OBG** *020 †30

PURI, Anuradha. 8101 HINSON FARM RD, STE 219 22306 #495-45-1994 L1998 **IM** *100 †20

RAJAN, Narain Prasad. 6355 WALKER LN, STE 406 22310 #036-07-1984 L1990 **CD** *020 †20

REDDING, Michael Alan. 8109 TISWELL DR, STE 511 22306 #010-02-1987 L1989 **FM** *020 †18 ‡

REDDING, Richard James. 1609 FORT HUNT CT 22307 #010-02-1965 L1966 **FM** *020 †18

REDDY, Manoj Soma. 2616 SHERWOOD HALL LN, STE 209 22306 #041-02-1996 L2003 **NEP IM** *020 †20,55

REHMAN, Amir. ■ 22306 #704-21-1988 L2003 **P ADP** *020

REX, Stephen Williard. 8101 HINSON FARM RD # 417 22306 #038-40-1990 L1994 **FM** *020 †18

RHAME, Richard Coleman. 2616 SHERWOOD HALL LN, STE 304 22306 #010-01-1954 L1962 **U** *020 †95

RICH, William L, III. 6355 WALKER LN, STE 405 22310 #010-02-1972 L1976 **OPH** *020 †35

RICHARDSON, Judith Yoland. ■ 22312 #010-03-2006 **GS** *012

RICHEY, Alan Ward. 6303 LITTLE RIVER TPKE 22312 #010-02-1983 L1991 **IM** *020 †20

RIVERS, Michael Brian. 6355 WALKER LN, STE 502 22310 #035-20-1985 L1991 **OPH OS** *020 †35

ROBERTSON, Sandy Jo. 8101 HINSON FARM RD, MOUNT VERNON PRIMARY CARE 22306 #051-01-2002 L2002 **FM** *020 †18

ROBSON, Scott Malcolm. 2501 PARKERS LN 22306 #060-01-1967 L1977 **IM FM** *020

ROSENBLATT, Arnold J. 6355 WALKER LN, STE 406 22310 #010-01-1975 L1982 **CD IM** *020 †20

ROTHSCHILD, Peter Gordon. 6355 WALKER LN STE 508, NORTHERN VA GYNECOLOGISTS 22310 #010-01-1981 L1984 **OBG** *020 †30

RUEBUSH, Trenton K, II. ■ 22315 #023-01-1971 L1972 **IM** *020 †20

RUSSELL, William Ashley. 1451 BELLE HAVEN RD, KIDZ DOCS 22307 #025-07-1984 L1987 **PD** *071 †55

SACHSE, Kathleen Terrenoi. ■ 22315 #041-12-2004 L2004 **AN** *012

SADAYA-CONDA, Janice G. 7906 ANDRUS RD STE 8 22306 #748-11-1987 L1995 **IM** *020 †20

SADDLER, Stephen Chas. 8101 HINSON FARM RD, STE 100 22306 #005-02-1988 L1995 **OSM** *020 †40

SADEGHIAN, Feri. ■ 22309 #517-01-1959 L1967 **GYN OS** *071

SAIDI, Iyad Salam. 6355 WALKER LN, STE 308 22310 #048-04-1994 L1999 **OTO FPS** *020 †45

SALAMA, Joseph Saml. ■ 22307 #330-02-1949 L1963 **GP IM** *075

SANDBERG, Michele Lee. ■ 22307 #028-03-1993 L1995 **CHP** *020 †75

SANDERS, Valerie Efonda. ■ 22308 #041-15-2000 L2008 **FM** *100 †18

SANNER, M Que. ■ 22312 #041-12-1951 L1958 **GP** *071

SANTIAGO, Jennifer Rabor. 6355 WALKER LN STE 408 22310 #033-06-1999 L2004 **OBG** *020 †30

SATTAR, Shamima. ■ 22303 #160-06-1997 L2006 **IM** *100 †20

SCHEFKIND, Mark Jerrold. 8101 HINSON FARM RD 22306 #041-01-1985 L1989 **OPH** *020 †35

SCHIFFMAN, Joel Howard. ■ 22306 #035-19-1961 L1968 **ORS** *020 †40

SCHREIBER, Alan G. 6355 WALKER LN, GREATER METROPOLITIAN 22310 #010-02-1981 L1991 **ORS** *020 †40

SCHREINER, Christina. 8101 HINSON FARM RD, STE 31 22306 #010-01-1980 L1984 **EM IM** *020 †16

SCHULMAN, Jeff Eric. ■ 22312 #033-06-2001 L2007 **ORS** *020

SCHWARTZ, Benjamin Joel. ■ 22307 #051-04-2002 L2007 **ORS** *100

SEIDMAN, David Jay. 6355 WALKER LN, STE 405 22310 #041-01-1982 L1987 **OPH PO** *020 †35

SHABSHAB, Samir F. 2616 SHERWOOD HALL LN, STE 209 22306 #605-01-1987 L1995 **IM** *020 †20

SHAPIRO, Stephen Franklin. ■ 22308 #010-02-1987 **FM** *020

SHARMA, Vandana Raj. 6371 LITTLE RIVER TPKE 22312 #495-23-1985 L1991 **N P** *020 †75

SHAUER, Alan Bruce. 2616 SHERWOOD HALL LN, STE 205 22306 #561-01-1968 L1972 **GE IM** *020 †20

SHEN, Cynthia Ann. 1451 BELLE HAVEN RD, KIDZ DOCS 22307 #023-01-1994 L1997 **PD** *020 †55

SHERMAN, Janette Bigelow. PO BOX 4605 22303 #025-07-1964 L1988 **IM OM** *050

SHIN, Ken Suck. 7900 ANDRUS RD UNIT ONE 22306 #583-04-1968 L1977 **GP** *020

SHOKOOHI, Hamid. ■ 22307 #517-11-2001 L2004 **EM** *100

SIDERIDIS, Andreas D. 6355 WALKER LN, STE 401 22310 #035-48-1993 L2005 **PD** *020 †55 ‡

SIDHU, Gurmeet Singh. 2616 SHERWOOD HALL LN, SHERWOOD HALL IMAGING CENT 22306 #495-45-1974 L1980 **DR VIR** *020 †80

SILIS, George Peter. 5115 FRANCONIA RD STE G 22310 #016-42-1991 L1994 **IM** *020 †20

SILIS, Manny P. 5115 FRANCONIA RD STE G 22310 #016-42-1991 L1994 **IM** *020 †20

■ = Address Information Privacy Protected

SILVERSMITH, Peter. 8101 HINSON FARM RD # 217 22306 #035-06-1970 L1977 **PS** *020 †65
SIMPAO-IGNACIO, Rosario D. 7906 ANDRUS RD S10 22306 #748-01-1966 L1984 **IM EM** *020
SIMPSON, John Alva. 6355 WALKER LN, STE 307 22310 #045-04-1981 L1990 **AI PD** *020 †55,03
SINHA, Vivek Pratap. ■ 22310 #665-01-2002 L2003 **FM** *100 †18
SMIRNIOTOPOULOS, Thomas T. 6355 WALKER LN, STE 300 22310 #010-02-1978 L1979 **PUD IM** *020 †20
SMITH, Anita Rochelle. ■ 22303 #001-06-2002 L2004 **IM** *020 †20
SMITH, Keisha S. ■ 22309 #010-02-2008 *012
SMITH, Leroy Fleming, Jr. 8101 HINSON FARM RD, STE 315 22306 #012-01-1960 L1967 **HEM ON** *071 †20
SNEDECOR, Michael R. ■ 22308 #048-04-1987 L1988 **GPM** *030 †70
SOLL, Robert Walter. 5306 MT VERNON MEMORIL HWY 22309 #018-03-1956 L1981 **N A** *071
SOURYAL, T Henry. 2501 PARKERS LN 22306 #330-02-1949 L1967 **GS CD** *071 †85
SOZI, Samson S. ■ 22306 #010-03-2008 *012
STAS, Michelle Plagata. 6355 WALKER LN, STE 508 22310 #051-01-1994 L1994 **OBG** *020 †30
STEIN, Jerome. 6355 WALKER LN, STE 408 22310 #035-08-1961 L1968 **GYN** *020 †30
STEPHENS, Ronald Todd. ■ 22309 #012-01-1990 L1991 **PM** *020 †60
STONE, Nancy Walker. ■ 22303 #021-05-1949 L1979 **P ADP** *071 †75
STONE, William E. ■ 22303 #021-05-1949 L1987 **CHP P** *071 †75
STONE, William M. 5263 WINTER VIEW DR 22312 #035-19-1952 L1966 **IM CD** *071 †20
STREET, James Howard, III. ■ 22309 #045-01-2000 L2005 **CCS** *100 †85
STRILKA, Richard John. ■ 22303 #041-14-1998 L2001 **VS** *020 †85
SUMMER, David Benj. 8101 HINSON FARM RD 22306 #025-07-1971 L1977 **OPH** *020 †35
SUNEW, John Young. 6355 WALKER LN, STE 406 22310 #035-08-1994 L2001 **IC CD** *020 †15
SWAN, Harvey Frank. 2616 SHERWOOD HALL LN 22306 #024-05-1972 L1973 **D A** *020 †15
SWEDO, Gregory James. 2501 PARKERS LN 22306 #016-01-1982 L1986 **PTH** *020 †50
SYMINGTON, John Sante. 7910 ANDRUS RD, STE 4 22306 #028-34-1986 L1991 **ID IM** *020 †20
SZEWCZYK, Celeste C. 2501 PARKERS LN, MT VERNON HOSPITAL 22306 #035-01-3975 L1978 **EM IM** *020 †20,16
TACKTILL, Norman. 6355 WALKER LN, STE 408 22310 #165-06-1976 L1979 **OBG** *020 †30
TAHMASSEBI, Nasser. 3117 WOODLAND LN 22309 #409-25-1962 L1976 *020
TALBOT, Frank James. 2501 PARKERS LN 22306 #010-02-1953 L1962 **CD IM** *020 †20
TAYLOR, Priscilla Renee. 3111 TELEGRAPH CORNER LN, STE 100 22310 #036-05-1996 L1996 **FM** *020 †18
TEBYANIAN, Naghmeh. 6355 WALKER LN, STE 406 22310 #010-01-1993 L1996 **CD** *020 †20
TEITELBAUM, Marc J. 6275 FRANCONIA RD 22310 #035-08-1995 L1997 **OBG** *020
THAM, Irene Morgwan. 7015C MANCHESTER BLVD, THE PEDIATRIC GROUP 22310 #012-05-2004 L2007 **PD** *100 †55
THOMPSON, Jennifer Carter. 1451 BELLE HAVEN RD, KIDZ DOCS 22307 #010-02-1996 L2006 **PD** *020 †55
TINKER, Bruce Purdy. 8101 HINSON FARM RD, STE 408 22306 #025-07-1971 L1976 **CD IM** *020 †20
TITUS, Jonathan. 2501 PARKERS LN, MT VERNON HOSPITAL HBO UNI 22306 #008-01-1965 L1967 **FM UM** *020 †18
TOLBERT, Charone Tennille. ■ 22315 #016-02-2006 L2006 **PD** *012
TOLENTINO, David Cruz. 2501 PARKERS LN, DEPT OF ANESTHLGY 22306 #038-40-2001 L2005 **AN** *020 †05
TRACY, Christopher Lee. ■ 22309 #023-12-2008 *012
TRAN, Christine L. 6355 WALKER LN, STE 508 22310 #051-04-1995 L1995 **OBG** *020 †30
TRINH, Truc Thithanh. ■ 22312 #051-01-1999 L1999 **GE** *100 †20
TRIVEDI, Divyang Janakray. 8101 HINSON FARM RD # 211 22306 #495-76-1979 L1990 **ON HEM** *020 †20
TSAI, Shi Ko. ■ 22310 #385-01-1966 L1972 **GP N** *020
TSE, William. 2501 PARKERS LN, MOUNT VERNON HOSPITAL 22306 #008-01-1987 L1993 **PD PHO** *050 †05
TURNER, Christine. ■ 22310 #051-01-2004 L2004 **IM** *100 †20
TYLENDA, Carleen. 8109 HINSON FARM RD, STE 504 22306 #010-02-1981 L1984 **GP IM** *020 †20
UBELHART, Chas Robt, III. 6355 WALKER LN, STE 202 22310 #020-12-1969 L1972 **ORS HS** *020
VAN, Phillip Leefong. ■ 22310 #010-02-2008 *012
VANMILDER, Shirley Anne. ■ 22303 #035-08-2002 L2006 **OBG** *020
VASILOPOULOS, Basil John. 8101 HINSON FARM RD, STE 31 22306 #010-02-1989 L1992 **EM** *020 †16
VERDERESE, John Paul. ■ 22307 #024-16-2005 L2005 **IM** *012
VILLAR, Victoria. ■ 22308 #748-01-1954 L1989 **P IM** *071
VOGT, Megumi Murakami. ■ 22315 #023-12-2000 L2002 **N** *020 †75
WAGNER, Robert Harrison. 6355 WALKER LN, STE 507 22310 #051-07-1995 L1995 **PM PMM** *020 †60 ‡
WALLACH, Corey James. ■ 22308 #005-19-2000 L2007 **ORS** *100
WALLER, Rachel Rebecca. 8109 HINSON FARM RD, STE 504 22306 #051-04-1999 L2001 **IM** *020 †20
WATTENDORF, Daniel John. ■ 22315 #010-01-1996 L1999 **MG** *020 †18,19
WATTENDORF, Nicole C. ■ 22315 #023-12-1997 *100
WEAVER, James Mac. ■ 22307 #016-06-1947 L1967 **PTH** *020 †50
WERTHEIMER, Barry Marvin. 2501 PARKERS LN, ANESTHESIA DEPARTMENT 22306 #010-03-1986 L1991 **AN** *020 †05
WESLEY, Keea Michelle. ■ 22310 #047-07-2002 L2003 *100
WHERRY, Sean Patrick. ■ 22308 #023-12-2006 L2006 **FP** *012
WHITMIRE, Norman, Jr. 8109 HINSON FARM RD, STE 504 22306 #008-01-1995 L1999 **IM** *020
WILLIAMS, Leslie Barnes. 8101 HINSON FARM RD, STE 112 22306 #012-05-1978 L1985 **N IM** *020 †20,75
WILLIAMS, Stephen J. 6412 BEULAH ST, STE 100 22310 #561-01-1975 L1982 **IM** *020 †20
WILLIS, Andrea Degeoris. 6303 LITTLE RIVER TPKE, STE 300 22312 #010-02-1998 L1999 *020 †55
WILSON, John Keddy. 8850 RICHMOND HWY, STE 202 22309 #051-04-1998 L2002 **P** *020 †75
WINELAND, Robert K. 1451 BELLE HAVEN RD 22307 #010-01-1951 L1955 **PD** *071 †55
WISE, Andrew Edmund. 6160 FULLER CT, FRANCONIA FAMILY MEDICINE 22310 #036-07-1986 L1988 **FM** *020 †20
WOHLER, Brett Alan. 6160 FULLER CT, FRANCONIA FAMILY MEDICINE 22310 #051-01-1986 L1988 **FM** *020 †18
WRIGHT, Kaadze Mamaa. 2501 PARKERS LN, FAIR OAKS ANESTHESIA ASSOC 22306 #051-01-1998 L2003 **AN** *020 †20
YACOUB, Mina Maurice. ■ 22303 #915-04-1994 L2002 **CCM** *020 †20

YADAO, Melissa Ann. 2616 SHERWOOD HALL LN, STE 104 22306 #051-04-1997 L1997 **OSM** *020
YANCEY, Joseph Ryland. ■ 22315 #051-07-2005 L2005 **FP** *012
YANG, Steven D. 6412 BEULAH ST, STE 100 22310 #010-02-1989 L1991 **IM** *020 †20
YAO, Wen-Jeng. ■ 22309 #033-06-2006 **OPH** *012
ZAIDI, Syed I H. ■ 22312 #704-02-1981 L1987 **P** *012 †20

ALTAVISTA – CAMPBELL

CARTER, Francis Coleman. 1280 MAIN ST 24517 #051-01-1979 L1980 **FM** *020
KENT, James P. 525 7TH ST 24517 #051-04-1934 L1934 **FM** *071
KINLAW, James Brady. ■ 24517 #041-13-1943 L1962 **PHP** *071
PIERUCCI, Louis. ■ 24517 #041-02-1955 L1991 **GS TS** *071 †85,90

AMELIA COURT HOUSE – AMELIA

HUNT, Clark Curtis. 8920 OTTERBURN RD, AMELIA HEALTH CARE CENTER 23002 #051-01-1973 L1982 **FM** *020 †18
MARTINEZ, Jesus Alfredo. ■ 23002 #847-10-1965 L2007 **ORS GP** *071 †40
PADEN, Scott Wood. 15415 PATRICK HENRY HWY, RAPID RESPONSE, LLC 23002 #036-05-1988 L1990 **EM** *020
SEQUEIRA, Debra Marie. 8920 OTTERBURN RD, AMELIA HEALTH CARE CENTER 23002 #495-96-1993 L2004 **P** *020 †18 ‡
YUSI-LENN, Almira U. 8631 NAMOZINE RD 23002 #748-01-1967 L1996 **IM** *020 †20

AMHERST – AMHERST

ARNOLD, Sidney R. PO BOX 40 24521 #020-02-1943 L1946 **GP** *071
KOHLI, Priya. PO BOX 1320, 124 AMBRIAR CT 24521 #539-06-1999 L2004 **FM** *020 †18
LAMBDIN, William M. ■ 24521 #051-01-1954 L1970 **GP** *020
LEONARD, Gordon Kyle. 816 S MAIN ST 24521 #051-01-1964 L1964 **GP** *071
PELFREY, David Allen. 124 AMBRIAR COURT 24521 #051-01-1988 L1989 **FM** *020 †18
RAINE, Dudley Allen, Jr. 842 S MAIN ST, AMHERST FAM PRAC, INC. 24521 #023-01-1966 L1989 **A FM** *020 †18

AMISSVILLE – CULPEPER

HENEGHAN, Margery Ann. ■ 20106 #035-15-1976 L1997 **DR PDR** *020 †80
TAPPIN, Charles Percival. ■ 20106 #407-12-1962 L1992 **P** *071 †75
WEBB, Martin Gilder, Jr. ■ 20106 #041-13-1948 **AM** *071 †70

ANNANDALE – FAIRFAX

ABOFREKA, Reffat K. 5047 BACKLICK RD STE A, SPRINGDALE PROF CTR 22003 #915-02-1968 L1989 **OBG** *020
ADAMS, Pamela Lynn. ■ 22003 #010-01-1982 L1991 **IM** *020 †20
AKAGAMI, Ryojo. 3301 WOODBURN RD, STE 202 22003 #065-01-1993 L1999 *020
ALMOAYED, Boshra Abdul-Ra. 3340 WOODBURN RD, FFX-FC CSB 22003 #797-02-1988 L2006 **P** *100 †75
ALVIR, Rene Ma B. ■ 22003 #748-02-1960 L1972 **U** *071 †95
AMBARDAR, Sujata H. 3289 WOODBURN RD, INFECTIOUS DISEASES 22003 #041-13-1990 L1995 **ID** *020 †20
ASKEW, Allyson Ann. 3301 WOODBURN RD STE 205 22003 #021-01-1982 L1989 **PDS GS** *020 †85
AZIZI, Wali. 4317 ROBERTS AVE 22003 #305-01-2000 L2004 **IMG** *020
BABINGTON, Parker William. ■ 22003 #051-07-2008 *012
BAER, Andrew Mitchell. ■ 22003 #305-01-1986 L1988 IM *075
BAHRANI, Ann. 7501 LITTLE RIVER TPKE, STE 302 22003 #528-01-1957 L1968 **P** *020 †75
BAIG, Mirza Saud. 7501 LITTLE RIVER TPKE, STE 104 22003 #704-02-1987 L1994 **IM** *020 †20
BAKER, Alan Robt. 3301 WOODBURN RD, STE 209 22003 #024-01-1966 L1994 **GS SO** *020 †85
BENJAMIN, William, III. 6930A LITTLE RIVER TPKE, STE A 22003 #010-03-1983 L1989 **FM** *020 †18
BICHER, Annette. 3289 WOODBURN RD 22003 #025-01-1987 L1990 **GO** *020 †30
BOWEN, Patrick J. 3301 WOODBURN VLG DR # 304 22003 #539-02-1956 L1971 **IM** *071 †20
CACHAY PITA, Antonio Jose. 3289 WOODBURN RD STE 85 22003 #737-01-1966 L1973 **OTO HNS** *020 †45
CAESAR, Anne E. ■ 22003 #010-01-1983 **IM** *020
CAMPBELL, Mary Irene. 7501 LITTLE RIVR TPKE #203 22003 #023-07-1977 L1986 **GYN** *020 †30
CAPOTORTO, Vito Antonio. 7617 LITTLE RIVER TPKE, STE 600 22003 #561-01-1991 L1996 **MPD** *020 †55,20
CASEY, William C. ■ 22003 #539-04-1955 L1960 **IM** *020 †20
CASSIDY, Michael Patrick. 3301 WOODBURN RD #010-02-1979 L1984 **OAR** *020 †40
CASTRO, Ernesto V. 3301 WOODBURN RD, NEURO LOGICAL SURGERY 22003 #649-01-1947 L1959 **NS** *071 †18
CHANG, Jennifer Burgos. ■ 22003 #036-05-1996 L1999 **IM** *062 †20
CHARLES, Eugenie. 3299 WOODBURN RD, STE 230 22003 #010-01-1999 L1999 **PD** *020 †55
CHO, Byoung-Suen. 4600 JOHN MARR DR, STE 201 22003 #583-02-1971 L1981 **PM** *071 †60
CHO, Young Hei Lim. 7501 LITTLE RIVER RD, STE 101 22003 #583-08-1968 L1978 **PD** *020 †55
CHUNG, Ingrid I. 7008 LITTLE RIVER TPKE # A 22003 #583-08-1988 L1993 **IM** *020 †20
COCKERHAM, Elaine G L. 7805 BYRDS NEST PASS 22003 #010-01-1972 L1975 **PD** *071 †55
COOGAN, E Anthony. ■ 22003 #539-04-1949 L1958 **GP** *071
CROSS, Garfield, IV. ■ 22003 #023-01-2005 L2007 *100
DEARTH, Christine Marie. 3289 WOODBURN RD, STE 100 22003 #035-03-1992 L1999 **AN** *020 †05
DILORENZO, Paul Edward. 3301 WOODBURN RD, STE 301 22003 #051-01-1980 L1981 **CD IM** *020 †20
DI PINTO, Teresita C. 3340 WOODBURN RD 22003 #132-09-1974 L1982 **P** *020
DITTO, Kara Evangeline. 3340 WOODBURN RD, FAIRFAX-FALLS CHURCH CSB-W 22003 #051-04-1998 L2003 **P** *020 ‡

DO, Thien Minh. 7611 LITTLE RIVER TPKE, STE 108W 22003 #010-01-1990 L1991 **CD** *020 †20

DO, Thieu Minh. 3815 DADE DR 22003 #051-07-1991 L1993 **PCC** *020 †20

DOBRANSKI, Andrew I. 3301 WOODBURN RD 22003 #759-03-1954 L1965 **ORS HS** *071 †40

DOPPELHEUER, John David. 3299 WOODBURN RD, STE 370 22003 #010-01-1978 L1981 **OBG REN** *020 †30

ELKAS, John Christopher. 3289 WOODBURN RD 22003 #035-09-1993 L2005 **OBG** *020 †30

ELLINI, Ahmad. 7501 LITTLE RIVER TPKE, 202 22003 #517-01-1970 L1987 **PD** *020 †55

ESCORCIA, Eduardo. ■ 22003 #264-03-1962 L1980 **IM OS** *100

FAN, Zuoheng. ■ 22003 #243-47-1984 L2005 **IM** *020 †20

FOLEY, Francis E. ■ 22003 #035-45-1949 L1952 **IM** *071 †20

FRANCO, Paulo E. 3299 WOODBURN RD STE 37 22003 #264-03-1960 L1970 **GS** *020 †85

FRASER, Denise Mack. 3299 WOODBURN RD, STE 360 22003 #035-45-1985 L1990 **GS** *020 †85

FRENCH, James Harold, Jr. 3299 WOODBURN RD STE 490 22003 #021-05-1974 L1985 **PS** *020 †65

FRIEDLER, Edward Michael. 7617 LITTLE RIVER TPKE 22003 #005-06-1977 L1986 **FM** *020 †18

GARCIA, Julio. 3289 WOODBURN RD, STE 06 22003 #042-01-1975 L1993 **NM IM** *020 †20,28

GIANG, Van Vu. ■ 22003 #941-01-1972 L1982 **GP** *020

GOFREED, Deborah Lynne. 3289 WOODBURN RD, STE 360 22003 #023-01-1980 L1984 **SME IM** *020 †20

GOLDSTEIN, Stafford S. 3301 WOODBURN RD STE 10 22003 #010-01-1976 L1978 **GE IM** *020 †20

GONZALEZ, Nelly Mercedes. 7617 LITTLE RIVER TPKE, STE 600 22003 #319-01-1977 L1999 **FM** *020 †18

GORSEN, Robert Marc. 3301 WOODBURN RD, STE 211 22003 #041-02-1982 L1988 **NS** *020

GRAHAM, Garth Nigel. ■ 22003 #008-01-2001 L2001 **IM** *100 †20

GREER, Douglas Fielder. 7023 LITTLE RIVER TPKE 22003 #035-01-1966 L1973 **OPH IM** *020 †35

HAFIZI, Ghazaleh. 3301 WOODBURN RD, STE 307 22003 #010-03-1990 L1996 **OBG** *020 †30

HAN, Chung Wan. 5105 BACKLICK RD # C 22003 #583-10-1962 L1995 **IM FM** *020

HAND, Colton M, Jr. 3340 WOODBURN RD, NORTHWEST CENTER FOR COMMU 22003 #051-01-1988 L1997 **P** *020 †75

HANFLING, Carl. ■ 22003 #869-04-1957 L1963 **FM PD** *020 †55,18

HARDMAN, George White. 7601 LITTLE RIVER TPKE, GROUP HEALTH ASSOC INC 22003 #023-07-1958 L1965 **PD** *071 †55

HARDY, Michael Rob. 3299 WOODBURN RD, STE 450 22003 #011-02-1978 L1984 **U** *020 †95

HARRIS, Bernard. 3289 WOODBURN RD, STE 100 22003 #038-40-1990 L1994 **AN** *020 †05

HART, Robert Russell. 3299 WOODBURN RD, STE 450 22003 #017-20-1986 L1988 **U** *020 †95

HAWKEN, Samuel Mc Comas. 3301 WOODBURN RD 22003 #010-02-1972 L1977 **ORS** *020 †40

HEIBY, James Richard. ■ 22003 #023-07-1971 L1973 **IM** *020

HELBING, Claus Karl L. 4534A JOHN MARR DR 22003 #407-16-1963 L1970 **AI PDA** *071 †55,03

HELMKAMP, Boyd Frederick. 3289 WOODBURN RD 22003 #035-20-1971 L1984 **ON OBG** *020 †30

HO, Thuy Nguyen. 4330 EVERGREEN LN STE G 22003 #941-01-1966 L1981 **OBG** *020 †30

HONG, Mu Kyung. 7004 LITTLE RIVER TPKE, STE A 22003 #010-02-1989 L1990 **GE** *020 †20

HORN, Henry J. 4540 JOHN MARR DR 22003 #010-01-1950 L1956 **FM PHP** *071 †18

HSIAO, Tony Yulea. 7501 LITTLE RIVER TPKE, STE 103 22003 #023-01-1988 L1994 **IM PHP** *020 †20

HUENE, Phyllis Anne. ■ 22003 #035-09-1959 L1964 **D** *062

ISAAC, Alexander Shalom. 3299 WOODBURN RD, STE 400 22003 #016-42-1998 L2002 **P** *020 †75

IVES, Julia Alana. ■ 22003 #130-01-2000 *100

JACKSON, Rochelle P. 3340 WOODBURN RD 22003 #035-47-1979 L1990 **P** *020 †75

JAVEDAN, Mehrdad. 7501 LITTLE RIVER TPKE, STE 202 22003 #517-01-1960 L1969 **PD** *020

JEAN, Cheo M. 7501 LITTLE RIVER TPKE 22003 #244-06-1969 L1975 **FM EM** *020 †16

JONES, Walter Arthur, III. ■ 22003 #047-05-1990 *100

KELLEY, Kathleen Ruth. 3299 WOODBURN RD STE 230, INOVA PEDIATRIC CENTER 22003 #023-01-1973 L1979 **PD** *020 †55

KENNEDY, Colleen A. 3301 WOODBURN RD 22003 #010-01-1979 L1986 **ORS** *020 †40

KHALIFA, Falah Abdalla. ■ 22003 #915-02-1969 L1980 **OBG** *020 †30

KHIN KHIN, Eindra. ■ 22003 #051-01-2006 L2006 **P** *012

KIM, Hee Shin. 6928 LITTLE RIVER TPKE # B 22003 #583-10-1969 L1978 **IM NEP** *020 †20

KIM, Hyung Lyull. 7002 LITTLE RIVER TPKE # F 22003 #583-06-1966 L1978 **GP** *020

KIM, Peter Donsung. 7002 LITTLE RIVER TPKE, STE F 22003 #583-04-2000 L2004 **FM** *020

KISTLER, Aaron Michael. 3289 WOODBURN RD STE 60, WOODBURN NUCLEAR MED 22003 #041-14-1982 L1983 **NM** *020 †20,28

KOLVEREID, Edward Ronald. 7501 LITTLE RIVER TPKE, STE G2 22003 #038-40-1960 L1969 **OBG** *020 †30

KRASICKY, Gary Alan. 8306 CHAPEL LAKE CT 22003 #025-01-1981 L1989 **DR NM** *020 †80

KREBS, Hans Bartold. 3289 WOODBURN RD 22003 #409-21-1973 L1980 **GO OBG** *020 †55

LACAYO PALLAIS, Edgard. ■ 22003 #682-01-1965 L1973 **OS** *020

LE, Connie Diemkhanh. 4208 EVERGREEN LN, STE 214 22003 #010-01-2000 L2005 **IM** *020 †20 ‡

LE, Khanh Nha. 4208 EVERGREEN LN, STE 213 22003 #010-01-1998 L2000 **OBG** *020 †30

LEE, Lesley H. 4209 EVERGREEN LN 22003 #583-03-1987 L1997 **P** *020

LIBRE, Eric Anthony. 3289 WOODBURN RD STE 350 22003 #010-02-1990 L1997 **IM** *020 †20

LIU, Ann Juyin. 5003 ROSLYN RD 22003 #021-01-1998 L2001 **PD** *020 †55

LORIO, Joseph Philibert. 4400 NEWDALE DR 22003 #010-02-1966 L1972 **P** *071

MAGONE, Maria Teresa. 3299 WOODBURN RD, STE 150 22003 #409-23-1994 L1999 **GS** *020 †35

MARTINS, Eduina Alice. 3340 WOODBURN RD, WOODBURN CMHC 22003 #043-01-1990 L1997 **P CHP** *020 †75

MATTHEWS, Robert Geo. 3299 WOODBURN RD, STE 450 22003 #025-01-1968 L1973 **CD** *020 †20

MATTICH, Angelo. 3340 WOODBURN RD, WOODHRR CENTER FOR COMM 22003 #957-01-1963 L1977 **P** *020

MAUNEY, Donald Lee. 3289 WOODBURN RD, STE 100 22003 #036-01-1995 L2001 **AN** *020 †05

MAY, Russell Leon. 3289 WOODBURN RD 22003 #047-05-1956 L1965 **OBG** *071 †30

MC DOWALL, James Douglas. 4503 HOLBORN AVE 22003 #038-41-1960 L1964 **PD** *071 †55

MC FALLS, James Casper. 7483 LITTLE RIVER TPKE 22003 #051-01-1964 L1964 **GYN** *020 †30

MC HALE, Kathleen Ann. 3301 WOODBURN RD, STE 309 22003 #041-07-1975 L1982 **ORS** *020 †40

MC MAHON, Doreen E. 7617 LITTLE RIVER TPKE, ANNANDALE FAMILY MEDICINE 22003 #023-01-1986 L1987 **FM** *072 †18

MILLER, Robert Wayne. 3340 WOODBURN RD, WOODBURN CENTER 22003 #017-20-1970 L1979 **P** *020 †75

MILLO, Corina Madalina. 3289 WOODBURN RD, STE 06 22003 #550-02-1992 L2005 **NM** *020 †28

MISHRA, Poonam. 3289 WOODBURN RD, STE 375 22003 #495-47-1993 L2004 **IM** *020

MOINFAR, Mohamad Reza. 7501 LITTLE RIVER TPKE, STE 202 22003 #517-01-1957 L1970 **PD** *020 †55

MORENO, Jose D. ■ 22003 #748-02-1939 L1980 **GP** *020

MORRISON, Allan Jos, Jr. 3289 WOODBURN RD, INFECTIOUS DISEASES 22003 #051-01-1980 L1985 **ID EP** *020 †20

MOYNIHAN, John Jos, Jr. 3301 WOODBURN RD STE 109 22003 #010-02-1980 L1982 **GS** *020 †85

NGUYEN, Dong So. 4330 EVERGREEN LN 22003 #941-01-1967 L1983 **EM FM** *020 †18

NGUYEN, Ngocha Thi. 7202 POPLAR ST 22003 #023-07-1993 L1996 **IM** *020 †20

NGUYEN, Quan Quoc. 4217 EVERGREEN LN BX 638 22003 #941-01-1969 L1980 **IM IMG** *020

NICKODEM, Anne M. 3299 WOODBURN RD, STE 340 22003 #010-02-1984 L1991 **PS** *020 †65 ‡

NORBY, Eric Hans. 3289 WOODBURN RD, STE 06 22003 #051-04-1980 L1987 **NM PTH** *020 †50,28

O'BRIEN, John Terence. 3299 WOODBURN RD STE 20 22003 #010-02-1977 L1984 **CD IC** *020 †20

OCTAIN, Bikan Singh. 4540B JOHN MARR DR 22003 #495-21-1982 L1991 **FM** *020 †18

OH, Yong Whan. 7008 LITTLE RIVER TPKE, STE E 22003 #583-03-1971 L1992 **FM AN** *020 †05,18

O'HALLORAN, Laurence Roe. 3299 WOODBURN RD STE 300 22003 #025-01-1988 L1994 **OTO** *020 †45

OZBERKMEN, Vacit Yakup. 3301 WOODBURN RD STE 307 22003 #902-10-1955 L1967 **OBG** *071 †30

PACHECO, Deborah Yvonne. 3340 WOODBURN RD, HEALTH SERVICES 22003 #048-12-1985 L1989 **P** *020 †75

PAIK, Seung Wook. 4200 DANIELS AVE 22003 #583-03-1972 L1978 **ORS** *020 †40

PARK, James Ki. 4600 JOHN MARR DR, STE 101 22003 #016-02-1995 L1999 **OPH** *020

PARK, Virginia Sunkyung. ■ 22003 #051-04-2007 **GS** *012

PARTHASARATHY, Ramaswamy. 5133 LIPSNER CT, KIDNEY&INTERNAL MEDICINE 22003 #495-33-1975 L1996 **IM NEP** *020 †20

PARVER, David Leland. 3289 WOODBURN RD 22003 #550-02-1998 L2003 **OPH** *020 †35

PARVER, Leonard Martin. 3289 WOODBURN RD 22003 #067-01-1970 L1978 **OPH** *020 †35

PEARSON, Jean H Horrigan. ■ 22003 #010-02-1952 L1956 **OBG** *020

PECK, Charles Albert, Jr. ■ 22003 #038-41-1965 L1965 **OS GS** *030 †85

PEI, Wanzheng. 3301 WOODBURN RD, STE 102 22003 #243-47-1988 L2002 **OBG** *020 †30

PEREZ, Steven John. 6715 LITTLE RIVER TPKE, STE 201A 22003 #005-06-1978 L1995 **IM** *020 †20

PHAM, Hoang Nguyen. 4326 EVERGREEN LN STE A 22003 #051-04-1986 L1989 **D** *020 †15

PILLAI, Sasikala. 3299 WOODBURN RD, STE 150 22003 #495-27-1967 L2001 **OPH** *020 †35 ‡

PIPAN, Catherine Mary. 7617 LITTLE RIVR TPKE #710 22003 #051-01-1991 L1994 **FM** *020 †18 ‡

PORETZ, Donald Martin. 3289 WOODBURN RD, INFECTIOUS DISEASES 22003 #051-04-1966 L1966 **ID IM** *020 †20

PRICE, Dudley Randolph. 3340 WOODBURN RD, WOODBURN MHC 22003 #036-07-1961 L1974 **P AM** *072 †70

PRICE, Gordon Wesley. 3299 WOODBURN RD, STE 490 22003 #036-05-1977 L1984 **PS** *020 †85,65 ‡

QUINTOS-GOMEZ, Mercedes G. 7617 LITTLE RIVER TPKE, STE 710 22003 #748-16-1988 L1993 **FM** *020 †18

QUION, Jun Anthony. 3299 WOODBURN RD, STE 200 22003 #748-02-1989 L1998 **CD** *020 †20

RAMAN, Rajesh C. 3299 WOODBURN RD, STE 230 22003 #033-05-2002 L2006 **PD** *020 †55

RAO, Lakshmi D. 8305 UPPER SPRING LN, DEWITT ARMY COMMUNITY HOSP 22003 #495-45-1987 L1995 **P** *020 †75

REING, Cornelius M. 3301 WOODBURN RD STE 309 22003 #010-02-1973 L1979 **ORS PD** *020 †55,40

RIUS, Ricardo A. 3340 WOODBURN RD 22003 #132-01-1980 L2002 **P** *020

RIXINGER-HARRIS, Ann. 3289 WOODBURN RD, INFECTIOUS DISEASES 22003 #024-01-1980 L1999 **ID IM** *020 †20

ROGAN, Kevin Michael. 3299 WOODBURN RD, STE 200 22003 #024-07-1981 L1990 **CD IM** *020 †20

ROGERS, John Raymond. 3340 WOODBURN RD, WOODBURN CENTER 22003 #056-06-1960 L1978 **P** *020 †75

RUBIO, David R. 7617 LITTLE RIVER TPKE, STE 600 22003 #035-03-1989 L1993 **IM PD** *020 †55,20

RULEY, Edward Jerome. 3289 WOODBURN RD 22003 #023-01-1964 L1993 **PN PD** *071 †55

SAADULLA, Lawand A. ■ 22003 #665-01-2006 L2006 **IM** *012

SALIH, Hassan A. 7501 LITTLE RIVER TPKE 22003 #528-01-1958 L1968 **P CHP** *020 †75

SCHEIDEMANDEL, Heinz H E. 3299 WOODBURN RD STE 300 22003 #407-04-1955 L1961 **OTO HNS** *020 †45

SCHIAVONE, Andrew A, Jr. 7369 MCWHORTER PL STE 410 22003 #041-09-1980 L1986 **P N** *020 †75

SCHMIDT, Mary Elizabeth. 3289 WOODBURN RD, STE 200 22003 #041-07-1984 L1988 **ID IM** *020 †20,55

SEDGHI, Roya. 7501 LITTLE RIVER TPKE, STE 303 22003 #051-07-1993 L1995 **IM** *020 †20

SHAMBUREK, Roland H. ■ 22003 #056-05-1953 L1977 **GP AM** *071 †70

SHREEVE, Stephen Martin. ■ 22003 #050-02-2002 L2005 **ON** *012 †20

SILVERSTEIN, Ross Stuart. 3299 WOODBURN RD STE 490 22003 #035-06-1981 L1985 **P** *020 †75

SIMONIAN, Simon J. 3301 WOODBURN RD, STE 306 22003 #917-30-1957 L1990 **GS** *071 †85

SMITH, Philip Scott. 3340 WOODBURN RD 22003 #001-02-1997 L1997 **CHP P** *020 †75

SOUTTER, Alexander D. 3301 WOODBURN RD, STE 205 22003 #035-01-1988 L2001 **PDS UP** *020 †85

SPILIOTIS, Bessie Grekas. ■ 22003 #418-01-1976 L1978 **PDE PD** *020 †55

STEG, James Anthony. 3299 WOODBURN RD STE 4 22003 #030-05-1981 L1984 **P CHP** *020 †75

STEPHENS, Robert Frederic. 3289 WOODBURN RD 22003 #028-02-1971 L1980 **OPH** *020 †35

STINGER, Robert B. 3340 WOODBURN RD 22003 #010-02-1981 L1985 **ORS** *020 †40

STRANGE, Robert Edward. 3340 WOODBURN RD, WOODBURN CENTER 22003 #017-20-1957 L1973 **P** *020 †75

SUGASTTI, Oscar F. 3299 WOODBURN RD, STE 230 22003 #176-01-1983 L2006 **PD** *020 †55

SUNNENBERG, Cecilia M. 3299 WOODBURN RD STE 400 22003 #038-40-1990 L1994 **P** *020 †75

SUSEMIHL, Lida Patricia. 3299 WOODBURN RD, STE 230 22003 #001-02-2001 L2001 **PD** *020 †55

SVOBODA, Jeff Thos. 3340 WOODBURN RD 22003 #016-11-1982 L1994 **P** *020 †20,75
TAVALLALI, Morad. 3299 WOODBURN RD STE 310 22003 #010-02-1985 L1993 **PS GS** *020 †65
THAHANE, Lineo Keneuoe. ■ 22003 #028-02-2001 L2003 **PD** *020 †55
TIMMES, Joseph J, Jr. 3301 WOODBURN RD STE 204 22003 #010-02-1969 L1970 **OPH** *020 †35
TRAMMEL, Demaree Lisa. 3340 WOODBURN RD 22003 #036-07-1997 L2006 **P** *020
TRAN, Vinh Binh. 7611 LITTLE RIVER TPKE, STE 108W 22003 #010-02-1992 L1995 **ORS** *020 †40
TSAO, Maria Santiago. 3340 WOODBURN RD, WOODBURN CTR 22003 #010-02-1994 L1998 **P** *020
TSAPOS, Michael John. ■ 22003 #418-01-1957 L1965 **GYN** *071 †30
TSITOS, Tony A. 7501 LITTLE RIVER TPKE 22003 #902-01-1957 L1966 **P CHP** *071
USMAN, Antonio K. 5101C BACKLICK RD 22003 #561-11-1990 L1993 **IM** *020 †20
VALENTI, Branko Sergio. 3301 WOODBURN RD, STE 211 22003 #561-09-1953 L1960 **OBG** *071 †30
VARA, Anthony Richard. 3299 WOODBURN RD, STE 450 22003 #010-02-1985 L1991 **U** *020 †95
VEJCIK, Scott Mark. ■ 22003 #422-01-2004 L2007 **FM** *100 †18 ‡
VERGNE, Raymond. 3301 WOODBURN RD, STE 301 22003 #035-08-1971 L1990 **CD CCM** *020 †20
VILLAVICENCIO, Olmedo. 7617 LITTLE RIVER TPKE, STE 600 22003 #319-01-1962 L1967 **PD FM** *071 †55,18
VONPECHMANN, Walter S. 3289 WOODBURN RD 22003 #010-01-1996 L2000 **OBG** *020 †30
WEINGARTEN, Elizabeth Ann. 7617 LITTLE RIVER TPKE, STE 600 22003 #035-06-2004 L2004 **FM** *020 †18
WELGOSS, Jeffrey Alan. 3289 WOODBURN RD 22003 #041-02-1986 L1998 **OBG OS** *020 †30
WHEELER, David Allen. 3289 WOODBURN RD, INFECTIOUS DISEASES 22003 #051-01-1982 L1996 **IM** *020 †20
WILSON, Jerry Scott. 3340 WOODBURN RD, WOODBURN CENTER FOR COMMUN 22003 #047-20-2003 L2007 **P** *020
WRIGHT, Thomas Patrick. 3289 WOODBURN RD, STE 390 22003 #051-01-1982 L1984 **GS CRS** *020 †85,10
YEN, Edwina. ■ 22003 #065-01-1979 L1994 **FM** *071
ZADEH, Hugh Bozorg. 7611 LITTLE RIVER TPKE, STE 101E 22003 #023-01-2004 L2007 **OMF** *020
ZAHIR, Lubna Varcie. 3301 WOODBURN RD STE 202 22003 #495-01-1993 L2001 **IM** *020 †20
ZOLGHADR, Mojgan Michelle. 3299 WOODBURN RD, STE 380 22003 #422-01-1999 L2002 **IM** *020 †20

APPALACHIA – WISE

AUGUSTINE, Paul. 507 W MAIN ST, APPLACHIA FAMILY HEALTH CE 24216 #495-52-1982 L1999 **IM NEP** *020 †20
PARANTHAMAN, Subramaniam. 508 W MAIN ST 24216 #495-04-1965 L1975 **PUD CCM** *020 †20 ‡

APPOMATTOX – APPOMATTOX

POWELL, Kenneth Allen. 24522 #051-04-1974 L1975 **FM** *020 †18
SMITH, Larry Francis. PO BOX 666, 181 OLD COURT HOUSE RD 24522 #051-01-1976 L1977 **IM GPM** *020

ARLINGTON – ARLINGTON

ABEDI, Masomeh Seyeda. 2001 15TH ST N, APT 1108 22201 #063-01-2006 **IM** *012
ABELE, Jennifer Ann. 1701 N GEORGE MASON DR, MEDICAL STAFF OFFICE 22205 #010-01-1999 L2002 **EM** *020 †16
ABRAHA, Tilahun Haile. ■ 22204 #913-18-1991 **P** *012
ACEVEDO, Miguel A. 3833 FAIRFAX DR, GUMC AT BALLSTON 22203 #429-01-1966 L1972 **OTO HNS** *020 †45
ADAMS, Hunter Doherty. ■ 22213 #051-04-1971 L1972 **GP** *030
ADAMS, Nikki Lee. 46 S GLEBE RD STE 103, RENASSENCE CTR 22204 #016-42-1986 L1998 **P OBG** *020 †75
AGHAEGBUNA, Onochie A C. 4201 WILSON BLVD # 110/612, ATTN: JOE MONAHAN 22203 #690-04-1994 L2001 **FM** *020 †18
AHMED, Mohammed. 22201 #495-21-1964 L1971 **IM END** *020 †20
AHMED, Navera Rashid. 1635 N GEORGE MASON DR, STE 220 22205 #160-02-1994 L2004 **RHU** *020 †20
AKBAR, Mohammad. 611 S CARLIN SPRINGS RD, SUIR 401 22204 #308-11-1985 L1991 **IM** *020 †20
ALATTAS, Elias Ali. ■ 22209 #010-01-2003 **IM** *100
ALBERT, Catherine Michell. ■ 22209 #010-02-2008 *012
ALBRIGO, John Louis. 2445 ARMY NAVY DR 22206 #035-15-1970 L1976 **ORS** *020 †40
ALEXANDROVA, Natalia A. 611 S CARLIN SPRINGS RD, STE 208 22204 #913-99-1991 L2000 **IM** *020 †75
ALI, Gholam H. 4040 FAIRFAX DR, STE 140 22203 #528-01-1975 L1996 **CD** *020 †20
ALI, Raziuddin. 22201 #051-07-2005 L2005 **DR** *012
ALIKHAN, Roohi. 46 S GLEBE RD, STE 103 22204 #748-10-1990 L2001 **P** *020
ALKIRE, Rebecca Ann. 22201 #055-01-2005 L2005 **PD** *012
ALLCOCK, Edward G. 1715 N GEORGE MASON DR 22205 #035-75-1992, ▲ L2004 **PM** *020 †60
ALLEN, Cyril Anthony. 2111 JEFFERSON DAVIS HWY, APT 508N 22202 #036-01-1974 L1976 **IM ON** *020
ALLEN, David Franklyn. 46 S GLEBE RD, STE 103 22204 #803-02-1969 L1991 **P** *020 †75
ALSADOON, Nawaf Khalid. ■ 22201 #010-01-2004 *100
ALVARADO, Gilberto Jose. 1715 N GEORGE MASON DR, STE 504 22205 #042-01-2001 L2006 **OSM** *020
ALVIS, Colette Raeann. ■ 22204 #010-02-2005 L2005 **OBG** *012
AMEDEO, Ralph Michael. 1715 N GEORGE MASN DR #306 22205 #010-02-1979 L1981 **IM** *020 †20
AMINI, Dennis. 1715 N GEORGE MASON DR, STE 302 22205 #010-02-1998 L1998 **OBG** *020 †30
ANDERSON, Edward Lee. 1611 N KENT ST, STE 1100 22209 #010-02-1976 L1978 **IM OM** *030 †20

ANDRE, Jason Lionel. ■ 22206 #010-03-2008 *012
ANSARI, Iradj. ■ 22209 #517-05-1968 L1976 **U** *020 †95
ANTONETTI, David Michael. 1715 N GEORGE MASON DR, UITE 108 22205 #010-02-2002 L2002 **IM** *100 †20
APPLEMAN, Gregory Michael. ■ 22204 #010-02-2004 L2006 **AN** *012
ARCHER, Wm Reynolds, III. 2445 ARMY NAVY DR 22206 #048-02-1980 L1984 **OBG** *020 †30
ARMBRUSTMACHER, Vernon W. ■ 22203 #025-01-1964 L1965 **FOP** *071 †50
ARNOLD, Lauren Elizabeth. ■ 22209 #010-02-2008 *012
ARSHI, Manpreet Kaur. 4840 31ST ST S STE B 22206 #496-46-1997 L2003 **IM** *020 †20
ARTMAN, Christian Eric. ■ 22201 #041-15-2000 L2001 **RNR** *100
ARZADON, Joseph M. 611 S CARLIN SPRINGS RD, STE 308 22204 #008-02-1994 L1996 **OMF CS** *020
ASCUNCE, Gil. 1715 N GEORGE MASN DR #410 22205 #847-10-1973 L1978 **GE IM** *020 †20
ASHTON, Wesley Scott. 2300 9TH ST S, GRIFFIN & SZIPL PC 22204 #041-09-1991 L1998 **PD** *020 †55
AVERY, Gordon L. 1635 N GEORGE MASON DR, STE 310 22205 #035-06-1974 L1980 **ORS** *020 †40
AWAN, Mushtaq Ahmad. 4040 FAIRFAX DR 22203 #704-01-1969 L1986 **GS GP** *020 †85
AZARMAHAN, Roya M. 1715 N GEORGE MASON DR 501 22205 #517-08-1984 L1994 **IM** *020 †20
AZEVEDO, Romeu Manuel. ■ 22201 #033-06-2004 L2005 **IM** *100 †20
BACARRA, Abraham Viste. 1701 N GEORGE MASON DR 22205 #748-08-1960 L1974 **AN** *020
BACHHUYNH, Thiengiang. 1715 N GEORGE MASON DR, STE 102 22205 #010-01-2001 L2001 **END** *012
BACKER, Joseph Anthony. 1701 N GEORGE MASON DR 22205 #017-20-1965 L1973 **R** *020 †80
BAILEY, Sally Joo. ■ 22205 #011-04-1998 L1998 **AI** *020 †55,03
BAIRD, Dean Eliot. 1701 N GEORGE MASON DR, VIRGINIA HOSP CTR DEPT RAD 22205 #023-12-1987 L1998 **DR** *020 †80
BAJAJ, Komal. ■ 22201 #010-01-2003 L2006 **PD** *100 †55
BAKER, Janna Elizabeth. ■ 22205 #041-12-2004 L2005 **EM** *012
BAKER, Omar Azzam. ■ 22209 #010-01-2008 *012
BALDOVICH, Kevin Joseph. ■ 22202 #041-14-2005 L2007 **FP** *012
BALDRATE, Christine Zilin. 1701 N GEORGE MASON DR 22205 #008-02-1999 L2004 **PD** *020 †55 ‡
BALL, Kirsten Vansteenber. ■ 22205 #010-01-2000 L2000 **GP** *020
BALLON, Lawrence Marc. 1715 N GEORGE MASON DR, STE 104 22205 #010-02-1972 L1975 **P PYA** *020 †75
BANKS, David Alan. 1701 N GEORGE MASON DR, STE 2D 22205 #049-01-1988 L1992 **AN** *020 †05
BARHAM, William Bruce. ■ 22201 #051-04-1984 L1985 **ID IM** *075
BARKDULL, Thad Joseph. 1715 N GEORGE MASON DR, STE 504 22205 #023-12-2000 L2000 **FSM** *020 †18
BARNES, Adelaide Elise. ■ 22209 #010-01-2008 *012
BARNES, Steven Lindsay. ■ 22201 #056-06-1987 L1989 **OM FM** *030 †70,18
BARTON, Bette Lee. ■ 22207 #010-01-1978 L1980 **CLP** *071 †50
BASAVARAJ, Ashwin. ■ 22209 #035-09-2007 L2007 **IM** *012
BASELGA, Christina Isabel. 1625 N GEORGE MASON DR 22205 #041-09-1995 L1997 **IM** *020 †20
BASHIAN, Ronald Stephen. ■ 22203 #035-08-1972 L1977 **PD** *071 †55
BATHIJA, Chela Ram. ■ 22203 #118-01-1978 **P** *100
BATSEL, Tanis Minette. ■ 22201 #023-12-1993 L1994 **GPM** *020 †70
BAUER, George Brian. ■ 22205 #038-41-1985 L1986 **IM IMG** *074
BAUMBUSCH, Clark Case. ■ 22201 #010-01-2007 L2007 **ORS** *012
BAYAZIT, Lutfi Y. ■ 22202 #902-03-1955 L1997 **GP IM** *071
BELCHER, Justin Miles. ■ 22201 #041-15-2004 L2004 **IM** *100 †20
BENJAMIN, Crystal Anne. ■ 22206 #021-05-2004 L2005 **AN** *012
BENNETT, Caroline Griffis. ■ 22203 #010-02-2008 *012
BENTHIN, Cody Jens. ■ 22209 #010-02-2006 L2006 **IM** *012
BERGAMINI, Paula Marie. 1635 N GEORGE MASON DR, STE 490 22205 #051-07-1991 L1992 **IM** *020 †20
BHAGVATHULA, Lakshmi R. 611 S CARLIN SPRINGS RD, STE 310 22204 #495-50-1997 L2002 **IM** *020 †20
BHAT, Inder Krishan. 611 S CARLIN SPRINGS RD, STE 503 22204 #495-51-1970 L1979 **CRS GS** *020 †10,85
BHATT, Rakesh Ravindra. 601 S CARLIN SPRINGS RD 22204 #495-76-1984 L1998 **AN PME** *020
BLACK, Christina Marie. ■ 22205 #041-14-2004 L2004 **OBG** *012
BLANCATO, Louis S. ■ 22201 #035-09-1945 L1947 **AN** *071 †05
BLEI, Carol Lynne. 601 S CARLIN SPRINGS RD 22204 #005-15-1969 L1977 **NM DR** *071 †80,28
BLOOM, Allyson Greer. 1701 N GEORGE MASON DR, MEDICAL STAFF OFFICE 22205 #010-01-2002 L2002 **EM** *100
BLOOM, Robert Leslie. 1715 N GEORGE MASON DR, STE 106 22205 #024-07-1973 L1976 **PUD CCM** *020 †20
BLUMENTHAL, Kevin Bryce. ■ 22206 #051-07-2003 L2004 **U** *012
BOLAND, Brian John. 1715 N GEORGE MASON DR, STE 406 22205 #051-01-1971 L1977 **IM VM** *020 †20
BONDY, Harold Eugene. 611 S CARLIN SPRINGS RD, STE 203 22204 #055-01-1969 L1976 **U** *020 †95
BORGES, Alberto Andres. 1635 N GEORGE MASON DR, STE 480 22205 #308-08-1983 L1986 **HO IM** *020
BORILLO, Romeo Bisquera. 46 S GLEBE RD, STE 100 22204 #748-01-1964 L1972 **GP PTH** *020
BORN, Kathryn. 1701 N GEORGE MASON DR, OBGYN 22205 #035-46-2002 L2002 **OBG** *100
BORUCHOW, Lillibeth B. 1715 N GEORGE MASON DR, STE 409 22205 #038-40-1963 L1971 **P** *020
BOWES, Joan Elizabeth. ■ 22207 #010-02-1990 L2000 **IM** *020 †20
BOXER, Daniel Ethan. ■ 22202 #422-01-2005 L2005 **IM** *012
BOYETTE, Lisa Blackburn. ■ 22209 #051-01-2007 *012
BRADY, Steven Carl. ■ 22207 #028-03-1981 **P** *100
BRANCHE, George C, III. 2445 ARMY NAVY DR 22206 #010-03-1982 L1987 **ORS** *020 †40
BRISCOE, Donald. PO BOX 15429 22215 #539-06-1983 L1990 **PTH** *020 †50
BRITTON, Vicki Viveros. ■ 22203 #011-02-2006 L2006 **IM** *012
BRIX, Kelley Ann. ■ 22205 #025-01-1978 L1979 **OM PHP** *040 †70
BROHL, Andrew Scott. ■ 22203 #011-02-2006 L2006 **IM** *012
BROMLEY, Nicholle Daniel. ■ 22201 #010-01-2008 *012

BRUNER, Denise E. 5015 LEE HWY STE 201 22207 #010-03-1979 L1980 **NTR FM** *020

BRYAN, Louis. 601 S CARLIN SPRINGS RD 22204 #047-05-1952 L1968 **AN** *071 †05

BUCAYCAY, Eleanor F. ■ 22204 #748-10-1978 L1999 **IM** *020 †20

BUCHANAN, Matthew M. 2445 ARMY NAVY DR, STE 300 22206 #038-40-1998 L2004 **ORS** *020 †40

BUCK, Alfred Sands. ■ 22202 #035-20-1962 L1963 **OS U** *071 †85,95

BUCKLEY, Robert Hobson. ■ 22209 #004-01-1988 L1988 **PD** *020 †55

BUEK, John David. 1701 N GEORGE MASON DR 22205 #041-13-1993 L2001 **OBG** *020 †30

BUESING, Mary A. 1635 N GEORGE MASON DR 22205 #036-07-1978 L1988 **ID IM** *030 †20

BULLOCK, Robert Graham. ■ 22207 #010-01-1954 L1960 **IM IMG** *071 †20

BURKA, Jennifer Mara. ■ 22201 #010-01-2003 L2005 **OPH** *012

BURKE, Amy Lynn. 3833 FAIRFAX DR, AT BALLSTON 22203 #021-01-1997 L1997 **MPD** *020 †20,55

BURKE, Kevin Michael. ■ 22209 #010-02-2008 *012

BURKE, Thomas John. 2111 WILSON BLVD STE 700 22201 #007-02-1982 L1996 **P** *062 †70,75

BUSH, Kelvin Nathanvana. ■ 22202 #010-01-2008 *012

BUTLER, Thomas Parke. 1635 N GEORGE MASON DR, STE 170 22205 #038-06-1971 L1978 **ON HEM** *020 †20

CADSAWAN DE LUCIANO, M T. ■ 22202 #748-02-1939 L1965 **AM GP** *071

CALISTE, Xzabia Annette. ■ 22201 #023-12-2006 L2006 *012

CAMPBELL, Jill Miriam. ■ 22204 #047-20-2006 L2006 **PD** *012

CAMPBELL, Kevin Charles. 1701 N GEORGE MASON DR, MEDICAL STAFF OFFICE 22205 #051-04-1993 L1995 **EM** *020 †16

CANADAS, Rafael. 3800 FAIRFAX DR STE 3, TOWER VILLAS 22203 #319-01-1968 L1984 **OBG** *020

CANADAS, Rodrigo Eduardo. ■ 22203 #319-01-1971 **OBG** *020

CANTER, Maria Pettit. 1625 N GEORGE MASON DR, STE 475 22205 #010-02-1999 L1999 **OBG** *100 †30

CARPOUSIS, Dean Peter. 2001 COLUMBIA PIKE, STE 131 22204 #041-09-1979 L1982 **CD IM** *020 †20

CARROLL, Charles P H. 1701 N GEORGE MASON DR 22205 #010-02-1961 L1976 **NTR N** *072

CASEY, Catherine Sue. 1715 N GEORGE MASON DR, STE 205 22205 #051-04-1974 L1977 **PD** *020 †55

CASKIE, Sandra. 1715 N GEORGE MASON DR, STE 305 22205 #010-01-1982 L1984 **OBG** *020 †30

CHAIKIND, Michael Harry. 1701 N GEORGE MASON DR, STE 2D 22205 #048-04-1987 L1991 **AN** *020 †75

CHALMETA, Alberto. 611 S CARLIN SPRINGS RD, STE 208 22204 #847-04-1961 L1972 **N CHN** *020 †75

CHANG, Yonmee. ■ 22201 #033-05-2007 L2007 **IM** *012

CHAUDHARY, Amita. 1635 N GEORGE MASON DR, STE 430 22205 #495-30-1983 L2000 **IM** *020 †18

CHAUDHARY, Aseem. 1635 N GEORGE MASON DR, STE 430 22205 #495-55-1980 L1996 **IM** *020 †20

CHEN, Sharon Man-Heng. ■ 22203 #048-02-2007 L2007 **IM** *012

CHEYNEY, Kathleen Frances. 601 S CARLIN SPRINGS RD, NORTHERN VA DOCTORS HOSP 22204 #041-02-1974 L1985 **TS CD** *020 †85,90

CHHABRA, Adhuna. 3835 9TH ST N, APT 402E 22203 #051-04-2004 L2004 **AI** *012 †20

CHIARELLO, Robert Jos. 1800 N OAK ST APT 1820 22209 #035-45-1979 L1980 **P** *020 †75

CHIEN, Thomas Suehwa. ■ 22203 #010-01-2005 L2005 **IM** *100

CHMIEL, Andrew Jos. 3033 WILSON BLVD 22201 #017-20-1965 L1970 **P PYA** *020 †75

CHO, Henry Heechang. 2116 N BRANDYWINE ST 22207 #051-04-1997 L1997 **FM** *020 †18

CHREA, Siphath. 3215 COLUMBIA PIKE 22204 #215-01-1972 L1984 **GP** *020

CHU, Jeanine Ngoc-Anh. 1635 N GEORGE MASON DR, STE 490 22205 #010-01-1991 L1994 **IM** *020 †20

CHUN, William Jung. ■ 22201 #035-09-2004 L2005 **IM** *100 †20

CHUNG, Wook. ■ 22201 #583-10-1967 L1976 **OBG** *071 †30

CIFALOGLIO, Claire Marie. 3033 WILSON BLVD, STE 600B 22201 #041-07-1974 L1991 **PD** *020 †30

CIOFALO, Carol Ellen. ■ 22205 #010-02-1978 L1981 **OBG** *071 †30

CLAPP, Deborah Gray. 1701 N GEORGE MASON DR 22205 #051-04-1978 L1981 **PD** *020 †55

CLARK, Bradley Charles. ■ 22204 #033-05-2008 *012

CLARK, Robert Alan. ■ 22201 #048-12-1981 L2007 **EM IM** *020 †20,16

COBBS, Gwendolyn Patterso. 1715 N GEORGE MASON DR 22205 #010-02-1992 L1992 **OBG** *020 †30

COCILOVO, Costanza. ■ 22207 #035-09-1996 L2000 **CRS** *020 †85,10

COHEN, Emil Israel. ■ 22207 #010-01-1998 L2004 **VIR** *012 †80

COHEN, Sylvie Israel. ■ 22205 #010-01-1995 L1995 **OM PLM** *030 †55,70

COLIN, Caroline Marie. ■ 22201 #010-02-2003 L2008 **OBG** *100

COLLEN, Jacob Fredrick. ■ 22209 #023-12-2002 L2003 **IM** *012

CONLEY, Diane H. 1701 N GEORGE MASON DR 22205 #048-14-1983 L1987 **DR** *020 †80

CONNALLY, Nathaniel T, Jr. 3563 N ABINGDON ST 22207 #051-01-1962 L1962 **IM** *020 †20

CONNOLLY, Catherine Ann. ■ 22213 #539-04-1991 L1999 **IMG** *100

CONTIS, George. 1716 WILSON BLVD 22209 #010-01-1958 L1969 **PHP PD** *071 †55

COOPER, Betsy Jane. 927 S WALTER REED DR, STE 12 22204 #047-07-1974 L1982 **P** *020 †75

COPPA, Nicholas Daniel. ■ 22201 #010-02-2002 L2002 **NS** *012

CORDERO, Steven Caldwell. ■ 22206 #023-12-2008 *012

CORNEJO YUMPE, Christian. 3045 COLUMBIA PIKE STE A 22204 #737-06-2000 **PD** *020 †55

CORRENTY, Patrick Anthony. 1715 N GEORGE MASON DR 22205 #041-14-1995 L1995 **IM** *020 †20

COUDON, Wilson Levering. 1400 S JOYCE ST, STE 126 22202 #051-01-1970 L1970 **PUD IM** *020 †20

COVERT, Caroline R. ■ 22201 #064-01-1977 **OS** *020 †05

COVEY, Carlton James. ■ 22201 #023-12-2006 L2007 **FP** *012

COX, Justin Michael. ■ 22206 #028-03-2004 L2007 *100 †20

COX-IYAMU, Roxanne. 5232 LEE HWY, WWC-NOVA 22207 #010-03-1986 L2000 **ID** *020

CRASSWELLER, Karen Doell. ■ 22205 #010-02-1988 L1992 **P** *020 †75

CRAVEN, Katherine Leslie. ■ 22202 #010-01-2008 *012

CROGHAN, Thomas Woodward. 1200 S HAYES ST, `AND CORPORATION CENTER 22202 #055-01-1981 L1984 **IM RHU** *075 †20

CROSSLAND, Stanley Gramch. 611 S CARLIN SPRINGS RD, STE 302 22204 #010-01-1971 L1972 **VS GS** *020 †85 ‡

CROWTHER, Mary Elizabeth. 1635 N GEORGE MASON DR, STE 185 22205 #143-01-1974 L2001 **OBG** *020

CURA, Fernando Adrian. ■ 22201 #132-01-1990 L2000 *100

CUTLER, John Robt. 4401 WILSON BLVD, STE 700 22203 #028-02-1980 L1981 **N** *020 †75

CZANDER, Eric Walter. 611 S CARLIN SPRINGS RD, STE 208 22204 #033-05-1991 L2000 **N** *020 †75

DACEY, Michael Jos, Jr. 1801 CRYSTAL DR 22202 #010-01-1990 L1994 **CCM** *020 †20

DAGGLE, Lindsey Elizabeth. ■ 22201 #010-02-2008 *012

DAHLINGHAUS, Erin Kathlee. ■ 22203 #038-43-2006 L2006 **PD** *012

DALEY, Timothy Horton. 1715 N GEORGE MASON DR, CASEY DALEY 22205 #010-02-1957 L1963 **PD** *071 †55

DALLABETTA, Gina Ann. 4401 WILSON BLVD, # 700 22203 #023-07-1983 L2001 **ID** *020 †20

DALLAS, Olympia P. 601 S CARLIN SPRINGS RD 22204 #051-04-1980 L1981 **FM** *020 †18

DALTON, Henry Tucker. 3801 FAIRFAX DR, STE 74N 22203 #051-01-1972 L1972 **OPH** *020 †35

DANACEAU, Steve Marc. 2501 N GLEBE RD, STE 101 22207 #051-04-1992 L1999 **ORS** *020 †40

DANIELS, John R. ■ 22207 #038-40-1950 L1983 **GP OS** *020

DANNIS, Marjorie Faith. 1625 N GEORGE MASON DR, STE 425 22205 #035-46-1991 L2004 **IM** *020 †20

DAS, Vincent Suneja. 5512 8TH ST S 22204 #010-03-1990 L1993 **FM** *020 †18

DAUD, Faisal Ahmad. ■ 22201 #036-05-2007 L2007 **IM** *012

DAVE, Yogen Arunkumar. ■ 22202 #041-13-2004 L2005 **IM** *100

DAVIS, Lonnie Darnell. 1715 N GEORGE MASON DR, NIRSCHL ORTHOPAEDIC CENTER 22205 #051-01-2000 L2005 **OSM** *020

DAVIS, Stephen Lawrence. ■ 22209 #048-12-2007 L2007 **ORS** *012

DEBASS, Brickte Lyn. 3833 FAIRFAX DR, STE 200 22203 #023-01-1996 L1999 **IM** *020 †18

DELANGE, Susan Marissa. ■ 22203 #016-43-2007 L2007 **IM** *012

DELANGE, Tyler Cameron. ■ 22204 #049-01-2004 L2007 **EM** *020

DE MUTH, Susan A Shultis. 3045 COLUMBIA PIKE STE A, ARLINGTON PEDIATRIC CENTER 22204 #041-01-1973 L1985 **PD** *072 †55

DENDULURI, Neelima. 1635 N GEORGE MASON DR, STE 170 22205 #021-06-1999 L1999 **ON** *100 †20

DESAI, Anish Sumant. ■ 22204 #020-02-2001 L2004 **IM** *100 †20

DESAI, Ramesh M. 611 S CARLIN SPRNGS RD #310 22204 #495-23-1965 L1975 **GE IM** *020 †20

DEUTSCH, Nina. ■ 22207 #048-14-1999 L2003 **PAN** *020 †05

DEVICK, Heather Nicole. ■ 22203 #011-02-2006 L2006 **IM** *012

DHIR, Rohit Robert. ■ 22201 #010-02-2008 *012

DIAZ, Adolfo Leon. 3801 FAIRFAX DR 22203 #264-01-1959 L1968 **FM** *020

DIEP, Lien. ■ 22201 #010-03-2002 **N** *012

DI MATTINA, Michael. 46 S GLEBE RD STE 301 22204 #051-04-1980 L1982 **REN OBG** *020 †30

DITTMAR, Elke Gertrud. ■ 22202 #409-22-1999 L2002 **PD** *100

DO, Thi Khoa. ■ 22201 #036-01-2005 **N** *012

DOAN, Phuoc Kim. 1220 N HUDSON ST 22201 #942-01-1969 L1982 **IM GP** *020

DODEK, Oscar Irving. 1635 N GEORGE MASON DR, STE 155 22205 #010-01-1956 L1992 **GYN** *020 †30

DRYER, Amy Louise. ■ 22203 #035-01-2003 L2006 **PD** *100 †55

DUARTE, Victor M. ■ 22209 #010-02-2008 *012

DUCIC, Mariana. 1625 N GEORGE MASON DR, STE 494 22205 #957-01-1992 L1995 **PD** *020 †55

DUGGAN, Francis Paul. ■ 22201 #010-02-1995 L1997 **EM** *020 †20

DUHAMEL, David Raymond. 1400 S JOYCE ST 22202 #010-02-1995 L1995 **PCC** *020 †20

DUNCAN, Loretta La Verne. ■ 22204 #010-03-1977 L1989 **P PHP** *020 †75

DUNWOODY, William James. 2786 S ARLINGTON MILL DR 22206 #010-01-1985 L1990 **DR** *062 †80

DUONG, Dinh Hung. 1220 N HUDSON ST 22201 #941-02-1969 L1982 **GP PTH** *020

DUVAL, Jules Riel. ■ 22207 #050-02-1996 L2004 **FM** *020 †18

DVORAK, Josef. 1635 N GEORGE MASON DR, STE 350 22205 #286-02-1969 L1976 **END IM** *020 †20

DVORAK, Vera Cermin. 1635 N GEORGE MASON DR 22205 #286-02-1970 L1976 **IM ID** *020 †20

EDWARDS, Christopher Stan. ■ 22201 #010-02-2008 *012

ELGART, Mervyn L. ■ 22203 #035-20-1957 L1971 **D DMP** *071 †15

ELLIOTT, John Jeffrey. 1635 N GEORGE MASON DR, STE 300 22205 #010-02-1977 L1981 **OBG** *020 †30

ELLIS, Ruth Dora. 2530 24TH ST N 22207 #016-11-1988 L1998 **FM** *020 †18

ELLISON, Adam Covino. ■ 22204 #026-08-2004 L2007 **ORS** *012

ELSAWAF, Mohamed Ashraf. ■ 22209 #033-06-2002 L2002 **PCC** *012 †20

ENDRES, Jennifer Katherin. ■ 22201 #033-06-2007 L2007 **PD** *012

ENGLAND, Dahlia Lisa. 1701 N GEORGE MASON DR, VIRGINIA HOSPITAL CENTER 22205 #035-15-1995 L2006 **EM** *020 †16

ENOS, William F, III. 601 S CARLIN SPRINGS RD 22204 #010-01-1976 L1983 **PTH** *020 †50

ERICKSON, Kevin Furman. ■ 22209 #041-01-2006 **IM** *012

ESKANDARI, Sara. ■ 22201 #025-07-2007 L2007 **EM** *012

ESPINEL, Carlos Hugo. 1715 N GEORGE MASN DR #401 22205 #264-06-1963 L1974 **IM CD** *020 †20

EVERS, Joseph Chas. 1701 N GEORGE MASON DR 22205 #010-02-1955 L1958 **PD OS** *020

EZMERLI, Nissrin Mahmoud. ■ 22213 #010-01-2003 L2005 **GE** *012 †20

FALO, Pablo Antonio. 1625 N GEORGE MASON DR, STE 474 22205 #132-01-1967 L1972 **GYN** *020 †30

FAND, R Sally Bogolub. 1701 N GEORGE MASON DR 22205 #016-02-1952 L1992 **FM IM** *071 †18

FARLEY, Nicole C. ■ 22204 #023-01-1995 L1998 **FM** *020 †18

FARRELL, Timothy Paul. 1625 N GEORGE MASON DR, STE 414 22205 #010-02-1987 L2004 **IM** *020 †20

FARRELLY, Erin Elizabeth. ■ 22201 #010-01-2007 **ORS** *012

FAVOT, Mark Joseph. ■ 22201 #010-02-2008 *012

FELICIANO, Josephine Loue. ■ 22209 #010-02-2004 L2004 **IM** *100 †20

FENDER, Gary Richard. 1701 N GEORGE MASON DR 22205 #033-05-1979 L1982 **IM** *020 †20

FERDOWSIAN, Hope Ridvan. ■ 22207 #039-01-2001 L2005 **IM** *100 †70,20

FERIOZI, Dan John. 2221 N BUCHANAN ST 22207 #036-07-1948 L1951 **PTH PD** *030

FERNANDEZ, Miguel Angel. 1625 N GEORGE MASON DR, STE 474 22205 #011-02-1990 L1994 **OBG** *020 †30

FIGUEROA, Armando B. ■ 22201 #748-08-1960 L1968 **IM CD** *020

FILIPESCU, Nicolae. 3801 FAIRFAX DR, STE 31 22203 #010-01-1975 L1976 **OBG** *020 †30

FINDLEY, Andrew L, Jr. 1700 N MOORE ST STE 1200, TRICARE REGIONAL OFFICE NO 22209 #001-06-1985 L1985 **GS SO** *020 †85

FIROOZBAKHT, Farshid. ■ 22202 #539-06-2004 L2004 **IM** *100 †20

FITZPATRICK, Brendan Mich. ■ 22204 #010-02-2007 L2007 **IM** *012

FITZPATRICK, Kelly West. ■ 22204 #010-02-2006 L2006 **IM** *012

FLACK, Thelma U. 3033 WILSON BLVD, ARLINGTON COUNTY DHS 22201 #748-10-1965 L1984 **PD HEM** *074

FLECKER, Kathleen Ann. ■ 22201 #010-01-2005 L2007 **PD** *012

FLORES, Carlos Alberto. ■ 22209 #010-02-2008 *012

FLORES, Gilbert Eduardo. ■ 22205 #176-04-1997 L2004 **GS** *100 †85

FLOREZ, Gerson Bruce. ■ 22206 #010-02-2008 *012

FOULKE, Charles Wm. ■ 22207 #010-01-1953 L1956 **IM OS** *020

FOX, Irina Jessica. ■ 22204 #010-01-2008 *012

FRAGA, Juan Reynaldo. 1701 N GEORGE MASON DR 22205 #275-01-1950 L1964 **PD** *071 †55

FRAKE, Paul Christopher. ■ 22201 #010-01-2008 *012

FRANK, Randolph A, Jr. 1715 N GEORGE MASON DR, STE 304 22205 #010-02-1986 L1988 **P PYG** *020 †75

FRANKLIN, William Geo. 1715 N GEORGE MASON DR, NO 107 22205 #051-01-1971 L1971 **CD** *020 †20

FREEMAN, Kenneth Ashton. 921 N QUINCY ST 22203 #036-01-1981 L1989 **IM** *020

FRICKA, Kevin Bradley. 2445 ARMY NAVY DR 22206 #010-01-1999 L2006 **ORS** *100

FRIEDMAN, Loren Louis. 1635 N GEORGE MASON DR, ARLINGTON PALLIATIVE CARE 22205 #035-46-1988 L1991 **PLM** *020 †18

FRIEDMAN, Mark Scott. ■ 22209 #035-08-2005 L2005 **IM** *012

FRILOUX, Louis A, III. 2786 S ARLINGTON MILL DR, INSIGHT IMAGING CENTER OF 22206 #016-02-1981 L1990 **DR** *020 †80

FUA, Frances Pioquinto. ■ 22203 #051-04-2007 L2007 **IM** *012

FURLONG, Wm Benedict, Jr. 1635 N GEORGE MASON DR, STE 440 22205 #041-12-1981 L1991 **ID IM** *020 †20

GAETA, Miguel Mauricio. ■ 22209 #005-14-2003 **GS** *012

GAITATZES, Chrysanthe G. ■ 22201 #024-05-2000 L2002 **NPM** *100 †55 ‡

GALAL, Fathy Sayed. ■ 22207 #915-02-1954 L1975 **RO** *071 †80

GALE, Seth Alan. ■ 22203 #051-04-2008 *012

GALLAGHER, Mary Ellen. 606 S TAYLOR ST 22204 #422-01-1997 L2003 **MPD** *100

GALLINEK, Wilfred Ernest. ■ 22207 #010-01-1955 L1962 **IM** *020

GALLOWAY, Thomas James. ■ 22209 #011-03-2005 L2005 **RO** *012

GANDY, Charles Lewis, III. 1701 N GEORGE MASON DR, DEPT OF ANES 22205 #010-01-1976 L1982 **AN** *020 †05

GARADA, Hazem S. 601 S CARLIN SPRINGS RD 22204 #584-01-1988 L1995 **IM** *020

GARRETT, Mary Gudaitis. 1715 N GEORGE MASON DR 22205 #001-02-1985 L1989 **PD** *020 †55

GASPAR, Maurice Leonard. 1635 N GEORGE MASON DR, STE 100 22205 #035-46-1977 L1980 **OPH** *020 †35

GAYDOS, Lawrence Alfred. 1701 N GEORGE MASON DR 22205 #010-02-1957 L1964 **IM OS** *030 †20

GEORGE, Maura Rose. ■ 22203 #016-06-2006 **IM** *012

GHARAVI, Mohammad Hossein. 611 S CARLIN SPRINGS RD, STE 206 22204 #422-01-1998 **PME** *071

GHAZVINI, Nasser. ■ 22213 #517-03-1969 L1997 **AN PME** *071 †05 ‡

GIACOMETTI, Andrea R. 1701 N GEORGE MASON DR, VIRGINIA HOSP CTR 22205 #010-02-1987 L1996 **DR RNR** *020 †80

GIORDANO, Maryann. 611 S CARLIN SPRINGS RD, STE 405 22204 #051-07-1994 L1994 **IM** *020 †20

GLICK, Brian Neal. 611 S CARLIN SPRINGS RD, STE 405 22204 #035-47-1986 L1993 **CD IM** *020 †20

GOLD, Liza Hannah. 2501 N GLEBE RD, STE 204 22207 #035-19-1986 L1991 **P** *020 †75

GOLDMAN, Michael Haim. 1635 N GEORGE MASON DR, STE 150 22205 #008-01-1975 L1988 **CD** *020 †20

GOLDMAN, William David. 1715 N GEORGE MASON DR 22205 #010-01-1975 L1981 **PD** *020 †55

GOLDSTEIN, Alben Glazer. 611 S CARLIN SPRINGS RD, STE 202 22204 #035-15-1971 L1977 **RHU IM** *020 †20

GOOD, Lauren Rebecca. ■ 22202 #010-02-2008 *012

GOODY, Allan John. 1715 N GEORGE MASON DR, STE 1 22205 #010-02-1996 L1997 **NEP** *020

GOPALAN, Ramanath. 1701 N GEORGE MASON DR 22205 #495-17-1976 L1993 **P** *020

GORDON, John David. 46 S GLEBE RD, STE 301 22204 #036-07-1989 L1999 **OBG OS** *020 †30

GORRELICK, Jennifer Lisa. 200 N GLEBE RD, STE 300 22203 #035-20-1998 L2001 **IM** *020 †20

GOVAKER, David A. ■ 22209 #019-02-1982 L1983 **FM MDM** *020 †18

GRANT, Kathryn Eileen. 1701 N GEORGE MASON DR, DEPARTMENT PHYSICAL MEDICI 22205 #051-04-1976 L1981 **PM RPM** *020 †60

GREEN, Elaine Reeves. 3224 S UTAH ST 22206 #019-02-1974 L1978 **P CHP** *020 †75

GRIFFITH, Renny. 1315 14TH ST N, SAFE SEDATION, PLLC 22209 #041-13-1992 L1997 **AN** *040 †05

GRUVER, Robert H. 4650 WASHINGTON BLVD 22201 #051-01-1952 L1952 **IM** *071

GUARDIANI, Elizabeth Anne. ■ 22209 #010-02-2007 L2007 **OTO** *012

GUARNIZO, Carlos. 5275 LEE HWY STE G1 22207 #264-01-1962 L1971 **PD** *071

GUDDETI, Muralidhar Reddy. ■ 22206 #495-70-1986 L2006 **GS** *012

GUIDI, Eric Jordan. 1715 N GEORGE MASON DR, STE 504 22205 #035-03-1987 L1992 **ORS** *020 †40

GUO, Sydney Shuoyi. 1701 N GEORGE MASON DR, STE 288 22205 #035-19-1997 L2006 **VS** *020 †85

GUPTA, Ambrish Kumar. 611 S CARLN SPRNGS RD #504 22204 #495-08-1981 L1983 **CD IM** *020 †20

GUPTA, Jyotsna. 611 S CARLIN SPRINGS RD, STE 504 22204 #495-08-1981 L1984 **IM** *075

HAAS, Melvyn Robt. 1101 S ARLINGTON RIDGE RD 22202 #010-02-1964 L1969 **P** *030 †75

HADDAD, Elizabeth Mary. 1701 N GEORGE MASON DR, STE 2D 22205 #035-47-1997 L2002 **AN** *020 †05

HAGAN, Robert Stewart. ■ 22207 #024-01-2007 *012

HAGEN, Laura Carrol. ■ 22201 #010-01-2008 *012

HAHN, Matthew Taehee. ■ 22204 #010-02-2008 *012

HALES, Deborah Jean. 1000 WILSON BLVD STE 1825, APA 22209 #038-06-1977 L1983 **P ADL** *040 †55,75

HALES, Jeff Bowen. 1400 S JOYCE ST, STE 126 22202 #047-05-1996 L2002 **PCC** *020 †20 ‡

HALL, Matthew Douglas. 4200 WILSON BLVD STE 1100 22203 #041-09-1987 L1988 **OM** *020 †70

HALLOIN, Noelle E Bach. ■ 22204 #026-04-2005 L2007 **PD** *012

HALVERSTADT, Matthew Edwa. ■ 22203 #010-02-2008 *012

HAMEED, Zahid. 1400 S JOYCE ST, APT 436 22202 #704-04-1988 L1999 **EM IM** *020 †20

HAMILTON, William George. 2445 ARMY NAVY DR 22206 #038-41-1997 L2002 **ORS** *020 †40

HANLAN, Derick Anthony. 1701 N GEORGE MASON DR, VIRGINIA HOSPITAL CENTER 22205 #950-01-1969 L1980 **RO R** *071 †80

HANN, Milka L. 5633 8TH ST N 22205 #957-01-1952 L1982 **P** *020 †75

HANNA, Erin Marie. ■ 22204 #010-02-2008 *012

HANNA, Jennifer Spalding. 1701 N GEORGE MASON DR, DEPARTMENT OF ANESTHESIA 22205 #041-02-1990 L1997 **AN** *020 †05

HANNA, Nicholas Nabil. ■ 22202 #021-06-2006 L2006 **IM** *012

HANNAN, Catherine Mary. ■ 22201 #010-02-2005 L2005 **PS** *012

HAQUE, Madina. 1635 N GEORGE MASON DR, STE 410 22205 #160-08-1988 L1999 **HEM** *020 †20

HARELICK, Marjorie Alma. ■ 22205 #038-40-1969 L1972 **CHP P** *020 †75

HARRINGTON, Erin Kathleen. ■ 22201 #051-07-2003 L2003 **AN** *100

HARSH, Veronica Leigh. ■ 22209 #055-01-2001 L2001 **P IM** *020 †75,20

HARTWELL, Patricia. ■ 22203 #034-01-1981 L1990 **AN** *020 †05

HASHIDA, Yoshie. ■ 22203 #572-13-1955 L1964 **ATP** *071 †20

HASSAN, Kamel J. ■ 22203 #010-02-1952 L1958 **AN** *071 †05

HATAM, Marie F. ■ 22202 #035-20-1979 L1980 **ORS OM** *062 †40

HAY, Mackenzie David. ■ 22207 #016-11-2006 **GS** *100

HAYES, Thomas Adrian. ■ 22203 #016-43-1958 L1971 **GP** *071

HEAD, Jimmy Dale. ■ 22201 #021-05-1964 L1964 **EM** *100

HEINLE, Colin Christopher. ■ 22201 #010-02-2008 *012

HENRY, Kurt A. ■ 22209 #422-01-1988 L2005 **CCM IM** *050 †20

HERBERT, Courtney Regan. 1715 N GEORGE MASON DR, STE 406 22205 #010-02-1999 L1999 **D** *020 †15 ‡

HERNANDEZ, Jennifer Loret. ■ 22207 #010-02-2008 L2008 *012

HERZLICH, Alexandra Andre. ■ 22209 #010-02-2008 *012

HERZLICH, Barry Chas. ■ 22209 #056-06-1976 L1978 **IM** *040 †20,03

HESHAM, Hosai Nargis. ■ 22207 #035-03-2004 L2004 **OTO** *012

HIGGINSON, Daniel Smith. ■ 22202 #023-07-2007 L2007 **IM** *012

HOARE, Raymond Robert. 3833 FAIRFAX DR, STE 200 22203 #010-02-1962 L1968 **CD IM** *071 †20

HOLMAN, Robert Paul. 1635 N GEORGE MASON DR, STE 180 22205 #010-02-1982 L1985 **IM ID** *020 †20

HOLTZ, Jonathan Eric. ■ 22206 #010-02-2008 *012

HONG, Sunok. ■ 22207 #583-03-1962 L1970 **PD** *020 †55

HOPKINS, Marc Douglas. ■ 22201 #041-13-2003 L2005 **GE** *012 †20

HOPKINS, Scott Patrick. ■ 22206 #010-02-2008 *012

HOQUE, Mohammad Ezazul. 2022 S NELSON ST, MOHAMMAD E HOQUE 22204 #160-02-1986 L2001 **GE** *020 †20

HOVANEC, Brenda Michelle. ■ 22204 #010-02-2007 L2007 **IM** *012

HOYME, Jane Carol. 3801 FAIRFAX DR 22203 #051-01-1977 L1979 **IM** *020 †20

HUANG, Caroline B. 1715 N GEORGE MASON DR, STE 102 22205 #025-12-2000 L2000 **END** *020 †20

HUANG, Gloria Schuching. ■ 22203 #010-01-2008 *012

HUGHES, Marjorie Helgans. ■ 22207 #035-20-1950 L1957 **PD PHP** *071

HULTZEN, Christopher A. 1701 N GEORGE MASON DR 22205 #011-02-1974 L1984 **NPM PD** *050 †55

HUNT, Lillian Browne. 4501 ARLINGTON BLVD, APT 120 22203 #047-05-1982 L1984 **IM** *020

HUTCHISON, Paul Joseph. ■ 22201 #010-02-2008 *012

HUYCKE, Edward Carl. ■ 22207 #019-02-1978 L2006 **CD IM** *020 †20 ‡

HUYNH, Tuan Huy. ■ 22209 #010-01-2002 **EM** *020

IBE, Comfort Nneze. ■ 22203 #016-02-2008 **OBG** *012

IQBAL, Mohammad Zafar. 1715 N GEORGE MASON DR #20 22205 #704-04-1967 L1975 **OTO A** *020 †45

JABBARPOUR, Yalda. ■ 22206 #010-02-2008 *012

JACKSON, Charles B. 2501 N GLEBE RD STE 201 22207 #010-02-1968 L1974 **ORS OSM** *020 †40

JACOB, Annamma J. 3801 FAIRFAX DR STE 72 22203 #495-27-1972 L1982 **A NPM** *020 †55

JACOB, Roshney Rose. ■ 22202 #894-01-2001 L2006 **IM** *012 †20

JACOB, Thomas N. 1635 N GEORGE MASON DR, STE 240 22205 #495-08-1970 L1978 **P** *020 †75

JACOUB, Irene Atef. ■ 22201 #041-15-2005 **PD** *012

JAISWAL, Arti Chander. ■ 22209 #035-09-2003 L2005 **PD** *100 †55

JAJODIA, Kamal. 2501 N GLEBE RD, STE 303 22207 #495-08-1971 L1999 **P** *020 †75

JALLA, Girja R. 611 S CARLIN SPRINGS RD, STE 509 22204 #495-51-1975 L1983 **IM** *020

JAMIESON, Timothy Allen. 1701 N GEORGE MASON DR, DEPARTMENT OF RADIATION ON 22205 #051-01-1994 L2008 **RO** *020 †80

JAYARAMAN, Uma. ■ 22206 #038-44-2004 L2006 **FM** *100 †18

JENKINS, Koren Michelle. ■ 22201 #051-07-2005 L2005 **IM** *012

JILLA, Yasmin Dara. 1200 N VEITCH ST, APT 925 22201 #051-01-2003 L2004 **CHP** *012

JIMENEZ, Jesus Gonzalez. 2726 S UHLE ST 22206 #847-04-1958 L1970 **FM IM** *020

JINDAL, Anjuli Sone. ■ 22204 #041-15-2005 L2005 **P** *012

JOEL, Andrew Burns. 1701 N GEORGE MASON DR, VHC-MEDICAL STAFF OFFICE 22205 #024-05-1997 L1997 **U** *020 †95

JOHANSEN, John Andrew. ■ 22206 #038-41-2004 L2004 **ORS** *012

JONES, John Ryan. 1701 N GEORGE MASON DR, MEDICAL STAFF OFFICE 22205 #010-01-1999 L2000 **PEM** *020 †16

JONES, Judith Karen. 1616 FORT MYER DR, STE 1430 22209 #048-04-1966 L1984 **PA IM** *071 †20

JORDAN, Jennifer Sue. ■ 22205 #011-04-2001 L2006 **AN** *020

KADEKAR, Sheela Maria. ■ 22201 #048-14-2004 L2005 **FM** *012

KADER, Abraham. 1625 N GEORGE MASON DR, STE 445 22205 #023-07-1987 L2002 **NS** *020 †25

KAHLER, Elizabeth Sartor. ■ 22206 #010-01-1940 L1941 **GP** *071

KAKKAR, Amit Mohan. ■ 22209 #012-21-2007 L2007 **IM** *012

KALIDINDI, Sowjanya Bhupa. ■ 22202 #495-61-2000 L2005 **IM** *020

KAMA, Ndeye Fatou. ■ 22207 #010-02-2008 *012

KANTAK, Sumeeta A. ■ 22209 #038-44-2005 L2005 **IM** *012

KAO, William Wan. ■ 22204 #051-04-2004 L2005 **U** *012

KAPADIA, Monesh Jaykumar. ■ 22202 #010-01-2004 **PTH** *012

KAPLAN, Anne K. 1701 N GEORGE MASON DR 22205 #018-75-1981, ▲ L1983 **GPM** *071

KARAM, Sana Dole. ■ 22205 #010-02-2008 *012

KARIM, Aleya. 2501 N GLEBE RD, STE 303 22207 #160-01-1989 L2003 **CHP** *020

KARIM, Yasmin Khadija. ■ 22202 #010-02-2005 L2005 **IM** *012
KARLITZ, Jordan J. 1635 N GEORGE MASON DR, STE 485 22205 #067-01-2000 L2006 **GE** *020 †20
KARWOSKI, Bethany A. ■ 22201 #010-02-2007 L2007 **TY** *012
KEEVE, J Philip. ■ 22201 #035-19-1952 L1989 **OM** *071 †55,70
KELLER, Jennifer Mendillo. ■ 22206 #016-06-2003 L2003 **OBG** *100
KERN, Melissa Dee. 1635 N GEORGE MASON DR, STE 100 22205 #021-01-1988 L1995 **OPH** *020 †35
KHAJAVI, Kamiar. ■ 22209 #041-01-2000 L2001 **IM** *020 †20
KHALEQUZZAMAN, Md. ■ 22204 #160-01-1981 **PTH** *012
KHANDELWAL, Susan K. 1701 N GEORGE MASON DR 22205 #048-15-1999 L1999 **PD** *020 †55
KHOURY, Maroun N. ■ 22204 #010-01-1985 **IM** *100
KHOURY, Michael Nabil. ■ 22202 #048-02-2008 *012
KHOURY, Randa Rajai. ■ 22202 #010-01-2008 *012
KHURANA, Charanjit Singh. 1701 N GEORGE MASON DR 22205 #495-01-1989 L2003 **IC CD** *020 †20
KIESEL, Robert D. 601 S CARLIN SPRINGS RD 22204 #010-02-1954 L1960 **OPH** *071 †35
KIESSLING, Brenda Robin. 5275 LEE HWY 22207 #010-01-1972 L1984 **FM** *071 †18
KIESWETTER, Caren. 6006 20TH ST N 22205 #051-07-1992 L1997 **OBG** *062 †30
KILLILEA, Bridget Rose. ■ 22206 #023-12-2008 *012
KILMER, Jennifer Lynn. 1625 N GEORGE MASON DR, STE 465 22205 #041-14-1978 L1982 **OBG** *020 †30
KIM, Chin Hee. ■ 22201 #041-14-2003 L2005 **IM** *100 †20
KIM, Nancy C. 1715 N GEORGE MASON DR 22205 #041-02-1992 L1996 **PD** *020 †55
KIM, Susan Jin. ■ 22209 #010-02-2006 L2006 **IM** *012
KIM, Taeho. 1715 N GEORGE MASON DR, STE 102 22205 #051-01-1982 L1987 **IM** *020 †20
KINDER, Cindy. ■ 22203 #038-44-2004 L2004 **OBG** *012
KIRKEL, Dean Mark. ■ 22201 #836-01-1999 L2006 **HO HO** *012 †20
KLEIN, Peter. ■ 22201 #036-07-2006 *012
KLUNK, Kathryn Ann. ■ 22205 #010-01-2008 *012
KNIGHT, Kevin Bergeson. ■ 22207 #010-02-2008 *012
KNOWLAN, Donald Michael. 1701 N GEORGE MASON DR 22205 #028-34-1954 L1963 **CD IM** *071 †20
KOCH, Edward Graeme. 1635 N GEORGE MASON DR 22205 #010-01-1969 L1973 **GYN GPM** *020 †30
KONG, Hey Jin. 200 N GLEBE RD, STE 300 22203 #051-01-1992 L1995 **IM** *020 †20
KOTECHA, Amy Vinod. 3801 FAIRFAX DR 22203 #041-15-1999 L2008 **OPH** *020 †35
KOTHARY, Deepali N. 1715 N GEORGE MASON DR, STE 406 22205 #496-30-1993 L2003 **OBG** *020
KRAFT, Harold H. 2020 14TH ST N, STE 700 22201 #010-02-1981 L1988 **AN** *020 †05
KRIMSHTEIN, Nina Susan. ■ 22201 #012-01-2004 L2005 **IM** *100 †20
KRISHNAN, Anasuya. ■ 22201 #041-14-2005 L2005 **PD** *012
KRUGER, Robert Mark. 1400 S JOYCE ST # 12 22202 #038-41-1992 L1999 **PCC IM** *020 †20
KUGEL, Robert B. ■ 22203 #025-01-1946 L1978 **PD** *071 †55 ‡
KUMAR, Sudha Lata. 1701 N GEORGE MASON DR, HOSPITAL CENTER-ARLINGTON 22205 #496-07-1982 L1988 **NPM** *020 †55
KURZBARD, Stephen Jay. ■ 22207 #035-46-1962 L1965 **GP R** *071
KUSCHNER, Robert Alan. ■ 22201 #035-48-1984 L1986 **ID IM** *020 †20
LAL, Ashish. ■ 22201 #010-01-2008 *012
LAMBERT, Eugene Jos. 1635 N GEORGE MASON DR, STE 430 22205 #010-02-1982 L1990 **IM GP** *020 †20
LAMBERTI, James Paul. 1715 N GEORGE MASON DR, STE 106 22205 #041-01-1980 L1985 **PUD IM** *020 †20
LANDIS, Glen Austin. 1701 N GEORGE MASON DR 22205 #010-02-1962 L1967 **NM IM** *071 †28
LANG, Edward Robert. 1701 N GEORGE MASON DR 22205 #008-01-1960 L1965 **NS** *071 †25
LANGLOH, John Thos. 3179 KEY BLVD 22201 #010-01-1967 L1967 **ORS OP** *071 †40
LASHGARI, Susanne Daria. 1635 N GEORGE MASON DR, STE 300 22205 #010-02-2000 L2000 **OBG** *020
LAX, Allison. ■ 22201 #035-46-2000 L2001 **MSR** *100 †80 ‡
LEAVITT, Willis Todd. ■ 22204 #025-07-1991 L1993 **P** *020 †75
LEE, David D. 1701 N GEORGE MASON DR, NICU 22205 #051-01-1985 L1990 **AN** *020 †05
LEE, Esther E. ■ 22204 #038-44-2005 **IM** *012
LEE, Joseph Paul. 1635 N GEORGE MASON DR, STE 250 22205 #028-02-2000 L2006 **OTO** *020 †45
LEE, Mary Rachel. 5232 LEE HWY, WHITMAN WALKER CLINIC 22207 #035-01-1989 L1996 **P** *020 †75,20
LEFTON, Charles Stuart. 1635 N GEORGE MASON DR, ORTHOPAEDICS & REHABILITAT 22205 #025-07-1971 L1978 **ORS** *020 †40
LEITCH, Jeffrey Adam. ■ 22201 #045-04-2008 *012
LEMMERMAN, Kathryn Ann. 5275 LEE HWY, KAPLAN CLINIC OF 22207 #016-01-1987 L1990 **FM** *020 †18
LEONARD, Matthew Madison. ■ 22207 #051-01-2004 L2007 **EM** *020
LEVY, Warren Seth. 1635 N GEORGE MASON DR, STE 190 22205 #010-01-1982 L1989 **CD IM** *020 †20
LI, Sumin. ■ 22201 #010-02-2008 *012
LIGETI, Marianne Beata. 1635 N GEORGE MASON DR, STE 430 22205 #473-01-1971 L1977 **IM** *020
LILIENFIELD, Lisa Joan. 5275 LEE HWY, KAPLAN CLINIC OF 22207 #010-01-1982 L1998 **FM** *020 †18
LIMAYE, Suresh Raghunath. 611 S CARLIN SPRINGS RD, STE 404 22204 #496-38-1962 L1972 **OPH** *020 †35
LIN, Kenneth Joyce. 3833 FAIRFAX DR, STE 200 22203 #051-04-1993 L1996 **IM** *020 †20
LIN, Kenneth Wensen. 200 N GLEBE RD, STE 300 22203 #035-19-2001 L2005 **FM** *020 †18
LISCHWE, Catherine Ann. 1715 N GEORGE MASON DR, STE 205 22205 #016-11-1974 L1981 **PD** *020 †55
LITTLE, Paul B. 2511 JEFFERSON DAVIS HWY, BOX 31 22202 #036-08-1985 L1988 **FM** *062 †18
LIU, Peter Futz. 1701 N GEORGE MASON DR, ATTN: MEDICAL STAFF OFFICE 22205 #023-01-1998 L2001 **EM** *020 †16
LONG, John A, Jr. 1701 N GEORGE MASON DR, ARLINGTON HOSP 22205 #010-02-1973 L1980 **DR** *020 †80
LORICA, Victor Emmanuel G. 1635 N GEORGE MASON DR, STE 215 22205 #748-02-1989 L1994 **NEP** *020 †20
LOVALLO, Jeffrey Leonard. 2445 ARMY NAVY DR 22206 #008-02-1981 L1993 **ORS HS** *020 †40
LOZANO, Emily Ariana. 6013 25TH RD N 22207 #056-05-1996 L2002 **PDC** *020 †55 ‡
LU, Johnny Tan. 600 ARMY NAVY DR, RM E-2015 22202 #748-02-1982 L1999 **IM** *020 †20

LUCAS, Chaikitch V. ■ 22201 #891-02-1965 L1972 **GS GP** *075 †85
LUCK, Steve Chas. 601 S CARLIN SPRINGS RD 22204 #010-02-1990 L1995 **AN** *020 †05
LUNDEEN, William Bruce. 1701 N GEORGE MASON DR, DEPT RAD 22205 #051-04-1955 L1955 **RO R** *020 †80
LUNG, Audrey Eliza. ■ 22201 #005-18-2005 L2006 **PD** *012
LUSE, David Mackenzie. ■ 22202 #010-01-2004 L2005 **IM** *100 †20
LYONS, Sidney. ■ 22201 #051-04-1941 L1941 **FM** *071
MAC DONALD, Linda Drake. 1635 N GEORGE MASON DR, STE 300 22205 #003-01-1979 L1982 **OBG** *062 †30
MACHADO, Juan Gilberto. 3833 FAIRFAX DR, STE 400 22203 #275-01-1956 L1980 **GYN** *020 †30
MACLEAN, Marion E. ■ 22204 #010-01-1949 L1963 **OBG** *071
MAHGOUB, Siham Mohieldin. ■ 22203 #848-01-1991 L2006 **ID IM** *050 †20
MAJOR, Mary Jane. 1715 N GEORGE MASON DR, STE 204 22205 #035-03-1977 L1980 **IM** *020 †20
MALETTE, Terah Jean. ■ 22209 #010-02-2008 *012
MALIN, Sean Christopher. ■ 22205 #010-01-2007 L2007 **IM** *012
MANN, Karen Elizabeth. ■ 22201 #010-01-2008 *012
MANSOUR, Amira. ■ 22201 #605-01-1965 L1984 **ATP PCP** *020 †50
MAR, Doreen Hung. 4141 N HENDERSON RD, 4141 N HENDERSON RD 1019 22203 #017-20-1984 L1989 **EM IM** *020 †20
MARKS, Ursula Marion. 1701 N GEORGE MASON DR 22205 #011-03-2001 L2004 **AN** *020 †05
MARQUEZ, Esteban Antonio. 1701 N GEORGE MASON DR, MEDICAL STAFF OFFICE 22205 #010-01-1994 L1995 **CD IM** *020 †20
MARQUEZ, Maria Luisa. 1701 N GEORGE MASON DR, PEDIATRIC DEPT 22205 #935-01-1990 L1995 **PD** *020 †55
MARSHALL, John Lindsay. ■ 22205 #020-02-1988 L1989 **ON** *020 †20
MARSHALL, Joseph K, Jr. 1625 N GEORGE MASON DR, STE 414 22205 #048-02-1968 L1975 **CD IM** *020 †20
MARTIN, Elizabeth Thiele. 601 S CARLIN SPRINGS RD, DEPT PATHOLOGY 22204 #051-01-1977 L1988 **PTH PCP** *020 †50
MARTIN, Lee Baldwin, Jr. 601 S CARLIN SPRINGS RD 22204 #041-01-1969 L1970 **OS GP** *020
MARTINEZ, Julian Esteban. 1625 N GEORGE MASON DR, STE 325 22205 #132-01-1997 L2003 **OBG** *020
MARTINEZ, Marina I. 1625 N GEORGE MASON DR 22205 #041-13-1978 L1983 **OBG** *020 †30
MARTINS, Raymond Catarino. 1715 N GEORGE MASON DR 22205 #010-01-2000 L2005 **IM** *020 †20
MARTY, Aileen Maria. 1550 CRYSTAL DR, STE 601 22202 #011-02-1982 L1986 **ID PTH** *050 †50
MASEL, Holly Loretta. 1635 N GEORGE MASON DR, STE 185 22205 #422-01-2002 L2002 **OBG** *020
MATHER, Jacques P. ■ 22202 #010-01-2008 *012
MATHEW, Maya Mary. ■ 22201 #021-01-2006 **IM** *100
MATTAR, Mark Christopher. ■ 22203 #051-04-2004 L2006 **GE** *012 †20
MATURI, Martha Marie. 611 S CARLIN SPRINGS RD, STE 411 22204 #024-05-1980 L1983 **IM** *040 †20
MATUS, Alicia Mercedes. 3033 WILSON BLVD 22201 #682-01-1970 L1985 **P** *020
MAUCK, Christine Klein. 1611 N KENT ST, STE 806 22209 #025-01-1981 L1982 **OBG PHP** *050 †70
MAYES, James Thos. 1701 N GEORGE MASON DR, VIRGINIA HOSPITAL CENTER 22205 #016-02-1979 L2006 **GS OS** *020 †85
MC AULEY, James Patrick. 2445 ARMY NAVY DR, ANDERSON ORTHOPEDIC CLINIC 22206 #064-01-1980 L1996 **ORS** *020 †40
MC CABE, Thomas A. 1715 N GEORGE MASON DR, STE 106 22205 #010-02-1970 L1977 **PUD CCM** *020 †20
MC FARLAND, John W. ■ 22207 #048-02-1977 L1981 **P** *020
MC GAVIN, Thomas A. 1701 N GEORGE MASON DR 22205 #041-13-1944 L1948 **OBG** *071
MC GRATH, Francis John. 1625 N GEORGE MASON DR, STE 414 22205 #010-02-1975 L1977 **CD** *020 †20
MC GREEVY, John R. ■ 22203 #035-01-1950 L1954 **P** *072
MC KIBBEN, Linda Jean. ■ 22202 #012-01-1982 L1986 **GPM** *020 †55,70
MC LAREN, Rodney Anthony. 1635 N GEORGE MASN DR #190, MATERNAL FETAL MEDICINE 22205 #024-07-1983 L1988 **MFM** *020 †30
MCLAUGHLIN, Patrick Micha. ■ 22201 #010-01-2008 *012
MC MANUS, Christopher P. 2525 10TH ST N 22201 #051-01-1983 L1991 **IM** *020 †20
MC MANUS, Reginald Paul. 2525 10TH ST N, C.P. AND R.P. MCMANUS, MD, 22201 #010-01-1956 L1961 **GP R** *020
MC NAMARA, John Micheal. 1100 WILSON BLVD, MINE SAFETY AND HEALTH 22209 #010-01-1980 L1998 **OM EM** *020 †70
MC PHERSON, Archie. 1701 N GEORGE MASON DR, EXECUTIVE SUITE 22205 #068-01-1958 L1962 **MDM PHP** *071 †75,70
MC PHERSON, Merle Mac Rae. ■ 22209 #068-01-1960 L1962 **PHP PD** *030 †70
MC PHERSON, Scott L. ■ 22205 #051-04-1996 **IM** *100
MC WEY, Russell Eugene. 1701 N GEORGE MASON DR 22205 #045-01-1983 L1987 **DR NM** *020 †80,28
MC WILLIAMS, Thomas G. 1701 N GEORGE MASON DR 22205 #010-02-1950 L1959 **R** *071 †80
MEI-TAL, Varda. ■ 22203 #550-01-1958 L1976 **P OS** *040 †75
MELKI, Toufic S. 1715 N GEORGE MASON DR, STE 101 22205 #010-02-1986 L1989 **OPH OS** *020 †35
MEMOLI, Matthew James. ■ 22201 #422-01-2002 L2005 **ID IM** *100 †20
MENKHAUS, Chrisanthy. ■ 22206 #010-02-2008 *012
MERLO, Christian Avery. 1400 S JOYCE ST, STE 126 22202 #010-02-1996 L1997 **PCC** *100 †20
MESSINGER, Paul Stein. ■ 22207 #023-07-1957 L1961 **GYN** *074 †30
MEYER, Jamie Lynn. ■ 22209 #010-01-2008 *012
MEZA, Rene S. 601 S CARLIN SPRINGS RD 22204 #847-04-1964 L1981 **GP OM** *020
MILLER, Abbiemae Buck. 1715 N GEORGE MASON DR 22205 #038-06-2002 L2005 **IM** *100 †20
MIN, Ellie Ho-Young. 3833 FAIRFAX DR, STE 200 22203 #010-01-1993 L2002 **IM** *020 †20
MIRZA, Sajida M. ■ 22202 #704-06-1968 L2001 **AI IM** *071
MITTAL, Monica Tina. ■ 22201 #048-16-2003 L2003 **EM** *100
MOAWAD, Gaby. ■ 22206 #605-03-2002 2007 **OBG** *012
MOE, Kathleen Marie. ■ 22204 #010-02-2003 L2004 **D** *100
MOLAIY, John Hossein. 1635 N GEORGE MASON DR, STE 480 22205 #654-01-1996 L2002 **FM** *020 †18
MOLINA, Hector Guillermo. 7101-J ROCK RIDGE LN 22215 #429-01-1989 L2000 **AN** *100
MONSERRATE, Nicole Marie. 1715 N GEORGE MASON DR, STE 108 22205 #010-02-1997 L1997 **IM** *040 †20
MOORE, Gregory Chas. ■ 22207 #035-09-1960 L1963 **OPH** *071 †35

MORDKIN, Robert Mark. 1701 N GEORGE MASON DR, MEDICAL STAFF OFFICE 22205 #005-06-1992 L1994 **U** *020 †95

MOREYRA, Eduardo. ■ 22206 #132-02-1987 L1993 **CD** *020 †20

MORRIS, Andrea Marie. ■ 22209 #010-01-2008 *012

MORRIS, Oriel Carlin. 1701 N GEORGE MASON DR 22205 #143-05-1945 L1974 **FM** *071 †18

MORRISSEY, Wm Fitzgerald. 2001 COLUMBIA PIKE 22204 #010-01-1957 L1961 **IM CD** *071

MOSHIRY, Bahram Tafreshi. 1715 N GEORGE MASON DR, STE 502 22205 #517-01-1957 L1997 **TS GS** *020 †85,90

MOSS, Audrey. 3033 WILSON BLVD 22201 #010-02-1980 L1985 **P** *020 †18,75

MOSTAFA, Naglaa. 611 S CARLIN SPRINGS RD, STE 406 22204 #915-02-1965 L1992 **OBG** *071 †30

MOTSINGER, Charles Duke. 2034 N CLEVELAND ST 22201 #023-12-1997 L1999 **FM** *020 †18,75

MUELLER, John B. 1635 N GEORGE MASON DR, ATTN EMERGENCY DEPT 22205 #035-03-1975 L1978 **EM IM** *020 †20,16

MUHS, Amanda Leigh. ■ 22201 #016-11-2006 L2006 **GS** *100

MUIR, Timothy David. 1715 N GEORGE MASON DR 22205 #010-02-1997 L2000 **IM** *020 †20

MULLAN, Paul Christopher. ■ 22207 #035-20-2004 L2004 **PD** *100 †55

MUNASAFI, Talal Ahmad. 1635 N GEORGE MASON DR, STE 380 22205 #528-01-1971 L1982 **PS** *020 †65

MYERS, Scott Nagel. ■ 22209 #017-20-1999 L1999 **PHO** *02u †55

MYERS, Trevor Perrin. 1701 N GEORGE MASON DR, DOMINION ANESTH CTR 22205 #023-07-1995 L1999 **AN** *020 †05

NABI, Anissa Amel. ■ 22201 #125-04-1997 L2004 **IM** *020 †20

NADEL, Carolina. ■ 22202 #033-05-1992 **PTH** *100

NAGDA, Sameer Hemant. 2445 ARMY NAVY DR, STE 400 22206 #016-42-2000 L2007 **ORS** *100

NARROW, William Erwin. 1000 WILSON BLVD, STE 1825 22209 #041-13-1983 L1983 **P EP** *050 †75

NASR, Nadim Munir. ■ 22209 #051-04-2003 L2003 **RO** *012

NATIVIDAD, Mariabella G. 3801 FAIRFAX DR, STE 11 22203 #043-01-1991 L1994 **IM** *020 †20

NAVID, Ebrahim. 611 S CARLN SPRNGS RD #409 22204 #517-03-1961 L1972 **GP PTH** *020 †50

NEAL, Kelly Ryan. ■ 22209 #036-01-2006 L2006 **IM** *012

NELSON, Arthur Derry. ■ 22205 #041-13-1957 L1958 **PHP FM** *071

NEMATZADEH, Fatemeh. 2501 N GLEBE RD, STE 303 22207 #517-01-1992 L2001 **CHP** *020

NEUFELD, Steven Keith. 2445 ARMY NAVY DR STE 300 22206 #041-09-1995 L2001 **ORS OFA** *020 †40

NGO, Thuan Dinh. 3801 FAIRFAX DR, STE 52 22203 #941-01-1963 L1979 **GP** *071 ‡

NG SUI HING, Ng You Kwong. ■ 22202 #919-05-1976 *100

NGUYEN, Michelle Chau. 1625 N GEORGE MASON DR, STE 474 22205 #051-01-1997 L1997 **OBG** *020 †30

NIEMTZOFF, Mariana J. 3801 FAIRFAX DR STE 10 22203 #132-01-1983 L1999 **P** *020 †75

NIEMYER, Judith Anne. 4100 FAIRFAX DR, STE 1150 22203 #041-09-1988 L1993 **IM** *020

NIRSCHL, Robert Phillip. 1715 N GEORGE MASON DR, STE 504 22205 #056-06-1958 L1965 **ORS OSM** *071 †40

NORRIS, Lorenzo. ■ 22203 #038-06-2001 L2006 **P** *100

NORTON, Robert Olon, Jr. ■ 22205 #021-01-1945 L1971 **OBG** *020

NORTON, Thomas David. ■ 22201 #010-02-2006 L2006 **IM** *012

NOTARIANNI, Michael P. 1625 N GEORGE MASON DR, STE 414 22205 #041-09-1993 L1993 **CD** *020 †20

OBICAN, Sarah Gloria. ■ 22203 #011-02-2006 L2006 **OBG** *012

O'CONNOR, Timothy James. ■ 22201 #010-02-2008 *012

O'DONNELL, Christopher Ma. ■ 22209 #010-02-2006 L2006 **IM** *012

O'DONNELL, Philip Jos. 1635 N GEORGE MASON DR, STE 314 22205 #010-02-1987 L1989 **IM** *020

O'HARA, Martin James. 1715 N GEORGE MASON DR, STE 107 22205 #539-04-1976 L1993 **CD IM** *020 †20

OHERN, Candice Briana. ■ 22203 #010-02-2007 L2007 **OBG** *012

OLIN, Lisa Cole. ■ 22201 #041-02-2005 L2005 **IM** *012

OMOJOKUN, Olanrewaju Omol. ■ 22201 #051-01-2005 L2007 **PD** *012

ONYIKE, Ahamefula Elemuwa. 3356 2ND ST S 22204 #033-05-1999 L2003 **OAR** *020

OPISSO, Anthony M. RR 3 ROGERSVILLE, NB CANADA EOA2TO 22210 #016-43-1950 L1954 **OS** *071

OPULENCIA, Alejandro P. ■ 22204 #748-10-1973 L1983 **OTO** *020

ORANGE, David Todd. 1701 N GEORGE MASON DR, VIRGINIA RADIOLOGICAL 22205 #011-02-1999 L2005 **DR** *020 †28,80

O'REGAN, Maureen. 1625 N GEORGE MASON DR, STE 474 22205 #010-02-1972 L1973 **GYN OBS** *020

OREILLY, Michael James. ■ 22203 #010-02-2002 L2003 **ORS** *012

ORSINGER, William Hubert. ■ 22207 #010-01-1947 L1948 **GP** *071

OSBORNE, Mildred Bynoe. 1725 N GEORGE MASON DR, DREWRY CENTER 22205 #051-04-1988 L1989 **P** *020 †75

OSHA, Judith Paul. 1701 N GEORGE MASON DR, PEDIATRICS DEPT 22205 #010-02-1971 L1973 **PD** *071 †55

OSIH, Regina Beloe. ■ 22201 #869-05-1998 L2003 **ID** *100 †20

OVERDECK, Kimberlee Horto. 1701 N GEORGE MASON DR, VIRGINIA RADIOLOGICAL ASSO 22205 #025-07-1997 L2006 **DR** *020 †80

PACKARD, Lisa Kay. ■ 22201 #010-02-2008 *012

PAIK, Kenneth Eugene. ■ 22209 #010-02-2008 *012

PAKULL, Barton. ■ 22209 #035-15-1961 L1970 **P** *071

PAL, Saikat. ■ 22201 #016-42-2005 L2005 **PD** *012

PALMER, Kathryn Mary. 1701 N GEORGE MASON DR, RADIOLOGY DEPARTMENT 22205 #041-01-1989 L1999 **RNR DR** *020 †55,80

PAPAILIAS-LAMERA, E C. ■ 22203 #418-01-1958 L1960 **PD** *071

PAPAKONSTANTINOU, K C. ■ 22209 #418-01-1992 L1998 **GS** *100

PAPALI, Alfred C. ■ 22201 #067-01-2007 L2007 **IM** *012

PAPPAS, Sam Peter. 1715 N GEORGE MASON DR 22205 #041-14-1995 L2004 **IM** *020

PARENTE, Antonio Rocco. 1625 N GEORGE MASON DR, STE 414 22205 #010-02-1984 L1986 **CD IC** *020 †20

PARISER, Anne Ruggles. 1635 N GEORGE MASON DR, STE 490 22205 #010-02-1988 L1991 **IM** *020 †20

PARK, Susan. 200 N GLEBE RD, STE 300 22203 #051-01-2002 L2006 **MPD** *100 †20,55

PARKS, Annalisa Mulhollen. 2506 23RD RD N, STE 140 22207 #041-13-1983 L1986 **GYN** *020 †30

PARVARESH, Kaveh. 611 S CARLIN SPRINGS RD, STE 409 22204 #305-01-2001 L2005 **FM** *100 †18

PATEL, Jayanti Lalbhai. 601 S CARLIN SPRINGS RD, HOSPITAL 22204 #495-22-1991 L1997 **IM** *020 †20

PATEL, Pranav Dhaneshkuma. ■ 22209 #048-16-2003 L2004 **HO** *012 †20

PATTAKOS, Gregory. ■ 22201 #010-02-2007 L2007 **GS** *012

PAWLAK, W J. 2455 ARMY NAVY DR, COLUMBIA PENTAGON CITY HOS 22206 #759-09-1963 L1983 **DR** *020 †80

PAZ-SOLDAN, Gonzalo J. 3045 COLUMBIA PIKE STE A, ARLINGTON PEDIATRIC CENTER 22204 #008-01-1991 L1995 **PD** *020 †55

PEARL, Jonathan Patrick. ■ 22203 #025-07-1999 L2003 **GS** *020 †85

PEASE, Alison Fast. 1715 N GEORGE MASON DR 22205 #008-02-1999 L2004 **PD** *020 †55

PEDEN, Sean Coenen. ■ 22208 #028-02-2008 *012

PENG, Justin. ■ 22206 #024-05-2005 L2005 **IM** *012

PEPEK, Joseph M. ■ 22201 #010-02-2003 L2006 **GS** *020

PETROVIC, Marija. ■ 22204 #957-02-1997 L2006 **P** *020 †75

PHAN, Duc Hong. ■ 22209 #010-01-2008 *012

PIEPERGERDES, James C. 1635 N GEORGE MASON DR, STE 250 22205 #007-02-1971 L1995 **OTO A** *020 †45

PINESS, Jane E. 1635 N GEORGE MASON DR, STE 185 22205 #010-02-1986 L1990 **OBG** *020 †30

PINZON, Jean-Paul. 1635 N GEORGE MASN DR #115 22205 #035-75-2002, ▲ L2005 **PLM IM** *012 †20

PODELL, Daniel Mark. ■ 22209 #010-02-2005 L2005 **P** *012

POLLACK, Seth Michaels. ■ 22203 #010-01-2005 L2005 **IM** *012

PORTER, Amy. 1625 N GEORGE MASON DR, STE 474 22205 #051-01-1996 L1996 **OBG** *020 †30

PORTNOY, Stuart Marlon. ■ 22205 #010-01-1991 L1992 **IM** *020

PRASAD, C M. 611 S CARLIN SPRINGS RD, STE 301 22204 #649-33-1984 L1987 **P N** *020 †20

PRASAD, Shanti. 2001 COLUMBIA PIKE, STE 131 22204 #495-37-1986 L2000 **IM** *020 †20

PRATT, Valerie S W. 1048 N STAFFORD ST 22201 #010-01-2002 L2005 **END** *100 †20

PRIMM, Annelle. 1000 WILSON BLVD, STE 1825 22209 #010-03-1980 L1982 **P** *020 †75

PROMINSKI, John E. ■ 22207 #010-02-1952 L1956 **R NR** *071 †80

PROMINSKI, William Edmund. 1701 N GEORGE MASON DR, RADIOLOGY DEPARTMENT 22205 #010-02-1983 L1987 **DR** *020 †80

PROSKY, Martin Gary. 1635 N GEORGE MASON DR, STE 485 22205 #035-08-1985 L1990 **GE HEP** *020 †20

PUTCHAKAYALA, Sashi. ■ 22209 #010-01-2006 L2006 **P** *012

PUTHAWALA, Khalid. 3 JOYCE ST, STE 126 22202 #038-06-2000 L2006 **PCC** *100 †20

QUIAOIT, Ysmaeljohn Anche. ■ 22201 #016-42-2004 L2007 **NEP** *012 †20

QURESHI, Mashuq Ahmad. 611 S CARLIN SPRINGS RD, NO-104 22204 #704-01-1954 L1975 **CD IM** *020 †20

RABIN, Rebecca Frances. ■ 22201 #041-01-2008 *012

RACZYNSKI, Carolina. ■ 22213 #010-01-1999 L1999 **PD** *020

RADIN, Robert P. 3801 FAIRFAX DR STE 21 22203 #035-20-1967 L1975 **P** *020 †75

RAHMAN, Naila Tasneem. 600 ARMY NAVY DR, RM E-2015 22202 #160-06-1985 L1993 **IM** *030 †20

RAHMAN, Nazia Henna. ■ 22202 #010-02-2008 *012

RAMAGOSA, Ryan Burke. ■ 22201 #010-02-2007 L2007 **IM** *012

RAMASWAMY, Isabel Jamili. 3801 FAIRFAX DR STE 44 22203 #748-01-1963 L1972 **PD** *020 †55

RANA, Hajira Izhar. ■ 22206 #055-01-2007 L2007 **PD** *012

RANA, Irmindra S. 611 S CARLIN SPRINGS RD, STE 511 22204 #308-13-1998 L2002 **NEP** *020 †20

RANA, Jeevindra Singh. 611 S CARLIN SPRINGS RD, STE 511 22204 #495-99-1994 L1998 **IM** *020 †20

RANA, Preeti. 611 S CARLIN SPRINGS RD, STE 511 22204 #495-23-1996 L2004 **IM** *020

RANDOLPH, Norman Dennis, Jr. ■ 22209 #010-02-2007 **IM** *012

RANKIN, Robert Avran M. ■ 22205 #047-06-1963 L1963 **P** *071 †75

RAO, Usha Sathishchan. ■ 22203 #047-05-2007 L2007 **TY** *012

RAOFI, Vandad. ■ 22201 #016-11-1995 L2008 **GS** *020 †85

RASMUSSEN, Kristine Marie. ■ 22203 #010-01-2008 *012

RATANAWONGSA, Rithi. ■ 22209 #010-02-1992 **PD** *100

RAUCH, Harry Ben. ■ 22202 #039-01-1981 L1983 **CHP P** *020 †75

RAYA, Vikram. ■ 22202 #012-01-2004 L2005 **IM** *100 †20

RAYANI, Shayan. ■ 22204 #038-44-2007 L2007 **IM** *012

REED, John Chas. 5275 LEE HWY, KAPLAN CLINIC OF 22207 #041-01-1970 L1999 **MDM FM** *030 †18 ‡

REESE, David John, II. 1715 N GEORGE MASON DR, DAVID J. REESE, M.D. 22205 #036-01-1968 L1971 **PD** *040 †55

REGIER, Darrel Alvin. 1000 WILSON BLVD, STE 1825 22209 #017-20-1970 L1971 **P EM** *020 †75

REGIER, Janet Friesen. 4201 WILSON BLVD RM 265, HEALTH UNIT 22230 #024-01-1981 L1997 **FM** *020 †18

REILLY, Elizabeth Rose. ■ 22204 #041-15-2006 L2006 **IM** *012

RENAUD, Nicole Kyongnan. 2805 COLUMBIA PIKE, STE 2B 22204 #010-01-1996 L2001 **OPH** *020

RENNERT, Wolfgang P. 4940 36TH ST N 22207 #409-05-1985 L1992 **PD** *020 †55

RICE, Dana Clark. ■ 22209 #010-01-2007 L2007 **GS** *012

RICHARDS, Eric Preston. ■ 22209 #010-02-2008 *012

RICHTER, Geraldine K. 2200 WILSON BLVD, PMB 547 22201 #010-02-1973 L1977 **ORS** *020 †40

RICKERICH, Charles L. ■ 22201 #035-08-1952 L1958 **GS** *071 †85

RIEDEL, Charles Jess. 1625 N GEORGE MASON DR, STE 445 22205 #038-41-1984 L1995 **NS** *020 †25

RIMICCI, Anthony James. 1635 N GEORGE MASON DR, STE 430 22205 #033-06-1999 L1999 **IM** *020 †20

RIVERA, Michelle Antonia. 1635 N GEORGE MASON DR, STE 400 22205 #035-20-1980 L1986 **D** *020 †15

RIVERA, Pedro N. 2107 WILSON BLVD 22201 #042-01-1971 L1971 **PD AM** *062 †55

RIZO, Ivania Maritza. ■ 22209 #010-02-2007 L2007 **IM** *012

ROBERTS, Esther Pearl. 4201 WILSON BLVD, STE 110351 22203 #047-07-1968 L1968 **P OS** *071 †75

RODILOSSO, Philip Thos. 1400 S JOYCE ST, STE 126 22202 #010-02-1958 L1963 **IM** *071 †20

RODRIGUEZ, Lorna Ivette. ■ 22201 #042-02-2001 L2007 **OBG** *100 †30

RODRIGUEZ, Patricia A. 1635 N GEORGE MASON DR, STE 170 22205 #035-46-1987 L1995 **ON** *020 †20

ROJAS, Juan Carlos. ■ 22201 #010-01-2001 L2005 **OBG** *020

ROKOSKE, Leslie Dustin. 1725 N GEORGE MASON DR, DREWRY CENTER 22205 #036-07-1991 L1995 **P** *020 †75

ROLAND, Laura Marie. 1701 N GEORGE MASON DR, STE 2D 22205 #010-02-2001 L2006 **AN** *020 †05

ROMNESS, Joseph O. 1715 N GEORGE MASN DR #108 22205 #016-06-1949 L1955 ORS *071 †40

ROSENBAUM, Faye R. 611 S CARLIN SPRINGS RD, STE 208 22204 #016-01-1984 L1988 N *020 †75

ROSENSTEIN, Gladys. 1600 S JOYCE ST, RIVER HOUSE/SUITE 1506 22202 #041-09-1944 L1966 IM GE *062

ROSSI, Christopher Thomas. ■ 22209 #035-06-2003 PTH *100

ROSSI, Gustavo Alberto. 1625 N GEORGE MASON DR, STE 325 22205 #132-01-1968 L1974 OBG *020 †30

ROTCHFORD, James Patrick. ■ 22207 #010-02-1953 L1966 D *071 †15

ROY, Sion Kumar. ■ 22201 #051-04-2007 L2007 IM *012

RUBIN, Arthur A. 3833 FAIRFAX DR, STE 200 22203 #010-02-1972 L1978 IM *020 †20

RUDMAN, Amanda Kate. ■ 22201 #041-14-2008 *012

RUDOLPH, Richard. 1417 KEY BLVD L2007 #010-02-1978 L1982 DR *020 †80

RUNKLE, Beatriz Pamela. 1701 N GEORGE MASON DR #PD 22205 #010-02-1975 L1985 NPM PD *020 †55

RYAN, Robert Francis. 1715 N GEORGE MASON DR, ARLINGTON HOSP MEDICAL BLD 22205 #010-02-1961 L1966 IM *020

RYAN, Robert Henry. ■ 22205 #050-02-1972 L1981 IM *020 †20

RYSCAVAGE, Patrick Amadeu. ■ 22209 #010-02-2004 L2004 IM *100 †20

SABERINIA, Massoud. 1715 N GEORGE MASON DR, STE 408 22205 #517-08-1979 L1993 END IM *020 †20

SABRI, Joseph Aziz. 1715 N GEORGE MASON DR, STE 202 22205 #605-01-1946 L1956 OTO *071 †45

SACKS, Tamara Eva. 1635 N GEORGE MASON DR, STE 115 22205 #010-01-1999 L2002 PLM IM *020 †20

SACOTO, Maria. 5555 COLUMBIA PIKE STE 209 22204 #319-04-1991 L2000 PD *020

SAENZ, Cesar Lenin. ■ 22202 #047-07-2003 L2007 ORS *012

SALEEM, Ahmed Mustafa. 1701 N GEORGE MASON DR, VIRGINIA HOSPITAL CENTER 22205 #528-01-1994 L2000 IM *062 †20

SANTANGELO, Robert Paul. 1635 N GEORGE MASON DR, STE 350 22205 #035-46-1965 L1982 END IM *020 †20

SANZ, Luis E. 1625 N GEORGE MASON DR, STE 475 22205 #010-02-1976 L1977 GYN *020 †30

SAPPINGTON, Richard F, Jr. 611 S CARLIN SPRINGS RD, STE 511 22204 #010-02-1960 L1966 PUD IM *071 †20

SCHAEFER, Craig John. 1701 N GEORGE MASON DR, MEDICAL STAFF OFFICE 22205 #035-03-1974 L1975 GS VS *020 †85

SCHALLHEIM, Jason Matthew. ■ 22203 #049-01-2003 L2005 PTH *012

SCHAPS, Sanford Howard. 1701 N GEORGE MASON DR, STE 2D 22205 #023-07-1985 L1990 AN CCA *020 †05

SCHESSEL, David Arthur. 1715 N GEORGE MASON DR ST4, VIRGINIA NEUROSURGEONS 22205 #035-46-1985 L1998 OTO *020 †45

SCHLESSER, John Francis. ■ 22205 #010-02-1985 L1988 EM *020 †16

SCHMIDT, Howard Joel. 1505 N KENILWORTH ST, VCU MEDICAL CENTER, PEDIAT 22205 #051-04-1984 L1985 PD *020 †55

SCHMIDT, Sung-Ji. ■ 22203 #041-13-2002 PCC *100

SCHNABEL, John Francis. 1101 ARLINGTON BLVD, # 810 SOUTH BLDG 22209 #041-15-2001 L2001 IM *100

SCHNEIDER, Kristy Ann. ■ 22201 #010-02-2008 *012

SCHNEIDER, Mark Thomas. 2001 15TH ST N 22201 #654-01-2008 *100

SCHOENGOLD, Jeffrey David. ■ 22209 #010-02-2008 *012

SCHREINER, David Allen. 611 S CARLN SPRNGS RD #405 22204 #033-05-1978 L1980 IM IMG *020 †20

SCHUMAN, Daniel C. 1600 N OAK ST, APT 527 22209 #024-07-1966 L2000 P *020 †75

SCHUM-BRADY, Marie Louise. ■ 22201 #010-01-1993 L1996 GP *020

SCHWAB, Frederick Jos. 1625 N GEORGE MASON DR, VIRGINIA HOSPITAL CENTER 22205 #041-14-1981 L1982 DR *020 †80

SCHWARTZ, Gary Philip. 600 ARMY NAVY DR, STE 2015 22202 #035-15-1968 L1996 IM GM *071 †20

SCHWARTZ, Jill. 1611 N KENT ST, STE 806 22209 #035-47-1991 L1994 OBG *020 †30

SCHWARTZ, William. 1725 N GEORGE MASON DR 22205 #056-06-1955 L1968 P *071 †75

SCOTTI, Michael J, Jr. ■ 22207 #010-02-1965 L1965 FM IMG *040 †20,18 ‡

SCULLY, James Henry. 1000 WILSON BLVD, STE 1825 22209 #021-01-1969 L1992 P GP *030 †75

SCULLY, William Francis, III. ■ 22201 #010-02-2008 *012

SEAMAN, Rachel Marie. ■ 22201 #039-01-2004 L2005 IM *100 †20

SEILER, Angele Carolyn. 1635 N GEORGE MASON DR, STE 490 22205 #010-02-1995 L1995 IM *020 †20

SEMAAN, Roy W. ■ 22207 #051-04-2008 *012

SHAFAI, Mandana. 1401 WILSON BLVD, STE 1007 22209 #038-45-1992 L1992 IM *020 †20

SHAH, Binit Jagdish. ■ 22203 #038-44-2003 L2004 P *012

SHAH, Koonj Ashvin. ■ 22201 #048-13-2006 L2006 IM *012

SHAH, Rupa. ■ 22203 #038-44-2006 L2006 OPH *012

SHAHAB, Syed Tariq. 1715 N GEORGE MASON DR, STE 301 22205 #704-02-1984 L2000 CD IM *020 †20

SHAHZAD, Saeed. 611 S CARLIN SPRINGS RD, STE 514 22204 #704-04-1979 L2006 N *020

SHARMA, Ashok Kumar. 601 S CARLIN SPRINGS RD 22204 #495-45-1967 L1982 R *020 †80

SHARMA, Mudit. ■ 22201 #035-06-2001 L2001 NS *020

SHARP, Trueman Winfield. ■ 22205 #051-01-1984 L2000 GPM *020 †70

SHARPE, Richard Earnest, Jr. ■ 22203 #035-01-1938 IM END *071 †20

SHERBER, Daniel Allan. ■ 22203 #035-01-1938 IM END *071 †20

SHETH, Sheetal Gaurang. ■ 22201 #035-06-2006 L2006 OBG *012

SHIH, Shirley Shiuhleei. ■ 22202 #035-03-2002 L2003 GS *012

SIBAY, Mounzer Fawzi. 611 S CARLN SPRNGS RD #304 22204 #875-01-1955 L1960 OTO ALI *071

SIDDIQUE, Shahzad Abid. 1701 N GEORGE MASON DR, VIRGINIA MEDICAL HOSPITAL C 22205 #028-34-2001 L2001 HO *012 †20

SIDDOWAY, Donald Ray. ■ 22201 #010-02-2008 *012

SIEBER, Otto Frank, Jr. 2107 WILSON BLVD STE 900 22201 #038-41-1958 L1958 PD PDI *030 †55

SIEGEL, Rubin Louis. ■ 22207 #803-09-1936 L1937 P PYA *071 †75

SILVESTRO, Stephen Robert. ■ 22204 #010-02-2006 PD *012

SIMON, Stephanie Lynn. ■ 22204 #010-01-2005 L2005 PD *012

SINCOCK, Matthew Curren. ■ 22206 #041-02-2005 L2005 IM *012

SINGH, Inder Paul. ■ 22209 #051-04-2006 IM *012

SMITH, Jacqueline Anne. ■ 22205 #051-01-1999 L1999 EM *020 †16

SMITH, Kathryn Marie. ■ 22201 #048-12-2007 L2007 OBG *012

SNYDER, Bertram C. 611 S CARLIN SPRINGS RD 22204 #010-02-1949 L1954 IM IMG *071 †20

SOOFER, Stephanie. 1701 N GEORGE MASON DR, ARLINGTON HOSPITAL 22205 #020-02-1992 L1999 PCP *020 †50

SOON, Anny Chunhui. ■ 22202 #010-01-2008 *012

SOR, Murat Halit. 1701 N GEORGE MASON DR, DEPARTMENT OF RADIOLOGY 22205 #010-01-1991 L1995 DR VIR *020 †80

SOTHINATHAN, Renuka. 1635 N GEORGE MASON DR, STE 215 22205 #539-03-1992 L1997 NEP *020 †20

SOWERWINE, Kathryn Jean. ■ 22206 #422-01-2006 L2006 IM *012

SPAGNOLI, Scott David. 1635 N GEORGE MASON DR, STE 250 22205 #025-01-1979 L1984 OTO *020 †45

SPANGLER, Jason Michael. ■ 22201 #041-14-1998 L2003 GPM *020 †70

SPINKS, Jeremy G. ■ 22202 #048-12-2004 L2007 EM *100

SPITZER, Trimble Bailey. ■ 22207 #051-07-2005 L2005 OBG *012

SPIVACK, Gary Robt. 2501 N GLEBE RD STE 303 22207 #033-06-1974 L1977 PYM CHP *020 †75

SPOONT, M Lawrence. 3033 WILSON BLVD STE 300B, ARLINGTON CTY AGING & DIS 22201 #016-06-1956 L2000 P PYG *020 †75

SREENIVASAN, Meera Veda. ■ 22203 #050-02-2005 L2005 IM *012

SRIMANUNTHIPHOL, Jun. ■ 22204 #891-01-1994 L1997 END *020 †20

SRINIVASAN, Sriraman Ram. ■ 22206 #422-01-2006 L2006 IM *012

STANFORD, Julia L. 200 N GLEBE RD STE 300, PHYSICIANS, P.C. 22203 #010-02-1998 L1998 MPD *020 †20,55

STAY, Ellsworth James. 1701 N GEORGE MASON DR, DEPT PTH 22205 #025-12-1973 L1978 PTH CLP *020 †50

STEIN, Lawrence Mark. 1400 S JOYCE ST STE 126, SUITE 126 22202 #035-08-1985 L1991 PUD IM *020 †20

STEMPLE-ZECK, Margaret. ■ 22207 #016-01-1940 L1942 FM *071

STEVENS, Barbara Ann. 3833 FAIRFAX DR STE 201 22203 #051-07-2002 L2002 PD *020

STEVENS, Kyleeann. ■ 22204 #037-01-2003 L2003 P *100

STEVENSON, Eugene O S. 2150 N POLLARD ST 22207 #010-01-1960 L1968 GS PDS *020 †85

STEWART, Donald H, Jr. ■ 22202 #028-02-1961 L1994 NS *071 †25

STINE, Terrill Mc Roe. 611 S CARLIN SPRINGS RD, STE 508 22204 #020-02-1981 L1986 ID IM *020 †20

STOKER, Martin Lawrence. 5015 LEE HWY 22207 #041-13-1954 L1958 IM *071 †20

ST PIERRE, Patrick. 1715 N GEORGE MASON DR, STE 504 22205 #023-12-1987 L2001 OSM ORS *020 †40

SUARDI, Enrico Mario Anto. ■ 22206 #561-03-2000 L2007 P *012

SUBHASH, Shree. 1635 N GEORGE MASON DR, STE 130 22205 #495-15-1968 L1979 U *020 †95

SULLIVAN, Caitlin Joyce. ■ 22209 #010-02-2008 *012

SUMIDA, Kevin David. 1635 N GEORGE MASON DR, STE 310 22205 #020-12-1996 L2003 ORS OSM *020 †40

SUTTON, Loree Kimberly. ■ 22207 #005-12-1985 L1987 P *030 †75

SVERHA, John Paul, II. 1625 N GEORGE MASON DR, EMERGENCY DEPARTMENT 22205 #008-01-1995 L1999 EM *020 †16

SYED, Amena Tabasum. ■ 22201 #025-07-2004 L2007 IM *020 †20

TABBARAH, Rami Zuhayr. ■ 22206 #605-01-2004 L2007 OBG *012

TAGGART, Rex R. 1600 S JOYCE ST # A910 22202 #019-02-1949 L1952 OS *020

TAHIRA, Mussarat. 611 S CARLIN SPRINGS RD, STE 514 22204 #704-21-1992 L1996 IM *020 †20

TAITANO, Cheryl Lim. 601 S CARLIN SPRINGS RD, ARLINGTON URGENT CARE CENT 22204 #748-02-2001 L2004 FM *100 †18

TANDATNICK, Joseph W. ■ 22209 #024-15-1943 L1943 PTH *020 †50

TANDY, Marlene Karen. ■ 22209 #010-01-1981 L1982 IM *062

TAYLOR, Nora Robinson. ■ 22206 #051-07-2003 L2006 IM *012

TCHABO, Jean-Gilles. 1701 N GEORGE MASON DR 22205 #067-02-1972 L1979 OBG PD *020 †30

TEPORDEI, Geraldine M P. ■ 22204 #781-01-1968 PHP *071

TERESCHUK, Michele Lynn. ■ 22202 #033-05-2006 PD *012

TERLINSKY, Alan S. 611 S CARLIN SPRNGS RD #411 22204 #010-02-1975 L1976 IM NEP *020 †20

THAKKAR, Anita P. ■ 22204 #422-01-2004 L2004 PD *020 †55

THATHAGARI, Neeraja. 611 S CARLIN SPRINGS RD, STE 504 22204 #495-62-1997 L2005 IM *100

THENAPPAN, Arunachalam. ■ 22204 #035-06-2006 L2006 GS *012

THINT, Ivy. ■ 22202 #209-01-1958 L1977 IM *071

TIBBITS, Paul Andrew. 1931 JEFFERSON DAVIS HWY, BUSINESS MODERN & SYSTEMS 22240 #021-01-1971 L1971 MDM OS *030 †20

TON, Chau That. 1701 N GEORGE MASON DR, ARLINGTON HOSPITAL 22205 #941-01-1973 L1986 AN *020 †05

TOUSTER, Michael David. ■ 22207 #035-19-1961 L1966 IM GE *071

TRIVEDI, Shriprakash Nand. 1701 N GEORGE MASON DR, MEDICAL STAFF OFFICE 22205 #495-76-1981 L2005 IM *020

TUHOLSKI, Nancy Lee. ■ 22205 #010-02-1982 L1988 PTH PD *020

TYROLER, Sidney Austin. 601 S CARLIN SPRINGS RD 22204 #038-40-1948 L1954 IM DIA *071 †20

UDUPA, Kodettoor R S. ■ 22204 #495-09-1970 L1987 ORS HS *020 †40

UDWIN, Michael Ronald. 1715 N GEORGE MASON DR, STE 302 22205 #039-01-1991 L1998 OBG *020 †30

VADOR, Gunjan Mukesh. 611 S CARLIN SPRINGS RD, VIRGINIA, SUITE 504 22204 #495-17-1988 L2002 IM HOS *020 †20

VALESANO, Adrienne Maria. ■ 22201 #010-01-2007 L2007 IM *012

VANCE, John Clair, Jr. 1701 N GEORGE MASON DR, RADIOLOGY DEPARTMENT 22205 #041-02-1959 L1967 DR *020 †80

VAN DER VLUGT, Gerold V. ■ 22204 #040-02-1963 L1966 PHP GPM *030 †70

VAN HERPE, Leo Bryant. 1715 N GEORGE MASON DR 22205 #010-01-1955 L1962 ORS *071 †40

VAN HOEK, Robert. ■ 22207 #035-01-1953 L1979 OS IM *071 †20

VARGA, Stephen Earl. ■ 22201 #010-02-2006 L2006 GS *012

VARGHESE, Reuben K. 800 S WALTER REED DR 22204 #043-01-1991 L2002 GPM *020 †20,70

VAUGHEY, Ellen Clarke. 1715 N GEORGE MASON DR, STE 106 22205 #010-02-1987 L1993 IM *020 †20

VELIGETI, Hari Veena. 601 S CARLIN SPRINGS RD, ARLINGTON URGENT CARE CENT 22204 #495-50-1997 L2007 IM *020 †18

VERGARA, Alfonso. 1815 N GEORGE MASON DR, # 410 22207 #847-04-1967 L1971 IM *071

VERSHEL, Genevieve. 1020 N QUINCY ST # 1915 22201 #026-04-1976 L1978 R *100

VICTOR, Gina Smith. ■ 22215 #010-03-2003 L2006 **FM** *100

VIGIL, Luis Humberto. 1635 N GEORGE MASON DR 22205 #737-06-1991 L2005 **IM** *100 †20

VILLAZON SALEM, Salvador. ■ 22204 #649-62-1985 L2005 *100

VILLEDA, Ruben Antonio. 4840 31ST ST S STE B 22206 #341-04-1997 L2003 **IM** *020 †20

VILLIVALAM, Arun Kumar. ■ 22201 #041-02-1998 L2008 **FM** *020 †18

VINH, Lam Vien. 2536 S ARLINGTON MILL DR 22206 #165-03-1976 L1981 **PS** *020 †85,65

VO, Phuong-Thu Thi. 3033 WILSON BLVD 22201 #942-01-1980 L2000 **P** *020

VOLK, William Robert. ■ 22202 #010-01-2007 **ORS** *012

WAGNER, Robert C. 1635 N GEORGE MASON DR, STE 140 22205 #010-02-1975 L1978 **GS** *020 †85

WAI, Homan Henry. ■ 22202 #005-18-2006 **IM** *012

WAI, Kitman. ■ 22202 #041-14-2005 L2007 **PD** *012

WALDMAN, Carl Jay. 611 S CARLIN SPRINGS RD, STE 208 22204 #016-06-1993 L1993 **CN** *020 †75

WALDROP, Danielle Renee. ■ 22201 #016-45-2006 **OBG** *012

WALSH, Christopher M. 1625 N GEORGE MASON DR, STE 334 22205 #010-02-2001 L2004 **IM** *020

WALSH, M Scott. 1701 N GEORGE MASON DR, VIRGINIA HOSPITAL CENTER 22205 #035-47-1981 L1982 **AN** *020 †20,05

WANIDWORANUN, Chingchai. 4001 9TH ST N, SUITE 228 22203 #891-01-1980 L1998 **IM** *020

WASHINGTON, Stanley Blair. 1701 N GEORGE MASON DR, RADIOLOGY DEPARTMENT 22205 #010-01-1997 L2003 **VIR DR** *020 †20

WATERHOUSE, Emily. ■ 22203 #010-02-2008 *012

WEAVER, Neill Kendall. ■ 22205 #024-01-1944 L1974 **OM IM** *071 †20,70,03

WEI, Lisa Lynn. 2700 CLARENDON BLVD, E-412 22201 #008-01-1996 L2000 **OPH PO** *020 †35

WEINER, Joshua Aaron. 2009 14TH ST N, STE 602 22201 #010-01-1998 L2000 **CHP** *020 †75

WELLBORN, Colvin C. 1715 N GEORGE MASON DR, STE 504 22205 #035-01-1993 L1995 **ORS** *020 †40

WELLS, Lanashia. ■ 22204 #010-03-2008 *012

WELTER, Drew C. ■ 22201 #035-15-2003 L2007 **AN** *100

WEST, Kristoffer Richard. ■ 22207 #010-01-2007 **ORS** *012

WHITE, Mattie Davis. 1435 N COURTHOUSE RD 22201 #025-12-1983 L1988 **CHP P** *020

WHITEHAIR, Curtis Lee. 3833 FAIRFAX DR, NRH REGIONAL REHAB 22203 #305-01-2000 L2000 **PM PRS** *020 †60

WHITING, Bradley Lodge. ■ 22204 #010-01-2008 *012

WIJETILLEKE, Padma P. 611 S CARLIN SPRNGS RD #10 22204 #220-01-1971 L1981 **PD** *020 †55

WILCOX, Clifton James. ■ 22201 #051-07-2008 *012

WILKINS, Luke Reinhart. 4650 WASHINGTON BLVD, BLVD #726 22201 #021-01-2007 L2007 **IM** *012

WILLCOX, Mark Emerson. ■ 22203 #010-02-2007 L2007 **IM** *012

WILLIAMS, Andrea Ellen. 1715 N GEORGE MASON DR 22205 #024-05-1990 L1994 **OBG** *020 †30

WILLIAMS, Matthew David. 1715 N GEORGE MASON DR, STE 106 22205 #051-04-1997 L1998 **PCC** *020 †20

WILTZ, Jonas Paul. ■ 22206 #021-01-2006 L2006 **IM** *012

WILTZ, Othon. 1625 N GEORGE MASON DR, VIRGINIA HOSPITAL CENTER 22205 #035-01-1985 L2006 **CRS GS** *020 †85,10

WINTER, David Brooks. 927 N KENMORE ST 22201 #055-75-1981, ▲ L1982 **GP OMM** *020

WISE, Alan. 1715 N GEORGE MASON DR 22205 #010-02-1968 L1970 **GS** *071 †85

WITTIG, Suzanne Herten. 1715 N GEORGE MASON DR, STE 307 22205 #010-02-1998 L1998 **IM** *020 †20

WOHLRAB, Juliette. 1701 N GEORGE MASON DR 22205 #035-15-1995 L1995 **PCC IM** *020 †20

WOLFF, Andrew Barrett. 1715 N GEORGE MASON DR, STE 504 22205 #028-02-2002 L2008 **OSM** *012

WRIGHT, Donald Carothers. 1625 N GEORGE MASON DR, STE 445 22205 #051-04-1975 L1999 **NS** *020 †25

WRIGHT, Donald John. ■ 22205 #048-02-1982 L1983 **FM** *020 †70,18

WU, Wendell. ■ 22203 #048-13-2004 L2004 **P** *012

WYCHERLY, Benjamin John. ■ 22206 #021-01-2005 L2005 **OTO** *012

YANOFSKY, Andrew Evan. ■ 22204 #033-05-2006 L2006 **IM** *012

YASSIN, John Gerald. 1715 N GEORGE MASON DR 22205 #024-07-1960 L1970 **OPH PS** *071 †35

YEH, Meng-Che. 4650 WASHINGTON BLVD 22201 #244-02-1989 L2000 **PTH** *020 †50

YI, David Husung. 1625 N GEORGE MASON DR, STE 425 22205 #051-04-2002 L2002 **IM** *100 †20

YOUSSEFI, Bijan. 611 S CARLN SPRNGS RD #402 22204 #517-01-1964 L1979 **OPH** *020 †35

YU, Jeannie Hyunju. ■ 22202 #011-02-2007 L2007 **IM** *012

YZER, Natalie Simone. ■ 22206 #016-06-2007 L2007 **P** *012

ZAHALSKY, Howard P. 1715 N GEORGE MASON DR, STE 501 22205 #043-01-1994 L1997 **IM** *020

ZAHEER, M Rafiq. 611 S CARLN SPRNGS RD #201 22204 #118-01-1981 L1995 **CD** *020 †20

ZINN, Edward. 601 S CARLIN SPRINGS RD 22204 #035-09-1966 L1970 **P** *020 †75

ZISMAN, Gilat. ■ 22206 #010-01-2008 *012

ZUBERI, Jamshed Ahmad. ■ 22201 #010-01-1996 L2000 **GS TRS** *020 †85

ZUNICH, Kathryn Margaret. ■ 22207 #035-15-1978 L1998 **IG IM** *050 †20,03

ZWEIG, Louis Kenneth. 1715 N GEORGE MASN DR #204 22205 #038-40-1998 L1998 **IM** *020 †20

ARRINGTON — NELSON

BROWN, Benjamin Timothy. 4038 THOMAS NELSON HWY, BLUE RIDGE MEDICAL CENTER 22922 #051-01-1980 L1981 **FM** *020 †18

BUNI, Tracy Mc Ginnis. 4038 THOMAS NELSON HWY, BLUE RIDGE MEDICAL CENTER 22922 #051-01-1994 L1994 **FM** *020 †18

WILLING, Stephen Alan. 4038 THOMAS NELSON HWY 22922 #023-01-1983 L1987 **FM FPG** *020 †18

YOUNG, Rebecca Brown. 4038 THOMAS NELSON HWY 22922 #055-02-1993 L1993 **FM** *020 †18

ASHBURN — LOUDOUN

ABDELBAKEY, Ayman A. 20905 PROFESSIONAL PLZ, STE 220 20147 #915-04-1987 L2001 **P** *020 †75

ACOURY, Nahla E. ■ 20147 #915-04-1978 L1993 **PTH** *020 †50

ALLEN, Harold Hayes, Jr. 20098 ASHBROOK PL, STE 190 20147 #051-01-1976 L1980 **ORS** *020 †40

ARASTU, Khusro Y. 43833 LAUREL RIDGE DR, VA MEDICAL CTR 20147 #495-21-1989 L1993 **P** *020

BASHARMAL, Ahmad Omar. ■ 20148 #759-04-2002 L2007 **IM** *100

BELOY, Amie Angelita G. 20955 PROFESSIONL PLZ #200, ASHBURN PEDIATRICS 20147 #748-02-1991 L2000 **PD** *100 †55

BHATTI, Fazal Rehman. 22930 OLYMPIA DR 20148 #704-20-1994 L2001 **IM** *020

BORRA, Madhu. ■ 20148 #495-50-1994 L2006 **PD** *100 †55

BUNGER, Margriet A. 20925 PROFESSIONAL PLZ, PLAZA #340 20147 #409-16-1978 L1989 **PD** *020 †55

CANCINO, Jennifer O. 44110 ASHBURN SHOPPING PLZ, UNIT 176 20147 #035-15-1997 L2000 **FM** *020 †18

CARROLL, Maura Katharine. 20955 PROFESSIONAL PLZ, STE 200 20147 #010-02-1998 L1998 **PD** *020 †55

CASOLARO, Mario Anthony. 21300 REDSKIN PARK DR, REDSKIN PARK 20147 #010-02-1980 L1983 **PUD IM** *020 †20

CHAMBERLAIN, Louise J. 20925 PROFESSIONAL PLZ, STE 340 20147 #023-01-1998 L2004 **PD** *020 †55

CHAR, George Uthuan. 21785 FILIGREE CT, STE 202 20147 #010-01-1997 L2003 **OPH** *020

CHENG, Katrina Woo. ■ 20147 #035-15-1994 L1999 **IM AN** *100

CHRISTIAN, Shirley L. 44050 ASHBURN SHOPPING PLZ 20147 #051-04-1999 L1999 **PD** *020 †55

CHUNG, Eugene. ■ 20147 #035-08-2003 L2007 **PD** *020 †55

COHN, Jeffrey Alan. 20925 PROFESSIONAL PLZ, BROADLAND FAMILY PRACTICE 20147 #038-41-2000 L2000 **FM** *020 †55

COOK, Randolph Bryant. 21785 FILIGREE CT, STE 103 20147 #051-01-1989 L1990 **ORS** *020 †85,40

COOPER, Jamille Tonia. ■ 20147 #010-03-1995 L2006 **PD** *074 †55

DARWISH, Dina H. 20925 PROFESSIONAL PLZ, STE 320 20147 #915-02-1990 L1998 **IM** *020 †20

DAVIS, Resa Elizabeth. 44075 PIPELINE PLZ, STE 210 20147 #038-45-2000 L2003 **PD** *020 †55

DOANE-WILSON, Cathleen O. 20925 PROFESSIONAL PLZ, PERFECTLY FEMALE WMNS HLT 20147 #050-02-1980 L2002 **OBG** *020 †30 ‡

DORSCH, Steve Stewart. 44340 PREMIER PLZ, STE 200 20147 #051-04-1997 L1997 **OMF** *020

DOSHI, Nitinkumar. ■ 20148 #495-22-1980 L2006 **IM** *020

EL- ARINI, M Osama. ■ 20148 #330-02-1961 L2002 **HO** *020 †18,20

FARUQI, Ambreen. ■ 20147 #051-07-2007 **PD** *012

FAZAL, Mohammed Q. ■ 20147 #704-01-1968 L1975 **P GP** *020

FEIERSTEIN, Saul. ■ 20147 #869-07-1963 L1965 **FM** *071 †18

GOEL, Neeta. 20600 GORDON PARK SQ, STE 130 20147 #495-12-1992 L2002 **FM** *020 †18

GONZALES, Maria Carmen Ve. ■ 20148 #748-01-1987 L2006 **CHP** *020 ‡

GOUD, Ravi Chandra. ■ 20147 #038-40-2004 L2007 **GPM** *100

GOWDA, Padma. 43962 MAIDEN CREEK CT, DEWITT-FAMILY HEALTH CENTE 20147 #495-21-1973 L1991 **IM IMG** *020

HABIB, Mahsin. 20925 PROFESSIONAL PLZ, STE 100 20147 #917-10-1993 L2000 **IM** *020 †20

HART, John Terrence. 20925 PROFESSIONAL PLZ, STE 100 20147 #051-01-1977 L1998 **OBG** *020 †30

HASSASSIAN, Sassan. 21785 FILIGREE CT, STE 103 20147 #051-07-1992 L2000 **PMM AN** *020 †05

HAYNESWORTH, Renee Piggee. 20608 GORDON PARK SQ, STE 170 20147 #020-02-1998 L1998 **PD** *020 †55

HOFFMAN-CROWLEY, Theresa. 20955 PROFESSIONAL PLZ, STE 200 20147 #051-07-1984 L1987 **PD** *030 †55

IVEY-CROWE, Gloria Jean. 44110 ASHBURN SHOPPING PLZ, UNIT 228 20147 #010-02-1994 L1995 **OBG** *020 †55

JARVIS-ECKERT, Marilyn. ■ 20147 #026-04-1950 L1964 **FM** *071 †18

JONES, Lisa Marsha. ■ 20147 #036-07-2006 L2006 **IM** *012

KATSNELSON, Arkady. ■ 20147 #913-01-1957 L1983 **FOP** *020 †50

KHAN, Bashir A. 44121 HARRY BYRD HWY, STE 215 20147 #495-51-1984 L1993 **PD** *020 †55

KHAN, Mahfuzul Haque. ■ 20147 #025-07-2003 L2003 **END** *012 †20

KIM, Cindy Hong. 44050 ASHBURN SHOPPING PLZ, STE 189 20147 #051-04-2001 L2001 **PD** *020 †55

KRZEPICKI, Jacek E. ■ 20147 #422-01-1994 L1995 **IM** *020

KURA, Shashikalaa. ■ 20148 #495-65-1999 L2008 **IM** *100 †20

LEE, Nicole Jennifer. 44050 ASHBURN SHOPPING PLZ, STE 189 20147 #041-15-1999 L2005 **PD** *020 †55

LY, Tam Thanh-Thi. 20211 KIAWAH ISLAND DR 20147 #051-04-2002 L2005 **ID** *020 †20

MALATI, Nabil. 43480 YUKON DR STE 100, KAISER PERMANENTE 20147 #915-04-1978 L1992 **PD** *020 †55

MANKAD, Mehul Vipul. 44110 ASHBURN SHOPPING PLZ, UNIT 251 20147 #016-06-1998 L2007 **P PFP** *020 †75

MARAGH, Sherry L H. 45155 RESEARCH PL, STE 140 20147 #023-01-2000 L2007 **PRD D** *020 †15 ‡

MC DONALD, Ruth Isabel. 44081 PIPELINE PLZ, STE 125 20147 #067-01-1978 L1982 **PD** *020 †55

MIRYALA, Shyamala. ■ 20147 #495-65-1993 L2000 **IM** *020 †20

MOJADIDI, Nafisa Khjazada. ■ 20147 #118-01-1964 L1976 **OBG** *020

MOJADIDI, Qudratullah. ■ 20147 #118-01-1965 L2002 **OBG** *020 †30

MOSHIRFAR, Ali. 21785 FILIGREE CT STE 103, CTR FOR ADVANCED ORTHO 20147 #041-01-1998 L2003 **OSS ORS** *020 †40 ‡

MUNRO, Alan Bruce. ■ 20147 #012-05-1957 L1957 **OBG** *071 †30

NGUYEN, Vananh Thi. 21785 FILIGREE CT 20147 #051-04-2001 L2007 **FM** *020

OCHIAI, Derek Hidehiko. 21785 FILIGREE CT, STE 103 20147 #038-06-1997 L2002 **ORS OSM** *020 †40

OELRICH, Leanna L. 21785 FILIGREE CT STE 10, NOVA MEDICAL GROUP 20147 #028-03-1995 L2008 **FM** *020 †18

PAGAN, Emily E B. 20955 PROFESSIONAL PLZ, STE 200 20147 #010-02-1997 L1997 **PD** *020

PASTERNAK, Laura Ann. 20925 PROFESSIONAL PLZ, STE 340 20147 #035-08-1989 L1994 **PD** *020 †55

PIERCE, Victoria C. 20955 PROFESSIONAL PLZ 20147 #023-01-1997 L1997 **PD** *020 †55

RASUL, Cecilia A. 44110 ASHBURN SHOPPING PLZ, UNIT 228 20147 #748-10-1983 L1997 **OBG** *020 †30

RATTNER, Susan Lynn. 44110 ASHBURN SHOPPING PLZ, UNIT 228 20147 #010-01-1982 L1984 **OBG** *020 †30

■ = Address Information Privacy Protected

ROACH, Alice Jeannette. ■ 20147 #048-12-1971 L1992 **R IM** *020 †80
RODRIGUEZ, Kelly Michael. 20905 PROFESSIONAL PLZ, BROADLAND FAMILY PRACTICE 20147 #041-13-2000 L2000 **FM** *100 †18
SALEEM, Gulrukh. 44075 PIPELINE PLZ, STE 200 20147 #704-01-1995 L2002 **IM RHU** *020 †20
SAMII, Abdol Hossein R. ■ 20147 #517-01-1964 L1998 **N** *020 †75
SAMII, Steven S.. ■ 20147 #759-06-2001 L2003 **IM** *012
SANUSI, Saida Morenike. 43480 YUKON DR STE 206 20147 #010-03-1997 L1997 **PD** *020 †55
SAVAGE, Margaret Ann. ■ 20148 #010-01-1994 **GPM** *040 †70
SHOWALTER, Andra Genese. ■ 20147 #051-04-1997 L1997 **RHU** *020 †20
SIRLIN, Scott Michael. 21785 FILIGREE CT STE 201 20147 #035-47-1980 L2000 **PG** *020 †55
SPENCER, Jeremy Thomas. ■ 20147 #010-01-2005 L2007 **PTH** *012
USMAN, Adil. 44121 HARRY BYRD HWY, STE 210 20147 #035-01-2000 L2004 **D** *020 †15
VENKATACHALLAM, Sunitha. ■ 20147 #495-09-1996 L2005 **IM** *020 †20
WADHWA, Jagdish Chandra. 20925 PROFESSIONAL PLZ, STE 100 20147 #495-47-1964 L2005 **OBG** *020 †30 ‡
WILDER, Jennifer Slack. 20905 PROFESSIONAL PLZ, BROADLAND FAMILY PRACTICE 20147 #010-02-2000 L2000 **FM** *100 †18
WILLIAMS, Irving Cardinal. ■ 20146 #047-07-2000 L2004 **PD** *020
WILLIAMS, Lisa Carol. 43480 YUKON DR, STE 206 20147 #041-12-1998 L1998 **PD** *020 †55
WILSON, Christine Talbott. ■ 20147 #045-01-1998 L1998 **PD** *020 †55
WOHLGEMUTH, Stephen A. ■ 20147 #036-07-1968 L1980 **IM** *020
WONG, Manhar. ■ 20148 #243-81-1986 **PTH** *100
YALAMANCHILLI, Haritha. ■ 20147 #495-70-1996 L2005 **FM** *100 †18

ASHLAND – HANOVER

BOWERS, Robert Mc Quilkin. 14160 HICKORY OAKS LN 23005 #048-04-1965 L2003 **GS** *020 †85
BOWMAN, Valerie Lynn. 9547 KINGS CHARTER DR 23005 #010-03-1990 L1993 **PD** *020 †55
CARLSON, Michael. 635 N WASHINGTON HWY, THERESA THOMAS MEDICAL CEN 23005 #035-06-1995 L1995 **IM** *020 †20
CARTER, Hill, Jr. 100 MEDICAL DR 23005 #051-01-1972 L1972 **FM** *020 †18
GANLEY, Donald Thos. 201 N WASHINGTON HWY, STE 306 23005 #035-08-1988 L1989 **IM** *020 †20
HAMILL, Carroll Francis. 104 BEVERLY RD 23005 #048-04-1961 L1978 **IM** *020
HANLEY, Robert Hayes. 635 N WASHINGTON HWY, THERESA THOMAS HEALTH CARE 23005 #041-01-1973 L1976 **FM** *020 †20
HUBBARD, Thomas Michael. 100 MEDICAL DR 23005 #051-04-1988 L1989 **FM** *020 †18
IRVIN, Natalie Rachelle. 11015 LEADBETTER RD, AIR PARK MEDICAL 23005 #048-13-1998 L1998 **FM OM** *020 †18
JONES, Donald Kenneth. ■ 23005 #035-09-1958 L1970 **P** *071
KERN, Marguerite Ann. 714 S CENTER ST 23005 #051-04-1962 L1963 **GP PD** *071
MARCINKIEWICZ, Marek. ■ 23005 #759-11-1988 L2007 **FP** *012
MOON, Christopher Sean. 100 MEDICAL DR 23005 #305-01-2001 L2001 **FM** *020 †18
SNEAD, Lawrence O, Jr. ■ 23005 #051-04-1950 L1950 **R** *071 †80
TRSIC, Yugo M. ■ 23005 #957-02-1951 L1969 **P N** *071
TWEEL, Wm Theodore, Jr. 12312 WASHINGTON HWY 23005 #051-04-1974 L1984 **PHP FM** *030 †18,70
WILLIAMS, Cheryl Yvette. 12300 WASHINGTON HWY 23005 #051-01-1992 L1992 **P** *020 †75
YOUNG, Christine M. 635 N WASHINGTON HWY 23005 #051-04-2004 L2007 **IM** *100 †20

ATKINS – SMYTH

OBREGON, Fausto. ■ 24311 #649-17-1949 L1958 **GS AS** *020

ATLANTIC – ACCOMACK

FLETCHER, Donald F, Jr. ■ 23303 #051-04-1951 L1951 **FM GP** *071

AXTON – HENRY

BESTLER, J Michael. ■ 24054 #035-45-1960 L1966 **PS OTO** *071 †45
FINE, Edward K. ■ 24054 #041-02-1958 L1981 **OBG** *020 †30
PARRENT, Phyllis Ann. ■ 24054 #051-04-1979 L1982 **EM** *020 †16

AYLETT – KING WILLIAM

GWATHMEY, Owen. ■ 23009 #051-04-1945 L1946 **CD OBS** *071 †85,90
LEWIS, Augustine W, III. 7864 RICHMOND TAPPHNCK HWY 23009 #051-04-1969 L1969 **FM PD** *020 †18 ‡
LONGEST, Donald Benson. ■ 23009 #051-04-1962 L1962 **FM** *020 †18 ‡
ROSENBERG, Mark Jacob. PO BOX 124 23009 #051-04-1978 L1991 **FM** *020 †18
TSUI, Allen Yatcheung. 11814 KING WILLIAM RD 23009 #010-01-1993 L2001 **FM** *020 †18

BAILEYS CROSSROADS – FAIRFAX

PRUNA, Olga R. ■ 22041 #275-01-1946 L1975 **PM** *071 †60

BARBOURSVILLE – ORANGE

FRENCH, David Marshall. 6129 SPOTSWOOD TRL 22923 #010-03-1948 L1961 **PHP** *030 †85

BASSETT – HENRY

LEWIS, David Howe. 324 T B STANLEY HWY 24055 #035-45-1962 L1967 **GS** *020 †85

BASTIAN – BLAND

DAVIS, Philip Joel. RR 1 BOX 2G 24314 #064-01-1971 L1983 *020

GRUBE, Richard Dennis. 12301 GRAPEFIELD RD 24314 #035-03-1997 L2000 **FM** *020 †18

BEALETON – FAUQUIER

KING, Diane Lynn. 6200 STATION DR 22712 #051-07-1987 L1990 **FM** *020 †18
ROBINSON, Ralph Miles. 6398 VILLAGE CENTER DR 22712 #051-04-1954 L1979 **NR GS** *020 †85

BEAVERDAM – HANOVER

CAMPBELL, Michael L. 16151 TRAINHAM RD 23015 #051-04-1992 L1993 **FM** *020 †18
HUFFMAN, Stanton Vance. ■ 23015 #051-04-1953 **GP** *071
MEROLA-CARVAJAL, Mary L. PO BOX 98 23015 #561-01-1978 L1982 **FM** *071 †18 ‡
NELSON, Mark Theodore. ■ 23015 #019-02-1989 L2003 **AN** *020 †05
STAIRS, Paul Whitney. ■ 23015 #051-04-1986 L1987 **FM** *020 †18

BEDFORD – BEDFORD

AMPARAN, Aquiles. ■ 24523 #649-01-1956 L1963 **GS** *071
AUSBAND, Stephen Claburn. ■ 24523 #036-08-1995 L1997 **EM** *020 †16
BEAHM, Linda Sue. 1613 OAKWOOD ST, STE 201 24523 #051-04-1985 L1986 **FM PLM** *020 †18 ‡
BIANCHINO-NIGRO, Darlene. 171 W MAIN ST 24523 #018-75-1990, ▲ L1995 **IM** *020
BUCHANAN, Brian Damien. 1710 WHITFIELD DR 24523 #028-34-1977 L1980 **IM** *020 †20
CABALLERO, Cesar Evaristo. 1613 OAKWOOD ST, BEDFORD MEM HLTH EMGY DEPT 24523 #737-06-1978 L1990 **FM EM** *020 †18 ‡
DENEKAS, Alan M. 1613 OAKWOOD ST 24523 #048-13-1987 L1990 **FM** *020 †18
DOVE, Erin H. 1613 OAKWOOD ST, BEDFORDMEMORIAL HOSPITAL 24523 #021-01-1997 L1997 **FM** *020 †18
GHOBRIAL, Samir Geo. 1615 OAKWOOD ST, CARILION OB/GYN BEDFORD 24523 #915-04-1969 L1977 **OBG** *020
HANUSIK, Frances Dorothy. 1203 ROUNDTREE DR 24523 #010-02-1953 L1956 **PD** *071
HUBACH, Kurt Wm. 1613 OAKWOOD ST, STE 201 24523 #010-01-1988 L1989 **FM** *020 †18
HUTCHISON, Wayne Thos. 1613 OAKWOOD ST, STE 201 24523 #007-02-1975 L1976 **FM** *020 †18
JOSLYN, Emerson Allen. 1613 OAKWOOD ST, STE 201 24523 #016-11-1983 L1986 **IM EM** *020 †20
KERR, John Martin, Jr. 1615B OAKWOOD ST 24523 #051-04-1986 L2005 **GS** *020 †85
KESSLER, Henry G. ■ 24523 #047-06-1938 L1939 **GP** *071
KRZYZANOWSKI, Suzanne K. 1613 OAKWOOD ST, BEDFORD MEMORIAL HOSPITAL 24523 #012-05-1995 L2002 **FM** *020 †18
LILLY, Paul Howard, Jr. 6485 FALLING CREEK RD 24523 #051-04-1964 L1964 **FM AM** *020 †18
LOWE, Eugene Walper, Jr. 1621 WHITFORD DR 24523 #051-04-1989 L1994 **GS** *020 †85
MATHEW, Mathew. 838 OLE TURNPIKE DR 24523 #495-27-1975 L1986 **NEP IM** *020 †20
MCLAREN, Barbara. 1615 OAKWOOD ST, STE D 24523 #035-03-1997 L2007 **OBG** *020
RHODES, Herbert Paul, Jr. 1613 OAKWOOD ST 24523 #051-04-1966 L1967 **DR NM** *020 †80,28
ROWELL, Diane Louise. 1368 AMERICAN WAY 24523 #051-07-1989 L1990 **FM** *020 †18
SMITH, Paula Renee. 171 W MAIN ST, BEDFORD MEDICAL, INC. 24523 #047-20-1998 L1998 **FM** *020 †18
TANNER, Russell Edward. 1613 OAKWOOD ST, EDFORD MEMORIAL HOSPITAL 24523 #025-07-1977 L1993 **OBG** *020
TEMELES, Daniel Stewart. 1621 WHITFIELD DR, STE A 24523 #041-14-1984 L1986 **IM** *020 †20
WEDDLE, William Elliot. 1613 OAKWOOD ST, BEDFORD MEMORIAL HOSPITAL 24523 #051-04-1975 L1978 **FM EM** *020 †18
WENGER, John Robert, Jr. 1613 OAKWOOD ST 24523 #051-04-1962 L1962 **FM OS** *071
WENTE, John Anthony, Jr. 1613 OAKWOOD ST 24523 #020-02-1962 L1970 **GS EM** *071 †85
WOODROOF, Kerry Colston. 412 N BRIDGE ST 24523 #051-04-1973 L1979 **OPH** *020 †35

BELLE HAVEN – ACCOMACK

DOSS, Otis Wm. ■ 23306 #051-04-1959 L1959 **GS** *071 †85
KOENIG, Carol Lynn. 15249 ARTHURS CT 23306 #051-07-1983 L1984 **FM** *071 †18
RIOPEL, David James. 9159 FRANKTOWN RD, CHILDREN'S HEALTH CENTER 23306 #051-01-1988 L1992 **IM PD** *020 †20,55

BENT MOUNTAIN – ROANOKE

PERRY, Alvis Tederrall. 10816 BOTTOM CREEK RD 24059 #036-01-1980 L1998 **AN GS** *020 †05
TURNER, Jeffrey David. ■ 24059 #047-20-1995 L1998 **EM** *020 †16

BERGTON – ROCKINGHAM

GEHMAN, Linford Kulp. 20055 BROCKS GAP RD 22811 #041-02-1963 L1970 **FM** *020 †18

BERRYVILLE – CLARKE

AIELLO, Christine Marie. 115 S CHURCH ST 22611 #011-02-1999 L1999 **FM** *020 †18
DELERY, Alfred A. 901 COOL SPRING LN 22611 #024-07-1944 L1982 **IM** *072 †20
FOUST, Linda Kay. 322 N BUCKMARSH ST 22611 #046-01-1979 L1991 **IM** *020 †20
IDEN, Thomas Carroll. 115 S CHURCH ST 22611 #051-04-1944 L1944 **GPM** *071 †18
KAISER, Sherif Z. 115 S CHURCH ST, BERRYVILLE MED ASSOC 22611 #915-02-1990 L1993 **FM** *020 †18 ‡
SALATA, Kimberly Heidig. 322 N BUCKMARSH ST 22611 #051-07-1994 L1994 **PM** *072 †60
SANTILLANO, Antonio B. ■ 22611 #748-01-1957 L1995 **CLP** *072 †50
STEUER, Kathryn L Knutzen. 13 W MAIN ST 22611 #028-02-1988 L2004 **D** *020 †15

BIG STONE GAP – WISE

BASS, Rhonda K. 3169 2ND AVE E 24219 #051-01-1998 L2007 **CHP PD** *100

■ = Address Information Privacy Protected

BATES, Gayle Catherine. 1980 HOLTON AVE E STE 203, LONESOME PINE PEDIATRICS 24219 #051-07-2004 L2007 **PD** *020 †55

BECHTEL, Robert Williams. 1990 HOLTON AVE E, LONESOME PINE HOSPITAL 24219 #012-05-1986 L1992 **IM** *020 †20

BELLAMY, Candace Lynese. PO BOX 759, 272 DOGWOOD DR 24219 #047-20-1997 L1997 **FM** *020 †18

COOPERSTEIN, Elizabeth C. 1 CLOVERLEAF SQ, STE F1 24219 #047-20-1997 L1997 **FM** *020 †18

DINGUS, Donald Elmer, II. 205 E 19TH ST N, ACROSS THE TRACKS HEALTHCA 24219 #051-01-1989 L1990 **FM** *020 †18

DUNWIDDIE, Walter C. 1990 HOLTON AVE E, LONESOME PINE HOSPITAL 24219 #051-04-1981 L1982 **AN** *020 †20

FLEENOR, Lawrence J. 1990 HOLTON AVE E 24219 #051-01-1966 L1966 **FM AI** *020 †18

FORD, Michael Benj. 1980 HOLTON AVE E STE 1 24219 #051-04-1970 L1970 **FM LM** *020 †18

GOPALAN, Srikumar. ■ 24219 #495-37-1974 L1983 **DR NM** *020 †80

KANWAL, Gurcharan Singh. 1990 HOLTON AVE E 24219 #495-03-1963 L1971 **IM** *020

LAGRIMAS, Fernando C. PO BOX 167, 309 SHAWNEE AVE E 24219 #748-08-1972 L1991 **GYN** *020

LEE, Dane. 272 DOGWOOD DR, WALLENS RIDGE STATE PRISON 24219 #027-01-1993 L1996 **FM** *020 †18

MANOHARAN, Edakandiyil. 1980 HOLTON AVE E, STE 301 24219 #495-44-1966 L1972 **OBG** *020 †30

MC CLANE, John Raymond. 1990 HOLTON AVE E 24219 #020-12-1965 L1979 **R** *020 †80

PARTHASARATHY, T K. 24219 #495-61-1966 L1973 **GS EM** *020 †85

RAMAKRISHNAN, M R. 1745 VALLEY VIEW DR E, MEDICAL DOCTOR 24219 #495-53-1974 L1979 **R** *020 †80

RENFRO, Thomas Edward. 1990 HOLTON AVE E 24219 #051-01-1985 L1986 **IM** *020 †20

RUSS, Mark David. 1980 HOLTON AVE E, STE 202 24219 #010-01-1993 L1993 **ORS** *020

SAHA, Subhash Chandra. 1990 HOLTON AVE E 24219 #160-05-1967 L1977 **R NM** *020 †80

SLATER, Kenneth C. 1990 HOLTON AVE E 24219 #748-08-1971 L1994 **IM** *020 †20 ‡

STRICKLAND, Robert D. 1990 HOLTON AVE E, P O DRAWER 1 24219 #047-20-1987 L1998 **GE** *020 †20

TAYLOR, Mark Michael. 1 CLOVERLEAF SQ, STE F1 24219 #051-04-1997 L1997 **FM** *020 †18

VACCO, Michael Charles. 1980 HOLTON AVE E 24219 #305-01-1984 L2005 **PD** *020 ‡

VITO CRUZ, Marissa Galvez. 1990 HOLTON AVE E 24219 #748-29-1994 L1996 **FM** *020 †18

BISHOP — TAZEWELL

DE MESA, Isabelita T. BISHOP MC RT 16 DRAW D 24604 #748-07-1964 L1983 **PD** *020

BLACKSBURG — MONTGOMERY

ABEL, Gary Stephen. ■ 24060 #055-01-1986 L1992 **FM** *075 †18

ANNADATA, Satish. 700 UNIVERSITY CITY BLVD, NEW RIVER VALLEY COMMUNITY 24060 #495-21-2001 L2004 **P** *012

ARONSON, Michael Roger. 2001 S MAIN ST, STE 1 24060 #051-04-1989 L1990 **DR** *020 †80

BAKER, Richard Holden. ■ 24060 #035-06-1961 L1987 **GYN GP** *071 †30

BARRANCO, S D. 3706 S MAIN ST, STE B 24060 #030-06-1966 L1973 **ORS OSM** *020 †40

BARRY, Fredrick Michael. 3700 S MAIN ST 24060 #021-01-1977 L1980 **IM** *020 †20

BECK, Matthew Todd. TECH UNIVERSITY, MCCOMAS HALL, VIRGINIA 24061 #011-03-1991 L1995 **FM** *020 †18

BIRCH, Bruce Mc Kinley. 820 UNIVERSITY BLVD, STE 2 24060 #051-01-1967 L1967 **IM END** *020 †20

BISHOP, Thomas Harman. ■ 24060 #036-01-2001 L2005 **VIR** *020 †80

BIVINS, Don Howard. 2265 KRAFT DR 24060 #047-06-1976 L1978 **N PME** *020 †75

BOATWRIGHT, Charles Lee. 901 PLANTATION RD 24060 #051-04-1953 L1953 **FM** *071 †18

BOERTH, Scott R. 3698 S MAIN ST 24060 #001-06-1997 L2000 **IM END** *020 †20

BOWMAN, Robert Lee. 3706 S MAIN ST, STE B 24060 #051-04-1962 L1962 **ORS HS** *071 †40

BOWMAN, Robert Rowley, Jr. 3700 S MAIN ST 24060 #038-41-1969 L1978 **FM** *020 †18

CALLAHAN, Cathleen Marie. 2265 KRAFT DR 24060 #036-01-1998 L2005 **OBG** *020 †30

CHRISTOPHER, Mark Earl. 3700 S MAIN ST, MONTGOMERY REGIONAL HOSPIT 24060 #038-40-1985 L2007 **PCP** *020 †50

CINCO, Narcissa C. 200 PROFESSIONAL PARK DR., THE CASCADE GROUP 24061 #748-11-1991 L1997 **CHP** *020

CLAY, Heidi Alexandra. 700 UNIVERSITY CITY BLVD 24060 #048-12-1988 L1992 **P SME** *020 †75

COLPITTS, Terence James. RR 460 SOUTH, MONTGONERY REGIONAL HOSP 24060 #036-01-1982 L1984 *020

COOKE, Circe Dee. 700 UNIVERSITY CITY BLVD, NRU COMM SVCS 24060 #034-01-1997 L2004 **CCP OS** *020 †55,75

COWLEY, Larry Allen. ■ 24060 #021-05-1967 L1985 **OTO** *020 †45

CRAMER, Jill B. 817 DAVIS ST, STE A 24060 #010-02-1998 L2005 **IM** *020 †75

DRYSDALE, Daniel Brian. 3645 S MAIN ST 24060 #036-07-1974 L1978 **OPH** *020 †35

EPSTEIN, Robert D. ■ 24060 #047-05-1940 L1940 **IM HEM** *071 †20

FARRIER, Paul Henry, Jr. VIRGINIA TECH, SCHIFFERT HEALTH CENTER 24061 #051-01-1962 L1962 **GP OM** *030 †70

FRASCA, Dominic. VIRGINIA TECH MCCOMAS HALL, SCHIFFERT HEALTH CENTER 24061 #035-15-1982 L1994 **EM FM** *020 †18

FRASCA, Linda Olsen. 3700 S MAIN ST, ACADEMIC PRIMARY CARE ASSO 24060 #035-15-1982 L1994 **EM** *020 †18

FREEBORN, Ethan Ray. ■ 24060 #051-01-2004 L2007 **EM** *020

FREEMAN, Jeremy Harmon. 1420 N MAIN ST, CARILION FAMILY MEDICINE 24060 #047-05-1999 L1999 **FM** *020 †18

FRIEBEN, Joseph Milan. ■ 24060 #035-45-2002 L2005 **P** *100

GRUBBS, Philip E. 817 DAVIS ST, STE 2 24060 #048-12-1985 L1994 **PS GS** *020 †85,65

GWYNN, Eric Stephen. ■ 24060 #051-04-2002 L2007 **U** *100

HANLINE, Philip Emerson. 2001 S MAIN ST, STE 1 24060 #035-09-1998 L2003 **DR** *020 †80

HASSEN, Elham. ■ 24060 #016-01-2002 **OBG** *100

HEDGES, David Joe. 110 PROFESSIONAL PRK DR SE, STE 5 24060 #051-04-1979 L1980 **OPH** *020 †35

HENDRICKS, Wm Tillman. 901 PLANTATION RD 24060 #048-04-1973 L1974 **FM** *020 †18

HENSHAW, Jolene Bryner. ■ 24060 #043-01-2002 L2007 **GS** *020

HUDGINS, David Michael. 901 PLANTATION RD, CARILION FAMILY MEDICINE 24060 #051-04-1982 L1983 **FM** *020 †18

ISENHOUR, Wm Apperson. 3708 S MAIN ST, STE B 24060 #047-06-1969 L1973 **OBG** *020 †30

JENKINS, Hulannie Andrew. 3700 S MAIN ST 24060 #011-03-1979 L2000 **EM OM** *062 †16

JONES, Belle Bonita. 805 DAVIS ST, WYTHE-BLAND PEDIATRICS 24060 #051-04-1996 L1998 **PD** *020 †55

JORDAN, Christine Drombet. 3698 S MAIN ST 24060 #051-07-2004 L2004 **IM** *020 †20

LAGAN, Henry Duane. VIRGINIA TECH, STUDENT HEALTH SERVICES 24061 #039-01-1964 L1988 **GP FSM** *020 †18

LANDER, David Henry. 3700 S MAIN ST 24060 #038-01-1975 L1981 **EM IM** *020 †20,16

LESTER, Randall Vaughn. 801 DAVIS ST STE 1 24060 #051-01-1977 L1998 **GS** *020 †85

LIVINGSTON, David Barker. ■ 24060 #001-06-1981 L1982 **EM** *020 †16

LO, Hing-Har. 2001 S MAIN ST STE 1 24060 #035-06-1974 L1981 **DR NM** *071 †28,80

LONG, Mary Tom Bunting. ■ 24060 #051-04-1943 L1943 **PHP** *071

MAC MILLAN, David T. 1901 S MAIN ST, STE 2 24060 #048-04-1976 L1994 **GS** *020 †85

MANDELSTAMM, Maria T. 3700 S MAIN ST 24060 #407-24-1955 L1974 **IM EM** *071 †16

MC COY, Catherine Wallace. ■ 24060 #051-01-1983 L1985 **IM** *020 †20

MERTES, Chris Paul. 901 PLANTATION RD, CARILION FAMILY MED 24060 #016-06-1993 L2005 **FM** *020 †18

MORROW, Linda. 901 PLANTATION RD, CARILION GYN ASSOCIATES 24060 #054-04-1984 L1996 **OBG** *020 †30

MOSTAGHIMI, Arash. ■ 24060 #024-01-2007 L2007 **IM** *012

NEELY, Julie. MCCOMAS HALL (0140), SCHIFFERT HEALTH CTR 24061 #038-40-1993 L1994 **IM** *020 †20

NEWMARK, Bertram Jeffrey. 2001 S MAIN ST, STE 1 24060 #038-40-1970 L1976 **DR NR** *020 †80

OSIMANI, Daniel Anthony. 830 HOSPITAL DR 24060 #016-11-1988 L2004 **CD IM** *020 †20

PAYNE, Jon Michael. 810 HOSPITAL DR 24061 #011-03-1973 L1978 **IM** *020 †20

POGONOWSKA, Magdalena J. 2001 S MAIN ST STE 1 24060 #759-01-1951 L1960 **R DR** *071 †80

POLITANO, Amani Dale. 604 HARRELL ST 24060 #051-01-2008 *012

PRABHU, Sunil Kumar. ■ 24063 #496-01-1990 **PD** *100

RABUN, Ellen Irene. 708 N MAIN ST STE 200 24060 #051-04-1984 L1996 **FM EM** *020 †18

RASUL, Kamran. 3700 S MAIN ST, MONTGOMERY REGIONAL HOSPIT 24060 #704-01-1991 L2001 **IM IMG** *020 †20

ROBERSON, Arthur Edward. 3700 WEST RIDGE DR 24060 #047-06-1996 L2000 **IM** *020 †20

ROBERTS, David Jos. 1997 S MAIN ST, CARILION OB/GYN 24060 #035-48-1990 L1994 **OBG** *020 †30

ROBINSON, Lucian Dabney. 901 PLANTATION RD, CARILION FAMILY MEDICINE 24060 #051-04-1972 L1972 **FM** *020 †18

SALINAS, Orlando F. ■ 24060 #176-03-1957 L1962 **OM FM** *071

SCHIFFERT, Charles Wilson. ■ 24060 #041-09-1946 L1950 **GP** *071

SHEPHERD, Richard De Witt. 901 PLANTATION RD, CARILION FAMILY MEDICINE 24060 #051-04-1979 L1980 **EM** *020 †16,18

SIEGEL, Marc Saml. 120 PROFESSIONAL PRK DR SE, STE 7 24060 #012-01-1979 L1984 **ORS OSM** *020 †40

SLAYTON, Michael Edward. 820 UNIVERSITY CITY BLVD, STE 2 24060 #051-01-1966 L1966 **IM** *071 †20

SOWINSKI, Kazimierz M. 105 MCDONALD ST 24060 #759-06-1973 L1977 **FM** *020

SPRAGUE, Patty Anne. STUDENT HEALTH SERVICE, VIRGINIA POLYTECHNIC INST 24061 #051-01-1978 L1981 **PD** *074

STAPLETON, Christopher P. 805 DAVIS ST 24060 #051-01-1988 L1990 **PD** *020 †55

STEPHENSON, Keith Richard. 901 PLANTATION RD, CARILION SURGICAL CARE 24060 #041-12-1983 L2002 **GS OS** *020 †85

STOCKBURGER, Robt Walker. 1420 N MAIN ST, CARILION FAMILY MEDICINE 24060 #051-04-1974 L1975 **FM** *020 †18

STOECKLE, David Bruce. 820 HOSPITAL DR 24060 #035-01-1972 L1978 **GS TS** *020 †85

STONE, James Hexie. ■ 24060 #051-04-1974 L1975 **EM OM** *020 †18

STRELKA, Eugene Paul, Jr. 3708 S MAIN ST 24060 #016-43-1967 L1973 **ORS** *071 †40

SULLIVAN, Karen Ann. 901 PLANTATION RD, CARILION FAMILY MED-BLACKS 24060 #051-04-1995 L1998 **FM** *020 †20

TEMPLE, Alton Davis. ■ 24060 #055-01-2007 **GS** *012

TEMPLETON, Nina. ■ 24060 #056-06-1977 L1994 **AN** *075 †05

THOMPSON, Chad Randal. 901 PLANTATION RD, CARILION FAMILY MEDICINE 24060 #051-07-1983 L1984 **FM** *020 †18

THRASH, Nehemiah, Jr. ■ 24060 #051-07-2006 L2006 **IM** *012

TSUI, Camilla Kamming. 901 PLANTATION RD, CARILION FAMILY MEDICINE 24060 #051-04-1995 L1995 **FM** *020 †18

WEISEMAN, Jane Stansel. 3700 S MAIN ST, EMERG ROOM 24060 #036-05-1986 L1987 **EM** *020 †16

WHEELING, Holly May. 3700 S MAIN ST, MONTGOMERY REGIONAL HOSP 24060 #051-04-1996 L2004 **EM** *020 †16

WILDER, J Edwin. 810 HOSPITAL DR 24060 #035-19-1976 L1992 **CD IM** *020 †20

WILLIAMS, Richard Tate. 2265 KRAFT DR 24060 #036-08-1986 L1992 **IM PD** *020 †20,55

WILLIAMS, Sarah Knopp. 700 UNIVERSITY CITY BLVD 24060 #036-08-1988 L1992 **P** *020 †75

WILSON, Richard Lee, Jr. 3708 S MAIN ST, STE F 24060 #055-02-1993 L1999 **PM OM** *020 †60

WINTERS, Adam D, III. UNIV STUDENT HLTH SERVICES, AND STATE UNIV 24061 #051-04-1976 L1978 **PA** *040 ‡

WUNSCH, Martha Jane. 200 PROFESSIONAL PRK DR SE, PARK DRIVE 24060 #023-12-1983 L1997 **ADM PD** *050 †55

YADRANDJI, Soheila. 3700 S MAIN ST 24060 #517-03-1988 L1999 **PTH** *020 †50

YOUNG, Robert James. 901 PLANTATION RD, CARILION GYN ASSOCIATES 24060 #051-01-1976 L1993 **OBG** *020 †30

ZHANG, Chunxiao. 817 DAVIS ST, STE A 24060 #243-36-1987 L2005 **CN** *020 †75

BLACKSTONE — NOTTOWAY

AZMI, Malalai. 920 S MAIN ST 23824 #305-01-2001 L2001 **FM** *020 †18

BERKLE, Keith Patton. 920 S MAIN ST 23824 #051-04-2003 L2003 **OBG** *012

BRADNER, Melissa Kay. 820 S MAIN ST 23824 #035-01-1996 L1997 **FM** *020 †18

CAO, Bichhuyen Luong. 820 S MAIN ST 23824 #036-08-1995 L1995 **FM** *100

CHOI, Jill Soonock. 920 S MAIN ST 23824 #305-01-2002 L2002 **FM** *100

CROWDER, Lina Sue. 920 S MAIN ST, BLACKSTONE FAMILY PRACTICE 23824 #051-04-1991 L1991 **FM** *040

HAHESY-CALHOUN, Marian A. 920 S MAIN ST, BLACKSTONE FAMILY 23824 #010-03-1996 L1996 **FM** *020 †18

HARRIS, James Selden. 920 S MAIN ST, PRACTICE CENTER INC 23824 #051-01-1960 L1960 **FM** *071 †18

ROSENBAUM, Charles I. 920 S MAIN ST 23824 #051-04-1984 L1986 **FM** *040 †18

SANDLIN, Sherry Ann. 920 S MAIN ST, BLACKSTONE FAMILY PRACTICE 23824 #051-07-1985 L1986 **FM PHP** *020 †18

SPENCE, Steven Nally. 920 S MAIN ST, BLACKSTONE FAMILY 23824 #051-01-1977 L1979 **FM** *020 †18

SWAN, Dennis Dwain. 920 S MAIN ST 23824 #665-01-2004 L2005 **FP** *012

WERTZ THOMAS, C Marcy. 820 S MAIN ST 23824 #020-12-1983 L1984 **AN FM** *020 †05,18

WHITE, Stuart Bruce. 820 S MAIN ST, BLACKSTONE FAM PRAC CTR 23824 #051-04-1957 L1957 **FM** *071 †18

BLACKWATER — SCOTT

HILL, R Michael. RR 1, BOX 53 24221 #031-01-1990 L1990 **FM** *020

BLUE RIDGE — BOTETOURT

LINICK, Kelli Lynn. PO BOX 200, 460 AT LAYMANTOWN RD 24064 #038-40-1994 L1995 **FM** *020 †18

NAVAB-BOUSHEHRI, Abdol H. ■ 24064 #517-01-1956 L1983 **ORS** *020

BLUEFIELD — TAZEWELL

ALI, Raza. 9 WESTWOOD MEDICAL PARK #704-21-1987 L1997 **NEP** *020 †20

ASBURY, Donald Walter. 1240 HOCKMAN PIKE 24605 #055-02-1987 L1994 **AI IM** *020 †20,03

CHOPRA, Kamlesh Kapoor. ■ 24605 #495-30-1964 *100

CHOPRA, Surrinder Kumar. 2113 COLLEGE AVE STE 23, CHOPRA PLASTIC SURGERY 24605 #495-03-1958 L1979 **PS** *020 †65

CHUN, Yong Kwon. ■ 24605 #583-09-1965 L1974 **P** *020

CICENAS, Ryan Richard. 106 HUFFARD DR 24605 #055-02-2000 L2004 **MPD** *020 ‡

DE GRAY, Stephen Alan. 7 WESTWOOD MEDICAL PARK 24605 #050-02-1975 L1986 **FM** *020 †18

DIAB, Anas. ■ 24605 #875-01-1985 L2000 **NEP** *020 †20

FIGUEROA, Oscar Fernando. 103 WESTWOOD CMN 24605 #737-06-1983 L2003 **PUD SME** *020 †20

GROUSE, David Scott. 19 WESTWOOD MEDICAL PARK 24605 #005-18-1980 L1984 **N** *020 †75

HARRIS, David Maxwell. 3 WESTWOOD MEDICAL PARK 24605 #065-01-1976 L1983 **OTO** *020 †45

IQBAL, Mohammad Khalid. 2221 W CUMBERLAND RD 24605 #704-15-1976 L1992 **PDC PD** *020 †55

JAIN, Sonia. ■ 24605 #051-01-2005 L2005 **PD** *012

JOHNSON, Frank Jos, Jr. 106 HUFFARD DR 24605 #012-01-1980 L1984 **FM** *020 †18

KHOKAR, Shahid Munif. 4 WESTWOOD MEDICAL PARK 24605 #704-15-1980 L2001 **PD PEM** *020 †55

LESNETT, James Curtis. 12 WESTWOOD MEDICAL PARK 24605 #055-01-1978 L1986 **FM** *020 †18

MILLER, Thomas Edward. 108 TITLEIST DR 24605 #035-01-1986 L2005 **DR** *020 †80

MOUNZER, Assaad. 17 WESTWOOD MEDICAL PARK 24605 #605-02-1977 L1988 **U OS** *020 †95

MYERS, Thomas C. 110 HUFFARD DR 24605 #028-78-1981, ▲ L2003 **D** *020

PETERSON, Phillip Allen. 106 HUBBARD DR 24605 #018-03-1985 L1988 **FM** *020 †18

QAZI, Naeem Akhtar. 9 WESTWOOD MEDICAL PARK 24605 #704-01-1972 L1987 **CD IM** *020 †20

RANA, Mohammad Javed. 2003 LEATHERWOOD LN 24605 #704-01-1984 L1997 **CD** *020 †20

RANA, Shahnaz. 9 WESTWOOD MEDICAL PARK 24605 #704-06-1975 L1978 **IM** *075 †20

RASKIN, Stephen Paul. 2000 LEATHERWOOD LN 24605 #024-01-1970 L1977 **R** *020 †80

RAZA, Quasir. 2111 COLLEGE AVE 24605 #496-01-1995 L1997 **IM** *020 †20

RIAZ, Riaz Uddin. 15 WESTWOOD MEDICAL PARK 24605 #495-21-1970 L1987 **P GP** *020 †75

ROBERTSON, Philip Brunner. 105 WESTWOOD CMN, PSYCH ASSOC/THE VIRGINIAS 24605 #048-13-1984 L1989 **P CHP** *020 †75

SAFI, Ihsan Omar. 5 WESTWOOD MEDICAL PARK 24605 #875-01-1978 L1993 **END** *020 †20

SATHRE, Howard Paul. 4 RIVERMONT DR 24605 #038-43-1988 L1991 **EM** *020 †20

SULTANA, Razia. 11 WESTWOOD MEDICAL PARK 24605 #704-01-1974 L1984 **PD** *020 †55

TOLLIVER, David L. 110 HUFFARD DR 24605 #055-75-1988, ▲ L1996 **D** *020

TUMBOKON, Marietta B. ■ 24605 #748-01-1972 L1978 **FM** *100

VASUDEVAN, Cuddalore P. 2117 COLLEGE AVE 24605 #495-61-1974 L1985 **PUD IM** *020 †20

BLUEMONT — CLARKE

WISSMATH, Frank Sum. ■ 20135 #028-02-1943 L1943 **PD OS** *071 †55

BON AIR — CHESTERFIELD

BOHANNON, Thomas Wm. 2711 BUFORD RD, STE 201 23235 #051-04-1984 L1986 **AN** *020 †05

BOONES MILL — FRANKLIN

DAUGHERTY, Harry K, Jr. ■ 24065 #028-34-1998 L2008 **PTH PCP** *020 †50

GARNER, Dorothy Caroline. ■ 24065 #001-02-1985 L1986 **ID** *020 †20

LOUGHEED, M N. RT 916 24065 #067-01-1947 L1971 **RO** *071

BOWLING GREEN — CAROLINE

ADAMS, Barbara Jeanne. 18138 HARDING DR 22427 #051-04-2008 L2008 *012

MARTIN, Arthur J. PO BOX 485, 134 LAFAYETTE AVE 22427 #051-04-1951 L1951 **GP** *071

OVERMAN, Ilma Meade. ■ 22427 #051-04-1970 L1970 **GP GYN** *071

VALDESDAPENA, Antonio E. PO BOX 450, 121 COURTHOUSE LN 22427 #041-13-1988 L1995 **FM** *020 †18

WOODFORD, Daniel William. 121 COURTHOUSE LN 22427 #051-04-2002 L2002 **IM** *020 †20

BOYDTON — MECKLENBURG

DEVINE, Charles Jos. 434 WASHINGTON STREET 23917 #051-07-1979 L1982 **PHP EM** *071 †16

SHELTON, William A. ■ 23917 #051-04-1952 L1952 **FM** *071 ‡

BOYKINS — SOUTHAMPTON

NARANJO, Jorge A. ■ 23827 #319-03-1959 L1963 **FM GP** *071 †18

BRACEY — MECKLENBURG

BAILEY, Paul Allen. 9782 HIGHWAY 903 23919 #054-04-1986 L1987 **FM CCM** *020 †18

ELASSAL-MAXIMOUS, Mervet. PO BOX 456 23919 #915-02-1976 L1995 **PM** *074

KIRKPATRICK, Homer L, Jr. ■ 23919 #011-02-1970 L1973 **IM NEP** *075

MORBITZER, Kurt Max. ■ 23919 #407-04-1948 L1961 **P** *071

BRAMBLETON — LOUDOUN

COWAN, Michael Lynn. ■ 20148 #028-02-1969 L1973 **HNS HEM** *030 †20

LUONG, Dao Quynh. 42882 TRURO PARISH DR, STE 201 20148 #024-16-1998 L2004 **FM** *020 †18

MCCABE, Barbra. ■ 20148 #036-07-1994 L2006 **PD** *020 †55

MEEHAN, Patrick Joseph. ■ 20148 #010-02-2000 L2005 **EM** *020 †16

SIZEMORE, Richard Tom, III. ■ 20148 #055-01-1977 L1980 **OS OPH** *071 †35

BRANCHVILLE — SOUTHAMPTON

DICKERSON, Richard Rowlan. ■ 23828 #051-04-1974 L1976 **GP** *075

BRIDGEWATER — ROCKINGHAM

CLAGUE, Allen Manville. 200 HIGH ST 22812 #051-04-1959 L1959 **GP** *071 †18

CRAWFORD, Harry S. 114 S MAIN ST 22812 #051-07-1994 L1997 **FM** *020 †18

HOLTHAUS, Wallace Harold. ■ 22812 #018-03-1957 L1967 **PTH** *020 †50

HUA, Haiyin. ■ 22812 #243-76-1994 *100

HUFFMAN, Rufus Clyde. 200 HIGH ST 22812 #051-04-1975 L1976 **FM** *020 †18

SCHULTZ, Joyce A. ■ 22812 #010-03-1972 L1978 **PS** *020

SMITH, Bobby L. ■ 22812 #051-01-1953 L1953 **AN GP** *071 †05

SMITH, Richard H, Jr. ■ 22812 #051-04-1953 L1953 **EM** *071

THOMPSON, James Walker. 114 S MAIN ST 22812 #047-05-1966 L1968 **IM** *072

WINE, Jean Fennell. ■ 22812 #051-04-1944 L1944 **IM** *071

BRISTOL — BRISTOL

CANTWELL, Thomas Jos. ■ 24201 #649-14-1981 L1989 **P PYG** *020

CHENG, Chin-Lin. ■ 24201 #244-01-1968 L1975 **EM PTH** *020 †16

CROCKETT, Claude H, Jr. ■ 24201 #051-01-1961 L1961 **FPS** *071 †45

DERDEN, Paul J. 300 W VALLEY DR, CROSSROADS MEDICAL MISSION 24201 #048-13-1982 L1983 **EM FM** *020 †18

DOSS, Anthony Expedit J. 621 COMMONWEALTH AVE 24201 #220-01-1967 L1976 **P GP** *075

KEGLEY, James B, Jr. ■ 24201 #051-04-1952 L1952 **PHP P** *071 †70

LATY, Mark S. 103 NORTH ST, RIDGEVIEW PAVILION 24201 #875-01-1988 L2003 **P** *020

MERCER, Judith C. ■ 24201 #020-02-1970 L1991 **FM** *075 †50

WEDDINGTON, Deborah L. 1315 EUCLID AVE STE E17, BRISTOL FAMILY HEALTH 24201 #051-01-1996 L1998 **FM** *020 †18

BRISTOL — WASHINGTON

BOEVE, Thomas James. 3170 LINDEN DR STE 6, SURGICAL GROUP, PC 24202 #047-05-1993 L1999 **OTO** *020 †45

DAVIS, Russell Alan. 3170 LINDEN DR, STE 6 24202 #027-01-1975 L2004 **OTO** *020 †45

DE GROOT, Terry Ross. 3170 LINDEN DR, STE 6 24202 #025-12-1976 L2007 **OTO** *020 †45

GOLDSTON, Joseph Perry. ■ 24202 #055-01-1976 L1997 **EM PD** *020 †55,16

GULDSETH, David Paul. 3177 LINDEN DR STE E6 24202 #005-12-1999 L1999 **FM** *020 †18 ‡

HARMAN, Debra Lynn. 14270 LEE HWY, LEE HIGHWAY MED CTR 24202 #051-04-1994 L1995 **FM** *020 †18 ‡

LEE, Cristy Gillespie. 14270 LEE HWY 24202 #027-01-1996 L1998 **FM** *020 †18

LITTON, Darlene E B. 103 BRISTOL EAST RD, HORIZON FAMILY MED 24202 #051-04-1973 L1976 **FM** *020 †18

MULLINS, Benny Carroll. ■ 24202 #051-04-1973 L1974 **EM** *020 †18

RATCLIFF, David Hood. 22762 OSPREY RIDGE RD 24202 #041-09-1979 L2004 **EM FM** *020 †18

TOOTHMAN, Clara Jane. 2426 LEE HWY STE 100 24202 #055-01-1965 L1966 **FM** *020 †18

BRISTOW — PRINCE WILLIAM

ESBENSEN, Kari Leigh. ■ 20136 #010-02-2008 *012

MACKINTOSH, Alan. ■ 20136 #539-01-1954 L1958 **FM** *020 †18

SENGUPTA, Shomik. ■ 20136 #143-02-1993 L2004 **U** *100

SEO, Jin Seok. ■ 20136 #583-02-1968 L2007 **AN** *071 †05

SHEA, Karen Ruth Olsen. ■ 20136 #005-12-1959 L1960 **AN** *071

SHEA, William Henry. ■ 20136 #005-12-1958 L1959 **OBS GP** *074

BROADWAY – ROCKINGHAM

GLICK, John T, Jr. JR DR 22815 #051-04-1950 L1950 GP *071
HOTCHKISS, William J. HWY 259 1 MILE EAST OF 22815 #051-04-1951 L1951 GP *071
MAST, Mark Miller. ■ 22815 #051-04-1998 L2001 FM *020 †18
PAUL, Priyanka. ■ 22815 #495-31-2001 L2007 IM *020 †20
REID, James Robt, IV. 12515 TIMBERWAY, BROADWAY FAM PRAC, P.C. 22815
    #051-01-1990 L1991 FM *020 †18

BROOKNEAL – CAMPBELL

CAMPBELL, John White. 104 CAROLINA AVE 24528 #051-01-1961 L1961 GP *020
CARWILE, Donald Eldridge. 104 CAROLINA AVE 24528 #051-04-1975 L1976 FM *020 †18
JONES, William Garnett. 104 CAROLINA AVE 24528 #051-04-1980 L1981 FM *020 †18
REILLY, Sharon Anne. 104 CAROLINA AVE 24528 #051-04-1997 L1997 FM *020 †18

BUCHANAN – BOTETOURT

GLENNEY, Robert Jess. 18080 MAIN ST, CARILION FAMILY MEDICINE 24066
    #037-01-1987 L2005 FM *020 †18
HARRIS, L Martin. ■ 24066 #051-04-1960 L1960 P OS *071 †75

BUCKINGHAM – BUCKINGHAM

KAPADNIS, Chandra D. 108 YOGAVILLE WAY 23921 #422-01-1995 IM *100
MC LANAHAN, Sandra Martin. RR 1 BOX 1680 23921 #025-07-1973 L1980 FM GP *020 †18

BUENA VISTA – BUENA VISTA CITY

CUNNINGHAM, Michael John. 2252 MAGNOLIA AVE 24416 #028-34-1978 L1980
    FM EM *020 †18
DUBIT, Scott Brian. 2252 MAGNOLIA AVE 24416 #047-05-1989 L1993 MPD *020 †20,55
HAMILTON, Thomas Francis. 2252 MAGNOLIA AVE 24416 #026-04-1979 L1983 FM *020 †18

BUMPASS – LOUISA

GEORGE, Eugene Donald. ■ 23024 #035-15-1964 L1986 NS *071 †25

BURGESS – NORTHUMBERLAND

BEATLEY, Robert Eugene. 740 JESSIE DUPONT MEM HWY 22432 #051-04-1965 L1965 GP *071
WALKER, Andrew Farley. PO BOX 400, BAY HARBOR MEDICAL CENTER 22432
    #051-04-1997 L1997 FM *020 †18
WOLSKI, Eugene Jos. PO BOX 250, 1257 GREENFIELD RD 22432 #023-01-1963 L1976
    FM A *071 †18

BURKE – FAIRFAX

ABISOUROUR, Iman. ■ 22015 #624-05-2006 IM *012
ALTMAN, Robert Michael. ■ 22015 #035-08-1977 L1986 P *020 †75
ANDERSON, Glenn. 9409 OLD BURKE LAKE RD, BURKE FAMILY PRACTICE 22015
    #010-02-1977 L1978 FM *020 †18
ANDRAWIS, Nabil S. 5631 BURKE CENTRE PKWY, STE A 22015 #915-04-1976 L1995
    IM *020 †20
ANTOINE, Rose Valentine. ■ 22015 #041-15-2004 L2007 *020
ARNOLDSON, Jorge O. 8988 FERN PARK DR 22015 #847-04-1964 L1968 PD ADL *020
BAIG, Mirza Shamim. ■ 22015 #704-02-1968 L1989 ORS *020 †40
BALSAMO, Pat A. 8988 FERN PARK DR 22015 #016-43-1957 L1959 PD *072 †55
BARBANO, Edward Francis. 8996 BURKE LAKE RD, STE 102 22015 #036-07-1989 L1993
    IM *020 †20
BARMAK, Leonard Geo. 9000 CROWNWOOD CT 22015 #035-19-1971 L1977 OPH *020 †35
BATTAD, Orson R. ■ 22015 #748-10-1978 L1992 FM *100
BEAN, Joseph Sumner. ■ 22015 #051-01-2006 †012
BETTINI, Robert John. 9004 CROWNWOOD CT, BURKE PROFESSIONAL CTR 22015
    #010-02-1965 L1968 GYN *020 †30
BLAKE, Jennifer Cherpes. 5765F BURKE CENTRE PKWY, STE 124 22015 #041-02-2000 L2006
    FM *020 †18
BOYKIN, Keith Baron. 5999 BURKE COMMONS RD, PEDIATRICS DEPT/KAISER PER 22015
    #051-07-1985 L1989 PD IM *020 †55
BROWN, Margaret Ann. 5999 BURKE COMMONS RD, KAISER PERMANENTE BURKE 22015
    #035-06-1967 L1971 PTH *071 †50
CARPENTER, Karen Reece. 5921 OAK RIDGE CT 22015 #048-04-1980 L2005 PD AM *020 †55
CASEY, Daniel Boyd. ■ 22015 #010-02-2006 L2006 MPD *012
CLAYTON, Nancy Miriam. ■ 22015 #028-34-1998 L2006 P *020 †75
COX, Elizabeth Anne. ■ 22015 #036-07-2008 †012
DEJO, Julio Alberto. 8998 FERN PARK DR 22015 #737-01-1970 L1978 IM CD *020
DOUGHERTY, Janet Marie. 9409 OLD BURKE LAKE RD, BURKE FAMILY PRACTICE 22015
    #051-01-1989 L1992 FM *020 †18
EHDAIE, Behfar. ■ 22015 #010-02-2005 L2005 U *012
ENELOW, Robert Stewart. 6035 BURKE CENTRE PKWY, STE 120 22015 #021-01-1985 L1988
    IM *020 †20
EPPS, Carla Lynn. 5999 BURKE COMMONS RD, BURKE MEDICAL CENTER 22015
    #032-01-1985 L2001 PD *020 †55
ESLAMI, Frank F. 5202 LYNGATE CT 22015 #517-01-1965 L1971 AI *020 †55,03
FEISEE, Seddigheh Alavi. 9554 OLD KEENE MILL RD 22015 #396-11-1963 L1975
    IM IMG *020 †20
GABRA, Nashwa W. 5631 BURKE CENTRE PKWY # A 22015 #915-04-1983 L2001 IM *020 †20
GARNER, Fredric Bruce. 8988 FERN PARK DR, BALSAMO, ARNOLDSON AND REE 22015
    #051-04-1966 L1966 PD *020 †55

GHALI, Emil Zaki. ■ 22015 #915-03-1968 L2001 IMG *020
HENOCHOWICZ, Stuart. 6035 BURKE CENTRE PKWY, STE 120 22015 #035-08-1981 L1989
    AI IM *020 †20,03
HENRY, Julie Patricia. 9004 FERN PARK DR 22015 #010-02-1985 L1989 D *020 †15
HUYNH, Marie. 5999 BURKE COMMONS RD 22015 #051-01-1995 L1997 IM *020 †20
KELLEHER, Janna J. ■ 22015 #047-06-2002 L2006 PCP *100 †50
KHAN, Mushtari. ■ 22015 #704-02-1975 L1995 GS *100
KHANDKER, Samiur Rahman. ■ 22015 #051-04-2008 *012
KIRKER, Rebecca Anne. ■ 22015 #051-07-2006 L2006 PD *012
KRAVITZ, Paul Howard. 9004 FERN PARK DR 22015 #010-01-1972 L1978 D *020 †15
LAHTI, Corrine Elizabeth. ■ 22015 #035-45-1977 L1988 EM IM *020 †20,16
LEE, Bong-Kee. ■ 22015 #583-02-1952 L1974 P *071
LEE, David Daewon. ■ 22015 #051-01-2004 L2004 DR *012
LENHARDT, Kimberly M. 5999 BURKE COMMONS RD 22015 #051-04-1997 L2001
    OBG *020 †30
LOCKETT-EVANS, Anya. ■ 22009 #024-05-1982 L1991 FM GP *071
MAYUGA, Ronaldo S. 5999 BURKE COMMONS RD, NEPHROLOGY SECTION 22015
    #748-02-1985 L1997 IM NEP *020 †20
MC BRIDE, Charles Edward. 9259 OLD KEENE MILL RD, # 100 22015 #010-02-1989 L1991
    GE IM *020 †20
MC MAHON, Mark Robt. 5201 LYNGATE CT, STE A 22015 #040-02-1981 L1993
    OAR OSM *020 †40
MOLES, Ken Lee. 9409 OLD BURKE LAKE RD, BURKE FAMILY PRACTICE 22015
    #051-01-1989 L1992 FM *020 †18
MORGAN, Ezra Marcelo. 10000 MARSHALL POND RD 22015 #682-03-1994 L2004 FM *020
MOSHELL, Alan Nathan. 9004 FERN PARK DR 22015 #035-19-1971 L1979 D OM *030 †15
MURPHY, Laurence John. 5212 LYNGATE CT 22015 #010-02-1977 L1979 PD AI *020 †55
NARAYAN, Puneet. 9291 OLD KEENE MILL RD 22015 #642-15-1977 L1993 IM *020 †20
NELSON, Lawrence Merle. ■ 22015 #041-12-1973 L1977 OBG REN *020 †30
NIE, Jingjiang. ■ 22015 #243-58-1986 L2006 NEP *012 †20
NOBU, Amy Yoshiko. 9409 OLD BURKE LAKE RD, BURKE FAMILY PRACTICE 22015
    #035-03-1986 L1987 FM *020 †18
OSTROWSKI, Cheryl A. ■ 22015 #023-12-1992 L1993 FM *020 †18
OWRUTZKY, Michele Enid. ■ 22015 #035-46-1976 L1983 PD *074 †55
POSNER, Robert Bruce. 9289 OLD KEENE MILL RD 22015 #035-08-1981 L1987 IM *020 †20
QUTUB, Hania. 5999 BURKE COMMONS RD 22015 #016-11-1996 L1996 OBG *020 †30
REES, William Chas. 8988 FERN PARK DR 22015 #010-02-1972 L1974 PD MDM *020 †55
RODRIGUEZ, Oscar. 5201 LYNGATE CT 22015 #264-05-1964 L1975 ORS HS *071 †40
RUSHIN, Audrey Maria. 5280 LYNGATE CT 22015 #025-12-1996 L2003 P *020 †75
RYAN, Christopher Patrick. 5999 BURKE COMMONS RD 22015 #010-02-1990 L1993
    FM *020 †18
SALEH, Nagui Naguib. 5999 BURKE COMMONS RD, BURKE MEDICAL CENTER 22015
    #915-04-1978 L2000 FM *020 †18
SONDRUP, Paul Robt. ■ 22015 #049-01-1963 L1968 FM *071
STAATS, Stacey Hollands. 5212 LYNGATE CT 22015 #051-04-1990 L1993 PD *020 †55
STAHL, Neil Ira. 6035 BURKE CENTRE PKWY, STE 280 22015 #024-05-1973 L1978
    RHU IM *020 †20
STEARNS, Laurel R. ■ 22015 #028-78-2006, ▲ L2007 TY *012
TRAN, Tam Xuan. ■ 22015 #041-02-2008 *012
WARTENBERG, Katja Elfried. ■ 22015 #408-30-1998 L2004 IM *100 †75
WEINGOLD, Daniel Elliot. 5201 LYNGATE CT, STE A 22015 #023-01-1991 L2001 ORS *020 †40
WEISSHAAR, Paul Howard. 5206 ROLLING RD STE A 22015 #033-05-1975 L1976 GYN *020 †30
WILSON, William Allen. 9261 OLD KEENE MILL RD 22015 #017-20-1982 L1985 IM *020 †20
WOLDE, Daniel Jemal. 5999 BURKE COMMONS RD 22015 #366-03-1992 L2002 NEP *020 †20
YISHAK, Aklilu Ashagrie. 5999 BURKE COMMONS RD 22015 #366-01-1992 L1996
    NEP *020 †20
ZIMMER, Bruce Stuart. 5201 LYNGATE CT 22015 #051-04-1981 L1983 ORS *030 †40

BURKEVILLE – NOTTOWAY

DONOVAN, Eugene Anthony. PO BOX 385 23922 #028-34-1978 L1980 IM *020 †20
FALCON, Hugo Derlis Gaona. ROUTES 360 & 460 23922 #726-01-1959 L1969 PYG *020
FALCON, Soledad M. HWY 360 460 23922 #726-01-1962 L1969 P *071
FLORES, Rosario Mayor. ■ 23922 #748-02-1941 L1978 IMG *071
MUNOZ, Anthony Jos. ROUTES 360 & 460 23922 #847-08-1951 L1956 GS TS *072 †85
SEPDHAM, Taweesuk B. ROUTES 360 & 460 23922 #891-03-1966 L1976 N P *020 †75 ‡
TRAN, George M. 412 NAMOZINE ST 23922 #010-01-1982 L1990 FM *020 †18

CALLAWAY – FRANKLIN

HASKINS, Paul A. ■ 24067 #035-03-1994 L1997 EM *020 †16
PHILPOTT, Benjamin Mark. 1559 FOOTHILLS RD 24067 #012-01-1996 L2003 FM *020 †18

CAPE CHARLES – NORTHAMPTON

BIBBINS, Betty Brown. ■ 23310 #051-07-1982 L1985 OBG *020 †30
CLARKE, Mark Gregory. 216 MASON AVE 23310 #041-12-1984 L1985 FM *020 †18
FRASER, Kiesha Nikuze. ■ 23310 #005-12-2001 L2004 PD *020 †55
KING, Rosa. PO BOX 191, 4206 MATTIE AVE 23310 #012-21-1991 L1998 FM *020 †18
MENDELSOHN, Barry Loeb. ■ 23310 #005-11-1968 L1981 P CHP *020 †75
RANDALL, Shirley Mason. 2987 BUTLERS BLUFF DR 23310 #051-01-1981 L1982 AN *020

CAPRON – SOUTHAMPTON

APPLEWHITE, Sarah Anrae. ■ 23829 #051-07-2005 L2005 PD *012

CARDINAL – MATHEWS

JENNETTE, Arthur Harris. ■ 23025 #041-01-1960 L1966 AN *071 †05

CARROLLTON – ISLE OF WIGHT

BASCO, Mary Frances. 13478 CARROLLTON BLVD, STE D 23314 #035-48-1998 L1998 IM *020 †20

CHADWICK, Jonathan Lyons. ■ 23314 #041-14-2006 L2006 *012

GASINK, Emmeline Cenizal. 13478 CARROLLTON BLVD, UNIT D AND E 23314 #051-07-2004 L2004 FM *020 †18

KNUST, Lisa Marie. 13478 CARROLLTON BLVD, UNIT D AND E 23314 #051-04-2003 L2003 FM *020 †18

CARTERSVILLE – CUMBERLAND

WILSON, Jo Myers. ■ 23027 #051-04-1992 L1999 FM *020 †18

CASANOVA – FAUQUIER

LAWRENCE, George J, Jr.■ 20139 #041-01-1938 OBG *071 †30

CATAWBA – ROANOKE

FODOR, Frank. PO BOX 200, CATAWBA HOSPITAL 24070 #473-01-1947 L1960 P *071

HURT, John Omohundro, Jr. 5525 CATAWBA HOSPITAL DR, CATAWBAS HOSPITAL 24070 #051-01-1964 L1964 P *020 †75

JABBARPOUR, Yadollah M. PO BOX 200, CATAWBA HOSP 24070 #051-01-1989 L1997 CHP *030 †75

NOGA, John Thos. PO BOX 200, CATAWBA HOSPITAL 24070 #010-01-1987 L1991 OS PYG *020 †75

NORTHWALL, Karl Walter. 5525 CATAWBA HOSPITAL DR, CATAWBA HOSPITAL 24070 #030-06-1978 L2006 P *020 †75

CATLETT – FAUQUIER

COYNER, Debra Sue. ■ 20119 #005-12-1982 L2004 FM *020 †18

GREINER, Hansel Matthias. ■ 20119 #051-04-2005 N *012

SEGAL, Henry Albert. ■ 20119 #041-01-1946 L1955 P PYA *071 †75

CEDAR BLUFF – TAZEWELL

MURTHY, Yelameli S. PO BOX 787 24609 #495-33-1961 L1973 GYN *020 †30

NASSIF, Sami Iskander. PO BOX 196 24609 #605-01-1957 L1976 PD PDC *071 †55

CENTREVILLE – FAIRFAX

ADEGOROYE, Oluseyi A. 14001A SAINT GERMAIN DR 20121 #690-02-1985 L1992 IM GP *020 †20

ALFONSO, Raymundo Palad. ■ 20120 #748-02-1953 L1961 GP *020

ANDERSON, Elizabeth F. 6211 CENTREVILLE RD, STE 700 20121 #036-08-1992 L1997 IM GS *020 †20

ATWAL, Navneet Kaur. 14204 ROYAL OAK LN 20120 #913-89-1992 L2001 P *100

BAHADORI, Robert Shahram. 6201 CENTREVILLE RD, STE 400 20121 #035-20-1989 L1996 PDO *020 †45

BARMADA-MAZID, Seirin. 6211 CENTREVILLE RD, STE 100 20121 #875-02-1988 L1995 PD *020 †55

BARTLETT, Donald E, Jr. 6134 REDWOOD SQ CTR, STE 101 20121 #051-01-1984 L1986 FM *020 †18

BELL, Scott Irwin. 6211 CENTREVILLE RD STE 70 20121 #035-03-1998 L1998 IM *020 †20

BENHEIM, Alan Eric. 5900 FORT DR, STE 410 20121 #010-02-1987 L1993 PDC PD *020 †55

BERGMAN, Kenneth Robt. 13890 BRADDOCK RD, STE 206 20121 #035-45-1967 L1975 AI IM *020 †20,03

BOWLES, Richard B, Jr. 13890 BRADDOCK RD STE 201 20121 #051-01-1970 L1970 FM *020 †18

BROWN, Janine Renee. 6201 CENTREVILLE RD, STE 10 20121 #038-44-2001 L2001 FM *020 †18

BYRNES, Laura E. 6211 CENTREVILLE RD, STE 100 20121 #010-01-1994 L1997 PD *020 †55

CARROLL, Brian Hurd. 5645 STONE RD, ROCKY RUN FAMILY MEDICINE 20120 #422-01-1987 L1992 FM *020 †18

CARTER, William H, Jr. 6201 CENTREVILLE RD 20121 #016-06-1976 L1977 FM OBS *020 †18

CHON, Andy Ki. ■ 20120 #051-04-2008 *012

COSENTINO, Raymond F. ■ 20120 #010-02-1965 L1968 GE IM *071 †20

DAY, Lenore Aileen. 6201 CENTREVILLE RD 20121 #056-06-1993 L1996 FM *020 †18

DECOSIMO, Lillian M. 6134 REDWOOD SQ CTR, STE 101 20121 #308-10-1986 L1995 GYN *020 †30

DO, Khanh Tu. ■ 20121 #010-01-2006 L2006 IM *012

DOLAN, Michael Francis. ■ 20121 #035-09-1957 L1990 PTH *020 †50

DOYLE, Deborah Joan. 6201 CENTREVILLE RD, STE 400 20121 #021-01-1988 L1994 OTO FPS *020 †45

DUBINSKY, Diane E. 6211 CENTREVILLE RD, STE 100 20121 #010-01-1982 L1984 PD *020 †55

ELGUERA, Elizabeth Denise. 13890 BRADDOCK RD, STE 103 20121 #008-01-1993 L1997 OBG *020 †30

ERIKSSON, Maura E. 13880 BRADDOCK RD, STE 201 20121 #051-04-1991 L1994 PD *020 †55

ERIKSSON, Wayne Richard. 13880 BRADDOCK RD, STE 201 20121 #051-04-1990 L1992 PD *020 †55

ESCALERA, Robert B, II. 5900 FORT DR, STE 410 20121 #010-02-2000 L2007 PDC *020 †55

FARAH, Bassam E. 6201 CENTREVILLE RD, STE 200 20121 #528-01-1989 L1996 IM *020 †20

FILAK, Michael Andrew. 6201 CENTREVILLE RD 20121 #010-01-1980 L1986 FM *020 †18

GRAZIANO, Thomas Raymond. 6211 CENTREVILLE RD, STE 700 20121 #035-09-1984 L1988 IM *020 †20

GRIMM, Samuel Oliver, III. 5675 STONE RD, VIRGINIA GYNECOLOGISTS 20120 #023-01-1980 L1988 OBG *020 †30

GVOZDJAN, Dragoslav Mihaj. ■ 20120 #957-07-1983 L2004 P *012

HASHEMI, Neda. 6201 CENTREVILLE RD, STE 700 20121 #051-04-1998 L2002 OBG *020 †30

HEPNER, Seymour I. 5900 FORT DR, STE 410 20121 #010-02-1972 L1976 PDC PD *020 †55

HOBBS, Lori Michele. 13880 BRADDOCK RD, STE 301 20121 #010-03-1992 L2002 D *020 †15

HONG, Sa-Yun. ■ 20121 #051-01-2008 *012

IYER, Akila Vasanthan. 6201 CENTREVILLE RD, STE 200 20121 #495-96-1995 L2004 FM *020 †18

JO, Vickie Young. ■ 20120 #051-01-2006 L2006 PTH *012

JOSHI, Vasudha V. 6201 CENTREVILLE RD, STE 200 20121 #496-07-1980 L1987 IM *020 †20

KARR, Sharon Switzman. 5900 FORT DR, STE 410 20121 #035-19-1986 L1992 PDC *020 †55

KEYES, Janice Lynn. 13890 BRADDOCK RD STE 201 20121 #051-04-1983 L1986 FM *020 †18

KILLIAN, Shoshana H. 13880 BRADDOCK RD STE 20 20121 #041-15-2002 L2002 PD *020 †55

KIM, Karl Hyo Seung. ■ 20120 #035-20-2000 DR *020

KRAFSIG, Luz Ayda. ■ 20121 #264-01-1992 FM *100

KUA, Ka Em. ■ 20120 #748-02-1977 L1984 PD NPM *020 †55

LASNER, Lance Alan. 6211 CENTREVILLE RD, STE 500 20121 #041-07-1989 L1997 GE *020 †20

LEE, Choong-Hee. ■ 20120 #583-02-1965 L1973 OBG *020 †30

LEE, Margaret Chong Ok. ■ 20121 #583-04-1958 L1971 AN PD *020 †55

LENNON, Frederick F. 6211 CENTREVILLE RD, STE 700 20121 #041-13-1984 L1989 IM *020 †20

LEVINSTONE, Alan Robt. 5895 TRINITY PKWY, STE 20 20120 #038-40-1973 L1993 IM N *020 †20,75

LOCKETT, Tammy Marie. 13880 BRADDOCK RD, STE 307 20121 #021-05-1996 L2005 OBG *020 †30

LUMABAN, Julita Arrobio. ■ 20121 #748-01-1959 P *075

MAK-FUNG, Michele W. 13880 BRADDOCK RD, STE 301 20121 #008-01-2000 L2004 D *020 †15

MALKOFF, Donald Burton. ■ 20120 #041-12-1960 L1961 OS N *062 †75

MARKIN, Laurie Susan. 5645 STONE RD 20120 #035-47-1993 L1996 FM *020 †18

MATTAY, Neerja Rao. 13880 BRADDOCK RD STE 301, DERM ASSOC OF NO VA 20121 #051-04-1988 L1991 D *020 †15

MC BRIDE, Timothy Paul. 6201 CENTREVILLE RD, STE 400 20121 #051-01-1977 L1990 OTO *020 †45

MC KENZIE, Bryan Anthony. 6201 CENTREVILLE RD, STE 400 20121 #023-07-1988 L1996 OTO *020 †45

MERO, James H. 13890 BRADDOCK RD, STE 209 20121 #010-02-1967 L1972 R OS *020 †80

MUGOL, Richard Gonzales. 5645 STONE RD 20120 #051-04-1993 L1994 FM *020 †18

NEWMAN, Ira Clifford. 14631 LEE HWY, STE 207 20121 #550-02-1994 L1994 P *020

OHRINER, Jamie E. 6211 CENTREVILLE RD, STE 100 20121 #049-01-1987 L1992 PD *020 †55

OHRINER, William David. 6211 CENTREVILLE RD, STE 100 20121 #035-06-1987 L1991 PD *020 †55

OVERHOLTZER, Julie Faye. 6201 CENTREVILLE RD 20121 #035-15-1987 L1990 FM *020 †18

PACE, John Hall. 6623 PELHAMS TRCE, PACE MEDICAL SERVICE 20120 #051-07-1991 L1992 FM FSM †18

PAISO, Jose Martin S. ■ 20121 #748-01-1990 L1997 ORS *100

PARK, Jin H. 5900 FORT DR, STE 410 20121 #036-01-1996 L2002 PDC *020 †55

PATEL, Piyush Raojibhai. 13880 BRADDOCK RD STE 208 20121 #495-23-1978 L1991 FM IM *020

RICHARDSON-MC KENZIE, Patr. 5895 TRINITY PKWY, STE 100 20120 #005-12-1997 L2005 FM *100 †18

ROBERTS, George Tregson. ■ 20120 #917-04-1969 L1994 PTH *020

RONCAL, Johnny Jeff Panla. ■ 20120 #748-24-1988 *100

RUBINSTEIN, Mark Isaac. 6201 CENTREVILLE RD, STE 400 20121 #041-02-1983 L1989 OTO FPS *020 †45

RUIZ, Rex B. 6201 CENTREVILLE RD 20121 #043-01-1996 L1999 FM *020 †18

SCHMITT, Thomas Edward. 5675 STONE RD, VIRGINIA GYNECOLOGISTS 20120 #038-40-1972 L1975 OBG *020 †30

SCHULMAN, Jeffrey Michael. 5675 STONE RD, VIRGINIA GYNECOLOGISTS 20120 #010-01-1977 L1979 OBG *020 †30

SHANMUGAM, Sangeetha. ■ 20121 #496-23-1995 L2007 IM IMG *020 †20

SHERLING, Sharon Camille. 5645 STONE RD 20120 #051-07-1999 L2002 FM *020 †18

SIDHU, Chandanjeet Kaur. ■ 20121 #051-04-1996 L2000 PD *020

SIEGER, Charles Elias. ■ 20120 #035-09-1956 L1957 R *071 †80

SINGH DHILLON, Balraj. ■ 20121 #495-03-1993 P *100

SOLEIMANI, Faramarz M. ■ 20120 #517-01-1967 AN OBG *100

TALANIN, Nikolai Y. 13880 BRADDOCK RD, STE 301 20121 #913-21-1985 L2002 D *020 †15

TAWFIK, Sherif Salah El-D. 5900 FORT DR, STE 410 20121 #915-06-1977 L1992 PD *020 †55

TSAI, John Tzong. 6211 CENTREVILLE RD, STE 100 20121 #010-01-1998 L2005 PD *020 †55

VILLANUEVA, Eusebio L, Jr. ■ 20120 #748-01-1959 L1982 GP *075

WALDMAN, Jeffry Todd. 6201 CENTREVILLE RD 20121 #008-02-1991 L1994 FM *020 †18

WHEELER, Julia Christine. 6201 CENTREVILLE RD, STE 200 20121 #051-01-1997 L1998 IM *020 †20

YOUN, Sugkee. 13880 BRADDOCK RD, STE 102 20121 #583-06-1982 L2003 NEP *020 †20

CHANTILLY – FAIRFAX

AKULA, Anand Mohan. 14408 CHANTILLY CROSSNG LN, # 703 20151 #495-21-1992 L1997 IM *020 †20

CHUNG, Luke Sooil. ■ 20151 #583-10-1967 L1995 DMP PTH *020 †50

ECCLES, Randy Lee. 3975 VIRGINIA MALLORY DR, NORTHROP GRUMMAN CORP 20151 #010-01-1996 L2003 IM OS *062 †20

EVANS, David Lee. 14155 NEWBROOK DR, STE 400 20151 #048-13-1987 L1991 IM *020 †20

FISHER, Dawn M. 3914 CENTREVILLE RD # 250 20151 #048-14-1996 L2000 FM *020 †18

FLINT, Joan Michelle. ■ 20151 #051-01-2008 L2008 *012

FUGATE, Candace Sue. 3914 CENTREVILLE RD, THE PEDIATRIC GROUP 20151 #020-02-1996 L1996 PD *020 †55

FURLANETTO, Richard Wm. 14225 NEWBROOK DR, DIVISION OF PEDS ENDO 20151 #016-02-1973 L2005 PDE PD *020 †55

GORLE, Vijaya Lakshmi. 4080 LAFAYETTE CENTER DR, STE 110 20151 #495-11-1996 L2003 IM *020 †20

HIJAZI, Yasmine Mona. 14225 NEWBROOK DR, QUEST DIAGNOSTICS 20151 #605-01-1995 L1996 PTH PCP *020 †50

HWANG, Irving. 4080 LAFAYETTE CENTER DR, STE 170 20151 #051-01-1999 L1999 FM *020 †18

JONAS, Dervila S. 4200 PLEASANT VALLEY RD, FAIRFAX MED LAB 20151 #539-04-1971 L1980 PTH *020 †50

JONES, Joseph Shaw. 14121 PARKE LONG CT, STE 112 20151 #012-01-1984 L1989 **ADM PMM** *020 †20 ‡

KIM, Theodore Taehun. 4229 LAFAYETTE CENTER DR, STE 1760 20151 #010-01-1994 L2006 **AI IM** *020 †20,03

KRISHNAN, Ashok. ■ 20151 #051-04-2007 *012

LYNCH, G Michael. 3914 CENTREVILLE RD, STE 250 20151 #041-02-1978 L1979 **FM** *020 †18

MC CLAIN, Paul Henry. 4820 CROSS MEADOW PL 20151 #021-01-1982 L1990 **IM EM** *020 †20

PERKOWSKI, Dayna Marie. ■ 20151 #051-01-2008 *012

PHILLIPS, John Keith. 4080 LAFAYETTE CENTER DR, SOUTH RIDING FAMILY 20151 #051-04-2000 L2000 **FM** *020 †18

RILEY, Celeste Rita. 14225 NEWBROOK DR, AMER MED LABS 20151 #041-14-1992 L2001 **PTH** *020 †50

ROSARIO, Olimpia. 14143 ROBERT PARIS CT 20151 #308-06-1987 L2000 **CHP P** *020 †75

SHERMAN, Nathan. 14225 NEWBROOK DR 20151 #033-06-1978 L1984 **PTH** *020 †50

SISCO, Kenneth Lee. 14225 NEWBROOK DR 20151 #004-01-1971 L2007 **PTH** *030 †50

SOLOS-KOUNTOURI, Eleni. 4229 LAFAYETTE CENTER DR, STE 1425 20151 #023-01-1994 L1998 **OBG** *020 †30

SOMMESE, Teresa J. 14155 NEWBROOK DR, ACTIVE HEALTH MANAGEMENT 20151 #038-06-1982 L1985 **GPM** *020 †70

STATKUS, Joseph Kevin. 4455 BROOKFIELD CORPORT DR 20151 #023-12-1986 L1988 **PMM PME** *020

TURGUT, Ayse Nur. 4090 LAFAYETTE CENTER DR 20151 #902-05-1987 L1995 **FM** *020 †18

WASEEM, Samia. ■ 20153 #704-01-1987 L2005 **FM** *020 †18

CHANTILLY – LOUDOUN

FAY, Frederick J. ■ 20152 #041-02-1950 **GS P** *071

KOHLI-CHHABRA, Kavneet. ■ 20152 #495-37-2000 **P** *020

LLAMANZARES, Teodoro P. ■ 20152 #748-01-1963 **OTO** *020

MINO, Manuel Eduardo. ■ 20152 #319-01-1952 L1979 **OS GP** *071

NELSON, Carla. ■ 20152 #023-12-1991 L1992 *020

ONG, Ricardo De Jesus. ■ 20152 #748-08-1959 **GP** *071

RAMIREZ, Pedro J. ■ 20152 #043-01-1999 L2001 **GS** *020 †85

CHARLES CITY – CHARLES CITY

BLACKWELL, Brian Keith. 9950 COURTHOUSE RD 23030 #051-04-1990 L1991 **IM** *020 †20

FLEENOR, Ellen Whitlow. 9950 COURTHOUSE RD, CHARLES CITY REG HLTH SVCS 23030 #051-04-1992 L1996 **FM** *020 †18

NETICK, Joe. ■ 23030 #021-01-1955 L1982 **D** *020 †15

WISE, James Lafayette, Jr. ■ 23030 #021-05-1964 L1966 **GP** *071 †55

CHARLOTTE COURT HOUSE – CHARLOTTE

ALGEIER, Rhonda B. 165 LEGRANDE AVE, CHARLOTTE PRIMARY CARE 23923 #051-04-2001 L2001 **FM** *020 †18

DAVIS, Charles Stewart. PO BOX 470, 165 LEGRANDE AVE 23923 #035-15-1970 L1974 **GP PHP** *020 ‡

CHARLOTTESVILLE – ALBEMARLE

ABDOLLAHZADEH, Sara. ■ 22901 #051-01-2006 L2006 **GS** *012

ABI-JAOUDEH, Nadine. ■ 22911 #067-02-2002 L2007 **VIR** *012 †80

ABRAHAMSON, Annika Marie. 535 WESTFIELD RD, STE 200 22901 #028-03-2001 L2001 **FM** *020 †18

ADAMS, Robert Edgar, Jr. 183 SPOTNAP RD, STE D 22911 #051-01-1990 L1997 **N IM** *020 †75

ADAMSON, Nathaniel E, Jr. ■ 22901 #051-01-1944 L1944 **OS GS** *071 †85

AHMED, Farah Hena. ■ 22901 #033-06-2004 L2004 **IM** *012 †20

ALDRICH, C Knight. ■ 22911 #016-06-1944 L1973 **P FM** *071 †75

ALENEZI, Abdullah Mohsin. ■ 22911 #797-01-1994 L1999 **PCC** *100 †04

ALISANSKI, Susan Beth. ■ 22911 #035-15-2000 L2007 **PD** *100 †55

AL-SHAMMARI, Muhammad A. ■ 22901 #584-01-1990 L1996 **DR** *100

ALTSCHULER, Scott. ■ 22901 #024-05-2002 L2005 **IM** *100 †20

ANGLE, Carol Remmer. ■ 22901 #035-20-1951 L1999 **OS NEP** *050 †55

ANYALEBECHI, Chukwudi Bar. ■ 22911 #690-04-1992 L2007 **IM** *100 †20

ARNOLD, Michael Lee. 600 PETER JEFFERSON PKWY, GYNECOLOGY LTD 22911 #038-06-1990 L1994 **OBG** *020 †30

ARNOLD, Peter Bondurant. ■ 22901 #051-04-2004 L2004 **PS** *012

ASAO, Kiyoko. 3025 BERKMAR DR, STE 1 22901 #043-01-1985 L1986 **IM** *020 †20

AUTIO, Karen Anne. ■ 22901 #035-48-2007 L2007 **IM** *012

BAE, Dongsin. ■ 22904 #035-09-1995 L2003 **OBG** *020

BAJWA, Harman Preet. ■ 22901 #010-01-2004 L2005 **N** *012

BALTZ, Joseph George, Jr. ■ 22901 #051-01-2007 L2007 **IM** *012

BARBER, Virginia Gibbons. 1575 STATE FARM BLVD, STE 1 22911 #036-07-1985 L1989 **OBG** *020 †30

BARNETT, Martha Louise. 1410 INCARNATION DR 22901 #023-01-1985 L1997 **RHU IM** *020 †20

BARRON, Ruth Elliott. ■ 22901 #045-01-2003 L2003 **IM** *100

BASHIR, Mudhasir. ■ 22911 #495-51-1991 L2001 **PYG** *100 †75

BATEMAN, Bruce Gary. 595 PETER JEFFERSON PKWY 22911 #012-01-1970 L1980 **OBG GP** *020 †30

BATTLE, Martha Davitt. ■ 22901 #035-45-1987 L2007 **IM** *020 †20

BAXTER, Jennifer Lauren. ■ 22901 #036-07-2007 L2007 **P** *012

BAYLISS, E Virginia. 175 S PANTOPS DR 22911 #051-01-1983 L1986 **P** *020 †75

BECK, Gretchen Schroeder. 1469 GREENBRIER PL 22901 #035-47-1993 L2000 **AI** *020 †55,03

BELL, Derek Edward. ■ 22901 #035-15-2002 L2007 **PS** *012

BELLIZZI, Andrew Michael. ■ 22901 #016-06-2004 L2004 **PTH** *012

BENNETT, Daniel Kittelle. ■ 22901 #051-01-2008 *012

BERCU, Tracy Elizabeth. ■ 22901 #422-01-2005 L2005 **IM** *012

BERGER, Elizabeth Hope. 250 WESTBROOK PL, 1ST AND 3RD FLOOR 22901 #035-20-1988 L1992 **OBG** *020 †30

BERLE, Dana Christine. ■ 22901 #051-01-2008 *012

BERNHEIM, Joseph Wise. 1550 GRAY FOX TRL 22901 #041-13-1975 L1997 **FM FPG** *020 †18

BIRNBAUM, Richard Alan. 502 NOTTINGHAM RD 22901 #020-02-1996 L1999 **CD** *020 †20

BLACKMAN, James Allen. KCRC-2270 IVY RD 22901 #038-40-1976 L1989 **PD** *020 †55

BLANKENBAKER, Walter L. ■ 22901 #051-01-1955 L1955 **AN** *071 †05

BLEEKER, Jonathan Scott. ■ 22901 #018-03-2005 L2005 **IM** *012

BLIZZARD, Robert M. ■ 22901 #016-06-1952 L1974 **END PD** *071 †55

BLOMMEL, Julie Lynn. 1490 PANTOPS MOUNTAIN PL, STE 105 22911 #051-04-1985 L1988 **OBG** *020 †30

BOERSMA, Carol A. 900 RIO EAST CT 22901 #051-01-2002 L2002 **PD** *020 †55

BONACCI, Jeffrey Lynn. ■ 22901 #025-12-1996 L2000 **P** *020 †75

BOOZER, Jeffress Hannings. ■ 22901 #012-05-1961 L1966 **PHP** *071

BORG, Tyler Thure. ■ 22911 #021-01-2004 L2005 **AN** *012

BORIC, Lamia. ■ 22901 #040-02-2005 L2005 **IM** *012

BORLOZ, Matthew Peter. ■ 22901 #051-01-2008 *012

BOWER, Peter John. 504 ALBEMARLE SQ 22901 #008-02-1980 L1994 **OS FM** *050 †16,18

BRADLEY, Robert James. ■ 22901 #056-05-1945 L1973 **IM** *071

BRANDON, Michael Stephen. 244 HYDRAULIC RIDGE RD 22901 #028-34-1988 L1989 **AN** *020 †05

BRAZA, Rudy Maeda. ■ 22911 #024-07-1997 L1999 **DR** *020 †80

BRIX, William Karl. ■ 22911 #016-11-2004 L2004 **PTH** *012

BROOKS, Heather Dawn. ■ 22901 #051-07-2005 L2005 **IM** *012

BROWN, David Wayne. 535 WESTFIELD RD, STE 200 22901 #051-01-1979 L1980 **FM** *020 †18

BRYANT, John H. ■ 22911 #051-01-1953 L1960 **PHP IM** *071

BURNS, Amy Suzanne. ■ 22901 #051-01-2006 L2006 **U** *012

BUSH, Zachary Monroe. ■ 22911 #007-02-2002 L2002 **END** *012 †20

CALHOUN, Alice Oh. 1800 TIMBERWOOD BLVD 22911 #051-04-1997 L1997 **FM** *020 †18

CALHOUN, Robert Bentley. 1800 TIMBERWOOD BLVD 22911 #001-02-1996 L1996 **FM** *020 †18

CALLAND, James Forrest. ■ 22901 #035-47-1997 L1997 **CCS** *100 †85

CAMNITZ, Will Martin. ■ 22901 #036-08-2008 *012

CAMPBELL, Andrew A. ■ 22911 #048-14-2005 L2005 **AN** *012

CAMPBELL, Deborah Lynn. 416 ALBEMARLE SQ 22901 #001-06-1987 L1993 **FM** *020 †18

CAMPERLENGO, Vanessa A. 675 PETER JEFFERSON PKWY, STE 335 22911 #021-05-1988 L1989 **CHP P** *020 †75

CAPITO, Anthony Emil. ■ 22911 #055-01-2006 L2006 **PS** *012

CARLBERG, David James. ■ 22901 #023-01-2008 *012

CARMAN, Robert Hull. ■ 22901 #035-45-1956 **CLP BBK** *030 †50

CARPENTER, John Martin. 889B RIO EAST CT, RIO FAMILY MED 22901 #051-01-1985 L1986 **FM** *020 †18

CARR, Anne Harnsberger. ■ 22901 #047-06-2004 L2004 **OBG** *012

CARR, Thomas Martin. ■ 22901 #047-06-2004 L2004 **DR** *012

CARY, Freeman H. ■ 22901 #012-05-1950 L1983 **IM CD** *071 †20

CARY, Meredith Rae. ■ 22901 #028-46-2001 L2001 **PFP** *020 †75

CASAZZA, Brian Andrew. 199 SPOTNAP RD, STE 2 22911 #016-06-1991 L1996 **PM** *020 †60

CAUTHEN, Clay Adams. ■ 22901 #047-06-2005 L2005 **IM** *012

CHAN, Daniel Tak Chi. ■ 22911 #654-01-2006 L2007 **FP** *012

CHERRY, Kenneth J, Jr. ■ 22901 #051-01-1974 L1976 **VS GS** *020 †85

CHESLER, David Lawrence. 3025 BERKMAR DR, STE 1 22901 #038-06-1974 L1977 **IM IMG** *020 †20

CHISHOLM, Christian A. 250 WESTBROOK PL, 1ST AND 3RD FLOOR 22901 #023-01-1991 L1995 **MFM OBG** *020 †30

CHITWOOD, Sarah E Roberts. ■ 22901 #051-01-1948 L1948 **P** *071

CHO, Jai Jong. 3046 BERKMAR DR STE B 22901 #583-02-1973 L1982 **FM IMG** *020 †18

CHOU, Caroline Hsiao-Hua. ■ 22901 #704-16-1990 L2000 **PYG** *020

CHRISANT, Maryanne. ■ 22901 #035-09-1986 L2007 **PD** *020 †55

CHRIST, Constance B. 199 SPOTNAP RD, STE 1 22911 #016-11-1996 L1999 **NEP** *020 †20

CIUDIN, Daniel. ■ 22901 #781-01-1995 L2000 **P** *012

CLARK, James Robt. 3010 BERKMAR DR 22901 #016-42-1992 L1994 **IM** *020 †20

CLARKE, Christopher Josep. ■ 22911 #024-07-2004 L2007 **PDC** *012 †55

CLAVET, John. ■ 22901 #051-07-2006 L2006 **PM** *012

CLOUD, Jeffrey William. ■ 22901 #048-12-1999 L2006 **ID** *100 †20

COLLINS, Andrew Stuart. 626 BERKMAR CIR 22901 #036-05-1999 L1999 **OPH** *020 †35

COMBS, Luke. 184 ZAN RD 22901 #051-01-1957 L1957 **OPH** *071 †35

COPPOLA, Theresa Joan. 3025 BERKMAR DR, STE 1 22901 #051-01-1990 L1998 **FM** *020 †20

CRAIG, James Wm. ■ 22901 #038-06-1945 L1972 **IM** *071 †20

CULVER, James O'Barr. 600 PETER JEFFERSON PKWY, GYNECOLOGY LTD 22911 #036-01-1998 L2003 **OBG** *020

CUTCHINS, Alexis C.A.. ■ 22901 #012-05-2004 L2007 **IM** *100 †20

DAGLI, Alicia Vann. 1490 PANTOPS MOUNTAIN PL, STE 200 22911 #051-01-1995 L1995 **FM** *020 †18

DAGLI, Hakan Akat. 1490 PANTOPS MOUNTAIN PL, STE 200 22911 #051-01-1999 L1999 **FM** *020 †18

DAVID, Joseph Jordan. 535 WESTFIELD RD # 100 22901 #055-01-1979 L1983 **P LM** *020 †75

DAVIDSON, William David. 977 SEMINOLE TRL 22901 #036-07-1953 L1988 **P** *020

DAVISON, John Sullivan. 1800 TIMBERWOOD BLVD, FOREST LAKES HEALTH CENTER 22911 #008-02-1993 L1996 **FM** *020 †18

DE BOER, Mark Daniel. ■ 22901 #003-01-2000 L2000 **PDE** *100 †55

DEGNAN, Gregory Gerard. 414 ALBEMARLE SQ 22901 #051-07-1984 L1987 **GS ORS** *020 †40

DELIRI, Hamid. ■ 22901 #517-08-1997 L2006 **IM** *100 †20

DENG, Chunli. ■ 22901 #243-70-1983 L2006 **NR** *100

DESSOUKY, Dessouky Ahmad. ■ 22901 #330-04-1957 L1973 **OBG OS** *071 †30

DETMER, William Matthew. 1459 GOLDEN CHAIN LN 22901 #005-02-1987 L1988 **IM** *020 †20

DEVINCENTIS, Christina M. 199 SPOTNAP RD, STE 4 22911 #051-01-1988 L1991 **IM** *020 †20

DEVINE, Michael J. 630 PETER JEFFERSON PKWY, STE 100 22911 #041-02-1993 L1994 **HS ORS** *020 †40

DICKENS, Michael Douglas. 1522 INSURANCE LN, STE A 22911 #035-01-1972 L1973 **PD** *020 †55

DUNLAP, Neal Edward. ■ 22901 #038-41-2006 L2007 **RO** *012

DUTTA, Anindya. ■ 22901 #495-27-1982 **PTH** *100

EBY, Joshua Clark. ■ 22901 #005-11-2003 L2006 **ID** *012 †20

ELLIS, Amber Marie. ■ 22901 #036-07-2007 L2007 *012

ELWARD, Kurtis Scott. 1450 SACHEM PL 22901 #016-11-1983 L1985 **FM IM** *020 †20,18

ENKIRI, Sean Alexander. ■ 22901 #023-01-2006 L2006 **IM** *012

ESKANDAR, Nizar Samih. ■ 22911 #875-01-1991 L2005 **NEP** *012 †20

EVANS, Avery Jennings. ■ 22901 #036-07-1989 L1994 **DR** *020 †80

EVANS, Josephine B. ■ 22901 #036-07-1989 L1994 **DR** *100

FAGERLI, Julian Claus. 155 RIVERBEND DR, UROLOGICAL ASSOCIATES LTD 22911 #051-07-1994 L2000 **U** *020 †95

FALLS, Randall Keith. 2964 HYDRAULIC RD, RIDGE INC 22901 #051-04-1986 L1987 **OBG** *020 †30

FERTILE, Jay Christopher. 1490 PANTOPS MOUNTAIN PL, STE 100 22911 #051-01-1996 L1996 **DR** *020 †80

FIFE, Jason Dennis. ■ 22901 #056-06-2005 L2006 **AN** *012

FISCHER, Joshua James. 650 PETER JEFFERSON PKWY, STE 100 22911 #035-06-1996 L1996 **IC CD** *020 †20

FLICKINGER, Tabor. ■ 22901 #051-01-2007 L2007 **IM** *012

FOWLER, Dale Eric. ■ 22901 #041-02-1982 L1982 **CD** *020 †20

FOWLER, Dennis R. ■ 22901 #016-01-1985 L1986 **U** *050

FRANK, Miles Mcgehee. 887B RIO EAST CT 22901 #036-01-1996 L2002 **CHP** *020 †75

FRANTZEN, Donna R. 108 WHITEWOOD RD, STE 4 22901 #051-01-1969 L1969 **P** *020

FREEDMAN, William Bernis. 650 PETER JEFFERSON PKWY, STE 100 22911 #035-45-1968 L1973 **CD** *020 †20

FRENCH, Brian Steven. ■ 22901 #035-06-2004 *100

FRICK, Keith Andrew. 1410 INCARNATION DR, STE 205 22901 #045-01-1997 L2002 **RHU IM** *020 †20

FRIEND, Cristopher D. 650 PETER JEFFERSON PKWY, STE 100 22911 #051-01-1974 L1978 **CD IM** *020 †20

FROST, Barbara Jean. ■ 22901 #051-04-1991 L1995 **OM GPM** *020 †70

FULLER, Brian Gildas. ■ 22911 #005-14-1987 L2006 **RO** *020 †80

GALYSH, Roman Lubomyr, Jr. ■ 22901 #001-02-2002 L2002 **IM** *100 †20

GERGEN, John Andrew. ■ 22911 #024-01-1957 L2004 **P PYG** *071 †75

GETTLEMAN, Robert Aaron. ■ 22901 #016-11-1982 L1982 **NS** *020 †25

GIULIANO, Vincent Jos, Jr. 1410 INCARNATION DR, STE 205 22901 #041-01-1965 L1973 **RHU IM** *020 †20

GLOVER, Jason Michael. ■ 22901 #050-02-2004 L2004 **PD** *012 †55

GONCE, Mark Allen. 110 S PANTOPS DR 22911 #039-01-1990 L1994 **OPH** *020 †35

GONZALEZ-ENGLE, Brenda Li. ■ 22901 #051-01-2008 *012

GOODE, Roland Roderick. ■ 22901 #051-01-2008 *012

GREEN, Aval-Na'Ree Sian. ■ 22901 #048-16-2003 L2003 **IMG** *100 †20

GREGG-KAMATH, Vanessa H. ■ 22911 #010-01-2003 L2003 **OBG** *100

GUERRANT, John L. ■ 22911 #051-01-1937 L1937 **IM A** *071 †20

GUESS, George Albert. 233 HYDRAULIC RIDGE RD, STE 101 22901 #051-04-1973 L1976 **EM OS** *050

HA, Jinny Suk. ■ 22901 #051-01-2008 *012

HAIR, Amy Lynne. ■ 22901 #012-01-2006 L2006 **PD** *012

HAIR, Clark Daniel. ■ 22901 #012-01-2006 L2006 **IM** *012

HALAPIN, Philip Thos. 258 HYDRAULIC RIDGE RD 22901 #048-04-1975 L1976 **P CHP** *020 †75

HALL, John Napier. 414 ALBEMARLE SQ 22901 #051-01-1993 L2001 **ORS** *020 †40

HALL, Richard Delmar, Jr. ■ 22901 #048-12-2007 L2007 **IM** *012

HAMMILL, William Wallace. 2415 REDBUD LN 22911 #045-01-1989 L1993 **PDC PD** *020 †55

HAN, Joseph Kristian. 905 CHARTER OAKS DR, # 12 22901 #041-07-1997 L2003 **OTO** *020

HANN, Louisa. 2964 HYDRAULIC RD 22901 #067-01-2000 L2006 **FM** *020 †18 ‡

HAQ, Iftikhar Ul. ■ 22901 #704-04-1988 L1999 **NS** *100

HARBERT, Guy Morley, Jr. ■ 22911 #051-01-1956 L1956 **OBS NPM** *071 †30

HARDIE, Molly S. ■ 22901 #051-01-2000 L2000 **PD** *100

HARLE, Heather Danielle. ■ 22901 #041-02-2006 L2006 **N** *012

HARRIS, James Wilson. ■ 22901 #011-04-2005 L2005 **EM** *012

HARRIS, Thomas Joe. ■ 22901 #048-14-2003 L2006 **HO** *012 †20

HARTMAN, Nicholas Dwight. ■ 22901 #051-01-2008 *012

HAYES, James Westcott. ■ 22901 #023-01-1954 L1979 **PD HEM** *072 †55

HEDRICK, Traci Lynn. ■ 22901 #020-12-2002 L2002 **GS** *012

HEGARTY, Thomas Jos. ■ 22901 #041-02-1966 L1972 **P** *020 †75

HEIDER, Robert Roy. 600 PETER JEFFERSON PKWY, GYNECOLOGY LTD 22911 #051-04-1985 L1988 **OBG** *020 †30

HELMBRECHT, Gary David. 600 PETER JEFFERSON PKWY, STE 190 22911 #056-06-1984 L1994 **MFM OBG** *020 †30

HERBERT, Wm Norman Parke. 250 WESTBROOK PL, 1ST AND 3RD FLOOR 22901 #036-05-1972 L2000 **OBS GYN** *020 †30

HIBBARD, Kevin Michael. ■ 22901 #051-07-2008 *012

HIMOT, Linda J. ■ 22911 #041-12-1966 L2007 **P** *071 †75

HIRSH, Wendy Whitmer. ■ 22901 #005-02-1975 L1990 **PD** *020 †55

HOEHNER, Paul James. 120 FONTANA CT 22911 #023-07-1986 L1999 **AN CD** *020 †05

HOGE, Steven Kenny. 300 BARRACKS HL 22901 #025-01-1982 L1989 **P** *020 †75

HOKE, Tracey Rous. ■ 22901 #023-01-1995 L1995 **PDC** *020 †55

HOLDEN, Todd Smith. ■ 22911 #051-01-1982 L1984 **EM** *074 †16

HOLLAND, Benjamin Harris. ■ 22911 #012-22-2005 L2005 **IM** *012

HOLMES, Adam Kermit. 650 PETER JEFFERSON PKWY, STE 160 22911 #051-04-2004 L2004 **IM** *020 †20

HOLT, Sarah Elizabeth. ■ 22901 #012-01-2005 **PD** *012

HONG, Gregory Keepum. ■ 22911 #036-01-2007 L2007 **IM** *012

HONG, John Sa. 183 SPOTNAP RD, STE A 22911 #051-01-1993 L1995 **IM** *020 †20

HORNEFF, John Arthur. ■ 22911 #043-01-1975 L1979 **IM PTH** *020

HOSTETTER, Abram Martin. 22911 #041-02-1957 L2003 **P** *071 †75

HOWARD, Brandon Augustus. ■ 22901 #036-07-2006 L2007 **DR** *012

HUCEK, Andrew Michael. 600 PETER JEFFERSON PKWY, STE 220 22911 #045-01-1979 L1981 **P** *020 †75

HULLFISH, Kathie Lynn. 250 WESTBROOK PL, 1ST AND 3RD FLOOR 22901 #051-01-1992 L1992 **OBG** *020 †30

HUQ, Ashraful. ■ 22901 #160-01-1985 L2001 **P** *020 †75

HWANG, Jen-Chun. ■ 22901 #385-01-1962 **OBG** *020

JACKSON, Stephen Daniel. ■ 22901 #036-01-2008 *012

JAFFAN, Abdel Aziz Ahmad. ■ 22901 #605-02-2001 L2003 **DR** *012

JANA, Timothy David. ■ 22901 #028-46-2004 L2004 **P** *012

JANAVS, Anita. ■ 22901 #046-01-1984 L1985 **PTH** *062

JARRELL, James Carter. 977 SEMINOLE TRL # 179 22901 #055-01-1978 L1992 **CHP** *020 †20,75

JAVORSKY, Bradley Richard. ■ 22911 #056-05-2002 L2002 **END** *012 †20

JAYAKUMAR, Kaimal Anitha. 2018 MICHELANGELO CT 22911 #495-04-1987 L2006 **PDC** *020 †55

JAZAERI, Amir Anthony. 250 WESTBROOK PL, 1ST AND 3RD FLOOR 22901 #051-01-1996 L1996 **OBG** *020 †30

JOFFY, Sergei Lev. ■ 22901 #051-01-2003 L2003 **NEP** *012 †20

JOHNSON, Dewaran Marie. ■ 22901 #051-01-1978 *020

JOHNSON, Holly Ann. ■ 22901 #654-01-1985 L1988 **GP** *020

JOHNSON, Sheryl Lynne. 22911 #010-02-1999 L2000 **P** *100 †75

JONES, David Gerard. ■ 22901 #004-01-2002 L2005 **CD** *012 †20

JONES, John Allan. 595 PETER JEFFERSON PKWY, STE 320 22911 #046-01-1984 L2002 **GS OS** *020 †85

JULIEN, Matheau Antoine. ■ 22901 #012-05-2006 L2006 **GS** *012

KALTREIDER, Sara Alice. 630 PETER JEFFERSON PKWY, STE 140 22911 #051-04-1980 L1981 **OPH** *020 †35

KAPUR, Jaideep. ■ 22911 #495-45-1984 L1998 **N** *075 †75

KATZ, William Thang. 256 STATION 2, NEW COLLEGE MALONE 22904 #051-01-1997 *100

KELLAMS, Bryce Samuel. 3263 PROFFIT RD 22911 #005-02-1995 L1998 **FM** *020 †18

KELLY, Gwendolyn Valerie. 600 PETER JEFFERSON PKWY, STE 200 22911 #012-05-1995 L1999 **OBG** *020 †30

KELLY, Jean Alexandra. ■ 22911 #025-01-1962 L1971 **DR** *020 †80 ‡

KIEHNA, Erin Nicole. ■ 22911 #008-01-2006 L2006 **NS** *012

KIM, Taik Chae. 1927 SWANSON DR 22901 #583-01-1948 L1969 **OS IM** *072

KING, Erin Rebecca. ■ 22911 #035-15-2006 L2006 **OBG** *012

KIPE, Brian Jeremy. ■ 22901 #051-01-2008 *012

KLECAN, Ann Marie. 1340 STONY POINT RD, STE 100 22911 #035-48-1993 L1996 **FM** *020 †18

KOVAC, Michael John, Jr. 183 SPOTNAP RD, STE C 22911 #041-01-1970 L1977 **ORS** *020 †40

KOZOWER, Benjamin D. ■ 22901 #035-45-1997 L2006 **GS** *100 †85,90

KRAMER, Andreas H J. ■ 22911 #062-01-1997 L2005 *100

KRAMER, Catherine. ■ 22901 #051-01-1986 L1988 **AN** *020

KRAMER, Christopher M. 1650 GARTH GATE LN 22901 #005-02-1986 L1999 **CD** *050 †20

KRASNER, Brett Douglas. 215 WAYLES LN, STE 150 22911 #025-07-2000 L2004 **D** *020 †15

KRIGER, Paige Lee. 199 SPOTNAP RD, STE 5 22911 #051-01-1996 L2002 **OTO** *020

KUPERMINC, Michelle Naomi. ■ 22901 #035-09-2001 L2005 **DBP** *012 †55

LAMBRUSCHI, Cheryl Marie. ■ 22901 #051-01-2005 L2005 **AN** *012

LANDER, Christopher John. 2050 ABBEY RD STE A 22911 #035-06-1985 L1988 **AN PME** *020 †05

LANE, Richard Henry. ■ 22901 #035-19-1982 L2006 **DR** *071 †80

LAVELLE, John Christopher. ■ 22911 #001-02-2003 L2007 **PTH** *100

LE, Michael Sang. ■ 22901 #027-01-2004 L2007 **IM** *100 †20

LEE, Janet H. ■ 22901 #583-03-1951 L1961 **CHP P** *020 †75

LEISURE, George Stanley. 595 PETER JEFFERSON PKWY, STE 290 22911 #016-02-1987 L1992 **IM** *020 †20,05

LI, Yung Hua. 2647 HYDRAULIC RD 22901 #825-01-1989 L1998 **OSS** *100

LIEB, David Charles. ■ 22901 #051-01-2003 L2006 **END** *012 †20

LIEB, Emily White. 595 PETER JEFFERSON PKWY 22911 #051-01-2003 L2006 **FM** *020 †18

LIGUSH, John, Jr. 1490 PANTOPS MOUNTAIN PL, PL #100 22911 #041-12-1987 L2002 **VS** *020 †85

LINDSAY, Richard Walter. ■ 22911 #035-09-1960 L1963 **IMG FM** *071

LITTLE, Stewart Charles. ■ 22901 #012-01-2003 L2003 **OTO** *012

LOBO, Leonard Jason. ■ 22911 #051-01-2005 L2005 **IM** *012

LOCKMAN, Anne Elizabeth J. ■ 22901 #048-13-2004 L2004 **N** *012

LOCKMAN, Deborah Worch. 3350 BERKMAR DR 22901 #051-01-1991 L1991 **D** *020 †15

LOGAN, Ashley Ryan. ■ 22901 #051-01-2006 L2006 **PD** *012

LONG, Todd J. 676A BERKMAR CIR 22901 #051-01-1994 L1994 **OPH** *020 †35

LOPEZ-MOLINA, Carmen M. ■ 22901 #010-01-1965 L1997 **PD ADL** *020 †55

LU, Rommel Perillo. ■ 22901 #748-01-1999 L2006 **HO** *012 †20

LUPOLD, Chris Paul. 1450 SACHEM PL 22901 #041-02-2001 L2004 **FM** *020 †18

MACFARLAN, Duncan Andrew. 416 ALBEMARLE SQ 22901 #048-04-1979 L1982 **FM** *020 †18

MAC ILWAINE, Wm A, IV. 110 S PANTOPS DR 22911 #051-01-1975 L1980 **OPH** *020 †35

MAC KNIGHT, John Mark. 3424 TURNBERRY CIR 22901 #041-02-1992 L1993 **IM** *020 †20

MAC KNIGHT, Joseph Chas. ■ 22911 #035-01-1946 L1952 **IM FM** *072

MAIER, Rhonda Ann. 125 RIVERBEND DR 22911 #051-04-1996 **FM** *020 †18

MAJUMDAR, Sachin Kumar. ■ 22911 #035-45-2004 L2004 **END** *012 †20

MANDICHAK, Mark Joseph. ■ 22901 #041-02-2007 L2007 **IM** *012

MAROTTA, Raymond Paul. 1450 SACHEM PL, UNIT 201 22901 #051-01-1979 L1981 **FM** *020 †18

MARSHALL, Hubert Algernon. 626 BERKMAR CIR 22901 #051-01-1954 L1954 **OPH** *020 †35

MARTIN, Jeffrey Matthew. 125 RIVERBEND DR, FIRST MED 22911 #051-04-1998 L1998 **FM** *020 †18

MASLOFF, James Irvin. 155 RIVERBEND DR 22911 #051-01-1956 L1956 **U** *071 †95

MATHERS, Amy Jean. ■ 22901 #016-43-2002 L2006 **ID** *012 †20

MAYO, Mary Anne Sink. 900 RIO EAST CT, STE A 22901 #036-08-1993 L2000 **PD** *020 †55

MC DANIEL, Lynn Mc Kinney. 1751 WINTERBERRY CT, FLORIDA PEDIATRIC ASSOCIAT 22911 #045-01-1992 L2007 **PD** *020 †55

MC DONALD, Bryan Michael. ■ 22901 #051-01-2002 L2006 **PD** *020 †55

MC DONALD, Mary Ann. 2584 HOLKHAM DR 22901 #051-01-1982 L1985 **FM** *020 †18

MC GOVERN, John J. 3263 PROFFIT RD 22911 #051-01-1992 L1995 **FM** *020 †18

MCHUGH, Kimberly Elaine. ■ 22911 #045-01-2006 L2006 **PD** *012

MCKISIC, Michael Sean. ■ 22901 #031-01-2007 L2007 **GS** *012

MEDEL, Ricky. ■ 22911 #038-43-2007 L2007 **GS** *012

MEJIA, Rojelio. ■ 22901 #025-12-2006 L2006 **IM** *012

MENZE, Alexander Joseph. ■ 22911 #041-20-2006 L2006 **N** *012

MESSICK, Kyle Jason. ■ 22901 #041-14-2002 L2007 **ORS** *100

METTLER, Bret Allen. ■ 22901 #046-01-2000 L2007 **TS** *012 †85

MICHAEL, Fouad B N. ■ 22901 #330-02-1962 L1971 **OTO** *071 †45

MICHEL, Robert Scott. 900 RIO EAST CT, STE A 22901 #051-01-1987 L1991 **PD** *020 †55

MIKA, David Bedrick. 535 WESTFIELD RD # 100 22901 #051-04-1983 L1986 **P PYA** *020 †75

MIKA, Katherine Dalton. 1522 INSURANCE LN, STE A 22911 #051-04-1983 L1986 **PD** *020 †55

MILLER, Margaret E. ■ 22901 #051-01-1999 L1999 **IM** *020 †20

MOHLER, Daniel N, Jr. ■ 22901 #051-01-1953 L1953 **HEM IM** *071 †20

MONTGOMERY, Matthew Thos. 600 PETER JEFFERSON PKWY, GYNECOLOGY LTD 22911 #051-07-1983 L1990 **OBG** *020 †30

MOORE, Christopher M. ■ 22901 #036-07-2004 L2004 **IM** *020 †20

MOORS, William Richard. 103 S PANTOPS DR, STE 107 22911 #038-06-1984 L1987 **EM** *020 †18

MOREL, Christian Edward. ■ 22901 #021-05-2002 L2006 **RNR** *012 †80

MORTON, Richard Wm. 110 S PANTOPS DR 22911 #051-01-1984 L1985 **OPH PD** *020 †35

MOSCA, Alfon Bernard. ■ 22901 #051-01-1956 L1956 **IM** *071

MOYER, Laura Katherine. ■ 22901 #041-14-2006 L2006 **IM** *012

MUNOZ, Edwin Lim. ■ 22901 #748-02-1987 L1993 **PTH** *100

MUNSON, Amie R. 1149 SEMINOLE TRL 22901 #051-04-1993 L1998 **FM** *020 †18

MURRAY, William Howard. 3263 PROFFIT RD 22911 #045-04-1993 L1993 **FM** *020 †18

MYTINGER, John Robert. ■ 22901 #035-03-2005 L2005 **CHN** *012

NANDA, Mohit. 600 PETER JEFFERSON PKWY, STE 350 22911 #039-01-1986 L2004 **OPH** *020 †35

NANDA, Vandana Sood. 600 PETER JEFFERSON PKWY, STE 350 22911 #033-06-1987 L2005 **D** *020 †15

NATHAN, Robert Judd. ■ 22911 #016-11-1954 L1995 **P PYA** *071 †75

NAVIWALA, Tahira. ■ 22911 #704-16-1980 L2004 **IMG** *100 †20

NEAL, Lindsey Rose. ■ 22901 #051-01-2007 L2007 **FP** *012

NEELY, Sarah Denise. ■ 22901 #012-05-2006 L2006 **P** *012

NESBITT, Theresa Heisley. ■ 22901 #016-06-1990 L1994 **OBG** *100

NEZZER, Tanya Karen. ■ 22901 #026-08-1989 L1992 **D** *100 †15

NGUYEN, Duong Xuan. 650 PETER JEFFERSON PKWY, STE 100 22911 #036-01-1989 L1993 **CD IM** *020 †20

NIEBURG, Phillip. ■ 22901 #038-06-1970 L1973 **PDI PD** *062 †55

ODELEYE, Abiodun Abayomi. ■ 22911 #690-05-1981 L2003 **BBK** *020

ORLICK, Joseph Bruce. 674 BERKMAR CIR 22901 #051-04-1986 L1989 **IM** *020 †20

OROURKE, Ashli Karin. ■ 22911 #012-01-2005 L2005 **OTO** *012

ORR, William Allison. 155 RIVERBEND DR 22911 #051-01-1961 L1961 **U** *020 †95

OSBORNE, Robert Byron. 155 RIVERBEND DR, UROLOGICAL ASSOCIATES LTD 22911 #051-04-1985 L1991 **U** *020 †95

OVERDYKE, Jeffrey Tucker. ■ 22901 #021-06-2003 L2003 **PYG** *012

OWEN, John Atkinson, Jr. ■ 22901 #051-01-1948 L1948 **DIA IM** *072 †20

OWENS, Kelly Anne. 600 PETER JEFFERSON PKWY, GYNECOLOGY LTD 22911 #038-43-1997 L2001 **OBG** *020

OWENS, Lewis Vollintine. 1490 PANTOPS MT PL, STE 100 22911 #007-02-1990 L2001 **VS EM** *020 †85

OZBURN, Timothy Neal. ■ 22911 #012-01-1998 L2007 **DR** *100 †80

PARLETTE, Eric Christian. ■ 22901 #051-01-1998 L1999 **D** *020 †15

PASSARELLA, Mark Harold. 155 RIVERBEND DR, UROLOGICAL ASSOCIATES LTD 22911 #010-02-1997 L2003 **U** *020 †95

PATEL, Chetan Ashok. ■ 22911 #045-01-2006 L2006 **IM** *012

PATEL, Manojkumar Dalsukh. ■ 22901 #496-41-1994 L2004 **PCC** *100 †20

PEARCE, Hannah Phillips. 3350 BERKMAR DR 22901 #023-01-1992 L1993 **D DS** *020 †15

PETERSEN, Erik John. ■ 22901 #051-04-2003 L2004 **DR** *012

PETERSON, Kristine Marie. ■ 22901 #026-04-2001 L2001 **ID** *100 †20

PHILLIPS, Melissa Susan. ■ 22901 #023-07-2005 L2005 **GS** *012

PIETSCH, Richard Lake. 110 S PANTOPS DR 22911 #051-01-1966 L1966 **OPH** *071 †35

POEHAILOS, Anthony Walter. 887B RIO EAST CT 22901 #008-02-1987 L1991 **CHP P** *020 †75

POEHAILOS, Karen Dembeck. 125 RIVERBEND DR, STE 3 22911 #051-01-1989 L1991 **FM** *020 †18

POLLARD, William Bryan. 22901 #051-01-1958 L1958 **OM** *030

POPKIN, Arnold Barry. 3042 BERKMAR DR 22901 #041-01-1961 L1980 **OPH** *020 †35

PORTER, Ryan Gary. ■ 22901 #051-01-2008 *012

POWERS, Robert David. ■ 22911 #051-01-1979 L1981 **EM IM** *020 †20,16

PRAHASH, Arun. 650 PETER JEFFERSON PKWY, STE 100 22911 #495-27-1991 L2007 **IC CD** *020 †20

PRETTYMAN, Shane Thomas. ■ 22901 #055-01-2007 L2007 **OBG** *012

PUDHORODSKY, Gregory S. 1410 INCARNATION DR 22901 #023-07-1977 L1987 **RHU IM** *020 †20

PUGH, Ernest Olin. 889B RIO EAST CT 22901 #051-01-1985 L1991 **FM** *020 †18 ‡

QUILLIAN, Warren Creel. 1490 PANTOPS MOUNTAIN PL, STE 200 22911 #051-01-1999 L1999 **FM** *020 †18

RAKES, Gary Paige. 422 ALBEMARLE SQ 22901 #051-01-1989 L1993 **AI** *020 †55,03

RASAMNY, Jk John. ■ 22911 #051-01-2007 L2007 **OTO** *012

RAU, Shane Wyatt. ■ 22901 #020-12-2004 L2004 **P** *012

REGELIN, Cedric Corey. ■ 22911 #023-01-2007 L2007 **AN** *012

REMALY, Donald Alan. 147 ZAN RD 22901 #041-07-1978 L2003 **FM EM** *020 †18

RENFROW, David Martin. ■ 22901 #041-13-2003 L2003 **CHP** *012

REPP, Anita Lopes. 1484 MINOR RIDGE CT 22901 #025-01-2001 L2002 **END** *012

REYNOLDS, David Nevin. 1522 INSURANCE LN, STE A 22901 #010-02-1978 L1985 **PD** *020 †55

RICCIARDI, Laura. 3025 BERKMAR DR, STE 1 22901 #021-01-1995 L2000 **IM** *020 †20

RIDDICK, Geo Walton, Jr. ■ 22901 #051-01-1966 L1966 **OPH** *020 †35

ROCHMAN, Adam S. ■ 22901 #011-02-2002 L2003 **EM** *020 †16

RUSHIA, Edwin L. ■ 22901 #035-19-1942 L1970 **AN** *071 †05

RUSHIA, Mary Anna. ■ 22901 #019-02-1947 L1970 **P** *071

RYAN, Timothy James. ■ 22901 #024-01-2003 L2003 **GS** *100

RYDLAND, Eric Norman. 1921 COMMONWEALTH DR 22901 #011-02-1978 L2003 **PD NTR** *020 †55

SACHS, Matthew Aaron. ■ 22901 #051-04-2006 L2007 *012

SAINI, Indrani P. ■ 22911 #496-07-1963 L1982 **PD ADL** *020

SALLER, Devereux N, Jr. 520 WESTBROOK PL, 1ST AND 3RD FLOOR 22901 #041-02-1982 L2003 **MFM CG** *040 †30,19

SANSONE, Philip Andrew. 1 GARNET CENTER DR, GARNETT CENTER 22911 #035-15-1968 L1969 **P PD** *071

SANUSI, Hendra Augustinus. 535 WESTFIELD RD STE 200 22901 #051-01-1989 L1991 **FM** *020 †18

SANUSI, Irwan Daniel. ■ 22911 #506-02-1960 L1976 **PTH DMP** *040 †50

SANUSI, Marina Theresia. ■ 22911 #506-02-1959 L1976 **P** *071 †75

SARGENT, Jennifer E. 650 PETER JEFFERSON PKWY, STE 160 22911 #019-02-1994 L2000 **IM** *020 †20

SARIRIAN, Shahrzad. 2328 FINCH CT 22911 #067-02-2002 L2004 **FM** *100 †18

SAUER, Bryan Gordon. ■ 22901 #056-05-2002 L2003 **IM** *100 †20

SAVOLA, Kristen Letson. ■ 22901 #035-01-1995 L2002 **D** *100 †20,15

SAYEED, Muhammad Razi U. ■ 22901 #704-02-1990 L1995 **PYG** *100 †75

SAYETTA, Rona Beth. ■ 22911 #023-01-1981 L2006 **P PHP** *020 †70

SCHAUER, Ashley Hamilton. 626 BERKMAR CIR, BLUE RIDGE OPHTHALMOLOGY 22901 #005-14-1990 L1994 **OPH** *020 †35

SCHAUER, Jocelyn. 900 RIO EAST CT, STE A 22901 #005-14-1991 L1994 **PD** *020 †55

SCHEIDT, Stephanie Ann. ■ 22911 #051-01-2005 L2005 **OBG** *012

SCHIEDLER, Vivian. ■ 22911 #005-02-2001 L2007 **OPH** *100 †35

SCHMITT, Erica Lauren. ■ 22901 #041-12-2004 L2005 **AN** *012

SCHMITT, John W. 250 WESTBROOK PL, 1ST AND 3RD FLOOR 22901 #048-13-1983 L2002 **OBG** *020 †30

SCHMITT, Timothy Michael. ■ 22901 #030-06-1999 L2006 **GS** *020 †85

SCHMITZ, Stephen Earl. 155 RIVERBEND DR, UROLOGICAL ASSOCIATES LTD 22911 #026-04-1968 L1976 **U** *020 †95

SCHNEIDER, Edward M. ■ 22901 #038-41-1946 L1946 **GE IM** *071 †20

SCHODERBEK, Robert John. ■ 22901 #045-01-2003 L2003 **ORS** *012

SCHRECENGOST, Katherine M. ■ 22901 #051-01-2006 L2006 **PD** *012

SCHROEDER, Andrew Mark. ■ 22901 #056-05-2007 L2007 **AN** *012

SCOTT, Evelyn Steranka. ■ 22901 #041-12-1989 L2005 **IM** *020 †20

SHARKEY, Amy Elizabeth. ■ 22901 #048-14-2007 L2007 **AN** *012

SHARMA, Sucheta. ■ 22911 #495-12-1990 L2003 **NM R** *012

SHAW, Jane Reed. 416 ALBEMARLE SQ 22901 #047-01-1986 L1992 **FM** *020 †18

SHEAR, William Scovell. ■ 22901 #003-01-2004 L2004 **IM** *100

SHELTON, Bobby Leonard, II. ■ 22901 #030-06-1996 L2006 **AN** *020

SHILLINGER, Frederick Wm. ■ 22901 #010-01-1947 L1959 **PTH** *071 †50

SHIVARAM, Vidyullatha. 1445 RIO RD E 22901 #495-35-1986 L1993 **PD** *020

SHORT, Timothy Burns. 416 ALBEMARLE SQ 22901 #038-07-1984 L1986 **FM** *020 †18

SHRUM, Richard Coffman. ■ 22901 #051-01-1942 L1956 **GS CRS** *071 †85

SHUGART, Christine Stoehr. ■ 22901 #051-01-2005 L2005 **FP** *012

SHUSTERMAN, Blake Daniel. ■ 22911 #038-40-2004 L2004 **NEP** *012 †20

SIDDIQUI, Rasheed Akram. 183 SPOTNAP RD, STE B 22911 #051-04-1995 L1995 **APM** *020 †05

SIEFERT, Suzanne Amanda. ■ 22901 #051-01-2008 *012

SILVA, Neil Roy. ■ 22911 #008-02-1996 L1999 **NEP** *020 †20

SITZMAN, Thomas James. ■ 22904 #036-07-2006 L2008 **PS** *012

SLEDD, Andrew Timothy. ■ 22911 #005-15-2006 L2006 **PD** *012

SMITH, George Landon. ■ 22901 #051-01-2008 *012

SMITH, Ryan Patrick. ■ 22901 #051-01-2007 L2007 **GS** *012

SNUSTAD, Diane Gail. 100 COLONNADES HILL DR 22901 #026-04-1979 L1986 **IMG IM** *020 †20

SOMMERS, Linda Maureen. 595 PETER JEFFERSON PKWY, # 320 22911 #026-04-1986 L1995 **GS** *020 †85

SPIEKERMANN, Joy C. ■ 22901 #041-09-1987 L1993 **GP** *071

SPINELLI, Anthony William. 1490 PANTOPS MOUNTAIN PL, STE 100 22911 #035-03-1995 L2001 **VIR** *020 †80

SQUILLACE, Susan P. 2145 MEADOWFIELD WAY 22911 #051-01-1982 L1984 **FM AI** *040 †18

STANCZAK, Jeffrey David. 1490 PANTOPS MOUNTAIN PL, STE 100 22911 #010-02-1997 L1997 **R** *020 †80

STANLEY, Dirk Patrick. ■ 22901 #051-01-2007 L2007 **PTH** *012

STEINER, Hansueli. ■ 22901 #869-01-1962 L1968 **P PYA** *071

STEWART, Richard Alan. 199 SPOTNAP RD STE 1 22911 #051-01-1988 L1989 **IM** *020 †20

STONE, James Radford. 977 SEMINOLE TRL 22901 #051-01-2004 L2004 **DR** *012

STRAKA, Bonnie Ann. 3350 BERKMAR DR 22901 #008-02-1987 L1988 **D** *020 †15

STREICKER, Wm Francis. 1149 SEMINOLE TRL, PROMPT CARE INC 22901 #035-19-1973 L1974 **GP** *020

STUART, Menachem Mendel. ■ 22911 #028-02-2007 L2007 **OTO** *012

SUKOVICH, William. 600 PETER JEFFERSON PKWY, STE 170 22911 #041-02-1992 L2005 **ORS** *020 †40

SUTER, Emanuel. ■ 22911 #869-01-1942 **OS** *071

SWANSON, Jonathan Raymond. ■ 22901 #035-45-2002 L2002 **NPM PD** *012 †55

SWEENEY, Thomas Kevin. 103 S PANTOPS DR STE 107 22911 #028-02-1981 L1989 **FM** *020 †18

SWENSON, Brian Richard. ■ 22911 #041-14-2004 L2004 **GS** *012

TAFT, Mary Jo. 536 PANTOPS CTR, BOX 313 22911 #051-04-1989 L1998 **CHP** *075 †75

TALBOTT, Wm Garland, Jr. 125 RIVERBEND DR 22911 #019-02-1976 L1982 **EM** *020 †16

TALREJA, Jayant Prakash. ■ 22911 #051-04-2006 L2006 **IM** *012

TANG, Yang. ■ 22901 #243-03-1998 L2006 **DR** *012

TAYLOR, Jennie Webster. ■ 22901 #051-01-2007 L2007 **N** *012

THIELE, Robert Hill. ■ 22911 #047-05-2006 L2008 **GS** *012

THOMPSON, Richard Brad. 2484 ASPENWOOD RD 22911 #035-01-1999 L2006 **TS** *012

TOMPKINS, Dorothy G. 198 SPOTNAP RD, STE A1 22911 #051-01-1966 L1966 **ADM PD** *020 †55

TRIBASTONE, Andrea Denise. 3263 PROFFIT RD, FOREST LAKES FAMILY PRACTI 22911 #051-01-1997 L1997 **FM** *020 †18

TRUCKSESS, Amanda Britt. ■ 22911 #051-04-2004 L2004 **PM** *012

TRUESDALE, Aimee Elizabet. ■ 22901 #021-05-2004 L2007 **IM** *100 †20

TURNER, Stephen David. ■ 22901 #051-01-2005 L2005 **IM** *012

TURZA, Kristin Chakarian. ■ 22911 #010-01-2007 L2007 **GS** *012

TYNDALL, Roxane. ■ 22901 #051-01-1994 L1994 **OPH** *020

UTHLAUT, Brian Scott. ■ 22901 #036-01-2003 L2003 **IM** *100 †20

VANDENHOFF, Stephen Edwar. ■ 22901 #041-15-2006 L2007 **FP** *012

VARNER, John D. ■ 22911 #051-01-1949 L1949 **NS** *071 †25

VASTINE, Victoria L. 600 PETER JEFFERSON PKWY, STE 270 22911 #048-16-1990 L1996 **PS** *020 †65,85

VON OETTINGEN, Dieter R. ■ 22901 #407-10-1951 L1957 **GS** *071

VORENBERG, Andrew James. ■ 22901 #051-01-2003 L2006 **GS** *012

WADE, Roy, Jr. ■ 22901 #032-01-2007 L2007 **PD** *012

WAMHOFF, Christine Otis. 600 PETER JEFFERSON PKWY, STE 290 22911 #028-03-2004 L2004 **OBG** *012

WANG, Don. ■ 22901 #243-92-1986 L1996 **NP** *020 †50

WANG, Shuping. 89 OAK FOREST CIR 22901 #243-48-1982 L2001 **NEP** *020 †20

WARD, Michael David. 175 S PANTOPS DR 22911 #018-03-2002 L2006 **P** *100

WASSERSTROM, Gretchen L. 900 RIO EAST CT, STE A 22901 #048-12-1995 L1998 **PD** *020 †55

WEISS, Nancy Louise. ■ 22911 #041-13-1969 L2006 **GS OS** *020 †85

WEN, Janice. ■ 22911 #027-01-2003 **PTH** *100

WENK, Kurt Siegfried. ■ 22904 #051-01-2008 L2008 *012

WEST, Olin Leslie. 1160 PEPSI PL 22901 #035-01-1970 L1990 **P** *075 †75

WHEELER, Clara Belle. 1754 STONY POINT RD 22901 #051-04-1982 L1985 **HS ORS** *020

WHITE, Kerr Lachlan. 250 PANTOPS MOUNTAIN RD 22911 #067-01-1949 L1978 **IM EP** *071 †20

WHITWORTH, Claiborne, IV. 155 RIVERBEND DR, UROLOGICAL ASSOCIATES LTD 22911 #051-01-1991 L1993 **U** *020 †95

WILKINS, Paul Cole. 175 S PANTOPS DR 22911 #051-01-1973 L1974 **P** *020 †75

WILKINSON, Diane Louise. 300 BARRACKS HL 22901 #025-01-1981 L1989 **R** *020 †80

WILLIAMS, Christopher D. 595 PETER JEFFERSON PKWY, STE 390 22901 #051-01-1994 L2001 **OBG** *020 †30

WILLIAMS, Derek Justin. ■ 22901 #012-01-2005 L2005 **PD** *012

WILLIAMS, Stephanie Joann. 77 BARCLAY PLACE CT, # 63-E 22901 #005-12-2004 L2006 OBG *012

WILLMS, Ann Bagley. ■ 22901 #041-02-1987 L1991 DR *020 †80

WINCHESTER, David Edwin. ■ 22901 #011-04-2005 L2005 IM *012

WOMACK, Scott Gregory. 110 S PANTOPS DR 22911 #051-04-1999 L2007 OPH *020 †20

WONG, Mayin. ■ 22901 #035-75-2002, ▲ L2006 CHP *012

WOODS, William Anthony. 1849 KEISER RIDGE RD 22911 #041-12-1991 L1991 EM *020 †16,55

WRIGHT, Jeffrey Lowell. ■ 22901 #028-34-2007 L2007 AN *012

WRIGHT, Philip Robert. ■ 22901 #051-04-2006 L2006 DR *012

WYKER, Yvonne Townsend. ■ 22901 #035-01-1949 OS *075

YATES, Paul A. ■ 22901 #005-18-2001 L2002 OPH *100 †35

YEAZELL, Lauren Kara. ■ 22901 #038-40-2006 L2007 AN *012

YOUNG, Denise Stickley. 250 WESTBROOK PL, 1ST AND 3RD FLOOR 22901 #051-04-1989 L1994 OBG *020 †30

ZAVADSKAYA, Natalia Yuri. ■ 22901 #913-05-1979 L2002 *020

ZITNAY, Christopher G. 183 SPOTNAP RD, STE A 22911 #051-01-1991 L1992 END *020 †20

CHARLOTTESVILLE – CHARLOTTESVILLE CITY

ABAZARI, Azin. PO BOX 800715, DEPT OF OPH 22908 #517-01-2003 L2007 OPH *012

ABD ELAZEEZ KHALED, Mohama. PO BOX 800212, HEALTH SYSTEM 22908 #915-04-2001 L2007 NS *012

ABDEL-RAHMAN, Emaad M O. UVA HSC NEPHROLOGY, P O BOX 133 22908 #915-04-1982 L1996 NEP IM *020 †20

ABDULLAH, David Clifford. 430 ROCKS FARM DR 22903 #036-05-1978 L1979 DR *020 †80

ABEL, Mark Francis. 2270 IVY RD, REHABILITATION CENTER 22903 #021-01-1982 L1989 ORS *020 †40

ACOSTA, Lealani Mae Yanez. ■ 22903 #051-01-2007 L2007 N *012

ADAMS, Joshua D. PO BOX 800136, UVA 22908 #041-13-2003 L2003 DR *012

ADAMS, Kelly Kirsten. ■ 22902 #030-06-2006 L2006 PD *012

ADAMS, Reid Barton. 500 RAY C HUNT DR 22903 #051-01-1987 L1988 GS SO *020 †85

ADEN, Justin Mcdonald. PO BOX 800136, UNIVERSITY OF VIRGINIA MED 22908 #025-01-2006 L2006 AN *012

AGARWAL, Raj. ■ 22903 #051-01-2008 *012

AHMED, Hazem Mohammed. ■ 22903 #915-04-1989 L2004 NS *012

AJGAONKAR, Ashok Dinkar. 1100 E JEFFERSON ST 22902 #051-01-1971 L1974 FM *020 †18

AKHTER, Mahabuba. PO BOX 800136, UNIV OF VIRGINIA 22908 #160-05-1983 L2005 *100

AKINLI, Timur Can. PO BOX 800136, UNIVERSITY OF VIRGINIA MED 22908 #041-15-2006 L2006 P *012

AKOSAH, Kwame Osei. PO BOX 800158, DIV.OF CARDIOASCULAR MEDIC 22908 #010-03-1985 L1989 IM CD *020 †20

AKRAM, Imran. 1234 PEBBLEBROOKE LN # 20 22902 #704-01-1998 L2002 P *020

AL-AWABDY, Basil S. ■ 22902 #012-22-2006 L2006 IM *012

ALBERT, Martin Philip. 901 PRESTON AVE, STE 402-3 22903 #041-01-1968 L1978 FM EM *020

ALBERTS, Jeffrey Scott. 459 LOCUST AVE, MARTHA JEFFERSON HOSPITAL 22902 #016-01-1986 L1989 EM *072 †20

ALEXANDER, Whitney Smith. 2411 IVY RD 22903 #004-01-1996 L1996 PD *020 †55

ALFANO, Alan. 545 RAY C HUNT DR, STE 310 22903 #041-02-1988 L1992 PM *020 †60

ALFORD, Bennett Allae. 1218 LEE ST, UNIV OF VA HOSP RAD DEPT 22908 #001-02-1972 L1977 R PDR *020 †80

ALLAM, Souha Samir. PO BOX 800136, UNIV OF VIRGINIA MED SCH 22908 #605-02-2000 L2006 *100

ALLER, James David. 1100 E HIGH ST STE 2A 22902 #051-01-1975 L1978 IM GP *020 †20

AL-OSAIMI, Abdullah M S. UNIV OF VA, MED EDUC DEPT 22908 #797-01-1993 L2001 *020

ALSON, Amy Ruth. 400 BRANDON AVE 22908 #422-01-2002 L2002 MP *020 †20

ALTES, Talissa Ann. 1215 LEE ST 22903 #054-04-1996 L1996 DR *020 †80

ALTHOFF, Seth Owen. ■ 22903 #041-13-2006 L2006 EM *012

AMBROCIO, Deryll Ulep. ■ 22903 #014-01-2003 L2006 RHU *012 †20

AMIN, Angela Bipin. 504 ELLIOTT AVE 22902 #021-05-1998 L2001 PD *020 †55

ANDERSEN, Willie Albert. HOSPITAL DR, DEPT OB/GYN PRVT CLINIC BL 22908 #023-01-1970 L1976 GO GYN *020 †30

ANDERSON, Justin Darrell. ■ 22902 #026-04-2001 L2004 CD *012

ANDERSON, Mark Wm. LEE ST BOX 170, UNIV OF VIRGINIA HEALTH CT 22908 #005-14-1983 L1997 DR GS *020 †80

ANDERSON, Susan M. 2270 IVY RD, KLUGE CHILDRENS REHAB 22903 #033-05-1980 L1985 PD OS *020 †55

ANDREWS, Judith Ann. ■ 22903 #143-03-1968 GP *020

ANGLE, John Frederick. BOX 170, DEPARTMEMT OF RADIOLOGY 22908 #030-05-1986 L1991 DR *020 †80

ANTIPPA, Phillip Nicholas. PO BOX 291, U V A 22908 #143-02-1991 *100

ANTON, Toomas. ■ 22903 #913-94-1995 L2007 NS *100

ARAD, Eldad. PO BOX 511, DEPT MED 22908 #550-03-1988 L1998 END *100

ARCHBALD, Laurie Renee. ■ 22903 #047-05-2002 L2002 IMG *012 †20

AREGAWI, Dawit Gebremicha. ■ 22903 #366-03-1995 L2006 IM *100

ARGO, Curtis Kent. BOX 800708, UNIV OF VA HEALTH SYS 22907 #018-03-2000 L2004 HEP GE *020 †20

ARINGTON, Steven Brad. ■ 22903 #051-01-1991 *100

ARLET, Vincent Marie Jean. 400 RAY C HUNT DR, STE 330 22903 #396-37-1985 *100

ARMENGOL, Carlos Eladio. 1011 E JEFFERSON ST, PEDIATRIC ASSOC. OF CHARLO 22902 #011-04-1995 L1995 PD *020 †55

ARNOLD, Holly Elisabeth. ■ 22902 #045-01-2005 L2005 D *012

ARNOLD, William P, III. 500 RAY C HUNT DR 22903 #035-45-1967 L1977 AN *020 †05

ARONSOHN, Michael Valen. ■ 22903 #005-06-1991 L1991 P *012 †30

ARONZON, Denise Beth. ■ 22902 #035-45-2005 L2005 PD *012

ARORA, Narinder Singh. 308 10TH ST NE 22902 #495-03-1964 L1976 PUD IM *020 †20

ASHBY, Finlay Michael. 459 LOCUST AVE, MARTHA JEFFERSON HOSPITAL 22902 #051-04-1982 L1988 EM FM *020

ASKEW, Fletcher Comer, Jr. 1000 E HIGH ST, STE B 22902 #012-01-1970 L1976 D *020 †15

ASTHAGIRI, Ashok Rajappa. ■ 22908 #038-44-2001 L2001 NS *100

ATKINS, Kristen Audra. JEFFERSON PARK AVE 22908 #050-02-1996 L2000 ATP PCP *020 †50

ATTINGER, Ernst Otto. UNIV OF VA MED CTR, BOX 377 22908 #869-07-1950 L1970 OS *062

AYERS, Carlos Ray. UNIV OF VA MED CTR, BOX 146 22908 #051-01-1958 L1958 CD IM *040 †20

AYERS, Donald Mark. PO BOX 800136, UVA 22908 #016-02-2003 L2003 *100

BAGAYOKO, Namory Djigui. HEALTH SCIENC, UNIV OF VIRGINIA 22908 #023-07-2007 L2007 ORS *012

BAILEY, Andrew A, Jr. 1100 E HIGH ST STE 1B 22902 #051-01-1979 L1985 GS *020 †85

BAILEY, Charles Cabell. 2955 IVY RD 22903 #051-01-1937 L1937 DIA *072 †20

BAILEY, Russell Coyle. ■ 22903 #012-01-2003 L2003 N *012

BALABAN, David Howard. 1139 E HIGH ST, GASTROENTEROLOGY ASSOC 22902 #023-01-1990 L1993 GE *020 †20

BALABAN, Lori Wecker. 1011 E JEFFERSON ST, PEDIATRIC ASSOC OF CHARL , 22902 #036-01-1990 L1993 PD *020 †55

BALESTRIERI, Philip J. 459 LOCUST AVE 22902 #010-01-1987 L1989 AN *020 †05

BALINT, Bart Wesley. JEFFERSON PARK AVE 22908 #055-01-1985 L1996 AN PME *020 †05

BALLERT, John Andrew. ■ 22908 #020-02-2004 L2004 OTO *012

BALLERT, Natalie M. ■ 22902 #020-02-2005 L2005 AN *012

BALLEW, Kenneth Alan. 2955 IVY RD, STE 205 22903 #018-03-1988 L1992 IM *072 †20

BALOGUN, Rasheed Abiodun. 500 RAY C HUNT DR 22903 #690-01-1990 L2001 NEP *020 †20

BALOGUN, Seki Adetokunbo. 500 RAY C HUNT DR 22903 #690-01-1992 L2001 IMG *020 †20

BARBER, Jack Willard. 500 RAY C HUNT DR 22903 #048-13-1981 L1985 P *020 †75

BARCIA, John Peter. 1224 W MAIN ST, STE 701 22903 #028-34-1990 L2001 PN *020 †55

BARKER, Bill J. ■ 22902 #038-43-1999 L2005 PCC *012 †20

BARKER, Kathryn Elizabeth. ■ 22902 #051-01-2007 PD *012

BARKER, Sarah Jane. ■ 22902 #055-01-2006 L2006 EM *012

BARNETT, B Lewis, Jr. BOX 414 U VA SCH OF MEDICI, DEPARTMENT OF FAMILY PRACT 22908 #045-01-1949 L1977 FM *071 †18

BARR, Michelle Snively. 500 RAY C HUNT DR 22903 #051-01-1990 L2001 DR *020 †80

BARRETT, Eugene Jos. 450 RAY C HUNT DR, BOX 801410 22903 #035-45-1975 L1991 END *050 †20

BARRETT, Kevin Michael. HOSPITAL DRIVE, DEPARTMENT OF NEUROLOGY, P 22908 #011-02-2002 L2006 VN *100 †75

BARRETT, Matthew James. ■ 22903 #051-01-2005 L2006 N *012

BARRETT, Matthew Michael. JEFFERSON PK BOX 291 22908 #305-01-2005 L2006 P *012

BARROSO, Luis Francis, II. ■ 22902 #011-04-2002 L2002 ID *012 †20

BARTELT, Luther August. PO BOX 800136, UNIVERSITY OF VIRGINIA MED 22908 #018-03-2006 L2006 IM *012

BASDEMIR, Demet. ■ 22903 #902-01-1992 L1997 PDE *100

BASHORE, Randall Thos. JEFFERSON PARK AVE 22908 #041-02-1982 L1983 IM IMG *020 †20

BASSIGNANI, Matthew John. 500 RAY C HUNT DR 22903 #024-05-1991 L1996 DR *020 †80

BATCHELET, Andrew Richard. ■ 22903 #051-01-2008 L2008 *012

BATTIG, Charles Guido. ■ 22906 #021-01-1961 L2004 AN *071 †05

BATTISTON, John Joseph, Jr. VIRGINIA HEALTH, UNIVERSITY OF 22908 #050-02-2003 L2003 DR *012

BATTLE, Robert Webb. LEE S, 4TH FLOOR. HOSPITAL EXPANS 22908 #051-01-1984 L2007 CD IM *020 †20

BAUER, Todd W. RM 4579, HOSPITAL DRIVE, CLINICAL DEPT. WING, 4TH F 22908 #041-01-1995 L2005 SO GS *020 †85

BAUM, Victor Curtis. 500 RAY C HUNT DR 22903 #047-05-1974 L1994 AN CCP *020 †55,05

BAUMAN, Kimberley Lisa. 2955 IVY RD, STE 205 22903 #048-02-1991 L1993 IM *020 †20

BAWEJA, Harpreet Singh. RADIOLOGY DEPT,P.O BOX 800, UNIVERSITY OF VIRGINIA 22908 #495-28-1990 L2006 DR *100 †80

BAWEJA, Manpreet Kaur. 459 LOCUST AVE, DEPT OF EMERGENCY MEDICINE 22902 #041-14-1998 L2006 EM *020 †16

BAYLOR, Michael Randel. 459 LOCUST AVE, MARTHA JEFFERSON HOSPITAL 22902 #045-04-1998 L1998 EM *020 †16

BEACH, Scott Richard. ■ 22902 #051-01-2006 L2006 P *012

BECKER, Daniel Martin. BOX 8000744, DEPT OF GENERAL MEDICINE 22908 #028-02-1975 L1984 IM *040 †20

BEDELL, Wallace C. ■ 22903 #024-01-1944 GS *071 †85

BEDFORD, Robert Forrest. O 800710, 1 HOSPITAL DRIVE P 22908 #035-20-1968 L1977 AN *020 †05 ‡

BEHM, Brian Winters. PO BOX 800708, MULTISTORY BLDG ROOM 2141 22908 #051-01-1999 L2003 IM *020 †20

BEHM, Carolyn Zesk. PO BOX 800136, UNIV OF VIRGINIA 22908 #051-01-2000 L2003 CD *020 †20

BEHM, William Edwin. DEPARTMENT OF RADIOLOGY, 1215 LEE STREET-NEW HOSPIT 22908 #047-06-2002 L2007 DR *020 †80

BELL, Kristin Clontz. 400 BRANDON AVE, UVA HLTH CTR BOX 800760 22908 #045-01-1994 L1994 IM *020 †20

BELLER, George Allan. UNIV OF VA HLTH SYS, HOSP EXPNSN BLDG RM 4035 22908 #051-01-1966 L1966 CD IM *020 †20

BELLER, Jennifer Perrine. PO BOX 800136, UNIVERSITY OF VIRGINIA MED 22908 #035-48-2006 L2006 IM *012

BELZILE, Etienne Louis. PO BOX 800136, UVA 22908 #067-01-1997 L2002 OAR *100

BENNETT, James Pepper, Jr. UNIV OF VA MEDICAL SCHOOL, DEPT NEURO 22908 #023-07-1974 L1981 N *020 †75

BERG, Carl Lansing. 500 RAY C HUNT DR 22903 #028-02-1986 L1997 GE IM *020 †20

BERGIN, James Danl. 1215 LEE ST RM 4059, HOSPITAL EXPANSION 22908 #024-07-1984 L1990 CD IM *020 †20

BERRY, Frederic A. 500 RAY C HUNT DR 22903 #051-01-1959 L1959 AN *040 †55,05

BERTRAM, Edward H, III. UNIV OF VIRGINIA MED CENTE, DEPT OF NEUROLOGY BOX 394 22908 #036-01-1980 L1981 N IM *050 †75

BEVELOCK, Laura Marie. ■ 22902 #033-06-2007 L2007 IM *012

BHARDWAJ, Hem Lata. ■ 22902 #051-01-2006 L2006 IM *012

BICKSTON, Stephen Jos. BOX 145, UVA HEALTH SCIENCES CENTER 22908 #036-01-1988 L1995 GE *020 †20

BIEDERMANN, Gregory Bruce. ■ 22902 #028-34-2001 L2005 RO *012

BILLANTE, Mark Joseph. PO BOX 800136, UVA MEDICAL CENTER 22908 #047-05-2001 L2006 ORS *012

BINDAL, Meenakshi. DEPT OF ANESTHESIOLOGY, UNIV OF VIRGINIA HLTH SYST 22908 #041-15-2003 L2007 PMM *012

BINDER, Alan Jay. UVA HEALTH SYS BOX 800158 22908 #035-15-1973 L2001 CD *020 †20

BIRCHENOUGH, Shawn Arthur. ■ 22903 #051-01-2002 L2002 PS *012

BISSRAM, Melisha. ■ 22902 #036-01-2003 L2003 NEP *012 †20

BITTL, Markus. PO BOX 800136, UNIVERSITY OF VIRGINIA 22908 #409-16-1992 L2003 *020

BIVENS, Mary-Margaret Cam. PO BOX 800718 22908 #051-01-2006 L2007 D *012

BIZZELL, Anton Che. ■ 22903 #051-01-1998 FM *100

BLACK, Jonathan Steven. ■ 22908 #030-05-2007 L2007 PS *012

BLACK, Katherine Lauren. ■ 22908 #045-01-2006 L2007 IM *012

BLACKHALL, Leslie Jackson. 1224 W MAIN ST, 2ND FLOOR, STE 201 22903 #035-19-1984 L2001 **IM** *020 †20

BLACKMON, Anna Kathryn. ■ 22903 #051-01-1999 L1999 **CD** *020 †20

BLANK, Susan Kuhn. ■ 22903 #024-01-2001 L2004 **END** *012

BLATMAN, Robert Nathan. ■ 22903 #051-01-1988 L2005 **OBG** *020 †30

BLOCH, Roman Christopher. 1215 LEE ST, BOX 800170 22902 #035-45-2002 L2007 **DR** *100 †80

BLOM, Berna Jean Romyn. ■ 22903 #660-04-1965 L1974 **D** *020

BLOUNT, Kevin John. ■ 22903 #008-02-2003 L2004 **DR** *012

BLUTEAU, Catherine Ann. PO BOX 800136, UNIVERSITY OF VIRGINIA 22908 #025-01-2005 L2005 **AN** *012

BOACHIE-ADJEI, Yaw Dwomoh. ■ 22903 #024-07-2006 L2006 **ORS** *012

BOATWRIGHT, Evelyn Juanit. ■ 22902 #038-06-2007 L2007 **PD** *012

BOBBITT, Oliver B. PO BOX 6128 22906 #051-01-1943 L1943 **CLP** *071 †50

BOEDEFELD, Robyn Lynn. ■ 22902 #020-12-1999 L2006 **PCC SME** *020 †20

BOEDEFELD, William M, II. ■ 22902 #030-06-1999 L2006 **TS** *020 †85

BOGDONOFF, David Leonard. 500 RAY C HUNT DR 22903 #035-45-1981 L1986 **AN GS** *020 †85,05

BOLTON, Warren Kline. 500 RAY C HUNT DR 22903 #051-01-1969 L1969 **IM NEP** *040 †20

BONDS, Denise Elaine. HOSPITAL WEST COMPLEX, 3RD FL RM 3181 22908 #030-06-1992 L2007 **IM** *020 †20

BOREK, Heather Ashley. ■ 22902 #008-02-2007 L2007 **EM** *012

BORISH, Lawrence Craig. MR4 BLDG RM 5041 LANE RD, UNIV OF VIRGINIA, BOX 8013 22908 #024-05-1979 L1999 **AI IM** *050 †20,03

BOROWITZ, Stephen Mark. UNIVERSITY OF VA 22908 #016-01-1980 L1988 **PD GE** *020 †55

BOST, Michael Anthony. 500 RAY C HUNT DR 22903 #051-01-1976 L1977 **EM FM** *020 †18,16

BOURNE, Thomas D. UNIV OF VIRGINIA, DEPT OF PATHOLOGY/BOX 8002 22908 #048-14-2001 L2001 **NP** *012

BOVE, Christina Marie. 1101 E HIGH ST UPPR LEVEL, BLUE RIDGE HEART & VASCLR 22902 #035-45-1996 L1999 **CD** *020 †20

BOYD, James Clark. 500 RAY C HUNT DR 22903 #028-02-1973 L1978 **CLP PTH** *020

BOYD, Jason Keith. PO BOX 800696 22908 #012-22-2003 L2004 **HO** *012 †20

BOYER, James Edward. 459 LOCUST AVE 22902 #051-01-2000 L2006 **HO IM** *020 †20

BOYLE, Robert John. PO BOX 800386, UVA HEALTH SYSTEM 22908 #023-07-1973 L1983 **NPM PD** *040 †55

BRACIALE, Thomas Jos. UNIVERSITY OF VIRGINIA, HEALTH SCIENCES CENTER 22908 #041-01-1975 L1992 **IG PTH** *020

BRADDOCK, Stephen Robt. PO BOX 800386, UNIV OF VA HLTH SYS 22908 #028-03-1988 L2006 **MG PD** *020 †19,55

BRAITHWAITE, S. 500 RAY C HUNT DR 22903 #051-04-1991 L1992 **EM** *020 †16

BRAKKE, Nathan Ryan. ■ 22903 #046-01-2002 L2005 **AN** *012 †55

BRANT, William Edward. 1215 LEE ST, NEW HOSPITAL UVA RADIOLOGY 22908 #005-02-1972 L2001 **DR AM** *040 †80

BRANTLEY, Elizabeth Ann. ■ 22903 #051-01-2007 L2007 **PD** *012

BRANTLEY, Richard Kirven. 916 E HIGH ST, STE 1 22902 #047-05-1997 L1997 **IM** *020 †20

BRASHEAR, H Robert, III. 500 RAY C HUNT DR 22903 #036-01-1979 L1981 **N** *050 †75

BRAYMAN, Kenneth Lewis. 500 RAY C HUNT DR 22903 #041-01-1981 L2002 **GS DIA** *050 †85

BRENBRIDGE, Norman A G. 459 LOCUST AVE, CHARLOTTESVILLE RADIOLOGY 22902 #035-19-1970 L1974 **DR** *020 †80

BRENIN, Christiana M. UVA BOX 800716 22908 #035-09-1990 L2002 **HO** *020 †20

BRENIN, David Rubin. HOSPITAL DRIVE, PRIVATE CLINICS BLDG./4TH 22908 #035-09-1990 L2002 **GS** *020 †85

BREWER, James L, III. 459 LOCUST AVE 22902 #051-01-1980 L1981 **EM** *020 †16

BREWER, Richard James. 459 LOCUST AVE 22902 #035-20-1970 L1973 **GS TS** *071 †85

BRILL, Louis Beverly, II. ■ 22902 #051-01-2005 L2006 **PTH** *012

BRIM, Shannon Elynn. ■ 22902 #051-01-2007 L2007 **OBG** *012

BRITT, Steven G. U OF VA SCHL OF MED PTH 22908 #048-02-1986 *100

BROCK, Andrew Sam. ■ 22902 #045-01-2003 L2003 **IM** *100 †20

BRODRICK, Brooks Barrett. ■ 22903 #051-01-2008 *012

BROOKS, Martha Jane. 1005 E HIGH ST 22902 #016-06-1959 L1964 **OPH** *075

BROWN, Alaina Marie. ■ 22902 #025-12-2006 L2006 **PD** *012

BROWN, Kelly Anne. ■ 22902 #025-12-2006 L2006 **PD** *012

BROWN, Morry Duvall. ■ 22903 #051-01-2000 L2000 **RNR** *012 †80

BROWN, Robert Stanley. 1 BOARS HEAD PL, # 101 22903 #051-01-1967 L1967 **P PFP** *071 †75

BROWN, Robert Stanley, Jr. 505 FAULCONER DR STE 1B 22903 #051-01-1981 L1983 **P IM** *020 †20,75

BROWN, Sue Alison. PO BOX 801406, 450 RAY C HUNT DR 22908 #051-01-1995 L2005 **IM** *020 †20

BROWN, Thomas Edwin. 400 RAY C HUNT ST, STE 33 22908 #045-01-1991 L1998 **OAR** *020 †40

BRUCK, Nathan. PO BOX 800136, UNIV OF VIRGINIA 22908 #550-01-1999 L2006 *100

BRUNNER, Carolyn Marie. UVA MEDICAL CENTER, RHEUMATOLOGY-UVA 22903 #010-02-1964 L1969 **RHU IM** *071 †20

BRUNS, David Eugene. 500 RAY C HUNT DR 22903 #028-34-1973 L1978 **CLP PCH** *050

BRUNTON, Lance Michael. ■ 22903 #041-12-2003 L2003 **ORS** *012

BRYANT, Mary Gayle. 545 RAY C HUNT DR #240, POB XO 801004 22908 #051-04-1993 L1993 **PM** *020 †60

BRYER, Bridget Marie. ■ 22903 #051-01-2007 L2007 **IM** *012

BUCKMAN, John. 500 RAY C HUNT DR 22903 #917-24-1950 L1966 **P** *040

BUDGE, Loren Passey. PO BOX 800662, 1215 LEE ST 22908 #010-01-2004 L2004 **CD** *012 †20

BULLOCK, Grant Carl. UNIV OF VIRGINIA, DEPT OF PATHOLOGY/BOX 8002 22908 #018-03-2001 L2001 **PTH** *100

BUMPASS, David Benjamin. ■ 22903 #051-01-2008 *012

BURGER, Christina Marie. ■ 22902 #005-12-2006 L2006 **EM** *012

BURKET, Roger Clair. JEFFERSON PARK AVE 22908 #010-01-1981 L1997 **CHP P** *071 †75

BURKHOLDER, Burton Von. 1000 E HIGH ST STE B 22902 #051-01-1997 L1997 **D** *020 †15

BURNETTE, Brent Richard. PO BOX 800136, UNIVERSITY OF VIRGINIA 22908 #047-07-2002 L2005 **IM** *100 †20

BURNS, Ted Michael. 500 RAY C HUNT DR 22903 #019-02-1994 L1995 **CN** *020 †75

BURWELL, Lawrence Rogers. 500 RAY C HUNT DR 22903 #038-06-1963 L1975 **CD IM** *020 †20

BUSHEN, Oluma Yoseph. PO BOX 801379, UNIVERSITY OF VIRGINIA 22908 #366-03-1991 L2002 **ID** *100 †20

BUSS, William Claude. 500 RAY C HUNT DR 22903 #005-12-1967 L1989 **DR NM** *020 †80,28

BUTLER, Paris Desoto. PO BOX 800136, UNIVERSITY OF VIRGINIA 22908 #051-01-2004 L2004 **GS** *012

CACHAT, Francois. PO BOX 800903 22908 #869-05-1991 L1999 **PN** *100

CAIRNS, Jerico Brian. ■ 22902 #054-04-2007 L2007 **EM** *012

CALDWELL, Stephen Hugh. 500 RAY C HUNT DR 22903 #036-05-1983 L1984 **IM GE** *020 †20

CAMPA, Justiniano F. 400 10TH ST NE, # A 22902 #847-04-1960 L1960 **N EM** *020 †75

CAMPANELLI, David Michael. 500 RAY C HUNT DR 22903 #035-20-1991 L1994 **IM** *020 †20

CAMPBELL, Bruce D, Jr. 459 LOCUST AVE 22902 #051-01-1980 L1983 **FM** *020 †18

CAMPBELL, Chris Alan. PO BOX 800376, HEALTH SYSTEM 22908 #036-01-2003 **PS** *012

CANLAS, Aurora Juliana. GME BOX 800136, UNIV OF VIRGINIA HLTH 22908 #422-01-2007 L2007 **FP** *012

CANNON, Laura Lee. ■ 22903 #051-01-2007 **FP** *012

CANON SALAZAR, Nicolas Da. GME BOX 800136, UNIV OF VIRGINIA 22908 #264-04-2004 L2007 **P** *012

CANTERBURY, Randolph Jack. HSC BOX 623, UNIV OF VA HOSPITAL 22908 #055-01-1979 L1979 **P PYM** *040 †20,75

CANTRELL, Robert Wendell. PO BOX 800789, MCKIM HALL 3007 22908 #010-01-1960 L1976 **HNS OTO** *071 †45

CARBONELL, Warren Shawn. ■ 22902 #051-01-2006 *012

CAREY, Robert Munson. 2955 IVY RD 22903 #047-05-1965 L1973 **END IM** *030 †20

CARFRAE, Bick Thi. 311 10TH ST NE, ALBEMARLE ANESTHESIA 22902 #018-03-2001 L2006 **AN** *020 †05

CARPENTER, Johnson T, Jr. 2955 IVY RD 22903 #051-01-1955 L1955 **HEM** *040 †20

CARPENTER, Martha Alma. 500 RAY C HUNT DR 22903 #051-01-1959 L1959 **PDC PD** *020 †55

CARRICABURU, Sarah Luz. LEE ST, PRIMARY CARE CENTER, 1221 22908 #016-06-2004 L2004 **FM** *100 †18

CARSON, Eric Ward. PO BOX 800159, UNIVERSITY OF VIRGINIA 22908 #016-11-1989 L2004 **OSM** *020 †40

CARTER, Bruce Christian. 1101 E JEFFERSON ST, STE 3 22902 #051-01-2001 L2001 **OPH** *020 †35

CARTER, Bruce Thos. 1101 E JEFFERSON ST, STE 3 22902 #051-01-1970 L1970 **PO** *020 †35 ‡

CARTER, Charles Thos. 500 RAY C HUNT DR 22903 #049-01-1988 L1993 **EM IM** *020 †20,16

CARTER, Cullen O'Neill. ■ 22903 #051-01-2008 *012

CARVER, Deborah Jeanmean. 500 RAY C HUNT DR 22903 #023-07-1989 L1998 **CCP** *020 †55

CASADABAN, Bridgett Leigh. ■ 22902 #056-06-2006 L2006 **OBG** *012

CASEY, Catherine Frances. ■ 22903 #035-06-2004 L2004 **FM** *020 †18

CASTRO, Barbara Ann. 500 RAY C HUNT DR 22903 #016-06-1990 L1993 **AN** *020 †05,55

CATHRO, Helen Paula. 500 RAY C HUNT DR 22903 #836-02-1984 L1997 **PTH** *020 †50

CAUGHRON, Samuel Dan. 901 PRESTON AVE, STE 300 22903 #019-02-1971 L1978 **FM OM** *020 †18

CAYCEDO, Francisco Jose. 400 RAY C HUNT DR, STE 330 22903 #264-05-1981 L2000 **OFA** *020 †40

CHAMBERS, Kathleen Marie. ■ 22903 #028-34-1989 L2002 **PD** *020 †55

CHAMPANERI, Shivam Amrut. ■ 22902 #051-01-2005 L2005 **IM** *012

CHAN, Donald P K. 500 RAY C HUNT DR 22903 #209-01-1960 L1993 **ORS** *020 †40

CHANCE, Joseph Franklin. 500 RAY C HUNT DR 22903 #047-05-1977 L1980 **IM EM** *020 †20,16

CHANG, Han Soo. JEFFERSON PK, BOX 291 22908 #572-03-1983 **NS** *100

CHANGAPPA, Reshma Baduvan. ■ 22903 #036-08-2007 L2007 **IM** *012

CHANKAEW, Ekawut. PO BOX 800136, UNIV OF VA 22908 #891-04-1999 *100

CHARIF, Pija M H. ■ 22908 #869-04-1958 L1962 **PD** *020 †55

CHARLTON, George Thomas. ■ 22902 #041-12-2006 L2006 **IM** *012

CHARLTON, Jennifer Richar. ■ 22903 #011-04-2004 L2007 **PN** *012 †55

CHATMAN, Micaela Tegan. ■ 22902 #051-01-2008 *012

CHAUDHRY, Omer A. PO BOX 800136, DEPT OF INFECT DIS 22908 #028-46-2002 L2005 **ID** *012 †20

CHEN, Donna Tewei. ■ 22903 #005-02-1994 L1998 **P** *020 †75

CHEN, Philip Ga-Houng. PO BOX 800713, HEALTH SYSTEM 22908 #038-06-2007 **OTO** *012

CHEVALIER, Robert Louis. VIRGINIAHEALTH SYSTEM, UNIV OF 22908 #016-02-1972 L1978 **PD PN** *030 †55

CHHABRA, Abhinav. 400 RAY C HUNT DR STE 330 22903 #051-01-1995 L1995 **HS ORS** *020 †40

CHIOZZA, Stefano. 291 E JEFFERSON ST, UNIV OF VA MED CTR 22902 #561-09-1993 L1995 **P** *100

CHITWOOD, Edmund Madison. 2874 MORGANTOWN RD 22903 #051-01-1997 L1999 **EM** *020 †16

CHOA, Mark Lewis. ■ 22908 #051-01-2008 *012

CHOI, Luke Seungho. PO BOX 800136, UNIVERSITY OF VIRGINIA 22908 #028-03-2004 L2004 **ORS** *012

CHONG, Daniel Gene. ■ 22903 #051-01-2008 *012

CHOUDHRI, Asim Fiaz. ■ 22902 #047-06-2004 L2005 **DR** *012

CHRISTENSEN, Marisa F. ■ 22903 #051-01-2001 L2005 **IMG** *020 †18

CHRISTIANSEN, Jonathan P. ■ 22908 #671-02-1994 L1999 **CD** *100 †20

CHRISTIANSON, Lisa Marie. 400 BRANDON AVE., ELSON STUDENT HEALTH CENTE 22908 #051-01-1999 L1999 **GPM** *012

CHRISTOPH, Richard Allen. UVA MED CTR, BOX 523 22908 #047-06-1976 L1985 **EM PD** *020 †55,16

CHRISTOPHEL, John Jared. PO BOX 800136, UNIVERSITY OF VIRGINIA 22908 #051-01-2004 L2004 **OTO** *012

CHUA, Dave Yu. RM 2766, 1215 LEE STREET 22908 #016-01-2000 L2004 **CD** *012 †20 ‡

CHUTE, Deborah Jean. PO BOX 800214, UNIVERSITY OF VIRGINIA 22908 #041-01-2003 L2003 **PTH** *100 †50

CIAMBOTTI, Jonathan M. 1852 EDGEWOOD LN, RADIOLOGY DEPT 22903 #041-12-1994 L1994 **DR** *020 †80

CICCHETTI, Michael Scott. ■ 22903 #051-01-2005 L2005 **PM** *012

CIFARELLI, Christopher Pa. PO BOX 800136, UNIVERSITY OF VIRGINIA 22908 #041-02-2005 L2005 **NS** *012

CLARK, Badie Travis, III. UVA CHILDREN'S HOSP, HOSP DR BARRINGER BLDG-5TH 22908 #036-08-2003 L2007 **CCP** *012

CLARK, David S. 1138 ROSE HILL DR, STE 20 22903 #051-04-1951 L1998 **IM NEP** *071

CLARKE, Margaret. PO BOX 800300, HEALTH SYSTEM 22908 #016-11-2001 L2001 **GS** *012

CLARKE, William Linus. UNIV OF VA MED CTR 22908 #047-05-1971 L1978 **DIA PDE** *050 †55

CLARY, Rebecca Ann. ■ 22908 #051-04-2005 L2005 **IM** *100

CLAXTON, Rene Noelle. ■ 22903 #011-03-2005 L2005 **IM** *012

CLAYTON, Anita L Hammer. 2955 IVY RD, NORTHRIDGE STE 210 22903 #051-01-1982 L1985 **P OS** *020 †75

CLAYTOR, Tedra Michelle. 1111 MILLMONT ST, # 115 22903 #055-02-2001 L2001 **ID** *100

CLEAVELAND, Erin Catherin. ■ 22902 #048-15-2006 L2006 **EM** *012

CLEMONS, Bruce Daniel. 310 OLD IVY WAY 22903 #018-03-1997 L1998 **IM** *020 †20

CLINES, Gregory Adam. ■ 22903 #048-12-1999 L2002 **END** *100 †20

COHEN, Bruce Jeffrey. 500 RAY C HUNT DR 22903 #023-07-1989 L1993 **P PFP** *020 †75

COHEN, Michael Arthur. 1215 LEE ST, DEPARTMENT OF RADIOLOGY 22908 #048-02-1974 L2003 **DR** *020 †80

COHN, Steven Mark. 500 RAY C HUNT DR 22903 #028-02-1985 L1998 **GE IM** *020 †20

COLE, Charles Jamesedward. 500 RAY C HUNT DR 22903 #023-01-1992 L1995 **FM EM** *020 †18

COLE, Jonathan Brandon. ■ 22902 #001-02-2003 L2007 **NEP** *012

COLEMAN, Sarah Slater. ■ 22903 #051-01-2003 L2003 **U** *100

COLLINS, Stephen Randolph. PO BOX 800136, UNIVERSITY OF VIRGINIA HEA 22908 #051-01-2005 L2007 **GS** *012

COLLINS, Tina. 459 LOCUST AVE 22902 #041-02-1995 L1997 **IM** *020 †20

COLLINS, Tyler Christian. ■ 22903 #005-06-2007 **ORS** *012

COMINELLI, Fabio. 500 RAY C HUNT DR 22903 #561-06-1983 L1992 **IM GE** *030

COMMINS, Scott Palmer. ■ 22903 #045-01-2004 **AI** *012 †20

CONDRON, Steven Lloyd. ■ 22902 #035-09-2001 L2005 **MPD** *100 †20

CONSOLVO, David Alan. RR 1 BOX 135A 22903 #051-01-1984 **NTR** *062

CONSTABLE, William Chas. JEFFERSON PK AVE, BOX 8003836 UVA HEALHT SYS 22908 #803-03-1955 L1969 **RO** *071 †80

CONWAY, Brian. WEST COMPLEX RM 2815, UNIV OF VA EYE CENTER 22908 #010-02-1968 L1978 **OPH** *040 †35

CONWAY, John Wm, III. ■ 22903 #264-01-1960 L1961 **P GP** *075

COOK, Christopher Donovan. PO BOX 800170, UNIV OF VA HEALTH SYSTEM 22908 #051-01-2001 L2001 **RNR** *020 †80

COOK, Laura Dziedzic. 1 JEFFERSON PARK AVE, OLD MEDICAL SCHOOL BLD RM 22908 #051-01-1999 L1999 **OPH** *020 †35 ‡

COOL, Amy Elizabeth. ■ 22902 #051-04-2005 L2005 **PD** *012

COOPER, Charles Morgan. 311 10TH ST NE 22902 #051-01-1985 L1988 **AN** *020 †05

COOPER, Philip Hart. 2955 IVY RD 22903 #05-14-1968 L1978 **DMP PTH** *020 †50

COPLAND, Andrew Pate. ■ 22903 #051-01-2008 *012

CORBETT, Eugene Chas, Jr. UVA BOX 800744, DEPT OF MEDICINE 22908 #016-02-1970 L1971 **IM GP** *020 †20

CORNELL, Eugenia. 918 9 1/2 ST NE 22902 #024-16-1980 L2003 **P** *020 †75

COSTABILE, Raymond A. HEALTH SYSTEMS, UNIVERSITY OF VIRGINIA 22908 #010-02-1984 L1991 **U GS** *020 †95

COURTNEY, Andrea Ursulla. 500 RAY C HUNT DR 22903 #051-01-1997 L1997 **FM** *020 †18

COUSAR, John Bradley. 500 RAY C HUNT DR 22903 #051-01-1973 L1976 **PTH CLP** *020 †50

CRABTREE, Shana Alexander. ■ 22903 #020-02-2007 L2007 **PD** *012

CRADDOCK, George B, Jr. 500 RAY C HUNT DR 22903 #051-01-1968 L1968 **CD** *020 †20

CRADDOCK, William E. 2955 IVY RD 22903 #352-07-1944 L1951 **DR** *071

CRAIN, Noreen Marie. PO BOX 800386, OF PEDS CHILDREN'S MED CTR 22908 #023-01-1995 L2001 **CCP** *020 †55

CRAMPTON, Richard S. 158 MEDICAL CTR 22908 #051-01-1956 L1956 **CD** *020 †20

CRANE, Andrew Paul. ■ 22908 #035-15-2006 L2006 **DR** *012

CROOK, Margaret Kawecki. ■ 22903 #051-01-2003 L2006 **END** *012 †20

CROPLEY, Thomas Geo. PO BOX 800718, DEPT OF DERMATOLOGY 22908 #051-01-1984 L2007 **D** *020 †15

CROSBY, Ivan Keith. 1215 LEE ST 22908 #143-05-1963 L1972 **TS** *020 †85,90

CROWE, Sheila Eileen. UNIV OF VIRGINIA, 2091MSB, DIV OF GASTROENTEROLOGY 22908 #065-10-1982 L2001 **GE** *020 †20

CROWLEY, Richard Webster. PO BOX 800136, UNIVERSITY OF VIRGINIA 22908 #010-01-2005 L2005 **NS** *012

CUI, Quanjun. ■ 22903 #243-38-1984 L1999 **OAR** *100

CUMMINGS, Mark Williams. ■ 22903 #036-08-2005 L2005 **PD** *012

CUMMINGS, Peter Mark Edwa. PO BOX 800136 22908 #539-06-2004 L2004 **NP** *100

CURTAIN, William Anthony. ■ 22903 #038-41-1943 L1995 **OAR** *100

CUSTALOW, Catherine B. P P BOX 800699, UVA HEALTH SYSTEM 22908 #051-04-1994 L1999 **EM** *020 †16

DABROWSKI, Susan Marie. ■ 22903 #035-06-2005 L2005 **PD** *012

DACUS, Angelo Rashard. ■ 22902 #051-01-2001 L2007 **HS** *100

DAHLE, Nathan Andrew. ■ 22902 #049-01-2006 L2006 **AN** *012

DAHMAN, Mohamed Ibrahim Y. JEFFERSON PK BOX 291 22908 #915-04-2001 L2005 **GS** *012

DAKE, Michael David. LEE ST, DEPT. OF RADIOLOGY; ROOM 1 22908 #048-04-1978 L2005 **DR PUD** *020 †20,80

D'ALESSANDRO, Frank Thos. 459 LOCUST AVE 22902 #020-02-1971 L1972 **AN PME** *020 †05

D'ALESSANDRO, Gloria J G. ■ 22903 #020-02-1971 L1972 **PD** *071

DALKIN, Alan Craig. 500 RAY C HUNT DR 22903 #025-01-1984 L1991 **END IM** *020 †20

DALLDORF, Carolyn Jo. 310 OLD IVY WAY, STE 201 22903 #036-01-1993 L1993 **IM** *020 †20

DAMERON, Zachariah C, III. 500 RAY C HUNT DR 22903 #051-01-1989 L1991 **P IM** *020 †20,75

DAMMANN, John F, Jr. 2955 IVY RD 22903 #038-41-1943 L1962 **CD OS** *071

DANDRIDGE, Wm Robt, Jr. 1149 ROSE HILL DR STE B 22903 #051-01-1971 L1971 **FM** *020 †18

DANIEL, Thomas Moore. JEFFERSON PARK AVE 22908 #051-01-1964 L1964 **GS TS** *071 †85,90

DARBY, Andrew Edward. PO BOX 800696, UVA MED CNTR LEE STREET 22908 #051-01-2002 L2002 **CD** *012 †20

DAUENHAUER, Laura Elsbeth. PO BOX 800136, UNIVERSITY OF VIRGINIA 22908 #056-06-2005 L2005 **P** *012

DAVIS, Christopher Kent. PO BOX 800136, MEDICAL STAFF & RESIDENCY 22908 #051-01-2000 L2000 **PDC** *100 †55

DAVIS, Jeffrey Dean. 1011 E JEFFERSON ST, STE 202 22902 #051-01-1991 L1994 **IM** *020 †20

DAVIS, John Staige, IV. 325 KENT RD 22903 #041-01-1957 L1961 **RHU IM** *030 †20

DAVIS, Sheila Frost. 1011 E JEFFERSON ST, CHARLOTTESVILLE, LTD 22902 #051-01-1991 L1994 **PD** *020 †55

DAVIS, Walter Sherwood. 545 RAY C HUNT DR, DEPT PHYSICAL MED & REHABI 22903 #036-05-1991 L1999 **GPM** *020 †60

DEAN, Peter Nelson. ■ 22903 #051-01-2008 *012

DEANGELIS, Gia Ann. SCIENCES CTR, UNIV OF VA HLTH 22908 #035-09-1985 L1991 **DR** *020 †80

DE ARRUDA NETO, Eurico. ■ 22908 #187-10-1982 L1994 **PTH** *100

DEE, Paul Michael. UNIV OF VA MED CTR, BOX 170 22908 #352-04-1959 L1978 **R OS** *020 †80

DE FREITAS, Edward Albert. 311 10TH ST NE, ALBERMARLE ANESTHESIA 22902 #051-04-1979 L1980 **AN** *020 †20,05

DEGRANDIS, Jessica. ■ 22903 #023-01-2008 *012

DE LANGE, Eduard Ellis. SCIENCES CTR, UNIV OF VA HEALTH 22908 #660-03-1972 L1985 **DR** *020

DEMARTINI, Nicholas Andre. ■ 22902 #032-01-2007 L2007 **IM** *012

DEMAZUMDER, Deeptankar. ■ 22903 #051-04-2006 L2007 **IM** *012

DENGEL, Lynn Elizabeth. ■ 22902 #010-02-2005 L2005 **GS** *012

DEN HARTOG, Julia Rebecca. ■ 22903 #041-01-2008 *012

DENSMORE, Jeanne M. 310 OLD IVY WAY, STE 201 22903 #051-01-1993 L1993 **IM** *020 †20

DENSMORE, John Jos. 500 RAY C HUNT DR 22903 #051-01-1995 L1995 **HO** *020 †20

DENT, John Martin. 500 RAY C HUNT DR 22903 #035-01-1986 L1992 **IM** *020 †20

DERDEYN, Amalie Shaffner. PO BOX 800718, UVA 22908 #051-01-2003 L2003 **D** *020 †15

DESOUZA, Duncan G. PO BOX 800710, DEPARTMENT OF ANESTHESIOLO 22908 #065-05-1991 L2005 **CCA** *100 †05

DETMER, Don Eugene. UNIV OF VIRGINIA, HEALTH SYSTEM BOX 800717 22908 #019-02-1965 L1987 **GS** *030

DIAMOND, Paul Thos. 500 RAY C HUNT DR 22903 #051-01-1986 L1992 **IM PM** *020 †20,60

DIAZ, Erik. 1325 W MAIN ST # A-1 22903 #051-01-2004 L2004 **AN** *012

DIAZ, Francis Livy, Jr. ■ 22902 #041-02-2003 L2004 **DR** *012

DI BENEDETTO, Margarete. 545 RAY C HUNT DR, STE 240 22903 #407-04-1951 L1989 **PM** *030 †60

DIBU, Raja Geo. ■ 22903 #605-01-1983 L1986 **N** *020

DIDUCH, David Randall. 500 RAY C HUNT DR, BOX 800159 22903 #024-01-1988 L1989 **ORS OSM** *020 †40

DI FAZIO, Cosmo Americo. JEFFERSON PARK AVE, UNIV OF VA MED CTR 22908 #036-01-1961 L1964 **AN** *020 †05

DILLINGHAM, Rebecca Anne. 500 RAY C HUNT DR 22903 #028-03-1999 L1999 **ID** *100 †20

DI MARCO, John Philip. 500 RAY C HUNT DR 22903 #038-06-1975 L1981 **CD PA** *020 †20

DIPIERRO, Charles Gian. PO BOX 800736, UVA DEPT OF PHYSIOLOGY 22908 #051-01-1994 L1994 **NS OS** *074

DISCEPOLO, Antonietta. GME BOX 800136, UNIVERSITY OF VIRGINIA HEA 22908 #561-05-1992 L2007 **NR** *012

DITTER, Susan Marie. 876 SWAN RDG 22903 #012-05-1980 L2004 **PFP** *100 †75

DIXON, Mark Shepherd. ■ 22903 #051-01-2003 L2003 **DR** *012

DOBRATZ, Eric John. ■ 22903 #051-07-2003 L2003 **OTO** *012

DONOWITZ, Gerald Richard. 500 RAY C HUNT DR 22903 #041-01-1974 L1977 **IM ID** *020 †20

DOULL, Gregory Harrison. 1011 E JEFFERSON ST, STE 202 22902 #038-06-1988 L1989 **IM** *020 †20

DOUVAS, Michael Gregory. ■ 22908 #051-01-1996 L2005 **PHO** *100 †20,55

DOVGALYUK, Jacqueline Mor. ■ 22903 #051-01-2007 L2007 **EM** *012

DOWELL, Joshua David. HLTH SYSTEM, UNIV OF VIRGINIA 22908 #017-20-2006 L2007 **DR** *012

DRAKE, David Bartleson. JEFFERSON PARK AVE, UVA BOX 800376 22908 #020-12-1983 L1988 **PS HS** *020 †85,65

DRAKE, Whitney Breckinrid. ■ 22903 #024-16-2005 L2005 **PD** *012

DROUIN, Christine. ■ 22908 #067-03-1997 L2003 **PCC** *100

DU, Xinli. PO BOX 800136, UNIVERSITY OF VIRGINIA 22908 #243-03-1998 L2007 **N** *012

DUARTE, Melissa Susan. ■ 22903 #008-02-2003 L2003 **OBG** *100

DUDLEY, Thomas Henry, Jr. 459 LOCUST AVE, MARTHA JEFFERSON HOSPITAL 22902 #045-01-1986 L1991 **PTH PCP** *020 †50

DUMONT, Aaron Sean. UVA PO BOX 800212, DEPT OF NEUROSURGERY 22908 #060-02-2000 L2000 **NS** *040

DUNCAN, Kara Lee. ■ 22908 #051-01-2003 L2003 **PTH** *100

DUNN, Michelle Beth. ■ 22903 #051-01-2004 L2007 **PD** *100 †55

DUNSMORE, Kimberly Panter. PEDIATRICS DEPARTMENT, BOX 386 22908 #012-05-1985 L1993 **PHO PD** *020 †55

DUONG, Vu Hong. ■ 22903 #051-01-2005 L2005 **IM** *012

DURBIN, Charles G, Jr. 500 RAY C HUNT DR 22903 #023-07-1973 L1978 **AN CCA** *040 †05

DURTAN, Lindsay Jane. 1224 W MAIN ST STE 201, UVA HEALTH SYSTEM 22903 #036-07-2004 L2007 **IM** *100 †20

DUSSAULT, Robert Gerard. PO BOX 800170, UNIV OF VA 22908 #067-06-1971 L1992 **R** *020

DUSTIN, Simone Marie. ■ 22903 #051-05-2008 *012

EAGLESON, Christine A. 500 RAY C HUNT DR 22903 #023-01-1996 L1996 **END** *020 †20

EASTHAM, R Jack, III. 1000 E HIGH ST STE A 22902 #051-01-1970 L1970 **OTO** *020 †45

EASTON, Brian Thomas. 101 WOODROW ST 22903 #051-01-1997 L1997 **FM** *020 †18 ‡

EDEN, Clara S. 459 LOCUST AVE, MARTHA JEFFERSON HOSPITAL 22902 #051-01-1988 L1991 **IM** *020 †20

EDGERTON, Milton T, Jr. 2955 IVY RD 22903 #023-07-1944 L1970 **PS HNS** *071 †85,65

EDREES, Burham Mohammed. UNIV OF VA MED CTR, DEPT PN 22908 #797-01-1980 L1995 *100

EISENHUTH, Kathryn Leigh. ■ 22903 #051-01-2006 L2006 **PD** *012

EISENHUTH, Scott Alan. PO BOX 800159, UNIVERSAITY OF VIRGINIA, D 22908 #051-01-2005 L2005 **ORS** *012

EISENMENGER, Michael Jose. ■ 22902 #030-05-2004 L2004 **AN** *012

EL-AHDAB, Fadi M. Fadel. PO BOX 800136, UNIVERSITY OF VIRGINIA 22908 #605-01-2000 L2004 QD *100

ELAMIN, Saadiq Farid, III. PO BOX 800136, UVA 22908 #041-15-2003 L2003 **ORS** *012

ELBIRLIK, Kemal Hamdi. 2955 IVY RD 22903 #902-01-1946 L1972 **P** *020

ELDER, Deborah Mc Fadden. 1101 E HIGH ST, STE 230 22902 #051-01-1990 L1991 **D** *020 †15

ELGJO, Geir Ivar. UNIV VA HEALTH SYSTEMS, DEPT ANESTH BOX 800710 22908 #693-01-1987 L2004 **AN** *020 †10

ELIAS, William Jeffrey. UNIV OF VA HEALTH SCIENCES 22908 #051-01-1994 L1994 **NS** *020 †25

ENFIELD, Kyle Byron. ■ 22903 #039-01-2003 L2003 **PCC** *012 †20

ENGLISH, Preska Melissa. ■ 22908 #012-22-2000 L2000 **P** *012

EPSTEIN, Robert M. UNIV OF VIRGINIA SCH OF ME, DEP OF ANESTHESIOLOGY 22908 #025-01-1951 L1972 **AN** *071 †05

ERWIN, Rebecca Jane. 1215 LEE STREET 22908 #036-08-2004 L2004 **N** *012

ESAU, Sharon Ann. 500 RAY C HUNT DR 22903 #025-07-1976 L1982 **PUD IM** *020 †20

ESSIG, Garth Fredric, Jr. ■ 22902 #038-40-2003 L2003 **OTO** *012

EVANS, Jonathan Michael. 500 RAY C HUNT DR 22903 #026-08-1989 L2001 **IM IMG** *020 †20

EVANS, William Smith. 500 RAY C HUNT DR 22903 #051-01-1974 L1975 **END IM** *050 †20

FAIRCHILD, Karen Diane. HOSPITAL DR., PEDIATRICS BOX 800386 22908 #036-07-1989 L2004 **NPM** *020 †55

FALAH, Mohammed Falah. PO BOX 800394, UNIVERSITY OF VIRGINIA 22908 #155-01-1996 L2004 **CN** *100

FALK, Leo J, Jr. ■ 22903 #035-08-1949 L1955 **IM PHP** *071

FARMER, Mark Nefflen. PO BOX 800636, UNIVERSITY OF VIRGINIA 22908 #010-01-2003 L2003 **HO** *012 †20

FARR, Barry Miller. UNIV OF VA MED CTR 22908 #028-02-1978 L1978 **ID IM** *071 †20

FASOULIOTIS, Tania. ■ 22903 #005-19-2006 **EM** *012

FECHNER, Robert Eugene. ■ 22902 #028-02-1960 L1975 **ATP** *071 †50

FEDORUK, Lynn M. PO BOX 800679, UNIV OF VIRGINIA HEALTH SY 22908 #060-01-1988 L2005 **TS** *100

FELDMAN, Philip Seymour. U OF VA MED CTR PATH 22908 #067-01-1965 L1978 **PTH** *020 †50

FENGLER, Brian Thomas. ■ 22903 #035-15-2005 L2005 **EM** *012

FERGUSON, John Dawes. 500 RAY C HUNT DR 22903 #836-02-1990 L2001 **ICE CD** *020

FERGUSON, Wayne W. 500 RAY C HUNT DR 22903 #035-01-1966 L1968 **GS** *020 †85

FERRARI, Lauren Michelle. ■ 22903 #047-06-2006 L2006 **PD** *012

FERRISS, James Stuart. ■ 22903 #021-05-2003 L2007 **OBG** *100

FIGG, Gregory Michael. STE 316, 545 RAY C HUNT DRIVE 22908 #038-40-2003 L2007 **PMM** *012

FIGG, Katie Marie. PO BOX 800136, UVA MEDICAL CENTER 22908 #038-40-2005 L2006 **AN** *012

FIGUEROA, Valentina Johan. ■ 22902 #036-05-2007 L2007 **PD** *012

FINNERTY, James Jos. 500 RAY C HUNT DR 22903 #035-09-1955 L1987 **OBG** *040 †30

FISCHER, Renee Louise. 1011 E JEFFERSON ST, STE 202 22902 #035-15-1996 L1998 **IM** *020 †20

FISHER, Joseph Douglas. 500 RAY C HUNT DR 22903 #051-01-1992 L1995 **PD** *020 †55

FITZ, Eric William. PO BOX 800715, UNIV OF VA 22908 #023-01-2001 L2002 **OPH** *100 †35

FLETCHER, Kenneth Charles, Jr. ■ 22908 #001-02-2001 L2001 **OTO** *020 †45

FLICKINGER, Charles John. PO BOX 800732 22908 #024-01-1964 **OS** *050

FLOHR, Tanya Ross. PO BOX 800136, UNIVERSITY OF VIRGINIA MED 22908 #041-15-2006 L2006 **GS** *012

FLOYD, Tom Sledge, Jr. UVA HEALTH SYSTEM, DEPT OF SURGERY RM 2803 WE 22908 #027-01-2007 L2007 **GS** *012

FORD, Autumn Leigh. ■ 22903 #047-07-2003 L2003 **AI** *012 †55

FORD, Justin Gregor. ■ 22903 #038-40-2006 L2007 **TY** *012

FORD, Raymond Foust. 1011 E JEFFERSON ST, JEFFERSON MEDICAL BUILDING 22902 #036-07-1966 L1971 **PD** *071 †55

FORT, Daniel. BOX 386, DEPARTMENT OF PEDIATRICS 22908 #045-01-1987 L1994 **PD** *020 †55

FORTENBERRY, Frazier, Jr. 1011 E JEFFERSON ST, STE 203 22902 #021-05-1985 L1990 **U** *020 †95

FOSTER, Eugene A. ■ 22903 #028-02-1951 L1961 **PTH** *071 †50

FOSTER, Wm Christopher. 500 RAY C HUNT DR 22903 #051-04-1976 L1980 **ORS** *020 †40

FOUNTAIN, Nathan Benj. 500 RAY C. HUNT DRIVE, P.O.BOX 80394 22908 #018-03-1989 L1992 **N CN** *020 †75

FOWLER, Donald Edward, III. ■ 22903 #051-01-2008 *012

FOX, Jonah Erik. PO BOX 800136, UNIVERSITY OF VIRGINIA 22908 #051-04-2004 L2005 **PM** *012

FOX, Kurt Johannes. ■ 22902 #407-16-1951 L1957 **GP** *071

FOX, Michael Gregory. PO BOX 5611 22905 #028-46-1992 L2006 **DR** *020 †80

FOX, William Edward. 916 E HIGH ST, STE 1 22902 #041-01-1994 L1994 **IM OS** *020 †20

FRACASSO, Paula Marie. COMPLEX.,P.O.BOX 800716, 1228 LEE ST,WEST 22908 #008-01-1984 L2007 **ON IM** *050 †20

FRANTZ, David Justin. ■ 22902 #051-01-2005 L2005 **IM** *012

FREEDMAN, Louis Allen. UVA, OX 800710 DPT OF ANESTHLGY 22908 #012-01-2000 L2001 **AN** *020 †05

FREILICH, Aaron Michael. ■ 22902 #051-01-2004 L2004 **ORS** *012

FRENCH, Jonathan Peter. ■ 22903 #030-05-2004 L2005 **PM** *012

FRIEBEN, Michelle. P.O.BOX 8001076, DEPARTMENT OF PSYCHIATRIC 22908 #035-45-2002 L2005 **CHP** *020 †75

FRIEL, Charles Mc Claskey. 500 RAY C HUNT DR 22903 #024-01-1993 L2001 **GS** *020 †85,10

FRIERSON, Henry F, Jr. 500 RAY C HUNT DR 22903 #045-01-1981 L1985 **ATP** *050 †50

FROH, Deborah Kay. 500 RAY C HUNT DR 22903 #016-02-1982 L1998 **PD PDP** *020 †55

FU, Kaiming Gregory. PO BOX 800212, HEALTH SYSTEM 22908 #035-46-2004 L2004 **NS** *012

FU, Shu-Man. U VA DIV RHE, BOX 412-MED 22908 #005-11-1970 L1988 **IM** *050 †20

FURMAN, Katherine Diane. ■ 22902 #016-42-2007 L2007 **PD** *012

GAL, Thomas Jos. PARK AVE, SYSTEM, BOX 80070JEFFERSON 22908 #041-02-1968 L1975 **AN** *020 †05

GALAZKA, Sim Stevens. UNIV OF VA HEALTH SYS, DEPT OF FAM MED POB 800729 22908 #025-01-1975 L1998 **FM FPG** *040 †18

GALGANO, Mary Todd. UNIV OF VIRGINIA, DEPARTMENT OF PATHOLOGY/P. 22908 #010-01-2002 L2002 **PCP** *012 †50

GAMPPER, Thomas Jos. 500 RAY C HUNT DR 22903 #019-02-1985 L1991 **PS GS** *050 †65

GANGAL, Kaanchan Subhash. ■ 22903 #041-02-2007 L2007 **N** *012

GANT, Alexa Andrea. ■ 22902 #045-01-2007 L2007 **P** *012

GARCIA, Daniel Vincent. PO BOX 800136, UNIVERSITY OF VIRGINIA 22908 #048-02-2005 L2005 **EM** *012

GARCIA, Lleowell Matthew. HEALTH SYSTEM, UNIV OF VIRGINIA 22908 #028-34-2002 L2007 **VS** *012

GARCIA, Omar Marcel. ■ 22908 #270-02-2001 L2002 *100

GAROZZO, Stephanie Anne. ■ 22903 #041-02-2006 **OBG** *012

GARRISH, Hazel G. ■ 22902 #036-01-2007 L2007 **PD** *012

GARSON, Arthur, Jr. UNIVERSITY OF VIRGINIA, 3027 MCKIM HALL 22908 #036-07-1974 L2002 **PDC PD** *020 †55

GASCO TAMARIT, Jaime. PO BOX 800136, UNIVERSITY OF VIRGINIA 22908 #847-08-2001 L2005 **NS** *012

GASKIN, Christopher M. PO BOX 800170, DEPT OF RAIOLOGY 22908 #011-03-1997 L2004 **DR** *020 †80

GASTON, Benj Mc Tyeire. UNIV VIRGINIA HLTH SCI, DEPT PEDS 22908 #051-01-1983 L1985 **PD** *020 †55

GAUGHEN, John Raymond, Jr. HEALTH SYSTEM, UNIV OF VIRGINIA 22908 #051-01-2002 L2002 **RNR** *012 †80

GAY, Spencer Bradley. BOX 170, DEPT OF RADIOLOGY 22908 #051-01-1983 L1986 **DR** *020 †80

GAZEWOOD, John Day. HEALTH SYSTEM LEE STREET, FAMILY MEDICINE UVA 22908 #047-05-1987 L1997 **FPG** *020 †18

GAZONI, Farnaz Milani. PO BOX 800710 22908 #051-01-2004 L2004 **AN** *012

GAZONI, Leo Mabuchi. ■ 22903 #051-01-2003 L2003 **GS** *012

GEILKER, Joyce Bechter. 2955 IVY RD, STE 205 22904 #051-01-1990 L1993 **IM** *020 †20

GELDMACHER, David Stephen. JEFFERSON PARK AVE 22908 #035-15-1986 L2002 **N** *020 †75

GENDRON, Valerie Ellen. ■ 22903 #051-01-2008 *012

GERAGHTY, Scott Ryan. ■ 22903 #007-02-2005 L2006 **DR** *012

GESSNER, Maxwell William. ■ 22902 #037-01-2000 L2001 **PMM** *012 †05 ‡

GHAEMMAGHAMI, Chris A. 500 RAY C HUNT DR 22903 #011-02-1993 L1998 **EM** *020 †20,16

GHAZI, Nicola George. ■ 22903 #605-01-1996 L2001 **OPH** *100

GIBSON, Robert Stephen. 500 RAY C HUNT DR 22903 #051-01-1975 L1979 **IM TS** *020 †20

GILDERSLEEVE, Stacey M. BOX 800870, UNIVERSITY OF VIRGINIA HEA 22908 #047-05-1992 L1992 **END IM** *020 †20

GILL, Laura Eleanor Andre. HEALTH SCIENC, UNIV OF VIRGINIA 22908 #162-01-1998 L2007 **ORS** *012

GILLENWATER, Heidi Joanne. RM 6251, 6TH FLOOR-MULTISTORY BLDG 22908 #054-04-1993 L2000 **HO** *020 †20

GILLENWATER, Jay Merritt. 2955 IVY RD, STE 303 22903 #054-04-1993 L2000 **PD** *020 †55

GILLENWATER, Jay Young. JEFFERSON PARK AVE 22908 #047-06-1957 L1965 **U** *071 †95

GILLIS, Jennifer Elizabet. UVA HEALTH SYSTEM, DEPT OF SURGERY RM 2803 WE 22908 #050-02-2007 L2007 **GS** *012

GIMPLE, Lawrence Wayne. 500 RAY C HUNT DR 22903 #024-01-1983 L1989 **IM CD** *020 †20

GLEASON, Charles Henry. ■ 22903 #051-01-1957 L1957 **PD** *071 †55

GLENNON, Tara Elizabeth. ■ 22903 #051-01-2006 L2006 **FP** *012

GOHIL, Vishal Bhagwandas. ■ 22903 #495-23-2003 L2006 **FP** *012

GOINS, Kathryn Mc Glynn. ■ 22903 #051-01-2006 L2006 **AN** *012

GOINS, Matthew Dean. ■ 22903 #051-01-2005 L2005 **AN** *012

GOLDBECK, Amy Lynn. ■ 22903 #041-13-2007 L2007 **IM** *012

GOLDBERG, Mark. 500 RAY C HUNT DR 22903 #024-05-1981 L1997 **FM** *020 †18

GOLDFARB, Adam Nathan. 500 RAY C HUNT DR 22903 #024-07-1986 L1998 **PTH** *020 †50

GOLDSTEIN, Gerald. 2955 IVY RD 22903 #041-01-1952 L1962 **ON IM** *071

GOLISH, Stanley Raymond. PO BOX 800159, UNIVERSITY OF VIRGINIA 22908 #005-14-2004 L2004 **ORS** *012

GOMEZ, Carlos Felipe. UNIV OF VA, BOX 177 22908 #051-01-1991 L1994 **IM** *020 †20

GOMEZ, Diego Alonso. 1139 E HIGH ST, GASTROENTEROLOGY ASSOC 22902 #051-07-1988 L1989 **IM** *020 †20

GOMEZ, Roberto Ariel. MR4 2001 UNIVERSITY OF VA, DEPARTMENT OF PEDIATRICS 22908 #132-01-1975 L1984 **NEP PD** *050 †55

GONIAS, Steven Larry. 500 RAY C HUNT DR 22903 #036-07-1984 L1987 **PTH** *020 †50

GOODKIN, Howard Parker. 500 RAY C HUNT DR 22903 #028-02-1995 L2002 **CHN** *020 †75

GOODMAN, Andrew Louden. ■ 22903 #051-01-2008 *012

GOODMAN, Matthew Joel. 500 RAY C HUNT DR 22903 #048-12-1988 L1991 **IM** *020 †20

GORDIAN, Amparo L. HLTH SYSTEM, UNIV OF VIRGINIA 22908 #041-15-2004 L2007 **RHU** *012 †20

GORDON, Grider Glen. 545 RAY C HUNT DR 22903 #048-78-2001, ▲ L2007 **DR** *100 †80

GORSCH, Stefan Michael. 459 LOCUST AVE, CTR FOR CNCR CRE 22902 #033-06-1988 L1994 **HO IM** *020 †20

GOSAIN, Sonia. ■ 22902 #051-01-2007 L2007 **IM** *012

GOSS, Larry Zane. ■ 22902 #051-01-1969 L1969 **IM** *062 †20

GRAHAM, Kelly Calder. ■ 22902 #051-07-2007 L2007 **N** *012

GRANT, John Leland. UVA P.O. BOX 800212, DEPARTMENT OF NEUROSURGERY 22908 #038-40-1975 L1985 **NS** *020 †25

GRANT, William Thos. 908 E JEFFERSON ST STE 101 22902 #028-02-1981 L1984 **ORS OSM** *020 †40

GRAW, Katherine Suzanne. ■ 22902 #010-02-2006 L2006 **GS** *012

GRAY, Alrich Livingston. ■ 22908 #010-03-2003 L2007 **CD** *012 †20

GRAY, Lloyd Sherwood, Jr. 500 RAY C HUNT DR 22903 #008-02-1978 L1985 **BBK** *050

GREEN, Jaime Susan. ■ 22902 #033-05-2005 L2005 **IM** *012

GREER, Kenneth Edward. 500 RAY C HUNT DR 22903 #051-01-1967 L1967 **D** *020 †15

GRENFELL, Raymond Frederi, III. PO BOX 800136, UNIVERSITY OF VIRGINIA 22908 #027-01-2005 L2005 **IM** *012

GREYSON, Charles Bruce. SCI CTR, UNIV OF VIRGINIA HLTH 22908 #035-15-1973 L1974 **P** *050 †75

GRIFFIN, Mary Pamela. 500 RAY C HUNT DR 22903 #027-01-1978 L1990 **NPM PD** *062 †55

GRIGG, Roger Gordon. ■ 22903 #143-05-1989 L1998 **OTO** *100

GROSCHEL, Dieter Hans Max. UNIV OF VA HLTH SCI CTR, DEPT PATH BOX 214 22908 #407-22-1957 L1959 **MM ID** *071

GROSH, William Wangerin. UVA-BOX 800716 CANCER CTR 22908 #035-01-1974 L1988 **ON IM** *020 †20

GROSS, Charles Wayne. 500 RAY C HUNT DR 22903 #051-01-1961 L1989 **OTO PDO** *071 †45

GROSSMAN, Leigh Barbara. HOSPITAL DR BARRINGER WING, UNIV OF VA HLTH SYS RM4423 22908 #041-07-1975 L1979 **PD ID** *020 †55

GROVES, Danja Strumper. PO BOX 800710 22908 #409-24-1999 *100

GRUNSFELD, Alexander A. ■ 22902 #033-06-2002 L2002 **IM** *100 †75

GUERRANT, Richard L. UNIV OF VA MED CTR, DEPT MED 22908 #051-01-1968 L1968 **ID IM** *050 †20

GUISE, Theresa Ann. 500 RAY C HUNT DR 22903 #041-12-1985 L2002 **END IM** *050 †20

GUMUSCU, Burak. ■ 22902 #492-10-1997 L2007 **PD** *012

GUO, Chang Yue. JEFFERSON PK BOX 291 22908 #243-65-1983 L2003 **GS** *100

GUPTA, Naren. ■ 22902 #496-09-1992 L2005 **GS** *012

GUTGESELL, Howard P, Jr. UNV VA MED CTR BOX 800386 22908 #056-05-1968 L1984 **PDC** *050 †55

GUTGESELL, Margaret E K. UNIV OF VA MED CTR, BOX 501 22908 #056-05-1968 L1984 **PD** *040 †55

GUZIK, Amy Katherine. ■ 22903 #035-03-2007 L2007 **N** *012

GWALTNEY, Jack Merrit. UNIV OF VA MED CTR 22908 #051-01-1956 L1956 **IM ID** *050 †20

GWATHMEY, Frank Winston, Jr. ■ 22902 #051-07-2007 L2007 **ORS** *012

GYPSON, Ward Glenn, III. 545 RAY C HUNT DR STE 310, UNIVERSITY OF VIRGINIADEPT 22908 #035-09-1989 L2004 **PM** *020 †60

HABERMAN, Cara Jean. ■ 22902 #032-01-2007 L2007 **PD** *012

HACKWORTH, Jordan Merrill. ■ 22903 #054-04-2006 L2007 **AN** *012

HAGSPIEL, Klaus Dieter. ■ 22903 #409-16-1988 L2007 **VIR** *020 †80

HALEY, Elliott Clarke, Jr. NEUROLOGY-800394 22908 #021-01-1974 L1978 **N IM** *020 †20,75

HALL, Colin Robt. UNIV OF VA MED CTR, # ANES 22908 #917-30-1971 **AN** *020

HALL, Courtney Nelson. ■ 22902 #001-06-2004 L2004 **IM** *012

HALL, Keri Kathleen. DAVIS 2315, HOSPITAL WEST, UNIVERSITY OF VIRGINIA HEA 22908 #055-02-1998 L1998 **ID IM** *012

HALL, Lauren Elizabeth. ■ 22902 #045-01-2006 L2007 **AN** *012

HALL, Snowden Cowman. PO BOX 4242 22905 #036-07-1965 L1972 **GE IM** *020 †20

HALPERN, Miriam Elyse. 501 FAULCONER DR, STE 2D 22903 #035-45-1980 L2006 **CHP** *012 †55

HALSEY, Jacqueline Kaye. 1139 E HIGH ST, STE 101 22902 #051-01-1978 L1980 **GYN** *020 †30

HAM, Peter Slagle. OF FAMILY MEDICINE, UNIVERSITY OF VIRGINIA DEP 22908 #051-01-2000 L2000 **FM** *020 †18

HAMILL, Robin Jane. 545 RAY C HUNT DR, STE 316 22908 #010-01-1980 L1988 **AN PME** *020 †05

HAMILTON, David Kojo. ■ 22908 #051-01-2003 L2003 **NS** *012
HAMILTON, David Vincent. ■ 22903 #005-06-2005 L2005 **P** *012
HAMMOND, William R. 415 8TH ST NE 22902 #051-04-1977 L1980 **PUD A** *020 †20
HANKS, John Bright. UNV VA DEPT SURG, BOXZ 800709 22908 #035-45-1973 L1982 **TS GS** *020 †85
HANNA, George Russell. UVA MEDICAL CENTER, NEUROLOGY-UVA 22903 #067-01-1956 L1958 **N** *071 †75
HARNOF, Sagi. PO BOX 800136, UNIV OF VIRGINIA MEDICAL S 22908 #550-02-1999 L2006 *100
HARPER, Michael Roy. 500 RAY C HUNT DR 22903 #051-04-1974 L1975 **FM** *020 †18 ‡
HARRIS, Jeffrey Keith. ■ 22908 #055-02-2007 L2007 **PD** *012
HARRIS, Mark Morrow. 311 10TH ST NE 22908 #041-13-1978 L1985 **AN EM** *040 †05
HARRISON, Madaline Burr. SCIENCES CTR, UNIV OF VA HLTH 22908 #011-02-1983 L1988 **N** *020 †75
HARTHUN, Nancy Lynn. 500 RAY C HUNT DR 22903 #008-01-1992 L1992 **VS VIR** *020 †85
HARVEY, Jennifer. 500 RAY C HUNT DR 22903 #003-01-1988 L1993 **DR** *020 †80
HASAN, Emad M. ■ 22903 #048-15-2000 L2007 *100
HASHISAKI, George Thos. 500 RAY C HUNT DR 22903 #054-04-1981 L1994 **OTO** *020 †45
HASHISAKI, Teresa Helen. 1011 E JEFFERSON ST, CHARLOTTESVILLE, LTD 22902 #051-01-1990 L1994 **PD** *020 †55
HASTINGS, Ramin Shayegan. ■ 22903 #051-01-2008 *012
HAUCK, Fern Robin. 500 RAY C HUNT DR 22903 #028-34-1978 L2000 **FM GPM** *050 †18
HAWBOLDT, Geoffrey S. 545 RAY C HUNT DR, STE 316 22903 #064-01-1994 L1999 **APM** *020
HAWK, Angela Fisher. ■ 22903 #012-01-2006 L2006 **OBG** *012
HAWK, Harris Emory. ■ 22903 #012-01-2006 L2006 **DR** *012
HAWKES, David Lee. 2411 IVY RD 22903 #051-01-1982 L1985 **PD** *020 †55
HAYDEN, Frederick Glen. HOSPITAL DR COBB HALL, RM 1033 22908 #005-11-1973 L1978 **ID CLP** *050 †20
HAYDEN, Gregory Francis. PO BOX 800386, DEPT. OF PEDIATRICS 22908 #036-01-1972 L1979 **PD** *020 †55
HAYDEN, Meredith Ellen. 1224 W MAIN ST, STE 701 22903 #045-01-2001 L2001 **PN** *100 †55
HAYNES, Robert Clark, Jr. UNIV OF VA MED CTR 22908 #028-02-1948 **OS** *100
HEALD, Evan Barnard. 500 RAY C HUNT DR 22903 #041-14-1991 L1994 **IM** *020 †20
HEALEY, Deborah Elizabeth. 100 E SOUTH ST STE 2 22902 #917-09-1978 L1985 **P** *020 †55,75
HEAVEY, Jonathan David. PO BOX 800699 22908 #047-05-2003 L2003 **EM** *100 †16
HEHIR, Michael Kevin. ■ 22902 #035-45-2005 L2005 **N** *012
HEILBRONNER, David Mark. 914 E JEFFERSON ST STE 102 22902 #025-07-1977 L1983 **ORS OP** *020 †40
HEIM, Steven Wayne. PO BOX 800729, UVA HLTH SYS DEPT FAM MED 22908 #051-01-1994 L1999 **FM** *020 †18
HEINAN, Kristen Colleen. ■ 22902 #051-07-2007 L2007 **PD** *012
HELLEMS, Martha Ann. 500 RAY C HUNT DR 22903 #051-01-1998 L1998 **PD** *020 †55
HELLER, Jay Ronald. 1020 E JEFFERSON ST 22902 #007-02-1972 L1973 **CHP P** *020 †75
HELM, Gregory Anthony. 500 RAY C HUNT DR 22903 #051-01-1988 L1995 **GS** *020 †25
HELM, Kristin Dasher. DIV OF ENDOCRLGY, PO BOX 401408 22908 #023-07-2002 L2005 **END** *012 †20
HELMS, Adam Steven. ■ 22903 #051-01-2005 L2005 **IM** *012
HELMS, Lauren B. ■ 22903 #051-01-2005 L2005 **PD** *012
HENDLEY, J Owen. U VA SCH MED PED BOX 386 22908 #041-01-1963 L1970 **ID PD** *050 †55
HENDRIX, John David, Jr. 902 E JEFFERSON ST, STE 201 22902 #036-01-1988 L1990 **DS D** *020 †15
HENDRIX, Sylvia Sutton. 459 LOCUST AVE, M JEFFERSON HOSP CNCER CTR 22902 #036-01-1988 L1992 **RO** *020 †80
HENRY, Gary W. 1 HOSPITAL DRIVE, 800710, UNIV OF VA HLTH SYSTEMS 22908 #917-02-1983 *100
HENRY, Thomas Dix. 1215 LEE STREET- NEW HOSPI, U.VA. DEPT. OF RADIOLOGY 22908 #047-06-2001 L2006 **DR** *100 †80
HEPGUR, Mehmet Fatih Gokh. ■ 22908 #902-10-1999 L2007 **OTR** *100
HERNDON, Steve Everett. PO BOX 800546, HEALTH SYSTEM 22908 #654-01-2004 L2007 **PCC** *012 †04
HERRINGTON, Pamila Ann. RIC MEDICINE BOX 623 HSC, UNIVERSITY OF VA DEPT PSYC 22908 #051-01-1993 L1993 **P** *020 †75
HESS, Charles Edwin. 500 RAY C HUNT DR 22903 #051-01-1959 L1959 **HEM ON** *020 †20
HEUSER, Cara Christina. ■ 22903 #051-01-2004 L2004 **OBG** *012
HEWLETT, Erik Lane. JEFFERSON PARK AVE, UNIV VA BOX 419 DEPT MED 22908 #023-07-1972 L1980 **END GE** *050 †20
HEYMANN, Peter Walter. 500 RAY C HUNT DR 22903 #038-06-1973 L1978 **AI PD** *050 †55,03
HICKS, Raymond H. ■ 22902 #011-02-2007 L2007 **AN** *012
HIGGINBOTHAM, Jack Wayne, Jr. 459 LOCUST AVE 22902 #051-04-1999 L1999 **DR** *020 †80
HIGGINS, Kristen Balkcum. ■ 22908 #036-05-2004 L2005 **D** *012
HILL, Duncan Lambert. 459 LOCUST AVE, MARTHA JEFFERSON HOSPITAL 22902 #036-01-2002 L2002 **IM** *020 †20
HILL, Kasey Thomas. ■ 22903 #021-05-2007 L2007 **PM** *012
HILLIARD, Bridget Ann. ■ 22902 #023-01-2003 L2003 **FM** *020 †18
HILLMAN, Bruce Jay. 500 RAY C HUNT DR 22903 #035-45-1973 L1991 **R** *030 †80
HIRSCH, Jack Saml. 1101 E JEFFERSON ST 22902 #051-04-1966 L1966 **OBG** *071 †30
HO, Christopher Pattrin. ■ 22902 #051-01-2004 L2004 **DR** *012
HO, Henry Chinchih. ■ 22902 #033-06-2006 L2006 **IM** *012
HOBBS, Brian Daniel. ■ 22903 #051-01-2008 *012
HOBBS, William Ralph. BOX 623, U OF VIRGINIA MEDICAL CENT 22908 #055-01-1970 L1979 **P N** *020 †75
HOBGOOD, Cassandra Daniel. PO BOX 801012, UNIVERSITY OF VIRGINIA 22908 #539-06-2004 L2005 **P** *012
HOGAN, Macalus Vinson. PO BOX 800159 22908 #010-03-2006 L2006 **ORS** *012
HOKE, George Martin. 1222 JEFFERSON PARK 2ND FL, UNIV OF VA BOX 800744 22908 #023-01-1995 L1995 **HOS** *020 †20
HOLLAND, Paul Reginald. PO BOX 800715, DEPT OPHTHALMOLOGY 22908 #014-01-2005 L2006 **OPH** *012
HOLROYD, Suzanne. 500 RAY C HUNT DR 22903 #051-01-1986 L1992 **P PYG** *050 †75
HOLSTEGE, Christopher P. JEFFERSON PARK AVE 22908 #025-07-1993 L1998 **EM ETX** *020 †16
HORNER, Julie Lynn. PO BOX 800710, UNIV OF VIRGINIA MED CTR 22908 #041-12-2004 L2004 **AN** *012
HOSTLER, Sharon Lee. 2270 IVY RD, KLUGE CHILDRENS REHAB CTR 22903 #050-02-1965 L1970 **PD OS** *040 †55
HOULIHAN, Christine Murra. 2270 IVY RD 22903 #010-02-1995 L1995 **PD** *020 †55

HOUPT, Eric Robert. MR4 BUILDING, RM 2115, UV-DIV OF INFECTIOUS DISEA 22908 #012-05-1996 L1999 **ID** *020 †20
HOWARDS, Stuart S. 500 RAY C HUNT DR 22903 #035-01-1963 L1971 **U OS** *071 †95
HOYER, Andrew William. 500 RAY C HUNT DR, UNIVERSITY OF VIRGINIA 22903 #024-16-2000 L2006 **PD** *100 †55
HSU BLATMAN, Karen Shon. ■ 22903 #018-03-2005 L2005 **IM** *012
HU, Yuhning Linda. ■ 22903 #051-01-2008 *012
HUANG, Chun-Hsiung. UNIV OF VA MED CTR, DEPT ORS 22908 #244-01-1968 **ORS** *100
HUANG, Michael Yu-Ting. ■ 22903 #011-04-2006 L2006 **DR** *012
HUBER, Albert Leopold. 910 E HIGH ST 22902 #035-09-1957 L1969 **A PUD** *020 †03,18
HUDAK, Christopher Eric. ■ 22902 #048-16-2008 *012
HUFF, John Stephen. 500 RAY C HUNT DR 22903 #017-20-1979 L1987 **EM N** *040 †75,16
HUFFMAN, Matthew Wampler. ■ 22902 #051-01-2006 L2006 **IM** *012
HUGHES, Kevin Richard. ■ 22903 #049-01-2006 L2006 **AN** *012
HUGHES, Molly Ann. 500 RAY C HUNT DR 22903 #047-05-1996 L1999 **ID** *020 †20
HUNT, John Fuller. 2955 IVY RD 22903 #010-01-1992 L1998 **AI** *100 †55,03
HUNT, William Bryce, III. 459 LOCUST AVE, EMERGENCY DEPT 22902 #051-01-1986 L1989 **EM** *020 †16
HURT, Charles Wm. PO BOX 8147 22906 #051-01-1954 L1954 **GP GS** *020
HUTCHESON, Grace Autumn. 459 LOCUST AVE 22902 #023-07-1993 L1996 **IM** *020 †20
HWANG, Kathleen. ■ 22903 #035-09-2004 L2004 **GS** *100
IBRAHIM, Kaissar S. ■ 22905 #396-04-1957 L1965 **GS CD** *071
ILLIG, Lisa Christine. 459 LOCUST AVE 22902 #056-05-1997 L2002 **IM PLM** *020 †20
INDIHAR, Maria Veronica. 459 LOCUST AVE 22902 #132-01-2002 L2002 **IM** *100 †20
INNES, Donald John. 500 RAY C HUNT DR 22903 #008-02-1977 L1981 **CLP PTH** *020
INTAGLIATA, Nicolas Micha. ■ 22902 #036-05-2007 L2007 **IM** *012
IRVINE, Eleanor S Gould. ■ 22903 #021-01-1951 L1956 **PTH** *071 †50
ISAAC, Mitchell Gareth. ■ 22902 #019-02-2003 L2007 **CN** *012
ISBELL, Benjamin Tobias. PO BOX 800136, UNIVERSITY OF VIRGINIA 22908 #036-01-2005 L2005 **OBG** *012
ISZKULA, Erik Richard. ■ 22902 #041-02-2007 L2007 **EM** *012
JACKSON, Marilyn J Black. JEFFERSON PARK AVE 22908 #010-03-1968 L1971 **AN** *020 †05
JAEGER, James Michael. DEPT. OF ANESTHESIOLOGY, HEALTH SCIENCES CENTER 22908 #050-02-1987 L1991 **CCA** *012 †05
JAFFE, Katherine Greer. ■ 22903 #051-01-2003 L2003 **IM** *100 †20
JAHRSDOERFER, Robt Albert. 500 RAY C HUNT DR 22903 #051-01-1961 L1961 **OTO** *020 †45
JAMESON, Mark James. PO BOX 800713, UVA HEALTH SYSTEM 22908 #045-01-2001 L2001 **OTO** *100 †45
JANE, John Anthony. 500 RAY C HUNT DR 22903 #016-02-1956 L1969 **NS** *020 †25
JANE, John Anthony, Jr. ■ 22903 #051-01-1996 L1997 **NS** *020
JARJOUR, Wael N. 500 RAY C HUNT DR 22903 #875-01-1982 L1998 **RHU** *020 †20
JEFFUS, Susanne Kurth. ■ 22903 #004-01-2007 L2007 **PTH** *012
JEHLE, Alexander Brockman. ■ 22902 #019-02-2000 L2007 **CD** *020 †20
JENKINS, Alan Deloss. DEPT OF UROLOGY BOX 422, UNIV OF VA SCHOOL OF MEDIC 22908 #024-05-1975 L1977 **U** *020 †95
JENKINS, Jeffrey Gwin. STE #240, 545 RAY C HUNT DRIVE 22908 #010-02-1998 L1998 **PM** *020 †60
JENKINS, Megan Clare. PO BOX 800136, UNIVERSITY OF VIRGINIA 22908 #032-01-2004 L2005 **AN** *012
JENKS, John Story. 141 EDNAM DR, INSTITUTE OF QUALITY HEALT 22903 #041-09-1978 L1996 **NTR IM** *020 †18
JENNINGS, Robt Hutchings. 459 LOCUST AVE 22902 #051-01-1956 L1956 **IM A** *071 †20
JENSEN, Mary E. 500 RAY C HUNT DR 22903 #051-04-1982 L1984 **RNR** *020 †80
JEUN, Bryan Su-Hyun. ■ 22903 #051-01-2008 *012
JOHNSON, Bankole A. ■ 22902 #919-05-1982 L2005 **P** *040 †75
JOHNSON, Charles Mc Coy. 1000 E HIGH ST STE A 22902 #023-07-1972 L1984 **PDO OTO** *040 †45
JOHNSTON, Karen Chodack. PO BOX 800394, UNIV OF VA 22908 #035-45-1991 L1995 **N OS** *020 †75
JONES, David Randolph. 500 RAY C HUNT DR 22903 #055-01-1989 L1999 **TS** *020 †85,90
JONES-QUAIDOO, Sean M. PO BOX 800136, UNIVERSITY OF VIRGINIA 22908 #005-14-2005 L2005 **ORS** *012
JOSEPHTHAL, Danl Herbert. 503 FAULCONER DR, STE 9A 22903 #035-45-1960 L1965 **PYA P** *020
JOYCE, Richard Alvis. ■ 22902 #051-01-1984 L1987 **FM** *020 †18
JUST, Joseph Scott. 500 RAY C HUNT DR 22903 #051-01-1996 L1996 **EM** *020 †16
KAHALEH, Michel. 500 RAY C HUNT DR 22903 #165-01-1994 L2001 **IM** *020 †20
KAHLER, David Marc. 500 RAY C HUNT DR 22903 #021-01-1985 L1990 **ORS OSM** *040 †40
KAHN, Sidney Lowell, IV. PO BOX 800170, UNIVERSITY OF VIRGINIA 22908 #012-05-2003 L2004 **DR** *012
KAJDASZ, Stephen Thomas. ■ 22903 #032-01-2006 L2006 **AN** *012
KALANTARINIA, Kambiz. 500 RAY C HUNT DR 22903 #517-05-1990 L2000 **IM NEP** *040 †20
KALINEY, Ryan William. ■ 22903 #016-06-2005 L2006 **DR** *012
KAMITYO, Toshifumi. 1620 JEFFERSON PRK AVE #2B 22903 #572-31-1981 L1991 **RNR** *020
KANAAN, Imad Udin N I. 13TH VENABLE CT APT #8 22903 #875-01-1976 *100
KANNARKAT, George Joy. 1256 FOX CREST WAY 22902 #033-05-2003 L2003 **HO** *012 †20
KANTOR, Edward Mark. UVA HEALTH SYSTEM, BOX 22908 #041-09-1995 L1995 **P PYM** *040 †75
KAPNADAK, Siddhartha Guru. ■ 22902 #040-02-2007 L2007 **IM** *012
KASHMER, David Matthew. ■ 22902 #041-15-2001 L2001 **GS** *020 †85
KASHMER, Laurissa Lynn. ■ 22902 #041-15-2002 L2002 **PDE** *012 †55
KASSEL, Mortimer H. ■ 22902 #869-05-1942 L1984 **GP** *071
KASSELL, Neal Frederic. 500 RAY C HUNT DR 22903 #041-01-1972 L1984 **NS** *020 †25
KATTWINKEL, John. U OF VA DEPT OF PEDS 22908 #024-01-1968 L1974 **NPM PD** *040 †55
KATZ, Adam Judd. JEFFERSON PARK AVE, UVHS - DEPT OF PLASTIC SUR 22908 #025-01-1993 L2001 **PS** *020 †65
KAUFMAN, David Alan. 500 RAY C HUNT DR 22903 #041-12-1990 L1998 **NPM** *020 †55
KAUSHIK, Anjan Pavani. ■ 22903 #051-01-2008 *012
KAVANAUGH, James Gibboney. 2955 IVY RD 22903 #051-01-1962 L1962 **CHP P** *020 †75
KAWWASS, Jennifer Fay. ■ 22903 #051-01-2007 *012
KEATS, Theodore Eliot. UNIV OF VA HLTH SCI CTR, DEPT RAD BOX 170 22908 #041-01-1947 L1964 **DR PDR** *071 †80
KECK, Leslie Elizabeth. ■ 22903 #012-01-2007 L2007 **IM** *012
KEDES, Dean Hamilton. RM 7069, JORDAN HALL, BOX 800734 22908 #008-01-1988 L1999 **ID** *020 †20

KEELEY, Ellen Catherine. PO BOX 800158, UNIV OF VA HEALTH SYSTEMS 22908 #041-02-1990 L2006 **CD** *020 †20
KEELEY, Meg Graham. 500 RAY C HUNT DR 22903 #051-01-1992 L1995 **PD** *020 †55
KEENAN, Geoffrey Scott. ■ 22903 #023-12-1999 L2007 **PM** *012
KELLER, Thomas Christian. ■ 22903 #051-01-2008 *012
KELLY, Heather Conrades. PO BOX 800710, UVA HEALTH SYS 22908 #011-02-1991 L2002 **AN** *020 †05
KELLY, Maria Denise. SYS JEFFERSON PARK AVE, RAD ONC BOX 800383 UVA HEA 22908 #539-02-1983 L1989 **RO** *071 †80
KELLY, Thaddeus Elliott. 500 RAY C HUNT DR 22903 #045-01-1963 L1975 **MG PD** *020 †55,19
KENNER, Rebecca Marie. 459 LOCUST AVE, MED RECORDS BOX 130 22902 #028-03-2002 L2002 **IM** *020 †20
KENNER, Thomas J. UNIV OF VA MED CTR, BOX 224 22908 #154-07-1956 *075
KENNEY, John Gale. 914 E JEFFERSON ST STE 202 22902 #041-12-1975 L1982 **PS** *071 †85,65
KENT, Katherine Warner. 2955 IVY RD STE 304, UNIV OF VIRGINIA DEPT OBGY 22903 #051-01-1998 L2004 **OBG** *020 †30
KERN, John Allen. 500 RAY C HUNT DR 22903 #051-01-1988 L1989 **TS** *020 †85,90
KERR, Sarah Elizabeth. PO BOX 800136, UNIVERSITY OF VIRGINIA 22908 #056-06-2005 L2005 **PTH** *012
KERRIGAN, Deirdre Casey. PO BOX 801004, 545 RAY C HUNT DR 22908 #024-01-1987 L2002 **PM** *020 †60
KESSER, Bradley William. ■ 22903 #051-01-1993 L1993 **OTO** *072 †45
KETCHERSIDE, Christopher. ■ 22902 #028-03-2004 L2004 **OPH** *012
KHAN, Niaz Ahmed. 310 OLD IVY WAY, STE 104 22903 #704-02-1989 L1998 **CHP** *020
KIM, Flora Sewon. ■ 22903 #051-01-2008 *012
KIMPEL, Donald Lee. HOSPITAL DRIVE, OMS ROOM 5777 22908 #038-40-1986 L2003 **RHU IG** *020 †20
KINGSLEY, Lauren Anne. ■ 22903 #051-01-2008 *012
KIRK, Mark Alan. 1222 JPA, BLUE RIDGE POISON CRT 22908 #020-12-1985 L2002 **EM ETX** *040 †16
KIRK, Susan Ellen. 500 RAY C HUNT DR 22903 #033-06-1987 L1994 **END** *040 †20
KIZER, Lillian Davies. ■ 22902 #012-22-2004 L2004 **IM** *012 †20
KLEINER, Daniel Eduard. JEFFERSON PK BOX 291 22908 #143-04-2001 L2004 **GS** *012
KLYM, Sondra Emily. UNIVERSITY OF VIRGINIA, OBSTETRICS AND GYNECOLOGY 22908 #040-02-2007 L2007 **OBG** *012
KNAUS, William A. UNIVERSITY VA SCH MEDICAL, BOX 600 22908 #055-01-1972 L1973 **CCM** *050 †20
KNIGHT, James Gregory. 1100 E HIGH ST 22902 #012-01-1975 L1977 **IM** *020 †20
KNIGHT, William Schley. ■ 22902 #011-03-2007 L2007 **IM** *012
KNOBLE, Jeanna Lynn. ■ 22902 #038-40-2002 L2006 **HO** *012 †20
KNOX, Laura Katherine. 500 RAY C HUNT DR 22903 #039-01-1988 L1994 **PS** *020 †65
KNUDSEN, Karen Lynn. ■ 22903 #008-02-2004 L2007 **END** *012 †20
KOCH, Matthew Allen. ■ 22902 #051-01-1979 *100
KOENIG, Steven Michael. PO BOX 800546, UNIV OF VA HLTH SYS 22908 #041-01-1984 L1994 **PUD CCM** *020 †20
KOEZE, Ursula Gailliot. 459 LOCUST AVE, MARTHA JEFFERSON HOSPITAL 22902 #051-01-1995 L1995 **EM** *020 †16
KOHLI, Anita. ■ 22902 #051-01-2006 L2006 **IM** *012
KOK, Mitchell Patrick. HEALTH SYSTEM, UNIV OF VIRGINIA 22908 #012-01-2000 L2007 **RNR** *012 †80
KOLB, Noah Allan. ■ 22903 #024-16-2008 *012
KOONTZ, Megan Kathleen. ■ 22903 #016-42-2007 L2007 **EM** *012
KOPLIK, Andrew Dwight. PO BOX 800136, UNIVERSITY OF VIRGINIA MED 22908 #033-06-2005 L2006 **AN** *012
KORBON, Gregg Allen. 459 LOCUST AVE, MARTHA JEFFERSON HOSPITAL 22902 #036-07-1976 L1981 **AN GP** *020 †05
KOZLOW, Wende Michele. ■ 22903 #056-06-2000 L2001 **END** *100 †20
KREPS, Carly Ellen. PO BOX 800136, UNIVERSITY OF VIRGINIA MED 22908 #051-01-2006 L2006 **PM** *012
KRIPALANI, Sanjay Bhagwan. HEALTH SYSTEM, UNIV OF VIRGINIA 22908 #036-05-2007 L2007 **EM** *012
KRISHNAN, Arthi Radha. ■ 22902 #012-01-2005 L2005 **PD** *012
KRON, Irving Louis. 500 RAY C HUNT DR 22903 #056-06-1975 L1981 **GS TS** *020 †85,90
KUBERSKY, Lee Ivan. ■ 22902 #033-06-2004 L2004 **N** *012
KUBIAK, Kendra L. PO BOX 800716, DEPT. OF INTERNAL MEDICINE 22908 #048-12-2000 L2003 **HO** *100 †20
KUHLMANN, Thomas Paul. 500 RAY C HUNT DR 22903 #037-01-1979 L1982 **IM EM** *020 †20,16
KUMARESAN, Hari Ganapathy. ■ 22903 #496-28-2000 L2007 **CHP** *020 †75
KWON, Michael S. PO BOX 800136, UNIVERSITY OF VIRGINIA 22908 #041-15-2002 L2004 **ORS** *012
LACY, Hilton Roy. 300 PRESTON AVE STE 308 22902 #004-01-1983 L1992 **CHP P** *020 †18,75
LAFRATTA, Kimrie Donovan. UNIV VA HLTH SYS, DEPT PEDS 22908 #038-06-1993 L1999 **PD** *100 †55
LAI, Victor Tinfung. ■ 22903 #035-48-2006 L2006 **OTO** *012
LAMBERT, Drew Leon. ■ 22902 #023-07-1999 L1999 **DR** *020 †80 ‡
LAMBERT, Vaia Abatzis. ■ 22902 #023-07-1999 L1999 **AN** *071 †05 ‡
LANDES, Daniel Abraham. 916 E HIGH ST STE 2, CHARLOTTESVILLE ENT ASSOCI 22902 #036-01-1990 L1990 **OTO** *020 †45
LANE, Susan Marie. PO BOX 800136, UVA 22908 #038-44-2000 L2000 **CD** *012 †20
LANFORD, Jeremiah W. PO BOX 800136, UNIVERSITY OF VIRGINIA 22908 #048-14-2002 L2003 **CN** *020
LANFORD, Randolph Ewing. 459 LOCUST AVE 22902 #051-04-1979 L1980 **GP** *020
LANGDON, Robert Godwin. JEFFERSON PARK AVE MED 22908 #016-02-1945 **OS** *050
LANGER, Jennifer Ellen. ■ 22902 #035-45-2005 L2005 **N** *012
LANHAM, John Louis. 1149 ROSE HILL DR 22903 #028-03-1980 L1982 **FM** *020 †18
LA PAR, Damian James. UVA HEALTH SYSTEM, DEPT OF SURGERY RM 2803 WE 22908 #007-02-2007 **GS** *012
LARNER, Andrew Chas. ■ 22903 #051-01-1982 L1988 **PTH** *071 †50
LARNER, James Mitchell. HEALTH SCIENCES CENTER, UNIVERSITY OF VIRGINIA 22908 #051-01-1980 L1983 **RO ON** *020 †20,80
LASHLEY, Susan Leonora. 1215 LEE ST 22908 #035-08-1997 L2004 **OBG** *020
LASSEN, Kari Elizabeth. ■ 22903 #051-01-2008 *012
LAU, Christine Lynn. ■ 22903 #032-01-1995 L2007 **TS GS** *020 †85,90
LAURENCIN, Cato Thos. 400 RAY C HUNT DR 22903 #024-01-1987 L2003 **ORS** *020 †40 ‡
LAURIE, Susan Mary. 2955 IVY RD, NORTHRIDGE UNIV OF VIRGINI 22903 #067-01-1984 L1993 **P** *020 †75,20
LAWRENCE, Erika L. ■ 22903 #030-05-2007 L2007 **AN** *012
LAWSON, Edgar Clifford. 337 15TH ST SW 22903 #051-01-1957 L1957 **OPH** *071 †35
LEAVELL, Byrd Stuart, Jr. 1139 E HIGH ST, GASTROENTEROLOGY ASSOC 22902 #051-01-1977 L1980 **GE IM** *020 †20
LEDOUX, Matthew Ronald. ■ 22902 #654-01-2003 L2007 **CCP** *012
LEE, Bonmyong Bora. ■ 22903 #051-01-2005 L2006 **DR** *012
LEE, Haidy Lauren. PO BOX 800383, UNIVERSITY OF VIRGINIA 22908 #005-15-2004 L2005 **RO** *012
LEE, James Douglas. 2496 OLD IVY RD STE 400, BLUE RIDGE 22903 #024-07-1980 L1989 **P** *020 †75
LEE, Laura. JEFFERSON PARK AVE 22908 #041-01-2000 L2006 **CCP** *020 †55
LEE, Laura Wonkyung. 545 RAY C HUNT DR, REHABILITATION 22903 #024-01-1994 L1994 **PM** *020 †60
LEE, Nora Grace. ■ 22903 #051-01-2008 *012
LEE, Stephen Daesup. ■ 22903 #051-01-2008 *012
LEE, Vanessa Daisy. 1215 LEE ST, UNIV OF VA MED CTR 22908 #041-02-2003 L2003 **IM GE** *012 †20
LEFKO, Andrew Geo, Jr. ■ 22902 #041-12-1964 L1970 **GP CHP** *020 †75
LEHMAN, Benjamin John. ■ 22903 #038-40-2005 L2005 **EM** *012
LEHMAN, Richard Emil. PO BOX 800386, DEPT OF PED. UVA HLTH SVC 22908 #422-01-2002 L2006 **CCP** *012
LEINER, John Grout. CARE CENTER RM 3416, UNIVERSITY OF VIRGINA PRIM 22908 #051-04-1991 L1999 **IM** *020 †20
LENG, Tong Khim. ■ 22908 #825-01-1992 L2001 **CD** *100
LEONE, Kenneth Vincent. HOSPITAL DRIVE, NEUROLOGY, BOX 800394 22908 #047-05-1992 L1992 **N CN** *020 †75
LEPSCH, Mark Anthony. ■ 22902 #051-01-2002 L2002 **FM** *020 †18
LESLIE, Catherine A. UNIV OF VA MED CTR, BOX 623 22908 #051-01-1982 L1987 **P IM** *020 †20,75
LEVINE, Paul Albert. DEPT. OF OTOLARYNGOLOGY—H, UVA HEALTH SYSTEMS 22908 #035-03-1973 L1984 **HNS** *020 †45
LEVITT, Helena Elizabeth. PO BOX 800136, UNIVERSITY OF VIRGINIA 22908 #041-12-2005 L2005 **IM** *012
LEWIS, Janet Elaine. 500 RAY C HUNT DR 22903 #038-43-1987 L1993 **RHU IM** *050 †20
LEWIS, Jason James. ■ 22902 #035-15-2004 L2004 **IM** *012 †20
LI, Dayuan. ■ 22908 #243-83-1987 L2007 **IM** *100 †20
LIM, David Scott. 500 RAY C HUNT DR 22903 #026-08-1996 L2002 **PDC CD** *020 †55
LIN, Anna Susan. ■ 22903 #017-20-2007 L2007 **FP** *012
LIN, Christine. ■ 22902 #036-08-2005 L2005 **IM** *012
LIN, Christine Maylyn. ■ 22903 #005-18-2007 **IM** *012
LIN, Janet Chan-Yue. ■ 22903 #051-01-2008 *012
LIN, Kant Yuankai. P.O. BOX 376, JEFFERSON PARK AVENUE 22908 #035-47-1984 L1992 **PS** *020 †65
LINDSTROM, Katherine May. ■ 22902 #018-03-2004 L2004 **PTH** *012
LIPINSKI, Michael Joseph. ■ 22902 #051-04-2006 L2006 **IM** *012
LIPPER, Maurice Harold. 500 RAY C HUNT DR 22903 #836-02-1957 L1978 **DR RNR** *020 †80
LIPPERT, Marguerite C. JEFFERSON PARK AVE UROL 22908 #041-14-1977 L1980 **U OS** *020 †95
LISLE, Turner Courtney. ■ 22903 #007-02-2004 L2004 **GS** *012
LITTLEWOOD, Keith Earl. 500 RAY C HUNT DR 22903 #035-15-1983 L1990 **AN PHP** *020 †05
LITVINAS, Lee Dennis. 459 LOCUST AVE, MARTHA JEFFERSON HOSPITAL 22902 #051-07-1990 L1993 **IM** *020 †20
LIU, Zhenqi. 450 RAY C HUNT DR 22908 #243-76-1983 L1998 **END** *020 †20
LOBO, Peter Isaac. BX 133 RENCL DIV 22908 #905-01-1966 L1975 **NEP IM** *020 †20
LOCH, Michelle Marie. JEFFERSON PK BOX 291 22908 #422-01-2005 L2005 **IM** *012
LOCKMAN, Andrew Robt. 500 RAY C HUNT DR 22903 #051-01-1991 L1994 **FM** *020 †18
LOGIN, Ivan Stewart. 500 RAY C HUNT DR 22903 #035-20-1971 L1979 **N IM** *050 †75 ‡
LONERGAN, Cheryl L. PO BOX 800718, DEPT OF DERM 22908 #051-01-2003 L2005 **D** *012
LOPES, Maria Beatriz S. JEFFERSON PARK AVE 22908 #187-04-1982 L1998 **NP ATP** *020 †50
LOPEZ, David. ■ 22902 #011-02-2007 L2007 **IM** *012
LOPIANO, Jillian Kaye. ■ 22902 #010-01-2007 L2007 **OBG** *012
LOUIS, Robert George, Jr. PO BOX 800681, 3801 W COMPLEX 22908 #654-01-2007 L2007 **GS** *012
LOVE, Sherie Lynn. ■ 22902 #023-01-2006 L2006 **PD** *012
LOVRIA, Erik Robert. ■ 22902 #035-45-2007 L2007 **GS** *012
LOWDON, Joseph Devon. 1011 E JEFFERSON ST, STE 202 22902 #051-01-1980 L1997 **IM** *020 †20
LOWE, William Wayne. 129 OVERLOOK DR 22903 #025-01-1979 L1997 **NPM** *020 †55
LOWSON, Stuart Martin. HEALTH SCIENCES CENTER, UNIV OF VIRGINIA 22908 #917-19-1982 L1995 **CCA** *020 †05
LUNARDINI, David Joseph. ■ 22903 #051-01-2008 L2008 *012
LYMAN, Sean James. ■ 22902 #036-01-2007 L2007 **GS** *012
LYNCH, Carl, III. 500 RAY C HUNT DR 22903 #035-45-1978 L1981 **AN** *050 †05
MA, Shen Ying. PO BOX 800136, UNIVERSITY OF VIRGINIA 22908 #051-01-2005 L2005 **ORS** *012
MACGLOIN, Siobhan Maire. UNIV OF VIRGINIA MED CTR, DEPT OF FAMILY MED 22908 #010-01-2007 L2007 **FP** *012
MACIK, Barbara Gail. 500 RAY C HUNT DR 22903 #048-13-1983 L1997 **HEM IM** *020 †20
MAC ILWAINE, Wm Andrew. ■ 22903 #051-01-1947 L1947 **IM** *071
MAC MILLAN, R Hunt, III. 459 LOCUST AVE, MARTHA JEFFERSON LAB 22902 #045-01-1983 L1984 **PTH** *020 †50
MADARAS, Megan Lisa. ■ 22908 #051-01-2008 *012
MAGEE, Anna Mary. 1101 E HIGH ST, STE 230 22902 #045-01-1990 L1994 **D** *020 †15
MAHADEVA, Branavan. ■ 22902 #422-01-2002 L2006 **N** *100
MAHADEVAN, Mani S. 500 RAY C HUNT DR 22903 #065-09-1986 L2002 *020
MAHAJAN, Anshu. PO BOX 800136, UNIVERSITY OF VIRGINIA 22908 #051-07-2005 L2005 **IM** *012
MAHAPATRA, Srijoy. CARDIOLOGY P.O. BOX 80015, UNIVERSITY OF VIRGINIA HE 22908 #024-07-1999 L2006 **CD IC** *100 †20
MAHMOOD, Aamir. ■ 22903 #704-02-1996 L2004 **CHP** *012
MAHONEY, David Blair. ■ 22902 #036-01-2007 L2007 **FP** *012
MAITLAND, Hillary Susan. ■ 22902 #041-13-2008 *012
MALGARI, Amanda Elizabeth. ■ 22903 #024-16-2008 *012
MALHOTRA, Rohit. 851 FIELDHAVEN DR 22903 #038-41-2000 L2000 **CD** *012 †20
MALONEY, William James. 313 2ND ST SE STE 300, DOWNTOWN FAMILY HLTHCARE 22902 #005-14-1987 L1989 **IM FM** *020 †20

■ = Address Information Privacy Protected

MALPASS, Howard Charles, III. ■ 22903 #036-01-2006 L2006 **IM** *012

MAMMEN, Tony. SECOND FLOOR, HOSPITAL DRIVE 22908 #056-05-2001 L2007 **U** *100

MANDELL, Gerald Lee. 500 RAY C HUNT DR 22903 #035-20-1962 L1969 **ID IM** *050 †20

MANDELL, James Wm. 500 RAY C HUNT DR 22903 #035-20-1992 L1994 **NP** *020 †50

MANES, Amritpal Kaur. PO BOX 800729, DEPT OF FAMILY MED 22908 #495-29-2003 L2006 **FP** *012

MANGRUM, Amy Jenkins. BOX 133 LEE SE., INTERNAL MEDICINE 22908 #047-06-1993 L1996 **NEP** *020 †20

MANGRUM, James M. PO BOX 800158, UNIVERSITY OF VIRGINIA HOS 22908 #047-06-1993 L1996 **CD** *020 †20

MANIS, Jeanne Hammond. 501 FAULCONER DR STE 2A 22903 #051-04-1989 L1993 **P** *020

MANNING, Bradley Bowker. 310 OLD IVY WAY, SUITE 104 22908 #051-01-2002 L2002 **CHP** *020

MARANO, Anthony Jos. ■ 22903 #035-06-1943 L1978 **ORS** *071 †40

MARCINIAK, Emily Kathleen. ■ 22903 #017-20-2007 **TY** *012

MARRI, Maaya Reddy. ■ 22903 #051-01-2006 L2006 **EM** *012

MARRI, Rama Lakshmi. 400 LOCUST AVE 22902 #495-65-1974 L1981 **PUD IM** *020 †20

MARSH, John Otho. 500 RAY C HUNT DR 22903 #051-07-1983 L1985 **FM AM** *020 †18

MARSHALL, John Crook. UNIV VA HLTH SCI CTR, BOX 612 DEPT MED 22908 #917-08-1965 L1990 **END IM** *050 †20

MARTIN, Marcus Lewis. EMERGENCY DEPARTMENT, UNIVERSITY OF VIRGINIA 22906 #051-07-1976 L1978 **EM** *020 †16

MARTINEZ, Horacio Duarte. ■ 22902 #264-01-1945 L1962 **GPM AN** *071

MARTINEZ, Lisa Christina. ■ 22902 #011-02-2007 L2007 **IM** *012

MARTINEZ, Sean James. ■ 22902 #011-02-2007 L2007 **IM** *012

MARTINSON, Heidi E. 117 HARTFORD CT 22902 #041-13-2003 L2003 **PD** *020 †55

MARTZ, Gabriel Ustin. ■ 22902 #024-16-2003 L2007 **CN** *012

MARZANI-NISSEN, Gabrielle. RM 3146, DEPT OF PSYCHIATRY LANE RO 22908 #035-48-1998 L1998 **P IM** *020 †20,75

MASON, Jane Holland. ■ 22903 #051-01-1998 L1998 **AN** *020

MASON, John Currie. 916 E HIGH ST, STE 2 22902 #036-01-1992 L1992 **OTO** *020 †45

MASON, Joseph Thos. 1008 E JEFFERSON ST 22902 #051-04-1988 L1989 **P** *020 †75

MASON, Matthew David. ■ 22902 #035-15-2008 *012

MASSARO, Thomas Andrew. PO BOX 800802, UNIV OF VA HLTH SYS 22908 #056-05-1977 L1981 **CCM NPM** *020 †55

MASSEY, Julie Elizabeth. ■ 22902 #045-01-2007 L2007 **IM** *012

MATHERNE, G Paul, Jr. JEFFERSON PK AVE, BOX 386 22908 #048-16-1982 L1988 **PD PDC** *050 †55

MATHES, Donald D. 932 E JEFFERSON ST 22902 #048-02-1987 L1990 **AN IM** *020 †20,05

MATHEW, Mammen M. 515 RAY C HUNT DR 22903 #495-08-1968 L1984 **PM** *020 †60

MATSUMOTO, Alan Hiyoshi. 500 RAY C HUNT DR 22903 #036-05-1980 L1991 **R IM** *020 †20,80

MATSUMOTO, Julie Ann. 500 RAY C HUNT DR 22903 #018-03-1983 L1991 **DR RNR** *020 †80

MAUGHAN, Karen Lesley. 500 RAY C HUNT DR 22903 #067-01-1991 L1993 **FM** *020 †18

MAUREMANN, Michelle Lynn. PO BOX 800394, UVA 22908 #018-03-2002 L2002 **CN** *012

MAY, Joseph Walton. 1149 ROSE HILL DR 22903 #051-01-1970 L1970 **FM** *020 †18

MC ALLISTER, John Joseph. UNIVERSITY OF VIRGINIA, DEPARTMENT OF ANESTHESIOLO 22908 #041-14-2002 L2002 **AN** *020

MC ALPINE, Marcia Jean. 310 OLD IVY WAY, STE 201 22903 #035-08-1986 L1993 **FM** *020 †18

MC ALPINE, Steven Lee. 459 LOCUST AVE, EMERGENCY DEPARTMENT 22902 #035-08-1986 L1990 **EM PD** *020 †20

MC CALL, Anthony Leo. 500 RAY C HUNT DR 22903 #056-06-1972 L2001 **END IM** *050 †20

MC CARTNEY, Christopher R. 500 RAY C HUNT DR 22903 #027-01-1996 L1999 **END** *020 †20

MC CARTY, Gale Anne. OMS ROOM 95777-HOSPITAL DR, DIVISION OF RHEUM/IMMUNOLO 22908 #036-07-1974 L2000 **RHU OS** *050 †20 ‡

MCCLAIN, Richard William. ■ 22903 #051-01-2008 *012

MC CONNELL, Kevin Robt. 925 E JEFFERSON ST 22902 #010-01-1983 L1997 **NEP IM** *020 †20

MC CUE, Frank Cyrus. UNIV OF VA HOSPITAL 22908 #051-01-1956 L1956 **HS ORS** *071 †40

MC CULLOCH, Michael A. ■ 22902 #048-13-2001 L2001 **PDC** *012 †55

MC DANIEL, Nancy Lee. UNIV VA HSC BOX 386 PED 22908 #051-01-1983 L1987 **PD CD** *020 †55

MC DERMOTT, Lisa A. 459 LOCUST AVE, INPATIENT SERVICES 22902 #048-12-2000 L2003 **IM** *020

MC DUFFIE, Marcia J S. UNIV OF VA HLTH SCIENCES C, DEPT OF MICROBIOLOGY 22908 #036-01-1981 L1993 **PD** *050 †55

MC ELEARNEY, Shannon Noel. ■ 22902 #028-02-2001 L2001 **GS** *012

MC GAHREN, Eugene Dewey. 500 RAY C HUNT DR 22903 #051-01-1984 L1985 **PDS** *020 †85

MCGINTY, Jasmin Lara. ■ 22902 #051-01-2004 L2004 **ORS** *012

MCGOWAN, James Austin. PO BOX 800136, UNIVERSITY OF VIRGINIA MED 22908 #051-01-2006 L2006 **AN** *012

MC ILHENNY, Joan. 500 RAY C HUNT DR 22903 #041-01-1977 L1985 **PDR PD** *020 †80,55

MCINTOSH, Alyson Lease. ■ 22902 #041-13-2005 L2005 **RO** *012

MCKECHNIE, Martha Dobson. ■ 22903 #026-04-1990 L1993 **EM** *020 †16

MC LAREN, Nancy Miller. 500 RAY C HUNT DR 22903 #012-05-1985 L1999 **PD NPM** *020 †55

MC LAUGHLIN, Robt Eugene. 545 RAY C HUNT DR, STE 120 22908 #041-02-1961 L1968 **ORS** *020 †40

MCLEOD, Matthew Doyle. ■ 22902 #012-22-2008 *012

MC LEOD, Susan Lee. PO BOX 7546 22906 #036-05-1974 L1976 **PHP** *030 †70

MCLINSKEY, Nancy A. 500 RAY C HUNT DR, NEUROLOGY 22903 #305-01-2001 L2007 **N** *020

MC MASTERS, Mary Gresham. UVA BOX 801024 STE 201 22908 #025-12-1996 L2004 **ADM** *020 †20

MC MINN, Brooke Elizabeth. 1305 WERTLAND ST APT 8-9 22903 #051-01-1998 L1998 **IM** *100

MC MULLEN, John Laird, III. ■ 22903 #011-04-2002 L2007 **VIR** *012 †80

MCMURTREY, Richard Jay. ■ 22902 #007-02-2008 *012

MC NAMARA, Coleen Ann. HEALTH SCIENCE CTR, BOX 80, UNIVERSITY OF VIRGINIA 22908 #038-43-1986 L1990 **IM CD** *020 †20

MC NAMARA, Stephen Jacobs. 300 PRESTON AVE STE 214 22902 #051-01-1991 L1992 **P** *020 †75

MEAKEM, Timothy Dean. 459 LOCUST AVE, MARTHA JEFFERSON HOSPITAL 22902 #051-01-1987 L1993 **AN** *020 †05

MEALOR, Augustus Everett. ■ 22902 #047-06-2008 *012

MEHRAD, Borna. ■ 22903 #917-12-1991 L2006 **PCC** *020 †20

MEHTA, Sachin Hemant. PO BOX 800710, DEPT OF ANSTHS UNIVERSITY 22908 #041-01-2002 L2007 **AN** *100

MENDELSOHN, Mark Jeffrey. PO BOX 800386, UNIV. OF VIRGINIA CHILDREN 22908 #028-03-1986 L1996 **PD** *020 †55

MERKEL, Richard L, Jr. 2955 IVY RD STE 210, PSYCHIATRIC CLINICAL RESEA 22903 #051-01-1979 L1990 **P** *020 †75

MERTZ, Christopher Macdon. ■ 22903 #051-01-2008 *012

MESSINGER, Richard Benjam. PO BOX 800136, UNIVERSITY OF VIRGINIA 22908 #055-01-2004 L2005 **AN** *100

METH, Sharon Laura. 310 OLD IVY WAY, STE 201 22903 #024-07-1999 L1999 **IM** *020 †20

METZGER, Rosemarie. PO BOX 800136, UNIVERSITY OF VIRGINIA 22908 #056-05-2004 L2004 **GS** *012

MEUSE, Michael Anthony. PO BOX 800136, UNIVERSITY OF VIRGINIA 22908 #032-01-2004 L2005 **DR** *012

MEYER, G Andrew. 308 10TH ST NE 22902 #038-06-1982 L1991 **DR** *071 †80

MEZEY, Lillian. 1021 MILLMONT ST, VALLEY COMMUNITY SERVICES 22903 #035-01-1990 L1998 **P** *020 †75

MICHAEL, Glen Elwin. ■ 22902 #005-02-2007 L2007 **EM** *012

MIHALKO, William Michael. 400 RAY C HUNT DR, STE 330 22903 #051-04-1993 L2005 **ORS OAR** *020 †40

MILLER, Bradley Bryan. ■ 22902 #051-04-1998 L1998 **NP** *020

MILLER, Charles Willard. 500 RAY C HUNT DR 22903 #051-01-1969 L1969 **ORS** *020 †40

MILLER, Chealon Dain. PO BOX 800136, UNIVERSITY OF VIRGINIA MED 22908 #024-01-2006 L2006 **ORS** *012

MILLER, Mark D. 500 RAY C HUNT DR 22903 #023-12-1987 L2000 **ORS** *020 †40

MILLER, Nikki Marie. ■ 22902 #038-43-2006 L2006 **PD** *012

MILLER, Stephen Edward. PO BOX 800136, UNIVERSITY OF VIRGINIA 22908 #010-01-2004 L2004 **GS** *012

MILLER, Susan Apperson. 545 RAY C. HUNT DR. SUITE, UVA BOX 801004 22908 #051-01-2002 L2002 **PM PME** *020 †60

MILLS, Anne Mcgehee. ■ 22903 #051-01-2008 *012

MILLS, James Dean. JEFFERSON PK BOX 291 22908 #654-01-2002 L2004 **NS** *012

MILLS, Stacey Earl. 500 RAY C HUNT DR 22903 #051-01-1977 L1980 **PTH** *040 †50

MINASI, John Salvatore. P.O. BOX181, U OF VIRGINIA HLTH SCI CEN 22908 #051-01-1985 L1986 **GS** *020 †85

MINOR, George Ridgway. 2955 IVY RD 22903 #051-01-1940 L1940 **TS PUD** *071 †85,90

MINTZ, Paul David. OLD MEDICAL SCHOOL RM 3810 22908 #035-45-1974 L1979 **BBK IM** *062

MIRZA, Mohd Ayoub. ■ 22903 #495-51-1995 L2005 **CD** *012 †20

MISHRA, Rajnish. PO BOX 800708, UNIVERSITY OF VA HLTH CNTR 22908 #495-45-1997 L2005 **IM** *100 †20

MISSAGHI, Nizamid-Din B. 1215 LEE STREET 22908 #051-04-2002 L2002 **AN** *020 †05

MISTRY, Dilaawar Jal. 454 RAY C HUNT DR, UNIT 240 22903 #495-16-1985 L1995 **PM** *020

MOBASHAR, Naseer Ahmad. ■ 22902 #704-01-1971 L1975 **GP** *020

MODESITT, Susan Carnall. ■ 22903 #051-01-1995 L2006 **OBG** *020 †30

MOGA, David Benj. 820 E HIGH ST STE B 22902 #056-06-1964 L1972 **ORS** *071 †40

MOHRMANN, Margaret E. ■ 22903 #045-01-1973 L1987 **PD PN** *040 †55

MOLONEY, Michael Thomas. 311 10TH ST NE 22902 #038-40-2001 L2004 **AN** *020 †05

MOMBEYARARA, Rudo. PO BOX 800136, UVA MEDICAL CENTER 22908 #305-01-2006 L2006 **FP** *012

MONSON, Katherine Annalis. PO BOX 800710, UNIV OF VIRGINIA MED CTR 22908 #030-05-2007 **AN** *012

MONTEITH, Stephen James. GME BOX 800136, UNIVERSITY OF VIRGINIA HEA 22908 #671-02-2005 L2007 **NS** *012

MONTELEONE, Peter Philip. ■ 22903 #024-07-2007 L2007 **IM** *012

MONTGOMERY, Howard Arthur. 2955 IVY RD, STE 304 UVA NORTHRIDGE 22903 #038-41-1961 L1968 **GYN** *071 †30

MOODY, David Tipton. 800 PRESTON AVE 22903 #048-14-1979 L1980 **P** *020 †75

MOONEY, Joseph. 201 SUNSET AVE 22903 #051-01-1969 L1971 **P CHP** *020 †75

MOORMAN, Joseph Randall. 500 RAY C HUNT DR 22903 #027-01-1978 L1990 **CD IM** *020 †20

MORAN, Ruth Eleanor. BOX 170, UVA HLTH SCI CTR 22908 #035-46-1987 L1993 **DR** *020 †80

MORGAN, Raymond F. 500 RAY C HUNT DR 22903 #055-01-1976 L1982 **PS HS** *020 †65

MORGAN, Walter Edward, III. ■ 22903 #035-01-1961 L1967 **OPH** *071 †35

MORI, Takahiro. JEFFERSON PK BOX 291 22908 #572-38-2001 L2007 **FP** *012

MORRIS, David Lyttelton. 1100 E HIGH ST, STE 2B 22902 #051-01-1975 L1978 **IM ID** *020 †20

MORRIS, Gordon Leigh. 459 LOCUST AVE 22902 #051-01-1978 L1984 **HEM ON** *020 †20

MORRIS, John Richard, III. 1100 E HIGH ST 22902 #051-01-1972 L1972 **GS** *020 †85

MOSELEY, Chas Dameron, III. 400 W HIGH ST 22902 #051-04-1969 L1969 **P GP** *020

MOSKALUK, Christopher A. JEFFERSON PARK AVE 22908 #036-07-1990 L1996 **PTH** *050 †50

MOUNSEY, Anne Leathes. 500 RAY C HUNT DR 22903 #917-21-1982 L2007 *020

MOUNSEY, John Paul. 500 RAY C HUNT DR 22903 #917-09-1987 L1993 **CD** *020

MOURAD, Shadi Michel. ■ 22903 #913-96-1997 L2006 **NEP** *012 †20

MOXLEY, Michael Dennis. 500 RAY C HUNT DR 22903 #051-01-1991 L1995 **OBG** *020 †30

MUCH, Jason William. PO BOX 800136, UNIVERSITY OF VIRGINIA 22908 #041-01-2005 L2006 **OPH** *012

MULHOLLAND, John Henry. ■ 22903 #023-07-1959 L1959 **IM ID** *071 †20

MULLER, William H, Jr. ■ 22908 #036-07-1943 L1954 **TS GS** *071 †85,90

MUNNELLY, Sean William. ■ 22903 #017-20-2002 L2002 **P** *100

MURRAY, Latham Brundred. 459 LOCUST AVE 22902 #051-01-1981 L1995 **GS VS** *020 †85

MURRAY, Rhunelle Camille. ■ 22903 #422-01-2003 L2007 **CN** *012

MUT, Melike. UVA BOX 800212 22908 #902-05-1995 L2003 *020

MYERS, Lisa Carol. ■ 22903 #036-01-2005 L2005 **PTH** *012

MYERS, Sara Elizabeth. ■ 22902 #045-01-2007 L2007 **PM** *012

NADKARNI, Mohan Moreshwar. 1222 JEFFERSON PARK AVE, BOX 800744 22903 #041-01-1990 L1991 **IM** *020 †20

NADLER, Jerry Lee. 500 RAY C HUNT DR 22903 #011-02-1978 L1999 **END IM** *020 †20

NAGJI, Alykhan. ■ 22902 #048-12-2006 L2006 **GS** *012

NAMBIAR, Ashwin Prabhakar. ■ 22903 #051-01-2008 *012

NAPLES, Robin Michelle. 511 N 1ST ST 22902 #041-13-2004 L2004 **EM** *100

NASS, Ralf Manfred. ■ 22902 #409-35-1988 L1998 *020

NATHAN, Barnett Ross. PO BOX 800394, NEUROLOGY 22908 #041-09-1992 L1993 **N** *020 †75

NAVA, Guillermina. PO BOX 800136, UNIVERSITY OF VIRGINIA 22908 #035-45-2001 L2001 **PS** *100

NEESE, Brian Harrison. 1215 LEE ST., UVA HEALTH SYSTEM 22908 #550-04-2005 L2005 **FP** *012

NEMERGUT, Edward Charles. 500 RAY C HUNT DR 22903 #017-20-1998 L1999 **AN** *020 †05

NEWSOM, Nancy Elizabeth. ■ 22903 #010-02-1987 L1989 **OBG** *020 †30

NEWTON, Joshua Spencer. PO BOX 800715, UNIV OF VA HLTH SYSTEM 22908 #012-01-2005 L2006 **OPH** *012

NGUYEN, Maria Nhatkhoa. ■ 22903 #051-07-2003 L2005 **PMM** *012

■ = Address Information Privacy Protected

NGUYEN, Quynhnhu. ■ 22908 #010-01-2001 L2003 **RO** *100
NGUYEN, Tam Nhu. ■ 22903 #051-01-2008 *012
NICHOLSON, Angela Marie. 545 RAY C HUNT DR, SUITE 240 BOX 801004 22908 #049-01-2002 L2003 **GS** *100 †60
NICHOLSON, Brandi Tamara. JEFFERSON PARK AVE 22908 #018-03-2000 L2001 **DR** *020 †80
NICHOLSON, Robert Marion, IV. ■ 22903 #025-01-2008 L2008 *012
NIELSEN, Niels Christian. ■ 22902 #187-08-2001 **P** *012
NIKPEY, Pari P. 400 LOCUST AVE STE 4 22902 #517-03-1978 L1994 **CN N** *020 †75
NITZ, Matthew David. ■ 22903 #051-01-2008 *012
NOLAN, Norris J. PO BOX 800136, UNIV OF VIRGINIA MED 22908 #048-02-2006 L2006 **PTH** *012
NOLAN, Stanton Peelle. 2955 IVY RD 22903 #051-01-1959 L1959 **TS** *071 †85,90
NOLD, Brian Michael. ■ 22903 #051-01-2000 *100
NORRELL, Nelly Prescilla. ■ 22902 #004-01-2007 L2007 **P** *012
NORTHUP, Patrick Grant. JEFFERSON PARK AVE 22908 #051-04-1994 L1995 **GE** *020 †20
NORTON, Patrick Terrance. ■ 22903 #035-03-2000 L2001 **DR** *100 †80
NORWOOD, Kenneth Westcott. 2270 IVY RD, UNIVERSITY OF VIRGINIA 22903 #036-05-1983 L1999 **PD** *020 †55
NORWOOD, Victoria Fay. MR-4, RM 2010, UNIV OF VA HLTH SCIENCES C 22908 #021-01-1985 L1992 **PN** *050 †55
OBEMBE, Olufolajimi O. ■ 22903 #036-07-2004 L2005 **DR** *012
OBENG, Rebecca Cynthia. ■ 22903 #051-01-2008 *012
OBLINGER, Michael John. 1139 E HIGH ST, GASTROENTEROLOGY ASSOC 22902 #051-01-1976 L1981 **IM GE** *020 †20
O'BRIEN, William Michael. 2955 IVY RD 22903 #008-01-1956 L1968 **RHU IM** *020
OGAN, James L. 500 RAY C HUNT DR 22903 #024-01-1991 L1996 **PD** *020 †55
OGUNYEMI, Abayomi O. U OF VA M C, BOX 394 22908 #690-02-1975 **OS** *100
OH, Laura. HEALTH SYSTEM, UNIV OF VIRGINIA 22908 #025-01-2007 L2007 **EM** *012
OKUSA, Mark Douglas. BOX 133 DIV OF NEP 22908 #051-04-1982 L1983 **NEP IM** *050 †20
OLIVER, M Norman. 500 RAY C HUNT DR 22903 #038-06-1994 L1998 **FM** *050 †18
OLIVIERO, Jason Anthony. PO BOX 800136, UNIVERSITY OF VIRGINIA 22908 #051-01-2003 L2003 **ORS** *012
OLSAKOVSKY, Leslie Ann. 2955 IVY RD, STE 300 22903 #041-12-1988 L1995 **OPH** *020 †35
OOGHE, Robert Barksdale. 505 FAULCONER DR STE 1A 22903 #051-01-1957 L1957 **IM** *020 †20
ORNDORFF, Douglas George. PO BOX 800136, UVA 22908 #007-02-2003 L2003 **ORS** *012
OSBORN, Tiffany Medlin. PO BOX 800699, 1215 LEE ST 22908 #048-13-1997 L2002 **EM** *020 †16
OSHRINE, Benjamin Reed. ■ 22903 #051-01-2008 *012
OSKOUIAN, Christen Beasle. ■ 22902 #018-03-2001 L2001 **PD** *020 †55
OSKOUIAN, Rod. ■ 22902 #005-14-2001 L2005 **NS** *012
OSTHEIMER, Nathan Allen. ■ 22903 #051-01-2007 *012
OTERO-LOPEZ, Antonio M. PO BOX 800136, UNIVERSITY OF VIRGINIA 22908 #042-01-1998 L2004 **OAR** *100 †40
PADIA, Shetal Harshadray. ■ 22903 #036-08-2000 L2000 **END** *100 †20
PAJEWSKI, Thomas N. 500 RAY C HUNT DR 22903 #048-14-1988 L1991 **AN** *020 †05
PAK, Anna Seong Hee. JEFFERSON PARK AVE 22908 #041-15-2002 L2004 **PD** *020 †55
PAK, Susan Julia. JEFFERSON PK BOX 291, UNIV OF VA MED CTR 22908 #041-02-1999 L2002 **GS** *100
PAMBIANCO, Daniel John. 1139 E HIGH ST, GASTROENTEROLOGY ASSOC 22902 #654-01-1982 L1985 **GE IM** *020 †20
PANCHAL, Amiesha Salina. ■ 22903 #025-07-2005 L2005 **FP** *012
PANKRATZ, Lauren Ann. ■ 22902 #038-40-2005 L2005 **PD** *012
PARK, Jennifer Jin-Woo. JEFFERSON PK BOX 291 22908 #539-02-2005 L2005 **IM** *012
PARK, Stephen Sungwon. 500 RAY C HUNT DR 22903 #051-01-1994 L1994 **FPS PS** *020 †45
PARKER, Kay C. 311 10TH ST NE 22902 #011-04-1976 L1993 **IM AN** *050 †20,05
PARKER, William Davis, Jr. 500 RAY C HUNT DR 22903 #011-04-1974 L1979 **CHN N** *050 †75
PARLETTE, Harry L, III. 500 RAY C HUNT DR 22903 #010-02-1968 L1978 **D** *071 †15
PARMAR, Jaywant Philip. HEALTH SYSTEM, UNIV OF VIRGINIA 22908 #055-01-2001 L2002 **VIR** *012 †80
PARSONS, Chris Hamilton. PO BOX 800734 22908 #038-06-1998 L2001 **ID** *020 †20
PATEL, Amit Ramesh. ■ 22903 #012-05-2000 L2006 **CD** *100 †20
PATEL, Daksha N. BOX 623 HSC, UVA/DEPT OF PSY MED 22908 #665-01-1996 L2006 **P** *020 †75
PATEL, Rajan Amish. HEALTH SCIENC, UNIV OF VIRGINIA 22908 #005-11-2000 L2003 **CD** *100
PATTERSON, James W. BOX 134 MEDICAL CENTER 22908 #051-04-1972 L1973 **DMP D** *040 †15
PAWLOWSKI, Sean William. 1215 LEE ST. 22908 #048-14-2004 L2007 **ID** *012 †20
PAYNE, Spencer Cranston. 500 RAY C HUNT DR, UNVERSITY OF VIRGINIA-HSF 22903 #035-48-2001 L2007 **OTO** *020 †45
PEAKE, Lilian Ruth. 1138 ROSE HILL DR, RAPPAHANNOCK RAPIDAN HEALT 22903 #051-01-1999 L1999 **IM** *062 †10
PEARCE, R Scott C. 800 PRESTON AVE 22903 #051-01-1986 L1989 **P** *020 †75
PEARSON, Justin David. PO BOX 800136, UNIVERSITY OF VIRGINIA HEA 22908 #056-06-2006 L2006 **EM** *012
PEARSON, Richard Dale. MEDICAL SCHO, UNIV OF VIRGINIA 22908 #025-01-1973 L1980 **ID IM** *050 †20
PEELER, Benjamin Banks. 500 RAY C HUNT DR 22903 #047-05-1991 L1998 **VS** *020 †85,90
PELTON, Ernest Williams. 400 LOCUST AVE STE 4A 22902 #051-01-1965 L1965 **N OS** *020 †75
PENDLETON, Amber Lynette. 1251 FOX CREST WAY, UNIVERSITY OF VIRGINIA 22902 #020-12-2005 L2005 **PD** *012
PENDLETON, Michael Eli. ■ 22902 #020-12-2005 L2005 **FP** *012
PENNOCK, Erin. ■ 22902 #041-02-2006 L2006 **N** *012
PERI, Cristian Valentin. PO BOX 800136 22908 #781-06-1982 L2001 *100
PERINA, Debra Gallo. 500 RAY C HUNT DR 22903 #055-01-1983 L1995 **EM** *020 †16
PERRIELLO, Vito A, Jr. 1011 E JEFFERSON ST, PED. OF ASSOC CHARLOTTESVI 22902 #036-07-1966 L1971 **PD** *020 †55
PETERS, Craig Andrew. PO BOX 800422, UNIVERSITY OF VIRGINIA HEA 22908 #023-07-1981 L2006 **UP** *020 †95
PETERSON, Christine M. U VA MED CTR STU HL, BX 378 22908 #024-07-1976 L1987 **OBG P** *030 †30
PETERSON, Kent Wright. 901 PRESTON AVE STE 400, OCCUPATIONAL HLTH STRATEGI 22903 #041-01-1968 L1971 **OM GPM** *062 †70 ‡
PETRI, William Arthur, Jr. JEFFERSON PARK AVE 385 22908 #051-01-1982 L1988 **ID IM** *050 †20

PEURA, David Allan. 500 RAY C HUNT DR 22903 #050-02-1971 L1990 **GE** *020 †20
PEYTON, Victor Colt. 459 LOCUST AVE 22902 #051-01-1991 L1998 **DR** *020 †80
PHILLIPS, Clifford D. BOX 170, DEPARTMENT OF RADIOLOGY 22908 #055-02-1984 L1986 **RNR** *020 †80
PHILLIPS, Frank Harrison. 500 RAY C HUNT DR 22903 #051-04-1969 L1969 **AN** *020 †05
PHILLIPS, Lawrence H, II. UNIV OF VIRGINIA MEDICAL C, DEPT OF NEUROLOGY BOX 8003 22908 #055-01-1974 L1981 **N CN** *020 †75
PHULL, Amit. ■ 22903 #051-01-2008 *012
PINSK, Maury Nelson. 300 LANE RD, RM 2010 MR-4 BUILDING 22908 #065-01-1997 L2001 **PD** *100 †55
PINTO, Luis Enrique. ■ 22908 #270-02-1983 **PD NPM** *020
PLATTS-MILLS, Thomas A. BOX 225, DEPT OF MEDICINE 22908 #917-09-1967 L1976 **IM AI** *050
PLAUTZ, Claire Marie U. JEFFERSON PARK AVE 22908 #011-02-2001 L2001 **EM** *020 †16
PLEWS-OGAN, Margaret L. 500 RAY C HUNT DR 22903 #024-01-1991 L1996 **IM** *020 †20
PLITT, David Calvin. ■ 22903 #041-14-2007 L2007 **IM** *012
PLUNKETT, Julia Lynn. ■ 22903 #020-02-2005 L2005 **EM** *012
POLITIS, George Demetri. 500 RAY C HUNT DR 22903 #035-20-1985 L1992 **AN PD** *020 †05,55
POLLAK, Peter Michael. ■ 22903 #051-01-2005 L2005 **IM** *012
POST, Barbara T Tyl. 2955 IVY RD STE 205, NORTHRIDGE INTERNAL MED 22903 #016-11-1983 L1989 **IM** *020 †20
POST, John Hazen, III. 908 E JEFFERSON ST 22902 #011-02-1980 L1981 **ORS** *071 †40
POSTHUMUS, Jonathon Brian. ■ 22903 #033-06-2007 L2007 **IM** *012
POURATIAN, Nader. ■ 22903 #005-14-2003 L2003 **NS** *012
POWELL, Steven Mark. 300 LANE RD MR-4 BLDG RM 1, DIV. OF GASTRO. & HEPATOL. 22908 #017-20-1987 L1996 **GE IM** *020 †20
PRESLEY, Alison E. UNIV OF VIRGINIA, DEPARTMENT OF PATHOLOGY/P. 22908 #016-06-2002 L2002 **PCP PTH** *012 †50
PRESTON, Mary Brown. 500 RAY C HUNT DR 22903 #008-02-1979 L1998 **IM** *020 †20
PRITCHARD, Robert Sydney. 459 LOCUST AVE, CENTER FOR CANCER CARE 22902 #028-34-1987 L1997 **HEM** *020
PROCACCINI, Nicholas J. ■ 22903 #051-01-2003 L2003 **IM** *100 †20
PRUETT, Timothy Lane. 500 RAY C HUNT DR 22903 #048-04-1976 L1987 **OS GS** *020 †20,85
PRUM, Bruce Edward, Jr. 500 RAY C HUNT DR 22903 #032-01-1988 L1995 **OPH** *020 †35
PUNJA, Mohan. ■ 22903 #051-01-2008 *012
PUNYANITYA, Visespong. 411 8TH ST NE 22902 #891-03-1969 L1980 **ORS** *020 †40
PUNYANITYA, Voranoot. 411 8TH ST NE 22902 #891-01-1965 L1976 **GYN** *020
PUROW, Benjamin Warren. ■ 22908 #023-07-1996 L2006 **PHO** *020 †55
QUIGG, Mark Stephen. UNIV OF VA MED CTR, DEPT MED 22908 #051-01-1990 L1994 **N IM** *020 †75
QUILLIAN, Heather Roberts. 2955 IVY RD, STE 303 22903 #051-01-1999 L1999 **PD** *020 †55
QURESHI, Hina Shafique. ■ 22903 #704-02-1995 L2004 **DMP PCP** *100
RABINOWITZ, Seymour. ■ 22902 #024-01-1958 L1969 **PYA P** *071 †75
RAGHAVAN, Prashant. PO BOX 800136, UNIVERSITY OF VIRGINIA 22908 #495-16-1997 L2004 **RNR** *100
RAGOSTA, Michael. 500 RAY C HUNT DR 22903 #043-01-1985 L1994 **CD IM** *020 †20
RAHIMI, Robert Shahram. ■ 22903 #016-42-2006 L2006 **IM** *012
RAJ, Ramona. ■ 22903 #035-15-2004 L2007 **END** *012 †20
RAJAGOPALAN, Pradeep. 459 LOCUST AVE 22902 #036-07-1995 L2000 **DR** *020 †80
RAMIREZ, Antonio Miguel. PO BOX 800710, UVA 22908 #051-01-2002 L2002 **AN** *020
RAMIREZ, Colin Edward. 400 BRANDON AVE, ELSON STUD HLTH POB 800760 22908 #051-07-1982 L1988 **PD ADL** *020 †55
RAMOS, Michelle Aguilar. ■ 22903 #051-01-2008 *012
RANNEY, Anne Marie. 2955 IVY RD, STE 303 22903 #035-15-1991 L1995 **PD** *020 †55
RAPHAEL, Jacob. UVA HEALTH SYSTEM BOX 8007, DEPARTMENT OF ANESTHESIOLO 22908 #550-01-1997 *100
RAYNOR, Laura Lee. OF MED, UNIV OF VIRGINIA SCH 22908 #036-01-2004 L2007 **NPM** *012 †55
READ, Paul Wm. JEFFERSON PARK AVE, RAD DNC BOX 800383 22908 #051-01-1990 L1997 **RO** *020 †80
REAMES, David Leroy. ■ 22902 #045-01-2007 L2007 **GS** *012
REARDON, Michael Anthony. ■ 22903 #051-01-2008 *012
REDICK, Dana Louise. 2955 IVY RD STE 304, UNIVERSITY PHYSICIANS FOR 22903 #040-01-1998 L2002 **OBG** *020 †30
REDINGTON, Maura Eileen. 1221 LEE ST., UVA DEPT. OF FAMILY MEDICI 22908 #016-43-2003 L2003 **FM** *100 †18
REDZINIAK, Daniel Edward. ■ 22902 #033-06-2002 L2006 **OSM** *012
REED, Sean William. ■ 22902 #024-16-2004 L2004 **FM** *100 †18
REHM, Patrice Koch. PO BOX 800170, UNIV OF VIRGINIA HLTH SYS 22908 #008-01-1981 L1999 **R NM** *020 †80,28
REIBEL, James Francis. UVA MED CTR 1 HOSPITAL DR, DEPT OF ORL-HNS BOX 800713 22908 #051-01-1975 L1977 **OTO** *020 †45
REIN, Michael Frank. UNIV OF VA HEALTH SYS, DIV-INF DISEASE BOX 80059 22908 #024-01-1969 L1975 **ID IM** *040 †20
REISER, Robert C. 500 RAY C HUNT DR 22903 #010-02-1988 L1997 **EM** *020 †16
REMBOLD, Christopher Mark. 500 RAY C HUNT DR 22903 #016-06-1981 L1984 **CD IM** *050 †20
REYNOLDS, Robert Edgar. JEFFERSON PARK AVE 22908 #024-01-1964 L1988 **IM GPM** *030 †70
REYNOLDS, Sarah Elizabeth. ■ 22903 #051-01-2007 L2007 **PTH** *012
RHEUBAN, Karen Schulder. UVA HEALTH SYSTEM, DIV PED CARDIO POB 800711 22908 #038-40-1974 L1980 **PD PDC** *030 †55
RHEUBAN, William Jay. 910 E HIGH ST 22902 #038-40-1973 L1975 **P** *020 †75
RICCIARDI, Daniel R. 2735 MILTON RD 22902 #045-01-1996 L2000 **EM** *020 †16
RICH, George Frederick. 500 RAY C HUNT DR 22903 #049-01-1985 L1988 **AN** *020 †05
RICH, Tyvin Andrew. JEFFERSON PK ST P O BOX 80, UNIV OF VIRGINIA HSC 22903 #051-01-1973 L1995 **RO** *020 †80
RICHMOND, Erick Jose. DEPARTMENT OF PEDIATRICS,, UNIVERSITY OF VIRGINIA, BOX 22908 #270-01-1993 L1998 **PDE PD** *100
RIDDERVOLD, Hans Olav. BOX 170 UNIV VA MED CTR 22908 #693-01-1951 L1976 **DR** *071 †80
RIDDLE, Cheryl Denise. 109 RUNNING FOX LN 22902 #047-05-2001 L2004 **IM** *020
RIJKE, Arie Marie. BOX 170 UNIV VA MED CTR 22908 #660-01-1978 **DR** *020
RION, David Butts. ■ 22903 #051-01-2008 *012
RIPBERGER, Frank M, Jr. BOX 378 MEDICAL CENTER 22908 #051-01-1947 L1947 **PD** *020 †55
RIVERA, Jorge Rodolfo, Jr. ■ 22903 #051-01-2007 L2007 **IM** *012

RIZK, Alex Hikmat. 500 RAY C HUNT DR 22903 #051-04-1990 L1991 **FM** *020 †18

ROBBINS, Mark Kenneth. 500 RAY C HUNT DR 22903 #036-01-1987 L1994 **PUD CCM** *020 †20

ROBERTS, Jennifer Lynn. ■ 22902 #051-01-2007 L2007 *012

ROBINSON, Elizabeth Ann. 225 LARKSPUR WAY, WEILL MEDICAL COLLEGE OF C 22902 #051-04-1999 L2006 **MPD** *020 †55,20

ROCHE, James Kenneth. PO BOX 801317, UNIV OF VIRGINIA HEALTH SC 22902 #041-01-1969 L1987 **GE IM** *050 †20

ROCHESTER, Dudley F. UVA MEDICAL CENTER, PULMONARY & CRITICAL CARE 22903 #035-01-1955 L1976 **PUD IM** *071 †20

RODGERS, Bradley Moreland. BOX 181/UNIV VA MED CTR 22908 #023-07-1966 L1981 **PDS GS** *050 †90,85

ROGOL, Alan David. 500 RAY C HUNT DR 22903 #036-07-1970 L1975 **PDE PD** *020 †55

ROME, Rachel Claudet. ■ 22902 #047-06-2006 L2006 **AN** *012

ROMNEY, Davis Alvin. ■ 22908 #051-01-2002 L2002 **RO** *020

ROSE, Charles Edward, Jr. 500 RAY C HUNT DR 22903 #020-02-1972 L1979 **PCC IM** *020 †20

ROSNER, Mitchell Howard. PO BOX 800133, UNIVERSITY OF VIRGINIA HSC 22908 #012-01-1996 L1996 **NEP** *020 †20

ROSS, Pamela Andrea. 500 RAY C HUNT DR 22903 #012-05-1991 L1994 **EM PEM** *020 †16

ROSS, William Tyler, Jr. BOX 300710 JEFFERSON PARK, DEPT OF ANESTHESIOLOGY 22908 #051-01-1964 L1964 **AN** *020 †05

ROTTKAMP, Daniele Monique. PO BOX 800136, UNIVERSITY OF VIRGINIA MED 22908 #041-01-2006 L2006 **IM** *012

ROUSSILLON, Kristin Curry. ■ 22903 #023-01-2006 L2006 **IM** *012

ROWE, David Mark. 459 LOCUST AVE, MARTHA JEFFERSON HOSPTIAL 22902 #051-04-1996 L1996 **DMP** *020 †50

ROY, Ornob Proteek. PO BOX 800422, OF MED 22908 #047-05-2005 L2005 **U** *012

ROY, Rupali. ■ 22902 #003-01-2006 L2006 **IM** *012

RUDE, Mary Katherine. ■ 22903 #051-01-2008 *012

RUFFIN, Marshall De G, Jr. 300 WELLINGTON DR, RUFFIN INFORMATICS, INC 22903 #024-01-1978 L1981 **IM MDM** *030 †20

RUSSELL, Mark Anthony. PO BOX 800718, DEPT DERM 22908 #038-40-1993 L1999 **D DMP** *020 †15

RUST, Robert Stanley, Jr. 500 RAY C HUNT DR 22903 #051-01-1981 L1999 **CHN PD** *020 †55,75

SABEEN, Samia. 1215 LEE STREET, UNIV OF VIRG HOSP;POBOX 80 22908 #160-01-1991 L2000 **PYG** *020 †75

SABHARWAL, Pooja. PO BOX 800136 22908 #905-02-2003 L2005 **P** *012

SABRI, Saher Salim. HEALTH SYSTEM, UNIV OF VIRGINIA 22908 #575-01-2000 L2007 **VIR** *012 †80

SADIK, Karim Walid. JEFFERSON PK BOX 291 22908 #539-06-2002 L2005 **GS** *012

SALEH, Khaled Jamal. PO BOX 800159, 400 BAY C HUNT DR STE 330 22908 #065-06-1991 L2004 **ORS OAR** *020 †40

SALERNO, Johnvito. PO BOX 800136, UNIVERSITY OF VIRGINIA 22908 #035-08-2000 L2005 **VIR** *100 †20

SALERNO, Michael. ■ 22902 #051-01-2003 L2008 **CD IM** *012 †20

SAMS, Walter Augustus. PO BOX 800715, UNIVERSITY OF VIRGINIA 22908 #012-01-2004 L2005 **OPH** *012

SANDRIDGE, Layne C. PO BOX 800136, UNIVERSITY OF VIRGINIA 22908 #021-05-1999 L2005 **VS** *020

SANFEY, Hilary Anne. JEFF PR AVE, SURG DEPT BOX 800709 22908 #539-03-1976 **GS** *020

SANSUR, Charles Adel. ■ 22903 #023-01-2002 L2002 **NS** *012

SANTEN, Richard Jos. 450 RAY C HUNT DR RM 2313, UNIVERSITY OF VIRGINIA 22908 #025-01-1965 L1995 **END IM** *020 †20

SANTULLI, Michael Edward. 400 LOCUST AVE 22902 #051-01-1986 L1991 **END** *020 †20

SARALKAR, Reshama Kishor. UNIVERSITY OF VIRGINIA, OBSTETRICS AND GYNECOLOGY 22908 #041-01-2007 L2007 **OBG** *012

SAREBAHI, Shikha. HLTH SYSTEM, UNIV OF VIRGINIA 22908 #495-84-1998 L2007 **RHU** *012 †20

SARTI, Marc. PO BOX 800170, 1215 LEE ST 22908 #005-18-1999 L2005 **DR** *100 †80

SASAKI, Tsutomu. PO BOX 800212, UNIV OF VA HLTH SYS 22908 #572-03-1997 L1998 **NS** *100

SATYANARAYANA, Gowri. ■ 22902 #038-40-2007 L2007 **IM** *012

SAULSBURY, Frank Timothy. MEDICAL CENT, UNIV OF VIRGINIA 22908 #030-05-1972 L1979 **PD** *050 †55

SAVANI, Aman Anil. PO BOX 800136, UNIVERSITY OF VIRGINIA 22908 #051-07-2004 L2004 **N** *012

SAWYER, Dan Wayne. 400 LOCUST AVE 22902 #024-07-1981 L1984 **ID IM** *020 †20

SAWYER, Robert Grant. 500 RAY C HUNT DR 22903 #025-01-1986 L1987 **TTS ID** *020 †85

SCANELLI, John Anthony, III. ■ 22903 #051-01-2007 L2007 **ORS** *012

SCHAFER, Katherine Rachel. ■ 22902 #036-01-2005 L2005 **IM** *012

SCHECHTMAN, Joel Martin. 1222 JEFFERSON PARK AVE, UMA - 3RD FLOOR 22903 #024-05-1981 L1999 **IM** *040 †20

SCHEEL, John Robert. ■ 22903 #005-18-2006 L2007 **DR** *012

SCHELD, William Michael. 500 RAY C HUNT DR 22903 #035-20-1973 L1976 **ID IM** *050 †20

SCHENK, Worthington G, III. 500 RAY C HUNT DR 22903 #036-07-1974 L1982 **GS TS** *020 †85

SCHIFF, David. 1335 LEE ST 22908 #024-01-1988 L2001 **N** *020 †75

SCHILDWACHTER, Thos Legge. 914 E JEFFERSON ST STE 102 22902 #051-01-1975 L1977 **ORS OSM** *020 †40

SCHIRMER, Bruce. JEFFERSON PARK AVE 22908 #036-07-1978 L1985 **GS** *020 †85

SCHLAGER, Theresa Ann. 500 RAY C HUNT DR 22903 #038-06-1984 L1990 **ID PD** *020 †55

SCHNEIDER, Bernard F. DEPT RADIATION ONCOLOGY, UNIVERSITY OF VIRGINIA 22908 #051-01-1991 L1991 **OS** *020 †80

SCHNEYER, Mark Stein. ■ 22903 #023-01-2006 L2006 **OTO** *012

SCHOEFFEL, Cynthia D. ■ 22903 #041-01-2008 L1978 **FM** *074 †18

SCHOEFFEL, Mark Edwin. 311 10TH ST NE 22902 #016-42-1978 L1983 **AN** *020 †05

SCHOFIELD, William Peter. 500 RAY C HUNT DR 22903 #919-03-1973 L1982 **P** *020 †75

SCHORLING, John Bales. 500 RAY C HUNT DR 22903 #038-40-1980 L1984 **IM GPM** *050 †20

SCHROEN, Anneke Theresa. HOSPITAL DRIVE, PVT CL BLDG 4TH FL RM 4527 22908 #048-12-1994 L2002 **GS** *020

SCHULT, Alexander. 459 LOCUST AVE, BOX # 3 22902 #539-05-1991 L1999 **PCC** *020 †20

SCHWENZER, Karen Jean. 500 RAY C HUNT DR 22903 #035-08-1982 L1986 **AN CCM** *020 †05

SCOTT, Christopher Mark. 1000 E HIGH ST, STE B 22902 #036-08-2003 L2007 **D** *020 †15

SEALE, Daniel Logan. 459 LOCUST AVE, MARTHA JEFFERSON HOSPITAL 22902 #051-01-1963 L1963 **DR** *071 †80

SEIDER, Nir. ■ 22908 #550-03-1992 L2003 *100

SEIDMAN-ZAGER, Michael. ■ 22903 #023-12-2008 *012

SEKHON, Harjot Singh. PO BOX 800136, UNIVERSITY OF VIRGINIA 22908 #495-43-2002 L2004 **CHP** *012

SEKHON, Rajneet Kaur. GME BOX 800136 22908 #305-01-2006 L2007 **FP** *012

SELDEN, Robert Francis. JEFFERSON PARK AVE 22908 #051-01-1958 1958 **PD PUD** *040 †55

SEMLER, Matthew Wall. ■ 22908 #051-01-2008 *012

SETO, Craig Kailani. 500 RAY C HUNT DR 22903 #051-07-1988 L2000 **FM FSM** *020 †18

SHADA, Amber Leigh. ■ 22908 #056-05-2007 L2007 **GS** *012

SHAFFER, Hubert Adams, Jr. UNIV OF VIRGINIA HOSPITAL, RADIOLOGY, P.O. BOX 800170 22908 #055-01-1965 L1970 **DR R** *020 †80

SHAFFREY, Catherine. 3325 ROSEDELL LN, ANESTHESIOLOGY 22903 #032-01-1988 L1993 **AN PME** *020 †05

SHAFFREY, Christopher I. ■ 22908 #051-01-1986 L1993 **NS OSS** *020 †25,40

SHAFFREY, Mark Edwin. UNIVERSITY OF VIRGINIA HEA, DEPT OF NEUROSURGERY BOX 8 22908 #051-01-1987 L1988 **NS** *020 †25

SHAH, Jasmine Ajit. PO BOX 800546, UNIVERSITY OF VIRGINIA 22908 #495-22-1999 L2006 **PCC** *012 †20

SHAH, Satu Jayant. ■ 22903 #011-02-2004 L2005 **IM** *012

SHAIKH, Shaziya Gul. ■ 22903 #051-01-2007 L2007 **PD** *012

SHAKOOR, Akbar. PO BOX 800715, DEPT OF OPH 22908 #704-25-2002 L2007 **OPH** *012

SHAMI, Vanessa Marie. HOSPITAL W LEE ST, UNIV OF VIRGINIA POB 80070 22908 #051-01-1996 L1996 **GE** *020 †20

SHARROW, Christopher Mich. 311 10TH ST NE, ALBEMARLE ANESTHESIA 22902 #051-01-2004 L2005 **AN** *012

SHAW, William Edward, Jr. 459 LOCUST AVE 22902 #016-11-1990 L1994 **OPH** *020 †35

SHEEHAN, Jason Patrick. ■ 22903 #051-01-1998 L1998 **NS** *020

SHELL, Troy L. ■ 22902 #051-07-2008 *012

SHEMO, John Palmer D. 2496 OLD IVY RD STE 400, BLUE RIDGE 22903 #055-01-1975 L1979 **P PYG** *020 †75 ‡

SHEMO, Mary Carroll. 2496 OLD IVY RD STE 400 22903 #055-01-1976 L1979 **P** *020 †75

SHEN, Francis Haotso. PO BOX 800159 22908 #051-01-1996 L1996 **OSS** *020 †40

SHERMAN, Jonathan Harris. ■ 22902 #012-01-2003 L2003 **NS** *012

SHILLING, Alfred Tanner. ■ 22903 #051-04-2003 L2003 **DR** *012

SHILLING, Ashley Matthews. JEFFERSON PK BOX 291 22908 #051-01-2001 L2001 **AN** *100 †05

SHIM, Yun Sup. ■ 22903 #051-04-1998 L2004 **PCC** *020 †20

SHIN, Kyungmin. ■ 22903 #036-05-2007 L2007 **IM** *012

SHIN, Thomas Arnold. ■ 22902 #023-01-2003 L2003 **DR** *100 †80

SHIPLEY, Patricia Jean. 914 E JEFFERSON ST, STE 204 22902 #010-02-1989 L1994 **N** *020 †75

SHONKA, David Charles. ■ 22903 #051-01-2004 L2004 **OTO** *012

SHORT, Robert Franklin. ■ 22903 #051-01-2006 L2006 **DR** *012

SHOUSHTARI, Asal Namaki. PO BOX 800136, UNIVERSITY OF VIRGINIA MED 22908 #016-42-2006 L2006 **RO** *012

SHRODE, Charles Willard. ■ 22902 #017-20-2007 L2007 **IM** *012

SHRUM, John Richard. 1100 E HIGH ST STE 1C 22902 #051-01-1977 L1981 **D** *020 †15

SHUMAKER, Nathan Ralph. PO BOX 800136, UNIVERSITY OF VIRGINIA 22908 #020-12-2004 L2004 **PTH** *012

SHUTT, Leslie Ernest. UNIV OF VA MED CTR, # ANES 22908 #917-10-1969 *100

SHUTTER, Jamie D. PO BOX 800136, UNIVERSITY OF VIRGINIA 22908 #035-15-2001 L2005 **PTH** *100 †50

SIBRE, Kelly Elizabeth. ■ 22903 #051-07-2007 L2007 **IM** *012

SIDHU, Harneil Singh. PO BOX 800136, UNIVERSITY OF VIRGINIA 22908 #065-06-2000 L2005 **VIR** *100 †80

SILVA, Anjali. 400 BRANDON AVE, UNIV OF VA STUDENT HEALTH 22908 #008-02-1996 L1999 **IM** *020 †20

SILVER, David Freeman. 800 PRESTON AVE 22903 #036-01-1976 L1985 **P** *020 †75

SIMMERS, Mary Elizabeth. ■ 22903 #041-14-2006 L2006 **IM** *012

SIMNAD, Virginia Irana. 500 RAY C HUNT DR, FONTAINE ADULT NEUROLOGY 22908 #036-01-1993 L1997 **N** *020 †75

SINGH, Karen Elizabeth. ■ 22902 #017-20-2006 L2006 **AN** *012

SINGH, Raman Preet. PO BOX 800300 22908 #495-08-1996 L2002 *100

SINGH A/L RANJIT SINGH, Ra. 237 COLONNADE DR, APT 23 22908 #539-06-2000 L2003 **GS** *012

SINHA, Tushar. ■ 22902 #665-01-2005 **IM** *012

SINKIN, Robert Alan. ■ 22902 #035-45-1980 L2006 **NPM PD** *030 †55

SIPE, William H. ■ 22903 #051-01-1951 L1951 **U** *071 †95

SIRAGY, Helmy M. 500 RAY C HUNT DR 22903 #915-07-1976 L1984 **END IM** *020 †20

SIRIWETCHADARAK, Rapipen. PO BOX 800136, UNIVERSITY OF VIRGINIA MED 22908 #891-02-1999 L2006 **APM** *100

SIZEMORE, Alecia Whitaker. HLTH SYSTEM, UNIV OF VIRGINIA 22908 #017-20-2006 L2007 **DR** *012

SLAWSON, David Craig. 500 RAY C HUNT DR 22903 #025-01-1981 L1983 **FM** *040 †18

SLINGLUFF, Craig L, Jr. OLD MED SCHOOL BLDG., UNIV OF VIRGINIA HLTH SCI 22908 #051-01-1984 L1991 **SO GS** *050 †85

SLITT, Gavin Tyler. ■ 22903 #008-02-2007 L2007 **IM** *012

SMITH, Justin Bracewell. DEPT OF PSYCH, UNIV OF VA HEALTH 22908 #051-01-2007 L2007 **P** *012

SMITH, Karl Danl. 459 LOCUST AVE, PERRY BROWN MED ADMIN 22902 #051-04-1983 L1987 **EM** *020 †20

SMITH, Philip William. ■ 22902 #051-01-2003 L2003 **GS** *012

SMITH, Robert Lee, II. ■ 22902 #048-13-2000 L2000 **TS** *012 †85

SMOLYAK, Nelly Alex. ■ 22903 #023-01-2004 L2002 **END** *012 †20

SNAVELY, Nicholas R. PO BOX 800718 22908 #048-04-2006 L2007 **D** *012

SNEED, Benjamin Phillip. BOX 800909, UNIVERSITY OF VIRGINIA HEA 22908 #054-04-2004 L2004 **IM** *100 †20

SNIDER, Cynthia Brigitte. ■ 22902 #049-01-2005 L2005 **IM** *012

SNOW, Rodney English. PO BOX 800136, UNIVERSITY OF VIRGINIA 22908 #047-06-2005 L2005 **IM** *012

SNUFFIN, William J, Jr. 459 LOCUST AVE, MARTHA JEFFERSON HOSPITAL 22902 #022-75-1985, ▲ L1994 **EM** *020 †16

SOLENSKI, Nina Jean. UVA DEPT OF NEUROLOGY-8003 22908 #041-02-1989 L1990 **N NS** *050 †75

SOLOMON, Hemant. PO BOX 800136, UNIVERSITY OF VIRGINIA 22908 #917-19-1995 L2005 **CD** *012

SOUTHERLAND, Andrew Meban. ■ 22902 #036-08-2006 L2007 **N** *012

SPAULDING, Cynthia Anne. 459 LOCUST AVE, MARTHA JEFFERSON HOSPITAL 22902 #051-01-1982 L1985 **RO** *020 †80

SPEARS, Nickie Melinda. 914 E HIGH ST 22902 #001-02-1989 L1990 **P** *020 †75

SPIEKERMANN, Burkhard F. 1224 W MAIN ST 22903 #041-09-1989 L1993 **AN IM** *020 †05

SPINELLI, Laura Lynn. 459 LOCUST AVE, MARTHA JEFFERSON HOSPITAL 22902 #035-03-1995 L2001 **PCP** *020 †50

SPRADLIN, Wilford Wayne. SCHOOL OF MEDICINE BOX 623, DEPT OF PSYCHIATRIC MED 22908 #051-01-1957 L1957 **P** *030 †75

SPRING, Gabriel Brett. ■ 22903 #051-01-2008 *012

STADLER, Brett Thomas. 311 10TH ST NE 22902 #025-01-1995 L1996 **AN** *020 †05

STADLER, Sarah Ann. 914 E JEFFERSON ST, STE G4 22902 #025-01-1995 L1996 **OBG** *020 †30

ST AMANT, Jeffrey Scott. ■ 22903 #001-02-2006 L2006 **EM** *012

STAMPS, Sarah Marguerite. ■ 22903 #051-01-2008 *012

STARNES, Trevor T. PO BOX 800159, UNIVERSITY OF VIRGINIA 22908 #017-20-2004 L2004 **ORS** *012

STAY, Rourke Mcquire. ■ 22902 #051-01-2004 L2005 **DR** *012

STEERS, William D. PO BOX 800422, UNIV OF VA SCHOOL OF MEDIC 22908 #038-43-1980 L1988 **U** *050 †95

STELOW, Edward Benjamin. ■ 22902 #056-06-1998 L2004 **PCP** *100 †50

STEPHAN, Scott James. PO BOX 800136, UNIVERSITY OF VIRGINIA 22908 #047-05-2005 L2005 **OTO** *012

STEPHEN, Siobhan Marie. ■ 22902 #024-01-1997 L2007 **OMF** *020

STEVENSON, Richard D. 2270 IVY RD, AND RESEARCH INSTITUTE 22903 #051-01-1984 L1989 **PD** *050 †55

STOKES, Jayme Bruce. ■ 22902 #036-08-2005 L2005 **GS** *012

STOKES, Melissa Carin. 2219B CENTER AVE 22903 #051-01-2006 L2006 **P** *012

STOKES, Robert L, Jr. 459 LOCUST AVE 22902 #051-01-1984 L1985 **FM** *020 †18

STOLER, Mark Howard. 500 RAY C HUNT DR 22903 #035-45-1980 L1993 **PTH PCP** *020 †50

STONE, David Deaderick. UNIV OF VA MED CTR 22908 #051-01-1958 L1958 **GE IM** *020 †20

STONE, David J. BOX 238 22908 #035-19-1978 L1980 **AN CCM** *020 †20,05

STRAUSS, Stephanie. ■ 22903 #032-01-2002 L2007 **GS** *100

STRAYER, Scott Merle. 500 RAY C HUNT DR 22903 #051-04-1994 L1994 **FM** *020 †18

STRIETER, Robert Martin. PO BOX 800466, CHAIR, DEPT OF INTER MED 22908 #025-12-1983 L2003 **PUD CCM** *050 †20

STRINGER, Janet Lynn. U OF VA SCH MED 394 NEURO 22908 #051-01-1984 L1986 **N** *050

STURGILL, Thomas Wayne. BOX 577, UNIV OF VIRGINIA SCH OF ME 22908 #051-01-1978 L1982 **IM** *020

SUBRAMANIAN, Natrajan Raj. ■ 22902 #056-06-2001 L2004 **CD** *012 †20

SUDHIR, Amita. ■ 22902 #051-01-2004 L2004 **EM** *100

SULLIVAN, Spencer Kemp. ■ 22903 #036-01-2005 L2005 **PD** *012

SUNDARARAJAN, Sripriya. ■ 22903 #495-16-1997 L2006 **PD** *012

SURATT, Paul Michael. 500 RAY C HUNT DR 22903 #038-06-1970 L1974 **PUD IM** *050 †20

SUTHERLAND, Sara Faill. 459 LOCUST AVE 22902 #005-14-1983 L2007 **EM** *030 †16

SUTPHEN, James Leonard. 500 RAY C HUNT DR 22903 #035-01-1972 L1981 **PD** *020 †55

SUTTON, Jocelyn Terry. ■ 22903 #033-06-2007 L2007 **PTH** *012

SUTTON, Thomas Grant. PO BOX 800710, UNIV OF VIRGINIA MED CTR 22908 #047-06-2007 L2007 **AN** *012

SWANK, Jessica F. ■ 22902 #055-01-2007 L2007 **FP** *012

SWEE, Warren. HEALTH SYSTEM, UNIV OF VIRGINIA 22908 #010-01-2001 L2002 **VIR** *012 †80

SYDNOR, Thomas Austin, Jr. 1000 E HIGH ST STE A 22902 #051-01-1956 L1956 **OTO PS** *071 †45

SYNAN, Matthew James. ■ 22903 #041-02-2007 L2007 **IM** *012

SYVERUD, Scott Alan. 500 RAY C HUNT DR 22903 #035-15-1981 L1992 **EM** *020 †16

SZELES, Robert Joseph. ■ 22903 #033-06-2006 L2006 **IM** *012

TACHE LEON, Carlos Albert. PO BOX 800136, UNIVERSITY OF VIRGINIA 22908 #264-01-1994 L2004 **GS** *012

TAFT, William Carlisle. ■ 22908 #048-14-1998 L1998 **N** *020

TAIGEN, Tyler Louis. PO BOX 800136, UNIVERSITY OF VIRGINIA 22908 #008-02-2003 L2003 **IM** *020 †20

TATAR, Steven Andrew. 1011 E JEFFERSON ST, STE 202 22902 #016-11-1967 L1974 **IM** *020 †20

TATE, Laura Allison. ■ 22902 #011-03-2004 L2004 **P** *012

TAYLOR, Angela Marie. UNIV OF VA HOSP EXP BLDG, 1215 LEE ST 22908 #045-01-1997 L2001 **IC CD** *100 †20

TAYLOR, Frank E. ■ 22903 #051-01-1950 L1950 **IM** *071 †20

TAYLOR, Latoya Danielle. ■ 22903 #051-01-2007 L2008 *100

TAYLOR, Lauren Leigh. ■ 22903 #047-06-2005 L2005 **EM** *012

TAYLOR, Peyton Troy, Jr. JEFFERSON PARK AVE, UNIV OF VA, P.O. BOX 80071 22908 #001-02-1968 L1969 **GO OBG** *020 †30

TAYLOR, Samuel Andrew. ■ 22903 #051-01-2005 L2005 **N** *012

TCHOUAFFI-NANA, Florence. HLTH SCIENCES, UNIV OF VIRGINIA 22908 #165-07-1996 L2007 **ID** *012 †20

TEATES, Charles David. UNIV VIRGINIA MED CTR, BOX 170 22908 #051-01-1963 L1963 **NM R** *071 †80,28

TEJA, Jagdish Singh. 1224 W MAIN ST STE 710 22903 #495-03-1960 L1974 **P OS** *071

TEKOLA, Bezawit Dejene. ■ 22903 #051-01-2008 *012

TEMPLE, Joel David. PO BOX 800386, UNIV OF VA HEALTH SYSTEMS 22908 #016-02-1991 L1998 **PDC** *012 †20

TEMPLETON, Dennis J. 500 RAY C HUNT DR 22903 #005-18-1984 L2001 **OS PTH** *050 †50

TESORIERE, Paul Joseph. 459 LOCUST AVE, MARTHA JEFFERSON HOSPITAL 22902 #051-07-2000 L2000 **HOS** *012

THEODORESCU, Dan. UVA 2ND FLOOR RM 2570, DEPT OF UROLOGY/ UNIV OF V 22908 #065-06-1986 L1995 **U** *020 †95

THIAGARAJAH, Siva. 1101 E JEFFERSON ST, STE 1 22902 #220-01-1968 L1974 **OBG MFM** *020 †30

THIELE, Arthur L. ■ 22903 #005-12-1947 L1954 **R** *071 †80

THOLPADY, Sunil Shantigod. PO BOX 800136, UNIVERSITY OF VIRGINIA 22908 #051-01-2005 L2005 **PS** *012

THOMAS, Andree Raymonde. ■ 22903 #396-06-1956 L1966 **CD IM** *071

THOMAS, Christopher Y. PO BOX 800716, 6TH FL MULTISTORY BLDG 600 22908 #019-02-1974 L1981 **ON HEM** *020 †20

THOMAS, Joylene W. ■ 22903 #047-07-2007 L2007 **ORS** *012

THOMAS, Kenneth Ryan. ■ 22903 #027-01-2006 L2006 **U** *012

THOMAS, Vinoo S. PO BOX 800136, UNIVERSITY OF VIRGINIA MED 22908 #035-15-2002 L2006 **APM** *020 †05

THOMPSON, Elizabeth Dell. ■ 22903 #051-01-2008 *012

THOMPSON, Hope Sherie. ■ 22903 #051-07-1999 L2001 **GS** *020 †85

THOMSON, James A, Jr. 1224 W MAIN ST 22903 #051-01-1973 L1975 **P** *020 †75

THORNER, Michael Oliver. 450 RAY C HUNT DR 22903 #917-26-1970 L1979 **END IM** *050

TIAN, Fang. PO BOX 800136 22908 #243-76-1991 L2006 **PM** *012

TIEDEMAN, James Stuart. 500 RAY C HUNT DR 22903 #036-07-1977 L1992 **OPH** *020 †35

TIEDEMAN, John Stuart. PO BOX 800136, UNIVERSITY OF VIRGINIA 22908 #051-01-2004 L2005 **AN** *012

TILLACK, Thomas Warner. 1215 LEE ST HOSP EXPY#3070, DEPT OF PATH RM 3070 22908 #008-01-1963 L1976 **ATP** *040 †50

TILTON, Elisha Peter. PO BOX 800715, UNIVERSITY OF VIRGINIA 22908 #050-02-2004 L2004 **OPH** *012

TIMOFEEV, Julia. ■ 22903 #011-03-2006 L2006 **OBG** *012

TING, Paul H. 500 RAY C HUNT DR 22903 #011-02-1992 L2000 **AN** *020 †05

TIOURIRINE, Mohamed. ■ 22903 #125-01-1988 L2004 **AN** *020 †05

TODOROVIC, Slobodan M. 800710 MAIL BOX, DEPT OF ANESTHESIOLGY 22908 #957-02-1982 L2001 **AN** *075 †05

TOLEDANO, Roulhac Darby. ■ 22903 #036-05-2004 L2004 **AN** *012

TOMPKINS, Wm Fraser, III. 310 OLD IVY WAY, STE 201 22903 #051-01-1966 L1966 **GE IM** *020 †20

TOWNSEND, Gregory Clarke. 500 RAY C HUNT DR 22903 #051-01-1986 L1990 **ID** *020 †20,55

TRACY, Chad Robert. ■ 22903 #018-03-2003 L2003 **U** *012

TRAHAN, Katherine M. 459 LOCUST AVE, MARTHA JEFFERSON SURGICAL 22902 #051-04-1998 L2007 **GS** *020 †85

TRAHAN, Michael David. 459 LOCUST AVE 22902 #048-15-1996 L2007 **GS** *020

TRAUL, Christine Sipp. ■ 22902 #038-43-2003 L2003 **CHN** *100 †55

TRAUL, David Edison. ■ 22902 #038-43-2003 L2003 **N** *100

TRITT, Shawn Eric. ■ 22902 #012-01-2005 L2006 **GS** *100

TROPELLO, Steven Patrick. ■ 22903 #051-01-2007 L2007 **EM** *012

TROWBRIDGE, Elisa Rodrigu. ■ 22902 #023-01-1997 L2007 **OBG OS** *020 †30

TROWBRIDGE, Matthew John. ■ 22902 #012-05-2000 L2000 **PD** *100 †55

TRUE, Barbara Sterchak. ■ 22903 #051-07-1989 L1991 **RHU IM** *100 †20

TRUGMAN, Joel Michael. PO BOX 800394, MCKIM HALL RM 2026 HOSPITA 22908 #024-05-1979 L1985 **N** *020 †55

TRUNDLE, Ashby Robert. 1011 E JEFFERSON ST 22902 #051-01-2001 L2001 **PD** *020 †55

TRUWIT, Jonathon Dean. 500 RAY C HUNT DR 22903 #010-02-1983 L1989 **PUD IM** *020 †20

TSANG, Katrina Wai Kay. JEFFERSON PK BOX 291 22908 #462-02-2004 L2006 **FP** *012

TUBB, Angela Rae. ■ 22905 #048-16-2003 L2006 **RHU** *012 †20

TUCKER, Amy Leigh. 500 RAY C HUNT DR 22903 #036-01-1986 L1989 **IM CD** *020 †20

TUCKER, Jim Boyce. 310 OLD IVY WAY, DIV OF CHILD & FAMILY PSYC 22903 #036-01-1986 L1989 **CHP P** *020 †75

TUNG, Kenneth Sik-Kwong. UNIV. OF VIRGINIA BOX 214, DEPT PATHOLOGY 22908 #143-02-1959 L1991 **PTH OS** *050 †50

TURBA, Ulku Cenk. PO BOX 800170, UNIV OF VA 22908 #902-22-1992 L2004 **NR** *100

TURMAN, Kimberly Ann. ■ 22903 #030-05-2002 L2007 **OSM** *012

TURNER, Adrienne Elizabet. ■ 22903 #048-16-2005 L2005 **P** *012

TURNER, James Cary. 500 RAY C HUNT DR 22903 #056-05-1976 L1978 **IM** *020 †20

TURNER, Ronald Bruce. PO BOX 800386, UNIV DEPT OF PEDIATRICS 22908 #016-45-1976 L2000 **PD ID** *050 †55

UHT, Rosalie Marie. 500 RAY C HUNT DR 22903 #035-48-1990 L2000 **NP** *050 †50

UNION, Nancy Ann. 565 BLOOMFIELD RD, EAST-WEST MEDICINE, P.C. 22903 #032-01-1980 L2001 **IM** *020

VADEN, Edwin Booth. ■ 22903 #051-01-1945 L1945 **PD** *072 †55

VALDELIEVRE, Sixtine-Pacif. ■ 22903 #051-01-2008 *012

VALIVETI, Prakash. ■ 22902 #055-02-2002 L2004 **DR** *012

VANCE, Mary Lee. 500 RAY C HUNT DR 22903 #021-05-1977 L1981 **END IM** *020 †20

VANDE POL, Scott Brian. P.O.BOX 800904, UNIVERSITY OF VIRGINIA 22908 #005-18-1985 L2003 **ATP OS** *050 †50

VAN DER SOMMEN, Lynda D. ■ 22903 #065-01-1977 L1978 **GP** *040

VANDYCK, Kofi Besebro. ■ 22903 #051-01-2007 L2007 **GS** *012

VAN HORN, Sandra Anne. ■ 22903 #051-01-2008 *012

VAUGHN, Christopher N. ■ 22903 #045-01-2002 L2002 **HO** *012 †20

VEBER, Lara C. ■ 22903 #045-01-2002 L2003 **FM** *100

VEHSE, Nico Walter. ■ 22902 #409-23-2002 L2007 **PD** *100 †55

VENSKO PINKERTON, Jo Ann. 2955 IVY RD STE 104 22903 #051-04-1981 L1983 **OBG** *020 †30

VERGHESE, George M. ■ 22903 #036-07-1993 L2002 **CCA** *020 †20

VOLKAN, Vamik Djemal. 2955 IVY RD 22903 #902-03-1956 L1962 **PYA P** *030

VOSS, John D, III. 500 RAY C HUNT DR 22903 #051-01-1984 L1989 **IM** *020 †20

WABIN, Jennifer. PO BOX 800623, UNIVERSITY OF VIRGINIA 22908 #048-12-2004 L2004 **P** *012

WAGGONER, Linda Ann. JEFFERSON PARK AVE, DEPT OF PEDIATRICS BOX 386 22908 #018-03-1989 L1992 **PD ID** *040 †55

WAGNER, Yasmin Isabel. PO BOX 800136, UNIVERSITY OF VIRGINIA 22908 #051-04-2005 L2005 **PTH** *012

WAHAB, Raed Ali. ■ 22903 #605-03-2000 L2005 **PCC** *012 †20

WALDRON, Peter Edmund. 500 RAY C HUNT DR 22903 #042-01-1983 L1985 **PHO PD** *020 †55

WALDROP, Christine Sandif. ■ 22902 #027-01-2004 L2004 **AN** *012

WALKER, James C. ■ 22903 #008-01-1951 L1983 **PD GP** *071 †55

WALKER, Shetarra Earnette. 411 VALLEY ROAD EXT 22903 #024-05-2003 L2006 **PDC** *012 †55

WALLACE, Karl Kenneth, Jr. RADIOLOGY DEPT, UNIV OF VA SCHOOL OF MED 22908 #051-04-1958 L1958 **DR NM** *071 †80,28

WALLENBORN, White M. ■ 22903 #051-01-1955 L1955 **OTO AM** *071 †45

WALTERS, Dustin Matthew. ■ 22903 #051-01-2007 L2007 **GS** *012

WANG, Andrew Yung-Ching. ■ 22902 #051-01-2001 L2007 **GE** *100 †20

WANG, Gwo-Jaw. JEFFERSON PK AVE, DEPT ORS 22908 #385-01-1966 L1975 **ORS** *020 †40

WARD, George Wm, Jr. UNIV OF VA MED CTR, DEPT OF INTERN MED BOX 225 22908 #010-01-1963 L1964 **A IM** *071 †03,20

WARD, Mary Dearing. SCI CENTER, UNIV OF VA HEALTH 22908 #051-01-1977 L1982 **IM** *020 †20

WARREN, Bertram Lee. ■ 22903 #051-01-1959 L1959 **GYN** *071 †30

WATSON TROJAN, Rebecca L. PO BOX 800136, UNIVERSITY OF VIRGINIA 22908 #026-04-2003 L2003 **FM** *100 †18

WAY, Denise Ann. ■ 22903 #035-03-2003 L2003 **FM** *100 †18

WEARY, Peyton Edwin. 1224 W MAIN ST, UNIV OF VA HOSP 22903 #051-01-1955 L1955 **D** *071 †15

WEAVER, Brad Ashby. ■ 22903 #051-01-2004 L2006 **NEP** *012 †20

WEAVER, William Ronald. 459 LOCUST AVE, ALBEMARLE ANESTHESIA, PLC 22902 #028-34-1996 L1997 **AN CCA** *012 †20

WEBB, Jeffrey Walker. PO BOX 800386, DEPARTMENT OF PEDIATRICS 22908 #012-01-2003 L2003 **PD** *020 †55

WEEKS, Ruth Bley. ■ 22902 #051-01-1960 L1960 **P CHP** *071

WEHRLI, Gay. ■ 22908 #005-06-1994 L2007 **CLP BBK** *020 †50

■ = Address Information Privacy Protected

WELLONS, Harry Albert, Jr. PO BOX 800679, UVA 22908 #051-04-1961 L1961 TS GS *071 †85,90

WELLS, Mary Kathryn. ■ 22905 #051-01-2008 *012

WERNER, Erika Franklin. ■ 22903 #051-04-2004 L2004 OBG *012

WEST, Amy Marisa. ■ 22903 #051-01-2003 L2003 CD *012 †20

WEST, John Jason. ■ 22903 #047-05-2000 L2004 ICE *012 †20

WEYNAND, Beth A. PO BOX 800136, UNIVERSITY OF VIRGINIA MED 22908 #048-14-2006 L2006 AN *012

WHEBY, Munsey Stephen. UNIVERSITY VA BOX 800711, DEANS OFFICE SCHOOL OF MED 22908 #051-01-1955 L1955 HEM NTR *040 †20

WHEELER, Lauren Michelle. ■ 22902 #051-04-2005 L2005 OBG *012

WHITE, James Lee. 500 RAY C HUNT DR 22903 #036-05-1986 L1988 AN *020 †05

WHITEHEAD, Matt Thomas. PO BOX 800136, UNIVERSITY OF VIRGINIA 22908 #047-06-2004 L2005 DR *012

WHITEHILL, Richard. 500 RAY C HUNT DR 22903 #051-01-1972 L1978 ORS GS *040 †40

WHITING, J D. 459 LOCUST AVE, MARTHA JEFFERSON HOSPITAL 22902 #051-01-1993 L1995 EM *020 †16

WICK, Mark Robt. 500 RAY C HUNT DR 22903 #056-05-1978 L1999 PTH DMP *062 †50

WILCOX, Susan Mary. 311 10TH ST NE 22902 #917-14-1982 L1995 AN *020

WILDER, Robert Phillips. 545 RAY C HUNT DR, DEPT OF PHYSICAL MED & REH 22903 #051-01-1988 L1989 PM *020 †60

WILHELM, Morton C. DEPT OF SURGERY BOX 181, UNIV OF VA MEDICAL CTR 22908 #051-01-1947 L1947 GS *071 †85

WILLENBORG, Melissa Dawn. PO BOX 800159, UVA ORTHOPAEDIC SURGERY 22908 #018-03-2006 L2006 ORS *012

WILLIAMS, Bernard Moore. ■ 22903 #051-01-1964 L1964 P *020 †75

WILLIAMS, Elizabeth K. 2411 IVY RD 22903 #051-01-1983 L1987 PD *020 †55

WILLIAMS, Freddie Maxine. ■ 22903 #024-01-2003 L2006 CD *012 †20

WILLIAMS, Gaylord Stone. 2955 IVY RD 22903 #051-01-1960 L1960 PS GS *020 †85,65

WILLIAMS, John Greiner. 1100 E HIGH ST 22902 #051-01-1985 L1986 GS *020 †85

WILLIAMS, Mark Edward. 1224 W MAIN ST, 2ND FLOOR, STE 201 22903 #036-01-1976 L1999 IMG IM *020 †20

WILLMS, Christopher D. 459 LOCUST AVE, MARTHA JEFFERSON SURGICAL 22902 #048-12-1990 L2006 TS *020 †85,90

WILLS, Thomas Luke. 1101 E JEFFERSON ST 22902 #051-01-1990 L2002 OBG *020 †30

WILLS, Wendi Rebecca. PO BOX 800729 22908 #010-02-1998 L2003 FM *020 †18

WILLSON, Douglas F. UNIV OF VA, DEPT OF PEDIATRICS 22908 #035-08-1977 L1983 CCP AN *020 †55,05

WILSON, Barbara B. 500 RAY C HUNT DR 22903 #051-01-1978 L1979 D *020 †15

WILSON, David Cole, III. 500 RAY C HUNT DR 22903 #051-01-1977 L1984 CHP P *020 †75

WILSON, Edward Croft. ■ 22903 #051-04-1958 L1958 GE IM *071

WILSON, William Grady. PO BOX 800386, UNIV OF VIRGINIA HEALTH SY 22908 #036-01-1974 L1979 PD MG *020 †55,19

WIMER, Mary Catherine. 1 BOARS HEAD LN 22903 #048-02-1981 L1985 P PYA *020

WINEMAN, Robert Wade. ■ 22902 #027-01-2003 L2003 DR *012

WINTER, William C. 400 10TH ST NE 22902 #012-05-1999 L1999 N SME *020

WINTHER, Birgit. UVA HEALTH SYSTEM, BOX 800, DEPT OF OTOLARYNGOLOGY 22908 #297-01-1979 L1991 OTO *020

WISMAN, Paul Pence, Jr. 1011 E JEFFERSON ST, JEFFERSON MEDICAL BUILDING 22902 #051-01-1990 L1993 PD AI *020 †20

WISPELWEY, Brian. BARRINGER WING 2409, HOSPITAL DRIVE 22908 #033-05-1982 L1989 ID IM *020 †20

WITMER, David Scott. 912 E HIGH ST 22902 #051-04-1989 L1993 ORS *020 †40

WITTMANN, Annemarei. PO BOX 800291, UVA 22908 #041-14-1999 L2000 IM *020

WOLANSKI, Edward Theodore. 400 LOCUST AVE 22902 #051-01-1982 L1986 OBG *020 †30 ‡

WOLF, Andrew Michael. 500 RAY C HUNT DR 22903 #051-01-1984 L1993 IM *040 †20

WOLF, Todd Earl. 459 LOCUST AVE, H.O.P.E. 22902 #654-01-1999 L2000 HO *020 †20

WOLFE, Karyn Elizabeth. 1011 E JEFFERSON ST, JEFFERSON MEDICAL BUILDING 22902 #051-01-2002 L2002 PD *020 †55

WONG, Emily Joy. 2955 IVY RD STE 303, UNIVERSITY OF VIRGINIA 22903 #005-18-1995 L2003 PD PDI *020 †55

WONG, Matthew H. ■ 22902 #065-10-2004 L2006 *012

WOODARD, Charles Ryan. ■ 22903 #047-07-2005 L2005 OTO *012

WOODS, Andrew Michael. BOX 238 22908 #011-03-1979 L1982 AN *020 †55,05

WOOTEN, Geo Frederick, Jr. POB 200394, DENT OF NEUROLOGY 22908 #035-20-1970 L1971 N *020

WORRALL, Bradford Burke. UVA HEALTH SYSTEM #800394, DEPT OF NEUROLOGY 22908 #012-05-1993 L1997 N VM *050 †75

WRENTMORE, Amy Lynn. ■ 22903 #041-14-2001 L2001 PD *020 †55

WYATT, Christopher Harris. ■ 22903 #027-01-2005 L2005 AN *012

WYATT, Julie Porter. ■ 22903 #027-01-2005 L2005 D *012

WYKER, Arthur W, Jr. PO BOX 800422 22908 #035-01-1949 L1960 U *071 †95

YANG, Zequan. JEFFERSON PK BOX 291 22908 #243-47-1987 L2005 GS *012

YEATON, Paul. 500 RAY C HUNT DR 22903 #055-01-1986 L1992 IM *020 †20

YEMEN, Terrance Allan. 500 RAY C HUNT DR 22903 #068-01-1979 L1990 *020

YOO, Heannie Young. ■ 22903 #041-14-2005 L2006 AN *012

YOSHIDA, Cynthia Michi. 902 E JEFFERSON ST, STE 201 22902 #019-02-1987 L1993 GE *020 †20

YOUEL, John Kenneth, Jr. 1011 E JEFFERSON ST 22902 #025-01-1960 L1967 GS *071 †85

YOUNG, Harold Edmund. NORTHRIDGE, GENERAL MEDICINE-UVA 22903 #051-01-1974 L1975 GP *020

YOUNG, Jeffrey Seth. LEE ST, UNIV OF VA HEALTH SYSTEM-S 22908 #051-04-1988 L1994 GS TRS *020 †85

YOUNG, Jennifer Lynette. ■ 22903 #045-01-2002 L2006 OBG *100

YOUNG, Kisha Janelle. ■ 22903 #051-01-2008 *012

YOUNGER, Deborah Anne. 2 BOARS HEAD PL # 240 22903 #011-04-1979 L1980 P CHP *020

ZANELLI, Santina Agnes. DEPT PEDS BOX 800386, UNIV VIRGINIA 22908 #396-14-1998 L2003 NPM *100 †55

ZAVAREI, Keyvan. 22908 #654-01-1997 L2001 PM *100 †60

ZAWODNY, Sarah Rose. ■ 22903 #056-06-2007 L2007 ORS *012

ZAZAKOS, Christopher. 459 LOCUST AVE, CENTER FOR CANCER CARE 22902 #035-08-1972 L1978 ON HEM *020 †20

ZHU, Zheng. ■ 22903 #027-01-2007 L2007 IM *012

ZIA, Saqib. ■ 22908 #704-01-2001 L2008 GS *100

ZIVONY, Adam Seth. PO BOX 800744 22908 #012-01-2006 L2006 IM *012

ZLUPKO, Michael C. ■ 22903 #041-01-2007 L2007 IM *012

ZUO, Zhiyi. 500 RAY C HUNT DR 22903 #243-21-1983 L1996 AN *020 †05

ZWANG, Oren Banjamin. ■ 22902 #010-02-1998 L2006 EM *012 †20

CHASE CITY – MECKLENBURG

CHILDREY, Stephen. ■ 23924 #051-04-1947 L1947 PHP OS *071

GIVEN, Frederick True, Jr. ■ 23924 #051-04-1953 L1953 GO GYN *071 †30

MOORE, Earle Winston. 946 N MAIN ST 23924 #051-04-1969 L1969 FM *020 †18

SUSLICK, Randall Hugh. 946 N MAIN ST 23924 #051-04-1973 L1980 GP OBG *020

CHATHAM – PITTSYLVANIA

AFZAL, Asma. 4 MAIN ST, HEALTH CENTERS OF PIEDMONT 24531 #704-05-1992 L2000 FM *020 †18

SHAH, Mineshkumar Rameshc. 19144 US HIGHWAY 29 24531 #495-89-1995 L2004 FM *020 †18

WHITEHEAD, Betty G Willis. ■ 24531 #051-01-1941 L1941 PD *071 †55

CHECK – FLOYD

CLARKSON, William David. ■ 24072 #045-01-1958 L1969 P *071

CHESAPEAKE – CHESAPEAKE CITY

ADLEBERG, Jon Michael. 1230 PROGRESSIVE DR, STE 100 23320 #041-09-1990 L1997 OPH *020 †35

ALIMARD, Ramin. 736 BATTLEFIELD BLVD N 23320 #051-04-1994 L1997 IC CD *020 †20

ALNAIF, Bunan. 3806 POPLAR HILL RD, STE B 23321 #528-01-1983 L1999 OBG U *020 †30

AMABILE, Anthony Thos. 712 OLD FIELDS ARCH 23320 #033-06-1988 L1991 IM *020 †20

AMIN, Biral Sanjay. ■ 23320 #051-07-2000 L2005 RO *020 †80

ANDERSON, Abraham S N. 1013 EDEN WAY N, STE A B & C 23320 #010-03-1965 L1971 OBG OS *020 †30

ANGLIN, Victor T, Jr. 736 BATTLEFIELD BLVD N 23320 #010-03-1979 L1982 IM EM *020 †20,16

ARNTSON, Thomas Leigh. 424 GALIES POINTE LN 23322 #005-12-1968 L1988 DR AM *020 †80

ARORA, Reeta Mendhiratta. 3301 TAYLOR RD 23321 #047-01-1997 L2002 PM *020 †60

ASHHURST, John C. ■ 23321 #047-07-1947 L1951 PTH *040

ATLAS, Barry Foster. 805 BATTLEFIELD BLVD N, STE 111 23320 #016-02-1977 L1982 OPH *020 †35

ATWOOD, Ronald Wayne. 108 KNELLS RIDGE BLVD #100 23320 #051-07-1987 L1989 FM *020 †18

AULICINO, Pat Louis. 200 MEDICAL PKWY, STE 210 23320 #035-09-1975 L1982 HS ORS *020 †40

AUMAN, James Richard. 4037 TAYLOR RD, STE A 23321 #036-01-1971 L1994 U *020 †95 ‡

BACHER, Ave. 736 BATTLEFIELD BLVD N, CHESAPEAKE RADIOLOGISTS 23320 #053-03-1986 L2003 R AR *020 †80

BAGALKOTKAR, Pamela M. 637 KINGSBOROUGH SQ STE D, CHESAPEAKE PEDIATRICS, INC 23320 #051-07-1992 L1992 PD *020 †55

BAIKO, Kevin Patrick. 801 VOLVO PKWY # 109-144 23320 #051-07-1995 L1996 FM *020 †18

BAKER, Robert E. 3206 CHURCHLAND BLVD 23321 #051-04-1968 L1968 OPH *020 †35

BAKSH, Masud. 1604 CLARKS CIR 23321 #160-01-1984 L2000 IM *020 †20

BALDERSTON, Rosemary S. 129 HANBURY RD W STE 103, HANBURY FAMILY MEDICINE 23322 #917-30-1981 L1984 FM *020 †18

BALLARD, Dorothy Marie. 300 MEDICAL PKWY, STE 100 23320 #025-07-2002 L2002 PD *020 †55

BALLESTERO, Juliana. 736 BATTLEFIELD BLVD N, CHESAPEAKE RADIOLOGISTS 23320 #041-07-1997 L2003 DR *020 †80

BARGER, Jennifer Lynn. ■ 23320 #023-12-2004 L2005 PCC *012

BARKLEY, Dominique Renee. 733 VOLVO PKWY, STE 200 23320 #038-45-2001 L2004 PD *020 †55

BARNES, Hal Wade. 213 RIVER WALK PKWY, STE 101 23320 #045-01-1986 L1990 FM *020 †18

BARNUM, Michael Joseph. 905 BATTLEFILD BLVD N #103 23320 #041-09-1993 L1999 ORS *020 †40

BARNWELL, Henri Maria. 1104 MADISON PLZ STE 102 23320 #051-01-1991 L1992 PD *020 †55

BAROT, Ikshvanku Amrutlal. 637 KINGSBOROUGH SQ, STE E 23320 #051-07-2001 L2005 N *020 †75

BARR, Lisa Binder. 637 KINGSBOROUGH SQ, STE D 23320 #051-07-1983 L1984 PM FM *020 †60

BASS, Lawrence Adrian. ■ 23320 #036-01-2001 L2005 OBG *020 †30

BAUCOM, Sandra S. 4012 RAINTREE RD STE 200A 23321 #036-01-1982 L1989 PD *020 †55

BELTRAN, Romulo Garcia. ■ 23321 #748-01-1955 L1978 P CHP *071

BENHAM, Claude Carter. 736 BATTLEFIELD BLVD N 23320 #051-01-1961 L1961 FM *071

BERMISA, Rosario V G. 110 AMERICAN LEGION RD 23321 #748-02-1974 L1995 PD *020 †55

BESHANY, Philip Bliss. 713 VOLVO PKWY, STE 100 23320 #051-07-1984 L1986 FM FSM *020 †18

BILLET, Adam. 300 MEDICAL PKWY, STE 316 23320 #023-01-1978 L1985 PS HS *020 †65

BLAIR, Billie Yvonne. 1239 CEDAR RD, PATIENT FIRST CEDAR ROAD 23322 #051-04-1999 L1999 IM *020

BLAIR, Keisha Natasha. ■ 23324 #047-07-2004 L2006 *100

BLOIR, Michael J. ■ 23322 #038-75-2007, ▲ L2007 *012

BLOWE, Vanessa Arnethia. 633 BATTLEFIELD BLVD S, SUTIE 300 23322 #033-05-1985 L1986 FM *020 †18

BOOSE, Wesley David. ■ 23322 #023-12-2008 *012

BOUSTANY, Marc Kamel. 113 GAINSBOROUGH SQ, STE 203 23320 #028-02-1994 L1999 GS *020 †85

BOWMAN, Carole Lynn. ■ 23322 #051-07-2001 L2001 PD *020

BOYLE, Daniel Edward, Jr. 4037 TAYLOR RD STE A 23321 #041-09-1973 L1999 U GP *020 †18,95

BREARD, John Patrick. ■ 23323 #021-06-2003 L2003 GS *012

BREIN, Jonathan R. 300 ESPLANADE PL 23320 #041-07-1982 L1986 AN *020 †05

BRENNER, Joel Stephen. 733 VOLVO PKWY 23320 #035-06-1994 L1994 PSM ADL *020 †55

BRICCETTI, Christine E. 520 TENNIS DR 23320 #010-02-1995 L1998 **PD** *020 †55

BROOKS, Jared Lawrence. 113 GAINSBOROUGH SQ, STE 203 23320 #010-01-1996 L2002 **GS** *020 †85

BROWN, Julie Ann. 736 BATTLEFIELD BLVD N, DEPT OF EMERGENCY MEDICINE 23320 #016-11-1995 L2000 **FM** *020

BROWN, Samuel Isaac. 700 BATTLEFIELD BLVD N, STE C 23320 #051-04-1979 L1989 **ORS** *020 †40

BROWN, William Peyton. 736 BATTLEFIELD BLVD N, CHESAPEAKE GENERAL HOSP 23320 #055-01-1976 L1979 **AN** *020 †05

BUCH, Robert Jefferson. 2864 GREENWOOD RD 23321 #038-41-2001 L2002 **AN** *020

BUGARIN, Lopito B. 200 MEDICAL PKWY, STE 315 23320 #748-07-1980 L1999 **PD** *020 †18

BUNDY, Joel Thos. 736 BATTLEFIELD BLVD N 23320 #036-05-1988 L1993 **NEP** *020 †20

BUNTING, Lisa Bradley. 733 VOLVO PKWY, STE 200 23320 #051-07-1995 L1995 **PD** *020 †55

BURFOOT, Keisha L. 817 GREENBRIER PKWY, STE B 23320 #041-09-1996 L2000 **OBG** *020 †30

BUSH, Richard Gordon. 429 MILL STONE RD 23322 #067-01-1974 L1984 **AN** *020 †18,05

BUTLER, Ralph Elbert. 3200 LYNNHURST BLVD 23321 #051-07-1996 L1995 **CRS** *020 †85

CAINES, Michael Andrew. 4057 TAYLOR RD 23321 #038-06-1992 L2001 **ORS OS** *020 †40

CAMPBELL, Charles Ladoue. ■ 23320 #021-05-1999 L2006 **FM** *020

CARIDEO, Louis N. 808 BATTLEFIELD BLVD S 23322 #041-09-1974 L1977 **IM** *020 †85

CARLSON, Daniel Wm. ■ 23321 #038-40-1972 L1975 **AN LM** *062 †05

CARLSON, Richard Edward. 109 WIMBLEDON SQ 23321 #016-43-1965 L1972 **OPH AM** *020 †35

CARPIO, Luis Gimpaya. 111 COASTAL WAY 23320 #748-07-1978 L1997 **IM** *020

CARR, Paula. 111 MILL CREEK PKWY, STE 300 23323 #043-01-1997 L1997 **FM** *020 †18

CARTWRIGHT, Kevin Douglas. ■ 23322 #051-07-2008 *012

CAWTHORN, John Walker. 733 VOLVO PKWY, STE 200 23320 #051-07-1992 L1993 **PD** *020 †55

CHALLA, Surya Narayana. ■ 23320 #495-53-1991 L2000 **GS** *020 †85

CHAMBERLAIN, Chas Richard. 1239 CEDAR RD 23322 #051-01-1957 L1957 **ATP** *040 †50

CHANG, Amos Hwei-Cheh. 736 BATTLEFIELD BLVD N 23320 #038-06-1973 L1978 **PTH PCP** *020 †50

CHAUDHURI, Mohan Lal. 4037 TAYLOR RD STE B 23321 #495-38-1964 L1978 **OTO** *020 †45

CHENAULT, Oran Ward, Jr. 4037 TAYLOR RD STE A 23321 #021-01-1959 L1976 **U** *071 †95

CHERRY, Alka Patel. 733 VOLVO PKWY STE 200, CHESAPEAKE PEDIATRICS 23320 #051-07-1993 L1997 **PD** *020 †55

CHO, Shao-Ru. 736 BATTLEFIELD BLVD N, CHESAPEAKE RADIOLOGISTS 23320 #244-03-1965 L1978 **DR** *020 †80

CHRISTENSON, Pamela Jane. 675 BATTLEFIELD BLVD N 23320 #005-12-1999 L2000 **IM** *020 †20

CHRISTIAN-TAYLOR, Alison. 3253 TAYLOR RD, STE 200 23321 #051-04-1996 L1996 **FM** *020 †18

CLARKSON, Sarah Bull. 300 MEDICAL PKWY 23320 #045-01-1979 L1988 **RHU** *020

CORNEY, Margie. 817 GREENBRIER PKWY STE B 23320 #033-06-1979 L1983 **OBG** *020 †30

COSTA, Boniface Santosh. 4037 TAYLOR RD STE D 23321 #160-02-1971 L1979 **GE IM** *020

CRAVEN, Richard Allen. 932 PROFESSIONAL PL, # 201 23320 #041-14-1981 L1984 **OM EM** *020 †70,16

CREEF, Michael Seldon. 1201 JACKSON AVE, INTEGRATED MEDICAL SERVICE 23324 #051-07-1987 L1989 **FM** *020 ‡

CRETEUR, Christian E. 3038 TYRE NECK RD 23321 #165-03-1952 L1958 **AN PUD** *071 †05

CROSS, Gregory Hachikian. ■ 23321 #025-07-1956 L1976 **GS** *071 †85

CUNNINGHAM, Joseph W, Jr. ■ 23322 #036-05-1990 L1997 **AN** *020 †05

CURLEY, Timothy Martin. 111 MEDICAL PKWY, STE 201 23320 #041-02-1995 L2004 **NEP** *020 †20

CURRAN, Chas Walter, Jr. 736 BATTLEFIELD BLVD N 23320 #041-01-1986 L1988 **AN** *020 †05

CURRY, Michelle Talley. 1021 EDEN WAY N, STE 123 23320 #051-07-1990 L1992 **PD** *020 †55

CUTTING, Jonathan Paul. ■ 23323 #023-12-1983 L1988 **DR PDR** *030 †80

DAJAO, Ragaciano Macairan. 4053 TAYLOR RD 23321 #748-11-1972 L1976 **GP** *020

DAJAO, Rise Faith Espina. 4053 TAYLOR RD 23321 #748-11-1972 L1976 **GP** *020

DANDALIDES, Steven M. 112 GAINSBOROUGH SQ, STE 200 23320 #047-05-1982 L1987 **GE IM** *020 †20

DANGL, Kurt S. ■ 23322 #051-07-1994 L1995 **GS** *020

DAUGHDRILLE, John Ernest. 736 BATTLEFIELD BLVD N, CHESAPEAKE RADIOLOGISTS 23320 #025-07-1970 L1983 **R NM** *020 †80,28 ‡

DAVIS, Frederick Carr. 2125 SMITH AVE, STE 202 23320 #051-01-1957 L1957 **PTH** *071 †50

DAVIS, Kimberly Noelle. ■ 23321 #035-48-2004 L2007 **PD** *020 †55

DAVIS, Leonard Leslie, Jr. ■ 23321 #004-01-1954 L1954 **GP** *071

DEBNATH, Chinmayee. 3253 TAYLOR RD, STE 200 23321 #160-04-1979 L1993 **FM** *020 †18

DEGUZMAN-BERUBE, Eleanor. 108 KNELLS RIDGE BLVD, STE 100 23320 #422-01-1995 L1998 **FM** *020 †18

DENIO, Alfred Elon, III. 300 MEDICAL PKWY 23320 #041-12-1981 L1987 **RHU IM** *020 †20

DERRING, Eldridge H, Jr. 110 WIMBLEDON SQ, STE A 23320 #051-04-1971 L1972 **PUD IM** *020 †20

DEUTSCH, Brian Douglas. 688 KINGSBOROUGH SQ, EAR NOSE & THROAT LTD 23320 #051-01-1988 L1990 **OTO FPS** *020 †45

DE VANTIER, Wayne Roger. 805 BATTLEFIELD BLVD N, STE 111 23320 #010-02-1980 L1987 **OPH** *020 †35

DEXTERS, Yvonne L. ■ 23321 #165-03-1951 L1966 **PD** *071 †55

DHAWAN, Rajnish. 300 MEDICAL PKWY, STE 208 23320 #495-45-1993 L2005 **PCC** *020 †20

DHAWAN, Vandana. 300 MEDICAL PKWY, STE 208 23320 #495-45-1994 L2005 **IM** *020 †20

DIGGS, Leslie David. ■ 23323 #010-03-1999 *100

DIXIT, Brinda Mayur. 637 KINGSBOROUGH SQ, STE D 23320 #041-02-1998 L2003 **RHU** *020

DO, Annie Trucanh Mong. 4037 TAYLOR RD STE C, PROVIDENCE HOSPITAL 23321 #654-01-2003 L2007 **OBG** *020

DOBBS, Laura A. ■ 23320 #048-02-2006 L2006 **PD** *012

DORADO, Jose Antonio. ■ 23322 #847-01-1960 L1975 **GP** *020

DORBAD, David Gordon. 4012 RAINTREE RD, STE 200A 23321 #051-07-2002 L2002 **PD** *020

DOROFI, David Bryant. 688 KINGSBOROUGH SQ, EAR NOSE & THROAT LTD 23320 #036-01-1995 L1995 **OTO** *020 †45

DOUGLAS, William W. ■ 23322 #001-02-1953 L1976 **P** *072

DUMARAN, Raymund Silos. 4041 TAYLOR RD, STE G 23321 #051-01-1992 L1995 **IM** *020 †20

DU PUY, Theodore Erwin. ■ 23321 #041-13-1963 L1982 **HS** *071 †40

DURBIN, Darcy M. 805 FOX RIDGE TRL, 805 FOX RIDGE TRAIL 23322 #012-01-1996 L2002 **CCP** *020

DZIATKIEWICZ, Jowita Ewa. 109 WIMBLEDON SQ STE D 23320 #759-10-1966 L1977 **PD** *020 †55

EARL, Keisha Archelleth. ■ 23321 #036-01-2008 *012

EDMONDS, John Thos, Jr. 805 BATTLEFIELD BLVD N, STE 111 23320 #051-07-1987 L1995 **OPH** *040 †35

EICHELBERGER, Michelle D. 733 VOLVO PKWY, CHESAPEAKE PEDIATRICS INC 23320 #051-07-1986 L1993 **PD** *020 †55

EICHELBERGER, Scott P. 733 VOLVO PKWY STE 200 23320 #051-07-1986 L1990 **PD** *020 †55

ELLIOTT, Dawn Owen. ■ 23321 #047-01-1990 L1992 **FM** *071

EMEJURU, Ogubuike. 513 BAYLOR CT 23320 #654-01-1982 L1987 **PD** *020 †55

ENNEN, Christopher Scott. ■ 23321 #023-12-2002 L2003 *020 †30

EPSTEIN, Cynthia Esther. 733 VOLVO PKWY 23320 #035-06-1995 L1995 **PDP** *020 †55

EURE, Gregg Rountree. 676 BATTLEFIELD BLVD N, STE B 23320 #051-04-1985 L1986 **U** *020 †95

EZIEME, Jonah Anyaogu Ulu. 736 BATTLEFIELD BLVD N 23320 #020-02-1997 L2006 **IM** *020 †95

FABRIZIO, Michael Dean. 676 BATTLEFIELD BLVD N, STE B 23320 #051-04-1992 L1999 **U** *020 †95

FAGERLUND, Robert Waino. ■ 23323 #024-07-1974 L1979 **END** *075 †20

FANTASKEY, Amy Patricia. ■ 23322 #041-14-1995 L2004 **ATP** *040

FARPOUR, Alireza. 113 GAINSBOROUGH SQ, STE 103 23320 #041-07-1990 L1995 **GS** *020 †85

FATEHI, Nasrollah. 300 MEDICAL PKWY, STE 210 23320 #517-01-1968 L1985 **NS** *020 †25

FEREBEE, Angela. 713 VOLVO PKWY 23320 #036-01-1991 L1993 **OBG** *020 †30

FERNANDEZ, Alfred E. 512 ALBEMARLE DR 23322 #748-10-1976 L1995 **IM** *020

FERRELL, John Leslie, III. 705 BATTLEFIELD BLVD N, PATIENT FIRST BATTLEFIELD 23320 #041-14-2003 L2004 **GS** *020

FITZHARRIS, Gregory Paul. 3205 CHURCHLAND BLVD 23321 #036-07-1990 L2006 **GS** *020 †10,85

FLOTTEN, Andrew Stan. ■ 23322 #016-02-2007 L2007 *012

FORBES-HAMILTON, Susan. ■ 23323 #020-12-2003 L2003 **IM** *100

FORREST, Elizabeth D. 4020 RAINTREE RD, STE B 23321 #055-01-1985 L1988 **IM** *020 †20

FOX, James Thos, Jr. ■ 23320 #041-07-1990 L1999 **VS GS** *020 †85

FOX, Patrick Thomas. ■ 23320 #051-07-2008 *012

FRANASIAK, Frank Eugene. 920 BATTLEFIELD BLVD S, STE 101 23322 #035-06-1977 L1977 **OBG** *020 †30

FRANKLIN, Quentin James. 732 EDEN WAY N, LASIKPLUS, GREENBRIER VILL 23320 #023-12-1995 L2004 **OPH** *020 †35

FRANTZ, Frazier Woodrow. 600 ARCHER CT 23322 #036-07-1988 L1991 **PDS** *020 †85

FRAZER, Julia Paige. 300 MEDICAL PKWY, STE 222 23320 #051-07-1999 L1999 **PD** *020 †55

FREEMAN, Elias Thos, III. 1016 JUSTIS ST, INDIAN RIVER FAMILY 23325 #051-04-1984 L1985 **FM** *020 †18

FREEMAN, Eric Jonathan. 4053 TAYLOR RD STE N 23321 #051-04-1971 L1973 **PUD IM** *020 †20

FRUMKIN, Kenneth. 736 BATTLEFIELD BLVD N, CHESAPEAKE GENERAL HOSPITA 23320 #041-09-1978 L1991 **EM** *020 †16 ‡

FULP, David Ralph. 736 BATTLEFIELD BLVD N 23320 #051-07-1981 L1982 **IM** *020 †20

GALLO, James John. 736 BATTLEFIELD BLVD N, CHESAPEAKE GEN HOSP 23320 #033-06-1984 L1990 **AN** *020 †05

GELLMAN, Michael Danl. 736 BATTLEFIELD BLVD N 23320 #033-05-1980 L1984 **AN** *020 †05

GELPI, Barbara Ann. 745 BATTLEFIELD BLVD N 23320 #037-01-1989 L1996 **NEP** *020 †20

GERBUS, Patrick Michael. 300 MEDICAL PKWY, STE 222 23320 #030-05-1991 L1994 **PD** *020 †55

GHOBRIAL, Mohib Naguib I. 109 WIMBLEDON SQ STE C 23320 #915-03-1979 L1991 **GS** *020 †85

GIBSON, Richard Borden. ■ 23323 #024-01-1953 L1958 **TS** *071 †85,90

GIROUX, Arthur Steven. 736 BATTLEFIELD BLVD N 23320 #010-02-1969 L1987 **PTH HEM** *020 †20,50

GIVEN, Robert Wilkins. 676 BATTLEFIELD BLVD N, STE B 23320 #051-04-1988 L1990 **U OS** *020 †95 ‡

GOBER, John David. ■ 23320 #021-05-1984 L1996 **AN GP** *020 †05

GOLDIN, Nathan Paul. 3105 WESTERN BRANCH BLVD 23321 #051-01-1977 L1984 **U** *020 †95

GOLDMAN, Milton S. ■ 23322 #041-01-1943 L1943 **GP OS** *020

GOLDSBY-MITCHELL, Cherubim. ■ 23320 #028-34-1982 L2008 **PD** *020 ‡

GONZAGA, Rufina B Cruz. 4323 INDIAN RIVER RD STE D, NOW CARE MEDICAL CENTER 23325 #748-08-1959 L1982 **IM** *071

GORMLEY, Robert Arthur. 705 BATTLEFIELD BLVD N, PATIENT FIRST BATTLEFIELD 23320 #038-40-1973 L1976 **IM MDM** *020 †20 ‡

GOSS, David Glenn. 700 BATTLEFIELD BLVD N, STE C 23320 #051-01-1995 L2001 **ORS** *020 †40

GOWEN, Marilyn Alley. 733 VOLVO PKWY 23320 #051-04-1979 L1990 **PDP PDA** *020 †55

GRAHAM, Mary Olive. 736 BATTLEFIELD BLVD N, CARDIAC REHABILITATION PRO 23320 #051-07-1984 L1988 **FM** *020 †18

GRAHAM, Scott James. 736 BATTLEFIELD BLVD N 23320 #012-01-1983 L1993 **HEM GS** *020 †50

GRAY, Latanya Denise. 3105 AMERICAN LEGION RD #F 23321 #051-07-1998 L1998 **FM** *020 †18

GREGUS, Thomas John. ■ 23322 #035-09-1987 L1991 **AN** *020 †05

GRIFFETH, Bradley Christo. ■ 23320 #051-07-2006 L2006 **DR** *012

GRIFFEY, Paul Michael. 508 BAYLOR CT, STE C 23320 #051-07-1995 L1995 **GS** *020

GRIFFEY, Richard Thos. 508 BAYLOR CT, STE C 23320 #055-01-1967 L1972 **OPH** *020 †35

GRIFFIN, Alesia Wright. 2147 OLD GREENBRIER RD, STE A 23320 #051-07-1998 L2000 **FM** *020 †18

GRIFFIN, Stacy Sirmar. ■ 23320 #004-01-2006 L2007 *012

GROSS, Fredric Jay. 109 WIMBLEDON SQ STE E 23320 #028-02-1986 L1991 **OPH** *020 †35

GROSS, Jerome S. 710 LIBERTY ST 23324 #051-04-1952 L1952 **FM** *071

GRUSHA, Donna Susan. 4012 RAINTREE RD, STE 100A 23321 #051-04-1983 L1989 **PD** *020 †55

GUILARAN, Eddie Z. ■ 23325 #748-01-1962 L1974 **FM GS** *071 †18

GYURICSKO, Eric Ormonde. 733 VOLVO PKWY 23320 #008-02-1995 L1995 **PDE PD** *020 †55

HABEEB, Edward David. 300 MEDICAL PKWY, STE 304 23320 #035-15-1974 L1979 **ORS** *020 †40

HALL, Caroline Ann. 733 VOLVO PKWY, CHESAPEAKE PEDIATRICS 23320 #025-12-2000 L2006 **MPD** *020 †55 ‡

HALL, James Henderson, III. 705 BATTLEFIELD BLVD N, PATIENT FIRST BATTLEFIELD 23320 #012-01-1966 L1973 **N AM** *020 †75

HAMMETT, Mark Edward. 1328 DANIELLE CT 23320 #048-15-1997 L1998 **DR** *020 †70

HANKINS, Priscilla Ann. ■ 23322 #021-05-1986 L1990 **P** *020 †75

HANNA, Edward Stanley. 633 BATTLEFIELD BLVD S, STE 300 23322 #041-02-1978 L1983 **FM** *020 †18 ‡

■ = Address Information Privacy Protected

HAREWOOD, Dionne Nicole. 4012 RAINTREE RD, STE 200A 23321 #012-21-1993 L1993
PD *020 †55

HARRELL, Jeffrey Lynn. ■ 23323 #051-07-2008 *012

HARRINGTON, Thomas Alfred, Jr. 2994 CHURCHLAND BLVD, CHURCHLAND INTERNAL 23321
#050-02-1979 L1982 IM *020 †20

HARRIS, Charles Larry. 736 BATTLEFIELD BLVD N 23320 #051-07-1981 L1982 FM *020 †18

HARTLINE, Steven Michael. 633 BATTLEFIELD BLVD S, STE 300 23322 #041-13-1996 L2005
FM *020 †18

HARVEY, Valerie Magloire. 733 VOLVO PKWY 23320 #051-01-1999 L2005 D *020 †15

HAYWARD, Catherine Z. 300 MEDICAL PKWY, STE 208 23320 #041-02-1979 L2006 GS *020 †85

HERNANDEZ, Humberto. ■ 23321 #308-01-1986 L1991 FM *020

HEYWOOD, Richard E. ■ 23321 #022-75-2004, ▲ L2005 *100

HIGGINS, Christine D. 113 GAINSBOROUGH SQ 23320 #051-07-1995 L1996 IM *020 †20

HILL, Richard. 860 GREENBRIER CIR, STE 100 23320 #011-04-1990 L1998 CHP P *020

HILLIARD, Allyson Marie. #051-07-2007 L2007 OBG *012

HOFFMAN, Charles Jacobs. 2994 CHURCHLAND BLVD 23321 #010-01-1963 L1968 IM *071 †20

HOFFMAN, Kellye Arianna. ■ 23320 #047-06-2005 L2006 *100

HOFSTRA, Jennifer Anne. ■ 23322 #051-07-2007 L2007 IM *012

HOGAN, Angela Duff. 733 VOLVO PKWY 23320 #051-07-2008 *012
#050-02-1987 L1994 AI PD *020 †03,55

HOLDEN, Richard Theodore. 700 BATTLEFIELD BLVD N, STE C 23320 #033-05-1975 L1982
ORS *020 †40

HOLLAND, Jennifer Mary. 300 MEDICAL PKWY, STE 222 23320 #051-07-1994 L1994
PD *020 †55

HOOD, Antoinette B Foote. 733 VOLVO PKWY 23320 #047-05-1967 L2001 D DMP *020 †15

HOOD, Richard Jeffrey. 688 KINGSBOROUGH SQ, EAR NOSE & THROAT LTD 23320
#001-02-1995 L1995 OTO *020 †45

HOWARD, Robert Thomas. #051-01-2000 L2000 IM *100

HSU, Helen Hwa. 736 BATTLEFIELD BLVD N 23320 #038-44-1997 L2002 EM *020 †16

HUNTE, Noel Lukanus. 4020 RAINTREE RD, STE B 23321 #035-20-1996 L1999 IM *020 †20

HUTCHISON, Stephanie Luci. 23322 #055-02-2006 L2006 OBG *012

IACOBUCCI, Mark John. 805 BATTLEFIELD BLVD N, STE 111 23320 #036-07-1996 L1996
OPH OS *020 †35 ‡

IGLECIA, Raymond. 4310 INDIAN RIVER RD 23325 #847-10-1963 L1978 P N *020 †75

IGLECIA, Raymond, Jr. 4310 INDIAN RIVER RD STE 4 23325 #041-02-1995 L1998 FM *020/

IGNACIO, D G. 1013 EDEN WAY N, STE A B & C 23320 #748-01-1957 L1969 OBG *071 †30

IGNACIO, Eleodora Merle. 1200 S MILITARY HWY 23320 #748-08-1963 L1971 FM IMG *020 †18

IGNACIO, Luis Faustino. ■ 23320 #748-01-1973 L1990 P *020 †75

IIAMS, Gordon John. 700 BATTLEFIELD BLVD N, STE C 23320 #051-07-1982 L1984
ORS HS *020 †40

ISAAC, Jos Wm Alexander. ■ 23320 #010-03-1971 L1975 OBG *071 †20

ISLAM, Anwarul. 736 BATTLEFIELD BLVD N 23320 #160-01-1972 L1982 IM *020

JACOB, Lionel Newman. 736 BATTLEFIELD BLVD N 23320 #001-06-1993 L1994 PTH *020 †50

JAMALI, Ali Reza. 200 MEDICAL PKWY STE 111 23320 #517-03-1968 L1977 ORS *020 †40 ‡

JAMIAS, Perla Modesta C. ■ 23321 #748-01-1970 L1983 PD *020

JENNINGS, Walter S. 736 BATTLEFIELD BLVD N 23320 #051-04-1951 L1951 FM *020 †18

JEZIOR, James Ritchie. 1209 HANNA ROSE CT 23320 #023-12-1989 L1999 U *020 †95

JOHNSON, Dominic A. 736 BATTLEFIELD BLVD N 23320 #038-44-1991 L1993 EM *020 †16

JOHNSON, Jennifer Lynne. ■ 23320 #051-07-2007 IM *012

JOHNSON, Tara Clarinda. ■ 23320 #051-01-2002 L2006 AN *020 †05

JOHNSTON, Vincent Boyd. 1239 CEDAR RD, PATIENT FIRST CEDAR ROAD 23322
#019-02-1991 L1995 FM UM *020 †18

JONES, Karen Levette. ■ 23321 #010-02-1998 L2001 FM *020 †18

JORDAN, Gerald Henry. 676 BATTLEFIELD BLVD N, STE B 23320 #048-13-1977 L1985
U *020 †95

JORDAN, Khadijah Yasin. 111 MEDICAL PKWY, STE 202 23320 #012-21-1991 L1995
OBG *020 †30

JULIAN, William Alexander. 3105 WESTERN BRANCH BLVD 23321 #020-12-1969 L1991
U *020 †95

JURKO, Robert Michael. 3101 AMERICAN LEGION RD, STE 15 23321 #038-41-1979 L1985
IM EM *020 †20

KAGAN, Harvey Jay. 300 MEDICAL PKWY, STE 222 23320 #010-02-1974 L1975 PD *020

KAGAN, Larry Howard. 1016 JUSTIS ST, INDIAN RIVER FAMILY 23325 #020-12-1979 L1980
FM *020 †18

KAKANI, Ramanaiah. 300 MEDICAL PKWY, CARDIOLOGY CONSULTANTS 23320
#495-58-1981 L1985 CD IM *020 †20

KALAFSKY, John Thomas. 688 KINGSBOROUGH SQ, EAR NOSE & THROAT LTD 23320
#041-13-1983 L1985 OTO HNS *020 †45 ‡

KALAGAYAN-THOMPSON, Dinah. 1317 BALLAHACK RD STE 100, NORTHWEST CLINIC 23322
#055-01-1992 L1997 FM *020 †18

KAPOOR, Sonia. 111 MILL CREEK PKWY, STE 300 23323 #496-04-2000 L2003 FM *020 †18

KAUFMAN, Steven Howard. 736 BATTLEFIELD BLVD N 23320 #036-01-1973 L1980
PUD IM *020

KELLY, Cynthia Szelc. 733 VOLVO PKWY 23320 #025-07-1985 L1994 PD AI *050 †55,03

KENDRA, Stephen John. 748 BATTLEFIELD BLVD N 23320 #041-02-1957 L1980 PHP *030 †70

KENNEDY, Joseph Davy. 3209 MORNINGSIDE DR, NAVAL MED CT PORTMOUTH 23321
#038-41-1971 L1997 IM IMG *020 †18

KENNEDY, Lisa Shea. 1021 EDEN WAY N STE 109 23320 #043-01-1983 L1986 FM *020 †18

KEVERLINE, Michael R. 3206 CHURCHLAND BLVD 23321 #041-12-1997 L2001 OPH *020 †35

KEYES, Alan Scott. 200 MEDICAL PKWY, STE 205 23320 #051-04-1988 L1989 OTO *020 †45

KIM, Mi Yeun. ■ 23320 #051-07-2008 *012

KIM, Susan Foley. 713 VOLVO PKWY, STE 100 23320 #050-02-1988 L1996 FM *020 †18

KING, Valeria Ammons. 1239 CEDAR RD, PATIENT FIRST CEDAR ROAD 23322
#056-05-1988 L1995 FM *020 †18

KING-JONES, Patricia Y. 1101 MADISON PLZ, STE 100 23320 #047-07-1989 L1991 P *020

KISA, Erik Harold. 736 BATTLEFIELD BLVD N, CHESAPEAKE GEN EMGY DEPT 23320
#051-01-1984 L1985 EM *020

KLING, Timothy Geo. 1101 MADISON PLZ, VIRGINIA CENTER FOR WOMEN 23320
#018-03-1971 L1997 OBG *020 †30

KNAUFT, Richard David. 4057 TAYLOR RD 23321 #005-12-1967 L1974 HS ORS *071 †40

KOBAK, Gregory Evan. 733 VOLVO PKWY 23320 #041-09-1997 L2003 PG *020 †55

KOENIG, Craig Stephen. 528 ALBEMARLE DR, ALLERGY AND ASTHMA SPECIAL 23322
#056-06-2000 L2004 AI *020 †20,03

KONIKOFF, Michael Ross. 733 VOLVO PKWY 23320 #047-05-2000 L2006 PG *020 †55

KOTHMANN, Daniel Scott. 736 BATTLEFIELD BLVD N, CHESAPEAKE RADIOLOGISTS 23320
#051-01-1990 L1996 DR *020 †80

KOUTOUFAS, Elizabeth Ann. 4113 STEPHANIE BOYD DR 23321 #051-04-2008 *012

KOVALCIK, Paul Jerome. 3105 AMERICAN LEGION RD #A 23321 #010-02-1969 L1980
CRS *020 †85,10 ‡

KOZEN, Buddy Gene, Jr. ■ 23320 #023-07-2000 L2001 EM *020 †16

KRISHNAGIRI, Sarala. 2994 CHURCHLAND BLVD, CHURCHLAND INTERNAL 23321
#495-04-1988 L1998 IM *020 †20

KWAN, Fenney. 817 GREENBRIER PKWY STE B 23320 #035-08-2002 L2007 OBG *020

LAIBSTAIN, Robert Bernard. 1016 JUSTIS ST, INDIAN RIVER FAMILY 23325 #051-04-1975 L1976
FM *020 †18

LANG, Deborah Bowers. 736 BATTLEFIELD BLVD N, PEACEHEALTH MEDICAL GROUP 23320
#050-02-2000 L2003 IM *020 †20 ‡

LAPEYROLERIE, Donna A. 675 BATTLEFIELD BLVD N 23320 #035-08-1991 L1994 IM *020

LA ROCQUE, James Calvin. 3205 CHURCHLAND BLVD 23321 #016-11-1974 L1982
END IM *020 †20

LAURENT, Jeffrey John. ■ 23322 #051-01-1999 L1999 NS *100

LEADBEATER, Jeannine M. 2845 CEDAR RD 23323 #035-03-1998 L1998 FM *020 †18

LEAO, Zennette Denise. 112 GAINSBOROUGH SQ 23320 #051-07-2000 L2003 OBG *020

LEE, John E. 637 KINGSBOROUGH SQ STE C 23320 #051-04-1977 L1977 OBG GP *071 †30

LEE, Patterson Ong. 736 BATTLEFIELD BLVD N, CHESAPEAKE GENERAL HOPITAL 23320
#748-20-1993 L2001 IM *020 †20

LEE, Rachel Deloris. ■ 23321 #047-06-2002 L2002 OBG *020

LEGALL, Elizabeth Langsto. ■ 23320 #051-07-2003 L2003 PM *100

LEGASPI, Amante Galace. 417 MILL STONE RD, CHESAPEAKE ANESTHESIOLOGIS 23322
#748-08-1968 L1981 AN *020

LEGASPI, Jane P. ■ 23322 #748-08-1969 L1985 OS P *071

LEGUM, Larry Landis. 113 COASTAL WAY, GREENBRIER MEDICAL CENTER 23320
#051-01-1972 L1972 D *020 †15

LEHEW, Willette Lewis. 300 MEDICAL PKWY, STE 308 23320 #051-01-1961 L1961
OBG *020 †30

LEHMAN, Robert David. 1421 KEMPSVILLE RD, STE A 23320 #051-07-1982 L1987 PD *020 †55

LEIBOVICI, Samuel. 3906 BAINEBRIDGE BLVD, SERVICES PL 23324 #305-01-2001 L2004
IM *100 †20

LEONCIO, Jose Dabu. 1061 GEORGE WASHNGTN GWY N 23323 #748-01-1970 L1976 GP *020

LEONE, Louis Michael, III. 1130 MERCHANTS CT, APT 2A 23320 #748-21-2002 L2007 P *012

LESLIE, Ann Debra. 736 BATTLEFIELD BLVD N 23320 #021-05-1983 L1987 PD *020 †55

LEVI, David Scott. 637 KINGSBOROUGH SQ, STE D 23320 #051-07-1998 L2003 PM *020 †60

LEWINSKI, Steven V. 745 BATTLEFIELD BLVD N 23320 #023-12-1986 L1993 NEP IM *020 †20

LEWIS, Victor D, III. 736 BATTLEFIELD BLVD N 23320 #041-01-1981 L2004 DR IM *020 †80

LEYVA, Fernando Frederick. ■ 23320 #023-12-2001 L2003 FM *020 †18

LIBBY, Brent Dalee. ■ 23322 #056-06-2001 L2001 *100

LIGOURI, Adrienne Lynn. ■ 23321 #035-47-2007 *012

LINDNER, Paul Ira. 612 KINGSBOROUGH SQ, STE 200 23320 #028-03-1993 L2001
OBG *020 †30

LIS, Barbara Diane. 1239 CEDAR RD, PATIENT FIRST CEDAR ROAD 23322 #051-07-1997 L1997
FM *020 †18

LOCKEMER, Hillary Elizabe. ■ 23320 #051-07-2006 L2006 PD *012

LOGRONIO, Jesus Malit. ■ 23322 #748-11-1974 L1986 GP *020

LONG, Linda Marie. 112 GAINSBOROUGH SQ, STE 100 23320 #051-01-1990 L1993
OBG *020 †30

LOWELL, William Grayson. 3105 AMERICAN LEGION RD, STE F 23321 #056-05-1970 L1977
PD GPM *020 †55

LOXLEY, Sidney S. 501 BATTLEFIELD BLVD N 23320 #010-01-1968 L1975 ORS *074

LUCIANO-PEREZ, Ernesto. 4057 TAYLOR RD 23321 #021-01-1986 L1991 ORS *020 †40

LUCKENBACH, Martha W. ■ 23320 #020-12-1977 1989 OPH *035

LUTGENDORF, Monica Ann. ■ 23322 #023-12-2004 L2005 OBG *020

LYNCH, Donald Francis, Jr. 676 BATTLEFIELD BLVD N, STE B 23320 #051-01-1971 L1971
U REN *020 †95 ‡

MAC KINNON, Roderick R. 4041 TAYLOR RD STE G 23321 #011-02-1980 L1983 IM *020 †20

MACPHERSON-SMITH, Malcolm. 2100 STEPPINGSTONE SQ, TRAINING CENTER 23321
#919-01-1976 L1982 EM FM *020 †18

MADDEN, Lawrence Declan. 3105 AMERICAN LEGION RD, STE 2 23321 #041-12-1987 L2001
AN *020

MAGIER, Igor. 2332 WOODHURST LN, FIRST FLOOR 23322 #051-01-1967 L1967 P *020 †75

MAGIER, Nina G. ■ 23322 #759-05-1938 L1975 P PD *071 †75

MALIK, Pramod R. 112 GAINSBOROUGH SQ, STE 200 23320 #495-23-1992 L2001
GE IM *020 †20

MALLEY, Ross Anthony. 736 BATTLEFIELD BLVD N 23320 #008-02-1983 L1991 AN *020 †05

MAMEDOVA, Tamara Nariman. 705 BATTLEFIELD BLVD N, PATIENT FIRST BATTLEFIELD 23320
#913-19-1983 L2003 FM *020 †20

MANDELL, Barry Alan. 805 BATTLEFIELD BLVD N, STE 111 23320 #051-04-1987 L1998
OPH *020 †35

MANOLIO, Richard Lee. 736 BATTLEFIELD BLVD N, EMER DEPT CHESAPEAKE HOSP 23320
#010-02-1980 L1991 EM *020 †16

MANSFIELD, Erika Lynne. 1239 CEDAR RD 23322 #539-04-1997 L2004 FM UCM *020 †18 ‡

MANSOOR, John Victor. 3210 CHURCHLAND BLVD, STE 2 23321 #021-06-1990 L1996
RHU IM *020

MARIONEAUX, Stephanie A J. 300 MED PKWY STE 108 23320 #024-01-1984 L1987
OPH *020 †35

MARTIN, Lourdes E. 736 BATTLEFIELD BLVD N, BLVD, NORTH 23320 #308-02-1986 L1994
IM *020 †20

MASON, Joel Andrew. 300 MEDICAL PKWY, STE 206 23320 #041-02-1962 L1969 ORS *071 †40

MATHEWS, Molly Robinson. 736 BATTLEFIELD BLVD N 23320 #055-02-1996 L2004
EM PD *020 †55,16

MATIASEK, April Sample. ■ 23322 #020-02-2005 L2006 GS *020

MATIASEK, Matthew R. ■ 23322 #041-13-2003 L2005 GS *100

MAYES, Kenneth Lee. ■ 23322 #007-02-1962 L1973 OTO *071 †45

MC CAMMON, Kurt Anthony. 676 BATTLEFIELD BLVD N, STE B 23320 #038-43-1992 L1992
U *020 †95

MCCAULLEY, Amanda Colleen. ■ 23320 #032-01-2006 L2006 *012

MCDIVITT, Jonathan Denlea. ■ 23320 #023-12-2006 L2007 *012

MCKEITHAN, Roisin M. 129 HANBURY RD W STE 103, HANBURY FAM MEDICINE 23322
#539-04-1976 L1983 FM *020 †18

MCMULLEN, Susan Victoria. ■ 23322 #051-07-2008 *012

MC PHEE, Joseph Roderick. ■ 23322 #035-47-1996 L1997 GS *020 †85

MENDEZ, Prudencio. 680 KINGSBOROUGH SQ STE A 23320 #042-01-1967 L1987
OTO FPS *020 †45

MILLENDEZ, Maridelle Bond. ■ 23320 #023-12-2007 *012

MILLER, Bernard H. 113 GAINSBOROUGH SQ, SUITE 300 23320 #051-04-1952 L1952
IM *071 †20

MILLER, Gabriella Lynn. ■ 23322 #051-07-1997 L1997 FM *020 †18

MILLER, Julius Saml. 113 GAINSBOROUGH SQ 23320 #051-07-1988 L1991 IM HOS *020 †20

MILLER, Thomas Wesley. 736 BATTLEFIELD BLVD N 23320 #038-43-1995 L1995 IM *020 †18,20

MILLER-COLEMAN, Alfreda. 3105 AMERICAN LEGION RD, STE D 23321 #045-01-1999 L2003
AN *020 †05 ‡

MISTRY, Farookh Dinshaw. 3802 POPLAR HILL RD, STE C 23321 #495-65-1970 L1981
OBG *020 †30

MITREV, Peter Vladimir. 680 KINGSBOROUGH SQ, STE A 23320 #007-02-1989 L1999
OPH *020 †35

MOBLEY, Cynthia H. 3802 POPLAR HILL RD, STE C 23321 #051-07-1984 L1987 OBG *020 †30

MONTAG, Thomas Wm. 109 WIMBLEDON SQ, STE F 23320 #026-04-1978 L1999
GO OBG *020 †30

MONTERO, Juan Murillo, II. ■ 23322 #748-11-1965 L1971 GS TS *071 †85

MOORE, Glen Leslie. 3205 CHURCHLAND BLVD 23321 #051-07-1983 L1989 GS *020 †85

MOORE, Matthew Douglas. ■ 23323 #023-12-2007 PD *012

MOORE-MAXWELL, Crystal A. ■ 23320 #051-04-1999 L2006 PTH *020 †50

MORALES, Lawrence R. 200 MEDICAL PKWY, STE 111 23320 #869-05-1969 L1979
ORS *020 †40

MORALES, Maripaz B. 733 VOLVO PKWY 23320 #748-01-1991 L1998 PD *020 †03,55

MORALETA-RODRIGUEZ, Anna. 736 BATTLEFIELD BLVD N 23320 #748-10-1989 L2002
IM *020 †20

MORELAND, Michael Emmet. 4041 TAYLOR RD STE H 23321 #030-06-1973 L1977 D *020 †15

MORRIS, Anthony Austin. 736 BATTLEFIELD BLVD N 23320 #045-01-1989 L1993 FM *020 †18

MORRIS, Sequita Magnolia. 213 RIVER WALK PKWY, STE 101 23320 #036-01-2001 L2006
FM *020

MOULTON, Patti Gayle. 1215 VOLVO PKWY STE 202 23320 #051-07-1984 L1987 P *020 †75

MUNN, Gary Leslie. 4816 CONDOR DR 23321 #035-09-1988 L1990 P *020 †75

MUNOZ, Marc Edward. 736 BATTLEFIELD BLVD N, BLVD., NORTH 23320 #016-43-1998 L2004
IM *020 †20

MUNTER, David Wm. ■ 23322 #023-12-1982 L1983 EM GP *030 †16

MUNTHALI, Rachel. 490 LIBERTY ST, SOUTH NORFOLK HLTH CTR 23324 #775-01-1990 L1998
IM *020 †20

MURDEN, Ernest Aubrey, Jr. 4020 RAINTREE RD, STE C 23321 #051-04-1963 L1963
OTO A *071 †45

MURILLO, Jaime Eduardo. 300 MEDICAL PKWY, CARDIOLOGY CONSULTANTS 23320
#264-03-1991 L2001 IM *020 †20

MUSAPATIKE, Josphat S. ■ 23322 #012-05-1986 L1989 FM EM *020 †18

MUSSELMANI, Zattam M. 1422 POINDEXTER ST 23324 #605-01-1994 L1999 IM *020 †20

MYERS, John Baggarly. 1446 CHESAPEAKE AVE 23324 #051-01-1959 L1959 GP *071

NASH, Margaret Ridgely. 1421 KEMPSVILLE RD, STE A 23320 #051-07-1995 L1995 PD *020 †55

NAUMANN, Dan Andrew. 675 BATTLEFIELD BLVD N, MEDICAL ASSOCIATES 23320
#051-04-1987 L1990 FM *020 †18

NAVARRO, Ramon G, Jr. 200 MEDICAL PKWY, STE 315 23320 #748-08-1962 L1970 PD *071 †55

NAYLOR, Martha Ellen. ■ 23325 #051-07-2002 L2002 NPM *012 †55

NEDELKA, Michele Anne. ■ 23320 #051-07-2008 RO *012

NEFF, Robert Swanson. 300 MEDICAL PKWY, STE 206 23320 #041-12-1965 L1972
ORS *020 †40

NELSON, Timothy Scott. 736 BATTLEFIELD BLVD N, BLVD, NORTH 23320 #041-02-1996 L2007
EM *020 †16

NEWMAN, John Benj. 3205 CHURCHLAND BLVD, TIDEWATER SURGICAL SPECIAL 23321
#023-12-1992 L1993 GS *020 †85

NEWSOM, Roger Winfield. 805 BATTLEFIELD BLVD N, STE 111 23320 #051-07-1992 L1997
OPH *020 †35

NICHOLS, Glenn Whitfield. 200 MEDICAL PKWY, STE 111 23320 #010-01-1979 L1984
ORS *020 †40

NIZHARADZE, Maia. ■ 23322 #912-02-1998 L2008 IM *012

OCA, Agripino Rebong. ■ 23320 #748-02-1942 L1979 GP PHP *020

O DONNELL, Brian Francis. 113 GAINSBOROUGH SQ 23320 #024-05-1987 L1996 IM *020 †20

OKAFOR, Nneka Catherine. 736 BATTLEFIELD BLVD N, CHESAPEAKE HOSPITALISTS, P 23320
#690-04-1998 L2006 IM *020 †20

OKHRAVI, Hamid Reza. 713 VOLVO PKWY, STE 100 23320 #517-04-1990 L2006
IM IMG *020 †20

OLD, Forrest Paul, Jr. 736 BATTLEFIELD BLVD N, CGH MEDICAL STAFF OFFICE 23320
#051-07-1983 L1984 IM GP *020 †20

O'NEILL, Laurie Ann. 633 BATTLEFIELD BLVD S, STE 300 23322 #024-16-1997 L2001
FM *020 †18 ‡

OREDEIN, Olugbenga Soga. 3253 TAYLOR RD, STE 200 23321 #010-03-1974 L1987
OBG *020 †30

ORTIZ, Evelyn. ■ 23321 #024-05-1988 *100

ORTIZ, Kenneth John. ■ 23322 #033-06-1996 L2002 PS *020 †85,65

OSBORNE, Tommy T, II. 612 KINGSBOROUGH SQ, STE 202 23320 #051-04-1992 L1993
ORS *020

OSTROFF, Edward B. 4037 TAYLOR RD, STE A 23321 #023-01-1967 L1974 U GP *071 †95

PALMISANO, David V. 129 HANBURY RD W, STE 103 23322 #665-01-2002 L2002 FM *020 †18

PALTING, Arlene. 213 RIVER WALK PKWY, STE 101 23320 #748-01-1983 L1994 FM *020 †18

PANIGRAHI, Gunadhar. 300 MEDICAL PKWY, CARDIOLOGY CONSULTANTS 23320
#495-79-1973 L1983 CD *020 †20

PAPARIELLO, Steven Gerald. 801 VOLVO PKWY, STE 111 23320 #041-14-1985 L1986 GP *020

PARSONS, Jerome Michael. 3105 WESTERN BRANCH BLVD, COMPLEX ONE STE 4A 23321
#051-04-1981 L1983 D DMP *020 †15

PASQUALE-NIEBLES, Kimberly. 4020 RAINTREE RD, STE D 23321 #012-01-1995 L2001
OTO *020 †45

PATEL, Sanjay M. 734 BATTLEFIELD BLVD N, CHESAPEAKE RADIOLOGY 23320
#965-01-1988 L2002 VIR *020 †20,80

PATEL, Vandana Apurva. 4053 TAYLOR RD STE N 23321 #495-23-1984 L1992
PUD CCM *020 †20

PATHAK, Minesh Babul. 736 BATTLEFIELD BLVD N, BOULEVARD NO. 23320
#305-01-2000 L2000 NEP *012 †20

PATTERSON, Henry David. ■ 23322 #030-05-1967 L1973 GS *071 †85

PAYNE, Charles Franklin. 4057 TAYLOR RD STE S 23321 #036-05-1958 L1967 D DMP *020 †15

PECSOK, James Louis. 736 BATTLEFIELD BLVD N 23320 #036-05-1982 L1987 AN *040 †05

PEEPLES, Vernita Newby. 1104 MADISON PLZ, STE 102 23320 #051-07-1989 L1990
PD *020 †55

PENNINGTON, Tracey Odeta. 700 BATTLEFIELD BLVD N, STE C 23320 #021-01-1995 L2001
PM *020 †60

PERWAIZ, Javaid Akhtar. 109 WIMBLEDON SQ 23320 #704-04-1973 L1980 OBG *075 †30 ‡

PETRUSCHAK, Michael J, Jr. 736 BATTLEFIELD BLVD N, CHESAPEAKE HOSP DEPT RAD 23320
#033-05-1975 L2005 DR *020 †80

PETTICREW, Jeffrey B. 3105 WESTERN BRANCH BLVD, BON SECOURS MEDCARE CTR 23321
#017-20-1975 L1976 EM GP *071 †16 ‡

PETTWAY, Sharon Kay. 4012 RAINTREE RD STE 100A, RENAISSANCE PEDIATRICS 23321
#038-40-1998 L2001 PD *020 †55

PHAM, Angela Oanh. ■ 23320 #051-07-2006 IM *012

PINKSTON, John Wayne. 736 BATTLEFIELD BLVD N, CHESAPEAKE RADIOLOGISTS 23320
#051-04-1979 L1990 R *020 †80

PITROLO, David Andrew. 736 BATTLEFIELD BLVD N, CHESAPEAKE GENERAL HOSPITA 23320
#055-01-1980 L1983 EM IM *020 †20,16

PITSENBARGER, Robert Paul. 224 GREAT BRIDGE BLVD, CHEASAPEAK COMM SVCS
BRD 23320 #051-01-1992 L1997 P *020 †75

POLICKY, Kevin Joe. ■ 23322 #030-05-1999 L2005 AN *100

PONTIER, Paul Jeffrey. 713 VOLVO PKWY, STE 100 23320 #048-02-1984 L1987
NEP IM *020 †20

POSNER, Irvin Leonard. 109 WIMBLEDON SQ, STE E 23320 #051-01-1958 L1958 OPH *071 †35

POST, Christopher Raymond. 705 BATTLEFIELD BLVD N, PATIENT FIRST BATTLEFIELD 23320
#041-14-1992 L2005 FM *020 †18

POWELL, Drusilla Saunders. 637 KINGSBOROUGH SQ, STE D 23320 #051-04-1986 L1988
PD *020 †55

POWELL, Stanley H. ■ 23321 #051-04-1932 L1932 GP GS *071

POWERS, Steven Brian. 612 KINGSBOROUGH SQ, STE 200 23320 #051-07-1986 L1987
OBG *020

PUGH, Scott Michael. ■ 23320 #036-05-2004 L2004 *020

PUGH, Suzanne Koziol. ■ 23320 #036-05-2004 L2005 OBG *012

QUAST, Robert Francis. 413 WOODCLIFF ARCH 23320 #028-02-1988 L1990 AN *020 †05

QUATE, Larry J. 100 WIMBLEDON SQ 23320 #041-01-1980 L1985 PUD CCM *020 †20

QUIDWAI, Asima Saleem. ■ 23320 #704-06-1997 L2006 IM *100 †20

QUIDWAI, Muhammad S. 224 GREAT BRIDGE BLVD, CHESAPEAKE COMMUNITY SERVI 23320
#704-16-1986 L2007 P *100

RAJAN, Soundar. 1015 EDEN WAY N STE B 23320 #495-70-1969 L1989 HEM ON *020 †20

RAKOWSKI, Daniel Anthony. 745 BATTLEFIELD BLVD N, TIDEWATER KIDNEY SPECIALIS 23320
#041-15-1999 L2000 NEP *020 †20

RAMIREZ, Ray Thomas. 3205 CHURCHLAND BLVD 23321 #051-07-1993 L1993
CRS *020 †85,10

RAMIREZ, Renato Fajardo. 3205 CHURCHLAND BLVD 23321 #748-02-1960 L1967
CRS *020 †10

RAMOLIA, Mansukhlal R. 4053 TAYLOR RD 23321 #495-48-1972 L1979 GP *020

RAND, William Kenan, III. 824 GREENBRIER PKWY # 100 23320 #051-01-1978 L1982
GYN *020 †30

RAPPAPORT, Leonard Arthur. 805 BATTLEFIELD BLVD N, STE 111 23320 #010-01-1988 L1998
OPH *020 †35 ‡

RAWLINGS, Brad Andrew. ■ 23320 #012-22-2006 L2006 OTO *012

RAY, Dipes Kumar. 113 GAINSBOROUGH SQ, STE 201 23320 #495-02-1976 L2004 IM *020 †20

RAY, Sulekha. 113 GAINSBOROUGH SQ # 201, PREMIER PRIMARY CARE PIC 23320
#495-02-1977 L1999 FM *100 †18 ‡

RAYMOND, Patricia Lynn. ■ 23320 #051-04-1986 L1990 GE IM *020 †20

RECTOR, George, Jr. 612 KINGSBOROUGH SQ 23320 #051-07-1981 L1985 OBG *020 †30

RHODES, Amanda E. 860 GREENBRIER CIR, STE 100 23320 #048-14-1998 L2002 P *020

RICOHERMOSO, Alfonso Z. ■ 23325 #748-01-1953 L1961 GP *071

RIEDER, Nancy Barbara. 705 BATTLEFIELD BLVD N, PATIENT FIRST BATTLEFIELD 23320
#051-04-1976 L2006 PD CHP *020 †55

RILES, Nathan L, Jr. 648 INDEPENDENCE PKWY, STE 300 23320 #035-15-1983 L1989
FM *020 †18

RINALDI, James Jude. 736 BATTLEFIELD BLVD N, CHESAPEAKE RADIOLOGISTS 23320
#010-02-1988 L1993 DR *020 †80

RITZMAN, Thomas Alexander. ■ 23320 #024-01-1940 L1943 PYA OBG *071 †30

ROBERTSON, Scott Alan. 300 MEDICAL PKWY, CARDIOLOGY CONSULTANTS 23320
#051-01-1993 L1993 CD *020 †20

ROBERTSON, Wm Clayton. ■ 23321 #051-04-1946 L1946 OPH *071 †35

ROBEY, Edwin Lee. 676 BATTLEFIELD BLVD N, STE B 23320 #036-05-1980 L1985 U *020 †95

ROCHE, John P. 688 KINGSBOROUGH SQ, EAR NOSE & THROAT LTD 23320
#041-09-1993 L1999 OTO *020 †45

RODRIGUEZ, William. ■ 23322 #042-01-2001 L2005 P *020

ROGERS, Lori M. ■ 23322 #023-12-1994 L1995 PTH *020

ROHN, Reuben David. 733 VOLVO PKWY 23320 #035-09-1971 L1976 PDE ADL *020 †55

ROMASH, Michael Martin. 100 WIMBLEDON SQ # A 23320 #041-13-1974 L1988
ORS EM *020 †40

ROWLAND, Robt Cutchin, Jr. 736 BATTLEFIELD BLVD N, CHESAPEAKE RADIOLOGISTS 23320
#051-07-1977 L1979 DR *020 †80

RULAND, Robert Thos. 100 WIMBLEDON SQ 23320 #051-07-1988 L1997 ORS *020 †40

RYDER, Rebecca Margaret. 112 GAINSBOROUGH SQ 23320 #036-01-1989 L1994
GYN *020 †30

SADR, Hooman. 1417 BATTLEFIELD BLVD N, BLDG 1 23320 #051-07-2001 L2001 NEP *020

SAENZ, Enrique Antonio. 676 BATTLEFIELD BLVD N, STE A 23320 #264-04-1961 L1975
GS *071 †85

SAINI, Kanwarpreet. 736 BATTLEFIELD BLVD N 23320 #305-01-2001 L2004 IM *020 †20

SALIB, Victor Fahim. 675 BATTLEFIELD BLVD N 23320 #915-05-1991 L2002 FM *020 †18

SAMPLE, Kenneth Maurice. ■ 23322 #020-02-1984 L1986 GS *020 †85

SANTOS, Josefino Santos. 736 BATTLEFIELD BLVD N 23320 #748-08-1967 L1978 IM *020

SATIN-SMITH, Marta S. 733 VOLVO PKWY 23320 #035-08-1989 L1996 PDE *020 †55

SAUNDERS, Milton A, Jr. ■ 23321 #033-05-1965 L1970 D OS *071 †15 ‡

SAVOY-WHITFIELD, Ivy V. 1417 BATTLEFIELD BLVD N, STE 360 23320 #010-03-1982 L1986
FM *020 †18

SCACCIA, Michael Paul. 4012 RAINTREE RD, STE 200A 23321 #035-03-1996 L1996
PD *020 †55

SCHAAF, William Edward, Jr. 704 RAPIDAN RIVER CT, APT E 23320 #041-15-2003 L2004
DR *012

SCHELLHAMMER, Paul F. 676 BATTLEFIELD BLVD N, STE B 23320 #035-20-1966 L1974
U *020 †95

SCHILZ, Justin Leo. ■ 23323 #056-05-2006 L2006 *012

SCHLOSSBERG, Steven Mark. 676 BATTLEFIELD BLVD N, STE B 23320 #035-20-1979 L1986
U *020 †95

SCHULWOLF, Alfred Morton. 300 MEDICAL PKWY, STE 100 23320 #051-01-1958 L1958 PD *020

SCIALES, Christine Ann. ■ 23320 #051-07-2008 *012

SELDEN, Samuel T. 200 MEDICAL PKWY STE 309 23320 #036-01-1977 L1981 **D IMG** *020 †15

SHAH, Dharmesh Kaniayalal. 710 LIBERTY ST, RIVERSIDE WALTER REED FAMI 23324 #496-25-1999 L2005 **FM** *020 †18

SHAH, Rasesh Mahendra. 736 BATTLEFIELD BLVD N 23320 #050-02-1986 L2001 **VS GS** *020 †85

SHAH, Sanjay Gunvantlal. 300 MEDICAL PKWY, CARDIOLOGY CONSULTANTS 23320 #495-76-1985 L1995 **CBG** *020 †20

SHAUGHNESSY, John Francis. 4323 INDIAN RIVER RD STE D, NOWCARE I 23325 #011-02-1981 L1984 **GP** *020

SHEA, Daniel Francis, Jr. 2301 SAINT BRIDES RD W 23322 #027-01-1985 L2007 **AN IM** *020 †05

SHETH, Parthiv Jesing. 4608 BERETTA CT 23321 #495-76-1990 L2000 **PYG** *020 †75

SHIPE, Timothy Ray. 736 BATTLEFIELD BLVD 23320 #041-14-1985 L1991 **AN** *020 †05

SHOEMAKER, Benjamin Moore. ■ 23320 #051-01-2006 **IM** *020

SHROYER, Michael Neil. 688 KINGSBOROUGH SQ, EAR NOSE & THROAT LTD 23320 #051-01-1987 L1993 **OTO** *020 †45

SIEGEL, Fred Harris. 700 BATTLEFIELD BLVD N 23320 #051-04-1978 L1983 **PS** *020 †65

SIEREN, Leah Marie. ■ 23320 #018-03-2006 L2006 **GS** *012

SIMKOVICH, Joan Wanda. ■ 23321 #010-02-1977 L1981 **OBG** *020 †30

SLADE-BYRD, Lynelle W. 300 MEDICAL PKWY, STE 100 23320 #051-04-2002 L2002 PD *020 †55

SLINGSBY, Brett Andrew. ■ 23320 #041-02-2007 L2007 **PD** *012

SMITH, Pamela Beth. 713 VOLVO PKWY 23320 #020-02-1987 L1990 **OBG** *020 †30

SNIDER, Gilbert Martin. 300 MEDICAL PKWY STE 212 23320 #025-01-1975 L1982 **N OS** *020 †75

SNYDER, Steven Keith. 109 WIMBLEDON SQ, STE D 23320 #023-01-1988 L1995 **OPH PO** *020 †35

SOKOLIK, Corinne Frances. ■ 23322 #023-01-2004 L2004 **EM** *020

SOOD-KHANDPUR, Roopam. 224 GREAT BRIDGE BLVD, CHESAPEAKE CSB 23320 #035-48-1997 L2004 **P** *020

SORIANO, Alfredo P. 610 LIBERTY ST 23324 #748-01-1964 L1971 **IM** *020

SOTOSKY, Michael Alan. 676 KINGSBOROUGH SQ, STE B 23320 #041-12-1983 L1984 **FM FPG** *020 †18

SPAUR, William Hamilton. 4323 INDIAN RIVER RD STE D 23325 #038-40-1960 L1981 **OM IM** *071

STABLEY, Robert Conrad. 1239 CEDAR RD, PATIENT FIRST 23322 #023-12-1994 L2007 **PTH** *100

STAMBAUGH, Robert Edward. ■ 23321 #023-12-1992 L1994 **EM** *020 †16

STENICKA, Francis John. 3800 POPLAR HILL RD 23321 #539-04-1962 L1975 **GP EM** *020 ‡

STERNLICHT, Ludwig. 110 WIMBLEDON SQ STE E 23320 #869-01-1970 L1979 **ON HEM** *020 †20

STEWART, James Alan. 4041 TAYLOR RD, STE G 23321 #055-01-1973 L1975 **IM** *020 †20

STRAUSS, Patricia M. 300 MEDICAL PKWY, STE 222 23320 #051-07-1984 L1988 **PD** *020 †55

STROHKORB, Jerry Eugene. 748 BATTLEFIELD BLVD N, CHESAPEAKE HLTH DEPT 23320 #051-07-1998 L2000 **OM** *030 †70

SUCHON, Gregory Paul. ■ 23320 #035-03-2004 L2004 **PD** *012 †55

SUN, Beryl Kuo Gee. 2147 OLD GREENBRIER RD, STE D 23320 #243-16-1955 L1976 **OBG** *020 †30

SUTTON, Daniel Matthew. ■ 23321 #023-12-2003 L2003 **GS** *020

SZOKE, Peter. 308 CEDAR LAKES DR 23322 #051-07-1986 L1988 **FM** *020 †18

TAMAYO, Sally Gene. ■ 23322 #023-12-1996 L1998 **CD** *020 †20

TAN, Desiree Co. 713 VOLVO PKWY, STE 100 23320 #748-01-2001 L2002 **FM** *020 †18

TAN, Domingo C. 736 BATTLEFIELD BLVD N, CHESAPEAKE RADIOLOGISTS 23320 #748-01-1968 L1972 **R** *020 †80

TAN, Johannes Hian Tjo. ■ 23320 #506-01-1959 L1998 **ATP CLP** *071 †50

TAN, Regina. 675 BATTLEFIELD BLVD N 23320 #026-04-1988 L1989 **IM** *020 †20

TAN, Valiant C. 300 MEDICAL PKWY, STE 314 23320 #748-01-1986 L1998 **HO ON** *020 †20

TANDY, Thomas Kind, III. 705 BATTLEFIELD BLVD N, PATIENT FIRST BATTLEFIELD 23320 #041-02-1986 L1993 **EM** *020 †16

TERRY, A Nicholas, Jr. 113 GAINSBOROUGH SQ 23320 #030-05-1974 L1976 **IM** *020 †20

THOMAS, Thomas William, Jr. ■ 23323 #023-12-2007 L2007 *012

THOMPSON, Michael Julian. 907 LIVE OAK DR STE A, OPERATION BLESSING 23320 #055-01-1994 L1997 **FM** *020 †18

THORNTON, Charlotte Lynn. 4120 MAPLE DR 23321 #001-02-1999 L1999 **FM** *020 †18

THOROGOOD, Michael Robt. 2100 STEPPINGSTONE SQ 23320 #917-06-1981 L1992 **FM** *020 †18

TIESENGA, Sidney Wilson. 110 AMERICAN LEGION RD 23321 #025-01-1966 L1967 **ORS** *020 †40

TIFFANY, Julie Trainer. 300 MEDICAL PKWY STE 100, TIDEWATER'S CHILDREN'S ASS 23320 #036-08-1998 L1998 **PD** *020 †55

TIONGCO, Felix P. 112 GAINSBOROUGH SQ, STE 200 23320 #748-02-1992 L1999 **GE** *020 †20

TO, Stephen See. ■ 23320 #748-01-2000 L2004 **FM** *020 †18

TOOLE, Wendy J. ■ 23320 #008-02-1994 L1995 **EM** *020 †16

TOPALLI, Krishna Brahma S. ■ 23321 #495-37-1992 L2007 *100

TREHERNE, Annyce Christin. ■ 23321 #047-07-2007 **GS** *012

TSEREDIANI, Giorgi. ■ 23322 #912-02-1998 L2008 **IM** *012

TSOU, Victor Marc. 733 VOLVO PKWY 23320 #025-07-1984 L1991 **PG PD** *020 †55

TUCKER, Ruby Margaret. ■ 23325 #033-05-1995 L2000 **IM** *020 †20

TURNER, Douglas Michael. ■ 23321 #041-14-2006 L2007 *012

UBEDEI, Emily Secheyangel. ■ 23321 #048-04-1999 L1999 **IM** *020

UY, Gregorio C. 2147 OLD GREENBRIER RD, STE D 23320 #748-01-1965 L1973 **OBG** *020 †30

VACCARELLA, Joseph Edward. 213 RIVER WALK PKWY, STE 101 23320 #051-07-1992 L1993 **FM** *020 †18

VAID, Arun Kumar. 710 LIBERTY ST 23324 #352-04-1967 L1973 **IM CD** *020 †20

VARGAS, Gustavo. 3906 BAINBRIDGE BLVD 23324 #737-01-1956 L1965 **FM** *020 †50

VARGAS, Honesto Belaro. ■ 23321 #748-07-1955 L1964 **GP OS** *071

VENKATARAMAN, Mythili T. 4053 TAYLOR RD, STE N 23321 #495-59-1986 L2001 **PCC IM** *020 †20

VILLASIS, Felipe C. 736 BATTLEFIELD BLVD N 23320 #748-01-1966 L1974 **N OS** *020 †75

WANCHICK, Kara Beth. ■ 23322 #038-43-2006 L2006 *012

WARREN, Pamela Delaine. 801 SANDERSON RD 23322 #047-07-1995 L2000 **IM** *020

WATERS, Louis Napoleon. ■ 23321 #051-01-1943 L1943 **GYN** *072 †30

WATSON, Francis Edward. 736 BATTLEFIELD BLVD N 23320 #030-05-1973 L1974 **EM** *020 †16

WAXMAN, Gary Jay. ■ 23322 #023-01-1975 L1999 **AN** *020 †05

WELCH, Nancy Mae. 748 BATTLEFIELD BLVD N 23320 #036-07-1972 L1977 **PHP PD** *030 †55,70

WELLS, Brian Patrick. ■ 23320 #023-01-1995 L1996 **GPM** *020 †70

WERTHEIMER, Richard Isaac. 300 MEDICAL PKWY STE 212 23320 #165-06-1978 L1987 **N** *020 †75

WEST, David John. 113 GAINSBOROUGH SQ 23320 #051-01-1985 L1988 **IM IMG** *020 †20

WHITELOCK, Leland D, Jr. 508 BAYLOR CT, STE C 23320 #023-01-1961 L1968 **OPH** *020 †35 ‡

WHITTED, Matthew Louis. 713 VOLVO PKWY STE 200, GREENBRIER OBSTETRICS AND 23320 #036-01-1986 L1989 **OBG** *020 †20

WILKINS, Howard Boykin. 3105 WESTERN BRANCH BLVD 23321 #051-04-1956 L1965 **OPH** *020

WILLIAMS, Clemmie Lee. ■ 23321 #047-07-1974 L1980 **FM** *020 †18

WILLIAMS, Fred Aaron. 1013 EDEN WAY N, STE A B & C 23320 #051-07-1995 L1998 **OBG** *020

WILLIAMS, Judith Virginia. 733 VOLVO PKWY 23320 #041-14-1984 L2000 **D** *020 †55,15

WILLIAMS, Margaret Yvonne. ■ 23321 #051-07-2008 *012

WILLIAMS, Melissa Lauren. ■ 23320 #021-06-2007 L2007 **EM** *012

WILLIAMS, Michael Brandon. ■ 23323 #048-13-2003 L2003 **U** *012

WILLIS, Lauren Kiely. 733 VOLVO PKWY 23320 #001-02-1993 L1999 **PD PG** *020 †55

WINGFIELD, Frank Q. 2125 SMITH AVE, STE 202 23320 #051-04-1952 L1952 **PTH** *020 †50

WINKE, Beth Marie. 700 BATTLEFIELD BLVD N, STE C 23320 #018-03-1988 L1995 **PM** *020 †60

WINSTON, York Edward. 745 BATTLEFIELD BLVD N, STE 103 23320 #051-04-1972 L1976 **OBG** *020 †30

WOLD, Stephen Michael. ■ 23323 #038-45-2005 L2005 **OTO** *012

WONG, Michelle Mai-Shung. 309 WOODARDS FORD RD 23322 #024-07-2008 *012

WOOD, Robin Elaine. 620 RIVER STRAND 23320 #023-12-1990 L1992 **OBG** *020 †30

YANCEY, Eric Leon. 2147 OLD GREENBRIER RD, YAMEIKA SURGICAL GROUP, PC 23320 #051-04-1991 L1999 **GS** *020 †85

YOUNG, Elisa Marie. ■ 23320 #047-06-2007 L2007 **PD** *012

ZAMAN, Imtiaz. 1015 EDEN WAY N, STE E 23320 #495-45-1981 L1992 **IM PUD** *020 †20

ZEV, Mohammad Z. 2994 CHURCHLAND BLVD, CHURCHLAND INTERNAL 23321 #160-01-1987 L1996 **IM** *020 †20

ZEV, Shirin Fatema. 2994 CHURCHLAND BLVD, CHURCHLAND INTERNAL 23321 #160-01-1989 L2004 **IM** *020 †20

ZHITAR, Sergey. 3241 WESTERN BRANCH BLVD, BAYVIEW PHYSICIAN SERVICES 23321 #913-50-1988 L2001 **IM** *020 †20

ZUNIEGA, Leah. 4053 TAYLOR RD, STE N 23321 #748-02-1990 L2000 **PUD** *020 †20

CHESTER – CHESTERFIELD

ABDULLAH, Anwar Kamal. ■ 23836 #495-05-1961 L1992 **IM PUD** *020

AGADA, Raphael Iwebunor. 4094 CREEK WAY 23831 #690-06-1984 L1999 **IM** *020 †20

AGARWAL, Rakesh. ■ 23836 #051-04-2001 L2001 **DR** *100 †80

AGYEMAN, Kwabena Osei. 13034 RIVERS BEND RD, VIRGINIA HEART GROUP, LTD 23836 #051-07-1991 L2002 **CD** *020

AKBAR, Salman Mughul. 12101 S CHALKLEY RD 23831 #051-07-1993 L1996 **IM** *020 †20

ALI, Rukhsana Fatima. ■ 23836 #495-21-1975 L1986 **AN** *075 †05

APONTE, Yolanda. ■ 23831 #308-03-1982 L1985 **GP** *020

BAROT, Ghanshyam C. 13038 RIVERS BEND RD 23836 #496-11-1980 L1998 **FM** *020 †18

BECKWITH, Douglas Earl. 12901 BRIGGS RD 23831 #051-07-1988 L1990 **FM** *020 †18

BERMANT, Michael Alan. 11601 IRON BRIDGE RD, IRONBRIDGE MED PK STE 201 23831 #016-06-1978 L1996 **PS HS** *020 †65

BORN, Ana Maria. ■ 23831 #010-01-2008 *012

BRANLY, Louis Phillip. ■ 23831 #047-06-1975 L1976 **P** *075

BROWN, Linda Kay. 12801 IRON BRIDGE RD 23831 #007-02-1994 L2005 **OBG** *020 †30

BURIJON, Brian Grieg. 12801 IRONBRIDGE RD, STE 200 23831 #051-04-1994 L1994 **FM** *020 †18

CAMPBELL, Kevin Michael. 4707 BUCKINGHAM CT 23831 #051-04-1983 L1984 **PD** *020 †55

CAROTHERS, Thomas Scot. 11601 IRON BRIDGE RD, STE 200 23831 #048-12-1996 L1996 **OPH** *020 †35

CHOU, Yi-Nan. 12600 IRON BRIDGE RD 23831 #385-04-1967 L1972 **CD AMI** *020 †20

CIOFLEC, Daniela. 13223 RIVERS BEND BLVD 23836 #781-04-1985 L1996 **IM** *020 †20

CIURASH, John Silvius. 12801 IRONBRIDGE RD, STE 300 23831 #781-04-1979 L1994 **FM** *020

CLAY, John Aubrey. ■ 23831 #051-04-2007 L2007 **FP** *012

CLEMENTS, Kim Carol. 12101 S CHALKLEY RD, PATIENT FIRST CHESTER 23831 #051-04-2001 L2001 **FM** *020 †18

COBAUGH, Donn Stephen. 12801 IRON BRIDGE RD, STE-200 23831 #051-04-1975 L1976 **FM FPG** *020 †18

COLINA, Mervyn Francis. ■ 23836 #051-04-1989 L1990 **FM** *020 †18,05

CROSS, Elizabeth Mc Gill. 4707 BUCKINGHAM CT, CHESTER PEDIATRICS 23831 #036-05-1987 L1990 **PD** *020 †55

DINICOLA, Anthony Paul. ■ 23831 #055-01-2006 L2006 **PM** *012

DUNCAN, Phillip B. 13034 RIVERS BEND RD 23836 #010-03-1978 L1983 **CD IM** *020 †20

EDWARDS, Monica Pamela. 13015 CHIPSTEAD RD 23831 #033-05-1988 L2000 **AN** *020 †05

FOREMAN, Lynne Helms. ■ 23836 #051-04-1989 L1992 **CHP** *020 †75

GALLIPOLI-STEELE, Kerri A. 4707 BUCKINGHAM CT 23831 #036-05-1996 L1996 **PD** *020 †55

GAY, George Mantovani. 11824 CLUB RIDGE DR 23836 #011-03-1990 L2000 **HO** *020

GORADIA, Vipool Kirit. 281 E HUNDRED RD 23836 #039-01-1993 L1999 **ORS OSM** *020 †40

GORE, Vincent Myron. 12101 S CHALKLEY RD, PATIENT FIRST CHESTER 23831 #023-12-1984 L2000 *020

GUPTA, Prabha U. ■ 23836 #010-01-2002 L2002 **IM** *020 †20

HABIB, Saima Zehra. 12702 OLD SAINT ANDREWS PL 23836 #704-21-1995 L2007 **FP** *012

HOLLAND, John Alfred, Jr. ■ 23836 #047-07-1976 L1977 **FM** *020 †18 ‡

JACOBS, Erwin M. ■ 23831 #036-05-1948 L1977 **N P** *072 †75

JENKINS, Elizabeth M. 12101 S CHALKLEY RD, PATIENT FIRST-CHESTER 23831 #007-02-1996 L2002 **FM** *020 †18

JONES, Wondiful Aubrayai. 12101 S CHALKLEY RD, PATIENT FIRST CHESTER 23831 #051-04-2002 L2002 **FM** *020 †18

KHANDAT, Amaresh B. ■ 23836 #496-38-1995 L2004 **P** *100 †75

LEE, Chao-Te. 11919 CLUB RIDGE DR 23836 #041-01-1970 L1976 **AN EM** *020

LEMITE, Gregory Keith. 1714 E HUNDRED RD, STE 104 23836 #035-47-1992 L2003 **GE IM** *020 †20

LEWIS, Cyrus Patrick. ■ 23831 #051-01-1957 L1957 **FM** *071 †18

LEWIS-BLACKWELL, Robbie L. ■ 23831 #051-04-1991 L1993 **PD** *020

MASOOD, Ali Khaja. ■ 23831 #422-01-2003 L2007 **IM** *100 †20

ORMSSMITH, Jessica Leah. 12900 JEFFERSON DAVIS HWY 23831 #051-04-2003 L2003 **FM** *020 †18

OSA, Osaguona Osamuederhu. ■ 23831 #010-03-2001 L2001 **IM** *020 †20

OTOVO-LEAH, Earnestine W. ■ 23831 #005-02-1976 L2005 **P PD** *020 †55

POLANSHEK, Mark Mumford. 4707 BUCKINGHAM CT 23831 #051-04-1995 L1987 **PD** *020 †55

PORT, Brian Richard. 12801 IRON BRIDGE RD, STE 200 23831 #035-03-1980 L1981 **FM** *020 †18

PUSTER, Geo Valentine, Jr. 12801 IRON BRIDGE RD, STE 200 23831 #051-04-1975 L1976 **FM** *020 †18

RAHMAN, Faiz-Ur. 12101 S CHALKLEY RD, PATIENT FIRST 23831 #704-02-1995 L2000 **IMG** *020 †20

ROBERTS-BOYD, Nicole E. 12101 S CHALKLEY RD, PATIENT FIRST CHESTER 23831 #023-01-1997 L1997 **IM** *020 †20

ROSE, Andrew Lee. 11601 IRONBRIDGE RD, STE 117 23831 #051-07-1994 L1997 **FM** *020 †18

SANBORN, George E. 11601 IRON BRIDGE RD, STE 200 23831 #051-01-1971 L1971 **OPH AM** *020 †35

SARRAF, Sadik Abdul. ■ 23836 #528-01-1958 L1974 **PD** *020 †55

SCHROEDER, Mark Alan. 11601 IRON BRIDGE RD # 117, IRON BRIDGE FAMILY PRACT 23831 #051-04-2002 L2002 **FM** *020 †18

SHAH, Amit R. ■ 23836 #495-23-1983 L1992 **P** *020 †75

SHAH, Tushar Chandravadan. 13121 RIVERS BEND BLVD 23836 #495-23-1992 L2000 **FM** *020 †18

SHAYNE, Robert Steven. 4707 BUCKINGHAM CT 23831 #023-01-1978 L1981 **PD** *020 †55

SIDHU, Baljit S. 13225 RIVERS BEND BLVD 23836 #495-03-1973 L1979 **ORS** *020 †40

STENNETT, Thomas R, III. 12801 IRON BRIDGE RD, STE 200 23831 #051-04-1981 L1982 **FM** *020 †18

STOGNER, Kimberly Ann. ■ 23831 #045-01-2006 L2006 **PTH** *012

VILLANUEVA, John Galen T. ■ 23836 #748-08-1991 L2000 **FM** *020 †18

VUYYURU, Lokesh Babu. 110 OLD BERMUDA HUNDRED RD 23836 #495-50-1983 L1991 **GE** *020 †20

VUYYURU, Sujatha. 13223 RIVERS BEND BLVD 23836 #495-50-1985 L1994 **RHU** *020 †20

WADDILL, James Thos. ■ 23831 #051-04-1965 L1965 **GP** *071

WALTON, George Clifford. 12101 S CHALKLEY RD, PATIENT FIRST CHESTER 23831 #051-04-1994 L1994 **FM** *020 †18

WILSON, Timothy Ratnam. 12901 BRIGGS RD 23831 #422-01-1997 L2002 **FM** *020 †18

YARATHA, Sridhar. ■ 23831 #306-01-1995 L2004 **P IM** *020

YEATTS, Donald Eric. 12101 S CHALKLEY RD, PATIENT FIRST CHESTER 23831 #051-04-1990 L1991 **FM** *020 †20

ZAIDI, Saima Imran. 713 CLUB CREST BLVD 23836 #704-02-2000 L2006 **FP** *012

ZHAO, Wei. ■ 23836 #243-75-1983 L2001 **AI PD** *100 †55,03

CHESTERFIELD — CHESTERFIELD

AHMAD, Akber. ■ 23838 #051-04-2002 L2005 **IM** *020 †20

AJJARAPU-JENNES, Esther S. ■ 23832 #306-01-2004 L2005 **FP** *012

ANNIS, Karen Kay. ■ 23832 #051-04-2005 L2005 **IM** *012

APPLETON, Darryn Lewis. ■ 23832 #671-02-2001 L2005 **IM** *012

BAIRD, Roger Pryor, III. 6801 LUCY CORR CT 23832 #051-01-1988 L1989 **P** *020 †75

BALA, Meena Elthia. 9501 LUCY CORR CIR, CHESTERFIELD HEALTH DEPT 23832 #495-20-1974 L1984 **FM** *020

BELSHEIM, Julie Nicole. ■ 23832 #016-43-2007 L2007 **FP** *012

BRINSER, Paul W, III. ■ 23838 #051-04-1995 *100 **EM**

CATOLICO, Maria Angela A. 6801 LUCY CORR CT, CHESTERFIELD COMMUNITY SER 23832 #748-10-1992 L2006 **P** *020 †75 ‡

CHAPARALA, Padmaja. PO BOX 92, 6801 LUCY CORR BLVD 23832 #495-58-1981 L1995 **PYG** *020

COX, Diane Renee. ■ 23832 #048-13-2005 L2005 **GS** *012

ESTRERA, Annabella. ■ 23838 #748-09-1972 L1983 **P** *020

ESTRERA, Clemente S, Jr. ■ 23838 #748-11-1972 L1977 **GP EM** *020

FISKE, Lauren Cameron. ■ 23832 #051-04-2007 L2007 **MPD** *012

FRIEDMAN, Robin Lynn. 9512 IRON BRIDGE RD, STE 100A 23832 #051-07-1994 L1994 **FM** *020 †18

FULCHER, James William. ■ 23832 #051-04-2004 L2006 **PTH** *012

GARRETT, Caroline Sue. ■ 23832 #020-12-2005 L2005 **MPD** *012

GARRETT, Charles Justin. ■ 23832 #047-06-2001 L2001 *020

GOWDA, Madhu Shivaramaiah. ■ 23832 #496-39-1999 L2006 **PHO** *012 †55

HENDRY, Travis Michael. ■ 23832 #010-01-2004 L2004 **ORS** *012

JONES, John Kipling. 9844 LORI ST, STE 100 23832 #051-04-1973 L1982 **CHP OS** *040 †75

KRAUSSE, Heather K. ■ 23832 #051-04-2003 L2003 **CHP** *012

LATHER, Robert Keith. ■ 23838 #023-12-1992 L1994 **EM** *020 †16

LIU, Pung Show. ■ 23838 #244-02-1953 L1975 **P GP** *071 †75

LOVELAND, Kerry Lee. ■ 23832 #054-04-2007 L2007 **ORS** *012

MAHONEY, Brent Paul. 6933 COMMONS PLZ, # 235 23832 #021-01-2004 L2005 **RO** *012

MISHRA, Asha. 6801 LUCY CORR CT, CHESTERFIELD COMM SVCS 23832 #496-07-1978 L1982 **P PYG** *020 †75

MITCHELL, Troy Michael. 13906 ORCHID DR, TROY M MITCHELL, MD, PC, I 23832 #051-04-2001 L2002 **FM** *100 †18

NAGARAJA GOWDA, Soundarya. ■ 23832 #495-99-2005 L2007 **N** *012

NELSON, William Richard, Jr. 9501 LUCY CORR CIR, P O BOX 100 23832 #051-04-1976 L1979 **PHP OBG** *062 †70

PATHAK, Satish Kumar. 9519 OWL TRACE DR 23838 #045-01-1990 L1993 **CD** *020 †20

PLOTKIN-HAN, Joan. 6801 LUCY CORR CT, P O BOX 92 23832 #051-04-1985 L1988 **P CHP** *020 †75

QUINN, Aaron Robert. 10613 RIDGERUN RD 23832 #051-07-2003 L2003 **EM** *020 †16

RAMIREZ, Raul Enrique. ■ 23832 #042-01-1981 L2007 **PDE** *020 †55

REYNOLDS, Todd Jos. 10107 KRAUSE RD STE 100 23832 #051-04-1992 L1993 **FM** *020 †18

SHAIKH, Tahir A. ■ 23832 #035-75-2005, ▲ L2005 **IM** *012

SIEGMUND, Rita Wiegner. ■ 23838 #028-34-1978 L1983 **PD** *020 †55

SINGH, Neena Gurpal. 6801 LUCY CORR CT 23832 #495-08-1974 L1982 **P** *020 †75

SRIRAM, Radhika. 6801 LUCY CORR CT 23832 #495-33-1991 L1995 **CHP** *020 †75

STEPHENSON, Meagan Leigh. ■ 23838 #051-04-2007 L2007 **IM** *012

UNKEL, John Henry. ■ 23838 #051-04-2008 *012

WITTE, Darren Samuel. 6433 CENTRALIA RD, INTERNAL MEDICINE&PEDIATRI 23832 #051-04-1996 L1996 **MPD IM** *020 †20,55

CHILHOWIE — SMYTH

JONKERS, Jennifer Ann. 403 CHILHOWIE ST 24319 #051-04-1998 L2002 **MPD** *020 †20,55

MURPHY, Gerard Howard. 403 CHILHOWIE ST, FAMILY CARE OF CHILHOWIE D 24319 #008-02-1994 L1996 **FM** *020 †18

CHINCOTEAGUE — ACCOMACK

AMRIEN, Donald Jos. 3741 WILLOW ST 23336 #154-02-1957 L1960 **GP OS** *020

GO, Ma. Carmelita Capon. 4049 MAIN ST, CHINCOTEAGUE ISL COM HOSP 23336 #748-26-1990 L2001 **IM FM** *020 ‡

NGUYEN, My Gia. ■ 23336 #041-02-1999 L2006 **FM** *020 †18

PAWELSKI, Richard Jos. ■ 23336 #041-01-1959 L1960 **R** *071 †80

PESANIELLO, Kimberly. 6455 MADDOX BLVD 23336 #023-07-1989 L2001 **P** *020 †75

SCOTT, Paul Anderson. 4049 MAIN ST 23336 #051-04-1975 L1987 **GP** *072

WOLFFE, Glenn Barnett. 6295 TEAL LN, ISLAND MEDICAL CENTER 23336 #038-41-1985 L1986 **FM** *020 †18

CHRISTIANSBURG — MONTGOMERY

AGNESS, Melisa Moore. 2900 TYLER RD 24073 #036-01-1987 L2001 **DR** *020 †80

AIKIN, Kent R. 2900 TYLER RD, STE 250 24073 #041-09-1977 L1995 **FM** *020 †18

AMONETTE, Wilbur F. 2900 LAMB CIR 24073 #051-04-1948 L1948 **IM OS** *020

AUBREY, Donna Lawson. 2900 TYLER RD 24073 #020-12-1987 L1991 **DR** *020 †80

BADILLO, Leslie Elvis. 205 ROANOKE ST, CARILION FAMILY & 24073 #042-01-1980 L1986 **FM OBG** *020 †18 ‡

BAKER, William Bradford. 2900 LAMB CIR, STE 335 24073 #035-19-1975 L1980 **IM NEP** *020

BARTA, Joseph Arthur, Jr. 2900 LAMB CIR 24073 #055-01-1964 L1972 **OPH** *020 †35

BENNETT, Lawrence Eric. 3425 COUNTRY MEADOW DR 24073 #035-19-1974 L1975 **FM** *020 †18

BILLUE, Angela Renee. 2900 TYLER RD 24073 #012-01-1987 L1989 **AN** *020 †05

BISSELL, Charles David. 2900 LAMB CIR 24073 #025-01-1990 L2001 **GS** *020 †85

BISSELL, Noelle Scaldara. 2900 LAMB CIR, STE 250 24073 #023-01-1990 L2001 **IM** *020 †20

BRADFORD, Sarah Reylea. 205 ROANOKE ST, CARILION FAMILY & 24073 #065-01-1994 **FM** *100

BROOKS, Jeffrey C. 2900 LAMB CIR STE 1871A, OF RADFORD INC. 24073 #036-05-1991 L1995 **AN** *020 †05

CAMPBELL, Sanam Emami. 2900 LAMB CIR, CARILION OB/GYN NEW RIVER 24073 #047-06-1993 L1993 **OBG** *020 †30

CHAVIS, Timothy Vaughn. 2900 LAMB CIR, CARILION SURGICAL CARE 24073 #047-06-1983 L1984 **GS** *020 †85

CHEUNG, Ada. 2900 LAMB CIR, STE L760 24073 #008-01-1992 L2003 **ORS** *020 †40

CHOUBEY, Sudhendu. 2900 LAMB CIR, STE 210 & 230 24073 #496-06-1986 L1998 **CD IM** *020

CHUNG, Jey-Dea. 2900 TYLER RD 24073 #243-50-1970 L1975 **AN** *020 †05

COLBY, John Christopher. 2875 BARN RD STE 200, SVPW OB/GYN 24073 #012-01-1991 L2004 **OBG** *020 †30

CONATSER, Michael Keith. 2900 LAMB CIR, STE 250 24073 #017-20-1988 L1992 **IM** *020 †20

COOK, Andrew Michael. 2900 LAMB CIR, CARILION NEW RIVER VALLEY 24073 #051-07-2003 L2003 **EM** *020 †16

COOK, William Henry, Jr. 2900 LAMB CIR, STE 160 24073 #051-01-1963 L1963 **PD** *020 †55

CRUISE, Rodell E, Jr. 2900 LAMB CIR 24073 #051-04-1995 L1995 **FM** *020 †18

CUBE, Ernesto Milla. 2900 LAMB CIR 24073 #748-01-1956 L1962 **OPH GS** *071 †35

DANYI, John Jos. 2900 TYLER RD 24073 #038-40-1983 L2002 **AN IM** *020 †05

DAVIE, Steven Ames. 2900 LAMB CIR STE 150 24073 #047-06-1968 L1969 **OTO** *071 †45

DAVIS, Thomas Philip. 10 HICKOK ST, STE 101 24073 #051-01-1961 L1961 **FM PDS** *020

DOWNING, La Miere Jos. 2900 LAMB CIR, CARILION VASCULAR CARE 24073 #025-01-1992 L2001 **VS GS** *020 †85

DOWNS, David A, Jr. 2900 LAMB CIR, CARILION BEHAVIORAL HLTH 24073 #030-05-1984 L2003 **PYG P** *020 †75

DUMS, Robert Mark. 205 ROANOKE ST 24073 #036-01-1996 L1996 **FM** *020 †18

ELSWICK, Ronald Kenneth. 2900 LAMB CIR 24073 #051-04-1955 L1955 **GYN** *071 †30

GEORGES, Theodore N. 2900 LAMB CIR, EMERGENCY DEPARTMENT 24073 #051-04-1973 L1974 **EM PUD** *020 †20,16

GIESEN, John W. 2900 LAMB CIR 24073 #051-04-1952 L1952 **IM** *071

GOLDSCHMIDT, Jerome Henry. 2900 LAMB CIR, STE 200 24073 #036-01-1998 L2005 **HO** *020 †20

GOODRICH, Michael D. 2900 TYLER RD 24073 #048-15-1990 L1999 **AN PME** *020 †55,05

GRABOYES, Arnold Bruce. 2900 TYLER RD, CARILION NEW RIVER VLY MED 24073 #051-04-1973 L1978 **EM IM** *020 †20,16

HANNAH, Carl Robert. 6 HICKOK ST 24073 #064-01-1981 L2003 **GP** *020

HARMAN, Ann Marie. 2900 TYLER RD 24073 #035-48-1987 L1990 **AN IM** *020 †05

HAWLEY, Rollin James, Jr. 2900 LAMB CIR 24073 #041-09-1967 L1991 **N CN** *020 †75,20 ‡

HERSHEY, J Henry. 210 PEPPER ST STE A 24073 #051-07-1982 L1983 **FM PHP** *030 †70,18

HIJAZI, Ali Atef. 2900 LAMB CIR, STE 250 24073 #605-01-1994 L2001 **IM** *020 †20

HLUSKO, George Paul, Jr. 2900 LAMB CIR 24073 #055-01-1967 L1983 **CHP P** *020 †75

HOLLIMAN, Daniel Rhodes. ■ 24073 #051-04-1981 L1984 **IM** *075 †20

HOWELL, Tamera Lynn. 2900 LAMB CIR STE 150 24073 #038-43-1993 L1999 **OBG** *020 †30

HUDGINS, John Stephen. 10 HICKOK ST STE 201 24073 #051-04-1985 L1989 **OPH** *020 †35

JAMISON, Thomas S. 95 PONDEROSA DR 24073 #048-12-1986 L1991 **IM** *020 †20

JOHN, Ajo. 2900 LAMB CIR, RADIOLOGY CONSULTANTS, INC 24073 #035-15-2001 L2007 **RNR** *020 †80

JONES, Kenneth Earl. 6 HICKOK ST 24073 #051-04-1974 L1975 **FM** *020 †18

KHAN, Arif Ali. 2900 LAMB CIR STE 250, CARILION NEWRIVER VALLEY M 24073 #704-09-1987 L2001 **IM** *020 †20

KISHORE, Anand Tunuguntla. 2900 LAMB CIR STE 320 24073 #495-21-1977 L1990 **GE IM** *020 †20

KOEHLER, Anthony J, Jr. 2875 BARN RD STE 200 24073 #005-12-1994 L1998 **OBG** *020 †30

KWAK, Kristina Lynne. 2955 MARKET ST 24073 #038-45-1999 L2006 **AI** *020 †55

LAMBERT, Reed Richard. 205 ROANOKE ST, CARILION FAMILY & 24073 #051-01-1987 L1990 **FM** *020 †18

■ = Address Information Privacy Protected

LESLIE, John W, Jr. 2900 LAMB CIR, CARILION PULMONOLOGY 24073 #051-04-1988 L1990 PCC IM *020 †20
MARSHALL, Linda R. 2900 LAMB CIR, STE 160 24073 #041-12-1975 L1989 PD *071 †55
MC COY, Harry Ellington. 2900 LAMB CIR, STE 200 24073 #051-01-1985 L1988 ON HEM *020 †20
MHATRE, Pradnya Yashavant. ■ 24073 #495-17-1997 L2005 DR *100 †80
MIGLANI, Jasdeep Singh. 2900 LAMB CIR, CARILLION BEHAVIORAL HEALT 24073 #495-08-1996 L1999 P *020 †75
MISHRA, Tanuja. 2900 LAMB CIR STE 260, NEW RIVER NEPHROLOGY ASSOC 24073 #495-47-1983 L2000 NEP IM *020 †20
MOGEN, Thomas Charles. 205 ROANOKE ST, CARILION FAMILY & 24073 #051-01-1986 L1988 FM *020 †18
MOREHOUSE, Ivan Roger. 2900 TYLER RD 24073 #020-12-1971 L1988 DR PD *020 †55,80
MOREHOUSE, Nancy E Wetzel. 3020 COUNTRY MEADOW DR 24073 #020-12-1971 L1988 PD *020 †55
NOBLE, Thomas Edward. 110 AKERS FARM RD 24073 #035-09-1972 L1993 GE IM *020 †20
PARAS, Norberto Espino. 2900 LAMB CIR, STE 250 24073 #748-01-1990 L2005 IM *020 †20
PATEL, Bharat Raojibhai. 2900 LAMB CIR, NRVMC X RAY DEPT 24073 #495-23-1971 L1979 R *020 †80
PENNELL, Wayne Estel. 2875 BARN RD, STE 200 24073 #036-05-1966 L1989 OBG *020
PRUSSIN, Aaron Justin. 2955 MARKET ST STE C4 24073 #011-02-1989 L1994 OTO HNS *020 †45
PUCKETT, Tedd Randal. 2900 LAMB CIR 24073 #023-12-1988 L1999 OPH *020 †35
RAJA, Jogesh Chhotalal. 2900 LAMB CIR, STE 250 24073 #495-96-1983 L1995 IM *020 †20
REUWER, John Francis. ■ 24073 #051-01-1980 L1982 EM GP *020 †16
RINGOLD, Mark Anthony. 110 AKERS FARM RD 24073 #047-06-1989 L1999 GE *020 †20
RIVERO, Jose M. 1201 ELM ST, HEART SPECIALST OF VIRGINI 24073 #654-01-1984 L1997 CD *020 †20
ROTCHE, Brigitte K. 6 HICKOK ST, CHRISTIANSBURG FAMILY PRAC 24073 #016-01-1989 L2000 PD *020 †55
SHAFFER, Charles Edwin. 95 PATRICIA LN NE 24073 #306-01-1988 L1998 EM *020 †18
SMITH, James H. ■ 24073 #047-06-1952 L1953 GP *071 †18
SMITH, James Randall. PO BOX 724 24068 #039-05-1986 L1998 FM *020 †18
SMUSZ, Tina Louise. 2900 LAMB CIR, CARILION PALLIATIVE 24073 #016-45-1986 L1989 FM EM *020 †18
SOLOMON, Robert Chas. 2900 LAMB CIR 24073 #051-07-1983 L1988 IM *020 †20
SONNIER, Christopher Shan. 90 COLLEGE ST, STE B 24073 #654-01-2000 L2001 END *020
STEPHENSON, Robert Brian. 2900 LAMB CIR 24073 #041-01-1982 L1988 ORS OSM *020 †40
SYPOLT, Susan Marie. 2900 TYLER RD 24073 #055-01-1987 L1994 R *020 †80
TAN, Alex A. 10 HICKOK ST, STE 102 24073 #748-11-1966 L1972 GS *071 †85
TAURO, Allen Patrick. 2900 LAMB CIR, STE 250 24073 #495-72-1995 L2001 IM *020 †20
TAYAL, Krishan Kumar. 2900 TYLER RD, # 330 24073 #495-77-1969 L1979 GS VS *020 †85
TODD, Mark Edward. 2900 LAMB CIR, CARILION NRV MEDICAL CENTE 24073 #051-04-1987 L1988 FM *020 †18
TRIVEDI, Bhairvi Ketan. 2900 LAMB CIR, STE 335 24073 #495-17-1982 L1992 IM NEP *020 †20
TUNUGUNTLA, Lakshmi. 2900 LAMB CIR, STE 320 24073 #495-21-1977 L1990 IMG IM *020 †20
WEIMERSKIRCH, Peter John. 2900 LAMB CIR 24073 #051-04-1982 L1987 EM GP *020 †16
WESTON, James Stuart. 2900 LAMB CIR, STE 330 24073 #051-01-1979 L1989 OBG *020 †30
WHITE, John James. 1305 RADFORD ST 24073 #027-01-1980 L1986 IM PUD *020 †20
WYNE, Amjad Uzair. 2900 LAMB CIR 24073 #704-01-1972 L1980 CD *020 †20
YAGER, Elizabeth Anne. ■ 24073 #030-05-1979 L2006 P *020 †75
ZAPATERO, Jose Miguel. 2900 TYLER RD 24073 #035-48-1995 L2006 FM *020 †18
ZEDALIS, Donald. 2955 MARKET ST, STE B1 24073 #020-12-1979 L1990 AI SME *020 †20,03

CHURCH ROAD – DINWIDDIE

HOLT, Mark Edgar, Jr. ■ 23833 #051-01-1946 L1946 IM OS *020 †20

CHURCHVILLE – AUGUSTA

ALEXANDER, Dawn. 252 DOE HILL DR, EAST ROCKINGHAM HEALTH CEN 24421 #055-02-1998 L2001 FM *020 †18

CLARKSVILLE – MECKLENBURG

HUNDLEY, Susan Dupuy. 61 BURLINGTON DR 23927 #051-01-1997 L1997 FM *020 †18
HUNDLEY, Willoughby S, III. 61 BURLINGTON DR 23927 #051-04-1981 L1982 FM EM *020 †16,18
ROSS, James Stanley. 115 COLLEGE ST 23927 #018-03-1992 L1996 FM *020 †18
THOMAS, Johnna Sue. 115 COLLEGE ST 23927 #036-08-1997 L2004 FM *020 †18
ZWILLING, Gregory Vincent. 115 COLLEGE ST 23927 #036-05-1994 L1997 FM FSM *020 †18

CLIFTON – FAIRFAX

ADEYEMI-BERO, Oluyemisi G. ■ 20124 #690-02-1988 L2008 FM *100 †18
BAROT, Lydia M. ■ 20124 #748-08-1962 L1975 PD OS *071
BRUCE, Julia Anne. 6709 CLIFTON RD 20124 #051-01-1994 L1997 FM *020 †18
CRAWFORD, Raymond S, III. ■ 20124 #004-01-1971 L1989 GS MDM *062 †85
DUGGAN, Michael. ■ 20124 #051-01-2006 L2006 AN *012
FRAMSTAD, Mark Alan. ■ 20124 #023-12-1993 L2006 AN *020 †05
GARCIA-RANGEL, Jorge Luis. ■ 20124 #275-01-1951 L1973 GP *020
HANNON, Mary Cecilia. 6400 WOODLAND RUN CT 20124 #035-46-2008 *012
HIGGS, Elizabeth Seale. ■ 20124 #051-01-1987 L1988 ID *050 †20
JIN, Young S. ■ 20124 #583-12-1983 L1995 PTH BBK *020
MC CARTY, Dennis P. ■ 20124 #051-01-1946 L1946 GS *071 †85
NOWELL, John Francis. ■ 20124 #023-01-1956 L1959 OPH *071 †35
SARODI, Sikander Sultana. ■ 20124 #704-04-1978 L1986 PD *020
SCANLAN, David Harold, III. 6506 STONEDALE LN 20124 #030-05-2007 PD *012

CLIFTON FORGE – ALLEGHANY

ALLEN, Edward G. 1701 RIDGEVUE AVE, FOREST HILL 24422 #035-03-1952 L1970 R *071 †80,28
BOYD, William Everett, Jr. ■ 24422 #051-07-1983 L1987 PD *020 †55
CLATERBAUGH, Raymond. PO BOX 544 24422 #036-05-1972 L1974 FM *020
DENIUS, Larry Richard. ■ 24422 #056-05-1964 L1967 FM *020 †18
FINESTONE, Alvin Wm. ■ 24422 #041-13-1948 L1958 DR *071 †80
GOINGS, Ronald Steven. 609 CHURCH ST 24422 #018-03-1978 L1981 FM FSM *020 †18
HALL, Aubrey Carlyle. PO BOX 547 24422 #051-04-1966 L1966 FM *020 †20
HULL, James Gregory. ■ 24422 #051-01-1965 L1965 ATP CLP *020 †50
NUNLEY, Wallace Clay. ■ 24422 #051-01-1948 L1948 FM *071
SIMANIS, Juris. PO BOX 547 24422 #010-02-1967 L1974 IM CD *020 †20

CLINTWOOD – DICKENSON

AJI, Sarmad. HOSP DR, DICKENSON COUNTY MED CTR 24228 #875-01-1983 L1994 VS GS *020 †85
ALDERMAN, Kurtz Edward. RR 1, CARE OF DICKENSON CLINIC 24228 #051-01-1955 L1955 GP *071
ARORA, Mohinder Partap. PO BOX 1389 24228 #495-03-1970 L1982 FM EM *020
IBRAHIM, Rimon. PO BOX 2071 24228 #875-01-1988 L1994 IM *020 †20
MISSAK, Samir Samuel. PO BOX 1040 24228 #915-03-1979 L1991 IM *020 †20
RATLIFFE, Norman C. PO BOX 280 24228 #051-04-1953 L1953 GP IMG *020
SINGH, Ram. 203 HOSPITAL DR 24228 #495-03-1962 L1980 GP EM *075
VANOVER, Patricia Joyce H. ■ 24228 #051-04-1974 L1975 GP *020

COEBURN – WISE

DAIUTO, Gerald Michael. 10839 NORTON-COEBURN RD 24230 #038-40-1985 L1996 IM *020

COLLINSVILLE – HENRY

JESNECK, Edward Jos. 2682 VIRGINIA AVE 24078 #051-04-1976 L1977 FM *020
LEGA, Robert Eugene. 203 KINGS MOUNTAIN RD, VAUGHAN PEDIATRIC CENTER 24078 #020-02-1973 L1995 PD *020 †55

COLONIAL BEACH – WESTMORELAND

BOULWARE, Alfred Larry. 700 MCKINNEY BLVD, STE 12 22443 #038-06-1975 L2004 IM *020 †20
FORRESTER, J Colin. 222 WILDER AVE 22443 #051-07-1982 L1983 FM IMG *075 †18
NADER, Jafar. 700 MCKINNEY BLVD 22443 #517-01-1958 L1970 FM GS *020 †18

COLONIAL HEIGHTS – COLONIAL HEIGHTS CITY

AHMED, Irshad. 2801 BOULEVARD, STE B 23834 #704-16-1987 L1998 IM *020 †20
ALEMAN, Christopher T. 320A CHARLES H DIMMCK PKWY 23834 #041-02-1995 L1995 D *020 †15
ALLAUDDIN, Tahir. 2905 BOULEVARD 23834 #704-02-1990 L2001 PUD *020 †20
ARMSTRONG, Brent Andrew. 3512 BOULEVARD 23834 #422-01-1995 L1995 MPD *020 †20,55
ARRIETA, Mary Cathrine. 400 SOUTHPARK BLVD, STE D 23834 #748-11-1974 L1984 PD NPM *020 †55
AULT, Peter N, Jr. 3512 BOULEVARD 23834 #051-04-1977 L1978 IM *020
BOODRAM, Kadarnath S. 436 CLAREMONT CT STE 105 23834 #422-01-1995 L2000 IM *020 †20
BOWLES, James William. 430 CLAREMONT CT, STE 121 23834 #051-04-1976 L1977 OPH *020 †35
BOYCE, Franklin D, Jr. ■ 23834 #051-04-1979 L1980 FM *020 †18
CALDWELL, Melaney A. 2425 BOULEVARD STE 6, CALDWELL PEDIATRICS AND WE 23834 #010-02-1993 L1993 PD *020 †55
CARL, Joan Rountree. 320A CHARLES H DIMMCK PKWY 23834 #051-04-1989 L1992 D *020 †15
CHIU, Grace Hsin-Ying. 241 DIMMOCK PKWY, STE 6 23834 #306-01-2001 L2002 FM *020 †18
CHIU, Ming S. 2905 BOULEVARD 23834 #244-04-1969 L1978 PUD IM *020 †20
CONCODORA, Joseph Anthony. 436 CLAREMONT CT, VIRGINIA UROLOGY CENTER 23834 #051-04-1973 L1975 U *020 †95
DABHI, Kishor Shankerji. 3628 BOULEVARD 23834 #495-76-1991 L1998 IMG *020 †20
DAVIS, Robert S. 2905 BOULEVARD 23834 #020-02-1964 L1965 EM GP *071
DAVIS, Robert Stephen. 2905 BOULEVARD 23834 #051-04-1980 L1983 IM PUD *020 †20
DIGGS, Arleeta Monee. 241 CHARLES H DIMMOCK PKWY, PRIME CARE FAMILY 23834 #051-07-1999 L1999 FM *020 †18
DIZON, Hermes. 210 TEMPLE AVE 23834 #748-07-1975 L1992 PD *020
DOEREN, Brian Richard. 241 DIMMOCK PKWY, STE 6 23834 #048-02-1993 L2007 FM *020 †18
DUBOSE, Don Antonio. ■ 23834 #045-04-2007 P *012
EAPEN, Sari G. 430 CLAREMONT CT, SYCAMORE BUILDING, STE 122 23834 #495-31-1976 L1982 PM *020 †60 ‡
ELEY, Kerry Williams. ■ 23834 #051-04-2006 L2006 FP *012
EMILIANI, Nicholas A. 3236B BOULEVARD 23834 #264-04-1970 L1977 P ADP *020 †75
FEMINELLA, John Geo, Jr. 430 CLAREMONT CT, STE 214 23834 #035-09-1966 L1972 U *020 †95 ‡
FEORE, John Colman. 3660 BLVD, STE H 23834 #539-02-1970 L1977 OBG REN *020 †30
FERGUSON, Willard R. ■ 23834 #048-02-1950 L1957 PD *071
GEORGE, Leelamma. ■ 23834 #495-63-1984 L2003 IM *020 †20 ‡
GLAZIER, David Brendan. 436 CLAREMONT CT, VIRGINIA UROLOGY CENTER 23834 #539-06-1990 L2001 U *020 †95
GOLDBERG, Jay Stephen. 3731 B BLVD 23834 #010-01-1970 L1971 GP OS *020
GONZALES, Patricia D. 210 TEMPLE AVE 23834 #748-01-1969 L1975 PD *020
GRIZZARD, William Samuel, Jr. 439 JENNICK DR 23834 #051-04-1943 L1943 OBG *071 †30
GRIZZARD, Wm Saml, Jr. 439 JENNICK DR, RIVERVIEW PHYSICIANS FOR 23834 #051-04-1980 L1983 OBG *020 †30

■ = Address Information Privacy Protected

GUPTA, Pranay. 3660 BOULEVARD, STE I 23834 #023-01-1997 L2001 **OPH** *020 †35
HARRY, Frederick Peter. 3403 BOULEVARD 23834 #051-04-1978 L1981 **IM** *020 †20
HAWKINS, Teresa Margaret. 436 CLAREMONT CT, HEALTH CARE PLUS 23834 #051-04-1996 L1996 **FM** *020 †18
HAWTHORNE, Tawni Frank. 3236 BOULEVARD, STE B 23834 #035-06-1976 L1978 **CHP** P *020 †75
HERRERA-MARTELA, Jolanta. 436 CLAREMONT CT, STE 105 23834 #759-12-1986 L2000 **IM** *020 †20
HOWARD, Richard K. 320B CHARLES H DIMMCK PKWY, STE 5 23834 #035-03-1977 L2003 **GS** *020 †85
HOWELL, Malcolm Lawrence. 3660 BOULEVARD, STE H 23834 #051-04-1984 L1987 **OBG** *020 †30
IQBAL, Jawed. 16011 KAIROS RD 23834 #704-16-1988 L1997 **PD** *020 †55
ISHIZAWAR, Yorckay Chang. 211 TEMPLE AVE 23834 #244-05-1969 L1979 **GS VS** *020 †85
JOHNSON, Lydia Jones. 320A CHARLES H DIMMCK PKWY, STE 7 23834 #051-01-1997 L1999 **D** *020 †15
JOHNSON, Robert Alexander. ■ 23834 #051-04-1971 L1974 **GP** *020
JOHNSON, Russell Anthony. 430 CLAREMONT CT, STE 122 23834 #041-13-1979 L1990 **PUD IM** *020 †20
JONES, Tracey Neal. 439 JENNICK DR, RIVERVIEW PHYSICIANS FOR 23834 #051-04-1990 L1993 **OBG** *020 †30 ‡
KHAN, Nadeem Anwar. 430 CLAREMONT CT, STE 212 23834 #704-01-1993 L2003 **PMM** *100 †60
KING, James Willard. ■ 23834 #021-05-1976 L1977 **NEP** *050 †20
KOHLI, Ravinder Singh. 89 SHERWOOD DR 23834 #495-29-1976 L1992 **IC IM** *020 †20
KOVACIC, Joseph H. ■ 23834 #561-11-1955 L1961 **ORS** *071 †40
LEMING, Joseph Atkins. 241 CHARLES H DIMMOCK PKWY, PRIME CARE FAMILY 23834 #051-07-1983 L1984 **GP** *020 ‡
LIN, Hsing-Wu. 436 CLAREMONT CT 23834 #385-04-1967 L1980 **CD IM** *071 †20
MC DONALD-JOHNSON, Rolanda. 430 CLAREMONT CT, STE 211 23834 #041-14-1996 L1996 **PD** *020 †55
MILLER, Bruce Allen. 3512 BOULEVARD 23834 #051-04-1983 L1984 **FM** *020 †18 ‡
MILLER, Carlton Edwin. 430 CLAREMONT CT, STE 122 23834 #051-07-1983 L1987 **RHU IM** *020 †20
MOHAGHEGHI, Hassan Ali. 3701 BOULEVARD, STE C 23834 #517-01-1959 L1979 **AI PDA** *020 †55
MOORE, De Saussure P, III. 3512 BOULEVARD 23834 #051-04-1976 L1977 **FM** *020 †18
MOORE, Desaussure P, Jr. 3512M BOULEVARD 23834 #036-07-1952 L1955 **GP** *071 †18
MURTHY, Gurunanjappa S. 400 SOUTHPARK BLVD, STE D 23834 #495-09-1959 L1973 **PD GP** *071 †55
NUGARAM, Rekha. 89 SHERWOOD DR 23834 #495-21-1991 L2004 **END** *100 †20
O'DONNELL, Philip Patrick. 2905 BOULEVARD 23834 #023-01-1974 L1979 **N** *020 †75
OGBURN, Christopher Wade. 241 CHARLES H DIMMOCK PKWY, PRIME CARE FAMILY 23834 #051-04-1997 L1997 **FM** *020 †18
PANZARELLA, Kim Marie. 320A CHARLES H DIMMCK PKWY 23834 #035-01-1993 L2001 **D** *020 †15
PRAKASH, Karanvir. 131 JENNICK DR, COLONIAL ORTHOPAEDICS 23834 #495-36-1982 L1990 **ORS PM** *020 †40
PRATT, Laura Lee. 320A CHARLES H DIMMCK PKWY 23834 #023-12-1988 L2001 **D** *020 †15
PUTHUMANA, Kochurani C. 215 TEMPLE AVE 23834 #495-63-1987 L1994 **IM** *020 †20
REARDON, Patrick A. 83 SHERWOOD DR 23834 #051-04-1959 L1959 **PD** *071 †55
RESKALLA, Totmes Tewfik. ■ 23834 #330-02-1953 L1995 **OBG** *071
REYES, Maria Rocio. 3701- A BOULEVARD 23834 #051-04-1998 L2002 **AI** *100 †20,03
ROBERTS, Keith Mc Duffie. 439 JENNICK DR, RIVERVIEW PHYSICIANS FOR 23834 #051-04-1996 L1996 **OBG** *020 †30
ROSENBERGER, William, II. 430 CLAREMONT CT, STE 121 23834 #051-04-1989 L1993 **OPH** *020 †35
ROSS, James Wilson. 436 CLAREMONT CT, STE 109 23834 #011-03-1977 L1978 **OM IM** *020 †20,70
SHAH, Amar Rajendra. ■ 23834 #654-01-2003 L2007 **FM** *020 †18
SHAH, Ramesh Ambalal. 3801 ORKNEY RD, RAMESH A SHAH 23834 #495-22-1961 L1977 **P IMG** *071
SHAHAB-UDDIN, Ahmed. 16011 KAIROS RD 23834 #704-16-1985 L1997 **PD** *020 †55
SHINDLER, Elliott Ronald. 3522 BOULEVARD, STE B 23834 #018-03-1969 L1975 **PD** *020
SHOU, Phillip Yeu Shing. 2801 BOULEVARD 23834 #243-33-1976 L1987 **IM PD** *020 ‡
SMITH, Brent Elliot. 430 CLAREMONT CT STE 121, VIRGINIA EYE INSTITUTE 23834 #024-05-1979 L1981 **OPH** *020 †35
SMITH, Charles William, III. 439 JENNICK DR, DBA/RIVERVIEW PHYSICIANS F 23834 #051-07-1985 L1989 **OBG** *020 †30
SMITH, Sandra Maurita. 436 CLAREMONT CT, STE 100 23834 #051-04-1990 L1991 **FM UCM** *020 †18
SQUIRES, William Ashley. 430 CLAREMONT CT 23834 #051-01-1979 L1980 **FM** *020 †18
SRIVASTAVA, Praveer. 131 JENNICK DR, COLONIAL ORTHOPAEDICS 23834 #495-45-1985 L2001 **ORS OAR** *020 †40
TALEGAONKAR, Shantaram K. 430 CLAREMONT CT, STE 121 23834 #495-34-1961 L1976 **OPH** *071 †35
TALEGAONKAR, Sunita S. 400 SOUTHPARK BLVD, STE D 23834 #495-01-1975 L1993 **PD** *020 †55
TANWI, T Bah, IV. 2905 BOULEVARD 23834 #654-01-1992 L1996 **N** *020
VAKIL, Amanollah Homayoun. PO BOX 554 23834 #517-01-1971 L1991 **AN CCM** *020 †05
VINIEGRA-SIBAL, Amabel. 801 JENNICK DR, STE A 23834 #748-10-1984 L1992 **PD** *020 †55
WALSH, Margaret Dahmus. 3660 BOULEVARD, STE J 23834 #041-14-1982 L1993 **OBG DR** *020 †80,30
WASCHLER, William. 430 CLAREMONT CT, STE 121 23834 #011-02-1984 L1986 **OPH** *020 †35
WEATHINGTON, Lee, II. 3512 BOULEVARD 23834 #021-01-1969 L1972 **FM** *020 †18 ‡
WILES, Howard Olen, III. 3660 BOULEVARD, STE H 23834 #020-12-1981 L1990 **OBG** *020 †30

COLUMBIA – GOOCHLAND

CARCHMAN, Evie Harvell. ■ 23038 #051-04-2006 L2006 **GS** *012
CARCHMAN, Susan Harvell. ■ 23038 #051-04-1983 *074
MONCURE, Charles Withers. PO BOX 14 23038 #051-04-1963 L1963 **CLP PTH** *071 †50
SHULMAN, Suzanne Gail. ■ 23038 #010-01-2001 L2007 **DR** *100 †80
WIECKING, David Kerndt. ■ 23038 #023-07-1960 L1960 **FOP LM** *071 †50

COPPER HILL – FLOYD

FRENCH, Lorraine Marie. 9104 FLOYD HWY N 24079 #011-03-1981 L2003 **OBG** *020 †30
JOHNS, Kathryn Louise. 1376 GRAYSVILLE RD SE, SOUTHWEST EMERGENCY PHYSIC 24079 #035-03-1999 L1999 **EM** *020

COURTLAND – SOUTHAMPTON

BOWLING, Donald Bruce. 22708 MAIN ST, COURTLAND MEDICAL CENTER 23837 #051-04-2005 L2005 **FP** *012
LAMBDIN, James W. ■ 23837 #051-04-1944 L1944 **IM** *071

COVESVILLE – ALBEMARLE

AULD, Richard M. ■ 22931 #023-07-1952 L1981 **FM PD** *020 †55,18

COVINGTON – COVINGTON CITY

ADRALES, Mamerto B. ■ 24426 #748-08-1965 L1972 **GS** *020
ALDEA, Erlinda Doncello. 2501 VALLEY RIDGE RD 24426 #748-01-1965 L1972 **PD** *020 †55
HADDADI, Gita. 2501 VALLEY RIDGE RD, JACKSON RIVER PEDIATRICS 24426 #517-06-1993 L2002 **PD** *100
KEDDIE, Suzanne Marcella. 620 ADDAMS ST 24426 #021-06-1985 L1999 **AN PME** *020 †05
LEWIS, John W. 411 W RIVERSIDE ST 24426 #055-75-1998, ▲ L1998 **GP FPG** *020 ‡
LUKE, Maryjane. RR 5 24426 #051-01-1952 L1952 **CD PD** *071 †55
MAYS, Gregory Chas. 201 INTERSTATE DR 24426 #038-43-1992 L1997 **OPH** *020 †35
ROBLETE, Beulah V. 529 W PARKLIN DR 24426 #748-08-1964 L1973 **OBG** *071 †30
SANKAR, Krishna. 201 INTERSTATE DR 24426 #495-33-1961 L1972 **OPH** *020
SHAMMA-OTHMAN, Zainab. 529 W PARKLIN DR, GREENBRIAR PHYSICIANS INC 24426 #528-01-1979 L1998 **PUD IM** *020 †20
WALKER, James Howard. 2419 VALLEY RIDGE RD, VALLEY RIDGE FAMILY MEDICI 24426 #023-12-1984 L2000 **FM** *020 †18
YU, Norma Ching. 1008 S MONROE AVE 24426 #748-08-1963 L1975 **IM EM** *020

CREWE – NOTTOWAY

GODSEY, Ralph Edwin. CREWE MEDICAL CTR 23930 #051-04-1962 L1962 **GP** *071
HALL, Clarence Edward, II. 12522 W COLONIAL TRAIL HWY 23930 #051-04-1998 L1998 **FM** *020 †18
MARSTON, Jonathan Eric. PO BOX 528 23930 #051-04-1995 L1995 **FM** *020 †18

CROSS JUNCTION – FREDERICK

MAJEWSKI, Patricia Ann. ■ 22625 #011-03-1981 L1986 **P** *020 †75
NELSON, David Luther. ■ 22625 #019-02-1970 L2008 **PD A** *020 †55,03

CROZET – ALBEMARLE

ACHAREKAR, Bela Arun. 1646 PARK RIDGE DR, CROZET FAMILY MEDICINE 22932 #038-43-2000 L2000 **FM** *020
BAISDEN, Joseph Myers. ■ 22932 #055-01-2003 L2004 **RO** *012
BARKER, Jeffrey Ryan. ■ 22932 #048-15-2006 L2006 **AN** *012
BOURQUE, Jamieson M. ■ 22932 #036-07-2003 L2006 **CD** *012 †20 ‡
CASSADA, William Abraham. ■ 22932 #051-04-1955 L1955 **R** *071 †80
COHEN, Sheldon. ■ 22932 #016-11-1955 L1956 **IM** *071 †20
HAMZA, Maged. 1260 BAYBERRY CT 22932 #915-02-1988 L2000 **APM** *020 †05
HARRISON, James H, Jr. ■ 22932 #045-01-1983 L2005 **PTH PA** *020 †50
HENDRICKS, Daniel Ewell. ■ 22932 #051-01-2003 L2003 **DR** *012
HENDRICKS, Krista Jean. ■ 22932 #051-01-2005 L2005 **AN** *012
HERRING, Russell E, Jr. ■ 22932 #051-04-1950 L1950 **R** *071
KEELEY, Mark Stephen. 1646 PARK RIDGE DR, CROZET FAMILY MEDICINE 22932 #051-01-1990 L1995 **FM** *020 †18
KENNEDY, Jamie Lynnwebb. ■ 22932 #017-20-2005 L2005 **IM** *012
KIRBY, Jennifer Leigh. ■ 22932 #051-01-2004 L2004 **IM** *012 †20
KOVARSKY, Joel. 1839 CLAY DR, STE B 22932 #018-03-1972 L1996 **RHU IM** *071 †20
LACHANCE, Jason Adams. ■ 22932 #010-02-2001 L2005 **OBG** *100
LAUB, Harvey Morris. 1646 PARK RIDGE DR 22932 #051-04-1981 L1982 **FM** *020 †18
LEISURE, Marketa K. 5674 THREE NOTCHED RD 22932 #016-02-1987 L1989 **PD** *020 †55
MARRARO, Howard W. ■ 22932 #035-01-1953 L1990 **IM** *071 †55
MICHAELSEN, Veronica E. ■ 22932 #018-03-1993 L1998 **EM** *074
MORGAN, Hallee Perkins. ■ 22932 #016-42-1978 L1982 **OBG** *020
NNAMANI, Ijeoma Nnechi. ■ 22932 #051-01-2008 *012
OBER, William Chas. PO BOX 487, 6818 JARMANS GAP RD 22932 #051-01-1974 L1976 **FM** *062
RICHARDSON, Donald Ray. ■ 22932 #051-01-1962 L1962 **D** *071 †15
ROWLINGSON, John C. 5006 LAKE TREE LN 22932 #035-06-1974 L1977 **AN PME** *020 †05
SAWYER, Russell C. 1646 PARK RIDGE DR, CROZET FAMILY MEDICINE 22932 #035-03-1988 L1990 **FM** *020 †18
SKELTON, Brandon Wayne. ■ 22932 #027-01-2005 L2006 **DR** *012
SMITH, Phillip Joshua. ■ 22932 #036-08-2007 L2008 **IM** *012
STEWART, Corrine Rene. 937 BRAEBURN ST 22932 #051-07-2002 L2002 **NPM** *012 †55
STRASSER, Heinz Jorg. ■ 22932 #154-02-1953 L1958 **FM** *072
WISE, Lily Sonia. 1646 PARK RIDGE DR, CROZET FAMILY MEDICINE 22932 #033-06-1996 L1996 **FM** *020 †18

CROZIER – GOOCHLAND

MONTICELLI, Jonathan D. PO BOX 156 23039 #051-07-2000 L2000 **IM** *020 †20

PORTER, Frederick S, Jr. ■ 23039 #023-07-1952 L1976 **PD** *071 †55
TOWNSEND, Mark David. ■ 23039 #051-04-2000 L2000 **MPD** *100 †20,55

CULPEPER – CULPEPER

BACCHUS, Bebi Samantha. 100 SAUNDERS ST 22701 #033-06-1994 L2006 **PD** *020 †55
BALDWIN, Thomas Alan. 633 SUNSET LN, STE F 22701 #051-07-1986 L1997 **GS** *020 †85
BAQAIE, Wahid Manzur. 663 SUNSET LN 22701 #024-05-1998 L2000 **ORS** *020
BEIER, Karl Martin. 541 SUNSET LN, STE 301 22701 #041-07-1978 L1981 **OBG** *020 †30
BEIER, Teressa Cotton. 501 SUNSET LN 22701 #051-07-1980 L1982 **GP** *020
BREAR, David Russell. 633 SUNSET LN, STE E 22701 #048-14-1978 L1984 **OPH FM** *020
BURNS, James Earl. 640 LAUREL ST, CULPEPER HEALTH DEPT 22701 #020-12-1971 L1978 **PD** *030 †55
BUSH, Anne Elizabeth. 1200 SUNSET LN, STE 2111 22701 #027-01-1986 L1997 **GE** *020 †20
BUSH, John Morris. 19170 EQUESTRIAN 22701 #047-06-1992 L1998 **IM** *020 †20
CALL, Thomas David. 501 SUNSET LN 22701 #041-13-1970 L1971 **CD IM** *071 †20
CHILES, Morton Perrin, III. 1200 SUNSET LN, STE 2210 22701 #051-01-1975 L1976 **FM** *020 †18
CIRENZA, Emanuel. 501 SUNSET LN, BOX 592 22701 #035-15-1984 L1985 **HEM ON** *020 †20
COOK, James Bryon. 1043 OAKLAWN DR 22701 #051-04-1976 L1977 **IM** *020 †20
DOLAN, Gail Lynn. 633 SUNSET LN, STE A 22701 #051-01-2000 L2003 **PD** *020 †55
GALA, Hemlata Kantilal. 206 S MAIN ST 22701 #496-38-1970 L1982 **GP PTH** *020
GLOUDEMAN, Mark Bernard. 541 SUNSET LN, STE 303 22701 #016-06-1984 L1989 **GS VS** *020 †85
GODFREY, Peter Edward. 541 SUNSET LN, STE 301 22701 #023-01-1979 L1983 **OBG** *020 †30
GOLUB, Robert Alan. 541 SUNSET LN, STE 303 22701 #035-46-1981 L2004 **GS CRS** *020 †10,85
GONZALEZ, Amauri. 1200 SUNSET LN, STE 2210 22701 #051-04-1984 L1986 **FM** *020 †18
GRAVATTE, Leroy T, IV. 471 JAMES MADISON HWY, STE 101 22701 #051-04-1985 L1988 **FM OS** *020 †18
HAQ, Sami Ul. 100 SAUNDERS ST, CMA 22701 #495-21-2000 L2005 **IM** *100
KILBY, Walter Bluford. 633 SUNSET LN, STE A 22701 #051-04-1969 L1969 **PD GP** *020
LEADBETTER, Robert Annon. 1100 SUNSET LN, STE 1310 22701 #055-01-1983 L1985 **P PHM** *050 †75
LEE, Insook Ina. 501 SUNSET LN, CULPEPER REGIONAL HOSPITAL 22701 #583-09-1984 L1990 **IM** *020 †20
MATHEWS, Karen Leigh. 100 SAUNDERS ST 22701 #051-07-1987 L1989 **OBG** *020 †30
MC HARGUE, Chauncey Ared. 1100 SUNSET LN, STE 1212 22701 #038-43-1986 L1990 **D** *020 †15
MENDLOW, Stephanie. 545 SUNSET LN, STE 102 22701 #035-08-1971 L1986 **CD** *020 †20
MITCHELL, Thomas Soren. 1100 SUNSET LN, STE 1211A 22701 #005-12-1966 L1999 **U** *020 †95
MOWATTLARSSEN, Eric. 501 SUNSET LN, EMERGENCY DEPT 22701 #051-04-1998 L2001 **EM** *020
MULUGETA, Yemisrach. 501 SUNSET LN 22701 #366-01-1989 L2001 **IM** *020 †20
NICHOLS, Kimberley Renett. 501 SUNSET LN 22701 #036-01-2000 L2004 **AN PME** *020 †05 ‡
PFEFFER, David Michael. 1100 SUNSET LN STE 1211A 22701 #028-02-1983 L1991 **U** *020 †95
POOLE, Joel Richard. 1043 OAKLAWN DR 22701 #051-04-1965 L1965 **IM END** *071
REDMON, Robert Bruce. 541 SUNSET LN, STE 102 22701 #051-04-05-1978 L1983 **OTO** *020 †45
REIGEL, Craig Alan. 663 SUNSET LN, VIRGINIA ORTHOPAEDIC CTR 22701 #041-07-1989 L2003 **OSM** *020 †40
REYNOLDS, Thomas Earl. 1200 SUNSET LN, STE 2210 22701 #051-01-1977 L1978 **FM** *020 †18
ROSEN, Robert A. 501 SUNSET LN 22701 #033-06-1975 L2005 **EM GP** *030 †16
ROSHANDEL, Ahmad Z. ■ 22701 #409-39-1998 L2006 **CD** *020 †20
RUTKOWSKI, Robert. 663 SUNSET LN 22701 #035-06-1976 L1981 **ORS OSM** *020 †40
SAID, Khaled Fathy Ahmed. 501 SUNSET LN 22701 #915-04-1995 L2003 **FM** *020 †18
SINGER, Grace Taryn. ■ 22701 #308-03-1981 L2007 **IM END** *020 †20
STEIN, Charles A. 633 SUNSET LN, STE C 22701 #051-01-1980 L1983 **PD** *020 †55
STERGIS, George Nicholas. 610 LAUREL ST 22701 #028-02-1979 L1991 **N NS** *020 †75
SUTER, Charles Francis, Jr. 1043 VAHLAWN DRIVE 22701 #051-01-1975 L1981 **IM IMG** *062 †20
SUTTON, Steven Glenn. 1100 SUNSET LN, STE 1211A 22701 #036-08-1991 L2004 **U** *020 †95
TRAYLOR, Amy Hocutt. ■ 22701 #036-05-1992 L2000 **N** *020 †75
WALLACE, Matthew B. 1200 SUNSET LN 22701 #051-01-1973 L1974 **FM** *020 †18
WEAVER, Robert Gregory. 633 SUNSET LN STE B 22701 #012-05-1974 L1997 **OTO** *020 †45
WERNER, Susan Jane. 633 SUNSET LN, STE C 22701 #041-09-1982 L1989 **PD** *020 †55
WHITEHURST, Lawrence Rowe. 471 JAMES MADISON HWY, STE 101 22701 #051-04-1974 L1976 **FM AM** *020 †18
WRIGHT, Thelma Bernice. 501 SUNSET LN, CULPEPER REGIONAL HOSPITAL 22701 #010-03-2001 L2002 **APM** *105
YI, Sok. 610 LAUREL ST, STE 3 22701 #023-01-1991 L2002 **PUD IM** *020 †20

CUMBERLAND – CUMBERLAND

LOMBANA, Alfonso. RR 3 BOX 284, THE CUMBERLAND CLINIC 23040 #132-02-1961 L1970 **IM OSS** *071 †20
PARMENTER, Robert E. ■ 23040 #021-05-1949 L1969 **GPM PHP** *071
PEREZ, Justo T. 1758 ANDERSON HWY, MEDICAL CENTER OF CUMBERLA 23040 #737-01-1952 L1962 **IM FM** *071

DAHLGREN – KING GEORGE

DI DONATO, A Jean Breaux. ■ 22448 #023-01-1972 L1979 **EM** *020
THOMAS, Elizabeth K. 17457 CAFFEE RD STE 217, NAVAL BRANCH HEALTH CLINIC 22448 #023-01-2001 L2003 **FM** *020 †18

DALE CITY – PRINCE WILLIAM

ABDULLE, Abucar Adan. 14409 HEREFORD RD 22193 #561-17-1984 L1991 **IM** *020 †20
ALIDOOST, Nosrat Ali. 4158 DALE BLVD 22193 #517-01-1972 L1990 **IM** *020

ALLEYNE, Aminah Latonya. ■ 22193 #010-01-2008 *012
BERAME, Belinda Berdin. 4158 DALE BLVD 22193 #748-11-1989 L1997 **FM** *020 †18
KANCIR-AZER, Ljubica M. 4158 DALE BLVD 22193 #957-01-1968 L1976 **ID** *020
KHAN, Najma Jahangir. 14009 MINNIEVILLE RD 22193 #704-09-1969 L1978 **PD ID** *020
SALENE, Kimberly J. 4158 DALE BLVD 22193 #035-45-1995 L2005 **IM** *020
SHAH, Rakesh Kumar. 4233 DALE BLVD 22193 #495-20-1970 L1981 **AN** *020

DALEVILLE – BOTETOURT

BERTHOLF, Max Erwin. ■ 24083 #005-11-1954 L1954 **FM GYN** *020 †18
DENNIS, Larry Glenn. ■ 24083 #041-09-1977 L1990 **MFM OBG** *020 †30
GALE, James Cofer. ■ 24083 #051-04-1943 L1943 **PTH** *071 †50
JONES, Daniel Ralph. 46 WESLEY RD, CARILION FAMILY MEDICINE 24083 #051-04-1974 L1975 **FM FPG** *020 †18
POLK, Elizabeth Lynn. 46 WESLEY RD, CARILION FAMILY MEDICINE 24083 #051-01-1995 L1996 **FM** *020 †18
SPROLES, John Hammitt. ■ 24083 #051-04-1943 L1943 **OBG** *071 †30
STIDHAM, Gregory Alan. 46 WESLEY RD, CARILION FAMILY MEDICINE 24083 #051-04-1983 L1984 **FM** *020 †18
WATSON, Brian Wesley. ■ 24083 #051-04-2001 L2007 **PTH** *100

DAMASCUS – WASHINGTON

KUDYADI, Deepti Satish. PO BOX 456 24236 #496-25-1997 L1999 **IM** *020 †20
LOGAN, Cynthia Ann. 20471 AZEN RD 24236 #036-01-1994 L1999 **FM** *020 †18
LUCK, James Thos. 306 SHADY AVE 24236 #051-01-1972 L1972 **FM** *071 †18

DANVILLE – DANVILLE CITY

ABRAHAM, Deepa. 125 EXECUTIVE DR, STE E 24541 #023-07-1995 L2002 **OPH** *020 †35
AHMED, Syed Aftab. 125 EXECUTIVE DR STE K 24541 #704-02-1967 L1976 **CD IM** *020 †20
ALABANZA, Tomas M. 990 MAIN ST, STE 204 24541 #748-01-1965 L1972 **IM** *020
AL-JASSAR, Muhanad M. Jas. ■ 24541 #528-01-1990 L2005 **IM** *100 †20
ALVAREZ, Orlando Mario. 800 MEMORIAL DR, DOMINION EYE CENTER 24541 #021-05-1987 L1998 **OPH** *020 †35
ANDREWS, Michael Jos, Jr. 1040 MAIN ST 24541 #036-07-1972 L1981 **U** *020 †95
ASHBY, B R. 1124 MAIN ST, POST OFFICE BOX 32749 24541 #051-01-1965 L1965 **P** *020 †75 ‡
ASWATH, Mugabala Byrappa. 130 GRAY ST 24541 #495-33-1978 L1998 **N CN** *020 †75
BABIERA, Rodolfo V. 1114 MAIN ST 24541 #748-11-1967 L1977 **AN** *071
BALDEMOR, Anita Baisas. 258 W MAIN ST 24541 #748-08-1961 L1977 **CHP P** *072
BEAVER, Lenworth Anthony. 159 EXECUTIVE DR STE E, MAGNOLIA OB/GYN ASSOCIATES 24541 #041-09-1983 L1991 **OBG** *020 †30
BELK, Christopher Charles. 125 EXECUTIVE DR STE L, DANVILLE RADIOLOGISTS, INC 24541 #019-02-1995 L2006 **DR** *020 †80
BELLES, Bettina Li. 142 S MAIN ST 24541 #011-02-1991 L2002 **DR** *020 †28,80 ‡
BERRETH, Kyla. 201 S MAIN ST STE 2100 24541 #018-75-1998, ▲ L2001 **PD** *020 †55
BIRD, Mark Allen. 159 EXECUTIVE DR, STE B 24541 #036-01-1996 L2005 **GS** *020 †85
BOND, Glen Morris. 949 PINEY FOREST RD, IMMEDIATE CARE 24540 #051-01-1962 L1962 **GP** *072
BROACH, Wm Edward, III. 101 HOLBROOK ST, OB GYN ASSOCIATES OF 24541 #001-02-1981 L1985 **OBG** *020 †30
BROTHERTON, Timothy Wayne. 125 EXECUTIVE DR, STE J 24541 #018-03-1982 L1991 **IM HO** *020 †20
BROUGHTON, Robert Edward, Jr. 201 S MAIN ST, STE 201 24541 #028-03-1975 L1994 **PD GE** *020 †55
BROWN, James Allen. 159 EXECUTIVE DR STE B, SOUTHSIDE SURGICAL SPEC 24541 #045-01-1978 L1984 **GS** *020 †85
BUIE, Thomas Edison, Jr. 382 TAYLOR DR 24541 #036-05-1961 L1977 **P** *071 †75
BURGBACHER, James Stanley. 990 MAIN ST, STE 201 24541 #051-04-1969 L1969 **P** *020
CALDWELL, David Clark. 125 EXECUTIVE DR, STE J 24541 #036-05-1980 L1986 **IM HO** *020 †20 ‡
CAMPBELL, Joseph C, Jr. 125 EXECUTIVE DR, DANVILLE ORTHOPEDIC 24541 #051-01-1990 L1991 **ORS** *020 †40
CAMPBELL, Joseph Cameron. 125 EXECUTIVE DR, STE A 24541 #051-04-1959 L1959 **R OS** *071
CAPLAN, Michael Alan. 125 EXECUTIVE DR, STE H 24541 #023-01-1983 L1986 **IM** *020 †20
CHAUHAN, Ajit Singh. 1045 MAIN ST, STE 1 24541 #495-22-1978 L1986 **CD** *020 †20
CHEEK, Vincent Kilmer. 142 S MAIN ST 24541 #036-01-1983 L1998 **EM FM** *020 †18
CHIZHIKOV, Mikhail O. 1045 MAIN ST STE 5 24541 #913-15-1985 L2000 **P** *020 †75
CLARK, Kanchan P. 231 CROSLAND AVE 24540 #045-01-1986 L1998 **CHP P** *020 †75
COBBLE, Clark Robt. 515 RISON ST, DANVILLE EYE CENTER INC 24541 #047-05-1970 L1978 **OPH** *020 †35
DALLARA, John James. 142 S MAIN ST 24541 #051-04-1987 L1988 **EM IM** *050 †70,20
DAROVSKY, Boris Marat. 173 EXECUTIVE DR, CANCER CENTER OF THE PIEDM 24541 #913-72-1981 L2000 **ON HEM** *020
DAVIDSON, Eric Norman. 125 EXECUTIVE DR, STE H 24541 #010-03-1976 L1979 **IM** *020
DAVIS, Stephen Van. 200 DEER RUN RD 24540 #051-01-1981 L1985 **CD** *020 †20
DECHURCH, Frances E. 142 S MAIN ST 24541 #036-05-1986 L2007 **IM IMG** *020
DE LAS ALAS, Reuben. 142 S MAIN ST 24541 #748-02-1975 L1982 **EM FM** *020 †16
DEYTON, Walter Edward. 142 S MAIN ST 24541 #036-01-1955 L1963 **R NM** *071 †80,28
DICKERSON, William Jos. ■ 24541 #039-01-1955 L1957 **P** *071 †75
DUPREY, Patricia Ann. 4500 RIVERSIDE DR, STE A 24541 #011-03-1981 L1992 **D** *020 †15
EASLEY, Charles Allen, Jr. ■ 24541 #051-04-1932 L1932 **GS CRS** *071 †85
ECONOMO, George. 125 EXECUTIVE DR STE L, BOX 2129 24541 #067-01-1976 L1981 **DR** *020 †80
ELIACIN, Louis Edgard. 513 PINEY FOREST RD 24540 #440-01-1974 L1987 **OBG** *020
EMBREY, Richard Penn. 201 S MAIN ST, STE 3200 24541 #023-07-1983 L1995 **TS** *020 †85,90
ENSMINGER, Jason Leslie. 101 HOLBROOK ST, OB GYN ASSOCIATES OF 24541 #033-06-1998 L2002 **OBG** *020 †30
ERASMO, Ramon Rondobio. 130 GRAY ST 24541 #748-09-1961 L1972 **NS** *020
ESCARIO, Mar Tan. 142 S MAIN ST 24541 #748-11-1967 L1973 **AN PME** *020 †05
ESTEVEZ, Jose Manuel. 212 S MAIN ST, STE 4 24541 #275-01-1960 L1965 **PTH HMP** *020 †50

■ = Address Information Privacy Protected

EVANS, Eugene M, Jr. ■ 24541 #036-07-1953 L1957 **D** *071 †15
EVANS, Robert Lou. 404 AIRPORT DR, STE 8 24540 #028-79-1968, ▲ L1999 **FM** *020
FAHMI, Muna Nazar Shakir. 142 S MAIN ST, DANVILLE REGIONAL MEDICAL 24541 #528-04-1990 L2005 **IMG** *100
FALGUI, Vicente T. 990 MAIN ST STE 204 24541 #748-01-1966 L1972 **IM** *020
FRAIFELD, Eduardo M. 142 S MAIN ST 24541 #048-14-1986 L1997 **AN PMM** *020 †05
FRASER, Hugh E, III. 212 S MAIN ST, STE 4 24541 #036-05-1982 L1997 **PTH IM** *062 †50
GADDY, Clifford Garland. 101 HOLBROOK ST 24541 #036-05-1947 L1951 **IM CD** *071 †20
GARCIA, Florencio B, Jr. 1040 MAIN ST 24541 #748-02-1993 L2000 **IM NEP** *020 †20
GERENA, Gail Theresa. 142 S MAIN ST, DANVILLE REGIONAL MEDICAL 24541 #035-47-1978 L2003 **ID PUD** *020 †20
GIBSON, Noah Francis. 201 S MAIN ST 24541 #036-05-1972 L1978 **PD** *020 †55
GOMEZ, Ramon Joson. 142 S MAIN ST 24541 #748-10-1978 L1984 **EM GP** *020
GRAY, Traci Nicole. 159 EXECUTIVE DR, STE E 24541 #047-07-2002 L2006 **OBG** *020
GRIGORYEV, Leon Mark. 4500 RIVERSIDE DR, STE B 24541 #913-16-1976 L1996 **PM** *020 †60
GROSS, Alton Frank. 125 EXECUTIVE DR STE A 24541 #041-13-1963 L1971 **ORS** *071 †40
GUANZON, Cesar Sancha. 142 S MAIN ST 24541 #748-01-1963 L1972 **GS GP** *020
HALE, Phillip Douglas. 723 PINEY FOREST RD 24540 #023-12-1982 L1985 **FM** *020 †18
HARDY, Thomas Jos. 212 S MAIN ST, STE 4 24541 #025-01-1975 L1979 **PTH** *020 †50
HARRIS, Sydney Madison. ■ 24541 #051-04-1996 L1999 **FM** *020 †18
HARVIE, Edwin James, Jr. 142 S MAIN ST 24541 #051-01-1958 L1958 **IM** *020 †20
HEIST, Cynthia S. 927 S MAIN ST 24541 #051-07-1982 L1986 **OBG** *075 †30
HENDERSON, Wm Warren, IV. 159 EXECUTIVE DR 24541 #051-01-1978 L1983 **PUD IM** *020 †20 ‡
HERMANN, Mark Christopher. 125 EXECUTIVE DR, DANVILLE ORTHOPEDIC 24541 #010-02-1985 L1990 **ORS** *020 †40
HICKSON, William Elliot. 110 EXCHANGE ST, STE F 24541 #051-07-1982 L1984 **IM** *020 †20
HODGES, Ronald Eugene. ■ 24541 #038-40-1972 L1998 **ORS HS** *071 †40
HONEA, Robert Harold. 159 EXECUTIVE DR, STE B 24541 #048-14-1981 L1982 **GS GP** *020 †85
HOOKER, Timothy H. 949 PINEY FOREST RD 24540 #051-04-1970 L1970 **PD GP** *020 †55
HUNGARLAND, John David. 4545 RIVERSIDE DR STE A 24541 #004-01-1997 L1999 **FM** *020 †18
HURTADO, Rafael V. 129 BROAD ST STE B 24541 #308-01-1986 L2005 **N** *020 †75
JANNACH, Stephan Henry. ■ 24541 #011-02-1998 L2004 **FM** *100
JONES, Corliss Laverne. 326 TAYLOR DR 24541 #035-09-1984 L1994 **PD** *020
JOSEF-GUANZON, Patrocinio. 326 TAYLOR DR, DEPT. 24541 #748-01-1962 L1972 **PD** *020
KANIEFSKI, Walter Joseph. 142 S MAIN ST, ER DEPT 24541 #014-01-1993 L1997 **EM** *020 †16
KARDON, Evan Peter. 142 S MAIN ST 24541 #035-08-1982 L2006 **EM** *020 †20
KHANIFAR, Aziz Alexander. 800 MEMORIAL DR, DOMINION EYE CENTER 24541 #005-06-2002 L2006 **OPH** *100
KOTLABA, David. 159 EXECUTIVE DR, STE K 24541 #286-13-1988 L1999 **CD** *020 †20
KOZLOWSKI, Douglas Lloyd. 103 DYERWOOD PL 24541 #023-01-1978 L1987 **U** *020 †95
KRAMER, Stuart Jeffrey. 125 EXECUTIVE DR, DANVILLE ORTHOPEDIC 24541 #035-15-1981 L1986 **ORS GS** *020 †40
KROME, Jonathan. 125 EXECUTIVE DR, DANVILLE ORTHOPEDIC 24541 #023-01-1992 L2004 **ORS OSM** *020 †40
KUENNEN, Michael Bradley. 101 HOLBROOK ST 24541 #018-03-1996 L1999 **IM** *020 †20
LAHTI, Gary Robert. 201 S MAIN ST, STE 3300 24541 #028-79-1992, ▲ L1997 **GS** *020
LAHTI, Stacy Lynette. 927 S MAIN ST, DANVILLE WOMEN'S CARE, PC 24541 #028-79-1992, ▲ L1997 **OBG** *020
LASAKI, Abiose O. 404 AIRPORT DR, STE 8 24540 #690-01-1973 L1995 **FM PHP** *020 †18
LASSITER, Max Errington. 201 S MAIN ST, STE 2100 24541 #036-05-1957 L1962 **PD** *071 †55
LAZO, Ivan Eduardo. 441 PINEY FOREST RD, STE B 24540 #308-03-1983 L1994 **FM** *020 †18
LE BLANC, Robert Edward M. 103A PINEY FOREST RD, CORNERSTONE COMPLETE CARE, 24540 #063-01-1989 L2000 *020
LEIDER, Peter John. 188 S MAIN ST 24541 #005-19-1995 L2000 **RO** *020 †80
LEKWUWA, Okafor Mang. 142 S MAIN ST, ER DEPT 24541 #036-07-1979 L1986 **FM** *020 †18
LEVINE, Max Phillip. 1037 MAIN ST 24541 #016-42-1968 L1992 **VS GS** *020 †85
LIN, Yi-Shien. 1114 MAIN ST, DANVILLE ANESTHESIOLOGISTS 24541 #244-01-1968 L1978 **AN** *071
LIPPERT, John Chas. 142 S MAIN ST 24541 #038-41-1971 L1979 **DR GP** *020 †80
LONG, Gwynn Douglas. 125 EXECUTIVE DR, DANVILLE HEMATOLOGY & ONCO 24541 #036-05-1983 L2003 **IM** *020 †20
MADAAN, Arvind. 159 EXECUTIVE DR, STE C 24541 #495-69-1994 L2004 **AI** *020 †55,03
MADDUX, Dugan Wiess. 1040 MAIN ST 24541 #036-01-1984 L1988 **NEP IM** *020 †20
MADDUX, Franklin Webster. 1040 MAIN ST, DANVILLE UROLOGIC 24541 #036-01-1983 L1988 **IM NEP** *020 †20
MAHMOUD, Hatim Ahmed. 201 S MAIN ST, STE 3400 24541 #848-01-1989 L2003 **END** *020 †20
MALLARE, Melchor Pulido. 1037 MAIN ST, MARTIN DONELSON JR 24541 #748-02-1954 L1962 **GP GS** *072 †85
MANHEIM, Arnold. 1114 MAIN ST 24541 #050-02-1959 L1966 **AN PUD** *071 †05
MAUTE, Frederick C. 927 S MAIN ST 24541 #036-08-1982 L1986 **OBG** *020 †30
MAY, Douglas Russell. 142 S MAIN ST 24541 #051-01-1986 L1993 **DR** *020 †80
MEADEMA, Samuel Jos. 159 EXECUTIVE DR, STE C 24541 #038-40-1978 L1979 **OTO HNS** *020 †45
MEADOWS, Glenn Irwin. 142 S MAIN ST 24541 #051-01-1981 L1982 **FM** *020 †18
MIER, Jose F, Jr. 142 S MAIN ST, ER DEPT 24541 #748-01-1965 L1972 **EM** *020 †16
MILAM, James Thos. 110 EXCHANGE ST STE F 24541 #051-01-1990 L1992 **FM** *020 †18
MILLER, Gary Price. 159 EXECUTIVE DR STE K 24541 #051-04-1976 L1977 **CD IM** *020 †18,20
MOHSIN, Faisal. 245 HAIRSTON ST, DANVILLE PITTSYLVANIA COMM 24540 #704-02-1994 L1999 **P** *020
MOORE, Michael Allan. 142 S MAIN ST, DANVILLE REG MED CTR 24541 #036-01-1970 L1979 **NEP IM** *020 †20
MURPHY, Katrina Gwendolyn. 201 S MAIN ST STE 3100 24541 #005-18-1997 L2004 **NS** *100
MUSGRAVE, Robert Edward. 142 S MAIN ST 24541 #047-06-1946 L1957 **ORS OS** *071 †40
NAZMUL, Mohammed Naser. 142 S MAIN ST, DANVILLE REGIONAL MEDICAL 24541 #160-03-1997 L2003 **IM** *020 †20 ‡
NEAL, Randolph Voss. 101 HOLBROOK ST, OB GYN ASSOCIATES OF 24541 #051-04-1992 L1997 **OBG** *020 †30
NEWELL, Alice Bowman. 101 HOLBROOK ST, OB GYN ASSOCIATES OF 24541 #051-07-1999 L1999 **OBG** *020 †30
NIGAM, Mukesh. 120 NEWBURY WAY 24541 #495-20-1980 L2002 **AN** *020 †05
OATES, Thomas Mc Kee, Jr. 159 EXECUTIVE DR, STE B 24541 #045-01-1980 L2002 **GS** *020 †55,85
OBERHEU, Victor Louis. 125 EXECUTIVE DR, DANVILLE RADIOLOGISTS INC 24541 #016-11-1958 L1972 **DR** *071 †80
OBOYLE, Joseph Eugene. 125 EXECUTIVE DR, STE E 24541 #024-07-1987 L1996 **OPH** *020 †35
ODOM, Terry David. 800 MEMORIAL DR 24541 #036-05-1979 L1984 **OPH** *020 †35
OMOJI, Bassey Ujah. 140 PINEY FOREST RD, STE B 24540 #422-01-1982 L1994 **PD** *020
O'NEILL, Thomas Jos. 159 EXECUTIVE DR, STE F 24541 #051-01-1971 L1971 **PUD IM** *020 †20 ‡
O'TOOLE, David Andrew. 150 W MAIN ST, PIEDMONT CENTER FOR SPINAL 24541 #011-04-1999 L2005 **APM** *020
OWENS, Harold Burley. ■ 24541 #036-01-1967 L1984 **DR** *071 †80
OWUSU, Nada Baah. 201 S MAIN ST 24541 #412-01-1987 L1995 **PD** *020 †55
OWUSU-YAW, Victor. 129 BROAD ST STE B 24541 #412-01-1987 L1994 **N** *020 †75
PACHECO, Elmer J. 125 EXECUTIVE DR STE J, DANVILLE CANCER CENTER 24541 #042-01-1981 L2005 **ON IM** *020 †20,28
PAGANO, Richard Ralph. 142 S MAIN ST 24541 #030-06-1972 L1999 **AN** *020 †05 ‡
PANDYA, Bhushan Hiralal. 501 RISON ST STE 130 24541 #495-45-1978 L1984 **GE IM** *020 †20
PANDYA, Parag Arunkumar. 142 S MAIN ST 24541 #495-22-1988 L2002 **AN PME** *020 †05
PASCASIO, Ernesto A. 109 DEER RUN RD 24540 #748-08-1966 L1983 **FM** *020
PATEL, Chandrakant M. 212 S MAIN ST STE 2 24541 #495-23-1980 L1984 **P GP** *020 †75
PATEL, Mukesh B. 501 RISON ST, STE 130 24541 #495-23-1990 L1997 **IM GE** *020 †20
PATEL, Pravinchandra C. 382 TAYLOR DR 24541 #495-23-1973 L1978 **P** *020 †75
PATEL, Suresh M. 382 TAYLOR DR, SOUTHERN VA MH INSTITUTE 24541 #495-63-1971 L1978 **P** *020
PATTERSON, John Richard. ■ 24541 #036-01-1958 L1965 **OBG** *071 †30
POMPOSINI, Daniel Lee. 125 WATSON ST, DANVILLE IM INC 24541 #012-01-1985 L1989 **IM** *020 †20
PRADHAN, Pradeep K. 949 PINEY FOREST RD 24540 #495-15-1988 L1995 **IM** *020 †20
PRASAD, Renuka N. 212 S MAIN ST STE 3 24541 #495-33-1969 L1979 **P** *020 †75
ROL, Cornelis. 142 S MAIN ST 24541 #660-01-1949 L1958 **OTO** *071 †45
ROMAN, Renato Marcelino B. 1040 MAIN ST 24541 #748-10-1991 L1996 **IM NEP** *020 †20
SEEPE, Carolyn Sue. 441 PINEY FOREST RD, PROVIDENCE FAMILY & SPORTS 24540 #024-07-1991 L1997 **FM** *020 †18
SEKYEMA, Yao-Foli. 1040 MAIN ST, DANVILLE UROLOGICAL CLNC 24541 #412-01-1987 L1999 **NEP** *020 †20
SETTLE, Paul Cox. 404 AIRPORT DR, STE A 24540 #020-02-1978 L1986 **FM** *020 †18
SHIFLETT, Douglas Wayne. 101 HOLBROOK ST 24541 #036-05-1974 L1975 **GE** *020 †20
SILVERMAN, Herbert R. ■ 24541 #051-01-1946 L1946 **GS** *071 †85
SIMMONS, Robert Geo. 142 S MAIN ST 24541 #036-01-1966 L1973 **GYN** *071 †30
SINGER, Joel Michael. 201 S MAIN ST, STE 3100 24541 #033-05-1975 L1989 **NS** *020 †25
SIZER, Kenneth Brown. 917 W MAIN ST 24541 #051-04-1956 L1956 **OM** *071
SLOAN, David Mapp. 800 MEMORIAL DR, STE A 24541 #045-01-1981 L1989 **OPH** *020 †35 ‡
SMITH, Richard Alan. 142 S MAIN ST, ER DEPT 24541 #051-07-1983 L1984 **EM FM** *020 †18
SOYANGCO, Alfredo Lopez. ■ 24540 #748-08-1960 L1972 **AN** *071
SOYANGCO, Florlisa Gamelo. ■ 24540 #748-08-1960 **IM CD** *075
SPAINHOUR, Jack Bryan, Jr. 101 HOLBROOK ST 24541 #036-05-1969 L1973 **GE IM** *020 †20
SPENCER, George Michael. 142 S MAIN ST 24541 #036-08-1989 L1995 **DR** *020 †80
SPENCER, Joanne Stryker. 404 AIRPORT DR, STE 8 24540 #036-08-1989 L1995 **PD** *020 †55
SPRINKLE, James Dean. ■ 24541 #038-40-1955 L1963 **GS TS** *020 †85,90
STEVENS, James Eugene. 142 S MAIN ST, DANVILLE REG MED CTE 24541 #051-01-1984 L1989 **EM** *020
STONEBURNER, Frances M. 142 S MAIN ST 24541 #051-04-1951 L1951 **ADL** *075
STONEBURNER, John M. 142 S MAIN ST 24541 #051-04-1950 L1950 **GS TS** *020 †85,90
TALTS, Karl Herbert. 142 S MAIN ST 24541 #035-20-1986 L1994 **AN** *020 †05 ‡
THOMPSON, Stephen Carter. 142 S MAIN ST 24541 #051-07-1994 L2000 **MPD** *020 †20,55 ‡
TORRES, Michael Hansen. 100 VICAR PL, STE A 24540 #748-10-1989 L1996 **FM** *020 †18
TRIVEDI, Rajendra S. 501 RISON ST STE 120, MEMORIAL FAMILY CARE INC 24541 #495-89-1984 L1995 **FM** *020 †18
TSUI, Edward Shung-Ching. ■ 24540 #243-21-1960 L1976 **AN** *071 †05
TURNER, Frank Graber. 115 S MAIN ST 24541 #051-01-1955 L1955 **GYN** *020 †30
TURNER, Jack Cocke. 425 HAWTHORNE DR 24541 #051-04-1973 L1977 **PTH BBK** *071 †50
VASIREDDY, Sabitha. 1955 MEMORIAL DR, DANVILLE PATIENT CARE INC 24541 #495-57-1989 L1996 **IM** *020 †20
VASIREDDY, Venugopal K. 1955 MEMORIAL DR, DANVILLE PATIENT CARE INC 24541 #495-57-1989 L1997 **IM** *020 †20
WANG, Laurence Shuchung. 603 COLQUOHOUN ST 24541 #010-03-1996 L1999 **FM** *020 †18
WATERS, Michael Geo. 723 PINEY FOREST RD 24540 #051-04-1985 L1990 **FM** *020 †18
WHITE, Michael Craig. 990 MAIN ST STE 202, GATEWAY ASSOC PLANS 24541 #051-04-1981 L1989 **D** *020 †15 ‡
WHITLEY, Thomas H, Jr. 501 RISON ST STE 120 24541 #036-01-1968 L1975 **DIA END** *020 †20
WILLIAMS, Della Christine. 159 EXECUTIVE DR, STE D 24541 #051-01-1973 L1979 **SME N** *020 †75
WILLIAMS, Keith Horace. 125 EXECUTIVE DR, STE H 24541 #041-09-1986 L1993 **IM** *020 †20
WINFIELD, Albert Carl, II. 441 PINEY FOREST RD, PROVIDENCE FAMILY SPORTS & 24540 #036-01-1988 L2002 **OS** *020 †18
WONG, Francis Patrick. 130 ENTERPRISE DR, EAGLE PHYSICIANS 24540 #566-01-1982 L1992 **FM EM** *020 †18
WORTHY, Edwin, Jr. ■ 24541 #024-05-1982 *100
YEE, Kim Brian. 200 DEER RUN RD 24540 #025-12-1982 L1988 **GS TS** *020 †85
ZAKHARY, Boshra Geo. 505 RISON ST 24541 #915-04-1982 L1989 **CD IM** *020 †20

DAYTON – ROCKINGHAM

MARSH, Michael Steven. 15 KILLDEER LN 22821 #011-03-1980 L1982 **FM** *020 †18
PENCE, Robert Paul. HWY 42 22821 #051-01-1991 L1994 **FM** *020 †18
RIDDEL, Clifford T, Jr. ■ 22821 #023-01-1949 L1950 **EM** *071
SCHUBERT, Ronald Lee. 15 KILLDEER LN 22821 #012-01-1978 L1983 **FM** *020 †18

DELAPLANE – FAUQUIER

ROY, Wayne R. ■ 20144 #010-03-1979 L1981 **OBG** *020

DELTAVILLE – MIDDLESEX

HENLEY, Marlene E Bolling. ■ 23043 #051-04-1959 L1959 **FM** *020 †18

■ = Address Information Privacy Protected

HOYE, Clara L. ■ 23043 #051-01-1934 L1934 **OS P** *071 †75
RANSONE, Sterling N, Jr. PO BOX 916, 16681 GENERAL PULLER HWY 23043 #051-04-1992 L1993 **IM** *020 †18
TERREBONNE, Mae E Smith. ■ 23043 #021-05-1974 L1996 **PD** *020 †55

DILLWYN — BUCKINGHAM

GARLAND, Charles M, Jr. ■ 23936 #051-01-1944 L1944 **OBG PHP** *072 †30
RUPP, Theresa Anne. PO BOX 20, 65 BRICKYARD RD 23936 #036-01-1988 L1990 **FM** *020 †18

DINWIDDIE — DINWIDDIE

ASHBY, Chas Chandler, Sr. ■ 23841 #051-04-1956 L1956 **FM** *071

DISPUTANTA — PRINCE GEORGE

KING, Tony Roosevelt. ■ 23842 #051-07-1991 L1993 **FM** *020 †18

DOSWELL — HANOVER

BOARDMAN, N Douglas. ■ 23047 #041-01-1992 L2000 **OAR** *020 †40

DUBLIN — PULASKI

CAMPBELL, David Wayne. PO BOX 1526 24084 #036-08-1994 L1994 **FM** *072 †18
CASSELL, Stuart Kent, Jr. 401 E MAIN ST 24084 #051-01-1966 L1967 **PD** *020 †55
CHEEK, Linda Sue. 28 TOWN CENTER DR 24084 #048-13-1992 L1993 **FM** *020 †18
CLARY, Donald Wayne. 4820 BARTON DR 24084 #051-07-1988 L1989 **FM** *020 †18
FARISS, Bruce Lindsay. PO BOX 638, 4655 CLEBURNE BLVD 24084 #051-01-1961 L1961 **END DIA** *020 †20
GEHRZ, Richard Campbell. PO BOX 1753, 5562 COUGAR TRAIL RD 24084 #026-04-1972 L1993 **PD IG** *020 †55
GROVER, Harish. 118 BROAD ST 24084 #495-03-1985 L2002 **GE** *020 †20
HALL, Glenn Claire, Jr. 401 E MAIN ST 24084 #051-01-1948 L1948 **PD** *071 †55
MAYO, William Fitzhugh. PO BOX 1269, 4676 LEE HWY 24084 #051-04-1975 L1976 **FM** *020 †18
OGBURN, John Francis. 401 E MAIN ST 24084 #047-05-1973 L1976 **PD** *020 †55
PATEL, Shriti Bharat. ■ 24084 #051-07-2006 **P** *012
ROYAL, Orren Le Royce. ■ 24084 #001-02-1956 L1981 **P** *071 †75
SAMPLES, Randall Gary. 5562 COUGAR TRAIL RD 24084 #047-06-1980 L1981 **PD** *020 †55
SHAFFER, Weldon Francis. 200 DUBLIN PARK RD 24084 #041-13-1989 L1990 **OBG** *020 †30
SKEWES, David Jessop. 5843 HANKS AVE 24084 #051-04-1956 L1956 **GP** *020
SKEWES, William Matthew. PO BOX 1799, DUBLIN MEDICAL CLINIC 24084 #051-04-1984 L1987 **IM** *020 †20
STILL, Gregory Lewis. 4676 LEE HWY, P.O.BOX DRAWER 1269 24084 #051-01-1982 L1983 **FM** *020 †18
STOUGH, Robert Clarence. 5749 JONES DR 24084 #041-01-1980 L1984 **FM NPM** *020 †05,18

DUFFIELD — SCOTT

FONSECA, Olimpo Fernando. 373 CECIL D QUILLEN DR, T 24244 #042-01-1977 L1979 **EM GP** *020
NORTON, Bennette Edward. PO BOX 88, 153 ROSS CARTER BLVD 24244 #027-01-1987 L1990 **FM** *020 †18

DULLES — LOUDOUN

ANDRE, Mc Kenzie. ■ 20189 #010-03-1998 L2001 **GPM** *100
BATCHA, Sithara. ■ 20189 #010-02-2004 *100
BRAVO, Herbert Fernando. 21010 DULLES TOWN CIR, STE 120 20166 #270-02-1987 L1992 **PD** *020 †55
BROWNRIDGE, Rose M Vaughn. ■ 20189 #016-11-1983 L1986 **IM** *020 †20
COTE, Timothy Raymond. ■ 20189 #010-03-1987 L1988 **PTH** *020 †70,50
COWLEY, Peter. ■ 20189 #048-04-1988 L1992 **IM** *020
DAVID, Panakkal Ukkuru. ■ 20189 #495-44-1972 L1983 **P** *020 †75
DE LAY, Paul Ruddy, Jr. ■ 20189 #005-19-1975 L1978 **FM GPM** *074 †70
DEROCHE, Tom Carlo. ■ 20189 #028-34-2005 L2005 **PTH** *012
DUBOIS, Amy Elizabeth. ■ 20189 #025-07-1991 L1996 **GS** *020 †85
FERNANDEZ-MIRANDA, John A. 44845 PACKAGE CT 2ND FL, UNITED AIRLINES MED DEPT 20166 #010-01-1976 L1983 **IM AM** *020
FUKUDA, Keiji. ■ 20189 #050-02-1984 L1985 **OS IM** *050 †20
GREENE, Carolyn M. ■ 20189 #043-01-1998 L2000 **IM** *020 †20
IMTIAZ, Rubina. ■ 20189 #704-06-1980 L1983 **IM OS** *020
JAFARI, Hamid S. ■ 20189 #704-16-1982 L1988 **PD OS** *020 †55
KILLAM, William Perry. ■ 20189 #036-01-1991 L2000 **OBG** *020 †30
KILPATRICK, Kevin Jos. ■ 20189 #016-01-1992 L1993 **IM PD** *020 †55,20
KNIGHT, Nancy Watson. ■ 20189 #036-01-1998 L1999 **FM** *020 †18
MAKOUS, Marina. 7030 ALMATY PL 20189 #041-07-1990 L1992 **FM P** *020 †18
MERMIN, Jonathan Harry. ■ 20189 #005-11-1992 L1993 **GPM** *020 †20,70
MORAN, John Schilling. 7030 ALMATY PL 20189 #005-15-1980 L1981 **PHP ID** *050 †70 ‡
NAHLEN, Bernard Lee. ■ 20189 #004-01-1983 L1983 **PHP FM** *050 †18
O'BRIEN, Katherine. 3410 PORT OF SPAIN PL 20189 #067-01-1988 L1992 **PD** *020 †55
PERINO, Louis J. ■ 20189 #048-15-2004 L2005 **EM** *100
SHEPARD, Colin W. ■ 20189 #036-05-1998 L1999 **IM** *020 †20
SINGER, Darrell Eugene. ■ 20189 #023-12-1995 L1996 **GPM** *020 †70
SPARKS, Lloyd Albert. ■ 20189 #473-04-1993 L1994 **P GP** *071
SPIEGEL, Paul Bradley. ■ 20189 #065-01-1991 L1996 **GPM** *020 †70
STONEHILL, Laura Louise. ■ 20189 #017-20-1982 L1997 **OBG** *074
STRUMINGER, Bruce H. ■ 20189 #023-07-1998 L2002 **IM** *020 †20

SUMMERS, Frederick J. ■ 20189 #024-07-1973 L1974 **P CHP** *020 †75
THIGPEN, Michael Craig. ■ 20189 #047-05-1997 L1999 **ID** *020 †20
WELCH, John Jos, Jr. ■ 20189 #035-06-1997 L1997 **PHO** *020 †55
WIERSMA, Steven Todd. ■ 20189 #025-07-1987 L1989 **PHP EM** *030 †70
WIKTOR, Stefan Zbyszko. ■ 20189 #041-14-1980 L1983 **IM** *020 †20

DUMFRIES — PRINCE WILLIAM

CHAMBERS, Zerline Evelyn. 3775 FETTLER PARK DR 22025 #033-05-1980 L1986 **OBG** *020
CHANDLER, Allen Eugene. ■ 22026 #041-02-1961 L1962 **PD PHP** *071 †55
DUROCHER, Frances A. ■ 22025 #041-07-1970 L1979 **IM** *071 †20
GREENHALGH, John Smith. 3928 LANSING CT 22026 #041-13-1963 L1967 **GP** *020
KHAN, Naeem. 3763 FETTLER PARK DR 22025 #704-09-1994 L2005 **FM** *020 †18
SINHA, Indira. 17618 MAIN ST 22026 #046-14-1985 L1998 **PD** *020
VIRTUDES, Loreto Pagador. 17459 JEFFERSON DAVIS HWY, DAVIS HIGHWAY 22026 #748-01-1977 L1990 **IM EM** *020 †20

DUNGANNON — SCOTT

CASSEL, Todd Andrew. 17633 VETERANS MEMORIL HWY 24245 #041-07-1982 L1985 **FM** *020 †18
MICHAEL, Gary Eugene. 17633 VETERANS MEMORIL HWY 24245 #041-07-1987 L1990 **FM** *020 †18

DUNN LORING — FAIRFAX

KALLAR, Surinder Kaur. ■ 22027 #495-69-1965 L1975 **AN** *075 †05
KIM, Sun Yong. ■ 22027 #041-14-1988 L1990 **NM** *020 †28
KUMARAPPAN, Uma. ■ 22027 #496-32-1993 L2007 **P** *100
LENERT, Jeffrey Thos. ■ 22027 #048-04-1989 L1990 **GS** *020 †85
YOON, Sung Won. 7863 FRICK WAY 22027 #583-10-1966 L1986 **D** *020 ‡

DUTTON — MATHEWS

CRAUN, Galen Glick. ■ 23050 #051-01-1974 L1981 **OAR** *020 †40

EAGLE ROCK — BOTETOURT

BOYD, William Everett. ■ 24085 #051-04-1955 L1956 **PD** *071 †55

EARLYSVILLE — ALBEMARLE

ALEXANDER, H C, III. ■ 22936 #051-01-1959 L1959 **RHU IM** *062 †20
ATTRIDGE, Joshua. ■ 22936 #017-20-2000 L2000 **NPM** *100 †55
LEE, Abigail Jane. ■ 22936 #023-12-2003 L2007 **D** *020 †15
MYERS, Charles Edgar. 690 BENT OAKS DR, OF THE PROSTATE, PLC 22936 #041-01-1969 L1994 **IM ON** *030 †20
TAYLOR, Gervas S, Jr. ■ 22936 #051-04-1944 L1944 **ORS OSM** *071 †40

EASTVILLE — NORTHAMPTON

LINGLE, David M. ■ 23347 #028-34-1991 L1997 **GS** *020 †85
PHILPOT, Linda Gotthardt. PO BOX 35 23347 #051-07-1987 L1988 **IM IMG** *020 †20

ELKTON — ROCKINGHAM

LOHKAMP, Irene Stavrou. 13737 SPOTSWOOD TRL 22827 #048-04-1986 L1987 **FM** *020 †18
OVIEDO, Raul Gabriel. PO BOX 46 22827 #451-01-1955 L1975 **IM** *020
STURGEON, Howard Elbert. 22827 #023-01-1956 L1957 **EM GP** *071
TALBOT, Asa Richard. 22827 #017-20-1965 L1971 **OTO A** *071 †45
TIMMONS, John Wesley. 13737 SPOTSWOOD TRL 22827 #051-04-1987 L1989 **FM** *020 †18
WRIGHT, Jack Leslie. 13737 SPOTSWOOD TRL, E ROCKINGHAM HEALTH CENTER 22827 #051-01-1982 L1992 **FM** *020 †18

EMORY — WASHINGTON

BHATTI, Tajammul Hussein. ■ 24327 #704-01-1960 L1971 **P NS** *075 †75

EMPORIA — GREENSVILLE

ANDERSON, Michael Spencer. 6 DOCTORS DR 23847 #051-01-1988 L1989 **FM** *020 †18
ASSAD-FALTAS, Marie T H. 6 DOCTORS DR 23847 #915-04-1977 L1988 **UM** *020
BAIG, Mirza Khalid. 727 N MAIN ST, SOUTHERN VIRGINIA REGIONAL 23847 #495-77-1986 L2004 **IM** *020 †20 ‡
BISHAI, Adel Gendy. 6 DOCTORS DR, EMPORIA MED ASSOCIATES PC 23847 #915-02-1975 L1986 **PD GP** *020
EAPEN, George. 306 WEAVER AVE 23847 #495-31-1973 L1982 **CD IM** *020 †20
FLOWERS, Adolph Vernon. 6 DOCTORS DR 23847 #010-03-1984 L1990 **FM** *020 †18
FLOWERS, Delores Carlene. 306 WEAVER AVE 23847 #010-03-1986 L1990 **OBG** *020
GARRETT, Herman A, Jr. 727 N MAIN ST 23847 #001-06-1988 L1990 **AN** *020 †05
GILLIAM, Theopolis, Jr. 6 DOCTORS DR 23847 #010-03-1984 L1987 **GE IM** *020 †20
GRILLON, Michael Stephen. 511A BELFIELD DR, SOUTHERN VIRGINIA MEDICAL 23847 #024-16-1985 L1997 **GS VS** *020 †85
LE GROW, Wynne Vinson E. 201 WEAVER AVE 23847 #038-40-1972 L1979 **NEP IM** *020 †20
LOGANATHAN, Sri. 727 N MAIN ST 23847 #495-04-1970 L1976 **PD** *020 †16
MARCELIN, Fitzgerald. 137 BAKER ST 23847 #041-07-1997 L2001 **MPD** *020 †20,55

MASRI-IMADI, Fetnat Faye. 410 SHORE DR, 6 DOCTORS DR 23847 #875-02-1981 L2006 FM *020 †18

MERCHANT, Wilson Caton, III. 301 MARKET DR, VIRGINIA UROLOGY CENTER 23847 #051-01-1977 L1983 U GS *020 †95

MORENO, Dale Edward. 306 WEAVER AVE 23847 #025-07-1992 L1998 GS *020

POWELL, Michelle Denise. ■ 23847 #051-04-1996 L1996 FM *100

PRINCE, John Stuart. 219 WEAVER AVE 23847 #051-04-1952 L1952 GP *020

PRIVALOV, Denis G. 511A BELFIELD DR 23847 #913-81-1996 L2002 NEP *020 †20

QUITIQUIT, Elfren A. 6 DOCTORS DR, EMPORIA MEDICAL ASSOCIATES 23847 #748-08-1964 L1972 GS *020

SALEEBY, Manhal. 727 N MAIN ST, SOUTH CENTRAL VA PAIN CTR 23847 #875-02-1988 L2002 AN PME *020 †05

SHRESTHA, Sanjib Das. 511A BELFIELD DR 23847 #495-73-1985 L2008 IMG *020 †20

SINGH, Iqbal. 214 WEAVER AVE, GREENSVILLE MEMORIAL HOSPI 23847 #495-03-1966 L1990 EM IM *020 †16

SOOD, Rakesh Kumar. 727 N MAIN ST, DEPT OF PSYCHIATRY 23847 #495-45-1977 L1988 P SME *020 †75

SPENCER, Beverly Elaine. 306 WEAVER AVE 23847 #024-01-1986 L1991 IM *020 †20

SQUIRE, Peter W. 219 WEAVER AVE, PRINCE SQUIRE MED CTR 23847 #051-04-1952 L1952 FM *020 †18

SQUIRE, Robert Hall. 219 WEAVER AVE, PRINCE SQUIRE MED CTR 23847 #051-04-1989 L1990 FM *020 †18 ‡

TCHOUKINA, Inna Faisovna. 511A BELFIELD DR 23847 #913-81-1996 L2004 CD *020 †20

THOMPSON, Levester. 205 HICKSFORD AVE 23847 #016-45-1975 L1983 FM *020

WALKER, Thomas Andrew. 6 DOCTORS DR 23847 #051-04-1957 L1957 FM *071 †18

ESMONT – ALBEMARLE

BUBB, Lori Catherine. 2256 IRISH RD, SOUTHERN ALBEMARLE FAMILY 22937 #024-16-1998 L2002 MPD *020 †20,55

HOBSON, Margaret Joan. 2256 IRISH RD 22937 #051-01-1986 L1990 IM PD *020 †20,55

UPCHURCH, Charles Thompso. ■ 22937 #036-01-2004 L2007 IM END *012 †20

WILLIAMS, Maryanne Denise. 2256 IRISH RD 22937 #051-01-1983 L1987 IM *020 †20

ETTRICK – PETERSBURG CITY

TRIPATHI, Sarika Shreyank. 20901 CHESTERFIELD AVE 23803 #495-76-2000 L2004 ID *020

EWING – LEE

BELL, James A, III. PO BOX 159, WESTERN LEE COUNTY HEALTH 24248 #036-01-1984 L1990 FM *020 †18

JOHNSON, James Byrd. GENERAL DELIVERY 24248 #051-01-1955 L1958 GP *020

EXMORE – NORTHAMPTON

FOLEY, John Albert, Jr. 3297 BROAD ST 23350 #051-04-1980 L1984 OPH *020 †35

FREUND, Jerome Robt. ■ 23350 #028-02-1990 L1991 FM *071 †18

PASSAGLIA, Lelio Narciso. ■ 23350 #561-01-1952 IM CD *071 †20

FAIRFAX – FAIRFAX

AARONSON, Charles Martin. 8301 ARLINGTON BLVD, CHARLES M AARONSON MD LTD 22031 #010-01-1955 L1963 D A *071 †15

ABDALLA, Wagida A. STUDENT HEALTH CENTER, GEORGE MASON UNIVERSITY 22030 #915-03-1972 L1980 ADL PD *020 †55

ABOUSY, Khalid Abbas. 8505 ARLINGTON BLVD, STE 350 22031 #041-13-1991 L1998 CD *020 †20

ABRAHAM, Sheena. 12255 FAIR LAKES PKWY 22033 #496-07-1992 L1997 IM *020 †20

ABU-HAMDA, Eyad M. 8301 ARLINGTON BLVD, STE T5 22031 #915-02-1990 L2000 PCC IM *020 †20

ADAMS, Ellen D. 3650 JOSEPH SIEWICK DR, STE 108 22033 #024-07-2000 L2004 AN *020 †05

ADAMS, Tonya Lynn. 3700 JOSEPH SIEWICK DR, STE 308 22033 #038-43-1995 L2001 GE *020 †20

AGRAWAL, Shantanu Kumar. 3600 JOSEPH SIEWICK DR, DEPARTMENT OF EMERGENCY ME 22033 #035-20-2004 L2008 EM *012

AHMED, M W Muhiuddin. 12255 FAIR LAKES PKWY, FAIR OAKS MEDICAL CENTER 22033 #160-03-1980 L1997 IM *020 †20

AHMED, Robert Frank. 4001 FAIR RIDGE DR, STE 304 22033 #010-02-1987 L1992 GS *020 †85

AHUJA, Neeta. 12255 FAIR LAKES PKWY, KAISER PERMANANTE 22033 #495-53-1985 L1988 ON HEM *020 †20

AIN, Brent Roger. 3650 JOSEPH SIEWICK DR, STE 300 22033 #021-01-1972 L1977 ORS *020 †40

AKRAM, Javed. 3700 JOSEPH SIEWICK DR, STE 205B 22033 #704-15-1991 L2004 IM *020 †20

AL-ATTAR, Adel Mohammed. 2740 PROSPERITY AVE 22031 #528-01-1962 L1972 PD *020 †55

AL-AWWA, Izzat. ■ 22032 #875-02-1983 NEP *100 †20

ALBANO, Maria Candida P. 8505 ARLINGTON BLVD, STE 130 22031 #024-07-1996 L2002 DR *020

ALBERS, William Richard. 10560 MAIN ST STE 221 22030 #010-02-1955 L1970 AM IM *071

ALBERT, Moses K. 3020 HAMAKER CT, STE 504 22031 #028-02-1978 L1981 D *020 †15

ALBUERNE, H M. SUITE 305, 3801 ARLINGTON BLVD 22031 #275-01-1960 L1967 GS *071 †85

ALEXANDER, Mary Anne. 4080 CHAIN BRIDGE RD, OCCUPATIONAL HEALTH CENTER 22030 #020-02-1997 L2003 IM *020 †20

AL-FAHIM, Abdul Karim I. ■ 22030 #010-01-1994 FM *100

ALFERT, Jonathan Eric. 8505 ARLINGTON BLVD, STE 130 22031 #035-08-1996 L1997 NM *020 †20

ALIJANI, Mohammad Rasool. 8503 ARLINGTON BLVD, STE 200 22031 #517-03-1962 L1981 TTS GS *020 †85

ALJUBURI, Amer Zeki S S. 10680 MAIN ST STE 100 22030 #528-01-1968 L1989 U PHP *020 †95

AL-KOUATLY, Huda Bachir. 3020 HAMAKER CT, STE 501 22031 #605-01-1994 L2004 OBG OBS *020 †30

ALLEN, Terry Andrea. 10721 MAIN ST STE 200 22030 #051-01-1996 L2000 OBG *020 †30

ALMASSIAN, H Peter. 3600 JOSEPH SIEWICK DR 22031 #517-01-1962 L1972 OTO GS *071

ALSAADI, Ayad Abdulilah. 4211 FAIRFX CRNR EST AVE A, STE 230 22030 #528-01-1991 L2002 IM *020 †20

AL-SHKAKI, Ghiath Abdul. ■ 22033 #528-02-1984 L2006 GS *020

ALYKHAN, Fuad. 12011 LEE JACKSON MMRL HWY, STE 102 22033 #704-04-1990 L1999 MPD *020

ANAND, Kanchan. 8301 ARLINGTON BLVD, STE T10 22031 #496-02-1992 L2002 NEP *020 †20

ANANDAN, Vasuki. ■ 22031 #495-04-1988 L2007 PTH *100

ANDERSEN, Fritz Herman. 8503 ARLINGTON BLVD, STE 120 22031 #132-01-1965 L1972 CD IM *020 †20

ANDERSEN, Glenna R. 8501 ARLINGTON BLVD # 300 22031 #051-01-1981 L1985 OBG *020 †30

ANDERSON, Marie Arnold. 11135 LEE JUDICIAL HWY 22030 #010-02-1989 L1993 OBG *020 †30

ANDREOLI, H-Marcelo. 8550 ARLINGTON BLVD, STE 201 22031 #924-01-1992 L1993 OBG GP *020 †30

ANEZ, Osvaldo. 3700 JOSEPH SIEWICK DR, STE 100 22033 #132-03-1976 L1983 GS OS *020 †85

APPLEWHAITE, Osbert Mark. 3225 GALLOWS ROAD, EXXON MOBIL RM FI P322 22037 #041-01-1976 L1981 IM *071 †20

APUD, Jose A. 8303 ARLINGTON BLVD # 205 22031 #132-05-1975 L1995 P *050 †75

ARAM, Anthony Nguyen. 3700 JOSEPH SIEWICK DR, STE 205 22033 #023-01-1992 L1997 ORS OTR *020 †20

ARBATOVA, Karina. ■ 22032 #035-47-2006 PS *100

ARDAIZ, Michael Jose. 4080 CHAIN BRIDGE RD PS 22030 #010-01-1994 L1996 GPM *012 †20

AROGUNDADE, Kareematula O. 3650 JOSEPH SIEWICK DR, STE 400 22033 #010-03-2006 L2006 FP *012

ASEEM, Wali Mohammed. ■ 22033 #118-01-1958 L1976 TS VS *071 ‡

ASUNCION, Odita D. 2740 PROSPERITY AVE 22031 #748-01-1963 L1976 CHP *020

ATIGA, Walter Lawrence. 8503 ARLINGTON BLVD, STE 120 22031 #005-12-1990 L2001 ICE *020 †20

ATIYEH, Ghassan Naim. 10657 BRADDOCK RD, CHILDRENS MED ASSOC OF 22032 #010-01-1999 L2002 PD *020 †55

AULAKH, Pavitar P. 8550 LEE HWY 22031 #495-03-1981 L1995 P *020 †75

AUSTIN, Cynthia Iheoma. 12011 LEE JACKSON HWY 22033 #051-07-1989 L1996 OBG *075 †30

AWADELKARIM, Faisal A. 10520 JUDICIAL DR 22033 #848-02-1990 L1998 P *020 †75

AZIZ, Waseem Ismail. 3650 JOSEPH SIEWICK DR, STE 205B 22033 #704-01-1987 L2005 GE HEP *020 †20

BAIG, Mirza Sajid Raza. ■ 22031 #704-02-1983 P *012

BAJWA, Gurpreet Singh. 8316 ARLINGTON BLVD, STE 514 22031 #036-05-1998 L1999 FM *020 †18

BALDINGER, John Chas. 3025 HAMAKER CT, STE 101 22031 #047-05-1980 L1986 OPH *020 †35

BALL, Robert Alan. 8503 ARLINGTON BLVD # 310 22031 #041-02-1985 L1992 U SO *020 †95

BANSON, Norbertina Laurea. ■ 22030 #041-12-1991 L2003 DR *020 †80

BANTA, Maureen Theresa. 4211 FAIRFX CRNR EST AVE A, STE 225 22030 #010-02-1993 L1998 PD *020 †55

BARATS, Lev L. 13065 AUTUMN WILLOW DR 22030 #047-06-1992 L2001 IM NTR *020 †20

BARKER, William Jay. 3600 JOSEPH SIEWICK DR 22033 #051-01-1981 L1984 EM *020 †16

BARLOW, Haven Jesse, Jr. 8501 ARLINGTON BLVD, STE 420 22031 #649-33-1981 L1991 PS HS *020 †65

BARONE, Anthony E. 3015 WILLIAMS DR, STE 200 22031 #035-03-1989 L2000 DR *020 †80

BASILE, John Jos. 3020 HAMAKER CT STE B111 22031 #051-04-1981 L1988 U *020 †95

BASKURT, Erol. 8261 WILLOW OAKS CO DR, CORPORATE DRIVE 22031 #051-01-1998 L2003 RNR *100 †80

BASTANI, Hoda. ■ 22031 #041-14-2007 L2007 PD *012

BAUGH, James Richard. 3020 HAMAKER CT 22031 #010-01-1980 L1989 PD *020 †55

BAVEJA, Rajiv. 2730 PROSPERITY AVE STE B, FAIRFAX NEONATAL ASSOCIATE 22031 #496-09-1995 L2007 NPM *100 †55

BAZEMORE, Andrew William. 3650 JOSEPH SIEWICK DR, FAIRFAX FAMILY PRACTICE 22033 #036-01-1997 L2005 FM *020 †18

BEACH, John Ernest W. 12255 FAIR LAKES PKWY 22033 #051-01-1985 L1991 PUD CCM *020 †20

BEAKES, Douglas Edwin. 3700 JOSEPH SIEWCK DR #402, GADDE ALLERGY/IMMUNOLOGY 22033 #041-09-1982 L2000 AI *020 †20,03

BEALL, Michael Edgar. 8503 ARLINGTON BLVD, STE 310 22031 #010-01-1972 L1974 U GP *020 †20

BEARGIE, Richard John. 3700 JOSEPH SIEWICK DR, STE 206 22033 #016-43-1955 L1976 GS VS *020 †85

BEAVER, Harry Carl. 4827 PINEY BRANCH RD 22030 #010-01-1963 L1972 OBG MDM *071 †30

BECK, Lucille Singer. 3020 HAMAKER CT STE B 22031 #016-06-1980 L1982 GE IM *020 †20

BECK, Robert B. 2730 PROSPERITY AVE STE B 22031 #016-43-1979 L1983 NPM PD *020 †55

BECKER, Andrew Moss. 9901 BRADDOCK RD, NORTHERN VIRGINIA TRAINING 22032 #035-15-1985 L1991 N IM *030 †20,75

BECKNER, Kara Marie. 8505 ARLINGTON BLVD, STE 130 22031 #010-02-1996 L1996 DR *020 †80

BEIRAMEE, Bahram. 8261 WILLOW OAKS CO DR, CORPORATE DR. 22031 #517-05-1965 L1974 DR *020 †80

BEKENSTEIN, William Leon. 3020 HAMAKER CT STE 200 22031 #051-04-1959 L1962 PD *020

BELL, Margaret H. 3020 HAMAKER CT, STE 401 22031 #038-43-1986 L1995 ICE PDC *020 †55,20

BELMAN, A Barry. 8501 ARLINGTON BLVD 22031 #016-06-1964 L1981 UP U *020 †95

BENALFEW, Yodit Belay. 12255 FAIR LAKES PKWY, KAISER PERMANENTE 22033 #759-04-1988 L1997 IM *020 †20

BERGER, Myron Paul. 3700 JOSEPH SIEWICK DR, STE 208 22033 #010-02-1964 L1967 U *071 †95

BERGMAN, Gary Jay. 10657 BRADDOCK RD, CHILDRENS MED ASSOC OF 22032 #035-47-1976 L1979 PD *020 †55

BERKEY, Barry Robt. ■ 22030 #041-12-1961 L1966 P *071 †75

BERMAN, Elise Lynn. 8505 ARLINGTON BLVD, STE 130 22031 #024-07-1995 L2001 DR *020 †80

BERMAN, Steven Franklin. 12011 LEE JACKSON HWY 22033 #041-01-1986 L1998 IM *020 †20

BERRY, David Bradley. 8316 ARLINGTON BLVD, STE 420 22031 #047-05-1987 L1990 OBG *020 †30

BERRY, John Christopher. ■ 22030 #023-12-2008 *012

BETHEL, Sonya Nadine. 9901 BRADDOCK RD, NORTHERN VIRGINIA TRAINING 22032 #011-03-1982 L1987 **FM** *020 †18

BEVERIDGE, Roy Ainsworth. 8503 ARLINGTON BLVD, STE 400 22031 #035-20-1983 L1988 **ON IM** *020 †20

BHATNAGAR, Richa. 3650 JOSEPH SIEWICK DR 4TH, RESIDENCY DEPT 22033 #023-01-2006 L2006 **FP** *012

BICKEL, Rudolf Gustav. 3600 JOSEPH SIEWICK DR 22033 #024-01-1963 L1973 **FM** *020 †18

BIEGELSEN, Elizabeth S. 12011 LEE JACKSON HWY, KAISER PERMANENTE, CARDIOL 22033 #024-01-1991 L2005 **IM** *020

BIELAMOWICZ, Anne M. 8501 ARLINGTON BLVD, STE 550 22031 #005-14-1990 L1998 **AN** *020 †05

BIGBEE, John Albert. 2740 PROSPERITY AVE 22031 #023-01-1967 L1996 **FM** *020 †18

BITAR, George John. 8501 ARLINGTON BLVD, STE 500 22031 #010-01-1993 L1998 **PS** *020 †65

BLAKEMORE, Laurel C. 8501 ARLINGTON BLVD, 2ND FL 22031 #001-02-1991 L2004 **ORS** *020 †40

BLECHER, Lee Irwin. 3650 JOSEPH SIEWICK DR, FAIRFAX FAMILY PRACTICE 22033 #051-04-1998 L2002 **FM OBG** *020 †18

BOCHENEK, Krzysztof Marek. 8505 ARLINGTON BLVD, STE 130 22031 #041-07-1996 L2005 **DR RNR** *020 †75,80

BON TEMPO, Carl Prescott. 3650 JOSEPH SIEWICK DR, STE 206 22033 #010-02-1969 L1970 **CD IM** *020 †20

BOOKS, Heather Lynn. 13151 MORNING SPRING LN 22033 #021-01-2001 L2006 **PD** *020 †55

BORD, Leslie Ann. 8505 ARLINGTON BLVD, STE 130 22031 #010-03-1995 L2005 **PDR R** *020 †80

BORO, Thomas James. ■ 22033 #051-04-2005 L2005 **GS** *012

BRANDT, Volker. ■ 22031 #035-20-1957 L1963 **OBG** *071 †30

BRANNIGAN, Robin C. 10721 MAIN ST, STE 2350 22030 #010-02-1992 L1996 **P** *020 †75

BRENNER, Richard V. 4001 FAIR RIDGE DR STE 304 22033 #043-01-1991 L1993 **GS** *020 †85

BRONSKY, George Frederick. 3020 HAMAKER CT, STE 501 22031 #165-06-1977 L1980 **MFM OBG** *020 †30

BROOKS, Michael Anthony. 8505 ARLINGTON BLVD, STE 130 22031 #016-42-1984 L2003 **DR** *020 †80 ‡

BROWN, Jennifer Allyn. 11135 LEE HWY 22030 #036-05-1999 L2007 **OBG** *020 †30

BROWNE, Paulette E. 12011 LEE JACKSON MMRL HWY, STE 480 22033 #023-01-1993 L1999 **REN OBG** *020 †30

BRUCHALSKI, John Thaddeus. 11135 LEE HWY 22030 #001-06-1987 L1989 **OBG** *020 †30

BRYAN, Candace Victoria. 3020 HAMAKER CT 22031 #041-12-2003 L2007 **N** *020

BUERY, Samantha Dominique. 3020 HAMAKER CT, STE B105 22031 #035-01-1994 L1999 **OBG** *020 †30

BURROUGHS, Susan Hobbs. 3650 JOSEPH SIEWICK DR, FAIRFAX FAMILY PRACTICE 22033 #051-01-1985 L1987 **FM** *020 †18

BURWELL, James Abraham. 2722 MERRILEE DR STE 230 22031 #023-01-1956 L1962 **R** *071 †80

BUSSEY, Christine D. 3650 JOSEPH SIEWICK DR, STE 206 22033 #041-01-1996 L2002 **CD** *020 †20

BUTCH, Rodney James. 8505 ARLINGTON BLVD, STE 130 22031 #008-01-1975 L1986 **R** *020 †20,80

BYRNE, Patrick John. 3020 HAMAKER CT, STE 101 22031 #038-40-1975 L1979 **ON** *020 †20

CALVA-CERQUEIRA, Daniel. ■ 22031 #018-03-2005 L2005 **GS** *012

CANTWELL, Mary Elizabeth. 8501 ARLINGTON BLVD, JONES INSTITUTE 22031 #035-47-1988 L1992 **AN** *020 †05

CAPLAN, Jill Lindsay. ■ 22033 #010-01-2004 **ORS** *012

CARLSON, David Roland. 8316 ARLINGTON BLVD 22031 #010-01-1960 L1964 **OBG** *020 †30

CARNES, Robert Scott, III. 10560 MAIN ST, STE 221 22030 #005-06-1977 L1980 **FM AN** *020 †05

CARTAGENA, Alicia Marie. 8261 WILLOW OAKS CORPRT DR 22031 #024-07-1988 L1989 **DR RNR** *020 †80

CASTRO, Marco Davis. 3020 HAMAKER CT 22031 #010-02-1991 L1992 **N CN** *020 †75

CERVA, Donald Stuart, Jr. 8505 ARLINGTON BLVD, STE 130 22031 #016-42-1977 L2001 **DR** *020 †80,16

CHAE, Seung Eun. ■ 22033 #018-03-1996 L1998 **FM** *020 †18

CHAMBERS, Theodore P. 8505 ARLINGTON BLVD, STE 130 22031 #047-05-1987 L1997 **VIR** *020 †80

CHANACHOTE, Udom. 3600 JOSEPH SIEWICK DR 22033 #891-02-1955 L1973 **OBG** *020 †30

CHANDANI, Ali Kassamali. 3998 FAIR RIDGE DR, STE 320 22033 #034-01-2000 L2006 **AN** *020 †05

CHANG, Alice Chialing. 8505 ARLINGTON BLVD # 420 22031 #048-12-1986 L1992 **ICE CD** *020 †20

CHANG, Carol Soo Jung. 13135 LEE JACKSON HWY, STE 135 22033 #033-06-1999 L2006 **NEP** *020 †20

CHANG, Craig K. 8505 ARLINGTON BLVD, STE 450 22031 #035-19-2000 L2006 **N** *100 †75

CHANG, Raymond. 8505 ARLINGTON BLVD 22031 #033-06-1999 L2006 **RNR** *100 †80

CHAO, Catherine Singwen. 3700 JOSEPH SIEWICK DR, STE 308 22031 #041-12-1991 L1997 **PG** *020 †55

CHARLESWORTH, Russell W. ■ 22033 #041-07-1988 L1990 **RHU** *075 †20

CHASE, Sandra Mae. ■ 22030 #041-07-1971 L1972 **OS FM** *020 †18

CHEN, Jing Selia. 8505 ARLINGTON BLVD, STE 130 22031 #024-01-2001 L2007 **DR** *020 †80

CHEN, Mei-Lieu Wu. 8622 LEE HWY 22031 #243-21-1941 L1970 **PD** *071

CHEN, Sun. 8505 ARLINGTON BLVD, STE 130 22031 #025-01-1984 L2006 **R IM** *020 †80

CHEN, Vincent Chimin. 13071 AUTUMN WILLOW DR 22030 #010-01-1987 L1999 **IM** *020 †20

CHERIYAN, Ranjit V. 3930 WALNUT ST 22031 #496-11-1979 L1987 **NEP IM** *020 †20

CHERRICK, Abraham Alan. 3031 JAVIER RD, STE 210 22031 #028-03-1980 L1983 **PM** *020 †60

CHHITWAL, Nandita. ■ 22030 #051-04-2004 L2004 **GS** *012

CHILDS, Ronald Clayton. 8501 ARLINGTON BLVD, STE 400 22031 #010-03-1983 L1993 **OSS ORS** *020 †40

CHILES, John Hall. 3998 FAIR RIDGE DR, STE 320 22033 #045-01-1983 L1996 **AN PME** *020 †05

CHO, Sook Tae. ■ 22033 #583-03-1956 L1983 **OBG** *020

CHOE, Jong Woo. 2826 OLD LEE HWY, STE 300 22031 #023-01-1986 L1992 **U GS** *020 †95

CHOI, Brian Kwang. 8505 ARLINGTON BLVD, STE 130 22031 #041-13-1997 L2004 **RNR** *020 †80

CHOI, Richard Jongho. 8505 ARLINGTON BLVD, STE 130 22031 #024-05-1995 L2000 **DR** *020 †80

CHOI, Su Jin. 8303 ARLINGTON BLVD, STE 110 22031 #055-01-1996 L2000 **FM** *020

CHOW, Chak Lam. ■ 22030 #385-03-1969 L1981 **GP** *075

CHRISTIE, Robert Jos. 3028 JAVIER RD, STE 500 22031 #051-04-1990 L2000 **HO** *020 †20

CHU, Joseph Lee. 3600 JOSEPH SIEWICK DR, FAIR OAKS EMERGENCY DEPART 22033 #041-02-2001 L2003 **EM** *020 †16

CHU, Tu-Anh. 3600 JOSEPH SIEWICK DR, FAIR OAKS HOSP DEPT PATH 22033 #010-02-1983 L1988 **PTH** *020 †50

CHUNG, Michael S. 2826 OLD LEE HWY, STE 201 22031 #583-15-1987 L1997 **PM** *020 †60

CHUNG, Sandy Lee. 3650 JOSEPH SIEWICK DR 22033 #051-01-1997 L1997 **PD** *020 †55

CHUNG, Simon Sinmin. 8503 ARLINGTON BLVD 22031 #041-09-1987 L1989 **U** *020 †95

CIRILLO, Nicholas B. 10328 SAGER AVE UNIT 322, MAILING ADDR/P.O.BOX 89 22030 #010-02-1965 L1971 **IM** *020 †20

CLARK, Craig Chas. 3650 JOSEPH SIEWICK DR, FAIRFAX FAMILY PRACTICE 22033 #028-34-1979 L1985 **FM** *020 †18

CLAYTON, David Owen. 3959 PENDER DR STE 320, THE CHILD & FAMILY COUNSEL 22030 #028-34-1997 L2002 **P CHP** *020 †75

CLAYTON, James Ernest. 2730 PROSPERITY AVE, STE A 22031 #030-06-1976 L1986 **PUD PD** *020 †55

CLAYTON, Wm Ellis, Jr. 3701 PENDER DR STE 500, TROY SYSTEMS INC 22030 #051-01-1965 L1965 **OS A** *062 †95

CLOSE, James Mc Clay. 8501 ARLINGTON BLVD # 300 22031 #023-01-1955 L1965 **OBG** *020 †30

COCHRAN, John Wesley. 8316 ARLINGTON BLVD, STE 310 22031 #041-02-1973 L1978 **N IM** *020 †20,75

COCKERHAM, John Taylor. 8501 ARLINGTON BLVD, 2ND FL 22031 #051-01-1980 L1988 **PDC** *020 †55

COGEN, Fran Rosenberg. 8501 ARLINGTON BLVD, PROSPERITY MEDICAL COMPLEX 22031 #035-01-1979 L1996 **PD** *020 †55

COHEN, Cynthia Goldstein. 8301 ARLINGTON BLVD # 505 22031 #041-14-1985 L1988 **P** *020 †75

COICA, Maria. ■ 22031 #781-04-1996 L2002 **PYM** *020 †75

COLE, Katherine Joyce. 3650 JOSEPH SIEWICK DR, FAIRFAX FAMILY PRACTICE 22033 #020-12-1980 L1987 **FM** *020 †18

COLEMAN, Eva. 3650 JOSEPH SIEWICK DR #303 22033 #198-01-1992 L2001 **IM** *020

COLVIN, Donald Bernard. 2710 PROSPERITY AVE, FAIRFAX COLON & RECTAL SUR 22031 #011-03-1975 L1984 **CRS GS** *020 †10,85

CONIGLIO, Susan J. 8501 ARLINGTON BLVD, STE 200 22031 #011-03-1983 L2001 **PD** *020 †55

COOLEY, David Mark. 8261 WILLOW OAKS CO DR, CORPORATE DR. 22031 #051-04-1982 L1997 **DR** *020 †80

CORRIGAN, Kathleen. 8505 ARLINGTON BLVD, STE 130 22031 #010-02-1986 L1988 **DR** *020 †80

COSSA, Nicholas A. 8503 ARLINGTON BLVD, STE 120 22031 #035-03-1980 L1983 **CD** *020 †20

COSTA, Jack Michael. 3650 JOSEPH SIEWICK DR, STE 202 22033 #010-01-1971 L1977 **D** *020 †15

CRANE-LEE, Kathleen T. 3911 OLD LEE HWY, STE 41C 22030 #035-48-1986 L1996 **FM** *020 †18

CRANTZ, Joanne Gittleson. 8316 ARLINGTON BLVD, NOVAMED ASSOCIATES 22031 #010-01-1979 L1985 **IMG IM** *020 †20

CROSS, Catherine Marie. 3700 JOSEPH SIEWICK DR, STE 300 22033 #005-14-2002 L2007 **PD** *020 †55

CROSSMAN, Steven Hovis. 3650 JOSEPH SIEWICK DR, FAIRFAX FAMILY PRACTICE 22033 #051-04-1995 L1998 **FM** *020 †18

CUEVO, Raymund Serrano. 8501 ARLINGTON BLVD # 340 22031 #008-01-1986 L1999 **ON** *050 †20

CUMBERLIN, Richard Lee. 10301 DEMOCRACY LN, ASSOCIATES IN RADIATION ON 22030 #016-11-1974 L2003 **RO** *020 †80

CURCIO, Christopher M. 8261 WILLOW OAKS CO DR, CORP DRIVE 22031 #023-07-1978 L1990 **OS DR** *020 †80

CURRY, Charlene Andrea. 8505 ARLINGTON BLVD, STE 130 22031 #010-01-1994 L2000 **DR** *020 †80

CURTIS, Kathleen. 3998 FAIR RIDGE DR 22033 #051-07-1994 L1994 **FM** *020 †18

CVETKOVICH, Lorna Lynn. 11135 LEE HWY, CARITAS CENTER WOMEN'S HEA 22030 #019-02-1977 L2000 **OBG** *020 †30

DABLING, Heather Anne. ■ 22031 #422-01-2007 L2007 **OBG** *012

DADE, Rodney Barnard. 3031 JAVIER RD, STE 100 22031 #025-07-1990 L1995 **PM** *020 †60

DAR, Rizman Qadir. 10721 MAIN ST, STE 2500 22030 #704-05-1985 L1991 **NEP** *020 †20

DAVID, Lynn M. 8261 WILLOW OAKS CO DR, KAISER PERMANENTE IMAGING 22031 #050-02-1989 L1998 **DR** *020 †80

DAVIS, Carolyn Florence. 8501 ARLINGTON BLVD, GLENNA R ANDERSON MD & 22031 #038-45-1988 L1992 **OBG** *020 †30

DAVIS, Mary Margaret. 8550 ARLINGTON BLVD # 201 22031 #051-01-1977 L1978 **OBG** *020 †30

DAVIS, Victoria Edmond. 8505 ARLINGTON BLVD, STE 130 22031 #005-18-1997 L1997 **DR** *020 †80

DEAN, Jennifer Beck. ■ 22032 #036-05-2001 L2007 **PHO** *020 †55

DEAN, Nathan Patrick. ■ 22032 #036-05-2001 L2001 **PD** *100 †55

DEI CAS, Ronald. 12011 LEE JACKSON HWY, STE 305 22033 #016-06-1989 L1995 **OPH PS** *020 †35

DEKKER, Jan J. 8316 ARLINGTON BLVD 22031 #660-07-1971 L1985 **GS** *020 †85

DEL NEGRO, Albert Anthony. 3020 HAMAKER CT, STE 401 22031 #010-02-1969 L1990 **ICE CD** *020 †20

DEMPSEY, Eugene Calvin. ■ 22030 #047-07-1942 L1942 **IM GP** *072

DEMPSEY, William Chas. 3600 JOSEPH SIEWICK DR 22033 #035-08-1955 L1977 **PS** *071 †85,65

DEWITT, Laura Ann. 3998 FAIR RIDGE DR 22033 #038-41-1991 L1995 **AN** *020 †05 ‡

D'HEUREUX, Sharon. 8505 ARLINGTON BLVD, STE 130 22031 #038-06-2000 L2006 **DR** *020 †80

DHINAKARAN, Geetha. 3600 JOSEPH SIEWICK DR, STE 180 22033 #495-16-1991 L1998 **AN** *020 †05

DIANGELO, Constance Rose. 9797 BRADDOCK RD # 100, NOVA OCME 22032 #056-06-1992 L2005 **FOP PTH** *020 †50

DIBADJ, Kourosh. 13135 LEE JACKSON MMRL HWY, STE 135 22033 #517-01-1995 L2007 **IM** *020 †20

DICICCO, Barry Shelton. 3650 JOSEPH SIEWICK DR, STE 307 22033 #036-01-1979 L1980 **PUD CCM** *020 †20

DINTIMAN, Brenda Jean. 3700 JOSEPH SIEWICK DR, STE 403 22033 #051-04-1985 L1991 **D** *020 †15

DLOTT, Tracy R. 12255 FAIR LAKES PKWY, KAISER PERMANENTE 22033 #048-13-1993 L2005 **OBG** *020 †30

DOAN, Ba Van. 2740 PROSPERITY AVE, FAMILY HLTH CTR OF FAIRFAX 22031 #941-01-1966 L1985 **IM NEP** *020

DOAN, Nhat Minh. 10721 MAIN ST STE 3400 22030 #010-01-1997 L1999 **IM ID** *020 †20

DOBRZYNSKI, Anne M. 8316 ARLINGTON BLVD, STE 420 22037 #422-01-1999 L1999 **OBG** *020 †30

DOBRZYNSKI, Dennis A. 3650 JOSEPH SIEWICK DR, STE 106 22033 #422-01-1999 L2005 **HO** *020 †20

DONOVAN, Robert J, II. ■ 22031 #045-01-1995 L1997 **EM AM** *020 †16

DOPPALAPUDI, Suma. 12255 FAIR LAKES PKWY, FAIR OAKS MEDICAL CENTER 22033 #495-21-1994 L2001 **IM** *020 †20

DOSOVA, Noemi. 3650 JOSEPH SIEWICK DR #10 22033 #286-04-1968 L1985 **PD** *020 †55

DOUGHERTY, Lynda Sue. 2710 PROSPERITY AVE, STE 200 22031 #038-43-1993 L1999 **CRS** *020 †85,10

DRESSLER, Linda Ann. 12011 LEE JACKSON HWY #305 22033 #024-01-1982 L1986 **OPH** *020 †35

DREW, P Jean. 9683A MAIN ST 22031 #041-07-1988 L1991 **FM** *020 †18

DROOZ, Alain Thos. 8505 ARLINGTON BLVD, STE 130 22031 #036-01-1984 L1999 **VIR** *020 †80

DUC, James. 8505 ARLINGTON BLVD # 420 22031 #023-07-1992 L1995 **ICE CD** *020 †20

DUNNING, David Marshall. 8503 ARLINGTON BLVD, STE 400 22031 #051-04-1979 L1990 **ON HEM** *020 †20

DUONG, Hon Quang. 8318 ARLINGTON BLVD, STE 301 22031 #941-02-1973 L1985 **OPH PTH** *020

DURR, Paul Gregory. 3600 JOSEPH SIEWICK DR 22033 #010-02-1996 L2000 **IM** *020 †20

DURRANI, Sarfraz Ali K. 3020 HAMAKER CT, STE 401 22031 #495-51-1990 L1999 **ICE** *020 †20

EARLE, Rona Harthill. 3020 HAMAKER CT, STE B102 22031 #010-02-1983 L1987 **IM** *020 †20

EARLS, James Patrick. 8505 ARLINGTON BLVD, STE 130 22031 #035-19-1988 L1999 **DR** *020 †80

EBERLY, Lewis Baker. 8316 ARLINGTON BLVD, STE 310 22031 #048-12-1985 L1990 **N SME** *020 †75

EDGEWORTH, Lewis Anson D. 3600 JOSEPH SIEWICK DR 22033 #065-01-1969 L1976 **GP OS** *020

EDMISTON, Kirsten Kilborn. 4001 FAIR RIDGE DR, STE 304 22033 #041-13-1988 L1997 **HO GS** *020 †85

EHRLICH, Thomas Paul. 3650 JOSEPH SIEWICK DR, STE 400 22033 #010-02-1990 L1991 **FM** *040 †18

EISENBAUM, Marc Allen. 3700 JOSEPH SIEWICK DR, STE 203 22033 #010-01-1981 L1987 **IM** *020 †20

ELA ONDO, Bruno. 8505 ARLINGTON BLVD # 420, THE CARDIO GRP 22031 #396-11-2000 *062

ELLISON, Oscar, III. 3022 JAVIER RD, STE 200 22031 #010-02-1980 L1982 **PD** *020

ELLWOOD, Leslie Clive. 3600 JOSEPH SIEWICK DR 22033 #011-03-1968 L1975 **PD OS** *020 †55

EMDADI, Trissana Lee. 3650 JOSEPH SIEWICK DR, STE 400 22033 #010-01-2005 L2005 **FP** *012

EPSTEIN, Bethany Catherin. 3700 JOSEPH SIEWICK DR, STE 300 22033 #051-04-2000 L2000 **PD** *100 †55

ERGENER, John Erdogan. 12011 LEE JACKSON HWY, 4TH FL 22033 #041-02-1992 L1992 **ORS OSS** *020 †40

ESPOSITO, Aldo Richard. 12011 LEE JACKSON HWY 22033 #010-02-1980 L1985 **CD IM** *020 †20

ESSEPIAN, John Phillip. 9936 MAIN ST 22031 #010-02-1988 L1994 **OPH** *020 †35

ESTABROOK, Dawn Mcqueen. 10657 BRADDOCK RD, CHILDRENS MED ASSOC OF 22032 #010-01-1997 L1997 **PD** *020 †55

EVANS, Jay Mark. 8501 ARLINGTON BLVD, STE 400 22031 #041-01-1985 L1991 **HS ORS** *020 †40

FALLS, Mark David. 3020 HAMAKER CT, STE 503 22031 #041-02-1987 L1990 **OPH** *020 †35

FANBURG, Susan Jennifer. 3700 JOSEPH SIEWICK DR, STE 300 22033 #010-01-1995 L1998 **PD** *020 †55

FARKHANI, Hasan. ■ 22030 #517-06-1992 L2004 **IM** *020

FARRELL, Walter John, Jr. 2722 MERRILEE DR 22031 #038-06-1960 L1967 **R** *071 †80

FAVRET, Anne Marie. 8503 ARLINGTON BLVD, STE 400 22031 #041-13-1993 L1994 **IM** *020 †20

FAZEL, Ali. 8501 ARLINGTON BLVD, STE 525 22031 #517-08-1991 L2005 **GE IM** *020 †20

FECANIN, Peter J. 3020 HAMAKER CT STE 403 22031 #010-02-1976 L1978 **IM** *020 †20

FEIGERT, John Morris. 3028 JAVIER RD, STE 500 22031 #035-20-1983 L1991 **HO ON** *020 †20

FERGUSON, Katherine A. 10721 MAIN ST, STE 307 22030 #010-01-1979 L1988 **P** *020 †75

FERNANDO, Lorency. 11204 WAPLES MILL RD, INOVA KELLAR CTR 22030 #495-59-1993 L2001 **CHP P** *020 †75

FIELD, Frances P. 9797 BRADDOCK RD # 100 22032 #308-03-1978 L1985 **FOP** *020 †50

FIELDS, Michael Jay. 2730 PROSPERITY AVE STE A, THE PEDIATRIC LUNG CENTER 22031 #036-07-1997 L2006 **PD** *020 †55

FIELDS, Richard Lee. 8316 ARLINGTON BLVD 22031 #017-20-1956 L1964 **OTO** *071 †45

FILDES, Robert Duane. 8505 ARLINGTON BLVD, STE 100 22031 #165-01-1978 L1983 **PN PD** *020 †20

FILIPESCU-TURNER, Laura C. 3600 JOSEPH SIEWICK DR, FAIR OAKS ANESTH ASSOC 22033 #010-01-2001 L2001 **AN** *020

FILLA, Rebecca Dawn. 12255 FAIR LAKES PKWY, KAISER FAIR OAKS 22033 #056-05-1990 L1996 **OBG** *020 †30

FINCH, Elizabeth Lathrop. 10470 ARMSTRONG ST 22030 #038-41-1978 L1983 **CHP P** *020 †75

FISH, Samantha Hope. ■ 22030 #035-15-2007 L2007 **PD** *012

FISK, Daniel Richard. 11135 LEE HWY 22030 #016-06-1989 L2000 **OBG** *020 †30

FOGARTY, Thomas Michael. 10369 DEMOCRACY LN STE A 22030 #010-02-1982 L1988 **P IM** *020 †20,75

FOLEY, Kerry Ann. 10306 EATON PL, STE 180 22030 #010-02-1982 L2002 **EM** *020 †16

FORREST, Scott Tobias. 10721 MAIN ST, STE 200 22030 #051-04-1996 L1996 **OBG** *020 †30

FORT, Milton Leonard. ■ 22032 #016-11-1957 L1958 **IM CD** *071 †20

FOWLER, Mark David. 2730 PROSPERITY AVE, STE B 22031 #011-02-1988 L1996 **NPM** *020 †20

FRANKE, Mark Edward. 3600 JOSEPH SIEWICK DR, DEPT OF EMERGENCY MEDICINE 22033 #035-09-1996 L1996 **EM** *020 †16

FREITAG, David Stephen. 8503 ARLINGTON BLVD # 150 22031 #010-02-1980 L1989 **D PS** *020 †15

FRENCH, Kathleen B. 3020 HAMAKER CT STE B104 22031 #024-05-1980 L1988 **NS** *020 †25

FRIEDLIS, Mayo Frederick. 3031 JAVIER RD, STE 100 22031 #025-07-1979 L1983 **PM PMM** *020 †60 ‡

FRIEHLING, Linda Ann. 10657 BRADDOCK RD, CHILDRENS MED ASSOC OF 22032 #016-42-1976 L1988 **PD NPM** *020 †55

FRIEHLING, Ted David. 3020 HAMAKER CT, STE 401 22031 #016-42-1976 L1988 **CD ICE** *020 †55,20

GALLAGHER, Edward James. 10090 MAIN ST, EDWARD J GALLAGHER MD LTD 22031 #065-09-1952 L1956 **IM DIA** *071

GARDE, Rachana Vasant. 12011 LEE JACKSON MMRL HWY, STE 302 22033 #045-01-1999 L2006 **OBG REN** *020

GARREAU, Elizabeth Ann. 3020 HAMAKER CT STE B105 22031 #033-06-1986 L1988 **OBG** *020 †30

GARVERT, Terry Ann. 3650 JOSEPH SIEWICK DR, STE 400 22033 #051-04-2004 L2004 **FM** *020 †18

GAVORA, Les Hugh. 3020 HAMAKER CT STE 403 22031 #010-01-1983 L1986 **EM** *020 †20

GELLER, Daniel Mark. 12011 LEE JACKSON HWY, STE 305 22033 #035-47-1992 L1992 **OPH** *020 †35

GELMAN, Howard Kenneth. 8316 ARLINGTON BLVD 22031 #016-11-1968 L1970 **OTO FPS** *071 †45

GENEVA, Edward Frank. 3600 JOSEPH SIEWICK DR, EMERGENCY DEPARTMENT 22033 #038-40-1976 L1985 **EM** *020 †16

GENNARO, Margaret Mary. 10560 MAIN ST PH 22030 #035-09-1987 L1999 **PD** *020 †55

GENTRY, David Wm. 3600 JOSEPH SIEWICK DR, EMERGENCY DEPT 22033 #023-01-1992 L1995 **EM** *020 †16

GEOLY, Kenneth Lucian. 8316 ARLINGTON BLVD 22031 #035-08-1968 L1972 **NEP IM** *020 †20

GEORGE, Swapna. 2740 PROSPERITY AVE, FAMILY HEALTH CENTER OF FA 22031 #495-44-1995 L2000 **IM** *020 †20

GHAZAL, Talal Moiffak. 3998 FAIR RIDGE DR, STE 320 22033 #305-01-2001 L2007 **APM AN** *020 †05

GLOVER, William Lloyd, Jr. 10875 MAIN ST STE 208 22030 #047-06-1965 L1972 **U SO** *020 †95

GODWIN, Ira David. ■ 22030 #036-01-1955 L1961 **PTH NM** *071 †50,28

GOEL, Raven Abhilasha. 13135 LEE JACKSON MMRL HWY, STE 135 22033 #023-01-2002 L2007 **IM** *100 †20

GOLDBERG, Andrew Gregg. 3700 JOSEPH SIEWICK DR, STE 301 22033 #033-05-1984 L1991 **PS GS** *020 †85,65

GOLDEN, John Seth. 12011 LEE JACKSON HWY, DEPARTMENT OF CARDIOLOGY 22033 #033-06-1985 L1991 **CD IM** *020 †20

GOLDMUNTZ, Ellen Anne. 8501 ARLINGTON BLVD 22031 #035-46-1986 L1993 **PD PPR** *020 †55

GOLDSTEIN, Leonard Steven. 8316 ARLINGTON BLVD, STE 600 22031 #010-02-1972 L1976 **P OS** *020 †75

GOLEMBIESKI, Michael E. 12255 FAIR LAKES PKWY 22033 #023-01-1972 L1974 **IM** *030 †20

GONZALES, Federico Carlos. 3700 JOSEPH SIEWICK DR, STE 402 22033 #737-01-1971 L1977 **IM** *020 †20

GOODMAN, Stephen Joel. 8505 ARLINGTON BLVD, STE 130 22031 #035-19-1967 L1973 **R** *020 †80

GOODWIN, Lyndon Keith. 8505 ARLINGTON BLVD, STE 130 22031 #023-01-1979 L1987 **OS DR** *020 †80

GOPAL, Sarita. 4001 FAIR RIDGE DR 22033 #041-07-1988 L1992 **OBG** *020 †30

GORAYA, Kamalinder Kaur. 8550 LEE HWY 22031 #495-29-1991 L2000 **CHP** *020 †75

GORDON, Brigid Annejulia. 8505 ARLINGTON BLVD, STE 130 22031 #010-02-1991 L1998 **DR** *020 †80,28

GORNY, Eric Russell. 2722 MERRILEE DR, STE 230 22031 #010-02-1999 L1999 **DR** *020 †80

GOVIL, Kanika. 3650 JOSEPH SIEWICK DR, STE 400 22033 #495-82-2001 L2006 **FP** *012

GOWDA, Murliya D. 10721 MAIN ST, STE 3400 22030 #051-04-2001 L2005 **ID** *020

GOYA, Garbine. 3020 HAMAKER CT, STE 401 22031 #847-11-1983 L2006 **ICE** *020 †55

GOYAL, Anjali. 3022 WILLIAMS DR STE 300 22031 #495-56-1988 L2002 **IM** *020 †20

GOYAL, Shalini. 3600 JOSEPH SIEWICK DR, INOVA FAIR OAKS HOSPITAL 22033 #041-02-1998 L2005 **IM** *020 †20

GRADY, Christopher Kevin. 2722 MERRILEE DR, SUTIE 230 22031 #041-02-1993 L1999 **DR** *020 †80

GRADZKA, Malgorzata I. 3700 JOSEPH SIEWICK DR, STE 200 22033 #759-03-1984 L1997 **IM RHU** *020 †20

GRAHAM, Charles Mc Donald. ■ 22030 #051-04-1959 L1959 **OBG** *071 †30

GRASS, David Bruce. 3020 HAMAKER CT, STE 400 22031 #035-08-1974 L1985 **N** *071 †75

GREENBERG, Jay. 8301 ARLINGTON BLVD, STE 209 22031 #041-01-1976 L1986 **PHO** *050 †55

GREENE, Michael David. 3700 JOSEPH SIEWICK DR, STE 203 22033 #010-02-1980 L1987 **IM** *020 †20

GREENHOUSE, Stephen. 12011 LEE JACKSON MMRL HWY, STE 302 22033 #023-01-1991 L1992 **OBG** *020 †30

GREENSPAN, Robert Edward. 13135 LEE JACKSON MMRL HWY, STE 135 22033 #023-01-1971 L1978 **NEP** *020 †20

GRIFFITH, Bernice Desiree. 8505 ARLINGTON BLVD, STE 130 22031 #035-47-1993 L2002 **DR** *020 †80

GRIGGS, Weishen Dai. 8505 ARLINGTON BLVD, STE 130 22031 #016-02-2001 L2007 **DR** *020 †80,28

GRISMER, Linda E M. 3022 WILLIAMS DR, STE 100 22031 #016-11-1994 L2005 **RHU** *020 †20

GRONINGER, James Hunter. 9300 LEE HWY, STE 200 22031 #051-01-2002 L2002 **IM** *100 †20

GRUEN, Jeffrey Myron. ■ 22031 #016-06-1980 L1987 **PD** *062 †55

GRUMBACH, Kathryn. 8505 ARLINGTON BLVD, STE 130 22031 #041-01-1979 L1999 **DR** *020 †80

GRUNDLEHNER, Marietta F. 3700 JOSEPH SIEWICK DR, STE 305 22033 #041-02-1974 L1980 **NEP IM** *050 †20

GUARNACCIA, Steven Paul. 12011 LEE JACKSON HWY 22033 #024-07-1985 L1995 **U** *020 †95

GUDAVALLI, Harini. 12255 FAIR LAKES PKWY, INTERNAL MEDICINE 22033 #495-14-1993 L1997 **IM** *020 †20

GUPTA, Anu. 10301 DEMOCRACY LN, ASSOC.IN RADIATION ONCOLOG 22030 #051-07-1992 L1995 **RO** *020 †80

GUPTA, Manish. 8503 ARLINGTON BLVD, STE 200 22031 #041-13-1995 L2004 **GS TTS** *020 †85

GUPTA, Pradeep Kumar. 8301 ARLINGTON BLVD # 405 22031 #010-03-1988 L1989 **GE** *020 †20

GUPTA, Praveen Kumar. 4080 CHAIN BRIDGE RD 22030 #690-06-1988 L1996 **IM** *020 †20

GURIAN, Karen Vernof. 4001 FAIR RIDGE DR, STE 202 22033 #026-08-1988 L1995 **OBG** *020 †30

HABIB, Christine Mary. 4001 FAIR RIDGE DR, STE 304 22033 #038-44-1998 L2006 **GS** *020 †85

HAFNER, Gordon Harold. 4001 FAIR RIDGE DR, STE 304 22033 #010-01-1983 L1984 **GS SO** *020 †85

HAFNER, Nancy Lynn. 8550 ARLINGTON BLVD, STE 201 22031 #010-01-1984 L1987 **OBG** *020 †30

HALLAL, F Joseph. 3650 JOSEPH SIEWICK DR, STE 206 22033 #041-01-1966 L1974 **OS** *071 †20

HAMANDI, Wadie J. ■ 22031 #528-01-1952 **CRS** *071 †10

HAN, Michael Young. 8503 ARLINGTON BLVD, STE 310 22031 #025-01-1999 L2001 **U** *020 †95

HANWAY, Jeffrey Lynn. 8501 ARLINGTON BLVD, STE 200 22031 #024-01-1988 L1994
ORS *020 †40

HARE, Kathryn Wilson. 3650 JOSEPH SIEWICK DR, STE 400 22031 #010-02-2006 L2006
FP *012

HARKLESS, Kia Eretha. 3700 JOSEPH SIEWICK DR, STE 300 22033 #051-04-2001 L2001
PD *100 †55

HARPER, Lisa R V. 8301 ARLINGTON BLVD, STE 404 22031 #869-05-1980 L1983 **IM** *020

HARPER, Sarah Jane. 8316 ARLINGTON BLVD # 310 22031 #041-12-2005 L2005 **IM** *012

HARRIS, Dale Anne. 8550 LEE HWY 22031 #064-01-1979 L1982 **P** *020 †75

HARRISON, Kenneth. 8261 WILLOW OAKS CO DR, CORPORATE DRIVE 22031
#051-07-1987 L1998 **DR** *020 †80

HARSHAW, William Geo, Jr. 2722 MERRILEE DR, STE 230 22031 #051-01-1962 L1962
R *020 †80

HARTZELL, Heather Dianne. 3650 JOSEPH SIEWICK DR, STE 303 22033 #028-02-1996 L2006
OPH *035

HARTZELL, William Osborn. 3600 JOSEPH SIEWICK DR 22033 #051-04-1992 L2006
IM *020 †20

HATTWICK, Michael A W. 8501 ARLINGTON BLVD, PROSPERITY PRIMARY CARE 22031
#048-04-1968 L1977 **IM PHP** *020 †20,70

HEAD, Gordon Lawrence. 8505 ARLINGTON BLVD, STE 130 22031 #005-14-1971 L1979
DR *020 †80

HEARNS, Rhonda Maria. 3015 WILLIAMS DR STE 202, GENETICS & IVF INSTITUTE 22031
#010-02-1993 L2004 **OBG** *020 †30

HEATH, Christine Mary. 8501 ARLINGTON BLVD, STE 200 22031 #041-07-1998 L2005 **N** *020

HEFTER, Lawrence G. 11150 MAIN ST, STE 501 22030 #016-02-1963 L1970
PTH DMP *020 †50,28

HEIT, Howard Allen. 8316 ARLINGTON BLVD, STE 232 22031 #041-12-1971 L1978
GE IM *020 †20 ‡

HELD, Arthur Christian. 12011 LEE JACKSON HWY, MEMORIAL HWY 22033
#025-01-1978 L2000 **CD** *020 †20

HERMAN, Gabriel Bryan. 8301 ARLINGTON BLVD # 41 22031 #010-02-1973 L1979
GE IM *020 †20

HERMES, Marjorie Liese. 3650 JOSEPH SIEWICK DR, FAIRFAX FAMILY PRACTICE 22033
#010-01-1988 L1990 **FM** *020 †18

HERRMAN, Joanne. 8324 PROFESSIONAL HILL DR, # 8 22031 #041-12-1979 L1982
OBG *020 †30

HILLIARD, Janet Karen. 2730 PROSPERITY AVE STE B, FAIRFAX NEONATAL ASSOCIATE 22031
#041-77-1973, ▲ L1978 **NPM PD** *020 †55

HIRANI, Sushma Sanjay. 10640 MAIN ST, STE 300 22031 #495-37-2001 L2006 **FM** *020 †18

HIRSCHMAN, Bernardo. 8303 ARLINGTN BLVD #NO-205 22031 #132-01-1955 L1973
P *020 †75

HO, Garry Waikurng. 3650 JOSEPH SIEWICK DR, STE 400 22033 #010-02-2003 L2003
FSM *100 †18

HODGES, Walter James, Jr. 4001 FAIR RIDGE DR STE 202 22033 #010-02-1989 L1993
OBG *020 †30

HODZIEWICH, Cassandra Mar. 3650 JOSEPH SIEWICK DR, STE 400 22033 #023-01-2006 L2006
FP *012

HOERNER, Kathleen M. 3600 JOSEPH SIEWICK DR 22033 #041-02-1984 L1989 **IM** *020 †20

HOLLCRAFT, Charles Martin. 3022 WILLIAMS DR, STE 200 22031 #023-12-1991 L2004
DR *020 †80

HONG, Sharon S. 3600 JOSEPH SIEWICK DR 22033 #035-15-2000 L2003 **PD** *020 †55

HOPE, Donald Gerard. 3016 WILLIAMS DR, CTR FOR CRANIAL & SPINALSR 22031
#023-01-1982 L1987 **NS** *020 †25

HORN, Marianna. 8301 ARLINGTON BLVD, PEDIA. HEMAT. & ONCOL. OF 22031
#035-47-1981 L1996 **PD** *075 †55

HORN, Martin Seth. 10721 MAIN ST, STE 3100 22030 #010-01-1977 L1981 **D** *020 †15

HORTON, Jack Donald. 3650 JOSEPH SIEWICK DR, STE 206 22033 #041-01-1971 L1979
CD *020 †20

HOWARD, Thomas Michael. 3650 JOSEPH SIEWICK DR, FAIRFAX FAMILY PRACTICE 22033
#023-12-1984 L1986 **FM** *020 †18

HOWELL, Suzanne White. 4211 FAIRFAX CORNR EST AVE, STE 225 22030 #047-06-1996 L2000
PD *020 †55

HRYVNIAK, Michael Russell. 4001 FAIR RIDGE DR, STE 305 22033 #033-05-1984 L1986
P *020 †75

HSIEH, Chifeng. ■ 22031 #051-04-2003 L2003 **FM** *020 †18

HUGHES, Mark Carroll. 3600 JOSEPH SIEWICK DR 22033 #051-07-1998 L1999 **EM** *020

HUH, Charles. 3700 JOSEPH SIEWICK DR, STE 201 22033 #038-43-1996 L2002 **GE** *020 †20

HUNTER, Nota A. 3998 FAIR RIDGE DR, STE 270 22033 #047-06-2000 L2001 **FM** *020 †18

HUNTINGTON, Daniele F. 3020 HAMAKER CT, STE 300 22031 #010-02-1971 L1976
PD NPM *020 †55

HUQ, Shameem Ara. 3600 JOSEPH SIEWICK DR, DEPT OF MEDICINE 22033
#160-02-1982 L2002 **IM IMG** *020 †20

HURLEY, John Kevin. 12255 FAIR LAKES PKWY, KAISER PERMANENTE 22033
#035-08-1969 L1981 **PD OS** *030 †55

HUSSNY, Emman. 4001 FAIR RIDGE DR, STE 101 22033 #038-06-1998 L2001 **FM** *020 †18

HUYNH, Luong Quang. ■ 22030 #941-01-1968 L1984 *100

HWU-YUN, Rosanna Wan Rou. 3998 FAIR RIDGE DR, STE 320 22033 #051-04-1984 L1987
AN *020 †05

HYMEL, Kent Paul. 8505 ARLINGTON BLVD # 100, INOVA PEDIATRIC SPECIALTY 22031
#016-45-1980 L2000 **PD** *020 †55

HYMES, Robert Allen. 8503 ARLINGTON BLVD, STE 200 22031 #005-02-1994 L2001
ORS *020 †40

HYNES, John Jos. 3600 JOSEPH SIEWICK DR, FAIR OAKS HOSP 22033 #308-08-1983 L1986
AN *020 †05

INMAN, Patricia S. 3998 FAIR RIDGE DR, STE 280 22033 #012-05-1978 L1992 **FM** *020 †18

ISHAQ, Syed Naveed. 2826 OLD LEE HWY STE 250 22031 #704-01-1985 L1996 **NEP** *020

ISKANDER, Mona Theresa. 12255 FAIR LAKES PKWY, KASIER PERMANENTE 22033
#055-01-2002 L2006 **FP** *012

IVY, Michael Warren A. 3600 JOSEPH SIEWICK DR 22033 #010-03-1963 L1964 **OBG** *071 †30

JACKMAN, Jeffrey Alan. 3700 JOSEPH SIEWICK DR, STE 102 22033 #011-02-1997 L1998
CD *020 †20

JACKSON, Kenneth Wm. 12255 FAIR LAKES PKWY, KAISER-PERMANENTE 22033
#033-05-1979 L1985 **ORS GS** *020 †40

JACKSON, Larry Kent. 8316 ARLINGTON BLVD STE 5 22031 #036-01-1963 L1986
CD IM *071 †20

JAVATE, Bartolome Arrieta. 8301 ARLINGTON BLVD 22031 #748-02-1961 L1970 **PD** *071 †55

JAVATE, Rosy Tablante. 3998 FAIR RIDGE DR, STE 320 22033 #748-01-1958 L1976 **AN** *071 †05

JEBRAILI, Sean Shahin Ali. 2750 PROSPERITY AVE, STE 120 22031 #051-04-1994 L1994
N NS *020 †25

JEFFERIES, Kara Lynn. 3905 RAILROAD AVE STE 100 22030 #051-01-2000 L2004 **OBG** *020

JENKINS, Ellen Marie. 3022 WILLIAMS DR, STE 204 22031 #041-04-1985 L1991 **RHU** *020 †20

JENKS, Michael Allan. 3600 JOSEPH SIEWICK DR, ATTN: EMERGENCY DEPT 22033
#051-04-2002 L2005 **EM** *020 †16

JEON, Sang Joong. ■ 22033 #583-01-1969 L2003 **AN** *020 †05

JERATH, Nakul. 8505 ARLINGTON BLVD, STE 130 22031 #016-02-1993 L2000 **PDR R** *020 †80

JIMENEZ, Antonio S. 2740 PROSPERITY AVE 22031 #010-03-1992 L1996 **FM** *020 †18

JOHAL, Jasbir Santokh. 11150 MAIN ST, STE 501 22030 #495-12-1975 L1997 **PP** *020 †50

JOHNS, Thomas Todd. 3022 WILLIAMS DR, STE 204 22031 #041-13-1978 L1985 **DR** *050 †80

JOHNSON, Britta Lynn. 3650 JOSEPH SIEWICK DR, STE 400 22033 #010-02-2004 L2004
FM *020 †18

JOHNSON, Clarion Ellis. 3225 GALLOWS RD, MOBIL OIL CORP 22037 #008-01-1976 L1988
CD IM *030 †20,70

JOHNSON, Derek Kendall. 3700 JOSEPH SIEWICK DR, STE 101 22033 #010-01-1995 L2001
AI *020 †55,03

JOHNSON, Lisa Koch. 3015 WILLIAMS DR STE 200, WASHINGTON RADIOLOGY ASSOC 22031
#010-02-1992 L1992 **DR** *020 †80

JONES, Emily Margaret. 3650 JOSEPH SIEWICK DR, STE 400 22033 #024-16-2005 L2005
FP *012

JONES, Jeffrey Stephen. 9836 LEE HWY 22030 #011-03-1970 L1977 **GS** *071 †95

JONES, Samuel Moseley. 3650 JOSEPH SIEWICK DR, FAIRFAX FAMIL PRACTICE CTR 22033
#051-04-1979 L1986 **FM** *040 †18

JONSSON, Johann. 8503 ARLINGTON BLVD, STE 200 22031 #484-01-1979 L1986
TTS GS *020 †85

JOSEPH, Allen Eliot. 8505 ARLINGTON BLVD, STE 130 22031 #024-05-1984 L1993
VIR DR *020 †80

JOSHUA, Sudhir Danl. ■ 22031 #023-01-1986 L2003 **IM** *020 †20

JUBURI, Rudy Husam. 8301 ARLINGTON BLVD, STE 100 22031 #528-01-1987 L1998
IM *020 †20

JUNEJA, Vinni. 3020 HAMAKER CT STE 101 22031 #041-15-2000 L2006 **ON HEM** *050 †20 ‡

KACEDAN, James Patrick. 10680 MAIN ST, STE 190 22030 #017-20-1987 L1991 **OBG** *020 †30

KAISER, Dierich Mark. 8550 LEE HWY STE 300, MERRIFIELD BEHAVIORAL HEAL 22031
#051-01-1997 L1997 **P** *020 †75

KAISER, Reem Zoheir. 3700 JOSEPH SIEWICK DR, STE 403 22033 #051-04-1995 L1995
D *020 †15

KALAGA, Sharma Srinivas. 3998 FAIR RIDGE DR, STE 320 22033 #495-21-1985 L1999
AN *020 †05

KALES, Arthur Norman. 8503 ARLINGTON BLVD, STE 400 22031 #016-02-1965 L1973
ON HEM *020 †20

KALLEY, Aida Aissatou. 3600 JOSEPH SIEWICK DR, INOVA FAIROAKS HOSPITAL ED 22033
#041-09-1997 L2002 **EM** *020 †16

KALRA, Sunil Kumar. 3600 JOSEPH SIEWICK DR 22033 #495-45-1986 L2000 **IM** *020 †20

KAMAT-NERIKAR, Riva. 12255 FAIR LAKES PKWY, 4962 COLLIN CHASE PLACE 22033
#047-07-1993 L1998 **PD** *020 †55

KANG, Mi Hwa. 3998 FAIR RIDGE DR, STE 320 22033 #583-01-1981 L1985 **AN** *020 †05

KANG, Shin Wook. ■ 22033 #583-01-1980 L1982 **OPH** *020

KANKAM, Collins F. 11150 MAIN ST, STE 501 22030 #412-01-1975 L1986 **CLP** *020 †28,50

KANTOR, Scott Douglas. 12011 LEE JACKSON HWY, DEPT OF UROLOGY 22033
#035-09-1975 L1980 **U** *020 †95

KAPOOR, Aarti. 10527 BRADDOCK RD, THE PEDIATRIC GROUP 22032 #422-01-2001 L2005
PD *020 †55

KAPOOR, Sunil Amrit. 2730 PROSPERITY AVE STE A 22031 #035-48-1995 L2001 **PDP** *020 †55

KARNAZE, Michael Geo. 8505 ARLINGTON BLVD, STE 130 22031 #019-02-1982 L1987
VIR R *020 †80

KARP, Steven Mitchell. 3998 FAIR RIDGE DR, STE 320 22033 #036-05-1988 L1992 **AN** *020 †05

KASACI, Arda. 4505 FOREST HILL DR, 4505 FOREST HILL DR 22030 #902-09-1990 L1998
P *020 ‡

KASSA, Lishan. 10520 JUDICIAL DR 22030 #366-01-1989 L1999 **IM** *020 †20

KATUSHA, Kathy. 8503 ARLINGTON BLVD, STE 140 22031 #041-09-1986 L1989 **IM** *020

KAUSHIVA, Anjali. 3650 JOSEPH SIEWICK DR 4TH, PRACTICE CTR 22033 #023-01-2005 L2005
FP *012

KAW, Daniel Go. 12255 FAIR LAKES PKWY 22033 #748-02-1975 L1992 **NEP IM** *020 †20

KAY, G Gordon. 10721 MAIN ST 22030 #038-06-1960 L1963 **IM CD** *071

KAZAKIS, Alexandra Mary. 3022 WILLIAMS DR STE 101 22031 #051-01-1983 L1987 **D** *020 †15

KAZMI, Salman O. 8503 ARLINGTON BLVD, STE 310 22031 #704-03-1967 L1976 **U** *020 †95

KEFALE, George Gebre. 3020 HAMAKER CT, STE 300 22031 #366-01-1974 L1987
NPM *020

KELLER, Andrew Jay. 8316 ARLINGTON BLVD, STE 300 22031 #422-01-1981 L1988
CD CCM *020 †20

KELLMAN, Gary Michael. 8505 ARLINGTON BLVD, STE 130 22031 #025-07-1981 L1992
DR *020 †80

KELLOFF, Gary Joe. ■ 22031 #007-02-1967 L1976 **OS IM** *050

KELLY, Kathleen A. 12255 FAIR LAKES PKWY, KAISER PERMANENTE 22033
#048-13-1992 L1996 **MPD** *020 †55,20

KELLY, Melinda K. 3700 JOSEPH SIEWICK DR, STE 302 22033 #041-01-1994 L1998
OBG *071 †30

KELTY, Jenny Lee. 2730 PROSPERITY AVE, STE A 22031 #023-01-1998 L2004 **PDP** *020 †55

KEREKES, Arpad. ■ 22037 #065-01-1976 L1978 *020

KESSLER, Chester Wm. 8301 ARLINGTON BLVD, STE T5 22031 #025-07-1971 L1973
FM *020 †18

KHAN, Adnan Rahman. ■ 22030 #051-04-2008 *012

KHAN, Fareeha I. 2826 OLD LEE HWY, STE 100 22031 #704-02-1987 L1996 **CD** *020 †20

KHAN, Mubarik Ahmad. 3650 JOSEPH SIEWICK DR, STE 205B 22033 #704-21-1994 L1999
IM *020 †20

KHAN, Nassar Farid. 2826 OLD LEE HWY STE 110 22031 #704-02-1985 L1995 **ON** *020 †20

KHAN, Sadia A. 8505 ARLINGTON BLVD, STE 450 22031 #704-09-1989 L2006 **CN** *100

KHANNA, Urmilla. 10515 WEST DR 22030 #495-19-1958 L1975 **PD CHP** *071 †55

KHAPRA, Asma Poonawala. 3700 JOSEPH SIEWICK DR, STE 308 22033 #023-07-2000 L2007
GE IM *020

KHEIRBEK, Tareq. ■ 22033 #875-01-2005 **GS** *012

KHORRAMI, Ali Ahmad. 9452 MAIN ST, MED FIRST URGENT CARE 22031 #118-01-1980 L1997
FM *020 †18

KHOURY, Alfred. 3020 HAMAKER CT STE 501 22031 #605-01-1978 L1987 **MFM OBS** *020 †30
KIERNAN, Joseph Mortimer. 8503 ARLINGTON BLVD, STE 120 22031 #051-04-1982 L1988 **IC CD** *020 †20
KIM, Albert Ho-Sien. 8505 ARLINGTON BLVD, STE 200 22031 #051-04-1994 L1994 **IC CD** *020 †20
KIM, Andrew Yongsuk. 10730 MAIN ST 22030 #035-09-1998 L1999 **AN** *020 †05
KIM, Chul Wha. 10730 MAIN ST, FAIRFAX SURGERY CENTER 22030 #583-01-1967 L1980 **AN** *020 †05
KIM, Chung-Kook. 8301 ARLINGTON BLVD # 510 22031 #583-01-1960 L1981 **OBG** *020
KIM, Gil U. 8316 ARLINGTON BLVD, STE 514 22031 #051-01-1991 L1995 **IM** *020 †20
KIM, Jennifer Megan. ■ 22033 #010-02-2008 *012
KIM, John Jungkyum. 12924 STARTERS LN 22033 #041-13-1999 L2004 **OSM** *020 †40
KIM, Mi Yong. 10400 EATON PL STE 5, NOVA HEALTHCARE 22030 #583-08-1966 L1973 **GYN** *020 †30
KIM, Michael Donhyun. 10801 MAIN ST, STE 700 22030 #051-04-1995 L2002 **FM** *020 †18
KISHI, Roman. 10657 BRADDOCK RD, CHILDRENS MED ASSOC OF 22032 #875-01-1988 L1997 **PD** *020 †55
KITAY, Kaleen. 8503 ARLINGTON BLVD, STE 140 22031 #035-08-1991 L1995 **IM** *020 †20
KLAYTON, Ronald Jay. 12011 LEE JACKSON HWY, PULMONARY MEDICINE DEPT 22033 #035-08-1969 L1981 **IM PUD** *020 †20
KLINE, Timothy Alexander. 3020 HAMAKER CT, FAIRFAX NEONATAL ASSOCIATE 22031 #036-05-1999 L2005 **NPM** *020 †55
KODALI, Lavanya. 3998 FAIR RIDGE DR, STE 320 22033 #495-50-1995 L2004 **AN** *020 †05
KODAMA, Teruaki. 8316 ARLINGTON BLVD # 410 22031 #030-06-1989 L1992 **GS** *020 †85
KOEHLER, Rolf Alfred. 3600 JOSEPH SIEWICK DR 22033 #407-32-1953 L1958 **IM** *071
KOHN, Susan Ellen. 10400 EATON PL, STE 410 #051-04-1984 L1986 **PD ADL** *020 †55
KOLACHANA, Padmaja. 8316 ARLINGTON BLVD, STE 104 22031 #495-11-1992 L1997 **NEP** *020 †20
KOLOLGI, Bina S. 12011 LEE JACKSON MMRL HWY, STE 102 22033 #051-04-1993 L1993 **IM** *020 †20
KOLOLGI, Sunil V. 12011 LEE JACKSON MMRL HWY, STE 102 22033 #496-15-1981 L1988 **GS** *020
KOO, Andrew Lee-Wah. ■ 22032 #051-01-2005 L2005 **P** *012
KOONS, Gregory Mark. 3905 RAILROAD AVE STE 100 22030 #010-02-1973 L1976 **OBG** *020 †30
KORNBLUTH, Ralph Ross. 8303 ARLINGTON BLVD, STE 207 22031 #067-01-1964 L1969 **P** *020
KORTUM, Laurel Diane. 3998 FAIR RIDGE DR 22033 #030-05-2002 L2006 **AN** *020 †05
KORTUM, Robert Leonard. ■ 22033 #030-05-2006 *012
KOSCIUK-ROWE, Teresa Anna. 4211 FAIRFAX CORNR EST AVE, PED PARTNERS OF N VA #225 22030 #048-12-1987 L1990 **PD** *020 †55
KOUYOUMDJIAN, Marc A. 12255 FAIR LAKES PKWY, 4TH FL 22033 #067-01-1991 L2000 **ORS** *020 †40
KRAUSE, Peter Carl. 8503 ARLINGTON BLVD # 200, INOVA OUTPATIENT CENTER 22031 #005-11-1996 L2005 **ORS** *020 †40
KRISHNAMURTHY, Bhanumathy. 9506 LEE HWY B 22031 #495-53-1973 L1998 **CHP** *075 †75
KRISHNAN, Kartik. ■ 22031 #035-01-1999 L2001 **PHO** *100 †55
KRIST, Alexander Headley. 3650 JOSEPH SIEWICK DR, FAIRFAX FAMILY PRACTICE 22033 #051-01-1996 L1996 **FM** *020 †18 ‡
KRISZTINICZ, Thomas I. 12011 LEE JACKSON HWY 22033 #035-20-1985 L1991 **OAR OTR** *020 †40
KULANGARA, Sara. 8503 ARLINGTON BLVD, STE 120 22031 #005-14-1990 L1997 **CD** *020 †20
KULSHRESTHA, Sunita. 3015 WILLIAMS DR, INSTITUTE 22031 #041-01-1994 L1994 **OBG** *020 †30
KURTZKE, Robert Nevin. 3020 HAMAKER CT 22031 #010-02-1985 L1990 **N CN** *020 †75
KWON, Tae-Sung. ■ 22031 #010-01-2007 *012
LACKAMP, Jeanne Marie. ■ 22031 #038-44-2003 L2007 **PYM** *012
LADER, Clifford David. 8505 ARLINGTON BLVD, STE 130 22031 #041-13-1977 L1983 **R** *050 †80
LAGOC, Annemarie Torredes. ■ 22030 #010-03-1996 L2003 **PD** *020 ‡
LANE, Herbert Edward, III. 8501 ARLINGTON BLVD # 400 22031 #010-02-1978 L1983 **ORS** *020 †40
LANGLEY, Roy William. 3650 JOSEPH SIEWICK DR, STE 305 22033 #016-43-1994 L2004 **IM** *020 †20
LAVENSTEIN, Bennett Louis. 8501 ARLINGTON BLVD, 2ND FL 22031 #023-01-1970 L1976 **CHN N** *020 †55,75
LAZARTE, Raul A. 3020 HAMAKER CT, STE 300 22031 #737-03-1974 L1981 **NPM PD** *020 †55
LE, Uyenphuong Ho. ■ 22030 #041-15-2006 L2006 **IM** *012
LEE, Brent R. 3998 FAIR RIDGE DR, STE 320 22033 #043-01-1993 L2002 **AN PHP** *020 †05
LEE, Charles Churlmin. 3998 FAIR RIDGE DR, STE 320 22033 #583-03-1987 L1997 **AN** *020 †05
LEE, Christine Hyunsook. 8501 ARLINGTON BLVD, PROSPERITY PRIMARY CARE 22031 #024-07-2003 L2003 **FM** *020 †18
LEE, Chun Sheng. 8301 ARLINGTON BLVD # 309 22031 #385-01-1967 L1973 **OBG** *020 †30
LEE, Gil Song. ■ 22033 #583-10-1971 L1984 **NS** *071
LEE, Ho Song. 8505 ARLINGTON BLVD, STE 130 22031 #051-04-1993 L2000 **RNR** *020 †80
LEE, Jai Keun. 3600 JOSEPH SIEWICK DR, FAIR OAKS HOSPITAL 22033 #583-03-1973 L1981 **AN** *040 †20
LEE, John Hun. 8505 ARLINGTON BLVD, STE 130 22031 #019-02-2000 L2000 **PDR** *020 †80
LEE, Patty. 8316 ARLINGTON BLVD, OTOLARYNGOLOGY ASSOCIATES 22031 #028-02-1989 L1994 **OTO** *020 †45
LEE, Peter, Jr. 3022 WILLIAMS DR, STE 301 22031 #056-05-1994 L1997 **PG** *020 †55
LEE, Ray Wang. ■ 22033 #051-04-1988 L2002 **EM** *020 †16
LEE, William Matthias. 3600 JOSEPH SIEWICK DR, EMERGENCY DEPT 22033 #030-06-1970 L2000 **EM** *020 †16
LEIDELMEYER, Reinald. ■ 22031 #660-03-1953 L1954 **EM** *071
LEONARD, David Drake. 3911 OLD LEE HWY STE 41C 22030 #051-04-1986 L1988 **FM FPG** *020 †18
LESSELROTH, Lawrence Z. ■ 22030 #035-09-1965 L1973 **CHP P** *050
LEWANDA, Amy Feldman. 8505 ARLINGTON BLVD, STE 100 22031 #035-47-1988 L1994 **PD MG** *020 †19,55
LEWIS, Edward Josiah. 3650 JOSEPH SIEWICK DR, STE 400 22033 #051-01-2004 L2004 **FSM** *012 †18
LEWIS, Kerry Randall. 10560 MAIN ST STE 210 22030 #051-04-1976 L1977 **FM IMG** *020 †18
LIAW, Winston Ronyu. 3650 JOSEPH SIEWICK DR 4TH, MEDICINE RE 22033 #048-04-2006 L2006 **FP** *012
LIBBY, Russell Clark. 3020 HAMAKER CT STE 200 22031 #010-01-1979 L1981 **PD** *020 †55
LIM, Jae Yun. 8501 ARLINGTON BLVD, STE 330 22031 #008-01-1994 L2006 **NS** *020 †25
LIM, Wang Ki. 4310 CANNON RIDGE CT # D 22033 #583-03-1969 L1983 **IM CD** *020

LINCOLN, Stephen Reece. 3015 WILLIAMS DR, STE 202 22031 #004-01-1986 L1999 **REN OBG** *020 †30
LINDE, Debby A. 3913 OLD LEE HWY, STE 31C 22030 #062-01-1992 L1998 **P CHP** *020 †75
LINDSTROM, Cheryl Ann. 8505 ARLINGTON BLVD, STE 130 22031 #056-05-1982 L1992 **DR OS** *020 †80
LINGERFELT, Brian Michael. ■ 22032 #051-04-2006 L2006 **IM** *012
LINK, Kathleen Mary. 3020 HAMAKER CT, STE 502 22031 #016-45-1976 L1979 **PDE** *020 †55
LIPPS, David Chas. 12011 LEE JACKSON HWY 22033 #010-01-1984 L1993 **N IM** *020 †75
LIU, Wei. 8303 ARLINGTON BLVD, STE 203 22031 #243-47-1991 L2002 **IM** *020 †20
LOFTUS, Andrew Wm. 8261 WILLOW OAKS CO DR 22031 #035-19-1981 L2002 **DR** *020 †80
LONCAR, Dragutin. 3020 HAMAKER CT STE 202 22031 #957-01-1980 L2007 **PHO HO** *020 †55
LONG, George Everett. 4033 MURDSTONE CT 22033 #051-04-1973 L1981 **EM** *071 †16
LORICO, Ruth S. 10697 DUDLEY HEIGHTS CT, INOVA FAIR OAKS HOSPITAL 22030 #748-10-1988 L1995 **PD** *020 †55
LOVGREN MORITZ, Arthur St. 3600 JOSEPH SIEWICK DR, FAIRL OAKS HOSPITALIST GRO 22033 #051-04-1990 L1995 **IM** *020 †20
LOWY, Naomi. ■ 22032 #035-09-2002 L2005 **END** *100 †20
MAANAVI, Darya Berta. 8501 ARLINGTON BLVD, GLENNA R ANDERSON MD & 22031 #051-07-1987 L1990 **OBG** *020 †30
MABATID, Heidi Flores. ■ 22033 #748-09-1973 L1979 **GS** *075
MACKIE, Lora Elise. 12255 FAIR LAKES PKWY, INTERNAL MEDICINE 22033 #010-01-1981 L1988 **FM** *020 †18
MACKOW, Robert Carey. 8501 ARLINGTON BLVD # 100 22031 #033-06-1979 L1980 **NEP IM** *020 †20
MADDOX, John Frank, III. 8316 ARLINGTON BLVD # 420 22031 #005-02-1977 L1984 **OBG** *020 †20
MAHADEVAPPA, Hunasikatti. 2826 OLD LEE HWY, STE NO330 22031 #495-72-1975 L1998 **IM PCC** *020 †20
MAHENDIRAN, Gajan Ananda. 3998 FAIR RIDGE DR, STE 320 22033 #305-01-2001 L2005 **AN** *020
MAHONEY, David Lucas. 3700 JOSEPH SIEWICK DR, STE 305 22033 #024-05-1985 L1990 **NEP** *020 †20
MAILLOUX, Benjamin Bruce. 3650 JOSEPH SIEWICK DR, STE 400 22033 #032-01-2005 L2005 **FP** *012
MAINKAR, Tanuja Avinash. 3998 FAIR RIDGE DR, STE 320 22033 #496-38-1986 L2001 **AN PMM** *020
MAJD, Kurosh. 8505 ARLINGTON BLVD, STE 130 22031 #010-01-1996 L2002 **DR** *020 †80
MAKKAWI, Hoda K. 8301 ARLINGTON BLVD STE 10 22031 #915-03-1990 L1998 **FM** *020 †18 ‡
MALEKGHASEMI, Malek M. 10520 JUDICIAL DR 22030 #308-10-1986 L1995 **IM ID** *020 †20
MALIK, Pankaj. 2740 PROSPERITY AVE STE 20 22031 #495-36-1986 L1987 **IM** *020 †20
MANEM, Suneetha. 2826 OLD LEE HWY, STE 330 22031 #495-62-1995 L2004 **IM** *020 †75
MANGALMURTI, Chaitanya S. 12255 FAIR LAKES PKWY, KAISER PERMANENTE 22033 #048-04-1992 L1999 **GS** *020 †85
MANGUIKIAN, Dertad. 9936 MAIN ST 22031 #605-01-1966 L1973 **OPH** *020 †35
MANTLE, Belinda Anne. 8316 ARLINGTON BLVD, STE 300 22031 #001-02-2000 L2007 **OTO PDO** *020 †45 ‡
MARAZZO, Donald Peter. 3015 WILLIAMS DR, GENETICS & IVF INSTITUTE 22031 #010-02-1978 L2004 **OBG END** *050 †19,30
MARKO, Emily Kathleen. 3905 RAILROAD AVE, STE 100 22030 #065-09-1988 L1994 **OBG** *020 †20
MARTIN, Jerry Wayne. 3600 JOSEPH SIEWICK DR 22033 #051-01-1970 L1970 **FM EM** *020 †18
MARTIN, John Oliver. ■ 22030 #010-01-1955 L1956 **GP** *071
MASER, Karen Roberta. 8505 ARLINGTON BLVD, STE 410 22031 #010-01-1994 L1994 **OBG** *020 †30
MASON, Patrick William. 3650 JOSEPH SIEWICK DR, STE 305 22033 #051-04-1993 L2001 **PDE PD** *020 †55
MASOOD, Khairunnisa. 3650 JOSEPH SIEWICK DR, STE 205B 22033 #496-27-1998 L2005 **IM** *100 †20
MATHER, Mary. 3700 JOSEPH SIEWICK DR, STE 403 22033 #023-12-1991 L1992 **D** *020 †15
MATHEWS, John Jos, Jr. 10721 MAIN ST STE 1500 22030 #010-02-1977 L1985 **IM** *020 †20
MATROS, Todd Gregg. 3650 JOSEPH SIEWICK DR, STE 206 22033 #021-01-1998 L1998 **CD** *020 †20
MATTES, Carol Elizabeth. 3998 FAIR RIDGE DR, STE 270 22033 #041-12-2000 L2003 **FM** *020 †18 ‡
MAUSHSHIR, Suhayl. 8501 ARLINGTON BLVD, THE MUASHER CENTER 22031 #605-01-1976 L1983 **OBG** *020 †30
MAYER, Thom Alan. 10306 EATON PL, STE 180 22030 #036-07-1977 L1980 **EM PD** *020 †16
MAZO, Fern Rosalyn. 3020 HAMAKER CT, STE 300 22031 #024-07-1975 L1980 **NPM PD** *020 †55
MC CLINTOCK, Wm Morris. 8501 ARLINGTON BLVD 22031 #051-01-1978 L1988 **CHN P** *020 †55,75
MCCONVILLE, Barry B. 10730 MAIN ST, FAIRFAX SURGICAL CENTER 22030 #021-01-1979 L1989 **AN** *020 †05
MC CORMALLY, Terence J. 3650 JOSEPH SIEWICK DR, FAIRFAX FAMILY PRACTICE 22033 #018-03-1978 L1987 **FM IMG** *020 †18
MC DONALD, David B. 3020 HAMAKER CT STE B100 22031 #016-02-1979 L1982 **IM** *020 †20
MC ELFISH, Karen Roberts. 10657 BRADDOCK RD, CHILDRENS MED ASSOC OF 22032 #005-18-1986 L1989 **PD** *020 †55
MC FARLAND, Sally Ann. 10529 BRADDOCK RD STE B 22032 #051-01-1984 L1993 **IM** *020 †20
MC KENNA, Thomas J. ■ 22031 #041-12-1940 L1941 **OPH** *071 †35
MC MURRER, James P, Jr. 8316 ARLINGTON BLVD, STE 600 22031 #010-02-1967 L1974 **CHP P** *020 †75
MC SWAIN, Robert Lawrence. 8505 ARLINGTON BLVD # 420 22031 #012-01-1996 L1997 **ICE CD** *020 †20
MEDINA, Oswaldo. 9119 GLENBROOK RD, ROUTE 9 22031 #935-07-1967 L2005 **GS** *020 †85
MEHFOUD, David Patrick, Jr. 8505 ARLINGTON BLVD, STE 130 22031 #051-04-1997 L2003 **RNR** *020 †80
MEHRYAR, Gholam Reza. 3650 JOSEPH SIEWICK DR, STE 310 22033 #517-06-1966 L1972 **N** *020 †55
MEHTA, Mala. 12255 FAIR LAKES PKWY, KAISER PERMANENTE 22033 #021-06-1990 L2000 **RHU** *020 †20
MEISTER, Robert Jay. 8503 ARLINGTON BLVD, STE 400 22031 #038-40-1975 L1978 **ON HEM** *020 †20
MELISI, James Wm. 8316 ARLINGTON BLVD, STE 640 22031 #035-08-1986 L1993 **NS SCI** *020 †25
MELLA, Barbara A. 3251 OLD LEE HWY 22030 #051-01-1960 L1960 **N** *071 †75

MENEZES, Geetha Aurelia P. 11150 MAIN ST, STE 501 22030 #495-52-1991 L2001 PTH *020 †50

MENTZ, Cindy. 3650 JOSEPH SIEWICK DR, FAIRFAX FAMILY PRACTICE CE 22033 #010-01-1999 L1999 FM *020

MERKEL, Victoria L. 3650 JOSEPH SIEWICK DR #40, FAIR OAKS PROFESSIONAL BLD 22033 #045-01-1981 L1982 FM *020 †18

MERLINO, Robin Beth. 3020 HAMAKER CT STE B106 22031 #025-01-1980 L1983 IM *020 †20

MEYERS, Steven Andrew. 2722 MERRILEE DR, SUTIE 230 22031 #036-07-1987 L1993 DR *020 †80

MICHEL, Ernest Lee. 3600 JOSEPH SIEWICK DR, FAIR OAKS ANESTHESIA 22033 #035-19-1995 L2005 AN *020

MIHALACHE, Monica Sorina. 3915 OLD LEE HWY, STE 21C 22030 #781-01-2000 L2005 FM *020 †18

MILANI, Kavian Sadeghzade. 9401 LEE HWY, STE 400 22031 #051-01-1995 L1995 FM *020 †18

MILLER, John Alfred. 8503 ARLINGTON BLVD, STE 400 22031 #035-45-1976 L1981 IM ON *071 †20

MILLER, Lawrence Allan. 8503 ARLINGTON BLVD, STE 120 22031 #035-06-1976 L1983 CD IC *020 †20

MILLER, Paul Ira. 8501 ARLINGTON BLVD, PROSPERITY PRIMARY CARE 22031 #023-01-1974 L1979 GE IM *020 †20

MILLER, Richard K. 10777 MAIN ST STE 203 22030 #030-05-1945 L1969 PHP GPM *030

MINSHEW, Philip Tyler. 2722 MERRILEE DR, FAIRFAX RADIOLOGICAL CONSU 22031 #010-01-1999 L1999 RNR *020 †80

MINTZ, Marshall Craig. 8505 ARLINGTON BLVD, STE 130 22031 #035-20-1977 L1988 DR *020 †80

MIRALIAKBARI, Reza. 8501 ARLINGTON BLVD, STE 420 22031 #041-13-1996 L2008 PS *020 †85,65

MIRKHEL, Ahmadshah. 4094 MAJESTIC LN PMB 29, VIRGINIA EMERGENCY MED. AS 22033 #305-01-2003 L2006 IM *100 †20

MIRZA, Farhat Hasan. ■ 22031 #495-45-1994 L2001 IM *100

MITCHELL, Michele M. 3998 FAIR RIDGE DR, STE 280 22033 #025-01-1996 L2007 FM *020 †18

MIZE, James Russell. 11150 MAIN ST, STE 501 22030 #051-01-1999 L1999 PTH *062 †50

MOAZZEZ, Amir Housheng. 3650 JOSEPH SIEWICK DR, STE 309 22033 #016-42-1996 L1996 GS *020 †85

MODAK, Prema. ■ 22031 #033-05-2002 L2006 IM *100 †35

MODAK, Rohit Mukund. ■ 22031 #033-05-2002 L2006 ID *020 †20

MODI, Anjali. ■ 22033 #495-29-2003 L2005 PD *012

MOESER, Thomas Eugene. 12011 LEE JACKSON HWY, 4TH FL 22033 #010-01-1970 L1992 OBG *071 †30

MOGHISSI, Jasmine Wanda. 9401 LEE HWY, STE 400 22031 #051-04-1988 L1989 FM *020 †18

MOON, Young Sun. ■ 22032 #583-08-1950 L1968 PD FM *020 †18

MORTON, Robert Edmund. 8301 ARLINGTON BLVD 22031 #036-07-1968 L1975 GE *020 †20

MOYLE, Henry. 8501 ARLINGTON BLVD, STE 330 22031 #005-14-1995 L2008 NS *020 †25

MUASHER, Lisa Coates. 8501 ARLINGTON BLVD, GLENNA R ANDERSON MD & 22031 #036-08-1995 L1995 OBG *020 †30

MUFTI, Salman. 2722 MERRILEE DR, STE 230 22031 #033-06-1998 L2004 VIR *020 †80

MULLER, Christian Thomas. 8505 ARLINGTON BLVD, STE 130 22031 #035-15-1999 L2004 RNR *020 †80

MULLER, Ryan David. ■ 22031 #045-04-2007 L2007 TY *012

MUNIS, Raiqa. 10803 MAIN ST, STE 800 22030 #704-23-1984 L1997 IM *020 †20

MURATORIO, Jose Luis. 8303 ARLINGTON BLVD # 205 22031 #132-01-1944 L1976 P *071 †75

MURPHY, Bernadette Mary. 3650 JOSEPH SIEWICK DR, DRIVE #101 22033 #033-06-1990 L1993 PD *020 †55

MURPHY, Robert P. 8505 ARLINGTON BLVD, STE 300 22031 #016-06-1969 L1998 OPH *020 †35

MURTHY, Arvind Sreedhara. ■ 22031 #051-04-2008 *012

MUSIO, Franco. 13135 LEE JACKSON MMRL HWY, STE 135 22033 #010-02-1985 L1998 NEP IMG *020 †20

MYAING, Alfred Chit. 8303 ARLINGTON BLVD, STE 106 22031 #209-01-1968 L1980 IM CD *020

MYRIE WILLIAMS, Carmen. 9005 STONELEIGH CT 22031 #035-19-1974 L1989 D DMP *071 †15,50

NA, Kimberly Brown. 3998 FAIR RIDGE DR, STE 320 22033 #018-03-2001 L2005 AN *020 †05

NAAHIELUA, Kimberly Kamak. 3600 JOSEPH SIEWICK DR, FAIR OAKS HOSPITAL,HOSPITA 22033 #550-04-2003 L2005 IM *100 †20

NAGHSH-TABRIZI, Nasrin. 2740 PROSPERITY AVE 22031 #654-01-1986 L1990 IM *020 †20

NAGI, Haramol K. 12255 FAIR LAKES PKWY 22031 #495-03-1989 L1997 ID *020 †20

NAIR, Suja J. 8501 ARLINGTON BLVD, SECOND FLOOR 22031 #422-01-1997 L2005 PDP *020 †55

NAKKA, Kavitha Kishore. 3022 WILLIAMS DR, STE 100 22031 #495-21-1994 L2003 IM *020 †20

NARSETE, Eugene M. ■ 22030 #016-43-1945 L1946 VS PDS *071 †85

NASRULLAH, Sameena Fareed. 8505 ARLINGTON BLVD, STE 130 22031 #028-46-1993 L2002 DR *020 †80

NASSIRY, Akbar Muhammad. ■ 22030 #051-04-2008 *012

NAU, Ernest Virgil. ■ 22031 #048-02-1958 L1958 GP OS *020

NAYER, Hassan. 11150 MAIN ST, STE 501 22030 #517-08-1990 L2004 HMP *100 †50

NAZAM, Samir. 13037 LEE JACKSON HWY # D, CHANTILLY WALK-IN CLINIC 22033 #875-02-1977 L1984 FM *020

NAZZAL, Jenny Jamileh N. 13135 LEE JACKSON MMRL HWY, STE 135 22033 #010-02-1983 L1987 NEP IM *020 †20

NEITHAMER, Calvin D, Jr. 8505 ARLINGTON BLVD, STE 130 22031 #041-12-1977 L1988 VIR DR *020 †80

NELSON, Alan Ray. ■ 22033 #016-06-1958 L1963 IM END *071 †20

NEVIASER, Thomas Jay. 3650 JOSEPH SIEWICK DR, STE 300 22033 #010-01-1966 L1973 ORS OSM *020 †40

NGO, Duc M. ■ 22032 #942-01-1973 L1994 IM *020

NGUYEN, Ben Lam. 8501 ARLINGTON BLVD, STE 330 22031 #024-01-1992 L1999 NS *020 †25 ‡

NGUYEN, Nghi Vinh. 2740 PROSPERITY AVE, FAMILY HEALTH CENTER OF FA 22031 #305-01-2000 L2001 FM *020 †18

NGUYEN, Phong Dong. 12011 LEE JACKSON HWY 22033 #041-13-1992 L1994 IM *020 †20

NICHOLS, Markyia Shanell. 10400 EATON PL, STE 515 22030 #023-01-2001 L2006 OBG *020 †30

NIES, Barbara May. 3020 HAMAKER CT, STE 501 22031 #025-12-1984 L1988 OBG MFM *030

NOEL, Roger A. 8316 ARLINGTON BLVD, STE 234 22031 #010-02-1968 L1969 IM *020 †20

NONAS, Constantine James. 12011 LEE JACKSON HWY, 4TH FL 22033 #024-07-1959 L1982 GS VS *071 †85

NORTH, John Michael. 2730 PROSPERITY AVE STE B 22031 #050-02-1981 L1989 NPM *020 †55

NOTES, David Raymond. 10721 MAIN ST, STE 206 22030 #010-01-1966 L1969 OPH *020 †35

NUKALA, Manjulatha. ■ 22030 #495-58-2003 L2008 IM *100 †20

NUNES, Mark Eugene. 8505 ARLINGTON BLVD, PEDIATRIC SPECIALTY CENTER 22031 #023-12-1989 L2002 MG PD *020 †19,55

NUNEZ, Daniele Mauricette. 3911 OLD LEE HWY # 41C, STE 41C 22030 #396-35-1980 L1997 FM *020 †18 ‡

O'BRIEN, Lynn Murphy. 3650 JOSEPH SIEWICK DR #40, FAIR OAKS PROFESSIONAL BLD 22033 #041-02-1983 L1984 FM *020 †18

O'CONNELL, Robert Stephen. 8505 ARLINGTON BLVD, STE 130 22031 #035-20-1975 L1983 DR *020 †80

OKORIE, Charles I. 12713 SHOPPES LN 22033 #690-04-1986 L1994 IM CCM *020 †20

OLIVERIO, Patrick J. 8505 ARLINGTON BLVD, STE 130 22031 #055-01-1988 L2000 RNR R *020 †18

ONG-VIRTUDES, Julieta. 3998 FAIR RIDGE DR, STE 320 22033 #748-01-1977 L1984 AN *040

ORAHOVAC, Zamira. 3600 JOSEPH SIEWICK DR, FAIR OAKS INOVA HOSP 22033 #957-08-1975 L2003 AN *020

ORHUE, Vbenosa. ■ 22031 #024-07-2007 GS *012

ORLOFF, Gregory Joshua. 8503 ARLINGTON BLVD, HEMATOLOGY/ONCOLOGY, P.C. 22031 #008-01-1986 L1995 ON HEM *020 †20

OSAE-ADDO, Gloria A. 10777 MAIN ST, STE 203 22030 #021-01-1994 L1999 GPM *020

OSBORN, John P. 2730 PROSPERITY AVE, STE A 22031 #035-06-1989 L1996 PDP *020 †55

OTCHY, Daniel Peter. 2710 PROSPERITY AVE, FAIRFAX COLON & RECTAL SUR 22031 #033-05-1980 L2001 CRS GP *020 †10,85

OVERDECK, Daniel Lombard. 8505 ARLINGTON BLVD, STE 130 22031 #028-02-1997 L2004 DR *020 †80

OVERTON, Eugene Willis. 4001 FAIR RIDGE DR, STE 101 22033 #051-01-1971 L1971 FM *020 †80

PAGGI, Stacy A. 3959 PENDER DR, STE 320 22030 #035-15-2001 L2001 CHP *020

PAIK, Haines K.. ■ 22033 #028-46-2006 ORS *012

PAIK, Ji Eun. 2826 OLD LEE HWY, STE 306 22031 #010-02-2001 L2002 OBG *100

PALAZZO, Lisa Maria. 3998 FAIR RIDGE DR, STE 320 22033 #016-02-1986 L1997 AN GS *020 †05

PALUMBO, Elizabeth J. 10527 BRADDOCK RD, THE PEDIATRIC GROUP 22032 #048-04-1996 L1999 PD *020 †20

PARAGUYA, Maria Fe. 9901 BRADDOCK RD, NORTHERN VIRGINIA TRAINING 22032 #748-01-1973 L1987 PD GP *020

PARK, Jonathan J. 10530 ROSEHAVEN ST, STE 111 22030 #041-12-1998 L2000 OS CFS *020

PARK, Juliana Youngmin. 3020 HAMAKER CT STE B103 22031 #038-06-1991 L1996 OPH *020 †35

PARK, Kyung Suk. 2740 PROSPERITY AVE, FAIFAX BEHAVRL HLTH CLC 22031 #583-03-1971 L1988 CHP P *020

PARK, Soo Woong. 10680 MAIN ST STE 130 22030 #583-02-1969 L1975 IM NEP *020 †20

PARTHASARATHY, Srinivason. 11166 FAIRFAX BLVD, STE 202 22030 #048-04-1988 L1999 OSM PM *020 †60

PATEL, Sunil V. 3020 HAMAKER CT, STE B111 22031 #033-05-1998 L2002 U *020 †95

PATEL-DONNELLY, Dipti. 3650 JOSEPH SIEWICK DR, STE 200 22033 #035-47-1996 L2003 HO IM *020 †20

PATNAIK, Bella D. 3020 HAMAKER CT, STE 503 22031 #051-01-1997 L1997 OPH *020 †35

PAYNE, Renee. 8316 ARLINGTON BLVD, STE 600 22031 #308-02-1988 L1996 P *020

PEARL, Phillip Lawrence. 8501 ARLINGTON BLVD, DEPT OF NEUROLOGY, SECOND 22031 #023-01-1984 L1990 CHN N *020 †75,55

PEEREBOOM, Gerrit. 3600 JOSEPH SIEWICK DR 22033 #660-03-1950 L1964 GS *071 †85

PEEREBOOM, Maud Joshua. ■ 22031 #660-03-1951 L1968 AN *071 †05

PERDAHL-WALLACE, Eva B. 8301 ARLINGTON BLVD, STE 209 22031 #858-04-1981 L1992 PHO PD *020 †55

PEREZ, Carol Bezirganian. 8301 ARLINGTON BLVD, STE 505 22031 #035-47-1988 L1993 P *020 †75

PERGOLIZZI, Richard. 8505 ARLINGTON BLVD, STE 130 22031 #038-44-1993 L2001 DR RNR *020 †80

PERRY, Lowell Wesley. 8318 ARLINGTON BLVD, STE 250 22031 #041-13-1960 L1969 PDC *071 †55

PEYTON, Randall Sutton. 3600 JOSEPH SIEWICK DR 22033 #051-04-1989 L1995 OAR OSM *020 †40

PEYTON, Vanessa Billstone. 4001 FAIR RIDGE DR, STE 101 22033 #051-07-1994 L1999 FM *020 †18

PFEFFER, Bruce Wm. 3700 JOSEPH SIEWICK DR, STE 300 22033 #023-01-1967 L1974 PD *020 †55

PFEIFFER, Cynthia W. 3650 JOSEPH SIEWICK DR, STE 400 22033 #051-04-1994 L1994 FM *020 †18

PHAM, Sean. ■ 22031 #051-04-2007 *012

PHILLIPS, Karen Diane. 4001 FAIR RIDGE DR, STE 304 22033 #038-43-1995 L2007 GS *020 †85

PHILLIPS, Robert Leroy, Jr. 3650 JOSEPH SIEWICK DR, FAIRFAX FAMILY PRACTICE 22033 #011-03-1995 L2000 FM *050 †18

PHUNG, David. ■ 22031 #051-01-1988 L1989 DR *020 †80

PIATT, Carol Lynn. 8301 ARLINGTON BLVD, STE 501 22031 #041-09-1981 L1982 D FM *020 †18,15

PICKFORD, Laura T. 4001 FAIR RIDGE DR 22033 #051-01-1995 L1998 OBG *020 †30

PIEN, Edward H. 3015 WILLIAMS DR 22031 #010-02-1981 L1997 DR *020 †80

PIGG-STANY, Alma R. 3905 RAILROAD AVE, STE 100 22030 #020-12-2001 L2005 OBG *020

PIPER, James Blandin. 8503 ARLINGTON BLVD, STE 200 22031 #018-03-1984 L2001 TTS GS *020 †20

PIRACHA, Samia Rashid. 8505 ARLINGTON BLVD, STE 130 22031 #055-01-2000 L2006 DR *100 †80

PLATOFF, Gennady E. ■ 22032 #024-05-1947 L1977 IM RHU *071

POLIN, Richard Sanders. 8318 ARLINGTON BLVD, STE 305 22031 #051-01-1991 L1991 NS *020 †25

PONTZ, Bradford Scott. 8316 ARLINGTON BLVD, NOVAMED ASSOCIATES 22031 #041-13-1995 L1996 IM *020 †20

PORTER, Meredith Lynn. 3650 JOSEPH SIEWICK DR, FAIRFAX FAMILY PRACTICE 22033 #051-04-1996 L1997 FM *020 †18

POTARAZU, Sreedhar V. 3650 JOSEPH SIEWICK DR, STE 102 22033 #010-01-1988 L1995 OPH *020 †35

POTTERTON, Victoria Kathr. ■ 22030 #008-01-2007 *012

POURNARAS, Stephen W, Jr. 3650 JOSEPH SIEWICK DR, STE 300 22033 #051-01-1980 L1984 ORS HS *020 †40

PRAH, Anthony J. 3600 JOSEPH SIEWICK DR, PEDIATRIC DEPARTMENT 22033 #412-01-1996 L2000 **PD** *020 †55

PRAHLAD, Ashok. 12011 LEE JACKSON HWY 22033 #495-33-1975 L1985 **GS** *030 †85

PRASAD, Kamla Kant. 3600 JOSEPH SIEWICK DR, FAIR OAKS ANESTH ASSOC 22033 #008-02-1986 L1994 **AN PME** *020 †05

PREMKUMAR, Ahalya. 3015 WILLIAMS DR STE 200 22031 #495-17-1978 L1989 **DR** *020 †80

PRICE, Susan Laura. 8550 LEE HWY, C/O KAISER PERMANENTE 22031 #048-13-1977 L1984 **P IM** *020 †75

PROCHAZKA, Marta Anna K. ■ 22030 #286-04-1962 L1969 **P** *020

PULERWITZ, Todd Cory. 3650 JOSEPH SIEWICK DR, STE 206 22033 #024-01-1999 L2006 **CD** *020 †20

PUTMAN, Christopher Mark. 8505 ARLINGTON BLVD, STE 130 22031 #023-07-1988 L2001 **RNR** *020 †80

QIU, Qiu. 3600 JOSEPH SIEWICK DR 22033 #243-21-1982 L1997 **IM** *020 †20

RAFI, Esmail. 10195 MAIN ST STE H 22031 #517-01-1957 L1968 **IM CD** *071 ‡

RAJ, Vijay. 2740 PROSPERITY AVE 22031 #495-45-1974 L1983 **GP IM** *020

RAMAKRISHNA, Gautam. 3700 JOSEPH SIEWICK DR, STE 102 22033 #035-47-1997 L2005 **CD** *020 †20

RAMERTH, Teresa Stathas. 11200 WAPLES MILL RD, STE 180 22030 #020-12-1993 L2001 **P PFP** *020 †75

RAMILO, Paul B. 3700 JOSEPH SIEWICK DR, STE 209 22033 #305-01-1999 L2004 **ID** *020 †20

RAMIREZ, Juanita Carmona. 3650 JOSEPH SIEWICK DR, STE 400 22033 #041-15-2004 L2004 **FM** *020 †20

RAMSEY, Ricky Lee. 3998 FAIR RIDGE DR, STE 320 22033 #021-06-1983 L1990 **AN PD** *020 †05

RANARD, Richard Craig. 3020 HAMAKER CT, STE 102 22031 #010-02-1982 L1984 **GE IM** *020 †20

RANDOLPH, Donna Ann. 10529 BRADDOCK RD STE B 22032 #003-01-1986 L1987 **IM** *020 †20

RASHID, Haroon. 8505 ARLINGTON BLVD # 420 22031 #704-01-1988 L1999 **CD ICE** *020 †20

RATTERMAN, Sandra Lynn. 3650 JOSEPH SIEWICK DR, FAIRFAX FAMILY PRACTICE 22033 #038-41-1993 L1994 **FM** *020 †18

RAYBUCK, Bryan D. 3650 JOSEPH SIEWICK DR, STE 206 22033 #041-14-1979 L1988 **CD IM** *020 †85

RECIO, Alfredo Hernandez. 11322 WESTBROOK MILL LN, UNIT 301 22030 #275-01-1952 L1967 **GP** *071

REDLIN, William Lloyd. 8318 ARLINGTON BLVD, STE 200 22031 #025-01-1969 L1975 **DR** *071 †80

REESE, Whitney Elizabeth. 3022 WILLIAMS DR STE 300 22031 #035-01-1990 L1991 **IM** *020 †20

REID, Robert Lawrence. 3650 JOSEPH SIEWICK DR, STE 200 22033 #033-06-1987 L1996 **IM** *020 †20

RENARD, Mary Riley. 3650 JOSEPH SIEWICK DR, STE 400 22033 #010-01-2004 L2004 **FM** *020 †18

RESTA, Lee Philip. 8501 ARLINGTON BLVD, STE 340 22031 #036-07-1999 L2008 **ON HEM** *012 †20

REWARI, Mona. 12255 FAIR LAKES PKWY 22033 #041-07-1996 L2002 **PD** *020 †55

REYNOLDS, Elizabeth Maier. ■ 22030 #030-05-1968 L1985 **CHP P** *020 †75

RHEE, Jonathan Jonghwa. ■ 22030 #010-01-2004 L2004 **GS** *100

RHODES, Glen Robt. 8303 ARLINGTON BLVD, OF NORTHERN VIRGINIA INC 22031 #036-07-1972 L1984 **VS** *020 †85

RICHARD, Robert. 3020 HAMAKER CT STE 400, NEUROLOGY CENTER OF FAIRFA 22031 #024-07-1991 L1996 **N** *020 †75

RIEDY, Karen Sue. 8505 ARLINGTON BLVD, STE 130 22031 #019-02-1985 L1991 **DR** *020 †80

RIETH, Kenneth Gerard. 8505 ARLINGTON BLVD, STE 130 22031 #028-34-1973 L1978 **RNR** *020 †80

RIGSBY, Christopher Mark. 8505 ARLINGTON BLVD, STE 130 22031 #035-06-1980 L1987 **DR** *020 †80

RIVES, James Vell. 8316 ARLINGTON BLVD # 600 22031 #001-02-1995 L1999 **P** *020 †75

RIZWAN, Sofia. 8550 LEE HWY 22031 #704-16-1990 L2005 **P** *020 †75

RIZZO, Patricia Conrad. 8501 ARLINGTON BLVD, STE 340 22031 #010-02-1990 L1992 **HO** *012 †20

ROBBINS, Peter Howard. 3959 PENDER DR STE 320 22030 #035-01-1982 L1987 **CHP P** *020 †75

ROBERT, Nicholas James. 8503 ARLINGTON BLVD, STE 400 22031 #067-01-1974 L1991 **ON HEM** *020 †20,50

ROBERTS, Teresa Lee. ■ 22033 #010-01-2003 L2007 **AN** *020

ROBINSON, Damon Frank. 3031 JAVIER RD, STE 100 22031 #010-01-2001 L2007 **PMM** *012

ROCHMIS, Ann. 3027 JAVIER RD 22031 #041-13-1965 L1970 **P** *020

ROCHMIS, Paul Gregor. 3027 JAVIER RD, STE 2 22031 #035-46-1964 L1970 **RHU OS** *020 †20

ROGACZ, Suzanne. 3020 HAMAKER CT, STE 502 22031 #036-01-1980 L1983 **END IM** *020 †20

ROLL, William E, Jr. 3650 JOSEPH SIEWICK DR, STE 309 22033 #010-01-1960 L1968 **GS** *071 †85

ROMANO, Michele Alana. 3998 FAIR RIDGE DR 22033 #051-04-1984 L1985 **FM** *020 †18

ROMERO-GUTIERREZ, Maritza. 3600 JOSEPH SIEWICK DR, FAIR OAKS HOSPITAL PATHOLO 22033 #270-01-1988 L2004 **PTH** *020 †50

ROMNESS, Mark Jos. 8501 ARLINGTON BLVD, STE 400 22031 #016-06-1987 L2001 **OP ORS** *020 †40

ROSENBLATT, Cheryl C. 3700 JOSEPH SIEWICK DR, STE 101 22033 #035-06-1969 L1987 **AI PD** *055,03

ROSS, Peter Stephen. 3650 JOSEPH SIEWICK DR, STE 305 22033 #024-01-1973 L1976 **END DIA** *020 †20

ROY, Camille Asseo. 3650 JOSEPH SIEWICK DR, FAIRFAX FAMILY PRACTICE 22033 #067-02-1997 L1997 **FM** *020 †18

RUFF, John Cullen. 8505 ARLINGTON BLVD, STE 130 22031 #036-01-1992 L1999 **DR** *020 †80

RUSTGI, Vinod Kumar. 8316 ARLINGTON BLVD, STE 515 22031 #023-07-1979 L1981 **GE** *020 †20

RUTLAND, Costanza Dieceka. 3921 POPLAR CREEK CT 22033 #010-03-2002 L2006 **OBG** *020

RYAN, Mary C. 10777 MAIN ST, STE 203 22030 #035-19-1963 L1969 **PD PHP** *020 †55

SAAVEDRA-DELGADO, Ana M. 8318 ARLINGTON BLVD, ALLERGY CLINIC STE 308 22031 #042-01-1975 L1996 **A AI** *020 †20,03

SACHDEVA, Shabnam. 10560 MAIN ST, STE 409 22030 #496-07-1990 L2001 **FM** *020 †18

SADR, Manijeh. 3650 JOSEPH SIEWICK DR, FAIRFAX PED ASSOC PC 22033 #917-28-1961 L1979 **PD** *020 †55

SAFFAN, David Sol. 12011 LEE JACKSON MMRL HWY, STE 302 22033 #012-01-1978 L1982 **REN GYN** *020 †30

SAFKO, Anne M. 8503 ARLINGTON BLVD # 120 22031 #010-02-1981 L1983 **CD IM** *020 †20

SAKSENA, Devendra Swarup. 3541 CHAIN BRIDGE RD # 6A 22030 #495-19-1960 **TS IM** *100 †85,90

SAKSENA, Shubhra. 4001 FAIR RIDGE DR, STE 101 22033 #036-05-1999 L2002 **FM** *020 †18

SALAM, Abdus. 11150 MAIN ST, STE 501 22030 #160-02-1983 L2005 **PTH** *100

SALAMOUN, Walid Alex. ■ 22030 #605-01-1976 L1990 **GS** *020

SALL, Richard Kenneth. 3700 JOSEPH SIEWICK DR, STE 209 22033 #024-05-1983 L1986 **ID IM** *020 †20

SALLOUT, Hisham Ibrahim. 1338 FIELDLARK CT 22033 #797-03-1987 L1997 **GE** *020 †20

SALMON, Chevonne Tenille. 3650 JOSEPH SIEWICK DR, STE 400 22033 #051-01-2005 L2005 **FP** *012

SAMI ZAKHARI, Iman R. 8501 ARLINGTON BLVD, STE 200 22031 #848-01-1979 L1990 **PD PDP** *020 †55

SANDERS, Enoch Marvin, Jr. 4001 FAIR RIDGE DR, VIRGINIA SURGERY ASSOCIATE 22033 #041-15-2001 L2007 **GS** *020

SANDHIR, Ajai K. ■ 22033 #495-08-1986 L1991 **IM OM** *020

SANKARAN, Kumaresan. 8301 ARLINGTON BLVD # 310 22031 #495-42-1978 L1998 **IM** *020 †20

SANTORO, Jennifer Mattucc. 8301 ARLINGTON BLVD, STE 505 22031 #035-45-2001 L2005 **P** *020 †75

SANTOS-ILAGAN, Emelina R. 11200 WAPLES MILL RD, MEIER CLINICS FAIRFAX 22030 #748-02-1979 L1992 **P** *020

SARMA, Amitabha. 3650 JOSEPH SIEWICK DR, STE 200 22033 #048-04-1998 L2005 **ON HEM** *020 †20

SARNES, Martin Howard. 8301 ARLINGTON BLVD, STE 509 22031 #165-04-1971 L1976 **CHP P** *020 †75

SATOURI, Raja'A. 10777 MAIN ST, STE 203 22030 #065-10-1997 L1999 **FM PHP** *030 †18

SAVOCA, Paul Eugene. 2710 PROSPERITY AVE, FAIRFAX COLON&RECTAL SURGI 22031 #035-08-1985 L1993 **CRS GS** *020 †85,10

SCHECHTERMAN, Steven Neil. 12255 FAIR LAKES PKWY, FAIR OAKS MEDICAL CENTER 22033 #051-01-1999 L1999 **ON** *100 †20

SCHEROKMAN, Barbara J. 12011 LEE JACKSON MMRL HWY, KAISER PERMANENTE NEURO 22033 #012-01-1975 L1993 **N IM** *020 †75

SCHMELING, John Wm. 4315 CHAIN BRIDGE RD 22030 #010-02-1985 L1988 **IM EM** *020 †20

SCHNEIDER, Ingrid Kvam. 8505 ARLINGTON BLVD, STE 130 22031 #051-04-1993 L1994 **DR** *020 †80

SCHORIN, Marshall Allen. 8505 ARLINGTON BLVD, STE 100 22031 #041-01-1975 L2007 **PHO PD** *020 †55

SCHRATZ, Lorraine M. 8501 ARLINGTON BLVD 22031 #035-03-1989 L1995 **PDC** *071 †55

SCHUFFLER, Carol Susan. 8301 ARLINGTON BLVD, STE 308 22031 #007-02-1978 L1985 **GE IM** *020 †20

SCHULMAN, Joseph Danl. 3015 WILLIAMS DR, INSTITUTE 22031 #024-01-1966 L1984 **OS** *071 †55,19,30

SCHUMANN, Harry Arie. 10721 MAIN ST, STE 1500 22030 #056-06-1975 L1978 **IM** *020 †20

SCHUPP, Daniela Janet. ■ 22030 #409-10-2003 L2005 **GS** *012

SCHWARTZBACH, Cary C. 8503 ARLINGTON BLVD, STE 200 22031 #035-01-1984 L1989 **ORS** *020 †10

SCOTT, Kevin Robt. 3700 JOSEPH SIEWCK DR #400, EYE PLASTIC ASSOCIATES PC 22033 #051-04-1985 L1991 **OPH PS** *020 †35

SEESTEDT, Richard C, Jr. 3020 HAMAKER CT 22031 #041-02-1993 L1999 **N IM** *020 †75

SEGALL, Errol Alan. 8316 ARLINGTON BLVD, STE 600 22031 #056-05-1975 L1979 **P ADM** *020 †75

SELVAGGI, Nina. 3022 WILLIAMS DR, STE 300 22031 #067-01-1970 L1988 **IM END** *020 †20

SEMENDY, Valeri Purnell. ■ 22031 #495-63-1970 L1980 **FM** *020 †18

SENNESH, Joel David. 11150 MAIN ST, STE 501 22030 #041-09-1978 L1982 **PTH ATP** *020 †50

SERVIDEO, Joseph Gerard. 3600 JOSEPH SIEWICK DR 22033 #041-14-1974 L1975 **EM FM** *020 †18,16

SETHI, Hercharan Kaur. 3700 JOSEPH SIEWICK DR, STE 207 22033 #495-29-1967 L1983 **OBG** *020 †30

SHAH, Soloman. 3700 JOSEPH SIEWICK DR, STE 401 22033 #051-07-1993 L1999 **GE** *020 †20

SHAOOL, Nomi. ■ 22032 #047-07-1997 L1999 **EM** *020

SHAPIRO, Alan David. 3600 JOSEPH SIEWICK DR, DEPT OF ANESTHESIOLOGY 22033 #024-05-1986 L1990 **AN** *020 †05

SHARMA, Gopesh Kumar. 8303 ARLINGTON BLVD, STE 203 22031 #495-18-1971 L1979 **OTO FPS** *020 †45

SHARRETT, Carol Sampson. 10777 MAIN ST STE 203, HLTH DIRECTOR 22030 #051-04-1968 L1968 **PHP** *030

SHAVER, Timothy R. 4001 FAIR RIDGE DR, STE 304 22033 #047-06-1982 L1993 **GS AS** *020 †85 ‡

SHEPHERD-BENIGAN, Daniel. 3650 JOSEPH SIEWICK DR 4TH, MEDICINE RE 22033 #011-02-2006 L2006 **FP** *012

SHERBER, Harvey S. 3650 JOSEPH SIEWICK DR, STE 206 22033 #024-07-1969 L1977 **CD IM** *020 †20

SHERER, Michael Abraham. 9901 BRADDOCK RD 22032 #024-05-1979 L1982 **P N** *020 †75

SHIH, Marianne Tienju. 8505 ARLINGTON BLVD, STE 130 22031 #028-02-2000 L2006 **DR** *020 †80

SHIN, Hyunki. 2826 OLD LEE HWY, STE 306 22031 #048-15-1991 L1997 **OBG** *020 †30

SHIRALI, Swati Sudheer. 12255 FAIR LAKES PKWY, DEPT. OF ORTHOPAEDICS4TH F 22033 #038-44-1990 L1999 **HS** *020 †40

SHMORHUN, Eugene Andrew. 3027 JAVIER RD 22031 #023-01-1982 L1988 **FM** *020 †18

SIDDIQI, Humaira Adeeb. ■ 22032 #704-26-1998 **P** *012

SIGMUND, Linda S. 3020 HAMAKER CT 22031 #010-02-1981 L1988 **N** *020 †75

SILAS, Glen Howard. 8316 ARLINGTON BLVD, STE 420 22031 #016-42-1997 L1997 **OBG** *020 †30

SILK, Alan Edward. 2730 PROSPERITY AVE STE B, FAIRFAX NEONATAL ASSOCIATE 22031 #033-05-1982 L1987 **NPM PD** *020 †55

SILVERI, Christopher P. 3650 JOSEPH SIEWICK DR, STE 300 22033 #041-01-1989 L1996 **ORS OSS** *020 †40

SILVERMAN, Robert Alan. 8316 ARLINGTON BLVD, STE 524 22031 #051-01-1977 L1987 **D** *020 †55,15

SIM, Yvonne Seekay. 8505 ARLINGTON BLVD, STE 130 22031 #035-20-1997 L1999 **DR** *020 †80

SINGER, Jerald Gary. 12255 FAIR LAKES PKWY 22033 #010-01-1990 L1996 **OBG** *020 †30

SINGH, Baikunth Kumar. 10721 MAIN ST 22030 #495-19-1961 L1971 **CD IM** *020 †20

SINGH, Balbir. 10721 MAIN ST, STE 3200 22030 #053-03-1981 L1991 **CD** *020 †20

SINGH, Sadhna N. 4001 FAIR RIDGE DR, STE 303 22033 #496-07-1982 L1993 **OBG** *020 †30

SINGH, Surjit K. 10560 MAIN ST, STE 215 22030 #496-07-1967 L1986 **IM** *020

SIRAK, Tseday Eyasu. 8505 ARLINGTON BLVD, STE 350 22031 #550-04-2002 L2007 **CD** *012 †20

SKLAR, Eric Bruce. 8505 ARLINGTON BLVD, STE 450 22031 #041-13-1998 L2003 **N VN** *020 †75

SLACK, James Walter. 12255 FAIR LAKES PKWY, FAIR OAKS CENTER 22033
#041-01-1984 L2000 **OPH** *020 †35

SMELTZER, Emily Rebecca. ■ 22032 #051-04-2008 *012

SMITH, Asha Patton. 8550 LEE HWY, 5TH FL 22031 #051-07-2001 L2002 **CHP** *020 †75

SMITH, Douglas Gregory. 3600 JOSEPH SIEWICK DR, DEPT OF EMGY MED 22033
#051-07-1998 L2001 **EM** *020 †16

SMITH, Jack Wayne. ■ 22031 #051-01-1978 L1981 **MDM FM** *030 †18

SMITH, Joseph M. 8503 ARLINGTON BLVD, ARRHYTHMIA INSTITUTE 22031
#024-01-1987 L2000 **CD ICE** *020 †20

SNYDER, Roger Alan. 8316 ARLINGTON BLVD, STE 602 22031 #041-01-1965 L1974
N OPH *020 †75

SOBHANI, Siavash C. 3700 JOSEPH SIEWICK DR, STE 402 22033 #010-02-1990 L1994 **IM** *020

SOKOYA, Olufunmilola M. 3020 HAMAKER CT STE 300 22031 #690-01-1990 L1993
NPM PD *020 †55

SOLTANY, Mark. 8316 ARLINGTON BLVD, STE 300 22031 #051-07-1987 L1991 **GS** *020 †45

SOLTANY, Ray A. 10721 MAIN ST 22030 #517-01-1951 L1962 **OTO** *071 †45

SONI, Depak. 3650 JOSEPH SIEWICK DR, STE 307 22033 #012-01-1984 L1991
PUD CCM *020 †20

SONI, Marsha Diane. 3700 JOSEPH SIEWICK DR, STE 209 22033 #012-01-1984 L1991
ID *020 †20

SOTO, Theresa Hickey. 3020 HAMAKER CT STE B105 #035-06-1992 L1999
OBG *020 †30

SPINOSA, David Jos. 8505 ARLINGTON BLVD, STE 130 22031 #024-07-1984 L1988
DR *020 †80

SPIRA, Alexander Illya. 8503 ARLINGTON BLVD, STE 400 22031 #035-19-1997 L2003
ON *020 †20

SPURR, Stephen Geo. 3600 JOSEPH SIEWICK DR, FAIR OAKS HOSP 22033
#919-05-1979 L1988 **NPM PD** *020 †55

SRABSTEIN, Jorge Carlos. 8501 ARLINGTON BLVD 22031 #132-01-1966 L1988
CHP *020 †55,75

STAGE, Thomas B. 12011 GOVERNMENT CNTR PKWY, FAIRFAX-FALLS CHURCH 22035
#038-40-1974 L1974 **P OS** *030 †75

STANTON, Larry Wayne. 2722 MERRILEE DR, STE 230 22031 #017-20-1959 L1961 **R** *071 †80

STASHOWER, Mitchell E. 3700 JOSEPH SIEWICK DR, STE 404 22033 #010-02-1992 L1993
D *020 †15

STERN, Eric. 3554 CHAIN BRIDGE RD, STE 302 22030 #010-01-1969 L1975 **OBG** *020 †30

STERN, Harvey Jay. 3015 WILLIAMS DR, INSTITUTE 22031 #035-46-1982 L1989
MG PD *020 †55,19

STERN, Lawrence Edward. 2710 PROSPERITY AVE, STE 200 22031 #051-01-1996 L2004
CRS GS *020 †85,10

STEVENSON, Fern L Davis. 3600 JOSEPH SIEWICK DR 22033 #065-06-1945 L1973 **IM** *071

STEWART, Donald F, Jr. 4080 CHAIN BRIDGE RD, FAIRFAX CO OCCUPATIONAL HE 22030
#019-02-1980 L1991 **AM EM** *020 †70

STONE, Amy Renee. 3020 HAMAKER CT 22031 #011-03-1995 L1995 **N** *020 †75

STONE, Deborah Lynn. 3600 JOSEPH SIEWICK DR, DEPARTMENT OF PEDIATRICS 22033
#011-03-1991 L1997 **PD CG** *020 †19,55

STROUSE, David Abraham. 3020 HAMAKER CT STE 401, 3020 HAMAKER CT 401 22031
#023-01-1995 L2002 **ICE** *020 †20

SUAREZ, Alfred. 8316 ARLINGTON BLVD 22031 #869-04-1957 L1963 **OPH** *020 †35

SUATENGCO, Domingo E. 3700 JOSEPH SIEWICK DR, STE 206 22033 #748-01-1978 L1987
U GS *020 †95

SUES, Anjali Mittra. 8501 ARLINGTON BLVD, PROSPERITY PRIMARY CARE 22031
#036-01-1992 L2005 **FM** *020 †18

SUGHRUE, Maura Jean. 3650 JOSEPH SIEWICK DR, FAIRFAX FAMILY PRACTICE 22033
#023-01-1979 L1983 **FM** *020 †18

SUH, Hwi-Yol. 8550 LEE HWY, 2 22031 #583-02-1961 L1988 **P** *071 †75

SUH, James. 2826 OLD LEE HWY, SUTIE 250 22031 #051-01-1988 L1990 **IM** *020 †20

SUH, Yongsook. 8503 ARLINGTON BLVD # 130, VICTORIA PLASTIC SURG CTR 22031
#035-09-1990 L1998 **PS** *020 †65

SUTINGCO, Alexander-Nichol. ■ 22032 #010-01-2001 L2005 **EM** *020 †16

SWOBODA, Ishild Johanna. 3612 DORADO CT 22031 #407-33-1963 L1969 **PD** *030 †55

SZUHAY, Gabor. 8501 ARLINGTON BLVD, CHILDRENS OUTPATIENT CENTE 22031
#067-01-1996 L2006 **CHN** *020 †75

TAJICK, Alireza Ghaemieh. ■ 22031 #305-01-2002 L2005 **IM** *020 †20

TAKAGI, Yasuaki. 8636 ARLINGTON BLVD 22031 #572-13-1957 L1965 **PD** *020

TANENBAUM, Mark Paul. 3700 JOSEPH SIEWICK DR, STE 102 22033 #010-02-1986 L1988
CD IM *020 †20

TARSIN, Mahmoud Saad. ■ 22033 #915-02-1969 L2005 **OS U** *100

TASHMAN, Hunter Scott. 3700 JOSEPH SIEWICK DR, STE 201 22033 #035-08-1980 L1983
OBG *020 †30

TERMINI, John Edward. 3600 JOSEPH SIEWICK DR 22033 #010-02-1962 L1971
IM PUD *071 †20

TESCHER, Todd Brian. 8316 ARLINGTON BLVD # 514 22031 #016-42-1992 L1998 **U** *020 †95

TESFAZION, Isaias. 12255 FAIR LAKES PKWY, FAIR OAKS MED CENTER 22031
#366-01-1980 L1992 **ON** *020

TESSITORE, Andrew. ■ 22031 #010-02-1945 L1951 **FM** *071 †18

THEISS, Mark Monroe. 8316 ARLINGTON BLVD, STE 414 22031 #010-02-1975 L1984
ORS OSM *020 †40

THIBODEAUX, Brent C. 3600 JOSEPH SIEWICK DR 22033 #021-06-1995 L1995 **PD** *020 †55

THIEL, James Michael. 3225 GALLOWS RD, RM FP089 22037 #035-20-1979 L1981
IM OM *030 †20,70

THOMAS, Sonia C.. 11204 WAPLES MILL RD, INOVA KELLAR CENTER 22030
#496-15-1995 L2005 **CHP** *020

TILDON, Toni Ola. 3020 HAMAKER CT STE 200, VIRGINIA PEDIATRIC GROUP L 22031
#051-04-2000 L2003 **PD** *020 †55

TINTLE, Scott Matthew. ■ 22033 #023-12-2006 L2008 **ORS** *012

TIRMIZI, Syed Mohamed N. ■ 22033 #495-77-1977 L1985 **IM** *020 †20

TISSERA, Jose Saul. 8301 ARLINGTON BLVD, STE 305 22031 #132-09-1968 L1972
OBG *020 †30

TO, Vivien Ngahtse. 3650 JOSEPH SIEWICK DR, STE 400 22033 #038-40-2005 L2005 **FP** *012

TOPIWALA, Vatsala N. 2740 PROSPERITY AVE, FAMILY HEALTH CTR OF FAIRF 22031
#495-89-1974 L1991 **FM** *020 †18

TORRES, Jomari Sheila. ■ 22033 #056-06-1998 L2006 **PD** *020 †55

TRACHMAN, Susan B. 8301 ARLINGTON BLVD # 505 22031 #048-14-1986 L1988 **P** *020 †75

TRAN, Doan. 8303 ARLINGTON BLVD # 107 22031 #941-01-1966 L1980 **OS** *071

TRIBBLE, Linda Gay. 3020 HAMAKER CT, STE 300 22031 #001-02-1988 L1995
NPM PD *020 †55

TRIPP, Jennifer Alison. ■ 22033 #051-01-2008 *012

TRIVEDI, Ketan Kirit. 3700 JOSEPH SIEWICK DR, STE 102 22033 #036-01-1995 L1997
CD *020 †20

TSUN, Michael N. 3600 JOSEPH SIEWICK DR 22033 #010-02-1979 L1982 **IM PUD** *020 †20

TU, Ho Chung. 3913 OLD LEE HWY STE 31B 22031 #941-02-1971 L1991 **NPM PD** *020

TURNER, James Witcher, Jr. 3600 JOSEPH SIEWICK DR 22033 #036-07-1964 L1971
IM HO *020 †20

TWIBLE, Dana Arnold. 8505 ARLINGTON BLVD, STE 130 22031 #051-01-1978 L2006 **R** *020 †80

TYROLER, Jay Cary. 3650 JOSEPH SIEWICK DR, STE 204 22033 #051-04-1985 L1993
IM *020 †20

UNDERWOOD, Reed Stockton. 3998 FAIR RIDGE DR, STE 320 22033 #051-04-1986 L1997
AN *05

URBAN, Bruce Andrew. 8505 ARLINGTON BLVD, STE 130 22031 #056-05-1988 L2000
DR *020 †20

USCINSKI, Ronald H. 8505 ARLINGTON BLVD 22031 #010-02-1968 L1983 **NS** *020 †25

UY-LEE, Corazon. 8301 ARLINGTON BLVD # 401 22031 #748-01-1965 L2000 **PD PDA** *020 †55

VALENTINE, Allison Marie. ■ 22033 #036-01-2007 L2007 *012

VALLONE, Eric Santo. 3911 OLD LEE HWY STE 41C, FAIRFAX 22030 #010-02-1997 L1997
IM *020 †20

VAN KIRK, Robert John, Jr. ■ 22030 #038-43-2002 L2007 **PCP** *020 †50

VARANELLI, Michael John. 2722 MERRILEE DR STE 230, FAIRFAX RADIO CNSLTS PC 22031
#041-12-1996 L1996 **DR AR** *020 †80

VARBLOW, Karin Forman. 10400 EATON PL STE 410, CAPITAL AREA PEDIATRICS 22030
#010-01-1998 L1998 **PD** *020 †55

VARMA, Jay D. 8505 ARLINGTON BLVD, STE 130 22031 #023-01-1996 L2003 **DR VIR** *020 †80

VARMA, Supriya. 10400 EATON PL, STE 510 22030 #496-07-1989 L1998 **OBG** *020 †30

VELCHIK, Michael Geo. 8505 ARLINGTON BLVD, STE 130 22031 #035-08-1977 L1990
NM DR *020 †80,28

VILASI, Vincent John. 3998 FAIR RIDGE DR, STE 320 22033 #036-07-1986 L1992
AN IM *020,05

VILLANUEVA, Pedro. 8303 ARLINGTON BLVD, STE 206 22031 #451-01-1984 L1993 **IM** *020 †20

VINAYEK, Rakesh. 4001 FAIR RIDGE DR STE 205 22033 #495-36-1974 L1987 **GE IM** *050 †20

VINH, Luc. ■ 22030 #396-04-1960 L1978 **FM** *071 †18

VITEK, Brantley Paul. 8501 ARLINGTON BLVD, STE 400 22031 #023-01-1961 L1968
ORS *020 †40

VITEK, Brantley Paul, Jr. 8501 ARLINGTON BLVD, STE 400 22031 #051-04-1990 L1993
ORS *020 †40

VOLBERG, Frank M, Jr. 8505 ARLINGTON BLVD, STE 130 22031 #036-07-1969 L1990
PDR *062 †80

VON FRICKEN, Manfred A. 8505 ARLINGTON BLVD, STE 300 22031 #028-02-1975 L1980
OS OPH *020 †35

VU, Khoi The. 12255 FAIR LAKES PKWY, KAISER FAIR OAKS 22033 #035-46-1976 L1981
OBG *020 †30

WAHBA, Leina Mamdouh. 8301 ARLINGTON BLVD, STE 206 22031 #915-04-1996 L1997
PD *020 †55

WALLIS, Denise Desiree. 3650 JOSEPH SIEWICK DR, STE 400 22033 #308-05-1998 L2005
P *100

WALTER, Barry Frederick. 4001 FAIR RIDGE DR, STE 304 22033 #012-01-1991 L1991
GS *020 †85

WARD, Kendria V. ■ 22030 #035-15-2003 L2003 **PD** *100

WEAVER, Elizabeth Mary. 4001 FAIR RIDGE DR, STE 101 22033 #023-01-1999 L2002
FM *020 †18

WEBSTER, Ella Mae. 12011 LEE JACKSON HWY, FAIR OAKS MEDICAL CENTER 22033
#011-03-1980 L1997 **IM** *020 †20

WEICHOLD, Katrin C. 8505 ARLINGTON BLVD, STE 410 22031 #913-89-1986 L1998
OBG *020 †30

WEIL, Marcie Karen. 8301 ARLINGTON BLVD, STE 209 22031 #024-05-1988 L1994
PHO *020 †55

WEINROTH, Stephen Edward. 10721 MAIN ST, STE 3400 22030 #010-01-1989 L1990
ID IM *020 †20

WEINSHANK, Herbert S. 10721 MAIN ST, STE 2300 22030 #165-02-1958 L1961 **P PYA** *020

WEINSTEIN, Samuel. 3020 HAMAKER CT STE 200 22031 #035-01-1969 L1987
PD CHP *020 †55

WEINTRAUB, Lauren Amy. 8505 ARLINGTON BLVD, STE 100 22031 #041-12-2001 L2008
PN *100 †55

WENDEL, George Erwin. ■ 22030 #016-06-1944 L1947 **IM** *071

WERNESS, Bruce Anthony. 3600 JOSEPH SIEWICK DR, INOVA FAIR OAKS HOSPITAL 22033
#007-02-1984 L1993 **PTH** *062 †50

WERTHEIM, Ray Allen. 4001 FAIR RIDGE DR 22033 #036-01-1976 L1982 **OBG GYN** *020 †30 ‡

WHIPPLE, George Albert. 3650 JOSEPH SIEWICK DR, GEORGE A WHIPPLE MD LTD 22033
#035-45-1957 L1964 **PS** *072 †65

WHITTENBERG, Beverly A. 3031 JAVIER RD, STE 100 22031 #041-15-2001 L2006 **PM** *100 †60

WILKENFELD, Morris Jack. 3022 WILLIAMS ST, STE 100 22031 #010-01-1973 L1979
RHU *020 †20

WILKINSON, Mary Judith. 8501 ARLINGTON BLVD # 340, OF NO. VA LTD. 22031
#005-11-1983 L1991 **ON HEM** *020 †20

WILLIAMS, Raenell Cristal. 3998 FAIR RIDGE DR 22033 #036-05-2003 L2003 **FM** *020 †18

WISH, Marc. 3020 HAMAKER CT STE 401 22031 #024-05-1979 L1982 **ICE CD** *020 †20

WISOTSKY, Jennifer Stepha. ■ 22032 #035-19-2005 L2007 **AN** *012

WOESSNER, Sarah Elizabeth. 3650 JOSEPH SIEWICK DR, STE 400 22033 #023-01-2004 L2004
FM *020 †18

WOLF, Kathy Eileen. 10680 MAIN ST, STE 190 22030 #010-02-1993 L1993 **OBG** *020 †30

WOLFE, Pierre Patrick. 12011 LEE JACKSON HWY 22033 #051-04-1973 L1974
PUD CCM *020 †20

WONG, Randall Vernon. 3025 HAMAKER CT, STE 101 22031 #041-02-1988 L2002 **OPH** *020 †35

WOODRING, Phyllis Mcgee. 8316 ARLINGTON BLVD, STE 515 22031 #036-01-1984 L1991
AN *020 †05

WOODSIDE, Jack R. ■ 22031 #041-02-1949 L1951 **AN LM** *071 †05

WOOLF, Steven Herbert. 3650 JOSEPH SIEWICK DR, FAIRFAX FAMILY PRACTICE 22033
#012-05-1984 L1993 **FM PHP** *050 †70,18

WROBEL, Jerzy W. 12011 LEE JACKSON HWY 22033 #759-07-1963 L1986 **CD IM** *020 †20

WU, Jane Jiachiann. 3650 JOSEPH SIEWICK DR, STE 307 22033 #041-07-1992 L2000
PCC *020 †20

WU-CHEN, Mei-Ling A. 8622 LEE HWY STE D 22031 #244-01-1972 L1976 **PD** *020 †55

WYNN, Alancia Christine. 8316 ARLINGTON BLVD, STE 234 22031 #048-04-1993 L1996
FM *020 †18

WYRE, Harry W., Jr. 3700 JOSEPH SIEWICK DR, STE 404 22033 #004-01-1970 L1985 D DMP *020 †15

YAKUB, Y Nabil. 3700 JOSEPH SIEWICK DR, STE 305 22033 #605-01-1968 L1980 NEP IM *020 †20

YANG, Debbie. ■ 22031 #051-04-2006 PD *012

YANG, Ling. 3601 CHAIN BRIDGE RD STE D 22030 #243-47-1989 L1999 FM *020 †18

YAO, Luke L. 8505 ARLINGTON BLVD, STE 130 22031 #051-01-2001 L2002 DR *100 †80

YAO, Lynne Pei-Lan. 8505 ARLINGTON BLVD, STE 100 22031 #010-01-1989 L2000 PN PD *020 †55

YARBORO, Timothy Everett. 3700 JOSEPH SIEWICK DR, STE 401 22033 #041-07-1980 L1982 FM *020 †18

YAUN, Amanda L. 8501 ARLINGTON BLVD, STE 200 22031 #021-01-1997 L2006 NS *020

YAZDANI, Ataollah. 2740 PROSPERITY AVE, FAMILY HEALTH CTR OF FAIRF 22031 #517-07-1971 L1989 PD *020

YAZDANINAJAFABADI, Kambiz. 8505 ARLINGTON BLVD, STE 350 22031 #693-01-1996 L2004 CD *100 †20

YOHANNES, Mulai Teklu. 8301 ARLINGTON BLVD, T5 22031 #366-01-1990 L1999 CCM *020 †20

YOHO, David Scott. 10721 MAIN ST, STE 3400 22030 #038-40-1991 L1992 ID *020 †20

YOON, Eleanor Helen. 8501 ARLINGTON BLVD, GLENNA R ANDERSON MD & 22031 #051-01-1995 L2003 OBG *020 †30

YOUNG, Cecilia Therese. 8316 ARLINGTON BLVD, NOVAMED ASSOCIATES 22031 #023-01-1991 L1999 IM *020 †20

YOUNG, Ira Sanders. 8503 ARLINGTON BLVD, STE 310 22031 #010-01-1959 L1965 U IM *020 †95

YOUNG, William Wai Choy. 8505 ARLINGTON BLVD # 100 22031 #030-06-1977 L1999 N EM *020 †55,75

YOUSUF, Asma. ■ 22030 #704-02-1982 L1995 N *100

YUN, Dennis. 3998 FAIR RIDGE DR, FAIR OAKS ANESTHESIA ASSOC 22033 #051-07-2002 L2007 APM *020 †05

ZACKRISON, Leila Haddad. 11166 MAIN ST, STE 405 22030 #005-12-1988 L1990 IM RHU *020 †20

ZAITA, Jamie L. 4001 FAIR RIDGE DR STE 202 22033 #024-05-1992 L1992 OBG *020 †30

ZAND, Dina Jane. 8501 ARLINGTON BLVD 22031 #016-06-1995 L2003 OS *020 †19

ZARCHIN, Lawrence Edward. 3020 HAMAKER CT STE 400 22031 #056-06-1972 L1977 N *020 †75

ZEH, Debra Anne. 8303 ARLINGTON BLVD # 201 22031 #035-08-1979 L1981 PD *020 †55

ZIA, Farah Zeba. 12255 FAIR LAKES PKWY 22033 #010-01-1997 L1999 IM *020

ZICHERMAN, Jason Marc. 8505 ARLINGTON BLVD, STE 130 22031 #033-06-2000 L2007 RNR *100 †80

ZIEGLER, Henry Dearborn. ■ 22033 #067-01-1970 L1971 PHP IM *020 †20

ZIEMER, Martina Kukolja. 8503 ARLINGTON BLVD, STE 140 22031 #017-20-1986 L1993 IM *020 †20

ZIMMONS, Paul Stanley. 8261 WILLOW OAKS CO DR, CORPORATE DR 22031 #010-01-1967 L1975 R OS *020 †80 ‡

FAIRFAX STATION – FAIRFAX

ANCHETA-DATOC, Minda C. ■ 22039 #748-02-1961 L1981 PTH CLP *020 †50

BAIG, Sheima. ■ 22039 #704-02-1969 L1989 ORS AN *020 †60

BAKSHI, Anita Kaur. ■ 22039 #051-04-2007 L2007 IM *012

BAUMAN, Dorothy Mae Hodil. ■ 22039 #041-07-1969 L1970 R RO *020 †80

BIGGAR, Sallie Ann. ■ 22039 #051-04-1983 L1986 PD *020

BUETHE, Robert Andrew, Jr. ■ 22039 #016-06-1964 L1966 AM OBG *030

CHANDRA, Amit. ■ 22039 #051-07-2006 L2008 EM *012

CHEN, Paul Tsin Chung. ■ 22039 #242-29-1940 L1957 FM *071

CLARK, Charles H, Jr. ■ 22039 #010-03-1982 L1986 GS *020

CORINALDI, Greg Austin. 6661 RUTLEDGE DR, KAISER PERMANENTE 22039 #033-06-1982 L1985 IM *020 †20

GUJRAL, Shireen. ■ 22039 #051-04-2005 L2005 AN *012

HUNNELL, Denise Jackson. ■ 22039 #048-12-1985 L1986 FM *020 †18

IKO, Benny Onuoha. 5812 HANNORA LN, FAIRFAX COUNTY HEALTH DEPT 22039 #409-35-1973 L1991 R *020 †80

JARBADAN, Ignaz Papa. 9015 SILVERBROOK RD, STE 106 22039 #748-08-1964 L1972 IM UCM *020

JARBADAN, Ignaz Roy. ■ 22039 #654-01-2002 L2008 IM *100

KAFAJI, Ahmed Hadi. 8006 BRANDT CT 22039 #528-05-1989 L2002 IM *100 †75

KILPATRICK, Michael E. ■ 22039 #034-01-1969 L1976 ID IM *050

LEE, Sang-Hoon. ■ 22039 #583-01-1970 L1976 IM ON *020 †20

LO PRESTI, Joseph Michael. ■ 22039 #010-02-1945 L1976 R PD *020 †55,80

O'CONNOR, Janet Lyn. ■ 22039 #035-15-1985 L1991 AN *020 †05

PATEL, Sohini. ■ 22039 #495-22-1971 L1977 PM GPM *020

PATEL, Usha Thakorbhai. ■ 22039 #495-23-1970 L1987 PD *020 †55

POTTS, Matthew Bryan. ■ 22039 #005-02-2007 GS *012

PREUSS, Harry Geo. ■ 22039 #051-20-1959 L1967 IM PTH *050

ROARK, John W. ■ 22039 #021-01-1949 L1954 CD IM *071 †20

ROSENBERG, Andrea. ■ 22039 #041-14-2005 IM *012

SAENGER, Arleen Meyer. ■ 22039 #005-19-1979 L2002 GPM *070

SCHMITT, Anne Marie. ■ 22039 #051-04-2007 L2007 IM *012

SHEA, Jennifer Ann. ■ 22039 #051-04-2007 L2007 IM *012

SINGLA, Manish. ■ 22039 #010-01-2006 L2007 IM *012

TAILLON, Donald Lionel. ■ 22039 #023-12-1991 L1993 PTH *020 †50

TIDABACK, Dale Roger. ■ 22039 #016-45-1983 L1988 GPM *020 †18,70

WOLFSON, Wendy Sue. ■ 22039 #035-09-1985 L1988 OBG *070 †30

ZIKRIA, Emir Ahmad. ■ 22039 #023-07-1956 L1956 TS VS *071 †85,90

FAIRFIELD – ROCKBRIDGE

PECK, Thomas Stuart. 33 RED HILL RD 24435 #010-01-1977 L1986 FM *020 †18

FAIRLAWN – RADFORD

DALRYMPLE, David J. 7516 LEE HWY, P O BOX 3608 24141 #422-01-1995 L1996 P *020 †75

FALLS CHURCH – FAIRFAX

ABBOTT, James R. 5201 LEESBURG PIKE, STE 1511 22041 #048-15-1999 L2008 FM *020 †18

ABRAMOWITZ, Michael David. 3300 GALLOWS RD, FAIRFAX HOSP 22042 #836-01-1972 L1985 AN OS *020 †05

ABULARRAGE, Christopher J. 3300 GALLOWS RD, INOVA FAIRFAX HOSPITAL 22042 #010-02-2001 L2001 GS *020 †05

AD, Niv. 2921 TELESTAR CT STE 140 22042 #550-02-1991 FM *020

ADAMS, Dawn Raquel. 3300 GALLOWS RD, DEPT. OF EMERGENCY MEDICIN 22042 #010-01-1998 L1999 EM *020 †16

AGARWAL, Swati. 3300 GALLOWS RD 22042 #036-07-2000 L2007 CCP *020 †55 ‡

AHARI, Jalil Ebrahimzadeh. 3300 GALLOWS RD, MEDICAL OFFICE 22042 #517-05-1999 L2004 PCC *012

AHLUWALIA, Ajit Singh. ■ 22042 #495-17-2001 L2007 IM *020 †20

AHMAD, Kaiser Amir. 2980 FAIRVIEW PARK DR, SECOND FLOOR 22042 #704-22-1989 L2000 PCC *020 †20

AHMAD, Shahzad. 3300 GALLOWS RD, LUNG TRANSPLANT CLINIC 22042 #704-01-1987 L2002 PCC *020 †20

AHRONOVICH, Margot Davis. 3300 GALLOWS RD, DEPT OF NEONATOLOGY 22042 #550-02-1985 L1990 NPM PD *020 †55

AKINGBA, Ajibola George. 3300 GALLOWS RD 22042 #690-02-1995 L2003 GS *020

AKROUT, Jamel E. 3300 GALLOWS RD 22042 #396-06-1973 L1986 TS EM *020

ALAPARTHI, Mohanbabu. ■ 22042 #495-99-1990 L2006 GS *012

ALARIF, Adhid Ismail. 3300 GALLOWS RD 22042 #038-06-1979 L1981 HEM IM *050 †20

ALATHARI, Husam Kais. 3302 GALLOWS RD 22042 #528-01-1991 L1997 P ADM *020 †75

AL-ATTAR, Ali. 3400 PAYNE ST, LLC 22041 #605-01-1989 L1995 IM *020 †20

ALBUS, Robert Alan. 2980 FAIRVIEW PARK DR, SECOND FLOOR 22042 #038-40-1972 L1989 TS *071 †85,90

ALDAGHLAS, Tayseer Atieh. ■ 22041 #010-01-2003 L2003 GS *012

ALEXANDER COLE, Corinne. 6565 ARLINGTON BLVD, STE 500 22042 #016-02-2003 L2005 IM *100 †20

ALHARIRI, Saad O. 3400 PAYNE ST, STE B100 22041 #528-01-1973 L1994 PD *020 †55

ALI, Alliyia Battul. ■ 22042 #035-06-2004 L2004 PEM *012 †55

AMOS, Wm Cardwell, Jr. 3300 GALLOWS RD 22042 #051-04-1952 L1952 IM CD *020

ANDERSON, Frank H. 7799 LEESBURG PIKE, THE NEUROLOGY CENTER 22043 #061-01-1963 GE *020

ANDREASEN, Arthur Cory. 3300 GALLOWS RD 22042 #047-05-1971 L1982 PD ADL *075 †55

ANDRES, Francis D. 3300 GALLOWS RD, INOVA FAIRFAX HOSPITAL 22042 #010-02-1960 L1961 P *020 †75

ANDREWS, Curtis Jay. 3300 GALLOWS RD 22042 #016-11-1995 L2001 AN *020 †05

ANDROS, Thomas G. 3300 GALLOWS RD, FAIRFAX ANESTHESIOLOGY 22042 #010-01-1986 L1996 AN AM *020 †05

ANGOSO, Manuel. 3300 GALLOWS RD 22042 #847-04-1958 L1963 IM CD *020

ARDAY, David Richard. 5111 LEESBURG PIKE, SKYLINE 5 STE 810 (OCMO) 22041 #038-06-1983 L1983 PHP OM *030 †70

ARMENGOL, Raul Enrique. 3300 GALLOWS RD, FAIRFAX HOSP DEPT EMERG ME 22042 #010-01-1981 L1988 EM IM *020 †16

ASCHER, David Peter. 3300 GALLOWS RD, FOR CHILDREN 22042 #036-01-1982 L2004 PD *020 †55

ASKEW, Kim Lee. 3300 GALLOWS RD, EMERGENCY DEPARTMENT 22042 #036-05-2003 L2006 PEM *012 †16

ATHARI, Freydoon. 3300 GALLOWS RD, FAIRFAX HOSP DEPT PATH 22042 #517-03-1961 L1970 PTH BBK *071 †20

ATIYEH, Maurice Nicola. 6400 ARLINGTON BLVD, STE 960 22042 #605-01-1960 L1986 GE IM *020 †20

AUERBACH, Peter Stamm. 3300 GALLOWS RD, INOVA FAIRFAX HOSPITAL 22042 #041-01-1998 L2004 EM PE *020 †16

AVSTREIH, Dan B. 3300 GALLOWS RD, IFH/EMERGENCY DEPT. 22042 #043-01-2002 L2006 EM *020 †16

AZIH, Chinelo Ifeyinwa. 3300 GALLOWS RD, DEPT OF INTERNAL MEDICINE, 22042 #016-43-2005 L2005 IM *012

BABU, Nimmagadda V R. 6319 CASTLE PL, STE 3D 22044 #495-57-1969 IM *100

BADE, Maseer Abdullah. 2921 TELESTAR CT, STE 140 22042 #017-20-1996 L2005 VS *020 †85

BALL, Michael Francis. 3300 GALLOWS RD 22042 #010-02-1959 L1973 END DIA *071 †20

BANASZAK, Damian Allen. 3300 GALLOWS RD 22042 #038-40-1986 L1991 EM GS *020 †16

BANK, Ronald Stephen. 3300 GALLOWS RD 22042 #023-01-1993 L1998 AN *020 †05

BARSANTI, Ardwin H. 3300 GALLOWS RD 22042 #035-19-1947 L1954 PD *071 †55

BARTH, Robert Lewis. 3300 GALLOWS RD 22042 #041-01-1970 L1974 AN *020 †05

BASSALI, Adel Wadie. 3300 GALLOWS RD 22042 #915-03-1983 L1996 AN *020 †05

BAUER, Elizabeth Anne. 3300 GALLOWS RD, INOVA FAIRFAX HOSPITAL 22042 #041-02-2002 L2002 PD *020 †55

BECK, Jeffery Arthur. 3300 GALLOWS RD, DEP. OF ANESTHESIOLOGY 22042 #041-13-1993 L1997 AN *020 †05

BELAY, Anteneh Mahari. 3300 GALLOWS RD, IFH/EMERGENCY DEPARTMENT 22042 #038-40-2003 L2006 IM *020 †16

BENNETT, Sharon Ann. 6400 ARLINGTON BLVD, STE 940 22042 #048-14-1997 L2005 NEP PN *020 †20,55

BERGER, Kenneth W. 3300 GALLOWS RD 22042 #051-01-1952 L1952 A ID *020 †03,20

BERGH, Arthur F. 3300 GALLOWS RD, DEPT OF ANESTHLGY 22042 #048-14-1993 L1998 AN PME *020 †05

BERISH, Robert Frank. 3300 GALLOWS RD 22042 #041-13-1965 L1973 AN PME *071 †05

BERTRAN, Jorge Luis. 6201 LEESBURG PIKE STE 410 22044 #275-01-1949 L1965 IM A *020

BEYENE, Eskender. 3300 GALLOWS RD, INOVA CENTRALIZED CREDENTA 22042 #010-01-1999 L2000 PCC *100 †20

BEZIRGANIAN, George. ■ 22042 #605-01-1953 L1962 P *071 †75

BIERMA, Edward Thomas. 3300 GALLOWS RD 22042 #023-01-2007 L2007 GS *012

BOKHARI, Farhat Jabbar. 3400 PAYNE ST STE 2 22041 #704-01-1978 L1992 PS HS *020 †65

BORKAR, Rajendra J. 3300 GALLOWS RD, INOVA FAIRFAX HOSPITAL, KA 22042 #495-37-1985 L1996 IM *020 †20

BORTNICK, Ronald Jack. ■ 22042 #010-01-1959 L1964 NS *071 †25

BOSLEY, Brooke Nicole. ■ 22044 #041-12-2005 L2005 OTO *012

BRALLIER, David Ronald. 3300 GALLOWS RD 22042 #018-03-1968 L1983 RNR R *020 †80

BRANTON, Philip Andrew. 3300 GALLOWS RD, FAIRFAX HOSP PATH DEPT 22042 #023-07-1987 L1997 PTH *020 †50

BRATSLAVSKY, Gennady. 3300 GALLOWS RD, DIANN 22042 #035-03-2000 L2005 U *100

BRENNT, Charles Edward. 3300 GALLOWS RD 22042 #040-02-1988 L1994 **IM** *020 †20

BRETT, Catherine Elizabet. ■ 22043 #028-46-2006 L2006 **OBG** *012

BRITO, Albert Veiga. 3300 GALLOWS RD, DEPT. OF PEDIATRICS 22042 #023-12-1986 L1998 **PD** *020 †55

BRITTON, John Thos. 3300 GALLOWS RD, DEPT OF ANESTHLGY 22042 #050-02-1979 L1992 **AN** *020 †05

BROOKS, Kenneth Mark. 3300 GALLOWS RD 22042 #021-01-1978 L1983 **CD IM** *020 †20

BROWN, Barrett Bolton, Jr. 3300 GALLOWS RD, FAIRFAX HOSP DEPT PATH 22042 #010-01-1987 L1992 **PTH** *020 †50

BROWN, Erica Stevens. 3300 GALLOWS RD 22042 #020-12-2002 L2006 **PD** *100 †55

BROWN, Steven Edward. 3300 GALLOWS RD DEPT AN 22042 #005-14-1978 L1988 **AN** *020 †05

BRUDNO, Douglas Spencer. 3300 GALLOWS RD, FAIRFAX HOSP/INOVA HLTH SY 22042 #012-01-1977 L2001 **NPM** *020 †55

BRUNO, Christina A. 6231 LEESBURG PIKE, STE 608 22044 #041-14-1996 L2007 **OPH** *020 †35

BRUTHER, Lawrence James. 3300 GALLOWS RD 22042 #033-05-1963 L1969 **EM OS** *020 †16

BUCUR, John C. 6305 CASTLE PL 22044 #041-12-1951 L1957 **NS** *075 †25

BUI, My Q. 7297 LEE HWY, STE B 22042 #941-01-1968 L1984 **GP** *020

BUI, Nghi Huu. 6060 ARLINGTON BLVD, FALLS CHURCH MEDICAL 22044 #035-19-1992 L1994 **IM** *020 †20

BURKA, Paul Stephen. 3300 GALLOWS RD, INVOA WOMEN'S CENTER/DEPAR 22042 #010-02-1974 L1977 **OBG** *020 †30

BURNHAM, Robert C. 3300 GALLOWS RD 22042 #035-09-1941 L1948 **PYA P** *071 †75

BURTON, Nelson Avard. 2921 TELESTAR CT, STE 140 22042 #049-01-1975 L1988 **TS GS** *020 †85,90

BUSTOS, Osvaldo. 5501 SEMINARY RD APT 1611S 22041 #132-01-1965 L1988 **FM** *062 †18 ‡

CAMACHO-FUENTES, Jaime J. 6201 LEESBURG PIKE STE 410 22044 #737-06-1982 L1998 **IM** *020 †20

CAMPANA, Jorge L. 6201 LEESBURG PIKE STE 200 22044 #011-04-1980 L1989 **OPH** *020 †35

CAMPBELL, Corder Compton. 3300 GALLOWS RD 22042 #054-04-1968 L1987 **PD OS** *020 †55

CANADAS, Antonio Lucio. 3429 FARM HILL DR 22044 #319-01-1952 L1957 **GS** *071

CANTWELL, Michael Nelson. ■ 22043 #041-12-2000 L2000 **P** *100

CARTER, Meredith Lynn. 3300 GALLOWS RD, INOVA FAIRFAX HOSPITAL (PE 22042 #010-02-1999 L2006 **PD** *020 †55

CATES, Robert Judson. 3300 GALLOWS RD, INOVA FAIRFAX HOSP DEPT EM 22042 #017-20-1971 L1975 **EM IM** *062 †20

CAVANAGH, Michael Jos. ■ 22041 #035-08-1945 L1955 **GS** *071 †85

CAY, Emin Seref. 6720 ARLINGTON BLVD 22042 #051-04-1986 L1987 **GP UCM** *020

CAY, Mehmet Nuri. 6720 ARLINGTON BLVD 22042 #902-03-1946 L1959 **IM GP** *071

CAZAN, Matthew John G, Jr. ■ 22041 #051-04-1982 L1984 **AN GS** *020

CENTENERA, Judy S. 3300 GALLOWS RD, DEPT ANESTHESIOLOGY 22042 #748-01-1966 L1972 **AN** *020 †05

CHAMBERLAIN, John Loomis. 3300 GALLOWS RD 22042 #051-01-1957 L1957 **PD** *071 †55

CHANDRA, Ramesh Gattu. 2841 HARTLAND RD STE 401 22043 #495-65-1975 L1983 **ORS OSM** *020 †40

CHANDY, Joby Joseph. 3300 GALLOWS RD, DEPT. OF ANESTHESIOLOGY 22042 #035-48-2003 L2008 **AN** *020

CHEEMA, Arshad P. 6712 ARLINGTON BLVD 22042 #704-21-1982 L1998 **FM** *020 †18

CHEIFETZ, Craig Evan. 3300 GALLOWS RD, DEPT OF MED 22042 #035-06-1995 L1997 **IM** *020 †20

CHEN, D W. 5113 LEESBURG PIKE, SKYLINE 4, SUITE 901 22041 #024-07-1991 L1992 **GP PHP** *020 †70

CHERAYIL, Gerald George. 3300 GALLOWS RD, DEPT OF ANES 22042 #056-01-1996 L2001 **AN** *020 †05

CHESTER, Marc Andrew. 3300 GALLOWS RD, DEPT OF PEDIATRICS 22042 #422-01-2003 L2003 **PDP** *012

CHHABRA, Dev Raj. 2841 HARTLAND RD 22043 #495-69-1979 L1991 **IM** *020 †20

CHHABRA, Susan Kaur. 3300 GALLOWS RD, FAIRFAX HOSPITAL 22042 #010-01-1995 L1995 **PD** *020 †55

CHOI, Elmer Kwon. 3300 GALLOWS RD, INOVA FAIRVAX HOSP ANES DP 22042 #035-19-1999 L2004 **AN CD** *020 †05

CHOUDHURY, Tripti. ■ 22042 #495-20-1970 L1994 **IM** *100

CHOWDHRY, Parveen. 6712 ARLINGTON BLVD 22042 #704-06-1964 L1991 **PD NPM** *020 †55

CHOWDHRY, Yasmin. 6712 ARLINGTON BLVD 22042 #704-05-1981 L1990 **PD** *020 †55

CHU, Michelle T. 6400 SEVEN CORNERS PL # J 22044 #051-01-1993 L1996 **FM** *020 †18

CLOUGHERTY, Patrick W. 3300 GALLOWS RD 22042 #041-12-1982 L1987 **AN PME** *020 †05

COBURN, Michael Bertram. 3302 GALLOWS RD, NORTHRN VA MENTL HLTH INST 22042 #016-11-1964 L2002 **P LM** *020 †70

COLEMAN, Robert L. 3300 GALLOWS RD 22042 #051-01-1984 L1987 **AN** *020 †05

COLLAZO, Lucas Ramon. 2921 TELESTAR CT, STE 140 22042 #035-06-1989 L1999 **TS PCS** *020 †85,90

COMUNALE, Robert Anthony. 3300 GALLOWS RD 22042 #051-04-1971 L1972 **FM** *020 †18

COOK, Elizabeth J. ■ 22044 #048-04-2002 L2004 **PD** *020 †55

COOK, Marci Krop. 3300 GALLOWS RD 22042 #035-06-1987 L1996 **OBG REN** *020 †30

COOPER, James Nelson. 3300 GALLOWS RD 22042 #035-19-1963 L1968 **GE IM** *071 †20

CORCORAN, Theodore P. 6319 CASTLE PL, STE 1E SEVEN CORNERS PROF 22044 #041-12-1989 L1993 **GS** *020

COSTESCU, Sanda. ■ 22042 #781-01-1957 L1981 **IM** *071 †20

COURT, Oliver. 3300 GALLOWS RD, INOVA FAIRFAX HOSPITAL 22042 #067-01-1995 *100

CRIMM, Carl Eugene. 3300 GALLOWS RD 22042 #051-04-1956 L1959 **FM** *071 †18

CROCK, Thomas Rankin. 2946 SLEEPY HOLLOW RD, SEVEN CORNERS MEDICAL ARTS 22044 #010-01-1973 L1974 **PD** *020 †55

CRONE, Catherine Chang. 3300 GALLOWS RD 22042 #041-02-1987 L1991 **P** *020 †75

CURCIO, Edward P. 2251 PIMMIT DR, STE C3 22043 #010-02-1967 L1973 **P** *020 †75

CURRY, John Lamar. 6231 LEESBURG PIKE STE 200 22044 #048-04-1967 L1975 **FM** *020

DALY, Jeanne A. ■ 22041 #051-01-1980 L1982 **GP** *020

DANG, Huong. 6319 CASTLE PL STE 2A 22044 #942-01-1979 L1997 **P** *020

DANG, Thao Phuong. 7297 LEE HWY STE F 22042 #941-01-1974 L1982 **OBG GP** *020 †30

DANTON, Peter Alvarez. 3300 GALLOWS RD, INOVA FAIRFAX HOSP-SURG 22042 #010-02-1975 L1980 **GS CRS** *020 †85,10

DAUBER, Henry Malcolm. 3300 GALLOWS RD, DBA INOVA PEDIATRIC 22042 #035-09-1971 L1979 **PTH** *020 †50

DAY, Sharon Lisa. 3300 GALLOWS RD, FAIRFAX HOSPITAL 22042 #010-02-1988 L1994 **EM PE** *020 †55,16

DECAREAU, Khanh Tran. ■ 22042 #010-01-2002 **IM** *100 †20

DELENICK, Peter J. 7787 LEESBURG PIKE 22043 #041-12-1978 L1985 **ORS** *020 †40

DELLA-SANTINA, C P. 3300 GALLOWS RD, KAISER OFF C/O FAIRFAX HOS 22042 #021-01-1989 L1994 **IM** *020 †20

DEL RIO, Robespierre M. 3302 GALLOWS RD, NORTHERN VIRGINIA MH INSTI 22042 #308-12-1984 L1997 **PFP LM** *020 †75

DENNEY, Roger Alan. 3300 GALLOWS RD, DEPARTMENT OF ANESTHESIOLO 22042 #028-03-1987 L1992 **AN PME** *020 †05

DERSHEWITZ, Norman J. ■ 22041 #010-02-1968 L1974 **N OM** *071

DESAI, Shashank Shailesh. 3300 GALLOWS RD, INOVA HEART AND VASCULAR I 22042 #016-02-1994 L2006 **CD** *020 †20

DEYE, Katherine P. 3300 GALLOWS RD, DEPT OF PEDS INOVA FAIRFX 22042 #041-02-1995 L2006 **PD** *020 †55

DIETZE, Claus Jochen. 6201 LEESBURG PIKE 22044 #407-01-1945 L1963 **CHP P** *020

DILLON, Peter John, Jr. ■ 22043 #010-02-2007 L2007 **FP** *012

DINIEGA, Benedict Macario. 5111 LEESBURG PIKE, DEPT OF DEFENSE 22041 #014-01-1976 L1978 **PHP FM** *030 †18,70

DIPAOLO, Francis. 6201 LEESBURG PIKE, STE 200 22044 #010-02-1989 L1992 **OPH** *020 †35

DOCKERY, William Keith. 3300 GALLOWS RD, FAIRFAX HOSPITAL 22042 #012-01-1981 L1985 **CCP PD** *020 †55

DODDI, Krishna P. 3300 GALLOWS RD, IFH/EMERGENCY DEPARTMENT 22042 #495-50-1982 L2006 **EM FM** *020 †18,16

DOGAN, Huseyin. 6400 ARLINGTON BLVD 22042 #902-10-1977 L2003 **NEP** *020 †20

DOLE, Polly Teophola. 3300 GALLOWS RD, FAIRFAX HOSP.- EMERGENCY M 22042 #041-15-2001 L2004 **EM** *020 †16

DOMANN, John Thos. 3300 GALLOWS RD 22042 #010-01-1956 L1961 **AN** *071

DOUNIS, William Achilleas. 3300 GALLOWS RD 22042 #023-01-1990 L1994 **AN** *020 †05

DRUCKENBROD, Glenn Geo. 3300 GALLOWS RD, FAIRFAX HOSPITAL 22042 #010-02-1986 L1989 **EM** *020 †16

DRYSDALE, Jonathan Robert. 3300 GALLOWS RD, DEPT OF INTERNAL MED 22042 #010-02-1997 L1997 **IM** *020 †20

DUNCAN, David Courtney. 3300 GALLOWS RD, DEPT OF MEDICINE 22042 #012-01-1992 L1994 **IM** *020 †20

DURR, Michael Jos, Jr. 7659 LEESBURG PIKE 22043 #010-02-1960 L1962 **P** *020 †75

DWYER, Kevin Michael. 3300 GALLOWS RD, DIVISION OF TRAUMA 22042 #010-02-1984 L1994 **CCS** *020 †85

EBEID, Rasha Abdel Monem. 3300 GALLOWS RD, OB CLINIC-INOVA FAIRFAX 22042 #915-02-1996 L2001 **OBG** *100

EBRAHIM, Hassan Mahmoud. ■ 22041 #915-03-2001 L2006 **HEM** *012 †20

EDDY, Orin Lee. 3300 GALLOWS RD 22042 #033-05-1998 L1999 **EM** *020 †16

EDER, Edward Ernest, III. 3300 GALLOWS RD, FAIRFAX HOSPITAL /CATS 22042 #715-01-1977 L1983 **IM** *020 †20

ELHASSAN, Ihab Omar. ■ 22041 #010-03-2007 **GS** *012

ELLAHHAM, Samer Helmi. 3701 S GEORGE MASON DR, STE C1 22041 #605-01-1986 L1989 **CD IM** *020 †20

ELREFAI, Ahmed, Jr. 3300 GALLOWS RD, FAIRFAX ANESTHESIOLOGY 22042 #010-03-1998 L2004 **AN PAN** *020 †05

EL-SABAAWI, Mohamed A. 3302 GALLOWS RD 22042 #915-03-1972 L1993 **P PYG** *020 †75

ELWIR, Jamal S. 5707 SEMINARY RD 22041 #915-05-1983 L1993 **PD** *020 †55

EMERY, Janice. 3300 GALLOWS RD 22042 #018-03-1975 L1979 **OBG** *020 †30 ‡

ENGELS, Emil David. 3300 GALLOWS RD, INOVA FAIRFAX HOSPITAL 22042 #008-01-1994 L1999 **AN** *020 †05

ENTERS, Sarah Jane. ■ 22043 #010-02-2008 *012

EPPARD, Leonard Calvert. 3300 GALLOWS RD 22042 #051-01-1961 L1961 **OBG** *071 †30

ERAGAN, Mehmet Arif. ■ 22041 #902-10-1952 L1970 **A IM** *071

ERARIO, Madeline. 3300 GALLOWS RD, INOVA FAIRFAX HOSP DEPT OF 22042 #010-02-1994 L1994 **IM** *040 †20

ERICKSON, Carol Frances. 3300 GALLOWS RD, FAIRFAX ANESTHESIOLOGY ASS 22042 #036-05-1981 L1989 **AN** *020 †05

FAKHRY, Samir Majid. 3300 GALLOWS RD, INOVA FAIRFAX HOSP 22042 #605-01-1981 L1984 **GS TRS** *020 †85

FARRELL, Christopher John. 3300 GALLOWS RD, DEPT OF ANESTHESIOLOGY 22042 #010-02-1994 L1998 **AN** *020 †05

FARZAN, Sattar. ■ 22041 #517-03-1956 L1998 **IM PUD** *040 †20

FATA, Paola. 3300 GALLOWS RD, DEPT OF TRAMA SVCS 22042 #067-01-1995 L2003 *020

FAUZIA, Mutahar. 5697 COLUMBIA PIKE, STE 100 22041 #704-06-1979 L1984 **OBG** *020

FEOLA, John Patrick. 6400 ARLINGTON BLVD, STE 940 22042 #010-02-1990 L1994 **IM** *020 †20

FISCHER, Greg David. 3300 GALLOWS RD, DEPARTMENT OF ANESTHESIOLO 22042 #041-12-1993 L1998 **AN PME** *020 †05

FISHELBERG, Jeremy Frankl. 3300 GALLOWS RD, FAIRFAX HOSP 22042 #550-02-2000 L2000 **PD** *020 †55

FLEET, Sara Elizabeth. 3300 GALLOWS RD, DEPT OF MEDICINE 22042 #056-05-2001 L2003 **CCM** *020

FOLEY, Erin Patricia. 3300 GALLOWS RD 22042 #043-01-1988 L1997 **AN** *020 †05

FOX, Eduardo Raul. 2946 SLEEPY HOLLOW RD 22044 #051-01-1995 L1999 **PD** *020 †55

FRASER, Jarrod Todd. 3300 GALLOWS RD 22042 #035-15-1993 L1998 **AN** *020 †05

FRAYNA, Cristina F. 6231 LEESBURG PIKE, STE 203 22044 #748-10-1982 L1995 **PD** *020 †55

FREEDY, Alicia Stacey. 3300 GALLOWS RD 22042 #550-02-2002 L2002 **PD** *020 †55

FREEMAN, Victor Geo. 3300 GALLOWS RD 22042 #005-11-1992 L1999 **IM** *030

FRENKEL, David Scott. 6073 ARLINGTON BLVD 22044 #010-01-1978 L1978 **P** *020 †75 ‡

FRIEDMAN, Evan Brady. ■ 22044 #035-06-2005 L2005 **OBG** *012

FRIEDMANN, Susan. DEPT.OF EMERGENCY MEDICINE, FAIRFAX HOSPITAL 22033 #010-01-1988 L1989 **EM** *020 †16

FULCHER, Thomas Montague. 3300 GALLOWS RD 22042 #051-01-1956 L1956 **TS VS** *071 †90,85

FULENWIDER, Ann Kathleen. 3300 GALLOWS RD 22042 #011-02-1983 L1986 **PTH** *020 †50

FULLERTON, Katherine Tsao. 3300 GALLOWS RD, INOVA FAIRFAX HOSPITAL, DE 22042 #035-47-2002 L2008 **PEM** *012 †55

FUSELIER, Michelle L. 6305 CASTLE PL, STE 1D 22044 #019-02-2003 L2006 **FM** *100

FUTTERMAN, Craig Alan. 3300 GALLOWS RD DEPT PED 22042 #051-07-1981 L1987 **CCM PD** *040 †55

GAJEWSKI, Donald Andrew. 3300 GALLOWS RD, INOVA FAIRFAX HOSPITAL 22042 #041-13-1994 L1996 **ORS** *020 †40

GALKIN, Lloyd Anson M. ■ 22042 #067-01-1972 L1975 **GP FM** *020

GAMBARDELLA, Josephine. 3300 GALLOWS RD, FAIRFAX HOSPITAL 22042 #035-03-1991 L1995 **AN** *020 †05

GARCIA, Ramon. 3156 HOLMES RUN RD 22042 #847-03-1955 L1960 **AN** *071 †05

GARRETT, John Richard. 2921 TELESTAR CT 22042 #001-02-1979 L1989 **TS VS** *020 †85,90

GARST, Paul Dimitre. 5111 LEESBURG PIKE STE 810, TRICARE REGION NORTH 22041 #016-11-1978 L2006 **MDM LM** *030 †20

GARTSIDE, Roberta Lee. 3300 GALLOWS RD 22042 #041-13-1981 L1988 **PS HS** *040 †85,65

GARZA, Alexander Gerard. ■ 22043 #028-03-1996 L1997 **EM** *020 †16

GAUSE, Paul Edward. ■ 22041 #048-04-1975 L1976 **IM** *020 †20

GAUSS, Cynthia Lynn. 3300 GALLOWS RD 3RD FL, FAIRFAX HOSP DEPT OF PSCH 22042 #051-04-1989 L1992 **P** *020 †75

GEBARA, David Jos. 6201 LEESBURG PIKE STE 308 22044 #035-15-1965 L1971 **P PYG** *020 †75

GEORGE, Anu Rachel. 6045 ARLINGTON BLVD, SEVEN CORNERS MEDICAL CENT 22044 #495-31-1994 L2000 **IM** *020 †20

GHEZZI, Keith Thos. 3300 GALLOWS RD, INOVA FAIRFAX HOSP 22042 #010-02-1982 L1983 **EM TRS** *030 †16

GIBNEY, Sheila A. 3300 GALLOWS RD 22042 #023-01-1972 L1982 **PD** *071 †55

GILL, Saumya Nagarajan. ■ 22043 #051-04-2007 L2007 **IM** *012

GIRARDI, Luigi Stefano. 6860 MCLEAN PROVINCE CIR 22043 #010-02-1987 L1990 **ID** *030 †20

GLOSSA, Jean Susan. 6196 ARLINGTON BLVD, COMMUNITY HEALJD CARE NETW 22044 #011-04-1993 L1997 **IM** *020 †20

GLYNN, Simone A. 3300 GALLOWS RD 22042 #067-01-1986 L1987 **FM** *020 †18

GOLOMB, Herbert Stanley. 6060 ARLINGTON BLVD, FALLS CHURCH MEDICAL 22044 #035-08-1960 L1964 **D** *071 †15

GONDOS, Brian Kenneth. 7659 LEESBURG PIKE 22043 #035-46-2002 L2006 **P** *020

GONDOS, Gordon Morris. 7659 LEESBURG PIKE 22043 #051-04-1970 L1970 **P CHP** *020 †75

GONZALEZ, Julio Cesar. 2841 HARTLAND RD STE 207 22043 #341-01-1974 L1982 **N PMM** *020

GORDON, Emily Rebecca. 3300 GALLOWS RD, DEPT. OF EMERGENCY MEDICIN 22042 #010-01-2001 L2005 **EM** *100 †16

GORDON-GRAY, Ana-Maria Cr. 3300 GALLOWS RD, DEPT OB/GYN CLINIC 22042 #035-48-1992 L1996 **OBG** *020 †30

GOSWAMI, Trishna. 3300 GALLOWS RD, INOVA MEDICAL STAFF OFFICE 22042 #041-15-2003 L2003 **HO** *012 †20

GRABMAYER, Josef Peter. 3300 GALLOWS RD, DEPT OF ANESTHESIA 22042 #035-08-1991 L1995 **AN** *020 †05

GRAHAM, Cheryl Fossum. 3130 FAIRVIEW PARK DR, BIOMETRIC RESEARCH INS INC 22042 #034-01-1977 **IM CD** *050

GRAHAM, Deborah Brauer. 3300 GALLOWS RD, FAIRFAX HOSPITAL/DEPT. OF 22042 #051-07-2004 L2005 **IM** *020 †20

GRAND, Bernard. ■ 22044 #035-19-1962 L1969 **PUD CCM** *071 †20

GRANGER, Stephen Ireland. 3300 GALLOWS RD 22042 #010-01-1958 L1961 **P PD** *074

GRAUSZ, Hannah M. 3300 GALLOWS RD, NORTHERN VIRGINIA 22042 #023-07-1996 L2003 **EM** *020 †16

GRAY, Brigid Catherine. 3300 GALLOWS RD 22042 #035-48-1995 L1997 **FM** *020 †18

GREEN, Neil A. 6404 SEVEN CORNERS PL, STE F 22044 #047-05-1975 L1979 **ORS** *020 †40

GREIG, Thomas West. 5111 LEESBURG PIKE, STE 601 22041 #047-06-1990 L1990 **GPM** *020 †70

GRIFFEN, Margaret Mary. 3300 GALLOWS RD, TRUAMA DIVISION 22042 #020-12-1993 L2006 **GS** *020 †85

GRUNDL, Peter Dominic. 3300 GALLOWS RD, 1 NOVA HOSPITAL 22042 #056-06-1982 L1995 **PD** *020 †55

GUPTA, Neeru R. ■ 22041 #024-05-2004 L2004 **OBG** *012

GUPTA, Ravindra Dayal. 3300 GALLOWS RD, DEPARTMENT OF MEDICINE 22042 #051-01-2000 L2005 **IM** *020 †20

GUTIERREZ, Fe Mendiola. 6245 LEESBURG PIKE, STE 500 22044 #748-01-1955 L1977 **PD PHP** *020

GWYNN, Lucas Kidd. 6408 SEVEN CORNERS PL # J 22044 #051-04-1996 L2000 **FOP DMP** *020

HAFSA- BELHARETH, Samira. 3300 GALLOWS RD 22042 #895-01-1998 L2004 **PD** *020 †55

HALL, Allan. 3300 GALLOWS RD 22042 #010-01-1952 L1957 **GS** *075 †85

HALMI, Marianne Leovy. ■ 22044 #473-01-1979 L1984 **BBK OS** *020

HANFLING, Dan G. 3300 GALLOWS RD, INOVA FAIRFAX HOSPITAL 22042 #043-01-1992 L1993 **EM** *020 †16

HANNAWAY, Christine D. 3300 GALLOWS RD, DEPT OF SURGERY 22042 #051-07-1998 L2000 **GS** *020

HANNON, John Francis. 2946 SLEEPY HOLLOW RD # 1 22044 #010-02-1953 L1960 **OPH** *071 †35

HANSON, Dianah Thelma. ■ 22041 #033-05-2003 L2006 **EM** *020

HAQUE, Salma Shamsul. ■ 22044 #021-06-2005 **IM** *012

HART, Richard Jos. 6400 ARLINGTON BLVD # 940 22042 #008-01-1967 L1973 **IM CD** *020 †20

HAUDA, William Edward, II. 3300 GALLOWS RD, DEPT OF EMERGENCY MEDICINE 22042 #056-05-1992 L1995 **EM PE** *020 †16

HEGGI, Abdulwahab Hashem. 3400 PAYNE ST, DOMINION CLINIC 22041 #575-02-1995 L2004 **IM** *100 †20

HEISEL, Nancy Jane. 6565 ARLINGTON BLVD, STE 500 22042 #040-02-1989 L2003 **IM** *020 †20

HELU, Nicholas. 3300 GALLOWS RD 22042 #308-01-1950 L1955 **IM** *020

HENDERSHOT, Kimberly M. 3300 GALLOWS RD, TRAUMA SERVICES-FAIRFAX HO 22042 #038-45-1999 L1999 **CCS** *100

HENRIKSON, Susan Elizabet. 3300 GALLOWS RD 22042 #025-01-2002 L2005 **PD** *100 †55

HENSLEE, Warren P. 6400 SEVEN CORNERS PL # M 22044 #048-13-1997 L2001 **FM** *020

HENSON, Jesus Anibal. 3300 GALLOWS RD, INOVA FAIRFAX HOSPITAL 22042 #042-03-1993 L1996 **IM** *020 †20 ‡

HERMES, Daniel J. 3300 GALLOWS RD, DEPT. OF EMERGENCY MEDICIN 22042 #010-01-1990 L1995 **EM** *020 †16

HERNANDEZ, Agdel Jose. ■ 22044 #042-01-2004 **P** *012

HERNANDEZ, Antonio. 5501 SEMINARY RD, APT 2508S 22041 #132-01-1962 L1973 **OBG GYN** *071 †30

HESSAMFAR, Afaneh. 3300 GALLOWS RD, INOVA FAIRFAX HOSPITAL 22042 #517-01-1981 L1986 **NPM PD** *020 †55

HILL, Mathilde Tissot. 3300 GALLOWS RD, FAIRFAX ANESTHESIOLOGY ASS 22042 #051-01-1999 L1999 **AN** *020 †05

HO, Hien Van. 6079 ARLINGTON BLVD 22044 #941-01-1972 L1984 **DM GP** *020 †55

HO, Hoa Van. 6079 ARLINGTON BLVD 22044 #305-01-1999 L2003 **PD** *020 †55

HOANG, My Dinh. 3300 GALLOWS RD, FAIRFAX HOSPITAL 22042 #033-05-1996 L1998 **IM** *020 †20

HOLT, Kerrie Lynn. 3302 GALLOWS RD, HEALTH INSTITUTE 22042 #032-01-1993 L1994 **P** *020 †75

HOLT, Ronald Rhodes. 3300 GALLOWS RD, FAIRFAX ANESTHESIOLOGY ASS 22042 #004-01-1972 L1978 **AN** *020 †05

HOWELL, John Mark. 3300 GALLOWS RD, INOVA FAIRFAX HOSPITAL 22042 #010-02-1982 L1987 **EM** *020 †16

HOYLE, Kelly Elizabeth. 3300 GALLOWS RD, DEPARTMENT OF MEDICINE 22042 #012-01-2003 L2003 **IM** *100 †20

HWANG, Vivian. 3300 GALLOWS RD, FAIRFAX HOSPITAL 22042 #051-01-1997 L2004 **PEM** *020 †16

HYUN, Robert. 3300 GALLOWS RD, FAIRFAX ANESTHESIOLOGY ASS 22042 #041-07-1992 L2000 **AN** *020 †05

IACONETTI, Dominick Jay. 3300 GALLOWS RD, DEPARTMENT OF ANESTHESIOLO 22042 #033-05-1988 L1991 **AN** *020 †05

IM, Dukjin. 3300 GALLOWS RD, DEPT OF REHABILITATION 22042 #525-01-1990 L2003 **PM** *020 †60

JACKSON, William Lorenzo. 2980 FAIRVIEW PARK DR, 2ND FL 22042 #056-05-1983 L1984 **HEM IM** *020 †20

JACOBSON, Cecil Bryant. 3300 GALLOWS RD 22042 #010-01-1964 L1976 **OS OBG** *075

JAMIL, Mouhamad Ghyath. 3300 GALLOWS RD 22042 #875-02-1994 L2003 **PCC** *020 †20

JANCZEWSKI, Mark Geo. 5209 LEESBURG PIKE STE 817, OASD/HA INFO MGMT DIR 22041 #051-07-1986 L1987 **FM AM** *062 †70,18

JASANI, Archana Balubhai. 2946 SLEEPY HOLLOW RD, SEVEN CORNERS MED ARTS BLD 22044 #010-02-1987 L1991 **PD** *020 †55

JEFFER, Edward Kenneth. 3701 S GEORGE MASON DR 22041 #005-06-1966 L1995 **P** *020 †75 ‡

JOHNSON, Dara Flagg. 3300 GALLOWS RD, FAIRFAX HOSPITAL 22042 #023-01-2002 L2002 **PD** *020

JOHNSON, Kathryn Lee. 2941 FAIRVIEW PARK DR, STE 100 22042 #023-12-1981 L1985 **OM PHP** *020 †70

JOHNSON, Pamela Carol. 3300 GALLOWS RD, INOVA FAIRFAX HOSPITAL, ER 22042 #041-07-1991 L2004 **FM GP** *020

JOHNSON, Robert W. 2251 PIMMIT DR, STE C3 22043 #016-11-1980 L1984 **P** *020 †75

JOLLY, Brantley T, Jr. 3300 GALLOWS RD 22042 #036-05-1987 L1990 **EM** *020 †16

KAMDAR, Faisal Majeed. 3448 DIEHL CT 22041 #010-12-2000 L2006 **AN** *020 †05

KASENETZ, Iver. 6060 ARLINGTON BLVD, FALLS CHURCH MEDICAL 22044 #016-42-1975 L1980 **U** *020 †95

KAYE, Joseph T. ■ 22042 #010-01-1948 L1964 **ORS** *071 †40

KEBAISH, Adel Soliman. 7787 LEESBURG PIKE, # B 22043 #915-02-1975 L1987 **ORS HEM** *020 †40

KELLER, Stephen Richard. 3300 GALLOWS RD, FAIRFAX HOSP DEPT PED 22042 #051-04-1978 L1982 **PD CCP** *020 †55

KELLY, Lawrence F. 3300 GALLOWS RD 22042 #010-02-1968 L1970 **PD** *020 †55

KENDERS, Kathryn L. 3300 GALLOWS RD 22042 #010-01-1970 L1972 **EM PE** *020 †16

KENNEDY, Stephen Francis. 3300 GALLOWS RD, FAIRFAX HOSPITAL 22042 #010-02-1973 L1975 **AN PME** *020 †05

KHANDHAR, Sandeep J. 2921 TELESTAR CT STE 140 22042 #016-06-1999 L2007 **TS GS** *020 †85

KHAWAND, Nabil Youssef. 3300 GALLOWS RD 22042 #915-02-1979 L1988 **U TTS** *020 †95 ‡

KHAYATMOFID, Forouzandeh. 3300 GALLOWS RD 22042 #010-01-1994 L1997 **FM** *020 †18

KIERNAN, Paul Darlington. 2921 TELESTAR CT, STE 140 22042 #010-02-1974 L1982 **TS** *020 †85,90

KILFEATHER, John Edward. 3300 GALLOWS RD 22042 #041-02-1961 L1968 **IM PUD** *020

KILICAL, Baran. 3300 GALLOWS RD, MEDICAL STAFF OFFICE 22042 #010-01-2002 L2005 **CD** *012 †20

KIM, Chin Moon. ■ 22043 #583-02-1952 L1967 **PD** *071 †55

KIM, Jean H. 2946 SLEEPY HOLLOW RD, STE 4B 22044 #035-15-2000 L2006 **END IM** *100 †20

KIM, Kenneth Su. ■ 22043 #021-01-1981 L2003 **IM** *020 †20

KIM, Suk Kew. 5884 LEESBURG PIKE 22041 #583-02-1960 L1976 **AN GP** *072

KLEIN, David Nahum. 3300 GALLOWS RD 22042 #010-01-1988 L1989 **EM** *020 †16

KLEIN, Jonathan. 6400 ARLINGTON BLVD, STE 940 22042 #561-03-1983 L1986 **IM IMG** *020 †20

KLING, Robert P. ■ 22042 #041-01-1952 L1965 **OPH RP** *020 †35

KOCH, James Frederick. 3300 GALLOWS RD 22042 #016-02-1981 L1986 **IM** *020 †05

KOHILAS, Konstantino T. 3300 GALLOWS RD, EMERG DEPT 22042 #023-01-2001 L2004 **EM** *020 †16

KOLIA, Gulam-Mohmed M. 6408 SEVEN CORNERS PL 22044 #495-22-1968 L1977 **CD IM** *020 †20

KONIGSBERG, James Louis. 3300 GALLOWS RD, DEPT OF ANESTHESIA FAIRFAX 22042 #010-01-1981 L1982 **AN IM** *020 †20,05

KOPACK, Gregory Edward. 3300 GALLOWS RD, EMERGENCY DEPT 22042 #010-02-1997 L1997 **FM** *020 †18

KORCAK, Jerome Michael. ■ 22041 #017-20-1961 L1979 **FM OS** *020 †18

KORNHAUSER, Michael James. 3300 GALLOWS RD 22042 #048-02-1962 L1969 **IM** *071

KOU, Maybelle. 3300 GALLOWS RD, INOVA FAIRFAX HOSP 22042 #010-01-1993 L1993 **EM PE** *020 †16

KRIEGER, Elizabeth Ann. ■ 22043 #010-02-2005 L2005 **IM** *012

KRONEN, Michael Robt. 3300 GALLOWS RD, INOVA FAIRFAX HOSPITAL 22042 #033-06-1987 L1994 **P** *020 †75

KUHN, Robert Edward. 3300 GALLOWS RD, FAIRFAX HOSPITAL 22042 #005-02-1997 L2000 **IM** *020 †16

KURZ, Otto A. 3300 GALLOWS RD 22042 #407-15-1951 L1956 **IM IMG** *071

LA BELLE, Ellen Jones. ■ 22041 #010-01-1974 L1978 **P** *020 †75

LAM, Hiu Fung. 3300 GALLOWS RD, DEPT OF EMERGENCY MEDICINE 22042 #024-05-1998 L1999 **EM** *020 †16

LAPHAM, Timothy Robert. 3300 GALLOWS RD, DEPARTMENT OF SURGERY 22042 #051-04-2001 L2001 **GS** *100

LAQUINTE, Vanessa. 3300 GALLOWS RD 22042 #041-12-2004 L2004 **PD** *020

LASHKERI, Taher S. 3300 GALLOWS RD, INOVA FAIRFAX HOSPITAL 22042 #665-01-2003 L2005 **PEM** *012 †16

LASOTA, Jon Francis. 3300 GALLOWS RD, FAIRFAX HOSPITAL 22042 #041-02-1992 L1996 **AN** *020 †05

LATCHIS, Erika M. 3300 GALLOWS RD, JNOVA FAIRFAX HOSPITAL 22042 #407-16-1963 L1970 **OBG** *020

LATKIN, Peter Chas. 6201 LEESBURG PIKE STE 300 22044 #035-09-1968 L1973 **PDA** *020 †55,03

LAWSON, Karen Ac. 6060 ARLINGTON BLVD, FALLS CHURCH MED CTR 22044 #010-02-1988 L1989 **IM** *020 †20

LE, Tru Van. 6404 SEVEN CORNERS PL # F 22044 #942-01-1974 L1995 **PD** *020 †55

LEARY, Patrick J. ■ 22044 #010-01-1953 L1955 **OBG OS** *071 †30

LEE, Eugene Kim. 3300 GALLOWS RD, DEPT OF EMERG MED 22042 #016-06-2002 L2005 EM *020 †16

LEE, Samuel Suckjae. 3300 GALLOWS RD, INOVA FAIRFAX HOSPITAL 22042 #023-01-1996 L2003 AN *020 †20,05

LEE, Seo Ryong. 3300 GALLOWS RD 22042 #583-10-1972 L1984 OBG *020 †30

LENCZYK, Michael Edward. 3300 GALLOWS RD, FAIRFAX HOSPITAL 22042 #033-06-1988 L1996 AN *020 †05

LETO, Carl Jos. 3300 GALLOWS RD 22042 #024-07-1980 L1984 OPH *020 †35

LEVORSON, Rebecca C. ■ 22041 #021-06-2004 L2007 PDI *012 †55

LEVY, Chauncey F, Jr. ■ 22043 #010-03-1950 L1998 OPH *071 †35

LIMAYE, Nirmala Suresh. ■ 22042 #495-17-1961 L1974 GYN *071 †30

LISBOA, Keilla Amorim. 3300 GALLOWS RD, DEPT OF GENERAL SURGERY 22042 #010-01-2006 L2006 GS *012

LOTFI, Ali. 3300 GALLOWS RD 22042 #517-01-1962 L1987 OBG R *020 †30

LOVICH, Susan Kim. 3300 GALLOWS RD 22042 #035-01-1989 L1997 PD *020 †55

LUSSOS, Steven Alexander. 3300 GALLOWS RD, FAIRFAX HOSPITAL 22042 #010-02-1987 L1991 AN *020 †05

LYONS, William S. ■ 22041 #010-01-1951 L1960 TS GP *071 †85,90

MAC MANUS, Quentin. 3300 GALLOWS RD 22042 #028-02-1970 L1979 TS VS *071 †85,90

MAGUIRE, John Francis. 3300 GALLOWS RD, EMERG DEPT - C/O KRISTI HU 22042 #010-02-1997 L2001 EM *020 †16

MAHANEY, Kevin Jos. 3300 GALLOWS RD, EMERGENCY DEPRTMENT 22042 #033-05-1990 L1991 EM *020 †20,16

MAHER, Jennifer Gail. 3300 GALLOWS RD, FAIRFAX HOSPITAL 22042 #055-01-1986 L1990 AN *020 †05

MAHER, Virginia Ellen. 6400 ARLINGTON BLVD, STE 940 22042 #041-13-1986 L1988 HEM *020 †20

MALEKZADEH, Alireza. 3300 GALLOWS RD, DEPARTMENT OF ORTHOPEDAEDI 22042 #010-01-1999 L2005 OTR *020 †40

MALIN, Edward Walter, IV. 3300 GALLOWS RD 22042 #010-01-2003 L2003 GS *012

MALKA, Jeffrey S. 3300 GALLOWS RD 22042 #869-04-1963 L1973 ORS OS *020 †40

MANALO, Bayani L. 6400 SEVEN CORNERS PL # G 22044 #748-02-1967 L1972 GE *020 †20

MANTHRIPRAGADA, Gopi Kris. 3300 GALLOWS RD, DEPARTMENT OF MEDICINE 22042 #016-06-2004 L2004 IM *100 †20

MARDELLI, Pierre G. 3300 GALLOWS RD 22042 #028-34-1991 L1992 OPH OS *020 †35

MARGULIES, David Mervyn. 3300 GALLOWS RD 22042 #016-06-1961 L1969 OBG *020 †30

MARTIN, Edward Dana. 5203 LEESBURG PIKE, STE 506 22041 #019-02-1970 L1988 PD *030

MASRI, As'Ad M. 5673 COLUMBIA PIKE, STE 200 22041 #051-01-1962 L1963 P *075 †75

MASSIMIANO, Paul Stephen. 3300 GALLOWS RD 22042 #010-02-1978 L1990 CD VS *020 †85,90

MASTERS, Emine Cay. 6720 ARLINGTON BLVD 22042 #010-02-1983 L1984 GYN GP *020 †30

MASTROTA, Francis M. ■ 22041 #010-02-1946 L1956 IM PD *071 †55

MAW, Khin Thet. 3302 GALLOWS RD, HEALTH INSTITUTE 22042 #209-01-1978 L1987 P *100

MAYRANT, Stephanie Renee. ■ 22041 #012-21-2006 P *012

MAZHARI, Ramesh. 3300 GALLOWS RD, OFFICE OF MEDICAL STAFF 22042 #665-01-1999 L2004 IC *100 †20

MAZID, Mohamed Rani. 3300 GALLOWS RD, KAISER OFFICE INOVA FAIRFA 22042 #875-02-1982 L1995 IM *020 †20

MCCAULEY, Meredith Marlin. 3300 GALLOWS RD, MED CRITICAL CARE SERVICE 22042 #028-34-2000 L2007 PCC *020 †20

MC CONNELL, Brian Alan. 3300 GALLOWS RD 22042 #041-14-1992 L1998 AN PME *020 †05

MCFADDEN, Devin Patrick. ■ 22043 #028-34-2007 L2007 FP *012

MC INERNEY, Ellen Rose. 3300 GALLOWS RD, DEPT OF MEDICINE 22042 #051-07-1996 L1998 IM *020 †20

MECHANICK, Judith. 3300 GALLOWS RD, FAIR FAX HOSPITAL 22042 #041-01-1982 L1985 IM *020 †20

MECKLENBURG, Fred Emil. 3300 GALLOWS RD - OB, INOVA FAIRFAX HOSP 22042 #026-04-1960 L1981 GYN *030 †30

MEHTA, Yoginkumar P. ■ 22043 #495-22-1965 L1975 U *071 †95

MELMED, Allan Stanley. 7659 LEESBURG PIKE 22043 #021-01-1972 L1975 P *020 †75

MELTZER, Andrew Charles. 3300 GALLOWS RD, INOVA FAIRFAX HOSPITAL EME 22042 #035-08-2002 L2006 EM *100 †16

MERCER-DALY, William. 5205 LEESBURG PIKE, STE 1500 22041 #539-02-1950 PHP OM *030

MESROBIAN, Robert Bennett. 3300 GALLOWS RD, DEPT OF ANES 22042 #016-43-1976 L1983 AN PD *020 †55,05

MEYER, Richard Selig. 6404 SEVEN CORNERS PL, STE F 22044 #041-09-1971 L1993 ORS *020 †40

MEZA, Griselda. 3300 GALLOWS RD 22042 #048-14-2007 L2007 PD *012

MGHIR, Rim. 6073 ARLINGTON BLVD 22044 #875-02-1983 L1993 P *020

MIAN, Ayesha Manzoor. ■ 22041 #010-01-2006 L2006 P *012

MIAN, Uzma Amer. 3535 S JEFFERSON ST, RIOMEDICAL LLC 22041 #704-06-1988 L2007 IM *020 †20

MICHALOWICZ, Joleen Marie. ■ 22041 #010-02-1991 *071

MICHETTI, Christopher P. 3300 GALLOWS RD, TRAUMA SERVICES 22042 #041-13-1994 L2001 TRS CCS *020 †85

MILAM, Mallory, Jr. 3300 GALLOWS RD, DEPT OF ANESTHESIOLOGY 22042 #010-01-1997 L2001 AN *020 †05

MILTEER, Regina Melinda. 3300 GALLOWS RD, INOVA FAIRFAX HOSP FOR CHI 22042 #051-04-1979 L1982 PD *030 †55

MISHRA, Alita. 3300 GALLOWS RD, DEPT OF MEDICINE 22042 #056-06-2000 L2000 IM *020 †20

MITCHELL, William A. 6312 SEVEN CORNERS CTR, PMB 302 22044 #041-01-1974 L1995 P *020 †75

MODE, Arthur Sander. 6073 ARLINGTON BLVD 22044 #038-41-1962 L1979 P *020 †75

MODLINGER, Paul Steven. ■ 22043 #035-19-1997 L2001 NEP *020 †20

MONIZ, Albert. 6060 ARLINGTON BLVD 22044 #010-02-1956 L1960 PD *071 †55

MOORE, Jennifer Dorothy. 6565 ARLINGTON BLVD, STE 500 22042 #016-43-1997 L2004 IMG *020

MOORE, Stephen Lee. ■ 22042 #024-07-1983 L1988 FM *020 †18

MORILLO, Segundo A. 5669 COLUMBIA PIKE 22041 #737-06-1976 L1987 FM *020

MORJARIA, Mukund M. 6408 SEVEN CORNERS PL # D 22044 #496-15-1969 L1975 IM *020

MOSES, Wm Russell Wallace. ■ 22044 #010-01-1939 L1946 GS *071 †85

MUIR, James Cameron. 6565 ARLINGTON BLVD # 500 22043 #051-01-1993 L2002 HO *020 †20

MUKHERJEE, Dipankar. 2921 TELESTAR CT, STE 140 22042 #495-36-1976 L1989 VIR AS *020 †85

MURIAS, Juan L Suarez. ■ 22044 #275-01-1950 L1964 PD AI *071

MYERS, Boyd Douglas. 3300 GALLOWS RD 22042 #023-01-1967 L1972 OPH *071 †35

MYRUSKI, Kimberly Sue. 3300 GALLOWS RD, FAIRFAX ANESTHESIOLOGY 22042 #010-01-1999 L2003 IM *020 †05

NABHA, Linda. ■ 22041 #010-02-2007 L2007 IM *012

NAM, Jae Joong. 6408 SEVEN CORNERS PL, STE K 22044 #583-03-1973 L1979 OTO *020

NAM, Myoung Ho. 3300 GALLOWS RD, INOVA FAIRFAX HOSPITAL 22042 #583-02-1981 L1986 PTH *020 †50

NANCHERLA, Suchithra A. 2946 SLEEPY HOLLOW RD 22044 #495-21-1981 L1987 END IM *020 †20

NASR, Mohamed Zaki M. 3302 GALLOWS RD, NORTHERN VIRGINIA MENTAL H 22042 #915-03-1966 L1989 P *020

NATHAN, Steven Dale. 3300 GALLOWS RD, INOVA TRANSPLANT CTR 22042 #836-01-1981 L1994 PUD CCM *020 †20

NECHIN, Kenneth Michael. 3300 GALLOWS RD 22042 #010-01-1981 L1982 AN *020 †20,05

NEPTUNE, Dominique. ■ 22041 #010-02-2002 L2002 P *100

NGUYEN, Dung. 6404 SEVEN CORNERS PL, STE M 22044 #941-01-1970 L1986 IM *020

NGUYEN, Dung Duc. 3300 GALLOWS RD 22042 #041-09-1994 L1997 AN *020 †05

NGUYEN, Giang Tuong. 6408 SEVEN CORNERS PL, STE F 22044 #941-01-1969 L1981 OBG *020 †30

NGUYEN, Henriette Tong. 6400 SEVEN CORNERS PL # N, SEVEN CORNERS PROF PK 22044 #840-01-1964 L1973 GP PTH *020

NGUYEN, Kim-Dung Thi. 6305 CASTLE PL, STE 3D 22044 #942-01-1990 L2000 IM *020 †20

NGUYEN, Lang Hai. ■ 22042 #051-01-2008 *012

NGUYEN, Long Thanh. 6408 SEVEN CORNERS PL # C 22044 #941-01-1970 L1986 PM GP *020

NGUYEN, Michael N. 3300 GALLOWS RD, KAISER PERMANENTE OFFICE 22042 #396-18-1981 L1998 IM *020 †20

NGUYEN, Minh-Chau Thi. 3300 GALLOWS RD, DEPT OF PSYCH 22042 #942-01-1983 L2005 P PYG *020

NGUYEN, Tung Duc. 6404 SEVEN CORNERS PL # J 22044 #941-01-1979 L1987 PD *020

NGUYEN, Van Hoang. 3300 GALLOWS RD, DEPT OF PSYCHIATRY 22042 #942-01-1982 L2005 P *100

NISSELSON, Catherine L. ■ 22041 #051-04-1978 L1984 AN *020

NITZSCHKE, Stephanie Lynn. 3300 GALLOWS RD 22042 #016-43-2005 L2005 GS *012

NOBARIAN, Rayehe A. 3300 GALLOWS RD 22042 #517-01-1953 L1978 PD OS *071 †55

NOVAK, David Joseph. 3300 GALLOWS RD 22042 #010-02-1995 L1995 ORS *020 †40

O'CONNOR, Donald James. 3302 GALLOWS RD, INST 22042 #010-01-1987 L1988 FM *020 †18

ODEND'HAL, Fortune, IV. 3300 GALLOWS RD 22042 #023-01-1960 L1966 EM GP *020

O'DONNELL, Francis L. 5113 LEESBURG PIKE, STE 901 22041 #035-08-1969 L1970 GPM ID *030 †20,70

O'DONNELL, Mary Beck. 2960 SLEEPY HOLLOW RD, DOMINION HOSPITAL 22044 #010-02-1989 L1991 IM *020 †20

O'DONNELL, Mary Therese. 3300 GALLOWS RD, FAIRFAX HOSPITAL 22042 #010-02-1984 L1987 IM PCC *062 †20

O'DONNELL, Maureen Susan. 3300 GALLOWS RD, DEPT. OF SURGERY 22042 #016-11-1997 L1997 GS *020 †85

O'HARA, Collin Joy. ■ 22043 #038-45-2005 PTH *012

OKOSUN, Stanley Eromonsel. 3300 GALLOWS RD 22042 #690-06-1997 L2003 GS *012

O'NEILL, Wm James, Jr. 7115 LEESBURG PIKE STE 224 22043 #010-01-1980 L1986 GS *020

ONG, Janus Po. 3300 GALLOWS RD, ATTN: MEDICAL STAFF OFFICE 22042 #748-02-1993 L2001 GE *020 †20

O'SHAUGHNESSY, Matthew J. ■ 22043 #026-04-2008 *012

OSHINSKY, Arnold Lawrence. 6060 ARLINGTON BLVD, FALLS CHURCH MEDICAL 22044 #023-01-1975 L1979 OPH *020 †35

PAGANUSSI, Peter J. 3300 GALLOWS RD, DEPT OF EMERGENCY MED. 22042 #010-02-1985 L1989 EM *020 †16

PALMER, Emily Davis. 2956 SLEEPY HOLLOW RD, SLEEPY HOLLOW PEDIATRICS 22044 #036-08-2000 L2000 PD *020 †55

PAN, Jeff J S. 6408 SEVEN CORNERS PL # L 22044 #244-04-1979 L1987 U NO *020 †95

PARK, Tong Soo. 3300 GALLOWS RD, INOVA FAIRFAX HOSPITAL 22042 #583-02-1971 L1979 NPM *020 †55

PASTERNAK, Lewis Reuven. 3300 GALLOWS RD, INOVA FAIRFAX HOSP 22042 #036-07-1977 L1979 AN CCM *030 †05

PASTORE, Lucia. 3300 GALLOWS RD 22042 #035-15-1977 L1980 PTH BBK *020 †50

PATE, Muhammad Ali. ■ 22043 #690-03-1990 L2001 ID *020 †20

PATEL, Chetankumar R. 3300 GALLOWS RD, INOVA FAIRFAX HOSPITAL 22042 #495-89-1984 L1999 AN CCA *020 †05

PATEL, Minal. 3300 GALLOWS RD, INOVA FAIRFAX EMERGENCEY D 22042 #422-01-1997 L2002 PEM *020 †20

PATLA, Venkataramana Rao. 3300 GALLOWS RD, FAIRFAX ANESTHESIOLOGY ASS 22042 #495-65-1983 L2001 AN CCA *020 †05

PAUZE, Denis Robert, Jr. 3300 GALLOWS RD, DEPT OF EMERGENCY MEDICINE 22042 #010-02-1995 L1998 PEM *100 †16

PERACHA, Hameed. 3400 PAYNE ST STE 200 22041 #704-02-1980 L1995 OPH NM *020 †35

PETERS, Leslie Lawrence. ■ 22041 #473-04-1948 L1957 OS GP *071

PETIT, Joshua Henry. 3300 GALLOWS RD, REDICTION ONCOLOGY ASSCOIA 22042 #023-01-2002 L2007 *100

PETTRONE, Frank Angelo. 3300 GALLOWS RD 22042 #010-02-1969 L1974 ORS OSM *020 †40

PHILLIPS, Jeffrey Howard. 6404 SEVEN CORNERS PL, STE F 22044 #035-46-1974 L1978 ORS *020 †40

PHO, Van Ngoc. 6400 SEVEN CORNERS PL # J 22044 #941-01-1971 L1983 GP *020

PIRZADEH, Solmaz. 2393 WATTERS GLEN CT 22043 #023-07-2008 *012

PO, Heng-Tsui. 3300 GALLOWS RD 22042 #242-10-1948 L1960 AN *020

POLLNER, Jane Hildy. 3300 GALLOWS RD 22042 #038-40-1988 L1990 ID IM *020 †20

POTTANAT, Cissy Paul. 6319 CASTLE PL, STE 3D 22044 #495-63-1989 L1995 FPG *020 †18

POTTER, Michael Chas. 3300 GALLOWS RD 22042 #010-02-1969 L1971 GS *020 †85

POWELL, Beverly Ann. 3300 GALLOWS RD 22042 #010-02-1975 L1978 PD OS *020 †55

PRASAD, Kalpna. ■ 22043 #495-98-1998 L2004 FM *020

PRICE, Kathleen Robinson. 2946 SLEEPY HOLLOW RD, STE 4B 22044 #025-01-1977 L1984 RHU IM *020 †20

PRICE, Philip Ashley. 3300 GALLOWS RD 22042 #010-02-1984 L1988 AN *020 †05

PRINZ, Ulrich Bernd. 3705 S GEORGE MASON DR, STE C65 22041 #051-01-1987 L1990 IM IMG *020 †20

PRINZ, Werner. ■ 22041 #407-32-1952 L1956 GP *071

PULLARKAT, Ranjit Raju. 3300 GALLOWS RD, INOVA FAIRFAX HOSPITAL TRA 22042 #024-05-1994 L2007 GS CCS *020

PURDY, Deborah Rachel. ■ 22043 #024-07-2005 L2005 PD *012

■ = Address Information Privacy Protected

PURKERT, William John. 3300 GALLOWS RD 22042 #010-02-1979 L1983 **GS** *020 †85
QUINONES-MAESO, Lorraine. 3300 GALLOWS RD, INOVA FAIRFAX HOSP-EMERG D 22042 #042-01-1987 L2001 **EM** *020 †16
RAFIQ, Nila. ■ 22042 #305-01-2004 L2007 **IM** *012 †20
RAHMAN, Shahzad. 3302 GALLOWS RD 22042 #495-24-1979 L1994 **P** *020 †75
RAMACHANDRAN, Sathya. ■ 22043 #496-32-2000 L2008 **OBG** *020
RANDHAWA, Gurvaneet S. ■ 22043 #495-03-1991 **IM** *100
RAO, Somashekar Narayana. 3300 GALLOWS RD, KAISER HSM/INOVA FAIRFAXHO 22042 #495-33-1991 L1994 **IM** *020 †20
RAVANI, Ali. ■ 22041 #517-01-1964 **CLP PTH** *050
REARDON, William John. 6060 ARLINGTON BLVD 22044 #010-02-1948 L1957 **FM** *071
RECINOS, Adrian, Jr. 6060 ARLINGTON BLVD 22044 #035-01-1945 L1950 **PD** *071 †55
RECKER-DUFFY, Sabine. 3300 GALLOWS RD, DEPARTMENT OF ANESTHESIOLO 22042 #409-24-1987 L2006 **AN** *05
REDDITT, Julie Catherine. 7659 LEESBURG PIKE 22043 #187-55-1982 L1988 **CHP P** *020
REDDY, Archana K. 3300 GALLOWS RD, DEPARTMENT OD 22042 #016-11-2004 L2005 **EM** *012
REED, James Todd. 3300 GALLOWS RD 22042 #035-15-1988 L1991 **IM** *020 †20
REINES, Howard David. 3300 GALLOWS RD, BASEMENT TOWER BLDG 22042 #050-02-1972 L1989 **GS CCS** *030 †85
REMY, Terri Federline. 6060 ARLINGTON BLVD, FALLS CHURCH MEDICAL 22044 #010-01-1989 L1991 **IM** *020 †20
RENTIA, Sameera Naser. 5651 COLUMBIA PIKE 22041 #495-28-1991 L1996 **PD** *020 †55
RHYMERS, Kurt Lee. 3300 GALLOWS RD 22042 #010-01-1977 L1978 **OBG** *020 †30 ‡
RIBEIRO, Gilberto H V. 3300 GALLOWS RD 22042 #462-01-1962 L1980 **AN** *040 †05
RICE, Diane Beach. 3300 GALLOWS RD, FAIRFAX HOSP DEPT PATH 22042 #055-01-1981 L1983 **PTH HMP** *020 †50
RIVERA, Antonio Rafael. 6319 CASTLE PL, STE 1E 22044 #737-01-1981 L2001 **NEP** *020 †20
RIZVI, Carol Anne Spencer. 3302 GALLOWS RD 22042 #038-40-1959 L1972 **P** *071
RIZZO, Anne Grace. 3300 GALLOWS RD, DEPARTMENT OF TRAUMA 22042 #035-06-1989 L2004 **CCS TRS** *020 †85
ROBERTSON, Jason Wade. 2946 SLEEPY HOLLOW RD, SLEEPY HOLLOW PEDIATRICS 22044 #023-07-2000 L2005 **PD** *020
ROSE, Gaylord S. 3300 GALLOWS RD, WOMEN'S AND CHILDREN'S, DE 22042 #048-15-1987 L2007 **OBG** *020 †30
ROSEMBLAT, Aldo Mario. 6316 CASTLE PL STE 2E 22044 #132-01-1973 L1982 **NS OM** *020 †25
RUCKSTUHL, Lily. 3300 GALLOWS RD 22042 #869-04-1954 L1958 **CD IM** *071
RUSSO, Eugene P. 3300 GALLOWS RD, TRAUMA SVCS DEPT OF SURG 22042 #010-02-1971 L1978 **TRS CCS** *020 †85
SAAD-EL-DEEN, Mustafa A. 5205 LEESBURG PIKE, STE 209 22041 #915-02-1978 L1996 **IM END** *020
SACHS, Sharona. 6565 ARLINGTON BLVD 22042 #035-06-1988 L2008 **PUD** *020 †20
SACIRBEY, Aziza A. ■ 22043 #957-01-1955 **P OBG** *074
SACIRBEY, Nedzib. ■ 22043 #957-01-1955 L1974 **P PHP** *071
SADAK, Karim Thomas. 3300 GALLOWS RD, PEDIATRIC RES PROGRAM 22042 #010-01-2006 L2006 **PD** *012
SADEGHI, Farideh. 3300 GALLOWS RD, KAISER OFFICE FAIRFAX HO 22042 #517-01-1976 L1991 **IM** *020 †20
SAKRAN, Joseph Victor. 3300 GALLOWS RD 22042 #550-04-2005 L2005 **GS** *012
SALAZAR, Delfin B. 3300 GALLOWS RD 22042 #748-01-1954 L1961 **AN OS** *020
SALTER, Fredric Louis. 6404 SEVEN CORNERS PL, STE F 22044 #041-09-1981 L1987 **ORS** *020 †40
SANDOVAL, Fabian. ■ 22042 #649-14-2003 *100
SASVARI, Jennifer Lynne. 3300 GALLOWS RD, INOVA-FAIRFAX HOSPITAL 22042 #033-05-2002 L2006 **EM** *100
SAWAYA, Sam Elie. ■ 22043 #048-04-2006 L2006 **IM** *012
SAWHNEY, Jasmine Kaur. ■ 22044 #051-04-2006 **P** *012
SCHACHNER, Stephen Harold. 3300 GALLOWS RD 22042 #030-06-1961 L1968 **END** *071 †20
SCHEIDLINGER, Jeffrey A. 3300 GALLOWS RD 22042 #035-46-1982 L1988 **AN CCM** *020 †20,05
SCHLOFF, Lizann. 7659 LEESBURG PIKE 22043 #010-01-1994 L1995 **P OS** *020 †75
SCOTT, Hugh Patrick. 5201 LEESBURG PIKE, STE 701 22041 #041-77-1964, ▲ L1965 **OTO FPS** *062
SCOTT, Susan J Argyle. 3507 RUSTIC WAY LN 22044 #051-01-1986 L1995 **PDC** *050 †55
SCRIBNER, James Thomas. ■ 22042 #010-02-2008 *012
SELMONOSKY, Carlos A. ■ 22041 #132-01-1956 L2002 **GP CD** *071 †85,90
SEMCHYSHYN, George O. 7659 LEESBURG PIKE 22043 #010-02-1963 L1971 **P** *020 †75
SENECA, Russell P. 3300 GALLOWS RD, DEPT OF SURGERY 22042 #010-02-1967 L1967 **GS CCS** *040 †85
SEOUDI, Hani Muhammad S. 3300 GALLOWS RD, INOVA FAIRFAX HOSPITAL 22042 #915-04-1984 L2002 **GS CCS** *020 †85
SHAIKH, Farook Ahmed. 6305 CASTLE PL STE 3C 22044 #496-38-1983 L1987 **IM ADM** *020 †20 ‡
SHAKOOR, Mohammed Abdus. 3300 GALLOWS RD, THE FAIRFAX HOSPITAL 22042 #495-21-1962 L1977 **AN OS** *071
SHAMIM, Noman. ■ 22041 #704-27-2000 **P** *012
SHANMUGAM, Natesa Pandian. 3300 GALLOWS RD, MEDICAL STAFF OFFICE 22042 #495-59-1990 L2004 **IM** *020 †20
SHAPPELL, Cynthia M. 3300 GALLOWS RD 22042 #048-13-1987 L2006 **PYM** *020 †75
SHAVER, Benjamin Alfonza. ■ 22042 #008-01-1956 L1965 **PD** *071 †55
SHEN, Irving. 2921 TELESTAR CT, STE 140 22042 #040-02-1988 L2006 **GS** *020 †85,90
SHERIDAN, Andrew J. 3300 GALLOWS RD 22042 #010-02-1970 L1976 **OPH** *071 †35 ‡
SHERIDAN, Charmayne T. ■ 22042 #143-03-1966 L1972 **EM FM** *075
SHIN, Wan. 3300 GALLOWS RD 22042 #583-01-1968 L1979 **PM** *020 †60
SHLOBIN, Oksana. 3300 GALLOWS RD, INOVA FAIRFAX HOSPITAL 22042 #010-02-1999 L2004 **PCC OS** *020 †20
SHUMAN, Lawrence Henry. ■ 22041 #016-42-1954 L1963 **OBG OS** *020 †30
SIGNORE, Caroline Cox. ■ 22043 #011-03-1992 L1994 **OBG** *071 †30
SIMMONS, Rachel Caroline. 3300 GALLOWS RD, EMERGENCY DEPT/C/O THOM MA 22042 #010-01-1996 L1997 **EM** *020 †16
SINGER, Steven Alan. 3300 GALLOWS RD 22042 #550-02-2007 **GS** *012
SIPES, James Norton. 2946 SLEEPY HOLLOW RD 22044 #051-01-1970 L1970 **IM CD** *020 †20
SIVALINGAM, Rukmani. ■ 22042 #917-08-2000 L2007 **IM** *100 †20
SKIBBIE, David Franklin. 3300 GALLOWS RD, INOVA FAIRFAX HOSP EMGY MD 22042 #010-01-1995 L1999 **EM** *020 †16
SPANIER, Holly Elizabeth. 3300 GALLOWS RD 22042 #023-01-2005 L2005 **PD** *012

SPEIR, Alan Mc Bain. 2921 TELESTAR CT, STE 140 22042 #012-01-1975 L1981 **TS VS** *020 †85,90
SPINELLA, Giovanna Maria. ■ 22042 #041-09-1980 L2005 **CHN PD** *020 †55
SPRISSLER, Greg Thos. 3300 GALLOWS RD, OF ANES 22042 #035-15-1973 L1978 **AN** *020 †05
STABILE, Jack Anthony. 3300 GALLOWS RD, FAIRFAX ANESTHSLGY ASSOC 22042 #024-01-1989 L1993 **AN** *020 †05
STAGLIANO, David Richard. ■ 22041 #051-04-2003 L2005 **PD** *100 †55
STEPHENS, Brian Osborne. 3300 GALLOWS RD 22042 #836-01-1980 L1996 **ORS** *020 †40
STIEGLER, Charles F. 6060 ARLINGTON BLVD 22044 #035-19-1940 L1948 **PD** *071
STITH, Rosa Bell. 5111 LEESBURG PIKE, SKYLINE 5 SUITE 810 22041 #051-04-1975 L1975 **FM** *030 †18
STONE, Richard Wayne. ■ 22041 #165-04-1980 L1986 **DR** *020 †80
STOTZ, William H. 3300 GALLOWS RD, CHILDREN - PEDS CCM 22042 #051-01-1995 L2003 **CCP** *020 †55
SUTHERLAND, Valerie Hope. 3300 GALLOWS RD, INOVA FAIRFAX HOSPITAL 22042 #005-06-2002 L2003 **IM** *100 †20
SUTTON, Richard Geo. 3258 VALLEY LN 22044 #010-02-1974 L1982 **P** *020 †75
TABATABAI, Babak. ■ 22042 #051-04-2007 L2007 **TY** *012
TAZANU, Abila Violet. 3300 GALLOWS RD DEPT PED 22042 #010-03-1996 L1996 **PD** *020 †55
TENHUNDFELD, Lynda Ardell. 7659 LEESBURG PIKE 22043 #007-02-1985 L1994 **CHP P** *020 †75
THAI, Cam-Tu Thi. 6316 CASTLE PL, STE 301 22044 #396-02-1986 L1996 **IM** *020
THOMAS, Gregory Lee. 5109 LEESBURG PIKE, C/O GNA 22041 #010-03-1976 L1979 **DR EM** *020 †18
THORNTON, Dawn Marie. 3300 GALLOWS RD, DEPT OF EMERGENCY MEDICINE 22042 #010-01-1994 L1997 **EM PE** *020 †20
THU, Tin Moe. 6400 SEVEN CORNERS PL, STE F 22044 #209-01-1986 L1997 **IM** *020 †20
TILDON-ARCHER, Donna L. ■ 22041 #010-03-1982 L1990 **NPM PD** *020 †55
TJAHJANA, Mingliarti. 6305 CASTLE PL, STE 3D 22044 #016-06-1997 L2004 **IM** *020
TOBIAS, Mitchell David. 3300 GALLOWS RD, ANESTHESIOLOGY INOVA FRFX 22042 #550-02-1984 L2001 **AN PME** *020 †05
TON, Camvan Nu. 6107 ARLINGTON BLVD, STE AB 22044 #942-01-1972 L2000 **IM** *020 †20
TONNESEN, Glenn Lorin. 3300 GALLOWS RD, RADIATION ONCOLOGY DEPT. 22042 #049-01-1973 L1981 **RO** *020 †80
TON-THAT, Han. 6305 CASTLE PL, STE 1A 22044 #023-01-1991 L1997 **GE** *020 †20
TRABERT, Richard Eric. 2946 SLEEPY HOLLOW RD, STE 3B 22044 #010-02-1965 L1970 **PD** *020 †55
TRAN, De Dinh. 3705 S GEORGE MASON DR 22041 #941-01-1947 L1970 **OS GYN** *071
TRAN, Kevin. ■ 22042 #051-01-2007 **IM** *012
TRAN, Quang Truc. 7309 ARLINGTON BLVD # 314 22042 #941-01-1978 L1987 **IM** *020
TRAN, Sang Van. 6319 CASTLE PL, STE 2A 22044 #941-01-1977 L1994 **IM** *020 †20
TRAN, Tam Thu. 6408 SEVEN CORNERS PL, STE M 22044 #942-01-1980 L1998 **IM** *020 †20
TREICHLER, Howard P. ■ 22044 #010-01-1946 L1957 **GYN** *071 †30
TRIPATHI, Paul C. 3300 GALLOWS RD, DEPT. OF EMERGENCY MEDICIN 22042 #024-05-2000 L2004 **EM** *020 †16
TRIVEDI, Vaishali H. 3300 GALLOWS RD 22042 #048-13-2006 L2006 **GS** *012
TSOU, Anthony Ying. 6400 SEVEN CORNERS PL 22044 #847-01-1966 L1976 **GP** *072
TU, Lan Chau Hang. 6404 SEVEN CORNERS PL # G 22044 #409-24-1979 L1990 **AI PD** *020 †55,03
TU, Richard Phay. 6404 SEVEN CORNERS PL # G 22044 #941-01-1972 L1990 **IM AN** *020,05
TULLOCH, Earl F, Jr. 3300 GALLOWS RD 22042 #036-05-1967 L1971 **IM EM** *020 †20
TUTUNCUOGLU, Suleyman O. ■ 22043 #902-07-1987 L2004 **PCP** *100
TYSZ, Samantha Anne. 3300 GALLOWS RD, EMERGENCY DEPT 22042 #047-06-1994 L1994 **EM** *020 †55,16
UNDERWOOD, Paula Kay. 5111 LEESBURG PIKE STE 538, OFF OF THE SURG GEN 22041 #007-02-1984 L1988 **PHP** *020 †70
UY, Adrian Thaddeus A L. 6060 ARLINGTON BLVD, FALLS CHURCH MEDICAL 22044 #748-10-1992 L2003 **IM** *020 †20
UZER, Matt A. 3300 GALLOWS RD, EMERGENCY DEPT 22042 #054-01-1985 L1988 **IM** *020 †20
VAN OEVEREN, Edward L. ■ 22044 #051-04-1995 L1997 **GP GPM** *020 †70
VARGA, John Henry. 5205 LEESBURG PIKE 22041 #038-40-1981 L1996 **OPH MDM** *071 †35
VIDWANS, Neil Mohan. 6060 ARLINGTON BLVD, FALLS CHURCH MEDICAL 22044 #025-01-1998 L2003 **IM** *020 †20
VILLAVICENCIO, Jorge E. 3300 GALLOWS RD, STE 1100 22042 #319-01-1951 L1956 **GP** *020
VIORRITTO, Erick Nathan. ■ 22043 #010-01-2007 L2008 **PD** *012
VISH, Michael George. 3300 GALLOWS RD 22042 #025-07-1999 L2006 **CCP** *100 †55
VISH, Nora Labiano. 3300 GALLOWS RD, DIVISION OF PEDIATRICS 22042 #025-07-2001 L2006 **PD** *020 †55
VOURLEKIS, Jason Sotos. 3300 GALLOWS RD, INOVA FAIRFAX HOSPITAL 22042 #016-06-1991 L2003 **IM PCC** *020 †20
WAH, Robert. 3160 FAIRVIEW PARK DR 22042 #040-02-1983 L1986 **OBG REN** *062 †30
WAHAB, Abdul. 6400 ARLINGTON BLVD 22042 #118-01-1982 L1992 **NEP IM** *020 †20
WAKED HAMMOUD, Tarek Moha. 3300 GALLOWS RD 22042 #605-01-2006 L2007 **GS** *012
WARREN, Marjorie Johnson. 6045 ARLINGTON BLVD 22044 #010-03-1982 L1984 **P DR** *075
WATSON, Joseph Clark. 3300 GALLOWS RD, IHVI STE 3100 22042 #005-18-1991 L1991 **NS** *020 †25 ‡
WEINBERG, Richard Lewis. 6565 ARLINGTON BLVD, STE 500 22042 #025-01-1978 L2005 **IM** *020 †20
WEIR, Nargues A. 3300 GALLOWS RD, INOVA FAIRFAX HOSPITAL 22042 #010-01-1996 L2002 **PCC** *020 †20
WHITE, Molly Jeanne. ■ 22042 #028-34-2007 L2007 *012
WILLNER, Henry Steven. 6565 ARLINGTON BLVD, STE 501 22042 #008-01-1975 L1978 **FM PLM** *020 †18
WIN, Sein. 6400 SEVEN CORNERS PL # F 22044 #209-01-1988 L1995 **PD** *020 †55
WINDREICH, Randy Marc. 3300 GALLOWS RD 22042 #550-02-2005 L2005 **PD** *020
WISE, Thomas Nathan. 3300 GALLOWS RD 22042 #036-07-1969 L1970 **P** *020 †75
WLADYKA, Christopher Geor. ■ 22043 #010-02-2004 L2005 **DR** *012
WONG, Charissa Joanwai. 6231 LEESBURG PIKE, STE 608 22044 #036-01-1997 L1997 *020
WRIGHT, John Jos. ■ 22043 #016-06-1981 L1988 **IM ON** *020 †20
WU, Peter Kim. 3300 GALLOWS RD 22042 #023-07-1997 L1997 **AN** *020 †05
YARNALL, David Chas. 3300 GALLOWS RD, FAIRFAX HOSPITAL DEPT ANES 22042 #041-14-1990 L1991 **AN PAN** *020 †05
YAZDI, Hamid A. 3300 GALLOWS RD, INOVA FAIRFAX HOSPITAL, EME 22042 #306-01-1995 L2007 **EM** *020

YERKOVICH, Stephen A. 3300 GALLOWS RD 22042 #035-06-1974 L1982 **EM IM** *020 †20,16

YOON, Albert Sukchul. 3302 GALLOWS RD 22042 #583-01-1963 L1981 **P** *020 †75

YOON, Hang Jin. 3300 GALLOWS RD 22042 #583-01-1968 L1977 **AN** *020

YOUNOSSI, Zobair M. 3300 GALLOWS RD, CENTER LIVER DISEASES 22042 #035-45-1989 L2000 **HEP GE** *020 †20

YUZEFOVICH, Michael. ■ 22042 #305-01-2003 L2003 **OBG** *020

ZAMAN, Syed Ashrafuz. 3300 GALLOWS RD, PATHOLOGY DEPARTMENT 22042 #160-02-1983 L1993 **PTH** *020 †50

ZIAI, Mohsen. 3300 GALLOWS RD, EMERITUS, PEDRC 22042 #023-07-1952 L1982 **PD** *071 †55

ZIMMERMAN, Harold Baer. 3300 GALLOWS RD 22042 #035-06-1958 L1967 **DR** *071 †80

ZIMMET, Steven Michael. 3300 GALLOWS RD 22042 #051-01-1968 L1968 **PUD CCM** *020 †20

ZUNDEL, Nathan Stewart. ■ 22042 #010-01-2008 *012

FALLS CHURCH – FALLS CHURCH CITY

ADIB, Houtan. 201 N WASHINGTON ST 22046 #517-01-1962 L1982 **DR** *020 †80

AHMED, Humaira Farhat. 402 S OAK ST 22046 #495-65-1991 L2000 **IM** *020 †20

AKHAVAN, Melody. 201 N WASHINGTON ST 22046 #035-48-2003 L2007 **AN** *020

ALBERTS, Wayne Wm. 201 N WASHINGTON ST 22046 #025-01-1966 L1980 **GS PDS** *071

ALEXANDER, Mary Pamela. 201 N WASHINGTON ST, KAISER PERMANENTE 22046 #051-07-1993 L2002 **IM** *020 †20

ANGOSO, Manuel Roberto. 313 PARK AVE STE 201 22046 #847-11-1986 L1989 **IM** *020 †20

ATIYEH, Bassam A. 107 N VIRGINIA AVE, NORTHERN VA PEDIATRICS 22046 #605-01-1985 L1995 **PD** *020 †55

AUSTIN, Frank Hutches, Jr. ■ 22040 #048-12-1948 L1991 **AM OM** *071 †70

AWAD, Elias Bruce. 201 N WASHINGTON ST, FALLS CHURCH MEDICAL CENTE 22046 #051-01-1999 L2002 **FM** *020 †18

BACHA, Frieda E. 201 N WASHINGTON ST, KAISER PERMANENTE MEDICAL 22046 #035-15-1985 L1993 **PTH ATP** *020 †50

BAE, Allison Junghwa. 131 E BROAD ST, STE 102 22046 #051-04-1996 L1998 **FM** *020 †18

BANAJI, Mridula. 101 N WASHINGTON ST, MAPMG /AFTER HOURS CARE 22046 #495-37-1994 L2002 **FM PD** *020 †55,18

BARAKAT, Amin J. 107 N VIRGINIA AVE 22046 #605-01-1967 L1976 **PD NEP** *020 †55 ‡

BARTRAM, Scott Fox. 407 N WASHINGTON ST, STE 104 22046 #016-06-1979 L1980 **FM** *020 †18

BAYES, Beverley Joan. 107 N VIRGINIA AVE 22046 #065-01-1961 L1969 **PD** *020 †55

BEACH, Douglas Matthew. ■ 22046 #051-04-2000 L2007 **PCC** *020 †20

BEACH, Jennifer Lehman. ■ 22046 #051-04-2000 L2000 **IM** *020

BEHARI, Ashish. 201 N WASHINGTON ST 22046 #041-02-1997 L1999 **U** *020 †95

BERGIN, Patrick Finley. ■ 22046 #028-02-2005 **ORS** *012

BERRY, Jacqueline R. 201 N WASHINGTON ST, FALLS CHURCH 22046 #010-03-1981 L1987 **IM UCM** *020 †20

BOARDMAN, Barbara. 201 N WASHINGTON ST, KAISER PERMANENTE PEDIATRI 22046 #041-13-1982 L1988 **PD PHP** *020 †55

BOLDT, Leigh Sangone. 201 N WASHINGTON ST 22046 #010-01-1990 L1996 **IM** *020 †20

BORRERO, Jaime. ■ 22046 #264-03-1953 L1989 **IM** *020 †20

BRONSTHER, Oscar L. 201 N WASHINGTON ST 22046 #035-08-1978 L2001 **GS OS** *020 †85

BUJANAUSKAS, Paul. 201 N WASHINGTON ST, 3RD FL 22046 #008-02-1990 L2007 **D** *020 †15

BULL-HENRY, Kathy P. 201 N WASHINGTON ST, DEPT OF GASTROENTEROLOGY 22046 #024-05-1981 L2003 **IM** *020 †20

BUNTEN, Bradley Leblang. 201 N WASHINGTON ST, FALLS CHURCH MEDICAL CENTE 22046 #010-01-1995 L2007 **AN** *012 †16

BUZZELL, Dawn Marie. 201 N WASHINGTON ST 22046 #010-01-1987 L1990 **OBG** *020 †30

BYER, Barry. 131 E BROAD ST STE 102 22046 #011-02-1969 L1970 **FM** *020

BYER, David Leland. 115 GRESHAM PL 22046 #010-02-2008 *012

CALIGTAN, Emma Alvaro. 201 N WASHINGTON ST, C/O DEPT OF ANESTHESIOLOGY 22046 #748-08-1966 L1984 **AN** *020 †05

CARDINAL, Linda. 201 N WASHINGTON ST 22046 #050-02-1986 L1999 **GS** *020 †85

CARLSON, Marysusan D. 201 N WASHINGTON ST 22046 #010-02-1985 L1989 **OPH** *020 †35

CARTER, Renee Yvonne. 201 N WASHINGTON ST, KAISER PERMANENTE-FALLS CH 22046 #045-04-1991 L2005 **PD** *020 †20

CATALANO, Christa Lynn. 201 N WASHINGTON ST, FALLS CHURCH MEDICAL CENTE 22046 #024-05-2000 L2000 **DR** *020 †80

CHAN, Dao Huy. ■ 22040 #692-01-1952 L1974 **OBG** *020

CHAUDARY, Maleeha Rahmat. 201 N WASHINGTON ST, DEPT OF URGENT CARE 22046 #704-15-1992 L2000 **FM** *020 †18 ‡

CHETTA, Sidney Guyol. 201 N WASHINGTON ST 22046 #021-05-1977 L1987 **ORS** *020 †40

CHIANG, Jeanne Tsenglai. 101 W BROAD ST, GEORGE MASON SQUARE 22046 #010-01-1992 L1994 **FM** *020 †18

CHRISTIANSON, Charles S. 103 W BROAD ST, STE 200 22046 #040-02-1943 L1945 **PUD IM** *071 †20

CLANOR, Teodora-Rowena B. 201 N WASHINGTON ST 22046 #748-01-1991 L2001 **PD** *020 †55

DANIEL, Elena. 201 N WASHINGTON ST, KAISER - OTOLARYNGOLOGY 22046 #036-05-1999 L2005 **OTO** *020 †45

DAVIDOV, Michael. 500 N WASHINGTON ST 22046 #957-02-1961 L1969 **CD IM** *071

DEMISSIE, Pupi. 201 N WASHINGTON ST, DEPT OF PEDIATRICS 22046 #010-03-1995 L2008 **PD** *020 †55

DENETTO, Michelle Ann. 201 N WASHINGTON ST 22046 #917-26-1992 L2004 **IM** *020 †20

DEREN, Susan Elizabeth. 201 N WASHINGTON ST, KAISER PERMANENTE 22046 #033-05-1995 L1998 **IM** *020 †20

DEWEY, John Bradford. 201 N WASHINGTON ST 22046 #024-05-1975 L1977 **ORS OAR** *020 †40

DIBBLE, Robin Li. ■ 22046 #051-01-1985 L1998 **GPM** *020

DIM, Bomen Hifzi. 405 N WASHINGTON ST 22046 #902-01-1955 L1964 **P** *020 †75

DO, Nhan Van. ■ 22046 #051-01-1994 L1996 **IM** *020 †20

DOUGLASS, Frances Alberta. 201 N WASHINGTON ST 22046 #010-03-1970 L2007 **PD** *020 †55

DRAKE, Stanley David. 201 N WASHINGTON ST 22046 #021-01-1985 L1990 **GE** *020 †20

DUVALL, Weijia Zhou. 201 N WASHINGTON ST, FALLS CHURCH MEDICAL CENTE 22046 #051-07-1994 L1994 **AN** *020 †05

DVORAK, Cecily Susan. 900 S WASHINGTON ST, STE 300 22046 #056-06-2002 L2002 **FM** *100 †18

ECONOMON, Straty Harry. 313 PARK AVE 22046 #023-01-1960 L1965 **P** *071

FARZANEH, Iraj. 201 N WASHINGTON ST 22046 #517-06-1967 L1985 **PD** *020 †55 ‡

FERMIN, Cyrelda Ramirez. 201 N WASHINGTON ST 22046 #748-08-1984 L1997 **PD** *020 †55

FIALCO, Marc Ira. 201 N WASHINGTON ST 22046 #038-41-1965 L1985 **OBG** *020 †30

FLEMING, Bryan W, Jr. 201 N WASHINGTON ST, KAISER PERMANTE FALLS CHUR 22046 #023-07-1962 L2000 **ORS OS** *071 †40

FORMAN, Alyson Rachel. 201 N WASHINGTON ST, FALLS CHURCH MEDICAL CENTE 22046 #051-04-1999 L2002 **PD** *020 †55

GARLING, Andrew C. ■ 22046 #024-01-1972 L1977 **OS EM** *030 †16

GILBERT, Roberta M. 313 PARK AVE STE 308 22046 #035-06-1962 L1987 **P** *062 †75

GONDHALEKAR, Smita S. 201 N WASHINGTON ST, FALLS CHURCH ADMINISTRATIO 22046 #495-28-1976 L1987 **PD** *020 †55

GORDON, Gary Hart. 201 N WASHINGTON ST, DEPT OF RADIOLOGY 22046 #010-02-1960 L1987 **DR NR** *020 †80

GRANOVSKY, Monica O. 201 N WASHINGTON ST 22046 #024-07-1992 L1999 **PD HO** *020 †55

GRESINGER, Thomas Hamlin. 900 S WASHINGTON ST, STE 300 22046 #010-01-1961 L1967 **OBG** *020 †30

GUPTA, Devika Padgaonkar. 201 N WASHINGTON ST, FALLS CHURCH MEDICAL CENTE 22046 #495-27-1987 L1996 **IM** *020 †20

GUZHVA, Olena O.. ■ 22046 #913-05-1993 L2007 **RHU** *012 †20

HALPIN, Diane Linda. 107 N VIRGINIA AVE 22046 #010-02-1995 L1995 **PD** *020 †55

HATA, Tracie Fumiko. 201 N WASHINGTON ST, KAISER PERMANENTE 22046 #014-01-1998 L2005 **FM** *020 †18 ‡

HAWKINS, Katrina Dafnis. ■ 22046 #010-01-2005 L2005 **IM** *012

HENTZ, Robert Douglas. 201 N WASHINGTON ST, KAISER PERMANENTE FALLS CH 22046 #010-01-1999 L1999 **FM** *020 †18

HERBERT, Henry Regis, Jr. 201 N WASHINGTON ST, KAISER-PERMANENTE 22046 #010-02-1960 L1981 **IM OM** *071 †20,70

HUANG, Angeline Hooiteen. 201 N WASHINGTON ST 22046 #005-12-1985 L1988 **FM** *020 †18

JAIN, Geeta. 201 N WASHINGTON ST, FALLS CHURCH MEDICAL CENTE 22046 #496-04-1978 L1994 **PD** *020 †55

JIN, Tina Aram. 131 GREAT FALLS ST STE 101 22046 #001-06-1996 L2003 **P CHP** *020 †75

JONES, Myriam Irma. 201 N WASHINGTON ST 22046 #005-14-1991 L1997 **IM** *020 †20

KARICKHOFF, John Robt. 313 PARK AVE 22046 #036-07-1964 L1970 **OPH** *020 †35

KELLY, Lisa Stehli. 107 N VIRGINIA AVE, N VIRGINIA PED ASSOC 22046 #038-06-2000 L2001 **PD** *020

KIM, Chul. 201 N WASHINGTON ST 22046 #583-02-1968 L1979 **OBG** *020 †30

KING, Don Wayne. ■ 22046 #048-02-1969 L1969 **N** *020 †75

KRUSE, Katherine Legare. 107 N VIRGINIA AVE 22046 #036-05-1998 L1998 **PD** *020 †55

KWAN, Alex M. 201 N WASHINGTON ST, SURGERY CENTER 22046 #748-02-1967 L1990 **AN** *020 †05

LAGRENADE, Alana Anne. 201 N WASHINGTON ST 22046 #010-03-1982 L1989 **PTH U** *062 †50

LEE, Donna. 201 N WASHINGTON ST, KAISER PERMANENTE 22046 #035-48-1990 L1993 **IM** *020 †20

LEE, Taisheng. 201 N WASHINGTON ST, KAISER FALLS MED CTR ENDO 22046 #047-06-1988 L1999 **END IM** *012 †20

LEGASPI, Alfredo Lacuna. FAIRFAX HOSPITAL, DEPARTMENT OF ANESTHESIA 22046 #748-01-1963 L1971 **AN** *071 †05

LIANG, Chitsui Vivia. 201 N WASHINGTON ST, FALLS CHURCH MEDICAL CENTE 22046 #051-04-2002 L2006 **OBG** *020

MAGNANT, George Arthur. 201 N WASHINGTON ST 22046 #010-02-1954 L1959 **PD** *020 †55

MAJETE, Lisa Kim. 201 N WASHINGTON ST, KAISER PERMANENTE 22046 #010-03-1997 L2001 **IM** *020 †20

MARTIN, George Wm. ■ 22046 #045-01-1947 L1957 **GP OBG** *071

MARTIN, Joilyn Stinson. 201 N WASHINGTON ST 22046 #038-41-1990 L2001 **OBG** *020 †30

MERENSTEIN, Daniel Jon. 103 W BROAD ST, FAMILY PHYSICIANS OF ARLIN 22046 #041-02-1997 L1997 **FM** *020 †18

MILLEA, Paul Jos. 101 W BROAD ST, DEPARTMENT OF INTEGRATIVE 22046 #056-06-1984 L2006 **FM** *020 †18

MOHANTY, Nivedita. 201 N WASHINGTON ST, KAISER PERMANE NE. 22046 #495-13-1983 L2000 **FM** *020 †18

MOUCHAHOIR, Ely George. 107 N VIRGINIA AVE 22046 #051-01-1998 L2004 **PD** *020 †55

MYERS, Lynne Beth Davis. 107 N VIRGINIA AVE 22046 #035-08-1971 L1974 **PD** *020 †55

NEAS, Gregory Alan. 201 N WASHINGTON ST 22046 #847-06-1979 L1984 **OTO** *020 †45

NGUYEN, Hoang-An Ngoc. 201 N WASHINGTON ST, FALLS CHURCH MED CTR 22046 #051-01-1997 L2003 **IM** *020 †20

NGUYEN, Khoa Quoc. 821 W BROAD ST 22046 #941-01-1972 L1985 **D PTH** *020 †50,15

NGUYEN, Vincent. 201 N WASHINGTON ST, KAISER PERMANENTE 22046 #047-06-1989 L1991 **FM** *020 †18 ‡

NGUYEN, Vu The. 201 N WASHINGTON ST, ATTN: CREDENTIALS DEPT 22046 #010-01-1996 L1998 **IM** *020 †20

OH-TAN, Hanita Therese. 407 N WASHINGTON ST, STE 100 22046 #010-01-2000 L2006 **PD** *020 †55

ONDER, Mehmet Hami. 200 LITTLE FALLS ST, STE 301 22046 #902-01-1949 L1968 **IM CD** *020

OSBORN, June Elaine. ■ 22046 #038-06-1961 L1961 **PD IM** *030 †55

OSWALD, Leticia Ann. 201 N WASHINGTON ST 22046 #748-01-1967 L1981 **PD** *071 †55

PHOENIX, Janet Arnetha. ■ 22046 #010-03-1989 **PHP** *020

PIERCE, Amy L. 201 N WASHINGTON ST, STE 100 22046 #035-15-1998 L2002 **PD** *020 †55

PIERRE, Karen Suzette. 201 N WASHINGTON ST 22046 #048-13-1986 L2003 **PTH** *020 †50

PILLAY, Jaya. 201 N WASHINGTON ST 22046 #495-33-1971 L1979 **OBG** *020 †30

POBLETE, Pio Ferrer. 131 E BROAD ST STE 103 22046 #748-02-1963 L1963 **IM** *020 †20

REDDY, Gita Susan. 201 N WASHINGTON ST, KAISER PERMANENTE 22046 #054-04-2001 L2006 **PD** *020 †55

REED-LINTON, Melinda M. 201 N WASHINGTON ST, KAISER PERMANENTE 22046 #047-07-1998 L2005 **FM** *020 †18

REILLY, Michael Jos. ■ 22046 #010-02-1956 L1963 **IM PUD** *071 †20

ROGART, Rochelle Epstein. 201 N WASHINGTON ST, INTERNAL MEDICINE DEPT 22046 #035-46-1975 L1997 **IM ID** *050 †20

ROLAND, Miriam Woodall. 200 LITTLE FALLS ST STE 20 22046 #048-02-1976 L1980 **P** *020 †75

ROTH, Daniel Jay. 201 N WASHINGTON ST, MAPMG-FALLS CHURCH MEDICAL 22046 #041-09-1991 L1997 **PD** *020 †55

RUIZ, Gil Madrigal. 200 LITTLE FALLS ST 22046 #748-01-1963 L1973 **IM A** *020

SALSBURY, Carl Allen. 407 N WASHINGTON ST, STE 100 22046 #051-04-1965 L1965 **PD A** *020 †55

SAROFF, Donald Avram. 201 N WASHINGTON ST 22046 #047-05-1992 L2002 **ORS** *020 †40

SCHILLER, Wilma Sue. 201 N WASHINGTON ST, ANESTHESIOLOGY DEPT. 22046 #043-01-1979 L1995 **AN IM** *020 †20,05

SCHMIEG, Andrea Marie. 407 N WASHINGTON ST, STE 104 22046 #041-02-1998 L1998 FM *020 †18

SCHWARTZ, Wendy N. 103 W BROAD ST STE 120 22046 #035-45-1978 L1981 FM *020 †18

SCOTT, Thomas Walter. 106 LITTLE FALLS ST 22046 #010-01-1975 L1977 OBG *020 †30

SEGAL, Lydia Sharon. 101 W BROAD ST, STE 300 22046 #003-01-1985 L1994 FM *020 †18

SHAHIDI, Firoozeh H. 313 PARK AVE STE 202 22046 #308-10-1986 L1991 END IM *020 †20

SHAW, Charles Holmes. ■ 22046 #025-07-1968 L2006 ORS *071 †40

SHERER, David Jonathan. 201 N WASHINGTON ST, DEPT OF ANESTHESIA 22046 #024-05-1984 L1992 AN *020 †05

SHIFFMAN, Jeanne Willis. 103 W BROAD ST STE 120 22046 #010-02-2001 FM *020 †18

SIMMONS, Steven Parker. 201 N WASHINGTON ST, KAISER PERMANENTE 22046 #047-06-1993 L1998 IM *020 †20

SJOGREN, Robert Wm, Jr. 201 N WASHINGTON ST 22046 #051-04-1971 L1993 GE HEP *020 †20

SMITH, Ronald Earl. 140 LITTLE FALLS ST 22046 #048-12-1971 L1997 PYA P *020 †20,75,16

SNYDER, Mark Harvey. 201 N WASHINGTON ST, KAISER PERMANENTE 22046 #041-02-1979 L1982 ID IM *030 †20

STALLINGS, James H, Jr. 107 N VIRGINIA AVE 22046 #010-01-1952 L1955 PD *071 †55

STERN, Neil. 201 N WASHINGTON ST 22046 #041-07-1981 L1986 OTO *020 †45

SY, Rody Gan. ■ 22046 #748-02-1974 L1980 CD *020

TERRIS, Mark Howard. 201 N WASHINGTON ST, KAISER PERMANENTE/ADMIN OF 22046 #005-02-1989 L1995 OTO *020 †45

THEISZ, Gordon Walker. 104A E BROAD ST 22046 #051-01-1998 L1998 FM *020 †18 ‡

THOMPSON, Curtis R. 520 N WASHINGTON ST, STE 101 22046 #038-45-1988 L1992 P *020 †75

TODD, Nushin F. 201 N WASHINGTON ST, ADMINISTRATION OFFICE 22046 #010-02-1993 L1999 HO *020

TRINIDAD, Cristina L. 201 N WASHINGTON ST 22046 #748-11-1968 L1990 IM *020 †20

TSONG, Edward Deyee. 201 N WASHINGTON ST 22046 #035-19-1999 L2008 OTO *100 †45

TURKUS, Joan A. 200 LITTLE FALLS ST STE 20 22046 #010-01-1959 L1980 P PFP *020 †28,75

TWENTYMAN, Scott Sheldon. 1207 OFFUTT DR 22046 #051-04-1982 L1983 PYA P *020 †75

VALASES, Charles. 201 N WASHINGTON ST 22046 #418-02-1982 L1989 GS *020 †85

VASWANI, Nari P. 200 LITTLE FALLS ST STE 20 22046 #495-17-1948 L1959 P *020

WALECKI, Jan K. 201 N WASHINGTON ST 22046 #759-01-1957 L1985 DR *020 †80

WATKIS, Patricia Ann. 201 N WASHINGTON ST, KAISER PERMEMENTE 22046 #036-07-1981 L1990 DR *020 †80

WATSON, Charles Henry. 407 N WASHINGTON ST, STE 100 22046 #025-01-1957 L1965 PD *071 †55

WAXMAN, Phyllis Gail. 407 N WASHINGTON ST, STE 100 22046 #023-01-1987 L1991 PD *020 †55

WEBB, Jennifer Lindy. ■ 22046 #023-07-2007 PD *012

WRIGHT, Marlene Victoria. 201 N WASHINGTON ST 22046 #051-07-1983 L1996 PD *020 †55

YU, Dan. 201 N WASHINGTON ST, KAISER PERMANENTE MED CTR 22046 #243-72-1985 L1998 IM *020 †20

ZHANG, Jianyi. 900 S WASHINGTON ST, STE 303 22046 #243-47-1982 L1998 GPM IM *020

ZWIRB, Mary E Wall. 201 N WASHINGTON ST 22046 #010-02-1985 L1987 IM *020 †20

FANCY GAP — CARROLL

ASHBY, Evan H, Jr. CASCADE MOUNTAIN RESORT 24328 #051-01-1951 L1951 OS GP *071

TRACY, John Wm. ■ 24328 #036-01-1982 L2004 FM *020 †18

FARMVILLE — PRINCE EDWARD

ABBAS, Magdi Ahmed. 800 OAK ST, SOUTHSIDE COMM HOSP -ER 23901 #915-02-1974 L1994 EM IM *020 †20

AGEE, Robert L, IV. 800 BUFFALO ST 23901 #051-01-1983 L1984 OBG *020 †30

AL-SHAMMAA, Hussien A. 300 E 3RD ST, FARMVILLE PEDIATRICS 23901 #915-02-1983 L1993 PD EM *020 †55

ANDERSON, George Edward. 800 OAK ST, DEPARTMENT OF ANESTHESIA 23901 #047-06-1982 L1986 AN *020 †05

BONAGIRI, Vara Prasad. ■ 23901 #495-57-1982 L1996 IM *020 †20

BROWNING, Joseph Edward. 833 BUFFALO ST, STE 200 23901 #021-06-1996 L1999 OBG *020 †30

CAPATI-DIONISIO, Teresita. 502 BEECH ST 23901 #748-08-1969 L1983 PD *020 †55

COLLMANN, Warren X. 108 4TH ST 23901 #041-01-1950 L1969 GS GP *071 †85

CORBETT, Timothy Wiley. 324 COMMERCE RD, STE A 23901 #047-07-1984 L1998 FM FPG *020 †18

DONKOR, Kwabena Agyarko. 800 OAK ST 23901 #412-01-1975 L1991 PUD IM *020 †20

DONOVAN, Mary Burleson. 800 OAK ST 23901 #028-34-1978 L1980 FM *020 †18

DUNN, J Wayland. 800 OAK ST 23901 #051-04-1957 L1957 GP *020

EISENSTEIN, Steven B. 108 CARSON MILLS DR 23901 #016-02-1990 L1996 P *020 †75

GOLDBERGER, Stephen H. 808 BUFFALO ST 23901 #024-05-1973 L1998 OTO A *020 †45

GOODFRIEND, David Peter. 100 POPLAR FOREST RD APT G 23901 #023-01-1991 L1999 GPM *020 †70

GORDON, Edward I. 800 OAK ST 23901 #023-01-1971 L1973 FM PD *020

GOTTFRIED, Irving Sass. 800 OAK ST 23901 #422-01-1981 L1986 GE IM *020 †20

HANEY, Ronald Loyde. 1509 W 3RD ST 23901 #011-02-1964 L1973 ORS *020

HEMLER, Paul Martin. 800 OAK ST 23901 #010-02-1954 L1956 AN *072 †05

HUBER, Kirsten Lynn. 800 OAK ST, STE 3-105 23901 #011-02-1986 L1996 GS *020 †85

JANES, Donald Nelson, Jr. ■ 23901 #005-15-2002 L2007 EM *020 †16

KONA, John Andrew. 800 OAK ST, ORTHOPEDIC AND REHABILITAT 23901 #051-07-1981 L1983 ORS *020 †40

LA ROCHE, Ripon Wilson. PO BOX 506 23901 #045-01-1978 L1981 OPH *020 †35

LENTZ, Gary Dean. ■ 23901 #038-40-1969 L1986 GS *071 †85

MAMURIC, Janette Ann A. 800 OAK ST 23901 #748-08-1992 L1998 PD *020 †55

MARTINEZ, Jesus A, Jr. 800 OAK ST 23901 #308-03-1996 L2001 IM *020 †20

MC DEVITT, Michelle Leigh. ■ 23901 #036-01-2001 L2007 AN *020

MENDEZ, Hedley Norman, III. 800 OAK ST 23901 #011-02-1970 L1971 EM *071 †16

NASH, H Robert. ■ 23901 #041-13-1977 L1981 PTH *020 †50

PATEL, Pravinbhai. 800 OAK ST, DEPT ER 23901 #495-20-1972 L1994 AN *020

PRUITT, David E. 833 BUFFALO ST, STE 200 23901 #305-01-1998 L1999 FM *020 †18

PUROHIT, Girish. 800 OAK ST 23901 #905-01-1970 L1976 CD IM *020 †20

ROTHFELS, Peter Lewis. PO BOX 414 23901 #060-01-1981 L1984 *020

SAN, Luke C. 202 AGEE ST 23901 #422-01-1989 L1992 IM *020

SHCHELCHKOV, Evgueni A. 800 OAK ST 23901 #913-36-1996 L2003 N LM *020 †75

SINNATAMBY, Diane S. 800 OAK ST, SOUTHSIDE COMMUNITY HOSPIT 23901 #220-03-1991 L2004 ID IM *020 †20

STAIGER, Linda Faye. 808 BUFFALO ST 23901 #051-07-1977 L1982 ORS *075 †40

TAN, Anjanette Sia Lin. 800 OAK ST, SOUTHSIDE COMMUNITY HOSPIT 23901 #748-02-1998 L2003 END *020 †20

TURNER, John Mills, III. ■ 23901 #051-04-1961 L1961 OBG *071 †30

VARNER, Lawrence Callie. 400 LONGWOOD AVE, FAMILY MED OF FARMVILLE 23901 #051-04-1982 L1983 FM FPG *020 †18

WILLS, James Michael. ■ 23901 #055-01-1979 L2006 DR *020 †80

WILSON, Chas Staples, Jr. 808 BUFFALO ST 23901 #051-04-1978 L1979 OPH *020 †35

WINE, John Robert. 800 OAK ST 23901 #051-04-1976 L1977 FM *020 †18

WITTEN, Vilma Camomot. 420 E 3RD ST, THE PROFESSIONAL BUILDING 23901 #748-11-1972 L1983 FM OBG *020 †18

FERRUM — FRANKLIN

ROYCROFT, Elizabeth Weick. 9388 CHARITY HWY 24088 #035-03-1963 L1971 PD *020 †55

FINCASTLE — BOTETOURT

ANDREWS, Clarke Butler. 36 BOTETOURT RD, PC FAMILY PRACTICE 24090 #051-07-1979 L1981 FM *020 †18

BAILEY, Dewey James. ■ 24090 #041-02-1955 L1958 IM *071 †20

BALABAN, James Bryce. ■ 24090 #008-02-1989 IM *100

HAYS, David R, Jr. 6025 OLD FINCASTLE RD 24090 #035-19-1949 L1991 OM IM *020

NGANELE, Charlotte Nutt. PO BOX 268, 108 E MAIN ST 24090 #035-09-1990 L2004 P *020 †75

FISHERSVILLE — AUGUSTA

ANDERSEN, Charles Frederi. 70 MEDICAL CENTER CIR, STE 110 22939 #028-02-1968 L1974 ORS *071 †40

ANDERSEN, Moira B. PO BOX 1000, AUGUSTA MEDICAL CENTER 22939 #051-01-1993 L1997 EM *075 †16

ANDERSON, J Powell. 96 MEDICAL CENTER DR 22939 #036-07-1949 L1954 FM FPG *071 †18

BARNES, David Milton. 17 N MEDICAL PARK DR 22939 #051-01-1988 L1995 OPH *020 †35

BARRETT, Michael Arthur. 78 MEDICAL CENTER DR, AMC. HOSPITALIST 22939 #010-01-1986 L1988 HOS IM *020 †20

BEEBE, Lucius Courtenay. 70 MEDICAL CENTER DR, STE 208 22939 #045-01-1978 L1988 U NM *020 †95

BENDFELDT, Carlos F. 9 S MEDICAL PARK DR 22939 #047-20-1995 L1999 OBG *020 †30

BOATRIGHT, Kenneth Allen. 70 MEDICAL CENTER DR, ORTHOPEDIC ASSOCIATES LTD 22939 #028-34-1977 L1983 ORS OSM *020 †40

BRANDT, Nicholas Carsten. 78 MEDICAL CENTER DR, AMC HOSPITALISTS 22939 #024-07-1999 L1999 IM *020 †20

BRIGHT, Richard Homer. 94 LONGVIEW CIR 22939 #038-06-1956 L1997 IM *020

BROOKS, Charles Harris. 70 MEDICAL CENTER CIR, STE 207 22939 #045-01-1973 L1978 NEP IM *020 †20

BROOKS, Mark P. 9 S MEDICAL PARK DR 22939 #030-06-1987 L1990 OBG *020 †30

BRYAN, Phillips R, Jr. 70 MEDICAL CENTER CIR 22939 #051-01-1969 L1969 U *020 †95

BUCHANAN, Patricia Kay. 78 MEDICAL CENTER DR 22939 #051-04-1986 L1989 DR *020 †80

BUCKLEY, Carie Dan, III. 70 MEDICAL CENTER CIR 22939 #004-01-1976 L1981 U *020 †95

BURGESS, David A. 70 MEDICAL CENTER DR, ORTHOPEDIC ASSOCIATES LTD 22939 #012-01-1980 L1989 ORS *020 †40

CAMPBELL, Garland Adam. ■ 22939 #051-01-2004 L2007 NEP *012 †20

CANADY, Sita S. 22 N MEDICAL PARK DR 22939 #051-01-1999 L2003 PD *020 †55

CARMICHAEL, Donald Corwin. 70 MEDICAL CENTER CIR, STE 213 22939 #010-02-1986 L2004 GS *020 †85

CASTELLO, Fred Mark. 78 MEDICAL CENTER DR 22939 #051-07-1980 L1983 PD *020 †55

CAULKINS, Charles W, Jr. 96 MEDICAL CENTER DR 22939 #051-04-1947 L1947 GS *071 †85

CAULKINS, David Whitney. 70 MEDICAL CENTER CIR 22939 #051-04-1980 L1985 GS *020 †85

CHACKO, Jacob M. 96 MEDICAL CENTER DR, AUGUSTA MEDICAL CENTER 22939 #917-18-1981 L1982 AN *020 †05

CHALDARES, Louis Steven. 78 MEDICAL CENTER DR 22939 #055-01-1977 L1981 AN *020 †05

CHRISTENSEN, Darin Lee. 70 MEDICAL CENTER CIR, STE 201 22939 #049-01-1990 L1991 P *020 †75

COMAR, James Shine. 96 MEDICAL CENTER DR, DEPARTMENT OF ANESTHESIOLO 22939 #045-01-1969 L1975 AN *020 †05

CRAMER, John David. 78 MEDICAL CENTER DR, AMC HOSPITALIST 22939 #012-01-1998 L2003 NEP *100 †20

DAMERON, Rebecca Doull. 78 MEDICAL CENTER DR 22939 #051-01-1989 L1994 DR *020 †80

DARRACOTT, Mixon Milford. 1161 BARRENRIDGE RD 22939 #045-01-1963 L1970 GYN *020 †30

EARLY, Stephen Vest. 70 MEDICAL CENTER CIR, STE 302 22939 #051-01-1984 L2001 PDO OTO *020 †45

EISENBERG, Edward F. 78 MEDICAL CENTER DR 22939 #011-02-1982 L1990 AN P *020 †75,05

ESCANELLAS, Jaime. 70 MEDICAL CENTER CIR, STE 211 22939 #042-02-1988 L1994 CD *020 †20

ESTEBAN, Felicia. 91 TINKLING SPG DR, ABC CHILDREN'S HEALTH CENT 22939 #045-01-1997 L2005 PD *020 †55

ESTEBAN, Ramon Corpus. 78 MEDICAL CENTER DR 22939 #045-01-2000 ORS *020 †40

FARLEY, Benjamin Gates. 535 S MEDICAL PK DR, AUGUSTA FAMILY PRACTICE 22939 #045-01-1995 L1998 FM *020 †18

FAULKENBERRY, William L. 70 MEDICAL CENTER DR, STE 213 22939 #051-07-1978 L1980 GS AS *020 †85

FERGUSON, Melinda Louise. 9 S MEDICAL PARK DR 22939 #048-02-1992 L1992 OBG *020 †30 ‡

FLATHER, Margaret Dubose. 39 BEAM LN 22939 #035-45-1989 L1992 OBG *020 †30

FUTRELL, Thomas Walter. 907 GOOSE CREEK RD, STE 103 22939 #047-06-1972 L1998 OTO *020 †45

GHAEMMAGHAMI, Maya. 78 MEDICAL CENTER DR, AMC CANCER CENTER 22939 #038-44-1990 L1998 HO *020 †20

GILDERSLEEVE, Roger Finch. 78 MEDICAL CENTER DR 22939 #051-01-1995 L1995 **IM** *020 †20

GILLOCK, Charles Buckley. 70 MEDICAL CENTER CIR 22939 #051-01-1990 L1991 **U** *020 †95

GOFF, Charles Daley. 70 MEDICAL CENTER CIR, STE 213 22939 #036-05-1992 L1992 **VS** *020 †85

GRAY, Thomas Glen. 907 GOOSE CREEK RD, STE A03 22939 #036-08-1986 L1998 **IM** *020 †20

GRICE, D Preston. 70 MEDICAL CENTER CIR, STE 305 22939 #048-13-1996 L1996 **APM** *020 †60

GRICE, Darlinda Mae. 70 MEDICAL CENTER CIR, STE 305 22939 #017-20-1989 L1996 **PM** *020 †60

GUNTHER, Robert Carl. 22 N MEDICAL PARK DR 22939 #041-14-1981 L1984 **PD** *020 †55

HAMMERSBERG, Jon Robt. PO BOX 1000 22939 #011-03-1968 L1971 **EM GP** *020

HENSON, Geoffrey Alan. 78 MEDICAL CENTER DR 22939 #012-01-2000 L2006 **AN** *020 †20

HERRING, David S. 907 GOOSE CREEK RD STE A03 22939 #024-05-1989 L1993 **IM** *020 †20

HOFFMAN, Michael Alan. 96 MEDICAL CENTER DR 22939 #016-01-1979 L1983 **P PME** *020 †75 ‡

HOGENMILLER, Matthew S. 57 N MEDICAL PARK DR, STE 101 22939 #048-14-1994 L1995 **RHU** *020 †20,55

HOOVER, John Karsten, II. 9 S MEDICAL PARK DR 22939 #051-01-1991 L1995 **OBG** *020 †30

HUGGINS, James Boyd. 78 MEDICAL CENTER DR 22939 #051-07-1979 L1982 **DR NM** *020 †80

JENSEN, Douglas Robt. 78 MEDICAL CENTER DR 22939 #025-01-1978 L1994 **AN IM** *020 †45,05

JONES, William Rowland. 70 MEDICAL CENTER CIR 22939 #051-01-1995 L2001 **U** *020 †95

KANCLER, Erika Nellie. 78 MEDICAL CENTER DR 22939 #051-04-1979 L1982 **AN** *020 †05

KANE, Timothy Joe. 57 N MEDICAL PARK DR, STE 109/POBOX 1138 22939 #051-01-1992 L1993 **P** *020 †75

KARAFFA, David Matthew. 70 MEDICAL CENTER CIR, SHENANDOAH VLY NEURO 22939 #051-04-1999 L1999 **N** *020 †75

KEELER, Richard F. ROUTE 250 22939 #051-01-1964 L1964 **PM PHP** *075

KEIM, Melvin N. 53 S MEDICAL PARK DR 22939 #051-04-1968 L1968 **FM** *020 †18

KHANDELWAL, Shiv Raj. 78 MEDICAL CENTER DR, ANC CANCER CENTER 22939 #051-04-1987 L1988 **RO** *020 †80

KING, Jennifer Marie. PO BOX 1000, 78 MEDICAL CENTER DR 22939 #041-02-2001 L2001 **EM** *020 †16

KIRK, Tripuraneni Deepa. ■ 22939 #036-01-2000 L2006 **END** *100 †20

KNOPP, James M. ROUTE 250 22939 #051-01-1947 L1947 **P** *071 †75

KOLLAR, Kevin T. AUGUSTA MEDICAL CENTER 22939 #035-08-1975 L1981 **EM IM** *020 †20,16

LICHTENSTEIN, Gary Bruce. 78 MEDICAL CENTER DR 22939 #051-04-1979 L1980 **DR NR** *020 †80

LINDBECK, George Harris. 78 MEDICAL CENTER DR 22939 #023-01-1986 L1988 **EM IM** *020 †20,16

MAHMOODIAN, Mohammad S. ■ 22939 #517-05-1965 L1972 **OBG PHP** *020 †30

MAHNESMITH, Randolph C. 9 S MEDICAL PARK DR 22939 #051-01-1977 L1978 **OBG** *020 †30

MANNING, Lee Link. 78 MEDICAL CENTER DR 22939 #051-01-2001 L2001 **AN** *020 †05

MANNING, Preston Cocke. 93 MEDICAL CENTER DR 22939 #008-01-1956 L1965 **GS** *072 †85

MATTERN, John Q. 78 MEDICAL CENTER DR, AUGUSTA MEDICAL CENTER 22939 #018-75-2000, ▲ L2003 **IM** *020 †20 ‡

MC DONALD, Jay Adams. 78 MEDICAL CENTER DR 22939 #001-02-1983 L1989 **PD** *020 †55

MC KIBBIN, Douglas Wm. 70 MEDICAL CENTER CIR 22939 #023-07-1977 L1983 **GS** *020 †85

MC KIBBIN, William Blake. 70 MEDICAL CENTER CIR, STE 309 22939 #001-02-1999 L2006 **GS** *020 †85

MC MAHON, Robert Wm. 70 MEDICAL CENTER CIR, STE 206 22939 #051-01-1985 L1988 **N UM** *020 †75

MC MILLAN, Daniel Burnes. 39 BEAM LN, AUGUSTA HEALTH CARE FOR WO 22939 #011-04-1978 L1981 **OBG** *020 †30

MERRITT, Clinton Thomas. 78 MEDICAL CENTER DR, AUGUSTA MEDICAL CENTER 22939 #051-07-2000 L2000 **IM** *100 †20

MILLER, Theresa Layne. 907 GOOSE CREEK RD STE A03 22939 #005-02-1992 L1994 **IM** *020 †20

MORRISS, Albert W. 78 MEDICAL CENTER DR 22939 #047-05-1972 L1978 **AN** *020 †05

MURPHY, Douglas Paul. WOODROW WILSON REHAB CTR 22939 #033-05-1983 L1990 **PM** *020 †60

MURRAY, Gary Chas. 70 MEDICAL CENTER CIR, STE 211 22939 #051-01-1977 L1980 **CD IM** *020 †20 ‡

NITZSCHE, Timothy Jay. 78 MEDICAL CENTER DR 22939 #030-05-2000 L2000 **AN** *020 †05 ‡

OLSON, Scott Gregory. 78 MEDICAL CENTER DR, AUGUSTA MEDICAL CENTER 22939 #055-01-2003 L2007 **MPD** *020 †20,55

ORR, William King. 71 FIRST ST 22939 #051-04-1955 L1955 **GP** *071

OTTENI, Jack Frederick. 78 MEDICAL CENTER DR, ORTHOPEDIC ASSOCIATES LTD 22939 #051-01-1997 L2003 **ORS** *020 †40

OZINAL, Ulku. PO BOX 1500 22939 #902-04-1963 L1978 **IM** *020

PAREKH, Jajashree S. 78 MEDICAL CENTER DR 22939 #495-17-1983 L1991 **NM** *020 †28

PAREKH, Shashank C. 78 MEDICAL CENTER DR 22939 #495-17-1982 L1991 **DR** *020 †80

PASZKOWIAK, Jacek Janusz. 70 MEDICAL CENTER CIR, STE 213 22939 #759-10-1996 L2006 **VS** *100 †85

PATEL, Rachna Dinubhai. 17 N MEDICAL PARK DR 22939 #035-46-1994 L1995 **OPH** *020 †35

PATRIARCO, Anthony G. 78 MEDICAL CENTER DR 22939 #024-01-1984 L1989 **PD** *020 †20,55

PATTERSON, Thos Reynolds. PO BOX 968, 53 S MEDICAL PARK DR 22939 #051-04-1978 L1994 **FM** *020 †18

PERELES, Thomas Richard. 70 MEDICAL CENTER DR, ORTHOPEDIC ASSOCIATES LTD 22939 #024-01-1990 L1995 **ORS OAR** *020 †40

PERKINS, Paul Hening. 7 S MEDICAL PARK DR 22939 #051-04-1962 L1962 **OBG** *071 †30

PINKSTON, J Elizabeth. 91 TINKLING SPRING DR 22939 #035-15-1984 L1987 **PD** *020 †55

PLAUTZ, Michael Robert. 70 MEDICAL CENTER CIR, STE 302 22939 #011-02-2000 L2000 **OTO** *020 †45

PLUMBLEY, Julie Ann. 70 MEDICAL CTR CIR STE 309, BLUE RIDGE PATH 22939 #051-01-1994 L2005 **HMP ATP** *020 †50

POLLARD, Matthew Elliott. 70 MEDICAL CENTER CIR, STE 103 22939 #045-04-1997 L2003 **ORS** *020 †40

RANZINI, Joseph Lange. 70 MEDICAL CENTER CIR 22939 #051-01-1986 L1992 **GS** *020 †85

SCHEEL, Gaytri P. 78 MEDICAL CENTER DR 22939 #005-14-2001 L2007 **FM** *020 †18

SHAPIRO, Matthew Paul. 78 MEDICAL CENTER DR 22939 #024-05-1980 L2003 **DR** *020 †80

SHEPHERD, Michael L. 79 N MEDICAL PARK DR, COMPREHENSIVE HEALTH SYSTE 22939 #033-06-1991 L1996 **P PYG** *020 †75

SHIELDS, Marc Douglas. 17 N MEDICAL PARK DR 22939 #020-02-1998 L1999 **OPH** *020 †35

SIMMONS, Jessica Nehrling. 22 MEDICAL CTR DR, AUGUSTA PEDIATRICS 22939 #023-01-2002 L2002 **PD** *020 †55

SPAHR, John. 70 MEDICAL CENTER CIR, STE 309 22939 #041-14-1975 L1979 **PTH** *030 †50

SPENCER, Timothy D. 70 MEDICAL CENTER DR, STE 213 22939 #051-04-1978 L1983 **VS TS** *020 †85

SPICUZZA, Thomas Jos. 70 MEDICAL CENTER CIR 22939 #051-04-1964 L1964 **N OS** *020 †55

STRASBURG, David. 78 MEDICAL CENTER DR 22939 #038-06-1994 L1995 **AN** *020 †05

SUTTON, Angela Vames. 70 MEDICAL CENTER CIR, STE 108 22939 #045-01-2002 L2007 **END** *100 †20

TEMPKIN, David Lawrence. 78 MEDICAL CENTER DR 22939 #048-12-1978 L1993 **DR** *020 †80

THOMPSON, Robert Bell. 9 S MEDICAL PARK DR 22939 #036-05-1984 L1995 **OBG** *020 †30

THOMPSON, William George. 70 MEDICAL CENTER CIR, STE 213 22939 #041-12-1985 L1994 **GS** *020 †85

TIPLER, Bradley Moore. 78 MEDICAL CENTER DR 22939 #001-02-1978 L1980 **DR NM** *020 †80

TOOMY, William Nicholas. 70 MEDICAL CENTER CIR, STE 301 22939 #010-01-1963 L1967 **IM** *020

TUCKER, Sally Irene. 96 MEDICAL CENTER DR, AUGUSTA MEDICAL CENTER 22939 #051-01-1987 L1991 **EM** *020 †16

ULMER, John David. 78 MEDICAL CENTER DR 22939 #012-05-1990 L2005 **AN** *020 †05

WACHSPRESS, Daniel Ira. ■ 22939 #008-02-1986 L1991 **FM** *020 †18

WENGER, Evan James. 70 MEDICAL CENTER CIR, STE 206 22939 #051-04-1999 L1999 **N** *100 †75

WOODRUM, George Orris. 78 MEDICAL CENTER DR 22939 #041-14-1987 L1991 **AN** *020 †05

ZUMSTEG, Thomas Archie. 78 MEDICAL CENTER DR 22939 #041-02-1983 L1990 **R** *020 †20,80

FLINT HILL – RAPPAHANNOCK

BROSGOL, Franklin Leonard. ■ 22627 #041-09-1965 L2001 **IM** *071 †20

FLOYD – FLOYD

HARRIS, Marcia Applegate. 911 E MAIN ST, CARILION FAMILY MEDICINE 24091 #001-06-1995 L1995 **FM** *020 †18

MARSHALL, Lawrence Vinton. 260 WEBBS MILL RD N 24091 #051-01-1964 L1964 **GP** *071

MOSER, Albert Wm. ■ 24091 #051-04-1956 L1956 **P N** *071

FOREST – BEDFORD

BROMAN, George Ellis. ■ 24551 #028-02-1958 L1965 **GS** *071 †85

BUTLER, John Marshall. 15421 FOREST RD, STE B 24551 #051-07-1982 L1988 **U** *071 †95

CARMACK, John Ford. 1175 CORPORATE PARK DR, PHYSICIANS 24551 #422-01-1987 L1990 **FM** *020 †18

COGGIN, Charles Haley, III. 1175 CORPORATE PARK DR, PHYSICIANS 24551 #045-04-1996 L1999 **FM** *020 †18

DODD, Jarrett Spencer. 1175 CORPORATE PARK DR, PHYSICIANS 24551 #051-04-1992 L1993 **FM** *020 †18

EPPES, Thomas Walton, Jr. 1175 CORPORATE PARK DR, PHYSICIANS 24551 #051-01-1978 L1979 **FM** *020 †18

FOREMAN, William Sidney. ■ 24551 #051-01-1957 L1957 **OBG** *071 †30

GOLDSTEIN, Seymour. 324 BAYBERRY CV 24551 #660-01-1960 L1980 **OBG** *071

HARMAN, David M, II. 1042 GRAVES MILL RD 24551 #051-01-1984 L1988 **OPH** *020 †35

HICKS, Christopher Mahood. 15421 FOREST RD 24551 #051-04-1981 L1984 **U** *020 †95

HINKLE, Leah Helen. 1175 CORPORATE PARK DR, PHYSICIANS 24551 #035-15-1996 L1999 **FM** *020 †18

KIM, Jong Won. ■ 24551 #583-01-1951 L1972 **PD GP** *071

KLEINER, Mark Anthony. 1175 CORPORATE PARK DR, "CVFP, INC-TIMBERLAKE FAMI 24551 #041-02-1998 L2006 **FM** *020 †18

ROBERT, Laura M. 1088 NEW LONDON RD 24551 #036-01-1995 L1995 **FM** *020 †18

ROBERTSON, Michael Scott. 2007 GRAVES MILL RD, FOREST WOMENS CENTER 24551 #028-34-1979 L2005 **OBG** *020 †30

ROGERS, Rebecca Glenn. 3431 WATERLICK RD, SEVEN HILLS VET HOSPITAL 24551 #024-01-1992 L1992 **OBG** *020 †30

SHUWARGER, Don. 2007 GRAVES MILL RD, FOREST WOMENS CENTER 24551 #048-04-1981 L1994 **OBG REN** *020 †30 ‡

SLOAN, Frederick Wm. ■ 24551 #035-15-1974 L1976 **EM IM** *020 †20,16

SMITH, David Middleton. 2103 GRAVES MILL RD 24551 #051-04-1978 L1979 **FM** *020 †18

STOWERS, Richard F, Jr. 1088 LONDON LINKS DR, CENTRAL VIRGINIA FAMILY PH 24551 #051-01-1979 L1980 **FM EM** *020 †18

URAY, Maria Semiha. 2007 GRAVES MILL RD, FOREST WOMENS CENTER 24551 #035-08-1987 L1998 **OBG** *020 †30

VAN BUSKIRK, Eric Ralph. 300 ENTERPRISE DR, STE E 24551 #051-01-1985 L1996 **PS** *020

WIDMEYER, Jeffrey Howard. 300 ENTERPRISE DR, STE E 24551 #051-04-1991 L1993 **VS** *020 †85

WILSON, David Coleman. 2203 GRAVES MILL RD, STE A 24551 #051-04-1982 L1984 **D IM** *020 †20,15

FORT BELVOIR – FAIRFAX

ADKINS, John Henry. 9501 FARRELL RD # GC11 22060 #030-05-1979 L2005 **EM** *020 †16

ALBANEZE, Philip Anton. 9501 FARRELL RD STE B408, USA MEDDAC, MCXA-QM 22060 #023-12-1999 L2000 **GS** *020 †85

AVERBACH, Marc L. 9501 FARRELL RD STE GC11, MDDAC - MCXA-P1CREDENTIAL 22060 #654-01-1998 L1993 **IM** *020 †20

BAENS, Aida Santillan. 9501 FARRELL RD STE GC11, DEWITT ARMY COMM HOSP 22060 #748-02-1971 L1984 **CHP P** *020 †75

BALDWIN, Edward L, Jr. 9501 FARRELL RD STE B408, DEWITT ARMY COMM HOSP 22060 #051-01-1989 L1995 **CHP** *020 †75

BARBER, David Wayne. 9501 FARRELL RD, ATTN: CREDENTIAL OFFICE 22060 #023-12-1994 L1995 **ORS** *020 †40

BERNSTEIN, Gregory M. 9501 FARRELL RD B408, DEWITT ARMY COMM HOSP 22060 #024-05-1998 L1999 **U** *020 †95

BLOOM, Marvin Eugene. 9501 FARRELL RD STE GC11, DEWITT ARMY COMM HOSP 22060 #041-12-1965 L1970 **IM END** *020

BOMAR, W Lamar, Jr. 9501 FARRELL RD STE B408, DEWITT ARMY COMM HOSPITAL 22060 #010-03-1969 L1976 **IM** *020

BUGGS, Adrienne Marie. 9501 FARRELL RD STE B408, DEWITT ARMY COMM HOSP 22060 #051-01-1991 L1992 **EM** *020 †16

BUISING, Nori Patricia. 9501 FARRELL RD RM B408, DEWITT ARMY COMM HOSP 22060 #023-12-1992 L1994 **FM** *020 †18

CHUNG, Youn Kee. 9501 FARRELL RD STE B408, DEWITT ARMY COMM HOSP 22060 #583-04-1969 L1975 **DR NM** *020 †28,80

CUNANAN, Erlinda Danao. 9501 FARRELL RD STE B408, DEWITT ARMY COMM HOSP 22060 #748-07-1963 L1972 **PD FM** *020 †55

DAUGELA, Mary Zibute. 9501 FARRELL RD, DEWITT ARMY COMM HOSP 22060 #010-02-1957 L1970 **ADL PD** *020 †55

DE GUZMAN, Ronald Dijamco. 9501 FARRELL RD STE B408, DEWITT ARMY COMM HOSP 22060 #010-02-1991 L1993 **AI IM** *020 †03,20

DELMONTE, Mary E. 9501 FARRELL RD STE B408, DEWITT ARMY COMM HOSP 22060 #023-12-1992 L1993 **FM** *020 †18

DICKMAN, Michael M. ■ 22060 #022-75-2006, ▲ L2006 *012

DOBSON, Craig Pritchard. 9501 FARRELL RD STE B408, DEWITT ARMY COMMUNITY HOSP 22060 #010-01-2000 L2002 **PDC** *012 †55

DOVE, Otto Eric. 9501 FARRELL RD STE B408, DEWITT ARMY COMM HOSP 22060 #041-02-1978 L1999 **PD** *020 †55

DUNHAM, Michael Rennel. 9501 FARRELL RD STE B408, MDDAC-MCXA-P1 CREDENTIAL O 22060 #041-09-1983 L1988 **GS** *020 †85

EDMONDSON, Jeffrey M. 9501 FARRELL RD RM B408, DEWITT ARMY COMMUNITY HOSP 22060 #048-13-1993 L1994 **FM** *020 †18

FEIGHNER, Brian Hershel. 9501 FARRELL RD # GC11 22060 #048-04-1983 L1984 **FM** *071 †70,18

FRIEDEL, Steven Paul. 9501 FARRELL RD STE B408, MDDAC - MCXA-P1 CREDENTIAL 22060 #023-12-1989 L1999 **ORS** *020 †40

GAFFNEY, Cherry Lynn. 9501 FARRELL RD STE GC11, ATTN: CREDENTIAL OFFICE-MC 22060 #045-01-1979 L1982 **FOP OS** *020 †50

GONZALEZ, Rodney Shawn. 9501 FARRELL RD RM B408, DEWITT ARMY COMM HOSP 22060 #035-09-1998 L2005 **FSM** *100 †18

GRANT, Randolph Odell, Jr. 9501 FARRELL RD STE B408, DEWITT ARMY COMM HOSP 22060 #047-07-1966 L1966 **GP DR** *020

GREENE, Colin M. 9501 FARRELL RD STE GC11, DEWITT HEALTH CARE NETWORK 22060 #041-13-1984 L1985 **FM** *030 †18

GRIGGS, Amelia Garcia. 9501 FARRELL RD RM B408, DEWITT ARMY COMMUNITY HOSP 22060 #023-12-1985 L2001 **PD** *020 †55

GULATI, Krishan Kumar. 9501 FARRELL RD STE B408, DEWITT ARMY COMMUNITY HOSP 22060 #495-43-1976 L1989 **PD IM** *020 †55

GUNDRY, Raymond Leslie. 9501 FARRELL RD STE GC11, MDDAC - MCXA-P1 CREDENTIAL 22060 #056-06-1993 L2000 **GS** *020 †18

HODGE, Joshua Allen. 9501 FARRELL RD STE GC11, DEWITT HEALTH CARE NETWORK 22060 #016-02-2000 L2000 **FM** *040 †18

HORN, Charles Stokes. 9501 FARRELL RD, DEWITT COMMUNITY HOSPITAL 22060 #051-01-1979 L1986 **PD** *020 †55

HOWARD, Leonard Nathaniel. 9501 FARRELL RD, USAMEDDAC/DEPT OF PATHOLOG 22060 #023-12-1987 L1998 **PTH** *020 †50

JACOCKS, John M. 9501 FARRELL RD STE B408, MDDAC - MCXA-P1 22060 #021-01-1984 L1990 **FM AM** *030 †18

JANUSZIEWICZ, Alan Andrew. 9501 FARRELL RD STE B408, ATTN: CREDENTIAL OFFICE 22060 #023-12-1986 L2007 **FM** *030 †18

JAROTZKY, Vladimir. DEWITT ARMY COMM HOSP PATH 22060 #132-01-1965 L1995 **PTH CLP** *020 †50

JOHNSON, Walter Carl. 9501 FARRELL RD, DEWITT ARMY COMMUNITY HOSP 22060 #016-11-1970 L1973 **EM IM** *020 †20,16

JUDE, Bonita L. 9501 FARRELL RD, STE GC11 22060 #041-09-1993 L1996 **PD** *020 †55

JUNNILA, Jennifer Lee. 9501 FARRELL RD STE GC11, USA MEDDAC, MCXA-PL; 22060 #056-06-1993 L1994 **FM** *040 †18

KALISH, Virginia B. 9501 FARRELL RD STE G-C11, DEWITT ARMY COMMUNITY HOSP 22060 #010-01-1991 L1998 **FM** *020 †18

KARIM, Nasiba. 9501 FARRELL RD STE B408, DEWITT ARMY COMM HOSP 22060 #704-02-1977 L1996 **IM** *020

KELLY, Matthew James. 9501 FARRELL RD, DIVISION OF ORTHOPEDAEDIC 22060 #041-14-1996 L1997 **ORS** *020 †40

KIM, Jun Woong. 9501 FARRELL RD STE B408, DEWITT ARMY COMM HOSP 22060 #023-01-1994 L1996 **FM** *020 †18

KIM, Suk Hee. 9501 FARRELL RD STE B408, DEWITT ARMY COMMUNITY HOSP 22060 #583-02-1958 L1970 **PD HEM** *020

KIM-AHN, Gina Jieyang. 9501 FARRELL RD, DEWITT ARMY COMMUNITY HOSP 22060 #023-12-1994 L2007 **DR** *020 †80

KUGLER, John Peter. 9501 FARRELL RD STE GC11 22060 #005-14-1977 L1994 **FM FPG** *030 †18

KULAS, Patricia Maria. 9501 FARRELL RD RM B408, DEWITT ARMY HOSP 22060 #051-04-1994 L1996 **DR** *020 †80

LANDIS, Anja Octavia. 9501 FARRELL RD 22060 #041-02-2001 L2001 **FM** *100 †18

LEE, Robert Yoon Sung. 9501 FARRELL RD STE B408, DEWITT ARMY COMM HOSP 22060 #010-01-1948 L1960 **GS OS** *071

LETTIERI, Christine H. 9501 FARRELL RD RM B408, DEWITT ARMY COMMUNITY HOSP 22060 #023-12-1998 L1999 **FM** *020 †18

LYON, Tracey Flanagan. 9501 FARRELL RD STE GC11, DEWITT ARMY COMMUNITY HOSP 22060 #023-12-1999 L2003 **AN** *020

MACDONNELL, Jason Alexand. ■ 22060 #039-01-2008 *012

MAGPANTAY, John-Rico B. 9501 FARRELL RD STE B408, DEWITT ARMY COMM HOSPITAL 22060 #010-01-1997 L1999 **IM** *020 †20

MARINKOVICH, Gregory A. 9501 FARRELL RD STE 408B, DEWITT ARMY COMM HOSP 22060 #005-06-1988 L1991 **NPM OS** *030 †55

MASCETTE, Alice Marie. 9501 FARRELL RD # GC11 22060 #010-02-1980 L1983 **CD IM** *050 †20

MATTESON, Gary Norman. 9501 FARRELL RD RM B408, ATTN: CREDENTIAL OFFICE 22060 #050-02-1978 L1980 **AM FM** *030 †70,18

MC KENNEY, Ann Stewart. 9501 FARRELL RD STE B408, DEWITT ARMY COMM HOSP 22060 #051-04-1980 L1981 **D IM** *020 †20,15

MCKENZIE-GARNER, Pearline. 9501 FARRELL RD STE B408, DEWITT ARMY COMM HOSP 22060 #023-07-1991 L1994 **GPM** *020 †70

MC LEOD, Ian Keith. 9501 FARRELL RD B408, DEWITT ARMY COMM HOSP 22060 #023-12-1997 L1998 **OTO** *020 †45

MC PHERSON, Mark Kenneth. 9501 FARRELL RD RM B408, DEWITT ARMY COMM HOSP 22060 #045-04-1995 L1997 **FM** *020 †18

MEYER, Joel Edwardlee. 9501 FARRELL RD B408, DEWITT ARMY COMMUNITY HOSP 22060 #023-12-1994 L2007 **FM** *020 †18

MILUSZUSKY, William J. 9501 FARRELL RD STE B408, DEWITT ARMY COMM HOSP 22060 #039-01-1986 L1987 **AN** *020 †05

MONCRIEF, Wm Henry, Jr. ■ 22060 #012-05-1944 L1944 **OS TS** *071 †85,90

MOORE, Kevin Earl. 9501 FARRELL RD, BLDG 808 22060 #023-12-1995 L1997 **FM** *020 †18

MOSELY, Dan Sage, III. 9501 FARRELL RD RM B408, DEWITT ARMY COMMUNITY HOSP 22060 #023-12-1996 L1997 **EM** *020 †16

NIDHIRY, Gracy Emmanuel. 9501 FARRELL RD STE B408, DEWITT ARMY COMMUNITY HOSP 22060 #495-52-1970 L1999 **PD** *020 †55

O CONNOR, Francis Gerald. 9501 FARRELL RD B408, DEWITT ARMY COMMUNITY HOSP 22060 #035-15-1985 L1991 **FM FSM** *020 †18

OLMSCHEID, Mary Agnes. 9501 FARRELL RD, DEWITT ARMY MEDICAL CENTER 22060 #026-04-1999 L2001 **FM** *020 †18

O'NEAL, Nona Hilner. 9501 FARRELL RD # GC11 22060 #010-03-1966 L1970 **AN CCM** *020

OSTRONIC, Thomas Danl. 9501 FARRELL RD STE B408, DEWITT ARMY COMMUNITY HOSP 22060 #010-02-1989 L1992 **CD IM** *020 †20

OTTO, Wayne Rupert. ■ 22060 #016-06-1947 L1983 **AM** *071

PEHRSON, Felicia Figa. 9501 FARRELL RD B408, DEWITT ARMY COMMUNITY HOSP 22060 #035-09-1987 L1990 **PD PDC** *030 †55

PENG, Suzette Weiann. 9501 FARRELL RD B408, DEWITT ARMY COMM HOSP 22060 #011-04-2002 L2004 **RHU** *012 †20

PONTIUS, Chaeim Santos. 9501 FARRELL RD STE B408, DEWITT ARMY COMM HOSP 22060 #023-12-1987 L2004 **DR** *020 †80

POWERS, John M. 9501 FARRELL RD STE B408, DEWITT ARMY COMMUNITY HOSP 22060 #035-09-1977 L1983 **FM FPG** *030 †18

PRIDGEON, Rhonda Marie. 9501 FARRELL RD STE B408, MDDAC - MCXA-P1 CREDENTIAL 22060 #048-02-1978 L1985 **N** *020 †75

RAFEY, Ernest Geo. 9501 FARRELL RD STE GC11, MDDAC - MCXA-P1 CREDENTIAL 22060 #051-01-1954 L1954 **FM** *020 †18

RENOM DE LA BAUME, Henri. 9501 FARRELL RD, DEWITT ARMY COMMUNITY HOSP 22060 #042-01-1984 L1986 **GE IM** *020 †20

RENZ, Marisa. 9501 FARRELL RD STE B408, DEWITT ARMY COMMUNITY HOSP 22060 #748-10-1981 L1999 **FM** *020 †18

REPETA, Richard Joseph, Jr. 9501 FARRELL RD, ATTN: EMERGENCY DEPT 22060 #024-07-1997 L2005 **EM** *020 †16

REYES, Gabriel. 9501 FARRELL RD STE GC11, DEWITT ARMY COMM HOSP 22060 #035-47-1989 L1992 **EM** *020 †16

RIDDLE, Jay Allen. 9501 FARRELL RD STE B408, ATTN: CREDENTIAL OFFICE 22060 #051-04-1988 L1996 **OPH** *020 †35

ROWE, John Roderick. 9501 FARRELL RD B408, DEWITT ARMY COMM HOSP 22060 #023-12-1988 L1989 **AM FM** *020 †70

SAGLIO, Jack Wm. ■ 22060 #024-07-1957 L1996 **PD** *030 †55

SALEEM, Tariq. PO BOX 583, STIMSON AT PETTRACA STREET 22060 #704-02-1962 L1991 **P** *020

SANCHEZ PICA, Ida S. 9501 FARRELL RD # GC11 22060 #847-01-1965 L1969 **OM PHP** *020

SCORZA, Keith Alan. 9501 FARRELL RD B408, DEWITT ARMY COMMUNITY HOSP 22060 #023-12-2003 L2003 **FM** *020 †18

SIAL, Kishwar S. 9501 FARRELL RD STE B408, ARMY, USA MEDDAC, MXCA-PI 22060 #704-06-1976 L1994 **IM** *020 †20

SODHI, Parminder. 9501 FARRELL RD, GI CLINIC DEWITT ARMY HOSP 22060 #496-07-1976 L1991 **IM GE** *020 †20

SPROAT, David B. 9501 FARRELL RD STE B408, ATTN: CREDENTIAL OFFICE 22060 #041-13-1988 L1990 **FM** *020 †18

TALBOT, Shelagh K. 9501 FARRELL RD, STE GC-11 22060 #041-07-1977 L1978 **OBG** *020 †30

TAYLOR, Albert William, II. 9501 FARRELL RD RM B408, DEWITT ARMY COMMUNITY HOSP 22060 #023-12-1994 L1996 **OBG** *020 †30

TENEZA, Brigilda Cocos. 9501 FARRELL RD STE B408, DEWITT ARMY COMM HOSPITAL 22060 #023-12-1997 L1999 **PD** *020 †55

VAN NESS, Madge Bruce. 9501 FARRELL RD # GC11 22060 #021-06-1976 L1981 **FM** *020

WILKERSON, Carol James. 9501 FARRELL RD STE GC11, MDDAC - MCXA-P1 CREDENTIAL 22060 #036-01-1981 L2004 **FM PHP** *020 †18

WILLIAMS, Sonia Michelle. 9501 FARRELL RD, DEPARTMENT OF EMERGENCY ME 22060 #016-45-1999 L2001 **EM** *020

WINN, Gregory M. 9501 FARRELL RD STE B408, MDDAC-MCXA-P1 CREDENTIAL 22060 #016-42-1983 L1983 **FM** *062 †18

WYMAN, Mary Jane. 9501 FARRELL RD, ATTN: CREDENTIAL OFFICE 22060 #010-01-1986 L1988 **FM FPG** *020 †18

FORT DEFIANCE – AUGUSTA

HANNA, H Michael, Jr. PO BOX 8 24437 #051-04-1968 L1968 **GP** *020

FORT EUSTIS – NEWPORT NEWS CITY

BAGALKOTKAR, Prashant B. 576 JEFFERSON AVE, MCXH-DCS-QM 23604 #051-07-1992 L1993 **FM** *020 †18

BAUTISTA, Rodolfo E. ■ 23604 #748-08-1966 L1980 **PD GP** *030 †55

BINDER, Lelia Parikh. 576 JEFFERSON AVE, MCXH-DCS-QM 23604 #010-01-1992 L1993 **PD** *020 †55

BOSTON, Edward G. FORT EUSTIS 23604 #047-07-1977 L1998 **OBG GP** *020 †30

CHESHIRE, Glenn Barron. FORT EUSTIS 23604 #051-07-1999 L1999 **FM** *020 †18

DAVID, Joseph. 576 JEFFERSON AVE, MCXH-DCS-QM 23604 #440-01-1965 L1976 *020

DEVLIN, Sanaz Bayati. 576 JEFFERSON AVE, ATTN: CREDENTIAL OFFICE 23604 #023-12-2000 L2002 **PD** *020 †55 ‡

DUCH, Paul. 576 JEFFERSON AVE, MCDONALD ARMY HOSPITAL 23604 #023-12-1989 L1993 **FM** *020 †18

FERMIN, Romeo Cruz. 576 JEFFERSON AVE, MCDONALD ARMY COMMUNITY HO 23604 #748-01-1965 L1997 **PD NPM** *020

GLAESER, Richard David. 576 JEFFERSON AVE, SURGERY-DERMATOLOGY CLINIC 23604 #047-06-1970 L2000 **GS** *020 †85

GOODWIN, George Raymond, Jr. 576 JEFFERSON AVE, MCXH-DCS-QM 23604 #023-12-1996 L1998 **IM** *020 †20

GRIFFITHS, Glenn Chas. 576 JEFFERSON AVE, MCXH-DCS-QM 23604 #041-12-1981 L1988 **FM** *020 †18

GROW, Jeffrey Douglas. 576 JEFFERSON AVE, DEPT OF FAMILY PRACTICE, M 23604 #409-05-1984 L1985 **FM** *020 †18

GUTIERREZ, Miguela T. 576 JEFFERSON AVE, MCXH-DCS-QM 23604 #748-01-1961 L1975 **FM** *020 †18

HENDRICKSON, Chad Scott. ■ 23604 #023-12-2002 L2006 **D** *020 †15

JAMES, Christopher Kramer. 576 JEFFERSON AVE 23604 #045-01-1997 L1997 **FM** *020 †18

JOHNSON, Anthony Eugene. 576 JEFFERSON AVE #005-14-1998 L2000 **ORS OSM** *020 †40

JORDAN, Wm Pritchard, Jr. 576 JEFFERSON AVE, MCDONALD ARMY HEALTH CENTE 23604 #036-05-1964 L1972 **D** *020 †15

MEARS, Craig Timothy. ■ 23604 #048-02-1982 L1983 **P** *020 †18

MYERS, Danny Wadell. 575 JEFFERSON AVE, WOMEN'S HEALTH CLINIC 23604 #047-07-1974 L1991 **OBG** *020

NIXON, Richard Dean. ■ 23604 #051-04-1990 L1992 **FM** *020 †18

PACIA-RANTAYO, Preciosa P. 576 JEFFERSON AVE, ATTN: CREDENTIAL OFFICE 23604 #748-01-1991 L1998 **FM** *020 †18

RICE, Leonard Otis. 576 JEFFERSON AVE, CREDENTIALS COORDINATOR 23604 #041-01-1996 L2001 **FM** *020 †18

ROACH, Christopher James. ■ 23604 #038-40-1999 L2005 **ORS** *020 †40

ROWE, Russell S. PO BOX Z, FLIGHT CONCEPTS DIVISION 23604 #048-04-1993 L2003 **FM** *020 †18

SAMAHA, Richard Geo. 576 JEFFERSON AVE, URGENT CARE CENTER 23604 #051-04-1984 L1987 **EM GP** *062 †16

SCOTT, Albert, Jr. 577 STERNBERG AVE, FORT EUSTIS VA 23604 #038-06-1983 L1984 **OBG** *020 †30

STADER, Richard O. FORT EUSTIS 23604 #041-02-1953 L1988 **ORS** *071 †40

VILLARIN, Alfredo C, Jr. 576 JEFFERSON AVE, MCXH-DCS-QM 23604 #748-01-1968 L1972 **GP EM** *020

ZILAI, Janet Ann. 576 JEFFERSON AVE, MACDONALD ARMY HTLH CTR 23604 #051-04-1985 L1986 **END IM** *020 †20

FORT LEE — PRINCE GEORGE

BUCKNER, Arthur Benj, Jr. 700 24TH ST, ATTN: CREDENTIAL OFFICE 23801 #005-11-1981 L1983 **DR IM** *020 †20,28

COLINA, Jose Fajardo, Jr. 700 24TH ST, KENNER ARMY HEALTH CLINIC 23801 #748-01-1961 L1971 **FM GP** *020

GAGON, Eleanor Law. 700 24TH ST, KENNER ARMY HEALTH CLINIC 23801 #012-05-1976 L1986 **P** *020 †75

HARTMAN, John B Leith. ■ 23801 #041-09-1947 L1949 **PS GP** *020

HUDGENS, Robert Oscar. 700 24TH ST, ATTN: CREDENTIAL OFFICE 23801 #051-04-1953 L1953 **PD** *071 †55

JEFFERIES, Michael Lewis. 700 24TH ST, USAMEDDAC-KAHC; ATTN:BHS-D 23801 #023-01-1976 L2004 **P PD** *030 †55,75

KHALID, Rana. 700 24TH ST, KENNER ARMY HEALTH CLINIC 23801 #704-02-1986 L2001 **FM** *020 †18

LIMBO-PEREZ, Zenen C. 700 24TH ST, PEDIATRICS HEALTH CLINIC 23801 #748-02-1963 L1975 **PD** *071 †55

NAVAL, Icarangal Alzona. 700 24TH ST, KENNER ARMY HEALTH CLINIC 23801 #748-08-1959 L1996 **FM IM** *071 †18

REDDY, Satti Suresh. 700 24TH ST 23801 #063-01-1989 L1998 **FM** *020 †18

ROST, Keith John. 700 24TH ST, ATTN: CREDENTIAL OFFICE 23801 #016-42-1979 L2003 **AM** *020 †20

SINAGUINAN, Eduardo. 700 24TH ST, ATTN: CREDENTIALS (CIVILIA 23801 #748-10-1976 L2003 **PD** *020 †55

WASHINGTON, Larry Hancock. 700 24TH ST BLDG 8130, KENNER ARMY HEALTH CLC 23801 #010-03-1982 L1992 **FM** *020 †18

WILKERSON, Vivian Myrtle. BLDG 8130 23801 #051-04-1958 L1958 **PD** *071 †55

YOOK, John Y. 700 24TH ST, ATTN: CREDENTIAL OFFICE 23801 #583-04-1966 L1989 **OM GP** *020

FORT MONROE — HAMPTON CITY

BARR, Andrew M. ■ 23651 #048-12-1994 L1995 **FM** *020 †18

CROSS, Peter D. 60 INGALLS RD, BLDG 82 23651 #305-01-1993 L1993 **FM** *020 †18

PLACE, Michael Leroy. ■ 23651 #023-12-1991 L1994 **FM** *020 †18

FORT MYER — ARLINGTON

NGUYEN, Duong. 401 CARPENTER RD BLDG 525, A RADER US ARMY HEALTH CLI 22211 #942-01-1970 L1979 **FM PHP** *020 †70,18

SCHOOMAKER, Eric Bradley. ■ 22211 #025-01-1975 L1986 **HEM IM** *030 †20

FRANKLIN — FRANKLIN CITY

BIDWELL, Glenn Porter, Jr. 102 FAIRVIEW DR, STE B 23851 #051-04-1971 L1972 **FM** *020 ‡

BOYLE, Susan V. 102 FAIRVIEW DR STE B, FAMILY PRACTICE ASSOCIATES 23851 #051-07-1997 L1998 **FM** *020 †18

BRANTLEY, Aurelius Walter. 1524 CLAY ST, 1524 CLAY STREET 23851 #051-04-1970 L1970 **FM** *020

CAPATI, Bienvenido B. 100 FAIRVIEW DR 23851 #748-01-1968 L1973 **GS** *020

CICERO, Michael Anthony. 106 FAIRVIEW DR STE C 23851 #056-06-1971 L1987 **PD** *020 †55

CLAPP, Henry Woodard, Jr. ■ 23851 #025-01-1963 L1981 **AN** *071 †05

CLINGENPEEL, J Floyd. 100 FAIRVIEW DR, STE 100 23851 #051-04-1968 L1968 **GYN** *020

EDWARDS, Alan Woodrow. ■ 23851 #051-04-1974 L1975 **IM** *030 †20

EDWARDS, Robert Gary. 100 FAIRVIEW DR 23851 #051-01-1961 L1961 **IM** *020

FULLER, Earl W, Jr. 102 FAIRVIEW DR, CARDIOLOGY CONSULTANTS 23851 #051-04-1968 L1968 **CD** *020 †20

GOODMAN, Benjamin M, Jr. 102 FAIRVIEW DR STE F, SOUTHAMPTON PRIMARY CARE 23851 #036-01-1963 L1967 **GP** *020

HARRIS, Alvin Eugene. SOUTHAMPTON MED BLDG 23851 #051-07-1978 L1981 **IM** *020

HIGHLANDER, William H. 102 FAIRVIEW DR STE G 23851 #051-07-1992 L1992 **N IM** *020 †75

JOHNSON, Gregory Leon. 102 FAIRVIEW DR 23851 #011-03-1979 L2007 **GS** *020 †85

JOHNSON, Stacey L. 100 FAIRVIEW DR, APOGEE PHYSICIANS 23851 #047-07-1993 L2006 **IM CCM** *020 †20

KETOFF, Nabila R. 104 FAIRVIEW DR, STE 104 23851 #704-02-1991 L1997 **PUD** *020 †20

KOKIC, Olga D. ■ 23851 #957-02-1953 **IM OBG** *071

KOKICH, Rudy Emil. 110 SOUTHAMPTON RD 23851 #308-03-1983 L1986 *020

KONEFAL, Joseph John. 100 FAIRVIEW DR, STE 103 23851 #024-05-1977 L1981 **U** *020 †95

MC NEELY, Irwin Hollar. 34040 UNION CAMP DR, MED DEPT INTL PAPER 23851 #036-07-1953 L1956 **GP OM** *071

MITROVIC, Nebojsa. 102 FAIRVIEW DR, STE F 23851 #957-02-1990 L1997 **IM** *020 †20

OLSON, William Bryan. 121 OAKWOOD DR, DBI RADIOLOGY, INC. 23851 #021-01-1973 L1975 **DR NM** *020 †80 ‡

ONA, Maria Annella M. 100 FAIRVIEW DR, STE 201 23851 #748-08-1990 L1998 **PD** *020 †55

PATEL, Manish Arun. 106 FAIRVIEW DR STE A, SOUTHHAMPTON ORTHOPAEDIC&S 23851 #041-15-2000 L2006 **ORS** *100 ‡

PEAK, Daniel Keene, Jr. 100 FAIRVIEW DR 23851 #051-01-1979 L1982 **IM** *020

PINTO, Carlos. SOUTHAMPTON MEDICAL BLDG, CARROLL & PINTO INC MD 23851 #187-13-1954 L1963 **ATP CLP** *071 †50

PONDER, James Michael. 100 FAIRVIEW DR 23851 #051-04-1979 L1979 **FM** *020 †18

POWELL, Clarence Leslie, Jr. 102 FAIRVIEW DR STE B 23851 #051-04-1975 L1976 **FM** *020 †18

PUTZE, Robert Leroy. 100 FAIRVIEW DR, STE 100 23851 #051-04-1959 L1959 **OBG** *071 †30

ROGERS, Richard O, Jr. ■ 23851 #051-04-1952 L1963 **IM** *071 †20

ROMANO, Frank Richard. 102 FAIRVIEW DR, STE H 23851 #035-09-1976 L1982 **OPH IM** *020 †20,35

SCOTT-BROWN, Itrish J. PO BOX 26 23851 #051-07-1999 L2002 **IM** *020 †20

SHEFFIELD, Sharon Lyvonne. 104 FAIRVIEW DR, STE 100 23851 #051-07-1992 L1992 **OBG** *020 †30

WILLIAMS, Charles Pierre. 104 FAIRVIEW DR, STE 200 23851 #036-01-2000 L2006 **GS** *020 †85

FRANKTOWN — NORTHAMPTON

BERNART, William Francis. ■ 23354 #035-01-1954 L1958 **IM CD** *071 †20

CARTER, Arthur Treherne. ■ 23354 #038-41-1975 L1980 **OBG** *071 †30

DOOLEY, Parker Clark. 9197 FRANKTOWN RD, EASTERN SHORE RURAL HEALTH 23354 #005-19-1975 L1978 **IM GP** *030 †20

HENDERSON, Edmund M. ■ 23354 #051-01-1942 L1942 **GP** *071

MACKLER, Stuart Fred. 7336 GULL POINT RD 23354 #035-09-1963 L1973 **ORS** *020 †40

REASON, H John. 8411 CREEK ST, OB/GYN ASSOCIATES 23354 #065-06-1971 L2004 **OBG** *020 †30

WILLIAMS, Frances A Holla. 7518 BAYSIDE RD, HILLCREST 23354 #007-02-1990 L2001 **FM** *020 †18 ‡

FREDERICKSBURG — FREDERICKSBURG CITY

ABDULLAH, Omer. 1965 JEFFERSON DAVIS HWY, STE 100 22401 #704-09-1991 L2000 **FM IM** *020 †20

ACCOUSTI, Kenneth Joseph. 3310 FALL HILL AVE, FREDERICKSBURG ORTHOPAEDIC 22401 #010-02-2000 L2006 **ORS** *020

ADKINS, Tonya Marie. 1101 SAM PERRY BLVD, STE 215 22401 #047-07-1993 L2001 **OBG** *020 †30

AGUILERA, Arnold J. 220 EXECUTIVE CENTER PKWY, STE 1627 22401 #018-03-1979 L1995 **N** *020 †75

AHMED, Zarmina. ■ 22401 #704-27-2000 L2007 **IM** *020 †20

AHUJA, Avnit Kaur. 2216 PRINCESS ANNE ST, ST,STE 203 22401 #495-43-1998 L2007 **RHU** *100 †20

ALATTAR, Maha. 1101 SAM PERRY BLVD, STE 414 22401 #047-06-1997 L1998 **N SME** *100

ALBERT, L Thos. 3312 FALL HILL AVE, PLASTIC SURGERY SVCS OF 22401 #020-12-1970 L1982 **PS GS** *020 †65 ‡

ALI, Awol Yimer. 1101 SAM PERRY BLVD # 307, MARY WASHINGTON HOSPITAL 22401 #366-01-1990 L2004 **ID** *100

ALLEGRETTI, Roxanne Marie. 331 PARK HILL DR 22401 #005-18-1991 L2000 **PD** *020 †55

ALLEN, Donald Miller. 1001 SAM PERRY BLVD 22401 #011-02-1971 L1972 **R** *020 †80

ALTAFFER, Lawrence F, III. 1701 FALL HILL AVE 22401 #051-01-1974 L1985 **U** *020 †95

ALTAMIRANO, Leo Cardenas. 1001 SAM PERRY BLVD, MARY WASHINGTON HOSP 22401 #748-08-1992 L2006 **PD** *100

AMIN, Jyoti Surendra. 1001 SAM PERRY BLVD, NEONATOLOGY OFFICE 22401 #495-23-1971 L1979 **NPM PD** *020 †55

ANAND, Mohit. 1101 SAM PERRY BLVD, STE 204 22401 #913-33-1996 L2005 **IM** *020 †20

ANDERSON, Duane Claude. 1601B OLD WILLIAM ST 22401 #005-12-1980 L1982 **OBG** *020 †30

ANZELMO, Thomas A. 1001 SAM PERRY BLVD 22401 #654-01-1989 L1996 **AN PME** *020 †05

ARMITAGE, John Marshall. 1201 SAM PERRY BLVD, STE 230 22401 #047-06-1979 L1994 **TS** *020 †85,90

ARORA, Balvant P. 1101 SAM PERRY BLVD, STE 314 22401 #495-23-1984 L2008 **PS** *020 †65

ASHTON, Sheryl Renee. 2300 FALL HILL AVE, STE 207 22401 #010-03-1994 L1997 **IM** *020 †20

ASIF, Muhammad. 1001 SAM PERRY BLVD, FHG, P.C, ATTEN: UNCHU KI 22401 #704-21-1997 L2006 **IM** *020 †20

ASKEW, Jeffrey Edward. 1201 SAM PERRY BLVD, STE 280 22401 #010-02-1995 L2006 **CD** *020 †20

AWADH, Abla Abed. 1001 SAM PERRY BLVD, MARY WASHINGTON HOSPITAL 22401 #951-01-1992 L2005 **IM** *020 †20

BAKER, Bruce Edward. 1001 SAM PERRY BLVD 22401 #016-43-1968 L1975 **P DR** *075 †75

BANKER, Michael C. ■ 22401 #035-48-1985 L2005 **TS** *020 †85,90

BARABASZ, Amy Lynn. 1001 SAM PERRY BLVD, F E M A 22401 #039-01-2000 L2005 **EM** *020 †16 ‡

BAUTISTA, Harold Clement. 3312 FALL HILL AVE, PLASTIC SURGERY SVCS OF 22401 #035-09-1986 L1992 **PS GS** *020 †85,65

BEAMON, Charles Ralph, Jr. 1101 SAM PERRY BLVD, STE 219 22401 #023-01-1968 L1972 **U IM** *020 †95

BECKER, Elmore James, Jr. 1051 CARE WAY 22401 #051-04-1991 L1992 **U** *020 †95
BELLAR, Helen Rose. 1001 SAM PERRY BLVD 22401 #036-01-1994 L2000 **CCA** *020 †05
BELLOTTI, Gerald A. ■ 22401 #561-01-1976 L1980 **AN** *071 †05
BERGER, Shana Ariel. ■ 22401 #008-02-2005 L2005 **P** *012
BERLAD, Lee. 1101 SAM PERRY BLVD, STE 321 22401 #048-02-1979 L2003 **NS** *020 †25
BERNSTEIN, Norman David. 1101 SAM PERRY BLVD # 307 22401 #036-05-1973 L1988 **ID IM** *020 †20
BIDDULPH, John Thos. 1201 SAM PERRY BLVD, STE 201 22401 #041-14-1986 L1988 **ORS** *020 †40
BIGONEY, Rebecca Moore. 1001 SAM PERRY BLVD 22401 #051-04-1979 L1980 **IM** *020 †20
BLANCHARD, Darlene Kay. 1101 SAM PERRY BLVD, STE 211 22401 #012-05-1998 L2007 **GS** *020 †85
BONIFACE, John, Jr. 2601 FALL HILL AVE 22401 #011-03-1970 L1972 **GE IM** *020 †20
BOYKIN, Arlene Risk. 1001 SAM PERRY BLVD, ATTN: NEONATOLOGY OFFICE 22401 #038-44-1996 L2003 **NPM** *020 †55
BRADSHAW, Brenda Anne. 2300 CHARLES ST, ABC PEDIATRICS PLLC 22401 #051-01-1996 L1998 **PD** *020 †55 ‡
BRODER, Robert Irving. 301 PARK HILL DR, STE 8 22401 #561-01-1969 L1976 **D** *071
BROSCHE, William Scott. 1001 SAM PERRY BLVD 22401 #016-02-1988 L1993 **AN** *020 †05
BROWN, Andrea Denise. 1001 SAM PERRY BLVD, MEDICAL SUPPORT SERVICE 22401 #012-21-1998 L1998 **PD** *020 †20
BUCKLEY, Brian John. 603 KENMORE AVE 22401 #010-02-1990 L2000 **IM** *020 †20 ‡
BURAS, Robert Richard. 1101 SAM PERRY BLVD 22401 #016-02-1981 L1998 **GS ON** *050 †85
BURKE, Patrick Declan. 1420 CENTRAL PARK BLVD, STE 200 22401 #539-05-1962 L1968 **OBG AN** *020 †30
CANIZARES, Teresita Cacha. 608 JACKSON ST, RAPPAHANNOCK AREA HLTH DIS 22401 #748-08-1966 L1973 **OBG** *020
CAREY, Peter Oxenham. 1051 CARE WAY 22401 #051-01-1983 L1984 **U** *020 †95
CASTILLE, Molly Martha. 321 PARK HILL DR 22401 #038-40-2000 L2003 **FM** *020 †18 ‡
CHANDRA, Harish Ramnandan. 1201 SAM PERRY BLVD, STE 280 22401 #495-23-1992 L2007 **IC CD** *020 †20
CHANG, Norman Anyi. 611 JEFFERSON DAVIS HWY, STE 201 22401 #012-01-1995 L1998 **IM** *020 †20
CHANG, Wayne Weiyuan. 250 EXECUTIVE CENTER PKWY 22401 #051-04-1998 L1998 **P** *020 †75
CHIANCONE, Giancarlo. 1101 SAM PERRY BLVD STE 20 22401 #561-10-1977 L1982 **OTO** *020 †45
CHIANG, Fuyu. ■ 22401 #010-01-1998 L2001 **ID IM** *020 †20
CHILDRESS, James M. 2216 PRINCESS ANNE ST, STE 21 22401 #051-04-1977 L1980 **PD** *020 †55
CHUNG, Raymond Kimpon. 2800 WELLFORD ST, STE 100 22401 #041-02-1994 L1996 **ORS** *020 †40
CLEMO, Simon Henry. 1201 SAM PERRY BLVD, STE 280 22401 #051-01-1987 L1988 **IM** *020 †20
COBB, Audrey Denise. 1001 SAM PERRY BLVD, MARY WASHINGTON HOSPITAL 22401 #028-02-1981 L1983 **NPM PD** *020 †55
COHEN, Murry Jos. 2217 PRINCESS ANNE ST 22401 #016-42-1965 L1991 **P** *020
COLOPY, Paul M. 220 EXECUTIVE CENTER PKWY, STE 1627 22401 #038-41-1978 L1980 **N CN** *020 †75
CONSTANTINE, Kostas J. 3310 FALL HILL AVE, ORTHOPAEDIC ASSOCIATES 22401 #051-01-1993 L1999 **HS** *020 †40
COOK, Wilson. 120 EXECUTIVE CENTER PKWY, RAPPAHANNOCK FAMILY PHYSIC 22401 #055-01-1993 L1996 **FM** *020 †18
CORRADO, Julia Ann. 1001 SAM PERRY BLVD, MEDICAL STAFF OFFICE 22401 #010-01-1994 L1998 **OBG** *020 †30
COSSENTINO, Mark James. 1031 CARE WAY 22401 #010-02-1996 L2001 **GE** *020 †20
CRAIG, Seth C, III. 1300 THORNTON ST, STE 200 22401 #035-06-1970 L1974 **PD AI** *020 †55,03
CROUSE, Sandra Dawn. 1001 SAM PERRY BLVD, TOMPKINS MARTIN MEDICAL PL 22401 #051-07-2002 L2007 **N** *020 †75
CRUZ, Francisco Philomel. 1101 SAM PERRY BLVD, STE 305 22401 #748-02-1995 L2006 **END** *020 †20
CURRIE, Randall Byron. 1101 SAM PERRY BLVD, STE 411 22401 #027-01-1975 L1987 **PUD IM** *020 †20
DABROW, Robert Craig. 1001 SAM PERRY BLVD, PEDIATRIC HOSP OFFICE 22401 #051-04-1984 L1985 **PD** *020 †55 ‡
D'ADDIO, Victor James. 1101 SAM PERRY BLVD, STE 211 22401 #021-01-1992 L2005 **VS GS** *020 †85
DALBERG, Rickard Karl. 1001 SAM PERRY BLVD, DEPT OF EMERGENCY MEDICINE 22401 #041-09-1989 L1994 **EM** *020 †16
DANIEL, James Richard. 1701 FALL HILL AVE, STE 105 22401 #021-01-1978 L1989 **GS ON** *020 †85
DANIELS, James Ray, Jr. 1101 SAM PERRY BLVD, STE 203 22401 #033-06-1996 L2002 **GS** *020 †85
DASHTIZAD, Nariman. 1708 FALL HILL AVE, STE 100 22401 #010-02-1999 L1999 **OTO** *020 †45 ‡
DETRANE, Frank Jos. 210 EXECUTIVE CENTER PKWY 22401 #041-13-1985 L1987 **GE IM** *020 †20
DOHERTY, Richard Donald. 1001 SAM PERRY BLVD 22401 #051-04-1997 L1997 **DR** *020 †80
DORMAN, Bruce H, Jr. 1001 SAM PERRY BLVD 22401 #036-07-1986 L2005 **AN** *020 †05
DUCHIN, Louis Karl. 600 JACKSON ST, RAPPAHANNOCK AREA COMMUNIT 22401 #035-09-1986 L1997 **P** *020 †75
DUMONT, Matthew David. 1051 CARE WAY 22401 #051-04-1998 L1998 **U** *020 †95
DUPUY, Dudley Armand, Jr. 1001 SAM PERRY BLVD 22401 #016-11-1990 L1996 **PTH** *020 †50
EARNHARDT, Richard Craig. 1101 SAM PERRY BLVD, STE 211 22401 #036-07-1989 L1990 **GS VS** *020 †85
ECKENBERGER, Jill Renee. 1001 SAM PERRY BLVD, ALLEGHENY GENERAL HOSPITAL 22401 #051-04-2005 L2008 **EM** *012
EDWARDS, Leroy Paul. 1001 SAM PERRY BLVD 22401 #005-12-1989 L1996 **AN CCA** *020 †05
EGLEVSKY, Andre, Jr. 2201 CHARLES ST 22401 #024-07-1969 L1977 **ORS** *020 †40
ERWIN, Richard P. 220 EXECUTIVE CENTER PKWY 22401 #010-02-1981 L1989 **N** *020 †75
ESSIG, Le Roy John. 240 EXECUTIVE CENTER PKWY 22401 #038-40-1969 L1973 **ON IM** *020 †20
FERGUSON, Joseph Michael. 2300 CHARLES ST, STE 201 22401 #023-07-1994 L1996 **IM** *020 †20
FERNANDO, Nimali E. 321 PARK HILL DR 22401 #041-12-1999 L2005 **PD** *020 †55
FIERO, Richard Alan. 521 PARK HILL DR, PULMONARY ASSOCIATION OF F 22401 #035-48-1988 L2000 **CCM PUD** *020 †20

FILIBERTO, Jeffrey Dohre. 300 PARK HILL DR 22401 #021-05-1992 L2007 **PM** *020 †60
FINES, Robert Evans, Jr. 1001 SAM PERRY BLVD 22401 #051-07-2001 L2004 **EM** *020 †16
FLYNN, Rod Leon. 1101 SAM PERRY BLVD, MARY WASHINGTON HOSPITAL 22401 #023-01-1996 L2006 **GS** *020 †85
FORTUNE, Thomas Patrick. 101 PARK HILL DR 22401 #010-02-1980 L1986 **NEP IM** *020 †20
FRANCHI, Diane. 1101 SAM PERRY BLVD, BLVD.,STE 307 22401 #008-02-1993 L1996 **ID** *020 †20
FRANCK, Thomas Geo. 608 JACKSON ST, RAPPAHANNOCK HLTH DIST 22401 #051-01-1989 L1990 **GPM** *030 †18,70
FRANZ, David Andrew. 1708 FALL HILL AVE, CENTER OF FREDERICKSBURG 22401 #051-01-1992 L1992 **OTO** *020 †45
FRAZIER, Jeffrey Ashley. 1001 SAM PERRY BLVD 22401 #036-08-1999 L2004 **DR** *100 †80
FULLER, Philip Stuart. 521 PARK HILL DR, PULMONARY ASSOCIATES OF FR 22401 #041-02-1973 L1982 **PUD IM** *020 †20
GARTH, David Michael. 1001 SAM PERRY BLVD 22401 #041-02-1995 L1998 **EM** *020 †16
GARVIE, Andrew Alphonsus. 1001 SAM PERRY BLVD, MARY WASHINGTON HOSPTIAL 22401 #051-04-1995 L1999 **EM** *020 †16
GEORGE, Jennifer M. 1965 JEFFERSON DAVIS HWY, VA MCGUIRE CLINIC 22401 #023-07-1995 L1996 **IM** *020 †20
GERTNER, Randy Alan. 101 PARK HILL DR 22401 #041-14-1998 L2003 **NEP** *020 †20
GEYER, Anne Huggins. 1001 SAM PERRY BLVD 22401 #036-05-1993 L2000 **PCP** *020 †50
GINESTRA, Todd Philip. 3312 FALL HILL AVE 22401 #016-11-1992 L2008 **PS** *020 †85,65
GLASSER, David Lawrence. 1001 SAM PERRY BLVD 22401 #011-04-1994 L1999 **DR** *020 †80
GONZALES, George T. 1212 POWHATAN ST 22401 #748-01-1966 L1972 **FM GP** *020
GONZALES, Manuel Tendero. 1212 POWHATAN ST, GONZALES MEDICAL CLINIC 22401 #748-08-1972 *020
GRAY, F Bradley. 1101 SAM PERRY BLVD STE 2 22401 #051-01-1962 L1962 **U** *020 †95
GREBOSKY, James Michael. 1001 SAM PERRY BLVD 22401 #041-14-1989 L1990 **FM** *030 †18
GREEN, Neil Brian. 1001 SAM PERRY BLVD 22401 #048-04-1993 L1998 **DR** *020 †80,28
GUACENA, Gonzalo F, Jr. 1001 SAM PERRY BLVD 22401 #748-02-1961 L1972 **EM GP** *020 †16
GUNN, James W. 1001 SAM PERRY BLVD, FREDERICKSBURG ANESTHESIA 22401 #020-12-1981 L1984 **AN** *020 †05
GUPTA, Vikas. 2216 PRINCESS ANNE ST, STE 201 22401 #023-01-1991 L1996 **IM** *020 †20
HAMILTON, William A. 619 JEFFERSON DAVIS HWY, STE 101 22401 #019-02-1986 L1995 **OBG** *020 †30 ‡
HARRY, Philip Scott. 501 PARK HILL DR 22401 #051-01-1988 L1999 **ORS** *020 †40
HARRY, Robert Roger. 1101 SAM PERRY BLVD, STE 211 22401 #036-01-1973 L1979 **GS VS** *071 †85
HEALY, Brian Francis. 1001 SAM PERRY BLVD 22401 #010-02-1985 L1997 **CCA** *020 †05
HEPPE, Howard Paul. 3312 FALL HILL AVE, PLASTIC SURGERY SVCS OF 22401 #051-01-1983 L1990 **PS** *020 †85,65
HERMAN, Sol. 1320 CENTRAL PARK BLVD, STE 205 22401 #035-08-1958 L2001 **P PYA** *072 †75
HERNANDEZ, Rafael Octavio. 120 EXECUTIVE CENTER PKWY 22401 #308-02-1986 L1992 **FM** *020 †18
HINE, Paul Forrest. 1001 SAM PERRY BLVD 22401 #038-40-1974 L1978 **PTH** *020 †50
HOFFMAN, Daniel Mark. 1051 CARE WAY 22401 #041-12-1989 L1996 **U** *020 †95
HOLDEN, Norman B, Jr. 600 JACKSON ST 22401 #051-04-1974 L1974 **P** *020 †75 ‡
HOLLISTER, William, Jr. 1001 SAM PERRY BLVD 22401 #023-01-1955 L1959 **GS** *071 †85
HOLLS, William Martin, III. 1101 SAM PERRY BLVD, STE 319 22401 #010-02-1977 L1982 **MFM OBG** *040 †30
HUESGEN, Christopher T. 1001 SAM PERRY BLVD 22401 #036-07-1991 L1995 **EM** *020 †16
IVES, Nadine Susan. ■ 22401 #023-12-1987 L1989 **HMP PTH** *020 †50
JAFRI, Farrukh Majid. 1101 SAM PERRY BLVD 22401 #704-02-1978 L2004 **GE** *020 †20
JAMES, Christopher Shayne. ■ 22401 #008-01-2001 **NS** *100
JOHNS, Montgomery Newman. 623 JEFFERSON DAVIS HWY, # 101 22401 #005-14-1978 L1986 **GYN** *020 †30
JOHNSON, David Lewis. 2300 FALL HILL AVE, STE 207 22401 #035-06-1972 L1975 **FM** *020 †18
JOHNSON, Douglas Russell. 1001 SAM PERRY BLVD, FREDERICKSBURG EMERG MED 22401 #016-11-1986 L1988 **EM AM** *020 †16
JOHNSON, Marriott C, Jr. 1001 SAM PERRY BLVD 22401 #035-20-1963 L1970 **ORS** *071 †40
JONES, Raymond Stanley. 2216 PRINCESS ANNE ST 22401 #566-01-1961 L1967 **PD** *020 †55
KALLAY, Nicholas. 521 PARK HILL DR, PULMONARY ASSOCIATES OF FR 22401 #001-02-1995 L2001 **PCC IM** *020 †20
KATZ, Edward N. 1231 JEFF DAVIS HWY 22401 #035-08-1983 L1987 **RHU PPR** *020 †20
KEAR, Moses Dargba. 1001 SAM PERRY BLVD 22401 #610-01-1987 L2003 **IM** *020 †20
KELSEY, Ronald Leon. 1001 SAM PERRY BLVD 22401 #016-11-1963 L1977 **PTH PCP** *071 †50
KENNEWEG, Donald John. 607 WILLIAM ST, RADIOLOGIC ASSOC 22401 #051-01-1958 L1958 **R RO** *071 †20
KHALID, Omar Mohammed. 1101 SAM PERRY BLVD, STE 415 22401 #528-01-1992 L2006 **PDC** *100 †55 ‡
KHAN, Monsurul Haque. 1001 SAM PERRY BLVD, FREDERICKSBURG HOSPITALIST 22401 #913-07-1991 L2004 **IM** *020 †20
KIL, H Jae. 1101 SAM PERRY BLVD, STE 413 22401 #051-07-1988 L1993 **OBG** *020 †30
KIM, Andrew Seungmo. 1300 THORNTON ST STE 200 22401 #051-04-2000 L2005 **AI** *020 †20,03
KIN, Jeffrey Danl. 1001 SAM PERRY BLVD 22401 #010-01-1989 L1996 **FM** *020 †18
KING, Bradford Lynn. 1101 SAM PERRY BLVD, STE 211 22401 #048-12-1994 L2001 **GS VS** *020 †85
KING, Lisa J. 1320 CENTRAL PARK BLVD, STE 310 22401 #047-07-1995 L1995 **IM** *020
KIRCHMIER, Raymond S, Jr. 2800 WELLFORD ST, STE 100 22401 #051-04-1988 L1994 **ORS OSS** *020 †40
KOHLER, Stewart Edwin. 2301 FALL HILL AVE, MEDICAL ARTS BLDG SUITE 20 22401 #036-07-1966 L1972 **RHU IM** *020 †20
KOTECHA, Tarulata L. ■ 22401 #905-01-1970 L1998 **PD GP** *020 †55
LANDSNES, David George. 1001 SAM PERRY BLVD 22401 #033-06-1994 L2001 **NR** *020 †80,28
LARSON, Kurt Roland. 2800 WELLFORD ST, STE 100 22401 #005-06-1985 L1992 **ORS OSM** *020
LEE, Lawrence Borden, Jr. 1965 JEFFERSON DAVIS HWY, STE 100 22401 #045-01-1998 L2002 **P** *020 †75
LEONARD, Tammy Joann. 621 JEFFERSON DAVIS HWY, STE 201 22401 #051-01-1997 L1998 **OBG** *020 †30
LESTER-SIMMONDS, S. 1101 SAM PERRY BLVD, STE 314 22401 #033-05-1995 L2000 **OBG** *020 †30
LEWIS, Arlene Denise. 609 JEFFERSON DAVIS HWY, STE 201 22401 #051-04-1997 L2001 **GYN** *020 †30
LIESER, John David. 1708 FALL HILL AVE, STE 100 22401 #041-14-2001 L2001 **OTO** *020 †45

LLOYD, Thomas Stacy, Jr. 1701 FALL HILL AVE 22401 #051-04-1948 L1948 **OBG** *071 †30

LOMEO, Rosalia M. ■ 22401 #041-07-1984 L1989 **RHU** *020 †20

LUO, Xiaodong. 1001 SAM PERRY BLVD, FREDERICKSBURG HOSPITALIST 22401 #243-16-1988 L2000 **IM** *020

MA, Steven Jebum. 605 JEFFERSON DAVIS HWY, STE 201 22401 #041-09-1997 L2002 **FM** *020 †18

MAC ARTHUR, Angus. 1001 SAM PERRY BLVD 22401 #919-03-1961 L1978 **FM** *071

MANCINI, P Maras. 321 PARK HILL DR, P.L. PEDIATRICS, P.L.L.C 22401 #035-48-1982 L1989 **PD** *055

MANDELL, Maurice S, Jr. 1001 SAM PERRY BLVD 22401 #020-12-1981 L1982 **IM** *020 †20

MANGES-ZALEGOWSKI, Krista. 1001 SAM PERRY BLVD 22401 #041-02-1988 L1996 **AN** *020 †05

MARCUS, Rebecca Kay. 1001 SAM PERRY BLVD 22401 #051-07-1977 L1979 **EM FM** *020 †18,16

MARKS, Frank Wayland. 1101 SAM PERRY BLVD, STE 101 22401 #051-04-1970 L1970 **IM** *020 †20

MARTYAK, Thomas E. 1201 SAM PERRY BLVD, STE 280 22401 #010-02-1981 L1990 **CD IM** *020 †20

MASSEY, Caleb Rosser, III. 1708 FALL HILL AVE, STE 100 22401 #051-01-1974 L1979 **OTO PS** *020 †45

MASTRI, Thomas Alexander. 2601 FALL HILL AVE, ASSOCIATES 22401 #033-06-1985 L2000 **GE** *020 †20

MAUNG, M Ohn. 2216 PRINCESS ANNE ST, STE 106 22401 #209-02-1985 L2002 **IM** *020 †20

MAURER, Charles L. 231 PARK HILL DR 22401 #035-15-1994 L2000 **HO** *020

MC DERMOTT, Michael P. 1001 SAM PERRY BLVD 22401 #038-41-1992 L1997 **DR** *020 †80

MC LAUGHLIN, John Jos. 1001 SAM PERRY BLVD 22401 #035-06-1984 L1999 **DR** *020 †80

MC MANUS, Patrick John. 2501 CHARLES ST 22401 #051-01-1985 L1988 **IM** *020 †20

MEDSKER, Thomas T. 1001 SAM PERRY BLVD 22401 #038-41-1978 L1979 **DR** *020 †80

MENACHERY, Sudeep J. 231 PARK HILL DR 22401 #422-01-1999 L2002 **HO** *020 †20

MEYER, Christopher M. 1001 SAM PERRY BLVD 22401 #051-04-1998 L2004 **DR** *020 †80

MEYER, Leslie S. 1071 CARE WAY, STE 101 22401 #051-04-1998 L2004 **OBG** *020 †30

MICHIELSON, Bradley John. 1001 SAM PERRY BLVD 22401 #051-04-1992 L1992 **AN** *020 †05

MILLER, Mark Dana. 1001 SAM PERRY BLVD 22401 #035-48-1981 L1986 **P** *020 †75

MIN, Aye. 1001 SAM PERRY BLVD 22401 #051-04-2000 L2000 **DR** *020 †80

MIRZA, Brian. 1101 SAM PERRY BLVD, STE 230 22401 #875-01-1992 L2007 **GS AS** *020 †85

MONAHAN, David Warren. 2601 FALL HILL AVE 22401 #036-05-1981 L1986 **GE IM** *020 †20

MORRIS, Terri Phipps. 2216 PRINCESS ANNE ST, STE 204 22401 #010-01-1986 L1998 **D ID** *020 †15

MOTER, Lawrence Russell. 1701 FALL HILL AVE 22401 #051-04-1960 L1960 **GS OS** *020 †85

MOULTON, Andrea Gililland. 1101 SAM PERRY BLVD, STE 413 22401 #051-07-2000 L2006 **OBG** *020

MOULTON, Stacy James. 1001 SAM PERRY BLVD 22401 #051-07-2000 L2006 **DR** *100 †80

MOZENA, Jonathan Daniel. 1001 PICKETT ST 22401 #018-03-2002 L2002 **AI** *100 †20,03

MUIR, William Angus. 231 PARK HILL DR, FREDERICKSBURG, INC. 22401 #038-06-1970 L1985 **HO** *020

MULAGHA, Eneya Hugh. 1320 CENTRAL PARK BLVD, STE 310 22401 #041-13-1995 L2001 **IM** *020 †20

MUNDY, Charles B. 1001 SAM PERRY BLVD 22401 #035-19-1950 L1954 **OS** *030

MUNKAILA, Ibrahim Abu. 1001 SAM PERRY BLVD, FREDERICKSBURG HOSPITALIST 22401 #902-01-1995 L2003 **IM** *020 †20 ‡

MURALIDHARAN, Visvanathan. 2601 FALL HILL AVE, FALL HILL GASTROENTEROLOGY 22401 #495-16-1994 L2007 **IM GE** *020 †20 ‡

MURRAY, Patricia Lee. 221 PARK HILL DR 22401 #010-01-1981 L1983 **GYN** *020 †30

NEWBERG, Barbara E. 1001 SAM PERRY BLVD 22401 #016-42-1995 L1999 **IM** *020 †20

NICCOLINI, Robert. 600 JACKSON ST 22401 #025-07-1966 L1971 **P ADP** *030 †75

NOWACEK, George E. 221 PARK HILL DR, GYNECOLOGY ASSOCITES OF FR 22401 #051-01-1995 L2006 **OBG** *020 †30

O'BRIEN, Michael Bradner. 501 PARK HILL DR 22401 #051-01-1983 L1983 **ORS** *020 †40

OFFICER, James David. 9. 101 PARK HILL DR 22401 #010-02-1981 L1984 **IM NEP** *020 †20

OLSOVSKY, Gregory D. 2500 CHARLES ST, CARDIOLOGY ASSOCIATES OF F 22401 #048-15-1998 L2007 **ICE** *020 †20

PALMER, Richard Shane. 2601 PRINCESS ANNE ST, STE 200 22401 #004-01-1995 L2003 **GS** *020 †85

PAPIER, Kenneth Scott. 1001 SAM PERRY BLVD 22401 #048-78-1991, ▲ L2000 **AN CCA** *020 †05

PARAB, Reshma Sunil. 1001 SAM PERRY BLVD 22401 #496-38-1998 L2006 **END** *100

PATEL, Zeenat Sanjay. 1011 CARE WAY, STE 200 22401 #665-02-2001 L2005 **OBG** *020 †20

PCSOLYAR, Dale Wilton. 220 EXECUTIVE CENTER PKWY, NEUROLOGY ASSOCIATES 22401 #041-14-1980 L1987 **N CN** *020 †75

PERUSSE, Kevin Robt. 1001 SAM PERRY BLVD 22401 #023-12-1990 L2002 **DR** *020 †80

PHILLIPS, Frederic Alden. 1001 SAM PERRY BLVD 22401 #041-02-1959 L1964 **PD LM** *062

POFFENBARGER, Glen J. 1101 SAM PERRY BLVD # 207, TOMPKINS MARTIN MEDICAL PL 22401 #010-02-1992 L2005 **NS** *020 †25

PYATAK, Peter Steven. 1011 CARE WAY, STE 200 22401 #033-05-1982 L1997 **OBG REN** *030 †30 ‡

RACKLEY, Justin Hamway. 1001 SAM PERRY BLVD, FREDERICKSBURG ANESTHESIA 22401 #051-01-2004 L2005 **AN** *012

RAGHU-OBLESHWAR, Balaji. 1001 SAM PERRY BLVD, FREDERICKSBURG HOSPITAL GR 22401 #495-21-1991 L2000 **IM** *020 †20

RANELS, Richard Eugene, Jr. 2301 FALL HILL AVE, STE 202 22401 #051-04-1975 L1978 **N LM** *020

REED, Donald Lloyd. 600 JACKSON ST 22401 #051-04-1961 L1962 **P CHP** *071

REHM, Jeffrey Ronald. 521 PARK HILL DR, PULMONARY ASSOCIATES OF FR 22401 #023-01-1987 L1995 **PUD CCM** *020 †20

RICE, David Blair. 1101 SAM PERRY BLVD 22401 #051-01-1964 L1964 **GE IM** *020 †20

RICKABAUGH, Coleen Ann. 1001 SAM PERRY BLVD, FEMA MARY WASHINGTON HOSP 22401 #041-14-1993 L1998 **EM** *020 †16

ROBBINS, Clement Jay, III. 619 JEFFERSON DAVIS HWY 22401 #051-04-1957 L1959 **OBG** *071 †30

ROBERTS, Lawrence H. 1001 SAM PERRY BLVD, TRAUMA SERVICES 22401 #010-01-1982 L2007 **GS TRS** *020 †20

ROYSTER, Clarence Edward. 621B JEFFERSON DAVIS HWY 2, SNOWDEN OFFICE PARK 22401 #051-04-1968 L1968 **OBG** *020 †30

RYAN, Bradley Calvin. 1101 SAM PERRY BLVD, STE 211 22401 #048-14-2001 L2006 **GS** *020 †85

RYAN, John Thos. 120 EXECUTIVE CENTER PKWY, RAPPAHANNOCK FAMILY PHYSIC 22401 #051-04-1972 L1973 **FM** *030 †18

RYCZKO, Barbara Ann. 1101 SAM PERRY BLVD, STE 311 22401 #035-06-1985 L1990 **GS** *020 †45

SACKS, Henry Gerard. 2301 FALL HILL AVE, STE 106 22401 #023-01-1971 L1976 **D** *020 †15

SAMPSON, Mitzi Jean. 2301 FALL HILL AVE, STE 302 22401 #051-04-1990 L1991 **FM** *020 †18

SATO, Shinichi. 1001 SAM PERRY BLVD, FREDERICKSBURG EMERGENCY M 22401 #051-04-1998 L2001 **EM** *020 †16

SCHLESINGER, James John. 1001 SAM PERRY BLVD, MARY WASHINGTON HOSP 22401 #035-06-1986 L1991 **EM** *020 †16

SCHUSTER, James John. 1001 SAM PERRY BLVD 22401 #041-14-1986 L1991 **DR** *020 †80

SCOTT, David Wm, Jr. 1001 SAM PERRY BLVD 22401 #051-01-1940 L1940 **IM CD** *071 †20

SCOTT, David Wm, III. 1001 SAM PERRY BLVD 22401 #051-01-1967 L1967 **DR** *020 †80

SCOTT, David Wright. 607 WILLIAM ST, RADIOLOGIC ASSOC 22401 #020-02-1958 L1959 **IM** *071

SELL, Scott Michael. 1051 CARE WAY 22401 #056-05-1990 L1999 **U** *020 †95

SEN, Devashish. 2800 WELLFORD ST, STE 100 22401 #495-47-1989 L2008 **PM APM** *020 †20,60

SHEETS, Clifton Avery. 1001 SAM PERRY BLVD, MARY WASHINGTON HOSPITAL 22401 #051-04-1983 L1989 **EM** *020 †16

SHERWOOD, John Timothy. 1201 SAM PERRY BLVD, STE 230 22401 #035-06-1994 L2006 **TS** *100 †85,90

SHORTER, Lia Dorthea. 1101 SAM PERRY BLVD, STE 314 22401 #036-08-2002 L2007 **OBG** *020 †30

SHUMAN, Mary Susan. 1071 CARE WAY, STE 101 22401 #039-01-1996 L2000 **OBG** *020 †30

SIMON, Robert Lee. 1001 SAM PERRY BLVD, PEDIATRIX MEDICAL GROUP, P 22401 #165-03-1977 L1994 **NPM PD** *020 †55

SIMS, Adam Hale. ■ 22401 #023-12-1997 L2008 **EM** *020 †16

SMITH, Peter Renick. 511 PARK HILL DR 22401 #035-45-1965 L1972 **A IM** *020 †20,03

SMITH, Renick Mathew. 1995 JEFFERSON DAVIS HWY, STE 100 22401 #051-04-1996 L2002 **GE** *020 †20

SNEDDEN, Michael Hawley. 501 PARK HILL DR 22401 #041-02-1979 L2002 **ORS** *020 †40 ‡

SOFIS, George Thomas. 1001 SAM PERRY BLVD, RADIOLOGIC ASSOCIATES OF F 22401 #045-01-2000 L2006 **DR** *020 †80

SOUTHWORTH, Lawrence Earl. 1001 SAM PERRY BLVD 22401 #051-04-1964 L1964 **R** *071 †80

SPIVEY, John Carl, Jr. 210 EXECUTIVE CENTER PKWY 22401 #051-01-1967 L1967 **GE IM** *020 †20

SPRINKLE, James Dean, Jr. 1001 SAM PERRY BLVD 22401 #051-04-1991 L1992 **RNR** *020 †80

SPRINKLE, Whitney Leigh. 331 PARK HILL DR 22401 #051-04-1993 L1995 **PD** *020 †55

STADULIS, Jerome M. ■ 22402 #041-02-1952 L1985 **OM** *071

STARLING, John Lewis. 1708 FALL HILL AVE STE 100 22401 #051-01-1967 L1967 **OTO** *071 †45

STATLER, John Daniel. 1001 SAM PERRY BLVD 22401 #041-02-1994 L2007 **DR VIR** *020 †80

STEBBING, Geo Ernest Thos. 608 JACKSON ST, RAPPAHANNCK AREA HLTH DIST 22401 #010-02-1961 L1964 **GPM** *071 †70

STELMACK, Victor Ralph. 1101 SAM PERRY BLVD, STE 203 22401 #035-09-1980 L2006 **GS** *040 †85

STEPHENS, Wesley G. ■ 22401 #047-06-1953 L1957 **EM** *071 †16

STERN, Donald Ray. 608 JACKSON ST 22401 #034-01-1979 L1981 **AI EP** *030 †70

STEVENS, Michael Peter. 1300 THORNTON ST 22401 #021-01-1969 L1976 **D** *020 †15

STEVENS, Patricia E P. 1300 THORNTON ST 22401 #021-01-1970 L1971 **D PHP** *020 †15

SUSSDORF, Claudia Ellen. 2300 FALL HILL AVE, STE 290 22401 #035-20-1986 L1993 **PD** *020 †15

SUTHAR, Bhavin Shashikant. 301A PARK HILL DR, VIRGINIA INTERVENTIONAL SP 22401 #021-05-1996 L2006 **PM PME** *020 †60

SZLYK, Gregory Richard. 1051 CARE WAY 22401 #010-01-1997 L1999 **U** *020 †95

TANVEER, Asra. 1001 SAM PERRY BLVD, PEDIATRIX MEDICAL GROUP, P 22401 #917-23-1987 L1996 **PD NPM** *020 †55

TARTER-WILLIAMS, Yasmin. 1701 FALL HILL AVE STE 105 22401 #010-03-1984 L2000 **FM** *020 †18

THOMPSON, Richard Niles. 1101 SAM PERRY BLVD, STE 121 22401 #047-06-1965 L1974 **GS** *020 †85

TOMZAK, Thomas Jos. 608 JACKSON ST 22401 #030-06-1973 L1985 **OBG** *020 †18,30

TOPPS, Jacinta White. 2300 FALL HILL AVE, STE 290 22401 #010-01-1998 L1998 **PD** *020 †55

TRIBLE, Waring, Jr. 1995 JEFFERSON DAVIS HWY, STE 100 22401 #051-04-1984 L1988 **GE IM** *020 †20

TRICE, Jerry Ashby. 521 PARK HILL DR 22401 #051-04-1959 L1959 **IM PUD** *020

TRUONG, Anne Nguyen. 2216 PRINCESS ANNE ST, STE 203 22401 #031-01-1993 L2000 **PM** *020 †60

TUCKER, Frederick C, Jr. 111 PARK HILL DR, STE B 22401 #038-40-1977 L1997 **HO ON** *020 †75,20

TUCKER, Susan. 111 PARK HILL DR, STE B 22401 #473-01-1972 L1998 **P** *020 †75

VAN HORN, Lori L. 1001 SAM PERRY BLVD 22401 #021-01-1987 L1994 **PD** *020 †55

VILLALOBOS, Linda Ann. 603 KENMORE AVE, SOPHIA MEDICAL ASSOCIATES, 22401 #165-01-1984 L1993 **IM** *020 †20

VOSSENBERG, Frans Albert. 1101 SAM PERRY BLVD # 415, VIRGINIA CARDIO CONSULT 22401 #041-02-1982 L1983 **IC CD** *020 †20

VRANIAN, Robert Brown. 1201 SAM PERRY BLVD, STE 280 22401 #008-01-1971 L1973 **CD IM** *020 †20

VU, Anh Duy. 2500 CHARLES ST, MOUNT VERNON CARDIOLOGY AS 22401 #010-01-1999 L2005 **CD MPD** *020 †20

WAKATSUKI, Rachel. 2300 FALL HILL AVE 22401 #010-01-1997 L2003 **IM** *020

WALKER, Scott Edward. 1101 SAM PERRY BLVD, TOMPKINS-MARTIN STE 401 22401 #025-01-1995 L2004 **OBG** *020 †30

WANG, Dennis Sheryung. 1101 SAM PERRY BLVD # 219 22401 #040-02-1988 L2005 **GS TRS** *020 †85

WANG, Nancy Liching. 120 EXECUTIVE CENTER PKWY, RAPPAHANNOCK FAMILY PHYSIC 22401 #035-15-1991 L1999 **FM** *020 †18

WARE, Paul Dudley. 1001 SAM PERRY BLVD 22401 #051-04-1991 L1996 **AN PME** *020 †05

WARGOVICH, Thomas Jos. 1201 SAM PERRY BLVD, STE 280 22401 #041-02-1982 L2003 **CD IM** *020 †20

WEBER, Timothy Dickson. 1001 SAM PERRY BLVD, FEMA MARY WASH HOSP 22401 #025-07-1998 L1998 **EM** *020 †16

WELHAM, Jenny H. 331 PARK HILL DR 22401 #014-01-1998 L2001 **PD** *020 †55

WENGER, Mark Alan. 511 PARK HILL DR, ALLERGY & ASTHMA ASSOCIATE 22401 #051-01-1997 L1997 **AI IM** *020 †20,03

WEXLER, Brian Scott. 1001 SAM PERRY BLVD, FEMA MARY WASHINGTON HOSPI 22401 #035-19-2000 L2004 **EM** *020 †16

WHEELER, Robert Clews, II. 1101 SAM PERRY BLVD, STE 204 22401 #024-01-1961 L1967 IM CD *020 †20

WHEELER, Thomas Earl. 1201 SAM PERRY BLVD 22401 #051-04-1975 L1978 CD IM *020 †20

WICKER, Donna Cuneo. 621 JEFFERSON DAVIS HWY, B 22401 #021-01-1985 L1989 OBG *020 †30

WICKER, Henry Sindos, Jr. 1101 SAM PERRY BLVD 22401 #021-01-1985 L1989 GS *020 †85

WILSON, Bonita Wesley. 511 PARK HILL DR 22401 #010-03-1976 L1985 AI PD *020 †55,03

WOHLER, Kurt Wade. 1001 SAM PERRY BLVD 22401 #051-04-1993 L1993 AN *020 †05

WOLANSKA, Bozena Danuta. 2216 PRINCESS ANNE ST, FREDERICKSBURG INC #107 22401 #759-09-1987 L2002 IM *020 †20

WONG, Peter Wing K. 201 EXECUTIVE CENTER PKWY, GASTROENTEROLOGY ASSOCIATE 22401 #051-01-1992 L1995 GE IM *020 †20

WOOD, Garrett Wilbur. 1001 SAM PERRY BLVD 22401 #030-06-1986 L1994 AN IM *020 †20,05

WORKMAN, Keith Robert. 1001 SAM PERRY BLVD 22401 #010-02-1994 L2003 PTH *050 †50

WRIGHT, Melville G, III. 621 JEFFERSON DAVIS HWY, STE 101 22401 #051-04-1971 L1976 PD *020 †55

YONKER-SELL, Anna Edwina. 1001 SAM PERRY BLVD, MARY WASHINGTON HOSP RD DP 22401 #056-05-1991 L1999 AN *020 †05

YOUNG, Scott A. 600 JACKSON ST 22401 #011-03-1988 L1999 CHP P *020 †75

FREDERICKSBURG – SPOTSYLVANIA

AARONSON, Allen Edward. 12101 CAROL LN 22407 #041-14-1974 L1977 PD PDC *020 †55

ABATE, Gerard. 4008 MOSSY BANK LN 22408 #308-07-1981 L1987 CD IM *020

AHMED, Syed Shoaib. 12000 KENNEDY LN, STE 100 22407 #704-21-1989 L2001 P *100

ALBO, Cecilio E. 6103 BLACKSTONE BLVD 22407 #748-11-1968 L1972 FM *020

ALLY, Nishat Fatima. ■ 22407 #051-04-2008 *012

AMEEN, Richard John. 4900 PLANK RD STE 101 22407 #051-04-1980 L1985 IM IMG *020 †20

AMORY, Charles Victor, Jr. 12006 KILARNEY DR 22407 #051-07-1994 L2000 PDP *020 †55

ANDERSON, Andrew S. 115 BLUFF POINT RD, ANESTHESIA AND CRITICAL CA 22407 #047-06-1976 L1980 AN OS *071 †20

ANDERSON, John Ryan, Jr. 12101 CAROL LN, PRATT MEDICAL CENTER 22407 #051-07-1985 L1986 FM *020 †18

BAILEY, Ryan Michael. 10703 SPOTSYLVANIA AVE, STE 101 22408 #023-01-2002 L2007 OMF *020

BANZON, Raymund Dennis. 12101 CAROL LN 22407 #047-07-1989 L1992 FM *020 †18

BLEY, Donald Edward. ■ 22407 #036-07-1972 L1977 FM *020 †18

BOULWARE, Valerie Hawkins. 6330 FIVE MILE CENTRE PARK, STE 400 22407 #038-06-1976 L2004 P *020

BROCK, Jay David. 4304 LAFAYETTE BLVD 22408 #067-01-1972 L1980 FM *020 †18

BROCK, Lee Richard. 4304 LAFAYETTE BLVD 22408 #035-15-1973 L1980 OPH *020 †35

CALLAHAN, Mary Patricia. 4550 EMPIRE CT 22408 #010-01-2004 L2004 PD *020

CAO, Lynn Kimthi. 1139 HEATHERSTONE DR, CHILDREN'S HEALTH, PC 22407 #051-04-1999 L1999 PD *020 †55

CARR-MALONE, Rosemary G. ■ 22408 #045-01-1997 L1997 P *020 †75

CHOUDHARY, Nivedita. 4107 PLANK RD STE A, PEAK MENTAL HEALTH SERVICE 22407 #917-20-1995 L2007 P *020

CLARK, Catherine Leah. 3429 JEFFERSON DAVIS HWY 22408 #056-06-1977 L1978 FM *020 †18

COSTA, Michael Jos. 3429 JEFFERSON DAVIS HWY, MEDIC ONE 22408 #035-46-1987 L1995 FM *020 †18

DANG, Diemngoc Tran. 3916 PLANK RD 22407 #011-02-1998 L2002 OPH *020 †35

DARDEN, Daryle Leighton. 10401 SPOTSYLVANIA AVE, STE 200 22408 #041-12-1999 L2005 RNR *020 †80

FAUSTINO, Edgardo F. 4107 LAFAYETTE BLVD, STE 3 22408 #748-01-1977 L1985 IM NEP *020 †20

FERNANDO, Neville Anthony. ■ 22407 #220-02-1968 L1975 AN *071 †05

FIORE, Paul Anthony. 11507 KINGSWOOD BLVD, FREDRICKSBURG ID CONSULTAN 22408 #041-12-1971 L1999 ID IM *020 †20

FISH, George Dennis. 10401 SPOTSYLVANIA AVE, FREDERICKSBURG LEE HILL 22408 #051-04-1984 L1988 DR *020 †80

FITZSIMMONS, Patrick J. 9530 COSNER DR, STE 200 22408 #051-07-1995 L2004 IC *020 †20

GALLOWAY, Shelby Jean. ■ 22408 #036-05-1965 L1965 DR *071 †80

GAMACHE, Donna Jean M. 125 OLDE GREENWICH DR, STE 220 22408 #050-02-1995 L1999 FM *020 †18

GLASS, Ted Alan. ■ 22407 #051-01-1977 L1979 DR *020 †80

GOEDEN, Michael J. 2511 SALEM CHURCH RD 22407 #030-05-1975 L1985 EM *020 †16

GOEDEN, Nancy Cornwell. 12101 CAROL LN, JILL E RYLAND 22407 #038-41-1980 L1985 EM *075 †55

GONZALEZ, Conrado C, Jr. 6105 HEALTH CENTER LN 22407 #748-08-1969 L1979 RO *020 †80

GOODLETT, Allison Houck. 12101 CAROL LN 22407 #012-22-1999 L2005 PD *020 †55

GOOSE, Pam Williams. 10401 SPOTSYLVANIA AVE, FREDERICKSBURG LEE HILL 22408 #023-01-1986 L1991 DR *020 †80

GORMAN, John Rossier. 10671 COURTHOUSE RD 22407 #019-02-1954 L1987 GP AM *030

GULATI, Harpreet Singh. 4343 PLANK RD STE 110 22407 #690-06-1990 L2001 IM PM *020 †60

GURFINKEL, Alexander E. 10600 SPOTSYLVANIA AVE, PERFERED PEDIATRICS 22408 #913-15-1996 L2006 PD GS *020 †55

HEBRON, Desiderio L, Jr. 992 BRAGG RD 22407 #748-02-1962 L1972 GP GS *071

HEWITT, Michael John. 10401 SPOTSYLVANIA AVE, STE 200 22408 #035-45-1978 L1982 DR *020 †80

HOLLOWELL, Monica Lynn. ■ 22407 #051-07-2005 L2006 PTH *012

JOHN, James E, Jr. ■ 22408 #051-01-1952 L1952 OM PTH *071

JOHNSON, Thomas Mark. 3916 PLANK RD 22407 #065-06-1994 L2001 OPH *020 †35

JOHNSON, William Blake. 12101 CAROL LN 22407 #041-01-1995 L2004 PD *020 †55

KALCHUK, Frank F. ■ 22407 #035-03-1943 L1959 GP *071

KAUFFMAN, Gregory John. 9530 COSNER DR, BLDG 1/2 22408 #033-06-1987 L1990 IM *075 †20

KIM, Jiyeon. 10600 SPOTSYLVANIA AVE 22408 #051-04-1991 L1991 PD *020 †55

KIN, John William, Jr. 12101 CAROL LN 22407 #051-07-2001 L2002 FM *020 †18

KOLEGA, Bruno. ■ 22408 #561-17-1951 L1967 FM *072

LASERNA, Oscar Magno. 4103 LAFAYETTE BLVD 22408 #748-01-1966 L1976 OBG *020 †30

LASERNA, Rosario Guanzon. 4103 LAFAYETTE BLVD 22408 #748-01-1965 L1975 OBG *020 †30

LEWIS, Richard Alan. 9530 COSNER DR, STE 200 22408 #023-07-1978 L1981 CD IM *020 †20

MALONE, Ricky Dee. ■ 22408 #048-12-1985 L1986 P OM *020 †70,75

MANSOURI, Arash. 3916 PLANK RD 22407 #051-04-1995 L1995 OPH *020 †35

MARIETTA, Joseph Michael. 2511 SALEM CHURCH RD 22407 #005-12-1986 L1995 EM *020 †16

MASI, Jeffrey Neil. ■ 22407 #005-02-2006 L2008 DR *012

MC CLANAHAN, Mark Allen. 10711 SPOTSYLVANIA AVE 22408 #051-04-1986 L1987 END IM *020 †20

MC LAUGHLIN, Job Jos. 4718 CARR DR 22408 #035-01-1933 L1946 IM *071

MUSSEY, Steven Walter. 4107 LAFAYETTE BLVD, STE 4 22408 #010-01-1985 L1993 IM IMG *020 †20

NAIR, Jayalekshmi. 4552 EMPIRE CT 22408 #495-31-1990 L2006 FM *020 †18

NGUYEN, Dien Van. 1129 HEATHERSTONE DR, FREDERICKSBURG CHRISTIAN 22407 #051-07-1996 L2005 IM *020 †20

NGUYEN, Hong Thuy. 12006 KILARNEY DR 22407 #023-01-1991 L1993 IM *020 †20

NOORI, Alice C. 4550 EMPIRE CT, KENNEBEC PEDIATRICS 22408 #748-08-1983 L2007 PD *020 †55

O'BRIEN, Julie Elizabeth. 10600 SPOTSYLVANIA AVE 22408 #030-06-1990 L1999 PD *062 †55

PAQUETTE, Joseph David. 12101 CAROL LN 22407 #051-04-1979 L1981 FM *020 †18

PENICK, Chas Garland, Jr. 8 RIVER OAK PL, 8 RIVER OAK PLACE 22407 #051-04-1979 L1982 EM *020 †16

POWELL, Timothy Andrew. 1129 HEATHERSTONE DR 22407 #051-04-1989 L1993 IM PD *020 †20,55

PURCELL, Linda M. 10600 SPOTSYLVANIA AVE 22408 #041-77-1991, ▲ L1994 PD *020 †55

REESE, William Andrew. 10620 SPOTSYLVANIA AVE 22408 #051-04-1986 L1992 GP EM *020 †16

SAMBAT, Paulino D, Jr. 106 FALCON DR 22408 #748-01-1965 L1972 GP GS *020 †85

SANDERS, Margaret M M. 12101 CAROL LN 22407 #051-04-1975 L1976 RNR *020 †80

SARBER, Lisa J. 4107 LAFAYETTE BLVD, STE 4 22408 #041-07-1988 L1995 IM *020 †20

SEIDNER, Scott Jeffrey. 9530 COSNER DR, STE 200 22408 #035-19-1982 L2003 CD IM *020 †20

SELLERGREN, Kim Roy. 12101 CAROL LN 22407 #024-01-1976 L1985 ORS *020 †40

SHARMA, Sunil. 4117 PLANK RD 22407 #495-45-1980 L1989 *020

SNOW, Frank Richard. 9530 COSNER DR, STE 200 22408 #051-04-1982 L1983 CD IM *020 †20

STADULIS, Leedyln H. ■ 22407 #012-01-1994 L2001 OBG *030

STOKER, Donald Riley. ■ 22407 #021-05-1958 L1972 OBG *071

SURESH, Sumana. 12000 KENNEDY LN, STE 100 22407 #495-50-1989 L2005 P *020

SWING, John Patrick, III. 4107 LAFAYETTE BLVD STE A 22407 #012-01-1997 L2001 P *020 †75

TAMANA, Feroz. ■ 22407 #118-01-1988 L2004 FM *020 †18

THOMAS, Ruby. 3920 PLANK RD, STE 120 22407 #496-32-1996 L2005 CHP *020 †75

WALSH, Laura. 7117 SALEM FIELDS BLVD 22407 #035-15-1998 L1998 PD *020 †55

WELLS, Bernadette N. 4107 LAFAYETTE BLVD, STE 2 22408 #017-20-1978 L1989 PD *074 †55

WOLFE, Warren. 10620 SPOTSYLVANIA AVE 22408 #041-77-1963, ▲ L2003 FM OS *020 ‡

ZIA, Jamal Uddin. 10620 SPOTSYLVANIA AVE 22408 #308-11-1986 L2006 FM *020

FREDERICKSBURG – STAFFORD

ALBERTSON, Anna-Jane. PO BOX 9072 22403 #041-07-1951 L1958 PHP GPM *071 †70

AZEZ, Ali Kahtan. ■ 22406 #528-01-1994 L2000 CHP *100

BRANDEL, George Pearson. ■ 22405 #038-06-1962 L1985 AM OS *071 †70

BRANTLEY, Julian T. 20 HEARTFIELDS LN, # 317 22405 #024-01-1944 L1944 OBG *071 †30

CAGGIANO, Maria A. 386 KINGS HWY 22405 #023-12-2004 L2005 P *012

CAINE, Robert Alan. 110 CAMBRIDGE ST 22405 #008-01-1974 L1980 OPH *020 †35

CHERWEK, Michael L. ■ 22405 #051-01-1971 L1971 IM CD *020 †20

COLEMAN, William Peach. 110 CAMBRIDGE ST 22405 #051-04-1972 L1976 OPH *020 †35

COX, Philip A. ■ 22405 #010-01-1941 L1976 GP GS *071 †85

FALKENBERG, Thomas. 10 CHATHAM HEIGHTS RD 22405 #041-02-1987 L1996 OPH *020 †20,35

GHALIB, Luma Mudhafar. ■ 22405 #528-01-1992 L2007 END IM *020 †20 ‡

GLOVER, Clarence Kinsey. 10 WHITE OAK RD 22405 #051-04-1956 L1956 OPH *071 †35

HAPPEL, Margaret Ashley. ■ 22405 #045-04-1997 L2007 GP *020 †20

HARRINGTON, F Baldwin. ■ 22405 #051-01-1958 L1958 ORS *071 †40

JANI, Binoy Rohit. 10 CHATHAM HEIGHTS RD 22405 #041-07-1996 L2001 OPH CS *020 †35

JOSEPH, Cherian. 46 TOWNES PL, FREDERICKSBURG GERIATRIC M 22405 #495-63-1993 L2007 IMG *020 †20

KING, Joseph Austin. ■ 22405 #047-05-1958 L1959 IM HEM *071

KLEINBERG, David C. ■ 22406 #654-01-1985 L1986 FM *075 †18

LI, Paul Xiaopu. 20 PLANTATION DR STE 105, MEDIC-1 22406 #243-16-1982 L2005 FM *100 †18

MASSAD, Louis Benedict. ■ 22405 #051-04-1958 L1958 GS OS *071 †85

MULDOON, Daniel Gregory. 418 CHATHAM SQ PARK OFC 22405 #010-02-1995 L1995 FM *020 †18

PARK, Sangil. ■ 22406 #051-01-2008 *012

PARMELEE, Warren Earl. 20 PLANTATION DR 22406 #005-12-1964 L1983 FM OM *020 †16

ROBBETT, William F X. ■ 22406 #010-02-1947 L1954 OTO OS *071 †45

RODRIGUEZ, David. ■ 22406 #035-15-1971 L1972 OTO *020 †45

SASSER, William Dudley. ■ 22405 #036-01-1971 L1972 GS VS *071 †85

SLOAN, Geoffrey David. 12 CHATHAM HEIGHTS RD 22405 #051-04-1979 L1982 AN *020 †05

VOSS, Carol Ann. 11 SMOKEHOUSE DR, STE 101 22405 #005-18-1989 L2007 FM *020 †18

WILLIAMS, Richard Stuart. ■ 22405 #051-04-1979 L1982 GPM *020 †85,70

WILLIS, Amos Johns. 10 CHATHAM HEIGHTS RD 22405 #035-08-1970 L1974 OPH *071 †35

WOO, Jean So-Chun. 20 PLANTATION DR 22406 #143-07-1969 L1973 *071

YARBROUGH, Frank Lee. ■ 22405 #020-02-1949 L1949 IM *071

FREE UNION – ALBEMARLE

DANIEL, William Warren. HILLTOP RD # 1 22940 #024-01-1941 L1986 GS ADM *071 †85

HENDRIX, John David. ■ 22940 #011-03-1967 L1970 D *071 †15

IEZZONI, Julia C. ■ 22940 #010-28-1987 L1992 PTH ATP *050 †50

MARR, John Stuart. ■ 22940 #035-09-1967 L2001 IM OM *030 †20,70

TURNER, Ulysses Grant, III. ■ 22940 #051-01-1966 L1966 GYN *071 †30

FRIES – GRAYSON

VANDYKE, Kelly S. 109 CARROL DR 24330 #051-01-1991 L1992 IM *020 †20

■ = Address Information Privacy Protected

FRONT ROYAL – WARREN

ALLI, Chaitanya. 140 W 11TH ST, FAMILY PRACT 22630 #495-65-2003 L2005 **FP** *012

BALL, Thomas Alan. 140 W 11TH ST 22630 #051-01-1990 L1993 **FM** *020 †18

BARRERE, Philip William. ■ 22630 #038-43-2002 L2004 **FM** *100

BARRON, Jennifer B. 140 W 11TH ST 22630 #051-04-1996 L1998 **FM** *020 †18

BERNARD, Barbara Therese. 841 N SHENANDOAH AVE, SKYLINE FAMILY PRACTICE 22630 #051-04-1997 L1997 **FM** *020 †18

BERRY, Colin. 1000 N SHENANDOAH AVE, MEDICAL AFFAIRS OFFICE 22630 #023-12-1988 L1990 **OBG** *020

BRADD, Floyd, III. 841 N SHENANDOAH AVE 22630 #051-07-1979 L1984 **FM EM** *020 †18

CHANDER, Mahesh. 315 W 10TH ST, FRONT ROYAL INTERNAL 22630 #495-03-1963 L1972 **IM NEP** *071 †20 ‡

DALY, Patricia Ann. 315 W 10TH ST, FRONT ROYAL INTERNAL 22630 #054-04-1983 L2001 **END IM** *020

DENNEHY, Francis Xavier. 140 W 11TH ST, FRONT ROYAL FAMILY PRACTIC 22630 #010-02-1987 L2003 **FM EM** *020 †18

DUNN, Deborah Ellen. 315 W 10TH ST, FRONT ROYAL PEDS 22630 #035-47-2001 L2005 **PD** *020 †55

FAVAREAU, James E. 318 N ROYAL AVE 22630 #010-02-1975 L1981 **ORS** *020 †40

FINK, Alan Jeffrey. 56 CHESTER ST 22630 #045-01-1983 L1987 **OPH** *020 †35

FREDERICKSEN, Judith S. 135 N ROYAL AVE, SHENANDOAH MEDICAL ASSOC, 22630 #035-48-1996 L1996 **FM** *020 †18

FREILICH, James William. 1000 N SHENANDOAH AVE 22630 #051-01-1997 L2002 **EM FM** *020 †18

GREEN, Shannan Arnita. 140 W 11TH ST 22630 #051-04-2002 L2002 **FM** *020 †18

HAWARI, Samer Fathi. 140 W 11TH ST 22630 #198-01-1996 L2005 **FM** *020 †18

HUBER, Charles Mac. 1000 N SHENANDOAH AVE 22630 #051-04-1968 L1968 **IM** *071 †20

HUMMEL, Keith B. 1000 N SHENANDOAH AVE 22630 #306-01-1985 L1999 **EM** *020

IRANI, Furadoon Adi. 135 N ROYAL AVE 22630 #495-04-1961 L1970 **IM** *071 †20

KANAL, Nirmal. 1096 N SHENANDOAH AVE 22630 #495-45-1969 L1980 **OPH** *020 †35

KARMY, Robert John. 1000 N SHENANDOAH AVE 22630 #005-12-1973 L1978 **OBG** *020 †30

KENNEY, Nancy Torhan. 842 N SHENANDOAH AVE, STE 2 22630 #041-07-1987 L2006 **IM IMG** *020 †20 ‡

KERNS, John William. 140 W 11TH ST 22630 #051-01-1975 L1976 **FM** *020 †18

LANDIS, John Dennis. 1000 N SHENANDOAH AVE 22630 #010-01-1966 L1972 **GS** *020 †85

LEITZ, Edward Martin. 315 W 10TH ST, FRONT ROYAL INTERNAL MED A 22630 #011-04-1998 L1998 **IM** *020 †20

MAJOR, William Berkeley. 1000 N SHENANDOAH AVE 22630 #051-01-1976 L1987 **ON HO** *020 †20

MALCOLM, Sharon E. 315 W 10TH ST, FRONT ROYAL INTERNAL 22630 #043-01-2000 L2003 **IM** *020

MARTIN, Larisa Grigorievn. 140 W 11TH ST, FAMILY PRACT 22630 #913-07-1985 L2006 **FP** *012

MC NEILL, Donald Hanson. 240 LOCUST DALE RD 22630 #051-04-1954 L1954 **GP OM** *072

MELTVEDT, Robt Carney, Jr. 1077 N SHENANDOAH AVE # A 22630 #005-18-1979 L1996 **GS** *020 †85

MONCADA, Victoria Yasmin. ■ 22630 #051-07-1992 L1999 **IM** *020

NANNA, Richard Thos. 1000 N SHENANDOAH AVE 22630 #051-04-1984 L1988 **EM FM** *020 †18

PATTESON, Thomas Earl, III. 315 W 10TH ST, FRONT ROYAL INTERNAL 22630 #051-04-1971 L1972 **GE IM** *020 †20

PHAM, Daniel Hoang. 140 W 11TH ST, SHENANDOAH VALLEY FAMILY P 22630 #305-01-2005 **FP** *012

PURI, Rajesh. 920 N SHENANDOAH AVE 22630 #496-09-1980 L1991 **NPM PD** *020 †55

PURUSHOTHAMALU, Jayashree. 1077 N SHENANDOAH AVE, STE B 22630 #495-59-1997 L2005 **FM** *020 †18 ‡

SEIPEL, Wayne David. 135 N ROYAL AVE STE B 22630 #041-02-1965 L1972 **U** *020

SERRANO, Jocelyn T. 140 W 11TH ST 22630 #748-20-2000 L2004 **FM** *020 †20

SUBEDI, Guna R. 135 N ROYAL AVE, SHENANDOAH MEDICAL ASSOCIA 22630 #243-72-1990 L1995 **IM** *020 †20

SUDIREDDY, Ramashilpa. 140 W 11TH ST, FRONT ROYAL FAMILY PRATICE 22630 #496-01-2002 L2006 **FP** *012

TRIPP, Mark David. 100 S SHENANDOAH AVE, WARREN MEMORIAL HOSPITAL 22630 #038-40-1986 L1996 **EM** *020 †16

VOORHEES, Michael Blaine. 1000 N SHENANDOAH AVE 22630 #055-01-1983 L1990 **EM** *020 †18

WALTER, Barbara Jean. 1077 N SHENANDOAH AVE, STE A 22630 #041-07-1983 L2006 **GS CCS** *020 †85

WENZINGER, Elaine Maria. 1000 N SHENANDOAH AVE 22630 #055-01-1984 L1985 **AN** *020 †05

WENZINGER, Patrick Jos. 451 LOCUST DALE RD 22630 #031-01-1980 L1983 **AN EM** *020 †05

WESTFALL, Roger Kyle. 140 W 11TH ST 22630 #055-01-1977 L1980 **FM FPG** *020 †18

WHISENANT, Sherry Ann. 140 W 11TH ST 22630 #001-06-1990 L1993 **FM** *020 †18 ‡

WOOD, Roy Stanley. ■ 22630 #036-07-1959 L1976 **PD** *075 †55

WRIGHT, David Kent. 1000 N SHENANDOAH AVE 22630 #051-04-1984 L2002 **IM EM** *020

ZIMET, Daniel Leonard. 842 N SHENANDOAH AVE, STE C 22630 #041-01-1978 L2003 **ORS** *020 †40 ‡

GAINESVILLE – PRINCE WILLIAM

ABDELFATTAH, Marwa Mohame. ■ 20155 #915-03-2002 L2007 **IM** *100

AGGARWAL, Sanjeev Kumar. 7901 LAKE MANASSAS DR 20155 #051-04-1994 L2002 **RO** *020 †80

AKBERZIE, Mohammad Ehsan. ■ 20155 #118-01-1965 L1980 **P PTH** *020

BARLETTA, Arthur Carl. 13864 CRABTREE WAY 20155 #010-02-1954 L1991 **OBG** *071 †30

BENDIGO, Leopoldo Lopez. PO BOX 345 20156 #748-11-1972 L1981 **ORS** *020 †40

BRODIE, Dorothy R Maupin. ■ 20155 #010-01-1953 L1955 **R** *071 †80

BRUHN, Donald Frederick. ■ 20155 #030-06-1958 L2001 **OBG OS** *071 †30

BURGIN, John Gregory. ■ 20155 #016-43-1967 L1996 **FM** *030 †18

CADAY, Antonio T. ■ 20155 #748-08-1965 L1980 **IM** *020

CALLAHAN, Patrick Francis. 7330 HERITAGE VILLAGE PLZ, UNIT 102 20155 #035-15-1990 L2001 **PD** *020 †55

CHAUDRI, Reema A. 7200 HERITAGE VILLAGE PLZ, SUITES 101&102 20155 #422-01-1997 L2000 **IM** *020 †20

CHOI, Chung Shin. ■ 20155 #583-08-1958 L1972 **OPH** *071 †35

CHOI, Kwang Yeul. ■ 20155 #583-01-1962 L2006 **PD** *071 †55

CHUNG, Philip Ryong. 7300 HERITAGE VILLAGE PLZ, SUITE 101 & 102 20155 #048-02-1999 L2006 **OPH** *020 †35

COBB, Valencia Janay. 7110 HERITAGE VILLAGE PLZ, STE101 INTERNAL MED 20155 #041-14-2001 L2004 **IM** *020

COHEN, Radha Reddy. 7330 HERITAGE VILLAGE PLZ, UNIT 102 20155 #001-02-1996 L2003 **PD** *020 †55

DE LA PENA, Cordell Amado. ■ 20155 #748-01-1958 L1964 **PTH BBK** *030 †50

ELLIS, John Wesley, Jr. ■ 20155 #017-20-1960 L1986 **OM FM** *030 †70,18

FEGLEY, Michelle Lee. 7508 GARDNER PARK DR 20155 #041-14-1994 L1994 **OBG** *020 †30

GALIOTO, Frank Martin, Jr. 7330 HERITAGE VILLAGE PLZ, UNIT 102 20155 #035-09-1968 L1977 **PDC** *020 †55

GUIEB, Adelaida De Guzman. 14535 JOHN MARSHALL HWY, STE 105 20155 #748-08-1963 L1972 **FM** *071 †18

GUPTA, Alok. 7350 HERITAGE VILLAGE PLZ, UNIT 101 20155 #495-45-1992 L2004 **IM** *020 †20

GUPTA, Alok Kumar. 7350 HERITAGE VILLAGE PLZ, PLAZA #101 20155 #495-21-1979 L1992 **FM** *020 †18

HACKETT, Jason Vanvliet. 14370 LEE HWY, STE 105 20155 #305-01-2002 L2002 **FM** *020 †18

HAMMONDS, Victoria C. 14540 JOHN MARSHALL HWY, STE 104 20155 #025-07-1993 L2000 **FM** *020 †18

HAN, Soo-Bong. ■ 20155 #583-10-1966 L1973 **P** *020 †75

IBRAHIM, Muhammad. ■ 20155 #704-02-1969 L1974 **PD** *020 †55

JOSEPHS, Taja Helen. 7508 GARDNER PARK DR 20155 #035-20-1999 L2003 **OBG** *020

KANG, Christopher. ■ 20155 #008-02-2003 L2007 **OMF** *020

KHAN, Ejaz Mohammad. 14370 LEE HWY, STE 104 20155 #704-09-1992 L2006 **ICE** *020 †20

KIM, Chung Whan. ■ 20155 #583-04-1964 L1972 **GS TRS** *071 †85

KIRBY, William Clark. 7330 HERITAGE VILLAGE PLZ, UNIT 102 20155 #017-20-1975 L1986 **PDC PD** *020 †55

LEE, Won Jay. ■ 20155 #583-01-1961 L2005 **DR AR** *071 †80,28

LILLIS, Christopher. 7110 HERITAGE VILLAGE PLZ, STE 101 20155 #010-02-2000 L2005 **IM** *020

LINDSEY, Jennifer H. 7330 HERITAGE VILLAGE PLZ, UNIT 102 20155 #051-01-1992 L1997 **PDC** *020 †55

LUKOWSKY, Gerhard Hans. ■ 20155 #407-12-1952 L1958 **IM CD** *071 †20

MANCINI, Robert C. 14535 JOHN MARSHALL HWY, STE 105 20155 #010-01-1990 L1996 **FM** *020 †18

MICHALSKI, Stephen Alan. ■ 20155 #051-04-1983 L1986 **GS CCS** *020 †85

MILLIS, David Howard. 8373 TENBROOK DR 20155 #010-03-1983 L2005 **P** *020 †75

MIN, James Byeongwoo. 14540 JOHN MARSHALL HWY, STE 104 20155 #035-08-1998 L2001 **FM** *020 †18

NAU, Jennifer Lauren. 14370 LEE HWY, STE 105 20155 #051-04-1995 L1999 **FM FPG** *020 †18

NEAL, Kathleen R. 7508 GARDNER PARK DR 20155 #049-01-1983 L2006 **GYN** *020 †30

NOISETTE, Bernadette E. ■ 20155 #035-46-1979 L2005 **PD** *020 †55

PHANG, James C. ■ 20155 #583-02-1967 L1976 **DR** *020 †80

PRIETO, Danl Corneja, Jr. ■ 20155 #748-02-1963 L1972 **EM GS** *071 †85,16

REDDY, Balemula Kusuma P. ■ 20155 #495-57-1976 **GP AN** *020

REDDY, G V. ■ 20155 #495-09-1961 L1972 **ORS GS** *071 †85

ROARK, George W, Jr. 13525 RYTON RIDGE LN 20155 #041-12-1950 L1956 **P PYA** *071 †75

ROSENTHAL, Joanna Beth. 7330 HERITAGE VILLAGE PLZ, UNIT 102 20155 #041-01-2001 L2007 **PDC** *100 †55

SAHAI, Harish S. ■ 20155 #495-75-1982 L1995 **IM** *020

SHAPIRO, Stephen Robt. 7330 HERITAGE VILLAGE PLZ, UNIT 102 20155 #035-19-1967 L1973 **PDC PD** *020 †55

SIDDIQUI, Mohammed F. ■ 20155 #495-53-1994 L2007 **FM** *020 †18

SIGMON, Douglas Harold. 14370 LEE HWY, STE 105 20155 #036-01-1996 L1999 **FM** *020 †18

SMITH, Chari Vaughnese. 7508 GARDNER PARK DR 20155 #016-45-1997 L2001 **OBG** *020 †30

TABANDEH, Hassan. 14370 LEE HWY, STE 104 20155 #517-12-1993 L2003 **CD IM** *020 †20

TAKANTI, Anuradha T. 7521 VIRGINIA OAKS DR, STE 200 20155 #495-21-1986 L1994 **PD** *020 †20

TANG, Steven J. 14540 JOHN MARSHALL HWY, STE 104 20155 #056-05-1998 L2001 **FM** *020 †18

TELEP, James Daniel. 7330 HERITAGE VILLAGE PLZ, UNIT 102 20155 #041-15-1999 L2005 **PDC** *020 †55

THOMPSON, James Alan. 7330 HERITAGE VILLAGE PLZ, UNIT 102 20155 #036-01-1994 L2001 **PDC** *020 †55

TURKINGTON, Susan Lea. 14370 LEE HWY, STE 105 20155 #019-02-1991 L2002 **FM** *020 †18 ‡

TYLKA, Christine Teresa. ■ 20155 #036-05-2008 *012

WEAVER, Albert Junior. 14535 JOHN MARSHALL HWY, STE 105 20155 #010-01-1976 L1978 **IM** *020 †20

YAZDANI, Shahram. 14370 LEE HWY, STE 104 20155 #035-19-1991 L2000 **CD IM** *020 †20

GALAX – CARROLL

AREY, Jo Ann H. 199 HOSPITAL DR STE 5 24333 #036-07-1975 L1976 **FM** *020 †18

AREY, Vaughn Ray. 199 HOSPITAL DR STE 5 24333 #036-01-1975 L1976 **FM** *020 †18

BLATTNER, Carlos Jesus. 227 HOSPITAL DR 24333 #051-04-1979 L1980 **OBG** *020 †30

BOLEN, John Wm, Jr. 110 VALLEY ST 24333 #051-01-1985 L1986 **DR** *020 †80

BRITTON, James C, III. 200 HOSPITAL DR 24333 #001-02-1982 L1991 **ATP PTH** *020 †50

BROCK, Jack Gilbert, Jr. 110 VALLEY ST, GALAX RADIOLOGY 24333 #045-01-1978 L1984 **DR** *020 †80

BUTLER, Amy E. 199 HOSPITAL DR STE 7, GALAX AND HILLSVILLE 24333 #036-05-1995 L2002 **FM** *020 †18

CARMODY, John Wm. 502 S MAIN ST 24333 #035-09-1976 L2002 **ORS** *020 †40 ‡

CHASTANET, Rachel Irene. 200 HOSPITAL DR 24333 #041-02-1987 L1989 **IM FM** *020 †18,20

CLARK, Kenneth Alan. 199 HOSPITAL DR, STE 7 24333 #011-04-1986 L1987 **IM** *020 †20

CUENCO, Napoleon. 200 HOSPITAL DR 24333 #748-10-1983 L1993 **P** *020 †75

ESTRELLA, Fernando S. ■ 24333 #748-10-1994 L2006 **IM** *020 †20

FANT, Palmer Willis. 199 HOSPITAL DR STE 10 24333 #045-01-1957 L1967 **R** *072 †80

FANT, Vanessa Sturgill. 199 HOSPITAL DR, FAMILY MEDICINE 24333 #051-01-2000 L2003 **FM** *020 †18

FIRGAU, Manuel Guillermo. 199 HOSPITAL DR, CARILION MEDICAL 24333 #024-05-1997 L1999 **IM** *020 †20

GARLAND, Landon W, Jr. 110 VALLEY ST 24333 #051-01-1981 L1993 **DR** *020 †80

GILLESPIE, Cameron A. 104 DOCTORS PARK 24333 #051-01-1974 L1975 **OTO FPS** *030 †45

GOAD, Bradley Jackson. 199 HOSPITAL DR, STE 5 24333 #055-75-2000, ▲ L2002 **IM** *020 †20 ‡

GRIFFETH, James Kenneth. 200 HOSPITAL DR 24333 #011-03-1984 L1987 **AN** *020 †05

IRVIN, Stephen Brooks. 199 HOSPITAL DR, STE 7 24333 #051-04-1968 L1968 **GP** *020 †18

JOHNSON, Barbara Louise. 225 HOSPITAL DR, BOLEN MEDICAL PARK 24333 #012-01-1993 L2000 **GS** *020

KAPP, John Paul. ■ 24333 #036-07-1963 L1963 **NS** *071 †25

KIGONYA, Peter Martin. ■ 24333 #880-01-1997 L2006 **IM** *020

KINCADE, Tamara Kay. 106 DOCTORS PARK 24333 #048-13-1994 L1998 **OBG** *020 †30

KING, James Peter. 104 DOCTORS PARK 24333 #051-01-1958 L1958 **OTO A** *020 †45

LASTINGER, Len Brooks, Jr. 199 HOSPITAL DR STE 5, SUITE A 24333 #012-05-1970 L1980 **IM HEM** *020 †20

LASTINGER, Linda Terry. 961 E STUART DR, INC. DBA GALAX FAMILY CARE 24333 #036-07-1976 L1980 **IM** *020

LAWS, Allen Maurice. 199 HOSPITAL DR STE 5 24333 #036-05-1984 L1987 **IM** *020 †20

LAZO, Robert Linden. 199 HOSPITAL DR STE 7 24333 #051-01-1993 L1995 **FM** *020 †18

LIEBRECHT, Paul Conrad. 333 HOSPITAL DR 24333 #033-05-1980 L1986 **ORS** *020 †40

LUAGUE, Samuel Y Balana. 401 N JEFFERSON ST 24333 #748-02-1964 L1975 **OPH OS** *020 †35

MADHUNAPANTULA, Sridhar. 200 HOSPITAL DR 24333 #496-24-1996 L2005 **IM** *020

MATTSON, Mark Warren. 225 HOSPITAL DR, BLUE RIDGE SURGICAL 24333 #016-06-1977 L1979 **GS** *020 †85

MCGUIRE, Maria B. 106 DOCTORS PARK 24333 #759-06-1982 L1998 **PD** *020 †55

MC KINLEY, Donald R. 227 HOSPITAL DR 24333 #018-03-1982 L1982 **OBG** *020 †30

MEYERS, Mary Cassebaum. 106 DOCTORS PARK, PEDIATRIC CARE CTR 24333 #035-01-1975 L1988 **PD PDE** *020 †55

MILLER, Donald Lee. 200 HOSPITAL DR 24333 #018-03-1975 L1994 **EM FM** *020 †18

NEAL, Ashley Elizabeth. ■ 24333 #008-01-2008 L2008 *012

NUCKOLLS, James Garland. 199 HOSPITAL DR STE 5 24333 #036-07-1966 L1972 **IM** *020

OKARO, Nnaemeka Freddy. 200 HOSPITAL DR, TWIN COUNTY REGIONAL HOSPI 24333 #690-04-1991 L2006 **IM** *100 †20

PEERY, William Wade. 225 HOSPITAL DR, BLUE RIDGE SURGICAL 24333 #051-01-1976 L1978 **GS** *020 †85

PRYOR, Robert E. 199 HOSPITAL DR STE 5 24333 #048-04-1986 L1989 **IM** *020 †20

RHOADES, Alan Raymond. 200 HOSPITAL DR, TWIN COUNTY REGIONAL HOSPI 24333 #422-01-2000 L2003 **IM** *020 †20

RIGOLIZZO, Donna. 140D LARKSPUR LN, MT ROGERS COMM SVC BOARD 24333 #010-02-1987 L2003 **P** *020 †75

RIOS, Juan Francisco. 199 HOSPITAL DR STE 5 24333 #649-01-1957 L1965 **DS** *071

ROGERS, Tate Mosley. 961 E STUART DR, OCCUMED URGENT CARE 24333 #036-01-1976 L1979 **FM** *020 †18

ROLDAN, Rodrigo Colete. 225 HOSPITAL DR, BLUE RIDGE SURGICAL 24333 #748-14-1989 L2006 **GS** *020 †85

SIRK, Rodney Allen. 103 DOCTORS PARK 24333 #055-02-1995 L1998 **FM** *020 †18

STEELE, Robert Leon. 200 HOSPITAL DR, TWIN COUNTY REGIONAL HEALT 24333 #308-10-1990 L2003 **AN** *020 ‡

STETLER, Robert Howard. 225 HOSPITAL DR 24333 #036-05-1979 L1986 **GS** *020 †85

TATE, Glen Edward. 200 HOSPITAL DR 24333 #051-01-1981 L1982 **FM** *020 †18

WHITTLE, Thomas Slade, Jr. 200 HOSPITAL DR 24333 #045-01-1965 L1978 **PTH** *020 †50

WILSON, Martha L. 104 E STUART DR 24333 #012-01-1980 L2001 **D IM** *020 †20,15

YOUNG-LIGHTBODY, Karon So. 106 DOCTORS PARK 24333 #566-01-1996 L2003 **PD** *020 †55 ‡

ZAKI, Kareem Ahmed. 105 DOCTORS PARK, LOTUS UROLOGIC GROUP 24333 #051-04-1993 L1993 **U** *030 †95

GATE CITY — SCOTT

STRANGE, John Edward. ■ 24251 #020-02-1987 L1994 **FM** *020

WHITT, James Dwight. ■ 24251 #051-01-1947 L1947 **GS ORS** *071

WOLFE, James Wallace. 390 KANE ST 24251 #051-01-1974 L1975 **FM** *020 †18

GLADE HILL — FRANKLIN

MERTEN, John Robinson. 7490 OLD FRANKLIN TPKE 24092 #051-04-1988 L1989 **FM** *020 †18

TAYLOR, Tiffany Ann. 845 DUNDEE RD 24092 #051-07-1992 L1993 **FM** *020 †18

GLADE SPRING — WASHINGTON

POTE, Douglas Allyn. 636 S MONTE VISTA DR, GLADE SPRING COMMUNITY CLI 24340 #051-07-1979 L1982 **FM** *020 †18

GLASGOW — ROCKBRIDGE

DEEM, John Richard. ■ 24555 #051-04-1957 L1957 **FM GP** *071

SAILER, Jane Pisarchick. 730 MCCULLOCH ST 24555 #041-02-1992 L1993 **FM** *020 †18

SAILER, Jay Gordon. 730 MCCULLOCH ST, MAURY RIVER FAM PLACT LLC 24555 #041-02-1992 L1993 **FM** *020 †18

STIKES, Henry Phillip. ■ 24555 #001-06-1979 L1985 **PHP** *030 †70

GLEN ALLEN — HENRICO

ABRAHAM, Mariana Lynn. ■ 23060 #051-04-2001 L2001 **PRD** *100 †15

AGGARWAL, Atul. ■ 23059 #008-02-1997 L2006 **NM** *100 †80,28 ‡

AHMED, Mateen. ■ 23060 #704-02-1989 L1998 **PCC** *020

ANAND, Aravindakshakarup. ■ 23059 #495-73-2004 L2005 **IM** *020 †20

ANDERSON, Stephanie Sin-Y. ■ 23060 #038-44-2004 L2007 **EM** *020

ARKIN, David Lawrence. 3990 STILLMAN PKWY 23060 #056-06-1977 L1979 **PD ADL** *020 †55

AYERS, Christopher Allen. ■ 23060 #051-04-2005 L2005 **PD** *012

BALLUM, Ryan Lee. ■ 23059 #051-04-2004 L2004 **PD** *020 †55

BEIRNE, Edward Bliley, Jr. 5000 COX RD 23060 #051-04-1966 L1966 **FM EM** *020 †18

BETHEA, Shea West. ■ 23059 #051-04-2005 L2005 **IM** *012

BOGGS, Cassie Leanne. ■ 23060 #012-01-2007 L2007 **PTH** *012

BOSTWICK, David Granger. 4355 INNSLAKE DR 23060 #023-01-1979 L1999 **PTH** *020 †50

BROOKS, Bryan Michael. 4600 COX RD, STE 120 23060 #051-04-1998 L1999 **OPH** *020

BROWN, Stephen E. 5324 TWIN HICKORY RD, STE 103 23059 #012-01-1999 L2000 **P** *100

BRUSILOVSKY, Ilia. ■ 23060 #051-04-2008 L2008 *012

BUGBEE, Linda. 4101 COX RD, STE 340 23060 #041-12-1986 L1991 **P** *020 †75

BURAKGAZI-DALKILIC, Evren. ■ 23060 #902-07-1996 L2005 **CN** *020 †75

BUSHAN, Y M S. ■ 23060 #495-33-1961 L1989 **GS EM** *020 †85

BUSTON, Jameson Geo, II. 4121 COX RD STE 110 23060 #051-04-1963 L1963 **FM OS** *020 †18

CAMDEN, Sharon Sullivan. 5201 HICKORY PARK DR STE A 23059 #051-04-1986 L1987 **D** *020 †15

CARTY, Sandra Jean. 5324 TWIN HICKORY RD, STE 102 23059 #051-04-2000 L2004 **P** *020 †75

CASSIDY, Amy Lucille. ■ 23060 #051-04-2004 L2004 **AN** *012

CHAMBERS, John Willis. ■ 23060 #036-07-1975 L1982 **IM GPM** *075

CHANG, Nevan Naiwen. 4370 BELFAST RD 23060 #051-04-1993 L1993 **EM** *020 †16

CHEUNG, Onpan. ■ 23059 #035-15-2003 L2003 **IM** *100 †20

CHOI, Sungwon. 9168 CENTERWAY DR 23059 #025-07-1999 L2001 **PHO** *100 †55

COOK, Sallie Hart S. 4510 COX RD STE 400 23060 #051-04-1976 L1978 **PTH BBK** *030 †50 *020 †75

DAHLVANI, Salim A. 11113 CARRINGTON GREEN DR, GLEN ALLEN 23060 #704-16-1980 L1993 **P** *020 †20

DAILEY, Tina Marie. ■ 23059 #038-45-2005 L2006 **OPH** *012

DANIEL, Ronsard. ■ 23059 #041-14-1997 L1998 **SCI** *020

DANIELS, Robert Mason. 5360 TWIN HICKORY RD, FAMILY PHYSICIANS-WYNDHAM 23059 #051-04-1993 L1996 **FM** *020 †18

DARA, Suvarchala Devi. ■ 23059 #495-21-1998 L2004 **CD** *012 †20

DATLA, Ravi Varma. ■ 23060 #496-31-2001 L2008 **IM** *012

DAVIE, Frank Marion. ■ 23059 #010-03-1959 L1959 **GS FM** *071

DERCO, Keith Andrew. 11551 NUCKOLS RD, STE F 23059 #041-12-1977 L1995 **PD** *020 †55

DEWIRE, Thomas Merrill. 3974 SPRINGFIELD RD 23060 #041-02-1979 L1981 **PS** *020 †85,65

DIETZ, Mark John. ■ 23059 #026-08-1984 L1989 **DR** *020

DURANT, Sharon Jean. PO BOX 5621 23058 #010-03-1977 L1980 **OBG** *020

EPPERSON, Thomas Irving. ■ 23060 #051-04-2004 L2004 **AN** *012

ERDMAN, Robt Livingstone. ■ 23059 #041-02-1966 L1969 **R** *071

ESPINOSA, Bialines A. ■ 23059 #308-03-1986 L2003 **OBG** *020

FERGUSON, James Grier, Jr. 4600 COX RD STE 120 23060 #048-04-1969 L1975 **OPH** *071 †35 ‡

FERLAND, Louise Diane. 4050 INNSLAKE DR STE 310 23060 #065-06-1984 L1999 **PS HS** *020

FERNICOLA, Catherine Anne. ■ 23059 #045-04-2007 L2007 **P** *012

FLICKINGER, Marc William. 4050 INNSLAKE DR, DRIVE SUITE308 23060 #041-14-1994 L2007 **FM** *020 †18

FLOWERS, Tami Ann. ■ 23060 #051-04-2005 L2005 **OPH** *012

FULTON, Charles Albert. ■ 23060 #051-04-1978 L1981 **FM** *020 †18

GERARD, Jody. 6013 BRITLYN CT, E.D. MANAGEMENT, LLC 23060 #035-03-1987 L2005 **EM** *020 †16

GHAEMMAGHAMI, Bernadette. 10571 TELEGRAPH RD, STE 210 23059 #051-04-1996 L1999 **FM** *020 †18

GORADIA, Laura Jane. 3990 STILLMAN PKWY 23060 #051-01-1995 L1999 **PD** *020 †55

GUPTA, Vidhi Aggarwal. ■ 23060 #011-04-2000 L2000 **DR** *020 †20,80

HAAS, Richard Jarman. 10571 TELEGRAPH RD, STE 110 23059 #051-01-1973 L1976 **PD** *020 †55

HADDAD, Raymond. 5000 HARVEST GLEN CT, VCU HEALTH SYSTEM 23059 #605-02-1963 L1971 **IM PUD** *072 †20

HASSAN, Aalya Mahreen. ■ 23059 #051-01-2001 L2001 **CD** *012

HEINZ, Eric Robert. ■ 23059 #051-04-2007 L2007 **GS** *012

HELOU, Marieka Ann. ■ 23060 #047-06-2006 L2006 **PD** *012

HIRSCH, Ari Ben. ■ 23059 #051-04-2004 L2004 **IM** *100

HOLMES, Kimberly Joy. ■ 23060 #036-05-2008 *012

HONG, Young Ki. ■ 23060 #051-04-2008 *012

HULCHER, Julius C. ■ 23060 #051-04-1941 L1941 **OTO** *071 †45

HUTTON, Jamie Sue. ■ 23060 #051-04-2005 L2005 **PD** *012

ISELIN, Elizabeth Leigh. ■ 23060 #051-04-2004 L2004 **CCP** *012 †55

JAIN, Reena. ■ 23059 #496-07-1989 L2004 **PTH** *020 †50

JONES, Susan Webber. 5213 HICKORY PARK DR, STE A 23059 #051-04-1989 L1992 **CHP** *020 †20

JOSEFSON, Deborah. 4355 INNSLAKE DR, BOSTWICK LABORATORIES 23060 #550-02-1993 L2003 **ATP IM** *050 †20,50

JOSEPH, Christie Susan. ■ 23059 #001-06-2006 L2007 **IM** *012

KALAHASTY, Gautham. ■ 23059 #024-05-1996 L2003 **ICE** *020 †20

KALIKI, Vasavi. ■ 23060 #495-70-1995 L2000 **PTH** *100

KAPA, Nandita. ■ 23059 #496-22-1999 L2003 **PD** *020

KARIM, Khalid. ■ 23059 #704-17-1989 L2006 **IM** *020 †20 ‡

KASSAMALI, Rahim. ■ 23059 #704-02-1997 L2006 **IM** *020 †20 ‡

KAST, David Andrew. ■ 23060 #007-02-2006 L2006 **AN** *012

KELLEY, Joseph Randall. ■ 23060 #045-01-2003 L2004 **RO** *012

KELLY, Leonard Wm, Jr. 201 CONCOURSE BLVD, STE 110 23059 #051-01-1966 L1966 **D** *071 †15

KHAN, Mohd Rehan Raza. ■ 23059 #704-25-1994 L2002 **DR** *020 †80

KIKEN, Michael Stephen. ■ 23059 #041-12-1969 L1998 **OBG** *072 †30

KLUK, Matthew William. ■ 23059 #051-04-2007 *012

KREISLER, Leslie Stephen. ■ 23059 #041-09-1969 L1976 **OTO** *071 †45

KROTTAPALLI, Kavitha. ■ 23059 #496-24-1997 L2002 **FM** *020 †18

KUMAR, Dhiren. ■ 23059 #051-01-2002 L2002 **IM** *020 †20

LAKDAWALA, Mayuri V. ■ 23059 #051-01-2004 L2004 **PD** *100 †55

LAMM, Tita C. 4355 INNSLAKE DR 23060 #748-08-1978 L1990 **PTH GP** *020 †50

LAPLANTE, Justin Kyle. ■ 23059 #051-04-2008 *012

LARNER, Joseph. 4851 LAKE BROOK DR, ALLOMED PHARMACEUTICALS 23060 #035-01-1945 **DIA** *050

LEBMAN, Ronald Ivins. 9905 ROSIER CREEK WAY 23060 #041-13-1974 L2004 **EM OM** *020 †16

LEE, John Chueniou. 5213 HICKORY PARK DR, STE A 23059 #051-04-1997 L1999 **P** *020 †75

LERNER, Alla. 5213 HICKORY PARK DR, STE A 23059 #306-01-2000 L2001 **P** *020 †75

LIPSTOCK, Kenneth David. 10120 WEST BROAD ST, STE E 23060 #051-04-1981 L1982 **OPH** *020 †35

LOPEZ, Gerardo St Tomas. ■ 23060 #748-07-1963 L1977 **FM** *071 †18

LOVE, Karen. 10120 W BROAD ST, STE R 23060 #047-07-1993 L1994 **D** *020

LU, Leo. 4355 INNSLAKE DR, BOSTWICK LABORATORIES 23060 #209-01-1973 L2005 **ATP PCP** *020 †50

LUCAS, Kathleen Brighid. ■ 23059 #051-04-2008 *012

MACASAET, Francisco F. 4355 INNSLAKE DR 23060 #748-08-1963 L1983 **PTH** *071 †50
MAC MILLAN, David Wishart. 4600 COX RD STE 120, MERCER PLAZA 23060 #051-01-1963 L1963 **OPH** *071 †35
MAC SEARRAIGH, Oisin. 10299 WOODMAN RD, HENRICO MENTAL HEALTH CTR 23060 #539-05-1973 L1975 **P** *071
MAHATA, Mini. ■ 23060 #051-04-2004 L2004 **IM** *100 †20
MALIK, Shabbaz Asif. ■ 23060 #051-04-2007 L2007 **IM** *012
MANASWI, Abhijit. ■ 23060 #495-15-1994 L2006 **OTR** *012
MANNING, Anthony Paul. 3974 SPRINGFIELD RD 23060 #051-04-1996 L1996 **AN** *020 †05
MC DANIEL, Kent Galen. 10299 WOODMAN RD, RETARDATION SERVICES 23060 #038-44-1993 L1993 **P** *020
MC DONALD, Kelly Brandon. 10150 STAPLES MILL RD, STE E 23060 #051-04-1995 L1995 **MPD** *020 †20,55
MOHAMED ABDEL MEGUID, A. ■ 23059 #915-03-1988 L1996 **P** *100 †75
MOLLAH, Ali Ayub. 5310 TWIN HICKORY RD, EXPRESS MED URGENT AND PRI 23059 #496-21-1993 L2000 **FM** *020 †18 ‡
MORISHETTY, Nalini. ■ 23059 #496-24-1997 L2002 **IMG** *100
MOUNASAMY, Varatharaj. ■ 23060 #495-04-1990 L2005 **OTR** *100
MUKKAMALA, Jhansi Rani. ■ 23060 #422-01-2001 L2001 **CHP** *020
MUNJAL, Sagar. ■ 23059 #496-40-1998 *100
NAGARAJAN, Rakesh. ■ 23060 #028-02-2002 *100
NAIR, Gayathri Velayudhan. ■ 23059 #495-31-1996 L2006 **NPM** *020 †55
NAKAS, Nermina. 5128 REIDS POINTE RD 23060 #957-08-1982 L2000 **PN PD** *050
NANNAPANENI, Srikant. ■ 23059 #495-62-1998 L2006 **IM** *100 †20
NERALLA, Sirisha. 10120 W BROAD ST, STE E 23060 #041-15-2001 L2007 **IM** *020 †20
NG, Allen Jongying. ■ 23059 #016-02-1991 L1995 **AN** *020 †05
O'CONNOR, Heather Marie. ■ 23060 #031-01-2003 L2006 **OBG** *020
PARHAM, Melanie Jean. 5360 TWIN HICKORY RD 23059 #036-05-1997 L1997 **FM** *020 †18
PARIHAR, Prem Singh. ■ 23060 #495-74-1983 L2005 **N** *012 †20
PATHAN, Muhammad Hanif. ■ 23059 #704-17-1984 L2007 **HMP** *012
PFEIFER, John Sterling. 12300 GREENWICH DR 23059 #047-05-1975 L1981 **GS VS** *020 †85
PINSKER, M Craig. 11956 MONTFORT CIR 23059 #012-01-1979 L1980 **AN** *020 †05
PURI, Puneet. ■ 23060 #495-30-2000 L2004 **GE** *012 †20
PUSHKIN, Yaacov Rabi. 12320 MORNING CREEK RD 23059 #055-02-1987 L1991 **P** *020 †75
RAHMAN, Saud Saqib. ■ 23060 #036-05-2005 L2005 **PTH** *012
RAJAB, Bashar M.. 3944 SPRINGFIELD RD 23060 #051-04-2008 *012
RAMESH, Seela. 9612 CENTERWAY DR 23059 #306-01-2000 L2003 **GE** *020
RAO, Ramesh D.. ■ 23060 #048-13-1997 L2007 **OS** *072 †80
RATHNAM, Punitha Ida. ■ 23060 #495-27-1995 L2002 **CHP** *012
READ, Stephen Geo. 10571 TELEGRAPH RD, STE 210 23059 #051-01-1984 L1987 **FM** *020 †18 ‡
REDDY, Pingle Swaroop. ■ 23059 #495-21-1978 L2007 **AN** *020 †05
REDDY, Seshamma Thikkavar. ■ 23060 #654-01-1998 L2004 **PTH** *020
REDMON, Julie Ann. 5219 HICKORY PARK DR, STE C 23059 #051-01-1992 L1993 **OTO** *020 †45
REHMAN, Haroon Ur. ■ 23059 #704-02-1992 L2005 **IM** *020 †20
REHMAN, Noma Amir. ■ 23059 #704-02-1992 L2003 **N** *100
REID, William Ferguson. ■ 23060 #010-03-1948 L1948 **GS ADM** *062 †85
ROBERT, Alina Mihaela. ■ 23060 #051-04-2008 *012
ROBINSON, William Luke. ■ 23060 #051-04-2006 L2006 **PM** *012
RUBIS, Paul John. ■ 23059 #051-04-1980 L1981 **R** *020 †80
RYLAND, Jill Elaine. 100 CONCOURSE BLVD, WEST SHORE 1 STE 111 23059 #051-04-1992 L1994 **PD** *020 †55
SANJEEVI, Arthi. ■ 23060 #495-04-1998 L2006 **GE** *100 †20
SEYMORE, Dominic Shay. ■ 23059 #047-20-2006 L2007 **PM** *012
SEYMORE, Kisa Waddell. ■ 23059 #047-20-2004 L2007 **IM** *100
SHAH, Suhasini Nitin. ■ 23059 #495-76-1972 L1994 **P** *020
SHAW DE PAREDES, Ellen S. 4480 COX RD, PAREDES INSTITUTE FOR WOME 23060 #055-01-1978 L1979 **DR** *020 †80
SHETTY, Kuthethoor S. ■ 23059 #495-09-1971 **P** *100
SINGH, Vikrant. ■ 23060 #051-04-2007 L2007 **IM** *012
SMITH, Michael Willis, Jr. 4480 COX RD STE 100 23060 #051-04-2000 L2000 **DR** *020 †80
SOWERS, Richard P, III. 5000 COX RD STE 100, PATIENT FIRST 23060 #051-04-1970 L1970 **EM** *020
SPILLMAN, Kimberly Rose. ■ 23059 #011-05-2007 **IM** *012
STADLER, Carlton L. ■ 23059 #048-16-2005 L2005 **EM** *012
STADLER, Teresa S. 4101 COX RD, STE 301 23060 #035-03-1995 L1995 **FSM OSM** *020 †18
STEVENS, Todd Miller. ■ 23059 #010-02-2001 L2006 **AN** *100 †05
SUMLER, Michele Leigh. ■ 23059 #051-04-2005 L2005 **AN** *012
SUTHERLAND, Tamara Albert. 11551 NUCKOLS RD STE F 23059 #035-06-2000 L2000 **PD** *020 †55
SUTTON, Valvin Earl, IV. ■ 23060 #010-03-1963 L1966 **IM** *071
SYLVEST, Vernon Martin. 4355 INNSLAKE DR 23060 #021-05-1966 L1974 **HMP** *020 †50
TAN, Ruby R. ■ 23059 #748-10-1991 L2007 **PD** *020 †55
TANG, Wozhan. ■ 23059 #243-77-1985 L2005 **HMP** *020 †50
THOMAS, Pendleton Emmett. 6200 MANAFORD CIR 23059 #051-04-1954 L1954 **GYN** *020 †30
TINANA, Adrienne Marie. 5000 COX RD, STE 100 23060 #010-01-2004 L2004 **IM** *012 †20
TRAN, Hau Minh. ■ 23059 #305-01-2005 L2006 **FM** *100
TURBAT-HERRERA, Elba Ana. ■ 23060 #001-02-1985 L1986 **PTH** *020 †50
VALENTE, Albert L. 3970 SPRINGFIELD RD 23060 #022-75-1992, ▲ L1993 **IM** *020 †20
VAUGHN, Keesha Dawn. 11551 NUCKOLS RD 23059 #041-15-2004 L2005 **PD** *020 †55 ‡
VILLAVICENCIO, Raquel. ■ 23059 #017-20-2006 L2006 **IM** *012
VYAS, Neha D. 10571 TELEGRAPH RD STE 210, C/O BROOK RUN FAMILY PHYS 23059 #048-04-1998 L2002 **FM** *020 †18
WASHINGTON, Alvin Keith. ■ 23060 #010-01-2002 L2002 **PD** *100
WASIK, Theodore Peter. 10299 WOODMAN RD, PSYCHIATRIST, HENRICO AREA 23060 #051-04-2003 L2003 **P** *020
WIESINGER, Herbert. 4600 COX RD STE 120 23060 #154-07-1950 L1956 **OPH** *071 †35
WILEY, Edward James, III. 3990 STILLMAN PKWY 23060 #051-04-1990 L1993 **PD NPM** *020 †55
WILLIAMS, William C, III. 4435 WATERFRONT DR, STE 101 23060 #051-04-1978 L1979 **FM** *020 †18
WILSON, Cameron Weber. ■ 23059 #051-04-2007 L2007 **GS** *012
WILTSHIRE, Gennifer Anne. ■ 23060 #051-04-2005 L2005 **IM** *012
YAPLE, Ross Albert, IV. ■ 23059 #035-06-2003 L2003 **CHP** *012

ZAMEROSKI, Natalie Anne. ■ 23060 #051-04-2008 *012
ZAVELSKY, Ilya. ■ 23059 #913-19-1984 L1993 **PD** *020 †55

GLOUCESTER – GLOUCESTER

ARNOLD, Fredrick Sanders. 7552 HOSPITAL DR STE 302 23061 #051-04-1974 L1985 **U** *020 †95
BACKER, Joel Evan. 7547 MEDICAL DR, STE 1200 23061 #051-04-1996 L2000 **OBG** *020 †30
BARTOL, Dennie Thomasson. 7519 HOSPITAL DR 23061 #051-01-1981 L1982 **DR OS** *020 †80 ‡
BAYLOUS, James Donald. 7519 HOSPITAL DR 23061 #055-02-1993 L2001 **VIR** *020 †80
BEAVERS, William J. 7519 HOSPITAL DR 23061 #027-01-1984 L1985 **DR R** *020 †80
BURTON, Albert Andrew. 7547 MEDICAL DR, STE 2100 23061 #021-05-1988 L1998 **CD** *020 †20
CHU, Edward. 7547 MEDICAL DR, STE 2100 23061 #043-01-1986 L1997 **IC** *020 †20
CROSS, Robert David. ■ 23061 #025-01-1989 L1992 **IM** *020 †20
CROWDER, Richard F. 7547 MEDICAL DR, STE 2200 23061 #051-04-1973 L1974 **IM OS** *020 †20
CURRAN, Valentine William. 7519 HOSPITAL DR 23061 #010-02-1995 L1995 **DR GS** *100 †80
DAIMLER, John C. 7519 HOSPITAL DR 23061 #035-06-1971 L1980 **DR** *020 †80
DAVIS, Robert Thos. 7547 MEDICAL DR, STE 2200 23061 #051-04-1974 L1976 **IM** *020 †20
DEMEO, Jonathan Harry. 7519 HOSPITAL DR 23061 #051-04-1986 L1990 **DR** *020 †80 ‡
EBBERS, Sarah Marie. PO BOX 1130, 7519 HOSPITAL DR 23061 #051-07-2004 L2007 **IM** *020 †20
GILLEN, William Stanley. 7547 MEDICAL DR, STE 2100 23061 #041-02-1988 L1994 **CD** *020 †20
HAMZEH LANGROUDI, Mehrdad. ■ 23061 #165-01-1993 L2005 **AN** *020 †05
IRBY, Steven Mark. 7519 HOSPITAL DR 23061 #012-05-1982 L2000 **DR** *020 †80 ‡
JONES, Harold D, III. ■ 23061 #051-07-1981 L1993 **IMG** *020
LANGDON, Daniel Curtis. 7547 MEDICAL DR, STE 2100 23061 #048-04-1971 L1980 **CD IM** *020 †20
LIANG, Yizhi. 7519 HOSPITAL DR 23061 #243-16-1988 L2004 **DR** *020 †80
MARSHELL, Carol Mae. ■ 23061 #001-06-2001 **FM** *100
MC CORMICK, Hugh Bernard. 7547 MEDICAL DR, STE 2100 23061 #033-05-1967 L1974 **CD** *020 †20
MOLLE, Jeffrey Scott. 7547 MEDICAL DR, STE 1500 23061 #038-40-1989 L1995 **GS** *020 †85
MOYLAN, Brian Lee. 7560 HOSPITAL DR, STE 101 23061 #023-01-1983 L1984 **IM** *020 †20
NEWSOME, Janice M. 7519 HOSPITAL DR 23061 #035-47-1994 L1994 **VIR** *020 †80
O'DONOHUE, Neil Francis. 7519 HOSPITAL DR 23061 #035-20-1968 L1993 **DR** *020 †80
OUTTEN, Sharon J. 7519 HOSPITAL DR 23061 #051-07-1982 L1987 **DR** *020
PEACH, William Fennell. 11 BRUTON AV NEWPORT NEWS, HAMPTON ROADS NEUROSURGERY 23061 #051-04-1958 L1958 **NS** *071 †25
PHELAN, Westell Carew. 7519 HOSPITAL DR 23061 #030-06-1976 L1994 **DR** *020 †80 ‡
PHILLIPS, Joseph Donald. 7580 HOSPITAL DR, STE 201 23061 #041-12-1964 L1981 **P** *020 †75
PINCUS, Thomas Andrew. 7519 HOSPITAL DR 23061 #048-14-1996 L2002 **RNR** *020 †80
RAY, Gaylord White. ■ 23061 #051-04-1976 L1977 **EM FM** *071 †16,18
REGAN, John Jos. 6876 MAIN ST, UNIT 4 23061 #024-07-1968 L1981 **IM ON** *020 †20
RESSLER, Melvin Wayne. 7554 HOSPITAL DR, STE 303 GLD D 23061 #041-13-1990 L2000 **GS** *020 †85
ROWE, Henry Carmichael. 7544 HOSPITAL DR, BLDG A 23061 #051-01-1973 L1974 **GP FM** *020
SARGEANT, Daniel Trigg. 7363 WALKER AVE, COURTHOUSE PEDIATRICS 23061 #051-01-1975 L1981 **DR PD** *020 †55,80
SCHENGBER, David John. 7519 HOSPITAL DR 23061 #028-34-1990 L1995 **DR** *020 †80 ‡
SHELBY, Melridge R. ■ 23061 #025-12-1975 L1978 **NPM** *020 †30
SIKES, Randall Arthur. 7519 HOSPITAL DR 23061 #012-05-1975 L1986 **DR AM** *040 †80
THOMAS, Geoffrey Hamilton. 7547 MEDICAL DR, STE 2200 23061 #051-04-1978 L1979 **IM** *020 †20
VAUGHAN, Charles Myers. 7547 MEDICAL DR, STE 2100 23061 #036-05-1986 L1988 **CD** *020 †20
WATKINS, Roger Alan. 7547 MEDICAL DR, STE 2200 23061 #051-07-1985 L1986 **IM** *020 †20
WEAVER, David Lee. 7519 HOSPITAL DR 23061 #024-07-1978 L1982 **DR** *020 †80
WENDELL, John M, Jr. 7519 HOSPITAL DR 23061 #035-06-1971 L1974 **R** *020 †80 ‡
WEST, Francis Thornton. 7547 MEDICAL DR, STE 2300 23061 #051-07-2004 L2007 **FM** *100 †18
YOUNG, Thomas Howard. 7547 MEDICAL DR, STE 2200 23061 #051-04-1976 L1977 **IM** *020 †20
ZULLO, Peter J. 7547 MEDICAL DR, STE 2200 23061 #010-02-1981 L1987 **IM** *020 †20

GLOUCESTER POINT – GLOUCESTER

BARTOK, Stephen P. PO BOX 400 23062 #869-01-1965 L1973 **NM RO** *020 †80,28

GOOCHLAND – GOOCHLAND

BAIN, Francis N. 2948 RIVER RD W 23063 #051-04-1977 L1978 **FM** *020 †18
HAGAN, Christine Donart. 2948 RIVER RD W 23063 #051-01-1978 L1980 **OM** *071 †18
JOHNS, Sonja Maria. 2841 RIVER RD W, VA CORRECTIONAL CTR/WOMENS 23063 #010-03-1978 L1983 **FM AM** *020
RAVIOTTA, Joseph John. 5246 RIVER RD W, P O BOX 217 23063 #021-05-1971 L1991 **OBG** *020 †30

GOODE – BEDFORD

BRYANT, Stephen Robt. 5410 OLD CIFAX RD, 1615 24556 #051-01-1974 L1975 **PD NPM** *020 †55

GORDONSVILLE – ORANGE

ANAMA, Emmanuel Desling. ■ 22942 #748-08-1959 L1975 **GP** *075

CLAYTON, Michael T. 17590 BLUE RIDGE TPKE, 17590 BLUERIDGE TURNPIKE 22942 #016-11-1980 L1985 **IM** *020 †20
COX, David Baxter. 501 N MAIN ST 22942 #051-01-1980 L1981 **FM** *020 †18
CRUISE, Michael Wayne. ■ 22942 #051-01-2007 L2007 **PTH** *012
GRABEEL, William S. PO BOX 482 22942 #051-04-1960 L1960 **FM** *071 †18
KING, Joshua David. ■ 22942 #041-14-2006 L2006 **IM** *012
OGG, William Garrett. ■ 22942 #027-01-2006 L2006 **IM** *012
ROBERSON, Porsche Brown. ■ 22942 #047-20-2007 L2007 **PD** *012

GRAFTON – YORK

CAVEN, Robert Emerson. 101 YORK CROSSING RD, MEDCARE 23692 #041-12-1964 L1996 **FM OM** *020 †18 ‡
HERRMANN, Louis Andrew. ■ 23692 #041-12-1954 L1977 **OM AM** *071
JONES, Kamlyn Grey. 2855 DENBIGH BLVD 23692 #036-08-2003 L2006 **FM** *020 †18
MAA, Mingtyh. ■ 23692 #051-07-2004 L2007 **PCC** *012 †20
REED, W Glenn. ■ 23692 #041-12-1946 L1952 **PTH** *071 †50

GREAT FALLS – FAIRFAX

ABUSITTA, Nasser I. ■ 22066 #915-03-1982 L1993 **EM** *020 †20
AFKHAMI, Amir Arsalan. ■ 22066 #010-01-2003 L2005 **IM** *020
AL-HUSSAINI, Muayad. 1002 EVONSHIRE LN 22066 #528-01-1957 L1992 **U** *062 †95
AN, Jeanie Jimi. ■ 22066 #016-06-1993 L1996 **PD** *071
BAKER, Stephen Robt. ■ 22066 #048-04-1965 L1971 **P** *020 †75
BERGER, Robert Martin. 411 CHESAPEAKE DR 22066 #035-15-1976 L1980 **UP U** *020 †95
BERGIN, William Frank. ■ 22066 #024-01-1956 L1958 **GS** *071 †85
CERRATO, Rebecca Amy. ■ 22066 #016-02-2001 L2004 **ORS** *100
CUSICANQUI MONRROY, Miriam. ■ 22066 #132-07-2001 L2007 **FM** *020 †18
DAVID, Ryan Douglas. ■ 22066 #035-46-2007 **EM** *020
DOERMAN, Randall Lindley. 10135 COLVIN RUN RD, STE 220 22066 #028-34-1976 L1979 **IM** *020 †20
DUNN, C Gibson. ■ 22066 #024-01-1973 L1976 **P** *020 †75
DWORK, Amy Gail. ■ 22066 #035-15-1975 L1980 **OBG** *020 †30
EDWARDS, Tanise Indra. ■ 22066 #041-01-1985 L1991 **EM** *020 †16
FEISEE, Jalalodin T. ■ 22066 #517-03-1961 L1987 **ATP GP** *075 †50
FURLONG, Lynne Kozlowski. ■ 22066 #028-34-1982 L1992 **D IM** *020 †15
GUILLEN, Manuel. 10134 COLVIN RUN RD STE D 22066 #341-01-1976 L1980 **A PDA** *020 †55
JAZAYERLI, Nabil. 10403 VAN PATTEN LN 22066 #875-01-1970 L1989 **CD IM** *020 †20
KADIAN, Rajeshwar Singh. ■ 22066 #495-73-1973 L1993 **GE IM** *020
KIM, John Suk. ■ 22066 #035-20-1991 L1994 **IM** *020 †20
KLOTE, Mary Mc Nerney. ■ 22066 #023-12-1999 L2000 **AI** *100 †20,03
LITWIN, Frederick Peter. ■ 22066 #041-13-1957 L1974 **PTH** *071 †50
MALONE, Timothy John. 731 WALKER RD STE F 22066 #019-02-1979 L1987 **OPH FPS** *020 †35
MC DONALD, Gerald Owen. PO BOX 1007 22066 #016-06-1947 L2004 **GS** *030 †85
MOHTASHEMI, Manucher. ■ 22066 #869-05-1958 L1967 **TS CD** *071 †85,90
MORSE, Martin A. 10132 COLVIN RUN RD, STE F 22066 #036-07-1983 L1995 **PS HS** *020 †65 ‡
NOROZIAN, Faraz Mohammad. ■ 22066 #305-01-1999 L2006 **CCP** *020 †55 ‡
OLIVER, Edward Raymond. ■ 22066 #025-01-2005 L2005 **DR** *012
PAPPAS, Gregory. ■ 22066 #038-06-1986 L1988 **PHP IM** *020
PRICE, Neel J. ■ 22066 #039-01-1942 L1956 **OBG** *071 †30
PRIMEGGIA, Jennifer. ■ 22066 #051-07-2006 L2006 **IM** *012
PSACHAROPOULOS, Helen T. 737 WALKER RD 22066 #418-01-1964 L1988 **PD GE** *071 †55
RAJAEE, Shahabeddin. ■ 22066 #517-05-1966 L1973 **OBG** *071 †30
ROY, Rita Teresa. ■ 22066 #010-01-1994 L1997 **GS** *050
RUSSO, Vojislava C. 737 WALKER RD STE 4 22066 #035-08-1973 L1978 **PD** *020
SALERNO, Judith Alyce. ■ 22066 #024-01-1985 L1987 **IMG IM** *020 †20
SARIS, Demetrius S. ■ 22066 #041-09-1950 L1951 **GS** *071 †85
SCHEPERS, Gerrit Willem H. 9513 LOCUST HILL DR 22066 #836-01-1939 L1963 **PTH OM** *071
SCHERPING, Steven C, Jr. ■ 22066 #035-15-1992 L1999 **ORS** *020 †40
SEIF-ZADEH, Atih Amanda. ■ 22066 #306-01-1997 L2000 **CHP** *100
SHANMUGAM, Victoria. ■ 22066 #917-33-1999 L2003 **RHU** *100 †20
STASIUK, Demetrius. ■ 22066 #035-01-1969 L1970 **N** *020 †75
SWINTON, Brian Burns. ■ 22066 #051-04-2008 *012
TAMJIDI, Panteha. 1211A TOWLSTON RD 22066 #010-01-1999 L2001 **D** *020 †15
TIPPETT, Peter Steven. ■ 22066 #038-06-1983 L1983 **IM EM** *020
VALK, Thomas Heyward. 10890 WOODLEAF LN 22066 #010-01-1974 L1979 **P AM** *030 †75
ZARET, Jessica Heller. ■ 22066 #035-19-2000 L2001 **OBG** *020 †30

GREENBACKVILLE – ACCOMACK

BENOR, Isaac Saml. ■ 23356 #010-01-1992 L1993 **GYN** *020 †30

GREENWOOD – ALBEMARLE

MORTON, Emma Brown. ■ 22943 #036-01-2001 L2004 **END** *100

GRETNA – PITTSYLVANIA

DUFFER, Rufus Randolph. 107 HENRY ST 24557 #051-04-1972 L1973 **FM** *020 †18
EAKIN, Stephen Wayne. 1220 W GRETNA RD 24557 #041-13-1981 L1988 **FM** *020 †18

GROTTOES – ROCKINGHAM

STEINBAUER, David Jerome. 24441 #023-01-1966 L1966 **OTO PS** *071 †45

GRUNDY – BUCHANAN

ARORA, Vasudev. PO BOX 2685 24614 #495-03-1957 L1970 **FPG IM** *071

CASTILLO, Probo Herrera. RR 5 BOX 20, BUCHANAN GEN HOSP 24614 #748-10-1968 L1976 **EM PD** *020 †55,18,16
ESTEBAN, Granwel Aquino. ■ 24614 #748-01-1961 L1976 **GP** *020
JAGUN, Olabisi A. RR 5 BOX 20, BUCHANAN GENERAL HOSPITAL 24614 #690-05-1979 L1991 **IM** *020 †20
MC DONALD, Thomas D. RR 5 BOX 20 24614 #051-01-1953 L1953 **PD FM** *071 †18
PATEL, Dinkar N. 20757 RIVERSIDE DR, TRI STATE CLINIC 24614 #495-23-1977 L1982 **IM** *020
PATEL, Haresh J. 20757 RIVERSIDE DR, TRI-STATE CLINIC 24614 #495-23-1974 L1995 **IM** *020 †20
PATEL, Jashbhai Nathabhai. 20757 RIVERSIDE DR 24614 #495-23-1972 L1981 **GS** *020 †85
PATEL, Jashubhai G. 20755 RIVERSIDE DR, STE 100 24614 #495-23-1979 L1991 **IM PUD** *020 †20
PATEL, Rajnikant R. 20757 RIVERSIDE DR, TRI STATE CLINIC 24614 #495-23-1970 L1976 **PD A** *055
QAZI, Amer Ghias. RR 5 BOX 20 24614 #704-01-1985 L1990 **EM GP** *020
REDDY, Cheruku Bhaskar. RR 5 BOX 20 24614 #495-21-1982 L2004 **AN** *100
SUTHERLAND, Clinton Hale. RR 5, BUCHANAN GEN PROF BLD 24614 #055-02-1990 L1993 **IM** *020 †20
TEDLA, Tesfamariam Mebrah. RR 5 BOX 20, ST. MARY'S HOSPITAL 24614 #366-01-1987 L2004 **FM** *020 †18
VISHAKANTAIAH, Nagaraja. 101 US ROUTE 460 E, COMMUNITY MED CTR 24614 #495-09-1984 L1999 **FM** *020
ZAMZAM, Salih M. DR ZAMZAM CLINIC 24614 #605-01-1967 L1976 **GS FM** *075 †85
ZIAKAS, Georgios. 1532 SLATE CREEK RD, STE 207 24614 #418-04-1996 L2007 **GS** *100

GUM SPRING – GOOCHLAND

HADEN, Charles Benj. 3207 BROAD STREET RD 23065 #051-01-1982 L1983 **FM** *020 †18
TAYLOR, Nancy Elizabeth. ■ 23065 #051-01-2003 L2003 **BBK** *012 †50

HALIFAX – HALIFAX

MASSIMI, Gregory Joseph. ■ 24558 #561-17-1992 L1997 **PTH** *020 †50
MOHTASHAM, Farzana. ■ 24558 #704-06-1984 L1998 **PP PTH** *020 †50
WILLIS, Calvin Johnson. 1000 LAKESHORE DR, P O BOX 387 24558 #051-04-1960 L1960 **GP** *020
WRAY, Frank Grove. ■ 24558 #051-04-1967 L1967 **GP** *020

HAMILTON – LOUDOUN

LEWIS, Michael. ■ 20158 #028-02-1976 L2007 **OBG** *020 †30
ROGERS, Joseph Megeath. ■ 20158 #023-01-1947 L1950 **EM** *071
SMITH, Ronald Edward. ■ 20158 #010-01-1966 L1975 **NM R** *071 †80

HAMPTON – HAMPTON CITY

ACOSTA, Carlos F. 2100 HARTFORD RD 23666 #042-01-1964 L1968 **OS** *020 †18
ACOSTA, Somi Marie. ■ 23664 #891-02-1971 L1978 **OBG** *020
ADCOCK, Ollie T, Jr. 2148 W MERCURY BLVD, RIVERSIDE MERCURY WEST MED 23666 #036-05-1979 L1983 **FM** *020 †18
ADDISON, Therese Jean. ■ 23669 #025-01-1978 L1996 **IM** *020 †20
AKANJI, Abimbola Olufunke. 600 MEDICAL DR, SUITES A&B 23666 #690-14-1991 L2005 **P** *020 †75
ALERTE, Marie-Claude. ■ 23666 #396-01-1975 L1982 **AN** *020
ALLISON, Kelley Zacharias. 3000 COLISEUM DR, WOMEN'S IMAGING CENTER 23666 #051-04-1998 L1998 **DR** *020 †80
AMARE, Helina. 100 EMANCIPATION DR, PRIMARY CARE DEPARTMENT 23667 #366-01-1990 L1998 **IM** *020 †20
ANGELELLI, Matthew Scott. 200 MEDICAL DR 23666 #051-07-1998 L2000 **P** *020
ANGUS, Sherwin. ■ 23666 #011-03-1999 L2003 **AN** *020 †05
ARUL, Gnanamani. 100 EMANCIPATION DR, VA MEDICAL CENTER 23667 #495-16-1976 L1981 **IM** *020 †20
ATCHLEY, Wm Doyle, Jr. 4000 COLISEUM DR, STE 350 23666 #051-07-1983 L1988 **IM** *020 †20
AUDEH, Nicholas. 3120 VICTORIA BLVD 23661 #033-06-1990 L1995 **AN** *020 †05
AYODEJI, Olayiwola B. 501 BUTLER FARM RD, PENINSULA KIDNEY ASSOC 23666 #690-02-1979 L1991 **NEP IM** *020 †20
AYRES, Stephen M. ■ 23664 #035-20-1955 L1985 **CD PUD** *071 †20
BACHTELL, Dana Lynne. 2100 HARTFORD RD 23666 #051-04-1988 L1991 **FM** *020 †18
BACON, Geoffrey Ware. 2206 EXECUTIVE DR STE F 23666 #035-03-1987 L1992 **OTO GS** *020 †45
BADDAR, Nader Talat. 530 ABERDEEN RD 23661 #051-07-1983 L1985 **EM GP** *020 †70
BAINES, Tyrone R, II. 21 E QUEENS WAY STE A 23669 #036-01-1995 L1999 **AN** *020 †05
BAKER, Christopher Lee. 3000 COLISEUM DR 23666 #051-01-1998 L2001 **EM** *020 †16
BARRIOS RENO, Leticia B. ■ 23669 #748-09-1968 L1985 *020
BARRON, Natalie Addington. 191 FOX HILL RD, STE A 23669 #051-07-1998 L1998 **FM** *020 †18
BASHEKIMOGLU, Melih Etem. 100 EMANCIPATION DR 23667 #902-01-1950 L1964 **IM** *020
BASTANI, Alan Matthew. 100 EMANCIPATION DR 23667 #517-01-1958 L1968 **ON HEM** *020 †20
BAUER, Paul Richard. ■ 23664 #036-05-1956 L1965 **GYN** *071 †30
BAYNE, David P. 2204 EXECUTIVE DR, STE E 23666 #010-03-1980 L1987 **U GS** *020 †95
BEAZLIE, Thomas Mcconaghy. 501 BUTLER FARM RD, STE I 23666 #051-04-1975 L1976 **IM NEP** *020 †20
BEN OTHMANE, Kamel. 850 ENTERPRISE PKWY, STE 1400 23666 #895-01-1990 L1998 **N** *020 †75
BERG, Samuel Wm. 3130 VICTORIA BLVD, HAMPTON HEALTH DEPT 23661 #017-20-1970 L1996 **PHP ID** *030 †20,70
BINGOL, Mehmet Mutahhar. 2115 EXECUTIVE DR STE 5A 23666 #902-01-1952 L1965 **PD** *020
BLAKE, Khashana Amois. ■ 23669 #051-07-2006 L2006 **FP** *012
BODNER, Bruce Ira. 2101 EXECUTIVE DR 23666 #051-01-1971 L1971 **OPH** *020 †35
BORGMEYER, Matthew Ryan. 77 NEALY AVE, 1ST MEDICAL GROUP/SGHC 23665 #028-03-2003 L2007 **OBG** *020
BOTTONI, Thomas Nicholas. 3000 COLISEUM DR 23666 #041-09-1993 L1994 **EM** *020 †16

BOWERS, Leo Clayton. 26 WINE ST 23669 #051-04-1978 L1981 **FM EM** *020 †18
BOYER, Debra. 191 FOX HILL RD, STE A 23669 #041-02-1983 L1984 **FM** *020 †18
BRADSHAW, Erica. 100 EMANCIPATION DR, MENTAL HEALTH & BEHAVIOURA 23667 #033-06-1988 L1992 **P** *020
BRAGG, Leroy P. 3120 VICTORIA BLVD 23661 #051-04-1950 L1950 **IM** *072
BRISCOE, Gregory Wm. DEPT OF PSYCHIATRY 116A, VETERAN'S ADMINISTRATION H 23667 #020-12-1989 L1995 **P** *020 †75
BROWN, Loretta Port. VA MEDICAL CIR 590/170 23667 #051-07-1981 L1983 **IM** *020
BRYANT, Alvin. 2000 KECOUGHTAN RD 23661 #010-03-1970 L1975 **GS EM** *020 †85
BURGER, Ray Edward. 100 EMANCIPATION DR 23667 #051-01-1972 L1977 **GS** *020 †85
BURKE, Erwin Lewis. 100 EMANCIPATION DR 23667 #067-01-1955 L1990 **GE IM** *071 †20
BURNS, Richard Lee. 2244 EXECUTIVE DR, RIVERSIDE BEHAVIORAL HEALT 23666 #047-06-1983 L2004 **CHP P** *020 †75
CALENDINE, Raelyn M. 45 PINE ST, 1ST MEDICAL GROUP/SGQ 23665 #051-07-1999 L2002 **FM** *020 †18
CARAHER, Timothy William. ■ 23666 #051-04-2007 L2007 **FP** *012
CARTER, Leo Rondus. 2115 EXECUTIVE DR STE 2D 23666 #025-12-1975 L1978 **OTO** *020
CATERINE, Anthony James. 2244 EXECUTIVE DR, HEALTH 23666 #016-43-1988 L2002 **P PYG** *020 †75 ‡
CHAI, Christy Yoon-Hee. 45 PINE ST, 1 FW HOSPITAL / SGOSG 23665 #005-12-2001 L2006 **GS** *020 †85
CHAI, Hyoun Chul. 3000 COLISEUM DR STE 101 23666 #583-01-1956 L1968 **TS PUD** *071 †85,90
CHAUDHURI, Tapan Kumar. 304 RUDISILL RD 23669 #495-32-1966 L1975 **NM GE** *020 †28
CHEMPLAVIL, Joseph K. 2115 EXECUTIVE DR STE 1A 23666 #495-63-1971 L1979 **END DIA** *020 †20
CHEUNG, Dominic Kui-Kong. 100 EMANCIPATION DR, HAMPTON VA MED CTR 23667 #023-07-1974 L1983 **HNS GS** *020 †85
CHINNERY, Lind Walter. 2115 EXECUTIVE DR STE 4B 23666 #047-07-1982 L1987 **IM** *020 †20
CHOI, Koo Young. ■ 23669 #583-03-1963 L1973 **PD** *071 †55
CLARK, Mark Wayne. 2112 HARTFORD RD STE B 23666 #024-01-1974 L1977 **CD IM** *020 †20
CLARK, Richard Franklin. ■ 23669 #051-04-1958 L1958 **PTH** *071 †50
CLOUD, Harold Ed. 2726 W MERCURY BLVD 23666 #649-22-1979 L1989 **FM** *020 †18
COHEN, Alan Paul. 21 E QUEENS WAY STE A 23669 #051-04-1963 L1963 **AN** *020 †05
COKER, Leslie Robin. 2115 EXECUTIVE DR STE 3A 23666 #051-04-1999 L1999 **D** *020 †15 ‡
COKER, William Luther, Jr. 2115 EXECUTIVE DR, STE 3A 23666 #045-01-1963 L1970 **D** *071 †15
COLE, Andrew Bruce. 3000 COLISEUM DR 23666 #051-07-1990 L1993 **EM** *020 †16
CONAGE, Thomas James. 110 COLISEUM XING, STE 142 23666 #007-02-1975 L1988 **OM FM** *020 †70 ‡
CONNELL, Hewlette Collier. 3000 COLISEUM DR 23666 #012-01-1957 L1994 **RO** *071 †80
COOPER, Elizabeth Ann. 2117 HARTFORD RD 23666 #028-34-1986 L1993 **IM** *020 †20
CORBETT, Robin L. 501 MEDICAL DR, HAMPTON ROADS 23666 #024-05-1989 L1995 **GE** *020 †20
CORNUM, Kory Gene. ■ 23665 #023-12-1986 L1988 **ORS GP** *020 †40
CORTINA, Jorge Alberto. 100 EMANCIPATION DR 23667 #051-01-1986 L1987 **P** *020 †75
COYLE, Cheri L. 101 EATON ST, STE 300 23669 #035-48-1987 L1991 **OBG** *020 †30
CRUFF, Dennis Michael. 4000 COLISEUM DR, STE 320 23666 #043-01-1985 L1987 **GS** *020 †85
CUI, Marie Pola I. 1786 OLD BUCKROE RD 23664 #748-11-1970 L1977 **GP EM** *020
CUSTALOW, Linwood Webster. 1832 TODDS LN 23666 #051-04-1964 L1964 **PS** *020 †45
DAHDAH, Khalil Boutros. 501 BUTLER FARM RD, STE B 23666 #308-05-1989 L1997 **IM** *020 †20
DENNIS, Phillip Martin. 2021A CUNNINGHAM DR, STE 7 23666 #023-01-1976 L1977 **PUD IM** *020 †20
DILLARD, Robert Lee. VET ADMIN HOSP, DEPT PATH 23667 #051-01-1975 L1982 **PTH** *040 †50
DO, Tam Thi Minh. 100 EMANCIPATION DR, VAMC 23667 #941-01-1975 L1990 **IM** *020 †20
DOSHI, Ramesh D. 100 EMANCIPATION DR 23667 #495-48-1966 L1979 **R FM** *071 †80
DUDLEY, David Watson. 200 MEDICAL DR STE B, COMMUNITY RESOURCE CENTER 23666 #051-07-1985 L1994 **P** *020 †75
DURHAM, Megan Elizabeth. ■ 23669 #020-02-2004 L2006 **PD** *100 †55
EDWARDS, Richard Ralph. 3000 COLISEUM DR 23666 #051-07-1984 L1985 **CD IM** *020 †20
EISNER, Jonathan David. 501 MEDICAL DR, HAMPTON ROADS 23666 #035-08-1989 L1994 **GE IM** *020 †20
ENRIQUEZ, Manuel H. 100 EMANCIPATION DR 111, VETERANS AFFAIRS MEDICAL C 23667 #748-10-1979 L1987 **PUD IM** *020 †20,70
ERDMAN, Charles William. 3000 COLISEUM DR 23666 #023-12-1993 L1994 **EM** *020
ERVIN, Harry Lennon, Jr. 77 NEALY AVE, 1MDG/SGHC 23665 #023-12-1993 L2007 **AN** *020 †05
FAMILANT, Joseph Waddell. 3120 VICTORIA BLVD 23661 #051-01-1965 L1965 **PD** *020 †55
FEE, Eric Chas. 2148 W MERCURY BLVD 23666 #041-14-1990 L2000 **FM** *020 †18
FIELDS, Branch Tucker, Jr. VA MED CTR 23667 #004-01-1963 L1983 **IM ID** *071 †20
FINDLAY, Colin Lawrie. 3000 COLISEUM DR, STE 350 23666 #051-07-2000 L2000 **IM** *020 †20
FINK, Sidney. ■ 23669 #035-01-1952 L1983 **GE EM** *020 †20,18
FISHER, Anthony Philip. 200 EATON ST 23669 #051-04-1998 L1998 **FM** *020 †18
FITZGERALD-SHELTON, Karen. 850 ENTERPRISE PKWY, STE 1200 23666 #025-01-1991 L1997 **OPH** *020 †35
FLEMING, Mark Tyrone. 3000 COLISEUM DR, STE 104 23666 #038-43-1999 L2006 **HO** *020 †20
FLETCHER, Alan. 2108 HARTFORD RD 23666 #352-07-1953 L1968 **U OS** *071 †95
FOREST-LAM, James Way. 100 EMANCIPATION DR, VAMC HAMPTON 23667 #051-07-1988 L2003 **IM** *020 †20
FRANCIS, Albert Hall, Jr. 2104 EXECUTIVE DR 23666 #051-07-1981 L1983 **FM** *020 †18
FRANCIS, Vernon Raphael. 2112 HARTFORD RD STE B 23666 #010-02-1979 L1982 **CD** *030 †20
FRANKLIN, William A. 4000 COLISEUM DR, STE 200 23666 #047-07-1972 L1974 **IM** *020
FRAZIER, Maurice W. ■ 23663 #010-03-1944 L1946 **GP OS** *020
FREDA, Franklin Lawrence. 3120 VICTORIA BLVD 23661 #051-04-1971 L1977 **OPH** *020 †35
FREDIANI, Alexander Wm. ■ 23669 #041-02-1938 L1939 **AM** *071
FRIEND, Clarence W, Jr. 3000 COLISEUM DR, STE 200 23666 #010-03-1987 L1989 **FM** *020 †18 ‡
GALDOS, Manuel. 4000 W MERCURY BLVD 23666 #737-01-1968 L1974 **OBG** *020 †30
GALLANOSA, Anacleto Gamit. ■ 23666 #748-01-1973 L1979 **IM OM** *020
GARELICK, Robin Beth. 3000 COLISEUM DR 23666 #051-07-1996 L1997 **EM** *020 †16
GARRISON, Jason Timothy. 3000 COLISEUM DR 23666 #051-07-1986 L1987 **EM** *020 †16
GHAZINOUR, Jamal. 100 EMANCIPATION DR 23667 #517-01-1970 L1989 **PM GP** *020 †60
GIBNEY, Paul Vincent. 3000 COLISEUM DR 23666 #035-48-1995 L2002 **EM** *020 †16
GILL, Baljit Singh. 100 EMANCIPATION DR 23667 #495-03-1981 L1984 **P ADP** *020 †75 ‡
GILL, Baltej Singh. 200 MEDICAL DR STE B 23666 #495-03-1978 L1982 **P CHP** *020 †75
GINGRAS, Michel Paul. 2208 EXECUTIVE DR STE E 23666 #067-03-1967 L1990 **P MDM** *020 ‡
GOLDMAN, Arthur Joel. 21 E QUEENS WAY STE A 23669 #041-02-1976 L1985 **AN** *020 †05
GORDON, James Marshall. 2101 EXECUTIVE DR 23666 #026-04-1966 L1967 **OPH** *071 †35
GRANT, Ilham C. 4000 COLISEUM DR, STE 350 23666 #655-03-1997 L2006 **IM** *020 †20
GRAY, Frederic Wood. ■ 23669 #008-01-1949 L1954 **GS TS** *071 †85
GREEN, Melvin Gaddis, Jr. 304 MARCELLA RD STE D 23666 #026-04-1973 L1974 **IM** *020 †20
GREEN, Stephen Lloyd. 2112 EXECUTIVE DR 23666 #036-01-1970 L1977 **ID IM** *071 †20 ‡
GREEN, Tamara Marie. ■ 23669 #036-01-1999 L2007 **EM** *020 †16
GREENBERG, Martin Taylor. 530 ABERDEEN RD 23661 #051-04-1967 L1967 **IM** *020
GREENE, Arthur David. 4000 COLISEUM DR, STE 100 23666 #010-03-1970 L1977 **ORS** *020 †40
GROSS, Leroy Patrick. 2 EATON ST STE 708 23669 #010-03-1975 L1980 **AM OM** *020 †70
GRUNOW, William Agur. HAMPTON VA HOSP CHIEF PATH 23667 #028-02-1969 L1969 **CLP PTH** *030 †50
GUDA, Sivakoti Nagireddy. ■ 23666 #495-21-2000 L2006 **IMG** *020 †20
GUYON, Martha S. 100 EMANCIPATION DR, DEPT OF PSYCH HAMPTON VAMC 23667 #011-04-1980 L1987 **P** *020 †75
HAAS, Christopher Arnold. 45 MIZZEN CIR 23664 #021-05-1994 L1999 **EM** *020 †16
HAGA, Edward Wayne. 9 MANHATTAN SQ, # A 23666 #036-08-1988 L1989 **FM** *020 †18
HAM, Suk Hee S. 100 EMANCIPATION DR, VA MEDICAL CENTER 23667 #583-10-1984 L1990 **IM** *020 †20
HAMID, Khalid M. 2020 N ARMISTEAD AVE, 157 NORTH MAIN STREET 23666 #849-01-1985 L1996 **IM** *020 †20
HAN, Soo Woong. 2021 CUNNINGHAM DR, STE 303 23666 #583-10-1968 L1977 **P CHP** *020 †75
HANDY, Richard Davis. 100 EMANCIPATION DR, VETERANS AFFAIRS MEDICAL C 23667 #024-05-1971 L1982 **IM NEP** *020 †20
HANSON, George K. 21 E QUEENS WAY STE A, ATTN: LEIGH CROSS 23669 #051-04-1977 L1980 **AN** *020 †05
HASSAN, Hassan A. 501 MEDICAL DR, HAMPTON ROADS 23666 #875-03-1991 L2002 **GE IM** *020 †20
HASSELQUIST, Arne. ■ 23664 #041-77-1983, ▲ L2005 **GPM** *071 †70
HECHT, James Lee. 3000 COLISEUM DR 23666 #051-04-1980 L1981 **EM** *020 †16
HEIMANN, Steven Walter. 600 MEDICAL DR, 2501 WASHINGTON AVE 23666 #051-07-1990 L1991 **CHP** *020 †75 ‡
HELM, Deborah Laverne H. 2110C HARTFORD RD, STE C 23666 #051-01-1975 L1977 **FM** *020
HENDERSON, Janet Lynn. 100 EMANCIPATION DR, VA MEDICAL CTR-HAMPTON 23667 #051-07-1985 L1991 **EM** *020 †16
HERCULES, Warren I. 4000 COLISEUM DR, STE 200 23666 #010-03-1980 L1984 **GS** *020 †85
HIGDON, Patrick Brian. 2115 EXECUTIVE DR, MULTISPECIALITY GROUP 23666 #051-07-1994 L1994 **FM** *020 †18
HILBURGER, Jill. 3000 COLISEUM DR, SENTARA CAREPLEX 23666 #025-07-1989 L2004 **AN** *020 †05
HILL, Monte Thomas. 4000 COLISEUM DR, STE 350 23666 #020-02-1998 L2001 **FM** *020 †18
HILL, Robert Middleton. 2115 EXECUTIVE DR, STE 9A 23666 #051-01-1984 L1985 **OBG** *020 †30
HITCHINGS, Lloyd Powell. 100 EMANCIPATION DR, HAMPTON VETRANS HOSP 23667 #051-07-1986 L2000 **N** *020 †75
HOEFER, Richard A. 3000 COLISEUM DR 23666 #041-77-1977, ▲ L1991 **SO** *020 †85
HOFFLER, Richard W, Jr. 100 EMANCIPATION DR, VA MEDICAL CENTER 23667 #047-07-1970 L1973 **IM** *020
HOLMAN, Mark Edward. 2115 EXECUTIVE DR STE 10A, PEDIATRIC CENTER PC 23666 #051-07-1988 L1990 **PD** *020 †55
HONG, Young Sook. 501 MEDICAL DR, HAMPTON ROADS 23666 #583-03-1964 L1973 **PM IMG** *020
HONG, Young-Sung. 501 MEDICAL DR 23666 #583-01-1961 L1972 **GE GP** *020 †20
HOWARD, Robert Edwin, Jr. 3000 COLISEUM DR 23666 #038-41-1961 L1968 **OBG REN** *071 †30
HOWELL, Hannibal Eldredge. 55 E TYLER ST 23669 #051-01-1958 L1958 **IM CD** *072 †20
HUGGINS, Clarence Lee. ■ 23664 #047-07-1958 L1958 **GS OM** *020 †85
HUNTER, Robert Hampton. 3000 COLISEUM DR, STE 200 23666 #051-04-1979 L1983 **FM** *020 †18
HUNTER, William Mills. 3000 COLISEUM DR 23666 #038-41-1970 L1975 **EM IM** *020 †20,16
HYMAN, Lawrence Craig. 2114A HARTFORD RD 23666 #045-01-1978 L1981 **FM** *020 †18
IGNACIO, Romeo Yap. ■ 23666 #748-02-1945 L1978 *100
INNES, Ruth Helen. 2115 EXECUTIVE DR, MULTISPECIALITY GROUP 23666 #305-01-2000 L2000 **FM** *020 †18
JENSEN, Beth Ann. 3000 COLISEUM DR, STE 200 23666 #050-02-1997 L1997 **IM** *020 †18
JOHNSON, Jeffrey David. 3000 COLISEUM DR 23666 #051-07-2001 L2005 **EM** *020 †16
JOHNSON, Melvin Russell. 3000 COLISEUM DR 23666 #047-07-1972 L1979 **IM PUD** *020
JOHNSON, Sandra S. 3000 COLISEUM DR STE 200, COLISEUM MEDICAL ASSOCIATE 23666 #055-01-1985 L1988 **IM** *020 †20
JOHNSON, Shonna Jene. 191 FOX HILL RD STE D, ELIZABETH LAKES FAMILY PRA 23669 #051-01-2003 L2003 **FM** *020
JOLY, Thomas John. 2101 EXECUTIVE DR 23666 #035-06-1997 L2005 **OPH** *020 †35
JONES, Harriett Hundley. 2117 HARTFORD RD, FAMILY PRACTICE OF HAMPTO 23666 #051-07-1983 L1985 **FM** *020 †18
JONES, John Paul. 2115 EXECUTIVE DR STE 1B 23666 #051-01-1969 L1969 **CD IM** *020 †20
JONES, Samuel Burnett, Jr. 9A MANHATTAN SQ, HAMPTON FAMILY PRACTICE 23666 #051-07-2001 L2003 **FM** *020 †18
JOYNES, Michael Hope. 9 MANHATTAN SQ, # A 23666 #051-04-1974 L1976 **FM** *020 †18
KAMEOKA, Judy Yuko. 110 COLISEUM XING 23666 #045-01-1989 L2001 **AN** *020 †05
KANTER, Mark Jos. 4000 COLISEUM DR, STE 110 23666 #051-07-1985 L1987 **PS CS** *020 †65
KAPOOR, R C. 100 EMANAPALIAN DR, VETERANS AFFAIR MED PROB 23667 #496-16-1980 L1998 **IM** *020 †20
KAUSHIK, Shaifali. 100 EMANCIPATION DR, CLINICAL DIR MRI 23667 #913-89-1987 L2000 **DR MSR** *020 †80
KEAN, Daniel Gardner, II. 4000 COLISEUM DR, SUTIE 350 23666 #047-07-2001 L2006 **PM** *100
KEEL, Brian Michael. 850 ENTERPRISE PKWY, STE 1200 23666 #004-01-1986 L1999 **OPH** *020 †16,35 ‡
KHAKEE, Sam. 3512 KECOUGHTAN RD 23661 #917-18-1965 L1977 **PD HEM** *020
KIM, Gregory Yungsuk. 4000 COLISEUM DR, STE 320 23666 #038-40-1996 L1996 **GS** *020 †85
KIM, Myung Woong. 501 MEDICAL DR, HAMPTON ROADS 23666 #583-01-1968 L1979 **GE IM** *020 †20
KINGSTON, Colin Matthew. 901 ENTERPRISE PKWY, STE 900 23666 #023-12-1991 L2003 **ORS** *020 †40

■ = Address Information Privacy Protected

KLUGER, Daniel Martin. 3000 COLISEUM DR 23666 #048-04-1995 L2000 **ID IM** *020 †20
KOCHHAR, Ruby. 100 EMANCIPATION DR, VA MEDICAL CENTER 23667 #495-45-1984 L1993 **HO** *020 †20
KOH, Woon Hi. 3116 VICTORIA BLVD STE 2 23661 #583-01-1961 L1974 **IM CD** *020 †20
KRUGER, Scott. 3000 COLISEUM DR, STE 104 23666 #041-02-1985 L1995 **HEM ON** *020 †20
KUMAR, Priesh lassavante. 100 EMANCIPATION DR, BLDG 110B 23667 #045-01-1996 L1996 **IM** *020 †20
KWON, Young Bae. 100 EMANCIPATION DR, VETERANS AFFAIRS MEDICAL C 23667 #583-01-1961 L1971 **U** *020 †95
LAFALCE, Christian Anthon. 4000 COLISEUM DR STE 350, COLONIAL PULMINARY AT CARE 23666 #305-01-2002 L2008 **PCC** *012 †20
LAPINEL, Stephen Elliott. 4000 COLISEUM DR, STE 350 23666 #035-08-1982 L1983 **OS** *020 †20
LECHMAN, Michael John. 100 EMANCIPATION DR, HAMPTON VA MED CTR 23667 #041-02-1971 L1988 **TS GS** *020 †85,90
LEDBETTER, Tamar C. 2115 EXECUTIVE DR, STE 4A 23666 #035-45-1990 L1993 **PD** *020 †55
LEE, Benjamin Patrick. 2112 HARTFORD RD STE B 23666 #051-04-1997 L1997 **ICE** *020 †20
LEE, Frank Wallace. 100 EMANCIPATION DR, VETERANS MEDICAL CENTER 23667 #051-04-1992 L1999 **IM** *020 †20
LEVIN, Leslie Michael. 3000 COLISEUM DR 23666 #051-07-2002 L2006 **EM** *020 †16
LEWIS, John Edward, Jr. 3000 COLISEUM DR 23666 #010-03-1999 L2004 **EM** *020
LINDBLOM, Laurie Beth. 100 EMANCIPATION DR 1, VETERANS'ADMINISTATION HOS 23667 #056-05-1989 L1992 **PM** *020 †60
LIPSHY, Kenneth A. ■ 23667 #048-14-1988 L1994 **GS SO** *020 †85 ‡
LIVINGSTONE, John N, II. 850 ENTERPRISE PKWY, STE 1400 23666 #012-01-1990 L1994 **N** *020 †75
LLOYD, Kermit Alvin. 850 ENTERPRISE PKWY, STE 1400 23666 #036-01-1989 L1990 **N** *020 †75
LOCKHART, Terri Gillis. 100 EMANCIPATION DR 23667 #012-01-1988 L1990 **IM** *020 †20
LOWERY, Kevin Moore. 501 BUTLER FARM RD 23666 #051-07-2002 L2002 **NEP** *020 †20
LUCAS, Elliott W, Jr. ■ 23666 #010-03-1983 L1988 **OBG** *071 †30
MAHADEVAN, Harihara Iyer. 100 EMANCIPATION DR 23667 #495-31-1967 L1977 **R** *020 †80 ‡
MAHMOUD, Alaa-Eldin M. 100 EMANCIPATION DR, VAMC DEPT PSYC SVC 23667 #915-02-1977 L1997 **P PYG** *020 †75
MALIXI, Edwin. 100 EMANCIPATION DR, VAMC HAMPTON 23667 #748-02-1973 L1978 **GP FM** *020 ‡
MALKANI, Vikram J. ■ 23669 #495-23-1981 L1990 **FM** *020 †18
MARSTELLER, Howard Blair. 850 ENTERPRISE PKWY, STE 1400 23666 #051-01-1981 L1984 **N** *020 †75
MATURI, Mary Frances. 100 EMANCIPATION DR 23667 #016-06-1978 L1987 **CD IM** *020 †20
MAXEY, Ellis F. 2400 CUNNINGHAM DR STE 900 23666 #051-04-1952 L1952 **OPH** *071 †35
MC ADAM, Richard Bernard. 2102 EXECUTIVE DR 23666 #036-01-1967 L1975 **NS** *020 †25
MC CORD, Jennifer. 9A MANHATTAN SQ, HAMPTON FAMILY PRACTICE 23666 #043-01-2001 L2001 **FM** *020 †18
MC CORMICK, Brian Chas. 9A MANHATTAN SQ 23666 #051-07-1989 L1993 **FM** *020 †18
MC CULLEN, Michael Arthur. 3000 COLISEUM DR, ATTN: MEDICAL HOSPITAL SER 23666 #051-07-2001 L2001 **IM** *020
MCQUEEN, Ryan Gerrard. ■ 23666 #051-04-2008 *012
MEADOWS, Robert Steven. 850 ENTERPRISE PKWY, STE 1400 23666 #036-05-1997 L2005 **N** *020 †75
MENON, Padman A. 2208 EXECUTIVE DR 23666 #495-44-1967 L1972 **D PD** *020 †55,15 ‡
MERTI, Gregory Edward. 3000 COLISEUM DR, SENTARA CARE PLEX HOSPITAL 23666 #041-12-1989 L2005 **IM** *020 †20
MICK, Brooks Allen. 3000 COLISEUM DR, STE 200 23666 #038-40-1966 L1989 **IM** *020 †20
MILLER, Jess Peck. 3120 VICTORIA BLVD 23661 #051-01-1957 L1957 **IM IMG** *071 †20
MIXON, James Henry. 2013 CUNNINGHAM DR, STE 203 23666 #041-13-1979 L1981 **FM** *020 †18
MIZUKI, Mikiso, Jr. HAMPTON VAMC, DEPT PM & R 23667 #039-01-1991 L1992 **PM** *020 †60
MODALI, Vidyasagar Venkat. 100 EMANCIPATION DR 23667 #495-21-1978 L2000 **GP** *020 †18
MOLINA, Manuel Jose. ■ 23669 #275-01-1955 L1961 **IM** *071
MONROY, Nelson Gonzalo. BEHAVIORAL SCIENCES, MENTAL HEALTH AND 23667 #341-01-1987 L2000 **P** *020 ‡
MOORE, Verba Ann. 2 EATON ST STE 708 23669 #021-01-1983 L2006 **AM** *020 †70
MOSTEK, Walter A. VET ADMIN MED CTR 23667 #038-40-1964 L1964 **P** *020 †05
MOSTEK, Walter Anthony. 100 EMANCIPATION DR, VA MED CTR 23667 #011-02-1976 L1982 **P** *020 †75
MOTHERSHEAD, Jerry Lynn. 2 EATON ST STE 800 23669 #028-03-1980 L1987 **EM** *020 †16
MOTLEY, Vickie Cortessa. 2200 EXECUTIVE DR STE D 23666 #051-04-1982 L1985 **PD** *020 †55
MOY, Peter Ming-Sue. 4000 COLISEUM DR, STE 310 23666 #035-19-1980 L1994 **TS CD** *020 †85,90
NABIH, Ramzy Nasr. VA MED CTR 23667 #915-02-1947 L1980 **SCI FM** *020 †18
NADARAJAH, Kamalini. 4000 COLISEUM DR, STE 350 23666 #919-01-1997 L2008 **IM** *020 †20
NETTO, I C Vernon. 100 EMANCIPATION DR 23667 #495-39-1957 L1971 **U** *020 †95
NGUYEN, Tan Phuong. VA MEDICAL CENTER 23667 #941-01-1974 L1982 **AN** *020
NIEMI, Sacha Zuleika. 2115 EXECUTIVE DR STE5C, TIDEWATER PHY MULTI SPEC 23666 #035-03-2000 L2006 **FM** *020 †18
NIEVES, Jose Edwin. 100 EMANCIPATION DR, MEDICAL CTR 23667 #308-02-1985 L1988 **P** *020 †75 ‡
NOBLE, Estrellita A B. 300 MEDICAL DR, FL 2 23666 #748-01-1965 L1986 **GP P** *020
NOCHIMSON, Geofrey David. 3000 COLISEUM DR 23666 #051-01-1988 L1992 **EM** *020 †16
NOGUES, Cristobal Andres. 2244 EXECUTIVE DR, HEALTH 23666 #308-06-1983 L1993 **P CHP** *075
NUSSEN, Jana Christine. 2117 HARTFORD RD 23666 #051-07-2002 L2005 **FM** *020 †18
O'CONNELL, Timothy Andrew. 101 EATON ST, STE 300 23669 #051-04-1982 L1983 **OBG** *020 †30
ODOM-AUSTIN, Angela. 2002 KECOUGHTAN RD 23661 #036-07-1989 L1991 **PD** *020 †55
ONGKINGCO, Jose Ramon. 23 MANHATTAN SQ, HAMPTON ROADS PEDIATRICS 23666 #748-02-1983 L1993 **PD PN** *020 †55
OPPENHEIM, Seth Herbert. 850 ENTERPRISE PKWY, STE 1200 23666 #011-02-1981 L1985 **OPH** *020 †35
ORTIZ, Miguel A. 100 EMANCIPATION DR, VA MED CTR 23667 #847-04-1958 L1961 **FM EM** *020
OSBORNE, Paul Dion. 3000 COLISEUM DR 23666 #011-04-1982 L1987 **EM** *020 †16
O'SHEA, Jeremiah Kimball. 3000 COLISEUM DR 23666 #051-01-2001 L2004 **EM** *020 †16
OSTAPKO, Stacy Jayne. 23 MANHATTAN SQ, CMG/HAMPTON ROADS PEDIATRI 23666 #035-15-2000 L2000 **PD** *020 †55 ‡
OTTE, Ray Chas. ■ 23661 #038-06-1956 L1964 **R** *071 †80
PAGE, Myron Ellsworth, III. 2108 HARTFORD RD 23666 #028-03-1971 L1979 **U** *020 †95
PARCELLS, Patrick R. 850 ENTERPRISE PKWY, STE 1400 23666 #024-05-1976 L1981 **N** *020 †75
PARHAM, Louis Danl, Jr. ■ 23669 #051-04-1965 L1965 **FM** *071
PARK, Soon Ok. VET ADMIN HOSP 23667 #583-03-1962 L1973 **GP** *075
PATTERSON, Frederick A. 850 ENTERPRISE PKWY, STE 1400 23666 #051-01-1994 L1995 **N** *020 †75
PAYNE, Loel Zachary. 901 ENTERPRISE PKWY, STE 900 23666 #036-01-1989 L1995 **OSM** *020 †40
PETOE, George. 100 EMANCIPATION DR 23667 #017-20-1963 L1988 **PTH ATP** *071 †50
PHILLIPS, James Laughton. 901 ENTERPRISE PKWY, TIDEWATER ORTHOPAEDIC ASSO 23666 #036-01-1965 L1973 **ORS** *020 †40
PILE, Wendell James. 2211 TODDS LN 23666 #016-11-1945 L1950 **P N** *020 †75
POTTER, Michael William. 3000 COLISEUM DR 23666 #051-07-1993 L1993 **EM** *020 †16
POWELL, David Michael. 3000 COLISEUM DR, STE 104 23666 #051-07-1992 L1994 **HO** *020 †20
PROPERT, David Boyd. VA MEDICAL CTR MED SVC 23667 #041-02-1958 L1969 **IM CD** *040 †20
RAIU, Camelia. 2115 EXECUTIVE DR, STE 5C 23666 #781-01-1994 L2008 **IM** *100 †20
RANGAPPA, Jai Kumar. 105 REFLECTION LN 23666 #495-34-1965 L1975 **AN IM** *020 †05
RAPOSO, Carlos Alberto. 4000 COLISEUM DR, STE 300 23666 #770-03-1970 L1976 **NEP IM** *020
REAGAN, Thomas Jos. 850 ENTERPRISE PKWY, STE 1400 23666 #035-06-1963 L1977 **N NP** *020 †75
REED, Matthew Daniel. 850 ENTERPRISE PKWY, STE 1200 23666 #033-05-1999 L2006 **OPH** *020 †35
REID, Bruce W. 2202 EXECUTIVE DR STE C 23666 #010-03-1979 L1984 **ORS** *020 †40
REIFF, Theodore Robt. 2 DIAMOND HILL RD 23666 #035-19-1954 L1955 **IM OS** *071 †20
REND, Charles Ambrose. 3130 VICTORIA BLVD, HAMPTON VERGINIA 23661 #005-02-1964 L1986 **OBG** *020 †30
RICCIARELLI, Giacomo. 3000 COLISEUM DR, STE 103 23666 #407-24-1968 L1978 **GS** *020
RIDLEY, Derrick Emerson. 4000 COLISEUM DR, STE 100 23666 #047-07-1980 L1981 **CD IM** *020 †20
RIVERO, Weimar. 100 EMANCIPATION DR 23667 #176-02-1965 L1977 **GS** *020 †85
RIZVI, Nahid Z. 100 EMANCIPATION DR, DEPT OF INTERNAL MED 23667 #704-02-1986 L1994 **IM** *020 †20
ROBERT, Frank Chambers. 3120 VICTORIA BLVD 23661 #012-01-1967 L1968 **FM IM** *020 †18
ROBERTSON, Kenneth John. 3000 COLISEUM DR 23666 #051-04-1974 L1976 **EM FM** *020 †16
ROBINSON, Joy Dixon. 100 EMANCIPATION DR, VETERANS AFFAIRS MEDICAL C 23667 #010-03-1983 L1987 **OPH** *020 †35
ROSENTHAL, Henry Fred. 100 EMANCIPATION DR 23667 #165-06-1977 L1996 **EM** *020
ROSSHEIM, Brooke Weinger. 100 EMANCIPATION DR, VETERANS AFFAIRS MEDICAL C 23667 #051-04-1993 L1996 **GPM** *020 †20,70
ROTHFUSS, Henry L. 2115 EXECUTIVE DR STE 2A 23666 #051-07-1980 L1981 **IM** *020 †20
RUSSOTTO, Joseph Anthony. ■ 23669 #010-02-1958 L1974 **OM NM** *020 †55,28
SABONYA, Linda Marie. 2208 EXECUTIVE DR, STE A 23666 #033-06-1980 L1988 **P** *030
SALE, Thomas W. 3120 VICTORIA BLVD 23661 #051-04-1952 L1952 **GS** *071 †85
SAN AGUSTIN, Lourdes C. ■ 23666 #748-02-1939 L1977 **FM** *074
SAN CLEMENTE, Joseph P. 100 EMANCIPATION DR 23667 #024-05-1973 L1989 **P** *030 †75
SANDERS, Kevin Wayne. 2108 HARTFORD RD 23666 #051-04-1989 L1994 *100 †95
SANDOW, Bruce A. 100 EMANCIPATION DR, VA MEDICAL CENTER 23667 #051-07-1999 L1999 **DR** *020
SARRETT, Kemper Davis. ■ 23669 #041-09-1956 L1958 **OBG** *071 †30
SATTERWHITE, Cynthia K. 410 MARCELLA RD, STE A 23666 #047-07-1979 L1980 **GE IM** *020 †20
SAVAS, Paul Evans. 901 ENTERPRISE PKWY, STE 900 23666 #051-04-1992 L1992 **ORS** *020 †40
SCHELBLE, Anita Marie. ■ 23665 #038-45-2002 L2006 **OBG** *020
SCHLOBOHM, Josefina T. 2244 EXECUTIVE DR 23666 #748-01-1972 L1983 **CHP** *020
SCHLOBOHM, Philip Geo. 2244 EXECUTIVE DR, HEALTH 23666 #748-01-1972 L1976 **P** *020 †75
SCHMIDT, Gilbert F, Jr. 3000 COLISEUM DR 23666 #025-07-1980 L1982 **EM LM** *020 †16
SCHNEIDER, Linda G P. 2019 CUNNINGHAM DR, STE 202 23666 #051-07-1979 L1983 **EM FM** *020 †16,18
SCOPER, Stephen Vincent. 2101 EXECUTIVE DR 23666 #027-01-1984 L1990 **OPH OS** *020 †35
SEARSON-NORRIS, Latrise P. 2100 HARTFORD RD 23666 #010-03-1996 L2000 **PD** *020 †55
SHAAR, Gretchen S. 45 PINE ST, 1ST MEDICAL GROUP/SGQ 23665 #025-12-1993 L1993 **EM** *020 †16
SHAH, Mukesh Harilal. 200 MEDICAL DR, # A 23666 #495-01-1978 L1984 **P** *020
SHAH, Pragna Nina. 3000 COLISEUM DR, STE 200 23666 #495-20-1967 L1977 **FM FPG** *020 †18
SHAHEEN, Edward Adeeb. ■ 23664 #051-01-1991 L2000 **EM** *020 †16
SHEPPARD, John Danl, Jr. 2101 EXECUTIVE DR 23666 #043-01-1978 L1988 **OPH ID** *020 †35
SHIPMAN, Deborah Anne. 200 EATON ST, OLD HAMPTON FAMILY PRACTIC 23669 #051-04-1994 L1994 **FM** *020 †18
SIBLEY, Anthony F. 2204 EXECUTIVE DR STE BCD 23666 #010-03-1979 L1987 **U** *020 †95
SIBLEY, Rosalind I Mc Coy. 2204 EXECUTIVE DR, STE B 23666 #027-01-1979 L1989 **DR** *020 †80
SIGRIST, Stephen Lee. 3000 COLISEUM DR 23666 #038-40-1996 L2006 **EM** *020 †16
SIMMONS, Benjamin Frankli, III. ■ 23666 #010-03-2008 *012
SIMPSON, Melvin Ross. 1999 W PEMBROKE AVE 23661 #047-07-1955 L1957 **GP** *071
SINGH, Gunwant. 3000 COLISEUM DR, SENTARA CAREPLEX HOSPITAL 23666 #495-03-1996 L2002 **IM** *020 †20
SINGH, Maninder G. 100 EMANCIPATION DR, VAMC 23667 #495-08-1984 L1995 **P** *020 †75
SIU, Joanne C. 501 BUTLER FARM RD 23666 #010-02-1996 L2002 **NEP** *020 †20
SMITH, Joshua R. 3000 COLISEUM DR 23666 #011-02-2002 L2005 **EM** *020 †16
SMITH, Wm Henderson, Jr. 2115 EXECUTIVE DR 23666 #020-02-1960 L1967 **OTO A** *071 †45
SNYDER, Jonathan D. 21 E QUEENS WAY STE A, HAMPTON, LTD 23669 #035-03-1990 L1994 **AN** *020 †05
SOOBERT, Karin Luule. PRIMARY CARE 590/170, DEPT VETERANS AFFAIRS 23667 #051-07-1984 L1985 **IM** *020 †20
SOROUR, Hani Mohamed. 4000 COLISEUM DR, STE 350 23666 #915-02-1997 L2007 **FM** *020
SPERRY, Bobbie Jo. 9 MANHATTAN SQ # A 23666 #055-02-2005 L2005 **FP** *012
STIFF, Minnie Zenovia A. 2110 HARTFORD RD STE C 23666 #010-03-1972 L1975 **PD** *020 †55
STOKES, Parker Rea. 9 MANHATTAN SQ, # A 23666 #051-04-1975 L1976 **FM** *020 †18
STOTT, Geraldine Ann. 3000 COLISEUM DR 23666 #036-05-1985 L1987 **ID IM** *020 †20
STROHHOFER, Anton. ■ 23669 #407-16-1949 L1956 **IM** *075 †20
SULLY, Ivory Ulysses, Jr. ■ 23669 #010-03-1952 L1953 **OM GP** *071

■ = Address Information Privacy Protected

SUTINGCO, Nicanor C. 2214 EXECUTIVE DR, STE B 23666 #748-08-1971 L1977 **PTH** *020

TALIBI, Mazhar Ali. 2108 HARTFORD RD 23666 #704-02-1961 L1972 **U** *020 †95 ‡

TAMAYO MATOS, David. 100 EMANCIPATION DR, BEHAVIORAL SCIENCE SERVICE 23667 #042-03-1986 L1996 **P** *020

TENHOLDER, Michael F. 100 EMANCIPATION DR, 100 EMANCIPATION DRIVE 23667 #038-41-1973 L1999 **PUD IM** *040 †20

THOM, Douglas. 101 EATON ST, STE 300 23669 #917-24-1975 L1985 **OBG REN** *020 †30

THOMAS, Fred Nicholas, III. 2115 EXECUTIVE DR, MULTISPECIALITY GROUP 23666 #051-07-1997 L2005 **IM** *020

THURLBY, Jefferson Robert. 77 NEALY AVE 23665 #004-01-1998 L2007 **AN AM** *020 †05

TOMPKINS, Kenneth James. 2208 EXECUTIVE DR 23666 #041-02-1982 L1991 **D EM** *020 †15 ‡

TREFTS, Lori Ann. 850 ENTERPRISE PKWY, STE 1400 23666 #028-34-2002 L2007 **N** *020 †75

TREHERNE, Katherine A. 2207 EXECUTIVE DR, STE A 23666 #047-07-1980 L1984 **D** *020 †15

TREHERNE, Robert Morton. 2207 EXECUTIVE DR STE A 23666 #047-07-1980 L1985 **OBG** *020 †30

TRIPURANENI, Naga S. 4000 COLISEUM DR, STE 350 23666 #495-21-1996 L2006 **CCM** *100 †20

ULLMAN, James Irwin. 21 E QUEENS WAY STE A 23669 #017-20-1969 L1977 **AN** *020 †05

UPTON, Elwin Gilbert. 2244 EXECUTIVE DR, RIVERSIDE BEHAVIORAL HEALT 23666 #062-01-1976 L1998 *020

VAN DER SPUY, Benjamin H. 3000 COLISEUM DR 23666 #660-03-1955 L1963 **GP OS** *071

VAZ, Stephanie Renee. 352 N FIRST ST 23664 #041-09-1998 L1998 **OBG** *020 †18,30

VOSS, Mary Kim. ATTN AMB CARE 170, V.A. MEDICAL CENTER 23667 #030-05-1979 L1981 **IM** *050 †20

WALKER, Paul. 2115 EXECUTIVE DR STE 4A 23666 #051-07-1979 L1982 **UCM PD** *020

WALLER, Kenneth Wm. 100 EMANCIPATION DR, VAMC HAMPTON 23667 #051-04-1985 L1986 **N** *020 †75

WALLINGFORD, Walter R. 2115 EXECUTIVE DR STE 6C 23666 #041-13-1962 L1973 **RHU IM** *020 †20

WALTON, Aaron Lea. ■ 23661 #036-07-1999 L2006 **ID** *100 †20

WALTON, Ava Bernadette. ■ 23666 #051-07-2002 L2003 **P** *020

WARD, Joseph Lawson. 9 MANHATTAN SQ, STE A 23666 #051-04-1975 L1977 **FM** *020 †18

WARD, Oscar Wilde, Jr. 3120 VICTORIA BLVD 23661 #051-04-1942 L1942 **GP OM** *071

WEINBERG, Samuel Edward. ■ 23664 #051-04-1964 L1964 **GS TS** *071 †85

WEISMAN, Todd Andrew. 200 EATON ST, OLD HAMPTON FAMILY PRACTIC 23669 #051-04-1979 L1988 **FM** *020 †18

WHITE, Earl Dowdy, II. 4000 COLISEUM DR, STE 100 23666 #051-04-1965 L1965 **ORS** *071 †40

WILKINSON, James W. ■ 23669 #051-04-1970 L1971 **FM P** *071

WOLOSHIN, Kimberley. 2113 HARTFORD RD, STE C 23666 #025-01-1993 L2004 **FM** *020 †18

WORNOM, Paul H. 3120 VICTORIA BLVD 23661 #051-01-1950 L1950 **IM A** *071

WUESTE, Michelle Marie. 77 NEALY AVE, 0001 MEDICAL GROUP 1 MDG/S 23665 #056-06-2000 L2005 **PD** *020 †55 ‡

YILLAR, Mehmet Kemal. 2208 EXECUTIVE DR, HAMPTO MENTAL HEALH ASSOCI 23666 #902-01-1959 L1979 **P** *020 †20

YOUNG, Maurice Edgar. 7 QUARRY CIR 23669 #038-45-2000 L2005 **OBG** *020 ‡

YOUNGER, Sarah Ann. 2117 HARTFORD RD, FAMILY PRACTICE OF HAMPTON 23666 #051-07-1996 L1996 **IM** *020 †20

ZHU, Jian. 100 EMANCIPATION DR, MEDICAL CTR 23667 #243-16-1987 L2001 **IM DIA** *020 †20

ZIEBER, Steven Roger. 45 PINE ST, 1ST MEDICAL GROUP/SGQ; 23665 #038-43-2000 L2006 **DR** *020 †80

ZIMMERMAN, Charles H, Jr. 4000 COLISEUM DR, STE 220 23666 #051-01-1964 L1964 **OBG** *071 †30

HAMPTON – NEWPORT NEWS CITY

DEVRIES, Katherine Meliss. ■ 23605 #051-04-2006 L2006 **FP** *012

HAMPTON – POQUOSON CITY

WILLIAMS, Martha Ferguson. ■ 23662 #051-07-1985 L1991 **EM** *020 †16

HANOVER – HANOVER

CROSS, Wirt Whitfield, Jr. ■ 23069 #051-04-2004 L2004 **GS** *100

HARDY – FRANKLIN

BALL, William Flinn. 13423 BOOKER T WSHNGTN HWY 24101 #036-08-1984 L1985 **FM** *020 †18

BUNN, Norris Dudley. ■ 24101 #041-09-1957 L1958 **GS** *071 †85

BURGESS, Henry E. 274 WESTLAKE RD 24101 #048-16-1998 L2001 **FM** *020 †18

CRAYE, Cornelis Kirk. 13205 BOOKER T WSHNGTN HWY, CARILION INTERNAL 24101 #305-01-1997 L1998 **IM** *020 †20

HELMS, Lee Thomas. 13295 BOOKER T WSHNGTN HWY, EYE CARE & SURGERY 24101 #051-04-1978 L1983 **OPH** *020 †35

JAWHAR, Mahmoud Omar. 13205 BOOKER T WSHNGTN HWY, CARILION INTERNAL 24101 #051-07-1996 L2001 **GS** *020 †85

LEMBERG, Bonnie Gail. ■ 24101 #035-20-1981 L1983 **DR** *020 †80

LIPSCOMB, Jeffrey Blake. ■ 24101 #051-04-1990 L1992 **IM** *020 †20

THELAN, Kenneth M. 13205 BOOKER T WSHNGTN HWY, CARILION INTERNAL 24101 #025-01-1975 L2004 **IM** *020 †20

THELAN, Virginia Blevins. 13205 BOOKER T WSHNGTN HWY, CARILION INTERNAL 24101 #055-02-1982 L2004 **IM** *020 †20

HARDYVILLE – MIDDLESEX

ATIENZA, Fernando C. ■ 23070 #748-08-1962 L1989 **PD** *071 †55

HARRISONBURG – HARRISONBURG CITY

AAMODT, Leonard Wortley. 119 UNIVERSITY BLVD, STE B 22801 #048-04-1986 L1993 **OBG** *020 †30 ‡

ADAM, Nazir Ahmed. 235 CANTRELL AVE 22801 #036-01-1994 L1997 **EM** *020 †16

ADAMSON, Nathaniel E, III. 370 NEFF AVE, STE S 22801 #051-01-1983 L1985 **DR NM** *020 †80

ALEXIOU, Jerri Alley. 2054 PRO POINTE LN 22801 #020-12-1996 L2001 **D** *020 †15

ALEXIOU, Michael Arthur. 2062 PRO POINTE LN, VALLEY ENT HEAD & NECK SUR 22801 #019-02-1996 L2001 **OTO** *020 †45

ARTHUR, Rodney Saml. 1871 EVELYN BYRD AVE 22801 #023-01-1984 L1991 **NEP IM** *020 †20

ASHBY, Jeffrey Alan. 1831 RESERVOIR ST 22801 #051-07-1993 L1999 **FM** *020 †18

BAE, Young Hoon. 1931 MEDICAL AVE, VALLEY BEHAVIORAL MEDICINE 22801 #583-02-1975 L2004 **P** *020 †75

BAER, Alexander Beckers. 235 CANTRELL AVE 22801 #051-01-1999 L1999 **EM** *020 †16

BAHLEDA, Thomas Anthony. 235 CANTRELL AVE, INPATIENT SERVICES 22801 #422-01-2002 L2005 **IM** *020 †20

BALINT, Tara Douglas. 3320 EMMAUS RD, HARRISONBURG SURGICAL 22801 #035-08-1998 L2006 **VS** *020 †20

BANNISTER, Warren Dale. 235 CANTRELL AVE 22801 #017-20-1981 L1989 **PTH IM** *020 †50

BARCH, Frank Jerry. 640 S MAIN ST 22801 #041-07-1975 L2002 **SME PCC** *020

BARNES, Brett C. 4165 QUARLES CT, HESS ORTHOPAEDICS & 22801 #048-04-1987 L2001 **ORS OSM** *020 †40

BARNES, John V, III. 1871 EVELYN BYRD AVE 22801 #051-04-1981 L1988 **CD** *020 †20

BATTAGLIA, Todd C. 235 CANTRELL AVE 22801 #035-06-1999 L1999 **ORS OSM** *020 ‡

BEHL, Joseph Wm, Jr. 235 CANTRELL AVE 22801 #051-04-1980 L1981 **DR NM** *020 †80

BELYEA, Brian Chipman. ■ 22801 #051-01-2004 L2004 **PD** *012 †55

BENTREM, George A. 235 CANTRELL AVE 22801 #051-01-1990 L1996 **FM** *020 †18

BERGER, Bary Mayer. 644 UNIVERSITY BLVD, STE A 22801 #023-01-1987 L1993 **U** *020 †95

BILL, Timothy James. 2058 PRO POINTE LN, VALLEY PLASTIC SURGERY, PC 22801 #051-01-1996 L1996 **HS** *020 †65

BILLINGSLEY, Thaine E. ■ 22801 #019-02-1953 L1955 **GP** *071

BING, Herbert Earl, Jr. 2291 EVELYN BYRD AVE 22801 #051-01-1974 L1978 **OBG** *071 †30

BLAY, Andrew Brian. 2323 GRACE CHAPEL RD, COOK'S CREEK CLINIC 22801 #065-01-1976 L1977 **EM** *020 †16,18

BOTTICELLI, Michael J. 2291 EVELYN BYRD AVE, HARRISONBURG OB/GYN ASSOC. 22801 #051-04-1994 L1994 **OBG** *020 †20

BOTTICELLI, Rebecca L. 1992 MEDICAL AVE, LIDEE ANESTHETICS&GYNECOLO 22801 #051-04-1995 L1995 **FM** *020 †18

BOULANGER, Philip Charles. 168 CHESTNUT RIDGE DR # C 22801 #016-11-1996 L1997 **FM** *020

BRADSHAW, Douglas Mark. 1733 ERICKSON AVE, ERICKSON PROF PARK 22801 #051-04-1982 L1992 **FM** *020 †18

BRANUM, Gene D. 3320 EMMAUS RD, HARRISONBURG SURGICAL 22801 #036-07-1986 L2001 **GS** *050 †85

BROOK, Gail Susanne. ■ 22801 #023-01-1984 L1994 **PD** *040 †55

BROWN, Gerald La Vonne. 847 CANTRELL AVE, VETERANS AFFAIRS PRIM CARE 22801 #036-07-1967 L1972 **P CHP** *050 †75

BRUNK, James Robt. 1031 S MAIN ST 22801 #051-01-1954 L1956 **IM PUD** *071

BUNDRICK, Thomas John. 370 NEFF AVE STE S 22801 #035-08-1978 L1982 **DR** *020 †80

BURGE, Joseph John. 373 NEFF AVE 22801 #036-07-1974 L1980 **RHU IM** *071 †20

BURTNER, Lawrence Danl. ■ 22801 #051-04-1954 L1954 **P** *071 †55

CALDWELL, Paul Chas. ■ 22801 #051-04-1970 L1970 **DR OS** *071 †80

CALDWELL, Roumiana Hristo. 235 CANTRELL AVE, PPT MED INPATIENT PHYS 22801 #198-01-1988 L2003 **IM** *020 †20

CALE, William F, III. 544 S MAIN ST 22801 #051-04-1977 L1982 **PUD CCM** *020 †20

CALLAHAN, Donald Morris. ■ 22801 #051-04-1954 L1954 **R RO** *071 †80

CAMPER, Harry Green, III. 1992 MEDICAL AVE, L'IDEE AESTHETICS & GYNECO 22801 #055-02-1981 L1985 **OBG** *020 †30

CANADY, Robert Grayson. 1871 EVELYN BYRD AVE 22801 #051-01-1999 L2004 **NEP** *020 †20

CANTER, Noland M, Jr. 235 CANTRELL AVE 22801 #051-04-1947 L1948 **R** *071

CAPSTACK, Ronald Edward. 1921 MEDICAL AVE 22801 #010-02-1978 L1983 **OPH** *020 †35 ‡

CARROLL, Dale Alan. 235 CANTRELL AVE, ROCKINGHAM MEMORIAL HOSPIT 22801 #045-01-1975 L2001 **FM PHP** *030 †70,18

CASSIDY, Megan Kathleen. 119 UNIVERSITY BLVD, STE B 22801 #051-01-2003 L2003 **OBG** *020

CHALAM, Ramesh. 235 CANTRELL AVE, ROCKINGHAM MEMORIAL HOSPIT 22801 #495-27-1974 L1981 **AN** *020

CHANG, Henry Honli. ■ 22801 #041-02-1999 L1999 **IM** *020 †20

CHAPPELL, Geo Edward, Jr. 644 UNIVERSITY BLVD, STE B 22801 #051-04-1971 L1973 **ORS** *020 †40

CHAPPELL, George Edward. ■ 22801 #051-04-1953 L1953 **GP** *072

CHOW, Felicia Cheshuen. ■ 22801 #023-07-2007 L2007 **IM** *012

CLINE, Ross Lee. ■ 22801 #055-01-1969 L1995 **DR** *071 †80

COHEE, Brian Michael. ■ 22801 #023-07-2008 *012

COHEN, David Ahron. 1661 S MAIN ST 22801 #051-04-2001 L2007 **OSM** *020

CONELL, Lawrence Jos. 752 OTT ST 22801 #051-07-1977 L1981 **P PYG** *020 †75

DALTON, Claudette Ellis H. 235 CANTRELL AVE, ROCKINGHAM MEMORIAL HOSPIT 22801 #051-01-1974 L1988 **AN** *030 ‡

DANISA, Olumide Ayodele. 4165 QUARLES CT, HESS ORTHOPAEDICS & 22801 #051-01-1990 L1990 **ORS** *020 †40

DAVIS, Sarah Marie. 1200 PARK RD 22802 #041-14-2006 L2007 **OBG** *012

DAY, Philip Wayne. 235 CANTRELL AVE, HARRISONBURG INTERNAL 22801 #055-01-1981 L1989 **IM** *020 †20

DEFREESE, Marcia Sharon. 4059 QUARLES CT 22801 #033-06-1992 L1995 **PD** *020 †55

DEGENE, Aklilu Mersha. 544 SOUTH MAIN STREET 22807 #366-03-1991 L2005 **PCC** *020 †20

DEPUTY, Glenn Edward. 1871 EVELYN BYRD AVE 22801 #051-01-1985 L1989 **N** *020 †75

DIDUCH, Barry Kent. JAMES MADISON UNIVERSITY, DEPT. OF SPORTS MEDICINE M 22807 #051-01-1992 L1993 **FM** *020 †18

DOTSON, Gary Wesley. 1661 S MAIN ST 22801 #051-01-1980 L1983 **EM IM** *020 †20

DUMLER, John Chas, Jr. 2054 PRO POINTE LN 22801 #023-01-1965 L1970 **D** *020 †15

EAGLE, John Russell. 370 NEFF AVE STE H 22801 #051-01-1963 L1963 **P** *020 †75

EGGLESTON, Robert Bolling. 3344 EMMAUS RD 22801 #024-01-1962 L1968 **OPH** *071 †35

ETRE, Mouline Haddy. MSC 7901, JAMES MADISON UNIV 22807 #018-03-1989 L1992 **FM** *020 †18

EVANS, James Dewitt. 3322 EMMAUS RD 22801 #055-01-1970 L1975 **FM** *020 †18

FELDMAN, Tomer. 235 CANTRELL AVE 22801 #016-43-1994 L1997 **EM** *020 †16

FENDLEY, Morris Jackson. 3320 EMMAUS RD, HARRISONBURG SURGICAL 22801 #012-05-1998 L2003 **GS** *020 †85

FINCH, John Mark. 1751 ERICKSON AVE 22801 #051-04-1992 L1994 **FM** *020 †18

FLETCHER, William Paul. 1015 QUINCE DR 22801 #051-04-1953 L1953 **FM OBG** *071

FOLSOM, Kent Regan. 235 CANTRELL AVE, ROCKINGHAM MEMORIAL HOSP 22801 #048-02-1992 L1994 **EM ETX** *020 †16
FOX, Frederick Louvane. ■ 22801 #024-05-1968 L1970 **ORS OTR** *071 †40
GARDNER, Joseph Erskin. ■ 22802 #051-04-1953 L1953 **FM** *071
GARWOOD, Robert Allen. 3320 EMMAUS RD, HARRISONBURG SURGICAL ASSO 22801 #041-14-2001 L2001 **GS** *100 †85
GATES, Charles Wayne. 3360 EMMAUS RD 22801 #021-05-1980 L1985 **OTO FPS** *020 †45
GEARING, Frank W, Jr. 1931 MEDICAL AVE, PEDIATRIC ASSOCIATES 22801 #051-04-1944 L1944 **R OS** *071 †80
GILLESPIE, Ritchie Peery. 1320 S MAIN ST, STE A 22801 #051-01-1974 L1988 **NS N** *071 †75,25
GLICK, John Thos. 1820 COUNTRY CLUB RD # I 22802 #051-04-1978 L1979 **FM OS** *020 †18
GODSHALL, Stephen Edward. 1751 ERICKSON AVE 22801 #041-14-1997 L2003 **FM** *020 †18
GOOD, Lois Anita. ■ 22802 #041-01-1958 L1961 **PD** *071
GORDON, Alexia Leontyne. 847 CANTRELL AVE, STE 100 22801 #041-07-1995 L2006 **FM** *020 †18
GORDON, Kenneth Wm. 235 CANTRELL AVE, FOR ANESTHESIOLOGY INC 22801 #051-01-1992 L1992 **AN** *020 †05
GORSUCH, Heidi Dries. 530 NEFF AVE, ROCKINGHAM MEM HOSP 22801 #023-01-1984 L2008 **GS** *020 †85
GRAYSON, David Edward. 370 NEFF AVE STE S 22801 #012-01-1997 L2005 **DR** *020 †80
GREEN, Walter F, III. 51 N LIBERTY ST 22802 #051-04-1957 L1957 **GP** *020
GREY, William Hugh. COMMUNITY SERVICE BOARD, HARRISONBURG - ROCKINGHAM 22802 #051-04-1948 L1951 **P** *072
GUERRERO, Tracy. 235 CANTRELL AVE, FOR ANESTHESIOLOGY INC 22801 #016-11-1996 L2001 **AN** *020 †05
HALEY, James Adams. 1751 ERICKSON AVE 22801 #051-04-1984 L1985 **FM** *020 †18
HAMID, Sadia. 235 CANTRELL AVE 22801 #704-20-2001 L2006 **IM** *020 †20 ‡
HARDIGREE, Gregory Keith. 4165 QUARLES CT, HESS ORTHOPAEDICS & 22801 #045-01-1988 L2004 **ORS** *020 †40
HARPER, Eugene Jutson. ■ 22801 #036-07-1967 L1974 **GS** *071 †85
HARPER, George W, III. 1661 S MAIN ST, HARRISONBURG 22801 #051-04-1977 L1978 **FM** *020 †18
HEARN, John T. ■ 22802 #051-01-1953 L1953 **GP** *071
HEATWOLE, Kenneth M. ■ 22802 #051-04-1951 L1951 **PUD** *071
HEATWOLE, Stanley Elmer. 755A CANTRELL AVE 22801 #051-04-1967 L1967 **EM** *020 †16
HELBERT, Hollen G. 235 CANTRELL AVE 22801 #051-01-1941 L1941 **IM** *071
HENDERSON, Charles Henry. 370 NEFF AVE STE S 22801 #051-01-1965 L1965 **R** *071 †80
HENDREN, Douglas Hardy. 4165 QUARLES CT, HESS ORTHOPAEDICS & 22801 #038-06-1982 L1996 **ORS** *020 †40
HERNANDEZ, Maria A. 129 UNIVERSITY BLVD, STE E 22801 #308-01-1978 L2001 **IM** *020 †20
HESS, Irvin Eugene. 4165 QUARLES CT 22801 #051-04-1964 L1964 **ORS** *020 †40
HEYAT, Perviz. 235 CANTRELL AVE, RMH INPATIENT PHYSICIANS 22801 #902-10-1982 L1999 **IM RHU** *020 †20
HORNER, Barry Eugene. 235 CANTRELL AVE, FOR ANESTHESIOLOGY INC 22801 #048-12-1994 L2002 **AN** *020 †05
HOSTETTER, Alden Lynn. 235 CANTRELL AVE, ANATOMIC PATHOLOGY 22801 #051-07-1982 L1987 **PTH PCP** *020 †50
HOTCHKISS, Jerome Jordan. 1661 S MAIN ST 22801 #051-04-1995 L1999 **FM** *020 †18
HUFFMAN, Harold Ezra. 235 CANTRELL AVE 22801 #051-04-1966 L1966 **FM** *020
ILAGAN, Michael Castillo. 235 CANTRELL AVE 22801 #047-07-1995 L2003 **EM** *020 †16
IUDICA, Anthony Christian. 1831 RESERVOIR ST 22801 #023-01-1998 L1998 **FM** *020 †18
JENKINS, Harold Samuel. 235 CANTRELL AVE 22801 #051-01-1974 L1975 **FM EM** *020 †16
JESTEADT, Gregory Charles. 1831 RESERVOIR ST 22801 #041-12-2000 L2000 **FM** *020 †18 ‡
JOHNSON, Lois E Boswell. ■ 22801 #016-11-1956 L1957 **PD ADL** *020 †55
JOHNSON, Wm Raymond, Jr. ■ 22801 #051-04-1953 L1953 **GP** *071
KASTANEK, Jill Anne. 235 CANTRELL AVE, FOR ANESTHESIOLOGY INC 22801 #041-07-1984 L2002 **AN** *020 †05
KEETON, Robert Edward. 235 CANTRELL AVE 22801 #051-04-1975 L1994 **FM** *020 †18
KENNEL, Elmer Elwood. 3320 EMMAUS RD, HARRISONBURG SURGICAL 22801 #023-07-1968 L1975 **GS** *020 †85
KERN, Charles Edward. 235 CANTRELL AVE, FOR ANESTHESIOLOGY INC 22801 #017-20-1985 L1989 **AN** *020 †05
KILBY, William Irvin. 3302 RESERVOIR ST 22801 #051-01-1980 L1983 **PD** *020 †55
KIME, Robert Clarence, III. 4165 QUARLES CT, HESS ORTHOPAEDICS PLC 22801 #036-07-1989 L1999 **ORS** *020 †40
KINGERY, Lou Gene. 1241 N MAIN ST, HRC-COMMUNITY SERVICE BOAR 22802 #055-02-1983 L1985 **P OS** *020 †75
KINI, Ganesh Devdas. ■ 22801 #422-01-2002 L2002 **IM** *020 †20
KISELICA, Daria. 1790 E MARKET ST STE 64B, RHM/CENTER FOR CORPORATE H 22801 #041-14-1984 L1988 **IM OM** *020 †20,70
KNISS, Mark Allan. ■ 22802 #041-09-1956 L1967 **FM** *071 †18
KOFELDT, Linda Marie. 304 NEFF AVE 22801 #041-13-1994 L1994 **ID** *020 †20
KOHRING, Regis Clarke. 235 CANTRELL AVE 22801 #035-15-1963 L1968 **AN** *071 †05
KRAMER, Eric Daniel. 235 CANTRELL AVE 22801 #010-01-1992 L1994 **EM** *020 †16
KRAUS, Harry Lee. ■ 22801 #051-04-1955 L1955 **FM** *071 †18
KRAUS, Harry Lee, Jr. 3320 EMMAUS RD 22801 #051-04-1986 L1991 **GS** *020 †85
KYLER, Robert Matthew. 100 E GRACE ST 22801 #051-01-1985 L1986 **RO** *020 †80
LALL, Madhulika. 235 CANTRELL AVE 22801 #305-01-2001 L2004 **IM** *020
LAMBERT, Lynn David. 3302 RESERVOIR ST 22801 #051-01-1976 L1979 **PD OM** *020 †55
LANCASTER, Luke. 370 NEFF AVE STE S 22801 #023-01-1988 L1994 **DR** *020 †80
LANDES, Timothy Chas. 1871 EVELYN BYRD AVE 22801 #051-07-1983 L1993 **GE IM** *020 †20
LAREAU, Eugene Raymond. 3320 EMMAUS RD, HARRISONBURG SURGICAL 22801 #010-02-1966 L1971 **GS** *020 †85
LEE, William Irvin. 1871 EVELYN BYRD AVE 22801 #051-04-1975 L1976 **CD IM** *020 †20
LEICHTY, Kerry Dale. 1751 ERICKSON AVE 22801 #018-03-1992 L1995 **FM** *020 †18
LEPLEY, Shawn Michael. 1661 S MAIN ST 22801 #038-41-1997 L2000 **FM** *020 †18
LI, Robert Chialin. 235 CANTRELL AVE, FOR ANESTHESIOLOGY INC 22801 #051-04-1993 L1993 **AN** *020 †05
LIBERACE, Val Joseph. 235 CANTRELL AVE, DEPARTMENT OF RADIOLOGY 22801 #041-13-2001 L2007 **NM** *020 †80,28
LIGHTNER, Jeffrey Kass. 752 OTT ST 22801 #041-01-1966 L1986 **P** *020 †75
LINDBERGH, John Robert. 235 CANTRELL AVE 22801 #051-07-1997 L1997 **EM** *020 †20,16
LOYNES, James Thomas. 100 E GRACE ST, RMH REGIONAL CANCER CENTER 22801 #045-01-1997 L2003 **HO** *020 †20
LOYNES, Maribeth P. 2291 EVELYN BYRD AVE 22801 #045-01-1996 L2003 **OBG** *020 †30
MAGRUDER, Eileen Enosaki. ■ 22801 #051-01-1975 L1976 **PHM** *050
MALIK, Vipin. 544 S MAIN ST, RMH PULMONARY ASSOCIATES 22801 #495-45-1993 L2006 **PUD CCM** *020 †20
MALONE, Jonathan. MSC 7901, JAMES MADISON UNIV HEALTH 22807 #041-13-1971 L1977 **ORS** *020 †40
MANSFIELD, John Bristow. 1012 RESERVOIR ST STE B 22801 #018-03-1974 L1979 **GS VS** *020 †85
MARRA, Steven Wm. 235 CANTRELL AVE 22801 #038-43-1988 L2007 **TS GS** *020 †85,90
MARTIN, Don Richard. 1931 MEDICAL AVE, THE JOHNS HOPKINS HOSPITAL 22801 #051-04-1983 L2007 **RHU IM** *020 †20
MARTIN, Joseph Alan. 235 CANTRELL AVE, FOR ANESTHESIOLOGY INC 22801 #051-04-1983 L2006 **AN** *020 †05
MC CORMICK, Robert Scott. 3344 EMMAUS RD 22801 #012-01-1997 L2000 **OPH** *020 †35
MC DONALD, Robert Melvin. 235 CANTRELL AVE 22801 #051-04-1953 L1956 **PD** *040 †55
MC GOWAN, John Alphonsus. 1871 EVELYN BYRD AVE 22801 #004-01-1980 L1987 **NEP IM** *071 †20
MC INTYRE, Kenneth Mark. 563 NEFF AVE STE A, BON SECOURS DEPAUL MEDICAL 22801 #305-01-1984 L2001 **UM IM** *020 †20
MC LAUGHLIN, David Paul. 1871 EVELYN BYRD AVE 22801 #041-14-1986 L1990 **IC** *020 †20
MC NAMARA, Jos Gerard M. 563 NEFF AVE, STE A 22801 #539-04-1983 L1986 **FM EM** *020 †18
MC NETT, Wayne Franklin. 1661 S MAIN ST, HARRISONBURG 22801 #036-01-1978 L1979 **FM** *020 †18
MILLER, Carolyn Ilene. 2061 EVELYN BYRD AVE STE C 22801 #038-44-1993 L1998 **D** *020 †15
MILLER, Kenlyn Shawn. 1921 MEDICAL AVE 22801 #038-44-1993 L1998 **OPH** *020 †35
MONTGOMERY, Gregory Flack. 3320 EMMAUS RD, HARRISONBURG SURGICAL 22801 #035-15-1978 L1985 **GS VS** *020 †85
MORGAN, Alan James. 1661 S MAIN ST, HARRISONBURG 22801 #048-14-1984 L1985 **FM** *020 †18
MORGAN, David B. 100 E GRACE ST, RMH REGIONAL CANCER CTR 22801 #023-12-1986 L1995 **RO** *020 †80
MORRA, Marcus Napoleone. 644 UNIVERSITY BLVD # A, HARRISONBURG UROLOGY ASSOC 22801 #010-02-1984 L1993 **U GS** *020 †95
MORRIS, Sherry Lynn. 235 CANTRELL AVE 22801 #036-01-1987 L1991 **DR** *020 †80
MORRISON, Arna Glenn. 235 CANTRELL AVE 22801 #051-01-1973 L1974 **PTH** *020 †50
MOSS, Jonathan David. 235 CANTRELL AVE, ROCKINGHAM MEMORIAL HOSPIT 22801 #011-02-1979 L1988 **FM** *020 †18
MOYER, Erin Andrea. ■ 22802 #041-02-2005 **ORS** *012
NEAL, Danny Alan. 333 LUCY DR 22801 #051-01-1984 L1986 **OTO HNS** *020 †45
NELSEN, Louis Edward, III. 2291 EVELYN BYRD AVE 22801 #051-07-1986 L1988 **OBG** *020 †30
NESBIT, Mark William. 235 CANTRELL AVE 22801 #036-01-1994 L2001 **EM GS** *020 †16
NEWCITY, James Francis. 235 CANTRELL AVE, HARRISONBURG PHYSICIANS FO 22801 #010-01-1986 L1988 **AN** *020 †05
NEWSOME, Susan Lynn. 3302 RESERVOIR ST, VALLEY CHILDRENS CLINIC 22801 #051-04-1984 L1990 **PD** *020 †55
NIO, Deborah Agnes Maria. 1831 RESERVOIR ST 22801 #051-04-1996 L1996 **FM** *020 †18
NIPE, George Maynard. 235 CANTRELL AVE 22801 #051-04-1946 L1947 **OBG** *071
NORRIS, Burl Fleet, Jr. 370 NEFF AVE 22801 #047-20-1991 L2001 **DR** *020 †80
OVERBY, Terry Lyn. 1871 EVELYN BYRD AVE 22801 #036-01-1974 L1978 **NEP IM** *020 †20
PARRIS, Addison Roger. 235 CANTRELL AVE, DEPARTMENT OF MEDICINE 22801 #305-01-2001 L2006 **ID** *020
PATEL, Ketan M. 235 CANTRELL AVE 22801 #495-23-1993 L2001 **IM** *020 †20
PENCE, Roger Steven. 1967 MEDICAL AVE 22801 #051-01-1991 L1993 **AI** *020 †55,03
PERDUE, Judith Susan. ■ 22801 #051-04-1981 L1985 **PD** *020 †55
PERDUE, Zack Taylor, III. 1931 MEDICAL AVE, RMH NEUROLOGY 22801 #051-04-1981 L1985 **N** *020 †75
PEREZ, Jose Ramon. ■ 22801 #264-05-1962 L1971 **U OS** *071 †95
PHILLIPS, Stephen Lee. 1790 E MARKET ST, STE 64B 22801 #051-04-1978 L1980 **FM OM** *020 †70,18
PITTS, Christopher D. 235 CANTRELL AVE, FOR ANESTHESIOLOGY INC 22801 #048-04-1991 L2005 **AN** *020 †05
POLLOCK, Stewart Gregory. 1871 EVELYN BYRD AVE 22801 #038-06-1985 L1991 **CD IM** *020 †20
POU, Javier Antonio. 1871 EVELYN BYRD AVE 22801 #042-02-2000 L2003 **GE** *020 †20
REILLY, Harold Francis. 1871 EVELYN BYRD AVE, HARRISONBURG MEDICAL ASSOC 22801 #010-02-1984 L1987 **GE IM** *020 †20
REISH, William Edwin. 4060 S MAIN ST 22801 #051-04-1954 L1954 **GP** *071
RENICK, Phillip Miles. 4059 QUARLES CT 22801 #041-07-1994 L2001 **PD** *020 †55
RIZVI, Reena. 235 CANTRELL AVE, ROCKINGHAM MEMEORIAL HOSPI 22801 #704-16-1990 L1999 **FM** *020 †18
ROBINSON, Brian Edward. 100 E GRACE ST, RMH REGIONAL CANCER CENTER 22801 #023-01-1983 L1990 **HEM IM** *020 †20
RODGERS, Stephen Quarles. HEALTH CENTER, MSC 7901 22807 #039-01-1970 L1973 **PD EM** *020 †55
ROHRER, Dennis Gilbert. 370 NEFF AVE 22801 #051-04-1981 L1982 **DR** *020 †80
ROUSSEL, Geo Albert, IV. 235 CANTRELL AVE, HARRISONBURG INTERNAL 22801 #021-05-1970 L1975 **IM** *020
RUST, John Newton. 235 CANTRELL AVE 22801 #051-01-1972 L1978 **PTH** *020 †50
SALAM, Tanvir U. 1931 MEDICAL AVE 22801 #704-21-1991 L2000 **PUD PCC** *020 †20
SCHULTZ, Robert Gwynn. ■ 22801 #051-04-1944 L1944 **OBG** *071 †18
SCHWARTZ, James Ruben. 4165 QUARLES CT, HESS ORTHOPAEDICS & 22801 #023-07-1971 L1978 **OSS ORS** *020 †40
SEASE, James Richard. 725 S MASON ST 22801 #051-04-1956 L1956 **GS GYN** *071 †85
SEASE, Robert Hammond, Jr. 1871 EVELYN BYRD AVE 22801 #051-04-1981 L1982 **GE IM** *020 †20
SEASE, William Craig. 644 UNIVERSITY BLVD, STE A 22801 #051-04-1980 L1985 **U** *020 †95
SEDWICK, Richard Elmer N. 1885 PORT REPUBLIC RD 22801 #051-04-1975 L1977 **OBG** *020 †30
SEEFRIED, Richard Andrew. 1921 MEDICAL AVE, ROCKINGHAM EYE PHYSICIANS 22801 #038-41-2001 L2005 **OPH** *020 †35
SENFIELD, Richard Maxon. 1840 E MARKET ST 22801 #008-01-1959 L1975 **AN** *071 †05
SHAFQAT, Syed Imran. 1951 EVELYN BYRD AVE, STE I 22801 #704-16-1987 L2001 **CCM** *020 †20
SHANK, David Lee. 235 CANTRELL AVE, ROCKINGHAM MEMORIAL HOSP 22801 #051-01-1977 L1978 **FM** *020 †18,16
SHEAP, Christopher N. 1741B ERICKSON AVE 22801 #051-04-1971 L1972 **D** *020 †15 ‡

SHENK, Jonathan David. 1661 S MAIN ST 22801 #051-04-1982 L1985 **FM** *020 †18
SHERRY, John E H, II. 2034 PRO POINTE LN 22801 #035-08-1991 L1994 **APM** *020 †05
SHOWALTER, Carl Robt. 235 CANTRELL AVE 22801 #051-01-1963 L1963 **P PFP** *071 †75
SHOWALTER, Samuel G. 235 CANTRELL AVE 22801 #051-04-1969 L1969 **FM** *071 †18
SLIPKA, Colleen Grant. JAMES MADISON UNIV, VARNER HSE MSC 0801 22807
 #038-40-2003 L2003 **P** *100
SLUSHER, Mary Catherine. 2291 EVELYN BYRD AVE 22801 #055-02-1988 L1989 **OBG** *020 †30
SMITH, Joseph D. 1751 ERICKSON AVE 22801 #051-04-1977 L1978 **FM** *020 †18
SMITH, Michael Eugene. 370 NEFF AVE STE S, MALL CENTRE 22801 #051-04-1977 L1977
 DR *020 †80
SMITH, Nina Kay. 235 CANTRELL AVE 22801 #055-02-1981 L1984 **GYN** *020 †30
SMITH, Susan Beth. 1947 MEDICAL AVE 22801 #055-01-1994 L2001 **PD** *020 †55
SMULKA-BELL, Kathleen. ■ 22801 #035-06-1987 L1990 **IM** *020 †20
STAGG, Paul Lynwood. 3365 MANNHEIM CT 22801 #036-05-1968 L1998 **END** *030 †20
STEINES, Ian Edwin. 235 CANTRELL AVE 22801 #023-01-2000 L2004 **EM** *020 †16
STELLER, Frank. 2322 BLUE STONE HILL DR, STE 260 22801 #297-01-1980 L1985
 FM EM *020 †18
STICKLEY, William Sproul. 235 CANTRELL AVE 22801 #036-05-1959 L1963 **AN GP** *071 †05
ST JOHN, Kathleen Marie. 1831 RESERVOIR ST 22801 #023-01-1998 L1998 **FM** *020 †18
STORY, William Henry. 1840 E MARKET ST 22801 #035-15-1966 L1971 **AN** *071 †05
STOUGH, Rick Allen. 755 CANTRELL AVE 22801 #004-01-1994 L1994 **OTO** *020
SUMMERS, Christopher J. 235 CANTRELL AVE, FOR ANESTHESIOLOGY INC 22801
 #036-01-1995 L2001 **AN** *020 †05
SWALLOW, Elizabeth Fink. 530 NEFF AVE 22801 #008-02-1983 L1987 **OBG** *071 †30
SYPTAK, John Michael. 1831 RESERVOIR ST, HARRISONBURG FAMILY PRACTI 22801
 #051-01-1994 L1994 **FM** *020 †18
TALBOT, William Hanna, Sr. ■ 22801 #051-04-1945 L1946 **CLP ATP** *071 †50
TRAN, Johanna Elizabeth. 235 CANTRELL AVE, ROCKINGHAM MEMORIAL HOSPIT 22801
 #024-07-2000 L2003 **PM** *020 †20
TSIKATA, Kafui Vida. ■ 22802 #051-04-2001 L2003 **FM** *100 †18
UNDERWOOD, Robert Michael. 235 CANTRELL AVE 22801 #045-04-1998 L2001 **EM** *020 †16
URBANSKI, Christine Marie. 100 E GRACE ST, RMH REGIONAL CANCER CENTER 22801
 #010-02-1997 L2002 **IM** *020 †20
VEST, Timothy Keith. 1871 EVELYN BYRD AVE 22801 #051-01-1976 L1982 **GE IM** *020 †20
VISGER, Jennifer Melissa. 119 UNIVERSITY BLVD STE B 22801 #051-01-2002 L2002 **OBG** *020
VISVALINGAM, Nando. 1931 MEDICAL AVE 22801 #035-03-1994 L1994 **N** *020 †75
WAGNER, Andrew Linn. 235 CANTRELL AVE 22801 #011-04-1992 L1999 **RNR** *020 †80
WALIGORA, Andrew. 1871 EVELYN BYRD AVE 22801 #759-01-1986 L1999 **NEP IM** *020 †20 ‡
WALSH, John Francis. 1871 EVELYN BYRD AVE 22801 #024-05-1987 L1999 **CD IM** *020 †20
WARNER, Mark Francis. 1871 EVELYN BYRD AVE 22801 #051-01-1977 L1980 **IM** *020 †20
WEIDIG, George Louis. 1831 RESERVOIR ST 22801 #051-04-1973 L1974 **FM** *020
WESTON, Lucy Allen. 235 CANTRELL AVE, FOR ANESTHESIOLOGY INC 22801
 #051-04-1991 L1991 **AN** *020 †05
WESTWOOD, Craig Alan. 235 CANTRELL AVE, FOR ANESTHESIOLOGY INC 22801
 #025-01-1991 L1995 **OS** *020 †05
WHITE, Heather Anne. ■ 22801 #028-03-1999 L2001 **RO** *020 †80
WHITEHEAD, David Calloway. 1831 RESERVOIR ST 22801 #051-04-1973 L1973 **FM** *071
WHITTEN, Carl Larry, Jr. 2291 EVELYN BYRD AVE 22801 #012-01-1978 L1987 **OBG** *020 †30
WHONDER-GENUS, Hillary G. 1951 EVELYN BYRD AVE, SUTIE I 22801 #035-03-1989 L2007
 PD *020 †55
WIDRA, Kenneth Alan. 1241 N MAIN ST 22802 #016-11-1985 L1987 **P** *020 †75
WILLIAMS, Gerald A. ■ 22802 #010-01-1949 L1957 **END IM** *071 †20
WILLISON, Crystl Dove. ■ 22802 #055-01-1987 L1996 **NS** *020 †25
WITMAN, John Andrew. 1751 ERICKSON AVE, ROCKINGHAM FAMILY PHYSICIA 22801
 #051-07-1996 L1996 **FM** *020 †18
WITMER, Daniel Gene. ■ 22802 #041-01-1964 L1974 **OBG** *071 †30
WITT, Mary Helen. 100 E GRACE ST 22801 #051-04-1995 L1998 **HO** *020 †20
YODER, Gene Lee. 235 CANTRELL AVE, HARRISONBURG INTERNAL 22801 #051-04-1975 L1978
 IM *020 †20
YODER, Paul Roy, Jr. 1921 MEDICAL AVE 22801 #051-01-1967 L1967 **OPH** *020 †35
YODER, Paul Timothy. ■ 22802 #010-01-1955 L1961 **FM** *072 †18
ZAPANTA, Conrado R. 831 CANTRELL AVE, PROFESSIONAL COMPLEX 22801
 #748-10-1965 L1972 **OTO FPS** *020 ‡

HARTFIELD — MIDDLESEX

FAIRBROTHER, Paul Francis. ■ 23071 #917-09-1966 L1978 **GYN** *020 †30
KAUFFMAN, Chester Thos. 816 WILTON CREEK RD 23071 #041-13-1963 L1997
 FM FPG *020 †18 ‡

HAYES — GLOUCESTER

BLALOCK, Julian Harward. 3055 GEORGE WSHNGTN MM HWY 23072 #051-04-1983 L1985
 PD *020 †55
BLANCHARD, Margaret V. 3055 GEORGE WSHNGTN MM HWY 23072 #051-04-1993 L1993
 PD *020 †55
BRODERICK, Elizabeth K. 3055 GEORGE WSHNGTN MM HWY 23072 #051-04-1993 L1994
 MPD *020 †55,20 ‡
BRZESKI, Richard Raymond. 3055 GEORGE WSHNGTN MM HWY 23072 #051-07-1982 L1984
 PD *020 †55
DRAPER, Amanda M. 3055 GEORGE WSHNGTN MM HWY 23072 #021-06-1999 L2008
 PD *020 †55
GRIFFITHS, Jon David. 3055 GEORGE WSHNGTN MM HWY 23072 #041-09-1995 L2003
 PD *020 †55
HOGG, John Roger. 3055 GEORG WSHNGTN MMRL 23072 #051-04-1963 L1963 **PD** *071 †55
JONAK, James Paul. 2246 GEORGE WSHNGTN MM HWY, MEMORIAL HIGHWAY 23072
 #035-15-1976 L1993 **FM** *020 †18
KARANDANA, Kamani Nirmala. 2348 YORK CROSSING DR, GLOUCESTER MEDICAL
 ASSOCIA 23072 #220-01-1993 L2007 **FM** *100
KAUFMAN, Patricia Lynn. 3055 GEORGE WSHNGTN MM HWY 23072 #035-06-1987 L1994
 PD *020 †55
KOERNER, Thomas Herbert. 3055 GEORGE WSHNGTN MM HWY 23072 #035-15-1986 L1990
 PD *020 †55

MAC ARTHUR, Wm John C, Jr. ■ 23072 #062-01-1969 L1994 **OTO** *020
MUENCH, Daniel Michael. 2246 GEORGE WSHNGTN MM HWY, MEMORIAL HWY 23072
 #038-41-1994 L2001 **FM** *020 †18 ‡
PACKER, Gerald Allen. 2348 YORK CROSSING DR 23072 #051-04-1978 L1979 **EM IM** *020 †16
STOCKBERGER, Lynn Paul. 3055 GEORG WSHNGTN MMRL 23072 #051-04-1968 L1968
 PD *071 †55
TANKERSLEY, Kenneth Lee. 2656 GEORGE WSHNGTN MM HWY, UNIT D 23072
 #041-12-2001 L2008 **GS** *071
WASSERMAN, L Leslie, Jr. 2348 YORK CROSSING DR 23072 #036-07-1966 L1972
 OBG *020 †30
WINELAND, Richard Hunter. 2348 YORK CROSSING DR 23072 #051-04-1982 L1983
 FM *020 †18

HAYMARKET — PRINCE WILLIAM

ALBARRACIN, Aurora B. ■ 20169 #748-01-1961 L1973 **PD OS** *020 †55
ANTUS, John Lawrence. 6611 JEFFERSON ST, HAYMARKET MEDICAL CR 20169
 #010-01-1968 L1973 **IM** *020 †20
BARTOLOME-DUFFY, Gloria. ■ 20169 #748-01-1965 L1993 **CHP P** *020 †75
CAMARCA, Mary Anna. ■ 20169 #051-07-1989 L1996 **PD** *020 †55
GARCES-VINLUAN, Andrea M. ■ 20169 #748-01-1965 L1981 **PD** *020
LIPE, J Steele. ■ 20169 #047-05-1965 L1967 **AN** *072 †05
MC EACHERN, Bryan Wallace. ■ 20169 #010-02-1990 L1994 **PD** *020 †55
MEHRA, Sheila. ■ 20169 #422-01-2004 L2007 **IM** *100
PATTERSON, Robert Harry. ■ 20168 #011-01-1969 L1970 **PTH** *071 †50
PELTIER, Jennifer Louise. ■ 20169 #010-02-2000 L2006 **IM** *020 †20
SHUPE, Theresa Belben. 15111 WASHINGTON ST, STE 121 20169 #010-01-1990 L1998
 FM *020 †18
WHITE, Thomas Donald. ■ 20169 #020-02-1959 L1960 **CHP P** *020

HEATHSVILLE — NORTHUMBERLAND

BALLINTINE, Elmer J. ■ 22473 #038-06-1949 L1949 **OPH** *072 †35
DANIEL, John Griffith. 8152 NORTHUMBERLAND HWY, CHESAPEAKE MEDICAL GROUP 22473
 #051-04-1981 L1982 **FM** *020 †18
EICHACKER, Walter C. ■ 22473 #035-08-1944 L1974 **FM** *071 †18
JOHNSTON, Robert Maynard. ■ 22473 #023-07-1968 L1974 **OPH** *020 †35
RENNIE, Laurie Earl. ■ 22473 #051-04-1954 L1954 **N IM** *071 †20,75

HERNDON — FAIRFAX

AHMAD, Ishtiaq. ■ 20171 #160-10-1987 L2000 **N** *020 †75
AHMAD, Mobashar. 1110A ELDEN ST, STE 102 20170 #704-04-1983 L1993 **HEM** *020 †20
AIJAZI, Mahmood G. 13900 PARK CENTER RD 20171 #704-16-1987 L2002 **PTH PCP** *020 †50
ALI, Muhammad Ashraf. ■ 20170 #704-16-1982 L2008 **IMG** *100 †20
AL-MUDHAFAR, Shayma Jafar. ■ 20170 #528-01-1998 L2007 **IM** *100
ANDERSON, Michael Hunter. ■ 20171 #023-12-1983 L1985 **FM** *030 †18
ARICHANDRAN, Narmatha. 2579 JOHN MILTON DR 20171 #021-01-1991 L1999 **PD** *020 †55
BADE, Asima. ■ 20170 #005-14-1997 L2007 **FM** *100
BAGARES, Fredrick B. ■ 20170 #003-75-2007, ▲ L2007 *012
BALINT, Virgil Aurel. 150 ELDEN ST, STE 240 20170 #781-04-1980 L1988 **PM PMM** *020 †60
BANDOPADHAY, Ratna. ■ 20171 #495-32-1987 L1998 **AN** *020
BEG MIRZA, Abdul Rahman. ■ 20172 #306-01-1994 *071
BELLEGARRIGUE, Maria C. 13900 PARK CENTER RD, LAB CORP OF AMERICA 20171
 #341-01-1962 L1988 **PTH PCP** *071 †50
BENNETT, Dean R. 13350 FRANKLIN FARM RD, STE 301 20171 #041-12-1978 L1984
 ORS *020 †40
BRESCAN, Debra Walker. ■ 20170 #038-06-1988 L2004 **P** *020
BROWN, Michael J. 297 HERNDON PKWY STE 101 20170 #011-02-1990 L2000 **PS** *020 †65 ‡
CARLETON, Robin Ann. 106 ELDEN ST, STE 13 20170 #051-04-1982 L1983 **AN IM** *020
CHANG, Victor C. ■ 20171 #023-12-2003 L2005 *100 †18
COOPER, Jason Adam. 555 HERNDON PKWY, HERNDON FAMILY MEDICINE 20170
 #023-01-1995 L1995 **FM** *020 †18
DAMMOJU, Sabita. ■ 20171 #495-53-1996 L2007 **OBG** *100
DANGVU, Anh Phuong. 112 ELDEN ST STE E 20170 #036-07-1987 L1991 **D** *020 †15
DAY, Krista Redd. ■ 20171 #051-04-2008 L2008 *012
DELANEY, W Allen Glover. 1330 SUMMERFIELD DR 20170 #011-03-1974 L1985 **AN** *020 †05
DE LA ROSA, Cindy G. 131 ELDEN ST, STE 312 20170 #748-02-1998 L2005 **PD** *020 †55
DOMBROWSKI, Robert M. 13350 FRANKLIN FARM RD 20171 #038-06-1993 L1993
 ORS *020 †40
EHSAN, Tajammul. 722 GRANT ST, DULLES NEUROLOGY CLINIC 20170 #704-02-1982 L2002
 N *020 †75
EKMAN, Donald Quentin. ■ 20171 #010-01-1954 L1969 **GP** *020
ENGTOW, Della Joyce. 2315 WOODLAND CROSSING DR, STE H 20171 #047-07-1993 L1993
 PD *020 †55
FERRER, Jennifer Peake. 2579 JOHN MILTON DR, STE 310 20171 #041-07-1986 L1990
 PD *020 †55
FRENCH, Elizabeth Gaines. ■ 20171 #024-07-1944 L1947 **AN EM** *071 †55,05
GANESHAN, Anita. 555 HERNDON PKWY, HERNDON FAMILY MEDICINE 20170
 #051-04-1992 L1994 **FM** *020 †18
GARDNER, Richard Edward. 150 ELDEN ST, STE 235 20170 #048-04-1994 L1995 **OTO** *020 †45
GARONE, Michael Alan. 100 ELDEN ST, STE 12 20170 #035-03-1980 L1981 **GE IM** *020 †20 ‡
GASSMAN, Audrey Lynn. 1544 YOUNGS POINT PL 20170 #051-07-1989 L2001
 OBG REN *020 †30
GURIAN, Josef Emanuel. 150 ELDEN ST, STE 235 20170 #024-16-1989 L1995 **OTO** *020 †45
HARRER, David Stanley. 13900 PARK CENTER RD 20171 #016-02-1965 L1970
 CLP PTH *072 †50 ‡
HASAN, Shabih U. 722 GRANT ST, STE F 20170 #704-01-1988 L1997 **N** *020 †75
HAZEL, William Andrew, Jr. 13350 FRANKLIN FARM RD, STE 220 20171 #036-07-1983 L1986
 ORS *020 †40
HEGAB, Ahmed Mohamed I. 100 ELDEN ST, STE 12 20170 #915-02-1991 L1995
 IM GE *020 †20

HEIDELBERG, Stephanie M. 1000 MONROE ST 20170 #021-05-1969 L1977 **P** *020 †75
HERMANSEN, Karen Lee. 150 ELDEN ST STE 235 20170 #051-04-1976 L1980 **OTO** *020 †45
HILL, Alvin Jos. 150 ELDEN ST, STE 200 20170 #011-02-1982 L1985 **AN** *020 †05
HORNER, Cynthia Joan. 555 HERNDON PKWY, STE 100 20170 #061-01-1989 L1991 *071
HOWE, Allen Kinne, Jr. 2579 JOHN MILTON DR STE 20 20171 #051-04-1978 L1979 **FM** *020 †18
HUSAIN, Sara Jafri. 131 ELDEN ST, STE 312 20170 #704-02-1999 L2007 **PD** *100
IMAM, Shamim A. 504 ELDEN ST, STE 3 20170 #704-06-1979 L1991 **FM** *020 †18
INGENITO, Gary Gerard. 13921 PARK CENTER RD, STE 100 20171 #041-02-1983 L2004 **N OS** *020
JAIN, Ranjana. 131 ELDEN ST, STE 312 20170 #051-04-1999 L2002 **PD** *020 †55
JAVED, Fawzia Noreen. ■ 20171 #021-06-2002 L2005 **IM** *020 †20
JOSEPH, Cyril. 106 ELDEN ST, STE 10 #495-52-1992 L1999 **IM** *020 †20
JOSEPH, Jacob. 106 ELDEN ST, STE 10 #495-52-1974 L1982 **FM FPG** *020 †16,18
KHANNA, Rajeev. 13505 DULLES TECHNOLOGY DR, STE 1A 20171 #495-43-1985 L1997 **IM** *020 †20
KIM, Byungki. 100 ELDEN ST, STE 12 20170 #035-20-1993 L2000 **GE** *020 †20
KING, Jennifer B. ■ 20171 #012-01-1991 L1995 **EM** *020 †16
KUMAR, Priya. ■ 20170 #035-19-2003 **DR** *012
LAPIS, Peter. 13900 PARK CENTER RD 20171 #473-01-1980 L2006 **DMP** *020 †50
LATIF, Aamir Anwar. 13044A LAUREL TREE LN 20171 #012-01-2000 L2003 **EM** *020 †16
LEAVENS, Deborah Irene. 555 HERNDON PKWY, HERNDON FAMILY MEDICINE 20170 #051-04-1979 L1980 **FM FPG** *020 †18
LINDE, Richard Emil. 150 ELDEN ST STE 235 20170 #051-04-1964 L1964 **OTO** *020 †45
MAHALLATI, Salaheddin. ■ 20170 #517-05-1959 L1967 **PD** *071 †55
MANNING, Clyde Vernon, Jr. 3329 STONE HEATHER CT 20171 #027-01-1994 L1994 **IM** *020 †20
MARCANTONIO, Domenica. ■ 20170 #051-07-2006 L2006 **EM** *012
MARION, Edward David. 150 ELDEN ST, STE 235 20170 #010-01-1972 L1976 **OTO** *020 †45
MARTINI, Carlos Jose M. 1709 ASCOT WAY 20190 #132-01-1960 **GPM** *030
MAYA, Nair. 2315 WOODLAND CROSSING DR, STE 4 20171 #495-31-1994 L1999 **PD** *020 †55
MC VEARRY, Ingrid Marie. 104 ELDEN ST, STE 16 20170 #010-02-2001 L2002 **OBG** *020 †30
MIRKIN, Kenneth Robt. 100 ELDEN ST, STE 12 20170 #025-07-1976 L1983 **GE IM** *020 †20
NAIR, Vivek Vasudevan. ■ 20170 #422-01-2002 L2006 **IM** *020
NEBERAI, Salah Mohamed. 110 ELDEN ST 20170 #915-04-1985 L1997 **PD** *020 †55
OPPENHEIM, Josh Paul. 150 ELDEN ST, STE 235 20170 #036-05-1982 L1987 **OTO** *020 †45
PANGAN, Zanita S. ■ 20170 #748-02-1955 L1965 **OBG** *020 †30
PATEL, Tushar Chandrakant. 13350 FRANKLIN FARM RD, STE 210 20171 #041-01-1989 L2000 **ORS OSS** *020 †40
PAYLING-WRIGHT, Charles R. 106 ELDEN ST, STE 10 20170 #917-30-1965 L1983 **FM** *020 †20
PERLMUTTER, Susan Jo. 106 ELDEN ST, STE 17 20170 #035-20-1988 L1997 **CHP** *020 †75
PETERSON, Joseph Alan. ■ 20170 #025-01-1984 L1993 **EM** *020 †16
PHOLERIC, John F, Jr. 1120 CLINCH RD 20170 #041-02-1974 L1975 **OTO A** *071 †45
PLESCIA, Marc Gian. 555 HERNDON PKWY, HERNDON FAMILY MEDICINE 20170 #033-06-1983 L1984 **FM** *020 †18
QUAYE, Ernest Nii-Amu. 110 ELDEN ST STE D 20170 #412-01-1976 L1988 **PD** *020 †55
RAGLAND, Janice Eileen. 555 HERNDON PKWY, HERNDON FAMILY MEDICINE 20170 #051-04-1992 L1994 **FM** *020 †18
RASHEED, Afzal Unissa. ■ 20170 #496-27-1996 L2006 **FM** *020 †18 ‡
RASHEED, Zafar Abdur. ■ 20170 #306-01-1997 L2006 **CHP** *020
ROBINSON, Brett Malcolm. 13350 FRANKLIN FARM RD, STE 100 20171 #021-01-1995 L1998 **AN** *020
ROBINSON, David Scott. ■ 20171 #023-12-2006 L2007 **FP** *012
ROHATGI, Ashish. ■ 20170 #495-45-1994 **GS** *100
SAFI, Farhad. ■ 20170 #010-01-2007 *012
SCHULMAN, Carol Brimberg. 131 ELDEN ST, STE 312 20170 #010-02-1970 L1974 **PD** *071 †55
SCHUSTER, Donna L F. 100 ELDEN ST STE 10 20170 #011-02-1972 L1980 **AI PD** *020 †55,03
SCUDERA, Peter Leonard. 100 ELDEN ST, STE 12 20170 #035-20-1984 L1991 **GE IM** *020 †20
SELF, Kristy K. ■ 20171 #048-14-2001 **EM** *100 †16
SHAFFER, Brian Carl. ■ 20170 #051-07-2005 L2008 **IM** *012
SHAH, Mita Deven. 12932 CEDAR GLEN LN, OAKHILL ANESTHESIA PC. 20171 #495-76-1990 L2002 **AN** *020 †05
SHARMA, Divya. ■ 20171 #034-01-2003 L2003 **IM** *100 †20
SHULL, Owen Clay. 1039 STERLING RD, STE 103 20170 #051-04-1958 L1958 **GP** *071
SILVERSTEIN, Michael A. 555 HERNDON PKWY, HERNDON FAMILY MEDICINE 20170 #051-04-1982 L1985 **FM** *040 †18
SINGH, Devna. ■ 20171 #495-14-1992 L2006 **FM** *100 †18
SMALL, Elizabeth Joy. ■ 20171 #047-05-1997 L2005 **OBG** *020 †30
SUPANEKAR, Jyoti Harsh. ■ 20170 #495-82-1993 L2001 **P** *020
SURI, Rama Krishnaveni. ■ 20171 #495-50-1999 L2005 **FM** *100
TALIB, Zohray Moolani. ■ 20171 #060-01-2002 L2005 **IM** *100 †20
TAN, Jeremias Chua. 100 ELDEN ST, STE 12 20170 #010-01-1999 L2000 **GE** *020 †20
TEMELES, Lawrence. ■ 20170 #041-12-1946 L1947 **P PYA** *071 †75
TEMELES, Margaret Stewart. ■ 20170 #024-07-1948 L1954 **P OS** *071
TETTEYFIO, Geoffrey Anang. 110 ELDEN ST STE D 20170 #412-01-1975 L1985 **PD NPM** *020 †55
TRAN, Hien Tien. 131 ELDEN ST, STE 150 20170 #941-02-1976 L1983 **CHP** *020 †75
TRAN, Ngoc Thi Bich. 100 ELDEN ST, STE 10 20170 #023-01-1995 L2000 **AI** *020 †20,03
TRAN, Quincy Khoi. ■ 20171 #051-04-2008 *012
TSAI, David M C. ■ 20170 #385-01-1962 L1972 **IM CD** *071 †20
VU GIA, An. ■ 20171 #941-01-1960 L1983 **PD GP** *071
WEAVER, Kevin Michael. 555 HERNDON PKWY, HERNDON FAMILY MEDICINE 20170 #023-01-1983 L1985 **FM FSM** *020 †18
WIJETILLEKE, Rohini. 100 ELDEN ST STE 14 20170 #220-02-1967 L1983 **FM PD** *020 †55
WISOR, Douglas William. 150 ELDEN ST, STE 240 20170 #035-06-1994 L1995 **PM PMM** *020 †60
WITTMANN, Stephan John. 487 CARLISLE DR STE A 20170 #023-01-1966 L1969 **AN** *071 †05
WOODS, John Dennis. 12458 OLIVER CROMWELL DR 20171 #654-01-1991 L1999 **FM** *020 †18

HIGHLAND SPRINGS — HENRICO

ALDHIZER, Theodore Gerard. 1001 W NINE MILE RD 23075 #051-04-1968 L1968 **FM FPG** *020 †18
COSTER, Caroline Victoria. ■ 23075 #055-01-2004 L2004 **P** *012
HARWOOD, Chas Pinchbeck. ■ 23075 #051-04-1953 L1953 **GP** *071

KHAN, Shujauddin. 5 W NINE MILE RD, HIGHLAND SPRINGS PRIMARY C 23075 #495-77-1988 L1999 **IM** *020 †20
OWEN, Fletcher Bailey, Jr. ■ 23075 #051-04-1959 L1959 **OS** *071

HILLSVILLE — CARROLL

DE BOE, James Henry. 523 N MAIN ST 24343 #051-04-1971 L1973 **FM OS** *020 †18
ELMASRY, Medhat Nagi. 430 W STUART DR, P O BOX 1805 24343 #915-02-1977 L1996 **IM** *020 †20
LYNCH, James Michael. 347 SPENCERS MILL RD 24343 #016-43-1963 L1974 **GP AM** *020
MARTIN, Moir Glenwood. ■ 24343 #051-04-1953 L1953 **FM** *071
MAYBERRY, Barry Marshall. RR 1 BOX 415, CENTER 24343 #036-05-1975 L1980 **FM** *020 †18
MC PHERSON, David P. PO BOX 38 24343 #051-04-1976 L1977 **FM** *020 †18
RAINEY, James Mc Iver. ■ 24343 #045-01-1976 L1977 **OBG** *020 †30
SILBER, Gershon. PO BOX 1328, 160 TRAINING CENTER RD 24343 #016-11-1970 L1982 **P GPM** *020
WILSON, Ohlen Rudolph. HWY 58, FAMILY MEDICAL CARE INC 24343 #051-04-1954 L1954 **FM OS** *072 †18
WYNNE-ROBERTS, Caroline R. PO BOX 1748 24343 #917-28-1961 L1992 **RHU IM** *071

HIWASSEE — PULASKI

WESTON, Don L. ■ 24347 #051-01-1962 L1962 **P** *071

HONAKER — RUSSELL

BISHOP, Raymond Oscar. PO BOX 741 24260 #051-04-2001 L2001 **FM** *020
CHAUDHRY, Faisal Tufail W. PO BOX 1020 24260 #704-01-1987 L1994 **IM** *020 †20
VALLEY, Mary Hamilton. 2261 CORN VALLEY RD, VALLEY INTERNAL MEDICINE 24260 #051-07-1995 L1995 **IM** *020

HOPEWELL — HOPEWELL CITY

ABBASI, Gohar Maqsood. 1000 RIVER RD, RIVESIDE REGIONAL JAIL 23860 #704-20-1990 L1999 **IM** *020 †20
AGARWAL, Kamala. 207 N 4TH AVE 23860 #495-34-1966 L1977 **P** *020 †75
ANDREW, Theodore C. 411 W RANDOLPH RD 23860 #028-44-1941 L1948 **GP GYN** *071
BARNARD-DUPREE, Dafferlin. 1000 RIVER RD, LIBERTY FORENSIC UNIT-RRJ 23860 #010-02-1984 L1997 **P** *020 †75
BASKER, Muralidharan Raje. 411 W RANDOLPH RD, GEISINGER HEALTH SYSTEM 23860 #495-04-1991 L2007 **GS CRS** *020 †20
BUSH, James Albert. 815 W POYTHRESS ST, HOPEWELL MEDICAL CENTER 23860 #051-04-1997 L1997 **MPD** *020 †20,55
CANGCUESTA, David C. 406 N 6TH AVE 23860 #748-11-1974 L1984 **OTO HNS** *020 †45
DAVE, Kamlesh Nandlal. 5303 PLAZA DR, STE 102 23860 #495-48-1979 L1988 **CD IM** *020 †20
DURRANI, Waheed. 1012 WINSTON CHURCHILL DR 23860 #704-08-1965 L1977 **GP PD** *020
ELLENBERG, Russell C. 301 W BROADWAY, HOSPEWELL DIALYSIS CENTER 23860 #030-06-1980 L1987 **NEP IM** *020 †20
FAROOQ, Mohammad. 602 N SIXTH AVE 23860 #704-19-1986 L1997 **IM PUD** *020 †20
FUREY, Sheila Mary. 207 N 4TH AVE 23860 #030-06-1992 L2000 **P** *020 †75
GADANI, Manu Ramji. 5303 PLAZA DR, STE 102 23860 #496-38-1978 L1995 **IM** *020 †20
GANDHI, Yogesh K. 411 W RANDOLPH RD STE 101 23860 #495-23-1989 L1994 **HO IM** *020 †20 ‡
GATES, Beverly Diane. 411 W RANDOLPH RD 23860 #021-05-1980 L1981 **PTH** *020 †50
GERMANO, Di Sciascio. 602 N 6TH AVE 23860 #561-11-1973 L1978 **CD IM** *020 †20
HAIDER, Agha S. 602 N 6TH AVE 23860 #704-16-1988 L1998 **CCM** *020 †20
HANNA, Constance Rickard. 411 W RANDOLPH RD 23860 #041-09-1982 L1983 **IM OM** *020 †20,70
JADHAV, Gopinath Rao. 208 N 4TH AVE 23860 #495-16-1973 L1983 **GE IM** *020 †20
JENSEN, Edward Walter. 712 W BROADWAY AVE 23860 #038-06-1958 L1964 **IM** *020
JOHNSON, Norris J. 401 HOPEWELL ST 405 23860 #010-03-1977 L1978 **FM OS** *071 †18
KHAN, Mubashir Ahmed. 247 E CAWSON ST 23860 #704-08-1975 L2001 **N** *020 †75
LAYMAN, David Arthur. 308 N 6TH AVE 23860 #051-04-1965 L1965 **FM** *020 †18
LEE, Ming-Shoei. 306 W BROADWAY 23860 #244-04-1967 L1977 **PD A** *020 †55
LEE, Russell Dennis. 411 W RANDOLPH RD, JOHN RANDOLPH GENERAL SURG 23860 #033-05-1992 L2006 **GS** *020 †18
LEE, Shin. 411 W RANDOLPH RD, JOHN RANDOLPH HOSPITAL 23860 #038-41-1996 L2003 **AN** *020 †05 ‡
LICEN, Vicente Soco. 308 N 4TH AVE, CHILD & ADOLESCENT CLC 23860 #748-11-1983 L2000 **PD** *020 †55
LIU, Ming. 411 W RANDOLPH RD, JOHN RANDOLPH MEDICAL CENT 23860 #243-62-1982 L2002 **AN** *020 †05
MAGNIN, Albert. 815 W POYTHRESS ST 23860 #308-03-1981 L1985 **IM** *040
MAKHOUL, Raymond Geo. 411 W RANDOLPH RD 23860 #016-02-1982 L1991 **VS GS** *020 †85
MILBY, Willard P, III. 411 W RANDOLPH RD 23860 #051-04-1984 L1985 **PTH NM** *062 †50
MILLER, Ronald Edward. 815 W POYTHRESS ST 23860 #051-04-1957 L1957 **FM** *020 †18
MOHIUDDIN, Abdul Qadir. 1012 WINSTON CHURCHILL DR 23860 #704-16-1988 L1999 **FM** *020 †18 ‡
MUGHAL, Zahid Ikhlaq. 602 N 6TH AVE 23860 #704-21-1990 L2004 **PUD SME** *020 †20
MUJEEBUDDIN, Mohammad. 1012 WINSTON CHURCHILL DR 23860 #495-65-1978 L1988 **IM** *020 †20
NEIFELD, David Michael. 308 N SIXTH AVE 23860 #035-15-1979 L1982 **FM** *020 †18
NIO, Hok Boen. 301 N THIRD AVE 23860 #506-01-1962 L1975 **P** *020 †75
OBUSAN, Aida Ong Ante. 308 N 4TH AVE 23860 #748-10-1974 L1997 **PD** *020 †55
PATEL, Kiran Bhai B. 503 N 3RD AVE 23860 #495-23-1978 L1986 **AN PME** *020 †05
PATEL, Nagindas L. 1060 RIVER RD, FEDERAL CORRECTIONAL CMPLE 23860 #495-23-1955 L1972 **P** *071 †75
PAVAN, Jay. 106 N MAIN ST 23860 #495-37-1989 L1999 **PM** *020 †60
PERERA, Francis. 411 W RANDOLPH RD, JOHN RANDOLPH MEDICAL CENT 23860 #220-01-1966 L1974 **AN** *020 †05
SARAYBA, Alberto A. 247 E CAWSON ST 23860 #748-01-1968 L1973 **GS** *075 †85

■ = Address Information Privacy Protected

SHEIKH, Tariq M. 505 N 6TH AVE, INFANT JESUS CHILDRENS CLI 23860 #704-02-1974 L2003 PD CG *020 †55
SHIM, Jaimoon. 406 N 6TH AVE 23860 #583-01-1972 L1980 OTO A *020 †45
SHIM, Young Soon. 602 N 6TH AVE 23860 #583-08-1972 L1979 IM IMG *071 †20
SIDDIQUI, Salman. 207 N 4TH AVE 23860 #704-02-1989 L2000 P CHP *020 †75
SIRIWATHARANGOON, C. 308 N 4TH AVE 23860 #891-04-1974 L1980 PD *020 †55
SKAGGS, Jerome D. 308 N 6TH AVE 23860 #028-02-1960 L1963 FM *071 †18
SUBRAMANIAM-MOOTHATHU, P. 411 W RANDOLPH RD 23860 #495-31-1973 L1987 N *071 †75 ‡
SUMMERVILLE, John William. 411 W RANDOLPH RD 23860 #056-05-1984 L1987 PTH NM *071 †50
SUPETRAN, Virgilio Conlu. 411 W RANDOLPH RD 23860 #748-01-1960 L1972 OBG *071 †30
SWARTZ, Steven Eugene. 411 W RANDOLPH RD 23860 #048-04-1983 L1991 GS *020 †85
TAWFICK, Mohammed A. 411 W RANDOLPH RD 23860 #915-02-1950 L1975 ORS HS *071
THOMAS, Carolyn Edmunds. 411 W RANDOLPH RD 23860 #051-04-1972 L1976 PTH *071 †50
TUASON, Evelyn T. 5303 PLAZA DR, STE 106 23860 #748-11-1983 L1994 PD *020 †55
TUNSTALL, June Rebecca. 401 HOPEWELL ST 405 23860 #047-07-1974 L1978 FM *020 †18
WRAY, Michael Doran. 411 W RANDOLPH RD 23860 #003-01-1975 L1981 PTH *050
YERBY, Phillip C, III. 23860 #051-04-1952 L1952 GP *071
YU, Lanping. 308 N 4TH AVE 23860 #055-01-2000 L2000 PD *020 †55

HOT SPRINGS — BATH

ALEXANDER, Clyde W, Jr. 24445 #027-01-1964 L1999 AN *071 †05
DAMEWOOD, Geo Pearis, IV. RT 220 24445 #051-04-1992 L1993 FM *020 †18
FREED, Daniel M. PO BOX 1070, 9232 SAM SNEAD HWY 24445 #012-01-1999 L1999 FM *020 †18
KANITHANON, Pongpijit. 24445 #891-02-1970 L1976 GS *020
MYERS, Donald S. PO BOX 1307 24445 #051-04-1950 L1950 OS GP *071
REDINGTON, James Franklin. PO BOX 797 24445 #051-07-1985 L1986 FM FPG *020 †18

HUDDLESTON — BEDFORD

CROFT, Patti Elaine. 24104 #024-16-1986 L2005 P *020 †75
KERN, Kathryn Eustance. 24104 #035-45-1956 L1987 PHP PD *071
KERN, William Albert. 24104 #035-45-1956 L1987 IM *071 †20
SPENCER, Edward Monroe. 2299 CAPEWOOD DR 24104 #016-02-1960 L1986 PD *040 †55

HUNTLY — RAPPAHANNOCK

KREBSER, Werner. RR 2 BOX 101 22640 #010-01-1958 L1959 GP *071

HURT — PITTSYLVANIA

BOWERS, Darin Kent. 527 POCKET RD 24563 #055-02-1987 L1993 OPH IM *020 †20,35
ELLIOTT, Robert Irvin. 527 POCKET RD, PHYSICIANS 24563 #051-01-1984 L1985 FM *020 †18
GANSER, Gail Laurie. 527 POCKET RD 24563 #047-05-1992 L1998 PO OPH *020 †35
HEY, Daniel Spurgeon. 527 POCKET RD 24563 #027-01-1997 L1997 FM *020 †18

INDEPENDENCE — GRAYSON

GRUBB, Stephen Allen. 304 DAVIS ST, SPINE CENTER 24348 #016-06-1974 L2000 ORS *020 †40
LOVELACE, Nance Ann. 217 S INDEPENDENCE AVE 24348 #041-77-1993, ▲ L2001 FM *020 †18
WRIGHT, Scott Alan. 24348 #016-45-1982 L1985 EM IM *020 †20,16

IRONTO — MONTGOMERY

TOMELTY, Joseph Patrick. 3401 HALF ACRE OF ROCKS RD 24087 #051-04-1973 L1974 R *100 †80

IRVINGTON — LANCASTER

GRAVATT, Arthur B. 22480 #051-04-1941 L1941 FM *071
HARNSBERGER, James Power. 22480 #051-04-1947 L1947 OM GP *071
KEY, Marcus M. 22480 #035-01-1952 L1975 OM D *071 †15,70
RITCHIE, George G, Jr. 22480 #051-04-1950 L1950 P *071
WILLIAMS, Mortimer Lee. 22480 #051-01-1947 L1947 OTO PUD *071 †45

IVY — ALBEMARLE

CONLEY, Robert Bryan. 22945 #036-01-1986 *075
SINKS, Lucius Frederick. 22945 #041-02-1957 L1977 ON PD *071 †55

JAMESVILLE — NORTHAMPTON

BRAUNSTEIN, Paul Wm. 23398 #024-01-1947 L1983 GS *071 †85

JARRATT — GREENSVILLE

MUGHAL, Amjad Iqbal. 901 CORRECTION WAY, GREENSVILLE CORRECTIONAL C 23870 #704-21-1986 L2003 IM *020 †20

JEFFERSONTON — CULPEPER

ATHAR, Khalid. 22724 #704-02-1994 L2008 AN *020

JOHNSTON, Russell G. 17390 BERKSHIRE DR 22724 #041-02-1971 L1977 AN *020 †05

JETERSVILLE — AMELIA

COOK, Sarah. 23083 #023-01-1945 L1951 PD *071

JONESVILLE — LEE

HARDIN, David Burton. RR 2 BOX 2258 24263 #016-11-1985 L2008 PM APM *020
MOPARTHY, Suhasini. 24263 #495-21-1995 L2005 PD *020
RICARDO, Luzviminda V. 24263 #748-08-1968 L1974 AN *020
SADER, Alicea Margaret. 24263 #041-15-2001 L2004 IM *100
SIDDIQUI, Mohammad S. RR 4, BOX 4369 24263 #704-16-1986 L2002 GS *020 †85
WATTS, Thomas Duval. 24263 #051-04-1935 L1935 GS OS *071 †85

KEEZLETOWN — ROCKINGHAM

BRUBAKER, Alta Lois. 22832 #539-06-1980 L1990 CHP P *020 †75

KENBRIDGE — LUNENBURG

BAUGH, Emerson Danl, Jr. 306 E 6TH AVE 23944 #051-01-1954 L1954 FM *071 †18
POWERS, David Carl. 306 E 6TH AVE 23944 #051-04-1989 L1990 FM *020 †18
POWERS, Graham Henderson. 306 E 6TH AVE 23944 #051-04-1986 L1988 FM EM *020 †18
REYNOLDS, Michael Keith. 306 E 6TH AVE 23944 #051-01-2001 L2004 FM *020

KENTS STORE — FLUVANNA

HUGHES, William Foster. 23084 #051-04-1978 L2007 OBS *020 †30

KESWICK — ALBEMARLE

ALLEN, Emile Anthony. 22947 #016-06-1986 L1986 U *071 †95
BASKERVILLE, Ashanti Neal. 22947 #051-01-2004 L2007 FM *020 †18
BECHAMPS, Michon. 22947 #051-07-2004 L2005 IM *012
BILCHICK, Kenneth Charles. 22947 #023-07-1999 L2007 ICE *100 †20
BURGESS, Cathleen E Cobb. 22947 #004-01-1975 L1975 AN *020 †05
CRENSHAW, Randy Wayne. 22947 #047-06-1969 L2000 EM *020 †16
FISHMAN, Robert. 22947 #869-05-1951 L1954 DR *071
HUNTER, Anne E Fulcher. 22947 #023-07-1941 L1959 PYA *020
LANE, Kristin Teunis. 22947 #051-01-2007 *012
MAHAN, Jack Delano. 22947 #051-01-1961 L1961 R *071 †80
MC CULLOUGH, Christopher. 3227 AVEBURY LN, WVU SCHOOL OF MEDICINE 22947 #051-01-1978 L1993 GS TTS *020 †85
MC MAHON, Edward P. 22947 #041-09-1971 L1996 IM *071 †20
MILLER, Harry Chas. 22947 #008-01-1954 L1974 U OS *071 †95
NICHOLAS, Claire Susan. 22947 #012-05-2008 *012
PAGET-BROWN, Alix O. 22947 #041-02-1999 L1999 NPM *012 †55
PORTERFIELD, Hubert Wm. 22947 #041-02-1955 L1955 PS *071 †65
RANNINGS, Dolores Ann. 22947 #048-02-1959 L1988 PD *071 †55
ROWE, William Jos. 22947 #038-41-1954 L2001 IM *071 †20
ROZAN, Gerald Henry. 22947 #041-13-1956 L1997 P OS *071 †75
SANDERS, Timothy Gene. 22947 #012-01-1984 L2003 DR *020 †80 ‡
STEMLAND, Christopher J. 22947 #010-02-2002 L2007 PAN *100 †05
WELLS, Lynda Torfreda. 22947 #917-28-1983 L2005 AN *020 †05
WILLIAMS, Timothy Richard. 22947 #051-01-1999 L1999 IM *020 †20

KEYSVILLE — CHARLOTTE

MOORE, Teresa Anne Fears. 312 KINGS HWY 23947 #036-05-1994 L1994 FM *020 †18

KILMARNOCK — NORTHUMBERLAND

ANTONIO, David Richard. 95 HARRIS RD # 5 22482 #566-01-1973 L1982 ORS *020 †40 ‡
BAYLOR, Richard Norton. 115 DMV DR 22482 #051-04-1946 L1946 IM RHU *071 †20
BESSLER, Joseph Chas. 107 DMV DR, BAY INTERNISTS INC 22482 #051-01-1988 L1994 IM *020 †20
BRYANT, James Edwin. HARRIS DR 22482 #036-05-1977 L1988 IM *020 †20
COPLEY, Genrose Desimone. 22482 #002-02-1953 L1987 GPM PHP *071 †70
DESCHAMPS, John. 107 DMV DR, BAY INTERNISTS INC 22482 #047-07-1981 L1992 IM *020
GLESSNER, Steven F. 107 DMV DR, BAY INTERNISTS INC 22482 #051-01-1977 L1986 IM *020 †20
GOODE, Harvey W, Jr. 40 CLIFTON AVE 22482 #051-04-1952 L1953 FM *020
HAMILTON, James Franklin. HARRIS DR 22482 #051-04-1979 L1980 OBG *020 †30
HARRIS, David Lea. HARRIS DR 22482 #016-06-1968 L1973 U *020 †95
HOOD, Thomas Robin. RR 1 BOX 247 22482 #019-02-1939 PHP *075 †70
HUFFMAN, Richard Myall. 22482 #010-01-1955 L1962 IM *071 †20
MC GRATH, Kevin John. 107 DMV DR, BAY INTERNISTS INC 22482 #035-06-1992 L1995 IM *020 †20
MONGE-MEBERG, Patricia K. 107 DMV DR, BAY INTERNISTS INC 22482 #051-04-2001 L2001 IM *020 †20
OLTERMANN, Steven Jarrell. PO BOX 1955 22482 #048-12-1981 L1986 GS *020 †85
POOLE, Robert Wm. 95 HARRIS RD, RAPPAHANNOCK ORTHOPAEDICS 22482 #010-01-1974 L1976 ORS *020 †40
PRICE, Charles Danl, III. 107 DMV DR, BAY INTERNISTS INC 22482 #051-01-1970 L1970 CD IM *020
SHIVERS, Gregg Allen. PO BOX 1449, 101 HARRIS DR 22482 #033-06-1990 L1993 IM *020 †20
STALLINGS, William R. 22482 #051-04-2003 L2006 FM *020 †18

■ = Address Information Privacy Protected

SUTHERLAND, Paul Alan. PO BOX 1449 22482 #051-04-1983 L1988 **EM FM** *030 †18
TINGLE, Norman Rock, Jr. HARRIS DR 22482 #051-07-1983 L1986 **FM** *020 †18
VOGEL, Matthew Frederick. 95 HARRIS RD BLDG 2 22482 #028-34-1988 L1992 **GYN** *020 †30
WEILER, Harold Hauser. 101 TECHNOLOGY PARK DR 22482 #051-04-1969 L1969
   OPH AM *020 †35

KING GEORGE – KING GEORGE

ANSARI, Nather Baqir. 11463 RIDGE RD, LLC 22485 #528-04-1984 L1998 **IM IMG** *020 †20
CANIZARES, Roberto Ramos. 11399 RIDGE RD 22485 #748-08-1966 L1974 **GS GP** *020
DEDWYLDER, Rosier Davis. 16463 DAHLGREN RD 22485 #036-07-1982 L1983 **FM** *020 †18
FADUL, Abdul Hamid. 11463 RIDGE RD, LLC 22485 #528-01-1961 L1972 **CD IM** *020 †20
HARRINGTON, Christopher C. 4483 JAMES MADISON PKWY 22485 #051-01-1986 L1989
   FM *020 †18
MCCRAY, Ayanna Johnson. 7967 KINGS HWY 7969, KING GEORGE PEDIATRICS 22485
   #051-07-2001 L2004 **PD** *020 †55

KING WILLIAM – KING WILLIAM

ENGLISH, Lucas Bolton. ■ 23086 #035-47-1999 L2006 **EM** *020

KINGSTOWNE – FAIRFAX

STEWART, Erin Elizabeth. 6901 S VAN DORN ST 22315 #010-01-2002 **IM** *100
SUBRAMANIAM, Deepa. ■ 22315 #495-59-1993 L2004 **HO** *100 †20

KINSALE – WESTMORELAND

DECKER, Henry Chesley. 1601 KELLY RD 22488 #051-04-1947 L1947 **IM OM** *071

LAKE RIDGE – PRINCE WILLIAM

ADESHINA, Yewande Olaseni. 12449 HEDGES RUN DR 22192 #690-01-1987 L2002
   FM *020 †18
MANN, Rajvinder Kaur. 12449 HEDGES RUN DR, URGENT MED/ CARE OF LAKE R 22192
   #495-03-1982 L1989 **IM** *020

LANCASTER – LANCASTER

NAULTY, Stephen John. ■ 22503 #041-02-1972 L2006 **AN** *020 †05
NICKERSON, Michael David, Jr. ■ 22503 #051-04-2008 *012

LANGLEY – HAMPTON CITY

THOMPSON, Troy William. LANGLEY AFB 23665 #016-45-1996 L1997 **IM** *020 †20

LANGLEY AIR FORCE BASE – HAMPTON CITY

ACEVEDO, Steven John. 45 PINE ST, 1ST MEDICAL GROUP/SGHC 23665 #048-02-2003 L2005
   PD *020
ADINARO, Joseph Thomas, IV. 77 NEALY AVE, 1ST MEDICAL GROUPGSGHC 23665
   #051-07-2000 L2002 **CD** *020 †20
BALDWIN, Sharolyn H. 45 PINE ST, 1ST MEDICAL GROUP/SGQ 23665 #007-02-1999 L2000
   IM *020 †20
BAUGHER, Julie Glenn. 45 PINE ST, LANGLEY AFB 23665 #038-45-2000 L2002 **IM** *020 †20
BAYER, Steven Lindsey. 45 PINE ST, 1MDG 23665 #023-12-1994 L1996 **OBG** *020 †30
BOETIG, Bradley John. 77 NEALY AVE, 1ST MEDICAL GROUPGSGHC 23665
   #023-12-2001 L2008 **PD** *020 †55
BOSTOCK, Deborah Jean. 45 PINE ST, 1ST MEDICAL GROUP/SGQ 23665 #036-05-1985 L2007
   FM FPG *030 †18
BREWER, Nathan Hall. 45 PINE ST, 1ST MEDICAL GROUP/SGQ 23665 #024-05-2003 L2006
   FM *020 †18
BRIDGES, Matthew Allen. 45 PINE ST, 1ST MEDICAL GROUP/SGHC; 23665 #051-01-1999 L1999
   OTO FPS *020 †45 ‡
BURKETT, Edwin Keith. 45 PINE ST, 0001 MEDICAL OPERATONS SQ 23665
   #023-12-1991 L2008 **FM** *030 †18
CONNER, Gary John. 45 PINE ST, 1ST MEDICAL GROUP/SGQ 23665 #035-47-1977 L1978
   OBG OS *040 †30
DAHLE, James Melvin. 45 PINE ST 23665 #049-01-2003 L2007 **EM** *020 †16
DICPINIGAITIS, Paul A. 77 NEALY AVE, 1ST MEDICAL GROUP/SGHC 23665 #035-19-1995 L2005
   ORS *020 †40 ‡
FALESKI, Edward J. 45 PINE ST, 1ST MEDICAL GROUP/SGQ 23665 #033-05-1977 L1979
   DR *020 †80
FENTON, Ann Sresthadatta. 45 PINE ST, 1ST MEDICAL GROUP/SGQ 23665
   #021-01-1999 L2001 **U** *020 †95
FISCHER, Robert J. 45 PINE ST, 1ST MEDICAL GROUP/SGQ 23665 #023-12-1984 L1986
   OBG *020 †30
GADY, Joshua Sol. 45 PINE ST, 1ST MEDICAL GROUP/SGQ 23665 #043-01-1998 L2000
   GS *020 †85
GRAVES, Sandra L. 77 NEALY AVE, 1ST MEDICAL GROUP/SGHC 23665 #047-20-1996 L1998
   GS *020
GRUTTER, Paul William. 77 NEALY AVE, 1ST MEDICAL GROUP/SGHC 23665
   #028-03-1999 L2003 **ORS** *020 †40
HARVEY, Richard Robert. 45 PINE ST, 1ST MEDICAL GROUP/SGQ 23665 #050-02-1995 L2005
   OPH *020 †35
HOUGLAN, David Carl. 45 PINE ST, 1ST MEDICAL GROUP CD 23665 #026-04-1980 L1985
   FM *030 †18
HUNTZINGER, Dustin George. 45 PINE ST, 1ST MEDICAL GRP/SGQ 23665 #056-06-1998 L1999
   FM *020 †18

IDDINS, Carol Jane. 77 NEALY AVE, 1 MEDICAL GROUP/SGHC 23665 #047-06-1993 L2006
   OBG *020
JOHNSON, Gregory Wm. 162 DODD BLVD 23665 #016-01-1990 L1992 **FM A** *030 †18
JONES, Loren Matthew. 77 NEALY AVE, 1ST MEDICAL GROUP/SGHC 23665
   #010-02-1999 L2000 **GS** *020
JOYCE, Kathleen Mary. 49 SPRUCE ST 23665 #051-01-2000 L2001 **D** *020
KNEE, Daniel Scott. 45 PINE ST, 1ST MEDICAL GROUP/SGHC 23665 #020-02-1998 L1999
   NPM *020 †55
KNIGHT, Kenneth Karl. 45 PINE ST, 1 MDG/SGHC 23665 #048-02-1990 L1991 **FM AM** *020 †70
KOERTNER, Adam Clay. 77 NEALY AVE, 1ST MEDICAL GROUP/SGHC 23665
   #034-01-2004 L2007 **EM** *020
LAWSON, Bradley Joe. 77 NEALY AVE, 1ST MEDICAL GROUP/SGOSO 23665
   #048-13-1994 L1996 **ORS** *020
LEGAN, Joseph James, Jr. 45 PINE ST, 1ST MEDICAL GROUP/SGQ 23665 #023-12-1990 L1992
   ORS *030 †40
LEIS, Aaron Daniel. 192 SWEENEY BLVD, INDEPENDENT CONTRACTOR 23665
   #017-20-2002 L2002 **AN** *020 †05
LYBECK, Dustin Oliver. 45 PINE ST, 1ST MEDICAL GROUP/SGHC 23665
   #018-03-2005 L2005 *020
MARBAS, Laurie L. 45 PINE ST, 1ST MEDICAL GROUP/SGQ 23665 #048-15-2003 L2004
   FM *020 †18
MOORE, Charlotte A. 77 NEALY AVE, BETHEL CLINIC 23665 #018-75-1999, ▲ L1999
   FM *020 †18
MORVANT, Jason Charles. 45 PINE ST, GENERAL SURGERY (SGOSG) 23665
   #021-05-2001 L2006 **GS** *100 †85
MYNES, Michael Scott. 77 NEALY AVE, 1ST MEDICAL GROUP/SGHC 23665 #055-01-1999 L2007
   AN *020
NASSIR, Mark Andrew. 77 NEALY AVE, 1ST MEDICAL GROUPGSGHC 23665
   #023-12-1997 L1999 **GPM** *020 †18,70
NAUMOVSKI, Nicolche J. 77 NEALY AVE, 1ST MEDICAL GROUP/SGHC 23665
   #957-04-1981 L1992 **P** *020
NIEMI, Matthew Gregory. 45 PINE ST 23665 #035-03-2000 L2006 **DR** *020 †80
O'BRIEN, David Michael. 77 NEALY BLVD, 1ST AMDS/CC 23665 #016-43-1987 L1989
   AM OM *030 †70
SIMMONS, Michael David. 45 PINE ST, 1ST MEDICAL GROUP/SFQ 23665
   #041-07-1998 L1999 *020
STEINER, Carol Marie. 77 NEALY AVE, 1ST MEDICAL GROUP/SGHC 23665 #010-02-1993 L2006
   PD *020 †55
TOPOLSKI, Mark Steven. 77 NEALY AVE, 1ST MEDICAL GROUP/SGHC 23665
   #051-01-2002 L2007 **ORS** *020
TRACHIER, Joseph A. 45 PINE ST, 1ST MEDICAL GROUP/SGQ 23665 #048-14-1996 L2000
   FM *020 †18

LANSDOWNE – LOUDOUN

ABEDIN, Tareq. 19415 DEERFIELD AVE, STE 213 20176 #051-04-1994 L1994 **IM** *020 †20,55
AGGARWAL, Rajiv Kumar. 19415 DEERFIELD AVE, STE 103 20176 #495-73-1988 L2002
   FM EM *020 †18
AKULA, Neeraja. 19450 DEERFIELD AVE, STE 365 20176 #495-21-1996 L2006 **IM** *020 †20
ALVI, Khadija Imran. 19450 DEERFIELD AVE 20176 #045-04-2000 L2008 **IM** *100 †20
ANDRABI, Seemi. 19455 DEERFIELD AVE # 306 20176 #704-06-1991 L1997 **ID IM** *020 †20
BAGRI, Harjit Singh. 44125 WOODRIDGE PKWY, STE 180 20176 #495-29-1988 L2002
   IM *020 †20
BESS, Angela C. 19450 DEERFIELD AVE, STE 445 20176 #041-13-1996 L2004 **OBG** *020 †30
CASABONA, Albert C. ■ 20176 #041-12-1951 L1963 **ORS** *071 †40
CHAND, Banti David. 19450 DEERFIELD AVE, STE 300 20176 #024-05-1994 L1997 **IM** *020 †20
CHANG, Phillip Jingo. 19450 DEERFIELD AVE, STE 275 20176 #035-45-1992 L2000 **PS** *020 †65
CHAPMAN, James E. ■ 20176 #010-01-1949 L1963 **IM** *071
CHEN, Donald. ■ 20176 #385-02-1951 L1969 **OTO HNS** *071
CHOI, Jenna Han. 19450 DEERFIELD AVE, STE 365 20176 #023-01-2002 L2007 **IM** *020 †20
DESTA, Hiwot B. 19450 DEERFIELD AVE # 150 20176 #051-01-1998 L2004 **GE** *020 †20
DULAI, Sarbjot Singh. 19415 DEERFIELD AVE, STE 310 20176 #051-04-1993 L1993 **N** *020 †75
GARG, Rajat. 19455 DEERFIELD AVE, STE 306 20176 #495-14-1996 **IC CD** *020 †20
GILL, Satinder S. 19415 DEERFIELD AVE # 213 20176 #422-01-1997 L2000 **IM GE** *020 †20
GREWAL, Ravneet. 19415 DEERFIELD AVE, STE 107 20176 #495-03-1994 L1999 **HO** *020 †20
HACKENBERG, Virginia M. 19465 DEERFIELD AVE, STE 205 20176 #012-05-1983 L1990
   GYN *020 †30 ‡
JOHNSON, David Charles. 19455 DEERFIELD AVE, STE 312 20176 #051-01-1996 L2002
   OSM *020
JOHNSON, Timothy Sterling. 19455 DEERFIELD AVE, STE 312 20176 #008-01-1996 L2005
   ORS OSM *020 †40
MALIK, Qudsia Iqbal. 19450 DEERFIELD AVE, STE 150 20176 #704-08-1997 L2002 **FM** *020 †18
MANCINI, Thomas John. 44055 RIVERSIDE PKWY, STE 216 20176 #055-01-1985 L1989
   IM *020 †20
MANGAT, Tara S. 19415 DEERFIELD AVE, STE 310 20176 #649-33-1986 L2002 **PYG** *020
MERRILL, Sarah Anne. 19441 GOLF VISTA PLZ, STE 320 20176 #010-02-1998 L1998
   OPH *020 †35
NASRULLAH, Abu Ahmed. 19415 DEERFIELD AVE # 106 20176 #047-06-1997 L2002
   OPH *020 †35
ODUTOLA, Jennifer. 19415 DEERFIELD AVE # 106 20176 #690-02-1995 L2003 **RHU** *020 †20
PALUVOI, Sobha Rani. 19415 DEERFIELD AVE, STE 210 20176 #495-70-1982 L2003 **P PYG** *020
PARAMESWARAN, Mahesh S. 19415 DEERFIELD AVE, STE 105 20176 #033-06-1997 L2002
   OTO *020
RENNERT, Douglas Andrew. 44055 RIVERSIDE PKWY, STE 204 20176 #035-01-1984 L1989
   PUD CCM *020
ROBERTS, Michelle Yvonne. 19455 DEERFIELD AVE, STE 204 20176 #023-01-1996 L2001
   OBG *020 †30
SABHARWAL, Charu. 19420 GOLF VISTA PLZ, STE 110 20176 #495-37-2000 L2006 **IM** *020 †20
SANDHU, Mandeep Pirthipal. 19415 DEERFIELD AVE, STE 115 20176 #495-23-1992 L1999
   IM *020 †20
SANTINI, Angela M. 19450 DEERFIELD AVE # 175 20176 #048-12-1989 L1995
   ORS OSS *020 †40
SEGURA, Edgard Andres. 19450 DEERFIELD AVE, STE 300 20176 #025-01-1995 L2001
   MPD *020 †20,55

SIDHU, Preetika Kaur. 19455 DEERFIELD AVE, STE 207 20176 #041-14-1993 L1998
OBG *020 †30
SILVA, Andrew Benedict. 19455 DEERFIELD AVE, STE 301 20176 #030-06-1991 L2000
OTO *020 †45
SINGH, Harmeet. 19455 DEERFIELD AVE # 211, CLINICAL NEUROLOGY 20176
#495-43-1987 L1999 N *020
SINGH, Karnail. 19415 DEERFIELD AVE, STE 115 20176 #495-03-1988 L1998 IM *020
SPOONER, Annemarie A. 19465 DEERFIELD AVE, STE 205 20176 #043-01-1998 OBG *020 †30
TUWINER, Seth Mitchell. 19450 DEERFIELD AVE, STE 175 20176 #550-03-2001 L2005
N NMN *020 †75
WALSH, Carolyn Mc Donough. 19415 DEERFIELD AVE, STE 307 20176 #032-01-1991 L2002
IM *020 †20
WASAN, Anita Nanda. 19450 DEERFIELD AVE # 335 20176 #001-06-1999 L2005 AI *020 †55,03
ZIENKOWICZ-GUCWA, I W. ■ 20176 #539-02-1952 GP OS *020

LAWRENCEVILLE – BRUNSWICK

BISHOP, William Branch. 319 W CHURCH ST 23868 #051-04-1944 L1944 GP *071
CLEMENTS, Boyd Mawhinney. 1607 PLANTERS RD, LAWRENCEVILLE CORRECTIONAL 23868
#051-04-1972 L1973 FM *020 †18
HARRISON, William Henry. 319 W CHURCH ST 23868 #051-04-1984 L1985 FM *020 †18
WYNN, Erica Larae. PO BOX 459, 203 SHARP ST 23868 #051-01-2000 L2000 PD *020

LEBANON – RUSSELL

AHMED, Tahir. 360 W MAIN ST 24266 #704-04-1996 IM *020 †20 ‡
BAILEY, Dwight Lawrence. 128 FLANAGAN AVE, 143 W. MAIN STREET 24266
#025-01-1977 L1980 FM FPG *020 †18
CHENG, Matthew Dee. 383 HIGHLAND DR 24266 #748-10-1991 L2001 IM PCC *020 †20
COMBS, Kevin Scot. ■ 24266 #020-75-2004, ▲ L2004 OMM *020
DREYZEHNER, Jana Kaye. 160 ROGERS ST, CUMBERLAND MOUNTAIN COMMUN 24266
#016-11-1991 L1997 CHP P *020 †75
DREYZEHNER, John J. 155 ROGERS ST BOX 2347, CUMBERLAND PLATEAU HLTH 24266
#016-11-1989 L1991 OM *030 †70
ELLIOTT, James Wm. TATE & CARROLL STS 24266 #051-04-1936 L1936 GP OS *071
KETRON, Samuel Gilmer. TATE & CARROLL STS 24266 #051-04-1963 L1963 OM *020 †18
MELTON, Samuel Hughes. PO BOX 2377 24266 #051-01-1993 L1993 FM *020 †18
REXRODE, Norman Leon, Jr. 505 FINCASTLE ESTATES CIR 24266 #055-01-1978 L1979
EM FM *020 †16
SABINO, Joycelyn A. 344 OVERLOOK DR, LEBANON PEDIATRICS 24266 #748-10-1991 L1996
PD *020 †55
SIDDIQI, Haya Waseem. 360 W MAIN ST, LEBANON PROFESSIONAL BUILD 24266
#704-06-1993 L2002 IMG *020 †20
SIDDIQI, Waleed Waseem. 360 W MAIN ST 24266 #704-01-1995 L2000 IM *020 †20
TACASTACAS, Joselin De Lu. PO BOX 128, COMMUNITY MEDICAL CARE 24266
#748-02-1994 L2004 IM IMG *020 †20
TOWNSEND, Charlotte Ann. 495 E MAIN ST, C-HEALTH 24266 #051-07-2001 L2001
FM *020 †18
WOLFE, Walter Woods, Jr. 128 FLANAGAN AVE, OF SW VA P.C. 24266 #051-04-1960 L1969
R *071
YOUSUF, Samina. 142 HIGHLAND DR, COMMUNITY MEDICAL CARE 24266 #704-02-1983 L1996
IM *020 †20

LEESBURG – LOUDOUN

ABDALLAH, Hala M. 705 E MARKET ST STE F 20176 #575-01-1983 L1999 PD *020 †55
ABEDIN, Mehnur. 40777 CANONGATE DR 20176 #704-01-1966 L1994 PD *020 †55
AHMAD, Tahir. 44045 RIVERSIDE PKWY 20176 #704-21-1991 L2002 IM *020 †20
AKBAR, Farooq. 105 LOUDOUN ST SW, # 505 20175 #704-01-1969 L1974 OBG *020 †30
AL-DABBAGH, Hiba Adnan. 20175 #575-01-1993 END *012
ALI, Khurram Nawaz. 20175 #654-01-2003 L2007 FM *020
ALLEN, Jane Diesner. 116C EDWARDS FERRY RD NE, JANE D ALLEN MD FACOG 20176
#016-43-1994 L2001 OBG *020 †30
ALWAN, Affan Othman. 44045 RIVERSIDE PKWY, LOUDEREN HLTCARE HOSP 20176
#330-04-1958 L1979 PD NPM *020 †55
AMARI, Salvatore N. 211 GIBSON ST NW 20176 #561-01-1958 L1974 IM *071
AMMANN, Kathleen M. 44045 RIVERSIDE PKWY, INOV LOUDOUN HOSP CTR LAB 20176
#017-20-1981 L1986 PTH PCP *020 †50
ANDERSON, W Edward. ■ 20177 #051-04-1955 L1956 AM PHP *071
ANDREW, John Alan. 222 CATOCTIN CIR SE, STE 200 20175 #047-05-1983 L1984
IM CCM *020 †20
ANDREW, Lori Rothstein. 722 E MARKET ST, STE 202 20176 #047-05-1983 L1985 PD *020 †55
AQUILINA, Thomas Carl. ■ 20175 #036-05-1990 L2006 AN *020
ARBABI, Niloofar. 44045 RIVERSIDE PKWY 20176 #517-08-1997 L2002 PD PEM *020 †55
AU, Kin-Sing. 44035 RIVERSIDE PKWY, STE 100 20176 #023-07-1981 L1991 RO IM *020 †20,80
AUSTIN, Eva Maria. 224 CORNWALL ST NW 20176 #759-09-1993 L1994 IM *020 †20 ‡
AZIE, William Ndekoum. 44045 RIVERSIDE PKWY, LOUDOUN EMERGENCY DEPT 20176
#010-03-1999 L2003 EM *020 †16
BAECHLER, Martin F. 44045 RIVERSIDE PKWY, MEDICAL STAFF 20176 #023-12-1993 L2005
ORS *020
BAEZA, Oscar R. ■ 20176 #231-01-1965 L1974 TS *020 †85,90
BAHRU, Menbere. ■ 20176 #005-14-2003 L2006 IM *020 †20
BARKHORDARI, Nasser. ■ 20176 #517-01-1957 L1973 DR *020
BEGUN, David Lawrence. 5 WIRT ST SW STE 2 20175 #010-01-1986 L1989 P *020 †75
BELOTE, Larry Pierce. 224 CORNWALL ST NW 20176 #051-04-1980 L1981 FM *020 †18
BELOTE, Robert Keith. 211 S KING ST 20175 #051-04-1975 L1976 FM *020 †18
BENCZE, Robert Francis. 44055 RIVERSIDE PKWY 20176 #036-07-1978 L1979 FM *020 †18
BERENGUT, Bakhruza. ■ 20176 #913-19-1975 P *100
BOUTON, Brian Barrett. ■ 20176 #035-45-1965 L1974 P CHP *020 †75
BOYER, Richard Coar. ■ 20175 #030-05-1937 L1937 R NM *071 †80,28
BRANDT, Dorthe Sophie. 44055 RIVERSIDE PKWY, STE 108B 20176 #035-20-1990 L1990
VIR *020 †80

BRANDT, Jan Julius. ■ 20176 #051-04-1990 L1992 FM *020 †18
BROWN, Anne Barbara. 116C EDWARDS FERRY RD NE 20176 #036-05-1990 L1994
OBG *020 †30
BUTLER, Kathleen G. 19455 DEERFIELD AVE, STE 102 20176 #010-02-1979 L2004
PDR *020 †80
CALIHAN, Martha Stowell. 116P EDWARDS FERRY RD NE 20176 #010-02-1982 L1983
FM *020 †20
CALLAHAN, Flinton, II. 20 DAVIS AVE SW 20175 #051-01-1972 L1972 OPH GP *020 †35
CECIL, Mary Alice. 44055 RIVERSIDE PKWY, STE 110 20176 #051-04-1990 L1991 FM *020 †18
CHAKURKAR, Mrunalini. 19455 DEERFIELD AVE, STE 206 20176 #496-38-1988 L2002
PUD *020
CHANDRA, Sandhya. 19455 DEERFIELD AVE, STE 306 20176 #495-05-1990 L1996 IM *020 †20
CHAREN, Jonathan David. 44055 RIVERSIDE PKWY, STE 110 20176 #035-46-2002 L2002
FM *020 †18
CHEZEM, Angela Louise. 44055 RIVERSIDE PKWY, STE 110 20176 #051-01-2001 L2001
FM *020
CHIANTELLA, Christopher L. 211 S KING ST 20175 #561-01-1981 L1991 FM *020 †18
CHIANTELLA, Virginia. 821 S KING ST, STE D 20175 #036-05-1983 L1988 GS *020 †85
CHOPIVSKY, Peter John. 114 EDWARDS FERRY RD NE 20176 #010-01-1978 L1990
FM *020 †18
CHOUDHARY, Sarfraz Ahmed. 44045 RIVERSIDE PKWY 20176 #704-05-1988 L2000
ID *020 †20 ‡
COOK, John Henry, III. 44055 RIVERSIDE PKWY, STE 116 20176 #008-01-1977 L1979
IM IMG *020 †20
CROSS, Cecil Bernard. 44055 RIVERSIDE PKWY, STE 246 20176 #051-04-1982 L1988
GS *020 †85
CROWLEY, Anthony Edward. 116 EDWARDS FERRY RD NE, STE Q 20176 #051-04-1984 L1986
FM *020 †18
DAGHIGH, Behnam. 44125 WOODRIDGE PKWY # 180 20176 #055-01-1996 L1996
AI IM *020 †20,03
DAR, Ajay. 44045 RIVERSIDE PKWY, STE 300 20176 #496-09-1986 L2001 ON IM *020 †20
DASTGHEYB, Mitra. 821 S KING ST STE A 20175 #517-05-1985 L1995 END IM *020 †20
DELA PAZ, Adrianne M. ■ 20176 #748-02-1994 OPH *012
DE RUSSO, Deanna Mary. 116A EDWARDS FERRY RD NE 20176 #041-09-1993 L1994
IM *020 †20
DE RUSSO, Franklin John. 116A EDWARDS FERRY RD NE 20176 #041-09-1960 L1988
TS *020 †85,90
DE SIMONE, Ralph Stephen. 751 MILLER DR SE, STE E3 20175 #051-04-1986 L1987
PTH *020 †20
DOGAN, M Ezel. ■ 20176 #902-01-1960 L1974 NS *071 †25
DUGGAL, Roopa Malpani. 19415 DEERFIELD AVE, STE 202 20176 #010-01-2000 L2000
OBG *020 †30
DULAI, Ramandeep. 19415 DEERFIELD AVE # 213, LANSDAWNE OB-GYN PLLC 20176
#038-44-1993 L1997 OBG *020 †30
ELIEZER, Elaine Teresa. 823 S KING ST STE A 20175 #051-04-1981 L1983 D DMP *020 †50,15
FALKENSTEIN, Richard, II. 224 CORNWALL ST NW 20176 #034-01-1983 L1988 FM *020 †18
FELTER, Christian Tilen. ■ 20176 #038-43-2001 IM *100
FELTER, Robert A. ■ 20176 #010-02-1973 L2005 PD OS *030 †50
FIELDS, Robia Ann. 104 DRY MILL RD SW, STE 102 20176 #028-03-1989 L1998 CHP P *020 †75
FINIZIO, Joseph P. 19455 DEERFIELD AVE, STE 102 20176 #010-02-1971 L1973 DR *020 †80
FLETCHER, Page Moss. 224 CORNWALL ST NW 20176 #051-01-1989 L1994 PYG P *020 †75
FOSTER, Douglas Goddard. 201 S KING ST 20175 #008-02-1984 L1986 P *020 †75
FOSTER, Gavin Neil. 44055 RIVERSIDE PKWY, STE 238 20176 #019-02-1985 L1994
OBG *020 †30
FRANCISCO, Edgardo Cruz. 42009 VICTORY LN 20176 #748-07-1964 L2004 P CHP *020 †75
FRANKEL, Robert Saul. 19455 DEERFIELD AVE, STE 102 20176 #038-06-1970 L1975
DR NM *020 †28,80
FRUITERMAN, Jan Paul. ■ 20176 #010-02-1972 L1978 OBG *071 †30
GARCIALA-JACOMINO, Jorge. 19455 DEERFIELD AVE, STE 102 20176 #025-12-1975 L1986
DR *020 †80
GARDNER, Jennifer Anne. 44045 RIVERSIDE PKWY, INOVA LOUDON HOSPITAL 20176
#035-01-1999 L1999 PD *020 †55
GATES, Thomas Jarman. 116A EDWARDS FERRY RD NE 20176 #051-04-1967 L1967
GS *071 †85
GAVIN, Matthew Bernard. 19 FORT EVANS RD NE, STE C 20176 #010-02-1985 L1989
ORS OSM *020 †20
GILBERT, George Elbanks. 19455 DEERFIELD AVE, STE 102 20176 #010-03-1969 L1972
DR *020 †80 ‡
GLICK, Howard Aaron. 102 HERITAGE WAY NE 20176 #025-12-1973 L1980 P CHP *020
GOMEZ, Jaime Leon. ■ 20175 #264-01-1956 L1969 GS EM *071
GORDON, Nina J. 19455 DEERFIELD AVE, STE 102 20176 #008-01-1993 L2001 DR *020 †80
GRAUERHOLZ, John Edward. ■ 20177 #474-03-1973 L1984 FOP *075 †50
GREAVES, Kondeh Augusta. ■ 20176 #047-07-1998 L2003 OBG *020 †30
GRIFFITH, Frederick P, III. 224 CORNWALL ST NW 20176 #051-04-1978 L1980 FM *020 †18
GROEBER, Sandra J. 823 S KING ST STE F 20175 #041-14-1990 L1993 PD *020 †55
GUPTA, Sunil. 44045 RIVERSIDE PKWY, INOVA LOUDOUN HOSPITAL 20176 #495-45-1983 L1985
NPM EM *020 †55
HA, Van Trong. 19415 DEERFIELD AVE, STE 314 20176 #036-07-1994 L1998 D *020 †15
HALL, Donald Penn, Jr. 40915 SPECTACULAR BID PL 20176 #010-02-1990 L1997 P *020 †75
HAN, Pum Suk. ■ 20176 #583-02-1942 PHP *075
HAZEN, Brian Allen. 44045 RIVERSIDE PKWY, INOVA LOUDOUN HOSPITAL 20176
#035-45-1994 L1994 IM *030 †20
HAZLETT, Sara Bradshaw. 44045 RIVERSIDE PKWY, LOUDOUN HOSPITAL 20176
#023-07-2003 L2005 EM *020 †16
HETZEL, Robert Lowell. 44055 RIVERSIDE PKWY, STE 110 20176 #051-07-1999 L2002
FM *020 †18
HIBBEN, Herbert Arthur. ■ 20175 #047-06-1948 L1964 PHP *071
HOGAN, Nicholas James. 44045 RIVERSIDE PKWY, MEDICAL STAFF OFFICE 20176
#035-03-2003 L2003 EM *020 †16
HYUN-PARK, Younghae Lisa. 19455 DEERFIELD AVE # 204, STE 204 20176
#041-07-1990 L1994 OBG *020 †30
IDRIS, Azza Hussein. 823 S KING ST STE F 20175 #035-47-2001 L2007 PD *020 †55
IRWIN, George Norton. ■ 20176 #005-06-1955 L1956 CD IM *071 †20
KARP, Cathy. 19115 DALTON POINTS PL, LANSDOWNE PEDIATRICS 20176 #010-01-2000 L2003
PD *020 †55
KAVANAGH, Michael Andrew. 19 FORT EVANS RD NE, STE C 20176 #010-02-1980 L1985
ORS *020 †40

KEMERER, Verne F, Jr. 19455 DEERFIELD AVE, STE 102 20176 #023-01-1980 L1985 DR NM *020 †80

KHAN, Imran Ahmad. 44055 RIVERSIDE PKWY, STE 104 20176 #041-02-1999 L2007 ORS HS *020 †40

KHAN, Naveed Mazhar. 44035 RIVERSIDE PKWY, STE 360 20176 #011-02-1993 L2003 OBG *020 †30

KIM, Richard Youngkeun. 44055 RIVERSIDE PKWY, STE 116 20176 #051-04-1994 L1997 IM *020 †20

KISSI, Ludmila Marie. 51 CATOCTIN CIR NE, NOVA MEDICAL GROUP 20176 #010-02-1999 L1999 IM *020 †20

KOH, Hanjong. 19450 DEERFIELD AVE, STE 365 20176 #056-06-1990 L1994 IM *020 †20

KORKOWSKI, Martin Anthony. 44055 RIVERSIDE PKWY, STE 216 20176 #038-43-1989 L1992 IM *020 †20

KOWARSKI, David. 19455 DEERFIELD AVE, STE 102 20176 #041-01-1986 L2006 DR *020 †80

KRIEGER, Mitchel D. 44045 RIVERSIDE PKWY 20176 #035-03-1985 L1997 PS *020 †85,65

KRISHNAN, Bhanumathi. 44055 RIVERSIDE PKWY, STE 244 20176 #495-04-1982 L2000 CD IM *020 †20

KRISS, Brita D. 44055 RIVERSIDE PKWY, STE 246 20176 #038-44-1989 L1994 GS *020 †85

KULA, Katherine Reiff. 44055 RIVERSIDE PKWY, STE 220 20176 #010-02-2002 L2005 OBG *020

LAFSKY, Robert David. 44055 RIVERSIDE PKWY, STE 226 20176 #041-01-1975 L1980 GE IM *020 †20

LAW, Gregory Alan. 44055 RIVERSIDE PKWY, STE 248 20176 #010-01-1990 L1998 CHP *020 †75

LEE, Joseph Yim. 211 GIBSON ST NW, STE 206 20176 #001-06-1995 L1998 FM *020 †18

LEE, Nathan William. ■ 20176 #051-04-2007 L2007 GS *012

LESNIEWSKI, James Andrew. 44055 RIVERSIDE PKWY, STE 246 20176 #041-01-1997 L2004 GS *020 †85

LEWIS, Andrew Morris, Jr. ■ 20176 #036-07-1961 L1961 OS PD *050

LILLIS, Frederick Patrick. 823 S KING ST STE B 20175 #010-01-1966 L1972 IM PUD *020

LINDSEY, Mercedes. 224 CORNWALL ST NW 20176 #033-05-1978 L2004 ON HEM *050 †20

LING, Jean C. 44045 RIVERSIDE PKWY, INOVA LOUDOUN HOSP/ED 20176 #024-05-1991 L1997 EM *020 †16

LONDNER, Michael Stephen. 44045 RIVERSIDE PKWY, ATTN: EMERGENCY DEPARTMENT 20176 #033-06-1996 L2004 EM *020 †16

LONGMORE, James Lyon. 209 GIBSON ST NW, STE 202 20176 #010-01-1976 L2006 FM *020 †18

LUY, Jeffrey Steven. 44035 RIVERSIDE PKWY, STE 150 20176 #056-06-1994 L2003 CD IM *020 †20

MA, Ann I. 2 CARDINAL PARK DR SE, STE 102B 20175 #038-41-1985 L1994 GE IM *020 †20

MA, Felix Yiho. 116P EDWARDS FERRY RD NE 20176 #038-06-1997 L2003 FM *020 †18

MAGHAK, Basil. 44035 RIVERSIDE PKWY, STE 410 20176 #035-09-1990 L2001 OBG *020 †30

MALACHIAS, Zachary N. ■ 20176 #041-12-1992 L2000 EM *020 †16

MAN, Philip Shu-Hoi. 19455 DEERFIELD AVE, STE 102 20176 #065-01-1979 L1987 R *020 †80

MANSOUR, Sam E. 211 GIBSON ST NW STE 103 20176 #065-10-1986 L2002 OPH OS *035

MC DOW, Russell Edward, Jr. 44055 RIVERSIDE PKWY, STE 102 20176 #051-01-1976 L1981 GS *020 †85

MCILWAINE, Benjamin H. 44045 RIVERSIDE PKWY 20176 #051-04-1975 L1976 FM *020 †18

MC LEOD, Harry Ronald. 116C EDWARDS FERRY RD NE 20176 #051-04-1968 L1968 OBG *020 †30

MECHERIKUNNEL, Ann. 44045 RIVERSIDE PKWY 20176 #495-52-1995 L1999 IM *020 †20

MELMED, John Richard. 19455 DEERFIELD AVE, STE 102 20176 #836-02-1970 L1978 DR *020 †80

MENDIGUREN, Ignacio Inaki. 44055 RIVERSIDE PKWY 20176 #024-07-1984 L1989 PUD CCM *020 †20

MENDLOWITZ, Abbe Dov. 44055 RIVERSIDE PKWY, STE 108B 20176 #023-01-1982 L1986 DR *020 †80

MIAN, Hina. ■ 20176 #704-06-2000 L2005 FM *020 †18

MOORE, Clen Damon M. 722 E MARKET ST, STE 202 20176 #023-07-1992 L1997 PD *020 †55

MORELAND, Roberta Maureen. 19415 DEERFIELD AVE, STE 314 20176 #051-01-1989 L1993 D *020 †15

MORGAN, John Irvin, IV. 239 EDWARDS FERRY RD NE 20176 #051-01-2000 L2003 EM *020 †16

MOUNTCASTLE, Timothy S. 44055 RIVERSIDE PKWY, STE 246 20176 #010-03-1999 L2006 PS *020 †85

NAGELL, Scott Howard. 44055 RIVERSIDE PKWY 20176 #035-08-1984 L1988 FM EM *020 †18

NAIR, Seema Saralakumari. 222 CATOCTIN CIR, LOUDOUN MEDICAL GROUP 20175 #654-01-2000 L2005 FM *020 †18

NAPOLITANO, Stephen Jos. 44055 RIVERSIDE PKWY 20176 #030-06-1971 L1974 FM *020 †18

NAYERI, Farid. ■ 20177 #517-03-1963 L1980 PM GP *020

NGUYEN, Jane Trang. 19455 DEERFIELD AVE, STE 306 20176 #041-01-1999 L2006 D *020 †15

NGUYEN, Thuan T. 41030 CANONGATE DR, WELLMONT LONESOME PINE HOS 20175 #422-01-1994 L1997 IM *020 †20

NOVACKI, Visnja. 102 HERITAGE WAY NE 20176 #957-01-1983 L1996 P *020 †75

O'CONNOR, James Patrick. 602 BATTERY TER NE 20176 #028-34-1982 L1994 OBG *062 †30

OSTROW, Lawrence D. 102 HERITAGE WAY NE 20176 #035-06-1971 L1975 P *020 †75

PARK, Young Don. 44055 RIVERSIDE PKWY, STE 244 20176 #023-01-1997 L2003 IM *020 †20

PARVA, Behzad. 2 CARDINAL PARK DR SE, STE 102A 20175 #041-13-1988 L1997 PS *020 †85,65

PATEL, Anil Jayanthlal. 2 CARDINAL PRK DR SE #103A 20175 #495-22-1984 L1990 IM *020 †20

PILLAI, Geetha. 44055 RIVERSIDE PKWY, STE 116 20176 #496-28-1993 L1999 IM *020 †20

PLONK, Wm Mcguire, Jr. 209 GIBSON ST NW STE 2, CAPITAL HOSPICE 20176 #051-01-1989 L2002 IMG *100 †18

POLLOCK, Dean Michael. 44035 RIVERSIDE PKWY, STE 150 20176 #003-01-1978 L1986 CD IM *020 †20

POONAWALA, Rahib Mansoor. 44055 RIVERSIDE PKWY, STE 110 20176 #051-01-2000 L2003 FM *100 †18

PUCCIO, Edward Vincent. 44045 RIVERSIDE PKWY, LOUDOUN HOSP CTR 20176 #041-12-1990 L1995 EM *030 †16

PULIZZI, Michael Jeffery. 44055 RIVERSIDE PKWY 20176 #041-09-1998 L2002 EM *020 †16

RAJENDRA, Rangappa. 44055 RIVERSIDE PKWY, STE 224 20176 #495-52-1981 L1988 IM HO *020 †20

RANA, Khalid Rashid. 44035 RIVERSIDE PKWY, BUILDING #2 SUITE 340 20176 #704-01-1982 L2003 N *020 †75

RANA, Naila Naureen. ■ 20176 #704-06-1986 L2002 CN *100 †75

RAPHAELSON, Marc Issac. 107 ROYAL ST SW, STE G 20175 #041-01-1978 L1988 N CN *020 †20

RAPPAPORT, Patricia Finn. 823 S KING ST STE F 20175 #051-04-1991 L1994 PD *020 †55

RETHY, Janine Abrams. ■ 20175 #035-47-2000 L2006 GPM PD *020 †55

RIAR, Amjad. 209 GIBSON ST NW, STE 202 20176 #704-08-1992 L2006 IM *020 †20 ‡

ROBERSON, Yvette Darlene. 44055 RIVERSIDE PKWY, STE 116 20176 #005-19-1990 L1993 IM *020 †20

ROBINSON, James Wesley. ■ 20176 #024-01-1944 L1949 RHU IM *071 †20

ROSECAN, Arthur Scott. 44055 RIVERSIDE PKWY 20176 #010-01-1986 L1988 PYG P *020 †75

ROWAN, George Peter. ■ 20176 #041-09-1958 L2006 ORS *072 †40

ROYCHOUDHURY, Anya Kamal. 19450 DEERFIELD AVE, STE 200 20176 #051-01-2003 L2006 PD *020 †20

RUDDEN, George Thos. 44045 RIVERSIDE PKWY, LOUDOUN HOSPITAL CENTER 20176 #010-02-1973 L1978 EM *020 †16

RUSSELL, Laura Jane. 721 E MARKET ST RM 111 20176 #017-20-1975 L1989 MG PD *020 †55,19

SABELLA, Donald A. 224 CORNWALL ST NW 20176 #010-02-1974 L1974 EM *020 †16

SAMPANG, Heidi Lapid. 823 S KING ST STE F 20175 #748-31-2000 L2005 PD *020 †55

SAUNDERS, Robert Paul. 19450 DEERFIELD AVE, STE 265 20176 #010-01-2001 L2001 FM *020 †18

SCHRUEFER, John Michael. ■ 20175 #010-02-1991 L2005 EM *020 †16

SEID, William. 2 CARDINAL PARK DR SE, STE 102B 20175 #016-11-1978 L1991 GS *020 †10,85

SHAH, Deepa M. 44045 RIVERSIDE PKWY, LOUDOUN HOSPITAL 20176 #010-01-1999 L2003 PD *020 †55

SHARMA, Anil Kumar. 44055 RIVERSIDE PKWY, 2LOUDOUN HOSP CTR 20176 #495-47-1978 L1992 PD NPM *020 †55

SIDIKI, Yasmin Hanif. 44055 RIVERSIDE PKWY, STE 104 20176 #704-08-1974 L1987 AN *020 †05

SILBERMAN, William Chas. ■ 20177 #010-01-1961 L1966 PTH *071 †50

SILVA, Anita. 821 S KING ST STE H 20175 #030-06-1991 L2002 OBG *020 †30

SIMMS, Elisabeth B. 44045 RIVERSIDE PKWY, STE 300 20176 #024-05-1972 L1979 ON *020 †20

SIMONDS, Mark Fletcher. 102 HERITAGE WAY NE, STE 302 20176 #047-05-1991 L2001 CHP P *020 †75

SKOLOFF, Joseph Stephen. 19450 DEERFIELD AVE 20176 #041-02-1970 L1976 PD *071 †55

SMITH, Edward Reed, Jr. ■ 20176 #010-02-2000 L2000 EM *020 †16

SPENCER, Donnie. 44045 RIVERSIDE PKWY, EMERGENCY DEPARTMENT 20176 #016-42-2000 L2002 EM *020 ‡

STEWART, Anne Margaret. 116Q EDWARDS FERRY RD NE, INTEGRTVE FAM MED CTR 20176 #051-07-1999 L2003 FM NTR *020 †18

STEWART, David Wayne. 209 OLD WATERFORD RD NW, WHOLE HEALTH FAMILY & SPOR 20176 #051-07-1999 L2003 FM FSM *020 †18

STOKES, Chauncey C. 44055 RIVERSIDE PKWY, STE 220 20176 #047-07-1981 L1991 OBG *020 †30

SUKHANI-MANKAD, Vaishali. 19465 DEERFIELD AVE, STE 101 20176 #016-11-1998 L2007 AI *100 †55,03

SULLIVAN, Katharyne Mary. 161 FT EVANS RD NE, STE 205 20176 #035-06-1992 L2002 CHP P *020 †75

SUMMERS, Anne Elizabeth. 44055 RIVERSIDE PKWY, STE 244 20176 #041-07-1980 L1985 CD IM *020 †20

TANG, Nancy Lee. 823 S KING ST STE F 20175 #023-01-1983 L2002 PD *020 †55

THAI-KEMPROWSKI, Huong Ng. 44125 WOODRIDGE PKWY, STE 180 20176 #051-04-1998 L2000 AI IM *020,03

THOMAS, Daphne G Z. 44055 RIVERSIDE PKWY, DEPT 7 EMERENCY MEDICINE 20176 #038-43-1991 L1996 EM *020 †16

THOMAS, Petra Joanne. 44055 RIVERSIDE PKWY, STE 204 20176 #041-13-1990 L2003 PUD IM *020 †20

TRIPPEL, Michele Denise. 19420 GOLF VISTA PLZ, STE 130 20176 #051-04-1995 L1995 IM *020 †20

UJEVIC, Neven A. 44055 RIVERSIDE PKWY, STE 116 20176 #957-01-1982 L1991 IM *020 †20

VIGLIANTE, Craig E. 19440 GOLF VISTA PLZ, STE 130 20176 #041-01-2000 L2003 *020

VIRMANI, Pranav. ■ 20176 #010-03-1999 L2003 EM *020 †16

VO, Nghia M. ■ 20176 #941-01-1974 L1978 GS VS *020 †85

WALDROP, Ronnie D. 44045 RIVERSIDE PKWY, INOVA LOUDOUN HOSPITAL 20176 #048-02-1987 L2007 PD PEM *020 †55

WARNER, Mary Patricia. ■ 20176 #041-12-1942 L1943 PD PHP *071

WATTENMAKER, Ian Michael. 19 FORT EVANS RD NE, STE C 20176 #041-01-1986 L1993 ORS GS *020 †40

WEINER, Paul L. 19455 DEERFIELD AVE, STE 102 20176 #010-02-1971 L1972 DR *020 †80

WENZEL, Michael Thomas. 44045 RIVERSIDE PKWY 20176 #051-04-1991 L1992 FM *020 †18

WEVER, Kim Marie. 116C EDWARDS FERRY RD NE 20176 #051-07-1997 L1998 OBG *020 †30

WILLOUGHBY, Michael Hill. 116C EDWARDS FERRY RD NE 20176 #021-01-1967 L1969 OBG *020 †30

WRIGHT, Colleen Kelly. 44055 RIVERSIDE PKWY, STE 110 20176 #025-01-1982 L1983 FM *020 †18

WRIGHT, Thomas M. 2 CARDINAL PARK DR SE, STE 102B 20175 #051-01-1951 L1951 GS *071 †85

YAGER, Jonathan E. 44055 RIVERSIDE PKWY, STE 244 20176 #024-01-1997 L2005 CD *020 †20

YORK, William Byrne, Jr. ■ 20176 #049-01-1968 L1969 PTH OS *020 †50

YOUNG, Yvette Shawntell. 44055 RIVERSIDE PKWY, INOVA LOUDOUN HOSPITAL 20176 #023-01-1998 L2003 PEM *012 †55

ZIAI, Niloofar. 19441 GOLF VISTA PLZ, STE 320 20176 #035-20-1985 L1992 OPH *020 †35

ZLOTKIN, David Michael. 19450 DEERFIELD AVE, STE 200 20176 #024-05-1997 L2000 PD *020 †55

LEXINGTON – ROCKBRIDGE

ARNOLD, Colleen M. 1 HEALTH CIR 24450 #041-09-1983 L1989 FM EM *020 †18

BECKNER, William W, Jr. PO BOX 1046, ROCKBRIDGE PROFESSIONAL BL 24450 #051-04-1950 L1957 OPH *071 †35

CARLSEN, Andrew Bert. 1 HEALTH CIR, CREDENTIALING DEPARTMENT 24450 #067-01-1965 L2004 CD *020 †20

CHEWNING, Mark William. 110 HOUSTON ST, LEXINGTON OB/GYN 24450 #051-07-2001 L2005 OBG *020

CLAGUE, Michael D. 1 HEALTH CIR, STONEWALL JACKSON HOSPITAL 24450 #038-06-1977 L1978 DR *020 †80 ‡

COPELAND, David Lynn. 448 INSTITUTE HL, VA MILITRAY INSTITUTE 24450 #038-06-1980 L1985 IM ADL *020 †20

COTHRAN, Malcolm L, Jr. 108 HOUSTON ST STE A 24450 #045-01-1969 L1975 **IM** *020 †20
CREWS, James Randolph. 204 E WASHINGTON ST 24450 #051-01-1978 L1981 **IM** *020 †20
DENT, Cynthia Hall. 130 WALKER ST, BLUE RIDGE DERMATOLOGY 24450 #036-01-1985 L1986 **D** *020 †15
DICK, W Barton. ■ 24450 #036-07-1966 L1974 **ORS** *071 †40
EDMUNDS, Frederick T. ■ 24450 #023-01-1950 L1975 **OBG** *071
ELLINGTON, David Alan. 102 SPOTTSWOOD DR 24450 #051-04-1975 L1984 **FM** *020 †18
ELLIS, Percita Loren. 108 HOUSTON ST STE E, STONEWALL PEDIATRICS 24450 #010-01-1986 L2001 **PD CHP** *020 †55
FEDDEMAN, Frederick A. 2 E WASHINGTON ST 24450 #041-02-1949 L1951 **GP OS** *071
FINTEL, William Allen. 108 HOUSTON ST, SECOND FLOOR 24450 #026-04-1983 L1984 **ON IM** *020 †20
HANSEN, Anne V Edmunds. ■ 24450 #047-05-1990 L2005 **NM** *074
HARRALSON, John David. ■ 24450 #020-12-1970 L1976 **OBG** *071 †30
HEMPHILL, Edward Stiles. 1 HEALTH CIR 24450 #038-41-1984 L1995 **ORS** *020 †40
HIRSH, Philip Reid, Jr. 59 UNION RUN, CENTRAL VA MENTAL HLTH CTR 24450 #041-02-1964 L1965 **P** *020 †75
HORTON, Jane T. 204 W WASHINGTON ST, WASHINGTON & LEE UNIV 24450 #050-02-1983 L1985 **IM** *020 †20
IRONS, Robert P. 100 SPOTTSWOOD DR 24450 #051-01-1945 L1946 **GYN GS** *071
IRONS, Robert Price, Jr. 100 SPOTTSWOOD DR 24450 #051-01-1972 L1972 **GS GYN** *020 †85
KERSCHL, Walter Charles. 204 E WASHINGTON ST, STE C 24450 #032-01-1993 L1993 **IM IMG** *020 †20
KNOELL, Keith. 130 WALKER ST, BLUE RIDGE DERMATOLOGY 24450 #033-06-1995 L1996 **D** *020 †15 ‡
KORNEGAU, Laura Post. 108 HOUSTON ST, STE A 24450 #051-01-1990 L1996 **IM** *020 †20
LANEHART, William Henry. 102 SPOTTSWOOD DR 24450 #021-06-1980 L1992 **PTH** *020 †50 ‡
LANIER, Laura Winn. 146 S MAIN ST, LEXINGTON FAM PRACT 24450 #051-04-1996 L1996 **FM** *020 †18
LARSEN, George Douglas. 300 WHITE ST, DISTRICT OF VIRGINIA 24450 #051-01-1969 L1971 **OBG** *020 †30
LUDER, Everett Kirk. 120 W NELSON ST 24450 #019-02-1985 L1999 **P** *020 †75
LYNCH, Jane M. 130 WALKER ST, BLUE RIDGE DERMATOLOGY 24450 #051-04-1998 L1998 **D DMP** *020
LYONS, Karen Ann. 108 HOUSTON ST STE A 24450 #023-01-1982 L1985 **IM EM** *020 †20
MC CLUNG, John Houston. ■ 24450 #051-01-1947 L1947 **GP** *071
MC CLUNG, William Lyle. 204 E WASHINGTON ST, ROCKBRIDGE INTERNIST INC. 24450 #051-04-1996 L1996 **FM** *020 †18
MEARS, William W. 130 SPOTTSWOOD DR, ROCKBRIDGE PROF BLDG 24450 #041-02-1960 L1987 **OPH PO** *020 †35
MOORE, Richard Henning. 102 SPOTTSWOOD DR 24450 #051-04-1980 L1984 **FM PD** *020 †55,18
NUNNELEY, Sarah A. ■ 24450 #026-04-1967 L1968 **AM** *071 †70
PAULY, Charles Roman. 130 WALKER ST, BLUE RIDGE DERMATOLOGY 24450 #016-43-1973 L1977 **D DMP** *020 †15
PECK, Dawn Hughes. ■ 24450 #010-01-1977 L1986 **PD** *020 †55
PICKRAL, Robert Moore. 146 S MAIN ST 24450 #051-04-1975 L1979 **FM GP** *020 †18
PRICE, Frank W. ■ 24450 #051-01-1953 L1953 **PD PHP** *071 †55
SAYRE, William James. 108 HOUSTON ST STE A, LEXINGTON INTERNISTS 24450 #051-01-1996 L2000 **IM** *020 †20
SCHIRMER, Patricia Lee. 1 HEALTH CIR, DEPT EMERGENCY 24450 #047-05-1989 L1993 **IM PD** *020 †20,55
SCHMIEG, Anthony Luke. ■ 24450 #030-05-1989 L1992 **EM FM** *020 †18
SEDOVY, John David. 100 SPOTTSWOOD DR 24450 #041-13-1994 L1994 **GS** *020 †85
SINCLAIR, Mary Beth. 25 NORTHRIDGE LN, STE 2 24450 #016-02-1990 L2005 **PD** *020 †55
TERHUNE, Charles Bunnell. ■ 24450 #035-01-1947 L1950 **P PYA** *071 †55
THOMAS, Andrew Ralsten. ■ 24450 #055-01-2007 L2007 **TY** *012
TOWNSEND, Irene. ■ 24450 #041-09-1974 L1985 **END PDE** *020
TROISE, Joseph. 110 HOUSTON ST, LEXINGTON OB/GYN 24450 #041-13-1992 L1996 **OBG** *020 †30
WERCHOWSKI, Jeffrey L. 1 HEALTH CIR 24450 #038-41-1980 L2001 **PUD CCM** *020 †20
YEILDING, Ruth Hill. ■ 24450 #001-02-2007 **TY** *012

LINCOLN — LOUDOUN

MARION, Warren Jos. PO BOX 22 20160 #005-15-1969 L1995 **ON IM** *020 †20

LINDEN — WARREN

ARNETT, Brenda Marie. ■ 22642 #055-01-2002 L2002 **IM** *100 †20
SMITH, Mark A H, Jr. ■ 22642 #010-01-1963 L1968 **MDM ORS** *071 †40

LINVILLE — ROCKINGHAM

BOYKO, Michael John. 9421 CHERRY GROVE RD 22834 #010-02-1980 L1985 **EM FM** *020 †16,18 ‡
SELLERS, Clay Lewis. 8233 JOES CREEK RD 22834 #047-06-2005 L2006 **U** *012

LOCUST GROVE — ORANGE

BELINSKY, Samuel Michael. ■ 22508 #010-01-1959 L1963 **OBG** *071 †30
JOHNSON, Kenneth Scott. 4444 GERMANNA HWY, STE 310 22508 #005-12-1988 L1998 **FM** *020 †18
PRASSE, Robert Hart, II. 35070 GERMANNA HEIGHTS DR, STE A 22508 #055-02-1992 L1998 **FM FPG** *020 †18
STUBBE, Herman Gerald. 4376 GERMANNA HWY 22508 #042-01-1974 L1993 **FM FPG** *020 †18
SWAIN, Garrett M. ■ 22508 #010-01-1945 L1954 **LM NS** *071 †25
SWAIN, Shirley Cath Towey. ■ 22508 #010-01-1945 L1959 **PD PHP** *071
TROWBRIDGE, John N. ■ 22508 #010-01-1989 L1992 **RHU** *075 †20
VANDERMEID, Maria Tabora. 36097 GOODWIN DR 22508 #051-07-1992 L1994 **FM** *020 †18 ‡

VANDERMEID, Peter Michael. 36097 GOODWIN DR 22508 #051-07-1992 L1998 **FM** *020 †18
WILSON, William Rosser. ■ 22508 #035-01-1964 L1986 **OTO HNS** *020 †45

LOCUST HILL — MIDDLESEX

GALE, Virginia W. ■ 23092 #036-01-1990 L2000 **FM** *020 †18

LORTON — FAIRFAX

BEDNAR, Stephen Jos. ■ 22079 #041-01-1964 L1966 **IM EM** *020 †20,16,18 ‡
BERRO, Eva Teresa. ■ 22079 #759-03-1982 L1985 **IM CCM** *020 †20
CHOW, Caroline Chialin. ■ 22079 #036-07-1989 L1994 **DR** *062 †80
CHUKWU, Cecilia Uzoamaka. ■ 22079 #690-04-1984 L2002 **IMG** *020 †20
CHUTUAPE, Arthur D. 8988 LORTON STATION BLVD, STE 204 22079 #035-19-1990 L1998 **IM** *020 †20
CIAMPI, Frank Peter. 9500 RICHMOND HWY 22079 #010-02-1985 L1987 **FM** *020 †18
FATEMA, Kaniz. ■ 22079 #160-01-1995 L2007 **FM** *020 †18
GALLINI, Marc Robt. 9502 RICHMOND HWY 22079 #025-01-1972 L1976 **FM** *020 †18
GARG, Rishi. ■ 22079 #051-04-2001 L2001 **IM** *100
HARRIS, Mark David. ■ 22079 #005-12-1991 L1992 **GPM** *020 †70,18
IPAKCHI, Ramin. ■ 22079 #041-01-1999 L2004 **OTO** *100 †45
KIM, Michelle Sunmee. ■ 22079 #010-01-2002 **OBG** *020 †30
LEE, David Wooyoung. 8988 LORTON STATION BLVD, LORTON STATION FAMILY 22079 #051-01-2001 L2001 **FM** *020 †18
LEE, William Hyong-Sok. 8350C TERMINAL RD, TRISTIN MED LAB 22079 #583-01-1957 L1988 **PTH GP** *020 †50
LONG, James Eugene. 8988 LORTON STATION BLVD, STE 100 22079 #036-08-1997 L1997 **IM** *020 †20
MARIN, Lucianne. ■ 22079 #042-01-2002 L2005 **PD** *020 †55
MICHEL, Claude A. ■ 22079 #649-14-1979 **PD** *020 †55
MOON, Deepti Suresh. ■ 22079 #023-12-2005 L2005 *100
RALEIGH, Meghan Frances. ■ 22079 #041-02-2007 L2007 **FP** *012
REEVES, Glen Irving. 8211 TERMINAL RD, UNIT1000 22079 #035-01-1972 L2004 **RO AM** *030 †80,70
RYDER, Mary Teresa. 9500 RICHMOND HWY 22079 #035-46-1985 L1995 **FM** *020 †18
WALKER, Sherrie Lee. 8988 LORTON STATION BLVD, STE 204 22079 #051-04-1987 L1996 **ID** *020 †20
WALLACE, Justin Robert. ■ 22079 #005-14-2008 *012
WEINTRITT, David Charles. 8988 LORTON STATION BLVD, STE 202 22079 #011-03-1993 L2001 **GS** *020 †85
WOSU, Uchechi Nneoma. 8988 LORTON STATION BLVD, STE 100 22079 #010-01-2002 L2005 **IM** *100 †20

LOUISA — LOUISA

DANIEL, Evelyn Patton. ■ 23093 #051-04-1950 L1950 **GP** *071
DANIEL, Griffith B. ■ 23093 #051-04-1950 L1950 **GP** *071
GREEN, Matthew Peter. 575 INDUSTRIAL DR, P O BOX 947 23093 #038-40-2002 L2002 **FM** *020 †18
GUARINO, Matthew G. ■ 23093 #409-40-1985 L1992 **PD** *020 †55
KINKADE, Josie Michelle. 6045 YANCEYVILLE RD, P O BOX 2204 23093 #051-04-1986 L1990 **FM** *020 †18
LAMB, William Robt. ■ 23093 #038-06-1964 L1965 **P CHP** *071 †75
SCHPER, Rachil K. ■ 23093 #759-03-1939 **FM GPM** *071
SCHWARTZ, David. 115 JEFFERSON HWY 23093 #025-07-1970 L1975 **FM** *020 †18
SOUTHALL, Alger Rixey, III. 101 WOOLFOLK AVE, LOUISA MEDICAL CENTER 23093 #051-04-1980 L1981 **FM** *020 †18
WESTFIELD, Wendy Kay. ■ 23093 #041-07-1996 L1996 **IM PD** *020 †20,55
ZIMMERMANN, Jay Adam. PO BOX 947, 575 INDUSTRIAL DR 23093 #025-01-2001 L2001 **FM** *100 †18

LOVETTSVILLE — LOUDOUN

KIMBALL, Robert W P. ■ 20180 #035-08-1949 L1973 **IM OS** *020 †20
RIDDICK, David Haydon. ■ 20180 #051-01-1966 L1972 **IM ON** *020 †20

LOVINGSTON — NELSON

DERDEYN, Andre Philip. PO BOX 338 22949 #048-12-1963 L1970 **CHP P** *030 †75

LOW MOOR — ALLEGHANY

BALLOU, Charles F. 1 ARCH LANE 24457 #024-07-1953 L1959 **IM PUD** *071 †20
BALLOU, James Elon. EMMETT MED SURGICAL CLINIC 24457 #051-07-1982 L1984 **IM** *020 †20
BALLOU, Michele Krick. 1 ARCH LANE 24457 #051-07-1982 L1984 **IM PUD** *020 †20
DAKERMANDJI, Farid. 1 ARCH LANE 24457 #875-02-1973 L1977 **AN** *020 †05
DEL TORO, I Cristina. PO BOX 233 24457 #649-14-1977 L1997 **PD** *020 †55
DUDLEY, Joann C. STE 300, ONE ARH LANE 24457 #010-02-1985 L2007 **GYN OBS** *020 †30
EDMUNDS, Meade C, Jr. PO BOX 174 24457 #051-01-1952 L1952 **GS** *020 †85
HWANG, Daniel. ■ 24457 #035-09-1996 L2001 **OTO** *020 †45
MADALENGOITIA, Jose. 1 ARCH LANE 24457 #737-01-1953 L1979 **PTH** *071 †50
MC COIG, James Austin. PO BOX 235, HIGHLANDS ORTHOPEADICS & S 24457 #051-01-1985 L1991 **ORS GS** *020 †40
POWELL, Unity Monger. 1 ARCH LANE 24457 #051-04-1945 L1946 **GP** *071
ROCOVICH, Sue Ellen B. U.S. INTERSTATE 64, ALLEGHANY REGION HOSP ER 24457 #055-75-1982, ▲ L1984 **EM IM** *071
SADJADI, Parviz-Mohsen. 1 ARCH LANE 24457 #517-01-1964 L1972 **TS GS** *020 †85,90
SHUMATE, George Ronald. 1APH LANE, STE 201 24457 #041-01-1969 L1976 **GS** *020 †85
SNYDER, James Leigh. 1 ARCH LANE 24457 #041-02-1961 L1976 **U** *071 †95

STRAUSBAUGH, Paul Lee. 1 ARCH LANE 24457 #038-40-1978 L1982 **OTO A** *020 †45

LURAY – PAGE

ALLEN, Gregory Wm. 200 MEMORIAL DR, PAGE MEMORIAL HOSPITAL 22835 #023-01-1988 L1991 **EM FM** *020 †18

BRENNWALD, Frederic W. ■ 22835 #869-02-1946 L1969 **GP GPM** *071

FEELEY, James Wm, III. 250 MEMORIAL DR STE B 22835 #035-20-1982 L1988 **FM EM** *020 †18 ‡

FEIT, Jeffrey Michael. 125 MEMORIAL DR, PAGE HEALTH CARE 22835 #051-01-1995 L1995 **FM** *020 †18

GEORGE, Francis H. 511 E MAIN ST 22835 #023-01-1977 L1982 **NM** *050 †28

HORNG, Fang-Shuh. 218 W PAGE ST 22835 #385-05-1965 L1973 **GS FM** *020 †85

HOWARD, Walter Wesley. 200 MEMORIAL DR, PAGE MEMORIAL HOSP 22835 #038-40-1977 L1984 **IM EM** *020 †20,16

KUBOTA, Richard Tadashi. 200 MEMORIAL DR, PAGE MEMORIAL HOSP RADIOLO 22835 #016-02-1982 L1983 **DR** *020 †80

LAUER, John A, Jr. RR 2 BOX 283D 22835 #005-12-1950 L1973 **GP** *071

LAWTON, George Marion. ■ 22835 #025-07-1958 L1970 **OM GPM** *071 †70

MILLER, David Brooke. 250 MEMORIAL DR, C 22835 #051-01-1986 L1987 **FM** *020 †18

RAKARIC, Ilija Steven. 250 MEMORIAL DR, STE A 22835 #957-01-1978 L1996 **IM** *020 †20

ROSS, George Gregory. 50 MEMORIAL DR 22835 #045-04-1986 L1988 **IM** *020 †20

SWITZER, David Scott. 125 MEMORIAL DR 22835 #051-01-1994 L1994 **FM** *020 †18

THOMAS, Wm Nathaniel, Jr. 200 MEMORIAL DR 22835 #051-01-1942 L1942 **DR** *071 †80

WINER, Stephen Frank. 250 MEMORIAL DR STE C 22835 #025-07-1967 L2006 **GS** *020 †85

LYNCH STATION – CAMPBELL

COHEN, Leonard Joel. 10102 LEESVILLE RD 24571 #165-02-1974 L1976 **FM** *020 †18

PHILLIPS, Jessicah Susann. ■ 24571 #051-01-2005 L2007 **IM** *012

LYNCHBURG – LYNCHBURG CITY

ADAMS, Scott Brackenridg. 2811 LINKHORNE DR, LIGHT MEDICAL 24503 #038-40-1995 L1995 **FM** *020 †18

ADENIJI, Margaret Yeside. 320 FEDERAL ST, CENTRA HEALTH 24504 #690-02-1977 L1997 **FM** *020 †18

AGARD, Winifred Venida. ■ 24503 #008-01-1997 L2008 **EM** *020

AHMAD, Syed Moizuddin. 100 BEACON HILL PL, ATLANTIC CITY MED CTR-NEON 24503 #704-02-1991 L2007 **PD NPM** *020 †55

ALBERS, Gregg Richard. ■ 24503 #038-43-1980 L1983 **FM** *020 †18

ALBERTSON, Thomas Howard. 1212 MCCONVILLE RD 24503 #036-07-1959 L1965 **PD A** *071 †03,55

ALDERFER, Raymond Jay. 1833 CLAYTON AVE 24503 #051-01-1982 L1998 **P IM** *020 †20,75

ALEXANDER, Eben, III. 4223 HILTON PL, FOCUSED ULTRASOUND SURGERY 24503 #036-07-1980 L2006 **NS OS** *020 †25

ALEXANDER, Margaret C. 20293 TIMBERLAKE RD 24502 #045-01-1981 L2001 **DR OS** *020 †80

ALFIERI, John L. 1901 TATE SPRINGS RD 24501 #041-09-1993 L1987 **FM** *020 †80

ALTY, C Gregory. 1911 THOMSON DR 24501 #051-04-1986 L1987 **GS VS** *071 †85 ‡

ANDERSON, Brian Allen. 1901 TATE SPRINGS RD 24501 #036-05-1989 L1992 **EM** *020 †16

ANDREWS, Wm Cooke, Jr. 1914 THOMSON DR, PIEDMONT ORTHO SURGERY INC 24501 #036-07-1980 L1981 **ORS** *020 †40

APONTE, Juan Pablo. 2215 LANDOVER PL 24501 #033-05-1997 L2000 **IM** *020 †20

ARMOCK, Robert Kenneth. 1901 TATE SPRINGS RD 24501 #025-12-1998 L1998 **FM** *020 †18

ARNOLD, John Byrd. 1212 MCCONVILLE RD, F READ HOPKINS PEDIATRIC 24502 #048-12-1967 L1973 **PD PHO** *020 †55

ASHRAF, Mohammed Khairul. 103 CLIFTON ST 24501 #160-02-1980 L2000 **NEP IM** *020 †20

ASHRAF, Nazma Yasmin. ■ 24502 #160-02-1981 L2000 **IM** *020 †20

BAKER, Albert Moton. 2011 TATE SPRINGS RD 24501 #051-01-1989 L1990 **PCC IM** *020 †20 ‡

BAKER, William Frank. 114 NATIONWIDE DR 24501 #051-04-1986 L1986 **OBG** *020 †30

BALDWIN, Monroe Glass, Jr. 725 CHURCH ST 15TH FL 24504 #051-01-1964 L1964 **U** *020 †95

BARNARD, John Wm, Jr. 2019 TATE SPRINGS RD 24501 #051-04-1989 L1995 **ORS** *020 †40

BARNES, David Wright. ■ 24501 #047-06-1964 L1965 **GP** *030

BARNEY, William H. ■ 24503 #051-04-1946 L1946 **IM PUD** *071

BASS, Robert Carlyle. 1911 THOMSON DR 24501 #051-04-1989 L2001 **GS** *020 †85

BAUER, Laura Lynn. 1901 TATE SPRINGS RD 24501 #051-04-2000 L2004 **IM** *020 †16

BELL, George Milton. 1900 THOMSON DR, LYNCHBURG HLTH DEPT 24501 #051-01-1961 L1961 **PUD IM** *020 †20

BETZ, Peter. 3300 RIVERMONT AVE 24503 #012-01-1996 L2001 **P PYG** *020 †75 ‡

BEVERLY, Walter Bryant. 2215 LANDOVER PL, MEDICAL ASSOCIATES OF CENT 24501 #051-01-1976 L1978 **EM** *020 †16,18

BIESEMIER, Karl William. 1905 ATHERHOLT RD, PATHOLOGY CONSULTANTS OF 24501 #018-03-1989 L1994 **PTH** *020 †50

BLACKBURN, James Edward. 1901 TATE SPRINGS RD 24501 #047-05-1959 L1966 **ORS** *072 †40

BLACKMAN, William Allison. 3300 RIVERMONT AVE 24503 #051-01-1980 L1984 **IM** *020 †20

BOND, Julia Preston. 3300 RIVERMONT AVE 24503 #051-07-1994 L2002 **CHP** *020 †75

BOWDEN, Robert Henry, Jr. 1900 THOMSON DR, VIRGINIA DEPARTMENT OF HEA 24501 #051-01-1959 L1959 **GYN GS** *071 †30

BOWEN, Robert Richardson. 320 FEDERAL ST, ATTN: CREDENTIALS DEPT 24504 #051-04-1956 L1956 **ORS** *071 †40

BRANSON, Donald Gene. 3300 RIVERMONT AVE 24503 #051-04-1964 L1964 **OM FM** *062 †18

BRENNAN, Robert Owen. 2215 LANDOVER PL 24501 #051-01-1978 L1984 **IM ID** *020 †20

BRENNAN, Teresa Lynch. 1912 MEMORIAL AVE, BLUE RIDGE THERAPY ASSOCIA 24501 #023-07-1978 L1984 **PD OS** *020 †55

BRINDLE, Robert Sean. 24502 #011-04-2007 L2007 **TY** *012

BROOKS, Laura Michelle. 1212 MCCONVILLE RD, F READ HOPKINS PEDIATRIC 24502 #051-01-1994 L2008 **PD** *020 †55

BROWN, Lawrence P. 1914 THOMSON DR, PIEDMONT ORTHOPAEDIC SURG 24501 #035-45-1963 L1967 **ORS** *020 †40

BROWN, William David. 1901 TATE SPRINGS RD 24501 #036-08-1983 L1984 **FM EM** *020 †18

BROWN, William Martin. 2410 ATHERHOLT RD 24501 #051-04-1974 L1975 **CD IM** *020 †20

BRUNSTETTER, David Byron. 2235 LANDOVER PL, CENTRAL VA COMMUNITY SERVI 24501 #036-05-1993 L1997 **P** *020 †75

BRUST, Stuart Wm. 2323 ATHERHOLT RD 24501 #025-01-1968 L1973 **D** *020 †15

BUCK, Frank Neville, Jr. ■ 24505 #051-04-1941 L1941 **U** *071 †95

BUCKLEY, Neil Holland. 1901 TATE SPRINGS RD 24501 #051-04-1995 L2003 **EM** *020

BUDDE, Jason Macrae. 2410 ATHERHOLT RD 24501 #012-05-1996 L2007 **TS** *020 †85,90

BURGER, Wilbur France. ■ 24503 #051-01-1963 L1963 **ON HEM** *071 †20

BURNHAM, Karen Armstrong. 2401 ATHERHOLT RD 24501 #023-12-1989 L2001 **AN PME** *020 †05

BURTON, Jennifer Orndorff. 2401 ATHERHOLT RD 24501 #055-75-1992, ▲ L1993 **PAN AN** *020 †05 ‡

CABIGAS, Verna Luz. 2097 LANGHORNE RD 24501 #748-10-2003 L2005 **FP** *012

CALLICOTT, Joseph H, Jr. 1905 ATHERHOLT RD 24501 #036-01-1962 L1968 **PTH PCP** *071 †50

CALVERT, George Edward. ■ 24503 #051-04-1947 L1947 **CRS FM** *071

CANNON, David Robt. 2215 LANDOVER PL 24501 #036-07-1976 L1981 **IM** *020 †20

CAPRISE, Peter A, Jr. 1914 THOMSON DR 24501 #036-01-1995 L2004 **ORS** *020 †40

CAREY, Daniel. 2410 ATHERHOLT RD, P O BOX 11889 24501 #024-01-1986 L1997 **CD IC** *020 †20

CARLTON, Soni Sangha. 1330 OAK LN, STE 101 24503 #048-14-1998 L2002 **D** *020 †15

CARRICO, Thomas Jos. 3300 RIVERMONT AVE, CENTER FOR WOUND CARE 24503 #051-04-1978 L1980 **PS OS** *020 †85,65

CARVAJAL, William. 101 ARCHWAY CT 24502 #051-04-2001 L2001 **GS** *020

CATALANO, Charles John. 121 NATIONWIDE DR 24502 #011-02-1976 L1982 **GE IM** *020 †20

CAULKINS, Michael Kennedy. 20304 TIMBERLAKE RD, TIMBERLAKE FAMILY PRACTICE 24502 #051-04-1982 L1984 **FM** *020 †18

CAULKINS, Pamela Marston. 20304 TIMBERLAKE RD, TIMBERLAKE FAMILY PRACTICE 24502 #051-04-1982 L1984 **FM** *020 †18

CEBALLOS, Elizenda M. 2402 ATHERHOLT RD, PIEDMONT EYE CENTER 24501 #012-05-1996 L2001 **OPH** *020 †35

CHAPMAN, Donald Redding. 1901 TATE SPRINGS RD, LYNCHBURG GENERAL HOSPITAL 24501 #005-14-1976 L1985 **EM FM** *020 †18,16

CHARLTON, Jennifer E. 2401 ATHERHOLT RD 24501 #036-01-1994 L1999 **AN** *020 †05

CHATANI-HINZE, Mayumi. 2097 LANGHORNE RD 24501 #572-31-2001 L2007 **FP** *012

CHEATWOOD, William Henry. 2085 LANGHORNE RD 24501 #051-01-1999 L1999 **FM** *020 †18

CHI, Louis G. 2215 LANDOVER PL, MED ASSOC OF CENTRAL VIRGI 24501 #035-09-1997 L2000 **IM** *020 †20

CLAPP, Clinton Earl. ■ 24503 #051-01-1981 L1990 **GS VS** *071 †85

CLARK, Donovan Deryl. 3300 RIVERMONT AVE 24503 #045-01-1983 L1998 **CHP** *020 †75

CLARK, Hal Clifford. 21556 TIMBERLAKE RD, STE D 24502 #422-01-1983 L1987 **IM** *020 †20

CLARK, Joe Lynn. 2321 ATHERHOLT RD 24501 #036-07-1966 L1974 **OTO PS** *071 †45

CLARK, Larry Edward, Jr. 121 NATIONWIDE DR 24502 #012-01-1999 L1999 **GE** *020 †20

CLARK, Shawn Broxton. 2138 LANGHORNE RD 24501 #011-02-1993 L2002 **NS** *020 †20

CLAY, Lucius Dubignon, III. 1900 TATE SPRINGS RD, STE 3 24501 #051-01-1979 L2003 **GS CRS** *020 †10,85 ‡

CLOWER, Robert Dean. 2542 LANGHORNE RD 24501 #012-01-1979 L1984 **U** *020 †95

COGGIN, Susan S. 2091 LANGHORNE RD 24501 #045-04-1998 L1999 **FM** *020 †18

COMBS, Kimberly H. 2091 LANGHORNE RD, STE 2 24501 #051-01-1996 L1996 **FM** *020 †18

COOK, Elizabeth Ann. 2215 LANDOVER PL 24501 #047-05-1998 L1999 **FM PLM** *020 †18

COOK, George Woods. 1905 ATHERHOLT RD, PATHOLOGY CONSULTANTS OF 24501 #051-04-1993 L1993 **PTH** *020 †50

COOK, Michael Robert. 1901 TATE SPRINGS RD 24501 #305-01-2000 L2000 **FM** *020 †18

COOK, Robert Dawson. 2542 LANGHORNE RD 24501 #051-04-1987 L1992 **U** *020 †95

COOK, William A, Jr. 1901 TATE SPRINGS RD 24501 #051-04-1951 L1951 **GYN** *071 †30

COOK, William Agee, III. 114 NATIONWIDE DR 24502 #051-04-1982 L1989 **OBG** *020 †30

COOPER, Alan Michael. PO BOX 1098 24505 #051-04-1976 L1977 **P** *020 †75

COURVILLE, Timothy. 2321 ATHERHOLT RD, BLUE RIDGE ENT & PLASTIC 24501 #021-05-1989 L1994 **OTO** *020 †45

COX, James M. 1901 TATE SPRINGS RD 24501 #051-01-1968 L1968 **NEP IM** *030 †20

CRESSON, David Homer, Jr. 1905 ATHERHOLT RD, PATHOLOGY CONSULTANTS OF 24501 #047-06-1981 L1987 **ATP CLP** *020 †50

CROW, William Cecil, Jr. 2097 LANGHORNE RD, LYNCHBURG FAMILY MEDICINE 24501 #051-04-1971 L1971 **FM** *040 †18 ‡

CROWDER, R Vincent, Jr. ■ 24503 #051-01-1949 L1949 **IM** *071 †20

CURE, James Dillon. 3300 RIVERMONT AVE 24503 #051-04-1982 L1983 **IM** *020 †20

DABNEY, Lewis Puller. 2728 OLD FOREST RD 24501 #051-01-1997 L1997 **GYN** *020 †30

DARRAH, Carol Joy N. 20293 TIMBERLAKE RD 24502 #019-02-1974 L1999 **DR** *020 †80

DE GUZMAN, Cesar V. PO BOX 1098, CENTRAL VIRGINIA TRAINING 24505 #748-10-1962 L1976 **GS GP** *020

DELANEY, Thomas John. 1901 TATE SPRINGS RD, LYNCHBURG GENERAL HOSPITAL 24501 #035-20-1975 L1994 **IM** *020

DE MARCHENA, Octavio. 1933 THOMSON DR 24501 #023-07-1976 L1991 **N IM** *020 †20,75

DIAMOND, Sharon Louise. ■ 24503 #051-07-2004 L2004 **FM** *100 †18

DICE, Robert Andrew. 1901 TATE SPRINGS RD 24501 #016-11-1997 L2000 **EM** *020 †16

DI GIULIO, Robert. 1901 TATE SPRINGS RD, CENTRA HEALTH 24501 #654-01-1990 L1999 **IM EM** *020 †20

DILLARD, Powell G, Jr. 113 NATIONWIDE DR 24502 #051-01-1947 L1947 **DR** *071 †80

DIMINICK, Michael Joseph. 1914 THOMSON DR 24501 #024-01-1993 L1998 **ORS** *020 †40

DONEGAN, Martha F. 2401 ATHERHOLT RD 24501 #010-01-1975 L1979 **AN** *020 †05

DOYLE, Joseph O'Brien. ■ 24503 #051-01-2005 L2005 **OBG** *012

DRISCOLL, Charles Edwin. 2097 LANGHORNE RD, LYNCHBURG FAMILY MEDICINE 24501 #018-03-1971 L1999 **FM FPG** *020 †18 ‡

DRISKILL, Robert Leroy. 3300 RIVERMONT AVE, P O BOX 3017 24503 #051-01-1987 L1988 **RO** *020 †80

DRISKILL, Wm Lawson, Jr. ■ 24503 #051-04-1954 L1954 **GYN** *071 †30

DUNLOP, Michael Craig. 1901 TATE SPRINGS RD 24501 #051-04-1995 L1998 **EM** *020 †16

DUNSTAN, James Cummings, Jr. 3300 RIVERMONT AVE 24503 #051-01-1976 L1979 **ORS HS** *020 †40

EDMUNDS, Benjamin P, Jr. ■ 24503 #051-01-1960 L1960 **IM** *071

EDWARDS, Preston Hill. 20255 TIMBERLAKE RD 24502 #051-05-1974 L1975 **FM** *020 †18

ELWELL, Daniel Robert. 3300 RIVERMONT AVE 24503 #036-01-2002 L2006 **AN** *020 †05

ERDLY, Ralph P. ■ 24503 #041-09-1952 L1953 **GP** *071

ESCHENROEDER, Harry C, Jr. 2019 TATE SPRINGS RD, ORTHOPAEDIC CTR CENT VA 24501 #028-03-1981 L1981 **ORS** *020 †40

FEINMAN, Maxwell Carlton. 2321 ATHERHOLT RD, ENT AND PLASTIC SURG INC 24501 #051-01-1954 L1954 **OTO AI** *071 †45

FENTON, Denise Lee. 1212 MCCONVILLE RD, F READ HOPKINS PEDIATRIC 24502 #041-12-1999 L2002 **PD** *020 †55
FENTON, Edward Brian. 1901 TATE SPRINGS RD 24501 #041-12-2002 L2002 **EM** *020 †16
FIELDS, Linda Gonsky. 1901 TATE SPRINGS RD, LYNCHBURG GENERAL HOSPITAL 24501 #012-05-1990 L1994 **AN** *020 †05
FILIPOVA, Hana. ■ 24501 #286-05-1986 L2005 **FP** *012 ‡
FISHER, John Gregory. 3300 RIVERMONT AVE 24503 #051-04-1987 L1988 **CHP** *020 †75
FISHER, Ronald James. 2542 LANGHORNE RD 24501 #018-03-1992 L1997 **U** *020 †95
FITZGERALD, Paul Francis. 1914 THOMSON DR 24501 #035-19-1964 L1971 **ORS** *071 †40
FLOREA, Robert Andrei. ■ 24502 #305-01-2007 L2007 **FP** *012
FORD, Kiah Thornton, III. ■ 24503 #051-01-1969 L1969 **DR** *071 †80
FOSTER, Matthew Robert. 1905 ATHERHOLT RD, PATHOLOGY CONSULTANTS OF 24501 #036-01-1996 L2001 **PCP** *020 †50
FOX, Parham Russell. 113 NATIONWIDE DR, RADIOLOGY CNSLTS/LYNCHBURG 24502 #051-04-1971 L1976 **DR NM** *020 †80
FRANTZ, David W. 2410 ATHERHOLT RD, THORACIC SURGERY 24501 #024-07-1976 L1989 **TS** *020 †85,90
FULLER, Samuel Prioleau. 1330 OAK LN, PLASTIC SURGERY 24503 #012-05-1973 L1980 **PS** *020 †65 ‡
FUNK, Susan E. 2215 LANDOVER PL 24501 #048-14-1988 L1990 **IM** *020 †20
GAGEN, Rachel Valiant. ■ 24503 #051-01-2003 L2007 **PD** *100 †55
GALLAGHER, James Wilson. 3300 RIVERMONT AVE 24503 #056-05-1998 L2002 **P** *020 †75
GARCIA, Frank George. 2091 LANGHORNE RD 24501 #036-08-1993 L1995 **FM** *020 †18
GARDNER, Robert D. 3300 RIVERMONT AVE 24503 #051-01-1953 L1953 **P** *071 †75
GARRETT, Thomas Scott. 2255 LANGHORNE RD STE 4 24501 #051-01-1984 L1988 **GS VS** *020 †85 ‡
GAYLE, William Earle, Jr. 1911 THOMSON DR 24501 #051-04-1965 L1965 **GS** *071 †85
GEZEN, Murat Tahir. 2215 LANDOVER PL 24501 #051-01-1998 L1998 **FM** *020 †18
GIANAKOS, Dean George. 2097 LANGHORNE RD, LYNCHBURG FAMILY MEDICINE 24501 #051-01-1984 L1986 **IM** *020 †20
GIBBS, Lucy V Hodnette. ■ 24505 #051-01-1961 L1961 **PM** *020
GILES, Richard Dixon. 103 CLIFTON ST 24501 #051-01-1969 L1969 **NEP IM** *020 †20
GILKEY, John Millard. 2728 OLD FOREST RD 24501 #036-01-1972 L1976 **GYN** *020 †30
GILMER, Graham, III. 1330 OAK LN, ASSOCIATES 24503 #023-01-1969 L1978 **OTO AM** *020 †45
GLENN, Robert Lee. ■ 24503 #051-01-1957 L1957 **IM GE** *071 †20
GONDI, Gautham. 2019 TATE SPRINGS RD, CENTRAL VIRGINIA ORTHOPEDI 24501 #045-01-1992 L1997 **OFA OSM** *020 †40
GONDI, Heidi Burg. 1922 THOMSON DR, POST OFFICE BOX 2659 24501 #012-05-1993 L1997 **AN** *020
GRAHAM, Louis Binford. 20304 TIMBERLAKE RD, TIMBERLAKE FAMILY PRACTICE 24502 #051-04-1975 L1976 **FM IMG** *020 †18
GREEN, Kevin Finnie. 2542 LANGHORNE RD 24501 #051-01-1979 L1980 **U** *020 †95
GREEN, Robert Lorenza, Jr. 113 NATIONWIDE DR 24502 #036-01-1983 L1988 **R VIR** *020 †80
GREGORY, David Steven. 2097 LANGHORNE RD, LYNCHBURG FAMILY MEDICINE 24501 #051-04-1994 L2001 **FM** *040 †18
GRESS, Daryl Ray. 1933 THOMSON DR 24501 #028-02-1982 L2002 **N EM** *020 †75
GUANZON, Angelo Patrick. 1901 TATE SPRINGS RD 24501 #051-04-2003 L2003 **EM** *020
GUGLIELMETTI, John Louis, Jr. 1801 THOMSON DR 24501 #036-08-1997 L2003 **GS** *020 †85
GUTHROW, Clyde Earl, Jr. 1330 OAK LN, STE 203 24503 #041-01-1969 L1980 **END IM** *071 †20
HACKENBRACHT, Jason M. 2410 ATHERHOLT RD 24501 #038-40-1997 L1997 **CD** *020 †20
HALL, James Allen, Jr. 113 NATIONWIDE DR 24502 #051-04-1979 L1981 **DR RNR** *020 †80 ‡
HALPIN, John J. 1937 THOMSON DR, LYNCHBURG HEMATOLOGY 24501 #010-02-1971 L1978 **ON HEM** *020 †20
HANCOCK, Edward H. 1980 THOMSON DR, LYNCHBURG HEALTH DEPT 24501 #051-01-1953 L1953 **PD** *071 †55
HANLEY, Matthew Lawrence. 1901 TATE SPRINGS RD 24501 #036-07-1998 L2001 **EM** *020 †16
HARDISON, Jeremy Leonard. 2011 TATE SPRINGS RD 24501 #036-07-2000 L2006 **PCC** *020 †20
HARRIS, David Langston. ■ 24502 #010-03-1959 L1964 **GP GS** *020
HARRIS, Joanna Hackman. 1900 THOMSON DR BOX 60, CENTRAL VIRGINIA HLTH DIST 24501 #051-01-1965 L1968 **PHP OBG** *020
HARRIS, Norman Stuart. 1901 TATE SPRINGS RD 24501 #051-01-1964 L1964 **IM PUD** *071 †20
HARRIS, Stuart Horsley. 1911 THOMSON DR 24501 #051-01-1957 L1957 **GS TS** *071 †85,90
HARWOOD, Rosemary. 320 FEDERAL ST 24504 #665-01-2003 L2003 **FM** *020 †18
HASAN, Nael. 117 MARGUERITE DR 24502 #051-04-1999 L2003 **EM** *020 †16
HATINOGLOU, Simon. 1330 OAK LN, PLASTIC SURGERY 24503 #024-05-1991 L1996 **GS** *020 †65
HAYES, Shawn Michael. 1901 THOMSON DR, LOWER LEVEL 24501 #051-01-1995 L1998 **IM** *020 †20
HEADLEY, Robert Nelson. 1937 THOMSON DR, LYNCHBURG HEMATOLOGY 24501 #036-01-1983 L1988 **ON HEM** *020 †20
HELLEWELL, Sarah C. 2011 TATE SPRINGS RD 24501 #051-04-2000 L2000 **PCC** *020 †20
HELLEWELL, Timothy Brooks. 113 NATIONWIDE DR 24502 #051-04-2001 L2001 **DR** *020 †80
HENDRICKSON, John Lauri. 3300 RIVERMONT AVE 24503 #051-04-1992 L1992 **CHP** *020 †75
HENGERER, James Russell. 1330 OAK LN, ASSOCIATES 24503 #035-03-1971 L1980 **OTO** *020 †45
HENGST, Arno Diedrich. ■ 24502 #407-21-1947 L1960 **P** *071
HERBERT, Pamela Gray. 119A TRADEWYND DR, BLUE RIDGE AESTHETICS CENT 24502 #010-02-2003 L2003 **FM** *020 †18
HICKMAN, Janet Gratner. 1330 OAK LN, STE 101 24503 #024-01-1971 L1979 **D** *020 †15 ‡
HICKMAN, Robert Edward. 121 NATIONWIDE DR, STE A 24502 #024-01-1971 L1979 **GE IM** *020 †20
HICKS, Kevin Oliver. 1901 TATE SPRINGS RD 24501 #051-04-1998 L2003 **DR** *020 †80
HILL, David Bennett. ■ 24503 #036-07-1957 L1961 **GS TS** *071 †85
HILL, Ronald Gene. 1900 TATE SPRINGS RD, STE 3 24501 #051-04-1975 L1982 **GS TS** *020 †85
HILLIARD, Anita Joy. 3300 RIVERMONT AVE 24503 #021-05-1989 L1994 **RO** *020 †80
HINDERLITER, Stacey Ann. 2097 LANGHORNE RD, LYNCHBURG FAMILY MEDICINE 24501 #041-01-1983 L1993 **PD PHP** *020 †55 ‡
HITE, Kenneth Clarke. ■ 24503 #051-04-2000 L2000 **DR** *100 †80
HOARD, Martin Alan. 101 ARCHWAY CT, CENTRAL VA ORAL & FACIAL S 24502 #051-04-1977 L1979 **PS** *020
HOBBS, William Alexander, Jr. 2108 LANGHORNE RD 24501 #051-04-1968 L1968 **OPH** *020 †35
HODGES, Joel Thomas. 3300 RIVERMONT AVE 24503 #422-01-2004 L2004 **FM** *020 †18
HOFFMAN, John Allen. 2091 LANGHORNE RD 24501 #055-02-1986 L1987 **FM** *020 †18
HOLLAND, Walter R. ■ 24503 #035-08-1947 L1954 **AN** *071 †05
HOPKINS, Jay Everett. 1906 THOMSON DR 24501 #036-07-1968 L1976 **ORS OSM** *020 †40
HOSTETLER, Joseph Dee. 2097 LANGHORNE RD, MED RESIDENCY 24501 #011-02-2007 L2007 **FP** *012
HOUCK, Peter Wm. 320 FEDERAL ST 24504 #051-01-1965 L1965 **PD FM** *020 †55
HOWARD, Lawrence Max. 1901 TATE SPRINGS RD 24501 #051-04-1947 L1947 **IM** *020
HOYT, Chad Alan. 2410 ATHERHOLT RD 24501 #023-01-1993 L1999 **CD** *020 †20
HUERTA, Joyce Lynn. 2019 TATE SPRINGS RD 24501 #007-02-1999 L2004 **PM PMM** *020 †60
HUNTER, James Gordon. 3300 RIVERMONT AVE 24503 #023-07-1959 L1965 **DR** *071 †20,80
HURT, George Adams. 2138 LANGHORNE RD 24501 #051-01-1964 L1964 **NS** *020 †25
HUTCHISON, Joseph Lynn. 3300 RIVERMONT AVE 24503 #018-03-1995 L2000 **OTO** *020 †45
IRONS, Raymond Jack. 3300 RIVERMONT AVE 24503 #051-04-1953 L1956 **OBG** *020 †30
JACKSON, Gabrielle Kori G. 2215 LANDOVER PL 24501 #051-01-1999 L1999 **FM** *020 †18
JARRETT, Harry Walthall. 2919 CONFEDERATE AVE 24501 #051-01-1965 L1965 **OBG** *071 †30
JOHNSEN, David Edward. 113 NATIONWIDE DR 24502 #051-04-1987 L1990 **DR** *020 †80
JOHNSON, Eileen El Dorado. 1003 5TH ST 24504 #869-04-1957 L1967 **GP P** *071
JOHNSON, Matthew Aaron. 2091 LANGHORNE RD, STE 2 24501 #005-12-1997 L1997 **FM** *020 †18
JOHNSON, Stephen Morgan. 3300 RIVERMONT AVE, CENTER FOR RESTORATIVE CAR 24503 #036-07-1978 L1984 **PUD PCC** *020 †20
JONES, James Barrett. ■ 24503 #051-01-1947 L1947 **ORS** *071 †40
JONES, John Paul. 1901 TATE SPRINGS RD 24501 #012-01-1991 L1994 **FM** *020 †18
JOSEPH, Charles Robt. 1933 THOMSON DR 24501 #041-13-1977 L1980 **N NRN** *020 †75
JUDD, Michael E. 3300 RIVERMONT AVE, PIEDMONT PSYCHIATRIC CENTE 24503 #305-01-1987 L1997 **P** *020 †75
KACZYNSKI, Rafal Piotr. 3300 RIVERMONT AVE 24503 #759-07-1998 L2005 **FP** *012
KALAFIAN, Michael Jeffrey. 1901 THOMSON DR, LYNCHBURG INTERNAL MEDICIN 24501 #051-01-1996 L2000 **IM** *020 †20
KAUPPI, Alan Conrad. ■ 24503 #012-05-1999 L2003 **END** *020 †20
KENNY, Eric Richard. 2025 TATE SPRINGS RD 24501 #036-01-1985 L1986 **RHU IM** *020 †20
KEYMER, Marjorie E. 700 MAIN ST 24504 #060-01-1970 **FM** *030
KHOURY, Joseph Benjamin. 2011 TATE SPRINGS RD 24501 #051-01-1994 L1998 **PCC SME** *020 †20
KIDD, Kristi G. 114 NATIONWIDE DR 24502 #051-07-1994 L1994 **OBG** *020
KIERNAN, Drew Edward. 2019 TATE SPRINGS RD, CENTRAL VA ORTHOPAEDICS 24501 #035-08-1994 L2000 **ORS HS** *020 †40
KIM, Eugene Lee. ■ 24504 #038-06-2002 L2007 **FP** *012
KIND, Heidi. 1007 SHEFFIELD DR, PHYSICIANS TREATMENT CENTE 24502 #035-75-1988, ▲ L2004 **FM** *020 †18 ‡
KING, C Sidney. 1901 TATE SPRINGS RD 24501 #051-04-1946 L1946 **IM OS** *071 †20
KITTRELL, Andrea. 1330 OAK LN, ASSOCIATES 24503 #036-05-1993 L1999 **OTO** *020 †45
KITTRELL, William Lloyd. 1801 THOMSON DR 24501 #016-45-1993 L1999 **CRS GS** *020 †85,10
KUHNLEY, Edward John. 2215 LANGHORNE RD STE 101, CNTRL VA COMM SERV CHD-FAM 24501 #051-01-1976 L1978 **P CHP** *040 †75 ‡
KUMAR, Shiv. 103 CLIFTON ST 24501 #495-36-1992 L2007 **NEP** *020 †20
LANE, Richard Allan. 1971 UNIVERSITY BLVD 24502 #023-01-1982 L1989 **ADL OM** *020 †70
LARKIN, Lawrence Douglas. ■ 24503 #034-01-1974 L1979 **DR** *071 †80
LARKIN, Lisa Marie. ■ 24501 #654-01-2006 L2007 **FP** *012
LARZELERE, Henry B. 1901 TATE SPRINGS RD 24501 #016-06-1944 L1969 **GS TS** *071 †85,90
LEE, Parker Hall, Jr. 3300 RIVERMONT AVE 24503 #051-01-1944 L1944 **OPH** *071 †35
LEE, Rick Don. 2401 ATHERHOLT RD 24501 #019-02-1997 L1999 **AN** *020 †05
LEFFKE, David W. 2542 LANGHORNE RD 24501 #035-06-1974 L1979 **U** *020 †95
LESKO, John Michael. 1922 THOMSON DR, STE D 24501 #422-01-2003 L2006 **AN** *020
LEWIS, Christopher W. 2410 ATHERHOLT RD 24501 #032-01-1999 L2002 **CD** *020 †20
LEWIS, Danielle Simon. 2215 LANDOVER PL, MEDICAL ASSOC OF CENTRAL V 24501 #035-19-1998 L2002 **IM** *020 †20
LOCKRIDGE, Robert S, Jr. 103 CLIFTON ST 24501 #051-04-1975 L1976 **NEP IM** *020 †20
LOTANO, Remo Andrea. 2402 ATHERHOLT RD 24501 #869-05-1968 L1972 **OPH GP** *071
LOWRY, E Kathryn. 3300 RIVERMONT AVE 24503 #055-01-1982 L1985 **AN** *020 †05
LU, Jack I Ning. 2215 LANDOVER PL 24501 #422-01-2003 L2006 **IM** *020 †20
LUEDKE, George Wm. 3300 RIVERMONT AVE 24503 #008-01-1976 L1980 **P ADP** *020 †75
LYNDE, James Lawrence. 20293 TIMBERLAKE RD 24502 #051-04-1957 L1957 **R NM** *020 †80,28
MACCALLUM, Cecilia Mermel. 1937 THOMSON DR, LYNCHBURG HEMATOLOGY 24501 #010-01-1999 L2003 **HO** *020 †20
MAC CORMAC, Michael Lloyd. 1901 TATE SPRINGS RD, DEPT OF ANESTHESIA 24501 #051-01-1984 L1987 **AN** *020 †05
MAC NEILL, John L. 1937 THOMSON DR, LYNCHBURG HEMATOLOGY 24501 #036-01-1984 L1989 **GO** *020 †20
MAFFEI, Loretta. 121 NATIONWIDE DR, STE A 24502 #041-14-1984 L1990 **GE IM** *020 †20
MAJEWSKI, Allen David. 3300 RIVERMONT AVE 24503 #021-05-1971 L1979 **PD** *020 †55
MALCOLM, Bradley Scott. 105 RICHESON DR, RICHESON DR PEDIATRICS 24501 #038-40-1975 L1979 **PD** *020 †55
MANDEVILLE, Brian William. ■ 24503 #056-06-1996 L2005 **IM** *020 †20
MANDEVILLE, Morgan Sturm. 105 RICHESON DR, RICHESON DR PEDIATRICS 24501 #010-01-1996 L1997 *020 †55
MARRACCINI, Christine A. 114 NATIONWIDE DR 24502 #023-01-1995 L1999 **OBG** *020 †30
MASSIE, William Mc Kinnon. ■ 24503 #051-01-1956 L1956 **IM OS** *020 †20
MATHIAS, Joseph E. 1901 TATE SPRINGS RD 24501 #051-04-1951 L1951 **U** *071 †95
MAWN, Christopher Brian. 2321 ATHERHOLT RD, BLUE RIDGE ENT & PLASTIC 24501 #012-01-1992 L1994 **OTO FPS** *020 †45
MC ANDREW, Brian P. 101 ARCHWAY CT 24502 #051-04-1999 L1999 **GS** *020
MC CABE, William Otey. 2091 LANGHORNE RD 24501 #051-04-1956 L1956 **FM GP** *071
MC CRARY, Morris E, III. 2138 LANGHORNE RD 24501 #051-01-1981 L1989 **NS** *020 †25
MC CURLEY, R Skyler. 1212 MCCONVILLE RD, F READ HOPKINS PEDIATRIC 24502 #036-01-1996 L1999 **PD** *020 †55
MC ROY, Lynn Louese. 1911 THOMSON DR 24501 #051-04-1987 L1992 **GS** *020 †85
MEADOWS, James Wesley. 2215 LANDOVER PL, P O BOX 11889 24501 #012-01-1992 L2000 **IM** *020 †20
MEADOWS, Kappa Peddy. 1330 OAK LN, STE 101 24503 #012-01-1992 L2000 **D** *020 †20,15
MEANS, Traci Michele. ■ 24503 #023-07-2007 **MPD** *012
MESSIER, Robert H, Jr. 2410 ATHERHOLT RD, THORACIC SURGERY 24501 #010-02-1988 L1990 **TS** *020 †85,90
METZGER, Edward Eugene. 1922 THOMSON DR STE D, LYNCHBURG INC 24501 #038-43-1995 L1996 **IM** *020 †05

■ = Address Information Privacy Protected

MEYER, Thomas Michael. 2410 ATHERHOLT RD 24501 #047-05-1997 L2005 **CD** *020 †20

MILAM, Michael Glenn. 1906 THOMSON DR 24501 #051-04-1982 L1988 **PUD CCM** *020 †20

MILANOVICH, Robt Anthony. 105 RICHESON DR 24501 #035-06-1968 L1975 **PD** *020 †55

MILES, Robert Milton. 1901 TATE SPRINGS RD 24501 #051-04-1968 L1968 **AI PD** *071 †55,03

MILLER, Richard Anthony. 3300 RIVERMONT AVE 24503 #038-40-1996 L1999 **IM** *020 †20

MILLER, Terry Oliver. 901 JEFFERSON ST, APT 6E 24504 #038-06-1964 L1970 **ORS** *071 †40

MOBAIDEEN, Ali Saleh. ■ 24502 #913-04-1993 L2006 **P** *012

MODJESKA, Gerald S. ■ 24503 #016-11-1949 L1989 **OS PD** *071 †55

MOFFATT, Lawrence S, Jr. 103 CLIFTON ST, LYNCHBURG NEPH PHYS 24501 #047-20-1987 L2000 **NEP IM** *020 †20

MOORE, Carl Alvin. 2410 ATHERHOLT RD 24501 #012-01-1980 L1986 **CD IM** *020 †20

MORRIS, John Franklin. PO BOX 678 24505 #051-04-1938 L1938 **AN** *071 †05

MORRIS, Richard Clagett. 105 RICHESON DR, RICHESON DR PEDIATRICS 24501 #051-01-1976 L1979 **PD** *020 †55

MORRIS, Willie Herman. 1901 TATE SPRINGS RD 24501 #051-01-1954 L1954 **GS** *071 †85

MUDRICK, Paul R. 1901 TATE SPRINGS RD, LYNCHBURG GENERAL HOSPITAL 24501 #051-01-1978 L1979 **AN** *020 †05

MUMPER, Elizabeth Anne. 2015 TATE SPRINGS RD, LOWR LEVEL 24501 #051-04-1980 L1984 **PD** *040 †55

MUTCH, Justin Andrew. 1212 MCCONVILLE RD, F READ HOPKINS PEDIATRIC 24502 #036-01-2000 L2003 **PD** *020 †55

NEIMAN, Wade Albert. 114 NATIONWIDE DR 24502 #041-09-1984 L1988 **OBG** *020 †30

NELSON-MADISON, Lori Ann. ■ 24502 #051-01-2006 L2006 **FP** *012

NEWTON, Grace Ann. 2007 TATE SPRINGS RD 24501 #027-01-1984 L1988 **D DMP** *020 †15 ‡

NEWTON, Richard Lynn. 113 NATIONWIDE DR, RADIOLOGY CONSULTANTS 24502 #027-01-1984 L1988 **R DR** *020 †80

NICHOLS, Katherine V. 1900 THOMSON DR, LYNCHBURG HEALTH DEPT VDH 24501 #016-06-1985 L1991 **NPM PD** *020 †55

NILES, Richard Allen. 2919 CONFEDERATE AVE 24501 #035-20-1962 L1970 **GYN** *071 †30

NUNN, Chalmers Morton, Jr. 121 NATIONWIDE DR 24502 #036-07-1980 L1999 **GE IM** *020 †20

NYGAARD, Thomas Wm. 2410 ATHERHOLT RD 24501 #047-05-1978 L1981 **CD IM** *020 †20

O'BRIEN, Peter Kenneth. 2410 ATHERHOLT RD 24501 #051-01-1994 L1994 **CD** *020 †20

OCHSNER, Frederick C. 1922 THOMSON DR 24501 #021-01-1972 L1976 **AN** *071 †05

OGRAM, John Donald. 2235 LANDOVER PL, CVCS ADULT /FAMILY SERVICE 24501 #033-05-1979 L1981 **P** *020 †75

OKIN, Michael Allen. 2091 LANGHORNE RD, STE 2 24501 #051-01-1980 L1987 **FM** *020 †18

OLDHAM, Dwight Stephen. 1937 THOMSON DR, LYNCHBURG HEMATOLOGY 24501 #051-04-1976 L1977 **ON HEM** *020 †20

OLIVER, Richard Wayne. 3300 RIVERMONT AVE 24503 #038-06-1969 L1971 **P** *020 †75 ‡

OLMSTED, John Bartow, III. 2811 LINKHORNE DR 24503 #047-20-1998 L1998 **FM** *020 †18

PADILLA, Michael Richard. 105 RICHESON DR, RICHESON DR PEDIATRICS 24501 #035-08-1996 L2005 **PD** *020 †55 ‡

PAINTER, William Edward. 2007 TATE SPRINGS RD 24501 #036-07-1957 L1967 **R NM** *071 †80,28

PALYS, Kenneth Stuart. 1901 TATE SPRINGS RD 24501 #041-02-1994 L2000 **EM** *020 †16

PARIKH, Nipun O. 2832 CANDLERS MOUNTAIN RD 24502 #495-23-1972 L1978 **GP PTH** *020 †50 ‡

PAUL, Kathleen Phillips. 1937 THOMSON DR, LYNCHBURG HEMATOLOGY 24501 #051-04-2000 L2002 **HO** *020 †20

PAULSEN, Suzanne Margaret. ■ 24503 #054-04-1959 L1964 **P CLP** *071 †50,75

PEDE, Roger Jos. 205 WINDY RIDGE DR 24503 #012-01-1992 L2001 **AN** *020 †05

PERROTTO, Judith A R. 1330 OAK LN, BREAST IMAGING 24503 #041-14-1985 L1997 **DR** *020 †80

PERRY, Donald Avant. 2401 ATHERHOLT RD 24501 #001-02-1976 L2001 **AN** *020 †18,05

PERRY, John Michael. 1905 ATHERHOLT RD, PATHOLOGY CONSULTANTS 24501 #001-02-1966 L1974 **PTH** *071 †50

PETRY, Craig John. 102 ARCHWAY CT, WYNDHURST FAMILY MEDICINE 24502 #056-06-1996 L1999 **FM** *020 †18 ‡

PHEMISTER, David Andrew. 114 NATIONWIDE DR 24502 #007-02-1990 L1994 **OBG** *020 †30

PIGGOTT, James Albert. 1905 ATHERHOLT RD 24501 #051-01-1961 L1961 **PTH** *020 †50

PITTARD, James Donald, Jr. 2215 LANDOVER PL, MEDICAL ASSOC OF CENTRAL V 24501 #051-04-1989 L1992 **FM** *020 †18

PLANKEEL, John Frederik. 2011 TATE SPRINGS RD 24501 #038-40-1996 L2001 **PCC** *020 †20

PLETKE, Patricia Anne. 2097 LANGHORNE RD, LYNCHBURG FAMILY MEDICINE 24501 #051-07-1979 L1980 **FM** *020 †18

PODOSEK, Alan M. 113 WIGGINGTON RD 24502 #035-06-1970 L1973 **FM D** *020 †18

POLETTI, Lawrence Francis. 1911 THOMSON DR 24501 #051-04-1993 L1995 **VS GS** *020 †85

POND, Trellou Jos, Jr. 2215 LANDOVER PL 24501 #047-05-1966 L1970 **IM CD** *071 †20 ‡

PORTER, Norman De Anguera. ■ 24503 #016-06-1965 L1985 **GYN** *071 †30

POTTER, Laura Jean. 213 WINDY RIDGE DR 24503 #007-02-1995 L2001 **EM** *020 †16

PRAHINSKI, John Robt. 1906 THOMSON DR 24501 #051-01-1992 L1993 **ORS** *020 †40

PRICE, Jerry Theodore. 1901 TATE SPRINGS RD 24501 #036-08-1986 L1987 **FM EM** *020 †18

PURVEZ, Akhtar. 3300 RIVERMONT AVE, CENTER FOR PAIN MANAGEMENT 24503 #495-51-1981 L1995 **APM PMM** *020 †05

RAFFERTY, Moira Anne. 2215 LANDOVER PL 24501 #051-04-1989 L2001 **IM** *020 †20

RAKHERAM, Geeta. 2215 LANDOVER PL 24501 #038-43-1995 L1998 **IM** *020 †20

RAMSEY, William Edward. 3300 RIVERMONT AVE 24503 #051-01-1971 L1971 **IM EM** *020 †20

RANK, Harb Leo. 113 WIGGINGTON RD 24502 #051-04-1994 L1994 **FM** *020 †18

RASO, Dominic Salvatore. 1905 ATHERHOLT RD, PATHOLOGY CNSLT OF CTRL VA 24501 #045-04-1991 L1998 **PTH PCP** *020 †50

RAYOS, Julie Rosete. 100 THORNFIELD DR 24502 #748-01-1976 L1984 **GP PD** *020

READ, Louis John. 3300 RIVERMONT AVE 24503 #051-04-1956 L1956 **FM** *071

REDMOND, James Seymour. 113 NATIONWIDE DR 24502 #036-07-1957 L1962 **R** *071 †80

REDMOND, Larry Hollis. 113 NATIONWIDE DR 24502 #036-05-1968 L1974 **DR** *020 †80

REID, David Lyle. 1901 TATE SPRINGS RD, LYNCHBURG GENERAL HOSPITAL 24501 #028-46-1988 L1999 **EM** *020 †16

RENNINGER, Valerie R. 320 FEDERAL ST 24504 #011-04-1991 L1992 **FM** *020 †18

RICHARDS, Robert D, Jr. 121 NATIONWIDE DR 24502 #051-04-1985 L1986 **GE IM** *020 †20

RICHARDS, William Davis. ■ 24502 #045-01-1948 L1953 **P** *071

RILEY, Harold Lee, III. 1933 THOMSON DR 24501 #051-01-1959 L1959 **N** *071 †75

RIORDAN, John Philip. 2225 LAKESIDE DR, STE C3 24501 #051-04-1992 L1995 **EM** *020 †16

RISHER, John Calhoun. 1330 OAK LN STE 201 24503 #051-01-1936 L1936 **OTO OS** *071

ROBERTSON, James W. 1901 TATE SPRINGS RD 24501 #036-01-1997 L1999 **FM** *020 †18

ROBERTSON, John Mott, Jr. ■ 24501 #051-01-1966 L1966 **IM** *071 †20

RODMAN, James Mulligan. 2137 LAKESIDE DR, STE 100 24501 #020-12-1976 L1977 **FM** *020 †18

ROONEY, Kara Mayer. 3300 RIVERMONT AVE 24503 #005-12-1993 L2005 **P CHP** *020 †75

SACKETT, Charles H. 2215 LANDOVER PL 24501 #051-01-1951 L1951 **IM CD** *071 †20

SACKETT, Matthew Clinton. 2410 ATHERHOLT RD 24501 #051-01-1994 L2000 **ICE** *020 †20

SALMON, John M, IV. 1905 ATHERHOLT RD, PATHOLOGY CONSULTANTS OF 24501 #051-04-1995 L2000 **PTH** *020 †50

SALVAGGIO, Mark Anthony. 1911 THOMSON DR, SEVEN HILLS SURGICAL ASSOC 24501 #041-09-1980 L2005 **GS VS** *020 †85

SCANLON, Nicole Rene. 2097 LANGHORNE RD 24501 #051-07-2003 L2003 **FM** *020 †18

SCHARF, Stephen Francis. 1901 TATE SPRINGS RD, LYNCHBURG GENERAL HOSPITAL 24501 #051-04-1987 L1991 **AN** *020 †05

SCHENBERG, Brian Mark. 1212 MCCONVILLE RD, F READ HOPKINS PEDIATRIC 24502 #035-08-2002 L2005 **PD** *020 †55

SCHEPENS, Daniel William. 113 NATIONWIDE DR 24502 #027-01-2000 L2006 **DR** *100 †80

SCHIETINGER, Brian Joseph. 2410 ATHERHOLT RD, THE CARDIOVASCULAR GROUP 24501 #047-06-2001 L2001 **CD** *100

SCHMIDT, Anita Ellen. 114 NATIONWIDE DR 24502 #035-45-1986 L1987 **GYN** *020 †30

SCOTT, Randall Abell. 3300 RIVERMONT AVE 24503 #051-04-1987 L1989 **P PFP** *020 †75

SENDI, Christopher Alan. 1901 TATE SPRINGS RD 24501 #010-02-1992 L1995 **IM** *020 †20

SESSOMS, George Wm. ■ 24503 #051-01-1954 L1954 **AN** *071

SHERBAN, Kenneth Anthony. 1901 TATE SPRINGS RD, LYNCHBURG GENERAL HOSPITAL 24501 #035-03-1977 L1980 **AN** *020 †05

SHUPTRINE, John Robt. 1901 TATE SPRINGS RD, LYNCHBURG GENERAL HOSPITAL 24501 #038-40-1981 L1988 **AN** *020 †05

SIDHU, Jaisimaran Kaur. 2097 LANGHORNE RD, MEDICINE RESI 24501 #422-01-2005 L2006 **FP** *012

SILVESTER, Timothy James. 1330 OAK LN, PLASTIC SURGERY 24503 #036-05-1974 L1979 **PS** *020 †65

SLUSHER, Ralph Chas. 1901 TATE SPRINGS RD 24501 #051-04-1957 L1957 **FM** *071 †18

SMITH, James Arthur, III. 1801 THOMSON DR 24501 #001-02-1964 L1974 **GS OS** *071 †85

SOLYOM, Antal Endre. 1066 KANAWA LN 24503 #473-02-1960 L1989 **P CHP** *071 †75

SONG, Soon Bock Kim. 2801 SEDGEWICK DR 24503 #583-01-1964 L1972 **PD** *020

SORENSON, Eric John. 2542 LANGHORNE RD 24501 #039-01-1964 L1969 **U** *020 †95

STEINMAN, Sharon Ann. 2215 LANDOVER PL 24501 #033-05-1997 L2001 **IM** *020

STEM, Jesse Lee. 2019 TATE SPRINGS RD 24501 #055-01-1995 L2001 **ORS** *020 †40

STEWART, Gary Schaake. 1212 MCCONVILLE RD 24502 #012-01-1983 L1984 **PD PHP** *020 †55

STEWART, Kathryn E P. 114 NATIONWIDE DR 24502 #012-01-1980 L1984 **OBG** *020 †30

STOKES, Brenda Lynn. 2097 LANGHORNE RD, LYNCHBURG FAMILY MEDICINE 24501 #023-01-1996 L1996 **FM** *040 †18

STOLL, Edward J. 1901 TATE SPRINGS RD 24501 #051-01-1951 L1951 **FM** *072 †18

STUTESMAN, Andrea Allen. 1319 ENTERPRISE DR, STE B 24502 #021-06-1983 L2005 **PM** *020 †60

STUTESMAN, James L. 105 RICHESON DR STE B 24501 #048-14-1983 L2005 **PM PMM** *020 †60

SUBLETT, James Wilson, Jr. 1922 THOMSON DR, STE D 24501 #051-01-1970 L1970 **AN** *071 †05

SULLIVAN, Robert Andersen. 1212 MCCONVILLE RD, F READ HOPKINS PEDIATRIC 24502 #045-04-1993 L1997 **PD** *020 †55

SULLIVAN, Stephanie K. 1212 MCCONVILLE RD, F READ HOPKINS PEDIATRIC 24502 #045-04-1993 L1997 **PD** *020 †55

SUPPA, Julie Ann. ■ 24503 #051-01-2005 L2005 **FP** *012

SUTTENFIELD, Chas Madison. 3300 RIVERMONT AVE 24503 #051-04-1962 L1962 **OPH** *071 †35

SYDNOR, Robert Wingfield. 2019 TATE SPRINGS RD 24501 #051-04-1975 L1976 **ORS** *020 †40

SYDNOR, Walton Kirkham. 2215 LANDOVER PL 24501 #036-01-1983 L1987 **IM** *020 †20

TATOM, Mathew Wayne. 2832 CANDLERS MOUNTAIN RD 24502 #035-75-1990, ▲ L1991 **FM** *020 †18

TAYLOR, Barron Keith. 3300 RIVERMONT AVE 24503 #051-07-1990 L1992 **NPM PD** *020 †55

TEAGUE, Francis B, Jr. 1901 TATE SPRINGS RD 24501 #036-05-1960 L1969 **GS TS** *071 †85,90

TEEL, Joseph Ryan. 320 FEDERAL ST, JOHNSON HEALTH CENTER 24504 #041-01-2003 L2006 **FM** *020 †18

THOMPSON, Stephen Lee. 2091 LANGHORNE RD 24501 #051-01-1965 L1965 **FM** *020

THOMPSON, Terry John. 1901 TATE SPRINGS RD 24501 #035-06-2001 L2001 **FM** *040

THOMSON, Chris Michael. 1901 TATE SPRINGS RD 24501 #051-04-1996 L1999 **EM** *020 †16

TOMPKINS, Matthew John. 2728 OLD FOREST RD 24501 #038-40-1995 L1995 **OBG** *020 †30

TORBERT, John V. ■ 24503 #051-01-1953 L1953 **IM** *071 †20

TRUITTE, David Brian. 2410 ATHERHOLT RD 24501 #041-12-1986 L1993 **CD IM** *020 †20

UZSOY, Namik Kemal. ■ 24503 #902-01-1948 L1973 **IM CD** *071

VALENTINE, Carl Michael. 2410 ATHERHOLT RD 24501 #051-01-1984 L1990 **CD IM** *020 †20

VANDERBURGH, Elizabeth A. 114 NATIONWIDE DR, WOMENS HEALTH SVCS 24502 #023-12-1988 L2003 **OBG** *020 †30

VANDEWATER, James Carl. 2091 LANGHORNE RD 24501 #051-04-1975 L1976 **FM** *020 †18

VAN DYKE, Kyle Gerard. 2919 CONFEDERATE AVE 24501 #016-02-1995 L1995 **FM** *020 †18

VAN DYKE, William Howard, Jr. 2410 ATHERHOLT RD 24501 #051-04-1978 L1979 **CD** *020 †20

VAUGHAN, David Allen. ■ 24503 #051-04-1973 L1974 **LM** *030 †20

VAUGHN, David Robinson. 2401 ATHERHOLT RD 24501 #051-01-2001 L2001 **AN** *020 †05

VOGEL, Robert Brian. 2402 ATHERHOLT RD, PIEDMONT EYE CENTER 24501 #011-02-1988 L1989 **OPH** *020 †35

VON ELTEN, Christopher B. 2137 LAKESIDE DR 24501 #051-04-1998 L2003 **FM** *020 †18

VON OESEN, Henry Davis. 1914 THOMSON DR 24501 #035-20-1970 L1977 **ORS** *020 †40

VOTH, Michael Kimberly. 1901 TATE SPRINGS RD 24501 #051-01-1977 L1978 **EM FM** *020 †16,18

VYAS, Vishnu K. 792 FARFIELDS DR, CENTRAL VIRGINIA TRAINING 24502 #495-23-1955 L1967 **GP OBG** *071

WADE, James Scott. 2215 LANDOVER PL, P O BOX 11889 24501 #020-12-1983 L1988 **ID IM** *020 †20

WALLACE, Pamela Waldron. 1933 THOMSON DR 24501 #026-08-1976 L1979 **P** *075 †75

WALLACE, William Miles. 1933 THOMSON DR 24501 #051-04-1973 L1979 **N** *020 †75

WALLER, Brenda Sue. 1935 THOMSON DR, PRIS, PLC. 24501 #041-12-1985 L1997 **PM EM** *020 †60

WEBB, Christopher Coffin. 2215 LANDOVER PL 24501 #051-04-1976 L1979 **IM IMG** *020 †20

WHEELOCK, Tracy Allen. 114 NATIONWIDE DR 24502 #051-01-1988 L1992 **OBG** *020 †30

WHISNANT, Robert Andrew. 2108 LANGHORNE RD 24501 #051-01-1986 L1988 **U GS** *020 †95

WHISNANT, Robt Alexander. 2108 LANGHORNE RD 24501 #051-04-1961 L1961 **OPH** *020 †35

WHITEHOUSE, Francis R. ■ 24503 #051-01-1938 L1938 **IM** *071 †20

WHITMORE, Charles W. 1330 OAK LN, STE 101 24503 #051-01-1947 L1947 **D OM** *072 †15

■ = Address Information Privacy Protected

WHITMORE, Mary C Gossage. 1330 OAK LN, STE 101 24503 #048-02-1948 L1953 **D** *020 †15
WILGUS, Alexander M. 2097 LANGHORNE RD, LYNCHBURG FAMILY MEDICINE 24501 #036-01-1993 L1995 **FM** *020 †18
WILL, Michael David. 2215 LANDOVER PL 24501 #051-01-1983 L1986 **IM** *020 †20
WILLIAMS, John Edward. 2091 LANGHORNE RD, STE 2 24501 #051-04-1982 L1983 **FM** *020 †18
WILLIAMS, Nathan Ramon. 2215 LANDOVER PL 24501 #036-08-1985 L1990 **IM** *020 †20
WILLIAMSON, Robert James. 2401 ATHERHOLT RD 24501 #023-07-1974 1982 **AN IM** *020 †15
WILLINGER, Samuel M. 3300 RIVERMONT AVE, VIRGINIA BAPTIST HOSP 24503 #165-03-1979 L1989 **NPM** *020 †20
WILSON, Jeffrey W. 2025 TATE SPRINGS RD, LYNCHBURG RHEUMATOLOGY CLC 24501 #036-07-1972 L1978 **RHU IM** *020 †20
WILSON, John Milton. 3300 RIVERMONT AVE 24503 #016-11-1984 L1997 **P** *020 †75
WISNIEWSKI, Lisa. ■ 24506 #050-02-1991 L1995 **END** *020 †20
WISNIEWSKI, Ralph Michael. 121 NATIONWIDE DR 24502 #041-09-1992 L1995 **GE** *020 †20
WODICKA, David Michael. 2091 LANGHORNE RD, STE 2 24501 #017-20-1977 L1984 **FM** *020 †18
WOLANSKI, Eugene Geoffrey. 2215 LANDOVER PL 24501 #051-01-1973 L1992 **IM** *020 †20 ‡
WOMBWELL, Jos Henry, III. 1906 THOMSON DR 24501 #020-12-1980 L1988 **ORS** *020 †40
WORETA, Solomon G. 2097 LANGHORNE RD, MEDICINE RESI 24501 #759-06-2004 L2006 **FM** *100
WORTLEY, George Cornelius. 2097 LANGHORNE RD, LYNCHBURG FAMILY MEDICINE 24501 #035-15-1977 L1987 **FM FSM** *020 †18
WRIGHT, James Wayne. 700 MAIN ST, FIRST COLONY LIFE INS CO 24504 #051-01-1976 L1979 **IM END** *062 †20
WRIGHT, Ronna Kim. 2091 LANGHORNE RD 24501 #039-05-1987 L1990 **FM** *020 †18
WU, Samuel. ■ 24502 #242-43-1957 L1968 **IM GPM** *071
WYNNYK, Patrick Jerome. 1901 TATE SPRINGS RD 24501 #023-01-1994 L1999 **IM** *020 †16,20
YODER, Daryl Hoak. 3209 FOREST BROOK RD 24501 #038-40-1973 L1977 **P** *020 ‡
YORK, Carrie Elizabeth. 1971 UNIVERSITY BLVD 24502 #036-01-2003 L2006 **FM** *020 †18
YOUNT, Laura Elizabeth. ■ 24503 #012-05-2004 L2007 **IM** *100 †20
YU, Pearl Lee. 3300 RIVERMONT AVE 24503 #026-04-1995 L2003 **PDP SME** *020 †55

MACHIPONGO – NORTHAMPTON

SHORT, Cathy Ellen. ■ 23405 #051-01-1987 L1992 **PD** *020 †55
WEISHAAR, Richard Jay. ■ 23405 #035-20-1952 L1985 **GYN** *071 †30

MADISON – MADISON

ELBERT, Bethanne. 2503 S SEMINOLE TRL, MADISON FAMILY MEDICINE 22727 #051-01-1996 L1996 **IM** *020 †20
FRYE, Patricia Carol. ■ 22727 #023-01-1981 L1982 **PD** *020 †55
HANSON, Maury Lloyd. ■ 22727 #035-20-1955 L1966 **NS** *100 †25
LAFFOND, William T. 2503 S SEMINOLE TRL 22727 #024-16-1985 L1997 **FM** *020 †18
LOGAN, Anne Jones. 125 N MAIN ST 22727 #051-04-1976 L1985 **FM** *020 †18
MARTENS, Vernon E. ■ 22727 #028-34-1937 L1971 **PTH CLP** *071
MOSCOE, Jay Edward. 125 N MAIN ST, P O BOX 587 22727 #020-12-1976 L1977 **FM** *020 †18
SCHENCK, Marcus David. 125 N MAIN ST, P O BOX 587 22727 #027-01-1978 L1981 **FM IMG** *020 †18
SEALANDER, John Yates. 2503 S SEMINOLE TRL 22727 #036-08-1985 L1996 **FM EM** *020 †18

MADISON HEIGHTS – AMHERST

BAUTISTA, Divinia Maliwat. 521 COLONY RD 24572 #748-01-1965 L1982 **PD** *020 †55
BENDALL, Richard A, Jr. PO BOX 1060, 4262 S AMHERST HWY 24572 #051-04-1976 L1977 **FM** *020 †18
CHANG, Wei Liang. 521 COLONY RD 24572 #244-04-1966 L1977 **PTH** *020 †50
DOBYNS, Thomas Elroy. 4579 S AMHERST HWY 24572 #051-04-1981 L1982 **FM** *020 †18
GARRETT, Calvin Sampson. ■ 24572 #051-04-1953 L1953 **GS** *074 †85
HAGA, David Shotwell. PO BOX 1060, 4262 S AMHERST HWY 24572 #051-04-1984 L1985 **FM** *020 †18
METZLER, Keith Alan. 200 AMELON SQ 24572 #036-08-1986 L1987 **FM** *020 †18
PARIKH, Surekha Nipun. 521 COLONY RD 24572 #495-22-1974 L1979 **GP** *020 ‡

MAIDENS – GOOCHLAND

APPELBERG, Maria. ■ 23102 #051-04-1974 L1977 **AN** *020
CHRISTIE, Laurence Glenn. 12433 KILLIGAY LN 23102 #051-04-1957 L1957 **GS VS** *020 †85
EARLY, Warren Luther. 1604 MAIDENS RD 23102 #041-13-1957 L1978 **R NM** *072 †80,28
GAGON, Terry Ersel. ■ 23102 #049-01-1966 L1972 **P PYA** *030 †75

MANAKIN SABOT – GOOCHLAND

BUGBEE, George Washington. ■ 23103 #041-12-1985 L1991 **AN** *020 †05
CROSS, Kieran Gorman. ■ 23103 #051-01-1990 L1993 **DR** *020 †80
GLASSER, Robert Michael. ■ 23103 #011-02-1962 L2007 **HEM IM** *072 †20
GORMLEY, William Thos. ■ 23103 #038-43-1977 L2000 **PTH FOP** *062 †50
HELLAMS, Ralph D, Jr. 294 RIVER RD W 23103 #051-07-1995 L1995 **FM** *020 †18
HERZOG, John Paul. 721 MEADOW RIDGE VW 23103 #024-05-1963 L1998 **END IM** *071 †20
HOFFMAN, Zachary Todd. ■ 23103 #051-04-2007 L2007 **IM** *012
KIRVEN, Leo Edwin. PO BOX 146 23103 #045-01-1954 L1963 **P** *030
PASCO, Hayden Merrill. ■ 23103 #051-04-2008 *012
RAO, Jaikar Sudhakar. ■ 23103 #495-37-1963 L1972 **EM** *071
RAO, Sybil P Nazareth. ■ 23103 #495-37-1961 L1975 **IM** *071 †20
SOLOMON, Stuart. ■ 23103 #051-04-1969 L1969 **PD** *071 †55
VANICHKACHORN, Greg Sukit. ■ 23103 #051-04-2005 L2006 **FP** *012
VIOL, Anthony William. 700 WOODSON PL 23103 #051-07-2000 L2000 **PS** *012 †85
ZEMMEL, Neil Jason. 406 WELLFIELD RD, RICHMOND AESTHETIC SURGERY 23103 #051-01-1998 L1998 **PS HS** *020 †65

MANASSAS – MANASSAS CITY

ABDELKADER, Maha Mohamed. 8680 HOSPITAL WAY, PRINCE WILLIAM HOSPITAL 20110 #915-02-1995 L2001 **P** *020
ADAMS, Selwyn Alexander. 9320 LEE AVE, REGIONAL ADULT DETENTION C 20110 #035-06-1988 L1993 **FM** *020 †20
ADEVOSO, Lauro Lavengco. ■ 20108 #748-01-1954 L1964 **AN** *071 †05
ALBERTSON, Keith Sumner. 9379 FORESTWOOD LN, PRINCE WILLIAM ORTHO CTR 20110 #041-02-1983 L2004 **ORS GS** *020 †40
ALISUAG, Andres, Jr. 9001 DIGGES RD STE 201 20110 #748-01-1967 L1978 **CD IM** *020 †20
AMY, Jonathan Robt. 8650 SUDLEY RD STE 309 20110 #010-02-1982 L1984 **N** *020 †75
ANBARASAN, Malarmathi T. 9161 LIBERIA AVE, STE 102 20110 #495-16-1996 L2002 **FM** *020 †18
ANDRIES, Luke Dumitru. 8700 SUDLEY RD 20110 #781-01-1987 L2006 **AN** *100
ARIAS, Joanna Dolores. 9001 DIGGES RD, STE 205 20110 #051-01-1979 L1994 **PS** *020 †65
AULT, Wendy Chickering. 9384 FORESTWOOD LN STE A 20110 #051-04-1976 L1979 **PD** *020 †55
AZIM, Mohammed Haroon. 8694 CENTREVILLE RD 20110 #495-53-1983 L1993 **IM** *020 †20
BAJNOK, Thomas Andrew. 8700 SUDLEY RD, MANASSAS ANESTHESIA 20110 #038-44-1987 L1991 **AN** *020 †20
BANKS, Aaron Elijah. 9550 SURVEYOR CT 20110 #005-14-2000 L2006 **PDC** *020
BARNES, Katina Geiger. 8700 SUDLEY RD, PRINCE WILLIAM HOSPITAL 20110 #036-01-2000 L2007 **FM** *020 †55
BARONI, Darren Scott. 8650 SUDLEY RD 20110 #023-12-1993 L2006 **GE** *020 †20
BARTOLOZZI, Mark Andrew. 9001 DIGGES RD, STE 204 20110 #035-09-1987 L1992 **GS VS** *020 †85
BASSAM, Deeni. 8525 ROLLING RD, STE 200 20110 #051-01-1997 L2004 **APM AN** *020 †05
BAZACO, Geo Constantine. 8650 SUDLEY RD, STE 212 20110 #561-11-1970 L1974 **IM PCC** *020 †20
BOLVARI, Joseph J. ■ 20110 #473-03-1953 L1960 **OBG** *071 †30
BRADY, John Wm. 8650 SUDLEY RD STE 310 20110 #010-01-1965 L1969 **D** *020 †15
BRODIE, Robin Elizabeth. 8650 SUDLEY RD, STE 306 20110 #051-01-1989 L1992 **P** *020 †55
BROOKS, Michelle Marie. 9001 DIGGES RD, STE 106 20110 #051-01-1998 L2002 **PD** *020 †55
BROWN, Toby Louis. 8629 SUDLEY RD STE 102, VIRGINIA RADIOLOGY ASSOC 20110 #036-01-1971 L1979 **R EM** *020 †80
BUCHINSKY, Elizabeth Anne. 8650 SUDLEY RD 20110 #035-15-1991 L1995 **FM** *020 †18
BUCHINSKY, Vincent Jos. 8691 STONEWALL RD 20110 #041-14-1980 L1982 **FM** *020 †18 ‡
CAMPBELL, Susan Keller. 8650 SUDLEY RD, SUTIE 306 20110 #051-01-1991 L1994 **FM** *020 †18
CARMOSKY, Donna Josephine. 8680 HOSPITAL WAY 20110 #035-47-1989 L1999 **P PYG** *020 †75
CARY, John Francis. 8700 SUDLEY RD 20110 #023-01-1984 L1987 **IM** *020 †20
CASANOVA, Edda Noelia. 8680 HOSPITAL WAY 20110 #042-04-1980 L2002 **P CHP** *020
CHAKURKAR, Ashwin B. 8700 SUDLEY RD, ATTN: CREDENTIALS DEPT 20110 #495-01-1985 L2001 **PDC** *020 †55
CHAMBERS, Joseph F. 8640 SUDLEY RD, STE 203 20110 #035-15-1999 L2002 **FM** *020 †18
CHOI, Myung Whan. 8650 SUDLEY RD, STE 410 20110 #051-04-1995 L1995 **IM** *020 †20
CHOWHAN, Anika Zaka. 8700 SUDLEY RD, MEDICAL STAFF OFFICE 20110 #048-04-1996 L2003 **PD** *020 †55
CHUNG, Andrew Keun. 8700 SUDLEY RD 20110 #025-01-1995 L2004 **U** *020 †95
CHUNG, Tae Sung. 9001 DIGGES RD, STE 206 20110 #051-04-1995 L1997 **FM** *020 †20
CLEARY, John Brian. 8650 SUDLEY RD, STE 212 20110 #010-01-1971 L1975 **PUD CCM** *020 †20
CONNER, Alvin Eugene. 9201 PORTNER AVE 20110 #051-04-1953 L1953 **PD** *071 †55
DEBS, Anthony. 8701 STONEWALL RD STE A 20110 #330-03-1967 L1976 **ORS** *020 †40
DEHAL, Stacy Annmarie. 9304 FOREST POINT CIR, MANASSAS OB/GYN 20110 #041-13-1994 L1998 **OBG** *020 †30
DELAWTER, Teresa Lynne. ■ 20110 #016-42-1990 L1994 **P ADP** *020 †75
DE LEON, Remedios L. 8910 CENTREVILLE RD, FAMILY MEDICAL CENTER 20110 #748-08-1977 L1993 **IM** *020 †20
DEMIDOV, Vladimir. 8700 SUDLEY RD 20110 #913-36-1981 L1999 **P PYG** *020 †75
DE ROSA, Gary Angelo. 8640 SUDLEY RD STE 203 20110 #010-02-1979 L1980 **FM** *020 †18
DESPER, Paul Carlton. 9608 CHAMPION CT 20110 #051-01-1961 L1961 **IM END** *071
DJAFARI, Valla Haji. 9378 FORESTWOOD LN 20110 #041-09-1997 L2004 **OPH** *020 †35
DOTSON, Thomas Charles. 9590 SURVEYOR CT, C/O DR. IRWIN 20110 #055-01-1995 L2000 **IM** *020 †20
DRUKER, Alla George. 8700 SUDLEY RD, MANASSAS ANESTHESIA 20110 #913-06-1984 L1999 **AN** *020 †05
EGGE, Alan Chester. 8640 SUDLEY RD, STE 207 20110 #051-01-1976 L1984 **OPH** *020 †55,35
ERDAG, Namik. 8401 DORSEY CIR, STE 101 20110 #902-04-1989 L2005 **DR** *100 †80
ESCANO, Michael C. 8569 SUDLEY RD, STE B 20110 #047-06-1999 L2005 **CD** *020 †20
FAROOQUE, Abdullah Al. 9001 DIGGES RD, STE 101 20110 #160-02-1989 L2000 **IM** *020 †20
FARR, Joseph Gerald. 8650 SUDLEY RD STE 206 20110 #012-05-1982 L1986 **GS VS** *020 †85
FELDMANN, Spencer Geo, Jr. 8640 SUDLEY RD STE 203 20110 #035-06-1977 L1980 **FM** *020 †18
FLOWER, Anita Rebecca. 9384 FORESTWOOD LN STE A 20110 #012-05-1986 L1989 **PD** *020 †55
FLOWERS, O Wendell. ■ 20110 #010-03-1981 L2006 **PD** *020 †55
FOLEY, Maura Patricia. 8650 SUDLEY RD, STE 212 20110 #035-06-1994 L1994 **PCC SME** *020 †20
GEHO, David Hurst. 10900 UNIV BLVD, M S 4E3 20110 #038-06-2001 L2006 **ATP** *050 †50
GIANCOLA, Frank James. 8640 SUDLEY RD, STE 306 20110 #010-02-1986 L1988 **PD** *020 †55
GIL MONTERO, Guillermo H. 8700 SUDLEY RD 20110 #132-02-1962 L1967 **U** *071 †95
GIYANANI, Ravi Mulchand. 8401 DORSEY CIR, STE 101 20110 #041-02-1994 L2000 **DR** *020 †80
GLASS, Kevin Lee. 8650 SUDLEY RD, STE 212 20110 #041-12-1991 L1998 **PUD** *020 †20
GLUCK, Gabriel. 8702 SUDLEY RD 20110 #067-01-1972 L1977 **ORS** *020 †20
GONZALEZ, John. 9304 FOREST POINT CIR, VIRGINIA WOMEN'S HLTH. ASS 20110 #035-19-1983 L1985 **OBG** *020 †30
GOODMAN, Laura Jean. 8700 SUDLEY RD, MANASSAS ANESTHESIA 20110 #051-01-1988 L1999 **AN** *020 †05
GORBACH, Jonathan Samuel. 8700 SUDLEY RD 20110 #024-07-1993 L1993 **DR** *020 †16
GOWER, Arthur Gaillard. 9001 DIGGES RD STE 107 20110 #051-01-1958 L1958 **PD** *020 †55 ‡
GRANADOS, Erik Gabriel. 9384 FORESTWOOD LN STE A, MANASSAS PEDIATRICS 20110 #429-01-1988 L1999 **PD** *020 †55

GUERRERO, Victor N. 9036 SUDLEY RD 20110 #748-10-1965 L1972 **ORS** *020 †40
GULERIA, Anshu Singh. 8525 ROLLING RD, STE 220 20110 #038-44-1988 L1991 **U** *020 †95
GUPTA, Arun Kumar. 8428 DORSEY CIR STE 101 20110 #495-90-1992 L2000 **IM** *020 †20
GUPTA, Neeraj. 9380 FORESTWOOD LN, STE F 20110 #038-44-1986 L1991 **OTO HNS** *020 †45
GUTLIPH, Jo Anne. 8640 SUDLEY RD, STE 303 20110 #035-06-1981 L1989 **GYN** *020 †30
HA, Cuong Trong. 8650 SUDLEY RD, STE 310 20110 #051-01-1999 L2003 **D** *020 †15
HACHICHO, Hoda Mihieddine. 8650 SUDLEY RD STE 300 20110 #913-01-1991 L2002 **N** *020 †75
HAILE, Lydia. 8700 SUDLEY RD, ATTN: MEDICAL STAFF OFFICE 20110 #016-11-1998 L2001 **EM** *020 †16
HARANGOZO, Ivan Ferenc. 8700 SUDLEY RD, MANASSAS ANESTHESIA 20110 #035-06-1987 L1991 **AN** *020 †05
HARVAN, David. 8625 SUDLEY RD 20110 #010-02-1977 L1981 **OPH** *020
HAY, Andy. 8717 DIGGES RD 20110 #023-07-1987 L1996 **OPH** *020 †35
HEATH, John Francis. 9300 FOREST POINT CIR 20110 #010-02-1955 L1959 **P CHP** *020
HEATON, Christopher Rees. 8691 STONEWALL RD 20110 #305-01-2001 L2004 **FM** *020 †18
HIGHFILL, Christopher S. 8644 SUDLEY RD, STE 308 20110 #023-01-1994 L2000 **ORS** *020 †40
HILLMAN, Todd H. 8401 DORSEY CIR, STE 101 20110 #023-01-1984 L1990 **DR** *020 †80
HORTON-THOMPSON, Camille. 8640 SUDLEY RD, STE 203A 20110 #033-06-2000 L2004 **FM** *020
HOSICK, William Bartley. 8644 SUDLEY RD, STE 308 20110 #051-04-1986 L1992 **ORS OSM** *020 †40
HUFF, William Thos, Jr. ■ 20110 #036-01-1960 L1963 **AN** *020
HUQ, Hassan Iqbal. 8401 DORSEY CIR, STE 101 20110 #051-01-1999 L1999 **DR** *020 †80
HUSAIN, Mohsin Akber. 8401 DORSEY CIR, STE 101 20110 #023-01-2000 L2006 **DR** *020 †80 ‡
IRWIN, Gilbert Raymond. 9590 SURVEYOR CT 20110 #033-05-1968 L1973 **IM ID** *020
ISIDRO, Hermenegildo N. 8703 STONEWALL RD 20110 #748-01-1966 L1974 **GP** *020
JACOBS, Jennifer Hayes. 8640 SUDLEY RD, STE 207 20110 #033-06-1992 L1998 **OPH** *020 †35
JIMENEZ, Daniel Estabillo. 8700 SUDLEY RD 20110 #748-10-1973 L1977 **EM** *020 †16,70
JOCSON, Dante Nazareno. 8910 CENTREVILLE RD 20110 #748-08-1968 L1975 **FM** *071
JOHNSON, Ingrid Denise. 8640 SUDLEY RD, STE 306 20110 #051-01-1997 L1997 **PD** *020 †55
JOSSAN, Subir Singh. 8525 ROLLING RD, STE 300 20110 #051-04-1993 L1993 **ORS HS** *020 †40
KALUS, Morton E, Jr. 8569 SUDLEY RD, STE B 20110 #023-07-1981 L1993 **CD NM** *020 †20
KANG, Amy. 8640 SUDLEY RD, STE 303 20110 #017-20-2000 L2005 **OBG** *020 †30
KANG, Byong Kuh. 8703 STONEWALL RD, STE 2B 20110 #010-03-1997 L2000 **FM** *020 †18
KANG, Margaret. 8629 SUDLEY RD, STE 102 20110 #051-04-2000 L2006 **DR** *100 †80
KAO, Janet Wenyun. 8700 SUDLEY RD, PRINCE WILLIAM HOSPITAL 20110 #028-02-1995 L1998 **PD** *020 †55
KARANTH, Shantharama. 8700 SUDLEY RD 20110 #495-09-1979 L1988 **PD NPM** *020 †55
KASIRSKY, Jennifer Lee. 8700 SUDLEY RD, OB/GYN HOSPITALIST OF PRIN 20110 #041-09-1994 L2005 **OBG** *020 †30
KATZ, David Harold. 8640 SUDLEY RD, STE 306 20110 #043-01-1990 L1994 **PD** *020 †55
KELLY, John Stephen. ■ 20110 #016-43-1947 L1993 **FM CRS** *071
KERR, Michael Keller. 8700 SUDLEY RD, C/O PRINCE WILLIAM HOSPITA 20110 #054-09-1993 L1996 **EM** *020 †16
KHAN, Huma Khalil. 8680 HOSPITAL WAY 20110 #704-20-1990 L2004 **P** *020 †75
KHOT, Vikram S. 8680 HOSPITAL WAY 20110 #495-33-1981 L1988 **P** *020 †75 ‡
KIM, Edward Chul. 8650 SUDLEY RD 20110 #041-02-1989 L1990 **GE IM** *020 †20
KIM, Edwin Hyunjin. 8401 DORSEY CIR, STE 101 20110 #016-02-1987 L2000 **DR** *020 †80
KIM, Eugene Hyun. 9378 FORESTWOOD LN, STE E 20110 #010-03-1999 L2003 **NEP** *020 †20
KOEPKE, James Robt. 8401 DORSEY CIR, STE 101 20110 #051-07-1991 L1997 **DR** *020 †80
KRENYTZKY, Stephen Marc. 9394 FORESTWOOD LN 20110 #019-02-1971 L1976 **PD** *020 †55
KROEGER, Leah Dawn. 8650 SUDLEY RD, STE 309 20110 #051-04-2001 L2006 **CN** *020 †75
KRUSE, David Matthew. 8700 SUDLEY RD 20110 #036-05-1995 L1998 **EM** *020 †16
LAMBA, Sanjay. 8600 ROLLING RD, STE 100 20110 #496-09-1991 L1997 **PD** *020 †55
LATIMER, Robert A W, Jr. 8640 SUDLEY RD, SUTIE 203 20110 #010-02-1982 L1988 **FM** *020 †18
LAWANDE, Ratnakar L. 8703 STONEWALL RD 20110 #495-17-1966 L1972 **OTO** *071 †45
LAWANDE, Rekha Ratnakar. 8700 SUDLEY RD, MANASSAS ANESTHESIA 20110 #495-17-1968 L1978 **AN** *020
LEET, Christopher Julian. 8569 SUDLEY RD, STE B 20110 #012-01-1972 L1973 **CD IM** *020 †20
LEHMAN, Robert Francis. 9379 FORESTWOOD LN 20110 #041-02-1964 L1971 **ORS** *071 †40
LEVIN, Norman Wm. 8700 SUDLEY RD 20110 #041-13-1973 L1986 **RHU IM** *020 †20
LIAO, Michael Shangte. 8650 SUDLEY RD, STE 303 20110 #012-05-2002 L2006 **OBG** *100 †30
LING, Judith. 8805 SUDLEY RD STE 200 20110 #005-11-1981 L1998 **PD** *020
LO RUSSO, Thomas James. 8650 SUDLEY RD, STE 212 20110 #035-15-1987 L1993 **PCC SME** *020 †20
LOUIE-NG, Eugene Junmien. 8650 SUDLEY RD STE 303 20110 #035-08-1995 L2001 **OBG** *020 †30
LYON, Everett Carter, Jr. 9301 LEE AVE, PRINCE WILLIAM HEALTH DIST 20110 #051-04-1960 L1960 **GP** *020
MACKIE, Susanne B. 8700 SUDLEY RD, EMERGENCY DEPT. 20110 #010-01-1995 L1995 **PD** *020 †55
MAC NAY, Donald Longwell. 8805 SUDLEY RD, PIEDMONT ORTHOPEDIC CLINIC 20110 #065-05-1962 L1969 **ORS** *075
MAGALSKI, Joseph John, Jr. 9001 DIGGES RD, STE 204 20110 #041-13-1994 L1999 **GS** *020 †85
MARANIAN, Ara Matthew. 8569 SUDLEY RD STE B, PRINCE WILLIAM CARDIOLOGY 20110 #010-02-1997 L2006 **CD** *020 †20
MARK, Frank Rudolf. 8700 SUDLEY RD 20110 #869-02-1953 L1982 **GP PHP** *071
MARKERT, Douglas James. 8401 DORSEY CIR, STE 101 20110 #051-07-1994 L1999 **VIR** *020 †80
MAROCHNIK, Sergei L. 8700 SUDLEY RD, MANASSAS ANESTHESIA 20110 #913-09-1983 L1998 **AN PME** *020 †05
MARSH, Robert Lee. 8640 SUDLEY RD, STE 302 20110 #016-11-1982 L2000 **ON HEM** *020 †20
MARTIN, Pamela Leigh. 8401 DORSEY CIR, STE 101 20110 #051-04-1992 L2002 **DR** *020 †80
MASON, Marsha Nagurney. 9384 FORESTWOOD LN STE A 20110 #051-07-1977 L1979 **PD** *020
MASSEY, Philip Norwood. 8401 DORSEY CIR, STE 101 20110 #023-01-1978 L1982 **DR** *020 †80
MATHEWS, J Lee, Jr. 8700 SUDLEY RD 20110 #051-04-1960 L1960 **FM EM** *071
MC CUE, Raymond Leo, III. 9304 FOREST POINT CIR, MANASSAS OB GYN 20110 #010-02-1979 L1987 **OBG** *020 †30
MC GLOTHLIN, William Geo. 8421 DORSEY CIR, STE 102 20110 #051-04-1978 L1994 **CHP P** *020
MC KENZIE, Andrea Elese. 8650 SUDLEY RD, STE 309 20110 #010-01-1987 L1994 **IM** *020 †20
MCPHERSON, Luz G. 8700 SUDLEY RD 20110 #748-10-1988 L2003 **NPM PD** *020 †55
MILLER, Stephen Lawrence. 8401 DORSEY CIR, STE 101 20110 #048-04-1981 L1986 **DR** *020 †80
MOHSENI, Alex Shokouhi. 8700 SUDLEY RD, PRINCE WILLIAMS HOSPITAL - 20110 #023-01-2003 L2005 **EM** *100 †16
MORALES, Edmundo G. 9202 CENTREVILLE RD, MANASSAS MEDICAL CENTER 20110 #649-17-1945 L1953 **GP EM** *071
MUKHARA, Hemalatha. 8680 HOSPITAL WAY, PRINCE WILLIAM HOSPITAL 20110 #495-95-1993 L2007 **CHP** *020 †75
MURTAZA, Syed Jawaid. 8680 HOSPITAL WAY, PRINCE WILLIAM HOSPITAL 20110 #704-02-1991 L2005 **SME** *020 †75
MUTHIAH, Annamalai. 8629 SUDLEY RD, STE 102 20110 #495-04-1959 L1999 **R AR** *062 †55
MUTHIAH, Annamalai, Jr. 8629 SUDLEY RD, STE 102 20110 #035-09-1992 L1992 **DR** *020 †80
NANCE, Larry Allen. 8650 SUDLEY RD, STE 200 20110 #038-40-1977 L1984 **OBG** *020 †30
NAROJI, Syamala K. 8701 DIGGES RD 20110 #495-11-1974 L1989 **OBG** *020 †30
NATOVITZ, Jodi Robin. 8640 SUDLEY RD, STE 306 20110 #035-06-1992 L1996 **PD** *020 †55
NEMIROVSKY, Eduard. 8700 SUDLEY RD, PRINCE WILLIAMS HOSPITAL 20110 #913-15-1987 L2003 **AN** *020 †05
NOONAN, Daniel J. 9380 FORESTWOOD LN STE B 20110 #035-19-1979 L1980 **OBG** *020 †30
NOORI, Ahmad Osman. 8694 CENTREVILLE RD 20110 #495-53-1985 L1994 **NEP IM** *020 †20
NUAR, Aime Louise. ■ 20110 #025-07-1977 L1978 **FM** *020
OCAMPO, Carlos Adalberto. 8700 SUDLEY RD, PRINCE WILLIAM HOSPITAL/ME 20110 #264-18-1993 L2006 **AN** *020
OMOJOKUN, Morayo Olufunso. 8691 STONEWALL RD 20110 #051-01-2002 L2005 **FM** *020 †18
PACE, Maria Elena. 8401 DORSEY CIR, STE 101 20110 #051-07-1994 L2002 **DR** *020 †80
PALOMBI, Joseph John. 8424 DORSEY CIR STE 102, SUDLEY PARK PROFESS CTR 20110 #035-03-1968 L1981 **CHP P** *020
PARK, Jinhong. 8650 SUDLEY RD 20110 #422-01-1996 L2003 **GE** *020 †20
PARKER, Frederick Wm, III. 8640 SUDLEY RD, STE 203 20110 #010-01-1972 L1973 **FM FSM** *020
PATEL, Trupti Bhailalbhai. 8640 SUDLEY RD, STE 203 20110 #051-07-1995 L2004 **FM** *020 †18
PEDERSON, Judith Cameron. 8700 SUDLEY RD, MEDICAL STAFF OFFICE 20110 #051-04-1987 L2003 **PD PHP** *020 †55
PELTIER, Kevin Edward. 8644 SUDLEY RD, STE 308 20110 #010-02-2000 L2006 **ORS** *100
PENNA, Anna Marie. 8700 SUDLEY RD, MANASSAS ANESTHESIA 20110 #032-01-1987 L2000 **AN** *020 †05
PEREZ, Michael David. 8640 SUDLEY RD, STE 203 20110 #038-43-1987 L1988 **FM** *020 †18 ‡
PERLMUTTER, David Michael. 8629 SUDLEY RD STE 102, VIRGINIA RADIOLOGY ASSOCIA 20110 #041-02-1995 L2001 **DR** *020 †80
PETRILLI, Edmund S. 8640 SUDLEY RD, STE 302 20110 #041-12-1969 L1972 **GO GYN** *020 †30
PHATAK, Nina. 8650 SUDLEY RD 20110 #035-45-1999 L2006 **GE** *020 †20
PITTMAN, James Allen. 8640 SUDLEY RD STE 411 20110 #027-01-1964 L1989 **OBG MDM** *030 †30
POLICARPIO, Cristina Nata. 8691 STONEWALL RD 20110 #748-01-1996 L2005 **FM** *020 †18
PREMOLI, Juan Jose. 9580 SURVEYOR CT 20110 #132-04-1966 L1976 **U** *020
PRICE, Douglas Sterling. 8650 SUDLEY RD 20110 #048-13-1978 L1989 **GE** *020 †20
QASIMYAR, Ahmad Zaky. 8694 CENTREVILLE RD, EMERGENCY USA 20110 #305-01-2001 L2004 **FM** *020 †18
QI, Dan Yi. 8700 SUDLEY RD, PATHOLOGY DEPARTMENT 20110 #243-78-1983 L2003 **HMP** *020 †50
QUETULIO-DEL PILAR, L C. 8700 SUDLEY RD, PRINCE WILLIAM HOSPITAL 20110 #748-02-1964 L1972 **AN** *020 †05
RAHMAN, Rashida Khatoon. 9378 FORESTWOOD LN STE E 20110 #965-01-1977 L1985 **IM NEP** *020 †20
RAMIREZ, Enrique Humberto. 8700 SUDLEY RD, MEDICAL STAFF OFFICE 20110 #042-01-2004 L2005 **EM** *012
RATCHFORD, Francis Xavier. 8640 SUDLEY RD, STE 203 20110 #035-15-1992 L1996 **FM** *020 †18
RATHKE, Charles Ernest. 9001 DIGGES RD, STE 107 20110 #035-45-1963 L1968 **PD** *072 †55
REDDY, Swarna B. 8700 SUDLEY RD, PRINCE WILLIAM HOSPITAL 20110 #495-70-1991 L2000 **PYG** *020
REGAN, Robert Michael. 8650 SUDLEY RD STE 411 20110 #010-01-1964 L1969 **OBG** *020 †30
REILLY, David Christopher. 8401 DORSEY CIR, STE 101 20110 #010-01-2000 L2000 **DR** *100 †80
RHEE, Thomas Ho. 8703 STONEWALL RD, STE 1B 20110 #035-09-1996 L2002 **OTO** *020 †45
RHOADS, John Chas. 9304 FOREST POINT CIR, MANASSAS OB GYN 20110 #010-01-1956 L1966 **GYN** *072 †30
RIDINGER, Robin Ann. 9001 DIGGES RD STE 206 20110 #018-03-1986 L1989 **FM** *020 †18
ROBINS, Michael Bruce. 8401 DORSEY CIR, STE 101 20110 #016-43-1983 L1989 **DR** *020 †80
ROSS, Scott Alan. 8640 SUDLEY RD, STE 203 20110 #010-02-1994 L1994 **FM FSM** *020 †18 ‡
SAJADI, Ali Mohseni. 9580 SURVEYOR CT, PRINCE WILLIAM UROLOGY 20110 #051-01-1996 L1996 **U** *020 †95
SALIS, Ari I. 8401 DORSEY CIR, STE 101 20110 #033-06-1995 L2006 **VIR** *020 †80
SANDOVAL, Yvette Cecilia. 8650 SUDLEY RD, STE 300 20110 #003-01-1989 L1999 **N** *020 †75
SEHN, James Thos. 9580 SURVEYOR CT 20110 #010-02-1972 L1978 **U IM** *062 †95
SEITZ, Georg Karl. ■ 20110 #407-33-1955 L1959 **OBG** *071 †30
SETHI, Meera. 8424 DORSEY CIR, STE 102 20110 #495-05-1991 L2005 **CHP** *020
SHAHZEB, Hassan. 8700 SUDLEY RD, PRINCE WILLIAM HOSPITAL 20110 #704-02-1983 L2002 **P** *100
SHERMAN, Thomas Marshall. 8650 SUDLEY RD 20110 #008-02-1987 L1994 **GE** *020 †20
SHOAGA, Atinuke Towobola. 8700 SUDLEY RD, PWH/MEDICAL STAFF OFFICE 20110 #690-01-1986 L2002 **CCP** *100 †55
SHUMAN, Marla Lynn. 8650 SUDLEY RD, STE 212 20110 #051-07-1985 L1990 **PUD IM** *020 †20
SHURBERG, Jonathan Louis. 8650 SUDLEY RD STE 410 20110 #045-01-1972 L1976 **GE IM** *020 †20
SIEGEL, David Alan. 8700 SUDLEY RD, PRINCE WILLIAM HOSPITAL 20110 #035-09-1976 L1980 **PD** *020 †55
SINGH, Andrew Harjeet. 8700 SUDLEY RD, PWH/ OCCUPATIONAL MEDICINE 20110 #028-34-2000 L2005 **GPM** *100 †70
SIROTKIN, Igor. 8401 DORSEY CIR, STE 101 20110 #035-06-2000 L2006 **RNR** *100 †80
SKOVRONSKY, Jeffrey J. 8700 SUDLEY RD, PATHOLOGY DEPARTMENT 20110 #035-15-1971 L1975 **PTH NM** *020 †50
SMITH, Patricia De Camp. 8625 SUDLEY RD, VIRGINIA EYE CENTER 20110 #023-07-1980 L1991 **OPH** *020 †35
SRIVASTAVA, Sangeeta. 8401 DORSEY CIR, STE 101 20110 #496-02-1989 L2005 **DR** *020 †80

■ = Address Information Privacy Protected

STARKIE, Carrie Jane. 9430 FORESTWOOD LN, STE 100 20110 #005-06-1998 L1998 PD *020 †55

STEPHAN, Donn Paul. 8700 SUDLEY RD, ATTN: MEDICAL STAFF OFFICE 20110 #023-07-1982 L1985 GS *020

SUMMERVILLE, David Alan. 8700 SUDLEY RD, PATHOLOGY DEPARTMENT 20110 #011-02-1980 L1995 PTH NM *020 †28,50

SUNKARA, Vijaya Lakshmi. 9303 FOREST POINT CIR, MANASSAS INTERNAL MED 20110 #495-50-1995 L2004 IM *020 †20

SWARTZ, Matthew Owen. 9378 FORESTWOOD LN STE C 20110 #016-42-1977 L1983 RHU *020 †20

SWIFT, Richard Allender. 8650 SUDLEY RD, STE 212 20110 #048-13-1990 L1991 PUD *020 †20

SY-HUI, Rossana T. 8700 SUDLEY RD, C/O PRINCE WILLIAM HOSPITA 20110 #748-02-1980 L1990 PD NPM *020 †55

TALLAPRAGADA, Jyotsna K. 8700 SUDLEY RD 20110 #495-65-1982 L1997 NPM *020 †55

TAM, Pilar G. 8700 SUDLEY RD, PRINCE WILLIAM HOSPITAL. E 20110 #737-06-1987 L2005 PD PDI *020 †55

TAVANI, Nicholas John, Jr. 8620 ROLLING RD 20110 #010-02-1980 L1989 FM *020 †18

THEODORE, Nihil Chand. 8691 STONEWALL RD 20110 #024-07-2002 L2005 FM *020 †18

THOMAS, Sabrina Hammett. 8735 PLANTATION LN 20110 #035-06-1997 L2002 OBG *020 †30

TRAVERS, Richard David. 8650 SUDLEY RD 20110 #008-01-1971 L1974 GE IM *020 †20

TUCKER, Steven Richard. 9001 DIGGES RD STE 206 20110 #038-40-1986 L1989 FM *020 †18

TURNER, Lewis John, Jr. 8629 SUDLEY RD, STE 102 20110 #051-01-1963 L1963 R *071 †80

VACHHER, Prehlad Singh. 8703 STONEWALL RD, ANXIETY STRESS CENTER PC 20110 #495-03-1956 L1966 P N *020 †75

VAN DER WOUDE, Harmen. 9380 FORESTWOOD LN, STE B 20110 #660-04-1952 L1958 GYN OS *020

VASSALLO, Michael. 8700 SUDLEY RD 20110 #024-07-1953 L1961 PTH NM *071 †50,28

VU, Duyanh The. 8401 DORSEY CIR, STE 101 20110 #023-01-1994 L1999 RNR *020 †80

WADLEY, John Kenneth. 9380 FORESTWOOD LN STE F 20110 #047-06-1959 L1973 OTO *071 †45

WALL, John Douglas. 9304 FOREST POINT CIR, MANASSAS OB GYN 20110 #010-02-1983 L1990 OBG *020 †30

WAMPLER, J Paul. 8709 DIGGES RD 20110 #051-04-1958 L1958 GS *071 †85

WARGO, Jennifer T. 8401 DORSEY CIR, STE 101 20110 #023-01-1996 L2001 DR *020 †80

WARNER, Michael Ray. 9304 FOREST POINT CIR, LTD., 20110 #051-04-1983 L1985 OBG *020 †30

WASIMUDDIN, Khalid. 9001 DIGGES RD, STE 201 20110 #495-77-1974 L1994 IM *020 †20

WEBB, Michelle Alanea. 8565 SUDLEY RD STE B, PRINCE WILLIAM CARDIOLGY 20110 #035-06-1993 L1993 CD *020

WEBBER, Matthew Joseph. 8401 DORSEY CIR, STE 101 20110 #051-04-2001 L2001 DR *100 †80

WEBER, David Ryan. 8401 DORSEY CIR, STE 101 20110 #011-03-1985 L1996 DR *020 †80

WEINSTEIN, Raymond Saul. 10900 UNIVERSITY BLVD, MS 18H 20110 #054-04-1980 L1993 FM OS *020 †18

WERNER, Wallace James. 8575 SUDLEY RD STE B 20110 #016-06-1970 L1972 FM GP *020

WESTNEY, Irving Vaughan. 8700 SUDLEY RD, EMERGENCY DEPT 20110 #023-01-1989 L1997 EM *020 †16

WHITE, James Latham. 8650 SUDLEY RD STE 206 20110 #051-04-1962 L1962 GS *071 †85

WILLIAMS, Anastasia L. 9430 FORESTWOOD LN, STE 100 20110 #051-01-1998 L2001 PD *020 †55

WINICK, Adam. 8401 DORSEY CIR, STE 101 20110 #033-05-1989 L1996 VIR *020 †80

ZAZZARO, Patrick Francis. 8401 DORSEY CIR, STE 101 20110 #033-06-1975 L1977 DR *020 †80 ‡

ZELDES, Geoffrey. 8700 SUDLEY RD, MEDICAL STAFF OFFICE 20110 #030-05-1988 L2002 EM FM *020 †18

MANASSAS – PRINCE WILLIAM

ABBOTT, Katherine A. 10623 CRESTWOOD DR 20109 #048-04-1987 L1990 PD *020 †55

ABEL, Marilyn K. ■ 20112 #016-11-1970 L1993 OPH GP *071 †35

ABISOGUN, Akinwunmi O. 11730 SUDLEY MANOR DR, KAISER PERMANENTE 20109 #690-02-1980 L1997 OBG *020 †30

ADAMS, Valencia D. 7320 SUDLEY RD 20109 #041-01-1980 L1996 IM *020 †20

ASHAI, Afshan. ■ 20109 #704-24-1998 L2002 P *020 †75

BARAZI, Kairy. 10530 LINDEN LAKE PLZ, STE 305 20109 #055-02-1998 L1999 OPH *020

BYRNES, Gordon Andrew. 10530 LINDEN LAKE PLZ, STE 305 20109 #023-12-1983 L1986 OPH *020 †35

CHU, Keith Hyong. 8100 ASHTON AVE, STE 200 20109 #041-09-1992 L1998 CD IM *020 †20

DABREU, Michelle Maria. 8100 ASHTON AVE, PRINCE WILLIAM FAMILY 20109 #041-02-1995 L2004 FM *020 †18

DESAI, Parimal C. 8100 ASHTON AVE, PRINCE WILLIAM FAMILY 20109 #495-37-1989 L1996 FM *020 †18

DIGLISIC, Gordana. 11730 SUDLEY MANOR DR, ATTN: CREDENTIALS DEPT 20109 #957-02-1984 L2001 IM *020 †20

DVONCH, Louis Adam. ■ 20112 #016-43-1945 L1946 GP OS *071

FITZGERALD, Susan K. 8100 ASHTON AVE STE 207, ASHTON AVENUE FAMILY MEDIC 20109 #010-01-1996 L1998 FM *020 †18

FRIEDMAN, George R. 7900 SUDLEY RD, STE 416 20109 #010-02-1975 L1989 R *020 †80

GHAFOURI, Mohsen. 8100 ASHTON AVE STE 215 20109 #517-05-1993 L2002 RHU IM *020 †20

GILL, Aman. 8100 ASHTON AVE, PRINCE WILLIAM FAM MED 20109 #495-29-2000 L2002 FM *020 †18

GONDI, Appaji. 7818 DONEGAN DR 20109 #495-50-1981 L2006 AI *020 †55,03

HARNUM, Lisa. 10623 CRESTWOOD DR 20109 #041-14-1988 L1989 PD *020 †55 ‡

HEMM, Stephanie E. 10623 CRESTWOOD DR 20109 #017-20-2003 L2006 PD *020 †55

KATZ, Harry M. ■ 20111 #001-02-1950 L1952 FM *071 †18

KC, Lilly. 8100 ASHTON AVE, PRINCE WILLIAM FAMILY 20109 #041-02-1992 L1995 FM *020 †18

KIM, Chin-Oh. 7524 DIPLOMAT DR 20109 #132-01-1997 L2006 IM *100

KRASZEWSKA, Anna A. 11730 SUDLEY MANOR DR 20109 #422-01-1995 L2002 IM *020 †20

KRAYTERMAN, Irina. 7320 SUDLEY RD 20109 #913-77-1962 L1985 EM IM *020

LEE, Gerald K. 7806 SUDLEY RD, STE 205 20109 #016-42-1996 L1998 GPM *020 †70

MAGHSOUDI, Alireza. 8100 ASHTON AVE, STE 200 20109 #051-04-1999 L1999 CD *100 †20

MAGUIRE, Jennifer. 10623 CRESTWOOD DR 20109 #422-01-1997 L2001 PD *020 †55

MASON, Mark Stephen. ■ 20112 #036-05-1973 L1975 GS VS *071 †85

MESBAHI, Kavoos. 10535 CRESTWOOD DR, STE 101 20109 #517-01-1970 L1985 GS CRS *020 †85,10

MITCHELL, John Wayne, Jr. 11730 SUDLEY MANOR DR 20109 #010-01-1969 L1971 PD *071 †55

NARAYANAN, Sharat. 11730 SUDLEY MANOR DR, MANASSAS MEDICAL CENTER 20109 #495-04-1981 L1999 IM *020 †20

PAUSWINSKI, John Robt. ■ 20109 #033-05-1967 L1970 FM AM *071 †18

PFISTER, Beverly Jean. 11730 SUDLEY MANOR DR 20109 #038-43-1981 L1988 IM *020 †20

RAMIREZ, Gilma Franklin. ■ 20111 #024-07-1980 L1998 GP *020

RUELAZ, Evelyn Anna. 11730 SUDLEY MANOR DR 20109 #041-01-1994 L1998 OBG *020 †30

SANDESARA, Chirag Mahendr. 8100 ASHTON AVE STE 200 20109 #305-01-1999 L2008 CD *100 †20

SIAHPOOSH, Sohrab. 8140 ASHTON AVE 20109 #517-05-1981 L1991 CHP P *020

SRINVASAN, Priyadarshi. ■ 20112 #048-02-1999 PD *020 †55

STARK, Randolph Wilkinson. 10680 CRESTWOOD DR STE B 20109 #051-04-1971 L1984 D *020 †15 ‡

STONEROCK, Grace Janine. 10696 CRESTWOOD DR STE B 20109 #036-05-1989 L1990 FM OM *020 †18

TAHERI, Hamid. 8100 ASHTON AVE, STE 200 20109 #048-13-1993 L1995 CD *020 †20

WARDAK, Khalil Satar. ■ 20111 #305-01-1999 L2006 FOP *012

WEEBER, Thomas Allen. ■ 20112 #025-01-1961 L1962 FM *071 †18

WELLS, Staci Taunton. ■ 20109 #012-01-2000 L2000 FM *020 †18

WINSTON, Janet Salome. ■ 20112 #035-06-1988 L2004 PTH *020 †50

MANASSAS PARK – PRINCE WILLIAM

WOODARD, Dean Harris. 8499 EUCLID AVE 20111 #055-02-1985 L1987 EM *020

MARION – SMYTH

ABAD, Jose Villalon. ■ 24354 #748-01-1955 L1962 IM *075

ALI, Shaheda. 340 BAGLEY CIR 24354 #704-02-1983 L2005 P *020

AMPUDIA, Roberto Jose. 1122 CULBERT DR 24354 #018-03-1994 L2000 GS *020 †85

ANGLIKER, Colin C J. PO BOX 1027, M CT C 24354 #918-01-1962 L1988 P PFP *020

ARMBRISTER, Douglas K. 592 RADIO HILL RD, MEDICAL ARTS BLDG 24354 #051-01-1959 L1959 GS ORS *020

ASBURY, Wesley Lee, Jr. 1048 TERRACE DR 24354 #047-20-1992 L1998 DR *020 †80

BAUMAN, Lyle Wayne. 1203 SNIDER ST 24354 #041-14-1987 L1993 GS HNS *020 †85

BETETA, Juan Carlos. 590 RADIO HILL RD, STE 1 24354 #429-02-1994 L2006 PD *020 †55

BLANKENSHIP, Joe Glenn. ■ 24354 #051-04-1980 L1983 DR FM *020 †18,80

BOLTER, Delano Woodrow. 1114 SNIDER ST 24354 #010-01-1961 L1965 P *071 †55

BOTTONE, Mary Elizabeth. 1583 N MAIN ST, STE B 24354 #051-04-1981 L1983 OTO *020

BOURHILL, Graham H. 110 ROBINHOOD DR 24354 #803-03-1945 L1953 IMG P *071

BROWN, Paul Garland. 1046 TERRACE DR 24354 #051-04-1982 L1983 FM *020 †18 ‡

CATALAN, Mandlita O. 502 E MAIN ST 24354 #748-01-1960 L1977 IM *020

CEBALLOS, Rodolfo B. 1122 CULBERT DR 24354 #748-01-1966 L1974 GS GP *020

CERVANTES, Alfredo. 340 BAGLEY CIR, HLTH INST 24354 #649-14-1982 L1997 P *020 †75

CLAMPITT, Robert Van. 1154 SNIDER ST, FAMILY PHYSICIAN OF MARION 24354 #048-02-1984 L1990 FM *020 †18

CRISP, Jonathan Gentry. 340 BAGLEY CIR, SOUTHWESTERN VIRGINIA MENT 24354 #045-01-1989 L2006 P *020 †75

DAVIS, Timothy Mark. 1114 SNIDER ST 24354 #051-01-1986 L2007 HO HEM *020 †20

DERIAN, Paul S. ■ 24354 #051-01-1951 L1951 ORS LM *071 †40

DIBBLE, Jos Franklin, II. 340 BAGLEY CIR, SWVMHI 24354 #011-04-1974 L1997 FM *020 †18

ELLER, Joseph J. ■ 24354 #012-05-1940 L1946 D *071

EVANS, Robert Bruce. 565 RADIO HILL RD, EMERGENCY DEPT 24354 #051-04-1987 L1988 FM EM *020 †18

FRANCIS, Linda. 340 BAGLEY CIR 24354 #035-06-1991 L2003 P PFP *020 †75

GARZON, Fernando Luis. 1122 CULBERT DR 24354 #132-02-1954 L1960 IM CD *020 †20

GORDON, Jeffrey Daryl. ■ 24354 #051-04-1997 L1997 ADP *020 †75

GRAHAM, Marlon Anthony. ■ 24354 #051-04-1982 L1986 P *020 †75 ‡

HALE, Robert Lee. 1116 SNIDER ST 24354 #016-11-1971 L1976 FM *020

HALL, Clifford Thaddeus. 340 BAGLEY CIR 24354 #021-05-1976 L1994 P PYA *020 †75

HAMMAN, Chelsea Coffey. 1046 TERRACE DR 24354 #036-01-2003 L2005 FM *100 †18

HARDEN, Amy Jo. 1020 TERRACE DR STE 101 24354 #051-01-1992 L2004 PD *020 †55

HODGES, Lily Handal. 340 BAGLEY CIR 24354 #649-14-1980 L1987 P *020

HUMSI, Ramzi Kamil. 1070 TERRACE DR, MEDICAL DOCTOR INC 24354 #605-01-1970 L1979 OBG *020

INOCALLA, Marilou V. 416 E MAIN ST 24354 #748-08-1974 L1992 P *020

JONES, George Frederick M. 590 RADIO HILL RD 24354 #041-01-1966 L1977 PD *020 †55

KISER, William David. 1128 N MAIN ST 24354 #051-04-1978 L1982 OPH *020 †35

KONRAD, Karl Wm. 340 BAGLEY CIR 24354 #041-01-1979 L1980 FM *020 †18

LEBITA-CEBALLOS, Victoria. ■ 24354 #748-11-1966 L1972 IMG GP *071

LEE, Linda Ann. 340 BAGLEY CIR 24354 #045-01-1993 L1994 P *020 †20,75

MARINE, Jean Marie. 1209 SNIDER ST, SMYTH REGIONAL ORTHOPEDICS 24354 #024-07-1979 L1993 ORS HS *020 †40

MARTIN, George Randolph. 340 BAGLEY CIR, SOUTHWESTERN VIRGINIA MENT 24354 #045-01-1974 L2005 CHP P *020 †75

MC DOWELL, Alice Williams. 590 RADIO HILL RD, STE 1 24354 #051-04-1973 L1975 PD *075 †55

MC DOWELL, James Everett. 1046 TERRACE DR 24354 #051-04-1973 L1975 FM *020 †18 ‡

MONE, Andrew Paul. 565 RADIO HILL RD, SMYTH COUNTY COMMUNITY HOS 24354 #038-41-1997 L2005 IM *020

MONTERO, Raul Eloy. 590 RADIO HILL RD, MEDICAL ARTS BUILDING 24354 #649-01-1954 L1961 PD *020 †55

MORELOS, Rodolfo Magdato. 335 PANORAMA DR 24354 #748-01-1953 L1974 ADL P *020 †55

OLMSTED, Thomas Russell. 340 BAGLEY CIR, SOUTHWESTERN VA MENTAL HEA 24354 #021-06-1984 L2004 P *020 †75

PARKER, Cindy J. 1070 TERRACE DR, SMYTH REGIONAL OB/GYN 24354 #017-20-1989 L2006 OBG *020 †30

PARKS, Ralph Aaron. 1209 SNIDER ST 24354 #011-02-1971 L2004 ORS *020 †40

PATTERSON, James Edwin. 1152 SNIDER ST, BMA SMYTH COURNTY 24354 #051-01-1957 L1957 EM FM *071 †18

RAYNAUD-HORNA, Alfred M. 502 E MAIN ST, MARION CORR TREATMENT CTR 24354 #847-10-1969 L1991 P *071

REACH, Ralph Thos. 700 PARK BLVD 24354 #045-04-1986 L1987 **FM** *020
REID, Judith Ellen. 340 BAGLEY CIR 24354 #051-01-1975 L1982 **IM AMI** *020 †20
REYNOLDS, Wayne Calvin. 700 PARK BLVD 24354 #051-04-1984 L1987 **IM** *020 †20
RICE, David Timothy. 1128 SNIDER ST 24354 #047-20-1985 L1990 **PTH** *020 †50
RICHARDSON, Emmett V, Jr. 224 RIDGEWAY RD 24354 #051-04-1960 L1960 **GP** *020
ROGERS, Rachel Marie. 1020 TERRACE DR, STE 101 24354 #036-08-1997 L2001 **PD** *020 †55
ROSENFELD, Michael Jay. PO BOX 1062 24354 #033-05-1991 L2004 **AN** *020 †05
SACKNOFF, Eric Jon. 1201 SNIDER ST 24354 #024-07-1971 L2006 **IM** *020 †95
SHEROWSKY, Ronald C. 565 RADIO HILL RD, DEPARTMENT OF RADIOLOGY 24354
  #017-20-1981 L1989 **DR** *020 †80
SINGER, Jerry R. 565 RADIO HILL RD, SMYTH COUNTY COMMUNITY HOS 24354
  #048-13-1983 L1984 **IM** *020 †20
SMITH, Oscar Orton, Jr. ■ 24354 #051-04-1944 L1944 **AS GS** *071
SQUIRES, Anne-Charlotte. 1118 SNIDER ST, SMYTH REGIONAL INTERNAL ME 24354
  #012-01-1996 L1999 **IM** *020 †20
STEED, Thomas Arthur. 1070 TERRACE DR 24354 #065-01-1969 L1990 **OBG** *020
STIEFEL, Brian Harris. 1020 TERRACE DR, STE 200 24354 #047-20-1999 L1999 **FM** *020 †18
STIEFEL, Jennifer Q. 1046 TERRACE DR 24354 #047-20-1996 L1996 **FM** *020 †18
SULLIVAN, Harvey E, III. 1048 TERRACE DR, SMITH COUNTY RADIOLOGY, IN 24354
  #047-06-1969 L1979 **R IM** *020 †80
SWAN, Forrest, Jr. 1114 SNIDER ST 24354 #016-11-1978 L1996 **HO IM** *020 †20
VERNON, Samuel David. 1118A SNIDER ST 24354 #051-04-1973 L1974 **IM** *020 †20
VESCE, James Jos, Jr. 340 BAGLEY CIR, SOUTHWESTERN VA MENTAL HLT 24354
  #043-01-1987 L1999 **P** *020
WASSUM, Chas Stevens, III. 700 PARK BLVD, SMYTH COUNTY HOSPITAL 24354
  #051-01-1965 L1965 **EM PD** *071 †55,16
WILLIAMS, Andrew Lee. 1128 SNIDER ST 24354 #051-01-1963 L1963 **PTH** *020 †50

MARSHALL – FAUQUIER

HOEBEL, Elizabeth Ann. 8452 RENALDS AVE 20115 #041-09-1990 L1993 **FM** *020 †18 ‡
HOUSKA, Robert Bradford. 8452 RENALDS AVE, COUNTRYSIDE FAM PRAC/BX337 20115
  #051-04-1988 L1989 **FM** *020 †18
ROYSTON, Norris A. PO BOX 337 20116 #051-04-1973 L1973 **FM** *020 †18

MARTINSVILLE – MARTINSVILLE CITY

AARON, Caren T. 314 FAIRY STREET EXT, STE A 24112 #051-04-1997 L1997 **IM** *020 †20
AARON, Maureen. 314 FAIRY STREET EXT, STE A 24112 #068-01-1968 L1984 **FM FPG** *020 †18
ABDUL-MBACKE, Makunda. 312 FAIRY STREET EXT # 201, PIEDMONT PREFERRED
  WOMEN'S 24112 #008-01-1998 L2007 **OBG** *020 †30
ADAMS, Samuel Webster. ■ 24112 #010-01-1946 L1950 **FM** *071
AIN UL HAQ, Ahmad Tayyab. 26 BROAD ST 24112 #704-04-1977 L1993 **IM** *020 †20
ALBANESE, Robert. 320 HOSPITAL DR 24112 #010-02-1960 L1963 **EM** *071 †16
BELL, Maurice Harold, III. PO BOX 204 24114 #051-04-1993 L1993 **AN** *020 †05
BERGMAN, Stuart Michael. 15 CLEVELAND AVE 24112 #035-20-1973 L1976 **U SO** *020 †95
BERRY, Thomas K. 314 FAIRY STREET EXT, STE B 24112 #051-04-1977 L1988 **GS** *020 †85
BETHEA, Charles Darnell. 1107 BROOKDALE ST, CARILION MEDICAL 24112
  #045-01-1980 L1983 **FM** *020 †18
BHATT, Dinesh Kumar. 287 COMMONWEALTH BLVD W 24112 #917-08-1977 L1992 **IM** *020 †20
BOTTON, Jacques Ephraim. 320 HOSPITAL DR 24112 #869-04-1955 L1958 **NS N** *074 †25
BRIDGES, Henry Edward, Jr. ■ 24112 #036-01-2001 L2002 **PM** *020
BUCHANAN, Linda Ann. 1107 BROOKDALE ST, CARILION MEDICAL 24112 #051-07-1989 L1990
  IM *020
BUHR, Robert H. 1100 SPRUCE ST 24112 #068-01-1968 L1995 **FM** *020
CAMBARERI, Richard Jos. 1107 BROOKDALE ST, RAVENEL ONCOLOGY CENTER ME 24112
  #010-02-1975 L1977 **ON HEM** *020 †20 ‡
CAMPBELL, Michelle. 319 HOSPITAL DR, STE 210 24112 #033-06-2001 L2004 **FM** *020 †18
CAMPELL, Henry Simon. PO BOX 3151 24115 #036-07-1960 L1969 **OPH** *071 †35
CASSIDY, John Edward. ■ 24115 #010-02-1942 L1943 **PD DIA** *071 †55
CHUMBLE, Shubhangi Atul. 101 CLEVELAND AVE, STE A 24112 #495-28-1992 L2001
  N *020 †75
COUGHLIN, Christopher T. 320 HOSPITAL DR, RADIATION ONCOLOGY DEPT 24112
  #024-01-1973 L2000 **RO ON** *020,80
CZITO, Brian Gary. 320 HOSPITAL DR, MEMORIAL HOSP OFMARTINSVIL 24112
  #012-01-1996 L2001 **RO** *020 †80
D'ORO, Louis. 319 HOSPITAL DR, STE 208 24112 #041-13-1984 L2006 **GS VS** *020 †85
EASON, Margie Beazley. ■ 24112 #036-01-1988 L1992 **P** *075 †75
EASON, Paul Richard. 1107A BROOKDALE ST, CARILION MEDICAL ASSOCIATE 24112
  #036-01-1988 L1992 **IM** *020 †20
EKUBAN-GORDON, Edna. 320 HOSPITAL DR 24112 #016-01-1996 L1998 **EM** *020 †16
ELLER, Myron Edward, Jr. 445 COMMONWEALTH BLVD E 24112 #051-01-1981 L1983
  FM IMG *020 †20
ENGEL, John Joseph. 15 CLEVELAND AVE, CHILDRENS MEDICAL CENTER 24112
  #033-05-1967 L1973 **PD** *020 †55
FINCH, Robert Delmar. 320 HOSPITAL DR 24112 #004-01-1964 L1969 **R NM** *071 †80,28
GEHRKEN, Geo Andrew, Jr. 101 CLEVELAND AVE STE C 24112 #012-01-1979 L1985 **U** *020 †95
GILMOUR, Ian James. 485 SAINT JOHNS CIR 24112 #062-01-1969 L1997 **AN CCM** *020
GRAYSON, Donald Michael. 749 E CHURCH ST 24112 #017-20-1974 L1979 **OPH** *020 †35
GREEN, Gordon Martin. 295 COMMONWEALTH BLVD W 24112 #065-05-1982 L1995
  FM *020 †18
GRISALES, Asur. 320 HOSPITAL DR 24112 #264-05-1959 L1964 **PTH** *020 †50
HAMDY, Kareem Adel. ■ 24112 #915-03-1994 L2007 **GS** *020 †85
HARCUS, Sinclair John, Jr. 1107 BROOKDALE ST 24112 #051-01-1981 L1983 **FM EM** *020 †18
HASSAN, Babar Navid. 319 HOSPITAL DR, STE 103 24112 #704-21-1985 L1998
  PUD PCC *020 †20
HASSAN, Zujajah. 319 HOSPITAL DR, STE 202 24112 #704-06-1992 L1998 **IM** *020 †20
HOLSINGER, Donald Rider. 15 CLEVELAND AVE 24112 #051-04-1955 L1955 **IM** *071 †20
HOLUBOWITCH, Edward John. 445 COMMONWEALTH BLVD E 24112 #035-01-1981 L1983
  FM *020 †18
HOLYFIELD, Paul Alfred. 315 HOSPITAL DR STE 201 24112 #036-05-1973 L1977 **OBG** *020 †30
HORTON, Jeffrey Wayne. ■ 24112 #007-02-1995 L1999 **EM** *020 †16
HURT, George Saml, III. 15 CLEVELAND AVE STE 15 24112 #051-01-1980 L1981 **U** *020 †95

INGRAM, Sally Sockwell. 320 HOSPITAL DR, DEPT. OF RADIATION ONCOLOG 24112
  #036-01-1988 L1993 **RO** *020 †80
INMAN, Barry Eugene. ■ 24112 #012-01-1990 L1993 **IM** *020 †05
IRBY, Jethro Hurt. 320 HOSPITAL DR 24112 #051-01-1942 L1942 **GP** *071
ISERNIA, James Michael. 319 HOSPITAL DR, STE 102 24112 #035-06-1993 L1996 **IM** *020 †20
ISRAEL MARDIROSIAN, Noobar. ■ 24112 #528-03-1989 L2006 **IM** *020
JONES, Vincent Keith. 1856 VIRGINIA AVE 24112 #422-01-1994 L2001 **IM** *020 †20
KING, Laurie Ellen. 320 HOSPITAL DR, MEM HOSP OF MARTINSVILLE 24112
  #035-03-1985 L1997 **EM** *020 †16
KING, Mervyn Robt. 320 HOSPITAL DR 24112 #051-01-1959 L1959 **AN IMG** *071
KIRKPATRICK, John P. 320 HOSPITAL DR, MEMORIAL HOSPITAL 24112 #048-13-1999 L2004
  RO *020 †80
LAFAVE, John Bradley. 15 CLEVELAND AVE, CHILDRENS MEDICAL CENTER 24112
  #050-02-1961 L1966 **PD** *020 †55
LAUZAU, Frank Justin. 1044 E CHURCH ST 24112 #036-01-1981 L1982 **IM** *020
LAYTON, James Edward. ■ 24112 #012-04-1964 L1964 **OM** *071
LEWIS, David Owen. 828 TURNER ASHBY RD, 828 TURNER ASHBY ROAD 24112
  #051-04-1972 L1973 **EM FM** *020 †16,18
LEWIS, William Benton. 1107 BROOKDALE ST, CARILION MEDICAL 24112 #051-01-1980 L1983
  IM *020 †20
LEWIS, Wm Dulaney, Jr. ■ 24112 #051-01-1945 L1945 **IM** *071 †20
LIM, May Joy David. 1107 BROOKDALE ST, CARILION MEDICAL ASSOCIATE 24112
  #748-17-2001 L2007 **FM** *020 †18
LISZKA, Bozenna Maria. 315 HOSPITAL DR STE 101 24112 #065-06-1977 L1996 **FM** *020 †18
MADONIA, Eugene C. 101 CLEVELAND AVE STE A 24112 #010-02-1976 L1979 **N** *020 †55
MAHONEY, John Stephen. 1100 E CHURCH ST 24112 #048-14-1983 L1988 **ORS OSM** *020 †40
MAHONEY, Mark T. 312 FAIRY STREET EXT # 101 24112 #005-76-2001, ▲ L2004 **FM** *020
MARKS, Lawrence Bruce. 320 HOSPITAL DR BOX 4788, MEM'RL HOSP OF MARTINSVILL 24112
  #035-45-1985 L1991 **RO** *020 †80
MARSHALL, Charles B. ■ 24112 #035-15-1949 L1957 **OBG** *071 †30
MARTIN, Michael Tregilgas. 320 HOSPITAL DR, VILLE AND HENRY COUNTY 24112
  #041-02-1998 L2000 **EM** *020 †16
MAZUREK, Bruce Edward. ■ 24112 #055-01-1987 L1990 **EM** *020 †16
MC CONNELL, David Brooke. ■ 24112 #041-02-1969 L1990 **EM GS** *071 †85,16
MC GEE, John Patrick. 1100 E CHURCH ST 24112 #051-01-1985 L1988 **ORS** *020 †40
MC GINN, James Sylvester. 445 COMMONWEALTH BLVD E, CARILION SURGICAL CARE 24112
  #050-02-1965 L1973 **GS** *071 †85
MOORMAN, John Hope, Jr. 320 HOSPITAL DR 24112 #051-04-1940 L1940 **OBG** *071 †30
NADEAU, Claude. 1107B BROOKDALE ST, CARILION CARDIOLOGY 24112 #067-03-1975 L1992
  CD *020
NOONAN, Mary Elizabeth. 15 CLEVELAND AVE, CHILDRENS MEDICAL CENTER 24112
  #057-07-1994 L1994 **PD** *020 †55
O'NEIL, Scott Mark. 319 HOSPITAL DR, STE 208 24112 #041-13-1992 L1998 **GS** *020 †85
PAINTER, Jack Allan. 319 HOSPITAL DR, STE 202 24112 #051-04-1987 L1988 **IC CD** *020 †20
PETERSON, Jon Thos. PO BOX 4783 24115 #005-06-1978 L1995 **EM** *020 †16
PIAT, Robert David. PRESTON RD 24112 #023-01-1963 L1984 **GS** *020
POIRIER, Leonard Scott. 320 HOSPITAL DR 24112 #005-14-1985 L1993 **DR VIR** *020 †80
PORRETTA, Jerome C. ■ 24112 #035-06-1972 L1978 **AN** *020 †05
PRINCE, William D, III. 1107 BROOKDALE ST, CARILION MEDICAL 24112 #051-04-1977 L1980
  IM *020 †20
RACHNER, Thomas Edward. 320 HOSPITAL DR 24112 #038-40-1986 L1999 **DR VIR** *020 †80
RICHMAN, Donald Wm. 320 HOSPITAL DR 24112 #010-01-1956 L1962 **OPH** *020 †35
ROYCROFT, David Wm. PO BOX 5308 24115 #035-03-1963 L1971 **PTH** *020 †50
SCOURAS, George Pete. 320 HOSPITAL DR 24112 #051-01-1958 L1958 **FM GP** *020
SEAMON, David Walter. 15 CLEVELAND AVE, CHILDRENS MEDICAL CENTER 24112
  #051-04-1987 L1990 **PD** *020 †55
SELF, Kathryn Cabot. 15 CLEVELAND AVE, CHILDRENS MEDICAL CENTER 24112
  #051-07-1999 L1999 **PD** *020 †55
SELL, Jarrett Keller. 1107 BROOKDALE ST, CARILION MEDICAL 24112 #051-01-2000 L2002
  FM *020 †18
SELMAN, John Wm. 435 COMMONWEALTH BLVD E 24112 #012-01-1975 L1977
  OTO A *020 †45
SILVERMAN, David Louis. 1103 BROOKDALE ST, STE D 24112 #051-07-1991 L1995
  OPH *020 †35
SINGH, Surinder Dayasingh. 1107 BROOKDALE ST, CARILION MEDICAL 24112
  #495-19-1985 L2005 **FM** *020 †18
SLEEPER, Arthur Michael. 320 HOSPITAL DR, RAVENEL ONCOLOGY CENTER 24112
  #011-02-1987 L1994 **ON IM** *020 †20
SMITH, John Randolph. PO BOX 3911 24115 #051-04-1956 L1956 **IM CD** *071 †20
SPREHE, Samuel Edward. 319 HOSPITAL DR, STE 201 24112 #039-01-1983 L2006
  OTO A *020 †45
SPRINKLE, Edward Pierre. MED CTR STE 203 24112 #051-01-1955 L1955 **GP** *071
SPRINKLE, Philip M. 209 HOSPITAL DR 24112 #051-01-1953 L1953 **HNS OTO** *072 †45
STAMBAUGH, Merris Alden. 1107 BROOKDALE ST, CARILION MEDICAL 24112
  #051-01-1996 L1998 **FM** *020 †18
SZULECKI, Judith Marie. 209 CLEVELAND AVE 24112 #033-05-1969 L1973 **D IM** *020 †15
THORNBERRY, Christa Marie. 15 CLEVELAND AVE, CHILDRENS MEDICAL CENTER 24112
  #045-01-1995 L1998 **PD** *020 †55
TOLER, Howis Yvette. ■ 24112 #019-02-2004 L2007 **FM** *020 †18
TOMS, Bate C, Jr. ■ 24112 #023-01-1950 L1956 **GS ORS** *071 †85
TORRES, Jose R. 1107 BROOKDALE ST, CARILION MEDICAL 24112 #042-02-1985 L1992
  OBG *040 †30
UDOETUK, Gabriel George. ■ 24115 #198-05-1995 L2007 **IM** *020 †20
VANGANI, Veena Nevand. 1107 BROOKDALE ST, CARILION MEDICAL 24112
  #496-03-1984 L2000 **IM** *020 †20
WAGNER, Karl Thos, Jr. 315 HOSPITAL DR, STE 105 24112 #041-02-1977 L1982 **ORS** *020 †40
WALLACE, George Lamar. 320 HOSPITAL DR 24112 #012-05-1955 L1960 **IM** *071
WALLACE, Pat Barrow. ■ 24112 #012-05-1955 L1960 **IM** *071
WALSH, Francis Xavier. 101 CLEVELAND AVE, STE A 24112 #036-05-1986 L1990 **N** *020 †75
WELHAM, Richard Thos. 319 HOSPITAL DR, STE 204 24112 #041-13-1965 L1991
  OBG GP *020 †30
WENKSTERN, Michael Grant. 1100 E CHURCH ST 24112 #011-04-1978 L1983 **ORS** *020 †40
WINIKUR, Lawrence Jay. 314 FAIRY STREET EXT STE C, PEIDMONT PAIN MEDICINE, PC 24112
  #051-04-1988 L1999 **AN** *020 †05
WOOLARD, Douglas Winfield. 320 HOSPITAL DR 24112 #051-01-1981 L1985 **DR** *020 †80
YATES, Matthew Chas. 320 HOSPITAL DR 24112 #048-02-1984 L1992 **DR** *020 †80

ZIMMER, William John. 1107 BROOKDALE ST, CARILION MEDICAL 24112 #056-06-1986 L1989 IM *020 †20

MATHEWS – MATHEWS

BOGAEV, Leonard Rocklin. ROUTE 611, MATHEWS HEALTH DEPARTMENT 23109 #041-01-1954 L1987 U *071 †95

BRADFIELD, Bruce Maynard. PO BOX 1360, 28 CHURCH ST 23109 #051-07-1988 L1989 FM *020 †18

GRISWOLD, Steven M. PO BOX 747, MATHEWS MEDICAL CENTER 23109 #043-01-1992 L1997 FM *020 †18

HUDGINS, Hubert Bland. MAIN ST 23109 #051-04-1965 L1965 GP *071

PORZIO, Raymond Joseph. ■ 23109 #033-05-1962 L1979 P CHP *071 †75

SADLER, William Anderson. ■ 23109 #051-04-1944 L1944 GP *071

MAURERTOWN – SHENANDOAH

CARITHERS, Jeffrey Scott. ■ 22644 #018-03-1981 L2007 FPS *071 †45

COTTRELL, John Austin, Jr. ■ 22644 #021-05-1970 L1976 IM *071 †20

KIRKLAND, Nathaniel C. 24160 OLD VALLEY PIKE 22644 #051-01-1972 L1972 FM *020 †18

PIERCE, Mark Rainer. ■ 22644 #012-01-1980 L1985 EM *020 †16

MAX MEADOWS – WYTHE

BAKANE, Neela Ramesh. 245 FORT CHISWELL RD, STE D 24360 #495-83-1969 L2005 FM *020 †18

STOKER, Michael Hughes. 791 FORT CHISWELL RD STE A 24360 #051-04-1983 L1987 FM *020 †18

MC GAHEYSVILLE – ROCKINGHAM

ASHTON, Christopher A. 9982 SPOTSWOOD TRL 22840 #055-01-1990 L1996 PD IM *020 †55

BRADSHAW, Susan Smith. 9982 SPOTSWOOD TRL 22840 #051-04-1985 L1988 PD *075 †55

BURT, Leslie Stephen. 9982 SPOTSWOOD TRL 22840 #041-14-1973 L1977 PD *020 †55

COMER, F Edward. 9982 SPOTSWOOD TRL 22840 #051-04-1964 L1964 PD *020

GEARING, Frank Wilson, III. 9982 SPOTSWOOD TRL 22840 #051-04-1975 L1978 PD *020 †55

HANON, Kelli. 9982 SPOTSWOOD TRL 22840 #005-12-1997 L2004 PD *020 †55

SEFCZEK, Donna Maria. ■ 22840 #016-42-1981 L2007 DR *020 †80

SEFCZEK, Robert John. ■ 22840 #016-11-1980 L2007 DR *020 †80

TOMEI, Jon Richard. 9982 SPOTSWOOD TRL 22840 #051-01-1995 L2001 PD *020 †55

MC KENNEY – DINWIDDIE

BELLO, Nicolas B. ■ 23872 #748-02-1949 L1975 FM EM *075

HARRISON, Denise Winfield. 19915 OLD WHITE OAK RD 23872 #051-04-1992 L1993 FM *020 †18

MC LEAN – FAIRFAX

ABDELMALEK, Samia Boutros. ■ 22101 #915-02-1958 L1975 FM *071

ABUJRAB, Claude. ■ 22101 #875-01-1990 L1998 RHU *020 †20

ADLER, Adrienne Cecile. ■ 22101 #047-06-1965 L1968 GP *071

AKBARI, Stephanie R. 6845 ELM ST STE 708, CTR FOR BREAST HLTH PC 22101 #041-01-1991 L2000 GS *020 †85

ALAGIA, Damian P, III. 6845 ELM ST, STE 600 22101 #010-02-1982 L1986 OBG GS *020 †30 ‡

AL AHMADI, Mamdouh D. ■ 22101 #797-02-1992 L1999 TS *100 †85,90

ALAOUI, Abderr A. ■ 22102 #396-19-1967 L1991 TS *020 †85

AL-DALLI, Mohammed A. 1515 CHAIN BRIDGE RD, STE 302 22101 #528-01-1985 L1997 IM *020 †20

ALMS, William John. 6731 WHITTIER AVE, STE B200 22101 #023-01-1995 L1999 D *020 †15

AMBROGGIO, Jennifer Dunde. ■ 22101 #036-01-2008 *012

AMINI, Maryamolsadat. ■ 22101 #517-08-1999 IM *012

AMINI, Shohreh. ■ 22101 #517-01-1984 L1992 IM *020 †20

AMOROSI, Leo David. 1515 CHAIN BRIDGE RD, STE 314 22101 #010-02-1955 L1962 OBG GYN *020 †30

ANDERSON, Michael Harold. 1364 BEVERLY RD, STE 303 22101 #017-20-1976 L1998 P *020 †75

ANEZ, Yasmin Khidou. 8365 GREENSBORO DR # A 22102 #528-01-1976 L1983 PD *020

ANNIBALI, Joseph Andrew. 1489 CHAIN BRIDGE RD STE 2 22101 #041-14-1982 L1987 P PYA *020 †75

ARDEN, Jonathan Levi. ■ 22101 #025-01-1980 L2003 FOP *062 †50

ARMSTRONG, Norman Alva. 6845 ELM ST, STE 600 22101 #010-03-1970 L1975 OBG OS *020 †30

ASHINY, Zelalem Aberra. ■ 22102 #366-01-1997 L2006 IM *020 †20

AVERY, Anthony Lee. ■ 22102 #010-02-2006 ORS *012

BAJOGHLI, Mehran. 1201 ALPS DR 22102 #305-01-1995 L2002 NM *020 †28

BALBA, Gayle Phadungchai. ■ 22102 #010-02-1998 L1998 ID *020 †20

BALBA, Nader H. ■ 22102 #008-02-1997 L1997 GE *020 †20

BANNON, Patricia Zita. 6845 ELM ST, STE 600 22101 #051-01-1997 L1997 OBG *020 †30

BARRICK, E Frederick. 1499 CHAIN BRIDGE RD, NO 100 22101 #041-01-1966 L1976 ORS *020 †40

BARTIS, Lois C. 1515 CHAIN BRIDGE RD, STE 312 22101 #035-08-1974 L1980 IM *020 †20

BASHIR-ELAHI, Abbas. ■ 22101 #517-01-1956 L1962 IM GE *075

BASNAYAKE, Shalika Kumari. ■ 22101 #010-02-2004 L2004 ID *012 †20

BEHNAM, Marcelina Benafsh. ■ 22102 #051-01-2006 L2007 EM *012

BERNABE-QUION, Nathalie P. ■ 22102 #748-10-1988 L1999 PD *020 †55

BICKSEL, James Lyle, Jr. 6714 WHITTIER AVE 22101 #012-01-1999 L2004 N *020 †75

BIGGS, Jennifer Mathews. ■ 22101 #010-02-2006 L2006 OBG *012

BIR, Christopher Todd. 1497 CHAIN BRIDGE RD, STE 105 22101 #001-02-2000 L2000 CHP *020 †75

BLOCK, David Alan. 1314 VINCENT PL 22101 #023-07-1972 L1975 CHP P *020 †75

BOAZ, Thurmond D, Jr. ■ 22101 #021-05-1940 L1965 PHP *071 †70

BORCHERDING, Donald Lee. ■ 22101 #018-03-1958 L1967 OM GP *030 †70,18

BROWNSTEIN, Willis Edwin. 8371A GREENSBORO DR 22102 #051-04-1965 L1965 D *020 †15

BRUCKNER, Nancy E V. 6731 WHITTIER AVE, STE B200 22101 #010-01-1976 L1980 D *020 †15

BRUNO, Peter Denis. 1499 CHAIN BRIDGE RD # 100 22101 #010-02-1975 L1980 ORS *020 †40

BUNCE, John D. ■ 22101 #010-02-1951 L1954 PD *071 †55

BYRNE, William Draper. ■ 22102 #010-02-1948 L1961 TS CD *071 †85,90

CAMPDEN-MAIN, Brian C. 1320 VINCENT PL 22101 #352-11-1942 L1953 P *071

CARTER, Robert Lee. 1515 CHAIN BRIDGE RD, STE 304 22101 #011-02-1961 L1963 D *020

CASAZZA, Lawrence J, Jr. 1629 SENECA AVE 22102 #035-06-1964 L1972 PHP *020 †55

CASSIDY, Susan Olevia. ■ 22101 #047-05-1979 L1980 IM OM *020 †20

CHA, Leanne Jiehea. 6715 WHITTIER AVE, STE 100 22101 #051-04-1999 L1999 FM *020 †18

CHAFFEE, Melissa Sue. 1317 VINCENT PL 22101 #035-06-1987 L1991 P *020 †75

CHAND, Nisha. 1012 EATON DR, GASTROINTESTINAL MEDICINE 22102 #495-37-1998 L1999 GE *020 †20

CHUSUEI, Oraphan C. 8373A GREENSBORO DR 22102 #891-02-1963 L1973 IM PD *020

CHUSUEI, Richard V. 8373A GREENSBORO DR 22102 #891-01-1962 L1970 PD CD *020 †55

COFFEY, Mary Lelia. ■ 22102 #010-02-1980 L1982 EM R *020 †16

COHEN, Claudia Sieger. 6845 ELM ST STE 611 22101 #055-01-1998 L2005 OPH *020 †35

COLINGO-FAHLBERG, Kelly. ■ 22102 #027-01-1989 L1998 AN *020 †05

COLLEA, Lisa Anne. 1515 CHAIN BRIDGE RD, STE G17 22101 #041-02-2003 L2003 OPH *020

CONRAD, Peter Walter. ■ 22101 #010-02-1954 L1961 TS CD *071 †85,90

CORLEY, Sarah Taylor. 6204 VERNON PALMER CT, INTERNAL MEDICINE ASSOCIAT 22101 #051-01-1986 L1988 IM OS *020 †20 ‡

CORMAN, Adam Ransford. ■ 22102 #051-07-2008 EM *012

COSTER, Laura O'Bryan. ■ 22101 #035-47-1994 ID *100 †20

CRANTZ, Frank Richard. 7921 JONES BRANCH DR, STE 320 22102 #023-07-1975 L1983 END *020 †20 ‡

DAHBAR, Jorge Eduardo. 6667A OLD DOMINION DR 22101 #132-02-1975 L1983 GP *020

DANACEAU, Henry Lawrence. ■ 22102 #038-04-1965 L1971 ORS *071 †40

DANIEL, David Gordon. 6850 ELM ST STE 200D&E 22101 #047-05-1982 L1986 P *050 †75

DAUCHER, James Andrew. ■ 22101 #305-01-2000 L2007 OBG *020 ‡

DAVOLI, Enrico. 6711 WHITTIER AVE 22102 #010-02-1956 L1960 PD PDA *071 †55

DEEKEN, John Frederick. ■ 22101 #010-02-2001 L2001 ON *050

DEYE, Gregory Alan. ■ 22101 #041-02-1995 L2006 ID *020 †20

DIDEHVAR, Mohammad R. 6262 OLD DOMINION DR, OLD DOMINION URGENT CARE 22101 #308-12-1986 L1995 FM *020 †18

DI PAOLO, Sanda F. 1515 CHAIN BRIDGE RD # 204, MCLEAN MEDICAL BUILDING 22101 #010-02-1989 L1991 OBG *020 †30

DORAN, Kelly Maureen. ■ 22101 #025-01-2007 EM *012

DREILING, Jennifer Lynne. ■ 22101 #051-01-2007 L2007 *012

DUDA, Gloria. 6845 ELM ST, STE 708 22101 #011-02-1984 L1986 PS *020 †85,65

DUFFY, Adrian Dominick. ■ 22101 #803-09-1957 L1971 P *072 †75

DUFFY, Eileen Josephine M. ■ 22101 #539-04-1956 L1972 P *072 †75

DURELL, Jack. ■ 22101 #008-01-1953 L1973 P *071

EJTEMAEE, Nasrin. 8375 GREENSBORO DR A 22102 #517-04-1981 L1999 FM *020 †18

ELLIS, Forrest James. ■ 22102 #017-20-1990 L2007 OPH *072 †35

EMPSON, Marianne Lober. ■ 22101 #297-01-1969 L1969 PD *062

ESTILO, Apolonia E. ■ 22101 #748-01-1953 L1972 AN PD *071

FAGAN, Landrey Milton. ■ 22102 #010-02-2008 *012

FALUDI, D Dennis. ■ 22101 #035-03-1977 L1983 HS ORS *020 †40

FARBOUDMANESCH, Ramin. 8100 LEWINSVILLE RD 22102 #010-01-1996 L1999 GE *020

FISHER, Nina Myerson. 6731 WHITTIER AVE, DERMATOLOGY ASSOC OF MCLEA 22101 #008-01-1997 L2002 D *020 †15

FOEGH, Marie Ladefoged. 1356 KIRBY RD 22101 #297-01-1969 L1982 IM GYN *050

FREEDMAN, Bruce Michael. 8180 GREENSBORO DR 22102 #036-07-1982 L1989 PS HS *020 †65

FRIED, William Andrew. 2010 CORPORATE RDG, STE 300 22102 #041-01-1976 L1982 PD *030 †55

FROELICH, Francis Edwin. 7405 WINDY HILL CT 22102 #047-05-1983 L1985 IM *100

GAB-ALLAH, Thonia Hafez. 8370 GREENSBORO DR, APT 818 22102 #915-04-1971 L1987 IM *071

GAILITIS, Sandra Ingrida. 6756 OLD MCLEAN VILLAGE DR 22101 #422-01-1982 L1985 IM *020

GANJEI, Ali Gholizadeh. ■ 22102 #051-04-1986 L1990 PM *020 †60

GARCIA, Robert Courtney. 1515 CHAIN BRIDGE RD, STE G12 22101 #010-01-1956 L1965 R NM *071 †80,28

GAVRILOVICH, Lillian. ■ 22102 #957-02-1966 L1974 IM *030

GAZALE, William J. ■ 22101 #396-04-1953 L1957 ORS *071 †40

GEORGOPOULOS, Dimitrios. 6842 ELM ST, STE 203 22101 #264-14-1987 L1996 P *020

GERMAIN, Timothy Justin. 1925 VALLEYWOOD RD, PLASTIC SURGERY ASSOCIATES 22101 #041-09-1998 L2005 PS *020 †65 ‡

GERONA-MACARANAS, Lucille. ■ 22102 #748-11-1993 L2007 PD *020 †55

GHAZIRAD, Mojgan. 7536 AMBERGATE PL, APT 5 22102 #517-01-1998 L2007 PD *012

GIBNEY, Matthew J, III. ■ 22102 #023-01-1972 L1982 PS GS *071 †85,65

GIRARDI, Alyce Marie. 1235 COLONIAL RD 22101 #010-02-1986 L1993 IM OM *020 †20

GOEL, Ranjana. ■ 22101 #495-67-1974 *074

GOLDENBERG, Robin Ira. ■ 22102 #010-02-1974 L1976 MDM ID *071 †55

GOLDMAN, George Saml. ■ 22102 #008-01-1929 L1991 P PYA *071

GORMAN, Barry Chas. 1483 CHAIN BRIDGE RD, STE 205 22101 #010-01-1971 L1976 P *020 †75

GRAY, Maribel Ocampo. 1580 SPRING GATE DR, P O BOX 11193 22102 #010-02-1997 L1997 EM *020 †16 ‡

GULATI, Gautam. ■ 22102 #010-01-2000 IM *100

GUO, Daqing. ■ 22101 #243-24-1987 L2004 NEP IM *100 †20

GURNEY, Ronald Edward. 6888 ELM ST STE 2A 22101 #035-08-1974 L1980 GE IM *020 †20

GURRALA, Joseph Parimal. ■ 22102 #053-06-2004 L2005 P *100

GUTIERREZ, Joseph Edward. ■ 22101 #056-06-1961 L1969 GS *072 †85

HADDADMASHAD, Afsane. 6858 OLD DOMINION DR, STE 104 22101 #010-02-1989 L1995 CD *020 †20

HAHN, Susan. ■ 22101 #010-01-2008 *012

HALES, Laura C. ■ 22101 #047-05-1996 L1999 PD *020 †55

HARBERT, John Chas. ■ 22101 #016-06-1963 L1969 GP *074 †28

HARRINGTON, Amy Lucile. ■ 22101 #041-15-2005 L2005 P *012

HARRIS, Forest Klaire. ■ 22102 #010-01-1953 L1974 IM *071 †20

■ = Address Information Privacy Protected

HAYRE, Nicole F. 8405 GREENSBORO DR STE 110 22102 #010-01-1998 L2003 **D** *020 †15
HEGDE, Ajit Kumar. ■ 22101 #495-99-1986 L2006 **AN** *020
HEILEN, Robert John. ■ 22101 #035-19-1964 L1971 **ORS** *071 †40
HELWIG, Amy Linn. ■ 22101 #056-06-1993 L2006 **FM MDM** *020 †18
HENICK, James H. ■ 22101 #024-07-1989 L1993 **PMM** *012 †05
HERRERA, James Fernando. 1497 CHAIN BRIDGE RD, STE 105 22101 #010-03-2000 L2005 **CHP** *020 †75
HIATT, David Ellis. 6845 ELM ST STE 710 22101 #067-01-1976 L1990 **P CHP** *020 †75
HO, Walter I Chie. ■ 22101 #065-01-1986 L2000 **GS** *020
HOLZMAN, Andrew Evan. 1750 TYSONS BLVD, STE 120 22102 #011-02-1987 L1989 **OPH** *020 †35
HORNE, Allen Bernard. 6715 WHITTIER AVE 22101 #051-04-1972 L1973 **FM** *020 †18
HUBACH, Frederick Willis. 6715 WHITTIER AVE, STE 100 22101 #010-01-1958 L1961 **FM** *020 †18
HUNTER, Lourdes B Cayosa. 1420 SPRING HILL RD, STE 350 22102 #023-01-1996 L1998 **AI IM** *020 †20,03
HURWITZ, William Eliot. ■ 22102 #005-11-1971 L1977 **IM PMM** *075
IBRAHIM, Sandy F. 6862 ELM ST, STE 700 22101 #025-07-2000 L2003 **FM** *020 †18 ‡
ISSA, Fuad. 6842 ELM ST, STE 104 22101 #875-02-1980 L1990 **P PYG** *020 †75
JACOBSON, Evan Lawrence. 1449 DOLLEY MADISON BLVD, STE H 22101 #041-02-2000 L2004 **P** *020
JAIPAUL, Chitra Komal. ■ 22101 #010-03-1991 L1997 **IM** *020 †20
JANDER, C Isabel Granja. 8365A GREENSBORO DR 22102 #033-05-2002 L2005 **PD** *020 †55
JEFFERY, Amy Ruth. ■ 22102 #035-06-1989 L1995 **PO** *072 †35
JENSEN, Kirk Bradley. 8220 GREENSBORO DR, STE 1150 22102 #016-11-1978 L1979 **EM** *020 †16
JONES, Sarah Elizabeth. ■ 22101 #051-01-2006 L2006 **DR** *012
JOSEPH, Colleen Anne. 1515 CHAIN BRIDGE RD # G17 22101 #010-02-1987 L1992 **OPH** *020 †35
KADA, Faiza. ■ 22101 #125-01-1989 L2003 **END** *020 †20
KAPLAN, Kenneth Lawrence. 6723 WHITTIER AVE STE 405D 22101 #016-02-1962 L1973 **CHP P** *020 †75
KARAM, Antoine Jean. ■ 22102 #010-01-1997 **OBG** *100 ‡
KARLIN, Kenneth Michael. 6845 ELM ST STE 611, EYE PHYSICIANS VA LTD 22101 #021-05-1980 L1985 **OPH** *020 †35
KERR, Christen Mccullough. 1307 DOLLEY MADISON BLVD 22101 #017-20-1984 L1996 **P** *020 †75
KETCHAM, Robert E. 1314 VINCENT PL 22101 #010-02-1973 L1978 **P** *020 †75
KHACHEMOUNE, Amor. ■ 22101 #125-03-1989 L2007 **PRD** *020 †15
KIM, Christine May. 1403 WOODHURST BLVD 22102 #028-34-2002 L2004 **OBG** *100
KIM, Ho Jin. 8371A GREENSBORO DR 22102 #051-04-1994 L2000 **D PMM** *020 †15
KIM, Jung Ja. ■ 22101 #583-03-1970 L1975 **AN** *020
KLAR, Ronald Martin. ■ 22102 #016-02-1971 **OS PHP** *030
KLETZ, Michael Robt. 1420 SPRING HILL RD, STE 350 22102 #033-05-1984 L1989 **AI** *020 †20,03
KOBYLSKI, Thomas Paul, Jr. 6760 OLD MCLEAN VILLAGE DR 22101 #041-14-1986 L1989 **CHP P** *020 †75
KRAKOWER, Brian Mark. 1515 CHAIN BRIDGE RD, STE 308 22101 #010-02-1988 L1990 **IM** *020 †20
LAM, Chau T. 6711 WHITTIER AVE, STE 101 22101 #048-14-1995 L1999 **MPD** *020 †55
LANE, Herbert Edward, Jr. ■ 22101 #010-02-1947 L1957 **ORS** *071 †40
LANING, Robert Comegys. ■ 22101 #041-02-1948 L1978 **GS** *020 †85
LANTER, Tracie Lee. 1515 CHAIN BRIDGE RD, STE 312 22101 #051-04-1992 L1995 **IM** *020 †20
LAWRENCE, Mark Allen. ■ 22102 #024-01-1965 L1971 **P** *020 †75
LAWSON, Carrie Danielle. 6845 ELM ST, STE 600 22101 #012-22-2003 L2003 **OBG** *020
LEBOWITZ, J Martin. 6845 ELM ST, STE 615 22101 #016-06-1963 L1976 **U UP** *020 †95
LEE, Tsang-Yui Rory. 1515 CHAIN BRIDGE RD 22101 #462-01-1961 L1972 **OPH** *071 †35
LENARD, Peter Dennis. 1485 CHAIN BRIDGE RD # 202 22101 #010-01-1968 L1974 **GS** *020 †85 ‡
LESSIN, Bruce Edward. 1313 DOLLEY MADISON BLVD, STE 207 22101 #025-01-1967 L1973 **IM NEP** *020 †20
LEVIN, Stephen Michael. ■ 22102 #035-08-1958 L1963 **ORS PM** *071 †40
LIBERMAN, Alberto Julio. ■ 22101 #132-01-1964 L1982 **OBG** *075 †30
LICAMELE, William Louis. 6760 OLD MCLEAN VILLAGE DR 22101 #010-02-1972 L1976 **CHP P** *020 †75
LICATA, Robert M. 6800 FLEETWOOD RD STE 111 22101 #010-02-1971 L1976 **P** *020 †75
LICHTMANN, Albert Laszlo. ■ 22101 #473-01-1953 L1960 **AN APM** *040
LILLRANK, Sonja Margareta. 1314 VINCENT PL, RM 6 22101 #374-05-1992 L1999 **P** *020 †75
LIN, Chiu Po. ■ 22101 #244-06-1967 L1992 **GP** *020
LIN, Jack Chi. ■ 22102 #654-01-2001 L2007 **GS** *100
LINDSTEDT, Jan Gustaf. 6708 MELROSE DR 22101 #858-02-1959 L1973 **DR NM** *020 †80
LINEHAN, Joseph David, Jr. 9111 FALLS RUN RD 22102 #051-04-1970 L1970 **ORS** *020 †40
LITTLE, Emily R. ■ 22101 #051-04-2008 L2008 **P** *012
LIU, Chang-Kai Lilly. 8377A GREENSBORO DR 22102 #244-02-1979 L1986 **PD** *020 †55
LOMAX, Peggy Jean. 6845 ELM ST, STE 710 22101 #010-02-1987 L1991 **P** *020
LORIA, Richard Claude. 6888 ELM ST, STE 301 22101 #847-11-1983 L1988 **A IG** *020 †20,03
LORICA, Arlenemarie A. 8365A GREENSBORO DR 22102 #748-02-1989 L1997 **PD** *020 †55
LOWRY, Elmer F, Jr. ■ 22101 #024-01-1943 L1956 **P** *071 †75
MACIULLA, Lori Jean. 6707 OLD DOMINION DR, STE 300 22101 #010-02-1985 L1988 **OBG** *020 †30
MAGASSY, Csaba Ladislao. 1300 CHAIN BRIDGE RD 22101 #030-06-1962 L1969 **PS** *020 †85,65 ‡
MAKORNWATTANA, Porawat. ■ 22102 #891-01-1995 L2001 **RHU** *100 †20,03
MARDINI, Mohamed Kamel. 6858 OLD DOMINION DR # 104 22101 #517-01-1968 L1973 **PDC** *020 †55
MARTIN, Dean H. ■ 22101 #010-01-1950 L1956 **OBG** *071 †30
MATISOFF, Andrew Jeffrey. ■ 22101 #051-01-2003 L2003 **AN** *100
MAYBURY, Rubie Sue. ■ 22101 #035-15-2007 L2007 **GS** *012
MAYCOCK, Wm Fredrick, Jr. 1418 MAYFLOWER DR 22101 #005-15-1966 L1996 **AN** *020
MAZAHERY, Behrang. ■ 22101 #051-04-2000 L2006 **ORS** *100
MAZZARELLA, I C. ■ 22101 #024-05-1956 L1971 **OS IM** *071
MC CARTHY, Catherine Lapp. 1307 DOLLEY MADISON BLVD, STE 3C 22101 #051-01-1996 L1996 **P** *020 †75
MC CURDY, Pamela Mary. 1307 DOLLEY MADISON BLVD, STE 3 22101 #039-01-1975 L1987 **CHP P** *020 †75

MC GINNIS, Jocelyn Ann. 6861 ELM ST, STE 4D 22101 #010-01-1984 L1994 **OBG** *020 †30
MC QUADE, Jennifer Ann. ■ 22101 #041-09-1998 L2005 **CRS GS** *100 †85,10
MCQUEEN, Sarah Rose. 8300 GREENSBORO DR STE 800 22102 #048-13-1992 L1994 **P** *020 †75
MEERASAHIB, Anish. 1521 SPRING GATE DR # 1030 22102 #495-31-2001 L2003 **HO** *012 †20
MERZ, Edwin Henry. ■ 22101 #028-02-1957 L1958 **IM** *020 †20
MILLS, Cathleen S. 1651 LA SALLE AVE, 8901 WISCONSIN AVE BETHESD 22102 #023-12-1996 L1997 **OBG** *020 †30
MISHKHAS, Nawal. ■ 22101 #704-02-1969 L1982 **P** *020
MISHRA, Bibhuti Bhlisman. 6714 WHITTIER AVE 22101 #495-27-1978 L1991 **N** *020 †75
MISHRA, Lopa Patel. 6714 WHITTIER AVE 22101 #917-28-1982 L2001 **GE IM** *020 †20
MOLEDINA, Nasimbanu R A. ■ 22102 #517-05-1979 L1982 **OS PD** *050
MOSELEY, James Alan. 626 CHAIN BRIDGE RD 22101 #011-02-1966 L1988 **FM EM** *020
MOTESHARREI, Bita. 1515 CHAIN BRIDGE RD, STE 314 22101 #011-02-1998 L1998 **OBG** *020 †30
MUSHTAQ, Ednan. 6845 ELM ST STE 303, METROPOLITAN E.N.T. 22101 #056-06-1989 L1997 **OTO FPS** *020 †45
NAJIB, Akram. 8343 GREENSBORO DR # A 22102 #528-01-1954 L1967 **VS CD** *071 †85,90
NAWAZ, Taimor. ■ 22101 #160-02-1982 L1991 **ID** *020 †20
NETTO, Georges Jabboure. ■ 22101 #875-01-1985 L1990 **PTH CLP** *020 †50
NEWMAN, Steven Alan. 1100 CHAIN BRIDGE RD 22101 #035-46-1973 L1981 **OPH NS** *040 †20,35
NGUYEN, Khanh Trang Thi. ■ 22102 #942-01-1978 L1999 **P** *020
NICKLAY, James Thos. ■ 22102 #038-40-1973 L1979 **OTO** *071 †45
NIMMAGADDA, R Rao. 1515 CHAIN BRIDGE RD, STE 212 22101 #495-70-1981 L1991 **GE** *020 †20
OMELON, Jerry Anthony. 1340 OLD CHAIN BRIDGE RD, STE 101 22101 #065-01-1968 L1994 **FM** *020
OSIFO, Nosakhare Guy O. ■ 22101 #690-01-1975 L1979 **PA** *071
OSSOFSKY, Helen Johns. ■ 22101 #023-07-1954 L1969 **P CHP** *071 †55
PANE, Gregg Anthony. ■ 22106 #025-01-1981 L1995 **EM OS** *040 †16
PARK, In Kwon. ■ 22101 #051-01-2005 L2005 **IM** *012
PARKASH, Amarender. ■ 22101 #496-43-1997 L2004 **AN** *020 †05
PARKER, John Sutherland. 1710 SAIC DR, SCIENCE APPLIC INTL CORP 22102 #010-02-1974 L1982 **TS CD** *050 †85,90
PASICOV, Benjamin. 1340 OLD CHAIN BRIDGE RD, STE 101 22101 #065-01-1968 L1976 **GP EM** *020
PASTER, Mark A. 6862 ELM ST, STE 700 22101 #051-07-2000 L2003 **FM** *020 †18 ‡
PAULSON, Michelle Louise. ■ 22101 #055-01-2002 L2005 **ID** *100 †20
PAYNE, John Dundee. 1314 VINCENT PL 22101 #016-06-1971 L1977 **P** *020 †75
PAYNE, Lillian Jones. 1314 VINCENT PL 22101 #016-06-1972 L1976 **CHP P** *020 †75
PECORA, David V. ■ 22101 #008-01-1941 L1968 **GS TS** *072 †85,90
PEREYRA, Vivian. ■ 22101 #308-02-1988 L1993 **GPM** *020
PHILLIPS, Yancy Y. 7005 GIRARD ST 22101 #001-02-1976 L1979 **PUD IM** *030 †20
PLATENBERG, Robert C. 1430 SPRING HILL RD, MED TEL INTL 22102 #010-02-1981 L1994 **RNR DR** *020 †80
PLEHN, Jonathan F. ■ 22102 #035-19-1977 L1978 **CD IM** *020 †20
POBLETE, Cristina. ■ 22101 #748-02-1965 L1972 **PD** *020 †55
PRESSMAN, Howard Ira. 6760 OLD MCLEAN VILLAGE DR 22101 #023-01-1973 L1979 **CHP P** *020 †75
PRUETT, Richard Kepley. ■ 22101 #005-14-1974 L1975 **ADM** *050
QAZI, Aisha Anjum. ■ 22101 #051-01-2007 L2007 **GS** *012
QUICK, Cedric Albert. 1350 BEVERLY RD # 230-115 22101 #946-01-1961 L1980 **OTO A** *071 †45
RADICE, Luis Carlos. ■ 22101 #132-01-1957 L1968 **OBG** *071 †30
RAJPAL, Rajesh Kumar. 8180 GREENSBORO DR, STE 140 22102 #051-04-1987 L1994 **OPH OS** *020 †35
REA, Edward L. ■ 22101 #010-01-1946 L1960 **IM CD** *071
REDINGTON, Kathleen Marie. 7314 YATES CT 22101 #035-20-1988 L1993 **N** *020 †75
RENFIELD, Marilyn Lewis. ■ 22101 #010-01-1965 L1972 **P PD** *072 †55
REYNOLDS, Arthur M, Jr. 1515 CHAIN BRIDGE RD, METRO OPHTHALMOLOGY ASSOCS 22101 #051-04-1953 L1953 **OPH** *071 †35
RIEMER, Melissa Ann. ■ 22102 #007-02-1994 *074
RIZVI, Monique Maria. 1340 OLD CHAIN BRIDGE RD, STE 101 22101 #422-01-1996 L2000 **IM** *020
ROBERTSON, Robert Hood. ■ 22101 #041-13-1948 L1964 **P** *071 †75
ROESEL, Thomas R. 7810 FALSTAFF RD 22102 #016-06-1981 L1991 **IM HEM** *020 †20
ROGART, Richard Barry. ■ 22102 #008-01-1978 L1998 **CD IM** *050
ROGO, Tanya Orie. ■ 22101 #021-01-2007 L2007 **PD** *012
ROSEN, Kathleen Nichols. ■ 22102 #010-02-1986 L1988 **EM** *020 †16
ROSENFELD, Susan Esther. 1317 VINCENT PL 22101 #041-13-1990 L1994 **P** *020 †75
ROSS, Michael A. 6861 ELM ST STE 4D, OB-GYN AND INFERTILITY 22101 #010-01-1975 L1977 **GYN OBG** *020 †30
ROTH, Richard Lee. 6845 ELM ST STE 210 22101 #016-06-1967 L1977 **P** *020 †75
RUBENSTEIN, Harvey Allan. 7921 JONES BRANCH DR, STE 320 22102 #035-15-1967 L1973 **END IM** *020 †20 ‡
RUIZ-CAMAUER, Raul. ■ 22101 #132-01-1971 L1978 **AN** *075
RUNGE, Jeffrey Wm. ■ 22102 #045-01-1981 L1982 **EM** *020 †16
SAADEH, Reem. ■ 22102 #010-02-2001 L2008 **MG** *020 †55,19
SABELLA, La Reine F. 6707 OLD DOMINION DR # 300 22101 #010-02-1975 L1976 **GYN** *020 †30
SABETPAYMAN, Arshia. ■ 22101 #010-01-2005 L2005 **IM** *012
SACKS, Charles Bernard. 1313 VINCENT PL 22101 #038-40-1965 L1977 **P** *020 †75
SAGER, Alan Robt. 6849 OLD DOMINION DR # 210 22101 #024-05-1969 L1976 **P** *020 †75
SANDERS, Jay Henry. 1317 VINCENT PL, THE GLOBAL TELEMEDICINE GR 22101 #024-01-1963 L2000 **IM AI** *062 †20,03
SANDERS, John A. 6845 ELM ST, STE 600 22101 #010-02-1953 L1960 **TS** *071 †30
SARIN, Seema. ■ 22101 #010-01-2003 L2006 **IM** *020 †20
SATTLER, Raymond Louis. 1483 CHAIN BRIDGE RD STE 3 22101 #038-06-1977 L1997 **CHP P** *020 †25,75
SCHAFER, Klaus Otto. ■ 22101 #018-03-1977 L1978 **FM AM** *030 †70,18
SCHEHL, Charles Anthony. ■ 22101 #041-13-1954 L1964 **IM** *071
SCHILLER, Maurice. 8620 BROOK RD 22102 #132-01-1963 L1968 **OBG** *071 †30
SEGEV, Gilead. 1313 DOLLEY MADISON BLVD, STE 302 22101 #048-15-1998 L2003 **IM** *020 †20
SETHI, Charanjit K. ■ 22102 #496-09-1977 **IM HEM** *071

■ = Address Information Privacy Protected

SETHI, Narinder Nitin. ■ 22102 #051-04-2003 L2004 **DR** *012

SEXTON, Jennifer Ann. ■ 22101 #028-03-2004 L2006 **GS** *012

SHAH, Monica R. ■ 22102 #043-01-1994 L2001 **CD** *020 †20

SHARMA, Karun Vashisht. ■ 22101 #051-04-2001 L2001 **VIR** *100 †80

SHASHATY, George Gabriel. ■ 22102 #010-02-1962 L1968 **HEM IM** *071 †20

SHASHATY, Nancy M Packert. ■ 22102 #035-08-1969 L1982 **DBP** *040 †55

SHEIKH, Nasreen Mazhar. ■ 22101 #704-02-1968 L1981 **FM EM** *020 †50

SHEIKH, Tehmina Moiz. 7490 CARRIAGE HILLS DR 22102 #704-06-1990 L2005 **P** *020

SHELBY, Gloria Dean. ■ 22102 #010-03-1984 L1991 **EM** *020

SHERMAN, Mark Elliot. ■ 22101 #016-02-1983 L1986 **PTH** *020 †50

SHILLING, Charles Utley. ■ 22101 #010-01-1955 L1962 **IM** *071 †20

SIMPSON, Frank B, III. 1320 OLD CHAN BRDG RD #310 22101 #051-04-1962 L1962 **P** *020

SKOPEK, Henry Adelbert. ■ 22101 #869-04-1961 L1982 **P** *020

SLIJEPCEVIC, Sinisa M. ■ 22106 #957-01-1956 L1972 **AN** *072

SMITH, John James. 1430 SPRING HILL RD, STE 500 22102 #051-01-1992 L1993 **DR LM** *020 †80

SMOAK, Maryfrances Brown. ■ 22102 #010-02-1995 L1997 **IM** *020

SMOKVINA, Marija Demsar. ■ 22101 #957-03-1959 L1972 **PM** *020

SOLACK, George A. ■ 22102 #010-01-1960 L1967 **R** *072 †80

SONI, Gurbax Singh. ■ 22101 #495-57-1967 L1986 **EM** *020

SOTEROPOULOS, Costa Georg. ■ 22101 #010-02-2007 **GS** *012

SOVEROW, Gary Jan. 6888 ELM ST, STE 3C 22101 #024-01-1972 L1977 **P** *020 †75

SOYSTER, Eliza Shumaker. ■ 22101 #010-01-1948 L1951 **OS** *074

SPRAGUE, James Baird. 1515 CHAIN BRIDGE RD 22101 #041-01-1969 L1984 **PO IM** *071 †35

STAIR, Sarah Jane. 1515 CHAIN BRIDGE RD 22101 #018-03-1988 L1993 **OPH** *020 †35

STECKLER, Eric Alan. 1483 CHAIN BRIDGE RD, STE 304 22101 #035-46-1971 L1978 **CHP P** *020 †75 ‡

STEG, John Paul. 6760 OLD MCLEAN VILLAGE DR 22101 #030-05-1970 L1973 **CHP P** *020 †75

STEIN, Robyn Marissa. 6723 WHITTIER AVE, STE 4050 22101 #051-07-1991 L1992 **P** *020

STERRETT, Henry H D, Jr. ■ 22102 #064-01-1947 L1953 **IM** *071

STRANNE, Steven Kent. ■ 22101 #036-07-1990 L1991 **GS** *100

STRAUCH, Barry Stuart. 1468 EVANS FARM DR 22101 #023-07-1965 L1973 **NEP IM** *020 †20

TABBARAH, Zuhayr A. ■ 22101 #605-01-1975 L1976 **IM** *020 †20

TANEN, Shlomo Mark. 7921 JONES BRANCH DR, STE 320 22102 #065-01-1983 L1989 **END DIA** *020 †20 ‡

TANG, Eric David. ■ 22101 #025-01-2005 *100

TARKINGTON, Mary Anne. ■ 22101 #010-02-1985 L1987 **U** *071 †95

TART, Nelson Monroe. ■ 22101 #010-01-1955 L1959 **OBG** *071 †30

TATTELBAUM, Adam Gaston. 6845 ELM ST, STE 300 22101 #035-01-1988 L1996 **HS** *020 †85,65

TAYLOR, George Peach, Jr. 1800 TYSONS BLVD 22102 #048-04-1978 L1978 **AM** *030 †70

TEUNIS, Bernard Scott. 1300 CHAIN BRIDGE RD 22101 #051-01-1962 L1962 **PS** *020 †85,65

THOMPSON, Suzy Ann. 1200 CAROL RAYE ST 22101 #036-01-1995 L2001 **PD** *020 †55

THORISDOTTIR, Kristin. ■ 22102 #484-01-1986 **D** *020 †15

TIGANI, Michael Carmine. 1515 CHAIN BRIDGE RD # G17 22101 #047-05-1983 L1987 **OPH** *020 †35

TSAO, Daniel. 1314 VINCENT PL 22101 #051-04-1989 L1993 **P** *020 †75

TURAK, Maryann. ■ 22102 #010-02-1968 L1973 **P CHP** *071 †75 ‡

UZER, Yuksel. ■ 22102 #902-03-1961 L1965 **GP** *071

WEBB, Kinari Eve. ■ 22101 #008-01-2002 L2004 **FM** *100 †18

WESSEL-MANITSAS, H. ■ 22101 #407-33-1951 L1975 **AN** *071

WHITE, Joseph Bruce. 1499 CHAIN BRIDGE RD, STE 100 22101 #055-01-1975 L1976 **OSS** *020 †40

WHITE, Paul William. ■ 22102 #028-02-2000 L2002 **VS** *012

WIJETILLEKE, Medhine Anus. ■ 22101 #051-04-2005 L2005 **PD** *012

WOO, Wendy Wingnei. ■ 22102 #051-04-2008 *012

WRIGHT, Diana C Dryer. ■ 22101 #041-01-1973 L1974 **GPM** *075 †70

WRIGHT, William Evan. ■ 22101 #041-01-1972 L1985 **OM IM** *030 †20,70

YAO, Lawrence. 1430 SPRING HILL RD, MED-TEL INTERNATIONAL 22102 #043-01-1985 L2000 **DR IM** *020 †20

ZAHIR, Tarique Moin. 1340 OLD CHAIN BRIDGE RD, MCLEAN IMMEDIATE CARE 22101 #055-02-2002 L2007 **IM** *020

ZANETTI, Christopher John. 1515 CHAIN BRIDGE RD, STE 308 22101 #033-06-1990 L1992 **IM** *020 †20

ZAPATA, Norma Lissette. 6835 CHURCHILL RD 22101 #042-01-1977 L2001 **OPH** *020 †35

ZAREK, Shvetha Murthy. ■ 22102 #051-01-2006 L2006 **OBG** *012

ZOHLMAN, Robert Stephen. 7337 HOOKING RD, STE 104 22101 #035-46-1968 L1998 **IM NEP** *071 †20

ZOHN, David Arthur. 1515 CHAIN BRIDGE RD 22101 #035-08-1955 L1967 **PM** *071 †60

ZOOK, Michelle Denise. ■ 22102 #010-02-2007 L2007 **IM** *012

ZUCKERMAN, Bram David. 8377A GREENSBORO DR 22102 #024-05-1981 L1988 **CD IM** *020 †20

ZUKEL, William J. ■ 22102 #041-09-1947 L1949 **CD OS** *071

ZWEIFEL, Samuel, Jr. ■ 22101 #019-02-1949 **FM** *071 †18

MEADOWS OF DAN – PATRICK

SPANGLER, Harold B. PO BOX 108 24120 #036-05-1948 L1949 **PD** *071

MEADOWVIEW – WASHINGTON

OWENS, Joanna M. ■ 24361 #041-07-1955 L1957 **PHP** *071

SIERCHIO, Gerald Peter. ■ 24361 #010-02-1956 L1971 **ORS** *071 †40

MECHANICSVILLE – HANOVER

ALEXANDER, Peter Arthur. 8220 MEADOWBRIDGE RD, STE 209 23116 #035-19-1996 L2002 **NS** *020 †25

ANDRAKO, John David. 8260 ATLEE RD 23116 #051-04-1975 L1975 **PD** *020

ARAIN, Sumaira Afzal. ■ 23116 #422-01-2004 L2007 **OPH** *012

ARAK, Gladys. 8220 MEADOWBRIDGE RD, STE 301 23116 #035-08-1967 L1970 **P PD** *020 †55

ARMENTI-KAPROS, Brenda M. 8220 MEADOWBRIDGE RD, STE 306 23116 #422-01-1996 L2000 **END** *020 †20

ARTZ, Ronald Paul. 8220 MEADOWBRIDGE RD, MEMORIAL MEDICAL CENTER 23116 #038-43-1973 L1978 **IM ID** *020 †20

BANDY, Maurice Edward. ■ 23111 #020-12-1969 L1975 **IM** *071

BATES, Kathryn Wellington. 8266 ATLEE RD, STE 318 23116 #051-01-1996 L1999 **PD** *020 †55

BERNSTEIN, Harold Adam. 7575 COLD HARBOR RD, BLDG 2 23111 #025-07-1996 1996 **OPH** *020 †35

BLACKBURN, Maurice L, Jr. 9376 ATLEE STATION RD 23116 #051-01-1986 L1989 **FM EM** *020 †18

BLAKE, Thomas Duvall. 7255 HANOVER GREEN DR 23111 #051-01-1979 L1982 **FM** *020 †18

BOWMAN, John David. 8266 ATLEE RD, MOB II STE 133 23116 #035-45-1975 L1976 **ORS** *020 †40

BRAGER, Robert Jay. 7485 RIGHT FLANK RD, STE 210 23116 #041-12-1990 L1996 **OTO HNS** *020 †45

BRANDT, Charles Wesley. 7571 COLD HARBOR RD 23111 #051-04-1961 L1961 **RHU IM** *020 †20

BRANT, Seth Evans. ■ 23111 #051-04-2003 L2003 **PCC** *012 †20

BRENNAN, James Francis. 6372 MECHANICSVILLE TPKE, STE 103 23111 #033-05-1975 L1977 **PD** *071 †55

BRICHTA, Robert Frank. 7016 LEE PARK RD, STE 100 23111 #028-34-1977 L1992 **D PD** *020 †55,15

BRODEUR, James Philip. 8201 ATLEE RD, STE B 23116 #051-01-1985 L1988 **RHU IM** *020 †20

BROOKS-WILLIAMS, Malinda. 9376 ATLEE STATION RD 23116 #051-04-1981 L1985 **FM** *020 †18

BROSNAN, Kathleen Angela. 8260 ATLEE RD 23116 #539-04-1949 L1978 **P OBG** *020 †75

BROWN, Jeffrey Alan. 8220 MEADOWBRIDGE RD, VIRGINIA SURGICAL 23116 #051-04-1989 L1991 **VS** *020 †85

BROWN, William Francis. 6509 STRAWBANK DR 23116 #041-14-1988 L1999 **AN** *020 †05 ‡

BUNDY, Graham Matthew. 8220 MEADOWBRIDGE RD, STE 303 23116 #051-04-1998 L2007 **TS** *020 †85,90

BURIJON, Laura Layman. 7571 COLD HARBOR RD 23111 #051-04-2002 L2005 **FP** *012

BURKE, Alan J. 7485 RIGHT FLANK RD, STE 210 23116 #917-25-1991 L2001 **OTO GS** *020 †45

BURKE, Melissa Anne. 8260 ATLEE RD 23116 #041-02-1994 L2004 **PCP SP** *050

BYRNE, J Daniel. 9097 ATLEE STATION RD, STE 220 23116 #001-02-1999 L2004 **P** *020 †75

CADER, Josephine B. 7347 BELL CREEK RD 23111 #748-01-1964 L1976 **A PD** *020 †55

CAMERON, Brian Martin. ■ 23111 #051-04-2001 L2001 **NS** *012

CAMPBELL, Robert M. ■ 23116 #036-07-1942 L1955 **OS PDS** *071 †85

CANE, James Howard. 8266 ATLEE RD, MOB 2: SUITE 215 23116 #010-03-1974 L1979 **OBG** *020 †30

CANNON, Mahlon Douglas. ■ 23111 #047-07-1973 L1975 **OBG** *075

CAPPELLO, Roger Wm. 7041 LEE PARK RD, LEE-DAVIS MEDICAL CENTER 23111 #036-07-1975 L1977 **IM** *020 †20

CARR, Jenifer Eileen. 8266 ATLEE RD, STE 226 23116 #036-05-1989 L1990 **FM** *020 †18

CHANDLER, David Alan. 7575 COLD HARBOR RD, BLDG 2 23111 #051-04-1988 L1992 **OPH** *020 †35

CONE, Stephen Wallace. ■ 23111 #045-01-2000 L2000 *100

CONLEY, Grace Ann. 8266 ATLEE RD, STE 318 23116 #033-05-1996 L1996 **PD** *020 †55

COOK, Patricia Taylor. 7238 MECHANICSVILLE TPKE, PATIENTS FIRST 23111 #051-04-2004 L2004 **MPD** *012

CORNETT, John Floyd. 7571 COLD HARBOR RD, FAMILY PHYSICIANS 23111 #051-04-2001 L2001 **FM** *020 †18

COTE, Eric Paul. 8228 MEADOWBRIDGE RD, VIRGINIA UROLOGY CENTER 23116 #045-01-1986 L1988 **U** *020 †95

COUCH, Brianna Rochelle. ■ 23111 #051-01-2006 L2006 **PD** *012

CROSS, David Scott. 8409 N RUN MEDICAL DR 23116 #051-04-1987 L1992 **OTO PDO** *020 †45

CURRY, William Lake. 8266 ATLEE RD, STE 318 23116 #051-04-1961 L1964 **PD** *071 †55

DABNEY, Thomas Todd, Jr. 8411 N RUN MEDICAL DR 23116 #051-01-1974 L1974 **OPH** *020 †35

DANIELS, Kennedy Scott. 8266 ATLEE RD STE 133, MEMORIAL REGIONAL MOB II 23116 #051-04-1982 L1983 **ORS** *020 †40

DAVIS, Thorp Jos. 8266 ATLEE RD, STE 133 23116 #051-01-1990 L1991 **ORS** *020 †40

DHRU, Aruna Digant. 9464 CHAMBERLAYNE RD, STE 101 23116 #495-22-1973 L1987 **PD** *020 †55

EADS, Robert Stephen. 8266 ATLEE RD, STE 330 23116 #051-07-1980 L1983 **OBG** *020 †30

ERICKSEN, Jeffery Jos. 8226 MEADOWBRIDGE RD 23116 #011-02-1990 L1998 **PM** *020 †60

EUGENIO, Emmanuel E. 6372 MECHANICSVILLE TPKE, STE 103 23111 #748-01-1983 L1997 **PD** *020 †55

FEDER, Ofer. 8266 ATLEE RD, STE 230 23116 #051-04-1997 L2003 **GE** *020 †20

FERGUSON, Jennifer Morris. 8220 MEADOWBRIDGE RD, MOB 1 STE 306A 23116 #051-04-1989 L1990 **IM** *020 †20

FLANDERS, Elaine Lizabeth. 8260 ATLEE RD 23116 #055-02-1986 L1989 **PTH** *020 †50

FOSTER, Brian James. 8220 MEADOWBRIDGE RD, MEMORIAL MEDICAL CENTER 23116 #018-03-2001 L2002 **IM** *020

FOSTER, Ida Marie. ■ 23116 #018-03-1999 L2003 **FM** *020 †18

FRANCO, Andres P, Jr. 7268 HANOVER GREEN DR, # B 23111 #748-01-1957 L1963 **PTH NM** *071 †28

FRIERDICH, Jenny Lynn. ■ 23116 #051-07-2004 L2004 **PM** *012

GALGANO, Kimberly Meyers. 8266 ATLEE RD, STE 330 23116 #051-01-2000 L2003 **OBG** *020

GATMAITAN, Genevieve A. 8266 ATLEE RD STE 319, PRIME DOC OF RICHMOND MEM 23116 #048-14-2002 L2002 **IM** *020 †20

GECKLE, David Stephen. 8220 MEADOWBRIDGE RD, STE 209 23116 #023-01-1989 L1997 **NS** *020 †25

GELRUD, Adam Keith. 8266 ATLEE RD, MOB 1 SUITE 306A 23116 #023-01-2000 L2003 **IM** *100

GIBELLATO, Charles M. 8254 ATLEE RD 23116 #038-43-1999 L2000 **PM** *060

GOGIA, Laura Elizabeth. ■ 23111 #051-04-2002 L2005 **OBG** *020

GONZALEZ, Michael Stephen. 7384 BEULAH CHURCH RD 23111 #048-14-1979 L1986 **EM FM** *020 †18,16

GOODMAN, Peter Lewis. 8220 MEADOWBRIDGE RD, STE 301 23116 #051-04-1968 L1968 **GE IM** *020 †20 ‡

GREWAL, Harpreet S. 8243 MEADOWBRIDGE RD 23116 #495-08-1983 L1994 **AN** *020 †05

HAGAN, Maura Kelly. 3351 SPILLWAY LN 23111 #051-07-1986 L1992 **ON HEM** *020 †20

HASSEN, Laura Kim. 7347 BELL CREEK RD, STE 150 23111 #051-04-2000 L2005 **PD** *020 †55

HAWKINS, John Woodruff. 8243 MEADOWBRIDGE RD, RICHMOND CARDIOLOGY ASSOCI 23116 #051-01-1983 L1984 **IC** *020 †20

HEATWOLE, Kenneth M. 7571 COLD HARBOR RD, BUILDIN 1 23111 #051-04-1984 L1985 **FM** *020 †18

HEDBERG, Victoria A. 7238 MECHANICSVILLE TPKE, PATIENTS FIRST 23111 #051-04-1987 L1988 **EM FM** *020 †18

HOLDAWAY, Brian Kendall. 8220 MEADOWBRIDGE RD 23116 #051-01-1987 L1989 **CD IM** *020 †20

HOLMES, James Hillman. ■ 23116 #004-01-1946 L1972 **P** *071

HOUGHTON, Micah Timothy. 8266 ATLEE RD, STE 226 MOB II 23116 #051-04-1995 L1995 **FM** *020 †18

HUTCHESON, Douglas Pauli. 8266 ATLEE RD, STE 330 23116 #051-04-1989 L1991 **OBG** *020 †30

HYLTON, Elizabeth G. ■ 23111 #154-07-1936 **GP OS** *071

JANNEY, Samuel M, II. 7041 LEE PARK RD 23111 #051-04-1977 L1978 **IM** *020 †20

JERNIGAN, James Elisha. 7255 HANOVER GREEN DR 23111 #011-03-1979 L1995 **FM** *020 †18

JOHNSON, Christopher R. 8222 MEADOWBRIDGE RD, MASSEY CANCER CENTER AT HA 23116 #051-04-1981 L1985 **RO** *020 †80

JONES, Drew G, IV. ■ 23116 #036-08-1998 L1998 **PCC** *100 †20

JONES, Matthew Lawrence. 7255 HANOVER GREEN DR, COLD HARBOR FAMILY MEDICIN 23111 #051-04-2002 L2002 **FM** *020 †18

KAHLER, Barbara Lyons. 7347 BELL CREEK RD, STE 100 23111 #051-01-1982 L1985 **PD** *020 †55

KAHN, Howard Donald. 8266 ATLEE RD, STE 230 23116 #051-04-1972 L1973 **GE IM** *020 †20

KAMINSKY, Brian Leonard. 8243 MEADOWBRIDGE RD, RICHMOND CARDIOLOGY ASSOCI 23116 #051-01-1980 L1986 **CD IM** *020 †20

KEIPER, John Robert. 7571 COLD HARBOR RD 23111 #048-02-1976 L1979 **IM** *020 †20

KELLEY, William Edwin. 8266 ATLEE RD, SUTIE 323 23116 #024-05-1973 L1980 **GS AS** *020 †85

KELLY, David Louis. 8220 MEADOWBRIDGE RD, MEMORIAL MEDICAL CENTER 23116 #051-04-1982 L1985 **IM** *020 †20

KERN, Kathryn E. 8266 ATLEE RD, STE 330 23116 #048-12-1988 L1991 **OBG** *020 †30

KING, Gretchen C Gerle. 8266 ATLEE RD STE 219, NEPHROLOGY SPECIALISTS 23116 #035-45-1985 L1990 **NEP IM** *020 †20

KIRBY, Karen Leigh. 7041 LEE PARK RD 23111 #051-04-1992 L1993 **IM** *020 †20

KLAAS, John Richard. 7347 BELL CREEK RD, STE 100 23111 #025-01-1993 L1996 **PD** *020 †55

KOEHN, Deborah Ann. ■ 23111 #051-04-2003 L2003 **IM** *100 †20

KRAMER, Marc Stephen. 8260 ATLEE RD, ER 23116 #051-04-1978 L1979 **FM** *020 †18

LA ROSA, Kathleen. 7347 BELL CREEK RD, STE 100 23111 #024-07-1995 L2000 **PD** *020 †55

LEE, Jason Pearce. 8220 MEADOWBRIDGE RD, MEMORIAL MEDICAL CENTER 23116 #036-05-1995 L1995 **IM** *020 †20

LOGIE, Brent Arlyn. 8266 ATLEE RD, STE 226 23116 #037-01-2001 L2002 **FM** *020 †18

LORDI, William M. ■ 23111 #035-08-1949 L1957 **P CHP** *071 †75

LOVE, Rodrick N. 8266 ATLEE RD, STE 330 23116 #047-07-1992 L1998 **OBG** *020 †30

MAC DOUGALL, Michael J. 8262 ATLEE RD 23116 #036-07-1993 L1998 **GS** *020 †85

MAGOVERN, Malcolm James. 7575 COLD HARBOR RD, BLDG 2 23111 #010-02-1963 L1971 **OPH OS** *020 †35

MARONEY, Timothy P. 6077 BARKERS MILL RD 23111 #016-43-1980 L1999 **DR** *020 †80

MARTIN, David Francis. 8250 ATLEE RD 23116 #016-42-2001 L2003 **EM** *020

MASTERS, Heather Bley. ■ 23116 #051-04-2003 L2003 **IM** *100 †20

MCATEE, Miriam Sanchez. 8266 ATLEE RD, STE 318 23116 #045-04-1999 L1999 **PD** *020 †55

MC TAMANEY, James Paul. 8220 MEADOWBRIDGE RD, VIRGINIA SURGICAL 23116 #023-07-1975 L1978 **GS VS** *020 †85

MEAD, Thomas Patrick. 8220 MEADOWBRIDGE RD # 205 23116 #035-06-1996 L2002 **OBG** *020 †30

MEHTA, Rajesh Vinodrai. 8220 MEADOWBRIDGE RD, STE 209 23116 #023-01-1997 L2003 **NS** *020 †25

MELZIG, Eric Perry. 8266 ATLEE RD, SUTIE 323 23116 #024-07-1972 L1975 **GS SO** *020 †85

MERSON, Mark Harold. 7016 LEE PARK RD 23111 #051-04-1988 L1989 **AN** *020 †05

MILLER, David Aaron. 8228 MEADOWBRIDGE RD, VIRGINIA UROLOGY CENTER 23116 #012-01-1992 L1998 **U** *020 †95

MONTAGUE, David Lee. 8266 ATLEE RD, STE 330 23116 #051-04-1974 L1977 **GYN** *020 †30

MOORE, Eric Stephen. ■ 23116 #001-02-2001 L2005 **CD** *012 †20

MOORE, Kenneth Edward. ■ 23116 #036-07-1989 L1990 **N** *020

MUTCHLER, Valerie Ann. ■ 23116 #051-01-1990 L1993 **FM** *075 †18

MYERS, Jennifer Lynn. ■ 23116 #051-04-2007 L2007 **IM** *012

NELSON, Kinloch. 8228 MEADOWBRIDGE RD, VIRGINIA UROLOGY CENTER 23116 #051-04-1998 L1999 **U** *020 †95

NELSON, Melissa Byrne. 8266 ATLEE RD, STE 318 23116 #051-04-1998 L2004 **PD** *020 †55

NICHOLS, Guy Eddy. 8260 ATLEE RD 23116 #051-01-1988 L1991 **PTH** *020 †50

NOBLE, Robert Earl. 7347 BELL CREEK RD, STE 100 23111 #035-06-1983 L1985 **PD** *020 †55

O'BIER, April Noel. ■ 23111 #051-01-2000 L2000 **EM** *020 †16

OVERMEYER, Richard Lee. 7041 LEE PARK RD 23111 #038-40-1979 L1980 **IM** *020 †20

PAYNE, Charles Frederick. 7041 LEE PARK RD 23111 #051-04-1994 L2000 **IM** *020 †20

PEAY, Clifton Lawrence. 8266 ATLEE RD, STE 224 23116 #035-06-1978 L1984 **OPH** *020 †35

PEDRAM, Sammy. ■ 23116 #048-15-2002 L2002 **PCC** *012 †20

PETRIZZI, Mark Gerard. 9376 ATLEE STATION RD 23116 #035-08-1989 L1990 **FM** *020 †18 ‡

PETRIZZI, Michael Jos. 9376 ATLEE STATION RD, HANOVER FAMILY PHYSICIANS 23116 #035-08-1983 L1987 **FM FSM** *020 †18

PHILLIPS, Kimberly Mcgroa. 7347 BELL CREEK RD, STE 100 23111 #045-01-1999 L1999 **PD** *020 †55

PILAND, Jethro H, Jr. 7255 HANOVER GREEN DR 23111 #051-04-1970 L1970 **FM** *020 †20

POULOS, Nicholas Geo. 7575 COLD HARBOR RD STE 1E 23111 #051-04-1955 L1955 **GS** *071 †85

POWERS, Monica Metzler. 8266 ATLEE RD, STE 330 23116 #048-14-1997 L2001 **OBG** *020 †30

POWERS, Patrick Lewis. 7347 BELL CREEK RD 23111 #051-04-1994 L1994 **AI** *020 †20,03

PRABHU, Shilpa Vilas. ■ 23111 #039-01-2006 L2006 **AN** *012

PRIVITERA, Christine M. 6372 MECHANICSVILLE TPKE, STE 103 23111 #035-06-1976 L1979 **PD GP** *020 †55

PUREWAL, Dilsheesh Kaur. 7016 LEE PARK RD, HANOVER OUTPT SURG CENTER 23111 #305-01-1998 L2004 **AN** *020

RATLIFF, James Ellis. 8228 MEADOWBRIDGE RD, VIRGINIA UROLOGY CENTER 23116 #048-04-1983 L1986 **U** *020 †95

RAVINDRA, P V. 8243 MEADOWBRIDGE RD 23116 #496-22-1988 L1993 **CD** *020 †20

RELPH, Natalie Gail. ■ 23111 #055-01-2003 L2006 **P** *020

REYNOLDS, Richard R. 8220 MEADOWBRIDGE RD, STE 303 23116 #012-01-1973 L1980 **TS** *020 †85,90

RICHARDSON, Dante Gacero. 9376 ATLEE STATION RD, HANOVER FAMILY PRACTICE RE 23116 #306-01-2002 L2003 **FM** *020

ROBERTS, Kenneth Hume. 7041 LEE PARK RD 23111 #051-04-1982 L1983 **IM** *020 †20

ROBERTSON, Ralph Herbert. 8260 ATLEE RD, MEMORIAL REGIONAL MEDICAL 23116 #051-07-1981 L1982 **EM IM** *020 †20,16

ROBERTSON, Thomas Carter. 7485 RIGHT FLANK RD, STE 210 23116 #051-04-2001 L2001 **OTO** *020 †45

ROBINSON, Jennifer Dee. 9111 DICKEY DR, HANOVER PEDIATRICS 23116 #048-02-2003 L2003 **PD** *100 †55

ROLFES, Robert Joseph. 7041 LEE PARK RD 23111 #038-41-1983 L1993 **IM GP** *020 †20

RYAN, Patricia Martin. 7238 MECHANICSVILLE TPKE, PATIENTS FIRST 23111 #041-14-1997 L1997 **IM** *020 †20

SAHLI, Kevin Jamil. 7571 COLD HARBOR RD 23111 #051-04-2003 L2003 **FM** *020 †18

SAHNI, K Singh. 8220 MEADOWBRIDGE RD, STE 209 23116 #517-05-1977 L1981 **NS** *020 †25

SALLEY, John Jones, Jr. 8260 ATLEE RD, EMERG DEPT MEM REG MED CTR 23116 #051-04-1996 L1997 **EM** *020 †18

SALVANT, Jackson Boland. 8220 MEADOWBRIDGE RD, STE 209 23116 #051-04-1988 L1994 **NS** *020 †25

SAUER, Jeremy Thomas. ■ 23116 #051-04-2007 L2007 **EM** *012

SCHLEIN, Paul Arthur. 6200 CHAMBERLAYNE RD 23111 #051-04-1975 L1977 **PD** *020

SCHRAA, Kristin Paul. 8266 ATLEE RD, STE 330 23116 #020-02-1994 L1994 **OBG** *020 †30

SCHWARZ, Maurice Chaskiel. 7501 RIGHT FLANK RD 23116 #051-04-1973 L1978 **ON IM** *020 †20

SEALAND, Robert Odaniel, II. ■ 23111 #047-06-2008 *012

SHABAN, Danny. 8220 MEADOWBRIDGE RD, STE 205A 23116 #305-01-1991 L2001 **OBG** *020

SHALF, Jerome Marshall. 6372 MECHANICSVILLE TPKE, STE 103 23111 #023-07-1970 L1975 **PD** *020 †55

SHUPACK, Ian Scott. 7571 COLD HARBOR RD, MECHANICSVILLE MEDICAL CEN 23111 #048-16-1995 L1995 **FM** *020 †18

SIMPSON, Kenneth R, Jr. 7255 HANOVER GREEN DR 23111 #051-01-1983 L1984 **FM** *020 †18

SLOTT, Jeffrey Howard. 8411 N RUN MEDICAL DR 23116 #067-01-1985 L1991 **OPH** *020 †35

SMITH, Estela Torres. 9179 BELLE FARM TER 23116 #042-01-1985 L1990 **DR** *020 †80

SMITH, Thomas Adrian. 8220 MEADOWBRIDGE RD, STE 308 23116 #051-04-1976 L1977 **N** *020 †75

SNEAD, Warren Leslie, Jr. 8266 ATLEE RD, STE 318 23116 #047-06-1988 L1991 **PD** *020 †55

SNODDY, John Wm. 8262 ATLEE RD STE 205, RICHMOND, LTD. 23116 #051-04-1973 L1976 **GS VS** *020 †85

SPASIC, Zvonko. 8220 MEADOWBRIDGE RD, STE 205 23116 #957-02-1990 L2002 **OBG** *020

SPRAGUE, Robert Ingram. 8260 ATLEE RD, MEMORIAL REG MED CTR 23116 #016-02-1984 L1986 **PTH** *020 †50

STEPHENS, Gregory Thomas. 9376 ATLEE STATION RD 23116 #051-04-1993 L1996 **FM** *020 †18

STILL, William John P. 8266 ATLEE RD, MOB 2 STE 322 23116 #051-04-1985 L1990 **NEP IM** *020 †20

TAN, Joseph Lai. 8266 ATLEE RD, MOB 2 STE 319 23116 #748-10-1990 L2003 **IM** *020 †20

THEDIECK, Charles G. 7575 COLD HARBOR RD, STE 2A 23111 #051-04-1953 L1953 **GYN** *020 †30

THOMPSON, James C, Jr. 8220 MEADOWBRIDGE RD, STE 306 23116 #045-04-1995 L2003 **IM** *020 †20

TIERNEY, William Andrew. 8220 MEADOWBRIDGE RD, VIRGINIA SURGICAL 23116 #051-04-1997 L1997 **VS** *020 †85

TIMMERMAN, William Richar. 7425 LEE DAVIS RD 23111 #026-04-1979 L1986 **CRS GS** *020 †10,85

TIPTON, Gary Alan. 7347 BELL CREEK RD, STE 100 23111 #025-07-1975 L1979 **PD** *020 †55

TODD, Robert M. 8260 ATLEE RD, MOB 2, STE 319 23116 #051-04-1985 L1988 **NEP IM** *020 †20

TRICARICO, Victor John. 7238 MECHANICSVILLE TPKE, PATIENTS FIRST 23111 #051-04-1974 L2005 **EM IM** *020 †20,16

TRUOG, Laurie A. ■ 23111 #028-46-2004 L2005 **CHP** *012

TUCKER, Stanley Cole. 8266 ATLEE RD, STE 315 23116 #051-01-1969 L1969 **CD** *020 †20

UHLE, Paul Harmon. 7016 LEE PARK RD, STE 100 23116 #051-04-1980 L1990 **D** *020 †15

UNDERWOOD, J Randall. 8101 VANGUARD DR 23111 #048-13-1994 L2003 **AN PME** *020

VANICHKACHORN, Ann. 8266 ATLEE RD, STE 330 23116 #035-47-1995 L1999 **OBG** *020 †30

VAUGHN, Warren Leslie, Jr. 8220 MEADOWBRIDGE RD, STE 203 23116 #028-02-1975 L1978 **IM IMG** *071 †20

WALKER, Kimberly Buresh. 9376 ATLEE STATION RD 23116 #051-04-2001 L2001 **FM** *020 †18

WASHINGTON-ALSTON, Louise. 6372 MECHANICSVILLE TPKE, STE 103 23111 #051-07-1988 L1991 **PD** *020 †55

WEBER, Matthew Elliot. 8266 ATLEE RD, STE 318 23116 #024-05-1997 L1997 **PD** *020 †55

WELLS, James Morgan. 8266 ATLEE RD, STE 318 23116 #051-04-1969 L1969 **PD** *020 †55

WENIG, Nora Anne. 8260 ATLEE RD, DEPT. EMERGENCY MEDICINE 23116 #055-01-1992 L1995 **EM** *020 †18

WHITE, William Richard. 8220 MEADOWBRIDGE RD, STE 209 23116 #035-20-1968 L1981 **NS** *020 †25

WILLIAMS, Carol Bascomb. 9113 DICKEY DR 23116 #010-03-1991 L1993 **PD** *020 †55

WILLIAMS, Mark Alexander. 8260 ATLEE RD 23116 #018-03-2002 L2002 **PCP** *012 †50

WILLS, Robert Douglas. 8266 ATLEE RD STE 133 23116 #051-04-1996 L2003 **ORS** *020 †40

WILSON, Claude Watson. 8220 MEADOWBRIDGE RD, STE 209 23116 #012-01-1973 L1978 **NS** *020 †25

WILSON, Jeffrey Kent. 8266 ATLEE RD STE 133 23116 #005-19-1978 L1983 **ORS** *020 †40

WITTKAMP, Michael Joseph. 8243 MEADOWBRIDGE RD 23116 #051-04-1999 L1999 **IC** *100 †20

WOLFGANG, Timothy Craig. 8220 MEADOWBRIDGE RD, STE 303 23116 #041-02-1972 L1979 **TS** *020 †85,90

WONG, Johnny Chungliang. 8220 MEADOWBRIDGE RD, STE 204 23116 #051-01-1986 L1987 **IM PCC** *020 †20

WOOD, Robert L. 5728 HILLVIEW RD 23111 #649-14-1966 L1971 **PHP OS** *030 †70

WOODFIN, Charlotte Louise. 9376 ATLEE STATION RD, HANOVER FAMILY PHYSICIANS 23116 #051-01-1995 L1995 **FM** *020 †18

WORREL, Laura Marjean. 8260 ATLEE RD 23116 #026-08-2001 L2005 **P** *020 †75

WRATCHFORD, Pamela. 7493 RIGHT FLANK RD, STE 400 23116 #011-02-1999 L2003 **FM** *020 †18

WRATCHFORD, Timothy Scott. 8249 CROWN COLONY PKWY, STE 103 23116 #055-01-1999 L2003 **MPD** *020 †20,55

WYSOR, Edwin Snead. 811 COLD HARBOR ROAD 23111 #051-01-1944 L1944 **GP OS** *071

YUCHA, Kim L Peeler. 7347 BELL CREEK RD, STE 100 23111 #036-08-1985 L1988 **PD** *020 †20

ZERATE, Calina B. 8260 ATLEE RD, MOB-S STE 319 23111 #748-07-1986 L2001 **IM** *020 †20

ZOCCO, Joseph James. 8220 MEADOWBRIDGE RD, STE 303 23116 #033-05-1973 L1976 **TS** *020 †85,90

MERRIFIELD – FAIRFAX

BUMGARNER, Robert L. PO BOX 3341 22116 #025-12-1974 L1979 PTH UM *030 †50
CHIOU, Andrew S. PO BOX 3900 22116 #035-03-1993 L1999 NS *020

MIDDLEBURG – LOUDOUN

DUBOVSKY, Elizabeth C. 21318 FOXCROFT RD, CHILDRENS NATIONAL MEDCIAL 20117 #051-07-1983 L1988 DR NR *020 †80
GARRINGER, Jacqueline A. 4 PENDLETON ST 20117 #038-43-1978 L2003 OPH *020 †35
KESLER, Richard Wm. 23499 MELMORE PL, RICHARD W KESLER MD 20117 #036-07-1967 L1974 PD PPR *071 †55
VON ARRAS, Joan A. 23451 CHASE HOLLOW LN, MIDDLEBURG PARTNERS 20117 #008-01-1983 L2003 DR NR *020 †80
WHITE, Frederick Rugaard. RR 1 BOX 329 20117 #025-01-1976 L1977 AN *040 †05

MIDLOTHIAN – CHESTERFIELD

AHMED, Nowsheen. 5955 HARBOUR PARK DR 23112 #160-02-1989 L2005 PD *020 †55
AL-MATEEN, Kevin B. 5306 CLIPPER COVE RD 23112 #010-03-1984 L1991 NPM PD *020 †55
ARCHULETA, Bobby Arnold. 13700 ST FRANCIS BLVD, PEDIATRIC ASSOCIATES PC 23114 #007-02-1975 L1978 PD *020 †55
ARENTS, Michelle Pittman. 10130 HULL STREET RD 23112 #051-04-1993 L1994 FM *020 †18
ARIAS, John Dimas. 23112 #660-03-1957 L1996 IM OS *075 †16
ASHAR, Manisha Satish. 13700 ST FRANCIS BLVD, STE 600 23114 #036-05-1993 L2005 CD *020 †20
AUERBACH, Barry Seth. 4902 MILLRIDGE PKWY E, BRAND ERMILL PEDIATRIC AND 23112 #023-01-1983 L1998 PD *020 †55
BAMPTON, James Frost. 13861 HULL STREET RD, PHYSICIANS OF FAMILY MEDIC 23112 #051-04-1994 L1994 FM *020 †18
BANKS, Marshall Dale. 13719 QUEENSGATE RD 23114 #047-07-1970 L1979 U *020
BANTLE, John Albert, III. ■ 23112 #039-01-2003 L2006 EM *020 †16
BARNES, John Gillespie. 13332 MIDLOTHIAN TPKE, VIRGINIA PHYSICIANS 23113 #051-04-1981 L1984 FM *020 †18
BAUTISTA, Genoveva A. ■ 23113 #748-01-1959 L1983 PD *071
BECKOM, Constance Waddell. 2367 COLONY CROSSING PL 23112 #051-04-1999 L1999 FM *020 †18 ‡
BELL, Zakia. ■ 23113 #035-06-1980 L1985 N *020 †75
BENNETT, Garrison Sol. 13332 MIDLOTHIAN TPKE 23113 #051-07-1998 L1998 FM *020 †18
BERKOWITZ, Leah Beth. ■ 23113 #010-01-2007 L2008 PD *012
BEVERIDGE, Clay Elliott. 13710 ST FRANCIS BLVD, PRIMEDOC OF ST. FRANCIS 23114 #051-04-1995 L1995 IM *020 †20
BHUIYAN, Md Badiul Alam. ■ 23114 #160-04-1985 FM SCI *020 †18
BINHAMMER, Harold Ewald W. 5001 W VILLAGE GREEN DR 23112 #065-05-1957 L1978 FM *071
BITTNER, Anna Kathryn. 13841 HULL STREET RD, STE 4 23112 #011-03-1985 L1989 FM *071 †18
BLEECHER, Kira Marie. ■ 23112 #051-04-2005 L2005 P *100
BLUMBERG, Michael Z. 14351 SOMMERVILLE CT 23113 #041-02-1971 L1977 AI PD *020 †55,03
BOHANNON, Josephine Sais. 2306 ROBIOUS STATION CIR 23113 #051-04-1984 L1986 D *020
BONES, Joseph Thos. 5955 HARBOUR PARK DR 23112 #051-04-1958 L1958 PD *020 †55
BORICH, Shawn Martin. 13710 ST FRANCIS BLVD 23114 #025-12-2001 L2003 EM *020 †16
BOURGUIGNON, Roger L. ■ 23112 #165-01-1954 L1973 ORS *071 †40
BOWERS, Jamelle Renee. 13710 ST FRANCIS BLVD, PRIMEDOC ST. FRANCIS 23114 #038-41-1997 L2003 NEP *020 †20
BOYCE, Edward L, Jr. 3000 WATERCOVE RD 23112 #051-04-1970 L1970 FM *020
BOYD, David Michael. ■ 23112 #305-01-2006 L2006 FP *012
BRICKHOUSE, Wm Darnell. 13700 ST FRANCIS BLVD, STE 605 23114 #010-01-1977 L1983 ORS *020 †40
BRIGHT, George Meredith. 13821 VILLAGE MILL DR, STE B 23114 #048-12-1961 L1968 AMI ADM *020 †55
BROWN, Frank Logan, Jr. ■ 23113 #008-01-1974 L1977 EM IM *020 †20,16
BROWN, James Sims, Jr. ■ 23113 #051-04-1990 L1997 P *020 †75
BROWN, Jennifer Blythe. 13332 MIDLOTHIAN TPKE, VIRGINIA PHYSICIANS 23113 #012-05-1987 L1988 FM *020 †18
BROWN, Robert David. 14051 ST FRANCIS BLVD, VIRGINIA UROLOGY CENTER 23114 #047-20-1984 L1990 U *020 †95
BUCKLER, Aileen Gretchen. ■ 23113 #051-04-1999 L2001 PTH *012
BURGET, Michele Doreen. 1521 HUGUENOT RD STE 10 23113 #041-12-2000 L2000 PD *020 †55
CAMPBELL, James Ashton, Jr. ■ 23112 #306-01-2003 L2006 FP *012
CAMPBELL, Wm Wesley, Jr. 13800 WINTERBERRY RIDGE 23112 #012-01-1970 L1981 N *020 †75
CARUSO, Anthony Cosmo. 13700 ST.FRANCIS BLVD, STE 600 23114 #010-02-1983 L1994 CD IM *020 †20
CASSANO, Anthony Dominick. ■ 23113 #033-06-1996 L1996 TS *020 †85,90
CASTILLO DIAZ, Camilo Mar. ■ 23112 #264-11-1996 L2007 GS *012
CELLA, Caroline Parker. 1807 HUGUENOT RD, STE 101 23113 #051-04-1985 L1988 FM *020 †18
CHAKRAVORTY, Devi. ■ 23114 #051-04-2003 L2003 OBG *020
CHISHOLM, Louis Randolph. 13332 MIDLOTHIAN TPKE, VIRGINIA PHYSICIANS 23113 #051-07-1977 L1978 FM *020 †18
CHRISTIAN, Lora Gill. 14400 SOMMERVILLE CT 23113 #048-13-1993 L1993 PD *020 †55
CIESLA, William Paul, Jr. ■ 23113 #010-02-1993 L1996 ID *020 †20
CLARK, David Anthony. 1316 ALVERSER PLZ, ADVANCED FAMILY PRACT 23113 #051-01-1979 L1980 FM *020 †16,18
COLLINS, Aimee Michel. ■ 23114 #020-02-2004 L2004 IM *100
COLLINS, Brian Jos. ■ 23112 #035-09-1961 L2004 PUD IM *071
COMPTON, Kyle Douglas. ■ 23112 #020-12-2006 FP *012
CONDRO, Alice Magner. 6510 HARBOUR VIEW CT, CHIPPENHAM PED & ADOL 23112 #023-01-1981 L1985 PD *020 †55
COOK, Adam Brett. 13141 RITTENHOUSE DR 23112 #051-04-2003 L2003 AN *012

COSTA, Giovanni Giacomo. 11020 HULL STREET RD, PATIENT FIRST GENITO 23112 #561-07-1953 L1974 IM ON *020 †20
CRICHIGNO, Gerardo A. 12201 OLD BUCKINGHAM RD 23113 #132-01-1966 L1974 CHP P *020
CRICHTON, James Wiley. 6510 HARBOUR VIEW CT 23112 #007-02-1968 L1969 FM *071 †18
CROSS, Robert Dixon. 13861 HULL STREET RD 23112 #051-01-1985 L1988 FM *020 †18
CROSSLAND, Clem C, Jr. 23113 #010-01-1946 L1951 GP *020
CULBERT, Danielle Jacquel. ■ 23112 #051-07-2006 L2006 IM *012
CULLEN, Elizabeth Marie. 1407 HUGUENOT RD 23113 #051-04-1994 L1997 PD *020 †55
DAND, Parul Pravin. 5955 HARBOUR PARK DR, MILESTONE PEDIATRICS PA 23112 #010-01-2000 L2007 PD *020 †55
DANEVA, Lozina Todorova. 2324 COLONY CROSSING PL 23112 #198-01-1983 L2002 NEP *020 †20
DAVIES, Thomas Clifford. 13146 MIDLOTHIAN TPKE, STE 12 23113 #064-01-1978 L1983 GP IMG *020
DEAL, Tracey Anne. 13700 ST FRANCIS BLVD, PEDIATRIC ASSOCIATES PC 23114 #051-01-1993 L1996 PD *020 †55
DE BLOIS, Mark Edwin. 4122 OLD GUN RD E 23113 #025-07-1980 L1984 ORS *020 †40
DEC, Katherine Louise. 5309 COMMONWEALTH CNTR PKWY, STE 100 23112 #025-12-1989 L1994 PM *020 †60
DECKER, Michael John. 13700 ST FRANCIS BLVD, STE 605 23114 #038-06-1971 L1975 PME PM *020 †60
DECKER, Raymond Gerard. 13911 ST FRANCIS BLVD, STE 101 23114 #051-04-1995 L1995 FM *020 †18
DEPALMA, Arpita Gupta. 11601 ROBIOUS RD, STE 100 23113 #045-01-1999 L2004 PD PDI *020 †55
DE PALMA, Michael James. 13700 ST FRANCIS BLVD, STE 400 23114 #045-01-1999 L2004 PM *020 †60
DE SILVA, Semage Melani B. 14400 SOMMERVILLE CT 23113 #836-01-1992 L2003 PD *020
DHARANIKOTA, Padmalatha. ■ 23114 #495-11-1998 L2004 IM *020
DHILLON, Manjit S. 6055 HARBOUR PARK DR, COLONIAL ORTHOPAEDIC INC 23112 #495-45-1986 L2000 ORS HS *020 †40
DIMITRIS, James C. ■ 23113 #418-01-1955 L1964 PFP P *071 †75
DOLORESCO, Mark Anthony. 13700 ST FRANCIS BLVD, STE 600 23114 #051-07-1989 L1992 CD *020 †20
DOMER, Jennifer Hollar. 6510 HARBOUR VIEW CT, CHIPPENHAM PEDIATRICS 23112 #051-01-1996 L1996 PD *020 †55
DORAN, Anne Spencer. 14366 SOMMERVILLE CT 23113 #051-04-1995 L1995 FM *020 †18
DUNN, Harold Paul. 13710 ST FRANCIS BLVD 23114 #035-15-1973 L1977 ATP CLP *062 †50
DWYER, James Henry. 5001 W VILLAGE GREEN DR, STE 107 23112 #051-04-1954 L1954 PD *072 †55
DWYER, Thomas Edward. 11020 HULL STREET RD 23112 #051-04-1984 L1985 FM *075 †18
EARASI, Madhavi. ■ 23113 #496-24-1996 L2007 AN *020 †05
EDSALL, Lisa Cseh. ■ 23113 #051-01-2004 L2004 D *012
EDWARDS, Eric Shawn. ■ 23112 #051-04-2008 *012
ELZEY, Mark Jason. ■ 23114 #051-04-2007 L2007 *012
ENGLISH, Eric Martin. ■ 23112 #051-04-1990 L1991 FM *020 †18
ESTRADA, Wilhelmina N. ■ 23113 #033-05-1987 L1992 NM *074 †20,28
EVANS, Eleanor Freed. ■ 23113 #051-04-1965 L1965 IM PA *020 †20
EVERETT, Joel Campbell. 13821 VILLAGE MILL DR 23114 #051-04-1981 L1983 PD *020 †55
FABRY, Howard Aldrich. 23114 #035-15-1963 L1966 PHP *074 †70
FANNON, Michael Shawn. ■ 23113 #051-04-1997 L1997 MPD EM *020 †20,55
FARRELL, Stella Brigid. ■ 23113 #004-01-1990 L1998 AN *020 †05
FEDYSZEN, Anne Catherine. 2820 WATERFORD LK DR 23112 #035-19-1991 L1994 CHP *020 †75
FERNANDEZ, Vivian Louise. 3000 WATERCOVE RD, MIDLOTHIAN FAMILY PRACTICE 23112 #035-15-1981 L1982 FM OM *020 †18 ‡
FIELDS, William Russell. ■ 23113 #055-01-1966 L1975 DR *071 †80
FIORE, Steven Mark. 13700 ST FRANCIS BLVD, STE 605 23114 #016-42-1986 L1988 OSS OTR *020 †40
FISCHER, George L. ■ 23112 #035-45-1951 L1963 IM GE *071 †20
FLYNN, Robert Steven. ■ 23112 #035-15-2004 L2004 GE *012
FOWLER, Michael Alan. ■ 23114 #422-01-2001 L2001 AN *100
FRANKS, Michael Edmond. 14051 ST FRANCIS BLVD, VIRGINIA UROLOGY CENTER 23114 #023-01-1996 L2006 U *020 †95
FRIEDEL, Robert Oliver. ■ 23112 #036-07-1964 L1977 P *071 †75
FRIERSON, John Hugh, Jr. ■ 23112 #045-01-1944 L1956 DR *071
GARRITY, Wendy Locke. 4902 MILLRIDGE PKWY E, BRANDERMILL PED & ADOL MED 23112 #035-15-1996 L1999 PD *020 †55
GAYLE, Richard Alexander. 2324 COLONY CROSSING PL 23112 #566-01-1993 L2002 IM NEP *020 †20
GAYLE, Sigsby Warren. 13700 ST FRANCIS BLVD, STE 600 23114 #051-04-1965 L1965 CD IM *071
GEHMAN, John Ernest. ■ 23112 #051-04-1964 L1964 FM *020
GEORGE, Anna. 11020 HULL STREET RD, PATIENT FIRST 23112 #495-72-1986 L2003 IM *020 †20
GIANOLA, Katherine Mary. ■ 23113 #051-04-1993 L1993 IM *020 †20
GIBBONS, Patrick J. 13700 ST FRANCIS BLVD, STE 500 23114 #036-01-1995 L1996 OTO *020 †45
GILL, Richard Russell. 13710 ST FRANCIS BLVD 23114 #051-04-1998 L2001 EM *020 †16
GIRERD, Rene J. ■ 23113 #396-03-1953 L1966 FOP *071 †50
GITOMIRSKI, Michael. 11020 HULL STREET RD, PATIENT FIRST GENITO 23112 #913-06-1988 L2004 FP *012
GIUSTI, Massimo. 13700 ST FRANCIS BLVD 23114 #561-06-1990 L1998 IM *020 †20
GLADUE, Karen Marie. 11020 HULL STREET RD, PATIENT FIRST GENITO 23112 #051-04-1987 L1988 FM *020 †18
GLASS, Kathryn Lyn. 14732 VILLAGE SQUARE PL, ATLANTIC PEDIATRIC SPECIAL 23112 #051-01-1998 L2000 PD *020 †55
GLAZIER, M Gina. 3000 WATERCOVE RD 23112 #539-03-1992 L2001 FM *020 †18
GOBLE, Sharon Ann. 14051 ST FRANCIS BLVD, FIRST FLOOR 23114 #051-04-1997 L1997 HO *020
GODDARD, Joseph Pannell. 13332 MIDLOTHIAN TPKE, VIRGINIA PHYSICIANS 23113 #051-01-1980 L1994 FM *020 †18
GONZALEZ, Andrea. 13700 ST FRANCIS BLVD, STE 601 23114 #264-05-1994 L2000 ID *020 †20
GRANT, Elton Lewis. 1600 HUGUENOT RD STE 1, RICHMOND 23113 #036-01-1986 L1990 PD *020
GRETH, Suzanne Michele. ■ 23112 #036-05-2003 L2007 PD *020

■ = Address Information Privacy Protected

GROCHOWSKI, Eugene Carl. ■ 23112 #016-06-1974 L1975 **NEP OS** *071 †20

GROSSBERG, Judith P. 1231 ALVERSER DR 23113 #051-04-1989 L1992 **PD** *020 †55

GU, Yaoming. 13700 ST FRANCIS BLVD, STE 400 23114 #243-72-1987 L2002 **PM** *020 †60

HAACKE-GOLDEN, Eric Jon. 2367 COLONY CROSSING PL, VIRGINIA FAMILY PHYSICIANS 23112 #026-04-1999 L1999 **FM** *020 †18

HAAS, Theron Henry. ■ 23112 #025-01-1945 L1951 **OBG** *071 †30

HALL, Andrea Lynn. ■ 23112 #661-02-2005 L2006 **FP** *012

HALLMANN, Clemens Erwin. 13911 ST FRANCIS BLVD, STE 101 23114 #065-01-1974 L1976 **FM EM** *020 †18

HARRINGTON, Arlene A. 5955 HARBOUR PARK DR 23112 #422-01-1996 L1999 **PD** *020 †55

HARRINGTON, William Gore. 14415 JUSTICE RD 23113 #051-04-1978 L1979 **FM** *020 †18

HARRISON, Henry Tucker. ■ 23113 #051-04-1954 L1954 **EM** *071

HARTMAN, Aaron Nathan. 13911 ST FRANCIS BLVD, STE 101 23114 #051-04-2000 L2000 **FM** *020 †18 ‡

HARVEY, Lorena Limon. 13861 HULL STREET RD 23112 #649-14-1980 L1985 **FM** *020 †18 ‡

HAWKINS, Hillary. 13700 ST FRANCIS BLVD, STE 400 23114 #051-04-1989 L1991 **PM** *020 †60

HENDRICKS, Glenna Pitman. 13630 HULL STREET RD 23112 #051-04-1999 L2000 **OBG** *100 †18

HENLEY, Robert W, Jr. 13700 ST FRANCIS BLVD, STE 600 23114 #051-01-1968 L1968 **CD IM** *020 †20

HESS, Samantha Leehastill. ■ 23113 #051-04-2007 L2007 **IM** *012

HEYMAN, Peter Steven. 14400 SOMMERVILLE CT 23113 #051-04-1993 L1993 **PD** *020 †55

HICKEY, Kenneth Scott. 13710 ST FRANCIS BLVD 23114 #051-04-2001 L2001 **EM** *020 †16

HICKS, Tracy Iezzi. 13700 ST FRANCIS BLVD, STE 305 23114 #051-07-1991 L1994 **OBG** *020 †30

HIGGS, Geoffrey Bessom. 13700 ST FRANCIS BLVD, STE 605 23114 #035-01-1988 L1999 **ORS OSM** *020 †40

HINSON, Claude R, Jr. 10130 HULL STREET RD 23112 #051-04-1979 L1981 **FM** *020 †18

HUDSON, David Lindsay. 11020 HULL STREET RD 23112 #143-03-1955 L1974 **FM AM** *071

INSLEE, Donald Ole. ■ 23113 #030-05-1956 L1973 **OM** *071

JACKSON, Lasandra Denise. 13700 ST FRANCIS BLVD, STE 510 23114 #033-06-1997 L2006 **GS** *020 †85

JACKSON, Paul Vernon. 13630 HULL STREET RD 23112 #051-04-1991 L1992 **FM** *020 †18

JESSUP, Douglas Eugene. 13700 ST FRANCIS BLVD, STE 605 23114 #017-20-1976 L1984 **ORS** *020 †40

JIMA, Bogale. 10130 HULL STREET RD 23112 #007-02-1995 L1995 **FM** *020 †18

JONES, Beverly. ■ 23112 #051-04-1949 L1949 **AN** *071

JONES, John Evan. ■ 23112 #049-01-1955 L1991 **IM END** *072 †20

JONES-DAGGETT, Sharron An. 13540 HULL STREET RD, ST FRANCIS FAMILY MED 23112 #661-02-2005 L2006 **FM** *020 †18

JOSHI, Prajwol Prasad. 13700 ST FRANCIS BLVD, STE 510 23114 #672-01-1992 L2006 **ID IM** *020 †20

KALLURI, Prakasam. 6055 HARBOUR PARK DR, COLONIAL ORTHOPAEDIC INC 23112 #041-13-1999 L2005 **OSS** *012

KAPADIA, Shaival Jayesh. 13700 ST FRANCIS BLVD, STE 600 23114 #051-04-1989 L1990 **CD** *020 †20

KAUL, Adam Thomas. 13354 MIDLOTHIAN TPKE 23113 #051-04-1996 L1996 **P** *020 †20

KEBLUSEK, Chas Winfield. 1409 HUGUENOT RD STE 101 23113 #051-04-1971 L1976 **OBG** *020 †30

KEEFFER, Karen Diane. ■ 23113 #039-01-1991 L1995 **P PFP** *020

KEEGAN, Jeffrey Michael. 1529 HUGUENOT RD 23113 #051-01-1982 L1985 **FM** *020 †18

KEETON, James M. ■ 23112 #038-41-1942 L1942 **GS** *071 †85

KELLETT, Gordon N, II. 13821 VILLAGE MILL DR 23114 #051-04-1972 L1975 **PD** *020 †55

KESARI, Madhuri. ■ 23113 #495-21-1997 L2004 **IM** *020

KIM, Thomas Jihan. 13710 ST FRANCIS BLVD, PRIMEDOC, ST.FRANCIS, PC 23114 #051-07-2000 L2000 **IM** *020 †20

KING, Derik Kent. 14541 KENMONT DR 23113 #028-46-1993 L1993 **EM** *020 †16

KING, Herbert Anacin, II. 3000 WATERCOVE RD 23112 #051-04-2000 L2002 **FM** *020 †18

KIRCHMIER, Raymond S. 14400 SOMMERVILLE CT 23113 #051-04-1963 L1963 **PD** *020 †55

KIRITSIS, Paul George. 13700 ST FRANCIS BLVD, STE 103 23114 #051-07-1994 L1994 **ORS** *020 †40

KIRKPATRICK, Barry V. 3641 OLD GUN RD E 23113 #051-04-1966 L1966 **PD NPM** *040 †55

KRAMOLOWSKY, Eugene V, II. 14051 ST FRANCIS BLVD, VIRGINIA UROLOGY CENTER 23114 #028-34-1980 L1987 **U** *020 †95

LEATON, Edward Montgomery. 14355 SOMMERVILLE CT 23113 #016-06-1979 L1984 **N** *020 †75

LEE, Chung Whan. ■ 23114 #583-02-1958 L1979 **P** *020

LEGHART, Gregory Francis. 13700 ST FRANCIS BLVD, STE 400 23114 #035-03-1985 L1990 **PM** *020 †60

LESTER, Barbara Thrush. 13911 ST FRANCIS BLVD, STE 101 23114 #051-07-1991 L1992 **FM** *020 †18 ‡

LEWIS, Richard Clark. 13700 ST FRANCIS BLVD, STE 600 23114 #038-41-1958 L1959 **P PYA** *020

LEWKOW, Lawrence Michael. 14051 ST FRANCIS BLVD 23114 #035-09-1975 L1993 **HO IM** *020

LONG, Frederick R, Jr. ■ 23112 #035-08-1943 L1943 **IM** *071

LOUCKS, Clay Ashley. 11020 HULL STREET RD, PATIENT FIRST-GENITO 23112 #048-14-2000 L2000 **FM** *020 †18 ‡

LYNAM, Michelle Catherine. 1555 CAMACK PL 23114 #051-04-1999 L1999 **AN** *020 †05

MACKEY, Kenton Lee. ■ 23112 #051-04-1989 †100

MAC QUEEN, Benjamin Rober. ■ 23112 #056-06-2005 L2005 **ORS** *012

MADDOX, Heather Elizabeth. 13861 HULL STREET RD, PHYSICIANS OF FAMILY MED 23112 #051-07-2000 L2000 **FM** *020 †18 ‡

MALHOTRA, Shailaja. 13841 HULL STREET RD, VILLAGE GREEN FAM MED PC 23112 #495-67-1986 L2001 **FM** *020 †18 ‡

MANNINO, Rosemarie. ■ 23112 #035-06-2000 L2000 **HO** *100 †20

MARINELLO, Mark Anthony. ■ 23113 #010-02-2003 L2003 **CCP** *012

MARINELLO, Melissa Lynn. ■ 23113 #010-02-2005 L2005 **GS** *012

MARQUEEN, Timothy John. 6055 HARBOUR PARK DR, COLONIAL ORTHOPAEDIC INC 23112 #051-04-1994 L1994 **OSM** *020

MARSHALL, Beth Christin. ■ 23114 #051-04-1997 L1997 **PDI** *100 †55

MARTIN, Wm Dabney, IV. 6500 HARBOUR VIEW CT 23112 #051-04-1984 L1985 **FM** *020 †18

MAUNG, Thein. ■ 23112 #209-03-1972 L2005 **IM** *100

MAY, James Terrell. 14051 ST FRANCIS BLVD 23114 #051-04-1973 L1974 **HO HEM** *020 †20

MAYFIELD, Robert Edward. 3000 WATERCOVE RD 23112 #051-01-1997 L1997 **FM** *020 †18

MCDONOUGH, Patrick Michae. ■ 23114 #056-05-2004 L2004 **PTH** *012

MC GHEE, Judith F. 4902 MILLRIDGE PKWY E 23112 #473-01-1976 L1979 **PD ADL** *020 †55

MC GOWAN, James Patrick. 13700 ST FRANCIS BLVD, STE 400 23114 #051-04-1990 L1993 **PM** *020 †60

MC LEOD, Jeff L. 5001 W VILLAGE GREEN DR, STE 108 23112 #065-01-1977 L1993 **FM** *020 †18

MC MURTRY, James Madison. 14051 ST FRANCIS BLVD, VIRGINIA UROLOGY CENTER 23114 #041-13-1983 L1988 **U** *020 †95

MC QUILKIN, Nancy A. 4902 MILLRIDGE PKWY E 23112 #748-02-1993 L1997 **PD** *020 †55

MILLS, Julia Hines. 13821 VILLAGE MILL DR 23114 #051-04-1977 L1980 **PD** *020 †55

MIN, John Kiho. 5001 W VILLAGE GREEN DR, STE 205 23112 #051-07-1990 L1993 **IM** *020 †20

MOHLIE, Steven Raymond. 11020 HULL STREET RD, PATIENT FIRST GENITO 23112 #023-07-1978 L1991 **FM** *020 †18

MOMIN, Atiya. 13861 HULL STREET RD, STE 200 23112 #160-02-1995 L2007 **FM** *020 †18

MOORE, James Anthony, III. ■ 23114 #051-04-2000 L2000 **DR** *100 †80

MORRISSETTE, W Philip, III. 13332 MIDLOTHIAN TPKE 23113 #051-01-1976 L1978 **FM** *020 †18

MUREN, Orhan. 2100 BRANDERMILL PKWY 23112 #902-10-1945 L1958 **PUD IM** *071 †20

MURON, David John. 13700 ST FRANCIS BLVD, STE 103 23114 #051-04-1987 L1990 **ORS OTR** *020 †40

MURPHY, Michael Edward. 13710 ST FRANCIS BLVD, PRIMEDOC OF ST. FRANCIS, P 23114 #036-07-2002 L2002 **MPD** *020 †20,55

MUSE, Raoul. 13540 HULL STREET RD, ST FRANCIS FAMILY MED 23112 #305-01-2005 L2006 **FP** *012

MYERS, Michael Allan. ■ 23112 #016-42-2005 L2006 **RO** *012

MYERS, Russell Henley. 3000 WATERCOVE RD 23112 #051-04-1982 L1983 **FM** *020 †18

NAKATSUKA, Mitsuru. 12906 MILL MEADOW CT 23112 #572-20-1964 L1980 **AN** *020 †05

NAZMI, Peyman. 14404 SOMMERVILLE CT 23113 #473-03-1990 L1995 **APM** *020 †05

NEELY, Brian Scott. 2367 COLONY CROSSING PL 23112 #051-04-1999 L1999 **FM** *020 †18

NOBLE, Earl W. ■ 23112 #035-06-1952 L1954 **IMG IM** *071 †20

NOFSINGER, Dennis E, Jr. 1407 HUGUENOT RD 23113 #051-04-1966 L1966 **PD** *020 †55

OKAY, Douglas Matthew. 13540 HULL STREET RD, ST. FRANCIS FAMILY MEDICIN 23112 #051-01-1998 L2001 **FSM** *020 †18

OTTO, Lisa R. 11020 HULL STREET RD 23112 #048-14-2001 L2001 **FM** *020 †18

PADILLA, Mary Teresa. ■ 23113 #003-01-2001 L2007 **PCP** *100 †50

PALEN, Ellen Marye. 2367 COLONY CROSSING PL 23112 #051-04-1998 L1998 **FM** *020 †18

PARRISH, Steven Thos. 13710 ST FRANCIS BLVD 23114 #051-04-1987 L1999 **EM** *020 †16

PASTORE, Dominick Jos. 13700 ST FRANCIS BLVD, PEDIATRIC ASSOCIATES PC 23114 #051-04-1989 L1992 **PD** *020 †55

PATEL, Pareshkumar B. ■ 23112 #495-22-1994 L2004 **IM** *020 †20

PAYNE, Kyle David. ■ 23112 #039-01-2005 L2006 **AN** *012

PELLICANE, James Vincent. 13700 ST FRANCIS BLVD, STE 510 23114 #041-12-1988 L1990 **GS** *020 †85

PHILLIPS, Ben Dixon, III. 2384 COLONY CROSSING PL 23112 #045-01-1999 L1999 **END** *020 †20

POLKAMPALLY, Pritam Rao. ■ 23114 #495-73-2003 L2007 **IM** *020

POWELL, Nancy Ann. ■ 23113 #051-04-1988 L1993 **FM** *020 †18 ‡

POWELSON, Stephen W. 13700 ST FRANCIS BLVD, STE 600 23114 #024-01-1977 L1980 **CD IM** *020 †20

PRASAD, Uma Rajendra. ■ 23113 #495-36-1972 L1984 **DR** *020 †80

PRINGLE, Tamara Raubitsch. 13700 ST FRANCIS BLVD, STE 305 23114 #051-04-2001 L2001 **OBG** *020 †30

PURCELL, Wm Vernon, III. 13540 HULL STREET RD 23112 #051-04-1980 L1981 **FM** *020 †18

RADCLIFFE, Jessica Jane. ■ 23113 #023-01-1978 L1986 **PDE DIA** *020 †55

RAO, Chudamani Kasuganti. ■ 23114 #496-34-2002 L2007 **NEP** *012 †20

RAVINDRAN, Vijaya. ■ 23112 #495-31-1957 L1972 **IMG IM** *020

RAZVI, Kulsoom. ■ 23113 #051-04-2006 L2006 **OBG** *012

REALUBIT, Jocelyn V. 14400 SOMMERVILLE CT 23113 #748-08-1980 L1993 **PD** *020 †55

REAMS, B Thomas. 1507 HUGUENOT RD STE 200 23113 #051-04-1975 L1977 **D** *020 †15

REECE, Steven Glenn. 13700 ST FRANCIS BLVD, STE 605 23114 #051-04-1994 L1994 **FM FSM** *020 †18

REID, Doris A. 1600 HUGUENOT RD, STE 121 23113 #047-07-1978 L1988 **FM** *020 †18

REMMERS, Rebecca King. ■ 23112 #047-06-1989 L1995 **PCP** *050 †50

REMUS, Elizabeth Leigh. ■ 23112 #051-04-2006 L2006 **FP** *012

RICHARDSON, Nathan Davis. 11020 HULL STREET RD, PATIENT FIRST GENITO 23112 #050-02-2005 L2005 **ORS** *012

RILEY, Paul Thos. 3000 WATERCOVE RD 23112 #051-04-1976 L1977 **FM OM** *020 †18

ROBERTS, Laura Lynne. ■ 23113 #021-05-2001 L2001 **FM** *020

ROBINSON, Frederick Danl. ■ 23113 #051-01-1958 L1958 **CD FM** *071 †20

ROGERS, Alfred Hodge. 13700 ST FRANCIS BLVD 23114 #047-06-1989 L1990 **IM** *020 †20

ROGERS, Joshua Barrett. 13710 ST FRANCIS BLVD 23114 #050-02-2002 L2005 **EM** *100 †16

ROLLINS, Kent Lawton. 14051 ST FRANCIS BLVD, VIRGINIA UROLOGY CENTER 23114 #045-04-1981 L1983 **U** *020 †95

ROSS, David Edward. 2621 PROMENADE PKWY, VA INSTITUTE OF NUEROPSYCH 23113 #051-04-1986 L1989 **P** *050 †75

ROWE, George Thos. 14400 SOMMERVILLE CT 23113 #051-04-1988 L1991 **PD** *020 †55

ROZATI, Fariba. 13841 HULL STREET RD, STE 4 23112 #496-01-1991 L2003 **IM** *020 †20

RYAN, Kristen D. 6510 HARBOUR VIEW CT, CHIPPENHAM PED & ADOL 23112 #038-40-1997 L2000 **PD** *020 †55

SABHARWAL, Vipal Kumar. 13700 ST FRANCIS BLVD, STE 600 23114 #027-01-1992 L1992 **CD** *020 †20

SALEEM, Rehan. 5931 HARBOUR PARK DR 23112 #704-01-1993 L2004 **PYG** *100 †75

SAMDANI, Attique. 14051 ST FRANCIS BLVD 23114 #704-09-1990 L1998 **HO** *020 †20

SANDERS, Donald Powell. 13332 MIDLOTHIAN TPKE, VIRGINIA PHYSICIANS 23113 #051-04-1972 L1973 **FM** *020 †18

SANTOSH, Padmini. 13700 ST FRANCIS BLVD, STE 502 23114 #495-59-1986 L2002 **OBG** *020 †30

SARAIYA, Sharadkumar. 6055 HARBOUR PARK DR, COLONIAL ORTHOPAEDIC INC 23112 #495-23-1975 L1984 **ORS** *020 †40

SAUNDERS, Martha Ann. 1407 HUGUENOT RD, HUGUENOT PEDS 23113 #051-04-1976 L1978 **PD** *020 †55

SCHARPF, Susan Julia. 13841 HULL STREET RD, STE 4 23112 #051-04-1989 L1992 **FM** *020 †18

SCHUL, Jeffery Lynn. 14351 SOMMERVILLE CT 23113 #028-02-1980 L1981 **AI PUD** *020 †20,03

SCHUNN, Gisa-Beate Angela. 14051 ST FRANCIS BLVD 23114 #409-16-1987 L2006 **HO IM** *040 †20

SEABURY, Charles A. 14051 ST FRANCIS BLVD, VIRGINIA UROLOGY CENTER 23114 #020-12-1997 L2003 **U** *020 †95

SEILER, Sigmund Placid. 1807 HUGUENOT RD, STE 101 23113 #051-04-1986 L1987 FM *020 †18

SHAH, Sonia Kaushik. 13700 ST FRANCIS BLVD, STE 510 23114 #035-06-1999 L1999 IM *020 †20

SHELTON, Bonnie Lee. ■ 23114 #011-02-1978 L1985 GS *074 †85

SHENOY, Ramakrishnan. 13354 MIDLOTHIAN TPKE #100 23113 #495-44-1963 L1974 P ADP *020 †75

SHEPHERD, George B. ■ 23112 #051-01-1960 L1960 PD *072

SHERMAN, Garrick Todd. ■ 23114 #020-12-2004 L2004 DR *012

SHERROD, John Philip. 13540 HULL STREET RD 23112 #051-04-1974 L1975 FM FSM *020 †18

SICAT, Jeffrey Mariano. 2384 COLONY CROSSING PL 23112 #051-04-1999 L1999 END *020 †20

SILVER, Timothy Milton. 13700 ST FRANCIS BLVD, STE 400 23114 #036-08-1997 L1998 PM PME *020 †60 ‡

SIMONS, Sandra Scott. ■ 23113 #008-01-2002 L2002 EM *100

SINGH, Anant Bir. ■ 23114 #495-08-1970 L2000 EM *020 †18,16

SIRI, Chakkris. 13700 ST FRANCIS BLVD, STE 502 23114 #891-04-1974 L1980 OBG *020 †30

SISON, Alfredo S, Jr. ■ 23113 #748-10-1979 L1996 IMG *020

SISON, Alfredo Yuson. ■ 23113 #748-01-1956 L1971 IM PTH *071

SLIWINSKI, Anthony M. 14051 ST FRANCIS BLVD # 2 23114 #010-02-1986 L1989 U *020 †95

SMITH, Jenny O. ■ 23112 #027-01-2004 L2004 GE *012 †20

SNOWDEN, Ransom G, III. 11601 ROBIOUS RD, STE 100 23113 #047-05-1990 L1998 PD *020 †55

SOMANATH, Muktha Lata. ■ 23112 #495-09-1969 DR *100

SPRING, Tammy Rochelle. ■ 23112 #020-12-2004 L2004 RHU *012 †20

STEIDLE, Karen Ann. 13700 ST FRANCIS BLVD, STE 400 23114 #041-01-1990 L2002 PM *020 †60

STEPHENS, Polly L. 14051 ST FRANCIS BLVD, STE 2210 23114 #021-01-1993 L1998 GS *020 †85

STRATTON, Dwayne Everette. 13710 ST FRANCIS BLVD 23114 #051-04-1996 L1999 EM *020 †16

STREHLER, Paul Mcgaffey. 6510 HARBOUR VIEW CT, CHIPPENHAM PED & ADOL 23112 #041-09-1986 L1988 PD *020 †55

STURROCK, Kelley Lyn. 13700 ST FRANCIS BLVD 23114 #035-03-2000 L2004 OBG *020 †30

TALIBI, Azhar Ali. 6510 HARBOUR VIEW CT, CHIPPENHAM PED & ADOL 23112 #051-04-1999 L1999 PD *020 †15

TAMINGER, David John. 2367 COLONY CROSSING PL 23112 #021-01-1999 L1999 FM *020 †18

TANNER, William Woodrow. ■ 23112 #051-04-1971 L1975 AN *020 †05

TEFERA, Mesfin Alemu. 13710 ST FRANCIS BLVD, PRIMEDOC ST. FRANCIS, PC 23114 #913-07-1986 L2006 IM *100 †20

TERRY, Charles Vaden. 14400 SOMMERVILLE CT 23113 #051-07-1983 L1986 PD *040 †55

THERUVATH, Harindran. ■ 23112 #495-44-1972 L1982 IM *020 †20

THORNTON, Nancy Hayden. ■ 23113 #051-04-1976 L1981 D IM *020 †20,15

TIDLER, Lillian Marie. ■ 23113 #023-01-1988 L1998 CHP PFP *020 †75

TOMENCHOK, Drew Martin. ■ 23113 #033-05-1991 L2004 PD *020 †55

VAN MANEN, John Wm. 13700 ST FRANCIS BLVD, STE 605 23114 #021-01-1981 L1992 OFA *020 †40

VERHEUL, John Willem. 13911 ST FRANCIS BLVD, STE 101 23114 #660-06-1984 L1986 FM OM *020 †18

VOORHEES, Philip H. ■ 23112 #035-20-1943 L1955 U *071 †95

VOORHIS, Adrienne Claire. 4902 MILLRIDGE PKWY E, PEDIATRIC ADOL MED PC 23112 #035-46-1993 L1993 PD *020 †55

WALKER, Jo Anne. 14051 ST FRANCIS BLVD, STE 1100 23114 #051-04-1988 L1993 RO *020 †80

WATKINS, Dawn Jayelynn. 11020 HULL STREET RD, PATIENT FIRST GENITO 23112 #051-04-2002 L2005 FM *100 †18

WATSON, Stuart Steve. ■ 23114 #048-02-1971 L1971 FM *071 †18

WATTERSON, William Kevin. 2410 PAGEHURST DR 23113 #051-04-1993 L1995 MPD *020 †20,55

WAYNE, Douglas Alan. 13700 ST FRANCIS BLVD, STE 605 23114 #025-07-1981 L1984 PM *020 †60

WESDOCK, James C. 13911 ST FRANCIS BLVD, STE 101 23114 #041-09-1985 L1993 FM OM *020 †70,18

WEST, Lisa Marie. 3738 WINTERFIELD RD, STE 100 23113 #051-07-1992 L1992 OBG *020 †30

WESTROL, Robert Steven. 13700 ST FRANCIS BLVD, STE 400 23114 #041-15-2002 L2006 PM *020

WHEELER, Robert Milton. 13911 ST FRANCIS BLVD, STE 101 23114 #051-04-1982 L1983 FM *020 †18

WHITE, Nathan James. ■ 23113 #025-07-2003 L2007 EM *100

WILD, Barton William. ■ 23114 #025-07-2005 L2006 AN *012

WIXTED, Dennis Damian. ■ 23113 #041-02-2000 L2000 IM *020 †20

WOLVER, Susan Elise. ■ 23112 #036-05-1989 L1990 IM *100 †20

WOOD, Monette Weaver. 11601 ROBIOUS RD, STE 100 23113 #051-07-1987 L1990 PD *020 †55

WORLAND, Richard Lynn. 13700 ST FRANCIS BLVD, STE 605 23114 #035-45-1970 L1977 ORS *020 †40

WRIGHT, R Lewis. ■ 23113 #051-04-1955 L1955 NS *071 †25

ZACHARY, John S. 1521 HUGUENOT RD STE 101 23113 #016-43-1979 L1983 PD *020 †55

ZASLAV, Kenneth Robt. 13700 ST FRANCIS BLVD, STE 605 23114 #035-46-1983 L1990 ORS OSM *020 †40

ZEBALLOS, Alvaro Ramiro. 13710 ST FRANCIS BLVD, EMERGENCY DEPARTMENT 23114 #048-15-1998 L2002 EM *020 †16

ZIEVE, Sandra L Turchick. ■ 23113 #026-04-1969 L1978 GP OM *040

ZIMBLE, James Allen. ■ 23112 #041-01-1959 L1960 OS OBG *071 †30

MILFORD – CAROLINE

CONLEY, John Ellis. 20500 EASTER SEAL DR 22514 #016-43-1980 L2007 P *020 †75 ‡

LEE, Yong Bum. 20500 REMUDA LN 22514 #023-01-1993 L1997 P *020 †75

MILLBORO – BATH

WILHITE, Philip A, Jr. ■ 24460 #051-04-1945 L1951 D *071

MILLWOOD – CLARKE

HOWE, John Prentice, III. 255 CARTER HALL LN, PROJECT HOPE 22646 #024-05-1969 L1970 CD IM *030 †20 ‡

PEAKE, James Benj. 255 CARTER HALL LN 22646 #035-20-1972 L1976 TS GS *020 †85,90

TALLEY, Lilburn Trigg. ■ 22646 #051-01-1954 L1954 R *071 †80

MINERAL – LOUISA

DOWNS, Peter Ellsworth. ■ 23117 #035-20-1957 L1968 EM CD *071 †85

HURLEY, Moira Rose. ■ 23117 #041-07-1969 L1980 EM *074

KOSMAHLY, Gerhard. ■ 23117 #407-30-1950 L1959 GP *071

MANZARI, John A. ■ 23117 #035-06-1964 L1965 PUD IM *071 †20

MC AVENEY, William Jos. ■ 23117 #035-08-1967 L1979 PD ADL *071 †55

PERO, Robert Thos. ■ 23117 #035-01-1984 L1985 OM PHP *020 †70

RICHARDSON, P Henderson. ■ 23117 #051-07-1979 L1980 GP *071

MINT SPRING – AUGUSTA

MOORE, H Lynn. PO BOX 6 24463 #051-04-1958 L1958 GP *020

MOLLUSK – LANCASTER

BLUEFELD, Curt, Jr. ■ 22517 #035-19-1945 L1948 IM CD *071 †20

MONETA – BEDFORD

ANZIULEWICZ, John Anthony. ■ 24121 #035-15-1961 L1979 R *071

BASKETT, Sarah J Kalb. 949 BOARDWALK DR 24121 #017-20-1965 L1988 P *020 †75

BEATTY, Susan Elaine. ■ 24121 #041-01-1972 L2003 PUD IM *075 †20

BLANKS, Virginia Luth. 4830 RUCKER RD, VILLAGE FAMILY PHYSICIANS 24121 #051-01-1988 L1990 FM *020 †18

BOONE, Owen Riley. 2448 MERRIMAN WAY RD, STE A 24121 #051-04-1961 L1961 GS *020 †85

BRAY, Charles Bunyan, Jr. RT 666 24121 #051-01-1944 L1944 ORS *071 †40

CHAMBERLAIN, Richard R. RR 5 BOX 252 24121 #023-07-1949 L1956 GYN *071 †30

CHAPMAN, Brent Wilson. 400 SCRUGGS RD, STE 2300 24121 #055-01-1985 L1991 IM *020 †20

CLAPSADDLE, Gene Edward. ■ 24121 #051-04-1952 L1952 OM *071 †18

DEHLI, Todd Herbert. 4830 RUCKER RD 24121 #024-06-1988 L1991 FM *020 †18

ELLETT, Rufus P, Jr. ■ 24121 #051-04-1944 L1944 OBG *071 †30

HUMPHREYS, Kathryn Luth. 4830 RUCKER RD 24121 #051-01-1982 L1983 FM *020 †18 ‡

KENNEDY, John David. ■ 24121 #539-05-1969 L1977 R *071 †80

KIRCHHOFF, Gary T. ■ 24121 #042-02-1984 L2001 AN *020 †05

LEWIS, Steven Teeford. 70 WESTWIND RD 24121 #018-03-1977 L1980 FM EM *020 †18

LUTH, Janice Elaine. 4830 RUCKER RD 24121 #051-01-1979 L1980 FM *020 †18

O'ROURKE, William Richard. ■ 24121 #028-03-1963 L1963 FM *071 †18

ROWELL, Thomas Robert. ■ 24121 #661-03-2004 L2005 P *012

SAADAT, Seyed Hessam. 70 WESTWIND RD, SML FAMILY PRACTICE 24121 #055-01-1994 L1998 FM VM *020 †18 ‡

STOWE, Mark Brian. ■ 24121 #038-43-1991 L1994 EM *020 †16

WELLER, William Franklin. ■ 24121 #067-01-1945 L1957 DR OS *071 †80

MONROE – AMHERST

BAWA, Balraj. 1073 FATHER JUDGE RD, OLD DOMINION JOB CORPS CEN 24574 #495-36-1967 L1977 PD *020 †55

MONTEREY – HIGHLAND

BIRD, Kimberly Hofmann. PO BOX 490 24465 #051-04-1993 L1993 IM *020 †20

TABATZNIK, Bernard. ■ 24465 #836-01-1949 L1971 CD IM *071

MONTPELIER – HANOVER

BAKHSHI, Virat. 16618 MOUNTAIN RD STE B, VCU MEDICAL COLLEGE 23192 #496-03-1987 L1997 IMG END *020

SASSER, Frank M, Jr. 16644 MOUNTAIN RD 23192 #051-04-1955 L1955 FM OM *072

SHELP, Frank Eugene. 13267 S ANNA LN 23192 #051-04-1984 L1993 P PYG *030 †75

MONTROSS – WESTMORELAND

MC CARTY, William Mason. ■ 22520 #024-01-1948 L1995 OPH *071 †35

WALSH, Christopher S. 15394 KINGS HWY 22520 #035-06-1985 L1989 RO *020 †80

MONTVALE – BEDFORD

OLAZAGASTI GONZALEZ, Juan. PO BOX 496 24122 #042-03-1987 L1990 PD *020 †55

MOON – MATHEWS

MORGAN, Elma A, Jr. ■ 23119 #051-04-1950 L1950 IM CD *071 †20

THOMPSON, James Edward. ■ 23119 #660-03-1957 L1958 OTO OS *071 †45

MOSELEY – CHESTERFIELD

HOLLISTER, Margaret E. ■ 23120 #051-04-2003 L2003 PD *012

■ = Address Information Privacy Protected

PAPINO, Maria Novella. ■ 23120 #561-07-2001 L2007 **FP** *012
PHILLIPS-WILLIAMS, Vanessa. ■ 23120 #051-07-2007 L2007 **PTH** *012
ROSENFIELD, Christine Ann. ■ 23120 #025-01-1978 L1996 **IMG IM** *020

MOUNT HOLLY – WESTMORELAND

GRIFFITH, Lloyd Tayloe. BOSCOBEL RT 202 22524 #051-01-1956 L1956 **FM** *020 †18

MOUNT JACKSON – SHENANDOAH

GROSE, Paul Sheridan. ■ 22842 #065-01-1959 L1976 **AN OS** *071
LONG, Keith Christian. 5173 MAIN ST, MT JACKSON FAM HLTH CTR 22842 #051-07-1995 L1995 **FM** *020 †18
MILLER, Charles Harner. 5173 MAIN ST 22842 #051-01-1965 L1965 **GP GS** *020 †85
MUIRURI, Kathleen Larson. 5173 MAIN ST, MT. JACKSON FAMILY HEALTH 22842 #025-12-1982 L1995 **FM** *020 †18

MOUNT SIDNEY – AUGUSTA

WHITE, Gordon Osler. PO BOX 308, 3064 LEE HWY 24467 #051-01-1962 L1962 **N** *071

MOUNT SOLON – AUGUSTA

TODD, John W, III. ■ 22843 #051-04-1947 L1951 **GS TS** *071 †85

MOUNT WEATHER – CLARKE

DINH, Ha. 19844 BLUERIDGE MOUNTAIN RD, HEALTH UNIT BLDG 403 FEMA 20135 #941-01-1966 L1981 **CD IM** *020 †20

NASSAWADOX – NORTHAMPTON

BOYER, A Stephen. 9507 HOSPITAL RD 23413 #041-01-1964 L1969 **GS** *020 †85
BULETTE, John Lawrence. ■ 23413 #041-13-1966 L1994 **P** *030 †75
DIXON, Henry Bryan, II. 9507 HOSPITAL RD 23413 #036-07-1961 1975 **CD IM** *020
FERGUSON, James Hunter. PO BOX 803, 9536 HOSPITAL AVE 23413 #919-05-1960 L1994 **ORS** *071
FRITZ, Arthur Livingston. NORTHAMPTON ACCOMACT MEM, DEPT OF RAD 23413 #036-01-1976 L1992 **DR** *020 †80
GOLDSTEIN, Charles David. SURGEONS, EASTERN SHORE PHYSICIANS & 23413 #035-09-1991 L1998 **GS** *020 †85
HOLCOMB, Harry S, III. 9507 HOSPITAL RD 23413 #008-01-1968 L1976 **ORS OFA** *071 †40
KELLAM, Lloyd Jos, III. 9507 HOSPITAL RD 23413 #051-01-1981 L1987 **CD IM** *020 †20
KELLAM, Marilyn Schneider. 9507 HOSPITAL RD 23413 #051-04-1982 L1983 **IM** *020 †20
MC DANIEL, James Lund. 9507 HOSPITAL RD 23413 #051-04-1976 L1982 **PUD IM** *020 †20
MOLERA, Federico Fernando. 9507 HOSPITAL RD 23413 #847-04-1972 L1984 **AN** *020
OLIVER, Lagora Arnette. PO BOX 77, EASTERN SHORE PHYSICIANS 23413 #010-03-2001 L2001 **PD** *020
ROGERS, Elizabeth Jane. EMERGENCY DEPT, SHORE MEMORIAL HOSPITAL 23413 #051-07-1984 L1989 **GS** *020
SNYDER, John Wilton, Jr. PO BOX 492 23413 #051-04-1979 L1980 **FM** *020 †18
STITH, Drury Martin. 9507 HOSPITAL RD 23413 #051-04-1969 L1969 **IM HO** *071 †20
TAVENNER, John Stephen. ■ 23413 #051-07-1980 L1984 **P** *020

NATHALIE – HALIFAX

BUCKMAN, Paul Stewart. 15210 L P BAILEY MEMRL HWY 24577 #051-04-1982 L1985 **FM** *050 †18
HAMLOR, Gahear Frederick. 15210 L P BAILEY MEMRL HWY 24577 #047-07-1976 L1978 **FM** *020 †18

NATURAL BRIDGE – ROCKBRIDGE

BROWNING, Louis Eugene. ■ 24578 #028-34-1943 L1943 **NM** *071

NELLYSFORD – NELSON

FLEISHER, Mitchell Allan. PO BOX 303 22958 #308-07-1981 L1984 **FM** *020 †18
GOLDMAN, Myla Denise. ■ 22958 #016-01-1999 L2000 **IM** *020 †8
MC CARTER, Danl Franklin. 2871 ROCKFISH VALLEY HWY 22958 #051-01-1987 L1989 **FM** *020 †18
POUTASSE, Eugene F. ■ 22958 #024-01-1943 L1964 **U** *071 †95
SELINE, Helen M Crabb. 13 CARDINAL LN 22958 #016-06-1961 L1991 **CHP** *071
SIMPSON, Allan Geo. 1381 MONOCAN DR 22958 #018-03-1973 L1980 **CD IM** *020 †20
WOOD, Maurice. ■ 22958 #917-04-1945 L1971 **FM** *071 †18

NEW CANTON – BUCKINGHAM

DWAN, Charles Martin. 606 CG WOODSON RD 23123 #025-01-1973 L1975 **FM IM** *020 †18,16

NEW CASTLE – CRAIG

MC INTYRE, Shelly. ■ 24127 #654-01-1996 L1997 **P SCI** *020

NEW KENT – NEW KENT

DAVIDOW, Daniel Nelson. 9407 CUMBERLAND RD 23124 #012-01-1977 L1982 **ADL PD** *020 †55
HOSFIELD, Richard H. 9407 CUMBERLAND RD 23124 #051-04-1972 L1972 **FM OM** *020 †18
REAMS, Patricia Ann. 9407 CUMBERLAND RD 23124 #051-04-1975 L1978 **PD** *020 †55

NEW MARKET – SHENANDOAH

STAUFFER, John Mark, Jr. ■ 22844 #051-01-1977 L1979 **FM** *020 †18

NEWBERN – PULASKI

GIBAS, Dinos. TOWES FERRY ROAD 24126 #418-02-1952 L1960 **U** *020 †95
VARESE, Yonne D. PO BOX 364, WILDERNESS RD 24126 #035-19-1950 L1953 **GP** *071

NEWPORT – GILES

MOLL, Anthonie Theodoor. ■ 24128 #660-02-1942 L1957 **OPH** *072
MOLL, Geertruida D J Z. ■ 24128 #660-03-1948 L1958 **GP** *071
MOLL, Jacob Theodoor. ■ 24128 #051-04-1969 L1969 **OM PHP** *071 †70
SPRAGUE, Dennis Michael. 2140 SPRUCE RUN RD 24128 #051-04-1977 L1980 **EM PD** *020 †16

NEWPORT NEWS – NEWPORT NEWS CITY

ABDALLAH, Adel Zuhdi M. 500 J CLYDE MORRIS BLVD, RIVERSIDE REGIONAL MED CTR 23601 #575-01-1982 L1994 **NPM PD** *020 †55
ABU AHMED, Tahanie. 500 J CLYDE MORRIS BLVD, DEPT OF MED EDUCATION 23601 #473-04-1998 L2007 **FP** *012
ADAMS, Kenneth Atwell. 11803 JEFFERSON AVE, STE 230 23606 #051-01-1976 L1981 **GE IM** *020 †20
AFSHARCHI, Foroozan. 500 J CLYDE MORRIS BLVD 23601 #517-01-1992 L2006 **FP** *012
ALBA, Norma Zamora. PO BOX 1034 23601 #748-01-1971 L1984 **GP** *020
ALDRIDGE, John William. 730 THIMBLE SHOALS BLVD 23606 #035-01-1997 L2002 **ORS OSM** *020 †40
ALEXANDER, Edward Lee, Jr. ■ 23606 #023-07-1952 L1958 **IM HEM** *020 †20
ALI, Alan Hassan. 11825 ROCK LANDING DR, ROCK LANDING PSYCHOLOGICAL 23606 #528-01-1977 L1984 **P CHP** *020 †75 ‡
ALLEN, Harry A, III. 2 BERNARDINE DR 23602 #036-05-1979 L1983 **DR** *020 †80
ALLEN, James Floyd. 730 THIMBLE SHOALS BLVD, STE 110 23606 #048-14-1981 L1984 **NS** *020 †25
ALLISON, Matthew Campbell. 11803 JEFFERSON AVE 23606 #051-04-1992 L1997 **DR** *020 †80
ANDERSON, Peter Bland. 10852 WARWICK BLVD 23601 #051-01-1978 L1981 **FM** *020 †18
ANDERSON, Richard Scott. 2 BERNARDINE DR 23602 #024-05-1986 L2003 **DR** *020 †80
ANDERSON, Thomas C. 2 BERNARDINE DR, DEPT OF PATHOLOGY 23602 #539-04-1982 L1993 **HEM** *020 †50
ANG, Choyan Lee. 416 J CLYDE MORRIS BLVD 23601 #748-09-1966 L1973 **PD** *020 †55
ANTON, Debra Cattell. 747 J CLYDE MORRIS BLVD 23601 #051-01-1993 L1993 **FM** *020 †18
APOSTOLES, Peter Steven. 4101 WASHINGTON AVE, NORTHROP GRUMMAN N.N. 23607 #051-04-1989 L1995 **OSM** *020
ASHBY, Kermit Bernard. 727 25TH ST 23607 #051-04-1980 L1984 **DR NR** *020
ASHBY, Samuel Kermit. 5100 MARSHALL AVE 23605 #010-03-1945 L1947 **GP OS** *071
ASPILI, Concepcion Santos. 4714 MARSHALL AVE 23607 #748-10-1984 L1993 **IM** *020 †20
ATIQ, Aida. 500 J CLYDE MORRIS BLVD, DEPT OF MED EDUCATION 23601 #704-16-2001 L2007 **FP** *012
AYRES, Nancy Carol. 703 THIMBLE SHOALS BLVD, STE B-4 23606 #025-01-1979 L1989 **FM** *020 †18
AZIZ, Ali S. 12725 MCMANUS BLVD, BLDG 2 23602 #915-04-1981 L2001 **P CHP** *020 †75
BABER, Bruce Allenby. ■ 23601 #051-04-1957 L1957 **AN** *071 †05
BADAVI, Aurora T. 4714 MARSHALL AVE 23607 #748-01-1975 L1993 **PD** *020 †55
BADDAR, Adrian Talat. 730 THIMBLE SHOALS BLVD 23606 #051-01-1997 L1997 **ORS** *020 †40
BAER, Robert Scott. 11842 ROCK LANDING DR #120 23606 #016-11-1978 L1993 **D** *020 †15
BAGGS, Wilbur J, Jr. ■ 23606 #051-04-1943 L1943 **GYN** *071 †30
BAINES, Bryan Nicholas. 13347 WARWICK BLVD, MULTISPECIALTY GROUP 23602 #051-07-1987 L1989 **FM** *020 †18
BAINES, Edward Francke. 11848 ROCK LANDING DR 23606 #051-04-1984 L1990 **AN** *020 †05
BANNING, Scott Justis. 12655 WARWICK BLVD, MULTISPECIALTY GROUP 23606 #051-04-1991 L1992 **FM** *020 †18
BARLASCINI, Cornelius, Jr. 704 THIMBLE SHOALS BLVD, STE 300A 23606 #051-01-1983 L1984 **END DIA** *020
BARNETT, Jewell Milton. 10510 JEFFERSON AVE, STE D 23601 #012-01-1970 L1972 **OBG** *020 †30
BASHKOFF, Eric Mark. 109 PHILIP ROTH ST 23606 #035-47-1988 L1993 **GS** *020 †85
BASS, Stuart Kenneth. 11848 ROCK LANDING DR, STE 303 23606 #051-04-1983 L1984 **AN EM** *020 †16,05
BASS, William Thos. 2 BERNARDINE DR 23602 #036-08-1982 L1987 **NPM PD** *020 †55
BAUST, Joseph A, Jr. 298 NAT TURNER BLVD S 23606 #047-07-2001 L2006 **PD** *020 †55
BAVUSO, Salvatore Karl. 12695 MCMANUS BLVD, BLDG 6 23602 #051-04-1999 L2006 **FM** *020 †18
BEASLEY, Darren Steele. 500 J CLYDE MORRIS BLVD, RIVERSIDE REGIONAL MEDICAL 23601 #025-07-2000 L2005 **EM** *012
BEAVERS, Tammy Jean. 1405 KILN CREEK PKWY STE K, JAMES RIVER FAMILY PARKWAY 23602 #010-02-1997 L2000 **FM** *020 †18
BEAZLIE, Frank S, Jr. 500 J CLYDE MORRIS BLVD 23601 #051-01-1943 L1943 **U** *071 †95
BERCASIO, Roland M. 11803 JEFFERSON AVE, STE 100 23606 #748-01-1991 L1996 **FM** *020 †18
BERCKMUELLER, Hugh Edward. 704 THIMBLE SHOALS BLVD, STE 100 23606 #038-41-1996 L1996 **OPH** *020 †35
BIDOT, Lianis Z. 11803 JEFFERSON AVE, STE 250 23606 #042-01-1982 L2000 **GS** *020 †85
BILLINGS, Brian Joseph. 109 PHILIP ROTH ST, STE 200 23606 #025-07-2001 L2007 **CRS** *020 †85

BLANCHARD, Thomas Randall. 895 MIDDLE GROUND BLVD, STE 300 23606 #051-04-1992 L1992 **PS** *020 †85,65

BLUM, Charles Timothy. ■ 23606 #035-06-1975 L1982 **AN** *075

BOBBITT, John Maxwell. NN SHIPBUILDING CO MED CLN 23607 #025-01-1952 L1981 **OM** *075 †95

BOENAU, Ioliene Beth. 500 J CLYDE MORRIS BLVD #033-05-1989 L1999 **EM** *020 †16

BOGGUS, Gary Walker. 972 NICKLAUS DR 23602 #051-07-1991 L1992 **P** *020

BOLDUC, Stephen Patrick. 11783 ROCK LANDING DR, STE 202 23606 #038-43-1979 L1983 **PD** *020 †95

BOOTH, Orin Watts. 321 MAIN ST 23601 #036-07-1943 L1948 **PD** *071 †55

BOSWORTH, David C. 500 J CLYDE MORRIS BLVD, RIVERSIDE REGIONAL MEDICAL 23601 #051-04-1972 L1978 **IM** *020

BOYD, John Wm. 101 PHILIP ROTH ST 23606 #036-08-1986 L1988 **IM** *020 †20

BRAGANZA, Teodoro. ■ 23601 #748-02-1952 L1976 **P** *072 †75

BRASSEL, Alfred L, Jr. 416 J CLYDE MORRIS BLVD, DEPARTMENT OF PUBLIC AFFAI 23601 #051-01-1969 L1969 **FM** *020 †18

BRAUCKMANN, Joan Louise. 11747 JEFFERSON AVE, STE 1B 23606 #038-41-1991 L1997 **AI** *020 †55,03

BROTHERS, William Geo. 11848 ROCK LANDING DR, JAMES RIVER ANESTHESIA 23606 #051-04-1981 L1985 **AN** *05

BROWN, Douglas Allen. 611 DENBIGH BLVD, PATIENT FIRST 23608 #422-01-1986 L1990 **FM EM** *020 †18

BROWN, Douglas Chas. 2 BERNARDINE DR 23602 #051-01-1984 L1995 **DR RNR** *020 †80

BROWN, Julia Ann. 12350 JEFFERSON AVE, STE 190 23602 #036-08-1994 L2001 **CHP** *020 †75

BUDDING, Jacobus. 640 DENBIGH BLVD STE 2 23608 #660-04-1956 L1977 **GS VS** *020

BURFORD, Amy Elizabeth. 500 J CLYDE MORRIS BLVD, RIVERSIDE REG MED CENTER 23601 #007-02-2000 L2003 **EM** *020 ‡

BURROWS, Jamie Patricia. 500 J CLYDE MORRIS BLVD 23601 #041-78-2004, ▲ L2004 **OBG** *012

BURTON, Allison Rae. ■ 23602 #305-01-2007 **FP** *012

BUSHEY, Sarah Margaret. 12655 WARWICK BLVD, MULTISPECIALTY GROUP 23606 #051-04-1985 L1986 **FM** *020 †18

BUTCHER, Brian Kevin. 298 NAT TURNER BLVD S 23606 #051-04-1997 L2000 **PD** *020 †55

BUTCHER, Robert Preston. 13347 WARWICK BLVD, MULTISPECIALTY GROUP 23602 #043-01-1990 L1997 **FM** *020 †18

BUXTON, Ernest Perry, III. 101 PHILIP ROTH ST 23606 #051-01-1967 L1967 **GE IM** *020 †20

CALDRONEY, Thomas Walter. 321 MAIN ST 23601 #035-20-1947 L1953 **PD** *020 †55

CALHOUN, Daniel M, Jr. 2 BERNARDINE DR 23602 #036-01-1971 L1978 **TS GS** *020 †85,90

CALLENDER, Ealena S. 500 J CLYDE MORRIS BLVD 23601 #023-01-2002 L2006 **OBG** *100

CAMPBELL, Amy Lynne. 12715 WARWICK BLVD, STE O 23606 #028-34-2002 L2002 **FM** *020 †18

CANTWELL, Danny Victor. 860 OMNI BLVD, MULTISPECIALTY GROUP 23606 #012-05-1971 L1992 **GS** *020 †85

CAPLAN, Carol Miegel. 500 J CLYDE MORRIS BLVD 23601 #041-12-1980 L1986 **PTH PCP** *020 †50

CARDELIA, James Marc. 11783 ROCK LANDING DR 23606 #041-02-1990 L2000 **OP** *020 †40

CARLSON, Jeffrey Robert. 751 J CLYDE MORRIS BLVD, ORTHOPAEDIC SURGERY & 23601 #010-01-1993 L1999 **ORS OSS** *020 †40

CARMINES, Henry Bradford. 12655 WARWICK BLVD, MULTISPECIALTY GROUP 23606 #051-07-1982 L1983 **FM EM** *020 †18

CARNEY, David Anthony. 11848 ROCK LANDING DR, VIRGINIA ANESTHESIA 23606 #051-04-1971 L1975 **AN** *020 †05

CARTER, Anthony Thos. 730 THIMBLE SHOALS BLVD 23606 #024-05-1987 L1994 **ORS** *020 †40

CARTER, Latisha Nicole. ■ 23606 #025-07-2002 L2004 **PD** *020 †55

CASANOVA, Lisa Ann. 401 OYSTER POINT RD STE A 23602 #043-01-1986 L1994 **OBG** *020 †30

CAVAZOS, Daniel Raymond. 730 THIMBLE SHOALS BLVD 23606 #023-12-1982 L1998 **ORS** *020 †40 ‡

CHAMBLAIN, Jenny. 500 J CLYDE MORRIS BLVD, DEPT OF MED EDU 23601 #422-01-2005 L2006 **FP** *012

CHAMBLEE, Denise R. 11800 ROCK LANDING DR 23606 #048-13-1988 L1993 **PO** *020 †35

CHANDLER, Walter Smith. 12652 JEFFERSON AVE, STE C 23602 #001-02-1982 L1983 **OM** *020 †70

CHANDRASEKHAR, C. 12420 WARWICK BLVD, BLDG 3 23606 #050-02-1994 L1998 **IM** *020 †20

CHATEH-NKENGTEGO, Nkengfac. 500 J CLYDE MORRIS BLVD, DEPT OF MED EDU 23601 #305-01-2005 L2006 **FP** *012

CHATTERSON, Michael P. 610 THIMBLE SHOALS BLVD 23606 #065-01-1972 L1997 **FM** *020 †18

CHEN, Maria Elizabeth. 11783 ROCK LANDING DR, STE 202 23606 #051-04-1993 L1996 **PD** *020 †55

CHESSEN, Douglas Howell. 12420 WARWICK BLVD, STE 7C 23606 #024-01-1969 L1973 **P ADP** *020 †75

CHILDS, George Goodwin, Jr. 608 DENBIGH BLVD 23608 #051-07-1979 L1986 **PUD CCM** *020 †20

CHILDS, Marcella Harris. 4714 MARSHALL AVE 23607 #010-03-1989 L2004 **PD** *020 †55

CHOU, Eric Jensen. 10833 JEFFERSON AVE, STE 110 23606 #041-14-1998 L2001 **IC** *020 †20

CHRISTIE, Joanne Lee. 13347 WARWICK BLVD, MULTISPECIALTY GROUP 23602 #033-05-1997 L1997 **FM** *020 †18

CICCONE, Christopher J. 12695 MCMANUS BLVD, TPMG FAM MED BLDG 6 STE A 23602 #051-07-1994 L1994 **FM** *020 †18

CLARK, Andrew T. 610 THIMBLE SHOALS BLVD, STE 520 23606 #065-01-1971 L1978 **FM** *020 †18

CLARK, Thomas W. 645 J CLYDE MORRIS BLVD 23601 #036-05-1988 L1994 **GS** *020 †85

CLEARY, Anastasia Dumbra. 500 J CLYDE MORRIS BLVD 23601 #038-43-2004 L2004 **FM** *020 †18

CLEM, Joseph Burton. ■ 23606 #023-12-1993 L1994 **CHP** *020 †75

CLOUD, Rose Joseph. 12695 MCMANUS BLVD STE 1D 23606 #495-73-1975 L1981 **PD** *020 †55

COATS, Stephen Dale. ■ 23601 #028-78-2005, ▲ L2006 *100

COCKERILL, Mark Lewis. 2 BERNARDINE DR 23602 #023-01-1987 L1997 **VIR** *020 †80

COHEN, Norman Katz. 11828 CANON BLVD, STE E 23606 #020-02-1953 L1954 **A OS** *071

COHEN, Nourollah Norman. ■ 23606 #517-01-1948 L1954 **IM** *020

COLEMAN, Martin Rade. 751 J CLYDE MORRIS BLVD, ORTHOPAEDIC SURGERY & 23601 #035-19-1976 L2002 **ORS OSM** *020 †40

COLLAROS, Victoria Irene. 858 J CLYDE MORRIS BLVD 23601 #038-41-1997 L1997 **FM** *020 †18 ‡

CONNITO, David John. 739 THIMBLE SHOALS BLVD, CENTER FOR RENAL MEDICINE 23606 #010-02-1982 L1987 **NEP IM** *071 †20

COOPER, Flora A Strehlman. ■ 23606 #028-34-1958 L1958 **PD OS** *071

COOPER, Wilson Jonathon. ■ 23606 #020-02-1956 L1957 **IM** *071

CORDES, Laura. 860 OMNI BLVD, STE 101 23606 #051-07-1999 L2003 **OBG** *020 †30

CORNELIUS, Pamela Beltran. 895 MIDDLE GROUND BLVD, DERMATOLOGY 23606 #051-01-1992 L1995 **D IM** *020 †20,15

COURTNEY, Cornelius B, Jr. ■ 23601 #051-04-1961 L1961 **GS VS** *071 †85

COVERDALE, David Bradley. 500 J CLYDE MORRIS BLVD 23601 #038-41-1999 L1999 **DR** *100

COWLING, Lawrence Stanley. 12420 WARWICK BLVD 23606 #051-04-1954 L1954 **GP** *071

COX, Kimberly Ann. 316 MAIN ST, FL 2 23601 #001-02-1999 L2001 **OBG** *020

CRAMER, Mark Steven. 2 BERNARDINE DR 23602 #025-07-1979 L1984 **DR** *075 †80

CROSBY, Scott James. ■ 23602 #051-07-2001 L2001 **FM** *020 †18

CROSS, John Armstrong, Jr. 109 PHILIP ROTH ST 23606 #051-04-1958 L1958 **GS** *020 †85

CROSS, Marshall Albert. 109 PHILIP ROTH ST, STE 200 23606 #051-04-1989 L1994 **GS** *020 †85

CUMMINGS, David Andrew. 2 BERNARDINE DR, DEPT OF PATHOLOGY 23602 #038-43-1998 L2003 **PTH** *020 †50

CURD, Lewis Howard, Jr. 11783 ROCK LANDING DR, STE 202 23606 #051-07-1980 L1983 **PD** *020 †20

CURTIS, Walter Robt S. 500 J CLYDE MORRIS BLVD 23601 #051-01-1972 L1972 **OBG** *020 †30

CYPRESS, Stanley Durant. 727 25TH ST 23607 #051-04-1974 L1977 **FM** *020

DANDEKAR, Meenal G. 500 J CLYDE MORRIS BLVD, RIVERSIDE REGIONAL MEDICAL 23601 #041-13-2003 L2003 **FM** *020 †18

DARBY, Eric Craig. 860 OMNI BLVD, MULTISPECIALTY GROUP 23606 #035-09-1992 L1998 **U** *95

DAS, Shantha. 856 J CLYDE MORRIS BLVD, STE A 23601 #496-34-2002 L2004 **FM** *020 †18

DAVIDSON, John Barry, Jr. 747 J CLYDE MORRIS BLVD 23601 #051-07-1991 L1993 **FM** *020

DAVIS, James Karnes. 500 J CLYDE MORRIS BLVD 23601 #036-07-1960 L1964 **R** *020 †80

DAVIS, Ronda W. 606 DENBIGH BLVD, STE 400 23608 #033-06-1997 L2000 **PD** *020 †55

DAYTON, Barry Dean. 11848 ROCK LANDING DR, JAMES RIVER ANESTHESIA 23606 #055-01-1990 L2003 **AN** *020 †05

DEDMOND, Daynelle Marie. 1051 LOFTIS BLVD, STE 100 23606 #051-07-2000 L2002 **GO** *020

DELAHOUSSAYE, Aladee R. 15425 WARWICK BLVD, STE H 23608 #036-05-1988 L1993 **IM** *020 †20

DE ROSA, Anthony John. 860 OMNI BLVD, MULTISPECIALTY GROUP 23606 #032-01-1992 L1997 **OPH** *020 †35

DEVENDORF, Deborah Jean. 2 BERNARDINE DR 23602 #051-04-1981 L1987 **NPM** *020 †55

DICKSON, Jeffrey Douglas. 856 J CLYDE MORRIS BLVD SU, DEPT OF EMERGENCY MEDICINE 23601 #051-07-1996 L1997 **EM** *020

DIMOFTE, Stefania. 10510 JEFFERSON AVE STE D, RIVERSIDE BRENTWOOD MED CT 23601 #781-02-1977 L2004 **OBG** *020

DINEEN, Mary Kay. 12700 MCMANUS BLVD, STE 102A 23602 #017-20-1976 L1982 **OBG** *020 †20

DUDLEY, Clarissa Marie. ■ 23608 #041-12-1995 L1999 **PD** *020 †55

DUGGAN, Todd Edward. 500 J CLYDE MORRIS BLVD, PENINSULA PULMONARY ASSOCI 23601 #035-06-2000 L2000 **PCC** *020 †20

DUHON, Denise Yvette. 12420 WARWICK BLVD 23606 #021-06-1986 L1989 **IM** *020 †20

DUMAS, Paul Alfred. 611 DENBIGH BLVD, PATIENT FIRST DENBIGH 23608 #067-03-1965 L1994 **GP PDC** *020

DURBHAKULA, Seetha Mahala. ■ 23606 #495-21-2003 L2007 **FP** *012

EDWARDS, James T, Jr. 12 BRUTON AVE 23601 #051-04-1975 L1976 **FM FPG** *020 †18

EDWARDS, Norman Ross. 500 J CLYDE MORRIS BLVD 23601 #030-06-1969 L1973 **GYN OS** *071 †30

EID, Mariam Ali. 500 J CLYDE MORRIS BLVD 23601 #605-01-1999 L2003 **OBG** *020

EL ALWANI, Mazen Ghassan. 500 J CLYDE MORRIS BLVD 23601 #605-01-2002 L2006 **OBG** *012

ELGIN, Robert Gregory. 11800 ROCK LANDING DR 23606 #036-01-1989 L1995 **OPH** *020 †35

ELKHOURY, Nabil Gergi. 500 J CLYDE MORRIS BLVD 23601 #913-96-2000 L2006 **OBG** *012

ELLIS, Charles Meyer, Jr. 416 J CLYDE MORRIS BLVD, STATE HEALTH DEPT PENINSUL 23601 #045-01-1966 L1972 **GS** *071

EVANS, Paul Lawson, Jr. 500 J CLYDE MORRIS BLVD, STE 602 23601 #051-07-1989 L1996 **TS** *020 †85,90

FAN, Dongsheng. 11848 ROCK LANDING DR, JAMES RIVER ANESTHESIA 23606 #243-46-1984 L2000 **AN** *020 †05

FARQUHAR, Charles Francis. ■ 23606 #017-20-1966 L1969 **FM** *020 †18

FARRAR, Howard Ashby. ■ 23602 #051-01-1960 L1961 **R** *071 †80

FATEH, Adnan Ali. 500 J CLYDE MORRIS BLVD, MEDICAL EDUCATION 23601 #051-07-2004 L2004 **DR** *012

FAULK, Charlie Micah. 704 GUM ROCK CT, STE 300 23606 #051-04-1978 L1978 **OBG** *020 †30

FEELY, Robert Everett, Jr. 704 THIMBLE SHOALS BLVD, STE 600A 23606 #011-03-1968 L1971 **FM** *020 †18

FELTHAM, Glen Thomas. 860 OMNI BLVD, STE 203 23606 #035-06-1994 L2001 **ORS** *020 †40

FENNELL, Marcia Lynn. 2 BERNARDINE DR 23602 #033-06-1981 L1990 **FM** *020 †18 ‡

FERNANDEZ, Elisa Victoria. ■ 23602 #308-05-2001 L2005 **OBG** *012

FERNANDEZ, Lin Lucy. 500 J CLYDE MORRIS BLVD 23601 #048-04-2000 L2003 **IM** *020 †20

FIAZ, Muhammad. 11711 JEFFERSON AVE, STE B 23606 #704-16-1987 L2001 **AI** *020 †20,03

FISH, James Alfred, Jr. 500 J CLYDE MORRIS BLVD 23601 #051-07-1977 L1978 **EM FM** *020 †18,16

FISHER, Chester L, Jr. 11747 JEFFERSON AVE, STE 1B 23606 #051-07-1979 L1980 **FM** *020 †70,18 ‡

FITHIAN, Thomas Edward. 730 THIMBLE SHOALS BLVD 23606 #035-01-1978 L1984 **ORS** *020 †40

FLANAGAN, Shawn Alan. 12720 MCMANUS BLVD, STE 304 23602 #023-01-1999 L2005 **FM** *020 †18

FLUHARTY, David Garrison. 610 THIMBL SHLS BLVD #100A 23606 #041-13-1956 L1964 **ADM** *071

FORBES, Sarah Elizabeth. 12420 WARWICK BLVD STE 5 23606 #051-04-1954 L1954 **GYN FPG** *020

FORD, Abby Kay. 714 THIMBLE SHOALS BLVD, STE B 23606 #041-09-1989 L1993 **OBG** *020 †30

FOX, John Alan. 11783 ROCK LANDING DR 23606 #035-01-1989 L1993 **OP OSS** *020 †40

FOXX, Elizabeth Cross. 11848 ROCK LANDING DR, STE 303 23606 #051-04-1991 L1992 **AN** *020 †05

FRANK, Robert J. 11747 JEFFERSON AVE, STE 2F 23606 #051-01-1950 L1950 **GS** *071 †85

FRANTZ, John F, II. 12420 WARWICK BLVD, STE 1D 23606 #041-02-1969 L1971 **OPH** *020 †35

FRAZIER, Charles Owen. 10510 JEFFERSON AVE, STE A 23601 #051-01-1987 L1989 **FM** *040 †18

FREEMAN, George Hartley. 11747 JEFFERSON AVE, STE 1B 23606 #051-04-1985 L1988 **OBG** *020 †30

FREEMAN, Rudolph, Jr. 500 J CLYDE MORRIS BLVD, RIVERSIDE REG MED CTR 23601 #051-04-1977 L1981 **PYG P** *030 †75

FULLER, Bruce Evans. 12695 MCMANUS BLVD, BLDG 3B 23602 #051-07-1985 L1990 **D** *020 †15

FUSTE, Rosa Maria. 1405 KILN CREEK PKWY, SUTIE E 23602 #041-02-1977 L1993 **PD** *020 †55

GABRIEL, Christos Andrew. 11783 ROCK LANDING DR 23606 #051-07-1981 L1984 **PD RHU** *020 †55

GALANTICH, Peter T. 895 MIDDLE GROUND BLVD, EAR NOSE & THROAT 23606 #035-09-1984 L1989 **OTO GS** *020 †45

GALLOWAY, Jacqulyn. 11783 ROCK LANDING DR, STE 202 23606 #001-06-1986 L1995 **PD** *020 †55

GALLUCCI, Charles L. ■ 23602 #041-12-1952 L1980 **OTO** *020

GALVIN, Kevin Patrick. 11848 ROCK LANDING DR, STE 303 23606 #011-04-1991 L2000 **AN PME** *05

GARCIA GONZALEZ, Maria Lo. 500 J CLYDE MORRIS BLVD, RIVERSIDE RED MED CTR 23601 #847-15-1993 L2006 **OPH** *100

GARDNER, Karen Bono. 316 MAIN ST, RIVERSIDE FAMILY PRACTICE 23601 #051-01-1994 L1996 **FM** *020 †20

GARNER, Wallace Kirby. 730 THIMBLE SHOALS BLVD, HAMPTON ROADS NEURO SPINE 23606 #051-01-1962 L1962 **NS** *020 †25

GAUTHIER, Michael Edward. 11848 ROCK LANDING DR, JAMES RIVER ANESTHESIA 23606 #051-04-1990 L2002 **AN PME** *020 †05

GEDDES, Karl Jonathan. 12420 WARWICK BLVD, BLDG 3 23606 #051-07-2000 L2003 **IM** *020 †20

GESSNER, Frederick Martin. 101 PHILIP ROTH ST 23606 #023-01-1985 L1991 **GE IM** *020 †20

GIANTURCO, Daniel Paul. 11848 ROCK LANDING DR, ANTHESIA ASSOCIATE OF HAMP 23606 #036-01-1991 L1995 **AN** *020 †05

GIBNEY, Lucy H Blackford. 11803 JEFFERSON AVE 23606 #051-07-1998 L2002 **EM** *020 †16

GILLESPIE, Lori King. 12100 WARWICK BLVD, STE 102 23601 #051-07-1993 L1993 **RO** *020 †80

GINSBURGH, Charles Lee. 704 THIMBLE SHOALS BLVD, STE 500A 23606 #051-07-1981 L1984 **FM** *020 †18

GISANRIN, Olumuyiwa. 10510 JEFFERSON AVE, STE A 23601 #038-45-2003 L2003 **FM** *100 †18

GIVENS, C Delp. 12420 WARWICK BLVD, STE 7A 23606 #051-01-1980 L1987 **PUD CCM** *020 †20

GIVENS, Paul Brown, Jr. 716 DENBIGH BLVD STE D1 23608 #051-04-1955 L1955 **FM** *071

GLICKMAN, Marc Harris. 1051 LOFTIS BLVD, STE 205 23606 #038-06-1975 L1981 **VS** *020 †85

GLUCKMAN, Jeffrey B. 11803 JEFFERSON AVE, STE 140 23606 #008-01-1966 L1976 **GE IM** *020 †20

GODBOUT, Jennifer Miller. ■ 23602 #051-07-2008 *012

GODFREY, Steven Donald. 11848 ROCK LANDING DR, JAMES RIVER ANESTHESIA 23606 #051-04-1986 L1990 **AN** *020 †05

GOLDSMAN, Helene. 500 J CLYDE MORRIS BLVD, PENINSULA PULMONARY ASSOCI 23601 #050-02-1987 L1988 **IM** *020 †20

GOLDWAG, Stuart Sol. 2 BERNARDINE DR 23602 #051-01-1990 L1995 **DR RNR** *020 †80

GOMUWKA, Patricia K. 12695 MCMANUS BLVD, BLDG 7A 23602 #060-01-1968 L1983 **PS GS** *020 †85,65

GONZALEZ, Rafael Javier. 500 J CLYDE MORRIS BLVD 23601 #308-03-2000 **FM** *100

GONZALO, Toti P. 716 DENBIGH BLVD, BLDG A 23608 #748-01-1965 L1977 **FM GS** *020 †18

GOODOFF, Kristina Marie. ■ 23606 #048-13-2008 *012

GOODWIN, Lori Marie. 11783 ROCK LANDING DR, STE 202 23606 #041-14-2003 L2003 **PD** *020 †55

GORE, David Leon, Jr. 109 PHILIP ROTH ST, STE 200 23606 #036-01-1978 L1984 **GS VS** *020 †85

GOWEN, Clarence Wm, Jr. 2 BERNARDINE DR 23602 #051-04-1979 L1990 **PD NPM** *020 †55

GRAFF, Michael Edward. 611 DENBIGH BLVD, PATIENT FIRST DENBIGH 23608 #041-12-1990 L1993 **FM** *020 †18 ‡

GRAHAM, Leroy. 15408 WARWICK BLVD, STONEYBROOK FAMILY PRACTIC 23608 #051-07-1997 L1998 **FM** *020 †20

GRANTHAM, Don Earl. J CLYDE MORRIS BLVD, RIVERSIDE HOSP/DEPT RAD 23601 #011-03-1970 L1970 **DR** *020 †80

GRASS, Gerald Wm. 11848 ROCK LANDING DR, STE 303 23606 #035-06-1983 L2006 **APM** *020 †05

GREEN, Kevin Bradley. 2 BERNARDINE DR, DEPT OF PATHOLOGY 23602 #048-13-2000 L2005 **PTH** *100 †50

GREER, Jeffrey Neal. 2 BERNARDINE DR 23602 #051-04-2000 L2003 **FM** *020 †18 ‡

GREGG, Karl Vardell. 500 J CLYDE MORRIS BLVD 23601 #045-01-1955 L1963 **OBG** *040 †30

GREMER, John Saml. 858 J CLYDE MORRIS BLVD 23601 #038-40-1965 L1969 **FM** *020 †18

GRETES, John Constantine. 739 THIMBLE SHOALS BLVD, CENTER FOR RENAL MEDICINE 23606 #036-07-1972 L1974 **NEP IM** *020 †20

GRIFFENHAGEN, Edna A. 2 BERNARDINE DR 23602 #051-07-1979 L2000 **DR** *020 †80

GROSS, Barry Lee. 401 OYSTER POINT RD, STE A 23602 #001-02-1975 L1978 **OBG** *020 †30

GUARDIA, Ricardo. 7320 WARWICK BLVD 23603 #649-01-1950 L1960 **FM GS** *071 †18

GUZMAN, Hector Romulo. ■ 23608 #176-02-1966 L1977 **PD EM** *071

HAGER, Harry Griffin, Jr. 813 DILIGENCE DR, STE 108 23606 #051-04-1960 L1960 **R** *020 †80

HAGGERTY, Patrick Geo. 500 J CLYDE MORRIS BLVD 23601 #051-07-1980 L1981 **ID IM** *020 †20

HALISTA, Kevin Danl. 2 BERNARDINE DR 23602 #041-02-1986 L1993 **DR** *020 †80

HALL, Debra Lynn. 11745 JEFFERSON AVE, STE 10A 23606 #051-01-1977 L1981 **GYN** *020 †30

HAMILL, James Foxgrover. 11848 ROCK LANDING DR, JAMES RIVER ANESTHESIA 23606 #025-07-1978 L1986 **AN** *020 †05

HANNA, Thomas Llewellyn. 401 OYSTER POINT RD, STE A 23602 #051-04-1979 L1987 **GYN** *071 †30

HARDEN, Elizabeth Ann. 1051 LOFTIS BLVD, # 100 23606 #036-07-1977 L1991 **HO ON** *020 †20

HARDING, Robert Ralph. 500 J CLYDE MORRIS BLVD 23601 #050-02-1986 L1989 **IM** *020 †20

HARMON, James Alexander. ■ 23606 #012-01-1961 L1968 **OM GP** *071

HARRIS, Jeffrey Emmett. 11747 JEFFERSON AVE, STE 4C 23606 #012-01-1981 L1993 **ID IM** *020 †20

HARRIS, William Overton. 500 J CLYDE MORRIS BLVD 23601 #051-04-1959 L1959 **N IM** *020 †20,75

HARRIS, William Overton. 11803 JEFFERSON AVE, STE 110 23606 #051-04-1988 L1995 **CD** *020 †20

HARRISON, Randolph Bryhn. ■ 23607 #051-04-1975 L1986 **PTH** *020 †50

HASAN, Seema Parveen. 500 J CLYDE MORRIS BLVD, MEDICAL EDUCATION 23601 #051-07-2004 L2004 **DR** *012

HATTEN, John Quackenbush. ■ 23606 #051-01-1948 L1948 **GYN OBG** *071 †30

HAYES, Gary Logan. ■ 23602 #010-02-1983 L1989 **ORS** *020

HAYNES, Boyd W, III. 751 J CLYDE MORRIS BLVD, ORTHOPAEDIC SURGERY & 23601 #051-04-1985 L1988 **ORS OSM** *020 †40

HEATWOLE, Eugene W. 25 HILTON TER 23601 #051-01-1952 L1953 **OPH** *071 †35

HELLMAN, Barry Harvey, Jr. 2 BERNARDINE DR, DEPT OF PATHOLOGY 23602 #010-01-1990 L1994 **ATP HMP** *020 †50

HELWIG, Warren Bowman. 500 J CLYDE MORRIS BLVD 23601 #051-04-1964 L1964 **PTH DMP** *020 †50

HENKE, Jeffrey Layne. 401 OYSTER POINT RD 23602 #019-02-1986 L1989 **OBG** *020 †30

HENLEY, Mark A. 2 BERNARDINE DR, MARY IMMACULATE HOSP 23602 #010-02-1987 L1990 **PD LM** *020 †55

HERRING, Angela. 710 DENBIGH BLVD 23608 #020-12-1978 L1979 **FM** *075 †18

HILL, Eurica Semon. 4714 MARSHALL AVE, P I C H 23607 #047-07-1986 L1988 **PD** *020

HJELKREM, Michael Carl. ■ 23606 #023-12-2002 L2007 **IM** *020 †20

HOFFMIER, Thomas Jos. 12720 MCMANUS BLVD, SUIRE 201 23602 #051-01-1975 L1979 **CD IM** *020 †20

HOGG, Carol Ann Campbell. ■ 23601 #048-04-1962 L1966 **PHP** *030

HOLZSAGER, David Jonas. 500 J CLYDE MORRIS BLVD 23601 #041-02-1971 L1992 **PD** *020 †55

HOPE, Phyllis Rhian. 2 BERNARDINE DR 23602 #011-03-1987 L1989 **PD** *020 †55

HOPSON, Steven Boyd. 860 OMNI BLVD, MULTISPECIALTY GROUP 23606 #041-07-1989 L1995 **GS VS** *020 †85

HORGAN, John Archibald. 500 J CLYDE MORRIS BLVD 23601 #051-01-1964 L1964 **CD IM** *020 †20

HOWELL, Matthew Douglas. 500 J CLYDE MORRIS BLVD, DEPT OF EMERGENCY MEDICINE 23601 #011-04-2001 L2007 **EM** *020 †16

HOWERTON, James Robt. ■ 23606 #047-06-1955 L1966 **P** *071 †75

HOYT, Philip Arthur, Jr. 2 BERNARDINE DR 23602 #010-02-1988 L1989 **FM FPG** *020 †18

HUFFMAN, Frank Harrison. 12715 WARWICK BLVD 23606 #051-04-1984 L1985 **FM** *020 †18

HUGHES, Gregory B. 11844 ROCK LANDING DR, STE B 23606 #023-12-1986 L1988 **END** *020 †20

HURT, Leslie Carone. 716 DENBIGH BLVD, COLONIAL OBGYN ASSOCIATES 23608 #011-03-2002 L2006 **OBG** *020 †30

HUYNH, Adric H. ■ 23602 #422-01-2006 L2007 **FP** *012

HYDE, Johnny, Jr. 1051 LOFTIS BLVD, STE 100 23606 #020-02-1999 L2006 **OBG** *020

IOBST, Joseph Saml. 10510 JEFFERSON AVE, STE D 23601 #041-13-1989 L2002 **OBG** *020 †30

IONESCU, Bogdan. 11825 ROCK LANDING DR, THE JAMES BUILDING 23606 #781-01-1973 L1997 **P** *020 †75

IRVIN, William Paul, Jr. 12100 WARWICK BLVD, STE 202 23601 #051-01-1989 L1992 **OBG** *020 †30

JAFRI, Naved Akhtar. 714 THIMBLE SHOALS BLVD, STE B 23606 #051-07-1996 L2000 **OBG** *020 †30

JAFRI, Obaid Hasan. 714 THIMBLE SHOALS BLVD, STE B 23606 #051-07-2001 L2001 **OBG** *020

JAMES, Kathleen Peyton. 11848 ROCK LANDING DR, JAMES RIVER ANESTHESIA 23606 #048-12-1986 L1988 **AN** *020 †05

JAMES, Ray Lester, Jr. 11747 JEFFERSON AVE, STE 5A 23606 #023-07-1980 L1986 **GE IM** *020 †20

JANOUSEK, John Thomas. 2 BERNARDINE DR 23602 #051-07-1994 L1995 **EM** *020 †16

JENKINS, Lisa. ■ 23606 #051-04-2006 L2006 **FP** *012

JOHNSON, Wm Randolph, III. 500 J CLYDE MORRIS BLVD 23601 #051-04-1991 L1993 **IM** *020 †20

JOLISSAINT, James Gregory. ■ 23602 #021-05-1986 L1986 **FM** *020 †20

JONES, Jacob Edward. 10510 JEFFERSON AVE, STE A 23601 #023-01-1983 L1988 **FM PHP** *040 †18

JONES, Kendall C, Jr. 109 PHILIP ROTH ST 23606 #051-01-1992 L1997 **GS** *020 †85

JONES, Rachel Mehall. 11848 ROCK LANDING DR, VIRGINA ANESTHESIA AND PER 23606 #048-13-2003 L2003 **AN** *100

JORDAN, Cassell Amanda. 10510 JEFFERSON AVE, STE E 23601 #047-07-1979 L1996 **PD ADL** *020 †55

JUSTIS, Gina B. 11848 ROCK LANDING DR, JAMES RIVER ANESTHESIA 23606 #035-06-1989 L1990 **AN** *020 †05

KALANTAR, Seyed Mohsen. 2 BERNARDINE DR 23602 #517-05-1970 L1989 **DR** *020 †80

KAMINER, Jon Jacob, Jr. 10510 JEFFERSON AVE, STE A 23601 #051-01-1996 L1996 **FM** *020 †18

KARIMOVA, Natavan Fakhrad. ■ 23606 #305-01-2005 L2007 **FP** *012

KARLOWICZ, Mitchell Gary. 2 BERNARDINE DR 23602 #023-07-1978 L1989 **NPM PD** *020 †55

KAROTKIN, Edward Harvey. 2 BERNARDINE DR 23602 #036-05-1971 L1979 **NPM PD** *020 †55

KASHTAN, Hillel Isaac. 11848 ROCK LANDING DR, JAMES RIVER ANESTHESIA 23606 #065-09-1982 L1993 **AN** *020 †05

KAUDER, Bruce Mitchell. 321 MAIN ST, CHILDREN'S CLINIC, LTD 23601 #051-01-1979 L1983 **PD** *071 †55

KAUDER, Donald Richard. 500 J CLYDE MORRIS BLVD 23601 #051-07-1980 L2006 **TRS** *020 †85

KAVIT, Gary Stuart. 500 J CLYDE MORRIS BLVD, DEPT EMERG MED/RIVERSIDE 23601 #051-07-1983 L1988 **EM PD** *020 †16

KAZ, Kian Monica. 12690 MCMANUS BLVD 23602 #016-43-1993 L1998 **OPH** *020 †35

KEILMAN, Clinton Gabriel. ■ 23602 #041-02-2003 L2006 **EM** *020

KESSLER, John Franklin. 1051 LOFTIS BLVD 23606 #055-01-1977 L1990 **ON HEM** *020

KHAN, Jawwad Jahangir. ■ 23606 #051-04-2005 L2005 **OBG** *012

KHAN, Shahbaz. 316 MAIN ST 23601 #704-04-1995 L2004 **FM** *020 †18

KHORSANDIAN, Rostam S. ■ 23606 #407-10-1956 L1961 **IM** *071

KIM, Michael Kihyun. 500 J CLYDE MORRIS BLVD 23601 #051-04-1998 L2001 **FP** *012

KING, Joseph Keithon. 606 DENBIGH BLVD, STE 701 23608 #036-08-2002 L2006 **OBG** *020

KING, Kenneth Raymond. 12695 MCMANUS BLVD 23602 #051-04-1969 L1969 **A PD** *020 †55,03

KINNISON, Elizabeth L. ■ 23608 #048-02-1988 L1989 **FOP** *020 †50

KINTIGH, James Wm. 13347 WARWICK BLVD 23602 #017-20-1967 L1970 **FM OS** *020 †18

KITAY, Steven Elliot. 11800 ROCK LANDING DR 23606 #041-12-1992 L2001 **OPH** *020 †35

KLEIN, Jeffrey Allen. 2 BERNARDINE DR 23602 #035-15-1971 L1988 **DR VIR** *020 †80

KNIGHT, Frank Sutton. 416 J CLYDE MORRIS BLVD, NEWPORT NEW HEALTH DEPT 23601 #047-06-1958 L1965 **OBG** *071 †30

KNOWLES, Yasmeen Kutty. 2 BERNARDINE DR 23602 #041-07-1998 L1998 **DR** *020 †80

KOPP, James Emidio. 500 J CLYDE MORRIS BLVD, C/O RIVERSIDE HOSP 23601 #055-01-1963 L1965 **N** *071 †75

KORNI, Roopa M. 500 J CLYDE MORRIS BLVD 23601 #495-09-1988 L2006 **FP** *012

KOSTINER, Geoffrey Brahm. 860 OMNI BLVD, MULTISPECIALTY GROUP #007-02-1996 L1996 **U** *020 *95

KRAMER, Benjamin Charles. ■ 23606 #028-02-2007 L2007 **TY** *012

LACEY, John Robt. 716 DENBIGH BLVD, STE C3 23608 #051-01-1965 L1965 **IM FM** *020

LAMBERSON, Robt Laurence. 11848 ROCK LANDING DR, JAMES RIVER ANESTHESIA 23606 #051-04-1980 L1983 **AN PD** *020 †05,55

LAMPEJO, Olubunmi T. 2 BERNARDINE DR, DEPT OF PATHOLOGY 23602 #473-01-1980 L2002 **PTH PCP** *020 †50

LAPETINA, Joanne E. 2 BERNARDINE DR 23602 #051-07-1989 L1991 **IM PD** *020 †20,55

LATIF, Zubair. 606 DENBIGH BLVD, STE 102C 23608 #704-02-1987 L1996 **IM** *020

LAUGHLIN, Carl Patrick. 11803 JEFFERSON AVE # 238 23606 #023-01-1956 L1964 **IM END** *020

LA VALLE, Gregory Jos. 11803 JEFFERSON AVE, STE 235 23606 #023-01-1981 L2005 **ON GS** *020 †85

LAWSON, Cheryl. ■ 23602 #005-11-1991 L1992 **EM** *020 †16

LAWSON, Richard Bland. 500 J CLYDE MORRIS BLVD 23601 #051-07-1980 L1983 **GS** *020 †85

LAYSER, Joseph Danl. 12100 WARWICK BLVD, STE 102 23601 #041-01-1977 L1983 **RO** *020 †80

LEBLANG, Steven Seth. 10510 JEFFERSON AVE, STE A 23601 #036-05-1981 L1982 **FM** *020 †18

LEDDY, Anne Lucia. 704 THIMBLE SHOALS BLVD, STE 300A 23606 #023-07-1969 L1987 **END IM** *020 †20

LEE, Daniel W. 716 DENBIGH BLVD STE C3 23608 #051-05-1981 L2006 **FM** *020 †18

LEE, Ralph Navero. 2010 27TH ST 23607 #010-03-1960 L1965 **GS** *020 †85

LEE, St George Tucker. 500 J CLYDE MORRIS BLVD 23601 #051-01-1972 L1972 **CD IM** *020 †20

LEEDIE, Linda Catherine. 2501 MARSHALL AVE, STE A 23607 #035-09-1982 L1992 **PD IM** *020 †55

LEE-JOHNSON, Maria C. 245 CHESAPEAKE AVE 23607 #010-03-1987 L1991 **PM** *020 †60

LEGIER, Jacques Frederick. 500 J CLYDE MORRIS BLVD, RIVERSIDE REG MED 23601 #165-02-1955 L1962 **PTH** *020 †50

LEIBOWITZ, Keith Alan. 860 OMNI BLVD, STE # 301 A 23606 #035-09-1985 L2005 **GE IM** *020 †20

LEICHTMAN, Lawrence Gene. 1405 KILN CREEK PKWY 23602 #048-15-1976 L1988 **PD MG** *020 †55,19

LEI-LIM, Beckilyn Lee. 298 NAT TURNER BLVD S 23606 #748-01-1981 L1992 **PD PEM** *020 †55

LENTHALL, Ronald Chas. 611 DENBIGH BLVD, PATIENT FIRST DENBIGH 23608 #041-12-1966 L1984 **FM EM** *020

LEWIS, Andrew Wm. 11800 ROCK LANDING DR, HAMPTON ROADS EYE ASSOC 23606 #023-12-1989 L2005 **OPH** *020 †35

LEWIS, Richard Gordon, Jr. 895 MIDDLE GROUND BLVD, STE 300 23606 #051-04-1998 **HS** *020

LEWIS, Wallace Emory, Jr. 610 THIMBLE SHOALS BLVD, STE 520 23606 #051-04-1976 L1977 **GP** *020

LIM, H Christopher N. 298 NAT TURNER BLVD S 23606 #748-01-1981 L1992 **PD N** *020 †55

LINK, Eugene Monroe. 12655 WARWICK BLVD, MULTISPECIALTY GROUP 23606 #051-04-1997 L1999 **FM** *020 †18 ‡

LLEWELLYN, Christine H. 11835 FISHING POINT DR, STE 203 23606 #033-06-1980 L1982 **DR** *020 †80

LOCKHART, John Lee. 827 DILIGENCE DR, STE 210 23606 #055-01-1970 L1976 **OBG** *020 †30

LOIACONO, Andrew Patrick. 2 BERNARDINE DR 23602 #422-01-2000 L2000 **DR** *100 †80

LOMBARDO, Anthony Paul. 11803 JEFFERSON AVE, STE 110 23606 #035-08-2000 L2007 **IC** *020 †20

LORENZO, David L. 4714 MARSHALL AVE 23607 #748-07-1980 L1993 **IM** *020 †20

LOVELUCK, Richard J B. 11848 ROCK LANDING DR, JAMES RIVER ANESTHESIA 23606 #011-02-1986 L1987 **AN** *020 †05

LOWE, Robert N. 2501 MARSHALL AVE, STE A 23607 #035-09-1982 L1992 **IM PD** *020 †55

LOWERY, Walter P. 747 J CLYDE MORRIS BLVD 23601 #051-04-1977 L1977 **FM** *020 †18

LUSTIG, Michael Robt. 10510 JEFFERSON AVE, RIVERSIDE BRENTWOOD FAMILY 23601 #051-04-1987 L1991 **FM** *020 †18

MAAROUF, Hoda Hussein. 500 J CLYDE MORRIS BLVD, RIVERSIDE HOSP 23601 #605-01-2000 L2004 **OBG** *012

MABALOT, Joel Verano. 11844 ROCK LANDING DR, STE B 23606 #748-08-1993 L2007 **END** *020 †20

MAC DONALD, Mark Edward. 10510 JEFFERSON AVE STE B 23601 #036-08-1989 L1990 **FM** *040 †18

MACKEL, Susan Elizabeth. 895 MIDDLE GROUND BLVD, DERMATOLOGY 23606 #017-20-1975 L1980 **D** *020 †15

MACKENZIE, Thomas A. 739 THIMBLE SHOALS BLVD, CENTER FOR RENAL MEDICINE 23606 #024-05-1978 L1979 **NEP IM** *020 †20

MACLAREN, George A. 500 J CLYDE MORRIS BLVD, RIVERSIDE INPATIENT INTERN 23601 #041-09-1986 L1992 **IM HOS** *020 †20

MAC PHERSON, Kerri Rae. 2 BERNARDINE DR 23602 #045-01-1988 L1991 **PD** *020 †55

MADDOX, John Coulter. 500 J CLYDE MORRIS BLVD 23601 #051-01-1976 L1980 **PTH HMP** *020 †50

MAIA, Diane Marie. 2 BERNARDINE DR, DEPT OF PATHOLOGY 23602 #048-04-1991 L2000 **PTH HMP** *020 †50

MAJUMDAR, Sohini. ■ 23602 #051-01-2006 L2006 **FP** *012

MALIN, David Russell. 2 BERNARDINE DR 23602 #047-06-1999 L1999 **RNR** *020 †80

MANES, Peter Rolf. 17579 WARWICK BLVD 23603 #050-02-1957 L1994 **P** *020

MARCUSON, Zantha Christin. 895 MIDDLE GROUND BLVD, DERMATOLOGY 23606 #051-04-1993 L1993 **DS** *020 †15

MARIANO, Robert Thomas. 2 BERNARDINE DR 23602 #041-09-1995 L2001 **DR** *020 †80

MARKOWITZ, Michael Paul. 11848 ROCK LANDING DR, JAMES RIVER ANESTHESIA 23606 #051-04-1975 L1976 **AN** *020 †05

MARSHALL, John Lyons. 12715 WARWICK BLVD, STE H 23606 #036-05-1971 L1973 **FM** *020 †18

MARTEL, Jeffrey Peter. ■ 23606 #036-01-2007 L2007 **TY** *012

MARTIN, Pierre Thos. 895 MIDDLE GROUND BLVD, STE 152 23606 #035-06-1988 L2006 **OTO HNS** *020 †45

MARTINEZ, Deborah Ann. 11803 JEFFERSON AVE STE 23, SURGICAL ONCOLOGY ASSOCIAT 23606 #007-02-1981 L2005 **GS** *020 †85

MATTERN, John Q A. 1051 LOFTIS BLVD, # 100 23606 #018-75-1968, ▲ L1973 **ON** *020

MATTHIAS, Dwight F. 11803 JEFFERSON AVE 23606 #422-01-1993 L2000 **END** *020 †20

MAUF, Patricia Rose. 2 BERNARDINE DR 23602 #046-01-1996 L1996 **PD** *020 †55

MAXWELL, David Baldwin. 11747 JEFFERSON AVE STE 4E 23606 #051-07-1980 L1981 **RHU IM** *020 †20

MBANU, Ibeawuchi Onu. 14703 WARWICK BLVD STE A 23608 #025-07-2001 L2005 **GPM** *020 †20,70

MC ALEER-LEAVEY, Laura E. 858 J CLYDE MORRIS BLVD, SUBURBAN FAMILY PRACTICE 23601 #030-06-1994 L2004 **FM** *020 †18

MC ARTHUR, Alexander, III. 895 MIDDLE GROUND BLVD, STE 300 23606 #041-02-1978 L1985 **PS** *020 †65,85

MCCALLA, Carlo Clarence. ■ 23602 #010-03-2002 L2007 **ID** *100 †20

MC CANN, Lalani Dainette. 500 J CLYDE MORRIS BLVD 23601 #051-07-1986 L1989 **FM** *020 †18

MC CANTS, Odell. 4714 MARSHALL AVE 23607 #010-03-1970 L1972 **OBG OM** *020 †30

MC CARTHY, Harry Smith. 309 MAIN ST 23601 #051-04-1973 L1978 **ORS** *020 †40

MC CHESNEY, Margaret B G. ■ 23606 #028-02-1949 L1970 **PD PHP** *071 †70

MC COIG, Forrest Danl. ■ 23602 #051-04-1963 L1963 **EM** *071

MC CRACKEN, Sharon Booker. 704 THIMBLE SHOALS BLVD, STE 600A 23606 #051-07-1995 L1995 **FM** *020 †18

MCFARLANE, Jacqualynne Ky. 500 J CLYDE MORRIS BLVD, OB/GYN 23601 #051-07-2007 L2007 **OBG** *012

MC GRATH, Janette Renee. 11848 ROCK LANDING DR, JAMES RIVER ANESTHESIA 23606 #010-02-1992 L1999 **AN** *020 †05

MC GRORY, Bruce Edward. 298 NAT TURNER BLVD S 23606 #045-01-1974 L1996 **PD** *020 †55

MC KEE, Brian Johnson. 704 THIMBLE SHOALS BLVD, STE 1 23606 #035-03-1983 L1987 **OPH** *020 †35

MCLEAN, Erika Lynn. 500 J CLYDE MORRIS BLVD 23601 #035-06-2002 L2005 **PD** *020 †55

MCLEAN, Robert James. 732 THIMBLE SHOALS BLVD, STE 602 23606 #010-03-1989 L1995 **FM** *020 †18

MCTAVISH, Jeffrey Donald. 2 BERNARDINE DR 23602 #065-01-1993 L2001 **DR** *020 †80

MEDFORD, Frank Eldridge. 11030 WARWICK BLVD 23601 #036-05-1961 L1967 **IM** *020 †20

MERCADO, Maria Luz C. 416 J CLYDE MORRIS BLVD, PENINSULA CHILD DEVT CLINI 23601 #748-01-1972 L1983 **PD** *020

MEYERS, Paul J. 4714 MARSHALL AVE 23607 #035-48-1986 L1991 **OBG OS** *030 †30

MICALE, Paul Joseph. 11803 JEFFERSON AVE, STE 110 23606 #012-05-1980 L1986 **CD** *020 †20

MICHAELIS, Nancy Gadams. 500 J CLYDE MORRIS BLVD 23601 #021-05-1990 L1991 **IM** *020 †20

MILES-RICHARDSON, Gurnel. ■ 23612 #033-06-1978 L1984 **HEM EM** *071

MILLER, Charles Anthony. 10510 JEFFERSON AVE, STE D 23601 #051-04-1990 L1991 **OBG GP** *020 †30

MILNE, Julia Hopper. 316 MAIN ST 23601 #045-01-2002 L2002 **FM** *100 †18

MINCKS, John Chas. 500 J CLYDE MORRIS BLVD 23601 #025-07-1982 L1986 **IM** *020 †20

MIRMELSTEIN, Alvin B H. 2 BERNARDINE DR 23602 #051-04-1946 L1952 **OTO** *071 †45

MISQUITTA, Andrea C. 2 BERNARDINE DR 23602 #067-01-1989 L2001 *020 †80

MITCHELL, George Stanley. 500 J CLYDE MORRIS BLVD 23601 #051-04-1954 L1954 **FM OS** *071 †18

MOHAMED KHALIL, Emad Said. 500 J CLYDE MORRIS BLVD 23601 #915-03-1989 **IM** *020 †20

MOORE, Jeffrey Dean. 860 OMNI BLVD, STE 203 23606 #051-04-1985 L1986 **ORS OSS** *020 †40

MOORE, Laurie Walker, Jr. 500 J CLYDE MORRIS BLVD 23601 #036-05-1963 L1970 **PUD IM** *020 †20

MOORE, Patrick David. 11800 ROCK LANDING DR 23606 #041-13-1966 L1968 **OPH** *071 †35

MORALES, Joselito B. 11825 ROCK LANDING DR, JAMES BLDG 23606 #748-02-1981 L1998 **P** *020 †75

MORGAN-MARSHALL, Anne E. 11842 ROCK LANDING DR, STE 105 23606 #048-13-2002 L2005 **OMF** *020

MORRIS, Thomas Ellsworth. 11835 FISHING POINT DR, STE 207 23606 #036-05-1959 L1965 **PD** *071 †55

MORRISON, J Donald. 716 DENBIGH BLVD STE B2 23608 #055-01-1967 L1971 **OBS** *071 †30

MORTENSEN, Wayne Marcus. ■ 23602 #010-02-2007 L2007 **TY** *012

MOSELEY, Heather Williams. 10510 JEFFERSON AVE 23601 #036-08-2005 L2005 **FP** *012

MRAVA, Diane Marie. 714 THIMBLE SHOALS BLVD, STE B 23606 #051-01-1993 L1997 **OBG** *020 †18

MUELLER, Lucas Andrew. ■ 23608 #028-34-2006 L2007 **OBG** *012

MULLINS, James M, III. 606 DENBIGH BLVD, STE 701 23608 #028-03-1983 L1991 **OBG** *020 †20

MULLINS, William James. 704 THIMBLE SHOALS BLVD 23606 #056-06-1958 L1969 **ORS** *071 †40

MULSON, Kimberly Dianne. ■ 23602 #422-01-2004 L2006 **PD** *020 †55

MURPHY, Allan Leslie. 11803 JEFFERSON AVE, STE 110 23606 #143-05-1973 L1989 **CD ICE** *020

MURPHY, Michael Anthony. ■ 23602 #011-03-2001 L2001 **CHP** *020 †75

MURRAY, Philip F. ■ 23602 #051-01-1946 L1954 **D** *071 †15

NACHBAR, James W. ■ 23606 #422-01-1997 L2000 **CHP** *020

NAGRAJ, Hoskote Subbaraya. 12695 MCMANUS BLVD, STE 1A 23602 #495-23-1971 L1976 **IM** *020 †20

NAHORMEK, Patricia Alice. 2 BERNARDINE DR 23602 #041-09-1973 L1981 **CD** *020 †20

NAPIER, Dennis Lee. 860 OMNI BLVD, STE 101 23606 #051-07-1976 L1978 **GYN** *020 †30

NARAYAN, Das Bangalore. 307 SAINT THOMAS ST 23601 #496-34-1996 L2006 **FP** *012

NAURATH, Rudolph Jos. ■ 23606 #407-20-1953 L1957 **FM IM** *071 †18

NELSON, Douglas Lloyd. 895 MIDDLE GROUND BLVD, STE 302 23606 #026-04-1977 L1980 **D** *020 †15

NICHOLS, Allen Bryant. 12720 MCMANUS BLVD, STE 201 23602 #051-01-1971 L1984 **CD IC** *020 †20

NORD, Peter William. 11803 JEFFERSON AVE, STE 140 23606 #065-10-1987 L1994 **FM FSM** *030

NORFLEET, Benj Elliott. 13347 WARWICK BLVD 23602 #051-04-1957 L1957 **FM** *071 †18

NORFLEET, Stephen Mangum. 13347 WARWICK BLVD 23602 #051-04-1973 L1974 **FM** *020 †18

NORMAN, Alan Patrick. ■ 23606 #051-07-1997 L2001 **MPD** *020 †20,55

NORMAN, Judith Ann. 12700 MCMANUS BLVD, STE 102A 23602 #051-07-1997 L2006 **OBG** *020 †30

NORTHAM, Drina Anne. ■ 23608 #759-06-2006 L2007 **OBG** *012

NUNEZ, Santiago. 708 MOBJACK PL 23606 #275-01-1957 L1963 **CHP P** *075

O'CONNELL, Kathy K. 11842 ROCK LANDING DR, STE 115 23606 #051-07-1988 L1992 **OBG** *020 †30 ‡

O'CONNELL, Leo Patrick. 11835 FISHING POINT DR 23606 #005-11-1969 L1973 **DR** *020 †80

O'CONNOR, Carolyn Fawn. 500 J CLYDE MORRIS BLVD 23601 #051-04-1991 L1997 **PTH** *020 †50

ODABASI, Lisa. 11803 JEFFERSON AVE, STE 230 23606 #035-48-1984 L1990 **GE IM** *020 †20

OELBERG, David Geo. 2 BERNARDINE DR 23602 #023-01-1978 L1993 **NPM PD** *020 †55

OLD, William Levi, III. 500 J CLYDE MORRIS BLVD, STE 602 23601 #051-01-1976 L1983 **TS** *020 †85,90

O'NEAL, Jerald Drew. 704 THIMBLE SHOALS BLVD, STE 700 23606 #020-12-1981 L1982 **EM FM** *020 †16,18

O'NEIL, Elizabeth Ann. 860 OMNI BLVD, MULTISPECIALTY GROUP 23606 #051-04-1987 L1993 **GS** *020 †85

O'NEIL, John Donald. 2 BERNARDINE DR 23602 #051-01-1985 L1991 **DR** *020 †80

O'NEILL, Dennis M. 1000 OLD DENBIGH BLVD 23602 #041-09-1977 L1978 **IM IMG** *020 †20

OPEITUM, Abiola Abiodun. 615 BLAND BLVD, SIEMENS 23602 #690-05-1981 L2004 *020

ORLINO, Robert Joseph. 500 J CLYDE MORRIS BLVD, INPATIENT INTERNAL MEDICIN 23601 #748-09-1981 L1984 **PUD IM** *020 †20

ORTIZ, Edward A. 500 J CLYDE MORRIS BLVD 23601 #051-04-1977 L1980 **EM** *020 †16

OZURUMBA, Onyeije Wil. ■ 23606 #010-03-2006 L2006 **FP** *012

PABBY, Ajay. ■ 23606 #024-05-1999 L2006 **GE** *020 †20

PAL, Joshua Sameer. 500 J CLYDE MORRIS BLVD, MEDICAL EDUCATION 23601 #051-07-2004 L2004 **AN** *012

PALANI, Amudha. 500 J CLYDE MORRIS BLVD, RIVERSIDE HOSP 23601 #496-32-1997 L2004 **FM** *020 †18

PANETTIERE, Anthony S. 12420 WARWICK BLVD, STE 7A 23606 #023-12-1986 L1999 **CN** *100 †75

PARKER, Dean Clifford. 858 J CLYDE MORRIS BLVD 23601 #010-03-1983 L1984 **PD IM** *075

PARSON, Michael Irvin. 4714 MARSHALL AVE, PENINSULA INST FOR COMM HE 23607 #010-03-1978 L1979 **FM** *020 †18

PASCHOLD, John C. 1051 LOFTIS BLVD, STE 100 23606 #036-05-1997 L1997 **HO** *020 †20 ‡

PAULSON, John Douglas. 606 DENBIGH BLVD, STE 701 23608 #051-01-1971 L1972 **GYN END** *020 †30

PAYNE, Thomas Wm. 500 J CLYDE MORRIS BLVD 23601 #036-01-1956 L1963 **PD** *020 †55

PEAK, Mimi I Noemi. 11000 JEFFERSON AVE 23601 #024-05-1982 L1997 **AM GP** *020

PELTZ, Edgar E. ■ 23602 #051-01-1952 L1952 **IM** *071

PERRY, Elaine. 416 J CLYDE MORRIS BLVD, PENISULA HEALTH DEPT 23601 #043-01-1995 L1996 **GPM** *020 †70

PERRY, Roger Hobart. ■ 23606 #051-01-1955 L1955 **PD** *071 †55

PETITJEAN, Sharon Linda. 10510 JEFFERSON AVE, STE A 23601 #038-45-1988 L1989 **FM FPG** *020 †18

PEYSER, Michael Bardo. 109 PHILIP ROTH ST 23606 #051-07-1994 L1994 **GS** *020 †85

PHILLIPS, Charles Kevin. 12 BRUTON AVE 23601 #051-04-1995 L1995 **FM** *020 †18

PHILLIPS, James W. 23607 #051-04-1933 L1933 **OPH** *071 †35

PHILLIPS, Paul Frederick. 708 MOBJACK PL 23606 #041-14-1976 L1978 **P** *075 †75

PHILLIPS, Roger Morgan. 755 THIMBLE SHOALS BLVD 23606 #008-01-1984 L1995 **FM** *020 †18

POITRAS, Jean-Maurice, Jr. 500 J CLYDE MORRIS BLVD, RIVERSIDE INPATIENT INTERN 23601 #023-01-1993 L2003 **IM** *020 †20

POLK, William H, Jr. 860 OMNI BLVD, STE 101 23606 #024-07-1975 L1980 **IM** *020

POMERANZ, Mark. 11848 ROCK LANDING DR, STE 303 23606 #035-75-1986, ▲ L1990 **AN** *020 †05

PORTER, Victoria Celeste. ■ 23606 #047-05-2007 **P** *012

POST, Ronald Holder. 109 PHILIP ROTH ST, STE 200 23606 #010-02-1996 L2005 **GS** *020 †85

POTTER, Michael B. 860 OMNI BLVD, STE 203 23606 #048-16-1996 L1996 **FM** *020 †18

POULSEN, Wendell T, Jr. 747 J CLYDE MORRIS BLVD 23601 #051-04-1978 L1979 **FM** *020 †18

POWELL, Douglas Oxley. ■ 23606 #051-04-1955 L1955 **ORS** *071 †40

POWELL, Wilson Albert, Jr. ■ 23601 #051-04-1947 L1947 **P** *071 †15

PRICE, Ralph. 500 J CLYDE MORRIS BLVD 23601 #869-04-1949 L1952 **GP** *075

PRICE, Walter S. ■ 23606 #041-01-1946 L1959 **PD** *071 †55

PRILLAMAN, Henry A, Jr. 309 MAIN ST, PENINSULA ORTHO ASSOCS PC 23601 #051-04-1964 L1964 **ORS** *075 †40

PRILLAMAN, Henry Melton. 11848 ROCK LANDING DR, STE 402 23606 #051-01-1992 L1992 **U** *072 †95

PROVENZANO, Jerome A. 7320 WARWICK BLVD 23607 #010-02-1990 L1992 **FM** *020 †18

PUSATERI, Robert Joseph. 739 THIMBLE SHOALS BLVD, CENTER FOR RENAL MEDICINE 23606 #055-01-1979 L1984 **NEP IM** *020 †20

PUTLAND, Kenneth Wm. 10852 WARWICK BLVD 23601 #011-02-1984 L1991 **FM** *020 †18

QUARLES, John Morton. 12 BRUTON AVE 23601 #051-04-1957 L1957 **GP** *071

QUEEN, Timothy Allen. 11842 ROCK LANDING DR, STE 100 23606 #051-01-1990 L1994 **OTO A** *020 †45

RADACK, Daniel Mark. 2 BERNARDINE DR 23602 #041-02-1991 L2000 **VIR** *020 †80

RAMOS, Emelita F. 12725 MCMANUS BLVD STE 2G, THERAPY ASSOC OF DENBIGH 23602 #748-08-1967 L1976 **P PYG** *020 ‡

RANSONE, Karen Ann. 610 THIMBLE SHOALS BLVD, STE 520 23606 #051-04-1992 L1995 **PD** *020 †55

RASHID, Alan Kareem. 10510 JEFFERSON AVE, STE E 23601 #048-15-2003 L2003 **PD** *100 †55

RASTOGI, Shivnandan P. 2 REGENTS COVE 23606 #495-12-1956 L1981 **NEP IM** *020 †20

RATCLIFFE, Kimberly Ann. 12420 WARWICK BLVD STE 4A, BLDG 3 23606 #021-01-1993 L2000 **IM** *020 †20

RATHOD, Rajendrasinh Jahu. 500 J CLYDE MORRIS BLVD 23601 #495-22-2002 L2006 **OBG** *012

RAYL, David Leroy. 10510 JEFFERSON AVE, STE D 23601 #019-02-1969 L1978 **OBG** *020 †30

READ, Bishop Porter. 895 MIDDLE GROUND BLVD, STE 108 23606 #051-01-1969 L1969 **U** *020 †95

REID, James Wm. 11015 WARWICK BLVD, REHABILITATION CENTER 23601 #021-01-1963 L1972 **IM** *020

REJZER, Ronald John. 2 BERNARDINE DR, MARY IMMACULATE HOSPITAL 23602 #041-09-1980 L1981 **EM FM** *030 †18,16

RENFORTH, Michael Edward. 2 BERNARDINE DR, MARY IMMACULATE HOSPITAL 23602 #055-01-1996 L1997 **EM UCM** *020 †12

RESO, Indrit. 11848 ROCK LANDING DR, JAMES RIVER ANESTHESIA 23606 #120-01-1989 L2000 **AN IM** *020 †20,05

RESTAINO, Irene G. 11783 ROCK LANDING DR 23606 #028-34-1984 L1992 **PD** *020 †55

RICHARDSON, Harrison H. 500 J CLYDE MORRIS BLVD, RIVERSIDE REGIONAL MEDICAL 23601 #020-02-1974 L2005 **EM** *020 †16

RIGAU, Felipe Alberto. 500 J CLYDE MORRIS BLVD, EMERGENCY MEDICINE 23601 #051-07-1980 L1981 **EM** *020 †16

RINALDI, Italo Pio. 11 BRUTON AVE 23601 #561-10-1951 L1957 **NS** *071 †25

ROBESON, Thomas N. 704 THIMBLE SHOALS BLVD, STE 700 23606 #051-04-1986 L1987 **FM** *020 †18

ROBINS, Richard Bailey. 895 MIDDLE GROUND BLVD, STE 152 23606 #051-04-1961 L1961 **OTO HNS** *071 †45

ROBINSON, Frederick L, II. 12655 WARWICK BLVD, MULTISPECIALTY GROUP 23606 #051-01-1976 L1977 **FM** *020 †18 ‡

RODGERS, Natalie Nicole. ■ 23608 #036-08-2007 L2008 **MPD** *012

ROGOWSKI, Michael. 2 BERNARDINE DR 23602 #041-09-1991 L1994 **EM** *020 †16

ROSS, Glenn Stuart. 11803 JEFFERSON AVE, STE 140 23606 #035-20-1987 L1991 **IM** *020 †20

ROSS, Mark Andrew. 245 CHESAPEAKE AVE 23607 #008-02-1984 L1987 **PM** *020 †60

RUCKER, Edmund Harrison. ■ 23609 #051-01-1954 L1954 **AN** *071 †05

RUFF, Mary Lee. 2 BERNARDINE DR 23602 #038-43-1979 L1983 **PD** *020 †55

RUSZKOWSKI, Ronald Jos. 1051 LOFTIS BLVD STE 100, VIRGINIA ONCOLOGY ASSOCIAT 23606 #056-06-1968 L2005 **ON HEM** *020 †20

SALLADE, Richard Lawrence. ■ 23606 #038-41-1955 L1964 **U** *071 †95

SAN AGUSTIN, Makaraig T. 416 J CLYDE MORRIS BLVD 23601 #748-02-1939 L1977 **GP AM** *020

SAN JUAN, Rodolfo Leongso. ■ 23606 #748-21-1993 L2005 **FP** *012

SARINO, Nelson Capati. 500 J CLYDE MORRIS BLVD, RIVERSIDE HOSP 23601 #422-01-2003 L2004 **FP** *012

SARKER, Rabeya. 10510 JEFFERSON AVE, RIVERSIDE FAMILY MEDICINE 23601 #160-14-2002 L2007 **FP** *012

SATCHWELL, Susan Hayward. 10510 JEFFERSON AVE, STE B 23601 #051-04-1975 L1976 **FM** *040 †18

SCHUELE, Werner K. 611 DENBIGH BLVD, PATIENT FIRST 23608 #048-04-2000 L2003 **FM** *020 †18

SCHULER, Frank August, III. 500 J CLYDE MORRIS BLVD 23601 #012-05-1968 L1970 **PS GS** *020 †65

SCHULZ, Joseph John. 1051 LOFTIS BLVD, # 100 23606 #051-01-1970 L1970 **ON IM** *020 †20

SCHWARTZ, Michael A. 500 J CLYDE MORRIS BLVD 23601 #051-15-1988 L2005 **PTH** *020 †50

SCORDALAKES, Geo Emmanuel. 15425 WARWICK BLVD, STE H 23608 #038-06-1971 L1990 **PD EM** *020 †55

SCOTT, Steven Sorrells. 109 PHILIP ROTH ST, STE 200 23606 #012-05-1989 L2006 **TS GS** *020 †85,90

SENEY, Franklin D, Jr. 704 THIMBL SHLS BLVD #500B, HAMPTON ROADS NEPHROLOGY 23606 #051-04-1978 L1991 **NEP IM** *020 †20

SETTINERI, Susan Marie. 2 BERNARDINE DR 23602 #041-14-1989 L1998 **PD NPM** *020 †55

SHACOCHIS, Thomas Jos. 858 J CLYDE MORRIS BLVD 23601 #051-04-1971 L1973 **FM** *020

SHAH, Meha Manoj. ■ 23606 #422-01-2005 L2005 **IM** *012

SHAHID, Sufia Begum. 1033 28TH ST, FIRST FLOOR 1 23607 #160-06-1979 L1986 **PD** *020 †55

SHARP-WARTHAN, Jennifer L. 13347 WARWICK BLVD, MULTISPECIALTY GROUP 23602 #051-07-1984 L1985 **FM** *020 †18

SHAW, James O Neil, Jr. 500 J CLYDE MORRIS BLVD 23601 #051-04-1970 L1970 **PUD IM** *071 †20

SHEGOG, James Howard. 12720 MCMANUS BLVD STE 308 23602 #038-40-1975 L1982 **IM IMG** *020

SHEPARD, Glenn Harvey. 895 MIDDLE GROUND BLVD, STE 300 23606 #051-01-1962 L1962 **PS** *020 †85,65

SHEPPARD, Forest Raymond. ■ 23606 #051-01-1998 L2005 **GS** *020 †85

SHIELDS, William Jennings. 2 BERNARDINE DR 23602 #051-04-1972 L1973 **D** *020 †15

SHWAYDER, Robert Craig. 716 DENBIGH BLVD 2 23608 #007-02-1972 L1978 **OBG** *020 †30

SIDDIKY, Muhammad Ali. 2 BERNARDINE DR 23602 #160-02-1972 L1980 **DR** *050 †80

SIDDIQUE, Ahsan. 500 J CLYDE MORRIS BLVD 23601 #305-01-2003 L2005 **FP** *012

SIMKO, Eric Jude. 895 MIDDLE GROUND BLVD, EAR NOSE & THROAT 23606 #023-12-1985 L2000 **OTO** *020 †45

SINGER, Gerard Anthony. 2 BERNARDINE DR, DEPT OF PATHOLOGY 23602 #051-04-1982 L1987 **PTH ATP** *020 †50

SINGH, Rajinder Pal. 802 LOCKWOOD AVE STE A 23602 #496-13-1981 L1987 **N** *020 †75

SMALL, Mary Esther. 416 J CLYDE MORRIS BLVD, PENINSULA HEALTH DISTRICT 23601 #051-04-1995 L1995 **OBG** *020 †30

SMITH, David Michael. 500 J CLYDE MORRIS BLVD 23601 #045-01-1990 L1996 **PTH** *020 †50

SMITH, Gerry Nieman. 245 CHESAPEAKE AVE 23607 #038-41-1988 L1993 **PM** *020 †60

SMITH, Omolara Louise. 2501 WASHINGTON AVE, HAMPTON-NEWPORT NEWS CSB 23607 #044-01-2001 L2005 **P** *020

SMITH, Ray Mc Kean, III. 2 BERNARDINE DR, DEPT OF PATHOLOGY 23602 #045-01-1973 L1982 **PTH** *020 †50

SMITH, Vincent John. 11848 ROCK LANDING DR, JAMES RIVER ANESTHESIA 23606 #016-01-1991 L1998 **AN** *020 †05

SNYDER, Robert James. 751 J CLYDE MORRIS BLVD, ORTHOPAEDIC SURGERY & 23601 #023-12-1981 L1994 **ORS AM** *020 †40

SOBHAN, Ajmal. 500 J CLYDE MORRIS BLVD 23601 #160-02-1971 L1976 **GS CD** *020 †85

SOLES, Donald Elwood, Jr. 10510 JEFFERSON AVE, STE A 23601 #051-04-1989 L1990 **FM** *020 †18

SOUTHER, Mark Edward. 12420 WARWICK BLVD STE 4A 23606 #028-03-1990 L1993 **IM** *020 †20

SPELLMAN, Steven Glenn. 12420 WARWICK BLVD 23606 #035-08-1982 L1986 **OPH** *020 †35

SPLAN, Thomas Paul. 11747 JEFFERSON AVE STE 3H 23606 #025-07-1970 L1979 **PUD CCM** *020 †20

STALLARD, Clinton W, Jr. ■ 23601 #023-01-1946 L1964 **OM PUD** *071 †70

ST CLAIR, Harvey Sheldon. 11783 ROCK LANDING DR 23606 #051-04-1978 L1984 **ORS** *020 †40

STEFFEY, William Rue. 12420 WARWICK BLVD, STE 4A 23606 #047-05-1966 L1971 **OTO** *075 †45

STEPHENS, Bertram E S. 4714 MARSHALL AVE 23607 #010-03-1970 L1975 **OBG EM** *020 †30

STEPHENS, John Robt. 101 PHILIP ROTH ST 23606 #023-01-1967 L1975 **GE** *020 †20

STIFF, Leroy Emmanuel. 4714 MARSHALL AVE, PICH 23607 #010-03-1971 L1975 **OBG** *020 †30

STILES, Thomas Marvin. 12720 MCMANUS BLVD, STE 311 23602 #004-01-1955 L1963 **ORS** *020 †40

STOLLE, Christopher P. 500 J CLYDE MORRIS BLVD, ADMINISTRATION 23601 #023-12-1992 L1994 **OBG** *020 †30

ST REMY, Carl Raphael. 11783 ROCK LANDING DR 23606 #035-01-1996 **OP** *020 †40

SUTTON, Thaddeus Geron. 2 BERNARDINE DR 23602 #036-08-1987 L1990 **IM** *020

SWENSON, Jon Hallie. 730 THIMBLE SHOALS BLVD 23606 #048-02-1985 L1990 **ORS GS** *020 †40

TAN, Teresa Xiaoping. ■ 23606 #051-04-2004 L2005 **OBG** *012

TANNER, Gary Alfred. 11800 ROCK LANDING DR 23606 #004-01-1986 L2006 **OPH** *020 †35

TAYLOR, Keith Erwin. 13347 WARWICK BLVD, MULTISPECIALTY GROUP 23602 #033-06-2000 L2000 **FM** *020 †18

TEMPLE, Thamer Eugene, Jr. 500 J CLYDE MORRIS BLVD, MEDICAL EDUCATION DEPT 23601 #012-01-1961 L1970 **END IM** *071 †20

TERRACINA, Anthony D. 645 J CLYDE MORRIS BLVD 23601 #027-01-1989 L2004 **GS** *020 †85

TEULE-HEKIMA, Nzinga Znia. 416 J CLYDE MORRIS BLVD, PENINSULA HEALTH DISTRICT 23601 #051-07-2001 L2001 **FM** *100

THORPE-BROOKS, Cherril An. 755 THIMBLE SHOALS BLVD 23606 #035-06-1977 L1984 **PTH EM** *020

TIFFANY, Kenneth Francis. 2 BERNARDINE DR 23602 #036-08-1999 L1999 **NPM** *020 †55

TILL, Heather Ashley. 500 J CLYDE MORRIS BLVD, DEPT OF MED EDU 23601 #422-01-2006 L2006 *012

TINSLEY, James Clifton. 13347 WARWICK BLVD, TIDEWATER PHYSICIAN MULTIS 23602 #051-07-2000 L2000 **FM** *020 †18

TITSCH, Marnie. 895 MIDDLE GROUND BLVD, DERMATOLOGY 23606 #011-03-1992 L1996 **D** *020 †15

TITUS, Mark Andrew. 101 PHILIP ROTH ST 23606 #033-05-1998 L2004 **IM** *020 †20

TRANDEL, Barbara Joy. ■ 23606 #051-01-1998 L2001 **FM** *020 †18

TRIESHMANN, Helmuth W, Jr. 751 J CLYDE MORRIS BLVD 23601 #035-45-1976 L1981 **ORS** *071 †40

TRIMBUR, Joanne Piazza. 11803 JEFFERSON AVE, STE 140 23606 #051-07-2002 L2002 **FM** *020 †18

TRIMUEL, Sharita Keiyatta. 500 J CLYDE MORRIS BLVD 23601 #010-02-2005 L2005 **FP** *012

TRUMP, David Haskell. 416 J CLYDE MORRIS BLVD, PENINSULA HEALTH DIST 23601 #041-02-1978 L1999 **PHP FM** *040 †70,18

TWEEDIE, Eric Lamont. ■ 23606 #064-01-1977 L2002 **AN** *020 †05 ‡

U, Tha Tho. 802 LOCKWOOD AVE, STE A 23602 #209-01-1987 L2003 **N** *020 †75

UMSTOTT, Charles Edward. 500 J CLYDE MORRIS BLVD, BLDG 1 23601 #051-04-1963 L1963 **TS CD** *020 †85,90

UNGER, Michael James. ■ 23608 #051-04-1982 **OBG** *074

VACHHANI, Ashish Amritlal. 2 BERNARDINE DR 23602 #051-07-1998 L1998 **DR** *020 †80

VALERIO, Hernani Abergas. 316 MAIN ST 23601 #748-29-1998 L2004 **FM** *020 †18

VAN BAVEL, James Olaf. 515 STERNBERG AVE, VET ADMIN MEDICAL CTR 23604 #041-02-1971 L1984 **P** *020 †75

VANDEN HOEK, Tien L. ■ 23602 #016-02-1987 L1991 **PD** *020 †55

VANDEN HOEK, Todd Lee. 316 MAIN ST, RIVERSIDE PEDIATRIC CENTER 23601 #016-02-1987 L1991 **EM** *020 †16

VAUGHN, Jennifer Ann. ■ 23606 #036-05-2008 **R** *012

VOLJAVEC, Alexander S. 218 MAXWELL LN 23606 #012-05-1985 L1994 **IM** *020 †20

VONU, Peter James. 895 MIDDLE GROUND BLVD, STE 300 23606 #038-43-1981 L1988 **FPS HS** *020 †65

VYAS, Barin Vishnu. ■ 23602 #473-04-2000 L2003 **P** *100

WARE, Henry Mc Wane. ■ 23601 #051-01-1955 L1955 **FM** *071 †18

WARREN, Daniel Churchman. 500 J CLYDE MORRIS BLVD 23601 #051-04-1964 L1964 **GPM PHP** *062 †70

WASH, Thomas Atwood. ■ 23601 #051-01-1955 L1955 **GYN** *071 †30

WASSUM, James Allen. 12100 WARWICK BLVD, STE 102 23601 #051-04-1972 L1973 **RO** *020 †80

WEAVER, Laurel G De Padua. 11848 ROCK LANDING DR, JAMES RIVER ANESTHESIA 23606 #748-10-1977 L1985 **AN** *020

WEINER, Eric Adam. 12420 WARWICK BLVD, STE 7A 23606 #007-02-1993 L1993 **PCC SME** *020 †20

WEISENFELD, Shirley. ■ 23601 #035-19-1946 L1979 **NM DIA** *071 †20,28

WEIXLER, Warren Paul. 12652 JEFFERSON AVE, STE A 23602 #422-01-1984 L1987 **FM** *020 †18

WETCHLER, Stewart James. 12700 MCMANUS BLVD # 102A 23602 #048-04-1977 L1977 **GYN** *020 †30

WETZLER, Kurt Henry. 2 BERNARDINE DR 23602 #010-02-1992 L1994 **VIR DR** *020 †80

WHANG, Jai Churl. ■ 23602 #583-02-1965 L2000 **GS** *020 †85

WHEAT, Thomas Adrian. 610 THIMBLE SHOALS BLVD, STE 520 23606 #047-06-1970 L1995 **GP GS** *020 †85

WHITE, Jonathan Curtis. 2 BERNARDINE DR 23602 #005-11-1988 L2006 **R NM** *020 †80

WILD, Charlotte. ■ 23604 #407-21-1953 L1962 **AN** *072

WILLIAMS, Harold L. ■ 23606 #036-07-1951 L1959 **GS** *071 †85

WILLIAMS, Mc Kim. ■ 23606 #036-07-1959 L1962 **AN** *071 †05

WILLIAMS, Verneeta L. 10510 JEFFERSON AVE, MEDICINE RESI 23601 #051-04-1994 L1999 **FM** *020 †18

WILLYARD, Kent Eric. 12695 MCMANUS BLVD, BLDG 6 23602 #051-07-1998 L1998 **FM** *020 †18

WILSON, H Alexander, III. 704 THIMBLE SHOALS BLVD, STE 300A 23606 #023-07-1974 L1987 **RHU** *020 †20

WILSON, Joseph Fredric. 895 MIDDLE GROUND BLVD, EAR NOSE & THROAT 23606 #045-01-1982 L1987 **OTO FPS** *020 †45

WINFIELD, Robert Shelby. 245 CHESAPEAKE AVE 23607 #051-01-1996 L1996 **PM** *020 †60

WINFREY, Raina. 716 DENBIGH BLVD STE C4 23608 #038-40-2000 L2000 **FM** *020 †18

WINGO, James Taylor. 11848 ROCK LANDING DR, JAMES RIVER ANESTHESIA 23606 #051-04-1985 L1986 **AN** *020 †05,18

WIRTH, John Clarence, Jr. 4101 WASHINGTON AVE, MEDICAL DEPT 23607 #041-02-1969 L1976 **OM** *020 †85

WOESSNER, William Harry. 401 OYSTER POINT RD, STE A 23602 #051-07-1988 L1991 **OBG** *020 †30

WOO, Robert. 11848 ROCK LANDING DR, STE 303 23606 #041-01-1980 L1991 **AN OS** *020 †05

WOOD, Bobby Terry. 500 J CLYDE MORRIS BLVD 23601 #051-01-1960 L1960 **D** *071 †15

WOOD, Harriett Evelyn. 12420 WARWICK BLVD 23606 #051-04-1956 L1956 **GYN** *071

WOOD, William Alexander, Jr. 860 OMNI BLVD, MULTISPECIALTY GROUP 23606 #036-05-1981 L1982 **DR** *020 †80 ‡

WOOLFOLK, Donald Irwin. 416 J CLYDE MORRIS BLVD 23601 #035-15-1961 L1987 **IM CD** *020

YAHYA, Fadi Bassam. 500 J CLYDE MORRIS BLVD 23601 #605-01-2003 L2007 **OBG** *012

YEATTS, Stanley Dail, II. 827 DILIGENCE DR, STE 210 23606 #051-07-1985 L1986 **OBG** *020 †30

YONKER, Kristin Faith. 11842 ROCK LANDING DR, STE 115 23606 #051-07-2001 L2004 **OBG** *020 †30

YOUNGER, Ross Martin. 895 MIDDLE GROUND BLVD, EAR NOSE & THROAT 23606 #051-01-1994 L1994 **OTO** *020 †45

YUENGERT, Mary A. 11835 FISHING POINT DR, STE 104 23606 #051-01-1981 L1987 **FM** *020 †18

ZAITOUN, Rafic H. 11803 JEFFERSON AVE, STE 110 23606 #051-04-1984 L1985 **CD IM** *020 †20

ZILLIOX, Ann Philomena. 11835 FISHING POINT DR, STE 107 23606 #028-34-1983 L1988 **AI PD** *020 †55,03

ZWICKLBAUER, Michael F. 895 MIDDLE GROUND BLVD, STE 300 23606 #035-03-1989 L1995 **PS** *020 †85,65

NICKELSVILLE – SCOTT

DE MOTTS, Gregory Lynn. 142 MEADE AVE 24271 #011-03-1978 L1979 **FM** *020 †18 ‡

NOKESVILLE – PRINCE WILLIAM

HEISLER, James Gerard. ■ 20182 #025-01-1967 L1968 **PTH** *020 †50

RALSTON, Sarah Anne. PO BOX 157 20182 #036-01-2006 **P** *012

RHODES, Deanne Nicole. ■ 20181 #010-02-2004 L2007 **PD** *012

NORFOLK – NORFOLK CITY

AARON, Demetria Lynne. ■ 23510 #012-21-2007 *012

ABESS, Alexander Tracy. 1562 MITSCHER AVE STE 250, CINCLANTFLT, NO2MC 23551 #045-01-2001 L2002 **AN** *012

ABOLHASSANI, Mohammad Rez. 23510 #305-01-2000 L2007 **IM** *020 †20

ABOUELHOSN, Loubna Adel. BOISSENVAIN AVE 23507 #605-02-1998 *100

ABU-HAMAD, Alfred Z. 825 FAIRFAX AVE, MATERNAL-FETAL MED-H.H., # 23507 #605-01-1985 L1992 **OBG MFM** *020 †30

ACKERMAN, Steven Bruce. 850 KEMPSVILLE RD, NDC MEDICAL CENTER 23502 #051-07-1990 L1991 **IM** *020 †20

ACOSTA, Anibal Argentino. ■ 23518 #132-02-1954 L1977 **REN GYN** *071 †30

ACRA, Wadi De Jesus. 150 KINGSLEY LN 23505 #308-01-1955 L1967 **GS OS** *020 ‡

ADAMS, Eric Arthur. 880 KEMPSVILLE RD STE 1300 23502 #001-02-1991 L1995 **OPH** *020 †35

ADAMS, Erin G. 1562 MITSCHER AVE STE 250, ATTN: CREDENTIAL OFFICE 23551 #051-04-2002 L2003 *020

ADAMS, Nehkonti. ■ 23503 #051-07-2008 *012

AFIFY, Mohamad Ahmad. 880 KEMPSVILLE RD, STE 2800 23502 #330-02-1964 L1974 **OTO** *020 †45

AGARWAL, Ashima. ■ 23507 #495-30-1992 L2002 **PTH** *100

AGOLA, John Christopher. 825 FAIRFAX AVE, STE 541 23507 #035-08-1987 L1994 **RNR N** *020 †80

AGRAWAL, Karen Kali. 600 GRESHAM DR RM 609 23507 #038-41-1996 L2003 **IM** *020 †20

AIELLO, Frank, III. 601 CHILDRENS LN 23507 #035-03-1983 L1993 **PD** *020 †55

AJMANI, Sheetal. 601 CHILDRENS LN, THE KING'S 23507 #051-07-2006 L2006 **PD** *100

ALADJ, Lawrence John. 600 GRESHAM DR 23507 #051-07-1981 L1984 **AN** *020 †05

ALBRECHT, Eric Jacob. ■ 23508 #033-06-2002 L2006 **AN** *020 †05

ALEMAYEHU, Dereje Tesfaye. 105 KINGSLEY LN, PRIMEDOC OF NORFOLK, PA 23505 #366-02-1987 L2006 **IM** *100 †20

ALEX, John Emery. 1562 MITSCHER AVE STE 250, US ATLANTIC FLEET 23551 #011-02-2005 L2006 *020

ALEXANDER, Shawn R. 229 W BUTE ST, STE 500 23510 #036-08-1996 L2004 **MPD** *020

ALLEY, William Daniel. 721 FAIRFAX AVE 23507 #051-07-2006 L2006 **EM** *012

ALMIRANTE, Cheryl Dabon. 855 W BRAMBLETON AVE, L STRELITZ DIABETES INST 23510 #748-10-1991 L2005 **IM** *020 †20

ALSPAUGH, John Steven. 844 KEMPSVILLE RD, STE 102 23502 #038-40-1982 L1986 **PS GS** *020 †85,65

ALY, Sarfraz. ■ 23507 #166-01-2003 L2007 **ID** *012 †20

AMAKER, Barbara H. 830 KEMPSVILLE RD 23502 #045-04-1990 L1996 **NP** *020 †50

AMARASINGHE, Disamodha C. 601 CHILDRENS LN 23507 #220-02-1968 L1975 **GS VS** *020 †85

AMIN, Sanjay M. 1529 INTERNATIONAL BLVD, STE 103 23513 #495-22-1971 L1979 **PD** *020 †55

AMIRI, Cyrus Shaghaghi. 901 HAMPTON BLVD, EAR NOSE AND THROAT LTD 23507 #517-03-1957 L1982 **OTO HNS** *071 †45

ANDERSON, Charles Wm. 600 GRESHAM DR 23507 #041-02-1948 L1951 **D PHP** *072 †15

ANDERSON, Freedolph Deryl. 601 COLLEY AVE, EASTERN VA MED SCH 23507 #026-04-1959 L1990 **GYN OS** *071 †30

ANDERSON, Mervan Oswald. 400 GRESHAM DR STE 504 23507 #010-03-1972 L1977 **OBG** *020 †30

ANDERSON, Scott Richards. 825 FAIRFAX AVE STE 510 23507 #051-07-2003 L2003 **OTO** *012

ANDREWS, Mason C. 601 COLLEY AVE, EASTERN V MED SCHOOL 23507 #023-07-1943 L1947 **REN GYN** *071 †30

ANDREWS, William Cooke. 880 KEMPSVILLE RD STE 2200 23502 #023-07-1947 L1951 **GYN OBS** *071 †30

ANGELES, M. Victoria Pela. PO BOX 1980, EASTERN VA MED SCH 23501 #748-20-2002 L2004 **P** *012

ANSARI, Armin. ■ 23510 #051-07-1993 L1993 **P ADM** *020 †75

ARCHER, David Fitzgerald. 601 COLLEY AVE, EASTERM VA MEDICAL SCHOOL 23507 #020-02-1960 L1987 **REN GYN** *030 †30

ARCHER, Lorenzo Pharr. 2539 CORPREW AVE 23504 #047-07-1966 L1973 **ORS OS** *071

ARCHER, Stephen Craig. 1562 MITSCHER AVE STE 250, OFFICE OF FLEET SURGEON NO 23551 #023-12-1983 L1985 **OBG** *020 †30

ARCHIE, Victor Cleavon. 5900 LAKE WRIGHT DR 23502 #036-01-1999 L2007 **RO** *020 †80

ARDELEAN, Monica Grace. 601 CHILDRENS LN 23507 #041-13-2005 L2005 **PD** *012

ARNETT, Stacy Michelle. 850 KEMPSVILLE RD, NDC MEDICAL CENTER 23502 #020-02-1997 L1997 **IM** *020 †20

ARORA, Harkesh. 358 MOWBRAY ARCH, DEPT OF MED EDU 23507 #495-28-2003 L2006 **IM** *012

ARRAGE, Antoine Abou. 1815 E LITTLE CREEK RD 23518 #330-03-1960 L1967 **IM GE** *071

ASLAM, Mahboob Ahmad. 825 FAIRFAX AVE, EVMS OFFICE OF GME 23507 #704-20-1987 L2005 **P** *012

AUSTIN, Warren Edward. 850 KEMPSVILLE RD, NDC MEDICAL CENTER 23502 #051-07-1998 L1998 **IM** *020 †20

AUZINS, Dace. ■ 23508 #025-01-1974 L1980 **IM** *020 †20

AVERY, Edward Stanley, Jr. ■ 23508 #036-01-1961 L1966 **PTH** *062 †50

AXELROD, Randy Craig. 600 GRESHAM DR 23507 #038-41-1982 L1997 **PD** *030 †55

AZAR, Hormoz. 600 GRESHAM DR, STE 8600 23507 #038-06-1964 L1979 **TS** *020 †85,90

■ = Address Information Privacy Protected

AZOURY, Ramez Said. 150 KINGSLEY LN, FL 3 23505 #605-01-1958 L1979 **OBG** *020 †30
AZOURY, Sharon Mary. ■ 23509 #051-07-2001 L2001 **IM** *100
BACANI, Geraldine R. 3755 E VIRGINIA BEACH BLVD, NORFOLK COMMUNITY SERVICES 23502 #748-09-1968 L1995 **P** *020
BACCUS, Frances R. ■ 23508 #048-12-1995 L2003 **AN** *020 †05
BADEMIAN, Robert Leo. 850 KEMPSVILLE RD, NDC MEDICAL CENTER 23502 #051-07-1983 L1984 **IM** *020 †20
BAHRANI, Otarod. 825 FAIRFAX AVE 23507 #036-05-1993 L1993 **IM** *020
BAJIT, Marieta Agawin. 150 KINGSLEY LN 23505 #748-01-1963 L1973 **AN** *020
BAKER, Frances Watt. ■ 23505 #023-07-1966 L1979 **PD** *075 †55
BAKER, Latricia A. 601 CHILDRENS LN 23507 #051-07-2003 L2003 **PD** *020 †20
BAKER, Lenox Dial, Jr. 600 GRESHAM DR, STE 8600 23507 #023-07-1966 L1979 **TS** *020 †85,90
BAKER, Sarah Flowers. ■ 23505 #051-07-2003 L2003 **FM** *100
BALAKRISHNAN, Mangales. 4301 E LITTLE CREEK RD 23518 #495-33-1976 L1984 **FM** *020 †18 ‡
BALAKRISHNAN, Sivara M. 850 KEMPSVILLE RD 23502 #220-02-1967 L1977 **IM IMG** *020 †20
BALINGIT, Joselito Sandov. 358 MOWBRAY ARCH, RM 203 23507 #748-02-1990 *100
BALMADRID, Christian Layn. ■ 23510 #056-06-2006 L2006 **EM** *012
BALSAMO, Luke H. ■ 23508 #035-45-1998 L1998 **OMO** *020
BALTUCH, Leigh. 100 KINGSLEY LN 23505 #041-02-1977 L1982 **P PYG** *071 †75 ‡
BANDFIELD, Andrea Janel. 700 W OLNEY RD, EASTERN VIRGINIA MEDICAL S 23507 #045-01-2004 L2004 **P** *012
BANKS, Alan Kirk. 844 KEMPSVILLE RD, CARDIOLOGY CONSULTANTS 23502 #035-09-1983 L1985 **CD** *020 †20
BAROCO, Allison Law. 825 FAIRFAX AVE, STE 410 23507 #001-06-2003 L2003 **ID** *012 †20
BAROCO, Patrick Edwin, Jr. ■ 23509 #001-06-2003 L2003 **OM** *020
BARR, Arnold Benj. ■ 23508 #010-01-1959 L1980 **PHP IM** *071 †20
BASTA, Baher Anwar. 825 FAIRFAX AVE 4TH FL, EVMS, DEPT. OF MEDICINE 23507 #915-03-1994 L2002 **IM** *020 †20
BASTA, Sameh A. 825 FAIRFAX AVE #915-03-1988 L1993 **IM** *020 †20
BAUMGARTNER, Timothy Scot. ■ 23510 #016-43-2006 L2006 **GS** *020
BAZIL, Megan Kyne. 601 CHILDRENS LN 23507 #023-01-2003 L2003 **PD** *020 †55
BECHER, John David. 850 KEMPSVILLE RD, NDC MED CTR 23502 #051-07-1976 L1978 **IM** *020 †20
BECK, Carty Elizabeth. ■ 23510 #051-07-2006 **EM** *012
BEER, Robert Markey. 1562 MITSCHER AVE STE 250, CINCLANTFLT/N02MC 23551 #023-12-2000 L2001 **ORS** *012
BEITINJANEH, Firas. 6161 KEMPSVILLE CIR, STE 315 23502 #875-01-1995 L2002 **CN** *020 †75
BELL, Joseph Sumner, III. 885 KEMPSVILLE RD STE 114, DIG & LIVER DIS SPECLTS 23502 #051-04-1976 L1982 **GE IM** *020 †20
BELLOVIN, Sabra Marie. ■ 23507 #051-07-1994 L1994 **FM** *071 †18
BELLUM, Venugopal. 358 MOWBRAY ARCH RM 2, EVMS - OFFICE OF GME 23507 #495-57-1999 L2003 **IM** *020 †18
BELTRAN, Natalie Carmen. 885 KEMPSVILLE RD, ROAD STE#200 23502 #051-01-1993 L1999 **PD** *020 †55
BEN YEHUDA, Yoram. 601 CHILDRENS LN, CHILDRENS HOSPITAL 23507 #550-03-1989 **PD** *100
BEPPLE, Jennifer Dawn. ■ 23507 #051-07-2004 L2004 **U** *012
BERGEN, Wayne Young. 600 GRESHAM DR 23507 #051-01-1985 L1986 **AN** *020 †05
BERGEVIN, Michael Allen. 800 W OLNEY RD 23507 #045-01-1982 L1989 **PTH** *020 †50
BERNABE, Maria Joyce. 721 FAIRFAX AVE, GHENT FAMILY PRACTICE CTR 23507 #748-17-1981 L2006 **FP** *012
BERNARD, Jacqueline Maher. 1562 MITSCHER AVE STE 250, NO2MC 23551 #023-12-1999 L2005 **R** *062
BERNARDO, Myrna. 207 E LITTLE CREEK RD, NORFOLK HEALTH DEPARTMENT 23505 #748-01-1973 L1980 **OBG PHP** *020
BERNERT, Lawrence A, Jr. ■ 23507 #051-01-1961 L1961 **P** *071 †75
BERNSTEIN, Robert Charles. 844 KEMPSVILLE RD, CARDIOLOGY CONSULTANTS 23502 #035-46-1983 L1990 **CD** *020 †20
BERRY, Tristan Teilhard. 400 W BRAMBLETON AVE, STE 100 23510 #051-04-2002 L2002 **U** *020
BEST, Heidi Amber. ■ 23507 #045-04-2006 L2006 **EM** *012
BETHEA, William Mc Laurin, Jr. 229 W BUTE ST, STE 700 23510 #012-01-1971 L1974 **IM** *020 †20
BETTS, Lawrence Stilwell. 600 GRESHAM DR 23507 #051-07-1986 L1996 **OM PTX** *030 †70
BEVAN, Herbert E, III. 601 CHILDRENS LN 23507 #028-02-1980 L1987 **PHO PD** *020 †55
BEWLEY, Mark Andrew. 160 KINGSLEY LN, STE 405 23505 #038-44-1997 L2002 **ORS** *020 †40
BIEDENBENDER, Rex David. 825 FAIRFAX AVE, STE 201 23507 #051-07-1997 L1997 **IM** *020 †20
BIEN, Richard Craig. ■ 23508 #012-01-2005 L2005 **PD** *012
BILDZUKEWICZ, Nikolai A. 1562 MITSCHER AVE STE 250, CINCLANTFLT, NO2MC 23551 #041-02-2001 L2003 **GS** *012
BILISOLY, Frank N, III. 850 KEMPSVILLE RD 23502 #051-01-1951 L1951 **IM N** *020 †20
BIRKENBACH, Mark Philip. 700 W OLNEY RD 23507 #035-01-1982 L2000 **ID PTH** *020 †50
BIUCKIANS, Andre. 600 GRESHAM DR, EASTERN VIRGINIA MED SCH 23507 #024-16-2001 L2006 **VS** *012
BJORNSSON, Hjalti Mar. ■ 23507 #484-01-1998 L2007 **EM** *012
BLAIS, David Paul. 600 GRESHAM DR 23507 #041-12-1985 L1986 **IM** *020 †20
BLAKE, David Paul. 825 FAIRFAX AVE 23507 #023-12-1990 L1999 **CCS** *012 †85
BLAKEY, David Neil. 601 CHILDRENS LN, DEPT OF ANESTHESIOLOGY 23507 #036-07-1981 L1989 **AN** *020 †05
BLANCO, Omar Anorico. 5040 E PRINCESS ANNE RD, STE A 23502 #051-07-1996 L1999 **PD** *020 †55
BLANKS, Allison Morgan. 208 E PLUME ST, STE 213 23510 #051-04-2004 L2004 **IM** *020 †20
BLAYLOCK, William Kenneth. 400 GRESHAM DR, STE 702 23507 #051-04-1985 L1990 **OPH FPS** *020 †35
BLUEMINK, Gary Groot. 600 GRESHAM DR 23507 #016-43-1964 L1975 **PTH** *040 †50
BLUESTEIN, Daniel Allen. 721 FAIRFAX AVE, ACADEMIC PHYS & SURGEONS 23507 #024-16-1975 L1981 **FM** *050 †18
BLYTHE, Diana Kate. ■ 23518 #051-07-2006 L2006 **PD** *012
BODNER, Kelly Marie. ■ 23508 #041-13-2001 L2001 **AI** *100
BOGARD, Shyrlena Laquonda. 601 COLLEY AVE STE 243, EVMS 23507 #016-42-2006 L2006 **OBG** *012
BOGGS, Sarah Rebecca. 601 CHILDRENS LN, DEPARTMENT OF PEDIATRICS 23507 #051-04-2003 L2003 **PD** *100 †55
BONAWITZ, Cara Ann. 825 FAIRFAX AVE, STE 541 23507 #041-14-1995 L2000 **DR** *020 †80

BORING, Wayne Douglas. 6160 KEMPSVILLE CIR, STE 203B 23502 #051-01-1958 L1958 **OBG** *071 †30
BORODKINA, Marina. PO BOX 1980, EASTERN VA MED SCH 23501 #422-01-2006 L2007 **PM** *012
BORYSEK, Dana. 150 KINGSLEY LN 23505 #286-09-1963 **PTH** *075
BOWERS, Daniel Leonard. ■ 23508 #023-07-2008 *012
BOWERS, John Thos. 850 KEMPSVILLE RD 23502 #050-02-1976 L1982 **PUD CCM** *020 †20
BOWLES, Mary Allison. 6161 KEMPSVILLE CIR # 315 23502 #030-05-1995 L2001 **N** *020 †75
BOYCE, Alison Marie. ■ 23507 #051-07-2006 L2006 **PD** *012
BRADLEY, Michael Joseph. ■ 23507 #051-07-2005 L2005 **IM** *012
BRAGG, Todd Michael. 1562 MITSCHER AVE STE 250, U.S. FLEET FORCES COMMAND 23551 #023-12-2005 L2006 *020
BRAGG, Winifred Diane. 6160 KEMPSVILLE CIR, SUITE 303-A 23502 #047-07-1991 L1995 **PM PMM** *020 †60
BRENNER, Michelle Game. 601 CHILDRENS LN, CHILDRENS HOSP 23507 #035-06-1995 L1995 **PD** *020 †55
BREWER, Herbert Martin. 600 GRESHAM DR 23507 #051-04-1960 L1960 **CD IM** *020
BREWER, Robert Francis. 150 KINGSLEY LN, WOUND CARE AND HYPERBARIC 23505 #020-12-1968 L1986 **PS GS** *020 †65
BRIDDELL, Kate Noel. ■ 23507 #051-01-2006 L2006 **PD** *012
BRIDGES, David Marvin. 6330 N CENTER DR, STE 220 23502 #012-01-1974 L1974 **DR** *071 †80
BRIDGES, Edward Ted. ■ 23507 #045-01-2005 L2007 **GS** *020
BRIGGS, Charles Samuel. ■ 23517 #051-07-2008 *012
BRINKLEY, Trimaine Monee. ■ 23507 #051-07-2008 *012
BRITT, L D. 825 FAIRFAX AVE, STE 610 23507 #024-01-1977 L1984 **GS** *030 †85
BRITT, Rebecca Caperton. 825 FAIRFAX AVE 23507 #051-07-1998 L2003 **GS** *020 †85
BROCK, William Allen. 600 GRESHAM DR, SENTARA NORFOLK GEN HOSP 23507 #041-12-1980 L2001 **IM CCM** *020 †20
BRODSKY, Ronald Clarke. 601 CHILDRENS LN 23507 #035-15-1981 L1985 **PAN** *020 †05 ‡
BROOKS, Chantal Neliya. 255 W BUTE ST 23510 #869-04-1980 L1982 **IM** *020
BROOKS, John, Jr. 255 W BUTE ST 23510 #045-01-1976 L1977 **IM** *020
BROOKS, Marechal-Neil. 930 MAJESTIC AVE 23504 #051-04-1985 L1989 **IM** *020 †20
BROOKS, Rebecca Anna. ■ 23507 #051-01-2007 L2007 **PD** *012
BROOKS, Whitney L. 885 KEMPSVILLE RD 23502 #010-01-1996 L2002 **GE IM** *020 †20
BROSCH, Gad Eliezer. 239 DUKE ST, UNIT 208 23510 #550-01-1964 L1971 **OBG GP** *020 †30
BROTHERTON, Jessica Anne. ■ 23507 #051-07-2008 *012
BROUGH, James Wm. SEWELLS PT BRAN CLINIC 23511 #025-07-1959 **AM** *100 †70
BROWDER, William Douglas. 358 MOWBRAY ARCH # 203, EVMS - OFFICE OF GME 23507 #051-07-2000 L2001 **EM** *020 †16
BROWER, Anne Clayton. 825 FAIRFAX AVE STE 541, EVMS HOFHEIMER HALL DPT RA 23507 #035-01-1964 L1970 **DR** *020 †80
BROWN, Anjeanette Tina. 1562 MITSCHER AVE STE 250, CINCLANTFLT 23551 #023-01-1998 L2001 **GS** *100
BROWN, Richard Coleman. 431 NEW HAMPSHIRE AVE 23508 #051-01-1963 L1963 **GPM NTR** *062 †70
BRUNER, David Ingram. ■ 23517 #051-01-2003 L2003 **EM** *012
BRUNER, Heather Crooks. ■ 23517 #051-01-2005 L2005 **EM** *012
BRUSH, John Elliott, Jr. 160 KINGSLEY LN, STE 200 23505 #051-01-1980 L1992 **CD** *020 †20
BRUSH, John Jos. 844 KEMPSVILLE RD, CARDIOLOGY CONSULTANTS 23502 #056-06-1970 L1972 **NEP** *020 †75
BUDORICK, Timothy E. 160 KINGSLEY LN, STE 405 23505 #016-43-1984 L1994 **ORS** *020 †40
BUESCHER, Edward Stephen. 855 W BRAMBLETON AVE, CENTER PEDS RESEARCH 23510 #023-07-1975 L1992 **PD** *020 †55
BUNDSCHUH, William Paul. 600 GRESHAM DR 23507 #035-15-1984 L1988 **AN** *020 †05
BURKE, Gene Hobbs. 850 KEMPSVILLE RD 23502 #051-01-1975 L1980 **CCM** *020 †20
BURWELL, Carolyn Smith. 830 SOUTHAMPTON AVE, STE 200 23510 #051-04-1976 L1979 **PD** *020
BUSH, Leah Linda. 830 SOUTHAMPTON AVE, STE 100 23510 #051-04-1984 L1985 **FOP PTH** *062 †50
BUTCHER, Joseph Mark. ■ 23503 #055-02-2007 **EM** *012
BUTLER, Thomas Edward, III. ■ 23507 #016-45-2006 L2006 **GS** *012
BYRD, J Abbott, III. 160 KINGSLEY LN, STE 405 23505 #051-04-1978 L1987 **ORS** *020 †40
BYRD, Rebecca Lee. 601 CHILDRENS LN 23507 #051-01-1975 L1981 **PHO** *020 †55
BYUN, Kathy. 6330 N CENTER DR, BLDG 13 23502 #035-15-2000 L2006 **NM** *020 †80
CALLENDER, Charles Wynter. 825 FAIRFAX AVE 23507 #051-04-1995 L2001 **PCC** *012
CALLENDER, David Michael. ■ 23507 #051-07-2008 *012
CAMP, Robert Michael. 902 GRAYDON AVE 23507 #012-01-1974 L1975 **IM** *020
CAMPBELL, Gloria Castillo. 420 N CENTER DR, STE 119 23502 #032-01-1980 L1991 **OBG** *071 †30
CAMPBELL, John Neil. 825 FAIRFAX AVE, STE 541 23507 #036-05-1998 L2005 **RNR** *020 †80
CAMPOS, Francisco E. 855 W BRAMBLETON AVE, CTR FOR PED RESEARCH 23510 #737-06-1990 L1997 **PD** *020 †55
CANTIN, Ira M. 160 KINGSLEY LN, STE 405 23505 #051-01-1951 L1951 **ORS** *071 †40
CAPLAN, Stephen Robert. 205 MEDICAL TOWER 23507 #051-01-1966 L1966 **GE IM** *020 †20
CARMAN, Claire Mager. 229 W BUTE ST STE 845 23510 #048-16-1985 L1992 **SO GS** *020 †85
CARMODY, James Bryan. ■ 23507 #051-01-2007 L2007 **PD** *012
CAROFF-KELL, Jessica Joy. 601 CHILDRENS LN, DPT ANESTHESIOLOGY 23507 #010-01-1999 L2003 **PAN** *020 †05
CARR, Gregory Charles. C/O HILDA HOBBS, EVMS - OFFICE OF GME 23507 #820-02-2006 L2007 **P** *012
CARSON, John F, II. 1562 MITSCHER AVE STE 250, OFFICE OF FLEET SURGEON/NO 23551 #026-04-1972 L1973 **FM UM** *020 †18
CARSON-JENKINS, Janice D. ■ 23509 #051-07-1994 L1994 **FM** *100
CARTER, Henry G. 825 FAIRFAX AVE, PSYCHIARTY 23507 #012-01-1950 L1971 **AN** *071 †05
CARTER, Russell Herman. 825 FAIRFAX AVE #010-03-1960 L1967 **GS ORS** *075
CARTY, James Walker, Jr. 850 KEMPSVILLE RD 23502 #023-01-1966 L1972 **IM** *020
CASELLA, Daniel Paul. ■ 23507 #051-07-2008 *012
CASTALDO, David James. 825 FAIRFAX AVE, STE 445 23507 #016-43-1993 L1993 **IM** *040 †20
CATALAN-AQUINO, Maria Ele. 358 MOWBRAY ARCH, EVMS-OFFICE OF GME 23507 #748-16-1989 L2006 **FP** *012
CAULEY, Dean Christopher. 1909 GRANBY ST STE A 23517 #016-11-1999 L1999 **PD** *020 †55
CAUTHEN, Cheryl G. 1005 MAY AVE, NORFOLK EYE PHYS & SURG 23504 #010-03-1981 L1982 **OPH** *020 †35
CECCHINI, John Matthew. 601 CHILDRENS LN 23507 #041-09-1998 L2000 *020 †05
CEJAS-ROSAS, Rodolfo. 1401 TIDEWATER DR STE I 23504 #275-01-1954 L1957 **IM** *020.

CELESTE, Francis Anthony. 601 CHILDRENS LN, THE KIN 23507 #023-01-2006 L2006 **PD** *012

CHACKO, Siju Thomas. 825 FAIRFAX AVE, HOFHEIMER HALL 23507 #495-63-1992 L2006 **ID** *012 †20

CHAI, Shirley Soonglen. 600 GRESHAM DR 23507 #051-04-2001 L2001 **FM** *020 †18

CHAKO, Alexander C. 110 KINGSLEY LN STE 310 23505 #035-48-1985 L1991 **DR** *020 †80

CHAMBERS, Donald Edwin. 600 GRESHAM DR 23507 #038-41-1954 L1959 **R** *020 †80

CHANDLER, H Lee, Jr. 600 GRESHAM DR 23507 #051-01-1955 L1955 **D** *020 †15

CHANIN, Edith Anne. ■ 23508 #035-48-1979 L1992 **IM OS** *040 †20

CHANTLER, Marcia Lynne. 600 GRESHAM DR 23507 #018-03-1996 L2002 **HO** *020 †20

CHAP, Alan David. ■ 23507 #038-41-2007 L2007 **GS** *012

CHAPMAN, Rees Cecil. 850 KEMPSVILLE RD 23502 #051-04-1954 L1954 **ON HEM** *020 †20

CHARETTE, Laura Alois. 6345 CENTER DR, BLDG 14 23502 #033-06-1989 L1991 **PD** *020 †55

CHAUDHRY, Abdul Wajid. 420 N CENTER DR, BLDG 11 23502 #704-21-1983 L1995 **NEP IM** *020 †20

CHAUDHURI, Krishna G. ■ 23517 #051-07-2007 L2007 **IM** *012

CHAUDHURI, Lakshmi Rani. 110 KINGSLEY LN, DEPAUL MEDICAL BUILDING, 2 23505 #051-07-1998 L2001 **FM** *071 †18

CHEN, Catherine. ■ 23517 #005-06-2001 L2004 **D** *012

CHEN, Ian Alps. 825 FAIRFAX AVE STE 410, EASTERN VIRGINIA MED SCHOO 23507 #027-01-1996 L1996 **IM** *020 †20

CHIAVARINI, Robert Louis. 6161 KEMPSVILLE CIR, MEDICAL CENTER RADS INC 23502 #025-07-1970 L1976 **DR** *071 †80 ‡

CHIDESTER, Paul Donald. 600 GRESHAM DR 23507 #041-12-1984 L1992 **NEP IM** *030 †20

CHILDERS, Adam Paul. ■ 23517 #051-07-2008 *012

CHIRICO, Christina Maria. ■ 23507 #038-44-2006 L2007 *012

CHO, Michael Sangjoon. ■ 23507 #055-01-2001 L2007 **IM** *100

CHOCANO, Jose F. 601 CHILDRENS LN 23507 #737-06-1983 L2005 **PDP** *020 †55

CHOI, Hin Sing. 850 KEMPSVILLE RD 23502 #041-02-1983 L1986 **IM** *020 †20

CHOLIS, Thomas Joseph, III. 601 CHILDRENS LN 23507 #010-02-1999 L2005 **CCP** *100 †55

CHOPRA, Kapil. PO BOX 1980 23501 #496-75-2003 **P** *012

CHOPRA, Kokil. 358 MOWBRAY ARCH STE 203 23507 #496-75-2003 L2007 **P** *012

CHRISTIAN, George Henry. 6330 N CENTER DR, BLDG 13 23502 #021-01-1966 L1974 **DR** *071 †80

CHU, Michael W. 825 FAIRFAX AVE STE 510, EASTERN VIRGINIA MED SCH 23507 #051-04-2006 L2006 **OTO** *012

CHUNG, Paul S. 1562 MITSCHER AVE STE 250, ATTN CREDENTIAL OFFICE 23551 #023-12-2004 L2005 *020

CICCONE, Alvin Jacob. 229 W BUTE ST, STE 500 23510 #051-04-1964 L1964 **FM** *071 †18

CICERO, Mark Xavier. 601 CHILDRENS LN, DEPARTMENT OF PEDIATRICS 23507 #035-06-2001 L2001 **PEM** *012 †55

CILENTO, Benjamin West. ■ 23508 #035-46-1998 L2008 **OTO** *020 †45

CIUFFO, Allen Anthony. 844 KEMPSVILLE RD, CARDIOLOGY CONSULTANTS 23502 #023-07-1978 L1985 **CD** *020 †20

CLARK, Damon Howard. ■ 23510 #024-01-2004 L2004 **GS** *012

CLARK, Scott Kevin. 600 GRESHAM DR 23507 #041-09-1984 L1990 **AN** *020 †05 ‡

CLARK, Victor Pierre. ■ 23505 #051-07-2007 L2007 **IM** *012

CLAYTON, Michelle. 935 REDGATE AVE 23507 #041-12-2000 L2000 **PD** *020 †55

CLEARY, Jeffrey Charles. ■ 23507 #023-12-1998 L1998 **PD** *020 †55

CLIFFORD, David Michael. 160 KINGSLEY LN, STE 405 23505 #010-01-1999 L2005 **ORS** *100 †40

CLIFFORD, Gregg Richard. 229 W BUTE ST, STE 700 23510 #051-01-1982 L1985 **IM** *020 †20

CLINGENPEEL, Joel Martin. 601 CHILDRENS LN, EMERGENCY MEDICINE 23507 #051-07-1998 L1998 **PE** *020 †55

COAKLEY, Timothy Alan. 1562 MITSCHER AVE STE 250, US ATLANTIC FLEET 23551 #016-42-1995 L1999 **EM FM** *020 †16

COHEN, Alan Mathew. 400 W BRAMBLETON AVE, STE 104 23510 #028-02-1982 L1988 **IM** *020 †20

COHEN, Bruce Allan. ■ 23504 #422-01-1981 L1982 **FM OM** *030 †18

COHN, Sheldon Laurence. 6275 E VIRGINIA BEACH BLVD, STE 300 23502 #051-01-1982 L1991 **OSM** *020 †40

COKER, Kyle Pelton. 358 MOWBRAY ARCH # 203 23507 #012-01-2004 L2004 **EM** *100

COLE, Eric Lowry. 400 W BRAMBLETON AVE, STE 301 23510 #036-07-1992 L2006 **PS OTO** *045,65

COLELLA, Peter Charles. ■ 23508 #051-07-2000 L2000 *020

COLEMAN, Claude Le Roy. 1216 GRANBY ST, STE 17 23510 #023-07-1974 L1994 **CHP P** *020 †75

COLEN, Lawrence Bruce. 6161 KEMPSVILLE CIR, STE 300 23502 #032-01-1975 L1990 **PS CS** *020 †85,65

COLLIE, Chris Thomas. ■ 23505 #028-78-2001, ▲ L2001 **AN** *100 †05

COLLINS, Jimmie Nelson. 825 FAIRFAX AVE, STE 610 23507 #005-15-1987 L1997 **GS TRS** *020 †85

COLLINS, Lajuana Marnita. 1500 E LITTLE CREEK RD, STE 205 23518 #051-07-1990 L1992 **P** *020 †75

COLTRIN, Diane Hamilton. 6315 N CENTER DR, STE 100 23502 #051-07-1990 L1994 **OBG** *020 †30

CONE, Richard Wayne. 358 MOWBRAY ARCH RM 203, EVMS - OFFICE OF GME 23507 #038-41-1983 L2002 **FM** *100

CONERY, John Patrick. ■ 23510 #041-13-1998 L1998 **PDR** *020 †80

CONKLING, Paul Robt. 5900 LAKE WRIGHT DR 23502 #038-40-1982 L1988 **ON HEM** *020 †20

COOK, John Jos. 600 GRESHAM DR 23507 #041-07-1979 L1986 **IM AN** *020 †20,05

COOKE, Tyler. ■ 23518 #051-07-2006 L2007 *020

COOPER, Ann Cameron. 400 W BRAMBLETON AVE, STE 201 23510 #051-04-1990 L1997 **FM** *020 †18

COOPER, Patricia Anne. 2539 CORPREW AVE 23504 #051-07-1978 L1983 **FM EM** *020 †18

COQUERAN, Adrienne Louise. 7924 CHESAPEAKE BLVD 23518 #038-06-1975 L1981 **GP EM** *020 †16

COTE, Nicole Lisa. 700 W OLNEY RD, STE 2054 23507 #036-07-2000 L2000 **PRD** *012 †15

COULTHARD, Stacy Lauren. ■ 23507 #051-07-2008 *012

COWART, Brandi Lynn. 358 MOWBRAY ARCH # 203 23507 #028-78-2004, ▲ L2004 **IFP** *012

CRABTREE, Daniel Wayne. 6161 KEMPSVILLE CIR, HALIFAX BLDG STE 215 23502 #025-07-1973 L1990 **FM** *030 †18

CRASS, Jeffrey Robt. 825 FAIRFAX AVE, STE 541 23507 #041-13-1976 L2002 **DR** *050 †80

CRISLER, Crile. ■ 8600 23507 #023-07-1962 L1971 **TS** *071 †85,90

CROCKFORD, Jon Lee. 250 W BRAMBLETON AVE, STE 202 23510 #051-01-1975 L1978 **OBG** *020 †30

CRONIN, Julia Almeida. 601 CHILDRENS LN 23507 #005-18-2005 L2005 **PD** *012

CROSS, James Parker. ■ 23507 #051-01-1957 L1957 **OTO** *020 †45

CROSS, Scott James. 5900 LAKE WRIGHT DR 23502 #038-40-1997 L2003 **HO IM** *020 †20

CROUCH, Earl R, Jr. 880 KEMPSVILLE RD STE 2500 23502 #051-04-1969 L1969 **OPH PO** *020 †35 ‡

CROUCH, Earl Russell. 880 KEMPSVILLE RD, STE 2500 23502 #051-07-1999 L2003 **OPH** *100 †35 ‡

CRUZ, Edwin. 150 KINGSLEY LN, DE PAUL MED CTR 23505 #035-08-1978 L1999 **IM PCC** *020 ‡

CULLEN, Richard L, Jr. 6161 KEMPSVILLE CIR, STE 225 23502 #056-06-1975 L1976 **IM** *020

CUNDIFF, David Michael. 850 KEMPSVILLE RD 23502 #051-04-1976 L1977 **EM IM** *020 †20,16

CUNDIFF, Maria Reeves. 830 KEMPSVILLE RD 23502 #051-07-1980 L1981 **PTH** *020 †50

CUNNINGHAM, Stephen Graha. ■ 23505 #051-07-2006 L2006 **P** *012

CUNNION, Kenji Mason. 601 CHILDRENS LN 23507 #036-07-1993 L1993 **PDI** *050 †55

CUTHERELL, Luke. DEPAUL MED ATRIUM STE 400 23505 #025-12-1981 L1981 **GS** *020 †85

DALE, Jamie Alexandra. 160 KINGSLEY LN, STE 405 23505 #038-41-1997 L2005 **ORS** *020

D'AMATO, Nicholas Anthony. 150 KINGSLEY LN, DEPT OF PATHOLOGY 23505 #021-01-1957 L1966 **PTH** *020 †20

DAMMAN, Julie Ann. 400 W BRAMBLETON AVE, STE 202 23510 #051-07-1988 L1991 **IM** *020 †20

DANIEL, Emad H. ■ 23510 #035-09-2007 *012

DANSO, Michael Anthony. 5900 LAKE WRIGHT DR 23502 #917-28-1996 L2007 **HO** *020 †20

DARROW, David H. 825 FAIRFAX AVE, STE 510 23507 #036-07-1987 L1994 **OTO PDO** *020 †45

DATTEL, Bonnie Joan. 825 FAIRFAX AVE, STE 310 23507 #005-18-1979 L1992 **MFM OBG** *020 †30

DAVENPORT, Katherine Paig. ■ 23508 #048-13-2005 L2005 **GS** *012

DAVIES, Sylvia Margaret. 721 FAIRFAX AVE, COMMUNITY MEDICINE 23507 #352-08-1959 L1990 **FM AN** *030 †18

DAVIES, Terence Carman. 721 FAIRFAX AVE 23507 #352-08-1959 L1990 **FM OS** *030 †18

DAVIES, Timothy O. 358 MOWBRAY ARCH, DEPT OF GME 23507 #065-05-2002 L2007 **U** *012

DAVIS, Dana Florine. ■ 23507 #051-07-2005 L2005 **IM** *012

DAVIS, Denise Michelle. 2844 GATE HOUSE RD 23504 #035-06-1985 L1988 **FM OM** *020 †18

DAVIS, Haywood Howard. 825 FAIRFAX AVE, STE 541 23507 #051-04-1975 L1977 **DR AM** *062 †80

DAVIS, Kirstin F. 825 FAIRFAX AVE, STE 541 23507 #010-02-1993 L1998 **DR** *020 †80

DAWANI, Surendra P. 850 KEMPSVILLE RD, NDC MEDICAL CENTER 23502 #045-01-1996 L1999 **IM** *020 †20

DEALLY, Carole. 358 MOWBRAY ARCH # 203, EVMS - OFFICE OF GME 23507 #062-01-1993 L2001 **GS** *020

DECLERCK, Matthieu Philip. ■ 23517 #005-06-2006 L2007 **EM** *012

DE FILIPPO, Christian Tin. EVMS OFFICE OF GME 23507 #270-02-2002 L2005 **P** *012

DE FREITAS, Steven M. 601 CHILDRENS LN 23507 #010-01-1998 L1999 *020 †05

DE GUZMAN, Maria R A P. 825 FAIRFAX AVE 23507 #748-10-1988 L1999 **PM** *020 †60

DE LA CRUZ, Manuela. 160 KINGSLEY LN STE 103 23505 #308-01-1980 L1988 **PUD IM** *020

DE LA TORRE, Ricardo. 825 FAIRFAX AVE, STE 541 23507 #264-10-1975 L1983 **DR** *020 †80

DEMARCANTONIO, Michael Al. ■ 23507 #041-14-2007 L2007 **OTO** *012

DEMKO, Lyudmila V. EVMS - OFFICE OF GME, C/O HILDA HOBBS, REGISTRAR 23507 #913-10-1995 L2007 **FP** *012

DERKAC, Wayne Michael. 600 GRESHAM DR, STE 8600 23507 #035-01-1974 L1983 **TS** *020 †85,90

DERKAY, Craig Steven. 601 CHILDRENS LN, EVMS DEPT OF OTO 23507 #051-04-1983 L1989 **OTO PDO** *020 †45

DERVAY, Joann Weber. 160 KINGSLEY LN, STE 405 23505 #051-07-1996 L1996 **PM** *020 †60

DE SOLMINIHAC, Marc C. 6330 NEWTOWN RD, NORFOLK PSYCHIATRIC 23502 #036-05-1982 L1989 **P** *020 †75

DE VECIANA, Margarita. 825 FAIRFAX AVE, STE 310 23507 #035-20-1988 L1994 **OBG MFM** *040 †30

DEVINE, Alicia Scott. ■ 23507 #051-07-2004 L2004 **EM** *020

DEVINE, Patrick Campbell. 600 GRESHAM DR 23507 #051-01-1953 L1953 **U** *071 †95

DEVITT, Charles Kent. 6330 NEWTOWN RD STE 523 23502 #020-02-1977 L1986 **CHP P** *020 †75

DEVITT, Susan Kay. 6330 NEWTOWN RD STE 523 23502 #020-02-1977 L1982 **P CHP** *020 †55

DIAGNE, Thiendella. 6210 HAMPTON BLVD 23508 #305-01-2004 L2004 **IM** *012

DICKERSON, John Wm. 400 GRESHAM DR, STE 308 THE MEDICAL TOWER 23507 #051-04-1958 L1958 **OPH** *071 †35

DIE, Jane Lesto. 601 CHILDRENS LN, 4TH FL 23507 #045-01-1984 L1996 **PD** *020 †55

DIEHL, Meredith Leigh. ■ 23517 #051-01-2003 L2003 **OPH** *020

DI LUSTRO, Joseph Frank. 601 CHILDRENS LN STE 5 23507 #051-07-1983 L1989 **NS NSP** *020 †25

DIMASSI, Adel Ahmad. 825 FAIRFAX AVE 23507 #654-01-1997 L2003 **IM** *020 †20

DIMESCU, Isabella Liliana. 850 KEMPSVILLE RD 23502 #781-01-1995 L2001 **IM** *020 †20

DISTASIO, Anthony J II. 600 GRESHAM DR, SENTARA DIV OR ORTHO TRAUM 23507 #010-02-1986 L1987 **ORS** *020 †40

DIXON, James Grayson. 825 FAIRFAX AVE 23507 #051-07-1981 L1982 **IM FM** *020 †20,18

DIXON, Marybeth R. 400 GRESHAM DR, STE 811 23507 #041-07-1989 L1992 **OBG** *020 †30

DOBBIE, Krista Rene. ■ 23518 #038-43-1998 L1998 **ON** *020 †20

DONATO, Lawrence Edward, Jr. 160 KINGSLEY LN, STE 405 23505 #041-77-2000, ▲ L2006 **OSM** *020

DONNAL, John Fitzpatrick. 825 FAIRFAX AVE, STE 541 23507 #051-01-1983 L1991 **DR** *020 †80

DORSAY, Theodore Arthur. 825 FAIRFAX AVE, STE 541 23507 #010-01-1991 L2002 **DR** *020 †80

DOWNEY, Laura Corbin. ■ 23510 #021-01-2006 L2006 **PD** *012

DOZIER, Peter Marquis. 601 CHILDRENS LN, DIVISION OF PSYCHIATRY 23507 #051-07-1984 L1987 **CHP P** *020 †75

DOZORETZ, Ronald Irving. 240 CORPORATE BLVD 23502 #035-06-1962 L1966 **P** *030

DREWES, Adam Lee. 601 CHILDRENS LN, DEPARTMENT OF PEDIATRICS 23507 #051-07-2003 L2003 **PD** *020 †55

DRUCKER, Jacob Ralph. 110 KINGSLEY LN, STE 509 23505 #051-04-1972 L1974 **U** *020 †95

DUCKETT, John Gerard. 850 KEMPSVILLE RD, NDC MEDICAL CENTER 23502 #010-02-1983 L1992 **IM** *020 †20

DUFFY, Erin Elizabeth. 1035 NIDER BLVD, STE 100 23521 #023-12-2001 L2001 **GP** *020

DUKES, Silena Christinee. ■ 23510 #038-44-2008 *012

DUMITRESCU, Adina. ■ 23508 #781-08-1998 L2005 **OBG** *012

DUNCAN, James Edward. 1562 MITSCHER AVE STE 250, OFF OF FLEET SURGEON/N02MC 23551 #036-07-1997 L1998 **CRS** *020 †85,10

DUNCAN, Mark Richard. 1562 MITSCHER AVE 23551 #055-01-1995 L1998 **FM** *020 †18

DUNKER, Robert Frey. 1007 S. WEBB CENTER 23529 #051-04-1983 L1984 **FM** *020 †18

DUQUE-JESOLVA, Merced. 2539 CORPREW AVE, NORFOLK COMM HOSP 23504 #748-01-1941 L1970 **GP GS** *020

DURAN, Eyup Hakan. 601 COLLEY AVE, EASTERN VIRGINIA MEDICAL S 23507 #902-05-1991 L2003 **OBG** *020

DUTKOSKY, Christine Marie. 358 MOWBRAY ARCH # 203, EVMS - GME OFFICE 23507 #017-20-2004 L2004 **GS** *012

DVORAK, Andrew William. 562 MITCHER AVE STE 250, OFFICE OF FLEET SURGEON/NO 23551 #016-42-2003 L2004 **OS** *020

DWORETZ, Arthur. 825 FAIRFAX AVE, DEPT PSYCH 23507 #036-01-1983 L1996 **P** *020 †75

EANES, Elizabeth Anne. 601 CHILDRENS LN, THE KIN 23507 #012-22-2006 L2006 **PD** *012

EAST, Mark A. 400 GRESHAM DR STE 50, CARDIOLOGY & ARRHYTHMIA CO 23507 #036-01-1995 L2003 **IC** *020 †20

EASTON, Richard Edwin. 830 KEMPSVILLE RD 23502 #019-02-1962 L1973 **OM IM** *020 †70

EDWARDS, Landon Shay. ■ 23510 #055-02-2006 L2007 **DR** *012

EGGERT, Michael Stewart. 850 KEMPSVILLE RD 23502 #036-01-1993 L2001 **PCC** *020 †20

EHRET, Melissa Anne. ■ 23507 #023-12-2007 L2007 **PD** *012

EL-BASHIR, Ahmed Hassan. ■ 23510 #915-03-1984 L1994 **P** *100

ELDER, Thomas David. 850 KEMPSVILLE RD 23502 #036-07-1957 L1965 **RHU IM** *071 †20

ELLIS, Alexander Reed. 601 CHILDRENS LN, DIV PEDIATRIC CARDIOLOGY 23507 #051-04-2000 L2007 **PDC IM** *100 †20,55

ELLIS, Neil James. ■ 23517 #051-07-2008 *012

ELLISON, Richard Carl, Jr. 1401 TIDEWATER DR STE 6 23504 #047-07-1958 L1967 **GS ORS** *020

EL-MAHDI, Anas Morsi. 600 GRESHAM DR 23507 #330-02-1959 L1971 **RO ON** *071 †80

ELSENRAAT, Abram John. 1468 INGRAM ST, U S MARINE CORPS FORCES CO 23551 #028-46-2002 L2002 **AN** *012

ELTAHAWY, Ehab Abdalla. PO BOX 1980 23501 #915-04-1995 **U** *100

ENG, Benjamin Peter. 721 FAIRFAX AVE 23507 #051-07-1977 L1980 **FM** *020 †18

ENNIS, Bryan Arthur. ■ 23517 #051-07-2008 *012

EPPERS, Anne Frances. 850 KEMPSVILLE RD 23502 #041-07-1996 L2004 **IM** *020 †20

ERWIN, Eleanor Anna. 600 GRESHAM DR, RALEIGH BLDG, ROOM 304 23507 #017-20-2003 L2003 **EM** *020 †16

ESCALANTE, Guido Roger. 112 BURLEIGH AVE 23505 #649-06-1950 L1957 **FM CD** *075

ESTRERA, Leonor Otadoy. 401 COLLEY AVE, TIDEWATER CHILD DEV CTR 23507 #748-02-1960 L1985 **PD OS** *020 †55

ETHERIDGE, Charles L. 600 GRESHAM DR 23507 #051-01-1985 L1988 **AN OS** *020 †05

ETHERIDGE, James E, Jr. 601 CHILDRENS LN, ROB 3 23507 #051-01-1955 L1955 **CHN N** *071 †55,75

EVANS, Donald Edward. 885 KEMPSVILLE RD, SUITE 101 AMELIA BUILDING 23502 #041-12-1977 L2003 **OPH** *020 †35

EVETT, Russell Dougherty. ■ 23510 #051-04-1957 L1957 **IM** *071 †20

FABISZEWSKI, Nina L. 825 FAIRFAX AVE, STE 541 23507 #024-16-1987 L1993 **R** *020 †80

FAIRFAX, Lindsay. ■ 23510 #051-07-2007 **GS** *012

FARABAUGH, Eric Anthony. 1562 MITSCHER AVE STE 250, ATTN: CREDENTIAL OFFICE, N 23551 #041-15-2003 L2004 *020

FARMER, Evan Ragland. 580 MOWBRAY ARCH 23507 #023-07-1970 L2001 **D DMP** *020 †15

FARSHIDI, Ali. ■ 23507 #051-07-2005 L2005 **IM** *012

FAUL, Lloyd J, Jr. 600 GRESHAM DR 23507 #051-01-1982 L1986 **AN** *020 †05

FAULCONER, Robt Jamieson. ■ 23508 #023-07-1947 L1954 **PTH** *071 †50

FAULKNER, Donald T. 641 REDGATE AVE, # 329 23507 #051-01-1943 L1943 **A IM** *071

FAVOR, Tatanisha. ■ 23507 #045-04-2006 L2006 **EM** *012

FAY, Shannon Elizabeth. 1562 MITSCHER AVE STE 250, US ATLANTIC FLEET 23551 #028-34-2006 L2007 *012

FAYTON, Charles Earl. 930 MAJESTIC AVE, STE 110 23504 #036-01-1979 L1982 **PD** *020 †55

FEKETE, Andrew Maurice. 7924 CHESAPEAKE BLVD 23518 #051-04-1956 L1956 **IM CD** *072

FELIBERTI, Eric Charles. 825 FAIRFAX AVE, EASTERN VIRGINIA MEDICAL S 23507 #048-02-1999 L2006 **GS** *020 †85

FERNANDEZ, Martha Theresa. 250 W BRAMBLETON AVE, STE 202 23510 #051-01-1989 L1992 **OBG** *020 †30

FERNANDO, Thomas Gamini. 110 MAYCOX AVE STE 2 23505 #220-01-1968 L1976 **P** *020 †75

FILE, Wilson Mc Call. ■ 23517 #045-04-2007 L2007 **PD** *012

FINCH, Albert B. 6345 CENTER DR, BLDG 14 23502 #035-06-1969 L1972 **PD** *030 †55

FINK, Fredric Neil. 885 KEMPSVILLE RD STE 200 23502 #051-01-1982 L1985 **PD** *020 †55

FINK, H Wm. 844 KEMPSVILLE RD STE 105 23502 #051-01-1938 L1938 **PD OS** *071 †55

FINK, Robert Alan. 885 KEMPSVILLE RD STE 200 23502 #051-01-1980 L1983 **PD** *020 †55

FISCHER, Andrew Michael. 600 GRESHAM DR 23507 #035-45-1985 L1989 **AN** *020 †05

FISH, Robert Norman. 1468 INGRAM ST, SERV SUP 23551 #049-01-2002 L2003 **AN** *012

FISHBACK, Nancy Fay. 600 GRESHAM DR, FL 5 23507 #017-20-1970 L1998 **PTH IM** *020 †20,50

FISHER, Randall Garth. 601 CHILDRENS LN 23507 #021-01-1988 L2000 **PD** *020 †55 ‡

FISHER, Stephen Irving. 830 KEMPSVILLE RD 23502 #034-01-1994 L2003 **HMP** *020 †50

FITCHETT, Claiborne W. 6160 KEMPSVILLE CIR, NORFOLK SURGICAL GROUP LTD 23502 #051-01-1947 L1947 **GS** *071 †85

FITZPATRICK, Emily Louise. 1909 GRANBY ST STE A, PEDIATRIC ASSOCIATES 23517 #035-06-2005 L2005 **PD** *012

FLATIN, Heidi Kathryn. 601 CHILDRENS LN 23507 #051-07-1989 L1992 **PD** *020 †55

FLEISCHER, Kirk Joachim. 600 GRESHAM DR, STE 8600 23507 #051-01-1991 L2000 **TS** *020 †85,90

FLEMMER, Mark C. 825 FAIRFAX AVE, STE 445 23507 #836-01-1978 L1993 **IM** *020 †20

FLENNER, Ronald Wayne. 825 FAIRFAX AVE, STE 410 23507 #051-07-1989 L1990 **ID** *020 †20

FLICK, Cynthia Shealy. 150 KINGSLEY LN 23505 #045-01-1987 L1991 **PM** *020 †60

FLYNN, Thomas Francis. ■ 23505 #010-02-1954 L1970 **EM GS** *071 †85

FOLEY, Christopher Kevin. 601 CHILDRENS LN, DIV OF CRITICAL CARE 23507 #050-02-1988 L1996 **CCP** *020 †55

FONTANA, Mark Ambrose. 6160 KEMPSVILLE CIR, STE 101B 23502 #023-12-1992 L1993 **GS** *020 †85

FOOTE, Frederick Odonnell. 1562 MITSCHER AVE STE 250, OFFICE OF FLEET SURGEON,N0 23551 #010-02-1986 L1988 **N** *020

FORD, Eugene Roland. 549 E BRAMBLETON AVE 23510 #047-07-1974 L1978 **FM** *075

FORTE, Bill Jeffrey. 3755 E VIRGINIA BEACH BLVD, MENTAL HLTH SVCS 23502 #035-46-1993 L1995 **P** *020 †75

FOSS, Clare Elizabeth. ■ 23505 #012-01-2007 L2007 **IM** *012

FOSTER, Maura Margrit. 601 CHILDRENS LN, THE KIN 23507 #051-07-2006 L2006 **PD** *012

FOWLER, Paul David. ■ 23508 #051-07-2008 *012

FRAME, Heather Ann. ■ 23505 #010-01-1999 L1999 **AN** *020

FREED, Gary Leland, Jr. ■ 23507 #051-07-2003 L2003 **OTO** *012

FREEMAN, Dana Nicole. 358 MOWBRAY ARCH, EVMS - OFFICE OF GME 23507 #654-01-2006 L2006 **IM** *012

FRIEDMAN, Asher Arthur. WAINWRIGHT BLDG 23510 #023-01-1947 L1954 **D** *071 †15

FRIEND, Kara Elizabeth. ■ 23507 #051-07-2008 L2008 *012

FRUCI, Carolyn Marie. 850 KEMPSVILLE RD, NDC MEDICAL CTR 23502 #047-05-1993 L2006 **PCC** *020 †20

FU, Diana Cheng Ting. 1468 INGRAM ST, US MARINE CORPS FORCES ATL 23551 #023-12-2000 L2001 **N** *012

FUHRMAN, Steven Andrew. 850 KEMPSVILLE RD 23502 #024-07-1982 L2001 **ID CCM** *020 †20

FURR, John H. ■ 23507 #051-01-1953 L1953 **P** *071

FUSSELL, James David. 825 FAIRFAX AVE 23507 #010-02-1966 L1972 **PUD IM** *071

FUSTINO, Nicholas John. 601 CHILDRENS LN, THE KIN 23507 #024-16-2005 L2005 **PD** *012

GABRIEL, Candice April. ■ 23505 #051-07-2007 L2007 **PD** *012

GABRIEL, Noelle Martha. ■ 23505 #051-07-2006 L2006 **PD** *012

GAL, Jonathan Stephen. ■ 23507 #051-07-2008 *012

GALICIA-CASTILLO, Marissa. 825 FAIRFAX AVE, STE 201 23507 #051-07-1997 L1997 **IM IMG** *020 †20

GALLO, David Alexander. 885 KEMPSVILLE RD 23502 #016-11-1963 L1968 **U** *071 †95

GAMSEY, Alan Jay. 160 KINGSLEY LN, STE 200 23505 #051-04-1975 L1978 **GE IM** *020 †20

GAO, Yan. 6330 N CENTER DR STE 220, MEDICAL CENTER RADIOLOGIST 23502 #243-39-1982 L2001 **DR** *020 †80

GARLINGTON, Wendy. 358 MOWBRAY ARCH, EVMS-OFFICE OF GME 23507 #143-11-2003 L2006 **IM** *012

GARNETT, Alfred R, Jr. 850 KEMPSVILLE RD 23502 #051-04-1979 L1980 **PUD CCM** *020 †20

GARRIS, Sheila Yvonne. 229 W BUTE ST, STE 221 23510 #041-13-1982 L1986 **IM** *020 †20

GARRISON, Bobby Joe. 1909 GRANBY ST STE A, CHILDRENS HOSPITAL OF THE 23517 #039-01-1980 L1983 **PD** *020 †55

GARY, Margaret Marshall. 160 KINGSLEY LN, STE 303 23505 #051-04-1982 L1991 **OBG** *020 †30

GATEWOOD, Edwin Edison. ■ 23518 #051-04-1993 L1993 **P** *020 †75

GAYLE, Robert Gordon. 600 GRESHAM DR, # 8620 23507 #041-12-1973 L1979 **VS** *020 †85

GEBREMEDHIN, Mulugeta. ■ 23510 #366-01-1994 L2006 **HOS IM** *100 †20

GECOLEA, Renato H. 6204 N MILITARY HWY 23518 #748-02-1968 L1977 **FM EM** *020

GEIB, Philip Oldham. 600 GRESHAM DR 23507 #041-13-1945 L1977 **OM GS** *071 †85

GELLER, D Michael. 825 FAIRFAX AVE, EASTERN VA MEDICAL SCHOOL 23507 #041-13-1980 L2003 **MDM IMG** *020 †20

GENSLER, Todd Wm. 250 W BRAMBLETON AVE, STE 101 23510 #041-09-1991 L2003 **VS** *020 †85

GEORGES, Leon Paul. 855 W BRAMBLETON AVE 23510 #869-04-1963 L1970 **IM END** *030 †20

GEORGI, Jennifer Nicole. ■ 23508 #036-01-2002 L2006 **AN** *020 †05

GIBBS, Colville Nigel. 850 KEMPSVILLE RD, NDC MEDICAL CENTER 23502 #422-01-1990 L2000 **PUD** *020 †20

GIBSON, David William. 1562 MITSCHER AVE STE 250, ATTN: CREDENTIAL OFFICE 23551 #011-02-1993 L1994 **GPM AM** *020 †70

GIBSON, Mark Alan. ■ 23505 #017-20-2003 L2003 **DR** *012

GIBSON, Wilford Keith. 160 KINGSLEY LN, STE 405 23505 #051-04-1985 L1986 **ORS OTR** *020 †40

GILBERT, Christian Lee. 601 CHILDRENS LN, CHILDREN'S HOSPITAL OF THE 23507 #041-13-1981 L2007 **GP** *020 †85,90

GILBERT, David Alan. 400 W BRAMBLETON AVE, STE 300 23510 #060-01-1971 L1979 **PS** *020 †65

GILL, Francesisa Mackey. ■ 23507 #051-07-2008 *012

GILLIS, Robert Clements. ■ 23517 #051-07-2007 **ORS** *012

GILLMAN, John Frederick. ■ 23517 #023-12-1992 L2007 **PM OSM** *020 †60

GILLMAN, Nicole Cherise. 825 FAIRFAX AVE, EVMS 23507 #047-07-2001 L2001 **OBG** *020 †30

GLASS, William F, II. 700 W OLNEY RD 23507 #048-13-1985 L1992 **ATP CLP** *020 †50 ‡

GLERUM, Steven Michael. ■ 23510 #023-12-2008 *012

GOAD, Lynn Carrico. 601 CHILDRENS LN, C/O NANCY VESPA PRIUTT, CS 23507 #020-12-2001 L2004 **PD** *020 †55

GOEI, Vita Lan-Ing. 601 CHILDRENS LN, DEPARTMENT OF PEDIATRIC GA 23507 #035-46-1986 L2007 **PD** *020 †55

GOEL, Anoj Kumar. ■ 23507 #495-73-1989 L2000 **END IM** *020 †20

GOFFMAN, Thomas E. 600 GRESHAM DR 23507 #041-09-1979 L1982 **RO** *040 †20,80

GOLDBERG, Martin Joseph. 100 KINGSLEY LN, CARDIOLOGY CONSULTANTS 23505 #051-04-1978 L1979 **CD IM** *020 †20

GOLDENBERG, Edward. 600 GRESHAM DR 23507 #020-12-1981 L1991 **P PFP** *020 †75

GOLDMAN, Charles Jay. 229 W BUTE ST, STE 500 23510 #051-04-1967 L1967 **IM END** *020 †20

GOLDSTICKER, Laurie A. 400 W BRAMBLETON AVE, STE 201 23510 #051-04-1992 L1993 **FM** *020 †18

GOLDSTICKER, Ralph David. ■ 23505 #051-04-1986 **PTH** *020

GOLOGAN, Olguta E. ■ 23505 #781-01-1996 L2003 **PCP** *100 †50

GOLPIRA, Elizabeth Baker. 400 GRESHAM DR, STE 811 23507 #051-07-1999 L1999 **OBG** *020 †30

GOMEZ, Luis Martin. 601 COLLEY AVE 23507 #737-01-1992 L2004 **OBG** *012

GOMEZ, Robert James. 601 CHILDRENS LN 23507 #005-14-1979 L1987 **PD CCP** *020 †55

GONZALES, Jose E. 110 KINGSLEY LN, STE 509 23505 #748-02-1967 L1979 **U** *020 †95

GOODMAN, Benjamin M, III. 825 FAIRFAX AVE, STE 445 23507 #051-07-2000 L2000 **IM** *020 †20

GOODWIN, Ambler Ray. ■ 23505 #051-04-1958 L1958 **PTH OS** *071 †50

GORETSKY, Michael Jay. 601 CHILDRENS LN STE 5B, CHILDRENS HOSP KINGS DAUGH 23507 #035-48-1991 L2000 **PDS** *020 †85 ‡

GOUGH, William Wood. 850 KEMPSVILLE RD 23502 #051-01-1967 L1967 **RHU IM** *020 †20

GOULD, Randolph J. 6160 KEMPSVILLE CIR, STE 101B 23502 #051-07-1978 L1983 **GS** *020 †85

GOULDIN, Thomas Winston. ■ 23518 #051-04-1954 L1954 **FM** *071 †18

GOWER, Elizabeth Jean. 6345 CENTER DR 23502 #051-07-1990 L1991 **PD** *020 †55

GRAHAM, Robert Michael. 150 KINGSLEY LN 23505 #035-19-1980 L1989 **ORS OFA** *020 †40

GRANOFF, Abbot Lee. 6330 NEWTOWN RD STE 316 23502 #047-06-1971 L1977 **P** *020 †75

GRANT, Thomas R, Jr. 721 FAIRFAX AVE 23507 #036-05-1982 L1984 **FM FPG** *071 †18

GRASSIA, Michael. 6160 KEMPSVILLE CIR, STE 302A 23502 #051-07-1997 L1998 **NEP** *020 †20

GRASSO, Susanne Ng. 825 FAIRFAX AVE, STE 541 23507 #051-07-1991 L1991 **DR** *020 †80

GRAY, Pamela J E. 6161 KEMPSVILLE CIR, STE 335 23502 #051-07-1979 L1979 **RHU IM** *020 †20 ‡

GREEN, Glen Alvin. 601 CHILDRENS LN, DAUGHTERS 23507 #035-15-1983 L1986 **NPM PD** *020 †55

GREEN, Jimmy Wade. 830 KEMPSVILLE RD 23502 #047-06-1980 L2007 **PTH FOP** *020 †50

GREENE, Garland Vestal. 1146 TOLER PL 23503 #036-05-1985 L1991 **IM FM** *020

GREENE, Krista Michelle. ■ 23507 #051-07-2008 L2008 *012

GREENSPAN, Mark. ■ 23509 #035-15-1960 L1968 **GS** *071 †85

GREGORY, Christopher Paul. ■ 23507 #036-08-2005 L2005 **IFP** *012

GRINNAN, Geo Lamb Buist. 600 GRESHAM DR, # 8600 23507 #051-04-1963 L1963 **TS** *071 †85,90

GROSS, Michael Leslie. 825 FAIRFAX AVE 23507 #021-01-1990 L1995 **D** *020 †15

GROVES, Cecil Dwight. 250 W BRAMBLETON AVE, STE 202 23510 #055-02-1981 L1982 **OBG** *020 †30

GRULKE, David C. 400 W BRAMBLETON AVE, STE 202 23510 #036-07-1975 L1978 **IM DIA** *020 †20

GRUNEIR, Richard Kenneth. ■ 23505 #065-01-1973 L1986 *020

GRUSENMEYER, Dennis P. 850 KEMPSVILLE RD 23502 #038-41-1997 L2003 **IM** *020 †20

GUINS, Theresa Ellen. 601 CHILDRENS LN 23507 #035-19-1989 L1995 **PD PEM** *020 †55

GUNAWARDENA, Ratnasiri M. 850 KEMPSVILLE RD, NDC MEDICAL CENTER 23502 #220-01-1994 L2005 **END** *020 †20

GUNTHER, Wendy Marie. 830 SOUTHAMPTON AVE, STE 1OO 23510 #005-06-1986 L2002 **FOP PP** *020 †50

GUR, Uri. EVMS - OFFICE OF GME, C/O HILDA HOBBS , REGISTRA 23507 #550-02-1997 **U** *012

GURTNER, Petra. 229 W BUTE ST, STE 800 23510 #409-16-1983 L1997 **NS** *020 †25

GUZMAN, Jojo-Anne A. 426 E FREEMASON ST, ASSOCIATES IN PRIMARY CARE 23510 #748-02-1994 L1998 **IM** *020 †20

GWATHMEY, Frank Winston. 6160 KEMPSVILLE CIR, STE 102A 23502 #036-01-1968 L1976 **HS ORS** *071 †40

HACKER, Anke. 600 GRESHAM DR 23507 #409-40-2000 L2001 **IM** *020 †18,20

HAFIZ, Mahmooda P. 7501 HONEYSUCKLE RD, MAHMOODA HAFIZ 23518 #704-04-1962 L1981 **P** *020

HAGGERTY, Ronald David. OFFICE OF FLEET SURGEON, ATTN: CREDENTIAL OFFICE 23551 #025-07-1995 L2000 **IM** *020 †20

HAHN, Jason Soochong. 600 GRESHAM DR 23507 #051-01-1999 L2002 **OTO** *020 †45

HAILE, Dereje Zewde. 850 KEMPSVILLE RD, NDC MEDICAL CENTER 23502 #051-07-1997 L1999 **IM** *020 †20

HAILES-WANKO, Tonya. 1815 E LITTLE CREEK RD 23518 #051-01-1998 L1998 **FM** *020 †18

HAJIMOMENIAN, Amir. 110 KINGSLEY LN E309 23505 #305-01-2000 L2000 **IM** *020 †20 ‡

HALLMARK, Robert James. 880 KEMPSVILLE RD, STE 2200 23502 #054-04-1990 L1998 **OBG** *020 †30

HALOL, Athena Jane. 358 MOWBRAY ARCH, DEPT OF GME 23507 #748-10-2000 L2007 **FP** *012

HAMAD, Karen Marieabu. 825 FAIRFAX AVE, STE 445 23507 #021-01-1995 L1999 **MPD** *020 †20,55

HAMBAZ, Nasser. 1477 NORVIEW AVE 23513 #517-08-1971 L1985 **GP** *020

HAMILTON, Colin W. 160 KINGSLEY LN, STE 405 23505 #010-02-1970 L1976 **OSS OMM** *071 †40

HANSON, Stephen Lloyd. 1035 NIDER BLVD, STE 100 23521 #026-04-1966 L2008 **FM** *020 †18 ‡

HAQUE, Ehteshamul. 150 KINGSLEY LN 23505 #704-02-1989 L2001 **IM** *020 †20

HARIHARAN, Selena L. 601 CHILDRENS LN 23507 #016-06-1996 L2003 **PEM PD** *020 †55

HARMS, Amy J. 171 KEMPSVILLE RD, BLDG B 23502 #056-05-2005 L2007 **PD** *100

HARRINGTON, John Walter. 601 CHILDRENS LN, GENERAL PEDIATRICS AT CHKD 23507 #035-09-1992 L2006 **PD** *020 †55

HARRIS, Alan Craig. 830 KEMPSVILLE RD 23502 #051-07-1981 L1984 **PTH HMP** *020 †50

HARRIS, Denise Lorraine. 250 W BRAMBLETON AVE, STE 202 23510 #047-05-2002 L2007 **OBG** *020

HARRIS, Tanya Shahzad. 400 GRESHAM DR STE 712 23507 #041-13-2002 L2006 **PM** *100 †60

HARROLD, Laprecious Liber. ■ 23507 #016-11-2006 L2006 **PD** *012

HARWELL, Courtney Amber. ■ 23510 #051-07-2008 *012

HASAS, Pedro D. 1815 E LITTLE CREEK RD, PEDRO D HASAS, MD, PLC 23518 #308-03-1985 L1994 **IM** *020 †20

HAUSER, Charlene Alma. ■ 23507 #021-01-2008 *012

HAYASHI, Konrad Edmund. 1562 MITSCHER AVE STE 250, OFFICE OF FLEET SURGEON/NO 23551 #023-12-1981 L1998 **GPM** *020 †70

HAYES, Henry Desmond. ■ 23508 #539-01-1954 L1958 **FPG FM** *071 †18

HEATWOLE, Katharine W. 850 KEMPSVILLE RD, NDC NEDICAL CENTER 23502 #051-07-1987 L1991 **N** *020 †75

HECHT, Gary Michael. ■ 23505 #024-01-1977 L1980 **IM** *075

HECK, Shannon Ione. ■ 23507 #051-07-2001 L2001 **D** *020 †15

HECKER, Susan Michelle. ■ 23505 #021-01-2003 L2005 **GS** *100

HEIDE, Robert Kay. 142 W YORK ST, INTERNAL MEDICINE 23510 #019-02-1962 L1968 **IM** *071 †20

HELFER, Sidney P. 8185 TIDAL RD 23518 #016-42-1948 L1959 **EM** *071

HENNELLY, Patrick Jos. 142 W YORK ST 23510 #010-02-1954 L1972 **IM** *071 †20

HENRY, Conrad Allan. 1881 E LITTLE CREEK RD 23518 #039-01-1971 L1981 **OPH** *020 ‡

HENRY, Deborah Mc Cauley. 601 COLLEY AVE, CLINICAL RESEARCH CENTER 23507 #036-05-1983 L1984 **IM** *020 †20

HENRY, Reginald B, Jr. 850 KEMPSVILLE RD 23502 #051-01-1950 L1950 **IM GE** *071 †20

HENRY, Reginald B, III. 850 KEMPSVILLE RD 23502 #051-01-1982 L1983 **D** *020 †15

HERRE, John Milton. 100 KINGSLEY LN, CARDIOLOGY CONSULTANTS 23505 #047-05-1977 L1983 **CD IM** *040 †20

HERRERA, Shannon Renee. 1562 MITSCHER AVE STE 250, US FLEET FORCES COMMAND, N 23551 #026-04-2005 L2006 **GS** *020

HERSH, Christopher Karrer. 6160 KEMPSVILLE CIR - SUI, SMITHFIELD BUILDING 23502 #019-02-1990 L1999 **HS** *040 †40

HESTER, Ryan Patrick. 825 FAIRFAX AVE STE 510, DEPT OTO-HNS 23507 #051-07-2002 L2002 **OTO** *100

HEYDARIAN, Cyrus Christop. ■ 23510 #055-02-2007 L2007 **PD** *012

HEYL, Peter Spencer. 825 FAIRFAX AVE RM 310, EVMS-MFM 23507 #036-05-1976 L1983 **MFM OBG** *020 ‡

HIGGINS, Heather Marie. ■ 23507 #023-12-2001 L2002 **EM** *012

HIGGINS, Thomas Stephen, Jr. ■ 23507 #020-02-2006 L2006 **OTO** *012

HINMAN, Timothy Stuart. 1562 MITSCHER AVE STE 250, CINCLANTFLT, NO2MC 23551 #019-02-1987 L1993 **FM** *020 †16

HO, Michael Nai Kong. 825 FAIRFAX AVE, STE 541 23507 #021-05-1990 L1993 **VIR** *020 †80

HOBGOOD, Sarah Ellis. ■ 23505 #024-01-2005 L2005 **IM** *012

HOCHMAN, Rodney Frank. 6015 POPLAR HALL DR # 300 23502 #024-05-1979 L1999 **RHU IM** *030 †20

HODEEN, Eric Carleton. 850 KEMPSVILLE RD, NDC MEDICAL CENTER 23502 #024-07-1968 L1972 **RHU IM** *020 †20

HODGE, Edwin Beaumont. 850 KEMPSVILLE RD 23502 #051-04-1958 L1958 **IM** *020 †20

HOERR, George Richard. 601 CHILDRENS LN 23507 #028-03-1984 L1989 **PS** *020 †65

HOFFMAN, George Charol. 6160 KEMPSVILLE CIR, STE 101B 23502 #024-07-1969 L1977 **GS SO** *020 †20

HOFFMAN, Richard Steven. 142 W YORK ST, INTERNAL MEDICINE 23510 #051-07-1987 L1988 **IM** *020 †20

HOGAN, Joseph. 6161 KEMPSVILLE CIR, STE 315 23502 #036-01-1985 L1992 **N IM** *020 †20,75

HOLDER, Francois Everton. 850 KEMPSVILLE RD, BLDG 850 23502 #035-19-1983 L1990 **ID IM** *071 †20

HOLLAND, Marie Tulou. 6161 KEMPSVILLE CIR, STE 315, HALIFAX BUILDING 23502 #051-07-1981 L1984 **N** *020 †75

HOLMES, Bert Wellington. 2539 CORPREW AVE 23504 #010-03-1974 L1979 **U FM** *071

HOLROYD, Timothy Joseph. 600 GRESHAM DR 23507 #051-01-1983 L1986 **AN** *020 †05

HOPKINS, John David. ■ 23502 #047-07-1958 L1975 **R NM** *071 †80

HORDEN, Harold Milton. 150 KINGSLEY LN 23505 #051-04-1962 L1962 **FM** *071 †18

HORNBUCKLE, Andrea C. 601 CHILDRENS LN 23507 #038-06-1993 L2001 **PD** *020 †55

HORNBUCKLE, Kelvin. 885 KEMPSVILLE RD 23502 #038-06-1994 L2001 **GE** *020 †20

HORTON, Charles Edwin, Jr. 601 CHILDRENS LN, 5TH FLOOR UROLOGY SUITE 23507 #051-07-1983 L1990 **UP U** *020 †95

HOUPT, Rhonda Spring. ■ 23505 #051-07-2005 L2005 **PD** *012

HOUSER, Edward Ross, II. ■ 23508 #036-01-2005 L2005 **U** *012

HOVLAND, William Neal. 110 KINGSLEY LN, DEPAUL MEDICAL BLDG SUITE 23505 #051-04-1974 L1975 **IM** *020 †20

HOWERTON, Douglas H. 600 GRESHAM DR 23507 #055-01-1987 L1993 **GE** *020 †20

HTWE, Tin Han. 850 KEMPSVILLE RD 23502 #209-01-1999 L2003 **ID** *020 †20

HUBBARD, George Wilkins. 6160 KEMPSVILLE CIR, STE 101B 23502 #051-01-1976 L1977 **GS TS** *020 †85

HUBBARD, Thomas Waite. 601 CHILDRENS LN 23507 #051-07-1976 L1980 **PD LM** *020 †55

HUGHES, Felix Austin. 825 FAIRFAX AVE, STE 541 23507 #047-05-1966 L1973 **DR** *071 †80

HUGHES, Gilbert Theodore. 400 GRESHAM DR, STE 811 23507 #051-07-1981 L1983 **OBG** *020 †30

HUJIC, Nirvana. 721 FAIRFAX AVE, PRACTICE RESIDENC 23507 #957-11-1994 L2005 **FP** *012

HUMADI, Sahira Ali Akbar. 825 FAIRFAX AVE, EVMS FAMILY & COMMUNITY ME 23507 #528-01-1983 L2000 **FM** *020 †18

HUMPHREY, William Trowell. 400 GRESHAM DR, STE 308 23507 #012-05-1962 L1972 **OPH** *071 †35

HUTCHENS, William Thomas. 825 FAIRFAX AVE, DEPARTMENT OF MEDICINE 23507 #035-03-1995 L2003 **PCC** *020 †20

HUTCHINSON, Kristin Kathe. 601 CHILDRENS LN, THE KING'S 23507 #051-04-2006 L2006 **PD** *012

HYDER, Huma Mahnaz. PO BOX 1980, EASTERN VA MED SCH 23501 #704-16-1992 L2001 **P** *020

IBARRA, Jorge. ■ 23518 #649-01-1951 L1962 **OS GS** *071

INAYET, Nadeem. 850 KEMPSVILLE RD, SENTARA MEDICAL GROUP 23502 #704-02-1992 L1999 **PUD** *020 †20

INGRAM, Ryan Willis. PO BOX 1980, DEPT OF PSYCHIATRY 23501 #051-07-2006 L2006 **P** *012

IRONS, Michele Anne. 825 FAIRFAX AVE, STE 410 23507 #041-15-2003 L2003 **IM** *020 †20

ISLAM, Selima Banu. 150 KINGSLEY LN 23505 #160-02-1970 *100

ISROW, Larry Alan. ■ 23509 #051-04-1971 L1972 **N** *075 †75

ITSKOVITZ, Joseph. 825 FAIRFAX AVE, HOFHEIMER HALL 6TH FLOOR 23507 #550-01-1977 L1986 *100

IVES, Charles Everett. 600 GRESHAM DR 23507 #016-06-1974 L1979 **GS** *020 †85

JACKSON, Robert Tyler. 600 GRESHAM DR 23507 #051-01-1971 L1972 **OTO** *075 †45

JAFFE, Alan Harvey. 160 KINGSLEY LN, 205 DEPAUL MEDICAL ATRIUM 23505 #051-04-1964 L1964 **GS** *020 †85

JAIN, Kirn. 229 W BUTE ST STE 500, WAINWRIGHT BUILDING, 23510 #051-01-2001 L2005 **MPD** *020 †20

JANKOSKY, Christopher J. 1562 MITSCHER AVE STE 250, ATTN: CREDENTIAL OFFICE 23551 #010-02-1990 L1992 **GPM** *020 †70,75

JENISON, Mark Walter. 850 KEMPSVILLE RD 23502 #036-01-1992 L1996 **D** *020 †15

JENKINS, Lisa C. 721 FAIRFAX AVE, GHENT FAMILY PRACTICE 23507 #012-21-1996 L1996 **FM** *020 †18

JIJAKLI, Amal. PO BOX 1980, EASTERN VA MED SCH 23501 #875-01-1990 L2004 **P** *012

JOHN, Justin Mathew. 601 CHILDRENS LN, JOE DIMAGGIO CHILDREN'S HO 23507 #495-37-1999 L2008 **AN PAN** *012

JOHNSEN, Jennifer Lynne. ■ 23510 #005-11-2003 *100

JOHNSON, David Allan. 885 KEMPSVILLE RD 23502 #051-04-1980 L1981 **GE IM** *062 †20

JOHNSON, Gretchen K. 1562 MITSCHER AVE STE 250, ATTN CREDENTIALS OFFICE 23551 #005-12-2004 L2004 *100

JOHNSON, Kaalan Erik. ■ 23505 #005-12-2004 L2004 **OTO** *012

JOHNSON, Lester Skolfield. 825 FAIRFAX AVE, STE 541 23507 #035-01-1995 L2001 **DR** *020 †80,28

JOHNSON, Steven Chas. 600 GRESHAM DR 23507 #041-07-1983 L1987 **AN** *020 †05

JOHNSON, William Thos. 825 FAIRFAX AVE 23507 #051-04-1959 L1959 **GP OS** *071

JOHNSTON, Mickaila James. ■ 23521 #023-12-2003 L2003 *020

JOHNSTON, Santa Joan. 601 CHILDRENS LN 23507 #041-07-1986 L1993 **CCP** *020 †55

JONES, Christopher Steven. ■ 23507 #051-07-2008 L2008 *012

JONES, Glenn Cartier. 229 W BUTE ST, DEDICATED CARE CENTER 23510 #016-02-1998 L2001 **IM** *020 †20 ‡

JONES, Howard Wilbur, Jr. 601 COLLEY AVE 23507 #023-07-1935 L1978 **OBG** *072 †85

JONES, Tamara Aletta. 825 FAIRFAX AVE, STE 410 23507 #051-07-2002 L2002 **IM** *020 †20

JONES, Tobin Jack. 201 GRANBY ST STE 103, NORFOLK COMMUNITY SERV BRD 23510 #034-01-1986 L1990 **P** *075 †75

JOYCE, John Owen. 1326 E LITTLE CREEK RD 23518 #051-07-1987 L1988 **FM** *020 †18

KALLEBERG, Kari Anne. ■ 23507 #051-07-2008 *012

KALMANOVICH, Yury. 400 GRESHAM DR, STE 301 23507 #913-09-1984 L2001 **NEP** *020 †20

KALOJI, Rajeshwari. 171 KEMPSVILLE RD, BLDG B 23502 #495-21-1988 L1999 **PD** *020 †55

KAPLAN, Arthur Sanford. 229 W BUTE ST STE 500 23510 #035-09-1948 L1953 **IM** *071 †20

KAPLAN, Ivor Barry. 400 W BRAMBLETON AVE, STE 300 23510 #836-01-1973 L1987 **PS** *020 †85,65

KAPUR, Gayatri. 601 COLLEY AVE 23507 #035-06-1992 L2001 **OBG** *020 †30

KARAKLA, Daniel Wm. 825 FAIRFAX AVE, STE 510 23507 #023-12-1986 L1999 **OTO HNS** *020 †45

KARNITSCHNIG, Ann Gaddum. 830 KEMPSVILLE RD 23502 #803-03-1956 L1964 **FM OS** *071 †18

KARP, Glenda Steinberg. 171 KEMPSVILLE RD, BLDG B 23502 #067-01-1980 L1983 **PD** *020 †55
KATZ, Paul Gary. 110 KINGSLEY LN, STE 509 23505 #067-01-1972 L1982 **U** *020 †95
KAYE, Robert Paul. 601 CHILDRENS LN 23507 #035-06-1985 L1990 **AN** *020 †05
KEFFER, Louis Henry. 420 N CENTER DR, BLDG 11 23502 #051-04-1951 L1951 **OBG** *071 †30
KELLOGG, Laura Crittenden. 721 FAIRFAX AVE 23507 #051-07-2002 L2002 **FM** *020 †18
KELLY, Joseph L, III. 110 KINGSLEY LN, STE 103 23505 #051-01-1984 L1985 **EM** *075
KELLY, Robert Edward, Jr. 601 CHILDRENS LN 23507 #023-07-1985 L1994 **PDS** *020 †85 ‡
KELLY, Ursula Marta. ■ 23507 #045-01-2007 L2007 **IM** *012
KERNER, Dawnielle J. 160 KINGSLEY LN, STE 300 23505 #035-46-1989 L1995 **OPH** *020 †35
KERSHNER, Nicole Allison. ■ 23507 #051-07-2008 *012
KESSLER, Charles August. 600 GRESHAM DR 23507 #043-01-1975 L1983 **IMG IM** *020 †20
KETTEN, Connie S. 601 CHILDRENS LN, CHILDREN'S SPECIALTY GROUP 23507 #051-07-1989 L2004 **PD** *020 †55
KEVERLINE, Sharon Rebecca. 250 W BRAMBLETON AVE, STE 202 23510 #041-12-1997 L2001 **OBG** *020 †30
KEVORKIAN, Constance M. 171 KEMPSVILLE RD, BLDG B 23502 #051-07-1979 L1982 **PD** *020 †55
KEYS-FREZZELL, Dana Jean. 850 KEMPSVILLE RD, NDC MEDICAL CENTER 23502 #038-06-1990 L2007 **IM** *020 †20
KHAN, Jamil Hakim. 601 CHILDRENS LN 23507 #051-01-1983 L1988 **NPM PD** *020 †55
KHARAZMI, Shervin Albert. 601 CHILDRENS LN, THE KIN 23507 #012-01-2005 L2005 **PD** *012
KIHLSTROM, Laura Jill. 600 GRESHAM DR 23507 #036-07-1998 L2002 **AN** *020 ‡
KIM, Manhyong. 110 KINGSLEY LN, STE 305 23505 #051-07-1982 L1984 **DR NR** *020 †80
KIM, Yoonah. 6330 N CENTER DR, BLDG 13 23502 #051-04-1997 L2004 **RNR** *020 †80
KIMBLE, Thomas Dudley. 601 COLLEY AVE, CRC-JONES INSTITUTE 23507 #010-03-2002 L2006 **OBG** *100
KING, John Winston. ■ 23502 #010-03-1947 L1948 **GS OM** *071 †85
KING, Paul Anthony. 825 FAIRFAX AVE, STE 410 23507 #051-07-2000 L2000 **IM** *020 †20
KING, Ronald Lester. 825 FAIRFAX AVE, STE 541 23507 #051-04-1966 L1966 **DR** *020 †80
KIPERS, Genevieve Louise. ■ 23510 #051-07-2008 *012
KIRCHNER, Frank H. 825 FAIRFAX AVE 23507 #021-05-1977 L1982 **P CHP** *040 †75
KIRKLAND, C Stokes, Jr. 110 KINGSLEY LN STE 202 23505 #051-07-1981 L1982 **FM** *020 †18
KIRVEN, Felix Moses. 6275 E VIRGINIA BEACH BLVD, STE 200 23502 #048-16-1988 L1996 **ORS** *020 †40
KLAFFKY, Erin Jeanne. ■ 23517 #051-07-2008 *012
KLEDZIK, Ronald Bruce. 809 BRANDON AVE, STE 311 23517 #051-01-1958 L1958 **PYA P** *020
KLEIMAN, Bruce. 850 KEMPSVILLE RD, NDC MEDICAL CENTER 23502 #649-02-1989 L2006 **IM** *020 †20
KLEVAN, Thomas. 100 KINGSLEY LN, CARDIOLOGY CONSULTANTS 23505 #008-01-1981 L1987 **CD** *020 †20
KLINE, Samuel Chas. 160 KINGSLEY LN, STE 405 23505 #017-20-1985 L1991 **HS ORS** *020 †40
KLINKHAMMER, Martin David. 150 KINGSLEY LN, EMERGENCY DEPARTMENT 23505 #026-08-2004 L2007 **EM** *020
KNAUER, Brenda K. PO BOX 1980 23501 #048-13-1998 L1998 **FM** *100
KNIGHT, Morris Reed, Jr. 6330 N CENTER DR, BLDG 13 23502 #011-03-1969 L1981 **R** *071 †80
KNOWLES, Robert Chas. 160 KINGSLEY LN, STE 400 23505 #036-05-1989 L1996 **GS** *020
KOCH, Laine Harlow. ■ 23517 #051-07-2005 L2005 **D** *012
KOEHL, George Wm. 1909 GRANBY ST STE A, PEDIATRIC ASSOC 23517 #056-06-1965 L1972 **PD** *020 †55
KOEN, Joseph Lee. 905 REDGATE AVE, STE 200 23507 #038-40-1993 L1999 **NS** *020 †25
KOLLINS, Kevin Michael. ■ 23507 #051-07-2007 L2007 **PD** *012
KONDYLIS, Filippos I. ■ 23518 #418-01-1989 L1996 **U** *100
KOO, Ellen Hoiyoung. ■ 23507 #051-07-2008 *012
KORPE, Poonum Satish. ■ 23517 #051-07-2008 *012
KOSARAC, Ognjen. PO BOX 1980, EASTERN VA MED SCH 23501 #957-08-1988 L2004 **PTH** *012
KREGER, David Lawrence. 160 KINGSLEY LN, STE 200 23505 #051-04-1972 L1973 **GE IM** *020 †20
KROP, Paul Nicholas. 160 KINGSLEY LN, STE 405 23505 #010-02-1969 L1975 **HS ORS** *020 †40
KRUGER, David B. ■ 23507 #051-01-1953 L1953 **P** *071
KUHN, Marcia Ann. 601 CHILDRENS LN, STE 5B 23507 #055-02-1996 L2005 **GS** *020 †85
KULBERG, Heidi Amanda. 425 W 20TH ST, PLANNED PARENTHOOD OF SE 23517 #003-01-1995 L2005 **FM** *020 †18
KUMAR, Anita. 100 KINGSLEY LN, STE 100 23505 #473-04-2000 L2006 **IM** *020
KURAMSHYNA, Iryna. EVMS - OFFICE OF GME, C/O HILDA HOBBS, REGISTRAR 23507 #913-13-1993 L2007 **FP** *012
KURTZ, Eleanor Judith. ■ 23510 #038-40-2007 L2007 **IM** *012
KUSHNER, David Chaim. 825 FAIRFAX AVE, STE 541 23507 #041-01-1971 L1998 **PDR PD** *020 †80
KWONG, Peter Onchung. 6333 CENTER DR, BLDG 16 23502 #051-04-1996 L2002 **U** *020 †95
LADAGA, Leopoldo Elio. 600 GRESHAM DR, SENTARA NORFOLK GEN HOSPIT 23507 #275-01-1954 L1960 **PTH** *071 †50
LAFORGIA, Audrone. PO BOX 1980 23501 #913-49-1991 L2006 **PD** *012
LALL-TRAIL, Joel K. 885 KEMPSVILLE RD 23502 #035-15-1995 L2000 **OPH** *020 †35
LANCE, Raymond Scott. 6333 CENTER DR, BLDG 16 23502 #023-12-1991 L2006 **U** *020 †95
LANOVE, Robert J, Jr. 160 KINGSLEY LN, STE 203 23505 #051-07-1985 L1990 **N IM** *020 †75
LAPLACE, Lea J. 426 E FREEMASON ST, ASSOCIATED IN PRIMARY 23510 #051-07-1998 L1998 **IM** *020 †20
LAPLACE, Peter Borsch. 426 E FREEMASON ST, ASSOCIATED IN PRIMARY 23510 #051-07-1999 L1999 **IM** *020 †20
LA ROCCO, Anthony, Jr. 825 FAIRFAX AVE, EASTERN VA MED SCH 23507 #010-01-1982 L1991 **ID** *020 †20
LARSON, Daniel Ander. ■ 23507 #038-41-2007 L2007 **OTO** *012
LASSETER, David Howell. 855 W BRAMBLETON AVE 23510 #038-41-1985 L1999 **END** *020 †20
LATHAM, Vicki Bernice. ■ 23517 #051-04-2002 L2004 **IMG** *100 †20
LA VAY, Donald Edward. 825 FAIRFAX AVE, STE 541 23507 #023-01-1977 L1989 **DR** *020 †80
LAZERNICK, Samara Dawn. ■ 23517 #051-07-2008 *012
LE, Dau Thanh. 249 S NEWTOWN RD 23502 #941-01-1975 L1988 **IM GP** *020 †20
LEAVEN, Trey Henry. 920 ELM CT 23502 #051-07-2004 L2004 **GS** *100
LECKY, Danielle Joy. ■ 23517 #051-07-2007 L2007 **PD** *012
LEDERMAN, Ira Robert. 7312 GRANBY ST 23505 #035-08-1962 L1963 **OPH** *071 †35
LEE, Albert H. 850 KEMPSVILLE RD 23502 #016-02-1987 L1992 **RHU IM** *020 †20
LEE, Bo Ryung. PO BOX 1980 23501 #583-10-1986 L2006 **FP** *012
LEE, John Jos. 1562 MITSCHER AVE, STE 200 23551 #056-05-1966 L1972 **P** *020 †75
LEE, Sarah Canfield. 171 KEMPSVILLE RD, BLDG B 23502 #055-01-2004 L2004 **PD** *020 †55
LEE, Travis. 721 FAIRFAX AVE, GHENT FAMILY PRACTICE CTR 23507 #038-45-1997 L2007 **FM SCI** *020
LEIDEL, Bernadette E. 6345 CENTER DR, BLDG 14 23502 #051-07-1991 L1993 **PD** *020 †55
LENTZ, Brian Keith. 1052 N SHORE RD, INOVA FAIRFAX HOSPITAL 23505 #021-01-1997 L2004 **OS** *020 †20,16
LESHER, Katrina Marie. 601 CHILDRENS LN, SIXTH FLOOR 23507 #051-04-2001 L2001 **PM** *100 †60
LESTER, Richard Garrison. EASTERN VA MEDICAL SCHOOL, DEPT OF RADIOLOGY 23501 #035-01-1948 L1961 **DR** *071 †80
LETTIERI, Christina Kay. ■ 23510 #055-01-2007 L2007 **PD** *012
LETTIS, Stacey Marija. ■ 23507 #051-07-2008 *012
LEVIN, David Martin. 120 CORPORATE BLVD, STE 400 23502 #043-01-1988 L1991 **FM** *020 †18
LEVY, Edward David. 6161 KEMPSVILLE CIR, STE 200 23502 #036-07-1942 L1947 **IM PD** *071
LEWIS, Donald Wray. 850 SOUTHAMPTON AVE 23510 #051-04-1979 L1983 **CHN PD** *020 †55,75
LEWIS-PRINCE, Marna T. 601 CHILDRENS LN 23507 #051-04-2002 L2002 **PD** *020 †55
LI, Wei. 825 FAIRFAX AVE, STE 646 23507 #243-72-1984 L2001 **PM** *020 †60
LIDMAN, Roger Wm. 6275 E VA BEACH BLVD, STE 200 23502 #023-07-1975 L1981 **RHU IM** *020 †20
LIEBIG, Tina Tran. ■ 23505 #023-12-1994 L1996 **DR** *020
LIEN, Buu T. 1529 INTERNATIONAL BLVD, STE 103 23513 #941-01-1971 L1981 **PD GP** *020 †55
LIESKE, Jonathan Michael. 1300 HELICOPTER RD, BLDG 3854 23521 #038-43-1998 L1999 **GPM** *020 †70
LIGHT, Robert Thomas. 1500 E LITTLE CREEK RD 23518 #654-01-1999 L1999 **P** *020 †75
LILLY, Edward Lewis. 229 W BUTE ST, STE 900 23510 #051-04-1968 L1968 **GE IM** *071 †20
LIN, Yen-Jwu Olive. ■ 23510 #036-08-2007 L2007 **EM** *012
LINA, Paula J. 3 COMMERCIAL PL, NORFOLK SOUTHERN CORPORATI 23510 #036-05-1987 L1988 **OM** *030 †70
LINE, Charles Genghis. 358 MOWBRAY ARCH # 203 23507 #051-01-2004 L2004 **FM** *020 †18
LINNAN, Brigid Mary. ■ 23505 #035-03-2005 L2005 **EM** *012
LIPSKIS, Donald Jos. 100 KINGSLEY LN, CARDIOLOGY CONSULTANTS 23505 #016-43-1977 L1983 **CD EM** *020 †20
LISNER, Charles Alan. 229 W BUTE ST, STE 700 23510 #051-01-1993 L1996 **IM** *020 †20
LIU, John Shieping. 110 KINGSLEY LN, STE 509 23505 #051-04-1991 L1997 **U** *020 †95
LIVINGOOD, Jennifer C. 1909 GRANBY ST STE A, PEDIATRIC ASSOCIATES 23517 #051-04-1999 L1999 **PD** *020 †55
LO, Bruce Mingyung. 600 GRESHAM DR 23507 #051-01-2001 L2004 **EM** *020 †16
LOBRAICO, Dayna Terese. ■ 23507 #016-01-2005 L2006 *100
LODICO, Matthew Jeanpaul. ■ 23502 #051-07-2008 L2008 *012
LOFGREN, Michael S. PO BOX 1980, DEPT OF SURGERY 23501 #051-07-2003 L2003 **GS** *012
LOGAN, Joshua Eugene. PO BOX 1980, EASTERN VA MED SCH 23501 #012-05-2006 L2006 **U** *012
LOIACONO, Patsy Julius. 6330 N CENTER DR, BLDG #13 STE 220 23502 #033-05-1966 L1968 **R NM** *020 †80,28
LONG, Lacy Marie. ■ 23517 #047-06-2006 L2006 **OBG** *012
LONGBOTHAM, Sonja. PO BOX 1980, DEPT OF RADIOLOGY STE 541 23501 #048-13-2004 L2005 **DR** *012
LOPATINA, Olga Alex. 252 W OCEAN VIEW AVE 23503 #051-04-2004 L2004 **DR** *012
LOVEGREEN, Mary Therese. ■ 23507 #051-07-2008 *012
LOVELL, Charles F. 142 W YORK ST STE 905 23510 #035-01-1972 L1976 **IM PHP** *020 †20
LOWE, Eric Jeffrey. 601 CHILDRENS LN 23507 #012-05-1998 L2004 **PHO** *020 †55
LUBIN, Barry Chas. 885 KEMPSVILLE RD STE 221 23502 #051-04-1975 L1979 **IM** *020 †20
LUEBBERT, Phillip David. 6330 N CENTER DR, BLDG 13 23502 #051-07-1987 L1988 **DR VIR** *020 †80
LUKBAN, James Chivian. 825 FAIRFAX AVE, STE 310 23507 #041-77-1991, ▲ L2005 **GYN** *020 †30
LUMSDEN, Nicholas Adam. ■ 23509 #051-07-2008 L2008 *012
LUSBY, Kristelle Elise. ■ 23517 #051-07-2007 **GS** *012
MACK, Bryan Douglas. 1468 INGRAM ST, CINCLANTFLT (GREEN SIDE) 23551 #051-07-2000 L2002 **AN** *020
MADREN, Lisa Kopec. 850 KEMPSVILLE RD 23502 #051-01-1996 L1996 **IM** *020 †20
MAGEE, Wm Preston, Jr. 400 W BRAMBLETON AVE, STE 301 23510 #010-01-1972 L1974 **PS OS** *020 †65
MAGLAYA, Fernando M. 850 KEMPSVILLE RD 23502 #748-01-1989 L2001 **IM** *020 †20
MAGNESS, Alfred P, II. 600 GRESHAM DR 23507 #038-40-1973 L1980 **NS** *020 †25
MAHAFFEY, Samuel Martin. 601 CHILDRENS LN, STE 5B 23507 #055-01-1979 L2005 **PDS** *020 †85
MAHON, Ellen Ruth. 2203 E LITTLE CREEK RD, ROOSEVELT FAMILY MEDICINE 23518 #041-07-1980 L1985 **FM** *040 †18
MAHONEY, Paul Dennis. 844 KEMPSVILLE RD, CARDIOLOGY CONSULTANTS 23502 #035-20-1993 L1999 **CD** *020 †20
MAJETHIA, Sheetal Arun. 358 MOWBRAY ARCH, DEPT OF GME 23507 #661-03-2006 L2006 **IM** *012
MAJITHIA, Rajiv Tushar. ■ 23508 #051-07-2007 L2007 **IM** *012
MALAKOOTI, Mark Ata. 1887 POWHATAN ST, NEPMU2 23511 #054-04-1989 L2001 **GPM** *062 †70
MALKMAN, Caryn. 1400 GRANBY ST, UNIT 218 23510 #051-04-2004 L2004 **OBG** *012
MANDEL, Lee Richard. 562 MITSCHER AVE SUITE 250, ATTN: CREDENTIAL OFFICE 23551 #011-02-1976 L1981 **IM AM** *020 †20,70 ‡
MANICKAVASAGAR, Marie J. 925 S MAIN ST 23523 #220-01-1965 L1973 **IM NEP** *020 †20
MANJONEY, Dawn Yvonne. 600 GRESHAM DR 23507 #051-07-1984 L1991 **CD IM** *071 †20
MANN, Jonathan Randall. 229 W BUTE ST, STE 500 23510 #654-01-2002 L2005 **IM** *020 †20
MANN, Robert Fletcher. 902 GRAYDON AVE 23507 #036-05-1959 L1969 **IM** *020 †20
MANNSFELD, Christian P. 150 KINGSLEY LN, DEPAUL MEDICAL CENTER 23505 #001-02-1993 L2004 **EM** *020 †16
MANSER, Thomas Jos. 825 FAIRFAX AVE 23507 #025-12-1981 L1984 **IM** *040 †20
MANSHEIM, Paul Adolph. 110 KINGSLEY LN, STE 401 23505 #056-05-1971 L1981 **CHP P** *020 †75
MAPANAO, Vivian Ubando. PO BOX 1980 23501 #748-16-2000 L2005 **FP** *012
MAPLES, Christopher John. 1562 MITSCHER AVE STE 250, OFFICE OF FLEET SURGEON 23551 #041-13-2001 L2001 **EM** *012
MARCINCZYK, Michael John. 600 GRESHAM DR, # 8620 23507 #033-06-1992 L2000 **VS** *020 †85
MARESH, Charles Geo. 110 KINGSLEY LN, STE 207 23505 #005-11-1970 L1976 **IM** *020 †20
MARGOLIUS, Alvin, Jr. ■ 23505 #035-01-1952 L1958 **ON HEM** *071 †20

■ = Address Information Privacy Protected

MARKHAM, Thomas Carl. 844 KEMPSVILLE RD STE 101 23502 #036-01-1975 L1981 ORS *020 †40 ‡

MARKS, Robert Murray. ■ 23503 #023-12-2003 L2004 PD *020

MARKWITH, Andrew Neil. ■ 23507 #051-07-2008 *012

MARSHALL, Timothy L. 930 MAJESTIC AVE 23504 #051-04-1977 L1978 CD IM *020 †20

MARSTELLER, Luisa Portal. 150 KINGSLEY LN 23505 #051-01-1981 L1987 DR *050 †80

MARTENS, Werner. 902 GRAYDON AVE 23507 #005-12-1968 L1972 IM *020

MARTON, Stephanie Ann. ■ 23507 #051-07-2004 L2004 PD *012 †55

MASCARINAS, Thelma C. 7665 SEWELLS POINT RD, NORFOLK HEALTH DEPT 23513 #748-01-1961 L1972 PD CD *071 †55

MASON, Cherral Jeanne W. ■ 23509 #021-01-1979 L1981 GP PD *020

MASON, Jon Donavon. 601 CHILDRENS LN 23507 #021-01-1978 L1995 EM PD *020 †55,16

MASON, Jonathan Richard. ■ 23509 #051-07-2008 *012

MASON, M Elizabeth. 855 W BRAMBLETON AVE 23510 #038-41-1984 L1989 IM *020 †20

MASON-LESLIE, Windy. 880 KEMPSVILLE RD, STE 2600 23502 #051-04-1997 L1997 PD *020 †55

MASOUD, Fatma Ramzi. 358 MOWBRAY ARCH, EVMS OFFICE OF GME 23507 #915-04-1975 L2006 FP *012

MATCHETT, Robert Michael. 600 GRESHAM DR 23507 #020-12-1977 L1980 AN *020 †05

MATSON, Christine Coberly. 721 FAIRFAX AVE, DEPT OF FAMILY & COMM MED 23507 #048-04-1978 L1993 FM *030 †18 ‡

MATSON, David Owen. 855 W BRAMBLETON AVE 23510 #048-04-1983 L1993 ID PD *040 †55

MATTHEWS, Karen Leigh. ■ 23507 #005-12-1997 L2007 DR *020 †70

MAURIELLO, Clifford Thoma. 601 CHILDRENS LN, THE KING'S 23507 #051-07-2007 L2007 PD *012

MAY, Shawno E. 1562 MITSCHER AVE STE 250, U.S ATLANTIC FLEET - NO2MC 23551 #021-01-1987 L1988 OPH GP *020

MAYER, Andrew Anthony. 600 GRESHAM DR 23507 #035-15-1959 L1965 R *020 †80

MC ARTOR, Robert Dennis. 601 CHILDRENS LN, DIVISION OF NEONATOLOGY 23507 #012-05-1966 L1970 NPM PD *020 †20

MC CARTHY, Mark Jos. 802 MEDICAL TOWER 23507 #018-03-1983 L1991 OPH IM *020 †20,35 ‡

MC COLE, Shannon Marie. 885 KEMPSVILLE RD 23502 #016-43-1993 L1993 OPH CS *040 †35

MC COY, Stephen Hartzell. ■ 23507 #021-01-1968 L1970 ORS *071 †40

MCCUNE, Thomas Robert. 1902 OMOHUNDRO AVE STE 100 23517 #051-07-1985 L1986 NEP OS *020 †20

MC DANIEL, Wm Windsor. 825 FAIRFAX AVE, 7TH FL 23507 #020-12-1982 L1985 P *020 †75

MCDAVIT, Michael Kent. ■ 23507 #035-09-2006 L2006 EM *012

MCDONALD, Douglas Rivingt. ■ 23508 #051-07-2008 *012

MCDOWELL, Christina Anne. ■ 23510 #051-07-2004 L2004 IM *012

MC ENTEE, Kathleen H. 825 FAIRFAX AVE 23507 #026-04-1975 L1981 IM *020 †20

MC GAUGHEY, Dean S, III. 5900 LAKE WRIGHT DR, VIRGINIA ONCOLOGY ASSOICAT 23502 #016-02-1994 L2000 HO *020 †20

MC GRATH, Michael Ford. 600 GRESHAM DR, STE 8600 23507 #010-02-1991 L1999 TS *020 †90,85

MC GRUDER, Jon Malley. 600 GRESHAM DR 23507 #051-01-1985 L1989 AN *020 †05

MC KENZIE, Susan E. 825 FAIRFAX AVE, STE 541 23507 #051-07-1981 L1982 DR *020 †80

MCLAIN, Kelly Lynn. ■ 23513 #055-02-2005 L2005 PD *012

MC LEOD, Melissa Mytyle. 601 CHILDRENS LN 23507 #036-01-1989 L1997 AN *020 †05

MC MONAGLE, Joseph S. ■ 23508 #048-14-2001 L2006 DR *012

MC NEIL, Kimberly Maureen. ■ 23507 #017-20-1991 L1992 DR *020 †80

MC NEILL, Douglas Hugh. 1562 MITSCHER AVE STE 250, OFFICE OF FLEET SURGEON/NO 23551 #035-01-1972 L1973 FM *020 †18

MC NULTY, Patricia Louise. ■ 23507 #051-07-2004 L2004 OBG *100

MCPADDEN, Kathleen Anne. ■ 23507 #051-07-2008 *012

MC PHEE, Hugh Thos. 6345 CENTER DR 23502 #001-02-1977 L1982 PD *020 †55

MEADE, Thomas Stanley, Jr. 160 KINGSLEY LN, STE 405 23505 #051-04-1973 L1977 ORS *020 †40

MEIER, Avi Zev. ■ 23517 #010-01-2005 L2006 OPH *012

MELIA, Michael Roy. ■ 23507 #023-12-2003 L2004 EM *012

MENEES, Stacy Bartnik. 885 KEMPSVILLE RD, STE 114 23502 #056-05-1999 L2006 GE *100 †20

MERCER, Angela M. 1401 TIDEWATER DR, STE 1 23504 #051-04-1977 L1984 IM *020

MEREDITH, Elizabeth Homes. 1909 GRANBY ST STE A, PEDIATRICS ASSOCIATES 23517 #051-07-1981 L1984 PD *020 †55

MIC KUNAS, Victor Herbert. 1909 GRANBY ST STE A, PEDIATRIC ASSOCIATES INC 23517 #011-03-1983 L1989 PD *020 †55

MIKLES, Bethany Michelle. ■ 23508 #011-04-2006 L2006 *012

MILLER, Brent Curtis. ■ 23507 #051-07-2008 *012

MILLER, Donald Harner. 6160 KEMPSVILLE CIR, STE 203B 23502 #051-01-1961 L1961 OBG *071 †30

MILLER, Jill Dana. 601 CHILDRENS LN 23507 #051-01-1997 L2003 PD PEM *020 †55

MILLER, Jonathan Wm. 6161 KEMPSVILLE CIR, STE 225 23502 #051-01-1975 L1980 IM *020 †20

MILLER, Newton Byrd. 160 KINGSLEY LN, STE 303 23505 #051-07-1977 L1978 OBG *020

MILLER, Norman. 885 KEMPSVILLE RD 23502 #165-01-1979 L1981 U *071 †95

MILLER, Richard H. 600 GRESHAM DR, NORFOLK GEN HOSP RADIOLOGY 23507 #011-03-1969 L1971 DR *071 †80

MILLER, Scott Arnold. 850 KEMPSVILLE RD 23502 #051-01-1977 L1982 IM ID *020 †20

MILLER, Stephen Franklin. 6330 CENTER DR, STE 220 23502 #047-05-1987 L1994 DR *020 †80

MINASIAN, Joanna Lu. 850 KEMPSVILLE RD, NDC-MEDICALCENTER 23502 #054-04-1996 L2006 IM *020 †20

MINER, James Monroe. 6330 NEWTOWN RD STE 625 23502 #005-15-1963 L1993 CHP ADM *071 ‡

MISTRY, Zarine. 850 KEMPSVILLE RD, C/O NDC-MEDICAL CENTER 23502 #220-01-1972 L1981 EM IM *020 †20,16

MITCHELL, Paul B, Jr. 400 GRESHAM DR, STE 200 23507 #023-12-1988 L2002 NS GP *020 †25

MOHAN, Ravinder. 721 FAIRFAX AVE, EASTERN VA MEDICAL SCHOOL 23507 #495-77-1979 L1999 FM *020 †18

MOHR, Melinda Richardson. ■ 23508 #051-07-2007 L2007 IM *012

MOLLIGAN, Harry Jos. 600 GRESHAM DR 2RP, SENTARA NORFOLK GENERAL HO 23507 #021-05-1983 L1987 OSS OTR *020 †40

MONEYMAKER, Carolyn Sue. 601 CHILDRENS LN, CHILDREN'S HOSPITAL 23507 #047-06-1983 L1995 PD *020 †55

MONTGOMERY, Thomas Robt. 850 SOUTHAMPTON AVE 23510 #010-01-1975 L1983 PD OS *020 †55

MOONEY, Martha Lynn. 850 KEMPSVILLE RD 23502 #051-07-1983 L1984 ID IM *020 †20

MOORE, Alfred Andrew D. 600 GRESHAM DR 23507 #352-07-1954 L1966 CD PDC *071 †55

MOORE, Andrew Wayne. ■ 23517 #051-07-2008 *012

MORA, Obiamaka N. 601 COLLEY AVE STE 243, EVMS 23507 #038-44-2006 L2006 OBG *012

MORENO, Leopold S D. ■ 23510 #132-01-1951 L1956 FM CD *072 †18

MOREWITZ, Jerry Howard. 825 FAIRFAX AVE 23507 #051-01-1975 L1977 CHP P *020 †75

MORIARTY, Richard Paul. 600 GRESHAM DR, 2ND FL 23507 #024-16-1975 L1980 PTH HMP *020 †50

MORINA, John Michael. 160 KINGSLEY LN, STE 405 23505 #051-01-1979 L1985 ORS *020 †40

MORRIS, Deborah Alissa. 825 FAIRFAX AVE STE 4, INTERNAL MEDICINE 23507 #011-03-2005 L2005 IM *012

MORSE, Jeffrey Hale. 930 REDGATE AVE 23507 #051-01-1982 L1983 P *020 †75

MORTON, Robert A. 1309 KEMPSVILLE RD 23502 #051-04-1952 L1952 IM FOP *071

MORTON, Terrence M. ■ 23504 #047-07-2001 L2001 GS *012

MORTON, Willie Alexander. 600 GRESHAM DR 23507 #035-08-1982 L1991 AN *020 †05

MOSQUERA, Guillermo. 400 W BRAMBLETON AVE # 100 23510 #264-01-1965 L1973 U *020 †95

MOSS, Burton Alan. 302A E LITTLE CREEK RD 23505 #051-04-1961 L1961 AI PDA *020 †55,03

MOUNTS, Jason Aaron. 601 CHILDRENS LN, THE KING'S 23507 #012-01-2002 L2002 PEM *012 †55

MUCCIARONE, James Joseph. 1840 COVE RD, NAVAL SPECIAL WARFARE GROU 23521 #023-12-2004 L2005 *100

MULDER, Erica Pearson. 601 CHILDRENS LN, CHKD 23507 #012-01-2004 L2004 PD *012 †55

MUNOZ, Cynthia Isela. 601 CHILDRENS LN 23507 #035-20-2002 L2007 AN *100

MURPHY, Thomas George. ■ 23510 #033-05-2005 L2006 *100

MURPHY-HIGGS, Shearin D. 229 W BUTE ST, STE 700 23510 #038-40-1999 L2003 IM *020 †20

MURRAY, Adam Mclean. ■ 23503 #051-07-2003 L2006 OBG *100

MURRAY, Kevin Patrick. 142 W YORK ST, INTERNAL MEDICINE 23510 #539-06-1970 L1973 IM IMG *020 †20

MURTHY, Anitha. 420 N CENTER DR, STE 128 23502 #496-39-1997 L2005 NEP *020 †20

MWAMBA, Theo Ndjongo. PO BOX 1980 23501 #266-03-2003 L2006 FP *012

MYERS, Lindsey Jo. ■ 23507 #051-07-2008 *012

MYRMOE, Jason Christopher. ■ 23507 #046-01-2007 L2007 IFP *012

NADIMI, Lida. 601 CHILDRENS LN, CHKD HOSPITAL 23507 #561-20-1995 L2005 APM *020

NAGAMANGALA, Vidya. EVMS - OFFICE OF GME, C/O HILDA HOBBS 23507 #496-37-1999 L2007 FP *012

NAHAR, Shamsun. 6161 KEMPSVILLE CIR, STE 225 23502 #160-01-1984 L2000 IM *020 †20

NALLS, Cecil Arthur, III. 6330 NEWTOWN RD, NORFOLK PSYCHIATRIC 23502 #051-04-1972 L1975 P *020 †75

NASIM, Suhail. 830 KEMPSVILLE RD 23502 #704-21-1982 L1993 PTH *020 †50

NASR, Munir Fares. 5900 LAKE WRIGHT DR, GYN ONCOLOGY 23502 #605-01-1965 L1987 OBG GO *020 †20

NATHAN, Matthew Lincoln. ■ 23508 #012-01-1981 L1982 IM *020 †20

NAYLOR, William Talbott. 902 GRAYDON AVE 23507 #051-04-1972 L1972 IM *020

NEAL, Richard King. ■ 23510 #054-04-1955 L1962 NS *071 †25

NEFF, Eric Swanson. 6275 E VIRGINIA BCH BLVD B 23502 #047-06-1998 L1998 ORS *020 †40

NEUGHEBAUER, Bogdan Ioan. 850 KEMPSVILLE RD 23502 #781-02-1992 L2003 ID *020 †20

NEWBY, James E, II. 930 MAJESTIC AVE, STE 220 23504 #051-07-1981 L1984 FM *020 †18

NEWBY, Keith Howard. 400 GRESHAM DR, STE 507 23507 #051-07-1990 L1994 CD *020 †20

NEWMAN, Rosanne. 825 FAIRFAX AVE STE 201, EASTERN VA MED SCH/INTERN 23507 #550-02-1983 L1990 IM IMG *020 †20

NEWTON, James Arthur, Jr. 850 KEMPSVILLE RD 23502 #004-01-1987 L1988 ID IM *020 †20

NEWTON, Joseph R, Jr. 600 GRESHAM DR, STE 8600 23507 #036-07-1984 L1991 TS *020 †85,90

NGUYEN, Chan Vuong. 825 FAIRFAX AVE, STE 541 23507 #041-12-1992 L1993 DR *020 †80

NGUYEN, Vinh Ngoc. 825 FAIRFAX AVE # 541, EVMS-DEPT. OF RADIOLOGY 23507 #005-15-2005 L2006 DR *012

NICORA BIA, Maria De Lour. 358 MOWBRAY ARCH, EVMS- OFFICE OF GME 23507 #924-01-1994 L2006 FP *012

NIE, Zhiqun. PO BOX 1980 23501 #243-97-1986 L2005 FM *100

NOFFSINGER, Daniel Lyle. 250 W BRAMBLETON AVE, STE 202 23510 #036-05-2001 L2001 OBG *030

NOGA, Josef Rudolfstan. ■ 23507 #051-07-2007 L2007 IM *012

NOORBAKHSH, Matthew Reza. ■ 23507 #051-07-2008 *012

NORDSTROM, Lindsey Morgan. ■ 23517 #051-07-2008 *012

NORRIS, David Michael. 601 CHILDRENS LN 23507 #014-01-1975 L1979 PD *020 †55

NORTHAM, Ralph Shearer. 850 SOUTHAMPTON AVE 23510 #051-07-1984 L1992 CHN N *020 †75,55

NOTTINGHAM, Carol White. 400 GRESHAM DR, STE 811 23507 #051-04-1981 L1983 OBG *020 †30

NOTTINGHAM, Scott Andrew. 171 KEMPSVILLE RD, BLDG B 23502 #051-07-1999 L2002 PD *020 †55

NOVOSEL, Timothy James. ■ 23507 #051-07-2000 L2000 CCS *100 †85

NOVOSEL, Tracy. 700 W OLNEY RD, DEPT OF DERM STE 2054 23507 #051-07-2000 L2001 D *012

NOWROOZI, Maryam Miriam. 110 KINGSLEY LN, STE 309 23505 #051-07-1999 L1999 IM *020 †20

NOWROOZI, Pouran Nadji. 150 KINGSLEY LN, FL 3 23505 #517-01-1966 L1982 OBG *020 †30

NUSS, Donald. 601 CHILDRENS LN, STE 5B 23507 #836-02-1963 L1977 PDS *020 †85

OAKLEY, Christopher Brand. 601 CHILDRENS LN 23507 #051-07-2005 L2005 PD *012

OBERMEYER, Phaik M. 400 W BRAMBLETON AVE, STE 201 23510 #038-44-1997 L2005 FM *020 †18

OBERMEYER, Robert John. 601 CHILDRENS LN STE B, CHILDRENS HOSPITAL OF THE 23507 #038-41-1997 L2005 PDS *020 †85

O'BRIAN, John Thos. 855 W BRAMBLETON AVE 23510 #050-02-1968 L1990 END DIA *020 †20

OBRIANT, David Miles. ■ 23517 #051-07-2008 *012

OEHNINGER, Sergio C. 601 COLLEY AVE 23507 #924-01-1980 L1987 REN *020

OELRICH, William Lyle. 229 W BUTE ST, STE 700 23510 #036-07-1972 L1976 CD IM *020 †20

OKOGWU, Ifeoma Felicia Lu. 358 MOWBRAY ARCH, STE 203 23507 #781-01-1997 L2005 IM *012

OLDFIELD, Edward Chas. 825 FAIRFAX AVE 23507 #051-01-1975 L1993 IM ID *020 †20 ‡

OLEINIK, Eveleen Mary. 825 FAIRFAX AVE, STE 541 23507 #035-01-1992 L2001 DR *020 †80

OLIVER, Jean Livesay. 1909 GRANBY ST STE A, PEDIATRIC ASSOCIATES 23517 #051-07-1995 L1995 PD *020 †55

OLSON, John Robt, Jr. 6330 CENTER DR 23502 #017-20-1968 L1973 R *071 †80

ONG, Arsenio Manlangit. 1232 W LITTLE CREEK RD, STE 300 23505 #748-10-1963 L1983 GP EM *020

OPPLEMAN, Leslie Barri. 2203 E LITTLE CREEK RD 23518 #051-01-1975 L1977 IM EM *020

ORDONEZ, Bernardo Jose. 400 GRESHAM DR, STE 200 23507 #023-01-1989 L1998 NS *020 ‡25

ORNELAS-STANECK, Mona R. ■ 23517 #041-13-2003 L2003 FM *020 †18

OSHEA, Kathy. ■ 23507 #051-07-2008 *012

O'SULLIVAN-MEJIA, Emeralda. ■ 23501 #051-07-2006 L2006 PTH *012

OWEN, William Conally. 601 CHILDRENS LN 23507 #036-05-1986 L1993 PHO PD *020 †55

OWENS, Michael Ray. 830 KEMPSVILLE RD, SENTANA LEIGH HOSPITAL 23502 #036-01-1968 L1989 HEM IM *020 †20

PAGE, Amy Melissa. ■ 23510 #051-07-2004 L2004 GS *012

PAGENKOPF, Eric Larue. ■ 23510 #023-12-1995 L1996 ORS *020

PAIK, Peter D. 358 MOWBRAY ARCH # 203 23507 #051-07-2004 L2004 FM *020

PAIK, Ronald Sungjean. ■ 23507 #051-07-2008 *012

PALMER, Dionne Yahmise. 601 CHILDRENS LN 23507 #010-03-1996 L1996 PD *020 †55

PANGALOS, Themistoklis. 880 KEMPSVILLE RD STE 2700 23502 #418-01-1956 L1962 A *020

PANGILINAN, Alicia Garcia. 825 FAIRFAX AVE STE 201, EVMS 23507 #748-16-1981 L2004 IM IMG *020 †20

PANNETON, Jean M. 600 GRESHAM DR, # 8620 23507 #067-02-1987 L2004 VS *020 †85

PAPANICOLAOU, Mary G. ■ 23505 #418-01-1937 IM *074

PARAGAS, Florence Vergara. 358 MOWBRAY ARCH RM 203, EVMS - OFFICE OF GME 23507 #418-13-1986 L2002 FM *020

PARIZHSKAYA, Maria. 830 KEMPSVILLE RD 23502 #913-09-1984 L2003 PP PTH *020 †50

PARK, Kip K. 825 FAIRFAX AVE, STE 541 23507 #017-20-1991 L2004 DR *020 †80

PARKER, Austin Lyle. 1562 MITSCHER AVE STE 250, OFF OF FLT SURGEON/NO2MC 23551 #023-12-2002 L2003 *020 ‡

PARKER, John Patrick. 844 KEMPSVILLE RD, CARDIOLOGY CONSULTANTS 23502 #038-40-1973 L1979 CD IM *020 †20

PARKER, Reina Haunanijan. ■ 23507 #035-03-2007 L2007 EM *012

PARKER, Sophie B. 400 GRESHAM DR 23507 #495-59-1982 L2005 CD *020 †20

PARSON, Angela Wynoma. ■ 23502 #010-03-2005 L2005 OBG *012

PARTINGTON, Jonathan P. 580 E MAIN ST, STE 200 23510 #038-06-1980 L1981 NS GS *020 ‡25

PASCHAL, James Richard. 330 E BAYVIEW BLVD 23503 #051-07-1980 L1983 IM *020

PASQUINELLI, Lawrence M. 171 KEMPSVILLE RD, BLDG B 23502 #041-02-1991 L1994 PD *020 †55

PATEL, Sheran S. 825 FAIRFAX AVE STE 423, HOFHEIMER HALL 23507 #028-79-1998, ▲ L2005 ID *100 †20

PATTERSON, Aaron Andreas. PROFESS AFFAIRS/NO2HC, OFF OF THE FLEET SURGEON 23551 #017-20-2000 L2001 GPM *012

PAVON, Humberto Francisco. 5700 LAKE WRIGHT DR, STE 101 23502 #726-01-1970 L1974 IM NEP *020 †20

PAYMAN, Gary H. 600 GRESHAM DR 23507 #035-45-1998 L2004 GE *020 †20

PAYNE, George Raymond, III. 160 KINGSLEY LN, STE 405 23505 #051-01-1983 L1989 ORS *020 †40

PAYNE, William Duncan. 160 KINGSLEY LN 23505 #051-04-1962 L1962 GS OS *020 †85

PECSOK, Thomas Richard. 229 W BUTE ST, STE 500 23510 #055-01-1985 L1989 IM *020 †20

PEGRAM, Linda Diane. 601 CHILDRENS LN 23507 #036-01-1995 L2004 PHO PD *020 †55

PELLEGRINO, Thomas Robt. 6161 KEMPSVILLE CIR, STE 315 23502 #020-12-1975 L1980 N *040 †75

PENIX, Jerry O'Don. 601 CHILDRENS LN, STE 5-A 23507 #021-01-1965 L1973 NS *020 ‡25

PERLMAN, Jerome David. ■ 23510 #051-01-1955 L1955 FM *071 †8

PERRY, Roger Ronald. 825 FAIRFAX AVE, EASTERN VA MED SCHOOL 23507 #041-01-1980 L1989 SO GS *020 †20

PESSAR, Marc L. 850 KEMPSVILLE RD 23502 #165-01-1976 L1981 R *040 †80

PETERMAN, Ellen Elizabeth. ■ 23507 #051-07-2007 L2007 IFP *012

PETERSEN, William Carl. 601 CHILDRENS LN 23507 #016-11-1971 L1983 PAN *020 †55,05

PETERSON, Charles Raymond. ■ 23509 #010-01-1955 L1982 PM *071 †60

PETRONIS, Kelli Ann. 601 CHILDRENS LN 23507 #018-03-1999 L2002 PEM *020 †55

PHILIPPAKIS, Spyros. 880 KEMPSVILLE RD 23502 #418-01-1958 L1965 GS *071 †85

PINCKENS, Cedric Durrell. 400 GRESHAM DR, STE 503 23507 #047-07-1985 L1994 GS *020 †85

PIRKLE, Giniene Margaret. 250 W BRAMBLETON AVE, STE 202 23510 #041-02-1999 L1999 OBG *020 †30

PLANAS, Roque Francisco. 208 E PLUME ST, SUTIE 213 23510 #847-06-1975 L1978 PUD CCM *020 †20

PLEASANT, William Andrew. ■ 23510 #051-07-2008 *012

PLEMMONS, John Kenneth. 358 MOWBRAY ARCH # 203, EVMS - OFFICE OF GME 23507 #051-07-2001 L2001 DR *020 †80

POE-ZEIGLER, Robin. 420 N CENTER DR, BLDG 11 23502 #051-07-1989 L1993 REN *020 †30

POFF, Sarah Beth. ■ 23507 #001-02-2007 L2007 PD *012

POHAR, Surjeet Singh. 600 GRESHAM DR, EASTERN VA MEDICAL SCHOOL 23507 #060-01-1985 L2006 RO *020 †80 ‡

POIRIER, Michael Patrick. 601 CHILDRENS LN 23507 #001-02-1990 L1996 PD PEM *020 †55

POLICARPIO, Danilo Ocampo. 825 FAIRFAX AVE, # 410 23507 #055-01-2002 L2003 IM *020 †20

POMICTER, Gregory Ryan. 1562 MITSCHER AVE STE 250, ATTN: CREDENTIAL OFFICE 23551 #050-02-2004 PD *100

POULIN, Nathaniel Robert. 358 MOWBRAY ARCH, STE 203 23507 #016-42-2005 L2005 GS *012

POWERS, Laura. 850 KEMPSVILLE RD 23502 #038-44-1998 L2001 IM *020 †20

PRESSWALLA, Faruk Behram. 401 COLLEY AVE STE A 23507 #495-01-1964 L1976 FOP PTH *062 †50

PRIBLE, Charles Ray. 3 COMMERCIAL PL, NORFOLK SOUTHERN CORP 23510 #017-20-1976 L1994 OM IM *030 †20

PRICE, Amy Louise. 825 FAIRFAX AVE, EVMS FAMILY & COMM MEDICIN 23507 #047-06-1999 L1999 FM *040 †18

PRICE, James Guy. ■ 23508 #051-01-1943 L1943 LM PM *062

PRICE-STEVENS, Lisa N. 885 KEMPSVILLE RD, STE 224 23502 #051-04-1993 L1993 IM *020 †20

PRIMICH, James Francis. 1562 MITSCHER AVE STE 250, CINCLANTFLT 23551 #024-05-1999 L2003 DR *100 †80

PROFFER, Dirk Stanton. 600 GRESHAM DR 2RP, SENTARA NORFOLK GENERAL HO 23507 #016-06-1984 L1993 ORS *020 †40

PROUD, Virginia Kent. 601 CHILDRENS LN, DEPT PEDS 23507 #051-01-1975 L1978 PD MG *020 †55,19

PUDUR, Sudhindra. ■ 23507 #495-65-1996 L2007 NEP *012

PURCHAS, Ivor Norman M. 5900 E VIRGINIA BEACH BLVD, STE 315 23502 #010-03-1976 L1982 GS *020 †85

PURITZ, Holly Suzanne. 250 W BRAMBLETON AVE, STE 202 23510 #024-07-1983 L1986 OBG *020 †30

QUARANTA, Anthony Jos. 850 KEMPSVILLE RD 23502 #422-01-1989 L1996 PCC SME *020 †20

QUARLES, Frederick N. 825 FAIRFAX AVE 23507 #010-03-1981 L1985 D *020 †15

QUIDGLEY NEVARES, Antonio. 825 FAIRFAX AVE, STE 646 23507 #042-01-1999 L1999 PMM *020 †60

QURESHI, Faiqa Aftab. 601 CHILDRENS LN 23507 #704-01-1973 L1978 PD PEM *020 †55

RAAFAT, Reem H. 601 CHILDRENS LN, CHILDREN'S SPECIALTY GROUP 23507 #575-01-1989 L2006 PN *020 †55

RABUSA, Melva Estoy. ■ 23507 #748-07-1972 *100

RACZYNSKI, Rebecca Ann. 601 CHILDRENS LN, DIVISION OF NEONATOLOGY 23507 #033-06-2004 L2004 PD *020 †55

RAGSDALE, Thomas Hall. 706 BALDWIN AVE, P O BOX 11560 23517 #047-06-1979 L1986 PS HS *020 †65,85

RAGULINCOYNE, Elizaveta. ■ 23505 #051-07-2008 *012

RAI, Aanmol Inderjeet Kau. EVMS OFFICE OF GME 23507 #495-29-1993 L2005 P *012

RAMEY, Erik Lynn. 1562 MITSCHER AVE STE 250, ATTN: CREDENTIAL OFFICE 23551 #023-12-2004 L2005 *020

RAMIREZ, Dana Erickson. 601 CHILDRENS LN 23507 #051-07-1998 L2005 PEM *020 †55

RANA, Lubna. 358 MOWBRAY ARCH # 203 23507 #704-06-1995 L2004 FM *020 †18

RANGAVAJHULA, Ramani N. EVMS - OFFICE OF GME, C/O HILDA HOBBS, REGISTRAR 23507 #495-57-1988 L2007 FP *012

RANKINS, Nicole Calloway. 825 FAIRFAX AVE, STE 310 23507 #051-07-2002 L2008 OBG *020

RAPLEY, James Carlos, III. ■ 23507 #024-01-2008 *012

RASHTI, Robert Aaron. 425 W 20TH ST, STE 6 23517 #048-02-1968 L1976 NS GP *030 ‡25

RAUSTOL, Ole Anton. ■ 23508 #043-01-2001 L2001 ORS *020

RAWLINGS, Ann Elizabeth. ■ 23505 #045-04-2000 L2003 GP *020

RAWLS, William Holland. 110 KINGSLEY LN, STE 509 23505 #051-07-1985 L1990 U *020 †95

REDA, Annette Williams. 885 KEMPSVILLE RD STE 101 23502 #016-11-1972 L1980 OPH *020 †35 ‡

REDD, Joan Louise. 150 KINGSLEY LN, DEPAUL MEDICAL CENTER-ACUT 23505 #051-01-1992 L2007 PM *020 †60

REDDEN, Timothy James. 600 GRESHAM DR, STE 203 23507 #028-34-2001 L2003 U *020

REDDING, Anne Denise. 160 KINGSLEY LN, STE 203 23505 #010-02-1987 L1992 N *020 †75

REDDY, Venkat Manoranjan. 400 GRESHAM DR, STE 308 23507 #016-02-1988 L1994 OPH *020 †35

REED, Jennifer Lucille. 8042 W GLEN RD 23505 #036-01-1994 L1998 PM *020 †60

REED, Scott Fredric. 825 FAIRFAX AVE 23507 #041-09-1997 L2002 GS *020 †85

REED, William Washington. 160 KINGSLEY LN, STE 505 23505 #051-04-1978 L1979 RHU IM *020 †20

REID, David Wm. 6320 N CENTER DR STE 101, CLINCL ASSOC OF TIDEWATER 23502 #025-01-1969 L1981 CHP P *020 †75

REIF, James Lawrence. 101 W 35TH ST 23504 #649-14-1971 L1976 P *020

REINA, Abdon. 1090 ALGONQUIN RD 23505 #264-05-1963 L1967 NS *071 ‡25

REMLEY, Karen Lynn. 601 CHILDRENS LN 23507 #028-46-1980 L1991 PD *020 †55

RENDA, Paul. 600 GRESHAM DR 23507 #035-47-1981 L1984 AN IM *020,05

RENINGER, Jennifer Rachel. 229 W BUTE ST STE 700, CONSULTANTS IN INTERNAL ME 23510 #041-01-1998 L2005 IM *020 †20

RENIVA, Faustino A. 249 S NEWTOWN RD 23502 #748-08-1986 L1994 IM *020 †20

REON, Julia F. 249 S NEWTOWN RD 23502 #011-02-1991 L1994 IM *020 †20

RESHEFSKY, Bonnie Louis. 7312 GRANBY ST 23505 #051-01-1967 L1967 OPH *071 †35

RICART, Esther Parada. ■ 23507 #847-12-1994 PDI *100

RICASA, Jocelyn Candelari. ■ 23508 #051-07-2007 L2007 IFP *012

RICCIO, Amy Davis. 171 KEMPSVILLE RD, BLDG B 23502 #051-07-1989 L1990 PD *020 †55

RICE, Marcus Chas. 160 KINGSLEY LN, STE 203 23505 #035-45-1976 L1979 N *020 †75

RICH, Jeffrey Brian. 600 GRESHAM DR, # 8600 23507 #016-02-1981 L1990 TS *020 †85,90

RICH, Thomas Jonathan. 600 GRESHAM DR 23507 #035-01-1983 L1991 AN *020 †05

RICHARDSON, Albert I. 600 GRESHAM DR, MED SCHOOL 23507 #012-22-2002 L2007 VS *012 †85

RICHARDSON, Donald W. 855 W BRAMBLETON AVE 23507 #051-04-1976 L1986 IM END *020 †20

RICHARDSON, Donald W. ■ 23505 #065-01-1966 L1979 PD P *020 †55

RICHMOND, Bill B. 6161 KEMPSVILLE CIR, STE 220 23502 #051-01-1973 L1982 ID IM *020 †20

RIEGLE, Carolyn Mary. 600 GRESHAM DR 23507 #051-07-1979 L1987 PD CCM *020 †55

RIGGS, Ryan Michael. 601 COLLEY AVE 23507 #039-01-2001 L2006 OBG *100

RIGGS, Stephen Boyd. 6333 CENTER DR BLDG 16 23502 #045-01-2001 L2008 U *100

RIJHWANI, Suresh Kumar. 830 KEMPSVILLE RD 23502 #704-02-1990 L2003 NEP *020 †20

RIMPLE, Hubert Mc Donald. ■ 23518 #010-03-1957 L1984 PHP IM *071

RIOS, Veronica Carranza. ■ 23507 #051-07-2004 L2004 EM *012

RIPPLINGER, Julie Lynn. 601 CHILDRENS LN, DIVISION OF NEONATOLOGY 23507 #051-07-2000 L2000 PD *020 †55

ROBERTSON, Charlene Marie. 426 E FREEMASON ST, ASSOCIATED IN PRIMARY 23510 #051-01-1994 L1994 IM *020 †20

ROBINETT, William L. 850 KEMPSVILLE RD, NDC MEDICAL CENTER 23502 #561-17-1978 L1980 EM *020 †20,16

ROBINSON, Daniel George. 601 CHILDRENS LN 23507 #020-12-2003 L2003 PD *020 †55

RODRIGUEZ, Jose Hiram. 300 E MAIN ST STE 1000, COMMANDER KQA 23510 #042-01-1978 L1996 PM *074 †18

ROGAN, Christopher J. 1562 MITSCHER AVE STE 250, ATTN: CREDENTIAL OFFICE 23551 #024-05-2004 L2004 GS *100

ROGERS, Anne Theresa R. 600 GRESHAM DR 23507 #919-05-1975 L1999 AN *020 †05

ROGERS, Henry Moore, Jr. ■ 23510 #036-05-1947 L1953 PD *071 †55

ROGERS, Jerry Ray. ■ 23505 #047-06-1959 L1964 EM GP *020

ROGERS, Lynette Sylvia. 7924 CHESAPEAKE BLVD, BAYVIEW MEDICAL CENTER 23518 #143-03-1967 L1974 GP IM *020

ROMULO, Rodrigo Luis Cruz. 6161 KEMPSVILLE CIR, STE 220 23502 #748-01-1983 L2003 IM *020 †20

RONO, Vicente N, Jr. 830 KEMPSVILLE RD 23502 #748-01-1964 L1972 FM *020 †18

ROPER, Albert L, II. 901 HAMPTON BLVD, EAR NOSE & THROAT LTD 23507 #036-01-1967 L1975 OTO FPS *071 †45

ROSEMAN, John Tyler, II. ■ 23507 #051-07-2008 *012

ROSS, Bertrand Alexander. 601 CHILDRENS LN 23507 #020-02-1977 L1988 PDC *020 †55

ROSS, C Denise Guinn. 830 KEMPSVILLE RD 23502 #048-12-1971 L1975 BBK PTH *075 †50 ‡

ROSS, Helen Rozella. 601 MEDICAL TOWER 23507 #028-03-1997 L2001 **D** *020 †15

ROURKE, Keith Francis. 400 W BRAMBLETON AVE, STE 100 23510 #064-01-1996 L2001 **U** *100

ROWE, Daniel Flaherty. ■ 23517 #051-07-2008 *012

ROWLAND, Leah Catherine. 885 KEMPSVILLE RD, STE 200 23502 #026-08-2003 L2007 **PD** *020 †55

ROWLEY, Dennis Alan. 830 KEMPSVILLE RD 23502 #019-02-1980 L1989 **PTH** *020 †50

ROYER, Thomas C. 3153 AZALEA GARDEN RD 23513 #051-04-1950 L1950 **GP AM** *020

RUIZ, Abelardo Antonio. 600 GRESHAM DR 23507 #051-01-1981 L1984 **AN** *020 †05

RUKA, Elizabeth Lynn. ■ 23508 #012-01-2005 **PD** *012

RUSHING, Gregory Duncan. 825 FAIRFAX AVE, STE 610 23507 #011-04-2002 L2002 **GS** *012

RUSSO, Anthony Ralph. 1326 E LITTLE CREEK RD, SENTARA MEDICAL CARE CENTE 23518 #035-15-1987 L1990 **FM** *020 †18

RUST, Harlan Curtis. 6160 KEMPSVILLE CIR, STE 302A 23502 #041-02-1998 L2005 **NEP** *020 †20

RUZICKA, Petr Oldrich. 601 CHILDRENS LN 23507 #026-04-1976 L2006 **PD NS** *020 †25

RYAN, Gordon Alan. 411 MEDICAL TOWER 23507 #649-33-1980 L1982 **IM** *020 †20

RYAN, Lawrence Brielman. PO BOX 14307 23518 #032-01-1999 L1999 **GP** *030

RYAN, Michael James. 885 KEMPSVILLE RD 23502 #051-07-1979 L1984 **GE IM** *020 †20

RYSZKIEWICZ, Rebecca Lynn. ■ 23508 #035-06-2008 *012

SAADEH, Ghandi M. 850 KEMPSVILLE RD, NDC MEDICAL CENTER 23502 #605-01-1983 L1992 **IM END** *020 †20

SABIR, Naheed Saleem. 825 FAIRFAX AVE STE 710, EASTERN VIRGINIA MEDICAL S 23507 #704-06-1993 L1998 **P** *020

SACHSE, Hans Paul Edward. 825 FAIRFAX AVE, STE 541 23507 #025-01-1971 L1997 **DR GS** *020 †80

SADJADI, Norie. ■ 23517 #051-07-2007 L2007 **OBG** *012

SAFFORD, Shawn David. 994 W OCEAN VIEW AVE 23503 #041-01-1997 L2005 **PDS** *012 †85

SAID, Lina Harbee. EVMS - OFFICE OF GME, C/O HILDA HOBBS, REGISTRAR 23507 #528-04-1993 L2007 **FP** *012

SALLAS, Ronald Kirkland. 601 CHILDRENS LN, DEPT OF NEONATOLOGY 23507 #051-07-1996 L1996 **PD** *020 †55

SAMPSON, Diane Elizabeth. ■ 23508 #051-07-1983 L1986 **PD** *020

SAMUELS, Derek Benjamin. ■ 23508 #035-06-2008 *012

SANCHEZ, Jose Enrique, Jr. 1562 MITSCHER AVE STE 250, CINCLANTFLT, N02MC 23551 #042-01-1994 L1996 **OTO** *020

SANDERS, Brian Patrick. 601 CHILDRENS LN 23507 #012-01-2001 L2001 **PEM** *012 †55

SANDERSON, Timothy Alonzo. 4101 GRANBY ST, STE 203 23504 #051-07-1980 L1981 **P PYA** *020

SANTACRUZ, N Daniel. 7428 TIDEWATER DR STE 100 23505 #726-01-1971 L1977 **IM NEP** *020 †20

SANTHER, Sharmini. 358 MOWBRAY ARCH, DEPT PSYCH 23507 #422-01-2006 L2006 **P** *012

SANTOS, Rosemarie Anne. ■ 23503 #055-02-2007 L2007 **PD** *012

SARAN, Preeti. PO BOX 1980 23501 #495-20-1990 L2006 **FP** *012

SARTORI, Suzanne Clair. 601 CHILDRENS LN 23507 #041-09-1996 L1996 **PD** *020 †55

SASS, Laura Ann. 601 CHILDRENS LN 23507 #010-01-1997 L1997 **PDI** *020 †55

SAUL, Slater Cumbermac. 400 GRESHAM DR # 705-6 23507 #010-03-1968 L1973 **OBG** *020 †30

SAUNDERS, Sheree Bernadet. 1562 MITSCHER AVE STE 250, PAC NO2HC 23551 #010-03-2005 L2006 *020

SAWYER, Ann Virae. ■ 23505 #028-78-2001, ▲ L2005 **END** *020 †20

SAYEGH, Paul Amin. 825 FAIRFAX AVE 23507 #051-01-1980 L1987 **P** *020 †75

SAYEGH, Susie Kelly. 825 FAIRFAX AVE STE 310, FETAL MEDICINE 23507 #051-01-1980 L1984 **OBG** *020 †30

SAYLES, John Minott. 6160 KEMPSVILLE CIR, STE 101B 23502 #016-11-1989 L2003 **GS** *020 †10,85

SCATARIGE, Carol A Sachs. 850 KEMPSVILLE RD 23502 #041-13-1972 L1986 **IM** *020 †20,70

SCHAEFER, John Chas. 6161 KEMPSVILLE CIR, STE 220 23502 #033-05-1970 L1974 **ID IM** *020 †20

SCHAFFER, John Jos. 160 KINGSLEY LN, STE 405 23505 #028-34-1982 L1988 **ORS OSM** *020 †40

SCHAUB, Nicholas Paul. 358 MOWBRAY ARCH, STE 203 23507 #023-01-2003 L2005 **GS** *012

SCHAUS, Kristina O'Neill. 601 CHILDRENS LN, THE KIN 23507 #026-04-2006 L2006 **PD** *012

SCHEIB, Sherry Ann. 229 W BUTE ST, STE 700 23510 #041-13-1994 L1994 **IM** *020 †20

SCHELLENBERG, Karl A. PO BOX 1980, EVMS PHYSIOLOGICAL SCI 23501 #023-07-1957 L1973 **PHM** *050

SCHLEGEL, Michael Stanley. OFFICE OF FLEET SURGEON/NO, ATTN: CREDENTIAL OFFICE 23551 #017-20-1990 L1992 **EM** *020 †16

SCHLOSSBERG, Matthew L. 600 GRESHAM DR 23507 #023-01-1996 L2002 **AN** *020 †05

SCHMIDT, James Malcolm. 601 CHILDRENS LN, CHKD CHILDREN'S HOSPITAL 23507 #036-01-1998 L2004 **PD** *020 †55

SCHNARRS, Robert Harold. 400 W BRAMBLETON AVE, HAGUE CNTR COSM&PLAS SURGE 23510 #041-14-1982 L1989 **PS HS** *020 †65,85 ‡

SCHNEIDER, James Joseph. 6160 KEMPSVILLE CIR, NORFOLK SURG GRP 23502 #028-34-1985 L2007 **GS SO** *020 †85

SCHOCK, Kim. 601 CHILDRENS LN 23507 #051-04-2001 L2001 **PD** *020 †55

SCHOEPF, Miriam Ulrike. 601 CHILDRENS LN, DEPT OF ANESTHESIOLOGY 23507 #409-16-1996 L2007 **AN PAN** *020 †05

SCHOLL, Gerald Stephen. 1562 MITSCHER AVE STE 250, OFFICE OF FLEET SURGEON/NO 23551 #020-12-1984 L1985 **AM** *030 †70

SCHREIBER, Jonathan L. 885 KEMPSVILLE RD, STE 224 23502 #036-07-1998 L2002 **D** *020 †15

SCHWAB, John Conrad. 6161 KEMPSVILLE CIR, STE 220 23502 #048-04-1985 L1998 **ID IM** *020 †20

SCHWARTZER, Joseph Simon. 3755 E VIRGINIA BEACH BLVD 23502 #011-03-1974 L1977 **P** *020 †75

SCIBELLI, Christopher D. 250 W BRAMBLETON AVE, BRAMBLETON MED CTR #101 23510 #041-13-1995 L1996 **VS** *020 †85

SCONIERS, Jacquelyn Miche. PO BOX 1980, DEPT OF SURGERY 23501 #047-07-2006 L2006 **GS** *012

SCOTT, Eric Christopher. ■ 23503 #018-03-2000 L2006 **VS** *012

SCOTT, Kimberly Atkins. 700 W OLNEY RD, DEPARTMENT OF DERMATOLOGY 23507 #051-04-2002 L2002 **D** *020 †15

SCOTT, Martha Howard. 721 FAIRFAX AVE 23507 #051-07-1989 L1990 **FM OS** *062 †18

SEAMON, Alex Reinemer. ■ 23508 #035-06-2008 *012

SEAWELL, Maureen C. 801 W LITTLE CREEK RD #104 23505 #051-07-1980 L1981 **IM** *020 †20

SEBRO, Nadew Simon. 358 MOWBRAY ARCH, EVMS-OFFICE OF GME 23507 #366-02-1999 L2006 **IFP** *012

SEKHON, Vijay Singh. 358 MOWBRAY ARCH, STE 203 23507 #041-15-2004 L2005 **DR** *012

SELLERS, John G. 1232 W LITTLE CREEK RD 23505 #036-07-1943 L1949 **OTO** *071 †45

SELLERS, Verna Reynolds. 249 S NEWTOWN RD, SENTURA LIFE CARE MEDICAL 23502 #010-03-1991 L1996 **IMG IM** *020 †20

SEWARD, Stephen William. 1562 MITSCHER AVE STE 250, OFFICE OF FLEET SURGEON/NO 23551 #038-40-1999 L2000 **IM** *020 †20

SHAFFER, Stephen Ernest. 601 CHILDRENS LN, CHILDREN'S HOSPITAL OF THE 23507 #038-43-1986 L2007 **PG PD** *020 †55

SHAIK, Shameem Sultana. 1443 N VEAUX LOOP, LAFAYETTE PSYCHIATRIC SERV 23509 #496-24-1995 L2001 **P** *020

SHALL, Lawrence M. 6275 E VA BEACH BLVD, STE 300 23502 #038-43-1980 L1986 **ORS OSM** *020 †40

SHAPIRO, Samuel Leon. ■ 23518 #051-01-1964 L1964 **N** *071 †75

SHARIFIAN, Ali. ■ 23510 #517-08-2000 L2007 **IM** *012

SHARMA, Nipun Raj. ■ 23507 #051-07-2008 *012

SHARPE, Larry Odell. 160 KINGSLEY LN, STE 504 23505 #051-04-1965 L1965 **D** *020 †15

SHARRY, Jessica Irene. 601 CHILDRENS LN, DIVISION OF EMERGENCY MEDI 23507 #048-13-2003 L2006 **PEM** *012

SHAVES, Mark Elliott. 600 GRESHAM DR, RADIATION ONCOLOGY & BIOPH 23507 #035-46-1989 L1991 **RO OBG** *020 †80

SHAVES, Sarah Carlson. 825 FAIRFAX AVE, STE 541 23507 #035-46-1989 L1995 **DR** *020 †80

SHEEDLO, Steven Todd. 1562 MITSCHER AVE STE 250, OFFICE OF FLEET SURGEON/NO 23551 #023-12-1996 L1998 **FM** *020 †18

SHELLINGTON, David K. ■ 23507 #023-07-2001 L2002 **CCP** *012 †55

SHELTON, Jean Elizabeth. 825 FAIRFAX AVE STE 646, DEPT OF PM & R 23507 #047-06-1972 L1976 **PM PD** *020 †55,60

SHENFELD, Ofer. 1915 COLONIAL AVE 23517 #550-02-1990 L1996 **U** *100

SHEPHEARD, Stuart L. 400 W BRAMBLETON AVE, STE 202 23510 #051-07-1981 L1986 **IM** *020 †20

SHERRILL, Richard W, Jr. 1005 MAY AVE 23504 #047-07-1960 L1977 **OPH** *020 †35

SHIAU, Danny Tenyen. 1887 POWHATAN ST 23511 #023-12-1997 L2007 **GPM** *020 †70

SHIELDS, Frank William, IV. ■ 23507 #051-07-2008 *012

SHIH, Chie-Youn. 601 CHILDRENS LN, DIVISION OF PEDIATRIC CRIT 23507 #010-01-1999 L2005 **CCP** *020 †55

SHIN, Susanna Hewon. ■ 23505 #051-07-2002 L2002 **GS** *012

SHOLTZOW, Melissa Joy. 358 MOWBRAY ARCH, OFFICE OF GME 23507 #041-02-2006 L2006 **PD** *012

SIBAL, Felix Palarca. ■ 23502 #748-02-1941 L1977 **N** *020

SIEMENS, Richard Lee. 1562 MITSCHER AVE, STE 250 23551 #055-02-1993 L1995 **PHP** *020 †70

SIGFRED, Sture Vivian, Jr. 6330 CENTER DR, STE 220 23502 #011-03-1969 L1969 **DR** *020 †80

SILVA, Carlos Adolfo. 160 KINGSLEY LN, STE 103 23505 #682-01-1982 L1990 **PUD IM** *020 †20

SILVERBERG, Marc Lindsay. 830 KEMPSVILLE RD 23502 #008-01-1991 L1999 **SP** *020 †50

SINACORI, John Todd. 601 CHILDRENS LN 23507 #035-15-1996 L2002 **OTO** *020 †45

SINESI, Christopher C. 150 KINGSLEY LN 23505 #024-05-1982 L1986 **RO** *020 †80

SINESI, Mark Sabino. 600 GRESHAM DR, DEPT OF RADIATION ONCOLOGY 23507 #024-05-1986 L1988 **RO** *020 †80

SINESI, Mathew Paul. 150 KINGSLEY LN 23505 #024-05-1983 L1986 **RO** *020 †80

SINGH, Ran Vijai Pratap. 400 GRESHAM DR, STE 607 23507 #495-67-1980 L2000 **NS** *020 †25

SKANSI, Viviana. 601 CHILDRENS LN 23507 #957-01-1963 L1970 **PD** *020 †55

SKEES, Mark Evan. 425 W 20TH ST, STE 1 23517 #051-07-1983 L1984 **FM** *020 †18

SKEPPSTROM, Richard H. ■ 23510 #051-01-1963 L1963 **N CHN** *020 †75

SKIDMORE, Grant Alan. 905 REDGATE AVE, STE 200 23507 #004-01-1989 L1995 **NS** *020 †25

SKOROPOWSKI, Garth C. 146 INGRAM ST HEALTH SERV, US MARINE CORPS FORCES COM 23551 #032-01-2002 L2003 *100

SKRINSKA, Ruta Jane. 885 KEMPSVILLE RD 23502 #038-06-1982 L1991 **OPH** *020 †35

SLY, Donald Eugene. 901 HAMPTON BLVD, EAR NOSE & THROAT LTD 23507 #051-01-1961 L1961 **OTO** *071 †45

SMILEY, Michael Robert. 1562 MITSCHER AVE STE 250, U.S. FLEET FORCES COMMAND, 23551 #028-34-2005 L2005 **EM** *012

SMITH, Claude Armistead. ■ 23507 #051-01-1960 L1960 **OBG** *071 †30

SMITH, James David. 830 KEMPSVILLE RD 23502 #036-08-1990 L2002 **HMP CLP** *020 †50

SMITH, Lamar Henry. 825 FAIRFAX AVE, STE 541 23507 #011-03-1974 L1999 **DR R** *020 †80

SMITH, Liam Robert. ■ 23507 #051-07-2007 L2007 **GS** *012

SMITH, Michael Lee. 601 CHILDRENS LN 23507 #051-01-1992 L1993 **PD** *020 †55

SMITH, Molly Kathleen. ■ 23504 #051-07-2001 L2001 **DMP** *100 †15

SMITH, Olga Marie. 1562 MITSCHER AVE STE 250, CINCLANTFLT, NO2MC 23551 #004-01-2001 L2001 **EM** *012

SNAMAN, Jennifer Malia. ■ 23507 #051-07-2008 *012

SNELL, Christine A S. 1560 BORDEAUX PL 23509 #041-14-1993 L1994 **EM** *020 †16

SNIDER, Gary Boyd. 229 W BUTE ST, STE 501 23510 #051-01-1977 L1979 **FM** *020 †18

SNYDER, James Glenn. 6053 RIVER CRES 23507 #051-01-1996 L1996 **GS** *020 †85

SODERDAHL, Douglas Wayne. 400 W BRAMBLETON AVE, STE 100 23510 #016-06-1991 L2002 **U** *020 †95

SOKOL, Richard Andrew. 229 W BUTE ST STE 500 23510 #051-04-1974 L1975 **FM FPG** *020 †18

SOLHAUG, Michael John. 700 W OLNEY RD, EASTERN VIRGINIA MED. SCHO 23507 #026-04-1975 L1979 **PD PN** *020 †55

SOLINAP, Daniel Tarrosa. 426 E FREEMASON ST, ASSOCIATED IN PRIMARY 23510 #748-01-1959 L1969 **FM EM** *020

SOLINAP, Perla Juaneza. 426 E FREEMASON ST, ASSOCIATED IN PRIMARY 23510 #748-01-1958 L1972 **FM** *020

SPEAR, Curtis Varnell. ■ 23505 #047-05-1956 L1961 **ORS** *071 †40

SPEAR, Leigh Margaret. 409 DUKE ST, STE 200 23510 #016-43-2006 L2006 **EM** *012

SPECHT, Adam Wayne. 825 FAIRFAX AVE, STE 541 23507 #025-01-1994 L1995 **DR** *020 †80

SPECKHART, Vincent Jos. 902 GRAYDON AVE STE 2 23507 #035-09-1958 L1969 **ON** *020

SPERLING, Michael Henry. 600 GRESHAM DR 23507 #041-07-1975 L1978 **GE** *020 †20

SPIEGEL, David Richard. 825 FAIRFAX AVE # 710 23507 #035-08-1989 L1993 **P** *020 †75

SPINGARN, Stephanie Ann. 830 KEMPSVILLE RD 23502 #005-02-1977 L1998 **PTH MM** *020 †50

SPITZE, Arielle Rhea. ■ 23507 #051-07-2007 L2007 **FP** *012

SPRINGER, Rhonda. ■ 23505 #039-01-1993 L1993 **FM** *020 †18

SQUATRITO, Robert C. 5900 LAKE WRIGHT DR, VIRGINIAONCOLOGY ASSOCIATE 23502 #051-04-1988 L1997 **OBG** *020 †30

SRIRAMA, Madhanika Laasya. 825 FAIRFAX AVE STE 71, EASTERN VIRGINIA MEDICAL S 23507 #894-01-2000 L2000 **P** *020 †75

STAEHR, Patricia Ann. 5425 ROBIN HOOD RD, STE 105 23513 #030-05-1982 L1987
FM *071 †18
STALLINGS, Amy P. 358 MOWBRAY ARCH # 203 23507 #036-08-2004 L2004 AI *012 †55
STALLINGS, Valerie Ann L. 830 SOUTHAMPTON AVE 23510 #036-01-1968 L1971
PHP PD *030 †55,70
STANECK, David Andrew. ■ 23517 #041-13-2003 L2003 U *012
STANLEY, James Bryan. ■ 23502 #051-07-1979 L1984 OBG AS *020 †30
STANLEY, Scott J. 830 KEMPSVILLE RD 23502 #016-43-1981 L1993 PTH *020 †50
STARLING, Suzanne P. 935 REDGATE AVE 23507 #036-08-1990 L2000 PD *020 †55
STECKER, John F, Jr. HAGUE MED CTR STE 100 23510 #010-02-1966 L1971 U *020 †95
STEIN, Emanuel. 721 FAIRFAX AVE, DEPT OF FAMILY & COMM MED 23507 #035-08-1959 L1981
CD IM *020 †20
STEINBERG, Amalia R. ■ 23505 #034-01-2005 L2005 OTO *012
STEINGOLD, Meyer. ■ 23505 #051-01-1936 L1936 GP GS *072
STEINHAGEN, Christine K. 825 FAIRFAX AVE 23507 #051-07-1995 L1995 P *020 †75
STENLUND, Roger Roy. 6330 CENTER DR, STE 220 23502 #056-05-1963 L2001
DR IM *020 †80
STEPHENS, Lisa Dawn. 171 KEMPSVILLE RD STE B 23502 #051-07-1997 L2000 PD *020 †55
STERNE, Justin Philip. ■ 23510 #051-07-2008 *012
STEVENSON, Donald V. 20 KOGER EXECUTIVE CTR 251 23502 #264-02-1958 L1976 PYA P *071
STEWARD, Keith Lamont. PO BOX 1980, EASTERN VA MED SCH 23501 #051-07-1997 *100
STEWART, Frank C, III. 601 CHILDRENS LN, DEPT OF ANESTHESIA 23507 #021-05-1978 L1996
AN CLP *062 †50,05
STEWART, John R, Jr. 1328 E LITTLE CREEK RD, LITTLE CREEK MEDICAL ASSOC 23518
#035-03-1980 L1986 FM OM *020 †70 ‡
STEWART, Virginia Annette. 160 KINGSLEY LN STE 400, DRS. IVES AND KNOWLES, INC 23505
#034-01-2000 L2006 GS *100
STILINOVIC, Lawrence M. ■ 23502 #028-03-1968 L1975 PS *020 †85,65
STINE, Ronald Arthur. 844 KEMPSVILLE RD, CARDIOLOGY CONSULTANTS 23502
#017-20-1978 L1983 CD IM *020 †20
STINER, Allan Ewing, Jr. 600 GRESHAM DR 23507 #041-02-1981 L1985 AN *020 †05
STITIK, Frederick Paul. 150 KINGSLEY LN, RADIOLOGY 23505 #033-05-1967 L1980 R *071 †80
STOLZ, Steven Michael. 885 KEMPSVILLE RD, STE 200 23502 #030-05-1986 L1992
PD ESM *020 †55
STRASNICK, Barry. 150 KINGSLEY LN 23505 #048-04-1985 L1993 NO OTO *020 †45
STRONGE, Elisabeth Rebecc. ■ 23518 #051-07-2006 L2007 IM *012
SU, Cynthia Chaosen. 5665 LOWERY RD 23502 #051-04-1994 L1999 IM *020 †60,20
SULLIVAN, Neil Michael. 850 KEMPSVILLE RD, NDC MEDICAL CENTER 23502
#032-01-1988 L1998 RHU *020 †20
SULLIVAN, Sean Daniel. ■ 23508 #033-06-1996 L2007 PG *020 †55
SUMMERFIELD, Douglas Tom. ■ 23505 #030-06-2007 L2007 IM *012
SUMMERFIELD, Melissa Mari. ■ 23505 #030-06-2006 L2007 OPH *012
SUR, Jennifer Felisilda. 601 CHILDRENS LN, THE KING'S 23507 #038-43-2007 L2007 PD *012
SUTTON, Roy Clifton, III. 600 GRESHAM DR, 2ND FL 23507 #051-04-1981 L1992 PTH *020 †50
SUTTON, Stuart Keith. 229 W BUTE ST, CONSULTANTS IN INTERNAL ME 23510
#020-02-1982 L1997 IM *020 †20
SUVATNE, Jimmy. ■ 23507 #016-42-2006 L2007 *012
SWANSON, Robert Benjamin. ■ 23508 #051-07-2008 *012
SZENTPETERY, Szabolcs. 600 GRESHAM DR, # 8600 23507 #473-01-1963 L1968
TS *020 †85,90
TADROS, Nabil T Mankarios. 110 KINGSLEY LN STE 411 23505 #915-03-1978 L1987
IM IMG *020 †20
TAHHAN, Hassan R. 830 KEMPSVILLE RD 23502 #605-02-1982 L1993 CLP BBK *020 †50
TAHHAN, Sami Georges. 825 FAIRFAX AVE, STE 445 23507 #051-07-1999 L1999 IM *020 †20
TAIT, Peter Haynesworth. ■ 23507 #051-07-2004 L2004 IFP *012
TALTY, Laureen Anne. 171 KEMPSVILLE RD, BLDG B 23502 #035-15-1983 L1986 PD *020 †55
TAVAKOLI, Hamid Reza. 110 KINGSLEY LN STE 2, LONG TERM CARE OF TIDEWATE 23505
#055-01-1998 L1999 P *020 †75
TAYLOR, Alex Persell. 1216 GRANBY ST STE 213, COMMUNITY FAMILY PRACTICE, 23510
#051-07-1997 L2001 FM *020 †18
TAYLOR, Helen Wickham. 641 REDGATE AVE UNIT 129 23507 #051-01-1943 L1943
GYN *071 †30
TAYLOR, John T. 8206 HAMPTON BLVD # 509 23505 #048-13-1991 L1993 AM *100 †18
TERZIS, Julia K. 330 W BRAMBLETON AVE STE 1 23510 #041-02-1970 L1981 PS GS *020 †65
TETALMAN, Bruce I. 880 KEMPSVILLE RD, STE 1100 23502 #038-41-1971 L1995 PM *020 †60
THAMES, Thomas Byron, II. 150 KINGSLEY LN 23505 #036-07-1982 L1988 IM MDM *030 †20
THOMAS, Desencia E. 6330 N CENTER DR, BLDG 13 23502 #048-12-1999 L2005 AR *020 †80
THOMAS, John Anthony. 1909 GRANBY ST STE A, CMG, INC D.B.A. PEDIATRIC 23517
#051-01-1967 L1967 PD *020 †55
THOMAS, Lea Anderson. 601 CHILDRENS LN, CHILDRENS SPECIALTY GROUP 23507
#051-07-1996 L1998 PD *020 †55
THOMAS, Richard John. 6330 N CENTER DR, STE 220 23502 #055-01-1997 L2003 DR *020 †80
THOMPKINS, Bennie Lee, Jr. ■ 23504 #020-02-1976 L1979 PD *075 †55,16
THOMPSON, George K. 601 CHILDRENS LN, ROB 3 23507 #048-14-1982 L1993 AN *020 †05
THOROGOOD, Christine Ann. 825 FAIRFAX AVE, STE 646 23507 #033-06-1996 L2001
PD *020 †55,60
THOTAKURA, Pratima. ■ 23507 #051-07-2007 L2007 IM *012
THRASHER, Patrick D. 6330 NEWTOWN RD, NORFOLK PSYCHIATRIC 23502
#051-04-1976 L1978 P *020 †75
THRIFT, Mary Crimora. ■ 23507 #051-04-1973 L1976 PD NPM *074
TOEWE, Clinton H, II. 721 FAIRFAX AVE, GHENT FAMILY PRACTICE 23507 #041-13-1963 L1980
FM *030 †18
TOMLINSON, James R, Jr. 850 KEMPSVILLE RD 23502 #051-01-1980 L1986
CCM PUD *020 †20
TON, Martin Vuthat. 600 GRESHAM DR 23507 #035-01-1989 L1993 AN *020 †05
TOOR, Svinder Singh. 850 SOUTHAMPTON AVE 23510 #495-03-1971 L1978
CHN PD *020 †75,55
TOOSI, Shakur Hamidi. 880 KEMPSVILLE RD, STE 1300 23502 #517-05-1973 L1980
OPH *020 †35
TOROSKY, Cyndi Michelle. 700 W OLNEY RD RM 2054, EASTERN VA MED SCHL 23507
#051-07-2003 L2003 D *012
TRAVER, Donald Jon. 358 MOWBRAY ARCH # 203 23507 #045-01-2004 L2004 PD *020 †55
TREECE, Wen-Hsuan. 6330 NEWTOWN RD, NORFOLK PSYCHIATRIC 23502
#244-04-1974 L1984 CHP P *020
TRENGOVE-JONES, Guy. 160 KINGSLEY LN, STE 202 23505 #836-02-1971 L1983 PS *020
TRUMAN, Christine Jane. 420 N CENTER DR, STE 141 23502 #035-01-2000 L2006 P *020 †75

TRZCINSKI, Douglas Robert. 825 FAIRFAX AVE STE 610, EVMS- DEPARTMENT OF
SURGER 23507 #001-06-1997 L2007 HS *020 †65
TSUCHITANI, Sara Naomi. ■ 23510 #051-01-2007 L2007 EM *012
TUANQUIN-GONZALEZ, Leilani. 850 KEMPSVILLE RD 23502 #055-01-2004 L2004 IM *020 †20
TUCKER, Billy Jack. 555 FENCHURCH ST, TOTAL HEALTH CARE 23510 #025-01-1962 L1965
GP OS *020
TUCKER, Michael Lynn. 400 GRESHAM DR STE 208 23507 #051-07-1988 L1992 FM *020
TURKIEWICZ, Witold A. 6275 E VIRGINIA BEACH BLVD, STE 200 23502 #001-06-1990 L1994
RHU IM *020 †20
TURNER, Samuel Duncan. 1468 INGRAM ST, SVCS SUPP 23551 #051-04-2001 L2002 *012
TYNES, William Vernon, II. 400 W BRAMBLETON AVE # 100 23510 #051-04-1962 L1962
U *071 †95
ULLAL, Jagdeesh. 855 W BRAMBLETON AVE 23510 #496-59-1999 L2004 IM *012
UMAR, Shaheen Ibrahim. 358 MOWBRAY ARCH # 203 23507 #028-34-2003 L2004 DR *012
UPCHURCH-BURROWS, Adayna. 930 MAJESTIC AVE, STE 110 23504 #010-03-1998 L2001
PD *020 †55
URBANO, Maria Rosina. 825 FAIRFAX AVE, PSYCHIARTY 23507 #051-07-1983 L1987
P CHP *040 †75
UROSKIE, Theodore W, Jr. 6161 KEMPSVILLE CIR, STE 300 23502 #041-09-1995 L1995
PS HS *020 †85,65
VAKILY ASL, Simin. PO BOX 1980 23501 #517-12-2000 L2006 FP *012
VALENZANO, Karen Lenz. 358 MOWBRAY ARCH, OFFICE OF GME 23507
#726-01-2004 L2007 *100
VALONE, James Austin, Jr. 400 GRESHAM DR STE 406 23507 #008-01-1974 L1980
OPH *071 †35
VANCE, Michael Scanlon. 601 CHILDRENS LN, CHILDRENS HOSPITAL 23507
#035-45-1986 L1998 PDC PD *020 †55 ‡
VAN SLYKE, Gary Lee. 957 W 21ST ST STE E, GHENT URGENT CARE 23517
#018-03-1967 L1982 FM EM *071 †18
VARGO, Stephen Thomas. ■ 23510 #038-40-1996 L1998 GS *020
VAUGHAN, Andrew Howard. ■ 23505 #051-07-2004 L2004 OTO *012
VAUGHAN, Mary Carver. 825 FAIRFAX AVE, SUITE 310, HOFHEINER HALL 23507
#051-07-1992 L1992 OBG *020 †30
VELAZQUEZ, Nivea Teresa. 6345 CENTER DR, PED DIAGNOSTIC CTR BLDG 14 23502
#024-05-1980 L1990 PD *020 †55
VENKATESAN, Ranganathan. 907 MEDICAL TOWER, 400 GRESHAM DR 23507
#495-04-1965 L1972 NEP IM *071 †20
VIA, James Dillard. ■ 23510 #051-01-1964 L1964 OBG *071 †30
VIJ, Subir. 3415 GRANBY ST 23504 #495-51-1994 L1998 IMG IM *020 †20
VIN R *012
VINCENT, David Anderson. 580 E MAIN ST, STE 200 23510 #021-06-1996 L1996 NS *020 †25
VINGAN, Harlan Lawrence. 825 FAIRFAX AVE, STE 541 23507 #035-08-1983 L1989
VIR R *012
VINIK, Aaron I. 855 W BRAMBLETON AVE 23510 #836-01-1960 L1990 DIA END *020 †20
VINSON, Alfred Mitchell. 600 GRESHAM DR, DEPT RAD 23507 #012-01-1965 L1971
DR *071 †80
VIRASORO, Ramon. ■ 23507 #132-01-1992 L2004 U *100
VISINTAINER, Catherine Ma. ■ 23507 #035-09-2006 L2006 EM *012
VLIAGOFTIS, Harissios. ■ 23508 #418-02-1987 L1992 AI *100 †20,03
VOLCHOK, Japa. ■ 23507 #022-75-2003, ▲ L2008 GS *012
VORA, Neti Nilesh. 358 MOWBRAY ARCH, EVMS - OFFICE OF GME 23507 #496-44-2003 L2006
IM *012
VORONA, Robert Danl. 600 GRESHAM DR, FL 5 23507 #051-01-1981 L1986 IM *020 †20
WADSWORTH, Jeffery T. 825 FAIRFAX AVE, NECK SURGERY, E VA MED SCH 23507
#011-04-1993 L1993 OTO *020 †45
WAGNER, John Stanley. 6275 E VA BEACH BLVD, STE 300 23502 #035-45-1973 L1977
ORS *020 †40
WAGNER, Michael Sean. ■ 23517 #051-07-2008 *012
WALDHOLTZ, Bruce David. 600 GRESHAM DR 23507 #041-12-1983 L1988 GE IM *020 †20
WALDROP, Bonnie B. ■ 23507 #051-04-1974 L1975 FM *071 †18
WALDROP, William Mc Guire. 6330 NEWTOWN RD, NORFOLK PSYCHIATRIC 23502
#051-04-1974 L1975 P OS *020 †75
WALKER, Clayton Lee. 600 GRESHAM DR 23507 #055-02-1982 L1989 AN *020 †05 ‡
WALKER, Robert. 825 FAIRFAX AVE, STE 646 23507 #016-42-1999 L2000 PM *020 †60
WALLIN, Gene Ambrose. 1468 INGRAM ST, HEALTH SERVICES SUPPORT) 23551
#047-06-1965 L1966 FM *020 †18
WALRATH, Benjamin David. 1562 MITSCHER AVE STE 250, US FLEET FORCES COMMAND
ME 23551 #016-01-2005 L2007 *020
WALTERS, Robert Edmond, Jr. 110 KINGSLEY LN, STE 307 23505 #021-01-1999 L2003
IM *020 †20
WANG, Jenny Qian. ■ 23507 #051-07-2007 L2007 OBG *012
WARD, Charles Arthur. 600 GRESHAM DR 23507 #020-12-1983 L1985 AN *020 †05
WARNER, John Francis. 850 KEMPSVILLE RD 23502 #036-01-1962 L1963 ID IM *040 †20
WARREN, Brian Butler. 600 GRESHAM DR 23507 #051-04-1993 L1993 APM *020 †05
WARREN, Paul Douglas. 6275 E VIRGINIA BEACH BLVD, STE 200 23502 #024-01-1991 L1998
ORS *020 †40
WARTHAN, Molly Mae. 601 MEDICAL TOWER 6TH FL 23507 #048-02-2004 L2005 D *012
WASTI, Nylah Fatima. 358 MOWBRAY ARCH 203 23507 #051-01-2004 L2005 DR *012
WATERS, David Carl. 905 REDGATE AVE, STE 200 23507 #025-01-1980 L1986 NS *020 †25
WATERS, Edward Thomas. 1562 MITSCHER AVE STE 250, U S FLEET FORCES
COMMAND/N 23551 #051-01-1993 L2001 PD *020 †55
WATRING, Nicole Jean. ■ 23508 #038-45-2005 L2005 EM *012
WEAVER, Jennifer Suzanne. 6330 N CENTER DR, BLDG 13 23502 #038-40-2000 L2006
DR *020 †80
WEBB, Charles Howard. 825 FAIRFAX AVE, STE 201 23507 #038-40-1973 L1983
IM IMG *020 †20
WEIRETER, Leonard J. 825 FAIRFAX AVE, STE 610 23507 #035-06-1980 L1987
GS TRS *020 †85
WEISMAN, Mark David. 229 W BUTE ST, STE 700 23510 #010-01-1997 L2000 IM *020 †20
WEISSBERGER, Marshall A. 825 FAIRFAX AVE, STE 541 23507 #010-01-1983 L1984
DR IM *020 †80
WEITZNER, Kenneth Bruce. PO BOX 1980 23501 #051-07-1984 P *020
WELLER, Amanda Lindsley. ■ 23507 #051-07-2008 *012
WELLS, Branden Lamaund. 144 WESTOVER AVE 23507 #011-03-1998 L1998 EM *020 †16
WENTWORTH, Jeffrey Martin. 250 W BRAMBLETON AVE, STE 202 23510 #036-08-1996 L2000
OBG *020 †30
WERNER, Alice Sheri. 600 GRESHAM DR 23507 #051-07-1980 L1987 PTH BBK *020 †50

■ = Address Information Privacy Protected

WERNER, Eric James. 601 CHILDRENS LN 23507 #041-02-1978 L1987 **PHO PD** *020 †55
WERTHEIMER, Michael Leona. ■ 23505 #001-06-2006 L2006 **OPH** *012
WEST, David Walter Martin. ■ 23505 #917-25-1964 L1980 **AN** *071
WEST, Stephanie Nicole. ■ 23507 #051-07-2007 L2007 *012
WESTMEYER, Frank C. 1208 ARMISTEAD BRIDGE RD 23507 #028-34-1975 L1977 **IM EM** *020 †20,16
WHALEN, Richard Mark. 249 S NEWTOWN RD 23502 #051-07-1985 L1986 **FM** *020 †18
WHEALTON, Edward Gordon. 23509 #051-07-1983 L1997 **FM** *020 †18
WHEELER, Jock Rodgers. 250 W BRAMBLETON AVE, STE 101B 23510 #051-04-1958 L1958 **OS GS** *030 †85
WHEELER, William Francis. 6330 CENTER DR, STE 220 23502 #051-01-1975 L1979 **DR** *020 †80
WHIBLEY, Theresa Waters. 400 GRESHAM DR, STE 811 23507 #051-07-1982 L1986 **OBG** *020 †30
WHITBECK, John Volkert. 825 FAIRFAX AVE, STE 541 23507 #041-02-1970 L1975 **DR** *020 †80 ‡
WHITE, John Phillips, III. ■ 23517 #023-01-1947 L1991 **GS** *072 †85
WHITE, Larry E. 850 SOUTHAMPTON AVE, 3RD FL 23510 #047-06-1976 L1980 **CHN** *020 †55,75
WHITE, Nicholas James. 601 CHILDRENS LN, EMERGENCY MEDICINE 23507 #033-06-1997 L2003 **PD PE** *020 †55
WHITEHURST, M Candace. 142 W YORK ST, INTERNAL MEDICINE 23510 #051-07-1985 L1987 **IM** *020 †20
WHITELOCK, Victoria P. ■ 23508 #023-01-1965 L1968 **OM FM** *071 ‡
WHITESIDE, Paul Francis. ■ 23510 #038-40-2007 L2007 **PD** *012
WHITLOCK, Lee Elias. ■ 23505 #051-01-1943 L1943 **GS** *020 †85
WHITMORE, Wm Harvey, Jr. ■ 23518 #051-01-1952 L1953 **GP OS** *071 †20
WILCOX, Clyde Wm, Jr. 6330 CENTER DR, BLDG 13 23507 #020-05-1968 L1977 **DR** *071 †80
WILDE, Wade Wallace. 1562 MITSCHER AVE STE 250, US ATLANTIC FLEET 23551 #023-12-1989 L2002 **EM PD** *020 †55
WILDER, Charles Durand. 600 GRESHAM DR 23507 #051-04-1982 L1985 **AN** *020 †05
WILDS, Preston L. 830 SOUTHAMPTON AVE 23510 #041-01-1953 L1978 **OBG MFM** *020 †30
WILEY, Kathleen E. ■ 23507 #051-07-2004 L2004 **PD** *020 †55
WILKES, Charlotte Marie. 600 GRESHAM DR 23507 #051-07-1984 L1984 **IM** *100
WILLARD, Richard Norman. 110 KINGSLEY LN, STE 508 23505 #051-04-1966 L1966 **OBG** *020 †30
WILLIAMS, Anderson J, Jr. 2539 CORPREW AVE 23504 #047-07-1952 L1965 **PTH** *020 †50
WILLIAMS, Annie Louise. 400 GRESHAM DR, 704 MEDICAL TWR 23507 #051-07-1979 L1982 **OBG** *020 †30
WILLIAMS, Armistead D. 6161 KEMPSVILLE CIR, STE 315 23502 #051-01-1972 L1972 **N** *020 †75
WILLIAMS, Audrea Doneta. 358 MOWBRAY ARCH # 203 23507 #010-03-2004 L2004 **PTH** *012
WILLIAMS, Christina Marie. 1468 INGRAM ST, ATTN CREDENTIAL OFFICE 23551 #012-21-2002 L2004 **FM** *020 †18
WILLIAMS, Olabode Alex. 600 GRESHAM DR 23507 #690-01-1985 L1998 **GE** *020 †20
WILLIAMS, Scott Seth. 600 GRESHAM DR, FL 1 23507 #035-06-1996 L2001 **RO** *020 †80
WILLIAMSON, John Adrian. 600 GRESHAM DR 2RP, SENTRA NORFOLK GENERAL HOS 23507 #019-02-1976 L1980 **ORS** *020 †40
WILLIAMSON, Sterling R. 6275 E VIRGINIA BEACH BLVD, STE 300 23502 #051-04-1965 L1971 **ORS** *071 †40
WILLIE, James Oliver. 549 E BRAMBLETON AVE 23510 #047-07-1948 L1950 **OS OBG** *071 †30
WILLIS, Jeff Robertson. 885 KEMPSVILLE RD 23502 #051-04-1990 L1999 **GE IM** *020 †20
WILSON, Addison Graves. 1840 COVE RD STE 100, NAB LITTLE CREEK 23521 #023-12-2005 L2007 **GS** *020
WILSON, Emily Nicole. ■ 23502 #051-07-2008 *012
WILSON, George Chas. 1120 BOTETOURT GDNS, SONAMEDSPA 23507 #011-02-1978 L1984 **CS** *020 †16
WILSON, Robert Marion. 5621 TIDEWATER DR 23509 #010-01-1966 L1969 **NEP IM** *020 †20
WILSON, Robert Maxwell. 6160 KEMPSVILLE CIR, STE 302A 23502 #027-01-1966 L1966 **AN** *071
WINSTEAD, Saundra E. 3415 GRANBY ST 23504 #051-07-1990 L1993 **FM** *020 †18
WISOFF, Carl P. ■ 23510 #024-01-1946 L1955 **DR NM** *071 †80,28
WOHLGEMUTH, Stephen David. 830 KEMPSVILLE RD 23502 #024-07-1983 L1988 **GS** *020 †85
WOLAN, Diana Lynne. 7924 CHESAPEAKE BLVD 23518 #051-07-1980 L1984 **IM** *020
WOLBURG, Julio. 4100 GRANBY ST, 4101 GRANBY ST #302 23504 #649-05-1957 L1972 **P** *030 †75
WOLCOTT, Hugh Dixon. 100 KINGSLEY LN, STE 400 23505 #016-06-1979 L1982 **OBG** *020 †30
WOLCOTT, James M. 327 W BUTE ST 23510 #051-01-1950 L1950 **GYN** *030 †30
WOMBOLT, Duane Geo. 400 GRESHAM DR, STE 402 23507 #018-03-1962 L1970 **NEP** *020 †20
WONG, Benjamin Chee-Man. 601 COLLEY AVE 23507 #060-01-1996 L2001 **OBG** *020 †30
WOO, Chee Keen. 825 FAIRFAX AVE, HOFHEIMER HALL 23507 #041-02-1998 L1998 **IM** *020 †20
WOODS, Gary Michael. ■ 23507 #051-07-2008 *012
WOODS, William French. 6330 NEWTOWN RD, NORFOLK PSYCHIATRIC 23502 #035-09-1970 L1973 **P** *020 †75
WOODSON, Frederick Gaston. 600 GRESHAM DR 23507 #051-01-1938 L1938 **P N** *071 †75
WOOLFITT, Robert Amos. 6330 CENTER DR, STE 220 23502 #055-01-1970 L1977 **DR** *020 †80
WOOTEN, William Isler, III. 601 CHILDRENS LN, THE KIN 23507 #036-08-2006 L2006 **PD** *012
WOOTTON, Frank Taylor, III. 885 KEMPSVILLE RD 23502 #051-07-1985 L1992 **GE** *020 †20
WORK, Granville Byron, III. 600 GRESHAM DR 23507 #025-01-1978 L1981 **AN** *020 †05
WRIGHT, Erin Leigh. ■ 23503 #039-01-2006 L2006 **PD** *012
WRIGHT, Kelly Lynn. 885 KEMPSVILLE RD, STE 200 23502 #051-07-2002 L2002 **PD** *020 †55
WRIGHT, Laura Schuetz. 601 CHILDRENS LN, 6TH FL 23507 #023-12-1997 L1999 **PD** *020 †55
WRIGHT, Richard O. 1401 TIDEWATER DR, STE 1 23504 #045-01-1984 L1992 **GS** *020
WRY, Diane J. 885 KEMPSVILLE RD 23502 #007-02-1979 L1980 **OPH** *020 †35
WURM, Alex Mark. 825 FAIRFAX AVE # 541, EASTERN VIRGINIA MEDICAL S 23507 #051-01-2003 L2003 **DR** *012
YACOB, Desalegn. 358 MOWBRAY ARCH RM 203, EVMS - OFFICE OF GME 23507 #051-01-2002 L2002 **PG** *012 †55
YAGEL, Scott Lee. 600 GRESHAM DR 23507 #041-09-1984 L2002 **GE** *020 †20
YAMASHIRO, Brent M. ■ 23507 #051-07-2008 *012
YAN, Jieming. 5700 LAKE WRIGHT DR, STE 131 23502 #243-49-1982 L2003 **IM** *020 †20
YAP, Teddy Mina. 358 MOWBRAY ARCH, DEPT OF MED EDU 23507 #748-19-1999 L2006 **IM** *012
YEATS, Alexander James, Jr. 358 MOWBRAY ARCH, OFFICE OF GME 23507 #422-01-2006 L2006 **EM** *012
YOUNG, James Douglas. 100 KINGSLEY LN, STE 404 23505 #051-04-1994 L1994 **U** *020 †95

YU, Bennett Winston. 600 GRESHAM DR, MEDICAL ONCOLOGY 23507 #025-01-1982 L2003 **HEM ON** *050 †20
YURACHEK, Mary Margaret. ■ 23508 #051-07-1990 L1991 **IM** *020 †20
ZABELL, Alan. 600 GRESHAM DR, FL 1 23507 #035-09-1976 L1978 **RO** *020 †20,80
ZAMFIR, Dan Adrian. PO BOX 1980, EASTERN VA MED SCH 23501 #781-01-1983 L2005 **P** *012
ZHAO, Wei. 400 GRESHAM DR STE 30 23507 #243-58-1995 L1999 **IM** *020 †20
ZHAO, Ying. PO BOX 1980 23501 #243-47-1986 L2003 **OBG** *020
ZIAIE, Ahmad Zia. 721 FAIRFAX AVE, GHENT FAMILY PRACTICE CTR 23507 #118-01-1993 L2006 **FP** *012
ZOLL, Ross Holman. 600 GRESHAM DR 23507 #011-02-1985 L2001 **AN** *020 †05
ZUKOWSKI, Anna. 358 MOWBRAY ARCH RM 203, EVMS - OFFICE OF GME 23507 #759-11-1982 L2002 **FM** *100
ZYDLEWSKI, Anthony Walter. 907 MEDICAL TOWER 23507 #024-07-1989 L1998 **NEP** *020 †20

NORTH – MATHEWS

DYAR, Kathryn Wilkin. BELMONT FARM - ROUTE 617 23128 #012-01-1970 L1975 **PD** *020 †55
KOZIOL, Dennis Frank. ■ 23128 #030-05-1971 L1975 **EM PD** *071 †55,16
REEVES, Alexander Garden. ■ 23128 #035-20-1963 L2002 **N** *071 †75

NORTH GARDEN – ALBEMARLE

BRAY, Megan Jane. ■ 22959 #041-02-1995 L1995 **OBG** *020 †30
BURT, David Russell. ■ 22959 #037-01-1999 L2003 **EM** *020
MASON, Pamela Kay. 2470 RED HILL RD 22959 #038-41-1999 L1999 **CD** *020 †20
REGAN, Kara Anne. ■ 22959 #036-08-2008 *012

NORTH TAZEWELL – TAZEWELL

GEE, Jeffry Travis. ■ 24630 #055-02-1996 L2000 **P** *020 †75
ODUNTAN, Omobola Oluwaseu. 583C E RIVERSIDE DR, TAZEWELL COMMUNITY HEALTH 24630 #690-01-1995 L2007 **FM** *100 †18

NORTON – NORTON CITY

ADONGAY, Luis Paco. ■ 24273 #748-10-1970 L1990 **AN** *100
ATYIA, Atif Abdel-Moneam. 100 15TH ST NW, NORTON COMMUNITY HOSPITAL 24273 #915-02-1982 L1998 **MPD PD** *020 †55
AWAN, Khalid Javed. 1921 PARK AVE SW 24273 #704-04-1964 L1972 **OPH** *020 †35
BANCHUIN, Pornpen S. ■ 24273 #891-02-1971 L1978 **GP** *020 †50
BANCHUIN, Thongdang. 280 VIRGINIA AVE NE, STE 102 24273 #891-02-1968 L1978 **GS** *020 †85
BANDY, Steven Martin. 100 15TH ST NW, NORTON COMMUNITY HOSPITAL 24273 #034-01-1997 L2000 **EM** *020 †16
BARONGAN, Amor A A. 280 VIRGINIA AVE NE, STE 107 24273 #748-01-1965 L1972 **IM** *020
BARONGAN, Pablo P. 280 VIRGINIA AVE NE, STE 107 24273 #748-08-1965 L1972 **IM GE** *020
BEGLEY, Charles Jeffrey. 340 ANDERSON HOLLOW RD, WISE REGIONAL MEDICAL 24273 #051-04-1983 L1986 **PD** *020 †55
BERARD, Marco. 100 15TH ST NW 24273 #067-02-1998 L2003 *020 †40
BHATTI, Mohammed A. 18 7TH ST NW, STE 306 24273 #308-10-1985 L1995 **N** *020
CAIZZI, Kathleen Ann. 98 15TH ST NW, STE 201 24273 #024-07-1975 L1985 **IM** *020
CALL, Frank Lloyd, II. 3RD ST N E 24273 #051-01-1963 L1963 **ON HEM** *071 †20
CAPALAD, Elpidio Fajardo. 100 15TH ST NW 24273 #748-07-1965 L1973 **GP** *020 †16
CARTAGENA, Rodolfo J S. 340 ANDERSON HOLLOW RD, WISE MEDICAL GROUP 24273 #748-01-1967 L1977 **GYN** *020
CONCEPCION, Nicanor B. 100 15TH ST NW 24273 #748-10-1970 L1984 **U P** *020
COX, Jack Kelson, II. 310 3RD ST NE 24273 #020-02-1987 L1991 **EM FM** *020 †18
CULLEN, Robert H. 280 VIRGINIA AVE NE, STE 107 24273 #748-08-1965 L1973 **GP AM** *075
CUSANO, Matthew Warner. 96 15TH ST NW, STE 104 24273 #041-13-1997 L2004 **IM** *020 †20
D'AMATO, Luciano. 100 15TH ST NW 24273 #561-04-1979 L1986 **GS** *020 †85
DE PONTE, Kathleen Ann. 935 VIRGINIA AVE NW, BOX 408 24273 #041-09-1980 L1983 **DR NM** *020 †20
DOZIER, Lance Cary. 98 15TH ST NW STE 201, NORTON SURGICAL CLINIC 24273 #041-02-1982 L1983 **GS** *020 †85
EHTESHAM, Uzma. 100 15TH ST NW 24273 #704-02-1993 L2003 **P** *020 †75
FAJARDO, Romulo Abrantes. 340 ANDERSON HOLLOW RD 24273 #748-01-1972 L1999 **IM** *020 †20
FEMI-PEARSE, Juni. 98 15TH ST NW, STE 201 24273 #690-02-1988 L1999 **GS** *020 †85
FULLER, Charles Irving. ■ 24273 #051-01-1945 L1945 **GP OS** *020 †55
HABRE, Antoine Georges. 340 ANDERSON HOLLOW RD 24273 #605-03-1994 L2006 **PCC** *020 †20
HAINES, Garland Thos. 101 15TH ST NW, DIAGNOSTIC IMAGING INC 24273 #051-07-1978 L1982 **DR** *020 †80
INGRAM, Ernagene F. ■ 24273 #038-40-1949 L1952 **PHP** *071
JAYNAL, Francis M A. 280 VIRGINIA AVE NE, STE 104 24273 #748-01-1964 L1991 **CD IM** *071
JOSHI, Anilkumar R. 616 PARK AVE NW, CARDIOVASCULAR ASSOCIATES 24273 #495-23-1974 L1982 **CD IM** *020 †20
LARKE, Daryl Sheldon. 96 15TH ST NW, STE 111 24273 #016-06-1976 L2006 **ORS** *020 †40
LERSCHLOLARN, Likit. 3RD ST N E 24273 #891-02-1968 L1977 **GS GP** *020 †85
LYLE, Lurton Braxton. 280 VIRGINIA AVE NE, STE 106 24273 #047-06-1962 L1964 **FM** *020 †18 ‡
MAINE, Charles Paul. 340 ANDERSON HOLLOW RD, WISE MEDICAL GROUP 24273 #051-04-1978 L1978 **IM** *020 †20
MC BRIDE, Timothy Oren. 340 ANDERSON HOLLOW RD, WISE REGIONAL MEDICAL 24273 #047-20-1997 L2000 **MPD** *020 †20,55
MEANS, Robert Earl. 96 15TH ST NW, STE 111 24273 #023-01-1979 L2006 **ORS** *020
MILLER, David Philip. 611 TRENT ST NE 24273 #041-12-1969 L1970 **ON HEM** *020 †20 ‡
MIRANDA, Prospero M. 100 15TH ST NW 24273 #748-10-1964 L1971 **GS GP** *020
MOLINA, Galileo Taquehan. 340 ANDERSON HOLLOW RD, WISE REGIONAL MEDICAL 24273 #748-08-1965 L1976 **GP EM** *071
MOORE, Raymond Michael. 280 VIRGINIA AVE NE, STE 101 24273 #051-01-1985 L1988 **FM** *020 †18

MULLINS, Emory Allen, Jr. 96 15TH ST NW STE 104 24273 #055-02-1994 L1997 **IM** *020 †20
MULLINS, Jennifer Erin. 102 15TH ST NW, STE 301 24273 #051-01-2000 L2000 **OBG** *020
NAUSS, David Cooper. 100 15TH ST NW, NORTON COMMUNITY HOSPITAL 24273 #041-13-1991 L1995 **AN** *020 †05
PATEL, Sapna R. 611 TRENT ST NE 24273 #306-01-1997 L2005 **ON** *020 †20
PIERCE, Daryl Wayne. 611 TRENT ST NE 24273 #021-06-1995 L2001 **HO** *020 †20
POTTER, James Thomas. 1014 PARK AVE NW 24273 #047-20-2000 L2002 **PD UCM** *020 †55 ‡
REED, Pauline Carvella. 96 15TH ST NW 24273 #047-20-1998 L1999 **FM** *020 †18
SAPRA, Parmod Kumar. 100 15TH ST NW 24273 #495-03-1971 L1975 **PD ADL** *020 †55
SHAMIYEH, Souhail Geo. 295 WHARTON LN NE 24273 #605-01-1985 L1987 **IM IMG** *020 †20 ‡
SHEPARD, Felix Eugene, Jr. 100 15TH ST NW 24273 #035-09-1993 L1993 **U** *020 †95
SREENIVASAN, C K. 1763 PARK AVE SW, ORTHOPEDIC CLINIC PC 24273 #495-02-1967 L1979 **ORS** *020 †40
STARNES, Christopher Todd. 98 15TH ST NW, STE 201 24273 #051-01-2002 L2004 **IM** *020 †20
STOKES, Myron Cornel. 96 15TH ST NW 24273 #018-03-2001 L2008 **GS** *100
VEDHANAYAKAM, Arunachalam. 96 15TH ST NW, STE 106 24273 #220-01-1964 L1973 **PD** *020
VEST, Gayle S. 102 15TH ST NW, STE 301 24273 #026-04-1974 L1980 **OBG** *020 †30
VEST, Steven Lee. 98 15TH ST NW STE 202, N C H MED ARTS BLDG #2 24273 #026-04-1974 L1980 **GE IM** *020 †20
WARD, J'Andre Okella. 100 15TH ST NW, NORTON COMMUNITY HOSPITAL 24273 #162-01-1994 L2000 **VIR** *100 †80
WHEATLEY, Michael Wayne. 295 WHARTON LN NE 24273 #051-01-1993 L1994 **FM** *020 †18 ‡
WILLIAMS, Gary Scott. 295 WHARTON LN NE 24273 #051-04-1979 L1980 **FM** *020 †18
ZIBDEH, Isam Tawfique. 102 15TH ST NW STE 301, MEDICAL ARTS BLDG #3 24273 #915-03-1971 L1978 **OBG** *020 †30

OAK HALL – ACCOMACK

BREHM, Hans Helmut. 8034 LANKFORD HWY, ATLANTIC MEDICAL CENTER 23416 #407-02-1956 L1980 **PD** *072 †55
HATCH, Richard Montague. 8034 LANKFORD HWY, ATLANTIC MEDICAL CENTER 23416 #051-07-1994 L1994 **FM** *020 †18
HOSHINO, David Ken. 8034 LANKFORD HWY, ATLANTIC COMMUNITY HEALTH 23416 #041-01-1980 L1983 **FM EM** *020 †18
ROLL, Jeanne Elizabeth. 8034 LANKFORD HWY, ATLANTIC MEDICAL CTR/PO BX 23416 #033-05-1978 L1993 **IM** *020 †20

OAK HILL – FAIRFAX

AL-KADIRI, Mohammed. ■ 20171 #473-03-1991 L2007 **FM** *020 †18
EVANS, Jennifer Elaine. ■ 20171 #016-01-2004 L2007 **EM** *020
KU, Jennifer. ■ 20171 #051-01-2007 L2007 *012
MILLWALA, Farida Noman. ■ 20171 #496-23-2000 L2002 **IM** *020 †20
WELCH, Timothy Steven. ■ 20171 #023-12-2003 L2005 **CD** *012 †20

OAKTON – FAIRFAX

ABBOT, David Munro. 2936 CHAIN BRIDGE RD 22124 #038-40-1970 L1971 **FM** *020 †18
ALLELY, Eric Bruce. ■ 22124 #007-02-1985 L1986 **MDM PHP** *050
ALLEN, Robert Monteith. ■ 22124 #041-02-1954 L1964 **R** *071 †80
ALLINGHAM, David Geoffrey. 2915 HUNTER MILL RD, STE 11 22124 #051-07-1985 L1991 **EM** *020
BENTON, Rebecca Lynn. ■ 22124 #036-01-1994 L2002 **PD** *020 †55
BIASSOU, Nadia Madelaine. ■ 22124 #016-02-2000 L2004 **RNR** *100
BURD, Terri Ellen. ■ 22124 #020-02-2007 *012
CHANG, Wellington Hancock. ■ 22124 #024-07-2000 **OPH** *100
DI SANDRO, Giovanni. ■ 22124 #561-19-1953 L1967 **U** *071
FANNING, Mary Major. 2914A CHAIN BRIDGE RD, OAKTON PRIMARY CARE CENTER 22124 #065-01-1977 L1997 **IM ID** *020 †20
FAUST, John Robert. ■ 22124 #010-01-2008 *012
FAYEZ, Jamil Abdul Latif. 2915 HUNTER MILL RD STE 11 22124 #704-02-1964 L2003 **END OBG** *020
HERLIHY, Summer Reid. ■ 22124 #051-01-2004 L2005 **DR** *012
IKHINMWIN, Magnus Kehinde. 10882 MIMOSA PL, NORTHERN VA NEPHROLOGY ASS 22124 #690-02-1985 L1998 **NEP IM** *020
KERMAN, Shelly Lynn. ■ 22124 #016-43-1977 L1980 **PTH CCG** *020 †19,50
KIM, Seung Wook. 2946 CHAIN BRIDGE RD STE N 22124 #654-01-1998 L2003 **FM** *100
KUSTRA, Kerri Lynne. 2942 HUNTER MILL RD 22124 #038-40-1997 L2007 **FM** *020 †18
LI, Sheryl G. ■ 22124 #041-02-1992 L1996 **PD** *020 †55
LUTENBERG, Stephen Paul. ■ 22124 #010-02-1974 L1979 **EM** *020
MALHOTRA, Divya Mehra. ■ 22124 #495-45-1993 L1997 **CD** *020 †20
MONGIA, Sumedha. ■ 22124 #041-12-1994 L1998 **PD** *062 †55
MUFTI, Shawana. ■ 22124 #704-01-1997 L2007 **OBG** *100
OWEN, Maryann Theresa. ■ 22124 #035-08-1990 L2002 **PCC** *020 †20
PETERSON-CREMER, Barbara. ■ 22124 #041-14-2008 *012
RUHL, Amy Parker. ■ 22124 #051-01-2006 **IM** *012
SZELE, George. ■ 22124 #473-01-1952 L1959 **AN OS** *020 †05

OAKWOOD – BUCHANAN

MODI, Kailas V. ■ 24631 #495-22-1971 L1978 **GP** *075
MODI, Vinodchandra D. US ROUTE 460 WEST, MINES MEDICAL CLINIC 24631 #495-23-1971 L1978 **IM** *075

ONANCOCK – ACCOMACK

BOSWORTH, Elam W, II. 19 MARKET ST 23417 #051-04-1952 L1953 **GP** *071
FEARS, Belle De Cormis. 23610 NORTH ST, # E5 23417 #051-04-1945 L1946 **PHP** *071
HOLLANDSWORTH, Thomas G. 20280 MARKET ST, ONLEY HLTH CTR 23417 #051-07-1996 L1999 **FM** *020 †18

LINGEN, Joan Kathryn. 20280 MARKET ST 23417 #016-42-1989 L1999 **GYN GP** *020 †30
SIVARAJAN, Muraleedharan. 20280 MARKET ST 23417 #495-31-1989 L2004 **PD** *055
STARK, Heather Roberta. 20280 MARKET ST, ONLEY COMMUNITY HEALTH CTR 23417 #065-10-1981 L1994 **GP** *020
TAYLOR, Jerome Henry. PO BOX 172, 196 MARKET ST 23417 #024-01-1981 L2005 **IM** *020 †20
WEYMANN, Donald R. ■ 23417 #035-08-1953 L1991 **CHP P** *072 †55,75

ORANGE – ORANGE

ALOI, Joseph Anthony. 661 UNIVERSITY LN 22960 #010-01-1988 L1991 **END** *020 †20
BARGMANN, Evelyn M. 661 UNIVERSITY LN, STE B 22960 #036-01-1977 L1991 **IM** *020 †20
BROWN, Marilyn A. 661 UNIVERSITY LN, STE A 22960 #047-07-1996 L2006 **PD** *020 †55
BRUCE, James Garnett, Jr. ■ 22960 #051-01-1940 L1940 **IM GP** *071
CONNELLY, Julia Elizabeth. 120 DOGWOOD LN, ORANGE COUNTY NURSING HOME 22960 #004-01-1977 L1983 **IM** *020 †20
COOLEY, Amy Aitcheson. ■ 22960 #055-01-2003 L2006 **FM** *100 †18
GASTON, Susan Marie. 661 UNIVERSITY LN, PEDIATRICS AT ORANGE 22960 #010-02-1983 L1996 **PD** *020 †55
GIESE, Matthew Richard. 13198 JAMES MADISON HWY 22960 #038-43-2001 L2001 **FM** *020 †18
HENDERSON, Deborah M. 661 UNIVERSITY LN, STE B 22960 #035-45-1995 L2004 **IM** *020 †20
KELLER, Lawrence Edward. 13198 JAMES MADISON HWY 22960 #051-01-1980 L1981 **FM** *020 †18
KINNEMAN, Robt Eugene, Jr. 458 MADISON RD, RAPPAH-RAPIDAN COMM SERV C 22960 #036-07-1955 L1985 **P AM** *071 †70
MARKS, Jennifer R. 661 UNIVERSITY LN STE B, ORANGE INTERNAL MEDICINE 22960 #023-01-1999 L1999 **IM** *020 †20
MERRICK, Randolph Vaughan. 303B MADISON RD, MERRICK FAMILY MEDICINE 22960 #051-04-1985 L1988 **FM** *020 †18
PAPPAS, Diane Elise. 661 UNIVERSITY LN, STE A 22960 #051-04-1991 L1992 **PD** *020 †55
PASTERNACK, Samuel. 362 MADISON RD 22960 #869-05-1972 L1978 **IM** *020
PAYNE, Nancy Jean. 661 UNIVERSITY LN, STE A 22960 #036-08-1997 L1997 **PD** *020 †55
PHILBRICK, John Tracy. 661 UNIVERSITY LN, STE B 22960 #024-01-1973 L1980 **IM EM** *020 †20,16
SCHINSTOCK, Elizabeth Ble. 661 UNIVERSITY LN, PEDIATRICS AT ORANGE 22960 #051-07-2000 L2000 **PD** *020 †55
SCHMITZ, Nancy Ann. 13198 JAMES MADISON HWY 22960 #016-11-1980 L1982 **FM** *020 †18
SEALANDER, Pamella Gregg. ■ 22960 #036-01-1985 **PD** *100
SHELTON, Rebecca A. 661 UNIVERSITY LN, PEDIATRICS AT ORGANGE UVA 22960 #051-04-1996 L1996 **PD** *020 †55
SILVESTER, Michael Jos. 13198 JAMES MADISON HWY 22960 #051-01-1976 L1979 **FM** *020 †18
SMYTH, Kathy. 661 UNIVERSITY LN, STE A 22960 #032-01-1990 L1997 **PD** *020 †55
WOLANSKI, Thomas Edward. 13198 JAMES MADISON HWY 22960 #051-01-1988 L1991 **FM** *020 †18

PAINTER – ACCOMACK

LUBS, Herbert A, Jr. ■ 23420 #008-01-1954 L1957 **MG** *071 †20,19

PALMYRA – FLUVANNA

ADAM, Jamie Lynn. 10 RIVERSIDE DR 22963 #035-45-2001 L2001 **PTH** *020 †50
BEAR, Edward Stafford. ■ 22963 #041-13-1962 L1971 **NEP IM** *020 †20
BOOTHE, Virginia Anne. ■ 22963 #040-02-1995 L1995 **IM** *020 †20
BROWN, Cynthia D. ■ 22963 #048-04-1999 L2007 **IM** *020 †20
CAMPBELL, Michael Olin. ■ 22963 #035-15-2006 L2007 **OPH** *012
CRIST, Matthew Brian. ■ 22963 #036-01-2004 L2005 **IM** *012
EVANS, Joseph Benjamin. 17 CENTRE CT, LAKE CTR PROFESS PK 22963 #041-09-1995 L1995 **IM** *020 †20
FERGUSON, Lauren Blythe. ■ 22963 #051-01-2007 L2007 **PD** *012
GENERELLY, Peter Roger. 1250 MOUNTAIN HILL RD 22963 #027-01-1970 L1985 **GP FM** *020 †16
HARMON, Robert Christophe. ■ 22963 #055-02-2005 L2005 **IM** *100
HOWARD, Laura Conklin. ■ 22963 #051-01-2004 L2004 **IM** *020 †20
JOHNSON, Elizabeth Amanda. ■ 22963 #001-02-2006 L2006 **P** *012
LOVELACE, Bruce Merle, IV. ■ 22963 #021-06-2002 L2002 **CHP** *012
LUTTERBIE, Mark Andrew. ■ 22963 #051-04-2005 L2005 **FP** *012
MARANKI, Jennifer Lee. ■ 22963 #041-13-2004 L2007 **IM** *100 †20
MAYER, Nancy Lynne. ■ 22963 #028-34-1985 L2003 **FM EM** *020 †18
MICELI, Kurt Phillip. ■ 22963 #041-15-2003 L2003 **MP** *012
MOORE, Susan J. 112 CROFTON PL, LAKE MONTICELLO INTERNAL M 22963 #051-01-1985 L1989 **IM IMG** *020 †20
NIEHAUS, Mark David. 17 CENTRE CT, PALMYRA MEDICAL ASSOCIATES 22963 #051-01-1999 L2003 **MPD** *020 †20,55
NOLTE, Paige Beattie. 17 CENTRE CT, C/O TRACY YANCEY 22963 #051-04-2001 L2005 **MPD** *020 †20,55
REIMERS, Gerald Floyd. ■ 22963 #025-01-1957 L1958 **FM PA** *071
RICHTER, James Anthony. ■ 22963 #045-04-2005 L2005 **IM** *012
SCALZO, David Carmine. ■ 22963 #050-02-2004 L2004 **AN** *012
SHERRELL, James C. ■ 22963 #047-06-2001 L2003 **ORS** *012
SMITH, Diana Alexis. ■ 22963 #045-01-2005 L2005 **P** *012
SMITH, Kenneth Gordon, Jr. ■ 22963 #021-05-2002 L2006 **NEP** *012 †20
STARR, Karen Lavoie. 17 CENTRE CT 22963 #023-01-1986 L1989 **IM IMG** *020 †20
STONE, Rebecca Youkey. ■ 22963 #041-01-2004 L2004 **OBG** *012
TAYLOR, Matthew David. ■ 22963 #041-13-2005 L2005 **GS** *012
WEISSMAN, Edward. ■ 22963 #016-42-1953 L1953 **IM IMG** *020 †20

PARKSLEY – ACCOMACK

GRAY, Patrick Bruce M. 19056 GREENBUSH RD, EASTERN SHORE BEHAV HLTH 23421 #803-05-1955 L1958 **P** *020

■ = Address Information Privacy Protected

GUBB, Geoffrey W. 17385 LANKFORD HWY 23421 #010-02-1970 L1977 **EM** *020
MC CLEAN-RICE, Nicholas T. PO BOX 1330, 19056 GREENBUSH RD 23421 #917-29-1980 L1986 **P** *040 †75
SCOTT, David Randolph. 17385 LANKFORD HWY 23421 #051-01-1983 L1988 **REN** *020 †30

PATRICK SPRINGS – PATRICK

BOYCE, William Henry, Jr. ■ 24133 #047-05-1944 L1989 **U** *071 †95
MEYER, Russell. ■ 24133 #017-20-1961 L1972 **OPH** *071 †35

PEARISBURG – GILES

ABRAMS, Margarita Angela. 602 WENONAH AVE 24134 #051-01-1992 L1996 **OBG** *020 †30
CECIL, William Byrnes, Jr. ■ 24134 #051-04-1946 L1946 **GP GS** *071
CULLEY, James Paul. 1 TAYLOR AVE 24134 #020-12-1966 L1990 **GS** *020 †85
DAVIS, Charles Young. 602 WENONAH AVE 24134 #010-01-1965 L1966 **GYN** *071 †30
DEVEREAUX, Robert Francis. 1611 WENONAH AVE, CARILION FAMILY MEDICINE 24134 #036-01-1982 L1986 **FM** *020 †18
HANSEN, Lori Leigh. 1611 WENONAH AVE, CARILION FAMILY MEDICINE 24134 #028-34-1997 L2000 **FM** *020 †18
HAYES, D Scott. 1611 WENONAH AVE, CARILION FAMILY MEDICINE 24134 #051-07-1986 L1987 **FM** *020 †18
HUDGINS, Laurie Pearse. 602 WENONAH AVE 24134 #051-04-1984 L1989 **OBG** *020 †30
MC GUIRE, Erma J Marra. 1 TAYLOR AVE 24134 #051-04-1951 L1951 **FM** *071 †18
MC GUIRE, George Oliver. ■ 24134 #051-07-1990 L1992 **IM** *100
MC GUIRE, Joseph F. 201 S WOODRUM ST 24134 #051-04-1951 L1951 **GP** *071
MC MAHON, Michael Alan. 1611 WENONAH AVE, CARILION FAMILY MEDICINE 24134 #051-04-1975 L1976 **FM** *020 †18
MEINCKE, David Lee. 602 WENONAH AVE 24134 #051-04-1973 L1976 **OBG** *020 †30
MELTON, Russell Winfree. 1611 WENONAH AVE, CARILION FAMILY MEDICINE 24134 #051-01-1994 L1997 **FM** *020 †18
NICHOLSON, Bradley W. 705 WENONAH AVE STE 4 24134 #051-04-1977 L1979 **GS CD** *020 †85
OLSON, Paul Alan. 219 BUCHANAN ST 24134 #047-05-1981 L1984 **IM** *020 †20
RIMON, Desiderio Jesus. 705 WENONAH AVE, CARILION SURGICAL CARE 24134 #023-01-1998 L1998 **GS** *020 †85
SHAWVER, Gregory Wayne. ■ 24134 #051-01-2002 L2007 **FM** *020 †18
SMITH, James Robt. 1 TAYLOR AVE, CARILION GILES MEMORIAL HO 24134 #051-04-1977 L1978 **FM** *020 †16,18
TAMMINEN, John L, III. 1 TAYLOR AVE 24134 #051-07-1983 L1987 **DR** *020 †80
WALKER, Kenneth Jos. 1611 WENONAH AVE, CARILION FAMILY MEDICINE 24134 #051-01-1975 L1976 **FM IMG** *020 †18
WERBLIN, Theodore Paul. 1 TAYLOR AVE, GILE MEMORIAL HOSPITAL 24134 #035-19-1972 L1985 **OPH IM** *020 †20,35 ‡
ZOLOVICK, George Thomas. 602 WENONAH AVE 24134 #036-05-1994 L2001 **OBG** *020 †30

PENHOOK – FRANKLIN

KIEHM, Leonard Yong Hee. ■ 24137 #005-12-1971 L1972 **GS** *071 †85
MC CLURE-SMITH, Pamela G. ■ 24137 #055-02-1987 L1991 **P** *020 †20
PERRY, Peter Linner. ■ 24137 #016-06-1968 L1976 **ORS** *071 †40
SYDNOR, J Brantley. ■ 24137 #051-01-1967 L1967 **OTO** *071 †45

PENN LAIRD – ROCKINGHAM

ROSE, A Lawrence. PO BOX 98 22846 #035-45-1959 L1983 **OPH** *071 †35

PENNINGTON GAP – LEE

AHSAN, Saira. 1800 COMBS RD, STE 4 LEE MEDICAL PLZ 24277 #704-25-1989 L1994 **PD** *020 †55
AHSAN, Syed Z. ■ 24277 #704-16-1983 L1994 **P CHP** *020 †75
ALI, Asghar. 1800 COMBS RD STE 3, LEE INT MED & FAM CARE 24277 #495-51-1997 L2005 **IM** *020 †20
ALMATARI, Abdullatief A. 1800 COMBS RD STE 12, LEE REGIONAL MEDICAL CTR 24277 #047-20-1996 L1999 **IM** *020 ‡
CANN, Braxton F, Jr. 1800 W MORGAN AVE 24277 #010-03-1961 L1990 **OTO HNS** *020 †45
CHENNAREDDY, Kiran Kumar. ■ 24277 #495-50-1995 L2002 **FM** *100 †18
DI TRAGLIA, Frank Jos. 1800 COMBS RD, MEDICAL STAFF OFFICE 24277 #748-01-1981 L1992 **RHU EM** *020 †20
FAIZE, Hossein. 1800 W MORGAN AVE 24277 #517-01-1967 L1974 **GS AS** *020 †85
GENERAL, Patricia Ann. 1800 W MORGAN AVE 24277 #051-04-1988 L1989 **P FM** *020 †18
GORE, Stephen Thos. 1800 COMBS RD, LEE REGIONAL MEDICAL CENTE 24277 #045-01-1981 L1994 **EM FM** *020 †18,16
KALANTAR MOTAMEDI, M R. 132 MAPLE AVE 24277 #517-01-1964 L1971 **GS ORS** *020
KAUL, Hitesh. ■ 24277 #495-73-1989 L2005 **GS** *020
KAUL, Zenia Peshin. ■ 24277 #495-84-1996 L2007 **AN** *020 †05
KOLODZIEJ, B Allen. 1800 W MORGAN AVE 24277 #422-01-1995 L2002 **EM** *020
LAUFER, Gabor Geysa. 1800 W MORGAN AVE 24277 #473-01-1972 L1982 **OBG** *020
LITTON, John Scott, Jr. 1800 COMBS RD, STE 7 24277 #051-01-2000 L2002 **FM** *020 †18
MOLONY, Patrick A. 1800 W MORGAN AVE 24277 #539-05-1969 L1972 **IM PUD** *020
OWENS, Beryl Henry. W MORGAN AVE 24277 #051-01-1954 L1954 **GP** *071
SULTAN, Shafi Ahmed. 132 MAPLE AVE 24277 #160-02-1970 L1980 **GS** *020
TURNBULL, James Mc Jannet. 430 INDUSTRIAL DR 24277 #917-29-1961 L1990 **P OS** *020 †75
VAN ZEE, Wayne Arthur. 602 W MORGAN AVE, STE 3 24277 #038-06-1973 L1976 **IM** *020 †20
VARANDANI, Chanda. 1800 W MORGAN AVE 24277 #495-49-1969 L1980 **PD** *020 †55
VARANDANI, Jai Krishin. 1800 W MORGAN AVE 24277 #495-49-1969 L1980 **IM GP** *020 †20

PETERSBURG – PETERSBURG CITY

ABEBEFE, David O. 801 S ADAMS ST 23803 #690-01-1987 L1993 **IM EM** *020 †20

AGARWAL, Ramesh Chandra. 20 W BANK ST 23803 #495-34-1963 L1973 **P GP** *020 †75 ‡
ALBRIGHT, David Wesley. W WASHINGTON ST 23803 #055-02-1986 L1989 **P** *020 †75
ALI, Mohammed Moinuddin. 801 S ADAMS ST 23803 #495-65-1966 L1979 **RO** *020 †80 ‡
AMARA, Chandra R. 510 S SYCAMORE ST 23803 #495-57-1978 L1993 **P CHP** *020 †75
BANKURU, Satish Kumar. 3400 S CRATER RD, STE B 23805 #495-21-1991 L2004 **NEP IM** *020 †20
BAUGH, Thomas A. 202 S SYCAMORE ST 23803 #010-03-1951 L1952 **GP** *072
BERGEN, Frederick D'Oench. 700 S SYCAMORE ST 23803 #035-20-1958 L1964 **TS GS** *071 †85,90
BIGLEY, Harry Alan, Jr. 700 S SYCAMORE ST STE 1 23803 #051-01-1968 L1968 **U** *020 †95 ‡
BUSCH, Joyce M Buffington. 200 S SYCAMORE ST 23803 #010-03-1961 L1967 **PD** *071
BUSCH, Samuel Edward. 200 S SYCAMORE ST 23803 #010-03-1961 L1967 **OBG OS** *075 †30
CAMPBELL, Cedric. 24 S ADAMS ST 23803 #016-11-1996 L1998 **AN** *012 †18
CHARITY-BROWN, Tamara A. 5 HOLLYHILL DR 23805 #051-01-2001 L2001 **PD** *020 †55
CHEN, Jin-Sheng. 2825 S CRATER RD 23805 #244-01-1970 L1975 **AN** *100 †05
CHIN, Judy Ling. 801 S ADAMS ST, VIRGINIA UROLOGY CENTER 23803 #051-04-1982 L1988 **RO IM** *020 †20,80
CHIRUMAMILLA, V. 3400 S CRATER RD STE B 23805 #495-58-1979 L1990 **IM NEP** *020 †20
COHEN, Alvin. 531 S SYCAMORE ST 23803 #051-01-1953 L1953 **IM NM** *020 †28
COHEN, Michael Robt. 531 S SYCAMORE ST 23803 #051-04-1984 L1987 **IM** *020 †20
CROWDER, Margaret E. ■ 23803 #010-03-1950 L1956 **IM OS** *071
CUMMINGS, Joan A. 3333 S CRATER RD, STE B 23805 #036-01-1977 L1980 **OBG** *020
DALTON, Fred Clinton. 510 S SYCAMORE ST, STE E 23803 #025-07-1947 L1979 **LM CHP** *071
DAWSON, Elizabeth Adams. 801 S ADAMS ST 23803 #051-07-1983 L1987 **DR** *020 †80
DEZZUTTI, Brian Peter. 801 S ADAMS ST, MEDICAL STAFF OFFICE 23803 #051-04-1994 L1998 **AN** *020
DI GIOVANNA, Thomas A. 801 S ADAMS ST 23803 #010-01-1982 L1983 **EM** *020 †16
DILLON, Edward Carpenter. 801 S ADAMS ST 23803 #041-01-1985 L1992 **EM IM** *020 †20
DUHART, Harold Bobby, Jr. 700 S SYCAMORE ST, STE 6 23803 #051-04-1991 L1993 **PD** *020 †55
DUNN, Richard Wade. 1888 S SYCAMORE ST 23805 #051-04-1977 L1978 **FM EM** *020 †18
EBELING, Thomas Andrew. PO BOX 4030 23803 #039-01-1989 L1991 **P** *020 †75
EHRENWORTH, Adolphe M. 801 S ADAMS ST 23803 #051-01-1951 L1951 **R** *071 †80
ENDE, Frederick Ivan. 121 S MARKET ST 23803 #051-04-1978 L1979 **IM** *020 †20
ENDE, Mark. 121 S MARKET ST 23803 #051-04-1981 L1983 **IM** *020 †20
FARNELL, Patrocinio M. ■ 23805 #748-02-1940 L1970 **IMG** *071
FEILD, Bolling Jones. 507 S SYCAMORE ST 23803 #051-04-1966 L1966 **IM CD** *020 †20
FOSTER, Orville Ryland. 1857A FORT MAHONE ST 23805 #038-40-1988 L1994 **AN IM** *020 †05,20
FREIHOFER, Erick Jean. 3277 S CRATER RD 23805 #038-41-1963 L1995 **D** *074 †15
FUKUMOTO, Donna M. 700 S SYCAMORE ST, STE 10 23803 #051-04-1977 L1979 **ON HEM** *020 †20
GIBBONS, Jonathan Myles. 350 POPLAR ST 23803 #023-12-1999 L2000 **ORS** *020 †05
GIBSON, Sandy Morton. 15 W OLD ST 23803 #051-04-1984 L1987 **NEP IM** *020 †20
GILL, Rajwinder Singh. 801 S ADAMS ST, SOUTHSIDE REGIONAL MEDICAL 23803 #495-99-1997 L2003 **AN** *020
GONZALES, Manuel Borja. PETERSBG PATH ASSOC STHSD 23803 #748-01-1963 L1976 **PTH** *020 †50
GRISWOLD, Martha Ann. 507 S SYCAMORE ST 23803 #051-04-1978 L1981 **IM OS** *020 †20
GUTIERREZ, Leo M. 801 S ADAMS ST 23803 #748-01-1968 L1985 **EM** *020 †85
HAINES, David Morrill. 541 S SYCAMORE ST, PETERSBURG ORTHOPAEDIC CTR 23803 #021-01-1969 L1976 **ORS GS** *071 †40
HARINDRAN, Usha J. 4030 WASHINGTON STREET 23803 #495-80-1978 L1982 **P** *020
HART, Kirby Thompson, Jr. 801 S ADAMS ST 23803 #024-01-1947 L1952 **PD NP** *071 †55
HEARST, Karen Ann. 301 HALIFAX ST, STE A 23803 #051-04-1990 L1991 **FM** *020 †18
HENRY, Brian Cornell. 801 S ADAMS ST 23803 #025-01-1987 L1988 **IM** *020
HOLDEN, Bobby G. 801 S ADAMS ST 23803 #051-04-1962 L1962 **GP** *071
HOWELL, Talmadge Rudolph. 510 S SYCAMORE ST 23803 #036-07-1958 L1964 **PDR R** *020 †80
HSU, Jong Chong. 801 S ADAMS ST, SOUTHSIDE REGIONAL MEDICAL 23803 #243-50-1969 L1979 **AN** *020
JUJJAVARAPU, Rayudu N. 700 S SYCAMORE ST 23803 #495-58-1977 L1989 **GS** *020 †85
KAO, Zen Leu. 1857 FORT MAHONE ST 23805 #385-04-1967 L1972 **AN** *020 †05
KASIRAJAN, Vigneshwar. 801 S ADAMS ST 23803 #495-04-1988 L2000 **TS** *020 †90,85
KEENE, Shenna Renee. 801 S ADAMS ST, PETERSBURG CLINIC COMPANY, 23803 #041-02-1999 L2005 **FM** *020 †20
KHAN, Khalid. 801 S ADAMS ST, EMERGENCY DEPARTMENT 23803 #704-02-1986 L2000 **IM** *020 †20
KHAN, Salman F. 801 S ADAMS ST 23803 #704-02-1990 L1998 **IM** *020 †20
KIM, Suel. 801 S ADAMS ST 23803 #023-01-1991 L1993 **END** *020 †20
KODURI, Ramesh Babu. 510 S SYCAMORE ST 23803 #495-65-1969 L1974 **P GP** *020 †75
KONDRAGUNTA, Butchaiah. 700 S SYCAMORE ST, STE 11 23803 #495-50-1985 L1999 **HO ON** *020 †20
KONDRAGUNTA, Sakuntla. 700 S SYCAMORE ST, STE 2B 23803 #495-50-1983 L1999 **IM** *020 †20
KRISHNAMURTHY, Kalale S. 801 S ADAMS ST 23803 #495-33-1961 L1978 **IM** *020
KUDARAVALLI, Krishna Rao. 510 S SYCAMORE ST STE B 23803 #495-58-1974 L1981 **OBG GYN** *020 †30
KUMAR, K L Ashok. 700 S SYCAMORE ST STE 10, P O BOX 2204 23803 #495-33-1978 L1985 **CD IM** *020 †20
LE, Lac Kiim. 26317 W WASHINGTON ST, CENTRAL STATE HOSPITAL 23803 #941-01-1975 L1982 **GP FM** *020
LEE, Young. 603 S SYCAMORE ST 23803 #583-10-1968 L1980 **GP PTH** *020
LITTAUA, Rebecca A. 801 S ADAMS ST 23803 #748-02-1981 L1996 **ID IM** *020
LIVINGSTONE, Robert C. ■ 23805 #023-01-1943 L1946 **ORS OM** *071
MACK, Debbie Mony. 350 POPLAR DR 23805 #051-07-1991 L1994 **CHP P** *020
MADDEN, Willis Mc Donald. 2719 S CRATER RD STE A 23805 #051-04-1981 L1984 **OPH** *020
MANALO, Fernando D. ■ 23805 #748-02-1931 *100
MASON, James D, Jr. 507 S SYCAMORE ST 23803 #051-01-1951 L1951 **IM** *071 †20
MASON, Marie Joy. PO BOX 4030, CENTRAL STATE HOSP 23803 #051-04-1957 L1957 **PHP** *020
MBAGWU, Adaku Joyce. ■ 23805 #047-07-2007 **OBG** *012
MC CARTER, Warren J. 801 S ADAMS ST 23803 #051-04-1982 L1983 **FM** *062 †18
MC CLURE, Phillip Hutson. ■ 23805 #012-05-1964 L1979 **R** *071 †80
MC CONAHEY, William M, III. 801 S ADAMS ST 23803 #026-04-1971 L1974 **EM ADM** *020

MC KENZIE, Norma Dee Ann. 20 W BANK ST 23803 #005-02-1971 L1987 **P** *020 †75

MC MILLAN, Jane E. 603 S SYCAMORE ST, COMMONWEALTH OB-GYN, PC 23803 #047-20-1998 L2002 **OBG** *020

MC MULLEN, Paul Eugene. ■ 23803 #038-40-1960 L1960 **GP** *071

MILITANA, Mark D. 801 S ADAMS ST 23803 #035-03-1989 L1990 **IM CD** *040

MISHRA, Raj Kumar. PO BOX 4030 23803 #495-55-1970 L1982 **IM GP** *020 †20

MOJA, Motsumi. 301 HALIFAX ST, STE A 23803 #010-03-1988 L1990 **IM** *020 †20

MORGAN, Jeffrey Todd. 801 S ADAMS ST 23803 #051-01-1993 L1999 **VIR** *020 †80

MOSCHLER, Edward Franklin. 510 S SYCAMORE ST, STE D 23803 #051-04-1990 L1995 **OBG** *020

MOSELEY, Charles Hilary. 801 S ADAMS ST 23803 #051-04-1956 L1956 **GYN** *071 †30

NGUYEN, Tu Huu. 801 S ADAMS ST 23803 #941-01-1973 L1983 **IM** *030 †20

NIKICICZ, Edward. 801 S ADAMS ST 23803 #759-04-1982 L1992 **PTH** *020 †50

OJEDIRAN, Olumuyiwa A. 734 S SYCAMORE ST 23803 #306-01-1997 L2002 **IM** *020 †20

OKELANA, Eniola. 801 S ADAMS ST 23803 #690-05-1984 L1995 **PUD** *020 †20

PASEOS, Erlinda T Sanchez. ■ 23805 #748-01-1957 L1996 **P OPH** *020

PETROCELLI, Dennis. 3335 S CRATER RD, CENTRAL STATE HOSPITAL 23805 #024-05-1994 L2000 **P PFP** *020 †75

RANDOLPH, David Marcus. 801 S ADAMS ST, VIRGINIA UROLOGY CENTER 23803 #051-07-1983 L1984 **RO** *020 †18,80

RANKIN, Kathryn Ann. 301 HALIFAX ST, PEIDMONT HEALTH DISTRICT 23803 #018-03-1985 L2005 **FM** *020 †18

REDDY, Pannala Jagan M. 510 S SYCAMORE ST, STE F 23803 #495-65-1964 L1977 **P** *020 †75

REDDY, Pannala Vijaya. 510 S SYCAMORE ST STE D 23803 #495-21-1965 L1978 **OBG** *020 †30

RICE, Benjamin Holt. ■ 23805 #051-04-1962 L1962 **GS** *071 †85

RICE, Benjamin Holt, Jr. ■ 23805 #051-04-1990 L1997 **GS** *020 †85

RICHARD, Louis E. ■ 23805 #021-05-1949 L1959 **R** *071 †80

ROEBUCK, Jerome Barland. 408 S SYCAMORE ST, PETERSBURG EYE CENTER LTD 23803 #021-01-1956 L1963 **OPH** *071 †35

ROSS, Raymond Thos. 700 S SYCAMORE ST, STE 12 23803 #051-07-1980 L1985 **GS VS** *020 †85

ROSTAFINSKI, Michael Jan. ■ 23805 #913-12-1947 L1960 **P AM** *020

ROYSTER, Michael Owen. 301 HALIFAX ST 23803 #036-07-1996 L2002 **GPM** *030 †70

RUHNKE, Edward Emeric, Jr. ■ 23805 #051-01-1963 L1963 **OBG** *071 †30

RUSSELL, Latonya Demetria. ■ 23803 #051-01-2006 L2006 **PD** *012

RYAN, George Leonard. ■ 23803 #051-04-1985 L1986 **GS** *020

RYANS, Miller M. W WASHINGTON ST 23803 #010-03-1953 L1955 **P** *071 †75

SAKHADEO, Shrihari S. H.W. DAVIS MEDICAL CENTER 23803 #495-28-1961 L1977 **EM PD** *075 †55

SARAIYA, Raksha S. 801 S ADAMS ST, SOUTHSIDE REGIONAL MEDICAL 23803 #495-23-1977 L1984 **AN PD** *020

SAUNDERS, Joyce L Herrin. W WASHINGTON ST 23803 #051-04-1959 L1959 **P** *040

SCRANAGE, Clarence, Jr. 3333 S CRATER RD, STE 3A 23805 #047-07-1982 L1985 **EM** *020 †16

SEO, Syng Pyo. THE CENTRAL STATE HOSPITAL 23803 #583-02-1963 L1980 **P** *020

SHAH, Saqib. 801 S ADAMS ST 23803 #019-02-1991 L2001 **IM** *020 †20

SHANDILYA, Loknath. 20901 CHESTERFIELD AVE 23803 #649-33-1985 L1995 **IM** *020

SHAVER, Kathryn Mc Ivor. 700 S SYCAMORE ST, STE 8 23803 #051-07-1984 L1986 **IM** *020 †20

SHIEH, Frank F. 603 S SYCAMORE ST 23803 #244-05-1969 L1976 **OBG FM** *071 †30

SIEGMUND, Brad Thomas. 801 S ADAMS ST 23803 #028-34-1976 L1982 **PTH CLP** *020 †50

SIMON, Thresa Helen. 510 S SYCAMORE ST STE F 23803 #495-16-1988 L1997 **CHP** *020 †75

SMITH, Barton Palmer. 801 S ADAMS ST 23803 #051-01-1982 L1985 **GS** *020 †85

SORMUS, Helju. W WASHINGTON ST 23803 #407-21-1946 L1957 **P** *071

STEELE, Richard F B, Jr. 51 S MARKET ST 23803 #051-04-1960 L1961 **GP OS** *020

STROTHER, Arnold Franklin. 26317 W WASHINGTON ST, BLDG 39 23803 #051-04-1958 L1958 **P CHP** *071

SVIDRO, Virginia Mary. 301 HALIFAX ST, CRATER HEALTH DIST VA DEPT 23803 #041-09-1977 L1984 **PD** *020 †55

THIGPEN, Calvin Herritage. 734 S SYCAMORE ST 23803 #051-01-1962 L1962 **GP LM** *071

THUNG, Nalda Sylvia. ■ 23805 #506-01-1955 L1970 **AN** *071 †55

TIETJEN, John Robt. ■ 23805 #035-03-1945 L1949 **PHP GPM** *071

TOLBERT, Shirlene. 24 S ADAMS ST, SOUTHSIDE FAMILY PRACTICE 23803 #033-05-1989 L1996 **FM** *020 †18

TOMLIN, Henry Louis. 600 S SYCAMORE ST 23803 #033-05-1975 L1977 **OBG** *020 †30

TORRE, Taryn Gayle. 801 S ADAMS ST, VIRGINIA UROLOGY CENTER 23803 #051-07-1994 L1995 **RO** *020 †80

TRAN, Thuy Thi. W WASHINGTON ST 23803 #051-07-1988 L1990 **FM** *020 †18

TRIVETTE, George A. 801 S ADAMS ST 23803 #051-07-1982 L1984 **RO** *020 †80

TUASON, Amenra F. RT 1 WASHINGTON ST, CENTRAL STATE HOSP 23803 #748-19-1983 L1987 **P PFP** *020

TYMOWSKI, Maciej. 801 S ADAMS ST 23803 #759-04-2000 L2000 **EM** *020 †16 ‡

VASA, Nirmala. SOOTHSIDE VA TRAINING CTR 23803 #495-50-1977 L1982 **IM** *020

VAUGHAN, Stephen F. 2731 S CRATER RD 23805 #051-04-1976 L1978 **FM** *020 †18

VICK, Clyde Whitley, Jr. 801 S ADAMS ST 23803 #023-07-1943 L1950 **GS GYN** *071 †85

WEBB, Robert B, Jr. 408 S SYCAMORE ST, PETERSBURG EYE CENTER LTD 23803 #051-01-1952 L1953 **OPH** *071 †35

WICKIZER, Boyd Roy, Jr. 801 S ADAMS ST, SOUTH SIDE REGIONAL MED CE 23803 #003-01-1975 L1982 **EM GS** *020 †85

WOOD, Isaac Keith. W WASHINGTON ST 23803 #051-04-1982 L1985 **CHP** *030 †75

WOOLDRIDGE, James Walter. 43 RIVES RD 23805 #051-07-1984 L1985 **CHP P** *020

WRIGHT, Luther Leroy. 801 S ADAMS ST, SOUTHSIDE HOSPITALIST GROU 23803 #305-01-2001 L2004 **IM** *100

WYATT, Davis Burton, Jr. 801 S ADAMS ST 23803 #051-04-1996 L2000 **EM** *020 †16

YELLINEDI, Sujatha. 700 S SYCAMORE ST, STE 11 23803 #495-50-1994 L2005 **HO** *020 †20

POQUOSON – POQUOSON CITY

BLACK, James N. ■ 23662 #047-06-1979 L1980 **OTO** *030 †45

BROOKS, Kevin Eugene. ■ 23662 #039-01-1984 L1986 **IM** *020 †70

FITHIAN, Ellen Capeci. ■ 23662 #051-01-1978 L1979 **D** *020 †15

FLYNN, Charles Laurence. ■ 23662 #035-20-1961 L1969 **GS** *071 †85

GROSS, Shari Lynn. ■ 23662 #051-01-2006 L2006 **FP** *012

IVATURY, Srinivas Joga. ■ 23662 #051-04-2006 GS *012

JUANG, Derek Kato. ■ 23662 #025-01-2008 *012

NETTO, Molly. ■ 23662 #495-04-1962 L1980 **OS PTH** *071 †50

PALMER, James David Keith. ■ 23662 #352-07-1948 L1982 **PM RHU** *050 †60

REMCHUK, Deborah Mary. ■ 23662 #051-07-2004 L2004 **IFP** *012

PORT HAYWOOD – MATHEWS

KENLEY, James B. ■ 23138 #051-01-1952 L1952 **PHP** *030 †70

PORTSMOUTH – PORTSMOUTH CITY

ABDELSHAHEED, Samir T M. 5911 PORTSMOUTH BLVD, FAMILY MEDICINE HEALTH CAR 23701 #915-03-1990 L2004 **FM** *020 †18

ACCETTOLA, Robert James. 3737 HIGH ST 23707 #048-02-1981 L1986 **IC CD** *020 †20

ADAMS, Jennifer Kash. 620 JOHN PAUL JONES CIR, ATTN: CREDENTIAL OFFICE 23708 #001-02-1991 L1995 **AN** *020 †05

ADRIANO, Elizabeth. 620 JOHN PAUL JONES CIR, NAVAL MEDICAL CENTER 23708 #023-12-1996 L2000 **OBG** *020 †30

AGRAZ, Javier, Jr. ■ 23704 #028-34-2005 *100

AKAM, Abu Reida Ali. 600 CRAWFORD ST, STE 300 23704 #848-01-1978 L2003 **FM HOS** *100

AKINS, David Lee. 301 GOODE WAY STE 101 23704 #012-01-1975 L1981 **IM** *020 †20

ALEGRE-IPANAG, Olivia Y. 664 LINCOLN ST 23704 #748-02-1978 L1999 **PD** *020 †55

ALETA, Elenita Farro. 4224 PORTSMOUTH BLVD 23701 #748-01-1965 L1993 **GP PTH** *020

ALEXANDER, Brian Andrew. 620 JOHN PAUL JONES CIR, ATTN: CREDENTIAL OFFICE 23708 #036-05-1990 L1991 **OPH** *035

ALEXANDER, James E, Jr. 3737 HIGH ST 23707 #047-05-1974 L1976 **GS OS** *030 †85

ALFONSO, Belina Rowena. 620 JOHN PAUL JONES CIR, CREDENTIAL OFFICE 23708 #051-07-1996 L1997 **P** *020 †75

ALONSO, Robert Anthony. 620 JOHN PAUL JONES CIR, NAVAL MEDICAL CTR PSYCH DE 23708 #020-02-1988 L1989 **P** *020 †75

ANDERSON, Paynesha Marie. 620 JOHN PAUL JONES CIR, DEPT OB 23708 #010-03-2005 L2006 *100

ANG-RABANES, Jose C. 620 JOHN PAUL JONES CIR, ATTN: CREDENTIAL OFFICE 23708 #748-01-1966 L1988 **N** *020

ANTONENKO, Alexander. 600 CRAWFORD ST, STE 300 23704 #913-13-1995 L2007 **FP** *012

ARBID, Elias Jos. 3640 HIGH ST, STE 2F 23707 #024-16-1987 L1999 **VS GS** *020 †85

ARNAOUT, Majd Mahmoud. 600 CRAWFORD ST, STE 300 23704 #875-03-1990 L2006 **FP** *012

ARSLAN, Gohar. 355 CRAWFORD ST, STE 102 23704 #704-21-1991 L2006 **HO** *020 †20

ARTRIP, John Henry. 3640 HIGH ST, STE 2D 23707 #025-07-1994 L2006 **TS** *020 †85,90

ASHAI, Shafqat Hamza. 850 CRAWFORD PKWY, BON SECOURS MEDICAL CENTER 23704 #704-19-1983 L1995 **IM** *020 †20

ASHAI, Shaista. 3300 ACADEMY AVE, CHURCHLAND PSYCHIATRIC ASS 23703 #704-06-1986 L1997 **P** *020

AUSTIN, Mark Wayne. 620 JOHN PAUL JONES CIR, NAVAL MEDICAL CENTER 23708 #048-04-1980 L1993 **OBG** *020 †30

AYRES, Allen Williams. 620 JOHN PAUL JONES CIR, ATTN: CREDENTIAL OFFICE 23708 #016-06-1971 L1972 **OBG** *020 †30

AZNAR, Sonia Ferry. EFFINGHAM ST 23708 #748-08-1967 L1979 **P** *020

BACAK, Velma Anne. 3300 ACADEMY AVE 23703 #051-01-1980 L1984 **CHP P** *020 †75

BACCUS, John Benjamin, III. 620 JOHN PAUL JONES CIR 23708 #048-14-1993 L2007 **APM** *100 †05

BACKENS, Matthew Vern. 600 CRAWFORD ST, STE 300 23704 #051-07-2006 L2006 **FP** *012

BAILEY, Philip Daniel, Jr. 620 JOHN PAUL JONES CIR, ATTN: CREDENTIAL OFFICE 23708 #022-75-1997, ▲ L1998 **PAN** *020 †05

BARAL, Dante A. 620 JOHN PAUL JONES CIR, ATTN: CREDENTIAL OFFICE 23708 #748-01-1964 L1976 **DR EM** *030

BARCLAY, Charles O, Jr. ■ 23704 #051-01-1950 L1950 **GP OS** *071

BARKER, Michael John. 620 JOHN PAUL JONES CIR, NMCP- DEPARTMENT OF SURGER 23708 #035-08-1998 L1998 **GS** *020 †85

BARNARD, John W. CRAWFORD PKWY AT FORT LANE 23704 #023-01-1949 L1950 **P** *071

BARRECA, Joseph Peter. 3640 HIGH ST, STE 2F 23707 #021-05-1956 L1977 **VS GS** *071 †85

BARROW, Richard Dowell, II. 620 JOHN PAUL JONES CIR, ATTN: CREDENTIAL OFFICE, N 23708 #036-08-2001 L2001 **EM** *012

BARTHEL, Robert Vincent. 620 JOHN PAUL JONES CIR, NAVAL MED CTR 23708 #023-12-1997 L2001 **ID** *020 †20

BASTIEN, John Louis. 620 JOHN PAUL JONES CIR, ATTN: CREDENTIAL OFFICE 23708 #023-12-1994 L2001 **FP** *020 †05

BAUCOM, Clairalyn Lois. 630 JOHN PAUL JONES CIR 23708 #047-06-2005 L2005 **PD** *012

BAUMGARTEN, Margaret. 600 CRAWFORD ST STE 30 23704 #913-15-1992 L1999 **FM** *020 †18

BECKMAN, William A, Jr. 620 JOHN PAUL JONES CIR, NAVAL MEDICAL CENTER 23708 #011-04-1996 L1998 **APM** *020 †05

BEHLMER, Patricia Maureen. 3640 HIGH ST, STE 1F 23707 #018-03-1979 L1984 **N** *020 †75

BELCHER, Richard L. 3214 VICTORY BLVD 23702 #409-10-1967 L1975 **FM OBG** *072

BERGER, Alexander. 2700 LONDON BLVD 23707 #869-07-1958 L1981 **FM IMG** *071 †18

BERGSTROM, Curt Alfred. ■ 23704 #023-12-2002 L2002 **AN** *012

BERMISA, Arthur V. 2701 ELLIOTT AVE, BERMISA & BERMISA MD PLC 23702 #748-08-1972 L2000 **FP** *020

BETTIS, Robert Michael. 620 JOHN PAUL JONES CIR, NAVAL MEDICAL CENTER 23708 #023-12-2004 L2004 **AN** *012

BEUTE, Trisha C. 620 JOHN PAUL JONES CIR, NAVAL MED CTR 23708 #023-12-2001 L2002 **D** *020 †15

BHOWMIK, Nihar R. 301 GOODE WAY STE 103 23704 #160-06-1980 L1993 **IM PD** *020 †20

BIBAY, Laarni Serquina. 301 GOODE WAY STE 203 23704 #748-02-1978 L1992 **PD** *020 †55

BIGGIO, Alice Elizabeth. ■ 23701 #051-07-2007 *012

BIKOWSKI, Richard Michael. 600 CRAWFORD ST STE 300 23704 #051-07-1979 L1982 **EM FM** *020 †18

BISCHOFF, Craig Ernest. 620 JOHN PAUL JONES CIR, ATTN: CREDENTIAL OFFICE, N 23708 #054-04-1980 L1990 **ORS** *020 †70

BISWAS, Abhik Kumar. 620 JOHN PAUL JONES CIR, NAVAL MEDICAL CENTER 23708 #054-04-1991 L1999 **CCP** *020 †55

BLACK, Kristina Rea. 620 JOHN PAUL JONES CIR, NAVAL MEDICAL CENTER 23708 #051-07-2005 L2006 *020

BLACKWELL, Steven Michael. 620 JOHN PAUL JONES CIR, MEDICAL STAFF SERVICES 23708 #001-02-1990 L2007 **AN** *020 †20

BLANTON, Michael Wallace. 355 CRAWFORD ST, STE 102 23704 #051-04-1983 L1991 **GS SO** *020 †85

BLASDELL, Steven Chas. 601 FREDERICK BLVD 23707 #035-45-1981 L1986 **ORS** *020 †40
BLOOM, David Charles. 620 JOHN PAUL JONES CIR, NAVAL MEDICAL CENTER 23708 #026-08-1994 L1995 **PDO** *020 †45
BLOOM, Tammy Lee. 620 JOHN PAUL JONES CIR, ATTN: PROFESSIONAL AFFAIRS 23708 #001-06-1994 L1996 **U** *020 †95
BOLANOS, Sandra. 600 CRAWFORD ST, STE 300 23704 #048-12-2007 L2007 **FP** *012
BONDY, Peter Carlton. 620 JOHN PAUL JONES CIR, ATTN: CREDENTIAL OFFICE 23708 #026-04-1987 L1992 **OTO FPS** *030 †45
BONTA, Marie Irene. ■ 23704 #045-04-2008 *012
BOZMAN, Raymond Elwood. 620 JOHN PAUL JONES CIR, NAVAL MEDICAL CENTER 23708 #010-01-1981 L1988 **DR MDM** *020 †80
BRAR, Harpreet Singh. 27 EFFINGHAM ST, NAVAL MED CTR 23708 #048-14-1985 L2000 **GS** *020 †85
BRASINGTON, Steve J. 620 JOHN PAUL JONES CIR, ATTN: CREDENTIAL OFFICE 23708 #011-02-1984 L1986 **CHP ADP** *020 †75
BRAWLEY, Stephen Craig. 620 JOHN PAUL JONES CIR, NAVAL MED CTR, MED SERV SU 23708 #048-12-2000 L2000 *020
BREAZEALE, Daniel Robert. 620 JOHN PAUL JONES CIR, ACADEMIC AFFAIRS/GME 23708 #023-12-1999 L2001 **OBG** *020 †20
BREEN, Suzanne Marie. 620 JOHN PAUL JONES CIR, ATTN: CREDENTIAL OFFICE 23708 #005-06-1996 L1997 **PD** *020 †55
BRITTMAN, Stanley Louis. 600 CRAWFORD ST, STE 300 23704 #051-04-1975 L1977 **FM FPG** *020 †18
BRITTON, Bruce Stuart. 600 CRAWFORD ST, STE 300 23704 #051-07-1990 L1991 **FM** *020 †18
BROWN, Christin Michele. 620 JOHN PAUL JONES CIR, NMC PORTSMOUTH 23708 #023-12-2000 L2000 *020
BROWN, William Melvin, III. 620 JOHN PAUL JONES CIR, NAVAL MED CTR 23708 #045-01-2002 L2003 **EM** *012
BRUKER, Charles Todd. 620 JOHN PAUL JONES CIR, NAVAL MEDICAL CENTER 23708 #012-01-2002 L2003 **PTH** *012
BRUMMETT, Richard Ralph. 355 CRAWFORD ST, STE 808 23704 #019-02-1987 L1993 **AN** *020 †05
BRYANT, Cynthia Maria. ■ 23708 #047-07-2000 L2001 **PD** *100 †55
BUI, Han Quang. 620 JOHN PAUL JONES CIR, PROFESSIONAL AFFAIRS 23708 #023-12-1997 L2006 **FM** *020 †20
BULLOCK, Karen E. 620 JOHN PAUL JONES CIR, DEPT OF INTERNAL MEDICINE 23708 #011-02-2002 L2003 **HO** *012 †20
BULLOCK, Nicole Patrice. ■ 23704 #036-01-2004 L2005 **PM** *012
BURKE, Rachel Ann. 620 JOHN PAUL JONES CIR, NAVAL MEDICAL CENTER PORTS 23708 #023-12-1997 L1997 **GS** *020 †85
BURNS, Ellie Lee. ■ 23707 #016-06-2004 L2004 *020
BUTLER, Annelore Fontane. 620 JOHN PAUL JONES CIR, ATTN: CREDENTIAL OFFICE 23708 #040-02-1967 L1998 **PD** *020 †55
CALLAN, James Edward. 620 JOHN PAUL JONES CIR, ATTN: CREDENTIAL OFFICE 23708 #005-12-1999 L2003 **EM** *020 †16
CALLAWAY, Robt Alonzo, Jr. 620 JOHN PAUL JONES CIR, ATTN: CREDENTIAL OFFICE 23708 #012-01-1970 L1994 **PUD IM** *020 †20
CAMERON, Matthew P. ■ 23707 #022-75-2007, ▲ *012
CANNON, David Lorne. 620 JOHN PAUL JONES CIR, ATTN: CREDENTIAL OFFICE 23708 #035-20-1991 L2005 **HS** *020 †40
CANONIZADO, Carmencita M. 620 JOHN PAUL JONES CIR, ATTN: CREDENTIAL OFFICE 23708 #748-07-1980 L1990 *020 †55
CAPLAN, Robert Bruce. 355 CRAWFORD ST STE 102 23704 #051-01-1963 L1963 **GS** *020 †85
CARLSON, Scott James. 620 JOHN PAUL JONES CIR, MEDICAL STAFF SERVICES 23708 #016-11-1995 L1999 **GS** *020
CARR, Donald Russell, Jr. 620 JOHN PAUL JONES CIR, ATTN: CREDENTIAL OFFICE 23708 #023-12-1993 L1994 **OSM** *020 †40
CARR, Michael Richard. 620 JOHN PAUL JONES CIR, NAVAL MEDICAL CENTER 23708 #016-43-1998 L1999 **PDC** *100 †55
CARTER, Eboni Xaivier. 600 CRAWFORD ST, STE 300 23704 #030-05-2001 L2001 **FM** *020 †18
CARTER, Falana Patrice. 600 CRAWFORD ST, STE 300 23704 #011-04-2001 L2001 **FM** *020 †18
CASTANARES, Antonietta M. 3235 ACADEMY AVE 23703 #748-11-1984 L1998 **NEP** *020 †20
CAUFIELD, Sean Patrick. ■ 23704 #016-43-2005 L2007 *020
CHAK, Sin-Pui. EFFINGHAM ST 23708 #243-21-1955 L1967 **NM PTH** *071 †50
CHAMP, David Wayne. 620 JOHN PAUL JONES CIR, NAVAL MEDICAL CENTER 23708 #023-12-1999 L1999 **EM** *020 †16
CHAMP, Raynido Alfonso. 620 JOHN PAUL JONES CIR, ATTN: CREDENTIAL OFFICE 23708 #051-04-1986 L1987 **IM** *071
CHAPEL, Ian Jonathan. 620 JOHN PAUL JONES CIR, NAVAL MED CTR 23708 #051-07-1998 L1999 **P** *020 †75
CHARISSIS, Michail. 620 JOHN PAUL JONES CIR, OUTPATIEN PSYCH CLINIC 23708 #023-12-1998 L1999 **P** *020 †75
CHASTANET, Robert Jos. 620 JOHN PAUL JONES CIR, NANVAL MED CTR 23708 #023-12-1987 L1999 **GS** *020 †85
CHAVIS, Cyril Vernon. 620 JOHN PAUL JONES CIR, ATTN: CREDENTIAL OFFICE 23708 #048-13-1987 L1999 **DR** *020 †80
CHEN, Chun-Ming. 3636 HIGH ST 23707 #244-05-1969 L1975 **AN** *071
CHIU, Che Wen. 3636 HIGH ST 23707 #244-05-1968 L1975 **GP** *020
CHOUDHURY, Ali Azam. 3235 ACADEMY AVE 23703 #160-02-1961 L1976 **NEP IM** *020 †20
CHOUGH, Dae Been. 3235 ACADEMY AVE, STE 201 23703 #583-01-1971 L1979 **CD** *020 †20
CHOUGH, Nam Hyun. 355 CRAWFORD ST, STE 808 23704 #583-02-1970 L1989 **AN GS** *020 †05
CHOY, Yoon Keun. ■ 23707 #583-02-1971 L1977 **AN** *020
CHUNG, Chung Ung. 2595 VICTORY BLVD 23702 #583-06-1969 L1976 **FM** *020
CHUNG, Jun Ki. 3235 ACADEMY AVE, STE 201 23703 #051-01-1990 L1997 **CD** *020 †20
CHUNG, Sung Ai Lee. ■ 23703 #583-03-1954 L1974 **OBG** *071 †30
CHUPP, Thomas Markham. 620 JOHN PAUL JONES CIR, DEPT OF FAM PRAC NAVAL MED 23708 #023-12-1993 L1999 **FM** *020 †18
CLARKE, Jonathan Eric. 620 JOHN PAUL JONES CIR, NAVAL MEDICAL CENTER 23708 #011-02-2002 L2002 **EM** *012
CLENNEY, Timothy Lee. 620 JOHN PAUL JONES CIR, ATTN: CREDENTIAL OFFICE 23708 #011-04-1992 L1994 **GPM** *020 †18
COBERY, Steven Thomas. 620 JOHN PAUL JONES CIR, NAVAL MEDICAL CENTER 23708 #043-01-2000 L2001 **NS** *020
COCHRAN, Donald Lee. 3706 WINCHESTER DR, STE 200 23707 #023-12-1985 L1993 **FM** *020 †18

COCHRAN, James Richard. 3300 HIGH ST, STE 6 23707 #051-01-1986 L1989 **IM** *020 †20
COLE, Jeffrey Brent. 620 JOHN PAUL JONES CIR, NAVAL MED CTR 23708 #023-12-1992 L2002 **IM** *020 †20
COLEMAN, Charles Stephen. 3640 HIGH ST, STE 3C 23707 #051-01-1979 L2000 **N SME** *020 †75
COLEMAN, Claude C, Jr. 3300 ACADEMY AVE 23703 #051-04-1946 L1947 **PS GS** *020 †65
COLLIER, Aldon Rockwell. 620 JOHN PAUL JONES CIR, DEPARTMENT OF PEDIATRICS 23708 #051-01-1992 L1995 **PD** *020 †55
COLLINS, Timothy Paul. ■ 23708 #010-02-1987 L1995 **HMP** *012 †18,50
CONKLIN, Michelle Ellis. 620 JOHN PAUL JONES CIR, PROFESSIONAL AFFAIRS/MSSP 23708 #051-04-2003 L2003 *020
CORDRAY, Douglas Roy. 3636 HIGH ST 23707 #021-01-1961 L1968 **PTH** *071 †50
CORREIA, Jennea Anthonett. 620 JOHN PAUL JONES CIR, NMC TRANSITIONAL INTERNS 23708 #033-06-2005 L2005 *100
COWAN, George Langstroth. ■ 23704 #023-12-2005 L2007 *100
COX, Harry Duffield. ■ 23703 #051-01-1946 L1946 **PD** *071 †55
CROSLIN, Artis Rayfort. 620 JOHN PAUL JONES CIR, NAVAL MEDICAL CENTER 23708 #010-03-1976 L1976 **HO** IM *020
CRUM, Frederick Clinton. 3235 ACADEMY AVE STE 10 23703 #011-04-1983 L1985 **FM** *020 †18
DAIL, Tonya Annette. 620 JOHN PAUL JONES CIR, WEE KARE PEDIATRICS 23708 #036-01-1998 L2001 **PD** *020 †55
DALESANDRO, Joy. 3640 HIGH ST, STE 1A 23707 #005-19-1991 L2002 **TS** *020 †85,90
DAMLE, Snehal Anant. 3235 ACADEMY AVE, STE 100 23703 #495-23-1988 L1998 **ON** *020 †20
DARDEN, Tarsha Joy. ■ 23707 #036-01-2005 L2005 **FP** *012
DATYNER, Anuradha K. 3640 HIGH ST, STE 2A 23707 #035-48-1991 L1996 **PM** *020 †60
DAVIS, Paul C. 355 CRAWFORD ST STE 102 23704 #495-31-1974 L1980 **DR** *020 †80
DAVIS, Regina Denise. ■ 23701 #051-04-1979 L1993 **FM** *020 †18
DAYANIM, Behrooz. 3235 ACADEMY AVE STE 304 23703 #517-01-1961 L1967 **GS** *071 †85
DEATON, Richard Thos. 3235 ACADEMY AVE 23703 #051-04-1964 L1964 **FM** *020 †18
DEBNATH, Kiran Sankar. 355 CRAWFORD ST, STE 808 23704 #160-02-1972 L1979 **AN** *020 †05
DECASTRO, Denise. 620 JOHN PAUL JONES CIR, NAVAL MED CTR 23708 #035-09-1984 L2007 **PD** *020 †55
DE LA CRUZ, Gloria V. 500 RODMAN AVE STE 5 23707 #748-08-1967 L1975 **PD** *020
DELANEY, Nancy Rita. 620 JOHN PAUL JONES CIR, ATTN: CREDENTIAL OFFICE 23708 #032-01-1994 L1995 **RHU IM** *020 †20
DE LA PENA, Jose Calixto. 620 JOHN PAUL JONES CIR, NAVAL HOSPITAL 23708 #847-03-1971 L1973 **FM IMG** *020 †18
DELONGA, David Matthew. 620 JOHN PAUL JONES CIR, PROFESSIONAL AFFAIRS 23708 #011-02-1998 L1998 **DR AM** *020 †70
DE LOS ANGELES, Jose T. 3703 COUNTY ST 23707 #748-08-1958 L1972 **GPM** *071
DELVECCHIO, David Michael. 620 JOHN PAUL JONES CIR, ATTN: CREDENTIAL OFFICE 23708 #010-02-1984 L1999 **PTH PCP** *020 †50
DEMAIO, Marlene. 620 JOHN PAUL JONES CIR, DEPT OF ORTHOPAEDIC SURG 23708 #041-09-1985 L1989 **ORS OSM** *020 †40
DEROO, Alta Jean. 620 JOHN PAUL JONES CIR, NMCP 23708 #011-03-2003 L2005 *100
DESAI, Dirghayu. 3703 COUNTY ST 23707 #495-23-1983 L1996 **IM** *020 †20
DEVLIN, John Joseph. 620 JOHN PAUL JONES CIR, ATTN: CREDENTIAL OFFICE, N 23708 #023-12-2000 L2005 **EM** *012
DOMINITZ, Illy. ■ 23703 #023-01-1998 L2000 **GPM** *020 †70
DONNELLY, Anne. 600 CRAWFORD ST STE 30 23704 #021-06-1990 L1991 **FM** *040 †18
DONOVAN, Erin A. 620 JOHN PAUL JONES CIR, DEPT OF HEM / ONOGOLOY 23708 #023-12-2000 L2001 **ON** *020 †20
DOSS, James Thomas. ■ 23707 #012-22-2004 L2005 **OPH** *012
DOSS, William Lafayette. 500 RODMAN AVE STE 1 23707 #010-03-1991 L1995 **PM** *020 †60
DOUGLAS, Brad H. 620 JOHN PAUL JONES CIR, DEPT OF OB/GYN 23708 #023-12-1997 L1998 **OBG AM** *020 †70
DOUGLAS, Thomas Joseph. 620 JOHN PAUL JONES CIR, NAVAL MEDICAL CENTER 23708 #023-12-2005 L2005 *020
DOWNS, Walter Maybury, Jr. 620 JOHN PAUL JONES CIR, ATTN: CREDENTIAL OFFICE 23708 #023-12-1991 L1992 **IM** *020 †20
DRINKWINE, Benjamin John. 620 JOHN PAUL JONES CIR, MEDICAL STAFF SERVICES 23708 #051-07-2004 L2005 *100
DRINKWINE, Jenifer Karine. ■ 23703 #023-12-2003 L2004 *100
DUNTON, Robert Frederick. 3640 HIGH ST 23707 #035-03-1981 L2007 **TS** *020 †85,90
DURICA, David Lewis. 601 FREDERICK BLVD 23707 #041-01-1964 L1971 **ORS OAR** *020 †40
DY, Aileen Amour. ■ 23704 #016-11-2004 L2005 *100
EARLEY, Angela Sue. 620 JOHN PAUL JONES CIR, NAVAL MEDICAL CENTER PORTS 23708 #038-41-1995 L2007 **CCS** *020 †85
EGGLESTON, Maurice K, Jr. 620 JOHN PAUL JONES CIR, ATTN: PROFESSIONAL AFFAIRS 23708 #051-04-1978 L1979 **OBG MFM** *020 †30
EICHELBERGER, Deborah Ann. 620 JOHN PAUL JONES CIR, NAVAL MEDICAL CENTER 23708 #041-13-1980 L1994 **GPM OM** *030 †70
EIZEMBER, Laura Ellen. 600 CRAWFORD ST, STE 300 23704 #017-20-1995 L2001 **FM** *020 †18
ELLIOTT, Ronald Eugene. ■ 23703 #047-07-1972 L1992 **OM IM** *072
ELLIS, Charles L. 620 JOHN PAUL JONES CIR, NMC PORTSMOUTH VA 23708 #010-02-1997 L1998 **OMF** *020
ENAD, Jerome Garciano. 620 JOHN PAUL JONES CIR, BONE&JOINT SPRTS MED INST 23708 #023-12-1992 L1998 **ORS OSM** *020 †40
ERDMAN, Jennifer Lee. ■ 23708 #023-12-1994 L1997 **IM** *020 †20
ESPINOSA, Octaviano. 620 JOHN PAUL JONES CIR, NMCP 23708 #033-05-2008 *012
FAIR, Ernest Lee, Jr. 620 JOHN PAUL JONES CIR, ATTN: CREDENTIAL OFFICE 23708 #041-09-1978 L1989 **GS** *020
FENTON, Michael Edwin. 620 JOHN PAUL JONES CIR, NAVAL MEDICAL CENTER 23708 #021-01-1997 L2007 **DR** *020 †80
FERRERA, Marc Huliganga. 620 JOHN PAUL JONES CIR, NAVAL MEDICAL CENTER 23708 #051-04-2003 L2006 **FM** *020 †20
FITCH, Jamie Lynn. ■ 23704 #047-06-2007 L2008 *012
FITZER, Margaret Vincent. 301 FORT LN 23704 #051-07-1985 L1986 **P** *020 †75
FLEENOR, Jonathan Todd. 620 JOHN PAUL JONES CIR, PROFESSIONAL AFFAIRS 23708 #023-12-1992 L1993 **PDC** *020 †55
FLYNN, Maria Christine. 620 JOHN PAUL JONES CIR, ATTN: CREDENTIAL OFFICE 23708 #021-01-1994 L2006 **DR P** *100 †80
FOLEY, Richard Walter. 620 JOHN PAUL JONES CIR, ATTN: CREDENTIAL OFFICE 23708 #050-02-1975 L1999 **TS GS** *071 †85,90
FOSSEE, Craig Thompson. ■ 23703 #041-15-2007 L2008 *012
FOSTER, David Thomas. 620 JOHN PAUL JONES CIR, NAVAL MEDICAL CENTER 23708 #048-14-2006 L2006 *012

■ = Address Information Privacy Protected

FOSTER, Stephen L. ■ 23703 #008-02-2000 L2005 *020

FOX, Bryan Alan. 620 JOHN PAUL JONES CIR 23708 #038-40-1996 L1996 **ORS** *100

FRANKLIN, Dean Edward. 3636 HIGH ST, MEDICAL STAFF OFFICE 23707 #051-07-2005 L2005 **EM** *012

FREIER, Grace Maria. 620 JOHN PAUL JONES CIR, ATTN: CREDENTIAL OFFICE 23708 #035-15-2002 L2005 *100 †55

FREITAG, Gregory Hans, Jr. 620 JOHN PAUL JONES CIR 23708 #023-12-2002 L2003 **GS** *020

FRIAS, Angelina Mendoza. 620 JOHN PAUL JONES CIR, ATTN: CREDENTIAL OFFICE 23708 #748-01-1979 L1994 **FM** *020 †18

FRICK, Edward James, Jr. 620 JOHN PAUL JONES CIR, ATTN: CREDENTIAL OFFICE 23708 #041-13-1994 L1999 **TS** *020 †85,90 ‡

FROIO, John Joseph. ■ 23708 #024-05-1996 L2002 **GS** *020 †85

FRY, Kimberly Sue. 620 JOHN PAUL JONES CIR, ATTN: CREDENTIAL OFFICE 23708 #011-04-1995 L1995 **GP** *020 †50

FTICSAR, James Eugene. 620 JOHN PAUL JONES CIR, ATTN: CREDENTIAL OFFICE 23708 #041-02-1972 L1998 **GS FM** *020 †85

FURMAN, David L. 620 JOHN PAUL JONES CIR, NAVAL MEDICAL CENTER 23708 #024-05-2004 L2005 *100 †20

GAGLIONE, Margaret E M. 620 JOHN PAUL JONES CIR, ATTN: CREDENTIAL OFFICE 23708 #041-14-1992 L1994 **IM** *020 †20

GALDINI, Angela Marie. 3706 WINCHESTER DR, STE 200 23707 #041-02-1982 L1983 **FM FPG** *020 †18

GALLAGHER, Kevin Lee. ■ 23703 #054-04-1983 L1984 **IMG IM** *020 †20

GANGOY, Leovigildo C. 620 JOHN PAUL JONES CIR, ATTN: CREDENTIAL OFFICE 23708 #748-09-1968 L1987 **PM GP** *020

GAO, Sam Wei. 620 JOHN PAUL JONES CIR, NAVAL MEDICAL CENTER 23708 #035-08-2002 L2002 **IM** *100 †20

GELPI, Jose Angel. 825 CRAWFORD PKWY 23704 #847-10-1963 L1967 **CHP P** *020 †75 ‡

GIACOBBE, Dean Thomas. 620 JOHN PAUL JONES CIR, MEDICAL STAFF SERVICES 23708 #032-01-1995 L2005 **AN CD** *100 †05

GIACOMAN, Jon C. 620 JOHN PAUL JONES CIR, ATTN:MEDICAL SERVICE SUPPO 23708 #048-14-2001 L2002 **AN** *020

GILFEATHER, Brian Michael. 620 JOHN PAUL JONES CIR, ACADEMIC AFFAIRS/GME 23708 #024-05-1986 L1988 **PTH** *020

GIRTELSCHMID, Michael. DEPT OB/GYN, PORTSMOUTH NAVAL HOSPITAL 23708 #286-04-1980 L1991 **OBG** *020 †30

GIUSEPPETTI, Mary M. 620 JOHN PAUL JONES CIR, DEPT OF PEDS-NMCP 23708 #023-12-1988 L1989 **NPM** *020 †55

GONZALEZ, Roberto Adrian. 620 JOHN PAUL JONES CIR, ATTN: PROFESSIONAL AFFAIRS 23708 #036-05-1998 L2001 **FM** *020 †18

GOPEZ, Angela Gessner. 620 JOHN PAUL JONES CIR, ATTN: CREDENTIAL OFFICE 23708 #041-02-1996 L2001 **DR** *020 †80

GORETZKE, Sean Everette. 620 JOHN PAUL JONES CIR, NAVAL MEDICAL CENTER 23708 #028-34-1997 L1998 **CHN** *020 †55

GOSNEY, James Earl, Jr. 600 CRAWFORD ST, STE 300 23704 #051-04-2000 L2005 **FM** *100

GRANT, Thomas Richard. 620 JOHN PAUL JONES CIR, ATTN:PROFESSIONAL AFFAIRS 23708 #023-12-2000 L2000 *020

GRIMSON, James Mccall. 620 JOHN PAUL JONES CIR, ACADEMIC AFFAIRS DEPT GME 23708 #005-18-1999 L2004 **R** *020 †80

GRIMWOOD, John Lee. 620 JOHN PAUL JONES CIR, ATTN: CREDENTIAL OFFICE, N 23708 #023-12-1994 L1995 **PTH** *020 †50

GROHOWSKI, Matthew Edwin. 620 JOHN PAUL JONES CIR, ATTN: CREDENTIAL OFFICE 23708 #035-08-1998 L2007 **DR** *020 †80

GUANZON, Rafael Fajardo. 704 LONDON ST 23704 #748-08-1969 L1976 **GP** *020

GUGGER, Douglas Robert. ■ 23704 #041-13-2007 *012

GUMPERT, Barton C. 620 JOHN PAUL JONES CIR, ATTN: CREDENTIAL OFFICE 23708 #047-05-1984 L1995 **CCM GP** *020 †20

GUPTA, Bhavdeep Kumar. 301 GOODE WAY, STE 102 23704 #495-45-1982 L1994 **CD** *020 †20

HAGANS, Jarita Arnette. 600 CRAWFORD ST, STE 300 23704 #010-03-2004 L2004 **FP** *012

HALL, Christian Carson. 620 JOHN PAUL JONES CIR, NAVAL MEDICAL CENTER PORTS 23708 #025-12-2000 L2006 **ORS OFA** *020

HALL, Harold Eugene. ■ 23703 #010-03-1959 L1960 **FOP PTH** *071 †50

HALL, R B, II. 620 JOHN PAUL JONES CIR, ATTN: CREDENTIAL OFFICE 23708 #051-01-1976 L1989 **FM OM** *020 †18

HANSEN, Robert Blaine, II. 3315 HIGH ST 23707 #010-01-1979 L1987 **N CCM** *020 †75

HAQUE, Mosta Gausel. 301 GOODE WAY, STE 201 23704 #160-02-1975 L1992 **NEP** *020 †20

HARDING, Brennan Reece. 620 JOHN PAUL JONES CIR, DEPT OF ANESTH 23708 #021-01-2001 L2001 **AN CD** *020 †05

HARGROVES, Andrew W, Jr. 850 CRAWFORD PKWY 23704 #051-01-1948 L1948 **R** *071

HARKLEY, Alfred Leon. ■ 23707 #036-01-1978 L1979 **P ADP** *020 †75

HARPEN, Martin Paul. 3235 ACADEMY AVE 23703 #038-40-1979 L1987 **NEP IM** *020 †20

HARRISON, Brooke Ann. ■ 23704 #051-07-2006 L2007 *012

HELM, John Wayne. 4700 GEORGE WASHINGTON HWY 23702 #051-01-1974 L1976 **FM** *020 †18

HELMERS, Scott Whittaker. 620 JOHN PAUL JONES CIR, ATTN: CREDENTIAL OFFICE 23708 #023-12-1990 L2002 **ORS** *020 †40 ‡

HELO, Kermit G. 620 JOHN PAUL JONES CIR, NMC PORTSMOUTH VA 23708 #021-06-2004 L2005 **PD** *020

HENAO, Jose. 620 JOHN PAUL JONES CIR, ACADEMIC AFFAIRS/GME 23708 #051-07-1999 L1999 **EM** *020 †16

HERBERT, Dwight Curtis. 620 JOHN PAUL JONES CIR, ATTN: CREDENTIAL OFFICE 23708 #010-03-1992 L1993 **FM** *020 †18

HERSH, Robert Eugene. 620 JOHN PAUL JONES CIR, ATTN: CREDENTIAL OFFICE 23708 #036-05-1986 L1992 **HS** *020 †85,65

HIGH, Tara Beth. 630 JOHN PAUL JONES CIR, GENL SRGY DEPT NVL MED CTR 23708 #023-12-2003 L2004 **GS** *020

HILL, James Bernard. 620 JOHN PAUL JONES CIR, NAVAL MED CTR 23708 #011-03-1996 L1998 **OBG** *020 †30

HINES, Neil Nigel. 620 JOHN PAUL JONES CIR, PSYCH DEPT 23708 #024-05-2005 L2006 *100

HINES, Scott W. 620 JOHN PAUL JONES CIR, MEDICAL STAFF OFFICE 23708 #008-01-1999 L1999 **EM** *100

HO, Van-Thong. 620 JOHN PAUL JONES CIR, ATTN: CREDENTIAL OFFICE 23708 #067-03-1985 L1993 **DR** *020 †80

HOGAN, Christopher James. 620 JOHN PAUL JONES CIR 23708 #051-01-1994 L1994 **HS** *020 †40

HOGG, Paul Sumpter. 3640 HIGH ST 23707 #051-04-1993 L2001 **GS** *020 †85

HOLLIS, Joseph Boniface. 1211 RODMAN AVE 23707 #028-34-1969 L1977 **GE** *020 †20

HOLLOWELL, John W. ■ 23703 #051-01-1946 L1946 **U** *071 †95

HOLMES, Francis Hammond. ■ 23705 #012-05-1942 L1968 **R** *071 †80

HOLTEL, Michael Ray. EFFINGHAM ST 23708 #023-12-1984 L1986 **OTO** *020 †45

HOLZER, Donald. 3315 HIGH ST 23707 #041-14-1977 L2003 **N PMM** *020 †75

HOOD, Bradley Stanton. 620 JOHN PAUL JONES CIR, NAVAL MEDICAL CENTER 23708 #021-06-1998 L2000 **PD** *020 †55

HOPKINS, Michael Thos. 620 JOHN PAUL JONES CIR, ATTN: CREDENTIAL OFFICE 23708 #016-42-1992 L2003 **HEM** *020 †20

HORTON, Todd. 620 JOHN PAUL JONES CIR, NAVAL MEDICAL CENTER 23708 #005-06-1998 L1998 **HS** *020

HUBERT, Amy Salness. 620 JOHN PAUL JONES CIR, NAVAL MEDICAL CENTER 23708 #051-07-2001 L2006 **EM** *012

HUFFORD, Dennis Lee. 620 JOHN PAUL JONES CIR, ATTN: CREDENTIAL OFFICE 23708 #038-40-1985 L2005 **FM** *020 †18

HUNT, Wesley Scott. 620 JOHN PAUL JONES CIR, MEDICAL STAFF SERVICES DEP 23708 #018-03-1976 L1979 **AN IM** *020 †20,05

HURST, William Milton, Jr. 620 JOHN PAUL JONES CIR, ATTN: CREDENTIAL OFFICE 23708 #051-07-1984 L1985 **FM** *020 †18

INOUYE, Lisa Suzanne. 620 JOHN PAUL JONES CIR, ATTN: CREDENTIAL OFFICE 23708 #041-12-1990 L1991 **IM** *020 †20

ISLAM, Mohammad Aminul. 3737 HIGH ST 23707 #704-03-1960 L1972 **IM GE** *050 †20

ISMAELI, Attiyah Tayseer. 600 CRAWFORD ST, STE 300 23704 #051-07-2006 L2006 **FP** *012

ISNER, Jennifer R. 620 JOHN PAUL JONES CIR, MEDICAL STAFF OFFICE 23708 #048-13-2004 L2004 *012

JACKSON, Leroy T. 620 JOHN PAUL JONES CIR, ATTN PROFESSIONAL AFFAIRS 23708 #047-07-1978 L1982 **END** *020 †20

JAKLIC, Beth Rachelle. 620 JOHN PAUL JONES CIR, DEPT OF SURG CODE 0511 23708 #051-01-1990 L1991 **CRS GS** *020 †10,85

JAN, Moore Hua. 620 JOHN PAUL JONES CIR, ATTN: CREDENTIAL OFFICE 23708 #023-12-1988 L1991 **GPM GP** *020 †70

JAO, Bienvenido O, Jr. ■ 23704 #748-09-1989 L2002 **AN** *020 †05

JAYANETTI, Sidath. 850 CRAWFORD PKWY 23704 #220-01-1967 L1979 **OBG DR** *020 †30

JODLOWSKI, Christopher Ri. ■ 23703 #016-43-2004 L2005 **AN** *012

JOHN, Sinoj Kanayamplacka. 61 PEPPERWOOD PL 23703 #495-63-1996 L2004 **IMG** *020

JOHNSON, Andrew Scott. 620 JOHN PAUL JONES CIR, ATTN: CREDENTIAL OFFICE, N 23708 #021-01-1992 L2004 **PMM** *020 †16

JOHNSON, Darlene Racquel. 620 JOHN PAUL JONES CIR, NAVAL MEDICAL CENTER 23708 #041-09-1997 L2002 **FM** *020 †18

JOHNSON, Wayne T. 3300 HIGH ST STE 1, ORTHOPEDIC SURGERY LTD 23707 #051-04-1977 L1987 **OP ORS** *020 †40

JOHNSTON, Michael Gwynne. 620 JOHN PAUL JONES CIR, NMC PORTSMOUTH-GEN SUR DPT 23708 #047-05-2003 L2004 **GS** *020

JONES, Jay Todd. 620 JOHN PAUL JONES CIR, NMC PORTSMOUTH VA 23708 #020-02-1999 L2004 **DR** *020 †80

JONES, Paul A. 3636 HIGH ST 23707 #010-03-1980 L1986 **OBS GYN** *020 †30

JONES, Ronald Homer. 5615A HIGH ST W 23703 #051-07-1982 L1984 **FM IM** *020

JULIANO, Michael Louis. 620 JOHN PAUL JONES CIR, DEPARTMENT OF 23708 #041-13-1999 L1999 **EM** *100

KAPFER, Stephanie Anne. 620 JOHN PAUL JONES CIR, PEDIATRIC SURGERY DIV 23708 #008-01-1995 L2006 **PDS GS** *020 †85

KAPLAN, Roy M. 355 CRAWFORD ST, STE 808 23704 #050-02-1978 L1986 **AN PD** *020 †55,05

KASTNER, Lee Norman. ■ 23703 #021-01-1948 L1953 **PD** *020 †55

KAY, Earl Danl, Jr. 3300 ACADEMY AVE 23703 #036-07-1965 L1972 **P PYG** *020

KENDALL, Shellie Marie. ■ 23704 #036-07-2007 L2007 *012

KERNER, Mark Bradley. 3640 HIGH ST STE 2A 23707 #035-46-1989 L1995 **ORS** *020 †40

KHAN, Muhammad Ali. ■ 23704 #049-01-2005 L2005 **PD** *012

KIM, Min Kwan. 620 JOHN PAUL JONES CIR, ACADEMIC AFFAIRS/GME 23708 #056-06-2000 L2005 **IM** *020

KIM, Sung Yong. 3409 SOUTH ST 23707 #583-04-1964 L1972 **PD** *020 †55

KING, Brian Scott. 620 JOHN PAUL JONES CIR, ATTN: CREDENTIAL OFFICE 23708 #051-07-2004 L2005 *100 †20

KIRK, Arthur Abbitt. 3636 HIGH ST 23707 #051-04-1941 L1941 **ORS** *071 †40

KITCHEN, Levi Kern. ■ 23704 #011-02-2007 L2007 *012

KNAPP, Robert Woodruff. 355 CRAWFORD ST, STE 102 23704 #012-05-1957 L1974 **GS** *020 †85

KNEE, Treyce S. 620 JOHN PAUL JONES CIR, ATTN: CREDENTIAL OFFICE 23708 #024-05-1991 L1992 **END** *020 †20

KNITTEL, Douglas Rolf. 620 JOHN PAUL JONES CIR, NAVAL MEDICAL CENTER 23708 #023-12-1985 L2000 **P FOP** *020 †50

KNOOP, Kevin Jos. 620 JOHN PAUL JONES CIR, NMC PORTSMOUTH VA 23708 #051-07-1985 L1987 **EM GP** *020 †16

KOSTINAS, John Eugene. 3636 HIGH ST 23707 #041-02-1958 L1973 **HEM IM** *071

KRAKUSIN, Ana Cristina. 620 JOHN PAUL JONES CIR, MEDICAL STAFF SERVICES 23708 #025-01-2000 L2002 **AN** *020 †05

KRASON, Moriah Susanne. 620 JOHN PAUL JONES CIR 23708 #010-01-2005 L2005 **PD** *100

KREBS, Gary Lynn. 620 JOHN PAUL JONES CIR, ATTN MEDICAL STAFF SERVICE 23708 #041*13-1977 L1983 **PD** *020 †55

KRENTZ, Michael Jos. 620 JOHN PAUL JONES CIR, ATTN: CREDENTIAL OFFICE 23708 #056-06-1973 L1974 **EM CCM** *030 †16,70

KROPCHO, Luisa Caterina. 620 JOHN PAUL JONES CIR, ATTN: GENERAL SURGERY DEPA 23708 #023-12-1998 L1998 **GS** *020 ‡

KUERSTEINER, Karl Arthur. PO BOX 1357 23705 #048-14-2007 L2007 *012

KUHN, Jeffery John. 620 JOHN PAUL JONES CIR, ATTN: CREDENTIAL OFFICE 23708 #051-01-1985 L2007 **OTO** *020 †45

KUO, Hwang Ren. 3235 ACADEMY AVE, STE 102 23703 #385-05-1965 L1972 **FM** *020 †18

KURTZ, Christopher Allen. 620 JOHN PAUL JONES CIR, ATTN: CREDENTIAL OFFICE 23708 #041-12-1993 L2003 **ORS** *020 †40

KUSHNER, David M. 620 JOHN PAUL JONES CIR, RADIOLOGY SERVICE LINE 23708 #038-06-1986 L1999 **DR NR** *020 †80

KWONG, Wai Hong. 3000 VICTORY BLVD 23702 #243-03-1957 L1972 **AN** *071

LAFRENIERE, Justin Paul. ■ 23704 #021-01-2007 **IM** *012

LANNIK, David Eliot. 601 FREDERICK BLVD 23707 #016-42-1976 L1983 **ORS HS** *020 †40

LANOUE, Elizabeth Dillon. 5615A HIGH ST W 23703 #051-07-1986 L1990 **GP** *020

LARYS, Robert Peter, Jr. 620 JOHN PAUL JONES CIR, NAVAL MEDICAL CENTER 23708 #047-20-1999 L2000 **OPH AM** *040

LAWRENCE, Duane Matthew. 620 JOHN PAUL JONES CIR, NAVAL MEDICAL CENTER 23708 #051-07-2004 L2005 *100

LAWSON, Robert Daniel. 620 JOHN PAUL JONES CIR, NAVAL MED CTR-PORTMNTH 23708 #023-12-2005 L2006 *100

LECLAIR, Lawrence Lee. 620 JOHN PAUL JONES CIR, ATTN: CREDENTIAL OFFICE 23708 #023-12-1990 L1991 **DR** *020 †80

LEE, Duk-Hyun. 355 CRAWFORD ST, STE 308 23704 #583-01-1960 L1973 **AN** *071

LEE, Jessica Jennifer. ■ 23704 #005-06-2005 L2006 **IM** *100

LEE, Rees L. 620 JOHN PAUL JONES CIR, DEPT OF PEDIATRICS 23708 #005-11-1996 L1997 **PDP PD** *020 †55

LEHEW, Karen Marie. 600 CRAWFORD ST, STE 300 23704 #016-01-1994 L1996 **FM** *020 †18

LEIBOWITZ, Beth Jan. ■ 23707 #041-07-1979 L1985 **IM** *020 †20

LENNARD, William Trevor. 620 JOHN PAUL JONES CIR, NMC PORTSMOUTH VA MED STAF 23708 #023-12-1999 L2005 **AN** *100

LEONARD, Kenneth Edwin. 620 JOHN PAUL JONES CIR, ATTN: CREDENTIAL OFFICE 23708 #010-01-1983 L1985 **GS** *020 †85

LESSMANN, Brett Haas. 620 JOHN PAUL JONES CIR, NMCP PSYCH CLNC 23708 #023-12-2005 L2007 **GP** *020

LEWIS-BROOKS, Chantal Den. 600 CRAWFORD ST, STE 300 23704 #010-03-2006 L2006 **FP** *012

LEXIER, Lenard Jay. 825 CRAWFORD PKWY 23704 #056-05-1968 L1974 **CHP P** *030 ‡

LI, Wei. 355 CRAWFORD ST, STE 808 23704 #243-48-1982 L1995 **APM** *020 †05

LIGHTFOOT, Jeffrey D. ■ 23704 #023-12-2002 L2003 **EM** *012

LIGNELL, Mark Douglas. 620 JOHN PAUL JONES CIR, ACADEMIC AFFAIRS/GME 23708 #012-01-1999 L1999 *020 †05

LIGOURI, Lorene Delia. 301 GOODE WAY, STE 206 23704 #035-47-1980 L2006 **OBG MDM** *030 †30 ‡

LIM, Sheila. ■ 23707 #209-01-1960 **PTH** *100

LIM, Wan Ngo. ■ 23707 #242-16-1945 L1959 **PD PDC** *020 †55

LINDSAY, Frank Gold, Jr. ■ 23705 #024-15-1942 L1945 **OM PHP** *071

LIPMAN, Ansel. ■ 23703 #051-04-1942 L1942 **R FOP** *071 †80

LIU, Michelle Ferdinand. 620 JOHN PAUL JONES CIR, MEDICAL STAFF SERVICES 23708 #043-01-2001 L2001 *020

LIZEK, Andrew Len. ■ 23707 #012-22-2007 L2007 *012

LOCKE, John Stephen. 620 JOHN PAUL JONES CIR, MEDICAL STAFF SERVICES OFF 23708 #023-12-1991 L1993 **ORS** *020 †40

LONG, Alvin Penrose, Jr. ■ 23704 #051-04-1948 L1948 **PTH** *071 †50

LOOMAN, Karen B. ■ 23704 #028-79-1998, ▲ L2002 **FOP** *012

LOPEZ-CARDONA, Alfonso. 825 CRAWFORD PKWY 23704 #264-10-1987 L1995 **CHP P** *020 †75

LOVKO, Kenneth Ray. 3636 HIGH ST 23707 #028-34-1963 L1979 **CHP** *020 †75

LUEKEN, Robert John. 620 JOHN PAUL JONES CIR, NAVAL MED CTR 23708 #051-07-2002 L2002 **EM** *012

LUNA CARO, Roberto. 301 FORT LN 23704 #649-17-1965 L1980 **CHP P** *020 †75

MA, Ju-Fang. 355 CRAWFORD ST, STE 808 23704 #243-16-1985 L2003 **AN** *020 †05

MAGDYCZ, William Paul, Jr. 620 JOHN PAUL JONES CIR, NAVAL MED CTR PORTSMOUTH 23708 #023-12-1989 L2006 **OTO HNS** *020 †45

MAGUIRE, Jason Douglas. 620 JOHN PAUL JONES CIR, ATTN: CREDENTIAL OFFICE, N 23708 #023-12-1992 L2007 **ID** *020 †20

MAHER, Jonathan Robert. ■ 23703 #041-02-2004 L2005 **GS** *100

MANIU, Calin Vasile. 3235 ACADEMY AVE, STE 201 23703 #781-01-1995 L2007 **CD IC** *020 †20

MANN, Kevan Ellary. 620 JOHN PAUL JONES CIR, GENERAL SURGERY DEPARTMENT 23708 #023-12-1996 L2004 **GS** *020 †85

MANOS, Gail Helen J. 620 JOHN PAUL JONES CIR, NAVAL MEDICAL CENTER 23708 #023-12-1990 L1992 **P** *020 †75

MARANAN-RAMOS, Lolita. 620 JOHN PAUL JONES CIR, ATTN: CREDENTIAL OFFICE 23708 #748-08-1967 L1973 **GP PD** *020 †55

MARCHEGIANI, Shannon Mari. 620 JOHN PAUL JONES CIR, NAVAL MED CTR 23708 #023-12-2005 L2005 **PD** *100

MARCHLEWSKI, Walter F, Jr. 620 JOHN PAUL JONES CIR, ATTN: CREDENTIAL OFFICE 23708 #041-02-1980 L1991 **PD** *020 †55

MARCUS, Spencer Dicker. 1801 PORTSMOUTH BLVD 23704 #051-01-1973 L1975 **CHP P** *020 †75 ‡

MARIANO, Ruth L. 620 JOHN PAUL JONES CIR, ATTN: CREDENTIAL OFFICE 23708 #748-08-1976 L1992 **PD** *020 †55

MARTIN, Merle Blair, II. 620 JOHN PAUL JONES CIR, MEDICAL STAFF OFFICE 23708 #005-06-2004 L2005 *100

MATSUSHIGE, Kouichi. 805 RODMAN AVE 23707 #572-58-1956 L1973 **IM** *020

MAZZILLI, Michael Aldo. 620 JOHN PAUL JONES CIR, NMC PORTSMOUTH VA 23708 #023-12-1990 L1995 **AN** *100 †05

MC BEE, Claude Matthew. 3640 HIGH ST 23707 #047-20-1990 L1996 **VS GS** *020 †85

MC BRIDE, Jeffrey Patrick. 620 JOHN PAUL JONES CIR, NAVAL MEDICAL CENTER 23708 #048-04-1973 L2000 **NM** *020 †18,80,28

MCCAIN, Arlene Santos. 600 CRAWFORD ST, STE 300 23704 #051-07-2007 L2007 **FP** *012

MCCRACKEN, Christopher Le. ■ 23704 #051-07-2008 L2008 *012

MC DONNELL, Shannon Marie. 620 JOHN PAUL JONES CIR, MEDICAL STAFF OFFICE 23708 #024-07-2000 L2001 **EM** *100

MCGOWAN, Peter Charles. 620 JOHN PAUL JONES CIR, NMC PORTSMOUTH VA 23708 #023-12-2004 L2005 **FM** *100

MC GUIRE, Jeffrey David. 620 JOHN PAUL JONES CIR, ATTN: CREDENTIAL OFFICE 23708 #023-12-1991 L1993 **AM** *020 †05

MC GUIRK, Timothy Dennis. 3636 HIGH ST 23707 #022-75-1984, ▲ L1986 **EM** *020 †16

MC KEE, James Michael. 620 JOHN PAUL JONES CIR, NMC PORTSMOUTH VA 23708 #028-34-1997 L2004 **DR** *020 †80

MCKENZIE, Chad Matthew. 3640 HIGH ST, STE 2F 23707 #039-79-1996, ▲ L2002 **VS GS** *020

MENTLER, Ellie Chiwon. ■ 23704 #023-12-2006 L2006 *012

MERRELL, Joseph Craig. 3690 HIGH ST, STE 3D 23707 #051-01-1977 L1983 **PS HS** *020 †65

MEYER, Gretchen Anne. 620 JOHN PAUL JONES CIR, ATTN: CREDENTIAL OFFICE 23708 #028-34-1988 L1990 **PD** *020 †55

MIELNICKI, Daniel Carl. 620 JOHN PAUL JONES CIR, ACADEMIC AFFAIRS/GME 23708 #023-12-1997 L1998 **EM** *020 †16

MILADI, Anis. 620 JOHN PAUL JONES CIR, NMC PORTSMOUTH VA 23708 #038-45-2004 L2005 *020

MILLER, James Richard. 620 JOHN PAUL JONES CIR, NAVAL MEDICAL CENTER 23708 #041-12-1985 L1987 **PDI PD** *020 †55

MILLER, Kyle Eric. ■ 23701 #023-12-2007 *012

MILLER, Steven Raymond. 620 JOHN PAUL JONES CIR 23708 #025-07-1995 L2004 **RO** *020 †80

MINGIONE, Donald Leo. 3300 ACADEMY AVE 23703 #030-06-1957 L1962 **P PMM** *020

MIROVSKI, Maxim V. 301 GOODE WAY STE 204 23704 #913-15-1992 L1999 **IM** *020 †20

MISA, Voltaire Santos. 355 CRAWFORD ST, STE 808 23704 #748-20-1993 L2005 **AN** *100

MITCHELL, Benj Sanford. 620 JOHN PAUL JONES CIR, NAVY ENVIRON HLTH CTR 23708 #021-05-1977 L1977 **PHP OM** *062 †70

MITCHELL, Eric Stephen. 620 JOHN PAUL JONES CIR, BLDG 1 23708 #012-22-1997 L1998 **IM** *020 †20

MODLO, Erik Joseph. 620 JOHN PAUL JONES CIR, NAVAL MEDICAL CENTER, PORT 23708 #038-44-2003 L2004 **IM** *100

MODZELEWSKI, Laura Nicole. 620 JOHN PAUL JONES CIR, NAVAL MEDICAL CENTER 23708 #041-02-1999 L2001 **EM** *020 †80

MOHON, Melissa Ann. 620 JOHN PAUL JONES CIR, STE 1100 23708 #023-12-1992 L1993 **OM GPM** *020 †70

MONTGOMERY, Demetria. 1701 HIGH ST, STE 102 23704 #036-07-1981 L2002 **IM** *020 †20

MOORE, Erin Marc. 620 JOHN PAUL JONES CIR, NMCP DEPT OF VASCULAR SURG 23708 #048-12-1994 L2005 **VS** *020 †80

MOORE, Sarah Fletcher. 3300 ACADEMY AVE, ACADEMEY CROSSING MEDICAL 23703 #051-07-1984 L1987 **P GS** *020 †75

MORALES, Lucia S Gongora. 620 JOHN PAUL JONES CIR, ATTN: CREDENTIAL OFFICE 23708 #748-07-1958 L1976 **OM** *071

MORRIS, Tod Andrew. 620 JOHN PAUL JONES CIR, ATTENTION: CRENDENTIAL OF 23708 #011-03-2005 L2006 *020

MUNN, Daniel Dudley. ■ 23708 #036-05-2000 L2000 **GS** *020

MURRELL, George Lee. 620 JOHN PAUL JONES CIR, ATTN: CREDENTIAL OFFICE 23708 #010-02-1987 L1990 **OTO GS** *020 †45

NAGABHIRAVA, Sowjanya. 355 CRAWFORD ST, STE 102 23704 #495-11-1995 L2006 **ON** *020 †20

NANCE, Benford O, Jr. 620 JOHN PAUL JONES CIR, NMC PORTSMOUTH 23708 #047-07-1994 L1998 **AN** *020 †05

NANYONGA, Alice Tabisa. 600 CRAWFORD ST, STE 300 23704 #010-03-2003 L2003 **FM** *100 †18

NARADZAY, Jerome Francis. 3636 HIGH ST, MEDICAL STAFF OFFICE 23707 #010-01-1990 L2007 **EM** *020 †16

NAVARRO, Guillermo A. 620 JOHN PAUL JONES CIR, ATTN: CREDENTIAL OFFICE 23708 #041-02-2000 L2000 *100

NAYAK, Sindhu R. 620 JOHN PAUL JONES CIR, NMC PORTSMOUTH 23708 #495-17-1956 L1979 **N** *020

NELSON, Andrew Alonzo. 620 JOHN PAUL JONES CIR, NAVAL MEDICAL CENTER PORTS 23708 #048-14-1985 L1986 **GPM** *020 †18

NEWMAN, Benjamin Goodrich. 620 JOHN PAUL JONES CIR, ATTN: CREDENTIAL OFFICE 23708 #038-41-1966 L2005 **FM EM** *020 †18

NIEDERHAUSER, Amy. 620 JOHN PAUL JONES CIR, PORTSMOUTH NAV HOSP OB/GYN 23708 #018-03-2002 L2003 **OBG** *020 †30

NSEKENENE, Kolongo. 2690 ELMHURST LN, HAMPTON ROADS REGIONAL JAI 23701 #781-01-1987 L2001 **IM** *020 †20

OBAYUWANA, Alphonsus O. 600 CRAWFORD ST, STE 300 23704 #010-03-1981 L1986 **OBG** *020 †30

O'BOYLE, Amy Leigh. 620 JOHN PAUL JONES CIR, NAVAL MED CTR, BLDG 1,RM C 23708 #021-01-1993 L1994 **OBG** *020 †30

O'BOYLE, John David. 620 JOHN PAUL JONES CIR, NAVAL MEDICAL CENTER 23708 #023-12-1992 L1999 **OBG** *020 †30

OBRIEN, Joseph Gorman, Jr. 620 JOHN PAUL JONES CIR, ATTN: CREDENTIAL OFFICE 23708 #051-07-1999 L1999 **AN** *020 †05

O'DONNELL, Robert Francis. ■ 23704 #051-07-2008 *012

OJO, Olukayode Oludapo. ■ 23703 #690-01-2000 L2005 **FP** *012

OKASINSKI, Michael J. ■ 23703 #038-44-2006 *012

O'MALLEY, Timothy Patrick. 620 JOHN PAUL JONES CIR, MEDICAL STAFF SERVICES OFF 23708 #010-02-1985 L2005 **OTO** *020 †45

ORBETA, Nelia Anarna. 620 JOHN PAUL JONES CIR, ATTN: CREDENTIAL OFFICE 23708 #748-08-1968 L1975 **GP** *020

ORENCIA, Rodolfo Tanabe. 620 JOHN PAUL JONES CIR, ATTN: CREDENTIAL OFFICE 23708 #748-07-1962 L1995 **FM** *020 †18

OWENS, John Elwood. 239 CONSTITUTION AVE 23704 #051-04-1971 L1975 **TS** *071 †85,90

PALMREUTER, Neal Earl. ■ 23705 #025-07-2007 *012

PARKER, Todd Allen. 620 JOHN PAUL JONES CIR, NAVAL MED CTR 23708 #051-07-2003 L2004 **EM** *012

PASCUAL, Reymond Guzman. 3636 HIGH ST 23707 #748-10-1973 L1980 **GS** *020

PATEL, Apurva Maheshbhai. 301 GOODE WAY, STE 102 23704 #495-23-1984 L1992 **IM** *020 †20

PATEL, Sugat Kiritkumar. 620 JOHN PAUL JONES CIR, BLGD 3, 1ST FLOOR 23708 #038-06-2000 L2006 **ID** *020 †20

PAULSEN, Leif Lamont. 620 JOHN PAUL JONES CIR, NAVAL MED CTR 23708 #056-06-2005 L2006 **FP** *012

PAVILACK, Mark Allan. 3603 COUNTY ST 23707 #047-05-1987 L2002 **OPH** *020 †35

PEEPLES, Margaret E Olsen. ■ 23703 #012-01-1943 L1968 **PD** *020

PEMBERTON, Arthur Samuel. 620 JOHN PAUL JONES CIR, NMC PORTSMOUTH VA 23708 #047-06-1997 L1998 **IM** *020 †20

PENALOSA, Leocadio B, Jr. 301 GOODE WAY 23704 #748-08-1967 L1974 **FM** *075 †18

PENNY, Michael Glenn. 620 JOHN PAUL JONES CIR, GME/ACADEMIC AFFAIRS 23708 #036-05-1994 L2000 **EM** *020

PERRY, Michael James. 620 JOHN PAUL JONES CIR, NAVAL MEDICAL CENTER 23708 #023-12-2003 L2003 **GS** *012

PET, Leo T. 620 JOHN PAUL JONES CIR, ATTN: CREDENTIAL OFFICE 23708 #748-07-1964 L1980 **FM** *071

PETERSEN, Christian Tyler. 620 JOHN PAUL JONES CIR, ATTN: CREDENTIAL OFFICE 23708 #026-04-1996 L2004 **AN** *020 †05

PETILON, Julio. 620 JOHN PAUL JONES CIR, NAVAL MEDICAL CENTER PORTS 23708 #047-07-2001 L2001 *020

PEZZELLA, Nickolas L, III. 3640 HIGH ST STE 2A 23707 #051-04-1996 L1996 **PM PRS** *020 †60

PICCIRILLI, Cynthia B. 620 JOHN PAUL JONES CIR, NAVAL MEDICAL CENTER 23708 #023-12-1988 L1995 **NS** *020 †25

PIERCE, Fletcher Nelson. 620 JOHN PAUL JONES CIR, ATTN: CREDENTIAL OFFICE 23708 #047-05-1996 L1998 **PCC** *020 †20

PIERCE, Jennifer L. 620 JOHN PAUL JONES CIR, NMC PORTSMOUTH VA 23708 #005-15-1997 L1999 **DR** *020 †80

PIERSON, Roger Victor. 3636 HIGH ST 23707 #352-07-1952 L1970 **P LM** *071
PISCHNOTTE, William Otto. ■ 23703 #035-08-1954 L1970 **R** *071 †80
POLK, Travis Martin. 620 JOHN PAUL JONES CIR, NMC PORTSMOUTH DEPT OF SUR 23708 #023-12-2001 L2001 **GS** *012
POPE, William Barrett, Jr. 3636 HIGH ST 23707 #051-04-1947 L1947 **GP** *071
POREA, Timothy Jos. 620 JOHN PAUL JONES CIR, ATTN: CREDENTIAL OFFICE 23708 #048-04-1992 L1994 **PHO** *020 †55
POSADAS, Luis Dila, III. 1801 PORTSMOUTH BLVD 23704 #748-10-1983 L1997 **P** *020 †75
PUTTLER, Krista Maren. 620 JOHN PAUL JONES CIR 23708 #023-12-2005 L2005 *100
PYLE, Wellden. 3636 HIGH ST 23707 #041-77-1956, ▲ L1972 **FM** *071
QUEEN, Thomas Allen. 3636 HIGH ST 23707 #028-02-1964 L1983 **GS** *020 †85
QUERRY, Amanda G. ■ 23704 #022-75-2007, ▲ *012
QUIGG, Robert Wm. 620 JOHN PAUL JONES CIR, ATTN: CREDENTIAL OFFICE 23708 #051-07-1981 L1985 **OM** *020
RANDOLPH, Robert Perry. 620 JOHN PAUL JONES CIR, ATTN: CREDENTIAL OFFICE 23708 #016-11-1970 L1973 **ORS** *020 †40
RAPP, Catherine Marie. ■ 23704 #016-45-2008 *012
RASCONA, Dominick Anthony. 620 JOHN PAUL JONES CIR, ATTN: CREDENTIAL OFFICE 23708 #023-12-1984 L1997 **CCM PUD** *020 †20
RAY, Quentin Patrick. 620 JOHN PAUL JONES CIR, NAVAL MED CTR 23708 #021-01-1999 L2000 **GE** *020 †20
READ, Mallory Jos, Jr. 5615 HIGH ST W 23703 #051-04-1970 L1970 **EM** *020 †16
RECTOR, James Thos. 620 JOHN PAUL JONES CIR, NAVAL MEDICAL CENTER 23708 #046-01-1987 L1999 **PTH** *050
REED, Sharon Budniak. 620 JOHN PAUL JONES CIR, ATTN: CREDENTIAL OFFICE 23708 #041-09-1997 L2008 **IMG** *020 †20
RENINGER, Charles W, III. 620 JOHN PAUL JONES CIR, BLDG 2 23708 #041-07-1997 L2005 **HO** *020 †20
RIBLET, Jeffrey L. 3640 HIGH ST, STE 2F 23707 #048-02-1987 L1993 **GS** *020 †85
RICCA, Robert Louis, Jr. 620 JOHN PAUL JONES CIR, ATTN: CREDENTIAL OFFICE 23708 #023-12-2000 L2000 **GS** *012
RICE, Doris Mable. 3921 KINGMAN AVE 23701 #008-02-1979 L1980 **RHU IM** *020 †20
RIDGWAY, Kirby Gail. 620 JOHN PAUL JONES CIR, ATTN: CREDENTIAL OFFICE 23708 #003-01-1979 L1980 **CLP** *040
RINDFLEISCH, Amy Elna. 620 JOHN PAUL JONES CIR, ATTN: CREDENTIAL OFFICE 23708 #024-05-1997 L2000 **PD** *020 †55
RINGLER, Robert L, Jr. 600 CRAWFORD ST, STE 300 23704 #023-12-1982 L2004 **FM** *040 †18
RINGQUIST, John Russell. 620 JOHN PAUL JONES CIR, NAVAL MEDICAL CENTER PORTS 23708 #023-12-2000 L2006 **EM** *012
RIPPLE, James Randal. ■ 23703 #012-01-2007 *012
RITCHIE, James Vivian. 620 JOHN PAUL JONES CIR, ATTN: CREDENTIAL OFFICE 23708 #027-01-1988 L1995 **AM** *020 †16
ROBERTS, Alfred M. 4700 GEORGE WASHINGTON HWY, MARYVIEW MEDCARE 23702 #036-07-1977 L1979 **FM** *020 †16
ROBERTS, Peter Frazier. 620 JOHN PAUL JONES CIR, ATTN: CREDENTIAL OFFICE 23708 #041-13-1992 L2004 **TS** *020 †85,90
ROBERTS, Timothy Arlen. 620 JOHN PAUL JONES CIR, PROFESSIONAL AFFAIRS 23708 #039-01-1995 L1996 **ADL** *020 †55
ROBINETT, Paul Ward. ■ 23703 #051-04-1945 L1948 **GS** *071 †85
ROBINSON, Ivan Frederick. 620 JOHN PAUL JONES CIR, DEPT OF RADIOLOGY 23708 #035-09-1986 L1994 **DR** *020 †80
ROCHE, Edward J, Jr. ■ 23703 #035-45-1950 L1951 **FM** *071
RODRIGUE, Tina Christiane. 620 JOHN PAUL JONES CIR, NAVAL MEDICAL CENTER 23708 #051-04-1997 L2007 **NS** *020 †25
ROGISH, Kristina Marie. ■ 23703 #055-01-2007 L2007 *012
ROLFE, Alan Ellis. 620 JOHN PAUL JONES CIR, ATTN: CREDENTIAL OFFICE 23708 #011-03-1984 L1986 **D IM** *020,15
ROMAN, Janice. 3640 HIGH ST, MARTHA DAVIS CANCER CENTER 23707 #010-02-1978 L1985 **RO** *020 †80
ROOS, Joel Andrew. 620 JOHN PAUL JONES CIR, DEPT OF EMGY MED NMCP 23708 #038-41-1989 L2002 **EM** *040 †16
ROSATI, Theresa H. 3636 HIGH ST, DEPT OF ANESTHESIOLOGY 23707 #051-04-2002 L2006 **AN** *100
ROSENBERG, Marc Joseph. 3235 ACADEMY AVE, STE 201 23703 #051-07-2001 L2007 **CD** *020
ROSS, William Bruce. EFFINGHAM ST 23708 #048-12-1971 L1975 **PTH BBK** *030 †50
ROSSLER, Darrin Joseph. 620 JOHN PAUL JONES CIR, MEDICAL STAFF SERVICES 23708 #048-14-2002 L2007 **EM** *012
ROTH, Jonathan Michael. 620 JOHN PAUL JONES CIR 23708 #035-19-2006 L2007 **ORS** *012
SAGER, Anita Louise. 620 JOHN PAUL JONES CIR, ATTN: CREDENTIAL OFFICE 23708 #051-07-1981 L1985 **FM** *020 †18
SALMON, Brittney Suzanne. ■ 23703 #051-07-2007 L2007 **PD** *012
SALZBRENNER, Stephen G. 620 JOHN PAUL JONES CIR, NMCP PSYCHIATRY 23708 #030-06-2001 L2002 **P** *020 †75
SANDVED, Karin Maria. 3300 HIGH ST STE 6, PORTSMOUTH 23707 #051-01-1991 L1996 **IM** *020 †20
SANTIAGO, Camilo. 620 JOHN PAUL JONES CIR 23708 #042-01-2003 L2004 **GS** *020
SARKAR, Dilip Kumar. 3640 HIGH ST STE 1F 23707 #160-02-1972 L1979 **GS VS** *071 †85
SARRIS, George Alexander. 3235 ACADEMY AVE, STE 201 23703 #035-47-1992 L2001 **CD** *020 †20
SASTRY, Topalli Krishna B. 3640 HIGH ST, STE 2A 23707 #495-37-1994 L1998 **PM** *020
SAUNDERS, James Tahlman. 301 GOODE WAY, STE 105 23704 #035-20-1974 L1977 **IM** *020
SAUTER, Bettina. 620 JOHN PAUL JONES CIR, NAVAL MEDICAL CENTER 23708 #016-76-2000, ▲ L2000 **EM** *012
SCHELZIG, Dietrich Werner. 620 JOHN PAUL JONES CIR, NAVAL MEDICAL CENTER 23708 #038-06-2003 L2004 *100
SCHINDLER, Lynnett L. 620 JOHN PAUL JONES CIR, NMC PORTSMOUTH VA 23708 #023-12-1998 L1999 **OBG** *020 †30
SCHMIEDER, Gregory Carl. ■ 23704 #016-45-2001 L2007 **VS** *012 †85
SCHROEDER, Ashley Anders. 620 JOHN PAUL JONES CIR, DEPT OTO-HNS 23708 #051-01-1993 L1994 **OTO** *020 †45
SCHROFF, Richard L, Jr. 620 JOHN PAUL JONES CIR, ATTN MEDICAL STAFF 23708 #041-13-1988 L1995 **GS** *020 †20
SCHWARTZMAN, Eric Lance. 620 JOHN PAUL JONES CIR, NAVAL MEDICAL CENTER PORTS 23708 #041-09-1993 L1994 **CD** *100 †20
SCOTT, Martin Noel. 620 JOHN PAUL JONES CIR, MEDICAL STAFF SERVICES 23708 #024-01-1998 L2003 **DR** *020 †80

SCUTERO, James Vincent. 3100 LONDON BLVD 23707 #030-06-1965 L1971 **PUD IM** *071 †20
SEARS, Richard Wm. ■ 23703 #041-12-1963 L1964 **OBG** *071 †30
SELLERS, Andrew Jackson. 620 JOHN PAUL JONES CIR, ATTN: CREDENTIAL OFFICE 23708 #023-12-1999 L2004 **FM** *020 †80
SEOK, John H. 620 JOHN PAUL JONES CIR, NAVAL MEDICAL CENTER 23708 #035-15-2001 L2001 **N** *020
SHABAZZ, Lloyd Aqeel. 355 CRAWFORD ST, STE 102 23704 #005-19-1987 L1998 **ON IM** *020 †20
SHAFER, Eric C. ■ 23704 #038-75-2007, ▲ *012
SHAFER, Robert Patrick. 620 JOHN PAUL JONES CIR, NMC PORTSMOUTH VA 23708 #036-05-2001 L2002 **AN** *100
SHAPIRO, Alan Robt. 620 JOHN PAUL JONES CIR, ATTN: CREDENTIAL OFFICE 23708 #035-19-2007 L2007 **AN IM** *020
SHARMA, Kshitij. ■ 23703 #011-04-2005 L2005 **IM** *012
SHARPE, Richard Powell. 620 JOHN PAUL JONES CIR, DEPT OF GENERAL SURGERY 23708 #023-12-1991 L1997 **CCS** *020 †85
SHELDON, Ingrid Victoria. 620 JOHN PAUL JONES CIR, NAVAL CENTER PORTSMOUTH 23708 #024-05-1997 L2006 **OBG FM** *020 †18
SHENENBERGER, Donald W. 620 JOHN PAUL JONES CIR, NAVAL MEDICAL CENTER PORTS 23708 #045-04-1996 L1999 **D** *020 †18
SHERROD, Peter D. 620 JOHN PAUL JONES CIR, ATTN: CREDENTIAL OFFICE 23708 #048-02-1985 L1986 **FM** *020 †18
SHOPE, Timothy Russell. 620 JOHN PAUL JONES CIR, ATTN: CREDENTIAL OFFICE 23708 #025-12-1990 L1993 **PD** *020 †55
SHORT, Patrick Leonard. ■ 23707 #023-12-2008 *012
SIDHOM, Magdy Kamile. 355 CRAWFORD ST, STE 808 23704 #915-04-1977 L1987 **AN IM** *020 †20,05
SIMMER, Edward David. 620 JOHN PAUL JONES CIR, NAVAL MED CTR 23708 #028-34-1990 L1991 **P PFP** *030 †75
SKRIP, Stephen Michael. 3636 HIGH ST 23707 #016-42-1988 L1991 **EM** *020 †16
SLAKEY, Joseph Bernard. 620 JOHN PAUL JONES CIR, ATTN: CREDENTIAL OFFICE 23708 #010-02-1987 L1988 **ORS OP** *020 †40
SMITH, Eddie Louis. 600 CRAWFORD ST 23704 #036-01-1984 L1992 **FM** *020 †18
SMITH, John Harold, Jr. 620 JOHN PAUL JONES CIR, ATTN: CREDENTIAL OFFICE 23708 #023-12-1997 L1998 **GE** *100 †20
SMITH, Thedia Jones. 4 CREEKSIDE CT 23703 #033-05-1983 L1990 **PD** *020 †55
SMITS, Robert Louis, Jr. 620 JOHN PAUL JONES CIR, NAVAL MED CTR PORTMOUTH 23708 #056-06-2001 L2001 **AN** *020 †05
SNYDER, Martin Lewis. 620 JOHN PAUL JONES CIR, ATTN: CREDENTIAL OFFICE 23708 #035-03-1978 L1999 **GS VS** *020 †85
SOE-HSIAO, Myint Myint. ■ 23707 #209-03-1979 L2007 **FP** *012
SONI, Parimalkumar J. 3235 ACADEMY AVE STE 30 23703 #495-23-1992 L2000 **IM** *020 †20
SORIA, Estanislao V, Jr. 620 JOHN PAUL JONES CIR, NAVAL MEDICAL CENTER 23708 #748-03-1970 L1987 **FM** *020
SORIANO, Franklin M, Jr. 4725 PORTSMOUTH BLVD 23701 #748-01-1956 L1987 **GS GP** *071
SOUTHERN, Fredrick Newell. 620 JOHN PAUL JONES CIR, NAVAL MED CTR PORTSMOUTH 23708 #019-02-1987 L1989 **VS GS** *020 †85
SPONAUGLE, Harlan Dale. 475 WATER ST 23704 #041-02-1961 L1970 **OPH** *071 †35
SPOONER, Michael Todd. 620 JOHN PAUL JONES CIR, ATTN: CREDENTIAL OFFICE 23708 #018-03-1999 L2007 **IM** *020
SRAY, William Andrew. 620 JOHN PAUL JONES CIR, DEPT OF OPTHLMGY 23708 #041-02-1991 L1992 **OPH** *020 †35
STABEN, Rebecca A. ■ 23704 #035-75-2005, ▲ L2006 *100
STANLEY, Jeff. ■ 23703 #051-04-1977 L1996 **N IM** *050 †20,16
STARKEY, Gary Lee. 3300 ACADEMY AVE 23703 #038-40-1981 L1988 **P** *071 †75
STAUDT, Anna Marie. 620 JOHN PAUL JONES CIR, ATTN: CREDENTIAL OFFICE 23708 #056-06-1990 L1992 **AN** *020 †05
STEWART, Joel David. 620 JOHN PAUL JONES CIR, ATTN: CREDENTIAL OFFICE 23708 #024-01-1993 L1994 **ORS** *020 †20
STEWART, Virginia Meredit. ■ 23702 #036-08-2008 *012
STILES, Margaret Montague. 3235 ACADEMY AVE STE 10 23703 #051-07-1997 L1997 **FM** *020 †18
STINSON, Darryl David. 620 JOHN PAUL JONES CIR, ACADEMIC AFFAIRS/GME 23708 #047-07-2002 L2005 **DR** *020 †80
STOKES, Ralph M, Jr. ■ 23701 #041-77-1944, ▲ *071
STONE, George Martin, II. ■ 23703 #011-03-1962 L1986 **OM AM** *071 †70
STONE, Kimberly Jordan. 620 JOHN PAUL JONES CIR, MEDICAL STAFF SERVICES DEP 23708 #035-48-1995 L2006 **FM** *020 †18
STRANGE, Robert George, Jr. 620 JOHN PAUL JONES CIR, NAVY MED CNTR PORTSMOUTH 23708 #051-04-1996 L2007 **TS CD** *020 †85
STRAYHORN, Earl C. 3636 HIGH ST 23707 #024-07-1975 L1983 **VS PME** *020 †85
STRUNC, Michael Jos. 620 JOHN PAUL JONES CIR, ATTN: CREDENTIAL OFFICE 23708 #028-34-1992 L1994 **PD** *020 †55,75
SU, Robert K. 2905 TANBARK LN 23703 #572-08-1965 L1973 **AN OS** *020
SURESH, Arati. 355 CRAWFORD ST, STE 808 23704 #495-72-1985 L1999 **AN** *020 †20,05
SUTTON, Joanne Mc Manaman. 620 JOHN PAUL JONES CIR, ATTN: CREDENTIAL OFFICE 23708 #011-02-1994 L1997 **PHO** *020 †55
TALBOT, Cynthia Lynn. 620 JOHN PAUL JONES CIR, ATTN: CREDENTIAL OFFICE 23708 #035-09-1998 L2004 **AN** *020
TAMMINGA, Cindy Lou. 620 JOHN PAUL JONES CIR, ATTN: CREDENTIAL OFFICE 23708 #016-01-1991 L1994 **ID** *020 †20
TANAKA, Zenji. ■ 23707 #021-01-1959 L1964 **AN** *071
TASSIN, Nadine Smith. ■ 23703 #047-07-2006 L2007 **TY** *012
TENEKJIAN, Vasken K. 3640 HIGH ST 23707 #605-01-1973 L1979 **VS TS** *020 †85,90
THAGARD, Andrew Sloane. ■ 23704 #011-03-2008 **OBG** *012
THANADAR, Abu Md Abdur R. 301 GOODE WAY STE 201 23704 #704-03-1962 L1974 **U** *020
THIEL, Robert P. 620 JOHN PAUL JONES CIR, NAVAL MEDICAL CENTER 23708 #035-09-1984 L1985 **PMM** *012 †05
THOMPSON, James Leslie. ■ 23703 #051-07-2008 *012
THOMPSON, Scott Stanfield. 4515 HIGH ST W 23703 #048-02-2001 L2002 **AN** *012
TIMBY, Jeffrey Wm. 620 JOHN PAUL JONES CIR, ATTN PROFESSIONAL AFFAIRS 23708 #041-13-1984 L1985 **IM PUD** *020 †20
TOBIAS, Imelda Victoria. 4224 PORTSMOUTH BLVD, P O BOX 65404 23701 #748-01-1971 L1980 **EM GP** *020
TONON, Elizabeth Ann. 620 JOHN PAUL JONES CIR, NMCP DEPT OF OPHTLMLY 23708 #050-02-1987 L1999 **OPH** *020 †35

TOPP, Shelby Gates. ■ 23704 #027-01-2007 L2007 *012
TRASK, John Douglas. 620 JOHN PAUL JONES CIR, ATTN: CREDENTIAL OFFICE 23708
#023-12-2002 L2003 **AN** *012
TSAI, Catherine M. 620 JOHN PAUL JONES CIR, NAVAL MED CTR GASTRO DEPT 23708
#005-14-1998 L2004 **GE** *020 †20
TURTON, David Bryan. 620 JOHN PAUL JONES CIR, ATTN: CREDENTIAL OFFICE 23708
#025-07-1982 L2001 **NM IM** *020,28
UNGER, Daniel Vernon, IV. 620 JOHN PAUL JONES CIR, ATTN: CREDENTIAL OFFICE 23708
#051-07-1984 L1987 **ORS AM** *020 †40
VALDES, Guido Francisco. 620 JOHN PAUL JONES CIR, ATTN:MEDICAL STAFF OFFICE 23708
#011-02-1992 L1995 **EM** *020 †16
VALDIVIESO, Jorge R. 3409 COUNTY ST 23707 #004-01-1947 L1971 **OPH** *071 †35
VANDENBOOM, Adam Michael. 620 JOHN PAUL JONES CIR 23708 #021-01-2007 L2007
HOS *012
VANDERPOL, Sarah Lynn. 620 JOHN PAUL JONES CIR, ATTN: CREDENTIAL OFFICE NM 23708
#038-06-2001 L2005 **OBG** *020 †30
VANHOOK, R Thomas. 620 JOHN PAUL JONES CIR, ATTN: CREDENTIAL OFFICE 23708
#004-01-2000 L2000 **EM** *020 †16 ‡
VAN HORN, Marilyn Ruth. 600 CRAWFORD ST, STE 300 23704 #051-07-2006 L2006 **FP** *012
VENTURA, Heather J. 620 JOHN PAUL JONES CIR, ATTN: CREDENTIAL OFFICER 23708
#023-12-2000 L2002 *020 †20
VENTURA, John C. ■ 23707 #051-07-2004 L2004 *100
VEST, Walter Edward, III. 3636 HIGH ST, MARYVIEW MEDICAL CENTER 23707
#051-04-1990 L1997 **IM** *020 †20
VIA, Darin Keith. 620 JOHN PAUL JONES CIR, MEDICAL STAFF SERVICES OFF 23708
#023-12-1991 L1993 **AN** *020 †05
VICENS, Jose Juan. 620 JOHN PAUL JONES CIR, ATTN: CREDENTIAL OFFICE, N 23708
#042-01-1976 L1980 **OBG** *020 †30 ‡
VIDARTE, Joseph D. 3640 HIGH ST STE 1D, MARYVIEW MEDICAL ARTS BLDG 23707
#737-01-1954 L1960 **OBG** *071
VIZCAINO, Federico. 3300 ACADEMY AVE 23703 #429-01-1973 L1979 **P** *020 †75
VOKOUN, Edward Scott. 620 JOHN PAUL JONES CIR, NAVAL MEDICAL CENTER 23708
#048-12-2001 L2002 **AN** *012
WAGNER, Alan Lewis. 620 JOHN PAUL JONES CIR, MEDICAL STAFF OFFICE 23708
#047-05-1982 L1986 **OPH R** *020 †35
WAGNER, Michael Robt. 620 JOHN PAUL JONES CIR, ATTN: CREDENTIAL OFFICE 23708
#010-02-1990 L1992 **N** *020 †75
WALKER, Jeffrey Bryan. 620 JOHN PAUL JONES CIR, ATTN: CREDENTIAL OFFICE 23708
#051-01-1998 L2000 **PTH** *020 †50
WALKER, Jennifer Marie. ■ 23707 #010-01-2008 *012
WALTERS, Janet Lee H. ■ 23704 #051-04-1978 L1987 **P** *020 †75
WALTON, Ruth Evelyn. 3300 ACADEMY AVE, CHURCHLAND PSYCH ASSOC 23703
#048-14-1996 L1998 **P CHP** *020 †75
WANG, Guofang. ■ 23707 #243-45-1982 L2007 **FP** *012
WANG, Junjie. 355 CRAWFORD ST, STE 808 23704 #243-69-1988 L2004 **AN** *020 †05
WARD, William Harrell. ■ 23704 #001-06-2007 L2007 *012
WARKENTIEN, Tyler Ernest. 620 JOHN PAUL JONES CIR, ATTN: CREDENTIAL OFFICE 23708
#017-20-2005 L2006 **IM** *012
WARNOCK, Alicia Lynn. ■ 23707 #023-12-2007 *012
WATSON, Erin Megan. ■ 23703 #051-04-2007 *012
WATSON, John K. 620 JOHN PAUL JONES CIR, MEDICAL STAFF SERVICES 23708
#023-12-1986 L1989 **PG PD** *020 †55
WATSON, Mary Mahany. 620 JOHN PAUL JONES CIR, ATTN: CREDENTIAL OFFICE 23708
#023-12-1986 L1989 **PD PDE** *071 †55
WEBSTER, Rebecca Marie. 620 JOHN PAUL JONES CIR, ATTN: CREDENTIAL OFFICE 23708
#035-45-2002 L2003 *020 †75
WECHSLER, Steven Michael. 620 JOHN PAUL JONES CIR, ACADEMIC AFFAIRS/GME 23708
#051-07-1999 L2001 **P** *020 †75
WELLS, Nicholas James. ■ 23704 #023-12-2006 L2006 *012
WELSH, Carey Anne. ■ 23704 #041-13-2006 L2006 *012
WHIDDON, David Richmond. 620 JOHN PAUL JONES CIR, DEPT. OF ORTHOPEDIC
SURGER 23708 #051-04-1998 L1998 **ORS** *100
WHITE, Sharese Michelle. 620 JOHN PAUL JONES CIR, ATTN:CREDENTIAL OFFICE 23708
#041-01-2001 L2001 **ORS** *012
WIESE, Deborah Jane. 620 JOHN PAUL JONES CIR, ATTN: PROFESSIONAL AFFAIRS 23708
#036-05-1986 L1990 **OBG** *020 †30
WILCOX KRUMREICH, Julie A. 620 JOHN PAUL JONES CIR 23708 #021-05-2002 L2003 **R** *040
WILDS, Harvey Bernard. 620 JOHN PAUL JONES CIR, DIV OPF RADIATION ONCLGY 23708
#023-12-1997 L1998 **RO** *020 †80
WILKENING, Robin M. 620 JOHN PAUL JONES CIR, ATTN: CREDENTIAL OFFICE 23708
#011-04-1997 L1984 **GPM** *020 †16,70
WILLIAMS, Michael Eugene. 620 JOHN PAUL JONES CIR, NAVAL MEDICAL CENTER 23708
#038-41-1979 L1983 **ON HEM** *020 †20
WILLIAMS, Ronald Murph. 620 JOHN PAUL JONES CIR, NAVAL MEDICAL CENTER 23708
#048-12-1997 L1997 **U** *100
WILSON, Kevin David. 3300 HIGH ST STE 6 23707 #041-12-1980 L1983 **IM** *020 †20
WINDSOR, Jimmy J. 3640 HIGH ST, STE 2D 23707 #011-02-1995 L2006 **CCA** *020 †05
WOLF, Jeffrey Stephen. 3235 ACADEMY AVE STE 200 23703 #051-04-1972 L1979
CRS *020 †10,85
WOOD, Kristi Megan. ■ 23704 #055-75-2006, ▲ L2007 *012
WRIGHT, Geoffrey Austin. 620 JOHN PAUL JONES CIR, MEDICAL STAFF SERVICES 23708
#041-13-1997 L1997 **ORS AM** *020
WRIGHT, Heath Daniel. 620 JOHN PAUL JONES CIR, NAVAL MEDICAL CENTER 23708
#023-12-2006 L2006 **PD** *012
WU, Shue Chen. 3636 HIGH ST 23707 #572-08-1967 L1976 **GYN** *071
WYATT, Armando Jabari. 600 CRAWFORD ST, STE 300 23704 #051-07-2002 L2002 **FM** *020 †18
YABLONSKY, Michael Jacob. ■ 23704 #051-01-1997 L2000 **D** *020 †16
YAMODIS, Nicolas Dimitri. 620 JOHN PAUL JONES CIR, MEDICAL STAFF OFFICE 23708
#035-15-1968 L1971 **NS** *020 †20
YANG, Tingwei. 620 JOHN PAUL JONES CIR, GME/ACADEMIC AFFAIRS 23708
#023-12-1998 L1999 **CD** *012
YANG, Xiaoping. 355 CRAWFORD ST, STE 808 23704 #243-53-1982 L1998 **AN** *020
YARBROUGH, Terry Pinckney. 3300 HIGH ST 23707 #051-04-1965 L1965 **IM CD** *020 †20
YEUNG, Eric Hoki. 620 JOHN PAUL JONES CIR, NAVAL MEDICAL CENTER 23708
#024-05-2006 L2007 *012
YEVICH, Steven Johannes. ■ 23703 #021-01-1980 L1980 **GPM IM** *020 †70

YOUNGBLOOD, Charles F. 620 JOHN PAUL JONES CIR, ATTN: CREDENTIAL OFFICE 23708
#030-06-2002 L2002 **AN** *012
YOWELL, Steven K. 620 JOHN PAUL JONES CIR, ATTN: PROFESSIONAL AFFAIRS 23708
#040-02-1975 L1976 **FM AM** *040 †18
YUN, Kab Yong. 355 CRAWFORD ST, STE 808 23704 #583-04-1968 L1992 **AN** *020 †05
YUNAS, Mohammad. 3003 HIGH ST 23707 #704-02-1970 L1974 **GP** *020 †18
ZAITOUN, Ghais Keith. 3235 ACADEMY AVE 23703 #051-01-1985 L1986 **IM** *020 †20
ZAWACKI, Kevin Edward. 620 JOHN PAUL JONES CIR, ATTN: CREDENTIAL OFFICE 23708
#023-12-1990 L1997 **CD IC** *020 †20
ZINTZ, Eric Jon. 620 JOHN PAUL JONES CIR, NAVAL MEDICAL CENTER 23708
#023-12-1986 L1988 **PDC ID** *020 †55

POTOMAC FALLS — LOUDOUN

ARCHER, Heidi Kambrod. 46165 WESTLAKE DR STE 100 20165 #010-02-1991 L1993
PM *020 †60
CHOUDHRY, Arshed Ahmed. 46161 WESTLAKE DR, STE 210 20165 #704-08-1970 L1987
OBG *020 †30
HESS, Christopher Lee. 21135 WHITFIELD PL, STE 103 20165 #056-06-1998 L1998 **PS** *100 †65
NAIR, Sharmila R. 46175 WESTLAKE DR STE 120 20165 #496-38-1990 L2000 **PD** *020 †55
NANCHERLA, Ananth Rao. 46161 WESTLAKE DR, LOUDOUN ANESTHESIA ASSOCI 20165
#495-21-1972 L1989 **AN** *020 †05
NOELLE, Holger. ■ 20165 #409-06-1997 L2005 **FM** *100 †18
RUSTOGI, Alok. 46090 LAKE CENTER PLZ, STE 201 20165 #496-09-1996 L2004 **IM** *100 †20
SCOTT, Lisa Marie. 46175 WESTLAKE DR, STE 120 20165 #036-07-2002 L2002 **PD** *020 †55
SEMLER, Douglas Cary. 46175 WESTLAKE DR, STE 410 20165 #038-41-1998 L2004 **D** *020 †15
THOMPSON, Jennifer Bracke. 46161 WESTLAKE DR, STE 210 20165 #051-01-1993 L1997
OBG *020 †30
TRUONG, Nhunga Thi. 46165 WESTLAKE DR STE 120 20165 #051-04-1991 L1992 **FM** *020 †18
VU, Tuan Anh. 46161 WESTLAKE DR, STE 220 20165 #023-01-1997 L2000 **EM** *020 †16
WASAN, Sanjeev Madanlal. 46090 LAKE CENTER PLZ, STE 201 20165 #048-13-1999 L2005
GE *020 †20
WILLIAMSON, Valerie C. 46165 WESTLAKE DR, STE 120 20165 #036-08-1987 L1990
FM *020 †18

POUND — WISE

BALUYOT, Virginia Acal. PO BOX 400, 11215 INDIAN CREEK RD 24279 #748-01-1973 L1986
GP EM *020
SAADO, Walid. 8350 MAIN ST, POUND COMPREHENSIVE CLINIC 24279 #875-01-1979 L1994
IMG *020

POUNDING MILL — TAZEWELL

DINO, Teodorico Reyes. ■ 24637 #748-01-1967 L1976 **EM** *020 †16
SINGH, Abhinav. ■ 24637 #495-20-2000 L2007 **IM** *020 †20

POWHATAN — POWHATAN

AMONETTE, Mark Steven. ■ 23139 #051-04-1986 L1987 **AI** *020 †18
BARNES, Sean. ■ 23139 #016-11-2000 **PTH** *100
BINFORD, Charles Alfred. ■ 23139 #011-03-1971 L1975 **P** *020 †75
BRADLEY, Robt Willoughbee. PO BOX 9 23139 #051-04-1947 L1947 **GP** *020
BROWN, Lester Webster, Jr. 2100 ACADEMY RD 23139 #051-01-1979 L1981 **FM** *020 †18
DUNCAN, David Arend. 1820 ANDERSON HWY 23139 #051-04-1984 L1985 **FM** *020 †18
EPPERSON, Thos Irving, Jr. 2891 ANDERSON HWY, MIDLOTHIAN FAMILY PRACTICE 23139
#051-04-1978 L1979 **FM** *020 †18
GRAHAM, Samuel Alan. ■ 23139 #045-01-1947 L1957 **PHP** *071
JAKOWSKI, Joseph Daniel. ■ 23139 #038-40-2004 L2007 **PCP** *012 †50
JOHNSON, Diane Lee. 1820 ANDERSON HWY 23139 #051-04-1996 L1999 **FM** *020 †18
NICKERSON, Richard George. ■ 23139 #010-01-1962 L2003 **PS GS** *071
PAN, Peter Hao-Hsiang. 260 PETERSBURG RD 23139 #051-07-1986 L1990 **AN IM** *020 †05
PRILLAMAN, Barbara Muller. 2891 ANDERSON HWY 23139 #051-04-1990 L1991 **FM** *020 †18
SOMERVELL, Pamela Mcghee. ■ 23139 #028-34-2006 L2007 **FP** *012

PRINCE GEORGE — PRINCE GEORGE

COOKE, Matthew Robert. ■ 23875 #051-04-2008 *012
CROSIER, Joseph Leo. ■ 23875 #051-04-1963 L1963 **ORS** *071 †40
DAVE, Akshay. 4205 CROSSINGS BLVD 23875 #495-22-1990 L1996 **IM** *020
DREWRY, David B. ■ 23875 #051-01-1952 L1952 **PD** *071 †55
GEFFERT-GERMAIN, G. 5842 ALLIN RD, PRINCE GEORGE ADULT &CHILD 23875
#051-04-1995 L1995 **CHN** *020
NEFF, David Andrew. 4260 CROSSINGS BLVD, # 2 23875 #051-04-1997 L1997 **FM** *020 †18
SMITH, Alan Michael. 5842 ALLIN RD 23875 #016-11-1978 L1980 **FM** *020 †18

PROVIDENCE FORGE — NEW KENT

DEVEAUX, Monique L. ■ 23140 #035-46-1996 L2006 **PD** *020 †55
GOKLI, Anup J. 9010 POCAHONTAS TRL 23140 #495-01-1981 L1988 **FM GS** *020 †18
THOMAS, Dennis Lee. 9010 POCAHONTAS TRL 23140 #051-04-1979 L1980 **FM** *020 †18

PULASKI — PULASKI

ACHARYA, Ajaykumar A. 4291 LEE HWY 24301 #495-23-1977 L1990 **CD IM** *020 †20
ACHARYA, Parasmani A. 4291 LEE HWY 24301 #495-23-1977 L1990 **AI** *020 †55,03
BAKANE, Ramesh Bhaurao. 2400 LEE HWY N 24301 #495-19-1967 L2005 **U** *020 †95
BRADLEY, David Daniel. 2460 LEE HWY N 24301 #005-15-1997 L2000 **IM** *020 †20
CHAN, Yung-Cheung. 2460 LEE HWY N 24301 #035-06-1973 L1979 **GS EM** *020 †85

CHAND, Yogesh. 2400 LEE HWY N, DBA PULASKI PHYSICIANS 24301 #010-02-1976 L1983 ORS HS *020 †40

D'AMICO, Paul Jos. 2460 LEE HWY N 24301 #051-04-1991 L1993 IM *020 †20

DAVIS, Glenn K, II. 1510 BOB WHITE BLVD 24301 #051-04-1982 L1983 OPH *020 †35

HASAN, Nasira Fatima. 2400 LEE HWY N 24301 #704-06-1954 L1978 OBG GP *075

HASSPIELER, Ralph Andre. 101 1ST ST NW 24301 #065-05-1985 L1998 FM *020 †18

HESS, Randal Orland. 2400 LEE HWY N, STE 100 24301 #051-04-1996 L1996 RO *020 †80

HYDUKE, J Frederick. 4556 1/2 PEAK CREEK RD 24301 #038-43-1985 L1989 AN *020 †05

HYLTON, James Moir. 25 4TH ST NW 24301 #051-01-1958 L1958 GP *071 †18

KAATZ, Matthew Saintjohn. 101 1ST ST NW 24301 #024-07-1996 L1997 FM *020 †18 ‡

KNARR, John Weidner. 2460 LEE HWY N 24301 #041-03-1970 L1974 IM CCM *020 †20

KNULL, Alan Franklin. ■ 24301 #038-43-1978 L1984 DR *020

LODERSTEDT, Gunther J. ■ 24301 #407-10-1955 L1958 GYN *071 †30

LOVELACE, James M. 2460 LEE HWY N 24301 #048-13-1990 L1997 ORS *020 †40

MC GUIRE, William F. 2460 LEE HWY N, P L BOX 112 24301 #051-01-1951 L1951 U *071 †95

OJOMO, Karanita Mary. 2400 LEE HWY N, ONCOLOGY HEMATOLOGY ASSOC 24301 #051-07-1986 L1999 RO *020

PENDERGRAST, Kenneth Roy. 2460 LEE HWY N 24301 #021-06-1987 L1988 IM *020 †20

QUINONES, Moises Eladio. ■ 24301 #308-03-1980 L1982 EM *020 †20,16

RAMAGE, Jay Newton. ■ 24301 #020-02-1997 L1998 FM *020 †18

ROGERS, John Warren. 2400 LEE HWY N, STE 100 24301 #021-05-1999 L2002 RO *020 †80 ‡

SALLABERRY, Jorge Luis. 2460 LEE HWY N 24301 #649-14-1999 L2007 IM *020 †20

SCHNELL, Donald Elmer. 2400 LEE HWY N 24301 #038-40-1961 L1982 PTH *020 †50

SETHNA, Dhun H. ■ 24301 #496-38-1972 L2008 AN CD *020,05

WIENKE, James Walter. ■ 24301 #005-02-1969 L1984 GS *020 †85

WILLIAMS, Dixon Caldwell. 2400 LEE HWY N, EMERGENCY DEPARTMENT 24301 #036-01-1979 L1980 FM *020 †18

YODER, Donald Eugene. 2460 LEE HWY N 24301 #051-04-1978 L1981 IM *020 †20

PUNGOTEAGUE — ACCOMACK

MAY, Madge Nickerson Dunn. ■ 23422 #051-04-1945 L1946 PD *071

PURCELLVILLE — LOUDOUN

ASSEFI, Ali Reza. 280 N HATCHER AVE, PURCELLVILLE DIALYSIS CTR 20132 #917-28-1984 L1990 NEP IM *020 †20

BAILEY, Frank F J. ■ 20132 #023-12-2007 L2007 *012

BARNWELL, Frank M. ■ 20132 #038-06-1950 L1950 IM *071

CHAPMAN, Val Loren. ■ 20132 #049-01-1979 L1983 FM EM *020 †18,16

CONNOLLY, Nicole P. 17336 PICKWICK DR, STE B 20132 #035-09-1997 L2000 PD *020 †55

FOX, Rebecca Rose. 17336 PICKWICK DR, STE B 20132 #019-02-1988 L1993 PD *020 †55

HARKRADER, Carol E. 170 W MAIN ST 20132 #051-01-1980 L1988 P *020 †75

HEGERICH, Thomas Jerome. 17336 PICKWICK DR, STE A 20132 #051-01-1994 L1994 FM *020 †18

HORNICK, Lawrence Ernest. 229 FRAZER DR 20132 #051-07-1984 L1985 FM *020 †18

IDREES, Irfan. 17336 PICKWICK DR 20132 #704-01-1995 L2002 IM *020 †20

IRVINE, Lisa Ann. 921 E MAIN ST STE B, PURCELLVILLE PEDIATRICS 20132 #023-07-2000 L2002 PD *020 †55

JOHNSON, Warren Evan. 441 E MAIN ST 20132 #050-02-1962 L1970 GP AM *030

KUSHNIR, Tatyana. 17336 PICKWICK DR, STE A 20132 #913-85-1983 L2004 FM *020 †18

LAMBERT, Paul Anthony. 17336 PICKWICK DR, STE B 20132 #051-07-1993 L1993 PS *020 †85,65

MADRID, Joel S. 17336 PICKWICK DR, STE B 20132 #748-02-1991 L1996 PD *020 †55

MARCELLIN, Lindsey N. 17336 PICKWICK DR 20132 #051-07-1984 L1986 IM FM *020 †20

MC COLLUM, Eric Douglass. ■ 20134 #051-04-2003 L2005 PD *020 †55

RAJU, Jamuna Dandu. 200 E MAIN ST 20132 #496-24-1988 L2004 P ADP *020

RASHID, Khurram. 17336 PICKWICK DR, BLDG #A, BOX 4 20132 #704-21-1983 L1994 OBG *020 †30

SCHRANKEL, Corinna. 17336 PICKWICK DR, STE B 20132 #409-02-1980 L1997 PD *020 †55

TOBACK, Seth Louis. 17336 PICKWICK DR, STE B 20132 #024-07-1997 L2006 PD *020 †55

TOOTELL, Rhodaline Demana. 740 E MAIN ST 20132 #051-04-2004 L2007 FM *100 †18

TOWE, James Halsey. 441 E MAIN ST 20132 #051-07-1994 L1994 FM *020 †18

TOWE, James Luther. 441 E MAIN ST 20132 #051-04-1962 L1962 GP *020

WESTON, Kathleen Shingler. ■ 20132 #041-13-1951 LM OS *071

QUANTICO — PRINCE WILLIAM

ARORA, Sudhir. 3259 CATLIN AVE, ATTN: CREDENTIAL OFFICE 22134 #495-49-1974 L1979 R *020 †80

COLAPIETRO, Vicki Jo. ■ 22134 #041-07-1993 L2005 FM *020 †18

DWYER, Timothy William. ■ 22134 #010-02-1996 L1998 *020 †55

HAYS, Russell Bennett, Jr. 3259 CATLIN AVE, NAVAL HEALTH CLINIC 22134 #011-02-1994 L1995 FM *020 †18

HOCTER, William Jos, Jr. ■ 22134 #016-43-1986 L1990 P PYG *020 †75

JONES, Richard Hughes. 3259 CATLIN AVE, ATTN: CREDENTIAL OFFICE 22134 #036-01-1995 L1996 FM *020 †18

KENNEDY, John Steven. 3259 CATLIN AVE, NAVAL HEALTH CLINIC 22134 #023-12-1994 L1995 P *020 †75

LIPSITZ, Robert Jeffrey. 3259 CATLIN AVE, QUANTICO MC BASE 22134 #025-07-1993 L1994 FM *020 †18

MENELEY, Bruce Coval. 3259 CATLIN AVE, ATTN: CREDENTIAL OFFICE 22134 #031-01-1986 L1989 EM *020 †16

MUELLER, Joseph James. 3259 CATLIN AVE, NAVAL MEDICAL CENTER 22134 #030-05-2005 L2005 *020

NASH, William Peter. 3259 CATLIN AVE, ATTN: CREDENTIAL OFFICE 22134 #016-11-1978 L2007 P *020 †75

PATEL, Dilip Devjeebhai. 3259 CATLIN AVE, NAVAL HEALTH CLINIC 22134 #495-01-1971 L1978 FM GP *020 †18

PEREZ, Marlow. ■ 22134 #007-02-1997 L1999 FM *020 †18

RYDER, Thomas John, Jr. 3259 CATLIN AVE, NAVAL HEALTH CLINIC 22134 #010-02-1996 L2006 FM *020 †18

SCHULTE, Douglas Robt. 3259 CATLIN AVE, QUANTICO MC BASE 22134 #051-01-1990 L1997 FM *020 †18

SHERMAN, Griselle. 3259 CATLIN AVE, QUANTICO MC BASE 22134 #042-01-1981 L2005 PD *020 †55

SHIVELEY, David Lee. 3259 CATLIN AVE, NAVAL HEALTH CLINIC 22134 #422-01-1982 L1997 IM *020 †70

TANNER, William John. 3259 CATLIN AVE, QUANTICO MC BASE 22134 #023-12-1991 L1992 FM *020 †18

QUANTICO — STAFFORD

REHE, Gregory Thos. HEALTH SERVICES UNIT, DEA TRAINING ACADEMY 22135 #023-12-1981 L1987 RHU IM *020 †20

QUINTON — NEW KENT

MURPHY, Christine Michell. ■ 23141 #051-04-2007 L2007 EM *012

VANDESAND, Jeffrey Allen. ■ 23141 #051-04-2003 L2004 DR *012

WINSOR, Stephanie Heather. 2955 POCAHONTAS TRL 23141 #065-01-1993 *100

RADFORD — RADFORD

BAADE, Wilhelm Michael. HERCULES INCORPORATED RAAP 24141 #154-02-1951 L1956 IM D *030

BEESE, Stephen Arthur. PO BOX 6899, STUDENT HEALTH SERVICE, MO 24142 #045-01-1982 L1990 FM *071 †18

BISHOP, William David. 106 WADSWORTH ST 24141 #017-20-1967 L1974 OTO *020 †45

BROWN, Ralph Danl, Jr. 2900 TYLER RD, CARILION NRVMC REHABLTN 24141 #016-11-1992 L2001 PM SCI *020 †60

BURK, Linda Ann. 200 8TH ST 24141 #051-04-1990 L1999 PD *020 †55

CHRISTIAN, William E. ■ 24141 #055-01-1966 L1972 AN *071 †05

CLAUSE, Harry Paul. PO BOX 1, RADFORD ARMY AMMUNITION PL 24143 #023-07-1955 L1963 TS CD *071 †85,90

DAVIS, Russell Lewis, Jr. 600 RANDOLPH ST 24141 #051-04-1961 L1961 FM *020 †18

DONNELLY, Kerry Bruce. 601 HARVEY ST 24141 #051-04-1984 L1989 ORS *020 †40

DUBNER, Neil Peter. ■ 24141 #035-46-1961 L1986 P *020 †75

GRAY, Kenneth Wayne. 601 HARVEY ST, RADFORD ORTHOPEDIC CTR 24141 #017-20-1979 L1984 ORS EM *020

GROVER, Leena. ■ 24141 #495-03-1989 L2003 DR *020 †80

HOWARD, Athena Auvil. 701 RANDOLPH ST, STE 210 24141 #055-01-1988 L1994 IM *020 †20

JOHNSON, Richard Roy. 614 E MAIN ST 24141 #051-01-1988 L1989 OPH *020 †35

JUDY, Charles Raeburn. 600 RANDOLPH ST 24141 #045-01-1992 L1993 FM *020 †18

KELLY, Daniel Raymond. 701 RANDOLPH ST, CARILION FAMILY MEDICINE 24141 #035-15-1985 L1986 FM *020 †18

KINCAID, Scott Allan. 701 RANDOLPH ST, CARILION FAMILY MEDICINE 24141 #051-07-1983 L1984 FM FSM *020 †18

KWON, Junbeom. ■ 24141 #010-01-2006 *012

LEE, Thaddeus Carmichael. 701 RANDOLPH ST, CARILION FAMILY MEDICINE 24141 #045-01-1970 L1976 FM *020 †18

LEVY, Jan Alfred. ■ 24141 #016-06-1964 L1969 GS *071 †85

MC ELROY, Paul Gregory. 200 8TH ST 24141 #051-01-2002 L2005 PD *020 †55

MEANS, Dennis Edward. PO BOX 5, CARILION NRV MED CTR 24143 #025-07-1979 L2007 MDM *030 †30

MOGEN, Florence Hart. 200 8TH ST 24141 #051-01-1987 L1990 PD *020 †55

MYERS, Ronald Lee. 106 WADSWORTH ST 24141 #038-41-1964 L1984 P *020 †75

PRICE, Linda Mc Wey. 700 RANDOLPH ST, RADFOR COMM HOSP PATH DEPT 24141 #045-01-1986 L1988 PTH PCP *074 †50

PRILLAMAN, William Watts. ■ 24143 #051-01-1961 L1961 IM RHU *020 †20

ROBERTSON, Richard Lee. 700 RANDOLPH ST 24141 #051-04-1959 L1960 IM GE *071

SNIDER, Zairha Gonzalez. 200 8TH ST, NEW RIVER VALLEY PEDIATRIC 24141 #341-01-1996 L2005 PD *012

SPILLMAN, James Blair. ■ 24141 #051-01-1954 L1954 PD *071 †55

STICKLEY, Robert F S. 200 8TH ST 24141 #051-01-1979 L1982 PD *020 †55

STONE, Gail R. 701 RANDOLPH ST, STE 120 24141 #051-04-1969 L1969 FM *020 †18

TARASIDIS, George C. 200 8TH ST 24141 #418-01-1952 L1961 GS TS *071 †85,90

TAYAL, Sudesh B. ■ 24141 #495-03-1967 L1980 OBG *020 †30

VACCARO, Paul Gerald, Jr. 200 8TH ST 24141 #021-05-1989 L2000 PD *020 †55

WALKER, Timothy Stuart. 200 8TH ST 24141 #051-04-1983 L1986 PD *020 †55

WALKER, Walter J, Jr. 700 RANDOLPH ST 24141 #021-01-1950 L1954 GP OS *071

RAPHINE — ROCKBRIDGE

HANCOCK, Philip Hurt. ■ 24472 #051-01-1960 L1960 OBG OS *071 †30

RAPIDAN — CULPEPER

ELLIOTT, Patricia L. ■ 22733 #025-01-1958 L1974 GP P *020

REEDVILLE — NORTHUMBERLAND

BRADLEY, Kenneth J. ■ 22539 #065-05-1963 L1994 FM *071 †85

ERNST, Angela Noel. ■ 22539 #048-14-1996 L1996 FM *020 †18

LEWIS, Turner Morrison. ■ 22539 #051-04-2001 L2002 RNR *100 †80

MAAN, Vikas. ■ 22539 #495-53-1992 L1996 IM *020 †20

RESTON — FAIRFAX

ADAMS, Diana M. 1850 TOWN CENTER PKWY 20190 #016-06-1984 L2002 OBG *020 †30

■ = Address Information Privacy Protected

AGUIAR, George, Jr. 1850 TOWN CENTER PKWY, STE 400 20190 #010-02-1995 L1995 ORS *020 †40

AHLGREN, Alice. 1850 TOWN CENTER PKWY, 1850 RESTON HOSP CTR/PATH 20190 #010-02-1977 L1982 PTH *020 †50

ALEMI, Behjat. 1850 TOWN CENTER PKWY, DEPT OF NEONATOLOGY 20190 #517-01-1972 L1989 NPM *020 †55

AL-HAMMOOD, Almouhannad I. 11445 SUNSET HILLS RD, ADMINISTRATION OFFICE 20190 #875-01-1986 L2000 IM *020 †20

ALI, Dima. 1801 ROBERT FULTON DR, STE 540 20191 #010-01-1996 L1998 FM *020 †18

ALI, Mohammad Karim. 1830 TOWN CENTER DR, STE 209 20190 #118-01-1974 L1989 OTO GS *020 †45

ALTALIB, Ilham Ismail. 11776 STRATFORD HOUSE PL, APT 1403 20190 #528-01-1965 L1978 OS GYN *020

ALTEMUS, Rosemary Martha. 1850 TOWN CENTER PKWY, ONCOLOGY 20190 #051-01-1988 L2003 RO *020 †80

AMBROSE, Julie Ann. 1860 TOWN CENTER DR, STE 110 20190 #041-02-2000 L2007 OBG *020 †30

AMMERMAN, Richard Gene. 1810 MICHAEL FARADAY DR, STE 200 20190 #024-07-1968 L1971 P GP *030 †75

ARNOLD, Janice Lee. 1830 TOWN CENTER DR # 301 20190 #016-02-1981 L1987 U *020 †95

ARONS, Michael James. 1810 MICHAEL FARADAY DR 20190 #036-07-1968 L1974 P *020 †75

ASCRIZZI, Vincent Paul. 1830 TOWN CENTER DR, STE 205 20190 #035-20-1990 L1993 PD *020 †55

AUKER, Charles Robt. ■ 20194 #010-02-1984 L1986 N *050 †75

AVERY, Janet. 1830 TOWN CENTER DR, STE 309 20190 #495-04-1971 L1980 FM IM *020 †18

AXELRAD, Andrew Marc. 11440 COMMERCE PARK DR, STE LL4 20191 #035-09-1989 L1995 GE *020 †20

BAILEY, Kathleen Marjorie. 11445 SUNSET HILLS RD, RESTON MEDICAL FACILITY 20190 #036-07-1977 L1992 IM EM *020 †20

BARAY, Ahmad. 12359 SUNRISE VALLEY DR, STE 200 20191 #118-01-1978 L1998 EM *020 †18 ‡

BAZAZ, Subash Bansi. 1830 TOWN CENTER DR, STE 201 20190 #035-03-1996 L2002 CD *020 †20

BEHRMANN, Arthur Edmund. 1760 RESTON PKWY STE 212 20190 #016-43-1978 L1979 P *020 †75

BENNETT, Geannie M. 11445 SUNSET HILLS RD, DEPT OB 20190 #038-40-1985 L1993 OBG *020 †20

BERG, Jeffrey Howard. 1860 TOWN CENTER DR, STE 300 20190 #024-05-1992 L1998 OSM ORS *020 †40

BERGMAN, Kenneth Robert. 1860 TOWN CENTER DR, STE 301 20190 #010-02-1998 L1999 OTO *020 †20

BHAT, Misha. ■ 20191 #858-01-2005 L2007 PD *012

BHUSHAN, Neeraj. 1850A TOWN CENTER PKWY, STE 410 20190 #495-45-1975 L1979 IM *020 †20

BISHOP, Robert Jos. 1800 TOWN CENTER DR STE 42 20190 #030-05-1982 L1986 P *020 †75

BLACKERBY, Louise Jeanne. ■ 20191 #396-06-1947 *074

BLANCHFIELD, Colleen Ann. 11150 SUNSET HILLS RD, STE 309 20190 #422-01-1985 L1992 P N *020 †75

BLITCH, James Bedford, Jr. 1810 MICHAEL FARADAY DR 20190 #051-04-1970 L1970 P *020 †75

BLOSSER, R Allen. 1850 TOWN CENTER PKWY 20190 #051-07-1988 L1989 GE *020 †20

BORNMANN, Robert Clare. ■ 20191 #041-01-1956 L1981 OM UM *071 †70

BOYD, Martha Bayles. ■ 20194 #024-05-1964 L1967 AN PUD *071 †05

BRADISH, Michael Scott. 1850 TOWN CENTER PKWY, ASSOCIATES PA 20190 #035-01-2000 L2003 AN *020 †05

BRANSCUM, Barton Anthony. 1875 CAMPUS COMMONS DR, AMEN CLINIC INC 20191 #023-12-1986 L1999 P *020 †75

BRODIE, Stephan Barry. 1850 TOWN CENTER PKWY, ASSOCIATES PA 20190 #010-01-1980 L1986 AN CCM *020 †05

BROWN, Carl Theodore. 11445 SUNSET HILLS RD 20190 #038-41-1976 L1990 OBG *020 †30

BROWN, Christopher Cooley. ■ 20190 #051-01-2008 *012

BROWN, Stephen Kenneth. 1850 TOWN CENTER PKWY, ASSOCIATES PA 20190 #005-18-1983 L2003 AN *020 †05

BRUCE, Thomas Alfred. 11445 SUNSET HILLS RD 20190 #035-09-1966 L1969 IM *020 †20

BUI, Tra P. 1850 TOWN CENTER PKWY, ASSOCIATES PA 20190 #048-04-1992 L2005 AN *020 †05

BURKHART, Gregory Allen. ■ 20191 #020-02-1981 L1992 FM *020 †18,70

BURTON, Leonard Eugene. ■ 20190 #039-01-1954 L1954 ORS *071 †40

BUXBAUM, James Curtis. 1850 TOWN CENTER PKWY, DEPT EM 20190 #010-01-1984 L1987 IM *020 †20

CAESAR, Lori Suzanne. ■ 20194 #010-01-2004 PD *012

CAMPBELL, Ellen Frances. 1860 TOWN CENTER DR, STE 160 20190 #010-01-1993 L1993 IM *020 †20

CAROME, Gail Rowlands. 11130 SUNRISE VALLEY DR, RESTON PED ASSOC STE 150 20191 #038-06-1987 L1994 PD *020 †55

CAUBLE, Kathleen. 1800 TOWN CENTER DR # 120 20190 #003-01-1981 L1989 OBG *020 †30

CHADHA, Vijay Kumar. 1800 TOWN CENTER DR # 214 20190 #495-45-1981 L1985 IM *020 †20

CHAU, Honghanh Thi. 11445 SUNSET HILLS RD, DEPT OB 20190 #010-01-1993 L1997 OBG *020 †30

CHEN, Natasha Lisa. 1850 TOWN CENTER PKWY 20190 #023-01-2001 L2005 IM *020

CHENG, Sam Siu Lun. 1850 TOWN CENTER PKWY, RESTON 20190 #035-47-1993 L1999 DR *020 †80

CHEREDDI, Kavitha. 1850 TOWN CENTER PKWY, MEDICAL STAFF OFFICE 20190 #495-70-1996 L2004 IM *100

CHERUKURI, Kavitha. ■ 20190 #010-01-1994 L1998 EM *020 †16

CHOLMONDELEY, Tessa Marie. 1800 TOWN CENTER DR, STE 212 20190 #008-02-1988 L1991 IM *020 †20

CHOU, Maria Chiyung. 1860 TOWN CENTER DR, STE 130 20190 #035-09-1999 L2002 RHU IM *020 †20

CHOW, David Kimkwong. 1830 TOWN CENTER DR, STE 210 20190 #012-05-1978 L1979 OPH *020 †35

CHRISTENSON, Douglas Mark. 1850 TOWN CENTER PKWY, ASSOCIATES PA 20190 #016-43-1992 L1998 AN *020 †05

CHUNG, Tae Joon. 1830 TOWN CENTER DR, STE 308 20190 #051-07-1993 L2001 RHU *020

CINTRON, Ruben. 12007 SUNRISE VALLEY DR, STE 120 20191 #036-05-1990 L1995 N *020 †75

CLOP, Stephanie Y. 1860 TOWN CENTER DR # 300 20190 #051-07-1996 L2003 PM *020 †60

COOPER, Tristan Simon. ■ 20194 #051-04-2008 *012

CORELLA, Augusto C. 1850 TOWN CENTER PKWY 20190 #010-03-1999 L2006 IM *020 †20

COURET, Ivette Anne. 1860 TOWN CENTER DR, STE 250 20190 #011-02-2000 L2000 OBG *020

DACHER, Elliott S. 1800 TOWN CENTER DR, STE 413 20190 #035-06-1970 L1975 IM *020 †20

DAVIS, James Henry. 1850 TOWN CENTER PKWY 20190 #017-20-1980 L1990 NPM PD *020 †55

DAY, Warner Brent. 11445 SUNSET HILLS RD, DEPT OB 20190 #021-05-1996 L1996 OBG *020 †20

DE SOUZA, Romaldo F X. 1850 TOWN CENTER PKWY 20190 #847-11-1973 L1977 IMG PCC *030 †20

DI PAOLA, Anthony Dominic. 1830 TOWN CENTER DR # 205 20190 #016-42-1970 L1975 PD *020 †55

DLOTT, Jeffrey S. ■ 20194 #048-13-1993 L2005 BBK *020 †50

DOLCICH, Augustine Andrew. 12110 SUNSET HILLS RD, TOWN CENTER FAMILY 20190 #010-03-1991 L1994 FM *020 †18

DOMSON, Paul Charles, Jr. 1850 TOWN CENTER PKWY, ASSOCIATES PA 20190 #051-04-1994 L1996 AN *020 †05

DONSKOY, Betty Schnur. 1800 TOWN CENTER DR, STE 420 20190 #036-01-1986 L1989 P *020 †75 ‡

DOUGHERTY, Charles Peter. 1850 TOWN CENTER PKWY, ASSOCIATES PA 20190 #041-07-1990 L2002 AN *020 †05

DU BOIS, David Edward. 1850 TOWN CENTER PKWY, RESTON 20190 #010-02-1996 L2001 DR *020 †80

DUDRO, Christopher D. 11349 SUNSET HILLS RD, FARRELL PEDIATRICS 20190 #051-01-2000 L2000 PD *020 †55

EAPEN, Annerose Navarro. 1860 TOWN CENTER DR, STE 230 20190 #035-20-1987 L1990 IM *020 †20

EDDINE, F S. 11862 SUNRISE VALLEY DR, # 101 20191 #875-01-1972 L1977 GP *075

EIERLE, Carl Christopher. 1850 TOWN CENTER PKWY, RESTON HOSPITAL CENTER 20190 #023-12-1996 L2007 ORS *020 †40

ELAMIN, Yasir Bannaga. 1850 CAMERON GLEN DR, COMMUNITY MENTAL HEALTH 20190 #915-04-1982 L2007 P *100

ELKOUSY, Mohammed Adel. 1830 TOWN CENTER DR, STE 101 20190 #038-43-1993 L2002 OBG MFM *020 †30

FAGAN, Lynne Lillian. 1800 TOWN CENTER DR, STE 212 20190 #035-46-1984 L1986 IM *020 †20 ‡

FAILLACE, Frank Anthony. 1850 TOWN CENTER PKWY, ASSOCIATES PA 20190 #035-06-1982 L1983 IM *020 †20,05

FARRELL, John David. 11349 SUNSET HILLS RD 20190 #041-12-1965 L1971 PD *071 †55

FARRELL, John David, Jr. 11349 SUNSET HILLS RD 20190 #051-01-1992 L1996 PD *020 †55

FELICE, Anthony Jos. 1860 TOWN CENTER DR, STE 460 20190 #035-08-1985 L1995 HO IM *020 †20

FIALK, Gary Stuart. 1860 TOWN CENTER DR # 180 20190 #008-02-1981 L1996 U *020 †95

FINGERHUT, Herbert Wise. 1850 TOWN CENTER PKWY, ASSOCIATES PA 20190 #012-01-1984 L1985 AN *020 †05

FISCHER, Leonard S. 1850 TOWN CENTER PKWY 20190 #010-02-1975 L1978 GE *020 †20

FITZSIMMONS, Lunei L. 1850 TOWN CENTER PKWY, RESTON HOSPITAL CENTER 20190 #748-10-1984 L2006 AN CCA *020

FLEETER, Thomas B. 1860 TOWN CENTER DR, STE 300 20190 #010-03-1979 L1981 ORS *020 †40

FLYNN, Peter Allan. ■ 20191 #008-01-1958 GS *071 †85

FORMAN, Martin Seth. 1850 TOWN CENTER PKWY 20190 #308-03-1981 L1984 PD *020 †55

FRUMAN, Stuart Alan. 1850 TOWN CENTER PKWY, RESTON 20190 #024-07-1988 L1994 DR *020 †80

GALLI, Suzanne Kim Doud. 1860 TOWN CENTER DR, STE 260 20190 #035-08-1997 L2003 OTO FPS *020

GANESHANANTHAN, Muttiah. 11445 SUNSET HILLS RD 20190 #220-02-1969 L1986 PD PDP *055

GARCES, Rafael. ■ 20191 #042-01-1955 AN *071 †05

GERKIN, Peter R. 1850 TOWN CENTER PKWY 20190 #010-01-1970 L1971 P *020 †75

GONZALEZ, Rodolfo Hector. 1860 TOWN CENTER DR, STE 350 20190 #737-06-1989 L1999 OBG *020 †30

GORMLEY, David Paul. 1850 CAMERON GLEN DR, COMMUNITY MENTAL HEALTH 20190 #016-02-1961 L1968 P CHP *020 †75

GOSPODINOFF, Alexia C. 1860 TOWN CENTER DR # 130 20190 #132-01-1991 L1997 RHU IM *020 †20

GOTTLIEB, Wendy Ruth. 1850 TOWN CENTER PKWY, STE 301 20190 #051-01-1996 L1999 GS *020 †65

GRIFFITHS, Jacqueline D. 12110 SUNSET HILLS RD, STE C50 20190 #025-01-1990 L1994 OPH *020 †35

GRIMM, Michael Andrew. 1850 TOWN CENTER PKWY, RESTON 20190 #011-04-1993 L2002 DR *020 †80

GURNEY, Robert Waring. 11315 SUNSET HILLS RD 20190 #010-02-1974 L1978 D PS *020 †15

HA, Mai C. 1850 CAMERON GLEN DR, STE 600 20190 #051-04-1993 L1998 P *020 †75

HADDAD, Ziyad Khalil. 1850 TOWN CENTER PKWY, RESTON 20190 #010-02-1997 L1997 DR *020 †80

HAGGERTY, Jean Marie. 11445 SUNSET HILLS RD, LOUDON PEDIATRIC ASSOCIATE 20190 #051-07-2000 L2003 PD *020 †55

HARDING, Andrew J. 12110 SUNSET HILLS RD, TOWN CENTER FAMILY 20190 #067-01-1985 L1992 FM *020 †18

HARKAVY, Kenneth Lee. 1850 TOWN CENTER PKWY, RESTON HOSPITAL CENTER 20190 #008-01-1971 L2003 PD NPM *020 †55

HARRISON, Stephen Gary. 1830 TOWN CENTER DR, STE 205 20190 #025-01-1975 L1977 PD *020 †55

HARTLEY, Mark Christopher. 1850 TOWN CENTER PKWY, STE 400 20190 #010-02-1984 L1988 ORS GS *020 †40

HASZ, Michael Wayne. 1831 WIEHLE AVE, FL 2 20190 #026-04-1986 L1993 ORS OSS *020 †40

HAYMES, Arthur Joel. 1894 PRESTON WHITE DR 20191 #024-05-1967 L1989 OBG *020 †30

HERBERT, Pamela Anne. 11654 PLAZA AMERICA DR, # 319 20190 #036-05-1989 L1995 EM *020 †16

HERON, Alva Roy, Jr. 1800 TOWN CENTER DR, STE 315 20190 #047-07-1977 L1979 OS *020

HERTZ, Linda Ellen. ■ 20190 #036-05-1991 L2002 GPM *020

HEYER, David Michael. 1800 TOWN CENTER DR, STE 460 20190 #025-01-1985 L1991 ON HEM *020 †20

HILL, Edward, III. 11921 FREEDOM DR STE 550, PMB 5501 20190 #047-07-1987 LM MDM *030

HONG, Chun. 11357 SUNSET HILLS RD 20190 #243-48-1985 L2002 **IM** *020 †20

HORWATH, Michael Jos. 1800 TOWN CENTER DR # 216 20190 #010-01-1983 L1985 END **IM** *020 †20

HURLEY, Brian Michael. 11160 S LAKES DR, # 183 20191 #005-06-2008 *012

IBIA, Itoro Ekopimo. 11701 BOWMAN GREEN DR 20190 #690-10-1986 L1999 **P** *020 †75

JACOBS, H Barry. ■ 20191 #035-19-1968 **LM GS** *075

JAMES, Edward Jos. 1850 TOWN CENTER PKWY, RESTON 20190 #041-01-1991 L2001 DR *020 †80

JARRELL, Laura Lee. ■ 20194 #051-04-2005 **IM** *012

JASTRZEBSKI, Geo Witold. ■ 20194 #041-12-1977 L1981 **EM** *020 †20

JONES, Alfreda. 1830 TOWN CENTER DR # 207 20190 #036-01-1987 L1991 **OBG** *020 †30

JOSHUA, Alan. 1800 TOWN CENTER DR, STE 118 20190 #660-03-1966 L1971 **IM NEP** *020

KABAL, John. 1712 CLUBHOUSE RD, STE 103 20190 #154-07-1975 L1982 **FM OM** *020 †18

KADAKIA, Reepa Suresh. 1860 TOWN CENTER DR, STE 140 20190 #024-05-2001 L2001 **OBG** *020 †30

KAMEL, Medhat Mohamed. ■ 20194 #330-02-1953 L1975 **GS** *071

KANERIYA, Perry P. 1860 TOWN CENTER DR, STE 400 20190 #041-02-1998 L2005 RNR *020 †80

KANU, John. ■ 20190 #051-01-2004 **GS** *100

KAPOOR, Shreeti. 11349 SUNSET HILLS RD, FARRELL PRDIATRICS 20190 #035-48-1995 L2001 **PD** *020 †55

KARTALIAN, George, Jr. 1860 TOWN CENTER DR, STE 300 20190 #035-06-1991 L2004 ORS *020 †40

KASHEM, Kamrul Islam. 1850 TOWN CENTER PKWY, MEDICAL STAFF OFFICE/ INPA 20190 #160-09-2001 L2006 **IM** *020 †20

KATARKI, Bijal Anil. 1830 TOWN CENTER DR 20190 #495-96-1995 L2003 **FM** *020 †18 ‡

KAUFMANN, Reto Werner. 1800 TOWN CENTER DR # 118 20190 #035-09-1962 L1964 **IM HEM** *071 †20

KELLEHER, Kevin John. 12040 S LAKES DR STE 190 20191 #035-06-1993 L1996 **FM** *020 †18

KENDALL, Martha Rugg. 1850A TOWN CENTER PKWY, INTERNAL MEDICINE 20190 #010-01-1976 L1978 **IM** *020 †20

KESSLER, Ellen Rosemary. 10701 PARKRIDGE BLVD, # 200 20191 #010-02-1978 L1987 **IM OM** *020 †20,70

KESSLER, Larry Scott. 1850 TOWN CENTER PKWY, RESTON 20190 #011-03-1991 L2001 DR *020 †80

KHANNA, Madhu Priya. ■ 20190 #067-01-1998 L2007 **U** *020 †95

KIM, Anje. 1474 N POINT VILLAGE CTR, # 318 20194 #041-01-1996 L2005 **NS** *020

KIM, Haijin. 12040 S LAKES DR, STE 195 20191 #005-12-1995 L1997 **FM** *020 †18

KLEIN, Thomas Jos. 1850A TOWN CENTER PKWY, STE 400 20190 #010-02-1984 L1988 ORS OSM *020 †40

KNECHTEL, Nishita. 11710 PLAZA AMERICA DR, STE 2000 20190 #495-15-1995 L2006 PYG *020

KREISBERG, Roderick Burns. 1850 TOWN CENTER PKWY, RESTON HOSPITAL CENTER 20190 #023-01-2002 L2005 **GE** *012 †20

KU, Karen Kai-Nan. 11349 SUNSET HILLS RD 20190 #010-02-1993 L2007 **PD** *020 †55

KUPERSCHMIT, Marcelo. 1850 TOWN CENTER PKWY, METROPOLITAN SURGICAL 20190 #132-01-1972 L1981 **GS** *020 †85

LAILAS, Nicholas Geo. 1860 TOWN CENTER DR # 150 20190 #010-02-1990 L1996 **U** *020 †95

LAKHANI, Shilen Vinodrai. 11440 COMMERCE PARK DR, STE LL4 20191 #055-02-2001 L2003 **GE** *020

LAREDO, James. 1830 TOWN CENTER DR STE 40, GEORGETOWN VASCULAR ASSOCI 20190 #023-01-1996 L2004 **VS PHL** *020 †85

LARSON, Steven Douglas. 12330 PINECREST RD, STE 250 20190 #010-01-1979 L1980 **FM** *020 †18

LATCHLEY, Aungel Elizabet. ■ 20190 #048-04-2006 L2006 **OBG** *012

LAURENT, A Daniel. 1860 TOWN CENTER DR # 180 20190 #041-01-1981 L1987 **U** *020 †95

LAWFORD, Thomas C, Jr. 2148 GLENCOURSE LN 20191 #051-01-1969 L1969 **OM IM** *030 †70

LEE, Byung-Boong. ■ 20194 #583-02-1963 L1973 **GS CD** *020

LEE, Edwin J. 1860 TOWN CENTER DR, STE 335 20190 #005-14-1998 L2004 OTO HNS *020 †45

LEE, Seon Huan. 1850 TOWN CENTER PKWY, MEDICAL STAFF OFFICE 20190 #010-02-1986 L2002 **EM** *020 †16

LERMAN, Martin Stewart. 11445 SUNSET HILLS RD 20190 #010-02-1973 L1976 **IM** *020 †20

LESHKO, Lidiya. 1850 TOWN CENTER PKWY, RESTON HOSPITAL CENTER 20190 #913-89-1996 L2007 **IM** *020 †20

LEVETT, Harry Lewis. ■ 20194 #016-06-1945 L1946 **OTO** *071 †45

LINDSEY, William Harold. 1800 TOWN CENTER DR, STE 320 20190 #051-01-1990 L1996 OTO *020 †45

LISKER, Heidi. 1830 TOWN CENTER DR # 307 20190 #024-05-1981 L1987 **OPH** *020 †35

LLANERAS, Rene Fernando. 1712 CLUBHOUSE RD 20190 #275-01-1960 L1973 **PD** *020

LONG, Geoffrey Stewart. 1800 TOWN CENTER DR, STE 118 20190 #028-34-1996 L1996 **IM** *020 †20

LUCAS, Susan J. 1830 TOWN CENTER DR, STE 218 20190 #010-01-1982 L1986 **OBG** *020 †30

LUSTBERG, Alex Michae. 11440 COMMERCE PARK DR, STE LL4 20191 #654-01-1996 L2002 **IM GE** *020 †20

MACKOUL, Paul Jos. 1860 TOWN CENTER DR, STE 215 20190 #024-07-1989 L1995 **OBG** *020 †30

MADDEN, Mark Patrick. 1850 TOWN CENTER PKWY, STE 400 20190 #010-02-1984 L1989 ORS *020 †40

MAGANIAS, Nicholas H. 1712 CLUBHOUSE RD 20190 #418-01-1955 L1967 **A GPM** *072 †55

MAHBOUBI, Ezzat. 11484 WASHINGTON PLZ W, STE 300 20190 #517-01-1961 L1991 **IM GP** *071

MALIK, Nidhi. 11445 SUNSET HILLS RD 20190 #495-08-1985 L1990 **IM** *020 †20

MAR, Alice. 11349 SUNSET HILLS RD 20190 #010-02-1997 L1997 **PD** *020 †55

MARQUARDT, Eveline B. 1800 TOWN CENTER DR, STE 319 20190 #010-01-1985 L1988 **OBG** *020 †20

MARTIN, Mami. 1850 TOWN CENTER PKWY, METROPOLITAN SURGICAL 20190 #010-02-1996 L1996 **GS** *020 †85

MASCATELLO, Vincent James. 1850 TOWN CENTER PKWY, RESTON 20190 #035-08-1970 L1976 **PDR DR** *020 †80

MASON, Kenneth Grant. 1850 TOWN CENTER PKWY, METROPOLITAN SURGICAL 20190 #010-03-1977 L1983 **GS** *020 †85

MASSEY, Robert Israel. 1850 TOWN CENTER PKWY, ASSOCIATES PA 20190 #045-01-1980 L1997 **AN CCA** *020 †05

MATCH, Joel Wayne. 1850 TOWN CENTER PKWY, STE 207 20190 #649-14-1978 L1987 **OBG OM** *020

MATHUR, Geeta V. 1850 TOWN CENTER PKWY, RESTON HOSPITAL CENTER MED 20190 #055-01-1993 L2001 **NPM** *020 †55

MAYUGA, Jocelynn L. 11130 SUNRISE VALLEY DR, STE 150 20191 #748-02-1987 L1997 PD *020 †55

MAZAREI, Nahid. 1850 TOWN CENTER PKWY, STE 309 20190 #010-01-1997 L2002 **OBG** *020 †30

MCENTIRE, Patricia Mouril. ■ 20194 #187-03-1990 L1998 **P** *020 †75

MEDOFF, Neil F. 11357 SUNSET HILLS RD 20190 #035-08-1968 L1971 **IM** *020 †20

MELLIS, Michael Geo. 1860 TOWN CENTER DR, STE 301 20190 #051-04-1986 L1988 OTO GS *020 †45

MERTENS, Michael Arthur. 1850 TOWN CENTER PKWY #RAD 20190 #005-06-1965 L1976 DR *020 †20

MILANI, Elle. 1800 TOWN CENTER DR # 316 20190 #051-04-2000 L2000 **OPH** *020 †35

MILES, Sara Strahan. 1850 TOWN CENTER PKWY, STE 209 20190 #024-16-1988 L1991 **IM** *020 †20

MILLER, David Robert. 1860 TOWN CENTER DR, STE 300 20190 #041-13-1995 L2001 HS ORS *020 †40

MILLS, Janete Marie. 1850 TOWN CENTER PKWY, DEPT RADIA/ONCOLOGY 20190 #041-13-1992 L1996 **RO** *020 †80

MOHAMMAD, Yar. 1850 CAMERON GLEN DR # 600, NW CTR FOR COMM MENTAL HLT 20190 #118-01-1965 L1995 **P** *020 †75 ‡

MOOLE, Padmalat Reddy. 1850 TOWN CENTER PKWY, MEDICAL STAFF OFFICE 20190 #495-62-1996 L2003 **IM** *020 †20

MORELL, Eva Maria. 1831 WIEHLE AVE, FL 2 20190 #759-07-1964 L1977 **FM** *020

MOULDS, Jefferson Eaddy C. 1850 TOWN CENTER PKWY, MID-ATLANTIC RADIATION ONC 20190 #051-04-1994 L1995 **RO** *020 †80

MUKHERJEE, Sara. 11445 SUNSET HILLS RD 20190 #005-18-1996 L2000 **IM** *020 †20

NANDEDKAR, Maithily A. 1801 ROBERT FULTON DR 20191 #035-20-1999 L2002 **D** *020 †15 ‡

NEDELCOVYCH, Pierre Sava. 1830 TOWN CENTER DR, STE 303 20190 #654-01-1983 L1984 **FM** *020 †18

NEIMAN, Harvey Louis. 1891 PRESTON WHITE DR, ACR 20191 #025-07-1968 L1969 DR *062 †80

NELSON, Christopher Mark. 11341 SUNSET HILLS RD, RESTON ANESTHESIA ASSOCIAT 20190 #023-12-1991 L2002 **AN** *020 †20

NGUYEN, Loan Thi. 11445 SUNSET HILLS RD 20190 #023-01-1988 L1992 **IM** *020 †20

NGUYEN, Phong Quang. 1860 TOWN CENTER DR, STE 130 20190 #011-03-1983 L1984 RHU *020 †20

NGUYEN, Thomas Tung. 1831 WIEHLE AVE 2ND FL, VIRGINIA SPINE INSTITUTE 20190 #051-07-1994 L1999 **FM** *020 †18

NICKLAS, Richard Austin. 1830 TOWN CENTER DR, STE 206 20190 #010-01-1964 L1974 AI IM *062 †03

NOGUERA, Eduardo C. 11440 COMMERCE PARK DR, STE LL4 20191 #132-02-1992 L2001 **GE** *020 †20 ‡

NORRIS, Alison. 11800 SUNSET HILLS RD, APT 1104 20190 #041-07-1980 L1983 **NEP IM** *020 †20

O'BRIEN, Walter Meyer. 1860 TOWN CENTER DR, STE 150 20190 #041-02-1983 L1985 **U** *020 †95

O CONNOR, Kevin Paul. 1860 TOWN CENTER DR, STE 150 20190 #010-02-1986 L1992 **U GS** *020 †95

O'NEILL, Thomas Michael. 11705 BOWMAN GREEN DR 20190 #010-01-1965 L1970 **D** *020 †15

OSPINA, Richard. 12007 SUNRISE VALLEY DR, STE 120 20191 #035-47-1998 L2003 **N** *020 †75

PAK, Seonae. 11445 SUNSET HILLS RD 20190 #016-11-1986 L1989 **IM** *020 †20

PALMER, Danica Damjanovic. 1850 CAMERON GLEN DR, COMMUNITY MENTAL HEALTH 20190 #957-02-1992 L1998 **P** *020

PALUVAI, Bharani R. 1830 TOWN CENTER DR, STE 309 20190 #495-04-1973 L1983 **IM** *020

PARHAR, Anvita. ■ 20194 #496-39-2000 L2007 **IM** *020 †20

PARKER, David Andrew. 1850 TOWN CENTER PKWY, STE 400 20190 #020-02-1999 L2005 ORS OSM *020 †40

PARRY, Gwilym. 1800 TOWN CENTER DR, DRIVE #212 20190 #007-02-1981 L1987 **IM FM** *020 †20

PATEL, Nisha Raman. 12110 SUNSET HILLS RD, STE C50 20190 #422-01-2001 L2007 **OPH** *020

PATHAK, Arvind Kumar. 1800 TOWN CENTER DR, STE 315 20190 #495-05-1964 L1984 **FM ID** *075 †55,18

PEREZ, Rafael Antonio. ■ 20190 #042-01-1971 L2004 **PTH HMP** *020 †50

PETERS, Jon David. 12007 SUNRISE VALLEY DR, STE 120 20191 #010-02-1980 L1982 **N** *020 †75

PINNAR, Eric David. 1850A TOWN CENTER PKWY, STE 301 20190 #051-04-1994 L1999 **GS** *020 †85

PINNAR, Robert Lloyd. 1850 TOWN CENTER PKWY, STE 301 20190 #033-05-1967 L1968 **GS** *020 †85

PLOTNER, Alan Jaime. 11440 COMMERCE PARK DR, STE LL4 20191 #035-47-1987 L1992 **GE** *020 †20

PODOLSKY, Robert Stephen. 1760 RESTON PKWY, STE 306 20190 #041-13-1988 L1996 **VS** *020 †85

POFFENROTH, Matthew Glen. 1850 TOWN CENTER PKWY, MEDICAL STAFF OFFICE 20190 #017-20-1994 L2005 **IM** *020 †20

POINDEXTER, Byron David. 1825 SAMUEL MORSE DR, AUSTIN WESTON CTR 20190 #017-20-1992 L1998 **PS** *020 †65

POWERS, Suzanne Marie. 1830 TOWN CENTER DR, STE 205 20190 #017-20-1998 L2004 **PD** *020 †55

PYENSON, Leslie R. 1875 CAMPUS COMMONS DR, SPECTAL, LLC, STE 100 20191 #020-02-1969 L1979 **IM OS** *050

RAGHURAM, Sheela. 1850 TOWN CENTER PKWY, INPATIENT SPECIALIST 20190 #495-09-1993 L2001 **IM** *020 †20

RAO, Neerada. 1850 CAMERON GLEN DR, COMMUNITY MENTAL HEALTH 20190 #495-21-1962 L1981 **P CHP** *020 †75

RAUSCH, Kathleen Ann. 1800 TOWN CENTER DR, STE 120 20190 #048-13-1988 L1992 **OBG** *020 †30

REGAN, Thomas Chas. ■ 20194 #035-06-1948 **GS OS** *071 †85

RETHY, Michael Charles. 1850 TOWN CENTER PKWY, RESTON 20190 #035-47-2000 L2006 DR *020 †80

ROBINSON, Emma Louise. 11445 SUNSET HILLS RD, RESTON MEDICAL CENTER 20190 #023-07-1992 L1997 **OBG** *020 †30

ROE, Leslie Parkman. 11800 SUNRISE VALLEY DR, STE 400 20191 #001-02-1985 L1986 **IM** *074

ROMERO, Gonzalo. 1860 TOWN CENTER DR, STE 350 20190 #264-01-1957 L1968 **GS** *020 †85

ROSENTHAL, Richard R. 1830 TOWN CENTER DR, STE 206 20190 #035-08-1966 L1973
A IM *020 †03
ROSENTHAL, Tammy Zelle. 11445 SUNSET HILLS RD, DEPT OF OB/GYN 20190
#010-01-1995 L1995 OBG *020 †30
ROSTAMI, Soheila. 1860 TOWN CENTER DR, STE 250 20190 #010-03-1994 L1997
OPH *020 †35 ‡
SAGER, Dennis Wayne. 1800 TOWN CENTER DR, STE 118 20190 #051-07-1978 L1981
IM *020 †20
SAHGAL, Avisesh. 1760 RESTON PKWY, STE 306 20190 #038-44-1995 L2003 VS *020 †85
SALVATORE, Tamra Jeanette. 11445 SUNSET HILLS RD, PEDIACTRICS 20190
#051-01-1988 L1995 PD *020 †55
SANDIFORD, John Alan. 1850 TOWN CENTER PKWY, METROPOLITAN SURGICAL 20190
#919-03-1970 L1977 GS *020 †85
SARTAWI, Ferdouse Tariq. 1860 TOWN CENTER DR, STE 110 20190 #038-45-2001 L2005
OBG *020
SCHECHTER, Genevieve A. ■ 20191 #025-07-1972 L1993 HEM ON *050 †20
SCHENK, Gregory Simon. 1860 TOWN CENTER DR, STE 150 20190 #035-08-1997 L2005
U *100 †95
SCHULER, Thomas Conrad. 1831 WIEHLE AVE, FL 2 20190 #017-20-1986 L1992 OSS *020 †40
SCHWARTZ, Anne Catherine. 1850 TOWN CENTER PKWY 20190 #036-05-1980 L1984
OPH *020 †35
SCHWEITZER, George Wm. 1850 TOWN CENTER PKWY, EMERGENCY DEPARTMENT 20190
#036-05-1973 L1976 EM GS *020 †16
SCOTT, Hope Taylor. 1830 TOWN CENTER DR, STE 205 20190 #010-01-1985 L1989
PD *020 †55
SEBASTIEN, Theodore S. 1800 TOWN CENTER DR, STE 415 20190 #067-01-1989 L1998
D *020 †15 ‡
SETHI, Malti. 1850 TOWN CENTER PKWY 20190 #495-41-1981 L1989 PTH *020 †50
SHAH, Meliha Hassan. 1850A TOWN CENTER PKWY, INTERNAL MEDICINE 20190
#051-01-1996 L1999 IM *020 †20
SHARARA, Fady Ihsan. 11150 SUNSET HILLS RD, STE 100 20190 #605-01-1986 L1998
OBG REN *020 †30
SHAW, Karla Smael. ■ 20191 #660-03-1962 L1967 P *074
SHEBARO, Issam Mahmoud. 11445 SUNSET HILLS RD 20190 #605-01-1982 L1990
OBG *020 †30
SHOR, Robert Alan. 1860 TOWN CENTER DR, STE 120 20190 #045-04-1982 L1989
CD IM *020 †20
SHOR, Samuel Mark. 1860 TOWN CENTER DR, STE 230 20190 #045-01-1982 L1984
IM *020 †20
SHUKLA, Padma Kant. 1860 TOWN CENTER DR # 210, PADMA K SHUKLA MD FACC 20190
#495-14-1976 L1985 CD IM *020 †20 ‡
SHUKLA, Sima. 1860 TOWN CENTER DR, STE 210 20190 #495-49-1988 L2000 IM *020 †20
SIA KIAN, Bing B. ■ 20194 #748-11-1965 L1975 ADL GP *071
SIGAL, Robert Keith. 1825 SAMUEL MORSE DR, AUSTIN WESTON CTR 20190
#041-02-1985 L1994 PS *020 †85,65
SIMON, Lawrence K. 1850 TOWN CENTER PKWY, EMERGENCY DEPARTMENT 20190
#011-02-1979 L1988 EM IM *020 †16
SIMSARIAN, James Parsons. 1830 TOWN CENTER DR 20190 #035-01-1966 L1973 N *020 †75
SINDHWANI, Sunanda Arora. 1850A TOWN CENTER PKWY, INTERNAL MEDICINE 20190
#495-69-1991 L2004 IM *020 †20
SIVO, Judit. 1850 TOWN CENTER PKWY 20190 #473-01-1977 L1996 PD *020 †55
SMOKVINA, Drago. 1800 TOWN CENTER DR, STE 212 20190 #957-01-1961 L1973
ORS PM *071
SOHAL, Darshan S. 11445 SUNSET HILLS RD 20190 #965-01-1985 L1994 IM *020 †20
SPARKS-JENET, Tammy Ruth. 1850 TOWN CENTER PKWY, ASSOCIATES PA 20190
#010-01-1993 L1993 AN *020 †05
SPEYER, Denita Faye. 1850 TOWN CENTER PKWY 20190 #005-12-1986 L1990 OBG *020 †30
SPITZER, Roger Earl. ■ 20191 #010-03-1962 L2000 NEP PD *050 †55
STEC, Heather Maria. 12040 SOUTH LAKES DR, STE 190 20191 #041-02-2001 L2001
FM *020 †18
STOKES, Richard L. 1830 TOWN CENTER DR # 207 20190 #010-03-1969 L1977 OBG *020 †30
STRASSBURGER, Terri Lynne. 12007 SUNRISE VALLEY DR, STE 120 20191
#023-01-1990 L1997 N *020 †20
SUBACH, Brian Robert. 1831 WIEHLE AVE, FL 2 20190 #025-01-1993 L2003 NS *020 †25
SUSCO, Michelle Skretny. 1830 TOWN CENTER DR, STE 205 20190 #035-06-1991 L1994
PD *020 †55
TAHERNIA, Amir Cyrus. ■ 20190 #517-01-1956 L1973 PDC PD *071 †55 ‡
TAWEEL, Fred Fadel. 1850A TOWN CENTER PKWY, INTERNAL MEDICINE 20190
#051-04-1988 L1991 IM *020 †20
TAYLOR, Erica Dianne. ■ 20191 #036-07-2006 L2006 ORS *012
TEKRONY, Mark Christopher. 1830 TOWN CENTER DR 20190 #033-06-1999 L2000 N *020 †75
THAL, Raymond. 1860 TOWN CENTER DR, STE 300 20190 #016-43-1984 L1988
ORS OSM *020 †40
THURSTON, Candace. 1850 TOWN CENTER PKWY 20190 #008-01-1979 L1983 OBG *020 †30
TITUS, Charles Cameron. 1810 MICHAEL FARADAY DR, NO 204 20190 #038-06-1960 L1980
P *020 †75
TORRENS, James Leo. 1850 TOWN CENTER PKWY, ASSOCIATES PA 20190
#010-02-1979 L1980 AN *020 †05 ‡
TRAD, Karim Sami. 1800 TOWN CENTER DR, STE 310 20190 #045-01-1986 L2006 GS *020 †85
TRAN, Nathan Ngo. 12110 SUNSET HILLS RD, STE LL20 20190 #051-04-2002 L2002
FM *020 †18
TREMOLS, Guillermo A. 1712 CLUBHOUSE RD, STE 101 20190 #847-10-1965 L1969
PD ADL *020
TRINIDAD, Juan. 1830 TOWN CENTER DR, STE 310 20190 #132-01-1959 L1967 GS OM *020
TURGEON, Daniel Gilles. 1800 TOWN CENTER DR, STE 312 20190 #010-02-1980 L1984
GS VS *020 †85
VALENTI, John Philip. 1850A TOWN CENTER PKWY, INTERNAL MEDICINE 20190
#010-02-1991 L1993 IM *020 †20
VALLE, Emil Frank. 11440 COMMERCE PARK DR, STE LL4 20191 #035-08-1994 L1998
GE *020 †20
VAN BUREN, John Miller. ■ 20190 #035-01-1947 L1954 NS *072 †25
VASILIADIS, Mark Emanuel. 12040 S LAKES DR, STE 190 20191 #051-01-1991 L1993
PD *020 †20
VASUDEVAN, Srinivasan. 1850 TOWN CENTER PKWY 20190 #495-45-1970 L1992
PUD CCM *020 †20
VICKERS, Mark Douglas. 1850 TOWN CENTER DR, STE 314 20190 #035-06-1986 L1987
IM *020 †20

WALKER, Thomas Mudd. 1850A TOWN CENTER PKWY, STE 400 20190 #010-02-1972 L1974
ORS *071 †40
WARD, Edward Duffy. 11445 SUNSET HILLS RD, KAISER-RESTON CENTER 20190
#051-04-1980 L1983 IM *020 †20
WATKIN, Terry. 12007 SUNRISE VALLEY DR, STE 120 20191 #165-01-1976 L1987
N CHN *020 †55,75
WEIR, Scott David. ■ 20190 #010-01-1995 L1996 EM *020 †16
WESTON, George Weedon. 1825 SAMUEL MORSE DR, AUSTIN WESTON CTR 20190
#001-06-1981 L1986 PS *020 †65
WILSON, Reina. 1830 TOWN CENTER DR # 101, RESTON FAM PRACT 20190
#748-10-1966 L1972 FM *020
WILSON, Robt Whiting, Jr. 1830 TOWN CENTER DR, STE 101 20190 #010-03-1974 L1980
FM *020 †18
WIN, Ommar. 11445 SUNSET HILLS RD 20190 #748-10-1989 L1996 IM *020 †20
WOLKE, Anita Marsha. 11440 COMMERCE PARK DR, STE LL4 20191 #045-01-1978 L1986
GE *020 †20
WORDEN, Jack L. ■ 20191 #005-16-1962 L1975 FM *071 †18
YALISOVE, Barbara Lee. 11445 SUNSET HILLS RD, KAISER PERMANENTE 20190
#010-01-1987 L1989 D *020 †15
YOUK, John Suk. 12330 PINECREST RD, FOX MILL FAM PRACT STE 250 20191
#051-01-2001 L2001 FM *020 †18
YOUNG, Delosa Anthony. 11445 SUNSET HILLS RD 20190 #021-05-1962 L1967 PD *020 †55
ZENZANO, Tatiana Adele. 11445 SUNSET HILLS RD 20190 #041-15-1999 L2004 PD *020 †55
ZHOU, Steven Kairong. 11693 N SHORE DR APT 22C 20190 #243-16-1982 *100
ZOLKIWSKY, Walter Richard. 1850 TOWN CENTER PKWY, RESTON HOSP CTR 20190
#649-14-1971 L1975 *030

RICE – PRINCE EDWARD

TAYLOR, Charles Dennis. ■ 23966 #051-04-1978 L1984 U *020 †95

RICHLANDS – TAZEWELL

ANSELMI, Kenneth Edward. 2949 FRONT ST 24641 #041-09-1973 L1977 OPH *071 †35
CHAVEZ, Rolando M. 2951 FRONT ST, CLINCH VALLEY UROLOGY 24641 #748-01-1966 L1979
U *020
CLAUSTRO, Daisy Senen. 2949 FRONT ST, DEPT OF ANESTHESIA 24641 #748-01-1971 L1983
AN *020
CLAUSTRO, Joseph Carino. 1 CLINIC DR, BOX CPI 24641 #748-01-1971 L1983 GS *020 †85
CLAUSTRO, Ludgerio Zabala. 2949 FRONT ST 24641 #748-01-1966 L1974 FM *020 †18
ERYILMAZ, Nurettin. PO BOX 1556 24641 #902-03-1955 L1973 R *020 †80
GUANLAO, Rolando A. 215 PLANTATION DR 24641 #748-08-1964 L1979 GS *020
HALEY, Frederick Lee. PO BOX CVPI, CLINCH VALLEY PHYS INC 24641 #047-05-1975 L2005
CD IM *020 †20
HILL, Kenneth Forbes. 2951 FRONT ST, STE 3850 24641 #045-01-1974 L2006 ORS HS *020 †40
HUNTER, William Crawford. PO BOX CVPI, THE CLINIC 24641 #649-14-1980 L1985
GE IM *020 †20
JAVED, Muhammad Ramzan. 2951 FRONT ST, STE 3100 24641 #704-04-1970 L1979
CD IM *020
KABARIA, Ramesh P. 2949 FRONT ST 24641 #495-48-1981 L1985 IM GP *020 †20
KHURI, Emile Isa. CLINIC VALLEY MED PLZ 1400 24641 #605-01-1968 L1975 GS TS *020
KNAPP, Edson Lee. 2949 FRONT ST, CLINCH VALLEY MEDICAL CENT 24641
#011-04-1997 L2005 DR *020 †80
KNAPP, Renda Kay. 2951 FRONT ST, STE 2900 24641 #011-04-1996 L2005 OBG *020 †30 ‡
LATIF, Azhar. 2951 FRONT ST STE 3100 24641 #704-01-1990 L2000 PD *020 †55
LUMBA, Ellen Grace N. ■ 24641 #748-01-1965 PM *100
MC VEY, James Hawver. 3150 CLINCH ST 24641 #051-01-1957 L1957 GP OS *071
MITCHELL, Larry Gilmer. 1 CLINIC DR, BOX CVPI 24641 #051-01-1980 L1981 FM *020 †18 ‡
MOORE, Ernest Eugene. 3150 CLINCH ST 24641 #023-01-1958 L1962 FM *071 †18
MOTOS, Ramon A. PO BOX 900 24641 #748-08-1966 L1974 FM *020 †18
MULLINS, Dowell E, Jr. PO BOX CVPI, CLINCH VALLEY PHYS INC 24641 #025-07-1989 L1993
OBG *020
NAGARAJA, Thimmojirao. 1 CLINIC DR, P O BOX CVPI 24641 #495-09-1970 L1988
OBG *020 †30
NIKAHN, Yaghoub. 2951 FRONT ST STE 1000, CLINC VALLEY PULMONARY 24641
#517-10-1987 L2004 IM *020 †20
ODUNTAN, Olusola. 3150 CLINCH ST, CLINCH PROFESSIONAL PHYSIC 24641
#690-01-1990 L2006 TS *100 †85,90
PARK, In Young. 2951 FRONT ST, CVMP STE 1600 24641 #583-02-1975 L1978 NEP IM *020 †20
PATEL, Binita. PO BOX CVPI, 1 CLINIC DR - CLAYPOOL 24641 #495-23-1977 L1981 PD *020
PATEL, Mahesh Babulal. 1246 CRESSWOOD DR 24641 #495-76-1980 L1984 IM *020
PATEL, Mina Meenaben D. PO BOX 1905 24641 #495-23-1976 L1982 P PTH *020 †75
PATEL, Mrugendra R. 2951 FRONT ST, STE 2400 24641 #495-89-1978 L1987 N P *020 †75
PATEL, Tushar Gordhanbhai. 3150 CLINCH ST STE 106 24641 #495-76-1981 L1985 IM *020 †20
PERALTA, Antonio M. 2949 FRONT ST 24641 #748-08-1966 L1979 FM IM *020
PILLAI, Madhavan V. 2951 FRONT ST, STE 1200 24641 #495-31-1966 L1980 ON HEM *020 †20
PIRIZ, Jose M. PO BOX CVPI, CLAYPOOL HILL 24641 #308-04-1988 L1996 CD *020 †20
PIRIZ, Toeya. PO BOX CVPI, 1 CLINIC DR 24641 #308-04-1988 L1996 IM *020
PRESNELL, Timothy Andrew. 1 CLINIC DR, P O BOX CVP1 24641 #036-01-1980 L1984
GYN *020 †30
REALICA, Buenaventura S. 200 WASHINGTON SQ 24641 #748-02-1936 L1976 EM IM *071
SAHYOUNI, Jamal I. 2949 FRONT ST 24641 #875-02-1983 L1991 IM *020 †20
SCHRADER, Guillermo J. 2949 FRONT ST 24641 #264-04-1953 L1969 GS TS *075
SCOTT, Howard Carlisle. 2949 FRONT ST 24641 #004-01-1953 L1957 FM U *071 †18
SHAW, Leon Richard. 2951 FRONT ST STE 36 24641 #836-01-1967 L2003 AN *020 †05
SHEIKH, Salman Saeed. 2951 FRONT ST, STE 1000 24641 #704-01-1995 L2004 PCC *020 †20
SHOOK, Daniel R. 2951 FRONT ST, STE 2900 24641 #010-02-1991 L1993 DR OS *020
SHOUKRY, Sherif Michail. 2949 FRONT ST, HHCV-ER 24641 #915-02-1980 L1990
IM EM *020 †20
STEFANINI, Mario. 2949 FRONT ST 24641 #561-17-1939 L1979 HO NM *020 †50 ‡
THOMSON, Roy Varghese. 1 CLINIC DR, THE CLINIC 24641 #495-63-1982 L1992
PD GP *020 †55
TITHA, Ravi Kumar. 3150 CLINCH ST, WASHINGTON SQUARE CLINIC 24641
#495-19-1996 L2003 IM *020 †20

TURJMAN, Dorid Kadri-Al. 2949 FRONT ST 24641 #875-01-1981 L1991 **PTH HMP** *020 †50
WEINACKER, Robert M, III. 2949 FRONT ST, CLINCH VALLEY MEDICAL CTR 24641 #001-02-1981 L1989 **RO LM** *020

RICHMOND – CHESTERFIELD

ABERNATHY, Ted Roger. 8719 FOREST HILL AVE 23235 #051-04-1970 L1970 **PD ADL** *020
ADAMS, Helen Bell. 6439 IRON BRIDGE RD 23234 #036-01-1995 L2006 **FM** *020 †18
ADAMS, Ruma Giantee. 9000 STONY POINT PKWY, VCU MEDICAL CENTER 23235 #919-05-1986 L1991 **FM** *020 †18
ADELAAR, Robert Stephen. 9000 STONY POINT PKWY, MCV 23235 #041-01-1971 L1976 **ORS HS** *071 †40
ADLEMAN, Jennifer Rebecca. ■ 23235 #051-04-2002 L2007 **FP** *012
AHMED, Zeenat Taj. ■ 23236 #495-15-1973 L1981 **GP IM** *020 †05
AHUJA, Rahul. ■ 23235 #305-01-2000 L2001 **IM** *100
AISENBERG, Laura Gray. 2500 POCOSHOCK PL, STE 104 23235 #051-04-2002 L2002 **FM** *020 †18
AKBAR, Faiza Salman. 2500 POCOSHOCK PL 23235 #704-09-1999 L2004 **FM** *100 †18
ALBERT, Moses Abey. 10800 MIDLOTHIAN TPKE, STE 265 23235 #051-04-1982 L1983 **AN PD** *030 †55,05 ‡
ALI, Muhammad Ashraf. ■ 23236 #704-01-1958 L1973 **PTH** *020 †50
ALLEN, Robert William. 9000 STONY POINT PKWY, MCV 23235 #051-04-1962 L1964 **PM** *020 †60
ALTER, Matthew Evan. 1051 JOHNSTON WILLIS DR, STE 200 23235 #035-06-1993 L1998 **GS** *020 †85
ANDERSON, James Corr. 2500 POCOSHOCK PL, WESTERFIELD FAM PRACTICE 23235 #051-01-1978 L1979 **FM** *020 †18
ANDERSON, Robert Charles. 10800 MIDLOTHIAN TPKE, #265, COMMWLTH ANESTH ASSOC 23235 #036-05-2000 L2000 **AN** *020 †05
ANDREWS, Jack Preston. ■ 23236 #051-04-1957 L1957 **PD** *071 †55
ANTIGUA-MARTINEZ, Maria T. 9105 STONY POINT PKWY 23235 #748-11-1983 L2002 **AN** *020 †05
ANTONIO, Eugenio V, III. 1401 JOHNSTON WILLIS DR, SURGICAL ASSOC RICHMOND 23235 #748-10-1966 L1976 **GS** *020 †85
ARCHER, John Stanard, Jr. ■ 23235 #051-04-1943 L1943 **OTO** *020
ARMISTEAD, Scott Thos. 1441 JOHNSTON WILLIS DR, PRIMARY HEALTH GROUP, INC 23235 #051-04-1991 L1994 **FM** *020 †18
ARMSTRONG, Michael, Jr. 8700 STONY POINT PKWY, STE 110 23235 #036-07-1989 L1995 **OTO FPS** *020 †45 ‡
ASHWORTH, Joel Thos, Jr. 7410 HULL STREET RD 23235 #051-04-1975 L1978 **FM** *020 †18
ASTRUC, Juan Antonio, Jr. 8700 STONY POINT PKWY, RETINA INST OF VIRGINIA 23235 #051-04-1996 L1996 **OPH** *020 †35
AYRES, John Wise, II. 1400 JOHNSTON WILLIS DR, STE A 23235 #051-04-1969 L1969 **ORS** *020 †40
BAGWELL, Charles Emmet. 9000 STONY POINT PKWY, MCV 23235 #036-05-1976 L1977 **PDS** *020 †85
BAKER, William Powell. 2602 BUFORD RD, RADIOLOGY ASSOCIATES OF 23235 #051-04-1986 L1987 **DR FM** *020 †80
BARNES, Tamera Counts. 1401 JOHNSTON WILLIS DR 23235 #051-04-1989 L1991 **EM** *020 †16
BAROT, Arvinder Kaur. 2500 POCOSHOCK PL, CHESTERFIELD FAMILY PRACTI 23235 #495-43-1979 L2004 **FP** *012
BARRETT, Francis E. ■ 23235 #051-01-1949 L1949 **IM FPG** *071 †20
BATES, Robley Dunglison. 1455 JOHNSTON WILLIS DR 23235 #051-04-1972 L1973 **U** *020 †95
BEAUCHAMP, Ray Alonzo. 2602 BUFORD RD, RADIOLOGY ASSOCIATES OF 23235 #048-02-1981 L1987 **DR** *020 †80
BELTRAN-KEELING, Joyce. 9000 STONY PT PKWY, WOMENS HEALTH CTR 23235 #051-04-1997 L1997 **IM** *020 †20
BENDHEIM, Stephen Howard. 10710 MIDLOTHIAN TPKE, STE 200 23235 #051-04-1989 L1992 **OBG** *020 †30
BENNETT, Audrey Kauffman. ■ 23235 #038-44-2001 L2001 **PTH** *020 †50
BENNETT, Joel Alan. 10800 MIDLOTHIAN TPKE, STE 265 23235 #041-09-1987 L1998 **AN** *020 †05 ‡
BENTLEY, Jack Kitchener. ■ 23236 #051-01-1956 L1958 **R OS** *071 †80
BEORN, Charles Frederick. 1233 MALL DR 23235 #051-04-1967 L1967 **IM** *020
BERGER, Meredith M. 1401 JOHNSTON WILLIS DR, STE 1200 23235 #055-02-1994 L1995 **END** *020 †20
BETTINGER, David Alan. 1051 JOHNSTON WILLIS DR, STE 200 23235 #051-04-1989 L1991 **GS** *020 †85
BINNS, Richard Lawrence. 1051 JOHNSTON WILLIS DR, STE 200 23235 #051-01-1982 L1984 **GS VS** *020 †85
BLAKE, Matthew Hadfield. ■ 23235 #045-01-2006 L2006 **ORS** *012
BLAKEY, Peter Patrick. 8719 FOREST HILL AVE 23235 #050-02-1977 L1980 **PD PSM** *020 †55
BLANCHARD, Lawrence E, III. 10710 MIDLOTHIAN TPKE, STE 401 23235 #028-02-1976 L1979 **D** *020 †15
BLANCHET, Nadia P. 9210 FOREST HILL AVE # B1 23235 #035-19-1981 L1983 **PS OS** *020 †85,65
BLEDOWSKI, Jozef Lech. ■ 23236 #051-04-2006 L2006 **P** *012
BONZON, Teotimo D. ■ 23236 #748-08-1961 L1971 **TS GYN** *075
BOWMAN, David Michael. 10800 MIDLOTHIAN TPKE, STE 127 23235 #021-05-2000 L2000 **OPH** *020 †35
BOWMAN, Wendy S. 1401 JOHNSTON WILLIS DR, STE 5000 23235 #051-04-2002 L2007 **OBG** *020
BRADSHAW, Brian Thomas. 2500 POCOSHOCK PL, STE 103 23235 #051-04-1986 L1988 **IM** *020
BRENGEL, George Richard. 9220 FOREST HILL AVE, STE A1 23235 #035-08-1978 L1979 **IM IMG** *020
BRENNER-VINCENT, Michele. 2602 BUFORD RD, RADIOLOGY ASSOCIATES OF RI 23235 #023-12-1993 L1995 **DR** *020 †80
BRENZIE, Mark Anthony. 8110 MIDLOTHIAN TPKE, PATIENT FIRST MIDLOTHIAN 23235 #305-01-2003 L2003 **N** *100
BROCK, Ellen Louise. 9000 STONY POINT PKWY 23235 #045-01-1981 L1984 **OBG** *020 †30
BROCK, Russell Lee. 8700 STONY POINT PKWY #100, STONY POINT SURG CTR 23235 #051-04-1989 L2003 **AN** *020 †05

BROOCKER, Warren Alan. 10710 MIDLOTHIAN TPKE, STE 200 23235 #041-13-1973 L1976 **OBG** *020 †30 ‡
BROWN, Edwin Merriman. ■ 23235 #050-02-1957 L1969 **PHP** *071 †70
BROWN, James La Velle. 2805 MCRAE RD, STE 1-A 23235 #051-04-1969 L1969 **OPH** *020 †35
BROWN, Patricia A Hoilman. 2410 CHANCELLOR RD, NO CURRENT OFFICE. THE LIS 23235 #050-02-1957 L1969 **P CHP** *020
BUCKLEY, Lenore Margaret. 9000 STONY POINT PKWY, MCV 23235 #035-45-1977 L1993 **RHU IM** *020 †20,55
BURACKER, Gary Keith. 1401 JOHNSTON WILLIS DR 23235 #051-04-1980 L1981 **FM EM** *075 †18
BURKE, Cynthia Anne. 2711 BUFORD RD, # 261 23235 #041-09-1988 L1995 **IM** *020 †20
BURKHARDT, Barry Webster. 1400 JOHNSTON WILLIS DR, STE A 23235 #024-07-1972 L1973 **ORS** *020 †40
BURRIS, Allen Stuart. 1401 JOHNSTON WILLIS DR, STE 1200 23235 #035-09-1981 L1988 **END IM** *020 †20
BUTTERY, Christopher M G. ■ 23235 #917-23-1955 L1956 **PHP FM** *071 †70
BYRNE, Joseph Thos. 8730 STONY POINT PKWY, STE 200 23235 #041-01-1943 L1947 **GP OS** *020
CALDWELL, John Beale H. 9000 STONY POINT PKWY 23235 #023-07-1963 L1970 **OPH** *071 †35
CAMP, Norman Marshall. 3105 STONY POINT RD 23235 #047-06-1966 L1974 **P PYA** *020 †75
CAMPBELL, Margaret R. 8719 FOREST HILL AVE 23235 #041-02-1988 L1990 **PD** *020 †55
CARDEA, John Alexander. 9000 STONY POINT PKWY, MCV 23235 #055-01-1966 L1973 **ORS OAR** *071 †40
CARPENTER, Jeanette Milln. 2500 POCOSHOCK PL 23235 #051-04-2004 L2004 **FM** *020 †18
CERNIGLIA, Frank Raymond. 8700 STONY POINT PKWY, STE 250 23235 #021-05-1982 L2005 **U UP** *020 †95
CHAPLIN, Robt Rogers, Jr. 1441 JOHNSTON WILLIS DR 23235 #051-04-1962 L1962 **FM** *071 †18
CHAUDHARY, Nazir Ahmad. 8133 FOREST HILL AVE 23235 #704-01-1971 L1977 **P** *020
CHO, Kathie Herryung. 9000 STONY POINT PKWY 23235 #051-04-1999 L1999 **IM** *020 †20
CLARK, Andrew Stone. 8700 STONY POINT PKWY 23235 #051-01-1980 L1982 **AN CCM** *020 †20
CLASBEY, Sheila D. 2500 POCOSHOCK PL, STE 103 23235 #051-07-2004 L2004 **IM** *020 †20
CLEMENT, Stephen. 1401 JOHNSTON WILLIS DR, STE 5600 23235 #051-01-1975 L1978 **GE IM** *020 †20
COBLE, Mary Lynn. 10710 MIDLOTHIAN TPKE, TURNPIKE #200 23235 #045-01-1999 L2004 **OBG** *020 †30
COHEN, Matthew Lewis. 2602 BUFORD AVE, RADIOLOGY ASSOCIATES OF RI 23234 #051-01-1998 L1998 **DR VIR** *020 †80
COLL, Jose D. ■ 23234 #051-04-1939 L1939 **OM GS** *071
COST, Christopher Paul. ■ 23235 #038-41-2006 **U** *012
COUTLAKIS, Peter James. 1401 JOHNSTON WILLIS DR, STE 4100 23235 #051-04-1994 L1994 **RHU** *020 †20
CRAGGS, Thos Franklin, III. ■ 23235 #051-04-1975 L1978 **FM** *020 †18
CUNNINGHAM, William Scott. 2602 BUFORD RD, RADIOLOGY ASSOCIATES OF 23235 #051-04-1980 L1982 **DR IM** *020 †80
CUTHBERT, Nathaniel West. 2602 BUFORD RD 23235 #051-04-1984 L1987 **DR** *020 †80
DANIEL, Jerome Madsen. 1441 JOHNSTON WILLIS DR 23235 #051-04-1976 L1977 **FM** *020 †18
DANIEL, John Spencer, III. 1913 HUGUENOT RD, STE 302 23235 #051-04-1981 L1989 **PTH** *020 †50
DAVENPORT, Philip Aaron. 1457 JOHNSTON WILLIS DR, JAMES RIVER NEUROLOGY 23235 #051-04-1985 L1995 **N CN** *020 †75
DAVIS, Jason Michael. 10800 MIDLOTHIAN TPKE, STE 265 23235 #051-01-2001 L2001 **AN** *020 †05
DAVIS, Leslie L. 10710 MIDLOTHIAN TPKE, STE 200 23235 #035-45-1994 L1998 **OBG** *020 †30
DAVIS, Rufus Cole. 201 WADSWORTH DR 23236 #051-01-1990 L2000 **GE** *020 †20
DE BLOIS, Georgean Graham. 1401 JOHNSTON WILLIS DR, JOHNSTON-WILLIS HOSP 23235 #025-07-1980 L1981 **PTH NM** *020 †50
DE GUZMAN, Edson. 1570 EARLY SETTLERS RD, CARDIOLOGY OF VIRGINIA 23235 #748-07-1986 L1998 **CD** *020 †20
DEITRICK, John C. 1051 JOHNSTON WILLIS DR, STE 200 23235 #025-01-1982 L1984 **GS VS** *020 †85
DELISIO, John Paul. 9105 STONY POINT PKWY, VIRGINIA UROLOGY CENTER, 23235 #035-09-1996 L1998 **U** *020 †95
DICKIE, Thomas Andrew. 10710 MIDLOTHIAN TPKE, STE 401 23235 #055-01-1976 L1981 **D** *020 †05,15 ‡
DIEHL, Earl H, Jr. 8700 STONY POINT PKWY 23235 #011-03-1969 L1978 **GE IM** *020 †20
DILLON, Mary Carney. 1401 JOHNSTON WILLIS DR 23235 #041-02-1985 L1992 **AN PAN** *020 †05
DITTO, John Lee, Jr. 8700 STONY POINT PKWY 23235 #028-03-1989 L1998 **OTO NO** *020 †45
DODD, Jeffrey Douglas. 1401 JOHNSTON WILLIS DR 23235 #051-04-1992 L1993 **FM** *020 †18
DOMMISSE, Martha O'Dell. ■ 23235 #051-04-2005 L2005 **FP** *012
DOOLEY, Mark Christopher. 107 WADSWORTH DR 23236 #035-09-1977 L1979 **GE IM** *020 †20
DOOLEY, Robert Kent. 10508 SYDELLE DR 23235 #051-04-1992 L1998 **EM** *020 †16
DORE, James Patrick, Jr. ■ 23235 #021-05-2002 L2002 **PAN** *100 †05
DOTY, Kimberly. 9211 GROUNDHOG DR 23235 #051-04-1991 L1995 **OPH** *020 †35
DUCK, George Bryan. 9105 STONY POINT PKWY 23235 #065-06-1975 L1986 **U** *020 †95
DUNN, Leo James. 9000 STONY POINT PKWY, MCV 23235 #035-01-1956 L1967 **OBG GO** *050 †30
EDELSTEIN, Michael C. 10710 MIDLOTHIAN TPKE, STE 331 23235 #028-02-1984 L1988 **REN** *020 †30
EDMONDSON, John David. 8700 STONY POINT PKWY, STE 250 23235 #051-04-1997 L1997 **GS** *020 †95
EICHLER, Thomas James. 1401 JOHNSTON WILLIS DR 23235 #051-04-1987 L1989 **RO** *020 †20
ELLEN, Joseph Harry. 10710 MIDLOTHIAN TPKE, STE 200 23235 #051-04-1973 L1979 **GYN** *020 †30 ‡
ELLETT, Henry Maxwell. 201 WADSWORTH DR 23235 #051-04-1988 L1989 **GE** *020 †20
EPPS, Stacey Lawrence. 165 WADSWORTH DR 23236 #010-02-1997 L1997 **N** *020 †75
EVANS, Martin Terry. 1051 JOHNSTON WILLIS DR, STE 200 23235 #021-01-1973 L1980 **VS GS** *020 †85
FAROOQI, Shazia Habib. 8110 MIDLOTHIAN TPKE, PATIENT FIRST MIDLOTHIAN 23235 #704-21-2000 L2003 **FM** *020 †18
FELSEN, Ruth Brenda. 1051 JOHNSTON WILLIS DR, STE 200 23235 #024-01-1990 L1996 **GS** *020 †85

■ = Address Information Privacy Protected

FIDLER, Melanie A. 2602 BUFORD RD, RADIOLOGY ASSOCIATES OF 23235 #051-04-1991 L1996 **DR** *020 †80

FOLIACO, Walter. 2500 POCOSHOCK PL 23235 #051-04-1994 L1994 **FM** *020 †18

FOXWORTH, Michael Kenneth. ■ 23235 #045-01-2006 L2006 **PD** *012

FRAKER, Robert Turnley. 9609 JEFFERSON DAVIS HWY, RICHMOND SOUTHSIDE TREATME 23237 #051-04-1975 L1976 **U OS** *020 †95

FRANK, Charles Gilbert. ■ 23236 #010-01-1975 L1990 **NPM PD** *020 †55

FREEMAN, James Robert. ■ 23236 #027-01-2006 L2006 **IM** *012

FREEMAN, Kathleen Hollis. ■ 23236 #027-01-2007 L2007 **IM** *012

FULLER, Richard Westwood. 2602 BUFORD RD, RADIOLOGY ASSOCIATES OF 23235 #051-04-1986 L1991 **DR** *020 †80

GADIWALLA, Seema A Asgar. 9000 STONY POINT PKWY, MCV ASSOCIATED PHYSICIANS 23235 #704-02-1991 L1997 **AN** *020 †20

GARA, Radha K. 2302 WILLIS RD 23237 #496-21-1991 L1997 **AN** *020

GARRETT, Algin Baylor. 9000 STONY POINT PKWY, THE PARK AT STONY POINT 23235 #041-14-1978 L1980 **D PRO** *020 †15

GARRETT, Allen Raye. 2502 ST REGIS DR, DEPT OF ANESTHESIA 23236 #041-13-1989 L1996 **AN** *020 †05

GENTRY, Cary Lofton. 8700 STONY POINT PKWY, STE 270 23235 #051-04-1995 L1995 **CRS** *020 †85,10

GEWANTER, Harry Lewis. 8719 FOREST HILL AVE 23235 #025-07-1976 L1983 **PPR PD** *020 †55

GHAPHERY, James Louis. ■ 23235 #051-04-1960 L1965 **AN** *071 †05

GIORDANO, Anthony M, Jr. 1405 JOHNSTON WILLIS DR, CENTRAL VIRGINIA 23235 #041-09-1976 L1981 **OTO HNS** *020 †45 ‡

GIREVENDULIS, Alexander K. 2602 BUFORD RD, RADIOLOGY ASSOCIATES OF 23235 #418-01-1972 L1977 **DR RNR** *020 †80

GIRERD, Philippe Henri. 9000 STONY POINT PKWY 23235 #033-05-1983 L1991 **OBG** *020 †30

GONZALEZ, Pablo Miguel. 1401 JOHNSTON WILLIS DR 23235 #132-02-1987 L1998 **HO** *020 †20

GOSPODNETIC, Marijan. 1401 JOHNSTON WILLIS DR, STE 5000 23235 #065-09-1971 L1978 **OBG** *020

GOULMAMINE, Redouane. ■ 23234 #125-01-1988 L2007 **PM** *020 ‡

GRAHAM, Sam D. 9105 STONY POINT PKWY 23235 #051-01-1946 L1946 **U** *071 †95

GREENFIELD, Scott Reid. 8110 MIDLOTHIAN TPKE, PATIENT FIRST MIDLOTHIAN 23235 #035-15-1980 L1983 **FM** *020 †18

GROSSMAN, Eric Corey. 9327 MIDLOTHIAN TPKE, STE 2C 23235 #051-07-2002 L2002 **AN** *020 †05

GRUEMER, Hanns-Dieter. ■ 23235 #407-23-1949 **PCH** *071

GUIRGUIS, Habib Habib. ■ 23236 #330-04-1964 L1971 **EM OS** *071

HA, Jonathan David. ■ 23235 #051-04-2006 L2006 **DR** *012

HADFIELD, Mark Halverson. 9210 ARBORETUM PKWY, STE 260 23236 #045-01-2000 L2000 **ORS** *020

HAQUE, Sheikh M.. 2500 POCOSHOCK PL, STE # 23235 #160-03-1984 L2005 **GS** *100

HARKRADER, Edward Rex. 1401 JOHNSTON WILLIS DR 23235 #051-04-1992 L1993 **FM** *020 †18

HARRISON, Jacquelin M. 1401 JOHNSTON WILLIS DR 23235 #051-01-1946 L1946 **GS OS** *071 †85

HARTENBERG, Michael A. 2602 BUFORD RD, RADIOLOGY ASSOCIATES OF 23235 #024-07-1976 L1980 **DR PDR** *020 †80

HAVERTY, Howard Onno, Jr. 8700 STONY POINT PKWY 23235 #051-07-1985 L1990 **GE IM** *020 †20

HAYDEN, George Douglas. 9000 STONY POINT PKWY, MCV 23235 #051-04-1945 L1950 **OTO** *071 †45

HAYES, Shelly Bowers. ■ 23235 #041-13-2002 L2007 **RO** *100

HELLER, Daniel Seth. 9240 STONY CREST CIR # 9 23235 #025-12-2003 L2007 **PMM** *012

HENDEL, Oscar Ferdinand. 1401 JOHNSTON WILLIS DR 23235 #051-01-1992 L1996 **AN** *020 †05

HENNESSEY, John Jos, IV. 1401 JOHNSTON WILLIS DR, THE ATRIUM STE 5300 23235 #051-04-1978 L1979 **N** *020 †75

HEPPNER, Gail Elizabeth. 10800 MIDLOTHIAN TPKE, STE 265 23235 #001-06-1993 L2005 **AN** *020 †05

HEYNER, Gregory James. 8133 FOREST HILL AVE 23235 #025-01-1963 L1969 **OPH** *071 †35

HICKMAN, Clifton Claude. 161 WADSWORTH DR 23236 #016-11-1976 L1981 **OTO** *020 †45

HINNANT, Ivan Darryl. 1401 JOHNSTON WILLIS DR, PHYSICAL MEDICINE & REHABD 23235 #010-03-1996 L1997 **PM** *020 †60

HITE, Paul David. 1401 JOHNSTON WILLIS DR 23235 #051-04-1981 L1984 **AN** *020 †05

HOFFMAN, Richard Henry. 2500 POCOSHOCK PL 23235 #051-04-1982 L1986 **FM** *020 †18

HOGGE, Jacquelyn Pointer. 2602 BUFORD RD, RADIOLOGY ASSOC. OF RICHMO 23235 #051-01-1990 L1992 **DR** *020 †80

HOLTHAUS, Lowrey Hunter. 2602 BUFORD RD, RADIOLOGY ASSOCIATES OF RI 23235 #051-04-1986 L1989 **DR** *020 †80

HORST, Anne Hedges. 2830 NEWQUAY LN 23236 #051-01-1996 L1996 **P** *020 †75

HUFF, Lawrence Richard, Jr. ■ 23235 #031-01-2007 L2007 **ORS** *012

HULL, Jeffrey Eaton. 2602 BUFORD RD, RADIOLOGY ASSOC. OF RICHMO 23235 #036-07-1984 L1993 **DR** *020 †80

HURT, Waverly Glenn. 1467 JOHNSTON WILLIS DR, CENTRAL VIRGINIA GYNE/ONCO 23235 #051-04-1964 L1964 **OBG** *020 †30

HUSSEINI, Abla Malek. 3000 STONY POINT RD, UNIT 2 23235 #605-01-1986 L2004 **FM PD** *020 †18

HYDE, Mark P. 10710 MIDLOTHIAN TPKE, STE 200 23235 #048-14-1989 L1993 **OBG** *020 †30

HYSLOP, John Wesley. 1401 JOHNSTON WILLIS DR, THE ATRIUM STE 1100 23235 #021-01-1977 L1980 **GS VS** *020 †85

IUORNO, Maria. 1401 JOHNSTON WILLIS DR, STE 1200 THE ATRIUM 23235 #016-06-1994 L1996 **END** *020 †20

JAIN, Anand. ■ 23236 #041-15-2008 *012

JAIRATH, Sanjeev Kumar. 8700 STONY POINT PKWY 23235 #495-73-1978 L1991 **GE IM** *020 †20

JAMES, Joseph Alexander. 1441 JOHNSTON WILLIS DR 23235 #035-46-1988 L1997 **IMG** *020 †20

JAMES, Walter Ennis. ■ 23235 #045-01-2007 L2007 **IM** *012

JARRELL, Shelby Edward. ■ 23236 #051-04-2004 L2005 **ORS** *012

JELLISON, Stephanie Eilee. ■ 23235 #051-01-2008 *012

JESSEE, Edgar Forrest, Jr. 1401 JOHNSTON WILLIS DR, STE 4100 23235 #051-04-1975 L1976 **RHU IM** *020 †20

JIRANEK, William Arthur. 9000 STONY POINT PKWY, DEPARTMENT OF ORTHOPAEDIC 23235 #051-01-1985 L1992 **ORS** *020 †40

JOHNS, Mark Edward. 1570 EARLY SETTLERS RD 23235 #051-04-1987 L1988 **CD** *020 †20

JOHNSON, Clyde Luther, Jr. 1051 JOHNSTON WILLIS DR, STE 200 23235 #010-02-1989 L1999 **TS** *020 †85

JOHNSON, Vanessa Oliver. 9211 BURGE AVE 23237 #051-04-1983 **FM OM** *020 ‡

JOHNSTON, Charles L, Jr. ■ 23235 #041-01-1953 L1965 **HEM CLP** *071

JONES, Christopher. 8110 MIDLOTHIAN TPKE, PATIENT FIRST MIDLOTHIAN 23235 #036-08-1989 L1993 **FM** *030 †18

JONES, George Robt. ■ 23235 #051-04-1945 L1946 **OBG** *071 †30

JONES, Mark Mcclellan. 1400 JOHNSTON WILLIS DR, STE A 23235 #051-04-1987 L1989 **ORS** *020 †40

KAMILAKIS, Peter Nikias. 10800 MIDLOTHIAN TPKE, STE 265 23235 #051-04-1999 L2001 **AN** *020 †05

KAZI, Syed S. ■ 23236 #495-21-1960 L1972 **FM EM** *020

KEATE, Ray Frederick. 8700 STONY POINT PKWY 23235 #021-01-1979 L2002 **GE IM** *020 †20

KHOKHAR, Manmohan Singh. 1427 JOHNSTON WILLIS DR 23235 #495-43-1981 L1986 **PM** *020 †60

KIM, David. 10800 MIDLOTHIAN TPKE, STE 265 23235 #051-04-1992 L1992 **AN** *020

KIM, Joseph Sang. 9210 ARBORETUM PKWY, STE 260 23236 #051-01-2001 L2008 **ORS** *020

KIRBY, Mathis Ann. 1401 JOHNSTON WILLIS DR 23235 #035-01-1981 L1986 **AN** *020 †05

KUMAR, Puneet. 8700 STONY POINT PKWY 23235 #495-73-1983 L2003 **IM GE** *020 †20

KUM-NJI, Philip. ■ 23234 #217-01-1977 L2000 **PD** *020 †55

KUNO, Helen Lee. 1401 JOHNSTON WILLIS DR, STE 1200 23235 #051-04-1988 L1989 **END IM** *030 †20

KUPERMINC, Denise Sasson. 9301 HULL STREET RD 23236 #132-01-1959 L1969 **PD** *071

KUTA, Arnold John. 2602 BUFORD RD, RADIOLOGY ASSOC OF RICHMON 23235 #018-03-1979 L1986 **RNR DR** *020,80

LACKNER, Flora Elisabeth. 1401 JOHNSTON WILLIS DR, STE 5000 23235 #051-04-2003 L2003 **OBG** *020

LADOCSI, Julie Humphrey. 1401 JOHNSTON WILLIS DR, STE 5000 23235 #051-04-1992 L1997 **OBG** *020 †20

LEAVITT, Shane Colby. ■ 23235 #031-01-2003 L2004 **ORS** *012

LEE, Alfred. 8700 STONY POINT PKWY 23235 #035-19-1980 L1981 **GE IM** *020 †20

LESLIE, Evan Joel. 1475 JOHNSTON WILLIS DR, STE 1475 23235 #011-02-1978 L1980 **OPH** *020 †35

LESZCZYSZYN, David John. 2529 PROFESSIONAL RD, BOX 980518 23235 #017-20-1994 L1994 **N CHN** *020 †75

LEVIN, Joshua Howard. ■ 23235 #051-04-2003 L2007 **PMM** *012

LI, Yih-Chang. 8424 SHERWOOD FOREST DR 23237 #021-06-2000 L2000 **AN** *100 †05

LINDSAY, Brenna Lynette. 1401 JOHNSTON WILLIS DR 23235 #023-01-1990 L1992 **IM** *020 †05

LONG, Georganne Wells. 1401 JOHNSTON WILLIS DR, STE 5000 23235 #001-02-1984 L1988 **OBG** *020 †30

LOVE, Virginia M. ■ 23234 #010-03-1950 L1955 **P** *071

LYNAM, Gregory Thomas. 8700 STONY POINT PKWY, STE 230 23235 #051-04-1998 L1998 **PS** *020 †65

LYONS, Christopher D. 223 WADSWORTH DR 23236 #051-04-1998 L1998 **GE** *020 †20

MAC DOUGAL, Lynn Ellen. 2602 BUFORD RD, RADIOLOGY ASSOCIATES OF RI 23235 #038-40-1990 L2005 **DR** *020 †80

MAC MILLAN, Ralph Victor. ■ 23235 #065-01-1960 L1978 **FM** *071

MALIK, Afshan Sahar. 3002 STONY POINT RD, STE A 23235 #704-16-1989 L2004 **FM** *100 †18

MANETAS, Michael Stephen. 8700 STONY POINT PKWY 23235 #051-04-1999 L1999 **GE** *020 †20

MANSILLA, Olivia Ana K. 235 WADSWORTH DR 23236 #429-01-1989 L2000 **IMG IM** *020 †20

MARGARON, Franklin Charle. ■ 23236 #032-01-2005 L2005 **GS** *012

MARTIN, George Wm. 2602 BUFORD RD, RADIOLOGY ASSOCIATES OF 23235 #051-04-1976 L1978 **DR OS** *020 †80

MATHE, Susanna A. 165 WADSWORTH DR 23236 #473-01-1983 L1985 **N** *020 †75

MATHEWSON, Wayne. 6439 IRON BRIDGE RD 23234 #051-04-1993 L1994 **FM** *020 †18

MATTINGLY, Thomas Kenneth. 10710 MIDLOTHIAN TPKE, STE 138 23235 #048-13-1998 L2004 **NS** *020

MAY, David Alan. 2602 BUFORD RD, RADIOLOGY ASSOCIATES 23235 #036-01-1988 L1998 **DR** *020 †80

MC CLERKIN, Dwayne Eric. ■ 23237 #045-01-2003 L2004 **ACA** *012

MC COOMER, Norman Eugene. ■ 23235 #020-12-2001 L2002 **PMM** *012 †60

MC CORMICK, Craig Daniel. 2602 BUFORD RD, RADIOLOGY ASSOCIATES OF 23235 #051-04-1997 L1997 **DR** *020 †80

MC GEE, Daniel Edward. 1401 JOHNSTON WILLIS DR, MEDICAL STAFF OFFICE 23235 #016-11-2003 L2006 **EM** *100 †16

MC KENZIE, Judith Jill. 1441 JOHNSTON WILLIS DR 23235 #011-02-1993 L2003 **IM** *020 †20

MC LAUGHLIN, Joseph Danl. 9327 MIDLOTHIAN TPKE, ASSOCIATES, P.C., STE 2-C 23236 #041-09-1990 L1994 **AN** *020 †05

MC LEAN, Christianne Pari. ■ 23235 #010-01-2005 L2005 **IM** *012

MC LEOD, David Allen. 9210 FOREST HILL AVE # B3 23235 #036-05-1985 L1987 **IM** *020 †20

MC NEER, Keith Wilson. 8700 STONY POINT PKWY, STE 220 23235 #051-04-1959 L1959 **PO** *020 †35

MEEKS, Thomas George. 161 WADSWORTH DR 23236 #038-40-1973 L1979 **OTO** *020 †45

MEUSSLING, Maria Michelle. 10710 MIDLOTHIAN TPKE, STE 200 23235 #051-01-2004 L2004 **OBG** *012

MIDDLETON, Paul. 1401 JOHNSTON WILLIS DR, STE 4100 23235 #051-04-1955 L1955 **OTO** *071 †45

MILLER, Grayson B, Jr. ■ 23235 #051-04-1969 L1969 **PHP ID** *030 †20

MILLER, James Wesley. 1447 JOHNSTON WILLIS DR 23235 #051-01-1977 L1979 **FM FSM** *020 †18 ‡

MITCHELL, Ellen Angle. 2500 POCOSHOCK PL 23235 #048-12-1983 L1988 **IM FM** *020 †20

MITCHELL, Martha E. 1401 JOHNSTON WILLIS DR 23235 #051-01-1990 L1997 **AN** *020 †05

MITCHELL, Patrick W. 2500 POCOSHOCK PL, STE 104 23235 #048-12-1988 L1988 **FM** *020 †18

MONAHAN, Mark Brown. 9105 STONY POINT PKWY, VIRGINIA UROLOGY CENTER 23235 #051-04-1995 L2000 **U** *020 †95

MONTGOMERY, Brett Langdon. ■ 23235 #051-07-2007 L2007 **IM** *012

MONTGOMERY, Margaret T. 1401 JOHNSTON WILLIS DR 23235 #051-04-1986 L1988 **AN** *020 †05

MORGAN, Carlisle Lee. 2602 BUFORD RD, RADIOLOGY ASSOCIATES OF 23235 #011-02-1973 L1979 **DR** *020 †80

MULLINS, Maurice Francis. 2602 BUFORD RD, RADIOLOGY ASSOC. OF RICHMO 23235 #539-02-1964 L1977 **DR NR** *071 †80

MULREANY, Patricia Rojko. 8719 FOREST HILL AVE 23235 #051-04-1984 L1987 **PD** *020 †55

NEDEFF, David Daniel. 1400 JOHNSTON WILLIS DR, STE A 23235 #055-01-1995 L2001 ORS *020 †40

NELSON, Bobby Wayne. 9200 FOREST HILL AVE, STE C2 23235 #051-04-1967 L1967 P *020 †75

NELSON, David Walter. 8110 MIDLOTHIAN TPKE, PATIENT FIRST MIDLOTHIAN 23235 #024-05-1982 L1989 FM *020 †18

NEWELL, Christopher Lee. 2500 POCOSHOCK PL, CHESTERFIELD FAMILY PRACTI 23235 #026-04-1999 L1999 AN *012 †18

NOTTINGHAM, Maurice, Jr. 1401 JOHNSTON WILLIS DR, # 5500 23235 #051-04-1960 L1960 CD IM *071

NUNLEY, Julia Annriley. 9000 STONY POINT PKWY, STONY POINT 2ND FLOOR 23235 #038-06-1983 L1984 D IM *020 †20,15 ‡

O'KEEFE, John Stewart. 8700 STONY POINT PKWY, STE 150 23235 #051-01-1998 L1998 OPH *020 †35

OLDER, Robert Alan. 9105 STONY POINT PKWY, VIRGINIA UROLOGY CENTER 23235 #036-07-1968 L1969 R *020 †80

O'SHANICK, Gregory John. 10710 MIDLOTHIAN TPKE, STE 125 23235 #048-02-1977 L1984 NUP OS *020 †75

OUTEN, Carl Dexter. 605 N COURTHOUSE RD, STE 101 23236 #051-04-1978 L1979 OPH *020 †35

OWEN, John Thos. 2500 POCOSHOCK PL, STE 104 23235 #051-04-1972 L1973 FM *020 †18

PAK, Yong Kun. ■ 23235 #583-01-1947 L1968 AN *075

PALOMBO, David Lee. 9105 STONY POINT PKWY, VIRGINIA UROLOGY CENTER 23235 #051-04-1994 L1995 AN *020 †05

PANTEN, Robert Richard, Jr. 1401 JOHNSTON WILLIS DR 23235 #051-04-1996 L1996 AN *020 †05

PARKER, Joel Floyd. 2602 BUFORD RD, OF RICHMOND 23235 #012-01-1969 L1986 DR *020 †80

PARR, Emily Luscher. 9711 KENDELWICK DR 23236 #051-04-1969 L1969 PD ADL *020 †55

PARTRIDGE, John Robt. 10710 MIDLOTHIAN TPKE, STE 200 23235 #036-01-1972 L1972 OBG *020 †30

PAYNE, Matthew William. 2500 POCOSHOCK PL, CHESTERFIELD FAMILY PRACTI 23235 #051-04-2004 L2004 FM *020 †18

PENBERTHY, David Rowley. 1401 JOHNSTON WILLIS DR, VIRGINIA RADIATION ONCOLOG 23235 #051-04-1994 L1995 RO *020 †80

PENCZAK, Robert Steven. ■ 23235 #041-07-1992 L1998 D *074 †15

PERDUE, Elizabeth Andrach. ■ 23237 #051-04-2006 L2006 EM *012

PERLMAN, Michael Romney. 161 WADSWORTH DR 23236 #019-02-1979 L1985 OTO *020 †45

PETRAS, Christodoulos M. 105 TWINRIDGE LN 23235 #045-01-1977 L1979 OPH PO *020 †35

PIEDRA, Joaquin Herculano. ■ 23236 #275-01-1944 L1963 IM GE *071

PIETERS, Philip C. 2602 BUFORD RD, RADIOLOGY ASSOC OF RICHMON 23235 #023-01-1988 L1994 DR *020 †80

PILLSBURY, Susan L. 2500 POCOSHOCK PL, STE 302 23235 #051-04-1977 L1980 PD *020

POLIQUIN, James R. 1401 JOHNSTON WILLIS DR, STE 5100 23235 #051-04-1979 L1981 GS VS *020 †85 ‡

POPE, Benjamin Wood. 1401 JOHNSTON WILLIS DR 23235 #067-01-1967 L1984 AN *020 †05

PRICE, Robert Lee. ■ 23235 #051-01-1946 L1946 PHP GPM *071 †70

PRINCE, Kelley Annett. 2500 POCOSHOCK PL 23235 #051-04-2005 L2005 FP *012

PROSSER, Ingrid Annemarie. 10710 MIDLOTHIAN TPKE, STE 200 23235 #024-05-1987 L1991 OBG *020 †30

QUTUBUDDIN, Abu Ali. 2802 STEMWELL LN 23236 #160-01-1978 L1998 PM *020

RACZ, Tracey Hickabee. ■ 23236 #036-01-2000 L2000 FM *020 †18 ‡

RADDIN, Ryan Stacer. ■ 23236 #051-04-2006 L2006 IM *012

RAMNANI, Dharamdas M. 9105 STONY POINT PKWY 23235 #495-23-1989 L1999 PTH *020 †50

RAMSEY, Edward J. 107 WADSWORTH DR 23236 #051-04-1973 L1979 GE *020 †20

RAMSEY, Tiffany Shannon. 1401 JOHNSTON WILLIS DR, STE 5000 23235 #051-04-1997 L2001 OBG *020 †30

RAWLES, John Gordon, Jr. 1400 JOHNSTON WILLIS DR 23235 #051-01-1976 L1978 HS ORS *020 †40

REBMAN, Jeffrey Allen. 1401 JOHNSTON WILLIS DR, # 4500 23235 #051-04-1983 L1985 U *020 †95

REECE, Gerry Lee. 2602 BUFORD RD, RADIOLOGY ASSOCIATES OF 23235 #036-07-1993 L1998 PDR *020 †80

REINHARDT, Stephen David. 229 WADSWORTH DR 23236 #051-04-1981 L1982 FM *020 †18

RETCHIN, Sheldon Michael. 9000 STONY POINT PKWY, MCV 23235 #036-01-1976 L1978 IM IMG *030 †20

REUTINGER, David Chas. 10710 MIDLOTHIAN TPKE, STE 200 23235 #048-14-1982 L1986 OBG *020 †30

RICHARDS, Amanoa Marilyn. 9000 STONY POINT PKWY, MCV WOMAN'S HEALTH CARE 23235 #836-02-1976 L1997 OBG *020

RICHARDS, Nelson G. ■ 23236 #051-01-1952 L1953 N CHN *071 †75

RIGBY, Peter Lawrence. 161 WADSWORTH DR 23236 #051-01-1988 L2006 OTO *020 †45

ROBERTO, Paul John, Jr. 1401 JOHNSTON WILLIS DR, # 4500 23235 #038-41-1992 L1998 U *020 †95

ROBERTSON, Giles M, Jr. 107 WADSWORTH DR 23235 #051-04-1968 L1968 GE IM *020 †20

ROPER, Barry Edward. 10800 MIDLOTHIAN TPKE, STE 127 23235 #020-02-1971 L1978 OPH *020 †35

ROSE, Amy Kathleen. 1051 JOHNSTON WILLIS DR, STE 200 23235 #047-05-1994 L2004 GS *020 †85

ROSE, David Michael. 1051 JOHNSTON WILLIS DR, STE 200 23235 #047-05-1991 L2004 GS SO *020 †85

ROSENBAUM, Peter Jon. 8700 STONY POINT PKWY, STE 100 23235 #028-02-1982 L2006 AN PME *020 †05 ‡

ROWELL, Craig Gorlick. 2602 BUFORD RD, RADIOLOGY ASSOCIATES OF 23235 #045-01-1986 L1990 DR *020 †80

RUCKER, Karen Snowden. 9000 STONY POINT PKWY, MCV 23235 #020-02-1985 L1986 PM *030 †60

RUDZINSKI, Dennis Jos. 1401 JOHNSTON WILLIS DR 23235 #008-01-1969 L1977 AN PD *040 †05

RYAN, Arthur Eugene. 9609 JEFFERSON DAVIS HWY 23237 #030-06-1947 L1973 OM AM *020

SABASTIN, Suja Maria. ■ 23236 #041-13-2007 L2007 FP *012

SALLEY, David Ross. 161 WADSWORTH DR 23236 #051-04-2003 L2003 OTO *012

SALOMONSKY, Anita B. ■ 23235 #048-12-1965 L1970 AN *071 †05

SAMDANI, Shaik. 1427 JOHNSTON WILLIS DR 23235 #495-62-1993 L2005 PM *020

SANDHU, Kulbir. 1401 JOHNSTON WILLIS DR, THE ATRIUM STE 1200 23235 #919-05-1992 L2005 IM *020 †20

SANTOSH, Venkataraman. 1051 JOHNSTON WILLIS DR, STE 200 23235 #495-53-1978 L2001 GS *020 †85

SCHANZER, Harriet. 6439 IRON BRIDGE RD 23234 #051-04-1983 L1986 FM *020 †18

SCHUNN, Christian D. 1401 JOHNSTON WILLIS DR, STE 200 23235 #409-16-1983 L2005 VS GS *020 †85

SCHWARTZ, Daniella Mualle. ■ 23235 #036-05-2007 L2007 PTH *012

SCHWARTZ, Owen Griffin. ■ 23235 #036-05-2007 L2007 IM *012

SCOTT, Cessar Lenia, Jr. ■ 23235 #010-03-2006 P *012

SCOTT-BREEDEN, Sara Marie. 6439 IRON BRIDGE RD 23234 #036-08-1993 L1993 FM *020 †18

SEELY, Georgia Ann. 10710 MIDLOTHIAN TPKE, STE 401 23235 #036-08-1989 L1992 D *020 †20,15

SHAW, Billy David. ■ 23235 #012-05-1992 L2005 PD *020 †55

SHAW, Chung I. ■ 23236 #244-04-1970 L1977 R *020 †80

SHAW, Sharon R. ■ 23235 #051-01-1994 L1997 PD *020 †55

SIDHU, Jatinder Kaur. 1427 JOHNSTON WILLIS DR, HOPEWELL ORTHOPEDIC CENTER 23235 #495-03-1974 L1982 PM *020 †60

SIEDLECKI, John Alexander. 1447 JOHNSTON WILLIS DR 23235 #051-04-1995 L1995 FM *020 †18 ‡

SILVA, Livia Pires. ■ 23235 #005-12-1999 L1999 IM *020 †20

SIMPSON, Barbara Ellen. ■ 23234 #051-04-2006 L2006 OBG *012

SISMANIS, Aristides. 8700 STONY POINT PKWY, STE 220 23235 #418-01-1973 L1980 OTO *020 †45

SMITH, Lindley Theodore. 8700 STONY POINT PKWY, STE 120 23235 #047-07-1966 L1974 OPH *020 †35

SMITH, William K, Jr. ■ 23235 #051-01-1953 L1953 CD IM *071 †20

SNYDER, James Frederik. 2602 BUFORD RD, RADIOLOGY ASSOCIATES OF 23235 #051-04-1991 L1992 DR *020 †80

SOBIESKI, Thomas J, III. 8700 STONY POINT PKWY 23235 #051-04-1977 L1978 GE IM *020 †20

SOMERS, Kara Elizabeth. 2500 POCOSHOCK PL 23235 #051-04-1988 L1991 PD *020 †55

SOMERVILLE, Ivia Jeanette. 8110 MIDLOTHIAN TPKE, PATIENT FIRST MIDLOTHIAN 23235 #051-04-1982 L1995 FM *020 †18

SPENCER, Brent Austin. ■ 23235 #048-02-2004 L2008 D PRD *012

SPINOS, Efstathios. 2602 BUFORD RD, RADIOLOGY ASSOCIATES OF 23235 #011-04-1980 L1984 VIR RNR *020 †80

SPRENKLE, Wilson Burnley. 1401 JOHNSTON WILLIS DR 23235 #051-04-1974 L1975 RO FM *071 †18,80

STANFORD, Sam R, Jr. 2711 BUFORD RD, BOX 372 23235 #051-04-1974 L1975 FM *020 †18

STANLEY, Holly Lyn. 2309 LOGAN ST, COORDINATED CARE FOR SENIO 23235 #011-03-1981 L1982 IMG *062 †20

STEIN, Ethan Alexander. 9237 MIDLOTHIAN TPKE, STE 2C 23235 #010-01-1992 L1997 AN *020 †05

STEINBERG, Amber Lynne. 1401 JOHNSTON WILLIS DR 23235 #041-02-1990 L1997 AN *020 †05

STEINGOLD, Kenneth Alan. 10710 MIDLOTHIAN TPKE, STE 331 23235 #051-04-1979 L1982 REN OBG *020 †30

STERN, Howard Gene. 1411 JOHNSTON WILLIS DR, LTD. 23235 #051-04-1987 L1989 ORS *020 †40

STEVENS, Garth, Jr. 8700 STONY POINT PKWY, STE 120 23235 #051-04-1978 L1987 OPH *020 †35

STOLTZFUS, Mark Charles. 10800 MIDLOTHIAN TPKE, STE 265 23235 #020-12-1998 L1998 AN *020 †05

STONE, Emily Joan. 10710 MIDLOTHIAN TPKE, STE 200 23235 #010-01-2002 L2006 OBG *020

STONE, James Walter, Jr. 1401 JOHNSTON WILLIS DR 23235 #051-01-1981 L1983 AN *020 †05

STRATON, Cary Sanford. 2602 BUFORD RD, RADIOLOGY ASSOCIATES/RICHM 23235 #051-01-1985 L1991 DR *020 †80

STRINGER, K Robert. 2500 POCOSHOCK PL, STE 103 23235 #005-12-1969 L1972 IM FM *020 †20

STUART, Joni Corine. ■ 23236 #051-04-2008 *012

SWETZ, Keith M. ■ 23235 #041-14-2003 L2007 PLM *012 †20

TABASSIAN, Ali Reza. 8700 STONY POINT PKWY, STE 150 23235 #051-04-1990 L1996 OPH *020 †35

TARASIDIS, Nicholas G. 161 WADSWORTH DR 23236 #051-04-1985 L1991 OTO *020 †45

TAYLOR, Gail Lynn. 1108 COURTHOUSE RD STE D 23236 #051-04-1988 L1990 FM *020 †18

TAYLOR, Timothy Royal. 2602 BUFORD RD, RADIOLOGY ASSOCIATES OF 23235 #011-03-1985 L1994 DR *020 †80

TEKLU, Abraham. 9030 STONY POINT PKWY, POINT 1, 23235 #366-01-1987 L2001 IM *020 †20

THAKKAR, Neha. 2500 POCOSHOCK PL 23235 #016-11-1993 L1998 IM *100 †20

THAKUR, Vasundhara M. 2602 BUFORD RD, RADIOLOGY ASSOCIATES OF 23235 #495-28-1970 L1986 NM *020 †28

THEODORIDIS, Dimitrios. ■ 23236 #418-02-1963 L1989 P N *071 †75

THOMPSON, Jeffrey Keith. 2602 BUFORD RD, RADIOLOGY ASSOCIATES OF 23235 #001-02-1990 L1994 DR *020 †80

TILGHMAN, Kenneth Gibson. 10442 MIDLOTHIAN TPKE 23235 #023-01-1990 L1996 PD *020 †55

TRIKHA, Gita. 1401 JOHNSTON WILLIS DR 23235 #495-37-1986 L1992 AN PME *020 †05

TUBBS, Jeffrey Thomas, Jr. ■ 23235 #016-45-2008 *012

TUCKEY-LARUS, Corinne N. 10710 MIDLOTHIAN TPKE, STE 2 23235 #041-02-1987 L1991 OBG *020 †30

TURNER, John Winbern. 1401 JOHNSTON WILLIS DR, DEPT FO 23235 #051-04-2002 L2006 DMP *020 †50

TYSON, Deidre L. 9000 STONY POINT PKWY 23235 #035-09-1986 L1992 PDE PD *020 †55

TYSON, James Callen. 161 WADSWORTH DR 23236 #035-09-1986 L1992 OTO *020 †45

UCCI, Bernadette Teresa. ■ 23235 #030-06-2002 L2002 IM *100 †20

UNDERHILL, Thomas Edward. 2602 BUFORD RD, RADIOLOGY ASSOCIATES OF 23235 #036-05-1994 L2000 RNR *020 †80

URQUIA, David Craig. 9210 ARBORETUM PKWY, STE 260 23236 #051-01-1983 L1989 ORS *020 †40

VAIDY, Kamala. ■ 23237 #495-04-1971 L1983 P *020

VAIDY, Mohan Thekke. 4924 COCHISE TRL 23237 #495-31-1962 L1970 GP PTH *020 †50

VAN PUTTEN-ADAMS, Darla N. 10800 MIDLOTHIAN TPKE 23235 #041-12-1984 L1989 FM EM *020 †18

VAUGHAN, Robert Wylder. 8110 MIDLOTHIAN TPKE, PATIENT FIRST MIDLOTHIAN 23235 #051-01-1980 L1981 FM *020 †18

VIVADELLI, Stephany C. 9310 WALHAES POINT 23236 #051-07-1985 L1986 GP IM *020 †20

■ = Address Information Privacy Protected

VOKAC, Charles William. 1400 JOHNSTON WILLIS DR, STE A 23235 #051-04-1993 L1993 PM *020 †60

WADDELL, Marion Crockett. ■ 23235 #051-04-1955 L1955 OPH *071 †35

WADSWORTH, James Douglas. 2602 BUFORD RD, RADIOLOGY ASSOC OF RICHKMO 23235 #038-41-1971 L1975 DR *075 †80

WAGNER, Christina Michele. 1401 JOHNSTON WILLIS DR, THE ATRIUM, STE 1200 23235 #051-04-2000 L2000 END *012

WALLACE, Timothy Jude. 9105 STONY POINT PKWY 23235 #051-04-2003 L2003 RO *012

WALLER, Richard Edmund. 1415 JOHNSTON WILLIS DR 23235 #051-01-1979 L1987 N PD *020 †55,75

WANG, Allen Yu-Lun. ■ 23235 #654-01-2003 L2006 FP *012

WATSON, T Lepierre. 1401 JOHNSTON WILLIS DR 23235 #051-04-1959 L1959 FM *071 †18

WEDD, George Gould, III. 6439 IRON BRIDGE RD 23234 #051-04-1975 L1980 FM *020 †18

WEMLINGER, Amanda Susan. ■ 23235 #016-45-2008 *012

WENLEDER, Rudolf Bernard. 9327 MIDLOTHIAN TPKE, STE 2C 23235 #011-02-1968 L1971 AN *071 †05

WEST, Randal John. 1423 JOHNSTON WILLIS DR, CENTRAL VA GYN/ONCOLOGY 23235 #039-01-1980 L1983 OBG *020 †30

WHITE, Robert Jerome. 165 WADSWORTH DR 23236 #051-04-1985 L1990 N *020 †75

WHITEHURST, Wm Westwood. 410 ADKINS RD 23236 #051-04-1958 L1958 IM P *071

WIEBE-KING, Steven M. 2602 BUFORD RD 23235 #051-04-1986 L1989 DR *020 †80

WILHITE, Anne C O'Brien. 10136 CHEROKEE RD 23235 #051-01-1985 L1986 AN *020 †05

WILKES, William Lee. 1405 JOHNSTON WILLIS DR, CENTRAL VIRGINIA 23235 #012-01-1967 L1969 OTO A *020 †45

WILKEY, Sonja Annette. 1401 JOHNSTON WILLIS DR, ATTN: MEDICAL STAFF OFFICE 23235 #024-07-2001 L2004 EM *020 †16

WILLIAMS, Marvin Thos. 1401 JOHNSTON WILLIS DR 23235 #051-04-1974 L1975 FM *020 †18

WILSON, Henry H, Jr. 1401 JOHNSTON WILLIS DR 23235 #051-01-1949 L1949 PS *071

WINKLER, Charles P, Sr. 2602 BUFORD RD 23235 #051-04-1955 L1959 R OS *020 †80

WINSLOW, Boyd Holden. 8700 STONY POINT PKWY #250 23235 #024-01-1974 L1981 UP *020 †95

WITTKAMP, Bernard Francis. 8710 CHOCTAW RD 23235 #051-04-1956 L1956 RHU IM *020

WOOD, William Christian. 10800 MIDLOTHIAN TPKE, STE 265 23235 #051-04-1988 L1989 AN *020 †05

WOOGEN, Scott D. 8700 STONY POINT PKWY 23235 #035-19-1981 L1982 GE IM *020 †20

WORARATANADHARM, Swaeng. 10710 MIDLOTHIAN TPKE, STE 200 23235 #891-01-1970 L1975 OBG *020 †30

WORTHAM, Edwin, V. 8700 STONY POINT PKWY, STE 210 23235 #016-06-1983 L1991 OPH PD *035

YARLAGADDA, Yamini P. 165 WADSWORTH DR 23236 #912-01-1993 L1996 N *020 †75

YODER, Mary Katherine. 2500 POCOSHOCK PL 23235 #011-03-2006 L2006 FP *012

YOUNG, Harold Francis. 9000 STONY POINT PKWY, MCV 23235 #038-40-1963 L1972 NS *020 †25

YOUNG, Stephen Chas. 1401 JOHNSTON WILLIS DR, STE 1200 23235 #051-04-1987 L1988 IM *020 †20

YOUNT, B Gerald, Jr. 2602 BUFORD RD, RADIOLOGY ASSOCIATES OF 23235 #035-01-1969 L1978 DR *020 †80

ZELENAK, James Jos. 2602 BUFORD RD, RADIOLOGY ASSOCIATES OF 23235 #051-04-1969 L1969 DR NM *020 †80

ZIMMER, Timothy James. 8700 STONY POINT PKWY, STE 280 23235 #038-41-1983 L1988 ORS OFA *020 †40

ZUELZER, Wilhelm A. 9000 STONY POINT PKWY, SPORTS SPINE AND SURGERY C 23235 #048-13-1975 L1980 ORS *020 †40

RICHMOND – HENRICO

ABOU ASSI, Souheil. 2369 STAPLES MILL RD, SUTIE 200 23230 #605-02-1995 L1998 GE *020 †20

ABOUTANOS, Michel B. 3042 MONTFORT LOOP 23294 #041-12-1993 L1998 CCS *020 †85

ACHAR, Vaj S. ■ 23230 #495-09-1956 L1976 N *020

ADAMS, Alan Howard. ■ 23230 #016-06-1958 L1966 N OS *020 †75

ADAMS, E Jane Beery. ■ 23230 #051-04-1944 L1944 OS *075

ADAWADKAR, Swati Sanghani. ■ 23228 #051-04-2007 L2007 OBG *012

ADESO, Mukong. ■ 23223 #010-03-2003 L2003 GS *012

AISIKU, Imoigele Kenneth. 4201 SEMINARY AVE 23227 #024-16-1997 L2002 PCC *012 †16

AKAN-ETUK, Uduak Etun. 1500 N 28TH ST, RICHMOND COMMUNITY HOSPITA 23223 #035-03-1992 L1993 IM *020 †20

AKERS, Latania Michelle. ■ 23223 #042-02-2007 L2007 FP *012

AKPAGU, Christina Unya. ■ 23230 #561-01-1966 L1972 PD *074 †55

AL-ABDULLA, Hamid M. 1602 SKIPWITH RD 23229 #528-01-1958 L1968 CD IM *020 †20

ALAVI, S Manucher. 8001 FRANKLIN FARMS DR 23229 #020-12-1964 L1969 DR OS *071 †80

ALBRECHT, Gerald Thomas. 7603 FOREST AVE STE 401 23229 #051-04-1983 L1988 PDC PD *020 †55

ALESI, Erin Renee. ■ 23223 #021-05-2007 L2007 IM *012

ALEXANDER, Richard Edwin. 7660 E PARHAM RD, STE 207 23294 #051-07-2002 L2007 OSM *012

ALFONSO, Alvaro. ■ 23230 #264-01-1949 L1959 PS GS *020 †85,65

ALI, Mir Taruj. 1603 SANTA ROSA RD, RM 101 23229 #496-27-1997 L2005 PCC SME *020 †20

ALLEN, Benj Randolph, Jr. 1651 N PARHAM RD 23229 #051-04-1961 L1961 NS *071 †25

ALLEN, Jeffery Duane. 10431 PATTERSON AVE, PATTERSON AVE FAMILY PRCTC 23238 #021-01-1988 L1996 FM *020 †18

ALLISON, Shelton, Jr. ■ 23233 #017-20-2006 L2006 P *012

ALMOND, Hilton Robinson. 7702 E PARHAM RD, STE 304 23294 #051-04-1965 L1965 GE IM *020 †20

ALPERT, David Harvey. 1602 SKIPWITH RD, EMERGENCY DEPT. 23229 #024-07-1983 L1985 IM *020 †20

ALPHIN, Thomas Henry. ■ 23230 #051-01-1947 L1947 OS PHP *071

AMENDOLA, Michael Fiore. ■ 23230 #051-04-2002 L2004 VS *012 †85

AMIN, Sabina. ■ 23233 #051-04-2008 *012

AMIRGHASSEMI, Bijan. 8040 VILLA PARK DR 23228 #517-03-1977 L1992 PTH *062 †50

ANANDABABU, Chellappan. 4906 CUTSHAW AVE STE 105 23230 #495-31-1968 L1982 P *020

ANASTACIO, Melissa Martin. ■ 23223 #051-01-2006 L2006 GS *012

ANDERSON, Amber Marie. ■ 23238 #035-06-2006 L2006 OBG *012

ANDERSON, William Robt. ■ 23238 #051-01-1982 L1985 IM *020 †20

ANNAN, Isaac Benjamin. ■ 23223 #412-01-1994 L2006 N *012

ANSELL, Burness Ferdinand. 6605 W BROAD ST 23230 #051-04-1957 L1957 IM HO *071 †20

APPLEBY, George Stephen. ■ 23230 #041-02-1943 L1946 GP GE *071

ARALU, Cletus Chudi. 1601 ROLLING HILLS DR, RM 200 23229 #690-07-1989 L2001 N *020

ARMENTROUT, Clement S. ■ 23233 #051-04-1940 L1940 GS GYN *075 †85

ARMSTRONG, Nancy Jamison. 7601 FOREST AVE, STE 228 23229 #051-04-1983 L1987 OBG *020 †30

ARRUA, Nestor Ruben. ■ 23230 #726-01-1969 L1975 IM *100

ASCARI, Clavio Mario. 1504 SANTA ROSA RD, RM 206 23229 #051-01-1999 L1999 AN *020 †05

ASHE, Stephen Maurice. 4000A GLENSIDE DR 23228 #051-07-1985 L1986 FM *020 †18

ASTRUC, Juan. 2105 E PARHAM RD, PARHAM MEDICAL VILLAGE 23228 #847-03-1957 L1986 N NP *071 †75

ATWILL, William Henry. 1602 SKIPWITH RD 23229 #051-01-1960 L1960 U GS *071 †95

AUBRECHTOVA, Hana. ■ 23223 #286-09-1991 L2005 N *012

AUSTIN, Raymond Francis. 8005 THOM RA 23229 #024-01-1959 L1989 R *071 †80

AVILES, Francisco Antero. ■ 23223 #275-01-1952 L1968 GP *071

AVULA, Danny Thejakumar. ■ 23223 #051-04-2004 L2004 GPM *012 †55

AYALA-SIMS, Veronica Ada. ■ 23223 #051-04-2004 L2004 MPD *012

BAGLEY, John Jos, Jr. 7601 FOREST AVE, STE 228 23229 #051-04-1967 L1967 GYN *020 †30

BAIRD, Todd Biery. 1510 WILLOW LAWN DR, STE 102 23230 #051-04-1999 L2005 DR *020 †80

BAKER, Jaimison Whitcliff. ■ 23223 #036-01-2006 L2006 AN *012

BALASANKAR, Atri Padmini. 1601 ROLLING HILLS DR, RM 201 23229 #495-15-1964 L1978 P CHP *020 †75

BALCOM, Robert Jos. 2810 N PARHAM RD 23294 #035-15-1979 L1990 NPM PD *030 †55

BALSAMO, Giuseppe. ■ 23230 #561-17-1952 L1960 PM *020 †60

BANERJE, Koduru. 3212 CUTSHAW AVE STE 303 23230 #495-21-1973 L1978 P *020 †75

BANERJEE, Deepak Dilip. 2309 LIGHTHOUSE CT 23294 #495-22-1996 L2001 IC *100 †20

BANERJEE, Suman Kumar. ■ 23233 #495-16-1991 L2006 PCP *020 †50

BANG, Ki Hong. ■ 23229 #583-06-1967 L1976 OBG *020 †30

BARBER, Letha Kay Foss. ■ 23230 #010-01-1968 L1968 PD *074

BARNES, Letcher Blackwell. ■ 23229 #051-04-1954 L1954 OM *071 †70

BARR, Mark Cameron. 10431 PATTERSON AVE 23238 #051-04-1980 L1983 FM *020 †18

BARRON, Deborah Mary. 1504 SANTA ROSA RD, RM 206 23229 #035-47-1989 L1997 AN *020 †05

BARTON, Ronald Miles. ■ 23223 #022-07-1973 L2004 PS GS *020 †85,65

BASHIR, Naim S. 2103 E PARHAM RD, STE 200 23228 #704-02-1982 L2005 PD PDP *020 †55

BATCHELDER, Allison Joy. 2305 N PARHAM RD, STE 2 23229 #011-02-1992 L2000 AN *020 †05

BATES, Hampton Robt. ■ 23238 #051-04-1957 L1957 PTH NM *071 †50,28

BATTISTA, Jos Victor, Jr. 7605 FOREST AVE STE 206 23229 #035-20-1968 L1974 OBG *071 †30

BAXTER, Robert Wallace. 7605 FOREST AVE STE 311 23229 #803-05-1945 L1959 GP OS *020 †05

BEARDEN, William Harvey, III. 1602 SKIPWITH RD 23229 #001-02-1998 L1998 OPH *020 †35

BECK, Tiffany Lee. ■ 23238 #051-04-2008 *012

BECKETT, Jeanne Plunkett. ■ 23229 #051-04-1958 L1958 OS PHP *074

BEDINGER, Robert W, Sr. ■ 23227 #051-04-1948 L1948 IM *071 †20

BEDINGER, Robt Wright, Jr. 7702 E PARHAM RD, STE 205 23294 #051-04-1978 L1981 IM *020 †20

BEHNKE, Robert. ■ 23223 #051-05-2007 L2007 PM *020

BEKENSTEIN, Jonathan W. 1400 WESTWOOD AVE STE 101 23227 #051-01-1991 L2000 N *020 †75

BELCHER, Henry V. ■ 23230 #051-04-1952 L1952 GS *071 †85

BELL, Joseph Huxley, III. ■ 23230 #051-01-1960 L1960 CD IMG *071

BENDER, Robert Roland. ■ 23230 #051-04-1954 L1954 GP *071

BERLINER, Jessica. 1508 WILLOW LAWN DR, STE 117 23229 #041-02-1995 L1999 VIR *020 †80

BERTRAND, Jos Gaspard M. ■ 23230 #065-09-1955 L1960 DR RO *071 †80

BESKIN, Robert Rekedal. 1508 WILLOW LAWN DR, DRIVE STE#117 23230 #021-01-1982 L1987 RNR DR *020 †80

BEZIRDJIAN, Diran Roger. 1602 SKIPWITH RD, DEPT OF RAD 23229 #605-01-1975 L1980 DR *020 †80

BHULLER, Gurpal S. 1510 N 28TH ST, COLONIAL ORTHOPAEDICS INC 23223 #495-08-1974 L1982 ORS *020 †40

BICHARA, Noble Lucien. 1602 SKIPWITH RD, DEPT ER 23229 #165-08-1980 L1981 IM *020 †20

BILLETT, Todd Evans. 7605 FOREST AVE, STE 206 23229 #051-04-1985 L1988 OBG *020 †30

BITTNER, Brian C. 3311 CHURCH RD, STE 100 23233 #051-07-1999 L1999 FM *020 †18

BLANTON, Erika Martha. 7605 FOREST AVE STE 313 23229 #407-24-1966 L1972 OBG *020 †30

BOARD, John Arnold. ■ 23227 #051-04-1955 L1955 REN OBG *071 †30

BOATWRIGHT, Joseph W, III. 1500 N 28TH ST 23223 #051-01-1975 L1978 PD *020

BOLTON, Susan Cross. ■ 23238 #051-04-2004 L2004 AN *012

BONAGA, Daniel Uri. ■ 23228 #748-16-1987 *100

BONNER, Charles Henderson. 5922 W BROAD ST 23230 #539-06-1976 L1980 PM OSM *020 †60

BOON, Franklin Fook Lin. ■ 23238 #825-01-1971 L1975 CHP P *020 †75

BOOTH, Jerry Clark. ■ 23229 #051-01-1963 L1963 D *071 †15

BOOTH, John Vincent. 1504 SANTA ROSA RD, RM 206 23229 #919-05-1989 L2002 AN *020

BOSWORTH, James E. 1508 WILLOW LAWN DR, STE 117 23230 #051-04-1977 L1978 DR *020 †80

BOULWARE, John Henry. ■ 23230 #045-01-1948 L1959 GP *020

BOWERS, William Hampton. 7858 SHRADER RD 23230 #051-04-1966 L1987 HS ORS *072 †40

BOWLES, Sally Marie. 9900 INDEPENDENCE PARK DR, STE 100 23233 #041-14-2004 L2007 PD *020

BOYD, Milton Alexander. ■ 23238 #010-01-1954 L1966 IM *071

BRADENHAM, Ben Persons. 2369 STAPLES MILL RD 23230 #041-02-1973 L1978 GE IM *020 †20

BRADSHAW, Randolph Graham. ■ 23230 #051-01-1948 L1948 R *071

BRAND, Mary Jane. ■ 23238 #041-07-1963 L1984 PD *071 †55

BRAND, William Thos, Jr. 2369 STAPLES MILL RD, GASTROINTESTINAL SPECIALIS 23230 #051-04-1981 L1984 GE IM *020 †20

BRAUN, Heidi Lisa. 7605 FOREST AVE, STE 411 23229 #051-04-1999 L1999 OBG *020 †30

BRAUN, Joel Edward. ■ 23238 #038-04-2004 L2005 PM *012

BRAWNER, Sandra Lee. 7601 FOREST AVE, STE 111 23229 #025-01-1982 L1986 OBG *020 †30

BREDRUP, Ole C, Jr. 1510 WILLOW LAWN DR # 102, COMMONWEALTH RADIOLOGY, PC 23230 #051-04-1960 L1960 R NM *071 †80,28

BRIGGS, Addie Jametta. 4744 FINLAY ST 23231 #051-04-1997 L2000 PD *020 †55

BRINSTER, Derek Ralph. ■ 23238 #041-01-1996 L2006 **TS** *100 †85,90
BRINSTER, Nooshin K. ■ 23238 #041-01-1996 L2006 **D DMP** *020 †15
BROADDUS, Reuben H, Jr. ■ 23229 #051-04-1959 L1959 **GP OM** *020 †18
BROCKBANK, Justin Clark. ■ 23228 #051-04-2005 L2005 **PD** *012
BROCKINGTON, Katina V. DEPT OF PRIMARY CARE, MCV HOSPITAL 23229 #051-04-1988 L1989 **IM** *020 †20
BRODIE, Owen Wingfield. ■ 23227 #051-04-1962 L1962 **P** *071 †75 ‡
BROMBERG, Daniel Herman. ■ 23230 #035-09-1966 L1972 **CD** *100
BROOKEMAN, Valerie Anne. 1508 WILLOW LAWN DR, STE 117 23230 #011-02-1984 L1986 **DR NM** *020 †80
BROOKS, James Webster, Jr. 7605 FOREST AVE STE 410 23229 #051-04-1980 L1986 **ID IM** *020 †20
BROWN, David Bryce. 9316 GAYTON RD 23229 #051-04-1999 L1999 **FM** *020 †18
BROWN, John Lewis. ■ 23230 #051-04-1943 L1943 **FM** *071
BROWN, Rosalind Carter. ■ 23227 #051-01-2002 *100
BROWN, Susan Gollobin. 7603 FOREST AVE STE 210 23229 #036-05-1984 L1990 **NPM PD** *020 †55
BROWNE, Judith Ellen. 616 HORSEPEN RD 23229 #051-04-1990 L1991 **EM IM** *020 †20
BRUCH, William Mark. ■ 23233 #051-04-1945 L1950 **PD** *071 †55
BRYSON, Gilbert Hamilton. ■ 23229 #051-04-1959 L1959 **GS** *071 †85
BUCHSBAUM, David Geoffrey. ■ 23233 #051-04-1976 L1977 **IM P** *020 †20
BUHLER, Catherine Marie. ■ 23294 #051-04-2006 L2006 **DR** *012
BUI, Minh Nguyen. 7603 FOREST AVE 23229 #041-13-1985 L1993 **CD GS** *020 †18,20
BUNTING, James Blair, Jr. 9536 OLDHOUSE DR 23238 #032-01-1996 L1997 **CHP** *020 †75
BURKE, George Wilson, III. 1603 SANTA ROSA RD, RM 101 23229 #051-04-1970 L1970 **PUD IM** *020 †20
BURNETT, William Franklin. ■ 23230 #051-01-1962 L1962 **GS TS** *020
BURTON, Mary Ann Bigger. ■ 23230 #051-04-1955 L1957 **OS** *071
BUTLER, Richard Harvey. ■ 23230 #021-01-1942 L1952 **OM AM** *071
BUTTERWORTH, Ann. ■ 23230 #051-01-1945 L1945 **IM** *075
BUTTERWORTH, John F, III. ■ 23229 #051-04-1952 L1952 **ORS** *071 †40
BYRD, Ann Carol. ■ 23229 #051-04-1980 L1983 **PD** *075 †55
CADER, A Martin. ■ 23238 #220-01-1968 L1976 **GPM** *030 †55 ‡
CALDWELL, Mary Mc Faden. 15000 CAPITAL ONE DR, ATTN 12078/HEALTH CTR 23238 #051-04-1981 L1982 **FM OM** *020 †18
CALL, Robert Somerville. 9920 INDEPENDENCE PARK DR 23233 #051-01-1987 L1992 **AI IM** *020 †20,03
CAMETAS, John Gus. 2307 N PARHAM RD 23229 #051-04-1969 L1969 **FM** *071 †18
CAMPBELL, James Ashton. 1127 N 29TH ST 23223 #010-03-1970 L1975 **FM R** *020
CAMPBELL, Kyle Dagan. ■ 23223 #051-04-2006 L2006 **AN** *012
CAMPBELL, Samuel Jacob. ■ 23294 #051-04-2006 L2006 **OBG** *012
CAOVAN, Dominique Bernard. ■ 23233 #051-01-2007 L2007 **IM** *012
CARMICHAEL, Miriam W. 1400 WESTWOOD AVE 23227 #051-04-1951 L1951 **N** *071 †75
CARR, Arthur Allen. ■ 23230 #051-04-1947 L1947 **PD** *071
CARTAGENA, Rafael, Jr. 1504 SANTA ROSA RD, RM 206 23229 #041-01-1999 L2005 **AN** *020 †05
CARTER, B Noland, II. ■ 23227 #023-07-1951 L1958 **GS CD** *071 †85
CARTER, Wesley Byrd. 3212 CUTSHAW AVE STE 30 23230 #051-04-1968 L1968 **CHP P** *020
CASPARI, Richard Bernard. 7650 E PARHAM RD, STE 301 23294 #011-03-1966 L1973 **ORS** *020
CASTELLO, Laura Anne. ■ 23223 #051-04-2008 *012
CASTLE, William Nicholas. 7603 FOREST AVE STE 407, UROLOGY SPECIALISTS OF RIC 23229 #051-01-1980 L1980 **U** *020 †95
CHAMBERS, Zachariah Winga. ■ 23294 #001-06-2007 L2007 **AN** *012
CHANG, Inja. ■ 23238 #583-03-1973 L1995 **GP** *020
CHANG, Jason Jinwoo. ■ 23223 #010-01-2008 *012
CHARLTON, Lei. 1122 N 25TH ST, STE A 23223 #047-07-1981 L1984 **IM OS** *020
CHAUDHARY, Shawn Ahmad. ■ 23229 #051-04-2008 *012
CHEHRAZI, Arash. ■ 23230 #051-04-2004 L2004 **DR** *012
CHEHRAZI, Claire Van Eenw. ■ 23229 #051-02-2005 L2005 **PD** *012
CHEN, Jeffrey H. 7702 E PARHAM RD, STE 102 23294 #041-09-1995 L2003 **GS** *020 †85
CHERNY, Roman Czerny. ■ 23230 #407-16-1950 L1957 **GP** *020
CHINAULT, John Curtis, Jr. 5711 STAPLES MILL RD, STE 100 23228 #045-04-1993 L1994 **RO** *020 †80
CHO, Suck Jae. ■ 23230 #583-04-1968 L1974 **OBG EM** *020
CHOUDHURY, Jayanta. 4705 E CARDINAL CT B 23228 #495-39-1994 L2003 **GE** *100 †20
CHOUFANI, Dani Ibrahim. ■ 23228 #605-03-2000 L2006 **IM** *100 †20
CHOWCHUVECH, Endliam. ■ 23230 #891-01-1956 L1974 **OPH** *020 †35
CHU, Josephine Shou-Chen. ■ 23229 #242-34-1945 L1964 **RO** *020 †20
CHUN, Walter Jhong-Wha. 9750 GAYTON RD 23238 #051-01-1995 L1998 **PD** *020 †55
CHUNG, Jiyearn. ■ 23228 #051-04-2003 L2004 **DR** *012
CISEK, James Edward. 1602 SKIPWITH RD, FOREST CAMPUS 23229 #025-07-1984 L1997 **EM** *020 †16
CLARK, Frederick A, Jr. ■ 23233 #017-20-1947 L1956 **OS** *071
CLARK, Pamela. 2201 WESTWOOD AVE, VIRGINIA BLOOD SERVICES 23230 #051-01-1982 L1986 **BBK CLP** *030 †50 ‡
CLARY, Beverley B, III. 7603 FOREST AVE, STE 403 23229 #051-04-1999 L2002 **OBG** *020 †30
CLEMENTS, Ernest Linwood. 7650 E PARHAM RD, STE 100 23294 #051-04-1959 L1959 **ORS** *071 †40
CLEMENTS, Richard K. ■ 23230 #051-04-1940 L1940 **OPH GP** *071 †35
COGBILL, Meagan Elizabeth. ■ 23223 #051-04-2008 *012
COHEN, Irwin Kelman. 1400 AQUA VISTA LN 23231 #036-01-1963 L1973 **PS GS** *071 †85,65
COHEN, Lawrence Franklin. 13252 BARWICK LN 23238 #035-08-1981 L1988 **OSS** *020 †40
COLE, Timothy John. 7702 E PARHAM RD STE 103 23294 #041-02-1988 L1991 **DR** *020 †80
COLEMAN, Joseph Emory. ■ 23229 #051-01-1957 L1957 **IM OS** *040
COLLEY, Amelia Holder. 9606 PATTERSON AVE 23229 #051-01-1983 L1988 **PD** *020 †55
COLLEY, John Lawrence. 2015 STAPLES MILL RD 23230 #051-01-1984 L1985 **OS** *030
COLSTON, John A C, Jr. ■ 23229 #051-01-1950 L1950 **U** *020 †95
COMEAUX, Jarmon Charles. ■ 23228 #010-03-2008 *012
CONRAD, Debra Dee. 2200 PUMP RD, STE 200 23233 #011-03-1982 L1983 **PD** *020 †55
CONSTANT, Tony. 1300 WATKINS LN 23227 #051-04-1956 L1956 **EM** *071 †16
CONYERS, Richard Mack. 4301 W BROAD ST, CONCENTRA MEDICAL CENTERS 23230 #051-04-1982 L1983 **FM** *020 †18
COOK, Douglas Eugene. 1508 WILLOW LAWN DR, STE 117 23230 #051-04-1980 L1982 **DR** *020 †80

COOK, James Stanley. 7660 E PARHAM RD, STE 100 23294 #051-07-1979 L1981 **FM** *075 †18
COOK, Kathleen Anne. 2205 N PARHAM RD, PATIENT FIRST PARHAM 23229 #051-07-1979 L1981 **GP** *020
COOKE, Charles Lee. 7700 E PARHAM RD 23294 #036-01-1963 L1966 **RHU IM** *020 †20
COOPER, Catherine L. 1201 CONFEDERATE AVE 23227 #036-01-1990 L1994 **AN** *020 †05
CORNELL, Christy E. ■ 23229 #051-04-1982 L1985 **P** *020 †75
COVINGTON, Damian L. 1510 N 28TH ST, STE 300 23223 #036-05-1999 L1999 **FM** *020 †10
COWANS, Rodney Harry. 7634 SPRENKLE CT 23228 #051-04-1992 L1994 **GP** *020
COX, William Henry. ■ 23227 #051-04-1943 L1943 **OBG** *071 †30
CRANE, Peter Duke. 1651 N PARHAM RD 23229 #654-01-1997 L2001 **APM** *020 †05
CRESS, Alicia Nacpil. 3311 CHURCH RD, STE 100 23233 #065-01-1991 L1994 **FM** *020 †18
CROGNALE, Elizabeth Jody. 7702 E PARHAM RD, STE 101 23294 #051-04-1997 L1997 **IM** *020 †20
CROSKEY, Djenabra Mayee. 2104 OLD PRESCOTT PL, OB HOSPITALISTS, INC. 23238 #010-03-1999 L2007 **OBG** *020
CROWL, Adam Christopher. 7858 SHRADER RD, ADVANCED ORTHOPEDIC CENTER 23294 #051-01-1999 L1999 **ORS** *100 †40
CULBERTSON, Leon R. ■ 23229 #051-01-1936 L1936 **U** *071 †95
DAGEFORDE, James Russell. 2200 PUMP RD, STE 100 23233 #048-04-1975 L1981 **FM** *020 †18
DAMEFF, Anton M. ■ 23230 #198-01-1963 L1974 **IM** *020 †20
D'ANDREA, Anthony Louis. ■ 23229 #561-17-1954 L1957 **FM OM** *072
DANIEL, John M, III. 7702 E PARHAM RD, STE 205 23294 #051-04-1977 L1978 **IM** *020 †20
DATTA, Harsh. ■ 23238 #913-09-1999 L2008 **PD** *012
DAUSCH, Susan M. 7603 FOREST AVE STE 101, COURTYARD MEDICAL OFFICE B 23229 #051-04-1996 L1996 **OBG** *020 †30
DAVIDSON, Donald Dale. 8911 SIERRA RD 23229 #041-01-1969 L1977 **ORS** *071 †40
DAVIS, Victoria. 7603 FOREST AVE, STE 101 23229 #051-04-1996 L1996 **OBG** *020 †30
DAVIS, William Bradley. ■ 23223 #051-04-2008 *012
DAVY, Mark Ferris. 7702 E PARHAM RD, STE 205 23294 #051-04-1978 L1979 **FM** *020 †18
DAWSON, Christopher Allen. ■ 23223 #055-01-2005 L2005 **PM** *012
DAWSON, Philip A J. 9606 PATTERSON AVE 23229 #067-01-1987 L1989 **PD** *020 †55
DAY, Jarrod Demetrius. 23231 #036-07-2002 L2002 *012
DEAL, Clifford Lanier, III. 8921 THREE CHOPT RD, STE 300 23229 #051-04-2000 L2000 **GS** *020 †85
DEARDEUFF, Michael Lane. ■ 23233 #051-01-2008 *012
DECHERT, Tracey Ann. ■ 23223 #041-13-2001 L2001 **GS** *012
DEEP, Anthony Abraham. 7605 FOREST AVE STE 3 23229 #051-04-1956 L1956 **OBG** *071 †30
DEEP, William Danl. 2809 EMERYWOOD PKWY, STE 140 23294 #051-04-1959 L1959 **HEM IM** *071 †20
DEIGNAN, Brian James. ■ 23223 #011-02-2007 L2007 **ORS** *012
DELLA TORRE, Thomas F. ■ 23223 #024-05-2002 L2007 **OTO FPS** *100
DEMOZ, Elias Gebrekidan. 8736 LANDMARK RD, NEW ERA VISITING PHYS LLC 23228 #366-01-1994 L2003 **IM** *020
DENISKO, Natalia Sergeevn. ■ 23238 #913-10-1984 L2000 **FM** *020 †18 ‡
DENNIS, Tiffani D. 7001 FOREST AVE, STE 2500 23230 #030-06-2004 L2004 **IM** *020 †20
DERBER, Catherine Jane F. ■ 23233 #051-07-1999 L2007 **IM** *020 †20
DERY, Frederick John. ■ 23223 #025-07-2005 L2006 **PM** *012
DESAI, Sanjay Shashikant. 7650 E PARHAM RD, STE 100 23294 #010-01-1984 L1994 **HS** *020 †40
DESCHAMPLAIN, Michelle L. ■ 23229 #051-04-2003 L2005 **GS** *012
DICKERSON, Tasha Brooks. 1510 N 28TH ST STE 300 23223 #051-04-2001 L2002 **FM** *020 †18
DIGGS, Tyra Lanee. ■ 23294 #010-02-2007 L2007 **IM** *012
DILLARD, Charles Maurice. ■ 23229 #051-04-2004 L2004 **PM** *012
DIMARTINO, Paul Peter. 7660 E PARHAM RD, STE 201 23294 #035-15-1975 L1997 **ORS** *020 †40
DINGLEDINE, William S. ■ 23238 #051-01-1951 L1951 **OM IM** *071 †20,28
DISLER, David Glenn. 1508 WILLOW LAWN DR, STE 117 23230 #024-01-1988 L1998 **DR** *020 †80
DISLER, Robin S. 7001 FOREST AVE, STE 2500 23230 #024-07-1988 L1998 **IM** *020 †20
DO, Khoi Ba. ■ 23228 #051-04-2004 L2004 **IM** *100 †20
DO, Marie Christine. ■ 23228 #051-04-2004 L2004 **PTH** *020
DOLBEARE, Dirk W. ■ 23228 #004-01-2004 L2005 **ORS** *012
DOTOLO, Joseph Ralph. ■ 23229 #051-01-1964 L1964 **IM CD** *020 †20
DOUGLAS, Michael Forbes S. 2201 E MAIN ST, STE 201 23223 #010-03-1977 L1983 **NEP IM** *020 †20
DRAPER, Walter. 2319 E BROAD ST 23223 #051-04-1955 L1955 **CHP P** *071 †75
DUCKWORTH, Paul Frederick. 2369 STAPLES MILL RD, STE 200 23230 #051-01-1984 L1985 **GE IM** *020 †20
DUFOUR, Jean. 1508 WILLOW LAWN DR, STE 117 23230 #165-01-1982 L1986 **DR** *020 †80
DULEY, Robert Kingston. 9207 RIVER RD 23229 #051-01-1955 L1955 **GP** *020
DULIT, Alan Michael. 2104 OLD PRESCOTT PL, SUMMIT OB-GYN 23238 #007-02-1995 L2007 **OBG** *020 †30
DUMVILLE, David Milton. ■ 23238 #051-04-1946 L1946 **IM CD** *071
DUNNAVANT, Siobhan Stolle. 7601 FOREST AVE, STE 228 23229 #051-07-1995 L1995 **OBG** *020 †30
DUNNINGTON, Judith E S. ■ 23229 #051-04-1972 L1976 **IM NEP** *062 †20
DUTZ-KOHOUT, Elfriede. ■ 23223 #154-07-1952 L1975 **PTH IG** *071 †50
ECHELBERGER, Mary Ann. ■ 23238 #051-04-1992 L1994 **IM** *020
EID, Ramy Youssef. 2369 STAPLES MILL RD, STE 200 23230 #605-03-1996 L2005 **GE** *020 †20
EKEY, David Price. 1508 WILLOW LAWN DR, STE 117 23230 #051-04-1976 L1980 **R** *020 †80
ELLIS, Robert. 1504 SANTA ROSA RD, RM 206 23229 #919-05-1975 L1986 **AN** *020 †05
ELLIS, Robert Gareth. ■ 23238 #051-04-2007 L2007 **IM** *012
ELSHOWAIA, Salwa Hassan S. ■ 23223 #848-01-1996 L2001 **PCP** *020 †50
EPSTEIN, Arnold Marvin. ■ 23229 #051-01-1958 L1958 **TS** *071 †85,90
ERNST, Arthur Clifford. 7700 E PARHAM RD, HEALTHSOUTH MEDICAL CENTER 23294 #051-04-1982 L1982 **IM** *020 †18
ERWIN, Michael Brune. 7605 FOREST AVE, STE 303 23229 #051-01-1997 L2005 **IC** *020 †20
ETTIGI, Prakash G. 4906 CUTSHAW AVE 23227 #495-35-1971 L1977 **P** *020 †75
EVERS, Joseph Peter. 6605 W BROAD ST 23230 #010-02-1987 L1990 **ON** *020 †20
EWANE, Kenneth A. ■ 23294 #051-04-2008 *012
FALIK, Adam Moshe. 1602 SKIPWITH RD 23229 #010-01-1997 L2000 **PD** *020 †55
FALTERMAN, Casey Gerard. 7603 FOREST AVE, STE 210 23229 #021-05-1976 L1988 **NPM PD** *020 †55
FALTERMAN, Mary L. 7603 FOREST AVE STE 401, PEDIATRIC CARDIOLOGY OF VA 23229 #045-01-1984 L1989 **PDC** *020 †55

■ = Address Information Privacy Protected

FARLEY, Emerson Dale, Jr. 2819 N PARHAM RD 23294 #041-12-1964 L1967 **IM RHU** *071 †20

FARRELL, Michael Thomas. 7603 FOREST AVE STE 306 23229 #051-01-1985 L1986 **GE IM** *020 †20

FARROW, C Creston, Jr. ■ 23230 #051-01-1951 L1951 **ATP CLP** *072 †50

FATANI, Yahya Imran F. ■ 23233 #051-04-2004 L2004 **IM** *012

FEATHERSTON, Edward W. ■ 23230 #051-04-1965 L1965 **OPH** *020

FERGUSON, Robert Thrift. ■ 23223 #051-04-2005 L2005 **GS** *012

FERGUSSON, Kevin W. 1600 WESTBROOK AVE, WESTMINSTER CANTERBURY CLN 23227 #051-04-1985 L1986 **FM MDM** *030 †18

FERIA, Argelio A. 1504 SANTA ROSA RD, RM 202 23229 #847-06-1975 L1979 **AN NS** *020

FERN, Stephen Edward. ■ 23229 #051-04-2004 L2004 **ORS** *012

FERRAR, William Lewis. 8923 THREE CHOPT RD, STE 101 23229 #041-01-1972 L1975 **IM** *020 †20

FETHIERE, William. ■ 23230 #440-01-1955 L1961 **PTH DMP** *071 †50

FIDLER, Robert Young, Jr. ■ 23238 #051-04-1991 L1996 **DR** *020 †80

FIELDS, Abbie Louise. 7603 FOREST AVE, STE 207 23229 #038-40-1987 L2005 **GO** *020 †30

FIERRO, A Gilberto S. PARHAM & QUIOCCASIN RDS 23229 #649-01-1959 **OS** *075

FIERRO, Anthony. 7605 FOREST AVE, STE 412 23229 #051-01-1976 L1977 **FM** *020 †18 ‡

FIERRO, Marcella F. ■ 23229 #035-06-1966 L1972 **FOP ATP** *062 †50

FINNEGAN, Maurice F, Jr. 1508 WILLOW LAWN DR, STE 117 23230 #051-04-1981 L1981 **DR VIR** *020 †80

FISHER, Dorothy G Calvert. ■ 23229 #065-06-1952 L1961 **P** *072

FISHER, Galen Hunt. 6603 W BROAD ST, STE 400 23230 #036-07-1997 L2005 **D** *020 †15

FITZPATRICK, Mark J. ■ 23230 #035-08-1953 L1959 **OBG GP** *075

FITZSIMMONS, Sharon Marie. 3600 W BROAD ST 23230 #038-40-1988 L2004 **PD** *020 †55

FLEET, Clifford B, Jr. ■ 23229 #051-01-1970 L1970 **OBG** *071 †30

FLETCHER, John David. ■ 23230 #051-01-1959 L1959 **PHP PD** *030 †55

FOGEL, William Martin. 8923 THREE CHOPT RD, STE 103 23229 #041-02-1964 L1974 **R** *071 †80,28

FOGELSON, Frederick S. 1602 SKIPWITH RD 23229 #024-01-1970 L1978 **ORS GS** *071 †40

FORMANEK, Gregory Andrew. 8919 THREE CHOPT RD, STE 2 23229 #033-05-1975 L2002 **ON IM** *020 †20

FORNARIS, Ernest Angel. 4792 FINLAY ST STE 1 23231 #035-15-1973 L1976 **IM** *020 †20

FORTH, Monica Jaye. 3311 CHURCH RD, STE 100 23233 #010-03-1998 L2005 **FM** *020 †18

FORTNER, Julie Weaver. 4786 FINLAY ST 23231 #051-04-1990 L1992 **PD** *020 †55

FOSTER, James Danl. 2200 PUMP RD, STE 100 23233 #051-04-1983 L1984 **FM** *020 †18

FOSTER-DRAIN, Robin Laroy. ■ 23229 #041-07-1991 **PHP** *100

FOUNTAIN-ELLIS, Tami J. 10431 PATTERSON AVE 23238 #051-04-1998 L1998 **FM** *020 †18

FOWLER, Franklin T. ■ 23238 #047-05-1943 L1961 **OS** *071

FOXMAN, Jan. 2511 COTTAGE COVE DR 23233 #023-01-1991 L1995 **EM** *020 †16

FOXX, Kenneth Reginald. 1510 N 28TH ST 23223 #010-03-2000 L2006 **GS** *020

FRAKES, Charles Ross. 7603 FOREST AVE, STE 210 23229 #048-02-1976 L1988 **NPM PD** *020 †55

FRASER, Rodger Alvin. 1511 STARLING DR 23229 #010-03-1974 L1995 **OBG** *075

FREED, Ivan Graham. ■ 23230 #051-04-1946 L1946 **ADL** *071 †55

FREEMAN, Jane. ■ 23230 #051-04-1951 L1951 **EM** *071

FREUND, Jack. 1701 FAIRFIELD WAY, MEDICAL DEPT 23223 #051-04-1946 L1946 **IM CD** *072 †20

FREY, Allen Arthur. 1500 N 28TH ST 23223 #023-01-1965 L1973 **DR** *071 †80

FRIEDMAN, Elke. 6605 W BROAD ST 23230 #056-06-1996 L1996 **HO** *020 †20

FRYE, Judson Matthew. ■ 23223 #051-04-2008 L2008 *012

FUN, Elizabeth. ■ 23294 #422-01-1996 L2003 **PD** *100

GALESKI, Joseph Salo, III. 7702 E PARHAM RD, STE 205 23294 #051-04-1976 L1978 **IM PLM** *020 †20

GAMOSO, Maribel. 1504 SANTA ROSA RD, RM 206 23229 #035-03-1995 L2000 **AN** *020 †05

GARAZO, Enrique. ■ 23230 #847-05-1950 L1967 **U** *020 †95

GARCIA, Pablo Belizario. ■ 23294 #748-01-1946 L1978 *071

GARCIA-OTERO, Jose A. ■ 23230 #275-01-1941 L1966 **R** *020

GARDNER, Clay Thos, Jr. 1602 SKIPWITH RD 23229 #051-04-1960 L1960 **END IM** *071

GATLING, H Bee. ■ 23230 #036-05-1960 L1971 **PHP** *020 †55

GELBER, Lawrence Elliot. 9920 INDEPENDENCE PARK DR, STE 100 23233 #308-07-1983 L1989 **A AI** *020

GELRUD, Louis Gerald. 2369 STAPLES MILL RD, STE 200 23230 #023-01-1971 L1976 **GE IM** *020 †20

GENTRY, Nicholas Lee. ■ 23294 #028-03-2007 L2007 **EM** *012

GEORGE, Theodore. ■ 23230 #051-04-1965 L1965 **GS GP** *071 †85

GERVIN, Alfred Spencer. 9702 GAYTON RD # 327, THE GERVIN GROUP 23238 #036-07-1969 L1983 **GS EM** *020 †16,85

GHARSE, Suresh P. 3900 MONUMENT AVE 23230 #496-38-1973 L1977 **CHP P** *020

GIANFORTONI, Joseph Gene. 7603 FOREST AVE STE 204 23229 #010-01-1978 L1988 **OBG REN** *020 †30

GIBSON, John Franklin, Jr. ■ 23230 #051-04-1940 L1940 **OS** *075

GIBSON-FRASIER, Gwendolyn. 9900 INDEPENDENCE PARK DR, STE 100 23233 #036-01-1996 L1996 **PD** *020 †55

GILLIAM, John Hilliard. 1601 ROLLING HILLS DR, RM 201 23229 #047-06-1974 L1984 **P** *040 †20

GLAZIER, Richard Lee. 7702 E PARHAM RD 23294 #051-01-1970 L1970 **IM ON** *020 †20

GLOWACKI, Keith Adam. 7858 SHRADER RD 23294 #041-02-1990 L1997 **ORS HS** *020 †40

GODSCHALK, Michael F. 400 WESTON WAY 23238 #055-01-1980 L1984 **END IM** *050 †20

GOLDING, John Vincent. ■ 23230 #010-03-1936 L1937 **GP OS** *071

GOLDSCHMIDT, Robert Alan. 1508 WILLOW LAWN DR, STE 117 23230 #056-05-1977 L1978 **DR PDR** *020 †80

GOMEZ, Humberto. 4906 CUTSHAW AVE STE 104 23230 #264-03-1955 L1972 **P CHP** *020 †75

GOMEZ, Mario Humberto. 4906 CUTSHAW AVE, STE 104 23230 #051-07-1983 L1988 **P PYG** *020 †75

GONZALEZ, Ernesto. 1504 SANTA ROSA RD, RM 205 23229 #132-02-1986 L1994 **PCC** *020 †20

GOOD, John Russell. ■ 23233 #051-04-1956 L1956 **FM P** *071

GOODMAN, Harold. ■ 23238 #051-04-1944 L1944 **R** *040 †80

GOODNER, John Wood. ■ 23233 #047-06-1956 L1966 **OBG** *071 †30

GOODWIN, Selwyn David. 1400 WESTWOOD AVE 23227 #836-02-1960 L1985 **FM** *071

GORMAN, Jerome Davis. ■ 23229 #051-02-1959 L1963 **GP EM** *071 †16

GOSSELIN, David Paul. 9900 INDEPENDENCE PARK DR, STE 100 23233 #051-04-1999 L1999 **PD** *020 †55

GOULD, Charles Frost. 7702 E PARHAM RD, STE 102 23294 #035-08-1973 L1990 **GS VS** *020 †85

GRAHAM, Ota Treville, Jr. ■ 23229 #051-04-1953 L1955 **FM** *075

GRAHAM, Richard Warwick. 7603 FOREST AVE, STE 407 23229 #051-04-1979 L1981 **U GS** *020 †20

GRANDIS, Stuart Victor. 4835 S LABURNUM AVE 23231 #051-04-1967 L1967 **FM OM** *020 †18 ‡

GRAVES, Ryan Benton. ■ 23223 #051-04-2008 *012

GREEN, Lonny Stenzler. 2240 JOHN ROLFE PKWY, VIRGINIA WOMEN'S CENTER 23233 #005-14-1987 L1993 **U** *020 †95

GREENWOOD, Carrilynn Addi. ■ 23228 #051-04-2008 *012

GREER, Chad Christopher. ■ 23228 #036-08-2005 L2005 **MPD** *012

GREGORY, James Stewart. 1904 BYRD AVE STE 200 23230 #064-01-1963 L1968 **CRS** *071 †10

GRIGGS, Douglas M. ■ 23230 #051-01-1953 L1953 **IM** *050 †20

GRINNAN, Daniel Charles. 7601 FOREST AVE, STE 106 23229 #051-04-2000 L2003 **PCC** *100 †20

GROMPONE, Antonio Mario. ■ 23230 #561-10-1963 L1967 **ORS** *020

GROOPMAN, David S. 4118 E PARHAM RD 23228 #035-19-1978 L1979 **EM IM** *020 †20,16

GROVER, Amelia. ■ 23229 #025-07-1996 L2004 **SO** *020 †85

GRUBB, George Lester. ■ 23230 #051-04-1943 L1943 **GYN** *020 †30

GUISTO, Donald Frank. 2340 HICKORY CREEK DR # 1B 23294 #005-02-1947 L1982 **GS EM** *071 †85

GULHAN, Adam Mehmet. ■ 23294 #902-22-1987 L1998 **CN** *020 †75

GUPTA, Shakun. ■ 23223 #051-04-2008 *012

GUTIERREZ, Julio B. ■ 23230 #176-02-1964 L1974 **IM** *100

HACKWORTH, William Andrew. ■ 23223 #051-04-2005 L2005 **IM** *012

HAENEBALCKE, Eline Elly. ■ 23223 #051-04-2006 L2006 **OBG** *012

HAFFIZULLA, Hope Andrea H. 719 N 25TH ST, VERNON J. HARRIS HEALTH CE 23223 #566-01-1999 L2002 **FM** *020 †18

HAFT, Kenneth Samuel. 1603 SANTA ROSA RD, RM 101 23229 #011-03-1995 L1995 **IM** *020 †20

HAGAN, Ralph Ernest. ■ 23238 #024-05-1961 L1970 **NS** *071 †25

HAGER, James Lawrence. ■ 23230 #051-04-1930 L1930 **OBG GP** *071

HAHN, Chiwon. 7605 FOREST AVE, STE 302 23229 #035-01-1987 L1997 **TS** *020 †85,90

HAISLEY-ROYSTER, Camille. 6603 W BROAD ST STE 400 23230 #036-07-1996 L1999 **D** *020 †15

HALABI, Rabih Samir. ■ 23294 #038-45-2006 L2006 **IM** *012

HALL, Royce Orion. ■ 23230 #051-01-1966 L1966 **OPH** *071 †35

HALLORAN, Randolph M. 1602 SKIPWITH RD 23229 #051-04-1965 L1965 **CD PUD** *071 †20

HAM, Catherine Brannon. ■ 23223 #051-04-2007 L2007 **IM** *012

HAMILTON, Stuart H, Jr. 1530 BATTERY HILL DR 23231 #051-04-1967 L1967 **OBG** *020

HAMPTON, Florine Kirk. ■ 23230 #051-04-1950 L1951 **GPM** *072

HAMRICK, Richard M, III. 1603 SANTA ROSA RD, RM 101 23229 #051-04-1982 L1985 **PCC IM** *020 †20

HANCOCK, William C. ■ 23238 #051-04-1949 L1949 **OBG** *071

HANRAHAN, Brian William. ■ 23230 #035-15-2004 L2004 **IM** *100

HARK, William Tucker. 9920 INDEPENDENCE PARK DR, STE 100 23233 #051-04-1993 L1993 **AI IM** *020 †20,03

HARP, William Lee. 9960 MAYLAND DR, STE 300 23233 #012-01-1975 L1977 **P PYG** *030 †75

HARPOLE, David H. ■ 23238 #047-06-1953 L1962 **TS GS** *071 †85,90

HARRELSON, Austin Barrow. 6603 W BROAD ST, STE 401 23230 #051-04-1962 L1962 **N** *071 †75

HARRINGTON, Gary Clayton. 1510 N 28TH ST, STE 301 23223 #028-02-1991 L1993 **GS** *020 †85

HARRINGTON, Sarah Elizabe. ■ 23233 #004-01-2003 L2008 **IM** *020

HARRISON, David Cushman. 4807 HERMITAGE RD, STE 102 23227 #051-04-1991 L1997 **IM** *020 †20

HARRISON, Melissa Leigh. ■ 23231 #051-04-2007 L2007 **IM** *012

HARRISON, Thomas Peyton. 1504 SANTA ROSA RD, RM 206 23229 #051-07-1996 L2003 **AN** *020 †05

HARVEY, John Edmund, III. ■ 23230 #017-20-1966 L1971 **AN** *020

HAUGETO, Sonja A. 9900 INDEPENDENCE PARK DR, STE 100 23233 #035-15-1998 L2001 **PD** *020 †55

HEAD, Mark Murdock. ■ 23223 #010-01-1982 L1994 *100

HEADLEY, Michelle Elder. 2300 E PARHAM RD, PATIENT FIRST WOODMAN 23228 #051-04-1993 L1993 **IM** *020 †20

HEMBERG, Francoise. ■ 23229 #165-04-1983 **PD** *074

HENDERER, Armistead Edmun. ■ 23229 #051-04-2005 L2005 **P** *012

HERMANN, Ernest Conrad. 3311 CHURCH RD 23233 #051-04-1953 L1953 **GP** *071

HERNANDEZ, Raul A. ■ 23230 #275-01-1955 L1960 **IM** *071

HERRELL, Jesse Lee, Jr. ■ 23223 #051-01-1945 L1952 **EM** *020

HERRICK, Benjamin Wright. ■ 23227 #051-04-2008 *012

HERRING, Marion Mcbride. 7858 SHRADER RD, ADVANCED ORTHOPAEDIC CENTE 23294 #036-01-1993 L1993 **ORS OSM** *020 †40

HESEN, John W, Jr. ■ 23230 #051-04-1950 L1950 **GP OS** *020

HILL, Cassandra J. ■ 23230 #045-01-1949 L1954 **P OS** *020

HILLELSON, Ruth Leanna. 9900 INDEPENDENCE PARK DR 23233 #050-02-1979 L1982 **PS** *020 †65

HILTON, Stephen Barry. ■ 23230 #035-19-1972 L1977 **P PA** *050

HODGES, Robert M. ■ 23230 #946-01-1953 L1963 **OBG** *030 †30

HOEKSTRA, John Arthur. 2809 EMERYWOOD PKWY, STE 140 23294 #016-11-1975 L1994 **IM** *050 †20,03

HOLCK, Susanne. ■ 23230 #297-01-1971 L1976 **PTH GS** *050 †50

HOLLAND, William Elisha. 7605 FOREST AVE STE 303 23229 #051-04-1962 L1962 **CD IM** *071 †20

HOLMES, Galen Raychelle. ■ 23223 #051-04-2008 *012

HOLOBER, Brian Chas. ■ 23230 #010-01-1969 L1976 **P IM** *020

HOLSEY, Royce L, Jr. ■ 23230 #051-01-1953 L1953 **FM GS** *020 †18

HOM, Mark. ■ 23230 #036-01-1988 L1992 **DR** *020 †80

HOOVER, Shelley Kae. 8600 STAPLES MILL RD 23228 #051-04-1994 L1994 **D DS** *020 †15

HOSSAIN, Anowar. ■ 23223 #913-92-1991 L2004 **N** *012

HOU, Andrew. ■ 23227 #051-04-2002 L2002 **PMM** *100 †60 ‡

HOU, Wei. ■ 23233 #243-72-1984 L2005 **GE** *012 †20

HOUSER, Aubrey A, Jr. ■ 23238 #051-04-1951 L1951 **DR GP** *071

HOWARD, Catherine. ■ 23233 #011-03-1984 L1985 **IM CD** *062 †20

HOWARD, Farrar W. 1300 WESTWOOD AVE 23227 #051-04-1953 L1954 **GP** *071

HOWELL, Hugh Richard. ■ 23233 #051-01-1957 L1957 **N** *071

HUBERT, Juergen. ■ 23238 #407-20-1953 L1957 **AN PMM** *072 †05
HUDSON, Charles F. ■ 23230 #051-04-1939 L1939 **IM CD** *071
HULL, David Jason. ■ 23223 #027-01-2003 L2007 **PTH** *100 †50
HULL, Kathryn Jessica. ■ 23223 #012-01-2006 L2006 **OBG** *012
HUNLEY, Richard Lee. 2105 E PARHAM RD 23228 #051-01-1974 L1975 **FM** *020 †18
HUNTER, Samuel Boykin. 1500 N 28TH ST DEPT PATH 23223 #047-07-1966 L1973 **CLP PTH** *020 †50
HURWITZ, Julius. 1602 SKIPWITH RD, DEPT RADIOLOGY HENRICO 23229 #836-01-1973 L1987 **R** *020 †80
HYDER, Ghouse Syed. 3208 CROSS COUNTRY CT 23294 #495-09-1960 L1993 **PD** *020
IATRIDIS, Angelos. ■ 23229 #418-02-1954 L1967 **PUD IM** *072
IMAIZUMI, Tsutomu. ■ 23294 #572-12-1973 L1983 **IM** *050 †20
IMHOLT, Megan Elizabeth. ■ 23223 #051-04-2005 L2005 **PD** *012
INGRAM, Phyllis Ray. ■ 23230 #023-01-1944 L1958 **GS** *075 †85
IRBY, Edward C, Jr. 7650 E PARHAM RD, STE 100 23294 #051-04-1981 L1987 **ORS** *020 †40
IRBY, Edward Claiborne. 7601 FOREST AVE, STE 228 23229 #051-04-1953 L1953 **OM IM** *072 †70
IRELAND, Hosea Dewain. ■ 23230 #051-04-1936 L1936 **PUD** *071
IRIONDO, Manuel Andres. ■ 23230 #275-01-1939 L1966 **AS FM** *071
IRWIN, Chas Fayette, III. 10431 PATTERSON AVE 23238 #024-01-1970 L1976 **FM** *020 †18
ISAAC, Malak. 2205 N PARHAM RD, PATIENT FIRST PARHAM 23229 #915-02-1997 L2005 **FM** *020
ISAACS, Edward Richard. 9030 THREE CHOPT RD STE C 23229 #051-04-1968 L1968 **N PME** *020 †75 ‡
ITSKOVICH, Rozana A. 7660 E PARHAM RD STE 204 23294 #913-50-1978 L1995 **IM** *020 †20
IUORNO, Joseph Daniel. 2010 JOHN ROLFE PKWY, DEPT. OF OPHTHALMOLOGY 23238 #422-01-2000 L2005 **OPH** *020 †35
IWASHYNA, Scott James. 9606 PATTERSON AVE 23229 #051-01-2004 L2004 **PD** *020 †55
JACEY, Robert Wayne. 2821 N PARHAM RD STE 105 23294 #016-11-1966 L1974 **OPH** *020 †35
JACKSON, Gustavus V, Jr. 2205 N PARHAM RD 23229 #051-04-1960 L1960 **OM FM** *030 †18
JACKSON, Richard Allen. 1510 N 28TH ST, STE 204 23223 #010-03-1977 L1979 **IM CCA** *020 †20
JACKSON, Sherri Taylor. ■ 23223 #023-01-2005 L2005 **IM** *012
JAFARI, Ghazaleh. ■ 23223 #051-04-2008 *012
JAFFE, Michael. 9606 PATTERSON AVE 23229 #064-01-1968 L1972 **PD** *020 †55
JAFFE, Sonia Ann. ■ 23230 #051-04-2007 L2007 **PD** *012
JAGGERS, Patricia Carol. 7700 E PARHAM RD, EMGY DEPT 23294 #001-02-1986 L1993 **EM IM** *020
JAIN, Gaurav. ■ 23228 #012-01-2004 L2007 **NEP** *012
JAMES, Charles Marion. 7650 E PARHAM RD, STE 100 23294 #036-07-1963 L1970 **ORS** *071 †40
JAMES, Keith Wm. ■ 23227 #352-03-1962 **OS** *040 †80
JARRELL, Shelby F, Jr. 7605 FOREST AVE, STE 212 23229 #051-04-1973 L1975 **OBG NPM** *020 †50
JESSE, Janice Kenney. 2201 WESTWOOD AVE, VIRGINIA BLOOD SERVICES 23230 #051-04-1989 L1993 **PTH** *020 †50
JESSEE, Robert W. ■ 23227 #047-06-1946 L1949 **GPM PHP** *030 †70
JEZIORSKI, Alison Marie. ■ 23223 #035-06-2008 *012
JOHNSON, Bartholomew Weng. ■ 23228 #051-04-2008 *012
JOHNSON, Bruce Earl. 7605 FOREST AVE 23229 #051-04-1974 L1976 **OBG** *020 †30
JOHNSON, Corey Morgan. ■ 23229 #020-12-2006 L2006 **U** *012
JOHNSON, Edgar Bruce. ■ 23228 #051-04-1972 L1983 **AN** *020 †05
JOHNSON, Katherine Hanbac. ■ 23223 #051-04-2005 L2005 **AN** *012
JOHNSON, Laura Meredith. ■ 23230 #051-04-1939 L1955 **PM PUD** *071
JOHNSON, Mariann H. 4 DAHLGREN RD 23238 #051-04-1978 L1980 **FM** *020 †18
JOHNSON, Ronald Harvey. 7660 E PARHAM RD, MOB #1 ,SUITE 104B 23294 #010-02-1987 L1996 **OBG** *020
JOHNSON, Walter Henry. ■ 23230 #028-44-1942 L1946 **GP** *075
JOHNSON, Zelda West. 1510 N 28TH ST, STE 305 23223 #023-01-1996 L1996 **FM** *020 †18
JOHNSON-THREAT, Yvette C. 1510 N 28TH ST STE 3 23223 #016-11-1991 L1996 **IM PD** *020 †20
JOHNSTON, William Burton. 3602 MONUMENT AVE, GAYLE SMITH SCHRIER 23230 #012-01-1954 L1957 **PD** *071
JOHNSTONE, Wm Thompson. 5 LOWER TUCKAHOE RD W 23238 #023-01-1962 L1970 **ORS** *020 †40
JONES, Anthony Darnell. ■ 23223 #051-07-2004 L2004 **IM** *020
JONES, Christine Marie. ■ 23227 #051-04-2001 L2001 **CD** *012
JONES, Sarah H Hoover. ■ 23229 #051-04-1943 L1943 **PD** *071
JONES, Sidney Rivers, III. 7001 FOREST AVE, STE 2500 23230 #051-04-1989 L1992 **IM** *020
JORDAN, Cheryl Denise. 4620 S LABURNUM AVE 23231 #051-04-1987 L1989 **FM** *020 †18
JOSEPH, Antony. 1601 ROLLING HILLS DR, RM 201 23229 #495-63-1971 L1978 **P** *020
JOVIN, Angelika. ■ 23230 #409-06-1994 L2006 **FM** *100 †18
JOVIN, Ion Serban. ■ 23230 #781-01-1990 L2002 **IC** *100 †20
JULIUS, Demetrios A. 7603 FOREST AVE STE 209 23229 #038-41-1971 L1981 **P SME** *020 †75
JUNCOS, Luis I. ■ 23230 #132-02-1963 L1966 **NEP IM** *075 †20
JUSTIS, Homer R. ■ 23230 #051-01-1946 L1946 **U** *071 †95
KACHUR, Edward. ■ 23223 #065-06-1996 L2001 **NS** *020
KARNITSCHNIG, Heinz H. ■ 23230 #539-11-1957 L1962 **FOP** *030 †50
KASE, Jonathan Andrew. ■ 23294 #038-43-2001 L2005 **OSM** *020
KASTELBERG, Eugene L, Jr. 719 N 25TH ST, VERNON J. HARRIS COMMUNITY 23223 #051-04-1989 L1990 **FM** *020 †18
KAVESKI, Maryann J. 1602 SKIPWITH RD 23229 #051-07-1984 L1988 **OBG** *020 †30
KAY, Deborah. ■ 23238 #051-04-1977 L1992 **PTH** *062 †50
KAY, Leslie L. ■ 23230 #561-17-1936 L1942 *072
KEENAN, Robert Edward. 5920 UPHAM DR, BELLEVILE BRANCH POSTAL 15 23227 #041-12-1963 L1979 **FM CD** *020 †18
KELLMAN, Neil Jay. ■ 23229 #035-03-1969 L1970 **GP** *020
KELLY, John Jackson, III. ■ 23227 #051-04-1948 L1948 **RHU IM** *071 †20
KENT, Richard Irwin. ■ 23238 #038-41-1958 L1964 **AN PUD** *071
KENYON, Barbara Ann. ■ 23230 #030-06-1959 L1973 **OTO GS** *020 †45
KENZAKOWSKI, Leo F. 1602 SKIPWITH RD, HDH HOSPITALISTS 23229 #041-02-1994 L2002 **IM PD** *020 †20,55
KESSLER, Stephanie Beth. ■ 23238 #051-04-2002 L2002 **RHU** *100
KEY, Wendell Wayne, Jr. 6610 W BROAD ST 23230 #051-04-1964 L1964 **IM NEP** *062 †20

KHAN, Mansoor Ahmed. 1510 N 28TH ST, STE 210 23223 #704-02-1989 L2000 **IM ID** *020 †20
KHATCHERESSIAN, James L. 6605 W BROAD ST, STE C 23230 #051-04-1998 L1998 **HO** *020 †20
KILLEEN, Karen Leann. 1510 WILLOW LAWN DR # 102 23230 #051-04-1994 L1994 **DR** *020 †80
KIM, Arnold Hyuneun. 1603 SANTA ROSA RD, RM 102 23229 #051-04-2000 L2004 **NEP** *020 †20
KIM, Roger Hoon. ■ 23223 #016-06-2000 L2007 **GS** *100 †85
KINDL, Brian Thomas. 7660 E PARHAM RD STE 207, OF VIRGIN 23294 #021-05-2002 L2007 **OSM** *012
KING, Audrey L Cox. ■ 23227 #035-08-1951 L1956 **PD** *071
KING, Carla Lynette. 719 N 25TH ST 23223 #023-01-1998 L2001 *020
KING, Donald Perry. 7702 E PARHAM RD 23294 #051-04-1956 L1956 **R** *071 †80
KING, Jerry Everett. ■ 23230 #040-02-1968 L1969 **R** *020 †80
KING, Robert Garland, Jr. 2821 N PARHAM RD STE 104 23294 #051-01-1962 L1962 **OPH** *020 †15
KISER, Pamela Elaine. 1508 WILLOW LAWN DR, STE 117 23223 #038-41-1979 L1981 **DR** *020 †80
KITCES, Edward Nathan. 7605 FOREST AVE, STE 205 23229 #051-04-1975 L1977 **D DS** *020 †15
KITCES, Eileen Cantor. 7605 FOREST AVE, STE 205 23229 #051-04-1976 L1977 **D** *020 †15 ‡
KLEIN, Andrew Mark. 10812 WEATHER VANE RD 23238 #030-05-1980 L1985 **OTO** *020 †45
KLINGER, Mary Matilda. ■ 23223 #021-05-1997 L2000 **IM** *040
KLUMB, Ivette Elise. ■ 23227 #033-05-2002 L2002 **GS** *100
KNAPP, Karen Elizabeth. 7603 FOREST AVE, STE 206 23229 #003-01-1985 L1988 **OBG** *020 †30
KNAYSI, George Albert. 8921 THREE CHOPT RD, STE 300 23229 #035-15-1965 L1973 **GS SO** *020 †35
KNIGHT, Yvonne. 3811 GASKINS RD 23233 #010-03-1977 L1980 **D** *020 †15
KOCKENTIET, Brett Robert. ■ 23228 #038-45-2005 L2006 **D** *012
KOLADE, Samuel Olayiwola. ■ 23230 #690-01-1967 L1977 **GS** *100 †85
KONERDING, Hazle S. 6603 W BROAD ST, STE 400 23230 #011-02-1973 L1975 **D** *020 †15
KONERDING, Karsten F. 1508 WILLOW LAWN DR # 117, COMMONWEALTH RADIOLOGY 23230 #016-06-1970 L1974 **DR** *020 †80
KOONTZ, Warren Sykes. 8923 THREE CHOPT RD, HENRICON INTERNISTS INC 23229 #051-04-1989 L1992 **IM** *020 †20
KOWALSKI, John Peter. 2660 NEW MARKET RD 23231 #051-01-1981 L1982 **FM** *020 †18
KOWALSKI, Marcin. ■ 23223 #035-09-2000 L2007 **ICE** *012 †20
KRAF, Anastasia. ■ 23230 #041-07-1941 L1947 **GP** *071
KRAFT, Colleen Anne. 8660 STAPLES MILL RD 23228 #051-04-1986 L1988 **PD** *020 †55
KRAUS, Shane James. 7660 E PARHAM RD, STE 200 23294 #051-04-1978 L1979 **FM OM** *020
KRAUT, Michelle Stevens. 24 E GLENBROOKE CIR, MICHELLE KRAUT, M.D., PLLC 23229 #034-01-1996 L2007 **DR** *020 †80
KRESHOVER, Seymour J. ■ 23230 #035-19-1949 L1950 **OS** *100
KRICKOVIC, Milan Piersol. 7605 FOREST AVE, STE 109 23229 #051-01-1964 L1964 **IM CD** *020
KUEBLER, Brandon Edward. ■ 23227 #055-01-2004 L2004 **MPD** *012
KULHANEK, Jan. ■ 23283 #286-13-1994 L2007 **IC** *012 †20
KUMAR, Kalyani Medicherla. 2103 E PARHAM RD 23228 #495-21-1974 L1979 **OBG** *020 †30
KUMAR, Medicherla Shyama. 2103 E PARHAM RD STE 200 23228 #495-21-1968 L1981 **IM CD** *020 †55,20
KURUP, Manikoth G. ■ 23238 #495-44-1962 L1972 **GS** *020 †85
KYRIAZIS, Aikaterini. ■ 23229 #418-02-1961 L1978 **PTH** *020 †50
LAHAR, Nicholas David. ■ 23223 #051-04-2008 *012
LAMBERT, Karen Rozelle. ■ 23231 #051-04-1994 L1994 **IM** *100
LANE, Michael Wendell. ■ 23227 #035-08-1999 L2004 **PM** *060
LANYI, Thomas Richard. 7601 FOREST AVE, STE 338 23229 #016-42-1964 L1981 **U** *020 †95
LAW, Brett Matthew. 2530 GASKINS RD, STE A 23238 #025-01-1995 L1996 **FM** *020 †18
LEARY, Jeffrey Marion. ■ 23233 #051-04-2008 *012
LEBAK, Nathan Matthew. ■ 23223 #056-05-2003 L2006 **AI** *012 †20
LEDAAL, Pal. ■ 23229 #693-01-1971 L1978 **PD** *100 †55
LEE, Chuan-Hsiang. ■ 23230 #242-09-1947 L1960 **R** *072 †80
LEE, David Younghwa. ■ 23228 #051-04-2008 *012
LEE, Kyung Ok Chi. ■ 23229 #583-03-1952 **PD** *071
LEE, Richard Mimms. ■ 23229 #051-04-1955 L1955 **PD GP** *071
LEE, Richard Youngsuk. ■ 23223 #051-04-2008 *012
LEFFLER, Susan Gail. 1508 WILLOW LAWN DR, STE 117 23230 #024-05-1992 L1995 **DR** *020 †80
LEIBOVIC, Stephen Jacob. 2819 N PARHAM RD STE 100 23294 #005-11-1983 L1990 **HS ORS** *020 †40
L'ENGLE, Camillus S, Jr. ■ 23230 #051-01-1943 L1943 **PD** *071
LETE, Serafina D. ■ 23230 #748-02-1940 L1960 **GP GS** *100
LEVINE, Jay Michael. 1508 WILLOW LAWN DR, STE 117 23230 #035-19-1972 L1977 **DR** *020 †80
LEVINE, Mark Jeffrey. 8600 DIXON POWERS DRIVE 23273 #035-46-1983 L1984 **PHP FM** *030 †18 ‡
LEVIT, Mikhail. ■ 23229 #035-75-2004, ▲ L2004 **OBG** *012
LEVITT, Robert Howard. 7702 E PARHAM RD, STE 106 23294 #023-01-1981 L1985 **CD IM** *020 †20
LEVY, Bernard G. ■ 23230 #010-02-1943 L1954 **PYA** *071
LEWIS, Edward Geo. ■ 23230 #051-01-1954 L1954 **GP** *071
LEWIS, Walter Jackson, III. ■ 23230 #010-01-1963 L1966 **IM CD** *071
LI, Rowena Tsung-Ying. ■ 23230 #242-09-1944 L1956 **AN** *071
LIDDINGTON, Chas Emerson. ■ 23230 #051-01-1943 L1943 **IM** *071
LINDNER, John D. ■ 23230 #051-04-1944 L1944 **FM** *020
LINDSEY-BOISSEAU, Sandra. 4620 S LABURNUM AVE 23231 #051-04-1977 L1980 **PD** *020 †55
LITCHFIELD, David Lee. 7700 E PARHAM RD 23294 #051-04-1958 L1958 **END NM** *071 †20,28
LITOS, Martha Toni. 2300 E PARHAM RD, PATIENT FIRST WOODMAN 23228 #051-01-1996 L1996 **FM** *020 †18
LITTLE, Margaret Ann. 7702 E PARHAM RD, STE 205 23294 #051-04-1994 L1995 **FM** *020 †18
LIVERMAN, Joan F Hulley. 4825 S LABURNUM AVE 23231 #051-01-1968 L1968 **P** *020
LLOYD, Katherine Page. 6605 W BROAD ST 23230 #051-04-1997 L1997 **HO** *020 †20
LOCKHART, Charles Gregory. 7605 FOREST AVE, STE 302 23229 #028-03-1977 L1986 **GS TS** *020 †85,90
LONG, James Walling. ■ 23230 #010-01-1943 L1949 **OS** *071
LONG, Jason David. ■ 23294 #051-04-2008 L2008 *012

■ = Address Information Privacy Protected

LONGACHER, Joseph Wm, Jr. 7702 E PARHAM RD, STE 304 23294 #051-04-1963 L1963 IM GE *020 †20

LONGAN, Robert C, Jr. 1600 WESTBROOK AVE # 277 23227 #051-04-1939 L1939 P *071 †75

LOPEZ, Roberto Valdez. 1504 SANTA ROSA RD, RM 202 23229 #748-01-1971 L1978 AN *020

LOTANO, Marc Anthony. ■ 23227 #051-04-2006 L2006 AN *012

LOWE, W Carter. ■ 23230 #051-01-1957 L1957 IM CD *071 †20

LOYA, Abdul Ghani. ■ 23229 #704-02-1959 L1977 FM *071 †18,16

LOYA, Asif. ■ 23229 #704-02-1998 L2004 PCP *100 †50

LOYA, Zakia I. 1602 SKIPWITH RD 23229 #704-02-1981 L1992 PD *020 †55

LUBLIN, Bernard Allan. 7660 E PARHAM RD, STE 208 23294 #035-19-1960 L1963 ORS *071 †40

LUCAS, Kenneth Wilson, Jr. 2205 N PARHAM RD, PATIENT FIRST PARHAM 23229 #051-04-1971 L1976 FM *020 †18

LYON-THOMAS, Lelia May. ■ 23230 #047-07-1923 L1930 OS *071

MAC IVOR, Duncan Campbell. 1602 SKIPWITH RD 23229 #038-40-1976 L1986 PTH *100 †30

MAESTRELLO, Steven Jos. 7702 E PARHAM RD, STE 304 23294 #051-04-1990 L1995 RHU *020 †20

MAGLIC-MURRAY, Gordana. ■ 23230 #957-02-1959 L1967 PD PDC *075

MAGOVERN, Linda Ludwig. 1602 SKIPWITH RD, STE 104 23229 #051-04-1989 L1994 PTH *020 †50

MAHNKE, James Henry. ■ 23229 #054-04-1960 L1966 NS *071 †25

MAHONEY, Lea Elizabeth. 7601 FOREST AVE, STE 100 23229 #051-04-2002 L2006 OBG *020

MAIZELS, Max Sam. 2017 OLD PRESCOTT CT 23238 #051-04-1975 L1976 OBG *020 †30

MALLIET, Jennifer Leone. ■ 23223 #035-09-1981 L1984 PD *020

MANETZ, Charles E. 7702 E PARHAM RD, MCGUIRE MEDICAL GROUP 23294 #010-01-1967 L1971 DR *071 †80

MANUTA, Carl. ■ 23230 #051-04-1939 L1939 GP *071

MARAIST, Adrienne Louise. 7603 FOREST AVE, STE 206 23229 #011-04-1984 L1988 OBG *020 †30

MARCHAL, Matthew Walter. 2530 GASKINS RD STE A 23238 #051-04-1997 L1997 FM *020 †18

MARKOWITZ, Sheldon M. ■ 23238 #051-04-1968 L1968 ID IM *071 †20

MARKS, Jon Stuart. 4786 FINLAY ST 23231 #036-05-1996 L1999 PD *020 †55

MARTIN, Stephanie Renee. ■ 23294 #051-04-2007 L2007 IM *012

MARTINEZ, Jose H. ■ 23230 #042-01-1967 L1970 IM END *020 †20

MARTIROSIAN, Edward D. 7702 E PARHAM RD, STE 106 23294 #051-04-1965 L1968 CD IM *020 †20

MASSAQUOI, Hawa Samanya. ■ 23238 #025-07-2004 L2004 MPD *012

MATHERN, Bruce Edward. 7650 E PARHAM RD, STE 200 23294 #038-41-1989 L1995 NS *020 †25

MATHEW, Elsa Varughese. ■ 23294 #495-37-2000 L2006 CN *100 †75

MATUSIAK, Barbara. 9960 MAYLAND DR, STE 300 23233 #033-05-1981 L2003 IM *062 †20

MAUCK, William Rutherford. 7650 E PARHAM RD, STE 100 23294 #051-04-1956 L1956 ORS *071 †40

MAXWELL-HORN, Angela Cher. ■ 23229 #016-01-2007 L2007 MPD *012

MAY, Boyd Hickman, Jr. 7702 E PARHAM RD 23294 #051-04-1956 L1956 AN *071

MAY, Linda Gale T. ■ 23229 #051-04-1973 L1974 PDA *071 †55

MAY, Virgil Robt, Jr. 2305 N PARHAM RD 23229 #051-04-1943 L1943 ORS *071 †40

MAYER, Alden Brigham. 8107 OVERHILL RD 23229 #051-04-1955 L1955 PD *071

MAYO, Edwin Aylette. ■ 23230 #051-01-1962 L1962 FM *071 †18

MAYR, Matthew Thomas. 1651 N PARHAM RD 23229 #008-01-1994 L2004 NS *020 †25

MCALLISTER, Robert Conrad. ■ 23223 #051-04-2003 *100

MC ALLISTER, Samuel Mark. ■ 23294 #422-01-1995 L2003 P *100

MC BRIDE, Robert Paul, III. 7605 FOREST AVE, STE 411 23229 #051-01-1979 L1983 OBG *020 †30

MC CAULEY, Charles Edward. ■ 23230 #010-02-1962 L1973 IM *050

MC CONNAUGHEY, John S. 9900 INDEPENDENCE PARK DR, STE 100 23233 #010-03-1982 L1985 PD *071 †55

MC CONNELL, Anabel H S. ■ 23230 #051-04-1942 L1942 OM OS *071

MC COY, Arch T. ■ 23230 #051-04-1953 L1953 U *030 †95

MC CULLOUGH, Johnnie A. ■ 23230 #051-01-1936 L1936 GS CD *071

MC CUTCHEON, Wm B, Jr. ■ 23230 #051-04-1952 L1952 TS CD *071 †85,90

MC DERMOTT, Thomas Paul. 7858 SHRADER RD 23294 #036-07-1991 L1998 ORS *020 †40

MC FALL, John S R. ■ 23230 #051-04-1942 L1942 AN *071

MC GEE, Francis E, Jr. 6603 W BROAD ST, STE 401 23230 #051-04-1964 L1964 N *020 †75

MC KEOWN, Joseph Edward. 420 N RIDGE RD, STE 100 23229 #041-13-1983 L1988 PS GS *020 †85,65

MCLEMORE, Aaron David. ■ 23227 #021-06-2007 L2007 IM *012

MC MULLAN, Francis H. ■ 23227 #051-04-1951 L1951 DMP *071 †15

MC NEER, Paul Randolph. 2303 N PARHAM RD, STE 2 23229 #051-04-1962 L1962 OPH *020 †35

MC QUILKIN, Bradford Ryan. 7603 FOREST AVE, STE 401 23229 #051-04-1996 L1997 PDC *100 †55

MEDEIROS, Milton O. ■ 23223 #187-12-1960 L1972 N OS *074

MEHFOUD, G Joseph. 8923 THREE CHOPT RD 23229 #051-07-1989 L1990 IM *020 †20

MEHRA, Anand. ■ 23294 #035-01-2007 *012

MENA, Osvaldo Del Carmen. ■ 23230 #308-01-1954 L1960 GS CRS *020

MENDEZ, Manuel Diaz. ■ 23229 #649-01-1952 L1961 GS GYN *071

MENDOZA, Carla Corazon. ■ 23238 #048-13-2007 L2007 PD *012

MENDOZA, Michelle L. ■ 23223 #035-19-2005 L2005 EM *012

MENKES, Harold Albert. ■ 23230 #061-01-1963 L1975 PUD *020 †20

MEYER, Andrew Duncanjosep. ■ 23223 #051-04-2004 L2004 MPD *012

MICHAEL, Andrew Jos. 2303 N PARHAM RD, STE 2 23229 #048-12-1987 L1997 OPH *020 †35

MICHAUX, Richard A. ■ 23227 #051-04-1937 L1937 GYN GS *071

MIDIS, Panos M. ■ 23238 #418-01-1954 L1960 AN *071

MIKSA, Andrea Kay. 1603 SANTA ROSA RD, RM 101 23229 #027-01-1984 L1985 PUD CCM *020 †12

MILLER, Amy Frey. ■ 23238 #038-43-2001 L2005 FM *020 †18

MILLER, Donald Mark. 7700 E PARHAM RD 23294 #038-43-2001 L2005 AN *020 †05

MILLER, Jay Richard. ■ 23230 #051-04-1964 L1964 GE IM *071 †20

MILLER, Lawrence Gordon. 8002 DISCOVERY DR, RM 101 23229 #051-04-1977 L1980 OBG *020 †30

MILLER, Michael J. 7702 E PARHAM RD, STE 304 23294 #051-04-1970 L1970 RHU IM *020 †20

MINNECI, Peter Vincent. 3370 PUMP RD, PATIENT FIRST SHORT PUMP 23233 #305-01-1987 L1997 FM *020 †18

MIRANDA, Danielle Ona. ■ 23294 #051-04-2008 *012

MIRKES, Melanie Dyan. ■ 23223 #051-04-2008 *012

MIRSHAHI, Sakina K. 3370 PUMP RD, PATIENT FIRST SHORT PUMP 23233 #704-02-1979 L1991 IM *020 †20

MISTRETTA, Michael A. 1603 SANTA ROSA RD, RM 101 23229 #035-48-1989 L1995 PUD *020 †20

MITCHELL, Andrew C. ■ 23230 #051-01-1951 L1951 FM IMG *071

MITCHELL, R Brian. 6605 W BROAD ST 23230 #036-07-1985 L1992 HEM IM *071 †20

MITCHELL, Richard Gardner. 7605 FOREST AVE, STE 211 23229 #021-01-1986 L1994 IM *020 †20

MITCHELL, Robert E, Jr. 7605 FOREST AVE STE 211 23229 #051-01-1950 L1950 GE IM *020 †20

MITCHELL, Robert E, III. 7605 FOREST AVE STE 211 23229 #051-04-1982 L1982 GE IM *020

MIZRACH, Glenn Brian. 4000 GLENSIDE DR A 23228 #021-01-1983 L1984 FM OM *020 †18

MOHANTY, Laxmi Bilasi. ■ 23238 #495-13-1963 L1975 PTH *071 †50

MOLDOVAN, Annamaria Zita. ■ 23233 #781-03-1981 L2004 P *012

MONGIA, Shella Kumar. ■ 23294 #495-45-1990 L2007 MGP *012

MONROE, Paul Sheldon. 2369 STAPLES MILL RD 23230 #016-02-1975 L1980 GE IM *020 †20

MONTEIRO, Gary Andrew. ■ 23294 #051-04-2007 AN *012

MOORE, Blake Walter. ■ 23223 #051-04-2007 L2007 GS *012

MOORE, Chas Coleman, Jr. 7601 FOREST AVE, STE 228 23229 #051-04-1971 L1973 OBG *020 †30

MOORE, Frederic Potts, II. 3602 MONUMENT AVE 23230 #035-01-1943 L1943 PD *071 †55

MOORE, Frederic Potts, III. 7601 FOREST AVE, STE 228 23229 #051-04-1979 L1985 OBG *020 †30

MOORE, William Francis. 4620 S LABURNUM AVE 23231 #004-01-1978 L1981 FM *020 †18

MOORE, William Thos. ■ 23229 #051-01-1938 L1938 OBG *071 †30

MOORESIDE, Douglas Edward. ■ 23230 #051-01-1966 L1966 PTH *030 †50

MORALES-THEODORE, Rosa Ma. ■ 23238 #016-11-2006 L2006 P *012

MORGAN, Raymond Ward. 2200 PUMP RD STE 100 23233 #051-04-1996 L1996 FM *020 †18

MORGAN, William Ritchie. 9351 W BROAD ST 23294 #051-04-1983 L1992 U *020 †95

MOROIANU, Mihail. 7702 E PARHAM RD, STE 101 23294 #781-01-1984 L2004 RHU *100 †20

MOSER-MALZONE, Ila F. ■ 23230 #051-04-1936 L1936 *071

MOUSSALLI, Colette. 8921 THREE CHOPT RD, STE 201 23229 #036-01-1980 L1981 END IM *020 †20

MUELLER, John Malcolm. 7702 E PARHAM RD, STE 101 23294 #051-04-1972 L1973 ON HEM *020 †20

MUILENBURG, Robert A. ■ 23230 #010-01-1944 L1950 IM *020

MULLEN, Edward Eugene. ■ 23230 #051-01-1941 L1941 IM *071 †20

MUMPOWER, Rebecca Yvonne. ■ 23231 #051-04-2003 L2003 IM *100 †20

MUNICHOODAPPA, Choodappa. ■ 23230 #495-17-1962 L1975 IM *100 †20

MUNIZ-SILVA, Adrian. ■ 23230 #042-01-1965 L1969 GE IM *020

MURPHY, David Patrick. 9351 W BROAD ST, VIRGINIA UROLOGY CENTER 23294 #035-19-1994 L2001 U *020 †95

MURPHY, Francis John. ■ 23230 #054-04-1955 L1970 NEP IMG *071

MURPHY, Thomas Jos. 2300 E PARHAM RD, PATIENT FIRST WOODMAN 23228 #308-11-1984 L1988 FM EM *020 †20

MURPHY, William Paul. 1504 SANTA ROSA RD, RM 202 23229 #036-05-2001 L2005 AN *020 †05

MURRAY, James S, Jr. ■ 23230 #051-01-1941 L1941 P GP *072

MURRAY, Vienne Karen. 7605 FOREST AVE, STE 411 23229 #051-01-1997 L1997 OBG *020 †30

MUSSMAN, Grant Mccann. 3602 MONUMENT AVE, MONUMENT AVE PEDIATRICS 23230 #051-01-2002 L2002 PD *020 †55

NAFICY, Sadeque S. ■ 23230 #517-01-1961 L1976 GS PTH *071

NAKANISHI, Eric Hideo. 1504 SANTA ROSA RD RM 206, ANESTHESIA ASSOCIATES OF R 23229 #038-43-1990 L2007 AN *020 †05

NALEPA, Michelle Patricia. ■ 23223 #021-06-2007 L2007 MPD *012

NARLA, Shireesha. 2427 LAKE LOREINE LN, MCGUIRE VETERANS HOSPITAL 23233 #495-21-1979 L1988 IM *020 †20

NAUMAN, Aisha. 2300 E PARHAM RD, PATIENT FIRST WOODMAN 23228 #704-06-1994 L2005 IM *020

NAZMY, Waleed N. 1601 ROLLING HILLS DR, RM 104 23229 #915-02-1991 L1997 N *020 †75

NEWSOME, Bobbette Linder. 1508 WILLOW LAWN DR, STE 117 23230 #051-01-1977 L1978 DR IM *020 †80

NG, Chi-Kin. 7702 E PARHAM RD, STE 302 23294 #244-02-1971 L2004 N *020 †75

NGUYEN, Hoang-Hai Ngoc. ■ 23223 #041-12-2003 L2003 NEP *012

NGUYEN, Jennifer L. ■ 23228 #051-04-2008 *012

NGUYEN, Tonytuan Huy. ■ 23228 #051-04-2008 *012

NIAZI, Saifullah Khan. 4906 CUTSHAW AVE, STE 105 23230 #704-01-1970 L1974 P GP *020

NICHOLLS, Aurelia Gill. ■ 23230 #051-04-1935 L1935 GP OS *071

NICHOLSON, Christopher S. 7702 E PARHAM RD, STE 106 23294 #017-20-1990 L1991 CD IM *020 †20

NICKENS, James Harold, Jr. ■ 23230 #010-03-1969 L1973 ADM GP *020

NISMAN, Richard Marc. ■ 23230 #051-04-1972 L1977 GE *020 †20

NOEL, Thomas Everett. ■ 23238 #011-03-2001 L2001 IC *012

NOGI, Jay. 10711 CHIPEWYAN DR 23238 #041-02-1971 L1972 OP *071 †40

NOLLER, Katherine Suzanne. ■ 23229 #051-04-2006 L2006 OBG *012

NOLLER, William Edward. 4620 S LABURNUM AVE 23231 #041-02-1970 L1987 FM *020 †18

NORDT, William E, III. 7650 E PARHAM RD, STE 100 23294 #033-06-1983 L1990 ORS *020 †40

NUCKOLS, Paula Louise. ■ 23233 #051-07-1995 L1995 FM *020 †18

O'CONNELL, Nan Gillespie. 7605 FOREST AVE STE 411 23229 #051-01-1990 L1993 OBG *020 †30

O'CONNOR, Robert Walter. 7660 E PARHAM RD 23294 #035-48-2002 L2006 OSM *012

O'DONOVAN, Sean Connell. 7605 FOREST AVE, STE 308 23229 #021-05-1987 L1989 CRS GS *020 †85,10

OH, Unsong. ■ 23229 #051-04-1999 L2003 N *100 †75

OHAI, Paul Chukwugozi. 4000A GLENSIDE DR, HEALTHSOUTH FAMILY PRAC 23228 #690-03-1979 L1994 FM *020

OHSLUND, Ronald Kermit. ■ 23230 #051-01-1961 L1961 AM *030 †70

O'KEEFE, Dorothy Ann. 3805 CUTSHAW AVE 23230 #035-15-1983 L1997 CHP P *020 †75

OLIFF, George Anthony. 1510 WILLOW LAWN DR # 102 23230 #051-04-1963 L1963 DR *071 †80

OPPENHIMER, William Mayo. 1602 SKIPWITH RD 23229 #051-01-1957 L1957 OBG *020 †30

ORDYNA, Nicholas John. ■ 23294 #051-04-2007 L2007 GS *012

ORTON, Vernon Alexander. ■ 23223 #051-04-2004 L2004 U *012

O'SULLIVAN, Susan Golda. 7702 E PARHAM RD, VIRGINIA PHYSICIANS INC 23294 #051-04-1994 L1994 **DR** *020 †80
OTERO, Francisco Jose. 7660 E PARHAM RD STE 207, OF VIRGIN 23294 #042-01-2000 L2005 **OSM** *020
OVERTON, Thomas P. ■ 23229 #051-04-1952 L1952 **PD** *071 †55
OWEN, Duncan Shaw, Jr. ■ 23229 #036-01-1960 L1965 **IM RHU** *071 †20
PACIOUS, Brian Jos. 1508 WILLOW LAWN DR, STE 117 23230 #010-02-1982 L1991 **DR** *020 †80
PADGETT, Alan Vaden. 1510 WILLOW LAWN DR # 102 23230 #051-01-1999 L1999 **DR** *020 †80
PADGETT, Julia K. ■ 23233 #051-01-1998 L1998 **D DS** *020 †15
PADUA, Fortunato Jos. ■ 23230 #021-05-1955 L1957 **GP** *075
PALMER, Celeste Dionne. ■ 23223 #010-01-2005 L2005 **PD** *012
PALMER, Dorothy Sue. ■ 23238 #051-07-2007 L2007 **PD** *012
PALMINTIER, Jon Stephen. 7605 FOREST AVE STE 308, LTD 23229 #021-05-1973 L1984 **CRS GS** *020 †85,10
PAPATERPOS, Nikiforos M. ■ 23230 #418-01-1951 L1961 **OS OBG** *074
PAREDES, Victor Manuel. 2530 GASKINS RD, STE B 23238 #132-02-1967 L1978 **OBG EM** *020 †30
PARK, Joon Oong. ■ 23229 #583-06-1967 L1979 **IM** *075
PARK, Nam Jin. ■ 23230 #583-06-1967 L1976 **P** *075
PARK, Sung Gohn. 9105 SPRING BROOK LN 23229 #583-03-1969 L1978 **AN** *020 †05
PARKER, Clifton Linwood. ■ 23227 #051-04-1965 L1965 **PUD IM** *071 †20
PARKER, Francis Power. ■ 23230 #051-01-1966 L1966 **ATP PCP** *020 †50
PATE, William Henry. ■ 23230 #051-04-1948 L1948 **GP** *071
PATRIZIO, John Anthony. 13520 REYNARD LN, RICHMOND COMMUNITY EMGCY A 23233 #654-01-1981 L1985 **EM** *020 †20
PAYNE, Kenneth N. ■ 23230 #035-01-1949 L1953 **PUD PHP** *075
PEBERDY, Mary Ann. 9813 RIDGE MEADOW PL 23238 #041-13-1984 L1993 **CD IM** *020 †20
PEDIGO, Elizabeth Burton. ■ 23223 #051-04-2005 L2005 **AN** *012
PEEBLES, Richard Charles. ■ 23227 #051-04-2001 L2001 **IM** *020
PEETS, Ayesha Kameela. ■ 23223 #047-07-2006 L2006 **MPD** *012
PEGRAM, Melvin Leon. 1537 HARPERS FERRY CT 23228 #047-07-1997 L1999 **FP** *012
PELECANOS, Nicholas T. ■ 23230 #418-01-1953 L1961 **TS CD** *071
PELKOFSKI, Elizabeth Benn. ■ 23223 #051-04-2008 *012
PELONERO, Anthony Leonard. 2221 EDWARD HOLLAND DR, MAIL DROP 43M 23230 #033-05-1983 L1984 **P** *030 †75
PENDLEBURY, Laura Karen. 7605 FOREST AVE, STE 411 23229 #051-04-2001 L2001 **OBG** *020 †30
PERAZA, Gustavo Jose. ■ 23230 #275-01-1955 L1961 **AN PTH** *020
PEREZ, Arturo. ■ 23230 #275-01-1954 L1962 **GS** *020
PEREZ, Eduardo David. 1530 E PARHAM RD 23228 #016-43-1980 L1988 **IM IMG** *050 †20
PERINI, Michael Anthony. 7605 FOREST AVE, STE 100 23229 #305-01-1996 L2001 **IM** *020 †20
PERKINS, Woodbury. ■ 23230 #035-01-1942 L1948 **OS PUD** *071 †20
PETCHETTI, Manjula Rani. ■ 23228 #495-11-1998 L2002 **PD** *100
PETERS, David Reid. 1511 STARLING DR 23229 #048-13-1994 L1994 **GYN** *020
PETERS, Patricia Marzol. ■ 23233 #051-04-2008 *012
PETRES, Robert Evan. 7601 FOREST AVE, STE 336 23229 #055-01-1965 L1970 **OBS MFM** *020 †30
PETTIT, Richard Jos. 8921 3 CHOPT RD STE 300 23229 #051-04-1978 L1980 **GS** *020 †85
PICCO, Christine Clara. ■ 23223 #051-04-2008 *012
PINSCHMIDT, Norman W. ■ 23230 #051-04-1949 L1949 **OPH** *071 †35
PITTS, Forrest Williford. PO BOX 27032 23273 #051-04-1947 L1947 **PHP IM** *030 †20
PLEASANTS, Gregory James. 2101 E PARHAM RD 23228 #051-04-1981 L1984 **IM** *020
POINDEXTER, John Saml, III. ■ 23229 #036-07-1963 L1971 **IM** *020 †20
POLE, Frank N. ■ 23229 #051-04-1936 L1936 **U** *071 †95
PORT, Carolyn Clayton. 4786 FINLAY ST 23231 #036-07-2001 L2001 **PD** *020 †55
PORTER, George Wm, Jr. 7001 W BROAD ST 23294 #051-04-1961 L1961 **FM OS** *071
POSEY, Jannelle Lynette. ■ 23228 #051-04-2008 *012
POTEET, James Edward. ■ 23230 #051-04-1962 L1962 **FM** *020
POTTER, Meredith A. ■ 23294 #048-14-2003 L2003 **PD** *100
POWELL, Jess A, Jr. ■ 23230 #051-01-1943 L1943 **GP** *071
POWELL, Tiffany Lasonya. ■ 23223 #025-07-2005 L2005 **NS** *012
POWERS, Kevin Larry. 4000A GLENSIDE DR 23228 #051-04-1992 L1993 **FM** *020 †18
PRABHAKAR, Shashi Kumar. 3370 PUMP RD, PATIENT FIRST SHORT PUMP 23233 #496-39-1994 L2002 **IM** *020 †20
PRATT, Dennis Cole. 1510 N 28TH ST 23223 #023-12-1988 L1994 **OPH** *020 †35
PRICE, Thomas Ransone. ■ 23229 #051-01-1960 L1960 **N** *050 †75
PRICE, Valarie Robins. 7209 W BROAD ST, ALLIED ANIMAL HOSPITAL 23294 #024-16-1993 L1996 **NEP** *020 †20
PRILLAMAN, Prescott Wade. 7605 FOREST AVE, STE 212 23229 #051-04-1994 L1997 **OBG** *020 †30
PRITCHARD, George Emmett. 1602 SKIPWITH RD 23229 #051-04-1960 L1960 **CD IM** *071
PRIU, Norberto Eduardo. ■ 23227 #132-01-1965 L1972 **NS** *020 †25
PUMAREN, Ralph Gavino. 3007 ANGLICAN PL, 3007 ANGLICAN PL. 23233 #748-10-1964 L1972 **AN GP** *020
PYLES, Alice Elizabeth. 3500 MECHANICSVILLE TPKE 23223 #051-04-1979 L1980 **FM** *020 †18
QUILLIN, Elizabeth Kathle. ■ 23227 #021-06-2007 **OBG** *012
QURESHI, Ghulam Dastgir. 7660 E PARHAM RD STE 102 23294 #704-01-1964 L1970 **HO IM** *020 †20
RABHAN, Nathan Henry. 7605 FOREST AVE, SE 206 23229 #012-01-1974 L1976 **OBG** *020 †30
RAFAL, Harold Sidney. ■ 23230 #051-04-1943 L1944 **GS** *071 †85
RAGAZZI, Helen N. 2027 E MAIN ST, CARMA 23223 #023-07-1991 L1999 **PD** *040 †55
RAGHEB, Samir Mikhail. ■ 23230 #330-01-1955 L1964 **TS CD** *020 †85,90
RAGLAND, Stuart, Jr. ■ 23230 #051-04-1950 L1950 **IM CD** *071 †20
RAHAL, Frederick. 5901 LAKESIDE AVE 23228 #051-04-1959 L1959 **PD FM** *071 †55
RANDOLPH, Charles L, Jr. ■ 23230 #051-04-1951 L1951 **R** *071 †80
RANJAN, Aparna. 8580 MAGELLAN PKWY, BON SECOURS RICHMOND 23227 #495-05-1993 L1999 **IM IMG** *020 †20
RANJBAR, Noshene Elaine. ■ 23229 #051-01-2002 L2007 **FM** *100
RAO, Yiping. 1871 IVYSTONE CT 23238 #243-74-1982 L2002 **GE** *100 †20
RAUSCH, Mark Austin. 7700 E PARHAM RD, BAYONNE MEDICAL CENTER 23294 #051-07-1997 L2005 **EM** *020 †16
RAWLS, John Ashburn. 7603 FOREST AVE 23229 #051-04-1960 L1960 **GS** *071 †85
RAY, Brenda Julia. 7660 E PARHAM RD, STE 205 23294 #051-04-1981 L1982 **IM** *020 †20
REED, William Clark, Jr. 1602 SKIPWITH RD, HENRICO DOCTORS HOSPITAL 23229 #051-04-2001 L2001 **FM** *020 †18
REESE, Dalinda Berk. 7700 E PARHAM RD 23294 #025-01-1981 L1982 **AN IM** *020 †20,05
REESE, Erin Lindsay. ■ 23231 #051-04-2007 L2007 **IM** *012
REESE, Mitchell Stuart. 1508 WILLOW LAWN DR, STE 117 23230 #012-05-1971 L1977 **DR N** *020 †80
REEVES, Juliana Eileen. ■ 23228 #051-01-2005 L2006 **OPH** *012
REEVES, Robert Legare. ■ 23230 #051-01-1946 L1946 **PA IM** *071 †20
REID, Natasha Ann. 314 N 25TH ST, # 2FL 23223 #021-05-2007 L2007 **OBG** *012
REIHL, Jeffrey Powers. 7700 E PARHAM RD 23294 #051-04-1993 L1994 **EM** *020 †18
RENTSCH, Saml Burton, Jr. ■ 23230 #051-04-1954 L1954 **IM OS** *071
REPASS, James Albert. ■ 23229 #051-04-1965 L1965 **IM NEP** *020 †20
REYNOLDS, Barbara K. ■ 23233 #035-09-1960 **PD PDC** *074
RHODES, Paul Gregg. ■ 23230 #154-02-1956 L1959 **PUD IM** *020 †20
RIAZ, Omer Junaid. ■ 23230 #051-04-2003 L2003 **GS** *012
RICE, Marion Lee, Jr. ■ 23228 #051-04-1944 L1944 **GE IM** *020 †20
RICE, Monica Louise. ■ 23238 #041-15-2000 L2003 **AN** *100 †05
RICHARD, Mary Martin Wade. ■ 23230 #051-01-1943 L1943 **OBG** *071
RICHARDSON, David W. ■ 23227 #024-01-1951 L1955 **CD IM** *071 †20
RICKMAN, Trudy Lynn. 1603 SANTA ROSA RD, FOREST PARK DIALYSIS CENTE 23229 #051-07-1996 L1999 **NEP** *020 †20
RISSER, Andreya Brianne. ■ 23223 #051-04-2008 *012
RIZK, Philip Hikmat. 1602 SKIPWITH RD, STE 201 23229 #051-04-1988 L1991 **IM** *020 †20
ROBERTS, Bobbie Lee. 7660 E PARHAM RD 23294 #010-01-1962 L1963 **R** *071 †80
ROBINSON, Edwin Gregg. 7702 E PARHAM RD, STE 301 MOB III 23294 #051-04-1984 L1985 **FM R** *020 †18
ROBINSON, Grover C. 4786 FINLAY ST 23231 #051-04-1972 L1972 **PD EM** *020 †55
ROBINSON, James Forrest. 7605 FOREST AVE STE 205 23229 #012-01-1972 L1973 **D** *020 †15
ROBINSON, Ronald Eric. 7702 E PARHAM RD, STE 103 23294 #051-04-1979 L1992 **DR** *020 †80
RODRIGUEZ, Colleen Graul. ■ 23233 #048-14-2007 L2007 **AN** *012
ROLLINS, James Andria. 7702 E PARHAM RD 23294 #030-06-1978 L1986 **FM** *020 †18
ROME, Alison M. ■ 23227 #021-06-2004 L2007 **HO** *012 †20
ROOKSBY, Susan Tuck. ■ 23230 #051-04-2007 L2007 **AN** *012
ROONEY, Mervyn Stuart C. 7605 FOREST AVE STE 311 23229 #539-03-1943 L1955 **AN** *075
ROSA, Samuel. ■ 23238 #847-04-1962 L1966 **GP** *030
ROSE, Leslie Wm, Jr. 7605 FOREST AVE STE 100 23229 #028-02-1943 L1949 **IM** *020 †20
ROSE, Leslie Wm, III. 7605 FOREST AVE STE 100 23229 #051-04-1979 L1980 **IM FM** *020 †20
ROSE, Vicki Holbrook. 1602 SKIPWITH RD, HENRICO DOCTOR'S HOSPITAL 23229 #020-12-1987 L2002 **NPM PD** *020 †55
ROSENBERG, Sanford M. 7603 FOREST AVE STE 301 23229 #008-02-1972 L1980 **REN GYN** *020 †30
ROSENBLUM, William I. 305 TARRYTOWN DR 23229 #035-19-1961 L1969 **NP ATP** *050 †50
ROWLAND, Harry S, Jr. 5 PARTRIDGE HILL FARM RD 23238 #023-01-1951 L1960 **U** *071 †95
ROWLES, David Mark. 7605 FOREST AVE, STE 410 23229 #051-04-1991 L2001 **ID** *020 †20
ROYAL, Frank Spencer. 1122 N 25TH ST 23223 #047-07-1968 L1969 **FM** *020
ROYAL, Frank Spencer, Jr. ■ 23227 #047-07-1997 **PYM** *020
ROYAL, Harry Willis. 1122 N 25TH ST, STE C 23223 #047-07-1966 L1970 **OBG** *020 †30
ROZAKI-SISMANI, Anna. 6605 W BROAD ST, CREDENTIALING-STE C 23230 #418-01-1973 L1980 **ON HEM** *020 †20
RUFFIN, David Monroe. ■ 23294 #055-01-2003 L2008 **AN** *100
RULA, Charles Arthur. 3370 PUMP RD, PATIENT FIRST SHORT PUMP 23233 #051-04-1973 L1974 **EM ORS** *020 †16
RUSSELL, John A. 513 FOREST AVE STE 206 23229 #056-06-1973 L1975 **P** *020 †75
RUSSO MENNA, Iolanda. ■ 23233 #561-17-1986 L2000 **AN** *020 †05
RUTLEDGE, Louise Ann. 7700 E PARHAM RD 23294 #016-06-1980 L1993 **N OM** *020
RYAN, Cynthia Shiloh. ■ 23223 #048-15-2001 L2001 **END** *020
SAEXINGER, Heribert Geo. ■ 23230 #154-07-1945 L1957 **P N** *030
SAIYED, Moin U. 1504 SANTA ROSA RD, RM 206 23229 #704-16-1982 L2004 **AN** *020 †05
SAIYED, Shama Begum. 3212 CUTSHAW AVE 23230 #704-02-1982 L2003 **P** *100
SALMAN, Nada. ■ 23294 #875-01-1992 L1998 **NPM** *100 †55
SANDIDGE, Roy P, Jr. ■ 23230 #051-01-1951 L1951 **ID** *071
SANTOS, Daniel Victor. ■ 23230 #051-04-2003 L2003 **OTO** *012
SARKER, Muhammad A. 4906 CUTSHAW AVE, CARY STREET FAMILY PRACTIC 23230 #160-05-1963 L1981 **FM** *020
SAVAGE, Bernard M. ■ 23229 #051-04-1951 L1951 **R** *071 †80
SCHEER, Cherie Eileen. 1510 WILLOW LAWN DR, STE 102 23230 #051-04-1980 L1982 **DR** *020 †80
SCHMIDT-ULLRICH, Brigitte. ■ 23229 #409-04-1971 L1990 **D** *020
SCHUKMAN, Jay S. 2221 EDWARD HOLLAND DR, ANTHEM BCBS VIRGINIA VA400 23230 #019-02-1975 L1999 **FM** *020 †18
SCHULMAN, Alan Eliot. ■ 23229 #036-01-2002 L2002 **N** *100 †75
SCHUTRUMPF, Andrew Clay. 7001 FOREST AVE, STE 2500 23230 #051-04-1989 L1997 **IM** *020 †20
SCHWARTEN, Donald E. ■ 23229 #016-06-1966 L1969 **R** *020 †80
SCHWARTZ, Jeffrey Veron. 2305 N PARHAM RD, STE 1 23229 #051-04-1992 L1993 **FM** *020 †18
SCHWARZSCHILD, Melissa W. 7605 FOREST AVE, STE 205 23229 #051-04-2002 L2002 **D** *020 †15
SCHWEIKER, Mary Michael. 3602 MONUMENT AVE, MONUMENT AVE PEDIATRICS 23230 #051-04-1994 L1994 **PD** *020 †55
SCOTT, Robert Bradley. 1400 WESTWOOD AVE, STE 106 23227 #051-04-1958 L1958 **IM IMG** *071 †20
SEEMAN, Irvin Jay. 2369 STAPLES MILL RD 23230 #012-01-1975 L1980 **GE IM** *020 †20
SEGURA, Victoria V. 8580 MAGELLAN PKWY, BON SECOURS HEALTH SYSTEM 23227 #748-02-1967 L1979 **OS PTH** *020 †50
SELPH, James Anderson. ■ 23229 #051-04-1957 L1957 **U** *020 †95
SENECAL, Kathryn Eileen. ■ 23223 #041-02-2006 L2006 **PD** *012
SENUOKE, Maxwell Olutilew. ■ 23228 #038-41-2005 L2005 **P** *012
SEQUEIRA, Deryk C. 7603 FOREST AVE STE 2, COURTYARD OFFICE BUILDING 23229 #495-01-1989 L2004 **NPM** *020 †55
SHAH, Vipul Ashok. ■ 23294 #038-43-2002 L2002 **NEP** *012 †20
SHAIA, Anthony Jos. 7650 E PARHAM RD, STE 100 23294 #051-04-1986 L1991 **ORS** *020 †40
SHAIA, Fred Thos. 8905 THREE CHOPT RD, # B 23229 #051-04-1965 L1965 **NO OTO** *072 †45
SHAIA, Harry Joseph. 7601 FOREST AVE, STE 228 23229 #051-04-1998 L2002 **ORS** *020 †40
SHAIA, Wayne Thomas. 10200 THREE CHOPT RD 23233 #051-04-1998 L1999 **OTO NO** *020 †45

SHANNON, George Ward. ■ 23230 #051-01-1945 L1945 **U** *071 †95

SHANOFF, Leslie Bernard. ■ 23230 #016-11-1959 L1975 **PS** *020 †65

SHARPE, Jewett Moncure. 4786 FINLAY ST 23231 #051-04-1983 L1989 **ADL PD** *020 †55

SHAUGHNESSY, Katherine T. 7605 FOREST AVE STE 212 23229 #051-04-1976 L1979 **OBG** *071 †30

SHAW, Eric Thomas. ■ 23294 #051-04-2008 *012

SHEEHAN, Michael Dale. 4620 S LABURNUM AVE 23231 #051-01-1978 L1979 **GP** *020

SHEPARD, William Alphonse. 3212 CUTSHAW AVE, STE 303 23230 #028-34-1977 L1979 **P CHP** *020

SHETTY, Ranjith. ■ 23223 #051-07-2003 L2003 **CD** *012 †20

SHIELDS, Charles P, III. 1602 SKIPWITH RD, HENRICO DOCTORS' HOSP 23229 #038-40-1982 L1984 **EM IM** *020 †20

SHINN, Laurie Lee. 6603 W BROAD ST, STE 400 23230 #051-04-1992 L1992 **D** *020 †55,15

SHOOK, Zachary Mark. 7700 E PARHAM RD 23294 #011-02-2003 L2003 **IM** *020 †20

SHUMADINE, Jason Thomas. ■ 23228 #051-07-2004 L2004 **RO** *012

SIDDIQUIE, Ambreen Sajjad. ■ 23228 #704-21-2002 L2008 **IM** *020 †20

SILVA-ROJANO, Norberto. ■ 23230 #264-02-1962 L1967 **GS EM** *071 †85

SILVERMAN, Gilbert. 1500 WESTBROOK CT 23227 #869-02-1960 L1967 **CHP PD** *075 †55,75

SIMCOX, Thomas Lloyd. ■ 23223 #051-04-2008 *012

SIMPSON, Kerri Anne. ■ 23223 #051-04-2008 L2008 *012

SINGER, Robert Perry. 1651 N PARHAM RD 23229 #035-20-1954 L1963 **NS** *071 †25

SINGH, Harinder Paul. ■ 23227 #495-29-1959 L1975 **AN IM** *071 †05

SKORAPA, Victor, Jr. ■ 23230 #051-04-1951 L1951 **R RO** *020 †80

SLATTON, David Sterling. 3781 WESTERRE PKWY, STE E 23233 #051-04-1991 L1998 **PS** *020 †85,65 ‡

SLOTKIN, Robert Irving. ■ 23230 #051-01-1961 L1961 **PD** *071 †55

SLUSS, James Roger, II. 10302 MEADBROOK PL 23230 #051-04-2001 L2001 **DR** *100 †80

SMALLWOOD, Katherine L. 7702 E PARHAM RD, STE 205 23294 #051-01-1980 L1983 **IM** *020 †20

SMITH, Crawford C. 7605 FOREST AVE, STE 308 23229 #041-02-1975 L1981 **CRS GS** *020 †10,85

SMITH, David Forsythe. ■ 23230 #010-01-1958 L1960 **TS CD** *071 †85,90

SMITH, Gayle S. 2200 PUMP RD STE 200 23233 #051-04-1990 L1993 **PD** *020 †55

SMITH, Joseph Chas. ■ 23230 #010-02-1947 L1951 **OS** *100

SMITH, Kimberly F. 12529 CAITLIN CIR 23233 #047-07-1991 L1993 **FM** *020 †18

SMITH, Lakeita Lynne. 1296 CONCORD AVE, PO OX 28690 23228 #051-04-1998 L2001 **PD** *020

SMITH, Larry Click. ■ 23229 #051-04-1956 L1969 **P** *071

SMITH, Marcus James. ■ 23228 #051-04-2007 L2007 **IM** *012

SMITH, Maurice J Vernon. 7601 FOREST AVE, STE 338 23229 #352-03-1956 L1968 **U** *071 †95

SMITH, Maynard Putney. ■ 23229 #051-01-1938 L1938 **AI OTO** *071 †45,03

SMITH, Paul Stelle. 7601 FOREST AVE, STE 228 23229 #033-05-1970 L1975 **OBG** *020 †30

SMITH, Tabathia. 1602 SKIPWITH RD, HENRICO DOCTORS HOSPITAL 23229 #025-01-1994 L1997 **EM** *020 †16

SMITH, William Scott. 1504 SANTA ROSA RD, RM 206 23229 #016-43-1976 L1984 **AN FM** *020 †18,05

SMITHSON, Lori V. 1508 WILLOW LAWN DR, STE 117 23230 #051-04-1980 L1981 **DR RNR** *020

SNODGRASS, Harold Wm. ■ 23230 #051-04-1943 L1943 **GS** *071

SNYDER, John Wilson. ■ 23233 #051-04-2004 L2004 **ORS** *100

SOBOTKA, Fred E. ■ 23230 #154-07-1958 L1967 **EM** *020

SOLTYS, Grace Regina. 3602 MONUMENT AVE, MONUMENT AVE PEDIATRICS 23230 #051-01-1990 L1993 **PD** *020 †55

SOMERVILLE, Matthew Chris. ■ 23238 #051-04-2008 L2008 *012

SOUTH, James Gregory. ■ 23238 #051-04-1973 L1975 **R** *071

SPARROW, Charles K, Jr. 2660 NEW MARKET RD, NEW MARKET MEDICAL CENTER 23231 #051-04-1985 L1986 **FM** *020 †18

SPENSIERI, Anthony M. 8002 DISCOVERY DR STE 41 23229 #305-01-1983 L1984 **IM** *020 †20

SQUEF, Ricardo. ■ 23230 #726-01-1984 L1987 **IM** *030

STALKER, Campbell Grieve. 100 W SQUARE DR 23238 #919-05-1963 L1976 **GS VS** *071 †85

STANGER, Richard Alan. ■ 23233 #035-46-2006 L2006 **GS** *012

STANLEY, Timothy Owen. 1504 SANTA ROSA RD, RM 206 23229 #016-42-1995 L2001 **AN** *020 †05

STARKMAN, Martin Tobias. 7603 FOREST AVE STE 303 23229 #056-06-1974 L1975 **NEP IM** *020 †20

STAUFFER, Richard Allen. 1504 SANTA ROSA RD, RM 202 23229 #041-14-1981 L2002 **AN** *020 †05

STEIN, David Brian. 2200 PUMP RD, STE 100 23233 #051-01-1990 L1993 **FM** *020 †18

STERN, Alan Glenn. 3850 GASKINS RD, STE 110 23233 #041-02-1997 L1997 **RHU** *020 †20

STEWART, William Bruce. 7605 FOREST AVE STE 308 23229 #033-05-1970 L1978 **CRS** *020 †85,10

STIRT, Joseph Avrum. 1500 N 28TH ST 23223 #005-14-1974 L1983 **AN GP** *040 †05

STOLK, Mordecai Jeremiah. ■ 23227 #550-04-2004 L2007 **NEP** *012 †20

STOLLER, Raymond. ■ 23230 #010-01-1946 L1954 **GP GS** *072

STOTTS, H Lyle. ■ 23238 #054-04-1952 L1953 **EM** *020 †16

STOUGH, Betty Dolores. ■ 23230 #051-04-1960 L1960 **GE IM** *075

STRACHAN, Michael Joel. 7702 E PARHAM RD, STE 101 23294 #051-04-1974 L1975 **RHU IM** *020 †20

STRAKER, Hilda Germaine. ■ 23230 #010-03-1940 L1940 **D** *071 †15

STRAZZULLO, John Francis. 3370 PUMP RD, PATIENT FIRST SHORT PUMP 23233 #051-01-1991 L1994 **FM** *020 †18

STRICKLAND, Susangeline S. ■ 23223 #051-04-2006 L2006 **EM** *012

STRUBLE, Stephen Graham. 7858 SHRADER RD, ADVANCES ORTHOPAEDIC CENTE 23294 #005-14-2002 L2006 **ORS** *100

SULLIVAN, Josephine Young. ■ 23230 #051-01-1949 L1949 **AN** *071

SUMMERS, John Tibbs, Jr. 7700 E PARHAM RD 23294 #051-01-1986 L1987 **AN** *020 †05

SUNDARAM, Usha T. 1602 SKIPWITH RD 23229 #495-53-1983 L1996 **MG PD** *020 †55,19

SUTTLE, Grace Ellis. 7605 FOREST AVE, STE 100 23229 #051-01-1964 L1964 **IM HEM** *020 †20

SUY, Sihong. ■ 23229 #036-01-2007 L2007 **GS** *012

SWINTECK, Brian James. ■ 23223 #036-05-2007 L2007 **ORS** *012

SZUCS, Richard Alexander. 1508 WILLOW LAWN DR, STE 117 23230 #041-02-1982 L1983 **DR** *020

TANKOOS, Amy. 11409 LINDENSHIRE LN 23238 #035-09-1975 L1977 **N CHN** *020 †75

TANNOUS, Manhal Mousa. ■ 23294 #875-01-1997 L2008 *020

TATE, Richard Steinbach. 8923 THREE CHOPT RD, STE 101 23229 #041-02-1991 L1992 **IM** *020 †20

TATINENI, Shanthi S. 3370 PUMP RD, PATIENT FIRST SHORT PUMP 23233 #496-33-1996 L2003 **FM** *020 †18

TAVLAN, Cemalettin. ■ 23230 #902-01-1955 L1964 **R OS** *020 †80

TAYLOR, Michael Paul. 10431 PATTERSON AVE 23238 #051-04-1978 L1983 **FM** *020 †18

TAYLOR, Richard N. ■ 23230 #051-01-1951 L1951 **CD GS** *071 †85

TEDESCHI, Kim Marie. 3602 MONUMENT AVE 23230 #051-04-1999 L1999 **PD** *020 †55

TEJADA, Hugo Higinio. ■ 23230 #308-01-1953 L1960 **GP** *071

TEKIN, Mustafa. ■ 23294 #902-03-1992 L1998 **MG** *100 †19

TEKLE, Fessehaie. 1500 N 28TH ST 23223 #366-01-1984 L1999 **IM** *020 †20

TESSIER, Jeffrey Michael. 3370 PUMP RD, PATIENT FIRST SHORT PUMP 23233 #035-06-1995 L1996 **ID** *100 †20

THEKKETHALA, Kuriakose V. ■ 23255 #495-31-1962 L1976 **FM** *071 †18

THOMAS, June. ■ 23238 #051-04-1950 L1950 **CHP P** *071 †75

THOMAS, Shelton Wayne. 7605 FOREST AVE 23229 #051-01-1979 L1984 **IC CD** *020 †20

THOMPSON, James Edward. ■ 23230 #051-04-2004 L2004 **IM** *100

THOMPSON, Louis Milton. 2240 JOHN ROLFE PKWY 23233 #051-04-1994 L1998 **OBG** *020 †30

THORNTON, John T, Jr. ■ 23230 #051-01-1939 L1939 **OS** *071

THORPE, Alice V. ■ 23229 #051-04-1949 L1949 **CD IM** *071

THORPE, Bruce Wayne. 3602 MONUMENT AVE, MONUMENT AVE PEDIATRICS 23230 #051-01-1977 L1994 **PD** *020 †55

THORPE, Curtis Wayne. PO BOX 27032, HENRICO HEALTH DEPT 23273 #051-04-1976 L1977 **PHP** *030 †70

THREAT, Daniel James, Jr. 1500 N 28TH ST, RICHMOND COMMUNITY HOSPITA 23223 #016-11-1991 L1994 **IM** *020 †20

TIDEY, George F, Jr. 7603 FOREST AVE STE 301, RICHMOND CENTER 23229 #051-04-1984 L1988 **END OBG** *020 †20

TIEDEMANN, Marie Therese. 4000A GLENSIDE DR 23228 #051-04-1980 L1983 **IM** *020 †20

TILLER, Katherine Elissa. PO BOX 28263 23228 #143-05-1990 L1997 **IM** *020 †20

TIPPLE, Margaret A. ■ 23233 #035-08-1971 L1974 **PHP PD** *020 †55

TORRES, Amado Protacio. ■ 23230 #748-07-1956 L1972 **IM GE** *020

TORRES, Patricio. 7605 FOREST AVE, STE 414 23229 #231-03-1966 L1981 **CHP P** *020

TORRES, William D. 1602 SKIPWITH RD 23229 #043-01-1983 L1984 **EM VM** *020

TOUBIA, Nagib Toubia. ■ 23294 #605-02-2002 L2006 **GE** *012 †20

TRAN, Minh Quoc. 7702 E PARHAM RD, STE 205 23294 #051-04-1996 L1996 **IM** *020 †20

TRAN, Thao Anh. 8600 STAPLES MILL RD, AFFILIATED DERMATOLOGIST O 23228 #051-01-1999 L2006 **D DS** *020 †15

TREICHEL, Siegfried R. ■ 23230 #407-10-1956 L1961 **P OS** *075

TRENT, David Ford. 6605 W BROAD ST 23230 #051-04-1984 L1985 **ON IM** *020 †20

TRENT, Jeanie Lee. 7700 E PARHAM RD 23294 #051-04-1986 L1988 **IM** *020 †20

TRICE, Ernest Randolph. ■ 23227 #051-04-1947 L1947 **D** *071 †15

TRUONG, Mireille Diemmy. ■ 23233 #051-04-2008 *012

TUCKER, Henry St Geo, III. 6605 W BROAD ST 23230 #051-01-1969 L1969 **HO HEM** *020

TUCKER, Wm Travis, Jr. 3311 CHURCH RD, STE 100 23233 #051-01-1980 L1981 **FM** *020 †18

TULL, Annemarie Gililland. 4786 FINLAY ST 23231 #051-04-2000 L2000 **PD** *020 †55

TUMMILLO, Marie E. ■ 23229 #422-01-1983 L1984 **OBG** *020 †30

TUNNER, William Sams. 9351 W BROAD ST, VIRGINIA UROLOGY CENTER 23294 #051-01-1960 L1960 **U PUD** *071 †95

TURNER, Elaine S. 7605 FOREST AVE, STE 103 23229 #041-07-1974 L1990 **AI IM** *020 †20,03

TURNER, Robert Thos. 7605 FOREST AVE, STE 100 23229 #051-07-1984 L1985 **IM** *020 †20

ULSHAFER, Chloe Bolgiano. ■ 23230 #023-07-1944 L1970 **OS** *071

UOTILA MABERRY, Arja A. ■ 23233 #374-05-1980 L2003 **PTH** *062 †50

URSO, James Anthony. 2235 STAPLES MILL RD, STE 104 23230 #051-04-1993 L2001 **VIR** *020 †80

VAFAI, Monireh. ■ 23230 #517-01-1969 L1974 **AN** *020

VANAM, Rajani. ■ 23238 #495-57-2003 L2006 **FM** *100

VANASIN, Boon. ■ 23230 #891-02-1964 L1972 **IM GE** *020 †20

VASTESAEGER, Maria R. ■ 23230 #165-01-1972 L1976 **IM EM** *030 †20

VAUGHN, Mark Edward. 1510 WILLOW LAWN DR # 102 23230 #051-04-2000 L2000 **DR** *020 †80

VEECH, Thomas Hayden. 3311 CHURCH RD, STE 100 23233 #051-04-2000 L2000 **FM** *020 †18 ‡

VELO, Anthony Gomez. ■ 23229 #847-04-1950 L1958 **NS** *071 †25

VERNON, Hazel Jane. 6603 W BROAD ST, STE 400 23230 #028-02-1983 L1989 **D** *020 †15

VIEAU, Colette Suzanne. 7605 FOREST AVE, STE 102 23229 #550-04-2004 L2007 **PD** *100 †55

VIGUE, Jason Todd. 1504 SANTA ROSA RD, RM 206 23229 #039-01-1999 L2003 **AN** *020 †05

VILSECK, Jos Richard, Jr. 7702 E PARHAM RD, STE 301 23294 #055-01-1966 L1971 **AI IM** *020 †03,20

VINEY, Reagan Dlynn. ■ 23294 #048-15-2007 L2007 **OBG** *012

VINSEL, Jeanne Marie. 7601 FOREST AVE STE 332 23229 #038-54-1980 L1985 **FM OBG** *020 †30

VITSKY, Maurice Sidney. 1300 WESTWOOD AVE 23227 #051-04-1942 L1942 **OBG** *071 †30

VOELKEL, Angelika Ingrid. ■ 23223 #407-21-1971 L1979 **PM** *020

VOELKEL, Norbert. ■ 23223 #407-21-1972 L1979 **PUD** *050

VOKAC, Vaclav Albert. 4835 S LABURNUM AVE 23231 #286-02-1952 L1973 **IM GE** *074

VRANIAN, Neshan M. 7702 E PARHAM RD, STE 205 23294 #051-04-1977 L1978 **IM** *020 †20 ‡

VU, Peter Dinh. 4301 W BROAD ST, CONCENTRA MEDICAL CENTER 23230 #561-17-1980 L2004 **IM OM** *020 †20

WADE, Terrill. ■ 23229 #143-06-1976 L1984 **FM** *075 †18

WARD, Deborah Williams. ■ 23238 #010-03-1978 L1982 **PD** *074 †55

WARKENTIN, John Raymond. 1603 SANTA ROSA RD, RM 101 23229 #035-03-1974 L1975 **PUD IM** *020 †20

WARNER, Dennis Anthony G. ■ 23230 #566-01-1973 L1985 **P** *020

WASTI, Suraiya Fatima. ■ 23238 #704-02-1973 L1980 **AN GP** *071

WATT, David Graham. ■ 23230 #803-03-1970 L1974 **OBG** *020.

WAX, Stuart Harold. ■ 23230 #051-01-1958 L1976 **OBG** *071 †30

WEATHERFORD, Shannon R. 7603 FOREST AVE, STE 206 23229 #051-04-1998 L1998 **OBG** *020 †30

WEDMORE, Sydney Melvin. ■ 23230 #050-02-1968 L1970 **IM** *020

WEIMER, George A. ■ 23223 #051-04-1952 L1952 **AN** *071 †05

WEIN, Barry Keith. 10431 PATTERSON AVE 23238 #041-02-1985 L1986 **FM** *020 †18

WEINBERG, Gregg David. 1508 WILLOW LAWN DR, STE 117 23230 #048-12-1991 L1998 **VIR** *020 †80

WEIRICK-SACKS, Gunvor E. ■ 23227 #051-04-1985 L1989 **PD** *020 †55

WEISS, Gregory Michael. ■ 23223 #051-07-2007 L2007 **AN** *012

WHEELER, Barton Scott. ■ 23227 #051-07-2008 *012

WHIPPLE, Terry L. 3407 OLD PARHAM RD 23294 #051-01-1971 L1971 **ORS** *020 †40
WHITAKER, Joyce Lafon. 1127 N 29TH ST 23223 #010-03-1970 L1975 **PD** *020
WHITE, John Prettyman. 4000A GLENSIDE DR, GLENSIDE MEDICAL ASSOCIATE 23228 #020-12-1986 L1987 **FM** *020 †18
WHITE, Kelley Elizabeth. 7001 FOREST AVE, STE 2500 23230 #036-01-1990 L1998 **IM** *020 †20
WHITTEN, Mark E. 2301 N PARHAM RD, STE 3 23229 #051-04-1977 L1978 **OPH** *020 †35
WICKHAM, Edmond Pryce, III. ■ 23227 #051-04-1995 L2004 **IM** *100 †20,55
WIJESOORIYA, Niran Romesh. ■ 23223 #051-01-2004 L2004 **PD** *100 †55
WILCOX, William A. ■ 23238 #016-06-1950 L1952 **R NM** *072 †80,28
WILEY, Edward James, Jr. 1602 SKIPWITH RD 23229 #051-04-1956 L1956 **PD** *071 †85
WILEY, James Hugh. ■ 23230 #051-04-1953 L1953 **ORS** *072 †40
WILKINS, William Thos. ■ 23238 #051-04-1959 L1959 **IM CD** *071
WILLIAMS, Carrington, Jr. ■ 23233 #024-01-1942 L1943 **GS GYN** *071 †85
WILLIAMS, Dean Climmon. 1500 N 28TH ST 23223 #051-04-1983 L1984 **EM IM** *020 †20
WILLIAMS, Louis H. 7605 FOREST AVE 23229 #036-07-1951 L1954 **OBG** *020 †30
WILLIAMS, Robert Kolbe. 7605 FOREST AVE STE 414 23229 #051-04-1948 L1948 **P** *071 †75
WILLIAMS, Robert Owen. ■ 23228 #051-04-1954 L1954 **IM** *071 †20
WILSON, Cristi Sanford. 7605 FOREST AVE STE 102 23229 #051-04-1987 L1990 **PD** *020 †55
WILSON, Robert M, Jr. ■ 23230 #051-04-1943 L1943 **R** *071 †80
WITT, Mary F. 2221 EDWARD HOLLAND DR 23230 #051-01-1978 L1988 **PD PDE** *030 †55
WOLTERS, Jeffrey P. ■ 23223 #021-01-2007 L2007 **GS** *012
WONG, Calvin Takchun. ■ 23223 #051-04-2004 L2004 **AN** *012
WONG, Vernon Genkin. 23230 #041-02-1958 L1971 **OPH** *050 †35
WONG, Wai Tuen. ■ 23229 #064-01-1960 L1969 **PME** *072 †05
WOOD, John David. ■ 23227 #047-05-1999 L1999 **OTO** *100
WOOD, John Thornton. ■ 23230 #051-01-1955 L1955 **P CHP** *020
WOODHOUSE, Sarah Wilson. ■ 23229 #051-04-1990 L1993 **P** *020 †75
WOODWARD, Edward, Jr. ■ 23230 #051-04-1951 L1951 **IM CD** *071 †20
WOODWARD, Patrick Malcolm. 7702 E PARHAM RD, STE 205 23294 #030-06-1997 L1997 **FM** *020 †18
WOOTTON, Jane P. 2805 W BROAD ST 23230 #051-04-1965 L1965 **PM** *071 †60
WORTHINGTON, Andrew Keith. 3105 W MARSHALL ST, STE 204 23230 #051-04-1982 L1986 **N** *020 †75
WORTHINGTON, Janette L. 1508 WILLOW LAWN DR, STE 117 23230 #051-04-1981 L1986 **DR** *020 †80
WOZENCRAFT, Colin Prior. ■ 23223 #051-04-2003 L2003 **IM** *100 †20
WRIGHT, Harry Vernon. ■ 23229 #051-04-2008 *012
WRIGHT, Tracy Stroma. 9900 INDEPENDENCE PARK DR, STE 100 23233 #051-04-2002 L2005 **PD** *020
YANCEY, Henry Alexander. 1300 WESTWOOD AVE 23227 #036-07-1957 L1968 **ORS** *020 †40
YAPLE, Elizabeth Ann. 4786 FINLAY ST 23231 #035-06-2003 L2003 **PD** *030 †55
YARBROUGH, Lee Cappel. ■ 23233 #021-06-2005 L2005 **D** *012
YEH, Juddi Chaolee. ■ 23233 #048-13-2002 L2002 **HO** *012 †20
YEMINI, Tamar. ■ 23233 #051-04-2005 L2005 **PD** *012
YOE, Klara Balajthy. ■ 23229 #473-04-1944 L1961 **PUD IM** *020
YOUSUFZAI, Bashir Ahmad. ■ 23229 #118-01-1982 L1997 **CN** *075 †75
YU, Jennifer Sungyu. ■ 23229 #035-01-2006 **RO** *012
YUAN, Xiang. ■ 23294 #243-47-1989 L2007 **GS** *100
YUNIS, Eduardo Jose. ■ 23230 #064-01-1954 L1962 **PTH OS** *040 †50
ZAITOUN, Fares Hamad. ■ 23255 #051-04-1991 L1993 **A** *020 †55,03
ZALIS, Oreste. ■ 23229 #396-06-1958 L1971 **P N** *062 †75
ZASLER, Nathan David. 3721 WESTERRE PKWY, STE B 23233 #016-42-1985 L1989 **PM** *020 †60
ZEEVI, Gary. 7605 FOREST AVE STE 404 23229 #008-01-1979 L1985 **CD IM** *020 †20
ZFASS, Hyman Saml. ■ 23221 #024-04-1942 L1944 **IM CD** *071
ZIMBERG, Yale H. 1602 SKIPWITH RD 23229 #051-04-1951 L1951 **TS GS** *071 †85,90
ZOLEN, Margaret H. ■ 23230 #051-04-1940 L1940 **P GYN** *071
ZURAVLEFF, Jeffrey John. 2807 N PARHAM RD, STE 100 23294 #041-12-1986 L1991 **OS OPH** *020 †35

RICHMOND – RICHMOND CITY

ABAYOMI, Olubunmi Kehinde. 401 COLLEGE ST BOX 980058, VA COMMONWEALTH UNIV MED 23298 #690-02-1972 L2001 **RO** *020 †80
ABBAS, Huma. PO BOX 980257 23298 #704-16-1990 L2005 **P** *012
ABBATE, Antonio. 1200 E BROAD ST, MCV - OFFICE OF GME 23298 #561-33-2000 L2004 **IM** *100 †20
ABBEY, Linda Jean. 1605 RHOADMILLER ST 23220 #036-07-1979 L1983 **FM** *020 †18
ABBOTT, James Easton. 2004 BREMO RD, STE 201 23226 #051-04-1976 L1977 **FM** *020 †18
ABERNATHY, Troy Van. PO BOX 980257, VA COMMONWLTH U HLTH 23298 #036-05-2006 L2006 **PD** *012
ABHISHEK, Kumar. ■ 23226 #496-09-2000 L2004 **IM** *020 †20
ABOUHASIRA, Mohamed M. 701 W GRACE ST 23220 #915-04-1983 L2003 **IM** *020 †20
ABRAHAM, Anil Thomas. 1200 E BROAD ST, MCV - OFFICE OF GME 23298 #016-42-2005 L2005 **AN** *012
ABRAMSON, Stephen N. 505 W LEIGH ST, STE 205 23220 #010-03-1979 L1983 **TS** *020 †20
ABRENIO, Jose Kempis. 400 E JACKSON ST, J ABRENIO MD OCME 23219 #748-09-1963 L1984 **PTH NM** *020 †50
ACKER, Christopher Gerard. 671 HIOAKS RD STE B, RICHMOND NEPHROLOGY ASSOC 23225 #041-12-1988 L1996 **NEP** *020 †20
ADAMS, Scott Mcdowell. 1200 E BROAD ST, MCV - OFFICE OF GME 23298 #036-05-2006 L2006 **ORS** *012
ADDESA, Anthony Emilio. 1201 BROAD ROCK BLVD, RADIATION ONCOLOGY(114A) 23249 #041-09-1990 L2004 **RO** *020 †80
ADEKOYA, Sulola D. 500 NORTH 10TH ST, RM 109 23219 #035-15-1989 L2001 **OBG** *020 †30
ADEM, Mukhtar. 1200 E BROAD ST, P O BOX 980102 23298 #024-16-2000 L2003 **IM** *020 †20
ADIELE, Moses Nkwachukwu. 600 E BROAD ST STE 1300, ASSISTANCE SVCS DEPT MED 23219 #010-03-1980 L1982 **OPH FM** *030 ‡
ADLER, Robert Alan. 1201 BROAD ROCK BLVD 23249 #023-07-1970 L1973 **END IM** *050 †20
ADLER, Stuart Phillip. 1605 RHOADMILLER ST 23220 #023-07-1971 L1979 **PD** *050 †55
AFROZ, Rownak. PO BOX 980257, VA COMMONWEALTH UNIV HLTH 23298 #160-08-1986 L2004 **P** *012
AGGARWAL, Avichal. PO BOX 980543, MED COLL OF VIRGINIA 23298 #913-07-1996 L2007 **PDC** *012

AGHDAMI, Aliasghar. DEPT OF ANESTHESIOLOGY, MED COLLEGE OF VIRGINIA 23298 #517-03-1957 L1973 **AN** *071 †05
AHMED, Hafeez Yusuf. ■ 23225 #051-04-2008 *012
AHMED, S M Anwar. MCV OFFICE OF GME 23298 #160-03-1982 L2002 **P** *020
AHMED, Shareef Basheer. ■ 23225 #051-04-2007 L2007 **IM** *012
AHMED, Syed M. 1200 E BROAD ST 23298 #160-06-1982 L2000 **PYG** *020 ‡
ALAM, Arif Syed. 7101 JAHNKE RD, STE 720 23225 #308-10-1985 L1993 **PD CCP** *020 †55
ALCANTARA, David Daniel. ■ 23220 #051-04-2008 *012
ALEMI, Lily. ■ 23226 #023-01-2004 L2004 **NS** *012
ALEXANDER, Alison Jean. 2421 CHAMBERLAYNE AVE 23222 #041-13-1991 L1996 **IMG PM** *020
ALFORD, Alison Eleanor. 1 E MARSHALL ST, VCUHS DEPT OF NEUROLOGY 23298 #041-02-2005 L2005 **CHN** *012
ALI, Usman. PO BOX 980257, VA COMMONWEALTH UNIV HLTH 23298 #704-02-1998 L2004 **P** *012
ALKHALIDI, Muna A. ■ 23221 #528-01-1972 L1995 **P** *100
ALLAN, Christine Diane. 1800 GLENSIDE DR STE 110, FAMILY PHYSICIANS LTD 23226 #051-04-1997 L1997 **FM** *020 †18
ALLEN, Douglas Roy. 1200 E BROAD ST 23298 #051-04-1995 L1995 **PDC** *020 †55
ALLEN, Frederick James. 3628 E BROAD ROCK RD 23224 #051-04-1965 L1965 **IM P** *020
AL-MATEEN, Cheryl S. 1605 RHOADMILLER ST 23220 #010-03-1989 L1989 **CHP P** *020 †75
AL-SAMSAM, Rim H. ■ 23298 #875-01-1989 L1996 **CCP** *020 †55
ALTIRKAWI, Khalid Ali. 1200 E BROAD ST, MCV - OFFICE OF GME 23298 #875-02-1982 L2004 **NPM PD** *020 †55
ALVANZO, Anika A. 1200 E BROAD ST, DIVQLTYHLTHCARE 980306 23298 #010-01-1999 L1999 **IM** *050 †20
AMENDOLA, Marco Aurelio. 1101 E MARSHALL ST, BOX 9804 23298 #924-01-1971 L1977 **DR** *071 †80
AMIN, Mitesh Satish. 6414 MIDLOTHIAN TPKE 23225 #051-04-1999 L2004 **CD** *012
AMIR, Abdul. 7110 FOREST AVE STE 203 23226 #305-01-2001 L2004 **IM** *020
ANDAYA, Cecilia Fe O O. 3603 GROVE AVE, PEDIATRIC & ADOLESCENT 23221 #748-10-1992 L2003 **PD** *020 †55
ANDERSON, Charles Collins. 7101 JAHNKE RD 23225 #012-05-1974 L1975 **EM** *020 †20,16
ANDERSON, Soni Jo. 1101 E MARSHALL ST, RM4-006 23298 #001-02-1998 L1998 **PTH** *100
ANDERSON-THOMAS, Mychal L. ■ 23219 #051-04-2008 *012
ANDRIANO, Joseph, Jr. 2621 GROVE AVE 23220 #305-01-1985 L1988 **IM** *020 †20
ANSARI, Baynazier. 1200 E BROAD ST, OFFICE OF GME 23298 #305-01-2007 L2007 **PD** *012
ANSCHER, Mitchell Steven. 401 COLLEGE ST, DEPARTMENT OF RADIATION ON 23298 #051-04-1981 L1982 **RO IM** *020 †20,80
APOSTLE, James Andrew. 1000 BOULDERS PKWY, STE 102 23225 #051-04-1995 L1995 **PCC** *020 †20
AQUILO, Melissa Dawn. 5801 BREMO RD, RICHMOND INPATIENT MEDICAL 23226 #051-04-1999 L2002 **IM** *020 †20
ARANCIBIA, Carlos U. 401 N 12TH ST, MEDICAL COLLEGE OF VA 23298 #231-03-1969 L1997 **AN** *020 †05
ARCHER, Gordon Lee. 1101 E MARSHALL ST, SANGER HALL, ROOM 1-018 23298 #051-01-1969 L1969 **IM ID** *050 †20
ARCHULETA, Felice Mary. 1007 HIOAKS RD 23225 #007-02-1978 L1979 **IM** *020 †20
ARMENDARIZ, Rebecca Teres. ■ 23221 #030-06-2008 L2008 *012
ARMSTRONG, Carl Wm. PO BOX 2448, MADISON BLDG RM 646 23218 #038-06-1975 L1980 **PHP ID** *030 †20,70
ARMSTRONG, Richard H. 112 N BOULEVARD 23220 #051-04-1961 L1961 **P** *020
ARNOLD, Gayle G. 3603 GROVE AVE 23221 #023-01-1945 L1951 **PD** *071 †55
ARNOLD, John Michael. PO BOX 980257 23298 #422-01-2007 L2007 **ORS** *012
ARNOLD, Paul Orphanidys. ■ 23225 #051-04-2003 L2003 **GE** *012 †20
ARORA, Tania Kaur. ■ 23221 #051-04-2004 L2004 **GS** *012
ARRIOLA-RODA, Elma Lou Y. 2621 GROVE AVE 23220 #748-08-1966 L1977 **AN** *020
ARROWOOD, James Alexander. 1200 E MARSHALL ST, GATEWAY BLDG 2-291 23298 #041-14-1980 L1984 **CD IM** *020 †20
ARTHUR, Amaterasha Nkumah. PO BOX 980257, DEPT OF PSYCHIATRY 23298 #047-07-2006 L2006 **P** *012
ARTHUR, Douglas Wm. 401 N 12TH ST, MEDICAL COLLEGE OF VA 23298 #036-05-1989 L1990 **RO** *020 †80
ARTHUR, Robert Miller. VET ADMIN HOSP 23249 #036-07-1954 L1970 **IM** *072 †20
ASHBY, Franklyn Henry. PO BOX 26603, PHILIP MORRIS USA 23261 #035-03-1954 L1975 **OM** *071
ASHRAFI, Abbas. ■ 23225 #306-01-2001 L2005 **FP** *012
ASHWORTH, John Sheriden. 3540 FLOYD AVE 23221 #035-01-1958 L1963 **IM** *020
ASI-BAUTISTA, Maria C. 7148 JAHNKE RD 23225 #036-08-1987 L1998 **CCP** *020 †55 ‡
ATIYEH, Wasfi A. ■ 23221 #605-01-1952 L1958 **OTO PS** *071 †45
ATKINS, Susan Edwin. 1011 HIOAKS RD, STE D 23225 #051-04-1985 L1991 **OP** *020 †40
ATKINS, William Marshall. ■ 23220 #051-04-1952 L1962 **FM** *071 †18
ATKINSON, Richard L, Jr. 800 E LEIGH ST STE 50, OBETECH OBESITY RESEARCH 23219 #051-04-1968 L1968 **NTR END** *030 †20
ATRI, Lakshmi Sundar. ■ 23221 #051-04-2006 L2006 **EM** *012
AULETTA, Ann Giovanna. 401 N 12TH ST, MEDICAL COLLEGE OF VA 23298 #041-02-1988 L1992 **DR** *020 †20
AURORA, Taruna Kaur. PO BOX 980401, 1250 E MARSHALL ST 23298 #495-08-1994 L2006 **OS** *020 †20,16
AYELE, Hana. 1201 BROAD ROCK BLVD, DEPT OF GERIATRICS & EXTEN 23249 #033-05-1990 L1994 **IMG** *020 †20
AYOOLA, Folahan Kolawole. ■ 23220 #048-12-2006 L2006 **GS** *012
BADIN, Nicholas. ■ 23226 #264-02-1954 L1960 **R OS** *071 †80
BAGGESEN, J Rand. 7101 JAHNKE RD, STE 550 23225 #051-04-1997 L1997 **FM** *020 †18 ‡
BAILIE, Allston Gibbes. ■ 23226 #035-06-1948 L1954 **PUD IM** *071
BAILIFF, Ronald Clyde. 2621 GROVE AVE, RETREAT HOSPITAL 23220 #020-12-1989 L2005 **AN** *071 †05
BAIRD, Charles Lewis, Jr. 205 N HAMILTON ST 23221 #051-04-1957 L1957 **CD IM** *020 †20
BAKER, Evelyn Louise. 400 WESTHAMPTON STA, VIRGINIA EYE INST 23226 #047-05-1999 L1999 **OPH** *020 †35
BAKER, Sherman, Jr. PO BOX 980230, HEMATOLOGY/ONCOLOGY DIVISI 23298 #024-16-1982 L1983 **HEM ON** *020 †20
BALDERGROEN, Mark Robert. 5875 BREMO RD, STE G5 23226 #051-04-1979 L1988 **TS CD** *020 †85,90
BALL, Michael John. 2621 GROVE AVE 23220 #035-08-1976 L1978 **CD IM** *020 †20
BANAS, Colin Andrew. 1300 E MARSHALL ST, MCV HOSP-NORTH HOSP 9TH FL 23298 #051-07-2002 L2002 **IM** *020 †20

■ = Address Information Privacy Protected

BARANI, Igor J. PO BOX 980257, VA COMMONWEALTH UNIV 23298 #035-15-2003 L2004 **RO** *012

BARBER, Nikol Angelic. 412 LIBBIE AVE STE 4, COMMONWEALTH NEONATOLOGY I 23226 #038-44-1999 L2005 **NPM** *020 †55

BARMAN, Ashish. PO BOX 980662, VCU DEPT OF PATHOLOGY 23298 #051-01-2006 L2006 **PTH** *012

BARON, Mark Stephen. 417 N 11TH ST, 5TH FL NEUROLOGY 23298 #012-01-1987 L2002 **N** *050 †75

BARR, Pamela Jane. 1200 E BROAD ST, MCV - OFFICE OF GME 23298 #305-01-2006 L2006 **PD** *012

BARRINGER, Michel Laron. 3603 GROVE AVE, ARNOLD BARRINGER HANZEL 23221 #036-05-1962 L1967 **PD PDA** *075 †55

BARSANTI, John Michael. 1501 MAPLE AVE, STE 301 23226 #051-04-1988 L1989 **AN PMM** *020 †05

BARTHOLOMEW, Matthew Ross. 401 N 12TH ST, MEDICAL COLLEGE OF VA 23298 #051-04-1997 L2000 **EM** *020 †16

BARTHOLOMEW, Theresa. 1001 HIOAKS RD, PEDIATRIC ASSOCIATES 23225 #051-04-1993 L1993 **MPD** *020,55

BARTO, Judith Ann. 7000 PATTERSON AVE 23226 #051-04-1998 L1998 **PD** *020 †55

BASAVARAJI, Durgada. 110 N ROBINSON ST STE 200 23220 #495-99-1973 L1990 **N** *020 †75

BASKERVILLE, Archer Lewis. 3223 HAWTHORNE AVE 23222 #051-04-1973 L1978 **CD IM** *020 †20

BATHAII, Seyed Mehdi. 1200 E BROAD ST, MCV - OFFICE OF GME 23298 #517-08-1999 L2006 **DR** *012

BAUER, Cheryl Elizabeth. ■ 23219 #051-04-2008 *012

BAUTISTA, Eliseo Acopio. 5855 BREMO RD, STE 506 23226 #005-12-1993 L1994 **GS** *020 †85

BAWCOMBE, Drew Philip. ■ 23219 #035-06-2005 L2005 **OPH** *012

BAYKAL, Ahmet. 1250 E MARSHALL ST, MED CLG OF VIRGINIA 23298 #902-04-1984 L2003 **DR** *020 †80

BEACH, William Richard. 1501 MAPLE AVE, STE 104 23226 #038-40-1986 L1991 **ORS** *020 †40

BEALES, Julie. 1201 BROAD ROCK BLVD, MCGUIRE VA HOSPITAL 23249 #051-04-1996 L1996 **IM IMG** *020 †20

BEAR, Harry Douglas. 401 N 12TH ST 23298 #051-04-1975 L1977 **GS SO** *020 †85

BEARMAN, Gonzalo Martin. 1200 E BROAD ST, VCU HEALTH SYSTEM 23298 #035-06-1997 L2003 **GPM** *020 †20,70

BEAULIEU, Andrew James. 671 HIOAKS RD, STE B 23225 #047-07-1991 L1991 **NEP** *020 †20

BEAZLEY, Wyatt S, III. 425 N BOULEVARD 23220 #051-04-1961 L1961 **GS** *020 †85

BECHARD, Daniel Earl. 1605 RHOADMILLER ST 23220 #035-15-1978 L1979 **PUD CCM** *040 †20

BECK, Ralph Edmund. 5801 BREMO RD 23226 #016-11-1957 L1959 **PTH** *071 †50

BECK, Roland Peter. 401 N 12TH ST 23298 #065-05-1955 L1990 **GYN OBS** *020

BECKER, Robert Brian. ■ 23298 #051-04-2008 *012

BECKWORTH, William Jeremy. ■ 23298 #005-12-2002 L2002 **PMM** *100 †60

BEDICHEK, Ellen Gracy. 671 HIOAKS RD STE B, RICHMOND NEPHROLOGY ASSOC 23225 #035-01-1986 L1988 **IM** *020 †20

BEDUSCHI, Ricardo. PO BOX 980257, MCV, ATTN: MARY ALICE 23298 #187-11-1992 L2001 **U** *100

BEIER, Bridget. ■ 23221 #041-78-2003, ▲ L2006 **END** *012 †20

BEKENSTEIN, Lori W. 1300 W BROAD ST, SPORTS MEDICAL BLDG,SUITE 23284 #051-01-1990 L1991 **CHP P** *020 †75

BELL, Patricia Evelyn. 1201 BROAD ROCK BLVD, H H MCGUIRE VAMC 23249 #028-02-1980 L1981 **IM NEP** *020 †20

BELL, Sandra La Verne. 101 COWARDIN AVE, #302 MANCHESTER PED ASSOC 23224 #051-04-1978 L1981 **PD** *020 †55

BELLE, Cheryl Michelle. 2809 NORTH AVE, STE 100 23222 #051-04-1990 L1993 **FM** *020 †18

BELLE, Walton Mc Neil. 2809 NORTH AVE 23222 #047-07-1958 L1963 **GP** *020 †85

BEN-EZRA, Jonathan Martin. 401 N 12TH ST, MEDICAL COLLEGE OF VA 23298 #024-05-1999 L1991 **HMP PTH** *020 †50

BENNETT, L P Robinson. 2809 NORTH AVE STE 201 23222 #047-07-1963 L1967 **PD** *020

BENNETT, Richard Leroy, Jr. 2809 NORTH AVE, STE 201 23222 #051-04-1999 L2002 **PD** *020

BENNETT, Susan Whitelock. 1101 E MARSHALL ST RM4-050, DEPT OF RADLGY VCU HLTH SY 23298 #051-07-1998 L1998 **DR** *020 †80

BENSON, Larry Leone. 500 HIOAKS RD, STE A 23225 #025-07-2001 L2008 **FSM** *100 †18

BENSON, William H. 401 N 11TH ST, FL 4 23219 #055-01-1986 L1991 **OPH** *020 †35

BERBESCU, Ema Ana. 1200 E MARSHALL ST, GATE WAY BLDG 6TH FL 23298 #781-01-1997 L2004 **PCP** *100

BERGH, Cecilia Catharina. ■ 23221 #041-15-2004 L2006 **IM** *012

BERMAN, Lorraine M Wolper. 1200 E BROAD ST 16TH FL, BOX 980108 23298 #008-02-1994 L2006 **VS GS** *020 †85

BERTANI, Peter A, III. 401 N 12TH ST, MEDICAL COLLEGE OF VA 23298 #010-02-1980 L1984 **DR GP** *020

BESWICK, Isca Rochelle. PO BOX 980257, MCV - DR. O'DONNELL 23298 #035-45-2001 L2001 **PDI** *100

BETTINGER, Cynthia Blain. 701 W GRACE ST 23220 #051-04-1989 L1990 **FM** *020 †18 ‡

BETTS, Martin Frederick. 1800 GLENSIDE DR, STE 103 23226 #917-02-1970 L1978 **PUD IM** *020

BHAT, Shridhar V. 110 N ROBINSON ST, STE 305 23220 #495-35-1970 L1979 **NEP IM** *071 †20

BHATIA, Gaurav. ■ 23220 #051-04-2008 L2008 *012

BHUSHAN, Anup. PO BOX 980257, DEPT OF INTERNAL MEDICINE 23298 #028-34-2005 L2005 **IM** *012

BICK, Michael Sagalyn. 5855 BREMO RD STE 407 23226 #020-02-1972 L1979 **P** *020 †75

BINDER, Andrew Jay. 1200 E BROAD ST, BOX 980102 23298 #041-15-2005 L2005 **IM** *012

BINDER, Anita Bhagat. 1200 E BROAD ST, MCV - OFFICE OF GME 23298 #496-37-2000 L2005 *012

BISKOBING, Diane M. 401 N 11TH ST, MCV NELSON CLINIC 23219 #056-05-1986 L1998 **END IM** *040 †20

BIZZELL, Kimberlee. 1200 E BROAD ST, MCV - OFFICE OF GME 23298 #038-40-2006 L2006 **IM** *012

BLACK, Joshua Gilbreath. 1200 E BROAD ST, GRADUATE MEDICAL EDUCATION 23298 #039-01-2005 L2005 **AN** *012

BLAIR, Charles Jos, III. 1001 E MARSHALL ST 23219 #051-04-1962 L1962 **OPH** *071 †35

BLANK, John Emmett. 1501 MAPLE AVE, STE 2 23226 #010-02-1990 L2002 **HS OTR** *020 †40

BLAYLOCK, Wilmer Kenneth. 1200 E BROAD ST, BOX 164 23298 #051-04-1958 L1958 **D IM** *020 †15

BLOUNT, Alston Wilcox. 5875 BREMO RD STE 601 23226 #041-01-1958 L1965 **CD IM** *071 †20

BLUM, Darrielle Valerie. 7101 JAHNKE RD, CJW MEDICAL CENTER 23225 #654-01-2001 L2001 **EM** *020 †16

BLUM, Joel Alan. 1201 BROAD ROCK BLVD, SECT 116-A 23249 #024-07-1968 L1987 **P** *020 †75

BLUNK, Karen Leigh. 401 N 12TH ST 23298 #051-07-1982 L1985 **IM** *020 †20

BOARDMAN, Cecelia Haines. 1101 E MARSHALL ST, VCUHS BOX 980034 23298 #041-01-1992 L2000 **GO OBG** *020 †30

BODURTHA, Joann Norma. PO BOX 980033, DEPT OF HUMAN GENETICS 23298 #008-01-1979 L1984 **PD MG** *020 †55,19

BOEHMLER, Jessica. ■ 23220 #041-15-2007 L2007 **IM** *012

BOHANNON, Arline Denise. 1300 E MARSHALL ST, P O BOX 980102 23298 #035-15-1988 L2003 **IMG IM** *040 †20

BOKINSKY, Gary Brooks. 5224 MONUMENT AVE, VIRGINIA UROLOGY CENTER 23226 #051-04-1971 L1973 **U GS** *020 †95

BOKKISAM, Srinivasa Chakr. 7101 JAHNKE RD, VIRGINIA HOSPITALISTS, INC 23225 #496-24-1994 L2006 **IM** *100 †20

BOLANOS, Rodrigo Antonio. 1200 E MARSHALL ST, THIRD FLOOR ROOM 3-225 23298 #011-02-2000 L2006 **ICE CD** *020 †20

BOLING, Peter Avery. 1200 E BROAD ST, VCU HEALTH SYSTEMS 23298 #035-45-1981 L1982 **IM IMG** *030 †20

BOLLERUP, Edwin J. 7101 JAHNKE RD, CJW MEDICAL CENTER-NICU OF 23225 #030-05-1975 L1995 **NPM PD** *020 †55

BONAPARTE, Kenneth Owura. ■ 23224 #041-13-2001 L2006 **IM** *020 †20

BONNER, Lloyd Arden. 505 W LEIGH ST, STE 303 23220 #025-01-1975 L1978 **IM** *020 †20

BOONE, Carolyn Jean. 505 W LEIGH ST 23220 #051-04-1980 L1985 **PD** *020 †55

BOONE, Elwood Bernard, Jr. 110 N ROBINSON ST, STE 403 23220 #047-07-1969 L1970 **U GS** *020 †95

BORDEN, Denise L. 1200 E BROAD ST, VCU HEALTH SYSTEM 23298 #010-03-1980 L1983 **IM** *020 †20

BORZELLECA, Joseph F, Jr. 401 N 12TH ST, P O BOX 980034 23298 #051-04-1981 L1985 **OBG** *040 †20

BOSCH, Herman Arthur. 1200 E BROAD ST, BOX 615 23298 #024-07-1967 L1979 **DR OS** *020 †80

BOSHER, Lewis Hinton, Jr. ■ 23226 #024-01-1940 L1950 **TS CD** *071 †85,90

BOSHER, Linwood Paul. 417 LIBBIE AVE, VIRGINIA SURGICAL 23226 #051-04-1974 L1975 **GS VS** *020 †85

BOSS, Michael John. ■ 23220 #051-04-2006 L2006 **AN** *012

BOU-HAIDAR, Doumit Semaan. 401 N 12TH ST, MEDICAL COLLEGE OF VA 23298 #605-03-1992 L1996 **GE** *020 †20

BOUNEVA, Iliana Simeonova. 1101 E MARSHALL ST, RM 12-011 23298 #198-01-1990 L2000 **IM GE** *020 †20 ‡

BOURLIER, Peter Frederick. 1201 BROAD ROCK BLVD 23249 #035-20-1965 L1968 **IM PUD** *071 †20

BOWEN, Henry Albert. 7301 FOREST AVE, STE 201 23226 #051-01-1978 L1984 **CHP P** *020 †75

BOWSER, Barrington H, Jr. 5500 MONUMENT AVE STE E 23226 #047-07-1982 L1988 **IM PHP** *020

BOYD, Carl John. 5855 BREMO RD, STE 100N 23226 #011-04-1999 L2001 **AN** *020 †05

BOYKIN, Joseph Vonzo, Jr. 2621 GROVE AVE 23220 #051-04-1976 L1977 **PS** *020 †85,65

BRADY-MORRIS, Angela Lynn. ■ 23220 #048-04-2003 L2004 **RO** *012

BRAJOVIC, Andrej. MED COLL VA-GME OFFICE 23298 #957-02-1998 L2002 **CHP** *020 †75

BRANDT, Andreas Martin. 7101 JAHNKE RD 23225 #051-04-1990 L1991 **FM** *020 †18

BRANNEN, Judy Lynn. 1201 BROAD ROCK BLVD, MCGUIRE VA HOSPITAL 23249 #051-04-1985 L1986 **IM** *020 †20

BRATH, Lisa Karen. 1200 E BROAD ST, MCV-PULMONARY OFFICE 23298 #048-12-1988 L1990 **PCC CCM** *020 †20

BREEDEN, Louis M. 7229 FOREST AVE, STE 112 23226 #051-04-1977 L1978 **FM** *020 †18

BREHMER, Charles Edward. 909 HIOAKS RD STE J 23225 #051-04-1973 L1974 **GP FM** *020 ‡

BRENDLINGER, Dirck Lowe. 7231 FOREST AVE STE 102 23226 #041-09-1963 L1986 **R** *020 †80 ‡

BRENGMAN, Matthew Lester. 5855 BREMO RD, STE 406 23226 #035-20-1993 L2004 **GS** *020 †85

BREWER, William Henry. 400 N 12TH ST, MEDICAL COLLEGE OF VA HOSP 23298 #047-05-1968 L1973 **DR** *020 †80

BRIERE, Russell Ovide. 7101 JAHNKE RD, NUCLEAR MED CHIPPENHAM 23225 #067-01-1957 L1966 **NM CLP** *071 †50,28

BROADDUS, Wm Clendenin. 417 N 11TH ST 23298 #038-06-1984 L1991 **NS** *020 †25

BROGA, Christopher Dwight. 5801 BREMO RD, ST MARY'S HOSPITAL PICU 23226 #051-07-2000 L2002 **PD** *020 †55

BROOKMAN, Richard Robt. 1001 E MARSHALL ST, 3RD FL 23219 #024-07-1969 L1981 **ADL PD** *040 †55

BROOKS, Cynthia Kay. PO BOX 980257, MCV 23298 #011-03-2001 L2002 **DR** *020 †80

BROOKS, George K, Jr. ■ 23226 #051-04-1942 L1942 **P PYG** *071 †75

BROOKS, James W. 1200 E BROAD ST, BOX 980136 23298 #051-04-1946 L1946 **TS** *020 †85,90

BROOKS, Jim Alphonso. ■ 23225 #051-04-2008 *012

BROOKS, Kenneth Phillip. 1000 BOULDERS PKWY, STE 202 23225 #035-03-1976 L1979 **P LM** *030 †75

BROWN, Cara Anne. ■ 23221 #051-04-2008 *012

BROWN, Donna Dodson. 400 WESTHAMPTON STA 23226 #047-20-1984 L1990 **OPH PO** *020 †35

BROWN, Kenneth Blair. 1800 GLENSIDE DR, STE 101 23226 #051-01-1983 L1985 **GS TTS** *020 †85

BROWN, Leon Julius. 101 COWARDIN AVE, STE 101 23224 #051-01-1974 L1977 **FM** *020

BROWN, Marcus Wendell. 1109 W MARSHALL ST, COMMONWEALTH CANCER INSTIT 23220 #051-04-1982 L1988 **RO** *020

BROWN, Melanie Antonietta. PO BOX 980257 23298 #422-01-2003 **GS** *012

BROWN, Melanie Kristine. 1200 E BROAD ST, MCV - OFFICE OF GME 23298 #019-02-2006 L2006 **MPD** *012

BROWN, Peter Wilcox. 417 LIBBIE AVE, VIRGINIA SURGICAL 23226 #012-05-1967 L1974 **GS SO** *020 †85

BRUCE, Kerry Elizabeth. 1201 BROAD ROCK BLVD 23249 #041-14-2009 L2001 **IM** *020 †20

BRUGH, Victor Miller. 701 EAST BYRD ST, FED RESERVE BANK OF RICHMO 23219 #051-04-1975 L1976 **EM FM** *020 †18,16

BRUZZESE, Joseph Dominic. MCGUIRE VAMC 23249 #023-01-1988 L1990 **IM RHU** *020 †20

BRUZZESE, Vivian L. 108 COWARDIN AVE, CROSS-OVER HEALTH CENTER 23224 #011-03-1988 L1989 **IM ID** *020 †20

BRYAN, Daphne Lynn. 4730 N SOUTHSIDE PLAZA ST 23224 #051-04-1990 L1991
FM *020 †18 ‡

BUCHANAN, Dana Marie. ■ 23226 #051-04-1988 L1989 **GS** *020 †05

BUCKMAN, Peter Danl. 2004 BREMO RD, STE 103 23226 #008-02-1986 L1995 **TS** *020 †85,90

BUETTNER, Karin W. 5875 BREMO RD STE 400 23226 #003-01-1988 L1991 **OBG** *020 †30

BULBULKAYA, Cevat. 23225 #902-01-1948 L1963 **DR** *075

BULLOCK, Henry A, Jr. ■ 23226 #051-04-1948 L1950 **OBG** *071

BULLOCK, John Paul, Jr. 5875 BREMO RD, STE 606 23226 #045-01-1974 L1979
OPH GP *020 †35

BUNDA, Michael Joseph. 7229 FOREST AVE, VIRGINIA CARDIOVASCULAR 23226
#035-09-1983 L1997 **CD** *020 †20

BUNDY, Walter E, Jr. VIRGINIA EYE INSTITUTE 23226 #051-04-1945 L1952 **PDA** *071 †55

BUNDY, Walter Edward, III. 400 WESTHAMPTON STA, VIRGINIA EYE INSTITUTE 23226
#051-04-1973 L1978 **OPH** *020 †35

BURCH, Charles Dick. 5801 BREMO RD 23226 #051-04-1954 L1954 **PD** *071 †55

BURCH, Karen Anne. PO BOX 980257, DEPT OF INTERNAL MEDICINE 23298
#051-04-2005 L2005 **IM** *012

BURKE, Arthur Wade, Jr. 7275 GLEN FOREST DR, STE 305 23226 #051-04-1960 L1960
RO ON *071 †80

BURKE, Leemore. 5855 BREMO RD, STE 605 23226 #012-05-1994 L2001 **OBG** *020 †30

BURKE, Patrick Kendall. 2621 GROVE AVE, STE 480 23220 #051-04-1968 L1968
END IM *020 †20,28

BURKE, Timothy Smith. 1201 BROAD ROCK BLVD, MCGUIRE VA MED CTR - RADIO 23249
#051-04-1976 L1980 **NM DR** *030 †80,28

BURKWALL, Patricia J. 7229 FOREST AVE STE 100 23226 #051-01-2000 L2003 **IM** *020 †20

BURNS, Carolyn A. 5875 BREMO RD, STE 501 23226 #041-12-1986 L1989 **CD IM** *020 †20

BURTON, Regina Saretta. PO BOX 980257, MCV - OFFICE OF GME 23298 #047-06-2003 L2003
PCP *012

BUTTERWORTH, Thomas Rives. 500 HIOAKS RD STE B 23225 #051-04-1955 L1955
ORS *071 †40

BUTTS, Clifton Daniel. ■ 23221 #047-20-1996 L1998 **PM** *100

CALABRESE, Vincent Paul. 5855 BREMO RD, STE 705 23226 #035-08-1965 L1972 **N** *071 †75

CALDWELL, Kimberly Ann. 101 COWARDIN AVE, STE 207 23224 #010-03-1986 L2005
PD ADL *020 †55

CALDWELL, Paul Estil, III. 1501 MAPLE AVE, STE 200 23226 #051-04-1999 L1999
OSM *020 †40

CALL, Theresa Justine. ■ 23221 #045-04-2008 *012

CAMEROTA, Anthony James. 5801 BREMO RD, PEDIATRIC ICU 23226 #023-12-1985 L1998
CCP *020 †55

CAMP, Teresa Randelle. ■ 23221 #051-01-2007 L2007 **EM** *012

CAMPBELL, Ruth F Williams. 401 N 12TH ST 23298 #051-04-1957 L1957 **PD PUD** *071 †55

CANONIZADO, Denise Grace. ■ 23220 #051-04-2008 L2008 *012

CAPLAN, Martin David. 7229 FOREST AVE, VIRGINIA CARDIOVASCULAR 23226
#041-09-1978 L1979 **CD IM** *020 †20

CAPONI, Domenico. 1201 BROAD ROCK BLVD, DIVISIONOF CARDIOLOGY 23249
#561-27-1986 L1994 **ICE** *020 †20

CAPUZZI, David M, Jr. 5801 BREMO RD, FL 2CD 23226 #041-02-1994 L1999
PCP PTH *020 †50

CARAVATI, Chas Martin, Jr. 5600 GROVE AVE 23226 #051-01-1963 L1963 **D** *071 †15

CARDONE, Jennifer Anne. 7159 JAHNKE RD 23225 #035-08-1994 L1994 **PD** *020 †55

CARDWELL, Chas Patteson. ■ 23220 #051-04-1955 L1955 **AN** *071

CARL, Daniel Eugene, II. ■ 23298 #035-06-2000 L2000 **NEP** *100

CARL, Neal Howard. 7101 JAHNKE RD, STE 550A 23225 #051-04-1998 L1998 **FM** *020 †18

CARLETON, David Eric. 1300 E. MARSHALL ST, HEALTH SYSTEM, P. O. BOX 23291
#051-04-2002 L2002 **RHU** *012 †20

CARMACK, John Timothy. 7101 JAHNKE RD 23225 #051-04-1989 L1990 **FM** *020 †18

CARRINGTON, Paul Weisz. 1201 BROAD ROCK BLVD, DEPT OF VETERANS AFFAIRS 23249
#649-01-1971 L1993 **BBK CLP** *030 †50

CARTER, Richard Ford. 1200 E BROAD ST, MCV - OFFICE OF GME 23298 #051-04-2005 L2005
GS *012

CARUCCI, Laura Rachel. 1250 E MARSHALL ST 23298 #035-15-1996 L2002 **DR** *020 †80

CASTELLUCCI, Robert Peter. 5875 BREMO RD STE 500 23226 #422-01-1982 L1985
END IM *020 †20

CASTILLO, Denis Flores. 1201 BROAD ROCK BLVD, HUNTER HOLMES MCGUIRE VAMC 23249
#748-02-1987 L1990 **SCI PM** *020,60

CAVALIERI, Stephen Lewis. 5855 BREMO RD, STE 403 23226 #041-04-1982 L1983 **IM** *020 †20

CAVEN, Dean Emerson. 7229 FOREST AVE, VIRGINIA CARDIOVASCULAR 23226
#051-01-1995 L1995 **CD** *020 †20

CECIL, Jane Ann. 1201 BROAD ROCK BLVD, EPIDEMIOLOGY, 111-C 23249 #035-20-1993 L2000
ID IM *020 †20

CERRETO, Madge Zacharias. 7159 JAHNKE RD 23225 #051-04-1984 L1986 **PD** *020 †55

CHADDERDON, Robert C. 1200 E BROAD ST, VCU HEALTH SYSTEM 23298
#032-01-2002 L2004 **ORS** *012

CHADHA, Vimal. 1101 E MARSHALL ST, P O BOX 980498 23298 #495-45-1983 L2002
PD NEP *100 †19

CHAFE, Weldon E. 1250 E MARSHALL ST 23298 #063-01-1975 L1994 **GO OBG** *020 †30

CHALKLEY, Matilda F D. 3011 MONUMENT AVE 23221 #020-02-1941 L1944 **GP** *071

CHAN, Lawrence Karluen. 23220 #056-06-2003 L2006 **GE** *012 †20

CHANG, Jamison William. ■ 23226 #051-01-2002 L2006 **NEP IM** *100 †20

CHANG, Michael George. 23221 #041-02-1997 L1998 **RO** *020 †80

CHAO, Bo Hua. PO BOX 980257, DEPT OF INTERNAL MEDICINE 23298 #026-04-2005 L2005
IM *012 †20

CHAPIN, Lucius Tyler. PO BOX 980257, MCV - OFFICE OF GME 23298 #051-04-2003 L2003
CHN *012

CHARITY, Cynthia M. 101 COWARDIN AVE, STE 207 23224 #035-01-1976 L1979 **PD** *071 †55

CHARITY, Renard Adkins. 101 COWARDIN AVE STE 208 23224 #047-07-1970 L1975
OBG *020 †30

CHARLES-MARCEL, Zeno L. ■ 23224 #010-03-1980 L1981 **IM GE** *030 †20

CHAUDRY, Ramesh Datta. 104 W FRANKLIN ST 23220 #308-11-1985 L1995 **PYG P** *020

CHEATHAM, Seth Adam. ■ 23298 #030-05-2003 L2003 **ORS** *012

CHEN, Christina Jiasheng. ■ 23220 #021-05-2007 L2007 **IM** *012

CHEN, Stephen Min. 5855 BREMO RD 23226 #051-04-1997 L1997 **PS** *020 †65

CHEN, Tao. PO BOX 980257 23298 #243-46-1990 L2006 **PM** *012

CHESLOCK, Sara Kirsten. 1200 E BROAD ST, MCV - OFFICE OF GME 23298
#055-01-2004 L2004 **GS** *012

CHESNEY, Alden Egaton. PO BOX 980257, MCV - OFFICE OF GME 23298 #275-01-1983 L2003
HMP *100

CHESTNUT, Lisa Dawn. 5801 BREMO RD, EMERGENCY DEPARTMENT 23226
#051-04-1990 L1994 **IM PD** *020 †55

CHIAPPETTA, Jason Achille. 400 WESTHAMPTON STA, VIRGINIA EYE INSTITUTE 23226
#045-04-1996 L1996 **OPH** *020 †35

CHILDRESS, Clarence G. 401 N 12TH ST 23298 #047-06-1995 L1995 **ID** *100 †20,55

CHIN, Theresa Lynn. ■ 23226 #051-04-2008 *012

CHONG, Kyong Un. ■ 23226 #055-02-2005 L2005 **IM** *012

CHOONG, Paul James. PO BOX 980257, MCV - OFFICE OF GME 23298 #036-05-2002 L2002
IM *020 †20

CHOWDHURY, Shamsur Rahman. 401 N 12TH ST, VCU HEALTH SYSTEM 23298
#160-01-1992 L2007 **PD** *020 †55

CHRISTENSEN, Jennifer Daw. 1201 BROAD ROCK BLVD, MCGUIRE VETERAN'S AFFAIRS 23249
#048-16-1998 L1999 **IM** *020 †20

CHRISTENSEN, John Stephen. 2201 GROVE AVE, DRS TITUS HENDRIX TURNER 23220
#051-04-1996 L1996 **IM** *020 †20

CHRISTMAS, James Taylor. 7101 JAHNKE RD 23225 #051-01-1983 L1989 **MFM OBG** *020 †30

CHRISTOPHER, Thomas David. 7101 JAHNKE RD STE 500 23225 #036-07-1981 L1991
TS CD *020 †90,85

CHUIDIAN, Francisco. 401 N 12TH ST, MEDICAL COLLEGE OF VA 23298 #748-10-1984 L1997
EM *020 †16

CHUNG, Connie Myong Soh. 401 N 11TH ST, PO BOX 980164 23219 #024-05-2003 L2004
D *100 †15

CHUNG, Harold Mooinn. 1101 E MARSHALL ST, SANGER HALL, ROOM 6-030 23298
#039-01-1994 L1997 **HO** *020 †20

CHUNG, Jennifer Annnicole. ■ 23221 #051-04-2008 *012

CHUNG, Theodore Dookjong. 401 COLLEGE ST 23298 #023-01-1991 L2000 **RO** *020 †80

CIFU, David Xavier. 401 N 12TH ST 23298 #024-05-1986 L1991 **PM** *020 †60

CILLO, Jason Alexander. 401 N 12TH ST 23298 #051-04-2000 L2003 **EM** *020 †20

CLAIBORNE, Herbert A, Jr. 5855 BREMO RD STE 205, ST MARY'S OFFICE BLDG 23226
#051-01-1947 L1947 **OBG** *071 †30

CLARK, Jennifer Diane. 7101 JAHNKE RD 23225 #047-06-1991 L1997 **PD** *020 †55

CLARK, Ralph Raymond, III. 1605 RHOADMILLER ST 23220 #051-04-1987 L1988 **IM** *020 †20

CLARKE, Mary Evadne. 110 N ROBINSON ST 23220 #035-45-1991 L1993 **IM** *020 †20

CLARKE, Wm Turkington. ■ 23221 #051-01-1957 L1957 **OTO** *062

CLARY, Richard Moncure. 425 N BOULEVARD 23220 #051-04-1974 L1983 **GS CRS** *020 †85

CLEMO, Frances Lynn. 1605 RHOADMILLER ST 23220 #051-01-1985 L1986 **IM** *020 †20

CLIMO, Michael Wm. 1201 BROAD ROCK BLVD, MEDICAL CENTERSECTION 111- 23249
#051-01-1989 L1990 **ID** *020 †20

CLORE, John Newton. 1605 RHOADMILLER ST 23220 #051-04-1982 L1983 **IM DIA** *020 †20

COBLE, William Lee, Jr. 7401 BEAUFONT SPRINGS DR, STE 100 23225 #045-01-2000 L2004
CD *020 †20

COCKE, Robert Wilford. ■ 23220 #051-04-2004 L2004 **EM** *020

COCKRELL, Charles Hunter. 401 N 12TH ST 23298 #051-04-1982 L1983 **DR** *020 †80

COGGINS, Claire Anne. 1101 E MARSHALL ST BOX 980, MCV CAMPUS,SANGER HALL
RM 23298 #036-07-1997 L2002 **DR** *020 †80

COHEN, Charles Albert. 3500 KENSINGTON AVE 23221 #869-05-1953 L1968 **PM IM** *072 †60

COHEN, Dennis Scott. 5855 BREMO RD, STE 506 23226 #041-12-1991 L1993 **GS** *020 †85

COHEN, Leslie Victoria. 2621 GROVE AVE, RETREAT HOSPITAL 23220 #051-01-1990 L2004
PS *020 †65 ‡

COHEN, Robert Jay. 7301 FOREST AVE, STE 300 23226 #051-04-1976 L1978 **N** *020 †75

COHEN, Stephen Alan. 401 N 11TH ST, NELSON CLINIC 6TH FL 23219 #051-04-1975 L1976
OBG *020 †20

COHEN, Wendy Stern. 1200 E BROAD ST, WEST HOSPITAL, 8TH FLR, N 23298
#041-01-1987 L2001 **P** *020 †75

COLE, Waverly Manson. 1001 E MARSHALL ST 23219 #051-04-1954 L1954 **AN** *071

COLEMAN, George Cameron. 401 N 11TH ST 23219 #051-04-1981 L1982 **FM FPG** *020 †18

COLEMAN, Peter Richard. 204 N HAMILTON ST, STE 204 23221 #671-01-1980 L1984
FM ADM *018

COLLINS, Heather Forbes. ■ 23220 #051-04-2008 *012

COLLINS, Phil. 107 S 5TH ST, RICHMOND BEHAVIORAL HEALTH 23219 #004-01-1963 L1968
P OS *020

COLQUHOUN, Alexander Davi. 401 N 12TH ST, MAIN HOSPITAL 5TH FLOOR 23298
#919-05-1978 *100

COLVIN, Mary Patricia. ■ 23298 #010-02-1998 L2000 **GS** *012

COMBS, James L. 7301 FOREST AVE, STE 200 23226 #051-04-1977 L1978 **OPH OS** *020 †35

CONDRO, Peter, Jr. 671 HIOAKS RD, STE B 23225 #035-06-1979 L1985 **IM NEP** *020 †20

CONKLIN, Robert Charles. PO BOX 980615 23298 #051-04-2003 L2003 **DR** *012

CONQUEST, Henry Fairfax. ■ 23221 #051-01-1954 L1954 **GS** *071 †85

CONRAD, William Scott. ■ 23226 #051-04-2002 L2002 **DR** *100 †80

CONSTANTINESCU, Florina M. 1112 E CLAY ST, BOX 980263 23298 #781-01-1998 L2006
RHU *100

CONTOS, Melissa Jeanne. 1101 E MARSHALL ST, MCV 23298 #051-04-1988 L1993
PTH *040 †50

COOK, Gary R. 401 N 11TH ST, DEPT OF OPHTHALMOLOGY-VCU 23219 #010-02-1976 L1983
OPH OS *020 †35

COOPER, Geoffrey Guy. 5875 BREMO RD STE 209 23226 #021-01-1981 L1983 **OPH** *020 †35

COOPER, Kevin Richard. 1605 RHOADMILLER ST 23220 #035-08-1973 L1974
PUD CCM *020 †20

COOTS-BROWN, Theodore R. 5 E CLAY ST 23219 #010-03-1951 L1952 **GP OS** *071

CORCORAN, James F T. 7107 JAHNKE RD, INSIGHT PHYSICIANS PC 23225
#035-20-1966 L1981 **P PFP** *020 †75

CORNMAN, Edmund Webster. 1800 GLENSIDE DR, STE 103 23226 #041-01-1990 L2002
N *020 †20

CORRIE, William Stephen. 5855 BREMO RD, STE 705 23226 #028-02-1966 L1987
OS N *075 †75

COTTERELL, Adrian Howard. 1200 E BROAD ST 23298 #036-07-1991 L2000 **GS TTS** *020 †85

COWLEY, Michael Jos. 417 N 11TH ST, MCV AMBULATORY CARE 23298 #001-02-1972 L1977
CD IM *020 †20

COXE, Jos Wentworth, III. ■ 23226 #023-07-1946 L1954 **GS** *071 †85

CRAMER, Samuel Keith. ■ 23220 #017-20-1972 L2005 **IM** *030 †20

CRANE, Joseph Thompson, IV. 2621 GROVE AVE 23220 #051-04-1997 L2000 **EM** *020 †16

CRAWFORD, Harry S, Jr. ■ 23226 #047-07-1951 L1955 **GS OS** *020

CRITTENDEN, David Gray. 3500 KENSINGTON AVE, HILL-DAVIS BLDG. 23221
#051-04-1964 L1964 **OTO** *071

CROSS, Steven Wayne. 2621 GROVE AVE 23220 #051-04-1979 L1980 **CD IC** *020 †20

CROSSEN, David Keith. 5855 BREMO RD STE 303 23226 #051-04-1986 L1987 **FM** *075 †18

■ = Address Information Privacy Protected

CUMMINGS, Charles Edward. 2809 NORTH AVE, STE 104 23222 #010-03-1962 L1963 **IM** *071

CUNNINGHAM, Kevin Patrick. 1201 BROAD ROCK BLVD, HOLMES MED CTR ANESTH SVC 23249 #041-14-1987 L1990 **AN** *020 †05

CURTIS, Richard Earl, Jr. 1000 BOULDERS PKWY, STE 202 23225 #051-04-1983 L1984 **P GP** *075

CUTTER, Douglas Nathan. 500 HIOAKS RD STE A 23225 #051-07-1985 L1986 **FM** *030 †18

CUTTINO, Charles Marsh. 401 N 12TH ST, P O BOX 80401 23298 #051-04-1994 L1997 **EM** *020 †16

CUTTINO, Laurie Wright. ■ 23225 #051-04-2001 L2001 **RO** *100 †80

CYRUS, Debra Ann. 7101 JAHNKE RD, VIRGINIA HOSPITALISTS INC. 23225 #024-16-2000 L2007 **PD** *020

DAFFERN, Pamela Jean. 2031 MONUMENT AVE, ASTMA ALERGRY/SINUS CTR 23220 #048-12-1985 L1999 **AI IM** *020 †20,03

DALTON, Gordon Vincent. 5899 BREMO RD STE A 23226 #051-04-1985 L1988 **ORS** *020 †40

DANELISEN, Daliborka M. 1200 E BROAD ST 6TH FL, MCVH - OFFICE OF GME 23298 #051-75-2007, ▲ L2007 **P** *012

DANG, Minh-Duyen Thi. 615 N 8TH ST 23298 #051-04-1997 **IM** *100

DANIEL, Donald Snead, Jr. 5801 BREMO RD 23226 #023-07-1958 L1958 **IM** *020

DANIELI, Sembua Samuel. 5801 BREMO RD, IMS HOSPITALIST PROGRAM 23226 #473-02-1993 L2004 **IM** *100 †20

DARDEN, James Ryland. 425 N BOULEVARD 23220 #051-04-1958 L1958 **GS GYN** *071 †85

DASH, Alok. ■ 23226 #051-04-2006 L2006 **GS** *012

DAUSCH, Robert James. 5855 BREMO RD, STE 207 23226 #023-01-1996 L1996 **IM** *020

DAVE, Akshay Vibhakar. 2010 BREMO RD, STE 128 23226 #048-04-1993 L1998 **OPH** *020 †35

DAVENPORT, Byrd Warwick. ■ 23226 #051-04-2005 L2005 **IM** *100

DAVIA, James England. 1200 E BROAD ST, BOX 980036 23298 #016-11-1962 L1997 **CD IM** *020 †20

DAVID, Daniel Wesley. 7110 FOREST AVE STE 201, RICHMOND PRIMARY CARE 23226 #051-04-2001 L2001 **FM** *020 †18

DAVID, Ronald Brian. 5875 BREMO RD STE 700 23226 #051-04-1964 L1964 **CHN PD** *071 †55,75

DAVIDSON, Martha Ellen. 2008 BREMO RD, STE 105 23226 #051-04-1985 L1993 **P PFP** *020 †75

DAVIS, Ivan Christopher. ■ 23221 #051-04-2007 L2007 **TY** *012

DAVIS, Ronald Kenneth. 417 LIBBIE AVE 23226 #051-04-1963 L1963 **VS GS** *071 †85

DAVIS, Susan Fischer. 109 GOVERNOR ST, VA DEPT OF HEALTH 23219 #032-01-1987 L1999 **EP** *062

DAVIS, Thomas Dewey, Jr. 5801 BREMO RD 23226 #051-04-1957 L1957 **GE IM** *071 †20

DAWKINS, Elizabeth Brooks. 1101 E MARSHALL ST, P O BOX 980160 23298 #051-04-1986 L1987 **IM** *020 †20

DAWSON, Mary Catherine. ■ 23221 #036-01-1998 L1998 **PD** *020 †55

DAY, Sarah E. 5855 BREMO RD, STE 302 23226 #035-46-1978 L1979 **PD** *075 †55

DAY, Tomeka G. 101 COWARDIN AVE STE 20 23224 #036-08-2003 L2003 **PD** *020

DE CONTI, Robert William. 7229 FOREST AVE, STE 101 23226 #051-01-1987 L1994 **GS** *020 †85,65

DE LA BURDE, Brigitte E. 401 N 12TH ST 23298 #407-15-1953 L1962 **PD** *072 †55

DELORENZO, Robert John. 401 N 12TH ST 23298 #008-01-1974 L1985 **N PA** *050 †75

DENLINGER, Bethany L. 1009 TAYLOR AVE 23225 #041-13-1989 L1990 **CD IM** *020 †20

DENT, Roy Wm. ■ 23226 #051-04-1959 L1959 **OS** *030

DESAI, Apurva Subodh. 1200 E BROAD ST - P, MEDICAL COLLEGE OF VIRGINI 23298 #495-01-1987 L2002 *020

DESCHNER, Bonnie Kay. 1250 E MARSHALL ST, DEPARTMENT OF ANESTHESIOLO 23298 #665-01-2000 L2002 **AN** *100 †05

DESCHNER, Steven Henry. 1223 E MARSHALL ST, DEPT. OF PHYSICAL MEDICINE 23298 #665-01-2000 L2002 **SCI** *020

DE SHAZO, Billy Wood. ■ 23221 #048-12-1956 L2000 **PS** *071 †65

DESTOUNIS, Nicholas P. VET ADMIN M C, DEPT PSYCH 23249 #418-01-1953 L1969 **P N** *030

DEVERNA, Charles John, III. ■ 23226 #051-04-2007 *012

DE WIT-HAHN, Marjolein. PO BOX 980050, 1200 E BROAD ST 23298 #024-07-1995 L1998 **PCC** *020 †20

DHILLON, Jasvinder Singh. 5801 BREMO RD, PICU, ST MARY'S HOSPITAL 23226 #495-03-1984 L2002 **PD** *020 †55

DIAZ, Sumac Dolores. 7107 JAHNKE RD 23225 #025-01-1999 L1999 **OBG** *020 †18,30

DI GIOVANNI, Susan R. 401 N 11TH ST, MCV NELSON CLINIC 23219 #051-04-1984 L1985 **NEP IM** *020 †20

DIGRAZIA, John Mark. 2621 GROVE AVE 23220 #023-01-1982 L1983 **CD IM** *020 †20

DIMAIO, Alexis Anne. ■ 23225 #035-48-2006 L2006 **EM** *012

DINARDO, Laurence Jos. 1201 E MARSHALL ST, STE 410 23298 #005-11-1986 L1991 **OTO** *020 †45

DIXON, Leon M. PO BOX 26227, MAIN POST OFFICE 23260 #010-03-1953 L1977 **IM OM** *020

DOBZYNIAK, Matthew Allan. 1501 MAPLE AVE, STE 200 23226 #025-01-1996 L2004 **ORS** *020 †40

DODD, Richard Wine. 5875 BREMO RD STE 303 23226 #051-04-1955 L1955 **OTO** *071 †45

DODSON, Austin Ingram, Jr. 5224 MONUMENT AVE 23226 #051-04-1946 L1947 **U** *071 †95

DODSON, Kelley Melissa. 1201 E MARSHALL ST STE 4, BOX 980146 23298 #010-01-2000 L2000 **OTO** *020 †45

DOHERTY, Matthew Thomas. ■ 23298 #051-04-2008 L2008 *012

DOLAN, Margaret Anne. 1200 E BROAD ST RM 1501, BOX 980107 23298 #038-06-1981 L1989 **PD EM** *020 †55

DOMSON, Gregory Froio. ■ 23221 #051-07-2000 L2000 **OMO** *100

DONAHUE, Christopher J. 2621 GROVE AVE 23220 #051-04-1993 L1998 **PTH** *020 †50

DOUGLAS, Ronald Maurice. ■ 23221 #051-04-1996 L2001 **FM** *020

DOUGLASS, Erin Ladd. ■ 23226 #051-04-2008 *012

DOW, Alan Wayne, III. 1200 E BROAD ST, MEDICAL COLLEGE VIRGINIA 23298 #028-02-2000 L2000 **IM** *020 †20

DOWNS, Robert W, Jr. 1605 RHOADMILLER ST 23220 #036-07-1974 L1983 **END IM** *020 †20

DRAPER, David Adrain. 401 N 12TH ST, MEDICAL COLLEGE OF VA 23298 #065-05-1958 L1964 **PD** *020 †55

DRAPER, Joy Caroline. 108 COWARDIN AVE, CROSSOVER HEALTH MINISTRY 23224 #051-04-1993 L1993 **OBG FM** *020 †18,30

DU, Beth Shioching. 5855 BREMO RD, STE 403 23226 #051-04-1997 L2000 **IM** *020 †20

DUANE, Therese Marie. 1200 E BROAD ST, VCU MEDICAL CENTER DIV OF 23298 #035-06-1995 L1995 **CCS** *020 †85

DUBOVOY, Arkadiy. 1200 E BROAD ST BOX 980695, WEST HOSPITAL 7N-105 23298 #913-13-1992 L2000 **PAN** *020 †05

DUNN, Nancy Lynne. 401 N 11TH ST STE 210, NELSON CLNC 23219 #035-06-1973 L1976 **PHO** *020 †55

DUNNINGTON, Gansevoort H. 7229 FOREST AVE, VIRGINIA CARDIOVASCULAR 23226 #051-04-1972 L1973 **CD IM** *020 †20

DWYER-ROBERSON, Margaret. 401 N 11TH ST, VCU HLTH SYSTEM ACC CLINIC 23219 #051-04-1989 L1990 **IM** *020 †20

DYE, James Clayton. 5801 BREMO RD, SAINT MARY'S HOSPITAL 23226 #051-01-1998 L2004 **IM** *020 †20

EAGLIN, Jaime Marie. ■ 23221 #051-07-2007 L2007 **OTO** *012

EBERSBERGER, Marc Lee. PO BOX 980257 23298 #422-01-2003 L2003 **ORS** *012

EBERT, Eleanore Margaret. 7301 FOREST AVE, STE 200 23226 #051-01-1995 L1992 **OPH OS** *020 †35

ECHOLS, Porter Burks, Jr. ■ 23221 #051-01-1958 L1958 **OPH** *071

ECKBERG, Dwain Lee. 1201 BROAD ROCK BLVD, MC GUIRE V. A. HOSPITAL 23249 #016-06-1963 L1977 **IM** *050 †20

EDDY, Janet Mary. 401 N 12TH ST 23298 #051-04-1987 L1988 **FM** *020 †18

EDMOND, Michael Bruce. ■ 23298 #055-01-1986 L1995 **ID IM** *030 †20

ELLEN, Elizabeth Fraser. ■ 23226 #010-01-2008 L2008 *012

ELLENBOGEN, Kenneth Alan. 1605 RHOADMILLER ST 23220 #023-07-1980 L1987 **CD IM** *020 †20

ELLIOTT, Anne Marita. ■ 23220 #016-45-2006 L2006 **PD** *012

ELLIOTT, Billie L Wright. 5855 BREMO RD, STE 304 23226 #051-04-1954 L1954 **P PA** *071 †75

ELLIOTT, David Cooper. 5855 BREMO RD STE 406 23226 #051-04-1983 L1986 **GS CCS** *020 †85

ELLIOTT, Gregory Randolph. 1250 E MARSHALL ST, MEDICAL COLLEGE OF VA 23298 #004-01-1977 L1990 **PDP ID** *020 †55

ELLISON, Elizabeth Hayes. 7101 JAHNKE RD, CJW MEDICAL CENTER-CHIPPEN 23225 #051-04-1999 L1999 **DR** *012 †20

EL-MASRI, Mohamad. 7101 JAHNKE RD STE 611, VIRGINIA HOSPITALISTS 23225 #305-01-2001 L2004 **IMG** *100

ELMORE, Stanley Mc Dowell. 500 HIOAKS RD 23225 #047-05-1958 L1966 **ORS** *071 †40

ENCK, Robin Ann. ■ 23225 #041-14-2006 L2007 **PM** *012

ERSKINE, Alistair Robert. PO BOX 980102, FAS OFFICE 23298 #051-04-1999 L2001 **MPD** *020 †55,20

ERVIN, William Sherman. 2621 GROVE AVE 23220 #051-07-1981 L1982 **EM** *020 †16

ESSAH, Paulina A. 1200 E BROAD ST, P O BOX 980102 23298 #023-07-1993 L1999 **IM** *020 †20

ESTES, Michael Dugan. 5855 BREMO RD, STE 100 23226 #051-04-1980 L1981 **AN PD** *020 †55,05

ESTRELLA, Jose Felipe. 7300 BEAUFONT SPRINGS DR, STE 101 23225 #649-06-1966 **ORS GS** *100

ESTRERA, Angelo O. PO BOX 981425 23298 #748-11-1981 L1995 **P** *100

ESTRERA, Nenita Otadoy. 107 S 5TH ST, RICHMOND BEHAVIORAL HLTH 23219 #748-11-1973 L1994 **CHP** *020 †75

EVANI, Renuka. 107 S 5TH ST, RICHMOND BEHAVIORAL HEALTH 23219 #495-47-1982 L1995 **P** *012

EVANS, Charles Garland, Jr. 2621 GROVE AVE 23220 #051-04-1981 L1982 **CD IM** *020 †20

EVANS, James Lawrence, III. 1220 BANK ST, VA DEPT OF MTL HLTH 23219 #041-02-1961 L1987 **P ADM** *030 †75

EVANS, Joseph John. 2621 GROVE AVE 23220 #041-02-1977 L1998 **ICE CD** *020 †20

EVANS, Seth Humphries. 1200 E BROAD ST, MCV - OFFICE OF GME 23298 #012-05-2005 L2005 **GS** *012

EVANS, Timothy Cave. 1201 E MARSHALL ST, VCU HEALTH SYSTEM 23298 #033-05-1983 L1997 **EM** *020 †16

EWING, Franklin R, III. ■ 23222 #051-04-1996 L1996 **FM** *020 †18

FAIRMAN, Ralph Paul. 1200 E BROAD ST, MCV BOX 980050 23298 #028-03-1972 L1975 **PUD IM** *020 †20

FALCUCCI, Octavio A. 401 N 12TH ST, MAIN HOSPITAL 5TH FLOOR 23298 #132-01-1991 L2002 **CCA** *020

FALLS, William Franklin. 5707 GROVE AVE 23226 #023-01-1959 L1966 **NEP IM** *071 †20

FANG, Gary Yunchun. ■ 23221 #051-04-2005 L2005 **MPD** *012

FANOUS, Ayman Hafez. 1300 E MARSHALL ST 23298 #051-04-1995 L1999 **P** *020 †75

FARHI, Raymond Sohbi. 7101 JAHNKE RD 23225 #264-01-1982 L1986 **NPM PD** *020 †55

FARRAN, Jamal Mohammad. 401 N 12TH ST, MAIN HOSPITAL 23298 #797-02-1992 L1995 **EM** *020 †16

FARRELL, Nicholas John. ■ 23220 #051-04-2000 L2000 **HO** *012

FAUSS, Brent Gerald. 5855 BREMO RD, STE 100 23226 #051-04-1982 L1985 **AN** *020 †05

FAYAZI, Azadeh Rose. 1200 E BROAD ST, MCV - OFFICE OF GME 23298 #038-45-2006 L2006 **PD** *012

FELDMAN, George Michael. 1201 BROAD ROCK BLVD, MCGUIRE VAMC 111G 23249 #035-19-1972 L1990 **IM NEP** *020 †20

FELDMAN, Michael John. ■ 23226 #051-04-2003 L2003 **PS** *012

FELTON, Warren Locker, III. 417 N 11TH ST, RANDOLPH MINOR HALL 23298 #039-01-1980 L1983 **N** *040 †75

FELTY, Danny Walker. 7101 JAHNKE RD, STE 550A 23225 #051-04-1998 L1998 **FM** *020 †18

FERNANDEZ, Antony. 1201 BROAD ROCK BLVD 23249 #495-59-1984 L1994 **P PFP** *030 †75

FERRELL, Benjamin Avant. ■ 23220 #051-04-2008 *012

FERRO, Thomas Jos. MCGUIRE VA MEDICAL CENTER, PULMONARY-111F 23249 #035-48-1980 L1998 **PUD IM** *020 †20

FERRY, Andrew Peter. MEDICAL COLLEGE OF VA, DEPT OF OPHTH 23298 #010-02-1954 L1978 **OPH** *040 †35

FIEDLER, Adam Julius. 7101 JAHNKE RD, STE 280 23225 #023-07-1969 L1971 **OBG** *020 †30

FIEDLER, Jean Hee. ■ 23298 #012-22-2008 L2008 *012

FIERRO, Robert John. 5875 BREMO RD STE 701, ST MARYS MED OFC BLDG 23226 #065-09-1968 L1975 **GYN REN** *020 †30

FISER, Steven Mark. ■ 23221 #003-01-1997 L1997 **TS** *020 †85

FISHER, Hugh P, Jr. ■ 23224 #051-04-1950 L1950 **IM** *020

FISHER, Robert Anthony. 401 N 12TH ST, MEDICAL COLLEGE OF VA 23298 #048-04-1980 L1991 **GS TTS** *020 †85

FITCH, Sarah Jean. PO BOX 980470, 1101 E MARSHALL ST 23298 #027-01-1978 L1998 **PDR** *020 †20

FITZGERALD, John Edmund. 7229 FOREST AVE, VIRGINIA CARDIOVASCULAR 23226 #051-04-1971 L1972 **CD** *020 †20

FITZHUGH, William Garth. 2000 BREMO RD, STE 205 23226 #051-04-1966 L1966 **OBG** *020 †30

FLAK, Keith S. 1200 E BROAD ST, VCU MED CTR 23298 #048-13-2004 L2004 **ORS** *012

FLANZENBAUM, Mark Adam. 5801 BREMO RD 23226 #035-06-1990 L1991 **EM PEM** *020 †20,55

FLEMING, William Kermit. 505 W LEIGH ST STE 307 23220 #047-07-1978 L1983 **ORS** *020 †40

FLETCHER, Devon Summers. ■ 23220 #027-01-2007 L2007 **IM** *012

FOGLE, Kelly Ashworth. 3500 KENSINGTON AVE, DAVIS EYE CENTER, LTD. 23221 #051-04-1974 L1975 **OPH IM** *020

FOHL, Richard Bell. 5855 BREMO RD, STE 309 23226 #051-04-1970 L1970 **D** *020 †15

FOLARIN, Hopemerlen Modup. ■ 23298 #038-06-2007 L2007 **IM** *012

FONSEKA, Componnage Piyum. 23220 #051-04-2008 *012

FORBES, Ronald Omega. 401 N 12TH ST 23298 #035-01-1975 L1980 **P** *020 †75

FORSSMANN-FALCK, Renate. 819 W BROAD ST B 23220 #409-25-1972 L1978 **P OS** *020 †75

FOSTER, Harriet Hutto. 1201 BROAD ROCK BLVD, MCGUIRE VA HOSPITAL 23249 #045-01-1981 L1984 **IM** *075 †20

FOSTER, Helen Montague. 2004 BREMO RD STE 106 23226 #051-04-1982 L1983 **P** *020 †75

FOSTER, Merritt W, Jr. 414 W FRANKLIN ST 23220 #051-04-1944 L1944 **P** *071 †75

FOSTER, Robin Lynn. 401 N 12TH ST, MEDICAL COLLEGE OF VA 23298 #051-04-1989 L1991 **PD** *020 †55

FOWLER, Alpha Alsbury, III. 1605 RHOADMILLER ST 23220 #012-01-1976 L1976 **PUD** *050 †20

FOX, Aaron David. ■ 23224 #051-04-2005 L2005 **IM** *012

FOX, Lindsay Arnoult. ■ 23226 #048-02-2004 L2004 **AN** *012

FOX, William Cory. ■ 23226 #048-02-2004 L2004 **DR** *012

FRABLE, Mary Ann Smith. ■ 23221 #016-06-1959 L1966 **OTO** *071 †45

FRABLE, William Jackson. 1605 RHOADMILLER ST 23220 #016-06-1959 L1966 **ATP PCP** *020 †20

FRANKS, Paul E. 5855 BREMO RD, STE 100N 23226 #051-04-1977 L1978 **AN** *020 †20,05 ‡

FRANZEN, Douglas Scott. ■ 23222 #025-01-2001 L2001 **EM** *020 †16

FRATKIN, Melvin Joel. 401 N 12TH ST, MEDICAL COLLEGE OF VA 23298 #051-04-1964 L1964 **NM END** *020 †20,28

FREDERICK, Louis Arnold. 7101 JAHNKE RD 23225 #051-04-1959 L1959 **U** *071 †95

FREDERICK, Louis Arnold. 5855 BREMO RD, STE 100N 23226 #051-04-1989 L1990 **AN** *005

FREDRICKSON, Sonja Karen. 1201 BROAD ROCK BLVD 151, MCGUIRE VA MED CTR 23249 #051-04-1997 L1998 **IM DIA** *020 †20

FREEMAN, Eric Bernard. 3800 PARKVIEW AVE 23222 #051-04-2002 L2005 **PD** *020 †55

FRENCH, Dorothy Mae. ■ 23226 #051-04-2000 **FM** *100

FRIEDEL, David Joseph. 1001 E MARSHALL ST 23219 #008-02-2000 L2000 **ID** *012 †20,55

FRIEDENBERG, Milton David. 5855 BREMO RD STE 412 23226 #051-04-1947 L1947 **P** *071

FRIEDMAN, Allan David. 1001 E MARSHALL ST, BOX 980506 23219 #023-01-1976 L2005 **PD** *030 †55

FULCHER, Ann Simpson. 401 N 12TH ST, DEPT OF RADIOLOGY 23298 #051-04-1987 L1990 **DR AR** *020 †80

FULCO, Frank Anthony. 1201 BROAD ROCK BLVD, MCGUIRE VA MEDICAL CENTER 23249 #055-01-1997 L1997 **IM PD** *020 †20,55

FULLER, Robert Ray. 5855 BREMO RD, STE 306 23226 #016-11-2000 L2007 **OBG** *040 †30 ‡

FUNKHOUSER, Laura. ■ 23226 #051-07-1978 L1982 **PD PM** *020 †55,70

FUQUAY, Maurice C. ■ 23221 #039-01-1952 L1952 **TS** *071 †85,90

FURMAN, Stanley Nelson. 5855 BREMO RD, STE 207 23226 #654-01-1981 L1985 **IMG PLM** *020 †20

GABICE, Bella Tari. ■ 23298 #051-04-2008 L2008 *012

GAERTNER, William Ronald. 5855 BREMO RD, INSIGHT PHYSICIANS PC 23226 #021-05-1979 L1983 **P** *020 †75

GAJJAR, Neha J. 7101 JAHNKE RD, STE 611 23225 #035-03-1994 L2003 **MPD** *020 †20,55

GARBEE, Michael Andrew. 1200 E BROAD ST, MCV - OFFICE OF GME 23298 #654-01-1998 L2006 **N** *012

GARCIA, Miriam P. 1201 BROAD ROCK BLVD, HUNTER HOLMES MCGUIRE VETE 23249 #748-10-1992 L1995 **CN** *020

GARDNER, David Franklin. 417 N 11TH ST, AMBULATORY CARE CTR 23298 #035-19-1971 L1978 **END IM** *020 †20

GARNETT, James Blair. 7401 BEAUFONT SPRINGS DR, STE 100 23225 #051-04-2000 L2000 **IC** *020 †20 ‡

GARNETT, Lockett Wooton. 5899 BREMO RD, STE 100 23226 #051-04-1979 L1980 **ORS** *020 †40

GARRETT, Carleton T. 401 N 12TH ST, MEDICAL COLLEGE OF VA 23298 #023-07-1966 L1993 **PTH OS** *071 †50

GARRETT, William Bradley. ■ 23225 #051-04-2005 L2005 **AN** *012

GARRIS-WALLACE, Sheila M. 7110 FOREST AVE, STE 201 23226 #047-07-1984 L1986 **IM** *020 †20

GATER, David Rex, Jr. 1201 BROAD ROCK BLVD, # 652/128 23249 #003-01-1992 L2007 **PM SCI** *050 †60

GATUSLAO, Hernan Tapia, Jr. 417 N 11TH ST, BOX 980599 23298 #748-10-1992 L1996 **N** *020 †75

GAZALA, Joseph Richard. 1001 E MARSHALL ST 23219 #528-01-1947 L1956 **OPH** *071 †35

GAZONI, Paulo Mabuchi. 401 N 12TH ST, DEPART. OF EMERGENCY MEDIC 23298 #051-04-2000 L2000 **EM** *020

GEBREGIORGIS, Abel Asnake. ■ 23220 #010-03-2007 L2007 **GS** *012

GEHR, Todd Wm. 1605 RHOADMILLER ST 23220 #051-05-1981 L1985 **NEP IM** *020 †20

GELDREICH, Randall M. 1200 E BROAD ST, VCU MEDICAL CENTER 23298 #051-01-2001 L2005 **EM** *012 †20,55

GELWIX, Christopher Clark. ■ 23226 #001-02-2007 L2007 **IM** *012

GENDALL, Kelly Ann. PO BOX 980257, DEPT OF INTERNAL MEDICINE 23298 #671-01-2004 L2005 **IM** *012

GENINA, Vera Yakovlevna. 1201 BROAD ROCK BLVD, VETERANS AFFAIRS MEDICAL C 23249 #913-54-1980 L1995 **IM** *020 †20

GENTILI, Angela. 1201 BROAD ROCK BLVD, VAMC (181) 23249 #561-14-1986 L1994 **IMG** *020 †20

GEORGE, Kimberly Creasy. 1200 E BROAD ST, BOX 980103 23298 #051-04-2002 L2002 **AI** *012 †20,55

GEORGE, Nedumkallel T. 1201 BROAD ROCK BLVD 171, MCGUIRE VA MEDICAL CENTER 23249 #495-52-1977 L2003 **IM** *020 †20

GERAYMOVYCH, Elena. ■ 23221 #051-04-2008 *012

GERGOUDIS, Richard Lewis. 1800 GLENSIDE DR STE 110 23226 #051-01-1986 L1989 **FM** *020 †18

GERLACH, Karen Elissa. PO BOX 980615 23298 #021-01-2003 L2007 **DR** *012

GERSZTEN, Enrique. 401 N 12TH ST, MEDICAL COLLEGE OF VA 23298 #132-01-1958 L1962 **ATP** *040 †20

GETTAS, Nick J. OLD CITY HALL, STE 120 23219 #065-01-1980 L1990 **FM** *030 †18

GEZEN, Burak Emin. ■ 23225 #051-04-2008 *012

GHAEMMAGHAMI, Paul Andrew. 5855 BREMO RD, STE 101 23226 #051-04-1993 L1999 **CRS** *020 †85,10

GHATAK, Nitya Ranjan. 401 N 12TH ST, MEDICAL COLLEGE OF VA 23298 #495-32-1957 L1976 **NP PTH** *040 †50

GHITIS, Joseph. 1200 E BROAD ST, MCV - OFFICE OF GME 23298 #048-02-2003 L2005 **DR** *012

GIBBS, John Elmore, II. 1223 E MARSHALL ST 23298 #036-08-2004 L2004 **PM** *012

GIBNEY, Eric Michael. ■ 23220 #012-05-1998 L2005 **NEP** *100 †20

GIBSON, Janice Lynn. 101 COWARDIN AVE STE 20 23224 #010-03-1983 L1987 **OBG** *020 †30

GIESSEL, Glenn Matthew. 1000 BOULDERS PKWY, SUITE102 23225 #048-04-1978 L1980 **PUD SME** *020 †20

GILL, Edward John, Jr. 1250 E MARSHALL ST, DEPT OF OB/GYN, PO BX 9800 23298 #024-07-1986 L1994 **OBG** *020 †18,30

GILL, John A. ■ 23226 #051-04-1946 L1946 **OTO** *072 †45

GILL, Joseph Patrick. 7101 JAHNKE RD 23225 #051-04-1982 L1985 **EM** *020 †20,16

GILL, Ranjodh S. 1200 E BROAD ST, RM 210 23298 #495-29-1987 L1995 **END** *020 †20

GILL, Sujoy. PO BOX 980257, MCV - OFFICE OF GME 23298 #055-01-2002 L2002 **PCC** *012 †20

GILLIAM, Darrell Kay. 7101 JAHNKE RD 23225 #051-04-1959 L1959 **FM** *071 †18

GILLIAM, Kari Lynn. 7159 JAHNKE RD, CHIPENHAM PEDIATRIC & ADOL 23225 #038-06-1992 L1995 **PD** *020 †55

GILLIGAN, David M. 2621 GROVE AVE 23220 #539-03-1983 L1994 **CD IMG** *020 †20

GILLIS, Howard, II. 706 W 24TH ST 23225 #016-06-1971 L1988 **OBG AM** *020 †30,70

GINDER, Gordon Dean. 401 COLLEGE ST, BOX 980037 23298 #023-07-1975 L1998 **IM** *040 †20

GIORDANO, Roger Gregory. ■ 23226 #041-13-1989 L2001 **PM** *020 †60

GLAUSER, Frederick Louis. 1605 RHOADMILLER ST 23220 #041-09-1963 L1977 **IM OS** *020 †20

GLENN, Daran Graham. 671 HIOAKS RD STE B, RICHMOND NEPHROLOGY ASSOCI 23225 #047-06-1998 L2006 **NEP** *020 †20

GLOVER, Trishana Wynette. 1201 BROAD ROCK BLVD 23249 #047-06-2000 L2000 **IMG** *020 †20

GLYNN, Francesca D. 7229 FOREST AVE, STE 109 23226 #051-04-1991 L1994 **IM** *020 †20

GODDER, Kamar. 1101 E MARSHALL ST, SANGER HALL 12-022 23298 #550-01-1980 L2005 **PD PHO** *020 †20

GODIN, Michael Scott. 410 LIBBIE AVE 23226 #021-01-1986 L1993 **FPS A** *020 †45

GOEL, Anika. ■ 23221 #496-21-2002 L2003 **N** *100

GOEL, Ruchi. ■ 23226 #051-04-2008 *012

GOGIA, Amit Narsne. 425 N BOULEVARD 23220 #051-04-2001 L2005 **GS** *020 †85

GOKHALE, Mandaar Arvind. 401 N 12TH ST, MEDICAL COLLEGE OF VA 23298 #035-19-1993 L1995 **EM** *020 †16

GOLDBERG, Aaron Ellis. ■ 23225 #051-04-2005 L2005 **OBG** *012

GOLDBERG, Stephanie Renee. ■ 23225 #051-04-2003 L2003 **GS** *012

GOLDIN, Michael Stanley. ■ 23225 #051-04-2008 *012

GOLDMAN, Stanley Allen. 5855 BREMO RD, STE 403 23226 #035-45-1961 L1968 **IM CD** *071 †20

GOLDMANN, Peter H. 5875 BREMO RD, STE 508 23226 #051-01-1974 L1975 **OPH** *020 †35

GOLDSTONE, Alvin I. 1800 GLENSIDE DR, CENTRAL VA 23226 #041-12-1965 L1969 **OTO** *020 †45

GONG, Pearl Jade. 107 S 5TH ST, HEALTH AUTHORITY 23219 #035-46-1983 L1991 **P CHP** *020 †75

GOODE, Lauren Hutton. PO BOX 980257, DEPT OF B/GYN 23298 #051-04-2006 L2006 **IM** *012

GOODWIN, David Alan. 412 LIBBIE AVE STE 4, COMMONWEALTH NEONATOLOGY, 23226 #023-12-1984 L1998 **NPM PD** *030 †55

GOPLERUD, Dean Roy. 401 N 12TH ST, MEDICAL COLLEGE OF VA 23298 #018-03-1955 L1973 **GO** *071 †20

GORDON, Courtnay E. 1200 E BROAD ST, O.O.BOX 980695 23298 #012-05-1999 L2004 **CCM** *020 †20

GORDON, Randolph Lee. 401 N 11TH ST, MCV NELSON CLINIC 23219 #051-04-1984 L1985 **PHP FM** *030 †70,18

GORECZNY, John Francis, Jr. ■ 23221 #051-04-2008 *012

GORMAN, Thomas Leo. 4906 FOREST HILL AVE 23225 #051-01-1956 L1956 **OPH** *075

GOSDIN, Craig Howard. 5801 BREMO RD, C/O MARY ANNE GRAF 23226 #021-01-1994 L1999 **PD** *020 †55

GOTTSCHALK, Robert B, Jr. 302 SENECA RD 23226 #012-01-1972 L1991 **P CHP** *020 †55

GOTTWALD, William. ■ 23226 #021-01-1976 L1977 **D** *075 †15

GOUDREAU, Evelyne. 1605 RHOADMILLER ST 23220 #067-02-1981 L1986 **IC** *020 †20

GOULD, David Wilfred, III. 1000 BOULDERS PKWY, STE 202 23225 #020-12-1985 L1990 **CHP P** *020 †75

GOWAN, Jimmy Lee. 7400 BEAUFONT SPRINGS DR, STE 330 23225 #045-01-1964 L2000 **GP** *020

GRADY, Victoria E. 1606 HULL ST 23224 #036-08-1993 L1997 **IM EM** *020

GRAHAM, Martin Frank. 1200 E BROAD ST RM 1501, BOX 529 23298 #836-02-1973 L1980 **GE PD** *050 †55

GRAHAM, Robert Scott. 1200 E BROAD ST, BOX 980631 23298 #051-04-1992 L1992 **NS** *020 †25

GRAHAM, Sam Dixon, Jr. 7135 JAHNKE RD 23225 #051-01-1974 L1975 **U** *020 †95

GRANT, Steven. 1605 RHOADMILLER ST 23220 #035-47-1973 L1987 **HEM ON** *050 †20

GRAY, Adam Mccoy. ■ 23226 #051-04-2001 L2007 **RNR** *020 †80

GRAY, Rashida Nzinga. 1300 E MARSHALL ST, MCV/VCU HEALTH SYSTEMS 23298 #041-15-2003 L2007 **P** *020

GREEN, David Adair. ■ 23221 #051-04-2003 L2003 **PCC** *012 †20

GREEN, Harold Thos, Jr. 2421 CHAMBERLAYNE AVE 23222 #010-03-1977 L1979 **IM** *020 †20

GREEN, Jeffrey Alan. 401 N 12TH ST, VA COMMONWEALTH UNIV HLTH 23298 #038-40-1996 L2001 **AN** *020 †05

GREENFIELD, Neal Stefan. 1200 E BROAD ST, BOX 981526 23298 #051-04-2005 L2005 **IM** *012

GREENFIELD, Victoria Anne. 1200 E BROAD ST, MCV OFFICE OF GME 23298 #051-04-2005 L2005 **IM** *012

GREER, Travis James. ■ 23225 #045-01-2007 L2007 **IM** *012

GREGG, Victoria Jenney. ■ 23225 #036-05-2001 L2001 **OP** *100

GRIMES, Margaret Mary. 401 N 12TH ST, MEDICAL COLLEGE OF VA 23298 #035-09-1975 L1979 **PTH** *020 †50

GRINNAN, Richardson. 2015 STAPLES MILL ROAD 23279 #051-04-1969 L1969 **PUD IM** *030 †20

GROB, Baruch Mayer. PO BOX 980118, VCU DIVISION OF UROLOGY 23298 #051-07-1987 L1989 **U** *020 †95

GROSSMAN, Catherine Elise. 1200 E BROAD ST, VCU MEDICAL CENTER HEALTH 23298 #041-02-2000 L2007 **PCC** *020 †20

GRUNER, George. 909 HIOAKS RD, STE A 23225 #016-06-1964 L1983 **NS N** *020 †25

GUERRY, Christopher Haski. ■ 23226 #041-01-2008 *012

GUIRKIN, Thomas Charles. 5801 BREMO RD, INTERCEDE HEALTH 23226 #051-04-2003 L2003 **IM** *100 †20

GULATI, Gauri Virindernat. 1001 E MARSHALL ST, P O BOX 980506 23219 #496-49-1997 L1999 *020

GULIANI, Sundeep Singh. ■ 23221 #011-03-2007 L2007 **GS** *012

GULLQUIST, Scott Duncan. 1200 E BROAD ST 23298 #010-02-1987 L1993 **PDC PD** *020 †55

GUMINSKY, April Lynn. 1200 E BROAD ST, MCV - OFFICE OF GME 23298 #045-01-2005 L2005 **MPD** *012

GUNNERSON, Kyle Jerome. 1200 E BROAD ST, DEPT OF ANESTHESIOLOGY 23298 #019-02-1996 L2003 **CCM EM** *020 †20,16

GUPTA, Atul K. PO BOX 980615 23298 #051-01-2003 L2003 **DR** *012

GUPTA, Shivani. ■ 23219 #051-04-2007 L2007 **IM** *012

GUTCHER, Gary Robt. 401 N 12TH ST, MEDICAL COLLEGE OF VA 23298 #023-07-1972 L1987 **NPM** *020 †55

HA, Chang Young. 1201 BROAD ROCK BLVD, RICHMOND VA HOSPITAL 23249 #583-09-1973 L1982 **SCI PM** *020 †60

HABEEB, Michael Patrick. PO BOX 980257, MCV - OFFICE OF GME 23298 #035-15-2002 L2003 **DR** *100 †80

HABIB, Adil. 1201 BROAD ROCK BLVD, CENTER 23249 #704-02-1991 L1994 **GE** *020 †20

HABIB, Aysha. 1101 E MARSHALL ST, RM 6-005 23298 #704-06-1997 L2007 **N** *012 †20

HABIBI, Mehran. 1200 E BROAD ST, VCU MEDICAL, DIV. OF ONCOL 23298 #517-12-1996 L2005 **GS** *020 †85 ‡

HABIB POUR, Ehsan. 1200 E BROAD ST, OFFICE OF GME 23298 #517-04-2005 L2007 **P** *012

HACKLER, Robert Hardin. DIV OF UROLOGY, MCV, DEPT OF SURGERY 23298 #036-01-1960 L1968 **U** *071 †95

HACKNEY, Mary Helen. 401 COLLEGE ST, BOX 980037 23298 #036-08-1988 L1989 **ON HEM** *020 †20

HADDAD, Joseph Benny. 5901 PATTERSON AVE 23226 #605-01-1972 L1975 **OBG** *020 †30

HADFIELD, Milton Gary. 401 N 12TH ST 23298 #049-01-1964 L1970 **NP** *040 †50

HAGAN, Michael P. 401 COLLEGE ST, DEPT RAD ONCOLOGY 23298 #048-04-1989 L1998 **RO** *020 †80

HAGEMANN, Timothy Wayne. 7229 FOREST AVE, VIRGINIA CARDIOVASCULAR 23226 #041-02-1983 L1992 **CD IM** *020 †20

HAGUE, John Randall. 401 N 12TH ST, MAIN 5 HOSPITAL 23298 #047-06-1975 L2003 **AN EM** *020 †55,05

HAHM, Jee Ho. 1201 BROAD ROCK BLVD, DEPT RADIOLOGY 23249 #583-01-1968 L1976 **R** *020 †80

HAIDER, Abdulrazzaq Zabun. ■ 23221 #528-02-1969 L1985 **NP PTH** *020 †50

HAITHCOCK, Roderick Ervin. 505 W LEIGH ST, STE 303 23220 #025-07-1975 L1978 **IM** *020 †20

HALIM, Sobia Hassan. PO BOX 980257, VA COMMONWLTH U HLTH SYS 23298 #704-16-1999 L2007 **PD** *012

HALL, Charles Edward, IV. 1000 BOULDERS PKWY, TUCKER PSYCHIATRIC CLINIC 23225 #051-04-2001 L2001 **CHP** *012 †108

HALVORSEN, Robert A, Jr. 1250 E MARSHALL ST 23298 #011-02-1974 L2002 **DR** *020 †80

HAN, Frederick Tehbek. ■ 23220 #010-02-2004 L2004 **CD** *012 †20

HAN, Jiho Joseph. 2621 GROVE AVE 23220 #035-06-1987 L1988 **CD IC** *012 †20

HANDY, Russell Lee. 5875 BREMO RD, STE 701 23226 #051-04-1980 L1984 **OBG** *020 †20

HANZEL, Jeffrey Sheldon. 3603 GROVE AVE, PEDIATRIC & ADOLESCENT 23221 #010-02-1969 L1976 **PD OS** *020 †55

HARBISON, John William. 1001 E MARSHALL ST, 4TH FL 23219 #018-03-1962 L1970 **N OPH** *040 †75

HARBOUR, John Richard. 5801 BREMO RD, FL 2CD 23226 #054-04-1977 L2005 **CLP HMP** *020 †50

HARD, Richard C, Jr. 1101 E MARSHALL ST, MCV 23298 #028-34-1958 L1967 **ATP** *050 †50

HARDY, Daniel Michael. 7301 FOREST AVE, STE 300 23226 #051-07-2000 L2004 **N** *020

HARGROVE, Marion D, Jr. 23221 #021-01-1954 L1993 **GE OS** *040 †20

HARKRADER, James Collin. 121 WYCK ST 23225 #051-04-1968 L1968 **OPH** *075 †35

HARLER, John Ashby. 110 N ROBINSON ST STE 305 23220 #051-04-1976 L1977 **IM** *020 †20

HARLFINGER, Erwin Herbert. 2621 GROVE AVE 23220 #051-04-1961 L1961 **GYN** *072

HARRIS, Barton. ■ 23221 #051-04-2002 L2007 **OAR** *012

HARRIS, Joseph Kim. 7301 FOREST AVE, STE 300 23226 #017-20-1981 L1982 **N** *020 †75

HARRISON, Mary Ellett. 3603 GROVE AVE, PEDIATRIC & ADOLESCENT 23221 #051-04-1985 L1988 **PD** *020 †55

HART, Alton, Jr. 1200 E BROAD ST, PO BOX 980306 23298 #012-01-1992 L2005 **IM** *020 †20

HARTIGAN, Sarah Marie. ■ 23221 #041-02-2007 L2007 **IM** *012

HARTWICH, Joseph Edmond. ■ 23220 #011-03-2006 L2006 **GS** *012

HASSAN, Zubair Ul. 5855 BREMO RD STE 101 23226 #704-01-1960 L1972 **CD IM** *020 †20

HASSANHUSSEIN, Abdurahman. 23298 #051-04-2007 L2007 **FP** *012

HASTILLO, Andrea Karen. 1605 RHOADMILLER ST 23220 #041-12-1969 L1972 **CD** *062 †20

HAWRYLUK, Gregory W J. 1200 E BROAD ST, MCV DEPT OF GME 23298 #060-01-2003 L2005 *100

HAYES, Curtis Woods. 1250 E MARSHALL ST, VCU HEALTH SYSTEM 23298 #033-05-1982 L1987 **DR** *020 †80

HAYNES, Jeffrey Harrison. 5855 BREMO RD, BOX X980015 23226 #051-04-1987 L1988 **PDS** *020 †85

HAZELRIGG, Monica Renee. 1201 BROAD ROCK BLVD 111, MCGUIRE VA MEDICIAL CENTER 23249 #051-04-1997 L1997 **IM** *020 †20

HEAD, Barbara B. 7101 JAHNKE RD 23225 #051-04-1993 L2001 **OBG** *020 †30

HEGAB, Ibrahim Mohamed. 110 N ROBINSON ST STE 105 23220 #915-02-1997 L2002 **N** *100

HEIMBACH, Curt Jarvis. 23220 #051-04-2003 L2003 **EM** *020

HELENTJARIS, Diana Ruth. 900 E MARSHALL ST, 3RD FL 23219 #025-12-1978 L1993 **GP** *030

HELLER, Andrew Jared. 1202 E MARSHALL ST, STE 401 23298 #035-46-1995 L1995 **OTO** *020 †45

HEMRAJANI, Reena Harish. ■ 23220 #011-05-2006 L2006 **IM** *012

HENCEROTH, William D, II. 110 N ROBINSON ST, STE 103 23220 #038-40-1973 L1975 **ORS** *020 †40

HENDRIX, Walter Clifford. 2201 GROVE AVE, DRS TITUS HENDRIX TURNER 23220 #051-01-1989 L1992 **IM** *020 †20

HENRY, Daniel Anthony. 1250 E MARSHALL ST, MAIN HOSP 3RD FL 23298 #028-34-1971 L1972 **DR PUD** *020 †80

HERBERT, Hadley Katharine. ■ 23219 #035-45-2007 L2007 **GS** *012

HERLIHY, Alice Nelson. ■ 23226 #051-04-2005 L2005 **IM** *012

HERMAN, Bernard Don. ■ 23220 #036-05-1957 L1977 **PD** *071 †55

HERRING, Aimee Elizabeth. ■ 23220 #023-07-2005 L2005 **EM** *012

HESS, Michael Lee. 1605 RHOADMILLER ST 23220 #041-12-1968 L1975 **CD IM** *020 †20

HETTEMA, John Michael. PO BOX 980126, VCU DEPT PSYCH 23298 #051-04-1996 L1996 **P** *050 †75

HEUMAN, Douglas Manning. 1605 RHOADMILLER ST 23220 #024-16-1977 L1979 **GE IM** *050 †20

HEWITT, Beth Barton. 5801 BREMO RD, MONUMENT PATHOLOGISTS INC 23226 #051-01-1992 L1992 **PTH** *020 †50

HEY, Jamie Cooper. 1000 BOULDERS PKWY, STE 200 23225 #041-02-1993 L2004 **PCC** *012

HEYBOER, James Peter. ■ 23225 #056-06-2006 L2006 **MPD** *012

HEYWOOD, James Robt. 3603 GROVE AVE, PEDIATRIC & ADOLESCENT 23221 #003-01-1971 L1995 **PD** *020 †20

HICKS, Kevin Andrew. 900 N HAMILTON ST, STE B 23221 #010-03-1997 L2005 **RHU** *020 †20

HIETALA, Sven Ola. 401 N 12TH ST, DEPT RADIOL 23298 #858-03-1966 L1976 **R** *040

HILL, John Edward. 5224 MONUMENT AVE 23226 #051-04-1947 L1947 **U** *071 †95

HILLNER, Bruce Ellis. 1101 E MARSHALL ST, VCU HEALTH SYSTEM 23298 #016-02-1979 L1984 **IM** *020 †20

HIRATA, Alice Jean. 7130 GLEN FOREST DR, STE 101 23226 #051-04-1987 L1989 **OBG** *030

HOFFMAN, Johanna A. 5700 W GRACE ST, STE 108 23226 #033-05-1960 L1978 **P** *030 †75

HOGAN, Christopher John. 7532 MARILEA RD 23225 #010-02-1998 L2002 **EM** *020 †16

HOLLAND, Henry Davis. 2008 BREMO RD STE 110 23226 #051-04-1966 L1966 **P PYA** *072 †75

HOLLOWAY, Kathryn Lois. 417 N 11TH ST, MEDICAL COLLEGE OF VA 23298 #033-06-1984 L1986 **NS OS** *020 †25

HOPE, Robert Lee, Jr. 401 N 12TH ST, MAIN HOSPITAL 5TH FL. 23298 #051-04-1999 L1999 **AN** *05

HORENSTEIN, Martin. 7101 JAHNKE RD 23225 #051-04-1968 L1968 **ON HEM** *071 †20

HORSLEY, John S. 401 N 12TH ST 23298 #051-01-1953 L1953 **GS OS** *071 †85

HORVATH, Brian D. ■ 23220 #036-07-2006 L2007 **D** *012

HOWELL, Halstead Dacosta. 221 E CLAY ST 23219 #010-03-1971 L1975 **GS** *020 †85 ‡

HOWELL, Keith Anson. PO BOX 981727, MCV CAMPUS 23298 #012-01-2001 L2002 **AN** *100 †05

HOYT, Jennifer Mary. 1200 E BROAD ST, MCV - OFFICE OF GME 23298 #051-04-2006 L2006 **EM** *012

HRISTOVA, Anna H. ■ 23225 #198-01-1988 L2006 **CN** *100

HUANG, Andrew Tsao. PO BOX 980146, VCU HLTH SYSTEM 23298 #011-02-2007 L2007 **OTO** *012

HUBER, Elizabeth Claire. 417 N 11TH ST, ACC SECOND FLOOR 23298 #036-01-1986 L1987 **IM** *020 †20

HUDGINS, Earl Maxwell. 7111 JAHNKE RD 23225 #051-01-1968 L1968 **D DMP** *071 †15

HUDSON, Joanne C. 4601 SULGRAVE RD 23221 #024-07-1971 L1987 **AN** *020 †05

HUGGINS, Adam Drew. ■ 23226 #001-02-2005 L2005 **OBG** *012

HUGHES, David G. 681 HIOAKS RD, STE H 23225 #012-01-1973 L1978 **CD IM** *020 †20

HUIZAR, Jose Francisco. 1201 BROAD ROCK BLVD, HUNTER HOMES MCGUIRE 23249 #649-13-1996 L2006 **CD** *020 †25

HULL, Jason Ray. 1007 PEACHTREE BLVD 23226 #051-04-1999 L1999 **OAR** *020 †40

HULSHOFF, John B. 7101 JAHNKE RD, STE 280 23225 #055-75-2003, ▲ L2006 **OBG** *020

HURT, Terry Wright. 2924 BROOK RD, CHILDRENS HOSP DEPT AN 23220 #047-06-1985 L1989 **AN** *020 †20

HUTCHER, Neil Edward. 5855 BREMO RD, ST MARY'S MED OFFICE BLDG 23226 #051-04-1965 L1965 **GS OS** *020 †85

HUYNH, Christine Nhu. 1200 E BROAD ST, PO BOX 980102 23298 #051-04-2003 L2006 **IM** *020 †20

HYDER, Haroon Syed. 4405 FOREST HILL AVE 23225 #496-35-2001 L2006 **FM** *020

IBRAHIMI, Said M. 1200 E BROAD ST, VA COMMONWEALTH U HLTH SYS 23298 #305-01-2004 L2006 **N** *012

IDEN, Thomas Carroll. PO BOX 980257, DEPT OF INTERNAL MEDICINE 23298 #051-04-2005 L2005 **IM** *012

IDOWU, Michael Ola. PO BOX 980662, DEPT OF PATHOLOGY 23298 #690-01-1995 L2000 **ATP PCP** *020 †50

IGLESIAS, Roberto Carlos. 7101 JAHNKE RD, CJW MEDICAL CENTER 23225 #005-14-2003 L2004 **GS** *012

IJAZ, Sadaf Sultana. PO BOX 980257 23298 #704-06-1987 L2006 **P** *012

IMAJO, Takeshi. ■ 23221 #572-45-1962 L1977 **NP PTH** *071 †50

IQBAL, Suleman Hameed. 1800 GLENSIDE DR, STE 103 23226 #422-01-2003 L2007 **SME** *012

IRANI, Anne-Marie A. 1112 E CLAY ST, MCGUIRE HALL 23298 #605-01-1978 L1984 **AI PPR** *050 †55,03

IRUNGU, Thomas Kimani. 109 GOVERNOR ST, VIRGINIA DEPARTMENT OF HEA 23219 #577-01-1989 L2005 **GPM** *020 †18,70

ISAACS, Christine R. 1250 E MARSHALL ST, DEPT. OB/GYN, P. O BOX 980 23298 #041-09-1997 L1997 **OBG** *020 †30

ISAACS, Jonathan Eric. 1200 E BROAD ST, BOX 980153 23298 #051-04-1996 L1996 **HS** *020 †40

ISENHOWER, Matthew Wilson. ■ 23221 #051-04-2008 L2008 *012

IVATURY, Rao Ramachandra. 1200 E BROAD ST, VCU MEDICAL CENTER 23298 #495-11-1970 L1998 **GS** *020 †85

IWASHYNA, Alexandra Nelso. ■ 23221 #051-01-2006 *012

JABEEN, Ruksana. 7101 JAHNKE RD, CHIPPENHAM CAMPUS 23225 #496-27-1996 L2006 **IM** *020 †20

JACKSON, Horace Jake. 505 W LEIGH ST STE 207 23220 #010-03-1976 L1983 **IM** *020 †20

JACOBSON, Eric Sheldon. ■ 23225 #056-05-1970 L1978 **ID IM** *071 †20

JAIN, Kunoor. ■ 23226 #051-04-2004 L2004 **GS** *012

JAIN, Rakesh Kumar. 7101 JAHNKE RD, STE 550 23225 #035-06-1982 L1987 **CD IM** *020 †20

JAIN, Sejal Virendra. ■ 23226 #495-22-2001 L2004 **CN** *012

JAIN, Vivek. ■ 23220 #051-04-2007 **TY** *012

JAMAL, Arifa. ■ 23220 #704-25-1991 L2000 **IMG** *100 †20

JAMDAR, Niteen Subhash. 7153 JAHNKE RD 23225 #422-01-2000 L2005 **IMG** *020 †20

JAMES, George Watson, IV. 110 N ROBINSON ST STE 401 23220 #051-01-1973 L1976 **ID IM** *020 †20

JANES, John Raymond, Jr. 5855 BREMO RD, STE 100N 23226 #016-11-1978 L1980 **AN** *020 †20

JANNUZZI, Daniel Marc. 108 COWARDIN AVE 23224 #051-07-1983 L1988 **FM** *020 †18

JASPERSE, Linda Marie. PO BOX 980710, DEPT OF PSYCHIATRY 23298 #422-01-2006 L2006 **P** *012

JAVEY, Golnaz. ■ 23219 #051-07-2004 L2004 **OPH** *012

JAWORSKI, Margie Louise. 1001 E MARSHALL ST, CHILDRENS PAVILLION 23219 #051-04-1980 L1984 **MG PD** *020 †55,19

JAYAWARDENA, Vidya. 1201 BROAD ROCK BLVD, SPINAL CORD INJURY UNIT VA 23249 #422-01-1993 L2000 **PM** *020 †60 ‡

JEFFERSON, Karen Walker. 7130 GLEN FOREST DR, STE 101 23226 #036-05-1994 L1994 **OBG** *020 †30

JENA, Tripti Bardhan. 1201 BROAD ROCK BLVD, DEPT 117 23249 #495-13-1968 L1980 **PM** *020 †60

JENNINGS, C Foster, Jr. 7229 FOREST AVE, VIRGINIA CARDIOVASCULAR 23226 #051-01-1982 L1982 **CD** *020 †20

JENNINGS, Torino Ravon. 2421 CHAMBERLAYNE AVE 23222 #051-04-2000 L2000 **FM** *020 †18

JENNINGS, Walter S, Jr. 1000 BOULDERS PKWY, STE 202 23225 #051-01-1981 L1982 **P** *020 †75

JENSKI, Christian A. PO BOX 980257, MCV - OFFICE OF GME 23298 #051-04-2003 L2003 **EM** *100

JEONG, Hong Sun. 1250 E MARSHALL ST, VCU HOSPITAL 23298 #011-04-2002 L2002 **CD** *012 †20

JESSE, Robert Louis. 1605 RHOADMILLER ST 23220 #051-04-1984 L1985 **CD IM** *020 †20

JESUDIAN, Alice. 1200 E BROAD ST, DEPT OF PSYCHIATRY 23298 #495-08-1973 L1989 **P** *020 †75

JETER, William Richard. 1800 GLENSIDE DR, STE 110 23226 #051-04-1973 L1976 **FM** *020 †18

JINKS, Jill Katherine. ■ 23226 #051-04-2005 L2005 **IM** *012

JOHNSON, Aleisha Janae. ■ 23225 #051-04-2005 L2005 **DR** *012

JOHNSON, Betty Anne. 1605 RHOADMILLER ST 23220 #024-01-1982 L1985 **IM** *020 †20

JOHNSON, Danna Elizabeth. 7101 JAHNKE RD, CHIPPENHAM MED CTR 23225 #035-15-1980 L1987 **PTH IM** *020 †20,50

JOHNSON, Douglas Allan. 1200 E MARSHALL ST, VCU HEALTH SYSTEM 23298 #051-04-2003 L2003 **END** *012 †20

JOHNSON, Randall Wayne. 7101 JAHNKE RD, . 23225 #051-04-1995 L2001 **NPM** *020 †55

JOHRI, Shilpa. 1000 BOULDERS PKWY, STE 102 23225 #495-54-1992 L2002 **PCC** *020 †20 ‡

JOLLES, Paul Richard. PO BOX 980001, VCU MEDICAL CTR 23298 #041-13-1983 L1991 **NM DR** *020 †20,28

JONES, Aaron Michael. ■ 23224 #051-04-2005 L2005 **PM** *012

JONES, Albert M, Jr. 1501 MAPLE AVE, STE 100 23226 #047-06-1983 L1984 **PM** *020 †60

JONES, Charles Milton, III. 5875 BREMO RD, STE G7 23226 #036-05-1983 L1989 **GO OBG** *020 †30

JONES, Elizabeth Anne. 410 N 12TH ST, MCV MAIN HOSPITAL 23298 #048-14-1991 L1996 **DR** *020 †80

JONES, Ethnie Small. 101 COWARDIN AVE STE 101 23224 #023-07-1987 L1989 **OPH** *020 †35

JONES, James Edward, Jr. 5875 BREMO RD STE 304 23226 #051-04-1975 L1982 **OBG** *020 †30

JONES, Steven Harris. 701 W GRACE ST 23220 #051-04-1976 L1978 **ORS** *020 †40

JONES, William Collins. 2809 NORTH AVE 23222 #047-01-1963 L1968 **OBG IM** *020 †30

JONES, Wm Russell, Jr. ■ 23226 #051-04-1941 L1941 **U** *071 †95

JOSEPH, Lenore Norene. 7301 FOREST AVE, STE 300 23226 #026-04-1992 L1998 **N** *020 †75

JOSEPH, Lerla Georgette. 1606 HULL ST 23224 #036-05-1977 L1983 **IM IMG** *020 †20

JOSEPH, Mary. ■ 23249 #495-53-1969 L1978 **P** *020 †75

JOY, Ajo. 1101 E MARSHALL ST, VCU DEPT OF NEUROLOGY 23298 #665-02-2004 L2005 **N** *012

JOYNER, Charles Allen. 2621 GROVE AVE 23220 #051-04-1994 L1994 **ICE** *020 †20

JULIUS, Aristides D. ■ 23221 #050-02-1951 L1976 **IM** *071

JUNG, Charlie. 5224 MONUMENT AVE, VIRGINIA UROLOGY CENTER, P 23226 #047-05-2002 L2007 **U** *020

KABOLIZADEH, Kamran. ■ 23226 #422-01-2005 L2006 **N** *012

KALLAHALLI MUNIYAPPA, Kish. 1200 E BROAD ST, 2ND FLOOR, RM 210 23298 #496-39-2000 L2006 **IM** *100 †20

KALLAR, Navreet Kaur. 1201 BROAD ROCK BLVD, PRIMARY CARE 171F 23249 #051-04-1999 L2003 **IM** *020 †20

KAMIN, Elizabeth Ann. ■ 23226 #051-07-2003 L2003 **AN** *100

KANCITIS, Indra Austra. 1001 E MARSHALL ST, CHILDRENS PAVILION 23219 #051-04-1997 L1998 **PD** *020 †55

KAPLAN, Brian Jay. 401 N 12TH ST 23298 #032-01-1990 L1998 **GS** *020 †85

KAPLOWITZ, Lisa Carol G. 109 GOVERNOR ST, RM 1331 23219 #016-02-1975 L1982 **ID IM** *040 †20

KAPOOR, Vashish. MED CTR OF VA 23298 #665-01-1998 **IM** *100

KAPROS, Mark John. 5855 BREMO RD, STE 100 23226 #422-01-1996 L2000 **AN PME** *020 ‡

KAPUR, Aarti Kamal. PO BOX 980257 23298 #654-01-2004 L2005 **P** *012

KARETI, Gautam B. 1101 E MARSHALL ST 23298 #654-01-2004 L2007 **N** *012 †20

KARJANE, Nicole Wood. 1250 E MARSHALL ST, P O BOX 980034 23298 #041-14-2000 L2000 **OBG** *020 ‡

KARLSSON, Jonas Patrik. 7101 JAHNKE RD 23225 #041-13-1995 L1996 **IM** *020 †20

KASZALA, Karoly. 1201 BROAD ROCK BLVD, 111 (73) 23249 #473-02-1993 L2006 **ICE CD** *020 †20

KATCHER, Jeremy Shawn. ■ 23224 #028-03-2005 L2005 **IM** *012

KATCHINOFF, Barry Lester. 7305 BOULDER VIEW LN 23225 #165-07-1977 L1983 **N** *020 †75

KATZ, Marc R. 5875 BREMO RD, STE G5 23226 #021-01-1981 L1981 **TS TTS** *020 †85,90

KAY, Grace Calef. ■ 23226 #035-09-1939 L1950 **OS** *071

KAYSER, Robert Granville. 1200 E BROAD ST, P O BOX 981792 23298 #033-05-2001 L2001 **IC** *012

KEARNEY, John Edward. PO BOX 981438, VCU/MCV CAMPUS 23298 #035-09-2002 L2002 **AN** *100 †05

KEIGHTLEY, Gerald Edward. 5320 PATTERSON AVE STE 200 23226 #051-04-1990 L1991 **NEP** *020 †20

KELLEHER, Alfred Brian. 7101 JAHNKE RD, CJW MEDICAL CENTER 23225 #035-19-1975 L1976 **EM IM** *020 †20,16

KELLEHER, Nicole Marie. PO BOX 980615 23298 #051-04-2005 L2005 **DR** *012

KELLEY, Brian Joseph. ■ 23298 #051-04-2008 *012

KELLUM, John Morgan, Jr. 1200 E BROAD ST 23298 #023-07-1969 L1983 **GS** *020 †85

KELLY, Brandon Reyes. 1200 E BROAD ST, MCV - OFFICE OF GME 23298 #035-19-2005 L2005 **NS** *012

KELLY, Frank R, Jr. 5801 BREMO RD 23226 #051-04-1943 L1943 **IM** *071

KELSO, Catherine M. 1300 E MARSHALL ST, MCV - N HOSP 23298 #051-04-1996 L1997 **IM** *020 †20

KENDLER, Kenneth Seedman. PO BOX 980126, MEDICAL COLLEGE OF VA 23298 #005-11-1977 L1983 **P** *050 †75

KENNEDY, Robert Moffatt. 23221 #045-04-2006 L2006 **DR** *012

KENNETT, Kelly Lynn. ■ 23225 #051-04-2008 *012

KERNITSKY, Lydia. 1001 E MARSHALL ST 23219 #035-20-1976 L1979 **CHN PD** *020 †55,75

KERNODLE, William Dwight. 1000 BOULDERS PKWY, STE 202 23225 #036-05-1972 L1975 **P** *020 †75

KERR, Gordon Hugh. 401 N 12TH ST 5TH FL, VCU DEPT OF ANESTHESIOLOGY 23298 #836-01-1977 L2006 *100

KESSEL, Ann Therese. 5855 BREMO RD, STE 703 23226 #021-01-1980 L1980 **PG** *020 †55

KHAN, Abid. 5801 BREMO RD, IMS HOSPITALIST PROGRAM/BS 23226 #704-02-1985 L1996 **IM** *020 †20

KHAN, Abid Raza. 5801 BREMO RD 23226 #704-25-1997 **IM** *100

KHAN, Asadullah. 1001 E MARSHALL ST, BOX 980264 23219 #704-25-1993 L2006 **PD** *020 †55

KHAN, Durre Nayab. 1200 E BROAD ST, MCV - OFFICE OF GME 23298 #704-02-1988 L2006 **P** *012

KHAN, Farrukh Abbas. PO BOX 980111, 1101 E MARSHALL ST 23298 #704-01-1994 L1999 **END** *012

KHAN, Hina Rahman. 1200 E BROAD ST 23298 #704-25-2003 L2006 **PD** *012

KHASAWINAH, Tariq A. PO BOX 980257, MCV - OFFICE OF GME 23298 #028-03-2003 L2003 **IM** *100 †20

KHWAJA, Tahir Nisar. PO BOX 980489, COMMONWEALTH UNIV 23298 #305-01-2002 L2007 **CHP** *012

KIBBLE, Holly Jason. PO BOX 842022, 1300 W BROAD STREET SUITE 23284 #038-06-1992 L2005 **GPM** *020

KIDD, Jason Michael. ■ 23221 #051-04-2008 *012

KIERCE, Jeannette Felicia. 401 N 12TH ST, MAIN HOSPITAL 5TH FLOOR 23298 #028-34-1992 L1998 **AN** *020 †05 ‡

KIEV, Jonathan. ■ 23298 #021-01-1989 L2003 **TS GS** *020 †90,85

KIM, Audrey Jeongah. PO BOX 980257 23298 #051-01-2006 L2006 **FP** *012

KIM, Caron Rahn. ■ 23221 #051-04-2008 *012

KIM, Christopher Kisok. 500 HIOAKS RD, STE B 23225 #051-01-1987 L2004 **OP** *020 †40

KIM, Hee Sung. 1200 E BROAD ST, MCV 23298 #583-02-1992 L2006 **PTH** *012

KIM, Jin-Tek. 701 W GRACE ST 23220 #583-02-1959 L1975 **P** *071

KIM, Moon Chul. 5855 BREMO RD, STE 100N 23226 #583-03-1969 L1978 **AN** *020

KIMMELSHUE, Katherine Nea. ■ 23221 #051-04-2005 L2005 **PTH** *012

KING, Anne Louise. 1605 RHOADMILLER ST 23220 #041-01-1980 L1981 **IM NEP** *020 †20

KING, Christopher Andrew. ■ 23226 #001-02-2003 L2006 **CD** *012 †20

KING, Terrence Lamont. ■ 23222 #051-04-2008 *012

KIPREOS, Barbara Ekker. ■ 23226 #660-03-1958 L1970 **PTH** *071 †50

KIRBY, Donald Francis. 1200 E BROAD ST, 6I DIVISION 23298 #010-01-1979 L1985 **GE NTR** *020 †20

KIRBY, Warren Byars. ■ 23226 #051-01-2007 L2007 **TY** *012

KIRKHAM, Daniel Welch. ■ 23225 #010-01-2002 L2002 **DR** *100 †80

KIRKHAM, John Charles. ■ 23225 #010-01-2004 L2004 **DR** *012

KISER, Robert Howard. 1250 E MARSHALL ST, MEDICAL COLLEGE OF VIRGINI 23298 #045-01-2000 L2005 **CD** *012 †20

KISHORE, Rekha Indira. ■ 23226 #051-04-2006 L2006 **DR** *012

KITCES, Suzanne Katherine. ■ 23225 #051-04-2004 L2004 **D** *012

KLADDER, Virginia William. 7229 FOREST AVE STE 112, PARTNER MD 23226 #051-04-2000 L2000 **IM** *020 †20

KLAFF, Justin. 1200 E BROAD ST, MCV - OFFICE OF GME 23298 #550-02-2005 L2005 **GS** *100

KLASSETT, Douglas V. 7110 FOREST AVE STE 201, RICHMOND PRIMARY CARE 23226 #051-04-1991 L1992 **FM** *020 †18

KLAUSNER, Adam Philip. 1200 E BROAD ST, VCU MEDICAL CENTER DIV OF 23298 #035-15-1996 L2002 **U** *020 †95

KLEIMAN, Deborah Gail. ■ 23221 #051-04-2008 L2008 *012

KLEIN, Wendy Simons. 1605 RHOADMILLER ST 23220 #038-06-1984 L1985 **IM** *020 †20

KLEINER, Elizabeth Anne. ■ 23225 #051-04-2002 L2002 **ID** *012 †20

KLINGENSMITH, William Cla. PO BOX 980257, MCV - OFFICE OF GME 23298 #422-01-2003 L2003 **PTH** *012

KLISCH, Gregory. ■ 23225 #051-04-2003 L2003 **DR** *012

KNOWLES, Scott Ennis. 110 N ROBINSON ST, STE 101 23220 #016-11-1978 L1979 **IM** *075

KOCH, William Calvin. 401 N 12TH ST, MEDICAL COLLEGE OF VA 23298 #051-01-1981 L1985 **PD ID** *020 †55

KOENIG, Karl G. 671 HIOAKS RD, STE B 23225 #041-09-1983 L1992 **NEP** *020 †20

KOGUT, Christopher Paul. ■ 23225 #051-04-2004 L2004 **P** *012

KOIRALA, Pradip. 1200 E BROAD 8TH FL, WEST HOSPITAL 23298 #672-01-2002 L2007 **P** *012

KOMOROWSKI, Daniel John. ■ 23221 #056-06-1999 L2004 **VIR** *100 †80

KONTOS, Hermes Apostolou. 1605 RHOADMILLER ST 23220 #418-01-1958 L1964 **CD** *030 †20

KONTOS, Michael C. 11TH & MARSHALL, MED COLLEGE OF VIRGINIA 23298 #051-04-1988 L1989 **CD** *020 †20

KOO, Harry Pontahk. 1200 E BROAD ST, P O BOX 980118 23298 #035-45-1987 L2002 **U** *020 †95

KOONTZ, Warren Woodson. ■ 23226 #051-01-1957 L1957 **U** *071 †95

KORNSTEIN, Michael J. 2621 GROVE AVE 23220 #035-15-1980 L1986 **PTH PCP** *020 †50

KORNSTEIN, Susan G. 401 N 12TH ST 23298 #043-01-1983 L1986 **P** *020 †75

KOROL, Vera Anatolyevna. 1101 E MARSHALL ST 23298 #913-32-1990 L2006 **CHN** *100

KORTE, Louisa Catherine. 401 N 12TH ST, MEDICAL COLLEGE OF VA 23298 #019-02-1982 L1998 **AN** *020 †05

KOWLER, Daniel Edward. 5855 BREMO RD STE 404 23226 #048-04-1975 L1977 **P** *020 †75

KOZIOL, Isaac. 5224 MONUMENT AVE, VIRGINIA UROLOGY CENTER 23226 #051-04-1969 L1969 **U** *020 †95

KRAVETZ, Robert Alan. 401 N 12TH ST, MEDICAL COLLEGE OF VA 23298 #038-06-1969 L1976 **AN IM** *072 †20,05 ‡

KRAWITZ, Seth Russell. 400 WESTHAMPTON STA, VIRGINIA EYE INSTITUTE 23226 #036-05-2002 L2007 **OPH** *020 †20

KRIPLANI, Leela Parsram. MCV CAMPUS 23298 #495-33-1968 L1998 **AN** *020

KROLL, Caleb Edward. 1200 E BROAD ST, MCV - OFFICE OF GME 23298 #051-01-2005 L2005 **IM** *020

KRYSTAL, Geoffrey Wolfe. 1605 RHOADMILLER ST 23220 #011-02-1982 L1988 **ON IM** *020 †20

KRYZANOWSKI, Leslie Jane. 1000 BOULDERS PKWY, STE 202 23225 #042-01-1984 L1987 **P PYG** *020 †75

KUEMMERLE, John Francis. 1605 RHOADMILLER ST 23220 #051-07-1984 L1987 **GE IM** *050 †20

KULKA, Gary Lawrence. 7400 BEAUFONT SPRINGS DR, STE 330 23225 #308-13-2001 L2005 **FM** *020 †18 ‡

KUMAR, Navita. PO BOX 980257 23298 #422-01-2007 **PD** *012

KUMARI, Sunita. PO BOX 980257 23298 #495-29-1999 L2005 **P** *012

KUMP, Cyrus Scott, III. 110 N ROBINSON ST STE 2 23220 #051-04-1994 L1995 **ORS** *020 †40

KUNDUR, Ramesh N. 2621 GROVE AVE 23220 #495-33-1990 L1999 **CD** *020 †20

KUNO, Ritsu. 1000 BOULDERS PKWY, STE 102 23225 #036-01-1988 L1989 **PCC IM** *020 †20

KUPERMINC, Mario. ■ 23226 #132-01-1959 L1967 **ON HEM** *071

KURZ, Michael Christopher. ■ 23225 #051-01-2003 L2006 **EM** *100

■ = Address Information Privacy Protected

KUSHINKA, Jeffrey Thomas. ■ 23220 #051-04-2002 L2002 **IM** *100 †20
KUZEL, Anton John. 401 N 11TH ST 23219 #016-11-1981 L1984 **FM** *030 †18
LABROPULOS, Stefanos V. PO BOX 980230, 1101 E MARSHALL ST 23298 #418-01-1988 L1998 **HO** *020 †20
LADD, Byron Scott. 400 WESTHAMPTON STA, VIRGINIA EYE INSTITUTE 23226 #017-20-1996 L2002 **OPH** *020 †35
LADOCSI, Lewis Thos, IV. 5899 BREMO RD, STE 205 23226 #051-04-1992 L1997 **PS** *020 †85,65
LAHAYE, Laura Ann. ■ 23221 #051-01-2006 L2006 **AN** *012
LAI, Guanhua. 1200 E BROAD ST, MCV 23298 #243-78-1986 L2006 **PTH** *012
LAKHANI, Sultan Ali K. 1300 E MARSHALL ST, NORTH HOSPITAL MCV 23298 #704-02-1979 L1994 **P PYG** *020 †20
LAMB, Charles Robt, Jr. 1201 BROAD ROCK BLVD 23249 #036-05-1963 L1966 **PM** *071 †60
LAMPS, Christopher A. PO BOX 980489, 515 N 10TH ST 23298 #047-05-1995 L2007 **CHP P** *020 †75
LANIER, Brock Justin. 1200 E BROAD ST, MCV - OFFICE OF GME 23298 #047-06-2006 L2006 **GS** *012
LANKFORD, Harvey Vernon. 7231 FOREST AVE, STE 103 23226 #051-04-1976 L1977 **END NM** *020 †20
LANNI, Susan Marie. 1101 E MARSHALL ST, BOX 980034 23298 #033-05-1992 L1998 **OBG MFM** *020 †30
LA ROSA, Francis A. 400 WESTHAMPTON STA, VIRGINIA EYE INSTITUTE 23226 #024-05-1995 L2000 **OPH** *020 †35
LATHAM, Bernice Grant. 505 W LEIGH ST 23220 #047-07-1971 L1973 **FM** *020 †20
LATHAM, Wiley Jacob. 505 W LEIGH ST, STE 301 23220 #047-07-1971 L1973 **IM** *020 †20
LAU, Christopher Yuyen. ■ 23219 #051-04-2002 L2006 **IM** *100
LAVER, Joseph. PO BOX 980646, MCV-DEPT. OF PEDIATRICS 23298 #550-03-1979 L1994 **PD PHO** *020 †55
LAVOIE, Suzanne Renee. 1101 E MARSHALL ST, BOX 980049 23298 #024-16-1986 L1990 **PD ID** *020 †20,55
LAWRENCE, Daniel C. 401 N 11TH ST STE 7 23219 #051-04-1980 L1981 **FM** *020 †18
LAWRENCE, Walter, Jr. 1200 E BROAD ST, BOX 980011 23298 #016-02-1948 L1966 **GS SO** *071 †85
LAYBOURN, Katherine A. ■ 23220 #048-02-1994 L1999 **GP** *020
LAYNE, Michael Steven. ■ 23220 #051-04-2008 *012
LEE, Allen Chongin. ■ 23298 #748-21-1997 L2001 **N** *100
LEE, Bennett Byunghun. 1200 E BROAD ST, P O BOX 980509 23298 #051-04-1994 L2006 **IM** *020 †20
LEE, Clifton Chulho. 7101 JAHNKE RD 23225 #051-04-1994 L1994 **PD PE** *020 †55
LEE, Hyung Mo. 401 N 12TH ST, MEDICAL COLLEGE OF VA 23298 #583-02-1949 L1957 **GS VS** *071 †85
LEE, Kangmin. 600 N 10TH ST, 310 RUDD HALL 23298 #051-04-2003 L2003 **NS** *012
LEE, Matthew Carter. 1200 E BROAD ST, MCV - OFFICE OF GME 23298 #051-04-2004 L2004 **GP** *100
LEE, Ruey-Min. ■ 23219 #244-02-1986 L2005 **ON** *020 †20
LEE, Sam Misung. 1200 E BROAD ST, 5TH FLOOR ROOM 5-110 23298 #012-01-1998 L2002 **PDC** *020 †20,55
LEE, Sophia Do-Hee. 1200 E BROAD ST, BOX 980645 23298 #035-45-1998 L1998 **GS** *100 †85
LEE, Sylvia Rozanski. ■ 23220 #051-04-2004 L2004 **PD** *020
LEFFLER, Christopher T. 401 N 11TH ST, FL 4 23219 #024-01-1993 L1995 **OPH** *020 †70,35
LEFFLER, Jessica Neidig. 1200 E BROAD ST, MCV - OFFICE OF GME 23298 #051-04-2005 L2005 **EM** *100
LEGESSE, Dereje. 7107 JAHNKE RD STE 611, VIRGINIA HOSPITALISTS 23225 #366-02-1994 L2003 *020 †20
LEICH, J Keith. 5855 BREMO RD STE 100N, HANOVER ANESTHESIA GRP INC 23226 #025-07-1985 L1986 **AN** *020 †05
LENCZOWSKI, Joi Michele. 7111 JAHNKE RD 23225 #036-07-1996 L2005 **D** *020 †15
LENETT, Stephen David. 2621 GROVE AVE, EMERGENCY DEPARTMENT 23220 #051-04-1975 L1976 **EM** *020 †18,16
LENNON, Michael James. PO BOX 980257, MCV - OFFICE OF GME 23298 #051-04-2002 L2002 **RNR** *012 †80
LESHNER, Robert Theodore. 417 N 11TH ST, 5TH FL 23298 #035-20-1969 L1981 **N CHN** *071 †75
LESSER, Steven Harry. 501 OLIVER HILL WAY, CHARITY HOSPITAL MEDICAL C 23219 #021-01-1982 L2007 **IM** *020 †16
LESTER, Denise De Shields. 1201 BROAD ROCK BLVD 110, MCGUIRE VA MEDICAL CENTER 23249 #033-05-1992 L1996 **AN** *020 †05
LEUNG, Anna Mary. 1200 E BROAD ST, MCV - OFFICE OF GME 23298 #051-04-2004 L2004 **GS** *012
LEUNG, Daniel Andreas. 1250 E MARSHALL ST, POB 980615-RADIOLOGY-VCUHS 23298 #869-07-1993 L2005 *020 †80
LEUTHAUSER, Amy Denise. ■ 23221 #051-04-2003 L2003 **GS** *100
LEVENSON, James Lloyd. 1200 E BROAD ST, BOX 980268 23298 #025-01-1977 L1982 **P PYG** *020
LEVIN, Leonard Leo. ■ 23226 #422-01-1983 L1986 **IM** *020
LEVY, James Robt. 1201 BROAD ROCK BLVD 23249 #038-06-1980 L1987 **END DIA** *050 †20
LEVY, Mark Morey. MEDICAL COLLEGE OF VA 23298 #041-01-1990 L1998 **VS** *020 †85
LEWELT, Wlodzimierz. 410 N 12TH ST, DEPT OF ANESTHESIOLOGY 23298 #759-06-1965 *100
LEWIS, Gregory Michael. PO BOX 980257, MCV - OFFICE OF GME 23298 #047-06-2001 L2002 **OPH** *020
LEWIS, Leigh Buchart. 5875 BREMO RD, STE 400 23226 #020-12-2001 L2005 **OBG** *020 †30
LEWIS, Neil Pendril. 1201 BROAD ROCK BLVD, RM 111H 23249 #917-24-1979 L1994 **CD** *020 †20
LEWIS, Richard Gordon. 681 HIOAKS RD, STE H 23225 #051-01-1968 L1968 **CD** *020 †35,20
LEWIS, Terry Dennis. 401 N 12TH ST, MEDICAL COLLEGE OF VA 23298 #051-04-1981 L1985 **DR** *020 †20
LI, Mengnai. 5801 BREMO RD, ST. MARY'S HOSPITAL, MEDIC 23226 #243-47-1995 L2003 **OP** *100
LIENG, Thanhtruc Thanh. ■ 23226 #051-04-2008 *012
LIM, Jin Soo. 5875 BREMO RD, STE 303 23226 #051-01-1999 L2004 **OTO** *071 †45
LIM, Jin Sung. 1011 HIOAKS RD STE A 23225 #035-19-1975 L2000 **OTO** *020 †45
LINAS, Phillip Aaron. 413 STUART CIR # 21 23220 #051-04-1980 L1980 **AN** *030 †05
LINDEMANN, Lillian C. 1310 W MAIN ST STE A 23220 #035-01-1949 L1952 **CHP P** *071 †55
LINER, Steven R. 401 N 11TH ST, MCV NELSON CLINIC 23219 #033-05-1977 L1979 **PD** *020 †55
LINK, Kurt. 3415 MONTROSE AVE 23222 #035-46-1961 L1978 **IM** *071

LINTON, Chike Michael. 1101 E MARSHALL ST, RM 6-005 23298 #024-07-2006 L2007 **N** *012
LINYEAR, Alice Strozik. 109 GOVERNOR ST 23219 #028-34-1965 L1981 **OBG PHP** *030
LIPPMAN, H Robt. VET ADMIN MED CTR LAB 113 23249 #035-19-1975 L1977 **PTH** *020 †50
LISZKA, Paul Victor. 1201 BROAD ROCK BLVD 23249 #473-03-1996 L2004 **IM** *100
LITWACK, Robert Simon. 1201 BROAD ROCK BLVD, MCGUIRE VAMC 110 23249 #026-04-1982 L1992 **AN** *020 †05
LIU, Chung-I. 1201 BROAD ROCK BLVD 23249 #385-03-1961 L1974 **DR** *071 †80
LOMBINO, Michael Joseph. 1200 E BROAD ST, MCV - OFFICE OF GME 23298 #035-19-2003 L2006 **IM** *100
LONDREY, Gregg Leslie. 417 LIBBIE AVE, VIRGINIA SURGICAL 23226 #051-04-1984 L1986 **GS VS** *020 †85
LONG, Stephen Paul. 1501 MAPLE AVE, STE 301 23226 #051-04-1986 L1988 **PME AN** *020 †05
LOTHE, Anand Prakash. 5855 BREMO RD, STE 403 23226 #036-05-1995 L1999 **IM** *020 †20
LOUGHRAN, Thomas P. 1300 W BROAD ST STE 113 23284 #051-04-1977 L1983 **ORS OSM** *020 †40
LOVELL, Blaise Meredith. ■ 23225 #051-04-2008 *012
LOVINGS, Vicki Denise. 5855 BREMO RD, STE 302 23226 #036-05-1983 L1986 **PD** *020 †55
LOWER, Richard Rowland. 108 COWARDIN AVE, CROSS OVER HEALTH CENTER 23224 #035-20-1955 L1965 **TS** *020 †90,85
LUCAS, Jerry Allen. 101 COWARDIN AVE, STE 208 23224 #047-07-1993 L1997 **OBG** *020 †30
LUKETIC, Velimir A C. 401 N 12TH ST 23298 #001-02-1985 L1988 **HEP GE** *040 †20
LUPPENS, Daniel Paul. ■ 23298 #047-05-2002 L2002 **PS** *012
LYCKHOLM, Laurel Jean. 401 N 12TH ST, MEDICAL COLLEGE OF VA 23298 #030-06-1985 L1985 **IM** *020
LYNCH, Alison M. 1300 E MARSHALL ST, DEPT OF PSYCH BOX 980710 23298 #836-01-1963 L1988 **P** *020 †75
MACHINIS, Theofilos. ■ 23298 #858-02-2003 L2006 **NS** *012
MAGHAKIAN, Cynthia J. 1201 BROAD ROCK BLVD # 116 23249 #396-24-1988 L1992 **P** *020
MAGNANT, Charles Donald. 5801 BREMO RD, ST. MARY'S HOSPITAL ED 23226 #051-04-1980 L1981 **IM EM** *020 †20,16
MAHAJAN, Satish. 2924 BROOK RD, CHILDRENS HOSP 23220 #496-09-1978 L1999 **PD** *020 †55
MAHER, James Wm. PO BOX 980519, VA COMMONWEALTH UNIV HLTH 23298 #011-03-1974 L2004 **GS** *020 †85
MAHONEY, Rhoda L Bland. 7113 THREE CHOPT RD 23226 #051-01-1982 L1984 **PD** *020 †55
MAIBERGER, Mary Piazza. ■ 23225 #051-04-2007 L2007 **IM** *012
MAIBERGER, Patrick Gibson. ■ 23298 #051-04-2006 L2006 **OTO** *012
MAKAROWSKY, Eugene. ■ 23225 #913-06-1941 L1955 **P** *071
MAKDAD, Bonita Jean. 412 LIBBIE AVE, STE 4 23226 #422-01-1984 L1988 **NPM** *020 †55
MAKHLOUF, Gabriel Michel. 1605 RHOADMILLER ST 23226 #352-06-1953 L1970 **GE IM** *050
MALHOTRA, Ajai Kumar. 1200 E BROAD ST 15TH FL, EAST WING, P.O. BOX 980454 23298 #495-67-1986 L2000 **CCS** *020 †85
MALUF, Daniel German. PO BOX 980572 23298 #132-02-1993 L2001 *020
MAMMO, Tigist Nigatu. ■ 23220 #020-12-2007 L2007 **MPD** *012
MANDEL, Michael David. 5855 BREMO RD, STE 403 23226 #051-04-1974 L1974 **IM ID** *020 †20
MANIKKARA, Reena. PO BOX 980257, DEPT OF INTERNAL MEDICINE 23298 #496-35-2001 L2006 **IM** *012
MANKAD, Anit Kaushik. PO BOX 980257, DEPT OF INTERNAL MEDICINE 23298 #033-06-2005 L2005 **IM** *012
MAPP, Jeffrey Stephen. 1001 E MARSHALL ST 23219 #051-04-2005 L2005 **PD** *012
MARCELINO, Victoria F. 1201 BROAD ROCK BLVD, SPINAL CORD SERV 128 23249 #748-09-1966 L1987 **PM** *020
MARKOWITZ, David Jeffrey. 6714 PATTERSON AVE 23226 #023-01-1980 L1987 **P CHP** *020 †75
MARKS, Cara Deckeman. 5801 BREMO RD, ST. MARY'S HOSPITAL 23226 #036-05-1996 L1999 **EM** *020 †16
MARKS, Lee Malcolm. 401 N 12TH ST, EMERGENCY MEDICINE DEPARTM 23298 #038-06-1993 L1996 **EM** *020 †16
MARSH, Kim Ernest. 413 STUART CIR # 21 23220 #028-02-1974 L1986 **NS N** *062 †25
MARSHALL, Kathy Lynn. 401 N 12TH ST, MAIN HOSPITAL 5TH FLOOR 23298 #027-01-1992 L1992 **AN** *020 †20
MARSLAND, David Wilson. 401 N 11TH ST, MCV NELSON CLINIC 23219 #035-03-1967 L1973 **FM PD** *030 †55,18
MARTIN, Caroline Coker. 1200 E BROAD ST, MCV - OFFICE OF GME 23298 #051-04-2005 L2005 **PTH** *012
MARTIN, Daniel C. 5899 BREMO RD STE 100 23226 #051-04-1985 L1987 **APM AN** *020 †05
MARTIN, Mary Jo. 1101 E MARSHALL ST RM 4-00, VIRGINIA COMMONWEALTH UNIV 23298 #055-02-1998 L1998 **NP FOP** *020
MARTIN, William Watkins. 2201 GROVE AVE 23220 #023-07-1954 L1958 **ON IM** *071 †20
MARTIROSIAN, Tovia Elizab. ■ 23298 #051-01-2006 L2006 **OBG** *012
MARWAHA, Vijay Rai. 5875 BREMO RD, STE 601 23226 #038-06-1999 L2002 **CD IC** *020 †20
MASON, Jonathan Keith. ■ 23219 #051-01-2007 L2007 **PD** *012
MASSEY, Charles Webster. ■ 23220 #051-04-1946 L1953 **R** *071 †80
MASSEY, Gita Vasers. 401 N 12TH ST 23298 #051-04-1981 L1986 **PHO ON** *020 †55
MASSEY, Hugh Davis. 1101 E MARSHALL ST, MCV 23298 #051-04-1996 L1996 **PTH** *020 †50
MASSIE, F Stanford. 2010 BREMO RD 23226 #036-07-1960 L1967 **AI A** *071 †55,03
MASTER, Sherman. 5700 W GRACE ST, STE 108 23226 #051-04-1961 L1961 **P** *020 †20
MATHERS, James Alexander. 1000 BOULDERS PKWY, SUITE102 23225 #035-01-1972 L1977 **PUD** *020 †20
MATTHEWS, Bradford James. 7229 FOREST AVE, VIRGINIA CARDIOVASCULAR 23226 #010-02-1989 L1991 **CD IC** *020 †20
MAUGHAN, George Topping. 425 N BOULEVARD 23220 #051-04-1981 L1986 **FM** *020 †18
MAYGLOTHLING, Julie Anne. 1201 E MARSHALL ST, 2ND FL 23298 #041-15-2001 L2006 **CCS** *020 †16
MC CALL, Calvin Odell. 401 N 11TH ST, BOX 980164 23219 #051-04-1983 L1984 **D** *020 †15
MC CARDELL, Kathleen Anne. 1201 BROAD ROCK BLVD #111K 23249 #051-04-1990 L1991 **HO** *020 †20
MC CARTER, Brenda Lynn. 7101 JAHNKE RD 23225 #051-04-1983 L1984 **FM** *020 †18
MC CARTY, John Michael. 1300 E MARSHALL ST, MAILSTOP 980157 23298 #035-47-1986 L1996 **HO IM** *020 †20
MC CLAIN, Joseph Michael. 1200 E BROAD ST, VIRGINIA COMMONWEALTH UNIV 23298 #030-05-1995 L2003 **TS** *020 †80
MC CLENAHAN, John L. ■ 23220 #041-01-1941 L1942 **R** *071 †80
MCCLUNG, Katherine Lynn. ■ 23225 #051-04-2005 L2005 **OBG** *012
MC CONNELL, Amy Constance. 5855 BREMO RD, STE 403 23226 #051-04-1999 L1999 **IM** *020 †20

MC CUE, Howard M, Jr. PO BOX 27601 23261 #051-04-1941 L1941 **OM IM** *071 †20

MC CULLOCH, Birgitta M. ▪ 23225 #051-04-2000 L2000 **IM** *020

MCCULLOCH, Madison, Jr. ▪ 23225 #051-04-2007 L2007 **GS** *012

MC DANIEL, Candice Odette. ▪ 23220 #005-15-2004 L2004 **ORS** *012

MCDONOUGH, Conan Murray. 5855 BREMO RD, STE 100N 23226 #051-04-2001 L2001 **AN** *075

MCDOWELL, Charles L. 2621 GROVE AVE 23220 #041-02-1959 L1963 **HS ORS** *020 †40

MC ELROY, Anne Howell. 7229 FOREST AVE, STE 104 23226 #038-06-1987 L1988 **OPH** *074

MC ENTIRE, Wesley Edward. 2002 BREMO RD, STE 201 23226 #051-04-1967 L1967 **P** *020 †75

MC GEHEE, Read F, Jr. ▪ 23226 #051-04-1961 L1961 **IM SME** *071 †20

MC GEHEE, Read Flournoy. 400 WESTHAMPTON STA, THE VIRGINIA EYE INSTITUTE 23226 #051-01-1989 L1994 **OPH** *020 †35

MCGHEE, Pamela Hall. 5875 BREMO RD STE 400 23226 #010-02-1989 L1990 **OBG** *020 †30

MC GLYNN, Fred Jos. 1501 MAPLE AVE, STE 200 23226 #051-01-1976 L1981 **ORS** *020 †40

MC GOVERN, John Jos. PO BOX 13101 23225 #051-01-1969 L1969 **PD** *071 †55

MC GOWAN, Gary Douglas. 7101 JAHNKE RD 23225 #051-01-1985 L1986 **EM** *020 †18

MC GRATH, Daniel Jos. 401 N 11TH ST, FL 4 23219 #016-45-1989 L1993 **OPH** *020 †35

MC GROARTY, David J. 5875 BREMO RD, STE 2018 23226 #010-02-1976 L1981 **GE IM** *020 †20

MCGUIRE, Antonio Martrell. ▪ 23224 #026-08-2007 L2007 **AN** *012

MC GUIRE, Hunter H, Jr. V A MED CTR SURG SERV 23249 #051-04-1955 L1955 **GS** *071 †85

MC GURL, John David. 1201 BROAD ROCK BLVD 23249 #051-04-1993 L1997 **IM** *020 †20

MC INTOSH, Georgia Nadia. PO BOX 981554, MCV 23298 #041-14-2000 L2000 **IM** *020

MC KAY, James. ▪ 23225 #803-01-1950 L1958 **GP** *071

MC KEITH, James John. 401 N 12TH ST, MEDICAL COLLEGE OF VA 23298 #041-02-1992 L1996 **EM** *020 †16

MC KEOWN, Charles E. ▪ 23221 #056-05-1941 L1946 **IM OM** *071

MCKILLEN, Julia Maria. ▪ 23225 #045-01-2006 L2006 **AN** *012

MC KINLEY, William Oscar. 1223 E MARSHALL ST, 4TH FL 23298 #035-03-1985 L1986 **PM** *020 †60

MC LANE, Shawn Creg. 1000 BOULDERS PKWY, STE 102 23225 #051-04-1993 L1994 **PCC** *020 †20

MC MANUS, Michael Charles. 1200 E BROAD ST, P O BOX 980118 23298 #007-02-2002 L2003 **U** *012

MCMURTRY, Cynthia Thomas. 1201 BROAD ROCK BLVD 23249 #041-02-1982 L1988 **IMG END** *020 †20

MC NAMEE, Shane. ▪ 23225 #038-43-2002 L2003 **PM** *020 †60

MC PHERSON, Richard Alan. 403 N 13TH ST, CLINICAL SUPPORT CTR 23298 #005-18-1973 L1994 **CLP** *030 †50

MEADORS, Evan Michael. ▪ 23221 #045-01-2004 L2004 **IM** *100 †20

MEADOWS, James Charles, Jr. 5855 BREMO RD, STE 100 23226 #011-02-1976 L1977 **AN IM** *020 †20,05

MEHRHOF, Austin I, Jr. 401 N 11TH ST STE 520, SURG, MCV STATION, BOX 980 23219 #035-03-1975 L1981 **PS** *040 †85,65 ‡

MELLIS, Peter Thos. 7101 JAHNKE RD 23225 #051-01-1980 L1984 **OS PD** *020 †55

MELOY, Linda Dianne. 1001 E MARSHALL ST, BOX 980506 23219 #033-06-1981 L1984 **PD OS** *040 †55

MELTON, Iain Craig. MCVA PO BOX 980053 23298 #671-01-1989 L1998 **ICE** *100

MENDEZ PICON, Gerardo P. 1800 GLENSIDE DR, STE 101 23226 #847-05-1966 L1974 **GS VS** *020 †85

MENKE, Nathan Benjamin. 401 N 12TH ST, BOX 980401 23298 #038-40-2002 L2002 **EM** *100 †16

MENNA, Gaetano Michele. 1250 E MARSHALL ST, MAIN HOSPITAL,5TH FLOOR 23298 #561-17-1987 L2003 **AN** *020

MERRELL, Ronald Clifton. 401 N 12TH ST 23298 #001-02-1970 L1999 **GS END** *020 †85

MERRILL, Cynthia Westneat. 110 N ROBINSON ST, STE 303 23220 #051-01-1972 L1976 **FM** *071 †18

MERRITT, Wyndell Hunt. 2002 BREMO RD STE 202 23226 #036-01-1966 L1975 **PS HS** *020 †65

MESSMER, James Michael. 401 N 12TH ST, MEDICAL COLLEGE OF VA 23298 #028-34-1972 L1981 **OS DR** *030 †80

METINKO, Andrew Paul. 5801 BREMO RD, TEMPLE UNIVERSITY CHILDREN 23226 #025-01-1985 L2008 **IM PD** *020 †20

MEYER, Marilyn Aileen. 5855 BREMO RD, STE 302 23226 #051-04-1981 L1983 **PD** *020 †55

MEYERHOFF, George Edward. 5855 BREMO RD, STE 208 23226 #051-04-1971 L1972 **IM CD** *020 †20

MEYERS, John Fredrick. 1501 MAPLE AVE, STE 200 23226 #038-40-1968 L1976 **ORS OSM** *020 †40

MICKELL, John Jos. 401 N 12TH ST, MEDICAL COLLEGE OF VA 23298 #035-01-1972 L1978 **CCP PDC** *020 †55

MIDDLETON, Angela Dawn. ▪ 23226 #051-04-2003 L2003 **FM** *020 †18

MIDHA, Meena. 1201 BROAD ROCK BLVD, MCGUIRE VET AFFAIRS MEDCTR 23249 #495-43-1969 L1980 **PM SCI** *071 †60

MIHAS, Anastasios A. 1201 BROAD ROCK BLVD 23249 #418-01-1967 L2000 **GE IM** *020 ‡

MIKLAVCIC, Amie Yvette. ▪ 23225 #041-15-2005 L2005 **OBG** *012

MILAM, William F. ▪ 23221 #038-40-1966 L2003 **PTH** *050

MILANESE, Simona M. 1201 BROAD ROCK BLVD, VA MEDICAL CENTER 23249 #561-16-1989 L1994 **HO** *020 †20

MILES, Michael Francis. 1217 E MARSHALL ST, TOXICOLOGY AND NEUROLOGY 23298 #016-06-1983 L2001 **N** *050 †75

MILLER, Ashley K. ▪ 23226 #047-06-2007 L2007 **P** *012

MILLER, David Wayne. 500 HIOAKS RD, WEST END ORTHO CLINIC 23225 #010-02-1988 L1990 **ORS** *020 †40

MILLER, John F. PO BOX 980230, MED COLL OF VIRGINIA/VCU 23298 #021-06-2004 L2006 **HO** *012 †20

MILLER, Kristin Bryant. ▪ 23225 #051-04-2004 L2004 **PCC** *012 †20

MILLER, Michael Benj. 1800 GLENSIDE DR, STE 103 23226 #748-08-1986 L2003 **PUD SME** *020 †20

MILLER, Susan Ann. 401 N 11TH ST, STE 742 23219 #005-14-1977 L1983 **FM** *020 †18

MILLER, Thomas Allen. 1201 BROAD ROCK BLVD, VA MED CTR SURG SRVC 112 23249 #041-13-1970 L2000 **GS GE** *020 †85

MILLIRON, Matthew John. ▪ 23220 #051-04-2008 *012

MILLS, Alan S. 401 N 12TH ST, MEDICAL COLLEGE OF VA 23298 #051-04-1977 L1979 **PTH** *050 †50

MINISI, Anthony Jos. 1201 BROAD ROCK BLVD, MCGUIRE VA MED CTR 23249 #041-01-1980 L1981 **CD IM** *020 †20

MINOR, Philip Lee Allen. ▪ 23222 #051-04-1947 L1947 **GYN OBS** *071

MITRA, Priya. ▪ 23220 #038-44-2004 L2007 **RO** *012 †20

MODJOROS, Melanie Elise. ▪ 23221 #041-12-2005 L2006 **IM** *012

MOFFATT, Thomas Lee. 671 HIOAKS RD, STE B 23225 #023-01-1975 L1977 **IM NEP** *020 †20

MOFOR, Achu Fongong. PO BOX 980257, DEPT OF INTERNAL MEDICINE 23298 #041-13-2006 L2006 **IM** *012

MOGOLLON, Andres Daniel. ▪ 23221 #649-14-1997 L2005 **GE** *012 †20

MOGYOROSI, Andras. 1201 BROAD ROCK BLVD - 5TH, VA MEDICAL CTR/MED SERVICE 23249 #473-01-1988 L1998 **NEP** *020 †20

MOHANTY, Pramod Kumar. 1201 BROAD ROCK BLVD, MCGUIRE V.A. MEDICAL CENTE 23249 #495-13-1963 L1973 **CD IM** *020 †20

MOHIUDDIN, Md Golam. PO BOX 980257 23298 #160-03-1982 L2004 **P** *012

MOHIUDDIN, Sohaib. ▪ 23220 #051-04-2007 *012

MOLLEN, Edward Leigh. 5855 BREMO RD, STE 702 23226 #051-04-1972 L1975 **AI PD** *020 †55,03

MONASTERIO, Eugenio A. PO BOX 980677, 1223 E MARSHALL ST 23298 #042-02-1995 L2001 **PM** *020 †60

MONGE, Teresa. ▪ 23225 #042-04-1992 L1996 **NEP** *020

MONROE, Sara. 1605 RHOADMILLER ST 23220 #016-01-1980 L1981 **ID IM** *040 †20

MONTANTE, Steven Joseph. 5855 BREMO RD 23226 #041-12-1995 L1995 **PS** *020 †65

MONTEIRO, Ildefonso C. 5855 BREMO RD, STE 100 23226 #748-07-1963 L1972 **AN GS** *071 ‡

MOON, Brian Bishop. ▪ 23298 #055-01-2007 L2008 **TY** *012

MOONEY, David James. ▪ 23219 #051-04-2008 *012

MOORE, Delores Cox. 7101 JAHNKE RD STE 611, C/O MARSHA O'NEIL -CHIPPEN 23225 #001-02-2001 L2005 **MPD** *100 †20

MOORE, Edward Weldon. 1605 RHOADMILLER ST 23220 #047-05-1955 L1970 **GE IM** *050

MOORE, Gregory Anthony. ▪ 23220 #048-13-2003 L2004 **PMM** *012

MOORE, Gregory Powell, II. 7101 JAHNKE RD, STE 280 23225 #051-04-1990 L1993 **OBG** *020 †30

MOORE, Robert Patrick. 1201 BROAD ROCK BLVD 23249 #051-04-1946 L1946 **IM PUD** *071

MOOTHATHU, Renuka S. 2006 BREMO RD, INSIGHT PHYSICIANS PC 23226 #495-59-1977 L1995 **P** *020 †75

MORALES-DOPICO, Lourdes. 1200 E BROAD ST - 6TH, MCVH - OFFICE OF GME 23298 #166-01-2006 L2007 **PD** *012

MORAN, Joel Benjamin. 1200 W BROAD ST 23284 #051-04-2004 L2004 **P** *012

MORANO, Gordon Shepard. ▪ 23221 #051-04-2005 L2005 **DR** *012

MOREL, Kelley Savage. ▪ 23225 #021-05-2007 L2007 **OBG** *012

MOREL, Thomas Devon. ▪ 23225 #021-05-2007 L2007 **EM** *012

MOREY, Dennis A J. ▪ 23225 #065-06-1950 L1955 **GE IM** *071 †20

MORITZ, Andrew James. ▪ 23220 #051-07-2006 L2006 **ORS** *012

MORLEY, Emily Mochrie. 1211 SHERWOOD AVE 23220 #352-04-1956 L1970 **IM PA** *050

MORLEY, John Wilson. 1605 RHOADMILLER ST 23220 #803-03-1951 L1970 **PUD IM** *040

MORRIS, Clifford Vincent. 2621 GROVE AVE 23220 #036-01-1989 L1992 **CD** *020 †20

MORRIS, Monica Reimers. 401 COLLEGE ST BOX 98058, MEDICAL COLLEGE OF VA 23298 #048-04-1993 L1998 **RO PLM** *020 †80

MORRIS, Randall Walker. 5801 BREMO RD, RICHMOND IMS 23226 #051-04-2001 L2001 **MPD** *020 †20,55

MORRISON, Allison Elise. 1200 E BROAD ST, MCV - OFFICE OF GME 23298 #045-01-2004 L2005 **D** *012

MORTON, Jessica Ray. 3000 FERNCLIFF RD 23225 #051-04-2004 L2004 **EM** *100

MORTON, Lawrence Danl. 1001 E MARSHALL ST, 1ST FL 23219 #035-08-1988 L1994 **CHN PD** *020 †55,75

MOSES, Leonard Carl. 1201 BROAD ROCK BLVD, STATION 111F 23249 #035-03-1987 L1989 **PUD CCM** *020 †20

MOSIERI, Jackmerry Chukwu. ▪ 23225 #690-01-1976 L2005 **GS** *012

MOSKOWITZ, Wm Bernard. 1200 E BROAD ST 23298 #011-04-1978 L1984 **PDC PD** *050 †55

MOXLEY, George. 1605 RHOADMILLER ST 23220 #028-02-1976 L1977 **RHU IM** *050 †20

MUASHER, Jamil Suheil. ▪ 23220 #051-04-2006 L2006 **DR** *012

MUELLER, Dawn G. 401 N 12TH ST 23298 #051-04-1972 L1975 **NPM PD** *071 †55

MUKAMANA, Grace. 1101 E MARSHALL ST, VCUHS DEPT OF NEUROLOGY 23298 #790-01-1989 L2004 **CN** *012

MUKHERJEE, Debraj. ▪ 23220 #032-01-2007 *012

MUKKAMALA, Sri Krishna. ▪ 23219 #051-04-2007 L2007 **IM** *012

MULLEN, Perry Wesley. 7229 FOREST AVE, HIGHLAND II BLDG 23226 #012-01-1979 L1985 **OPH** *020 †35

MULLER, John Garrett. 701 W GRACE ST 23220 #051-04-1978 L1979 **GPM** *020 †70

MULLINAX, Perry Franklin. 401 N 12TH ST, MEDICAL COLLEGE OF VA 23298 #051-04-1955 L1964 **IM RHU** *020 †20,03

MUMPER, James David. 7229 FOREST AVE, STE 112 23226 #051-01-1983 L1984 **FM** *020 †18

MURPHY, Cheryl Susanne. 108 COWARDIN AVE 23224 #016-43-1986 L1991 **FM** *020 †18

MURPHY, Geoffrey Scott. PO BOX 980401, DEPT. OF EMERGENCY MEDICIN 23298 #051-04-2004 L2004 **EM** *100

MURTAUGH, Heather Marie. ▪ 23225 #051-04-2008 *012

MUSTAFA, Shaheen F. PO BOX 980489 23298 #160-01-1981 L1992 **CHP** *020

MYER, Edwin Chas. 307 COLLEGE ST, VIRGINIA COMMONWEALTH UNIV 23298 #836-01-1956 L1973 **CHN N** *071 †55,75

MYERS, Troy Dean. ▪ 23221 #051-04-2001 L2001 **EM** *012

NADEEM, Tariq. 600 N 10TH ST, MCV STATION 23298 #704-01-1988 L1995 **P** *100

NAIR, Srikumar Pankajaksh. 1200 E BROAD ST - 6TH, MCVH - OFFICE OF GME 23298 #305-01-2007 L2007 **PD** *012

NAKONECZNA, Irene. ▪ 23225 #407-05-1949 L1962 **PTH** *071 †50

NAM, Marie Hae. PO BOX 980257, MCV - OFFICE OF GME 23298 #051-04-2001 L2002 **OBG** *100

NAMBIAR, Prabhakaran K. 1201 BROAD ROCK BLVD, MCGUIRE VA MED CTR 23249 #495-49-1975 L1985 **PM SCI** *020 †60

NANCE, Walter Elmore. 307 COLLEGE ST, RANDOLPH MINOR HALL 23298 #024-01-1958 L1976 **OS PD** *030 †19

NAPIANTEK, Karen Sue. 412 LIBBIE AVE, STE 4 23226 #051-07-1995 L1995 **NPM** *020 †55

NAPOLEON, Jay Louis. 1250 E MARSHALL ST, PO BOX 980541 23298 #051-04-1985 L1986 **AN PME** *020 †20

NARANG, Omprakash V. 5875 BREMO RD, STE 110 23226 #495-17-1974 L1993 **FM** *020 †18

NARLA, Lakshmama Das. 403 N 13TH ST, MEDICAL COLLEGE OF VA 23298 #495-50-1976 L1988 **PDR DR** *040 †80

NASSAR, Nabeel K. 2621 GROVE AVE 23220 #575-01-1989 L1998 **IM** *020 †20

NAVARRE, Angela Sims. ▪ 23225 #012-01-1975 L1978 **CHP P** *075 †75

NAYLOR, Elizabeth Miller. ▪ 23226 #041-02-2004 L2004 **IM** *100 †20

NEAL, M Pinson, Jr. 5855 BREMO RD, STE 705 23226 #047-06-1953 L1963 **DR** *071 †80

NEFF, Robert Swanson, II. ■ 23221 #051-04-2005 L2005 **ORS** *012

NEIFELD, James Paul. 1250 E MARSHALL ST 23298 #051-04-1972 L1978 **SO HNS** *020 †85

NEIL, Elmer Ewart. 1700 FRONT ST 23222 #010-03-1970 L1980 **R** *020

NEIL, Gregory Christopher. ■ 23298 #566-01-1989 L1998 **PS** *020 †65 ‡

NELSON, Charles M Kinloch. 5224 MONUMENT AVE 23226 #051-04-1969 L1969 **U GS** *020 †95

NELSON, Charles Wellman. 681 HIOAKS RD, STE H 23225 #051-01-1985 L1989 **CD** *020 †20

NELSON, Kirk Lee. 1201 BROAD ROCK BLVD, MCGUIRE VA MEDICAL CENTER 23249 #041-09-1977 L1986 **P IMG** *020 †75

NELSON, Robert Tyrone, Jr. 5224 MONUMENT AVE 23226 #005-14-1992 L1998 **U** *020 †95

NERALLA, Sridhar. 1000 BOULDERS PKWY, STE 102 23225 #016-76-1998, ▲ L2005 **PCC** *020 †20

NESTLER, John Edwin. 1605 RHOADMILLER ST 23220 #041-01-1979 L1980 **END IM** *020 †20

NEWBILL, Edward Thos. 5875 BREMO RD, STE 303 23226 #051-01-1979 L1983 **OTO** *020 †45

NEWSOME, Heber H, Jr. 1101 E MARSHALL ST, BOX 980565 23298 #021-01-1962 L1970 **GS NTR** *071 †85

NEWTON, Calvin Mark. 7401 BEAUFONT SPRINGS DR, STE 100 23225 #045-01-1981 L1982 **CD IM** *020 †20

NEWTON, George Broadie. 425 N BOULEVARD 23220 #048-04-1981 L1990 **VS GS** *020 †85

NEYMAN, Greg. ■ 23226 #051-04-2004 L2007 **EM** *100

NGO, Matthew Minh Tri. 681 HIOAKS RD, STE H 23225 #051-01-1999 L2006 **ICE** *020 †20

NGUYEN, Bichngoc Thi. ■ 23220 #051-04-2008 *012

NGUYEN, Kimanh Thi. ■ 23220 #051-04-2008 *012

NICHOLS, Catherine. 510 N ALLISON ST, # B 23220 #051-01-1997 L1997 **OBG** *020 †30

NICHOLS, Lydia Caroline. 1200 E BROAD ST - 6TH, MCVH - OFFICE OF GME 23298 #045-01-2003 L2007 **AN** *012 †55

NIENOW, Shalon Marie. ■ 23219 #051-04-2008 L2008 *012

NIXON, John Victor. 403 N 13TH ST N7077, MED COLLEGE OF VA 23298 #917-08-1965 L1986 **CD IM** *040

NOBLE, Jason Gregory. 401 N 12TH ST, VCUHS 23298 #041-09-1986 L1999 **AN** *020 †05

NOOR, Amra. ■ 23224 #704-05-1998 L2006 **IMG** *020 †20

NORDGREN, Aaron Dirk. PO BOX 980615 23298 #011-05-2006 L2006 **DR** *012

NORFLEET-MEGSON, Mary H. 7229 FOREST AVE STE 211 23226 #051-01-1978 L1984 **PD** *020 †20

NOVAK, Christopher Philip. 109 GOVERNOR ST, RM 530 23219 #062-01-1996 L2004 **GPM** *020 †70

NUARA, Joseph Carl. 2621 GROVE AVE 23220 #051-04-1969 L1969 **CD IM** *020 †20

NURNBERG, Ruth Diane. ■ 23220 #045-04-1992 L1993 **IM** *050 †20

O'BANNON, John Maurice. 7301 FOREST AVE, STE 300 23226 #051-04-1973 L1974 **N SME** *020 †75

OBERLANDER, Eric Kimball. ■ 23220 #051-04-2001 L2001 **NS** *012

ODULANA, Adebowale Ayoola. ■ 23226 #036-01-2006 L2006 **MPD** *012

OFOGH, Kaveh. 401 N 12TH ST, MEDICAL COLLEGE OF VA 23298 #517-10-1988 L1995 **IM** *020

OITICICA, Claudio. 7119 JAHNKE RD, PEDIATRIC SURGEONS OF VIRG 23225 #187-03-1968 L2002 **PDS** *020 †85

OJO, Peter Babatunde. 1200 E BROAD ST, 15TH FL 23298 #690-01-1995 L2007 **GS** *012 †85

OKEN, Donald Edward. 1605 RHOADMILLER ST 23220 #035-01-1954 L1975 **NEP IM** *050 †20

OKONJI, Eluojo Israel. 1201 BROAD ROCK BLVD 23249 #690-14-1992 L2007 **IMG** *012 †20

OLDHAM, Robert Lee. 1200 E BROAD ST, WEST HOSP, 8TH FLR, EAST W 23298 #001-02-2004 L2004 **P** *012

OLINGER, Mary Mc Lean. 2004 BREMO RD STE 106 23226 #028-02-1982 L1985 **P** *020 †75

OLSHANSKY, Kenneth. 5875 BREMO RD STE 212 23226 #051-04-1968 L1968 **PS** *020 †65

OMARZAI, Reza K. 2621 GROVE AVE 23220 #704-01-1987 L1998 **CD IM** *020 †20

O'NEIL, Timothy Earl. 1001 HIOAKS RD, PEDIATRIC ASSOCIATES 23225 #051-04-1990 L1992 **PD** *020 †55

ORHON, Asli Suzan. ■ 23225 #654-01-1999 L1999 **P** *020 †75

ORIA, Maria Josefina. 7101 JAHNKE RD, CJW MEDICAL CENTER 23225 #042-01-2000 L2000 **PD** *100 †55

ORNATO, Joseph P. 401 N 12TH ST, BOX 401 23298 #024-05-1971 L1985 **CD EM** *020 †20,16

OSTMAN, Henry Espino. ■ 23226 #748-20-1999 L2007 **PUD** *012

OUEDRAOGO, Ghislaine L. 12 N THOMPSON ST, PATIENT FRIST CARYTOWN 23221 #051-04-2002 L2002 **MPD OS** *020 †20,55

OWEN, Heth, Jr. ■ 23226 #051-04-1949 L1949 **AN** *071

PADE, Patricia A. 700 E FRANKLIN ST, STE 300 23219 #041-12-1978 L1981 **IM EM** *020 †20,16

PAHLE, Nancy Jo. 2201 GROVE AVE, DRS TITUS HENDRIX TURNER 23220 #047-06-1993 L1993 **END** *020

PAI, Ajit B. 1200 E MARSHALL ST, P O BOX 980661 23298 #041-15-2005 L2005 **PM** *012

PALANK, Brian Joseph, Jr. ■ 23220 #051-04-2007 L2007 **AN** *012

PALETTA, Laura Elizabeth. ■ 23226 #051-04-2003 L2003 **MPD** *100 †20,55

PALMORE, Randolph Harris. 900 N HAMILTON ST STE A 23221 #051-04-1990 L1991 **FM** *020 †18

PALUMBO, Michelle Lynn. ■ 23225 #051-04-2008 *012

PANCOAST, James White. 417 LIBBIE AVE 23226 #051-04-1960 L1960 **GS CD** *020 †85

PANDAK, William Michael. MCGUIRE VETERANS AFFAIRS M, DIVISION OF GASTROENTEROLO 23249 #051-04-1983 L1984 **GE IM** *050 †20

PANDURANGI, Ananda K. 401 N 12TH ST, MEDICAL COLLEGE OF VA 23298 #495-73-1975 L1984 **P** *020 †75

PANDYA, Arti Lalitkumar. 1101 E MARSHALL ST, MEDICAL COLLEGE OF VA 23298 #496-38-1983 L1991 **MG PD** *020 †19,55

PANDYA, Paras. 401 N 12TH ST 503, MAIN HOSPITAL MCV CAMPUS 23298 #035-06-1996 L1999 **EM** *020 †16

PANEBIANCO, Deborah Irr. 1201 BROAD ROCK BLVD, GEN MED BLDG 111B 23249 #051-04-1991 L1992 **IM** *020 †20

PAOLONI, Christopher E. ■ 23220 #035-15-2003 L2007 **OBG** *020

PAREKH, Vipul Vrajalal. PO BOX 980257 23298 #104-01-2005 **N** *012

PARIKH, Nikunj Dineshchan. 7101 JAHNKE RD, CHIPPENHAM MEDICAL CENTER 23225 #495-76-1996 L2003 **IM** *020 †20 ‡

PARISI, Richard Arthur. 1800 GLENSIDE DR STE 103, SLEEP DISORDER CTR OF VA 23226 #041-07-1980 L1999 **PUD SME** *050 †20

PARK, Haejoe. ■ 23220 #051-04-2006 L2006 **GS** *012

PARKER, George A. 5855 BREMO RD, STE 506 23226 #024-05-1972 L1980 **GS SO** *020 †85

PARKER, Mark Steven. 1250 E MARSHALL ST 3RD FL, POB 980615 23298 #051-07-1989 L2000 **DR** *020 †80

PATEL, Ashokkumar R. 2015 MONUMENT AVE 23220 #495-48-1981 L1985 **IM GP** *020

PATEL, Hitesh. ■ 23220 #051-04-2008 *012

PATEL, Hitesh Keshavbhai. 7101 JAHNKE RD, STE 611 23225 #495-22-1998 L2006 **IM** *020 †20 ‡

PATEL, Shital Kantilal. 5855 BREMO RD, STE 100N 23226 #305-01-1999 L2003 **AN** *020 †05

PATTERSON, James L, Jr. 401 N 12TH ST 23298 #051-04-1961 L1961 **FM GP** *030 †18

PATTERSON, Jennie Banner. ■ 23220 #051-04-2008 *012

PATTERSON, Ronald Halford. 1201 BROAD ROCK BLVD, HUNTER HOLMES VA MEDICAL C 23249 #051-04-1971 L1973 **ORS** *020 †40

PATTERSON, Tara Clare. ■ 23221 #033-05-1998 L2004 **P** *020 †75

PAULSEN, Walter H J. 1300 E MARSHALL ST 23298 #905-01-1969 L1979 **CD IM** *020 †20

PAWLOW, Lara Elizabeth. ■ 23225 #051-04-2008 *012

PEARSALL, Thomas Ballou. 5801 BREMO RD, ST. MARY'S HOSPITAL 23226 #051-01-2002 L2005 **IM** *020 †20

PEARSON, Suzanne. ■ 23298 #038-41-1995 L1995 **PTH** *100

PEAT, Austin Ellerbe. ■ 23221 #020-12-2007 L2007 **GS** *012

PEDYNKOWSKI, Alfred B. 1208 HULL ST 23224 #759-07-1965 L1976 **AN** *020

PEEL, Carolyn Ann. 401 N 11TH ST, BOX 980216 23219 #051-04-1992 L1995 **FM** *020 †18

PEERY, Sharon Eileen. ■ 23220 #016-06-1993 L2003 **IM** *020 †20

PELLOCK, John Michael. 1001 E MARSHALL ST 23219 #028-34-1971 L1978 **CHN N** *040 †75,55

PENBERTHY, Lynne T. ■ 23225 #025-01-1981 L1983 **GS** *020

PENDYAL, Kausalya. 7101 FOREST HILL AVE, UNIT 0 23225 #495-62-1997 L2007 **FM** *020 †18

PENG, Thomas Chih Cheng. 1101 E MARSHALL ST, P O BOX 980034 23298 #008-02-1980 L1989 **OBG IM** *020,30

PEPPIATT, Harry Brian. 671 HIOAKS RD, STE B 23225 #051-04-1983 L1989 **IM NEP** *020 †20

PEREZ, Francisco Jose. PO BOX 980053, MCV CAMPUS DEPT. ELECTROPH 23298 #042-01-2000 ICE 23298 **ICE** *020 †20

PERKINS, Edward Brent. 1101 E MARSHALL ST, MCV DIVISION OF HEM/ONCOLO 23298 #051-04-1996 L1996 **HO** *020 †20

PERVAIZ, Khurram. 1200 E BROAD ST, MCV - OFFICE OF GME 23298 #704-01-2002 L2005 **ORS** *012

PHAN, Laura T. 401 N 11TH ST RM 439, VIRGINIA COMMONWEALTH UNIV 23219 #051-04-2006 L2007 **OPH** *012

PHIEFFER, Laura Susanne. 420 LIBBIE AVE, AVENUES DERMATOLOGY PLLC 23226 #051-04-1997 L1997 **D** *020 †15

PHILLIPS, Charles William. 7229 FOREST AVE, VIRGINIA CARDIOVASCULAR 23226 #051-01-1977 L1980 **CD IM** *020 †20

PICONE, Carmela M. 401 N 12TH ST, MEDICAL COLLEGE OF VA 23298 #048-14-1983 L1990 **N** *020 †75

PIEDRA, Mariano Martin. 2008 BREMO RD STE 110 23226 #051-04-1982 L1983 **P** *020 †75

PIERCE, Catherine V. 7101 JAHNKE RD, DEPT PATHOLOGY/LABORARY 23225 #051-04-1990 L1994 **PTH** *020 †20

PIERCE, John Gerald, Jr. 403 N 11TH ST STE 600 23298 #011-03-1991 L1999 **OBG IM** *020 †20,30

PIERCE, Julian Thomas, Jr. ■ 23222 #051-04-2000 **IM** *100

PINKHAM, Rebecca Charlott. 28 WESTHAMPTON WAY, UFA 3694 23173 #051-04-2005 L2005 **P** *012

PINN, Melvin Thos, Jr. 600 E BROAD ST, STE 400 23219 #051-01-1976 L2003 **FM** *030 †18

PINSON, Andy Gilliam. 1605 RHOADMILLER ST 23220 #045-01-1987 L1990 **IM** *020 †20

PIZZANI, Eddy. 5855 BREMO RD STE 101 23226 #935-01-1962 L1975 **IM GE** *020

PIZZANI, Miriam Koller. 5855 BREMO RD, STE 101 23226 #051-04-1980 L1980 **P CHP** *020 †75

PLACIDE, Ricky James. 500 HIOAKS RD, STE B 23225 #051-07-1996 L2003 **ORS OSS** *020 †40

POKLEPOVIC, Andrew Stewar. ■ 23225 #011-04-2004 L2004 **IM** *100 †20

POLATTY, Rose Crystal. 1201 BROAD ROCK BLVD, STE 161 23249 #012-01-1977 L1978 **PUD CCM** *020 †20

POLINGER-HYMAN, David Jos. 1200 E BROAD ST, MCV - OFFICE OF GME 23298 #035-08-2003 L2005 **DR** *012

POLSKY, Michael Bruce. 1000 BOULDERS PKWY, STE 102 23225 #011-03-2001 L2007 **PCC** *020

POMMERSHEIM, William J. ■ 23221 #038-41-1998 L2004 **MSR** *020 †80

PONG, David Choy. 7229 FOREST AVE STE 100, PARTNER MD 23226 #005-02-1990 L1993 **FM** *020 †18

POPE, John Henry, Jr. 7127 JAHNKE RD 23225 #051-04-1975 L1976 **FM** *020 †18

POPPELL, Charles Dean. ■ 23225 #051-04-2007 L2007 **AN** *012

PORT, John Eric. ■ 23221 #051-04-2003 L2003 **IM** *100 †20

POSNER, Marc Philip. 401 N 12TH ST, MEDICAL COLLEGE OF VA 23298 #056-06-1976 L1983 **TTS VS** *020 †20

POWELL, Kristen Fischer. 7113 THREE CHOPT RD, STE 101 23226 #051-04-1997 L1997 **NPM** *020 †55

POWELL, Raleigh Cox. 12 N THOMPSON ST, PATIENT FRIST CARYTOWN 23221 #051-04-1968 L1968 **P** *020

POWELL, Robert Gilliam. 5801 BREMO RD, EMERGENCY DEPARTMENT 23226 #051-04-1974 L1976 **FM** *020 †18,16

POWERS, Cara Colleen. ■ 23298 #004-01-2003 L2003 **ORS** *100

POWERS, Celeste N. 1200 E MARSHALL ST, GATEWAY BLDG 6TH FL 23298 #048-14-1985 L1989 **PTH PCP** *020 †50

POWERS, Karen Lynne. 1200 E BROAD ST, MCV - OFFICE OF GME 23298 #025-01-2004 L2004 **PS** *012

POWERS, Karen Margaret. ■ 23220 #422-01-2002 L2006 **CHN** *012

POZEZ, Andrea L. 5855 BREMO RD 23226 #649-14-1980 L1986 **PS** *020 †65 ‡

PRADHAN, Shilpi. ■ 23226 #028-02-2004 L2004 **OPH** *012

PRINCE, John Stuart, Jr. 1201 BROAD ROCK BLVD, MCGUIRE VA MED CTR 23249 #051-04-1989 L1990 **IM** *020 †20

PRINZ, Andreas Werner. 1201 BROAD ROCK BLVD, CENTER /CARDIOLOGY SECTION 23249 #051-04-1990 L1990 **CD** *020 †20

PROCTOR, Jack Douglas. ■ 23221 #051-04-1962 L1962 **PA IM** *071 †20

PROTO, Anthony V, Jr. 401 N 12TH ST 23298 #008-01-1971 L1984 **DR** *062 †80

PURGASON, Polly Annette. 5875 BREMO RD, STE 606 23226 #036-05-1986 L1992 **OPH** *020 †35

PURYEAR, Douglas Wayne. 1000 BOULDERS PKWY, STE 102 23225 #051-04-1989 L1990 **PCC IM** *020 †20

PUSTILNIK, Sean David. ■ 23224 #051-04-2008 L2008 *012

PUTNEY, Scott Alexander. ■ 23220 #051-04-2008 *012

QUAGLIANO, Peter Vincent. 1201 BROAD ROCK BLVD, HOSPITAL RADIOLOGY-114 23249 #051-04-1990 L1992 **DR** *020 †80

QUEEN, Brenda Allyn. ■ 23226 #051-04-2007 L2007 **IM** *012

QUIRK, Gerald Lee. ■ 23220 #051-04-2008 *012

RABHAN, Walter Norton. 1501 MAPLE AVE STE 200, TUCKAHOE ORTHOPAEDIC ASSOC 23226 #012-01-1964 L1972 **ORS** *020 †40

RABINOWITZ, Rachel Alison. ■ 23220 #051-04-2008 *012

RADOW, Scott K. 1000 BOULDERS PKWY, STE 102 23225 #055-01-1977 L1978 PUD CCM *020 †20

RAJA, Muhammad Ishtiaq. 7101 JAHNKE RD, CJW MEDICAL CENTER 23225 #704-15-1994 L2004 IM HOS *020

RAMAMURTHY, Sujatha G. 7101 JAHNKE RD 23225 #048-13-2003 L2003 MP *012

RAMASWAMY, Anil Kumar. 1200 E BROAD ST, PO BOX 980140 23298 #495-33-1994 L2001 PDE *020 †55

RAMSEY, Frank Edgar. 2621 GROVE AVE 23220 #154-01-1974 L1984 EM *020 †16

RAMUS, Ronald Mark. 5855 BREMO RD, STE 306 23226 #016-02-1987 L2004 MFM OBG *020 †30

RANGAPPA, Shantaram. PO BOX 981701 23298 #051-01-1996 IM *020

RAO, Tangada Premasudha. 1201 BROAD ROCK BLVD, 111M 23249 #495-65-1984 L1992 RHU IM *020 †20

RAPP, Matthew Kendrick. ■ 23220 #010-01-2008 *012

RASH, Christopher Bradley. ■ 23226 #051-04-2004 L2004 CD *012 †20

RASHID, Omar Maen. ■ 23220 #036-07-2006 L2006 GS *012

RATANASEN, Rutt Mark. ■ 23220 #051-04-2008 *012

RAUSCH, Christine Ani. 5855 BREMO RD, SUITE 405 MOB NORTH 23226 #051-07-1997 L2005 D *020 †15

RAY, Catherine L Tissot. 7149 JAHNKE RD, TUCKER PSYCHIATRIC CLINIC 23225 #010-01-1958 L1964 GP P *071

RAYANI, Sujana Venkata. PO BOX 980257 23298 #495-50-1997 L2003 P *100

RAZA, Syed Arman. PO BOX 980036 23298 #704-02-2001 L2006 IM *020

RAZA, Syed Asad. PO BOX 980257 23298 #704-01-1998 P *012

RAZDAN, Amit. PO BOX 980257, MCV 23298 #495-67-1994 L2000 CHP *020 †75

RAZVI, Fatema. 5801 BREMO RD, ST. MARY'S HOSPITAL 23226 #033-06-1999 L1999 MPD *020 †20,55

READ, Edward James, Jr. 401 N 12TH ST, PO BOX 980401 23298 #041-02-1977 L2002 EM FM *020 †16,18

REDDY-MUNAGALA, Pallavi. PO BOX 980257, DEPT OF INT MED 23298 #001-02-2007 L2007 IM *012

REDMAN, Richard D. 7110 FOREST AVE STE 101 23226 #039-01-1972 L1982 PS *020 †85,65

REDWINE, Fay E. 5855 BREMO RD STE 306 23226 #051-04-1974 L1977 MFM OBG *020 †30

REDWOOD, Marcia Constance. ■ 23220 #051-04-2007 IM *012

REESE, George Walter. 701 W GRACE ST 23220 #051-04-1955 L1955 IM *020

REGAN, Laura Elizabeth. 420 LIBBIE AVE, AVENUES DERMATOLOGY 23226 #038-40-1999 L2005 DMP *020 †15

REGAN, William Whitfield. 900 N HAMILTON ST 23221 #028-02-1947 L1954 GE IM *071 †20

REHMAN, Syed Amir. 7101 JAHNKE RD, STE 611 23225 #704-02-1992 L2003 HO *020 †20

REID, Buffie Marie. ■ 23226 #011-04-2002 L2002 GE *012 †20

REID, Renee Donna. 401 N 12TH ST, DEPT OF EMERGENCY MEDICINE 23298 #038-06-1991 L1994 EM *020 †16

REINHARD, James Stewart. 1220 BANK ST, COMMONWEALTH OF VIRGINIA 23219 #016-11-1984 L1994 P PFP *030 †75

REITER, Evan Ralph. 1201 E MARSHALL ST, STE 401 23298 #024-01-1993 L1998 OTO *020 †45

RESNIK, Tracy Ruth. ■ 23226 #051-04-2000 L2000 EM *020

REYES, Carlos Alfonso. 23224 #264-05-1982 IMG *100

REYNOLDS, John Wallin. 7101 JAHNKE RD 23225 #048-02-1974 L1984 PTH *020 †50

RICH, Petrovia Morgan. 909 HIOAKS RD STE I 23225 #026-04-1980 L1985 OPH *020 †35

RICHARD, Stephen Ross. 110 N ROBINSON ST, STE 303 23220 #051-04-1984 L1987 FM *020 †18

RICHARDS, Charles N, Jr. 7101 JAHNKE RD 23225 #051-04-1950 L1950 GP OBG *071

RICHMOND, Michael A. 2000 RIVERSIDE DR 23225 #021-06-2004 L2004 AN *012

RIDDER, Thomas Stephen. ■ 23225 #051-04-2007 L2007 GS *012

RIGBY, Fidelma Burke. 1101 E MARSHALL ST, BOX 980034 23298 #051-01-1989 L1995 OBG *020 †20

RILEY, Christa Leigh. 1200 E BROAD ST, POB 980695 23298 #051-04-2005 L2005 AN *012

RILEY, Roger Steyer. 403 N 13TH ST, CSC BUILDING 665-E 23298 #055-01-1978 L1997 PTH *020 †50

RINDOS, Michelle. 5855 BREMO RD, STE 605 23226 #035-45-2002 L2002 OBG *020

RINEHARDT, Richard F. 7130 GLEN FOREST DR, STE 101 23226 #051-04-1985 L1988 OBG *020 †20

RITTER, Ann M. 7115 JAHNKE RD, PEDIATRIC NEUROSURGERY 23225 #048-04-1991 L1994 NS *020 †25

RIVERS, Cullen Bullard. 1000 BOULDERS PKWY, STE 200 23225 #012-01-1971 L1976 PUD IM *020 †20

RO, Kee Sung. ■ 23226 #583-08-1982 L1992 IM *020 †20

RO, Peter S. 2621 GROVE AVE 23220 #018-03-1985 L1991 CD IM *020 †20

ROBBINS, Brian Scott. 5801 BREMO RD, RICHMOND IMS HOSP PROG 23226 #550-02-2002 L2005 IM *100 †20

ROBERTS, David Walton. 401 N 12TH ST 23298 #012-01-1988 IM *020

ROBERTS, Elizabeth Brown. 5855 BREMO RD, STE 605 23226 #051-04-2001 L2005 OBG *020 †30

ROBERTS, John David. 1101 E MARSHALL ST, RM 6-030 23298 #041-01-1976 L1993 ON PD *050 †20,55 ‡

ROBERTS, Marigny Begue. 23225 #021-06-2005 L2005 PTH *012

ROBERTS, William Neal, Jr. 417 N 11TH ST, AMBULATROY CARE CTR MCV 23298 #051-01-1977 L1986 RHU IM *040 †20

ROBERTSON, Charles Henry. 5801 BREMO RD 23226 #051-04-1971 L1973 IM MDM *071 †20 ‡

ROBERTSON, Louise Wilkes. 1200 E BROAD ST 23298 #051-04-1960 L1960 PDC PD *071 †55

ROBERTSON, Wm Archibald. 5700 OLD RICHMOND AVE, STE 1 23226 #051-04-1964 L1964 TS VS *071 †85,90

ROBINSON, Bradford James. PO BOX 980257, MCV - OFFICE OF GME 23298 #048-02-2003 L2003 DR *012

ROBINSON, Robert Eugene. ■ 23220 #051-04-1960 L1960 OS IM *071

ROCKOWER, Brian Garrett. ■ 23220 #041-13-2001 L2001 P *020

RODRIGUEZ, Ramon, III. 1111 E MAIN ST 23219 #539-05-1990 L1999 FM LM *020 †18

ROGERS, Stephanie Paige. ■ 23220 #051-04-2007 IM *012

ROHATGI, Sameer. 7229 FOREST AVE, VIRGINIA CARDIOVASCULAR 23226 #035-20-1998 L2005 IC *020 †20

ROMHILT, Donald Wade. 1605 RHOADMILLER ST 23220 #036-07-1962 L1978 CD OS *020 †20

ROSANELLI, Peter. 5855 BREMO RD STE 305 23226 #051-04-1965 L1965 OBG *020 †30

ROSE, Lisa Jeannette. ■ 23220 #051-04-2007 IM *012

ROSS, Wanda S. 7101 JAHNKE RD 23225 #047-07-1978 L1984 PD *020 †55

ROTH, Todd Stuart. 1200 E BROAD ST, MCV - OFFICE OF GME 23298 #422-01-2006 L2006 PD *012

ROTHEMICH, Stephen F. 401 N 11TH ST 23219 #051-04-1989 L1990 FM *020 †18

ROWE, Bruce Clifford. 425 N BOULEVARD 23220 #038-06-1984 L1987 OBG *020 †30

ROWE, Douglas Stephen. 7301 FOREST AVE, STE 100 23226 #051-01-1967 L1967 PS GS *020 †85,65

ROWE, Joy P. 5855 BREMO RD, STE 403 23226 #051-04-1987 L1988 IM *020 †20

ROWSON, Melanie Viola. ■ 23225 #023-01-2007 P *012

ROYAL, Erica M. 5875 BREMO RD, STE 203-205 23226 #047-07-1994 L2000 OBG *020 †30

ROYAL, Pamela Jofrances. 505 W LEIGH ST STE 304 23220 #051-07-1986 L1989 D *040 †15

ROYSTER, Kristin Ethel. ■ 23225 #051-04-2006 FP *012

ROZYCKI, Henry Jos. 401 N 12TH ST RM 6-500 23298 #033-06-1981 L1988 NPM PD *020 †55

RUBATT, Jennifer Marie. PO BOX 980034, VIRGINIA HOSPITALS 23298 #056-06-2002 L2002 OBG *100

RUDDY, Shaun. 1605 RHOADMILLER ST 23220 #008-01-1961 L1974 RHU AI *020 †20,03

RUDLIN, Craig Reid. 4600 GROVE AVE 23226 #024-01-1978 L1979 PDE *020 †55

RUDNICK, Emily Frances. 23220 #051-04-2008 OTO *100

RUSSELL, Edward Clifton. 1101 E MARSHALL ST, BOX 980121 23298 #036-05-1970 L1971 PHO *020 †55

RUTHERFORD, Molly Stewart. ■ 23225 #051-04-2004 L2004 CD *012 †20

RYAN, Mark Hehman. 4730 N SOUTHSIDE PLAZA ST 23224 #051-04-2000 L2000 FM *020 †18 ‡

SABORIO, Pablo Jose. PO BOX 980498, CHILDREN'S MED CTR 23298 #270-01-1986 *100

SADATI, Sheler. PO BOX 980001 23298 #517-08-2001 L2004 EM *012

SAFWAT, Amira Moftah. PO BOX 980541, 410 N 12TH ST 23298 #330-02-1964 L1972 AN *071 †05

SAJID, Syed Hassan. 5855 BREMO RD STE 210 23226 #704-02-1992 L1997 P *020

SAKOWSKI, Anthony D, Jr. 400 WESTHAMPTON STA 23225 #051-04-1969 L1969 OPH *020 †35

SALAM, Sultana Ayubi. 1201 BROAD ROCK BLVD, MEDICAL CENTER 116A 23249 #915-02-1979 L1983 P *020 †75

SALLEY, Kelsey E S. ■ 23225 #051-04-2003 L2003 END *012 †20

SALOUR, Mozhdeh. 401 N 12TH ST, MEDICAL COLLEGE OF VA 23298 #051-04-1995 L1995 DR *020 †80

SALZBERG, Arnold David. 1200 E BROAD ST, BOX 980645 23298 #051-04-1998 L1998 GS *100 †85

SALZBERG, Elizabeth Leigh. 1200 E BROAD ST 16TH FL, BOX 980135 23298 #051-04-2003 L2003 GS *012

SAMBANDAM, Senthil Nathan. 1200 E BROAD ST, MCV - OFFICE OF GME 23298 #495-59-2000 L2007 OAR *012

SAMPSON, Deborah Alice. ■ 23298 #023-01-2007 L2007 GS *012

SAMUELS, Julie Anne. PO BOX 27401 23279 #051-07-1982 L1989 IM *030 †20

SANDERS, Karen Michele. 1201 BROAD ROCK BLVD, BLDG 507 WING B2 RM 6 23249 #035-09-1977 L1982 IM RHU *030 †20

SANDHU, Bimaljit Singh. 1200 E BROAD ST, 14TH FL 23298 #495-43-1995 *100

SANFORD, Kimberly W. 1101 E MARSHALL ST RM 4-00, VIRGINIA COMMONWEALTH UNIV 23298 #051-04-2001 L2001 PTH *100 †50

SANTIAGO, Yarima Sol. 1200 E BROAD ST, MCV - OFFICE OF GME 23298 #665-02-2007 L2007 MPD *012

SANYAL, Arun Jayant. 401 N 11TH ST, MCV NELSON CLINIC 23219 #495-45-1981 L1986 GE IM *020 †20

SARCIA, Marc Anthony. ■ 23220 #010-02-2006 L2006 GS *012

SATIJA, Bela. 2000 BREMO RD, STE 200 23226 #495-47-1988 L2003 OBG *020

SAUNDERS, Mary E S. ■ 23219 #051-04-1974 L1975 GP *075 †18

SAVAS, Jean Ann. 1201 BROAD ROCK BLVD, SURGICAL SVC 23249 #051-04-1990 L1995 GS *020 †85

SAYED, Hamdy Ibrahim. 7115 JAHNKE RD, JAMES RIVER FAMILY MEDICIN 23225 #062-01-1977 L1984 OM *040

SAYEED, Zabe Reza. PO BOX 980257, VA COMMONWEALTH UNIV HLTH 23298 #305-01-2006 L2006 P *012

SAYLOR, Edward Michael. 6508 EDGEHILL RD 23226 #041-14-1974 L1976 FM EM *020 †18

SCHATZKI, Peter F. 1201 BROAD ROCK BLVD 23249 #024-07-1952 L1968 PTH *071 †50

SCHEUER, Abigail Lee. PO BOX 980034, VIRGINIA HOSPITALS 23298 #045-01-2004 L2004 OBG *012

SCHIEKEN, Richard Merrill. 401 N 12TH ST, MEDICAL COLLEGE OF VA 23298 #041-01-1965 L1982 PDC PD *071 †55

SCHIESS, Florina Miura. ■ 23298 #654-01-2005 L2006 FP *012

SCHIFF, Graenum Robt. 1000 BOULDERS PKWY, STE 202 23225 #016-42-1959 L1973 P GP *020 †75

SCHLEICHER, William Frede. ■ 23226 #051-04-2007 L2007 *012

SCHLESINGER, Cory. ■ 23226 #010-02-1985 L2001 PTH *020 †50

SCHMIDT, Robert Skolfield. 1200 E BROAD ST, MCV - OFFICE OF GME 23298 #048-04-2005 L2005 GS *012

SCHMITT, James Kennith. 1201 BROAD ROCK BLVD 23249 #005-02-1971 L1994 IM END *050 †20

SCHNEIDER, Robert Kirwin. 401 N 12TH ST 23298 #012-05-1985 L1997 P IMG *020 †20,75

SCHOEFFLER, Edmund Dwight. 7130 GLEN FOREST DR, STE 101 23226 #051-01-1986 L1989 OBG *020 †30

SCHOOLS, Kimberly Anne. 1200 E BROAD ST, MCV - OFFICE OF GME 23298 #051-04-2004 L2004 IM *100 †20

SCHRODER, Gregory Louis. 5855 BREMO RD, STE 406 23226 #051-04-1987 L1988 GS *020 †85

SCHROEDER, Diane Lee. 1201 BROAD ROCK BLVD, MCGUIRE VA MEDICAL CENTER 23249 #051-04-1985 L1986 IM END *020 †20

SCHROEDER, Jason Lee. PO BOX 980257, MEDICAL COLLEGE OF VIRGINI 23298 #038-40-2001 L2001 NS *012

SCHUBERT, Mitchell Lee. 1605 RHOADMILLER ST 23220 #048-04-1977 L1979 GE IM *050 †20

SCHUFELDT, Susan Taich. 5801 BREMO RD 23226 #016-01-1979 L1982 FM *020 †18

SCHWARTZ, Charles Curtis. 1200 E BROAD ST, MEDICAL COLLEGE OF VIRGINI 23298 #025-07-1969 L1979 GE IM *071 †20

SCHWARTZ, Lawrence Barry. 1112 E CLAY ST, RM 4-110 23298 #028-02-1976 L1983 A IM *050 †20,03

SCIOSCIA, Thomas Neil. 5899 BREMO RD, STE 100 23226 #051-04-1998 L2002 ORS *100 †40

SCOGGINS, Robert Bruce. ■ 23220 #012-05-1958 L1966 D *071 †15

SCOTT, John Keith. 1800 GLENSIDE DR STE 110 23226 #051-04-2001 L2001 FM *020 †18

SEEDS, John Wm. 401 N 11TH ST, STE 500 23219 #051-01-1972 L1972 OBG *020 †30

SEITZ, Donald Geo. 5899 BREMO RD, STE A 23226 #056-06-1967 L1973 ORS *071 †40

SELBY-PENCZAK, Rachel M. 1300 E MARSHALL ST, P O BOX 980102 23298 #041-07-1995 L1998 IMG *020 †20

SELISKAR, Christine W. 7159 JAHNKE RD, CHIPPENHAM PEDIATRICS&ADOL 23225 #007-02-2003 L2004 PD *020 †55

■ = Address Information Privacy Protected

SELLMAN, James E. 6714 PATTERSON AVE, STE 204 23226 #051-04-1973 L1978 P CHP *020 †75

SEMIZIAN, Diane Marie. ■ 23226 #051-01-2005 L2005 EM *012

SESSLER, Curtis Neil. 1605 RHOADMILLER ST 23220 #038-41-1979 L1980 PUD CCM *020 †20

SETTLES, Jeffery Dirk. 1200 E BROAD ST, MCV - OFFICE OF GME 23298 #020-12-2006 L2007 DR *012

SEWARD, Robert Lewis. 1000 BOULDERS PKWY, STE 202 23225 #051-01-1995 L1995 P *020 †75

SEWELL, Nathan Alexander. ■ 23220 #047-05-1999 L1999 PS *020 †65

SHAFER, Wm Hamilton, Jr. 5801 BREMO RD, EMERGENCY DEPARTMENT 23226 #051-04-1979 L1980 FM EM *020 †18

SHAH, Jagdip B. 401 N 12TH ST, MEDICAL COLLEGE OF VA 23298 #495-76-1972 L1989 AN CCM *020 †05

SHAH, Mahendra D. 7101 JAHNKE RD 23225 #496-38-1982 L1990 PD GE *020 †55

SHAH, Rakesh Kumar. PO BOX 980257 23298 #160-07-2000 L2006 P *012

SHAH, Siddhi Jagdip. 401 N 12TH ST, MAIN HOSPITAL 5TH FLOOR 23298 #495-76-1975 L1989 DR *020 †80

SHAHABUDDIN, Sarah. 1800 GLENSIDE DR, STE 103 23226 #495-45-1989 L2001 PUD *020 †20

SHAKIN, Paul Charles. 5855 BREMO RD, STE 100 23226 #041-09-1982 L1997 AN *020 †05

SHAMASKIN, Ronald Gary. 5855 BREMO RD, STE 100N 23226 #051-04-1991 L1994 AN *020 †05 ‡

SHAPIRO, Jay Howard. 401 N 12TH ST, MCV PHYSICIANS 23298 #001-06-1985 L1989 AN *020 †05

SHAPIRO, Steven Malcolm. 1001 E MARSHALL ST, BOX 980211 23219 #041-12-1975 L1988 PD N *050 †55,75

SHARIFF, Zahra. ■ 23221 #539-02-2002 L2005 IM *020 †20

SHARMA, Amol. 23219 #051-04-2008 L2008 IM *012

SHARP, Robin Adair. ■ 23221 #021-06-2006 L2006 IM *012

SHARPE, Alton Rivington. 7231 FOREST AVE, THYROID SPECIALISTS INC 23226 #051-04-1954 L1954 NM END *071 †20,28

SHARPS, Chester Howard. 1501 MAPLE AVE, STE 200 23226 #041-09-1979 L1985 ORS *020 †40

SHAW, James Edward. 401 COLLEGE ST, MEDICAL COLLEGE OF VIRGINI 23298 #005-14-1985 L1986 HEM ON *020 †20

SHAW, Travis Laron. ■ 23225 #051-04-2004 L2004 OTO *012

SHEEHAN, Jennifer Lee. 5855 BREMO RD, STE 100N 23226 #051-04-2000 L2000 AN *100 †05

SHEEHY, Conor Joseph. ■ 23226 #051-04-2008 *012

SHEFFERLY, James Robt. 5801 BREMO RD, ST MARY'S HOSPITAL 23226 #025-01-1981 L1982 EM IM *020 †20,16

SHENEMAN, Daniel Paul. 401 N 12TH ST, MEDICAL COLLEGE OF VA 23298 #017-20-1988 L1989 P *020 †75

SHEORN, Keyhill. 1001 BOULDERS PKWY, STE 160 23225 #045-04-1985 L1986 P *020

SHEPARD, Richard Kesniel. 1200 E MARSHALL ST, GATEWAY BUILDING 3RD FLOOR 23298 #001-02-1987 L1994 CD *020 †20

SHEPHERD, Ray Wesley. PO BOX 980050, DIV OF PULMONARY/CRIT CARE 23298 #036-01-1996 L1996 PCC *100 †20

SHIELD, James Asa. 1000 BOULDERS PKWY, STE 202 23225 #051-01-1964 L1964 P *020 †75

SHIFFMAN, Mitchell L. 1605 RHOADMILLER ST 23220 #035-15-1983 L1984 GE IM *050 †20

SHIM, Chi Yun. 5855 BREMO RD, YOUN YOUNG-OK 23226 #583-01-1961 L1972 AN *071 †05

SHIPLEY, Jared Adam. PO BOX 980257, DEPT OF INTERNAL MED 23298 #041-15-2005 L2005 IM *012

SHOLAR, Elbert Frank. 107 S 5TH ST, RBHA 23219 #028-34-1987 L1991 P *020 †75

SHOOK, Jana Eileen. 7159 JAHNKE RD 23225 #011-02-2003 L2003 PD *020 †55

SHOWALTER, Henry B, Jr. 6325 JAHNKE RD, RADIOLOGY ASSOCIATES OF 23225 #051-04-1963 L1963 R *020 †80

SHREVE, James Mark. 7113 THREE CHOPT RD STE 10 23226 #055-01-1984 L1986 P *020 †55

SHUMAKER, Bradley Allen. 7101 JAHNKE RD, VIRGINIA HOSPITALISTS, INC 23225 #041-15-2000 L2001 IM *020 †20

SICA, Domenic Angelo. 1101 E MARSHALL ST, SANGER HALL ROOM 8-062 23298 #051-04-1975 L1976 IM NEP *020 †20

SILBERMAN, Henry K. ■ 23221 #035-19-1950 L1972 P RO *071 †75

SILVERMAN, Bruce Alan. 5320 PATTERSON AVE STE 200 23226 #051-04-1982 L1985 NEP IM *020 †20

SILVERMAN, Joel J. 1200 E BROAD ST 8TH FL, VCUHS BOX 980-710 23298 #019-02-1969 L1972 P *030 †75

SIMPSON, John Michael. 1501 MAPLE AVE, STE 200 23226 #038-43-1985 L1991 ORS OSS *020

SIRI, Kris Alexander. ■ 23220 #051-04-2008 *012

SIROT, Devra Michele. 5501 PATTERSON AVE 23226 #051-04-1987 L2001 FM EM *020

SISSON, Robert Franklin. 2621 GROVE AVE 23220 #051-04-1984 L2003 CD IM *020 †20

SLAGEL, Dale Everett. 330 S 4TH ST 23219 #056-06-1974 L1975 EM OM *020 †20,16

SMITH, Christie Lynn. ■ 23220 #051-04-2008 *012

SMITH, Gladstone Edward. 2621 GROVE AVE 23220 #051-04-1958 L1958 PTH *071 †50

SMITH, Jerome. 909 HIOAKS RD, STE B 23225 #010-02-1977 L1983 IM *020 †20

SMITH, Julious P, III. 5899 BREMO RD STE 100 23226 #051-01-1994 L1994 ORS OSM *020 †40

SMITH, Matthew Alan. 5801 BREMO RD, IMS RICHMOND 23226 #023-01-2002 L2005 IM *100 †20

SMITH, Ray Huey. 681 HIOAKS RD, SHELTON W THOMAS 23225 #051-04-1955 L1955 CD IM *071

SMITH, Robert Kevin. 7101 JAHNKE RD, # 280 23225 #001-02-1987 L1990 OBG *020 †30

SMITH, Rodney Hall. 1000 BOULDERS PKWY, STE 102 23225 #051-04-1970 L1970 PUD CCM *020 †20

SMITH, Stephanie E. PO BOX 980257 23298 #051-04-2001 L2003 NPM *100 †55

SMITH, Thomas Jos. 1101 E MARSHALL ST 23298 #008-01-1979 L1985 ON PLM *020 †20

SMITH, Wade Kilgore. 1200 E BROAD ST, DIV OF MED ONCOLOGY 23298 #023-07-1963 L1975 ON HEM *040 †20

SMITH, Wally Renee. 1200 E BROAD ST, 10TH FLOOR, W WING, RM 402 23298 #001-02-1981 L1991 IM *020 †20

SMITHSON, Peter Wm. 5801 BREMO RD 23226 #917-04-1978 L1980 FM *020 †18

SNEAD, Ronald Wilson. 515 N 10TH ST, P O BOX 980489 23219 #051-04-1968 L1968 CHP PD *072 †55,75

SNEED, Nathan Alexander. 1200 E BROAD ST, MCV - OFFICE OF GME 23298 #048-15-2005 L2005 GS *012

SNIDOW, Terri Moynihan. 701 W GRACE ST 23220 #051-04-1985 L1987 NPM PD *020 †55

SOLAN, Stuart M. 7229 FOREST AVE, STE 112 23226 #051-04-1977 L1978 FM *020 †18

SOLIMAN, Dina Emile. 1200 E BROAD ST, RM 7-10 23298 #915-02-1981 L1992 AN *020 †05

SOLIS, Edward Ariel. PO BOX 980049, UNIV SOM 23298 #005-06-2000 L2007 ID *012

SOLOMON, Susan M. 5855 BREMO RD STE 605 23226 #030-06-1981 L1986 OBG *030 †30

SOMMERS, Jefferson M. 7107 JAHNKE RD, INSIGHT PHYSICIANS PC 23225 #036-07-1986 L1996 P *020 †75

SONENKLAR, Neil Allen. 515 N 10TH ST, VIRGINIA COMMONWEALTH UNIV 23219 #025-01-1977 L1988 CHP P *040 †55,75

SONG, Shiyu. 401 COLLEGE ST, MCV MASSEY CANCER CTR BASE 23298 #243-32-1983 L2004 RO *020 †80

SONI, Manish. ■ 23221 #010-01-2001 L2007 CHP *025

SOOD, Aradhana Avasthy. 401 N 12TH ST, MEDICAL COLLEGE OF VA 23298 #495-34-1979 L1988 CHP *020 †75

SOROF, Suzanne Alise. 1200 E BROAD ST, ST,PO.BOX 980036 23298 #048-04-1998 L2006 IC *100 †20

SORRELS, Karen P Campbell. 7159 JAHNKE RD, CHIPPENHAM MEDICAL BLDG 23225 #036-01-1969 L1973 PD *020 †55

SOZER, Muammer. ■ 23220 #902-10-1945 L1972 PTH *020 †50

SPADAFORA, Shaun Andrew. 1700 BAYBERRY CT, CPC HOSPITALISTS DIVISION 23226 #024-16-2002 L2002 IM *020 †20

SPADAFORA, Suzanne Granad. 7111 JAHNKE RD 23225 #010-02-1999 L2003 D *020 †15 ‡

SPANIER, Elliott Jos. 1000 BOULDERS PKWY, STE 202 23225 #036-05-1972 L1978 P *020 †75 ‡

SPERRY, Robert Earle. 2621 GROVE AVE 23220 #019-02-1986 L1990 ICE CD *020 †20

SPIERS, Leon Otis, III. 7229 FOREST AVE STE 100 23226 #051-01-1982 L1982 FM *020 †18

SPIESS, Bruce Davis. 401 N 12TH ST, MEDICAL COLLEGE OF VA 23298 #016-01-1980 L1999 AN *020 †05

SPORN, I Norman. ■ 23226 #051-04-1957 L1957 IM NEP *071

SPRINGEL, Edward Henry. PO BOX 980034, MED COLL OF VIRGINIA HOSPS 23298 #051-04-2005 L2005 OBG *012

SREEDHAR, Sue S. 401 N 12TH ST, MEDICAL COLLEGE OF VA 23298 #495-42-1981 L1993 PD CCM *020 †55

SRIKULMONTREE, Thitinan. 1201 BROAD ROCK BLVD 111M, RHEUMATOLOGY SECT-HHM VAMC 23249 #891-03-1998 L2003 RHU IM *020 †20 ‡

SRIRAM, Thiruneermalai G. 1300 E MARSHALL ST, MCV - N HOSP 23298 #495-72-1979 L1993 P *020 †75

STACY, William Knox. V A MED CTR RICHMOND 23249 #045-01-1961 L1969 NEP IM *020 †20

STALLINGS, L Robert. MED COLLEGE OF VIRGINIA, DEPT. OF ANESTHESIOLOGY 23298 #051-04-1982 L1990 AN *020 †05

STARKWEATHER, Kathryn Jea. ■ 23220 #051-04-2008 L2008 *012

STEFANIK, Peter James. 5855 BREMO RD STE 207 23226 #051-04-1983 L1984 IM *020 †20

STENSLAND, Mark Steven. 5801 BREMO RD 23226 #026-04-1976 L1977 EM *020 †18,16

STEPHENS, Harvard W. PO BOX 26963, 6900 ATMORE DR 23261 #024-01-1975 L2004 IM *020 †20

STEPHENS, Kyle Wayne. 333 N 17TH ST, # 304 23219 #056-06-2004 L2004 GS *012

STERLING, Cheryl Patrice. ■ 23298 #024-05-2001 L2001 IM *100

STERLING, Richard Keith. 1200 E BROAD ST, BOX 980341 23298 #041-02-1988 L1989 IM HEP *020 †20

STEVENS, Michael Patrick. ■ 23221 #051-04-2004 L2004 IM *100 †20

STEVENSON, Rashida. 1200 E BROAD ST, MCV - OFFICE OF GME 23298 #023-01-2004 L2004 N *012

STEWART, Lauraine M. 10021 BROAD ROCK BLVD, MCGUIRE VA MED CTR BOX 110 23249 #016-11-1962 L1967 AN GE *040 †55,05

STIKE, Aaron Brondell. ■ 23219 #051-04-2006 L2006 U *012

STILL, Wm James Sangster. 401 N 12TH ST, DEPT PATH 23298 #803-01-1951 L1968 PTH *020

STONE, James Johnston. ■ 23226 #051-01-2001 GS *012

STONEBURNER, Frank D, Jr. 417 LIBBIE AVE, VIRGINIA SURGICAL 23226 #051-04-1982 L1984 VS GS *020 †85

STOVALL, Dale Wm. 1250 E MARSHALL ST, DEPT OF OB/GYN, MAIN HOSPI 23298 #048-15-1985 L1998 OBG REN *020 †30

STRATFORD, Thomas Peirson. 201 N HAMILTON ST 23221 #051-04-1953 L1953 OPH *071 †35

STRAVITZ, Richard Todd. 1200 E BROAD ST, SECTION OF HEPATOLOGY 23298 #035-19-1986 L1990 HEP GE *020 †20

STRIFE, Brian James. ■ 23220 #051-04-2007 L2007 IM *012

STRINGER, Warren Allison. 1250 E MARSHALL ST, DEPARTMENT OF RADIOLOGY 23298 #005-12-1979 L1989 RNR DR *020 †20,80

STROUBE, Robert Bruce. 109 GOVERNOR ST, VIRGINIA DEPT OF HLTH 23219 #051-04-1974 L1975 PHP *030 †70

STUART, James Ewellbrown. 500 HIOAKS RD, STE B 23225 #051-07-1989 L1990 ORS HS *020 †40

STUART, Kelly Anne. 7229 FOREST AVE STE 203, COMMONWEALTH NEONATOLOGY 23226 #051-07-1992 L1994 NPM *020 †55

STUART, William Thos. ■ 23226 #051-04-1954 L1954 U OS *075 †95

STUBBS, Pamela Hamilton. 5 E CLAY ST 23219 #047-07-1982 L1993 CHN *020 †55

STUCKEY, Charles Porter. 1201 BROAD ROCK BLVD, HUNTER HOLMES MCGUIRE VAMC 23249 #055-02-1984 L1985 IM IMG *020 †20

SUAREZ-WINOWISKI, Olga Ma. 1200 E BROAD ST RM 7102, WEST HOSPITAL RIGHT WING 23298 #649-28-1986 L2007 AN *012

SUBBEGOWDA, Roopa. 1101 E MARSHALL ST, VA COMMONWEALTH U 23298 #496-22-1992 L2001 N *020

SULAMAN, A.K.M.. PO BOX 980257, VA COMMONWEALTH UNIV HLTH 23298 #160-01-1993 L2005 P *012

SUMPTION, Kevin Francis. 1853 W GRACE ST 23220 #051-04-1993 L1996 IC *020 †20

SUN, Eugene Yo-Jen. 1250 E MARSHALL ST 23298 #654-01-2005 L2005 P *012

SUNDIN, Burton Mc Chesney. 5899 BREMO RD, STE 205 23226 #036-07-1997 L2004 PS HS *020 †65

SURATWALA, Sanjeev J. 1501 MAPLE AVE, STE 200 23226 #035-01-2001 L2008 ORS *020

SUREJA, Raj Nagji. 12 N THOMPSON ST, PATIENT FRIST CARYTOWN 23221 #051-04-2003 L2003 PMM *012

SURESH, Bangalore R. 412 LIBBIE AVE STE 4, COMMONWEALTH NEONATOLOGY I 23226 #495-33-1979 L1999 NPM PD *020 †55

SURI, Pawan. PO BOX 980401, 1250 E MARSHALL ST 23298 #495-45-1993 L2005 OS EM *020 †20,16

SUTER, Cary Grayson. 1101 E MARSHALL ST, MCV 23298 #051-01-1947 L1951 N OS *071 †75

SUTHERLAND, James Calvin. 900 N HAMILTON ST, STE B 23221 #051-04-1983 L1986 RHU IM *020 †20

SUTTLE, David Earl. 109 GOVERNOR ST 7TH FL, DIR OFF OF FAM HLTH SERV 23219 #027-01-1971 L2002 ADL PD *030 †55

SUTTON, Charles E, Jr. 10 E LEIGH ST 23219 #047-07-1982 L1987 N *020

SVOBODA, Joseph Robt. ■ 23226 #010-01-1963 L1964 **OPH OS** *071 †35
SWAINEY, Craig Walter. ■ 23298 #036-01-2002 L2002 **HO** *012 †20
SWANSTON, Nicole Marian. 1200 E BROAD ST, MCV - OFFICE OF GME 23298 #005-12-2005 L2005 **MPD** *012
SWAPP, Ryan Edward. ■ 23226 #051-04-2008 *012
SWEENEY, Ashley Brittingh. ■ 23225 #051-04-2008 *012
SWEENEY, Lori Barnett. ■ 23225 #051-04-2000 L2005 **END** *100 †20
SWITZ, Donald Mac Lean. ■ 23226 #016-02-1962 L1970 **GE IM** *071 †20
SYDNOR, Malcolm Kennedy. 1250 E MARSHALL ST, PO BOX 980615 23298 #051-04-1999 L1999 **VIR** *100 †80
SYED, Huzaefah Jeelani. ■ 23225 #051-04-2006 L2006 **IM** *012
TABER, Rex Eugene. 3126 W CARY ST # 237 23221 #028-46-1997 L1997 **CHP** *020 †75
TAKABE, Kazuaki. PO BOX 980011, WEST HOSPITAL 7-404 1200 E 23298 #572-15-1992 L2006 **GS** *100
TALMAN, Edward Armistead. ■ 23226 #051-01-1958 L1958 **GS** *071 †85
TARANT, Sandy Ives. 7101 JAHNKE RD, CHIPPENHAM HOSPITAL 23225 #033-06-1981 L1992 **PD NPM** *020 †55
TARKINGTON, Phillip E. 1201 BROAD ROCK BLVD 23249 #047-06-1996 L1996 **IM** *020 †20
TATE, Alexandra J. 7130 GLEN FOREST DR, STE 101 23226 #041-02-1991 L1994 **OBG** *020 †30
TATUM, James Luther. 1201 BROAD ROCK BLVD, MEDICAL CENTER 23249 #051-04-1973 L1978 **NM DR** *020 †80,28
TAVANAIEPOUR, Daryoush. PO BOX 980631, VCUHS/MCV 23298 #671-01-2003 L2004 **NS** *012
TAYLOR, Donald A. 5875 BREMO RD STE 310 23226 #047-06-1976 L1983 **CHN PD** *020 †55,75
TAYLOR, Gary Lynn. 5801 BREMO RD 23226 #001-06-1981 L1982 **EM** *020 †16
TAYLOR, John Richard. 701 W GRACE ST 23220 #036-05-1956 L1972 **N** *071 †75
TAYLOR, Mary Elizabeth. 5320 PATTERSON AVE, STE 200 23226 #021-05-1999 L2002 **NEP** *020 †20
TEASLEY, Jean Elizabeth. PO BOX 980211, 1001 E MARSHALL ST 23298 #012-01-1981 L1985 **OS CHN** *020 †55,75
TEEKAH, George Anthony. 505 W LEIGH ST 23220 #010-03-1975 L1983 **PUD IM** *020
TERRY, Susan White. MED COLL OF VA HOSPS 23219 #051-04-1980 *100
TEWARI, Susmeeta. PO BOX 980257, VA COMMONWEALTH UNIV HLTH 23298 #496-06-2002 L2004 **IM** *012
THAKRAL, Vibha. 401 N 12TH ST, MEDICAL COLLEGE OF VA 23298 #010-01-1995 L1995 **IM** *020 †20
THEOGARAJ, Janakibai. 1201 BROAD ROCK BLVD, MCGUIRE VETERAN AFFAIR MED 23249 #495-04-1963 L1978 **P** *020 †75 ‡
THOMAS, Arul Manuel. ■ 23225 #051-04-2008 *012
THOMAS, George Walter. 7101 JAHNKE RD 23225 #051-04-1972 L1974 **PTH** *020 †50
THOMAS, Harry, Jr. 7101 JAHNKE RD 23225 #051-04-1963 L1963 **OBG** *071 †30
THOMPSON, Ashley Nicole. 7101 JAHNKE RD 23225 #051-04-2001 L2006 **PD** *020 †55
THOMPSON, James Albert. 7229 FOREST AVE, VIRGINIA CARDIOVASCULAR 23226 #051-04-1975 L1976 **CD IM** *020 †20
THONGTRANGAN, Issada. ■ 23225 #891-07-1992 L2004 **ORS** *012
THORN, Radhika M.. ■ 23220 #051-04-2008 L2008 *012
THORNTON, John L. ■ 23225 #051-04-1949 L1955 **BBK NM** *071 †50,28
THURMAN, Alan Lee. 5875 BREMO RD, STE 311 23226 #047-06-1987 L1988 **EM UM** *020 †20
THURMAN, William Allen. 5900 MIDLOTHIAN TPKE 23225 #051-04-1956 L1956 **DR** *020 †80
THURSTON, Stephen Ellyson. 7301 FOREST AVE, STE 300 23226 #051-04-1979 L1980 **N** *020 †75
TIMMONS, Tracy Alane. ■ 23224 #051-04-2004 L2004 **GS** *012
TIPTON, Amanda Marie. ■ 23225 #047-06-2008 *012
TISDALE, Samuel Albert. 1211 SHERWOOD AVE 23220 #051-04-1954 L1954 **OS** *050 †55
TISNADO, Jaime R. 1200 E MARSHALL ST 3RD FL, MAIN HOSP-RADIOLOGY DEPT 23298 #737-01-1964 L1977 **R VIR** *020 †80
TISNADO, Jamie. ■ 23220 #051-04-2008 *012
TITUS, Cloyd Kent. 2621 GROVE AVE 23220 #051-01-1970 L1970 **IM RHU** *020 †20
TODD, William Mc Clintock. 1201 BROAD ROCK BLVD # 113 23249 #047-06-1978 L1983 **PTH HMP** *020 †50 ‡
TOLEDO, Jenny Rose. ■ 23224 #051-04-2008 *012
TOMPKINS, Lornel Garlita. 505 W LEIGH ST STE 207 23220 #023-01-1978 L1984 **PCC IM** *020
TONEY, Ronald Wayne. 418 LIBBIE AVE 23226 #051-04-1974 L1974 **FM** *020 †18 ‡
TONG, Lawrence Chungfai. 600 N 10TH ST 23298 #051-04-2006 *012
TOOMEY, Courtney Jane. ■ 23219 #051-04-2008 *012
TOOR, Amir A. 1101 E MARSHALL ST, BOX 980157 23298 #704-01-1990 L2007 **HO** *020 †20
TOPAZ, On. 1201 BROAD ROCK BLVD, DIV CARD MCGUIRE VA M C 23249 #550-02-1979 L1994 **CD** *020
TORRISI, Peter Francis. 1000 BOULDERS PKWY, STE 200 23225 #035-09-1980 L1983 **PUD IM** *020 †20
TORRONE, Maria Regina. ■ 23219 #051-04-2004 L2004 **DR** *012
TORTORELLA, Frank John. ■ 23225 #561-01-1969 L1976 **IM** *020
TOWNE, Alan Raymond. 1201 BROAD ROCK BLVD 23249 #396-11-1980 L1985 **N CN** *020 †75
TRAN, Nam Duy. PO BOX 980631, VCUHS/MCV 23298 #003-01-2003 L2003 **NS** *012
TRICE, Edmund Winston. 400 WESTHAMPTON STA, EYE SURGEONS OF RICHMOND I 23226 #051-04-1981 L1983 **OPH** *020 †35
TRICE, Robert Palmer. 701 W GRACE ST 23220 #051-04-1944 L1944 **GP** *071
TRIPATHI, Shreyank Dhanan. 671 HIOAKS RD, STE B 23225 #495-76-2000 L2004 **IM** *020
TRIVEDI, Ami Mukesh. PO BOX 980257, MCV - OFFICE OF GME 23298 #051-04-2003 L2003 **DR** *012
TROYER, Lisa Rochelle. 7130 GLEN FOREST DR, STE 101 23226 #030-06-1986 L1996 **OBG** *020 †30
TRUTIA, Alexandru Eugen. 1300 E MARSHALL ST, MCV - N HOSP 23298 #781-01-1991 L1996 **P** *020 †75
TSOGAS, Nickolaos. ■ 23298 #418-01-1991 L1999 **ID** *100 †20
TUCKER, Mary Guerry. 201 N HAMILTON ST 23221 #051-04-1986 L1987 **OPH** *020
TULOU, Nicholas Paul. 5855 BREMO RD, STE 207 23226 #051-04-1975 L1978 **IM** *020 †20
TURNER, Banks Whitaker. 2201 GROVE AVE, DRS TITUS HENDRIX TURNER 23220 #051-01-1989 L1993 **FM** *020 †18
TURNER, Mary Ann. 401 N 12TH ST, MEDICAL COLLEGE OF VA 23298 #001-02-1971 L1975 **DR** *040 †80
TUTEN, Hans Robt. 1501 MAPLE AVE, STE 200 23226 #051-04-1991 L1992 **ORS OP** *072 †40
TUTTON, Roger Headly. 410 N 12TH ST, MCV MAIN HOSPITAL 23298 #018-03-1955 L1997 **R** *071 †80
TYE, Gary William. 417 N 11TH ST 6TH FL, MCV CAMPUS/POB BOX 980631 23298 #051-04-1998 L1998 **NS** *100

UMALI, Maria Angela Tobia. 1200 E BROAD ST, MCV - OFFICE OF GME 23298 #748-01-2000 L2006 **PDC** *012 †55
UMBERHANDT, James Eddie. ■ 23225 #012-01-1971 L1972 **FM** *020
UMBERHANDT, Robert Cecil. ■ 23225 #012-22-2006 L2006 **ORS** *012
URBACH, John Richard. 1200 E BROAD ST, BOX 980710 23298 #025-01-1977 L1984 **P** *030 †75
USSERY, Carol Thos. 7101 JAHNKE RD, CHIPPENHAM HOSPITAL 23225 #051-04-1987 L1988 **FM** *020
VANICHKACHORN, Jed Sujit. 1501 MAPLE AVE, STE 200 23226 #051-04-1995 L1999 **ORS** *020 †20
VANNIER, Theresa. 12 N THOMPSON ST, PATIENT FIRST 23221 #035-08-1991 L1992 **IM** *020 †20
VANTUYLE, Jessica Lynn. 5875 BREMO RD, STE 203-205 23226 #041-02-1998 L1999 **OBG** *020 †30
VARANDANI, Anjali. ■ 23226 #051-04-2002 L2005 **NPM** *012 †55
VARGAS-ZAPATA, Rafael J. 7101 JAHNKE RD #649-02-1983 L1984 **FM** *020 †18
VARGHESE, Saji Sarah. 7101 JAHNKE RD STE 611, VIRGINIA HOSPITALISTS, INC 23225 #051-04-1999 L1999 **IM** *020 †20
VARMA, Amit. ■ 23220 #051-04-2006 L2006 **IM** *012
VASCONCELOS, Olavo M, Jr. 417 N 11TH ST, MCV AMBULATORY CARE 23298 #187-10-1990 L1995 **CN** *020 †75
VENNART, George P. 401 N 12TH ST 23298 #035-45-1953 L1965 **PTH** *040 †50
VETROVEC, George Wayne. 1200 E BROAD ST, RM 607 23298 #051-01-1970 L1970 **CD IM** *020 †20
VIEWEG, W Victor R. 401 N 12TH ST 23298 #010-01-1965 L1981 **P CD** *020 †20,75
VIGNESHWAR, Sucharitha. 5855 BREMO RD STE 206 23226 #495-04-1987 L2000 **OBG** *020 †30
VILLAR-GOSALVEZ, Carlos S. ■ 23225 #051-04-2004 L2005 **FP** *012
VINIK, Melvin. 401 N 12TH ST, MEDICAL COLLEGE OF VA 23298 #016-02-1960 L1967 **R** *020 †80
VINNIKOVA, Anna K. 1101 E MARSHALL ST, P O BOX 980160 23298 #913-01-1990 L1993 **NEP** *020 †20
VIOL, Geoffrey Wm. 1201 BROAD ROCK BLVD, MAIL DRP 111G MCGUIRE VAMC 23249 #143-06-1962 L1979 **NEP IM** *020 †20
VOGAN, Drummond Grant. ■ 23220 #051-04-2008 *012
VOHRA, Mohammad Ilyas. 1201 BROAD ROCK BLVD, VA MEDICAL CENTER 23249 #704-16-1990 L1999 **IM** *020 †20
VOLK, Stephan Carpenter. 2010 BREMO RD 23226 #051-04-1972 L1976 **OPH** *020 †35
VOZZA, Nestor Claudio. 2006 BREMO RD, INSIGHT PHYSICIANS PC 23226 #132-02-1969 L1976 **P** *020 †75
VRANIAN, Steven Craig. 7229 FOREST AVE, VIRGINIA CARDIOVASCULAR 23226 #051-04-1986 L1992 **CD** *020 †20
VU, Huan Nguyen. 401 N 12TH ST 23298 #048-15-1991 L2004 **GS** *072 †85
WACKER, Dorothea Marie. ■ 23222 #051-04-1960 L1960 **IM P** *020
WADE, Seaborn Mcdonald. ■ 23226 #051-04-2001 L2001 **HO** *020 †20
WAGLE, Sheetal Harish. 1200 E BROAD ST, VA COMMONWLTH U HLTH SYS 23298 #495-28-1993 L2006 **N** *012
WALKER, Joel Wayne. 515 N 10TH ST, VIRGINIA TREATMENT CENTER 23219 #041-09-1998 L2002 **CHP** *020 †75
WALKER, William Clement. 1223 E MARSHALL ST 23298 #051-04-1987 L1988 **PM** *020 †60
WALLER, Alene Howard. STUDENT HEALTH CENTER, UNIVERSITY OF RICHMOND 23173 #036-01-1987 L1989 **FM** *020 †18
WALLER, Susan Jervey. 401 NORTH 11TH ST, NELSON CLINIC, SUITE 200 23219 #051-04-2001 L2001 **P** *100 †75
WALLNER, Clare Francisco. ■ 23219 #051-04-2008 *012
WALSWORTH, Matthew Kevin. ■ 23220 #051-04-2007 L2007 **IM** *012
WAMPLER, Galen Lee. PO BOX 980230 23298 #051-04-1959 L1959 **ON** *020
WANG, Peng. PO BOX 980230 23298 #243-72-1982 L1998 **IM** *100
WARD, Bruce Horatio. 505 W LEIGH ST 23220 #010-03-1976 L1982 **CD IM** *020 †20
WARD, John David. 2924 BROOK RD 23220 #038-41-1970 L1976 **NS** *020 †25
WARD, Kevin Ralph. 401 N 12TH ST, BOX 980401 23298 #021-01-1989 L1998 **EM** *020 †16
WARD, Winfred O'Neil. ■ 23226 #051-04-1958 L1959 **P PYA** *071
WARE, Harry Hudnall, III. 5855 BREMO RD STE 205 23226 #051-01-1958 L1958 **OBG** *071 †30
WARE, James Latane. 5801 BREMO RD 23226 #051-04-1959 L1959 **PS** *071 †85,65
WARNER, Marc Thomas. 417 LIBBIE AVE, VIRGINIA SURGICAL 23226 #001-02-1996 L2002 **VS GS** *085
WASHINGTON, Sofia. 5801 BREMO RD 23226 #010-01-1997 L1997 **PD** *020 †55
WASSERMAN, Brian Mark. 7153 JAHNKE RD 23225 #051-04-1974 L1975 **IM** *020 †20
WATEMBERG, Nathan M. 1101 E MARSHALL ST, MED COLLEGE OF VIRGINIA 23298 #264-12-1981 L1997 **N** *020 †55,75
WATERHOUSE, Elizabeth J. 307 COLLEGE ST, RANDOLPH MINOR HALL 23298 #024-01-1988 L1992 **N** *020 †75
WATKINS, Jimmie Parks. 1201 BROAD ROCK BLVD, DEPT OF ANESTHESIOLOGY 110 23249 #001-02-1981 L1986 **AN OS** *020 †20
WEAVER, John Arthur. 1201 BROAD ROCK BLVD, RADIOLOGY DEPT 23249 #010-03-1978 L1982 **NM NR** *020 †80,28
WEAVER, Michael F. 1200 E BROAD ST 23298 #038-44-1993 L1994 **ADM PMM** *050 †20
WEAVER, Tureman Gayle. ■ 23226 #051-01-1957 L1957 **OS** *071
WEAVER, Yvonne Jackson. 2621 GROVE AVE 23220 #036-05-1974 L1978 **CD** *020 †20 ‡
WEBER, David Joel. 401 N 12TH ST, MEDICAL COLLEGE OF VA 23298 #041-02-1971 L1976 **P GP** *075 †75
WEBSTER, Elizabeth Belt. 400 E JACKSON ST, OFFICE OF MED EXAMINER 23219 #032-01-2002 L2002 **OBG** *012
WEIS, Ricardo Ariel. 1200 E BROAD ST, MCV-OFFICE OF GME 23298 #132-01-1995 L2006 **AN** *012
WEISBERGER, Robert. 5801 BREMO RD, EMER DEPT-ST MARYS HOSP 23226 #035-09-1978 L1979 **EM IM** *020 †20,16
WEISS, Elisabeth. 401 COLLEGE ST, DEPT OF RADIOLOGY ONCOLOGY 23298 #409-20-1990 *100
WEISS, Joshua Robert. 5855 BREMO RD STE 100N 23226 #011-04-1990 L1991 **AN** *020 †05
WELANDER, Charles Eric. 5875 BREMO RD, STE G7 23226 #016-02-1971 L1997 **GO ON** *012
WELTON, Steven John. 6714 PATTERSON AVE STE 103 23226 #026-04-1974 L1989 **P CHP** *020 †75
WENZEL, Richard Putnam. 401 N 12TH ST, MEDICAL COLLEGE OF VA 23298 #041-02-1965 L1972 **ID IM** *030 †20

■ = Address Information Privacy Protected

WERNER, John Gregory. 7113 THREE CHOPT RD, STE 101 23226 #051-04-1994 L1994 **PD** *020 †55

WEST, Janet. 1001 E MARSHALL ST, CHILDREN'S PAVILION 23219 #051-04-2003 L2003 **PD** *020

WESTIN, Margaret C. 1800 GLENSIDE DR, STE 110 23226 #051-04-1988 L1989 **FM** *020 †18

WETZEL, Ryan Andrew. ■ 23221 #017-20-2005 L2006 **PM** *012

WHEELER, William Edge. 5801 BREMO RD 23226 #051-04-1972 L1975 **DR PDR** *071 †80

WHELAN, James Francis. ■ 23224 #539-06-2000 L2007 **GS** *100 †85

WHITE, Diana Gay. ■ 23226 #048-13-1982 L1995 **FM** *020 †18

WHITE, Hubert Ruark, Jr. 2621 GROVE AVE 23220 #023-01-1960 L1967 **PTH CLP** *071 †50

WHITE, Michael Alexander. ■ 23226 #051-04-2008 *012

WHITE, Sara Lorraine. 5801 BREMO RD, HOSPITAL PICU 23226 #010-03-1977 L1993 **CCM PD** *020 †55

WHITE, Travis Wayne. ■ 23226 #048-13-1983 L1995 **FM FPG** *020 †18

WHITEHURST-COOK, Michelle. 1200 E BROAD ST, P O BOX 251 23298 #051-04-1979 L1980 **FM** *020 †18

WHITLEY, Brian T. 2427 W MAIN ST 23220 #051-04-1996 L1996 **CHP** *100

WIATEREK, Gregory. 1200 E BROAD ST 23298 #759-01-2007 L2007 **IM** *012

WICKHAM, James Robt. 2201 GROVE AVE 23220 #051-04-1960 L1961 **IM** *020 †20

WIGAND, James Peter. 7153 JAHNKE RD 23225 #051-04-1973 L1974 **END IM** *020 †20

WILBANKS, Peter Thornton. 5875 BREMO RD, STE 400 23226 #051-04-1989 L1992 **OBG** *020 †30

WILKES, Martin F. ■ 23298 #051-04-2007 L2007 **IM** *012

WILKINSON, David S. 1101 E MARSHALL ST 23298 #011-02-1978 L1981 **PTH ATP** *040 †50

WILLETT, Rita Mary. 401 N 12TH ST, MEDICAL COLLEGE OF VA 23298 #028-02-1981 L1988 **IM DIA** *020

WILLIAMS, Armistead M. 204 N HAMILTON ST 23221 #051-01-1952 L1952 **GS GYN** *071 †85

WILLIAMS, Charles Lee. 1902 PRINCE GEORGE RD 23225 #003-01-1986 L1987 **GS** *020 †05

WILLIAMS, Charles Lee. 7101 JAHNKE RD 23225 #051-04-1948 L1948 **FM** *071 †18

WILLIAMS, David Collin. 413 STUART CIR # 21 23220 #051-04-1960 L1960 **GP** *020

WILLIAMS, David Terrell. ■ 23222 #020-02-2007 L2007 **GS** *012

WILLIAMS, Debra M. PO BOX 981455, MCV MAIN HOSPITAL 23298 #014-01-1994 L1994 **CCP** *100

WILLIAMS, Elizabeth Ellen. 4701 LEONARD PKWY 23226 #051-04-1999 L1999 **PD** *020 †55

WILLIAMS, James Wesley. 1201 BROAD ROCK BLVD, MCGUIRE MEDICAL CENTER (11 23249 #048-04-1983 L1993 **PM OS** *020 †60

WILLIAMS, Makeba Lanell. ■ 23225 #047-07-2004 L2004 **OBG** *012

WILLIAMS, Mason Miller. 5899 BREMO RD, STE 205 23226 #051-04-1973 L1975 **PS** *020 †45,65

WILLIAMS, Robert Bruce. 901 E CARY ST, C/O ERNST & YOUNG 23219 #051-04-1976 L1977 **FM** *050 †18

WILLIAMS, Ted Arthur. 5855 BREMO RD, STE 703 23226 #055-01-1981 L1990 **GE PD** *062 †55

WILLIAMSON, Brian Richard. 6325 JAHNKE RD, RADIOLOGY ASSOCIATES OF 23225 #539-06-1965 L1976 **DR NM** *020 †80,28

WILLIS, Linda Griffin. 15 W CARY ST 23220 #051-04-1983 L1984 **IM** *020

WILLIS, Mark Catesby, Jr. 1200 E BROAD ST, DEPT OF ORTHO SURGERY 23298 #051-04-1994 L1996 **ORS** *020 †40

WILMS, Christopher C. 1201 BROAD ROCK BLVD 23249 #035-45-2001 L2001 **IM** *020 †20

WIND, Ante Liesbeth. 1200 E BROAD ST, MCV - OFFICE OF GME 23298 #051-01-2006 L2006 **PD** *012

WINTERS, Cleome Jane. 5801 BREMO RD, ATTN: PEDIATRIC HOSPITAL 23226 #051-01-1996 L1996 **PD** *020 †55

WISE, Christopher M. 417 N 11TH ST, AMBULATORY CARE CTR 23298 #036-01-1977 L1980 **RHU IM** *020 †20

WISGIRDA, Jean Alice. 5855 BREMO RD, STE 605 23226 #043-01-1979 L1982 **OBG** *020 †30

WITHERSPOON, John Michael. 1605 RHOADMILLER ST 23220 #036-07-1967 L1978 **IM PHP** *020 †20

WITTMAN, John Joseph, Jr. 7301 FOREST AVE, STE 300 23226 #051-04-1999 L1999 **N** *020 †75

WOLEBEN, Christopher M. 402 N 12TH ST, MCV STATION BOX 980401 23298 #051-04-1997 L1997 **PD PEM** *020 †55

WOLFE, Shannon Michael. 1501 MAPLE AVE, STE 200 23226 #038-44-1995 L2000 **OSM** *020 †40

WONG, Edward Sang. 1201 BROAD ROCK BLVD #111C 23249 #024-01-1976 L1983 **ID IM** *020 †20

WONG, Kenneth Mann. ■ 23220 #051-04-2008 *012

WONG, Roger Zhiguan. ■ 23220 #051-04-2008 *012

WOOD, Joseph Lyman. 413 STUART CIR # 21 23220 #051-04-1973 L1974 **IM** *020 †20

WOOD, Mark Allen. 1605 RHOADMILLER ST 23220 #047-06-1983 L1984 **CD IM** *020 †20

WOOD, Marnie A. 1200 E BROAD ST, VIRGINIA COMMON WEALTH 23298 #064-01-2002 L2007 **FOP** *012 †50

WOODHOUSE, Robert W, III. 7101 JAHNKE RD 23225 #051-04-1958 L1958 **OM** *072

WOODLIEF, Ray Marshall. 1201 BROAD ROCK BLVD 23249 #036-05-1964 L1974 **DR** *020 †80

WOODS, Lauren A. PO BOX 613, DEPT PHARM-VA COMM UNIV 23218 #025-01-1949 **OS** *071

WOODWARD, Ashley Paige. ■ 23225 #045-01-2005 L2005 **OBG** *012

WOOTTON, Percy. ■ 23226 #051-04-1957 L1957 **OB IM** *071

WORNOM, Issac Leake, III. 5899 BREMO RD, STE 205 23226 #051-01-1981 L1989 **PS** *020 †85,65

WRIGHT, David Nathaniel. PO BOX 5717 23220 #008-01-1982 *040

WRIGHT, Karen Celeste. 1201 BROAD ROCK BLVD 23249 #051-04-2003 L2006 **IM** *020

WU, Theodore Tsungyueng. 400 WESTHAMPTON STA, VIRGINIA EYE INSTITUTE 23226 #051-01-1999 L1999 **OPH** *020 †35 ‡

WYATT, Davis Burton. 1001 E MARSHALL ST 23219 #051-04-1955 L1955 **OPH PD** *071 †35

WYATT, Sheron Tomeeka. 7101 JAHNKE RD 23225 #051-04-2004 L2007 **IM** *100 †20

XENAKIS, Mark. 681 HIOAKS RD, STE H 23225 #035-08-1996 L2003 **CD IC** *020 †20

YAGHMAI, Pedram. ■ 23220 #041-15-2007 L2007 *012

YALAMANCHILI, Venkata R. ■ 23298 #010-01-1994 L1997 **EM** *020 †16

YANNI, Leanne M. 417 N 11TH ST, AMBULATORY CARE CENTER 23298 #035-15-1998 L1998 **IM** *020 †20

YEE, Allen. 401 N 12TH ST, MEDICAL COLLEGE OF VA 23298 #035-48-1994 L2000 **EM** *020 †16

YEN, Nancy. 1200 E BROAD ST, OF OR 23298 #041-15-2005 L2005 **ORS** *012

YOO, Jae-Hwi. 1201 BROAD ROCK BLVD, MCGUIRE MED CTR DEPT RAD 23249 #583-10-1971 L2001 **DR NM** *030 †28,40

YOUN, Young-Ok. 5855 BREMO RD, STE 100N 23226 #583-02-1963 L1973 **AN** *071 †05

YOUNG, Dale Christopher. 500 HIOAKS RD, STE B 23225 #036-07-1978 L1985 **ORS** *020 †40

YOUNG, Guy Thomas. 1250 E MARSHALL ST 23298 #012-01-2004 L2004 **AN** *012

YOUNG, Michael Minkyo. 2006 BREMO RD, INSIGHT PHYSICIANS PC 23226 #583-03-1980 L1994 **P CHP** *020

YOUNG, Paula Alethia. 412 LIBBIE AVE, STE 4 23226 #051-01-2000 L2005 **PD** *100

YOUNG, Reuben Barnes. 1223 E MARSHALL ST BOX 65, MED COLL OF VA 3RD FL 23298 #051-04-1957 L1957 **PDE PD** *071 †55

YOUNG, William H, III. 110 N ROBINSON ST STE 301 23220 #048-04-1982 L1983 **IM** *020 †20

YOUSUF, Hasan Mohammed. 1201 BROAD ROCK BLVD, HUNTER HOLMES MCGUIRE VA M 23249 #160-02-1989 L2005 **IM** *020 †20

YU, Jinxing. 1101 E MARSHALL ST, BOX 980470 23298 #243-33-1983 L2000 **DR** *020 †80

ZACHARIAS, Charles M, Jr. 2621 GROVE AVE 23220 #051-04-1973 L1974 **CD PUD** *020 †20

ZACHARIAS, Lawrence C. 7229 FOREST AVE, MEDICAL SPECIALISTS INC 23226 #051-04-1956 L1956 **IM GE** *020

ZACKO, Joseph Christopher. 1815 MONUMENT AVE # 1 23220 #051-04-2001 L2001 **NS** *012

ZACUR, Sharline Joyce. ■ 23221 #011-02-2001 L2001 **PS** *012

ZAKAIB, Edward Albert. 7101 JAHNKE RD 23225 #051-04-1962 L1963 **FM** *020 †18

ZALLER, Eli Jerrold. 5855 BREMO RD STE 404 23226 #051-04-1971 L1975 **P** *020 †75

ZAMBRANA, Benj Franklin. 4405 FOREST HILL AVE 23225 #051-04-1968 L1971 **FM PD** *020

ZAYDAN, Islam Mohsen. 417 N 11TH ST, P O BOX 980599 23298 #915-03-1995 L2003 **N OS** *100

ZECHMAN, Heather Marie. 5875 BREMO RD, STE 400 23226 #041-14-1999 L1999 **OBG** *020 †30

ZEDLER, Barbara K. 615 MAURY ST, PHILIP MORRIS USA RD & E 23224 #016-06-1980 L1981 **IM** *050 †20

ZEDLER, Peter Alfred. 7130 GLEN FOREST DR, STE 101 23226 #016-11-1980 L1982 **GYN** *020 †30

ZELENAK, James Kenneth. 7110 FOREST AVE STE 201 23226 #051-04-2001 L2001 **FM** *020 †18

ZFASS, Alvin Martin. 1605 RHOADMILLER ST 23220 #051-04-1957 L1958 **GE IM** *020 †20

ZHANG, Changxi. 1200 E BROAD ST, OFFICE OF GME 23298 #243-38-1984 L2006 *100

ZHANG, Jian. 5855 BREMO RD STE 100, WEST END ANESTHSIA GROUP I 23226 #243-47-1986 L2007 **AN** *020 †05

ZHAO, Shourong. ■ 23298 #243-46-1985 L2000 **HMP** *020 †50

ZIENTEK, Gary Michael. 5801 BREMO RD, MONUMENT PATHOLOGISTS 23226 #025-07-1984 L1989 **PTH** *020 †50

ZIEVE, Franklin Jos. 1201 BROAD ROCK BLVD 23249 #026-04-1971 L1979 **IM END** *050 †20

ZIMMERMAN, Barklie Waters. 1800 GLENSIDE DR STE 101 23226 #051-04-1980 L1986 **VS GS** *020 †85

ZIMMERMAN, Steven Mark. 2621 GROVE AVE 23220 #051-07-1983 L1986 **PTH** *020 †50

ZINSSER, John W. 5855 BREMO RD, STE 309 23226 #048-13-1991 L1998 **PS** *020 †65

RIDGEWAY — HENRY

PARK, Chanmin. 6460 GREENSBORO RD, FAMILY PRACTICE ASSOCIATES 24148 #034-01-1996 L2000 **FM** *020 †18

RILEYVILLE — PAGE

LORD, Lillian Reba. ■ 22650 #041-13-1949 L1966 **GS OS** *020

SELAWRY, Helena Pretorius. ■ 22650 #836-03-1960 L1971 **DIA IG** *071

RIXEYVILLE — CULPEPER

BATES, Harry Clark, Jr. ■ 22737 #010-01-1943 L1948 **IM OM** *071

CARMICHAEL, Elizabeth R. ■ 22737 #051-04-1957 L1957 **AN** *071 †05

REID, William Mitchell. 13237 BEECHWOOD LN, BOX 509 22737 #035-20-1956 L1964 **GS** *071 †85

SCORZELLI, Nicholas V. ■ 22737 #024-15-1942 **OM** *071

WALKER, Charles Bradford. ■ 22737 #001-02-1987 L1999 **AN IM** *020 †05

ROANOKE — ROANOKE

ABEL, Kimberly Duklewski. ■ 24018 #305-01-2004 L2007 **EM** *100

AHMAD, Bashiruddin Khalil. 4431 STARKEY RD 24018 #704-01-1974 L2000 **N OS** *020 †75

AHMED, Abdirizak Mohamed. ■ 24019 #473-04-1996 L2002 **IM** *020

AHMED, Saleem. ■ 24018 #915-05-1982 L1996 **AS GS** *100

ALBERT, Rudolf Franz. ■ 24018 #036-01-1964 L1970 **PTH** *071 †50

ALFONSO, Gabriel A. 2840 ELECTRIC RD, STE 111 24018 #308-08-1981 L1988 **PTH** *020

ALHADEFF, Joseph Edwards. 4064 POSTAL DR, ROANOKE ORTHOPAEDIC CENTER 24018 #033-05-1996 L2001 **ORS** *020 †40

ALI, Mohammad Rizwan. 4923 COLONIAL AVE, STE B 24018 #704-02-1988 L1994 **P** *020 †75

ALLEN, Margaret Anne. 5115 BERNARD DR, STE 201 24018 #026-08-2001 L2001 **PAN** *020 †05

ALLIGOOD, Roberta Bagwell. ■ 24018 #036-05-1990 L1991 **FM** *020 †18

ALTHOUSE, Douglas Glenn. 4040 POSTAL DR, CARILION PEDIATIC 24018 #055-01-1982 L1985 **PD** *020 †55

AMICK, Robert L, Jr. 6415 PETERS CREEK RD 24019 #045-01-1983 L1984 **FM** *020 †18

AMOROSO, Kathy. 4040 POSTAL DR, CARILION PEDIATIC 24018 #036-07-1984 L1994 **PD PPR** *020 †55

ANG-ALHADEFF, Angela. 1597 STRAWBERRY MOUNTN DR D 24018 #033-05-1997 L2002 **AI** *020 †55

ANUNOBI, Echezona. ■ 24018 #690-03-1998 L2007 **P** *012

AROGYASAMI, Roy M. ■ 24018 #035-01-2007 L2007 **TY** *012

ARTHUR, Christy Langlois. 3707 BRAMBLETON AVE, STE 2 24018 #051-01-2000 L2000 **FM** *020 †18

BADLISSI, John Kerry. ■ 24019 #422-01-2005 L2005 **IM** *012

BAETZ, William Richard. 5115 BERNARD DR, STE 201 24018 #038-06-1970 L1978 **AN** *020 †05

BARTLEY, Cavitt K. ■ 24018 #051-01-1953 L1953 **GP EM** *071

BASILE, Vincent Thos. 5304 INDIAN GRAVE RD SW, STE A 24018 #038-06-1970 L1976 **AN PUD** *005

BEAVERS, Aaron L, Jr. ■ 24019 #047-06-1960 L1961 **FM** *071 †18

BERDING, Herbert Chas, Jr. 5115 BERNARD DR, STE 201 24018 #012-01-1983 L1989 **AN** *020 †05 ‡

BERRY, Bradley D. ■ 24018 #041-02-1953 L1955 **GP IM** *071
BERRY, Robert Edward. 7620 AUTUMN PARK 24018 #041-02-1955 L1971 **GS TS** *071 †85,90
BHOWANSINGH, Roshan. ■ 24018 #894-01-1999 L2005 **IM** *012
BILBRA, Linda Joyce. ■ 24018 #047-06-1974 L1979 **EM PHP** *020
BISBAL-MURRUGARRA, O. ■ 24018 #737-06-1998 L2005 **GE** *100 †20
BLACKWELL, James Edward. 4504 STARKEY RD, STE 200 24018 #025-07-1972 L1980 **DR** *020 †80
BLAIR, Walter Bernard. 5115 BERNARD DR 24018 #035-09-1966 L1972 **P** *020 †75
BOATWRIGHT, John Chas. ■ 24018 #051-04-1982 L1983 **IM** *020 †20
BOBBA, Ravi Kiran. ■ 24018 #496-24-1996 L2002 **IM** *020
BOCKNER, Andrew Chas. 5115 BERNARD DR, STE 204 24018 #041-02-1969 L1976 **P** *020 †75
BOGGS, Charles H, Jr. ■ 24018 #016-06-1950 L1968 **GS** *071 †85
BONDURANT, Robert F. ■ 24018 #051-04-1944 L1944 **IM** *071
BRADY, Don Irvin. 3707 BRAMBLETON AVE, STE 2 24018 #036-05-1990 L1991 **FM** *020 †18
BRAILSFORD, Lucien Edward. ■ 24018 #045-01-1959 L1959 **GS TS** *071 †85,90
BRAVO, Cesar J. ■ 24018 #042-01-1999 L2005 **HS** *100 †40 ‡
BREINER, Michael Jos. 2965 COLONNADE DR, STE 140 24018 #051-07-1985 L1993 **PS** *020 †65
BRIGGS, Albert Leon, Jr. ■ 24018 #051-04-1985 L1991 **EM** *020 †16
BRIJBASSIE, Alan Auroon K. ■ 24018 #894-01-2003 L2006 **IM** *012
BROADWELL, Ronald Alan. 4504 STARKEY RD, STE 200 24018 #005-12-1989 L1994 **DR** *020 †80
BROCHERO ALEMAN, Alfonso. ■ 24018 #264-15-1997 L2006 **IM** *012
BROZYNA, Witold. 4504 STARKEY RD, STE 200 24018 #759-03-1982 L1985 **DR IM** *020 †20,80
BUTCHER, Christian Hayes. ■ 24019 #305-01-2000 L2006 **PCC** *020
CAMARDI, Michael James. 1615 SUNBERRY CIR, GERIATRICS 3RD FLOOR 24018 #308-03-1978 L2006 **IM** *020 †20
CAMDEN, Mary Elizabeth. ■ 24019 #051-07-2006 L2006 **OBG** *012
CARDENAS, Alexander F. 5115 BERNARD DR, STE 201 24018 #011-03-1990 L1991 **AN** *020 †05
CARMOUCHE, Jonathan J. 4064 POSTAL DR 24018 #010-01-2000 L2006 **ORS** *020
CARNEVALI, William Santo. 5115 BERNARD DR, STE 201 24018 #041-09-1992 L2000 **AN** *020 †05
CARTER, Sandra Lynn. 4504 STARKEY RD, STE 200 24018 #036-01-1991 L1999 **AN** *020 †05
CASHION, Bradley J. 5115 BERNARD DR, STE 201 24018 #035-45-2001 L2005 **AN** *020 †05
CHAMBERS, Carroll L, Jr. 5115 BERNARD DR, STE 201 24018 #012-01-1988 L1998 **PAN** *020 †05 ‡
CHANDEL, Leslie Marshall. ■ 24018 #016-01-1989 L1989 **P CHP** *074 †75
CHANDLER, James Thornton. 4064 POSTAL DR, ROANOKE ORTHOPAEDIC CENTER 24018 #012-01-1983 L1992 **ORS OFA** *020 †40
CLAPP, Debra Hart. 4231 COLONIAL AVE, STE 1 24018 #036-07-1981 L1985 **OBG** *020 †30
CLARK, Charles E, IV. 4504 STARKEY RD, STE 200 24018 #036-08-1992 L1996 **AN** *020 †05
CLARK, Joe F. 4504 STARKEY RD, STE 200 24018 #020-12-1981 L1984 **AN** *020 †05 ‡
COATES, Joseph Brandon. ■ 24018 #051-04-2006 L2006 **FP** *012
COLLINS, Steven Joseph. 3035 PETERS CREEK RD NW, STE C 24019 #035-03-1995 L1997 **FM** *020
COURY, George Sarkis. 5115 BERNARD DR, STE 201 24018 #038-40-1984 L1987 **AN PME** *020 †05
COUTURE, Stephen A. 5303 INDIAN GRAVE RD SW 24018 #045-01-1988 L1991 **IM** *020 †20
CRAFT, William Hugh, Jr. 4040 POSTAL DR, CARILION PEDIATIC 24018 #036-01-1979 L1985 **PD NPM** *040 †55
CRAGUN, William Hal. ■ 24018 #005-06-1976 L1981 **PUD IM** *040 †20
CRONAU, Leslie Henry, Jr. ■ 24018 #028-34-1961 L1961 **AN PA** *071 †05
CUESTA, Maximo Lopez. ■ 24019 #748-01-1957 L1972 **OBG** *072 †30
CURTISS, Ursula Mary. 5115 BERNARD DR, STE 201 24018 #034-01-1988 L1993 **AN** *020 †05
DALLAS, Robert Lewis. 5115 BERNARD DR, STE 201 24018 #012-01-1980 L1986 **AN** *020 †05
DANG, Minhchau Thi. 5115 BERNARD DR STE 201 24018 #051-01-1991 L1995 **AN** *020 †05
DANIEL, Catherine Ann. 4064 POSTAL DR, ROANOKE ORTHOPAEDIC CENTER 24018 #051-04-1998 L2004 **RHU IM** *020 †20
DASARI, Sireesha. ■ 24018 #495-58-2002 L2006 **FP** *012
DAVIS, Algernon Couch. 3922 ELECTRIC RD 24018 #051-04-1929 L1929 **OBG** *071
DAVIS, Algernon Gibson. 3922 ELECTRIC RD 24018 #051-04-1963 L1963 **GYN OS** *020 †30
DAVIS, Stacy Ann Marie. ■ 24018 #566-01-2001 L2005 **IM** *012
DE LEON, Dexter Guevarra. ■ 24018 #748-20-2002 L2006 **IM** *012
DEMEYTS, Daniel Dominique. 5115 BERNARD DR, STE 201 24018 #036-01-1999 L2005 **AN** *020 †05
DEMOTT, Chad Jason. ■ 24018 #025-07-1998 L2005 **IM** *020 †20
DENNEY, Jill Kimberly. 5115 BERNARD DR 24018 #051-04-1998 L2003 **AN** *020 †05
DEYERLE, Lisa Michelle. 4901 BRAMBLETON AVE 24018 #051-07-2000 L2003 **FM** *020 †18
DIVERS, Allison Kingrey. 4320 BRAMBLETON AVE STE B 24018 #051-07-1998 L1998 **D** *020 †15
DUCKWORTH, Elizabeth Hoye. 5115 BERNARD DR, STE 201 24018 #051-01-1977 L1981 **AN** *020 †05
DUDLEY, Alden W, Jr. ■ 24018 #036-07-1962 L1963 **PTH NP** *030 †50
DUGGAR, Robert Gerald, Jr. 5115 BERNARD DR, STE 201 24018 #001-02-1980 L1988 **AN** *020 †05
DUNNE, Bernard. ■ 24018 #016-06-1972 L1995 **IM** *020 †20
ECKERT, Richard Russell. 4370 STARKEY RD, STE 4C 24018 #033-05-1983 L1992 **ORS GS** *020 †40
ECKERT, Robert Thos. ■ 24018 #041-02-1945 L1946 **IM** *071
EDDINS, William Geo. 6600 NORTHSIDE HGH SCHL RD 24019 #051-04-1967 L1967 **FM GP** *020 †18
EDILLON, Guido Artes. ■ 24018 #748-11-1966 L1972 **AN** *071 †05
EDWARDS, Richard Thos, III. 7533 WILLIAMSON RD 24019 #051-01-1967 L1967 **IM** *020 †20
EL DIKA, Samer Sobhi. ■ 24018 #605-01-1997 L2007 **GE IM** *020 †20
ELIASON, David Andrew. ■ 24018 #005-15-2003 L2007 **OPH** *100
ELTON, James Francis. 4504 STARKEY RD, STE 200 24018 #012-05-1989 L1998 **AN** *072 †05
ENG, Eugene Hyseng. 1906 ELECTRIC RD 24018 #047-06-2003 L2007 **OPH** *020
ERDIM, Feyyaz. ■ 24018 #902-01-1954 L1962 **AN GP** *071
ESTRONZA, Nordeli. 4431 STARKEY RD, ROANOKE NEUROLOGICAL ASSOC 24018 #042-02-1992 L2000 **N CN** *020 †75
FABRICIUS, Thomas James. 3369 COLONIAL AVE SW 24018 #018-03-1998 L2001 **FM** *020 †18
FAWLEY, Pamela Marian. ■ 24018 #055-01-1977 L1977 **P FM** *075
FELDENZER, John Andrew. 2766 ELECTRIC RD, STE A 24018 #035-06-1983 L1989 **NS** *020 †25
FORBES, Dawn Elizabeth. ■ 24018 #051-01-1984 L1987 **PD** *071 †55
FORBES, Jeffrey Alan. 4504 STARKEY RD, STE 200 24018 #051-01-1986 L1990 **AN** *020 †05
FORBES, Lloyd Antoni. ■ 24018 #566-01-2004 L2007 *100
FORTH, Richard Vernon. 3235 ELECTRIC RD, STE 1A 24018 #036-07-1975 L1979 **GYN** *020 †30
FRANKO, James Benj. ■ 24018 #012-01-1984 L1985 **IM** *040 †20
FREDSTROM, Rene Darlene. ■ 24018 #037-01-2003 L2003 **IM** *100 †20
GADPAILLE, Charles Key. 5115 BERNARD DR, STE 201 24018 #021-06-1979 L2000 **AN** *020 †05
GANDEE, Ray Wayne. 4504 STARKEY RD, STE 200 24018 #055-01-1971 L1973 **DR** *020 †80
GLASGOW, Jean M Martin. ■ 24018 #051-01-1936 L1936 **P** *071
GOLDSCHMIDT, Jerome Henry. ■ 24018 #028-34-1969 L1997 **OPH** *071 †35
GONZALES, Tricia Charlene. ■ 24018 #894-01-2003 L2007 **IM** *012
GRANT, Charles Dean. ■ 24018 #051-01-2000 L2000 **DR** *100 †80
GRINSTEIN, Alberto. 4728 WEMBLEY PL SW 24018 #132-01-1964 L1999 **P** *020 †75
GUILFOYLE, Francis M. ■ 24018 #051-01-1985 *100
HAGAN, Hugh J, III. 4064 POSTAL DR 24018 #051-01-1980 L1987 **HS ORS** *040 †40
HAGY, John Albert, Jr. 3707 BRAMBLETON AVE, STE 1 24018 #051-01-1987 L1992 **GS** *020 †85
HAHN, Sung Sik. ■ 24019 #583-29-1996 L2005 **IM** *012
HANCHETT, Ross Howland. ■ 24018 #051-01-2007 L2007 **OBG** *012
HANNA, Amy Jean. ■ 24018 #056-05-2003 L2003 **GS** *012
HARRIS, Norman Ray, II. 5115 BERNARD DR, STE 303 24018 #019-02-1984 L1999 **PS HS** *020 †65
HARRIS, William Kent. 6415 PETERS CREEK RD 24019 #055-01-2000 L2000 **FM** *020 †18 ‡
HARRY SINGH, Nandi. ■ 24018 #894-01-2002 **IM** *100
HARTMAN, Michael James. ■ 24018 #056-06-1971 L1985 **ORS** *020
HATCHER, Natalie Nicole. ■ 24018 #036-08-2008 *012
HAUSER, John Bruce. 5318 BLACK BEAR LN 24018 #025-07-1965 L1977 **R NR** *020 †80
H'DOUBLER, Carolyn Loscal. 5146 REMINGTON RD 24018 #035-46-1991 L2000 **IM** *020 †20
HEDBERG, Ann Elizabeth. 4045 POSTAL DR 24018 #036-05-1990 L1993 **P** *020 †75
HEINDEL, Donald Jos. 5115 BERNARD DR, STE 201 24018 #056-05-1978 L1985 **AN** *020 †05
HENNING, George Durham. 4064 POSTAL DR 24018 #051-01-1965 L1965 **ORS** *020 †40
HENRY, James Allen. ■ 24018 #016-11-1989 L1996 **PTH PCP** *020 †50
HENSHAW, Timothy James. ■ 24018 #051-04-1987 L1997 **RHU** *020 †20
HESS, Darla Bakersmith. ■ 24018 #021-01-1979 L2007 **CD IM** *020 †20
HICKAM, George Lindsay. 4040 POSTAL DR 24018 #051-01-1966 L1966 **PD** *020 †55
HIPPEARD, Scott Crawford. 4901 BRAMBLETON AVE 24018 #051-01-1999 L1999 **GP** *020
HOBACK, Daniel Pflum. 7533 WILLIAMSON RD, STARMOUNT CLINIC 24019 #051-01-1961 L1961 **GP** *071
HOLLAND, Dwight Allen. ■ 24018 #051-01-2008 *012
HOLLANDER, Michael David. 4504 STARKEY RD, STE 200 24018 #010-02-1991 L2001 **DR** *020 †80
HORMEL, Barbara Ann. 6415 PETERS CREEK RD, CARILION NORTH ROANOKE CEN 24019 #051-04-1981 L1982 **IM** *020 †20
HUMERICKHOUSE, Edward Bar. ■ 24018 #654-01-2006 L2006 **IM** *012
HUNT, David Sterling. 5115 BERNARD DR, STE 201 24018 #012-05-1983 L1986 **AN** *020 †05
HUNT, Keith Kellogg, Jr. ■ 24018 #051-01-1962 L1962 **IM PUD** *071 †20
JENKINS, Todd Allan. ■ 24018 #051-07-2005 L2005 **GS** *012
JENNINGS, C Leon, Jr. 4231 COLONIAL AVE 24018 #051-04-1958 L1958 **OBG** *071 †30
JOHN, Christopher Kenyon. 4064 POSTAL DR, ROANOKE ORTHOPAEDIC CENTER 24018 #020-02-1998 L2004 **ORS OSM** *020 †40
JOHNSON, Frank Mitchell. ■ 24019 #051-01-1956 L1956 **GP OS** *071
JOINER, Murray E. 4519 BRAMBLETON AVE, STE 302 24018 #047-07-1987 L1991 **PM PME** *020 †60
JONES, Michael Lee. ■ 24018 #010-01-1987 L1988 **EM** *020 †16
JUTA, Jacob. ■ 24018 #035-47-2005 L2005 **GS** *012
KAKKAR, Sanjeev. ■ 24018 #496-09-1998 L2007 **FP** *012
KANG, Young Sup. ■ 24018 #583-02-1957 L1962 **PS** *071 †65
KANITHANON, Pitplearn. ■ 24019 #891-02-1969 L1976 **AN** *020
KARLEN, James Mark. 5115 BERNARD DR, STE 201 24018 #051-01-1984 L2001 **AN** *020 †05
KELLAM, Stephen John. 3369 COLONIAL AVE SW, CARILION FAMILY MEDICINE 24018 #051-04-1997 L2004 **FM** *020 †18
KELLEHER, Kevin Chas. 4901 BRAMBLETON AVE 24018 #038-43-1981 L1982 **FM** *020 †18
KELLY, James Alexander. 4231 COLONIAL AVE, STE 1 24018 #051-07-1976 L1977 **OBG** *020 †30
KESSEL, Jeffrey Scott. 5115 BERNARD DR, ANESTHESIOLOGY CONSULTANTS 24018 #055-01-1995 L2005 **AN** *100 †20,55,05
KHAN, Amanullah. ■ 24018 #704-16-1991 L2005 **PYG** *100
KIM, Young U. 3604 MORNING DOVE RD 24018 #583-01-1947 L1972 **EM** *071 †85
KISER, Jackson Wm. 4504 STARKEY RD 24018 #051-04-1990 L1997 **DR** *020 †20,80
KOVACH, David Aaron, II. 4504 STARKEY RD STE 200, C/O LEWIS-GALE MEDICAL CEN 24018 #051-01-1996 L1996 **AN** *020 †05
KRELL, Linda Sue. 5212 FALCON RIDGE RD, 5212 FALCON RIDGE RD 24018 #023-07-1976 L1982 **NPM PD** *020 †55
KUCHMAK, Olga. ■ 24018 #759-11-2001 L2007 **IM** *012
KUDUMALA, Anuradha. ■ 24018 #495-62-1994 L2001 **CHP** *020
KUMBASAR, Sadettin D. ■ 24018 #902-03-1989 **IM** *100
KUNKLE, Arthur Alfred. 4040 POSTAL DR, CARILION PEDIATIC 24018 #041-02-1972 L1973 **PD** *020 †55
KWAK, Dong Lin. ■ 24018 #583-02-1961 L1972 **R** *020 †80
LAKHDIR, Farahaba R. ■ 24018 #704-25-1988 L2004 **PD PN** *020 †55
LANDEY, Herbert Max. ■ 24018 #021-05-1958 L1969 **R OS** *020 †80
LANZARA, Gennard Thos. 4504 STARKEY RD STE 200, LEWIS-GALE MEDICAL CENTER 24018 #051-07-1984 L1988 **AN** *020 †05
LATIF, Razia. ■ 24019 #704-02-1974 L1985 **PD ID** *020 †55
LEE, Maxine Mae. 5115 BERNARD DR, STE 201 24018 #024-01-1988 L2000 **AN** *020 †05
LEIVY, Sander Warren. 2766 ELECTRIC RD STE A, MCVITTY EXECUTIVE CTR 24018 #041-02-1987 L1993 **NS** *020 †25
LEMON, George Lawton. ■ 24018 #051-04-1946 L1969 **EM** *071
LEONG, Kristie A. ■ 24018 #051-04-1990 L1992 **FM** *020
LEVITOV, Alexander B. ■ 24018 #913-06-1977 L2002 **IM CCM** *020 †20
LEWIS, Steven Ray. ■ 24018 #004-01-2004 L2007 **OBG** *040
LITWILLER, Roger Wayne. 5115 BERNARD DR, STE 201 24018 #011-03-1970 L1970 **AN** *020 †05
LONG, Charles Robt. 4504 STARKEY RD, STE 200 24018 #023-12-1987 L1996 **DR** *020 †80
LOOMER, Laura Jean. 4358 STARKEY RD, STE 2 24018 #051-01-1986 L1989 **OBG** *020 †30
LUCAS, George Jos. ■ 24018 #010-02-1955 L1976 **N** *071 †75

■ = Address Information Privacy Protected

MACDONALD, Neil Andrew. 5115 BERNARD DR, STE 201 24018 #025-01-1989 L1994 AN *020 †05

MACREA, Madalina Minciu. ■ 24018 #781-01-1997 L2004 PCC *020 †20

MALINCHAK, Marie Leslie. 3369 COLONIAL AVE SW, CARILION FAMILY MEDICINE 24018 #051-07-1995 L1995 FM *020 †18

MANGRAY, Mahendra. ■ 24018 #894-01-1999 L2004 IM *100

MANN, John Walter, III. 4064 POSTAL DR, ROANOKE ORTHOPAEDIC CENTER 24018 #051-01-1987 L1992 ORS *020 †40

MANOS, Ginger Lynne. ■ 24018 #654-01-2005 L2006 GS *012

MARIENFELDT, Hans F. ■ 24018 #154-02-1950 L1956 GP *071

MARTIN, Andrea Renee. 4231 COLONIAL AVE 24018 #028-03-2002 L2006 OBG *020 †30

MATSANGOU, Maria. ■ 24018 #917-13-2000 L2005 IM *012

MAYS DE PEREZ, Kimberly A. ■ 24018 #011-04-2004 L2004 OBG *012

MCBRIDE, Jeremy Frank. ■ 24018 #023-07-2007 L2007 TY *012

MC COWN, John G. ■ 24019 #051-04-1943 L1943 GP *071

MC FAGUE, Richard Francis. 4923 COLONIAL AVE, STE B 24018 #024-16-1984 L2000 PM *020 †60

MCFARLANE, Michelle A. PO BOX 20372 24018 #036-05-1997 L2007 PM *020 †60

MCISAAC, Jason Ian. ■ 24019 #550-04-2007 L2008 GP *012

MC LEOD, James Wm. ■ 24018 #039-01-1972 L1979 ORS *074 †40

MEKALA, Durga Prasad. ■ 24018 #495-70-1994 L2006 FP *012

MEYER, Michael Bernard. 4040 POSTAL DR, CARILION PEDIATIC 24018 #012-05-1974 L1979 PD *020 †55

MEYERS, Dawn C. ■ 24018 #010-03-1987 L1995 PTH *020 †50

MILLER, Thomas Kevin. 4064 POSTAL DR 24018 #041-12-1980 L1986 ORS PM *020 †40

MOORE, John Eiland. 89 SUMMERS WAY, CARILLION PEDIATRIC 24019 #036-05-1995 L2002 PD *020 †40

MOPARTY, Eswar. ■ 24018 #495-21-2005 L2007 FP *012

MORGAN, Stephen Alderton. 3369 COLONIAL AVE SW 24018 #051-01-1986 L1987 FM *020 †40

MOSKAL, Joseph Tuvia. 4064 POSTAL DR, ROANOKE ORTHOPAEDIC CENTER 24018 #028-02-1981 L1982 ORS *040 †40 ‡

MUELENAER, Penelope Ann. 6736 MALLARD LAKE DR 24018 #051-07-1979 L1992 PD PDI *050 †55

MULLET, James Goddard. 4504 STARKEY RD, STE 200 24018 #035-03-1984 L1985 DR *020 †80

MURDOCK, Robert Lawrence. 4923 COLONIAL AVE, STE B 24018 #035-03-1984 L1991 P *020 †75

MURRAY, Robert Louis. ■ 24018 #036-01-1956 L1962 R *071 †80

NAZLI, Ayesha. ■ 24018 #704-16-1991 L2006 FM *020 †18

NEMEC, Douglas Richard. 4519 BRAMBLETON AVE, STE 302 24018 #038-43-1985 L1996 AN APM *105

NIEDERLEHNER, James Robt. 5115 BERNARD DR, STE 201 24018 #051-01-1975 L1977 AN *020 †05

NOTTINGHAM, Clifford, III. 6415 PETERS CREEK RD 24019 #051-04-1978 L1979 FM *020 †18

NOURI, Labeed Sami. 4064 POSTAL DR, ROANOKE ORTHOPAEDIC CENTER 24018 #528-03-1994 L2004 ORS *020

O'CONNOR, Siobhan G. 4519 BRAMBLETON AVE, STE 302 24018 #539-06-1990 L2002 PM *020 †60

OJIE, Jude Ogochukwu. ■ 24018 #690-06-2002 L2006 IM *012

ORTON, Matthew David. ■ 24018 #051-01-2008 *012

OSBORN, Steven Ray. 5303 INDIAN GRAVE RD SW, CLEARBROOK URGENT CARE 24018 #019-02-1982 L2003 FM *020 †18

OSUORAH, Vivien Ifeyinwa. ■ 24019 #690-04-1999 L2006 FP *012

PACHECO, Patricia P. ■ 24018 #051-04-1989 L1990 DR *020 †80

PADMANABHAN, Hema. ■ 24018 #496-07-1980 L1998 IM *020 †20 ‡

PAGET, Charles Johnson. 3707 BRAMBLETON, STE 1 24018 #017-20-1990 L2002 GS *020 †85

PALMERTON, Todd Steven. 6415 PETERS CREEK RD 24019 #051-07-1985 L1986 FM *020 †18

PARASHAR, Amitabh. ■ 24018 #496-09-1999 L2005 IM *100 †20

PARK, Jong H John. 5335 SILVER FOX RD 24018 #583-04-1964 L1974 AN GS *071

PATEL, Vishal Dhiren. 5419 SUGAR LOAF MONTN RD R 24018 #496-41-2000 L2001 IM *020

PATTEN, Robert C, Jr. 3707 BRAMBLETON AVE, . 24018 #051-07-1988 L1989 FM *020 †18

PATTERSON, Abram M, Jr. 4504 STARKEY RD, STE 200 24018 #051-01-1968 L1968 R PDR *020 †55,80

PATTERSON, Mark A. 89 SUMMERS WAY, CARILLION PEDIATRIC 24019 #035-03-1989 L1992 PD *020 †55

PAXTON, Ben Eugene. ■ 24018 #023-07-2007 L2007 TY *012

PEARSON, Theodore John. 5115 BERNARD DR, STE 201 24018 #045-01-1993 L1993 AN *020 †05

PEREZ, Ana M. 2840 ELECTRIC RD, STE 111 24018 #275-01-1949 L1972 CLP PTH *071 †50

PEREZ, Antonio. ■ 24018 #275-01-1954 L1966 PTH CLP *071 †50

PEREZ, Antonio, III. 5115 BERNARD DR, STE 201 24018 #051-01-1984 L1988 AN *020 †05

PERKINS, Marvin E. 4502 STARKEY RD 24018 #024-01-1946 L1978 P PHP *071 †75

PHILLIPS, Joseph Thos, Jr. ■ 24018 #051-01-1937 L1937 GS GYN *071

PIERCE, Christopher A. 4040 POSTAL DR, CARILION PEDIATIC 24018 #051-01-1993 L1998 PD *020 †55

PODESCHI, Daniel Marc. 4504 STARKEY RD STE 200 24018 #016-11-1989 L1993 AN *020 †05

PORCIUNCULA, Jon Carlo. ■ 24018 #665-01-2006 L2007 IM *012

PRESSLEY, C Christopher. 5115 BERNARD DR, STE 201 24018 #036-01-1999 L2003 AN *020 †05

PRICE, Charles Wm. ■ 24018 #021-06-1975 L1989 R *075 †80

PUGH, Robert L, Jr. 4370 STARKEY RD, STE 1A 24018 #305-01-1991 L1994 IM *020

QUIOCO, Lydia Llanto. ■ 24018 #748-11-1971 L1980 IM *020 †20

REA, Wm Saml Gibson, Jr. ■ 24018 #008-01-1977 L2000 P *020 †75

REDDY, Pavan K. 7842 CEDAR EDGE RD 24018 #495-13-1992 L1993 P *020 †75

REEFE, William E. ■ 24018 #010-02-1949 L1953 IM IMG *071 †20

REFINETTI, Ana Paula Corr. ■ 24018 #187-03-2004 L2007 GS *012

REINER, Grant. ■ 24019 #654-01-2000 L2002 GS *100

REMANDABAN, Teodulo. 5115 BERNARD DR, STE 201 24018 #748-11-1973 L1977 AN *020

ROMAN-STEANS, Maria C. ■ 24018 #016-11-1997 L2007 IM *020

ROSENFELD, Peter. 4504 STARKEY RD STE 200, P O BOX 8849 24018 #035-15-1992 L1993 DR *020 †80

ROTH, Andrew Geo. ■ 24018 #035-45-1978 L1991 PS FPS *020 †85,65

SADEK, Mona. 4231 COLONIAL AVE, STE 1 24018 #047-05-1994 L1997 OBG *020 †30

SADIQ, Saima. ■ 24018 #704-09-1997 L2006 FP *012

SAGART, Elahe. 2727 ELECTRIC RD 24018 #517-19-1996 L2002 P *020 †75

SALTERS, Robert Edward. ■ 24018 #045-01-2004 L2007 EM *020

SAMARASINGHE, Gunasiri. 5372 FALLOWATER LN 24018 #220-01-1969 L1996 AN PME *105

SAROYA, Satinder Kaur. ■ 24018 #495-29-1995 L2006 FP *012

SARVAY, Thomas Long, Jr. ■ 24018 #051-04-1964 L1964 P *020 †20

SATHAPPAN, Sathappan S.. 4064 POSTAL DR, ROANOKE ORTHO CTR 24018 #917-02-1995 ORS *100

SCHERER, Christopher J. 4431 STARKEY RD 24018 #041-14-1991 L1997 N *020 †75

SCIALABBA, Mark Anthony. 4431 STARKEY RD 24018 #561-12-1982 L2001 N *020 †75

SEAMON, Jesse Brian. ■ 24018 #051-01-2008 *012

SHAFFER, Lee W, Jr. 4064 POSTAL DR 24018 #051-04-1950 L1957 ORS *071 †40

SHANNON, John Robt. 4504 STARKEY RD, STE 200 24018 #051-01-1988 L1992 AN *020 †05,20

SHERMAN, Christine G. 5115 BERNARD DR STE 201 24018 #036-01-1997 L2001 AN *020

SHETH, Pragna Dhimant. ■ 24018 #495-23-1993 L2003 PTH *020 †50 ‡

SILBERBLATT, Enrique A. 3505 BRAMBLETON AVE 24018 #035-09-1977 L1985 PS FPS *020 †85,65 ‡

SINGH, Harpreet. ■ 24018 #496-48-2003 L2006 FP *012

SISK, Michael Anthony. 4431 STARKEY RD, ROANOKE NEUROLOGICAL ASSOC 24018 #036-05-1967 L1971 CHN N *020 †55,75

SLONIM, Anthony Daniel. 5208 FOX RIDGE RD 24018 #035-09-1991 L2007 CCM PD *020 †55,20

SMALES, William Palmer. 6415 PETERS CREEK RD 24019 #036-05-1990 L1991 IM *020

SMITH, Abby Aspel. 4231 COLONIAL AVE, STE 1 24018 #035-45-1988 L1998 OBG *020 †30

SMITH, Donald Geo, Jr. 3707 BRAMBLETON AVE, BRAMB 24018 #051-04-1983 L1984 FM *020 †18

SMITH, Mark O'Dell. 3707 BRAMBLETON AVE, STE 4 24018 #036-05-1984 L1987 GS CCS *020 †85

SMITH, Martin T. 3825 ELECTRIC RD, 419 OFFICE CENTER STE C 24018 #055-75-1982, ▲ L1997 PHL D *020

SMITH, Susan Lee. 4040 POSTAL DR, PED ASSOC OF ROANOKE VALLE 24018 #036-01-1991 L1998 PD *020 †55

SORIANO, Maria Rosario. ■ 24018 #748-01-1990 L2007 PD *020 †55

SOUTHALL, Eugene P, III. 4504 STARKEY RD, STE 200 24018 #051-01-1992 L1997 DR *020 †80,28

SOWERS, Ann Branyon. 70 SUMMERFIELD CT 24019 #051-04-1979 L1984 OPH *020 †35

SPITZER, Janet Lee. 3536 BRAMBLETON AVE STE 4 24018 #051-04-1981 L1985 FM OS *020 †18

SRISUMRID, Sutin. ■ 24018 #891-01-1967 L1975 R *020 †20

STAVOLA, Anthony Robt. 6415 PETERS CREEK RD 24018 #035-08-1977 L1978 FM IMG *020 †18

STEANS, Stacy Theodore. ■ 24018 #030-05-1994 L2007 CCP *100 †55

STEFFE, John Wilson, Jr. 4504 STARKEY RD, STE 200 24018 #051-04-1981 L1982 DR *020 †80

STEVENS, Ward Wm, Jr. 4431 STARKEY RD 24018 #021-01-1960 L1968 NS *020 †25

STILTNER, Angela Renee. 5285 CRUMPACKER DR 24019 #051-01-2000 L2000 FPG *020 †18

STOECKER, Thomas Jeffrey. 4504 STARKEY RD, ROANOKE, PC - SUITE 200 24018 #025-07-1982 L1987 DR *020 †80

STRONG, Thomas Elisha. 4064 POSTAL DR 24018 #047-06-1956 L1963 ORS *071 †40

STURM, Charles Harveyford. 5115 BERNARD DR, STE 201 24018 #038-41-1994 L2000 AN *020 †05

SUMMERLIN, Daniel C. 4504 STARKEY RD, STE 200 24018 #036-01-1973 L1981 AN *020 †05

SURRUSCO, Richard Mark. 3232 PINELAND RD SW, ROANOKE, VA. 24018 24018 #561-01-1971 L1973 EM *020 †16

SWANSON, Cathy Jo. 5115 BERNARD DR, STE 201 24018 #036-01-1986 L1989 AN *020 †05

SWEENEY, Nina Keeley. 3369 COLONIAL AVE SW 24018 #051-01-1996 L1999 FM *020 †18

TEDLA, Wosenyelew Mulat. ■ 24018 #366-03-1997 L2004 IM *100 †20

TEED, Richard Russell, Jr. ■ 24019 #305-01-2007 L2007 GS *012

TERSHAK, Daniel Richard. 3707 BRAMBLETON AVE, CARILION SURG CARE 24018 #041-02-1995 L2000 GS *020 †85

THOMAS, Bruce Richard. 4504 STARKEY RD, STE 200 24018 #038-40-1973 L1974 DR VIR *020 †80 ‡

THOMPSON, David Earl. 5115 BERNARD DR, STE 201 24018 #028-02-1981 L1990 AN IM *020 †20,05

TINGLER, William Leon, II. 4431 STARKEY RD 24018 #047-20-1999 L1999 N *020

TORRE, Wayne Joseph. ■ 24018 #051-07-1979 L1983 PTH *074 †50 ‡

TRACY, Michael Kennedy. 3800 ELECTRIC RD, STE 307 24018 #035-01-1999 L2006 OPH *020 †35

TROSTLE, Thomas Frederick. 5115 BERNARD DR, STE 201 24018 #051-01-1973 L1975 AN *020 †05

TURNER, Robert Lander, Jr. ■ 24019 #045-01-1975 L1978 P *020

TWILLEY, Rush Matthew. ■ 24019 #051-07-2005 L2007 EM *012

UBESIE, Kanene Virginia. ■ 24019 #048-13-2007 L2007 GS *012

UNG, Chheany Walterchapm. 5372 FALLOWATER LN 24018 #041-14-2002 L2002 APM *020 †05

VARMA, Anjali. ■ 24018 #495-45-2000 L2008 P *012

VASCIK, James Michael. 5304 INDIAN GRAVE RD SW, STE A 24018 #016-11-1978 L1988 NS *020 †25

VIELAVICIUS, Mindaugas. ■ 24018 #913-96-1994 L1999 AN *020

VOHRA, Manjit Kaur. 2727 ELECTRIC RD, STE 100 24018 #495-43-1977 L2004 P *020 †75

VONGVORACHOTI, Joe. ■ 24018 #051-04-2007 L2007 IM *012

WALKER, Rome Haward. 3707 BRAMBLETON AVE 24018 #055-01-1974 L1979 GS *071 †85

WALTON, David Clark. ■ 24018 #051-04-1967 L1967 AI PDA *020

WANG, Moses. ■ 24019 #242-36-1934 L1978 IM *020

WARNER, Charles Hamilton. 4504 STARKEY RD, STE 200 24018 #036-07-1985 L1991 DR *020 †80

WEAVER, Edgar Newman. 5304 INDIAN GRAVE RD SW, STE A 24018 #051-01-1975 L1981 NS *020 †25

WHEELOCK, Franklin M. 3231 ELECTRIC RD 24018 #051-04-1987 OS *020

WHITE, Alan Preston. 5721 LONGRIDGE CIR, CARILION SURGICAL CARE-ROA 24018 #036-05-1974 L2004 GS *020 †85

WHITNEY, William Percy. 3369 COLONIAL AVE SW 24018 #035-15-1994 L1994 FM *020 †18

WILEY, Roger Paul, Jr. 4504 STARKEY RD, STE 200 24018 #041-12-1978 L1983 DR RNR *071 †80

WILKINS, Megan Lenore. ■ 24019 #665-01-2007 L2007 IM *012

WILKS, John Wm. ■ 24018 #047-06-1957 L1963 GYN *071 †30

WILSON, James Thos, III. 4431 STARKEY RD 24018 #051-04-1976 L1982 CHN N *020 †55,75

WINN, Thomas Meredith, Jr. 4231 COLONIAL AVE 24018 #051-04-1963 L1963 **OBG** *020 †30

WOLFF, Paul Ronald. 5115 BERNARD DR, STE 201 24018 #003-01-1981 L1990 **AN IM** *020 †05

XIA, Tian. ■ 24018 #243-76-1993 L2007 **FP** *012

YORK, William S. 5115 BERNARD DR, STE 201 24018 #048-15-1997 L1997 **GS** *020 †05

YOUNGBLOOD, Ella M D. 3390 COLONIAL AVE, ROANOKE FAMILY MEDICINE 24018 #051-04-1980 L1981 **FM** *020 †18

ZEBRO, Gebrehana Woldense. 3464 COLONIAL AVE, 3 24018 #366-02-1989 L2002 **OS** *100 †20

ZELENIK, Mary Ella. 4504 STARKEY RD STE 2 24018 #047-05-1978 L1981 **R** *020 †80

ROANOKE – ROANOKE CITY

ABO-HILAL, Mohammad. 1212 3RD ST SW, CARILION HEALTH SYSTEM 24016 #875-01-2000 L2004 **P** *100

ABRAHAM, Christina Marie. 1117 S JEFFERSON ST, ALLERGY AND ASTHMA ASSCOIA 24016 #051-07-2001 L2001 **AI** *100 †20,03

ABRAHAM, George A. 1117 S JEFFERSON ST 24016 #915-02-1972 L1985 **AI PD** *020 †55,03

ADAMS, Felicity Ann. ■ 24014 #036-01-2001 L2007 **CHP** *020

AKONG, Joanne Frances. 1906 BELLEVIEW AVE SE 24014 #894-01-2000 L2003 **IM** *100 †20

ALBERS, Jennifer Carol. 102 HIGHLAND AVE SE, OB/GYN EDUCATION 24013 #051-04-2002 L2002 **OBG** *100

ALBRIGHT, Chad Donald. 707 S JEFFERSON ST 24016 #041-14-1996 L1999 **OPH** *020 †35

ALGINO, Kenneth Martin. 101 ELM AVE SE, CARILION ROANOKE COMMUNITY 24013 #024-05-1989 L2007 **PTH HMP** *020 †50

ALI, Uzma Manzar. 4910 VALLEY VIEW BLVD NW 24012 #704-16-1990 L2005 **FM** *020 †18

ALLEN, John T. 1234 FRANKLIN RD SW 24016 #010-02-1971 L1975 **U** *020 †95

ALLEN, Robert Wilson, Jr. 101 ELM AVE SE, 6TH FLR-PEDIATRIX MED GRP 24013 #024-04-1969 L1969 **NPM** *071 †55

ALLT, Wm Ernest Charlton. PO BOX 13367 24033 #917-25-1943 L1978 **RO** *020

AMATO, Alise Mary. 21 HIGHLAND AVE SE, INC 24013 #003-01-1995 L2002 **PD** *020 †55

ANDROSSOV, Andrei. 1314 PETERS CREEK RD NW 24017 #913-39-1992 L2007 **FP** *012

ARIF, Saira. PO BOX 13367, CARILION ROANOKE MEM HOSP 24033 #704-02-1996 L2006 **P** *012

ARLISS, Jill Marie. 21 HIGHLAND AVE SE, STE 200 24013 #035-03-2001 L2005 **OBG** *012

ARNER, Mark Chas. 102 HIGHLAND AVE SE, STE 3 24013 #049-01-1973 L1987 **OBG** *030 †30

ARNOLD, William Scott. 2001 CRYSTAL SPRING AVE SW 24014 #051-01-1990 L1992 **TS** *020 †85,90

AULAKH, Mandeep. 1212 3RD ST SW 24016 #495-29-1998 **P** *012

AUSTIN, Joseph Lee. 127 MCCLANAHAN ST SW 24014 #051-04-1975 L1978 **CD IM** *020 †20

AZIZ, Sameh Gamil. 1906 BELLEVIEW AVE SE, CARILION ROANOKE MEMORIAL 24014 #915-04-1994 L2001 **PCC** *020

BABBAR, Jatinder Pal. 1212 3RD ST SW, CARILION HEALTH SYSTEM 24016 #495-73-2001 L2004 **P** *012

BAILEY, Dewey James, III. 1030 S JEFFERSON ST, STE 200 24016 #041-02-1987 L1988 **END IM** *020 †20

BAKER, Joseph Wilmer. 2001 CRYSTAL SPRING AVE SW 24014 #036-07-1982 L1984 **OS TS** *020 †85,90

BAKHIT, Cyrus Eros. 1316 S JEFFERSON ST, PAIN MANAGEMENT CENTER OF 24016 #036-05-1989 L1999 **PME IM** *020 †20,05

BALBIN-VALLESTEROS, G. 4615 HUNTRIDGE RD, LEWIS GALE CLC 24012 #748-02-1989 L1999 **PD** *020 †55

BANSAL, Pankaj. 1212 3RD ST SW 24016 #495-45-2002 L2005 **FP** *012

BARKSDALE, Robert C. 1722 JEFFERSON ST SE, EMERGENCY MEDICINE 24016 #001-06-1991 L2001 **EM** *020 †16

BARNES, Daniel Gilchrist. ■ 24014 #036-05-2004 L2007 **EM** *020

BARRITT, A Sidney, III. 202 DUKE OF GLOUCSTR SW 24014 #035-20-1968 L1973 **GE IM** *020 †20

BARTLEY, Homer. 101 ELM AVE SE 24013 #051-04-1936 L1936 **GP** *071

BARWICK, Elizabeth C. 1906 BELLEVIEW AVE SE 24014 #055-75-2007, ▲ L2007 **OBG** *012

BASILE, Michael Jos. 1310 3RD ST SW 24014 #038-40-1970 L1978 **IM** *020 †20

BAUER, Daniel Vincent. 1310 3RD ST SW 24016 #051-01-1996 L1999 **IM** *020 †20

BEACHAM, Brian Lee. ■ 24015 #665-01-2006 L2006 **GS** *012

BEIRNE, Renee Ann. 2001 CRYSTAL SPRING AVE SW, CARILION INTERNAL 24014 #051-04-1999 L1999 **IM** *020 †20

BELAK, Zenon A. 1212 3RD ST SW 24016 #759-12-2006 **IM** *012

BERDEEN, Thompson N, Jr. 210 CHURCH AVE SW 24011 #051-01-1971 L1972 **EM** *020 †16

BERRY, Michael Adair. 2001 CRYSTAL SPRING AVE SW, CARILION INTERNAL 24014 #051-04-1979 L1987 **IM** *020 †20

BHALLA, Narinder Pal. 2001 CRYSTAL SPRING AVE SW, STE 300 24014 #035-06-1988 L1999 **CD IM** *020 †20

BHANDARI, Arvin Sitaram. 1212 3RD ST SW 24016 #880-01-1981 L2003 **P** *020

BHARATHAN, Rajapillai K. 424 ELM AVE SW 24014 #495-66-1989 L1997 **IM** *020 †20 ‡

BINNS-LOVEMAN, Karen M. 101 ELM AVE SE 24013 #011-02-1997 L1999 **NPM** *020 †55

BIVENS, Carl Hill, Jr. 1030 S JEFFERSON ST, STE 200 24016 #051-04-1967 L1967 **END DIA** *020 †20

BLACK, Denise Sylvia. 1906 BELLEVIEW AVE SE, MED EDUCATION BUILD- 3 24014 #665-02-2006 L2007 **IM** *012

BLACKWOOD, Ralph A, Jr. 2001 CRYSTAL SPRING AVE SW, CARILION INTERNAL 24014 #047-06-1992 L1998 **MPD** *020 †55,20

BLADYKAS, Brian Francis. 16 WALNUT AVE SW, WALNUT AVE ASSOCIATES 24016 #654-01-1999 L1999 **P ADP** *020 †75

BLATCHFORD, Patrick Tyson. ■ 24014 #019-02-2003 L2003 **GS** *012

BLOUNT, Margaret Ann. 1314 PETERS CREEK RD NW 24017 #051-04-1998 L1998 **FM** *020 †18

BOGGESS, Howard Preston. 101 ELM AVE SE, COMMUNITY HOSP OF ROANOKE 24013 #036-07-1967 L1971 **PD** *040 †55

BOLINGER, Brian Scott. 1315 2ND ST SW, INTERNAL MEDICINE OF 24016 #038-06-1991 L1998 **IM** *020 †20

BOLTON, Thomas Bret. 1906 BELLEVIEW AVE SE, ROANOKE MEMORIAL HOSPITAL 24014 #051-05-1985 L1991 **EM** *020 †16

BONO, Joseph Albert. 1315 2ND ST SW 24016 #035-09-1965 L1974 **GS** *071 †85

BOSHRA, Soheir Seifein. 1314 PETERS CREEK RD NW 24017 #915-03-1981 L2000 **FPG** *020 †18 ‡

BOWLES, Paul Elwood. 21 HIGHLAND AVE SE, STE 100 24013 #051-04-1967 L1967 **PD** *071 †55

BRISLEY, Jon Philip. 707 S JEFFERSON ST 24016 #036-01-1988 L1992 **OPH** *020 †35

BROWN, Beverley Bernice. 2145 MOUNT PLEASNT BLVD SE 24014 #041-15-1999 L2004 **FM OBS** *040 †18

BRUBAKER, Herman W. 5501 WILLIAMSON RD 24012 #051-04-1953 L1953 **FM** *071 †18

BUCK, David Andrew. 2013 JEFFERSON ST SW, FL 1 24014 #051-04-1999 L1999 **RO** *020 †80

BUDIN, Robert Earl. 1906 BELLEVIEW AVE SE, CARILION ROANOKE MEMORIAL 24014 #041-14-1980 L2006 **PTH** *020 †50

BURCH, John Gordon. 2601 FRANKLIN RD SW, ROANOKE NEUROLOGICAL CENTR 24014 #060-01-1967 L1979 **N** *020 †75

BURNETT, William Thomas. ■ 24015 #045-04-1999 L2005 **EM** *020 †16

BURNSTEIN, Alan Vladimir. 202 DUKE OF GLOUCSTR SW 24014 #048-04-1975 L1982 **GE IM** *071 †20

BURTON, Floyd Randell. 21 HIGHLAND AVE SE, INC 24013 #017-20-1987 L2006 **PD** *020 †55

BUSHKAR, John Phillip. 127 MCCLANAHAN ST SW, STE 300 24014 #051-04-1975 L1976 **CD IM** *020 †20

BUTLER, Wm Wilson Saml. 101 ELM AVE SE 24013 #051-01-1980 L1982 **U** *030 †95

BYRNES, Timothy Raymond. 707 S JEFFERSON ST, STE 201 24016 #035-06-1995 L2001 **OPH** *035

CAIN, James Steven. 2602 FRANKLIN RD SW 24016 #051-07-1985 L1987 **NEP IM** *020 †20

CALLIS, James Timmons. 1234 FRANKLIN RD SW 24016 #047-05-1983 L1990 **VS GS** *020 †85

CAMPBELL, Alfred W. 101 ELM AVE SE, ASSOCIATES 24013 #048-14-1993 L1998 **PTH** *020 †50 ‡

CANELA, Christinne Dugang. 1212 3RD ST SW 24016 #748-11-2002 L2005 **OBG** *012

CANNON, Christopher E. 2001 CRYSTAL SPRING AVE SW, STE 300 24014 #036-08-1992 L2000 **CD** *020 †20

CAPELLA, Jeannette Marie. 101 ELM AVE SE 24013 #011-04-1993 L2002 **TRS CCS** *040 †85

CARMICHAEL, Elizabeth S B. 335 23RD ST SW 24014 #051-04-1974 L1975 **FM** *020 †18

CASTLE, James Richard. 1111 S JEFFERSON ST, STE A 24016 #055-01-1969 L1976 **PUD IM** *020 †20

CAVETT, Clinton Moore. 102 HIGHLAND AVE SE, STE 404 24013 #027-01-1973 L1992 **PDS GS** *020 †85

CHAND, Vikram K. 2013 JEFFERSON ST SW, FL 2 24014 #495-45-1991 L2006 **HO IM** *020 †20

CHEN, Jennifer Bickley. 920 S JEFFERSON ST, JEFFERSON COLLEGE OF HEALT 24016 #023-01-1989 L1994 **RHU IM** *020 †20

CHINNEPALLI, Himabindu. 1212 3RD ST SW 24016 #495-62-1998 L2003 **FM** *100 †18

CLARK, Carolyn. 1310 3RD ST SW 24016 #036-01-1987 L1998 **IM** *020 †20

CLARKE, Eugene Jos. 515 8TH ST SW 24016 #047-06-1955 L1976 **GPM** *030 †70

CLAYTOR, John Bunyan, Jr. ■ 24016 #047-07-1940 L1949 **OBG** *071

CLAYTOR, Richard Lamont. 1304 PLANTATION RD NE 24012 #051-01-1993 L1997 **CHP** *020

COBEY, Elwood Alexander. 3322 W RIDGE RD SW 24014 #023-01-1977 L1993 **GYN** *020 †30

COLLINS, Beth Ann. ■ 24015 #051-01-1965 L1965 **OBG** *071 †30

COLLINS, Robert Graham. 21 HIGHLAND AVE SE, STE 100 24013 #051-04-1989 L1992 **PD** *071 †55

CONLON, Barbara M. 4615 HUNTRIDGE RD, BONSACK FAMILY PRACTICE 24012 #539-06-1990 L1994 **FM** *020

CONRAD, John Christian. 1906 BELLEVIEW AVE SE, DEPT OF ANESTHESIA 24014 #036-05-1985 L1989 **AN** *020 †05

COOK, Lawrence S. 1906 BELLEVIEW AVE SE 24014 #051-75-2007, ▲ L2007 **OBG** *012

CORDLE, Richard Alan. 102 HIGHLAND AVE SE, STE 305 24013 #028-02-1991 L2002 **PG** *020 †55

CORREIA, Neil John. ■ 24013 #286-13-2005 L2006 **OBG** *012

COTHRAN, Donna S. 101 ELM AVE SE, 6TH FL 24013 #045-01-1989 L1992 **NPM PD** *020 †55

COTTER, Francis. 707 S JEFFERSON ST, VISTAR EYE CENTER 24016 #010-02-1984 L1987 **OPH** *020 †35

COX, Mary Ann. 21 HIGHLAND AVE SE, INC 24013 #036-08-1996 L2003 **PD** *020 †55

CRAWFORD, James Jos. 1906 BELLEVIEW AVE SE, DEPT OF ANESTHESIA 24014 #021-05-1982 L1989 **AN** *020 †05

CREEKMORE, Robert Sherman. 3601 PEAKWOOD DR SW 24014 #047-06-1961 L1962 **DR NM** *020 †80

CRICKENBERGER, Dallas P. 302 WASHINGTON AVE SW 24016 #051-01-1966 L1966 **ORS** *020 †40

CRISS, Tracey M. 213 MCCLANAHAN ST SW, STE 310 24014 #055-01-1991 L1995 **P** *020 †75

CROWGEY, Junius Ellett. 707 S JEFFERSON ST, VISTA EYE CENTER 24016 #051-01-1954 L1954 **OPH** *071 †35

CRUM, Jerry Brice. 1138 2ND ST SW 24016 #047-06-1959 L1967 **OPH** *071

CULPEPPER, Clifford Perry. 331 HERSHBERGER RD, FRIENDSHIP MANOR 24012 #036-05-1978 L1979 **NEP** *020 †20

CURTIS, Dianna Lee. 21 HIGHLAND AVE SE, STE 200 24013 #051-07-1996 L1996 **OBG** *020 †30

CUTTER, Edgar Burford. 1234 FRANKLIN RD SW 24016 #028-34-1954 L1962 **U** *071 †95

DALLAS, Apostolos P. 1906 BELLEVIEW AVE SE, CARILION ROANOKE MEMORIAL 24014 #051-04-1987 L1990 **IM** *020 †20

DANESHFAR, Bahrasm Daniel. ■ 24014 #048-15-2006 L2007 **GS** *012

DANIEL, Charles Douglas. 1234 FRANKLIN RD SW 24016 #051-04-1998 L2004 **U** *020 †95

DAUGHERTY, John F. 4910 VALLEY VIEW BLVD NW 24012 #016-42-1977 L1979 **FM OS** *020 †18

DAVENPORT, Roxanne R. 102 HIGHLAND AVE SE, STE 103 24013 #017-20-1996 L1996 **GS OS** *020 †85

DAVIDSON, Jesse T, III. 1234 FRANKLIN RD SW 24016 #051-01-1976 L1982 **VS GS** *020 †85

DAVIES, Ross Sander. PO BOX 13367, ROANOKE MEM HOSP 24033 #007-02-1969 L1992 **GS TS** *071 †85,90

DAVIS, Benjamin Cameron. 2524 ROSALIND AVE SW 24014 #305-01-2005 L2008 **FP** *012

DE GUZMAN, Gerard Placido. 512B MCDOWELL AVE NE, VALLEY OCCUPATIONAL MED 24016 #051-07-1995 L1995 **FM** *020 †18,70

DELANEY, John Patrick. 101 ELM AVE SE 24013 #051-01-1981 L1982 **AN** *020 †05

DELANEY, Martin D, III. ■ 24014 #021-01-1970 L1986 **CHP P** *020

DELAPP, Paul David. ■ 24015 #051-07-2005 L2005 **P** *012

DEMICCO, Deborah Diane. 2001 CRYSTAL SPRING AVE SW, STE 301 24014 #035-09-1978 L1986 **ID IM** *020 †20

DERESKA, Nina Holtzapple. 1030 S JEFFERSON ST, STE 109 24016 #011-03-1998 L2005 **OBG** *020 †30

DESAI, Jitendra Sumantrai. 16 WALNUT AVE SW 24016 #495-23-1972 L1980 **P** *020 †75

DESAI, Varsha Jitendra. 1101 1ST ST SW, PEDIATRIC CLINIC 24016 #495-23-1972 L1980 **PD** *020 †55

DE VERTER, John Scott. ■ 24014 #048-02-1967 L1973 **P** *020 †75

DIAZ-PAVON, Jose. ■ 24014 #847-13-1978 **ON** *100

DICKERSON, Shelby Clark. 101 ELM AVE SE 24013 #051-01-1972 L1972 **CD IM** *040 †20

DINSMORE, John E. 102 HIGHLAND AVE SE, STE 404 24013 #055-01-1992 L2006 **GS** *020 †85

DIXON, David Lloyd, III. 21 HIGHLAND AVE SE, STE 100 24013 #036-05-1976 L1981 PD *071 †55

DOHERTY, Debra Kay. ■ 24014 #048-13-2001 L2007 GS *100

DONATO, Antonio Tuason. 1125 S JEFFERSON ST 24016 #748-01-1962 L1972 GS VS *020 †85,90

DORSEY, Douglas Russell. 1111 S JEFFERSON ST STE A 24016 #051-01-1982 L1987 IM PUD *020 †20

DORSEY, Neil K. 2001 CRYSTAL SPRING AVE SW, CARILION INTERNAL 24014 #023-01-1982 L1993 IM *040 †20

DORSEY, Susan Boardwine. 1215 3RD ST SW 24016 #004-01-1987 L1993 D *020 †15

DOUGLAS, Deborah Krum. ■ 24014 #005-02-1977 L1982 PTH *020 †50

DREZALIU, Valentin Florin. 102 HIGHLAND AVE SE 24013 #781-01-2000 L2006 OBG *012

DROUGAS, James Geo. 1234 FRANKLIN RD SW 24016 #047-05-1989 L1997 VS GS *020 †85

DUCEY, Kevin Francis. 2001 CRYSTAL SPRING AVE SW, STE 201 24014 #024-07-1973 L1981 TS *020 †85,90

DUNKER, Ralph Otto, Jr. 1030 S JEFFERSON ST, STE 106 24016 #038-40-1970 L1990 NS GP *020 †25

DURHAM, Alfred Ainsley. 4910 VALLEY VIEW BLVD NW 24012 #041-13-1976 L1981 ORS †40

DYE, Kevin Randell. 1201 FRANKLIN RD SW 24016 #028-46-1981 L1986 GE IM *020 †20

DYE, Nancy Elizabeth. 101B MOUNTAIN AVE SW 24016 #028-46-1981 L1986 GS *020 †85

DZIDO, Grace Ann. 1906 BELLEVIEW AVE SE, CARILION ROANOKE MEMORIAL 24014 #305-01-1999 L2004 IM *020 †20 ‡

EAPEN, Saju S. 1505 FRANKLIN RD SW 24016 #495-31-1991 L2001 AI *020 †20,03

EDWARDS, Devin Shane. ■ 24012 #055-02-2004 L2004 GS *012

EDWARDS, John Reynolds. 2017 JEFFERSON ST SW 24014 #051-04-1974 L1978 ORS *040 †40

ELIAS, William Sliman. 1030 S JEFFERSON ST 24016 #047-05-1965 L1973 N SME *020 †20,75

ELIAS, Zev. 1030 S JEFFERSON ST, STE 106 24016 #041-13-1982 L2003 NS TRS *020 †25

ELLSWORTH, Sterling M. 902 S JEFFERSON ST 24016 #028-46-1984 L1998 OBS GYN *020 †30

ELRINGTON, Carol Mark. PO BOX 13367, CARILION ROANOKE MEMORIAL 24033 #566-01-1991 L2002 IM *100 †20

ENGLAND, Frank A, III. 127 MCCLANAHAN ST SW, PC 24014 #027-01-1982 L1983 CD IM *020

EPPLEY, Kurt Christian. 2145 MOUNT PLEASNT BLVD SE, CARILION SE FAMILY MED 24014 #021-05-2004 L2007 FP *012

ERWIN, William Swadley. JEFFERSON AT BELLEVIEW 24033 #051-01-1957 L1957 IM PUD *040 †20

ESCASINAS, Edgar R. JEFFERSON AT BELLEVIEW 24033 #748-11-1976 L1987 NEP IM *020 †20

ESKENAZI, Allen Elliot. 21 HIGHLAND AVE SE, INC 24013 #023-07-1982 L2000 HEM ON *020 †55

ESTRADA SANTIAGO, Wilber. ■ 24016 #264-15-1997 L2004 IM *100 †20

EVANS, Ryan Dale. 2602 FRANKLIN RD SW 24014 #041-14-2000 L2000 NEP *020 †20 ‡

EVETT, John Kirby. ■ 24014 #051-01-1989 L1991 EM *020 †16

FACCIANI, John Marcus. 707 S JEFFERSON ST, VISTAR EYE CTR 24016 #035-01-1999 L2004 PO OPH *035

FAHIM, Fahim. 2720 LIBERTY RD NW, BLUE RIDGE BEHAVORIAL HEAL 24012 #704-16-1988 L2000 CHP *020 †75

FARBER, Steven Lee. 213 MC CLANAHAN ST SW, STE 110 24014 #011-04-1979 L1980 OBG *020 †30

FARLEY, Jimmy Weldon. 375 HERSHBERGER RD 24012 #051-04-1960 L1960 OPH *020

FATHY, Dana B. 1906 BELLEVIEW AVE SE, C/O WENDY HEDRICK, PRACTIC 24014 #048-15-2003 L2007 DR *012

FEAR, Douglass Durston. 707 S JEFFERSON ST 24016 #023-07-1939 L1942 GS GYN *071 †85

FERNANDEZ FALCON, Cristian. ■ 24014 #132-01-1992 L2006 FPG *012 †18

FISHER, Joan Mistretta. 101 ELM AVE SE, CARILION MED CENTER CHILDR 24013 #005-11-1990 L1997 PHO *020 †55

FLOYD, Virginia Taylor. 21 HIGHLAND AVE SE, STE 200 24013 #051-04-1980 L1983 OBG *020 †30

FOGEL, Sandy Lewis. 213 MCCLANAHAN ST SW, STE 404 24014 #028-02-1979 L2007 GS *020 †85

FOSTER, James Edward, II. PO BOX 13367, BELLEVIEW AT JEFFERSON STR 24033 #041-09-1979 L1995 GS *020 †85

FOWLER, Hilton Lawrence. 802 OAKWOOD DR SW 24015 #035-20-1964 L1978 N *030 †75

FOWLKES, Jason Randall. ■ 24015 #045-01-2004 L2004 GS *012

FRALIN, Gordon Wayne. 1314 PETERS CREEK RD NW 24017 #051-04-1962 L1962 GP *020

FRANTZ, Paul T. 2001 CRYSTAL SPRING AVE SW, STE 201 24014 #010-02-1971 L1981 TS GS *020 †85,90

FRASER, John Colin. 1030 S JEFFERSON ST, STE 106 24016 #048-04-1976 L2004 NS *020 †25

FRAZIER, Arthur Benj. 24015 #051-04-1955 L1955 RO NM *071 †80

FRAZIER, John Richard. 2108 BROADWAY AVE SW 24014 #033-05-1962 L1973 CHP P *071 †75

GADDAM, Shravan Kumar Red. 1314 PETERS CREEK RD NW 24017 #495-37-1996 L2005 FP *012

GALLAGHER, John Storey. 1906 BELLEVIEW AVE SE, CARILION COMMUNITY HOSPITA 24014 #011-04-1979 L1983 NPM PD *020 †55

GARCIA, Jorge M. 213 MC CLANAHAN ST SW, STE 110 24014 #011-04-1980 L1981 OBG *020 †30

GARD, Robert Chesson. 21 HIGHLAND AVE SE, INC 24013 #036-01-1999 L2003 PD *020 †55

GARDNER, James Hugh. 1111 S JEFFERSON ST, JEFFERSON INTERNAL 24016 #051-01-1987 L1990 IM *020 ‡

GARST, Arthur H, Jr. 24014 #051-01-1960 L1960 OBG *071 †30

GAY, William Meriwether. 102 HIGHLAND AVE SE # 101 24013 #051-07-1980 L1984 PDC *040 †55

GAYLORD, John Freeman, III. 1315 2ND ST SW, STE 202 24016 #036-05-1986 L1989 IM *020 †20

GEORGE, Jeffrey Edward. 2001 CRYSTAL SPRING AVE SW, STE 201 24014 #055-01-1984 L2007 TS CD *020 †85,90

GEORGE, Sajid Melvin. ■ 24014 #496-21-2002 L2005 IM *012

GILBERT, Carol Marie. 1906 BELLEVIEW AVE SE, DEPARTMENT OF SURGICAL EDU 24014 #005-19-1978 L1982 GS TRS *040 †85

GILBERT, Monica Lynn. 391 HERSHBERGER RD, NORTH ROANOKE MEDICAL ASSO 24012 #051-01-1999 L1999 FPG *020 †18

GOLDMAN, Jill Hillmar. 101 ELM AVE SE 24013 #051-04-1987 L1988 FM *020 †18

GOODE, Jeffrey Edwin. 1906 BELLEVIEW AVE SE, INTERNAL MEDICINE MEDICAL 24014 #654-01-2004 L2004 FM *020 †18

GOODING, James J. 1906 BELLEVIEW AVE SE, JEFFERSON AVE 24014 #025-07-1981 L1988 IM *020 †20

GORDGE, William Noel. 1201 3RD ST SW, PHYSICANS TO CHILDREN 24016 #143-02-1952 L1957 PD *071 †55

GOULD, Natalie Sandra. 2110 CAROLINA AVE SW, 1ST FL 24014 #036-01-1994 L2005 OBG *020 †30

GRAYSON, Richard Jos, Jr. 201 MC CLANAHAN ST SW, ROANOKE EAR NOSE & THROAT 24014 #021-01-1963 L2007 OTO *020 †45

GREENAWALD, Joanne H. 2718 LIBERTY RD NW 24012 #051-01-1987 L1989 *062 †75

GREENAWALD, Mark Henry. 2145 MOUNT PLEASNT BLVD SE, SE ROANOKE FAM MED CTR 24014 #051-01-1987 L1989 FM *040 †18

GREER, William Crockett. 4910 VALLEY VIEW BLVD NW 24012 #051-01-1954 L1954 GP *071

GUILFOYLE, Francis M. 4910 VALLEY VIEW BLVD NW, STE 310 24012 #035-09-1960 L1966 PD *020 †30

GUIRGUIS, Ekram Gaballa. 5720 WILLIAMSON RD, STE 107 24012 #915-02-1974 L2005 FM *020 †18

GUNARATNAM, Magdalena Jey. 1310 3RD ST SW 24016 #539-06-2000 L2005 IM *020 †20

GUSTAFSON, Judy Skidmore. 1906 BELLEVIEW AVE SE, DEPT OF ANESTHESIA 24014 #049-01-1982 L1983 AN *020 †20,05

HACKER, John F. PO BOX 8293 24014 #407-12-1951 L1959 P *072

HAGY, John Albert. 2145 MOUNT PLEASNT BLVD SE 24014 #051-04-1960 L1960 FM *040 †18

HALEY, Harold Bernard. ■ 24014 #028-34-1946 L1973 GS ON *071 †85

HALLMAN, Kenneth Legree. 615 MCDOWELL AVE NW 24016 #045-01-1989 L1991 IM *020

HANABURY, Mark Richard. 707 S JEFFERSON ST, FL 5 24014 #051-04-1978 L1979 OTO FPS *020 †45

HANCOCK, John Dennis. 21 HIGHLAND AVE SE 24013 #027-01-1972 L1978 OBG *020 †30

HANLEY, Christopher Gerar. PO BOX 13367 24033 #759-12-2005 L2006 P *012

HARDEE, Gregory Deleslie. 102 HIGHLAND AVE SE, STE 304 24013 #045-01-1982 L1983 OBG *020 †30

HARDING, John Louis. 2110 CAROLINA AVE SW, THIRD FLOOR 24014 #041-15-2001 L2001 OBG *020

HARLESS, James Matthew. 101 ELM AVE SE 24013 #036-05-1991 L1998 EM *020 †16

HARRINGTON, Daniel Philip. 213 MCCLANAHAN ST SW, STE 310 24014 #055-01-1980 L1982 IM P *020 †20,75

HARRIS, Ronald B. 707 S JEFFERSON ST, VISTA EYE CENTER 24016 #065-01-1953 L1956 OPH *071 †35

HARRIS, Steven G. 1234 FRANKLIN RD SW 24016 #036-07-1984 L1993 PS *020 †85,65

HART, Michael Hugh. 102 HIGHLAND AVE SE # 305 24013 #030-05-1982 L1998 PG *020 †55

HARTER, Basil T. ■ 24014 #023-07-1950 L1957 OBG *071

HARTER, Geoffrey Thos. 1234 FRANKLIN RD SW 24016 #051-01-1984 L1990 OTO HNS *020 †45

HARTLEY, Hetzal. 101 ELM AVE SE, CARILION OCCUPATIONAL MED 24013 #016-11-1982 L1994 OM EM *020 †70

HARTMAN, David Wm. 213 MCCLANAHAN ST SW, LEWIS-GALE CLINIC 24014 #041-13-1976 L1982 P *020 †75

HARTRANFT, Craig Dwight. 707 S JEFFERSON ST 24016 #051-04-1985 L1988 OPH *020 †35

HASSAN, Imran. 1212 3RD ST SW 24016 #704-21-2004 P *012

HAYES, John Shomari Augus. 1212 3RD ST SW 24016 #566-01-1999 IM *012

HAYES, Joseph Michael. 1234 FRANKLIN RD SW 24016 #010-02-1979 L1980 U *075 †95

H'DOUBLER, William Zack. 1234 FRANKLIN RD SW 24016 #047-05-1989 L1990 GS *020 †85

HEATH, Robert Chas. 2013 JEFFERSON ST SW, FL 2 24014 #025-01-1981 L1988 RO IM *020 †20,80

HEERENS, Ann Terese. 101 ELM AVE SE, NICU OFFICE 6TH FLOOR 24013 #024-01-1996 L2002 IM *020 †55

HEFNER, Charles A. 213 MC CLANAHAN ST SW #206 24014 #023-01-1946 L1952 IM CD *071

HELLINGER, Karl H R. 1906 BELLEVIEW AVE SE, 3RD FL 24014 #051-01-1964 L1964 PTH NM *071 †28,50

HENRETTA, Thomas Ross. 1201 FRANKLIN RD SW 24016 #051-04-1962 L1962 GS OS *020 †85

HENRY, Chad Michael. ■ 24017 #665-01-2006 L2006 IM *012

HENRY, Charles Alan. 1017 2ND ST SW 24016 #012-01-1980 L1981 GS *020 †85

HESS, Leonard Wayne. 1906 BELLEVIEW AVE SE, CHAIR OB/GYN, CARILION ROA 24014 #051-04-1977 L1977 OBG MFM *020 †30

HILL, Stephen Laurence. 1125 S JEFFERSON ST 24016 #024-05-1976 L1983 GS VS *020 †85

HINES, John Len. 707 S JEFFERSON ST, VISTAR EYE CENTER 24016 #038-40-1985 L1989 OPH *020 †35

HIPPENSTEEL, Kirk Edward. 1111 S JEFFERSON ST, STE A 24016 #017-20-1971 L1979 PUD IM *020 †20

HOFFORD, Roger Allan. 1314 PETERS CREEK RD NW 24017 #051-01-1979 L1981 FM *040 †18

HOLLINGSWORTH, John H. JEFFERSON AT BELLEVIEW 24033 #012-05-1962 L1967 CD IM *071 †20

HUBBARD, Jennifer Owen. 1212 3RD ST SW 24016 #051-01-2001 L2001 OPH *100

HUGHES, Douglas Mark. 1722 JEFFERSON ST SE, ASSOCIATES 24014 #041-14-1990 L1995 HMP PTH *020 †50

HULL, George H. JEFFERSON AT BELLEVIEW 24033 #051-04-1952 L1966 P PYA *071 †75

HULL, Jane Renee. 1906 BELLEVIEW AVE SE, CARILION CLINIC CHILDREN'S 24014 #036-05-1993 L1996 PD *020 †55

HUMPHRIES, Marion K, III. PO BOX 28008 24014 #051-01-1966 L1966 OPH *071 †35

HUMPHRIES, Wm Howell, Jr. 2602 FRANKLIN RD SW, VALLEY NEPHROLOGY 24014 #012-01-1975 L1977 GP EM *072 †16

HURT, Alvin Judson. ■ 24014 #051-01-1954 L1954 OBG *071 †30

HUTCHESON, Jack Robert, Jr. 2013 JEFFERSON ST SW, FL 2 24014 #045-01-1973 L1979 ON HEM *071 †20

HYDE, Kelly Vaughan. ■ 24015 #048-14-2006 L2006 GS *012

IGBOKIDI, Oyidie. 127 MCCLANAHAN ST SW, PC 24014 #690-07-1994 L2006 CD *100 †20

IMAM, Khursheed. 2923 FRANKLIN RD SW 24014 #008-01-1994 L1995 DR *020 †80

IMAM, Naiyer. 2923 FRANKLIN RD SW, CENTER FOR ADVANCED IMAGIN 24014 #043-01-1990 L1998 RNR *020 †80

INHORN, Lowell Frank. 2013 JEFFERSON ST SW, CANCER CENTER OF S.W. VIRG 24014 #023-07-1982 L1988 ON HEM *020 †20

INOUYE, Alice Masami. 2145 MOUNT PLEASNT BLVD SE, SE ROANOKE FAM MED CTR 24014 #024-07-1978 L1990 FM *020 †18

IRVIN, Robert Wheary, Jr. 102 HIGHLAND AVE SE # 436, CARILION CTR FOR WOMEN & 24013 #051-04-1948 L1948 OBG *071 †30

JAEGER, Anne. 1111 S JEFFERSON ST, JEFFERSON INTERNAL 24016 #422-01-1989 L1994 IM IMG *020

JAMISON, Suzanna Connick. ■ 24014 #021-05-2004 L2004 MP *012

JANI, Kunal Pankaj. ■ 24014 #026-08-2008 *012

■ = Address Information Privacy Protected

JEFFERSON, Wm Emmett, III. 101 ELM AVE SE, ASSOCIATES 24013 #047-06-1986 L1988 PTH PCP *020 †50

JEREMIAH, Michael Patrick. 1314 PETERS CREEK RD NW, ROANOKE/SALEM 24017 #011-03-1990 L1995 FM *020 †18

JEREZ-MARTE, Jasmin Maria. 1603 FRANKLIN RD SW 24016 #308-04-1999 L2002 IM *020 †20

JIMENEZ, Consuelo T. ■ 24016 #748-01-1937 L1976 GP PD *020

JOFKO, John. JEFFERSON AT BELLEVIEW 24033 #021-01-1945 L1954 IM GP *071 †20

JOHNSON, Bruce Everett. 1906 BELLEVIEW AVE SE, DEPT OF MEDICINE 24014 #005-14-1976 L2008 IM IMG *040 †20 ‡

JOHNSON, Cynda Ann. 1906 BELLEVIEW AVE SE, VA TECH & CARILION MED SCH 24014 #005-14-1977 L2008 FM *030 †18

JOHNSON, David Hays. 101 ELM AVE SE 24013 #024-05-1999 L1999 FM *020 †18

JOHNSON, Earl Robt. 2006 WINDSOR AVE SW 24015 #051-01-1954 L1954 IM *071

JOHNSON, Harry I, Jr. 1315 2ND ST SW STE 101 24016 #051-04-1953 L1953 IM *071

JOHNSON, Robert Riley. 2001 CRYSTAL SPRING AVE SW 24014 #041-12-1977 L1987 RHU IM *071

JUVVA, Sowjanya. CARILION ROANOKE MEM HOSP, DEPT INT MED 24033 #495-11-2002 L2005 IM *012

KAGEY, David Andrew. 102 HIGHLAND AVE SE # 105 24013 #051-04-1998 L1998 U *020 †95

KAGEY, William Jos. 101 ELM AVE SE 24013 #051-01-1967 L1967 PD *020 †55

KAUFMAN, John Pearse. 2001 CRYSTAL SPRING AVE SW, STE 204 24014 #051-01-1970 L1970 D *020 †15 ‡

KAUSHAL, Ashutosh. 2001 CRYSTAL SPRING AVE SW, CARILION INTERNAL 24014 #495-29-1987 L1994 IM *020 †20

KAYROUZ, Thomas Martin. 102 HIGHLAND AVE SE, STE 435 24013 #020-02-1984 L1988 PD CCM *020 †55

KEELEY, Christopher C. 213 MCCLANAHAN ST SW, CARILION OB/GYN 24014 #051-01-1995 L1995 OBG *020 †30

KEELEY, Robert Carroll. 1111A S JEFFERSON ST 24016 #051-01-1980 L1985 PUD IM *020 †20

KEELEY, Robert Louis A. 1234 FRANKLIN RD SW 24016 #051-01-1944 L1944 GS TS *071 †85,90

KEENE, Carol Lynn Mullins. 21 HIGHLAND AVE SE, STE 200 24013 #051-04-1981 L1990 OBG MFM *020 †19,30

KEES, Donald W. 101 ELM AVE SE, 4TH FL 24013 #055-01-1985 L1988 PD *020 †55

KEILMAN, David Allen. 4910 VALLEY VIEW BLVD NW 24012 #041-12-1977 L1979 FM OBG *020 †18

KENNEDY, Stephen Smith. 2013 JEFFERSON ST SW, SECOND FLOOR 24014 #051-01-1973 L1981 ON HEM *071 †20

KENNETH, Arline Maiella. ■ 24014 #308-13-2003 L2005 MP *012

KERKERING, Thomas Michael. 2001 CRYSTAL SPRING AVE SW, CRYSTAL SPRING MEDICAL OFF 24014 #051-04-1974 L1975 ID *020 †20

KEYS, David Nilson. 707 S JEFFERSON ST, FL 5 24016 #036-07-1964 L1974 OTO *020 †45

KHACHIYANTS, Nina. 2017 JEFFERSON ST SW, ATTN: TOM MADDY 24014 #913-21-1980 L2006 P *012

KHAN, Kashan Raza. 2118 ROSALIND AVE SW 24014 #704-16-2000 L2007 FPG *012

KIM, Ae-Sik. 5720 WILLIAMSON RD, STE 107 24012 #583-03-1974 L1998 PM *020 †60

KIM, Yuhee. 1212 3RD ST SW 24016 #583-08-1986 L2006 FP *012

KING, Merritt Henry. 102 HIGHLAND AVE SE 24013 #665-01-2005 L2005 OBG *012

KINSLER, David Asbury. 707 S JEFFERSON ST 24016 #051-01-1983 L1987 OPH *020 †35

KISTNER, James Robt. 101 ELM AVE SE 24013 #016-43-1973 L1977 AN *020 †05

KLAWONN, Natalie Kate. 1906 BELLEVIEW AVE SE, CARILION ROANOKE MEMORIAL 24014 #665-01-2003 L2003 IM *100 †20

KLEPZIG, Dale Robert. ■ 24015 #048-14-2004 L2004 GS *012

KNOPF, Reuben De Loach. JEFFERSON AT BELLEVIEW 24033 #045-01-1954 L1960 DR *071 †80

KNOX, Cecil B, III. 1130 2ND ST SW, DICINE & REHAB 24016 #048-02-1983 L1988 PM PD *020 †65,65

KOCH, Michael Hartung. 1030 S JEFFERSON ST, STE 200 24016 #035-45-1975 L1981 END IM *020 †20

KOLMSTETTER, Siegfried J. ■ 24017 #407-04-1949 L1963 IM *071

KUEHL, Damon Ross. 1906 BELLEVIEW AVE SE 24014 #026-04-2000 L2006 GPM *100 †16

KUEHL, Karen Nolan. 1906 BELLEVIEW AVE SE 24014 #007-02-1999 L2006 EM *020 †16

KUPFNER, John G. PO BOX 13367 24033 #035-06-2005 L2005 P *012

LADENIKA, Adetokunbo Alex. PO BOX 13367, CARILION HLTH SYSTEM 24033 #305-01-2005 L2006 P *100

LAHOUD, Maha. 1314 PETERS CREEK RD NW 24017 #654-01-2000 L2002 P *012

LAMBERT, Brent Rogers. 451 KIMBALL AVE NE 24016 #051-07-1980 L1983 FM EM *062 †18

LAMPROS, Jim Nicholas. 310 1ST ST SW STE 402 24011 #051-04-1969 L1969 D *071

LANIER, Andrew Stephens. 101 ELM AVE SE 24013 #028-02-1946 L1973 PHP *071

LANTZ, Jeri Lynn. 2001 CRYSTAL SPRING AVE SW, STE 203 24014 #018-03-1993 L2001 MPD PD *020 †20,55

LARA-TORRE, Eduardo. 102 HIGHLAND AVE SE, STE 303 24013 #649-52-1996 L2008 OBG OS *020 †30

LEATHERLAND, Mary D. 101 ELM AVE SE, CARILION EMERG SVC INC 24013 #023-01-1997 L2007 FM *020 †18

LEIVY, Susan Roberts. 1906 BELLEVIEW AVE SE 24016 #036-01-1987 L1993 DR *020 †80

LE PETER, Alan Jos. 1138 2ND ST SW 24016 #010-02-1963 L1967 OPH *020 †35

LEWIS, Van Laney. 1906 BELLEVIEW AVE SE 24014 #027-01-1979 L1981 RNR VIR *020 †80

LI, Janet. 1030 S JEFFERSON ST, STE 109 24016 #067-01-1997 L2004 OBG *020

LLAVORE, Jo-Anne Adviento. ■ 24014 #748-01-2004 L2007 FP *012

LOCKHART, Estes Sage. 1212 3RD ST SW, CARILION HEALTH SYSTEM 24016 #422-01-2002 L2003 P *012

LOFRANCO, Eduardo Kiamco. 101 ELM AVE SE, PO12946 24013 #748-09-1971 L1977 GS *020

LOFTIN, Charles Ivey, III. 101 ELM AVE SE 24013 #036-01-1963 L1969 IM ON *020

LONG, Bruce A. 101 ELM AVE SE 24013 #001-02-1988 L1993 GS *020 †85

LOTHES, Christopher M. BELLVIEW & JEFFERSON STS, ROANOKE MEM HOSP/EMER DPT 24014 #055-01-1974 L1977 EM FM *020 †18,16

LOWE, Luther Burton. 3048 BRAMBLETON AVE SW 24015 #051-04-1934 L1934 FM D *071 †18

LUCAS, Robert Scott. 5501 WILLIAMSON RD 24012 #051-01-1986 L1989 FM *020 †18

LUCKTONG, Tananchai A. 213 MCCLANAHAN ST SW, STE 404 24014 #051-01-1995 L2002 GS *020 †85

LUNEAU, Scott Michael. ■ 24015 #473-04-2005 L2006 IM *012

LUNT, Tricia A. 1212 3RD ST SW 24016 #305-01-2004 L2004 OBG *012

LUSTIG, Michael Bruce. ■ 24014 #016-42-1985 L1994 IM *030 †16

LYSTASH, John Chester. 127 MCCLANAHAN ST SW, PC 24014 #041-02-1982 L1985 CD IM *020 †20

MADSEN, Keith Peter. ■ 24015 #051-04-2008 *012

MALLIDI, Padmaja V. 2013 JEFFERSON ST SW, FL 2 24014 #495-50-1995 L2003 HO *020 †20 ‡

MALPASS, Michael Alan. 1315 2ND ST SW, STE 101 24016 #047-05-1978 L1985 IM *020 †20

MANESH, Supreet Singh. 1212 3RD ST SW 24016 #495-29-2000 L2005 IM *012

MANETTA, Evelyn Walker. 101 ELM AVE SE 24013 #055-01-1979 L1982 EM *020 †16

MAO, Vivian Hweiwen. 102 HIGHLAND AVE SE, CARILION CLINIC 24013 #041-02-1995 L2000 OTO *020 †45

MARTE GRAU, Andres Carlos. 1212 3RD ST SW 24016 #308-05-1998 L2002 IM *100 †20

MARTIN, Elizabeth Rice. 21 HIGHLAND AVE SE, STE 200 24013 #051-04-1998 L1998 OBG *020 †30

MARTIN, John Albert. JEFFERSON AT BELLEVIEW 24033 #041-02-1944 L1952 DR *071 †80

MATHEWS, Jose. 1212 3RD ST SW, CARILION HEALTH SYSTEM 24016 #495-47-1982 P *012

MATHIS, John Milligan. 2923 FRANKLIN RD SW 24014 #047-05-1976 L1981 DR RNR *020 †80

MATOS, Luis Angel. 1505 FRANKLIN RD SW 24016 #042-01-1976 L1997 AI PDA *020 †55,03

MATTHEWS, Fletcher Garret. 2602 FRANKLIN RD SW 24014 #051-04-1995 L1998 NEP *020 †20

MAY, Terrence Patrick. 127 MCCLANAHAN ST SW, PC 24014 #033-06-1987 L1995 CD *020 †20

MAYBERRY, Alton Ray. 2314 OAK HILL LANE 24015 #020-02-1956 L1985 P *071 †75

MAYES, Daniel Charles. ■ 24014 #047-05-1986 L1987 DMP *100 †50

MAYSON, Preston B, Jr. ■ 24014 #010-01-1962 L1968 R *071 †80

MC ALLISTER, Mark S. ■ 24014 #028-46-1994 L2006 GS *012

MC BRIDE, Dane Carlos. 1505 FRANKLIN RD SW 24016 #025-07-1976 L1985 AI PD *020 †55,03

MCBRIDE, Mark Allen. 21 HIGHLAND AVE SE, INC 24013 #051-07-1991 L1994 PD *020 †55

MC CAUSLAND, Alexander. 1505 FRANKLIN RD SW 24016 #051-01-1937 L1937 A *071 †03

MC CUIN, Elizabeth Smith. 902 S JEFFERSON ST 24016 #036-01-1985 L1986 OBG *040 †30

MC KERNAN, Timothy B. 2617 WYCLIFFE AVE SW 24014 #025-07-1994 L1999 EM *020 †16

MC LUCKIE, Alan Earley. 127 MCCLANAHAN ST SW, PC 24014 #023-12-1987 L2002 CD IM *020 †20

MECK, Mandy Marie. 101 ELM AVE SE 5TH FL, PEDIATRIC HEMATOLOGY/ONCOL 24013 #051-07-1994 L2005 PHO *020 †20

MEHRA, Abhishek. PO BOX 13367 24033 #495-37-2001 L2005 P *012

MEYERS, Roy Lee, III. 202 DUKE OF GLOUCSTR ST SW 24014 #023-01-1987 L1995 GE *020 †20

MIERISCH, Cay Michael. 2017 JEFFERSON ST SW, CARILION ORTHOPAEDIC SURGE 24014 #409-36-1994 L1998 HS *100 †40

MIHALIK, Jennifer Erin. ■ 24012 #051-07-2006 L2007 GS *012

MILLER, Joelle De Vore. 102 HIGHLAND AVE SE, STE 404 24013 #011-03-1983 L1996 PDC PD *020 †55

MILLER, Karen Sue. 120 W KIRK AVE 24011 #025-01-1982 L1986 IM *020 †20

MINICHAN, David Parrish. 1234 FRANKLIN RD SW 24016 #051-01-1955 L1955 GS CRS *071 †85

MISICKO, Nancy Jo. 2145 MOUNT PLEASNT BLVD SE, BLVD., SE 24014 #041-14-1996 L2001 FM *020 †18

MITCHELL, William Craig. 1315 2ND ST SW, INTERNAL MEDICINE OF 24016 #036-05-1987 L1988 IM *020 †20

MONAHAN, Lawrence Keith. 1111 S JEFFERSON ST, JEFFERSON INTERNAL 24016 #019-02-1968 L1974 IM *020 ‡

MOORE, Barbara Carol. 1240 3RD ST SW, BRADLEY FREE CLINIC 24016 #020-12-1991 L1995 OBG *020 †30

MOORE, Christopher Benton. ■ 24013 #017-20-2006 L2007 GS *012

MOOSE, Susan C. 2001 CRYSTAL SPRING AVE SW, STE 203 24014 #020-75-2005, ▲ L2005 IM *012

MORGAN, John Edward. 202 DUKE OF GLOUCSTR ST SW 24014 #051-01-1970 L1970 GE IM *020 †20

MORGAN-BEDASSE, Andrea Va. ■ 24014 #566-01-2002 L2007 IM *012

MORRIS, James Culvin, III. 2233 SANFORD AVE SW 24014 #036-07-1962 L1970 PS *071 †85,65

MORTLOCK, David Henry. ■ 24014 #104-01-2006 L2007 FP *012

MOUNTCASTLE, Robert B, Jr. 1310 3RD ST SW 24016 #051-04-1979 L1984 IM END *020 †20

MUELENAER, Andre A, Jr. 1 RIVERSIDE CIR, STE 101 24016 #051-07-1979 L1991 PD PDP *062 †55

MULINDA, James. 1030 S JEFFERSON ST, STE 200 24016 #905-01-1988 L2005 END *020 †20

MUNSON, Keith Darrel. 1234 FRANKLIN RD SW 24016 #048-12-1981 L1999 CRS GS *020 †10,85

MURCHISON, Ross W. 1906 BELLEVIEW AVE SE, INTERNAL MED EDUCATION 24014 #048-14-2000 L2007 IM *020 †20

MUSGRAVE, Donna L. 21 HIGHLAND AVE SE, STE 200 24013 #051-01-1982 L1990 GYN IM *020 †30

MUTHUKRISHNAN, Vijai Brin. 1212 3RD ST SW 24016 #665-01-2007 GS *012

NATHAN, Geeta Viswa. PO BOX 13367, CARILION ROANOKE MEM HOSP 24033 #495-37-2004 L2008 P *012

NDEM, Stella Imo. 213 MCCLANAHAN ST SW, STE 310 24014 #690-10-1991 L1999 CHP *020 †75

NELSON, Kelly Kristine. 21 HIGHLAND AVE SE, INC 24013 #041-02-1997 L2005 PD *020 †55

NEWMAN, Brian Keith. 101 ELM AVE SE, ASSOCIATES 24013 #051-01-1993 L1993 PCP *020 †50

NEWTON, Richard Milton. 2129 ROSALIND AVE SW 24014 #051-04-1954 L1954 CD IM *020 †20

NGUYEN, Son Hoang. ■ 24014 #422-01-2005 L2006 IM *012

NOBLETT, Russell Don. 1310 3RD ST SW 24016 #048-12-1989 L1995 IM *020 †20

NOLAN, Donald Barry. 2601 FRANKLIN RD SW 24014 #051-01-1967 L1967 N *071 †75 ‡

O'BRIEN, Robert Francis. 2923 FRANKLIN RD SW 24014 #035-48-1989 L1994 DR *020 †80

OFFERMANN, Paul V, Jr. ■ 24014 #010-02-1985 L1986 EM *020 †16

OLAZAGASTI-GONZALEZ, Juan. 102 HIGHLAND AVE SE, STE 305 24013 #042-01-1992 L2001 R AR *020 †80

OLIPHANT, Beverly Ann. ■ 24012 #010-01-1969 L1971 IM GE *071 †20

OLSEN, Robin L. ■ 24017 #051-04-2005 L2005 FP *012

OMOTADE, Aderonke O. PO BOX 13367 24033 #041-12-2003 L2003 MP *012

PAGE, Paul Fielding. JEFFERSON AT BELLEVIEW 24033 #025-12-1981 L1985 IM *020 †20

PAREEK, Archana. 1906 BELLEVIEW AVE SE 24014 #496-02-2001 L2006 IM *100 †20

PASLEY, Faith R. 1231 S JEFFERSON ST, LEWIS GALE PHYSICIANS, LLC 24016 #051-04-1972 L1974 FM *040 †18

PASLEY, William Watson. 1231 S JEFFERSON ST 24016 #051-01-1975 L1976 GYN *020 †30

PASTERNAK, Steven Jerome. 410 26TH ST SW 24017 #017-20-1983 L1988 EM *020 †16

PATEL, Sona Manilal. 1906 BELLEVIEW AVE SE, ATTN: TAMMY HAGER 24014 #048-16-2003 L2006 END *012 †20

PATRICK, Michael Kevin. 1603 FRANKLIN RD SW 24016 #056-06-1996 L1999 **IM** *020 †20

PATTON, Larry Wayne. 4910 VALLEY VIEW BLVD NW 24012 #010-01-1984 L1987 **D** *020 †15

PAYNE, Jason Joseph. ■ 24014 #566-01-2004 L2007 **IM** *012

PEARLMAN, William Glenn. 1906 BELLEVIEW AVE SE, DEPT OF EMERGENCY MED. - O 24014 #036-08-1991 L1992 **FM** *020 †18

PEASE, Clinton Scott. ■ 24014 #051-01-2007 L2007 **TY** *012

PENDLETON, John W. 2001 CRYSTAL SPRING AVE SW 24014 #051-01-1977 L1981 **IM RHU**

PERALTA, Manuel Tee, Jr. 1314 PETERS CREEK RD NW, FAM PRAC RES PRG 24017 #748-10-1999 L2004 **FM** *020 †18

PEREGRINO, Manuel Angel. 101 ELM AVE SE 24013 #024-01-1991 L2004 **NPM PD** *020 †55

PETERSON, Charles H, Jr. 1111 S JEFFERSON ST, JEFFERSON INTERNAL 24016 #051-01-1956 L1956 **IM** *071

PHILLIPS, Stephen Gilmer. 127 MCCLANAHAN ST SW, PC 24014 #051-04-2000 L2000 **CD** *100 †20

PHILP, Allan Swayze. 1906 BELLEVIEW AVE SE 24014 #047-05-1995 L2007 **CCS** †85

PIERCE, Douglas Edward. 1201 3RD ST SW, PHYSICANS TO CHILDREN 24016 #047-06-1955 L1956 **PD** *071 †55

PILE, Christopher Wade. 1906 BELLEVIEW AVE SE 24014 #051-07-1996 L1996 **FM** *020 †18

PITTMAN, Jackson Lee. 1906 BELLEVIEW AVE SE, 3RD FL 24014 #036-05-1970 L1978 **PTH** *071 †50

POOLEY, Robert Earl. JEFFERSON AT BELLEVIEW 24033 #035-08-1960 L1967 **PTH** *071 †50

POWLEDGE, Darrell F. 512 MCDOWELL AVE NE, B 24016 #011-03-1974 L1976 **OM PHP** *020 †18,70

PRICE, William Griffin. 101 ELM AVE SE, ASSOCIATES 24013 #036-01-1986 L1990 **PTH** *020 †50

PUENTE-ESPEL, Jordi. 1212 3RD ST SW 24016 #649-01-2006 **GS** *012

PUTNAM, Adin T, II. 1906 BELLEVIEW AVE SE, DEPARTMENT OF SURGERY 24014 #023-01-1986 L2007 **GS** *020 †85

PUYANA, Richard B. 1906 BELLEVIEW AVE SE, DEPT OF ANESTHESIA 24014 #649-27-1985 L1993 **AN IM** *020 †05

RACE, Donald John. 707 S JEFFERSON ST, STE 102 24016 #041-12-1970 L1976 **OPH** *020 †35

RAHMAN, Sabreen Rubaida. 1212 3RD ST SW, CARILION HLTH SYS 24016 #306-02-2005 L2007 **P** *012

RAMACHANDRAN, K. 2001 CRYSTAL SPRING AVE SW, STE 300 24014 #495-04-1982 L1992 **CD** *020 †20

RANDOLPH, John Carlton. ■ 24014 #011-02-2007 L2007 **TY** *012

RANE, Santosh Gopal. 1908 BELLEVIEW AVE SE, MEDICAL EDUCATION-INTERNAL 24014 #495-96-1999 L2006 **IM** *020 †20

RE MINE, Stephen Gordon. 213 MCCLANAHAN ST SW, STE 404 24014 #026-04-1975 L2005 **GS SO** †85

RESK, Joan M. 5303 CLEARBROOK VILLAGE LN 24014 #016-76-1970, ▲ L1998 **GP OMM** *071

RICE, James Davies. ■ 24015 #038-40-1968 L1973 **R** *071 †80

RICHARDS, Ken Renard. 1234 FRANKLIN RD SW 24016 #023-01-1996 L2002 **GS** *020 †85

RIDOUT, Steven Burke. 4615 HUNTRIDGE RD 24012 #051-01-1993 L1994 **FM** *020 †18

ROBERTS, Christena Lynn. ■ 24012 #011-04-2000 L2007 **FOP** *020

ROGERS, Ethan Samuel. ■ 24011 #023-01-2007 L2007 **GS** *012

ROLLE, Anishka Shonique. ■ 24014 #894-01-2003 L2006 **IM** *012

ROLLER, Gerald Wm. JEFFERSON AT BELLEVIEW 24033 #051-04-1956 L1956 **IM RHU** *071 †20

ROSENOFF, Stephen Howard. 2013 JEFFERSON ST SW, FL 2 24014 #024-07-1969 L1974 **ON HEM** *020 †20

ROSSINI, Juan P. 1212 3RD ST SW, CARILION HLTH SYS 24016 #048-14-2006 L2007 **GS** *012

ROWE, Joseph Franklin, III. 2001 CRYSTAL SPRING AVE SW 24014 #051-04-1994 L2002 **TS** *020 †85,90

ROY, Soumen. 1212 3RD ST SW 24016 #495-73-2003 L2005 **FP** *012

RUDE, Robert Emerson. 127 MCCLANAHAN ST SW, STE 300 24014 #051-04-1974 L1975 **CD IM** *071 †20

RUTH, Gerald Jay. 101 ELM AVE SE 24013 #051-04-1962 L1962 **OBG** *071 †30

SAEED, Manzar. PO BOX 13367, ROANOKE MEM HOSP 24033 #704-01-1987 **IM** *100

SALAMA, Adel M. 1111 S JEFFERSON ST, JEFFERSON INTERNAL 24016 #915-03-1976 L1995 **IM** *020 †20

SALAMI, Oludamilola Adeni. 1212 3RD ST SW, CARILION HEALTH SYSTEM 24016 #690-22-2000 L2004 **P** *012

SAPRA, Mamta. 2118 ROSALIND AVE SW, HEALTHY AGING 24014 #496-07-2000 L2007 **PYG** *012

SARBIN, Adam Avram. 21 HIGHLAND AVE SE, INC 24013 #051-04-1991 L1993 **PD** *020 †55

SAVAGE, Rodney Wells. 127 MCCLANAHAN ST SW, STE 300 24014 #016-06-1978 L1981 **CD IM** *020 †20

SAVCHUK, Yuriy. PO BOX 13367, CARILION ROANOKE MEMORIAL 24033 #913-57-1992 *100

SCHEIDERER, David Jacob. 1328 2ND ST SW 24016 #038-40-1985 L1986 **P** *020 †75

SCHERTZ, Gerald Lee. 2013 JEFFERSON ST SW, 2ND FL 24014 #016-02-1971 L1977 **ON IM** *020 †20

SCHLEUPNER, Mark A. 615 MCDOWELL AVE NW, CARILION INT MED NW 24016 #051-01-1998 L1998 **IM** *020 †20

SCHMEDTJE, John F, Jr. 201 MCCLANAHAN ST SW, ROANOKE HEART INSTITUTE 24014 #016-06-1981 L1988 **CD IM** *020 †20

SCHMIDT, Tarin Anne. 2145 MOUNT PLEASNT BLVD SE, SOUTHEAST FAMILY PRACTICE 24014 #016-45-1995 L1995 **FM** *020 †18

SCHROYER, Daniel Christop. ■ 24016 #025-07-2007 L2007 **IM** *012

SCRIBNER, Dennis Ronald. 2110 CAROLINA AVE SW, 1ST FL 24014 #008-02-1993 L2004 **GO** *020 †30

SCRUGGS, Hugh Jarrard. 2013 JEFFERSON ST SW 24014 #047-06-1969 L1972 **RO** *020 †80

SEAMON, Robert H. 1603 FRANKLIN RD SW 24016 #023-01-1977 L1987 **IM** *020 †20

SEIBERT, Donald George. 202 DUKE OF GLOUCSTR ST SW 24014 #010-01-1977 L2001 **GE IM** *020 †20

SHAH, Narendra Champaklal. 101 ELM AVE SE 24014 #495-20-1967 L1975 **P** *020 †20

SHAHANE, Shirish S. 2728 COLONIAL AVE SW, THE CENTER FOR BARIATRIC M 24015 #495-20-1969 L1984 **IM** *075

SHARMA, Smriti Ishu. 24014 #160-12-2002 L2006 **IM** *012

SHARP, Brett Wallace. 213 MCCLANAHAN ST SW STE 2 24014 #049-01-1989 L2006 **PD P** *020 †75,55

SHARPE, Donna Estelle. 102 HIGHLAND AVE SE 24013 #035-47-1993 L2000 **OTO** *020 †45

SHAYLOR, Sara Daniel. 1906 BELLEVIEW AVE SE 24014 #051-04-2004 L2004 **DR** *012

SHEIKH, Saadia Ajmal. 1212 3RD ST SW, CARILION HEALTH SYSTEM 24016 #704-21-1999 L2004 **P** *012

SHELTON, John. 2729 AVENEL AVE SW 24015 #051-04-1980 L1981 **GP** *062

SHERMAN, James Merrill, Jr. 102 HIGHLAND AVE SE # 203, PULMONARY MEDICINE 24013 #011-04-1975 L2004 **PD PDP** *020 †55

SHINER, Philip Thompson. 127 MCCLANAHAN ST SW, PC 24014 #036-07-1964 L1971 **CD** *020 †20

SHOJAEE, Samira. ■ 24014 #286-03-2003 L2006 **IM** *012

SHORTRIDGE, Charles M. 707 S JEFFERSON ST 24016 #051-01-1960 L1960 **OPH** *071 †35

SHULER, Thomas Edwin. JEFFERSON AT BELLEVIEW, MED ED ORTHO 24033 #045-04-1986 L1994 **ORS OTR** *020 †40

SIMONDS, Gary Robt. 1030 S JEFFERSON ST, STE 106 24016 #033-06-1984 L2003 **NS** *020 †25

SINGER, Lewis Jay. 306 MCCLANAHAN ST SW 24014 #016-42-1973 L1982 **OPH** *020 †55,35

SLACKMAN, Robert Louis. 1030 S JEFFERSON ST, STE 109 24016 #005-18-1980 L1995 **REN OBG** *020 †30

SLATE, Garrick James. 102 HIGHLAND AVE SE, STE 303 24013 #473-04-2001 L2004 **OBG** *012

SLAUGHTER, Arthur Robt. ■ 24015 #051-01-1972 L1972 **FM** *071 †18

SLEMP, Andrew Alfred, Jr. 1101 1ST ST SW 24016 #047-06-1967 L1971 **GS** *020 †85

SLOCUM, Christopher Lee. ■ 24014 #038-40-2000 L2007 **NPM** *020 †55 ‡

SLOWIKOWSKI, Jacek. 2001 CRYSTAL SPRING AVE SW, STE 300 24014 #759-10-1981 L1992 **CD NM** *020 †20

SMITH, Elton Travis, Jr. 101 ELM AVE SE, ASSOCIATES 24013 #036-01-1991 L1998 **PTH HMP** *020 †50

SMITH, Jean Alice. 2001 CRYSTAL SPRING AVE SW, STE 301 24014 #051-04-1979 L2000 **IM ID** *020 †20

SMITH, Jemille. ■ 24016 #051-07-2006 L2007 **FP** *012

SMITH, Joseph Froelich. 611 MCDOWELL AVE NW, THE BURRELL CENTER 24016 #051-01-1987 L1998 **P** *020 †75

SMITH, Steven Ray. 1906 BELLEVIEW AVE SE 24014 #020-12-1998 L1998 **OBG** *020 †30

SNEAD, James Given. ■ 24014 #051-01-1944 L1944 **R** *071 †80

SOHI, Sukhpreit Kaur. 1212 3RD ST SW, CARILIOM HEALTH SYSTEM 24016 #495-37-2001 L2004 **P** *012

SPEAKER, Marcus Leon. 2145 MOUNT PLEASNT BLVD SE 24014 #055-01-2001 L2001 **FM** *020 †55

SPRUILL, William Austin. 21 HIGHLAND AVE SE, INC 24013 #036-08-1987 L1990 **PD** *020 †55

STACEY, Joanna Helms. 902 S JEFFERSON ST 24016 #048-13-2000 L2000 **OBG** *040 †30

STADNYK, John Michael. ■ 24014 #051-07-1999 L2000 **EM** *020 †16

STARR, John Walter. 127 MCCLANAHAN ST SW, PC 24014 #036-07-1972 L1977 **CD IM** *020 †20

ST CLAIR, Joseph. 5505 WILLIAMSON RD 24012 #396-26-1971 *100

STEINWEG, Donald Lee. 2001 CRYSTAL SPRING AVE SW, CARILION INTERNAL 24014 #023-01-1978 L2000 **IM** *020 †20

STEWART, Paul Jonathan. 1906 BELLEVIEW AVE SE 24014 #048-04-2005 L2005 *100

STOCKSTILL, Kurt Robt. 21 HIGHLAND AVE SE STE 200 24013 #051-04-1989 L1990 **OBG** *020 †30

STONE, Chandra Renae. ■ 24015 #005-12-2004 L2004 **IM** *100

STRAIN, Brian Mc Cullough. 2001 CRYSTAL SPRING AVE SW, STE 201 24014 #036-05-1982 L1987 **TS CD** *074 †85,90

STRELOW, Scott Andrew. 707 S JEFFERSON ST 24016 #047-05-1986 L1995 **OPH** *020 †35

SUBUHI, Tabassum. 1212 3RD ST SW 24016 #704-02-1992 L2003 **FM** *020 †18

SWANK, Gary Paul. 2001 CRYSTAL SPRING AVE SW, STE 300 24014 #422-01-1997 L2004 **IM** *020 †20

SWEET, Jon Michael. 2001 CRYSTAL SPRING AVE SW, STE 203 24014 #051-01-1993 L1995 **IM** *020 †20

SWEET, Mary Gayle. 1314 PETERS CREEK RD NW 24017 #051-01-1993 L2000 **FM** *040 †18

SWISHER, Eric David. 21 HIGHLAND AVE SE, STE 200 24014 #051-04-1993 L1995 **OBG** *020 †30

SZEGO, Ellen Zeichner. 101 ELM AVE SE, CARILION ROANOKE COMM. HOS 24013 #396-04-1974 L1992 **NPM PD** *020 †55

SZILAGYI, Michael S. 101 ELM AVE SE 24013 #654-01-1998 L1998 **FM** *020

TAMEZ, Joseph Regin. 102 HIGHLAND AVE SE, STE 203 24013 #048-14-1995 L2001 **PDP** *020 †55

TEAGUE, Nelson Stone. 1234 FRANKLIN RD SW 24016 #036-05-1962 L1970 **U** *071 †95

TEATERS, Chas Allen, Jr. 101 ELM AVE SE 24013 #051-04-1979 L1980 **EM GP** *020 †16

THOMAS, Barton Allan. 1118 1ST ST SW 24016 #035-05-1986 L1994 **PS OS** *020 †85,65

THOMAS, Linda Ann. PO BOX 13367, CARILION ROANOKE MEMORIAL 24033 #894-01-2001 L2002 **RHU** *020 †20

THOMPSON, James Edward. 2145 MOUNT PLEASNT BLVD SE, CARILION FAMILY MEDICINE 24014 #051-01-1993 L1994 **FM** *040 †18

TIMMERMANN, Paul C. 1215 3RD ST SW, STE 300 24016 #038-06-1986 L1988 **D** *020 †15 ‡

TIMS, Joseph Stuart. ■ 24014 #051-01-2007 L2007 **TY** *012

TODD, Jeffrey Scott. 127 MCCLANAHAN ST SW, PC 24014 #051-04-1988 L1993 **CD** *020 †20

TOEVS, Christine Carter. 1906 BELLEVIEW AVE SE, CARILION ROANOKE MEMORIAL 24014 #036-08-1992 L1994 **CCS** *020 †85

TORRE, Glenn Michael. 1906 BELLEVIEW AVE SE, DEPT OF ANESTHESIA 24014 #051-07-1995 L1995 **AN** *020 †05

TRAYNHAM, John Edward, III. ■ 24014 #051-01-1966 L1966 **ORS** *020 †40

TRINKLE, David Ball. 2118 ROSALIND AVE SW, AGING 24014 #051-01-1987 L1988 **P** *020 †75

TROTTA, Brian Michael. ■ 24014 #051-01-2007 L2007 **TY** *012

TU, Priscilla. ■ 24015 #028-79-2005, ▲ L2005 **FP** *012

TUCK, Kenneth Douglas. 707 S JEFFERSON ST 24016 #051-01-1958 L1958 **OPH** *020 †35

TUCKER, Forrest Lee. 101 ELM AVE SE 24013 #051-01-1980 L1983 **PTH PCP** *020 †50

TUCKER, Nadia Sandra. 1212 3RD ST SW 24016 #305-01-2005 L2005 **MP** *012

UREKE, Vitaliy Viktorovic. 1906 BELLEVIEW AVE SE 24014 #781-06-2000 L2007 **IM** *012

VAHABZADEH, Ali. 1906 BELLEVIEW AVE SE 24014 #166-01-2003 L2004 **IM** *100 †20

VAIL, Sydney Jay. 1906 BELLEVIEW AVE SE, DEPT OF SURGICAL EDUCATION 24014 #010-02-1989 L1997 **GS TRS** *020 †85

VANCE, Samuel Franklin. 101 ELM AVE SE, ASSOCIATES 24013 #051-04-1964 L1964 **PTH HMP** *071 †50

VASUDEVA, Sachinder. 213 MCCLANAHAN ST SW, STE 310 24014 #495-69-1994 L2005 **P** *020 †75

VASUDEVA, Shikha Sharma. 1906 BELLEVIEW AVE SE, MEDICAL EDUCATION 24014 #495-74-1998 L2006 **IM** *020

VERMILLION, Robert Lee. 21 HIGHLAND AVE SE, STE 200 24013 #051-04-1968 L1968 **GYN** *020 †30

VIA, Charles Timothy. 1906 BELLEVIEW AVE SE, ROANOKE 24014 #051-04-1982 L1983 **PTH** *062 †50

VIGH, Alexander G. 2001 CRYSTAL SPRING AVE SW, STE 300 24014 #022-75-1987, ▲ L2003 **CD** *020 †20

VOEKLER, Susanne Erika. 4615 HUNTRIDGE RD, BONSACK MEDICAL CENTER 24012 #010-01-1993 L1996 **IM** *020 †20

VOGELEY, Kevin John. ■ 24014 #051-04-2001 L2001 **PAN** *100 *05

WADE, Evelyn Henry Clark. ■ 24014 #051-04-1944 L1945 **P** *071

WADE, Walter Burke. ■ 24014 #047-06-1974 L1987 **U** *020 *95

WAGNER, George Crane. 2840 COLONIAL AVE SW, C-15 24015 #011-02-1978 L1994 **IM** *020 †20

WALL, George Hampton. ■ 24015 #036-05-1958 L1965 **GE IM** *071 †20

WALLENBORN, Peter A, Jr. JEFFERSON AT BELLEVIEW 24033 #051-01-1944 L1944 **OTO** *020 †45

WALSH, William Kevin. 2110 CAROLINA AVE SW, 3RD FL 24014 #016-45-2001 L2001 **OBG** *020

WARD, Thomas Sanders Robt. 1414 FRANKLIN RD SW 24016 #045-01-1955 L1963 **U OS** *071 †95

WARD, William Caldwell. 1009 OLD COUNTRY CLB RD NW 24017 #027-01-1972 L1974 **FM** *020 †18

WATTSMAN, Terriann. 102 HIGHLAND AVE SE, MED OFC BLDGE STE 404 24013 #035-15-1994 L1994 **GS PDS** *020 *85

WEIDENBACHER, Richard L. ■ 24014 #041-01-1956 L1957 **GS P** *075

WEISERBS, Dennis Barry. 202 DUKE OF GLOUCSTR ST SW 24014 #041-01-1978 L1979 **GE IM** *020 †20

WEISMAN, Joseph Steven. 1225 MAPLE AVE SW 24016 #036-07-1983 L1992 **OPH OS** *020 †35

WELCH, William James. 127 MCCLANAHAN ST SW, PC 24014 #016-45-1977 L1983 **ICE CD** *020 †20

WELLS, David Christopher. 2001 CRYSTAL SPRING AVE SW, STE 201 24014 #001-02-1980 L1987 **TS GS** *020 *85,90

WELLS, Hugh Haynsworth, Jr. 101 ELM AVE SE, PEDIATRICS MEDICAL GROUP 24013 #051-01-1975 L1979 **NPM PD** *020 †55

WERNER, Mark Jos. 1906 BELLEVIEW AVE SE, CARILION ROANOKE MEMORIAL 24014 #047-05-1984 L2003 **ADL** *030 †55

WHATLEY, Ralph Emerson. 2001 CRYSTAL SPRING AVE SW, CARILION INTERNAL MEDICINE 24014 #036-07-1979 L2007 **PUD IM** *050 †20

WHITE, Justin Bradley. PO BOX 13367 24033 #012-01-2004 L2004 **MP** *012

WHITE, Robert Marion. 101 ELM AVE SE, ASSOCIATES 24013 #045-01-1974 L1980 **PTH DMP** *020 †50 ‡

WHITESELL, Rebecca Tanner. 4582 FRANKLIN RD SW 24014 #051-04-1990 L1991 **PM** *020 †60

WHITLEY, Herbert Gaddy. 102 HIGHLAND AVE SE # 101, CARILION MC FOR CHILDREN 24013 #051-04-1979 L2001 **PDC PD** *020 †55

WIDMEYER, Robert Saml. ■ 24014 #023-01-1968 L1980 **ORS** *071 †40

WIGGINS, Diane. 1603 FRANKLIN RD SW, ROANOKE VALLEY MEDICAL CLI 24016 #051-01-1985 L1988 **IM** *020 †20

WIGINTON, Clark David. 1906 BELLEVIEW AVE SE 24014 #048-02-2004 L2004 **DR** *012

WIID, Michael. 1212 3RD ST SW, CARILION HEALTH SYSTEM 24016 #836-02-1996 L2001 **IM** *020

WILKES, Kenneth Trevor. 1906 BELLEVIEW AVE SE 24014 #051-01-2004 L2004 **AN** *012

WILLIAMS, David Edward L. 102 HIGHLAND AVE SE # 303 24013 #051-01-1973 L1975 **OBG** *040 †30

WILLIAMS, Edwin Leon, II. 213 MC CLANAHAN ST SW 24014 #051-04-1960 L1960 **GS VS** *071 †85

WILLIAMS, Eric. 127 MCCLANAHAN ST SW, PC 24014 #041-13-1990 L1999 **CD** *020 †20

WISMAN, William Robt. 1506 FRANKLIN RD SW 24016 #051-01-1959 L1959 **OBG** *020 †30

WOOD, John Robt. 375 HERSHBERGER RD, VISTAR EYE CTR 24012 #051-01-1975 L1981 **OPH** *020 †35

WRIGHT, Brian D. 1906 BELLEVIEW AVE SE 24014 #048-12-2004 L2004 **OPH** *012

YATES, Harry Robt, Jr. 2208 JEFFERSON ST SE 24014 #051-01-1951 L1951 **IM GE** *071 †20

YEARGAN, Jon Charles. ■ 24012 #041-02-1999 L2002 **FM** *020 †18

YOUNG, Wesley Robert. 3962 BOSWORTH DR SW, EMERGENCY MEDICINE 24014 #038-06-2005 L2008 **EM** *012

ZACHMANN, Gregory Carl. 1234 FRANKLIN RD SW, JEFFERSON SURGICAL CLNC 24016 #051-01-1994 L1994 **OTO** *020 †45

ZARELLA, Christopher Step. ■ 24014 #036-05-2005 L2005 **GS** *100

ZHU, Li. 1212 3RD ST SW 24016 #243-48-1989 L2005 **FP** *012

ZIMMERMAN, John Francis. 1310 3RD ST SW 24016 #041-13-1983 L2002 **IM FPG** *020 †20

ROCHELLE — MADISON

CARLSON, Shelly Rae. 40 COMMERCE LN STE D, MADISON PRIMARY CARE 22738 #051-01-2002 L2002 **FM** *020 †18

SIEGEL, Barry Leonard. 334 BAIRS TRAIL LN 22738 #016-02-1956 L1990 **PYA P** *020 †75

ROCKVILLE — HANOVER

HOLLIS, Michele. ■ 23146 #047-06-2000 L2000 **EM** *020 †16

KEES, Tanja. 11440 BIENVENUE RD 23146 #409-43-1999 L2001 **CHP** *100 *75

KLINGER, Rochelle Lynn. PO BOX 155 23146 #024-05-1982 L1986 **P** *020 *75

MCLAREN, Donald W. 16492 MLC LN, MEDICAL DEPARTMENT 23146 #048-02-1978 L2003 **PD** *062 †55

PATE, Doris Catherine. 16492 MLC LN, MEDICAL DEPT 23146 #036-08-1991 L2008 **FM** *020 †18

WILLIAMS, Van Wagner, III. 16492 MLC LN, MEDICAL DEPARTMENT 23146 #027-01-1969 L1989 **PHP PD** *030 †55

ROCKY MOUNT — FRANKLIN

AIGNER, Lyne Burke, Jr. 390 S MAIN ST, CARILION MEDICAL 24151 #051-07-1986 L1988 **FM** *020 †18

AMOS, Jesse Francis. 195 MAPLE AVE, CARILION FAMILY MEDICINE 24151 #051-01-1969 L1969 **FM** *020 †18

ANDERSON, Stanley Ladell. 390 S MAIN ST, CARILION OB/GYN ROCKY 24151 #028-34-2001 L2005 **OBG** *020

ARROYO, Matthew Luis. 230 S MAIN ST, CARILION INTERNAL 24151 #051-01-1992 L1997 **IM** *072 †20

ATIENZA, Vergel S. 390 S MAIN ST, CARILION MEDICAL 24151 #748-10-1976 L1994 **FM** *020 †18

BARRETT, Christine E H. 70 N MAIN ST 24151 #047-06-1973 L1978 **AS** *020 †85

BLAYLOCK, Wm Mc Gehee. 490 S MAIN ST 24151 #051-04-1967 L1967 **RHU IM** *020 †20

BOHON, Sonya Nicole. 390 S MAIN ST, CARILION MEDICAL 24151 #051-01-1999 L2002 **FM** *020 †18

BUMGARDNER, Jack Hood. 195 MAPLE AVE, CARILION FAMILY MEDICINE 24151 #051-04-1972 L1972 **FM** *020 †18

CARGO, Jon Darryl. 390 S MAIN ST, CARILION MEDICAL 24151 #051-01-1988 L2001 **IM** *020 †20

CASSIDY, Robert Edward. 230 S MAIN ST, CARILION BONE & JOINT 24151 #010-02-1966 L1995 **ORS** *020 †40

DULANEY, Kimberly Allison. 390 S MAIN ST, CARILION MEDICAL ASSOCAITE 24151 #051-07-2004 L2004 **FM** *020 †18

EARL, Peter Carpenter. 390 S MAIN ST, CARILION OB/GYN ROCKY 24151 #007-02-1984 L2001 **OBG** *020 †30

GARGES, Thomas William. 390 S MAIN ST, CARILION MEDICAL 24151 #041-15-1999 L1999 **FM** *020 †18

GUELZOW, Kurt Wm L. 395 S MAIN ST 24151 #048-04-1971 L1978 **OPH** *020 †35

KAHN, Ralph Y. 180 FLOYD AVE 24151 #583-01-1951 L1960 **DR** *071

LANE, Charles Jenkins. 180 FLOYD AVE, HOSPITAL 24151 #036-08-1989 L1996 **EM OS** *020 †16

LESKO, Edmund Michael. 100 ADAM PERRY RD 24151 #016-06-1964 L1971 **AN** *020 *05

MERTEN, Suzan R. 390 S MAIN ST, STE 103 24151 #045-01-1988 L1989 **ON** *020 †20

MISSLBECK, Margret Gene. 230 S MAIN ST 24151 #051-01-1990 L1991 **FM** *020 †18

MONTGOMERY, John E L, Jr. ■ 24151 #051-04-1968 L1968 **PD** *020 †55,16

PERMASHWAR, Vydia. 1035 FRANKLIN ST, STE 202 24151 #566-01-1994 L2000 **PD** *020 *55

QUIOCO, Heathcliff M. 70 N MAIN ST 24151 #748-11-1970 L1977 **SG** *020 *85

SCHUELLEIN, Paul Robt. 390 S MAIN ST, CARILION OB/GYN ROCKY 24151 #035-46-1989 L1992 **OBG** *020 †30

SHAH, Mikesh Chinubhai. 390 S MAIN ST, CARILION MEDICAL 24151 #495-01-1998 L2005 **IM** *100

SHERRARD, Lindsay Hill. 390 S MAIN ST, STE 201 24151 #036-01-2005 L2008 **FP** *012

STRONG, Robert Sinclair. 390 S MAIN ST, CARILION MEDICAL 24151 #051-01-1972 L1972 **FM** *020 †18

VAMENTA, Rene N. 681 S MAIN ST 24151 #748-09-1977 L1993 **PD** *020

WEIBEL, Donald Edwin. 529 S MAIN ST 24151 #561-01-1975 L1979 **FM** *020

WINESETT, Preston Steve. ■ 24151 #051-04-1968 L1968 **FM** *071 †18

ROSELAND — NELSON

BLUM, Allan David. ■ 22967 #869-05-1965 L1986 **OPH** *071 †35

JEFFRIES, Mary Katherine. ■ 22967 #051-01-1991 L1994 **PD** *020 †55

MASSIE, Samuel Powell. ■ 22967 #051-01-1964 L1964 **FM** *071

PRESTON, Ellen K Johnson. ■ 22967 #051-04-1950 L1950 **OS PHP** *071

ROUND HILL — LOUDOUN

ADWERS, James Robt. ■ 20141 #030-05-1969 L1975 **GS** *071 †85

ANTOLIK-HUDLER, Annette. 6 E LOUDOUN ST 20141 #041-77-1994, ▲ L1998 **IM** *020 †20

GUNDELFINGER, Benjamin F. ■ 20141 #005-02-1943 L1943 **PHP ID** *071 †70

HOFFMAN, Peter Frederic. ■ 20141 #051-04-1970 L1970 **IM AM** *030 †20,03

PHILLIPS, Lawrence V. ■ 20141 #010-01-1952 L1965 **FM GPM** *071

RUCKERSVILLE — GREENE

BOSTIC, Brooke Arledge. 140 STONERIDGE DR, STE 100 22968 #036-01-1989 L1993 **EM FM** *020 †18

CANTOW, Edward Francis. ■ 22968 #010-02-1961 L1972 **ON HEM** *071

COHEN, Arthur Edwin. ■ 22968 #038-01-1957 L1958 **OBG** *020 †30

DAME, Lien Thi. ■ 22968 #051-01-2006 L2006 **IM** *012

DUANI, David Simon. 140 STONERIDGE DR, STE 100 22968 #035-06-1980 L1982 **FM** *020 †18

MACK, David Adam. ■ 22968 #016-01-2001 L2001 **HO** *020

MCELROY, Amy Phillips. ■ 22968 #051-01-2005 L2005 **FP** *012

TAYLOR, Marsha Lynn. 140 STONERIDGE DR, GREENE FAMILY MEDICINE 22968 #051-01-2003 L2003 **FM** *020 †18

RURAL RETREAT — WYTHE

BASLER, Bonnie Newman. 7061 W LEE HWY 24368 #027-01-1997 L1997 **FM** *020 †18

MARTIN, Samuel. 120 N MAIN ST 24368 #027-01-1959 L1961 **FM** *071

RUSTBURG — CAMPBELL

SHAHADY, Gertrude Koch. PO BOX 69 24588 #036-01-1989 L2000 **FM** *020 †18

RUTHER GLEN — CAROLINE

GULATI, Sudhir. 17428 CENTER DR STE E, LADYSMITH URGENT CARE 22546 #495-73-1978 L2003 **GP TTS** *020

NAIR, Santhi Balakrishnan. 17470 CENTER DR, STE 4A 22546 #305-01-2000 L2006 **PD** *020 †55

RUSSELL, Sarah Anne. ■ 22546 #051-04-2007 L2007 **MPD** *012

SIMES, Rebecca Summitt. 17470 CENTER DR, STE 4A 22546 #051-04-1998 L1998 **PD** *020 †55

SPENCER, Frederick J. ■ 22546 #352-04-1945 L1951 **PHP OS** *072 †70

TREMENTOZZI, Daniel Paul. 18048 JEFFERSON DAVIS HWY, CAROLINE CHRISTIAN HEALTH 22546 #041-14-1994 L2001 **PD** *020 †55

SAINT PAUL — WISE

HOLLIDAY, Taylor Duke. PO BOX 338, RIVERSIDE COMMUNITY MED CL 24283 #048-13-1981 L1986 **FM** *020 †18

SAINT STEPHENS CHURCH – KING AND QUEEN

GWATHMEY, Pamela Lester. PO BOX 130 23148 #051-04-1984 L1985 **FM** *020 †18
GWATHMEY, William Brooke. PO BOX 130 23148 #051-04-1985 L1986 **FM** *020 †18

SALEM – SALEM

AHMADZADEH, Shahram. 1970 ROANOKE BLVD, VAMC-DIALYSIS (111D) 24153 #517-04-1991 L1999 **NEP IM** *020 †20
AKERS, Stephen Matthew. ■ 24153 #055-01-2008 *012
ALCANTARA, Cirle Sevilla. ■ 24153 #748-10-1990 L1997 **ID IM** *020 †20
ALLDREDGE, Karen J. 1802 BRAEBURN DR 24153 #048-13-1997 L2000 **EM** *020 †16
ALOUF, Gregory Alan. 1618 APPERSON DR 24153 #539-06-1998 L1998 **FM** *020 †18
ANAND, Vishal Sunil. 400 E BURWELL ST 24153 #495-17-1994 L2000 **P PFP** *020 †75
ASEBIOMO, Bankole Simbo. 1900 ELECTRIC RD 24153 #690-01-1989 L2007 **IM** *020 †20
AUJLA, Sarbjit Singh. 1970 ROANOKE BLVD, DEPT PYCH 24153 #495-29-1977 L1986 **P CHP** *020
AYYILDIZ, Vedii. 511 ROANOKE BLVD 24153 #902-01-1951 L1961 **GS AS** *071 †85
BADER, Geoffrey Michael. 1970 ROANOKE BLVD # 116A7 24153 #025-01-1989 L1990 **P** *020 †75
BAJAJ, Harminder Pal S. 1970 ROANOKE BLVD, VA MEDICAL CTR 24153 #495-29-1982 L1993 **IM** *020 †20
BANNING, Bruce C, Jr. 1900 ELECTRIC RD 24153 #023-01-1984 L1988 **DR** *020 †80
BARNHART, Karen Quinn. 2102 W MAIN ST 24153 #051-04-1978 L1979 **FM** *020 †18
BARON, George Paul. 1802 BRAEBURN DR, LEWIS-GALE CLINIC, LLC 24153 #050-02-1969 L1974 **AN** *020 †05
BARTON, Ben Reed. 1802 BRAEBURN DR, STE 1310 24153 #047-06-1980 L1981 **TS** *020 †85,90
BAUM, Joseph James, II. 2155 APPERSON DR 24153 #018-03-1964 L1981 **FM EM** *020 †16,18
BAYLISS, Garry Edward. 1802 BRAEBURN DR 24153 #036-01-1985 L1991 **RHU IM** *020 †20
BAYLOR, George Montgomery. 1802 BRAEBURN DR 24153 #055-02-1991 L2004 **APM** *020 †05
BEAZLEY, Luthur A, Jr. 1802 BRAEBURN DR, LEWIS-GALE CLINIC INC 24153 #047-05-1946 L1946 **PD** *071 †55
BEAZLEY, Luthur Abner. 1802 BRAEBURN DR 24153 #036-05-1977 L1980 **PD** *020 †55
BEESLEY, Joseph Ralph. ■ 24153 #067-01-1951 L1961 **P** *071
BELL, Victor Holloway. 511 BOULEVARD, STE B 24153 #020-02-1984 L1985 **FM** *020 †18
BERN, Merritt John. 1906 BRAEBURN DR 24153 #011-02-1982 L1987 **GE IM** *020 †20
BHATIA, Anil M. 1802 BRAEBURN DR, LEWIS-GALE LABORATORY SVC 24153 #496-38-1984 L1999 **IM** *020 †20
BIBRO, Mary Catherine. 1802 BRAEBURN DR 24153 #041-13-1976 L1986 **PTH** *020 †50
BINNINGS, Clement Burke. 2155 APPERSON DR, LEEHI MEDICAL CENTER 24153 #021-06-1984 L1985 **FM** *020 †20
BOLIN, Delmas John. 1935 W MAIN ST, WEST SALEM MEDICAL CTR 24153 #016-11-1996 L2002 **FM** *020 †18
BOLLU, Madhavi. 1970 ROANOKE BLVD, SALEM VA MED CTR 24153 #495-37-1999 L2002 **IM** *100 †20
BRADLEY, Joy Jolliffe. 1802 BRAEBURN DR, BLUE MOUNTAIN PATHOLOGY, P 24153 #051-04-1984 L1986 **PTH** *020 †50
BROWN, Esther L Clark. ■ 24153 #051-04-1945 L1946 **GP** *071
BULAS, Kristina Eva. 1970 ROANOKE BLVD, VAMC SALEM 24153 #759-10-1981 L1992 **OM IM** *020 †20
CAMDEN, Daniel Mc Clung. 1802 BRAEBURN DR 24153 #051-04-1978 L1981 **IM** *020 †20
CANNON, Mary Marcelyn. ■ 24153 #047-06-1962 L1966 **BBK IM** *071
CARR, James Bradley. 1802 BRAEBURN DR 24153 #016-06-1980 L1989 **ORS** *020 †40
CASTERN, Louis Jos. 2131 APPERSON DR, VALLEY OCCUPATIONAL MEDICI 24153 #025-07-1972 L1982 **OM EM** *020
CEPEDA, Anne Marie. 1970 ROANOKE BLVD, PSYCHIATRY SALEM VA MED 24153 #011-02-1978 L1982 **P** *020 †75
CEPULO, Andrew John. 1900 ELECTRIC RD 4TH FL 24153 #038-41-1987 L1991 **PM** *020 †60
CHAHIL, Ritu. 1970 ROANOKE BLVD, VETERANS AFFAIRS MEDICAL C 24153 #495-08-1997 L1998 **P IM** *020 †20,75
CHAKRAVORTY, Ranes C. 5049 CHEROKEE HILLS DR 24153 #495-38-1949 L1972 **GS HNS** *020
CHAUDRY, Muddasar. 1802 BRAEBURN DR 24153 #704-21-1987 L2006 **ID IM** *020 †20
CHEN, Kurt Yaohsun. 1924 BRAEBURN DR, CARILION CLINIC 24153 #023-01-1989 L1994 **OTO** *020 †45
CHITNAVIS, Vikas N. 1906 BRAEBURN DR, VALLEY GASTROENTEROLOGY 24153 #495-83-1977 L1999 **GE IM** *020 †20
CHOUDHURY, Arindam. 1970 ROANOKE BLVD, VETERANS ADMIN HOSPITAL 24153 #051-07-1985 L1987 **GS VS** *020
CHUN, Theresa Won Choon. ■ 24153 #583-03-1955 L1982 **PD GP** *072 †55
CLARK, John Robt, Jr. 1900 ELECTRIC RD 24153 #036-07-1942 L1947 **U** *071
CLOUGH, L Robert. ■ 24153 #047-06-1953 L1959 **FM** *071 †85
COFFEY, Maurice Eugene. ■ 24153 #039-01-1973 L1976 **PUD IM** *020 †20
COLE, John, Jr. 1970 ROANOKE BLVD, ENT CLINIC VAMC 24153 #051-01-1958 L1958 **OTO HNS** *071 †45 ‡
COLLIN, Gary Richard. 1970 ROANOKE BLVD, SALEM VAMC (112) 24153 #022-08-1985 L1994 **GS CCS** *020 †85
CORDERO, Christopher Eric. 1900 ELECTRIC RD, ANESTHESIOLOGY DEPT 24153 #048-12-1989 L1993 **AN PME** *020 †05 ‡
CROUSE, Charles David, II. 1802 BRAEBURN DR 24153 #036-01-1999 L1999 **OTO** *020 ‡
CRUSER, Fred S. 1970 BOULEVARD 24153 #051-01-1950 L1950 **PYG OS** *071
CUMMINGS, Joyce. 1802 BRAEBURN DR 24153 #035-06-1999 L2003 **PD** *020 †55
CURRIE, Mark Stuart. 1802 BRAEBURN DR 24153 #048-12-1978 L1997 **HO ON** *050 †20
DASTOOR, Firdaus Cawas. 1802 BRAEBURN DR 24153 #495-17-1972 L2004 **GE IM** *020 †20
DAUM, Conrad Henry. 400 E BURWELL ST 24153 #020-12-1971 L1973 **P PYG** *020 †75
DE GUZMAN, Placido H, Jr. 1802 BRAEBURN DR 24153 #748-01-1963 L1978 **DR** *020 †80
DELANEY, Russell Evans. 1802 BRAEBURN DR, LEWIS-GALE PHYSICIANS 24153 #051-01-1996 L1998 **PD** *020 †55
DE LEONNI STANONIK, Mateja. 1970 ROANOKE BLVD, DEPT OF PSYCHIATRY 24153 #665-01-2007 L2007 **P** *012
DEPRET-GUILLAUME, Serge E. 1935 W MAIN ST, PC 24153 #051-01-1991 L1992 **FM** *020 †18
DESSYPRIS, Emmanuel. 1970 ROANOKE BLVD 24153 #418-01-1970 L1992 **HO IM** *020 †20

DETWEILER, Mark Budd. ■ 24153 #561-23-1991 L1997 **PYG** *020 †75
DICHTEL, William Jos, Jr. 1924 BRAEBURN DR, CARILION CLINIC 24153 #023-01-1977 L1986 **OTO** *020 †45
DILLON, Ronald Williams. 426 W MAIN ST 24153 #051-04-1964 L1964 **OPH** *071 †35
DOWLING, Robert Emmett, IV. 1900 ELECTRIC RD 24153 #041-12-1997 L2000 **EM** *020 †20
DUCKWALL, Francis Jos. 1802 BRAEBURN DR 24153 #051-04-1963 L1963 **PD** *020 †55
EBARB, Jeanette Marie. ■ 24153 #004-01-2004 L2004 **EM** *020
EDMUNDS, Keith Castleton. 2155 APPERSON DR 24153 #051-04-1956 L1956 **FM** *072
ELDRIDGE, Thomas Haws. 1970 ROANOKE BLVD, VAMC 24153 #051-01-1972 L1972 **IM** *020 †20
ELECHI, Clement. 1802 BRAEBURN DR 24153 #690-01-1988 L2001 **N** *020 †75
ELESHO, Virginia Mary. 1970 ROANOKE BLVD, VA MEDICAL CENTER 24153 #305-01-2000 L2004 **IM** *020
ELLIS, Madge Elaine. 1802 BRAEBURN DR 24153 #566-01-1989 L2000 **GS** *020 †85
ESGUERRA, Amando V. 1970 ROANOKE BLVD, DEPT PATH 24153 #748-01-1965 L1974 **PTH** *020 †50
FAME, Thomas Michael. 1802 BRAEBURN DR, LEWIS-GALE PHYSICIANS, LLC 24153 #048-14-1984 L1992 **AI PD** *020 †55,03
FARMER, James Mastin. 1802 BRAEBURN DR 24153 #048-04-1997 L2007 **ORS** *020 †40
FISHER, Richard Harding. 103 E MAIN ST 24153 #051-04-1947 L1947 **ORS** *071 †40
FLETT, Bonnie Louise. 431 APPERSON DR 24153 #051-04-1993 L1993 **FM** *020 †18
FOREHAND, John Randolph. 1802 BRAEBURN DR 24153 #036-01-1974 L1978 **AI PUD** *020 †55,03
FURCONE, Janine. ■ 24153 #035-45-1994 L1994 **IM** *100
GARVIN, Dennis Deane. 1802 BRAEBURN DR, STE 2130 24153 #051-04-1973 L1976 **U** *020 †95
GARVIN, John Mc Vay, Jr. 1900 ELECTRIC RD, LEWIS-GALE MEDICAL CENTER 24153 #045-01-1970 L1970 **EM FM** *020 †20
GILLILAND, Charles Donald. 1900 ELECTRIC RD, LEWIS GALE MEDICAL CENTER 24153 #041-13-1971 L1975 **IM** *020 †20
GLONTZ, Gary Edwin. 1802 BRAEBURN DR, LEWIS GALE CLINIC 24153 #041-12-1962 L1968 **IM ID** *020 †20
GODWIN, Gene Arthur. 2102 W MAIN ST 24153 #051-04-1965 L1965 **GP** *020 †18
GOODRICH, Rana Q. 1898 BRAEBURN DR 24153 #051-07-1994 L1995 **FM** *020 †18
GRAY, William Gilman. 1902 BRAEBURN DR 24153 #051-04-1966 L1966 **CHP P** *075
GREENE, Nelson Brent. 1802 BRAEBURN DR 24153 #051-07-1980 L1982 **PUD CCM** *020 †20
GREWAL, Harleen. ■ 24153 #496-42-1999 L2006 **PYG** *100 †75
GRIFFETH, Benjamin Todd. 1970 ROANOKE BLVD, CODE 116A7 24153 #045-04-1996 L1996 **P** *020 †75
GROSS, Gary Paul. 1802 BRAEBURN DR 24153 #051-01-1976 L1978 **D** *020 †15
GROVE, Lucian Y, Jr. 1935 W MAIN ST, PC 24153 #051-01-1982 L1985 **IM** *020 †20
GULLAPALLI, Dakshinamurty. 1970 ROANOKE BLVD, VA MEDICAL CENTER 24153 #495-11-1987 L1996 **N** *020 †75
GUSTAFSON, Mark Worsham. 1802 BRAEBURN DR, LEWIS-GALE PHYSICIANS 24153 #051-04-1982 L1985 **OBG** *020 †30
GUZZARDI, Richard Woods. ■ 24153 #422-01-1987 L1993 **IM** *020 †20
HAAS, Cheryl Barbara. 1900 ELECTRIC RD, LEWIS-GALE MEDICAL CENTER 24153 #033-06-1994 L1997 **EM** *020 †16
HABIB, Roy Pierre. 1900 ELECTRIC RD, SALEM HOSPITALISTS, LLC 24153 #605-02-1992 L1997 **IM** *020 †20
HAGADORN, Jon Bruce. 1802 BRAEBURN DR, LEWIS-GALE CLINIC INC 24153 #035-03-1966 L1971 **OTO** *071 †45
HAGY, Mark Lindsay. 1900 BRAEBURN DR 24153 #051-04-1999 L2005 **ORS** *100 †40
HAIDER, Syed T. 1900 ELECTRIC RD 24153 #704-02-1991 L2000 **IM PLM** *020 †20
HANNA, Sameh Wadie. 1970 ROANOKE BLVD, SALEM VAMC 24153 #915-03-1980 L2001 **IM GP** *020 †20
HANNA, Suzanne Missak. 1970 ROANOKE BLVD, SALEM VAMC 24153 #915-03-1982 L2001 **FM** *020 †18
HARBOR, Cathryn Kaylor. 1930 BRAEBURN CIR, PC BRAEBURN FAMILY 24153 #036-01-1992 L1993 **FM** *020 †18
HARPOLD, Gary Joe. 1970 ROANOKE BLVD, DEPT NEUR 24153 #036-05-1976 L1985 **N AM** *020 †75
HERMINGHUYSEN, David C. 1942 BRAEBURN CIR, STE 101 24153 #021-06-1985 L2006 **END** *020 †20
HOOPER, William Edward. 101 KNOTBREAK RD 24153 #036-07-1983 L1984 **ORS** *020 †40
HOOVER, Gates Edgar. 2155 APPERSON DR, C LEE HI MEDICAL CENTER 24153 #021-05-1989 L1993 **AI MPD** *020 †20,55,03
HORMEL, Timothy Louis. 1904 BRAEBURN DR, ASSOCIATES, PC 24153 #028-34-1977 L1982 **N** *020 †18
HUTCHINS, Anne Cain. 1970 ROANOKE BLVD 24153 #045-01-1986 L1987 **IM** *020 †20
IRANMANESH, Ali. 1970 ROANOKE BLVD, DEPT ENDO 24153 #517-01-1969 L1979 **END IM** *020 †18
JAMISON, Gregory Martin. 1970 ROANOKE BLVD, VA MEDICAL CENTER 24153 #047-20-1985 L2004 **GP IM** *020
JARMUKLI, Nabil Fahmi. 1802 BRAEBURN DR 24153 #605-01-1982 L1992 **IM** *020 †20
JEREMIAH, John Spencer. 1802 BRAEBURN DR 24153 #539-01-1954 L1956 **EM** *030
JHA, Chetna. 1802 BRAEBURN DR 24153 #495-54-1992 L2002 **IM** *020 †20
JOHNSON, Brent Mitchell. 1900 ELECTRIC RD, STE 1040 24153 #051-04-1984 L1989 **ORS** *020 †40
JORNALES, Maria Janeta F. 1308 W MAIN ST, LONG TERM CARE-MEDICAL ASS 24153 #748-10-1987 L1995 **FM** *020 †18
JOSHI, Varuna. 1970 ROANOKE BLVD, DEPT OF PSYCHIATRY (116A7) 24153 #495-43-2002 L2006 **P** *012
KARAGEORGE, Lampros Steve. 1970 ROANOKE BLVD, LABORATORY SERVICE 113 24153 #051-04-1994 L1994 **PCP** *020 †50
KARRI, Vandana R. 1802 BRAEBURN DR 24153 #495-11-1996 L2005 **HO** *020 †20
KAZEMI, Mehdi M. 1970 ROANOKE BLVD # 19-B 24153 #036-01-1996 L1996 **IM** *020 †20
KESSLER, Alfred R. 1802 BRAEBURN DR 24153 #036-07-1945 **NS OS** *071
KESSLER, Allen Reif, II. 1898 BRAEBURN DR 24153 #051-07-1975 L1981 **GS** *020 †85 ‡
KHADILKAR, Nitin Arun. ■ 24153 #495-96-2003 L2006 **P** *012
KHAN, Mohammad Akhtar. 1970 ROANOKE BLVD 24153 #704-16-1982 L1995 **PM** *020
KHAWAM, Souha Jean. 2102 W MAIN ST 24153 #025-12-1998 L2001 **FM** *020 †18
KIM, Kye Young. 1970 ROANOKE BLVD, BLDG 7-1 24153 #583-01-1976 L1999 **PYG P** *020 †75
KINNISON, Susan L. 1802 BRAEBURN DR 24153 #038-44-1994 L1995 **GS** *020
KIRTLEY, Douglas Wade. 1906 BRAEBURN DR 24153 #051-07-1982 L1988 **GE IM** *020 †20
KOLESSOVA, Marina. 1970 ROANOKE BLVD, SALEM VAMC PRIMARY CARE 24153 #913-99-1986 L1997 **IM** *020 †20

KOVESDY, Csaba. 1970 ROANOKE BLVD, SALEM VAMC 111D 24153 #473-03-1995 L2000 NEP *020 †20

KUIKEN, Garry Henry. 1930 BRAEBURN CIR, PC BRAEBURN FAMILY 24153 #051-04-1975 L1976 FM *020 †18

LAMB, Charles Emerson. 2155 APPERSON DR, C LEE HI MEDICAL CENTER 24153 #051-04-1982 L1983 FM EM *020 †18

LEGGETT, Richard Preston. 1914 BRAEBURN DR 24153 #051-01-1986 L1993 P PFP *020

LEHMANN, Lauren Pate. 1970 ROANOKE BLVD 24153 #048-04-1983 L1993 P ADM *020 †75

LEIPZIG, James Mark. 1940 BRAEBURN CIR 24153 #005-14-1984 L1992 ORS *020 †40

LEMMER, Joseph Peter. 1802 BRAEBURN DR 24153 #035-06-1974 L1979 IM RHU *020 †20

LEONG, Apollo Yuen. 1930 BRAEBURN CIR, PC BRAEBURN FAMILY 24153 #051-04-1988 L1989 FM *020 †18

LEVEY, Myron Sandy. 1802 BRAEBURN DR 24153 #023-07-1974 L1977 IM *020 †20

LEWIS, Verna M. 1900 ELECTRIC RD 24153 #048-04-1984 L1988 PM *075 †60

LI, Junping. 1970 ROANOKE BLVD, EYE CLNC 24153 #243-52-1984 L2000 OPH *020 †35

LIPSCOMB, Larry Geo. 1970 ROANOKE BLVD, VETERANS ADMINISTRATION ME 24153 #021-05-1975 L1988 ORS *020 †40

MADAN, Ashok. 1970 ROANOKE BLVD, DEPT OF RADIOLOGY 24153 #913-06-1995 L2007 DR *100 †80

MAIOLO, Andrew Joseph. 1802 BRAEBURN DR 24153 #055-01-1994 L1995 CD *020 †20

MAKOUI, Cyrus. 1970 ROANOKE BLVD 24153 #517-01-1965 L1970 PTH *020 †50

MANALO, Buenaventura G. ■ 24153 #748-02-1951 L1980 IM *071

MARCUS, Leonard Jeffrey. VA MEDICAL CENTER, PSYCHIATRY SERVICE (116A) 24153 #021-05-1990 L1994 P *020 †75

MARK, Jennifer Lee. 1802 BRAEBURN DR, LEWIS-GALE PHYSICIANS 24153 #028-34-1999 L2003 MPD *020 †20,55

MARTIN, Thomas J. 1970 ROANOKE BLVD, SALEM VAMC 111 24153 #051-04-1987 L1998 PUD CCM *020 †20

MATTHEWS, James David. 1900 ELECTRIC RD, MEDICAL IMAGING SPECIALIST 24153 #051-04-1989 L1998 NM *020 †80,28

MAXFIELD, Donna Lynn. 1802 BRAEBURN DR, MEDICAL STAFF OFFICE 24153 #051-04-1984 L1988 OPH *020 †35

MAXYMIV, George Walter. 1802 BRAEBURN DR, DEPT. OF GYNECOLOGY 24153 #038-40-1978 L1979 OBG *020 †30

MCCARTHY, Joseph J. 1970 ROANOKE BLVD, SALEM VAMC 24153 #654-01-1989 L1997 IM *020 †20

MC CARTHY, Maureen Fay. 1970 BOULEVARD, # 14 24153 #024-16-1987 L1994 P *020 †75

MC CARTHY, Patrick John. 1970 ROANOKE BLVD 24153 #010-01-1972 L1986 ON HEM *071 †20

MC GUFFIN, Robert Odell. 1900 ELECTRIC RD 24153 #051-04-1971 L1972 EM *020 †16

MEHTA, Sachin Narendra. 1970 ROANOKE BLVD 24153 #496-36-2002 L2003 P *100

MENDOZA, Andronico S. ■ 24153 #748-01-1970 P *100

MENDOZA, Jose Luis. 1970 ROANOKE BLVD 24153 #737-01-1992 L2004 HO *020 †20

MEUNIER, Ronny Paul. 1970 ROANOKE BLVD, DEPT OF PSYCHIATRY 24153 #661-02-2006 L2007 P *012

MILLER, David S, II. 1802 BRAEBURN DR 24153 #051-04-1962 L1962 IM CD *071 †20

MILLER, John Milton. LEWIS GALE CLINIC 24153 #051-04-1958 L1958 HEM *020 †20

MINARIK, Harry J. ■ 24153 #012-05-1950 L1951 GP *071

MITCHENER, James Saml. 1970 ELECTRIC RD 24153 #036-07-1981 L1982 PS HS *020 †85,65

MOLES, James Kelly, Jr. V.A. MEDICAL CENTER 24153 #051-01-1986 L1988 IM P *020 †75,20

MOORE, Michael Judson. 1900 ELECTRIC RD 24153 #051-04-1948 L1948 IM *071 †20

MOORMAN, Warren L, Jr. ■ 24153 #051-04-1943 L1943 GS PS *071 †85,65

MOWERY, Deborah Thoren. 1900 ELECTRIC RD, VALLEY REHABILITATION INC 24153 #051-07-1989 L1990 PM *020 †60

MOYLAN, Robert Danl. 1906 BRAEBURN DR 24153 #051-01-1985 L1986 GE IM *020 †20

MULL, Sears Curtiss. 1802 BRAEBURN DR, LEWIS GALE CLINIC 24153 #041-12-1966 L1973 ORS OAR *020 †40

MYERS, Alonzo H, Jr. 1802 BRAEBURN DR 24153 #036-07-1959 L1966 ORS *020 †40

NAGY, Stephanie Elizabeth. 1970 ROANOKE BLVD, VA MEDICAL CENTER 24153 #016-02-1987 L1995 ID *020 †20

NAYYAR, Neha. 1970 ROANOKE BLVD 24153 #495-03-2005 L2007 P *012

NEATHAWK, Jacob Price. 1802 BRAEBURN DR 24153 #051-01-1973 L1977 CD *020 †20

NELSON, Joseph Lee, III. 1906 BRAEBURN DR 24153 #051-04-1978 L1979 GE IM *020 †20

NEMATBAKHSH, Soroor. 1970 ROANOKE BLVD # G111 24153 #016-42-1995 L2001 IM *020 †20

NEVIN, Marc Glenn. 1308 W MAIN ST, LONG TERM CARE-MEDICAL ASS 24153 #041-12-1975 L1976 FM *020 †18

NOBBEE, Vashist Varune. 1802 BRAEBURN DR, LEWIS-GALE PHYSICIANS 24153 #566-01-1991 L1997 IM *020 †20

NOLAND, Eugene B, Jr. 1802 BRAEBURN DR 24153 #051-04-1971 L1973 IM OS *020 †20

NORRIS, William Templeton. ■ 24153 #051-04-1955 L1955 P *071

OBERLENDER, Gary Harvey. MEDICAL CENTER, VETERAN'S ADMIN 24153 #041-09-1980 L1981 IM *020 †20

O'HAGAN, Gary George. 1930 BRAEBURN CIR, PC BRAEBURN FAMILY 24153 #047-06-1988 L1989 FM *020 †18

PAGE, Lourdes Maria. ■ 24153 #025-12-1981 L1985 IM *020 †20

PAINE, Robert Edward, Jr. ■ 24153 #051-04-1947 L1947 IM P *072

PARK, Donald Heedon. 1970 ROANOKE BLVD, SALEM VA HOSPITAL 24153 #583-15-1978 L2002 IM *020 †20

PARRISH, Thomas G. 1900 BRAEBURN DR, LEWIS-GALE HOSPITAL 24153 #047-07-1982 L1984 EM *020

PATEL, Bharatbhai G. 1970 ROANOKE BLVD 24153 #495-23-1993 L1998 IM *020 †20

PATEL, Himanshu S. 400 E BURWELL ST 24153 #495-23-1981 L1989 CHP ADP *020 †75

PATEL, Mukesh P. 405 KIMBALL AVE 24153 #495-23-1981 L1983 P *020 †75

PATOLIA, Harsukh P. 1900 ELECTRIC RD, SALEM HOSPITALISTS, LLC 24153 #495-23-1992 L1997 IM *020 †20

PAYNE, Robert Kenneth. 1802 BRAEBURN DR 24153 #004-01-1971 L1977 PD *020 †55

PEREZ, Enrique. 1970 ROANOKE BLVD, PSYCHIATRY DEPT -116A7 24153 #051-01-1986 L1990 P *020 †75

POFFENBERGER, Rodney J. 1900 ELECTRIC RD 24153 #025-01-1986 L1991 U *020 †95

POLLIO, Francis Vincent. 1970 ROANOKE BLVD 24153 #041-01-1982 L1985 IM IMG *020 †20

PREUSS, Jeffrey Michael. 1900 ELECTRIC RD 24153 #010-02-1988 L1995 EM *020 †16

PRIDDY, John Wilcox. 1935 W MAIN ST, PC 24153 #051-07-1987 L1989 FM *020 †18

PROKOPCHAK, Richard. 1802 BRAEBURN DR 24153 #010-02-1984 L1992 CD IM *020 †20

RAZA, Syed A. 3737 W MAIN ST, STE 102 24153 #704-02-1992 L2001 IM PLM *020 †20

REINHOLD, Sandra Lynn. 1802 BRAEBURN DR, BLUE RIDGE SURGERY CENTER 24153 #023-12-1993 L1994 AN *020 †05

RENICK, Ole Wibholm. 3531 KEAGY RD 24153 #051-04-1971 L1978 OTO HNS *020 †45

RICH, Deborah Arnetta. 1970 ROANOKE BLVD 24153 #010-03-1992 L1995 GP UCM *020

RICHARDS, Paul Douglas. 1900 ELECTRIC RD STE 100 24153 #021-01-1979 L1985 ON HEM *020 †20

RICHARDS, Steven D. 1970 ROANOKE BLVD, VETERANS ADMIN. MEDICAL CE 24153 #039-01-1976 L1985 CD AN *020 †05,20

RIEBEL, Gregory David. ■ 24153 #035-15-1987 L1998 OSS ORS *020 †40

RIPLEY, Robert Cameron. 1908 BRAEBURN DR, SALEM SURGICAL ASSOCIATES 24153 #051-04-1979 L1984 GS VS *020 †85

RIVERA-IRIAS, Jorge R. 1970 ROANOKE BLVD 24153 #187-11-1972 L1998 GS VS *020 †85

RIZK, Samir Noshy. 1970 ROANOKE BLVD, VETERAN AFFAIRS HOSPITAL 24153 #915-09-1976 L1996 IM *020 †20

RORRER, Michael D. ■ 24153 #051-04-1979 L1980 FM EM *020 †16

ROTH, Robert Frank. 1900 ELECTRIC RD 24153 #035-01-1955 L1973 PS GS *071 †85,65

ROZOS, Constantino A. ■ 24153 #051-04-1995 L1995 GE IM *020 †20

RUFFIN, Richard E. 1900 ELECTRIC RD, SALEM HOSPITALISTS, LLC 24153 #041-12-1995 L2000 IM *020 †20

RUTHERFORD, William Buren. 1900 ELECTRIC RD 24153 #051-04-1973 L1974 CD IM *020 †20

SADLER, John Edward, III. 1930 BRAEBURN CIR, PC BRAEBURN FAMILY 24153 #051-04-1991 L1992 FM *020 †18

SAINZ, Kenneth G. 1970 ROANOKE BLVD 24153 #308-03-1988 L1994 IM *020 †20

SAUL, Patton Bernard. 1900 ELECTRIC RD, # 200 24153 #051-01-1974 L1980 GO *020 †30

SAWH, Amar K. 1970 ROANOKE BLVD, MAIL RT 111G 24153 #566-01-1992 L1997 IM *020 †20

SAYERS, Marta Carolyn. 1802 BRAEBURN DR 24153 #045-01-1976 L1982 CD IM *020 †20

SCHMIDT, Mark Anderson. 1900 ELECTRIC RD, JEFFERSON SURGICAL CLINIC 24153 #012-01-1988 L1994 U *020 †95

SHARMA, Rajeev Kumar. 1802 BRAEBURN DR, LEWIS-GALE LABORATORY SVC 24153 #496-09-1984 L1993 IM *020 †20

SHARMA, Taralkumar Ravjib. ■ 24153 #496-61-2003 P IM *100

SHARP, Robert Bailey. 1970 BOULEVARD 24153 #025-01-1956 L1957 IM *020 †20

SHERIGAR, Rathnakara M. 1970 ROANOKE BLVD, VA MEDICAL CENTER 24153 #495-09-1996 L2002 IM *020 †80

SHERMAN, Howard Bruce. 1904 BRAEBURN DR, VALLEY NEUROLOGY ASSOC, P. 24153 #035-46-1983 L1990 N *020 †20

SHORT, Delmar Dean. 1970 ROANOKE BLVD, DEPT PSYCH 24153 #005-15-1982 L1986 P *030 †75

SIBLEY, Wm Langley, III. 1802 BRAEBURN DR 24153 #051-01-1956 L1956 GS TS *071 †85

SIMONENKO, Iouri Ivanovic. 1970 ROANOKE BLVD 24153 #913-64-1986 L2007 P *012

SINGH, Chand. 1970 ROANOKE BLVD, CLINIC 1 24153 #495-29-1975 L1978 IM EM *020 †20 ‡

SINGH, Surindra J. 1970 ROANOKE BLVD, CHIEF EMERGENCY MED 24153 #495-90-1974 L1977 CCM EM *020 †20

SMITH, Richard Allen. 1900 ELECTRIC RD 24153 #051-07-1992 L1997 DR *020 †80

SMITH, Samuel Nowell. 1802 BRAEBURN DR, LEWIS-GALE LABORATORY SVC 24153 #036-05-1968 L1972 FM *020 †18

SPETZLER, Bertram W. 1802 BRAEBURN DR 24153 #016-01-1975 L1980 ORS *020 †40

STAYKOV, Ivaylo Draganov. 1802 BRAEBURN DR 24153 #198-05-1998 L2004 CN *100

STEFFE, Lee Anne. 1802 BRAEBURN DR 24153 #051-04-1981 L1983 PD *020 †55

STEWART, Bruce Neal. 1802 BRAEBURN DR 24153 #011-03-1970 L1976 PUD SME *020 †20

STEWART, Thomas Woodruff. 2155 APPERSON DR 24153 #035-01-1945 L1952 AN OS *071 †05

SWANSON, Marc Alan. 1802 BRAEBURN DR 24153 #055-01-1980 L1991 PME AN *020 †16,05

SWARTZENDRUBER, F D. ■ 24153 #011-03-1975 L1992 GS VS *020 †85

SWARTZENDRUBER, Frederick. 1802 BRAEBURN DR 24153 #016-11-1947 L1948 GS VS *020 †85

TAN, Shen-Li. 1970 ROANOKE BLVD, SALEM VAMC; CARDIOLOGY 111 24153 #825-01-1997 L2006 IC *100 †20

TATULLI, Francesco. 1970 VA MEDICAL CENTER 24153 #561-21-1989 GS *100

TAYLOR, Clarence Waldo. 1900 ELECTRIC RD 24153 #051-04-1955 L1955 FM IMG *071 †18

TELLIAN, Frank Frederick. 1970 ROANOKE BLVD 24153 #023-07-1980 L1982 P PA *020

TILL, Jonathan Stanwood. 1802 BRAEBURN DR, LEWIS-GALE LABORATORY SVC 24153 #012-05-1982 L1986 OPH *020 †35

TIMS, Roger Dean. 1802 BRAEBURN DR, LEWIS GALE CLINIC 24153 #001-02-1971 L1976 EM UCM *071 †16

TORRE, Brian Anthony. 1802 BRAEBURN DR 24153 #051-04-1980 L1986 ORS HS *020 †40

TORRE, Mark Steven. 1900 ELECTRIC RD 24153 #051-07-1999 L1999 AN *020

TRAN, Tu Anh. 1802 BRAEBURN DR 24153 #020-12-1978 L1979 OTO HNS *020 †45 ‡

TRIPP, Henry F, Jr. 1802 BRAEBURN DR 24153 #036-07-1985 L2001 TS VS *020 †90,85 ‡

VALLESTEROS, Alfredo, Jr. 1900 ELECTRIC RD, SALEM HOSPITALISTS, LLC 24153 #748-02-1986 L1999 IM *020 †20

VAN DER LINDEN, Brian J. 1906 BRAEBURN DR, SOUTHWEST VIRGINIA, P.C. 24153 #030-06-1989 L1995 GE IM *020 †20

VIKELIDOU, Iphigenia. 1802 BRAEBURN DR, LEWIS-GALE CLINIC 24153 #418-02-1971 L1993 PD N *020 †75

VINCENT, Christopher K. 1802 BRAEBURN DR, LEWIS-GALE PHYSICIANS, LLC 24153 #025-01-1987 L2005 VS *020 †85,90

VIVIAN, Stephan Jos. 1802 BRAEBURN DR, LEWIS-GALE PHYSICIANS, LLC 24153 #038-41-1984 L2007 ICE CD *020 †20

WALDROP, Preston Adam. 1900 BRAEBURN DR, 101 KNORBREAK ROAD 24153 #051-01-1984 L1990 ORS OSM *020 †40

WATSON, Bruce Allen. 426 W MAIN ST 24153 #051-04-1973 L1974 OPH PD *071 †35

WATTS, Earl Wilson, Jr. 2155 APPERSON DR 24153 #051-04-1955 L1955 OM *071

WESLEY, Roger Lee. 1900 ELECTRIC RD, LEWIS GALE MEDICAL CENTER 24153 #051-04-1985 L1987 AN PME *020 †05

WHITE, Paul Fletcher. 1802 BRAEBURN DR 24153 #051-04-1964 L1964 AI PD *071 †55,03

WHITEHURST, Robert Morris. 1802 BRAEBURN DR, LEWIS-GALE CLINIC 24153 #036-07-1981 L1985 CLP ATP *020 †50

WICKHAM, James Randall. 1970 ROANOKE BLVD 24153 #051-01-1989 L1991 P *020 †75

WILLIAMS, Donald Richard. 2102 W MAIN ST 24153 #051-04-1962 L1962 FM *020 †18

WILLIAMS, Robert Barclay. 1908 BRAEBURN DR, SALEM SURGICAL 24153 #036-05-1987 L1993 GS *020 †85

WILLIAMS, Samuel J, II. 834 RED LN 24153 #038-40-1973 L1980 GS VS *071 †85

WILSON, Wayne Hilton. 1970 ROANOKE BLVD, VA MEDICAL CENTER 24153 #051-04-1964 L1964 GS *020 †85

WITTEN, James A. 1802 BRAEBURN DR 24153 #051-04-1972 L1975 PUD IM *020 †20

WRAY, Carol Ann. 2880 KEAGY RD 24153 #025-01-1982 L1988 PS HS *020 †65

YAZEL, J Joe. SALEM VA MED CTR RM 116A 24153 #038-40-1971 L1979 P IM *020 †20,75

YONEYAMA, Tatsuo. 1970 ROANOKE BLVD 24153 #572-29-1955 L1977 **ATP CLP** *020 †50
YOUNG, Deana Ann. 2102 W MAIN ST 24153 #051-01-1995 L2002 **FM** *020 †18
ZELLER, Robert Geo. 1802 BRAEBURN DR, RADIOLOGY DEPARTMENT 24153 #023-01-1976 L1996 **VIR DR** *020 †80

SALTVILLE – SMYTH

ALVARADO, Jacinto C. PO BOX 729, 308 W MAIN ST 24370 #319-02-1969 L1995 **GS ORS** *074
ELMORE, Karen A. 308 W MAIN ST, SALTVILLE MEDICAL CENTER 24370 #051-04-1998 L1998 **IM** *020 †20
FINNE, Charles O. PO BOX 1000, 308 W MAIN ST 24370 #047-06-1943 L1947 **FM ORS** *071
ODOM, Marshall Harrell. ■ 24370 #036-01-1975 L2001 **FM** *020 †16
WILLIAMS, Paul D. 308 W MAIN ST 24370 #047-20-1984 L1985 **FM** *020 †18

SALUDA – MIDDLESEX

LENGUA, Jose Antonio. PRINCE GEORGE 23149 #737-01-1962 L1974 **GP GS** *020
MUIR, Brockett, Jr. PO BOX 499, 820 GLOUCESTER RD 23149 #051-01-1962 L1962 **OBG** *020 †30

SANDSTON – HENRICO

HAKE, Gerald Wm. 6 E WILLIAMSBURG RD 23150 #308-07-1982 L1986 **IM** *020
MALLOY, Jessica Kristin. ■ 23150 #051-04-2007 L2007 **P** *012

SANDY HOOK – GOOCHLAND

BOWLES, James Harold. 2884 SANDY HOOK RD 23153 #047-07-1952 L1953 **GP** *020
BOWLES, James Harold, Jr. 2884 SANDY HOOK RD 23153 #051-01-1982 L1983 **FM** *020 †18
SHORT, Shelley Cronin. 2884 SANDY HOOK RD 23153 #051-04-1994 L1994 **FM** *072 †18

SCHUYLER – NELSON

SMIGRODZKI, Rafal Marek. 4323 CARTER RD, 4323 CARTER RD 22969 #759-12-1990 L2002 **N** *020 †75

SCOTTSVILLE – BUCKINGHAM

CAMPANELLI, Craig Paul. ■ 24590 #024-05-1991 L1993 **IM** *020
CELIN, John Frank. ■ 24590 #561-03-1972 **PS** *020
DIEHL, Laurie Ann. ■ 24590 #051-01-2007 L2007 **P** *012
DUFF, Pamela Beth. ■ 24590 #035-19-1972 L1995 **PD** *020 †55
REELE, Stots B. ■ 24590 #048-04-1971 L1971 **PA IM** *071 †20
SCHMIDT, Tim Totten. RR 1 BOX 269 24590 #017-20-1975 L1995 **ORS GS** *071 †40
WHITESIDE, Connie. ■ 24590 #041-07-1978 L1979 **IM** *030 †20

SEAFORD – YORK

KRAMER, David Timothy. ■ 23696 #023-12-1996 L1998 **FM** *020 †18
ROSS-CLUNIS, Hayden. ■ 23696 #051-04-1991 L1994 **IM** *020 †20
TRICE, Thomas Bernard. ■ 23696 #036-08-1994 L1996 **IM** *020

SHAWSVILLE – MONTGOMERY

HEMPHILL, Julia Tyra. 6920 ROANOKE RD 24162 #001-02-1997 L1997 **FM** *020 †18
SMITH, George Robt, Jr. PO BOX 187, 4330 PAIR O DOCS LN 24162 #024-01-1953 L1955 **FM** *071 †18

SHENANDOAH – PAGE

BROTHERS, Richard M. 424 S 3RD ST 22849 #051-04-1978 L1980 **FM** *020 †18

SHIPMAN – NELSON

GIOVANOLI, Ernest John. ■ 22971 #561-17-1958 L1960 **P** *020
GOETZ, Axel Armin. ■ 22971 #409-19-1966 **OS** *062
TURNER, Edwin Witcher. ■ 22971 #012-05-1941 L1995 **FM AM** *071 †18

SMITHFIELD – ISLE OF WIGHT

BARAKAT, Habib Khalil. 919 S CHURCH ST 23430 #605-03-1992 L1996 **IM PCC** *020 †20
BELVIN, David Glenn. 919 S CHURCH ST, INC 23430 #051-04-1983 L1985 **FM** *020 †18
BLACKNER, Kenneth Todd. ■ 23430 #049-01-2005 L2006 ***100
CAMPBELL, Laura Pendleton. ■ 23430 #051-07-1989 L1992 **CHP** *020
EICH, David Meeks. 919 S CHURCH ST 23430 #051-04-1984 L1985 **CD IM** *020 †20
FITZHARRIS, Joan Maychu. 919 S CHURCH ST, SMITHFIELD MEDICAL CENTER 23430 #036-07-1994 L2006 **IM** *020 †20
HEARN, Brian B. ■ 23430 #035-15-2003 L2006 **OBG** *020
HURST, Michael Eric. 919 S CHURCH ST, SMITHFIELD MEDICAL CTR, IN 23430 #051-07-1991 L1992 **PD** *020 †55
JAMISON, Bernard Francis. 60 RIVERSIDE DR 23430 #539-01-1954 L1959 **FM** *071
JUDSON, Preston Lyman. 919 S CHURCH ST 23430 #017-20-1963 L1980 **CD IM** *071 †20 ‡
KELLS, Douglas Ulring. 919 S CHURCH ST 23430 #051-04-1967 L1967 **ORS** *071 †40
LEAVEY, James Francis. ■ 23430 #030-06-1994 L2003 **PCC** *020 †20
LEE, Timothy Navero. 919 S CHURCH ST, SMITHFIELD MEDICAL CENTER 23430 #051-04-1990 L1991 **FM OM** *020 †70,18

LEE, Timothy Patrick. 919 S CHURCH ST 23430 #539-04-1948 L1958 **OM** *071
LONGFORD, Desmond John H. ■ 23430 #539-01-1956 L1958 **OM** *020
LOPRESTI, Bartholomew M. 919 S CHURCH ST, INC 23430 #051-07-1981 L1984 **UCM GP** *020
LO PRESTI, Susan Lum. ■ 23430 #051-07-1982 L1982 **CLP BBK** *040 †50
LUNDIE, Donald Wayne. 919 S CHURCH ST, INC 23430 #051-04-1972 L1973 **FM** *020 †18
MATHEW, Jennifer Susan. 919 S CHURCH ST, SMITHFIELD MED CTR 23430 #035-48-1999 L2004 **FM** *020 †18
MITCHELL, Allen Ormond. ■ 23430 #023-12-1992 L1993 **OTO** *020 †45
MITCHELL, Melanie W. ■ 23430 #023-12-1992 L2000 **GS** *020
PARK, Crawford Dick. ■ 23430 #041-01-1963 **VS** *071 †85,90
PERSONS, Jeffrey Brewster. 919 S CHURCH ST 23430 #035-03-1981 L1986 **ORS OSM** *020 †40
POPE, Shannon Miller. 201 GUMWOOD DR 23430 #051-07-1998 L2002 **MPD** *020 †20,55
POPE, Thomas Christopher. 201 GUMWOOD DR 23430 #051-07-1998 L2002 **MPD** *020 †20,55
PSIMAS, James N. 913 S CHURCH ST, STE C 23430 #051-01-1948 L1948 **GYN** *072 †30
QUINN, Stephen Michael. 405 GATLING POINTE PKWY 23430 #051-04-2001 L2004 **EM** *020 †16
SMALL, James Fentem, III. ■ 23430 #012-05-2007 L2007 **OBG** *012
STURGILL, Eric Darren. ■ 23430 #023-12-2002 L2003 *020
TOMPKINS, James L. 919 S CHURCH ST, INC 23430 #047-05-1974 L1976 **PD** *020 †55
WALKER, Miley Wesson. 919 S CHURCH ST 23430 #047-06-1972 L1978 **U** *020 †95
WEITZMAN, Douglas Keith. 919 S CHURCH ST, INC 23430 #041-09-1984 L1986 **FM OM** *020 †18

SOUTH BOSTON – HALIFAX

AH, Robert Wan. 2204 WILBORN AVE 24592 #012-01-1987 L1993 **EM** *020 †20
ANCHETA, Romulo Andres. 1129 N MAIN ST 24592 #748-10-1964 L1972 **GP** *062
BAJWA, Gurnam Singh. 2206A WILBORN AVE 24592 #495-03-1965 L1976 **GS** *020 †85
BASSIL, Habib F. 2232 WILBORN AVE 24592 #605-02-1980 L1989 **CD** *020 †20
BELL, William Robt. 2204 WILBORN AVE 24592 #035-03-1974 L1983 **GS** *020 †85
BIBBS, Charles Spencer. 2204 WILBORN AVE 24592 #026-08-1997 L2006 **FM** *020 †18
BROWNE, Roger Wayne. 2204 WILBORN AVE 24592 #041-09-1967 L1973 **IM** *020 †20
BRUNO, Dante S. 1020 BILL TUCK HWY STE 900 24592 #748-08-1968 L1996 **GP PTH** *020
BURNETT, Gerald Crain. 2204 WILBORN AVE 24592 #051-04-1966 L1966 **D DMP** *020 †15
CARBONE, Joseph Michael. 2045 HAMILTON BLVD 24592 #028-02-1993 L2000 **U** *020 †95
CHENNAREDDY, Srinivasa R. 2204 WILBORN AVE, HEART DEPARTMENT 24592 #495-50-1994 L2007 **IC** *020 †20
CROWDER, Thos Harold, Jr. 2212 WILBORN AVE, FULLER-ROBERTS CLINIC INC 24592 #036-07-1955 L1960 **PD** *071
CUEBAS-TORRES, Juan E. 2206 WILBORN AVE STE B 24592 #042-01-1995 L2001 **N** *020 †75
DAVIS, Richard Wm. 1627 SEYMOUR DR 24592 #649-14-1988 L1989 **IM** *075
DEVINE, Joan Wilson. 2212 WILBORN AVE 24592 #051-07-1979 L1982 **OBG** *020 †30
DURR, Robert Alan. 2210 WILBORN AVE 24592 #035-06-1980 L1981 **PUD IM** *020 †20
EBALO, Nonna Mendoza. 2212 WILBORN AVE 24592 #748-08-1992 L2002 **PD** *020 †55
EVANS, Frederick Carlyle. 2212 HALIFAX RD 24592 #051-04-1958 L1958 **GYN** *020
FERGUSON, Wilson Jos. 2045 HAMILTON BLVD 24592 #038-41-1976 L1984 **U** *020 †95
FOGARTY, Jacqueline Mary. 409 OAK LN 24592 #035-03-1974 L1983 **ORS** *020 †85,40
FREDERICKS, Michael Roy. 2045 HAMILTON BLVD 24592 #028-34-1977 L2002 **NEP IM** *020 †20
FULLER, W Allen. 2212 HALIFAX RD 24592 #051-04-1946 L1949 **GS OS** *071 †85
FULLER, William Allen, Jr. 2212 WILBORN AVE 24592 #051-04-1971 L1973 **GS** *020 †85
HAGOOD, Warren Cleaton. 2204 WILBORN AVE 24592 #051-04-1953 L1953 **FM** *071
HALL, Sherry Lene. 1129 N MAIN ST 24592 #036-07-1983 L1987 **IM** *020 †20
ISKANDAR, Said Bechara. 2204 WILBORN AVE, HALIFAX REGIONAL HOSPITAL 24592 #605-03-2000 L2006 **CD** *020
JAYATILAKA, Suresh Gehan. 2232 WILBORN AVE 24592 #422-01-1999 L2007 **GE** *020 †20
JONES, Michael Francis. 2204 WILBORN AVE 24592 #038-45-1985 L2003 **EM** *020 †16
KETCHERSID, Marie K. 2045 HAMILTON BLVD 24592, NEPHROLOGY CLINIC 24592 #048-12-1989 L1996 **IM** *020 †20
KETCHERSID, Terry L. 2204 WILBORN AVE 24592 #048-12-1986 L1996 **NEP** *020 †20
KING, Broderick Darryl. 2212 WILBORN AVE 24592 #047-07-1996 L2003 **IM** *020
KING, Samantha Yvette. 2212 WILBORN AVE 24592 #047-07-1993 L2003 **PD** *020 †55
KUMAR, Pankaj. 2204 WILBORN AVE 24592 #495-54-1996 L2002 **NPM** *020 †55 ‡
LEE, Sun Geun. 2204 WILBORN AVE 24592 #583-01-1961 L1976 **EM** *020
LENZEN, Jonathan M. 2210 WILBORN AVE 24592 #422-01-1986 L1992 **IM** *020 †20
MAC CARTY, William C, III. 422 HAMILTON BLVD 24592 #024-01-1971 L1978 **ORS HS** *020 †40
MORRIS, Mark John. 521 WEBSTER ST 24592 #051-01-1987 L1991 **OPH** *020 †35
MUNGO, Albert Joseph. 2204 WILBORN AVE 24592 #016-11-1996 L2003 **DR** *020
NEELAGIRI, Venkat Rama Kr. ■ 24592 #495-37-2001 L2005 **FP** *012
NOBLIN, Frances E. ■ 24592 #051-04-1936 L1942 **PUD** *071
OTERO-TRUITT, Tessie. 2232 WILBORN AVE STE 3 24592 #422-01-1989 L1995 **END IM** *020 †20
PAMBID, Leovigil D. 1129 N MAIN ST, SOUTHSIDE MED ASSOC PC 24592 #748-08-1965 L1973 **IM** *020 †18,20
PANICH, Banyat. 2212 WILBORN AVE 24592 #891-02-1968 L1978 **PD** *020 †55
PARIKH, Amar Anilkumar. 2045 HAMILTON BLVD 24592 #012-22-2002 L2007 **NEP AMI** *020 †20
PARKER, Charles Harrison. 1627 SEYMOUR DR, P O BOX 397 24592 #041-13-1986 L1987 **GE IM** *020 †20
PATEL, Babita B. 2232 WILBORN AVE 24592 #422-01-1995 L2003 **ID IM** *020 †20
PATEL, Bakul Kumar. 2204 WILBORN AVE 24592 #422-01-1996 L2003 **GE** *020 †20
PURVIS, Edward S, II. 2232 WILBORN AVE, STE E 24592 #051-04-1984 L1996 **GS** *020 †85
RANDHAWA, Devinderpal Sin. 2232 WILBORN AVE, STE D 24592 #495-29-1993 L2005 **HO** *020
ROBERTS, Lucien Wood, Jr. 2204 WILBORN AVE 24592 #051-04-1948 L1948 **OBG OS** *071 †30
ROSCHE, Charles W. 2200 BEECHMONT RD 24592 #021-06-1985 L1988 **OBS GYN** *020 †30
RUCKER, Morton Stanley. 424 HAMILTON BLVD, HALIFAX BEHAVORIAL HLTH CN 24592 #064-01-1964 L1981 **P PYA** *071 †75
SAN PEDRO, Elmer. 2204 WILBORN AVE 24592 #748-08-1988 L2002 **DR** *020 †28,80
SCHACHT, Neil F. 2232 WILBORN AVE, STE D 24592 #422-01-1982 L1998 **HEM IM** *020 †20
SOUZA, Cesar Augusto. 2204 WILBORN AVE, HALIFAX REGIONAL HOSPITAL 24592 #924-01-1967 L1977 **AN GS** *020
SPARKS, Paul Cornwell. 422 HAMILTON BLVD 24592 #041-09-1968 L1975 **ORS** *020 †40

STANLEY, Dennis Clark. 2204 WILBORN AVE, HALIFAX REGIONAL HOSPITAL 24592
#051-04-1974 L1976 **DR** *020 †80
THANAPORN, Prasit. 2212 WILBORN AVE 24592 #891-02-1968 L1973 **OBG** *020 †30
TORRES, Ma Precious T. 2212 WILBORN AVE 24592 #748-10-1989 1996 **PD** *020 †55
TRIEU, Duc Kien. 2204 WILBORN AVE 24592 #305-01-2002 L2002 **OBG** *020
TRUITT, Terrance J. 2210 WILBORN AVE 24592 #422-01-1989 L1995 **PUD CCM** *020 †20
TRUITT, Thomas Michael. 2232 WILBORN AVE 24592 #422-01-1989 L1996 **P** *020
TUCKER, Henry Jos. 2212 WILBORN AVE, FULLER-ROBERTS CLINIC INC 24592
#051-04-1958 L1958 **GS CRS** *071
URUETA, Enrique E. 2204 WILBORN AVE 24592 #264-05-1962 L1975 **GP PTH** *071 †50
WARD, Phillip Dale. 2212 WILBORN AVE, P O BOX 10 24592 #051-04-1973 L1975 **OBG** *020 †30
WHITLOW, Zachary Stewart. 2100 WILBORN AVE 24592 #051-01-1987 L1992 **GS VS** *020
WISEMAN, Floyd C. 3046 CARLBROOK RD 24592 #048-14-1982 L1986 **P PYA** *020 †75
WITKO, James F. 2210 WILBORN AVE, SOUTHSIDE VIRGINIA 24592 #561-07-1982 L1988
PUD IM *020 †20

SOUTH HILL — MECKLENBURG

ADAMS, Anthony Clay. PO BOX 90, 125 BUENA VISTA CIR 23970 #020-12-1993 L2005
EM *020 †18
ALLEN, Harry Richard. PO BOX 267 23970 #005-14-1964 L1966 **CHP P** *020 †55
ALLEN, Herbert R, Jr. 23970 #036-01-1985 L1986 **IM** *020 †20
BELMONTE, Winona Zenobia. 412 BRACEY LN 23970 #748-10-1993 L1998 **P PYG** *020 †75
BOUTROS, Samir. 125 BUENA VISTA CIR 23970 #915-04-1964 L1980 **U GS** *020 †95
BRAND, Rolf. ■ 23970 #143-08-1969 L1979 **FM** *020
BROWN, David Hamilton. 125 BUENA VISTA CIR, BOX 90 23970 #065-01-1972 L1992 *020 ‡
CRICHLOW, Brian Robert. 302 N MECKLENBURG AVE 23970 #036-07-1999 L2004
OPH *020 †35
CROWDER, Charles H, Jr. ■ 23970 #051-01-1952 L1952 **FM IM** *071 †18
DAW, Albert Lee. 833 W DANVILLE ST 23970 #023-01-1968 L1973 **GS GP** *071 †85
DE MOYA, Jose F. 416 DURANT ST 23970 #308-01-1977 L1996 **GS VS** *020 †85
DUGAR, Nidhi. ■ 23970 #495-37-1999 L2003 **IM** *100 †20
FOZDAR, Manish Amrish. 412 BRACEY LN 23970 #495-76-1988 L1998 **PFP** *020 †75
GEAR, Arthur Sewell. 516 W ATLANTIC ST 23970 #051-04-1959 L1959 **CD IM** *020
GOLI, Devainder. 125 BUENA VISTA CIR BOX 90, EMERGENCY MEDICINE 23970
#495-36-1974 L1997 **EM PTH** *020 †16
GULMATICO, Oscar B. 302 PETTUS ST 23970 #748-09-1968 L1977 **PD** *020
HORNE, Wallace Jennings. 125 BUENA VISTA CIR, P O BOX 90 23970 #051-04-1981 L1982
EM FM *030 †16,18 ‡
JONES, James David. 412 BRACEY LN 23970 #036-07-1954 L1998 **P PD** *020 †55,75
KAISER, Suzanne B. 202 E FERRELL ST 23970 #915-02-1961 L1991 **IM** *071
KAISER, Zoheir Jos. 125 BUENA VISTA CIR 23970 #915-02-1957 L1987 **OTO** *020
KEELING, Robert D. ■ 23970 #051-04-1946 L1947 **EM GP** *071
KILPATRICK, Kathryn Ann. 514 W ATLANTIC ST, SOUTH HILL FAMILY MEDICINE 23970
#051-04-1983 L1988 **PD** *020 †55
LACY, Matthew L, II. 125 BUENA VISTA CIR 23970 #051-04-1946 L1946 **GS** *071
LEWIS, Robert M, Jr. 125 BUENA VISTA CIR, COMMUNITY MEMORIAL HOSPITA 23970
#705-06-1983 L2005 **EM** *020
MICHIE, David Wayne. 514 W ATLANTIC ST 23970 #051-04-1997 L1997 **FM** *020 †18
MILLER, Michael Francis. 125 BUENA VISTA CIR 23970 #051-07-1984 L1991 **IM** *020 †20
NGUYEN, Phong Huu. 125 BUENA VISTA CIR, P O BOX 90 23970 #038-06-1996 L1996
FM *020 †18
NWAOKOCHA, Charles Ngozi. ■ 23970 #690-06-1990 L2005 **IM** *020 †20
POWELL, Mark Alan. 125 BUENA VISTA CIR, COMMUNITY MEM HEALTHCTR 23970
#041-12-1993 L1997 **AN** *020
POWERS, Linda Pacharzina. 516 W ATLANTIC ST 23970 #048-02-1985 L1986 **END IM** *062 †20
REPLOGLE, Corinne Ruth. 514 W ATLANTIC ST, LITTLETON FAMILY PRACTICE 23970
#041-14-1997 L2004 **FM** *020 †18
SADIGHIAN, Z Dean. 408 DURANT ST 23970 #517-01-1943 L1957 **GP PUD** *071
SAUNDERS, Thomas Archer. 401 DURANT ST, P O BOX 396 23970 #051-04-1948 L1948
GP OBG *071
SHELTON, Wm Alexander, Jr. 821 W DANVILLE ST, THOMAS A SAUNDERS DR OFC 23970
#051-04-1980 L1980 **FM** *072 †18
SIMON, Derron Mc Rae. 416 DURANT ST, CMH SURGICAL SERVICES, LLC 23970
#025-07-1996 L2002 **GS** *020 †85
SPORE, Richard Wayne. 125 BUENA VISTA CIR, EMERGENCY DEPARTMENT 23970
#047-06-1974 L1989 **EM FM** *020
STRUNK, John Robert. 125 BUENA VISTA CIR 23970 #649-14-1978 L1982 **IM CCM** *020 †20
STURMER, Frederick Chas. 833 W DANVILLE ST 23970 #012-01-1963 L1963 **GS** *071 †85
THOMPSON, Kimberly Ann. 516 W ATLANTIC ST 23970 #041-15-2000 **PD** *100
WASHBURN, Ronald Lee. 125 BUENA VISTA CIR 23970 #035-06-1973 L1979 **R OS** *020 †80
WILLIAMS, Carlos A. ■ 23970 #308-01-1980 L1994 **N OS** *040 †75
YORK, Lisa Michelle. 514 W ATLANTIC ST 23970 #051-01-2001 L2004 **FM** *020 †18

SOUTH RIDING — LOUDOUN

ASSEFA, Getu. 25499 DABNER DR 20152 #198-01-1989 L2001 **CD** *020 †20
COX, Karin Angelika. 26137 KENNYWOOD SQ 20152 #051-07-1991 L2003 **IM OM** *020 †70,20
FOGARTY, Lynn Darby. 43063 PEACOCK MARKET PLZ, STE 150 20152 #051-01-2000 L2000
PD *020 †55
HAMEED, Zahid. ■ 20152 #704-21-1991 L2005 **P** *020
MICHEL, Edward David. 43063 PEACOCK MARKET PLZ, STE 150 20152 #041-13-1992 L2000
PD *020 †55
PRICE, Shannon Elaine. 25055 RIDING PLZ, SOUTH RIDING PEDIATRICS 20152
#041-15-2000 L2003 **PD** *020 †55
REYNOLDS, Benjamin P. 43063 PEACOCK MARKET PLZ, STE 150 20152 #051-01-2001 L2004
PD *020 †55
STERN, Mindy Pasik. 43063 PEACOCK MARKET PLZ, FARRELL PEDIATRICS 20152
#025-01-1996 L2004 **PD** *020 †55
STEWART, Allan H. ■ 20152 #010-01-1952 L1959 **P PYA** *020 †75,18

SOUTHBRIDGE — PRINCE WILLIAM

SINGH, Ravinder Pal. 17193 WAYSIDE DR 22026 #495-10-1981 L1996 **PUD** *020 †20

SPOTSYLVANIA – SPOTSYLVANIA

APTER, Ronald Alan. ■ 22551 #010-01-1958 L1962 **CD IM** *071 †20
BROWN, Dana B. 10482 GEORGETOWN DR, RAPPAHANNOCK FAMILY PHYSIC 22553
#051-01-1997 L1997 **FM** *020 †20
FLOYD, Julie Mary. 10482 GEORGETOWN DR 22553 #035-15-1995 L2005 **FM** *040 †18
LOVELLO, Katherine T. 7307 BLOOMSBURY LN, STE 101 22553 #033-06-1984 L1993
EM GP *020 †16
RICHMAN, Suzanne. 10411 COURTHOUSE RD, STE A 22553 #041-02-1988 L1998 **PD** *020 †55
WALSH, Edward Gilbert. ■ 22551 #051-01-2004 L2004 **EM** *020

SPRING GROVE – SURRY

INGRAM, Rebecca Jill. ■ 23881 #051-01-2002 L2002 **P** *100

SPRINGFIELD – FAIRFAX

ABLES, Waylan, Jr. 6501 LOISDALE CT, MID ATLANTIC PERM MED GROU 22150
#010-03-1981 L1986 **GS** *020 †85
ADAM, Yehuda G. 6501 LOISDALE CT 22150 #550-01-1958 L1985 **GS** *071 †85
ADEWALE, Benjamin Adyson. 7011 CALAMO ST, STE 105 22150 #308-11-1987 L1996
P *020 †75
AHN, Peter Juhee. ■ 22150 #023-12-1992 L1994 **DR** *020 †80
ALBUERNE, Mercedes S. ■ 22009 #275-01-1960 L1966 **PD** *062
ALPAN, Oral. 6210 OLD KEENE MILL RD 22152 #902-05-1990 L2005 **AI** *020 †55,03
ASMAR, Jabib. ■ 22151 #308-01-1962 L1975 **NEP** *075
AZIZI, Percilla. ■ 22153 #496-07-1992 L2003 **IM** *020 †20
BALDO, Edna Reyes. 8136 OLD KEENE MILL RD, FAIRFAX COUNTY HLTH DEPT 22152
#748-01-1968 L1983 **GP** *020
BALL, Achana V. 8136 OLD KEENE MILL RD, STE A100 22152 #891-02-1969 L1988 **IM PUD** *020
BANKS, Gregory Charles. 6501 LOISDALE CT 22150 #010-03-1996 L2000 **FM** *020 †18
BARBASH, Andrew Jeffrey. 6501 LOISDALE CT, C/O KAISER PERMANENTE 22150
#016-06-1981 L1987 **N MDM** *030 †75
BAYLY, Timothy Clohessy. 5510 ALMA LN, STE 3 22151 #010-02-1972 L1983
PUD CCM *072 †20
BAZEL, Samaneh. 6501 LOISDALE CT 22150 #041-13-2001 L2003 **PD** *020 †55
BEDNOV, Yanina M. 6501 LOISDALE CT 22150 #913-05-1981 L1998 **PCP** *020 †50
BENNETT, Bruce H. 7470 SPRING VILLAGE DR, RC-215 22150 #010-01-1938 L1966
AM OM *071 †70
BERSOFF-MATCHA, Susan J. 6501 LOISDALE CT, SPRINGFIELD MEDICAL CENTER 22150
#010-02-1993 L1999 **ID** *020 †20
BOOTH, Alexandra Elaine. 6501 LOISDALE CT 22150 #041-12-1994 L2000 **GS** *020 †85
BRADLEY-NORTH, Carole J. 6501 LOISDALE CT 22150 #010-03-1972 L1983 **END IM** *020 †20
BRANDWIN, Leslie Martin. 7440 SPRING VILLAGE DR, GREENSPRING VLG MED CTR 22150
#028-34-1971 L1972 **RHU IM** *020 †20
BROWER, Gerry Lee. ■ 22150 #038-41-1988 L1990 **GPM** *020 †70,18
BUTTERFIELD, Betty Jean. 6501 LOISDALE CT 22150 #005-06-1982 L1987 **GE** *020 †20
CALHOUN, Stephen Marc. 6501 LOISDALE CT, CTR 22150 #010-02-1980 L1989
IM PUD *020 †20
CARLINI, Margaret Theresa. 8136 OLD KEENE MILL RD # A 22152 #010-02-1986 L1990
PM *020 †60
CARSJO, Alma Britt-Marie. 6501 LOISDALE CT, DEPT OF OB/GYN 22150 #858-03-1977 L1991
OBG GO *020 †30
CARTMELL, Jo Ellen. 7440 SPRING VILLAGE DR 22150 #017-20-1984 L1987 **IM** *020 †20
CASUGA-MARQUEZ, Erlinda. ■ 22150 #748-08-1973 L1990 **P CHP** *020
CHEEMA, Abdul Hanan. 6417 LOISDALE RD, STE 309 22150 #704-04-1996 L2006 **IM** *020
CHOI, Rosan Y. 6501 LOISDALE CT, DEPT-OPHTHALMOLOGY 22150 #051-04-1995 L1995
OPH *020 †35
CHRISTIE, Catherine M. 6501 LOISDALE CT 22150 #041-02-1984 L1989 **PD PDE** *020 †55
CIGTAY, Attila Sakir. 6501 LOISDALE CT, KAISER PERMANENTE 22150 #902-01-1956 L1967
DR *020 †80
COCCARO, Alfred Philip. 6128 BRANDON AVE, STE 205 22150 #035-15-1967 L1972
DR NM *020 †28,80
CONANT, Katherine Ellen. ■ 22150 #024-05-1987 L1988 **N** *020 †75
CORNET, Antoine Parnell. ■ 22151 #440-01-1974 L1982 **P N** *020
COSTENBADER, Cynthia Lou. 8136 OLD KEENE MILL RD, STE A 22152 #023-01-1982 L1984
PD *020 †55
COURTNEY, Gina Gayle. 6501 LOISDALE CT 22150 #010-03-1986 L1989 **PD** *020 †55
CRAIG, Thomas John. ■ 22152 #035-08-1963 L1969 **P GPM** *030 †70,75
CRIM, Lisa Margarethe. 8316 TRAFORD LN, VIRGINIA PEDIATRIC/ADOLSEC 22152
#038-41-1987 L1989 **PD** *020 †55
CURRALL, Victoria Regina. 5510 ALMA LN 22151 #010-02-1998 L1998 **IM** *020 †20
CURREY, N Carol Deangelis. 8346 TRAFORD LN, STE 101 22152 #051-04-1997 L1997
AI *020 †20,03
DALTNER, Lynn Ann. 5510 ALMA LN, VA MEDICAL ALLIANCE 22151 #036-05-1989 L1995
IM *020 †20
DAVACHI, Farzin. 8134 OLD KEENE MILL RD, STE 300 22152 #517-04-1961 L1994
PDC PD *071 †55
DAVIDSON, Stuart L. 5514 ALMA LN, STE 100 22151 #024-05-1976 L1983 **ORS** *020 †40
DAVIS, Mark Philip. 5501 BACKLICK RD, STE 105 22151 #051-04-1974 L1976 **EM** *020 †16
DAVISON, Rebecca Jane. 6501 LOISDALE CT 22150 #036-01-1990 L1991 **FM** *020 †18
DE ANGELIS, Robert Neal. 8346 TRAFORD LN 22152 #051-04-1968 L1968 **D DMP** *020 †15
DHARIA, Tarum Manilal. 6501 LOISDALE CT, KAISER PERMANENTE 22150 #495-17-1972 L1991
OBG *020 †20
DOAN, Minh-Phuong Lu. 6501 LOISDALE CT, KAISER PERMANENTE 22150 #010-01-2001 L2001
IM *020 †35
DONOVAN, Claudia K. 6501 LOISDALE CT, SPRINGFIELD MEDICAL CENTER 22150
#035-08-1987 L1990 **FM** *020 †18
ELCHURI, Swati Vijayaksh. ■ 22153 #051-01-2007 **PD** *012
ELLER, Marc Allan. 5510 ALMA LN, STE 2 22151 #011-02-1984 L1990 **FM** *020 †18
ERIM, Zeki. ■ 22152 #902-03-1953 L1958 **R** *071 †80
EZMERLI, Nahed Mahmoud. 6501 LOISDALE CT 22150 #010-01-1999 L1999 **OBG** *020 †30
FATTEH, Naaz. 6501 LOISDALE CT 22150 #041-07-1992 L1995 **IM ID** *020 †20

FEINBERG, Jeffrey Heyman. ■ 22152 #023-12-1997 L1998 **FM AM** *020 †18
FERRER, Rosario Cabrera. 6365 ROLLING MILL PL, STE 103 22152 #748-01-1977 L1985 **IM** *020
FISHER, Margaret E. 6501 LOISDALE CT 22150 #035-01-1983 L1991 **IM RHU** *020 †20
FITZ, Veronica Elizabeth. 6501 LOISDALE CT 22150 #016-42-1981 L1985 **PD** *020 †55
FRASER, Douglas J, Jr. 5411 BACKLICK RD STE A 22151 #010-02-1969 L1973 **OPH** *020 †35
FURST, Eric Jonathan. 5504 BACKLICK RD 22151 #048-04-1986 L1992 **OTO HNS** *020 †45
GABLE, Janice Ruth Fox. 7440 SPRING VILLAGE DR, GREENSPRING MEDICAL CENTER 22150 #017-20-1970 L1971 **FPG** *020 †18 ‡
GADOL, Judith. 8134 OLD KEENE MILL RD, EYE CONSULTANTS OF 22152 #023-01-1975 L1979 **OPH** *020 †35
GARDNER, Allen Stiles. 6128 BRANDON AVE, STE 201 22150 #010-01-1960 L1967 **IM GE** *020
GESICKI-WOOD, Laura M. 8134 OLD KEENE MIL RD #301, ACCREDITED ALLERGY CTR 22152 #051-01-1999 L2002 **AI** *020 †20
GIOIA, Adriana R. 5502 BACKLICK RD, VA MEDICAL URGENT CARE 22151 #011-02-1985 L1992 **FM** *020 †20
GOLDBERG, Michael Harvey. 8134 OLD KEENE MILL RD, EYE CONSULTANTS 22152 #010-02-1974 L1979 **OPH** *020 †35
GREEN, Ira. 6501 LOISDALE CT 22150 #035-08-1953 L1969 **IM** *050 †20
GREEN, Ira Joel. 6501 LOISDALE CT 22150 #869-05-1957 L1960 **DR R** *020 †80
GUSTAFSON, John Fowler. 7406 SPRING VILLAGE DR, HP309 22150 #035-20-1954 L1979 **IM CD** *071
HABTEMARIAM, Yonathan. 6334 SHAUNDALE DR 22152 #023-07-2008 *012
HALLE, Michael B. 6501 LOISDALE CT, KAISER PERMENENTE 22150 #021-01-1989 L1992 **IM** *020 †20
HAMILTON, Kathleen Marie. 6120 BRANDON AVE STE 203 22150 #010-01-1976 L1985 **PD PDC** *020 †55
HASHISH, Lama Abdulkader. ■ 22150 #875-01-1992 L1998 **RHU** *020 †20
HASSAN, Syed Siraj-Ul-. ■ 22153 #704-08-1970 L2000 **PD FM** *020 †55
HIRSCHHORN, Jessica Betsy. 6501 LOISDALE CT 22150 #010-02-1983 L1985 **ORS** *020 †40
HOANG, Jacqueline Kim. 5502 BACKLICK RD 22151 #051-04-1993 L1994 **PD** *020 †55
HOGAN, Martha L Wyrick. 8316 TRAFORD LN 22152 #010-02-1968 L1971 **PD** *020 †55
HOSSANIMADANI, Ahmad Reza. ■ 22153 #010-03-2008 *012
HUANG, Eric C. ■ 22151 #035-03-2005 L2005 **PTH** *012
IMBURG, Jerome. ■ 22150 #051-04-1947 L1947 **OS** *072 †55
IMMEL, Walter Wm. 5510 ALMA LN, STE 3 22151 #032-01-1981 L1986 **GE IM** *020 †20
JARRIS, Paul Edward. ■ 22153 #041-01-1984 L1985 **FM** *020 †18
JARVANDI, Mohammad. 8316 TRAFORD LN, CENTER, PC 22152 #305-01-1999 L2001 **PD** *020 †55
JEFFREY-COKER, Lami A. 6501 LOISDALE CT 22150 #010-03-1984 L1988 **OBG** *020 †30
JIN, Sang Ho. ■ 22152 #583-04-1953 **AN** *075
JOHNSON, Lester Dean, Jr. ■ 22150 #010-02-1947 L1956 **OBG** *071
JOHNSON, Paul Wm, Jr. 5510 ALMA LN 22151 #017-20-1976 L1980 **IM** *020 †20
JONES, Vonnegretc Jeanell. ■ 22152 #010-02-2008 *012
KAPLAN, Saul James. 6501 LOISDALE CT 22150 #001-02-1980 L1987 **HS ORS** *020 †40
KASMAN, Roberta Alene. 6501 LOISDALE CT 22150 #005-18-1988 L1996 **ORS** *020 †40
KATZ, Ernest. 6128 BRANDON AVE, STE 201 22150 #035-09-1978 L1987 **IM GE** *020 †20
KATZ, Stuart E. 6501 LOISDALE CT 22150 #024-07-1976 L1984 **U** *020 †95
KAWECKI, Janet K. 6501 LOISDALE CT 22150 #010-02-1976 L1979 **IM** *071 †20
KEIM, Daniel Edward. 8348 TRAFORD LN STE 301 22152 #008-01-1968 L1981 **ID OS** *020 †55
KHAN, Rais Ahmad. ■ 22152 #704-02-1988 L2007 **P** *100
KHINE, Mimi. 5537 HEMPSTEAD WAY 22151 #209-01-1973 L1989 **P** *020
KIM, Hie Chul. 8925 BURKE LAKE RD 22151 #583-06-1965 L1973 **PM PMM** *071 †60 ‡
KITCHEN, Robert Henry, Jr. 6501 LOISDALE RD 22150 #021-01-1976 L1988 **FM** *020 †18
KNOX, Henry Donald. ■ 22152 #041-02-1957 L1963 **PD** *071 †55
KOENIGER, Mark Andrew. ■ 22153 #023-12-1992 L1994 **FP** *020 †20
KRAMER, Dan. 6501 LOISDALE CT, KAISER PERMANENTE 22150 #051-01-1970 L1970 **R** *020 †80
KUHN, Amy L. ■ 22150 #038-06-1931 L1942 **PD GP** *071
LEE, Louis Choong. ■ 22151 #010-01-2006 L2006 **GS** *012
LEE-FAUST, Carol S. 8134 OLD KEENE MILL RD, EYE CONSULTANTS OF 22152 #041-07-1996 L2004 **OPH** *020 †35
LEJMAN, Elisabeth. 6501 LOISDALE CT 22150 #759-01-1975 L1989 **D** *020 †15
LITTLETON, Philip Ray. 6120 BRANDON AVE, STE 308 22150 #036-01-1967 L1972 **PD** *071 †55
LODHI, Tahira Irum. ■ 22152 #704-24-1999 L2007 **FP** *012
LOPEZ, Emigdio A, Jr. 6116 ROLLING RD, STE 216 22152 #748-02-1972 L1979 **IM** *020 †20
LU, Robert Rhett. 6120 BRANDON AVE, NOVA PEDIATRICS, LTD. 22150 #005-06-2004 L2007 **PD** *020 †55
LURIE, Marc Alan. 6501 LOISDALE CT 22150 #023-01-1977 L1983 **PD** *020 †55
MAGBUHOS, Celerino M. 6501 LOISDALE CT 22150 #748-02-1978 L1990 **IM** *020 †20
MAGEE, P F Adrian. 5514 ALMA LN, STE 200 22151 #539-06-1981 L1988 **CD** *020 †20
MAHDI, Saad Fakhri. 6370 SPRINGFIELD PLZ 22150 #528-05-1991 L2001 **IM P** *020 †20
MAI, Phuong Xuan. 6620 KEENE DR, VIRGINIA PAIN & REHABILITA 22152 #422-01-1998 L2002 **PM** *020 †60
MALHI-CHOULA, Navreet. 6501 LOISDALE CT, KAISER PERMANENTE 22150 #495-45-1993 L1998 **GE** *020 †20
MAMANA, John Philip. 5510 ALMA LN 22151 #024-05-1970 L1971 **IM** *020 †20
MANSFIELD, Kevin Jonathan. ■ 22152 #010-02-2008 *012
MARCUS, Norman Aaron. 8346 TRAFORD LN STE B-4 22152 #005-11-1978 L1983 **ORS HS** *020 †40
MARTZ, Douglas Gorr. ■ 22150 #041-01-1955 L1956 **PTH** *071 †50
MATHESON, John A. ■ 22150 #035-08-1944 L1947 **FM** *071 †18
MAYERGOYZ, Deborah Yokubo. 8348 TRAFORD LN, STE 301 22152 #913-05-1972 L1986 **PD** *020 †55
MCCLINTOCK, Benjamin Will. ■ 22152 #010-01-2008 *012
MC NALLY, Patricia Ann. 6501 LOISDALE CT 22150 #010-02-1987 L1990 **AI IM** *020 †20,03
MEMBER, Bernard J. ■ 22151 #035-19-1979 L1995 **CHP PD** *020 †55
MERCHANT, Aziz. ■ 22151 #041-02-2000 L2000 **GS** *012
MESSMAN, Kenny Wayne. 6501 LOISDALE CT, FAMILY PRACTICE DEPT 22150 #047-05-1969 L2000 **FM** *020 †18
MIRMIRANI, Nooreddin. 5537 HEMPSTEAD WAY 22151 #517-01-1970 L1977 **CHP** *020 †75
MOALEMI, Azita. 6136 BRANDON AVE, MOUNT VERNON CARDIOLOGY 22150 #023-01-1992 L1993 **CD** *020 †20
MOORE, Sharon Kelley. 8348 TRAFORD LN, STE 400 22150 #010-03-1993 L1999 **P** *020 †75

MORAN, Raul A. 8297 BARK TREE CT 22153 #748-10-1979 L1983 **AN** *020
MUELLER, Karl H. 6320 AUGUSTA DR 22150 #407-20-1955 L1967 **P** *071
NADEEM, Sumera. ■ 22150 #704-02-1996 L2002 **P** *020 †75
NEGRON RIVERA, Luis A. ■ 22153 #847-05-1964 L1981 **EM** *071 †16
NEKOBA, Jeffrey Kibe. 7489 HUNTSMAN BLVD, HUNTSMAN MEDICAL CENTER 22153 #051-04-1991 L1994 **FM** *020 †18
NELSON, Jennell Elizabeth. 6501 LOISDALE CT, DERMATOLOGY DEPT 22150 #047-07-1996 L2000 **D** *020 †15
NGUYEN, Liem Thanh. 6828 COMMERCE ST, STE 101 22150 #941-01-1972 L1985 **FM** *020 †18
OMARA, Timothy John. 8316 TRAFORD LN 22152 #010-02-1999 L1999 **PD** *020 †55
OSHRY, Stacy Yale. 5510 ALMA LN 22151 #023-01-1993 L1993 **IM** *020 †20
PALUCH, Simon. 6120 BRANDON AVE 22150 #407-04-1949 L1954 **IM** *071
PAPPOUS, Panagiotis. 5504 BACKLICK RD 22151 #418-01-1958 L1967 **OTO A** *020
PARELHOFF, Edward Samuel. 8134 OLD KEENE MILL RD, EYE CONSULTANTS OF 22152 #023-07-1978 L1984 **PO OPH** *020 †35
PARROTT, Marian A. 7400 SPRING VILLAGE DR, MEDICAL CENTER 22150 #032-01-1978 L1987 **IM IMG** *020 †20
PATTISON, Timothy Wilson. ■ 22153 #023-01-2001 L2002 **IM** *012
PHAM, Phu-Thu. 6116 ROLLING RD STE 104 22152 #748-10-1977 L1989 **FM** *020 †18
PRICE, Michael B. 5510 ALMA LN, STE 2 22151 #035-19-1978 L1983 **IM CD** *020 †20
RANGADHAM, Kuntimaddi. ■ 22152 #495-62-1977 *100
RAO, Chethana V. 7440 SPRING VILLAGE DR 22150 #495-33-1994 L2003 **IM IMG** *020 †20
REDDY, Amy Kansagra. 6501 LOISDALE CT, KAISER PERM-PEDIATRICS 22150 #021-05-2002 L2002 **PD** *020 †55
RICHARDS, Georgia A. 6501 LOISDALE CT, 12TH FL 22150 #010-03-1994 L2002 **GE** *020 †20
RICHMOND, David Russell. 6501 LOISDALE CT 22150 #023-01-1969 L1998 **FM FPG** *030 †18
ROATH, Michael Steven. 8322 TRAFORD LN STE D 22152 #024-01-1965 L1970 **P N** *020 †75
RODGERS, Allison. 6120 BRANDON AVE, STE 203 22150 #010-02-1996 L1999 **PD** *020 †55
RODRIGUEZ, Chalon. ■ 22150 #275-01-1943 L1963 **U** *030 †95
ROOK, Frederick Wm. 6807 SPRINGFIELD PLZ, STE 205 22150 #065-01-1944 L1953 **ORS** *071 †40
ROSENTHAL, Sheldon Jay. 6807 SPRINGFIELD PLZ 22150 #869-05-1964 L1971 **R** *071 †80
ROSSBACH, Christopher N. 8316 TRAFORD LN 22152 #051-04-1989 L1994 **PD** *020 †55
SCHUMANN, Deborah Jewell. 6501 LOISDALE RD, KAISER PERMANENTE 22150 #023-01-1975 L1986 **OPH** *071 †35
SEIDMAN, Laurence Alan. 6120 BRANDON AVE, STE 308 22150 #035-09-1986 L1988 **PD** *020 †55
SHAPS, Stephanie Hope. 5502 BACKLICK RD, PEDIATRIC ASSOCIATES OF SP 22151 #035-19-2002 L2006 **PD** *020
SHARMA, Mrinal. 5514 ALMA LN, STE 200 22151 #067-03-1988 L1996 **CD IM** *020 †20
SHENK, Ian Marshall. 6501 LOISDALE CT, KAISER PERMANENTE 22150 #023-07-1965 L1971 **GE IM** *020 †20
SHEPHERD, Stuart James. ■ 22152 #005-11-1991 L1996 **IMG IM** *075
SHERNOCK, Marsha. 8314 TRAFORD LN STE C 22152 #010-02-1976 L1979 **PD** *020 †55
SIDDIQUI, Sarwat Waqar. ■ 22153 #704-02-1994 **PTH** *100
SIDHU, Dilbagh Singh. 7839A ROLLING RD 22153 #495-36-1975 L1981 **EM GP** *020 †55 ‡
SINGH, Maneesha. 6501 LOISDALE CT 22150 #496-07-1980 L1983 **IM** *020 †20
SMITH, Heather Isobel. 6501 LOISDALE CT, SPRINGFIELD MEDICAL CENTER 22150 #064-01-1993 L2007 *020
SMITH, Michael Quintel. 6044 DEER RIDGE TRL 22150 #036-01-1985 L1989 **OBG** *020 †30
SOHEIL, Harriet. 8348 TRAFORD LN, MT VERNON CMH STE 400 22152 #517-03-1961 L1984 **P** *072 ‡
SONE, Julia Hee. 6501 LOISDALE CT, DEPARTMENT OF SURGERY 22150 #035-15-1990 L2004 **CRS** *020 †10,85
SOYER, Muharrem Tanju. 6501 LOISDALE CT 22150 #902-03-1965 L1975 **GS** *020 †85
STAM-CHEATHAM, Annick. 6501 LOISDALE CT 22150 #048-14-1995 L2005 **FM** *020 †18
SUDDARTH, Brian Nicholas. ■ 22150 #051-04-2005 L2005 **DR** *012
SUSKIEWICZ, Lewis. 5510 ALMA LN, STE 4 22151 #010-02-1972 L1975 **IM** *020 †20
TEFERA, Kirubel. ■ 22152 #051-07-2008 *012
THODIYIL THOMAS, Annie A. 6128 BRANDON AVE STE 201 22150 #690-01-1989 L1998 **IM** *020 †20
TUCKER, Alton G. 7489 HUNTSMAN BLVD 22153 #051-04-1977 L1978 **FM** *020 †18
TUNSTALL, Irene I. 8136 OLD KEENE MILL RD, STE A*205 22152 #021-01-1981 L1989 **D** *020 †15
VERMA, Anil. 8346 TRAFORD LN STE B-2 22152 #495-36-1974 L1979 **IM PUD** *020 †20
VINH, Dai. 6501 LOISDALE CT 22150 #941-01-1973 L1983 **GS** *020 †85
VINK, J De Meillon. ■ 22150 #836-02-1948 L1961 **FM** *071 †18
VOLIKAS, Lazaros T. 6501 LOISDALE CT 11TH, OPHTHALMOLOGY DEPARTMENT 22150 #041-14-2000 L2002 **OPH** *020 †35
VOLPE, Charles Robert. ■ 22151 #051-07-1994 L2004 **GS** *020
VOSS, Stephen Rieke. 6128 BRANDON AVE, STE 201 22150 #005-14-1979 L1983 **IM GE** *020 †20
VROOM, John R. 6501 LOISDALE CT 22150 #041-09-1965 L1984 **A PD** *020 †55,03
WANG, Ted T-C. ■ 22150 #244-02-1961 L1980 **GS GP** *020
WEISZ, Alice M. 6501 LOISDALE CT 22150 #561-23-1981 L1986 **END DIA** *020 †20
WHAYNE, Barbara. 6128 BRANDON AVE, STE 308 22150 #048-12-1984 L1990 **IM** *020 †20
WILLIAMS, Lacia Rochelle. ■ 22152 #017-20-2006 L2006 **FP** *012
WILSON, Simon Arn. 6501 LOISDALE CT 22150 #033-06-1984 L1997 **OBG** *020 †30
WINSTON, Bradley John. 6501 LOISDALE CT, KAISER PERMANENTE MED CTR 22150 #041-01-1979 L1982 **GE** *020 †20
WOOD, David John. 6551 LOISDALE CT STE 155 22150 #062-01-1966 L1985 **CHP** *020
YOUNES, Robert Paul. 6699 SPRINGFIELD CTR DR, MEDICAL EDUCATION CTR 22150 #067-01-1963 L1986 **PD** *071 †55 ‡
ZAMSKAYA, Anna. 6501 LOISDALE CT, SPRINGFIELD MEDICAL CENTER 22150 #048-02-2003 L2006 **IM** *100 †20

STAFFORD — STAFFORD

ABISELLAN, Georgina A. ■ 22554 #275-01-1960 L1972 **P** *071
AHMED, Asmat. 1075 GARRISONVILLE RD #115 22556 #160-05-1982 L2001 **IM** *020 †20
AL-KHOZAIE, Liqaa Said. ■ 22556 #528-04-1986 L2001 **FPG** *100 †18
ALMEFLEHI, Faisal Abdulla. ■ 22554 #473-01-1990 L2004 **IM** *100 †20
BROWN, Michael C. 385 GARRISONVILLE RD, ASSOCIATES IS 22554 #008-01-1993 L2000 **GE** *020 †20

BUSTIN, Frederick Bernard. 608 GARRISONVILLE RD 22554 #016-01-1978 L1981 FM EM *020 †18

CARLBERG, Matthew A. 44 MINE RD, STE 2 22554 #034-01-1989 L1991 FM GP *020 †18

CARR, William Michael. 385 GARRISONVILLE RD # 209, STAFFORD PEDIATRICS 22554 #012-01-1981 L1984 PD *020 †55 ‡

COHEN, Michael Eric. 24 ONVILLE RD STE 205 22556 #023-01-1975 L1981 N IM *020 †75,20

COLON, Hector Manuel. 385 GARRISONVILLE RD, STE 204 22554 #042-02-1998 L2002 OBG *020 †30

DE BLASI, Robert Francis. 90 GREENSPRING DR 22554 #008-01-1972 L1974 ORS *020 †40

DOUGHTY, Mark K. 385 GARRISONVILLE RD, STE 205 22554 #065-09-1984 L1996 FM *020 †18

ENRIGHT, Rosemary Theresa. 608 GARRISONVILLE RD 22554 #051-01-1979 L1980 FM *020 †20

FUSCO, Frank Danl. 16 CANTERBURY DR 22554 #010-02-1958 L1965 PUD IM *071 †20

GEBREYESUS, Yared Aytaged. 2712 JEFFERSON DAVIS HWY, STE 101, PO.BOX 1090 22554 #366-01-1988 L2005 IM *020

GRANGER, Sarah Lynne. ■ 22554 #010-01-2007 GS *012

HERNANDEZ, Carolina Maria. 2765 JEFFERSON DAVIS HWY, STE 109 22554 #737-06-1993 L2007 IM *020 †20

HOLLAND, Susan Jean. ■ 22554 #023-01-1985 L2002 IM *020 †20

HORTON, Jodie Melissa. 385 GARRISONVILLE RD, STE 204 22554 #051-04-2000 L2004 OBG *020

HUANG, Jack Chaujeh. 385 GARRISONVILLE RD, ASSOCIATES IS 22554 #035-19-1998 L2004 GE *020 †20

IGLESIA, Wenifredo N. ■ 22556 #748-01-1957 L1970 GS OS *071

JAN, Iffat. 608 GARRISONVILLE RD 22554 #495-51-1993 L2003 FM *020

JENET, Richard Neil. 385 GARRISONVILLE RD, STE 207 22554 #041-12-1984 L1985 OBG *020 †30

JOSEPH, George Arakal. 9 CENTER ST STE 101, GARRISONVILLE URGENT CARE 22556 #495-33-1989 L1997 IM *020

JOSOVITZ, Kenneth Neil. 385 GARRISONVILLE RD, ASSOCIATES IS 22554 #033-05-1991 L1996 GE *020 †20

KAHN, Enamul H. 237 GARRISONVILLE RD, STE 101 22554 #160-02-1981 L1993 MPD PD *020 †55,20

KIL, Hyung Joon. 422 GARRISONVILLE RD, STE 106 22554 #051-07-1983 L1987 OBG *020 †30

LOVING, Tamara Stevens. 422 GARRISONVILLE RD, STE 101 22554 #051-04-1991 L1993 PD *020 †55

MARATHE, Atul Vasant. 385 GARRISONVILLE RD, ASSOCIATES IS 22554 #010-03-1996 L2002 GE *020 †20

MC DERMOTT, Brian Thomas. 90 GREENSPRING DR 22554 #038-41-1997 L2002 ORS *020 †40

MENDEZ, Enrique. ■ 22554 #016-43-1954 L1982 OS IM *071 †20

MERCADO-FILES, Barbara. 422 GARRISONVILLE RD, STE 106 22554 #035-47-1995 L1999 OBG *020 †30

MOHANTY, Nibedita. 422 GARRISONVILLE RD, STE 108 22554 #051-04-1986 L1990 CD *020 †20

MUNIYAPPA, Ranganath. ■ 22554 #496-39-1992 L2004 END *020 †20

NEUSTATTER, Patrick. 392 GARRISONVILLE RD, STE 210 22554 #917-23-1970 L1986 FM *020 †18

PAUZE, John Alexander. 300 DESTROYER CV, AQUIA HARBOUR 22554 #051-01-1972 L1973 FM *020 †18

PICKARD, Sybil Dawn. 392 GARRISONVILLE RD, STE 210 22554 #036-05-1995 L2005 FM *020 †18

RAJEE, Haleh. 110 SOARING EAGLE DR 22556 #041-15-1999 L1999 PD *020 †55

REID, Yolanda G. 392 GARRISONVILLE RD, STE 210 22554 #010-03-1997 L1997 FM *020 †18

ROZO-SANMIGUEL, Alvaro. ■ 22554 #264-01-1952 PYA CHP *071

SCHUETTE, Joseph Peter. 422 GARRISONVILLE RD, STE 106-06-1989 L1997 FM *020 †18

SCHULTZ, David Michael. 422 GARRISONVILLE RD, STE 111 22554 #035-03-1980 L2007 FM *020 †18

SINGH, Balwinder. 9 CENTER ST, STE 101 22556 #495-03-1990 L1999 IM *020

SINGH, Sonia. 110 SOARING EAGLE DR, PEDIATRIC PARTNERS STAFFOR 22556 #055-02-2001 L2004 P *012 †55

SOKOLOW, David Philip. 90 GREENSPRING DR 22554 #041-01-1986 L1993 ORS *020 †40

SQUILLANTE, Robert G, Jr. 90 GREENSPRING DR 22554 #011-02-1989 L1995 OSS ORS *020 †40

VILLARREAL, Yvonne M. 608 GARRISONVILLE RD 22554 #003-01-1993 L2001 FM *040 †18

WILLIAMS, Russell Warren. 422 GARRISONVILLE RD, STE 101 22554 #032-01-1975 L1978 FM *020 †18

STANARDSVILLE – GREENE

KNIGHT, Donald Aubrey. ■ 22973 #051-04-1961 L1961 GP *071

STANLEY – PAGE

LEE, R David. 235 MEDICAL DR, PAGE RURAL HEALTH CENTER 22851 #051-04-1994 L1994 FM *020 †18 ‡

STANLEYTOWN – HENRY

BING, John Paul. ■ 24168 #051-04-1946 L1950 GP OS *071

STATE FARM – POWHATAN

RODRIGUEZ, Hugo Moises. 3600 WOODS WAY, POWHATAN CORRECTIONAL CENT 23160 #308-12-1994 L1999 IM *020

STAUNTON – STAUNTON CITY

ABELLERA, Rosito Pimentel. PO BOX 3500 24402 #748-07-1964 L1971 *020

ALEXANDER, Kerry Anthony. 42 LAMBERT ST, STAUNTON MEDICAL 24401 #038-43-1988 L1991 IM *020 †20

ALLEN, Kaye Rebekah. 40 LAMBERT ST, STE 413 24401 #005-02-1987 L1997 OM IM *020 †70

ANDERSON, Jonathan C. 1301 RICHMOND AVE, BOX 2500 24401 #051-07-1990 L1992 P *020 †75

BAKER, Brian Russell. ■ 24401 #023-01-2004 L2006 EM *020

BATES, Harry Clark, III. 1355 RICHMOND AVE BOX 4000, BOX 4000 24401 #051-04-1972 L1981 CHP P *020 †75

BILL, Caroline Shen. 1301 RICHMOND AVE, BOX 2500 24401 #051-01-1996 L1996 P IM *020 †20,75

BISCARDI, Frank Hugo. 42 LAMBERT ST, STE 511 24401 #051-04-1987 L1993 PUD *020 †20

BLUMENTHAL, Barry H. 1301 RICHMOND AVE BOX 250, WESTERN STATE HOSPITAL 24401 #051-04-1981 L2001 P *020 †75

BOURGEOIS, Francis John. 412 COMMERCE RD 24401 #021-01-1972 L1980 OBG IM *020 †20,30

BRANSCOME, William Carl. 401 N COALTER ST 24401 #008-01-1958 L1964 IM *071 †20

BROOKS, Stephanie R T. ■ 24401 #045-01-1973 L1975 PTH *100

CANTON, John Norman. ■ 24401 #047-06-1955 L1973 OBG *071 †30

CARR, Quintin O. ■ 24401 #051-01-1952 L1952 GP *071

CHERNOFF, David B. 40 LAMBERT ST STE 522, STAUNTON MEDICAL CTR 24401 #041-02-1985 L1987 FM *020 †18

CHHABRA, Sandhya. 1301 RICHMOND AVE, BOX 2500 24401 #010-02-1998 L1998 END *020 †20

COLEMAN, Richard L M. STE 211, STAUNTON MEDICAL CTR 24401 #051-01-1965 L1965 OBG *072 †30

DEGEN, Douglas Bennett. 42 LAMBERT ST, STAUNTON MEDICAL 24401 #051-04-1978 L1982 IM *020 †20

DOERR, Janet A. 24401 #038-41-1980 L1983 DR NM *020 †80

DORRIES, Olimpia V. ■ 24401 #781-04-1987 L1997 CHP *020

ERINC, Ismail Ethem. ■ 24401 #902-01-1955 L1973 IM PUD *020

FOWLER, Donald Richard. ■ 24401 #055-01-1963 L1974 GS VS *071 †85

FOX, William Earl. 1301 RICHMOND AVE, BOX 2500 24401 #051-01-1995 L2000 PYG *020 †75

GARDELLA, Lynn English. 1301 RICHMOND AVE, BOX 2500 24401 #041-13-1987 L1990 IM *020 †20

GARDELLA, Robert John. 1301 RICHMOND AVE, BOX 2500 24401 #051-01-1989 L1990 P *020 †75

GARDNER, Richard Ernest. 2010 N AUGUSTA ST 24401 #051-01-1964 L1964 OPH *071 †35

GARDNER, Rufus S, Jr. ■ 24401 #051-04-1948 L1948 IM PM *071

GLICK, Joseph Livingstone. 1301 RICHMOND AVE 24401 #051-04-1955 L1955 P *071

GOBAR, Asad. 1301 RICHMOND AVE 24401 #118-01-1953 L1984 P *071

GODETTE, George Austin. 108 MACTANLY PL 24401 #039-01-1983 L1993 ORS *020 †40

HANNA, Stevan Terrell. 13 TERRY ST 24401 #051-04-1970 L1970 OTO *062 †45

HARMAN, William E. ■ 24401 #051-01-1942 L1942 PD *071 †55

HARRELL, William Larry. ■ 24401 #051-01-1973 L1974 EM FM *020 †18,16

HARRISON, Carrington. 1524 N AUGUSTA ST 24401 #051-01-1969 L1969 ORS *071 †40

HASKINS, Barbara Gay. 1301 RICHMOND AVE, WESTERN STATE HOSPITAL 24401 #051-01-1983 L1985 P *020 †75

HEREFORD, William Lee. 108 MACTANLY PL 24401 #001-02-1983 L1989 ORS *020

HIGGINBOTHAM, Rachel E M. 85 SANGERS LN, VALLEY COMMUNITY SERVICE B 24401 #036-07-2002 L2006 P *020

HOM, Benjamin Karl. 1301 RICHMOND AVE, P O BOX 2500 24401 #005-06-2005 L2006 DR *012

HU, Jeannie Ching-I. PO BOX 4000, 1355 RICHMOND AVE 24402 #036-01-1997 L2002 P *020 †75

JAYNE, Thomas Mitchell. 1228 N AUGUSTA ST 24401 #051-04-1984 L1987 P *020 †75

JENSEN, Diana Alethea. 40 LAMBERT ST, STE 411 24401 #036-05-1988 L1991 FM *020 †18

JESSEE, Wayne Phillip. PO BOX 2372 24402 #051-01-1971 L1972 PTH CLP *020 †50

KEATTS, Ami Hiatt. 503 VICTORIA DR, THE WOMEN'S CENTER 24401 #051-07-1997 L1997 OBG *020 †30

KEEFE, Stephen Duval. ■ 24401 #051-07-1987 L1989 OTO HNS *020 †45

KRAG, James L. 1110 MONTGOMERY AVE 24401 #654-01-1986 L1987 P *020 †75

LANDAUER, Diane Snover. 934 N AUGUSTA ST 24401 #033-05-1986 L1994 FM *020 †18

LARRIVIERE, Daniel G. 1301 RICHMOND AVE, BOX 2500 24401 #048-04-1998 L1999 N *020 †75

LASER, Swen Ericson. 47 ROLLING GREEN DR 24401 #001-02-1985 L2000 AN *020 †05

LAWLER, Frederick Warren. 191 MIDDLE RIVER RD 24401 #036-01-1985 L2006 OTO *020

LENKER, Leon Edward. 40 LAMBERT ST, STAUNTON MEDICAL CTR, STE 24401 #051-04-1975 L1978 FM *020 †18

LINDSAY, Rebecca Jane. 1301 RICHMOND AVE, BOX 2500 24401 #055-01-1979 L1981 P *020 †75

MASSEY, David Quintin. 2009 N AUGUSTA ST 24401 #036-05-1984 L1985 FM *020 †18

MIZZI, Alex. ■ 24401 #561-13-1947 L1957 GP *071

MORRISON, Robert Lord. ■ 24401 #051-04-1943 L1943 AN *071 †05

MOSS, Mark. 1355 RICHMOND AVE, COMMONWEALTH CENTER FOR CH 24401 #051-01-1993 L1999 CHP *020 †75

NICHOLS, Stephen Andrew. 1301 RICHMOND AVE 24401 #051-01-1983 L1984 P *020 †75

O'BRIEN, Mary Agnes. 422 COMMERCE RD 24401 #051-04-1965 L1965 IM OS *020

OWENS, Patricia A. ■ 24401 #041-07-1981 L1985 FM *075 †18

PATE, Candace Rowland. 401 COMMERCE RD, STE 421 24401 #036-08-1993 L1993 PD *020 †55

PITSILOS, Stephanie Ann. 42 LAMBERT ST, STAUNTON MEDICAL 24401 #041-01-2002 L2002 IM *020 †20

POWELL, Heather Lynn. 1301 RICHMOND AVE, P O BOX 2500 24401 #047-06-2004 L2005 PM *012

RADOIU, Nicolas. ■ 24401 #067-03-1953 L1967 RHU IM *071

RICHARDSON, Alan Tines. ■ 24401 #039-05-1982 L1990 EM *020 †16

RICHARDSON, Peter Bruce. 42 LAMBERT ST, STAUNTON MEDICAL CENTER 24401 #045-01-1975 L1980 OPH *020 †18

RIDGES, Ryan Mark. 2010 N AUGUSTA ST 24401 #049-01-1997 L1998 OPH *020 †35

SAATHOFF, Gregory Brian. 1301 RICHMOND AVE 24401 #028-03-1983 L1986 P PD *040 †75

SACHNO, Roman, Jr. 40 LAMBERT ST, STE 321 24401 #051-04-1967 L1967 IM GP *020

SALOMON, Alexander E. 42 LAMBERT ST, STAUNTON MEDICAL 24401 #010-02-1994 L1996 IM *020 †20

SAUDER, Kurtis Lamar. 401 COMMERCE RD, BLUE RIDGE PED STE 421 24401 #051-01-1993 L1993 PD *020 †55

SHANNON, Carol C. 1301 RICHMOND AVE 24401 #051-07-1989 L1990 P *020 †75

SHAPCOTT, Thomas Aaron. 1429 N AUGUSTA ST, PO BOX 3205 24401 #045-01-1982 L1984 FM *020 †18

SHERWOOD, Cindy. 85 SANGERS LN, LANCASTER GENERAL HOSPITAL 24401 #016-11-1997 L1997 P *020 †75

■ = Address Information Privacy Protected

SIEGFRIED, George Earle. 165 MEADOW KNOLLS LN 24401 #051-04-1968 L1968
PS *020 †85,65
SIMAN, Margaret Chaffin. 1234 MIDDLEBROOK AVE, STE E 24401 #051-07-1994 L1995
FM *020 †18
SMITH, Kenneth Roy. ■ 24401 #010-01-1974 L1977 PS *071 †85,65
SMITH, Mary C Rehak. 1301 RICHMOND AVE 24401 #027-01-1983 L1991 P PD *030 †75
SOWERS, William Frederick. MEDICAL CENTER 24401 #051-04-1957 L1957 D *020 †15
SPROUL, A Erskine. ■ 24401 #051-01-1941 L1941 ATP PCP *071 †30
SPROUL, George Thos. 401 COMMERCE RD STE 421 24401 #051-01-1974 L1977 PD *020 †55
STATHOS, John Anthony, Jr. 2010 N AUGUSTA ST 24401 #051-01-1977 L1981 OPH *020 †35
STEELE, A Arthur. 424 COMMERCE RD 426 24401 #023-01-1971 L1990 IM END *071 †20
STEGALL, Brown Hampton. ■ 24401 #051-01-1965 L1965 GS *071 †85
SUTHERLAND, Jo Ann Jesse. 1301 RICHMOND AVE 24401 #023-01-1964 L1969 GE *071
SUTKER, Lawrence Henry. 1301 RICHMOND AVE, P O BOX 2500 24401 #045-01-1975 L1979
P PYG *020 †75
TENNEY, Malcolm. ■ 24401 #051-04-1959 L1959 PHP *030
THOMAS, Alexander R. 401 COMMERCE RD, STE 421 24401 #051-01-2003 L2007 PD *020
TYLER, Michael Julius J. 85 SANGERS LN 24401 #048-13-1984 L2002 P *020
WANGLER, John Geo, Jr. 1301 RICHMOND AVE, BOX 2500 24401 #051-01-1964 L1964
P *071 †75
WEISMAN, Charles Kahn. 42 LAMBERT ST STE 422, STAUNTON MEDICAL CENTER 24401
#665-01-1997 L2005 FM *020 †18
WYNNE, Marigail. 85 SANGERS LN 24401 #036-07-1968 L1971 P *020 †20,75
YOUNG, Jeffrey Bright. 114 WHITE OAK GAP RD 24401 #055-01-1979 L1983
EM PM *020 †16,18
ZADROZNY, John Henry. 42 LAMBERT ST, STAUNTON MEDICAL 24401 #036-05-1979 L1984
CD IM *020 †20
ZUUR, Peter J. ■ 24401 #660-03-1957 L1964 P PD *071

STEPHENS CITY – FREDERICK

BASHARMAL, Khodaidad H. 106 HYDE CT 22655 #118-02-1969 L2001 IM *020 †20
GRANT, Joel Timothy. 370 FAIRFAX PIKE, STEPHENS CITY FAMILY MEDIC 22655
#048-02-2001 L2001 FM *020 †18
MIDDELHOF, Charles Aldwin. ■ 22655 #270-02-2000 L2005 FP *012
RICKEL, Ralph E, Jr. 106 HYDE CT 22655 #055-01-1981 L1994 FM GP *020 †18

STEPHENSON – FREDERICK

MC ALLISTER, John Eldon. 233 BURNT FACTORY RD 22656 #051-04-1964 L1964 NS *020 †25

STERLING – LOUDOUN

ABDALLAH, Hasan I. 46396 BENEDICT DR, STE 310 20164 #575-01-1984 L1998 PDC *020 †55
AHDIEH, Jalal. ■ 20165 #517-01-1948 L1967 IM AN *071
AL-JAYOUSI, Zakieh. ■ 20164 #575-01-1985 L1991 PD *100 †55
AMIN, Shilpa Harshad. 21036 TRIPLESEVEN RD, NOVA MEDICAL GROUP 20165
#010-01-1996 L1998 FPG *020 †18
ANDERSON, James Edward. 21475 RIDGETOP CIR, STE 360 20166 #005-12-1965 L1968
OBG *020 †30
ANDREWS-VALLANCE, Mildred. 46440 BENEDICT DR, STE 207 20164 #055-01-1999 L2002
PD *020 †55
ASKHETA, Mazen. 47361 DARKHOLLOW FALLS TER 20165 #422-01-1993 L1999 IM *020 †20
BAKER, Janet Mary. 21475 RIDGETOP CIR, STE 150 20166 #023-07-1994 L2003 HS *020 †40
BARRETT, Diane Theresa. 21351 RIDGETOP CIR, STE 100 20166 #010-01-1998 L1998
OBG *020 †30
BENTZ, G D. 46440 BENEDICT DR STE 2 20164 #649-33-1988 L1991 FM *020 †18 ‡
BERMAN, David Elliot. 14 PIDGEON HILL DR, STE 100 20165 #065-05-1981 L1991
PS CS *020 †65 ‡
BHAN, Jason Mohan. 46440 BENEDICT DR, STE 107 20164 #011-02-2000 L2000 FM *020 †18
BHATIA, Madhu Subramanian. 6 PIDGEON HILL DR STE 260 20165 #495-45-1973 L1984
P CHP *020 †75
BOUTROS, Ayman. 21475 RIDGETOP CIR, STE 300 20166 #035-08-1985 L1989 OPH *020 †35
BROWN, Carlton Q. 21400 RIDGETOP CIR, STE 100 20166 #012-05-1978 L1986
AN PME *020 †05
BUTERA, Christina Lynn. 21475 RIDGETOP CIR, STE 300 20166 #038-43-1994 L2004
OPH PO *020 †35
CASUCCIO, John Richard. 46440 BENEDICT DR, STE 202 20164 #038-40-1976 L1988
PS OTO *020 †45,65
CHAUHAN, Ashok. 21525 RIDGETOP CIR, STE 280 20166 #496-09-1985 L1994
PUD IM *020 †20
CHAWLA, Arvinder Singh. 21495 RIDGETOP CIR, STE 102 20166 #495-43-1984 L1994
IM *020 †20
CHO, Hyegin Helen. 21135 WHITFIELD PL, STE 107 20165 #011-03-2000 L2005 FM *020 †18
CHOICE, Curtis Von. 4 PIDGEON HILL DR 20165 #038-43-2002 L2006 PAN *020
CHOPRA, Rajiv Kumar. 21351 RIDGETOP CIR, STE 100 20166 #020-02-1995 L2002
DR *020 †80
CHOUDHARY, Namrata K. 46165 WESTLAKE DR, STE 220 20165 #045-01-1992 L1997
OBG *020 †30
COCHRANE, William James. 21351 RIDGETOP CIR, STE 100 20166 #803-05-1964 L1972
OS *020 †30
COHEN, Lawrence. 204 LAKE DR 20164 #035-20-1965 L1972 ORS LM *062 †40
COHN, Howard Lewis. 207 E HOLLY AVE STE 215 20164 #035-47-1973 L1978 OBG *020 †30
COLEMAN, John H. 2 PIDGEON HILL DR, STE 400 20165 #017-20-1953 L1997
FM FPG *020 †18
COLEMAN, Linda Elaine. 2 PIDGEON HILL DR, STE 400 20165 #038-40-1984 L1987 IM *020 †20
CORRADO, Michael A. ■ 20164 #010-01-1952 L1959 CD IM *071
CRENSHAW, Joanne. 21135 WHITFIELD PL, STE 102 20165 #035-20-1991 L1998 OPH *020 †35
CRENSHAW, Ryan Paul. 46440 BENEDICT DR, STE 208 20164 #035-20-1991 L1998 IM *020 †20
CURRIER, Carol Anne. 46440 BENEDICT DR, STE 110 20164 #041-07-1972 L1987
OPH GP *020 †35,70
DANAO, Cecile Melanie. 14 PIDGEON HILL DR, CAPITAL AREA PEDIATRICS 20165
#038-43-2004 L2007 PD *100 †55

DOBROVIC, Nino Mario. 46400 BENEDICT DR, STE 1 20164 #010-01-1993 L1994 APM *020 †60
DONALD, Felicia Lyn. 21135 WHITFIELD PL STE 101, FOR WOMEN OB/GYN ASSOC 20165
#051-07-1982 L1987 OBG *020 †30
DORSCH, Grace Wilson. 4 PIDGEON HILL DR 20165 #045-01-1990 L1993 AN *020 †05
DUNN, Cheryl T. 6 PIDGEON HILL DR, STE 260 20165 #040-02-1972 L1976 P *020 †75
DUNNER, Peter Spencer. 21351 RIDGETOP CIR, STE 100 20166 #035-09-1976 L1982
DR *020 †80
ELANGOVAN, Anita. ■ 20166 #019-02-2002 L2002 IM *100 †20
ELLAURIE, Maadhava. 46440 BENEDICT DR STE 212 20164 #836-05-1975 L1998
AI PD *020 †55,03
FANDINO, Ernesto. 14 PIDGEON HILL DR, STE 130 20165 #264-04-1968 L1987
PD ADL *020 †55
FERGUSSON, Paula N. 46165 WESTLAKE DR, STE 210 20165 #051-04-1985 L1988 PD *020 †55
FLETCHER, Sarah Susan. 21135 WHITFIELD PL, STE 107 20165 #051-04-1986 L1994
FM *020 †18
FOX, Elisabeth Ann. 46090 LAKE CENTER PLZ #104 20165 #041-02-1984 L1999 OTO *020 †45
GARALA, Mehul Himat. ■ 20165 #051-04-2006 L2006 PM *012
GARSON, Ronald J. 6 PIDGEON HILL DR, STE 260 20165 #041-01-1974 L1977 P *020 †75 ‡
GLASSMAN, Leonard Mark. 21351 RIDGETOP CIR, STE 100 20166 #041-02-1969 L1982
DR R *020 †80
GRECO, Judith Lim. 2 PIDGEON HILL DR, STE 400 20165 #021-05-1993 L1995 IM *020 †20
GREENBERG, Julianne S. 21351 RIDGETOP CIR, STE 100 20166 #010-01-1988 L1993
DR *020 †80
HARRIS, William Paul. 4 PIDGEON HILL DR 20165 #010-02-1984 L1992 AN *020 †05
HASAN, Faisal. ■ 20165 #160-06-1988 *100
HASNAIN, Syed Sibtul. ■ 20164 #704-04-1978 L2002 P *100
HEBBAR, Jyotsna. ■ 20166 #011-04-2004 L2007 PD *100 †55
HENNESSEY, Francis B. ■ 20164 #024-07-1953 L1994 ORS *071 †40
HUANG, Cecil N. 4 PIDGEON HILL DR 20165 #005-11-2000 L2000 AN *100 †05
HUNTER, Noriko Sakai. 22636 GLENN DR, STE 101 20164 #010-01-1993 L1995 IM *020 †20
HUTTAM, Maher A. ■ 20164 #366-01-1991 L2007 GS *020 †85
INCATASCIATO, William A. 14 PIDGEON HILL DR 20165 #011-04-1991 L1994 PD *020 †55
IYER, Ravi R. 21495 RIDGETOP CIR, STE 102 20166 #496-14-1985 L1995 IM IMG *020
JAFFE, Russell Merritt. 14 PIDGEON HILL DR STE 300 20165 #024-05-1972 L1973
AI CLP *050 †50
JAHAN, Shaukat. 21495 RIDGETOP CIR, STE 203 20166 #160-02-1972 L1991 OBG *020 †30
KARAM, Claude Farid. 21155 WHITFIELD PL, STE 102 20165 #605-03-1989 L1997 PD *020 †55
KASLOFF, Ilene Merle. 20 PIDGEON HILL DR, STE 202 20165 #041-14-1982 L1990 PD *020 †55
KHAN, Smeena M. 21165 WHITFIELD PL, STE 106 20165 #011-02-1995 L2004 D *020 †20,15
KHEIR, Sonia M. 405 GLENN DR STE 10A 20164 #915-02-1972 L1986 PTH D *020 †50
KLADAKIS, Alexis Octavio. 21351 RIDGETOP CIR, STE 100 20166 #010-02-1995 L2000
DR *020 †80
KLAINER, Peter Scott. 46396 BENEDICT DR, STE 330 20164 #035-01-1988 L1997
PS *020 †85,65
KLEIN, Mark Elliot. 21351 RIDGETOP CIR, STE 100 20166 #035-08-1978 L1979 DR *020 †80
LEE, Wha-Young Cho. ■ 20165 #583-03-1965 GP *074
LEON, Ralph Albert. 21135 WHITFIELD PL, STE 207 20165 #011-04-1989 L2002 FM *020 †18
LINDLAU, Dana Su. 6 PIDGEON HILL DR STE 170 20165 #051-01-1999 L2002 PD *020 †55
LOPEZ, Lolita Amio. 45566 CHESWICK PARK CT 20166 #748-10-1988 L1998 PD *020 †55
MACHINENI, Praveena. ■ 20164 #496-24-1999 *100
MAHGOUB OSMAN, Safa Moham. ■ 20165 #848-05-1998 L2007 IM *020 †20
MANDOLESI, Gabriela Adria. 21475 RIDGETOP CIR, STE 360 20166 #051-04-2004 L2004
OBG *012
MANN, Ruth Avigan. 6 PIDGEON HILL DR, STE 170 20165 #067-01-1980 L1984 PD *020 †55
MARSHAK, Steven Peter. 21036 TRIPLESEVEN RD, 1ST FL 20165 #010-02-1995 L1995
IM *020 †20
MBAHI, Musa Adamu. ■ 20166 #690-09-1989 L2007 BBK *100 †50
MC CARTY, Patrick Peter. 45305 CATALINA CT STE 103 20166 #051-04-1994 L1994 OM *020
MC GORRY, Thomas Patrick. 46440 BENEDICT DR STE 207 20164 #041-09-1969 L1974
PD *020 †55
MECHERIKUNNEL, Paul T. 107 E HOLLY AVE, STE 3 20164 #023-07-1989 L1998
ORS HS *020 †40
MELAMUD, Alex. 21351 RIDGETOP CIR, STE 140 20166 #038-06-2001 L2007 OPH *020 †35
MIKHAIL, Eva Labib. 405 GLENN DR STE 10A 20164 #915-02-1969 L1976 PTH *020 †50
MILLER, Lorna M. 4 PIDGEON HILL DR 20165 #010-01-1990 L1994 AN *020 †05
MIRZA, Sobia Naz. 46409 SPRINGWOOD CT 20165 #704-01-2004 *100
NADERI, Shervin. 14 PIDGEON HILL DR, STE 100 20165 #041-15-1999 L2005 OTO *020 †45
NESBITT, C Phillip. 6 PIDGEON HILL DR 20165 #010-02-1992 L1994 AN *020 †05
NESBITT, Elizabeth H. 4 PIDGEON HILL DR 20165 #010-02-1992 L1995 AN *020 †05
NGUYEN, Anh-Dai Kim. 6 PIDGEON HILL DR STE 205 20165 #056-06-1996 L2003
AI *020 †20,03
NOVAK, Edward Andrew. 20650 MUDDY HARBOR SQ 20165 #010-02-1957 L1996
OPH *071 †35
OSMAN, Michael Humayun. 21351 RIDGETOP CIR, STE 140 20166 #010-02-1992 L1999
OPH *020 †35
OTT, Ingrid Lorentzen. 21351 RIDGETOP CIR, STE 100 20166 #024-01-1990 L1997
RNR *020 †80
PANITZ, Polly Jane. 2 PIDGEON HILL DR, STE 400 20165 #024-05-1984 L1993 PD *020 †55
PASTOR, Carmen L. 21475 RIDGETOP CIR STE 350 20166 #737-01-1986 L1995 END *020 †20
PATEL, Vikas Jayanti. 14 PIDGEON HILL DR, STE 340 20165 #036-07-2000 L2005 D *020 †15
PAYDAR, Mehdi H. ■ 20165 #517-05-1959 OBG *100 †30
PAYNE, Fred J. 1329 SHEPARD DR, STE 7 20164 #041-12-1949 L1978 PHP GPM *071 †70 ‡
PETERKIN, Ian. 21351 RIDGETOP CIR, STE 100 20166 #065-09-1989 L1994 DR *020 †80
RAAD, Bahman Siapoosh. ■ 20165 #517-01-1956 L2000 PD *071
RAILAN, Veena V. 101 E HOLLY AVE, STE 9 20164 #495-92-1974 L1979 GP PD *020
RAMASESHAN, Sujatha. ■ 20165 #496-39-2000 L2007 IM *100 †20
RAMASWAMY, Devanhalli. 21495 RIDGETOP CIR STE 102 20166 #495-33-1961 L1971
CD IM *071 †20
REESE, William Henry, Jr. 21475 RIDGETOP CIR, STE 302 20166 #051-04-1961 L1961
GP OS *071
REISNER, Darrell Steven. 21475 RIDGETOP CIR 20166 #008-02-1995 L1996 OPH *020 †35
RICHARDSON, Douglas S. 21495 RIDGETOP CIR STE 204 20166 #035-06-1971 L1973
D AM *020 †15
RODNEY, Kurt Gregory. 46440 BENEDICT DR, STE 107 20164 #041-09-1979 L1981 EM *020 †16
RODRIGUES, Lori Rose. 14 PIDGEON HILL DR, STE 130 20165 #023-01-2002 L2005
PD *020 †55

RODRIGUES, Rui Gaspar. 6 PIDGEON HILL DR, STE 170 20165 #010-03-2002 L2005 PD *020 †55

ROSE, Gary Leyton. 21351 RIDGETOP CIR, STE 100 20166 #056-06-1977 L1988 DR NM *020 †80,28

ROSENTHAL, Richard. 21525 RIDGETOP CIR, DEVAN VAS 20166 #028-02-1985 L1990 PUD IM *020 †20

SALVADOR, Juan Carlos. ■ 20164 #051-07-1997 L2000 IM *062

SCHISLER, John Quincy. 4 PIDGEON HILL DR 20165 #012-05-1982 L1990 AN *020 †05

SCHROEDER, Christie Lynn. ■ 20165 #005-12-2006 *012

SCHULTE, Charles John, III. 14 PIDGEON HILL DR, STE 130 20165 #035-03-1962 L1974 PD PHP *020 †55

SEDGEWICK, Jeffrey Hunt. 21475 RIDGETOP CIR, STE 220 20166 #010-02-1993 L2000 OPH *020 †35

SEGUE-ANDREWS, Andrea. 46440 BENEDICT DR, STE 107 20164 #025-07-1997 L2004 FM *020 †18

SETHI, Rupinder Kaur. 21475 RIDGETOP CIR, STE 210 20166 #495-29-1993 L2003 PD *020 †55

SHABAZZ, Dwana R. 14 PIDGEON HILL DR, STE 340 20165 #010-01-2002 L2006 D *020 †15

SIPE, Patrick Steven. 4 PIDGEON HILL DR 20165 #023-12-1997 L1998 AN PDI *020 *05

SLACK, Mark Raymond. 4 PIDGEON HILL DR 20165 #010-02-1986 L1989 AN *020 †05

SMITH, Janine Nicole. 46169 WESTLAKE DR, STE 130 20165 #023-01-1997 L2007 OPH PO *020 †35

SMITH, Joseph H, Jr. 4 PIDGEON HILL DR 20165 #010-02-1993 L1996 AN *020 *05

STEEL, Maxwell W, Jr. ■ 20165 #041-02-1944 L1944 IM GPM *071

ST RAYMOND, Philip Andre. 46440 BENEDICT DR STE 209 20164 #047-05-1982 L1987 U *020 †95

TERRITO, Pauline A P. ■ 20164 #041-09-1954 L1955 A PD *071

THOMAS, Albert Bruce, II. 46165 WESTLAKE DR, STE 100 20165 #038-43-1991 L1993 PM *020 †60

TILTON, Susan Hanley. 46440 BENEDICT DR, STE 110 20164 #048-04-1975 L2002 OM AM *075 †70

TODD, Michael Mclain. 46161 WESTLAKE DR, STE 300A 20165 #049-01-1999 L2004 D DS *020 †15

TONTHAT, Han. 21495 RIDGETOP CIR, STE 102 20166 #051-07-1995 L1996 IM *020

TRAN, Hoang Vi. 21165 WHITFIELD PL, STE 104 20165 #032-01-1993 L1998 IM *020 †20

TRIVEDI, Bhavini Vinod. 6 PIDGEON HILL DR, STE 205 20165 #041-02-1997 L2001 AI *020 †20,03

ULREY, Teresa M. 4 PIDGEON HILL DR 20165 #048-14-1988 L1994 AN *020 *05

VASQUEZ, Betsy. 14 PIDGEON HILL DR, STE 220 20165 #035-46-1986 L1995 OTO *020 †45

VLAHOS, Michael M. 21495 RIDGETOP CIR 20166 #010-02-1963 L1964 GP *020

WEINSTEIN, Jonathan Ira. 46440 BENEDICT DR, STE 207 20164 #035-06-1993 L1996 PD *075 †55

WILDER, Deborah Diane. 21135 WHITFIELD PL, STE 101 20165 #010-02-1989 L2004 OBG *020

WILSON, Lynnford Saml, Jr. 21475 RIDGETOP CIR, STE 150 20166 #012-05-1974 L1990 ORS FM *020 †18,40

YUN, Jungim Amy. 4 PIDGEON HILL DR 20165 #051-07-1990 L1994 AN *020 †05

ZANGENEH, Farhad. 46090 LAKE CENTER PLZ, STE 106 20165 #654-01-1997 L2002 END IM *020 †20 ‡

ZAPP, Elizabeth Anne. 21135 WHITFIELD PL, STE 107 20165 #041-02-1997 L2005 FM *020 †18

STONY CREEK – SUSSEX

MATHERLEE, Michael Dean. 12454 HARTLEY ST, HEALTH CENTER 23882 #051-04-1999 L1999 FM *020 †18

STRASBURG – SHENANDOAH

DWYER, Jennifer Bridget. 390 E KING ST STE 6 22657 #017-20-1998 L1998 FM *020 †18

LAYMAN, Rebecca Kay. 290 E KING ST, STE 6 22657 #051-04-1999 L1999 FM *020 †18

SAVAGE-OTEY, Tinea Joi. 105 STONY POINTE WAY # 210, SHENANDOAH PEDS 22657 #051-04-1998 L1999 PD *020 †55

WEST, Brian James. 357 BROWN ST 22657 #004-01-2000 L2001 FM *020 †18

STUART – PATRICK

COLE, Richard Claude. PO BOX 1019 24171 #051-01-1981 L1984 FM OBS *020 †18

FLOWERS, Jeanne Smith. 110 W BLUE RIDGE ST 24171 #036-08-1994 L1994 FM *020 †18

GHAURI, Adil Zahoor. 18877 JEB STUART HIGHWAY, PATRICK COUNTY FP 24171 #704-25-2000 L2005 IM *020 †20 ‡

HUFF, Steven Ronald. ■ 24171 #051-07-1992 L1995 FM PLM *020 †18

KAHAN, Barry Edward. 18688 JEB STUART HWY 24171 #036-01-1969 L1978 R *020

KIPREOS, Nicholas T. PO BOX 912, 797 WOODLAND DR 24171 #051-04-1990 L1993 FM *020 †18

KRAMER, Ralph Lewis. PO BOX 805 24171 #035-03-1976 L1986 OBG MFM *020 †30

MC NAMEE, Edwin T, Jr. ■ 24171 #021-01-1952 L1954 GP *071

STUARTS DRAFT – AUGUSTA

BEILER, Omar James. 113 1ST ST 24477 #051-01-1983 L1990 FM *020 †18

CLEVENSON, David Joel. 24 GLOUCESTER RD, STUARTS DRAFT FAMILY PRACT 24477 #051-04-1984 L1999 FM *020 †18

FORBES, John Wm, III. 24 GLOUCESTER RD 24477 #051-04-1963 L1963 FM *020 †18

HATTER, Dennis Lee. 24 GLOUCESTER RD 24477 #051-04-1975 L1978 FM *020 †18

HOSTETTER, Samuel. 24 GLOUCESTER RD 24477 #043-01-1996 L2000 FM *020 †18

MC LAUGHLIN, Timothy E. 24 GLOUCESTER RD 24477 #051-01-2001 L2001 FM *020 †18

MILLER, Richard Burkhart. 24 GLOUCESTER RD 24477 #041-14-1974 L1977 FM *020 †18

NOLLEY, Eugene Davis. ■ 24477 #051-04-1956 L1956 FM *071

SUFFOLK – SUFFOLK CITY

ABOULATTA, Hussein M. 2000 MEADE PKWY 23434 #915-04-1974 L1988 CD IM *020 †20

ABU-ABSI, Michael Samir. 2000 MEADE PKWY 23434 #038-43-1998 L2002 IM *020 †20

ADKINS, William Edward. 2000 MEADE PKWY, LAKEVIEW MED CTR INC 23434 #051-07-1979 L1982 OBG *020 †30

ADRIANO, Phillip Michael. ■ 23435 #023-12-1997 L2007 EM *012

APAKUPAKUL, Nakorn. 2800 GODWIN BLVD 23434 #891-01-1964 L1974 FM *020 †18 ‡

ARRIOLA, Christine Marie. ■ 23435 #051-07-2005 L2006 *100

AZHAR, Zahur Ullah. ■ 23435 #704-04-1963 L1978 GS GYN *071

BABINEAU, Teresa Wirth. 7077 CRITTENDEN RD 23432 #051-07-1990 L1991 FM *040 †18

BAKHT, Shoaib. 1030 HILLPOINT RD 23434 #160-06-1977 L1985 CD IM *020 †20

BARAKAT, Serena E. 2000 MEADE PKWY, LAKEVIEW MEDICAL CENTER 23434 #605-03-1993 L1999 IM *020 †18

BARNES, Rianna Colette. ■ 23435 #051-07-2007 L2007 PD *012

BAROT, Amrutlal Jethalal. 1540 BREEZEPORT WAY, STE 500 23435 #495-17-1973 L1981 FM P *020 †75

BASCO, Thomas Edward. 2790 GODWIN BLVD STE 36 23434 #035-48-1975 L1999 OBG *020 †30

BELGRAVE, Claude Donald. ■ 23434 #024-01-1984 L1996 OPH IM *020

BENSON-FOULK, Ernette Y. 4868 BRIDGE RD 23435 #051-04-1995 L1995 PD *020 †55

BERGFIELD, Thomas G. 2012 MEADE PKWY, ORTHOPAEDIC SPECIALIST OF 23434 #030-06-1978 L1983 HS ORS *020 †40

BLAKE, Michael Clarence. 2790 GODWIN BLVD, STE 230 23434 #051-04-1972 L1973 GS GYN *020 †85

BLEVINS, Judith Coffman. 2800 GODWIN BLVD, RADIATION ONCOLOGY 23434 #051-07-1989 L1993 RO *020 †80

BONO, Michael Jos. 2800 GODWIN BLVD 23434 #051-07-1983 L1984 EM *020 †16

BRADY, John Edward. 2050 HILLPOINT BLVD N 23434 #045-01-1992 L1999 FM *020 †18

BROWN, Stafford George, Jr. 2800 GODWIN BLVD, ATTN:DR. STAFFORD BROWN 23434 #051-01-1998 L1998 DR *020 †80

BUCHANAN, John Goodwin. 157 N MAIN ST, STE D 23434 #010-01-1964 L1974 P *071 †75

BURGER, Robert Henry. 2000 MEADE PKWY, LAKEVIEW MEDICAL CENTER IN 23434 #035-19-1954 L1983 U *020 †95

CAPUTO, Arthur Francis, Jr. 5100 STONEWALL CT 23435 #035-15-1999 L2001 OBG *012

CHALKLEY, Milton De Rohan. ■ 23434 #051-04-1955 L1955 GS *020

CHANG, Eugene Y. 104 PALMYRA DR, STE B 23434 #033-05-1993 L2001 GS *020 †85

CHIRICO, Dianne Mc Neill. 2000 MEADE PKWY 23434 #041-12-1997 L2004 PD *020 †55

CHRISTI, Rebecca Amelia. ■ 23435 #023-12-2007 L2007 *012

CLAWSER, Rory Adam. 2000 MEADE PKWY, LAKEVIEW MEDICAL CENTER, I 23434 #051-04-2003 L2003 OBG *020

COLLIER, J Porter, Jr. ■ 23433 #001-02-1958 L1978 ORS OS *071 †40

CORNELL, George Willett. 2000 MEADE PKWY, LAKEVIEW MED CTR INC 23434 #051-01-1971 L1972 OBG *020 †30

CURRY, Richard Lee. 2000 MEADE PKWY 23434 #055-01-1972 L1978 PD *020 †55

DAMLE, Anant Shreeram. 5818 HARBOUR VIEW BLVD, STE 240 23435 #495-23-1988 L1999 GE IM *020 †20

DE JESUS, Jose M. ■ 23435 #035-47-1984 L1989 AN *020 †05

DE LACEY, William A. 2000 MEADE PKWY, LAKEVIEW MEDICAL CENTER, I 23434 #010-02-1982 L1992 ICE CD *020 †20

DEMKOWSKI, Henry C. 2000 MEADE PKWY, LAKEVIEW MED CTR INC 23434 #051-07-1988 L1992 OBG *020 †30

DENNIS, William Ray. 6202 SPRINGHILL WAY 23435 #028-46-1998 L2001 EM *020 †16

D'HAEM, Robert John. 2800 GODWIN BLVD, SENTARA OBICI HOSPITAL 23434 #025-07-1981 L1982 DR *020 †80

DONAHUE, David Robert. ■ 23435 #016-76-2007, ▲ L2007 *012

DOWLING, Nequita Anjanett. ■ 23435 #051-07-2004 L2007 FM *020 †18

DOYLE, Mary Beth. ■ 23435 #020-02-2006 L2006 *012

DUNN, Chad Brian. ■ 23435 #041-02-2005 L2005 EM *012

DUNTEMANN, Thomas Jos. 5818 HARBOUR VIEW BLVD, STE 240 23435 #016-42-1980 L1996 GE IM *020 †20

EDWARDS, Kathryn Gail. 152 BURNETTS WAY, SUFFOLK PEDIATRICS 23434 #539-04-2003 L2003 PD *020 †55

ELGOHARY, Dina Farouk. ■ 23435 #023-01-2006 L2006 DR *012

ESMAILI, Haydeh. 2470 PRUDEN BLVD 23434 #517-04-1977 L1986 P *020 †75

ESMAILI, Hossain. 1750 KINGS FORK RD 23434 #517-03-1971 L1978 AN *020

ESPINOSA, Emilio M. ■ 23434 #847-04-1951 L1959 AN *071

EVANS, David Paul. ■ 23435 #051-07-2007 L2007 PD *012

EWELL, Cleve W. 2470 PRUDEN BLVD, SUFFOLK PSYCHIATRIC GROUP 23434 #047-07-1984 L1988 P *020 †20,75

FEDEI, Diana C. 2790 GODWIN BLVD, STE 375 23434 #051-07-1996 L2000 OBG *020 †30

FEDERICI, Benigno Dominic. 5833 HARBOR VIEW BLVD, STE C 23435 #041-02-1991 L1995 OBG *020 †30

FORMAN, Jeffrey David. 2000 MEADE PKWY 23434 #041-09-1988 L1995 PCC *020 †20

FORSSELL, Carol Ann. ■ 23434 #051-04-1984 L1987 DBP *020 †55

FTICSAR, Jennifer Megan. ■ 23435 #041-02-2004 L2005 OBG *100

GARCIA, Maria Lourdes. ■ 23434 #042-03-1986 L2007 *020

GARLAND, Daniel Wayne. 2800 GODWIN BLVD 23434 #051-07-1982 L1985 PTH PCP *020 †50

GARLAND, Joshua Paul. ■ 23435 #023-12-2005 L2006 *020

GARNETT, Michelle Lynn. 2800 GODWIN BLVD, OBICI HOSPITAL—RADIOLOGY 23434 #038-06-1995 L2004 DR *020 †80

GARRATT, Bruce Thos. 1900 N MAIN ST 23434 #051-04-1960 L1960 GP *071

GATZEK, Werner John. 3900 BREEZEPORT WAY, # 104 23435 #407-04-1948 L1955 OM *071

GAUDREAU, Philip Adrien, III. ■ 23434 #023-12-2008 *012

GEIGER, Phillip George. ■ 23434 #023-12-2002 L2002 AN *012

GOLDIN, Norman Ross. 5818 HARBOUR VIEW BLVD 23435 #051-01-1977 L1982 GE IM *020 †20

GOODWIN, Kimberley D H. ■ 23433 #040-02-1984 L1988 GP *020

GRAVES, Nikki La Shan. ■ 23435 #036-01-1999 L2001 FM *020 †20

GRAY, Eugenia M G. 2790 GODWIN BLVD, STE 205 23434 #036-07-1993 L1993 OTO *020 †45

GREEN, Dallis Louis. ■ 23434 #021-01-2007 L2008 *012

GREEN, Leslye H. ■ 23434 #021-01-2004 L2006 FM *100 †18

GREGORY, Douglas Blair. 4868 BRIDGE RD 23435 #051-04-1973 L1980 PD PSM *020 †55

GRENGA, Tad Edward. 5818 HARBOUR VIEW BLVD, STE 220 23435 #038-40-1979 L1987 PS HS *020 †65,85 ‡

GROSS, Melissa Faith. 1000 COMMERCIAL LN, MENTAL HLTH 23434 #051-04-1989 L1991 P ADM *020 †75

GROSSO, Peter Chas. 2000 MEADE PKWY 23434 #016-43-1986 L1988 PD *020 †55

GUARDA, Helena Maria. 5833 HARBOUR VIEW BLVD, STE B 23435 #033-06-1994 L2001 PS *020 †65

GUPTA, Dolly. 424 N MAIN ST, STE 2 23434 #496-07-1985 L1995 PD *020 †55

■ = Address Information Privacy Protected

HALL, Dena Raye. 2050 HILLPOINT BLVD N, FAMILY MEDICINE 23434 #004-01-1987 L1990 FM *020 †18

HAROLD, Yolanda Michelle. 2800 GODWIN BLVD 23434 #010-03-1989 L1998 AN *020 †05

HARRELL, Robt Riddick, III. 2000 MEADE PKWY, LAKEVIEW MEDICAL CENTER 23434 #051-04-1965 L1965 U *071 †95

HARRIS, Howard H. 2790 GODWIN BLVD, STE 225 23434 #028-03-1974 L2000 TS *020 †85,90

HAYEK, Craig Steven. 2401 GODWIN BLVD, STE 2 23434 #051-07-1996 L1996 FM *020 †18

HERMAN, Lora Marie. 2800 GODWIN BLVD 23434 #046-01-1986 L1996 PTH *020 †50

HICKS, Thomas Richardson. ■ 23435 #023-12-2003 L2004 *100 †20

HIGHTOWER, Howard Ernest. 1900 N MAIN ST, DEPT OF RADIOLOGY 23434 #051-07-1980 L1985 R DR *020 †80

HIOTELLIS, Apostolos Igna. ■ 23435 #051-07-2005 L2005 FP *012

HOAGLAND, Benjamin David. ■ 23435 #023-12-2007 L2007 *012

HOANG, David H. 5818D HARBOUR VIEW BLVD 23435 #038-75-1997 ▲ L2006 OSM ORS *020

HOLLERAN, James David. 2000 MEADE PKWY 23434 #051-07-1987 L1990 IM *020 †20

HOQ, Kasedul. 5622 BENNETTS PASTURE RD 23435 #160-03-1955 L1974 FM *020 †18

HOWELL, Donald Sherman. ■ 23434 #051-04-1956 L1956 ORS *071 †40

IOBST, Joseph Isidore. ■ 23435 #041-13-1947 L1948 IM GP *071 †20

JACKSON, Theresa Gill. 2050 HILLPOINT BLVD N, FAMILY MEDICINE 23434 #051-07-1989 L1993 PM *012 †18

JACKSON, William George. 2050 HILLPOINT BLVD N, FAMILY MEDICINE 23434 #051-07-1983 L1984 FM *020 †18

JAVIER, Rosa Maria. 5622 BENNETTS PASTURE RD, BENNETTS CREEK FAMILY MED 23435 #748-01-1998 L2006 FM *020 †20

JENKINS, David Raymond. 1217 N MAIN ST 23434 #023-07-1974 L1991 OBG OS *020

JOHNSON, Brian Logan. 2000 MEADE PKWY, LAKEVIEW MEDICAL CENTER IN 23434 #023-12-1986 L1988 D *020 †15

JONES, Shavon Cecil. 157 N MAIN ST 23434 #025-07-1995 L2003 FM *020

JONES-IVES, Norma Lee. 2790 GODWIN BLVD, STE 375 23434 #005-15-1997 L2006 OBG *020 †30

KALLEN, Lowell H. ■ 23434 #023-07-1968 L2003 P CHP *020 †55,75

KAPUR, Manohar Lal. ■ 23434 #495-36-1962 L1973 GP *020

KING, Brian Scott. 2000 MEADE PKWY, LAKEVIEW MEDICAL CENTER 23434 #010-02-1993 L1994 GS CCS *020 †85

KOCH, Richard Adam. ■ 23435 #051-07-2004 L2004 EM *012

KODURI, Prashanthi Borra. 3217 BRIDGE RD 23435 #495-70-1988 L1997 FM *020 †18

KODURI, Venu G. 2000 MEADE PKWY, LAKEVIEW MED CTR 23434 #495-11-1986 L1993 GE IM *020 †20

LADWIG, Corrine. ■ 23435 #018-03-2005 L2006 PD *012

LAMPTON, Lee David. 1900 N MAIN ST, LOUISE OBICI MEMORIAL HOSP 23434 #005-02-1968 L1979 R DR *020 †80

LASSEN, Lorenz Frederick. 4868 BRIDGE RD, LAKEVIEW MEDICAL CENTER 23435 #023-12-1981 L2005 OTO NO *020 †45

LAWSON, John Mark. 5818 HARBOUR VIEW BLVD, STE 240 23435 #012-05-1980 L1991 GE IM *020 †20

LAWSON, Lisa Janeen. ■ 23433 #047-20-2001 L2005 IM *020 †20

LEE, Monique Mc Carter. 157 N MAIN ST, STE A 23434 #047-07-2000 L2000 FM *020 †18

LEE, Ping Nga Allan. 4868 BRIDGE RD 23435 #748-01-1995 L1999 ID *020 †20

LEE, Rusty Joe. ■ 23435 #036-08-2007 L2007 EM *012

LEE, Soo Hwa. ■ 23433 #583-03-1953 L1982 PHP PD *071 †55

LEE, Vincent. 114 N MAIN ST, STE 200 23434 #051-07-1994 L1997 IM *020 †20

LEPORE, Michael A, Jr. 5818 HARBOUR VIEW BLVD, # C2 23435 #051-07-1982 L1985 OBG *020 †30

LEVERONE, Laura Isenhour. 152 BURNETTS WAY 23434 #051-07-1994 L1994 PD *020 †55

LEVIN, Beth Ezzell. 2000 MEADE PKWY, LAKEVIEW MEDICAL CTR 23434 #041-13-1983 L1991 OBG *020 †30 ‡

LIM, Henry Suh. 23433 #583-01-1953 L1982 AN *071 †05

LOEW, Albert Geo. ■ 23435 #010-02-1957 L1965 NS *071 †25

LYLE, John Patrick. 2790 GODWIN BLVD, STE 205 23434 #040-02-1977 L1981 OTO FPS *020 †45

MAHONEY, Michael Dennis. 2790 GODWIN BLVD, STE 255 23434 #041-09-1975 L1987 NEP IM *020 †20

MAILLOUX, Melanie Ann. 413 MARKET ST 23434 #050-02-1998 L2001 PD *020 †55

MANCUSO, Frank Smith. 4868 BRIDGE RD, LAKEVIEW MEDICAL CENTER 23435 #021-01-1963 L1967 PD *020 †55

MARLOW, Aaron Lee. 2012 MEADE PKWY, ORTHOPAEDIC SURGERY CENTER 23434 #065-10-1994 L2000 ORS OAR *020

MAXEY, Ellis Franklin, Jr. 1030 HILL POINT BLVD N 23434 #051-07-1978 L1981 PUD IM *020 †20

MC CORMICK, Kathryn Franc. ■ 23435 #030-05-2004 L2004 PD *020 †55

MC COY, Lisa Kay. ■ 23434 #041-01-1989 L2006 FM *020

MCLELLAN, Katrina Marie K. ■ 23434 #051-04-2005 L2005 PM *012

MENASHA, Moussa Youssef. 2000 MEADE PKWY, LAKEVIEW MED CTR INC 23434 #050-02-1969 L1984 GE IM *020 †20

MILLER, Kari M. 2800 GODWIN BLVD 23434 #051-07-2005 L2005 FP *012

MODI, Navita. 2790 GODWIN BLVD, STE 375 23434 #495-10-1996 L2004 OBG *020 ‡

MORGAN, Mokhtar Ould. 2050 HILLPOINT BLVD N, FAMILY MEDICINE 23434 #036-01-2000 L2000 FM *020 †18

MYINT, Maung Than. 1900 N MAIN ST, ANESTHESIOLOGY DEPT 23434 #209-01-1970 L1977 AN *020 †20

NANAVATY, Rajiv B. 150 BURNETTS WAY, STE 320 23434 #495-23-1992 L1997 N *020 †75

NAPORA, Casimir. 2463 PRUDEN BLVD, SUFFOLK EYE ASSOCIATES PC 23434 #021-01-1980 L1996 OPH *020 †35

NASEER, Nauman. 2000 MEADE PKWY 23434 #704-01-1998 L2007 IC *020 †20

NEUMANN, Daniel Adam. 5818 HARBOUR VIEW BLVD, STE 240 23435 #051-07-1997 L2003 GE *020 †20

NICHOLS, Keith Cameron. 1500 BREEZEPORT WAY, STE 100 23435 #036-01-1984 L1987 EM *020 †16

NOLD, Ralph John. ■ 23434 #028-34-1941 L1954 R *071

O'DWYER, Andrew J, Jr. 2016 MEADE PKWY 23434 #016-06-1968 L1971 OPH *020 †35

OMASTER, Jennifer Elder. ■ 23435 #051-07-2002 L2005 FM *100 †18

OSTMAN, David Lee. 2064 NICKLAUS DR 23435 #025-07-1982 L2001 GYN *020 †30

PAGADOR, Jennifer F. 2401 GODWIN BLVD, STE 3 23434 #748-01-1987 L2001 FM *020 †18

PATE, James Reedie. ■ 23435 #023-12-1992 L1994 GPM *020 †70

PATEL, Vishwas Jitendrabh. 505 RUSHWOOD CT 23435 #495-23-2001 L2008 IM *012

PELAUSA, Edilberto O. 2000 MEADE PKWY, LAKEVIEW MED CTR, INC 23434 #067-02-1979 L1998 OTO HNS *020 †45

PELCZAR, Andrew Joseph. ■ 23435 #023-07-1999 L1999 GS *100

PELLETIER, Erica Rose. 152 BURNETTS WAY 23434 #051-04-2003 L2003 PD *020 †55

PEREZ, Barbaro Jesus. 2012 MEADE PKWY 23434 #033-05-1999 L2005 OSM *020 †40

PERRY, Pamela Maria. ■ 23435 #016-06-1993 L2007 EM *020 †16

PILLAI, Thankom B. 5622 BENNETTS PASTURE RD 23435 #496-07-1965 L1972 FM *020 †18

PILLAI, Variathu B. 1890 N MAIN ST 23434 #495-38-1964 L1973 GS VS *071 †85

POOLE, Aaron Tanner. ■ 23435 #056-06-2006 L2007 *012

RAMOS, Remigio Mayuga. 2800 GODWIN BLVD 23434 #748-01-1969 L1974 PTH GP *020 †50

RAMSTAD, David Scott. 2000 MEADE PKWY 23434 #051-07-1980 L1982 IM OM *020 †20

RANSOM, Brandy Erin. ■ 23435 #051-07-2008 *012

RICH, David L. ■ 23435 #024-05-2004 L2004 *020

ROBERTO, Frank Andre. 1000 COMMERCIAL LN, COMMUNITY ML 23434 #056-05-1976 L1981 P CHP *020 †75

ROBERTSON, Jane Melinda. 152 BURNETTS WAY, MEDICAL GROUP 23434 #045-04-1993 L1993 PD *020 †55

ROLLINS, Dixon Michael. 2800 GODWIN BLVD, OBICI HOSP 23434 #051-04-1969 L1969 DR GP *020 †80

SAN DIEGO, Carmelita M. 2800 GODWIN BLVD 23434 #748-02-1963 L1972 PTH GP *020 †50

SANKARAN, K N Vijaya. 440 W WASHINGTON ST 23434 #495-45-1966 L1976 PD *020

SANKARAN, Nellie M. 440 W WASHINGTON ST 23434 #748-02-1969 L1976 PD ADL *020 †55

SAN ROMAN, Irene Paula. ■ 23435 #042-02-1993 L2006 IMG *020 †20

SARACHENE, Joseph Eugene. 2269 BRIDGE RD 23433 #038-44-1986 L1988 P *030 †75

SARRIS, Barbara Marie. ■ 23435 #035-47-1992 L1994 *020 †20

SAVEIKA, Joseph Andrie, III. 2000 MEADE PKWY 23434 #051-07-2003 L2003 PM *020 †20

SEAL, Robert Bennie. ■ 23433 #012-01-1960 L1966 PTH *071 †50

SEEMAN, Paul David. ■ 23436 #035-06-1993 L1994 GPM *020 †18,70

SERIANNI, Richard Paul. ■ 23434 #023-12-2001 *020 †05

SIDHOM, Mervat Emile. ■ 23435 #915-04-1978 L1987 P *020

SINCLAIR, Joseph Jefferds. 2016 MEADE PKWY 23434 #055-02-2003 L2007 OPH *020

SMITH, Karen Denise. 2897 BRIDGE RD 23435 #051-07-1996 L1996 FM *020 †18

SMITH, Stanley Bernard. 2790 GODWIN BLVD, STE 255 23434 #051-04-1977 L1978 NEP IM *020 †20

SMITH-GRIFFIN, Kimberly A. 4868 BRIDGE RD 23435 #041-12-1997 L1997 IM FM *020 †20,18

SPRUIELL, Linwood Ray. 2800 GODWIN BLVD, SENTARA OBICI HOSPITAL 23434 #047-07-1981 L1989 AN *020 †05

STARK, James J. 5835 HARBOUR VIEW BLVD, STE C 23435 #024-01-1971 L1977 ON HEM *020 †20

STARRETT-KELLER, Cheryl M. ■ 23435 #041-02-2007 *012

STOCKMAN, Lynne Wiser. 3217 BRIDGE RD, NORTH SUFFOLK FAMILY MEDIC 23435 #028-78-1989, ▲ L1990 FM *020 †18

STOKES, Monique Raney. 2604 N NANSEMOND DR 23435 #036-08-1994 L1994 FM *020 †18

STRUM, Daniel Geo. ■ 23435 #026-04-1972 L1989 PTH *020 †50

SU, Alexander Kuang-Chyi. 2800 GODWIN BLVD 23434 #244-04-1971 L1974 HO IM *020 †20

SUFYANI, Sylvia Hoq. 5622 BENNETTS PASTURE RD 23435 #051-07-1996 L1996 IM *020

SWEENEY, John Richard, Jr. 2453 PRUDEN BLVD 23434 #047-05-1976 L1979 AI PD *020 †55,03

TAN, Bethany Bragdon. ■ 23435 #051-07-1995 L1995 TS *020 †85

TANNOUS, Geoge Moussa. 5818 HARBOUR VIEW BLVD, STE B2 23435 #875-01-1989 L1998 IM *020 †20

TAYKO, Manuel Enfestan. ■ 23435 #748-01-1957 L1968 GS *020

TEPERA, Christopher M. ■ 23435 #023-12-2000 L2001 U *012

THAKRAL, Vikas. ■ 23435 #495-22-2002 L2006 IM *020 †20

THOMAS, Philip R. 112 KINGS HWY 23432 #051-04-1951 L1951 GP *020

THOMASON, Phillip Ray. 4868 BRIDGE RD, LAKEVIEW MEDICAL CENTER 23435 #004-01-1963 L1973 PD *020 †55

TRIKALSARANSUKH, C. ■ 23434 #891-04-1980 L1993 PD *020 †55

TURNBAUGH, Lois W. ■ 23434 #023-01-1969 L1977 GP EM *020 †16

TURNER, Thomas Wm. ■ 23438 #051-04-1975 ADM *071 *

VAUGHN, Lindsey Dewitt. 2050 HILLPOINT BLVD N, FAMILY MEDICINE 23434 #051-07-1989 L1990 FM *020 †18 ‡

VERDIRAME, Joseph L. 2000 MEADE PKWY, LAKEVIEW CLINIC INC 23434 #051-01-1974 L1977 IM CD *020 †20

WADDY, James Mitchell, Jr. 2800 GODWIN BLVD 23434 #051-04-1999 L1999 FM *020 †18

WALLER, David Franklin. 2050 HILLPOINT BLVD N, FAMILY MEDICINE 23434 #051-07-1989 L1991 FM *020 †18

WALSHE, Christopher J. 5838 HARBOUR VIEW BLVD, STE 290 23435 #050-02-1990 L2007 OBG *020 †30

WARDELL, Arthur Warren. 5818D HARBOUR VIEW BLVD, STE 150 23435 #035-20-1975 L1980 ORS *020 †40

WEBB, Leslie Anne. 2000 MEADE PKWY, LAKEVIEW MEDICAL CENTER, I 23434 #036-05-1996 L1996 CD IC *020 †20

WEINSTEIN, David J. 2800 GODWIN BLVD 23434 #035-06-1964 L1967 GP *071

WENTZEL, Carl Frank. 5818 HARBOUR VIEW BLVD, BON SECOURS HARBOUR VIEW H 23435 #051-07-1989 L1992 EM *020 †16

WILLIAMS, Bernard Andrew. ■ 23434 #566-01-1997 L2007 IM *100 †20

WILLIAMS, Karen T. 157 N MAIN ST 23434 #036-08-1993 L1993 FM *020 †18

WILLIAMS, Michael T. 114 N MAIN ST, STE 200 23434 #010-03-1978 L1981 IM *020 †20

WILSON, Matthew Ryan. ■ 23435 #021-01-2006 L2007 *012

WING, Edward Ellison. 2790 GODWIN BLVD, STE 375 23434 #035-08-1992 L2006 OBG *020 †30

WING, John E, III. 114 N MAIN ST, STE 200 23434 #041-12-1985 L1991 IM *020 †20

WUNDERLICH, Joanne Rue. 2000 MEADE PKWY, LAKEVIEW MEDICAL CENTER IN 23434 #055-02-1993 L1993 PD *020 †55

ZASADA, Andrew Peter. 2800 GODWIN BLVD 23434 #028-34-1980 L1989 DR *020 †80

ZEILER, David Zachary. 2000 MEADE PKWY 23434 #050-02-1980 L1994 GS *020 †85

ZHU, Qingyan. 1520 BREEZEPORT WAY, STE 600 23435 #243-69-1982 L1998 N *020 †75

SUTHERLAND – DINWIDDIE

PHIPPS, William James, Jr. 5609 CLAIBORNE RD 23885 #051-04-1986 L1987 FM *020 †18

SOUTHALL, Kirby Donaldson. 5609 CLAIBORNE RD 23885 #051-01-1983 L1986 FM *020 †18

SWOOPE – AUGUSTA

ELSEA, Richard Wm. ■ 24479 #051-07-1991 L1992 FM *020 †18 ‡

SYRIA – MADISON

MC COY, Kenneth Lowell. ■ 22743 #041-13-1942 L1959 **CLP PTH** *071 †50,28
PAYETTE, John Joy. GENERAL DELIVERY, INDIAN WINDS HOMESTEAD 22743
  #051-04-1958 L1958 **OBG OS** *071 †30

TABB – YORK

WILLIAMS, Tamara Lea. ■ 23693 #035-45-1989 L1990 **FM** *020 †18

TAPPAHANNOCK – ESSEX

BARNES, Cameron Ryan. 1396 TAPPAHANNOCK BLVD, VIRGINIA UROLOGY CENTER 22560
  #051-04-1998 L1998 **U** *020 †95
BENNETT, Robert Mc Intyre. 668 HOSPITAL RD, VIRGINIA CARDIOVASCULAR 22560
  #051-04-1972 L1974 **CD IM** *020 †20
BIGG, Michael John. 618 HOSPITAL RD, RIVERSIDE TAPPAHANNOCK HOS 22560
  #917-06-1975 L1983 **DR** *020
BRIGGS, Robert Edward. 658 HOSPITAL RD, STE 303 22560 #041-02-1984 L1986 **FM** *020 †18
BUCHER, Bruce Myron. 618 HOSPITAL RD 22560 #028-03-1964 L1980 **IM GP** *020
CHRISTENSON, Randy Wm. 618 HOSPITAL RD, RIVERSIDE TAPPAHANNOCK HOS 22560
  #040-02-1975 L2000 **R** *020
COLEMAN, Geoffrey. ■ 22560 #041-13-1984 L1996 **FM EM** *020 †18
DOROMAL, Noel Macairen. 659 HOSPITAL RD, BLDG A 22560 #748-01-1967 L1974
  GS *062 †85
DUDLEY, James Roane. 618 HOSPITAL RD, EMERGENCY DEPT 22560 #051-07-1985 L1986
  EM *020 †18
FERRANCE, Randy Joe. 618 HOSPITAL RD 22560 #051-04-1998 L1998 **MPD** *020 †20,55
FRANCIS, Michael Jos. 659 HOSPITAL RD, STE 203 22560 #035-09-1985 L1997
  CRS *020 †85,10
HADEN, Halcott T. ■ 22560 #047-05-1950 L1956 **IM** *071 †28,20
HASKINS, Jeffrey Milton. 668 HOSPITAL RD BLDG B, SUITE 300 22560 #010-01-1979 L1984
  U *020 †95
HOCKETT, William Jos. PO BOX 579 22560 #016-43-1947 L1960 **R** *071 †80
JENNINGS, Stewart Wayne. 618 HOSPITAL RD 22560 #051-07-1999 L1999 **MPD** *020 †20,55
KHAN, Irim Shahbaz. 618 HOSPITAL RD, HOSPITAL 22560 #035-09-1998 L2002 **IM** *020 †20
KINSEL, Vicki Arlene. 618 HOSPITAL RD 22560 #051-07-1989 L1991 **IM NEP** *020 †20
KROLL, Ronald Neil. 618 HOSPITAL RD 22560 #041-09-1967 L1971 **NEP IM** *071 †20
LUDEMAN, Douglas H, Jr. 1396 TAPPAHANNOCK BLVD, VIRGINIA UROLOGY CENTER 22560
  #051-04-1979 L1981 **U** *020 †95
MASON, Reginald Kai. 618 HOSPITAL RD 22560 #041-07-1995 L2004 **GS** *020 †85
MICHOS, John Aristides. 659 HOSPITAL RD, STE 100 22560 #051-07-1988 L1991
  PUD IM *020 †20
OSTER, Niels Henrik. 618 HOSPITAL RD 22560 #005-12-1961 L1966 **GS** *020
POLEVOY, Terry Alan. 618 HOSPITAL RD 22560 #025-07-1970 L1985 **EM** *020
RHAMY, Scott Jackson. 1396 TAPPAHANNOCK BLVD, VIRGINIA UROLOGY CENTER 22560
  #017-20-1997 L2006 **U** *020 †95
RODA, Prospero De La Cruz. 1269 TAPPAHANNOCK BLVD, HOSKINS CREEK PLACE 22560
  #748-07-1966 L1974 **GS EM** *071
ROUHIER, Charles Richard. 618 HOSPITAL RD, RIVERSIDE HOSP ED 22560
  #025-01-1978 L1985 **EM FM** *020 †18,16
SANDERSON, Jesse F, Jr. 618 HOSPITAL RD 22560 #036-01-1969 L1981 **RNR** *012 †80 ‡
SPIEGLER, Glenn Jay. PO BOX 1389, 659 HOSPITAL RD STE 202 22560 #035-09-1982 L1987
  ORS *020 †40
SPOONER, Myron Georges. 648 HOSPITAL RD, STE 305 22560 #016-06-1972 L1993
  OBG *071 †30
VALENZUELA, Gregg Anthony. RIVERSIDE TAPPAHANNOCK HOS, MEDICAL ARTS BLDG
  A 22560 #051-01-1978 L1984 **GE IM** *020 †20
WALES, Dennis S. 618 HOSPITAL RD, RIVERSIDE TAPPAHANNOCK HOS 22560
  #048-14-1997 L2005 **FM** *020 †18
WIND, Michael Allen, Jr. 953 OAKLAND RD 22560 #051-01-2002 L2008 **ORS** *020

TAZEWELL – TAZEWELL

BAKER, K Drew. 992 1/2 BEN BOLT AVE 24651 #051-04-1990 L1994 **PD** *020 †55
BOZUNG, Patricia Sue. 840 E FINCASTLE ST 24651 #025-01-1984 L1993 **IM PD** *020 †20
CARPIO, Pablo M. 141 BEN BOLT AVE 24651 #748-01-1983 L1994 **IM** *020 †20
DAVIS, John Evan. 141 BEN BOLT AVE 24651 #051-01-1977 L1979 **PD A** *020 †55
GOMEZ, Roy C. 141 BEN BOLT AVE 24651 #495-31-1972 L1999 **PD FM** *020 †55 ‡
JABOURIAN, Zaven. 141 BEN BOLT AVE 24651 #605-01-1980 L1989 **OTO** *020 †45
KWUN, Doo Yung. 141 BEN BOLT AVE 24651 #583-06-1969 L1973 **PD** *020 †55,18
MOORE, Kerry Francq. ■ 24651 #051-07-1981 L2006 **FM D** *020
MURRAY, William Olanda. PO BOX 230 24651 #047-06-1959 L1982 **FM** *075
OLINGER, David Phlegar. ■ 24651 #051-01-1959 L1959 **OBG** *071
PLAGATA, Eduardo D. 840 E FINCASTLE ST, P O BOX 852 24651 #748-08-1964 L1972
  GP GS *071 †85
RINEHART, Stephen Roy. 123 BEN BOLT AVE 24651 #051-01-1977 L1978 **FM** *020 †18
SHRADER, William Eric. 141 BEN BOLT AVE 24651 #041-02-1983 L1984 **FM** *020 †18
SMITH, Mary Anne Jane. 141 BEN BOLT AVE, TAZEWELL COMM HOSP 24651
  #748-01-1973 L1995 **IM FM** *020
TOLOSA, Eduardo T. PO BOX 837, KING CT 24651 #748-01-1962 L1972 **GP** *020
WILE, Ira Barnes. 306 E PINE ST 24651 #048-12-1963 L1980 **U** *071
ZILBERFARB, Bernard. ■ 24651 #010-02-1974 L1975 **ORS FM** *071

THE PLAINS – FAUQUIER

EDDY, Harrison P, III. ■ 20198 #035-01-1945 L1997 **P PYA** *071 †75
RUSSELL, William Michael. ■ 20198 #539-03-1969 L1976 **R** *020 †80

TIMBERVILLE – ROCKINGHAM

PERRY, Danny Lee. 165 NEW MARKET RD 22853 #048-02-1972 L1974 **FM** *020 †18

SHOWALTER, Brian Michael. ■ 22853 #051-04-2008 *012

TOANO – JAMES CITY

BURRI, Christopher Aaron. ■ 23168 #051-07-2005 L2005 **FP** *012
BURRI, Kristina Cohen. ■ 23168 #051-07-2007 L2007 **EM** *012

TRIANGLE – PRINCE WILLIAM

ABBAS, Saad Abd El-Moneim. ■ 22172 #915-05-1971 *100
AMPOSTA, Lustricia N. ■ 22172 #748-01-1956 L1983 **P** *030
BAIG, Mirza Mohammed Ali. ■ 22172 #704-27-1999 L2006 **IM** *100 †20
BATAILLE, Marie Francesse. ■ 22172 #649-38-1995 **IM** *020
CLAY, Tokzhan Kairatovna. ■ 22172 #913-29-1992 L2007 **FM** *020
HAFEEZ, Hammad. ■ 22172 #704-05-2000 L2005 **IM** *020 †20
LOU, Jeffrey Koon. ■ 22172 #051-04-2003 L2003 **GS** *100
SEIPEL, John H. ■ 22172 #024-01-1954 L1961 **LM N** *071

TROUTDALE – GRAYSON

POWERS, William Thos. 67 HIGH COUNTRY LN 24378 #051-01-1976 L1981 **IM CD** *020 †20

TROUTVILLE – BOTETOURT

ECHOLS, Charles Little. ■ 24175 #051-01-1959 L1959 **N NP** *071 †75
EVANS, O Norman. ■ 24175 #045-01-1959 L1968 **P** *072 †75
OVERSTREET, Ronald Boyd. 37 LAYMANTOWN RD 24175 #051-04-1976 L1977 **FM** *020 †18
REA, Catherine Gibson. 37 LAYMANTOWN RD 24175 #051-01-2001 L2001 **FM** *020 †18
ROBINSON, Carey William. 58 RIDGE RD, EYE CARE & SURGERY 24175 #021-06-1987 L1993
  OPH *020 †35
THOMPSON, William M, IV. 58 RIDGE RD, EYE CARE & SURGERY 24175 #051-01-1999 L1999
  OPH *020 †35
WOODFORD, Randall Lyndon. ■ 24175 #051-01-2006 L2006 **PTH** *012

TROY – FLUVANNA

BRASHERS, Valentina L. ■ 22974 #051-01-1982 L1988 **IM** *020 †20
CARFRAE, Matthew James. ■ 22974 #018-03-2001 L2006 **NO** *012 †45

UNIONVILLE – ORANGE

SEARLE, Robert E. ■ 22567 #051-01-1967 L1967 **OPH OTO** *020 †35 ‡

UNIVERSITY OF RICHMOND – RICHMOND CITY

DEANE, Lynne Pendleton. STUDENT HEALTH CENTER 23173 #051-04-1982 L1983 **FM** *020 †18
GLICK, Sarah Rachel. 28 WESTHAMPTON WAY, UR BOX 3346 23173 #035-20-2007 L2007
  PD *012

URBANNA – MIDDLESEX

KLUGE, Robert Carter. 23175 #051-04-1954 L1954 **PD** *071 †55
LADENDORF, Virginia C B. ROUTE 227 23175 #051-04-1949 L1951 **P** *020

VERONA – AUGUSTA

GREEN, Walter Howard. 2 FORT RIVER RD 24482 #051-01-1973 L1976 **EM IM** *020 †20,16
HENSLEY, George Thos. ■ 24482 #038-40-1957 L1957 **PTH** *071 †50
HIGGS, James Albert. 1 GREEN HILL DR 24482 #051-01-1954 L1954 **FM** *071
KENNEDY, Robert George. 1 GREEN HILL DR 24482 #051-01-2000 L2005 **FM** *100 †18
LEALE-CRAIG, Kirsta. 1 GREEN HILL DR 24482 #035-06-1995 L2000 **FM** *020 †18
LONGMIRE, Mack Harvey. 1 GREEN HILL DR 24482 #047-20-1995 L1995 **FM** *020 †18
PAINTER, William Graham. ■ 24482 #051-04-1945 L1946 **GP** *071

VICTORIA – LUNENBURG

BRIDGFORTH, Lewis Wm. PO BOX AF 23974 #051-04-1965 L1965 **FM GP** *020 †18
RIVAS, Juan Antonio. PO BOX 70, 1508 K V RD 23974 #033-05-1981 L1990 **FM** *020 †18

VIENNA – FAIRFAX

ABERNATHY, Margaret R. 1815 BEULAH RD 22182 #051-04-1964 L1964 **N** *020
AHAD, Abdul. 8701 WESTWOOD DR 22182 #704-04-1958 L1989 **P GP** *071
AL-BU-SAIDI, Noor. ■ 22182 #695-01-1994 L1997 **END** *100 †20
AL-HAZZAA, Selwa A F. ■ 22183 #797-01-1998 **OS** *075
AL-KADHI, Yusuf Abdullah. ■ 22182 #797-01-1990 L1997 **DR** *020 †80
ALMOHSEN, Ibrahim Zaid. 344 MAPLE AVE W 22180 #797-01-1987 **PD** *100 †55
ALTAMIRANO, Rene. 406 BRANCH RD SE 22180 #176-01-1951 L1960 **OPH** *020
ANDRINO, Barbara. 100 MAPLE AVE E, INOVA URGENT CARE CTR 22180 #003-01-1984 L2001
  FM *020 †18
ANNUNZIATA, Christina J. 8320 OLD COURTHOUSE RD, STE 100 22182 #010-02-2000 L2000
  ON *100 †20
ANNUNZIATA, Christopher C. 8320 OLD COURTHOUSE RD, STE 100 22182
  #010-02-1994 L1995 **ORS OSM** *020 †40
ARIA, James J. 8233 OLD COURTHOUSE RD, STE 150 22182 #517-01-1968 L1978
  REN GYN *020 †30

■ = Address Information Privacy Protected

ATTAR, Muhammed Ahmad. ■ 22182 #305-01-1989 **IM** *020
BAJOGHLI, Amir Ali. 8130 BOONE BLVD STE 340 22182 #051-04-1994 L1995 **D DS** *020 †20,15
BALIAD, Val Bathala. 100 MAPLE AVE E 22180 #025-07-1992 L2000 **IM** *020 †20
BALZARETT, Joseph Raymond. 8206 LEESBURG PIKE, STE 207 TYSONS PROF BLDG 22182 #010-02-1966 L1973 **CHP P** *020 †75
BARASH, Faith Ellen. 8300 OLD COURTHOUSE RD, STE 140 22182 #033-06-1986 L2004 **OBG** *020 †30
BARNARD, Marvin. 8000 TOWERS CRESCENT DR, STE 180 22182 #010-03-1979 L1997 **IM** *020
BARNETT, William Marc. ■ 22181 #041-12-1981 L2001 **EM** *020 †16
BARRY, Rebecca Rudd. 243 CHURCH ST NW, STE 200C 22180 #051-01-1996 L1997 **D** *020 †15
BARSANTI, Ronald G. 410 MAPLE AVE W 22180 #010-02-1953 L1958 **PD** *020
BAUTISTA, Maria Veronica. ■ 22182 #748-01-1991 L2004 **PDP PD** *020 †55
BEHSUDI, Faiz Mohammed. 1608 SPRING HILL RD, EMERGENCY USA 22182 #118-02-1976 L1984 **GS EM** *020
BEHSUDI, Homaira. 1608 SPRING HILL RD 22182 #118-01-1985 L1995 **FM** *020 †18
BENJELLOUN, Hind. ■ 22182 #051-07-2005 L2005 **P** *012
BERGER, Jonathan Henry. ■ 22180 #038-43-2008 *012
BITAR, John Geo. ■ 22182 #605-01-1960 L1986 **PD GE** *020 †55
BLANK, Melanie Jaye. 124 PARK ST SE, STE 202 22180 #035-09-1985 L1988 **NEP IM** *020 †20
BONACCI, Christopher E. 361 MAPLE AVE W, STE 200 22180 #035-01-1995 L1998 **OS** *020
BRADLEY, Joan Doerflinger. 115 PARK ST SE, VIENNA FAMILY MEDICINE 22180 #051-07-1995 L1995 **FM** *020 †18
BRANTLEY, Julian T, Jr. 2110 GALLOWS RD STE D 22182 #036-01-1975 L1978 **P** *020 †75
BUDHRANI, Sunil Sajan. ■ 22182 #010-01-1999 L2005 **EM** *020 †16
BULGER, Elizabeth Ann. ■ 22181 #010-02-1984 L1988 **ID IM** *020 †20
BULLIN, Joy Maria. ■ 22182 #051-04-2000 L2000 **PTH** *020 †50
BUYSE, Valerie Josephine. 2110 GALLOWS RD STE D 22182 #024-05-1972 L1985 **P ILI** *020 †75
CAMERON, Alan S, Jr. 2102 GALLOWS RD # B 22182 #039-01-1950 L1968 **P** *050 †75
CARDENAS, Francisco. ■ 22180 #264-03-1956 L1964 **GS** *071 †85
CARROLL, Patrick Anthony. 360 MAPLE AVE W 22180 #539-02-1954 L1960 **U** *071 †95
CASSIDY, William Michael. 410 MAPLE AVE W, STE 5 22180 #010-02-1970 L1975 **PD** *020 †55
CHAN, Oscar. 2235 CEDAR LN, STE 302 22182 #005-12-1991 L2004 **GS** *020
CHANG, Woody. 1934 OLD GALLOWS RD, STE 350 22182 #035-15-1997 L2000 **IM** *020 †20
CHATMAN, Anita S. 100 MAPLE AVE E 22180 #160-02-1981 L1995 **FM** *020 †18
CHEN, Richard. ■ 22182 #035-03-1992 L1995 **IM** *020 †20
CHHABRA, Sumeet Kumar. ■ 22182 #010-01-2006 L2006 **IM** *012
CHONG, John Yo-Han. ■ 22181 #010-01-2004 L2007 **OPH PO** *012
CHOW, Jimmy Alastair. 8150 LEESBURG PIKE, STE 910 22182 #462-01-1968 L1981 **HS PS** *020 †65
CLEMENS, Michael Avery. 8290 OLD COURTHOUSE RD # D 22182 #429-01-1981 L1989 **AN** *020
CORBO, Joseph. 301 MAPLE AVE W, BIRCH BLDG. STE C. 22180 #010-02-1975 L1978 **P** *020 †75
CROSS, Phyllis Anne. ■ 22182 #036-07-1977 L1982 **MDM FM** *030 †18 ‡
DAPPEN, Alan Wayne. 360 MAPLE AVE W STE E, DOCTOKR FAMILY MED 22180 #054-04-1979 L1992 **FM** *020 †18
DARWISH, Hussain M. ■ 22182 #704-02-1973 L1980 **AN** *075 †05
DEL VECCHIO, Michael A. 8296 OLD COURTHOUSE RD # D 22182 #010-02-1967 L1971 **P** *020 †75 ‡
DEMAKIS, John George. ■ 22181 #016-11-1962 L1999 **IM CD** *050 †20
DE PAOLA, Francesco. ■ 22180 #561-10-1949 L1955 **PD** *071
DIETZ, Richard Frederick. 130 PARK ST SE, STE 100 22180 #035-20-1965 L1967 **CD IM** *020 †20
DONNELLY, Kathleen M. ■ 22180 #036-07-1990 L2006 **CCP** *020 †55
DORNAN, Joyce Janette. 100 MAPLE AVE E 22180 #051-01-1999 L1999 **FM** *020 †18
DOUGLAS, Sibert Roy. ■ 22181 #035-45-1956 L1957 **IM** *071 †20
DUGGAN, Paul M. 8150 LEESBURG PIKE, STE 909 22182 #041-01-1960 L1966 **OPH** *071 †35
EDOUARD, Anna Juliette. 100 MAPLE AVE E 22180 #041-13-1997 L1999 **IM** *020
ELARINY, Hazem Ahmed. 2235 CEDAR LN, STE 301 22182 #021-06-1990 L1998 **GS AS** *020 †85
ELGIN, Virginia E. 401 CYNTHIA LN NE 22180 #005-19-1992 L1996 **PD N** *020 †75,55
ERDAG, Gulsun. ■ 22181 #902-05-1987 **PTH** *012
FAJARDO, Therese N. ■ 22181 #748-10-1996 **HO** *100 †20
FALLS, Richard Alfred. 8150 LEESBURG PIKE STE 9 22182 #035-06-1959 L1966 **OPH** *020 †35
FETTER, Theodore Walker. 201 PARK ST SE 22180 #041-02-1971 L1992 **OTO NO** *020 †45
FLANNERY, Frank Travers. 108 MAPLE AVE E 22180 #023-12-1981 L2002 **FM EM** *030 †18
FOULKE, John David. 8229 BOONE BLVD, STE 700 22182 #035-01-1959 L1963 **OM IM** *020 †70
FOX, Carol Cathleen. 410 MAPLE AVE W, STE 5 22180 #051-01-1995 L1999 **PD** *020 †55
FRAMM, Daniel Herschel. 302 MAPLE AVE W 22180 #023-01-1954 L1971 **OPH PD** *020 †55,35 ‡
FRANKLIN, Sherri Lovelace. 8300 OLD COURTHOUSE RD, STE 140 22182 #023-01-1992 L2001 **OBG** *020 †30
FRUCHT, David Martin. ■ 22182 #036-07-1991 L1994 **IM** *020 †20
FULTON, Rebekah Ryanne. ■ 22180 #036-01-2006 L2006 **IM** *012
GAERTNER, Richard Leo, Jr. 133 MAPLE AVE E STE 300 22180 #041-13-1965 L1971 **ORS** *020 †40
GARCIA, Alberto J. 926 FANWAY DR NE 22180 #041-13-1949 L1956 **OBG** *071 †30
GARCIA, Raul R. ■ 22180 #649-17-1949 L1959 **FM** *071
GARCIA, Robert D. ■ 22182 #748-01-1984 L1993 **PD** *100 †55
GARCIA, William John. 8233 OLD COURTHOUSE RD, STE 150 22182 #045-01-1980 L1988 **REN OBG** *020 †30
GILLANDERS, Robert James. 307 MAPLE AVE W, STE J 22180 #010-02-1964 L1970 **OBG OS** *020 †30
GINNAN, Shannon Roy. 1934 OLD GALLOWS RD, STE 500 22182 #035-15-2000 L2001 *020
GIROIR, Brett Paul. ■ 22180 #048-12-1986 L1987 **CCP CCM** *040 †55
GOGINENI, Sree Lakshmi. 124 PARK ST SE, STE 202 22180 #495-50-1994 L2001 **IM** *020 †20
GOMEZ, Miguel Jose. 307 MAPLE AVE W 22180 #264-14-1985 L1996 **OBG** *020
GREEN, Jon Norman. 8000 TOWERS CRESCNT DR #18 22182 #005-06-1977 L2001 **EM OM** *020 †16
GROSS, Frederick M, Jr. 403 NIBLICK DR SE 22180 #020-02-1949 L1957 **IM** *020
GUARINO, Walter Cesar. 2740 CHAIN BRIDGE RD, STE 105 22181 #924-01-1973 L1977 **P** *020 †75
HAIR, Joyce E P. 307 MAPLE AVE W STE C 22180 #010-01-1974 L1978 **GYN** *020 †30
HALL, Melinda Sue. 8300 OLD COURTHOUSE RD, STE 140 22182 #021-05-1981 L1982 **OBG** *071 †30
HAM, Tibor John. 135 CENTER ST S 22180 #051-04-1975 L1976 **IM** *020 †20
HAMILTON, Wilmer P. ■ 22180 #654-01-1982 **IM** *100
HASAN, Bazigha. 10205 WESTFORD DR 22182 #704-06-1980 L1998 **FM** *020 †18
HASSAN, Aishah Carol. ■ 22182 #056-06-1983 L1990 **OBG** *020 †30
HATTWICK, Emily Anne. 415 CHURCH ST NE, STE 101 22180 #010-01-1998 L2004 **ORS** *100
HERSH, Camilla Carroll. 8300 OLD COURTHOUSE RD, STE 140 22182 #025-01-1980 L1987 **OBG** *020 †30
HILMI, Khaldoon Ibrahim. 410 MAPLE AVE W STE 3 22180 #528-01-1952 L1986 **IM CD** *020 †20
HINES, Daniella Ernestine. 100 MAPLE AVE E 22180 #035-45-1989 L1992 **END** *020 †20
HOOPER, Tomoko Inadomi. ■ 22182 #005-02-1970 L1971 **GPM** *040 †70
HOSSEINKHAH, Fatemeh. ■ 22180 #409-06-1999 L2008 **FP** *012
HUANG, Jeffrey Debin. 115 PARK ST SE, VIENNA FAMILY MEDICINE 22180 #035-08-1999 L1999 **FM** *020 †18
HUGHES, John J. ■ 22182 #035-15-1952 L1957 **IM** *071 †20
HUGHES, Steven Samuel. 8320 OLD COURTHOUSE RD, STE 100 22182 #035-45-1985 L1986 **OSS** *020 †40
HUPPI, Joan W. 8245 BOONE BLVD STE 650 22182 #011-04-1979 L1984 **IM IMG** *030 †20
HUSSEIN, Maged H. 2555 CHAIN BRIDGE RD 22181 #915-04-1978 L1988 **IM NEP** *020 †20
HWANG, Minja Ma. ■ 22182 #583-03-1960 L1993 **AN** *071
INAE, Anthony Masaru. ■ 22180 #005-12-1994 L2003 **FM** *020 †18
INGRAM, Bethany Revak. 9500 LAGERSFIELD CIR 22181 #051-04-1999 L1999 **FM** *100 †18
JAIN, Bharti. 415 CHURCH ST NE, STE 101 22180 #495-05-1966 L1997 **R GP** *020
JAO, Archimedes E. ■ 22180 #748-01-1961 *100
JENKINS, James P, Jr. 115 PARK ST SE, VIENNA FAMILY MEDICINE 22180 #051-04-1984 L1991 **FM** *020 †18
JOFFEE, Micha. 243 CHURCH ST NW, STE 100C 22180 #012-05-2000 L2000 **FM** *020 †18
JOLLY, Jenora Hathaway. 100 MAPLE AVE E 22180 #054-04-1991 L2007 **IM** *020 †20
KAO, Leon William. ■ 22182 #051-04-2006 L2007 **IM** *012
KAR, Mitryan. ■ 22181 #010-01-2008 *012
KARP, Evan Brett. 410 MAPLE AVE W, STE 5 22180 #036-05-1989 L1993 **PD** *020 †55
KAWECKI, Anita E. ■ 22182 #759-12-1984 L1996 **IM** *020 †20
KAZI, Aneela. ■ 22181 #704-08-1997 L2007 **P** *012
KELL, Joseph Foster, Jr. ■ 22182 #008-01-1943 L1954 **NS** *071 †25
KELLEY, Victoire Elite. ■ 22182 #051-01-2004 L2006 **FP** *012
KHALIL, Zaid Hashim. 301 MAPLE AVE W, POPLAR BLDG STE C 22180 #528-01-1979 L1998 **FM** *020 †18 ‡
KHORRAMI, Fakhria Masumi. 100 MAPLE AVE E 22180 #118-01-1981 L1993 **FM** *020 †18
KIM, Choong-Hee. ■ 22181 #583-01-1947 **FM OS** *071
KING, Kevin Lee. ■ 22180 #051-04-1989 L1991 **IM** *020 †20
KLEIN, Gary Michael. 8536 HARVEST OAK DR, GARY M. KLEIN, MD, LLC 22182 #012-01-1992 L2006 **UCM OM** *020 ‡
KNERR, Robert James. ■ 22181 #038-40-1960 L1964 **PD** *071 †55
KNUDSON, Homer Ellsworth. 8308 OLD COURTHOUSE RD # A 22182 #010-01-1972 L1973 **OBG** *020
KONGSTVEDT, Peter Reid. 8000 TOWERS CRESCENT DR, STE 800 22182 #056-05-1977 L1990 **IM GP** *030 †20
KOUTROUVELIS, Panagiotis. 8320 OLD COURTHOUSE RD, STE 150 22182 #418-01-1956 L1959 **R NM** *020 †80
KUKICH, Stanka. 403 COUNCIL DR NE 22180 #957-02-1974 L1980 **IM** *020 †20
KURUP, Ajit Gopal Somasun. 100 MAPLE AVE E, INOVA URGENT CARE 22180 #496-37-1995 L2004 **FM** *020 †18
LARSEN, Janet Lynne. 100 MAPLE AVE E, UNIVERSITY OF MICHIGAN 22180 #049-01-2001 L2007 **FM** *020
LEE, Kenneth Hongchong. 115 PARK ST SE, VIENNA FAMILY MEDICINE 22180 #023-01-1992 L1995 **IM** *020 †20
LEIBOWITZ, Ian Howard. 1688 ABBEY OAK DR 22182 #422-01-1982 L1984 **PG PD** *020 †20,55
LEIGH, Julie Friedlin. 8150 LEESBURG PIKE STE 909 22182 #023-07-2002 L2007 **OPH** *020 †35
LENNEN, William Chas. 8320 OLD COURTHOUSE RD, STE 100 22182 #010-02-1988 L1992 **ORS** *020 †40
LETMANYI, Ilona Helga. ■ 22182 #028-34-2006 L2007 **FP** *012
LIESER, Rebecca Lore. ■ 22182 #051-01-1982 L1982 **OBG** *020
LITOVITZ, Gary Lane. 2110 GALLOWS RD 22182 #010-02-1978 L1982 **P** *020 †75
LOPATA, Aaron Michael. 410 MAPLE AVE W, STE 5 22180 #016-11-1997 L2004 **PD** *020
LOUIE, Adeline. 8320 OLD COURTHOUSE RD, STE 150 22182 #035-46-1984 L1991 **DR** *020 †80
LUX, Ann Mary. 2102 GALLOWS RD B 22182 #010-02-1964 L1973 **P** *020 †75
MACKIE, Barbara Mary. 311 MAPLE AVE W, STE H 22180 #010-02-1991 L1992 **A** *020 †18
MAHINPOUR, Siavash. ■ 22182 #517-08-1965 L1975 **ORS** *072 †40
MANDES, Thomas C. 370 MAPLE AVE W 22180 #649-02-1957 L1964 **IM** *020 ‡
MARDELLI, Paul. 10001 VALLEY CREEK LN 22182 #605-01-1976 L1979 **P** *020 †75
MARDER, Carey Miles. 130 PARK ST SE STE 100 22180 #041-02-1972 L1981 **CD IM** *020 †20
MARTEL, Leon Alphonse, Jr. 410 MAPLE AVE W 22180 #010-02-1947 L1953 **GYN** *071 †30
MARTIN, Michael Scott. 100 EAST ST SE, STE 301 22180 #035-46-2001 L2005 **PD** *020 †55
MASRI-FRIDLING, Gayle. 8320 OLD COURTHOUSE RD, STE 303 22182 #041-01-1989 L1991 **D** *020 †15
MC ANDREWS, Julie S. 410 MAPLE AVE W STE 5 22180 #010-02-1985 L1987 **PD** *020 †55
MCCALL, David. ■ 22181 #010-03-2007 **ORS** *012
MC CONNELL, John Patrick. 8320 OLD COURTHOUSE RD, STE 100 22182 #010-02-1978 L1981 **ORS** *020 †40
MC DONNELL, Marissa S. ■ 22181 #010-02-1993 L1993 **PD** *020 †55
MC LAUGHLIN, Theresa G. 8229 BOONE BLVD, COMPREHENSIVE HLT SVCS#700 22182 #041-14-1989 L1999 **IM** *030 †20
MILLER, Abbe Larry. 311 MAPLE AVE W STE H 22180 #660-03-1968 L1975 **A PDA** *020
MILNES, Roger Farnam. ■ 22181 #035-45-1947 L1948 **GS TS** *071 †85,90
MITCHELL, John David. 130 PARK ST SE, STE 300 22180 #051-01-1985 L1988 **OPH EM** *020 †16,35
MITCHELL, Joseph David. 2110 GALLOWS RD STE D 22182 #045-01-1984 L1986 **P** *020 †75
MOFRAD, Pirooz S. 2009 GALLOWS TREE CT 22182 #041-12-2000 L2000 **ICE** *020 †20
MORIN, Emily Louise. 130 PARK ST SE, STE 300 22180 #010-02-1999 L1999 **OPH** *020 †35 ‡
MORRIS, Edward Follett. 410 MAPLE AVE W, STE 5 22180 #035-19-1994 L1994 **PD** *020 †55
MUZZAMMEL, Al. 8292 OLD COURTHOUSE RD # C 22182 #160-02-1973 L1988 **OBG** *020 †30
MYERS, Ledamien Keith. ■ 22180 #038-45-2008 *012
NARAYANAN, Karuna. 100 MAPLE AVE E 22180 #495-44-1994 L2003 **FM** *020 †18
NASR, Ramy. ■ 22182 #010-03-2008 *012
NAYAK, Pradeep Ramnath. 130 PARK ST SE, STE 100 22180 #051-01-1986 L1993 **CD** *020 †20

NELSON, Stuart. ■ 22182 #035-08-1975 L1991 **IM** *020 †20
NEWTON, David Emory. ■ 22180 #051-04-1986 L1987 **FM PD** *020 †18
NGUYEN, Tuc Thi. ■ 22180 #051-04-2004 L2004 **PD** *012
NIMS, Linda P. 243 CHURCH ST NW, STE 200C 22180 #045-01-1973 L1977 **D** *020 †15
OCAMPO, Alexander Tongio. 360 MAPLE AVE W STE F 22180 #748-01-1968 L1979
    DMP PTH *020 †50
OGLE, Kathleen Yvonne. ■ 22182 #010-01-2008 *012
OLIVER, Cap H, Jr. ■ 22182 #048-02-1951 L1969 **RHU IM** *071 †20
ORTON, Gina M. ■ 22182 #041-09-1981 L1994 **P** *020 †75
PARENTE, Charles Lucas. 100 MAPLE AVE E 22180 #051-01-1995 L1999 **FM** *020 †18
PARKER, David P. 8381 OLD COURTHOUSE RD, STE 100 22182 #048-02-1992 L1999
    FM *020 †18
PATEL, Snehal R. ■ 22180 #035-01-2004 L2005 *100
PIKIS, Andreas Charis. 8320 OLD COURTHOUSE RD, STE 150-B 22182 #418-02-1983 L1998
    PD *020 †55
PISHDAD, Gholamreza. ■ 22181 #517-05-1971 L1976 **END IM** *050 †20
POTLURI, Satish Babu. ■ 22180 #496-24-2001 L2005 **IM** *100 †20
PUJOL, Jackie. 450 MAPLE AVE E STE 211 22180 #396-01-1962 L1973 **PD** *020 †55
QUITKIN, H Matthew. 415 CHURCH ST NE, STE 102 22180 #008-01-1995 L1997 **ORS** *020 †40
RAMAN, Ramesh. ■ 22182 #495-33-1981 L1987 **N** *020 †75
RAZIAN, Ali. ■ 22181 #517-01-1996 **IM** *100
REDBORD, Kelley Pagliai. 243 CHURCH ST NW, STE 200C 22180 #023-07-2002 L2007
    D PRD *020 †15 ‡
REISH, Andrew George. ■ 22182 #051-01-2008 *012
REYNOLDS, Louise D. 115 PARK ST SE, VIENNA FAMILY MEDICINE 22180 #041-09-1993 L1994
    FM *020 †18
RHEE, Henry H. ■ 22181 #043-01-1994 L1997 **ID** *020 †20
RICE, Roy Richard, Jr. 102 MAPLE AVE E, NAT'L NAVAL MEDICAL CENTER 22180
    #023-12-1993 L1994 **DR** *020 †80
RIMOLA, Sergio Romeo. 8302 OLD COURTHOUSE RD # A, SPANISH OB-GYN
    ASSOCIATES, 22182 #429-01-1979 L1997 **OBG** *020 †30
RODRIGUEZ FERNANDEZ, Luz. ■ 22181 #041-07-1991 L1996 **CRS** *100 †85
ROMNESS, David Wm. 8320 OLD COURTHOUSE RD, STE 100 22182 #051-07-1984 L1990
    ORS *020 †40
ROTTER, Fran S. 8301 OLD COURTHOUSE RD 22182 #023-01-1989 L1993 **D** *020 †15
ROTTER, Steven Marc. 8301 OLD COURTHOUSE RD 22182 #023-01-1986 L1992
    D OS *020 †15
SABA, Amer A. 2235 CEDAR LN, STE 301 22182 #875-01-1992 L2003 **PS HS** *020 †85,65 ‡
SAFA, Ali M. 301 MAPLE AVE W STE 3A 22180 #517-06-1969 L1987 **END DIA** *020 †20
SALADINO, Lawrence P. 8229 BOONE BLVD STE 700, COMPREVSE HLTH SERV INC 22182
    #010-02-1975 L1985 **OM IM** *030 †20
SALOUR, Arash. ■ 22181 #422-01-1997 **PD** *100
SAMSON, Justino Paras. ■ 22182 #742-02-1941 L1972 **GP** *071
SANAI, Reza. ■ 22182 #010-01-2005 L2005 **IM** *012
SAWCHUK, William Saml. 8320 OLD COURTHOUSE RD, STE 303 22182 #025-01-1981 L1986
    D *020 †15
SAWYER, Rebecca Gay. 410 MAPLE AVE W, STE 5 22180 #051-01-1991 L1992 **PD** *020 †55
SCHONZEIT, Darin Carla. 115 PARK ST SE, STE 300 22180 #033-06-1986 L1987 **FM** *020 †18
SCHWARTZ, Richard Harvey. 115 PARK ST SE, STE 203 22182 #010-02-1965 L1969
    PD OS *020 †55 ‡
SCHWEISTHAL, Paul Edward. 410 MAPLE AVE W STE 5, VIENNA MEDICAL WEST 22180
    #056-06-1967 L1972 **PD** *020 †55
SEBASTIAN, Mary Louise. ■ 22182 #051-01-2000 L2000 **GS** *100 †85
SEDDIQ, Mohammad Karim. ■ 22180 #118-01-1968 L2003 **GS CRS** *071 †85
SENNESH, Louise Mari. ■ 22180 #041-09-1978 L1982 **P** *020 †75
SERYAKOV, Michael George. 8292 OLD COURTHOUSE RD # C 22182 #913-09-1981 L1995
    OBG *020 †30
SHAHAN, Cimmie Lynne. ■ 22180 #010-01-2008 *012
SHAHIN, Bahman. 8294 OLD COURTHOUSE RD # A 22182 #517-01-1966 L1974
    PD PN *020 †55
SHEIFER, Stuart Ethan. 130 PARK ST SE, STE 100 22180 #036-07-1994 L1997 **CD** *020 †20
SHEPLER, Thomas Roberts. 415 CHURCH ST NE STE 101 22180 #023-07-1970 L1980
    ORS *020 †40
SHERIDAN, Elizabeth. ■ 22182 #065-01-1987 L2007 **FM** *020
SHINAISHIN, Furkan. ■ 22182 #035-03-2006 L2006 **EM** *012
SHOHAM, Myron Alan. 360 MAPLE AVE W STE E 22180 #024-05-1971 L1978 **GE IM** *020 †20
SILEO, Robert Peter. 201 PARK ST SE 22180 #035-08-1976 L1977 **IM** *020 †20
SINGH, Niku. ■ 22182 #010-01-2002 L2003 **P** *020
SKLAR, Lisa Framm. 302 MAPLE AVE W 22180 #051-07-1984 L1989 **OPH OS** *020 ‡
SKOVRONSKY, Daniel Moshe. ■ 22181 #041-01-2001 L2001 **PTH** *100
SKUFCA, Robert A. ■ 22182 #028-78-1959, ▲ L1988 **PHP** *012
SOFFER, Lynn Janet. 8229 BOONE BLVD, STE 700 22182 #035-06-1979 L1990 **IM** *050 †20
STOUT, Shannon. ■ 22181 #023-12-2007 L2008 **GS** *012
STUDNER, Alan. ■ 22182 #035-08-1958 L1994 **P** *020
SUAREZ, Sylvia Maria. 2236C GALLOWS RD 22182 #035-01-1987 L1997 **D** *020 †15
SUH, Ryung. ■ 22181 #010-02-1998 L2000 **OM** *020 †70 ‡
SULLIVAN, Thomas Stephen. 8245 BOONE BLVD, STE 401 22182 #010-01-1982 L1988
    FM *020 †18
SUMIDA, Nita. 8320 OLD COURTHOUSE RD, STE 100 22182 #020-12-1996 L2003 **RHU** *020 †20
SUN, Xinhui. ■ 22181 #243-64-1983 L2003 **PCP** *020 †50
TABRIZI, Mehdi Fakher. 8290 OLD COURTHOUSE RD # A 22182 #517-03-1957 L1967
    OBG *020 †30
TANCHEL, Nancy Ann. 8321 OLD COURTHOUSE RD, STE 110-LIBERTY LASER EYE 22182
    #012-05-1984 L2000 **OPH** *020 †35
TANDECIARZ, Sandra Ines. 115 PARK ST SE, VIENNA FAMILY MEDICINE 22180
    #041-14-1994 L1994 **FM** *020 †18
TAYLOR, John Kenyon. ■ 22182 #028-03-1975 L1977 **GS** *020 †85
TILTON, Frederick Elmore. ■ 22181 #034-01-1977 L1979 **OM AM** *030 †70
TIRADO, Sandra. 8233 OLD COURTHOUSE RD, STE 170 22182 #035-46-1980 L1985
    IM NEP *012
TRALKA, George Anthony. ■ 22181 #010-02-1956 L1970 **IM** *071 †20
TRAVIS, Tracy Leigh. 8150 LEESBURG PIKE, STE 400 22182 #051-07-1982 L1988 **EM** *020 †16
TUCK, Matthew Grayson. ■ 22182 #010-01-2006 L2006 **IM** *012
VELUGUBANTI, Gireesh. ■ 22182 #495-37-2002 L2004 **CHN** *012
VIVES, Mark Christopher. 130 PARK ST SE, STE 100 22180 #010-02-1997 L2004 **CD** *020 †20

WATTS, Elizabeth Jean. 410 MAPLE AVE W, STE 5 22180 #038-43-1985 L1988 **PD** *020 †55
WEAVER, Andrea Balas. 100 EAST ST SE, STE 301 22180 #047-06-1994 L1996 **PD** *020 †55
WEINBERG, Richard James. 8150 LEESBURG PIKE, STE 909 22182 #038-40-1967 L1978
    OPH *071 †35
WHANG, Jeongyeon. ■ 22181 #041-01-2000 L2007 **IM** *020 †20
WHITE, Robert M. 8320 OLD COURTHOUSE RD, STE 100 22182 #010-02-1968 L1973
    ORS *071 †40
WIDDER, Shlomo. 8230 LEESBURG PIKE, STE 630 22182 #550-03-1976 L1986 **PS** *020 †65
WOLDU, Gebrewahid. 100 MAPLE AVE E 22180 #038-45-1997 L2001 **FM** *020 †18
WOO, Chung Yul. 8075 LEESBURG PIKE STE 780 22182 #018-03-1992 L1993 **PHL FM** *020 †18
YANG, Nam Doh. ■ 22182 #583-04-1959 L1973 **OBG GP** *071
YI, Su Chin. 115 PARK ST SE STE 300, VIENNA FAMILY MEDICINE 22180 #051-04-1996 L2000
    MPD *020 †20,55
YOO, Jinny Kathleen. 100 EAST ST SE, STE 301 22180 #051-01-1997 L1997 **PD** *020 †55
YOUSEFI, Jamal. 502 MAPLE AVE W 22180 #051-04-1994 L1994 **PS HS** *020 †65 ‡
ZARRINNESHAN, Alan A. ■ 22180 #010-01-2008 *012
ZHANG, Xiaochun X. 2102 GALLOWS RD D 22182 #243-94-1983 L1996 **IM** *020 †20
ZHU, Xiaolan. 8206 LEESBURG PIKE STE 306 22182 #243-94-1977 L2002 **IM OS** *020 †20
ZIENERT, Karen Diane. 8300 OLD COURTHOUSE RD, STE 140 22182 #025-01-1994 L2007
    OBG *020 †30
ZORNIAK, Agnieszka Maria. 8308 OLD COURTHOUSE RD # B 22182 #759-07-1994 L1996
    P *020 †75 ‡

VINTON – ROANOKE

BEIRNE, Timothy Michael. 415 S POLLARD ST 24179 #051-04-1997 L1997 **FM** *020 †18
CANVIN, Joseph C. 204 S MAPLE ST 24179 #033-06-1997 L2001 **PM** *020 †60
CHAPMON, Trevar Ollie. 204 S MAPLE ST 24179 #045-04-2000 L2004 **PM** *020
IVEY, Henry Reese, Jr. 415 S POLLARD ST 24179 #051-01-1974 L1975 **FM** *020 †18
RHEA, Randall R. 415 S POLLARD ST 24179 #047-06-1981 L1982 **FM** *020 †18
TALIAFERRO, John Peyton. 415 S POLLARD ST, CARILION PARKWAY PHYSICIAN 24179
    #051-04-1995 L2008 **FM** *020 †18
WATTS, Earl Mark. 415 S POLLARD ST 24179 #051-01-1984 L1985 **FM** *020 †18
WOLFE, Michael Wayne. 204 S MAPLE ST, CARILION BONE AND JOINT CE 24179
    #051-01-1990 L2000 **ORS** *020 †40

VIRGINIA BEACH – VIRGINIA BEACH CITY

ABRAMS, Marc Jason. 134 BUSINESS PARK DR 23462 #041-12-2001 L2005 **AN** *020 †05
ABRISS, Richard Bruce. 984 FIRST COLONIAL RD, STE 302 23454 #041-12-1979 L1988
    OTO *020 †45
ADLER, Theodore. 1120 FIRST COLONIL RD #203 23454 #051-04-1955 L1955 **GS** *020 †85
AFLATOONI, Saeed. 780 LYNNHAVEN PKWY 23452 #517-01-1964 L1995 **P** *020 †75 ‡
AGUSTIN, Lourdes Alquiros. 1124 LYNNHAVEN PKWY 23452 #748-01-1958 L1978 **IM FM** *071
AKIN, Onat. ■ 23464 #902-01-1987 L1994 **PTH** *100 †50
ALBERICO, Thomas A. 1950 GLENN MITCHELL DR 23456 #055-01-1979 L1981
    HEM ON *020 †20
ALEXANDER, Burton F. 1950 GLENN MITCHELL DR 23456 #051-01-1992 L1992 **HO** *020 †20
ALFORD, William Lee, Jr. 289 INDEPENDENCE BLVD, STE 221 23462 #051-04-1976 L1978
    ADM PME *020 †80
ALLEN, Joseph Jethro. 1745 CAMELOT DR, STE 100 23454 #036-01-1957 L1971 **P** *071
ALLISON, Nancy Lynn. 740 INDEPENDENCE CIR 23455 #038-43-1978 L1988 **NEP IM** *020 †20
ALTAMIRANO, A Kimberly. 1800 CAMELOT DR, STE 200 23454 #051-01-1992 L1995
    NPM *020 †55
AMBERMAN, Geo Herbert, III. 1147 INDEPENDENCE BLVD 23455 #649-14-1977 L1983
    FM *020 †18
ANDERSON, Kathleen Hess. 4092 FOXWOOD DR STE 101 23462 #051-07-1994 L1994
    EM *020 †16
ANDERSON, Robin Nicole. 2017 PLEASURE HOUSE RD 23455 #051-07-2002 L2004
    FM *020 †18
ANSARI, Zaigham Hussain. 2580 POTTERS RD, DOMINION PSYCHIATRIC 23454
    #704-05-1987 L2001 **CHP** *020
ANTHONY, John Scott. 1200 FIRST COLONIAL RD, STE 200 23454 #038-41-1995 L2004
    D *020 †15
ANTONIO, Stephanie Moody. 933 1ST COLONIAL RD # 102 23454 #017-20-1995 L2004
    OTO NO *020 †45
ARBUCKLE, Jeffrey Keith. 527 N GREAT NECK RD 23454 #051-04-1989 L1999 **FM** *020 †18
ARDISON, Gary Winship. ■ 23456 #036-05-1965 L2006 **FM** *071 †18
AREZO, Shahwali. 1101 FIRST COLONIAL RD, STE 300 23454 #051-07-1995 L1995 **GE** *020 †20
ARLUK, Glen Marc. 1101 FIRST COLONIAL RD, STE 300 23454 #051-04-1998 L1999
    GE *020 †20
ARMADA, Manuel Alberto. 4092 FOXWOOD DR, STE 101 23462 #048-02-2000 L2000
    EM *020 †16
ASHBY, Charles C, Jr. 1708 OLD DONATION PKWY, CARDIOVASCULAR ASSOCIATES 23454
    #051-04-1979 L1980 **CD IM** *020 †20
ASHE, Allison Renee. 4092 FOXWOOD DR, EPT 23462 #665-01-1999 L1999 **EM** *020 †16
ASHMAN, Berton Wm. ■ 23451 #008-01-1964 L1969 **GE IM** *071
ASHMAN, Carol Amini. 4668 PEMBROKE BLVD, RIVERSIDE RADIOLOGY ASSOCI 23455
    #017-20-1990 L2007 **R RNR** *020 †80
ASHMAN, Rosemary Isabel. 1800 CAMELOT DR, STE 200 23454 #008-01-1995 L1998
    PD *020 †55
ASHMAN, Stuart. ■ 23451 #051-01-1954 L1954 **P** *071 †75
ASUNCION, Christopher W. 828 HEALTHY WAY, STE 350 23462 #035-03-1989 L1990
    FM *020 †18
AUSTIN MOORE, Lynnette M. 1920 ARLINGTON ARCH DR 23464 #012-21-1995 L1995
    IM FM *020 †20,18
AYERS, Richard Blair. 1080 FIRST COLONIAL RD, STE 200 23454 #044-01-1980 L1981
    FM *020 †18
BACANI-LONGA, Carolina. 5821 LANCELOT DR 23464 #748-07-1957 L1979 **IM HMP** *020
BAEZ, Ramon E, Jr. ■ 23455 #847-05-1972 L1975 **GP** *071
BAGON, Edrenalinda P. ■ 23455 #748-08-1970 L1977 **PD NPM** *071 †55 ‡
BAGON, Tomas M, Jr. ■ 23455 #748-08-1965 L1976 **AN** *071 ‡
BAKHSHI, Elizabeth D. 813 INDEPENDENCE BLVD, STE A 23455 #051-07-2002 L2002
    FM *020 †18

BAKHSHI, Raja Mcguffie. 303 35TH ST STE 102 23451 #051-07-2001 L2001 **FM** *020 †18

BALDERSTON, Scott Michael. 2117 MCCOMAS WAY, STE 105 23456 #051-01-1980 L1984 **PDC PD** *020 †55

BALLANTYNE, Peter Andrew. 4092 FOXWOOD DR, STE 101 23462 #051-07-1997 L1997 **EM** *020 †16

BARAKEY, Amiele Hassen. ■ 23451 #051-04-1971 L1976 **GS** *020 †85

BARBER, Gregory A. 397 LITTLE NECK RD, STE 100 23442 #023-12-1987 L1989 **VS** *020 †85

BARCHAS, Rebecca Elise. 780 LYNNHAVEN PKWY STE 400 23452 #038-06-1975 L1979 **P** *020 †75

BARCO, Eric Pakingan. 1060 FIRST COLONIAL RD, VIRGINIA BEACH GENERAL HOS 23454 #305-01-1998 L2002 **IM** *020 †20

BARRETT, Kevin Patrick. ■ 23454 #038-41-1991 L1993 **FM** *072 †18

BARRINGER, Margaret. 1450 KEMPSVILLE RD 23464 #065-10-1978 L1996 **FM** *071

BARTEL, Alan Gilbert. 1708 OLD DONATION PKWY, CARDIOVASCULAR ASSOCIATES 23454 #011-03-1966 L1973 **CD** *020 †20

BARTIMOCCIA, Michelle Lee. 2117 MCCOMAS WAY STE 103, GENERAL BOOTH PEDIATRICS 23456 #016-43-1999 L2003 **PD** *020 †55

BASON, William Martin. 800 INDEPENDENCE BLVD 23455 #035-08-1957 L1979 **PD** *020 †55

BATTE, W, Jr. 1060 FIRST COLONIAL RD 23454 #422-01-1987 L1995 **DR** *020 †80,28

BATTEN, James Vincent. 2301 GENERAL BOOTH BLVD, STE B 23456 #051-07-1991 L1994 **PD** *020 †55

BAZEMORE, Derek Glenn. ■ 23455 #035-19-2005 **EM** *012

BEASLEY, Walter Ewing. ■ 23464 #047-06-1958 L1982 **TS GS** *071 †85,90

BEATTY, Maxine Ruth. 1212 LAKE JAMES DR STE C 23464 #041-07-1973 L1974 **PD** *020 †55

BECHER, Elaine Marie. 2580 POTTERS RD, DOMINION PSYCHIATRIC 23454 #054-04-1985 L1987 **CHP** *020 †75

BELCHER, Birgit. 1860 COLONIAL MEDICAL CT 23454 #409-10-1966 L1974 **IM** *071 †20

BELL, Donald Banks. 1975 GLENN MITCHELL DR, STE 202 23456 #051-07-1981 L1983 **OBG** *020 †30

BERCOWITZ, Harvey Howard. ■ 23451 #005-11-1975 L1989 **IM** *020 †20,16

BERGER, James Seymour. 1120 FIRST COLONIAL RD 23454 #035-19-1946 L1954 **GS** *071 †85

BERGER, Jeffrey Jos. 5320 PROVIDENCE RD 23464 #051-07-1988 L1989 **GS** *020 †85

BERGER, Keith Edward. 1301 FIRST COLONIAL RD, STE 201 23454 #036-07-1976 L1981 **GE IM** *020 †20

BERGHOFF, Adar Taun. 1550 TOMCAT BLVD STE 150, OCEANA BRANCH MEDICAL CLIN 23460 #036-01-2001 L2003 **D** *012

BERMAN, Jacob Henry. 522 S INDEPENDENCE BLVD, STE 102A 23452 #033-06-1983 L1987 **P** *020 †75

BERMAN, Larry Wm. 5121 GREENWICH RD 23462 #051-01-1958 L1958 **PD** *071

BERRY, Billy Wayne, Jr. 1950 GLENN MITCHELL DR, STE 310 23456 #036-01-1991 L1996 **OTO** *020 †45

BEST, David Walker. 1800 CAMELOT DR STE 401 23454 #017-20-1971 L1976 **NEP IM** *020 †20

BEVERLY, Vernis Lowell, Jr. 5486 INDIAN RIVER RD, PATIENT FIRST INDIAN 23464 #051-01-1998 L2000 **MPD** *020 †55

BEYER, Gail Suzanne. 1020 INDEPENDENCE BLVD, STE 311 23455 #017-20-1981 L1997 **IM HEM** *020 †20

BHASIN, Mohit. 1708 OLD DONATION PKWY, CARDIOVASCULAR ASSOCIATES 23454 #012-05-1998 L2006 **CD** *020 †20

BHATTACHARRYA, Biswa R. 1060 FIRST COLONIAL RD 23454 #495-02-1982 L1988 **FM PTH** *020 †18

BIRK, Peter. 1821 OLD DONATION PKWY, STE 11 23454 #035-15-1977 L1978 **PUD IM** *020 †20

BISHOP, Barbara Muriel. ■ 23454 #016-06-1973 L1975 **FM FPG** *020 †18

BLACKMAN, Jerome Scott. 101 N LYNNHAVEN RD STE 204 23452 #021-01-1971 L1986 **PYA** *020 †75

BLACKWOOD, Robert Charles. 1201 LAKE JAMES DR, STE 200 23464 #060-02-1982 L1994 **FM** *020 †18

BLANCHARD, Peter Bernard. 1821 OLD DONATION PKWY 23454 #035-19-1962 L1975 **CRS GS** *071 †10,85

BLUMBERG, Mary C Le Blanc. 3396 HOLLAND RD 23452 #039-01-1984 L1995 **PTH** *020 †20,50

BOCCA, Silvina Maria. 800 INDEPENDENCE BLVD 23455 #051-07-1998 L1998 **OBG** *020

BOHAN, Michael Edward. 4616 WESTGROVE CT 23455 #010-01-1962 L1982 **IM** *020 †20

BOHLKE, Glen Leroy. 2580 POTTERS RD 23454 #018-03-1967 L1976 **CHP P** *071

BONNER, Kevin Francis. 5716 CLEVELAND ST, STE 200 23462 #010-02-1993 L1998 **ORS** *020 †40

BOONE, Luther Roy. 1020 INDEPENDENCE BLVD, STE 203 23455 #051-04-1968 L1968 **IM** *020

BOSSARD, Shane Philip. 2317 KINGBIRD LN 23455 #041-15-2001 L2001 **EM** *020 †16

BOUCHER, Ronald Robt. ■ 23455 #024-16-1992 L1999 **AN** *020 †05

BOUNDS, Kevin Bradford. 1815 COLONIAL MEDICAL CT 23454 #051-01-1982 L1989 **PS GS** *020 †85,65

BOYD, James Horace. ■ 23455 #047-07-1942 L1944 **GP** *071

BRAGG, Phyllis Anne. 4092 FOXWOOD DR, STE 101 23462 #051-07-1984 L1986 **EM** *020 †16

BRAUN, Tammy Linda. 1080 FIRST COLONIAL RD, STE 412 23454 #051-07-1991 L1992 **PD** *020 †55

BRAUNSTEIN, Paul Wm. 909 FIRST COLONIAL RD 23454 #024-16-1982 L1989 **TS** *020 †90,85

BRE, J Lionel. ■ 23455 #132-01-1959 L1967 **GS VS** *071 †85

BREWER, Robert Geo. 3701 PACIFIC AVE 23451 #010-01-1952 L1971 **GS NTR** *071 †85

BRIGGS, Jonathan Eugene. 1300 DIAMOND SPRINGS RD, STE 400 23455 #012-01-2002 L2002 **IM** *020 †20

BRIONES, Norman Yanzon. ■ 23456 #005-18-2003 L2005 **PTH** *020

BRITT, Charlene Marie. 816 INDEPENDENCE BLVD, STE 100 23455 #036-01-1995 L1995 **FM** *020 †18

BROADHEAD, Daniel D. 2580 POTTERS RD 23454 #036-05-1969 L1978 **P** *020 †75 ‡

BROCK, Macon Foscue. ■ 23454 #051-04-1930 L1931 **GP PUD** *071

BROGAN, John Chas. 3196 SILVER SANDS CIR 23451 #041-01-1961 L1992 **FM A** *030 †18

BROMBERG, Jonathan Fox. 332 NEWTOWN RD 23462 #051-07-1995 L1995 **FM** *020 †18

BROOKS, Shirlee Ann. 1290 DIAMOND SPRINGS RD 23455 #025-07-1981 L1981 **GP OM** *020

BROOME, Jesse Michael. 1000 FIRST COLONIAL RD, STE 101 23454 #020-12-1983 L1984 **IM** *071 †20

BROWN, Beryl Sandler. 5320 PROVIDENCE RD 23464 #051-07-1991 L1991 **GS** *020 †85

BROWN, Ronald Bayard. ■ 23451 #010-01-1967 L1970 **EM** *071 †16

BROWNING, Gary Micheal. 828 HEALTHY WAY, STE 330 23462 #020-12-1984 L1987 **GYN** *020 †30 ‡

BRUCKNER, Jana Terezie. 1748 SIR WILLIAM OSLER DR 23454 #286-02-1960 L1974 **FM OS** *071

BRUGH, Victor Miller, III. 1200 FIRST COLONIAL RD, STE 100 23454 #051-04-1996 L1996 **U** *020 †95

BRUNO, Alphonse H L, Jr. 828 HEALTHY WAY, STE 330 23462 #051-04-1965 L1972 **OBG** *020 †30

BRYAN, Curtis Russell. 760 LYNNHAVEN PKWY, STE 201 23452 #051-04-1976 L1988 **CHP P** *020 †75

BRYANT, Shawne R. 321 EDWIN DR, STE 102 23462 #010-03-1980 L1985 **GYN** *020 †30

BULLABOY, Charles Allen. 2117 MCCOMAS WAY, STE 105 23456 #036-05-1970 L1977 **PDC PD** *020 †55

BULLARD, George M, Jr. 1120 FIRST COLONIAL RD, STE 100 23454 #036-08-1983 L1984 **FM** *020 †18

BURGER, Robert Lindsay. 1950 GLENN MITCHELL DR 23456 #051-01-1967 L1967 **HO HEM** *020 †20

BURGESS, John Thompson. ■ 23454 #051-01-1984 L1987 **D** *020 †20,15

BURKE, Megan Elise. ■ 23464 #007-02-1999 L2008 **PHO** *100 †55

BURNS, Francis Gregory. ■ 23454 #051-04-1956 L1956 **ORS** *071 †40

BURNS, Mary A. 5320 PROVIDENCE RD, STE 100 23454 #422-01-1990 L1995 **OBG OS** *020 †30

BURT, Joe Howard. 1060 FIRST COLONIAL RD 23454 #036-05-1961 L1964 **GP** *020

BUTTS, Edward Barfield. 1020 INDEPENDENCE BLVD 23455 #051-04-1968 L1968 **NS** *020 †25

BYARS, Donald Vance, II. 4092 FOXWOOD DR, STE 101 23462 #051-07-1999 L1999 **EM** *020 †16

BYMAN, Eric M. 4660 HAYGOOD RD 23455 #051-07-2002 L2005 **FM** *100 †18

BYRD, Allison D. 2017 PLEASURE HOUSE RD, BAYSIDE FAMILY PRACTICE 23455 #051-04-1978 L1988 **IM** *074 †20

BYRD, John Abbott. ■ 23451 #051-04-1947 L1947 **IM** *071 †20

BYRD, Sharon J. 700 INDEPENDENCE CIR, STE 2A 23455 #033-06-1977 L1982 **GYN** *020 †30

BYRD, William Edward. 5241 PRINCESS ANNE RD 23462 #051-01-1942 L1942 **GYN** *071 †30

BYRNE, Brendan Terence. ■ 23451 #025-07-2007 *012

CAFIERO, Louis. 800 INDEPENDENCE BLVD 23455 #561-11-1973 L1977 **P** *020

CAJULIS, Leonard Robin. 1408 CRYSTAL PKWY 23451 #051-07-2001 L2001 **IM** *020

CALABRO, James Anthony. 4092 FOXWOOD DR, STE 101 23462 #039-09-1999 L1999 **EM** *020 †16

CALDERON, Celia Sayoc. ■ 23451 #748-02-1961 L1988 **PD HEM** *072 †55

CALDERON, Dominador C. ■ 23451 #748-02-1961 L1988 **IM PUD** *071 †20

CALILUNG, Dorotea Mangune. ■ 23464 #748-08-1979 L1991 **PD ADL** *020

CALLAHAN, Robert David. 3745 HOLLAND RD 23452 #056-05-1985 L1991 **FM** *020 †18

CAMACHO, Peligny L. 917 LEVEL GREEN BLVD 23464 #748-01-1952 L1970 **FM EM** *071

CAMPBELL, Brian Hardy. ■ 23451 #041-12-2006 L2007 **EM** *012

CAMPBELL, Robert Brick. 1800 REPUBLIC RD, STE 102 23454 #050-02-1984 L1994 **ORS OSM** *020 †40

CANNON, Michael Ross. 933 FIRST COLONIAL RD, STE 100 23454 #020-12-1999 L1999 **RHU** *020 †20

CANTON, Elsa Fe L. ■ 23455 #748-10-1963 L1971 **OBG** *071 †30

CAO, Xianghui. 968 FIRST COLONIAL RD, STE 103 23454 #243-47-1984 L2002 **CN** *020

CARBYN, Kevin Michael. 1201 LAKE JAMES DR, KEMPSVILLE FAMILY PRACTICE 23464 #064-01-1992 L1995 **FM** *020 †18

CAREY, Benjamin Arthur. ■ 23454 #036-07-1978 L1989 **ADP FOP** *020 †75

CARLEO, James O. 4092 FOXWOOD DR 23462 #035-09-1966 L1968 **EM FM** *020 †18,16

CARLSON, Charles E. ■ 23452 #038-06-1949 L1949 **CD IM** *075

CARLSTON, John Anthony. 1704 SIR WILLIAM OSLER DR 23454 #008-01-1958 L1967 **A** *071 †03

CARNEY, Marcia Denise. 968 FIRST COLONIAL RD, STE 105 23454 #035-20-1977 L1981 **OPH** *020 †35 ‡

CARNEY, Martin Jos. 1868 WILDWOOD DR, THE CARNEY CTR 23454 #041-02-1980 L1986 **PS** *020 †65

CARPENTER, David Thos. 1060 FIRST COLONIAL RD, CREDENTIALS DEPT- C/O BOLL 23454 #023-12-1992 L1994 **NPM** *020 †55

CARRAWAY, James Howard. 5589 GREENWICH RD, STE 100 23462 #051-01-1962 L1962 **CS PS** *020 †85,65

CARTY, Rebecca Lynn. ■ 23452 #051-01-2006 L2006 **GS** *012

CARWELL, Glenn Ray. 992 FIRST COLONIAL RD 23454 #047-05-1970 L1975 **PS HS** *020 †85,65

CASHION, Donald Thos. 1605 GENERAL BOOTH BLVD, PATIENT FIRST GENERAL 23454 #051-04-1974 L1975 **EM FM** *020 †18,16

CASTANEDA, Alberto J. 6025 PROVIDENCE RD, STE 110 23464 #264-01-1950 L1969 **FM** *020 †18

CASTLE, Robert Foster. 5700 THURSTON AVE STE 107, DISABILITY DETERMNTN SERV 23455 #038-06-1956 L1996 **PDC CD** *030 †55

CASWELL, Christopher C. 816 INDEPENDENCE BLVD, STE 2A 23455 #041-13-1985 L1991 **FM IM** *020 †05

CAUGHEY, Michael Thos. ■ 23451 #051-07-1990 L1991 **IM EM** *075

CENZON, Maria Regina G. 2580 POTTERS RD, DOMINION PSYCHIATRIC 23454 #748-10-1980 L1994 **P** *020 †75

CETRONE, Anthony C. 6632 INDIAN RIVER RD 23464 #041-02-1979 L1981 **EM GP** *020 †16

CHA, Jai-Chul. ■ 23454 #583-02-1968 L1976 *071 †50

CHAGANTY, Syamaladevi. 5301 PROVIDENCE RD 23464 #495-11-1983 L1993 **PD** *020 †55

CHAKER, Albert Eliot. ■ 23451 #023-12-2004 L2005 **AM GS** *020

CHAKRABORTTY, Saghana B. 1020 INDEPENDENCE BLVD 23455 #011-02-1983 L1998 **FM** *020 †18

CHANG, Lawrence Kuo. 1120 FIRST COLONIAL RD, STE 200 23454 #007-02-1995 L2000 **D** *020 †15

CHARLES, Michael Geo. 3745 HOLLAND RD, CHIMNEY HILL 23452 #051-04-1985 L1986 **FM** *020 †18

CHARLTON, William Jeffrey. 1120 FIRST COLONIAL RD, FIRST COLONIAL FAMILY PRAC 23454 #051-04-1983 L1984 **FM** *020 †18 ‡

CHIDESTER, Betty Brown. 4092 FOXWOOD DR, STE 101 23462 #041-12-1980 L1989 **EM GS** *020 †16

CHILDRESS, Lorenzo, Jr. ■ 23452 #047-06-1971 L1996 **GE IM** *020 †20

CHOE, Kyle Seung. 4400 CORPORATION LN, STE 102 23462 #035-45-1998 L2003 **FPS OTO** *020 †45

CHOI, Hyeon Duk. 933 FIRST COLONIAL RD, STE 112 23454 #051-01-1997 L2004 **PD** *020 †55

CHOW, Matthew Pui. 800 INDEPENDENCE BLVD, SBH/SENTARA MEDICAL GROUP 23455 #038-44-2002 L2006 **AN** *020 †05

CHU, Young-Kwon. 303 ATLANTIC AVE 23451 #583-03-1964 L1973 **AN** *020 †05

CHUPKA, Paul. 1060 FIRST COLONIAL RD, SENTARA VIRGINIA BEACH HOS 23454 #018-75-1995, ▲ L2002 **IM** *020 †20

CIRIC, Andrej Milan. 800 INDEPENDENCE BLVD 23455 #957-02-1968 L1972 **DR** *071 †80

CLARE, Robert Alan. 4092 FOXWOOD DR STE 101 23462 #041-12-1987 L1989 **EM** *020 †16

CLARK, William P, Jr. 1020 INDEPENDENCE BLVD, STE 111 23455 #010-02-1978 L1984 **ON HEM** *020 †20

CLARKE, John Palmore. ■ 23454 #051-04-1960 L1960 **TS VS** *071 †85,90

CLIFFORD, Thomas George, Jr. 840 FIRST COLONIAL RD, STE 102 23451 #051-07-1981 L1982 **GS** *020 †85

COHEN, David Michael. ■ 23455 #051-04-1988 L1990 **DR** *020 †80

COHEN, Edith Joann. 1270 DIAMOND SPRINGS RD, STE 110 23455 #041-12-1984 L1994 **IM** *020 †20

COLE, Charles Edward. 4092 FOXWOOD DR, STE 101 23462 #051-04-1983 L1984 **EM** *020 †16

COLEMAN, Samuel Richard. ■ 23451 #016-42-1941 L1941 **GP** *020

COLONNA, John Owen, II. 397 LITTLE NECK RD, 3300 S BLDG STE 100 23452 #051-04-1983 L1993 **OS GS** *020 †85

CONAWAY, Don Lee. 1716 SIR WILLIAM OSLER DR 23454 #055-01-1965 L1970 **IM END** *020 †20

CONKWRIGHT, Douglas Dewey. 527 N GREAT NECK RD 23454 #036-01-1954 L1955 **FM FSM** *020

COOPER, William R. 1008 FIRST COLONIAL RD, STE 103 23454 #051-01-1969 L1969 **PUD CCM** *020 †20

COTTON, Jacqueline Sue. 800 INDEPENDENCE BLVD 23455 #024-05-1985 L2000 **PD** *020 †55

COUNSELMAN, Francis Lee. 4092 FOXWOOD DR, STE 101 23462 #051-07-1983 L1984 **EM** *020 †16

COUSINS, Jaysun Kiziuk. 4092 FOXWOOD DR, STE 101 23462 #051-07-2000 L2000 **EM** *020 †16

CRISOSTOMO, Christen Cond. 6632 INDIAN RIVER RD 23464 #748-01-2000 L2004 **FM** *020 †18

CROTEAU, Louis John. 1024 FIRST COLONIAL RD 23454 #024-01-1976 L1977 **FM FSM** *020 †18

CROUCH, James Joseph. 4092 FOXWOOD DR, STE 101 23462 #045-01-2000 L2000 **EM** *020 ‡

CURULLA, Richard Michael. 1860 COLONIAL MEDICAL CT 23454 #030-06-1996 L2000 **MPD** *020 †20,55

CURULLA, Wendy Marie. 4092 FOXWOOD DR, STE 101 23462 #030-05-2000 L2000 **EM** *020

CUSHMAN, Jerry Francis. 1605 GENERAL BOOTH BLVD, PATIENT FIRST GENERAL 23454 #010-02-1985 L2007 **FM** *020 †18

DABNEY, Laura Fraser. 3084 BRICKHOUSE CT 23452 #051-07-1995 L1995 **P** *020 †75

DALTON, Catherine Anne. 816 INDEPENDENCE BLVD, STE 1H 23455 #051-04-1991 L1992 **IM** *020 †80

DALTON, Joseph Michael. 1975 GLENN MITCHELL DR, STE 302 23456 #035-01-1990 L1991 **GS VS** *020 †85

DANDALIDES, George. ■ 23455 #038-40-1955 L1955 **FM** *071 †18

DARBY, Daniel Lee. 1630 DONNA DR STE 102 23451 #047-06-1972 L1980 **P** *020 †75 ‡

DARDEN, James Edgel. ■ 23455 #007-02-1979 L1982 **FM** *020 †18,16

DARROW, Charlene D. 2100 LYNNHAVEN PKWY # 201, TRIACARE PRIME VA BEACH 23456 #035-19-1978 L2006 **FM** *020 †18

DAVIDSON, Deanna Starr. 1060 FIRST COLONIAL RD, RADIATION ONCOLOGY 23454 #019-02-1980 L2007 **RO** *020 †80

DAVIES, Nicola Jane. 816 INDEPENDENCE BLVD, STE 100 23455 #025-01-1992 L1996 **FM EM** *040 †18

DAVIS, Chas Stanley, Jr. 4501 N WITCHDUCK RD 23455 #028-34-1964 L1966 **U** *020

DAVIS, Harvey Danl. 1704 SIR WILLIAM OSLER DR 23454 #035-08-1967 L1971 **PDA IG** *020 †55,03

DAVIS, Jeffrey Michael. ■ 23462 #011-03-2005 L2006 **OPH** *012

DAVIS, Kenneth Brian. 1450 KEMPSVILLE RD 23464 #051-04-1989 L1990 **FM** *020 †18

DAVIS, Robert Elwyn. 1060 FIRST COLONIAL RD 23454 #041-12-1946 L1987 **OM GS** *071 †85

DAVIS, Steve Ward. 1005 CATON DR, VIRTUAL RADIOLOGIC 23454 #010-02-1993 L1998 **DR** *020 †80

DAVLIN, Lance Burroughs. 5501 GREENWICH RD, STE 200 23462 #021-01-1986 L1990 **HS** *020 †40

DEANE, Sandra A. 4092 FOXWOOD DR, STE 101 23462 #011-03-1995 L1995 **EM** *020 †16

DEBO, Richard F. 1080 FIRST COLONIAL RD, STE 307 23454 #023-12-1984 L1992 **OTO** *020 †45

DE DIOS, Jennifer Garcia. 1408 CRYSTAL PKWY, FIRST HEALTH MEDICAL PRACT 23451 #045-01-2000 L2000 **IM** *020 †20

DEITELL, Monica Terry. ■ 23454 #016-42-1981 L1995 **CHP P** *020 †75

DELFAUS, Carol Gizoni. 1060 FIRST COLONIAL RD, VIRGINIA BCH GEN HOSP 23454 #042-01-1980 L1987 **NPM** *020 †55

DELIANIDES, Aris Philip. 1012 FIRST COLONIAL RD 23454 #051-04-1988 L1992 **OPH** *020 †35

DEMASI, Richard James. 397 LITTLE NECK RD, STE 100 23452 #036-05-1986 L1993 **VS** *020 †85

DENK, Michael Jon. 1060 FIRST COLONIAL RD 23454 #035-06-1986 L1999 **PS CFS** *020 †65

DENNIS, Charles Henry. 816 INDEPENDENCE BLVD, STE 3H 23455 #016-11-1968 L1990 **OTO** *020 †45

DESAI, Gautam D. 800 INDEPENDENCE BLVD 23455 #495-01-1981 L1990 **FM** *020 †18

DESAI, Maulin. 1605 GENERAL BOOTH BLVD, PATIENT FIRST GENERAL 23454 #028-46-2000 L2000 **FSM** *020

DE SANTOS, Jorge T. ■ 23455 #748-01-1936 L1978 **GS GYN** *071

DESHMUKH, Suhas L. 1020 INDEPENDENCE BLVD, STE 110 23455 #495-83-1982 L2002 **GE** *020 †20

DE TRIQUET, John Michel. 100 CONSTITUTION DR, STE 217 23462 #041-13-1974 L1984 **PD** *040 †55

DE VERA-HIPOL, Rosario F. 701 INDEPENDENCE CIR 23455 #748-08-1965 L1978 **IM** *020

DEVEREUX, James Peter. 230 CLEARFIELD AVE, STE 124 23462 #539-04-1969 L1976 **ORS** *020 †40

DEVLIN, James Timothy. 1120 FIRST COLONIAL RD, STE 100 23454 #036-05-1966 L1969 **FM IM** *071 †18

DEWALT, Chester W, Jr. ■ 23454 #041-12-1950 L1951 **GP** *071

DHARAMSI, Aisha Amin. ■ 23464 #051-01-2008 *012

DHILLON, Rajinder S. 780 LYNNHAVEN PKWY 23452 #495-10-1983 L1990 **CHP P** *020 †75

DI BONA, Douglas Dante. 1080 FIRST COLONIAL RD, STE 300 23454 #033-05-1968 L1978 **OBG** *071 †30

DICKINSON, William Andrew. 1080 FIRST COLONIAL RD, JESSE W SAINT CLAIR III 23454 #036-07-1956 L1956 **CD IM** *071 †20

DICKINSON, William Andrew. 138 S ROSEMONT RD, STE 215 23452 #051-07-1988 L1994 **AN** *020 †55,05

DICKSON, Albert Maxcy. 1020 INDEPENDENCE BLVD, STE 104 23455 #041-01-1958 L1959 **FM** *020

DILEO, Leonard Michael. 780 LYNNHAVEN PKWY 23452 #561-01-1973 L1979 **P PYG** *020 †75

DILLON, James Daniel. 1080 FIRST COLONIAL RD, STE 400 23454 #047-05-1972 L1977 **NS** *020 †25

DOKMAK, Ahmed M. 1745 CAMELOT DR STE 200 23454 #915-03-1993 L2007 **P** *020 †75

DONEGAN, Catherine Sheila. ■ 23455 #035-09-1988 L1990 **IM** *020 †20

DONNELLY, John Emmitt. ■ 23451 #035-08-1958 L1995 **OM FM** *071 †18

DONNELLY, June F. ■ 23451 #035-08-1958 L1996 **PD** *020 †55

DORON, Isaac G. ■ 23451 #915-02-1955 L1974 **PD A** *071

DORR, Cynthia Elaine. 4092 FOXWOOD DR, STE 101 23462 #051-07-1993 L1993 **EM** *020 †16

DOUGLAS, Cromwell C. ■ 23451 #047-07-1947 L1948 **GP** *071

DOWD, James Edward. 5716 CLEVELAND ST, STE 200 23462 #041-12-1992 L1998 **ORS** *020 †40

DOWDY, Robert Louis. 1024 FIRST COLONIAL RD, STE 102 23454 #055-01-1992 L1995 **FM** *020 †18

DOWLING, Jean M. ■ 23454 #035-09-1954 L1970 **CHP P** *071

DOWNING, Carol Elaine. 1212 LAKE JAMES DR STE C 23464 #008-02-1985 L1992 **PD** *020 †55

DOWNS, Edward Jay. 2313 W GREAT NECK RD 23451 #051-04-1975 L1976 **EM UM** *020 †16

DOYLE, Brian Carpenter. 4092 FOXWOOD DR, STE 101 23462 #051-04-1996 L1996 **EM** *020 †16

DRAPER, Eric Bruce. ■ 23454 #023-12-2003 L2004 *100

DREW, Therese Ann. 1444 KEMPSVILLE RD 23464 #038-06-1995 L1996 **PM** *020 †60

DRZEWIECKI, Anna E. 1856 COLONIAL MEDICAL CT, PLASTIC SURGERY 23454 #065-09-1979 L1993 **ORS** *020 †65

DUNDON, Bruce Carroll. 1020 INDEPENDENCE BLVD, STE 312 23455 #038-06-1969 L1975 **D** *020 †15

DUNDON, Suzanne Ertzman. ■ 23451 #038-06-1974 L1976 **P** *020 †75

DUNFORD, Joseph Leonard. 4092 FOXWOOD DR, STE 101 23462 #051-04-1965 L1965 **EM** *020 †16

DUNNINGTON, Arthur R. 933 FIRST COLONIAL RD, STE 100 23454 #051-04-1973 L1974 **RHU IM** *020 †20

DUPRE-RIOS, Christopher S. 134 BUSINESS PARK DR, ATLANTIC ANESTHESIA 23462 #035-45-2001 L2006 **PAN** *100 †05

EARLEY, Chas Marion, Jr. 1060 FIRST COLONIAL RD 23454 #036-07-1953 L1958 **GS** *071 †85

EBINGER, Peggy Gail. 4417 CORPORATION LN # 250 23462 #034-01-1986 L1993 **CHP** *020 †75

EDINGER, Gregory John. 5320 PROVIDENCE RD, STE 100 23464 #041-02-1972 L1977 **EM FM** *020 †16,18

EDMONDS, Beatrix. 1157 FIRST COLONIAL RD, STE 300 23451 #021-05-1991 L1995 **D** *020 †15

EDMONDSON, William P, Jr. ■ 23455 #051-01-1960 L1960 **ID IM** *071 †20

EHSAN, Rashid. ■ 23455 #704-02-1990 L2007 **IMG** *012 †20

EIDLIN, Martin Alan. 3432 HOLLAND RD, PATIENT FIRST HOLLAND 23452 #035-08-1972 L1981 **FM** *020 †20

EL-BESHBESHY, Tarek Ahmed. 1569 LAKE JAMES DR, VA BEACH 23464 #915-04-1969 L1987 **NM GS** *020

ELLIS, Natalie Nicole. 291 INDEPENDENCE BLVD, STE 522 23462 #047-07-2001 L2006 **D** *020

ELLISON, Waldo Morse. 2580 POTTERS RD, DOMINION PSYCHIATRIC 23454 #038-41-1968 L1972 **P** *020 †75

ELSTEIN, Morris Milton. 1748 SIR WILLIAM OSLER DR 23454 #012-01-1977 L1979 **OBG** *020 †30

ENDERSON, Laurence W, III. 840 FIRST COLONIAL RD, STE 102 23451 #051-07-1981 L1986 **GS** *020 †85

ENGLERT, Robert Paul. 1060 FIRST COLONIAL RD, PEDIATRIX MEDICAL GROUP, P 23454 #023-12-1994 L2001 **PD** *020 †55

EPSTEIN, Edwin Stuart. 397 LITTLE NECK RD, STE 107 3400 BLDG 23452 #010-02-1977 L1992 **DS U** *020 †95

ESPADA-GARCIA, Francisco. 5320 PROVIDENCE RD 23464 #042-03-1981 L1989 **FM** *020 †18

ESPEJO, Guillarmo. 1020 INDEPENDENCE BLVD, HAYGOOD MEDICAL CENTER 23455 #737-01-1958 L1965 **CD IM** *071

ESPINOSA, Myrna Mendiola. 2020 S INDEPENDENCE BLVD, FAMILY & INTERNAL MEDICAL 23453 #748-08-1963 L1974 **GP EM** *020

ESPIRITU, Keith Alexander. ■ 23454 #748-20-2004 L2007 **FP** *012

EUSEBIO-ORDONEZ, Alice As. ■ 23456 #748-21-2002 L2003 **FM** *020

EVANS, James Gregory. 351 EDWIN DR, STE 102 23462 #051-04-1974 L1975 **FM** *020 †18

EVERETT, John Clayton. 303 35TH ST, STE 102 23451 #051-04-1973 L1974 **FM** *020 †18

EVERETT, Wm Clinton, Jr. ■ 23451 #051-01-1964 L1964 **PD** *071 †55

FANNEY, Daryl Richard. 4668 PEMBROKE BLVD, STE 109 23455 #051-01-1985 L1990 **DR** *020 †80

FARLAND, Melvin Standford. 1550 TOMCAT BLVD STE 150 23460 #036-01-2000 L2002 **FM** *020 †18 ‡

FARRAR, Susan Cable. ■ 23455 #021-01-2000 L2002 **OBG** *100

FEDRO, Randall Craig. 1368 N GREAT NECK RD 23454 #016-11-1983 L1984 **FM** *020 †18

FELDMAN, Howard Ronald. 1212 LAKE JAMES DR STE F 23464 #051-07-1981 L1983 **FM FPG** *020 †18

FELDMAN, William Edward. 2301 GENERAL BOOTH BLVD, STE B 23456 #051-04-1972 L1974 **PD ID** *020 †55

FELLNER, Dietrich Albert. 813 INDEPENDENCE BLVD, THE EYE SPECLTS LTD 23455 #041-14-1999 L1992 **OPH** *020 †35

FELTY, Caroline J. 5320 PROVIDENCE RD, STE 100 23464 #045-01-2000 L2007 **OBG** *020 †30

FENDERSON, Allen Rex. 351 EDWIN DR, MULTISPECIALTY GROUP 23462 #041-14-1975 L1976 **FM** *020 †18

FENTON, Leslie Hall. ■ 23454 #041-13-1982 L2006 **IM UM** *020 †20

FEUCHT, Christopher Lee. 1244 THOMPKINS LN 23464 #012-01-1976 L1994 **D** *062 †15

FICKENSCHER, Ben Alan. ■ 23452 #051-07-2005 L2005 **EM** *012

FINEMAN, Sheldon Paul. 134 BUSINESS PARK DR, ATLANTIC ANESTHESIA, INC 23462 #025-07-1979 L1982 **AN PME** *020 †05

FINK, Leo Jerome. ■ 23455 #025-07-1944 L1945 **P** *071

FIVEASH, Jos Gardner, Jr. 1000 FIRST COLONIAL RD, DEVINE-FIVEASH UROLOGY LTD 23454 #051-01-1960 L1960 **U** *071 †95

FLOOD, Jill T. 844 FIRST COLONIAL RD, STE 202 23451 #051-07-1982 L1986 **REN GYN** *020 †30

FOER, Warren Hillary. 909 FIRST COLONIAL RD 23454 #010-01-1963 L1979 **NS** *071 †25

FOLEY, Kelly Anne. 4092 FOXWOOD DR STE 1 23462 #047-07-1992 L1992 **EM** *020 †16

FONTANA, Christy Delaossa. 2117 MCCOMAS WAY 23456 #051-07-1991 L1992 **PD** *020 †55

FONTANARES, Arlene Jane. 828 HEALTHY WAY, STE 330 23462 #051-07-1990 L1994 **OBG** *020 †30 ‡

FORESTIERE, Joseph. 533 NEWTOWN RD STE 104 23462 #035-03-1971 L1976 **IM** *020 †20

FOSS MC CAMMON, Carol M. 1060 FIRST COLONIAL RD 23454 #038-43-1992 L1992 **EM** *020 †16

FOSTER, Christopher Willi. ■ 23452 #051-07-2005 L2007 **PD** *012

FRANCIS, John James. 1029 LUXFORD LN 23455 #649-01-1969 L1994 **GP** *071

FRANCISCO, Reynaldo M. 904 KEMPSVILLE RD STE 101 23464 #748-02-1970 L1977 **OPH GP** *020 †35

FRANK, L Matthew. 1080 FIRST COLONIAL RD, STE 400 23454 #008-02-1973 L1978 **CHN PD** *020 †55,75

FRANZI, Rebecca Anne. 1605 GENERAL BOOTH BLVD, PATIENT FIRST GENERAL 23454 #003-01-2004 L2004 **PM** *100

FRANZMAN, Craig. 1020 INDEPENDENCE BLVD, STE 111 23455 #035-19-1986 L1992 **ON HEM** *020 †20

FRAZIER, Robt Anthony, Jr. 1060 FIRST COLONIAL RD, VBGH DEPT PTH 23454 #047-06-1986 L1997 **PTH DMP** *020 †50

FREEMAN, Bruce Gregory. 5589 GREENWICH RD, STE 100 23462 #038-06-1975 L1976 **PS HS** *020 †65

FREER, Douglas Hall. 2408 SABINA WAY, 1855 EVERGREEN ST 23456 #021-06-1984 L1985 **FM** *030 †70,18

FRENKEL, Ronald Bert. 279 INDEPENDENCE BLVD 23462 #008-02-1982 L1989 **OPH** *020 †35

FREUND, Ronald Kenneth. 816 INDEPENDENCE BLVD, STE 3B 23455 #035-46-1978 L1985 **HS ORS** *040

FROEDE, Craig Brian. 3432 HOLLAND RD, PATIENT FIRST HOLLAND MED 23452 #023-01-1986 L1989 **IM** *020 †20

FROST, David Sidney. 23451 #020-12-1971 L2008 **FM** *020 †18

FULLER, Wayne Templeton. 3745 HOLLAND RD 23452 #051-04-1980 L1982 **IM** *020 †18

GAGLIONE, Jimdavid. 4445 CORPORATION LN, STE 115 23462 #041-14-1991 L1992 **FM** *020 †18

GAINES, Marc Irving. 1860 COLONIAL MEDICAL CT 23454 #038-40-1973 L1976 **IM** *020 †20

GALIOTOS, Jennifer Ann. ■ 23454 #051-07-2003 L2003 **PD** *100 †55

GALLANOSA, Mayorico G, Jr. ■ 23464 #748-01-1967 L1985 **PD GP** *020

GALUMBECK, Cynthia Diane. 1817 REPUBLIC RD 23454 #038-06-1989 L1992 **P CHP** *020 †75

GALUMBECK, Matthew Alan. 1817 REPUBLIC RD 23454 #036-07-1987 L1993 **PS** *020 †65

GALYON, Ronald Curtis. 23452 #051-07-1986 L2003 **ORS** *075 †40

GANDERSON, Alan Philip. 1101 FIRST COLONIAL RD, STE 300 23454 #051-04-1969 L1969 **GE IM** *020 †20

GARCIA, Gloria F. 23464 #748-07-1972 *074

GARRETT, Samuel N. 465 N GREAT NECK RD, VIRGINIA BEACH EYE CENTER, 23454 #051-07-1983 L1990 **OPH** *020 †35

GARRISON, Jack Stiles. 1020 INDEPENDENCE BLVD, STE 101 23455 #051-04-1955 L1955 **FM** *071 †18

GATA, Renato Junior Garci. 2020 S INDEPENDENCE BLVD 23453 #748-20-1998 L2004 **FM** *020 †18 ‡

GEISSINGER, Brent Wm. 1800 CAMELOT DR, STE 400 23454 #036-01-1991 L2003 **GE** *020 †20

GELFAND, Henry M. ■ 23462 #016-02-1950 L1953 **PHP** *071

GELLASCH, Tara Louise. 828 HEALTHY WAY, STE 330 23462 #067-01-2001 L2005 **OBG** *020 †30

GELPI, Juan Roberto. 5320 PROVIDENCE RD 23464 #010-01-1988 L1996 **CRS** *020 †85,10

GENCO, Michael Lee. 4092 FOXWOOD DR, STE 101 23462 #051-01-1997 L2000 **EM** *020 †16

GENTA, Valerio Maria. 1060 1ST COLONIAL RD 23454 #561-07-1970 L1981 **ATP CLP** *020 †50

GEORGE, Edward Richard. 1950 GLENN MITCHELL DR 23456 #011-02-1971 L1978 **HO ON** *020 †20

GEORGE, Jennifer Denise. 1975 GLENN MITCHELL DR, STE 202 23456 #051-01-2001 L2005 **OBG** *020 †30

GEORGE, Linda Joan. 1120 FIRST COLONIAL RD, FIRST COLONIAL FAMILY PRAC 23454 #035-48-1990 L1996 **FM** *040 †18

GERSHON, Steven Lloyd. 2020 GENERAL BOOTH BLVD, STE 110 23454 #035-08-1988 L1992 **PM** *020 †60

GIANVITTORIO, Joy Marie. 351 EDWIN DR, STE 102 23462 #041-13-1997 L2000 **FM** *020 †18

GIBERT, Christopher L. 4092 FOXWOOD DR, STE 101 23462 #004-01-1996 L1996 **EM** *020 †16

GILBERT, Stanley H, Jr. ■ 23454 #041-13-1953 L1990 **PD** *020 †55

GIVONETTI, Lori Ann. 4092 FOXWOOD DR, STE 101 23462 #035-15-1994 L1997 **EM** *020 †16

GLASSON, Sandra Elise. 968 FIRST COLONIAL RD, STE 101 23454 #036-07-1986 L1993 **ORS OSM** *020 †40

GOINS, Ernest Earl. 5486 INDIAN RIVER RD, PATIENT FIRST INDIAN 23464 #748-09-1978 L1980 **FM** *020 †18

GOLD, Edward Wm. 800 INDEPENDENCE BLVD 23455 #649-33-1983 L1984 **ORS** *020 †40

GOLDBERG, Eric Jason. 4480 HOLLAND OFFICE PARK, STE 225 23452 #041-02-1995 L2000 **CN** *020 †75

GOLDMAN, Ilene Garnick. 4092 FOXWOOD DR, STE 101 23462 #011-03-1992 L1992 **EM** *020 †16

GOLDSTEIN, Leanelle. 1080 FIRST COLONIAL RD, STE 200 23454 #060-02-1993 L2007 **GS** *020 †85

GOLPIRA, Pierre Hossein. 780 LYNNHAVEN PKWY, STE 400 23452 #051-07-2000 L2000 **P** *020 †75

GONZALES, Norman Manaois. 5320 PROVIDENCE RD 23464 #748-01-2001 L2002 **FM** *020 †18

GOODE, Vera Gonzella. 4654 HAYGOOD RD, STE B 23455 #047-07-1982 L1985 **IM** *020

GOTTIMUKKALA, Maruthi V. 1016 INDEPENDENCE BLVD 23455 #495-50-1977 L1987 **CD IM** *020 †20

GRABER, Stanley. BAYSIDE HOSP 23455 #035-08-1953 L1972 **PTH** *071 †50

GRAF, William Robert, II. ■ 23456 #041-02-1995 L1996 **P** *020 †80

GRAVENSTEIN, Mary Ann P. ■ 23455 #038-40-1982 L1983 **IMG** *062

GRAY, Nelson Turner. ■ 23454 #051-04-1962 L1962 **PD** *071 †55

GRAYSON, George Ira. 816 INDEPENDENCE BLVD # 2B 23455 #035-19-1965 L1980 **PUD IM** *020

GREENBERG, Seth Howard. 1008 FIRST COLONIAL RD, STE 103 23454 #035-08-1986 L1997 **PUD** *020 †20

GREGORY, Roger Thorpe. ■ 23455 #051-04-1965 L1965 **VS** *071 †85

GRIFFIN, Francis G. 1060 FIRST COLONIAL RD 23454 #051-01-1951 L1951 **GYN** *071 †30

GRIFFIN, John Jos, Jr. 1708 OLD DONATION PKWY, CARDIOVASCULAR ASSOCIATES 23454 #023-01-1976 L1984 **CD IM** *020 †20

GRIFFIN, Judi Dennise. 1060 FIRST COLONIAL RD 23454 #305-01-2001 L2004 **IM** *020

GRISWOLD, James Francis. 3143 MAGIC HOLLOW BLVD 23453 #065-09-1966 L1972 **P** *020

GRUBER, Brian Lewis. 4092 FOXWOOD DR, STE 101 23462 #051-01-1974 L1978 **EM FM** *020 †18,16

GRUBERT, Jaime Maclaybabe. ■ 23454 #051-07-2007 *012

GUANZON, Angelina. 281 INDEPENDENCE BLVD, STE 326 23462 #748-01-1970 L1997 **P** *075

GULBRANDSEN, Patricia H. ■ 23456 #041-01-1967 L1983 **GPM OM** *062 †60,70

GUNDLACH, David Carl. 4417 CORPORATION LN 23462 #038-40-1973 L1992 **IM** *030 †20

GURDZIEL, Gloria U Kreis. 3076 BRICKHOUSE CT 23452 #024-07-1973 L1985 **CHP P** *020 †75

GUSTAFSON, Keith Benj. 800 INDEPENDENCE BLVD, SMG ANESTHESIA-SBH 23455 #023-01-1988 L2002 **AN** *020 †05

GUTERMUTH, Melvin C, Jr. 868 NEWTOWN RD 23462 #023-01-1987 L1989 **AN** *020 †05

HAASE, Gregory Alan. 1856 COLONIAL MEDICAL CT 23454 #028-34-1972 L1974 **FM IM** *020 †18

HADEN, David Saml. 5505 INDIAN RIVER RD # 101 23464 #028-02-1987 L1990 **IM** *020 †20

HADRAMI, Salam Omar. 1060 FIRST COLONIAL RD, HOSPITAL 23454 #575-01-1996 L2002 **IM** *020 †20

HAMMOND, Sharon Lynette. ■ 23455 #035-15-1978 L2001 **PD** *020 †55

HAN, Caroline Kim. ■ 23454 #051-01-2000 L2000 **FM** *020 †18

HAN, Michael Sanghoun. ■ 23462 #035-19-1992 L2003 **AN** *020 †05

HAN, Min Kyu. ■ 23455 #036-05-1998 L1999 **OPH** *020 †35

HANSON, Lisbet Margareta. 5320 PROVIDENCE RD, STE 100 23464 #050-02-1982 L1986 **OBG** *020 †30

HARDT, Anthony Burk. 1024 FIRST COLONIAL RD, VA BEACH FAMILY PRACTICE L 23454 #038-44-1984 L1985 **FM** *020 †18

HARDY, Timothy Jos. 3720 HOLLAND RD, STE 101 23452 #051-07-1985 L1989 **OBG** *020 †30 ‡

HARR, George Chas, Jr. 1200 FIRST COLONL RD #200M 23454 #041-13-1979 L1982 **D EM** *020 †20,15

HARRIS, Edward Davis. ■ 23451 #051-01-1955 L1955 **GP** *030

HARRIS, Lisa Michelle. 1115 INDEPENDENCE BLVD, STE 118 23454 #041-09-1988 L1994 **DR NTR** *020 †80

HARRISON, H Courtenay. 1008 FIRST COLONIAL RD 23454 #036-07-1959 L1966 **END IM** *072 †20

HARRISON, H Courtenay, Jr. 1101 FIRST COLONIAL RD 23454 #051-01-1984 L1990 **END IM** *020 †20

HARRISON, Isabella. ■ 23454 #023-07-1938 L1976 **GS TS** *071 †85

HART, Karen Martin. 4660A HAYGOOD RD 23455 #051-04-1989 L1990 **FM** *020 †18

HARTMAN, Carl Wm. 1708 OLD DONATION PKWY, CARDIOVASCULAR ASSOCIATES 23454 #035-15-1969 L1975 **CD IM** *075 †20

HARTNECK, Joseph C. 4092 FOXWOOD DR, STE 101 23462 #026-04-1977 L1979 **EM IM** *020 †20,16

HASKELL, Edward G, Jr. ■ 23452 #036-07-1946 L1980 **FM** *071 †18

HATCHER, James J. 933 FIRST COLONIAL RD #203 23454 #051-01-1976 L1977 **PUD CCM** *020 †20

HATHWAR, Vasantha Kumar S. 1008 FIRST COLONIAL RD, STE 103 23454 #496-39-1994 L2002 **PCC SME** *020 †20

HAYES, Thomas Jos. 1101 1ST COLONIAL RD, STE 200 23454 #041-09-1979 L1989 **D** *020 †15

HEATH, Kirk William. ■ 23454 #051-07-2002 L2002 **GS** *020 †85

HECHT-LEAVITT, Charles M. 4668 PEMBROKE BLVD, MRI & CT DIAGNOSTICS 23455 #051-04-1980 L1987 **DR RNR** *020 †20

HEIBY, Laura Rae. 1821 OLD DONATION PKWY, STE 4 23454 #051-07-1979 L1980 **FM** *020 †18

HENDERSON, Michael Potter. 2580 POTTERS RD, DOMINION PSYCHIATRIC ASSOC 23454 #051-04-2001 L2007 **P CHP** *020 †75

HENRIQUEZ, Humberto Frias. 3145 VIRGINIA BEACH BLVD, ROSE HALL PROF BLDG #202 23452 #041-13-1979 L1989 **IM** *020 †20

HESS, John Milton. 1060 FIRST COLONIAL RD 23454 #041-02-1960 L1969 **AN** *071 †05

HEUSER, George Kelly. ■ 23455 #051-07-1984 L1987 **IM** *030 †20

HIGGINS, Michael Ross. 740 INDEPENDENCE CIR 23455 #803-03-1964 L1974 **NEP** *071 †20

HILL, Angela Lidia D. 4151 N WITCHDUCK RD 23455 #041-07-1966 L1974 **P** *071 †75

HILL, Trafford, Jr. 2580 POTTERS RD 23454 #051-01-1961 L1961 **P** *071

HINES, Michael John. ■ 23457 #048-04-1966 L1969 **OPH** *071

HINNANT, Lee Coleman. 4445 CORPORATION LN 23462 #051-07-2003 L2005 **FM** *020 †18

HIPOL, Manuel A. 701 INDEPENDENCE CIR 23455 #748-07-1963 L1978 **R U** *020

HIPPENSTIEL, Mark John. 5486 INDIAN RIVER RD, PATIENT FIRST INDIAN 23464 #041-02-1997 L2000 **FM** *020 †18

HIREGOUDAR, Mohan L. ■ 23455 #495-35-1965 L1979 **IM GE** *020

HLAVACEK, James Matthew. 134 BUSINESS PARK DR 23462 #030-05-1983 L1992 **AN** *020 †05

HOBEIKA, Elie Moubarak. ■ 23462 #605-03-2002 L2005 **OBG** *012

HOFFMAN, Michelle Ann. 3413 VIRGINIA BEACH BLVD 23452 #016-02-2004 L2004 **PD** *012

HOLLADAY, Jeff Gartman. 816 INDEPENDENCE BLVD, STE 1H 23455 #021-06-1991 L2002 **IM** *020 †20

HOLLAND, Clarence Adrian. 2017 PLEASURE HOUSE RD 23455 #051-04-1962 L1962 **GP** *071

HOLLAND, Deborah Ellen. 921 FIRST COLONIAL RD 23454 #051-07-1982 L1984 **PD** *020 †55

HOLLOWELL, Jean Gaye. 2117 MCCOMAS WAY, STE 105 23456 #036-01-1982 L2004 **U GS** *020 †95

HOLOTA, Paul Stuart. 4092 FOXWOOD DR, STE 101 23462 #035-15-1999 L1999 **EM** *020 †16

HOLT, David Brannon. 4660 HAYGOOD RD, STE A 23455 #014-01-1981 L1982 **FM** *072 †18

HONICK, Dana Lee. 4092 FOXWOOD DR STE 10, TIDEWATER, PLC 23462 #041-07-1995 L1999 **EM** *020 †16

HONIG, Mark Pieter. ■ 23451 #016-06-1985 L1999 **PS** *020 †65,85

HORNE, Melvin L. ■ 23451 #024-15-1938 L1944 **PA GP** *071

HOUSTON, Robert Edgar. 800 INDEPENDENCE BLVD, SMG ANESTHESIA - SBH 23455 #016-11-2002 L2006 **AN** *020

HUBBARD, Benj Arthur, Jr. ■ 23455 #051-04-1949 L1949 **GP PD** *071

HUBBARD, Thomas Jos. 329 PHILLIP AVE 23454 #028-02-1983 L1992 **PS OTO** *020 †45,65

HUBBELL, William Jos. 332 NEWTOWN RD, PATIENT FIRST NEWTON ROAD 23462 #025-01-1978 L1994 **FM** *020 †18

HUDSON, Sue B. 802 NEWTOWN RD 23462 #047-06-1976 L1983 **IM** *020 †20

HUGGINS-JONES, Dawn E. 1147 INDEPENDENCE BLVD, STE 103 23455 #041-09-1981 L1997 **OBG** *020 †30

HUGO, Jacobus Benjamin. 328 LOUISA AVE, STE 110 23454 #836-02-1970 L1992 **PS HS** *020 †65

HUNDLEY, Ann Elizabeth. ■ 23464 #051-07-2008 *012

HUNTER, Kenneth Stewart. 1120 FIRST COLONIAL RD, STE 200 23454 #051-07-1985 L1986 **D** *020 †15

HUNTLEY, Carolyn Joanne. 3396 HOLLAND RD STE 102, BEACH HEALTH CLINIC 23452 #019-02-1963 L1972 **PD N** *020 †55

HUOT, Rachel Irene. 5232 PROVIDENCE RD, DOCTORS ON CALL 23464 #021-06-2000 L2000 **FM** *020

HURWITZ, Richard Lewis. ■ 23456 #023-07-1967 L1976 **VS OS** *071 †85

IMAD, Melhem Abdul-Rahim. 1008 FIRST COLONIAL RD, STE 103 23454 #605-03-2000 L2007 **PCC** *020

IMBUR, Donald James. 1856 COLONIAL MEDICAL CT, STE B 23454 #056-06-1969 L1976 **U** *071 †95

IRVING, Declan P. ■ 23451 #539-04-1970 L1975 **VS GS** *020 †85
ISLER, Carmen M. ■ 23456 #847-02-1971 L1974 **GPM** *020
JACOBS, Jonathan S. 935 1ST COLONIAL RD 23454 #047-05-1973 L1978 **PS OS** *020 †65
JACOBSON, Peter Chas. 1800 REPUBLIC RD STE C 23454 #047-05-1981 L1987 **ORS** *020 †40
JAIN, Vivek. 1201 FIRST COLONIAL RD 23454 #055-01-1996 L1998 **OPH** *100 †35
JALBERT, Kristen Hoffman. 1080 FIRST COLONIAL RD, STE 200 23454 #051-07-1985 L1988 **FM** *020 †18
JAMALUDEEN, Abdul Hamid. 2501 JAMES MADISON DR, VIRGINIA BEACH CITY JAIL 23456 #010-03-1972 L1975 **IM** *020 †20
JAMES, Sarah Raquel. 600 INDEPENDENCE BLVD 23462 #041-02-1997 L2000 **AN** *020 †05
JANSON, Jan Albert. 1101 FIRST COLONIAL RD, STE 300 23454 #035-19-1984 L1990 **GE IM** *020 †20
JAVIER, Francis Valerian. 5320 PROVIDENCE RD, STE 101 23464 #748-01-2001 L2003 **FM** *020 †18
JAWORSKI, Mavis Webster. 351 EDWIN DR, STE 102 23462 #048-04-1989 L2008 **FM** *020 †18
JEFFREY, Clyde Grey, Jr. ■ 23454 #036-05-1961 L1961 **OM GP** *071 †70
JENKINS, Donald Denison. 1080 FIRST COLONIAL RD, STE 200 23454 #035-01-2000 L2007 **GS** *100 †85
JEROY, Harry Keirn. 138 S ROSEMONT RD, STE 215 23452 #051-04-1968 L1968 **AN** *071 †05
JO, Stephen Changkap. 1060 FIRST COLONIAL RD, SENTARA VIRGINIA BEACH GEN 23454 #005-12-1998 L2002 **IM** *020 †20
JOHNSON, Amour Fe. 5320 PROVIDENCE RD, STE 100 23464 #422-01-2002 L2006 **OBG** *020
JOHNSON, Bruce Ellsworth. 1008 FIRST COLONIAL RD, STE 103 23454 #051-04-1978 L1981 **PUD IM** *020 †20
JOHNSON, Curtis Merlin. ■ 23455 #026-04-1948 L1992 **PD PDA** *071 †55
JOHNSON, Jason Ryan. 1950 GLENN MITCHELL DR, STE 300 23456 #051-07-2002 L2006 **FM** *040 †18
JOHNSON, Peter Mathew. 2401 SHIPS WATCH CT 23451 #016-06-1992 L2003 **GS** *020 †18
JOHNSON, Robert Albert. 800 INDEPENDENCE BLVD 23455 #035-08-1971 L1976 **PD** *020 †55
JONES, Benita Watson. 3745 HOLLAND RD 23452 #051-04-1995 L1995 **FM** *020 †18 ‡
JONES, Daphne Michelle. 134 BUSINESS PARK DR, ATLANTIC ANESTHESIA 23462 #010-01-1999 L2006 **AN** *020 †05
JONES, David Fitzgerald. 844 FIRST COLONIAL RD, PEDIATRICS AT THE BEACH 23451 #051-01-1988 L1994 **PUD** *020 †20
JONES, Davis Benton, III. 1800 CAMELOT DR STE 200 23454 #041-12-1986 L1989 **PD** *020 †55
JONES, Eric Lloyd. 4654 HAYGOOD RD STE B, CHRISTIAN MEDICAL ASSOCIAT 23455 #047-07-1988 L1991 **IMG** *020 †20
JONES, Steven Richard. 1708 OLD DONATION PKWY, CARDIOVASCULAR ASSOCIATES 23454 #041-09-1985 L1991 **CD IM** *020 †20
JONES, Thomas Michael. 1120 FIRST COLONIAL RD, STE 100 23454 #051-07-1993 L1993 **FM** *020 †18
JORDAN, Cami Ullah. 1800 CAMELOT DR, STE 200 23454 #021-01-1996 L1996 **PD** *020 †55
JORDAN, Louis Charles. 5716 CLEVELAND ST, STE 200 23462 #021-01-1996 L1996 **OAR** *020 †40
JORDAN, Louis Robt. 5501 GREENWICH RD, STE 200 23462 #035-20-1963 L1971 **ORS** *071 †40
JOYCE, Michael Harrison. 5301 PROVIDENCE RD 23464 #051-01-1980 L1983 **PD** *020 †55
JOYNER, Sarah Elizabeth. 5700 CLEVELAND ST, STE 228 23462 #051-07-2002 L2002 **CD** *012 †20
JU, Wook Ja Lee. 5301 PROVIDENCE RD STE 60, PROVIDENCE SOUTH OFFICE BL 23464 #583-01-1962 L1974 **PD** *071
JUSKEVICH, Robert Stanley. 1080 FIRST COLONIAL RD, STE 300 23454 #016-43-1970 L1978 **OBG** *020 †30
KADAKKAL, Ramesh B. 1020 INDEPENDENCE BLVD, STE 304 23455 #495-31-1970 L1976 **U** *020 †95
KADAKKAL, Sreeja. 1020 INDEPENDENC BLVD #304 23455 #495-44-1975 L1980 **P** *020 †75
KAKRIA, Ramesh Champalal. ■ 23464 #495-01-1967 L1984 **RO** *071 †80
KALAGAYAN, Hector J. 5486 INDIAN RIVER RD, PATIENT FIRST INDIAN 23464 #748-01-1958 L1994 **GS GP** *020
KALANTAR, Seyed Babak. ■ 23451 #051-07-2004 **ORS** *012
KALOJI, Madhukar. 1020 INDEPENDENCE BLVD, STE 205 23455 #495-21-1986 L1999 **PUD** *020 †20
KANTER, Harry Lee. 1708 OLD DONATION PKWY, CARDIOVASCULAR ASSOCIATES 23454 #051-01-1986 L1994 **CD** *020 †20
KAROLL, Craig Alan. 641 LYNNHAVEN PKWY, STE 204 23452 #028-46-1987 L1991 **P** *020 †75
KARP, Nelson Marc. 460 S INDEPENDENCE BLVD 23462 #051-04-1981 L1982 **GP UCM** *020
KARPOV, Vladimir Alexande. 256 N WITCHDUCK RD, STE G 23462 #913-99-1997 L2000 **P** *020 ‡
KAUFFMAN, Jeffrey Harris. 1101 FIRST COLONIAL RD, STE 300 23454 #051-04-1991 L1992 **GE IM** *020 †20
KAY, David Lloyd. 1550 TOMCAT BLVD STE 150 23460 #023-12-2001 L2003 **AN** *020
KAYE, James Patrick. 1060 FIRST COLONIAL RD 23454 #016-06-1975 L1989 **PTH** *020 †50
KAYOTA, Stephen Walter. 837 FIRST COLONIAL RD, STE C 23451 #051-07-1993 L1993 **PM** *020 †60
KAZAKIS, Demetrios James. 1708 OLD DONATION PKWY, CARDIOVASCULAR ASSOCIATES 23454 #051-01-1988 L1994 **CD** *020 †20
KEATS, Matthew Mason. 4417 CORPORATION LN, STE 250 23462 #051-01-1980 L1984 **P** *020 †75
KELLY, Anne Chilton. 1080 FIRST COLONIAL RD, STE 412 23454 #005-06-2001 L2006 **PD** *020
KELSEY, Gerdi D. 1120 FIRST COLONIAL RD, STE 100 23454 #041-13-1967 L1969 **FM AM** *071 †18
KEMP, George Marshall. 1120 FIRST COLONIAL RD, STE 202 23454 #048-12-1977 L1983 **GO GYN** *020 †30
KEMP, Peter J. 1147 INDEPENDENCE BLVD 23455 #654-01-1988 L1993 **OBG** *020 †30
KENERSON, John Gerard. 1708 OLD DONATION PKWY, CARDIOVASCULAR ASSOCIATES 23454 #050-02-1977 L1982 **CD** *020 †20
KENNEDY, Gerard Dennis. 1550 TOMCAT BLVD 23460 #048-02-1979 L1979 **FM** *020 †18
KENNEDY, Kris Elaine. 1975 GLENN MITCHELL DR, STE 202 23456 #051-04-1984 L1988 **OBG** *020 †30
KERNS, Brian Lee. 4092 FOXWOOD DR STE 1 23462 #051-07-2002 L2002 **EM** *100 †16
KHAN, Abdur Rasheed. 4221 PLEASANT VALLEY RD 23464 #649-33-1984 L1988 **FM** *020 †18
KHAN, Ghazala Yasmin. 4221 PLEASANT VALLEY RD, STE 114 23464 #495-21-1977 L1988 **PD** *020 †55
KILLEN, Joseph F, Jr. 1120 FIRST COLONIAL RD, STE 100 23454 #051-07-1983 L1984 **FM** *020 †18

KINGSBURY, Michelle E. 1020 INDEPENDENC BLVD #103 23455 #023-12-1989 L1991 **FM OM** *020 †18 ‡
KNAPP, Barry John, II. 4092 FOXWOOD DR STE 101, EMERGENCY PHYSICIANS OF TI 23462 #035-15-1994 L1997 **EM** *020 †16
KNIGHT, Catherine P. ■ 23455 #047-06-1997 L2000 **IM** *020 †20
KNIGHT, Herbert. 4460 CORPORATION LN, STE 190 23462 #047-07-1990 L1991 **IM** *020
KOBUS, Wilhelm. ■ 23451 #660-04-1960 *071
KOEN, Leon. ■ 23451 #847-04-1956 L1968 **EM GS** *071
KOH, Hae Kyung Hong. 800 INDEPENDENCE BLVD 23455 #583-01-1969 L1974 **PTH** *075 †50
KOLLI, Madhu Krishna. 1157 FIRST COLONIAL RD, STE 200 23454 #038-06-1997 L2002 **NEP** *020 †20
KREIDER, Stanley J. ■ 23454 #016-02-1965 L1976 **P** *071 †75
KROP, Thomas Monroe. 1101 FIRST COLONIAL RD, STE 200 23454 #035-20-1972 L1977 **D** *020 †15
KRUP, Jennifer Fox. 2232 VA BEACH BLVD, STE 104 23454 #051-07-1978 L1979 **FM** *020
KUBICKI, Ted Marian. 1024 FIRST COLONIAL RD 23454 #060-01-1994 L1996 **FM** *020 †18 ‡
KULCZYCKY, Ihor Gregory. 5249 PROVIDENCE RD 23464 #065-09-1964 L1977 **GS** *020 †85
KUMAR, Achla. 5314 PROVIDENCE RD 23464 #496-07-1970 L1979 **PM** *020 †60 ‡
LABOCCETTA, Lydia Toon. ■ 23451 #051-07-2008 *012
LACKORE, Raymond C. 1101 FIRST COLONIAL RD, STE 100 23454 #011-04-1977 L1984 **OBG** *020 †30 ‡
LAGO, Dayna Marie. 465 N GREAT NECK RD 23454 #021-05-1989 L1994 **OPH** *020 †35
LAGUERTA, Nena Metra. 3660 BRANNON DR 23456 #748-29-1993 L2003 **P** *020
LAGUNDINO, Flordelino C. 5266 PRINCESS ANNE RD # D, PREMIER MEDICAL 23462 #010-03-1971 L1976 **R GP** *020
LAKE, Ann Hillery Wilson. 5700 THURSTON AVE 23455 #016-01-1985 L1989 **P** *062 †75
LAMARCHE, Donald E, Jr. 968 FIRST COLONIAL RD, STE 103 23454 #051-07-1991 L1995 **N** *020 †75
LA MARCHE, Donald Edward. 4588 VIRGINIA BEACH BLVD 23462 #035-09-1963 L1980 **OPH** *020 †35
LANDAKER, Edwin John. ■ 23456 #024-07-2003 L2003 **N** *020
LANDRY, Douglas Ramon. 4092 FOXWOOD DR, STE 101 23462 #032-01-1990 L1994 **GP EM** *020 †16
LANE, Penny Combs. 1080 FIRST COLONIAL RD, ATLANTIC PEDIATRIC SPECIAL 23454 #023-12-1989 L1991 **PD** *020 †55
LANG, Joseph Peter. 4092 FOXWOOD DR STE 101 23462 #051-07-2001 L2001 **EM** *020 †16
LANGILLE, David K C. 4536 BONNEY RD, C/O TIDEWATER EMERG MED 23462 #064-01-1984 L1988 **EM GP** *020 †16
LASTER, James Monroe. 3143 MAGIC HOLLOW BLVD, STE 200 23453 #016-06-1969 L1978 **P** *020 †75
LAW, Katherine Pinckney. 5320 PROVIDENCE RD STE 301, PROVIDENCE RD FAMILY PRACT 23464 #051-04-1982 L1983 **FM** *020 †18
LAWRENCE, Duane Arthur. 1020 INDEPENDENCE BLVD, STE 211 23455 #035-45-1965 L1974 **FM OS** *020 †18
LEAVY, Philip Gerard, Jr. 4092 FOXWOOD DR, STE 101 23462 #010-02-1969 L1971 **EM IMG** *020 †16
LEE, Michael Edward. 1950 GLENN MITCHELL DR 23456 #036-01-1988 L1995 **HEM** *020 †20
LEE, Millie. 205 BUSINESS PARK DR, STE 200 23462 #035-47-1992 L2000 **CD** *020 †20
LE PAGE, Joseph Francis. 1605 GENERAL BOOTH BLVD, PATIENT FIRST GENERAL 23454 #051-04-1993 L1994 **FM** *020 †18
LERNER, Martin. 5555 GREENWICH RD, STE 600 23462 #035-15-1962 L1964 **FM** *020
LESLIE, Lawrence F. 4092 FOXWOOD DR, STE 101 23462 #051-01-1998 L1998 **EM** *020 †16
LETTERLE, Susan J. 4092 FOXWOOD DR 23462 #025-01-1996 L2000 **EM** *020 †16
LEVIN, Janice. 1975 GLENN MITCHELL DR, STE 202 23456 #051-04-1988 L1990 **OBG** *020 †30
LEVIN, Laurence Leonard. 134 BUSINESS PARK DR, ATLANTIC ANESTHESIA, INC. 23462 #041-13-1981 L1985 **AN** *071 †05
LEVINE, Edgar Morris. 848 FIRST COLONIAL RD, FIRST COLONIAL EYE CARE 23451 #019-02-1990 L2001 **OPH GP** *020 †35
LEXIER, Melissa Rachel. 1950 GLENN MITCHELL DR, STE 304 23456 #051-07-2001 L2003 **PD** *020 †55
LEYTON, Matthew N. 816 INDEPENDENCE BLVD, STE 2C 23455 #030-06-1997 L1998 **PM** *020 †60
LIM, Angelita Agustin. 4501 N WITCHDUCK RD, STE D 23455 #748-01-1958 L1975 **IM CD** *020
LIM, Lilian Elizabeth A. 1060 FIRST COLONIAL RD, ATTN: PEDIATRIX MEDICAL G 23454 #748-02-1985 L2003 **NPM** *020 †55
LIN, Steven Kueiku. ■ 23464 #028-02-2005 **IM** *012
LIND, James Forest. 760 LYNNHAVEN PKWY, ACDMC PHYS & SURG ESTRN VA 23452 #065-05-1951 L1979 **GS** *071
LINDER, Paul Gary. 813 INDEPENDENCE BLVD, STE D 23455 #041-14-1984 L1985 **IM** *020 †20 ‡
LIPPS, Brian Joseph. 3061 BRICKHOUSE CT, STE 109 23452 #035-47-1996 L2004 **NEP** *100 †20
LIPSCOMB, Rebecca Michele. 4325 HUDGINS DR 23455 #051-07-2002 L2004 **EM** *020 †16
LIPTON, Eric Chas. 816 INDEPENDENCE BLVD, STE 100 23455 #035-15-1991 L1994 **FM** *020 †18
LISNER, Diana Ellerman. 844 FIRST COLONIAL RD, STE 204 23451 #051-01-1993 L1996 **PD** *020 †55
LISZKA, Marianne Zuggo. 1060 1ST COLONIAL RD 23454 #473-03-1994 L2003 **IMG** *020 †20
LITTLE, Lourdes Leuterio. ■ 23456 #748-02-1963 L1984 **OM** *030 †55
LLANO, Alfonso. 6025 PROVIDENCE RD, # 110 23464 #264-04-1992 L1995 **IM** *020 †20
LONGWATER, Adam Brian. 4092 FOXWOOD DR, STE 101 23462 #012-22-1999 L1999 **EM** *020 †16
LOPES, Jo Anne Marie. 5121 GREENWICH RD, STE 101 23462 #051-07-1989 L1994 **PS** *020 †65
LOUKA, Kamal Selim. 4867 BAXTER RD STE 105 23462 #915-02-1971 L1984 **FM FSM** *020
LOVE, Suzanne S. 4092 FOXWOOD DR, STE 101 23462 #047-05-1975 L1976 **EM** *020 †18,16,70
LOWDON, Jack, Jr. 1821 OLD DONATION PKWY # 9 23454 #051-01-1981 L1985 **DR** *020
LOWE, Scott Miller. 1728 VIRGINIA BEACH BLVD 23454 #047-07-1970 L1975 **OBG** *020 †30
LUISKUTTY, George C. ■ 23456 #039-01-2004 L2007 **EM** *020
LUNDIN-MARIANO, Jill Ann. 1800 CAMELOT DR, STE 200 23454 #041-09-1996 L2001 **PD** *020 †55
LUSTIG, Harry Raab, Jr. 4092 FOXWOOD DR 23462 #051-07-1980 L1981 **EM** *020 †18,16
LUTHRA, Ramesh C. 5283 CLUB HEAD RD 23455 #495-29-1960 L1970 **U GP** *020
LYONS, Dorothy Araline. 816 INDEPENDENCE BLVD, STE 2A 23455 #041-09-1979 L2006 **N CHN** *020 †20
LYTH, William Michael. 138 S ROSEMONT RD, STE 215 23452 #041-12-1985 L1989 **AN** *020 †05

■ = Address Information Privacy Protected

MACHAJ, Vincent Richard. 138 S ROSEMONT RD, STE 215 23452 #041-12-1976 L1983
AN *020 †05

MAC LAUGHLIN, Wm Wittmer. 1020 INDEPENDENCE BLVD, STE 111 23455
#035-09-1981 L1982 ON HEM *020 †20

MADREN, Eric Michael. 1925 GLENN MITCHELL DR, STE 100 23456 #051-01-1994 L1994
FM *020 †18

MAGNO, Elizabeth Lopez. 6632 INDIAN RIVER RD 23464 #748-08-1988 L1999 FM *020 †18

MAGPOC, Norma O. 1020 INDEPENDENC BLVD 23455 #748-01-1964 L1972 IM NEP *020

MAHINI, Abraham. 700 INDEPENDENCE CIR # 2C 23455 #517-01-1966 L1977 U *020 †95

MAHONEY, Robert Kevin. 5320 PROVIDENCE RD 23464 #051-01-1985 L1988 FM *020 †18

MAINALI, Elsie S. 1060 FIRST COLONIAL RD, PEDIATRIX MEDICAL GROUP, P 23454
#748-07-1984 L1995 PD *020 †55

MAIZEL, David R. 5555 GREENWICH RD STE 600, SENTARA MED GRP 23462
#033-06-1974 L1978 FM MDM *030 †18

MAKDISI, Walid. 824 DEVEREAUX DR 23462 #605-01-1985 L2004 IM *020 †20

MALIK, Rajul. 1860 COLONIAL MEDICAL CT, VBIM 23454 #495-23-1991 L2004 IM *020 †20

MALLENBAUM, Sidney. 1008 FIRST COLONIAL RD, STE 101 23454 #036-01-1986 L1990
N *020 †75

MANCHIKALAPUDI, P. 205 BUSINESS PARK DR, STE 200 23462 #495-21-1991 L2003
IC *020 †20

MANIAN, Swarna. 1860 COLONIAL MED CT, VA BCH INT MED 23454 #038-06-1997 L2002
IM *020 †20

MANICKAVASAGAR, S. 5555 GREENWICH RD STE 60 23462 #220-01-1958 L1974
EM U *020 †18

MANKE, Chad Richard. 230 CLEARFIELD AVE, SUITE124 23462 #025-07-1998 L1998
ORS *020 †40 ‡

MANNARINO, Kathy Lynn. 1147 INDEPENDENCE BLVD 23455 #051-04-1998 L1998
FM *020 †18

MAPP, John Alfriend. 1120 FIRST COLONIAL RD, STE 100 23454 #051-01-1958 L1958
FM *071 †18

MARCH, Melissa Irene. ■ 23452 #038-41-2007 L2007 OBG *012

MARKHAM, Harold Wm. 3432 HOLLAND RD, PATIENT FIRST HOLLAND 23452
#051-04-1972 L1973 FM *020 †18

MARKS, Charles Wesley. 917 NORTHWOOD DR 23452 #748-10-1977 L1983 IM EM *020

MAROTO, Felix. ■ 23464 #847-04-1957 L1966 AN *071

MARSHALL, Sheri Tamara. 5320 PROVIDENCE RD, STE 301 23464 #033-05-1996 L1996
FM *020 †18

MARTIN, Kristen O. 1101 1ST COLONIAL RD, STE 200 23454 #023-12-1995 L2006 D *020 †15

MARTIN, Stewart Wm. 4092 FOXWOOD DR, STE 101 23462 #051-07-1989 L1992 EM *020 †16

MARTIN, Trent Douglas. 1020 INDEPENDENC BLVD #110 23455 #060-01-1983 L1988
GE IM *075 †20

MARTIN, William Leroy. 5320 PROVIDENCE RD, STE 100 23464 #041-12-1963 L1969
OBG *020 †30

MARTIN DEL CAMPO, Matthew. ■ 23453 #016-11-2005 L2005 EM *012

MARTINELLI, Maurice Ivan. PO BOX 68065 23471 #143-05-1963 L1977 DR *020

MARTIRES, Jemma Charity. ■ 23462 #748-11-1994 L2007 PD *100

MASCARINAS, Teofilo C, Jr. 4501 N WITCHDUCK RD, STE D 23455 #748-01-1966 L1972
IM *020

MATON, Bruno Michel. ■ 23454 #396-08-1995 L2008 CN *020 †75

MATON, Kelly Maureen. ■ 23454 #041-13-1988 L1991 CHN *020 †55

MATTHEWS, Richard Eugene. 143 TOWER DR 23462 #051-04-1970 L1972 IM *020

MAY, William Heath. 5121 GREENWICH RD 23462 #051-01-1967 L1967 PD *071 †55

MC CABE, William Robt. ■ 23451 #039-01-1953 L1953 ID IM *071 †20

MC CAULEY, Janet Lynn. 277 BENDIX RD, ANTHEM BCBS 23452 #036-07-1984 L1987
OBG PHP *020 †30

MC CLUSKEY, Mary Therese. ■ 23462 #028-34-1986 L1988 IM *020 †20

MC CORMACK, Daniel Paul. 4092 FOXWOOD DR STE 101, TIDEWATER, PLC 23462
#033-06-1996 L2000 EM *020 †16

MC COY, Dawn Marie. 6477 COLLEGE PARK SQ, STE118 23464 #051-07-1994 L1994
PD *020 †55

MC CREADY, Daniel Roy. 1950 GLENN MITCHELL DR, STE 300 23456 #023-01-1970 L1976
FM *020 †18

MC CUNE, Frederick K. 1060 FIRST COLONIAL RD 23454 #010-01-1955 L1963 AN *071 †05

MC DANIEL, David Henry. 933 FIRST COLONIAL RD, STE 113 23454 #055-01-1978 L1983
D *020 †15

MC DERMOTT, Flordeliza M. 400 S WITCHDUCK RD 23462 #748-10-1977 L1982 N *020 †75

MC DERMOTT, Glenn Robt. 1368 N GREAT NECK RD 23454 #748-10-1977 L1988 IM FM *020

MC DERMOTT, Jos Patrick. 1975 GLENN MITCHELL DR, STE 302 23456 #035-09-1988 L1998
GS *020 †85

MC DERMOTT, Wayne Michael. 1543 AMBERLEY FOREST RD 23453 #748-10-1978 L1984
CRS GS *020

MC DONALD, Wilbur E, Jr. 4092 FOXWOOD DR, STE 101 23462 #051-01-1978 L1980
EM *020 †16

MC ENROE, Charles Scott. 113B 83RD ST 23451 #035-03-1982 L1989 VS GS *020 †85

MC GEEHAN, Karen Marie. 1080 FIRST COLONIAL RD, STE 200 23454 #030-06-1993 L1994
FM *072 †18

MC HUGH, Sean Patrick. ■ 23455 #041-09-1998 L2003 CCM *020 †20

MC INTYRE, Margaret Irwin. 2301 GENERAL BOOTH BLVD 23456 #051-07-1983 L1986
PD *020 †55

MC KECHNIE, Ronald Scott. 1708 OLD DONATION PKWY, CARDIOVASCULAR
ASSOCIATES 23454 #011-02-1997 L2004 IC *020 †20

MC LAUGHLIN, Debra Banks. 1080 FIRST COLONIAL RD, STE 200 23454 #051-07-1984 L1985
FM *020 †18

MC LAUGHLIN, Edwin W. 4092 FOXWOOD DR STE 101, TIDEWATER 23462 #051-07-1996 L1996
EM *020 †16

MEDDOWS, Michael John. ■ 23451 #051-07-2002 L2002 *020 †05

MEIN, Eric Alan. 1800 CAMELOT DR STE 300 23454 #051-07-1986 L1987 PM *020 †60

MENDELSON, Moss Harlan. 4092 FOXWOOD DR, STE 101 23462 #051-01-1990 L1994
EM *020 †16

MENDRINOS, Savvas E. ■ 23454 #418-06-1994 L2005 PTH *100 †50

MENEES, Daniel Stephen. 1708 OLD DONATION PKWY, CARDIOVASCULAR ASSOCIATES
#016-01-1999 L2006 IC *020 †20

MENEFEE, Stephen Andrew. 2859 VIRGINIA BEACH BLVD, LITTLE NECK MEDICAL
ASSOCI #649-40-1981 L1984 FM *020 †18

MEYER, Gregory Mc Bride. 1020 INDEPENDENCE BLVD, STE 311 23455 #308-03-1980 L1992
IM *020 †20

MICHAEL, Joel Craig. 4092 FOXWOOD DR, STE 101 23462 #055-01-1990 L1993 EM *020 †16

MIDIS, Nicholas Anthony. 5716 CLEVELAND ST, STE 200 23462 #051-04-1994 L2000
ORS *020 †40

MILLER, Edward Chas. 1708 OLD DONATION PKWY, CARDIOVASCULAR ASSOCIATES 23454
#028-02-1979 L1980 CD IC *020 †20 ‡

MILLER, Ira David. 813 INDEPENDENCE BLVD 23455 #035-46-1964 L1973 GS VS *020 †85 ‡

MILLER, James Richard. 1708 OLD DONATION PKWY, CARDIOVASCULAR ASSOCIATES 23454
#051-01-1993 L1995 CD *020 †20

MILLER, Mitchell Bruce. 2109 MCCOMAS WAY, STE 102 23456 #041-14-1979 L1980
FM *020 †18

MILLER, Stephen Allen. 1729 WILDWOOD DR STE 103 23454 #011-04-1981 L1982
OBG *020 †30

MINK, James Wm. 5121 GREENWICH RD 23462 #051-07-1984 L1987 PD *020 †55

MIRANDA, Josue Danl A. 5136 PRINCESS ANNE RD 23462 #748-02-1973 L1982 GS *020 †85

MIRANDA, Prospero Lumagui. 5136 PRINCESS ANNE RD 23462 #748-07-1952 L1982 GP *071

MIRENDA, Joseph Vincent. 138 S ROSEMONT RD, STE 215 23452 #016-06-1984 L1991
AN CCM *020 †05

MIRZA, Alamgir. ■ 23462 #160-07-1999 L2007 IM *100 †20

MITCHELL, Douglas Kent. 2117 MCCOMAS WAY STE 103, GENETZ BOOTH PEDS 23456
#025-01-1984 L1992 PD ID *020 †55

MITCHELL, Robt Elmer, Jr. 2580 POTTERS RD, DOMINION PSYCHIATRIC 23454
#041-09-1961 L1974 P OS *020

MITSCH, Matthew J. 1821 OLD DONATION PKWY, STE 6 23454 #035-03-1990 L1995
OPH *020 †35

MLADICK, Richard Anthony. 1037 FIRST COLONIAL RD, PLASTIC SURGERY CENTER INC 23454
#016-06-1959 L1968 PS *020 †85,65 ‡

MOAYERY, Massoum. 700 INDEPENDENCE CIR, STE 2D 23455 #517-01-1968 L1982
OPH *035

MODLINGER, Ronald Edwin. 1531 AMBERLEY FOREST RD 23453 #033-06-1976 L1984
CD IM *020 †20

MOHORN, Riikka Pauliina. 1020 FIRST COLONIAL RD, VIRGINIA BEACH SURG LTD 23454
#051-07-1999 L2006 GS *020 †85

MONI, Kochicheril N. 1020 INDEPENDENCE BLVD #31 23455 #495-31-1968 L1979
CD ICE *050 †20

MONTEJO, Migdonia. 6025 PROVIDENCE RD, # 110 23464 #264-11-1990 L1995 FPG *020 †18

MOON, Agnes Hyungnam. ■ 23451 #583-01-1964 L1995 PM *071 †60

MORGAN, Franklin Gill, Jr. 828 HEALTHY WAY, STE 330 23462 #012-01-1978 L1981
OBG *020 †30 ‡

MORIN, Scott Randall. 984 FIRST COLONIAL RD, STE 302 23454 #051-07-1986 L1992
OTO HNS *020 †45

MORO, Michael. 813 INDEPENDENCE BLVD, STE A 23455 #561-11-1970 L1974 FM *020 †18

MORRIS, Richard Louis. 848 FIRST COLONIAL RD 23451 #039-01-1966 L1975
PS GS *020 †85,65

MORRISON, Angela Sharnell. ■ 23455 #051-07-2006 L2006 OBG *012

MOSBY, Robert Thos, Jr. 5555 GREENWICH RD, STE 501 23462 #051-04-1961 L1961
PD *071 †55

MOSCOSO, Ricardo. 5320 PROVIDENCE RD 23464 #035-01-1991 L1997 GS *020 †85

MOSELEY, Elizabeth Hart. 2701 BLUEBILL DR, MEDICAL CENTER RADIOLOGIST 23456
#051-07-1994 L1994 DR *020 †80

MOSS, Gary Blair. 1704 SIR WILLIAM OSLER DR 23454 #051-04-1992 L1993 AI IM *020 †20,03

MOSURE, James Chas. 812 N VILLIER CT 23452 #038-44-1983 L1984 DR *020 †80

MOUNAIMNE, Marwan Wafik. 1020 INDEPENDENC BLVD #309 23455 #605-01-1977 L1981
N CHN *020 †75

MUHLENDORF, Ivan Kenneth. 828 HEALTHY WAY, STE 330 23462 #051-01-1973 L1977
GYN *020 †30 ‡

MULLEN, Joseph Terrance. ■ 23455 #024-05-1955 L1974 GS TS *071 †85,90

MURPHY, Noreen Elizabeth. ■ 23455 #016-01-2006 L2007 IM *012

MURPHY, Stephen P. 138 S ROSEMONT RD, STE 215 23452 #030-06-2001 L2006 AN *020 †05

MURRAY, Brian Philip P. 134 BUSINESS PARK DR, ATLANTIC ANESTH 23462
#024-05-1970 L1993 AN *071 †05

MURRAY, Glenn Chas. 1060 FIRST COLONIAL RD, ATTN: JUDITH KIEFER 23454
#035-19-1979 L2004 AN IM *020 †20,05

MURTHY, Papaiah Srinvasa. 134 BUSINESS PARK DR 23462 #495-33-1965 L1976 AN *020 †05

MYERS-POWELL, Brenda A. 1045 HORTON PL, VIRGINIA RETINA SPECIALIST 23454
#028-02-1994 L2005 OPH *020 †35

NAKAMOTO, Rona K. 3933 BONNEY RD 23452 #048-15-1983 L1994 AN *020

NAKANISHI, Junichiro Luke. 3333 VIRGINIA BCH BLVD #24 23452 #572-30-1955 L1960
GS OS *075

NARD, Jeffrey Howard. 1745 CAMELOT DR, STE 200 23454 #041-09-1987 L1989 P *020 †75

NASH, Robert Arthur. 5589 GREENWICH RD, STE 175 23462 #035-15-1973 L1974
N PMM *020 †75 ‡

NAYAK, Ramnath. 1020 INDEPENDENC BLVD #202 23455 #495-17-1956 L1975
END IM *020 †20

NEATROUR, George Peyton. 1201 FIRST COLONIAL RD 23454 #051-01-1984 L1986
OPH *020 †35

NELSEN, Alan C. 1450 KEMPSVILLE RD 23464 #165-03-1975 L1998 IM *075 †20

NELSON, Wilner Nels J, Jr. 2100 LYNNHAVEN PKWY, STE 201 23456 #018-03-1968 L1996
FM *071 †18

NEWBY, William E. ■ 23451 #051-04-1951 L1951 OPH *071 †35

NISSMAN, Harvey Leonard. ■ 23451 #035-19-1975 L1986 P *020 †75

NORTHROP, Michael Stewart. ■ 23451 #035-09-2005 L2005 PD *012

NORTON, Richard Howard. ■ 23452 #041-01-1958 L1981 AN *062 †05

O'CONNELL, Patrick Wm. 1800 REPUBLIC RD, STE 102 23454 #050-02-1983 L1989
ORS OSM *020 †40

O'CONNOR, Frank Jos. ■ 23462 #051-01-1959 L1959 U OS *071

O'GRADY, Martin Gabriel. 1975 GLENN MITCHELL DR, STE 302 23456 #056-05-1980 L1989
GS VS *020 †85

OH, Chang Kyeong. 1101 FIRST COLONIAL RD, STE 300 23454 #035-20-1999 L2006
GE *020 †20

OLD, Levi, Jr. ■ 23451 #051-04-1951 L1951 GS TS *071 †85,90

OLD, Wayne David. 1708 OLD DONATION PKWY, CARDIOVASCULAR ASSOCIATES 23454
#051-07-1982 L1983 CD IM *020 †20

OLDS, Francine Annette. 1080 FIRST COLONIL RD #403 23454 #036-01-1986 L1989
OBG *020 †30

OLEKSA, James Stephen. 800 INDEPENDENCE BLVD, SMG ANESTHESIOLGY/ SBH 23455
#011-02-2002 L2006 AN *100 †05

OLSON, Jeffrey John. 4092 FOXWOOD DR, STE 101 23462 #011-03-1985 L1986 **EM** *020 †16

OLSZAK, Rebbecca Lynn. 2117 MCCOMAS WAY, STE 103 23456 #030-06-2004 L2004 **PD** *020 †55

O'NEILL, Donald Andrew. 230 CLEARFIELD AVE, STE 124 23462 #035-01-1973 L1987 **ORS** *020 †40

ONG, Joseph George. 1080 FIRST COLONIAL RD, STE 400 23454 #041-13-1999 L2007 **NS** *020

ONSANIT, Addie Jitpapa. 1270 DIAMOND SPRINGS RD, STE 110 23455 #051-01-1998 L2003 **IM** *020 †20

ONSANIT, Tawachai. 1020 INDEPENDENC BLVD #204 23455 #891-01-1964 L1976 **CRS** *020 †10,85

ONUFER, John Robt. 1708 OLD DONATION PKWY, CARDIOVASCULAR ASSOCIATES 23454 #028-02-1984 L1991 **CD IM** *020 †20

OPET, Robert Francis. 138 S ROSEMONT RD, ANESTHESIA SPECIALISTS 23452 #041-13-1989 L1994 **IM** *020 †05

OPPENHEIM, Arnold R. 5320 PROVIDENCE RD 23464 #024-05-1974 L1981 **D GP** *020 †15

ORDONEZ, Marylin M P R. ■ 23455 #748-02-1970 L2006 **P RO** *020

OUELLET, Jeanne-Paule. ■ 23458 #067-04-1978 L1996 *020

PACKER, Richard T. 5320 PROVIDENCE RD, KATHERINE P LAW 23464 #065-10-1986 L1995 **FM** *020

PACKER, Tamar. 5320 PROVIDENCE RD, PROVIDENCE RD FAMILY PRACT 23464 #065-10-1987 L1995 **FM** *020

PADDISON, Richard M. ■ 23451 #036-07-1945 L1947 **N** *071 †75

PADMORE, Nicole Angelique. 1300 DIAMOND SPRINGS RD, STE 400 23455 #051-04-1995 L1995 **IM** *020

PAL, Joginder. 780 LYNNHAVEN PKWY 23452 #495-03-1973 L1981 **P** *020 †75

PALAT, Govindankutty K. 1020 INDEPENDENCE BLVD, STE 302 23455 #495-44-1969 L1977 **P N** *020 †75

PALAT, Meera Koyappalli. 1020 INDEPENDENCE BLVD, STE 302 23455 #495-44-1970 L1980 **PD** *020

PALTING, John Kenneth. 2859 VA BEACH BLVD 23452 #748-01-1984 L1995 **FM** *020 †18

PARDEE, Helen Roberts. 1113 GUNSTON RD, CHILD HOSP OF THE KING'S D 23451 #012-05-1990 L2000 **PD** *020 †55,19

PARENT, F Noel, III. 397 LITTLE NECK RD, 3300 S BLDG 23452 #041-02-1982 L1989 **VS** *020 †85

PARISER, David Michael. 1120 FIRST COLONIAL RD, STE 200 23454 #051-04-1972 L1972 **D DMP** *020 †15

PARISER, Robert Jay. 1120 FIRST COLONIAL RD, STE 200 23454 #051-04-1974 L1976 **D DMP** *020 †15

PARKER, Charles E, Jr. 5029 CORPORATE WOODS DR, STE 250 23462 #041-77-1968, ▲ L1975 **P CHP** *020 †75

PARKER, Lambert Titus K. 5041 CORPORATE WOODS DR, STE 200 23462 #561-25-1984 L2002 **IM OS** *020

PARKS, Barbara Lynn. ■ 23451 #056-06-1978 L1991 **IM** *020 †20

PARMAR, Meenakshi. 256 N WITCHDUCK RD 23462 #495-03-1989 L2004 **P** *012

PARRISH, Bernard L. ■ 23464 #051-04-1929 L1929 **GYN** *071

PATEL, Anil Nanubhai. 816 INDEPENDENCE BLVD, STE 3C 23455 #495-23-1980 L1988 **PUD IM** *020 †20

PATEL, Anilkumar. 1020 INDEPENDENCE BLVD, STE 102 23455 #495-23-1979 L1988 **CD IM** *020 †20

PATEL, Jitendra Manubhai. 2020 S INDEPENDENCE BLVD, FAMILY & INTERNAL MEDICAL 23453 #495-23-1979 L1985 IM *023 †20

PATEL, Nandini Anilkumar. 700 INDEPENDENCE CIR, STE 3D 23455 #495-23-1979 L1988 **P** *020

PATEL, Tushar R.. 780 LYNNHAVEN PKWY STE 400 23452 #306-01-1997 L2004 **P** *100 †75

PATTERSON, John Robt, II. ■ 23454 #051-03-1991 L1994 **FM** *020 †18

PAYNE, Jody Michelle. 23464 #051-07-2008 *012

PAYNE, Martin Allen. 4092 FOXWOOD DR, STE 101 23462 #051-07-1996 L1996 **EM** *020 †16

PEARMAN, Steven Dudley. 1380 TUSCANY DR 23456 #051-01-1982 L1983 **FM** *020 †18

PECHAN, B Warren. 1120 FIRST COLONIAL RD, STE 200 23454 #010-01-1973 L1980 **U OS** *020 †95

PENNELL, Kirsten Nadine. ■ 23456 #051-07-2006 L2006 **EM** *012

PETERSON, John Emerick. 340 WHITING LN 23456 #035-20-1954 L1959 **GS** *071 †85

PHILLIPS, James Wyatt. 533 NEWTOWN RD STE 104 23462 #051-04-1947 L1947 **OS GP** *071

PHOCAS, John Geo, III. 780 LYNNHAVEN PKWY 23452 #010-01-1991 L2003 **P** *020 †75

PIANIN, Stanley Lloyd. ■ 23454 #035-19-1956 L1994 **FM** *020 †18

PICARDI, Mary Catherine. 1120 FIRST COLONIAL RD, STE 100 23454 #023-01-1974 L1983 **FM** *020 †18

PICOU, Wally John. ■ 23464 #021-05-1959 L1970 **EM** *071

PIERCE, Gregory Wayne. 5486 INDIAN RIVER RD, PATIENT FIRST INDIAN 23464 #047-07-1983 L1992 **FM** *020 †18

PIKE, Irving Marvin. 1020 INDEPENDENCE BLVD, STE 110 23455 #012-01-1978 L1983 **GE IM** *020 †20

PIZARRO ROSARIO, Pablo D. ■ 23456 #042-01-1983 L2007 **CCA** *020 †18,05

PLATT, Gerald William. ■ 23452 #023-12-2001 L2002 **EM** *012

PLITT, Virginia Ruth. ■ 23464 #051-07-2008 *012

PLOTNICK, Stephen Edward. 3500 VIRGINIA BEACH BLVD, STE 300 23452 #024-05-1988 L1993 **RHU** *020 †20

PLUNKETT, Harry G, Jr. 4092 FOXWOOD DR, STE 101 23462 #051-04-1965 L1965 **EM FM** *071 †18,16

POLEY, J Rainer. 921 DOWNSHIRE CHASE 23452 #154-02-1956 L1978 **GE PD** *020 †55

PONCE, Juan Francisco. 4092 FOXWOOD DR, EMERG. PHSICIANS OF TIDEWA 23462 #028-02-1975 L1978 **EM** *020 †16

PONCE, Pamela Ann. ■ 23452 #028-02-1977 L1979 **PD** *071 †55

POSADA, Jaime. ■ 23456 #264-03-1949 L1992 **IM GE** *071

POUDEL, Atit. ■ 23462 #672-04-2003 *100

POULIN, Ronald Francis. 5741 CLEVELAND ST, STE 300 23462 #024-05-1974 L1996 **HEM ON** *020 †20

POWELL, Ian David. ■ 23454 #012-05-2005 L2007 **GS** *020

PRAKALAPAKORN, Daranee. ■ 23455 #891-01-1969 L1975 **PD GP** *020 †55

PRAKALAPAKORN, Yanyong. ■ 23455 #891-01-1969 L1976 **GP GS** *071

PRIEUR, Tara Hollen. 933 FIRST COLONIAL RD, STE 112 23454 #051-07-1998 L1998 **FM** *020 †55

PUGACH, Neil Lewis. 780 LYNNHAVEN PKWY STE 285 23452 #024-05-1980 L1995 **N** *020 †75

PYLE, Pamela Gail. 5320 PROVIDENCE RD, STE 100 23464 #051-07-1984 L1988 **OBG** *020 †30

QURESHI, Nabeel Asif. ■ 23456 #051-07-2008 *012

QURESHY, Hammad Ahmad. 1300 DIAMOND SPRINGS RD, STE 400 23455 #704-02-1995 L2007 **PCC IM** *020 †20

RACK, Robert Vincent. ■ 23452 #010-02-1958 L1983 **PD** *071 †55

RADIN, Robert Chas. 3386 HOLLAND RD STE 202 23452 #038-41-1977 L1979 **AI IM** *020 †20,03

RAHMAN, Ahmed Abdul. 1020 INDEPENDENC BLVD #308 23455 #495-31-1972 L1982 **GS VS** *020 †85

RAHMAN, Syed Habeebur. 4480 HOLLAND OFFICE PARK, STE 225 23452 #495-09-1973 L1985 **N** *020 †75

RAHNEMA, Mansur. 1856 COLONIAL MEDICAL CT 23454 #407-16-1956 L1970 **GS** *020 †85

RAJAB, Hussein A.. ■ 23462 #797-04-1997 L2004 **IM** *020 †20

RAJURKAR, Suman M. ■ 23455 #495-21-1961 L1985 **PTH** *075

RAMISCAL, Erlinda O R. ■ 23462 #748-01-1967 L1972 **PD** *020

RAMPONA, Douglas Mercer. 848 FIRST COLONIAL RD 23451 #048-04-1968 L1969 **OPH** *020 †35

RANDHAWA, Niti K. 816 INDEPENDENCE BLVD, STE 100 23455 #048-13-1996 L2001 **FM** *020 †20

RAO, Bhaskar G. 1147 INDEPENDENCE BLVD 23455 #495-16-1966 L1972 **ON HEM** *020 †20

RAO, Jyoti. 1147 INDEPENDENCE BLVD 23455 #496-07-1972 L1974 **FM** *020 †18

RASSOOL, Mohammad. 665 NEWTOWN RD, STE 114 23462 #517-03-1966 L1985 **IM** *020 †20

RAWLES, James White, Jr. 1101 FIRST COLONIAL RD, STE 300 23454 #051-04-1980 L1983 **GE IM** *020 †20

RAWLS, Harvey P. ■ 23451 #051-04-1952 L1952 **U** *071 †95

RAWLS, Harvey P, Jr. 4092 FOXWOOD DR, STE 101 23462 #051-07-1984 L1986 **EM** *020 †16

RAYMUNDO, Marivic C. 1212 LAKE JAMES DR, STE C 23464 #748-01-1985 L2001 **PD** *020 †55

RAZAVI, Ashkon. ■ 23454 #051-04-2008 *012

REAL, Jennifer Swisher. ■ 23453 #035-46-2003 L2007 **IM** *100 †20

RECTOR, Geo Harry Morris. 23454 #010-02-1948 L1953 **AN** *071 †05

REDFORD, Ramon N, Jr. 1060 FIRST COLONIAL RD 23454 #051-04-1961 L1961 **GYN** *071 †30

REED, Jennifer Masden. ■ 23454 #051-04-2001 L2001 **GS** *020 †85

REINGOLD, William N. 512 S INDEPENDENCE BLVD 23452 #051-01-1952 L1952 **OBG** *020 †30

REKANT, Evan Matthew. 409 CROATAN HILLS DR 23451 #041-02-1996 L1996 **EM** *020 †16

RENNER, Debra Ann. 1975 GLENN MITCHELL DR, STE 302 23456 #035-06-1991 L2006 **FM CLP** *062 †50,18

RHEE, Kyung Uk. 3500 VIRGINIA BEACH BLVD, LITTLE NECK TOWERS STE 303 23452 #583-02-1962 L1968 **GP** *020

RIDDICK, Joseph Henry, Jr. ■ 23451 #036-07-1962 L1964 **PTH OS** *071 †50

RIEDLER, John F. 780 LYNNHAVEN PKWY 23452 #030-05-1978 L1996 **P CHP** *020 †75

RING, Susan Elizabeth. 1004 FIRST COLONIAL RD, STE 102 23454 #051-07-1985 L1986 **IM** *020 †20

RIPOLL, Ignacio. 6025 PROVIDENCE RD, # 110 23464 #264-04-1971 L1975 **PUD CCM** *020 †20

ROBBINS, Joseph Allen. 1708 OLD DONATION PKWY, CARDIOVASCULAR ASSOCIATES 23454 #051-01-1977 L1980 **CD IM** *020 †20

ROBERTS, Anne Bryant. ■ 23455 #023-12-2005 **FM** *020

ROBERTS, Edward Franklin. 2020 S INDEPENDENCE BLVD, STE 5 23453 #051-07-1983 L1991 **OBG** *020 †30

ROBERTSON, Robert John. 935 FIRST COLONIAL RD, STE B 23454 #051-04-1956 L1956 **CD IM** *071

ROBICHAUD, Marie Ryhanych. 1380 TUSCANY DR, PRINCESS ANNE FAMILY PRACT 23456 #051-01-1994 L1994 **FM** *020 †20

RODEBAUGH, Justin Matthew. ■ 23455 #051-07-2008 *012

RODRIGUEZ, Linda P. 1453 KEMPSVILLE RD STE 103 23464 #748-07-1965 L1981 **PD PDC** *020 †55

ROGERS, Stacey Jean. 1950 GLENN MITCHELL DR 23456 #050-02-1993 L2003 **OBG** *020 †30

ROLL, Walter Arthur, Jr. 800 INDEPENDENCE BLVD, SENARA BAYSIDE HOSPITAL 23455 #033-05-1978 L1994 **IM** *020 †20

ROMERO, Aleli G. 6009 PROVIDENCE RD 23464 #748-01-1962 L1975 **FM** *020

ROMERO, Cynthia Corrine. 6009 PROVIDENCE RD 23464 #051-07-1993 L1994 **FM** *020 †18

ROMERO, Daniel Ochangco. ■ 23453 #748-08-1960 L1976 **GP** *071

ROSA, Miguel Angel. 134 BUSINESS PARK DR 23462 #024-05-1980 L1990 **AN PD** *020 †05

ROSE, Joan Helena. 233 BUSINESS PARK DR, STE 100 23462 #051-07-1981 L1984 **HS** *020 †85

ROSE, Meredith Bruce. 5320 PROVIDENCE RD, PROVIDENCE ROAD FAMILY PRA 23464 #051-04-1979 L1979 **FM** *020 †18

ROSENBLUM, Richard Scott. 2829 SHORE DR, STE 200 23451 #051-04-1992 L2000 **PS** *020 †45,65

ROSSO, Ritchie Oliver. 4092 FOXWOOD DR, STE 101 23462 #051-04-1974 L1975 **EM** *020 †18,16

ROURE, Rafael A. ■ 23454 #847-04-1962 L1988 **FM IM** *020

ROUSSIS, Vasilios. ■ 23454 #418-01-1965 L1985 **IM** *020

ROY, Kanak Ratan. 2020 S INDEPENDENCE BLVD, FAMILY & INTERNAL MEDICAL 23453 #495-38-1966 L1981 **FM IM** *020 †18

ROYSTER, Henry Page. ■ 23451 #051-04-1948 L1948 **GS** *071 †85

RUBENSTEIN, Brian Lee. 4092 FOXWOOD DR, STE 101 23462 #041-15-1998 L2002 **EM** *020 †16

RUBINO, Mary Catherine. 5486 INDIAN RIVER RD, PATIENT FIRST INDIAN 23464 #051-07-2002 L2002 **FM** *100 †18

RUDOLPH, William Garry. ■ 23454 #023-01-1983 L1986 **CRS** *062 †70

RUDOLPH, William Garth. 1080 FIRST COLONIAL RD, ROAD, STE#200 23454 #005-02-1995 L2007 **CRS** *020 †85,10

RUETZEL, Craig H. 1080 FIRST COLONIAL RD, RD # 300 23454 #048-13-1988 L1992 **OBG** *020 †30

RUFFIN, Willcox. 5720 GREENWICH RD 23462 #051-01-1956 L1956 **PS** *071 †65

RUSS, Clarke. ■ 23451 #035-03-1959 L1966 **ORS** *071 †40

RYAL, Jennifer Lynn. ■ 23452 #039-01-2003 L2003 **OS** *100 †18,20

SACK, David Michael. 6632 INDIAN RIVER RD 23464 #041-02-1981 L2005 **OM UM** *030 †70

SADR, Negar Nikki. 828 HEALTHY WAY, STE 330 23462 #051-07-2003 L2003 **OBG** *020

SALCEDO, Jacqueline. 1020 INDEPENDENCE BLVD, STE 110 23455 #035-47-1991 L1997 **IM GE** *020

SALEMI, Mehdi. ■ 23462 #517-07-2001 L2007 **IM** *020 †20

SALSANO, Alessio Carmen. 5301 PROVIDENCE RD STE 90 23464 #033-06-1979 L1983 **IM** *020 †20

SALTER, Oscar. 138 S ROSEMONT RD, STE 215 23452 #011-02-1985 L1990 **AN** *020 †05

SALUMBIDES, Cristina J. 3745 HOLLAND RD, CHIMNEY HILL MED ASSOC 23452 #748-01-1979 L1983 **FM** *020 †18 ‡

SAMARAS, Thomas A. 1120 FIRST COLONIAL RD, STE 100 23454 #023-01-1982 L1983 **FM** *020 †18

SAMPLE, Malena Cynthea. 700 INDEPENDENCE CIR, STE 3A 23455 #036-01-2002 L2006 **OBG** *100

SAMUELS, Garfield Hue. ■ 23456 #305-01-2002 L2006 **PCC** *100 †20
SANDFORT, Marni Aline. ■ 23451 #010-01-1998 **PTH** *100
SANGIRAY, Hayri E. 1120 FIRST COLONIAL RD, STE 200 23454 #035-75-1998, ▲ L2004 **D** *020 †15
SANTIAGO, Arthur Cajucom. 4551 PROFESSIONAL CIR 23455 #748-07-1962 L1977 **AN** *071
SANTOS, Amelia L. 134 BUSINESS PARK DR, ATLANTIC ANESTHESIA 23462 #748-10-1968 L1974 **AN** *020
SARRETT, David Lee. 1181 FIRST COLONIAL RD 23454 #041-09-1959 L1959 **OBG** *020 †30
SAVERY, Susan Goese. 332 NEWTOWN RD, PATIENT FIRST NEWTON ROAD 23462 #026-04-2001 L2001 **FM** *020
SCANLAN, Paul Gardner. ■ 23451 #051-07-2008 *012
SCHECHNER, Stephen Alan. 321 EDWIN DR STE 101, ATLANTIC SURGICAL ASSCS, P 23462 #051-04-1970 L1970 **GS** *020 †85
SCHEWE, William J. ■ 23454 #010-01-1943 L1952 **IM** *071
SCHICK, Eduardo Jorge. 3386 HOLLAND RD, STE 105 23452 #132-04-1951 L1962 **OBG** *020 †30
SCHINDERLE, David Brian. 138 S ROSEMONT RD, STE 215 23452 #025-12-1997 L2002 **AN** *020 †05 ‡
SCHINDLER, Kimberly Miche. ■ 23464 #051-07-2005 L2005 **PD** *012
SCHNEIDER, Daniel Scott. 2117 MCCOMAS WAY, STE 105 23456 #030-06-1979 L1991 **PDC PD** *020 †55
SCHOENFELD, Renee Binder. 297 INDEPENDENCE BLVD, PEMBROKE SIX STE 126 23462 #016-11-1974 L1975 **CHP R** *020
SCHREIBER, Douglas Ray. 1020 INDEPENDENC BLVD #306 23455 #025-07-1975 L1982 **ORS HS** *020 †40
SCHREIBER, Mark Traudt. 780 LYNNHAVEN PKWY STE 400, ATLANTIC PSYCHIATRIC SVCS. 23452 #028-02-1975 L1978 **P** *020 †75
SCHREINER, Carol A. 2580 POTTERS RD 23454 #041-13-1963 L1981 **P** *020 †75
SCHUBERT, Eric Brian. 1200 INDEPENDENCE BLVD 23454 #051-04-1997 L2003 **NS** *020
SCHULWOLF, Lauren Beth. ■ 23451 #035-08-2003 L2006 **PD** *100 †55
SCHUSTER, Rudolf Franz. ■ 23452 #407-16-1952 L1956 **IM OM** *072
SCOTT, Margery B Atkins. 1120 FIRST COLONIAL RD, STE 200 23454 #047-07-1971 L1979 **D PTH** *020 †15
SCOTT, Thomas Henry, Jr. 816 INDEPENDENCE BLVD # 2B 23455 #047-07-1971 L1978 **PUD IM** *020 †20
SEAGULL, Fanya Nori. 1080 FIRST COLONIAL RD, STE 412 23454 #033-05-1997 L2000 **PD** *020 †55
SEEHERMAN, Robert S. ■ 23451 #041-09-1949 L1970 **FM IM** *071
SEELEY, Richard John. ■ 23452 #024-07-1956 L1987 **GP AM** *071 †70
SERWATKA, Linda Mae. 1120 FIRST COLONIAL RD, STE 200 23454 #048-13-1979 L1995 **D** *020 †15 ‡
SHAH, Chirag Nalinchandr. 5555 GREENWICH RD, STE 600 23462 #051-07-1991 L1992 **FM** *020 †18
SHAH, Hemang. 4480 HOLLAND OFFICE PARK, STE 225 23452 #495-76-1987 L1996 **N** *020 †75
SHAH, Kalyani Kandarp. 700 INDEPENDENCE CIR, STE 1D 23455 #495-89-1981 L1988 **FM PTH** *020
SHAH, Kandarp Krishnalal. 700 INDEPENDENCE BLVD, # 1D 23455 #495-23-1980 L1986 **GE IM** *040 †20
SHAH, Kiritkumar N. 100 CONSTITUTION DR, STE 217 23462 #495-23-1970 L1976 **PD** *020 †55
SHAPIRO, Alan Isaiah. ■ 23464 #003-01-1975 L1977 **REN GYN** *020 †30
SHARATH, Murali-Dharan C. 4532 BONNEY RD, STE C 23452 #495-59-1970 L1980 **AI IM** *020 †20
SHELTON, Aubrey L. ■ 23451 #051-01-1941 L1941 **FM** *071
SHEN, You-Jun. 1060 1ST COLONIAL RD 23454 #243-16-1984 L2006 **PCP** *020 †50
SHENOUDA, Teresa Andrea. ■ 23455 #038-43-2000 L2001 **OPH** *100 †35
SHERWOOD, Janice Costilow. 933 FIRST COLONIAL RD, STE 100 23454 #051-07-1991 L1994 **RHU IM** *020
SHETTY, Udaya Kumar. 1745 CAMELOT DR, STE 200 23454 #495-35-1979 L1991 **CHP P** *020 †55
SHEWAN, Anne Margaret. 4624 PEMBROKE BLVD, STE 101 23455 #051-01-1990 L1993 **PD** *020 †55
SHIMABUKURO, Lynn Matsu. 2859 VIRGINIA BEACH BLVD, LITTLE NECK MEDICAL ASSOCI 23452 #051-07-1982 L1986 **IM PD** *020 †20,55
SHOAIBI, Ahmad. ■ 23451 #517-01-1956 L1967 **PD PHP** *020 †55
SHULMISTER, David. 4092 FOXWOOD DR, STE 101 23462 #027-01-1983 L1985 **EM** *020 †16
SHUR-ALLEN, Lyubov B. 1368 GREAT NECK VLG 23454 #913-64-1992 L1998 **FM** *020 †18
SIEGEL, Gary Richard. 933 FIRST COLONIAL RD #100 23454 #051-04-1980 L1983 **RHU IM** *020
SIEGEL, Jack Lawrence. 5716 CLEVELAND ST, STE 200 23462 #035-03-1986 L1988 **ORS OSM** *020 †40
SIEGEL, Lewis Howard. ■ 23451 #051-04-1989 L1990 **EM** *020 †16
SIEGFRIED, Brett Harris. 1060 FIRST COLONIAL RD, PEDIATRIX MEDICAL GROUP P. 23454 #041-12-1998 L2004 **PD NPM** *020 †55
SIMMONS, Monique Nichole. 1975 GLENN MITCHELL DR, STE 202 23456 #051-07-2001 L2004 **OBG** *020 †30
SINGH, Amar Jit. 1745 CAMELOT DR, STE 200 23454 #495-51-1976 L1983 **P** *020 †75
SINGH, Charanjit P. 700 INDEPENDENCE CIR 23455 #495-03-1975 1980 **P** *020
SINGH, Parbhur. 1020 INDEPENDENCE BLVD, NO 213B 23455 #495-03-1972 L1979 **OPH** *020 †35
SINGLETON, Clay Wendell. ■ 23462 #047-07-2003 L2003 **PM** *020
SINGSON, Florisa. 4551 PROFESSIONAL CIR, SUITE 201 ICA BUILDING 23455 #748-01-1982 L1994 **FM** *020 †18 ‡
SINTHUSEK, Hatai Jan. ■ 23451 #036-05-2001 L2001 **IM** *100
SIVAKUMAR, Vanitha Seetha. ■ 23464 #055-01-2008 *012
SKENDERIS, Basil Spiros. 1120 FIRST COLONIAL RD, STE 203 23454 #051-01-1988 L1998 **GS SO** *020 †85
SKORUPA, Amy Michelle. ■ 23452 #051-04-2000 L2007 **HO** *020 †20
SMITH, Howard Clayton, Jr. 1120 FIRST COLONIAL RD, STE 100 23454 #051-01-1979 L1980 **FM** *020 †18
SMITH, Joseph Paul. ■ 23456 #051-01-1955 L1955 **GP** *071
SMITH, Robert Lawrence. 1060 1ST COLONIAL RD 23454 #051-01-1962 L1962 **PTH PCP** *071 †50
SNIPES, Ramona S. 4092 FOXWOOD DR, STE 101 23462 #005-12-1999 L2003 **EM** *020 †16
SNYDERS, Glenn Chas. 1800 CAMELOT DR, STE 200 23454 #051-01-1982 L1986 **PD** *020 †55
SOORI, Mohammed K. ■ 23451 #913-01-1982 L2004 **P** *020 †75
SOTEROPOULOS, George C. 800 INDEPENDENCE BLVD 23455 #010-02-1976 L1977 **DR NR** *020 †80

SPAN, Kimberly Mary. ■ 23451 #051-07-2007 L2007 **IM** *012
SPECKHART, Michael Louis. ■ 23451 #036-05-2001 L2007 **IM** *020
SPERRY, Thomas Howard. 1024 FIRST COLONIAL RD, STE 102 23454 #051-04-1973 L1974 **FM** *071 †18
SPRAITZAR, Sarah Ruth. ■ 23462 #041-02-2007 L2007 **TY** *012
SPRINGER, Marianne Gail. 800 INDEPENDENCE BLVD 23455 #051-07-1983 L1986 **PD** *020 †55
SPRUIELL, Michael. 2020 S INDEPENDENCE BLVD, STE 5 23453 #047-07-1981 L1983 **OBG** *075 †30
SPULLER, Marc Edward. ■ 23455 #038-43-1979 L1982 **PD** *020 †55
STADTMAUER, Laurel Ann. 1744 SIR WILLIAM OSLER DR 23454 #035-46-1987 L2002 **OBG REN** *030 ‡
STALLINGS, William. 1120 FIRST COLONIAL RD, STE 100 23454 #051-01-1958 L1958 **FM** *071 †18
STARLING, Jay C. 933 FIRST COLONIAL RD, STE 105 23454 #023-01-1976 L1981 **OPH** *071 †35
ST CLAIR, Jesse Walton. 1708 OLD DONATION PKWY, CARDIOVASCULAR ASSOCIATES 23454 #041-02-1979 L1980 **CD** *020 †20
STEHLIK, John Mc Teer. 1200 FIRST COLONIAL RD # 2, THROAT LTD 23454 #041-02-1963 L1970 **OTO** *071 †45
STEIER, Howard Chas. 1004 FIRST COLONIAL RD, STE 102 23454 #035-20-1970 L1972 **IM** *020 †20
STEINBERG, Michael S. 1950 GLENN MITCHELL DR, STE 102 23456 #035-19-1970 L1982 **ON HO** *020 †20
STEPHENS, Mary L. ■ 23451 #051-01-1962 L1962 **FM PHP** *074
STERN, Kelly Luther. 3432 HOLLAND RD, PATIENT FIRST HOLLAND 23452 #010-01-1982 L1983 **FM** *020 †18
STEWART, Joan Rae. 1745 CAMELOT DR, STE 100 23454 #041-07-1981 L1984 **EM** *071
STICKLEY, Donna Elder. ■ 23454 #020-02-1988 L1990 **EM** *020 †16
STILLMAN, Barron H. 1821 OLD DONATION PKWY # 2 23454 #016-06-1958 L1965 **IM CD** *020 †20
STOCKWELL, David Hunt, III. 1101 FIRST COLONIAL RD, STE 300 23454 #035-20-1997 L2006 **GE** *020 †20
STOECKLEIN, Herbert Geo J. ■ 23451 #041-09-1943 L1949 **OS D** *071
STOKES, Gordon Kavanaugh. 397 LITTLE NECK RD, STE 100 23454 #041-02-1988 L1992 **GS** *020 †85
STOWELL, Jeremy Averill. 3500 VIRGINIA BEACH BLVD, STE 435 23452 #036-07-1967 L1970 **P ADM** *020 †75
STRASNICK, Victoria S. 933 FIRST COLONIAL RD, STE 112 23454 #048-04-1984 L1993 **PD** *020 †55
STRICKLEN, Rhaiannon. ■ 23464 #051-04-2007 L2007 **PD** *012
STROSAHL, Kurt Frederick. 1020 INDEPENDENCE BLVD, STE 102 23455 #041-13-1975 L2002 **CD IM** *020 †20
STROTMEYER, Pamela. 1060 FIRST COLONIAL RD 23454 #051-07-1977 L1980 **PD** *020 †55
STROUD, Stephen Briggs. 351 EDWIN DR, MULTISPECIALTY GROUP 23462 #051-04-1974 L1975 **FM** *020 †18
SUN, Tommy. 3396 HOLLAND RD STE 105, GREEN RUN FAMILY PRACTICE, 23452 #051-07-1979 L1981 **FM** *020 †18
SUYS, Sonia. ■ 23452 #165-04-1987 L2000 **GS** *020
SWINGLE, David Wayne. 2321 BAYVILLE RD 23455 #051-07-1981 L1991 **NS** *020 †25
TALREJA, Deepak Roshan. 1708 OLD DONATION PKWY, CARDIOVASCULAR ASSOCIATES 23454 #051-01-1997 L2004 **IC** *020 †20
TALREJA, Reena Roshan. 5320 PROVIDENCE RD, STE 100 23464 #047-05-1998 L2002 **OBG** *020 †30 ‡
TALREJA, Roshan S. 1805 COLONIAL MEDICAL CT 23454 #495-45-1967 L1974 **IM PHP** *020
TAN, James Hui Teck. ■ 23452 #005-12-1981 L2005 **FM MDM** *030 †18
TAN, Luke Y S. PO BOX 175, % DR LEE 23458 #748-08-1966 L1975 **P** *075
TAYLOR, Jack Borden. 4400 OCEAN FRONT AVE 23451 #036-07-1965 L1976 **CD** *071 †20
TAYLOR, Waller L, Jr. 1821 OLD DONATION PKWY 23454 #036-07-1963 L1966 **OPH** *020 †35
TEACHEY, William Swain. 1020 INDEPENDENCE BLVD, STE 313 23455 #036-01-1968 L1976 **OTO FPS** *020 †45
TENNANT, Bradley Franklin. 1120 FIRST COLONIAL RD, STE 100 23454 #051-04-1984 L1985 **FM** *020 †18 ‡
TERHAAR, Kenneth Albert. ■ 23462 #023-12-2001 L2002 **DR** *012
THOMAS, Brant Wayne. 1821 OLD DONATION PKWY, STE 4 23454 #051-04-1983 L1984 **FM** *020 †18
THOMAS, Edward Armistead. 1060 FIRST COLONIAL RD 23454 #051-04-1984 L1987 **IM CCM** *020 †20
THOMAS, Janelle Ann. 800 INDEPENDENCE BLVD 23455 #055-02-1998 L1998 **EM** *020 †16
THOMAS, Mariamma A. ■ 23454 #495-27-1956 L1957 **OBG END** *040 †20
THWEATT, Venita C Newby. 4452 CORPORATION LN, HEALTH, PEMBROOKE CORP CTR 23462 #036-01-1973 L1987 **PHP PD** *030
TIGNOR, Matthew Morgan. 923 FIRST COLONIL RD #1801 23454 #051-07-1976 L1978 **ID IM** *040 †20
TISDALE, Bradford W. 3745 HOLLAND RD, CHIMNEY HILL MEDICAL ASSOC 23452 #051-04-1981 L1982 **FM** *020 †18
TOLAND, Joseph. 5301 PROVIDENCE RD 23464 #539-04-1971 L1976 **PD** *020 †55
TOM, Eugene John. 1975 GLENN MITCHELL DR, STE 300 23456 #036-07-1995 L2006 **AN GS** *020 †05
TOMPKINS, Mary Jane. ■ 23455 #038-06-1959 L1965 **IM** *020 †20
TOROP, Andres Henry. 4668 PEMBROKE BLVD, STE 117 23455 #033-05-1992 L1998 **DR** *020 †80
TORRALBA, Apolinaris. 1300 DIAMOND SPRINGS RD, STE 400 23455 #748-01-1990 L2005 **IM** *020 †20
TRAN, Paul Hoa. ■ 23456 #051-07-2005 L2005 **GS** *012
TRANT, John Hill, III. ■ 23451 #036-07-1961 L1967 **OPH** *071 †35
TRAUGH, Cathy Hixenbaugh. 816 INDEPENDENCE BLVD, STE 100 23455 #055-01-1979 L1990 **FM** *020 †18
TROIANO, Raymond Gerard. 1060 FIRST COLONIAL RD 23454 #035-15-1973 L1977 **N** *030 †75
TROTMAN, Linda Ann. 308 HORACE AVE 23462 #051-07-1981 L1986 **FM** *020 †18
TSAO, Thomas K S. 780 LYNNHAVEN PKWY 23452 #041-09-1967 L1972 **P** *020 †75
TURNER, Philip. 700 INDEPENDENCE CIR, STE 3A 23455 #051-03-1971 L1974 **OBG OS** *071 †30
UDUAGHAN, Jacob Oritsenem. ■ 23454 #305-01-2005 L2005 **IM** *100
UNDERWOOD, Christina M. 1147 INDEPENDENCE BLVD, FAMILY MEDICAL PRACTITIONE 23455 #038-45-1994 L1999 **CHP** *020
UPADHYAY, Jyoti Jitendra. ■ 23451 #025-07-1994 L2007 **U** *020 †95
UTECHT, Lynn Marie. 1101 1ST COLONIAL RD, STE 200 23454 #051-07-1985 L1987 **D IM** *020 †15

■ = Address Information Privacy Protected

VALENTINE, Lawrence E. 2785 BROAD BAY RD 23451 #051-04-1963 L1963 **EM OM** *020 †16
VALENTINE, Richard Nelson. 800 INDEPENDENCE BLVD 23455 #025-07-1973 L1980 **OBG** *020 †30
VANDERVORT, Jay A. 1200 FIRST COLONIAL RD, STE 202 23454 #010-02-1998 L1999 **CS OMF** *020
VAUGHAN, Ingrid Irene. ■ 23454 #051-07-1987 L1991 **AN** *020 †05
VAZQUEZ, Ana Hilda. 1821 OLD DONATION PKWY, STE 4 23454 #024-07-1984 L1995 **FM PD** *020 †18
VENDETTI, Curtis Sergio. 1240 PERIMETER PKWY, STE 401 23454 #021-05-1995 L2004 **GS** *020
VENKATESAN, Saileela. 1020 INDEPENDENCE BLVD, STE 105 23455 #495-09-1969 L1975 **PD** *020 †55
VENNER, Robert B. ■ 23456 #030-05-1941 L1946 **GP** *071
VERFURTH, Francis T. 134 BUSINESS PARK DR, ATLANTIC ANESTHESIA 23462 #051-01-1985 L1991 **AN IM** *020 †20,05
VILLASECA, Miriam M. ■ 23456 #748-01-1964 **PD** *071
VINSON, Charlie Stephen. 1800 CAMELOT DR STE 200 23454 #045-01-1982 L1985 **PD** *020 †55
VIZOLLI, Thomas Leonard, Jr. 4092 FOXWOOD DR, STE 101 23462 #030-06-1998 L1998 **EM** *020 †16
VOGEL, Ruth. 4624 PEMBROKE BLVD, STE 101 23455 #550-01-1971 L1986 **PD PHO** *020 †55
VOSHELL, Thos Hammersley. ■ 23452 #041-02-1955 L1969 **GP** *072
VRETAKIS, George Nicholas. 138 S ROSEMONT RD, STE 215 23452 #035-19-1987 L1992 **AN** *020 †05
WADDELL, David Thos. 1000 1ST COLONIAL RD, STE 101 23454 #051-07-1985 L1988 **FM** *020 †18 ‡
WADDELL, Robert Wayne. ■ 23454 #051-04-1960 L1960 **ORS** *071 †40
WADSWORTH, Michele R. 2117 MCCOMAS WAY, STE 103 23456 #051-07-1991 L1993 **PD PEM** *020 †55
WAGENER, Gebhard. ■ 23451 #409-33-1993 **AN** *020 †05
WAGNER, Thomas Watts. 4092 FOXWOOD DR, STE 101 23462 #051-07-1988 L1991 **EM** *020 †16
WAITEKUS, John Raymond. 1380 TUSCANY DR, PRINCESS ANNE FAMILY PRACT 23456 #051-07-1998 L1998 **FM** *020 †18
WALLACE, Duncan Saron. ■ 23455 #007-02-1962 L1971 **P CHP** *071 †75
WALSH-WEINBERG, Howard N. 2859 VIRGINIA BEACH BLVD, LITTLE NECK MEDICAL ASSOCI 23452 #035-03-1976 L1984 **FM** *020 †18
WANG, Lina. 1008 FIRST COLONIAL RD, STE 101 23454 #243-36-1985 L2005 **N** *100 †75
WARDEN, Steven Scott. 1004 FIRST COLONIAL RD, STE 101 23454 #010-01-1975 L1979 **U** *020 †95
WARDEN, William Budd. 2017 PLEASURE HOUSE RD 23455 #010-01-1965 L1966 **FM** *020 †18
WARREN, David Lester. ■ 23451 #024-07-1948 L1981 **IM OM** *071 †20
WARSOF, Steven Lester. 1080 FIRST COLONIAL RD, TIDEWATER PERINATAL CENTER 23454 #008-01-1977 L1979 **MFM OBG** *020 †30
WARTH, Gregory James. 1860 COLONIAL MED CT 23454 #038-40-1973 L1976 **IM HOS** *020 †20
WATERBURY, Rex Gardner. 828 HEALTHY WAY, STE 330 23462 #036-05-1983 L1989 **OBG** *020 †30
WATSON, Tiffany Yvonne. ■ 23462 #028-46-2006 L2006 **IM** *012
WATTERS, John Albert, Jr. ■ 23452 #048-04-1965 L1976 **OS OPH** *030 †35
WEBB, Michael Andre. 6632 INDIAN RIVER RD 23464 #041-12-1986 L1989 **GS** *020
WEISS, Denton Dean. 272 BENDIX RD STE 100, CONVERGENCE CENTER III 23452 #056-06-1988 L2000 **PS HNS** *020 †45,65
WENTWORTH, Heather Yeiser. 4092 FOXWOOD DR, STE 101 23462 #051-07-1996 L2000 **EM** *020 †16
WENZEL, Paul David. 816 INDEPENDENCE BLVD, STE 100 23455 #051-01-1985 L1987 **FM** *020 †16
WERWATH, David Lee. 1788 REPUBLIC RD, STE 400 23454 #056-06-1981 L1982 **EM** *020 †16
WEST, Richard Duane. 840 FIRST COLONIAL RD, STE 102 23451 #041-01-1965 L1972 **GS** *020 †85
WESTON, Margrethe E. ■ 23464 #041-02-2002 L2003 **EM** *012
WETZLER-BERLIN, Samantha. ■ 23451 #051-04-1995 L1995 **PTH** *020 †50
WHELAN, Thomas Vincent. 1020 INDEPENDENCE BLVD, STE 211 23455 #038-41-1979 L1980 **NEP IM** *020 †20 ‡
WHITAKER, Guy D, III. 800 INDEPENDENCE BLVD, SMG ANESTHESIA - SBH 23455 #051-07-1982 L1989 **AN** *020 †05
WHITE, Kevin Thomas. 1101 FIRST COLONIAL RD, STE 300 23454 #035-47-1998 L2004 **GE** *020 †20
WHITE, Rolfe Downing. 1137 FIRST COLONIAL RD 23454 #051-04-1975 L1979 **GYN U** *020 †30 ‡
WHITEHEAD, William Odell. ■ 23455 #024-07-1961 L1968 **AM OPH** *071
WHITNEY, Hugh Raymond H. 800 INDEPENDENCE BLVD 23455 #539-06-1965 L1973 **AN** *071 †05
WICK, Nancy Ann. 200 GRAYSON RD, STE 101 23462 #051-04-1992 L2007 **PD** *020 †55
WILKES, Charles A. 828 HEALTHY WAY, STE 330 23462 #023-01-1980 L1981 **OBG REN** *020 †30 ‡
WILLIAMS, Frederick M. ■ 23451 #051-04-1949 L1949 **OPH** *020
WILLIAMS, Harry Thos. 2859 VIRGINIA BEACH BLVD, LITTLE NECK MEDICAL ASSOCI 23452 #041-09-1989 L1991 **FM** *020 †18
WILLIAMS, Janice Denise. 1405 PEBBLEBROOK WAY, AFTER 9/30/06 I RETIRE FRO 23464 #035-06-1977 L2002 **OBG OS** *071 †30
WILSON, Eugene Kramer, III. ■ 23464 #023-12-2002 L2003 **FP** *012
WILSON, James Andrew. 4092 FOXWOOD DR, STE 101 23462 #016-02-1994 L2001 **EM** *020 †16
WINGARD, Daren Murray. 1147 INDEPENDENCE BLVD 23455 #035-15-1995 L1996 **PM** *020 †60
WINKES, Adeline. 2100 LYNNHAVEN PKWY, TRI-CARE PRIME, KONIKOFF B 23456 #043-01-1998 L2007 **PD** *020 †55
WINTERS, Mark Richard. 351 EDWIN DR, MULTISPECIALTY GROUP 23462 #047-05-1980 L1981 **FM** *020 †18
WITTENBERG, Samuel Harris. 2859 VIRGINIA BEACH BLVD 23452 #041-01-1979 L1987 **FM** *040 †18
WOLF, Monford Anthony. 1975 GLENN MITCHELL DR, STE 300 23456 #023-01-1988 L2007 **AN** *020 †05
WOLFF, Kirsten Lyn. ■ 23456 #050-02-1993 L1998 **OBG** *020 †30
WOLFORD, Keith Harlow. ■ 23471 #051-04-1963 L1963 **EM FM** *072 †16,18
WOLOY, Eleanora Marie. ■ 23455 #025-01-1957 L1968 **PYA P** *020

WONG, George Sonny. 2017 PLEASURE HOUSE RD 23455 #051-04-1978 L1979 **FM** *020 †18
WOODARD, Laura Lee Love. ■ 23451 #051-01-1991 L1995 **EM** *020 †16
WOODARD, Robert Mason. 1120 FIRST COLONIAL RD #10 23454 #051-04-1990 L1995 **FM** *020 †18
WOODFORD, Renee Aline. 1060 FIRST COLONIL RD #102, ATLANTIC ANESTHESIA INC 23454 #055-01-1985 L1986 **AN PME** *020 †05
WOODHOUSE, Jessie Elnora. ■ 23452 #010-03-1978 L1981 **P** *020 †75
WOODS, David Wayne. 816 INDEPENDENCE BLVD, STE 100 23455 #021-06-1981 L1981 **FM** *020 †18
WOOLLETT, Ian Francis. 1708 OLD DONATION PKWY, CARDIOVASCULAR ASSOCIATES 23454 #007-02-1996 L2000 **CD** *020 †20
WRIGHT, Tracy Beth. 1975 GLENN MITCHELL DR, STE 202 23456 #051-01-1991 L1996 **OBG** *020 †30
WRUBEL, Chris Jos. 1080 FIRST COLONIAL RD, STE 412 23454 #051-01-1991 L1998 **PD** *020 †55
WYLES, Ronald Jos. 1200 FIRST COLONL RD #200M 23454 #038-06-1963 L1969 **D** *071 †15
YARWOOD, Julita Andrea. ■ 23462 #012-21-2008 *012
YATES, Gary Robt. 3268 STAPLEFORD CHASE 23452 #048-14-1981 L1982 **FM** *020 †18
YEH, Betty P Y. 1020 INDEPENDENCE BLVD, STE 211 23455 #051-04-1969 L1969 **NEP** *071 †20
YETTER, William Albert. 780 LYNNHAVEN PKWY 23452 #308-11-1983 L1987 **P PYG** *020 †75
YODER, Eric Monroe. ■ 23451 #036-07-1978 L2006 **FM EM** *020 †18
YOO, Hee Dong. 134 BUSINESS PARK DR, ATLANTIC ANESTHESIA, INC. 23462 #583-03-1967 L1977 **AN** *020 †05
YOUNG, Winfield Anthony. 1212 LAKE JAMES DR STE C 23464 #035-48-1984 L1986 **PD** *020 †55 ‡
YUE, Charles Chunghyup. 138 S ROSEMONT RD, STE 215 23452 #036-07-1991 L2005 **AN** *020 †05
ZAMZAM, Nancy Salih. 1181 FIRST COLONIAL RD, - SUI 23454 #305-01-2000 L2004 **OBG** *020
ZARATE, Jorge Mauricio. 6025 PROVIDENCE RD, # 110 23464 #264-11-1990 L1994 **FM** *020 †18
ZHANG, Da. ■ 23464 #243-73-1985 L2004 **FM** *020 †18
ZUNIGA, Basilio Domingo. ■ 23452 #748-07-1955 **GP GS** *020
ZUNIGA, Dorcas Asercion. 4660A HAYGOOD RD 23455 #051-07-1986 L1989 **FM** *020 †18
ZWEIFLER, Richard Marc. 816 INDEPENDENCE BLVD, STE 2H 23455 #021-01-1990 L2008 **N VN** *050 †75

WARE NECK – GLOUCESTER

HEINIG, Charles Frederick. ■ 23178 #035-15-1955 L1961 **ORS OS** *071 †40
TABB, Waller Crockett. PO BOX 178, 6102 WARE NECK RD 23178 #051-01-1959 L1959 **A PUD** *071 †03,20

WARM SPRINGS – BATH

CHESNUT, John Letcher. STAR RT A 420 24484 #047-06-1938 L1943 **IM** *072

WARRENTON – FAUQUIER

ABRAMS, Jeffrey Robt. 406 HOSPITAL DR 20186 #023-01-1986 L1995 **NEP IM** *020 †20
ALLEN, Benjamin Franklin. 500 HOSPITAL DR 20186 #024-07-1974 L1979 **ORS** *020 †40
ALLISON, David W. 384 HOSPITAL DR 20186 #422-01-1994 L2002 **PS** *020 †85,65
AMSTER, Michael Samuel. 559 FROST AVE, STE 101 20186 #016-11-1999 L1999 **PD** *020 †55
ANSA, Evelyn Maureen. 500 HOSPITAL DR, FAUQUIER HOSPITAL 20186 #412-02-1990 L2007 **AN** *020 †05
ARNSTINE, Kimberly Sara. 493 BLACKWELL RD, STE 202 20186 #038-41-1994 L1999 **FM** *020 †18
ARULTHIRUMARAN, Jeyaraman. 400 HOSPITAL DR, STE C 20186 #495-95-1991 L1996 **IMG** *020 †20
BANSON, Felice Laurea. 500 HOSPITAL DR 20186 #024-16-1998 L2004 **GE IM** *020 †20
BELL, Jeffrey Walton. 428 HOSPITAL DR 20186 #038-40-1989 L1993 **OBG** *020 †30
BORSODY, Frank J. 20187 #051-01-1960 L1960 **IM** *071
BROWN, Christopher Jos. 52 W SHIRLEY AVE 20186 #010-02-1983 L1986 **ORS OSM** *020 †40
BROWN, Joseph Adam. 432 HOSPITAL DR, DRS FARR WAMPLER HENSON 20186 #051-04-2001 L2001 **GS** *020 †85
BUNCH, John D, III. 500 HOSPITAL DR 20186 #045-01-1982 L1986 **FM EM** *075
CAMPBELL, Gina Elizabeth. 428 HOSPITAL DR, THE WOMEN'S GROUP 20186 #020-02-1999 L2007 **OBG** *020
CHALMETA, Diana. 20 ROCK POINTE LN 20186 #051-04-1995 L1995 **MPD** *020 †20,55
CHANDER, Nivedita. 406 HOSPITAL DR 20186 #024-07-1994 L2000 **NEP** *020 †20
CHANG, Christopher Yongsu. 550 HOSPITAL DR, FAQUIER ENT. CONSULTANTS 20186 #008-01-2000 L2004 **OTO A** *020 †45
CHHAY, Sinath. 500 HOSPITAL DR, FAUQUIER HOSPITAL 20186 #305-01-2001 L2005 **AN** *020 †05
CHIENKU, Constantine N. 45 N HILL DR, STE 202 20186 #217-01-1994 L2000 **PD** *020 †55
CHUN, Lorraine. 253 VETERANS DR 20186 #005-14-1996 L2007 **OBG** *020 †30
CONNOLLY, Christopher P. 528 WATERLOO RD 20186 #035-09-1996 L1999 **IM** *020 †20
COUK, David Edgar. 328 HOSPITAL DR 20186 #051-04-1963 L1963 **ORS** *071 †40
DANIEL, Linda E High. 500 HOSPITAL DR 20186 #030-05-1968 L1970 **DR** *071 †80 ‡
DART, Robert Cromwell. 52 W SHIRLEY AVE 20186 #021-05-1976 L1983 **ORS** *020 †40
DATTA, Nimai Chandra. 220 CULPEPER ST, FAUQUIER PROFESSIONAL BUIL 20186 #495-38-1958 L1974 **U TRS** *071
DAVID, Joseph Paul. 419 HOLIDAY CT, # 100 20186 #023-01-1989 L1990 **IM** *020 †20
DESAMOURS, Claudine. 500 HOSPITAL DR 20186 #396-19-1995 L2004 **AN** *020 ‡
DOUGHERTY, Cynthia A. 432 HOSPITAL DR, DRS FARR WAMPLER HENSON 20186 #038-43-1992 L1997 **GS** *020 †85
DRAKE, Le Earle Bobo. ■ 20186 #004-01-1946 L1954 **GS** *071
DUNN, Marianina Domingo. 35 HORNER ST STE 200 20186 #051-07-1999 L2000 **P** *020 †75
EGAN METZING, Christine. 528 WATERLOO RD 20186 #035-09-1987 L1992 **IM** *020 †20
EVANS, David Christian. 493 BLACKWELL RD, STE 202 20186 #051-04-1990 L1991 **FM** *020 †18
FARBER, Renee Carisio. 253 VETERANS DR, STE 210 20186 #012-05-1997 L2001 **OBG** *020 †30
FINKEL, Lawrence. 360 CHURCH ST 20186 #035-47-1982 L2000 **D DMP** *020 †50,15

GADDE, Jyothi. 493 BLACKWELL RD STE 305 20186 #495-65-1978 L1997 **AI IM** *020 †20,03
GARRETSON, Ralph Bonner. 52 W SHIRLEY AVE 20186 #028-02-1996 L2002 **ORS** *020 †40
GOHEEN, Susanna Michelson. 528 WATERLOO RD 20186 #048-04-2001 L2005 **MPD** *020 †20,55
GOLUB, Gregory Scott. 493 BLACKWELL RD STE 2, STE 202 20186 #010-02-1999 L2000 **FM** *020 †18
HELLEMS, Harper Keith, Jr. 7360 BEAR WALLOW DR 20186 #051-01-1966 L1966 **R** *071 †80
HENSON, Kenneth Irvin. 432 HOSPITAL DR, DRS FARR WAMPLER HENSON 20186 #051-04-1988 L1993 **GS** *020 †85
HOGGE, Charles Carson. 388 HOSPITAL DR 20186 #051-04-1985 L1989 **OPH** *020 †35
JAKUM, Joshua Adam. 20 ROCK POINTE LN 20186 #012-05-1998 L2003 **PD** *020 †55
JEFFRIES, Margaret N. 45 N HILL DR STE 2 20186 #051-04-1982 L1984 **PD** *020 †55
JUANPERE, Maria Eugenia. 20 ROCK POINTE LN 20186 #024-05-1994 L1996 **PD** *020 †55
KATCHER, Daniel. 400 HOSPITAL DR, STE C 20186 #050-02-1972 L1975 **ON HEM** *020 †20
KEENAN, Grace Lillian. 528 WATERLOO RD 20186 #063-01-1985 L1987 **IM** *030 †20
KILYK, Toni C. 210 W SHIRLEY AVE 20186 #032-01-1990 L1992 **FM** *020 †18
KIM, David. 52 W SHIRLEY AVE 20186 #033-05-1998 L2003 **PM** *020 †60
KORNETSKY, Kenneth Mark. 406 HOSPITAL DR 20186 #024-16-1974 L1978 **NEP IM** *071 †20
KRASKE, Gerhard Karl. 493 BLACKWELL RD, STE 201 20186 #010-01-1990 L2006 **IM AI** *020 †20
KROFCHECK, Joseph Lee. 4535 DEN HAAG RD 20187 #005-06-1958 L2002 **P PFP** *062
KULA, Alisan Gordon. 400 HOSPITAL DR, STE C 20186 #010-01-1990 L1999 **HO** *020 †20
LARSEN, Kenneth T, Jr. 500 HOSPITAL DR, LAUQUIER HOSPITAL 20186 #010-02-1970 L1971 **EM** *020 †16
LEE, Jae Young. 493 BLACKWELL RD STE 201, PIEDMONT INTERNAL MEDICINE 20186 #051-07-1994 L2001 **IM** *020 †20
LIN, Michael Tsui. 400A HOSPITAL DR, FAUQUIER FAMILY PRACTICE, 20186 #051-04-1998 L1998 **FM** *020 †18
LIN, Robert Tzu-Jun. 555 HOSPITAL DR 20186 #023-01-1998 L2001 **IM** *020 †20
LLOYD, Samuel Jos. 550 HOSPITAL DR 20186 #023-07-1968 L1975 **GYN** *020 †30
MAGUIRE, Raymond Charles. ■ 20188 #010-02-1962 L1967 **PTH NP** *071 †50
MANWARING, John Laurence. 550 HOSPITAL DR 20186 #051-01-1968 L1968 **OTO** *071 †45
MAOURY, Demetrius Stanley. 493 BLACKWELL RD, STE 201 20186 #051-01-1993 L1996 **IM** *020 †20
MARPU, Neelima Reddy. 528 WATERLOO RD 20186 #496-52-2001 L2006 **PM** *020 †20
MAURONER, Norman Lee, Jr. 555 HOSPITAL DR 20186 #021-06-1978 L1981 **IM** *020 †20
MAYBACH, Anita Marie. 381 STUYVESANT ST, STE 1 20186 #051-07-1998 L2001 **EM** *020 †16
MAYBACH, Eric Jon. 381 STUYVESANT ST, STE 1 20186 #026-04-1969 L1971 **FM EM** *020 †18
MC CARTHY, Kevin Chas. 493 BLACKWELL RD, STE 201 20186 #010-02-1992 L1995 **IM** *020 †20
MICHALSKI, Martha C. ■ 20186 #028-02-1978 L1984 **CHP** *020 †20
MORENO, Amy Kathleen. 493 BLACKWELL RD, STE 202 20186 #051-04-1999 L1999 **FM** *020 †18
MYERS, Thomas Edward. 428 HOSPITAL DR 20186 #055-01-1976 L1982 **OBG GYN** *020 †30
NEE, Robert. 406 HOSPITAL DR 20186 #041-13-1994 L2003 **NEP** *020 †20
ORLANDO, Michael M. 500 HOSPITAL DR, DEPT PATH 20186 #010-02-1973 L1974 **PTH CLP** *030 †50
PALUMBO, Patrick W. 75 W LEE HWY 20186 #010-02-1987 L1990 **GS FM** *020
PHILLIPS, David Anthony. 550 HOSPITAL DR 20186 #051-04-1992 L2002 **OTO HNS** *020 †45
PHILLIPS, Hannah. 528 WATERLOO RD, STE A-1 20186 #067-01-2004 L2007 **FM** *100 †18
PITTS, Suzanne Martel. 35 HORNER ST, STE 110 20186 #010-01-1990 L1994 **P** *020 †75
RAMSER, James Richard, Jr. 52 W SHIRLEY AVE 20186 #051-04-1987 L1990 **ORS OFA** *020 †40
REITER, Stephen Arthur. 340 HOSPITAL DR 20186 #016-11-1969 L1985 **P** *020 †75
RHAMES, Matthew Patrick. 6244 BRIGHTON CT 20187 #051-07-1998 L2001 **EM** *020 †16
RINGHOLZ, George M. 384 HOSPITAL DR, RIVER OAKS NEUROLOGY, LLC 20186 #048-04-1996 L2006 **N** *020 †75
SAMUEL, Lynn Harriet. 500 HOSPITAL DR 20186 #051-04-1988 L1989 **PTH GS** *020 †50
SEAL, Charles Nathaniel. 52 W SHIRLEY AVE 20186 #036-05-2001 L2007 **ORS OSS** *100
SHERMAN, Lisa Decossy. 493 BLACKWELL RD STE 316, WARRENTON DERMATOLOGY PC 20186 #008-02-1988 L1994 **D** *020 †15
SILBERSIEPE, Heinz-Otto G. 500 HOSPITAL DR, DEPT ANES 20186 #407-30-1950 L1956 **AN** *020 †05
SIMPSON, William L, Jr. 382 HOSPITAL DR 20186 #051-01-1990 L1992 **IM** *020 †20
SNYDER, David Michael. 52 W SHIRLEY AVE, BLUE RIDGE ORTHOPAEDIC ASS 20186 #023-01-1967 L1974 **ORS** *020 †40
SONG, Tae Sup. ■ 20187 #583-02-1949 L1971 **IM HEM** *071
STEPHENSON, Larry L. 440 HOSPITAL DR 20186 #051-04-1977 L1981 **N** *020 †75
TELFER, Nancy. ■ 20188 #041-07-1956 L1986 **NM IM** *071 †28,20
TRACE, Amy Lynn. 493 BLACKWELL RD, STE 101 20186 #038-40-1997 L2001 **IM** *071 †20
TRAN, Anh Hoang. 10 N HILL DR, STE 1-1B 20186 #051-07-1991 L1995 **AN** *020 †05
VON ELTEN, Steven Walter. 493 BLACKWELL RD STE 202 20186 #051-04-1976 L1977 **FM EM** *020 †16,18
WAMPLER, Guy Benjamin. 432 HOSPITAL DR, DRS FARR WAMPLER HENSON 20186 #051-04-1986 L1990 **GS VS** *020 †85
WARD, Christopher Michael. 493 BLACKWELL RD STE 202 20186 #038-40-1997 L2001 **MPD** *020 †20,55
WILLIAMS, John Polk. 432 HOSPITAL DR, DRS FARR WAMPLER HENSON 20186 #036-01-1992 L1999 **GS VS** *020 †85
WISE, Jeffrey Jonathan. 52 W SHIRLEY AVE, BLUE RIDGE ORTHO ASSOC 20186 #023-01-1993 L1999 **ORS OSS** *020 †40

WARSAW – RICHMOND

CLEARY, Thomas Leo, III. ■ 22572 #038-43-2004 L2004 **EM** *020
DUNN, Alison Marie. 16 DELFAE DR 22572 #051-04-1996 L1999 **PD** *020 †55
DUNN, Richard Kindley. 16 DELFAE DR 22572 #051-04-1996 L1999 **FM** *020 †18
KING, John Norman. 22572 #051-04-1959 L1959 **GS** *071 †85
RAY, Hallie A. 52 CAMPUS DR, STE 152B 22572 #048-02-1982 L1983 **GP** *040
STRICKLAND, Sharon Renee. 16 DELFAE DR 22572 #055-01-2000 L2003 **PD** *020 †55
TITUS, Frederick Preston. ■ 22572 #035-08-1940 L1946 **GYN** *072 †30

WASHINGTON – RAPPAHANNOCK

RIFAAT, Monira K. PO BOX 490 22747 #330-03-1961 L1969 **CLP PTH** *020 †50

WATER VIEW – MIDDLESEX

MONCURE, William B. ROUTE 640, GENERAL DELIVERY 23180 #051-04-1949 L1949 **AN** *071

WATERFORD – LOUDOUN

BEAVER, William Thos. ■ 20197 #035-20-1958 L1969 **PA** *071
IBRANYI, Gustav L. PO BOX 319 20197 #473-01-1945 L1949 **FM GYN** *071

WAVERLY – SUSSEX

AUSTIN, Ramona Louise. 344 W MAIN ST, WAVERLY MEDICAL CENTER 23890 #051-07-1994 L1996 **IM** *020
CHAMBERLAIN, Charles Wm. ■ 23890 #051-04-1964 L1964 **GP** *020 †18
EMRAN, K B M. 24414 MUSSELWHITE RD, SUSSEX STATRE PRISON 23891 #160-04-1989 L2002 **IM** *020 †20
ULEP, Benjamin T. 24427 MUSSELLWHITE DR, MEDICAL SERVICES DEPARTMEN 23891 #748-10-1969 L1999 **FM OS** *020

WAYNESBORO – WAYNESBORO CITY

AKIN, Claire Nishiimoto. ■ 22980 #051-01-2005 L2005 **FP** *012
ALDERFER, Richard D. 179 NOTTINGHAM LN 22980 #051-04-1970 L1970 **FM** *020 †18
ALLEN, Cynthia Schick. ■ 22980 #001-02-2001 L2007 **PCP** *020 †50
AYERS, Gilmer Cornelius. 428 S MAGNOLIA AVE 22980 #051-01-1962 L1962 **FM** *071 †18
BELL, Rudolph Mardre. 2611 W MAIN ST, EMERGICARE 22980 #012-05-1958 L1965 **GP** *071
BRAND, Laura. 41 STONERIDGE DR 22980 #041-01-1991 L1994 **FM** *020 †18
BRANDT, Matthew Todd. ■ 22980 #020-12-2004 L2005 *100
BROOKINGS, Michael E. 633 S WAYNE AVE, EMERGENCY DEPARTMENT 22980 #021-05-1988 L1992 **EM** *020 †18
CAMPBELL, John Stephen. 2611 W MAIN ST 22980 #021-06-1975 L1991 **FM PE** *020 †55,16
CHEEK, Kimberly Michelle. 2522 JEFFERSON HWY, STE 110 22980 #055-02-2003 L2003 **IM** *100 †20
CULP, Jeffrey Alan. ■ 22980 #038-41-2003 L2003 **AI** *012 †20
DAVIS, Gina Gibson. 15 BOYINGTON BLVD, STE AO1 22980 #051-04-1996 L1996 **FM** *020 †18
DEACON, James Douglas. ■ 22980 #051-01-1959 L1959 **AN** *071 †05
EGLESTON, Du Bose. ■ 22980 #045-01-1940 L1958 **OPH** *071 †35
ELBOGDADI, Daniel George. ■ 22980 #010-01-2001 L2007 **RHU** *020
FERN, Robert Jerome. 108 COMMUNITY DR, WAYNESBORO PEDIATRICS 22980 #051-01-1997 L2001 **PD** *020 †55
FISCHER, Ronald Allen. ■ 22980 #035-06-1968 L1972 **OTO** *075 †45
GILLESPIE, James Earnest. 425 S LINDEN AVE 22980 #035-45-1970 L1978 **OPH AM** *020 †35
HEATWOLE, John Paul. ■ 22980 #051-04-1954 L1954 **AN** *071
HECK, Christopher Chas. 428 S MAGNOLIA AVE 22980 #024-07-1981 L1999 **FM FPG** *020 †18
HENRY, Ann Katherine. 920 SHENANDOAH VILLAGE DR, STE 121 22980 #028-02-1978 L1979 **RHU IM** *020 †20
HORAN, Linda Kyle. ■ 22980 #051-07-1978 L1980 **OBG** *020 †30
HORNER, W Harry. 169 ENTRY SCHOOL RD 22980 #035-20-1982 L1984 **IM** *020 †20
HOSTETTER, Melissa Faith. 108 COMMUNITY DR, WAYNESBORO PEDIATRICS, PLC 22980 #034-01-2000 L2000 **PD** *020 †55
HOWLETT, Stephen Andrew. 1305 13TH ST, UNIT A-2 22980 #023-07-1967 L1974 **GE IM** *020 †20
INTRESS, Robert Harlan. ■ 22980 #018-03-1944 L1945 **GP EM** *071 †05
KAPPES, William Carl, Jr. 13TH AT MAGNOLIA 22980 #051-04-1956 L1956 **PD** *071 †55
LANGOUET-ASTRIE, Muriel. 2542 JEFFERSON HWY STE 106 22980 #396-35-1982 L1997 **AI PDA** *020 †55
LEE, Donald Wayne. 428 S MAGNOLIA AVE 22980 #051-01-1996 L1996 **FM** *020 †18
LONG, James Arthur. 13 MAGNOLIA LN 22980 #051-04-1970 L1970 **PUD IM** *020 †20
MUMBAUER, Steven Wayne. 1305 13TH ST, UNIT B-2 22980 #041-13-1994 L1998 **PD** *075 †55
NATHE, James Edward. ■ 22980 #026-04-1968 L1975 **DR** *071 †80
OZINAL, Gungor. ■ 22980 #902-10-1957 L1972 **IM FM** *071
PENN, Samuel Randolph. ■ 22980 #051-01-1946 L1946 **GS TS** *071 †85
REED, James Chilton. ■ 22980 #011-03-1963 L1971 **D OS** *071 †15
ROBINSON, Chas Randolph. ■ 22980 #051-01-1980 L1983 **PTH** *020 †50
ROSS, Wesley Jay. 428 S MAGNOLIA AVE 22980 #051-04-1978 L1981 **FM** *020 †18
SEATON, Scott Montgomery. 15 BOYINGTON BLVD, STE A01 22980 #023-07-1992 L1993 **IM** *020 †20
SHERRY, John Barry. 501 OAK AVE 22980 #065-01-1948 L1958 **PTH** *071
SMITH, Robert Scott. ■ 22980 #036-01-2005 L2006 **GS** *100
SMOLKIN, Mitchell Todd. 15 BOYINGTON BLVD, STE A01 22980 #023-01-1974 L1996 **IM** *020 †20
SNODGRASS, Shelley Lyne. 2522 JEFFERSON HWY, STE 110 22980 #023-01-1998 L2006 **IM** *020 †20
STEIN, Karlton Albert. 428 S MAGNOLIA AVE 22980 #051-04-1972 L1975 **FM** *020 †18
TALBERT, John Robt. ■ 22980 #051-01-1957 L1957 **OBG** *071 †30
TERRY, Fred. ■ 22980 #055-75-2005, ▲ L2006 **PM** *012
TYLER, David. ■ 22980 #051-04-1952 L1953 **OBG** *071
WALTHALL, David B, III. ■ 22980 #051-01-1961 L1961 **FM IM** *020 †18
WILLIAMS, Hazael Jos. ■ 22980 #051-04-1938 L1938 **FM** *071
WITT, Nancy May Garrett. 1504 13TH ST 22980 #051-04-1955 L1955 **P** *020
WOODS, Paul A. 362 S LAUREL AVE 22980 #005-12-1944 L1944 **AM FM** *071
YOBS, Anne C Roof. ■ 22980 #036-07-1953 L1957 **PHP PTH** *071
YOUNG, Scott Frederick. 428 S MAGNOLIA AVE 22980 #055-01-1999 L2002 **FM** *020 †18

WEBER CITY – SCOTT

ADKINS, Bruce Richard. 155 SHADY ELM LN 24290 #047-06-1961 L1962 **GP** *072 †18
ADKINS, Steven Mark. 1754 US HIGHWAY 23 N 24290 #051-04-1988 L1990 **FM** *020 †18
ARNETTE, Bryan Thomas. 1754 US HIGHWAY 23 N 24290 #051-01-2002 L2005 **FM** *020 †18
FRANKLIN, Lauren Brenci. 1754 US HIGHWAY 23 N 24290 #011-03-1995 L2005 **FM** *020 †18
GEER, Robert Mac. 1754 US HIGHWAY 23 N 24290 #016-06-1971 L1976 **FM** *071 †18

GRIGSBY, Holly Charlene. 1754 US HIGHWAY 23 NORTH, HOLSTON MEDICAL GROUP 24290 #305-01-2003 L2007 **FM** *020

HAGER, Shelton Philip. 222 US HIGHWAY 23 N 24290 #036-08-1998 L2005 **FM** *020 †18

MC COY, James Lowell. 1754 US HIGHWAY 23 N 24290 #051-04-1976 L1977 **FM** *020 †18

NOOR, Sidi Yousseff. 1754 US HIGHWAY 23 N 24290 #016-01-1983 L2007 **FM** *020 †18

WILSON, Larry Terrell. 1754 US HIGHWAY 23 N 24290 #033-06-1998 L2001 **FM** *020

WEEMS – LANCASTER

POLLARD, Richard Allan. 3983 BLACK STUMP RD 22576 #025-01-1958 L1989 **OS OM** *071 †70

WINTER, Phillip Emil. ■ 22576 #028-02-1960 L1990 **GPM MDM** *030 †70

WEST POINT – KING WILLIAM

CAPPS, Pamela Marlene. ■ 23181 #051-07-2000 L2000 **FM** *020 †18

CARVER, Donald Dickinson. PO BOX 232 23181 #036-01-1989 L1990 **FM** *020 †18

MELTON, Harvey Edward. ■ 23181 #051-04-1953 L1953 **GP** *071

OLSSON, Shirley Anne C. ■ 23181 #051-04-1952 L1956 **PHP** *072

WEYERS CAVE – AUGUSTA

BRAND, Asher. 51 AVIATION CIR, STE 208 24486 #051-04-1991 L1994 **EM** *020 †16

BUCKWALTER, Victor Lee. 1151 KEEZLETOWN RD, STE 101 24486 #041-13-1978 L1986 **FM** *020 †18

RAPP, Raymond Edward. ■ 24486 #010-01-1952 L1968 **AN** *071

WEIRICH, Gordon Dale. 1151 KEEZLETOWN RD 24486 #017-20-1979 L1982 **FM ADM** *020 †18

WHITE MARSH – GLOUCESTER

HOWARD, Vaughan Henry, Jr. ■ 23183 #051-04-1977 L1977 **EM FM** *071 †16,18

WHITE POST – CLARKE

JONES, Matthew Page. PO BOX 207, 1260 WESTFIELD FARM LN 22663 #051-01-1990 L1991 **HO** *020 †20

SIMMONS, Debra G. PO BOX 209 22663 #051-04-1977 L1982 **NEP IM** *020 †20

WHITE STONE – LANCASTER

BAGNALL, Richard David. ■ 22578 #051-04-1998 L1998 **FM** *020 †18

BANGEL, William M. ■ 22578 #051-04-1950 L1950 **OBG** *071 †30

BLOODWORTH, Leon Ponder. ■ 22578 #011-03-1969 L1972 **EM FM** *071

BRAY, Stuart Thos. ■ 22578 #051-04-1947 L1948 **NR R** *071 †28

CUBBAGE, Brian Keith. 30 SHADY LN 22578 #051-01-1999 L1999 **FM** *020 †18

DAFFEH, June Belinda. ■ 22578 #008-02-1996 L2004 **IM** *100

DUER, Ellen Ann. 347 COPPEDGE FARM RD 22578 #023-01-1964 L1994 **AN EM** *020

KIRBY, James Chasey. ■ 22578 #010-01-1955 L1961 **IM ID** *071 †20

MOORE, George, Jr. ■ 22578 #041-13-1947 L1970 **PHP GPM** *071 †70

NICHOLS, David Buell. 30 SHADY LN 22578 #067-01-1976 L1977 **FM EM** *020 †18 ‡

PERKINS, Stephen J. ■ 22578 #028-46-1984 L1998 **EM** *020 †16

WEBB-WRIGHT, Jennie. ■ 22578 #051-04-1995 L1998 **EM** *020 †16

WOLF-SMALL, Brigitte. ■ 22578 #654-01-1999 L2000 **FM** *020 †18 ‡

WRIGHT, James Lee. 285 CLARK POINT DR, DOC OUT OF THE BOX, LLC 22578 #051-04-1995 L1998 **FM** *020 †18

WICOMICO – GLOUCESTER

JUSTIS, David La Vern. ■ 23184 #038-41-1974 L2005 **EM GS** *071 †16 ‡

WICOMICO CHURCH – NORTHUMBERLAND

BRAND, Eugene D. ■ 22579 #024-01-1950 L1971 **PS HNS** *071 †75

THOMASON, Dustin Elliott. ■ 22579 #035-01-2003 *100

WILLIAMSBURG – JAMES CITY

ACKART, Richard Steeves. 120 KINGS WAY, STE 2200 23185 #036-05-1974 L1975 **PUD CCM** *020 †20

ADAWADKAR, Satish Prakash. 100 SENTARA CIR 23188 #051-01-2004 L2004 **AN** *012

ALEXANDER, Gordon M, Jr. 301 MONTICELLO AVE 23185 #010-02-1994 L1994 **IM** *020 †20

ALMIRANTE, James Vincent. 120 KINGS WAY STE 1500, DOCTORS SURGERY CENTER 23185 #748-02-1992 L2005 **APM AN** *020 †05

ALSTON, Rebecca Baker. 100 SENTARA CIR 23188 #051-04-1982 L1983 **PTH PHP** *020 †50

ALTMAN, Jennifer Jean. 1162 PROFESSIONAL DR 23185 #036-07-2001 L2005 **PD** *020 †55

ALVARADO, Carlos Alberto. 100 SENTARA CIR, WILLIAMSBURG EMERGENCY PHY 23188 #005-15-1982 L2006 **EM**

AMADEO, Javier. 217 MCLAWS CIR, STE 103 23185 #042-01-1994 L2006 **NS** *020 †25 ‡

AMSTADTER, Stephani Jane. 7151 RICHMOND RD, STE 405 23185 #016-06-1998 L2007

ANANTHRAM, Vasudev. 117 BULIFANTS BLVD, STE B 23188 #495-33-1989 L2002 **CD IM** *020 †20

ANDERSON, John A. ■ 23188 #010-03-1962 L1967 **LM R** *030 †80

ANDERSON, William Morris. ■ 23185 #028-02-1942 L1946 **IM** *071 †20

BAKER, James E. ■ 23185 #047-07-1952 L1986 **OS P** *071 †75

BAKER, John Harrison. 7151 RICHMOND RD, STE 403 23188 #036-01-1974 L1987 **OBG** *020 †30

BALL, John James, III. 4374 NEW TOWN AVE, STE 200 23188 #051-04-1976 L1977 **FM** *020 †18

BARRETT, Elizabeth G. 5249 OLDE TOWNE RD 23188 #036-01-2001 L2004 **FM** *020

BARTON, James Edwin. 5251 JOHN TYLER HWY, STE 15 23185 #051-04-1973 L1974 **EM OS** *020 †18,16

BASSIG, Ricardo Alarcon. 4601 IRONBOUND RD, EASTERN STATE HOSPITAL 23188 #748-01-1961 L1974 **EM GP** *020

BASTA, Barbara J. ■ 23185 #759-10-1967 L1983 **P** *071

BATMAN, Louisa Satchwell. ■ 23188 #051-04-1958 L1958 **OBG** *071 †30

BEDELL, Kevin R. 4622 ROCHAMBEAU DR 23188 #023-01-1976 L1987 **IM AM** *020 †20

BENEKE, William James. 5215 MONTICELLO AVE, # A 23188 #035-06-1986 L2004 **CD IM** *020 †20

BIERNACKI, Gregory James. 120 KINGS WAY, STE 1400 23185 #010-02-1985 L1988 **OM GP** *020

BIGLEY, Elmer C, Jr. ■ 23188 #041-02-1965 L1966 **ORS PM** *071 †40

BLANCHARD, Jeffrey Glenn. 7151 RICHMOND RD, MULTISPECIALTY GROUP 23188 #051-04-2002 L2002 **FM** *020 †18

BODNER, Theodore Herbert. ■ 23185 #035-19-1960 L1961 **ORS** *071 †40

BOLASH, Alan Michael. 101 ELIZABETH MERIWETHER, ANESTHESIA DEPT 23185 #025-07-1980 L1983 **AN** *05

BOOTH, Bruce Walter. 3901 TREYBURN DR, STE 2A 23185 #051-01-1971 L1971 **ON HEM** *020 †18

BOQUIST, Christopher Glen. 120 KINGS WAY, STE 1400 23185 #051-04-1998 L2005 **FM** *020 †18

BROWN, Howard Raymond. ■ 23188 #035-19-1959 L1986 **OM IM** *030

BROWN, Joseph Danl, III. 224 MONTICELLO AVE 23185 #051-01-1960 L1960 **GP** *020 †18

BROWN, Susan Mc Donald. 120 KINGS WAY STE 2700, WILLIAMSBURG NEUROLOGY 23185 #041-07-1984 L1990 **PTH** *020 †50

BROWN, Thomas Montford. ■ 23188 #008-01-1956 L1986 **ORS** *071 †40

BROWNE, Howard S. ■ 23188 #016-06-1949 L1997 **ORS OS** *071 †40

BRUBAKER, James Danl. ■ 23185 #041-02-1960 L1998 **FM PD** *072 †18

BUCHANAN, Camilla. 120 KINGS WAY, STE 3400 23185 #051-04-1976 L1979 **OBG** *020 †30

BUETOW, Elizabeth Ann. 100 SENTARA CIR, DEPARTMENT OF EMERGENCY ME 23188 #035-15-1996 L1998 **EM** *020 †16

BUNTING, Richard Fry. 5215 MONTICELLO AVE 23188 #051-01-1961 L1961 **OPH** *071 †35

BURGESS, Scott Vassar. 120 KINGS WAY, STE 402 23185 #028-03-1998 L2005 **U** *020 †95

BURKE, Melvin H. ■ 23185 #051-01-1952 L1952 **AN** *071

BURKEY, Elizabeth Ann. 3901 TREYBURN DR, STE 101 23185 #051-07-1999 L1999 **FM** *020 †18

CAMP, Thomas Carl. 100 SENTARA CIR 23188 #051-07-1981 L1985 **EM** *020 †16

CAMPANA, Richard Anthony. 312 2ND ST 23185 #051-07-1982 L1985 **GP ADM** *020 †70

CAMPBELL, Anh Nguyen-Duy. 5215 MONTICELLO AVE, STE A 23188 #010-02-1988 L1994 **CD** *020 †20

CAMPBELL, Glenn Clark. 5215 MONTICELLO AVE, ADVANCED VISION INSTITUTE 23188 #041-02-1986 L1994 **OPH GP** *020 †35

CAMPBELL, Russell Witter. 156 STRAWBERRY PLAINS RD, STE A 23188 #033-06-1982 L1991 **VS GS** *85

CAMPOLATTARO, Robert M. 5208 MONTICELLO AVE, STE 150 23188 #033-05-1998 L2003 **HS** *020 †40

CAPECCI, Kendall Louis. 6601 MOORETOWN RD 23188 #056-03-1987 L1992 **DR** *020 †80 ‡

CARLUCCI, Joseph. ■ 23188 #561-01-1952 L1960 **AN** *071 †05

CARR, Daniel Elwyn. 4125 IRONBOUND RD, MULTISPECIALTY GROUP 23188 #050-02-1980 L1994 **ORS GS** *020 †40

CARR, Ian Robert. ■ 23185 #917-24-1958 L1968 **PDC LM** *020

CARR, John Donald. 5429 OLDE TOWNE RD, OLDE TOWNE MEDICAL CENTER 23188 #917-29-1962 L1987 **FM** *020

CARROLL, William Jerome. 2125 LAKE POWELL RD 23185 #041-02-1959 L1969 **P CHP** *071

CASH, Paul David. 100 SENTARA CIR 23188 #051-04-1982 L1989 **EM** *020 †16

CATCHINGS, Timothy Titus. 500 SENTARA CIR, STE 100 23188 #012-05-1978 L1984 **CD IM** *020 †20

CHANG, Matthew Youmin. 217 MCLAWS CIR, STE 103 23185 #038-06-1999 L2005 **NS** *020 ‡

CHASTENEY, Edith Siegener. ■ 23185 #051-04-1947 L1957 *071

CHISAM, Mark Ewing. 3901 TREYBURN DR STE B, WILLIAMSBURG RADIATION THE 23185 #023-12-1994 L1996 **RO** *020 †80

CHOHANY, George J. 301 MONTICELLO AVE 23185 #473-01-1947 L1954 **GS GP** *071

CHUN, Kelly. 372 MCLAWS CIR, STE 1 23185 #583-01-1986 L1999 **P** *020 †75

CIRCEO, Richard Bernard. ■ 23185 #024-07-1961 L1976 **DR** *020 †80

CLARE, Frank Brian. 100 SENTARA CIR 23188 #422-01-1984 L1985 **EM** *020 †18

CLEVINGER, Roger Lee, Jr. 100 SENTARA CIR 23188 #051-04-1991 L1992 **IM** *020 †20

CLIPPINGER, Frank W, Jr. ■ 23185 #028-02-1952 L1952 **ORS** *071 †40

CONNELL, Alastair Mc Crae. 208 JONES MILL LN 23185 #919-05-1954 L1985 **IM** *071

CONVERSE, Joseph O. 457 MCLAWS CIR, # 1 23185 #055-01-1984 L1989 **GE** *020 †20

CORONADO, Gualberto Tulod. 4601 IRONBOUND RD 23188 #748-01-1956 L1992 **P CHP** *071

CORVETTE, Donna Marie. 5335 DISCOVERY PARK BLVD, STE A 23188 #010-03-1988 L1991 **D** *020 †20,15

CULLOM, Maryellen P. 120 KINGS WAY, STE 1300 23185 #025-01-1988 L1993 **OPH** *020 †35

CULLOM, Robt Douglas, Jr. 120 KINGS WAY, STE 1300 23185 #047-05-1987 L1998 **OPH** *020 †35

CUMMINGS, William Steven. 5251 JOHN TYLER HWY, STE 15 23185 #034-01-1971 L1972 **FM EM** *020 †18,16

DA COSTA, Christopher T K. 3901 TREYBURN DR, STE 201 23185 #965-01-1983 L2000 **IM ID** *020 †20

DAFASHY, David Derrick. ■ 23185 #051-04-1997 L2000 **IM** *020 †20

DAVIS, Charles Monroe. 4601 IRONBOUND RD 23188 #036-05-1966 L1967 **P PFP** *030 †75

DAVIS, Mark W. ■ 23188 #048-14-2002 L2004 **IM** *020 †20

DAVIS, Richard B. ■ 23188 #018-03-1953 L1956 **HEM IM** *071 †20

DE GRACIAN, Alicia B. PO DRAWER A 23185 #649-01-1944 L1964 **P IM** *020

DE LAURENTIS, Dominic A. ■ 23185 #041-13-1953 L1997 **VS GS** *071 †85

DE WITT, Gerald Wallace. 119 BULIFANTS BLVD 23188 #051-01-1969 L1969 **PD NPM** *020 †55

DHILLON, Avtar S. 1657 MERRIMAC TRL, COLONIAL SEVS BOARD 23185 #495-03-1977 L1983 **P ADM** *020 †75 ‡

DICKINSON, Daniel Jackson. 156 STRAWBERRY PLAINS RD, STE C 23188 #036-07-1985 L1992 **IM** *020 †20

DI MATTIA, Ralph Richard. 301 MONTICELLO AVE, SENTARA WILLIAMSBURG COMM 23185 #041-02-1981 L1984 **IM** *020 †20

DIMMETT, James David. 4601 IRONBOUND RD 23188 #017-20-1959 L1970 **P** *020

DONLAN, Charles Jos, Jr. 120 KINGS WAY, SIOTE 2200 23185 #051-04-1970 L1970 **PUD IM** *020 †20

DOWNEY, Mark Collins. 119 BULIFANTS BLVD 23188 #051-04-1996 L2001 **PD IM** *020 †20,55

DU BUY, Jean Bernard. 10117 SYCAMORE LANDING RD 23188 #023-01-1965 L1978 **EM ID** *072 †16

ELLER, Patricia Faria. 120 KINGS WAY, C 23185 #187-14-1996 L2003 **CN** *020

ELLIS, Mark Edward. 120 KINGS WAY, STE 3100 23185 #036-05-1977 L1989 **ON HEM** *020 †20

ENAYAT-POUR, Kazem M. 4601 IRONBOUND RD 23188 #517-05-1973 L1979 **P CHP** *020 †75

ERFE, Jose Asperin. 481 MCLAWS CIR STE 1 23185 #748-02-1962 L1972 **P N** *020 †75

ERFE, Purita F. ■ 23185 #748-10-1966 **P N** *020

ERGIN, Umit Cevdet. 109 JAMES LONGSTREET, TAZEWELL'S HUNDRED 23185 #902-01-1949 L1964 **P IM** *071 †75

ETZEL, Michael Allister. ■ 23188 #028-34-1984 L1988 **P** *100

FAJARDO, Jesus Eduardo. ■ 23188 #737-01-1967 L1972 **PD ID** *020 †55

FALCAO, Manoel Azevedo. ■ 23188 #187-03-1948 L1959 **ORS RHU** *071

FARKAS, Hazel D Martin. ■ 23188 #803-03-1962 L1998 **P** *071

FARRAR, John Thruston. ■ 23188 #028-02-1945 L1965 **GE OS** *062 †20

FITZPATRICK, Michael D. 120 KINGS WAY, STE 1400 23185 #051-04-1994 L1994 **FM** *020 †18

FLAGG, Elena Fernandez. 329 MCLAWS CIR, ARTH & RHEUMATIC DISEASE 23185 #048-15-1997 L1997 **RHU** *020 †20

FLETCHER, John Stevenson. ■ 23185 #051-01-1955 L1955 **PD** *071 †55

FLOYD, Jay Wm. 5231 JOHN TYLER HWY 23185 #023-01-1990 L2007 **FM** *020 †18 ‡

FOOS, Robert Edward, Jr. 100 SENTARA CIR 23188 #051-04-1976 L1977 **EM FM** *020 †18,16

FREE, Julianne. ■ 23188 #016-06-1955 L1956 **PD** *071 †55

FREYFOGLE, Edward B, Jr. ■ 23188 #016-11-1976 L2004 **U GP** *020 †95

GAJJAR, Tushar Umakant. 6601 MOORETOWN RD, WILLIAMSBURG COMMUNITY HOS 23188 #048-02-1991 L1995 **APM AN** *020 †05

GARRETT, Elena Cuticelli. ■ 23188 #051-04-2006 L2006 **EM** *012

GENTRY, Steven Edwin. ■ 23188 #051-01-1981 L2006 **PUD IM** *020 †20

GERAGHTY, Patricia Eileen. ■ 23185 #035-19-1959 L1994 **PTH** *020 †50

GIORGI-GUARNIERI, Deborah. ■ 23185 #051-07-1989 L2000 **P** *020 †75

GOO, Heidi. 5231 JOHN TYLER HWY 23185 #010-03-1996 L2005 **FM** *020 †18

GOTICO, Rustico Tolentino. 4601 IRONBOUND RD 23188 #748-01-1957 L1975 **GP** *020

GOTTFRIED, Linda Perkins. 1162 PROFESSIONAL DR, WILLIAMSBURG COMMUNITY MED 23185 #017-20-1992 L1995 **PD** *020 †55

GRAHAM, John James. ■ 23188 #030-06-1961 L1962 **OBG** *030 †30

GRAHAM, Maurice Edward. 4374 NEW TOWN AVE, STE 202 23188 #004-01-1974 L1981 **PD** *020 †55

GRASINGER, John Edward. 400 SENTARA CIR, STE 320 23188 #010-02-1964 L1976 **ORS** *020 †40

GRIFFIN, Harvey Lee, Jr. ■ 23185 #036-07-1956 L1965 **PTH** *071 †50

GRIMES, Stephen Arthur. 100 SENTARA CIR 23188 #051-04-1981 L1982 **EM GS** *020 †16

GROSSMAN, Ronald David. 4125 IRONBOUND RD, STE 200 23188 #041-02-1971 L2005 **FM FSM** *020 †18

GRUNDY, Jennifer Lynn. 5231 JOHN TYLER HWY 23185 #035-09-1997 L2001 **IM** *020 †20

GUARNIERI, Johnstuart M. 333 MCLAWS CIR STE 3, PLASTIC SURGERY PC 23185 #051-07-1985 L1987 **PS FM** *020 †65

GUTH, Lloyd. ■ 23188 #035-19-1953 L1969 **OS** *071

GYPSON, Ward Glenn. ■ 23188 #035-09-1959 L1963 **GYN** *071 †30

HAKIM, Christopher A. 219 MCLAWS CIR 23185 #024-16-1980 L1981 **RHU IM** *020 †20

HAMPERS, Douglas Anthony. 4125 IRONBOUND RD, MULTISPECIALTY GROUP 23188 #032-01-1998 L2007 **ORS** *020 †40

HAMRICK, John Douglas. 461 MCLAWS CIR STE 1 23185 #051-04-1973 L1975 **IM** *020 †20

HANCOCK, Susan Marie. 156 STRAWBERRY PLAINS RD, STE A 23188 #011-04-1998 L2007 **VS** *020 †85

HANGER, Keith Elwood. 120 KINGS WAY, STE 2500 23185 #051-04-1968 L1968 **CD IM** *020 †20

HARALDSTED, Alexander K. 120 KINGS WAY, STE 2200 23185 #297-02-1982 L2001 **PUD SME** *020 †20

HARDING, Patrick Neal. 120 KINGS WAY, C 23185 #051-07-1993 L1993 **N** *020 †75

HARTLE, Richard John. 457 MCLAWS CIR, # 1 23185 #051-04-1987 L1993 **GE** *020 †20

HENDERSON, Clifford E. ■ 23188 #051-04-1972 L1973 **FM** *020 †18

HENDERSON, June S. ■ 23188 #051-04-1972 L1973 **FM** *020

HERSHBERG, Robert Allen. 301 MONTICELLO AVE 23185 #056-06-1965 L1976 **PTH** *020 †50

HESS, James Brock. 5251 JOHN TYLER HWY, STE 15 23185 #051-04-1968 L1968 **IM EM** *020 †20,16

HESTER, Jill Nagel. 301 MONTICELLO AVE 23185 #011-04-1985 L1986 **AN FM** *020 †18,05

HIGDON, Laura Ellen. 7151 RICHMOND RD, STE 405 23188 #051-07-1995 L1995 **FM** *020 †18

HIGGINS, Michael E. 5208 MONTICELLO AVE, STE 150 23188 #035-15-2000 L2005 **ORS** *020

HILL, Mary Johannah. 7151 RICHMOND RD, MULTISPECIALTY GROUP 23188 #051-04-1988 L1989 **FM** *020 †18

HO, Jeffrey Hunbon. ■ 23188 #038-41-2002 L2006 **AN** *020 †05

HONABLUE, Richard Riddick. 243 MCLAWS CIR STE 102, FAMILY HLTH CARE LTD 23185 #047-07-1974 L1980 **FM EM** *020 †18

HOWARD, Hall Renfro. 120 KINGS WAY, STE 1500 23185 #021-05-1971 L1976 **GS** *020 †85

HSIA, Hung-Lun John. ■ 23185 #051-01-2007 L2007 **TY** *012

HUNDT, David Gordon. 3901 TREYBURN DR, STE 101 23185 #051-07-1999 L1999 **IM** *020 †20

HURT, David Langkop. 100 SENTARA CIR, SENTARA WILLIAMSBURG MED C 23188 #051-01-1974 L1975 **AN PUD** *020 †05

INGHAM, Tiffany Michelle. ■ 23188 #051-07-2000 L2000 **AN IM** *020 †20

INLOES, Benjamin H, Jr. 5638 BOATWRIGHT CIR, WILLIAMSBURG LANDING 23185 #023-01-1940 L1954 **GYN** *071 †30

IONESCU, Radu Teodor. 301 MONTICELLO AVE, SMG DIV.OF HOSPITAL MEDICI 23185 #781-04-1989 L2004 **IM** *100 †20

JACOBSON, Michael James. 400 SENTARA CIR, STE 300 23188 #007-02-1998 L2002 **OTO** *020

JAMES, John Forrest. ■ 23188 #023-12-1996 L1997 **GPM** *020 †70

JAMISON, Thomas Maxwell. 6601 MOORETOWN RD 23188 #017-20-1972 L1976 **DR** *020 †80

JAVERNICK, Michael Joseph. ■ 23185 #010-02-2004 L2006 **FP** *012

JENKINS, Daniel Geo. 1115 PROFESSIONAL DR 23185 #051-04-1972 L1977 **OBG** *020 †30

JOHNSON, Richard Bailey. 110 WORKINGTON 23188 #051-01-1981 L1985 **PHP IM** *020 †20

JOHNSON, Tommy. 1313 JAMESTOWN RD, STE 103 23185 #041-01-1978 L1987 **FM** *020 †18

JOHNSON, Wade Lane. ■ 23185 #051-04-1967 L1967 **P** *020 †75

JONES, Roger Wm. 1115 PROFESSIONAL DR 23185 #017-20-1972 L1976 **OBG** *020 †30

JONES, Webb Darden. 5700 WILLIAMSBURG LNDNG DR, LANDING MEDICAL CLINIC 23185 #051-04-1971 L1972 **FM** *020 †18

KAISER, John Robt. 100 SENTARA CIR 23188 #027-01-1973 L1980 **IM** *020 †20

KAMINER, Kimberly Leann. 301 MONTICELLO AVE, WILLIAMSBURG COMM HOSPITAL 23185 #051-01-1996 L1996 **EM** *020 †16

KANNA, Arvo. 400 SENTARA CIR STE 320 23188 #005-12-1986 L2007 **N NRN** *020 †20,75

KAROW, Juliette Seelye. STUDENT HEALTH SERVICE, WILLIAM & MARY COLLEGE 23185 #025-01-1951 L1974 **GP** *020

KATZ, Daniel Jacob. ■ 23188 #041-02-2006 L2006 **IM** *012

KELLER, Kristy Ann. ■ 23188 #025-01-2002 L2002 **OBG** *020

KERBIN, Laura Diane. 120 KINGS WAY, STE 3100 23185 #051-07-1994 L1994 **ON PLM** *020 †20

KERSH, Charles Ronald. 3901 TREYBURN DR 23185 #051-04-1982 L1983 **RO** *020 †80

KOZ, Gabriel. 4601 IRONBOUND RD, EASTERN STATE HOSPITAL 23188 #836-01-1958 L1993 **P** *030

KREMER, Richard Edward. ■ 23185 #008-01-1976 L1978 **IM** *020

KWON, Syn Whan Oh. ■ 23185 #583-08-1963 L1971 **CHP GP** *020

LA BELLE, Patrice. ■ 23188 #041-07-1975 L1980 **IM NEP** *050 †20

LAMBERT, Alexander Leroy. 5335 DISCOVERY PARK BLVD 23188 #010-03-1988 L1990 **ORS** *020 †40

LANGEBECK, Miguel. ■ 23188 #264-04-1961 L1967 **PTH CLP** *020 †50

LANZALOTTI, John Allen. 136 PROFESSIONAL CIR 23185 #041-01-1975 L1982 **GP GS** *020

LASKOWSKI, Stanislaw Z. 301 MONTICELLO AVE 23185 #759-04-1938 L1977 **IM P** *072

LAWLESS, Benjamin Richard. 120 MONTICELLO AVE 23185 #020-02-2000 L2007 **FM** *020 †18

LEE, Joanna Suzanne. ■ 23185 #051-04-2007 *012

LEFEBVRE, Jeanne Marie J. 3435 JOHN TYLER HWY, RIVERSIDE GREENSPRINGS MED 23185 #065-06-1986 L1998 **IM** *020 †20

LE NOACH, Philip Marcel. 400 SENTARA CIR, STE 320 23188 #165-03-1983 L2003 **ORS** *020 †40

LESNICK, James Edward. 120 KINGS WAY, STE 3500 23185 #035-45-1978 L1986 **NS** *020 †25

LEVINE, Michael Jesse. 5251 JOHN TYLER HWY, STE 17 23185 #008-02-1995 L2000 **OM** *020 †20,70

LILLY, Michael Charles. 500 SENTARA CIR STE 202, WILLIAMSBURG SURGERY 23188 #051-04-1994 L2004 **GS** *020 †85

LIMBER, Gerald Keck. ■ 23188 #041-12-1967 L1971 **PTH** *030 †50

LINK, Karen Wessel. 100 SENTARA CIR 23188 #051-07-1994 L1994 **EM** *020 †16

LONG, Leana S. 120 KINGS WAY STE 1300, HAMPTON ROADS EYE ASSO. 23185 #036-08-1999 L1999 **OPH** *020 †35 ‡

LONTKOWSKI, Susan Marie. 120 KINGS WAY, STE 3400 23185 #036-07-1988 L1991 **OBG** *020 †30

LUCAS, Christopher C. ■ 23188 #011-03-1995 L1997 **FM AM** *020 †70,18

LUNA, Ruben Villaflores. 133 OLD CARRIAGE WAY, EASTERN STATE HOSPITAL 23188 #748-02-1964 L1973 **GP** *020

MAHATME, Arvind. 500 SENTARA CIR, STE 202 23188 #011-04-1999 L2004 **SO GS** *020

MALONEY, Milford C. ■ 23185 #035-06-1953 L1991 **CD IM** *072 †20

MANEJWALA, Omar Sharif. 5477 MOORETOWN RD, WILLIAM J FARLEY CENTER 23188 #023-01-1997 L2006 **P** *020 †75

MARCHESCHI, David G. 100 SENTARA CIR 23188 #038-43-1992 L1997 **PTH PCP** *020 †50

MARCINKUS, Susan Rita. ■ 23185 #036-01-1992 L1996 **AN PAN** *020 †05

MARCUSON, Patricia Lynn. 400 SENTARA CIR, MULTISPECIALTY GROUP 23188 #035-09-1991 L1992 **IM** *020 †20

MARCUSON, Sanford Kent. 400 SENTARA CIR, MULTISPECIALTY GROUP 23188 #051-04-1994 L2000 **IM** *020 †20

MARES, Steven Chas. 4374 NEW TOWN AVE, STE 202 23188 #051-07-1992 L1993 **PD** *020 †55

MARK, Laura J. 194 WILSON DR 23188 #010-02-1981 L1995 **P** *020 †75

MARKS, Steven Edward. 120 KINGS WAY, STE 3200 23185 #036-05-1982 L1984 **U** *020 †95

MARSH, John Chas. ■ 23188 #008-01-1959 L1999 **ON HEM** *072 †20

MARTIN, Maurice H. ■ 23188 #030-06-1952 L1986 **OBG** *071 †30

MASSENGILL, Christopher L. 120 KINGS WAY STE 1400, RIVERSIDE WILLIAMSBURG FAM 23185 #051-04-1996 L1999 **FM** *020 †18

MASSEY, William Jos, III. 322 MONTICELLO AVE 23185 #036-07-1962 L1967 **IM** *071 ‡

MATHEWS, Hallett Holmes. ■ 23185 #051-04-1980 L1981 **ORS** *071 †40

MC ALLISTER, Wm H, IV. 217 MCLAWS CIR, STE 103 23185 #036-01-1992 L1998 **NS** *020 †25

MC BEATH, George Raymond. 132 PROFESSIONAL CIR, MULTISPECIALTY GROUP 23185 #051-04-1987 L1988 **FM** *020 †18

MC CARTHY, John J, III. 5208 MONTICELLO AVE, STE 180 23188 #010-02-1982 L2002 **ORS** *020 †40

MC CLELLAN, Jason E. 5249 OLDE TOWNE RD 23188 #051-01-1952 L1952 **IM HEM** *071 †20

MC CLURE, James N, Jr. ■ 23185 #028-02-1955 L1978 **P** *071 †75

MC CLURE, Sharon F. 4601 IRONBOUND RD, EASTERN STATE HOSPITAL 23188 #051-04-1979 L2000 **P** *020 †75

MC MENAMIN, Paul John. 1155 PROFESSIONAL DR 23185 #035-08-1987 L1991 **OPH** *020 †35

MENSCH, Lisa. ■ 23185 #051-07-2000 L2000 **P** *020 †75

MERCER, Christie Ann. 119 BULIFANTS BLVD, CMG - PEDIATRIC ASSOCIATES 23188 #030-05-1999 L1999 **PD** *020 †55

MILLER, Christopher N. ■ 23185 #020-12-2000 L2000 **EM** *020

MILLER, Thomas James. 301 MONTICELLO AVE, WILLIAMSBURG COMM HOSPITAL 23185 #026-04-1981 L1982 **AN IM** *020 †20,05

MONIZ, Mark P. 120 KINGS WAY STE 2800, WILLIAMSBURG SURGERY P C 23185 #048-14-1993 L1998 **GS** *020 †85

MONTILEONE, Michael S. 6601 MOORETOWN RD 23188 #654-01-1996 L1997 **DR** *020 †80

MOSES, Gail Anne. 107 BARLOWS RUN 23188 #051-07-1987 L1988 **IM** *020 †20

MOSS, Carrie Renee. 120 KINGS WAY, STE 2300 23185 #051-04-1989 L1995 **PM** *020 †60

MOUSSALLI, Clarice. 5251 JOHN TYLER HWY, STE 15 23185 #036-05-1979 L1983 **IM** *020 †16

MOWERY, David Bruce. ■ 23185 #001-02-1990 L1991 **FM** *020 †18

MUNZEL, Thomas Lee. 120 KINGS WAY, STE 2200 23185 #038-41-1972 L1980 **IM** *020 †20

MURPHY, Kyung-Mi Lim. 2732 HOLLY RIDGE LN 23185 #025-01-1995 L2000 **PD** *020 †55

MUSGRAVE, Jos Walker, Jr. 1139 PROFESSIONAL DR 23185 #021-01-1968 L1974 **D** *020 †15

MYERS, Julia Lynn. 100 SENTARA CIR, SMG DIV. OF HOSPITAL MEDIC 23188 #045-01-2001 L2004 **IM** *020 †20

NEAL, Berryman Voss. ■ 23185 #051-01-1955 L1955 **D** *071 †15

NGUYEN, Chan Duc. 4601 IRONBOUND RD 23188 #942-01-1972 L1992 **P** *020

NGUYEN, Diem Duc. 4601 IRONBOUND RD, EASTERN STATE HOSPITAL 23188 #941-01-1970 L1987 **FM** *020 †18

NORDLUND, John Richard. 113 BULIFANTS BLVD STE A, WILLIAMSBURG RETINA CTR 23188 #028-02-1986 L1992 **OPH** *020 †35

NOVERAS, Teresita L R. 4601 IRONBOUND RD, EASTERN STATE HOSPITAL 23188 #748-08-1974 L1983 **P** *020

OBIE, Eric Van. 5231 JOHN TYLER HWY, RWMA 23185 #024-05-1999 L1999 **FM** *020 †18

OH, Charles I. 4601 IRONBOUND RD 23188 #422-01-1988 L1999 **IM** *020 †20

OLIVER, Geo Jeffries, Jr. 301 MONTICELLO AVE 23185 #051-04-1947 L1947 **GS** *071

■ = Address Information Privacy Protected

OMBAC, Linda D. 4601 IRONBOUND RD 23188 #748-01-1974 L1982 **P IM** *020 ‡
OSHIKI, Michael Seiji. 107 BARLEY MILL PL 23188 #023-12-1998 L1998 **FM** *020 †18
PABBY, Ritu S. ■ 23188 #024-05-1999 L2002 **AI** *100 †20
PANBEHCHI, Mahmood. ■ 23185 #517-01-1955 L1967 **GP GS** *020
PARIKH, Pranav Hemant. 400 SENTARA CIR, MULTISPECIALTY GROUP 23188 #654-01-2000 L2004 **IM** *020 †20
PARK, Chan Suk. 120 MONTICELLO AVE, MEDEXPRESS WILLIAMSBURG 23185 #035-46-1985 L1989 **EM** *020 †16
PATEL, Mukesh M. 4601 IRONBOUND RD, EASTERN STATE HOSP BLDG 24 23188 #308-10-1988 L2000 **P** *020
PEARCE, David Christopher. 1115 PROFESSIONAL DR, GOVERNOR BERKELEY PROF CTR 23185 #036-01-1986 L1989 **OBG** *020 †30
PELTIER, Hubert Conrad. ■ 23185 #017-20-1948 L1969 **PD** *071 †55
PENG, Shane Hsuing. 400 SENTARA CIR, STE 450 23188 #065-10-1987 L1997 **FM EM** *020 †18
PERRY, John Curtis. ■ 23185 #051-04-1999 L1999 **PCC** *020
PERRY, Robert Peter. 301 MONTICELLO AVE, SMG-DIVISION OF HOSPITAL M 23185 #035-45-1976 L1977 **IM** *020 †20
PETER, Mohan. ■ 23185 #495-52-1970 L1978 **TS** *071 †85,90
PHARR, Scott Yorke. 120 KINGS WAY STE 2600 23185 #051-04-1972 L1977 **OTO** *020 †45
PIETRUSZYNSKI, Steven T. ■ 23185 #041-14-1999 L2007 **DR** *020 †80
PIOTROWSKI, Joseph John. 156 STRAWBERRY PLAINS RD, STE A 23188 #041-09-1983 L1998 **VS GS** *020 †85
PITMAN, John Mathews. 326 MONTICELLO AVE, 2ND FL 23185 #051-01-1959 L1959 **GS TS** *020 †85,90
PITMAN, John Mathews, III. 324 MONTICELLO AVE 23185 #051-01-1987 L1995 **PS HS** *020 †65
PLATON, Pablo Ticzon. ■ 23188 #748-01-1941 L1977 **IMG PHP** *020
PLOTT, Michael Francis. ■ 23185 #010-02-1964 L1996 **CD IM** *020 †20
POLEKSIC, Slobodan. ■ 23185 #396-08-1955 L1960 **PTH** *071 †50
PORTAL, Cynthia Thrush. 1162 PROFESSIONAL DR 23185 #051-01-1984 L1988 **PD** *020 †55
PORTAL, Jose Manuel. 120 KINGS WAY, STE 1300 23185 #051-01-1984 L2001 **OPH** *020 †35
POWELL, Kristina M. 119 BULIFANTS BLVD #035-15-1998 L2003 **PDP** *020 †55
POWERS, Thomas Jefferson. ■ 23188 #051-04-1972 L1973 **FM** *020 †18
PRESCOTT, Georgia Ann. 230 MONTICELLO AVE, PEDIATRIC ASSOC OF WILLIAM 23185 #051-04-1973 L1975 **PD** *020 †55
RAHMAN, Mahmood Aminur. 4601 IRONBOUND RD, EASTERN STATE HOSPITAL 23188 #704-25-1990 L2001 **P PFP** *020 †75
RAKHRA, Gursharn Singh. 400 SENTARA CIR STE 350, GASTROINTESTINAL & LIVER S 23188 #539-06-1988 L2007 **GE** *020 †20
RAUF, Khaliq Abdul. 100 SENTARA CIR, 2ND FL 23188 #010-01-2003 L2003 **IM** *020 †20
REAMS, Steven Henry. 1113 OLD COLONY LN 23185 #051-04-1970 L1970 **P** *020
REILLY, Paul David. 111 OLD COLONY LN 23185 #051-04-1983 L1987 **P** *020 †75
RENTO, Richard G, II. 120 KINGS WAY, STE 3200 23185 #043-01-1986 L1992 **U** *020 †95
RILEY, Gerald Terhahn. ■ 23188 #032-01-2002 L2005 **DR** *100 †80
RIVERS, Robert Jos. ■ 23188 #024-01-1957 L1973 **VS GS** *071 †85
ROBERSON, Emily Francis. 1115 PROFESSIONAL DR 23185 #051-07-1991 L1994 **OBG** *020 †30
ROBERTS, Katherine Ann. 301 MONTICELLO AVE 23185 #012-01-1997 L1997 **END** *020 †20
ROBUSTO, James Robt. 301 MONTICELLO AVE 23185 #023-07-1983 L1984 **FM EM** *020 †18 ‡
ROGOWSKI, Putul. 301 MONTICELLO AVE 23185 #041-13-1990 L1994 **AN** *020 †05
ROSSHEIM, Edgar Herbert. ■ 23185 #051-04-1957 L1957 **IM CD** *071
ROWLEY, Wilbur Francis. ■ 23188 #016-11-1959 L2001 **N P** *071 †75
SAMMONS, James Harris, Jr. 301 MONTICELLO AVE, CENTERA WM COMM HOSP 23185 #048-04-1978 L2005 **MDM OBG** *030 †30
SANCHEZ, Niria Dalila. 100 SENTARA CIR 23188 #264-01-1992 L2005 **ATP PCP** *100 †50
SANDERS, Donna Wheatley. 301 MONTICELLO AVE 23185 #051-04-1990 L1994 **AN** *020 †05
SANZ, Manuel O. 1105 QUEENS XING 23185 #847-04-1956 L1967 **P** *020 †75
SATKO, Frank Gregory. 301 MONTICELLO AVE 23185 #038-41-1967 L1973 **AN** *020 †05
SAWYER, Lois Taylor. ■ 23185 #036-05-1958 L1962 **AN** *071
SCHARLOP, Beth. 120 KINGS WAY, STE 3400 23185 #035-47-1980 L1985 **OBG** *020 †30
SCHECHTER, Gary Lee. ■ 23188 #035-15-1963 L1972 **OTO HNS** *071 †45
SCHLESINGER, Kimberly Wyn. 120 KINGS WAY, STE 3100 23188 #041-12-1997 L1997 **HO** *020 †20
SCHOONMAKER, Jeanette S. 104 FERNWOOD 23185 #035-15-1962 L1977 **P CHP** *071 †75
SCHRADER, Guillermo. 4601 IRONBOUND RD, EASTERN STATE HOSPITAL 23188 #264-04-1981 L1995 **P** *020
SCHULTZ, Roger Edward. 120 KINGS WAY, STE 3200 23185 #035-47-1980 L1985 **U** *020 †95
SCHUMANN, Keith William. 5309 DISCOVERY PARK BLVD 23188 #051-04-1996 L2000 **D** *020 †15
SCHWARTZ, Miles J. ■ 23188 #035-19-1951 L1952 **CD** *071 †20
SEAGER, Charles Arthur. 132 PROFESSIONAL CIR, MULTISPECIALTY GROUP 23185 #035-15-1983 L1984 **FM** *020 †18
SELVARAYAN, Philip. ■ 23185 #495-66-1973 L1983 **CD IM** *050 †20
SESSLER, Monique N. 118 BULIFANTS BLVD, STE A 23188 #187-13-1986 L1993 **FM** *020 †18
SHIELD, Stephen Wyatt. 1144 PROFESSIONAL DR 23185 #051-07-1988 L1993 **AI PD** *020 †55,03
SIM, Peter Alan. 230 N BOUNDARY ST, P O BOX 3700 23185 #051-01-1973 L1974 **EM FM** *020 †18,16
SIMO, Todd Edward. 312 2ND ST, FIRST MED 23185 #026-04-1993 L1994 **OM** *020
SINGH, Harbjajan. ■ 23185 #495-90-1954 *100
SKINNER, Bennie Alan. 6601 MOORETOWN RD 23185 #051-04-1995 L1995 **DR** *020 †80
SMERLIS, Nicholas A. 5208 MONTICELLO AVE, STE 150 23188 #023-01-2001 L2006 **HS** *020
SODERBERG, Kimberly Ingra. ■ 23185 #051-04-2003 L2007 **D** *020 †15
SOLOMON, Robert Irwin. 400 SENTARA CIR, STE 320 23188 #018-03-1981 L1985 **N OPH** *020 †20
SOUEIDAN, Shawke Abdel A. 120 KINGS WAY, C 23185 #605-01-1986 L1992 **N** *020 †75
SPARRER, James Preston. 100 SENTARA CIR 23188 #051-01-1991 L1991 **PTH** *020 †50
SPRAGUE, Peggy H. ■ 23185 #045-01-1952 L1967 **OS** *075
STECK, Audrey Elaine. 100 SENTARA CIR 23188 #051-01-1991 L1993 **PTH** *020 †50
STEPHAN, M Ilene. 3901 TREYBURN DR, WILLIAMSBURG RADIATION THE 23185 #051-01-1998 L1998 **IM** *020 †20
STEVENS, Kingsley Morton. ■ 23188 #024-01-1947 L1959 **IM** *071
STONEBRAKER, Angela Chu. 120 KINGS WAY, STE 1400 23185 #051-01-2000 L2005 **OTO** *100 †45
STOUTENGER, Wayne Allan. 7151 RICHMOND RD, STE 405 23188 #028-34-1983 L1994 **FP** *012

SULLIVAN, Robert Emmette. 2116 HARPERS ML 23185 #017-20-1976 L1992 **EM** *020 †16
SWARTZ, Edward Francis. ■ 23188 #041-02-1960 L1961 **GYN** *071 †30
TAN, Hoay Tjiang. ■ 23185 #660-03-1958 L1967 **U** *071 †95
TANSEY, Erin Elizabeth. ■ 23185 #035-19-2007 L2007 **IM** *012
TAYLOR, Anthony John. 120 KINGS WAY, STE 3200 23185 #028-34-1970 L1971 **U** *020 †95
TEASLEY, David G. 227 MCLAWS CIR 23185 #036-07-1978 L1984 **PS HS** *020 †65
TEASLEY, Jack Lamkin. ■ 23185 #036-07-1947 L1954 **PS** *071 †65
THEIS, Richard Braxton. 301 MONTICELLO AVE 23185 #051-04-1975 L1976 **FM** *020 †18
THIEL, Martin August. 301 MONTICELLO AVE 23185 #051-01-1969 L1969 **HS VS** *071 †85
THOMAS, Terrence Jos. ■ 23185 #051-03-1959 L1960 **GS** *071
TILLINGHAST, Guy W. 120 KINGS WAY, STE 3100 23185 #043-01-1992 L2001 **ON** *020 †20
TIMES, Terryl D. 500 SENTARA CIR STE 202, SENTARA MEDICAL GROUP 23188 #048-02-1986 L1988 **GS** *020 †85
TIRUMALASETTI, Fughik J. 4601 IRONBOUND RD, BLDG 33 23188 #495-11-1972 L2000 **P** *020 †75
TUCKER, Jane Lilian. 400 SENTARA CIR, STE 450 23188 #065-05-1987 L1997 **FM** *020 †18
VALENZUELA, Luis A. ■ 23188 #264-01-1962 L1970 **PTH OS** *071 †50
VEREB, Kathleen Ann. 301 MONTICELLO AVE, SMG DIV. OF HOSPITAL MEDIC 23185 #038-40-2000 L2006 **IM** *020
VIA, Dan Forrest. 4374 NEW TOWN AVE, STE 202 23188 #036-07-1994 L1997 **PD** *020 †55
VOLZ, Lawrence Robt. 120 KINGS WAY, STE 3200 23185 #041-01-1989 L1995 **U** *020 †95
VYAS, Hasmukh Amratlal. 4601 IRONBOUND RD, EASTERN STATE HOSP BLDG 2 23188 #495-22-1980 L1984 **P** *020
WALTER, Philip Stuart. 156 STRAWBERRY PLAINS RD #C 23188 #051-04-1987 L1990 **IM** *020 †20
WARD, Ann Marie. ■ 23185 #023-01-1955 L1955 **PD** *071
WARNER, Melissa Lee. 5477 MOORETOWN RD, WILLIAMSBURG PLACE 23188 #051-07-1983 L2000 **OS FM** *020 †18
WEIDIG, Jeffrey Chas. ■ 23188 #041-09-1971 L1972 **OS** *020 †20
WELLS, Christina Lee. 3901 TREYBURN DR, STE 2A 23185 #051-01-1992 L1992 **HO** *020 †20
WELLS, Virginia Denise. 287 MCLAWS CIR, # 2 23185 #048-02-1985 L1986 **IM ID** *020 †20
WENTT, Allan R, Jr. 5249 OLDE TOWNE RD 23188 #051-04-1985 L2002 **OBG** *020 †30
WILHELM, Charles Edwin. 5335 DISCOVERY PARK BLVD, STE B 23188 #051-04-1980 L1981 **ORS** *020 †40
WILHELM, Vicki S. ■ 23185 #051-07-1980 L1983 **IM** *030 †20
WILLIAMS, Robert G W, Jr. ■ 23188 #041-09-1946 **IM** *071
WILLIAMS, Valencia Jones. 5231 JOHN TYLER HWY 23185 #051-04-1995 L1995 **FM** *020 †18
WILSON, Jeffrey Scott. 156 STRAWBERRY PLAINS RD, STE A 23188 #051-07-1997 L2002 **VS** *100
WOLFF, Jennifer Ashley. 4374 NEW TOWN AVE, STE 100 23188 #422-01-2004 L2007 **FM** *020 †18
WOOD, Mark Donald. 4125 IRONBOUND RD, MULTISPECIALTY GROUP 23188 #041-14-1992 L2001 **GS** *020 †85
WOOD, Thomas B. ■ 23185 #051-04-1978 L1981 **FM** *075 †18
WOODWARD, Denton D. 5224 IVEY LN 23188 #011-02-1971 L1972 **R GP** *020 ‡
YOUNG, Robert B. ■ 23188 #019-02-1953 L1959 **FM CD** *071 †18
YOUSEF, Mashour Yousef. 120 KINGS WAY, STE 3100 23185 #875-03-1989 L2005 **HO IM** *020 †20
ZIEGLER, Penelope Proctor. 5477 MOORETOWN RD, THE WILLIAM J FARLEY CTR 23188 #010-01-1978 L1996 **P ADM** *020 †75

WILLIAMSBURG – WILLIAMSBURG CITY

BELL, Baxter Israel, Jr. ■ 23187 #051-04-1954 L1954 **GP** *071
ELLIS, Kimberly Telexa. ■ 23187 #018-03-1994 L2006 **FM P** *020 †18
JACOBY, William J, Jr. PO BOX 506 23187 #041-02-1950 L1984 **IM** *071 †20
KENDALL, Mark Acton. ■ 23187 #010-03-1965 L1976 **R** *020 †80,28

WILLIS – FLOYD

ENCARNACION, Maria D. 586 FERNEY CREEK RD NW 24380 #847-02-1980 L1988 **FM** *020 †18
MEADOWS, Linville Monroe. ■ 24380 #036-01-1982 L1984 **HEM IM** *020

WINCHESTER – FREDERICK

APOSTLE, Thomas Christ. ■ 22603 #028-02-1958 L1964 **AN** *071 †05
BERG, Mark Jonathan. 3202 VALLEY PIKE # 1 22602 #035-15-1984 L2001 **FM** *020 †18
BERRY, Wayne J, II. 199 GLENDOBBIN LN 22603 #051-07-1986 L2006 **FM** *020 †18
BROWN, Matthew G. ■ 22603 #041-02-1952 L1953 **FM** *071 †18
CREASY, Richard Alan. ■ 22602 #051-01-1973 L1977 **AN** *071 †05
DOERING, Mark Wm. 874 FOX DR, PREVENTIVE WOMENS HEALTH 22603 #065-01-1984 L1989 **OBG** *020 †30
FONTAINE, Juliette Savon. 141 FORT COLLIER RD, MEDKO 22603 #025-12-1989 L1997 **FM** *020 †18
GIUNTA, Joseph L. ■ 22602 #010-02-1963 L1986 **PS** *075 †85
GLOVER, Tamara Denise. ■ 22602 #051-07-2007 L2007 **FP** *012
GREEN, Howard Malcolm. 878 FOX DR, WINCHESTER ANESTHESIOLOGIS 22603 #024-05-1989 L2007 **AN** *020 †05
GREENBERG, Jerome H. ■ 22603 #010-02-1949 L1952 **PHP** *071 †70
HANSEN, Hobart Garfield. ■ 22603 #051-01-1957 L1957 **P** *071
HARBOURNE, Kevin Scott. 878 FOX DR 22603 #036-05-1990 L2000 **CCA** *020 †05
HARRY, David Kent. 160 EXETER DR 22603 #039-01-1985 L1989 **R** *020 †80
HYNES, Alla Golovkina. 129 FORTRESS DR 22603 #913-69-1996 L2004 **OPH** *020 †35
JACKSON, Randolph M. ■ 22603 #051-04-1946 L1946 **AN** *071 †05
KICZALES, Adolphe Chas. ■ 22603 #010-01-1955 L1964 **P** *071
LYNN, Hugh B. ■ 22603 #035-01-1940 L1941 **PDS** *071 †85
MADDOX, Joseph Edward. ■ 22602 #046-01-1962 L1962 **GYN** *071 †30
MATTSON, Daniel Henry. ■ 22603 #047-06-1952 L1952 **IM AI** *072 †20
MAYO, Fitzhugh. ■ 22603 #051-04-1955 L1955 **FM** *030 †18
MC CABE, Joseph G. ■ 22602 #051-01-1977 L1982 **DR** *020 †80
POLING, Harry Emerson. 878 FOX DR, ANESTHESIOLOGISTS INC 22603 #041-12-1971 L1974 **AN** *020 †05 ‡

REPASKY, Ronald Geo. 160 EXETER DR 22603 #038-06-1990 L1991 **DR** *020 †80
RIZZO, Richard John. 160 EXETER DR 22603 #041-02-1989 L1992 **DR AR** *020 †80
SACKL, Terri Lynn. ■ 22602 #038-43-1986 L1996 **PD** *020 †55
SAVARESE, Melchior F R. ■ 22602 #010-02-1949 L1955 **OBG** *071 †30
SHARMA, Sunil. 201 WOODFIELD LN, 201 WOODFIELD LANE 22602 #035-03-1991 L1995 **EM** *020 †16
SNOW, David Michael. 160 EXETER DR 22603 #051-07-1987 L1991 **DR VIR** *020 †80
THWING, Curtis Jeffrey. 160 EXETER DR 22603 #051-04-1995 L1995 **DR** *020 †80
VAUGHAN, Ward Pierman. 202 BROOKNEIL DR 22602 #041-09-1974 L1978 **OBG** *020 †30
VORSTER, Molly Cage. ■ 22602 #051-04-2006 L2006 **FP** *012
WATTS, Blake Howard. 160 EXETER DR 22603 #051-01-1985 L1986 **DR** *020 †80
WHITWORTH, Frank Dixon. ■ 22603 #023-01-1937 L1939 **GP** *072
WILLI, Francis Walter. 160 EXETER DR 22603 #010-02-1984 L1990 **DR** *020 †80
WOOD, John Lawrence. 160 EXETER DR 22603 #011-03-1973 L1985 **DR** *020 †80
YOUNG, Kyle Wilson. 160 EXETER DR 22603 #051-01-1998 L1998 **DR** *020 †80

WINCHESTER – WINCHESTER CITY

ABASSI, Imran. 1840 AMHERST ST, WINCHESTER MEDICAL CENTER 22601 #704-21-1993 L2007 **PYG** *020 †75
ABDUL-RAHMAN, Mustapha. 1840 AMHERST ST 22601 #913-32-1994 L2001 **END** *100
ABRAHAM, Yirgalem M. 1840 AMHERST ST, VALLEY HOSPITALISTS, PC 22601 #366-01-1988 L2003 **IM** *020 †20
AHMAD, Raheel. 1870 AMHERST ST, STE 2B 22601 #704-05-1991 L2001 **IM** *020 †20
APPIAH, Victor. 500 W JUBAL EARLY DR, STE 120 22601 #412-01-1995 L2003 **FM** *100 †18
ARMSTRONG, John Harry. 104 SELMA DR 22601 #025-01-1971 L1978 **ID IM** *020 †20
AVERILL, Katherine Ann. 212 LINDEN DR, STE 154 22601 #051-07-1994 L1998 **OBG** *020 †30
BACON, Anne M. 1730 AMHERST ST 22601 #051-01-1977 L1981 **RHU IM** *020 †20
BAGOUS, Trine N. 1330 AMHERST ST 22601 #297-01-1992 L2003 **OBG** *020 †30
BARCH, Cyril Allan. 104 SELMA DR, SELMA MED ASSOC 22601 #051-04-1974 L1990 **IM IMG** *020 †20
BASSO, Alessandro G. 20 S STEWART ST 22601 #561-06-1956 L1974 **U UP** *071 †95
BECHAMPS, Gerald Jos. 20 S STEWART ST, STE 100 22601 #010-02-1963 L1971 **GS SO** *020 †85
BENDER, William Jos. 1867 AMHERST ST 22601 #051-04-1986 L1987 **FM** *020 †18
BENKELMAN, Doug Wade. 1840 AMHERST ST 22601 #028-03-1995 L2002 **EM** *020 †16
BOGAERT, Maria Alicia. 1514 AMHERST ST, DERMATOLOGY ASSOCIATES, IN 22601 #308-02-1984 L1994 **D IM** *020 †20,15
BOTT, D Gregory. 1870 AMHERST ST 22601 #055-01-1977 L1980 **PD** *020 †55
BOWERS, Timothy K, Jr. 172 LINDEN DR, STE 105 22601 #051-04-1994 L1995 **GS** *020 †85
BOYD, Loretta Anne. 20 S STEWART ST, STE 100 22601 #051-01-1996 L2001 **GS** *020 †85
BRALY, Jimmy Lee. 423 WEST CORK ST 22601 #028-34-1970 L2005 **OS GP** *020
BRINK, William Clarence. ■ 22601 #041-13-1993 L1993 **IM** *020 †20
BROWN, J Dixon. 190 CAMPUS BLVD, STE 200 22601 #041-14-1979 L1984 **CD** *020 †20
BROWN, Stuart E, III. 1840 AMHERST ST 22601 #051-01-1984 L1986 **EM** *020 †16
BRUHN, Erich Wm. 190 CAMPUS BLVD, STE 410 22601 #021-01-1988 L2000 **GS** *020 †85
BURNS, Charles Leon, Jr. ■ 22601 #051-04-1959 L1959 **OPH** *071 †35
BURSLEM, Wm Ashworth, Jr. 1870 AMHERST ST, STE 2B 22601 #051-01-1969 L1969 **RHU IM** *071 †20
BYRD, Jessica P. 2913 VALLEY AVE STE 200, APPLE BLOSSOM FAMILY PRACT 22601 #055-01-1997 L1997 **FM** *020 †18
CAGGIANO, Gian B A. 607 E JUBAL EARLY DR 22601 #010-01-1968 L1977 **EM** *020 †16
CALDWELL, Anne B. 1840 AMHERST ST 22601 #143-08-1973 L1994 **EM IM** *020 †20
CALDWELL, Eston Robert. 190 CAMPUS BLVD, WINCHESTER PEDIATRIC 22601 #036-05-1976 L1983 **PD** *020 †55
CALL, Jason Thomas. 190 CAMPUS BLVD, STE 200 22601 #047-05-1998 L2005 **IC** *020 †20
CALL, Jillian Hurley. 1840 AMHERST ST 22601 #047-05-1998 L2005 **EM** *020
CAMERON, O Winston, Jr. 1840 AMHERST ST 22601 #027-01-1977 L1994 **ORS** *020 †40
CAPONE, Patrick Michael. 125 MEDICAL CIR, CONSULTANTS INC 22601 #035-06-1987 L1992 **N NRN** *020 †75
CARL, John Milton, III. 20 S STEWART ST 22601 #055-02-1993 L2000 **GS** *020 †85
CARTER, John Bocock. 190 CAMPUS BLVD 22601 #051-01-1984 L1990 **OPH** *020 †35
CATLETT, Richard Henry. 1400 AMHERST ST, WINCHESTER PULMONARY & 22601 #051-01-1984 L1992 **PUD IM** *020 †20
CHADDUCK, James Bickford. 1818 AMHERST ST, CONSULTANTS INC 22601 #051-01-1991 L1993 **NS** *020 †25
CHAMBERS, Beverly Noe. 1824 W PLAZA DR, STE D 22601 #051-04-1958 L1967 **OS** *071
CHEEMA, Rauf Aman. 1840 AMHERST ST 22601 #704-21-1988 L2002 **P** *020 †75
CHESSON, John Perry. 1104 AMHERST ST, STE 204 22601 #016-02-1999 L1999 **U** *100 †95
CHILDRESS, Stuart P, Jr. 1400 AMHERST ST, WINCHESTER PULMONARY & 22601 #051-04-1970 L1970 **IM PUD** *020 †20
CHO, Andrew Changyoun. 1840 AMHERST ST 22601 #035-09-2001 L2004 **IM** *100
CHOI, John Youngjoon. 125 MEDICAL CIR, CONSULTANTS INC 22601 #041-09-1992 L2006 **N** *020 †75
CHOWDHURY, Abdur Rouf. 1512 BROOKDALE CT 22601 #160-01-1980 L1999 **PD** *020 †55
CLAWSON, Teresa Louise. 1840 AMHERST ST 22601 #017-20-1990 L1996 **NPM** *020 †55
COOPER, Richard Coleman. 1818 AMHERST ST 22601 #048-02-1977 L1988 **NS** *071 †25
COURTNEY, Thomas Weldon. 128 MEDICAL CIR 22601 #008-01-2000 L2006 **ORS** *020
CRAFT, George Francis, II. 1870 AMHERST ST, STE 2E 22601 #051-04-1988 L1995 **OBG** *020 †30
CRESSY, Elizabeth Delpit. 1840 AMHERST ST, VALLEY HOSPITALISTS, PC 22601 #036-01-1992 L1993 **IM** *020 †20
CROWE, Neil Ward. 125 MEDICAL CIR, CONSULTANTS INC 22601 #020-12-1985 L1990 **NRN CN** *020 †75
CUMMINGS, Steven Paul. 1840 AMHERST ST, MOB I STE 2A 22601 #011-03-1985 L1996 **TS VS** *020 †85,90
DABINETT, Laura Nevins. 1820 W PLAZA DR 22601 #051-01-1986 L1989 **GYN** *020 †30
DAGUIO, Monina Fernandez. 1830 AMHERST ST 22601 #748-31-2000 L2005 **FP** *012
DAHIMENE, Mounira. 1002 AMHERST ST STE C, PEDIATRIC ASSOCIATES OF WI 22601 #125-01-1996 L2003 **PD** *020 †55
DALESSIO, Santa. 1400 AMHERST ST, WINCHESTER PULMONARY & 22601 #035-08-1993 L2001 **CCM** *020 †20
DAMRON, Joseph Mc Donald. 190 CAMPUS BLVD STE 400 22601 #051-04-1948 L1948 **PD** *020 †55
DAMRON, Joseph Mc Donald. 190 CAMPUS BLVD, WINCHESTER PEDIATRIC 22601 #422-01-1986 L1989 **PD** *020 †55
DANSIE, Chad L. 1840 AMHERST ST 22601 #049-01-1995 L1995 **PD** *020 †55
DAUGHERTY, Thomas Wilson. 1840 AMHERST ST 22601 #051-04-1970 L1970 **ORS** *020 †40
DAVIS, Cee Ann. 130 W PICCADILLY ST, BLUE RIDGE WOMENS CARE PC 22601 #051-01-1983 L1990 **OBG** *020 †30 ‡
DAVIS, John Edward, III. 1870 AMHERST ST, ANESTHESIOLOGISTS INC AT 22601 #055-01-1980 L1983 **AN PME** *020 †05
DEES, Charles Donald. 1840 AMHERST ST 22601 #051-01-1994 L2004 **EM** *020 †16
DEHAVEN, Kristin Denielle. 1330 AMHERST ST 22601 #055-01-1997 L2003 **OBG** *020 †30
DENNARD, Andrew Keith. 1870 AMHERST ST, ANESTHESIOLOGISTS INC AT 22601 #012-22-1999 L2004 **AN** *020 †05
DILLINGHAM, Robert Carter. 1840 AMHERST ST 22601 #011-03-1985 L1989 **PTH** *020 †50
DILLON, Savtanter S. 1840 AMHERST ST 22601 #506-04-1973 L1996 **P** *020 †75
DRAKE, Charles Roy, Jr. 1870 AMHERST ST, STE 2B 22601 #051-01-1979 L1983 **IM DIA** *020 †20
DUCK, Leda Ann. 190 CAMPUS BLVD, WINCHESTER PEDIATRIC 22601 #051-01-1996 L1999 **PD** *020 †55
DUCK, Robert William. 1104 AMHERST ST, STE 102 22601 #051-01-1995 L1999 **FM** *020 †18
DUMONT, James P. 20 S STEWART ST, STE 100 22601 #067-01-1988 L1995 **GS** *020 †85
EDWARDS, Jessica D. ■ 22601 #035-06-1999 L2002 **OBG** *020 †30
EDWARDS, Jessica P. 1330 AMHERST ST 22601 #048-13-2004 L2008 **AN** *012
EISELE, Nancy B. 1845 W PLAZA DR, EYE ASSOC OF WINCHESTER 22601 #028-46-1984 L1988 **OPH** *020 †35
EISENBERG, Dorothy Baker. 190 CAMPUS BLVD, WINCHESTER PEDIATRIC 22601 #036-07-1985 L1994 **PD** *020 †55
ELLIS, William Wallace. 1870 AMHERST ST STE 3D 22601 #024-01-1961 L1964 **IM** *071 †20
EPSTEIN, David Andrew. 1870 AMHERST ST, BLDG 1 22601 #038-40-1995 L2002 **VS** *020 †85
EVANS, Frances Russell. 1824 W PLAZA DR STE D 22601 #051-07-1991 L1993 **IM** *020 †20
FARRA, Frederic Thos. 190 CAMPUS BLVD, STE 200 22601 #023-01-1977 L1987 **CD IM** *020 †20
FERGUS, Allan Harold. 1818 AMHERST ST, CONSULTANTS INC 22601 #051-01-1996 L2002 **NS** *020 †25
FIEO, Richard Leonard. 1330 AMHERST ST, STE A 22601 #041-02-1972 L1978 **OBG** *020 †30
FIRDOUS, Shabana. 1812 W PLAZA DR 22601 #704-21-1989 L2002 **P** *020 †75
FITZSIMMONS, Daniel J. 1002 AMHERST ST, STE C 22601 #010-02-2001 L2001 **PD** *020 †55
FLAX, Bruce Laurence. 1870 AMHERST ST, STE B 22601 #010-02-1982 L1990 **RO** *020 †20,80
FOUST, Robert James. 322 W PICCADILLY ST 22601 #046-01-1980 L1991 **DR** *020 †80
FOWLER, Mariecken V. 125 MEDICAL CIR, CONSULTANTS INC 22601 #051-01-2001 L2005 **N** *100 †75
FOX, Preston Stuart. 1840 AMHERST ST, WINCHESTER RADIOLOGISTS, P 22601 #051-01-1985 L1990 **DR** *020 †80
FREDIEU, Andre. 125 MEDICAL CIR, CONSULTANTS INC 22601 #005-14-1998 L2005 **IM N** *020 †75
FREILICH, Vicki Simmons. 1002 AMHERST ST, STE C 22601 #051-01-1999 L2002 **PD** *020 †55
FUTRAL, Allen Ashley, Jr. 190 CAMPUS BLVD STE 200 22601 #051-01-1960 L1960 **CD IM** *071 †20
GAITHER, Neal Streater. 1840 AMHERST ST 22601 #051-04-1980 L1991 **CD IM** *020 †20
GALBRAITH, Mark. 104 SELMA DR 22601 #016-11-1976 L1988 **IM ID** *020 †20
GALL, Adam F, Jr. 1104 AMHERST ST STE 100 22601 #055-01-1981 L2004 **GS** *020 †85,65
GARDINER, James Estes. 190 CAMPUS BLVD, STE 300 22601 #051-04-1978 L1980 **GE IM** *020 †20
GAUNT, Hunter Marshall. ■ 22601 #051-04-1957 L1957 **GS VS** *071 †85
GAWALT, Susan Jane. 1002 AMHERST ST STE C 22601 #051-01-1994 L1997 **PD** *020 †55
GEIB, Kevin Shane. 148 LINDEN DR, STE 103 22601 #028-46-1994 L1995 **U** *020 †95
GEMMA, Nicholas Wm. 1870 AMHERST ST STE F 22601 #051-01-1985 L1987 **ON HEM** *020 †20
GHRAMM, John William. 1824 AMHERST ST 22601 #143-03-1972 L1977 **OBG** *075 †30
GIANGOLA, John. 607 E JUBAL EARLY DR, VRE, DBA URGENT CARE CENTE 22601 #561-01-1974 L1978 **EM** *020 †16
GIBBS, Thomas Avery. 104 SELMA DR, SELMA MEDICAL ASSOC 22601 #039-01-1995 L1998 **IM** *020 †20
GIBSON, Thomas Jesse. 20 S STEWART ST, STE 100 22601 #041-13-1972 L1977 **GS** *020 †85
GILDERSLEEVE, Gerald Alan. 1840 AMHERST ST 22601 #051-04-1958 L1958 **R OS** *071 †80
GILLIS, Laura Girandola. 1867 AMHERST ST 22601 #035-46-1994 L2001 **GPM** *020 †70
GLEMBOT, Troy Martin. 20 S STEWART ST 22601 #051-07-1991 L1991 **GS** *020 †85
GOFF, Rowland Daley, Jr. 20 S STEWART ST 22601 #036-01-1963 L1986 **TS GS** *071 †85,90
GOPAL, Alok. 190 CAMPUS BLVD, STE 420 22601 #496-09-1990 L2005 **APM** *020 †05
GOPAL, Meenakshi. 1440 AMHERST ST, PRACTICE PC 22601 #496-09-1992 L2005 **IM** *020 †20
GOSHEN, Charles Robt. 200 N WASHINGTON ST 22601 #055-01-1968 L1992 **CHP P** *020 †75
GUIRGUIS, Adel Bassily. 1712 AMHERST ST 22601 #330-01-1957 L1967 **U** *020 †95
GUSTIN, Harry N, III. 522 AMHERST ST, AMHERST FAMILY PRACTICE 22601 #051-04-1978 L1979 **FM** *020 †18 ‡
GUSTIN, Katherine Hawkins. 125 MEDICAL CIR, CONSULTANTS INC 22601 #051-04-1979 L1980 **N** *020 †75
HA, Mai Amy. 333 WEST CORK ST, FOURTH FLOOR 22601 #665-01-1997 L2003 **IMG** *020 †20
HAAG, Gary Allen. 1870 AMHERST ST, ANESTHESIOLOGISTS INC AT 22601 #018-75-1981, ▲ L2001 **AN** *020 †05
HAGAN, Charles Henry. 1870 AMHERST ST, ANESTHESIOLOGISTS INC AT 22601 #055-01-1975 L1983 **AN** *020 †05
HAGERTY, Mary. 1730 AMHERST ST 22601 #016-01-1982 L1992 **RHU** *020 †20
HALL, Robert Batson. 1800 W PLAZA DR 22601 #051-01-1958 L1958 **GYN** *020 †30
HAMIL, Rachel Williams. 1840 AMHERST ST 22601 #012-01-1996 L2003 **EM** *020 †16
HANCOCK, William Jos. 190 CAMPUS BLVD, STE 200 22601 #051-01-1958 L1958 **IM** *071 †20
HARRIS, Gregory Paul. 1870 AMHERST ST, ANESTHESIOLOGISTS INC AT 22601 #035-46-1983 L1988 **AN** *020 †05
HARRIS, Jeffrey Peden. 1839 W PLAZA DR 22601 #012-01-1972 L1974 **IM NEP** *020 †20
HAVRON, Milton Dean, Jr. 117 W BOSCAWEN ST, STE 201 22601 #051-01-1989 L1997 **FM** *020 †18
HELM, W Jackson. ■ 22601 #041-13-1957 L1958 **OS PUD** *071 †20
HENDREN, Michael Dale. 1840 AMHERST ST 22601 #051-07-1999 L1999 **EM** *020 †16
HETHCOAT, Gayland Oliver. 190 CAMPUS BLVD, STE 200 22601 #012-22-1993 L2001 **IM** *020 †20
HILL, Douglass Orville. ■ 22601 #051-04-1947 L1947 **IM PUD** *071
HILLYARD, Raymond W, Jr. 1712 AMHERST ST 22601 #041-02-1981 L1986 **U** *020 †95
HIRSCHBERG, Stanley M. 1818 AMHERST ST 22601 #010-01-1965 L1970 **PS** *020 †65

■ = Address Information Privacy Protected

HOFFMAN, Michael Anthony. 1712 AMHERST ST, UROLOGY CLINIC OF WINCHEST 22601 #041-14-1995 L2002 **U** *020 †95
HOUCK, William Albert, Jr. 1870 AMHERST ST STE F 22601 #051-01-1968 L1968 **ON HO** *020 †20
HOUCK, William Albert, III. 1870 AMHERST ST, STE F 22601 #051-04-1998 L1998 **HO** *020 †20
HOUSER, Archie W. 212 LINDEN DR STE 152 22601 #048-02-1993 L2000 **IM DIA** *020 †20
HOUSER, Patricia Murphy. 1867 AMHERST ST 22601 #048-02-1993 L2000 **FM** *020 †18
HUME, John Mitchell. 1840 AMHERST ST 22601 #041-01-1955 L1997 **P PFP** *020 †75
HYLTON, Paul Hampton, Jr. 1002 AMHERST ST STE C, PED ASSOC OF WINCHESTER 22601 #051-01-1960 L1960 **PD** *020
INGRAM, Richard Michael. 1870 AMHERST ST, STE F 22601 #035-15-1995 L1995 **HO** *020 †20
IRELAND, Patrick David. 1818 AMHERST ST, CONSULTANTS INC 22601 #036-05-1989 L1995 **NS** *020 †25
IRIANNI, Francisco Manuel. 1840 AMHERST ST 22601 #132-01-1967 L1987 **GYN REN** *020 †30
ISENHOWER, Nelson Nolan. 1870 AMHERST ST, ANESTHESIOLOGISTS INC AT 22601 #036-05-1974 L1983 **AN** *020 †05 ‡
IWANOW, Ingrid Christine. 142 LINDEN DR, STE 106 22601 #032-01-1996 L2001 **OTO** *020 †45
JAFARBAY, Ashkan. 1840 AMHERST ST, PRIMEDOC OF WINCHESTER, PC 22601 #305-01-2000 L2003 **IM** *020 †20
JOGLEKAR, Jairaj Suresh. 172 LINDEN DR, STE 100 22601 #894-01-2001 L2004 *020
JOHNSON, Helen Rebecca. 130 PEYTON ST 22601 #051-07-1991 L1992 **FM** *020 †18
JOHNSON, Peter Albrecht. 116 MEDICAL CIR 22601 #030-06-1981 L1982 **OTO AI** *020 †45
JOHNSTON, Tracy Marie. 1440 AMHERST ST, CITY HOSPITAL 22601 #051-04-1994 L2008 **FM** *020
JONES, David Joseph. 1840 AMHERST ST 22601 #305-01-2001 L2004 **IM HOS** *020
JONES, Jo Allen. 2057 CIDERMILL LN 22601 #055-01-1978 L1983 **FM** *020 †18
JONES, Robert Mark. 607 E JUBAL EARLY DR, URGENT CARE CENTER 22601 #055-01-1977 L1983 **EM FM** *020 †18,16
KALBIAN, Vicken V. 1440 AMHERST ST 22601 #605-01-1949 L1969 **IM CD** *020
KAREN, Matthew Evan. 116 MEDICAL CIR, WINCHESTER EAR NOSE THROAT 22601 #035-15-1993 L2001 **OTO** *020 †45
KAROLYI, Don Gary. 1867 AMHERST ST 22601 #012-01-1973 L1978 *071
KATARI, Sreelatha. 333 WEST CORK ST, UNIT 145 22601 #496-24-1992 L1999 **PM PME** *020 †60
KEENAN, Thomas P. 302 S CAMERON ST 22601 #010-02-1967 L1975 **OPH** *071 †35
KEIM, Douglas Brian. 190 CAMPUS BLVD, STE 200 22601 #051-01-1994 L1994 **IM** *020 †20
KEITH, Kimberly Davis. ■ 22601 #051-04-1986 L1989 **EM** *020 †16
KELLAMS, Ann Lenox. 1840 AMHERST ST 22601 #005-02-1995 L1998 **PD** *020 †55
KENDALL, Robert Gentry. ■ 22601 #051-04-1962 L1962 **CD NS** *071 †25
KESSLER, George H, Jr. 230 W BOSCAWEN ST 22601 #023-07-1960 L1967 **GE IM** *071 †20
KHAN, Ejaz A. ■ 22601 #704-25-1988 L1993 **PD** *020 †55
KHODR, Mohamed Ali. 150 W COMMERCIAL ST 22601 #605-01-1984 L1992 **GPM PHP** *030 †70
KIDD, Leslie S. 1840 AMHERST ST 22601 #047-06-1994 L1998 **OBG** *020 †30
KITCHIN, Llewellyn Irby. 190 CAMPUS BLVD, STE 300 22601 #051-01-1983 L1984 **GE IM** *020 †20
KLIEWER, David Joe. 1870 AMHERST ST, ANESTHESIOLOGISTS INC AT 22601 #023-07-1987 L2002 **AN** *020 †05
KORNREICH, Bryan Asher. 1002 AMHERST ST STE C, PEDIATRICS ASSOCIATES 22601 #023-07-1996 L1996 **PD** *020 †55 ‡
KOSCIUK, Martin. 1830 AMHERST ST 22601 #132-02-1998 L2005 **FP** *012
KOZLOWSKI, Frederick H. 190 CAMPUS BLVD, STE 200 22601 #051-01-1994 L1994 **IM** *020 †20
KUJALA, Gregory A. 1870 AMHERST ST STE 1D 22601 #041-02-1981 L1990 **RHU IM** *020 †20
LAIDLAW, James Carter. 190 CAMPUS BLVD, MEDICAL OFC BLDG STE 430 22601 #025-01-1963 L1970 **CD IM** *071 †20
LANDRIO, Julie Ann. 1870 AMHERST ST, STE 2B 22601 #024-07-1995 L1998 **IM** *020 †20
LANDRIO, Mark Allen. 905 CEDAR CREEK GRADE, STE 200 22601 #024-07-1993 L1998 **N** *020 †75
LEE, Don Dongsoo. 123 AMHERST ST 22601 #051-01-1988 L1993 **P** *020 †75
LEE, Edward Ingfei. 1840 AMHERST ST 22601 #036-01-1990 L1998 **NPM** *020 †55
LEONARD, Mark Thomas. 1870 AMHERST ST, STE 2E 22601 #051-04-1993 L1993 **OBG** *020 †30
LESKOVEC, William Conrad. 1840 AMHERST ST 22601 #035-06-1984 L1985 **IM** *020 †20
LESSAR, Jeffrey Scott. 1400 AMHERST ST, WINCHESTER PULMONARY & 22601 #048-13-2000 L2006 **PCC** *020 †20
LEVINSON, Mark Edward. 1712 AMHERST ST 22601 #041-02-1992 L1998 **U** *020 †95
LEWIS, Benj Franklin, Jr. 1400 AMHERST ST, WINCHESTER PULMONARY & 22601 #036-01-1975 L1981 **IM PUD** *020 †20
LIVERMON, Jefferson F, Jr. 1867 AMHERST ST 22601 #051-07-1983 L1994 **FM** *020 †18
LIZER, James Robt. 335 WESTSIDE STATION DR 22601 #025-01-1983 L1987 **P CHP** *020 †75
LOWDER, John Henry, Jr. 1870 AMHERST ST, STE 2E 22601 #036-08-1981 L1985 **OBG** *020 †30
LUDDEN, John Michael. 190 CAMPUS BLVD, STE 310 22601 #051-04-2000 L2003 **IM** *020 †20 ‡
LUONG, Linda Le. 440 W JUBAL EARLY DR, STE 240 22601 #051-04-1999 L2006 **FM** *020 †18
LUTZ, Roy Winston. ■ 22601 #051-01-1967 L1967 **PD NEP** *072 †55
LYONS, Lisa Anandi. 1840 AMHERST ST, WINCHESTER EMERGENCY PHYSI 22601 #051-07-2002 L2002 **EM** *100 †16
LYONS, Paul Damien. 125 MEDICAL CIR, CONSULTANTS INC 22601 #001-02-2000 L2001 **N** *020 †75
MAC ISAAC, Elaine Carol. 104 SELMA DR 22601 #064-01-1987 L1998 **FM** *020 †18
MAGARIK, David Eric. 1840 AMHERST ST, 161 CHEIFTON PL 22601 #028-02-1976 L2002 **DR** *020 †80
MARFING, Thos Edward, Jr. 190 CAMPUS BLVD STE 410 22601 #051-04-1980 L1989 **GS** *020 †85
MARINO, John J. 1840 AMHERST ST 22601 #010-02-1972 L1978 **AN** *071 †05
MARTENSON, Stephen H. 128 MEDICAL CIR 22601 #051-01-1978 L1983 **ORS OSM** *020 †40
MARTIN, Lewis K, II. PO BOX 3340, DEPT RADIOLOGY 22604 #051-01-1967 L1972 **R** *020 †80
MARTINEZ, Carlos Jaime. 1830 AMHERST ST 22601 #654-01-2004 L2005 **FP** *012
MARTINEZ, Mauricio Albert. 1840 AMHERST ST 22601 #035-08-1994 L2000 **EM** *020 †16
MATTHEWS, Marianne Parham. 1870 AMHERST ST, ANESTHESIOLOGISTS INC AT 22601 #051-04-1988 L1992 **AN** *020 †05
MATTSON, Melanie Danielle. 190 CAMPUS BLVD, STE 200 22601 #021-06-1987 L1988 **CD** *020 †20
MC AULIFFE, Michael John. 1840 AMHERST ST 22601 #010-02-1980 L2000 **EM** *020 †16
MC CLAUGHERTY, Glenn K. 335 WESTSIDE STATION DR 22601 #051-04-1989 L1993 **P** *020 †75
MC COY, Mary Cathleen. 1330 AMHERST ST STE A, WINCHESTER OB/GYN, P.L.C 22601 #038-40-1966 L1995 **OBG MFM** *020 †30
MC KELWAY, Russell Brick. 1812 W PLAZA DR 22601 #051-01-1984 L1985 **P IM** *020 †20,75
MC LELLAN, David Curtis. 1870 AMHERST ST, ANESTHESIOLOGISTS INC AT 22601 #021-01-1981 L1993 **AN GS** *020 †05
MC PHERSON, Lon Helton. 1840 AMHERST ST, OFFICE OF INTERNAL AFFAIRS 22601 #016-01-1985 L1988 **IM IMG** *030 †20
MC WHORTER, W David. 1330 AMHERST ST STE A 22601 #051-04-1960 L1966 **OBG** *071 †30
MIKUS, Joseph Leo. 142 LINDEN DR, STE 106 22601 #041-14-1990 L1995 **OTO** *020 †45
MINGHINI, Anita. 172 LINDEN DR STE 103, WINCHESTER BREAST CENTER, 22601 #051-07-1993 L1993 **GS** *020 †85
MOGILI, Lakuma Reddy. 1014 AMHERST ST, STE 202 22601 #496-01-1996 L2004 **P** *020
MONROE, Stuart Alan. 1840 AMHERST ST, PATHOLOGY 22601 #005-06-1962 L1985 **PTH** *030 †50
MOOMAU, George Benjamin. 607 E JUBAL EARLY DR 22601 #055-01-1979 L1986 **EM** *020 †18
MOORE, Richard C. 12 N BRADDOCK ST 22601 #005-14-1972 L1996 **FM OM** *030 †18
MUELLER, Paul Shipman. ■ 22601 #032-01-1997 L1999 **P** *020
MURPHY, Thomas Michael. 1400 AMHERST ST, WINCHESTER PULMONARY & 22601 #051-07-1983 L1991 **PUD IM** *020 †20
NASHED, James Khalil. 1870 AMHERST ST STE 2E 22601 #011-02-1997 L1997 **OBG** *020 †30
NATALE, Melissa Anne. 1840 AMHERST ST 22601 #041-13-1995 L2002 **EM** *020 †16
NEMEC, Richard Louis. 190 CAMPUS BLVD, STE 300 22601 #038-40-1982 L1991 **IM** *020 †20
NENE, Vaishali Vilas. 172 LINDEN DR 22601 #028-46-1994 L1995 **IM** *020 †20
NGUYEN, Thai Quang. 1840 AMHERST ST, DEPT OF EMERGENCY MEDICINE 22601 #021-05-1992 L2002 **EM** *020 †16
NUCKOLS, John Thos. 1840 AMHERST ST 22601 #051-04-1967 L1967 **P** *071 †75
O'DONNELL, Philip John. 104 SELMA DR, SELMA MED ASSOC INC 22601 #051-04-1976 L1977 **IM** *020 †20
OLIVER, Thomas Wright. 1712 AMHERST ST 22601 #065-05-1983 L1988 **U** *020 †95
O'MARA, Sean T. 1840 AMHERST ST 22601 #041-13-1997 L2006 **EM** *020
OMUNDSEN, Beth Ann. 1820 W PLAZA DR 22601 #041-14-1988 L1989 **FM** *020 †18
PARIKH, Gaurav Tarunkumar. 1840 AMHERST ST, VALLEY HOSPITALISTS, PC 22601 #495-23-1995 L2006 **IM** *020 †20
PARK, Sohyun Carolyn. 1840 AMHERST ST, PRIME DOC OF WINCHESTER, P 22601 #010-01-1997 L1999 **IM** *020 †20
PARKER, Kenneth Robt. 333 W CORK ST, UNIT 145 22601 #038-40-1974 L1979 **PM** *020 †60
PATTERSON, Paige E. 104 SELMA DR 22601 #010-02-1990 L1995 **FM** *020 †18
PATTERSON, Richard Jos. 347 WESTSIDE STATION DR 22601 #010-02-1990 L1995 **ORS** *020 †40
PETERSON, Wesley Harold. 1840 AMHERST ST 22601 #041-09-1967 L1973 **PD PHP** *020
PHILLIPS, George Lauren. 1870 AMHERST ST 22601 #035-15-1969 L1972 **AN** *020 †05
PIANALTO, David Bernard. 1840 AMHERST ST, WINCHESTER EMERGENCY PHYSI 22601 #051-07-2002 L2002 **EM** *020 †16
PILLAI, Shyama. 1440 AMHERST ST, PRACTICE PC 22601 #051-04-1994 L1996 **FM** *020 †18
POE, Joseph Worthy. 1840 AMHERST ST 22601 #055-02-1996 L2001 **RNR** *020 †80
POSS, Michael Joseph. 1818 AMHERST ST, WINCHESTER NEUROLOGICAL CO 22601 #036-05-1993 L2000 **PME AN** *020 †05
POTTER, John Crandall. 1840 AMHERST ST, EMERGENCY DEPT 22601 #051-04-1984 L1998 **NEP** *020 †20
POTTS, Eric Edward. 125 MEDICAL CIR STE A, PHYSICIAN 22601 #056-06-2003 L2007 **N** *100
POWERS, David Wm. 1840 AMHERST ST 22601 #051-04-1983 L1985 **EM** *020 †16
QUINN, John Chas. 190 CAMPUS BLVD, STE 200 22601 #051-04-1972 L1974 **CD IM** *020 †20
RAFTER, Jack R T. 104 SELMA DR 22601 #051-01-1970 L1970 **FM** *020 †18
RAJAN, Rajith. 1840 AMHERST ST 22601 #665-02-2003 L2004 **FM** *020 †18
RANA, Tayyib Shahzad. 1870 AMHERST ST, STE 3A 22601 #055-01-1998 L2004 **OPH** *020
REDDY, Gayathri Muthyala. 1440 AMHERST ST, PRACTICE PC 22601 #495-09-1999 L2006 **FM** *020 †18
REESE, Heather. 212 LINDEN DR, STE 158 22601 #055-01-1998 L2003 **OBG** *020 †30
RESTREPO, Nicolas C. 1712 AMHERST ST 22601 #051-01-1989 L1995 **U** *020 †95
REULING, Frank Harold, Jr. 302 S CAMERON ST 22601 #018-03-1963 L1969 **OPH** *020 †35
REZBA, Benjamin Victor. 1870 AMHERST ST, STE 2D 22601 #016-11-1970 L1973 **ORS** *020 †40
RICHARDSON, Don Harlor. 1840 AMHERST ST, WINCHESTER MED CTR 22601 #036-01-1959 L1965 **PTH CLP** *071 †50,28
RICHMAN, Marc Noah. 148 LINDEN DR, STE 103 22601 #035-06-1998 L2003 **U** *020 †95
RIZVI, Hil. 1840 AMHERST ST 22601 #038-45-1993 L1996 **EM IM** *020 ‡
ROBERTS, Charles Stewart. 1870 AMHERST ST 22601 #012-05-1986 L2000 **TS** *020 †85,90
ROCCA, Michelle Marie. 1870 AMHERST ST, STE 2B 22601 #018-03-1995 L1999 **NEP** *020 †20
ROGATNICK, Lewis Andrew. 380 MILLWOOD AVE 22601 #016-42-1986 L1998 **U GS** *020
RUSSELL, Paul J. 190 CAMPUS BLVD, WINCHESTER PEDIATRIC 22601 #055-01-1988 L1991 **PD** *020 †55
SALATA, James Andrew. 142 LINDEN DR STE 106 22601 #041-01-1991 L1991 **OTO** *020 †45
SCHIAVONE, Danl Chas, Jr. 337 WESTSIDE STATION DR 22601 #011-03-1975 L1978 **PD** *020 †55
SCHOPICK, Steven R. 1818 AMHERST ST, CONSULTANTS INC 22601 #035-46-1992 L2004 **NS** *020 †25
SCHOTT, Sherry K. 1870 AMHERST ST, SUITE 2-B MEDICAL OFFICE B 22601 #055-01-1991 L1994 **IM** *020 †20
SCHROEDER, Mark Douglas. 104 SELMA DR, WINCHESTER MEDICAL CONSULT 22601 #026-04-1978 L1982 **IM** *020 †20
SCHULTZ, Philip Andrew. 1002 AMHERST ST STE C, PEDICTRIC ASSOCIATES OF WI 22601 #051-01-1991 L2007 **PD** *020 †55
SCHWARZ, M Roy. ■ 22601 #054-04-1963 **OS** *030
SCHWENTKER, Andrew E. 190 CAMPUS BLVD, STE 200 22601 #041-14-1997 L1997 **IM** *020 †20
SEARS, Richard John. 190 CAMPUS BLVD, STE 300 22601 #036-05-1991 L1994 **GE HEP** *020 †20
SELZNICK, Lee Andrew. 1818 AMHERST ST, CONSULTANTS INC 22601 #028-02-2001 L2007 **NS** *020
SFEIR, Ramsey. 1870 AMHERST ST, ANESTHESIOLOGISTS INC AT 22601 #038-40-1984 L1989 **AN** *020 †05
SHABB, William Allan. 1870 AMHERST ST, ANESTHESIOLOGISTS INC AT 22601 #055-01-1981 L1985 **AN** *020 †05
SHANABROOK, Kevin Ray. 1840 AMHERST ST 22601 #041-12-1989 L1990 **EM** *020 †16
SHEPPARD, Geo Lester, Jr. 125 MEDICAL CIR STE A 22601 #045-01-1964 L1968 **N** *020 †75

■ = Address Information Privacy Protected

SHIH, Grace Loyu. 190 CAMPUS BLVD, STE 300 22601 #008-01-2000 L2006 **GE** *020 †20
SHYAMSUNDER, Archana K. 190 CAMPUS BLVD STE 310, WINCHESTER MEDICAL CONSULT 22601 #496-07-1996 L2004 **NEP IM** *020 †20
SIIRA, Richard Dana. 1840 AMHERST ST, WINCHESTER EMERGENCY PHYSI 22601 #036-05-1996 L2000 **EM** *020 †16
SINCLAIR, Terry Louis. 1840 AMHERST ST, WINCHESTER MEDICAL CENTER 22601 #025-01-1967 L1974 **GS** *030 †85
SINGER, William Howard. 1870 AMHERST ST, ANESTHESIOLOGISTS INC AT 22601 #041-01-1975 L2003 **AN** *020 †05
SISSON, David Edward. 190 CAMPUS BLVD, STE 310 22601 #033-05-1994 L1999 **NEP** *020 †20
SKILES, Jeffrey Allen. 104 SELMA DR, SELMA MEDICAL ASSOCIATES 22601 #055-01-1994 L1994 **CD** *020 †20
SMITH, Catherine Sarina. 142 LINDEN DR, STE 106 22601 #035-08-1993 L2000 **OTO** *020 †45
SMITH, Connie Lynn. 104 SELMA DR 22601 #055-01-1996 L2002 **PD ID** *020 †20,55
SMITH, Edward Paul. 190 CAMPUS BLVD, STE 200 22601 #010-02-1990 L1991 **IM** *020 †20
SMITH, Norman John. 1870 AMHERST ST, STE B 22601 #038-06-1970 L1971 **RO GP** *020 †80
SNELGROVE, Norman Eli. 104 SELMA DR 22601 #045-04-1986 L1991 **FM** *020 †18
SNOW, Nicholas David. 190 CAMPUS BLVD, STE 300 22601 #038-40-1985 L1995 **GE IM** *020 †20
STAFFORD, James H, Jr. 1870 AMHERST ST STE 2E 22601 #045-01-1964 L1971 **OBG** *020 †30
STAM, Marc Denton. 1870 AMHERST ST STE 2A, WINCHESTER CARDIO & VASCUL 22601 #035-09-1988 L1999 **TS VS** *020 †85,90
STANFORD, Gregory Gerard. 20 S STEWART ST 22601 #047-06-1982 L2004 **TRS CCS** *020 †85
STEFANO, John A. 142 LINDEN DR, STE 108 22601 #035-06-1975 L1982 **OPH** *020 †35
STEUER, Eric Raymond. 1840 AMHERST ST 22601 #028-02-1992 L2004 **OPH** *020 †35
STEWART, Kathleen Ann. 1870 AMHERST ST, STE F 22601 #051-01-1988 L1995 **HO** *020 †20
STRAUS, Karen Lizbeth. 1870 AMHERST ST, STE B 22601 #032-01-1982 L1990 **RO** *020 †80
SWOPE, Bernard Mc Claren. 347 WESTSIDE STATION DR 22601 #041-01-1967 L1983 **ORS HS** *020 †40
THOMPSON, Edward Guerrant. 116 MED CIR 22601 #051-01-1960 L1960 **OTO FPS** *071 †45
THOMPSON, Robert Dean. 1870 AMHERST ST, ANESTHESIOLOGISTS INC AT 22601 #041-15-1999 L2003 **AN** *020 †05
TIMBERLAKE, Byron Burton. ■ 22601 #038-40-1964 L1971 **OTO PS** *020
TOXOPEUS, Margaret E. 1840 AMHERST ST 22601 #025-01-1964 L1971 **R** *020 †80
TREFZGER, Elizabeth Carol. 123 AMHERST ST 22601 #051-04-1986 L1991 **CHP** *020 †75
TROUP, James Bannerman. 20 S STEWART ST, STE 100 22601 #803-01-1951 L1961 **ORS** *020 †40
TROXEL, James Roy. 117 W BOSCAWEN ST 22601 #023-01-1953 L1955 **FM** *071
TSCHIRGI, Laurel Dean. 1870 AMHERST ST, STE 1C 22601 #051-01-1978 L1982 **IM** *020 †20
TUCKER, Ashley Robt, III. 20 S STEWART ST, STE 100 22601 #028-03-1970 L1973 **TS VS** *020 †85,90
TURNBULL, Charles C. 1840 AMHERST ST 22601 #051-07-1999 L1999 **EM** *020 †16
ULICH, Paul John. 20 S STEWART ST 22601 #035-20-1984 L1989 **GS VS** *020 †85
VAN OSTEN, George Karl. 190 CAMPUS BLVD, STE 420 22601 #025-12-1975 L1977 **APM AN** *020 †05
VILAR, Nancy Fe. 420 W JUBAL EARLY DR 22601 #847-04-1983 L2005 **OPH OS** *020 ‡
VIRMANI, Ajay. 650 CEDAR CREEK GRADE, STE 213 22601 #010-01-1991 L1992 **CD VM** *020 †20
VITI, Anthony Jos. 1870 AMHERST ST STE 3B 22601 #055-01-1987 L1999 **OPH** *020 †35
VOLINSKY, John Bryant. 190 CAMPUS BLVD, WINCHESTER PEDIATRIC 22601 #051-01-1987 L1998 **PD** *020 †55
WADE, Karen Elizabeth. 212 LINDEN DR, STE 158 22601 #051-07-1986 L1987 **OBG OS** *020 †30
WAKE, Gary Wentworth. ■ 22604 #051-04-1965 L1965 **FM OM** *071 †18
WALK, J Frederick. ■ 22601 #041-01-1960 L1968 **OBG** *020 †30
WARNER, James G, Jr. 650 CEDAR CREEK GRADE, STE 213 22601 #055-01-1989 L1999 **CD** *020 †20
WARNER, John William. 1712 AMHERST ST 22601 #036-01-1998 L2000 **U** *020 †95
WATTS, Michael Edward. 1840 AMHERST ST 22601 #051-01-1998 L1998 **EM** *020 †16
WEBER, Lisa Kay. 212 LINDEN DR STE 152, WINCHESTER MEDICAL CONSULT 22601 #055-02-1995 L1998 **IM** *020 †20
WEHNER, Robert William. 190 CAMPUS BLVD 22601 #038-41-1985 L1991 **OPH IM** *020 †35
WHITACRE, Samuel N. 1867 AMHERST ST 22601 #051-01-1953 L1953 **GP** *071
WHITE, Andrew Adam. 104 SELMA DR 22601 #051-01-1978 L1997 **FM** *020 †18
WHITE, Henry George, Jr. ■ 22601 #051-04-1962 L1962 **ORS** *071 †40
WIEDOWER, James Steven. 20 S STEWART ST, BARIATRIC PROGRAM 22601 #004-01-1978 L1979 **GS OS** *020 †85
WILLEY, John Boyd. 1330 AMHERST ST, STE A 22601 #051-04-1972 L1973 **OBG** *020 †30
WILSON, Carolyn Scott. 1820 W PLAZA DR 22601 #051-04-1987 L1993 **GYN** *020 †30
WINTER, Curtis Andrew. 1104 AMHERST ST, STE 200 22601 #055-02-1982 L1987 **OBG** *020 †30
WISE, Dennis Watkins. 128 MEDICAL CIR 22601 #035-20-1967 L1974 **ORS HS** *020 †40
WISE, Thomas Watkins. 128 MEDICAL CIR 22601 #036-05-1995 L2000 **ORS** *020 †40
WOLFE, Gordon Keith. 1400 AMHERST ST, WINCHESTER PULMONARY & 22601 #055-01-1978 L1988 **PUD IM** *020 †20
YANG, Leonard Reid. 1840 AMHERST ST 22601 #016-11-1980 L2000 **EM** *020 †18,16
YIRGA, Rahel Gebrehiwot. 1840 AMHERST ST, VALLEY HOSPITALISTS, PC 22601 #023-01-1997 L2002 **IM** *020 †20
YORK, James R. 1824 W PLAZA DR, # D 22601 #051-04-1952 L1952 **FM** *020 †18
YOUNG, Chi Gene. ■ 22601 #028-34-2007 L2008 **GS** *012
ZIAYEE, Assadullah. 607 E JUBAL EARLY DR, URGENT CARE CENTER 22601 #118-01-1971 L1993 **FM** *020 †18
ZOLLER, John H, III. 128 MEDICAL CIR 22601 #038-43-1981 L1988 **ORS** *020 †40
ZONTINE, David Herbert. 125 MEDICAL CIR STE A 22601 #041-12-1964 L1974 **N** *071 †75

WINDSOR – ISLE OF WIGHT

MADDOCK, Stephen William. 70 E WINDSOR BLVD STE G 23487 #051-07-2000 L2001 **GP** *020

WIRTZ – FRANKLIN

BOURHILL, Eric Chas. 6675 BOOKER T WASHNGTN HWY 24184 #051-07-1984 L1988 **FM EM** *020 †18

CHACONAS, George Harry. 6675 BOOKER T WASHNGTN HWY, CARILION FAMILY MEDICINE 24184 #051-07-1984 L1985 **FM** *020 †18
PHILLIPS, Thomas Michael. ■ 24184 #010-02-1966 L1980 **FM IM** *071 †20,16
SHAPIRO, Joel Hirsch. ■ 24184 #041-01-1958 L1986 **R** *071 †80

WISE – WISE

AGARWAL, Anil. 716 SPRING AVE NE 24293 #495-05-1993 L2003 **PCC** *020 †20
CANTRELL, Eleanor Sue. 134 ROBERTS AVE SW 24293 #051-04-1980 L1984 **IM** *020
FARLAND, Andrew Matthew. ■ 24293 #051-04-2006 M #012
GONZALEZ, Ulysses S. ■ 24293 #748-01-1951 L1957 **IM** *020
JAIN, Sureshchand D. 716 SPRING AVE NE 24293 #495-34-1964 L1973 **PD** *020 †55
MAPHIS, Frederick D, Jr. ■ 24293 #051-04-1942 L1942 **PD** *071 †55
NORTH, Arthur W. ■ 24293 #048-12-1964 L1970 **OBG** *071
RAM, Tumkur Dayalu. PO BOX 3267 24293 #495-33-1962 **ORS** *100 †40
REZA, Farooq Mohammed. NORTON RD & HOSPITAL DR 24293 #495-56-1975 L1991 **GE IM** *020 †20
THOLPADY, Sudama S. 716 SPRING AVE NE, NCH OFFICE BLDG 24293 #495-52-1966 L1975 **IM** *020 †20

WOODBRIDGE – PRINCE WILLIAM

ABBASI, Mustafa A. 13552 MINNIEVILLE RD 22192 #704-01-1985 L1996 **IM** *020 †20
ABISUGA, Olakunle Olusiji. 14139 POTOMAC MILLS RD, WOODBRIDGE MEDICAL CENTER 22192 #198-01-1988 L1998 **IM** *020 †20
ABOLGHASEM-NEJAD, Ghassem. 2020 OPITZ BLVD STE B 22191 #517-01-1961 L1971 **ORS HS** *020 †40
ADAWADKAR, Prakash D. 4201 DALE BLVD, PRAKASH D. ADAWADKAR MD, P 22193 #649-33-1986 L1989 **PD DIA** *020 †55
ADLER, Alf Karl. 2296 OPITZ BLVD STE 350 22191 #010-01-1980 L1984 **OBG** *020 †30
AGGROIA, Abhay Vivek. 2296 OPITZ BLVD, STE 330 22191 #495-69-1979 L1994 **IM** *020
ALEJANDRO, Inocencio P. ■ 22191 #748-01-1990 L1995 **IM RHU** *100 †20
ALEMBIK, Marc C. 2296 OPITZ BLVD, STE 440 22191 #010-01-2990 L1994 **OBG** *020 †30
ALEMZADEH, Amir. 12604 LAKE RIDGE DR, MEDICINE ASSOCIATES 22192 #010-01-1998 L2001 **IM** *020 †20
ALEMZADEH, Nazanin. 12604 LAKE RIDGE DR, MEDICINE ASSOCIATES 22192 #660-03-1999 L2003 **IM** *020 †20
ALFILER, Joel P. 2300 OPITZ BLVD 22191 #748-02-1976 L1994 **AN** *020
AL-KHATEEB, Deana Ghassan. 2296 OPITZ BLVD, STE 330 22191 #528-01-1990 L2000 **IM** *020 †20
ARABSHAHI, Alidad. 2070 OLD BRIDGE RD, STE 103 22192 #010-01-1998 L2003 **OTO** *020
AUSTIN, Ernest. ■ 22193 #010-03-1961 **FM GPM** *071
AZIZ-SULTAN, Hamed. 14450 SMOKETOWN RD, FAMILY HEALTH CTR-WOODBRID 22192 #913-15-1968 L1995 **FM** *020 †20
AZZAM, Charles. 1916 OPITZ BLVD 22191 #605-02-1979 L1987 **NS** *020 †25
BAHADORI, Mohammad. 14904 JEFFERSON DAVIS HWY, STE 203 22191 #517-01-1967 L1995 **RHU IM** *020 †20
BAJOGHLI, Mehdi. 2200 OPITZ BLVD, STE 230 22191 #517-08-1956 L1984 **AI** *020 †55,03
BANE, Stephen Michael. 2300 OPITZ BLVD 22191 #016-43-1984 L1997 **OTO FPS** *020 †45
BARKEV, Banian. 14904 JEFF DAVIS 22191 #605-01-1974 L1978 **IM** *020 †20
BARRERA, Francisco R. ■ 22191 #748-01-1960 L1972 **IM** *020 †20
BAS, Mauricio D, Jr. 1970 OPITZ BLVD 22191 #748-07-1962 L1972 **TS VS** *020 †85
BATTAD, Clementina F. 14139 POTOMAC MILLS RD 22192 #748-10-1978 L1994 **PD** *030 †55
BELILES, Karen Elizabeth. 2296 OPITZ BLVD STE 270, THE POTOMAC CENTER 22191 #036-01-1989 L2001 **P** *020 †75
BENITO, Ruben T. 2300 OPITZ BLVD 22191 #748-01-1964 L1979 **FM** *020 †18
BENNETT, Elizabeth Ann. 14450 SMOKETOWN RD, FAMILY HLTH CTR OF WOODBRD 22192 #024-05-1995 L2004 **FM** *020 †18
BENSON, Robert Granger. ■ 22191 #028-02-1982 L2000 **IM MDM** *030 †20
BHATTI, Asmaa Ashraf. ■ 22191 #012-01-2006 L2006 **IM** *012
BOMMASANI, Reena Rao. 13168 CENTERPOINTE WAY, FAMILY CARE MEDICAL CENTER 22193 #496-34-1998 L2004 **IM** *020 †20
BOYETT, Douglas Henry. 2300 OPITZ BLVD, EMERGENCY DEPARTMENT 22191 #001-02-1989 L1994 **FM** *020 †18
BOYLAN, Susan E. 2296 OPITZ BLVD, STE 140 22191 #010-02-1981 L1986 **RO IM** *020 †20,80
BRADLEY, Lorelle Emmalene. 14139 POTOMAC MILLS RD, KAISER PERMANENTE-WOODBRID 22192 #041-01-1999 L2001 **PD** *020 †55
BRADY, Douglas Brian. 2296 OPITZ BLVD 22191 #035-09-1979 L1987 **OBG** *020 †30
BROWN, Susan Padama. 14139 POTOMAC MILLS RD, WOODBRIDGE MEDICAL CENTER 22192 #748-20-1983 L1999 **FM** *020 †18
BRYCE, Peter Alexander. 2296 OPITZ BLVD STE 250 22191 #010-03-1974 L1977 **OBG** *020 †30
BURDETT, V Renee. 13649 OFFICE PL, STE 102 22192 #001-02-1989 L1991 **CHP P** *020 †75
BURNS, Cynthia Anne. 2300 OPITZ BLVD, POTOMAC HOSPITAL 22191 #041-07-1995 L2006 **IM** *020 †20
CAFFEY, Soren. 2280 OPITZ BLVD STE 220 22191 #517-08-1994 L2005 **HO** *100 †20
CAMPBELL, Peter Lawrence. 12721 DARBY BROOK CT 22192 #065-01-1965 L1978 **P** *020 †75
CAPLAN, Michael Stuart. 1990 OLD BRIDGE RD, STE 101 22192 #024-05-1999 L2002 **PD** *020 †55
CARTER, William Thos. ■ 22192 #047-01-1973 L1983 **EM** *020
CASTLE, Robert Lewis. 2028 OPITZ BLVD, FAIRFAX OB/GYN ASSOCIATES 22191 #010-01-1976 L1978 **OBG** *020 †30
CEBALLOS, Josefino M. 2300 OPITZ BLVD, DEPT OF EMERGENCY MEDICINE 22191 #748-10-1962 L1972 **EM OM** *020 †85,18,16
CHANG, Nelson. 2300 OPITZ BLVD 22191 #051-01-1992 L1996 **FM** *020 †18
CHEEMA, Qasim Munir. ■ 22193 #056-06-2006 **IM** *012
CHEUNG, Albert Yen Kit. 14139 POTOMAC MILLS RD, KAISER PERMANENTE -WOODBRI 22192 #065-05-1994 L2004 **IM** *020 †20
CHHABRA, Yuskiran Kaur. 14450 SMOKETOWN RD, FHC OF WOODBRIDGE 22192 #496-07-1977 L1985 **PD FM** *020 †55
CHUTUAPE, Mariano Disini. 2010 OPITZ BLVD STE B 22191 #035-08-1989 L1996 **CD IM** *020 †20
CLINTON, Mark Jos. 2296 OPITZ BLVD STE 230 22191 #033-06-1986 L1992 **PUD CCM** *020 †20

COHEN, Robert Alan. 2296 OPITZ BLVD STE 260 22191 #024-05-1981 L1991 **GS** *020 †85
COLLETTI, Nicholas George. 14904 JEFFERSON DAVIS HWY 22191 #033-05-1962 L1964 **FM** *020 †18
COPE, Gerry A. 3401 COMMISSION CT, STE 201 22192 #010-01-1980 L1987 **FM** *020 †18
CORDERO, Jimmy P. 2300 OPITZ BLVD, EMERGENCY ROOM 22191 #748-02-1964 L1974 **EM GS** *020 †16
CORNEL-MANALOTO, Manolisa. 12710 DARBY BROOK CT 22192 #748-10-1988 L2002 **MPD** *020
DANIELS, Patience. 14139 POTOMAC MILLS RD, C/O AHC 22192 #041-02-1992 L1999 **FM** *020 †18
DE LOS SANTOS, Arturo F. 1968 OPITZ BLVD 22191 #748-01-1960 L1972 **GS** *071 †85
DENNIS, Beth Lyn. 14450 SMOKETOWN RD, PRINCE WILLIAM SQUARE 22192 #051-01-1991 L1992 **FM** *020 †18
DESAI, Pratik Shirish. 2296 OPITZ BLVD, STE 3300 22191 #055-01-1998 L2005 **U** *020 †95
DEWITT, Gerald Francis. 2296 OPITZ BLVD, STE 410 22191 #010-02-1983 L1992 **OPH** *020 †35
DIDUCH, Lesia Zoriana. ■ 22192 #847-10-1976 **FM** *040
DYKES, Reno Jackson. 15941 CARDINAL DR, STE 200 22193 #048-04-1967 L1972 **P** *020 †75
EISSLER, Corbin Geo. 14139 POTOMAC MILLS RD 22192 #051-01-1975 L1978 **FM** *020 †18
ELEY, Linda. 14139 POTOMAC MILLS RD, KAISER PERMANENTE HEALTH C 22192 #012-21-1987 L1992 **PD** *020 †55
ELHASSAN, Amir Omar. ■ 22193 #023-07-2007 **IM** *012
ELJAIEK, Luis F, Jr. 2300 OPITZ BLVD, POTOMAC HOSPITAL 22191 #051-07-1983 L1984 **EM IM** *020 †16
EL MAWAN, Mohamed Tarek H. 14904 JEFFERSON DAVIS HWY, STE 204 22191 #915-02-1976 L1998 **PD GP** *020 †55
ENGLISH, Dan Couch. 14139 POTOMAC MILLS RD, KAISER PERMANENTE 22192 #048-04-1955 L1988 **FM OS** *071 †85
ENJETTI, Pamela Enid. 2300 OPITZ BLVD 22191 #495-35-1975 L1987 **AN PME** *020
ESCARIO, Francisco Tan. 2300 OPITZ BLVD 22191 #748-11-1972 L1977 **AN** *020 †05
FANALE, Joachim Michael. 2028 OPITZ BLVD STE B 22191 #033-05-1977 L1979 **OBG** *020 †30
FARBER, Jon Matthew. 1990 OLD BRIDGE RD, STE 101 22192 #016-02-1977 L1985 **PD OS** *020 †55
FERLAZZO, Steve Lawrence. 2300 OPITZ BLVD 22191 #051-04-1966 L1966 **OTO AI** *071 †45
FINEMAN, Bill L. 2300 OPITZ BLVD 22191 #016-76-1955, ▲ L1955 **PM GP** *071
FRACASSO, Mark R. 12508 LAKE RIDGE DR 22192 #010-02-1981 L1982 **OBG** *020 †30
FRANCIS, Jamison K. 14904 JEFFERSON DAVIS HWY 22191 #041-09-1976 L1980 **D** *020 †15
FRIEDENTHAL, Amy Lynn. 12512 LAKE RIDGE DR STE D 22192 #024-07-1990 L1991 **IM** *020 †20
GALLARDO, Ernesto. 2300 OPITZ BLVD 22191 #748-10-1973 L1997 **PD GS** *020 †55
GARVEZ, Magdalena D. 2321 PRINCESS ANNE LN 22191 #748-09-1963 L1972 **GYN** *071
GEHANI, Mohini Taro. 2300 OPITZ BLVD 22191 #496-38-1968 L1975 **AN** *071
GHASEMZADEH, Roksana. 14573 POTOMAC MILLS RD 22192 #561-16-1993 L2002 **IM** *020 †20
GIANNUZZI, Vito Anthony. 12506 LAKE RIDGE DR, THE PEDIATRIC GROUP 22192 #010-01-1972 L1978 **PD** *020 †55
GILL, Naurang S. 14401 HEREFORD RD 22193 #495-03-1975 L1981 **N** *020
GOLESORKHI, Reza. 12506 LAKE RIDGE DR STE C 22192 #654-01-1998 L2002 **IM** *020 †20
GOYAL, Deepshikha. 14139 POTOMAC MILLS RD 22192 #495-30-1993 L1998 **PD** *020 †55
GROVER, Vijay Kumar. 14904 JEFFERSON DAVIS HWY, STE 309 22191 #495-03-1975 L1982 **IM** *020
GUERGUERIAN, Rosemary. 2300 OPITZ BLVD, EMERGENCY DEPARTMENT 22191 #047-05-2000 L2000 **EM** *020 †16
HALMI, Denis John. 2280 OPITZ BLVD STE 320 22191 #473-01-1979 L1983 **GS** *020 †85
HANNA, Joseph Ragy. 2028 OPITZ BLVD STE B, NOVA ORTHOPEDIC AND SPINE 22191 #038-40-2000 L2006 **ORS** *100
HANNA, Mona Mounir. 1690 OLD BRIDGE RD 22192 #915-02-1988 L2001 **PD** *020 †55
HASHISHO, Mazen M. ■ 22192 #605-01-1998 L1999 **VS** *100 †85,90
HATCHER, Ronald Allen. 2296 OPITZ BLVD, STE 440 22191 #051-04-1976 L1987 **OBG** *020 †30
HENSLE, Craig Lyndon. 14904 JEFFERSON DAVIS HWY 22191 #035-09-1976 L1978 **OPH EM** *020 †35 ‡
HERITAGE, Douglas Edwin. 2026 OPITZ BLVD STE A 22191 #051-04-1975 L1976 **OBG** *020 †30 ‡
HESSAMI, Tatjana. 2300 OPITZ BLVD, DEPARTMENT OF 22191 #409-33-2001 L2007 **EM** *100 †16
HETELEKIDIS, Stella. 2296 OPITZ BLVD, STE 140 22191 #035-45-1988 L1993 **RO** *020 †80
HEYDARIAN, Siamak M. 2200 OPITZ BLVD, STE 350 22191 #654-01-1987 L1992 **IM** *020 †20
HINDMAN, Hal Barton. 2300 OPITZ BLVD 22191 #033-05-1981 L1988 **OBG** *020 †30
HONG, Sam Kyung. 12209 REDWOOD CT 22192 #041-09-1991 L1992 **IM** *020 †20
HOPKINS, Stuart Quinzel. 14139 POTOMAC MILLS RD, KAISER WOODBRIDGE MED CTR 22192 #023-01-1995 L2001 **IM** *020 †20
HRICZ, Linda Parkhurst. 14450 SMOKETOWN RD, FHC OF WOODBRIDGE 22192 #012-05-1986 L1993 **FM** *020 †18
HUSSAIN, Nizar M. 2296 OPITZ BLVD, STE 330 22191 #528-01-1990 L2000 **IM** *020 †20
HWANG, Richard John. 2022 OPITZ BLVD, STE A 22191 #583-09-1967 L1987 **D PTH** *020 †50,15
ISRAEL, Lawrence Jason. 2300 OPITZ BLVD, POTOMAC HOSP DEPT OF RAD 22191 #023-01-1987 L1991 **DR** *020 †80
JABER, Marwan Riad. ■ 22192 #035-08-1999 L2007 **EM** *020 †16
JABER, Rolla Nabih. ■ 22192 #025-07-2003 L2007 **D** *020 †15
JADIDI, Ali R. 12722 DIRECTORS LOOP 22192 #422-01-1997 L2001 **PD** *020 †55
JAGHLIT, Mohammed Ali. 14139 POTOMAC MILLS RD 22192 #875-01-1968 L1985 **PD PHO** *071 †55
JERUZAL, Joanna Karolina. ■ 22193 #051-04-2008 *012
JEWETT, Heather Carmen. ■ 22193 #051-07-2003 L2007 **AN** *100
JOUBIN, Jahan. 2296 OPITZ BLVD STE 450 22191 #517-05-1965 L1972 **ORS GS** *020 †40
KANANI, Samir P. 2296 OPITZ BLVD, STE 140 22191 #048-02-1999 L2004 **RO** *020 †80
KANDAHARI, Masoom M. 2280 OPITZ BLVD, STE 220 22191 #495-36-1978 L1986 **ON HO** *020 †20
KANG, Jun H. 2300 OPITZ BLVD 22191 #583-02-1977 L1992 **NPM PD** *020 †55
KAPADIA, Atul P. 2280 OPITZ BLVD STE 210, SUITE #210 22191 #495-22-1990 L1998 **IM** *020 †20
KATO, Deirdre Umeyo. 14139 POTOMAC MILLS RD, DEPARTMENT OB 22192 #539-06-1999 L2004 **OBG** *020 ‡
KAW, Nellie Ong. 2300 OPITZ BLVD 22191 #748-02-1979 L1989 **PD** *020 †55
KAYE, Zachary Allan. 14904 JEFF DAVIS HWY, STE 305 22191 #038-40-1973 L1979 **END IM** *020
KELBERG, Robert Dana. 14139 POTOMAC MILLS RD 22192 #010-03-1971 L1999 **CD IM** *020 †20
KENT, James Carl. 2200 OPITZ BLVD STE 235 22191 #065-01-1974 L1977 **FM** *020
KESHMIRI, Abolhassan. 2300 OPITZ BLVD 22191 #517-01-1955 L1981 **AN** *020 †05
KHACHIKIAN, Zareh Hagop. 2296 OPITZ BLVD, STE 350 22191 #422-01-2002 L2006 **OBG** *020
KHOSRAVI, Hamed. 2010 OPITZ BLVD STE B 22191 #517-01-1991 L2004 **HEM** *020 †20
KO, Sang Wook. ■ 22191 #065-01-1994 L1997 *100
KOHLI, Sanjeev. 1912 OPITZ BLVD 22191 #495-90-1989 L1997 **IM** *020 †20
KOOCHEKZADEH, Azadeh. 1990 OLD BRIDGE RD, STE 101 22192 #024-05-1994 L2001 **PD** *020
KRAUSE, Craig Chas. 15941 DONALD CURTIS DR, STE 200 22191 #025-01-1987 L2002 **P PFP** *020 †75
KRIEGEL, Andrew V.. 2280 OPITZ BLVD, MS HERSHEY MEDICAL CENTER 22191 #913-12-1987 L2007 **PS** *020 †85
KRINGER, Sarah Virginia. 2300 OPITZ BLVD, C/O EMERGENCY DEPARTMENT 22191 #051-01-2002 L2005 **EM** *100 †16
KUMAR, Krishnan S. 1900 OPITZ BLVD STE A 22191 #495-98-1973 L1988 **PD** *020 †55
KUMAR, Nitin Arun. 2200 OPITZ BLVD 22191 #041-01-1994 L2001 **DR** *020 †80
KUMER, Virginia Mae. ■ 22192 #005-16-1962 L1975 **GP IM** *071
KWARTENG, Collins Amponsa. ■ 22192 #024-16-2007 **IM** *012
LABRIOLA, Paula Ann. 1924 OPITZ BLVD 22191 #041-12-1990 L1993 **PD** *020 †55
LAMBERT, Lawrence G. ■ 22192 #051-04-1975 **ORS** *020
LATEEF, Babur Bari. 14904 JEFFERSON DAVIS HWY, STE 308 22191 #038-44-1996 L2002 **OPH** *020 †35
LAURENT, Raymond Dohuuduc. 1950 OPITZ BLVD 22191 #396-03-1980 L1994 **N** *020
LAYFIELD, Richard Lee, III. 2028 OPITZ BLVD STE B 22191 #011-04-1997 L2003 **ORS** *020 †40
LAZAROAE, Susan E H. 1990 OLD BRIDGE RD, STE 101 22192 #017-20-1993 L1998 **PD** *020 †55
LEE, Kok Seah. 2296 OPITZ BLVD STE 210 22191 #825-01-1969 L1974 **GE IM** *020 †20
LEE, Sang Nam. 2296 OPITZ BLVD, STE 140 22191 #583-10-1965 L1977 **DR** *020 †80
LEVIN, Sara Beth. 14450 SMOKETOWN RD, WOODBRIDGE FAM HLTH CTR 22192 #023-01-1996 L1999 **PD** *020 †55
LONG, John Devlin, Jr. 14139 POTOMAC MILLS RD, OB/GYN DEPARMENT 22192 #051-04-1987 L1989 **OBG** *020 †30
LOPEZ, Rodolfo Lagmay. 2300 OPITZ BLVD, EMERGENCY ROOM 22191 #748-01-1965 L1972 **GS AS** *020 †16
LOPIANO, Mark Cameron. 2200 OPITZ BLVD 22191 #010-02-1982 L1989 **DR RNR** *020 †80
LORENZ, Richard Lawrence. 1924 OPITZ BLVD 22191 #010-02-1969 L1970 **PD** *020 †55
LORICO, Lee Eric S. 12285 PONDWATER CT 22192 #748-10-1988 L2000 **AN** *020 †05 ‡
LOTFI, Paymaun. 2028 OPITZ BLVD STE B 22191 #051-04-1994 L1999 **ORS** *020 †40
LOU, Ek Seng. 2296 OPITZ BLVD, STE 300 22191 #067-01-1970 L1976 **U** *020 †95
LOVE, Angela Yvonne. 14450 SMOKETOWN RD 22192 #010-03-1990 L1993 **IM** *020 †20
LOWERY, Wylie Donald, Jr. 2010 OPITZ BLVD STE C 22191 #036-01-1987 L1993 **ORS** *020 †40
LOWRY, Thomas Power. ■ 22193 #005-11-1957 L1958 **P** *071 †75
LUCERO, Bruce A. 14055 CROWN CT 22193 #007-02-1981 L1996 **FM FSM** *020
MADIRAJU, Krishna Prasad. 2024 OPITZ BLVD, STE A 22191 #495-21-1992 L1996 **PD** *020 †55
MAFI, Shahryar. 14901 JEFFERSON DAVIS HWY, STE 406 22191 #308-10-1987 L1997 **CD** *020 †20
MAGUIRE, Elizabeth Hope. 1924 OPITZ BLVD 22191 #045-01-2001 L2001 **PD** *020 †55
MAKIPOUR, Houshang. 2280 OPITZ BLVD STE 200 22191 #517-07-1968 L1987 **IM** *020 †20
MALEK GOUDARZI, Behnam. 2024 OPITZ BLVD STE C, VIRGINIA PULMONARY ASSOCIA 22191 #517-01-1996 L2005 **PCC SME** *020 †20 ‡
MALLOY, Lisa Kimberly. 5800 MAPLEDALE PLZ 22193 #051-04-1997 L2000 **FM** *020 †18
MANCHANDA, Prem Prakash. 14139 POTOMAC MILLS RD 22192 #495-45-1992 L1998 **IM** *020 †20
MANN, Jatinder Pal Singh. 14573 POTOMAC MILLS RD 22192 #495-03-1976 L1987 **IM FM** *020
MAREFAT, Saeed. 14908 JEFFERSON DAVIS HWY 22191 #010-02-1985 L1989 **OS PS** *020 †65
MARZBAN, Nader. 2300 OPITZ BLVD, POTOMAC HOSPITAL 22191 #517-01-1970 L1986 *075
MASON, Cheryl A. PO BOX 5323 22194 #010-03-1981 L1985 **OBG OS** *040 †30
MASSIE, Jean Marie. 1990 OLD BRIDGE RD, STE 101 22192 #051-07-1982 L1985 **PD** *020 †55
MC AFEE, Rebecca D. 2300 OPITZ BLVD, DEPART OF PATH POTOMAC HOS 22191 #048-13-1984 L2000 **PTH PCP** *020 †50
MC CARTHY, Wm Carroll. 2010 OPITZ BLVD STE A 22191 #010-02-1973 L1976 **FM** *020 †18
MC KINNEY, Jennifer L. 14139 POTOMAC MILLS RD 22192 #017-20-1976 L1979 **PD** *020 †55
MC KINNON, Harry Donald, Jr. ■ 22192 #024-05-1997 L1998 **FM** *020 †18
MC LAURIN, Mary Ann Maria. 2300 OPITZ BLVD, ATTN MEDICAL STAFF OFFICE 22191 #035-19-1982 L1989 **EM** *020 †16
MC LEOD, Francine Nicole. 2296 OPITZ BLVD, STE 440 22191 #041-13-1997 L2004 **OBG** *020 †30
MEHTA, Sameer Harshad. 2300 OPITZ BLVD, POTOMAC HOSPITAL 22191 #023-01-1999 L2004 **EM** *020 †16
MENDEL, Peter Allan. 3401 COMMISSION CT, STE 201 22192 #011-02-1981 L1985 **FM** *020 †18
MEYER, Tiffany Lynne. 1690 OLD BRIDGE RD 22192 #010-01-1997 L2006 **PD ADL** *020 †55
MITCHELL, Regina Marie. 2296 OPITZ BLVD, STE 440 22191 #010-01-1995 L1999 **OBG** *020
MOGHTADER, Ali. 14904 J DAVIS HWY STE 201 22191 #517-01-1959 L1966 **OTO FPS** *071 †45
MONTILLA, Lino Cueto. 2028 OPITZ BLVD, FAIRFAX OB/GYN ASSOCIATES 22191 #010-01-1992 L1995 **OBG** *020 †30
MOON, Sung Kil. 2300 OPITZ BLVD 22191 #583-02-1970 L1977 **AN** *020
MORTAZAVI, Ala Seyed. 2024 OPITZ BLVD STE C 22191 #308-10-1986 L1991 **PUD** *020 †20
MOUSAVI, Morteza. 2296 OPITZ BLVD STE 340 22191 #517-01-1968 L1982 **CD IM** *020 †20
MOUSSAVI, Sohail. 12604 LAKE RIDGE DR, MEDICINE ASSOCIATES 22192 #660-03-1999 L2003 **IM** *020 †20
MURPHY, Richard Jos. 14139 POTOMAC MILLS RD, WOODBRIDGE MEDICAL CENTER 22192 #041-09-1972 L2001 **EM** *020
MYERS, Catherine V. 2300 OPITZ BLVD, POTOMAC HOSPITAL 22191 #036-05-1995 L2006 **EM** *020 †16
NAFZINGER, Moses Le Roy. 12506 LAKE RIDGE DR 22192 #023-01-1954 L1955 **GP** *071
NAGIA, Aly Hassan. 2280 OPITZ BLVD, STE 225 22191 #915-04-1969 L1998 **AN APM** *020 †05
NAIN, Rajev Ishwar. 2296 OPITZ BLVD, STE 260 22191 #055-02-2000 L2006 **GS** *020 †85
NASREEN, Abida. 4001 PRINCE WILLIAM PKWY, # 302 22192 #704-02-1975 L1994 **DR** *020 †80
NEMATOLLAHY, Violet. 1690 OLD BRIDGE RD 22192 #517-01-1978 L1983 **PD** *020 †55
NICHOLLS, Kenwyn H. 14139 POTOMAC MILLS RD 22192 #010-03-1967 L1973 **PD** *050 †18
NKRUMAH, Jacklyn Akua. ■ 22191 #024-16-2005 L2008 **IM** *012
NUNEZ, Anne Marie. 14450 SMOKETOWN RD, OF WOODBRIDGE 22192 #396-35-1980 L2002 **FM** *020 †18 ‡

NWUFOH, Gabriel Obiorah. 12716 DIRECTORS LOOP 22191 #690-04-1983 L1998 **IM** *020 †20

O'DEA, Maureen Theresa. 2296 OPITZ BLVD, STE 410 22191 #010-02-1988 L1989 **OPH** *020 †35

OKKEMA, Julie Mae. 14139 POTOMAC MILLS RD, KAISER PERMANENTE 22192 #010-01-1981 L1987 **OBG** *071 †30

OLIN, Richard T. 1936 OPITZ BLVD STE A 22191 #051-04-1981 L1982 **FM** *020 †18

O'QUINN, William Esdorn. 14139 POTOMAC MILLS RD 22192 #045-01-1974 L2002 **FM** *020 †18 ‡

ORAEE, Samad. 2024 OPITZ BLVD STE B, NEUROLOGICAL CTR OF NVA 22191 #308-11-1986 L1993 **N PME** *020

OSKUIYAN, Hossein. 1978 OPITZ BLVD 22191 #649-33-1987 L1998 **IM** *020 †20

PAGE, David Elliott. 14139 POTOMAC MILLS RD, KAISER PERMANENTE 22192 #010-02-1978 L1981 **FM** *020 †18

PAPAS, Alexander. 14904 JEFFERSON DAVIS HWY, STE 302 22191 #418-01-1966 L1976 **CD IM** *071

PARK, Hyungsoon. 2296 OPITZ BLVD STE 255 22191 #583-02-1960 L1972 **P** *020

PATEL, Kirankumar. 14450 SMOKETOWN RD, FAMILY HLTH CTR OF WOODBRI 22192 #495-89-1983 L1994 **IM** *020 †20

PATTON, Ranjini V. 2300 OPITZ BLVD, ATTN:LUIS ELJAIEK 22191 #033-05-1995 L2004 **EM PE** *020 †16

PECK, Judith Eileen. 2300 OPITZ BLVD, POTOMAC HOSPITAL EMERGENCY 22191 #023-12-1999 L2006 **EM** *020 †16

PIERCE, Susan Michelle. 2296 OPITZ BLVD, STE 140 22191 #031-01-1984 L1993 **RO ON** *020 †80

POLE, Shriharsh L. 14904 JEFFERSON DAVIS HWY, STE 205 22191 #495-01-1979 L1992 **IM** *020 †20

POSTELNEK, David Lee. 2300 OPITZ BLVD, POTOMAC HOSPITAL ER 22191 #010-01-1993 L1994 **FM** *020 †20

PRASANNA, Swarnalatha. 1455 OLD BRIDGE RD, STE 206 22192 #495-33-1978 L2002 **P** *020 †75

PRATT, John Whetten. 12800 DARBY BROOK CT 22192 #047-07-2006 L2007 **IM** *100

PUGLISE, Joseph V. 1924 OPITZ BLVD 22191 #010-02-1967 L1971 **PD PDA** *071 †55

RAJURKAR, Madhusudan G. 14450 SMOKETOWN RD, WOODBRIDGE 22192 #495-20-1961 L1983 **PD** *020 †20

RAMLER, John Michael. 14450 SMOKETOWN RD, FAMILY HEALTH CENTER OF WO 22192 #051-04-1975 L1976 **FM** *020 †18

RAMSEY-KHOMAMI, Ali. 14904 JEFFERSON DAVIS HWY, STE 407 22191 #517-01-1969 L1976 **OBG** *020 †30

RATHINASAMY, Palanichamy. 2300 OPITZ BLVD 22191 #495-42-1973 L1980 **DR** *020 †80

RAZAVI, Mohammad H. 14904 JEFFERSON DAVIS HWY, STE 103 22191 #308-10-1985 L1993 **GE IM** *020 †20

REHA, William C. 2296 OPITZ BLVD STE 220 22191 #035-09-1981 L1982 **U** *020 †95

REKULAPELLI, Prasad. 1690 OLD BRIDGE RD 22192 #495-57-1990 L2001 **PD** *020 †20

ROBINSON, Richard Geo. 2296 OPITZ BLVD, STE 230 22191 #035-20-1975 L1978 **PUD CCM** *020 †20

RODD, Sam Changize. 4221 DALE BLVD 22193 #517-06-1980 L1993 **IM EM** *020 †20

RODRIGUEZ, Raul A. 2300 OPITZ BLVD, EMERGENCY DEPARTMENT 22191 #132-01-1972 L1979 **EM** *020 †16

ROSEN, Leonard Asher. 2028 OPITZ BLVD, FAIRFAX OB/GYN ASSOCIATES 22191 #010-01-1976 L1977 **OBG** *020 †30

ROUADY, William A. 2300 OPITZ BLVD 22191 #605-02-1959 L1967 **NS** *071 †25

SABET, Sina John. 2296 OPITZ BLVD STE 120 22191 #025-01-1993 L1997 **OPH** *020 †35

SALJUKI, Rafiq Mohammad. 14904 JEFFERSON DAVIS HWY, STE 302 22191 #409-21-1990 L2005 **IM** *020 †20

SALUJA, Ritu. 2300 OPITZ BLVD, DEPARTMENT OF EMERGENCY ME 22191 #036-05-2003 L2006 **EM** *020 †16

SANTOYO-LOPEZ, Jesus A. 12800 DARBY BROOK CT 22192 #935-01-1974 L1987 **FM PTH** *020 ‡

SARGENT, Donald L. 2241M TACKETTS MILL DR 22192 #051-04-1985 L1986 **FM OS** *020 †18

SEAH, Stanley Kin Kok. 2296 OPITZ BLVD, LEE KOK-SEAH MD FACG 22191 #062-01-1961 **IM OS** *020 †20

SEED, John Chas. 14450 SMOKETOWN RD, WOODBRIDGE 22192 #028-34-1969 L2000 **P PYG** *020 †75

SHAH, Tejas J. 4331 RIDGEWOOD CENTER DR 22192 #495-23-1994 L2003 **FM** *020 †18

SHAPIRO, Carol Sadie. 1940 OPITZ BLVD 22191 #041-07-1965 L1966 **PS** *020 †65

SHAREGHI, Khosro. 2200 OPITZ BLVD STE 310 22191 #409-02-1972 L1988 **CD IM** *020 †20

SHEIKH, Mazhar Ul-Haq. 14904 JEFFERSON DAVIS HWY, STE 306 22191 #704-02-1968 L1981 **CD IM** *020 †20

SIKORA, Robert Anthony, Jr. 2296 OPITZ BLVD, STE 401 22191 #016-42-1994 L1999 **AI** *020 †20,03

SINCLAIR, Jeffrey Scott. 2296 OPITZ BLVD, STE 260 22191 #051-04-1998 L2003 **GS** *020 †85

SINGH, Inderjit. 14904 JEFFERSON DAVIS HWY, STE 208 22191 #495-03-1976 L1992 **U** *020 †95

SIRH, Joseph Hongsuk. 2300 OPITZ BLVD 22191 #583-06-1956 L1971 **AN** *071 †05

SIRIPRAKORN, Prachak T. 1966 OPITZ BLVD # 09 22191 #891-04-1974 L1988 **CD** *020 †20

SMITH, David Alden. 14139 POTOMAC MILLS RD 22192 #005-02-1982 L1997 **FM MDM** *020 †18

SOBHANY, Manochehr. 2300 OPITZ BLVD 22191 #517-03-1963 L1970 **IM PUD** *071 ‡

SOYER, Aysegul. 1930 OPITZ BLVD, 2296 OPITZ BLVD #360 22191 #902-10-1980 L1985 **N** *020 †75

STANSFIELD, Sally K. ■ 22192 #054-04-1977 L1983 **PHP IM** *050 †20,16

STEELE, Barbara Dipietro. 4264 BERWICK PL 22192 #051-01-1987 L1991 **OBG** *074 †30

STEINGASZNER, Laszlo C. 2300 OPITZ BLVD 22191 #473-01-1952 L1961 **PTH** *071 †50

STERNBERG, Michael Ross. 3166 GOLANSKY BLVD STE 201 22192 #035-19-1983 L1985 **P** *020 †75

STICH, Matthew Thos. 14465 POTOMAC MILLS RD 22192 #051-04-1984 L1987 **OPH OS** *020 †35

STROOP, Deeann Marie. 14450 SMOKETOWN RD 22192 #047-05-1986 L1989 **FM** *020 †18

SULLIVAN, Thomas Jos. 1990 OLD BRIDGE RD, STE 101 22192 #033-05-1964 L1968 **PD** *020

SUMNER, Michael G. 2296 OPITZ BLVD, STE 360 22191 #041-09-1966 L1997 **P IM** *020 †20

TABIBI, Shahrzad. 12508 LAKE RIDGE DR 22192 #023-01-2001 L2005 **OBG** *020 †30

TAN-GATUE, Leonardo Gan. ■ 22193 #748-10-1962 L1972 **PD** *071 †55

TEFERA, Girma Kebede. ■ 22191 #366-02-1991 L2007 **IM** *020 †20

THETHI, Arveen Kaur. 2200 OPITZ BLVD, STE 230 22191 #025-07-1998 L2004 **AI** *020 †20,03

THOMAS, Pottayil Varkey. 2300 OPITZ BLVD 22191 #495-14-1968 L1972 **AN** *020 †05

TINSLEY, Charleen Bess. 14450 SMOKETOWN RD, WOODBRIDGE FAM HEALTH CENT 22192 #016-42-1978 L2001 **IM** *020 †20

TOAN, Quang Dam. ■ 22191 #941-01-1966 L1982 **GP** *072

TORRES, Eduardo. 2296 OPITZ BLVD, STE 350 22191 #042-01-2001 L2005 **OBG** *020

TOUCHETTE, Leonard Lee. 2296 OPITZ BLVD STE 510 22191 #051-07-1977 L1979 **PD** *020 †55

TRAN, Daniel Dinh. 2280 OPITZ BLVD, STE 320 22191 #005-12-1993 L2005 **GS CCS** *020 †85

TRAVIS, Lon Paul. ■ 22192 #011-03-1960 L1964 **P OS** *020

TRENT, Jocelyn D. 2296 OPITZ BLVD, STE 403 22191 #748-08-1978 L1990 **PD** *020 †55

TULSI, Priyadarsha Kaur. ■ 22193 #051-01-1998 L2004 **PD** *020 †55

UCHELLA, Sunday C. 14904 JEFFERSON DAVIS HWY, PEDITRIC CLINICAL SERVICES 22191 #690-04-1985 L1995 **PD** *020 †55

UPSHUR, Marshall Leroy. 14139 POTOMAC MILLS RD 22192 #012-01-1979 L1985 **PD ADL** *020 †55

VAYER, Arthur J. 2296 OPITZ BLVD, STE 260 22191 #043-01-1987 L1993 **GS CRS** *020 †85,10

VAZQUEZ-VELAZQUEZ, Jorge. ■ 22192 #308-12-1978 L1997 **PHP GP** *020

VELURI, Ravi Kumar. 13168 CENTERPOINTE WAY, STE 101 22193 #495-58-1976 L1990 **PD** *020

VELURI, Savithri-Chandana. 4331 RIDGEWOOD CENTER DR, NORTH VIRGINIA FAMILY PRAC 22192 #495-58-1996 L2008 **FM** *020 †18

VENTZEK, Albert Theodore. 2000 OPITZ BLVD 22191 #010-02-1960 L1965 **FM PD** *071 †18 ‡

WADDELL, Beverly Jane. 14139 POTOMAC MILLS RD 22192 #036-01-1986 L1990 **OBG** *020 †30

WADDELL, Nikki Rai. 1900 OPITZ BLVD STE F 22191 #036-08-2002 L2002 **IM** *020 †20

WARD, Kenneth Gerard. 2010 OPITZ BLVD STE C 22191 #033-05-1973 L1978 **ORS** *020 †40

WEISS, Juan E. 14450 SMOKETOWN RD 22192 #042-04-1982 L1985 **PD** *020 †55

WEISS, Michael Aron. 2200 OPITZ BLVD 22191 #035-19-1970 L1975 **DR NM** *020 †80,28

WELTMAN, Allyse Leigh. 2296 OPITZ BLVD, STE 440 22191 #050-02-1999 L1999 **OBG** *020 †30

WILLIAMS, Harvey Bernard. 12506 LAKE RIDGE DR STE C 22192 #016-43-1958 L1960 **GP** *020

WILLIAMS, James Thomas. 12506 LAKE RIDGE DR STE C 22192 #051-04-1998 L1999 **FM** *020 †18

WILMOT, Ben D. 12506 LAKE RIDGE DR 22192 #041-01-1956 L1961 **PD** *071 †55

WILSON, Melodi Lynette. 2028 OPITZ BLVD, FAIRFAX OB/GYN ASSOCIATES 22191 #024-05-1999 L2003 **OBG** *020

WOODARD, Emily Bernice. ■ 22193 #051-04-2004 L2007 **IM** *100

WYNN, Alan Howard. 1900 OPITZ BLVD STE F 22191 #035-20-1983 L1987 **IM** *020 †20

YADAO, Alex Peralta. 2300 OPITZ BLVD 22191 #748-01-1962 L1972 **GS OS** *020

YU, Benson Waisun. 14139 POTOMAC MILLS RD 22192 #010-02-1990 L1992 **IM** *020 †20

ZELLEKE, Makonnen K. 2300 OPITZ BLVD, POTOMAC HOSPITAL 22191 #366-01-1989 L2001 **PD** *020

ZHANG, Cindy Yihong. 14904 JEFFERSON DAVIS HWY, STE 305 22191 #243-72-1983 L2000 **APM** *020 †20

WOODLAWN – CARROLL

WORRELL, Dan Carlton. 22 TRAINING CENTER RD 24381 #051-04-1986 L1989 **FM** *020 †18 ‡

WOODSTOCK – SHENANDOAH

BRAUER, Marvin Donald. 761 S MAIN ST, VANDERBILT HALL 22664 #005-12-1987 L1990 **IM** *020 †20

BYRD, Gregory Sean. 761 S MAIN ST, WOODSTOCK INTERNAL 22664 #051-07-1990 L1995 **IM** *020 †20

CARDWELL, Elisabeth T. 761 S MAIN ST 22664 #051-01-1990 L1991 **IM** *020 †20

CARDWELL, Thomas M. 755 S MAIN ST STE 104 22664 #051-01-1990 L1994 **P** *020 †75

CARMAIN, Torr Erik. 755 S MAIN ST 22664 #056-06-1990 L1999 **GS** *020 †85

COLE, Scott Chas. 1065 S MAIN ST 22664 #023-12-1984 L1995 **PD** *020 †55

DAMAVANDY, Tania. 759 S MAIN ST 22664 #010-01-1999 L2003 **OBG** *020 †20

DECI, David Michael. 755 S MAIN ST 22664 #011-03-1980 L1985 **FM** *040 †18

DOFF, Michael Douglas. 227 S MAIN ST 22664 #056-06-2004 L2004 **GS** *100

GERMROTH, Jerry Alan. 761 S MAIN ST, WOODSTOCK INTERNAL 22664 #051-04-1979 L1982 **IM** *020 †20

HAUN, Eloise F Clymer. 755 S MAIN ST 22664 #051-04-1962 L1962 **P CHP** *020 †55,75

HAUN, Jacob, Jr. ■ 22664 #051-04-1972 L1972 **EM IMG** *071

HINDMAN, Donald Oliver. 755 S MAIN ST 22664 #010-01-1980 L1989 **EM FM** *020 †18

HOFFMAN, John Feland. 755 S MAIN ST STE 102 22664 #001-02-1980 L1981 **FM** *020 †18

JANSEN, Donald Grant. 759 S MAIN ST 22664 #060-01-1978 L1997 **FM** *030 †18

KLEINSCHMIDT, James C. 759 S MAIN ST 22664 #004-01-1986 L1997 **GS** *071 †85

KLEINSCHMIDT, Nancy Jane. 761 S MAIN ST, WOODSTOCK INTERNAL 22664 #004-01-1986 L1997 **IM** *020 †20

LOEWITH, Margaret Helene. 759 S MAIN ST, SHENANDOAH WOMENS CARE 22664 #041-13-1982 L1984 **OBG** *020 †30

MACLEOD, Scott. 1195 HISEY AVE STE 100 22664 #065-01-1977 L1995 **FM** *020 ‡

MARTEL, Michelle M. 755 S MAIN ST 22664 #067-06-1982 L1992 **OBG MFM** *020 †20

METHVIN, Claudia Hilburn. 759 S MAIN ST, WOODSTOCK FAMILY PRACTICE 22664 #021-01-1999 L2002 **FM** *020 †18

MILLER, Harold W, Jr. ■ 22664 #051-04-1951 L1951 **GS** *071 †85

MILLER, Stage Edmund. 755 S MAIN ST 22664 #051-04-1958 L1958 **FM** *071

MILLIGAN, Richard Patrick. 761 S MAIN ST, WOODSTOCK INTERNAL 22664 #038-45-1983 L1984 **IM** *020 †20

MULLIGAN, Edward Kieran. 150 S MAIN ST 22664 #539-03-1966 L1972 **FM** *020 †18

NERI, Anthony Robt, III. 1065 S MAIN ST, SHENANDOAH PEDIATRICS 22664 #041-02-1991 L2000 **PD** *020 †55

O'NEAL, Jonathan F. ■ 22664 #023-12-1985 L1992 **AN** *020 †05

PECK, Randall Jos. 755 S MAIN ST 22664 #051-04-1983 L1985 **AN** *020 †05

READ, Marc Edward. 759 S MAIN ST, SHENANDOAH MEDICAL IMAGING 22664 #011-02-1976 L1979 **DR NR** *020 †80

RICHARDS, Mark Allen. ■ 22664 #055-01-2008 *012

SNYDER, Lori Suzanne. 230 SHENANDOAH ST 22664 #041-02-1995 L2003 **OPH** *020 †35

STEVENS, Suzanne. 240 SHENANDOAH ST 22664 #041-14-1988 L1997 **ORS** *020 †40

WHITE, Duane Scott. 761 S MAIN ST, WOODSTOCK INTERNAL MEDICIN 22664 #051-01-1999 L2002 **IM** *020 †20 ‡

WYNN, Audrea Hitz, II. 240 SHENANDOAH ST 22664 #038-43-1984 L1989 **ORS** *020 †40

WOOLWINE – PATRICK

WEAVER, Richard Leonard. 926 RIDGE RD 24185 #011-03-1968 L1994 **NPM PD** *020 †55

WYTHEVILLE – WYTHE

ABELEDA, Maria Concepcion. 770 W RIDGE RD, STE 220 24382 #748-02-1974 L1991 **P CHP** *020

AGRAWAL, Bipin B. ■ 24382 #025-07-1977 L2000 **NEP IM** *071 †20

BALLENGER, Fred Jackson. 340 PEPPERS FERRY RD, WYTHE ARTIFICIAL KIDNEY CE 24382 #036-05-1975 L1976 **OS** *020 †20

BARTON, Walter Seignious. 1325 W RIDGE RD, FAMILY PHYS WYTHEVILLE LTD 24382 #051-04-1959 L1959 **GP** *071 †18

BEAVERS, Kyndal Ann. 100 EDGEMONT RD 24382 #047-07-1991 L1996 **IM** *020

BENNETT, Jennifer Lynn. 600 W RIDGE RD 24382 #055-02-1996 L2000 **FM** *020 †18

BOOKER, James Judson, III. 1375 W RIDGE RD 24382 #051-01-1968 L1968 **FM** *020 †18

BOSWELL, John Garland. 375 E PINE ST 24382 #055-02-1982 L2006 **PTH** *020 †50

CALLIHAN, William C, II. 590 W RIDGE RD, WYTHE BLAND PEDS 24382 #055-01-1976 L1989 **PD** *020 †55

CHO, Kyoung Soung. 360 VIRGINIA AVE 24382 #583-03-1964 L1974 **GS** *020

CHUN, Judy Lee. 1155 N 4TH ST, UROLOGY ASSOCIATES OF NEW 24382 #018-03-1997 L2003 **U** *020 †95

COOK, Keith Eric. 600 W RIDGE RD 24382 #035-09-1996 L2006 **DR** *020

DEAL, William Read. 590 W RIDGE RD, STE D 24382 #012-01-1975 L1980 **GS** *020 †85

DOONAN, Joyce Marie. ■ 24382 #041-07-1984 L1985 **AN** *020

DOVE, Scotty G. 710 W RIDGE RD 24382 #055-75-1993, ▲ L1997 **FM** *020 †18

ELKINS, Irving Barefoot. 1155 N 4TH ST, UROLOGY ASSOCIATES OF NEW 24382 #036-05-1969 L1985 **U** *020 †95

FARRELL, George Jos, III. 710 W RIDGE RD, STE F 24382 #011-02-1975 L1999 **OTO FPS** *020 †45

FOX, Elizabeth Ann. 600 W RIDGE RD 24382 #055-01-2000 L2004 **OBG** *020 ‡

FRYE, Jeanetta Walters. ■ 24382 #047-05-2007 **IM** *012

GRIFFIN, Kevin. 1155 N 4TH ST, UROLOGY ASSOCIATES OF NEW 24382 #048-13-1989 L1995 **U** *020 †95

HAPPEL, Richard Douglas. 590 W RIDGE RD STE I 24382 #045-01-1984 L1985 **CD IM** *020

HARRIS, Charles A. 590 W RIDGE RD, STE F 24382 #010-03-1979 L1985 **GS GP** *020 †85

HORNEY, Wayne D. 1375 W RIDGE RD 24382 #051-04-1977 L1979 **FM** *020 †18

JUSAY, Feliciano Juanillo. 360 VIRGINIA AVE 24382 #748-11-1966 L1973 **OBG** *020

KARNEI, Robert F, Jr. ■ 24382 #048-02-1960 L1992 **PTH CLP** *071 †50

KILGORE, William Tommy. PO BOX 652 24382 #051-01-1982 L1983 **OBG** *020 †30

KING, William Whitman. 1155 N 4TH ST, UROLOGY ASSOCIATES OF NEW 24382 #051-01-1964 L1964 **U** *020 †95

LANGLEY, Michael John. 1155 N 4TH ST, UROLOGY ASSOCIATES OF NEW 24382 #048-04-1984 L1985 **U** *020 †95

LANINGHAM, James E T. ■ 24382 #051-04-1966 L1966 **CLP PTH** *071 †50

LEE, Roberto Juan. 105 W PINE ST 24382 #748-01-1964 L1971 **GS** *020

MATHENA, Tracy Lee. ■ 24382 #051-07-2003 L2003 **OS** *020 †18,20

MC CONNELL, James Jos. 365 W RIDGE RD 24382 #051-04-1972 L1974 **IM** *020 †20

MOORE, Chimer Davis, Jr. 360 VIRGINIA AVE 24382 #051-01-1955 L1955 **FM OS** *020 †18

MORIN, Norman Paul. 1995 W RIDGE RD 24382 #007-02-1985 L1991 **ORS** *020

MOSES, Fredrick Mathi. 600 W RIDGE RD 24382 #308-07-1982 L1986 **EM P** *020 †18

PERONA, Barbara Piez. 600 W RIDGE RD, ATTN: CREDENTIALS DEPT 24382 #036-07-1990 L1996 **AN** *020 †05 ‡

RITCH, Karl Andrew. 600 W RIDGE RD, RADIOLOGY 24382 #036-07-1991 L1996 **DR** *020 †80

ROGNEY, Douglas Lloyd. 360 VIRGINIA AVE, WYTH MEDICAL ASSOCIATES IN 24382 #036-05-1970 L1976 **FM** *020 †18

ROTCHE, Robert Martin. 590 W RIDGE RD, STE L 24382 #016-11-1988 L1999 **HEM** *020 †20

SETTLOW, Gordon Jay. 600 W RIDGE RD, DEPT OF PATHOLOGY 24382 #020-02-1970 L1999 **PTH** *020 †50

SMITH, Donald Craig. MT ROGERS HLTH DISTRICT 24382 #051-04-1974 L1976 **PHP** *030

SMITH, Holly Lynn. 600 W RIDGE RD 24382 #051-07-1989 L1991 **FM** *020 †18 ‡

SPITZER, Kamila. 600 W RIDGE RD, WYTHE COUNTY COMMUNITY HOS 24382 #286-02-1990 L2003 **AN** *020 †05

STARK, Carl E. ■ 24382 #051-01-1952 L1953 **GP** *071

STONE, James B, III. 1375 W RIDGE RD 24382 #051-01-1968 L1968 **FM OBS** *020

TAYLOR, Beth Ann. 590 W RIDGE RD, STE E 24382 #001-06-1989 L2005 **GE IM** *020 †20

TOMIAK, William Matthew. 1375 W RIDGE RD 24382 #051-04-1998 L1998 **FM** *020 †18

ZIEGLER, Herman Frederick. ■ 24382 #038-41-1965 L1971 **R** *020 †80

YORKTOWN – YORK

ABIDI, Rabbiya Nasir. ■ 23693 #704-09-1997 L2004 **FP** *012

ADEYIGA, Adebunmi Olajunm. ■ 23693 #051-01-2005 L2005 **DR** *012

AMAKER, Raymond Davis. ■ 23693 #045-04-1990 L1996 **NPM** *020 †55

AMER, Mohammed Ashrafuddi. ■ 23693 #496-27-1996 L2007 **FP** *012

ARBOLEDA, Evelyn Duran. 205 HAMPTON HWY 23693 #748-01-1972 L1982 **P** *020 ‡

AYALA-JIMENEZ, Pablo. ■ 23693 #042-03-1980 L1984 **GP** *020

BAILEY, Robert Rives. ■ 23692 #051-01-1960 L1960 **FM** *071 †18

BATTAR, Saraswathy Sasha. ■ 23692 #495-65-1980 L1991 **IMG PLM** *020 †20

BRYANT, John Patrick. 307 COOK RD, MULTISPECIALITY GROUP 23690 #051-07-1979 L1980 **FM** *020 †18

CAMPBELL, Hawes, III. 307 COOK RD, MULTISPECIALITY GROUP 23690 #051-04-1964 L1964 **FM OS** *020 †18

CAMPOLATTARO, Annmarie. 307 COOK RD, MULTISPECIALITY GROUP 23690 #033-05-1998 L2000 **MPD** *020 †20,55

CHOI, Christina Y. ■ 23693 #048-02-1985 L1990 **IM** *020

CROCKER, Justin Adams. ■ 23692 #051-04-2008 *012

DE LEON-HALL, Teodora G. ■ 23692 #748-01-1957 L1978 **PD** *020 †55

DE LOS SANTOS, Gregorio R. ■ 23692 #748-01-1960 L1974 **GS** *071 †85

DOHERTY, Ernest F, Jr. ■ 23692 #041-02-1951 L1987 **GP** *071

DUNN, Melinda Martin. 3630 GEORGE WSHNGTN MM HWY, HWY STE#E 23693 #051-04-1991 L1995 **DR** *020 †80

EVANS, Paul Edward. 2855 DENBIGH BLVD 23692 #008-02-1979 L1981 **FM IMG** *020 †18

FINK, Stephen Adam. 3630 GEORGE WSHNGTN MM HWY, STE E 23693 #051-04-1980 L1982 **DR** *020 †80

FOELSCHE, Ruth. ■ 23692 #407-23-1939 L1968 **GP** *071

FOXX, Stephen Dell. 3630 GEORGE WSHNGTN MM HWY, STE E 23693 #051-04-1991 L1993 **RNR** *020 †80

GARRETT, Roland G, Jr. ■ 23692 #051-04-1958 L1958 **GS** *071 †85

GONZALEZ-ARROYO, Edwin. PO BOX 90, BRANCH MED CLN/NAV WEAPON 23690 #308-03-1979 L1982 **GP** *020

GRAHAM, Walter Hopkins. ■ 23692 #051-04-1960 L1960 **TS** *071 †85,90

GRIZZARD, John Dallas. 3630 GEORGE WSHNGTN MM HWY, MEM HWY 23693 #051-04-1979 L1983 **DR PD** *020 †80

GUAN, Yu. ■ 23693 #243-76-1992 L2007 **FP** *012

HALL, Steven Michael. 3630 GEORGE WSHNGTN MM HWY, STE E 23693 #051-04-1988 L1991 **DR** *020 †80

HASSAN, Cyrus. ■ 23692 #517-05-1966 L1973 **DR** *020

HOLLINGSWORTH, John D, Jr. 101 YORK LN, MULTISPECIALTY GROUP 23692 #051-04-1984 L1990 **FM** *020 †18

HOPSON, Sharon C. 505 SHIP POINT RD 23692 #036-08-1994 L1994 **ID** *020 †20

HYRE, Hugh Martin. 3630 GEORGE WSHNGTN MM HWY, MEM HWY 23693 #038-45-1986 L1990 **DR NR** *020 †80

IYER, Sowmya. ■ 23693 #051-04-2003 L2003 **D** *100

JACKSON, Gloria Moore. 101 YORK LN, MULTISPECIALTY GROUP 23692 #011-03-1986 L1989 **FM** *020 †18

LINDEMANN, Carl James. 307 COOK RD, MULTISPECIALITY GROUP 23690 #051-07-1994 L1995 **FM** *020 †18

LIZARZABURU, Jesus Luis. 101 YORK LN, MULTISPECIALTY GROUP 23692 #005-18-1998 L1998 **FM** *020 †18 ‡

LYNCH, Sean Roborg. ■ 23692 #836-01-1961 L1988 **IM ON** *020 †20

MC CONAUGHY, Teresa Lentz. 2855 DENBIGH BLVD 23692 #045-01-1991 L1992 **FM** *020 †18

MCREYNOLDS, Amber Christi. ■ 23692 #041-14-2008 *012

MEHROTRA, Surabhi. ■ 23692 #024-01-2006 **MPD** *020 †20,55

MEYER, Sabena. ■ 23693 #065-06-1995 L1997 **FM** *020 †18

MUFFELMAN, David Wm. 367 MOORE HOUSE RD 23690 #051-01-1975 L1976 **D IM** *020 †15,18,16

ORTIZ-NATOLI, Elizabeth. ■ 23692 #035-19-1986 L2000 **PD** *020 †55

POITRAS, Jean Maurice. ■ 23692 #035-08-1947 L1971 **PD EM** *071 †55

RAINES, Timothy Lee. 3212 HAMPTON HWY, # B 23693 #051-04-1990 L1991 **FM** *020 †18

RAJARAM, Suryakumar. ■ 23692 #495-16-1970 L1983 **PD EM** *020 †55

RAO, Gadahad Kishore. 3630 GEORGE WSHNGTN MM HWY, STE E 23693 #495-53-1970 L1975 **DR** *020 †80

RELTON, Sudhakar C. ■ 23693 #495-59-1980 L1988 **NEP** *020 †20

RITCHIE, William Wallace. 3630 GEORGE WSHNGTN MM HWY, STE E 23693 #051-04-1979 L1980 **DR** *020 †80

SCHLOSS, Robert William. ■ 23692 #024-01-2001 L2003 **DR** *100 †80

SHAMAIENGAR, Ravi Vijay. 3630 GEORGE WSHNGTN MM HWY 23693 #051-04-1996 L1996 **DR** *020 †80

SIFTON, Charles Leeman D. 5033 GEORGE WSHNGTN MM HWY 23692 #065-06-1968 L1998 **FM** *020 †18

SMITH, Kimberly Lynn. ■ 23692 #051-07-2008 *012

STACK, Kathleen Marie. ■ 23692 #047-06-1988 L1989 **P ADP** *020 †75

TRAPANI, Edward Tindal. 3630 GEO WASH HWY, C/O PER SE 23693 #051-07-2000 L2006 **DR** *100 †80

WARNIMENT, Crista Benson. ■ 23693 #048-16-2005 L2005 **FP** *012

WEBER, Suchong. ■ 23693 #035-09-2003 L2004 *100 †18

WOISARD, Kevin Keith. 3630 GEORGE WSHNGTN MM HWY, STE E 23693 #051-04-1983 L1989 **DR** *020 †80

YARLAGADDA, Atma Ram. ■ 23692 #913-89-1983 L2000 **P** *020

ZANONI – GLOUCESTER

ALLISON-BRYAN, Barbara. 7574 HOSPITAL DR, DRAWER 1846 23061 #041-14-1980 L1988 **PD ADL** *020 †55

BASS, Gregory. ■ 23061 #005-06-1996 L1999 **EM** *020 †16

BROWN, William Brushwood. ■ 23061 #051-04-1956 L1956 **FM OM** *071

BRYAN, Hugh M, III. PO BOX 646 23061 #041-14-1980 L1988 **ORS** *020 †40

CRAWFORD, Andrea Cecilia. PO BOX 646 23061 #051-04-1977 L1980 **ORS** *020 †40

EBERLE, Robert Chas. ■ 23061 #016-06-1954 L1997 **HNS OTO** *071 †85,45

FISHBURNE, Harriette B. 7363 WALKER AVE, DRAWER 800 23061 #051-01-1991 L1994 **PD** *020 †55

GEISERT, Todd. PO BOX 770 23061 #051-04-1979 L1983 **OPH** *020 †35

HAGOOD, William J, Jr. ■ 23061 #051-04-1943 L1943 **FM** *071 †18

JACKSON, Neville James. ■ 23061 #352-04-1953 L1974 **GS OS** *071 †85

KLINK, Robert Winfield. 7685 MEREDITH DR, GLOUCESTER WOMEN'S CLINIC 23061 #051-04-1971 L1975 **OBG AM** *020 †18

MYLES, John Turpin. ■ 23061 #051-04-1955 L1955 **DR NM** *071 †80

PARTIN, John Calvin. ■ 23061 #038-41-1959 L1991 **PD GE** *050 †55

ROSENDORF, Stanley B. ■ 23061 #010-01-1953 L1988 **GYN** *072 †30

STONE, Kearfott Mc Caull. 7590 HOSPITAL DR 23061 #051-01-1971 L1971 **OPH** *020 †35

TSCHAN, Donald Nelson. 7560 HOSPITAL DR, STE 101 23061 #041-13-1975 L1976 **FM** *020 †18

YUTZY, Carl Vernon. ■ 23061 #010-01-1960 L1965 **GS** *071 †85

CHARLOTTE AMALIE – SAINT THOMAS

ABBA, Boniface C. ■ 00801 #014-01-1976 L1986 **GS ON** *020
DASWANI, Chandra Ramchand. PO BOX 1511 00804 #825-01-1977 *100
FALLARIA, Orchid Ibanez. PO BOX 9426, KNUD HANSEN HOSP PO 00801 #748-01-1967 L1978 **EM GP** *020
HEATH, Alfred Oswald. ■ 00801 #041-02-1957 L1966 **GP GS** *020 †85
LESS, Garfield A. 1 3 6TH ST SUGAR ESTATE 00802 #566-01-1974 L1988 **GP** *020
MONSANTO, Didace S. ■ 00804 #396-06-1959 **PD PM** *071
MOORHEAD, John S. ■ 00804 #010-03-1930 L1951 **PHP GPM** *071 †70
PETERKIN, Rupert Augustus. 9149 ESTATE THOMAS, PARAGON MEDICAL BUILDING, 00802 #047-07-1972 L1986 **OBG** *020 †30
RAMOS, Evelyn Cristobal. PO BOX 9426, KNUD HANSEN HOSP PO 00801 #748-01-1967 **EM** *020
SAUNDERS, Edward. #10 SIXTH ST, SUGAR ESTATE 00802 #422-01-1984 L1989 **IM** *020
SCHNEIDER, Roy Lester. ■ 00804 #010-03-1965 L1986 **SO HNS** *020 †85
TAYLOR, William Edward C. PO BOX 1641 00804 #803-09-1938 **GS** *072
UY-BARRETTA, Cosme Baudin. KNUD HANSEN MEM HOSP 00801 #748-01-1959 L1975 **PD OS** *020

CHRISTIANSTED – SAINT CROIX

ALONSO, Francisca J. PO BOX 7903 00823 #748-01-1967 L1985 **PD** *020
ANDUZE, Alfred Lee. 4500 SION FARM, ISLAND MEDICAL CENTER 00820 #010-03-1974 L1978 **OPH** *020 ‡
BENN, Jamila Melanie. ■ 00820 #039-01-2003 L2004 **FM** *100 †18
BERKELEY, Michele Barbara. PO BOX 5377, SUITE 7 ISLAND MEDICAL CTR 00823 #010-02-1991 L2000 **OBG** *020 †30
BRISCOE, Warren. ■ 00821 #024-05-1985 L2006 **OBG** *020 †30
BUCHER, Robert Lawrence, Jr. 4007 ESTATE DIAMOND RUBY 00820 #026-04-1969 L1989 **END DIA** *020 †20
BURTON, Leslie Joshua, Jr. ■ 00823 #047-06-2001 L2005 **FM** *020 †18
CEBEDO, Alejandro C. ■ 00824 #748-01-1958 L1971 **GS GP** *020
CHIU, Yum-San. 4007 ESTATE DIAMOND RUBY 00820 #385-02-1951 L1965 **AN** *071
COUCH, Frances Gene. ■ 00820 #025-01-1977 L1980 **GYN** *020
DAWISKIBA, Wieslaw C. 4000 BEESTON HILL MED CTR, STE 4005 00820 #759-12-1974 L1994 **AN PMM** *020
DE CHABERT, Ralph A. ■ 00821 #869-05-1958 **OBG OS** *020
DIZON, Antonio F. ISLAND MEDICAL CENTER 00820 #748-08-1960 L1970 **IM** *071
DIZON, Michelle Najera. PO BOX 629, 1B JUDITH FANCY 00821 #012-21-1996 L2001 **END IM** *020 †20
D'SENA, Dorothy Kathleen. PO BOX 223055 00822 #495-02-1948 L1954 **OBG** *020 †30
EGNATINSKY, Jack. ■ 00824 #035-15-1965 L1966 **AN** *071 †05 ‡
FERNANDO, Cynthia C. ■ 00821 #748-01-1955 L1969
GALIBER, Andre A, Jr. 4500 SUNNY ISLE, STE 5 00820 #047-07-1984 L1987 **NM** *020 †80
GALIBER, Angelo Keith. 4500 SUNNY ISLE, STE 5 00820 #010-03-1984 L1987 **DR** *020 †80
GARDINER, Walter H. 5134 SUNDIAL PARK 00820 #035-01-1973 L1995 **NEP IM** *020
GIBBS, Richard T. ■ 00823 #566-01-1989 L2000 **PD** *020 †03,55
GUY, Richard Steele. 5000 CARDEN BEACH CONDS, UNIT 5425 00820 #047-07-1956 L1957 **GYN** *071 †30
HENDRICKS, Olaf G, Jr. 42-43 STRAND ST 00820 #010-03-1972 L1986 **P** *020
HENRY, Claudius L. ■ 00821 #010-03-1969 L1978 **ORS GS** *020 †40
HENRY, Lloyd Nasibu. PO BOX 1126 00821 #016-02-1964 L1971 **GS GP** *020
HODGSON, Carlton Roy. 17 ESTATE SOUTHGATE, GALLOWS BAYST CROIX US V1 00824 #869-01-1966 **ID PTH** *020
JETT, Gary Emil. 3022 EST GOLDEN ROCK 00820 #025-07-1983 L1999 **PM** *030 †60
JOHNSTON, Daniel Edwin. 4000 ESTATE BEESTON HL, STE 2 00820 #396-04-1979 L1983 **FM EM** *020 †18
KASIN, James Valiant. 4093 DIAMOND RUBY STE 7, PMB 199 00820 #143-07-1973 L2002 **PTH** *020 †50
KEFALOS, Kirana. ■ 00824 #038-06-1983 L2006 **IM** *020 †20
KING, Geraldine A. 00822 #041-01-1949 L1953 **N** *075 †75
KWON, Chung Yul. ■ 00820 #583-08-1957 **PD** *071
LEWIS, Coralee Ineta. 4500 SUNNY ISLE, STE 5 00820 #041-07-1980 L1999 **DR** *020
MANIBO, Jose Y. PO BOX 1593, 68 RUBY QUEENS QUARTER 00821 #748-01-1960 L1970 **U** *020
MANNINGS, Dawn Elizabeth. ■ 00823 #011-02-1997 L2001 **IM** *020 †20
MARSHALL, Bradford E. 4500 SION FARM STE 7, ISLAND MEDICAL CENTER 00820 #869-05-1958 L1969 **PM** *020
MATTHEW, Mavis Lorraine. 35 EST LA GRANDE PRINCESS 00823 #041-13-1984 L1988 **PD** *020 †55
MODY, Ila Suren. ■ 00821 #496-38-1960 L1975 **OBG** *020
MODY, Surendra Keshavlal. ■ 00821 #495-01-1961 L1976 **OPH** *020
MOORE, Trevena Bianca. ■ 00821 #024-01-1997 L2004 **PD** *020 †55
MOROWITZ, Joshua Alan. 4100 SION FARM SHOPP CTR 00820 #008-02-1979 L1983 **GS VS** *020 †85
NEUGART, Lourdes. 1000 KING ST, STE 4U 00820 #308-03-1983 L2001 **P CHP** *020 †75
OLANS, Richard Neal. PO BOX 216 00821 #024-07-1970 L1971 **ID IM** *020 †20
OMBRES, Severn R, Jr. 4500 SION FARM, P O BOX 5996 00820 #869-04-1973 L2000 **OPH** *020 †35
PEDERSEN, Walter John, Jr. PO BOX 7840, SUNNY ISLE 00823 #010-03-1975 L1986 **ORS** *020
PEREZ, John Charles. 4007 ESTATE DIAMOND RUBY 00820 #308-07-1980 L1998 **NEP IM** *020
PRASAD, Arakere B. 4000 BEESTON HILL MED CTR, STE 1 00820 #495-99-1978 L1983 **EM GP** *020 †16
RICKETTS, Anthony David. 4504 ESTATE DIAMOND, FLAGSTAR PROFESSIONAL BUIL 00820 #690-22-1990 L1999 **PD** *020 †55
ROMAN, Justo Manuelandres. 3009 ESTATE ORANGE GRV 00820 #308-01-1981 L1999 **PD** *020 †55
SANDERS, Herbert Lawrence. ■ 00824 #054-04-1974 L1975 **EM** *071
SLOMIN, Vincent Edward. ■ 00820 #035-03-1956 **FM** *071 †18
STARKEY, Thomas David. PO BOX 973 00821 #048-12-1982 L2005 **TS VS** *020 †85,90
SUH, Wook. ■ 00821 #583-04-1951 L1966 **GP GS** *071 †85
THOMAS, Bridget A. 4007 DIAMOND RUBY 00820 #566-01-1991 L1999 **IM** *020

THOMPSON, Jacqueline. 4200 UNITED SHOPP PLZ, STE 810 00820 #010-03-1989 L2000 **GS** *020 †85
THOMPSON, Robert H, III. ■ 00824 #010-03-1978 L1981 **IM OS** *020 †20
WEST, Kia Denise. ■ 00821 #010-03-2005 L2005 **FP** *012
WHITTEN, William Wiley. ■ 00820 #035-09-1947 L1950 **PD OS** *071 †55

CRUZ BAY – SAINT JOHN

MC MULLEN, Robert Chas. ■ 00831 #030-06-1977 L1989 **IM FM** *020
SAMBAT, Ricardo D. ■ 00831 #748-01-1961 L1971 **GS** *020

FREDERIKSTED – SAINT CROIX

BEAUCHAMP, Francisco M. PO BOX 1379, KINGSHILL STA 00841 #847-08-1975 L1986 **OBG** *020
CHRISTIAN, Cora Le Ethel. 40 ESTATE LA GRANGE 00840 #041-02-1971 L1975 **FM** *020 †18 ‡
GLENN, James Stokes. 117 HANNAH'S REST 00841 #017-20-1954 L1969 **PTH FOP** *071 †50
LOW-A-CHEE, Raymond Mervy. 516 STRAND ST 00840 #566-01-1972 L1993 **UCM** *020

KINGSHILL – SAINT CROIX

ANDERS, Ronald Lee. ■ 00850 #010-03-1973 L2000 **OBG** *020
CONNELL, Neville Kenneth. PO BOX 4546, CHARLES HARWOOD CLINIC 00851 #010-03-1971 L1989 **OM FM** *020
JAMERSON, Dorothy Aline. ■ 00850 #010-03-1975 L1980 **AN** *020
MC MAHON, Lisa Michelle. ■ 00851 #024-05-1996 L1999 **FM** *020 †18
MERRITT, Carolyn Cheatham. PO BOX 5240, 254-A ESTATE GLYNN # 3&4 00851 #010-01-1978 L2003 **D** *020 †15
POTTS, Michael Peter. ■ 00851 #010-03-1984 L1991 **CD CCM** *020 †20
SUBRAMANIAM, Babu. PO BOX 4471, 254A ESTATE GLYNN SUITE #1 00851 #495-59-1985 L2002 **N** *020 †75
TREASURE, Olivine Anne. PO BOX 4159, 9 BEESTON HILL MED CTR 00851 #011-02-1992 L1998 **OBG** *020 †30

SAINT CROIX – SAINT CROIX

AHMED, Mohammed Iqbal. PO BOX 8008, SUNNY ISLES 00823 #495-65-1968 L1986 **PD** *020
ALLEN, Adele Darlene. BOX A5, PEPPER TREE TERRACE 00820 #654-01-1989 *100
AUGUSTIN, Fermin. 61 HERMAN HILL 00821 #847-04-1952 **IM CD** *072
BATENGA, Rizalina R. ISLAND MEDICAL CENTER 00823 #748-01-1960 L1970 **PD** *075
BISHOP, Frank Thos. 4500 SION FARM, ISLAND MED CTR 00820 #051-04-1974 L1986 **FM** *020
BRASLOW, Charles Albert. GRANADA DEL MAR #301 00820 #023-07-1973 L2000 **AN PS** *020 †85
BUMANN, Robert Richard. 4007 DIAMOND RUBY 00820 #409-16-1992 L2002 **AN** *020 †05
CAMOES, Manuel Ferreira. 4500 SION FARM, ISLAND MEDICAL CENTER 00820 #770-01-1961 L1969 **OBG** *020 †30
CARR, Noel Austen Victor. BEESTON HILL MED CENTREE 00841 #010-03-1968 L1977 **OBG END** *020 †30
CARRILLO, Norma I. ■ 00820 #748-07-1961 L1981 **P PHP** *071
CINTRON ROSARIO, Raymond. 4007 ESTATE DIAMOND RUBY, CHRISTIANSTED 00820 #042-03-1984 L2000 **IM GE** *020 †20
EVANGELISTA, Tomas C. 42 KING ST, F'STED 00820 #748-01-1957 L1970 **IM GP** *020
GALIBER, Dante Pierre. 4500 SUNNY ISLE STE B4, ISLAND MEDICAL CENTER 00820 #017-20-1989 L1993 **CD NM** *020 †20
GARCIA GARCIA, Rafael. 7-A EAST WHIMFREDERIKSTED 00851 #847-01-1972 L1989 **GP** *020
JEROME, Marc Antoine. PO BOX 25537, 184 RUBY PLZ 00824 #440-01-1963 L1996 **OBG** *030 †30
LAKHRAM, Ramesh B. 4007 DIAMOND RUBY, CHRISTIANSTED 00820 #422-01-1987 L2006 **NEP IM** *020
MOORMAN, Gregory J. ■ 00824 #048-13-1993 L2001 **PS** *020 †65
OYAKE, Augustine Tamabor. DEPT OF OB/GYN, ST CROIX HOSPITAL 00823 #690-01-1969 L1973 **OBG** *020
WADE, Cheryl Denise. 1112 KING ST, CRISTIANSTED 00820 #035-19-1985 L1993 **GS** *020 †85
WILLIAMS, Wilbert. 3000 GOLDEN ROCK SHOPP CTR, CHRISTIANSTEAD 00820 #035-03-1978 L1983 **FM** *020

SAINT JOHN – SAINT JOHN

ZAMELIS, Robert Alexander. 5000 ESTATE ENIGHED 4A 00830 #035-15-1984 L1994 **IM** *020 †20

SAINT THOMAS – SAINT THOMAS

ALEXIS, Carlton Peter. 9800 BUCCANEER MALL, STE 8 00802 #010-03-1957 L1991 **IM** *072 †20
ALLA, Seshagiri Rao. SUGAR ESTATE, 1-3 6TH STREET 00801 #495-11-1975 L1984 *020
ALLA, Srinivasa Lakshmi. SUGAR ESTATE, 1-3 6TH STREET 00803 #495-50-1980 L1991 **FM** *020
AMARO, Luis Orlando. 9048 SUGAR EST 00802 #038-45-2001 L2005 **MPD** *100 †20,55
ANDERSON, Thos Gordon, Jr. 6500 RED HOOK PLZ, STE 205 00802 #045-01-1979 L2002 **FM** *020 †18
BACHAN, Rabindranath. ■ 00801 #566-01-1995 L2006 **HO** *020 †20
BAIRD, Gordon Jos. 13 FIRST AVE, SUGAR EST 00802 #010-03-1973 L1986 **OBG GP** *020
BISCOE, Byron Wm, Jr. 19 NISKY CTR, PEARLE VISION 00802 #012-21-1987 L1995 **OPH** *020
BOAZ, David Earnhardt. PO BOX 9887 00801 #036-07-1970 L1989 **EM OS** *020 †16
BROWN, Yvette. PO BOX 7278, HAVENSITE MALL UPPER LEVEL 00801 #035-19-1949 L1973 **AI** *071 †03
BUBB, Stephen Keith. ■ 00802 #019-02-1974 L1975 **ORS** *071 †40
BURNETT, Derek Michael. PO BOX 307679 00803 #041-14-1986 L2002 **PM** *020 †60
CAESAR, Hugo Victor. 9716 ESTATE THOMAS # 8-103, 9003 HAVENSIGHT MALL #320 00802 #010-03-1968 L1998 **ORS** *020 †40

■ = Address Information Privacy Protected

CALLENDER, Wilbur K. 52-A 10TH ST ESTATE THOMAS 00801 #010-03-1967 L1986 OBG *020 †30

CHASE, Jeffrey Michael. 9149 ESTATE THOMAS, PARAGON MEDICAL BLDG STE 1 00802 #041-13-1993 L1999 ORS *020 †40

CHEETHAM, Brian Curtis. 9162 ESTATE THOMAS, BAY 10 00802 #033-06-1985 L1989 GE IM *020 †20

CLAYTON, James P. 6500 RED HOOK PLZ STE 205, RED HOOK FAMILY PRACTICE 00802 #035-46-1984 L1990 FM D *020

COMISSIONG, Gilbert Keith. PO BOX 9401, #2-410 TH ST 00801 #020-02-1997 L2002 GS *020 †85

COMISSIONG, Sidney James. ■ 00803 #041-07-1985 L1991 GS *020

COMISSIONG, Thelma Ruth. 9149 ESTATE THOMAS, PARAGON MEDICAL BLDG 00802 #041-02-1979 L1991 EM IM *020 †20,16

CORBIN, John Alphonso S. 6006-5 ROSENDAHL ESTATE 00802 #010-03-1960 L1961 PHP *020

COUMARBATCH, Lauretta L. PO BOX 8868, UPPER HAVENSITE MALL 00801 #010-03-1991 L1998 GPM *020 †55

CURRERI, Peter A. PO BOX 6047 00804 #041-13-1948 L1966 GYN *071 †30

DASWANI, Murli. 46B ESTATE THOMAS, ABOVE 7-11,SUGAR ESTATE 00802 #495-30-1972 L1982 AMI *020

DAVIS, Kathryn Mary. ■ 00802 #016-06-1959 L1989 AN *071

DIAMANTE, Paula Anne. ■ 00802 #422-01-2001 L2005 PD *020

DOTTIN, Iris Elena. 4 MEDICAL COMPLEX STE 4 00802 #308-02-1991 L2005 PD *020

DUKES, Martin Walter, Jr. 11 MEDICAL COMPLEX, STE 11 00802 #030-05-1977 L2004 OBG *020 †30

DY, Cresencia. PO BOX 304986 00803 #748-11-1964 L1977 *020

FLOOD, Roy Devonne, Jr. ■ 00801 #036-01-1990 L2003 CD IC *020 †20

FRANKLIN, John Roland. 9003 HAVNSGHT SHP CTR #301, BLDG 3 00802 #035-01-1988 L2000 U *020 †95

GARBUTT, Neil. ■ 00801 #566-01-1975 L1989 GS U *020

GARDNER, Julia C. 9154 ESTATE THOMAS 00802 #048-13-1990 L1995 ORS *020 †40

GEORGE, Ezmin. ■ 00801 #041-12-2006 L2006 IM *012

GOLDMAN, Herbert Ira. 50 SUGAR ESTATES, STE 202 00801 #869-04-1966 L1993 IM ON *020 †20

GOLDMAN, Lawrence Norman. 9149 ESTATE THOMAS, STE 208 00802 #016-42-1971 L1975 GE IM *020 †20

HARTSHORN, Scott Linwood. 9149 ESTATE THOMAS, STE 203 00802 #045-01-1993 L1998 FM *020 †18

HOBDY, Erole. 9150 ESTATE THOMAS, STE 202 00802 #035-01-1998 L2005 ON *100 †20

HUNTE, Wishburne Irad. 10 BOLONGO BAY 00802 #308-07-1981 L1992 IM *020

JOHNSON, Archer C. ■ 00801 #010-03-1953 L1954 GP OS *020

JONES, Carolyn. 6500 RED HOOK PLZ, RED HOOK FAMILY PRACTICE 00802 #063-01-1994 L2004 FM PD *020 †18

JONES, Derrick Darnell. PO BOX 302866 00803 #012-21-1992 L1999 AN *020 †05

KEAN, Catherine Alisa. 50 SUGAR ESTATE, V.I. MED FOUNDATION BLD. 00804 #033-05-1991 L1997 OBG *020

KIM, Kab Kyun. PO BOX 8888 00801 #583-02-1954 L1965 R *020 †80

LAKE, Angel Anthony. ■ 00801 #025-12-2001 L2006 IM *020

LAPENNA, Lino M. 50 ESTATE THOMAS, STE 210 00802 #561-21-1952 L1991 P CHP *020

LINDSEY, Audria Blanche. 9149 ESTATE THOMAS, STE 202 00802 #047-07-1980 L1989 AI PD *020

LIVINGSTON, Mark D. 6500 RED HOOK PLZ, STE 205 00802 #048-15-1995 L2006 FM AM *020 †18

LLOYD, Christine Angela. 9149 ESTATE THOMAS, PARAGON MEDICAL BLDG. 00802 #035-01-1995 L1999 OBG *020 †30

LU, Leighmin. 9150 ESTATE THOMAS, STE 105 00802 #385-02-1960 L1973 P N *020 †75

LUI, Angela W K. 9150 ESTATE THOMAS, RM A211 00802 #041-09-1986 L1989 IM *020

MACARIOLA, Demetrio R, Jr. 6500 RED HOOK PLZ STE 20, RED HOOK FAMILY PRACTICE 00802 #748-26-1990 L2003 PDI PD *020 †55

MAYNARD, Paul Vendel. 45 1ST AVE 00802 #566-01-1976 L1978 *020

MC DONALD, Sylvester O. 2 BREWERS BAY, UVI HEALTH SERVICES 00802 #010-03-1949 GP ORS *071

MERCADO, Secundina G. 50 ESTATE THOMAS STE 201, VI MEDICAL FOUNDATION BLDG 00802 #748-08-1959 L1973 OPH OS *020

NIGAMATOV, Ilias. 9150 ESTATE THOMAS, MED FOUNDATION BLDG 00802 #913-06-1979 L1999 P *020

NIMMO, Ronald Clinton. PO BOX 12079, SPECIAL UNRESTRICTED LIC 00801 #033-05-1978 L1998 OBG *020

NUTTER, Marilyn Jo. ■ 00801 #020-02-1997 L2003 IM *020 †20

ODLUM, Frank Alphonso. PO BOX 12138, 2ND & 4TH 10TH ST 00801 #039-01-1990 L1997 GS *020 †85

OFOHA, Kenneth O. PO BOX 12199 00801 #308-10-1986 L1999 EM *020

OKIYE, Stephen E L. 50 EST THOMAS STE 106, VI MEDICAL FOUNDATION 00801 #036-01-1975 L1986 U VS *020

PAK, Hae Young. PO BOX 8888 00801 #583-03-1954 L1965 PD A *020

PETTY, Brenda A Gumbs. ■ 00801 #026-08-2000 *100

POBLETE, Evangelina. 9TH ST SUGAR EST, PROFESSIONAL CTR STE 1B 00801 #748-02-1960 L1986 PD OS *020

RAJANI, Chander Kanta. ■ 00803 #496-07-1950 L1976 OBG *020

RANDALL, Beverly Banks. ■ 00802 #023-07-1991 L2000 NPM *020 †55

RICHARDSON, Condon A. 9048 SUGAR EST, SCHNEIDER REGIONAL MEDICAL 00802 #566-01-1995 L2006 PHO *100 †55

RICHARDSON, Reva Abigail. ■ 00803 #048-04-1999 L2004 MPD *020 †20

ROBINSON, James Fletcher. 9150 ESTATE THOMAS 00802 #010-03-1965 L1986 D *020

RODRIGUEZ, Luis Maria. PO BOX 8704, 4TH STREET BIO-MEDICAL BLD 00801 #132-04-1955 L1966 FM IMG *020

RODRIGUEZ-L OFFICIAL, L. ■ 00801 #308-01-1972 L1992 PD *020

ROSAL, Joselito Posadas. PO BOX 9326 00801 #748-01-1984 L1985 *020

RUIVIVAR, Richard Borras. ■ 00801 #748-07-1975 FM *020

SALVO, Maria S. 6501 RED HOOK PLZ, STE 20 00802 #132-01-1990 L2005 CCA *020 †05

SHAPIRO, Adam Marc. 9149 ESTATE THOMAS, STE 308 00802 #010-01-1986 L2002 OTO FPS *020 †45

SMITH, C Warren. 55 PRINDSENS GADE 00801 #010-03-1944 L1944 PHP PD *072 †55

SPENCER, Derek Victor. 1026 TENTH ST, SUGAR ESTATE 00802 #010-03-1967 L1970 P PHP *020

SPRAUVE, Margaret E. 9149 ESTATE THOMAS, PARAGON MED BLDG STE 206 00802 #024-01-1990 L1998 OBG MFM *020 †30

TALAVERA, Perla Espiritu. PO BOX 304908, VETERANS DRIVE 00803 #748-07-1969 PD *100

TIZES, Bruce Randolph. PO BOX 7549 00801 #016-42-1984 L1984 OPH EM *020

VICTOR, Janice Debra. PO BOX 302094 00803 #038-45-1999 L2005 PME AN *020 †05

WRIGHT, Debra Lynn. 4605 TUTU PARK MALL, STE 207 00802 #024-01-1992 L2005 OBG *020 †30

YTBAREK, Brikti. 9048 SUGAR EST, THE ROY LESTER SCHNEIDER H 00802 #005-14-1998 L2004 IM *020 †20

ABERDEEN – GRAYS HARBOR

AUBERTIN, Danette Helen. 915 ANDERSON DR 98520 #007-02-1995 L2004 **FM** *020 †18

BASHANDY, Hany Gaber Abd. 915 ANDERSON DR 98520 #915-02-1998 L2006 **IM** *100 †20

BAUSHER, John Chas. 1020 ANDERSON DR STE 203 98520 #050-02-1976 L1979 **FM** *020 †18

BAUTISTA-AZORES, Richelle. 954 ANDERSON DR STE 1 98520 #748-08-1994 L2002 **PD** *020 †55

BENNETT, Lawrence N. 915 ANDERSON DR, SOUTH SOUND RADIOLOGY AT 98520 #036-01-1982 L1997 **DR** *020 †80

BERNEY, Timothy Grant. 1211 SKYVIEW DR 98520 #016-42-1997 L2002 **ORS** *020 †40

BOLIN, Rex Warren. 1104 BASICH BLVD 98520 #007-02-1981 L1984 **PUD IM** *020 †20

BONIFIELD, James Gee. 915 ANDERSON DR, SOUTH SOUND RADIOLOGY AT 98520 #048-12-1971 L1976 **DR GP** *020 †80

BRANDT, Kim B. 915 ANDERSON DR 98520 #018-03-1975 L2005 **FM** *020 †18

BROTTEM, John Leonard, III. 1104 BASICH BLVD 98520 #054-04-1971 L1980 **PUD SME** *020 †20

BUCK, Julie Marie. 915 ANDERSON DR 98520 #054-04-1999 L2004 **OS** *020 †20,16

CAGAN, Michael E. 1108 BASICH BLVD 98520 #035-08-1968 L1974 **DR** *020 †20

CARATAO, Rowena Maderazo. 1100 BASICH BLVD 98520 #748-11-1972 L1983 **PD** *020 †55

CHENAULT, Price M. 1211 SKYVIEW DR 98520 #035-03-1969 L1981 **ORS** *020 †40

CHRISTENSON, Jeffrey C. 1104 BASICH BLVD 98520 #035-01-1991 L1997 **PCC** *020 †20

CONN, David Eric. 1606 SIMPSON AVE 98520 #040-02-1975 L1987 **CD IM** *020 †20

DHANDA, Gurdarshan Singh. 915 ANDERSON DR, SOUTH SOUND RADIOLOGY AT 98520 #056-06-1994 L1999 **NM** *020 †80

DRASNIN, Stephen L. 1813 SUMNER AVE, HEALTH CTR 98520 #308-11-1985 L1991 **FM** *020 †18

ENGEL, Moshe David. 915 ANDERSON DR 98520 #017-20-1993 L1996 **EM** *020 †18

ERICKSON, Juliette K. 1020 ANDERSON DR, STE 203 98520 #048-04-1999 L2002 **FM** *020 †18

ESTALILLA, Francis V. 1720 SUMNER AVE 98520 #014-01-1990 L1994 **OPH** *020 †35

FAHEY, Matthew Gilbert. 915 ANDERSON DR 98520 #040-02-1987 L2003 **EM** *020 †16

FIELDS, Jack M. 915 ANDERSON DR, SOUTH SOUND RADIOLOGY AT 98520 #035-09-2000 L2005 **DR** *100 †80

FRANCISCOVICH, Robin Ann. 915 ANDERSON DR 98520 #018-03-1981 L1982 **AN** *020 †05

GALL, Jeffrey Allan. 915 ANDERSON DR 98520 #010-01-2001 L2005 **EM** *020 †16

GIBBS, Philip. 611 N F ST 98520 #917-08-1965 L1978 **CD NM** *020 †20,28

GIVENS, Barbara Lefler. 1020 ANDERSON DR STE 20 98520 #054-04-1992 L1992 **IM** *020

GROSECLOSE, Lydia Joy. 1412 ROBERT GRAY BLVD 98520 #035-18-1944 L2002 **PD** *020 †55

HANSEN, Stephen Michael. 1211 SKYVIEW DR 98520 #016-11-1999 L2004 **ORS** *100

HAUTALA, John William. 915 ANDERSON DR 98520 #054-04-1993 L1996 **EM** *020 †16

HOFMANN, William Peter. 915 ANDERSON DR, DEPT OF ANESTHESIOLOGY 98520 #649-31-1992 L2002 **AN PAN** *020

HOGG, Katherine Meiko. 1104 BASICH BLVD 98520 #048-14-1983 L1987 **PUD CCM** *020 †20

HOOT, Glenn P. 118 W 1ST ST, LASER CENTER 98520 #048-12-1987 L1994 **OPH** *020 †35 ‡

HUCK, Robert Love. 1104 BASICH BLVD 98520 #028-02-1978 L1983 **PUD IM** *020 †20

HUNT, Kenneth I. 1005 N BROADWAY ST 98520 #050-02-1970 L1972 **GE IM** *020 †20

HUTTON, William Steven. 1100 BASICH BLVD 98520 #048-02-1973 L1988 **PD** *020 †55

IANCU, Mihai Florin. 915 ANDERSON DR, SOUTH SOUND RADIOLOGY AT 98520 #781-01-1992 L2006 **DR** *020 †80,28

JOHNSON, Antoine Douglas. 501 N BROADWAY ST 98520 #047-07-1996 L2000 **FM** *020 †18

KAO, Ching-Pang. 1812 SUMNER AVE STE F 98520 #244-01-1970 L1982 **D** *020

KHURSHID, Muhammad Aijaz. 191 CONSTANTINE WAY, STAFFORD CREEK CORRECTIONS 98520 #704-16-1990 L2000 **ID IMG** *020

KILGORE, Wm Edson, II. 1020 ANDERSON DR STE 202, SUITE 202 98520 #049-01-1972 L1986 **OBG** *020 †30

KNACKSTEDT, Virgil Ernest. 915 ANDERSON DR, SOUTH SOUND RADIOLOGY AT 98520 #030-05-1974 L1982 **DR** *020 †80

LAYBOURN, Loren Earnest. ■ 98520 #054-04-2002 L2002 **DR** *020

LENGLE, Steven James. 915 ANDERSON DR 98520 #005-19-1986 L2004 **VIR DR** *020 †80

LEW, Ralph. 1720 SUMNER AVE, HARBOR OPHTHALMOLOGY 98520 #010-01-1966 L1972 **OPH** *071 †35

LIPSKI, Timothy Andrew. 915 ANDERSON DR 98520 #056-06-2003 L2007 **EM** *020

LLOYD, Deborah Amm. 954 ANDERSON DR STE 108 98520 #025-12-2002 L2007 **GS** *020

LUETKEHANS, Thomas James. 915 ANDERSON DR, SOUTH SOUND RADIOLOGY AT 98520 #016-11-1984 L1992 **VIR** *020 †80

MACS, Juris Miervaldis. 6317 OLYMPIC HWY, GRAYS HARBOR FIRE DISTRICT 98520 #054-04-1962 L1968 **GS** *020 †85

MAGSALAY, Edgardo Castro. 1020 ANDERSON DR, STE 204 98520 #748-10-1969 L1983 **PD** *020

MATSUBARA, Rodney Shigeo. 915 ANDERSON DR, SOUTH SOUND RADIOLOGY AT 98520 #054-04-1971 L2005 **DR** *020 †80

MAY, Gregory Kenneth. 1211 SKYVIEW DR 98520 #030-06-1990 L1995 **HS ORS** *020 †40

MCCANN, Bessie. 915 ANDERSON DR 98520 #056-06-2004 L2006 **EM** *020

MC CAULEY, Robert Leeroy. 915 ANDERSON DR 98520 #019-02-1992 L1995 **IM** *020 †20

MELVILLE, David Ernest. 915 ANDERSON DR 98520 #048-13-1971 L2004 **EM FM** *020 †18

MEMON, Mohammad Saleem. 1220 BASICH BLVD STE B, GRAYS HARBOR INT MED 98520 #704-16-1985 L1995 **IM** *020 †20 ‡

MERRIFIELD, Benjamin F. 1006 N H ST 98520 #038-06-1998 L2005 **GE** *020 †20

MILLER, John James. 105 S BROADWAY ST 98520 #040-02-1997 L2002 **N** *020 †75

MOORE, Chris Cd. 915 ANDERSON DR 98520 #005-02-1996 L2000 **EM** *020 †16

MORRIS, Ralph Louis. 1020 ANDERSON DR, STE 205 98520 #054-04-1960 L1978 **IM** *020 †20

NAUCK, Charles John. 915 ANDERSON DR 98520 #054-04-1985 L1990 **PTH** *020 †50

NEWTON, Thomas. 915 ANDERSON DR 98520 #040-02-1991 L2005 **FM** *020 †18

O'CONNELL, Dennis Michael. 1108 BASICH BLVD 98520 #040-02-1975 L1983 **DR** *020 †80

PARRINO, Tremont Vincent. 915 ANDERSON DR, SOUTH SOUND RADIOLOGY AT 98520 #023-12-1987 L1995 **DR** *020 †80

POLLOCK, Charles Anson. 915 ANDERSON DR 98520 #018-03-1957 L1958 **FM** *071 †18

PRESCOTT, Joanna Arcuni. 915 ANDERSON DR, SOUTH SOUND RADIOLOGY AT 98520 #035-09-1995 L2005 **DR** *020 †80

REED, Kevin Joseph. 915 ANDERSON DR, SOUTH SOUND RADIOLOGY AT 98520 #023-12-1988 L2000 **DR** *020 †80

REES, John Morris. 1020 ANDERSON DR STE 202, GRAYS HARBOR WOMEN'S CLINI 98520 #649-14-1978 L1988 **OBG** *020

RICE, Murray Newmyer. 915 ANDERSON DR 98520 #026-04-1980 L1981 **EM** *020 †16

RIMKUNOS, Linda Marie. 915 ANDERSON DR 98520 #033-05-1981 L1991 **EM FM** *020 †16,18

ROWE, Brent Jonathan. 954 ANDERSON DR, STE 107 98520 #054-04-1995 L2000 **GS** *020 †85

ROWLEY, Thomas Dean. 1108 BASICH BLVD 98520 #018-03-1971 L1974 **DR** *071 †80

RUSSELL, Tracy Lynne. 954 ANDERSON DR, STE 105 98520 #422-01-1996 L2006 **PD** *020

RUYLE, Susan. 207 S CHEHALIS ST 98520 #054-04-1985 L1991 **OPH** *020 †35

SAMADI-SOLTANI, Maryam. 1100 BASICH BLVD 98520 #517-11-1991 L2006 **PD** *100

SCHULTE, Terrence Anthony. 915 ANDERSON DR 98520 #026-04-1968 L1975 **PTH GP** *062 †50

SHEN, Charles Hao. 915 ANDERSON DR, SOUTH SOUND RADIOLOGY AT 98520 #043-01-2000 L2005 **DR** *020 †80 ‡

SINGHA, Navneet Kaur. 915 ANDERSON DR, SOUTH SOUND RADIOLOGY AT 98520 #016-11-1993 L1999 **VIR** *020 †80

SISSON, John Whiting. 915 ANDERSON DR 98520 #032-01-1998 L2007 **EM** *020 †16

STAGNONE, David. 915 ANDERSON DR, SOUTH SOUND RADIOLOGY AT 98520 #034-01-1987 L1998 **DR** *020 †20,80

SUI, Xingwei. 954 ANDERSON DR, STE 102 98520 #243-32-1984 L2003 **ON IM** *020 †20

THENG, Pei Shih. 1813 SUMNER AVE 98520 #063-01-2002 L2005 **FM** *020 †18

THOMPSON, Shahnaz. ■ 98520 #704-01-1956 L1974 **PD GP** *071 †55

TIMMS, Ian David. 915 ANDERSON DR, SOUTH SOUND RADIOLOGY AT 98520 #008-01-1990 L1997 **VIR** *020 †80

TROEH, Timothy Harry. 954 ANDERSON DR, STE 104 98520 #054-04-1993 L1996 **IM** *020 †20

TULLEY, Eric Brock. 915 ANDERSON DR 98520 #048-02-1999 L2003 **EM** *020 †20

VEGH, Julius. ■ 98520 #473-04-1951 L1959 **FM** *071

VERSCHUYL, Evert Jan. 915 ANDERSON DR, SOUTH SOUND RADIOLOGY AT 98520 #036-05-1988 L1993 **DR** *020 †80

WONG, Anne Marie. 615 N F ST, P O BOX 87 98520 #030-06-1991 L1995 **IM** *020 †20

WONG, H Jeffrey. 915 ANDERSON DR, GRAYS HARBOR COMMUNITY HOS 98520 #031-01-1983 L2002 **AN** *020 †05

WORTH, Robert Bruce. 1020 ANDERSON DR, STE 203 98520 #040-02-1977 L1980 **FM ADM** *020 †18

AIRWAY HEIGHTS – SPOKANE

BARKER, Michael J. ■ 99001 #048-13-2006 L2007 *020

HEMPEL, James Robert. ■ 99001 #023-12-1999 *020 †50

ALLYN – MASON

ROLLINS, William Harlan. ■ 98524 #054-04-1963 L1970 **U** *020 †95

WARTMAN, Calvin. 1250 E OLD RANCH RD 98524 #019-02-1946 L1954 **GS GP** *071

AMBOY – CLARK

MC WAYNE, W Robynne. ■ 98601 #031-01-1984 L1986 **AN** *020

ANACORTES – SAN JUAN

FERGUS, James Weldon. ■ 98222 #030-05-1957 L1957 **GYN** *072 †30

ANACORTES – SKAGIT

ADAMS, George Bryant. ■ 98221 #005-12-1971 L1974 **FM** *020

AHSAEI, Ramin. 5003 HEATHER DR 98221 #496-20-1991 L2002 **AN** *020

ALEXANDER, Andrew Geo. 2511 M AVE STE B 98221 #005-06-1982 L2007 **FM IM** *020 †18

ALEXANDER, John Maurice. ■ 98221 #035-01-1966 L1990 **PUD IM** *020 †20

AMOS, Deborah Ellen. 1220 22ND ST STE D 98221 #054-04-1991 L1995 **PM** *020 †60

ASHBACH, Matthew Nathan. ■ 98221 #054-04-2004 **OTO** *012

BACKMAN, Mark Steven. 1213 24TH ST 98221 #054-04-1978 L1981 **FM** *020 †18

BALESTRERI, Thos Michael. 1211 24TH ST, ISLAND HOSPITAL 98221 #054-04-1992 L1997 **AN** *020 †20

BAME, John David. 1211 24TH ST 98221 #038-41-1970 L1974 **DR** *071 †80

BARNETT, Blair Mercer. 2303 CASCADE CT 98221 #005-14-1964 L1982 **AN** *020

BAUMANN, William James. ■ 98221 #056-06-1961 L1962 **P CHP** *020 †75

BECKER, Dwight Lowell. ■ 98221 #048-40-1943 L1943 **OM IMG** *071

BECKER, Lawrence Dwight. 1211 24TH ST 98221 #038-40-1970 L1975 **AN** *020 †05

BENZ, Deborah Marie. 1017 20TH ST 98221 #003-01-1981 L1988 **OM** *020 †16

BETHKE, Richard Alan. 1211 24TH ST 98221 #028-34-1987 L1990 **EM** *020 †16

BJORSETH, Franklin E. 2511 M AVE HA 98221 #054-04-1992 L1992 **FM** *020 †18

BOGOSIAN, Armen James. 5010 TOTEM TRL, UNITED STATES 98221 #003-01-1974 L1977 **AN** *020 †05

BOLTON, Karen Michele. 1220 22ND ST, STE A 98221 #020-12-1983 L1997 **FM** *020 †18

BRIGHAM, Nathaniel Stephe. ■ 98221 #021-01-2005 L2006 **FM** *020

BROOKS, Thomas Pidduck. 1004 N AVE 98221 #054-04-1954 L1955 **FM** *071 †18

BROWN, Linda Ruth. 1213 24TH ST, STE 300 98221 #007-02-1986 L1990 **OPH** *020 †35

CHAMBERS, John Danl. 1004 COMMERCIAL AVE, APT 208 98221 #018-03-1963 L1968 **OPH** *071 †35 ‡

CLANCEY, Gary James. 2511 M AVE, STE D 98221 #038-06-1973 L1974 **ORS** *071 †40

COBB, Leonard C. ■ 98221 #010-01-1953 L1955 **GE** *071

CONNOR, Rory Kevin. 1213 24TH ST 98221 #030-06-1977 L1981 **N** *020

CONWAY, Claude Leslie. 1213 24TH ST 98221 #007-02-1974 L1977 **FM** *020 †18

CONYERS, William C. 1211 24TH ST 98221 #010-01-1986 L1993 **FM** *020 †18

CUI, Jimmy Y. 2511 M AVE, STE D 98221 #243-70-1982 L2001 **PM PMM** *020 †60 ‡

EIESLAND, Harold Lloyd. 2511 M AVE STE 100 98221 #054-04-1969 L1973 **IM ON** *020 †20

ELLIS, Kenneth Ronan. 1213 24TH ST, STE 300 98221 #005-15-1998 L2002 **OPH** *020 †35

ELY, Cecil Wilbur, Jr. 1213 24TH ST 98221 #025-01-1963 L1987 **OBG** *071 †30

ESPOSITO, Francis Anthony. 4912 PORTALIS WAY, POST OFFICE BOX 436 98221 #021-01-1960 L1977 **R** *020 †80

FEIN, Charles Lewis. 2511 M AVE, STE C 98221 #005-02-1992 L1997 **IM** *020 †20

FOWLER, Amber Dyane. ■ 98221 #056-06-2002 L2006 **D** *020 †15

GAHLER, Hans-Rudolf. ■ 98221 #869-07-1954 L1957 **FM** *071 †18

GALLANT, Ellen Marie. 2601 M AVE 98221 #035-01-1993 L2007 **CD** *020 †20

GARD, Kenley Eugene. ■ 98221 #054-04-1962 L1967 **A PD** *071 †03,55
GARDE, Kathleen Ann. 1213 24TH ST 98221 #038-06-1994 L2001 **OBG** *020 †30
GELLATLY, Thos Alexander. 5106 KINGSWAY 98221 #803-05-1959 L1990 **AN** *071 †05
GUNN, John Curry. ■ 98221 #016-11-1970 L2004 **PD** *062 †55,16
GURALNICK, Daniel Eric. 2601 M AVE 98221 #001-02-1998 L2000 **CD** *020 †20
HALL, Phillip Lee. ■ 98221 #054-04-1966 L1972 **CD IM** *020 †20
HANESWORTH, Danl Matthew. 2511 M AVE, STE D 98221 #054-04-1992 L1999 **ORS** *020 †40
HENEKS, Helen I Andreasen. ■ 98221 #018-03-1951 L1981 **GP PD** *071
HIGGINS, Robert W. ■ 98221 #054-04-1965 L1968 **FM** *071 †18
HOGGE, Jason Gregory. 1213 24TH ST 98221 #305-01-2003 L2006 **FM** *020 †18
HORESH, Allen Haron. 2511 M AVE, STE C 98221 #016-02-1993 L1999 **IM** *020 †20
HYLAND, Ansel Quigley. 7556 W SHORE DR 98221 #040-02-1970 L1975 **AN** *020 †05
JAMES, Michael Clinton. 2511 M AVE, STE A 98221 #054-04-1984 L1987 **FM** *020 †18
JONES, David W. 1018 FIDALGO AVE 98221 #060-01-1991 L1994 **FM** *020 †18
JORGENSEN, Raymond Andrew. ■ 98221 #028-34-1956 L1981 **OTO** *071 †45
KARTMAN, Adam Affron. 1211 24TH ST 98221 #003-01-1986 L1991 **EM EM** *020 †18
KECKLEY, Laurie A L. 2602 16TH ST 98221 #048-02-1995 L1999 **PD** *020 †55
KIRKWOOD, Charles Richard. 2511 M AVE STE A 98221 #054-04-1971 L1977 **FM GP** *071 †18
KOO, Kenny Ping-Kong. 1211 24TH ST 98221 #462-01-1976 L1995 **GS** *020
KRESS, Thomas Donald. 24TH ST & 111TH AVE, ISLAND HOSPITAL 98221 #035-15-1975 L1987 **EM** *020 †16
LAMME, Jacqueline Suzanne. ■ 98221 #023-12-2005 L2006 **FM** *020
LANG, Kaarsten Robin. 1017 20TH ST 98221 #005-12-1987 L1992 **ORS** *020 †40
LARSSON, Charles Evert. 1211 24TH ST 98221 #858-01-1978 L1985 **FM** *020 †18
LIVERMORE, James David. 1211 24TH ST 98221 #040-02-1977 L1982 **ORS** *020 †40 ‡
LLEWELLYN, Nancy Hoover. 2511 M AVE STE C 98221 #054-04-1988 L1990 **IM** *020 †20
LOHAVANICHBUTR, Kamol. 2601 M AVE 98221 #891-04-1988 L1998 **CD IC** *020 †20
MADENWALD, Malcolm B. ■ 98221 #054-04-1964 L1965 **ORS** *071 †40
MASTEN, Thomas Oliver. 1211 24TH ST 98221 #038-06-1994 L2001 **AN** *020 †05
MATHIS, John Robt, Jr. 1213 24TH ST STE 100 98221 #049-01-1991 L1993 **IM** *020 †20
MCDONALD, Alix Kathaleen. 2511 M AVE STE B, ANACORTES FAMILY MEDICINE 98221 #305-01-2004 L2007 **FM** *020 †18
MC GINTY, John Danl. PO BOX 655 98221 #025-01-1955 L1956 **IM CD** *071 †20
MULLINAUX, Ernest B. ■ 98221 #048-12-1945 L1979 **GP GS** *071
MURRAY, Bryan Hugh. 2511 M AVE, STE C 98221 #020-12-1988 L2004 **IM** *020 †20
NANOS, George Peter, III. ■ 98221 #051-04-1998 L2006 **GS** *020
NICOLLS, Richard Thos. ■ 98221 #005-15-1963 L1991 **GP** *071
OEFELEIN, Mary Rinko. ■ 98221 #038-06-1990 L2004 **IM** *020 †20
OETH, Dennis Arthur. ■ 98221 #018-03-1970 L1971 **FM** *071 †18
OLMSTED, Jeanne Burgess. 1213 24TH ST 98221 #005-02-1983 L1989 **PD** *020 †55
OSTLUND, James Albion. 1119 11TH ST 98221 #054-04-1958 L1959 **GP GYN** *020 †30
PAPRITZ, Jack Whitney. ■ 98221 #016-02-1956 L1961 **GP GS** *020
PASNICK, Marykay. 1211 24TH ST 98221 #054-04-1977 L1980 **EM PD** *020 †55,16
PAYNE, Patricia L Bruce. ■ 98221 #016-06-1952 L1953 **AN GP** *020
POWERS, Robert Walter. ■ 98221 #019-02-1955 L1958 **OBG GS** *071
PRINS, Robert Peter. 1213 24TH ST 98221 #023-07-1969 L1971 **OBG** *020 †30
RAMERMAN, Wayne Geo. 1213 24TH ST STE 100 98221 #054-04-1969 L1972 **IM** *071
REZVANI, Ezzatollah. 1220 22ND ST STE B 98221 #517-04-1962 L1971 **IM CD** *020 †20
RICHARDS, Marvin Lester. 1213 24TH ST 98221 #005-12-1980 L1991 **PD** *020 †55
RIEGER, Robert Paul. 2511 M AVE, STE A 98221 #054-04-1990 L1993 **FM** *020 †18
RODIN, Curtis Wayne. 2511 M AVE, STE D 98221 #040-02-1987 L1990 **ORS** *020 †40
SCHMALTZ, Kristine Ellen. 1213 24TH ST STE 700, ISLAND SURGEONS 98221 #005-14-1984 L1989 **GS** *020 †85
SCHOUWEILER, Heather Day. ■ 98221 #054-04-2008 *012
SCHWENK, Walter Gustav. 24TH ST M AVE 98221 #023-07-1961 L1964 **VS TS** *071 †85
SHAFER, Jonathan Boadu. 2511 M AVE, STE D 98221 #048-02-2001 L2007 **ORS** *100
SIBLE, Michael Dean. 1213 24TH ST STE 700 98221 #054-14-1984 L1989 **GS VS** *020 †85
SLAUGHTER, William H, III. ■ 98221 #035-15-1964 L1971 **ORS** *020 †40
SMITH, Stacia Ann. 1017 20TH ST 98221 #054-04-1987 L1992 **ORS OSS** *020 †40
SON, Julie Yoolee. ■ 98221 #033-06-2005 L2006 **P** *020
SPIRO, Saul Matthew. ■ 98221 #050-02-1956 L1962 **P** *071
SPONSELLER, Marie C. ■ 98221 #025-01-1985 L1991 **PD NEP** *020 †55
STALSBROTEN, Oliver Lars. 2511 M AVE STE B 98221 #040-02-1975 L1980 **FM** *020 †18
SWEENEY, Margaret Alicia. 2511 M AVE, STE A 98221 #017-20-1996 L1999 **FM** *020 †18
THOMPSON, Gina Biggs. 1101 22ND ST 98221 #048-12-1987 L1992 **P** *020 †75
TUCKER, Keith Benoit. ■ 98221 #054-04-1958 L1961 **GP EM** *071
WILLIAMS, Charles Everett. ■ 98221 #016-02-1961 L1992 **IM** *071 †20
WILLIAMSON, Richard V. 2511 M AVE, STE D 98221 #005-18-1983 L1987 **ORS OSM** *020 †40
ZAMBORSKY, Julie A. 1213 24TH ST 98221 #041-13-1996 L1999 **FM** *020 †18

ANDERSON ISLAND — PIERCE

GEIBERGER, Charles Robt. ■ 98303 #005-02-1954 L1955 **GS CD** *071 †85
HOLT, Charlene Poland. ■ 98303 #011-02-1963 L1979 **HO GPM** *071 †55

ARLINGTON — SNOHOMISH

BALLON, Bruce Jay. 903 MEDICAL CENTER DR #100 98223 #051-04-1988 L1992 **OPH** *020 †35
BECKNER, F James. 330 S STILLAGUAMISH AVE 98223 #005-14-1975 L1978 **IM GP** *020
BENNETT, Andrew Leon. 875 WESLEY ST STE 250 98223 #054-04-1984 L1991 **FM** *020 †18
BROWN, Gary Lee. 20302 77TH AVE NE, CASCADE MEDICAL GROUP 98223 #007-02-1971 L1973 **OTO PS** *020 †45
BURK, Phillip Scott. 330 S STILLAGUAMISH AVE 98223 #054-04-1993 L1996 **FM** *020 †18
BURKS, Donald Erwin. 330 S STILLAGUAMISH AVE 98223 #048-04-1973 L1980 **IM PUD** *075
CAMERON, Bruce D. 16404 SMOKEY POINT BLVD, STE 303 98223 #048-04-1991 L2001 **OPH** *020 †35
CARTWRIGHT, Jefferson J. 20218 77TH AVE NE STE B 98223 #048-12-1989 L2003 **ORS** *020 †40
CHAFFEE, Charles Turner. 7530 204TH ST NE 98223 #054-04-1973 L1974 **FM** *020 †18
COLLINS, James David. 330 S STILLAGUAMISH AVE 98223 #047-06-2000 L2000 **EM** *020 †16
COYNE, William Heath. ■ 98223 #028-34-1983 L1991 **IM PD** *020 †20,55
DAVIS, Frederick Jos. 328 S STILLAGUAMISH AVE 98223 #064-01-1968 L1970 **ORS** *020 †40

DUNNINGTON, David Arthur. 16410 SMOKEY POINT BLVD, STE 208 98223 #054-04-1977 L1979 **FM** *020 †18
FLETCHER, James Rodgers. 875 WESLEY ST STE 250 98223 #054-04-1984 L1988 **FM** *020 †18
GO, Rosana L. 330 S STILLAGUAMISH AVE 98223 #748-01-1981 L2003 **PD** *020 †55
GROSS, James Richard. 20302 77TH AVE NE, CASCADE MEDICAL GROUP 98223 #054-04-1980 L1982 **OTO FPS** *020 †45
HARMAN, Richard Lee. 903 MEDICAL CENTER DR, CASCADE REGIONAL EYE 98223 #011-02-1973 L1984 **OPH** *020 †35
HARRIS, Kevin Craig. 20302 77TH AVE NE, CASCADE MEDICAL GROUP 98223 #056-06-1998 L2003 **OTO** *020 †45
HARTLING, Ross Paul. 330 S STILLAGUAMISH AVE 98223 #040-02-1981 L1987 **DR** *020 †80
HEJAZI, Seyed Ali. 16410 SMOKEY PT BLVD, POINT BOULEVARD 98223 #902-07-1989 L2001 **IM** *020 †20
HENDERSON, James Roger. 875 WESLEY ST STE 130 98223 #024-01-1969 L1975 **PD PHO** *020
HENNING, Eric Norman. 330 S STILLAGUAMISH AVE 98223 #026-04-1984 L1987 **EM** *020 †18
HOOKE, Gerard. 330 S STILLAGUAMISH AVE 98223 #539-04-1971 L1972 **EM** *020
HUDEC, Bradley Wayne. ■ 98223 #054-04-1976 L1980 **EM** *020 †18
JANEWAY, David Ward. 875 WESLEY ST, STE 250 98223 #035-45-1998 L2000 **FM** *020 †18
JOBE, Richard Ray. 16410 SMOKEY POINT BLVD, STE 200 98223 #028-03-1961 L1965 **IM HEM** *020 †20
JOHNSON, Gary Kenneth. 20302 77TH AVE NE, CASCADE MEDICAL GROUP 98223 #054-04-1969 L1971 **OTO FPS** *020 †45
JOHNSON, Rodney E. 328 S STILLAGUAMISH AVE, IOWA ORTHO CTR PC 98223 #060-02-1975 L2007 **ORS** *020 †40
KAHM, Edward Lyle. ■ 98223 #054-15-1964 L1967 **GP** *071
KNOWLTON, Ekaterina. 875 WESLEY ST STE 230, CASCADE SURGEONS 98223 #026-04-1993 L1999 **GS** *020 †85
LOPEZ, Jena Marie. 330 S STILLAGUAMISH AVE 98223 #005-14-2000 L2007 **EM** *020
LOWDEN, Robert James. ■ 98223 #056-06-1945 L1949 **GYN** *071 †30
LUCIANNA, Mark Andrew. 7530 204TH ST NE, ARLINGTON FAMILY MEDICINE 98223 #016-43-1970 L1973 **FM** *020 †18
MALAN, Kennett Peck. 8400 207TH PL NE 98223 #023-01-1962 L1967 **OBG** *071 †30
MAXWELL, John Ronald. 19132 59TH DR NE, CASCADE RADIOLOGY CONSULTA 98223 #539-04-1963 L1970 **R** *020 †80
RILEY, David Allen. 20302 77TH AVE NE, CASCADE MEDICAL GROUP 98223 #054-04-1988 L1993 **OTO A** *020 †45
RONNING, Arnold Andreberg. 875 WESLEY ST, STE 130 98223 #054-04-1996 L2000 **PD** *020 †55
RUSHER, Jerry Llewllyn. 326 S STILLAGUAMISH AVE, CASCADE MEDICAL CENTER 98223 #054-04-1971 L1972 **GP** *020
SAYED, Muhammad A. 875 WESLEY ST STE 240, CASCADE VALLEY SLEEP DISOR 98223 #915-04-1988 L2004 **SME N** *020 ‡
SCHILLHAMMER, Gary Lee. 330 S STILLAGUAMISH AVE, NSCHS CENTRAL BILLING 98223 #050-02-1981 L1984 **FM** *020 †18
SPENCER, Mark Edward. 326 S STILLAGUAMISH AVE 98223 #054-04-1978 L1985 **FM IMG** *020 †18
STANLEY, Garrit Edward. 3131 SMOKEY POINT DR, STE J 98223 #054-04-1963 L1964 **GP** *020
STEFAN, Doina Alexandrina. 875 WESLEY ST, STE 130 98223 #781-01-1986 L1997 **PD** *020 †55
THULINE, Dale Nathan. 3131 SMOKEY POINT DR, STE J 98223 #028-02-1974 L1975 **OM** *020
WIETHARN, Bruce Edwin. 903 MEDICAL CENTER DR, CASCADE REGIONAL EYE 98223 #021-01-1995 L2004 **OPH** *020 †35
WOLFF, Peter. 875 WESLEY ST STE 230 98223 #016-06-1980 L1988 **GS VS** *020 †85
ZOOK, Norman Wilbur. 330 S STILLAGUAMISH AVE 98223 #040-02-1955 L1956 **GP** *071
ZYLSTRA, Philip James. 326 S STILLAGUAMISH AVE 98223 #025-07-1981 L1990 **FM** *020 †18

ASOTIN – ASOTIN

LOWTHER, James Marion. ■ 99402 #048-02-1963 L1971 **D** *071 †15

AUBURN – KING

AFLATOONI, Alfred. 3830 A ST SE, SOUTH AUBURN MEDICAL 98002 #030-05-1974 L1977 **FM** *020 †18
ANDERSON, Brian Lynn. 202 N DIVISION ST, STE 100 98001 #040-02-1983 L1989 **U** *020 †95
ANDERSON, Stephen Huntley. 202 N DIVISION ST 98001 #025-01-1981 L1984 **GS U** *020
ANSARI, Irfan A. 125 3RD ST NE, ELECTRODIAGNOSIS & REHAB 98002 #704-16-1988 L1995 **PM** *020 †20,60
ANSINGH, Herman R. ■ 98002 #660-03-1956 L1959 **GS** *071 †85
ARENDT, Steven Curt. 17225 SE 339TH ST 98092 #005-14-1983 L1984 **FM OS** *020 †18
AUSTIN, Daryl Marieg. 202 N DIVISION ST, PLAZA TWO STE 301 98001 #007-02-1993 L1997 **IM** *020 †20
AVERY, Marc Douglas. 2704 I ST NE 98002 #025-07-1985 L1993 **P** *020 †75
BALICH, Susan Mary. 202 N DIVISION ST 98001 #016-06-1992 L1998 **DR** *020 †80
BARTLETT, Eugene Fred. ■ 98092 #028-02-1958 L1974 **GS GP** *071 †85
BAUMAN, John Michael. 202 N DIVISION ST 98001 #023-12-1980 L2000 **DR NM** *030 †20,28,80
BAUTISTA, Luz Marinas. ■ 98002 #748-07-1967 L1984 **P** *071
BECKER, Virgil Victor, Jr. 125 3RD ST NE, EAR, NOSE, THROAT AND PLAS 98002 #005-06-1983 L1989 **GS OS** *020 †40
BEERS, Sidney Newton. 202 N DIVISION ST 98001 #035-09-1993 L2000 **EM** *020 †16
BEINS, Michael Howard. 202 N DIVISION ST 98001 #056-06-2001 L2004 **EM** *020 †16
BENFANTI, Cynthia Lynn. 816 F ST SE 98002 #023-12-1990 L2002 **CHP** *020
BESSLER, Robert Aaron. 202 N DIVISION ST, MEDICAL CTR 98001 #038-06-1997 L2000 **EM** *020 †16
BHASKAR, Padmini. 3830 A ST SE 98002 #495-04-1961 L1988 **END GYN** *040 †30
BIGLER, Charles R. 201 N DIVISION ST, VALLEY WOMENS HEALTH CARE 98001 #048-04-1987 L1991 **OBG** *020 †30
BIRSE, Stewart Craig. 202 N DIVISION ST, STE 301 98001 #048-02-1985 L1988 **IM** *020 †20
BOSAK, Peter. 202 N DIVISION ST, STE 301 98001 #286-06-1991 L2005 **IM** *020 †20
BOWEN, John Scott. 202 N DIVISION ST 98001 #048-04-1975 L1984 **DR VIR** *020 †80
BRETZ, Stephen William. 202 N DIVISION ST 98001 #025-01-1995 L2006 **EM** *020 †16
CARLSON, Robert E. 122 3RD ST NE 98002 #025-01-1992 L1998 **ORS** *020 †40

■ = Address Information Privacy Protected

CARUSO, Anthony Paul. 202 N DIVISION ST, PLAZA TWO SUITE 100 98001 #054-04-1994 L2000 U *020 †95

CHAMBERS, Camille Joy. 700 15TH ST SW, M/C 5F-08, 17-67 BLDG 98001 #035-47-1987 L1999 GPM OM *020 †70,18

CHEN, Alan Tsunwen. 122 3RD ST NE, CASCADE ORTHOPAEDICS 98002 #016-42-2002 L2007 PM *100 †60

CHEN, James Songjen. 202 N DIVISION ST 98001 #011-03-1997 L2003 DR *020 †80

CHU, Sammy. 202 N DIVISION ST 98001 #061-01-1995 L2001 RNR DR *020 †80

CHUN, Sam Yeol. 202 N DIVISION ST 98001 #061-01-1999 L2005 DR *100 †80

COVERT, Cristina Mai. 126 AUBURN AVE, STE 300 98002 #305-01-2002 L2006 FM *020 †18

CRIDDLE, Keith Jensen. 202 N DIVISION ST, STE 405 98001 #049-01-1975 L1978 FM *020 †18

CUNNINGHAM, Cord Wayne. ■ 98092 #023-12-2003 L2005 EM *020 †16

DAVIDOV, Jennifer Michele. ■ 98001 #054-04-2008 *012

DAWOOD, Ayad Amjad. 202 N DIVISION ST 98001 #528-01-1979 L2001 IM *020 †20

DEJNOZKA, Malcolm Martin. ■ 98092 #048-13-1983 L2006 MDM PD *030 †55

DIACONOU, John N. 202 N DIVISION ST, STE 402 98001 #418-01-1972 L1980 VS *020 †85

DOZOIS, Diane Nicole. 17500 SE 392ND ST, AUBURN COMMUNITY HEALTH CE 98092 #054-04-1995 L1997 FM *020 †18

ELIZAGA, Andrew Martin. 202 N DIVISION ST, PLAZA ONE 98001 #054-04-1993 L1995 AN *020 †05

EMCH, James Rae. 202 N DIVISION ST 98001 #054-04-1964 L1966 EM FM *020 †18,16

ENGLISH, David Todd. 202 AUBURN AVE, AUBURN DERMATOLOGY 98002 #054-04-1968 L1974 D DMP *020 †15 ‡

EYLANDER, Edward S. ■ 98071 #054-04-1951 L1952 AN *071 †05

FEATHERSTONE, Judith Ann. 126 AUBURN AVE STE 300 98002 #054-04-1986 L1990 FM *030 †18

FELIPE, Joel Deguzman. 1340 M ST SE, STE A 98002 #308-13-1998 L2003 FM *020 †18 ‡

FISHER, Robert Stanley. ■ 98001 #056-05-1948 L1950 AN *071

FLANERY, Mark Francis. 202 N DIVISION ST 98001 #046-01-1979 L1983 AN *020 †05

FORD, Ernest Lee. ■ 98092 #005-12-1973 L1990 EM *020 †16

FRERICHS, Robert Lawrence. 202 N DIVISION ST 98001 #030-05-1982 L1987 AN EM *020 †05

GEHRETT, Barbara Klotz. 202 N DIVISION ST, STE 400 98001 #008-01-1977 L1977 IM *020 †20

GEHRETT, Joseph Owen, Jr. 202 N DIVISION ST, STE 400 98001 #036-07-1977 L1979 IM *020 †20

GETTEL, Nadine Kay. 202 N DIVISION ST STE 301, PLAZA II 98001 #056-06-1994 L1997 IM *020 †20

GILBERT, Bruce R. 202 N DIVISION ST, PLAZA ONE 98001 #035-19-1978 L1981 NM IM *020 †20,28

GOLAN, Neil Edwin. 735 12TH ST SE 98002 #026-04-1995 L1998 FM *020 †18

GOLDBERG, Ronald Stephen. 222 2ND ST NE, STE B 98002 #024-01-1973 L1979 ON HEM *020

GOLDMAN, Jack. 803 E MAIN ST 98002 #062-01-1972 L1979 IM *020 †20

GREELY, Michael Jos. 735 12TH ST SE 98002 #054-04-1979 L1981 FM *020 †18

GREENMAN, Gordon F. 202 N DIVISION ST 98001 #017-20-1978 L1983 DR *020 †80

GREGG, Bruce Jay. 202 N DIVISION ST 98001 #048-12-1985 L1988 IM *020 †20

GUSLER, Jay K. 735 12TH ST SE 98002 #056-06-1993 L1996 FM *020 †18

HAHN, Frederick Lawrence. ■ 98002 #005-12-1948 L1948 FM GP *071

HARKINS, Karyn Irene. 735 12TH ST SE 98002 #054-04-1997 L2000 FM *020 †18

HARRISON, Harry, Jr. 4233 S 273RD PL, 4233 SO 273RD PLACE 98001 #056-05-1977 L1986 PD NPM *020 †55

HEATHCOCK, Robert Brian. 202 N DIVISION ST 98001 #005-12-1998 L2000 DR *020 †80

HENDOW, Raouf Gabriel. ■ 98071 #528-01-1948 P IM *071

HILL, Demetrice Lorraine. ■ 98092 #021-05-1995 L1997 OBG *020 †30

HSIEH, Yi Chang. 202 N DIVISION ST, STE 100 98001 #033-05-1997 L2003 U *020 †95

HUANG, I-Hua. 202 N DIVISION ST 98001 #051-04-2001 L2007 RNR *020 †80

HUIRAS, Michael Francis. 202 N DIVISION ST STE 405, PLAZA TWO 98001 #016-06-1982 L1988 FM *020 †18

JAHANPARVAR, Azadeh I. 202 N DIVISION ST, PLAZA 2 98001 #054-04-1996 L2000 IM *020 †20

JARAMILLO, Kenneth John. ■ 98001 #005-15-1993 L1995 AN *100 †18

JOHNSON, Timothy Robt. 735 12TH ST SE 98002 #025-01-1992 L1992 IM *020 †20

JOHNSTON, Robert Grant. 202 N DIVISION ST, STE 301 98001 #054-04-1970 L1974 IM *020 †20

JUSTUS, Mark Stephen. 202 N DIVISION ST 98001 #016-11-1995 L2006 DR *020 †80

KIM, Mark Seungbae. 735 12TH ST SE, AUBURN MULTICARE CLINIC 98002 #048-04-1997 L2000 FM VM *020 †18

KLAAS, Virginia Ellen. 202 N DIVISION ST 98001 #005-15-1989 L1995 NM DR *020 †80,28

KLEIN, Robert Ira. 202 N DIVISION ST 98001 #035-15-1969 L1974 DR *020 †80

KNEISL, Alison S. 17500 SE 392ND ST 98092 #005-02-1997 L1999 FM *020 †18

KROBER, Janet Chong. ■ 98001 #054-04-2008 *012

KUO, Stephen Jason. 222 2ND ST NE STE A 98002 #035-19-1982 L1983 RO IM *020 †20,80

LENG, Vuthy. ■ 98001 #305-01-2001 L2005 FM *020 †18

LEWIS, Gregory Elliot. 202 N DIVISION ST, AUBURN MEDICAL CTR 98001 #005-19-1999 L2002 EM *020 †16

LOVELL, Robert Walter. 2704 I ST NE, C/O VALLEY CITIES COUNSELI 98002 #561-15-1986 L1993 P CHP *020 †75

LUND, Philip Lee. 202 N DIVISION ST 98001 #020-02-1984 L1985 DR PDR *020 †80

MACCIO, Maryellen E, III. 201 N DIVISION ST, VALLEY WOMENS MEDICAL CARE 98001 #025-12-1985 L1989 FM *020 †18

MAC MAHON, Hugh Ronald. 20 2ND ST NE 98002 #051-04-1960 L1970 N *071 †75

MARTIN, Kevin Blaine. 202 N DIVISION ST STE 405, PLAZA TWO 98001 #038-06-1996 L1998 FM *020 †18

MARTIN, Richard Paul. 122 3RD ST NE 98002 #035-09-1989 L2006 OSM *020 †40

MCCLAUGHLIN, Patrick Owen. ■ 98002 #054-04-2008 *012

MCKAY, Noah Adam. 502 16TH ST NE STE 300, N AUBURN GENERAL MED CLINI 98002 #035-46-1983 L1985 GP *075

MC MONIGAL, Richard S. 202 N DIVISION ST 98001 #041-12-1992 L1995 EM *020 †16

MERCHANT, Rohinton K. 3830 A ST SE STE 204 98002 #495-73-1970 L1983 FM ADM *020

MICALI, Iliana D. 309 2ND ST SE, STE 100 98002 #737-01-1987 L1999 IM *020 †20

MOCERI, Jonathan David. 202 N DIVISION ST 98001 #054-04-1993 L1995 AN *020 †05

MOONEY, Maureen Ann. 921 HARVEY RD, STE B 98002 #026-04-1992 L2000 D DS *020 †15 ‡

MOORE, Milan Shannon. 126 AUBURN AVE STE 200 98002 #024-01-1990 L2001 ORS *020 †40

MORRISON, Jennifer Lynn. 202 N DIVISION ST 98001 #041-09-1994 L1999 DR *020 †80

MYERS, Loyd Milton. ■ 98092 #005-12-1982 L1992 OS *050

NAYAN, Marilyn Eduarte. 202 N DIVISION ST 98001 #748-20-1988 L2004 OM *020

NEELY, Bruce Kealan. 202 N DIVISION ST 98001 #054-04-1992 L1995 EM *020 †16

NELSEN, Michael Robert. 202 N DIVISION ST 98001 #054-04-1995 L1995 DR VIR *020 †80

NICOL, Ronald Frank. 202 N DIVISION ST 98001 #005-14-1976 L1987 DR *020 †80

OCHSNER, Jennifer Erin. 202 N DIVISION ST 98001 #038-41-2001 L2006 DR *100 †80

OGLESBY, John Sutherland. 202 N DIVISION ST, STE 300 98001 #038-43-1995 L2007 OBG *020 †30

OLMSTEAD, Steve Ralph. 202 N DIVISION ST, PLAZA ONE 98001 #054-04-1979 L1980 EM *020 †16

ORIEL, Bruce. 202 N DIVISION ST, STE 202 PLAZA 2 98001 #035-46-1993 L2000 PD *020 †55

PANG, Nancy Ck. 735 12TH ST SE 98002 #035-03-1995 L2002 FM *020 †18

PARKER, Aria M. 202 N DIVISION ST 98001 #495-17-1990 L2002 DR *020 †80

PERPUSE, Liza Anne. 126 AUBURN AVE, NUMBER 300 98002 #035-03-2002 L2005 FM *100 †18

PETERSON, Jolyon David. 202 N DIVISION ST 98001 #026-04-1970 L1972 EM FM *020 †18,16

PIATT, John David. 202 CROSS ST SE 98002 #038-41-1995 L2005 IM *020 †20

RASTELLI-LEE, Nora Lynn. 202 N DIVISION ST 98001 #016-01-1989 L1989 DR *062 †80

REEDY, R Graham. 1314 8TH ST NE, STE 101 98002 #495-15-1966 L1976 FM FSM *020 †18 ‡

REGER, Kenneth Mathew. 202 N DIVISION ST 98001 #040-02-1980 L1985 DR NR *020 †80

RICH, David Bruce. 202 N DIVISION ST, STE 405 98001 #054-04-1980 L2005 FM *020 †18

RICHARDS, Jon. 202 N DIVISION ST 98001 #005-12-1980 L1987 AN *020 †05

RICHLING, Robert Barrett. 202 N DIVISION ST 98001 #016-42-2002 L2006 EM *020 †16

ROE, Thomas Coombe, Jr. 20 2ND ST NE 98002 #041-02-1965 L1969 OPH *020 †35

ROGGEVEEN, Mark Justin. 202 N DIVISION ST 98001 #035-01-2001 L2007 DR *020 †80

SABBAGH, Emily Marie. 309 2ND ST SE STE 100 98002 #041-07-1990 L1994 *020

SABET, Ahad Abdollahi. 202 N DIVISION ST, DEPARTMENT OF INTERNAL MED 98001 #042-02-2000 L2005 MPD *020 ‡

SANCHEZ, German Alberto. 202 N DIVISION ST, PLAZA II STE 202 98001 #264-09-1990 L2006 PD *020 †55

SANTOS, Nilo S. 202 N DIVISION ST, STE 301 98001 #748-02-1992 L2001 IM *020 †20

SAYRE, James Randall. 202 N DIVISION ST 98001 #021-01-1983 L1993 DR *020 †80

SCALLON, Steven Eugene. 202 N DIVISION ST 98001 #041-01-1993 L2000 R *020 †80

SCHOENECKER, Steven A. 202 N DIVISION ST 98001 #007-02-1980 L1984 R *020 †80

SHOPE, Mark Leslie. 201 N DIVISION ST, VALLEY WOMENS HEALTH CARE 98001 #028-03-1979 L1989 OBG *020 †30

SIDDIQI, Sarosh. 13315 SE 333RD CT 98092 #704-04-1986 L2003 PCC PUD *020 †20

SILL, Howard Walter, Jr. 202 N DIVISION ST 98001 #041-12-1997 L2000 FM *020 †18

SMITH, Carolina Kato. ■ 98092 #025-01-1997 L2007 AN *020 †05

SMITH, Joel Reed. 202 N DIVISION ST, STE 301 98001 #054-04-1982 L1994 IM *020 †20

SMITH, Terry Glen. 122 3RD ST NE 98002 #049-01-1984 L2007 ORS *020 †40

SNYDER, Nolana Clara. ■ 98092 #016-42-1981 L1984 AN *020 †05

SNYDER, Rodney W. 202 N DIVISION ST, STE 302 98001 #063-01-1979 L1984 GYN OBG *020 †30

STEHR-GREEN, Jeanette Kay. ■ 98001 #048-13-1983 L1994 PHP *050

STRAFFORD, Brereton Bruce. 122 3RD ST NE 98002 #041-01-1986 L1992 ORS OSM *020 †40

SUNDARUM, Srini Vasan. 125 3RD ST NE, ELECTRODIAGNOSIS & REHAB 98002 #495-65-1988 L1998 PM IM *020 †20,60

SWEIGARD, Charles Bertram. 204 AUBURN AVE 98002 #041-01-1956 L1975 PD *020 †55

THOMAS, Gordon Geo. 101 2ND ST NE 98002 #018-03-1958 L1960 HNS OTO *071 †45

THOMAS, Lijo Karottu. 202 N DIVISION ST, STE 400 98001 #495-63-1998 L2004 IM *071 †20

TOOMEY, Kathie Pooler. 202 N DIVISION ST, PLAZA ONE 98001 #023-07-1998 L2001 EM *020 †16

TRIVEDI, Ashish Mahesh. 202 N DIVISION ST, STE 200 98001 #495-48-1991 L2001 N CN *020 †75

TUASON, Desmond Barreras. 3830 A ST SE, SOUTH AUBURN MEDICAL 98002 #748-08-1983 L1995 IM *040

TURNER, Jill. 202 N DIVISION ST, STE 400 98001 #035-19-1985 L1988 IM *020 †20

TYSON, Robert Neville. 225 N DIVISION ST 98001 #028-02-1965 L1967 N IM *071 †20,75

TYSON, Roger Lindelle. 735 12TH ST SE 98002 #010-01-1964 L1967 GP *071

WALIA, Jyotsana. 130 3RD ST NE 98002 #495-19-1975 L1984 FM *020

WANDLER, Bruce James. 735 12TH ST SE 98002 #016-06-1972 L1976 GS *020

WARD, Kevin Jos. 202 N DIVISION ST, STE 100 98001 #010-01-1984 L1990 U *020 †95

WARNER, Charles Wm. 202 N DIVISION ST STE 405, PLAZA TWO 98001 #054-04-1982 L1985 FM *020 †18

WEATHERS, Bailey G, Jr. 39015 172ND AVE SE 98092 #051-04-1960 L2007 FM *020 †18

WHELAN, Christopher G. 202 N DIVISION ST, STE 300 98001 #539-05-1959 L1965 U *071 †95

WILDE, George D. 735 12TH ST SE 98002 #054-04-1951 L1952 GP *020

WONG, Anna. 202 N DIVISION ST STE 200, AUBURN REG MED CTR 98001 #063-01-1994 L2006 N *020

WU, Lillian. 126 AUBURN AVE STE 300 98002 #041-02-1993 L1997 FM *020 †18

WUKASCH, David Eugene. ■ 98092 #048-02-1977 L1980 FM *020 †18

YAMASHITA, Hideo James. 200 AUBURN AVE 98002 #038-40-1986 L1992 GS *020 †85

ZERR, George Christian. 20 2ND ST NE 98002 #030-06-1960 L1967 P PYG *071

BAINBRIDGE ISLAND – KITSAP

ALMQUIST, Jon Richard. 380 WINSLOW WAY E, VIRGINIA MASON WINSLOW 98110 #008-01-1965 L1967 PD *020 †55

ARMSTRONG, Michael John. 13261 FAIRFIELD PL NE, WESTSOUND EMERGENCY PHYSIC 98110 #056-06-1994 L2006 EM *020 †16

AST, Robert Adam. ■ 98110 #007-02-1999 L2003 EM *020

BAKER, Neil Jeffrey. ■ 98110 #005-11-1977 L1992 P *020 †75

BAKER, Richard Martin. ■ 98110 #038-06-1965 L1972 FM P *020 †18

BENNETT, Chester G. ■ 98110 #018-03-1944 L1947 GS *071

BOHONOS, Joseph Jay. 14612 MISTY VALE PL NE 98110 #062-01-1988 L1998 EM *020 †16

BRENNER, Adam Michael. ■ 98110 #035-45-1997 L2007 EM UME *020 †16

CHAMPION, Wm Marshall. ■ 98110 #054-04-1961 L1963 PS *071 †65

CHEUNG, Jason C. 931 HILDEBRAND LN NE 98110 #067-01-1991 L1998 OPH PO *020 †35

CHEW, Felix Sze-Kway. ■ 98110 #011-03-1979 L2004 DR *020 †80

CHIN, Jean Yutfun. ■ 98110 #026-04-1988 L2005 FM *020 †18

CHU, Franklin. 1122 MADISON AVE N 98110 #023-07-1970 L1977 OPH FM *071 †35

CITRON, Michael Herbert. 321 HIGH SCHOOL RD NE, STE D3292 98110 #005-06-1973 L1974 GE *062

COWAN, David B. 380 WINSLOW WAY E, V M WINSLOW 98110 #008-01-1988 L1990 FM *020 †18

CROFT, David Winston. ■ 98110 #041-02-1954 L1955 OM GP *071

CURTIS, Frederick K. ■ 98110 #035-01-1956 L1961 **NEP IM** *071 †20

DU PEN, Stuart Leigh. 14555 WILD SWAN LN NE 98110 #028-34-1967 L1968 **AN OS** *020 †05

EKIN, Jennifer Ann. ■ 98110 #026-08-1993 L2001 **IM** *020 †20

FEIG, David Brian. 380 WINSLOW WAY E 98110 #012-05-2003 L2007 **FM** *100 †18

FEIGENBAUM, Joel Alvin. ■ 98110 #005-02-1962 L1998 **NS** *020 †25

FIELDING, Ira Martin. ■ 98110 #035-09-1962 L1969 **U** *020 †95

FIKE, William. ■ 98110 #035-01-1992 L2005 **FM** *020 †18

FISHER, Willa Ann. ■ 98110 #005-02-1965 L1969 **PHP PD** *071 †55

FORTNER, Robert Wm. 9631 SUMMER HILL LN NE 98110 #054-04-1967 L1968 **IM NEP** *071 †20

FOY, John Lynch. ■ 98110 #025-01-1977 L1981 **IM** *030

GEISERT, Frederick E. ■ 98110 #067-01-1953 L1954 **PTH** *071 †50

GOAD, Robert Frank. 5624 LYNWOOD CENTER RD NE, ANESTHESIOLOGIST 98110 #030-06-1973 L1990 **AN UM** *020 †05 ‡

HAGGAR, Thomas Donald. 380 WINSLOW WAY E, BOX 10787 98110 #026-04-1971 L1972 **FM** *020 †18

HATTNER, Robert Stephen. ■ 98110 #025-07-1965 L2003 **NM END** *071 †20,28

HEBARD, Don Wells. ■ 98110 #041-13-1968 L1969 **RO** *071 †80

HELMING, Charles Vernon. 380 WINSLOW WAY E, VIRGINIA MASON 98110 #035-01-1970 L1978 **ORS** *020 †40

HEMMEN, John Edward. 3609 POINT WHITE DR NE, BAINBRIDGE IS 98110 #005-19-1974 L1976 **EM** *020 †16

HENDLER, Jared M. 231 MADISON AVE S 98110 #005-14-1973 L1978 **FM** *020 †18

HEPWORTH, William Brad. 380 ERICKSEN AVE NE 98110 #005-02-1997 L1999 **GS** *020

HURLOW, Robert Scott. 945 HILDEBRAND LN NE, STE 100 98110 #054-04-1980 L1984 **FM OBG** *020 †18

IHLER, Garret Martin. ■ 98110 #041-12-1976 L1976 *030

JAMIESON, Marie Elizabeth. ■ 98110 #054-04-1987 L1989 **AN** *071 †05

KALLAS, Alexander Peter. ■ 98110 #005-06-1987 L2004 **EM** *020 †16

KEYES, Gregory Ernest. 231 MADISON AVE S 98110 #049-01-1975 L1981 **FM** *020 †18

KLEIN, Kenneth Bruce. ■ 98110 #024-01-1975 L1982 **GE** *050 †20

KOCH, Luis. ■ 98110 #231-03-1961 L1979 **AN** *020

KOHLI, Daniel Robt. ■ 98110 #016-06-1942 L1950 **IM P** *072

KOVAL, Maureen Allison. 945 HILDEBRAND LN NE, STE 100 98110 #054-04-1993 L1996 **FM** *020 †18

LEATHAM, L Kim. 380 WINSLOW WAY E 98110 #054-04-1988 L1990 **FM** *020 †18

LEITER, Elliot. ■ 98110 #035-19-1957 L1991 **U OS** *071 †95

LEWIS, Jack Leon. ■ 98110 #016-11-1954 L1955 **ORS OS** *071 †40

LIM, Andrew Khengann. ■ 98110 #036-01-1990 L2005 **IM** *020 †20

LINHARDT, Molly Sue. 380 WINSLOW WAY E, VIRGINIA MASON WINSLOW 98110 #539-06-2001 L2006 **PD** *020 †55

LUZZATTI, Luigi. ■ 98110 #026-04-1943 L1951 **PD OS** *071 †55,19

MICHAEL, Ellen V. ■ 98110 #016-43-1979 L1999 **P** *020

MICHALS, Arnold Alfred. ■ 98110 #005-12-1942 L1942 **GS TS** *071 †85,90

MONK, Thomas Ralph. 945 HILDEBRAND LN NE, STE 100 98110 #054-04-1982 L1986 **PD** *020 †55

MYERS, Lafe Hasty, Jr. ■ 98110 #054-04-1960 L1962 **OS P** *071 †75

NEPOM, Gerald Thos. 5388 CRYSTAL SPRINGS DR NE 98110 #054-04-1978 L1982 **IG** *050

O'HALLORAN, Albert. ■ 98110 #539-02-1949 L1959 **PTH** *071 †50

POPOVICH, Brana. ■ 98110 #957-02-1955 L1969 **PM** *071 †60

RANEY, James Oscar. 3335 PLEASANT BEACH DR NE 98110 #054-04-1961 L1964 **P PYA** *020

RAYL, Judith. 380 WINSLOW WAY E, VIRGINIA MASON MEDICAL CEN 98110 #054-04-1997 L2000 **FM** *020 †18

READY, Jodi. ■ 98110 #035-47-1998 L2001 **IM** *020 †20

REITER, Blake Edward. 14677 SIVERTSON RD NE 98110 #026-04-1985 L1986 **AN PME** *020 †05

RICHARDSON, John R Ford. ■ 98110 #040-02-1942 L1946 **GP** *071

RIZZA, Joseph Michael. ■ 98110 #407-20-1965 L1970 **PTH NM** *071 †50,28

ROGER, Jeffrey Philip. ■ 98110 #007-02-1999 L2005 **EM** *020

ROGERS, Sundance Loomis. 380 WINSLOW WAY E 98110 #011-03-1993 L1993 **IM** *020 †20

SANDLER, Harold. ■ 98110 #038-41-1955 L1958 **AM OS** *050

SANDRI, Piero Francis. ■ 98110 #028-34-1966 L1981 **IM** *071 †20

SATYA, Krishna Akella. 657 AZALEA AVE NE 98110 #035-48-1999 L2003 **EM** *020 †16

SMITH, Terri Graham. ■ 98110 #054-04-1990 L1990 **PD** *020 †55

STEMLER, Richard S. 8986 BARNCLIFF AVE NE 98110 #041-01-1953 L1963 **GE IM** *071 †20

ST LOUIS, Darsi Suzanne. ■ 98110 #054-04-1992 L1993 **IM** *020 †20

SWANSON, Paul Eric. ■ 98110 #040-02-1984 L2001 **ATP** *040 †50

THEMANN, Britt Joelle. ■ 98110 #021-01-2008 *012

THOMPSON, Gale Eugene. 175 PARFITT WAY SW, UNIT SR 98110 #054-04-1960 L1961 **AN OS** *071 †05

WALKER, Franklin Delano. ■ 98110 #017-20-1961 L1989 **P CHP** *020 †75 ‡

WALTERS, Frederick C. 9431 COPPERTOP LOOP NE # A, BAINBRIDGE PEDIATRICS 98110 #005-02-1999 L2001 **PD** *020 †55

WARREN, Linda Ann Shipley. 380 WINSLOW WAY E 98110 #024-01-1987 L1994 **PD** *020 †55

WILSON, David Otto. ■ 98110 #005-11-1958 L1984 **IM** *071 †20

BATTLE GROUND — CLARK

BOWES, Richard Kourtney. ■ 98604 #012-05-2004 L2006 **IM** *100 †20

DOERFLER, Eric Allan. 2005 W MAIN ST 98604 #040-02-1991 L1994 **FM** *020 †18

GEBBIE, Neil Wm. 720 W MAIN ST STE 115 98604 #028-34-1975 L1978 **FM** *071 †18

GOLDBERG, Lawrence David. 2210 W MAIN ST, STE 107-384 98604 #024-05-1979 L1981 **IM CD** *020

HAMPTON, James, Jr. 2005 W MAIN ST 98604 #028-02-1995 L1999 **FM** *020 †18

LEE, Elizabeth Ann. 1706 W MAIN ST, STE 113 98604 #012-01-1989 L1994 **FM** *020 †18

LOWER, Courtney Anne. 2005 W MAIN ST 98604 #025-07-1999 L2002 **FM** *020 †18

MC DONALD, Walter John. ■ 98604 #025-01-1964 L1965 **IM END** *071 †20

MOHANDESSI, Siyavash. 2005 W MAIN ST 98604 #054-04-2004 L2004 **FM** *020 †18

MOOR, Fred Bennett, Jr. ■ 98604 #005-12-1953 L1971 **ORS** *071 †40

SIMONS, Arthur James. 2005 W MAIN ST, VANCOUVER CLINIC 98604 #012-01-1989 L1994 **FM** *020 †18

BEAUX ARTS — KING

GAMMILL, Hilary Seglin. ■ 98004 #054-04-1999 L2006 **OBG** *100

JOHNSTON, Robin Reynolds. ■ 98004 #016-11-1957 L1960 **CD IM** *071 †20

JORDAN, Prescott, Jr. ■ 98004 #016-02-1941 L1956 **TS GS** *075 †85

SALTONSTALL, R. ■ 98004 #038-06-1976 L1977 **CHP PYA** *071 †75

WHATMORE, George Bernard. ■ 98004 #016-02-1948 L1950 **IM OS** *020

BELFAIR — MASON

BRAILE, Louis Emil. ■ 98528 #056-06-1945 L1946 **FM** *072

HARDY, William M. ■ 98528 #010-01-1949 L1950 **TS GS** *071 †85

LYON, Lawrence. 23460B STATE ROUTE 3 98528 #050-02-1997 L2001 **FM** *020 †18

NELSON, Carolyn Ruth. ■ 98528 #005-12-1965 L1966 **EM FM** *075 †16,18

RAUH, Jay Thos. ■ 98528 #023-01-1958 L1959 **OBG U** *072 †30

REASOL, Jose Jeffrey Turt. 140 NE STATE ROUTE 300, NORTH MASON MEDICAL CLINIC 98528 #748-11-1998 L2005 **IM** *100 †20

BELLEVUE — KING

AARONSON, Lewis Clarke. ■ 98008 #005-02-1948 L1961 **PD PDA** *071 †55

ACHESON, Marita Barbara. 1135 116TH AVE NE STE 250 98004 #917-09-1981 L1984 **DR** *020 †80

ACK, Diane Marie. 2700 NORTHUP WAY 98004 #010-02-1988 L1991 **PD** *020 †55

AGNANI, Santosh Arjun. 2820 NORTHUP WAY STE 10 98004 #495-23-1982 L1997 **P** *020 †75

AGRICOLA, Shelley. 1135 116TH AVE NE STE 310 98004 #049-01-1979 L1983 **AN CD** *020 †20,05

AGUSTIN, Christina Maria. 1035 116TH AVE NE, OVERLAKE HOSPITAL 98004 #054-04-2001 L2005 **P** *020

AHMADIAN, Mandana. 1380 112TH AVE NE STE 205 98004 #409-22-1995 L2005 **END** *020 †20

AHMED, Tariq. 15710 NE 24TH ST STE C, AMERICAN MEDICAL CLINIC, I 98008 #495-49-1981 L1993 **FM IM** *020 †70 ‡

AHN, Johan Kwanghee. 6237 155TH PL SE, JKA DIAGNOSTIC IMAGING, LL 98006 #035-09-1995 L2003 **DR** *020 †80

ALLEN, David Milton. ■ 98004 #035-19-1980 L1983 **PD** *050 †55

ALLEN, Frank H. 1035 116TH AVE NE, OVERLAKE HOSP 98004 #024-05-1960 L1973 **DR NM** *071 †20,28

AMIDON, Thomas Morton. 1135 116TH AVE NE, STE 600 98004 #036-07-1986 L1995 **IM CD** *020 †20

ANANTH, Aparna. 11808 NORTHUP WAY STE WES 98005 #496-38-2001 L2005 **AN** *100 †05

ANDERSON, Joan Lois. ■ 98007 #030-06-1985 L1988 **PD** *020

ANDERSON, Stephen Bowen. 1632 116TH AVE NE, STE A 98004 #054-04-1971 L1972 **FPS OTO** *020 †45

ANTON, Elisabeth Susan. 1535 116TH AVE NE, STE 100 98004 #005-02-1990 L1995 **OBG** *020 †30

APPELBAUM, Andrew Mark. 3080 148TH AVE SE, STE 115 98007 #836-04-1983 L1994 **FM** *020 †18

ARCAGA, Victoria Altavas. ■ 98005 #748-02-1970 L1979 **PD** *074 †55

ARSHAD, Mehreen. 10129 MAIN ST, APT 403 98004 #704-25-2006 **PD** *100

ASHLEY, Milton Miller. 27 100TH AVE NE 98004 #024-01-1945 L1952 **P IM** *071 †75

AU, David Hsiangshan. ■ 98006 #016-02-1993 L1996 **PCC** *020 †20

AUERBACH, Patricia C. 222 112TH AVE NE, MAIL STOP A-BLV 98004 #048-12-1992 L2001 **IM OM** *030 †20

AUSTIN, Jos John Michael. 1135 116TH AVE NE, STE 605 98004 #065-10-1982 L1991 **TS** *020 †85,90

AVILES, Ronnier J. 1135 116TH AVE NE STE 600, OVERLAKE INTERNAL MEDICINE 98004 #270-02-1995 L2006 **IC** *020 †20

AYARS, Garrison Hubert. 1605 116TH AVE NE, STE 111 98004 #054-04-1976 L1981 **A ID** *020 †20,03

AYERS, Gregory Martin. 11911 NE 1ST ST, STE B308 98005 #017-20-1992 **ICE CD** *030

BAILEY, Rea. ■ 98006 #038-41-1938 **GP** *071

BAJENOVA, Natalia. ■ 98004 #054-04-2008 *012

BAKER, Randall William. 1135 116TH AVE NE STE 310 98004 #054-04-1993 L1997 **AN** *020 †05

BAKER, Ray Merville, Jr. 12301 NE 10TH PL 98005 #005-15-1985 L1989 **PME AN** *020 †05

BALASSANIAN, Neron. 1654 180TH AVE NE 98008 #605-01-1960 L1980 **OM FM** *020 †55

BALDWIN, John Louis. 1310 116TH AVE NE STE C 98004 #030-05-1971 L1975 **RHU IM** *020 †20

BALFOUR, Robert Irving. 1135 116TH AVE NE 98004 #041-13-1966 L1967 **AN** *020 †05

BALLARD, Clark Tilton, Jr. 14929 SE ALLEN RD, STE 103A 98006 #048-02-1977 L1999 **P OM** *020 †75 ‡

BANKSON, Anne Marie. 1035 116TH AVE NE 98004 #024-05-1986 L1989 **FM** *020 †18

BARDARSON, Baird Milton. 13231 SE 36TH ST, STE 1500 98006 #054-04-1955 L1956 **GP** *020

BARDMAN, Nelly M. 1811 156TH AVE NE, STE 1A 98007 #913-21-1981 L2005 **IM** *020 †20

BARLOON, Andrew Saml. 2821 NORTHUP WAY STE 200, 2821 NORTHUP WAY STE 200 98004 #012-05-1987 L1992 **OPH** *020 †35

BARNES, Sharylee. 213 152ND PL SE 98007 #065-01-1971 L1999 *020

BARSS, Joseph Andrew. ■ 98004 #025-01-1946 L1958 **GS CD** *071 †85

BARUCK, David Albert. 13231 SE 36TH ST, STE 110 98006 #054-04-1967 L1969 **GP OS** *020

BASS, Ralph Lamar, II. 12826 SE 40TH LN 98006 #012-05-1964 L1968 **P** *071

BASSETT, Kent La Mar. 1300 116TH AVE NE, EYE CLINIC OF BELLEVUE 98004 #054-04-1979 L1980 **OPH** *020 †35

BATIK, Odette G. 14350 SE EASTGATE WAY, EASTGATE PUBLIC HEALTH 98007 #035-01-1985 L1986 **FM PHP** *020 †18

BAUMAN, Carla Jean. 1260 116TH AVE NE 98004 #024-01-1992 L1995 **D** *020 †15

BEALL, Joseph Hilary. ■ 98007 #054-04-1956 L1958 **GP** *071

BEAULIEU, Cassandra M. 2700 NORTHUP WAY 98004 #054-04-1998 L2000 **PD** *020 †55

BELLIS, Mark Yancy. 1035 116TH AVE NE 98004 #034-01-1998 L2003 **EM** *020 †16

BENDA, Sara Kristina. 4122 FACTORIA BLVD SE, STE 101 98006 #054-04-1997 L1999 **PD** *020 †55

BENTHUYSEN, James Lester. 11808 NORTHUP WAY, STE W120 98005 #016-02-1980 L1989 **AN** *020 †05

BERGMAN, James Jay. 13451 SE 36TH ST 98006 #005-14-1974 L1975 **FM** *020 †18

BERKOWICZ, Louise Ariele. 3080 148TH AVE SE STE 115 98007 #836-02-1973 L2001 **IMG UM** *020 †18

BERMAN, Michele Rhonda. 4689 174TH AVE SE 98006 #028-02-1981 L2001 **PD** *020 †55

BERNHARDT, Donald James. 1135 116TH AVE NE STE 310 98004 #056-06-1976 L1977 **AN** *020 †05

BIGGERS, Oliver Robt. 1370 116TH AVE NE STE 105 98004 #047-07-1975 L1976 **CRS GS** *020 †10,86
BILLINGTON, Bradley Ira. 1231 116TH AVE NE STE 100 98004 #054-04-1967 L1971 **ORS GP** *020 †40
BINGHAM, Margaret Nilsson. ■ 98004 #040-02-1940 L1946 **OS** *071
BIRNBACH, Charles David. 2821 NORTHUP WAY, STE 200 98004 #035-19-1992 L1996 **OPH** *020 †35
BJURSTROM, Robert Lee. 1135 116TH AVE NE, STE 610 98004 #054-04-1981 L1982 **IM PUD** *020 †20
BLANK, Chester Anthony. ■ 98006 #056-06-1937 L1938 **PHP** *071
BLOCK, Susan Sam. 1200 112TH AVE NE, STE B250 98004 #005-06-1981 L1993 **OBG** *020 †30
BLOOMER, Sarah Katherine. 1035 116TH AVE NE 98004 #024-01-1979 L1980 **PD** *020 †55
BOEHL, James E. 17057 SE 47TH CT 98006 #035-45-1998 L2001 **EM** *020 †16
BOIKO, Patricia. 13451 SE 36TH ST, FACTORIA MEDICAL CENTER 98006 #035-20-1980 L1985 **FM** *020 †18
BOLLES, Leo J. 15611 BELLEVUE REDMOND RD 98008 #056-06-1950 L1952 **GPM OS** *071
BOLLYKY, Jennifer Anne. 1035 116TH AVE NE 98004 #005-14-2000 L2004 **IM** *020 †20
BONTECOU, David Cannon. 1515 116TH AVE NE STE 307 98004 #035-45-1960 L1965 **IM N** *071
BONVALLET, Scott Thos. 1135 116TH AVE NE, STE 600 98004 #056-06-1986 L1993 **IM CCM** *020 †20
BOSWELL, James Everett. 1035 116TH AVE NE 98004 #035-03-2002 L2005 **IM** *020 †20
BOYD, Herschell H. 1370 116TH AVE NE, BOYD CLINIC FOR EYE CARE 98004 #047-05-1952 L1958 **OPH** *071 †35
BRANDES, Clayton B. 1135 116TH AVE NE, STE 510 98004 #005-06-1991 L1997 **ORS** *020 †40
BREITZ, Hazel Brenda. ■ 98004 #836-01-1974 L1981 **NM** *074 †28
BRODIE, Carl James. 14100 SE 36TH ST STE 105 98006 #028-34-1982 L1990 **RHU IM** *020 †20
BRONSTEIN, David. 1035 116TH AVE NE 98004 #005-18-1978 L1985 **EM** *020 †20,16
BROOKS, Charles N. ■ 98006 #025-07-1980 L1988 **ORS LM** *030 †40
BROWN, Alan Burchard. 1632 116TH AVE NE, STE C 98004 #025-01-1985 L1990 **GS ORS** *020 †40
BRUMM, Constance J. 1600 116TH AVE NE, STE 102 98004 #038-43-1979 L1983 **FM** *020 †18
BUNAS, Stanley Jon. 1515 116TH AVE NE, STE 307 98004 #036-01-1979 L1983 **D** *020
BUNIN, Alan. 12443 BEL RED RD STE 390 98005 #038-40-1968 L1969 **FM** *020 †18
BUNKER, William Hudson. 1220 116TH AVE NE 98004 #028-03-1970 L1972 **AN** *071 †05
BURGESS, Kathleen Hope. ■ 98005 #054-04-1999 L2002 **PM** *020 †60 ‡
BURKE, Matthew Joseph. 747 177TH LN NE 98008 #028-34-1995 L2000 **P** *020
BURKE, Theodore James. ■ 98006 #054-04-1989 L2006 **BBK** *020 †50
BURNS, Douglas Mc Call. 12301 NE 10TH PL, STE 101 98005 #054-04-1995 L1996 **PM** *020 †60
BUSKIRK, James Rollin. 1687 114TH AVE SE STE 125 98004 #026-04-1976 L1998 **P** *030 †75
BUTANI, Raj Chandru. 1135 116TH AVE NE, STE 560 98004 #041-07-1996 L2007 **GE IM** *020 †20
BUTENKO, Eugene Robt. ■ 98005 #054-04-1971 L1975 **DR** *071 †80
CABLE, Christopher John. 1216 W LAKE SAMMSH PKWY SE 98008 #005-14-1997 L1999 **IM** *020 †20
CAIN, Laura Rokusek. ■ 98008 #028-02-1987 L1987 **OM IM** *020 †20
CALINOIU, Ileana. 14030 NE 24TH ST, STE 104 98007 #781-01-1994 L2002 **CHP** *020 †75
CALLERO, Vern Louis. 4307 128TH AVE SE 98006 #054-04-1960 L1961 **FM** *072 †18
CAM, James L G. ■ 98007 #748-10-1967 L1984 **IM GP** *020
CAMPBELL, Patrick Michael. 1310 116TH AVE NE, STE C 98004 #016-02-1967 L1970 **RHU IM** *071 †20
CAMPBELL, Robert Jos. 375 118TH AVE SE STE 220 98005 #018-03-1963 L1965 **PYA CHP** *020 ‡
CAMPBELL, Robert Miller. ■ 98004 #025-01-1945 L1947 **OBG** *071 †30
CARLSEN, Ray Allen. 2330 130TH AVE NE, STE 201 98005 #008-01-1962 L1971 **D DMP** *020 †15
CARLSON, Dorothy Leavens. 11217 NE 15TH ST 98004 #041-07-1953 L1954 **P CHP** *071 †75
CARLSON, Gretchen W. 11201 SE 8TH ST STE 105 98004 #041-12-1998 L2000 **P** *020
CARTER, Amy Elizabeth. 2700 NORTHUP WAY, UNIV OF WA SOM GME RM C212 98004 #031-01-2004 L2004 **PD** *020 †55 ‡
CARTER, Ann Patricia. ■ 98005 #803-01-1960 **PHP** *072
CARY, Jeffrey Michael. 3208 111TH AVE SE 98004 #007-02-1972 L1976 **PUD IM** *020 †20
CASE, Kevin Jos. 1135 116TH AVE NE 98004 #030-05-1976 L1980 **DR** *020 †80
CASE, Mary Jean. ■ 98004 #030-05-1976 L1980 **PTH** *074 †50
CASTELL, Hugh Mc Farlane. 1035 116TH AVE NE 98004 #018-03-1963 L1967 **P OS** *075
CENTERWALL, Gillian Hacke. ■ 98004 #048-02-2008 *012
CHAMBERLAIN, Beatrice D L. 14858 LAKE HILLS BLVD 98007 #917-30-1970 L1978 *020
CHANG, David Hwayuan. 13033 BEL RED RD STE 120 98005 #056-06-1993 L1995 **APM** *020 †05
CHANG, Michael Wei. 12340 NE 8TH ST, STE 101 98005 #048-02-1988 L1992 **PM** *020 †60
CHAO, Ann Tien-Ling. 1135 116TH AVE NE STE 310 98004 #028-02-1982 L1983 **AN** *020 †05
CHEN, John Chihyeh. 13433 NE 20TH ST, STE D 98005 #028-34-1993 L1997 **IM** *020
CHEW, Ryan Bert. 1035 116TH AVE NE 98004 #016-06-1999 L2002 **IM** *020 †20
CHINN, Terrance Andrew. 1621 114TH AVE SE, TERRANCE A CHINN INC PS 98004 #054-04-1970 L1976 **P** *071 †75
CHO, Anthony Jaeyun. ■ 98004 #054-04-2004 L2005 **FP** *012
CHONG, Elaine Annyi. 1135 116TH AVE NE STE 310, OVERLAKE ANESTHESIOLOGISTS 98004 #041-12-2003 L2004 **AN** *020
CHOUDHURY, Neetilekha. 13231 SE 36TH ST, STE 110 98006 #496-18-1986 L2003 **IM** *020 †20
CHOY, Sun Hak. ■ 98015 #583-01-1945 L1989 **ATP DMP** *071 †50
CHUN, Edward S. 1035 116TH AVE NE, OVERLAKE HOSP PRACTICE 98004 #016-42-1995 L1998 **IM** *020 †20
CHUNG, Young Chun. 1687 114TH AVE SE, STE 150 98004 #583-04-1963 L1972 **GS CRS** *020 †85,10
CILIBERTI, John Ralph. 1035 116TH AVE NE 98004 #012-05-1969 L1971 **EM IM** *020 †20,16
CLARFELD, Richard Bruce. 1135 116TH AVE NE, STE 180 98004 #016-11-1974 L1975 **OS** *020 †85
CLARK, James Eric. 1632 116TH AVE NE, STE C 98004 #054-04-1987 L1993 **ORS GS** *020 †40
CODAY, Mary Pei-Ann. 1837 156TH AVE NE STE 201 98007 #024-01-1994 L1998 **OPH** *020 †35
COE, Ronald Leonard. 1535 116TH AVE NE, BELLEGROVE PROFESSIONAL PA 98004 #054-04-1970 L1974 **OBG** *020 †30
COKAN, France Z. ■ 98006 #957-03-1957 L1964 **IM** *071 †20
COLELLO, Joseph J. 1135 116TH AVE NE, STE 310 98004 #043-01-1983 L1987 **AN PD** *020 †55,05
COLLIER, John Tom. 1135 116TH AVE NE STE 310 98004 #048-12-1973 L1975 **AN** *020 †05
COLPITTS, Michael Ralph. 1551 116TH AVE NE 98004 #036-07-1971 L1972 **AN OS** *020 †05
CONDON, Joseph Vincent. 1600 116TH AVE NE, STE 206 98004 #011-02-1987 L1996 **CD** *020 †20
CONNER, Raymond Mize. 1535 116TH AVE NE # 10 98004 #027-01-1976 L1980 **OBG** *020 †30
COOLEY, Janine Rowley. 1200 112TH AVE NE STE C 98004 #054-04-1982 L1983 **FM** *020 †18
COSTELLO, John Anthony. 1135 116TH AVE NE STE 310 98004 #016-11-1993 L1995 **AN** *020 †05
COTTON, Elisabeth M. 1135 116TH AVE NE, STE 110 98004 #067-01-1984 L1995 **IM** *074 †20
COULON, Gabrielle. 1035 116TH AVE NE 98004 #021-01-1981 L1987 **EM** *020 †16
COURTNEY, Rachel Melanie. 14711 NE 29TH PL, STE 255 98007 #016-02-2002 L2002 **PD** *020 †55
COX, John Thos. 1600 116TH AVE NE, STE 302 98004 #054-04-1973 L1976 **FM EM** *071 †16,18
COYLE, J Terrence. 1300 116TH AVE NE, EYE CLINIC OF BELLEVUE 98004 #056-06-1957 L1962 **OPH** *071 †35
CRINITI, Amy Rebecca. 1545 116TH AVE NE, STE 102 98004 #017-20-1999 L2003 **OBG** *100
CRITTENDEN, Gretchen L. 1414 116TH AVE NE, STE E 98004 #040-02-1999 L2002 **IC** *020 †20
CROSBY, Ruth. 2700 NORTHUP WAY 98004 #048-12-1989 L1992 **PD** *020 †55
CROSSLAND, Kathryn D. 1135 116TH AVE NE STE 230 98004 #024-01-1984 L1985 **ON IM** *020 †20
CROUNSE, William Edward. 1035 116TH AVE NE, C/O OVERLAKE HOSP MED CTR 98004 #038-43-1979 L1981 **FM** *030 †18
CURTIS, William Edward. 11036 NE 24TH ST 98004 #007-02-1988 L1997 **TS** *020 †85,90
DADA, Arinola Fatunmota. 1310 116TH AVE NE, STE C 98004 #690-02-1995 L2001 **RHU** *020 †20
DAMANI, Sidhdharth K. ■ 98008 #495-23-1985 L2007 **NM** *012
DANOFF, Nancy Lynn. 14350 SE EASTGATE WAY 98007 #038-06-1986 L1988 **PD** *020 †55
DAVIS, Andrew Peter. 1300 116TH AVE NE, EYE CLINIC OF BELLEVUE, LT 98004 #024-05-1978 L1992 **OPH** *020 †35
DAVIS, David R. 411 108TH AVE NE, ONE BELLEVUE CENTER #1960 98004 #040-02-1951 L1960 **GS** *071 †85
DAYLO, Amado Abul, Jr. ■ 98007 #014-01-1998 L2005 **P** *020 †75 ‡
DECKER, Kathleen Patricia. 27 100TH AVE NE 98004 #005-11-1985 L1990 **P PFP** *020 †75
DEDOMENICO, Mark P. 4455 148TH AVE NE 98007 #028-34-1964 L1970 **GS CD** *072 ‡
DELLINGER, Evan Patchen. 1700 116TH AVE NE 98004 #024-01-1970 L1977 **GS ID** *020 †85
DICHARRY, Douglas Clark. 2025 112TH AVE NE STE 200 98004 #021-05-1979 L1991 **CHP P** *020 †75
DIPPEL, John Adam. 27 100TH AVE NE 98004 #054-04-1989 L1993 **P** *020 †75
DOAN, Allen Edward. 1515 116TH AVE NE, BELLEGROVE CARDIOLOGY 98004 #038-06-1959 L1963 **CD IM** *071 †20
DOBSON, Janice Lavoie. ■ 98004 #008-02-1983 L1998 **OBG** *071
DOBSON, Ronald Cole. 15325 SE 30TH PL, STE 220A 98007 #034-01-1974 L1975 **EM CCM** *071 †20,16
DOLAN, Edward A. ■ 98004 #030-06-1943 L1944 **R** *071 †80
DONLAN, Stacey Schauer. 2950 NORTHUP WAY STE 210 98004 #010-02-1991 L1995 **IM** *020 †20
DONNER, Neil Farrell. ■ 98006 #005-06-2003 L2007 **EM** *020
DOUCETTE, Joseph W. 1135 116TH AVE NE STE 600 98004 #024-01-1984 L1991 **CD IM** *020 †20
DRESCHER, Dean Anthony. ■ 98004 #056-05-1972 L1979 **FM** *020 †18
DREW, Annabel Joan. 1810 116TH AVE NE, EASTSIDE FAMILY MEDICINE 98004 #065-10-1979 L2004 **FM** *020
DREYFUSS, Paul Henry. 12301 NE 10TH PL STE 101 98005 #038-40-1988 L2001 **PM** *020 †60
DRUCKMAN, Hope Lynne. 1407 116TH AVE NE, STE 200 98004 #024-01-1976 L1979 **IM PD** *020 †55,20
EDWARDS, H Berryman. 14535 BEL RED RD, STE B200 98007 #051-01-1977 L1985 **P ADP** *020 †75
EGNAL, Antony Saul. 1200 112TH AVE NE 98004 #836-02-1985 L1992 **FM** *020 †18
EGRARI, Sepehr. 2950 NORTHUP WAY, STE 100 98004 #016-42-1992 L1999 **PS GS** *020 †85,65
EHSAN, Mitra. 1135 116TH AVE NE STE 200, OVERLAKE COLON & RECLT CLC 98004 #054-04-1996 L2001 **CRS GS** *020 †85,10
EINSPAHR, Larry Wm. 1370 116TH AVE NE, EASTVIEW PROF. BLDG #201 98004 #056-05-1975 L1978 **CHP** *020
EISNER, Andrea Savilla. 1135 116TH AVE NE STE 400, CHILDRENS BELLEVUE 98004 #005-11-1988 L1993 **CHP P** *020 †75
EL-GHAZZAWY, Adel Galal. 1135 116TH AVE NE, STE 550 98004 #019-02-1992 L2000 **GS** *020 †85
ELMAGHRABY, Mohamed A F. ■ 98006 #915-02-1947 L1972 **P** *071
ENCK, Robert Whitney. 10224 NE 10TH ST 98004 #016-11-1954 L1955 **GP** *020
ENGEL, Gregory Max. 1632 116TH AVE NE, STE C 98004 #054-04-1974 L1976 **ORS** *020 †40
ENRIGHT, Jill. 1135 116TH AVE NE, STE 110 98004 #036-07-1990 L1993 **IM** *020 †20
ERICKSON, Kathryn W. 14030 NE 24TH ST STE 202 98007 #054-04-1984 L1984 **D IM** *020 †20,15
ESCHBACH, Jos Wetherill. ■ 98004 #041-02-1959 L1961 **NEP IM** *071 †20
EWASKOW, Sandra Pauline. 1280 116TH AVE NE, STE 210 98004 #030-06-1991 L1993 **PCP** *020 †50
FAIRCHILD, Linda Marie. 222 100TH AVE NE 98004 #040-02-1978 L1982 **IM EM** *020 †20
FARINAS, Vicente. 1135 116TH AVE NE STE 310 98004 #021-01-1992 L1997 **AN AM** *020 †05
FAULKNER, Noreen C. 1200 112TH AVE NE, STE B250 98004 #025-01-1988 L1990 **OBG** *020 †30
FERRIN, David Bruce. 1600 116TH AVE NE STE 206 98004 #049-01-1972 L1979 **CD IM** *020 †20
FERRIS, Brian Lee. 1135 116TH AVE NE, STE 305 98004 #051-01-1995 L2003 **VS** *020 †85
FILARCA, Maria Santos N. 12507 BEL RED RD 98005 #748-01-1953 L1969 **GP** *071
FISHMAN, Mark Alan. 3080 148TH AVE SE, STE 115 98007 #025-01-1970 L1971 **FM A** *020 †18
FITZGERALD, Elizabeth. ■ 98006 #005-06-2005 L2005 **GS** *012
FLOWERS, Otero Vogt. 4122 FACTORIA BLVD SE #101 98006 #048-14-1983 L1984 **PD** *020 †55
FLUM, David R. 1700 116TH AVE NE 98004 #011-02-1991 L2000 **GS** *020 †85
FOSMIRE, Daniel Perry. 1231 116TH AVE NE, STE 203 98004 #016-42-1987 L1999 **N** *020 †75
FOWLER, Jeffrey Vernon. 1414 116TH AVE NE, STE E 98004 #054-04-1998 L1998 **ICE** *020 †20
FRANCIS, Julie Sleder. 14030 NE 24TH ST, STE 202 98007 #054-04-1984 L1985 **D PD** *020 †15
FREDRICKSON, Marvin Dale. 2210 132ND AVE SE 98005 #054-04-1968 L1972 **ON HEM** *020 †20
FREED, Forestine L Weller. ■ 98006 #054-04-1956 L1957 **OBG** *071
FREUDENBERGER, Todd Henry. 1135 116TH AVE NE, STE 600 98004 #054-04-1994 L1998 **PCC** *020 †20
FRIEDLAND, Eric Thomas. 1035 116TH AVE NE 98004 #054-04-1994 L1996 **EM** *020 †16

■ = Address Information Privacy Protected
9187

FUREDY, Ronald Lincoln. 1687 114TH AVE SE STE 125 98004 #005-06-1967 L1971 **PYA P** *020
FURRER, William, Jr. ■ 98005 #041-12-1965 L1970 **ORS LM** *071 †40
FURUYA, Clinton Masao. 1201 116TH AVE NE 98004 #028-34-1958 L1967 **OTO GP** *071 †45
GAILLOUR, Francine Renee. 15600 NE 8TH ST 98008 #034-01-1981 L1982 **IM** *020 †20
GALL, Chikit. 1135 116TH AVE NE STE 1 98004 #054-04-2004 L2007 **IM** *020
GAMRATH, James Herbert. 4122 128TH AVE SE STE 20 98006 #005-17-1962 L1975 **FM** *071
GAN, Chi Meng. 1811 156TH AVE NE STE 3 98007 #063-01-1976 L2003 **FM** *020 †18
GARLAND, Leslie Allison. 1035 116TH AVE NE 98004 #060-01-1992 L1997 **FM** *020 †18
GARRIE, Stuart Allen. ■ 98004 #005-06-1967 L1976 **D P** *071 †15,75 ‡
GAVRILA, Marian Daniel. 1135 116TH AVE NE 98004 #781-01-1991 L1999 **OBG OBS** *020 †30
GELTZER, Allen Jed. 1407 116TH AVE NE 98004 #024-07-1995 L1998 **IM** *020 †20
GEORGE, John Wm. 1035 116TH AVE NE 98004 #054-04-1969 L1972 **OBG** *020 †30
GEORGES, Britton Lee. 1515 116TH AVE NE STE 207 98004 #010-01-1972 L1975 **A** *020 †20,03
GEPHART, Harlan Reid. 2700 NORTHUP WAY, PEDIATRIC ASSOCIATES 98004 #016-02-1961 L1967 **PD** *020 †55
GIBSON, Kathleen D. 1135 116TH AVE NE STE 305 98004 #054-04-1994 L1998 **VS** *020 †85
GIGUERE, Laurie Jean. ■ 98005 #054-04-1996 L1999 **FM** *020 †18
GILBERT, Michael Lewis. 12301 NE 10TH PL, STE 200 98005 #048-04-1983 L1990 **OPH IM** *020 †35 ‡
GILMORE, Carol Ann. 1200 112TH AVE NE, STE B250 98004 #048-14-1983 L2006 **IM** *020 †20
GLYNN-THAMI, Maura. 13231 SE 36TH ST STE 110 98006 #054-04-1985 L1988 **FM** *020 †18
GOERTZ, Brian O. 11100 NE 8TH ST, STE 820 98004 #068-01-1979 L1989 **FM** *020
GOFMAN, John David. 1300 116TH AVE NE, EYE CLINIC OF BELLEVUE 98004 #005-11-1974 L1975 **OPH** *020 †35
GOGENOLA, Lawrence Jos. 1551 116TH AVE NE, BELLEVUE DERMATOLOGY CLINI 98004 #054-04-1982 L1987 **D** *020 †15
GOLDEN, Michael Paul. 2025 112TH AVE NE, STE 200 98004 #005-14-1973 L1990 **CHP PD** *020 †55,75
GOLDMAN, Peggy Lynn. 15395 SE 30TH PL 98007 #005-11-1975 L1978 **EM ID** *020 †20,16
GOLLNICK, Lea V S. ■ 98008 #054-04-1961 L1962 **GP PHP** *071 †18
GOLOB, Deborah Sue. 1600 116TH AVE NE, STE 304 98004 #038-43-1984 L2005 **END IM** *020 †20
GOMBERG, Bernard. ■ 98004 #016-11-1941 L1952 **OBG** *071 †30
GOODKIN, David Alan. ■ 98005 #035-15-1980 L2003 **NEP IM** *020 †20
GOODMAN, David Sanford. 1607 116TH AVE NE STE 102 98004 #011-02-1983 L1989 **APM GS** *020 †05
GORMAN, David Gregory. 1231 116TH AVE NE STE 203, OVERLAKE NEUROLOGY 98004 #034-01-1975 L2003 **N** *020 †75
GOTTESMAN, Eric Philip. 1135 116TH AVE NE, STE 600 98004 #035-08-1989 L2007 **PUD** *020 †20
GOZE, Nuri Mustafa. ■ 98007 #902-10-1954 **FM GP** *020
GRAHAM, Albert Richard. 1600 116TH AVE NE STE 104 98004 #005-12-1960 L1964 **OBG** *020 †30
GRAHAM, Gene Orloff. 1035 116TH AVE NE 98004 #028-02-1956 L1967 **OBG** *071 †30
GRAY, Deetta M. 4455 148TH AVE NE, THE SPA AT PRO SPORTS CLUB 98007 #068-01-1990 L1997 **D** *020 †15
GRIFFING, Lee Richards. ■ 98004 #038-41-1978 L1983 **EM** *075 †16
GRIMM, Ross Montgomery. ■ 98004 #028-34-1943 L1947 **GP** *071
GRINBERG, Yakov P. 1940 116TH AVE NE STE 200 98004 #913-27-1978 L1997 **IM** *020 †20
GROGAN, Melany Kirschen. ■ 98006 #041-02-2006 L2007 **AN** *012
GROHMAN, Marie Elisabeth. 12917 SE 38TH ST, STE 100 98006 #040-02-1992 L1997 **FM** *020 †18
GROSS, Christopher Andrew. 11004 NE 15TH ST 98004 #005-06-2001 L2005 **P** *020 †75
GRUBB, Donald James. 1300 114TH AVE SE STE 210 98004 #005-02-1972 L1975 **P** *020 †75
GUYETTE, Todd Michael. 1535 116TH AVE NE, STE 200 98004 #024-01-1997 L2003 **ORS** *020 †40
HACKETT, Carol Hedden. 1380 112TH AVE NE, STE 100 98004 #036-01-1966 L1974 **FM** *020
HACKETT, John P. 1603 116TH AVE NE, STE 112 98004 #010-02-1967 L1974 **D IM** *020 †20,15
HALL, Jonathan Bergh. 1035 116TH AVE NE 98004 #028-34-1991 L2002 **EM** *040 †16
HALPERIN, Mike Earl. 1035 116TH AVE NE, EMERGENCY DEPT 98004 #054-04-1990 L1994 **EM** *020 †16
HAMILTON, Thomas E. 2020 116TH AVE NE STE 100 98004 #049-01-1979 L1980 **GPM IM** *020 †20
HAMPSON, John Laurence. ■ 98004 #023-07-1946 L1960 **P** *030
HANNAN, John R. ■ 98006 #041-01-1939 L1941 **DR** *071
HANSEN, Jeffrey Theodore. ■ 98008 #005-12-2000 L2003 **FM** *020 †18
HANSEN, Mulloy Grigor. 14858 LAKE HILLS BLVD 98007 #060-01-1975 L1976 **FM** *020
HANSHEW, Evelyn Marie. 1515 116TH AVE NE STE 107 98004 #054-04-1987 L1989 **FM** *020
HANSON, Gwen Szwarc. 1409 140TH PL NE, STE 106 98007 #011-04-1986 L2002 **FM** *020 †18
HAO, Gene Yu. 1407 116TH AVE NE 98004 #025-01-1996 L2000 **IM** *020 †20
HARGER, Catherine Louise. 40 LAKE BELLEVUE DR, STE 100 98005 #016-06-1976 L1977 **CHP P** *020 †75 ‡
HARMS, G Lester. ■ 98007 #019-02-1956 L1964 **R NM** *071 †80
HARNISCH, James Philip. 1600 116TH AVE NE, STE 306 98004 #038-40-1969 L1974 **D ID** *020 †15
HARRINGTON, Kristi Marie. 1035 116TH AVE NE 98004 #007-02-1996 L2000 **GS OS** *020 †85
HASHISAKI, Peter Alan. 1200 116TH AVE NE STE D 98004 #054-04-1975 L1983 **ID IM** *020 †20
HAWKINS, Rodger Gilman. ■ 98005 #040-02-1964 L1981 **FM** *071 †18
HAYNES, Deborah Sue. 1309 114TH AVE SE STE 316 98004 #054-04-1983 L1985 **P** *020 †75
HAYNES DE REGT, Roberta. 1135 116TH AVE NE 98004 #043-01-1979 L1996 **OBS OBG** *020 †30
HAYWARD, Mark Alan. 12522 SE 48TH PL 98006 #062-01-1952 L1958 **GP** *071
HELLEKSON, Carla. 1300 114TH AVE SE STE 102 98004 #032-01-1974 L1975 **P OS** *020 †75
HEPWORTH, Claud Ira. 3417 1/2 122ND PL NE 98005 #025-01-1954 L1969 **R RO** *020 †80
HERMAN, Martin Allen. 11711 NE 12TH ST STE 1A 98005 #011-02-1975 L1981 **CRS GS** *020 †10,85
HERREID, Peter Anthony. 1280 116TH AVE NE, STE 210 98004 #031-01-1988 L1995 **DMP** *020 †50
HERSETH, Elizabeth Ann. 1810 116TH AVE NE 98004 #054-04-1983 L1984 **FM** *071 †18
HEYWOOD, J David. 1035 116TH AVE NE 98004 #016-02-1959 L1965 **IM HEM** *071 †20
HEYWOOD, John Alan. 1135 116TH AVE NE, STE 600 98004 #054-04-1989 L1996 **CD ICE** *020 †20
HIGHNESS, Joel Alfred. 15600 NE 8TH ST, PMB BL 98008 #054-04-1974 L1976 **AN** *020 †05
HILL, James Joseph. 1925 140TH AVE NE 98005 #054-15-1969 **GP** *020
HILLARD, Virany. 1700 116TH AVE NE 98004 #035-19-1999 L2006 **NS** *100
HING, Andrew Wm. 1280 116TH AVE NE, STE 210 98004 #028-02-1990 L2000 **SP** *020 ‡
HIRSCH, Melinda Schramm. ■ 98005 #010-01-1971 L1973 **P** *071
HOANG, Vu Trong. 1135 116TH AVE NE STE 605 98004 #011-03-1990 L2000 **TS** *020 †85,90
HOEDEMAKER, Frederick S. 1687 114TH AVE SE STE 125 98004 #067-01-1959 L1962 **P PYA** *071 †75
HOFFMAN, H Clark. ■ 98005 #016-06-1953 L1954 **GS HS** *071 †85
HOISTAD, Dick L. 1200 112TH AVE NE, STE B250 98004 #037-01-1989 L2000 **OTO** *020 †45
HOLDER, John Trimble. 1414 116TH AVE NE 98004 #004-01-1968 L1975 **CD IM** *020 †20
HOLLIDAY, William Chapman. 2300 130TH AVE NE, STE A211 98005 #038-40-1973 L1975 **P** *020
HOM, Michael. ■ 98007 #005-14-1984 L1985 **AN GS** *020 †05
HONG, Hui. 1407 116TH AVE NE 98004 #067-01-1995 L1998 **IMG** *020 †20
HORIBE, Mayumi. ■ 98006 #572-36-1984 L2005 **AN** *020 †05
HORTON, William Geo. ■ 98006 #035-19-1961 L1970 **AN** *071 †05
HOWSON, Tracey Linda. 14711 NE 29TH PL, STE 255 98007 #054-04-2002 L2002 **PD** *020 †55
HSUE, Kuyuen. 1135 116TH AVE NE, STE 310 98004 #054-04-1988 L1991 **IM** *020 †05
HUEHNERGARTH, R J, Jr. 1035 116TH AVE NE 98004 #041-13-1970 L1977 **PTH CLP** *020 †50
HUGHES, M Steven. 1632 116TH AVE NE, STE C 98004 #019-02-1987 L1990 **FM** *020 †18
HUNG, Linda S. 14711 NE 29TH PL, STE 255 98007 #056-06-2000 L2003 **PD** *020 †55 ‡
HURLBURT, Ward Bullard. ■ 98006 #010-01-1959 L1966 **OS GS** *030 †85,70
HWANG, Irene Y. 2700 NORTHUP WAY 98004 #017-20-1996 L2004 **PD** *020 †55
HWANG, Joo Ha. 1700 116TH AVE NE 98004 #016-02-1997 L1999 **GE** *020 †20
HYNES, John Kevin. 1414 116TH AVE NE, BELLEVUE CARDIOL CLINIC 98004 #054-04-1976 L1981 **CD IM** *020 †20
IACOLUCCI, Joseph Peter. ■ 98006 #056-05-1969 L1988 **IM** *020 †20
ISA, Sana. 1407 116TH AVE NE, STE 200 98004 #040-02-1995 L1999 **IM** *020 †20
ISRAEL, Lawrence Max. 1535 116TH AVE NE 98004 #054-04-1969 L1975 **OBG** *071 †30
ITO, Brian Masaru. 1511 NE 10TH ST 98004 #025-01-1981 L1982 **N** *020 †75
JABBUSCH, Mark Robt. 1035 116TH AVE NE 98004 #056-05-1973 L1976 **FM** *020 †18
JACKSON, Charles G. 1200 112TH AVE NE STE C210 98004 #035-06-1971 L1975 **AI PDA** *020 †55,03
JACOBS, Brian Coate. 1400 116TH AVE NE, BELLEVUE MEDICAL IMAGING, 98004 #054-04-1983 L1985 **DR IM** *020 †20,80
JACOBS, Cheryl Renee. 1200 112TH AVE NE, STE B250 98004 #024-07-1994 L1997 **IM** *020 †20
JACOBS, Teresa Ellen. 1540 140TH AVE NE, # 100 98005 #035-47-1985 L1992 **SME PUD** *020 †20
JACOBSEN, Judith Ann. 1925 140TH AVE NE 98005 #054-04-1982 L1986 **OBG** *020 †30
JANCZAKOWSKI, Wlodzimierz. ■ 98004 #759-07-1955 L1968 **AN** *071 †05
JENKIN, Peter John. 222 112TH AVE NE 98004 #065-10-1975 L1999 **D** *020 †15
JENSON, Kaleb Krueger. 11808 NORTHUP WAY, STE W120 98005 #056-06-2000 L2004 **AN** *100 †05
JEWITT, Steven Paul. 1601 114TH AVE SE, STE 180 98004 #046-01-1980 L1988 **P** *020 †75
JONES, Calvin Tod. 13033 BELLEVUE REDMOND RD 98005 #040-02-1983 L1986 **OM FM** *020 †70,18
JONES, James Blake. 40 LAKE BELLEVUE DR # 25 98005 #012-05-1984 L1988 **P** *020 †75
JONESCHILD, Edward David. 2700 NORTHUP WAY 98004 #054-04-1966 L1969 **PD OS** *020 †55
JOSLIN, Richard Scott. 2700 NORTHUP WAY 98004 #040-02-1972 L1975 **PD** *020 †55
JUERGENS, Steven Manley. 11201 SE 8TH ST, STE 105 98004 #026-08-1979 L1981 **P ADM** *020 †75
JUZVIK-LEVITZ, Inesa. 3006 NORTHUP WAY, STE 102 98004 #913-96-1988 L1996 **FM** *020 †18
KANDALA, Madhuri. 2015 116TH AVE NE 98004 #495-13-1998 L2003 **NEP** *020 †20
KANDIKONDA, Vijaya L. ■ 98006 #495-99-1991 L2006 **N** *020 †75
KANER, Richard Alan. 1750 112TH AVE NE 98004 #054-04-1984 L1987 **IM** *020 †20
KANG, Kalle. 1135 116TH AVE NE 98004 #035-19-1977 L1986 **GE** *020 †20
KANHOUWA, Meera. 15325 SE 30TH PL, STE 200 98007 #024-07-1988 L2000 **EM** *020 †16
KAPELA, Robert Farrell. 5652 132ND AVE NE, A.K.E. PATHOLOGISTS 98005 #054-04-1963 L1966 **PTH** *071 †50
KARANAM, Sambasivarao. 15921 NE 8TH ST, # C205 98008 #496-13-1980 L1984 **GP** *020
KARCH, David B. 15325 SE 30TH PL, STE 220A 98007 #010-01-1992 L1996 **EM** *020 †16
KEECH, Pamila R. 11711 NE 12TH ST, STE 2B 98005 #016-43-1987 L1989 **NEP IM** *020 †20
KELLOGG, Howard B, Jr. 2820 122ND PL NE 98005 #016-06-1956 L1957 **GS TS** *020 †85
KELLY, Sharon Brubaker. 14030 NE 24TH ST, STE 202 98007 #054-04-1984 L1985 **D** *030 †15
KENNY, Gerald Michael. ■ 98004 #016-06-1960 L1969 **U OS** *071 †95
KENT, Daniel L. 3005 112TH AVE NE, STE 100 98004 #035-45-1978 L1985 **IM IMG** *030 †20
KERR, Robert Franklin. 1380 112TH AVE NE STE 205, PACIFIC OFFICE PARK 98004 #025-07-1948 L1949 **FM GP** *071
KESTLE, Donald Gene. 1011 116TH AVE NE 98004 #028-02-1962 L1969 **IM ID** *071 †20
KHADEM, Saeed. ■ 98006 #517-01-1957 L1979 **PD** *071 †55
KHAN, Arifulla. 1900 116TH AVE NE STE 112 98004 #495-33-1976 L1984 **P** *020 †75
KHANNA, Neil K. ■ 98015 #665-01-1997 L2005 **CHP** *020 †75
KHECHOYAN, David Yurevich. ■ 98007 #054-04-2005 L2005 **GS** *012
KILCLINE, Bradford Andrew. 1035 116TH AVE NE 98004 #041-12-1997 L2002 **EM** *020 †16
KIM, Sang U. 1135 116TH AVE NE 98004 #054-04-1990 L1992 **GE** *020 †20
KIM, Young Min. 1515 116TH AVE NE, STE 101 98004 #583-10-1982 L1997 **OBG** *020 †30
KING, Kenneth Ray. 1687 114TH AVE SE STE 125 98004 #019-02-1973 L1977 **PYA CHP** *020 †75
KING, Philip John L. 2015 116TH AVE NE, STE B 98004 #143-03-1977 L1981 **N OS** *020
KING, Philip W, Jr. 2015 116TH AVE NE 98004 #748-02-1990 L2000 **NEP** *020 †20
KIPP, Gaylon Earl. 1900 116TH AVE NE, WELLNESS CENTER 98004 #054-04-1979 L1980 **FM** *020 †18
KLEIN, Nancy Allen. 1545 116TH AVE NE, STE 102 98004 #047-05-1985 L1993 **OBG** *040 †30
KNAPP, Leonard Wilbur. ■ 98006 #038-41-1959 L1959 **GP** *071
KNIPHER, Kurt Frederick. ■ 98005 #016-02-1978 L1980 **N** *074
KNOEPFLER, David Andrew. 1035 116TH AVE NE 98004 #054-04-1989 L1992 **IM** *020 †20
KNOEPFLER, Peter Tamas. 1035 116TH AVE NE 98004 #035-20-1955 L1970 **P OS** *062 †75
KNOTT, Russell Alan. ■ 98006 #030-05-1966 L1969 **ORS** *100 †40
KOBASHI, Kathleen Chizuko. 222 112TH AVE NE, STE 101 98004 #041-09-1992 L1999 **U** *020 †95
KOELEMAY, Kathryn Gail. 2700 NORTHUP WAY 98004 #021-05-1979 L1991 **PD** *020 †55
KOENIG, Kelan Richard. 1035 116TH AVE NE, OVERLAKE HOSPITAL 98004 #054-04-1995 L1997 **P** *020 †75
KOLE, Christian. 10845 MAIN ST 98004 #660-03-1952 L1956 **P** *072 †75
KONING, Frans. ■ 98006 #660-03-1955 L1958 **FM FPG** *071

■ = Address Information Privacy Protected

KOVACH, Nicholas Lee. 1135 116TH AVE NE STE 230, OVERLAKE INTERNAL MEDICINE 98004 #040-02-1984 L1987 **ON HEM** *020 †20
KOZLOWSKI, Christopher M. 1135 116TH AVE NE STE 600 98004 #010-02-1988 L1998 **CD** *020 †20
KRAFT, Denise Susan. 1200 112TH AVE NE STE C 98004 #054-04-1979 L1980 **FM OS** *020 †18
KRENGEL, Walter Franklin. 1231 116TH AVE NE, STE 100 98004 #040-02-1959 L1966 **ORS** *020 †40
KRISHNADASAN, Bahirathan. 6737 161ST AVE SE UNIT B, UNIVERSITY OF WASHINGTON 98006 #005-19-1996 L2002 **TS** *100 †85,90
KULPA, Peggy Jane. 4122 FACTORIA BLVD SE, STE 101 98006 #056-05-1980 L1988 **PD** *020 †55
KUMIN, Ivri Matthew. 12340 NE 8TH ST 98005 #021-01-1971 L1985 **PYA P** *020 †75
KUNTZ, Alice Lee. 1135 116TH AVE NE STE 500, BELLEVUE ENT CLINIC 98004 #005-02-1993 L1993 **OTO** *020 †45
KUO, Guy. 1135 116TH AVE NE STE 310, OVERLAKE ANESTHESIOLOGISTS 98004 #031-01-1989 L1992 **AN** *020 †05
KURES, Peter Rodney. 1600 116TH AVE NE, STE 206 98004 #016-02-1987 L1998 **CD** *020 †20
KUSTIN, Jim Isaac. 1370 116TH AVE NE, STE 100 98004 #143-08-1973 L1989 **GYN REN** *020 †30
KWON, Hower. 365 118TH AVE SE, STE 118 98005 #035-19-1993 L2003 **CHP** *020 †75
LAI, Edwin Jueyshiu. 1135 116TH AVE NE, STE 560 98004 #054-04-1999 L2007 **GE** *020 †20
LAM, Dickson. 1035 116TH AVE NE 98004 #054-04-2000 L2003 **IM** *020 †20
LAMPE, Ellen K. 14711 NE 29TH PL STE 2 98007 #048-12-1994 L1997 **PD** *020 †55
LARKINS ROBERTSON, Joan M. 4122 FACTORIA BLVD SE #101 98006 #028-02-1984 L1984 **PD** *020 †55
LARSEN, Jeanne Marie. 14711 NE 29TH PL STE 245, PEDIATRICS ASSOCIATES 98007 #054-04-1986 L1988 **PD** *020 †55
LAUTER, David Marc. 1600 116TH AVE NE STE 304 98004 #035-45-1986 L1992 **GS VS** *020 †85
LEAVITT, Kent Gaylord. 1135 116TH AVE NE STE 450 98004 #025-01-1984 L1991 **OPH** *020 †35 ‡
LEE, Joseph Insang. 1407 116TH AVE NE STE 200, OVERLAKE INTERNAL MEDICINE 98004 #005-12-1997 L2004 **IM** *020 †20
LEE, Shawn Joon. 1035 116TH AVE NE, OVERLAKE HOSPITAL 98004 #054-04-1998 L2001 **IM** *020 †20
LEFF, Michael Alan. 1600 116TH AVE NE STE 204 98004 #016-11-1965 L1975 **PS HS** *020 †65
LEGGETT, Gerald Hall. 7944 NE 32ND STREET 98004 #154-01-1974 L1978 **AN** *071
LEGGETT, James H, III. 1135 116TH AVE NE, STE 600 98004 #004-01-1982 L1984 **CD** *020 †20
LEONARD, Edward Earl, II. 1200 116TH AVE NE STE D 98004 #041-12-1994 L1996 **ID** *020 †20
LEOPOLD, Seth Samuel. 1700 116TH AVE NE 98004 #035-20-1993 L2002 **ORS** *020 †40
LEVIN, Aaron. 1135 116TH AVE NE STE 310, OVERLAKE ANESTHESIOLOGISTS 98004 #035-20-1994 L1998 **AN** *020 †05
LEVINE, Melvin David. ■ 98005 #024-07-1964 L1971 **ORS** *020 †40
LEYSER, Selig. 1199 116TH AVE NE, STE 3 98004 #836-02-1973 L1979 **PTH CLP** *020 †50
LIAW, Brandon Hongyin. ■ 98004 #035-09-2002 **P** *100
LIM, Pohlian. 1200 116TH AVE NE STE D 98004 #035-01-1991 L1999 **IM ID** *020 †20
LIN, Jules. ■ 98004 #024-01-1999 L2006 **TS** *012
LIN, Paul C. 1545 116TH AVE NE, STE 102 98004 #035-03-1994 L2001 **OBG** *020 †30
LING, Dorothy Hueilin. 1135 116TH AVE NE STE 310 98004 #016-06-1987 L1990 **AN** *020 †05
LINGAM, S Dharma. ■ 98006 #495-16-1971 L1977 **GE IM** *020 †20
LIPTON, Barbara Steiner. ■ 98004 #016-11-1943 L1945 **P** *071 †75
LIU, Yu-Chin. 1380 112TH AVE NE, STE 205 98004 #041-01-1984 L2000 **IM** *020 †20
LIZAK, Paula Frances. ■ 98006 #041-13-1990 L1995 **DR** *020 †80
LORANT, Zsolt Arpad. 14216 NE 21ST ST 98007 #473-02-1994 L2000 **P CHP** *020 †75
LOWE, Philip Neil. 1135 116TH AVE NE STE 190, WASHINGTON IMAGING SERVICE 98004 #016-42-1985 L1990 **DR** *020 †80
LU, Leslie. 1200 112TH AVE NE, STE B250 98004 #005-14-1993 L1993 **IM** *020 †20
LUSTGARTEN, Maurice V. 2200 112TH AVE NE, STE 140 98004 #005-15-1968 L1971 **P** *020 †75
LYLE, Ann Black. 2700 NORTHUP WAY 98004 #054-04-1978 L1978 **PD** *075
LYNCH, Robert Paul. 11711 NE 12TH ST, STE 1A/EASTSIDE SURG ASSOC 98005 #038-40-1982 L1992 **GS TRS** *020 †85
LYSONS, Donald F. 1135 116TH AVE NE STE 310 98004 #054-04-1967 L1968 **AN** *020 †05
MA, Jian Feng. 10037 NE 23RD ST 98004 #035-01-1999 L2005 **U** *020 †95
MAC DOUGALL, Roderick, Jr. 1035 116TH AVE NE 98004 #048-02-1971 L1978 **PD** *020 †55
MADHANI, Minakshi D. 2614 EVERGREEN POINT ROAD 98004 #495-65-1962 L1972 **GP** *075
MADHAVAN, Ernest Mohandas. 14030 NE 24TH ST, STE 104 98007 #041-15-2003 L2003 **P** *020
MADIGAN, Danl Michael, Jr. 1201 116TH AVE NE 98004 #016-43-1960 L1967 **OTO** *071 †45
MAGEE, Michael Scott. 2020 116TH AVE NE 98004 #038-40-1979 L1982 **END IM** *020 †20
MAHRER, Kenneth Neal. 222 112TH AVE NE, STE 101 98004 #005-06-1988 L1995 **CD IC** *020 †20
MAJID, Saniea Fatima. ■ 98008 #704-25-2002 L2004 **GS** *012
MANAM, Rajesh. ■ 98004 #495-11-1994 L2007 **GE** *100 †20
MANNER, Paul A. 1700 116TH AVE NE 98004 #067-01-1991 L2006 **ORS** *020 †40
MANULLANG, Theodore Radja. 1135 116TH AVE NE, STE 310 98004 #005-12-1994 L1999 **AN** *020 †05
MARASHI, S Mohammad. ■ 98006 #517-01-1963 L1970 **PD** *020 †55
MARGRET, Cecilia Patrica. ■ 98007 #495-04-1999 L2006 **P** *012
MARKUS, Stephen Peter. 1540 140TH AVE NE STE 100 98005 #051-07-1983 L1984 **FM A** *020
MARMORSTEIN, Barry Lyon. 1603 116TH AVE NE STE 112 98004 #016-11-1966 L1974 **PUD IM** *020 †20
MAROSAN, George. 11820 NORTHUP WAY, STE E190 98005 #016-01-1983 L1994 **PS GS** *020 †85,65
MARQUESS, Nanci Jayne. 14350 SE EASTGATE WAY 98007 #017-20-1982 L1990 **PD** *020 †55
MARSHALL, Jean Hornbrook. 13451 SE 36TH ST 98006 #007-02-1978 L1978 **FM** *020 †18
MARSHALL, Stephen Watt. 1035 116TH AVE NE 98004 #040-02-1982 L1986 **EM IM** *020 †20,16
MARTI, Laurie Alison. 3006 NORTHUP WAY, STE 102 98004 #654-01-1998 L2002 **FM** *020 †18
MARX, Larry Steven. ■ 98006 #028-46-1982 L2002 **CHP P** *020 †75
MASON-PLUNKETT, Jenna. 1035 116TH AVE NE 98004 #043-01-2001 L2005 **EM** *020 †16
MATHEWS, J Wayne. 2200 112TH AVE NE, STE 140 98004 #048-12-1966 L1979 **P** *020 †75
MATTHIES, Rich Johns. 1135 116TH AVE NE STE 190, WASHINGTON IMAGING SERVICE 98004 #025-12-1975 L1984 **R** *050 †80
MAURER, Stephen Harry. 1035 116TH AVE NE 98004 #049-01-1968 L1976 **PYA** *020
MAXWELL, John Alan. 1600 116TH AVE NE 98004 #024-01-1961 L1974 **GS** *020 †25
MC CABE, Kinne Darrow. 12501 BEL RED RD, STE 210 98005 #021-01-1970 L1979 **FM R** *020 †18
MC CALLIN, Paul Fonce. ■ 98004 #007-02-1947 L1964 **OBG** *071 †30
MC CLINTON, Leslie T. 1035 116TH AVE NE 98004 #016-11-1949 L1958 **GS** *071 †85
MC CLURE, Robert D. 1545 116TH AVE NE, STE 102 98004 #065-06-1968 L1990 **U** *020 †95
MC CONNELL, John Wm. 1135 116TH AVE NE STE 310 98004 #054-04-1987 L1990 **AN** *020 †05
MC CREADIE, Gordon Scott. 1035 116TH AVE NE, PUGET SOUND PHYSICIANS 98004 #061-01-1995 L1999 **EM** *020 †16
MCDERMOTT, Carmen Veronic. ■ 98006 #054-04-2004 L2004 **IM** *100 †20
MC FARLAND, David Kevin. 1035 116TH AVE NE 98004 #054-04-1984 L1985 **FM** *020 †18
MC GOUGH, Peter Myles. 13231 SE 36TH ST, STE 110 98006 #005-06-1979 L1980 **FM** *020 †18
MC HUGH, Carolyn Jean. ■ 98008 #054-04-2004 L2004 **IM** *100 †20
MCMILLAN, James Jos. 10050 NE 10TH ST, STE B 98004 #005-02-1990 L1994 **OPH** *020 †35
MC MILLAN, John Cameron. 10050 NE 10TH ST, C/O JAMES J. MCMILLAN, MD 98004 #030-06-1956 L1963 **R RO** *020 †80
MEDLOCK, Clyde C, Jr. 13231 SE 36TH ST, STE 110 98006 #012-01-1966 L1971 **PD** *071 †55
MEHTA, Sonali. ■ 98008 #063-01-1991 L1996 **PYG** *020 †75
MEISEL, John Lawrence. 1035 116TH AVE NE 98004 #041-01-1970 L1972 **GE IM** *071 †20
METZ, Stewart Arthur. ■ 98006 #008-01-1972 L1973 **END IM** *050 †20
MIKESELL, Kathryn A. 2700 NORTHUP WAY 98004 #023-01-1968 L1972 **PD** *020 †55
MILLER, Dan S. ■ 98009 #018-03-1944 L1950 **U** *071 †95
MILLER, John Leslie. 1370 116TH AVE NE, STE 206 98004 #017-20-1970 L1975 **P CHP** *020
MILLER, Thomas Thane. 1035 116TH AVE NE 98004 #001-02-1977 L1979 **IM** *020 †20,16
MILNE, Kristen Beth. 1035 116TH AVE NE 98004 #040-02-1994 L1998 **EM** *020 †16
MINAMI, Eiji. 1135 116TH AVE NE STE 550 98004 #005-12-1975 L1989 **GS** *020 †20,85
MINKIN, Stuart Allen. 2700 NORTHUP WAY 98004 #056-05-1968 L1970 **PD** *020 †55
MIRZA, Shazia Mahmood. ■ 98006 #704-01-1994 **IM** *100
MITCHELL, Graham Thomas. ■ 98006 #016-42-2007 **P** *012
MITCHELL, Marc Ronald. 1407 116TH AVE NE, STE 200 98004 #024-05-1993 L1995 **IM** *020 †20
MOHAN, Venkatachala. 1135 116TH AVE NE 98004 #495-45-1982 L1999 **GE IM** *020 †20
MONTGOMERY, Robert Bruce. ■ 98005 #036-07-1987 L1990 **ON** *020 †20
MONTGOMERY, Wendi Irene. 1035 116TH AVE NE 98004 #024-07-1987 L1987 **PD** *020 †55
MONTINE, Thomas J. ■ 98006 #067-01-1991 L2002 **PTH** *020 †50
MOORE, Heather August. 1535 116TH AVE NE, STE 100 98004 #028-03-1996 L2001 **OBG** *020 †30
MOORE, John Chas. 1035 116TH AVE NE 98004 #014-01-1979 L1982 **EM** *020 †16
MOORE, Mehri Damavandi. 1601 114TH AVE SE STE 180 98004 #517-01-1972 L1975 **CHP P** *020 †75
MOORHEAD, Dudley Thos. 1135 116TH AVE NE, STE 220 98004 #035-20-1969 L1978 **VS GS** *020 †85 ‡
MORRIS, Michael Edward. 222 112TH AVE NE, STE 101 98004 #005-15-1981 L1982 **ORS** *020 †40
MORTON, David Calvin. 1400 116TH AVE NE, BELLEVUE PROVIDENCE MEDICA 98004 #041-09-1979 L1982 **IM** *020 †20
MORTON, Kenneth Laurence. 14655 BEL RED RD STE 203 98007 #028-02-1983 L1990 **OPH** *020 †35
MOURADIAN, Wendy Elyse. 460 173RD PL NE 98008 #035-01-1977 L1978 **PD** *020 †55
MUKHTADIR, Shah Mohammad. ■ 98006 #160-04-1999 *100
MURAKAMI, Carol Sumi. 1135 116TH AVE NE STE 560, NORTHWEST GASTROENTEROLOGY 98004 #016-43-1985 L1988 **GE IM** *020 †20
MURDOCH, Mary Frances. 2700 NORTHUP WAY, PEDIATRICS ASSOC 98004 #054-04-2004 L2004 **PD** *020 †55
MUSNICK, David Jason. 1300 114TH AVE SE, SE STE 105 98004 #005-02-1986 L1988 **IM ISM** *020 †20
MYERS, Tiffany Lucille. 2700 NORTHUP WAY, PEDIATRIC ASSOCIATES INC P 98004 #038-41-1999 L2002 **PD** *020 †55
MYSTKOWSKI, Paul M. 1407 116TH AVE NE, STE 200 98004 #038-41-1994 L1998 **END** *020 †20
MYSTKOWSKI, Supriya. 1035 116TH AVE NE 98004 #016-06-1998 L2001 **IM** *020 †20
NADERSHAHI, Arash. 1035 116TH AVE NE 98004 #028-03-1996 L2001 **IM** *020 †20
NADIG, Daniel Erich. 1135 116TH AVE NE, STE 550 98004 #054-04-1994 L1999 **GS** *020 †85
NAINI, Hossein Jafari. PO BOX 487 98009 #517-01-1957 L1963 **IM DIA** *071
NAKAMOTO, Greg Isao. 222 112TH AVE NE, STE 101 98004 #005-18-1996 L1998 **ISM IM** *020 †20
NEE, Alex Chihming. ■ 98005 #038-41-2004 L2004 **N** *012
NEHRU, Padmini Chak. 4455 148TH AVE NE 98007 #055-01-1982 L1993 **AN** *020 †05
NELSON, John Raymond, III. 1035 116TH AVE NE 98004 #036-05-1985 L2000 **IM** *020 †20
NESS, Rhonda Lynn. 925 116TH AVE NE 98004 #030-06-1977 L1981 **PTH** *062 †50
NEUFELD, William Peter. 1035 116TH AVE NE 98004 #062-01-1976 L1978 **FM** *020 †18
NGUYEN, Cuc Thu. 4320 130TH PL SE 98006 #030-05-1987 L1989 **P** *020 †75
NGUYEN, Thi Cam. 12917 SE 38TH ST, SWEDISH PHYS-FACTORIA #100 98006 #010-01-1993 L1993 **FM** *020 †18
NOBIS, Catherine Ann. 2700 NORTHUP WAY 98004 #056-05-1993 L1993 **PD** *020 †55
NORDBY, Arthur Le Roy. ■ 98004 #054-15-1964 L1964 **AN** *071
NORDIN, David Denton. 1035 116TH AVE NE 98004 #026-04-1973 L1976 **PTH** *020 †50
NORSEN, Jason Paul. 222 112TH AVE NE, STE 101 98004 #054-04-1999 L1999 **IM** *020 †20
NORTH, Edward Ray. 1535 116TH AVE NE, STE 200 98004 #019-02-1971 L1981 **ORS HS** *020 †40
NUDELMAN, Mitchell Eric. 1535 116TH AVE NE, BELLEGROVE PROFESSIONAL PA 98004 #054-04-1988 L1991 **OBG** *020 †30
NUMRYCH, Amy Sue. 1600 116TH AVE NE, STE 102 98004 #016-11-1991 L1994 **FM OBS** *020 †18
NYGAARD, Christine E. 1414 116TH AVE NE STE C 98004 #025-12-1985 L1992 **PS** *020 †85,65
O'BRIEN, James Kilty. 1135 116TH AVE NE, STE 600 98004 #026-04-1987 L1997 **PCC** *020 †20
ODDERSON, Ib Rask. 1700 116TH AVE NE 98004 #047-05-1985 L1987 **PM** *020 †60
OKAMURA, Richard Ken. 1135 116TH AVE NE, STE 310 98004 #005-18-1987 L1991 **AN PME** *020 †05
OLIAEI, Sepehr. 1406 151ST AVE SE 98007 #021-01-2008 *012
OLSON, Ellen Tallerico. 677 120TH AVE NE # 109 98005 #007-02-1995 L2001 **APM** *020
OMBRELLARO, Mark. 1135 116TH AVE NE, STE 220 98004 #054-04-1987 L1996 **VS GS** *020 †85 ‡
O'QUIN, Ronald Jos. 1135 116TH AVE NE, STE 610 98004 #007-02-1976 L1980 **PUD IM** *020 †20
OSBORN, Robert Hooper. 1035 116TH AVE NE 98004 #018-03-1966 L1973 **OBG** *020 †30
OTTESON, Evan Logan. 1370 116TH AVE NE, STE 201 98004 #054-04-1964 L1965 **P** *020 †75
PADDISON, Patricia L. 1400 112TH AVE SE, STE 100 98004 #021-05-1982 L1990 **P** *020 †75

■ = Address Information Privacy Protected

PARAS, Leilani Dacalos. 1200 112TH AVE NE, SUITE160 BLDG C 98004 #028-03-2001 L2004 **FM** *020 †18
PARK, Kilhong. 1515 116TH AVE NE STE 307 98004 #583-02-1979 L2001 **FM** *020 †18
PARKER, James Lowell. 13231 SE 36TH ST, STE 110 98006 #030-06-1980 L1983 **FM** *020 †18
PASCALE, Michael Jos. 1135 116TH AVE NE STE 310 98004 #005-06-1990 L1991 **AN** *020 †05
PASCUALY, Ralph A. 12801 SE 38TH ST 98006 #035-48-1978 L1979 **P** *020 †75
PASOS, Leandro. 15650 NE 24TH ST, STE D 98008 #021-01-1954 L1986 **ORS OTR** *071
PASTOR, John Franciol. 2025 112TH AVE NE STE 2 98004 #021-05-1998 L2000 **P** *020 †75
PATEL, Ashit Chandrakant. 1135 116TH AVE NE STE 510, PROLIANCE ORTHO & SPORTS M 98004 #495-96-1986 L2003 **ORS** *020 †40
PATHY, Sumathy T. 1515 116TH AVE NE, STE 107 98004 #220-04-1997 L2003 **FM** *020 †18 ‡
PATTERSON, David John. 222 112TH AVE NE, STE 101 98004 #671-02-1976 L1985 **GE** *020 †20
PAZOUREK, Milan. ■ 98007 #286-02-1960 L1967 **OS GP** *071
PELMAN, Richard Stuart. 1135 116TH AVE NE STE 620, BELLEVUE UROLOGY ASSOC INC 98004 #054-04-1979 L1985 **U** *020 †95
PELTON, James Gordon. 1135 116TH AVE NE STE 160 98004 #030-05-1981 L1982 **RO** *020 †80
PEPPER, Daniel. 1135 116TH AVE NE, STE 305 98004 #016-01-1977 L1980 **VS GS** *020 †85
PERKINS, Carol L. 1309 114TH AVE SE STE 316 98004 #005-02-1985 L1986 **P** *020 †75
PERKINS, Harold Doyle. 4455 148TH AVE NE 98007 #803-03-1969 L1971 **OM** *020
PERKINSON, Bradley R. 1135 116TH AVE NE STE 310 98004 #005-18-1980 L1983 **AN** *020 †05
PERLMUTTER, Neal Steven. 1135 116TH AVE NE, STE 600 98004 #028-03-1983 L1989 **CD IM** *020 †20
PETRESCU, Constantin C. ■ 98008 #781-01-1967 L1994 **FM** *020 †18
PEVEHOUSE, Byron C. ■ 98005 #048-04-1952 L1952 **NS** *071 †25
PFLEGER, Mark John. 1135 116TH AVE NE STE 190, WASHINGTON IMAGING SERVICE 98004 #028-34-1986 L1997 **DR** *020 †80
PFLUG, Amos Eugene. ■ 98007 #040-02-1952 L1967 **AN** *071
PHAM, Rosalynhon N. ■ 98008 #054-04-2008 *012
PHAM, Tam Ngoc. ■ 98006 #005-18-1998 L2005 **CCS** *100 †85
PHAN, Tu. ■ 98004 #942-01-1977 L1989 **P** *020
PHILLIPS, Zaiga Alksnis. 2700 NORTHUP WAY 98004 #054-04-1959 L1960 **PD** *020 †55
PIEHL, Janet Howard. 13231 SE 36TH ST, STE 110 98006 #054-04-1996 L1999 **FM** *020 †18
PIERRE-JEROME, Frantz. 1135 116TH AVE NE STE 190, WASHINGTON IMAGING SERVICE 98004 #023-07-1987 L1998 **VIR** *020 †80
PINKERS, Lothar Herman. 1201 116TH AVE NE 98004 #028-02-1955 L1959 **GS TRS** *071 †85
PIPERS, James Thos. ■ 98006 #005-12-1960 L1972 **ORS** *071 †40
PITKETHLY, David Thos. 1600 116TH AVE NE, STE 302 98004 #036-07-1961 L1972 **NS** *071 †25
PLATZNER, Anne Marybartfa. 13231 SE 36TH ST, STE 110 98006 #035-03-1995 L1997 **FM** *020 †18
PLUNKETT, Richard J. ■ 98008 #047-05-1974 L1976 **EM** *020 †70,16
POMEROY, David Phipps. 2000 116TH AVE NE, STE 6 98004 #038-41-1976 L1977 **FM** *020 †18
PONZOO, Catherine. 15600 NE 8TH ST, STE B1 98008 #041-07-1989 L1999 **FM** *020 †18
PRATT, Collette Mary. 1925 140TH AVE NE 98005 #005-02-1994 L1996 **IM** *020 †20
PRELLER, Debra Ann. 1035 116TH AVE NE 98004 #054-04-1994 L1996 **IM** *020 †20
PRESTON, Diana Sue. 1370 116TH AVE NE, ADVANCED DERMATOLOGY 98004 #005-06-1988 L1998 **IM** *020 †20
PRITCHARD, William C. ■ 98004 #040-02-1948 L1950 **IM** *071 †20
PYFER, Howard Richard. 9941 LAKE WASH BLVD NE 98004 #054-04-1956 L1957 **PM GP** *071
QUAN, Richard Bing-Fong. ■ 98008 #035-19-1950 L1984 **OM CD** *071
RACKNER, Vicki Lynn. 1400 112TH AVE SE, STE 210 98004 #024-05-1988 L1990 **TS** *020 †85
RAINS, Anthony John. 12801 SE 38TH ST, HEALTHSOUTH - FACTORIA 98006 #054-04-1982 L1983 **GP** *072
RAMAIAH, Ramesh. ■ 98008 #495-98-1994 L2006 *100
RASKIN, Jack. ■ 98008 #035-46-1960 L1970 **CHP P** *071
RASKIND, Daniel Stephen. 1135 116TH AVE NE STE 101, OVERLAKE SENIOR HEALTH CEN 98004 #016-42-1995 L2001 **IM** *020 †20
REAVELL, George Thos. 1300 116TH AVE NE, EYE CLINIC OF BELLEVUE 98004 #011-03-1969 L1971 **OPH OS** *071 †35
REDDY, Saritha A. 14030 NE 24TH ST, STE 104 98007 #495-82-1997 L2001 **CHP** *020 †75
REEBS, Frederick Wm. ■ 98006 #054-04-1954 L1955 **FM** *071 †18
REED, James E. 1855 156TH AVE NE, STE 101 98007 #038-41-1994 L1997 **GS** *020
REED, John P, Jr. ■ 98004 #026-04-1949 L1954 **AN** *071 †05
REES-LUI, Georgia May. 1135 116TH AVE NE 98004 #049-01-1983 L1986 **GE IM** *020 †20
REHMAN, Khurram S. 1135 116TH AVE NE, STE 640 98004 #917-24-1995 L2007 **OBG** *100 †30
REID, James Alexander. 1035 116TH AVE NE 98004 #023-07-1955 L1960 **IM END** *071 †20
RICE, Sandra C. 1407 116TH AVE NE 98004 #054-04-1978 L1979 **IM** *020 †20
RICHARDS, Jennifer L. 1380 112TH AVE NE ST100 98004 #005-18-1992 L2004 **FM** *020 †18,75
RICKETTS, Dean Stratton. 1231 116TH AVE NE, STE 100 98004 #005-15-1967 L1979 **ORS GP** *020 †40
RIES, Harvey Allen. ■ 98015 #054-04-1968 L1971 **P GP** *071 †75
RIGGERS, Martha Ann. 3080 148TH AVE SE, STE 115 98007 #054-04-1995 L1998 **FM** *020 †18
RITZEN, Arlene Elizabeth. ■ 98006 #054-04-1995 L2005 **PD OS** *020 †55
ROBERTSON, Christine M J. 1607 116TH AVE NE, STE 102 98004 #054-04-1970 L1971 **IM** *020 †20
ROBIN, Joseph Jay. 1600 116TH AVE NE, STE 302 98004 #054-04-1971 L1977 **N** *020 †75
ROBISON, Maia Shinobu. ■ 98006 #041-14-2003 L2007 **CHP** *012
ROBLES AGUIRRE, Roberto. 705 136TH PL NE STEA2, ANESTHESIOLOGY FOR OUTPATI 98005 #429-01-1958 L1970 **AN** *020 †05
ROCK, Lewis Burnham, III. 17128 NE 5TH PL 98008 #051-01-1970 L1990 **FM** *020 †18
RODEY, Geoffrey Thos. 1135 116TH AVE NE, STE 310 98004 #028-03-1987 L1990 **AN** *020 †05
ROEBEN, Gregory Van. 11522 NE 21ST ST 98004 #024-16-1995 L1998 **P** *020 †75
ROEHR, John Nicol. ■ 98004 #040-02-1959 L1961 **R RO** *071 †80
ROGERS, Gary La Mar. 1600 116TH AVE NE STE 104 98004 #049-01-1971 L1974 **OBG** *020
ROMANICK-SCHMIEDL, Sue. 11522 NE 20TH ST 98004 #065-10-1982 L1991 **RHU** *020 †20
ROPER, John Walter. ■ 98006 #054-04-1968 L1969 **FM** *020 †18
ROSE, Eric. 13231 SE 36TH ST STE 110 98006 #035-46-1993 L1995 **FM** *020 †18
ROSE, Judy Ann. ■ 98006 #017-20-1987 L2006 **BBK** *020 †50
ROSE, Kamala. 1035 116TH AVE NE 98004 #005-11-1997 L2000 **EM** *020 †16
ROSELLE, David Marshall. 1035 116TH AVE NE 98004 #023-01-1982 L1987 **EM** *020 †20,16
SADRI, Azra. 1940 116TH AVE NE STE 20 98004 #517-03-1966 L1992 **GP** *020
SAHS, Jean A. 2700 NORTHUP WAY 98004 #030-05-1989 L1992 **PD** *020 †55
SALAMA, Sameh Michael. 1515 116TH AVE NE STE 205 98004 #054-04-1990 L1990 **GS** *020 †85
SALEHI, Atosa. 1035 116TH AVE NE 98004 #040-02-1994 L1998 **EM** *020 †16
SANDERSON, Aysel Kurda. 1310 116TH AVE NE STE A 98004 #048-02-1984 L1991 **PS HS** *020 †65
SANDMAN, Lester Mark. 2820 NORTHUP WAY, STE 250 98004 #056-06-1986 L1988 **P** *020 †75
SANTORO, Vincent Martin. 1601 116TH AVE NE, STE 111 98004 #008-02-1984 L1988 **ORS OSM** *020 †40
SASYNUIK, Michael Edwin. ■ 98008 #062-01-1955 L1967 **PTH** *071 †50
SATITPUNWAYCHA, Patricia. 1135 116TH AVE NE STE 310 98004 #035-45-1996 L2001 **AN** *020 †05
SAUNDERS, Michael David. 1700 116TH AVE NE 98004 #056-06-1993 L1995 **GE** *020 †20
SAWHNEY, Deepak. 1135 116TH AVE NE STE 310, OVERLAKE ANESTHESIOLOGISTS 98004 #036-01-1988 L1989 **AN** *020 †05
SAWYER, Kenneth D. 15227 NE 6TH ST 98007 #028-34-1975 L1982 **ORS OM** *020
SCALLON, Audrey Ming Yun. 5107 142ND PL SE 98006 #061-01-1993 L2001 *020
SCARBROUGH, Michael Dean. 11808 NORTHUP WAY STE W 98005 #005-12-1982 L1991 **AN** *020 †05
SCHAEFER, Robert Earl. 1201 116TH AVE NE 98004 #035-01-1958 L1964 **DR** *071 †80
SCHIESSER, Michael J. 1540 140TH AVE NE, STE 100 98005 #035-45-1994 L1996 **IM** *020 †20
SCHMIDT, Craig James. 777 108TH AVE NE STE 1200, SYNETRA FINANCIAL 98004 #040-02-1974 L1977 **IM** *030 †20
SCHNEIDER, Garry Stephen. 1035 116TH AVE NE 98004 #005-14-1972 L1973 **AN** *020 †05
SCHOCK, Peter Brooks. 1600 116TH AVE NE, STE 102 98004 #054-04-1974 L1975 **FM** *020 †18
SEAVER, Eric Bradford. 13451 SE 36TH ST, GROUP HEALTH - FACTORIA CL 98006 #054-04-1995 L2006 **IM** *020 †18
SEAVER, Gwen Edlund. 2700 NORTHUP WAY, PEDIATRIC ASSOCIATES, INC 98004 #054-04-1994 L2006 **PD** *020 †55
SEELIG, Michelle Dawn. 1309 114TH AVE SE 98004 #035-47-1999 L2006 **FM** *050 †18
SEKIJIMA, Haruto. ■ 98005 #054-04-1953 L1957 **AN** *020 †05
SELINGER, Roanne Rachel. 1135 116TH AVE NE STE 560, NORTHWEST GASTROENTEROLOGY 98004 #047-05-1998 L2000 **GE HEP** *020 †20
SENNEWALD, Frank Rainer. 1201 116TH AVE NE 98004 #065-06-1958 L1962 **OTO** *071 †45
SHAFFER, Nancy. ■ 98006 #035-03-1994 L2001 **DR** *020 †80
SHAMSA, Mandana. ■ 98006 #517-11-1993 L2007 **IM** *020 †20
SHANBHAG, Darshana G. 1407 116TH AVE NE 98004 #495-17-1987 L1996 **IM** *020 †20
SHANDS, Patricia A. 1632 116TH AVE NE, STE C 98004 #048-15-1991 L1997 **ORS** *020 †40
SHARPE, Matthew Richard. 320 106TH AVE NE 98004 #038-40-1992 L2006 **OPH** *020 †35
SHAW, Myle. ■ 98007 #054-04-2008 *012
SHERIDAN, Geoffrey Wm. 1632 116TH NE NO C 98004 #035-20-1972 L1975 **ORS** *071 †40
SHIFRIN, Donald Lee. 2700 NORTHUP WAY 98004 #010-02-1974 L1978 **PD** *020 †55
SHIH, Francis Davis. 2840 NORTHUP WAY STE 200, OVERLAKE BEHAVIORAL HEALTH 98004 #050-02-1997 L2006 **CHP P** *020 †75
SHIH, Scott Tafei. 1135 116TH AVE NE STE 310, OVERLAKE ANESTHESIOLOGISTS 98004 #035-01-1989 L1997 **AN** *020 †05
SHIU, Samuel Yun-Sang. 2000 116TH AVE NE STE 3A 98004 #462-01-1976 L1993 **FM** *020 †18 ‡
SHNEIDMAN, David Wm. 1280 116TH AVE NE, STE 210 98004 #005-14-1973 L1989 **DMP PTH** *020 †50
SHRIVER, Harry J, III. 13451 SE 36TH ST 98006 #017-20-1970 L1971 **FM** *030 †18
SILVER, Mark Allan. 1632 116TH AVE NE, STE C 98004 #024-05-1979 L1986 **ORS HS** *020 †40
SILVERMAN, Martin Saml. 1135 116TH AVE NE, STE 310 98004 #051-01-1985 L1986 **AN** *020 †05
SIMMONDS, Joseph Beachley. 27-100 NE 98004 #054-04-1955 L1959 **P** *071
SINDORF, John C. ■ 98006 #054-04-1986 L1988 **P** *020 †75
SINGER, Michael David. ■ 98005 #025-07-1980 L1987 **AN IM** *020 †05
SINGH, Randip. 1100 112TH AVE NE, STE 320 98004 #495-43-1999 L2005 **CN** *100 †75
SLOAN, Derek Dean. ■ 98006 #005-18-1999 **PTH** *100
SMALL, Robert Howard. 9816 NE 34TH ST 98004 #041-01-1977 L1986 **CHP P** *030 †75 ‡
SMITH, Eric Jay. 1135 116TH AVE NE, STE 310 98004 #054-04-1988 L1990 **AN** *020 †05
SMITH, John Walter. 1407 116TH AVE NE, STE 200 98004 #016-02-1976 L1978 **ON HEM** *020 †20
SMITH, Mason Arthur. 15325 SE 30TH PL STE 2, INC, PS 98007 #040-02-1971 L1979 **EM IM** *030 †20,16
SMITH, Meredith P. 1031 116TH AVE NE 98004 #023-01-1949 L1957 **GS** *071 †85
SMYTHIES, Christopher J. 1515 116TH AVE NE, STE 302 98004 #001-02-1983 L1993 **NS GS** *020 †25
SOBEL, Michael. 1700 116TH AVE NE 98004 #035-46-1975 L2001 **VS GS** *020 †85
SONG, James Yumin. 1600 116TH AVE NE, STE 302 98004 #243-57-1982 L2000 **N** *020 †75
SONG, Ki Taek. ■ 98005 #583-02-1950 L1967 **GS TS** *071 †85,90
SOULES, Michael Roy. 1545 116TH AVE NE, STE 102 98004 #005-14-1972 L1980 **REN OBG** *020 †30
SPERLING, Steven Danl. 1135 116TH AVE NE STE 190, WASHINGTON IMAGING SERVICE 98004 #019-02-1985 L1998 **DR** *020 †80
SPIEKER, Martha. 3023 137TH AVE NE 98005 #035-06-1989 L1997 **AN** *020 †05
STARK, Roger Allen. 1135 116TH AVE NE STE 605 98004 #030-05-1974 L1975 **TS GS** *020 †85,90
STEAD, Richard Barnett. ■ 98004 #005-11-1979 L1986 **IM HEM** *050 †20
STEPHENS, David R. 10687 NE 2ND ST 98004 #067-01-1984 L1995 **PS** *020 †65
STERLING, Ronald Murray. 12356 NORTHUP WAY STE 100 98005 #005-12-1972 L2000 **PYG** *020
STERN, Fredric Arlen. 1370 116TH AVE NE STE 102, AESTHETIC SURGERY 98004 #035-01-1981 L1982 **OPH** *020 †35
STESCO, David B J. ■ 98006 #065-02-1976 L1990 **EM** *020 †16
STEWART, Bertrand Fendley. 1700 116TH AVE NE 98004 #005-11-1986 L1990 **CD** *020 †20
STIMAC, Gary K. 12600 SE 38TH ST 98006 #018-03-1979 L1984 **DR RNR** *020 †80
STRIGENZ, Andrew Thos. 1135 116TH AVE NE STE 310 98004 #056-06-1987 L1991 **AN** *020 †05
STROH, James Eugene, Jr. 1605 116TH AVE NE STE 111 98004 #028-34-1961 L1962 **AI** *071 †03
STROM, Mark Gary. PO BOX 1608 98009 #035-46-1969 L1999 **TS** *071 †85,90 ‡
SU, Leonard Tsu. 1135 116TH AVE NE STE 305, DEPT. OF SURGERY, BOX 3564 98004 #041-01-1998 L2005 **VS** *020 †85
SUH, Erik Hosun. 1601 116TH AVE NE, STE 111 98004 #048-13-1997 L2001 **FM** *020 †18 ‡
SUH, Sang Ho. 2820 NORTHUP WAY STE 105 98004 #025-01-1995 L1997 **P** *020 †75
SUN, Hsiang-Chun. 1135 116TH AVE NE STE 13 98004 #308-10-1985 L1997 **FM** *020 †18
SUN, Steven Dapung. 1535 116TH AVE NE, STE 200 98004 #016-01-1993 L1998 **HS GS** *020 †40
SUTHERLAND, Donald Arthur. 1400 116TH AVE NE 98004 #035-45-1947 L1953 **PD PDA** *071 †55
SWARTZ, Debra Johnson. ■ 98008 #026-08-1991 **FM** *071

9190

■ = Address Information Privacy Protected

SWEENEY, Desmond. ■ 98006 #803-09-1944 L1966 **AN** *071 †05
SWENSON, Waylene Wang. ■ 98004 #005-12-1986 L2004 **RO IM** *020 †80
SWISTAK, Michael Alan. 1414 116TH AVE NE 98004 #024-07-1974 L1988 **CD IM** *020 †20
SZUCS, George Gyula. 1035 116TH AVE NE 98004 #473-04-1949 L1960 **FM** *071 †18
TADLOCK, Lauri M. 925 116TH AVE NE # 114 98004 #054-04-1981 L1984 **D IM** *020 †20,15
TAN, Lennart Cu. 1035 116TH AVE NE 98004 #017-20-1998 L2004 **PTH** *020
TANDON, Pooja. 2700 NORTHUP WAY, PEDIATRIC ASSOCIATES 98004 #043-01-1999 L2007 **PD** *020 †55
TARBET, Kristin Jones. 1810 116TH AVE NE, VIRGINIA MASON MEDICAL CEN 98004 #049-01-1992 L1999 **CS OPH** *020 †35
TASHAKKOR, Ezzatollah. 1811 156TH AVE NE, STE 3 98007 #902-10-1962 L1985 **GS FM** *071
TAYADE, Arti Sachin. 1750 112TH AVE NE, STE A101 98004 #495-83-1990 L2000 **IM** *020 †20
TEITZ, Carol Claire. 1700 116TH AVE NE 98004 #008-01-1974 L1975 **ORS** *020 †40
TERASAKI, Wesley Lawrence. 12917 SE 38TH ST STE 100 98006 #011-02-1981 L1982 **IM** *020 †20
THILO, Robert Glenn. 2200 112TH AVE NE, STE 100 98004 #018-03-1979 L1984 **P** *020 †05
THOMAS, Julie M. ■ 98008 #023-07-1992 L1995 **IM** *020 †20
THOMASSEN, Lisa Veva. 1035 116TH AVE NE 98004 #012-05-1992 L1996 **PTH** *020 †50
THOMPSON, Peter A. ■ 98007 #043-01-1984 L1986 **IM ON** *030 †20
THOMPSON, Robert Wilcox. 2200 112TH AVE NE, STE 140 98004 #056-05-1958 L1960 **P** *020
THORLAKSON, Neil F. ■ 98004 #024-01-1952 L1953 **OPH** *071 †35
THORLAKSON, Richard G. PO BOX 7518 98004 #028-34-1981 **OPH** *075
THUOT, Gayle Elizabeth. 13451 SE 36TH ST 98006 #054-04-1972 L1975 **PD** *020 †55
THYER, Angela Claire. 1545 116TH AVE NE, STE 102 98004 #038-41-1994 L2001 **OBG** *020 †30
TING, Karen Ru-Chien. 1200 112TH AVE NE STE B250, MINOR & JAMES MEDICAL PLLC 98004 #067-01-1993 L1993 **IM** *020 †20
TOLO, Jennifer Crowe. 1607 116TH AVE NE STE 115 98004 #054-04-1994 L1996 **FM** *020 †18
TORRES, Frank Wm, III. 1414 116TH AVE NE, BELLEVUE CARDIOLOGY CLINIC 98004 #005-02-1983 L1999 **CD** *020 †20
TRAN, Audrey Bach. 1135 116TH AVE NE, STE 16E 98004 #035-09-1999 L2004 **RO** *020 †80
TREXLER, Lillian Greenlee. 1611 116TH AVE NE, STE 201 98004 #036-01-1981 L1985 **P ADM** *020 †75
TRIGG, Douglas Jos. 222 112TH AVE NE, STE 101 98004 #017-20-1982 L1993 **IM** *020 †20
TRIMBLE, Lorne Doug. 1370 116TH AVE NE STE 101 98004 #062-01-1977 L1980 **HNS** *020
TRIONE, Marcus Anthony. 1035 116TH AVE NE 98004 #005-18-1997 L2001 **EM** *020 †16
TUNG, Millie Y. 2015 116TH AVE NE, STE B 98004 #041-07-1967 L1975 **NEP IM** *020 †20
TYLER, Scott Elliot. 1035 116TH AVE NE 98004 #054-04-1988 L1990 **FM** *020 †18
TYSON, Robert Leonard. 1687 114TH AVE SE, STE 125 98004 #035-01-1956 L2005 **PYA CHP** *020 †75
TZUNG, Shie-Pon. 1135 116TH AVE NE 98004 #244-02-1986 L1994 **GE** *020 †20
UEDA, Robert Kazuo. ■ 98006 #030-06-1993 L2004 **DR VIR** *020 †80 ‡
UMAR, Imran. ■ 98006 #704-21-1987 L2004 **NP** *100 †50
UPTON, Joseph W, III. 4455 148TH AVE NE 98007 #056-06-1992 L1992 **FM OS** *020 †18
URQUHART, Murray Linton. 1135 116TH AVE NE STE 310 98004 #011-03-1982 L1986 **AN** *020 †05
UYENO, Randall J. 4122 FACTORIA BLVD SE, STE 101 98006 #038-45-1981 L1987 **PD** *020 †55
VAIMAN, Irine L. 1940 116TH AVE NE, STE 200 98004 #913-21-1981 L1996 **FM** *020 †18
VAJZOVIC-NIZAMIC, Eldina. 14350 SE EASTGATE WAY, EASTGATE PUBLIC HEALTH CEN 98007 #957-08-1994 L2001 **FM** *020 †18
VANDE KROL, Laurie A. 1035 116TH AVE NE 98004 #016-01-1988 L1996 **EM** *020 †16
VANDERGRIFT, Ruth Schreck. ■ 98008 #017-20-1983 L1986 **FM** *020 †18
VAN HARE, Robert Steven. 1035 116TH AVE NE 98004 #048-04-1987 L1991 **EM** *020 †16
VAN PAASSCHEN, Frits R. 2700 NORTHUP WAY 98004 #660-03-1957 L1963 **PD** *030 †55
VAN PETTEN, Aleeta S. 1200 112TH AVE NE 98004 #016-11-1976 L1977 **FM** *020 †18
VANSANDT, Earl Max. 1231 116TH AVE NE 98004 #028-03-1963 L1969 **ORS** *071 †40
VAN ZYL, Mary Anne. 1400 116TH AVE NE, C/O PROVIDENCE MEDICAL GRO 98004 #047-05-1983 L1987 **PD** *020 †55
VERDUZCO, Maria. ■ 98008 #054-04-2008 *012
VINCENT, Lee Stevens. 2700 NORTHUP WAY 98004 #016-11-1957 L1962 **PD** *020 †55 ‡
WAGNER, Stacie Elizabeth. ■ 98004 #028-34-1987 L1992 **IM** *020 †20
WAHL, Tanya Austin. 1135 116TH AVE NE STE 230 98004 #036-07-1997 L2001 **ON HEM** *020 †20
WALKER, John H. ■ 98004 #025-01-1940 L1944 **R** *071 †80
WALL, Martin Jos. 1135 116TH AVE NE STE 620 98004 #016-11-1989 L1996 **U** *020 †95
WALL, Peter Davis. 1135 116TH AVE NE, STE 320 98004 #010-01-1994 L2004 **OBG** *020 †30
WALLUM, Brad J. 2020 116TH AVE NE, STE 150 98004 #046-01-1981 L1984 **END IM** *020 †20
WALSH, John Stuart. 2330 130TH AVE NE, STE 201 98005 #054-04-1991 L2001 **D IM** *020 †15
WANG, Charles Rung. 2025 112TH AVE NE, STE 200 98004 #654-01-1988 L1991 **CHP** *020
WARME, Winston John. ■ 98005 #023-12-1989 L2007 **OSM** *020 †40
WARREN, Daniel T. ■ 98006 #048-14-2000 L2001 **APM** *100 †05
WATTS, William Edward. ■ 98008 #024-01-1942 L1946 **IM** *071 †20
WATTS, William James. 1135 116TH AVE NE, STE 600 98004 #054-04-1975 L1979 **PUD IM** *020 †20
WEI, Jun. ■ 98007 #048-02-2008 *012
WEIL, Gary A. 11201 SE 8TH ST, STE 105 98004 #001-02-1981 L1982 **P** *020 †75
WEINER, Harry I. 17050 NORTHRUP WAY 98008 #016-11-1938 L1946 **OPH** *071 †35
WEINSTEIN, Loryn Patricia. 1535 116TH AVE NE, STE 200 98004 #043-01-1996 L2001 **HS** *020 †40
WEIR, Thomas Wilson. 4639 133RD AVE SE 98006 #028-03-1963 L1969 **D DMP** *020 †15
WEISSMAN, Robert Merrill. 1135 116TH AVE NE, STE 620 98004 #016-11-1973 L1985 **U** *020 †95
WELLS, Rebecca L. 1135 116TH AVE NE STE 310, OVERLAKE ANESTHESIOLOGISTS 98004 #056-06-1995 L1999 **AN** *020 †05
WELSH, Robert Lenhart. 1035 116TH AVE NE 98004 #054-04-1959 L1963 **OBG** *071 †30
WETMORE, Karen Elaine. ■ 98005 #011-02-1982 L1989 **PD** *020 †55
WEY, Chialin. 1135 116TH AVE NE, STE 110 98004 #016-11-1994 L1997 **IM** *020 †20
WIEGENSTEIN, John T. PO BOX 3433 98009 #024-01-1944 L1948 **OM IM** *071
WILKINSON, Cathy Green. 4122 FACTORIA BLVD SE, STE 101 98006 #001-02-1983 L1984 **PD NPM** *020 †55
WILLIAMS, Henry Jos. 1750 112TH AVE NE 98004 #003-01-1975 L1978 **IM FM** *020 †20
WILLIAMS, Laurie Michelle. 2700 NORTHUP WAY 98004 #016-43-2000 L2003 **PD** *020 †55
WINFIELD, John Leonard. 1551 116TH AVE NE 98004 #004-01-1961 L1968 **D** *020 †15
WINSTEAD, Ricard Burton. 3040 164TH PL NE 98008 #054-04-1979 L1980 **FM** *030 †18
WINTERS, George Ross, III. 1135 116TH AVE NE, STE 560 98004 #050-02-1993 L2005 **GE** *020 †20
WITKOP, Kimberly Annette. ■ 98006 #028-46-1991 L1993 **IM** *020 †20
WOLFE, William Alcott. ■ 98004 #016-06-1946 L1948 **IM** *071 †20
WONG, Jacqueline Yuenyeng. ■ 98008 #041-15-2006 L2006 **FP** *012
WOODS, Steven Kimble. 1600 116TH AVE NE, STE 104 98004 #054-04-1982 L1985 **OBG** *020 †30
WRIGHT, George E. ■ 98006 #040-02-1953 L1954 **AN** *020 †05
WRIGHT-WILSON, Cheryl S. 2700 NORTHUP WAY 98004 #023-01-1980 L1983 **PD** *020 †55
WU, Chensen. ■ 98006 #036-07-2004 *100
WU, Joyce Fangyen. 2700 NORTHUP WAY 98004 #035-09-2001 L2004 **PD** *100 †55
YANG, Stephanie Hailin. 1135 116TH AVE NE STE 310, OVERLAKE ANESTHESIOLOGISTS 98004 #048-04-2003 L2003 **AN** *020
YEH, Jane Yotsen. 1035 116TH AVE NE 98004 #024-05-1999 L2001 **IM** *020 †20
YEUNG, Rhinee W. 2210 132ND AVE SE 98005 #038-40-1974 L1977 **FM** *020 †18
YOUNG, Irene Anmei. 1750 112TH AVE NE, STE D258 98004 #025-07-1996 L2001 **PM PRS** *020 †60
YOUNG, Jacob Nathan. 1515 116TH AVE NE STE 302 98004 #036-07-1986 L1997 **NS** *020 †25
YOUNG, Josephine C. 2700 NORTHUP WAY 98004 #024-05-1991 L1997 **PD ADL** *050 †55
YU, Mujun. 1280 116TH AVE NE 98004 #243-69-1986 L2000 **PCP** *020 †50
YUNG, Pamela Mei. 13231 SE 36TH ST, STE 110 98006 #016-43-1993 L1996 **FM** *020 †18
ZAMPONA, Anna Antonios. ■ 98004 #198-01-1989 L1999 **FM** *020 †18
ZEIBER, Marina Sandra. 2700 NORTHUP WAY 98004 #035-45-1974 L1980 **PD** *020 †55
ZEMPLENYI, Jan. 1260 116TH AVE NE, STE 110 98004 #005-02-1980 L1987 **CS OTO** *020 †45
ZENRI, Shigeomi. 925 116TH AVE NE STE 2 98004 #572-28-1966 L1972 **GP** *020 †50
ZHANG, Michelle Ming. ■ 98004 #243-47-1988 L2006 **HO** *012 †20
ZIERLER, Robert Eugene. 1700 116TH AVE NE 98004 #023-07-1976 L1977 **VS GS** *040 †85
ZILZ, Nathan Douglas. 1135 116TH AVE NE STE 600 98004 #023-07-1994 L1996 **CD** *020 †20
ZIMMER, Harold Lewis. 1535 116TH AVE NE, STE 100 98004 #035-45-1976 L1980 **OBG** *020 †30
ZOBEL, Mark Steven. 1135 116TH AVE NE STE 190, WASHINGTON IMAGING SERVICE 98004 #028-02-1989 L1993 **DR PDR** *020 †80
ZUBAIR, Kaisera Jamil. 2700 NORTHUP WAY, PEDIATRIC ASSOCIATES 98004 #038-40-1994 L1997 **PD** *020 †55
ZUBAIR, Muhammad. 1135 116TH AVE NE STE 110, OVERLAKE MEDICAL CLINIC 98004 #704-01-1989 L2000 **IM** *020 †20 ‡

BELLINGHAM – WHATCOM

ADAMS, Ione Sharon. 4455 CORDATA PKWY 98226 #026-04-1986 L1988 **FM** *020 †18
ADRIANCE, Mark Loyd. 600 BIRCHWOOD AVE 98225 #030-06-1975 L1976 **FM** *020
ALAN, Robert Lupcho. 2979 SQUALICUM PKWY, STE 202 98225 #041-02-1964 L1972 **OPH** *020 †35
AMBROSE, Peter M. 3015 SQUALICUM PKWY, STE 220 98225 #054-04-1971 L1972 **EM OM** *020 †70,16
ANARADIAN, Mitchell Peter. 2621 S HARBOR LOOP DR # 5 98225 #005-15-1962 L1975 **FM** *020
ANDERSON, John Donald. 3015 SQUALICUM PKWY, STE 260 98225 #027-01-1965 L1973 **OPH** *071 †35
ANDERSON, William Howard. 2075 BARKLEY BLVD, STE 220 98226 #040-02-1988 L1994 **AI IM** *020 †20,03
ANDREWS, Stuart. 4280 MERIDIAN ST, STE 120 98226 #016-11-1977 L1980 **FM** *020 †18
ARNOLD, John W. 4545 CORDATA PKWY 98226 #008-01-1952 L1953 **IM N** *071 †20
ARVIN, Diane Mackel. 2901 SQUALICUM PKWY 98225 #017-20-1979 L1990 **OBG** *020
ATCHISON, Michelle Eunsun. 2901 SQUALICUM PKWY, VASCULAR SURGERY 98225 #005-12-2000 L2007 **VS** *020 †85
AUSTIN, Daniel Edmond. 2075 BARKLEY BLVD 98226 #032-01-1988 L1990 **FM** *020 †18
AUSTIN, Wayne W. 610 DUPONT ST STE I28 98225 #005-12-1953 L1954 **FM OS** *020
BAADER, William Michael. 3015 SQUALICUM PKWY, STE 240 98225 #016-11-1985 L1987 **PS** *020 †85,65
BACHMAN, Barbara Ann. 2940 SQUALICUM PKWY STE 1 98225 #016-42-1995 L2000 **GS** *020 †85
BAKER, David Edward. 710 BIRCHWOOD AVE, STE 101 98225 #021-01-1980 L1988 **NS** *020 †25
BAN, Steven. 4545 CORDATA PKWY 98226 #016-06-1973 L1976 **PD** *020 †55
BANJANIN, Milan. 3130 ELLIS ST 98225 #957-05-1976 L1993 **FM** *020 †18 ‡
BARNETT, Donald Curtis. 2901 SQUALICUM PKWY, STE 101 98225 #019-02-1968 L1974 **DR** *071 †80
BARNHART, Roger Alan. 2205 ERIE ST, 3149 ELLIS ST 98229 #040-02-1960 L1969 **OTO PS** *071 †45
BARR, Mary Louise. 3645 E MCLEOD RD 98226 #034-01-1984 L1990 **P** *020
BATT, Nathan. 2940 SQUALICUM PKWY # 20 98225 #061-01-1966 L2003 **OBG GP** *020
BAYLESS, Guy Walter. ■ 98229 #048-02-1968 L1977 **OBG** *071 †30
BEGLIN, Peter Alan. 2901 SQUALICUM PKWY 98225 #036-05-1991 L1999 **IM** *020 †20
BEISER, Claire. 3015 SQUALICUM PKWY, ASSOCIATES 98225 #010-02-1985 L1997 **ID IM** *020 †20
BELCASTER, Gary Michael. 4545 CORDATA PKWY 98226 #016-11-1990 L2003 **GE** *020 †20
BERGHOLZ, Warren E. ■ 98226 #054-04-1951 L1952 **GP** *071
BERGMAN, Gary Duane. 3149 ELLIS ST # 103 98225 #005-18-1981 L1982 **ORS HS** *020 †40
BERNER, Ruth M. 2901 SQUALICUM PKWY 98225 #008-02-1990 L2000 **EM** *020 †16
BERRY, Donald Fletcher. 4545 CORDATA PKWY 98226 #035-48-1979 L1985 **PUD IM** *020 †20
BHOLA, Rajesh. 4545 CORDATA PKWY 98226 #495-45-1990 L2005 **CD** *020 †20
BIGELOW, Bradley Dean. 2901 SQUALICUM PKWY, ST JOSEPH'S HOSP 98225 #025-07-1984 L1987 **EM** *020 †16
BILLING, Peter Samuel. 12 BELLWETHER WAY 98225 #026-04-1993 L2004 **GS** *020 †85
BINDER, Richard Hermann. 3015 SQUALICUM PKWY, STE 160 98225 #065-01-1991 L1994 **FM** *020 †18
BISCHOFF, Nancy Kay. 4545 CORDATA PKWY STE 1E 98226 #023-07-1994 L1997 **PD** *020 †55
BLACK, Jeffrey Buffum. 4291 MERIDIAN ST STE 101, CARE MEDICAL GROUP 98226 #005-19-1993 L1995 **FM** *020 †18
BLACK, Teresa Lynn Heidt. 12 BELLWETHER WAY, STE 223 98225 #018-03-1991 L1994 **P** *020 †75
BLACKBURN, James Howell. 3001 SQUALICUM PKWY, STE 5 98225 #021-05-1991 L1999 **PS HS** *020 †65 ‡
BLACKWELL, Linda Jean. 3015 SQUALICUM PKWY STE 1 98225 #028-03-1981 L1990 **FPG FM** *020 †18

BLAKER, Scott Nevin. 220 UNITY ST 98225 #035-01-1992 L1994 **FM** *020 †18
BLOOM, Edward William. 3500 ORCHARD PL 98225 #040-02-1997 L2005 **FM** *020 †18 ‡
BLOOM, Jessica Johnson. 3500 ORCHARD PL, FHA 98225 #025-01-1998 L2005 **FM** *020 †18
BLOOM, Steve Matthew. 3015 SQUALICUM PKWY 98225 #040-02-2000 L2003 **FM** *020
BOCHSLER, James J. 4545 CORDATA PKWY 98226 #035-01-1989 L1992 **PD** *020 †55
BODLEY, Don Howard. 4545 CORDATA PKWY, MADRONA MEDICAL GROUP 98226 #010-01-1969 L1998 **ORS** *020 †40
BOENIG, Thomas Edward. 3907 AARON CT 98226 #025-12-1987 L1992 **OBG** *020
BOERCKER, Geoffrey Keith. 1000 MCKENZIE AVE, STE 21 98225 #047-05-1976 L1989 **P CCM** *075 †05,75
BOLAND, Anthony Bradley. 2901 SQUALICUM PKWY, ST. JOSEPH HOSPITAL MEDICA 98225 #010-02-1979 L1985 **VS** *020 †85
BOWDEN, Bruce Allen. 2075 BARKLEY BLVD, STE 220 98226 #054-04-1977 L1982 **D DMP** *020 †15
BOYNTON, Solon R, Jr. ■ 98227 #041-09-1939 L1942 **GP GPM** *071
BRANIGAN, Emmett Francis. 2980 SQUALICUM PKWY, STE 103 98225 #055-02-1981 L1982 **OBG** *075
BRAUN, Frederic H. 3001 SQUALICUM PKWY # 6 98225 #067-01-1972 L1973 **CHN N** *020 †55,75
BRETTELL, Patti Jo. 710 BIRCHWOOD AVE, ASSOCIATES 98225 #016-42-2000 L2004 **N** *020
BUCHHOLZ, Robert Burman. 2901 SQUALICUM PKWY 98225 #038-40-1963 L1980 **PS OS** *071 †85,65
BUCKLEY, Timothy Neil. 2901 SQUALICUM PKWY, ST. JOSEPH HOSPITAL 98225 #056-06-1974 L1985 **FM** *020 †18
BUEHLER, Allan Louis. 2901 SQUALICUM PKWY 98225 #016-11-1972 L1975 **EM** *020 †16
BUETOW, Stephen John. ■ 98225 #010-02-1997 L2007 **DR** *100 †80
BURDEN, Anthony Jos. 1345 KING ST 98229 #047-05-1987 L1990 **FM** *020 †18
BURNS, Arlen Birk. 3001 SQUALICUM PKWY STE 8 98225 #024-01-1964 L1972 **U GP** *071 †95
CALDERON, Thomas Arpero. 4455 CORDATA PKWY 98226 #049-01-1995 L1998 **FM** *020 †18
CALLENDER, Thomas Bruce. 1050 LARRABEE AVE, STE 105 98225 #026-04-1972 L1978 **AN** *071 †05
CARPENITO, Gerardo. 336 36TH ST, # 303 98225 #061-01-1994 L1998 **NEP** *100 †20
CARRILLO, Monica. 4455 CORDATA PKWY, SEAMAR COMMUNITY HEALTH CL 98226 #005-11-1999 L2002 **FM** *020 †18
CESAR, Stephen Yap. 4545 CORDATA PKWY 98226 #748-01-1976 L1983 **GS** *020 †85
CHANG, Alan G Y. 2930 SQUALICUM PKWY, NORTHWEST 98225 #014-01-1989 L1998 **GE IM** *020 †20
CHANG, Heather Ann. 4280 MERIDIAN ST, STE 120 98226 #061-01-1981 L1993 **FM** *020
CHANG, Norman F. 4280 MERIDIAN ST, STE 120 98226 #061-01-1978 L1992 **FM** *020
CHASSON, Albert Leon. ■ 98225 #038-41-1954 L1954 **PTH** *071 †50
CHIAROTTINO, Gary Douglas. 2901 SQUALICUM PKWY 98225 #030-06-1964 L1969 **GP** *075 †18
CHOBANOV, Zeljka. 710 BIRCHWOOD AVE, ASSOCIATES 98225 #957-11-1996 L2005 **N** *020 †75
CHUA-GOO, Katherine Palao. 3149 ELLIS ST, NO 203 98225 #748-08-1984 L1999 **IM** *020
CLURE, Barbara Michele. 2901 SQUALICUM PKWY 98225 #007-02-1988 L1991 **FM** *020 †18 ‡
COLEMAN, Ronald Leslie. ■ 98229 #030-05-1974 L1976 **AN** *020
COLETTI, Andrew Thomas. 2901 SQUALICUM PKWY 98225 #035-46-1994 L2004 **CD** *020 †20
COLLINS, Heidi Ann. 2901 SQUALICUM PKWY 98225 #016-06-1998 L2002 **PM** *020 †60
COMESS, Keith Allen. 4545 CORDATA PKWY 98226 #003-01-1979 L1982 **CD IM** *040 †20
COOK, Hull Alden. 1600 F ST 98225 #030-05-1974 L1975 **OBG** *020 †30
COVERT-BOWLDS, Christopher. 220 UNITY ST, INTERFAITH COMM HLTH CTR 98225 #054-04-1991 L1993 **FM** *020 †18
CROSBY, G Kristin. 904 PUGET ST, MEDICAL MANAGEMENT DEPT 98229 #051-04-1978 L1999 **FM MDM** *020 †18
CUEVAS, Crescencio. ■ 98225 #847-08-1959 L1969 **NS N** *071
CUMMINS, Shari Owen. 4545 CORDATA PKWY, MADRONA MEDICAL GROUP 98226 #017-20-1987 L1992 **IM** *020 †20
CYR, Amy Elizabeth. 4545 CORDATA PKWY 98226 #030-05-2002 L2007 **GS** *020 †85
DABNEY, Sue Ann. 2075 BARKLEY BLVD 98226 #028-03-2003 L2003 **FM** *020 †18
DANENHOWER, Clay C. 2901 SQUALICUM PKWY 98225 #045-01-1998 L2004 **SP** *020
DANIELS, Mark. 2901 SQUALICUM PKWY 98225 #035-09-1986 L2000 **CD IM** *020 †20
DANK, Jan Peter. 3614 MERIDIAN ST, STE 200 98225 #007-02-1992 L1992 **D** *020 †20,15
DAVIS, Brantley Pierce. ■ 98225 #054-04-1953 L1955 **OS OM** *071
DAVIS, Marc Andrew. 2901 SQUALICUM PKWY 98225 #041-13-1988 L2002 **EM** *020 †16
DEGER, Grant Edward. 2103 BIRCH CIR 98229 #038-41-1965 L1970 **IM NEP** *071 †20
DELBECQ, Ronald Jerome. 2901 SQUALICUM PKWY 98225 #025-01-1978 L1979 **PTH** *020 †50
DERLETH, Thomas R. ■ 98229 #025-01-1968 L1972 **ON IM** *071 †20
DEROOK, Frances Anne. 4545 CORDATA PKWY 98226 #038-41-1987 L1992 **CD** *020 †20
DICKINSON, Katherine E. 1530 ELLIS ST 98225 #010-01-1985 L1996 **FM GYN** *020 †18
DIESTELHORST, James B. 4545 CORDATA PKWY 98226 #028-03-1996 L2002 **PCC** *020 †20
DILL, Clover Novia. 4545 CORDATA PKWY 98226 #654-01-2000 L2004 **IM** *020
DOHERTY, Mark Jos. 4545 CORDATA PKWY 98226 #030-06-1982 L1983 **D** *020 †15
DOUBT, Normadell. ■ 98226 #054-04-1951 L1953 **IM** *071 †20
DOUGLAS, James Marion, Jr. 2979 SQUALICUM PKWY 98225 #036-07-1978 L1994 **TS GS** *020 †85,90
DROBNICKI, David Wm. 3130 SQUALICUM PKWY STE 40 98225 #025-07-1985 L1986 **PM** *075
DUNCAN, William Yeats, III. ■ 98229 #035-01-1961 L1966 **U** *071 †95
ELKAYAM, David. 3015 SQUALICUM PKWY, STE 180 98225 #035-47-1982 L1988 **AI PD** *020 †55,03
ELLENDER, Willard Anthony. ■ 98225 #021-05-1968 L1978 **OPH** *071 †35
EMERT, Laurie Elizabeth. 4545 CORDATA PKWY 98226 #001-02-1999 L2003 **PD** *020 †55
ENGLAND, Benjamin Thomas. 4545 CORDATA PKWY 98226 #038-43-1999 L2004 **IM** *020 †20
FAIRBANKS, Eugene Fox. ■ 98226 #025-01-1945 L1948 **GP AN** *071 †05,18
FARRIER, James Allen. ■ 98229 #005-06-1967 L1968 **N** *071 †75
FILUK, Peter Eugene. 4545 CORDATA PKWY 98226 #054-04-1994 L1997 **PD** *020 †55 ‡
FINNIGAN, David Paul. 4545 CORDATA PKWY 98226 #010-02-1988 L1991 **PD** *020 †55
FISCHER, Benjamin P. 2901 SQUALICUM PKWY, ST. JOSEPH'S HOSPITAL 98225 #048-04-2000 L2004 **IM** *020 †20
FORD, Michael Carter. 2979 SQUALICUM PKWY, STE 202 98225 #048-04-1994 L1998 **OPH** *020 †35
FOSTER, Denis Gerald. 1815 C ST 98225 #018-03-1976 L1978 **FM** *020 †18
FOX, Anne Theresa. 4545 CORDATA PKWY 98226 #024-16-1997 L2002 **IM** *020 †20
FOX, Debora Jean. 4545 CORDATA PKWY, MADRONA MEDICAL 98226 #054-04-1994 L2000 **CRS GS** *020 †85,10
FRANKENFELD, Eric Ralph. 470 BIRCHWOOD AVE, STE A 98225 #005-15-1979 L1982 **END IM** *020 †20
FRAZIER, Wesley T. ■ 98226 #041-01-1961 L1970 **AN** *071 †05
FREDERICKS, Lillian E. ■ 98227 #041-07-1941 L1942 **AN PME** *072 †05
FREEMAN, Larry Spaulding. 119 N COMMERCIAL ST, STE 1360 98225 #005-02-1972 L1978 **CHP P** *020 †75
FREEMAN, William Le Clair. PO BOX 5293 98227 #054-04-1974 L1975 **FM PHP** *071 †70,18
GABAY, Elizabeth Lee. 220 UNITY ST, INTERFAITH COMMUNITY HLT C 98225 #056-05-1976 L1995 **IM ID** *020 †20
GALVIN, James A V M. ■ 98225 #035-03-1943 L1945 **P** *071 †75
GANNON, Michael Kevin. 3149 ELLIS ST # 103 98225 #018-03-1982 L1983 **ORS** *020 †40
GARDNER, Richard Lynn. 3614 MERIDIAN ST, STE 200 98225 #048-04-1962 L1973 **D GP** *020 †15
GARGANO, Charles Anthony. 4545 CORDATA PKWY 98226 #001-02-1999 L2003 **IM** *020 †20
GARVIN, James Elwood. ■ 98229 #016-06-1946 **IM** *071
GASS, Kenneth Brewer. 4545 CORDATA PKWY, MADRONA MEDICAL GROUP,PS 98226 #016-02-1974 L1975 **PD** *020 †55
GAUBATZ, Robert Wm. 3015 SQUALICUM PKWY # 100 98225 #007-02-1965 L1970 **FPG** *020 †18
GAVARESKI, David John. 3500 ORCHARD PL 98225 #054-04-1974 L1975 **FM** *020 †18
GAYDA, Edward Xavier. 609 N SHORE DR 98226 #054-04-1979 L1980 **P** *020 †18,75
GEIST, Michael John. 4545 CORDATA PKWY 98226 #054-04-1993 L1995 **IM** *020 †20
GIBB, Robert Pearse. 2901 SQUALICUM PKWY 98225 #028-02-1948 L1951 **CLP PTH** *071 †50
GIBSON, Emily Polis. 25 HIGH ST 9112, APT 100 98225 #054-04-1980 L1980 **FM** *020 †18
GILBERT, Stanley Craig. 3614 MERIDIAN ST, STE 200 98225 #019-02-1985 L1996 **D PHL** *020 †18,15
GILES, Roy Chas. ■ 98226 #917-30-1953 L1963 **AN** *071
GILLHAM, Martha Helen. 4545 CORDATA PKWY, MADRONA MEDICAL GROUP 98226 #054-04-1995 L1997 **IM** *020 †20
GOBER, Lorna Ann. 516 HIGH ST, MS 9132 98225 #054-04-1998 L2000 **FM** *020 †18
GOLDFOGEL, Gary Alan. 1500 N STATE ST 98225 #012-05-1984 L1985 **PTH FOP** *020 †50
GOLDMAN, David Lawrence. 710 BIRCHWOOD AVE, STE 101 98225 #028-03-1981 L1990 **NS** *020 †25
GOO, Eduardo Ho. 470 BIRCHWOOD AVE, STE B 98225 #748-10-1984 L1999 **IM** *020 †20
GOODMAN-WILSON, Gittle G. 11 BELLWETHER WAY STE 210, BELLINGHAM MEDICAL CLINIC 98225 #016-42-1993 L2001 **IM** *040 †20
GORDIN, Mendel Michael. ■ 98225 #913-16-1961 L1991 **FM P** *071
GORTON, Robert Eugene, Jr. ■ 98229 #649-33-1986 L1997 **FM** *020 †18
GRIGGS, William Phillips. 340 BIRCHWOOD AVE 98225 #001-02-1974 L1976 **U** *020 †95
GRUNNER, Anthony J. ■ 98225 #286-07-1965 L1983 **P CHP** *075
HAKEMAN, Susan Mackay. 1112 11TH ST, STE 301 98225 #048-04-1990 L1994 **P** *020 †75
HALE, Norman Olav. 1110 LARRABEE AVE STE 20 98225 #054-04-1990 L1994 **CHP** *020 †75
HALL, Deborah Ann. 3500 ORCHARD PL 98225 #005-02-1995 L2006 **FM** *020 †18 ‡
HALL, Thomas C. 809 E CHESTNUT ST 98225 #024-01-1949 L1992 **ON IM** *050 †20
HAMILTON, Robert Lee. ■ 98225 #019-02-1956 L1962 **GYN** *071 †30
HARELL, George S. 3725 TREE FARM LN 98226 #035-01-1963 L1999 **DR** *071 †80
HARLE, James Michael. 1326 E LAUREL ST 98225 #054-04-1998 L2001 **CHP** *020 †75
HARRIS, Robert Fleming, Jr. 2940 SQUALICUM PKWY # 203 98225 #021-01-1968 L1977 **OTO** *071 †45
HART, Nancy Rhea. 2901 SQUALICUM PKWY 98225 #020-02-1981 L1985 **OBG** *071 †30 ‡
HAVEMAN, Dale Edward. 2592 KWINA RD, LUMMI INDIAN HEALTH CLINIC 98226 #025-07-1973 L1978 **FM PD** *020 †55
HAVEMAN, Gregory Alan. ■ 98229 #054-04-2008 *012
HEAPS, David Kenneth. 1225 E SUNSET DR, STE 145 98226 #025-01-1963 L1970 **ORS** *071 †40
HECHT, Robert Emil. 2940 SQUALICUM PKWY, BELLINGHAM EAR NOSE & 98225 #054-04-1967 L1968 **OTO HNS** *020 †45
HECHT, Robert Harold. 2940 SQUALICUM PKWY, STE 203 98225 #035-45-1964 L1967 **ID IM** *020 †20
HEIN, Lee Chas. 1815 C ST STE K38 98225 #054-04-1973 L1976 **FM** *020 †18
HEISINGER, Dale Helton. 4545 CORDATA PKWY, MADRONA MEDICAL GROUP 98226 #028-02-1966 L1971 **PD** *020 †55
HELLIS, Samuel Dean. 2980 SQUALICUM PKWY, STE 301 98225 #005-11-1967 L1972 **OBG** *072 †30
HERDMAN, Stephen C. 3015 SQUALICUM PKWY, STE 120 98225 #040-02-1984 L1985 **FM** *020 †18
HESTON, Thomas F. 600 BIRCHWOOD AVE 98225 #028-34-1992 L1994 **NC NM** *020 †18,28
HEYDRICH, Alfred Laurent. ■ 98229 #275-01-1941 L1973 **GS GP** *071
HIERSCHBIEL, Ernst. ■ 98226 #407-10-1951 L1992 **R** *071 †80
HILL, John Warren, Jr. 2940 SQUALICUM PKWY, PARKWAY SURGICAL CENTER 98225 #017-20-1998 L2003 **GS** *020 †85
HILL, Leslie Victoria H. 4545 CORDATA PKWY 98226 #064-01-1983 L2003 **OBG** *020 †30
HINES, James Loel. 3001 SQUALICUM PKWY 98225 #021-05-1965 L1975 **PS** *020
HIPSKIND, Marcy Gibb. 3015 SQUALICUM PKWY, STE 120 98225 #028-02-1978 L1982 **FM** *020 †18
HIPSKIND, Stephen Gregory. 114 W MAGNOLIA ST, CONSULTING 4TH FLOOR 98225 #028-34-1978 L1981 **FM** *020 †18
HODGE, John Hartman. 1130 N FOREST ST 98225 #008-01-1955 L1956 **OPH** *071 †35
HODGES, Denise Dudley. 3015 SQUALICUM PKWY, NORTHWEST EYE CLINIC INC 98225 #054-04-1991 L2000 **OPH OS** *020 †35
HOEKEMA, Joel Richard. 2979 SQUALICUM PKWY, STE 203 98225 #054-04-1995 L2001 **ORS** *020 †40
HOFFMANN, Kelly. 4545 CORDATA PKWY 98226 #026-04-1998 L2005 **FM** *020 †18
HOFFMANN, Mark Douglas. 4545 CORDATA PKWY 98226 #026-04-1998 L2005 **FM** *020 †18
HOFFMEISTER, Robert Geo. 4545 CORDATA PKWY 98226 #016-11-1972 L1977 **IM EM** *020 †20 ‡
HOLROYD, John Bailie. 4545 CORDATA PKWY, MADRONA MEDICAL GROUP 98226 #036-05-1995 L1997 **IM** *020 †20
HOLTZMAN, Sherry Lee. 2980 SQUALICUM PKWY, STE 301 98225 #056-05-1987 L2000 **OBG** *020 †30
HOOD, Frederick R, Jr. ■ 98225 #041-01-1952 L1953 **GS TS** *071 †85,90
HOPPER, James Galvin. 2220 CORNWALL AVE 98225 #054-04-1984 L1999 **FM** *020 †18
HORN, Ronald Lee. 2530 KWINA RD 98226 #028-03-1974 L1976 **FM ADM** *020 †18
HORNING, John Arthur. 2901 SQUALICUM PKWY 98225 #016-06-1993 L2000 **EM** *020 †16
HORNUNG, Lessli Dorothea. 4545 CORDATA PKWY 98226 #054-04-2002 L2002 **PD** *020
HOUK, Harold Wayne. 1815 C ST STE J36 98225 #039-01-1955 L2001 **GP** *071

■ = Address Information Privacy Protected

HOWE, Warren Billings. 516 HIGH ST, WWU STUDENT HLTH MS-9132 98225 #028-02-1965 L1970 **FM FSM** *020 †18
HOYT, John Wesley. 3614 MERIDIAN ST, STE 100 98225 #054-04-1986 L1988 **PTH NP** *020 †50
HUGHES, Michael Damon. 3130 ELLIS ST 98225 #054-04-1995 L1997 **FM** *020 †18
ISON, Harry Cecil. ■ 98225 #020-02-1948 L1948 **GP** *071
JACOBS, Kellie Linwood. 3500 ORCHARD PL 98225 #032-01-1988 L1991 **FM** *020 †18
JACOBSON, Margaret Ann. 3015 SQUALICUM PKWY, STE 120 98225 #016-06-1983 L1986 **FM** *020 †18
JAGERMAN, Louis Stephen. ■ 98225 #035-15-1964 L1993 **OPH** *071 †35
JAMES, Helen Ann. 3001 SQUALICUM PKWY STE 5 98225 #671-01-1964 L1982 **PS HS** *020 †65
JAMES, Peter D F. 3130 ELLIS ST 98225 #803-03-1958 L1959 **GP** *071 †18
JAY, Burton. ■ 98226 #035-46-1960 L1963 **D OS** *071
JERNBERG, Kenneth Irving. 3015 SQUALICUM PKWY, STE 180 98225 #026-04-1954 L1958 **PD** *071 †55
JESSUP, David Blackwell. 2901 SQUALICUM PKWY 98225 #036-01-1997 L2004 **CD** *020 †20
JOHNSON, David Lee. 4545 CORDATA PKWY 98226 #054-04-1972 L1973 **PD** *020 †55
JONES, Noah Jesse. 2979 SQUALICUM PKWY 98225 #038-45-1999 L2007 **IC** *020 †20
JONES, Phillip Henry. PO BOX 935 98227 #030-05-1954 L1963 **PHP GPM** *030
JONES, Richard James. 3104 SQUALICUM PKWY, STE 101 98225 #056-05-1961 L1972 **GS TS** *020 †85
JONES, William David. 4545 CORDATA PKWY 98226 #040-02-1965 L1972 **IM** *020 †20
KAEPERNICK, Lisa Anne. 2980 SQUALICUM PKWY, PARKWAY #301 98225 #056-05-1999 L2003 **OBG** *020 †30
KAHLSTROM, Emily Jean. ■ 98226 #067-01-1963 L1964 **PD PUD** *020 †55
KAHN, Mitchell. 2980 SQUALICUM PKWY, STE 102 98225 #035-01-1975 L2006 **IM OS** *020 †20
KAHN, Robert Sylvan. 4029 NORTHWEST AVE 98226 #007-02-1975 L2000 **PME AN** *020 †55,05
KAISER, Frederick S. 3015 SQUALICUM PKWY, NORTHWEST EYE CLINIC INC 98225 #035-20-1978 L1983 **OPH** *020 †35
KAUFMAN, Cary Steven. 2940 SQUALICUM PKWY # 101 98225 #005-14-1973 L1975 **GS SO** *020 †85
KAZYMYRA, Marta S V. 3130 ELLIS ST 98225 #068-01-1977 L1980 **GP** *020
KEAY, Myoung Soo. ■ 98226 #583-02-1975 L1976 **OBG** *020
KELLY, Michael Thos. 3614 MERIDIAN ST, STE 100 98225 #017-20-1973 L2001 **CLP ID** *020
KELTY, Maureen. 3015 SQUALICUM PKWY, STE 280 98225 #046-01-1983 L1991 **OBG** *020 †30
KEVWITCH, Mansel Karl. 340 BIRCHWOOD AVE 98225 #025-01-1987 L1993 **U UP** *020 †95
KIM, James Min. 1130 N FOREST ST 98225 #005-06-2000 L2005 **OPH** *020 †35
KLEM, Kenneth Joseph. 4455 CORDATA PKWY, SEA MAR COMMUNITY HLTH CTR 98226 #060-01-1987 L2001 **FM** *020 †18
KLOEHN, Kenneth Winans. 2930 SQUALICUM PKWY 98225 #056-05-1967 L1970 **AN** *071 †05
KNOPS, Gail Gibb. 516 HIGH ST, W WASH U STUD HLTH CTR 98225 #028-02-1989 L1994 **FM** *020 †18
KNOPS, Joost Lawrence. 2940 SQUALICUM PKWY, BELLINGHAM EAR NOSE & 98225 #028-02-1989 L1994 **OTO** *020 †45
KNOWLES, Ann Marie. 3015 SQUALICUM PKWY 98225 #030-05-1993 L1998 **MPD** *020 †20,55
KNUDSEN, John Ralph. 4029 NORTHWEST AVE, STE 203 98226 #054-04-1970 L1973 **GP EM** *020
KOCH, David Allan. 1000 MCKENZIE AVE, STE 22 98225 #054-04-1971 L1973 **P** *020 †18,75
KOLODYCHUK, Leonard B. 4545 CORDATA PKWY 98226 #060-01-1984 L2002 **ORS OSS** *020 †18,40
KOONTZ, Judith Ann. 1133 RAILROAD AVE STE 100, CATHOLIC COMMUNITY SVC WW- 98225 #019-02-1975 L1998 **CHP P** *020 †75
KOOPMAN-BECHTEL, Maya Ann. ■ 98226 #035-08-1991 L2005 **CHP P** *020 †75
KORTH, Jurgen. ■ 98226 #407-12-1960 L1968 **GS** *020 †85
KOWALS, Daniel William. 412 GIRARD ST, KOWALLS PEDS 98225 #041-12-1996 L2004 **PD FM** *020 †55
KREBS, Richard Stewart. 3015 SQUALICUM PKWY STE 10 98225 #019-02-1974 L1978 **FM OM** *071 †18
KRONENBERG, Nathan W. 1000 MCKENZIE AVE 98225 #016-11-1951 L1971 **P** *072
KUIKEN, Ben Crawford. 4545 CORDATA PKWY, MADRONA MEDICAL GROUP 98226 #019-02-1966 L1970 **PD** *062 †55
KULLAS, Christopher D. 2979 SQUALICUM PKWY STE 20, BELLINGHAM EYE PHYSICIANS 98225 #067-01-1996 L2003 **OPH** *020 †35
KUTNERIAN, Karl Kegham. 4646 FIELDSTON RD 98225 #038-06-1960 L1964 **HEM IM** *071
LAINE, Erick John, Jr. 4545 CORDATA PKWY 98226 #056-06-1985 L1992 **IM** *020 †20
LAM, Kelvin Nhon-Tro. 4545 CORDATA PKWY 98226 #028-34-2001 L2007 **PCC** *020
LANDAU, Barry Jay. 710 BIRCHWOOD AVE, STE 101 98225 #008-02-1988 L2001 **NS** *020 †25
LANDERHOLM, Robert W. 12 BELLWETHER WAY 98225 #054-04-1986 L1989 **GS** *020 †85
LANDERS, Jeffrey Thomas. 12 BELLWETHER WAY 98225 #038-06-1997 L2004 **GS** *020 †85
LAUGHLIN, Pamela D. 4545 CORDATA PKWY 98226 #054-04-1999 L2001 **IM** *020 †20
LAWRENCE, George Warren. 4029 NORTHWEST AVE, STE 203 98226 #028-03-1977 L1991 **FM** *071 †18
LAWRENCE, Michael Scott. 710 BIRCHWOOD AVE, STE 101 98225 #040-02-1978 L1984 **NS** *020 †25
LAYNE, Robert Sheldon. ■ 98225 #005-02-1966 L1971 **EM FM** *020 †16
LEE, Josianne Weisbach. 4545 CORDATA PKWY 98226 #054-04-2000 L2003 **PD** *020 †55
LEONE, Richard J, Jr. 2979 SQUALICUM PKWY, STE 201 98225 #033-06-1994 L2004 **TS** *020 †85,90
LEPTIHN, Antje Hedda. ■ 98229 #005-02-1990 L1992 **IM** *020 †20
LE SAGE, Hui-Ying Theresa. 2075 BARKLEY BLVD 98226 #054-04-1994 L1996 **FM** *020 †18
LETINSKY, Daniel Mark. ■ 98225 #050-02-2006 L2006 **FP** *012
LEVENSON, Barry. 2930 SQUALICUM PKWY, NORTHWEST 98225 #067-01-1976 L1977 **GE IM** *020 †20
LEVINE, Henry Saml. 1112 11TH ST, STE 301 98225 #038-06-1972 L1973 **P PFP** *020 †75
LIN, Ming. 2901 SQUALICUM PKWY, ST. JOSEPH HOSPITAL ER 98225 #048-13-1989 L2003 **EM** *020 †16
LINDENBAUM, Mark. 3015 SQUALICUM PKWY, STE 100 98225 #016-11-1979 L1988 **IM IMG** *020 †20
LOHSE, James Richard. 3015 SQUALICUM PKWY # 250 98225 #030-05-1976 L1981 **GS CD** *020 †85
LOMBARD, William E. 410 BIRCHWOOD AVE, STE 200 98225 #041-13-1974 L1981 **NEP IM** *020 †20
LOMBARDI, William Louis. 2979 SQUALICUM PKWY, STE 101 98225 #021-01-1994 L2001 **CD IC** *020 †20
LONNER, Joseph Gunnar. 2980 SQUALICUM PKWY, STE 105 98225 #054-04-2001 L2005 **AN** *020 †05
LOTFI, Mary Elisabeth. 410 BIRCHWOOD AVE STE 200, MOUNT BAKER NEPHROLOGY 98225 #915-02-1998 L2006 **NEP** *020
LOWY, Jonathan. 2901 SQUALICUM PKWY 98225 #040-02-1996 L2003 **CD** *020 †20
LOWY, Leasa J. 3015 SQUALICUM PKWY STE 21 98225 #040-02-1996 L2003 **OBG** *020 †30
LUI, Kin Lun. 4545 CORDATA PKWY 98226 #023-01-1996 L1998 **IM** *020 †20
LUPCHO, Ambrose V. ■ 98229 #041-13-1931 L1932 **OS GP** *071
LYNCH, David Ashley. 600 BIRCHWOOD AVE 98225 #035-15-1975 L1976 **FM** *020 †18
MAC GREGOR, John Forbes. 2979 SQUALICUM PKWY, STE 101 98225 #032-01-1998 L2006 **ICE CD** *020 †20
MACKAY, Bruce Cole. 710 BIRCHWOOD AVE STE 201 98225 #048-12-1982 L2006 **N** *050 †75
MADEN, William Le Roy. ■ 98229 #047-06-1955 L1955 **P PYA** *071 †75
MADSEN, Douglas Lee. 3015 SQUALICUM PKWY, STE 140 98225 #054-04-1981 L1985 **OBG** *020 †30
MAHAL, Monika Ranjit. 4545 CORDATA PKWY, MADRONA MEDICAL GROUP 98226 #054-04-1995 L2003 **PD** *020 †55
MAKAN, Nizar R. 4545 CORDATA PKWY 98226 #035-08-1975 L1984 **D** *020 †15
MALLORY, Michael Jerome. 2980 SQUALICUM PKWY, STE 301 98225 #001-02-1992 L2000 **OBG** *020 †30
MALONE, Stephen Allen. 2901 SQUALICUM PKWY 98225 #048-13-1983 L1989 **CD IM** *020 †20
MAMOLEN, Margaret. ■ 98229 #005-02-1983 L1994 **FM PHP** *020 †18
MARSHALL, Garrett Lain. 2930 SQUALICUM PKWY # 101 98225 #054-04-1997 L1997 **PM** *020
MARTINDALE, Madeleine R. ■ 98226 #035-45-2000 L2002 **IM** *020 ‡
MATTEUCCI, Vincent E. 3015 SQUALICUM PKWY, NORTHWEST EYE CLINIC INC 98225 #021-01-1997 L2001 **OPH** *020 †35
MC AFEE, Don D. 2979 SQUALICUM PKWY, STE 101 98225 #005-02-1976 L1981 **CD IM** *020 †20
MC AFEE, Jennifer Lynn. 1000 MCKENZIE AVE 98225 #005-02-1975 L1981 **END** *020 †20
MC ALLISTER, Vermont H. 3500 ORCHARD PL 98225 #007-02-1968 L1970 **FM** *020 †18
MCCALLUM, Gary Jack. 2940 NEWMARKET PL STE 106, MEDICAL CLINIC 98226 #068-01-1974 L1997 **FM EM** *020 †18
MC CLENAHAN, Richard Ford. 3015 SQUALICUM PKWY, STE 120 98225 #016-06-1983 L1986 **FM** *020 †18
MC CULLOUGH, Kelly David. 2930 SQUALICUM PKWY, NORTHWEST 98225 #054-04-1999 L2001 **GE** *020 †20
MC GUINNESS, Scott Wm. 4545 CORDATA PKWY 98226 #054-04-1985 L1987 **PD** *020 †55
MC KINNEY, David Spencer. 4545 CORDATA PKWY 98226 #056-06-1992 L1995 **IM** *020 †20
MILLARD, Philip Ronald. 2980 SQUALICUM PKWY # 301 98225 #054-04-1963 L1964 **OBG** *071 †30
MILLER, James Philip. 2940 SQUALICUM PKWY, STE 204 98225 #005-12-2000 L2000 **GS** *020 †85
MONGUE, Robert Jos. 2901 SQUALICUM PKWY 98225 #025-01-1985 L1991 **EM** *020 †16
MOOKHERJEE, Saswati. ■ 98225 #054-04-1998 *100
MOORE, Craig Kevin. 2901 SQUALICUM PKWY 98225 #005-06-1978 L1989 **FM FSM** *020 †18
MOORE, Randall Wayne. 4280 MERIDIAN ST, STE 120 98226 #065-10-1983 L1992 **FM** *020 †18
MOORE, Tillman M, Jr. ■ 98225 #028-02-1953 L1953 **ORS GS** *072 †85,40
MORA, Carl Shayne. 2980 SQUALICUM PKWY, STE 301 98225 #011-03-1994 L1998 **OBG** *020 †30
MOREN, James Arthur. 2075 BARKLEY BLVD 98226 #012-05-1975 L1979 **FM** *020 †18
MORISON, David Scott. 4545 CORDATA PKWY 98226 #016-42-1994 L2004 **PCC** *020 †20
MORROW, Kenneth Avard. 3015 SQUALICUM PKWY STE 26 98225 #061-01-1959 L1993 **OPH** *071 †35
MORROW, Nathan G. 4465 CORDATA PKWY 98226 #036-07-1990 L1990 **IM** *020 †20
MOSS, Larry Eugene. 410 BIRCHWOOD AVE, STE 200 98225 #018-03-1986 L1992 **NEP IM** *020 †20
MOSTAD, Sara Blanche. 516 BAYSIDE RD 98225 #054-04-1999 L2000 **ID** *100 †20
MUMMA, John. 2980 SQUALICUM PKWY, BELLINGHAM SURGERY CENTER 98225 #005-02-1956 L1962 **AN GP** *071 †05
MURIBY, Nujud R. 809 E CHESTNUT ST 98225 #154-07-1962 L1972 **PS HS** *020
NELSON, Darl Dean. 3149 ELLIS ST, STE 301 98225 #017-20-1959 L1969 **GE** *020 †20
NESTOR, Patrick J. 4465 CORDATA PKWY 98226 #048-13-1997 L2003 **HO** *020 †20
NETBOY, David Ellis. 2901 SQUALICUM PKWY 98225 #005-02-1967 L1987 **EM IM** *020 †16
NEWELL, Astrid Marie. ■ 98229 #028-02-1992 L2004 **FM** *030 †18
NEWELL, Robert Calvin. ■ 98225 #028-02-1957 L1970 **OTO HNS** *071 †45
NG, Kai-Ling. 2930 SQUALICUM PKWY # 101, ATTN: BRANDY VAN DE KONP 98225 #061-01-2002 **DR** *100
NGUYEN, Tuyet Thi. 4545 CORDATA PKWY, MADRONA MEDICAL GROUP P S 98226 #067-02-1984 L1996 **PD** *020 †55
NIKOMBORIRAK, Jakdej. 4545 CORDATA PKWY 98226 #010-02-1990 L1998 **PCC** *020 †20
NOELL, Christopher N. 3645 E MCLEOD RD 98226 #035-06-1972 L1973 **P** *020 †75
O'KEEFE, Karen D. 2220 CORNWALL AVE 98225 #067-01-1996 L2002 **FM** *020 †18
O'KEEFE, S Casey. 340 BIRCHWOOD AVE 98225 #067-01-1996 L2002 **U** *020 †95
OKSENBERG, Deborah Ann. 4455 CORDATA PKWY 98226 #025-01-1997 L2005 **FM** *020 †18
OLIVER, Brian Nicholas. 3130 SQUALICUM PKWY # 300, BELLINGHAM ANESTHESIA ASSC 98225 #917-04-1961 L1972 **AN** *071 †05
OLIVER, Thomas Arthur. ■ 98225 #048-02-2000 L2006 **CD** *020 †20
OLSON, David Erik Lee. 2940 SQUALICUM PKWY, BELLINGHAM EAR NOSE & 98225 #026-04-1998 L2003 **OTO** *020 †45
OLSON, Robert Orville, Jr. 2950 NEWMARKET PL, 101-261 98226 #033-06-1974 L1979 **OBG** *020 †30
OTTO, Patricia Maxine. 470 BIRCHWOOD AVE STE A 98225 #056-05-1972 L1978 **OBG** *020 †30
OUELLETTE, Tracy Jenkins. 800 E CHESTNUT ST, STE 3A 98225 #026-04-1994 L2001 **PM** *020 †60
OWINGS, Raymond Mark. 2901 SQUALICUM PKWY, ST JOSEPH HOSPITAL 98225 #012-05-1979 L1982 **PTH** *062 †50
PARLATORE, Anselm Anthony. 1050 LARRABEE AVE, STE 204 98225 #030-06-1969 L1989 **P** *020 †75
PARRISH, Clark Owen. 4545 CORDATA PKWY 98226 #039-01-1978 L1987 **IM** *020 †20
PATTERSON, Brian Milton. 3130 ELLIS ST 98225 #061-01-1966 L1971 **FM** *020 †18
PAULI, Andrew Denzil. 1116 KEY ST, STE 200 98225 #005-18-1980 L1987 **P CHP** *020 †75
PEREZ, Jim. 2901 SQUALICUM PKWY 98225 #005-18-1988 L1991 **EM** *020 †16
PETTIT, John Mark. 340 BIRCHWOOD AVE 98225 #422-01-1981 L1987 **U** *020 †95
PHILLIPS, Gerald Henry. ■ 98226 #028-03-1977 L1977 **R** *020 †80
PHILLIPS, Robert Raymond. 2901 SQUALICUM PKWY 98225 #054-04-1995 L1997 **CD** *020 †20
PIATT, Martin Walter. 4545 CORDATA PKWY 98226 #025-12-1986 L2004 **FM** *020 †18
PIERSON, James Marcus. 2901 SQUALICUM PKWY 98225 #017-20-1976 L1980 **EM IM** *020 †20,16
PIETRO, Michael. 3015 SQUALICUM PKWY # 250 98225 #047-05-1985 L1986 **GS VS** *020 †85

■ = Address Information Privacy Protected
9193

PRICKETT, James David. 4545 CORDATA PKWY, MADRONA MEDICAL GROUP 98226 #005-11-1976 L1988 **RHU IM** *020 †20

PRITCHETT, Edwin Adams. 2901 SQUALICUM PKWY 98225 #065-06-1951 L1959 **GYN** *071 †30

QUICK, David William. ■ 98225 #003-75-2006, ▲ L2006 **IM** *012

RADVANY, Andris Edward. 1225 E SUNSET DR, STE 145 98226 #016-11-1996 L1999 **IM** *020 †20

RAJ L., George Stephan. 710 BIRCHWOOD AVE, STE 101 98225 #495-53-1998 L2007 **PM** *020

RANSOM, Jon Carlisle. 2901 SQUALICUM PKWY, ST JOSEPH HOSPITAL 98225 #048-12-1975 L1980 **NEP IM** *020 †20

RAPPE, Donald Lee. 2211 RIMLAND DR STE 1 98226 #007-02-1976 L1979 **FM** *030 †18

REITZ, Christoph R. 2930 SQUALICUM PKWY, NORTHWEST 98225 #409-10-1992 L2001 **GE** *020 †20

REMICK, Ronald Allen. 609 N SHORE DR A, LAKE WHATCOM RESIDENTIAL C 98226 #010-01-1974 L1991 **P** *020 †75

RICHARDS, Steven Craig. 4545 CORDATA PKWY, MADRONA MEDICAL GROUP, PS 98226 #001-06-1996 L2002 **IM** *020 †20

RICHARDS, Steven J. 4545 CORDATA PKWY 98226 #049-01-1989 L1993 **OBG** *020 †30

RIES, Jeffrey David. 2901 SQUALICUM PKWY 98225 #038-40-1981 L1983 **FM EM** *020 †16,18

RIGAS, Constantine J. 809 E CHESTNUT ST 98225 #025-01-1970 L1991 **CHP P** *020 †75

RINNE, Ralph Henry. ■ 98229 #028-34-1948 L1956 **GS** *071 †85

ROFKAR, George Albert. ■ 98225 #038-40-1965 L1968 **AN** *071 †05

ROSE, Robert Warren. 2901 SQUALICUM PKWY 98225 #049-01-1963 L1966 **DR NM** *071 †80

ROSQUIST, Jennifer Lynn. 4545 CORDATA PKWY 98226 #054-04-1995 L2006 **PD** *020 †55

ROSS, Elizabeth Katrina. 3614 MERIDIAN ST, STE 200 98225 #035-01-1997 L2004 **D** *020 †15

ROSS, James Alan. 3500 ORCHARD PL 98225 #054-04-1975 L1976 **FM** *030 †18

ROUTT, Audrey Patricia. ■ 98225 #028-02-2006 L2006 **IM** *012

RUBEY, Steven Allen. 3645 E MCLEOD RD 98226 #054-04-1967 L1968 **CHP P** *020 †75

RUF, Walter Norman. 3001 SQUALICUM PKWY STE 6 98225 #048-02-1968 L1974 **N GS** *020 †75

RUSSELL, Matthew Franklin. 2901 SQUALICUM PKWY 98225 #032-01-1998 L2001 **EM** *020 †16

SAKAHARA, April Mae. 800 E CHESTNUT ST STE 3A 98225 #054-04-1984 L1985 **PM** *020 †60

SAMRA, Ravinder. 1801 C ST 98225 #028-34-1994 L2006 **OBG** *020 †30

SANDENO, William Scott. 4545 CORDATA PKWY, % PAMARTINTA PARKWAY 98226 #054-04-1994 L1999 **IM** *020 †20

SANDHU, Harsimrat. 4455 CORDATA PKWY, MENTAL HEALTH, 2ND FLOOR 98226 #005-02-1990 L1993 **P** *020 †75

SAUNDERS, William Ryall. 4029 NORTHWEST AVE STE 203, NORTHWEST WALKIN HEALTH 98226 #003-01-1984 L1987 **FM** *020 †18

SCHAYES, Roy Milton. ■ 98225 #016-11-1960 L1967 **ORS** *071 †40

SCHIMKE, Melana Kay. 3500 ORCHARD PL 98225 #054-04-1994 L2002 **FM** *020 †18

SCHNECK, Dennis Wayne. ■ 98229 #060-01-1965 L1976 **GP** *020

SCHNEIDER, Thomas Franz. 3500 ORCHARD PL 98225 #054-04-1987 L1991 **FM** *020 †18

SCHOENECKER, James A, Jr. 2979 SQUALICUM PKWY, STE 301 98225 #048-14-1988 L2005 **GE** *020 †20

SCOTT, Maryanne Bartoszek. 4545 CORDATA PKWY, STE 2C 98226 #041-09-1981 L2001 **AI PD** *020 †55,03

SELTZER, Janet. 4545 CORDATA PKWY 98226 #005-11-1978 L1989 **IM PUD** *020 †20

SEMPLE, Henry Chas. ■ 98225 #021-05-1958 L1958 **OPH OS** *020 †35

SHAH, Ifat Ali. 2901 SQUALICUM PKWY 98225 #409-05-1971 L2002 **PTH** *040 †50

SHAPIRO, Miriam R. 3500 ORCHARD PL 98225 #048-04-1988 L1990 **FM** *020 †18

SHARF, Roger Evan. 3130 ELLIS ST 98225 #041-13-1984 L1991 **FM EM** *020 †18

SHAW, Janine. 220 UNITY ST, INTERFAITH COMMUNITY CLIN 98225 #025-12-1986 L1989 **FM P** *020 †18

SHAW, John B. 4455 CORDATA PKWY 98226 #005-16-1962 L1975 **GP** *071

SHAW, John B Northcote. 4455 CORDATA PKWY 98226 #016-43-1984 L1993 **FM** *020 †18

SHEINKOPF, Russell Hendel. 119 N COMMERCIAL ST # 290, BELLINGHAM TOWERS 98225 #005-06-1980 L1992 **P** *020

SHERMAN, Lora Coryell. 4455 CORDATA PKWY 98226 #038-06-1993 L1995 **FM** *020 †18

SHIELDS, Mary Ellen. 2901 SQUALICUM PKWY 98225 #003-01-1973 L1978 **PD** *020 †55

SHIELDS, Raymond Wayne. 2592 KWINA RD, LUMMI HEALTH CLINIC 98226 #005-06-1974 L1993 **FM EM** *030 †16

SHOKEIR, Cheryl Marie. 336 36TH ST 98225 #060-02-1991 L1997 *020

SHOKEIR, Marc Omar. 336 36TH ST 98225 #068-01-1991 L1996 **PTH** *020 †50

SHORT, Jason Tyler. 2075 BARKLEY BLVD 98226 #056-06-2000 L2000 **FM** *020 †18 ‡

SHURMAN, Alan James. 2901 SQUALICUM PKWY 98225 #054-04-1978 L2003 **CD** *030 †20

SIEMANOWSKI, Benjamin. 4545 CORDATA PKWY 98226 #041-02-2000 L2007 **GE** *020 †20

SKIBA, Grzegorz. 4029 NORTHWEST AVE, STE 301 98226 #759-08-1988 L2007 **APM** *020 †05

SMITH, Brenda L. 4545 CORDATA PKWY 98226 #034-01-1981 L1999 **OBG** *020 †30

SMITH, Eric Starheim. 3015 SQUALICUM PKWY # 22, WHATCOM OCCUPATIONAL HEALT 98225 #040-02-1981 L1982 **OM** *020 †70

SMITH, Gary Mark. 809 E CHESTNUT ST 98225 #028-02-1979 L1983 **P** *020 †75

SMITH, Robert Frederick. ■ 98229 #054-04-1960 L1961 **ORS** *071 †40

SMITH, Russell Frederick. 2901 SQUALICUM PKWY 98225 #025-01-1955 L1994 **FM ADM** *072

SNYDER, Gary Richard. 519 17TH ST 98225 #016-06-1966 L1967 **FM GS** *020 †18

SOKOL, Lanny Fred. 716 DONOVAN AVE 98225 #024-07-1985 L2003 **EM OS** *020 †16

SOLOVJEV, Vsevolod. 2901 SQUALICUM PKWY 98225 #048-04-1958 L1959 **P** *020

SPERRY, Robert Geo. 3130 ELLIS ST, ASSOCIATES IN FAMILY MEDIC 98225 #038-41-1992 L1996 **FM** *020 †18

SRINIVASAN, Murali. 3015 SQUALICUM PKWY 98225 #496-23-1993 L2006 **IM** *020 †20

STACKHOUSE, Thomas Logan. 2940 SQUALICUM PKWY, BELLINGHAM EAR NOSE & 98225 #025-01-1987 L1992 **OTO HNS** *020 †45

STERN, Gregory H. 509 GIRARD ST, WHATCOM COUNTY HEALTH DEPT 98225 #005-02-1984 L1990 **FM PHP** *030 †18

STEWART, James Andrew. 1000 MCKENZIE AVE 98225 #030-05-1966 L1970 **P** *020 †75 ‡

STIFF, Donald Wm S. ■ 98229 #024-05-1945 L1982 **R** *071 †80

STINER, Dana Bradford. 4545 CORDATA PKWY 98226 #054-04-1971 L1973 **GE IM** *020 †20

STOCKBURGER, John Scott. 1000 MCKENZIE AVE, STE 16 98225 #004-01-1997 L2000 **FM** *020 †18

STRATTON, Albert W. ■ 98226 #016-06-1948 L1948 **GS** *071 †85

SULLIVAN, Michael P. 2901 SQUALICUM PKWY 98225 #016-42-1991 L1995 **EM** *020 †16

SULLIVAN, Naomi Rebecca. 500 BIRCHWOOD AVE STE B, MOUNT AUBURN HOSPITAL 98225 #035-47-1997 L2007 **IM** *020 †20

SUN, Jian Yi. 2901 SQUALICUM PKWY 98225 #243-52-1978 L2004 **HOS** *020 †20

SURY, Mani N. 12 BELLWETHER WAY, STE 108 98225 #495-65-1971 L1998 **IM** *020 †20

SWAN, Jerome Wm. ■ 98225 #016-06-1958 L1959 **OPH** *071 †35

SWANSON, Dax Christopher. ■ 98226 #005-02-1995 L1997 **FM** *020 †18

SZALAY, Glenn Coleman. ■ 98228 #062-01-1956 L1963 **PD OS** *071 †55

TARLETON, Scott David. 3015 SQUALICUM PKWY, STE 120 98225 #005-19-1983 L1984 **FM** *071 †18

TAYLOR, Carolyn. 410 BIRCHWOOD AVE, STE 201 98225 #041-09-1989 L2000 **N** *020 †75

TAYLOR, Michael Andre. 3217 SQUALICUM PKWY 98225 #051-04-1989 L1992 **RO** *020 †80

TAYLOR, Roy Andrew. 3104 SQUALICUM PKWY, STE 103 98225 #040-02-1976 L1978 **VS TS** *020 †85

THOMPSON, Ian Lindsey. 3217 SQUALICUM PKWY 98225 #005-14-1974 L1976 **RO** *020 †80

THOMPSON, Michael Gregory. 4545 CORDATA PKWY 98226 #008-01-2003 L2003 **PD** *020 †55

THORNBERG, Teresa Ann. 1130 N FOREST ST 98225 #054-04-1989 L1989 **OPH** *020 †35

THORPE, Michael Alan. 3149 ELLIS ST, STE 103 98225 #018-03-1983 L1985 **ORS** *020 †40

TILLEY, John W, Jr. 2592 KWINA RD, LUMMI TRIBAL HEALTH CENTER 98226 #041-02-1982 L1992 **IM** *020 †20

TISDALL, John Robbie. 1815 C ST STE J35 98225 #060-01-1973 L1978 **OPH** *020 †35

TRAUTMAN, Walter Jacques. 2980 SQUALICUM PKWY 98225 #054-04-1993 L1996 **APM** *020 †05

TRIMINGHAM, J Loch. 4545 CORDATA PKWY, MADRONA MEDICAL GROUP 98226 #067-01-1966 L1967 **ORS** *020 †40

TROUPIN, Allan Stuart. ■ 98229 #035-01-1960 L1964 **N CN** *071 †75

TROUTMAN, James Leslie. 4545 CORDATA PKWY, MADRONA MEDICAL GROUP 98226 #036-07-1986 L1989 **PD** *020 †55

TU, Amy. 12 BELLWETHER WAY STE 219 98225 #045-01-1998 L2004 **OBG** *020 †30

TURK, David Jos. 4545 CORDATA PKWY, MADRONA MEDICAL GROUP 98226 #054-04-1988 L1990 **END** *020 †20

UNGS, Timothy John. 4029 NORTHWEST AVE 98226 #040-02-1977 L1978 **OM AM** *020 †70

VANDERBILT, Burton Lee. 2901 SQUALICUM PKWY 98225 #017-20-1977 L1978 **PTH CLP** *020 †50

VANDERBILT, Carletta Mary. 3015 SQUALICUM PKWY, STE 100 98225 #017-20-1976 L1979 **IM IMG** *020 †20

VANDER GRIEND, Keith J. 2940 SQUALICUM PKWY 98225 #047-05-1994 L1999 **GS** *020 †85

VANDER GRIEND, Orville K. 2940 SQUALICUM PKWY # 204 98225 #025-07-1967 L1968 **GS** *020 †85

VAN DER VLUGT, Theresa M. 2901 SQUALICUM PKWY 98225 #005-11-1997 L1998 **EM** *020 †16

VAN DYKE, Alexander C G. ■ 98225 #038-41-1956 L1989 **PD EM** *071 †55,16

VAN KOLKEN, Anne Maria. ■ 98229 #919-02-1971 L1981 **AN** *071

VAN KOLKEN, Richard James. ■ 98229 #025-01-1970 L1981 **DR** *071 †80

VAUPEL, Douglas Lee. 1316 KING ST STE 3 98229 #026-08-1978 L1987 **P CHP** *020 †75 ‡

VEITCH, Robert Lorimer. ■ 98229 #054-04-1970 L1976 **GE IM** *071 †20

VENNOS, Elizabeth Mary. 2075 BARKLEY BLVD, STE 230 98226 #010-02-1988 L1995 **D** *020 †15

VERNEUIL, Andrew C. 2940 SQUALICUM PKWY # 20 98225 #026-08-1996 L2007 **OTO** *020 †45

VERNIDHARAN, Jogaratnam. 220 UNITY ST 98225 #220-02-1990 L2004 **MPD** *020 †20,55

VERRET, Michel Rene. 3130 ELLIS ST 98225 #067-01-1968 L1977 **FM** *030 †18

VIEGAS, Aleixo Manuel. 2901 SQUALICUM PKWY 98225 #496-15-1993 L2002 **IM** *020 †20

WADLAND, Donald Wm. 2930 SQUALICUM PKWY, NORTHWEST 98225 #025-01-1967 L1970 **GE** *020 †20

WAKEFIELD PAGELS, April K. 2075 BARKLEY BLVD STE 105, NORTH SOUND FAMILY MEDICIN 98226 #019-02-2002 L2004 **FM** *020 †18

WALLACE, Steven Franklin. 4545 CORDATA PKWY 98226 #041-01-1990 L1990 **PD** *020 †55

WALTERS, Brian Harry V. 1050 LARRABEE AVE, STE 104 98225 #064-01-1960 L1965 **AN OS** *071 †05

WALTNER, William Ernest. 12 BELLWETHER WAY STE 222 98225 #030-06-1977 L1988 **PD PDP** *020 †20,55

WANNE, Rachel Miriam. 2220 CORNWALL AVE 98225 #041-15-2001 L2005 **FM** *020 †18

WATSON, Robert Eugene. 119 N COMMERCIAL ST # 1100 98225 #054-04-1971 L1972 **CHP P** *020

WATTERSON, Martin Neal. 1225 E SUNSET DR, STE 145 # 479 98226 #305-01-1997 L2000 **FM** *020 †18 ‡

WAYNE, Marvin Alan. 2901 SQUALICUM PKWY 98225 #025-01-1968 L1973 **EM** *020 †16

WEAVER, John Howard. 2220 CORNWALL AVE 98225 #918-01-1978 L1981 **FM** *020

WEBB, Zachary A. 1345 KING ST, NORTHSTAR ASSOCIATES 98229 #473-02-1998 L2005 **CN** *100 †75

WEICHE, Ralph Eugene. 2901 SQUALICUM PKWY 98225 #054-04-1997 L2004 **EM** *020 †20,16

WEIS, Mark Julian. ■ 98229 #020-12-1969 L1970 **FM IM** *020 †18

WELLS, Diana Guza. 4545 CORDATA PKWY 98226 #051-04-1985 L2006 **IM** *020 †20

WELSH, Anne Palmer. 4545 CORDATA PKWY, MADRONA MEDICAL GROUP, PS 98226 #054-04-1989 L1989 **PD** *020 †55

WELSH, Gregory Mark. 4545 CORDATA PKWY, MADRONA MEDICAL GROUP, PS 98226 #023-07-1989 L1991 **PD PHO** *020 †55

WERNER, Matthew Wayne. 3015 SQUALICUM PKWY 98225 #054-04-2001 L2003 **FM** *020 †18

WHIPPLE, Bruce Gordon. ■ 98229 #054-04-1965 L1967 **OTO** *020 †45

WHITE, Gerald W. ■ 98229 #917-04-1969 L1993 *020

WHITEHEAD, Brent Edward. 4545 CORDATA PKWY 98226 #005-12-2003 L2006 **FM** *020 †18

WHITNEY, Timothy Mark. 3001 SQUALICUM PKWY, STE 5 98225 #041-12-1984 L2003 **PS HS** *020 †85,65

WILLEY, T Ian. ■ 98225 #060-01-1955 L1967 **PTH** *071 †50

WILLIAMS, Eric Dean. 2901 SQUALICUM PKWY, EMERGENCY DEPARTMENT 98225 #056-06-1994 L2001 **EM** *020 †16

WILLS, Kristine Marie. 3015 SQUALICUM PKWY 98225 #017-20-1987 L2001 **FM** *020 †18

WINTER, William Wallace. 2901 SQUALICUM PKWY 98225 #054-04-1963 L1965 **GYN** *071 †30

WISNER, David Edward. 470 BIRCHWOOD AVE STE A 98225 #056-05-1972 L1978 **RHU IM** *020 †20

WISNER, Steven Paul. 4545 CORDATA PKWY 98226 #019-02-1974 L1981 **PD** *020 †55

WITTE, Todd Nolan. 2979 SQUALICUM PKWY, STE 301 98225 #051-04-1999 L2007 **IM** *020 †20

WOLGAMOT, Gregory Michael. ■ 98225 #054-04-2000 L2003 **DMP** *020 †50 ‡

WOODS, Stephen Preston. 2979 SQUALICUM PKWY 98225 #005-18-1982 L1990 **GE IM** *020 †20

WREGGIT, George Riley. 2901 SQUALICUM PKWY 98225 #025-01-1967 L1972 **GS** *071 †85

WU, Chao-Ying. 2075 BARKLEY BLVD 98226 #054-04-1988 L1990 **FM** *020 †18

WYNNE, Douglas Frederick. 2901 SQUALICUM PKWY 98225 #054-04-1972 L1973 **IM IMG** *020 †20

YEOSTROS, Janine Anne. 4280 MERIDIAN ST 98226 #011-03-2000 L2003 **FM** *020 †18

YI, Josh. 2901 SQUALICUM PKWY 98225 #038-41-2001 L2004 **IM** *020 †20

■ = Address Information Privacy Protected

YIN, Way. 2075 BARKLEY BLVD STE 110 98226 #035-01-1987 L1990 **PMM PME** *020 †05
YOOS, Jessica Rushmer. 2980 SQUALICUM PKWY, STE 105 98225 #035-45-2000 L2000 **AN** *020 †05
YOUNG, Karen Marie. ■ 98225 #035-19-1999 L2007 **FM** *100 †18,75
YOUNG, Lawrence Jos. 4204 MERIDIAN ST STE 101 98226 #061-01-1971 L1992 **IM GP** *071 †20
ZARZYCKI, Mark John. 2901 SQUALICUM PKWY 98225 #056-05-1984 L1987 **EM** *020 †16
ZECH, Edward Raymond. 2979 SQUALICUM PKWY # 30 98225 #030-06-1980 L1986 **TS GS** *020 †85,90
ZIBULEWSKY, Joseph. 2901 SQUALICUM PKWY 98225 #041-13-1987 L2006 **EM** *020 †16,55

BENTON CITY – BENTON

BRIGGS, Terri Harmon. 32509 E RED RD 99320 #054-04-1988 L1989 **IM** *020 †20
CLEAVES, John Thomas. ■ 99320 #023-12-2006 L2007 *012
MYERS, Roy Allen. PO BOX 603, 1105 DALE AVE 99320 #007-02-1994 L1998 **FM** *020 †18

BINGEN – SKAMANIA

SCHUEMANN, Karl Ernst. ■ 98605 #028-02-1991 L1991 **IM** *100

BLAINE – WHATCOM

ALLAN, David Hugh. 377 C ST, BAY MEDICAL CLINIC 98230 #068-01-1977 L1980 **FM** *020
BARNEBEE, James Hosea, III. 8693 GREAT HORNED OWL LN 98230 #048-15-1977 L1986 **FM AM** *020 †18
BISHOP, Rodney Philip. 4550 BIRCH BAY LYNDEN RD 98230 #917-25-1960 **GP** *020
BROBYN, Richard Dolde. 5635 WHITEHORN WAY 98230 #041-01-1957 L1960 **FM RHU** *050
CHIN, Wallace E. ■ 98230 #005-12-1949 L1972 **EM GP** *071
DOWER, Gordon Ewbank. BOX F110 232 98230 #352-11-1948 L1968 **CD OS** *040
FINLAY, J Graham. 4550 BIRCH BAY LYNDEN RD, # 1127 98230 #054-04-1950 L1952 **AN** *071
FLANAGAN-STEWARD, Mary L. 1733 H ST STE 330, PMB 553 98230 #061-01-1975 L1993 **AN** *020 †05
GILSON, Albert Jack. ■ 98230 #035-20-1957 L1998 **NM R** *062 †80,28
HARRISON, Katherine Alice. ■ 98230 #004-01-1977 L2006 **FM NM** *040 †28,18
HEPWORTH, Richard Gordon. ■ 98230 #917-05-1950 L1976 **U LM** *071
HUI, Frank Chiu-Wai. ■ 98230 #061-01-1973 L1979 **HS OS** *040
JOHNSON, Roderick L. ■ 98230 #054-04-1951 L1953 **CLP BBK** *071 †85
NARAYANAN, Rajnikanth. ■ 98231 #496-35-1997 L2002 **IM** *020 †20
NEWMAN, Harold Frank. ■ 98230 #007-02-1954 L1955 **GPM** *030 †70
PEYTON, Alton B. ■ 98230 #048-02-1942 L1958 **U** *071 †95
STAFFORD, Charles Michael. 377 C ST, BAY MEDICAL CLINIC 98230 #917-03-1952 L1989 **EM FM** *071
SU, Daniel Lung. 250 H ST 98230 #054-04-1995 L2000 **FM** *020 †18
THOMPSON, Rodney L B. 8097 HARBORVIEW RD 98230 #005-12-1995 L2000 **FM** *020 †18
VANDERWIELEN, Paulus. ■ 98230 #660-04-1952 L2007 **P** *071
WILLIAMS, Alan Loudon. 8463 POINTE RD N, THE EVERETT CLINIC 98230 #035-15-1970 L1982 **DR RNR** *020 †80
WOLF, Bruce John. ■ 98230 #054-04-1967 L1971 **OPH** *071 †35
YASAYKO, Harold Harry M. ■ 98230 #060-01-1966 L1977 **OM GP** *020

BONNEY LAKE – PIERCE

ARIGALA, Mythili R. 20639 STATE ROUTE 410 E, CASCADE MEDICAL CLINIC 98391 #495-16-1993 L1998 **IM** *020 †20
BARRETT, Sherri Elizabeth. 20825 STATE ROUTE 410 E, PMB 242 98391 #028-34-1990 L1995 **PM** *020 †60
HURLEY, Wayne Edward. 20503 127TH STREET CT E 98391 #005-12-1972 L1987 **EM** *020 †16
MEALER, Daren Roger. ■ 98391 #048-12-2000 L2003 **FM** *020 †18 ‡
SANTOS, Sharon H. 19820 HWY 410 E, STE 102 98391 #748-02-1992 L2001 **PD** *020 †55
SILVER, Haven. 19820 STATE ROUTE 410 E, STE 202 98391 #016-42-1972 L1973 **FM** *071 †18

BOTHELL – KING

BIDWELL, Donald Wellwood. 9315 NE 141ST PL 98011 #012-05-1958 L1958 **GP R** *071 †80
BLANK, Debby Jo. PO BOX 3003 98041 #024-07-1984 **OS IM** *030
BLUME, Gary Berns. 19125 NORTH CREEK PKWY, STE 204 98011 #016-06-1985 L1988 **FM** *020 †18
CAMPBELL, Lawrence F. ■ 98011 #025-01-1963 L1964 **R OS** *071 †80
CARLSON, Robert Lynn. 20140 106TH AVE NE 98011 #054-04-1962 L1963 **FM** *020 †18
CORDERO, Valerie Jean. 11913 NE 195TH ST 98011 #054-04-2002 L2004 **FM** *100 †18
DEYLE, David Roger. 9223 NE 193RD ST 98011 #026-04-2000 L2004 **MG** *100
DUNN, John Baker. 11913 NE 195TH ST, NORTHSHORE PEDIATRICS 98011 #016-06-1994 L1999 **PD** *020 †55
ECKERT, Buckley Allan. 10025 NE 186TH ST, LAKESHORE CLINIC 98011 #048-02-1986 L1990 **PD IM** *020 †20,55
ESSER, Sally Rene. 10025 NE 186TH ST, LAKESHORE CLINIC 98011 #054-04-1985 L1988 **FM** *020 †18
GARGARI DE NOCHLIN, Maria. ■ 98011 #649-01-1972 L1988 **P CHP** *020
GIN, Shan Yah. ■ 98011 #242-15-1931 L1959 **PD** *071 †55
GLASS, Michael Robt. ■ 98011 #010-03-1967 L1983 **P** *071 †75
HOCKEISER, Steven Philip. 11913 NE 195TH ST 98011 #033-06-1980 L1985 **FM** *020 †18
HOVSEPIAN, Nancy Bowling. 11913 NE 195TH ST, C/O GROUP HEALTH COOPERATI 98011 #039-05-1988 L1992 **IM** *020 †20
HUANG, Jane Chen. ■ 98011 #016-06-1990 L2000 **PTH** *020 †50
JELINEK, George Earl. ■ 98041 #034-01-1976 L1977 **U** *071 †95
KELLY, William Albert. ■ 98028 #038-41-1954 L1961 **NS** *071 †25
KENDRICK, Susan Shaw. 11913 NE 195TH ST 98011 #050-02-1987 L1990 **FM** *020 †18
LEONARDO, Lilaine C. 10025 NE 186TH ST, LAKESHORE CLINIC 98011 #054-04-1996 L1999 **FM** *020 †18

LEVIN, Floyd Dale. ■ 98041 #010-01-1946 L1948 **GP** *071
LIMARZI, Gary Irving. 10025 NE 186TH ST, LAKESHORE CLINIC 98011 #011-03-1972 L1975 **FM** *071 †18
LOCKNANE, Timothy Duane. 18518 BOTHELL WAY NE, STE C 98011 #056-06-1995 L1998 **FM** *020 †18
MAHTANI, Sarita Manu. ■ 98011 #054-04-2006 L2006 **IM** *012
MC AFEE, Scott Randall. 11913 NE 195TH ST 98011 #054-04-1989 L1989 **FM** *020 †18
MC ALISTER, Robert. 11913 NE 195TH ST 98011 #054-04-1961 L1965 **OS FM** *020 †18
MONAHAN, James Thomas. ■ 98011 #054-04-1958 L1959 **FM** *071 †18
MUSTAFA, Syed Kamal. 10634 E RIVERSIDE DR, STE 130 98011 #704-22-1984 L2000 **CHP** *020 †75
O'CONNELL, Mary. 12900 NE 180TH ST, STE 100 98011 #033-05-1985 L1989 **GYN** *020 †30
PARRIS, Lawrence Lyle. 14048 JUANITA DR NE 98011 #054-04-1976 L1979 **FM** *020 †18
PLATZ, Theresa Ann. 10025 NE 186TH ST, LAKESHORE CLINIC 98011 #054-04-1996 L1998 **FM** *020 †18
RUSSELL, Robert Michael. 16425 104TH AVE NE 98011 #054-04-1976 L1977 **EM** *020 †16
SEFTON, Peter Vanhoy. 10025 NE 186TH ST, LAKESHORE CLINIC 98011 #017-20-1982 L1989 **FM** *020 †18
STEPHANO, Paul Anthony. ■ 98011 #036-07-2004 *100
TERRANOVA, Regina E. 11913 NE 195TH ST 98011 #005-06-1988 L1998 **FM** *020 †18
WILSON, Thomas Albert. 10025 NE 186TH ST, LAKESHORE CLINIC 98011 #026-04-1984 L1987 **FM** *020 †18

BOTHELL – SNOHOMISH

ABRAMS, Paul Gordon. 3830 MONTE VILLA PKWY, STE 200 98021 #008-01-1976 L1985 **ON IM** *030 †20
ABRAMSKI, Stanley Francis. ■ 98012 #016-43-1969 L2003 **P** *020 †75
BEDAREV, Igor. 3804 155TH PL SE 98012 #913-67-1996 *100
BELL, John Philip. ■ 98021 #005-17-1962 L1975 **OBG** *071 †30
BRANDT, Gordon C. 3450 MONTE VILLA PKWY 98021 #005-02-1994 L1995 **IM** *050
BUSTEED, Frank F. ■ 98012 #054-04-1952 L1954 **PTH** *071 †50
CASTRO, Felipe Galvez. ■ 98021 #748-01-1950 **GP** *072
CHINN, Yum Hung. ■ 98012 #024-05-1990 L1992 **GS** *020
CROGHAN, Richard Alfred. ■ 98012 #036-01-1965 L1965 **OPH** *020
DRACHMAN, Jonathan G. 21823 30TH DR SE, UNIV OF WASHINGTON, BOX 35 98021 #024-01-1989 L1991 **ON** *050 †20
EDELSTEIN, Gerald. ■ 98012 #035-46-1960 L1962 **AN PD** *071 †55,05
EINSTEIN, Arunachalam. 18429 38TH DR SE 98012 #495-94-1991 L2006 **IM EM** *020 †16,20
FARAH, Rafic Jean. ■ 98012 #605-02-1997 L2005 **IM** *100 †20
FRUMKIN, Lynn Robt. 22021 20TH AVE SE, ICOS CORP 98021 #054-04-1984 L1985 **ID N** *050
FUNG, Kevin Y. ■ 98012 #036-05-2006 L2006 **AN** *012
GARRIGUES, Henry Bascum. ■ 98012 #024-01-1937 L1948 **CD GS** *071 †85
HOWATT, James Walter. 21540 30TH DR SE STE 400 98021 #005-02-1971 L2006 **FM** *030 †18
JENSEN, Mary E. ■ 98012 #018-03-1979 L1979 **DR** *020 †80
LEE, Jong Sung. ■ 98021 #583-02-1964 L1970 **P** *020 †75
MALIK, Muhammad Iqbal A. ■ 98012 #704-01-1962 L1992 **PUD IM** *020 †55,20
MASSEY, Timothy Hayes. 1629 220TH ST SE, # 201 98021 #016-11-1981 L1993 **ORS** *020 †40
MURPHY, Lisa C. 1909 214TH ST SE, STE 110 98021 #005-18-1989 L1989 **FM** *020 †18
NHOUNG, Sowaite. ■ 98021 #305-01-1994 *100
NOLAN-MONTELEONE, Jennifer. 22010 17TH AVE SE STE F, EVERGREEN MEDICAL CENTER 98021 #654-01-1998 L2002 **FM** *020 †18
O'BRIEN, Susan Marie. ■ 98012 #035-09-1983 L1991 **EM** *020 †16
PEDERSEN, Alf Hvide-Bang. ■ 98012 #016-06-1947 L1947 **GPM PHP** *071 †70
PORTER, Jennifer Kristine. ■ 98021 #054-04-2000 L2004 **OBG** *020 †30
QUAY, Steven Carl. 22026 20TH AVE SE STE 102 98021 #025-01-1977 L1995 **R DR** *050 †50 ‡
RAMOS, Manuel Felipe. ■ 98012 #748-09-1971 L1980 **GP** *020
ROBINSON, John W. 21540 30TH DR SE, STE 400 98021 #049-01-1980 L2004 **FM** *030 †18
SHOROFF, Srilatha. ■ 98012 #495-62-1991 L2005 **IM** *020 †20
SIEVERS, Eric L. 21823 30TH DR SE, SEATTLE GENETICS INC 98021 #043-01-1988 L1990 **PHO** *050 †55
TERPENING, Larry Russell. ■ 98021 #040-02-1969 L1974 **AN** *020 †05
VANCLEAVE, Mary Janelle. ■ 98021 #019-02-2003 L2007 **IM** *020 †20
YU, Albert Sungyin. 22021 20TH AVE SE, ICOS CORPORATION 98021 #054-04-1985 L1986 **IM** *020 †20

BOW – SKAGIT

BOETTNER, Donald H. ■ 98232 #016-06-1945 L1948 **IM GS** *071 †85
BOTT, Karlyn Gale. ■ 98232 #032-01-2007 **IM** *012
SELLS, Clifford Jerome. ■ 98232 #054-04-1963 L1966 **PD PHP** *071 †55
WOLFF, Virginia Ann. ■ 98232 #026-08-1984 L1986 **FM** *020 †18

BREMERTON – KITSAP

ABDULLAH, Bisher Adel. 2500 CHERRY AVE, STE 102 98310 #875-01-1989 L1998 **PG** *020 †55
ADAMS, Mark Chas. 1225 CAMPBELL WAY, STE 101 98310 #041-01-1979 L1981 **VS TS** *020 †85
AFARIN, Afshin Khodaram. ■ 98337 #017-20-2002 L2003 *020
AFLATOONI, Lila. 804 CALLAHAN DR, STE A 98310 #517-07-1967 L1987 *020
ANDERSEN, Karie Faye. 1 BOONE RD, C/O 83F, NAVAL HOSPITAL 98312 #028-03-1991 L1994 **PD** *020 †55
ANDERSEN, Karlyna L. ■ 98312 #023-12-1992 L1993 **FM AM** *020 †18
ANDERSON, Eric Wade. 1 BOONE RD, NHB DEPT. OF ANESTHESIOLOG 98312 #023-12-1998 L2004 **AN** *020 †05
ANDERSON, Gregory James. ■ 98311 #056-06-2005 L2007 **FP** *012
ANDREWS, James C. ■ 98337 #025-01-1949 L1950 **D PHP** *072 †15
ANDREWS, K Patricia M. ■ 98337 #025-01-1949 L1951 **AN** *071 †05
ARTHUR, John Scripture. 2528 WHEATON WAY, STE 101 98310 #035-03-1968 L1971 **VS TS** *020 †85
BAER, Karl Gunter. ■ 98312 #035-15-1968 L2003 **P** *020 †75
BALDWIN, Randy Lane. 1 BOONE RD, NAVAL HOSPITAL, C/083F 98312 #010-01-1992 L2006 **EM** *020 †16

BANZER, John Alfred. 2512 WHEATON WAY 98310 #016-42-1999 L2005 **CD** *020 †20

BARKIN, Karin. 5455 ALMIRA DR NE 98311 #409-10-1987 L2007 **P** *020 †75

BARTRAM, Linda Sessums. 2520 CHERRY AVE 98310 #023-01-1975 L1984 **IM NEP** *020

BAUER, William Monie. 2620 WHEATON WAY STE 1 98310 #049-01-1988 L1997 **IM** *020 †20

BECK, David Lawrence. 5455 ALMIRA DR NE, STE 421 98311 #054-04-1977 L1986 **IM ADM** *030 †20

BECKE, Ian Geoffrey. 2741 WHEATON WAY STE A 98310 #143-03-1970 L1996 **IM PLM** *020 †20 ‡

BECKER, Christopher Ryan. 2520 CHERRY AVE, EMERGENCY DEPARTMENT 98310 #054-04-2003 L2006 **EM** *020 †16

BELDING, Melvin Earl. 2520 CHERRY AVE 98310 #007-02-1962 L1969 **IM ID** *030 †20

BELL, Steven Andrew. 2700 CLARE AVE 98310 #056-05-1988 L1996 **DR VIR** *020 †80

BENNETT, Martin Andrew. 1211 CARVER ST W, KITSAP COUNTY EMS 98312 #539-06-1996 L2000 **IM** *020 †16

BENNETT, Steven Phillip. 2512 WHEATON WAY 98310 #001-06-1994 L2006 **PCC** *020 †20

BENOIT, Michael Jon. 2528 WHEATON WAY, STE 105 98310 #054-04-1974 L1980 **FM** *020 †18

BERGMAN, Sander Eugene. ■ 98312 #041-12-1971 L1976 **N** *071 †75

BERNI, George Albert. 1225 CAMPBELL WAY STE 101 98310 #054-04-1975 L1977 **TS TRS** *020 †85

BERNSTEIN, Jeffrey David. 2512 WHEATON WAY 98310 #016-42-1981 L1987 **VS GS** *020 †85

BIDANA, Azucena-Flor M. ■ 98311 #748-07-1968 *100

BIEDEL, Clark Wm. ■ 98310 #038-40-1943 L1945 **PD** *071 †55

BIRNBAUM, Jack Aaron. 2512 WHEATON WAY 98310 #005-14-1982 L1992 **DIA** *020 †20

BLACKMON, Griffith M. 1225 CAMPBELL WAY, STE 201 98310 #041-09-1988 L1989 **PCC** *020 †70,20

BOTHWELL, Linda Harriet. 1 BOONE RD, PROFESSIONAL AFFAIRS CODE 98312 #005-18-1983 L1994 **AM OM** *071 †35

BRAY, David Martin, III. 2520 CHERRY AVE 98310 #021-05-1970 L1973 **ATP CLP** *020 †50 ‡

BRIGHT, Donald Attridge. 2720 CLARE AVE, STE C 98310 #054-04-1992 L2000 **N** *020 †75

BRIGHT, Robert Bartineus. 245 4TH ST, ROBERT B BRIGHT MD INC PS 98337 #016-06-1946 L1949 **FM FPG** *071

BROSTOFF, Kathy Haskin. 3092 RIDGEVIEW DR NE 98310 #005-06-1987 L1992 **PLM IMG** *030 †20

BROWN, Bradley Don. 2700 CLARE AVE 98310 #045-01-1990 L1996 **DR** *020 †80

BUENVIAJE, Eric Martin. ■ 98312 #023-12-2002 L2002 **FP** *012

BURCH, Thomas Adams. ■ 98310 #005-06-1946 L1946 **PHP** *071

BURCKHARDT, William A, III. ■ 98311 #016-06-1968 L1990 **P** *020 †75

BURKE, Michael S. 5455 ALMIRA DR NE 98311 #016-42-1994 L1999 **P** *020 †75

CARBONE, Jerome Emile. 1225 CAMPBELL WAY, STE 201 98310 #005-02-1976 L1980 **PUD IM** *020 †20

CARMICK, Edward S. 2528 WHEATON WAY, STE 204 98310 #035-20-1962 L1968 **D** *020 †15

CASE, Austin Mc Clain. 6680 ILLAHEE RD NE 98311 #054-04-1954 L1958 **PYA P** *020

CAVINESS, James Alfred, Jr. 1 BOONE RD, NAVAL HOSPITAL, C/083F 98312 #023-12-1996 L1998 **OM** *100 †70

CHRISTEN, Bruce Robt. 1 BOONE RD, NAVAL HOSPITAL 98312 #005-06-1985 L1991 **GPM** *020 †70

CLEGG, Tiffin Carl. 616 6TH ST 98337 #550-02-1999 L2002 **FM** *020 †18

COGAN, Oscar Jerome. 2520 CHERRY AVE 98310 #016-11-1965 L1983 **IM NEP** *020 †20

COGEN, Kenneth Alan. 2771 HEMLOCK ST, STE 201 98310 #041-01-1973 L1977 **NEP IM** *020 †20

COLIGNON, Ward Brace. 2601 CHERRY AVE STE 315, KITSAP INTERNAL MEDICINE A 98310 #054-04-1980 L1985 **IM RHU** *020 †20

CORLEY, David Edward. 1225 CAMPBELL WAY STE 201, KITSAP CHEST CONSULTANTS 98310 #010-02-1990 L1992 **PUD CCM** *020 †20

COX, Richard Arrington. 2520 CHERRY AVE, DEPT OF PATH 98310 #038-06-1975 L1976 **PTH** *071 †50

COYLE, Joseph T. ■ 98310 #539-02-1927 L1930 **GP** *071

CREELMAN, Ernest W. ■ 98312 #024-01-1946 L1952 **IM CD** *071 †20

CROMWELL, Gordon N, Jr. 2600 CHERRY AVE STE 202 98310 #048-04-1970 L1974 **ORS** *020 †40

CROWLEY, John Walter. 1 BOONE RD, NAVAL HOSPITAL, C/083F 98312 #010-02-1982 L1992 **DR IM** *020 †80

DALY, Karen Ann. 1 BOONE RD, NAVAL HOSP MENTAL HLTH DEP 98312 #005-14-1984 L1986 **P FM** *020 †75,18

DAMRONGPIPATKIJ, Y. 2709 HEMLOCK ST 98310 #891-07-1993 L2003 **CD** *020 †20

DAVARN, Scott Patrick. 2520 CHERRY AVE, HARRISON MEDICAL CENTER 98310 #054-04-2004 L2007 **EM** *020

DAVIS, Gregory Ronald. 2520 CHERRY AVE 98310 #036-01-1992 L1998 **EM** *020 †16

DAVIS, Henry Fred. 1 BOONE RD, PROFESSIONAL AFFAIRS CODE 98312 #005-11-1962 L2003 **FM AM** *071 †18

DAVIS, Joe Jack. 2520 CHERRY AVE, WOUNDCARE SERVICES 98310 #048-12-1970 L1975 **GS** *020 †85

DHANANI, Salimah. 616 6TH ST, PENINSULA COMMUNITY 98337 #704-25-1998 L2004 **PD** *020 †55

DHAWAN, Mandeep Singh. 616 6TH ST, PENINSULA COMMUNITY 98337 #495-03-1998 L2005 **IM** *020 †20

DIAMOND, Angela. 1225 CAMPBELL WAY STE 101, OF KITSAP CO 98310 #054-04-1989 L1993 **VS TS** *020 †90,85

DIBBLE, Rolland Edward. 2025 WHEATON WAY, STE 102 98310 #539-01-1967 L1986 **AN OS** *020

DICK, Mark Lee. ■ 98312 #028-46-1993 L1994 **IMG** *020 †20

DOHODA, Richard Stanley. 1 BOONE RD, NAVAL HOSPITAL 98312 #023-12-1988 L2006 **OPH** *020 †35

DOMMERMUTH, Ronald Floyd. 1 BOONE RD, NAVAL HOSPITAL 98312 #023-12-1991 L1993 **FM** *020 †18

DORE, Frederick H, Jr. 2620 WHEATON WAY, STE 1 98310 #028-34-1984 L1985 **IM** *020 †20

DREW, Frederick Edgar. 2512 WHEATON WAY 98310 #021-05-1948 L1950 **FM** *072 †18

DROZ, Angela Marie. 1 BOONE RD, ATTN PROFESSIONAL AFFAIRS 98312 #011-02-1997 L2003 **FM** *020 †20

DUCKWORTH, Garrett W, Jr. 1400 FARRAGUT AVE, PSNS BHC CODE 063 98314 #028-46-1977 L2002 **OM GP** *020

DUFF, Gregory Paul. 2600 WHEATON WAY, # 311 98310 #024-01-1992 L1997 **ORS** *072 †40

DUGGAL, Narinder Mohan. 2520 CHERRY AVE 98310 #061-01-1994 L1998 **IM DIA** *020 †20

DUTKY, Paul Arthur. ■ 98312 #030-05-1977 L1986 **EM ORS** *020 †16

EADY, Karen A. 2771 HEMLOCK ST, STE 201 98310 #056-06-1984 L1989 **IM** *020 †20

EAGAN, Roger Kenneth. 1225 CAMPBELL WAY, STE 201 98310 #016-45-1999 L2006 **PCC SME** *020

EDER, Kenneth Walter. ■ 98310 #041-13-1963 L1972 **ORS** *071 †40

EISENBERG, Mark Howard. 2520 CHERRY AVE, EMERGENCY DEPARTMENT 98310 #038-06-1998 L2001 **EM** *020 †16

EKIN, Scott Thomas. 2520 CHERRY AVE, HARRISON HOSPITAL 98310 #026-08-1993 L1999 **EM** *020 †16

ERICKSON, Kimberly K. ■ 98337 #051-07-2001 L2001 *020

EVANOFF, George V, Jr. 2771 HEMLOCK ST, STE 201 98310 #021-06-1981 L1994 **NEP IM** *020 †20

FEINMAN, Jessica Ariel. ■ 98337 #054-04-1998 L2003 **P** *020 †75

FELDBAU, Gary Alan. 2520 CHERRY AVE 98310 #165-04-1971 L1975 **FM** *020 †18

FELTS, A Douglas. 616 6TH ST, PENINSULA COMMUNITY 98337 #019-02-1989 L1992 **FM** *020 †18

FERMAN, William Bradley. 1310 BERTHA AVE, # A 98312 #858-02-1983 L1989 **FM OBS** *020

FLEISCHMAN, Sally S. 2520 CHERRY AVE 98310 #550-02-1999 L2002 **FM** *020 †18

FRANZ, Ernest Andrew. 2520 CHERRY AVE, HARRISON MEMORIAL HOSPITAL 98310 #017-20-1985 L1988 **EM** *020 †16

FRUM, Daniel K. 2512 WHEATON WAY 98310 #040-02-1983 L1984 **D** *020 †15

GANNON, Michael John. 2741 WHEATON WAY, STE A 98310 #010-02-1990 L1996 **IM** *020 †20

GEORGE, Donald Lee. 2720 CLARE AVE, STE B 98310 #396-04-1982 L1987 **GS** *020 †85

GHOSH, Prabhakar C. BOONE ROAD 98312 #495-54-1965 L1992 **GS** *071 †85

GOULD, Robert Joseph. 1 BOONE RD, PROFESSIONAL AFFAIRS, C/08 98312 #030-06-2002 L2007 **IM** *012

GRABINSKY, Andreas. 2601 CHERRY AVE STE 304, PENINSULA PAIN CLINIC 98310 #409-23-1996 L2004 **AN** *020 †05

GRABOWSKI, Michael V. 2520 CHERRY AVE, HARRISON MEM HOSP PATHOL 98310 #056-06-1965 L1972 **PTH** *020 †50

GRAISY, Edward L. 3206 PINE RD NE 98310 #016-43-1953 L1954 **GP** *071

GREEN, Johnny Bert. 2528 WHEATON WAY STE 103, KITSAP COLORECTAL SURGERY, 98310 #054-04-1980 L1997 **CRS GS** *040 †10,85

GREENE, Garry Reid. 5050 STATE HIGHWAY 303 NE, STE 103 98311 #054-04-1978 L1983 **AN** *020 †05

GREENFELD, Bernard M. 1651 NE BENTLEY DR 98311 #005-11-1971 L1978 **EM OM** *020 †16

GRETCH, Gary Jos. 2620 WHEATON WAY, STE 1 98310 #028-02-1987 L1991 **IM** *020 †20

GREY, Nancy Briller. 2520 CHERRY AVE 98310 #041-14-1986 L1988 **AN** *020 †05

GROSS, Major Ryan. 2601 CHERRY AVE, STE 315 98310 #017-20-1988 L1995 **IM** *020 †20

GULDJORD, Knute Moe. 2655 WHEATON WAY 98310 #054-04-1961 L1967 **OPH** *071 †35

HABENER, Stephen Arthur. 2635 WHEATON WAY 98310 #005-14-1967 L1970 **OTO** *020 †45

HAGMANN, John Henry. 2520 CHERRY AVE, HARRISON MEMORIAL HOSPITAL 98310 #023-12-1980 L1989 **EM** *030 †10

HALL, George Mason. PO BOX 960, 400 WARREN AVE 98337 #054-04-1960 L1967 **OTO** *071 †45

HALLIGAN, William Keith. 2512 WHEATON WAY 98310 #005-06-1973 L1977 **GS** *020 †85

HALLMAN, Keith Oliver. 2520 CHERRY AVE, OLYMPIC MEDICAL LABS INC 98310 #011-02-1970 L1971 **PTH** *020 †50

HAMBLETON, Jeffrey David. 2520 CHERRY AVE 98310 #005-19-1978 L1979 **FM OBG** *020 †18

HAMBLETON, Jeffrey Scott. 2025 WHEATON WAY, STE 102 98310 #654-01-2001 L2003 **AN** *020 †05

HAMILTON, Andrew Russell. 1 BOONE RD, NAVAL HOSPITAL 98312 #056-06-1982 L2005 **FM** *020 †18

HAMMAR, Samuel Pitcher. 700 LEBO BLVD BOX 2171 98310 #054-04-1969 L1970 **PTH** *020 †50

HAMON, Charles Burr. 2601 CHERRY AVE, STE 315 98310 #024-05-1968 L1970 **IM** *020 †20

HAN, Susan Kwon. ■ 98311 #035-45-1992 L1992 **IM** *020 †20

HARDAWAY, John Victor. 1 BOONE RD, OPHTHALMOLOGY DEPT 98312 #023-12-1994 L1995 **OPH** *020 †35

HARPUR, Timothy John. 2601 CHERRY AVE 98310 #056-05-1999 L2003 **IM AN** *020 †05

HASHIM, Mohammad Jawad. 2520 CHERRY AVE 98310 #704-25-1994 L2002 **FM** *020 †18

HAVILAND, James West. ■ 98312 #023-07-1936 L1940 **IM ADL** *071 †20

HAYDU, Francis Eugene. 1651 NE BENTLEY DR 98311 #054-04-1976 L1994 **EM** *020 †16

HAYES, Jean C. 2025 WHEATON WAY, STE 102 98310 #041-02-1973 L1997 **AN** *020 †05

HEATH, Victor C. BOONE ROAD 98312 #005-14-1962 L1990 **PTH** *020 †50

HEBER, Kari Kent. 2720 CLARE AVE, STE C 98310 #023-12-1997 L1999 **N** *020

HEDGES, John Chas. 2500 CHERRY AVE, KITSAP UROLOGY ASSOCIATES 98310 #005-14-1974 L1980 **U EM** *020 †95

HEGEWALD, Michael Gerard. 2512 WHEATON WAY, THE DOCTORS CLINIC 98310 #054-04-1984 L1991 **CD IM** *020 †20

HENNES, David Michael. 2709 HEMLOCK ST 98310 #054-04-1964 L1966 **IM** *020 †20

HERMAN, Joseph James. 2601 CHERRY AVE, STE 315 98310 #005-06-1986 L1991 **ID IM** *020 †20

HERRERA, Mark Edward. 1 BOONE RD, MEDICAL STAFF SERVICES C/0 98312 #023-12-1996 L2004 **DR** *020 †80

HILBORN, Glen Alan. 2601 CHERRY AVE 98310 #031-01-1988 L1992 **AN** *020 †05

HILLYER, Jon Frederick. 2520 CHERRY AVE 98310 #019-02-1991 L1995 **AN** *020 †05

HINRICHS, Ward Lane. ■ 98311 #030-05-1958 L1959 **PD PDC** *071 †55

HOLDER, Curtis Hulon. 843 6TH ST, STE 230/240 98337 #021-01-1989 L1997 **P** *020 †75

HOLDREN, Dale Norman. 2655 WHEATON WAY 98310 #054-04-1990 L1994 **OPH** *020 †35

HOOVLER, Anthony Ray. 2512 WHEATON WAY, THE DOCTORS CLINIC 98310 #020-02-1992 L2006 **IM** *020 †20

HOPPER, Betty Ilene. ■ 98311 #028-02-1959 L1963 **P** *071

HOSTETTER, H Glenn. ■ 98310 #041-02-1960 L1966 **PD** *071 †55

HOUSTON, Harry Rollins. ■ 98311 #024-07-1955 L1968 **OBG** *071 †30

HRISSIKOPOULOS, Peter A. 2520 CHERRY AVE 98310 #048-02-1979 L1983 **AN** *020 †05

HSU, Nan-Shing. 1 BOONE RD, NAVAL HOSPITAL BREMERTON 98312 #306-01-1996 L2002 **FPG** *012 †18

HSU, Tsu-Liang. ■ 98311 #244-03-1958 L1981 **AN** *071

HUANG, Anthony Boohan. 2520 CHERRY AVE 98310 #244-06-1971 L1981 **OBG IM** *020 †30

HUSODO, Indrawan. 2601 CHERRY AVE 98310 #143-08-1979 L1991 **AN IM** *020 †05

HUTCHINSON, Chad Hunter. 2520 CHERRY AVE 98310 #054-04-1991 L1994 **AN** *020 †05

IVERSEN, Larry Dean. 840 CALLAHAN DR, STE C 98310 #054-04-1970 L1971 **ORS** *020 †40 ‡

JACK, Hayden Orin. 1 BOONE RD, NAVAL HOSPITAL, C/083F 98312 #010-03-1995 L1996 **DR** *020 †80

JACOBSON, Laura Belcove. 2520 CHERRY AVE, HARRISON MED CTR 98310 #016-11-1979 L2005 **PTH PCP** *020 †50 ‡

JANSEN, Perry Albert. 925 ADELE AVE 98311 #041-14-1991 L1994 **FM** *020 †18

JENSEN, Warren P. ■ 98312 #021-05-1947 L1953 **PD** *071 †55

JOHNSON, Christopher C. 2709 HEMLOCK ST 98310 #048-12-1983 L1985 **CD IM** *020 †20

JOHNSON, Frank Lewis. ■ 98312 #025-12-1972 L1983 **FM** *071 †18
JOHNSON, Joseph Lowell. 2720 CLARE AVE, STE A 98310 #021-01-1983 L1988 **ON HEM** *020 †20
JOHNSON, Larry Hugh. 1 BOONE RD, NAVAL HOSP, C/083F 98312 #024-07-1975 L1999 **FM** *020 †18
JOHNSON, Michael Lee. 2601 CHERRY AVE 98310 #038-43-1980 L1986 **AN EM** *020 †05
JUN, Stephan Frank. 1 BOONE RD, NAVAL HOSPITAL, C/083F 98312 #054-04-1987 L1993 **PTH GP** *020 †50
JUNGSCHAFFER, Dana Ann. 2655 WHEATON WAY 98310 #005-06-1991 L1999 **OPH** *020 †35
KAIN, Christopher C. 2500 CHERRY AVE, STE 304 98310 #010-02-1981 L1989 **ORS OSS** *020 †40
KATIGBAK, Amado M, Jr. 2741 WHEATON WAY STE A, OLYMPIC VIEW BUILDING 98310 #748-01-1989 L2001 **IM** *020 †20
KECK, Jeffrey Paul, Jr. 83F BOONE RD, NAVAL HOSPITAL BREMERTON 98312 #041-14-1999 L2001 **AN** *012
KERRIGAN, John Thomas. 2520 CHERRY AVE 98310 #422-01-1987 L1993 **AN GS** *020 †05
KILDUFF, James Thos. 2500 CHERRY AVE STE 301 98310 #025-07-1967 L1969 **U ID** *071 †95
KILLORAN, Sean Michael. 4373 MINARD RD W 98312 #016-06-1965 L1970 **P CHP** *020 †75 ‡
KIM, Jeong Hwan. 1 BOONE RD 31, NAVAL HOSP 98312 #051-07-1999 L2007 **IM GE** *020 †20
KING, Lonnie Tildon. USNH-BREMERTON OTO 98314 #054-04-1977 L1983 **OTO** *020 †45
KING, Robert C. 2771 HEMLOCK ST STE 100, HARRISON PHYSICIANS-CTS 98310 #039-01-1971 L1989 **ORS** *020 †40
KLIONS, Kenneth David. ■ 98312 #041-12-1985 L2003 **AN** *020 †05
KOTAS, Walter S. ■ 98310 #016-11-1938 L1947 **GP OS** *071 †70
KREMER, Paul Andrew. 2601 CHERRY AVE STE 2, SUITE 215 98310 #054-04-1988 L1993 **OPH OS** *020 †35
KRIEG, Margaret Mary. 1225 CAMPBELL WAY STE 201, KITSAP CHEST CONSULTANTS 98310 #012-05-1989 L1989 **CCM IM** *020 †20
KUHNER, Ben Richard. 1900 NE RIDDELL RD 98310 #040-02-1963 L1976 **P** *071 †75
LAMBERG, John David. 2512 WHEATON WAY 98310 #054-04-1971 L1979 **ON HEM** *071 †20
LANE, Brian William. 2520 CHERRY AVE 98310 #030-06-1988 L2005 **EM** *020 †16
LEAKE, Jeffrey Park. 2025 WHEATON WAY 98310 #038-40-1982 L1985 **AN** *020 †05
LEE, Arthur Bryant. 2709 HEMLOCK ST 98310 #054-04-1977 L1981 **CD IM** *020 †20
LEIST, Frederick Douglas. 2600 CHERRY AVE, STE 201 98310 #056-05-1967 L1969 **PS GS** *020 †85,65
LE THANH, Clement P N. ■ 98311 #396-31-1997 L2006 **PD** *020
LINDQUIST, Scott Wayne. 345 6TH ST 98337 #054-04-1992 L1996 **PD** *020 †55
LINDSTROM, Eric Richard. 2512 WHEATON WAY, DOCTORS CLINIC 98310 #028-02-1975 L1995 **IM** *020 †20
LIVINGSTONE, Bruce L. ■ 98337 #019-02-1949 L1971 **P N** *071 †75
LONG, Dawn Michelle. ■ 98312 #016-43-2006 L2007 **FP** *012
LOUTZENHEISER, Todd D. 2520 CHERRY AVE 98310 #050-02-1999 L2003 **AN** *020 †05
LUBETICH, John F, Jr. 2520 CHERRY AVE 98310 #019-02-1987 L1991 **AN** *020 †05
LUCAS, Peter Brown. 5002 KITSAP WAY # 106, GROUP HEALTH COOPERATIVE 98312 #038-06-1981 L1993 **P IM** *020 †75
LUCE, Ronda Fay. BOONE RD 98312 #024-01-1978 L1986 **EM FM** *020 †18
MARQUEZ, Luis Enrique. 1 BOONE RD, C/083F, NAVAL HOSP 98312 #042-03-1997 L2006 **EM** *020 †16
MARTENS, Jeffrey Steven. 1 BOONE RD, NAVAL HOSPITAL 98312 #023-12-2001 L2003 **PD** *020 †55
MATHESON, George Wm. 400 WARREN AVE, KPS HEALTH PLANS 98337 #054-04-1963 L1964 **MDM OBG** *030 †30
MC CLUSKEY, Donald J. 2512 WHEATON WAY 98310 #030-06-1955 L1958 **FM** *071 †18
MC COY, Brian Patrick. 1 BOONE RD, NAVAL HOSP PROFF AFFAIRS C 98312 #016-43-2000 L2006 **AN** *020 †05
MC CULLOUGH, Paul Singer. 2011 E 11TH ST 98310 #030-06-1959 L1965 **ORS** *071 †40
MC DOWELL, Michael P. ■ 98312 #001-02-2000 L2000 **OTO** *020 †45
MC GREGOR, Marianne E. ■ 98312 #054-04-1981 L1983 **GPM OS** *020
MC MANUS, Michael Sean. 2741 WHEATON WAY STE A, GROUP HEALTH COOPERATIVE 98310 #005-15-1983 L1986 **PUD OM** *020 †70
MEANS, James Franklin. NAVAL REG MED CTR, DEPT PED 98314 #040-02-1968 **PD** *020 †55
MERRILL, Barth Edward. 1 BOONE RD, NAVAL HOSPITAL BREMERTON 98312 #023-12-1991 L1992 **FM GP** *020 †18
MEYER, Roger Jess. ■ 98310 #028-02-1955 L1958 **PHP PD** *020 †55
MICHAELIS, Milton S. 2700 CLARE AVE 98310 #023-01-1964 L1970 **R** *020 †80
MILLER, Arthur V, Jr. 2512 WHEATON WAY 98310 #021-01-1941 L1964 **U** *071
MILSPAW, Jennifer Leigh. ■ 98310 #012-05-2002 L2005 **OBG** *020
MOON, Michael Robt. 900 SHERIDAN RD STE 109 98310 #040-02-1970 L1976 **AN** *071 †05
MOORE, Donna Elizabeth. 2528 WHEATON WAY, STE 206 98310 #016-42-1985 L1986 **PM** *020 †60
MORRIS, William David. 2520 CHERRY AVE, EMERGENCY MEDICINE 98310 #054-04-1998 L2002 **EM** *020
MOTUZ LEEN, Martha M. 2601 CHERRY AVE STE 215 98310 #043-01-1988 L1993 **OPH** *020 †35
MULDONG, Estelita T. ■ 98312 #748-01-1964 L1976 **IM NEP** *020
MURPHY, Ann Elizabeth. 2720 CLARE AVE, STE A 98310 #054-04-1987 L1990 **ON** *020 †20
NIAKAN, Enayat. 2720 CLARE AVE STE C 98310 #517-01-1973 L1987 **N** *020 †75
NICHOLSON, John C. ■ 98310 #048-16-1990 L1991 **OTO** *020 †45
NYQUIST, Brian O. 2601 CHERRY AVE 98310 #030-05-1980 L1986 **AN UM** *020 †05,18
OLSEN, Terrill Carlyle. 2601 CHERRY AVE, STE 215 98310 #026-04-1966 L1968 **OPH** *020 †35
ORTIZ, Donnaville Francis. 616 6TH ST 98337 #748-02-2001 L2007 **FM** *020 †18
PACIOTTI, Mark Vincent. 2709 HEMLOCK ST 98310 #026-04-1978 L1984 **CD** *020 †20
PARKER, Jay Robt. 2520 CHERRY AVE 98310 #003-01-1974 L1977 **GP GYN** *020
PICKETT, Mark Terry. 1 BOONE RD, MEDICAL STAFF SERVICES, C/ 98312 #023-12-1984 L1987 **AN** *020 †05
PIEDAD, Emerich Damo. 1 BOONE RD, ATTN: CREDENTIAL OFFICE, C 98312 #023-12-1996 L1998 **FM** *020 †18
POCUIS, David Leo. 2512 WHEATON WAY, DOCTORS CLINIC 98310 #025-12-1973 L1974 **FM** *071 †18
POHL, Stephen Eric. 1 BOONE RD, ATTN: MEDICAL STAFF SERVIC 98312 #017-20-1968 L1979 **EM AM** *020 †16
POPE, Sara Margaret. ■ 98310 #050-02-2007 **FP** *012
PRYDE, Katherine Anne. 2520 CHERRY AVE, EMERGENCY DEPARTMENT 98310 #016-42-1997 L2001 **EM** *020 †16
PULUKURTHY, Satyavardhan. 2709 HEMLOCK ST 98310 #495-62-1997 L2006 **CD** *020 †20
RAMIREZ, Hedim Obsum. 2601 CHERRY AVE 98310 #748-08-1974 L1980 **AN** *020
RASMUSSEN, Eric Ove. 2512 WHEATON WAY 98310 #005-19-1977 L1981 **D DMP** *020 †15
REICHARD, Scott Ray. 1651 NE BENTLEY DR, PROMP CARE 98311 #038-45-1989 L1998 **EM** *020 †16
REIMER, Ronald Robt. 2720 CLARE AVE, STE A 98310 #025-12-1973 L1980 **ON HEM** *020 †20
REINACH, Robert Chas. 5455 ALMIRA DR NE, KITSAP MENTAL HEALTH SERVI 98311 #016-11-1971 L1996 **P** *020 †75
REYES, Hector, Jr. 2512 WHEATON WAY, THE DOCTORS CLINIC OF EAST 98310 #748-08-1986 L2007 **IM** *020
RICHARDSON, John Rowe. 2520 CHERRY AVE 98310 #025-12-1973 L1974 **N IM** *020 †75
RICHARDSON, William B. 2512 WHEATON WAY 98310 #016-06-1951 L1951 **PD** *071
ROBERTS, William Michael. NAVAL HOSPITAL, ATTN: CREDENTIAL OFFICE 98314 #010-01-1979 L1981 **ORS** *020 †16
ROBERTSON, John S. ■ 98311 #035-15-2006 **FP** *012
ROHLFING, James Jeffrey. 2700 CLARE AVE 98310 #054-04-1986 L1991 **DR IM** *020 †80
ROSE, David Michael. 2025 WHEATON WAY STE 102 98310 #038-40-1973 L1983 **AN** *020 †05
ROWND, William Ernest, Jr. ■ 98310 #021-05-1942 L1944 **GP GS** *071
ROZENDAL, Robert Henry. 2520 CHERRY AVE 98310 #040-02-1966 L1985 **OS FM** *030 †18
RUBENSTEIN, Robert Scott. 2512 WHEATON WAY 98310 #005-18-1986 L1991 **N** *020 †75
SALMON, Chas Lester, Jr. ■ 98337 #051-04-1943 L1947 **GS** *071 †85
SAVAGE, Paul Jeffrey. 1 BOONE RD, C/083F 98312 #028-34-1987 L1994 **IM** *020 †20
SCHMIDT, Donald Le Roy. ■ 98310 #016-06-1954 L1956 **ON HEM** *071 †20
SCHMIDT, Kathryn Nicole. 1 BOONE RD 98312 #056-06-1994 L1995 **IM** *020 †20
SCHUBERT, Thomas W. 2520 CHERRY AVE 98310 #056-06-1952 L1953 **OPH** *071 †35
SCHULZE, Keith Alan. 2500 CHERRY AVE, KITSAP UROLOGY ASSOCIATES 98310 #020-02-1980 L1986 **U GS** *020 †95
SCHUMACHER, Cynthia Lynn. 1 BOONE RD, C/083F, NAVAL HOSPITAL 98312 #016-06-1989 L1992 **OM IM** *020 †70
SCHWEITZER, Erik John. 1 BOONE RD, ATTN PROFESSIONAL AFFAIRS 98312 #025-01-1994 L1996 **FM** *020 †18
SCOTT, Charles Mc Coy. 2520 CHERRY AVE 98310 #041-01-1958 L1986 **GYN** *020 †30
SEAL, William Clayborn. 2520 CHERRY AVE 98310 #005-15-1968 L1977 **IM IMG** *020 †20
SEVERSON, Jewell A. ■ 98312 #054-04-1953 L1956 **GP GYN** *072
SHAH, Jignesh S. 2709 HEMLOCK ST 98310 #496-38-1997 L2005 **ICE** *020 †20
SHARMA, Pankaj. 728 LEBO BLVD 98310 #495-34-1973 L1981 **GE IM** *020 †20
SHARMAN, Donald Lee. 2601 CHERRY AVE STE 213 98310 #005-12-1983 L1986 **IM** *020 †20
SHOQUIST, Devin Michael. 1 BOONE RD 98312 #054-04-1997 L2006 **P** *020 †75
SHULER, Gail Karen. 5002 KITSAP WAY STE 200 98312 #041-13-1980 L1989 **P** *020 †75
SMITH, Christopher Dunlap. 2601 CHERRY AVE 98310 #054-04-1993 L1996 **AN** *020 †05
SOLZE, Elizabeth Gail. 1 BOONE RD, C/083F 98312 #001-06-2002 L2005 **IM** *020 †20
SORENSEN, Kenton Scott. 2655 WHEATON WAY 98310 #016-43-1993 L2002 **OPH** *020 †35
SPIEKER, Michael Raymond. 1 BOONE RD, CODE 035 NAVAL HOSP 98312 #040-02-1981 L1982 **FM** *040 †18
SPIRO, Robert Timothy. 1 BOONE RD, C/083F, NAVAL HOSP 98312 #012-01-1968 L2006 **PD UM** *071 †55
SPRINGATE, Stephen C. 2520 CHERRY AVE 98310 #016-02-1986 L1991 **RO** *020 †80
STAEHELI, Christopher C. 1 BOONE RD, NAVAL HOSPITAL 98312 #054-04-1984 L1989 **CHP** *020 †75
STAKER, Lynn Le Roy. 900 SHERIDAN RD STE 105 98310 #049-01-1965 L1972 **ORS** *020
STA. MARIA, Anna Marie Ce. ■ 98312 #748-01-1998 L2007 **FM** *100
STANFORD, Alfred. 1 BOONE RD, MED STAFF SVS, C/083F, NAV 98312 #041-09-1976 L1991 **DR** *020 †80
STANLEY, John L P. 2512 WHEATON WAY 98310 #054-04-1951 L1953 **FM IM** *071
STEELE, Michael Bartolome. ■ 98311 #005-12-2002 L2003 *020 †20
STUMP, William John. 840 CALLAHAN DR STE C 98310 #041-14-1973 L1975 **N LM** *062 †75
SWIFT, John David. 2601 CHERRY AVE, STE 302 98310 #005-14-1982 L1986 **IM** *020 †20
SY, Benjamin C. 2512 WHEATON WAY 98310 #748-01-1997 L2006 **PCC** *020 †20 ‡
TAN, Rana Teresa. 2512 WHEATON WAY 98310 #005-19-1990 L1997 **PUD** *020 †20
TANNER, Craig Edward. ■ 98337 #054-04-1999 L2003 **OS** *020 †20
TAYLOR, Francee Jean. 2601 CHERRY AVE, STE 315 98310 #054-04-1989 L1993 **IM** *020 †20
TECHENTIN, Anna Louise. 1 BOONE RD, PROFESSIONAL AFFAIRS CODE 98312 #030-06-2002 L2003 **FM** *020 †18
THUT, David Christian. 1 BOONE RD, C/083F, NAVAL HOSPITAL 98312 #041-01-1995 L2004 **ORS** *020 †40
TIBBALS, Benjamin Vance. 2771 HEMLOCK ST STE 100 98310 #017-20-2001 L2002 **AN** *020 †05
TICE, Paul. 2520 CHERRY AVE, HARRISON HOSPITAL 98310 #005-18-1972 L1973 **EM GP** *020 †16
TINKER, David D. 2709 HEMLOCK ST 98310 #023-01-1977 L1982 **CD IM** *020 †20
TORRES, Joanne Marie. 2520 CHERRY AVE, HARRISON HOSPITAL 98310 #025-01-2001 L2007 **EM** *020 †16
TURPIN, Jack T. 2520 CHERRY AVE 98310 #016-06-1950 L1951 **FM GP** *075 †18
UNDERDOWN, William Edward. 2520 CHERRY AVE 98310 #011-03-1977 L1985 **FM EM** *020 †18
URBON, Richard Lyle, Jr. 2520 CHERRY AVE 98310 #056-06-1999 L2006 **IM** *020 †20
VAN DER WILDE, Robert. 3421 KITSAP WAY 98312 #660-03-1956 L1959 **GP FM** *020 †18
VARU, Vanraj C. 2520 CHERRY AVE, HARRISON MEDICAL CENTER 98310 #495-79-1975 L1993 **P** *020
VASIN, Dimitri. 840 CALLAHAN DR STE A 98310 #913-06-1988 L2000 **NEP** *020 †20
VENTURINI, Chrystel T. 2601 CHERRY AVE, STE 105 98310 #396-38-1994 L2001 **RNR** *020 †80
VIEK, Christa Von Reis. ■ 98311 #407-16-1953 L1959 **PD GYN** *075
WADDELL, Richard Allen. 1 BOONE RD, CODE 083F 98312 #012-05-1997 L2003 **EM** *020 †16
WALLS, David Louis. 4040 WHEATON WAY STE 203 98310 #017-20-1959 L1965 **D** *040 †15
WATSON, John A. ■ 98310 #016-01-1940 L1941 **GP** *071
WAYNE, Ronald Geo. 2601 CHERRY AVE 98310 #005-06-1978 L2002 **AN** *020 †05
WESLEY, Richard Bruce. 1225 CAMPBELL WAY, STE 201 98310 #023-07-1971 L1976 **PUD IM** *020 †20
WIGGINS, George E. 2512 WHEATON WAY 98310 #038-40-1980 L1987 **FM OBS** *020 †18
WILLERFORD, Dennis M. 2720 CLARE AVE STE A 98310 #028-02-1985 L1986 **HEM GS** *020 †20
WILLIAMS, Linda Lee. 2520 CHERRY AVE 98310 #041-07-1996 L2000 **P** *020 †75
WILSON, Harry R, Jr. BOONE RD 98312 #041-12-1945 L1990 **GYN** *071 †30
WINTER, Malcolm Wm. 2720 CLARE AVE, STE A 98310 #054-04-1981 L1989 **ON HEM** *020 †20
WOODMAN, Charles Albert. 2601 CHERRY AVE, STE 315 98310 #016-43-1974 L1977 **IM** *020 †20
WORTH, Michael Paul. 2601 CHERRY AVE 98310 #550-02-1997 L2001 **AN** *020 †05

■ = Address Information Privacy Protected

9197

YEE, Yuen San. 2771 HEMLOCK ST, STE 202 98310 #016-45-1983 L1991 **GE IM** *020 †20
YEKEL, Robert Lemoyne. 2512 WHEATON WAY 98310 #030-05-1958 L1959 **GS** *071 †85
YENNI, Lawrence Jon. 1 BOONE RD C/083F, NAVAL HOSPITAL 98312 #019-02-1996 L2006 **ORS** *020 †40
YOUNG, Sherwood Fredrick. 900 PACIFIC AVE 98337 #016-06-1965 L1974 **PM** *020 †60

BREWSTER – OKANOGAN

HAEGER, Eric Edward. PO BOX 577, 507 HOSPITAL WAY 98812 #005-12-1995 L2001 **FM** *020 †18
HANSON, Lindsay Keith. PO BOX 517 98812 #005-12-1978 L1988 **FM** *020 †18
HARDINGE, Mervyn G. ■ 98812 #005-12-1942 L1942 **NTR OS** *071
JENSEN, Joseph Lehigh, III. 703 N W 2ND ST 98812 #038-40-1971 L1974 **FM** *020 ‡
NIEHAUS, Linda Sue. ■ 98812 #026-08-1988 L1994 **FM** *020 †
STOUT, Harold B. PO BOX 517, 520 W INDIAN AVE 98812 #005-12-1938 L1940 **FM GP** *071 †18

BRIER – SNOHOMISH

CIHAK, Robert James. ■ 98036 #024-01-1966 L1971 **DR** *071 †80
MARTENS, Irvin Jos. ■ 98036 #028-34-1943 L1987 **TRS** *071
RAY, Lance Ira. 23824 BRIER RD 98036 #021-01-1970 L1971 **GS** *020 †85

BRINNON – JEFFERSON

MC CANN, Desmond. ■ 98320 #803-03-1959 L1962 **P** *071

BRUSH PRAIRIE – CLARK

EDLICH, Richard French. ■ 98606 #035-19-1962 L1969 **PS** *020 †85,65
JOHNSON, Robert Lee. ■ 98606 #026-04-1960 L1960 **RHU IM** *071 †20 ‡
KOHL, Steve. ■ 98606 #035-01-1970 L1973 **ID PD** *040 †55
PINNEY, Chas Tannert, Jr. ■ 98606 #040-02-1981 L1998 **EM GP** *020
ROMERO-GOERTZ, Peter L. ■ 98606 #040-02-1981 L1984 **AN** *020 †05

BUCKLEY – PIERCE

BREDIN, June Gweneth. 2120 RYAN RD, RAINIER SCHOOL 98321 #054-04-1984 L1990 **FM OS** *020 †18
CHUBBUCK, Jimmy Dean. 2120 RYAN RD, RAINIER SCHOOL 98321 #054-04-1980 L1982 **FM** *020 †18
DAHL, Christian Wm. 2120 RYAN RD, RAINIER SCHOOL RHC 98321 #026-01-1983 L1986 **FM AM** *020 †18
RUVALCABA, Rogelio. RAINIER SCHOOL 98321 #649-14-1957 L1964 **PD PDE** *071 †55
TAIT, Douglas Anthony. 738 MAIN ST 98321 #065-01-1956 L1959 **FM** *071 †18
WELSH, Michael A. 305 N RIVER AVE 98321 #028-46-1982 L1988 **FM** *020 †18

BURIEN – KING

ALCORN, Garrett Dale. 16251 SYLVESTER RD SW, DEPT PATH 98166 #016-11-1982 L1983 **PTH** *020 †50
AL-KUDSI, Razan Ragda. 16259 SYLVESTER RD SW, STE 401 98166 #875-01-1974 L1991 **NEP IM** *020 †20
ANDREWS, James Ernest. 16251 SYLVESTER RD SW, HIGHLINE COMMUNITY HOSPITA 98166 #024-05-1978 L1982 **FM** *020 †16
ARANCA, Andres Geo. 15217 8TH AVE S STE A 98148 #748-10-1975 L1983 **OBG OS** *020
ARBELO, Nilda Ruth. 457 SW 148TH ST, STE 202 98166 #042-01-1980 L1995 **FM** *020 †18
BAGATELL, Carrie Jo. 16259 SYLVESTER RD SW, STE 504 98166 #012-05-1984 L1987 **END IM** *050 †20
BAKER, Gordon Philo. 14203 AMBAUM BLVD SW 98166 #010-01-1955 L1963 **AI PDA** *020 †55,03
BARRONIAN, Alan Dirk. 16259 SYLVESTER RD SW, STE 501 98166 #054-04-1985 L1990 **ORS** *020 †40
BLATNER, Michael Eugene. 16259 SYLVESTER RD SW, STE 302 98166 #028-34-1987 L1993 **PS** *020 †65
BOCKOW, Barry Ira. 16122 8TH AVE SW STE D3 98166 #038-06-1975 L1979 **IM** *020
BUCK, Harper J. ■ 98166 #030-05-1961 L1973 **FM AM** *071 †18
BUNCH, Stephen Andrew. 16259 SYLVESTER RD SW #504, THREE TREE MEDICAL BLDG 98166 #054-04-1955 L1957 **IM** *071
BURNETT, Curtis Stowell. 16259 SYLVESTER RD SW, STE 401 98166 #014-01-1981 L1986 **CD IM** *020 †20
BUTLER, David John. 140 SW 146TH ST 98166 #049-01-1973 L1975 **FM** *020 †18
BUTTITTA, James Joseph. 16233 SYLVESTER RD SW #230, HIGHLINE INTERNAL MEDICINE 98166 #041-02-1994 L1996 **IM** *020 †20
BUTTITTA, Patricia F. 16110 8TH AVE SW STE A, SEAHURST MEDICAL CENTER 98166 #041-02-1992 L1995 **IM** *020 †20
CHIN, Edwin. 16233 SYLVESTER RD SW, STE 250 98166 #748-07-1987 L1996 **IM NEP** *020 †20
CHOCK, Alan Richard. 16251 SYLVESTER RD SW, HIGHLINE COMMUNITY HOSP 98166 #014-01-1980 L1983 **EM** *020 †16
CHOW, Robert K P. 13512 AMBAUM BLVD SW, # 100 98146 #067-01-1992 L1999 **D** *020 †15
CHOW, Tszming. 16259 SYLVESTER RD SW, STE 503 98166 #041-12-2001 L2001 **N** *020
CLARK, Robert Leon. 16251 SYLVESTER RD SW 98166 #654-01-1981 L1992 **PUD CCM** *020
CLARK, William Lincoln. 16259 SYLVESTER RD SW # 50 98166 #054-04-1988 L1995 **HS** *020 †40
CLEMENT, James Frederick. 16259 SYLVESTER RD SW, STE 504 98166 #032-01-1985 L1986 **IM** *020 †20
CONGER, Dean Michael. 14031 AMBAUM BLVD SW, UPPER LEVEL 98166 #010-01-1991 L1991 **OPH** *020 †35
DAVILA, Edward Danl. 629 SW 153RD ST 98166 #649-02-1987 L1990 **IM** *020 †20
DEAN, Thomas Andrew. 16251 SYLVESTER RD SW 98166 #054-04-1995 L2000 **PCP** *020 †50

DE GROOT, Jerry. 16122 8TH AVE SW STE E5 98166 #010-01-1960 L1962 **OBG** *071 †30
DIEM, Heidi Lori. ■ 98166 #054-04-1988 *100
DONG, Kenneth H. 14212 AMBAUM BLVD SW, STE 202 98166 #048-02-1994 L1997 **PD** *020 †55
DONOVAN, Janet Giardina. 16233 AMBAUM BLVD S, STE G40 98148 #041-09-1991 L1991 **FM** *020 †18
DOUGHTEN, Philip T, Jr. 140 SW 146TH ST 98166 #038-06-1978 L1984 **FM** *020 †18
DUNCAN, Christopher W. 16122 8TH AVE SW, STE E3 98166 #051-04-2001 L2007 **GE** *020 †20
DUNCANSON, Neil P. 14212 AMBAUM BLVD SW, STE 202 98166 #016-06-1958 L1962 **PD** *071 †55
ELAHI, Paymon. 14212 AMBAUM BLVD SW 98166 #021-01-1995 L1999 **PD** *020 †55
ERICKSON, Clayton Dale. 221 SW 153RD ST STE 258 98166 #054-04-1971 L1976 **OS FM** *075
ESCHBACH, Eugenie Marie. 1010 S 146TH ST 98168 #054-04-1986 L1996 **P** *020 †75 ‡
EVANS, Jeffrey Lewis. 16259 SYLVESTER RD SW, STE 303 98166 #048-04-2000 L2006 **U** *020 †95
FINKLE-WEAVER, Cedar. 16259 SYLVESTER RD SW, STE 301 98166 #056-06-1991 L1993 **OBG** *020 †30
FRANKEL, Jeffrey Marc. 16259 SYLVESTER RD SW, STE 303 98166 #054-04-1979 L1985 **U** *020 †95
GARCIA, Gregory Paul. 16251 SYLVESTER RD SW, EMERGENCY DEPARTMENT 98166 #005-06-2000 L2004 **EM** *020 †16
GHARIB, Salma Fatemeh. 16251 SYLVESTER RD SW 98166 #517-05-1997 L2002 **IM** *020 †16
GMEINER, Kjersten Elrida. 140 SW 146TH ST, GROUP HEALTH BURIEN 98166 #026-04-1998 L2000 **FM** *020 †18
GOTT, Paul Eric. 16122 8TH AVE SW, STE D1 98166 #021-01-1988 L2000 **GS** *020 †85
GOTTLIEB, Daniel William. 16259 SYLVESTER RD SW #401 98166 #024-05-1978 L1983 **CD IM** *020 †20
GRABOWSKI, Wm Stanley. 16251 SYLVESTER RD SW, HIGHLINE RADIOLOGY ASSOCIA 98166 #012-05-1975 L1992 **DR** *030 †80
GREEN, David Chas. 16259 SYLVESTER RD SW, STE 505 98166 #024-01-1985 L1990 **HNS OTO** *020 †45
GREENFIELD, Mark David. 16110 8TH AVE SW STE C2 98166 #020-12-1978 L1981 **PD ID** *020 †55
GREGORES, Basil John. 14212 AMBAUM BLVD SW 98166 #054-04-1953 L1956 **PD** *071 †55
GRIDLEY, Gary Douglas. 16251 SYLVESTER RD SW, MEDICAL STAFF OFFICE, HCH 98166 #011-03-1990 L1993 **AN** *020 †05
GRIFFITH, Robert Breen. 16233 SYLVESTER RD SW, STE 260 98166 #038-41-1964 L1966 **GP** *020
GRUNENBERG, Nicole Ann. 457 SW 148TH ST, STE 202 & 203 98166 #038-41-1994 L1996 **FM** *020 †18
GUNSUL, Alan Lane Webster. 216 SW 156TH ST 98166 #054-04-1955 L1956 **FM LM** *071 †18
HABIB, Sadia Farah. 16110 8TH AVE SW, STE A2 98166 #704-08-1999 L2006 **IM** *020 †20
HACKER, Lisa Marie. 1010 S 146TH ST, HIGHLINE W SEATTLE MENTAL 98168 #025-01-1985 L1986 **CHP P** *071 †75
HAMBURGER, Rena Mae. 203 SW 153RD ST 98166 #054-15-1964 **GP** *071
HANEY, Steven Thos. 1010 S 146TH ST, HEALTH CENTER 98168 #038-40-1977 L1988 **P** *020 †75
HANSEN, Dayne Dennis, Jr. 16259 SYLVESTER RD SW, STE 401 98166 #054-04-1976 L1977 **CD IM** *020 †20
HAPUTA, Andrew John. 16122 8TH AVE SW, STE D1 98166 #036-01-2000 L2004 **GS** *020 †85
HARTWELL, Peter Shattuck. 16122 8TH AVE SW STE E3 98166 #016-02-1981 L1982 **GE IM** *020 †20
HARTZLER, Edward Wm. 16233 AMBAUM BLVD S, STE G40 98148 #017-20-1970 L1973 **FM** *020 †18
HAZELTINE, Frederick G. ■ 98146 #054-04-1951 L1954 **PD** *071 †55
HELLER, Howard Frederick. ■ 98166 #016-06-1977 L1980 **FM** *030 †18
HENKLE, Esther. 16233 SYLVESTER RD SW, STE G40 98166 #847-04-1995 L2003 **FM** *020 †18
HENLEY, David Scott. 16259 SYLVESTER RD SW 98166 #005-06-1987 L1993 **DR IM** *020 †80
HENRY, Robert Earl. ■ 98146 #028-34-1963 L1963 **NM HEM** *071 †28,20
HINCHEY, James. ■ 98166 #024-05-2005 L2005 **EM** *012
HINELINE, Theresa Lynn. 14212 AMBAUM BLVD SW, STE 202 98166 #030-05-1991 L1996 **PD** *020 †55
HOLMAN, Joan Donovan. 140 SW 146TH ST, GROUP HEALTH COOPERATIVE 98166 #028-03-1988 L1990 **IM** *020 †20
HOUK, Joseph T. ■ 98166 #017-20-1949 L1956 **DR** *071 †80
HOWELL, William Brooks. 16259 SYLVESTER RD SW, GENERAL AND VASCULAR SURGE 98166 #054-04-1963 L1964 **GS VS** *020 †85
HUCHALA, Thomas James. 14212 AMBAUM BLVD SW, STE 201 98166 #054-04-1956 L1957 **GP** *071 †18
HULSE, Thomas Edward. 15211 8TH AVE S 98148 #748-08-1974 L1977 **FM** *020 †18
ISAACSON, Jeanne Manna. 16259 SYLVESTER RD SW 98166 #035-48-1991 L2000 **IM** *020 †20
JACKSON, Frederic Neven. 16259 SYLVESTER RD SW, STE 403 98166 #054-04-1976 L1981 **PUD CCM** *020 †20
JACOBUS, Ryland M. ■ 98166 #016-01-1940 L1948 **FM GP** *071
JAIN, Sapna. 140 SW 146TH ST 98166 #054-04-1999 L2001 **FM** *020 †18
JESSEN, Barbara Green. ■ 98146 #016-11-1958 L1989 **N PME** *062 †75 ‡
JOHNSON, Steele Raymond. 16110 8TH AVE SW 98166 #010-01-1972 L1980 **OBG** *071 †30
KELLER, David Wilson, III. 16259 SYLVESTER RD SW, STE 404 98166 #045-01-1988 L2000 **ID** *020 †20
KELLY, Megan Sue. 16251 SYLVESTER RD SW 98166 #025-01-1993 L1997 **OBG** *020 †30
KENNELLY, Michael M. 16122 8TH AVE SW, STE D1 98166 #054-04-1978 L1984 **GS VS** *020 †85
KHAN, Lubna Nawaz. 16233 SYLVESTER RD SW #230 98166 #704-06-1988 L2000 **IM** *020 †20
KNOPP, Douglas Kingston. 140 SW 146TH ST 98166 #054-04-1975 L1976 **FM** *020 †18
KREISMAN, Kent Newton. 16259 SYLVESTER RD SW, STE 401 98166 #028-03-1967 L1983 **IM** *020 †20
KRESSIN, Kimberly Ann. 16251 SYLVESTER RD SW, MEDICAL STAFF OFFICE 98166 #003-01-2000 L2003 **AN** *020 †05
LARSON, Roger Keith. 14212 AMBAUM BLVD SW, STE 201 98166 #054-04-1958 L1961 **FM GP** *020 †18
LEVENSON, Robert Montie. 16233 SYLVESTER RD SW, STE 110 98166 #020-02-1946 L1947 **CD IM** *071 †20
LEVENSON, Robt Monte, Jr. 16110 8TH AVE SW STE A3 98166 #054-04-1975 L1981 **ON IM** *020 †20
LEVINE, Martin Daniel. 140 SW 146TH ST 98166 #038-06-1997 L1999 **FM** *020 †18
LEVY, Elie. 13610 1ST AVE S 98168 #035-46-1991 L1997 **D DS** *020 †15 ‡
LEVY, Sarah Anne. 140 SW 146TH ST, GROUP HEALTH CO-OP BURIEN 98166 #005-02-1986 L1989 **FM** *020 †18

■ = Address Information Privacy Protected

LINDELL, Anita Kerstin. 140 SW 146TH ST 98166 #143-11-2005 L2006 **FP** *012
LOMBARDI, John Anthony. 16259 SYLVESTER RD SW, STE 501 98166 #038-44-1992 L2002 **ORS** *020 †40
LOONEY, Todd R. 16251 SYLVESTER RD SW 98166 #054-04-1981 L1982 **AN** *020 †05
LOUIE, Helen. 16122 8TH AVE SW, STE E5 98166 #041-07-1994 L1998 **OBG** *020 †30
LUTZ, Pamela Denice. 16259 SYLVESTER RD SW #301 98166 #038-41-1990 L1995 **OBG** *020 †30
MALETZKY, Avron Jos. 140 SW 146TH ST 98166 #035-01-1963 L1966 **PD PDC** *071 †55
MANOLE, Irina Mihaela. 16110 8TH AVE SW STE A1, SEAHURST FAMILY MEDICINE 98166 #781-02-1998 L2003 **FM** *020 †18
MARCUS, Gwen Elizabeth. 16110 8TH AVE SW STE C2, SEAHURST PEDIATRICS 98166 #422-01-1983 L2000 **NPM PD** *020 †55
MARSDEN, Judith Lee. 15209 8TH AVE S 98148 #016-11-1963 L1964 **GP** *020
MARTIN, Chuck Donald. 16251 SYLVESTER RD SW, HIGHLINE HOSPITAL 98166 #061-01-1992 L2003 **DR NM** *020 †80,28
MAURICE, Peter Fredric, III. 16259 SYLVESTER RD SW, STE 505 98166 #010-02-1998 L2004 **OTO PSH** *020 †45
MC CLEAN, Hugh Peter. 16259 SYLVESTER RD SW, STE 505 98166 #030-06-1954 L1955 **OTO** *071
MC CLEAN, Patrick Hugh. 16259 SYLVESTER RD SW, STE 505 98166 #054-04-1982 L1988 **OTO HNS** *020 †45
MC GREW, Deborah Ann. 16259 SYLVESTER RD SW, STE 403 98166 #034-01-1988 L2002 **PD** *020 †55
MENA, Michael Felix Marty. 16251 SYLVESTER RD SW, HIGHLINE HOSPITAL 98166 #001-02-1997 L2002 **IM** *020 †20
MERS, William Robin. 16110 8TH AVE SW, STE C3 98166 #048-02-1975 L1988 **PD** *020 †55
MEYER, Barbara Ann. 140 SW 146TH ST 98166 #025-01-1976 L1981 **FM** *020 †18
MEYER, Susan Leilani. 457 SW 148TH ST, STE 202 98166 #031-01-1983 L1998 **EM** *020 †16
MORENO, Megan A. ■ 98166 #010-01-2000 L2004 **ADL** *012 †55
MUONEKE, Vincent Nnaemeka. 16233 SYLVESTER RD SW 98166 #690-04-1980 L1990 **HS** *020 †65
NAKATA, Kenneth Michael. ■ 98166 #054-04-1981 L1985 **IM** *075
NEARY, Wendy Ingham. 16110 8TH AVE SW 98166 #056-05-1994 L1996 **FM** *020 †18
NGUYEN, David Duc. 137 SW 154TH ST 98166 #054-04-1998 L2000 **FM** *020 †18
NIELSEN, David Greer. 16525 MAPLEWILD AVE SW 98166 #026-04-1967 L1973 **OPH** *071 †35
NIXON, John Elliott. 16110 8TH AVE SW STE B 98166 #054-04-1955 L1956 **EM GP** *020 †16
OLSON, John Charles, Jr. 16233 SYLVESTER RD SW, STE G40 98166 #010-02-1998 L2000 **FM** *020 †18
OLTYAN, Karin Sue. 16233 SYLVESTER RD SW, STE G40 98166 #041-14-2002 L2005 **FM** *020 †18
ORY, Peter Alan. 275 SW 160TH ST, HIGHLINE IMAGING, LLC 98166 #048-04-1981 L1990 **DR IM** *020 †20,80
PARKER, David Paul. 16251 SYLVESTER RD SW, HIGHLINE COMM HSP EM DEPT 98166 #003-01-1990 L2002 **EM** *020 †16
PAVES, Alejandro De Guia. 16259 SYLVESTER RD SW, STE 301 98166 #748-02-1972 L1982 **GYN IM** *020 †30
PAVES, Anita V. 16110 8TH AVE SW, STE C2 98166 #748-02-1972 L1981 **PD PN** *020 †55
POLLAK, Arnold Jay. 16233 SYLVESTER RD SW, STE 260 98166 #050-02-1987 L2001 **CD NM** *020 †20
POWERS, Glenn Irving. 16251 SYLVESTER RD SW 98166 #012-21-1988 L1990 **AN** *020 †05
PUNGAN, Marian. 16251 SYLVESTER RD SW, HIGHLINE MEDICAL CENTER 98166 #781-01-1995 L2006 **IM** *020 †20
PURCELL, Nancy Lee. 16259 SYLVESTER RD SW 98166 #028-03-1967 L1971 **IM END** *020 †20
QUITIQUIT, Celeste. ■ 98146 #054-04-2008 *012
RABINOWITZ, Desmond Geo. 16110 8TH AVE SW, STE C3 98166 #836-02-1972 L1990 **PD** *020 †55
RANDOLPH, Robert Ernest. 16233 SYLVESTER RD SW, STE 110 98166 #023-07-1996 L1999 **ON** *020 †20
RANES, Paul Scott. ■ 98166 #007-02-1966 L1972 **GS** *071 †85
RECINTO, Christie Anne. 16259 SYLVESTER RD SW, STE 301 98166 #017-20-1993 L1998 **OBG** *020 †30
RIBAS MURGA, Mario. 14434 AMBAUM BLVD SW, SEAMAR COMMUNITY HEALTH CE 98166 #429-01-1977 L1988 **OM** *020
RICCI, Michael Thos. 16251 SYLVESTER RD SW, DEPT RADIOLOGY-HIGHLINE 98166 #016-11-1975 L1976 **DR** *020 †80
RICE, James W. 16251 SYLVESTER RD SW 98166 #024-07-1975 L1976 **EM** *020 †16
RICHARDSON, Robt Garratt. 16251 SYLVESTER RD SW 98166 #067-01-1968 L1973 **RO** *020 †20
RITCHIE, Kindred Aaron. 16251 SYLVESTER RD SW 98166 #054-04-1985 L1987 **CLP ATP** *020 †50
ROBERTS, Richard Wayne. ■ 98146 #054-04-1958 L1959 **P N** *071 †75
ROSEWATER, Frederick H. 13610 1ST AVE S, THE LEVY BUILDING 98168 #038-41-1965 L1974 **D** *020 †15
RYAN, Thomas Michael. 16251 SYLVESTER RD SW, COMMUNITY HOSPITAL 98166 #048-12-1979 L1980 **EM** *020 †16
SCHALLER, Gilbert K. 16110 8TH AVE SW STE A2 98166 #054-04-1952 L1954 **IM** *071
SCHLAMMINGER, Monika. ■ 98166 #408-31-2003 L2004 **FP** *012
SCHLITT, Michael James. 16259 SYLVESTER RD SW, STE 502 98166 #001-02-1978 L1989 **NS** *020 †25
SCHNEIDER, Barbara Ann. 16259 SYLVESTER RD SW, STE 504 98166 #047-05-1984 L1985 **IM** *020 †20
SFERRA, Lisa Lillian. 457 SW 148TH ST, STE 202 98166 #054-04-1997 L2003 **FM** *020 †18
SHAH, Viral Shashikant. 16251 SYLVESTER RD SW, HIGHLINE MEDICAL CENTER 98166 #495-22-2001 L2006 **NEP** *100 †20
SHIRMAN, Amos. 16110 8TH AVE SW, STE C1 98166 #550-04-1986 L1992 **FM** *020 †18
SHROFF, Mary. 16251 SYLVESTER RD SW 98166 #495-73-1976 L1997 **IM** *020 †20
SHUSTER, Patricia Ann. 16122 8TH AVE SW, STE E5 98166 #041-02-1986 L1992 **OBG** *020 †30
SKOGLUND, Rodney Dan. 16259 SYLVSTR RD #SW-504 98166 #023-07-1966 L1971 **END IM** *020 †20
SLAYMAKER, Scott Eugene. 16110 8TH AVE SW STE A 98166 #054-04-1976 L1984 **IM** *020 †20
SMITH, James Wm. 12101 AMBAUM BLVD SW 98146 #054-04-1953 L1954 **ADM FM** *020 †18
SPALEK, Nina. 12459 AMBAUM BLVD SW, STE A 98146 #748-01-1972 L1984 **GP ADM** *020
SPRAGUE, Marilyn D. ■ 98166 #014-01-1983 L1984 **AN** *071 †05
STEIN, Richard Edward. 16233 SYLVESTER RD SW, STE G20 98166 #016-11-1980 L1986 **GE IM** *020
STEINER, Michael Dennis. 16233 SYLVESTER RD SW, STE 220 98166 #035-20-1981 L1986 **OPH** *020

STRAYER, John Martin. 16251 SYLVESTER RD SW 98166 #038-40-1994 L1998 **EM** *020 †16
SUE, Donna. 16251 SYLVESTER RD SW, HIGHLINE COMMUNITY HOSPITA 98166 #061-01-1989 L1995 **EM** *020 †16
TAKASUGI, Bonnie Jean. 16233 SYLVESTER RD SW, STE 110 98166 #054-04-1978 L1986 **ON IM** *020 †20
TAMADDON, Sheri Mayron. 16251 SYLVESTER RD SW 98166 #035-45-1997 L1997 **AN** *020 †05
TATUM, Roger Perry, II. 16122 8TH AVE SW, STE D1 98166 #016-06-1995 L2001 **GS** *020 †85
TAYLOR, Cynthia L. 14212 AMBAUM BLVD SW 98166 #041-07-1981 L1988 **FM** *020 †18
TEICHER, Harry Lewis. 16122 8TH AVE SW, STE E3 98166 #035-19-1992 L1992 **GE** *020 †20
TESLER, Alan Scott. 16233 SYLVESTER RD SW # 1, SWEDISH CANCER INSTITUTE A 98166 #005-14-1972 L1984 **RO** *020 †20 ‡
TKHACHUK, Douglas Cameron. ■ 98166 #062-01-1978 *020
TOH, Jackie Chu. ■ 98166 #026-04-1972 L1980 **GP PM** *020 ‡
TRAN, Jacqueline Van. 16259 SYLVESTER RD SW, STE 503 98166 #032-01-1993 L1995 **N** *020 †75
VAN BODEGOM, John S. 16110 8TH AVE SW STE A2, SEAHURST MEDICAL CENTER 98166 #021-01-1971 L1972 **IM** *020 †20
VANDENBERG, James Jos. 322 SW 155TH ST 98166 #054-04-1954 L1956 **D** *071 †15
WATSON, John Tatum. 16110 8TH AVE SW, STE C1 98166 #045-01-1990 L1996 **FM** *020 †18
WILLEKES, Tonia Marie. 16251 SYLVESTER RD SW, HIGHLINE MEDICAL CENTER 98166 #018-03-1990 L2007 **EM** *020 †20
WILSON, Arthur Henry. 14031 AMBAUM BLVD SW, BURIEN EYE CLINIC 98166 #054-04-1954 L1958 **OPH** *071 †35
WONG, Jason Hueichiang. 140 SW 146TH ST 98166 #035-46-2000 L2002 **FM** *020 †18
WONG, Rena S. 17646 1ST AVE S 98148 #005-14-1985 L1996 **PS** *020 †65,85
ZERBY, Glenn Alan. 16251 SYLVESTER RD SW 98166 #041-02-1980 L1996 **EM IM** *020 †20,16
ZIPEROVICH, Daniel Pedro. 16233 SYLVESTER RD SW, STE 280 98166 #005-06-1983 L1988 **IM** *020 †20

BURLINGTON – SKAGIT

ABBOTT, Dale Romain. 835 E FAIRHAVEN AVE 98233 #054-04-1984 L1988 **FM EM** *020 †18
BAKER, Joel Wilson, Jr. ■ 98233 #054-04-1968 L1973 **GS** *020 †85
BERGER, Jeffrey Allen. 435 E GEORGE HOPPER RD, STE 106 98233 #017-20-1984 L1985 **P** *020
CREELMAN, Paul C. 712 S BURLINGTON BLVD 98233 #054-04-1976 L1977 **FM** *020 †18
JACOBSEN, Robert Ray. 1162 S BURLINGTON BLVD, DIETRICH & SMITH CLINIC 98233 #028-34-1993 L1999 **FM** *020 †18
KIZER, Danielle Lynne. 435 E GEORGE HOPPER RD, STE 106 98233 #038-41-1997 L1999 **PYG** *020 †75
LOHAVANICHBUTR, Pawadee. 835 E FAIRHAVEN AVE 98233 #891-04-1990 L2005 **FM** *020 †18
MOLLER, Jeffrey Lawrence. ■ 98233 #054-04-2008 *012
POWELL, Robert Lee. ■ 98233 #008-01-1956 L1985 **DR** *071 †80
SANCHEZ, James David. 435 E GEORGE HOPPER RD, STE 106 98233 #054-04-1988 L1991 **P** *020 †75
SARRO, Louis J. ■ 98233 #016-06-1942 L1946 **OPH** *071 †35
SHELTON, Melvin Dewey. 435 E GEORGE HOPPER RD, STE 106 98233 #039-01-1988 L2005 **P** *050 †75
SHILLING, David Douglas. 712 S BURLINGTON BLVD 98233 #024-01-1976 L1977 **FM** *020 †18
SMITH, David Edwards. 16442 COUNTRY CLUB DR 98233 #041-13-1960 L1969 **GS CD** *071 †85
STARK, Eric Richard. 835 E FAIRHAVEN AVE 98233 #005-11-1994 L1996 **FM** *020 †18
ZIMMERMANN, Timm Allen. ■ 98233 #056-05-1963 L1965 **IM NM** *071 †28,20

CAMANO ISLAND – ISLAND

BARTOK, Stephen Jos. ■ 98282 #005-02-1969 L1993 **DR** *020 †80
FINLEY, John Wm. ■ 98282 #024-01-1943 L1948 **GS** *062 †85
GRABILL, James Rodney. ■ 98282 #023-01-1952 L1982 **GP IM** *071
KREJCHA, James Jos. ■ 98282 #016-11-1960 L1996 **FM** *071 †18
KUYPERS, Marcus Eric. 891 SE CAMANO DR 98282 #048-14-1977 L1981 **EM GP** *020 †16
RAGDE, Haakon. 1080 UTSALADY RD 98282 #051-01-1957 L1966 **U OS** *020 †95
SODT, Peter Christian. ■ 98282 #016-06-1980 L1982 **PDC PD** *071 †55
TAO, Liang-Che. ■ 98282 #243-47-1954 **PCP** *040 †50
ZIELINSKI, Dorothy Ann. 370 NE CAMANO DR, STE 5 # 136 98282 #016-01-1982 L2002 **FM** *020 †18

CAMAS – CLARK

BADIEI, Basheer Alexis. 3400 SE 196TH AVE, STE 101 98607 #040-02-1989 L2000 **D** *020 †15
BERI, Meena. 19301 SE 34TH ST STE 104 98607 #495-65-1978 L1999 **OPH** *020 †35
CARAG, Henry R. ■ 98607 #016-02-1995 L2007 **DMP** *020 †50
COWAN, Christopher Lee. 1442 NW ILWACO CT 98607 #026-04-1982 L1999 **NM DR** *020 †80,28
DAVIS, David Benj, II. ■ 98607 #048-02-1959 L2001 **OPH** *071 †35
DHINGRA, Anshu. 3240 NE 3RD AVE 98607 #495-34-1994 L2005 **FM** *020 †18
FARRIS, Cathleen Lynn. ■ 98607 #016-42-1985 L1989 **N** *020
GASKELL, Arthur, III. 411 NE 6TH AVE 98607 #005-12-1983 L1985 **FM** *075 †18
GREENE, Nathan William. ■ 98607 #041-02-1995 L2003 **HS** *020 †40
HOLLEY, John Alan. ■ 98607 #050-02-1994 L2004 **FM** *020 †18
KUHLE, William Gerard. 1709 NW 40TH AVE, COLUMBIA IMAGING GROUP 98607 #005-14-1992 L2004 **VIR** *020 †80
KUZIS, Karl Anthony. 713 NE 4TH AVE, FAMILY DOCTORS OFFICE 98607 #040-02-1999 L2002 **FM** *020 †18
LIEM, Annie Lian-Foong. 713 NE 4TH AVE 98607 #005-12-1970 L1996 **PD** *020 †55
MILLER, Carole R. ■ 98607 #028-34-1992 L1995 **FM** *020 †18
NORRIS, Charles Walter. ■ 98607 #010-02-1957 L1959 **OBG OS** *071
ORCHARD, Michael James. ■ 98607 #040-02-1985 L1990 **AN GS** *020 †05
PAIK, David. ■ 98607 #005-12-2006 L2006 **FP** *012
PAO, Dorothy May. ■ 98607 #025-01-1999 L2004 **DR** *020 †80
PORTER, Henrik Petersen. ■ 98607 #035-20-1960 L1969 **IM ID** *071 †20
SHEN, Joseph Pius. ■ 98607 #025-01-1997 L2004 **DR** *020 †80

WU, Yaping. ■ 98607 #243-63-1983 L2005 **HMP** *100 †50

CAMP MURRAY – PIERCE

MALTZ, Ben Ray. BLDG 6, 10TH CST (WMD) 98430 #016-42-1986 L1993 **EM** *020 †16

CARNATION – KING

JENSEN, Ann. ■ 98014 #040-02-1972 L1976 **OBG** *020 †30
STEELE, Dean Wesley. 29923 NE TOLT HILL RD 98014 #028-02-1985 L1990 **EM** *020 †16

CARSON – SKAMANIA

BECKER, Robert L. 112 NEWPORT DR 98610 #005-12-1953 L1954 **GP** *071

CASHMERE – CHELAN

HOYER, Thomas V. ■ 98815 #025-01-1951 L1952 **P** *071 †75
KOLOKOFF, Valerie Ruth. 303 COTTAGE AVE 98815 #010-01-1981 L1984 **FM** *020 †18
MEYER, Edgar A. 303 COTTAGE AVE 98815 #018-03-1950 L1954 **FM** *071 †18
SCHNEIDER, Robert Lyle. 203 MISSION AVE STE 107 98815 #026-04-1963 L1993
  PM GP *020 †60

CASTLE ROCK – COWLITZ

AYOUB, Anwar Fayez. 341 FRONT AVE NW BOX 747 98611 #847-05-1975 L1997 **GS** *020
AYOUB, Reinhild E W. ■ 98611 #409-10-1982 L1989 **PD** *020 †55
JONES, Clarence W. ■ 98611 #005-12-1955 L1957 **ORS** *071 †40
TORRES, Emma Vergara. 1026 S ROAKE STREET 98611 #748-08-1974 L1983 *020

CATHLAMET – WAHKIAKUM

HAUGE, Arthur Lyddon. ■ 98612 #040-02-1962 L1970 **ORS** *062 †40
WRIGHT, Keith James. 335 UNA AVE 98612 #016-45-1992 L1995 **FM** *020 †18

CENTERVILLE – KLICKITAT

CHILES, Paul Allen. ■ 98613 #054-04-1971 L1976 **GP PHP** *075
CROCKER, John J. 366 SIMCOE MOUNTAIN RD 98613 #054-04-1980 L1981 **FM** *020 †18

CENTRALIA – LEWIS

ANDERSON, Keith Victor. 1900 COOKS HILL RD 98531 #035-45-1981 L1990 **ORS HS** *020 †40
BAN, Jong-Wook. 1121 HARRISON AVE 98531 #583-15-1997 L2004 **IM** *100
BECKFORD, Noel Donavan. 1900 COOKS HILL RD 98531 #035-08-1984 L1990 **AN** *020 †05
BILLINGS, Robert Eugene. 914 S SCHEUBER RD 98531 #025-07-1970 L1973 **EM** *020
BIRCHARD, Carl Russell. 1900 COOKS HILL RD 98531 #016-11-1968 L1977 **ORS** *071 †40
BIRCHARD, Keith Ray. 1900 COOKS HILL RD, WASHINGTON ORTHOPAEDIC CTR 98531
  #054-04-1999 L2002 **ORS** *020
BIXLER, David Loren. 914 S SCHEUBER RD 98531 #017-20-1974 L2004 **IM CCM** *020 †20
BLITMAN, Maury N. 1800 COOKS HILL RD, STE F 98531 #041-09-1986 L2007
  HEM AN *020 †20
BROWND, Richard Gordon. 914 S SCHEUBER RD 98531 #039-01-1974 L1989 **EM** *020 †16
BURDEN, Kenneth H. 914 S SCHEUBER RD 98531 #005-12-1953 L1973 **FM** *020 †18
CARTER, Gregory Thaddeus. 1809 COOKS HILL RD 98531 #016-43-1986 L1994
  PM GPM *050 †60
CASERTA, Kevin Todd. 1809 COOKS HILL RD 98531 #038-40-1999 L2003 **PM** *020 †60
COOPER, Loren Dale. 1800 COOKS HILL RD 98531 #005-12-1969 L1976 **IM CD** *020 †20
DALTON, Cynthia Kay. 1800 COOKS HILL RD, STE A 98531 #051-04-1987 L1993 **GS** *020 †85
DEMUN, Eric Murray. 1740 COOKS HILL RD 98531 #051-01-1995 L1997 **FM** *020 †18
EHLERS, Sally Maria. 1720 COOKS HILL RD 98531 #040-02-1991 L1997 **GS** *020 †85
EILAND, John E. 1000 S SCHEUBER RD 98531 #005-76-1999, ▲ L2004 *020
ESTRADA, Evelyn Sandico. 1000 S SCHEUBER RD 98531 #748-08-1961 L1979 **OBG** *020
FELL, Thomas E. 914 S SCHEUBER RD 98531 #016-02-1963 L1967 **AN** *020 †05
FERGUSON, Benjamin R, Jr. 1800 COOKS HILL RD, %LOWER COLUMBIA PATH 98531
  #007-02-1963 L1965 **PTH NM** *062 †50,28
FICK, David Lawrence. 1800 COOKS HILL RD 98531 #040-02-1978 L1979 **IM** *020 †20
FRITZ, Anthony Wolfgang. ■ 98531 #005-12-1988 L1991 **IM** *020 †20
GALVIN, Ross Mitchell. ■ 98531 #020-02-1943 L1944 **FM** *071
GENSOLIN, Dexter Mercurio. 1707 COOKS HILL RD, CENTRALIA SPECIALITY CENTE 98531
  #748-09-1985 L2001 **FM** *020 †18
GREEN, Philip Allen. 914 S SCHEUBER RD 98531 #054-04-2000 L2003 **EM** *020 †16
HARMON, David Kent. 1800 COOKS HILL RD 98531 #054-04-1971 L1976 **U** *071 †95
HAYDEN, Douglas Lee. 914 S SCHEUBER RD 98531 #054-04-1981 L1982 **EM** *020 †16
HENNESSEY, Stephen D. 1720 COOKS HILL RD, ASSOCIATED SURGEONS OF WA 98531
  #048-14-1983 L1988 **GS OS** *020 †85
HOLLAND, Jackson Riley. 1800 COOKS HILL RD 98531 #021-06-1973 L1974 **OTO** *020 †45
HULL, Larry Dale. 1900 COOKS HILL RD 98531 #054-04-1964 L1967 **ORS** *020 †40
KENNARD, Scott Carl. 914 S SCHEUBER RD 98531 #048-12-1979 L1980 **AN** *062 †05
KURTZ, Waldon V. ■ 98531 #007-02-1960 L1981 **GP** *071
LARSON, Mark Thos. 914 S SCHEUBER RD 98531 #012-05-1991 L1993 **EM** *020 †16
LOWE, Daniel Kingsley. 1720 COOKS HILL RD 98531 #040-02-1972 L2003 **GS TRS** *020 †85
LYNAM, Sheila Diane. 914 S SCHEUBER RD 98531 #039-01-1993 L1999 **PTH** *020 †50
MC CULLOUGH, Francis H. ■ 98531 #036-07-1943 L1957 **ORS** *071 †40
MC GILL, Charles Lewis. 208 W LOCUST ST, MEDICAL CNETER 98531 #005-12-1996 L2000
  FM *020 †18
MCINTYRE, Brenda Lenez. 230 WASHINGTON WAY 98531 #422-01-1997 L2003 **PD** *020 †55
NELSON, Chris E. 914 S SCHEUBER RD 98531 #005-12-1978 L1981 **PD** *020 †55

NELSON, Larry Ronald. 1800 COOKS HILL RD 98531 #054-04-1972 L1973 **IM** *020 †20
NISHIYAMA, Mark. 1900 COOKS HILL RD 98531 #005-12-1987 L2001 **OBG** *020 †30
OGDEN, Frank Wm. 914 S SCHEUBER RD 98531 #054-04-1961 L1965 **GS GP** *020
O'NEILL, Patrick Michael. 914 S SCHEUBER RD 98531 #020-02-1980 L1986
  EM FM *020 †18,16
PERKO, Kenneth Patrick. 1740 COOKS HILL RD, INC PS 98531 #054-04-1970 L1975
  FM *071 †18
POLITE, Brenda Lee. 1000 S SCHEUBER RD, CENTRALIA WOMEN'S CENTER 98531
  #005-12-1989 L2003 **FM** *020 †18
POPE, Isaac S. 230 WASHINGTON WAY 98531 #054-04-1974 L1975 **PD** *020
PRENTICE, Joseph Orlando. ■ 98531 #005-02-1975 L1981 **AN OS** *020
REISWIG, Marc Lowry. 914 S SCHEUBER RD, CENTRALIA FIRE DEPARTMENT 98531
  #005-12-1995 L1998 **EM** *020 †16
ROBINSON, Stanley Wade. 914 S SCHEUBER RD 98531 #019-02-2001 L2005 **EM** *020 †16
ROCO, Manuel N. 914 S SCHEUBER RD 98531 #748-01-1961 L1968 **GP PDE** *020
ROPKA, Mark Gilbert. 1720 COOKS HILL RD 98531 #005-12-1971 L1976 **GS** *020 †85
SCHLEGEL, Roy Walter. 2428 W REYNOLDS AVE, CASCADE MENTAL HEALTH CARE 98531
  #007-02-2000 L2005 **CHP** *020 †75
SCHUAL-BERKE, Danl Albert. 914 S SCHEUBER RD 98531 #035-09-1979 L1982 **EM** *020 †16
SHASHA, Khalil Ibraheam N. 914 S SCHEUBER RD 98531 #528-04-1992 L2002 **IM** *020 †20
SHERFEY, Justin J. 1900 COOKS HILL RD, WASHINGTON ORTHOPEDIC CENT 98531
  #005-76-1999, ▲ L2004 **ORS OAR** *020
SLATTERY, Scott Chas. 1900 COOKS HILL RD 98531 #005-12-1990 L1999 **ORS** *020 †40
SMITH, Floyd Dale. 1800 COOKS HILL RD 98531 #051-01-1979 L1982 **IM CD** *020 †20
SOUTHWELL, Craig L. 914 S SCHEUBER RD 98531 #067-01-1980 L1989 **EM** *020 †16
TAYLOR, Michael Verne. 914 S SCHEUBER RD, ANES. DEPT 98531 #028-02-1975 L2000
  AN *020
THAKKER, Atul. 1720 COOKS HILL RD 98531 #005-14-1992 L1997 **GS** *020 †85
UBANI, Chinweuba Enyinnay. 914 S SCHEUBER RD, PROVIDENCE CENTRALIA HOSPI 98531
  #690-10-1994 L2007 **IM** *020 †20
VORVICK, Linda Jean. 914 S SCHEUBER RD 98531 #054-04-1982 L1983 **FM** *040 †18
WILLIAMS, David Verne. 208 W LOCUST ST 98531 #054-04-1964 L1968 **FM** *071 †18
WILLIAMS, Paul David. 208 W LOCUST ST 98531 #035-03-1993 L1995 **FM** *020 †18
YARTER, Christopher Lee. 1740 COOKS HILL RD, INC PS 98531 #051-01-1995 L1998
  FM *018 †18

CHATTAROY – SPOKANE

BENNETT, David Allan. 34705 N NEWPORT HWY 99003 #041-12-1981 L1999 **PD** *020 †55
FULLER, Robert Lee, Jr. 25507 N REGAL RD, P O BOX 289 99003 #034-01-1978 L1985
  EM GP *020
STIME, Nathan Paul. 34705 N NEWPORT HWY, RIVERSIDE MEDICAL CLINIC 99003
  #054-04-1968 L1969 **FM** *020
WALLNER, Herman Charles. ■ 99003 #005-02-1962 L1978 **OBG** *071 †30

CHEHALIS – LEWIS

ADAMS, Jeanne M. 176 NE SCHOOL ST 98532 #016-43-1975 L1978 **FM** *020 †18
BUNGE, Paul David. 1299 BISHOP RD 98532 #028-03-1995 L2004 **IM OS** *020 †20
CHAN, Terence Tat Yin. 981 S MARKET BLVD 98532 #005-12-1979 L1986 **DR** *020 †80
CHAWLA, Jitesh Jagdish. 500 SE WASHINGTON AVE, VALLEY VIEW HEALTH CENTER 98532
  #436-03-2001 L2004 **FM** *020 †18
CHUNG, Iris Jungmin. ■ 98532 #005-12-1995 L2001 **FM** *020 †18
CHUNG, Paul Yosun. 2517 NE KRESKY AVE, PACIFIC CATARACT & LASER 98532
  #005-12-1991 L2001 **OPH** *020 †35
ELLOWAY, Simon. 155 N MARKET BLVD 98532 #005-12-1963 L1964 **FM IM** *020 †18
FRITZ, Helmuth Franz. ■ 98532 #005-12-1973 L1977 **IM CD** *071 †20
GANO, David Lee. 2517 NE KRESKY AVE, KAISER FOUNDATION HOSPITAL 98532
  #005-12-1993 L2007 **OPH** *020 †35
GAWLIK, Michael Mariusz. 1299 BISHOP RD, STECK MEDICAL CENTER 98532
  #759-01-2000 L2003 **IM** *020 †20
GIEBEL, Arthur Weldon. 2517 NE KRESKY AVE 98532 #005-12-1991 L2006 **OPH** *020 †35
GIMBEL, Hervey Willis. 1299 BISHOP RD 98532 #005-12-1955 L2001 **OM GPM** *020 †70
KNIGHT, Arthur L. ■ 98532 #064-01-1949 L1950 **OM** *071
KUGEL, Robert Dennis. 143 WOODCREST DR 98532 #005-12-1980 L1987 **GS** *071 †85
LE PROWSE, Conrad Robt. 370 S MARKET BLVD 98532 #034-01-1986 L1989 **PD** *020 †55
LOVIN, Jeffrey Douglas. 187 ALDERWOOD DR 98532 #054-04-1984 L1996 **DR OS** *020 †80
MC ELHANEY, Robert Dean, Jr. 4254 JACKSON HWY 98532 #025-12-1998 L2001 **FM** *020 †18
MILLER, Harley Daniel. 1299 BISHOP RD BOX 1267 98532 #005-12-1962 L1967
  GP RHU *020 †18.
NYGARD, Edward Andrew. 981 S MARKET BLVD, P O BOX 1201 98532 #005-12-1970 L1976
  DR *020 †80
PLASTER, Burton Clay. 709 NW PENNSYLVANIA AVE, P O BOX 1707 98532 #051-01-1986 L1988
  FM *020 †18
REISWIG, Robert A. 981 S MARKET BLVD 98532 #005-12-1966 L1974 **R** *020 †80
RITLAND, Sandra K. 500 SE WASHINGTON AVE 98532 #005-12-1981 L2004 **FM** *020 †18
SATTAR, Anjan Kazi. 135 W MAIN ST 98532 #913-89-1992 L2003 **P** *020
SLATTERY, Kristin Kuhlman. ■ 98532 #005-12-1990 L1991 **GP** *020
SMITH, Wayne M. ■ 98532 #054-04-1954 L1955 **GP** *071
STROHBACH, Michael W. 1299 BISHOP RD 98532 #005-12-1985 L1986 **FM** *030 †18
WILLIAMS, Ronald James. 1299 BISHOP RD 98532 #054-04-1981 L1985 **EM** *020
WOOD, Rachel Carus. 360 NW NORTH ST 98532 #007-02-1984 L1995 **FM PHP** *030 †18

CHELAN – CHELAN

BOYDSTUN, James Allen. 320 N EMERSON 98816 #004-01-1966 L1978 **P AM** *071 †75
CLEMENTS, Martin Joseph. ■ 98816 #020-02-2004 L2005 **FM** *020 †18
CRAMPTON, Susan Marie. PO BOX 368 98816 #040-02-1985 L1987 **FM** *020 †18
ENE-STROESCU, Valerica D. 503 E HIGHLAND AVE, LAKE CHELAN COMM HOSP 98816
  #781-01-1995 L2003 **P** *020
ETHIER, James William. 503 E HIGHLAND AVE, LAKE CHELAN COMM HOSP 98816
  #064-01-1980 L2001 **ADP P** *020 †75

FISHER, William Richard. ■ 98816 #048-04-1958 L1962 **FM** *071 †18
GAMELIN, Lili Marie. ■ 98816 #028-03-1983 L1987 **NEP** *020 †20
HUTTON, Amy Elizabeth. 219 E JOHNSON AVE 98816 #016-43-1999 L2002 **FM** *071 †18
JAMES, Charles Franklin. ■ 98816 #054-04-1964 L1969 **FM** *071 †18
KLINGNER, Mary Celeste. 106 EVERGREEN AVE 98816 #028-03-1998 L2003 **FM** *020 †18
KREMER, John Arthur, II. 219 E JOHNSON AVE 98816 #007-02-1978 L1979 **FM** *020 †18
TAGGE, Gordon Kent. 7375 RIDGEVIEW DR, C/O LAKE CHELAN CLINIC 98816
     #048-14-1985 L1996 **GS** *020 †85
TRAVERS, Michael Danl. PO BOX 368, 219 E JOHNSON AVE 98816 #025-12-1981 L1991
     FM *020 †18
WASZKEWITZ, Charles Jay. 219 E JOHNSON AVE 98816 #033-06-1981 L1987 **FM** *020 †18

CHENEY – SPOKANE

HOUGH, Charles Benj. 19 N 7TH ST 99004 #054-04-1980 L1981 **FM** *020 †18
KOESKE, Tom Jerome. 19 N 7TH ST 99004 #005-19-1985 L1986 **FM** *071
RAM, Pushpa Sangadala. 12205 W ORCHARD TER 99004 #495-37-1982 L1985 **FM** *020
STABEN, Jonathan Mark. 19 N 7TH ST 99004 #054-04-2000 L2002 **FM** *020 †18 ‡

CHEWELAH – STEVENS

BALDWIN, Gary Thos. 518 E CLAY AVE 99109 #048-12-1980 L2007 **OBG** *020 †30
BOONE, Thomas John. 500 E WEBSTER AVE 99109 #024-01-1975 L1977 **FM** *020 †18
BROCK, Sylvia Eunice. ■ 99109 #007-02-1974 L1977 **GP** *020
HOUSER, Glenn David. 1872 DRY CREEK RD 99109 #032-01-1982 L1987 **FM** *020 †18
JOHNSTONE, Kimberlyn Ann. 500 E WEBSTER AVE 99109 #005-06-1988 L1991 **FM** *020 †18
LINDEMAN, Donald Henning. ■ 99109 #030-05-1962 L1969 **GP** *071 †18
MOYER, Robin Nelson. 500 E WEBSTER AVE 99109 #041-14-1984 L1987 **FM OBG** *020 †18
SISCO, James Gregory. 500 E WEBSTER AVE 99109 #054-04-1991 L1994 **FM** *020 †18
ZUGEC, Maja. 500 E WEBSTER AVE, ST. JOSEPH'S HOSPITAL 99109 #957-01-1985 L1998
     IM *020 †20

CHIMACUM – JEFFERSON

DUFF, William R. 2481 ANDERSON LAKE RD, # 614 98325 #048-14-1975 L1978 **P OS** *071
HARPER, Jack Richard. 2481 ANDERSON LAKE RD, RM 643 98325 #019-02-1954 L1956
     GS *075

CITY OF SPOKANE VALLEY – SPOKANE

DE WITT, Harvey Jennings. ■ 99212 #010-01-1956 L1975 **ORS** *020 †40

CLARKSTON – ASOTIN

BAIRD, Thomas Douglas. ■ 99403 #035-15-1941 L1953 **PD GP** *071
BERG, Sara Amsterdam. 1623 5TH ST STE B 99403 #056-06-1987 L1991 **OBG** *020 †30
BLACK, Elizabeth L. 1267 BELMONT WAY 99403 #035-46-1997 L2005 **FM** *020 †18
CHIN, Donald Kenneth. 1221 HIGHLAND AVE, EMERGENCY ROOM 99403 #030-05-1973 L1989
     FM *020 †18
CHINCHINIAN, Harry. ■ 99403 #056-06-1959 L1964 **PTH FOP** *071 †50
CIHAK, Robert Wm. 1225 HIGHLAND AVE 99403 #005-14-1967 L1976 **PTH FOP** *020 †50
DE MEYERE, Aaron Marshall. 1623 5TH ST, STE A 99403 #003-01-1980 L1995 **OBG** *020
DRIVER, Michael Kirk. 1221 HIGHLAND AVE 99403 #040-02-1980 L1988 **FM** *020 †18
EGGLESTON, Mark Thomas. 500 PORT DR, EYE CARE SPECIALISTS 99403
     #030-06-1997 L2000 **OPH** *020 †35
EGGLESTON, Richard John. 500 PORT DR 99403 #019-02-1967 L1974 **OPH GP** *020 †35
ERNSTER, Allen Michael. 1422 15TH ST, HOUSE CALLS 99403 #048-15-1989 L1999
     FM *020 †18
FORE, Jane Ann. 1119 HIGHLAND AVE, STE 7 99403 #019-02-1979 L1998 **IM OS** *020 †20
GARCIA, Jose Yu, Jr. 1119 HIGHLAND AVE, STE 5 99403 #748-01-1979 L2000 **NEP IM** *020 †20
GARGES, Lawrence Marston. 1207 EVERGREEN CT, ALL-ASTHMA TRISTE CLINIC 99403
     #649-01-1965 L1970 **AI IM** *020 †20,03
GERWELS, John Walter. ■ 99403 #049-01-1968 L1974 **D DS** *071 †15
GREGGAIN, Donald James. 1271 HIGHLAND AVE 99403 #068-01-1980 L1994 **FM** *020
HALL, Richard Michael. ■ 99403 #025-12-2008 *012
HARRIS, Jeffrey Lynn. 1221 HIGHLAND AVE, TRISTATE MEDICAL CENTER 99403
     #056-06-1991 L1996 **IM** *020 †20
HERBERT, Wesley R, Jr. 617 DIAGONAL ST 99403 #041-09-1965 L1969 **OPH** *020
HYDE, Reed Warren. 1221 HIGHLAND AVE 99403 #067-01-1944 L1968 **OTO A** *072 †45
KOENEN, Carl Theodore. ■ 99403 #056-06-1958 L1964 **PTH** *071 †50
LAYTON, Rex G. ■ 99403 #039-01-1939 L1947 **OPH A** *075
MACKAY, Jayme Theodore. 1271 HIGHLAND AVE 99403 #060-01-1980 L1998 **FM** *020
MANNSCHRECK, John Wm. 1254 HIGHLAND AVE 99403 #054-04-1987 L1989 **DR** *020 †80
MARTYN, Kurt Richard. 1221 HIGHLAND AVE, TRI STATE MEM HOSP 99403
     #056-06-1973 L1993 **EM** *020 †16
MOUNTJOY, Dennis Gerry. 1271 HIGHLAND AVE 99403 #005-06-1976 L1994 **IM EM** *020
SEIBLY, Walter Willard. ■ 99403 #005-12-1945 L1947 **FPG GS** *071
SPENCER, David Alan. 2723 SCENIC HILLS DR 99403 #039-01-1964 L1972 **GS** *020 †85
STEIN, Matthew Alexander. 1254 HIGHLAND AVE, TWIN CITIES RADIOLOGY 99403
     #031-01-1992 L1998 **RNR** *020 †80
WEILAND, Richard John. 1207 EVERGREEN CT 99403 #054-04-1973 L1977 **GP IM** *020
WILLIAMS, Walter L. 1119 HIGHLAND AVE, STE 1 99403 #019-02-1996 L2002 **D** *020 †15

CLAYTON – STEVENS

MC CALLUM, James A. ■ 99110 #041-02-1959 L1961 **GP** *071

CLE ELUM – KITTITAS

ANDERSON, John Carl. 201 ALPHA WAY 98922 #054-04-1973 L1976 **FM** *020 †18

HOOVER, Mark Atwood. 201 ALPHA WAY 98922 #005-12-2001 L2007 **FM** *020 †18
JEROME, Jerome Tyrrell. 201 ALPHA WAY 98922 #054-04-1996 L1998 **FM** *020 †18 ‡
OWENS, Wendy Anne. 201 ALPHA WAY 98922 #038-45-2002 L2002 **FM** *020 †18
SCHMITT, Paul Michael. 201 ALPHA WAY 98922 #025-01-1973 L1977 **FM** *020 †18
WISE, Elizabeth Franzi. 201 ALPHA WAY 98922 #024-01-1978 L1981 **FM** *020 †18

CLINTON – ISLAND

BELL, Jack Wayne. ■ 98236 #054-04-1960 **GYN** *071 †30
COWGER, Marilyn Louise. ■ 98236 #030-05-1956 L1963 **PDE OS** *071 †55
EDWARDS, Georgia S. ■ 98236 #048-04-1973 L2006 **ON IM** *020 †20 ‡
FRIEND, Lena. ■ 98236 #023-12-1997 L1999 *020
GALLAGHER, Henry Fry, Jr. ■ 98236 #041-01-1961 L1962 **IM IMG** *071 †20
GOODWIN, Sally Ann. ■ 98236 #028-34-1979 L1985 **FM OS** *020 †18
LOOMIS, Ted Albert. 2707 GABELEIN RD 98236 #008-01-1946 L1949 **OS** *050
SWANSON, Clarence H, Jr. ■ 98236 #030-05-1954 L1987 **FM** *071 †18
WEEKS, Bradford Stillman. 6456 CENTRAL AVE 98236 #050-02-1989 L1993 **P** *020

CLYDE HILL – KING

AMIEL, Felix V. ■ 98004 #330-03-1954 L1960 **OTO A** *020 †45
ANDERSON, Richard Van. 1620 94TH AVE NE 98004 #028-34-1987 L1997 **TS** *020 †85,90
CONDON, Robert E. ■ 98004 #035-45-1957 L1959 **GS GE** *030 †85
ELLERING, Jerome B. ■ 98004 #056-06-1945 L1946 **GYN** *071
FANG, Michele Yumei. 8637 NE 17TH ST, PEDIATRIC ASSOCIATES, INC 98004
     #048-13-1989 L1992 **PD** *020 †55
GELMAN, Lois Margaret. ■ 98004 #003-01-1984 L1988 **AN IM** *020 †05
HONARI, Jamshid. 2808 95TH AVE NE 98004 #517-05-1962 L1969 **NEP IM** *020 †20
LEGGETT, Randi Smith. 2806 93RD AVE NE, UNIVERSITY OF WASHINGTON 98004
     #054-04-1981 L1982 **IM** *020 †20
ROSENBERG, Robert Harris. 8670 NE 17TH ST 98004 #026-04-1952 L1955 **DR** *071 †80
SMART, Thomas B. ■ 98004 #054-04-1951 L1953 **IM** *071
TOOLEY, George Edward. ■ 98004 #019-02-1937 L1949 **PTH** *071 †50

COLBERT – SPOKANE

BANK, Bernadine. ■ 99005 #016-06-1987 L1988 **OBG** *020 †30
BOYLE, Victor Delano. ■ 99005 #005-12-1960 L1961 **FM** *020 †18
BUSH, Gerald Davis. ■ 99005 #031-01-1980 L1981 **GS** *020
DEAN, Orval. ■ 99005 #054-04-1956 L1957 **OM GP** *075
JOHNSON, Bruce Elwin. 16905 N TRIPLE BUTTE CIR 99005 #026-04-1969 L1975 **EM** *071 †16
MORRISON, Charles Clayton. ■ 99005 #026-04-1966 L1982 **FM IMG** *020 †18
NASH, Michael John. ■ 99005 #026-04-1981 L1988 **IM** *020 †20
NERUD, William Alexander. ■ 99005 #030-05-1962 L1967 **ORS** *071 †40
WILLIAMS, Lynne Huie. 4518 E SILVER PINE RD 99005 #025-07-1969 L1981 **CHP P** *020 †55

COLFAX – WHITMAN

BARRETT, Andrea Jean. 1200 W FAIRVIEW ST, THREE FORKS ORTHOPAEDICS, 99111
     #054-04-1994 L1997 **ORS** *020 †40
FRENCH, Harold Graeme. 1200 W FAIRVIEW ST, THREE FORKS ORTHOPAEDICS P 99111
     #021-01-1980 L1988 **ORS** *020 †40
HAUGEN, Keith Allen. 1210 W FAIRVIEW ST 99111 #040-02-1996 L2003 **FM** *020 †18
HENWOOD, Wesley Chas. ■ 99111 #054-04-1957 L1959 **R** *020 †80
JOHNSON, Bryan Neal. 1210 W FAIRVIEW ST 99111 #028-34-1987 L1989 **IM** *020 †20
MELLOR, William Kimball. 1210 W FAIRVIEW ST 99111 #054-04-1985 L1987 **FM** *020 †18
PARSONS, Mark Edward. 1210 W FAIRVIEW ST 99111 #040-02-1992 L1992 **FM** *020 †18
SINGH, Govind. 1210 W FAIRVIEW ST, WHITMAN MEDICAL GROUP 99111 #495-37-1995 L2003
     FM FPG *020 †18
TULIN, Robert Wayne. 1210 W FAIRVIEW ST 99111 #054-04-1965 L1966 **OS IM** *071

COLLEGE PLACE – WALLA WALLA

BRYSON, Elmer J. ■ 99324 #005-12-1952 L1952 **GP** *071
DEAKINS, Charles David. ■ 99324 #005-12-2005 **IM** *012
FIELD, Sue Allison. ■ 99324 #005-12-1983 L1990 **AN** *074 †05
HAWKINS, Lawrence Richard. 374 SE HIGHLAND PARK DR 99324 #005-12-1961 L1974
     AN *020
KARSTENS, Andres Ingver. ■ 99324 #040-02-1943 L1945 **AM** *071 †70
KETTING, Samuel. ■ 99324 #005-12-1960 L1982 **FM** *020
KJELLSTRAND, Carl-Magnus. ■ 99324 #858-01-1962 L1999 **NEP IM** *020
KLEIN, James D. ■ 99324 #005-12-1953 L1953 **GP GS** *071
LAMBERTON, Harold W. ■ 99324 #005-12-1945 L1949 **FM** *071
SADOYAMA, James Anki. ■ 99324 #005-12-1957 L1958 **OTO** *071 †45
THRASHER, Thais Verdelle. ■ 99324 #005-12-1957 L1958 **P ATP** *071 †50,75
VERCIO, William Paul. ■ 99324 #005-12-1981 L1985 **OBG** *020 †30
WILKINSON, Stanley L. ■ 99324 #005-12-1952 L1960 **FM** *071
WILL, Albert. ■ 99324 #005-12-1956 L1958 **GP** *020

COLVILLE – STEVENS

ARTZIS, Samuel Alan. 1200 E COLUMBIA AVE, NORTHEAST WASHINGTON MEDIC 99114
     #030-06-1991 L1994 **FM** *020 †18
BACON, Barry John. 1200 E COLUMBIA AVE #005-12-1984 L1990 **FM** *020 †18
BALL, Angela Marie. 1200 E COLUMBIA AVE 99114 #054-04-1989 L1989 **FM** *020 †18
BARKER, Patrick Arrington. 143 GARDEN HOMES DR 99114 #051-01-1973 L1978 **IM** *020 †20
BATEMAN, Joseph R, III. ■ 99114 #010-01-1947 L1954 **IM OS** *071 †20
CANTO, Archimedes R. ■ 99114 #748-01-1962 L1971 **FM** *071 †18
CANTO, Ramon Guanzon. 143 GARDEN HOMES DR 99114 #748-01-1981 L1985
     IM PCC *020 †20

DOYLE, William Jerome. 1200 E COLUMBIA AVE 99114 #030-06-1963 L1966 **GP** *020 †18

FARAHMAND, Mehrdad. 1200 E COLUMBIA AVE, NORTHEAST WASHINGTON MED G 99114 #040-02-1992 L1998 **GS** *020 †85

FRLAN, John Richard. 1200 E COLUMBIA AVE, DBA NORTHEAST WASHINGTON M 99114 #054-04-1983 L1984 **IM** *020 †20

GOTTSCHALL, Marvin J. 370 N MAIN ST 99114 #005-12-1953 L1954 **R AM** *020 †80

GRAY, Edmund Wesley. 143 GARDEN HOMES DR 99114 #054-04-1953 L1954 **PHP OM** *030 †18

HATFIELD, Lon Marsh. 143 GARDEN HOMES DR, COLVILLE HEALING ARTS CENT 99114 #018-03-1973 L1975 **FM** *020 †18

HERMAN, John Philip. 143 GARDEN HOMES DR 99114 #018-03-1961 L1966 **FM GP** *020 †18

HOLLING, Karl Herman. 164 N MAIN ST 99114 #028-34-1981 L1984 **OPH** *020 †35 ‡

HUME, April Sunshine. 1200 E COLUMBIA AVE, NORTHEAST WASHINGTON MEDIC 99114 #054-04-2003 L2003 **FM** *020 †18

JOHNSON, Edward Douglas. 1200 E COLUMBIA AVE 99114 #054-04-1996 L1998 **FM** *020 †18

JOHNSON, Richard Grant. ■ 99114 #041-12-1972 L1974 **EM** *071 †16

LENG, Jason W. ■ 99114 #005-12-2006 L2008 **IM** *012

LIND, Bradley Clifford. 143 GARDEN HOMES DR 99114 #026-04-1976 L1984 **IM** *020 †20

MARKEL, Patrick Scott. 143 GARDEN HOMES DR 99114 #038-40-1980 L1999 **EM** *020 †16

MENDEZ-VIGO, Mark. 143 GARDEN HOMES DR 99114 #030-05-1978 L1986 **GE IM** *020 †20

MONTOWSKI, Deborah Ann. 1200 E COLUMBIA AVE 99114 #020-12-1998 L2002 **FM** *020 †18

MORENCY, Rene-Louis. ■ 99114 #067-03-1980 L1986 **OPH** *020 †35

MOULLET, Daniel Wells. 1200 E COLUMBIA AVE 99114 #031-01-1994 L1996 **FM** *020 †18

PONTECORVO, Eugene G. 1200 E COLUMBIA AVE 99114 #021-01-1985 L1994 **ORS** *020 †40

SCHAFER, Randal Edward. 1200 E COLUMBIA AVE, NE WASHINGTON MED GRP 99114 #005-12-1984 L2000 **GS** *020 †85

SCHLEGEL, Peter James. 143 GARDEN HOMES DR 99114 #016-01-1994 L1999 **HO** *020 †20

SHANNON, Patrick Jos. 1200 E COLUMBIA AVE 99114 #054-04-1981 L1982 **FM** *020 †18

SNOOK, Michael Dean. 1200 E COLUMBIA AVE 99114 #054-04-1979 L1980 **FM** *020 †18

WATERS, Leslie Ellen. 143 GARDEN HOMES DR 99114 #036-01-1980 L1988 **FM IM** *020 †18

WORTH, Lawrence Wayne. 164 S MAIN ST STE C 99114 #048-12-1968 L1974 **IM** *020 †20

CONCRETE — SKAGIT

GARCIA, Daniel Hector. 7438 S D AVE STE A 98237 #047-07-1979 L1981 **FM** *020 †18

CONNELL — FRANKLIN

MUNDALL, Jon Marcus R. ■ 99326 #005-12-1973 L1985 **GP GPM** *020

COPALIS BEACH – GRAYS HARBOR

BLOCK, Stanley Howard. ■ 98535 #005-14-1965 L1966 **P PYA** *071 †75

COULEE DAM – OKANOGAN

GROSS, Charles Gene. ■ 99116 #030-05-1957 L1990 **GS OS** *071 ‡

COUPEVILLE – ISLAND

ADAMS, Kelly Lynn. 101 N MAIN ST 98239 #011-75-1988, ▲ L1996 **EM FM** *020

AKINS, James Peter. ■ 98239 #026-04-1952 L1952 **GP AS** *071

ALEXANDER, Darren George. 101 N MAIN ST 98239 #028-03-1997 L2000 **EM** *020 †16

ALLGAIER, Jeffrey Todd. 101 N MAIN ST 98239 #036-05-2003 L2006 **EM** *020 †16

BARLOTTA, Flora Maria. ■ 98239 #033-05-1962 L1993 **HEM IM** *071 †20

BELL, John Wm. 305 SNAKELUM POINT RD 98239 #016-06-1946 L1948 **GS TS** *071 †85,90

BISHAI, Samir Farris. 101 N MAIN ST 98239 #005-12-1978 L1994 **EM GS** *020 †16

BOLLES, Frank Platt. ■ 98239 #050-02-1964 L2006 **FM** *071 †18

BORDEN, Mark Ethan. 101 N MAIN ST 98239 #038-06-1993 L1997 **EM** *020 †16

BOWMAN, Kevin R. 101 N MAIN ST 98239 #030-06-1993 L1997 **EM** *020 †16

BURNETT, Robert James. 107 S MAIN ST 98239 #030-06-1975 L1979 **OBG EM** *020 †30

CICHOWSKI, Mark Steven. PO BOX 1227 98239 #025-12-1976 L1982 **OPH** *020 †20,35

COOKS, Michael Ira. 101 N MAIN ST 98239 #550-02-1985 L2007 **IM OS** *020 †20

COPENHAVER, Jim Kevin. ■ 98239 #054-04-1989 L1992 **FM** *020 †18

CORTAZZO, Jeffrey Martin. 101 N MAIN ST 98239 #028-03-1986 L1992 **EM GP** *020 †16

DANNHAUER, Ann Cheryl. 202 N MAIN ST 98239 #035-45-1984 L1990 **GYN** *020 †30

DERETIC, Tatjana. 107 S MAIN ST STE B202 98239 #957-02-1991 L2004 **P** *020 †75

DWERSTEG, Jochen F. 101 N MAIN ST 98239 #068-01-1979 L1984 **AN** *020 †05

GOLDSTEIN, Richard Paul. 2230 SKYCREST DR 98239 #001-02-1964 L1990 **GYN** *020 †30

GONZALEZ, Julio Cesar. 101 N MAIN ST, SANTA BARBARA COUNTY PUBLI 98239 #025-01-1998 L2000 **IM ID** *050 †20

HAM, Jay. 101 N MAIN ST 98239 #038-06-1970 L1985 **AN** *020 †05

HEISTERKAMP, Georgia E. 101 N MAIN ST, P O BOX 1647 98239 #007-02-1990 L1999 **GS** *020 †85

HU, Benjamin T. 107 S MAIN ST, STE D101 98239 #054-04-1985 L1986 **U** *020 †95

JOHNSON, Donald Russell. PO BOX 900, 80 N MAIN ST 98239 #028-02-1995 L1999 **D** *020 †15

KIM, Chi-Na. 101 N MAIN ST 98239 #048-02-1994 L1998 **EM** *020 †16

KINSELLA, Helen Louise. ■ 98239 #012-05-1985 L1990 **CHP P** *020 †75

LA GASSE, Jeffrey Paul. 101 N MAIN ST 98239 #035-45-1984 L1995 **EM IM** *020 †16

LHAMON, Helene W. 101 N MAIN ST 98239 #025-12-1997 L2006 **EM** *020 †16

MC KEE, Douglas Mark. 101 N MAIN ST 98239 #054-04-1987 L1991 **EM** *020 †16

NAVIAUX, Nils Ward. 101 N MAIN ST 98239 #054-04-2000 L2006 **IM** *100 †16

OAKLAND, John Howard. 101 N MAIN ST, WHIDBEY GENERAL HOSPITAL 98239 #030-05-1972 L1993 **IM** *071 †20

O'NEILL, Patrice Julianne. 101 N MAIN ST 98239 #007-02-1972 L1973 **FM** *020 †18

OUTLUND, E Christopher. 101 N MAIN ST 98239 #018-03-1977 L2000 **AN** *020 †05

PLASTINO, John Bradley. 101 N MAIN ST 98239 #054-04-1988 L1991 **EM** *020 †18

RIEDERER, Mary Lucie. 101 N MAIN ST 98239 #019-02-1974 L1990 **OBG** *020 †30

ROBERTS, Christopher W. 101 N MAIN ST 98239 #008-01-1982 L1985 **IM EM** *020 †20 ‡

ROOF, Lee Whitney. PO BOX 746 98239 #048-04-1979 L1981 **IM** *020 †20

SCHMIDT, Grant C. 101 N MAIN ST 98239 #038-75-1996, ▲ L2002 **EM** *020

SKUBI, K Byron. 101 N MAIN ST 98239 #054-04-1971 L1979 **ORS** *020 †40 ‡

SLEPYAN, David Hayden. 107 S MAIN ST STE D101 98239 #035-20-1968 L1970 **PS GS** *020 †65

STRANDBERG, Arthur F. ■ 98239 #038-41-1955 L1961 **FM** *072 †18

TONG, Wendy Wai Yee. ■ 98239 #010-02-1996 L2008 **IM** *020 †20

VADER, Thomas Benj. 101 N MAIN ST 98239 #025-01-1971 L1976 **AN** *020 †05

WATERMAN, Bruce Allan. 101 N MAIN ST 98239 #005-12-1996 L1999 **FM EM** *020 †18

WESENBERG, Brent Curtis. 101 N MAIN ST 98239 #056-06-1986 L1991 **EM** *020 †16

WHITFORD, Mac Lewis. 101 N MAIN ST 98239 #040-02-1977 L1983 **OBG** *071 †30

WOLFMAN, Jacob N. ■ 98239 #062-01-1972 L2004 **N** *020 †75

ZAVERUHA, Paul A. 101 NE BIRCH ST, P O BOX 1080 98239 #010-02-1971 L1981 **GS** *020 †85

COVINGTON – KING

BAUER, Faron Jos. 17700 SE 272ND ST 98042 #005-15-1991 L1993 **FM** *020 †18

BLAUVELT, Roger Michael. 27121 174TH PL SE, STE 204 98042 #047-05-1989 L1997 **ORS HS** *020 †40

BOUCHARD, Todd Samuel. 16850 SE 272ND ST, COVINGTON PRIMARY CARE 98042 #054-04-1992 L1992 **FM** *020 †18

CANCRO, J Chriss. 27121 174TH PL SE, STE 204 98042 #041-09-1970 L1976 **ORS OSM** *020 †40

CHAN, Philip Yuethung. 16850 SE 272ND ST, STE 100 98042 #054-04-1995 L1997 **FM** *020 †18

CHANG, David Yeun Bin. 17700 SE 272ND ST 98042 #060-02-1993 L1997 **FM** *020 †18

CHUNG, Eunice Seunghee. 17700 SE 272ND ST STE 26, MS: 177-2-SURG 98042 #025-01-2000 L2007 *020

COBERT, Stephen Andrew. 17700 SE 272ND ST, STE 200 98042 #048-04-1988 L1994 **OTO** *020 †45

CORCORAN, Connie Lynne. 17700 SE 272ND ST, STE 440 98042 #039-01-1985 L2005 **PD** *020 †55

DE GUZMAN-ABAJERO, M O. 17700 SE 272ND ST, STE 270 98042 #748-01-1992 L2000 **FM** *020 †18 ‡

EVOY, Robert Jos. ■ 98042 #028-34-1945 L1946 **OBG** *071

GODBOUT, Regina Marie. 27005 168TH PL SE, STE 301 98042 #016-42-1994 L2001 **IM** *020 †20

GOPALAKRISHNAN, Thanuja. 27005 168TH PL SE, STE 301 98042 #495-59-1997 L2007 **IM** *020 †20

HERNER, Kimberley K. 16850 SE 272ND ST, STE 100 98042 #035-46-1992 L1992 **FM** *020 †18

HIATT, Daniel Deane. 16850 SE 272ND ST 98042 #017-20-1959 L1961 **GP** *020 †18

JACOBSON, Louis. 17700 SE 272ND ST, COVINGTON MULTICARE CLINIC 98042 #836-02-1973 L1983 **AN** *020 †05 ‡

LE CLAIR, Robert James. 17700 SE 272ND ST 98042 #054-04-1993 L2004 **PD** *020 †55

LIM, Helen U. 17700 SE 272ND ST STE 175, COVINGTON MULTICARE SURG 98042 #748-02-1972 L1979 **AN** *020 †05

MA, Chieh Chun. 27005 168TH PL SE, STE 201 98042 #056-06-2002 L2002 **IM** *020 †20

MANULLANG, Wellington O. 16850 SE 272ND ST 98042 #005-12-1964 L1976 **OBG** *071 †30

MATKO, Matthew John. 27005 168TH PL SE, STE 201 98042 #038-44-2000 L2003 **IM** *020 †20

MC ILROY, Richard H, Jr. 17700 SE 272ND ST 98042 #017-20-1966 U *020 †95

MORRISON, John Christoper. 17700 SE 272ND ST 98042 #038-06-2002 L2006 **MPD** *020 †20,55

MUIR, Vyrn Paul. 17700 SE 272ND ST 98042 #054-04-1969 L1970 **FM** *030 †18

NELSON, Nicholas L. 17128 SE 272ND ST 98042 #030-06-1953 L1954 **FM OBG** *072 †18

NIJJAR, Ravinder Singh. 16850 SE 272ND ST 98042 #654-01-1996 L2001 **FM** *020 †18

NISEVICH-LURIE, Natalia. 16850 SE 272ND ST, STE 100 98042 #913-15-1989 L2005 **FM** *020 †18

NOMMENSEN, Michael. 17700 SE 272ND ST, STE 240 98042 #016-11-2000 L2003 **FM** *020 †18 ‡

RAO, Gayathri Devi H. 17700 SE 272ND ST, STE 440 98042 #496-15-1994 L2000 **PD** *020 †55

ROLFE, Charles Lee. 17700 SE 272ND ST 98042 #055-01-1983 L1984 **EM IM** *020 †20

SANDBULTE, Wilbur Gene. 27121 174TH PL SE, STE 204 98042 #018-03-1969 L1977 **ORS** *020 †40

SIMPSON, Rebecca Ruth. 17700 SE 272ND ST, # 240 98042 #048-02-1998 L2001 **FM** *020 †18

SINGER, Karl Lawrence. 27121 174TH PL SE, STE 204 98042 #010-01-1964 L1968 **ORS AM** *071 †40

SLEETER, Tamara Jean. 16850 SE 272ND ST, STE 250 98042 #005-12-1976 L1981 **OBG** *020 †30

STRUNK, Michael Wm. 17700 SE 272ND ST, # 240 98042 #007-02-1986 L1997 **FM** *020 †18

TEUSINK, Timothy Ray. 16850 SE 272ND ST, COVINGTON 98042 #054-04-1979 L1980 **FM** *020 †18

WAKATAKE, Edward Etsuo. 17700 SE 272ND ST, MULTICARE URGENT CARE 98042 #005-12-1997 L2001 **FM** *020 †18

WARNER, Elizabeth Ann. 16720 SE 271ST ST STE 202 98042 #038-40-1983 L1995 **P** *020 †75

YAP, Eric W. 16850 SE 272ND ST, STE 210 98042 #043-01-1994 L2000 **GE** *020 †20

COWICHE – YAKIMA

THOMPSON, Clark Eugene. ■ 98923 #041-09-1958 L1961 **GS** *072 †18

DARRINGTON – SNOHOMISH

AUVIL, Arthur Danl. ■ 98241 #005-12-1983 L1985 **RO** *020

DAVENPORT – LINCOLN

CUTTER, Bruce Ahern. 100 3RD ST, DAVENPORT OUTREACH CLINIC 99122 #054-04-1982 L1983 **HO IM** *020 †20

NICHOLS, Joni Carol. 100 3RD ST, DAVENPORT OUTREACH CLINIC 99122 #036-07-1984 L1993 **HEM ON** *020 †20

REED, Frederick Joseph. 100 3RD ST STE 1, LINCOLN HOSPITAL 99122 #023-12-1997 L2007 **FM AM** *020 †18

ST CLAIR, Robert C. 100 3RD ST STE 1, NORTH BASIN MEDICAL CLINIC 99122 #654-01-1986 L1989 **FM** *020 †18

YOUNG, Donella Sue Graves. 100 3RD ST STE 1, DAVENPORT CLINIC 99122 #039-01-1980 L1989 **FM** *062 †18

DAYTON – COLUMBIA

EIDT, Laurence Allyn. 1012 S 3RD ST, COLUMBIA FAMILY CLINIC 99328 #019-02-1971 L1991 **FM** *020 †18
LUCE, Michael Eugene. 1012 S 3RD ST, COLUMBIA FAMILY CLINIC 99328 #025-12-1973 L1979 **FM** *020 †18
PITTMAN, Donald Wayne. 1012 S 3RD ST 99328 #040-02-1961 L1962 **FM** *071
SHIELDS, Heidi Elizabeth. 1012 S 3RD ST, COLUMBIA COUNTY HEALTH SYS 99328 #056-06-1991 L1994 **FM** *020 †18
SMITH, Eileen Pazderka. 1002 S 3RD ST, STE B 99328 #030-05-1990 L1997 **D** *020 †15

DEER HARBOR – SAN JUAN

KANIS, Lorraine Josephine. PO BOX 190 98243 #025-07-1978 L1981 **PM** *071 †60

DEER PARK – SPOKANE

DHILLON, Karam S. SOUTH FOREST & EAST D 99006 #495-02-1949 L1971 **GP OBG** *072
FIGUEROA, Edgar Angel. 1015 E D ST 99006 #042-01-1977 L1980 **FM** *020 †18
VANG, Cha Johnny. ■ 99006 #305-01-2004 L2004 **IM** *020 †20
WILLARD, Paul Arthur. PO BOX 742 99006 #054-04-1978 L1979 **IM** *020 †20

DEMING – WHATCOM

DILLER, Cathie Lynn. 3920 VALLEY HWY 98244 #051-07-1992 L1999 **FM** *020 †18

DES MOINES – KING

AMIRI, Fariba. 22000 MARINE VIEW DR S, STE 200 98198 #517-01-1990 L1999 **IM** *020 †20
BERSCH, Barry Jeffrey. 22000 MARINE VIEW DR S, STE 200 98198 #047-07-1973 L1986 **IM** *020
BROWN, Michael Chas. 22236 7TH AVE S 98198 #049-01-1966 L1990 **FM FPG** *020 †18
CHANG, Elaine Yilien. 22000 MARINE VIEW DR S, STE 200 98198 #041-12-1994 L1998 **OBG** *020 †30
CHANG, Morris Bosang. 22220 MARINE VIW DR S #200, COMPREHENSIVE SLEEP MEDICI 98198 #019-02-1992 L1998 **N EM** *020 †75
DAU, Quan Minh. ■ 98198 #054-04-2008 *012
DAVYDOW, Dimitry Samuel. ■ 98198 #028-46-2002 L2007 **P** *100
DEEVEY, Jo Augur. 22236 7TH AVE S 98198 #023-01-1973 L1994 **ADP P** *020
DIMBIL, Mumin Daud. 22000 MARINE VIEW DR S, STE 100 98198 #704-16-1998 L2007 **FM** *020 †18
DOSSETT, Michelle Leigh. ■ 98198 #054-04-2008 *012
EGGLIN, J Michael. ■ 98198 #054-04-1958 L1958 **ORS** *071
ENLOE, Garold Gene. 23600 MARINE VIEW DR S, # 435 98198 #054-15-1964 **AN** *071
FAHEY, Karen. 24027 26TH AVE S 98198 #049-01-1984 L1984 **IM** *020 †20
FALLON, William Michael. ■ 98198 #005-15-1965 L1971 **ORS** *071
GAUVIN, Normand Ernest. ■ 98198 #024-07-1954 L1955 **PD** *071 †55
HALL, Raney Dewey. 26225 PACIFIC HWY S 98198 #005-06-1985 L2004 **EM IM** *020 †20,55
HAVENS, Spencer Robert. ■ 98198 #056-06-2005 L2005 **PM** *012
HITCHMAN, Robert. ■ 98198 #056-06-1948 L1950 **GP** *071 †8
PITTIER, Michael Vincent. 22000 MARINE VIEW DR S, STE 100 98198 #005-27-1970 L1973 **IM GE** *020 †20
PUTNAM, John Danl. ■ 98198 #005-02-1970 L1977 **FM IM** *071 †20,18
SNYDER, Sean Michael. ■ 98198 #054-04-2007 L2007 **IM** *012
STUHRING, Donald H. ■ 98198 #035-01-1950 L1959 **AM OM** *071 †70

DUPONT – PIERCE

ADAMS, Brian Lee. ■ 98327 #023-12-2006 L2008 **TY** *012
AGOCHUKWU, Uzondu Francis. ■ 98327 #017-20-2007 **ORS** *012
ANGELIDIS, Matthew Stephe. ■ 98327 #023-12-2006 L2008 *020
ARTHURS, Zachary Marshall. ■ 98327 #039-01-2003 L2004 **GS** *012
BENTON, Katherine Bibb. 2035 GARRY OAKS AVE, UNIT C 98327 #012-05-2005 L2007 **PD** *012
BETTS, Aaron Michael. ■ 98327 #023-12-2007 **TY** *012
BOSTAPH, Andrew Scott. ■ 98327 #023-12-2000 L2007 **DR** *100 †80
CHANG, James H. ■ 98327 #016-42-1998 L2007 **DR PD** *100 †80
CHANG, Suzie. ■ 98327 #016-42-1998 L2004 **PD** *020 †55
CHIARA, Joseph Ahlstrom. ■ 98327 #028-34-2005 L2007 **OTO** *012
CLARK, Jason Christopher. ■ 98327 #056-05-2005 L2007 **FP** *012
CORCORAN, Shawn Patrick. ■ 98327 #010-02-2007 **IM** *012
CUBANSKI, Jeanne Yvette. ■ 98327 #016-43-2004 L2006 **OPH** *012
DE VITA, Diane. 1802 FISHER AVE 98327 #051-04-1996 L2002 **EM** *020 †16
DUKE, Angela Greaves. ■ 98327 #021-05-2002 L2006 **OBG** *020 †30
ECKERT, Matthew Joseph. ■ 98327 #016-43-2004 L2006 **GS** *012
EICHINGER, Josef Karl. ■ 98327 #041-13-2004 L2006 **ORS** *012
FALLOT, Andre. ■ 98327 #010-02-1995 L1998 **PDP** *020 †55
FARGO, Matthew Vernon. ■ 98327 #023-12-2001 L2003 **FM** *020
FAVERO, Michael David. ■ 98327 #023-12-2005 **IM** *012
FLAKE, Eric Melvin. ■ 98327 #023-12-2001 L2003 **DBP** *012 †55 ‡
FLANAGAN, Ryan Patrick. ■ 98327 #023-12-2007 **PD** *012
GAFFNEY, Daniel Lahiri. ■ 98327 #030-06-2005 L2005 *020
GLOYSTEIN, David Michael. ■ 98327 #048-13-2003 L2004 **ORS** *012
GRANT, Melissa Ann. ■ 98327 #045-04-2007 *012
HERBERT, Garth Stephen. ■ 98327 #008-01-2003 L2006 **GS** *012
HOBLET, Aaron Howard. ■ 98327 #038-40-2003 L2004 **ORS** *012
HOPKINSON, Monique O. ■ 98327 #010-01-2006 L2008 **GS** *012

HUDSON, Michael Jason. ■ 98327 #051-01-2007 **EM** *012
JOHNSON, Jeremy Daniel. ■ 98327 #023-12-2000 L2000 **FM** *020 †18
KUHN, Kenneth David. ■ 98327 #023-12-1999 L2001 **GPM** *012 †18
KWUN, Christopher Y. ■ 98327 #010-01-2002 L2003 **DR** *012
LALIBERTE, Bryan Donald. ■ 98327 #051-04-2007 **TY** *012
LEMMON, Keith Merle. ■ 98327 #019-02-1998 L2007 **ADL** *020 †55
LITTELL, Christopher T. ■ 98327 #028-79-1996, ▲ L1998 **GPM PD** *030 †70,55
LU, Kang. ■ 98327 #024-05-2005 L2007 **DR** *012
MANNING, Debra Ann. ■ 98327 #051-04-2001 L2002 **FP** *012 †18
MARTINDALE, Richard E, Jr. ■ 98327 #048-02-1965 L1975 **AN GP** *071 †05
MAZUR, Melissa Anne. ■ 98327 #038-06-2000 L2000 **PHO** *055
MCDONOUGH, Patrick Shanno. ■ 98327 #010-02-2006 L2008 **GS** *012
MOFFITT, John Charles. ■ 98327 #023-12-2007 **TY** *012
MORRIS, Brian L. ■ 98327 #048-13-1986 L1987 **OBG** *020 †30
NIJJAR, Upneet Kaur. ■ 98327 #023-12-2006 L2007 **FP** *012
OAK, Robert Lee. ■ 98327 #023-12-2004 L2005 *020
PAMPLIN, Jeremy Charles. ■ 98327 #023-12-2001 L2002 **IM** *020
PARADA, Stephen Arthurwea. ■ 98327 #038-45-2006 L2007 **ORS** *012
PERRY, Robert Jason Thoma. ■ 98327 #054-04-2004 L2006 **GS** *012
RABII, Amir Masoud. PO BOX 456 98327 #409-25-1984 L1997 **FM** *020 †18 ‡
RIVERS, Bruce Anthony. ■ 98327 #010-03-2004 L2006 **OPH** *012
RODGERS, Matthew Dale. ■ 98327 #023-12-2006 L2008 **FP** *012
RUNSER, Lloyd Austin Aaro. ■ 98327 #038-06-2005 L2006 **FP** *012
RYAN, Jenny Legaspi. ■ 98327 #023-12-2006 L2008 **IM** *012
SAUNDERS, Rhiana Dawn. ■ 98327 #010-02-2004 L2006 **OBG** *012
SEAQUIST, Derek Kevin. ■ 98327 #023-12-2002 L2004 **PTH** *100 †50
SOHN, Vance Young. ■ 98327 #010-02-2004 L2006 **GS** *012
SOLBERG, Jon S. ■ 98327 #037-01-2006 **EM** *012
SPEAR, Samuel Albin. ■ 98327 #023-12-2004 L2005 **OTO** *012
STEINMAN, Alan Mark. ■ 98327 #005-11-1971 L1974 **OM GPM** *030 †70
SUNDELL, Zoe Sarahestel. ■ 98327 #023-12-2006 L2008 **PTH** *012
TAYLOR, Leland Daniel. ■ 98327 #023-12-2005 L2006 **DR** *012
THEELER, Brett James. ■ 98327 #023-12-2005 L2007 **N** *012
VILLACORTA, Rachel Repuld. ■ 98327 #005-19-2005 L2006 **EM** *012
WHITE, Joseph Michael. ■ 98327 #016-42-2007 **GS** *012
WIDENER, Douglas Blair. ■ 98327 #012-01-2008 *012
WILHELM, Michael Joshua. ■ 98327 #023-12-2005 L2007 **OTO** *012
WILTON, Nouansy Khowong. ■ 98327 #051-07-2005 L2007 **IM** *012
WOJCIEHOWSKI, Angieszka O. ■ 98327 #023-12-2004 L2006 **IM** *012

DUVALL – KING

FERRIER, Jean Rakofsky. ■ 98019 #035-19-1964 L1970 **P** *075
FINCH, Lisa. ■ 98019 #054-04-2002 L2002 **OS** *012 †80
GREENLEAF, Richard C. ■ 98019 #035-01-1942 L1949 **IM PUD** *071 †20
LEE, Sherman. 14720 MAIN ST NE, STE 109 98019 #061-01-1988 L1998 **FM** *020 †18
STEWART, Harold V, III. 14304 275TH AVE NE 98019 #039-01-1974 L1983 **EM** *020 †16
WANG, Yu. 14720 MAIN ST NE, STE 109 98019 #243-76-1996 L2007 **FM** *100 †18

EAST WENATCHEE – DOUGLAS

ABBOTT, Michael Jeffrey. 100 HIGHLINE DR 98802 #054-04-1996 L1998 **FM** *020 †18
ABOUL-FATH, Nadine Mahmou. ■ 98802 #869-04-1999 **IM** *020
ASPLUND, Cici Bean. 100 HIGHLINE DR 98802 #054-04-1981 L1982 **FM** *020 †18
BANKEN, Joel Timothy. 100 HIGHLINE DR 98802 #054-04-1998 L2000 **FM** *020 †18
BOUSMAN, Ronald Lee. 100 HIGHLINE DR 98802 #018-03-1971 L1972 **FM** *020 †18
EISERT, Douglas Alan. 100 HIGHLINE DR 98802 #040-02-1985 L1988 **PD** *020 †55
FAGER, Donald B. ■ 98802 #016-06-1948 L1954 **PD OS** *071 †55
GARDNER, John Wendell. ■ 98802 #016-06-1954 L1960 **DR** *071 †80
GILLESPIE, Kelly Ryan. 100 HIGHLINE DR 98802 #023-12-2007 L2005 **FM** *020 †18
GRAVES, Roy Wm. ■ 98802 #054-04-1978 L1983 **EM** *020 †16
GROSDIDIER, Jason Mathias. 100 HIGHLINE DR, EAST WENATCHEE CLINIC 98802 #046-01-2000 L2004 **FM** *020 †18
HIMMEL, Peter David. ■ 98802 #007-02-1979 L1996 **VS GS** *071 †85
JOBE, Lance William. 230 GRANT RD, STE B6 98802 #054-04-1995 L1999 **EM** *020 †16
LAPO-HEDIN, Debra. 100 HIGHLINE DR 98802 #054-04-1984 L1998 **FM** *020 †20
LYNCH, Patrick Clarence. 100 HIGHLINE DR 98802 #028-34-1992 L1995 **IM** *020 †20
LYONS, Paul Harrell. ■ 98802 #004-01-1952 L1953 *071
MITRAKUL, Satu. 1761 MANHATTAN DR 98802 #891-01-1964 L2007 **NEP IM** *020 †20 ‡
PARNELL, Michael Allen. 2840 RIVERWALK PL 98802 #027-01-1976 L1977 **EM** *020 †16
RICHTSMEIER, Thos Elliott. ■ 98802 #018-03-1969 L1970 **CD IM** *020 †20 ‡
SCULL, Christine E H. ■ 98802 #054-04-1969 L1973 **GP** *071
SMITH, Donald Geoffrey. ■ 98802 #005-12-1961 L2003 **GP** *071
WILLIAMS, Richard G, Jr. 100 HIGHLINE DR 98802 #005-11-1973 L1999 **IM** *020 †20

EASTSOUND – SAN JUAN

BLACKADAR, Charles Samuel. ■ 98245 #023-12-1997 L1999 **FM** *020 †18
BOTELER, Diane Louise. ■ 98245 #007-02-1988 L1990 **FM** *020 †18
CASS, Vera Ashbaugh. PO BOX 4, STAR ROUTE 98245 #018-03-1948 L1949 **OBG** *071
FRAZER, Thomas Somjen. 7 DEYE LN 98245 #036-01-1983 L2007 **FM** *020 †18
KIRCHNER, Shannan Cole. 1286 MOUNT BAKER RD, STE B102 98245 #018-03-1996 L1999 **FM** *020 †18
MC KENZIE, Zona Ellen. ■ 98245 #038-06-1987 L1989 **CD** *020 †20
RUSSELL, David Lee. 7 DEYE LN 98245 #001-02-1997 L2003 **FM** *020 †18
SHINSTROM, David Clayton. 1286 MOUNT BAKER RD # B102, ORCAS FAMILY HEALTH CENTER 98245 #038-41-1976 L1979 **FM** *020 †18
TRUNKEY, Franklin Mc Atee. ■ 98245 #067-01-1960 L1966 **DR NR** *071 †80
WILLIAMS, Stanley Paul. PO BOX 278 98245 #020-12-1966 L1968 **GP EM** *020

EDGEWOOD – PIERCE

CROWLEY, James Noel. ■ 98371 #061-01-1966 L1967 **NS** *062 †25

■ = Address Information Privacy Protected

DENZLER, Charles Henry. ■ 98372 #017-20-1931 L1932 **GP** *071
HYMAN, Ann Brenneis. ■ 98372 #019-02-1986 L1995 **EM** *020 †16
MALTA, Vito J. ■ 98371 #005-15-1962 L1975 **GP** *071
MURPHY, Vincent M. ■ 98372 #030-06-1953 L1955 **AN** *020

EDMONDS - SNOHOMISH

ADAMS, Barrett Ford. ■ 98026 #054-04-2004 L2007 **EM** *020
ADELMAN, Robert Edward. 21601 76TH AVE W 98026 #016-06-1974 L1978 **EM IM** *020 †20,16
AHMAD, Afzal. ■ 98020 #704-20-1985 L1996 **GS** *100
ALBERTS, James Robert. 7320 216TH ST SW, STE 320 98026 #016-42-1997 L2003 **ORS** *020 †40
ALLEN, Jennie Michelle. ■ 98026 #054-04-2008 *012
ALLEN, Paul Albert. 21601 76TH AVE W 98026 #040-02-1973 L1976 **CCM IM** *020 †20
ALTHOUSE, Ralph Gerson. 7320 216TH ST SW, STE 210 98026 #917-09-1982 L1985 **CD IM** *020 †20
ANDERSON, Robert Arthur. 16010 73RD PL W 98026 #054-04-1957 L1959 **FM GPM** *040 †18
ARENTZ, Matthew John. 21601 76TH AVE W 98026 #016-43-2002 L2005 **PCC** *012 †20
AVAKIAN, Arpenik. 21616 76TH AVE W, STE 209 98026 #913-38-1983 L1998 **OPH** *020 †35
AVERSA, Guido Antonio. 21701 76TH AVE W, STE 201 98026 #561-10-1966 L1972 **P** *071 †75
AYENGAR, Nagamani. 7315 212TH ST SW, STE 201 98026 #495-09-1965 L1974 **GP** *020
BABCOCK, Judith. 21911 76TH AVE W, BIRTH & FAMILY CLINIC 98026 #005-19-1976 L1977 **FM** *020 †18
BAGNULO, Paul Aldo. 7315 212TH ST SW STE 101, EDMONDS FAMILY MED CLNCL 98026 #024-05-1969 L1974 **FM** *020 †18
BAXTER, Sandra Gogins. 7315 212TH ST SW STE 101, EDMONDS FAMILY MEDICINE CL 98026 #049-01-1988 L1991 **FM** *020 †18
BEAUPIED, Earl Francis. 21601 76TH AVE W 98026 #025-07-1979 L1982 **EM** *020 †16
BEGERT, Stephen Paul. 21911 76TH AVE W, BIRTH & FAMILY CLINIC 98026 #054-04-1983 L1986 **FM** *020 †18
BEHLA, Herman C, Jr. ■ 98020 #005-11-1950 L1951 **GP** *071
BEIGHTON, Murray Alan. 21601 76TH AVE W 98026 #062-01-1974 L1978 **GP** *020
BENNETT, Martha A S. 7315 212TH ST SW STE 101, EDMONDS FAMILY MEDICINE CL 98026 #005-19-1976 L1979 **FM** *020 †18
BETTIS, Robert Brent. 7315 212TH ST SW, STE 101 98026 #019-02-1973 L1974 **FM** *020 †18
BHATIA, Shailender. ■ 98026 #495-36-2000 L2004 **HEM** *100
BLAKENEY, Ginger Jaye. 7315 212TH ST SW STE 101 98026 #054-04-1996 L1998 **FM** *020 †18
BORG, Sandra Kay. 7315 212TH ST SW STE 203, EDMONDS FAMILY MED, INC, P 98026 #003-01-1981 L1982 **FM** *020 †18
BORROMEO, Raul Vargas. 21601 76TH AVE W 98026 #030-06-1993 L1996 **EM** *020 †16
BOURNE, Randolph Bennett. 21616 76TH AVE W, STE 205 98026 #047-05-2003 L2007 **OBG** *020
BRAY, Jeffrey Franklin. 21616 76TH AVE W STE 205 98026 #056-06-1996 L1996 **OBG** *020 †30
BRAY, Ronald Eugene. ■ 98020 #054-04-1960 L1963 **GYN** *071 †30
BRINKMAN, Jill Perry. ■ 98020 #023-01-2003 **GS** *100
BROBECK, Alan Geo. 21601 76TH AVE W 98026 #054-04-1964 L1966 **ORS** *020 †40
BRUNSKILL, Andrew J. ■ 98020 #917-04-1977 L1986 **PHP PD** *030 †55,70
BRUNSON, Linda Swenson. 7320 216TH ST SW, STE 200 98026 #024-07-1983 L2004 **IM** *020 †20
BRYANT, Tanya I.. 21906 76TH AVE W, EDMONDS FAMILY CARE PLLC 98026 #913-15-1978 L2004 **FM** *020 †18
BURRELL, John Allen. ■ 98020 #028-34-1955 L1960 **OS** *071
CAMERON, Brian Douglas. 7320 216TH ST SW 98026 #054-04-1993 L1999 **ORS** *020 †40
CAMPBELL, Richard Joseph. 21601 76TH AVE W 98026 #016-11-2003 L2003 **EM** *020 †16
CARDWELL, Thomas Ray. 21600 HIGHWAY 99 98026 #038-41-1970 L1975 **PD** *020 †55
CAREY, Ross Glen. 7315 212TH ST SW, STE 101 98026 #038-06-1984 L1986 **FM** *020 †18
CARTER, Stephen Thomas. 7315 212TH ST SW STE 101 98026 #041-09-1998 L2001 **FM** *020 †18
CAWTHON, David Franklin. 21616 76TH AVE W STE 211, STEVENS PROFESSIONAL CENTE 98026 #008-01-1978 L1986 **NS** *020 †75
CHAFFEE, Robert Geo. 21600 HIGHWAY 99 98026 #016-02-1971 L1973 **GE IM** *020 †20
CHAN, Clara Yankay. 7315 212TH ST SW STE 101 98026 #054-04-2002 L2004 **FM** *020 †18
CHANDLER, Melvin Eugene. 527 DAYTON ST, THE CENTER 98020 #018-03-1973 L1979 **FM** *020 †18
CHINN, Melissa S. 21616 76TH AVE W, STE 201 98026 #005-77-2001, ▲ L2004 **OBG** *020
CHRISTIANSEN, Janet K. 7315 212TH ST SW STE 203 98026 #054-04-1990 L1992 **FM** *020 †18
CHUANG, Rosalind Shengi. ■ 98026 #054-04-2003 L2003 **N** *100
CHUNG, Alexander C. 21601 76TH AVE W 98026 #054-04-1999 L2002 **IM** *020 †20
CLARK, Susan Loraine. 21601 76TH AVE W 98026 #054-04-1983 L1985 **CHP P** *075
CONNOLLY, Maeve Josephine. ■ 98020 #917-28-1966 L1970 **GP** *071
COSGROVE, Kennedy Michael. 21601 76TH AVE W 98026 #021-01-2000 L2002 **P** *020 †75 ‡
COX, Robert Edward. 7320 216TH ST SW, STE 20 98026 #048-04-1974 L1977 **PUD SME** *020 †16,20
CREALOCK, Frank W. 21601 76TH AVE W 98026 #062-01-1948 L1955 **OBS** *071
CRONRATH, Geordis May. ■ 98020 #065-01-1955 L1959 **AN** *071 †05
CRONYN, Maurene Patrice. 21911 76TH AVE W, BIRTH & FAMILY CLINIC 98026 #054-04-1980 L1983 **FM** *020 †18
CROTHERS, Marvin Dean. 23200 EDMONDS WAY STE A 98026 #054-04-1973 L1975 **OS FM** *071
CUSTER, Allen Leroy. ■ 98026 #041-13-1963 L1968 **OPH** *071 †35 ‡
DAMEROW, E Morgan. 21601 76TH AVE W 98026 #016-02-1960 L1962 **AN** *020
DEBLEY, Cara Kirks. 21600 HIGHWAY 99, STE 260 98026 #016-42-1998 L2001 **GE** *020 †20
DEGAN, Thomas J. 21600 HWY 99 STE 150 98026 #054-04-1976 L1980 **ORS** *020 †40
DEMING, Michael Geo. 21600 HWY 99, STE 210 98026 #039-01-1971 L1978 **P** *020 †75
DENKINGER, Todd Michael. ■ 98020 #054-04-1996 L1999 **EM** *020 †16
DINES, Gary Nelson. 21600 HIGHWAY 99 98026 #005-18-1983 L1987 **GE IM** *020 †20
DOO, Ella C. 21600 76TH AVE W, STEVENS HOSPITAL DEPT RADI 98026 #041-07-1978 L1980 **DR** *020 †80
DUDETSKY, Alexander Petro. 21906 76TH AVE W 98026 #913-21-1976 L2005 **IM** *020
EHNI, William Frederick. 21701 76TH AVE W, STE 200 98026 #054-04-1982 L1987 **ID IM** *020 †20
EIDE, Fernette Fang. 6701 139TH PL SW, EIDE NEUROLEARNING CLINIC 98026 #005-02-1988 L2001 **N** *020 †75
ENGEL, Winslow. 120 3RD AVE S STE 120, CHESED HEALTH CARE, PS 98020 #026-04-1980 L2000 **IM** *020 †20
ENGLISH, Margaret Jessica. 21600 HWY 99 STE 290 98026 #036-05-2001 L2004 **PD** *020 †55
ESPINOSA, Everardo J. 941 12TH AVE N 98020 #649-01-1954 L1960 **AN PME** *072 †05
EVERARD, Mark Joseph. 21601 76TH AVE W 98026 #026-04-1999 L2003 **AN** *020
FENNING, Walter Reid. 7320 164TH ST SW, STE 140 98026 #035-20-1982 L1983 **AN** *020 †05
FERENCE, Andrea Jon. 21601 76TH AVE W 98026 #041-07-1996 L2000 **AN PME** *020 †05
FLEMING, Robert S. 22727 HIGHWAY 99 STE 201 98026 #041-13-1961 L1965 **CHP P** *072 ‡
FORSTER, Gary Logan. 21701 76TH AVE W, STE 300 98026 #048-04-1970 L1980 **ORS** *020 †40
FUHRMANN, David Scott. 21911 76TH AVE W, BIRTH & FAMILY CLINIC 98026 #016-43-1995 L2000 **FM** *020 †18
FURSTOSS, James Allen. 7015 150TH PL SW, RETIRED 98026 #028-34-1967 L1974 **OTO** *020
FURTADO, Marina Clare. 15900 70TH AVE W 98026 #054-04-1997 L2004 **EM** *020 †16
GONCHAROFF, Bernard. ■ 98020 #054-15-1964 **GP** *020
GOODRICK, Wm Ian Michael. ■ 98026 #352-06-1957 L1962 **GS** *071 †85
GORDON, Michelle Leno. 21601 76TH AVE W 98026 #054-04-1998 L2000 **IM** *020 †20
GOSS, John Catlin, Jr. 21616 76TH AVE W STE 207 98026 #040-02-1963 L1969 **GS** *071 †85
GOWRI, Vasanthi. 21601 76TH AVE W 98026 #495-04-1986 L1998 **IM** *020 †20
GRAHAM, Cheryl Suzanne. 21601 76TH AVE W 98026 #025-07-1986 L1991 **AN** *071 †05
GRASSMAN, Eric D. 7320 216TH ST SW, STE 210 98026 #048-12-1977 L2003 **CD IM** *020 †20
GRIER, Douglas H. 21822 76TH AVE W, SOUND UROLOGICAL 98026 #010-01-1982 L1991 **U** *020 †95
GUO, Jinfeng. 21600 HIGHWAY 99 98026 #243-16-1982 L2000 **GE** *020 †20
GURVITZ, Michelle Zeena. ■ 98026 #005-14-1995 L2005 **PDC** *020 †20,55
GUSTAFSON, Belinda Jean. ■ 98020 #054-04-1991 L1994 **P** *020 †75
HANSON, Harlis Duane. ■ 98020 #026-04-1956 L1964 **PD** *071 †55
HANSON, Mark Turner. 7315 212TH ST SW STE 1, EDMONDS FAMILY MEDICINE CL 98026 #026-04-1973 L1974 **FM AM** *020 †18
HARDY, Steve Edward. 7320 164TH ST SW, STE 140 98026 #028-02-1998 L2002 **AN** *020 †05
HARMON, Kurt Everett. 7315 212TH ST SW STE 201 98026 #054-04-1995 L1998 **GS** *020 †85
HARRIS, Victoria Louise. 21601 76TH AVE W, STEVENS HOSPITAL 98026 #061-01-1989 L1991 **P** *020 †75
HEADLEY, John Lawrence. 21600 HWY 99 STE 280 98026 #005-14-1976 L1980 **D DMP** *020 †15
HEARD, David Leon. 21600 HWY 99 STE 255 98026 #054-04-1975 L1976 **PM OS** *020 †60
HELFING, Saul Herschel. 21600 HIGHWAY 99, STE 210 98026 #041-02-1983 L1992 **P PHP** *020 †75
HERTER, Christian Dupont. ■ 98026 #026-04-1986 L1989 **FM** *020 †18
HILL, Lucius Davis, III. ■ 98026 #051-01-1944 L1954 **GS CD** *071 †85,90
HOCHBERG, Henry Martin. 22721 76TH AVE W, STE B 98026 #035-46-1985 L1988 **FM GPM** *020 †18
HOLLISTER, Rachel S. 7315 212TH ST SW 98026 #054-04-1996 L1998 **FM** *020 †18
HORIUCHI, Myra Gaykeiko. 7315 212TH ST SW, STE 101 98026 #035-46-1995 L1997 **FM** *020 †18
HUBBARD, Stephen Thos. 7320 216TH ST SW, STE 210 98026 #005-02-1974 L1987 **CD IM** *020 †20
HUBER, Bertrand Russell. ■ 98026 #024-01-2006 L2006 **PTH** *012
HUNTER, C Gordon. 21616 76TH AVE W, STE 211-212 98026 #016-42-1974 L1978 **GYN** *020 †30
IJO, Elisabeth K. 21601 76TH AVE W 98026 #305-01-2003 L2005 **IM** *020 †20
INADOMI, David Paul. 21601 76TH AVE W 98026 #005-02-1991 L1994 **AN** *020 †05
INGRAM, Michael Alexander. ■ 98026 #054-04-1979 L1984 **IM EM** *020 †20,16
IVANJACK, Lisa Marie. 21601 76TH AVE W 98026 #026-08-1997 L2000 **IM** *020 †20
JACOBS, Jennifer. 23200 EDMONDS WAY 98026 #025-07-1976 L1982 **OS PHP** *071
JACOBSON, Laurie G. 21600 HIGHWAY 99, STE 280 98026 #016-11-1998 L2004 **DS D** *020 †15
JEFFERS, Robert Clark. 21616 76TH AVE W, STE 205 98026 #054-04-1967 L1972 **OBG** *071 †30
JENSEN, Christine Chen. ■ 98026 #054-04-2004 L2005 **GS** *012
JOH, Jung-Hyun. 21616 76TH AVE W, STE 211 98026 #583-01-1991 L1998 **NEP** *020 †20
JOHNSTON, Eileen Marie. 21605 76TH AVE W, STE 200 98026 #051-01-1991 L1999 **HO** *020 †20
JONES, David Bruce. 21600 HIGHWAY 99 STE 230 98026 #054-04-1967 L1974 **OPH GP** *071 †35
JONES, Marthlyn. 19231 88TH AVE W 98026 #028-03-1979 L1989 **FM** *020 †18
JONG, Elaine Claire. 1100 4TH AVE S 98020 #005-18-1974 L1975 **ID IM** *040
JURICH, Thomas J, Jr. 7315 212TH ST SW, STE 201 98026 #016-06-1986 L1991 **GS TS** *020 †85
KAJLICH, Aurel J. 21601 76TH AVE W 98026 #286-13-1966 L1973 **AN** *020 †05
KARR, Bradley Payne. 21601 76TH AVE W 98026 #054-04-1993 L1997 **AN** *020 †05
KEATON, Alan Louis. 21616 76TH AVE W, STE 112 98026 #040-02-1962 L1970 **OTO** *071 †45
KENT, Paul Richard. ■ 98026 #048-04-1977 L1978 *075
KIM, Anna Soohyung. 7320 216TH ST SW STE 220 98026 #050-02-1996 L2000 **OPH** *020 †35
KIM, Joohee. 21616 76TH AVE W, STE 211 98026 #583-01-1991 L1999 **IM END** *020 †20
KIM, Kyungju. 21601 76TH AVE W, UNIVERSITY OF WASHINGTON 98026 #054-04-2002 L2004 **AN** *020
KIMMEL, Ryan James. 21601 76TH AVE W, STEVENS HEALTHCARE 98026 #054-04-2001 L2005 **P** *020
KLEKOTKA, John Joseph. 21616 76TH AVE W, STE 108 98026 #041-13-1963 L1968 **PD** *071 †55
KNUTSON, Susan Silverness. ■ 98026 #041-13-1963 L1967 **PD** *020 †55
KRICHMAN, Kenneth Herman. 7935 216TH ST SW STE E 98026 #005-06-1972 L1977 **IM N** *020 †20
KUECHLE, David Karl. 21600 HIGHWAY 99 STE 150, KRUGER ORTHO CLNC 98026 #048-04-1989 L1995 **ORS** *020 †40
LAMKEE, Muriel Jean. ■ 98020 #030-05-1953 L1959 **OBG** *071 †30
LAU, Michael Pui Hing. 7315 212TH ST SW STE 204 98026 #462-01-1977 L1980 **GYN** *020 †30
LE BOEUF, Dorothy F Barta. ■ 98026 #028-03-1962 L1965 **FM** *071 †18
LEE, Justin Cheuk-Fun. 7315 212TH ST SW, STE 205 98026 #016-11-1999 L2003 **CD** *020 †20
LEE, Sang-Chol. ■ 98026 #654-01-2002 *100
LEE, Suji. 21616 76TH AVE W, STE 211 98026 #033-05-1999 L2004 **NEP** *020 †20
LEITE, Beverly Ann. 21601 76TH AVE W 98026 #038-06-1982 L1986 **ID IM** *020 †20
LESHCHINSKY, Felix V. 21601 76TH AVE W 98026 #005-02-2001 L2005 **EM** *100 †16
LIPPMAN, Laura Celise. 7315 212TH ST SW STE 203, EDMONDS FAMILY MEDICINE CL 98026 #041-07-1975 L1976 **FM** *071 †18
LITTLE, Timothy Eugene. 21600 HIGHWAY 99 STE 220, KRUGER CLINIC 98026 #005-06-1983 L1986 **GE IM** *020 †20
LLORENTE, Edward Hipolito. ■ 98026 #005-02-1978 **GP** *075

■ = Address Information Privacy Protected

LOCKARD, Gretchen Dee. 21911 76TH AVE W, BIRTH & FAMILY CLINIC 98026 #043-01-1999 L2001 **FM** *020 †18

LONGWAY, Ralph Ernest. ■ 98020 #005-12-1955 L1970 **OPH** *071 †35

LUKACS, Jozsef. 21601 76TH AVE W 98026 #005-02-1986 L1996 **DR** *020 †80

LUTHER, Keith Alexander. 7320 216TH ST SW STE 200 98026 #016-11-1993 L1999 **MPD** *020 †55,20

MAC FARLANE, Steven D. 7315 212TH ST SW, STE 201 98026 #054-04-1981 L1982 **AS VS** *020 †85

MACK, Adam George. 21601 76TH AVE W 98026 #030-05-2002 L2005 **IM** *100 †20

MALDAZYS, John David. 21822 76TH AVE W, SOUND UROLOGICAL 98026 #016-06-1975 L1991 **U** *020 †95

MALOTT, Ralph Justin. ■ 98020 #030-05-1954 L1964 **P** *071

MARIK, Francis. 21601 76TH AVE W 98026 #473-01-1960 L1977 **GS** *071 †85

MARKOWITZ, Daniel R. 21605 76TH AVE W, STE 200 98026 #005-11-1992 L1992 **ON HEM** *020 †05

MATHENY, Theodore Raymond. 23200 EDMONDS WAY # A, EVERGREEN CLINIC 98026 #005-06-1983 L2001 **FM** *020 †18

MAUK, Joyce Elaine. 7320 216TH ST SW, STE 310 98026 #048-13-1983 L1991 **N** *020 †75

MCCALLISTER, Erika Lyn. ■ 98026 #054-04-2004 **GS** *012

MC CALLISTER, Wren Vance. 7320 216TH ST SW, STE 320 98026 #054-04-2000 L2000 **HS** *020

MC CLELLAND, Richard K. 21601 76TH AVE W 98026 #028-46-1976 L1983 **IM EM** *020 †16

MC CORMICK, Matthew Jos. 21601 76TH AVE W 98026 #010-01-1988 L1997 **DR** *020 †80

MC COY, Claude Oliver. 555 DAYTON ST STE C 98020 #054-04-1963 L1964 **P** *020

MC COY, Robert Hays. 7320 216TH ST SW STE 20 98026 #028-34-1982 L1987 **PUD CCM** *020 †20

MC CULLOUGH, James Arthur. 7320 164TH ST SW, STE 140 98026 #054-04-1988 L1996 **AN** *020 †05

MC GEE, Richard Allan. 21605 76TH AVE W STE 200 98026 #023-07-1971 L1973 **ON HEM** *020 †20

MC KEE, William Mark. ■ 98020 #056-05-1960 L1963 **MDM IM** *071 †20

MERCER, James Kevin. 21601 76TH AVE W 98026 #040-02-1976 L1979 **EM** *020 †16

MILLER, Carolyn G. 7320 164TH ST SW, STE 140 98026 #054-04-1992 L1999 **AN** *020 †05

MILLER, Lee Gilbert. ■ 98026 #024-01-1956 L1962 **PD N** *020 †55

MITCHELL, Robert Jeatran. 21616 76TH AVE W, STE 205 98026 #041-02-1979 L1984 **OBG** *020 †30

MITO, Robert Ken. 7320 216TH ST SW, STE 210 98026 #054-04-1976 L1977 **CD IM** *020 †20

MODELL, Ellen M. 7320 216TH ST SW, STE 310 98026 #019-02-1990 L1994 **N** *020 †75

MOE, Donald George. 7315 212TH ST SW, STE 101 98026 #054-04-1987 L1989 **FM** *020 †18

MUSTIN, Henry Dutton. 7315 212TH ST SW, STE 101 98026 #028-02-1978 L1979 **OS PHP** *020 †70,18

NAGASAKA, Ayako. ■ 98026 #040-02-1958 L1964 **GP** *072

NANK, David Reinhardt. 21616 76TH AVE W, STE 102 98026 #035-01-1964 L1968 **ORS** *071 †40

NEILSON, Daniel. ■ 98020 #054-04-1977 L1978 **AN** *020 †05

NELSON, Marci Michele. 21911 76TH AVE W STE 110 98026 #005-18-2001 L2001 **FM** *020 †18

NEWITT, Thomas R. ■ 98020 #041-02-1949 L1949 **AN** *071 †05

NEWLYN, Thomas Patrick. 21701 76TH AVE W STE 3 98026 #143-01-1966 L1977 **CHP P** *020 †75

NGUYEN, Bichkhanh Thi. 7320 216TH ST SW, STE 200 98026 #040-02-1988 L1991 **IM** *020 †20

NICOLAS, Arcadio F. ■ 98026 #748-10-1965 L1972 **GP GS** *075

NILL, Leroy Martin. ■ 98020 #028-34-1973 L1980 **PD** *020 †05

NIRMAL, Kodavayour S. ■ 98026 #496-07-1984 L2006 **FM** *020 †18,20

O'BRIEN, Paul Emmet. 21616 76TH AVE W, STE 208 98026 #026-04-1961 L1965 **IM** *020

OLSEN, Michael Stewart. 21601 76TH AVE W 98026 #040-02-1973 L2005 **PUD IM** *020 †20

OLSON, Jon Brandon. 21701 76TH AVE W STE 301 98026 #047-05-1971 L1974 **AN PME** *020 †05

OLSSON, Roger Bryant. 7315 212TH ST SW STE 101, EDMONDS FAMILY MEDICINE CL 98026 #030-05-1975 L1976 **FM EM** *020 †18

OWINGS, Raymond Hays. ■ 98026 #012-05-1958 L1976 **PTH** *071 †50

PAK-GORSTEIN, Suzinne. 21600 HWY 99 98026 #025-12-2001 L2003 **PD** *020 †55

PAMES, James Edward. 21616 76TH AVE W, SWEDISH PHYSICIANS SUMMIT 98026 #028-03-1990 L1998 **CD** *020 †20

PEACEY, James Randolph. 22727 HIGHWAY 99, STE 107 98026 #054-04-1988 L1990 **CHP P** *020 †75

PECK, David Fraser. 21616 76TH AVE W, STE 110 98026 #016-06-1973 L1976 **OPH** *020

PETERSON, Jennifer Stacy. 7315 212TH ST SW STE 101 98026 #054-04-1994 L1996 **FM** *020 †18

PETRIN, Joseph Gerrard. 7315 212TH ST SW, STE 101 98026 #054-04-1975 L1976 **FM** *020 †18

PHILLIPS, Richard Claude. 111 MAIN ST, STE 106 98020 #005-11-1973 L1983 **TS** *020 †90,85

PROUDFOOT, Martin Lewis. 7315 212TH ST SW, STE 101 98026 #020-12-1975 L1978 **FM EM** *020

QUISTGAARD, Susanne U. 7315 212TH ST SW STE 207, EDMONDS FAMILY MEDICINE CL 98026 #036-05-1993 L1993 **FM** *020 †18

RAJENDRAN, Babu. 7320 164TH ST SW, STE 140 98026 #030-05-1993 L1994 **AN** *020 †05

RAMACHANDRAN, Vimala. ■ 98026 #038-06-2001 L2007 **HS** *020

RATTRAY, Mark C. ■ 98026 #054-04-1978 L1979 **OBG** *030 †30

REES, William James. ■ 98020 #028-34-1946 L1974 **D PA** *071

REICHLER, Robert Jay. 21827 76TH AVE W 98026 #035-46-1961 L1976 **CHP P** *020 †75

REINBOLD, Kirsten Lee. 21601 76TH AVE W, STEVENS HOSPITAL 98026 #054-04-1986 L1989 **AN IM** *020 †05

REMINGTON, Jeffrey Paul. 7320 216TH ST SW, STE 320 98026 #054-04-1973 L1978 **ORS** *020 †40

RIEGER, Jurgen Karl. 21601 76TH AVE W, STEVENS HOSP DEPT AN 98026 #038-40-1974 L1975 **AN IM** *020 †20,05

RODDY, Timothy Michael. 21822 76TH AVE W, SOUND UROLOGICAL 98026 #040-02-1982 L1989 **U** *020 †95

ROGERS, Catherine Alice. 21616 76TH AVE W STE 20, SOUND WOMEN'S CARE 98026 #034-01-1995 L1999 **OBG** *020 †30

ROSE, Roger Alan. 7416 212TH ST SW, COMPASS HTLH EXTENED SERV 98026 #016-11-1964 L1965 **CHP P** *020 †75

ROSEN, Irwin Chas. ■ 98020 #869-04-1956 L1972 **AN** *071 †05

ROSENSHEIN, Marc Steven. 21605 76TH AVE W STE 200 98026 #041-02-1973 L1978 **ON HEM** *020 †20

RUST, Richard E. 21601 76TH AVE W 98026 #018-03-1952 L1954 **FM** *071 †18

SANDLER, Richard Anthony. 21200 72ND AVE W 98026 #040-02-1968 L1971 **PM PMM** *020 †60

SARGENT, Christopher John. 7315 212TH ST SW, STE 101 98026 #054-04-1996 L1998 **FM** *020 †18

SCHAM, Stewart M. 911 9TH AVENUESOUTH 98020 #035-01-1960 L1967 **ORS** *071 †40

SCHENCK, Darius Stig. ■ 98020 #054-04-2001 *100

SCHLAMEUS, Jeffrey Floyd. 7315 212TH ST SW, STE 101 98026 #010-01-1975 L1976 **FM** *020 †18

SCHLESINGER, Teresa Marie. 21616 76TH AVE W STE 112 98026 #016-11-1985 L1990 **AN** *020 †05

SCHNEIER, Jason Ian. 21600 HIGHWAY 99 98026 #041-12-1976 L1977 **GE IM** *020 †20

SCHREIEGG GOUCH, Ellen D. 7935 216TH ST SW 98026 #407-16-1952 L1980 **GP OS** *071

SCHULTZ, Fordyce Emmeal. 21601 76TH AVE W 98026 #028-34-1955 L1956 **OPH** *071

SCISCOE, Debora I. 21616 76TH AVE W, STE 205 98026 #048-04-1982 L1991 **OBG** *020 †30

SCOTT, Jeffrey Robt. 21600 HIGHWAY 99 98026 #030-06-1978 L1996 **PD** *020 †55

SETO, Jane Mei-Chun. ■ 98020 #242-37-1951 **PHP IM** *020

SETO, Samuel K. 21911 76TH AVE W, STE 101 98026 #056-05-1991 L1995 **OPH** *020 †35 ‡

SEVERINGHAUS, Edwin C. 21601 76TH AVE W 98026 #035-20-1952 L1967 **P** *071 †75

SHAW, Russel Laverne. ■ 98026 #054-04-1956 L1958 **GP OS** *071

SHELTON, Roger Dean. 7315 212TH ST SW STE 204 98026 #003-01-1975 L1977 **GYN** *020 †30

SILBERMAN, Stanford Joel. ■ 98020 #054-04-1959 L1965 **GS** *020 †85

SILVER, Darcy Deetta. 7320 216TH ST SW 98026 #030-05-2001 L2006 **ORS** *020

SILVER, Mark Alan. 21616 76TH AVE W, STE 103 98026 #041-01-1979 L1984 **DIA END** *020 †20

SIMONS, C Edward, Jr. 21701 76TH AVE W 98026 #054-04-1951 L1957 **U** *071 †95

SKOVRON, Elizabeth Horan. ■ 98020 #035-03-1977 L1979 **IM** *020

SPIEGEL, James Francis. 21605 76TH AVE W, STE 100 98026 #008-02-1986 L1997 **RO IM** *020 †20,80

SPIRO, David Arthur. 21911 76TH AVE W, BIRTH & FAMILY CLINIC 98026 #054-04-1983 L1985 **FM** *020 †18

STAPLETON, William Jos. ■ 98026 #028-34-1945 L1946 **AN** *071 †05

STEEVES, Samuel Lloyd. ■ 98020 #060-01-1952 L1964 **AN GP** *071

STETSENKO, Galina Y. ■ 98026 #054-04-2004 L2006 **PTH** *012

STETSENKO, Yuriy Panteley. ■ 98026 #913-05-1973 **CD P** *071

STEWART, Cameron Allen. 21204 72ND AVE W 98026 #040-02-1955 L1960 **GP** *071

STOUT, Karen Kathleen. 21601 76TH AVE W 98026 #003-01-1996 L2000 **CD** *100 †20 ‡

STRONG, Linda Keene. 7320 216TH ST SW, STE 200 98026 #012-01-1991 L1994 **IM** *020 †20

SUTTON-WOLF, Annika. 21600 HWY 99, STE 290 98026 #005-19-2004 L2004 **PD** *020 †55

SWEDBERG, Steven Harold. 21600 HIGHWAY 99, STE 230 98026 #054-04-1992 L1995 **OPH** *020 †35

SZYMANSKI, Ronald John. ■ 98020 #056-05-1956 L1968 **AN** *071

TAIBLESON, David Edward. 7315 212TH ST SW, STE 2-3 98026 #007-02-1985 L1990 **FM** *020 †18

TAKAGI, Brian Keith. 21600 HIGHWAY 99 STE 230 98026 #041-12-1989 L1997 **OPH** *020 †35

TAPLIN, Susan Elizabeth. 21600 HIGHWAY 99, STE 290 98026 #054-04-1994 L1994 **IM** *020 †20

TAYLOR, Ronald Ernest. 21616 76TH AVE W, STE 205 98026 #054-04-1959 L1965 **IM** *071

TESCH, Donald Joseph. 7315 212TH ST SW STE 203 98026 #005-14-1988 L1996 **FM** *020 †18

THAKKAR, Rupin Raj. 21600 HIGHWAY 99, STE 290 98026 #056-06-2003 L2003 **PD** *020 †55

THAL, Ben. 21616 76TH AVE W, STE 111 98026 #054-04-1958 L1964 **OTO PS** *071 †45

THURMAN, Andrew Franklin. 7315 212TH ST SW, STE 203 98026 #005-14-1996 L1999 **FM** *020 †18

TIMMONS, J Daniel. 21616 76TH AVE W, STE 211-212 98026 #038-40-1956 L1962 **GYN** *020 †30

TODD, John Thos. 21601 76TH AVE W 98026 #028-34-1969 L1975 **OTO** *020 †45

TOLBERG, Maryellen. 7315 212TH ST SW STE 203 98026 #041-02-1989 L1989 **FM** *020 †18

TREANOR, Thomas Andrew. ■ 98026 #035-15-1954 L1957 **OBG OS** *071 †30

TROWBRIDGE, Janet Marie. 21600 HIGHWAY 99, STE 280 98026 #035-19-1999 L2006 **D** *100

TUURA, James L. ■ 98020 #056-05-1953 L1963 **D A** *071 †15

TYSON, Geoffrey Louis. 21701 76TH AVE W, STE 203 98026 #041-13-1982 L1983 **AN EM** *020 †05

UPTON, Kathryn Elizabeth. 221 4TH AVE N 98020 #056-06-1990 L1993 **FM** *020 †18

WALDBURGER, John Jos. 7320 164TH ST SW, STE 140 98026 #054-04-1982 L1983 **AN** *020 †05

WALTZ, Ronald Newman. 21616 76TH AVE W, STE 109 98026 #054-04-1972 L1974 **FM** *020 †18

WARD, Jeffery Charles. 21605 76TH AVE W, STE 200 98026 #054-04-1987 L1993 **HO IM** *020 †20

WEAKLY, Daniel Earle. 7315 212TH ST SW STE 101 98026 #028-34-1984 L1990 **FM** *020 †18

WEEKS, Gary Lawrence. 21616 76TH AVE W, SWEDISH PHYSICIANS SUMMIT 98026 #016-06-1980 L1990 **CD IM** *020 †20

WERNER, Ferdinand. ■ 98026 #041-01-1956 L1960 **GP** *071

WILLIAMS, John Bruce. 21616 76TH AVE W 98026 #040-02-1981 L1989 **IM** *020 †20

WILSON, Michelle J. 7315 212TH ST SW, STE 201 98026 #048-04-1991 L1992 **GS** *020 †85

WINANT, Leanna Kay. 21911 76TH AVE W, STE 110 98026 #039-05-1990 L1992 **FM** *020 †18

WONG, Agnes. 21600 HIGHWAY 99 98026 #056-05-1987 L1991 **PD** *020 †55 ‡

YARNALL, Stephen R. 617 5TH AVE S 98020 #035-45-1960 L1962 **IM NTR** *020 †55

YOON, Jay M. 7631 212TH ST SW, STE 106B 98026 #583-02-1971 L1998 **ON IM** *020 †20

YORE, Liam Thomas. 6528 136TH PL SW 98026 #016-06-1997 L2000 **EM** *020 †16

YRUMA, Emmanuel M. 21601 76TH AVE W 98026 #748-02-1990 L2000 **IM** *020 †20

ZAMMIT, Michael. 21616 76TH AVE W 98026 #627-01-1975 L1982 **VS** *020 †85

ZEH, Catherine. 21911 76TH AVE W, BIRTH & FAMILY CLINIC 98026 #016-11-2002 L2002 **FM** *020 †18

ZEITZ, Stanley Jesse. 21616 76TH AVE W STE 202 98026 #035-19-1958 L1963 **A IM** *071 †03,20

ZHOU, Dadong. 7320 216TH ST SW STE 310 98026 #243-48-1990 L2002 **N** *020 †75

ELK – SPOKANE

COVERT, Stanley B, Jr. ■ 99009 #035-09-1949 L1967 **OS** *020 †18

ELLENSBURG – KITTITAS

AKKER, Lee Roy. CHESTNUT & MANITOBA STS 98926 #016-11-1965 L1969 **FM** *071 †18

ARASMITH, Jessica Lynn. ■ 98926 #054-04-2007 **PD** *012

BOONE, Aretas Cephas. ■ 98926 #010-01-1954 L1955 **FM** *071

BOYS SMITH, John Wynn. 109 N PINE ST 98926 #917-21-1968 L1990 **OPH** *020 †35

BRUBAKER, Derick Scott. 107 E MOUNTAIN VIEW AVE, STE 1 98926 #041-14-1999 L2002 **FM** *020 †18

■ = Address Information Privacy Protected

BRUBAKER, Jennifer Erin. 107 E MOUNTAIN VIEW AVE, STE 1 98926 #041-14-1999 L2002 PD *020 †55

CARR, Marilynn Grace. 716 E MANITOBA AVE, VALLEY CLINIC LLP 98926 #054-04-1987 L1989 FM *020 †18

CRUZ, Frank Hernandez. 603 S CHESTNUT ST 98926 #005-12-1990 L1993 FM *020 †18

DE PALMA, Arthur Ernest. 400 E UNIVERSITY WAY 98926 #041-12-1966 L1974 FM FPG *020 †18

FENG, Jamin. 700 E MANITOBA AVE, STE 101 98926 #065-02-1988 L1992 IM *020 †20

FRIEDLAND, Thomas Walter. ■ 98926 #040-02-1966 L1971 U *071 †95

HANEY, Byron Lee. 107 E MOUNTAIN VIEW AVE, STE 1 98926 #017-20-1982 L1990 FM OBS *020 †18

HARRIS, Kenneth Allan. 700 E MANITOBA AVE 98926 #019-02-1976 L1977 GS *020 †85

HAZELWOOD, Kyle Jeffrey. ■ 98926 #016-43-2007 *012

HERBERT, Herbert J. ■ 98926 #030-06-1945 L1954 OPH OTO *071

HERMAN, Bruce Aaron. 716 E MANITOBA AVE, VALLEY CLINIC LLP 98926 #028-02-1986 L1990 FM OBS *020 †18

HERMAN, Elise Jill. 611 S CHESTNUT ST, STE E 98926 #041-13-1984 L1990 PD *020 †55

HIERSCHE, Daniel Louis. 700 E MANITOBA AVE STE 106 98926 #005-12-1979 L1985 ORS *020 †40

HOWELL, J Harden. 2205 W DOLARWAY RD, STE 3 98926 #036-01-1974 L1979 OTO *020 †45

JOHNSON, Richard Wm. 700 E MANITOBA AVE, STE 101 98926 #040-02-1977 L1984 IM *020 †20

JOHNSON, Robert G, Jr. 107 E MOUNTAIN VIEW AVE, STE 1 98926 #040-02-1995 L2001 FM *020 †18

JUEL, Randolph Wade. 603 S CHESTNUT ST 98926 #010-01-1972 L1973 EM *020 †16

LARSON, Mark Warren. 716 E MANITOBA AVE, VALLEY CLINIC LLP 98926 #019-02-1990 L1997 FM *020 †18

LONGO, Anthony James. 603 S CHESTNUT ST, KITTATAS VALLEY COMMUNITY 98926 #048-02-2002 L2007 ORS *020

LUNDY, David Andrew. 716 E MANITOBA AVE 98926 #054-04-1967 L1972 GP EM *071 †18

MANSON-HING, Collin James. 603 S CHESTNUT ST 98926 #001-06-1977 L1989 GP *020

MATTHEWS, Glenn Boyd. ■ 98926 #048-04-1959 L1986 OBG *071 †30

MERRILL-STESKAL, John J. 716 E MANITOBA AVE, VALLEY CLINIC LLP 98926 #040-02-1991 L1994 FM *020 †18

O'BRIEN, Timothy Jay. 700 E MANITOBA AVE STE 109 98926 #026-04-1966 L1984 GS OS *020 †85

OLDHAM, Brent Aldridge. 611 S CHESTNUT ST STE A 98926 #024-01-1976 L1977 PD *020 †55

PACE, William R, III. 700 E MANITOBA AVE STE 105 98926 #054-04-1974 L1975 ORS *020 †40

PEET, Andrew Chas. 603 S CHESTNUT ST 98926 #033-05-1985 L1987 EM IM *020 †20

PENNY, Janet Adele. 611 S CHESTNUT ST, STE E 98926 #033-06-1993 L2007 PD *020

POWELL, James Allen. 716 E MANITOBA AVE 98926 #028-03-1958 L1967 GS GYN *071

ROIS-ROMERO, Ricardo Andr. 611 S CHESTNUT ST STE A 98926 #264-21-1999 L2006 FM *020

SAND, John H. 611 S CHESTNUT ST STE B 98926 #005-19-1976 L1983 OBG *020 †30

SHIELS, Patrick Lawrence. 603 S CHESTNUT ST, KITTITAS VALLEY COMMUNITY 98926 #016-11-1974 L1979 GP *020

SINGH, Sawraj. 700 E MOUNTAIN VIEW AVE, STE 502 98926 #495-29-1970 L1987 GS GP *020 †85

SMITH, Patrick Henry. 2318 BRICK RD 98926 #054-04-1969 L1971 GP EM *020

SOLBERG, Don Alan. 716 E MANITOBA AVE, VALLEY CLINIC LLP 98926 #054-04-1973 L1978 FM *020 †18

TERPENNING, Buckley J. ■ 98926 #035-46-1984 L1986 RNR R *072 †80

VARNER, Cheryl L. 2205 W DOLARWAY RD, STE 3 98926 #003-01-1999 L2004 OTO *020 †45

VAUGHAN, Richard Dallas. 716 E MANITOBA AVE, VALLEY CLINIC LLP 98926 #016-06-1977 L1980 FM *020 †18

WELLS, Nancy Lucretia. 611 S CHESTNUT ST STE C 98926 #040-02-1990 L1992 FM *020 †18

WICKERATH, James. 603 S CHESTNUT ST, K V C H 98926 #054-04-1989 L1991 EM FM *020 †18

ZITTERMAN, Joseph, Jr. 611 S CHESTNUT ST, STE A 98926 #041-13-1993 L2002 IM *071

ENUMCLAW — KING

ANDERSON, A Kenneth. 3021 GRIFFIN AVE 98022 #054-04-1957 L1958 GP IM *071

ATKINSON, Stephen Grant. 2820 GRIFFIN AVE, STE200 98022 #048-14-1985 L2001 GS VS *020

BALLARD, Mary L. 718 GRIFFIN AVE, # 197 98022 #028-34-1983 L1988 IM IMG *020

BHASKAR, James R. 1450 BATTERSBY AVE 98022 #654-01-1987 L1994 FM *020 †18

BISHOP, David Harold. 2820 GRIFFIN AVE STE 210 98022 #054-04-1986 L1986 ORS *020 †40

BRITTON, Lisa Maureen. 1450 BATTERSBY AVE 98022 #005-02-1996 L1998 FM *020 †18

CARGILL, Samuel Earl. 3021 GRIFFIN AVE, ENUMCLAW MEDICAL CENTER 98022 #040-02-1988 L1993 GS *020 †85

CHUNG, Gary Whakuk. 2820 GRIFFIN AVE, STE 101 98022 #048-12-2000 L2000 OPH *020 †35

CLARK, James Elliott. 3021 GRIFFIN AVE 98022 #054-04-1972 L1973 FM *020 †18

DAY, Linda Elizabeth. 2820 GRIFFIN AVE, STE 101 98022 #035-46-1993 L1997 OPH OS *020 †18

DICKSON, Holly A. 3021 GRIFFIN AVE 98022 #048-13-1997 L2001 OBG *020

ERICKSON, John D. 2125 C ST 98022 #041-09-1951 L1952 GP OS *071

ERICKSON, Katrina Joanne. 1450 BATTERSBY AVE 98022 #021-01-2004 L2006 FM *020 †18

FEENEY, Deidre Louise. 1818 COLE ST, PLATEAU FAMILY MEDICINE 98022 #025-12-1985 L1986 FM *020 †18

FRERICHS, Luther Alan. 3021 GRIFFIN AVE 98022 #030-05-1975 L1978 FM *020 †18

GARDNER, Victor H, Jr. ■ 98022 #018-03-1951 L1954 ORS OS *020 †40

GHERMAY, Berhan. 1450 BATTERSBY AVE 98022 #005-18-1996 L2003 FM *020 †18

GRAMANN, Robert Conrad. 3021 GRIFFIN AVE 98022 #030-06-1973 L1976 OBG *020 †30

GUNDERSON, Paul Einar. 2820 GRIFFIN AVE STE 200 98022 #024-01-1970 L1977 GS *071 †85

HARBIN, Elizabeth Ann. 1450 BATTERSBY AVE 98022 #665-01-2004 L2006 FP *012

HAYNE, Lon Alan. 1450 BATTERSBY AVE, DEPT OF RADIOLOGY 98022 #007-02-1983 L1986 DR RNR *020 †80

HOSODA, Emitis Kourosh. 2820 GRIFFIN AVE STE 204 98022 #048-12-1995 L2002 IM *020 †20

HOUTZ, Jane Marie. 3021 GRIFFIN AVE 98022 #010-01-1990 L2000 IM *020 †20

JARSTAD, John Steven. 2820 GRIFFIN AVE, STE 101 98022 #054-04-1984 L1989 OPH *020 †35

JOHNSON, O Arthur. ■ 98022 #054-15-1964 GP *071

JOHNSON-BECKER, Nancy A. 1427 JEFFERSON AVE 98022 #005-76-1986, ▲ L1991 OTO FPS *020

KAEHLER, Mark R. 1450 BATTERSBY AVE, EMERGENCY ROOM 98022 #023-01-1984 L1989 EM FSM *020 †18

MAGLEY, George Randolph. 3021 GRIFFIN AVE, ENUMCLAW MEDICAL CENTER 98022 #054-04-1971 L1973 FM *020 †18

MAGLEY, Joseph Wilson. 3021 GRIFFIN AVE 98022 #048-15-2008 *012

MAY, Lance Arnold. 1450 BATTERSBY AVE 98022 #019-02-1993 L2000 IM *020

MERRILL, James Albert. 3021 GRIFFIN AVE 98022 #054-04-1975 L1976 FM *020 †18

RICE, David Harold. 1450 BATTERSBY AVE 98022 #019-02-1978 L1993 DR *020 †80

ROCKEY, Dean Mc Dowell. 2820 GRIFFIN AVE, STE 101 98022 #054-04-1957 L1959 OPH *071 †35

RUBIN, Jason Phillip. 1450 BATTERSBY AVE, ENUMCLAW COMMUNITY HOSPITA 98022 #028-34-1995 L1999 FM *020 †18

RUSH, Rebecca Brown. 1818 COLE ST, PLATEAU FAMILY MED PS 98022 #028-34-1985 L1986 FM *020 †18

RUSSELL, Charles Alan. 2820 GRIFFIN AVE STE 103 98022 #005-12-1978 L1985 HS *020 †40

SHAWCROSS, Dustin L I. 1450 BATTERSBY AVE 98022 #056-06-2003 L2005 EM *020 †16

TAYLOR, Brett N. 1450 BATTERSBY AVE 98022 #048-12-1989 L1989 EM UCM *020

TEPPER, Michael. 2820 GRIFFIN AVE STE 204 98022 #422-01-1993 L2003 IM *020 †20

TESTER, Robert Aaron. 2820 GRIFFIN AVE, STE 101 98022 #049-01-2000 L2004 OPH *020 †35

TROBAUGH, Gene Bryant. 3021 GRIFFIN AVE 98022 #040-02-1969 L1973 CD *020 †20

VANFOSSEN, Brenda Rae. 3021 GRIFFIN AVE 98022 #055-02-2001 L2004 PD *020 †55

VERZOSA, Jude Gerard Ditc. 3021 GRIFFIN AVE 98022 #748-01-1995 L2003 IM *020 †20

WILLIAMS, Shari Catherine. 1450 BATTERSBY AVE 98022 #005-06-1987 L1998 EM *020 †16

WILLNER, Andrew Noel. 3021 GRIFFIN AVE 98022 #054-04-1976 L1978 FM *020 †18

ZECH, Ralph K. ■ 98022 #030-06-1949 L1951 CRS GS *071 †85 ‡

EPHRATA — GRANT

ADAMS, Rocky Jay. ■ 98823 #024-07-2008 *012

ALLRED, Lowell C. 508 W DIVISION AVE 98823 #049-01-1980 L1981 FM *020 †18

BRZEZNY, Alexander. 220 NAT WASHINGTON WAY, COLUMBIA BOSIN FAMILY 98823 #286-04-1996 L2001 FM *020 †18

GREIG, Bradley J. 220 NAT WASHINGTON WAY, COLUMBIA BASIN FAMILY MED 98823 #060-01-1992 L1996 IM *020

KIRKHAM, W Brian. 220 NAT WASHINGTON WAY, COLUMBIA BASIN FAMILY MEDI 98823 #067-01-1976 L1992 FM *020

SAID, Mohammad Hassan. ■ 98823 #847-03-1967 L1980 FM IM *020 †20,18

EVANS — STEVENS

LANDES, Richard Dale. ■ 99126 #055-01-1965 L1986 NPM PD *020 †55

EVERETT — SNOHOMISH

ABSON, Paul Antony. 3901 HOYT AVE, EVERETT CLNC 98201 #054-04-1986 L1991 OTO GS *020 †45

ADAM, Julie Lynn. 3216 NORTON AVE, STE 201 98201 #054-04-1982 L1983 DR *020 †80

ADAM, Steven Franklin. 1717 13TH ST, PROVIDENCE REGIONAL CANCER 98201 #054-04-1975 L1976 RO R *020

ADAMS, Jeffery Robert. 3901 HOYT AVE, 3927 RUCKER AVE 98201 #054-04-1995 L2001 OTO *020 †45

AFLATOONI, Sarmad Jon. 1321 COLBY AVE 98201 #041-07-1997 L2003 NEP *020 †20

ALI, Syed Fasahat. 1330 ROCKEFELLER AVE # 310, C/O JULIE SALL, EVERETT CL 98201 #495-65-1997 L2002 IM *020 †20

ANDERSEN, Harold Frank. 900 PACIFIC AVE 98201 #018-03-1976 L2006 MFM OBG *030 †30

ANDERSON, Larry Simon. 3216 NORTON AVE, STE 201 98201 #024-01-1965 L1968 DR *020 †80

ANDERSON, William Floyd. 3327 COLBY AVE 98201 #054-04-1960 L1961 D *020 †15

ANDRE, Robert Earl. 900 PACIFIC AVE STE 500 98201 #040-02-1981 L1982 OBG *020 †30

ANDREWS, Carl Arthur. 4301 HOYT AVE 98203 #016-11-1970 L1975 ORS *020 †40

ARGUE, Leland R. 12800 BOTHELL EVERETT HWY, STE 160 98208 #026-04-1992 L1999 FM *020 †18

ARMSTRONG, Samuel Currie. 3901 HOYT AVE 98201 #035-06-1967 L1974 ON IM *071 †20

ATKINS, David Arthur. 3216 NORTON AVE, STE 201 98201 #005-12-1981 L1985 DR NR *020 †80

BABUSIS, Benis Paul. 3216 NORTON AVE, STE 201 98201 #005-15-1996 L2001 DR *020 †80

BAILEY, Christopher F. 1728 W MARINE VIEW DR, STE 109 98201 #010-02-1989 L2002 P *020 †75

BAILEY, Robert Michael. 12800 BOTHELL EVERETT HWY, STE 120 98208 #054-04-1993 L1997 FM *020 †18

BANFIELD, Matthew Adams. 900 PACIFIC AVE 98201 #030-06-2003 L2007 OBG *020

BARDIN, Earl Dan. 4225 HOYT AVE STE C 98203 #054-04-1981 L1983 U GS *020 †95

BARDSLEY, Nigel Donald. 9032 EASTVIEW AVE 98208 #917-23-1977 L1985 AN *020 †05

BARFORD, Donald Alun G. PO BOX 1067, (PAVILION) 900 PACIFIC AVE 98206 #917-23-1969 L1985 MFM OBG *020 †30

BARKER, Howard Barnum. 3102 COLBY AVE 98201 #005-11-1995 L2001 ORS *020 †40

BATSON, Jennie Lee. 1430 BROADWAY 98201 #023-07-1984 L1991 OBG *020 †30

BATSON, Oliver Andrew. 1717 13TH ST, PROVIDENCE REG CANCER PART 98201 #023-07-1984 L1991 ON HEM *020 †20 ‡

BECK, Niels Christian. 1001 N BROADWAY STE A11, PHYSICIAN 98201 #028-03-2003 L2007 EM *020

BECKLEY, Russell Brian. 1321 COLBY AVE 98201 #016-43-1988 L1994 IM *020 †20

BEEGLE, Earl Dennis. 12800 BOTHELL EVERETT HWY, STE 290 98208 #918-01-1978 L1982 FM *030 †18

BELL, Larry Edward. 3901 HOYT AVE, THE EVERETT CLINIC 98201 #005-11-1976 L1981 AN *020

BELNAP, Brian Knight. ■ 98208 #010-01-2005 L2006 AN *012

BERKOWITZ, Caryn Michelle. 12800 BOTHELL EVERETT HWY, STE 200 98208 #035-48-1985 L1997 GE HEP *020 †20

BIKHAZI, Paul Henry. 3927 RUCKER AVE, THE EVERETT CLINIC 98201 #005-18-1995 L2000 OTO *020 †45

BISLA, Tajinder Singh. 1912 EVERETT AVE 98201 #035-08-1995 L2001 PTH *020 †50

BLACKWELL, Jeffrey Scott. 1818 121ST ST SE 98208 #039-01-1985 L1992 FM *020 †18

BLUE, James Morton. 1330 ROCKEFELLER AVE # 220 98201 #012-01-1975 L1976 NS *071 †25

BOMMARITO, James Carl. 3901 HOYT AVE 98201 #025-07-1972 L1999 **AI PD** *020 †55,03
BOND, Eugene Cralle. 900 PACIFIC AVE 98201 #039-01-1948 L1957 **FM GS** *071
BORK, David Burton. 3216 NORTON AVE, STE 201 98201 #054-04-1974 L1979 **DR** *020 †80
BOWERS, Cindy Lou. 3901 HOYT AVE 98201 #005-15-1983 L1993 **FM** *020 †18
BREVIG, James K. 1330 ROCKEFELLER AVE, STE 400 98201 #035-01-1986 L1993
TS CD *020 †85,90
BRINKLEY, Charles Blane. 900 PACIFIC AVE, STE 501 98201 #056-06-1987 L1991
OBG *020 †30
BRODSKY, Richard Dean. 916 PACIFIC AVE 98201 #028-02-1972 L1984 **FM** *020 †18
BRONSTEIN, Andrew David. 3131 NASSAU ST, STE 102 98201 #024-01-1984 L1986
DR RNR *020 †80
BROOKS, Dean Kent. ■ 98203 #019-02-1942 L1984 **OS** *071
BRYSON, Jiho Huang. 4027 HOYT AVE 98201 #035-19-1995 L1997 **OM IM** *020 †20,70
BUONO, Grace. 3901 HOYT AVE 98201 #054-04-1986 L1988 **ICE CD** *020 †20
BURGOYNE, Brian. 3216 NORTON AVE, STE 201 98201 #005-06-1986 L1992 **DR** *020 †80
BURNSTEIN, Alan. 3901 HOYT AVE 98201 #067-01-1988 L2002 **OPH** *020 †35 ‡
BYRNES, Timothy Andrew. 1330 ROCKEFELLER AVE, STE 400 98201 #035-20-1982 L1990
TS *020 †85,90
CADENA-FORNEY, Gina. 916 PACIFIC AVE 98201 #264-22-2001 L2005 **FM** *020 †18
CALDWELL, Douglas Paul. 3216 NORTON AVE, STE 201 98201 #038-41-1997 L2003
DR *020 †80
CAMPBELL, Elizabeth Ann. ■ 98208 #030-06-2003 L2006 **PD** *100
CAMPBELL, Robert Alan. 3901 HOYT AVE 98201 #005-19-1973 L1987 **OPH EM** *020 †16,35
CANETE, Cherissa Ruiz. ■ 98208 #748-11-1977 *100
CARLSON, Kara L. 3216 NORTON AVE, STE 201 98201 #018-03-1992 L1998 **DR** *020 †80
CARTER, Alan Edward. 1818 121ST ST SE 98208 #038-06-1981 L1984 **FM CLP** *020 †18
CARTER, Susan Alene. 1818 121ST ST SE 98208 #040-02-1986 L2000 **FM** *020 †18
CASSELMAN, Edward S. 3216 NORTON AVE, STE 201 98201 #005-14-1971 L1979 **DR** *020 †80
CASTAGNO, Arthur A. 3216 NORTON AVE, STE 201 98201 #041-01-1980 L1986 **DR** *020 †80
CHALAKA, Sridar. 1330 ROCKEFELLER AVE, STE # 340, WWMG 98201 #035-48-1991 L1997
CCM *020 †20
CHAMBLIN, Dianna Lynn. 4027 HOYT AVE 98201 #054-04-1981 L1982 **PM** *020 †60
CHAN, Alan D S. 3216 NORTON AVE, STE 201 98201 #005-14-1994 L2000 **DR** *020 †80
CHANDRA, Ritik Satish. 1001 N BROADWAY, STE A11 98201 #028-02-2002 L2005 **EM** *020 †16
CHANG, Kevin Cheng-Yu. 3901 HOYT AVE, THE EVERETT CLINIC 98201 #244-02-1982 L2000
OPH *020 †35
CHANG, Suk Choo. 3802 BROADWAY STE B 98201 #583-02-1947 L2005 **P** *050 †75
CHATZKEL, Sherrie Lynn. 728 134TH ST SW, STE 120 98204 #041-13-1976 L1991 **R** *020 †80
CH'EN, Ian Y. 728 134TH ST SW STE 120, VANCOUVER RADIOLOGISTS, PC 98204
#035-45-1989 L1996 **DR** *020 †80
CHEN, San-Hwan. 4004 COLBY AVE, STE 101 EVERETT WA 98201 98201 #048-02-1995 L2000
D DMP *020 †15
CHEN, Steve Yuwen. 3216 NORTON AVE, STE 201 98201 #035-46-1999 L2005 **DR** *020 †80
CHEPURI, Vinaya Babu. 1330 ROCKEFELLER AVE, STE 540 98201 #026-04-1986 L1993
CD IM *020 †20
CHISHOLM, Dougal Roy. 3927 RUCKER AVE, THE EVERETT CLINIC 98201
#064-01-1977 L1994 *020 †18
CHO, Kisoon. 2930 MAPLE ST 98201 #035-48-1985 L1991 **FM** *020 †18
CHOCK, Devorah Alana. 125 130TH ST SE, FIRST FLOOR 98208 #010-02-1996 L2007 **GS** *020
CHONG, Maria. 3216 NORTON AVE, STE 201 98201 #054-04-1992 L1997 **DR** *020 †80
CHRISTIANSEN, Tawnya L. 4526 FEDERAL AVE BLDG 9, COMPASS HEALTH 98203
#054-04-1999 L2003 **P** *020 †75
CHUANG, Peter Pokai. 728 134TH ST SW, STE 120 98204 #026-04-1998 L2003 **DR** *020 †80
CHUN, Michael Raymond. 2320 RUCKER AVE, EVERETT NEUROLOGICAL CTR 98201
#056-05-1989 L1989 **N** *020 †75
CHUNG, Kiyon. 3901 HOYT AVE, THE EVERETT CLINIC - CARDI 98201 #026-08-1998 L2002
CD *020 †20
CLOSS-BREWER, Melissa. 12800 BOTHELL EVERETT HWY, STE 190 98208
#020-12-1995 L1999 **PD** *020 †55
CLYNE, Victoria Elizabeth. 12800 BOTHELL EVERETT HWY, STE 220 98208 #065-10-1979 L2002
FM *074 †18
CODSI, Michael Joseph. 3927 RUCKER AVE, CCF - DEPT OF ORTHOPEDICS 98201
#005-06-1999 L2007 **ORS** *100 †40
COHN, David Jonathan. 3216 NORTON AVE, STE 201 98201 #035-20-1978 L1980
N DR *020 †80
CONTRERAS, Ruben Anthony. 3901 HOYT AVE 98201 #005-06-1981 L1982 **FM** *020 †18
COOK, James Mc Donald, Jr. 3216 NORTON AVE, STE 201 98201 #048-12-1981 L1991
VS *020 †85
COOPER, Amy Marie. 1321 COLBY AVE, HOSPITAL TEAM 98201 #007-02-2000 L2003
IM *020 †20
CORWIN, Terry Spark. 4310 COLBY AVE, STE 203 98203 #048-12-1996 L2001 **U** *020 †95
COSTAS, Kimberly E. 1330 ROCKEFELLER AVE, STE 400 98201 #010-02-1998 L2003
TS *020 †85,90
COTTER, Mary-Ellen Leslie. 4526 FEDERAL AVE 98203 #065-10-1986 L1997 *020
COUGHENOUR, Mark Eaton. 1717 13TH ST, STE 300 98201 #019-02-1983 L1988
ON IM *020 †20
COURSEY, Emily Perry. ■ 98201 #027-01-2004 L2004 **AN** *012
COX, George John, Jr. 3927 RUCKER AVE 98201 #054-04-1985 L1986 **GE IM** *020 †20
CRAMER, John Francis, III. 1321 COLBY AVE 98201 #024-01-1974 L1979 **CCM IM** *020 †20
CURRAN, Catherine Maxwell. 916 PACIFIC AVE 98201 #054-04-1984 L1985 **FM** *020 †18
CZOP, Carol Lynn. 3207 WETMORE AVE, DEPT OF ANESTHESIA 98201 #036-01-1992 L1997
AN *020 †05
DACANAY, Leonardo M. 3930 HOYT AVE 98201 #005-14-2002 L2006 **OPH** *020
DALY, Charles Paul. 3216 NORTON AVE, STE 201 98201 #005-02-1990 L1992 **VIR** *020 †80
DASH, Harold. 3901 HOYT AVE, THE EVERETT CLINIC 98201 #024-01-1974 L1984
CD IM *020 †20
DASTVAN, Celia Mcardle. 12800 BOTHELL EVERETT HWY, STE 190 98208 #051-04-1990 L1993
PD *020 †55
DAVIDSON, Richard A. 3901 HOYT AVE, THE EVERETT CLINIC 98201 #035-20-1962 L1969
OPH *071 †35
DAVIS, Geoffrey Clemens. 3927 RUCKER AVE 98201 #024-05-1994 L2003 **GE** *020 †20
DAVIS, Gordon Bruce. 1111 PACIFIC AVE 98201 #054-04-1974 L1975 **PS** *020
DAVIS, Kent Stuart. 900 PACIFIC AVE, STE 501 98201 #019-02-1996 L2002 **OBG** *020 †30 ‡
DE BERARDINIS, Michael C. 3901 HOYT AVE 98201 #021-05-1967 L2003 **U GP** *020 †95
DECHADENEDES, Nicholas B. 12800 BOTHELL EVERETT HWY, STE 190 98208
#054-04-1982 L1986 **PD** *020 †55
DEFRANG, Robert Donald. 728 134TH ST SW, STE 120 98204 #056-06-1986 L1995 **VS** *020 †85
DE MARTINI, Joseph Rowell. 3216 NORTON AVE, STE 201 98201 #051-04-1997 L2003
DR *020 †80
DE PENDER, William James. 11001 31ST PL W, STE 1 98204 #054-04-1979 L1985 **FM** *020 †18
DERMODY, Richard Lee. 900 PACIFIC AVE, STE 500 98201 #016-45-1977 L2004 **OBG** *020 †30
DIAZ, George Arnold. 3901 HOYT AVE 98201 #039-01-1999 L2004 **ID** *020 †20
DICIRO, Dominic Theodore. 1001 N BROADWAY STE A11 98201 #028-03-1992 L2005
EM *020 †16
DICK, Ronald Larrabee. 916 PACIFIC AVE 98201 #024-16-1986 L1988 **PD** *020 †55
DICKEY, David Hueglin. 1818 121ST ST SE 98208 #035-09-1997 L2000 **IM** *020 †20
DILLINGER, Donald S. 10333 19TH AVE SE, STE 103 98208 #048-02-1978 L1979
IM PMM *020 †20
DILWORTH, John Andrew, IV. 3901 HOYT AVE 98201 #054-04-1969 L1976 **IM ID** *020 †20
DIMAS, Calixto Tanaka, III. 3131 NASSAU ST, STE 102 98201 #008-01-1985 L1995 **DR** *020 †80
DUONG, Michael Hungminh. 1330 ROCKEFELLER AVE, STE 540 98201 #026-04-1998 L2006
IC *100 †20
DURHAM-VOLD, Kyle Anne. 900 PACIFIC AVE STE 500 98201 #041-09-1993 L2001
OBG *020 †30
EHSAN, Mike M. 7601 EVERGREEN WAY STE B5, SUNRISE MEDICAL CARE 98203
#517-01-1959 L1966 **EM IM** *072
EIDE, Brock Leonard. 3927 RUCKER AVE 98201 #054-04-1988 L2001 **IM** *071 †20
EIFERT, Brian Edward. 3216 NORTON AVE, STE 201 98201 #027-01-1988 L2004
DR IM *020 †20,80
EISSMANN, Edward Wm. 3927 RUCKER AVE 98201 #031-01-1985 L1998 **GS ORS** *020 †40
ENGLISH, Gail L. 4027 HOYT AVE 98201 #054-04-1974 L1976 **IM** *020 †70
ENGUIDANOS, Enrique R. 1001 N BROADWAY STE A11 98201 #005-18-1996 L1999
EM *020 †16
ENRIGHT, James Robt. 3003 W CASINO RD, MS OY-75 98204 #026-04-1970 L1974
FM OM *020 †70,18
EPHRON, John H. 3927 RUCKER AVE, C/O JULIE SALL 98201 #035-15-1994 L1997 **DR** *020 †80
ERHARDT, James Bruce. 3216 NORTON AVE, STE 102 98201 #030-06-1979 L1984
OTO *020 †45
ERICKSON, David Loren. 1330 ROCKEFELLER AVE, STE 210 98201 #054-04-1979 L1980
GP *020
ESCHBACH, Virginia. 3216 NORTON AVE, STE 201 98201 #017-20-1980 L1999 **DR OS** *020 †80
EVANS, Philip Nolan. 3927 RUCKER AVE 98201 #023-07-1984 L1987 **AN** *020 †05
EYTINGE, Ernest Jos. ■ 98203 #028-02-1942 L1950 **IM** *071 †20
FACER, James C. 916 PACIFIC AVE 98201 #049-01-1960 L1970 **OTO** *071 †45
FAULHABER, Judith Ann. 1321 COLBY AVE 98201 #016-06-1981 L1982 **AN** *020 †05
FELICIANO, Philip D. 3216 NORTON AVE, STE 201 98201 #017-20-1985 L1997 **VS** *020 †85
FERGUSON, Geoffrey Stuart. 3216 NORTON AVE, STE 201 98201 #054-04-1974 L1975
DR *020 †80
FINDLAY, Laird Alan. 1330 ROCKEFELLER AVE, STE 210 98201 #040-02-1976 L1981
IM IMG *020 †20
FINK, Robert Ivan. 1728 W MARINE VIEW DR 98201 #026-04-1975 L1978 **P** *020 †75
FINLEY, J William. 1330 ROCKEFELLER AVE # 120, EVERETT CLINIC DEPT SURG 98201
#054-04-1996 L2003 **SO GS** *020 †85
FINLEY, Jimmy Garrett. 3901 HOYT AVE 98201 #047-05-1966 L1968 **GE IM** *030 †20
FINN, Shelly. 3901 HOYT AVE, THE EVERETT CLINIC 98201 #054-04-1987 L1990 **IM** *020 †20
FISK, Albert Wm. 3901 HOYT AVE 98201 #054-04-1983 L1984 **MDM** *030 †20
FLAKE, Brenda Lynn. ■ 98203 #005-12-1991 L1995 **OBG** *020 †30
FLEMING, Francis Xavier. 4225 HOYT AVE, STE B 98203 #048-14-1986 L1995 **PS HS** *020 †65
FORD, John Jos. ■ 98203 #005-02-1967 L1975 **VS GS** *075 †85
FRANKE, Randal Carl. 11001 31ST PL W 98204 #005-06-1981 L1986 **GP** *020 †70
FREED, Jeffrey Alan. 1321 COLBY AVE, PROVIDENCE EVERETT MED CTR 98201
#041-02-1983 L1996 **PTH BBK** *020 †50
FRITCHEN, Cathy Hollis. 3901 HOYT AVE 98201 #056-06-1976 L1985 **RHU IM** *020 †20
FROEHLICH, Hervey W, Jr. 2930 MAPLE ST 98201 #041-02-1981 L1982 **PD PDI** *020 †55 ‡
FROST, D Whitney. 3927 RUCKER AVE 98201 #046-01-1981 L1986 **ORS HS** *020 †40
FU, Yiu Kai. 3216 NORTON AVE, STE 201 98201 #462-01-1981 L2001 **DR** *020 †80
GABOUREL, Linda S. 4004 COLBY AVE, STE 101 98201 #040-02-1982 L1986 **D IM** *020 †20,15
GAHM, Sara Jo. 1001 N BROADWAY, STE A11 98201 #050-02-1993 L1996 **EM** *020 †16
GALLAGHER, William Jos. 3216 NORTON AVE, STE 202 98201 #016-02-1979 L1990
GS *020 †85
GALUSKA, Richard Dean. 916 PACIFIC AVE 98201 #026-04-1976 L1977 **AN** *020
GARDNER, Raymond Anson. ■ 98203 #005-12-1948 L1948 **AS GP** *071
GARHWAL, Sanjeev. 1330 ROCKEFELLER AVE, STE 540 98201 #035-19-1997 L2004
CD *100 †20
GEDDES, Cynthia. 3901 HOYT AVE 98201 #040-02-1987 L2002 **AN** *020 †05
GEIER, J Michael. 1330 ROCKEFELLER AVE, STE 220 98201 #019-02-1979 L1993 **NS** *020 †25
GERDES, Arthur James. PO BOX 1067, PROVIDENCE HOSPITAL 98206 #026-04-1959 L1966
RO R *071 †80
GHORAI, Sujoy Kumar. 12800 BOTHELL EVERETT HWY, STE 200 98208 #051-04-1996 L2002
GE *020 †20
GIERKE, Eric Paul. 3901 HOYT AVE 98201 #054-04-1990 L1992 **N** *020 †75
GIESECKE, Thomas F. 4301 HOYT AVE 98203 #012-05-1977 L1985 **FM GP** *020 †18
GIMLETT, David Myron. 3927 RUCKER AVE, THE EVERETT CLINIC 98201 #054-04-1961 L1963
FM *020 †18
GO, Greta Tan. 3216 NORTON AVE, STE 201 98201 #010-02-1987 L2000 **DR** *020 †80
GOLD, Elizabeth Sarah. 3901 HOYT AVE 98201 #008-01-1993 L1995 **CD** *020 †20
GOLDBAUM, Gary Mitchell. 3020 RUCKER AVE, FAMILY MEDICINE BOX 359846 98201
#007-02-1978 L1986 **PHP FM** *030 †70,18
GOLLER, Debra Ann. 3901 HOYT AVE, STE 120 98201 #005-18-1981 L1987 **GS OS** *020 †85
GOODMAN, Daniel Robt. 3125 COLBY AVE STE J 98201 #038-06-1981 L1986 **FM OBS** *020 †18
GOODMAN, John Lewis. 1330 ROCKEFELLER AVE # 120 98201 #056-06-1973 L1975
GS *020 †85
GOODMAN, Justin Samuel. 3927 RUCKER AVE, THE EVERETT CLINIC 98201
#005-18-1998 L2000 **GE** *020 †20
GORDON, Gavin Ian. 3927 RUCKER AVE 98201 #054-04-1990 L1992 **FM** *020 †18
GRAHAM, Deborah L. 3216 NORTON AVE, STE 201 98201 #041-07-1977 L1988
DR VIR *020 †80
GRAVES, Timothy Arthur. 1330 ROCKEFELLER AVE # 12 98201 #024-07-1994 L2001
GS *020 †85
GREEN, Cheryl Ann. 1728 W MARINE VIEW DR, STE 106 98201 #054-04-1996 L2000 **P** *020 †75
GREEN, Ronald Jeff. 1728 W MARINE VIEW DR, STE 106 98201 #035-01-1990 L1993
IM *020 †20

■ = Address Information Privacy Protected

WASHINGTON
EVERETT

GRIFFIN, Arthur Russell. 728 134TH ST SW STE 120 98204 #054-04-1955 L1957 **R** *071 †80
GROSSMAN, Arthur Saul. 4301 HOYT AVE 98203 #054-04-1973 L1977 **FM** *020 †18
GUILDNER, Charles Wayne. 916 PACIFIC AVE 98201 #030-05-1957 L1961 **AN** *071 †05
GULBAS, Diane S Mordaunt. 12800 BOTHELL EVERETT HWY, PROVIDENCE HEALTH CARE CEN 98208 #048-12-1975 L1995 **EM FM** *020
GUNDERSON, Todd Frederick. 3901 HOYT AVE 98201 #016-06-1992 L1996 **IM** *020 †20
GUNION, Mark William. 916 PACIFIC AVE 98201 #005-19-1999 L2003 **AN** *020 †05 ‡
GUNNING, Mark Eugene. 1330 ROCKEFELLER AVE, STE 450 98201 #539-03-1978 L2004 **NEP** *020 †20
HAAKENSTAD, Alan Otto. 3218 NASSAU ST, KIDNEY & ARTHRITIS CLNC 98201 #041-01-1967 L1971 **IG RHU** *050 †20
HABERMAN, Clayton R. 1912 EVERETT AVE 98201 #056-05-1949 L1950 **FOP ATP** *071 †50
HAFT, Lawrence Robt. 1330 ROCKEFELLER AVE, STE 540 98201 #041-09-1981 L1986 **CD IM** *020 †20
HALLAM, Paula S. 728 134TH ST SW STE 120, RADIA INC. PS 98204 #016-06-1993 L2000 **DR** *020 †80
HALLER, Ralph Thos. 1100 PACIFIC AVE 98201 #038-06-1981 L1986 **ORS** *020 †40
HALLGARTH, Brian Howard. 3927 RUCKER AVE 98201 #028-34-1980 L1981 **ORS** *020 †40
HAMMOND, George Steven. 3901 HOYT AVE, THE EVERETT CLINIC 98201 #048-02-1983 L1988 **END IM** *020 †20
HAN, Eldi Kyoung-Ok. 1330 ROCKEFELLER AVE, STE 210 98201 #305-01-2001 L2004 **IM** *020 †20
HAN, Steve. 3901 HOYT AVE, THE EVERETT CLINIC/JULIE S 98201 #016-43-1999 L2004 **U** *020 †95
HARMON, Ben Hugh. 3216 NORTON AVE, STE 201 98201 #004-01-1986 L1999 **DR FM** *020 †80
HARP, Karin Ila. 4004 COLBY AVE, THE EVERETT CLINIC-DERMATO 98201 #054-04-2001 L2002 **D** *020 †15
HART, Karen Marie. 1321 COLBY AVE 98201 #054-04-1988 L1991 **IM** *020 †20
HASSAN, Shukra Abdow Ibra. 2930 MAPLE ST 98201 #902-07-2002 L2006 **IM** *020 †20
HATHAWAY, Sarah Lynn. 12800 BOTHELL EVERETT HWY, STE 160 98208 #054-04-1991 L1993 **FM** *020 †18
HAUGEN, Ann E. 3901 HOYT AVE 98201 #054-04-1992 L2005 **PD** *020 †55
HAVENER, Todd Whitmore. 1100 PACIFIC AVE, STE 300 98201 #056-06-1998 L2004 **ORS** *020 †40
HAWKINS, Catherine C. 3901 HOYT AVE, THE EVERETT CLINIC 98201 #024-07-1979 L1991 **ID IM** *020 †20
HAWKINS, Robert A. 728 134TH ST SW STE 120, UPMC HORIZON 98204 #043-01-1997 L2007 **DR** *020 †80
HAYES, Elizabeth Jo. 3216 NORTON AVE, STE 201 98201 #025-01-1976 L1987 **DR NM** *020 †80
HECHT, William Helge. 3822 COLBY AVE 98201 #054-04-1962 L1964 **R** *071 †80
HECKER, Lonny Mitchell. 3927 RUCKER AVE 98201 #035-19-1985 L1990 **GE IM** *020 †20
HEISEN, Martin. 3901 HOYT AVE 98201 #409-40-1989 L2001 **CD IM** *020 †20
HELPHREY, Donald Matson. 10625 44TH AVE SE 98208 #054-04-1973 L1974 **FM** *020 †18
HENDERSON, Philip Edwin. 900 PACIFIC AVE STE 501, GYNECOLOGY 98201 #054-04-1980 L1984 **OBG** *020 †30
HENRIKSEN, George Arthur. 3216 WETMORE AVE, STE 3 98201 #054-04-1967 L1968 **P** *020 †75
HENRY, Larry Ward. 916 PACIFIC AVE, FLYNN CANCER CENTER 98201 #054-04-1975 L1976 **RO** *071 †80
HETTEL, Kathryn Louise. 5007 CLAREMONT WAY 98203 #038-43-1984 L1992 **PM** *020 †60
HINDS, Marvin Ward, Jr. 3020 RUCKER AVE STE 300 98201 #047-05-1970 L1974 **PHP GPM** *030 †70
HOLLENBECK, Phyllis A. 5007 CLAREMONT WAY, MMG CLAREMONT 98203 #043-01-1977 L1994 **FM NP** *020 †18
HORI, Kevin Michio. 916 PACIFIC AVE 98201 #005-14-1995 L1998 **EM** *020 †16
HORNUNG, Robin Louise. 4004 COLBY AVE, EVERETT CLNC 98201 #008-01-1990 L1999 **D GPM** *020 †70,15
HOWARD, Jane M. 1818 121ST ST SE 98208 #028-34-1981 L1987 **IM** *020 †20
HOWELL, Reginald S. ■ 98208 #010-03-1951 L1960 **P** *071
HOYLE, Rodney V. 3802 COLBY AVE 98201 #049-01-1962 L1968 **OPH** *020
HU, Kent Kang. 1321 COLBY AVE, 2ND FL 98201 #008-01-1998 L2001 **IM** *020 †20
HUANG, Bill K. 1100 PACIFIC AVE, STE 300 98201 #016-06-2000 L2007 **ORS** *100 ‡
HUANG, Deborah Lynn. 2930 MAPLE ST, GROUP HEALTH COOPERATIVE 98201 #010-01-2000 L2004 **IM** *020
HUANG, Emily Yalan. 1330 ROCKEFELLER AVE, STE 450 98201 #039-01-1996 L2001 **IM NEP** *020 †20
HUMMEL, William E. 4301 HOYT AVE 98203 #016-02-1949 L1956 **ORS** *071 †40
HUTCHINSON, Thomas Weston. ■ 98213 #025-01-1969 L1971 **ORS** *072 †40 ‡
JACOBSON, Robert Lee. 3901 HOYT AVE 98201 #056-05-1982 L1988 **FM** *020 †18
JALALI, Amir Shahriyar. 1330 ROCKEFELLER AVE, STE 350 98201 #028-03-1997 L2001 **PM** *020 †60
JIANG, Yin-Zheng. 1717 13TH ST, STE 300 98201 #243-20-1986 L2000 **ON** *020 †20
JOG, Shilpa. ■ 98203 #495-83-1995 L2007 **MPD** *020 †20
JOHANSEN, Kaj Henry. 3216 NORTON AVE, STE 201 98201 #054-04-1970 L1978 **VS TRS** *020 †85
JOHNSON, Gregory Alan. 916 PACIFIC AVE 98201 #048-04-1978 L1989 **PS** *075 †65
JOHNSON, Gregory Gordon. 1001 N BROADWAY, STE A11 98201 #054-04-2003 L2006 **EM** *020 †16
JONES, Diane Marie. 1721 HEWITT AVE, STE 605 98201 #041-13-1970 L1974 **GS** *071 †85
JONES, Jerry Clark. I1321 COLBY AVE 98201 #039-01-1963 L1965 **P** *020
JONES, Thomas Wm, Jr. 3930 HOYT AVE 98201 #030-06-1980 L1984 **OPH** *020 †35
JORDAN, John Dennis. 900 PACIFIC AVE, STE 500 98201 #038-06-1987 L1989 **OBG** *020 †30
JOSAFAT, Alice Brown. 728 134TH ST SW STE 120, C/O RADIA INC., P.S. 98204 #018-03-1998 L2004 **DR** *020 †80
JURAVSKY, Louis I. 728 134TH ST SW, STE 120 98204 #062-01-1984 L2005 **RNR** *100 †80
KAHN, Barry Todd. 1912 EVERETT AVE 98201 #028-02-1990 L1998 **PTH ATP** *020 †50
KAHN, Zevi Seth. 12800 BOTHELL EVERETT HWY 98208 #005-14-1985 L1988 **FM** *020 †18
KARR, Reynold Michael, Jr. 3128 NORTON AVE 98201 #023-01-1969 L1979 **A RHU** *020 †20,03
KATSH, Naomi. 3901 HOYT AVE 98201 #007-02-1979 L1982 **PD** *020 †55
KEENE, Lynn Marie Wilford. 2000 W MARINE VIEW DR, BRANCH NAVAL HEALTH CLINIC 98207 #011-03-1988 L2005 **PD** *020 †55
KELLY, Mary Mauriello. 3216 NORTON AVE, STE 201 98201 #054-04-1980 L1981 **DR** *074 †80
KENNEDY, John Bruce. 4225 HOYT AVE, EVERTT FAMILY PRACTICE CTR 98203 #054-04-1960 L1963 **GP** *075 †18
KIM, Paul Hyungbae. 1321 COLBY AVE, PROVIDENCE HOSPITAL 98201 #016-11-2004 L2006 **EM** *020
KIMBALL, Frederick James. 4301 HOYT AVE 98203 #054-04-1975 L1980 **FM EM** *020 †18
KINAHAN, Peter Joseph. 3102 COLBY AVE 98201 #061-01-1985 L2001 **ORS** *020 †40
KINARD, Kenneth Harold. ■ 98201 #035-01-1946 L1952 **IM** *071
KINGSLEY, Roy Edward. ■ 98201 #047-07-1944 L1946 **IM OS** *030
KLICPERA, James Anton. 1818 121ST ST SE, THE EVERETT CLINIC 98208 #016-02-1975 L1977 **PD** *020 †55
KNOLL, Paul Warren. 1717 13TH ST, # 300 98201 #054-04-1976 L1977 **ON IM** *020 †20
KOEHLER, Mary Frances. 3322 BROADWAY, COMPASS HEALTH 98201 #036-07-1982 L1985 **P** *020 †75
KOERNER, Michael Karl. 2320 RUCKER AVE 98201 #025-01-1977 L1987 **N** *020 †75
KOSCH, Wm Fredrich, III. ■ 98203 #041-01-1966 L1968 **GP** *020
KROL, Christopher Mark. 3216 NORTON AVE, STE 201 98201 #759-04-1998 L2004 **DR** *100 †80 ‡
KROLAK, James Douglas. 900 PACIFIC AVE, STE 501 98201 #016-06-1968 L1975 **OBG** *020 †30
KRUEGER, Ronald Allen. 3927 RUCKER AVE 98201 #026-04-1988 L1994 **OTO FPS** *020 †45
KUAN, Chia-Jen. 3218 NASSAU ST 98201 #244-02-1983 L1993 **NEP** *020 †20
KUMAR, Santosh. 3223 COLBY AVE, ELECTRODIAGNOSIS AND REHAB 98201 #495-36-1966 L1975 **PM PHP** *020 †60
KUO, Judith Hsinhsin. 12800 BOTHELL EVERETT HWY, STE 190 98208 #035-19-1997 L2000 **PD** *020 †55
KUTSY, Roman L. 2320 RUCKER AVE 98201 #913-39-1983 L1995 **N CN** *020 †75
LABIB, Mary Frances. ■ 98203 #054-04-2007 L2007 **IM** *012
LABIB, Salwa Ramzy. 1330 ROCKEFELLER AVE, STE 450 98201 #915-03-1974 L1985 **NEP IM** *020 †20
LAGOZZINO, Daniel Angelo. ■ 98203 #040-02-1943 L1946 **PD PDA** *071 †55
LAMMERT, Gary Karnosh. 3216 NORTON AVE, STE 201 98201 #038-06-1983 L1996 **DR** *020 †80
LAMUS, Bruce Barnard. I1321 COLBY AVE 98201 #049-01-1955 L1960 **IM PUD** *071 †20
LANDIS, Konnie Lynette. ■ 98201 #041-13-1996 L1998 **FM** *020 †18
LANK, Sylvia Salama. 9623 32ND ST SE, STE D106 98205 #056-06-1995 L1999 **OBG** *020 †30
LARSON, Duane Ramon. 3822 COLBY AVE 98201 #054-04-1957 L1958 **R** *071 †80
LARSON, Willard Alvin E. ■ 98203 #054-04-1957 L1958 **P OS** *020
LAU, George Tsun. 3901 HOYT AVE, TEC HOSPITALIST TEAM OFC 98201 #035-09-2000 L2003 **IM** *020 †20
LAUGHERY, Rory Michael. 1410 BROADWAY, COMMUNITY CLINICS OF SNOHO 98201 #005-14-1971 L1972 **FM** *020 †18
LEE, In Woo. ■ 98208 #583-02-1958 L1972 **P CHP** *071 †75
LEE, Katie Eunkyung. 1321 COLBY AVE, HOSPITALIST OFFICE 98201 #048-14-2000 L2004 **IM** *020 †20
LEE, Melissa. 2930 MAPLE ST, GROUP HEALTH COOPERATIVE 98201 #023-01-1992 L1995 **IM** *020 †20
LEE, Peter K. 3901 HOYT AVE 98201 #583-01-1985 L1991 **IM** *020 †50,20
LEE, Seunghyun. 5007 CLAREMONT WAY 98203 #583-15-1993 L2006 **PM** *020 †60
LEE, Suk Bo. 1330 ROCKEFELLER AVE # 310, THE EVERETT CLINIC 98201 #583-01-1984 L1990 **PM** *020 †60
LEIGHTON, Charles R, Jr. ■ 98203 #016-11-1952 L1953 **FM** *020
LEITZELL, James. 7601 EVERGREEN WAY, STE B6 98203 #049-01-1973 L1975 **NS OPH** *020 †16
LELLEID, Nancy Ann. 3901 HOYT AVE 98201 #040-02-1975 L1981 **N** *020 †75 ‡
LESTER, Jane Armstrong. 3901 HOYT AVE 98201 #054-04-1986 L1990 **PD** *020 †55
LI, Wai-Yuen. 728 134TH ST SW, STE 120 98204 #025-07-1969 L1973 **DR** *020 †80
LIAO, David C. 1330 ROCKEFELLER AVE, STE 330 98201 #035-09-1995 L1999 **END** *020 †20
LIEN, Marcus Chenchi. 1330 ROCKEFELLER AVE STE 3, 6TH FLOOR, CRITICAL CARE D 98201 #041-01-2001 L2007 **CCM** *020 †20
LIN, David Anson. 3901 HOYT AVE, THE EVERETT CLINIC 98201 #016-42-1997 L2002 **IM** *020 †20
LINDSTROM, David Olaf. 4301 HOYT AVE 98203 #038-41-1999 L2002 **FM** *020 †18
LINSCOTT, Nancy Lynn. 12800 BOTHELL EVERETT HWY, STE 160 98208 #036-01-1997 L2004 **FM** *020 †18
LIPO, James Francis. 1912 EVERETT AVE 98201 #056-06-1968 L1974 **PTH** *020 †50
LITTLE, Darren Jon. 916 PACIFIC AVE, FLYNN CANCER CENTER 98201 #005-12-1999 L2004 **RO** *020 †80
LITTLE, John Wesley. 3216 NORTON AVE, STE 201 98201 #035-45-1971 L1980 **DR** *020 †20,80
LIU, Sandra A. 3901 HOYT AVE 98201 #067-01-1989 L1992 **PD** *020 †55
LOCKETT, Cindy Ann. 3901 HOYT AVE 98201 #005-06-1995 L1998 **FM** *020 †18
LOFLAND, Donald Floyd. 3901 HOYT AVE 98201 #011-04-1983 L2002 **FM** *020 †18
LOURA, Friedrich Carl. 12800 BOTHELL EVERETT HWY, STE 200 98208 #005-18-1982 L1988 **GE IM** *020 †20
LOWELL, De Witt James. ■ 98206 #016-11-1954 L1955 **PTH GP** *071
LUBA, David Phillip. 1818 121ST ST SE, THE EVERETT CLINIC 98208 #024-16-1986 L1989 **PD** *020 †55
LUETH, Brian Dexter. 3930 HOYT AVE 98201 #010-02-1982 L1987 **OPH** *020 †35
LUSK, James Alexander. 3927 RUCKER AVE 98201 #025-01-1982 L1983 **IM** *030 †20
LY, Stacie Hien. 12800 BOTHELL EVERETT HWY, STE 18 98208 #007-02-2002 L2002 **IM** *020 †20
LYNCH, John Patrick. 1515 PACIFIC AVE 98201 #008-01-1962 L1964 **OTO** *071 †45 ‡
LYONS, Richard Morgan. PO BOX 5127 98206 #038-40-1967 L1974 **OTO** *020 †45
MACAULAY, Shane Edward. 3131 NASSAU ST, STE 102 98201 #005-18-1988 L1990 **DR** *020 †80
MADSEN, Robin Lynn. 3726 BROADWAY, STE 201 98201 #041-09-1995 L2005 **ORS** *020 †40
MAGARAM, David Lee. 728 134TH ST SW, STE 120 98204 #005-02-1976 L1999 **R** *020 †80
MAGNUS, Toshiko F. 916 PACIFIC AVE 98201 #008-01-1990 L1990 **IM** *020 †20
MAHONEY, Heather Lynette. PO BOX 1067, 1321 COLBY AVE 98206 #035-20-2000 L2002 **PD** *020
MAIN, Bruce Edward. 4301 HOYT AVE 98203 #025-01-1976 L1979 **FM** *020 †18
MALLOY, Henri Rembert. ■ 98204 #010-03-1939 L1944 **GS** *071
MANNING, Frederick C, III. 3901 HOYT AVE 98201 #048-04-1974 L1979 **FM** *040 †18
MARANDI, Patris S. 3216 NORTON AVE, STE 202 98201 #016-01-1991 L2000 **GS** *020 †85
MARASSI, Nicholas P. 3901 HOYT AVE 98201 #005-18-1980 L1986 **AN** *030 †05
MARKUS, Cynthia Ann. 1321 COLBY AVE 98201 #025-01-1974 L1975 **EM** *020 †16
MARLOW, David Christopher. 3216 NORTON AVE, STE 201 98201 #025-07-1998 L2004 **DR** *020 †80
MARSHALL, Elizabeth T. 3901 HOYT AVE, THE EVERETT CLINIC 98201 #032-01-1987 L1987 **FM** *020 †18
MARSIDI, Ignatius. 4225 HOYT AVE STE A 98203 #165-04-1974 L1980 **IM GE** *020 †20

■ = Address Information Privacy Protected

MASON, Jeff Richard. 1100 PACIFIC AVE 98201 #016-42-1988 L1993 **ORS GS** *020 †40
MASON, Lucille G Winkler. 1330 ROCKEFELLER AVE, STE 230 98201 #016-43-1955 L1958
  FM *071
MAXOOD, Sepehr Steve. 1330 ROCKEFELLER AVE, STE 540 98201 #012-01-1994 L2001
  CD *020 †20
MAYHLE, Mark Donald. 728 134TH ST SW STE 120, RADIA INC., P.S. 98204
  #054-04-1988 L1992 **DR** *020 †20
MC BRIDE, Paul Tessmer. 3901 HOYT AVE 98201 #049-01-1982 L1987 **IM AI** *020 †20,03
MC CALLIE, Brian James. 3216 NORTON AVE, STE 201 98201 #028-34-1991 L2001
  DR *020 †80
MCCLEAN, Janice Lorraine. 3901 HOYT AVE DEPT FAM, THE EVERETT CLINIC 98201
  #030-06-1991 L1991 **FM** *020 †18
MC CUTCHAN, Harold John. 3726 BROADWAY, STE 201 98201 #054-04-1985 L1989
  ORS HS *020 †40
MC DERMOTT, John Patrick. 1330 ROCKEFELLER AVE # 400 98201 #051-01-1970 L1991
  TS *020 †85,90
MC DONNELL, William M. 12800 BOTHELL EVERETT HWY, STE 200 98208 #028-34-1983 L1997
  GE IM *020 †20
MC DUFF, Tobae Galambos. 2320 RUCKER AVE 98201 #012-05-1979 L1980 **N** *020 †75
MC ELHANEY, Sean Kevin. 2930 MAPLE ST, GROUP HEALTH COOPERATIVE 98201
  #025-12-1994 L2000 **FM** *020 †18
MC FADDEN, Tiffany M. 900 PACIFIC AVE, STE 501 98201 #048-14-1995 L2000 **OBG** *020 †30
MC FADDEN, William A. 12800 BOTHELL EVERETT HWY, STE 120 98208 #048-14-1995 L2000
  FM *020 †18
MC GOWAN, John David. 3216 NORTON AVE, STE 201 98201 #030-06-1998 L2004
  DR *100 †50
MC INTYRE, Robt Campbell. 1509 32ND ST, PLANNED PARENTHOOD WESTERN 98201
  #010-01-1974 L1980 **FM** *030 †18
MC INTYRE, William Burley. 3216 NORTON AVE, STE 201 98201 #005-11-1992 L1996
  VS *020 †85
MC NAMARA, Thomas Jos. 1912 EVERETT AVE 98201 #005-02-1964 L1971
  CLP NM *071 †50,28
MC NAMARA, Timothy Edward. 3218 NASSAU ST, KIDNEY & ARTHRITIS CLINIC 98201
  #030-06-1970 L1979 **NEP IM** *020 †20
MC QUEEN-SMITH, Sidney J. 8609 EVERGREEN WAY 98208 #065-10-1977 L1991 **GP** *020
MC VITTIE, Jody L. 1330 ROCKEFELLER AVE # 330 98201 #038-06-1981 L1986 **FM** *071 †18
MEAGHER, Ronald Paul. 3207 WETMORE AVE 98201 #010-02-1958 L1962 **AN** *071 †05
MERRITT, Thomas Llewellyn. 3003 W CASINO RD 98204 #016-06-1978 L1979 **OM IM** *020 †20
MEYERS, Deborah Sue. 1818 121ST ST SE 98208 #054-04-1996 L1998 **IM** *020 †20
MICHAELSON, Robert Lynn. 125 130TH ST SE, NW WEIGHTLOSS SURGERY 98208
  #016-11-1995 L2001 **GS** *020 †20
MILEY, Elizabeth Marie. 1717 13TH ST, # 300 98201 #048-12-1994 L2002 **HO** *020 †20
MILLAN, Juan Alejandro. 3216 NORTON AVE, STE 201 98201 #010-03-1999 L2003 **DR** *020 †80
MILLER, Richard Elihu. 3216 NORTON AVE, STE 201 98201 #035-46-1978 L1983 **DR** *020 †80
MILLIE, Michael Perry. 1330 ROCKEFELLER AVE 98201 #030-05-1997 L2003 **GS** *020 †85
MILLIKAN, Peter Alfred. EVERETT GENEVAL HOSPITAL 98206 #005-19-1973 L1975
  EM *020 †16
MILNER, Judy Rea. 2230 RUCKER AVE 98201 #020-02-1984 L1997 **P** *020 †75
MIRZA, Rizvan Allen. 3216 NORTON AVE, STE 201 98201 #033-06-2001 L2007 **DR** *020 †80
MLODINOW, Steven Gary. 12800 BOTHELL EVERETT HWY, STE 160 98208 #005-18-1989 L1992
  FM *020 †18
MONTEFORTE, William James. 1912 EVERETT AVE 98201 #036-05-1972 L1975
  PTH CLP *020 †50
MONTGOMERY, Kevin Farrell. 125 130TH ST SE 1ST FL, NORTHWEST WEIGHT LOSS
  SURG 98208 #035-46-1986 L1989 **GS** *020 †85
MOORE, George Walter. 1330 ROCKEFELLER AVE # 330, WESTERN WASHINGTON MED
  GRP 98201 #039-01-1972 L2001 **END IM** *020 †20
MORRIS, Sundee Lee. 3901 HOYT AVE, THE EVERETT CLINIC 98201 #054-04-1982 L1987
  FM *020 †18
MORTON, Glynnis Mascha. 900 PACIFIC AVE, STE 501 98201 #028-34-1989 L1997
  OBG *020 †30
MOSER, Autumn Josephine. 1330 ROCKEFELLER AVE # 520 98201 #038-06-2000 L2003
  IM *020 †20
MU, James Z. 4225 HOYT AVE STE A, DEPARTMENT OF GASTROENTERO 98203
  #243-70-1985 L2000 **GE IM** *020 †20
MUELLER, Thomas Jacob. 1515 PACIFIC AVE, PACIFIC & COLBY BUILDING 98201
  #054-04-1982 L1987 **OTO A** *020 †45
MULUMUDI, Mahesh S. 3901 HOYT AVE, C/O JULIE SALL 98201 #495-62-1991 L2005
  IC *020 †20
MURPHY, Richard Ronan. 3901 HOYT AVE 98201 #919-03-1993 L1999 **N** *020 †75
MURPHY, Thomas Michael. ■ 98206 #005-02-1973 L1977 **N** *062 †75
MUSTO, Cynthia Lee. 1818 121ST ST SE, THE EVERETT CLINIC 98208 #041-07-1981 L1983
  OBG *071 †30
MYERS, Mary Lightfoot. 1001 N BROADWAY, STE A11 98201 #048-12-1989 L1993 **EM** *020 †16
NEHME, Tammam Naim. 3216 NORTON AVE, STE 201 98201 #605-01-1997 L2002 **DR** *020 †80
NEUBAUER, Nancy Huet. 3216 NORTON AVE, STE 201 98201 #025-07-1991 L2000
  DR *020 †80
NEUGER, Elizabeth Lee. 1330 ROCKEFELLER AVE # 120 98201 #024-05-1993 L1999
  GS *020 †85
NEWKIRK, Lee Jay. 3802 COLBY AVE 98201 #024-07-1999 L2003 **AN** *020 †05
NGO, Tuyen Van. 9017 EVERGREEN WAY # A 98204 #941-01-1971 L1984 **GP** *020 ‡
NGUYEN, Thuc Phung. 3927 RUCKER AVE 98201 #054-04-2001 L2001 **RHU** *020
NICOLOV, Laurent. 1818 121ST ST SE 98208 #054-04-1996 L1999 **OBG** *020 †30
NIETO, Alexander Frank. 1330 ROCKEFELLER AVE, STE 400 98201 #007-02-1978 L1980
  GS *020 †85,90
NOLAN, John Patrick. ■ 98208 #016-06-1959 L1965 **CD IM** *071 †20
NOSAL, Jane Maria. 3901 HOYT AVE 98201 #016-11-1989 L1995 **D** *020 †15
NOWAK, Delwyn James. ■ 98201 #016-06-1947 L1952 **IM GP** *020
NOWAK, Thomas Allen. ■ 98205 #028-34-1975 L1976 **IM FM** *020 †16
OCAMPO, Eugene Edward. 2930 MAPLE ST 98201 #005-18-1976 L1979 **FM** *020 †18
OCHS, Oliver Dietmar. 3216 NORTON AVE, STE 201 98201 #054-04-1993 L2001 **DR** *020 †80
O'CONNOR, Mary Catherine. 3901 HOYT AVE 98201 #017-20-1987 L1991 **IM PD** *020 †20,55
O'CONNOR, Timothy David. 3901 HOYT AVE, THE EVERETT CLINIC 98201 #016-11-1972 L1973
  PUD *020 †20
OEI, Melina Elizabeth. 4027 HOYT AVE 98201 #001-02-1997 L2001 **PM** *020 †60
O'HARA, David Dighton. 916 PACIFIC AVE 98201 #035-20-1960 L1967 **IM DIA** *071 †20

OLDENKAMP, Susan Eileen. 12811 8TH AVE W STE D109 98204 #054-04-1978 L1985
  D DMP *020
OLINGER, Eileen Marie. 1330 ROCKEFELLER AVE # 230 98201 #017-20-1980 L1983
  IM GP *020 †20
OLSON, Kathryn Knudsen. 1818 121ST ST SE 98208 #048-04-1997 L1997 **IM** *020 †20
OLSSON, Harold Eric. 3216 NORTON AVE, STE 201 98201 #035-45-1968 L1976 **DR** *020 †80
OSETINSKY, Michael V. 1724 W MARINE VIEW DR, STE 130 98201 #021-05-1984 L1992
  OPH GS *020 †35
OSETINSKY, Patricia Ann P. 12800 BOTHELL EVERETT HWY, STE 190 98208
  #021-05-1984 L1992 **PD** *074 †50
OSNIS, Robert. 3216 NORTON AVE, STE 201 98201 #035-19-1994 L2006 **DR VIR** *020 †80
OSTOLAZA, Martin Felix. 3014 HOYT AVE 98201 #028-34-1956 L1962 **OBG** *071 †30
OVERBECK, John Robert. 3216 NORTON AVE, STE 201 98201 #054-04-1995 L1997
  NM NC *020 †28
PACIFICO, Albert D. 1321 COLBY AVE 3RD FL 98201 #036-07-1990 L1990 **ID** *020 †20
PAPENHAUSEN, Mark David. 3216 NORTON AVE, STE 201 98201 #054-04-1997 L2005
  VS *020 †85
PARIKH, Sanjiv R. 3216 NORTON AVE, STE 201 98201 #495-23-1984 L1993 **DR** *020 †28,80
PARK, Kwang Hie. 3802 BROADWAY, STE B 98201 #583-01-1979 L2005 **P CHP** *020 †75
PARSONS, Terri Ann. 3216 NORTON AVE, STE 101 98201 #012-05-1986 L1990 **PM** *020 †60
PASCUAL, Frederick E. 3901 HOYT AVE 98201 #005-18-1995 L1998 **PCC** *020 †20
PATEL, Purnima Mahendra. 1330 ROCKEFELLER AVE, STE 210 98201 #422-01-2000 L2006
  IM *020 †20 ‡
PAULL, Laurence Gordon. 728 134TH ST SW, STE 120 98204 #016-06-1972 L1979 **DR** *020 †80
PAUTLER, Thomas Geo. 5007 CLAREMONT WAY, MEDALIA CLAREMONT CLINIC 98203
  #030-06-1967 L1969 **FM OM** *020 †18
PEAVY, Erica Vrai. 3901 HOYT AVE 98201 #054-04-1983 L1984 **OBG** *020 †30
PETERS, Donald Roy. 3216 NORTON AVE, STE 201 98201 #040-02-1973 L1979 **R RNR** *020 †80
PETERSEN, Randall Kurt. 3131 NASSAU ST, STE 102 98201 #023-07-1984 L1992 **DR** *020 †80
PETERSON, Darwin Lee. 3901 HOYT AVE, EVERETT CLINIC 98201 #047-06-1971 L1973
  IM *020 †20
PETRY, Sara Doll. 4526 FEDERAL AVE, OLYMPIC MENTAL HEALTH 98203 #038-06-1982 L1989
  P *020 †75
PHAM, Anne Ngocphuong. 1818 121ST ST SE, THE EVERETT CLINIC 98208
  #054-04-1993 L1993 **FM** *020 †18
PIEPER, Kevin Lee. 900 PACIFIC AVE, STE 501 98201 #056-09-1998 L2004 **OBG** *020 †30
PINKHAM, James R. 3901 HOYT AVE, THE EVERETT CLINIC 98201 #054-04-1968 L1970
  ORS AM *020 †40
POINTON, Martin John. 1912 EVERETT AVE 98201 #031-01-1986 L1990 **PTH** *020 †50
POLETTI, Pietro M. 3802 BROADWAY, STE B 98201 #561-03-1957 L1966 **P** *020
PRESHAW, Lawrence Edwin. 2432 VIEWCREST AVE 98203 #007-02-1976 L1988 **PTH** *020 †50
PRICE, Christopher Edward. 3901 HOYT AVE 98201 #030-06-1995 L2002 **CD** *020 †20
PRICE, Robert Houston. 10315 19TH AVE SE, STE 112 98208 #049-01-1983 L1988
  N SME *020 †75
PRINDLE, Kirk Hubbard, Jr. 3901 HOYT AVE 98201 #054-04-1965 L1969 **CD IM** *020 †20
QUAMMEN, Diane Louise. 900 PACIFIC AVE, STE 500 98201 #054-04-1983 L1987
  OBG *020 †30
QURAISHI, Mohammed F. 3216 NORTON AVE, STE 201 98201 #048-02-2000 L2005
  VIR *020 †20
RAEMONT, Lizabeth Maria. 3901 HOYT AVE 98201 #016-11-1987 L1991 **OPH** *020 †35
RAFII, Cyrus Karl. 1321 COLBY AVE 98201 #016-11-1986 L1994 **FM** *020 †18
RAFOTH, Richard Jon. 3927 RUCKER AVE 98201 #016-11-1970 L1977 **GE IM** *030 †20 ‡
RAHN, Kathryn Margaret. 12800 BOTHELL EVERETT HWY, SUITES 290 98208
  #054-04-1988 L1992 **P** *020 †75
RAJ, Sanjay Singh. 916 PACIFIC AVE 98201 #305-01-1999 L2002 **PD** *020 †55
READ, Mary Frances. 4027 HOYT AVE 98201 #054-04-1980 L1984 **FM** *020 †18
REES, Patricia Vanderlaan. 3216 NORTON AVE STE 202, WESTERN WASHINGTON
  MEDICAL 98201 #046-01-1982 L1990 **GS FM** *020 †18,85
REHSE, Dagmar Helga. 3927 RUCKER AVE, C/O JULIE SALL 98201 #007-02-1997 L2001
  PS *100 †85
REICHMANN, F Joseph. 4310 COLBY AVE # 301 98203 #054-04-1972 L1973 **GP** *075
REIMER, Randall Scott. 12800 BOTHELL EVERETT HWY, STE 18 98208 #025-12-1981 L1984
  IM *020 †20
RICHARDSON, Thomas Moore, Jr. 1330 ROCKEFELLER AVE, STE 540 98201
  #010-02-1999 L2005 **CD** *020 †20
ROBERTS, Joanne Carolyn. 1321 COLBY AVE 98201 #026-04-1985 L1997 **IM** *020 †20
ROBINSON, Jeffrey David. 3216 NORTON AVE, STE 201 98201 #026-04-1985 L1992
  DR R *020 †80
ROCCA, Paolo. 3901 HOYT AVE, ATTN: JULIE SALL 98201 #561-30-1991 L1996 **IM** *020 †20
ROEHL, Dean Randall. 2930 MAPLE ST 98201 #060-01-1987 L1998 **FM** *020 †18
ROGERS, Clifford Wyn. 1330 ROCKEFELLER AVE 98201 #054-04-1980 L1981
  OBG GYN *020 †30
ROMANO, Allan Jack. 3216 NORTON AVE, STE 201 98201 #054-04-1983 L1989
  DR NRN *020 †80
ROON, Anthony Jules. 1321 COLBY AVE, EMERGENCY DEPARTMENT 98201
  #005-11-1972 L1979 **VS GS** *020 †85
ROSE, Jeffrey Steven. 1330 ROCKEFELLER AVE, STE 225 98201 #040-02-1978 L1985
  CD IM *020 †20
ROSS, Stephen Carl. 1920 100TH ST SE 98208 #028-34-1981 L1984 **FM** *020 †18
ROUNTREE, Harlan Avery. 3927 RUCKER AVE 98201 #012-01-1990 L1990 **FM** *020 †18
ROY, Madhurina. 7601 EVERGREEN WAY, STE B6 98203 #495-13-1990 L1999 **IM** *020 †20
RUEBEL, Gayle Thos. 728 134TH ST SW STE 120, C/O RADIA INC., P.S. 98204
  #054-04-1968 L1972 **DR** *020 †80
RUNYON, Katherine Lynn. 3901 HOYT AVE 98201 #003-01-1978 L1979 **PD** *020 †55
RUSSIAN, David Alan. 1330 ROCKEFELLER AVE, STE 340 98201 #028-02-1990 L1994
  PUD SME *020 †20
RYAN, Patrick Edward, Jr. 1330 ROCKEFELLER AVE, STE 400 98201 #035-06-1987 L1997
  TS *020 †20
SAFFITZ, Mark Steven. 3927 RUCKER AVE 98201 #056-05-1979 L1982 **IM** *020 †20
SAIKALY, Elie Phillip. 1717 13TH ST, THE EVERETT CLINIC 98201 #018-03-1979 L2002
  ON HEM *020 †20
SALAMA, William Mikhail. ■ 98203 #915-03-1961 L1975 **GS** *020 †85
SAMSON, V Edward. 3927 RUCKER AVE 98201 #913-86-1976 L1997 **GE** *020 †20
SAMUELSON, Mindy Lisa. 4310 COLBY AVE, STE 203 98203 #048-04-2001 L2005 **U** *020 †95
SANTIAGO, Cristina Rigor. 1321 COLBY AVE, THE EVERETT CLINIC 98201 #748-10-1987 L2003
  IM *020 †20

SATRE, Richard Wm. 3216 NORTON AVE, STE 201 98201 #056-06-1982 L2003 **DR** *020 †80

SAVAGE, Emily Marton. 3901 HOYT AVE, THE EVERETT CLINC 98201 #005-06-1998 L2006 **IM** *020 †20

SAXBY, Charlotte Page. 2930 MAPLE ST, GRUP HLTH COOPERATIVE OF P 98201 #005-02-1987 L1992 **OPH** *020 †35

SCARR, Robert Alan. 3901 HOYT AVE 98201 #036-01-1979 L1980 **IM** *020 †20

SCHAAF, Scott A. 3927 RUCKER AVE, GUNDERSON BUILDING 98201 #016-76-1992, ▲ L1999 **ORS OAR** *020

SCHECTER, Lawrence Mark. 1321 COLBY AVE 98201 #041-09-1965 L2004 **GS** *085

SCHENCK, Stig Lennart. 916 PACIFIC AVE 98201 #858-03-1975 L1981 **AN** *020

SCHMIDT, Dieter Kurt Thom. 12800 BOTHELL EVERETT HWY, STE 260 98208 #836-04-1989 L2004 **D DS** *020 †15 ‡

SCHMITT, Christian J T. 3218 NASSAU ST, KIDNEY & ARTHRITIS CLNC 98201 #154-07-1962 L1975 **NEP IM** *020 †20

SCHMITT, Karin. 3218 NASSAU ST 98201 #407-07-1964 L1976 **RHU** *075 †20

SCHOCKET, Luanne E. 900 PACIFIC AVE, STE 501 98201 #021-01-1996 L2000 **OBG** *020 †30

SCHWAB, Sidney Mayer. 1330 ROCKEFELLER AVE # 120 98201 #038-06-1970 L1982 **GS** *071 †85

SEIB, Thomas Paul. 3216 NORTON AVE STE 101, REHABILITATION & SPINE CEN 98201 #054-04-1993 L1997 **PM** *020 †60

SEIBOLD, William Raymond. 916 PACIFIC AVE 98201 #056-05-1956 L1962 **OPH OS** *071 †35

SEKHON, Avtar Singh. 8609 EVERGREEN WAY 98208 #495-43-1997 L2007 **FM** *020 †18

SELOVE, Daniel Mc Leskey. ■ 98201 #011-03-1987 L1994 **FOP** *020 †50

SEMON, Richard Lonsbury. 1100 PACIFIC AVE, STE 300 98201 #054-04-1974 L1975 **ORS** *020 †40

SHAH, Seema Narayan. 3901 HOYT AVE 98201 #041-02-2002 L2006 **OBG** *020

SHALL, Matthew Bradley. 3216 NORTON AVE STE 101 98201 #038-43-2001 L2005 **PM** *020 †60

SHARMAHD, Steven Lloyd. 900 PACIFIC AVE STE 500 98201 #016-06-1979 L1980 **OBG** *020 †30

SHAW, Joshua Hamblen. 916 PACIFIC AVE 98201 #054-04-1978 L1983 **IM** *020 †20

SHEPHARD, Kyle Christophe. 2930 MAPLE ST, EVERETT MEDICAL CENTER 98201 #067-01-2002 L2005 **IM** *020 †20

SHERIDAN, Frank Mc Cain. 3901 HOYT AVE 98201 #021-06-1982 L1983 **CD** *020 †20

SHINOHARA, Michi Marie. 3901 HOYT AVE 98201 #054-04-2002 L2002 **D** *012 †20

SHOOK, Jennifer Eloise. 3216 NORTON AVE, STE 201 98201 #036-01-1993 L1998 **DR** *020 †80

SHULL, Brian Stephen. 1818 121ST ST SE 98208 #017-20-1994 L1997 **FM** *020 †18 ‡

SINGH, Ranjeet Bhagat. 3131 NASSAU ST, STE 102 98201 #143-08-1989 L2002 **R** *020 †80

SKALLEY, Thomas Copps. 3927 RUCKER AVE 98201 #021-01-1986 L1990 **ORS** *020 †40

SKALLEY, Thomas Waldo. 3901 HOYT AVE 98201 #021-04-1954 L1957 **OBG** *071 †30

SLACK, Shawn Lee. 3901 HOYT AVE 98201 #494-24-1992 L1992 **RHU** *020 †20

SLOSBERG, Edward Alan. 4225 HOYT AVE STE A, DEPT OF GASTROENTEROLOGY 98203 #035-47-1988 L1998 **GE IM** *020 †20

SMITH, Budge H. 1330 ROCKEFELLER AVE, STE 540 98201 #010-01-1982 L1983 **CD** *020 †20

SMITH, Dorsett David. 4310 COLBY AVE STE 201 98203 #041-01-1963 L1971 **PUD OM** *020 †20

SMITH, Jennifer Kay. 900 PACIFIC AVE, STE 500 98201 #054-04-1978 L1983 **OBG** *020 †30

SMITH, Shauna Marie. 14 E CASINO RD 98208 #016-02-1991 L1993 **FM** *020 †18

SMITH, Thomas Julius. 1330 ROCKEFELLER AVE # 120 98201 #024-07-1971 L2002 **GS** *020 †20

SMITH, William Edward. 3003 W CASINO RD BLDG 40-, COLUMN A 1.5 M/C OY-75 98204 #019-02-1988 L1998 **OM IM** *030 †20

SOBOTKA, Dale Frank. 2230 RUCKER AVE # 100 98201 #030-05-1980 L1981 **P** *020 †75

SOHN, Andrew S. 1330 ROCKEFELLER AVE, STE 330 98201 #583-02-1992 L1998 **RHU** *020 †20

SPENCER, Bob A. ■ 98203 #048-02-1946 L1948 **GP** *071

SPENCER, Tracy Neil, III. 1321 COLBY AVE 98201 #023-01-1969 L1976 **IM** *020 †20

SPRENKLE, Arthur C. 4310 COLBY AVE, STE 202 98203 #035-01-1971 L1974 **AI IM** *020 †20,03

STACK, Gary Michael. 4310 COLBY AVE STE 203 98203 #054-04-1972 L1972 **U** *020 †95

STALLINGS, Shirley K. 4526 FEDERAL AVE, OLYMPIC MENTAL HEALTH 98203 #018-03-1976 L1991 **CHP P** *030 †75

STAMBAUGH, Lloyd Frank. 728 134TH ST SW STE 120, RADIA INC. PS 98204 #036-07-1994 L2001 **DR** *020 †80

STARK, Thomas Frederick. 3726 BROADWAY, STE 201 98201 #048-02-1990 L2003 **ORS** *020 †40

STEFANEC, Milan. ■ 98205 #024-07-1993 L1997 **AN** *020

STEVENSON, Jill Janene. ■ 98208 #054-04-2006 L2007 **D** *012

STEWART, David James. ■ 98203 #007-02-1961 L1968 **CD IM** *020 †20

STOCKER, Victoria. 4301 HOYT AVE 98203 #054-04-1992 L1998 **FM** *020 †18

STOLLER, David Leedy. 3125 COLBY AVE, STE J 98201 #038-06-1982 L1993 **FM GPM** *020 †18

STONECIPHER, Thomas K. 3927 RUCKER AVE 98201 #016-43-1977 L1982 **ORS** *020 †40

STRANDJORD, Thomas Paul. 916 PACIFIC AVE 98201 #023-07-1983 L1984 **NPM PD** *020 †55

SU, Cynthia Wenyeng. 3927 RUCKER AVE 98201 #056-02-1994 L2001 **PS** *020 †65

SUBITCH, Thomas John. 3207 WETMORE AVE 98201 #056-05-1956 L1962 **AN PME** *071 †05

SUBRAMANIAN, Sanjay. 1321 COLBY AVE, THE EVERETT CLINC 98201 #495-27-1994 L2002 **CCM** *020 †20

SULLIVAN, Thomas Patrick. 3131 NASSAU ST, STE 102 98201 #005-14-1993 L1997 **RNR** *020 †80

SUMMERS, Gregory T. 1321 COLBY AVE, PROVIDENCE EVERETT MEDICAL 98201 #055-01-1988 L2001 **AN** *020 †05

SUN, Danny Da-Nie. 3229 HOYT AVE 98201 #308-12-1987 L1997 **PS HS** *020

SUTCLIFFE, Peter Douglas. 3901 HOYT AVE, THE EVERETT CLINC 98201 #041-01-1999 L2003 **CD** *020 †20

SUZUKI, Manaji Mary. 12800 BOTHELL EVERETT HWY, STE 190 98208 #028-03-1996 L1999 **PD** *020 †55

SWANDER, Jack Edward. 916 PACIFIC AVE 98201 #018-03-1943 L1948 **GP** *072

SWANSON, Wendy Sue. 3901 HOYT AVE 98201 #041-01-2003 L2003 **PD** *020 †55

SWYER, Mark Lewis. 210 128TH ST SE 98208 #033-06-1980 L1982 **IM** *020 †20

TABER, Roger Elliot. 3901 HOYT AVE, THE EVERETT CLINC 98201 #054-04-1994 L1996 **IM** *020 †20

TALLMAN, Carol Ann. 3216 NORTON AVE STE 101 98201 #054-04-1974 L1977 **PM** *030 †60

TAMBER, Michael Jonathan. 3901 HOYT AVE 98201 #021-01-2000 L2006 **END** *020 †20

TASWIN, Meldy. 2930 MAPLE ST, MEDICAL CENTER 98201 #506-03-1999 L2005 **IM** *020 †20 ‡

TATUR-KROL, Iwona M. 3901 HOYT AVE 98201 #759-04-1993 L2004 **IM** *020 †20 ‡

TAYLOR, Linh Cam. 3901 HOYT AVE 98201 #037-01-2000 L2004 **MPD** *020

TAYLOR, Steve Keith. 3216 NORTON AVE STE 101 98201 #054-04-1990 L1990 **PM** *020 †60

THIEL, Brent Graham. 3927 RUCKER AVE 98201 #056-06-1993 L1993 **ORS** *020 †40

THIERSCH, Norman John. 9509 29TH AVE W 98204 #054-04-1987 L1987 **FOP** *020 †50

THOMAS, Kevin Danl. 3901 HOYT AVE 98201 #023-12-1991 L1997 **FM** *020 †18

TJOELKER, Michael Lyle. 3327 COLBY AVE 98201 #028-34-1981 L1985 **D** *020 †15 ‡

TOCHER, Thomas Merson. 5929 EVERGREEN WAY, STE 200 98203 #054-04-1988 L1991 **IM** *020 †20

TOMPKINS, Richard Kelsey. 3901 HOYT AVE, C/O JULIE SALL 98201 #007-02-1965 L1978 **IMG** *071 †20

TORRANCE, Jonathan B. ■ 98201 #054-04-1950 L1954 **OM EM** *071

TRASK, Charles Hughes. I1321 COLBY AVE 98201 #067-01-1955 L1964 **GS TS** *071 †90,85

TRIVISONNO, Rodolfo A. 1728 W MARINE DR STE 109, BAY PSYCHIATRIC CENTERS 98201 #132-01-1986 L1997 **P** *020 †75

TRUE, Bevlorraine. 2930 MAPLE ST 98201 #018-03-1990 L1990 **FM** *020 †18

TRUONG, Thao Pham. 3901 HOYT AVE 98201 #024-01-1998 L2000 **NEP** *020 †20

TSAY, Robert Chii-Yong. ■ 98208 #244-03-1962 L1984 **GP** *071

TU, Yuanpo. 3901 HOYT AVE, THE EVERETT CLINIC 98201 #025-01-1987 L1989 **PUD IM** *020 †20

TURAL, Ahmet C. 1330 ROCKEFELLER AVE, STE 210 98201 #902-10-1987 L1997 **ID** *020 †20

VALENTINE, Mark Conrad. 3327 COLBY AVE 98201 #023-07-1974 L1979 **D** *020 †15

VAN BUSKIRK, Elmer J. ■ 98201 #005-12-1933 L1933 **OBG GP** *071

VANDERHEIDEN, Scott M. 3216 NORTON AVE, STE 201 98201 #030-06-1998 L2004 **DR** *020 †80

VANDERMEER, James Daggett. 12800 BOTHELL EVERETT HWY, STE 160 98208 #048-15-1983 L1993 **FM** *020 †18

VANDREE, John Chas. 1330 ROCKEFELLER AVE, STE 340 98201 #026-04-1972 L1977 **PUD** *020 †20

VAN HISE, Milton Lowell. 3216 NORTON AVE, STE 201 98201 #005-12-1994 L2000 **RNR** *020 †80

VEGA-BERMUDEZ, Francisco. 916 PACIFIC AVE 7TH 98201 #023-07-1993 L2004 **N** *020 †75

VIECO, Pedro Tomas. 728 134TH ST SW STE 120, RADIA INC PS 98204 #035-15-1985 L1996 **DR** *020 †80

VOLD, Leif G. 900 PACIFIC AVE, FL 5 98201 #033-06-1991 L2001 **OBG** *020 †30

WAGNER, Teresa Elizabeth. 1321 COLBY AVE 98201 #054-04-1997 L1999 **PCC** *100 †20

WAGNER, Willard Gene. 4225 HOYT AVE 98203 #005-12-1964 L1965 **GP GS** *071 †18

WALCZAK, Dariusz. 1728 W MARINE VIEW DR, STE 111 98201 #759-09-1987 L1998 **APM** *020 †05

WALDBAUM, Jerome Robt. 12800 BOTHELL EVERETT HWY, STE 200 98208 #030-05-1977 L1983 **GE** *020 †20

WALKER, Barbara Hegge. 3901 HOYT AVE 98201 #054-04-1986 L1990 **IM** *020 †20

WALKER, Luke Nathaniel. 4005 HOYT AVE, C/O JULIE SALL 98201 #039-01-1998 L2005 **HO** *020 †20

WALLIS, Walter Merle. 4526 FEDERAL AVE, COMPASS HEALTH 98203 #038-06-1972 L1975 **P PYA** *020 ‡

WANG, Ying. 3216 NORTON AVE, STE 201 98201 #243-21-1982 L2004 **DR** *020 †80

WANNER, Ann M. 3901 HOYT AVE, THE EVERETT CLINIC 98201 #008-02-1985 L1991 **AI IM** *020 †20,03

WARREN, Chad Allen. 3927 RUCKER AVE, DEPT. OF ORTHOPEDIC SURGER 98201 #005-06-1999 L2006 **ORS** *020 †40

WATKINS, Brad Michael. 125 130TH ST SE, NORTHWEST WEIGHT LOSS SURG 98208 #020-02-1991 L1998 **GS** *020 †85

WAY, Jenny Yannjen. 3901 HOYT AVE 98201 #005-02-2000 L2003 **IM** *020

WEAVER, Kelly Bernard. 1330 ROCKEFELLER AVE, STE 310 98201 #054-04-1996 L2000 **PM** *020 †60

WEICHT, Elizabeth A. 1410 BROADWAY, SNOHOMISH CO, EVERETT CLIN 98201 #010-02-1992 L1995 **PHP** *020 †18

WELCH, Joseph Danl. 916 PACIFIC AVE 98201 #010-01-1970 L1978 **HS PS** *071 †85,65

WELLENSTEIN, Gail Ann. 1920 100TH ST SE STE B 98208 #056-05-1981 L1986 **PD** *020 †55

WERTHEIMER, Clay Maurice. 1100 PACIFIC AVE, STE 300 98201 #038-06-1985 L1990 **ORS OSM** *020 †40

WERTHEIMER, Haskell M. ■ 98201 #048-02-1942 L1957 **GS** *071 †85

WESTCOTT, Stephen Edmund. 1330 ROCKEFELLER AVE, STE 210 98201 #010-01-1978 L1982 **IM** *020 †20

WESTMAN, David Gilbert. 3216 NORTON AVE, STE 201 98201 #065-06-1986 L2006 **DR** *020 †80

WETSTONE, Raymond Scott. MEDICAL DENTAL BLDG, STE 507 98201 #054-04-1968 L1969 **AN** *071 †05

WHALEN, Raymond Keith. 3901 HOYT AVE, DEPARTMENT OF UROLOGY 98201 #005-14-1985 L1992 **U** *020 †95

WHITELEY, Timothy Norman. 2930 MAPLE ST, EVERETT MEDICAL CENTER 98201 #054-04-1998 L2000 **FM** *020 †20

WIDLUND, Bengt Olov. 2731 WETMORE AVE STE 208B 98201 #858-02-1972 L1984 **AN** *020

WILHELM, Crispin Saml. 2320 RUCKER AVE 98201 #054-04-1981 L1986 **N** *020 †75

WILLIAMS, Dean Edward. 2028 WETMORE AVE, COMMUNITY HEALTH CENTER 98201 #026-08-1991 L1998 **FM** *020 †18

WILSON, Raymond Stephen. 3927 RUCKER AVE 98201 #023-07-1979 L1983 **GE** *071 †20

WINDLE, Brian H. 12800 BOTHELL EVERETT HWY, STE 260 98208 #060-02-1980 L2002 **PS HS** *020 †65

WINNINGHAM, Donald Gene. ■ 98203 #054-04-1963 L1966 **U** *071 †95

WINNINGHAM, Jefferey S. 3901 HOYT AVE, PROVIDENCE EVERETT MED CT 98201 #021-01-1994 L1997 **FM** *020 †20

WITRAK, Bonnie Jean. 3216 NORTON AVE, STE 201 98201 #026-08-1979 L1985 **DR GP** *020 †80

WITTE, Jonathan P. 3901 HOYT AVE 98201 #016-11-1977 L1982 **RHU IM** *020 †20

WONCIK, Karen S. 2320 RUCKER AVE 98201 #039-01-1980 L1986 **NS** *071 †25

WOOD, Julie Rae. 1330 ROCKEFELLER AVE, STE 340 98201 #021-05-1997 L1999 **PCC** *020 †20

WOODARD, Kristinza Renee. ■ 98204 #056-06-2006 L2007 **PTH** *012

WOODS, John O, Jr. ■ 98203 #041-12-1953 L1955 **PD** *071 †55

WRIGHT, Sanford Jos, Jr. 2320 RUCKER AVE, EVERETT NEUROLOGICAL CTR 98201 #054-04-1968 L1979 **NS** *020 †25

WROBLEWSKI, Kathleen Mary. 3218 NASSAU ST 98201 #035-03-1991 L1994 **NEP** *020 †20

WYGANT, Gerard Patrick. 12800 BOTHELL EVERETT HWY, PRACTICE 98208 #016-43-1974 L1977 **FM** *020 †20

YOKOE, Dawn Hisa. 3901 HOYT AVE, THE EVERETT CLINIC 98201 #005-11-1987 L1991 **OBG** *020 †20

YUEN, Albert Funmun. 5007 CLAREMONT WAY, CLAREMONT FP CLINIC 98203 #003-01-1990 L1993 **FM** *020 †18

■ = Address Information Privacy Protected

ZAK, Daniel Avram. 916 PACIFIC AVE 98201 #048-04-1984 L1987 **EM IM** *020 †20,16
ZERNGAST, Benjamin Andrew. 3025 RUCKER AVE 98201 #035-45-1996 L2000 **AN** *020 †05
ZIEDALSKI, Tomasz Marcin. 1330 ROCKEFELLER AVE, STE 340 98201 #054-04-1997 L1997 **PCC** *020 †20
ZIMMERMAN, John M. 3726 BROADWAY 98201 #054-04-1992 L1994 **FM** *020 †18
ZUNKEL, David Eugene. 3216 NORTON AVE, STE 201 98201 #007-02-1973 L1977 **DR** *020 †80

EVERSON – WHATCOM

CUENE, Sara Ann. ■ 98247 #056-05-1969 L1972 **PD** *075
GUNNINGHAM, Frederick J. 6884 HANNEGAN RD 98247 #054-04-1987 L1989 **FM** *020 †18
MURDOCK, Kenneth A, Jr. ■ 98247 #050-02-1960 L1962 **FM** *071 †18
SPADY, Kenneth Harold. 407 E MAIN ST 98247 #005-12-1955 L1956 **GP OBS** *020
STAVES, Diane Rosemary. 6760 MISSION RD, NOOKSALK CLINIC 98247 #008-02-1981 L1999 **IM EM** *020 †20

FAIRCHILD AIR FORCE BASE – SPOKANE

BAER, Jefferson Tomas. 701 HOSPITAL LOOP, ATTN: CREDENTIAL OFFICE 99011 #036-01-2001 L2005 **CD** *012
BROCKWAY, Leah Wilkinson. 713 HOSPITAL LOOP STE 300, 604 MDS 99011 #021-05-1983 L2002 **GS GP** *020
CARRELL, Matt Allen. ■ 99011 #038-45-1996 L1998 **FM** *020 †18
COX, Brian Christopher. 701 HOSPITAL LOOP 99011 #040-02-2005 L2005 **AM** *020
FLESHER, Stephanie Ann. 701 HOSPITAL LOOP, STE 132 99011 #028-46-1990 L1997 **DR** *020 †80
KELSTROM, Jared Christoph. 701 HOSPITAL LOOP, ATTN CREDENTIAL OFFICE 92M 99011 #005-12-2005 L2006 **IM** *020
KUHAR, Lisa Ann. 701 HOSPITAL LOOP STE 317, 92ND MDG 99011 #028-02-1984 L1989 **IM GP** *020 †20
SPARKMAN, Theresa B. 701 HOSPITAL LOOP STE 317, 92ND MEDICAL GROUP 99011 #001-06-1987 L1988 **P PD** *020 †55
TSCHIRHART, Alicia Louise. 701 HOSPITAL LOOP STE 317, 92ND MEDICAL GROUP 99011 #025-01-1995 L1997 **P** *020 †75
WHITE, Christy Leigh. 701 HOSPITAL LOOP, 92ND MDOS 99011 #001-06-2004 L2004 **FM** *020 †18
WHITE, Cicely Wilhite. 701 HOSPITAL LOOP, ATTN CREDENTIAL OFFICE 99011 #048-02-2002 L2002 **PD** *020

FAIRFIELD – SPOKANE

BALEK, Walter William. 210 MAIN ST, ASSOCIATES FAMILY 99012 #026-04-1972 L1973 **FM** *020 †18
MARKIN, Rom Jeffrey. 210 MAIN ST, ASSOCIATES FAMILY 99012 #054-04-1984 L1984 **FM** *020 †18
METCALF, Michael James. 210 MAIN ST, ASSOCIATES FAMILY 99012 #040-02-1972 L1973 **FM** *020 †18
RUSSELL, Paul Eugene. 210 MAIN ST, ASSOCIATES FAMILY 99012 #049-01-1973 L1974 **FM** *020 †18
ZERANSKI, Brian Bert. 210 MAIN ST, ASSOCIATES FAMILY 99012 #054-04-1993 L1996 **FM** *020 †18

FALL CITY – KING

CZYHOLD, Michael Wm. ■ 98024 #054-04-1966 L1971 **P** *074
LEIN, John Nave. ■ 98024 #054-04-1955 L1957 **OBG** *071 †30

FEDERAL WAY – KING

ABDULLAH, Sarmed. ■ 98023 #875-01-1999 L2004 **IM** *100
ABOY, Erlinda Sanchez. ■ 98023 #748-07-1975 *100
ABRAHAM, Linda P. 33501 1ST WAY S 98003 #016-01-2003 L2003 **IM** *020 †20
ADAIKKALAM, Aruna. ■ 98023 #495-42-1991 L2006 **IM** *020 †20
ALABASTER, Steven Lee. 34503 9TH AVE S, STE 130 98003 #047-06-1974 L1984 **GE IM** *020 †20
ALLEMAN, Allen Chas. 34616 11TH AVE S, STE 4 98003 #056-05-1971 L1976 **FM** *020 †18
ALLEY, Elizabeth Ann. 33501 1ST WAY S 98003 #016-45-1998 L2001 **AN** *020
ALPERT, Eryn Nicole. 34515 9TH AVE S 98003 #036-07-2003 L2007 **EM** *020
AMES, Gerard Wm. 1109 S 348TH ST, CENTER 98003 #016-42-1975 L1978 **IM NEP** *020 †20
ANDERSON, John Elwood. 34616 11TH AVE S STE 3 98003 #020-12-1966 L1972 **DR** *020 †80
ANDERSON, Lennart Lloyd. 34515 9TH AVE S STE 200 98003 #054-04-1961 L1962 **GP** *020
APOSTOL, John Malonzo. 34503 9TH AVE S STE 220 98003 #054-04-1997 L2003 **PD** *020 †55
AU, Allen Tak-Chiu. 34616 11TH AVE S, STE 3 98003 #242-21-1954 L1969 **R** *071 †80
AWAD, John Ayad. ■ 98023 #330-02-1956 L1970 **FM** *071
BADYAL, Mohinder Singh. 32124 1ST AVE S STE 100 98003 #306-01-1986 L1993 **PD** *020 †20
BAIRD, Emily Joanne. ■ 98023 #023-07-2005 L2005 **AN** *012
BALL, Terrence Jos. 33501 1ST WAY S 98003 #054-04-07-1969 L1975 **GE IM** *020 †20
BAUTISTA, Erleine Faye. ■ 98023 #010-02-2007 **OBG** *012
BAYLOR, C Ty. 34509 9TH AVE S, STE 104 98003 #019-02-2000 L2006 **PCC** *020 †20
BINTASAN, Sunida. 33516 9TH AVE S, STE 7 98003 #891-02-1971 L1984 **P CHP** *020 †75
BLACKBURN, Mary. 30809 1ST AVE S, STE B 98003 #008-02-1990 L1993 **FM** *020 †18
BLAKENEY, Sanders Sidney. 700 S 320TH ST, STE A 98003 #041-13-1975 L1981 **OBG** *020
BRENOWITZ, Gene Louis. 34515 9TH AVE S 98003 #041-12-1986 L1988 **AN PME** *020 †05
BRIDGE, Theodore Allen. 1014 S 320TH ST, FEDERAL WAY PEDIATRIC CLNC 98003 #054-04-1989 L1992 **PD** *020 †55
BROOKS, Maria Christina. 301 S 320TH ST 98003 #748-13-1981 L2002 **FM** *020 †18
BROWN, Janet Sue. ■ 98003 #007-02-1974 L1975 **PTH** *100
BRUSH, Michael Bernheim. 301 S 320TH ST 98003 #028-34-2000 L2004 **OPH** *020 †85
BUCHANAN, Thomas Mark. 1300 S 320TH ST 98003 #054-04-1967 L1973 **ID IG** *050 †20
BUCK, Charles Parkhurst. 34515 9TH AVE S 98003 #010-02-1998 L2000 **EM** *020 †16
CAIN, Marsha Lynn. 33516 9TH AVE S STE 7 98003 #021-05-1966 L1969 **P** *020 †75

CAMPBELL, John Andrew. 34515 9TH AVE S 98003 #025-07-1993 L1999 **EM** *020 †16
CHAFFEE, John Robt. 32018 23RD AVE S 98003 #024-01-1992 L1992 **FM** *020 †18 ‡
CHANG, Jonathan Huichong. ■ 98003 #748-01-1972 L1989 **AN** *075
CHEN, Hsi Hsuan. ■ 98023 #244-02-1948 L1990 **P PHP** *071 †75
CHINN, Mullan Arthur. ■ 98003 #054-04-1963 L1966 **AN PME** *071
CHO, Won-Jae. ■ 98093 #583-10-1976 L1985 *062
CHUNG, Christopher Y. 918 S 348TH ST STE B 98003 #005-02-1994 L2007 **PS CS** *020 †65
CHUNG, Chu Ho. ■ 98023 #583-02-1957 L1975 **IM FM** *071
CLEMENS, Todd Jos. 301 S 320TH ST, FEDERAL WAY MEDICAL CENTER 98003 #056-06-1992 L1992 **P** *020
COBB, Loren Mason. ■ 98003 #025-12-1976 L1992 **PDS** *020 †85
CUBE, Regino Padua. ■ 98023 #023-12-2007 **TY** *012
CURTIS, Mary Frances. 34503 9TH AVE S, STE 100 98003 #040-02-1984 L1990 **IM** *020 †20
CZUK, Mary Hardaway. 33501 1ST WAY S, DEPT OB 98003 #048-12-1995 L1999 **OBG** *020 †30
DAI, Lucia Yuanwei. 34515 9TH AVE S 98003 #243-16-1989 L2002 **AN** *020
DARBY, Patric J. 2505 S 320TH ST, STE 100 98003 #306-01-1992 L1998 **P CHP** *020 †20
DAVIDOV, Michael Sergei. 34509 9TH AVE S STE 207 98003 #913-01-1975 L1997 **OBG** *020 †30
DAVIS, Christopher James. 3455 S 344TH WAY, STE 210 98001 #010-01-1972 L1996 **EM IM** *071 †20,16
DAWSON, David J. 34509 9TH AVE S, DAVID R DAWSON ORTHOPEDIC 98003 #067-01-1975 **IM** *100 †20
DAWSON, David Richard. 32114 1ST AVE S STE 103 98003 #054-04-1980 L1986 **ORS** *020 †40
DE LA CRUZ, Fe Lillian. ■ 98093 #005-12-1983 L1984 **FM** *020 †18
DEV, Rajesh Kumar. ■ 98023 #054-04-2001 L2003 **END** *020
DHRU, Dhavalkirti. 34617 11TH AVE S, STE 202 98003 #495-23-1967 L1978 **OTO** *020 †45
DINI, Robert Michael. 32018 23RD AVE S 98003 #016-42-1997 L1999 **FM** *020 †18
DIONISIO, Anne Nubla. 301 S 320TH ST, GROUP HEALTH COOPERATIVE 98003 #030-06-1997 L2000 **PD** *020 †55
DORMAN, Thomas A. 2505 S 320TH ST STE 100 98003 #803-03-1965 L1996 **IM** *020 †20
DUNHAM, Jane Suzanne. 118 SW 330TH ST STE 300 98003 #054-04-1997 L2000 **IM** *020 †20 ‡
ELLINGSEN, Megan Briggs. 33501 1ST WAY S, VIRGINIA MASON FEDERAL WAY 98003 #054-04-2003 L2003 **IM** *020 †20
EMERY, Mark Benson. 34612 6TH AVE S, STE 200 98003 #065-05-1993 L1999 **OTO** *020 †45
ERLING, Carl Bertil. 301 S 320TH ST 98003 #026-04-1964 L1986 **FM** *020 †18
ESUABANA, Asuquo A. 308 S 330TH PL 98003 #913-22-1983 L1996 **FM OBS** *020 †18
FANG, Victoria Anne. 32018 23RD AVE S, U.W.P.N. 98003 #024-07-1983 L2001 **FM** *020 †18
FASULLO, Andrea Maynard. 33501 1ST WAY S 98003 #023-07-1995 L1998 **PD** *020 †55
FOSEN, Katina Melanie. ■ 98001 #011-02-2005 L2007 **EM** *012
FOX, Jonathan Ronald. 33501 1ST WAY S 98003 #005-19-1997 L2000 **PD** *020 †55 ‡
FOX, Samuel Ross. 34515 9TH AVE S 98003 #049-01-1956 L1957 **GS OS** *020 †85
FREDLUND, Paul Noel. 33501 1ST WAY S 98003 #024-01-1970 L1975 **DIA END** *020 †20
GARDNER, Summer Clem. ■ 98001 #001-02-2005 L2006 **AN** *012
GARVIN, Patrick Henry. 34515 9TH AVE S 98003 #030-06-1976 L1979 **EM** *020 †16
GASS, Michael Arthur, Jr. 34515 9TH AVE S 98003 #054-04-1980 L1983 **DR** *072 †80
GERDES, Erik Meinhard. 34515 9TH AVE S 98003 #038-06-2002 L2005 **EM** *020 †16
GIBSON, David Evan. 34515 9TH AVE S 98003 #020-02-1978 L1985 **EM** *020 †16
GODLEWSKI, Krystof Jan. 34509 9TH AVE S, STE 304 98003 #036-05-1983 L1987 **CD** *020 †20
GORDIENKO, Oleg E. 34509 9TH AVE S STE 308 98003 #913-53-1967 L1986 **FM** *020
GOULD, Richard Kent. 33501 1ST WAY S 98003 #025-01-1968 L1970 **PD** *020 †55
GOULD, Richard Raymond. 35418 4TH AVE SW 98003 #054-04-1986 L1988 **GS** *020 †85
GOVIER, Fred Everett. 33501 1ST WAY S 98003 #030-05-1979 L1987 **U** *020 †95
HAFTEL, Anthony Jacob. 34515 9TH AVE S 98003 #041-01-1971 L1976 **PD EM** *040 †16
HARRIS, Russle Herbert. 301 S 320TH ST 98003 #054-04-1970 L1975 **IM** *020 †20
HARROUN, Robert Victor. ■ 98023 #016-06-1948 L1957 **GS** *071
HART, Jeffrey Donovan. 33515 10TH PL S STE 16 98003 #034-01-1982 L1985 **P** *020 †75
HAYDEN, Daniel Taylor. 301 S 320TH ST 98003 #054-04-1959 L1961 **FM** *071 †18
HAYNES, Robert Ralph. 34503 9TH AVE S, STE 100 98003 #038-43-2000 L2003 **IM** *020 †20 ‡
HEGEWALD, Mark Douglas. 34612 6TH AVE S, STE 200 98003 #054-04-1983 L1988 **OTO HNS** *020 †45
HENRICHS, Wade Hemme. 3455 S 344TH WAY, STE 210 98001 #026-04-1984 L1987 **EM** *020 †16
HEPPENSTALL, Heather. 30809 1ST AVE S 98003 #061-01-1975 L1982 **FM** *072 ‡
HIRAI, Thomas Jun. 200 S 333RD ST ST150, NORTHMARK BLDG 98003 #187-04-1997 L2006 **GS** *020 †85
HOLDNER, Karen Marie. 34503 9TH AVE S STE 220 98003 #035-15-1987 L1990 **PD** *020 †55
HOPKINS, David S. 34503 9TH AVE S STE 100, MEDALIA HEALTHCARE AT 98003 #026-04-1960 L1961 **FM** *071 †18
HOUSER, James Belden. 1010 S 336TH ST, STE 110 98003 #016-06-1990 L1994 **P** *020 †75
HUNTER, Jeffrey Alan. 33501 1ST WAY S 98003 #038-41-1983 L1984 **GS** *020 †85
IMKAMP, Antonius W. 30620 PACIFIC HWY S, STE 103 98003 #660-03-1956 L1961 **GPM** *020
JAIN, Shaily. 34503 9TH AVE S, STE 130 98003 #496-04-1998 L2007 **GE** *020 †20
JIRANEK, Geoffrey Chas. 33501 1ST WAY S 98003 #032-01-1981 L1986 **GE IM** *020 †20
JOHNSON, Elsa Ann. ■ 98023 #011-03-1979 L1988 **PD** *020 †55
JOTWANI, Vijay M. 301 S 320TH ST 98003 #016-11-2003 L2006 **FM FSM** *020 †18
KANDALLU, Venkatesh R. 34509 9TH AVE S, STE 304 98003 #495-33-1988 L1997 **CD IM** *020 †20
KIM, Chi-Hyun. 33501 1ST WAY S 98003 #041-15-1999 L2001 **IM** *020 †20
KIM, Doug Shin. 31260 PACIFIC HWY S, STE 3 98003 #016-01-1985 L1990 **FM EM** *020 †20
KIM, Mark Kibong. ■ 98003 #583-02-1948 L1986 **OS AN** *071 †05
KIM, Michael Moonchul. ■ 98003 #054-04-2001 L2002 **OTO** *020
KIM, Pyong Chol. 533 S 336TH ST, STE C 98003 #003-01-2000 L2005 **DR** *020 †80
KIM, Young H. 34515 9TH AVE S 98003 #016-01-1986 L1990 **AN** *020 †05
KIRILUK, Anthony Wm. 33501 1ST WAY S 98003 #054-04-1980 L1983 **FM** *020 †18
KIRSCH, James Louis. 34509 9TH AVE S STE 104 98003 #054-04-1979 L1982 **PUD CCM** *020 †20
KLEEMANN, Douglas Karl. 30809 1ST AVE S 98003 #056-06-1995 L1998 **FM** *020 †18 ‡
KLOBY, Jay. 700 S 320TH ST STE D 98003 #010-02-1974 L1990 **DR** *020 †80
KNIPE, Thomas Albert. 34503 9TH AVE S, STE 230 98003 #054-04-2001 L2006 **OTO** *020 †45
KOHLER, Delphin G. 1305 S 312TH ST, PROFESSIONAL ARTS BLDG 98003 #030-06-1953 L1954 **FM** *071 †18
KORNBERG, Jacob Jos. 33838 PACIFIC HWY S, STE B200 98003 #005-15-1969 L1976 **GS AS** *020 †85
KOSS, George Wm. 720 S 320TH ST, STE A 98003 #005-16-1962 L1975 **GP AM** *020 †18
KOZIE, Daniel Walter. 34612 6TH AVE S, STE 200 98003 #016-43-1971 L1973 **OTO A** *071 †45
KRAFT, Debra M. 34515 9TH AVE S 98003 #031-01-1995 L1997 **FM** *020 †18

KUBEJA, Martin Allen. 34515 9TH AVE S 98003 #035-01-1996 L2000 **AN** *020 †05
LAMA, Michael Thomas. 32200 MILITARY RD S, S D301" 98001 #011-02-2005 L2006 **AN** *100
LAMBERT, Alain Louis. 34503 9TH AVE S STE 100 98003 #028-34-1987 L1990 **IM** *020 †20
LARSON, Charles Harold. ■ 98023 #054-04-1966 L1969 **FM** *072
LAUTMAN, Kirby James. 34612 6TH AVE S, STE 200 98003 #054-04-1982 L1987 **OTO** *020 †45
LEE, Yuri Anna. ■ 98023 #035-45-2008 *012
LEVINE, Sharon Ruth. 33431 13TH PL S, CENTER 98003 #024-16-1990 L1997 **FM** *020 †18
LEVY, Barbara Susan. 34503 9TH AVE S, STE 330 98003 #005-18-1979 L1981 **GYN REN** *020 †30
LI, Xuyang. 32114 1ST AVE S STE 203, FEDERAL WAY WOMEN'S HEALTH 98003 #048-12-2002 L2006 **OBG** *020
LUCAS, Andrea Paige. 30800 PACIFIC HWY S, CARE PLUS MEDICAL CENTER 98003 #041-15-2003 L2005 **FM** *100 †18
LYNCH, Edward Donald. ■ 98023 #067-01-1939 L1940 **AM A** *071
MALPASS, Thomas Wm. 33501 1ST WAY S 98003 #051-01-1975 L1978 **ON IM** *020 †20
MAYON, George Edward. 1705 S 324TH PL 98003 #005-15-1967 L1975 **ORS** *071 †40
MC DONALD, Brian Leigh. 33501 1ST WAY S 98003 #012-05-1977 L1978 **IM** *020 †20
MC LAUGHLIN, Robert Paul. 30800 PACIFIC HWY S 98003 #028-34-1978 L1986 **IM** *020 †20
MC NICHOLS, Kennard Dean. 33501 1ST WAY S, VIRGINIA MASON 98003 #005-14-1974 L1977 **FM** *020 †18
MEDANI, Danny Ignatius. 34716 1ST AVE S, SOUTH A 98003 #308-11-1986 L1991 **IM** *020
MESOLA, Rommel Paulo Pato. 301 S 320TH ST 98003 #748-11-2000 L2006 **FM** *020 †18
METCALF, Sharon Lee. 710 S 348TH ST, STE A 98003 #051-04-1995 L1999 **OBG** *020 †30 ‡
MIDDLETON, Robert Todd. 34515 9TH AVE S 98003 #040-02-1983 L1988 **CD IC** *020 †20
MILLER, Eduardo Antonio. 1300 S 320TH ST 98003 #025-01-2001 L2001 **FM** *020 †18
MILLER, Rosalie R. 33501 1ST WAY S 98003 #550-02-1985 L1992 **FM** *020 †18
MOMAH, Charles M. 1230 S 336TH ST 98003 #690-04-1980 L1993 **OBG** *020 †30
MOUSER, Pamela Lee. 301 S 320TH ST 98003 #005-14-1997 L2001 **PD** *020 †55
MUTHIAH, Vallikannu. 33501 1ST WAY S, VIRGINA MASON MEDICAL CENT 98003 #495-94-2000 L2005 **IM** *020
NGUYEN, Cuong Phuc. 33659 7TH CT SW 98023 #422-01-1999 L2002 **IM** *020 †20
NGUYEN, Giao Ngoc. 34515 9TH AVE S 98003 #028-46-1996 L2000 **EM** *020 †16
NUNES, Natalie L. 33431 13TH PL S 98003 #010-02-1995 L1997 **FM** *020 †18
OBREGON, Victor Lawrence. 728 S 320TH ST, STE F 98003 #048-12-1985 L1990 **OBG OS** *071 †30
OH, Ki Hyun. 200 S 333RD ST, STE 150 98003 #583-15-1977 L1990 **GS VS** *020 †85
OLLEE, Henry P, Jr. ■ 98023 #054-04-1974 L1975 **FM** *020 †18
ORY, Richard Edwin. 34503 9TH AVE S STE 220 98003 #048-04-1979 L1982 **PD** *020 †55
ORY, Robert Andrew. 34503 9TH AVE S, STE 100 98003 #048-14-1990 L1996 **IM** *020 †20
OTTO, Matthew D. 34515 9TH AVE S 98003 #025-07-2005 L2008 **EM** *012
PALADINETTI, Terry L. 34515 9TH AVE S, ST FRANSICS HOSPITAL 98003 #048-12-1992 L1993 **AN** *020 †05
PANLASIGUI, Leonico G. 34616 11TH AVE S, STE 6 98003 #748-08-1977 L1984 **IM** *020
PARK, Alexander Jungho. ■ 98023 #008-01-2008 *012
PEW, Mary Catharine. 33431 13TH PL S 98003 #041-01-1984 L1991 **PD OS** *020 †55
PHILIPSEN, Anne Elizabeth. 33431 13TH PL S, FEDERAL WAY COMM HLTH CTR 98003 #026-04-2001 L2004 **FM** *020 †18
PHILLIPS, Terry Lee. 34515 9TH AVE S 98003 #041-12-1976 L1977 **AN** *071 †05
POGUE, Larry Fay. 301 S 320TH ST 98003 #017-20-1967 L1970 **GP** *020 †18
POISSON, Sujata C. 34617 11TH AVE S, STE 100 98003 #495-19-1982 L1994 **N** *020 †75
POORE, Stephen E. 34515 9TH AVE S 98003 #023-12-1987 L1997 **OBG** *020 †30
POPE, Dana W. 34515 9TH AVE S 98003 #026-04-1984 L1989 **EM** *020 †20,16
QUDDUSI, Shaista. 34515 9TH AVE S 98003 #704-02-1988 L1995 **END** *020 †20
QUICK, Matthew Bernhard. 301 S 320TH ST 98003 #041-02-1993 L1999 **FM** *020 †18
RAI, Navdeep Singh. 34509 9TH AVE S, STE 104 98003 #038-40-1988 L2001 **CCM PUD** *020 †20
RANZENBACH, Meredith Roe. 181 S 333RD ST, STE 210C 98003 #023-07-1990 L1997 **DR** *020 †80
REAGAN, Patrick John. 33501 1ST WAY S 98003 #030-06-1972 L1977 **CD IM** *020 †20
REDDY, M S Prasad. 34515 9TH AVE S 98003 #495-50-1972 L1978 **AN** *020
REIBMAN, Stephen Jeffrey. 181 S 333RD ST, STE 210C 98003 #054-04-1969 L1970 **DR** *071 †80
RICHMOND, Jessica Broda. 33501 1ST WAY S 98003 #028-34-1987 L1990 **IM** *020 †20
RIESENBERGER, Timothy M. ■ 98023 #005-12-2001 L2005 **EM** *020 †16
ROCHIER, Dennis B. 34709 9TH AVE S, STE B200 98003 #048-12-1985 L1987 **IM IMG** *020 †20
ROE, Myong Jae. 710 S 348TH ST, STE A 98003 #583-01-1969 L1977 **OBG GP** *020 †30
ROGERS, James Eugene. 33501 1ST WAY S 98003 #054-04-1971 L1973 **PD** *020 †55
ROSCETTI, James Louis. 34616 11TH AVE S STE 4 98003 #016-11-1968 L1973 **FM** *020 †18
ROSHOLM, John. 34509 9TH AVE S, STE 204 98003 #030-05-1962 L1966 **GS** *071 †85
SAEED, Tabassum. 34616 11TH AVE S, ELECTRODIAGNOSIS & REHAB 98003 #704-06-1974 L1979 **PM** *075 †60
SAFAI, Zohreh E. 34515 9TH AVE S 98003 #046-01-1992 L1995 **FM** *020 †18 ‡
SALCEDO-WASICEK, Carolina. 34503 9TH AVE S, STE 320 98003 #264-04-1987 L1996 **GS** *020 †85
SANCHEZ, Raymond. 34515 9TH AVE S 98003 #034-01-1972 L1975 **EM FM** *020 †18
SANDERS, Elizabeth Juhan. 700 S 320TH ST STE D 98003 #027-01-1995 L2000 **DR** *020 †80
SCHAFFENBURG, Mark S. 34515 9TH AVE S 98003 #041-07-1988 L2007 **EM** *020 †16
SCHNEEWEISS, Daniel. 34515 9TH AVE S 98003 #014-01-1977 L1990 **AN P** *020 †75,05
SCHUMACHER, Kerry James. 33801 1ST WAY S, STE 101 98003 #047-06-1977 L2006 **DR OPH** *020 †80
SCHUMACHER, Walter. 34515 9TH AVE S 98003 #869-07-1973 L1975 **AN** *020 †05
SCHWAB, Henriette P. 34616 11TH PL S 98003 #660-03-1979 L1988 **D** *020 †18,15
SHAO, Yi. ■ 98001 #243-16-1982 *100
SHAW, David Michael. 34509 9TH AVE S, STE 104 98003 #008-01-1995 L2004 **PCC** *100 †20
SHELLEY, Peter Bennett. 32123 1ST AVE S 98003 #041-01-1970 L1981 **OPH PO** *020 †35 ‡
SILVA, William Andre Z. 34503 9TH AVE S, STE 330 98003 #061-01-1997 L2005 **OBG** *020 †30
SIMPSON, Timothy I. 34709 9TH AVE S, STE B200 98003 #048-12-1985 L1986 **GS** *020 †85
SLONIM, Samuel Lee. 34616 11TH PL S STE 5 98003 #005-06-1980 L1981 **FM** *020 †18
SMITH, David Warner. 31217 PACIFIC HWY S, # 128 98003 #036-01-2001 L2002 **GS** *100
SMITH, Karen Creighton. 33501 1ST WAY S 98003 #005-14-1982 L1983 **IM GP** *020 †20
SNYDER, Robert Jon. 710 S 348TH ST STE A, ST FRANCIS WOMEN'S HEALTHC 98003 #041-02-1980 L1992 **OBG** *020 †30
SOULIERE, Chas Robt, Jr. 34503 9TH AVE S, STE 230 98003 #008-01-1981 L1991 **OTO** *020 †45
SPORL, Laura Guinee. 33501 1ST WAY S 98003 #021-05-1992 L2006 **OBG** *020 †30
SRIKANTH, Myur S. 34509 9TH AVE S, STE 103 98003 #495-04-1988 L1996 **GS** *020 †85
STEMPEL, David Alan. 33501 1ST WAY S 98003 #038-41-1973 L1980 **PDA A** *020 †55,03
STONESIFER, Larry Dee. 34509 9TH AVE S STE 200 98003 #004-01-1976 L1984 **END IM** *020 †20
STRIDDE, Braden C. 918 S 348TH ST, STE B 98003 #016-06-1983 L1990 **PS** *020 †65
SUERO, James Anthony. 34509 9TH AVE S, STE 304 98003 #019-02-1992 L1995 **CD** *020 †20
SUTHERLAND, Eleanor Irene. ■ 98023 #407-19-1964 L1978 **FPG GP** *020 †18
SWART, Frans G. 34515 9TH AVE S 98003 #660-03-1986 L1991 **AN** *020 †05
TAKAHASHI, Corrie Linn. 33501 1ST WAY S, VIRGINIA MASON FEDERAL WAY 98003 #054-04-2002 L2005 **PD** *020 †55
TASNEEM, Mahmuda. 33501 1ST WAY S 98003 #495-04-1985 L1997 **IM** *020 †20
THAYER, Kimberly Ruth. 34515 9TH AVE S 98003 #018-03-2003 L2006 **EM** *100 †16
TORGERSON, Arthur Clement. 34509 9TH AVE S, STE 204 98003 #016-06-1957 L1958 **GS TS** *071 †85
TRAN, Thao Huynh. 710 S 348TH ST STE A, FMG-ST. FRANCIS WOMEN'S HE 98003 #035-46-1995 L1999 **OBG** *020 †30
TRANTHAM, James Gary. 402 S 333RD ST, STE 100 98003 #048-04-1975 L1980 **P PYM** *020 †75
TWYMAN, Marianne Louise. 1105 S 348TH ST, STE B103 98003 #005-12-1974 L1975 **GPM FM** *020 †18
UBEROI, Sunanda. 34515 9TH AVE S 98003 #495-36-1970 L1984 **RHU IM** *020 †20
VAUGHAN, Gregory Dean. 301 S 320TH ST 98003 #007-02-1975 L1980 **FM** *020 †18
VELASCO, Estrelino D, Jr. 34617 11TH AVE S, STE 202 98003 #748-01-1989 L2001 **FM** *020 †18
VELLING, David Anthony. 34509 9TH AVE S STE 203B 98003 #005-06-1990 L2002 **PME OS** *020 †05
VERRILLI, John Thomas. 34509 9TH AVE S, STE 104 98003 #035-46-2000 L2006 **PCC** *020 †20 ‡
VIRJI, Alnoor. ■ 98003 #422-01-1987 L1991 **FM** *072 †18
VORA, Yasmin. 1300 S 320TH ST 98003 #308-11-1985 L2005 **IM** *020
WAGNER, James Martin. 34509 9TH AVE S, STE 304 98003 #040-02-1976 L1982 **CD** *020 †20
WATANABE, Barbara Y. 34515 9TH AVE S 98003 #054-04-1983 L1983 **AN PD** *020 †55,05
WEIS, Kurt Richard. 700 S 320TH ST STE A 98003 #054-04-1972 L1978 **OBG** *020 †30
WELLS, J Denise. 34709 9TH AVE S, STE B500 98003 #004-01-1984 L1989 **ORS** *071 †40
WENDT, John Salem. 34503 9TH AVE S, STE 230 98003 #025-01-1975 L1988 **N** *020 †75
WIESTER, Rebecca Tritt. 33431 13TH PL S, DEPT PF PUBLIC HLTH 98003 #038-41-1979 L1985 **PD** *020 †55
WINTHER, John Bernard. 301 S 320TH ST 98003 #005-18-1977 L1982 **PD** *020 †55
WONG, Stacey C. 33501 1ST WAY S 98003 #038-06-1983 L1987 **DR** *020 †80
WULFESTIEG, Carl Wm. 33501 1ST WAY S 98003 #005-14-1971 L1979 **OTO** *020 †45
WUTHRICH, Daniel A. 34509 9TH AVE S, STE 304 98003 #025-07-1991 L1994 **CD** *020 †20
WYMAN, Charles Mahan. 33501 1ST WAY S 98003 #030-05-1972 L1973 **FM** *020 †18
YAMAKI, Estelle Ikuko. 2319 SW 320TH ST 98023 #035-03-1980 L1984 **OBG** *020 †30
YANG, Hui. 533 S 336TH ST STE C, VALLEY RADIOLOGISTS INC. P 98003 #018-03-1997 L2003 **DR** *020 †80
YOO, Eunjoo. 32018 23RD AVE S 98003 #056-05-2000 L2003 **FM** *020 †18 ‡
ZHOU, Kevin Yan Ting. 34509 9TH AVE S, STE 304 98003 #243-08-1984 L2003 **CD** *020 †20
ZIEMANN, Joy Louise H. 34616 11TH PL S, FEDERAL WAY FAMILY PRACTIC 98003 #028-34-1974 L1977 **FM** *020 †18

FERNDALE – WHATCOM

BATES, Jennifer Ann. 5580 NORDIC PL 98248 #054-04-1997 L1999 **IM** *020 †18
CARLISLE, Steven James. ■ 98248 #016-06-1959 L1964 **P** *020
EVERETT, Norman F. PO BOX 965 98248 #005-12-1948 L1949 **GP** *071
HANSEN, David A. 5580 NORDIC PL 98248 #043-01-2003 L2003 **FM** *020 †18
HRUBY, John. 5580 NORDIC PL 98248 #054-04-1976 L1978 **FM** *020 †18
LEWIS, Steve Arthur. 5580 NORDIC PL 98248 #028-34-1991 L1991 **FM** *020 †18
MC LAURIN, Jennie A. ■ 98248 #036-05-1985 L1988 **PD ID** *020 †55
SAFFORD, Bertha Louise. 5580 NORDIC PL 98248 #054-04-1976 L1978 **FM** *020 †18
SIGURDSON, Thorbjorg. ■ 98248 #054-04-1960 L1962 **N** *071
VOLK, Jon Michael. ■ 98248 #028-34-1962 L1968 **PD** *071 †55

FIFE – PIERCE

CASEY, Elmer Michael, Jr. 502 54TH AVE E 98424 #016-43-1973 L1998 **OM AM** *071 †70
HAASTRUP, Sarah Katherine. 2902 57TH AVENUE CT E 98424 #040-02-2004 L2004 **FM** *020 †18
MARTIN, Daniel John. ■ 98424 #005-12-2005 L2007 **DR** *012
NELSON, James Harvey. 502 54TH AVE E, MULTICARE HEALTHWORKS 98424 #007-02-1963 L1976 **OM GP** *071 †55,70
SCOTT, Floyd Earl, Jr. 5303 PACIFIC HWY E, # 278 98424 #045-04-1985 L2003 **CCS** *020 †85
SHAWEL, Getnet Estifanos. 2820 PACIFIC HWY E, APT 205 98424 #366-02-1987 L2002 **IM** *020 †20
URAGA, Nick Wm. 4703 PACIFIC HWY E 98424 #030-06-1973 L1977 **OM AM** *020
WISBEY, Erin Christi. ■ 98424 #005-12-2005 L2006 **OBG** *012

FIRCREST – PIERCE

ATKINSON, John Welsey. 1339 ALAMEDA AVE 98466 #054-04-1972 L1974 **FM** *020 †18
COMFORT, John F. ■ 98466 #028-34-1953 L1954 **GP** *071
DAVIES, Bruce G. 1033 REGENTS BLVD, STE 102 98466 #048-12-1988 L1992 **PD** *020 †55
DEBUSSCHERE, Paul Eugene. 1033 REGENTS BLVD STE 102, UNIVERSITY PLACE PEDIATRIC 98466 #054-04-1995 L1997 **PD** *020 †55
GALLUCCI, Ronald Gary. 1033 REGENTS BLVD STE 102 98466 #028-34-1965 L1970 **PD** *071
HAUTALA, John M. 1033 REGENTS BLVD, STE 102 98466 #054-04-1977 L1981 **PD ADL** *020 †55
HOYER, Louis Paul, Jr. ■ 98466 #041-01-1940 L1946 **OTO GS** *071
JACKSON, Michael Reid. 1339 ALAMEDA AVE 98466 #054-04-1980 L1981 **FM** *020 †18
MARTIN, Robert Jos. 1033 REGENTS BLVD STE 204 98466 #040-02-1968 L1976 **D DMP** *071 †15
PAGE, Brandi Rachel. ■ 98466 #035-03-2008 *012
RAMINS, Ira Vitols. ■ 98466 #594-01-1939 L1954 **GP** *071

9212

■ = Address Information Privacy Protected

RONE, Belinda Shunk. 1033 REGENTS BLVD STE 102, UNIVERSITY PLACE PEDIATRIC 98466
#054-04-1977 L1978 **PD** *020 †55
STRUTHERS, Megan. 1033 REGENTS BLVD, STE 102 98466 #005-18-1992 L1992 **PD** *020 †55
TORGENRUD, Terry Wayne. 1033 REGENTS BLVD STE 102 98466 #036-05-1968 L1971
PD ADL *020 †55
WILSON, Robert Harrison. 1401 REGENTS BLVD STE 1 98466 #005-19-1974 L1975
FM *020 †18
WILSON, Virginia Talcott. ■ 98466 #007-02-1952 L1953 **OS** *071

FORKS – CLALLAM

BOKHARI, Freeha Farhia. 530 BOGACHIEL WAY 98331 #704-21-1996 L2005 **FM OBS** *020 †18
DICKSON, Richard Lee. 530 BOGACHIEL WAY 98331 #054-04-1977 L1978 **FM** *020 †18
HARMON, Gary Dean. 590 BOGACHIEL WAY 98331 #025-01-1987 L1989 **CRS** *020 †85,10
KASHER, R Jerome. 590 BOGACHIEL WAY 98331 #030-06-1961 L1992 **GS** *071
KRIEBEL, Stephen Hepworth. 530 BOGACHIEL WAY 98331 #041-01-1972 L1973 **FM** *020 †18
ROHANI, Farrokh. ■ 98331 #308-11-1986 L1991 **FM** *062
ROMNEY, Kenneth Charles. 590 BOGACHIEL WAY, BOGACHIEL CLNC 98331
#049-01-1994 L1996 **FM OBS** *020 †18
SHIMA, John Martin. 460 W E ST 98331 #030-06-1978 L1981 **IM EM** *020 †20

FORT LEWIS – PIERCE

BENNETT, Leo Leon. ■ 98433 #038-40-1978 L1983 **CCM PUD** *020 †20
BERKENBAUGH, James Thos. ■ 98433 #010-02-1977 L1987 **NPM PD** *020 †55
CAUSEY, Marlin Wayne. ■ 98433 #012-01-2007 **GS** *012
JHAVERI, Mustansir D. ■ 98433 #495-22-1962 L1969 **U GS** *020 †95
JIRAU-ROSALY, Wanda D. ■ 98433 #042-03-2002 L2004 **FM** *020 †18
KOCADAG, Belen Latag. ■ 98433 #748-01-1976 †062
NIEVES-ROBBINS, Neris M. MADIGAN ARMY MED CTR, DEPT RAD ATTN: MCHJ-R 98431
#042-01-1997 L1998 **DR** *020 †80
REED, Harrell Lester, II. ■ 98433 #020-12-1979 L1989 **END IM** *030 †20

FOUR LAKES – SPOKANE

LOGAN, Junius Raymond. ■ 99014 #038-40-1994 **GS** *100

FOX ISLAND – PIERCE

BRAND, Timothy Charles. ■ 98333 #021-01-1999 L2007 **U** *020
FLASKERUD, Jeffrey J. ■ 98333 #035-01-1998 L2004 **PD** *100 †55
MAC DONALD, Bruce Guy. 1329 KAMUS WAY 98333 #054-04-1971 L1974 **OS FM** *030 †18
MARSHALL, Gerald. ■ 98333 #028-34-1963 L1963 **GP OS** *020 †50
TORRES, Rolando. ■ 98333 #023-12-1995 L2007 **PE** *020 †16
WOOD, Sandra Anne. ■ 98333 #054-04-1986 L1987 **PYG GP** *020 †75

FREELAND – ISLAND

BERGMANN, Barbara Ann. ■ 98249 #005-02-1971 L1977 **P** *020 †75
BOULWARE, Kathleen Gaines. PO BOX 1288 98249 #054-04-1978 L1979 **IM** *020
CUTCHER, Ann Boyd. 6339 WAHL RD 98249 #003-01-1985 L2002 **IM** *020 †20
ISAACS, Myron Michael. ■ 98249 #016-42-1957 L1995 **ORS** *020 †40
MC ANALLY, Thomas Paul. 5486 HARBOR AVE, SOUTH WHIDBEY HLTHCARE 98249
#021-01-1974 L2000 **IM ID** *020 †20 ‡
MONDA, George Damian. ■ 98249 #028-34-1958 L1968 **U** *071 †95
MORROW, James Wm. ■ 98249 #030-05-1952 L1952 **U** *071 †95
PETRAK, Zrinko. PO BOX 462, 5486 HARBOR AVE 98249 #132-01-1967 L1985 **IM CD** *020 †20
SHAPIRO, Marvin James. PO BOX 759 98249 #026-04-1944 L1944 **DR** *071 †80
SHAPIRO, Stephen Carton. 5522 FREELAND AVE 98249 #005-19-1974 L1975 **FM EM** *020
STRAYER, Marilynn A. ■ 98249 #038-40-1964 L2000 **P** *071 †75
WAGNER, Robert David. 1690 LAYTON RD 98249 #017-20-1976 L1983 **PD** *020 †55

FRIDAY HARBOR – SAN JUAN

AHBEL, Gertrude S. ■ 98250 #154-02-1949 L1974 **P** *071
DE FALCO, Alfred John. 223 HALVORSEN RD 98250 #035-45-1962 L1988 **U** *020 †95
DORPAT, Klarese Lere. ■ 98250 #054-04-1952 L1953 **GP** *074
DWYER, Regina Joan. 523 EGG LAKE RD 98250 #035-19-1986 L1988 **IM** *020 †20
EDWARDS, John Michael. ■ 98250 #030-06-1979 L1991 **OS LM** *020
FISHAUT, Jack Mark. ■ 98250 #005-18-1973 L2002 **IM PD** *050 †55 ‡
FRY, Barbara Carnahan. ■ 98250 #025-01-1948 L1956 **OBG** *071
GASKILL, William Marvin. ■ 98250 #005-12-1964 L1978 **TS** *071 †85,90
GASTALDO, Edward. ■ 98250 #005-14-1980 L1981 **GPM** *020 †70
GILSON, Betty St Cyr. ■ 98250 #026-04-1944 L1969 **PHP** *071
GOSSOM, John Burk. 550 SPRING ST 98250 #054-04-1977 L1980 **FM FPG** *020 †18
HAMILTON, Bobbi A C. PO BOX 492, 151 SKOTTOWE LN 98250 #041-07-1972 L1973
FM *071 †18
HERNDON, S Paul. 411 EAGLE COVE DR 98250 #010-01-1970 L1971 **PDC** *020 †55
HOLBROOKE, David Reese. 685 SPRING ST PMB 112 98250 #067-01-1969 L1976 **EM FM** *030
HUA, Li. 620 UNIVERSITY RD 98250 #243-43-1997 L2007 *100
JAMES, Frank Eugene. PO BOX 607, 145 RHONE ST 98250 #054-04-1984 L1985 **FM** *020 †18
JOHNSTON, David Alan. ■ 98250 #040-02-1981 L1985 **P** *020 †75
KETTERING, Harry Albert. ■ 98250 #040-02-1945 L1953 **OBG** *071 †30
LALLY, Robert Francis. ■ 98250 #041-09-1972 L1987 **EM** *020 †16
MAHONEY, Susan Marie. 550 SPRING ST 98250 #054-04-1994 L1996 **FM** *020 †18
MORAN, Gregory Chas. 550 SPRING ST 98250 #035-47-1990 L2002 **FM** *020 †18
ROBINS, D Stephen. PO BOX 2389 98250 #917-23-1967 **OS D** *062
SACKS, Jerome Henry. ■ 98250 #026-04-1957 L1957 **TS** *020 †85,90
SMITH, Edward L, II. ■ 98250 #024-01-1938 L1946 **GP** *071

SMITH, Marjorie Lou. ■ 98250 #016-11-1952 L1978 **EM OS** *071
SMULOVITZ, Jan M. 20 CLIPPER WAY 98250 #165-02-1971 L1995 **END DIA** *020 †20
TUTTLE, Douglas Richards. ■ 98250 #020-02-1973 L2007 **FM** *020 †16
VOM LEHN, Walter Otte. 1508 THREE MEADOWS LN 98250 #035-20-1957 L1977
FM ADL *071 †18
WELLINGS, Sefton Robt. ■ 98250 #054-04-1953 L1970 **PTH** *071 †50
WINGREN, Michael Dan. 550 SPRING ST 98250 #026-04-1987 L1991 **FM** *020 †18

GIG HARBOR – PIERCE

ABADULLAH, Ahmad. 4423 PT FOSDICK DR NW #200, PENINSULA INT MED ASSOC 98335
#704-02-1990 L1997 **IM OM** *020 †20
ALDRICH, Franklin Dalton. ■ 98332 #038-06-1962 L1962 **PTX IM** *071
BAERG, Richard Doran. 4725 OLD STUMP DR NW 98332 #054-04-1965 L1973 **GE IM** *020 †20
BAGEANT, Thomas Edgar. 10810 63RD AVE NW 98332 #010-01-1970 L1972 **AN** *071 †05
BAKER, James M. 6401 KIMBALL DR 98335 #035-06-1970 L1973 **FM** *020 †18
BARON, Jennifer Ahimsa. 4700 POINT FOSDICK DR NW, STE 219 98335 #041-02-2002 L2007
D *020 †15
BERGLUND, Karin Beth. ■ 98335 #056-05-2004 L2007 **PD** *020 †55
BOSELEY, Mark Edward. ■ 98332 #021-01-1995 L2006 **OTO** *020 †45
BOUTERSE, Susan Elizabeth. 6401 KIMBALL DR, STE 104 98335 #056-06-1990 L1997
PD *020 †55
BOYD, John Thos. 4545 POINT FOSDICK DR NW, GIG HARBOR CHILD EXPRESS 98335
#035-09-1975 L1980 **PD** *020 †55
BRACE, Melanie Jeanne. 3206 50TH STREET CT NW, STE A101 98335 #025-01-1990 L1993
CHP P *020 †75
BRAMHALL, James Litton. 6901 SOUNDVIEW DR 98335 #352-08-1951 L1961 **P PTH** *071 †50
BROCK, Doyle Lee, Jr. ■ 98335 #005-14-1974 L1983 **P GP** *020
BROWN, Garrick Daniels. 2727 HOLLYCROFT ST, STE 480 98335 #047-06-1997 L2003
GE *020 †20
BROWN, Tommy Allen. ■ 98335 #039-01-1994 L2003 **GS** *020 †85
BUSHLEY, David Matthew. 3712 31ST AVE NW 98335 #010-01-1997 L2005 **OPH** *020 †35
BYRNE, James Michael. 4700 PT FOSDICK DR NW, STE 102 98335 #422-01-1999 L2007
IM *020
CARROUGHER, John Gregory. 4700 POINT FOSDICK DR NW, STE 307 98335
#023-12-1985 L1988 **GE IM** *020 †20
COE, John Richard. ■ 98335 #028-78-1966, ▲ L1998 **FM OM** *071 †18
COLTER, Mary Lee. 4119 29TH AVE NW 98335 #049-01-1988 L1992 **IM** *020 †20
CRADDOCK, Mark Farabee. 4700 POINT FOSDICK DR NW, STE 220 98335 #054-04-1977 L1982
FM *020 †18
DAHLGREN, Timothy J. 8992 90TH AVE NW 98332 #035-06-1984 L1991 **EM** *020 †16
DAINTY, Louis Alan. ■ 98335 #023-12-1996 L1998 **OBG** *020 †30
DIMANT, John Stevens. 4700 PT FOSDICK DR NW, STE 211 98335 #016-01-1982 L1985
PD *020 †55
DONNER, Michelle Verena. ■ 98335 #409-16-1990 *075
FAHMY, Raed Nicola. 4700 POINT FOSDICK DR NW, STE 320 98335 #010-01-1985 L1999
CD *020 †20
FAULSTICH, Gary Geo. ■ 98335 #030-06-1975 L1998 **CHP P** *020 †75
FIELD, Dean Arden. 4700 PT FOSDICK DR NW, STE 202 98335 #003-01-1987 L1999
FM EM *020 †18
FINE, Betsy Lynn. 4700 POINT FOSDICK DR NW 98335 #010-01-1980 L1981 **FM** *020 †18
FINKLEMAN, Lowell C. 6718 144TH ST NW 98332 #062-01-1976 L1978 **GP** *020
FISHER, Lawrence Edward. ■ 98335 #025-01-1976 L1988 **PTH** *071 †50
FISHER, Olaf Lincoln. 5305 OLD STUMP DR NW, 11650 VALLEYCREST ROAD 98332
#005-15-1962 L1975 **GP OS** *020
FITZGERALD, Kerri Rebecca. ■ 98332 #038-43-2001 L2007 **NPM** *020 †55
FRIEDENBERG, Ralph Chas. ■ 98335 #016-06-1963 L1965 **END IM** *071 †20
FRIEDMAN, Mark Alan. 4700 PT FOSDICK DR NW, STE 111 98335 #016-02-2001 L2006
ORS *020
GARCIA, Joseph Casimir. ■ 98332 #028-34-2005 L2007 **PD** *100
GEISSLER, Francis T. 6401 KIMBALL DR, STE 203 98335 #054-04-1993 L1999
OPH FM *020 †35
GILBERT, Richard Ernest. 6401 KIMBALL DR, GIG HARBOR MEDICAL CLINIC 98335
#054-04-1970 L1971 **FM** *020 †18
GISKE, Aren A. ■ 98335 #050-02-2008 *012
GOETZ, Kathleen S. 4545 PT FOSDICK DR NW, MAILSTOP 4545-1-UC 98335
#039-01-1990 L1997 **PEM** *020 †55
GOTTLIEB, Bruce E. 4700 POINT FOSDICK DR NW 98335 #048-12-1982 L1990 **IM** *020 †20
GRAY, Richard Edward. 5801 SOUNDVIEW DR, STE 150 98335 #016-06-1984 L1990
ORS *020 †40
GROUSE, Jan Ellen. ■ 98332 #054-04-1973 L1989 **FM** *030 †18
GROUSE, Lawrence Douglas. ■ 98332 #054-04-1973 L1975 **IM** *062
GUINA, Maria Lourdes C A. 4700 PT FOSDICK DR NW, STE 320 98335 #748-01-1994 L2006
N *020
GUINTO, Rachelle January. 4700 POINT FOSDICK DR NW 98335 #748-10-2001 L2007
FM *020 †18
GUTIERREZ, Ricardo R. 5114 POINT FOSDICK DR NW, STE E 98335 #025-01-1981 L1990
EM *020 †16
HAGAMAN, Betty A. 5114 POINT FOSDICK DR NW, STE E 98335 #005-06-1970 L1975
OPH *020 †35
HAMMER, Carl Stevens. 4700 POINT FOSDICK DR NW, STE 320 98335 #067-01-1968 L1969
GS *020 †85
HASSAN, Douglas Matthew. 5801 SOUNDVIEW DR, STE 150 98335 #061-01-1987 L1997
HS *020 †40
HERRON, Thomas Michael. 6401 KIMBALL DR STE 104 98335 #054-04-1982 L1986
PD *020 †55
HERSHMAN, Arnold. ■ 98332 #028-79-1952, ▲ L1993 **OBG** *071
JIGANTI, John Jos. 5801 SOUNDVIEW DR, STE 150 98335 #016-43-1986 L1992
OAR OSM *020 ‡
KAHNG, Randall Sanghyuk. 4012 4TH ST NW 98335 #016-42-1999 L2003 **EM** *020 †16
KEITH, Julian Faison, III. ■ 98335 #036-05-1979 L1985 **NPM PD** *020 †55
KELLOGG, Will. 2912 91ST AVENUE CT NW, 2912 91ST AVENUE CT NW 98335
#025-01-1992 L1996 **AN** *020 †05
KEMP, John Edward. ■ 98332 #017-20-1963 L1968 **AN** *072 †05

KENNEDY, Timothy Raymond. ■ 98332 #025-12-1988 L1992 **PTH** *020 †50
KENNEY, George James. ■ 98335 #054-04-1961 L1965 **R OS** *071 †80
KESLING, Peter Robert. 2703 JAHN AVE NW STE C5 98335 #005-02-1969 L1972 GYN *020 †30 ‡
KHAN, Wajahat Ali. 6401 KIMBALL DR 98335 #704-02-1992 L2004 **FM** *020 †18
KHEMANI, Pravin Manohar. 4700 PT FOSDICK DR NW, STE 320 98335 #025-07-1999 L2005 N *100 †75
KIEMELE, Marissa F. 4700 PT FOSDICK DR NW, STE 208 98335 #060-01-1995 L2000 **FM** *020 †18
KIM, Dione Han. ■ 98335 #583-08-1965 L1974 **AN** *020 †05
KIM, Taehee Rosa. 6401 KIMBALL DR 98335 #034-01-1999 L2003 **IM** *020 †20
KIRKWOOD, Kenneth J. 4545 POINT FOSDICK DR NW, STE 145 98335 #035-47-1978 L1981 **FM UCM** *020 †18 ‡
KONICEK, Steven Jay. 6401 KIMBALL DR, GIG HARBOR MEDICAL CLNC 98335 #054-04-1986 L1995 **OS** *020 †20
KOZAK, Maurie-Lynn Carla. 6401 KIMBALL DR, GIG HARBOR MEDICAL CLINIC 98335 #060-02-1989 L1997 **FM** *020 †18
KRAMP, Stephen Gerard. 4700 POINT FOSDICK DR NW, STE 202 98335 #054-04-1992 L1994 **FM** *020 †18
KRETSCHMER, Louis Frank. 3017 89TH ST NW 98332 #040-02-1970 L1975 **ORS** *020 †40
KRONISCH, David Herbert. ■ 98332 #054-15-1964 **GP** *071
KULPA, Patty Jean. 7282 STINSON AVE STE C 98335 #056-05-1980 L1988 **GYN OS** *020 †30
KUNKLE, Robert Wm. 4545 POINT FOSDICK DR NW, STE 250 98335 #023-07-1981 L1990 ORS OSM *020 †40
LAMB, Joseph J. 9770 44TH AVE NW STE 102 98332 #051-04-1985 L2006 **IM** *050 †20
LARKIN, Hugh Anthony, Jr. 7717 110TH ST NW 98332 #054-04-1980 L1981 **R** *020
LAVELL, Louis Wm. ■ 98335 #054-15-1964 **FM** *071
LAVINDER, Imka Crystal. 4700 POINT FOSDICK DR NW, STE 211 98335 #005-76-1998, ▲ L2001 **PD** *020 †55
LEE, Jonathan Oliver. ■ 98332 #048-04-1965 L1995 **P ADM** *020
LERMAN, Robert Howard. 5800 SOUNDVIEW DR, FUNCTIONAL MEDICINE RESEAR 98335 #041-02-1966 L1998 **NTR IM** *062 †20
LEVERETT, Vincent Mark. 4700 POINT FOSDICK DR NW, STE 220 98335 #037-01-2001 L2004 **FM** *020 †18
LINDSTROM, Axel. ■ 98335 #858-02-1950 L1959 **GP OM** *071
LONG, Thomas Eugene. 1119 SEA CLIFF DR NW 98332 #023-01-1978 L1995 **EM** *020
LORBERBAUM, Herman A. ■ 98335 #005-02-1950 L1950 **PTH HEM** *071 †50
LURIA, Eric Walter. 4402 HUNT ST NW 98335 #035-45-1973 L1976 **FM** *020 †18
MALAPIRA, Amelito B R. 4700 PT FOSDICK DR NW, STE 320 98335 #748-10-1990 L2006 N *020 †75
MANLAPAZ, Eller Cunanan. ■ 98332 #748-20-1992 L2004 **IM** *020 †20
MARSHALL, Jay Richard. PO BOX 357 98335 #051-01-1969 L1969 **IM** *062
MARTIN, Lawrence Moorer. ■ 98335 #027-01-1969 L1991 **P CHP** *020 †75
MC CLELLAN, Michael Wayne. ■ 98335 #007-02-1986 L1989 **MG PD** *020 †19,55
MC CLELLEN, Jeffrey H. ■ 98335 #023-12-2001 L2003 **PD** *100
MC SHANE, Suzan Marie. ■ 98329 #041-07-1990 L1992 **IM** *020 †20
MEYER, Melissa Ayn. ■ 98335 #023-12-1995 L2007 **FM** *020 †18
MILLETT, David Walter. ■ 98332 #054-04-1961 L1964 **ORS** *071 †40
MORRELL, Michael Harris. ■ 98335 #035-19-1968 L1974 **ORS** *020 †40
MURPHY, Thomas O. 161 MAPLE LN NW, RAFT ISLAND 98335 #023-07-1949 L1951 **CD GS** *071 †85
MUSTAFA, Syed Khalid. 6401 KIMBALL DR, GIG HARBOR MEDICAL CLINIC 98335 #704-02-1989 L1997 **IM** *020 †20
NAASZ, Corrie Ainslee. 6401 KIMBALL DR 98335 #020-02-1992 L2002 **MPD PD** *020 †55,20
NIVEN, Alexander S. ■ 98335 #024-07-1995 L1996 **PCC IM** *020 †20
O'BRIEN, Mary Katherine. 4545 POINT FOSDICK DR NW 98335 #005-14-1984 L1992 **FM** *020 †18
OTA, Kay Kunio. 14020 188TH AVE 98335 #019-02-1948 L1950 **GP GS** *071
OZIMEK, Carl Dean. ■ 98332 #036-07-1977 L1988 **PD** *020 †55
PATTERSON, James Lewis. 4700 PT FOSDICK DR NW, STE 220 98335 #024-07-1977 L1978 **FM** *030 †18
PEARSON, Michael Roy. 5801 SOUNDVIEW DR STE 251 98335 #026-04-1971 L1976 **P CHP** *020 ‡
PUIG, Francis Javier. ■ 98332 #275-01-1948 L1966 **FM OM** *071
QUIRING, Dennis Lauren. 6501 KIMBALL DR 98335 #054-04-1970 L1979 **FM** *020 †18
RANKIN, Roland Eugene. ■ 98332 #005-02-1963 L1993 **OBG** *020 †30
RIFENBERY, James Dale. 4700 POINT FOSDICK DR NW, STE 320 98335 #054-04-1980 L1984 **GS** *020 †85
RITCHIE, William Thomas. ■ 98335 #016-06-1962 L1965 **OTO** *071 †45
ROBERTSON, Cliff Allen. 6401 KIMBALL DR, GIG HARBOR MEDICAL CLINIC 98335 #038-40-1989 L1991 **FM** *020 †18
ROME, Merit Sarah Ramzy. 4700 POINT FOSDICK DR NW, STE 302 98335 #019-02-1987 L1995 **P** *020 †75
ROMNEY, Michael Clark. 4700 PT FOSDICK DR NW, STE 102 98335 #049-01-1966 L2005 **EM** *020
ROSE, Jerman W. ■ 98335 #041-13-1943 L1961 **P CHP** *071 †75
RUBEL, Eric Jacques. PO BOX 1249 98335 #023-12-1991 L2006 **FM** *020 †18
RUE, Forrest Lee. ■ 98332 #005-12-1985 L1989 **AN** *020 †05
RURIK, Gregory Wm. 4700 PT FOSDICK DR NW, STE 211 98335 #028-02-1985 L1987 **PD** *020 †55
SADIQ, Raheela. 4423 POINT FOSDICK DR NW, STE 200 98335 #704-25-1992 L1999 **IM** *020 †20
SAMMS, John Marshall. 4700 PT FOSDICK DR NW, STE 220 98335 #041-02-1977 L1978 **FM** *020 †18
SCHMALTZ, Gregory Adam. 6718 144TH ST NW 98332 #060-02-1989 L1999 **FM** *020 †18
SCHNEIDER, Paul David. 4423 POINT FOSDICK DR NW, STE 200 98335 #054-04-1970 L1977 **NEP IM** *020 †20
SCHOEN, Richard Gordon. 5122 OLYMPIC DR NW, STE A203 98335 #017-20-1973 L1976 **EM** *020
SCHOLL, Rebecca Lynne. ■ 98335 #010-02-2007 L2007 **TY** *012
SCHORE, Robert Malcolm. 2727 HOLLYCROFT ST STE 39 98335 #025-01-1969 L1972 **FM OS** *020 †18
SCHULZE, Phillip Scott. 4700 PT FOSDICK DR NW 98335 #048-13-1975 L1979 **FM** *030 †18
SCHUTT, David Carlton. ■ 98335 #010-01-1975 L1980 **FM** *030 †18
SEVILLE, Paul Ruiz. 6401 KIMBALL DR, FMG-GIG HARBOR MEDICAL CLI 98335 #005-15-1996 L2007 **U** *020

SIEBOLD, Hans Klaus. ■ 98329 #407-15-1962 L1965 **AN** *071 †05
SIGMON, Michael Jeffery. ■ 98332 #038-06-1991 L2004 **GPM** *020 †18,70
SIMMS, Roger Scott. ■ 98335 #034-01-1979 L1980 **GP EM** *072 †16
SINGH, Niten. ■ 98335 #023-12-1997 L2007 **VS** *020 †85
SMITH, Jennifer Emily. 4700 PT FOSDICK DR NW, STE 220 98335 #054-04-1997 L2000 **FM** *020 †18
SORRELLS, Morris Lee. ■ 98335 #017-20-1963 L1963 **PD EM** *020 †55
STAGNER, Ralph Vernon. ■ 98335 #016-11-1955 L1956 **U** *071 †95
STEWART, John Denovan. 5801 SOUNDVIEW DR, STE 150 98335 #032-01-1977 L1982 **HS ORS** *020 †40
STUART, Robert. 4700 POINT FOSDICK DR NW, STE 305 98335 #038-40-1976 L1978 **FM EM** *020 †18
SULLIVAN, Kevin Jeremiah. 6401 KIMBALL DR, GIG HARBOR MEDICAL CLINIC 98335 #005-06-1996 L1999 **FM** *020 †18
TAN, Margaret Chan. ■ 98335 #005-12-1955 L1956 **GP** *020
TAN, Stephen. ■ 98335 #005-12-1956 L1957 *071
TAYLOR, Mark Wallace. 4700 POINT FOSDICK DR NW, STE 112 98335 #016-06-1992 L1996 **OPH** *020 †35
THOMAS, Max Stilwell. ■ 98329 #018-03-1939 L1946 **IM** *071
THOMAS, Sylvia M. 4700 POINT FOSDICK DR NW 98335 #005-12-1991 L2001 **FM** *020 †18
THOMPSON, Trula Jo. ■ 98332 #036-05-1979 L1993 **FM** *030 †18
TRIPP, Glenn Chas. 4700 POINT FOSDICK DR NW, PEDIATRICS NORTHWEST PS 98335 #004-01-1975 L1992 **PD** *020 †55
TSIMBEROV, Dmitry. 6316 106TH ST NW 98332 #913-09-1986 L1998 **IM** *020 †20
VAUGHAN, Patrick John. 5801 SOUNDVIEW DR, STE 150 98335 #010-02-1996 L2004 **ORS** *020 †40
VAUGHAN, Thomas Keith. 4700 POINT FOSDICK DR NW, STE 320 98335 #039-05-1984 L2005 D *020 †15
VILLANUEVA, Rosendo Real. ■ 98332 #748-07-1957 L1975 **P** *071
VON HERZEN, Josephine L M. ■ 98332 #030-06-1971 L1972 **OBG** *020 †30
WALCK, John Alfred. 6625 WAGNER WAY NW, STE 250 98335 #143-05-1976 L1997 **FM ADM** *020 †18
WALDRON, Frank Dennis. ■ 98335 #054-04-1962 L1964 **GE IM** *071 †20
WALLOCH, Antone Strejc. ■ 98335 #054-04-1953 L1954 **P** *071
WEINSTEIN, Gloria Ann. ■ 98335 #041-07-1975 L1978 **PD** *020 †55
WEINSTEIN, Sheridan Lloyd. ■ 98335 #035-46-1962 L1963 **PHP GP** *075
WORNELL, Douglas Paul. 5500 OLYMPIC DR, STE A105 98335 #011-02-1984 L1997 **NS** *020 †75
XUAN, Linli. 3410 A ST NW 98335 #243-16-1987 L2004 **HO** *020 †20
YANCEY, Robert Allen. 4700 POINT FOSDICK DR NW, HARBOR ORTHOPEDICS STE 111 98335 #024-01-1983 L1984 **ORS** *020 †40
ZIMA, Aaron Jude. ■ 98332 #025-01-2001 L2007 **RNR** *020 †80
ZOOK, Wayne Bowman. ■ 98332 #017-20-1953 L1956 **FM AM** *071 †18

GOLDENDALE – KLICKITAT

BOTHAMLEY, William C. 711 E COLLINS DR 98620 #061-01-1992 L1992 **FM** *020 †18
GARNETT, Michael Edward. 711 E COLLINS DR 98620 #040-02-1977 L1978 **FM EM** *020 †18
JONES, David William. 711 E COLLINS DR 98620 #054-04-2003 L2003 **FM** *020 †18
LENTZ, Jennifer Mccabe. 711 E COLLINS DR 98620 #007-02-2001 L2006 **FM** *020 †18
NGUYEN, Lan-Anh Khac. 711 E COLLINS DR 98620 #654-01-2001 L2004 **FM** *020 †18
RAJANI, Anil Pierre. 711 E COLLINS DR, FAMILY PRACTICE CLINIC 98620 #065-06-1993 L1996 **FM** *020 †18
RUSSO, Emilio Anthony. 711 E COLLINS DR 98620 #021-05-2005 L2005 **FP** *012
SHERPA, Nawang Karsang. 711 E COLLINS DR 98620 #243-4-1996 L2004 **FM** *030
SMITH, Russell Murat. 205 S COLUMBUS AVE RM 108, RM 108 98620 #054-14-1984 L1992 **GS** *020
SPOLAR, Trenton John. 711 E COLLINS DR 98620 #016-11-1966 L1970 **D IM** *020 †15
THOMPSON, Neal Rodney. ROOSEVELT & ALLYN STS 98620 #041-09-1960 L1962 **FM** *071 †18
TUPPER, Elsie A George. 400 S ROOSEVELT AVE 98620 #005-12-1953 L1955 **FM OS** *020 †18
TUPPER-STITES, Geraldine. ■ 98620 #005-12-1954 L1957 **PHP** *075 †70

GRAHAM – PIERCE

KIMURA, Irene Kimiyo. ■ 98338 #040-02-1992 L1992 **FM** *020 †18
MAOUD, Raouf F. PO BOX 1188 98338 #915-04-1985 L1995 **IM** *020 †20
MICHAEL, Sharon Jane. ■ 98338 #047-05-1977 L1981 **IM** *020
OLIVA, Anthony Joseph. ■ 98338 #048-02-2004 L2006 **IM** *020
SPIGER, Michael J. ■ 98338 #054-04-1969 L1974 **IM NM** *071 †20,28
WALTER, Arthur Lee. 25325 106TH AVE E 98338 #016-11-1971 L2003 **PD** *020 †55
WEIGEL, Keith M. ■ 98338 #054-04-1976 L1981 **IM** *020

GRAND COULEE – GRANT

CASTRODALE, Andrew Cecil. 411 FORTUYN RD, OKANOGAN HOSPITAL DISTRICT 99133 #054-04-1994 L1996 **FM** *020 †18
CHAFFEE, Jacob Petersen. 411 FORTUYN RD 99133 #054-04-2001 L2003 **FM** *020 †18
FERCHA, Mohammed E. 411 FORTUYN RD 99133 #396-06-1974 L2002 **GS** *020 †85

GRANDVIEW – YAKIMA

BIGGS, April R. 208 N EUCLID RD 98930 #004-01-2000 L2003 **FM** *020 †18
BUCKINGHAM, Ward Bruce. 1000 WALLACE WAY, MEDICINE DEPT 98930 #054-04-1969 L1973 **IM** *020 †20
DIETRICH, Sharon Arlene. 1000 WALLACE WAY 98930 #054-04-1983 L1986 **FM** *020 †18
DUBEK, Martin. 222 E 2ND ST 98930 #286-03-1996 L2003 **FM** *071 †18
FIEDLER, Albert E, II. 222 E 2ND ST 98930 #005-14-1980 L1990 **FM** *020 †18
KHAN, Sheik Nizam. 1000 WALLACE WAY 98930 #913-65-1990 L2002 **IM** *020 †20
LASSELLE, Donald Dale. 1000 WALLACE WAY 98930 #040-02-1973 L1998 **OBG** *020 †30 ‡
LOMBARDI, Mary Haywood. 1000 WALLACE WAY, CLINIC - GRANDVIEW CLINIC 98930 #035-03-1996 L2002 **PD** *020 †55

■ = Address Information Privacy Protected

MAGIER, Michael Gary. 1000 WALLACE WAY, CLINIC GRANDVIEW MED-DENTA 98930 #017-20-1993 L1996 **FM** *020 †18

MARX, Herman Benno. 1000 WALLACE WAY 98930 #429-01-1983 L1994 **FM** *020 †18

ORR, Flint Wood. 1000 WALLACE WAY, YAKIMA VALLEY FARMWORKERS 98930 #048-13-1997 L2002 **IM** *020 †20

SCHILLE, Tamera Lee. 1000 WALLACE WAY, YAKIMA VALLEY FARM WORKERS 98930 #054-04-1989 L1995 **PD** *020 †55

GRANITE FALLS – SNOHOMISH

KUSSY, James Chas. PO BOX 689 98252 #016-06-1954 L1961 **GP AN** *071 †50

SCHMIESING, Don Chas. ■ 98252 #026-04-1969 L1970 **OPH** *071 †35

GRAYLAND – PACIFIC

SEBREN, Joseph G. PO BOX 732, 1078 BONNIE LN 98547 #035-08-1951 L1955 **OBG** *071 †30

GREENACRES – SPOKANE

ALLAN, William Laird. PO BOX 9, 4023 S CONKLIN RD 99016 #041-13-1959 L1985 **CHP P** *071 †75

FUJINAGA, Kevin Hideo. ■ 99016 #005-06-1990 L1994 **AN** *020 †05

HARCUS, Ross R. ■ 99016 #008-01-1948 L1952 **R** *071 †80

GREENBANK – ISLAND

MULES, Janet E. ■ 98253 #023-01-1963 L1973 **P GPM** *071 †75

HANSVILLE – KITSAP

ALLEN, Robert Donkin. ■ 98340 #041-13-1942 L1943 **OS AN** *071

BERGY, Gordon G. ■ 98340 #025-01-1949 L1955 **IM** *071 †20

TALCOTT, Donald Alwyne. ■ 98340 #041-13-1962 L1967 **AN** *071 †05

WENDER, Esther Hyatt. ■ 98340 #040-02-1963 L2003 **PD CHP** *071 †55

WILLIAMS, Buerk. ■ 98340 #054-04-1956 L2004 **DR NM** *071 †80

HEISSON – CLARK

KALE, Howard F. ■ 98622 #054-15-1969 **GP GS** *071

HOODSPORT – MASON

IE, Sing Ong. ■ 98548 #506-02-1963 L1994 **PTH** *071 †50

HOQUIAM – GRAYS HARBOR

BALLARD, Robert Finch. ■ 98550 #040-02-1943 L1944 **GP** *071

LEWIS, Richard Dean. 815 K ST 98550 #054-04-1976 L1979 **FM** *020 †18

STRANGE, Melvin Karl. 815 K ST 98550 #051-01-1978 L1981 **FM** *020 †18

TEVELIET, Craig Joseph. 815 K ST 98550 #040-02-1977 L1980 **FM** *020 †18

TRUSCHEL, Timothy L. 205 8TH ST, EVERGREEN COUNSELING 98550 #041-12-1977 L1986 **P CHP** *020 †75

HUNTS POINT – KING

COBURN, Wallace A. 3235 84TH AVE NE 98004 #051-01-1951 L1952 **GYN GS** *071 †85

ENKEMA, Louis C, Jr. 8329 HUNTS POINT CIR 98004 #005-14-1973 L1979 **CLP PTH** *050

ILWACO – PACIFIC

ADAMS, Brandon Lowrie. OCEAN BEACH CLINIC 98624 #030-05-1963 L1989 **GP P** *020

FRIEDMAN, David Jonathan. PO BOX N, 176 1ST AVE 98624 #024-07-1980 L2007 **GS CRS** *020 †85

GARDNER, Wm James, III. FIRST & FIR 98624 #041-01-1954 L1991 **GS VS** *071 †85

SMITH, Kim York. PO BOX H, OCEAN BEACH HOSPITAL 98624 #054-04-1981 L1994 **EM** *020

SUTHERLAND, Frederick R. 117 SPRUCE ST 98624 #018-03-1952 L1953 **FM** *020

WALISER, Mark Jay. 1ST & FIR, OCEAN BEACH HOSP EMER DEPT 98624 #054-04-1982 L1987 **EM** *020 †16

WANG, Dan-Bing. PO BOX N, 176 FIRST AVE N 98624 #060-01-2000 L2002 *020

INDIANOLA – KITSAP

CAGLE, William Dubreuil. ■ 98342 #011-02-1978 L1985 **P** *020 †75

MC DONALD, Geo Butler, Jr. ■ 98342 #054-04-1963 L1966 **R NM** *020 †80,28

ISSAQUAH – KING

ALEXANDER, David. ■ 98027 #041-15-2002 L2003 **AR** *012 †80

AMARA, Sashi Bindu. 100 NE GILMAN BLVD 98027 #495-65-2000 L2002 **IM** *020 †20

ANDERSON, Sandra Jean. 1455 11TH AVE NW 98027 #054-04-1992 L1992 **FM OBS** *020 †18

BARCHET, Stephen. ■ 98027 #023-01-1956 L1984 **OBG** *071 †30

BARNICKEL, Sigrid. 22510 SE 64TH PL STE 130 98027 #054-04-1985 L1985 **FM** *020 †18

BARRALL, Janet Louise. 100 NE GILMAN BLVD 98027 #054-04-1989 L1992 **OPH PO** *020 †35 ‡

BEEKEN, Kelly Elizabeth. ■ 98029 #051-01-2008 *012

BELL, Allan Brooks. 780 NW JUNIPER ST, # 404 98027 #040-02-1938 L1939 **AN** *071

BICE, Steven Arthur. 13120 207TH AVE SE 98027 #026-04-1983 L1984 **AN** *030 *05

BILL, Kazuko Uno. ■ 98075 #041-07-1948 L1949 **DR** *071 †80

BRESSLER, Mark Franklin. 85 NW ALDER PL 98027 #041-14-1983 L1985 **D** *020 †15

BRUCKNER, James David. 600 NW GILMAN BLVD, STE E 98027 #030-06-1984 L1990 **ORS** *020 †40

BRUENDERMAN, Patricia A. 1455 11TH AVE NW 98027 #020-12-1984 L1993 **IM** *020 †20

BURGE, Daniel Jonathan. ■ 98075 #041-02-1986 L1999 **RHU** *020 †20

BUSHNELL, Jerome Leroy. 100 NE GILMAN BLVD 98027 #054-04-1978 L1979 **FM** *020 †18

CAO, Yunyu. 1455 11TH AVE NW 98027 #243-45-1994 L2004 **IM** *020 †20

CASTLE, Thomas Harmon, Jr. 600 NW GILMAN BLVD, STE E 98027 #008-02-1982 L1988 **ORS OSM** *020 †40

CHI, Thomas Daehun. 600 NW GILMAN BLVD, STE A 98027 #024-01-1994 L2000 **ORS** *020 †40

CLARKSON, Thomas Alan. 6520 226TH PL SE, STE 150 98027 #056-06-1990 L1998 **FM** *020 †18

CLAUSER, John Benson. ■ 98029 #017-20-1956 L1973 **AN PUD** *071

CLEMETT, John. 450 NW GILMAN BLVD, STE 105 98027 #035-45-1986 L1993 **DR IM** *020 †80

COUCH, Rex Dee. ■ 98029 #017-20-1956 L1956 **CLP ATP** *071 †50 ‡

CRAWFORD, Johnette L. 2005 NW SAMMAMISH RD 98027 #030-06-1997 L2001 **FM** *020 †18

CRENSHAW, William B. 450 NW GILMAN BLVD, STE 105 98027 #051-01-1987 L1997 **VIR** *020 †80

CROSSAN, Laurence T. 100 NE GILMAN BLVD 98027 #041-02-1987 L1992 **OBG** *020

EARLY, Jennifer L. ■ 98027 #048-12-2001 L2004 **IM** *020

EGE, David Leroy. 450 NW GILMAN BLVD STE 201 98027 #019-02-1989 L1992 **PD** *020 †55

ENGELBRECHT, Diane E. 450 NW GILMAN BLVD, STE 105 98027 #037-01-1987 L1993 **DR** *020 †80

EVANS, Elisabeth Lorna. 6520 226TH PL SE STE 12 98027 #054-04-1975 L1986 **OBG** *020 †30

FAN, Xiaohong. ■ 98029 #243-64-1986 **IM** *012

FREIMANIS, Imanta Edward. 6505 226TH PL SE 98027 #038-40-1979 L1987 **VS GS** *020 †85

GENTSCH, Thomas Otto. ■ 98027 #008-01-1953 L1955 **TS** *071 †85,90

GOPALAN, Dharini Yadhu. ■ 98027 #496-32-1993 L2002 **IM** *020 †20

GRAHAM, Kristin Beard. 450 NW GILMAN BLVD, OVERLAKE OB GYN PC 98027 #026-04-1986 L1991 **OBG** *020 †30

GRAY, John Merle. 1455 11TH AVE NW 98027 #054-04-1990 L1992 **FM** *020 †18

HAINES, James Donald. 450 NW GILMAN BLVD, OVERLAKE OB GYN PC 98027 #025-01-1973 L1977 **OBG** *020 †30

HARDY, Keith S. 3707 PROVIDENCE POINT DR SE, STE G 98029 #025-01-2003 L2003 **PM** *020

HASSANTASH, Seyed-Ahmad. ■ 98029 #517-08-1983 L1994 **GS** *100

HATZAKIS, Michael, Jr. 1505 NW GILMAN BLVD, STE 2 98027 #005-11-1995 L2001 **PM** *020 †60

HEARNE, Jessica Anne. ■ 98027 #054-04-2007 L2007 **FP** *012

HIEGEL, Traci Lynn. 22526 SE 64TH PL, STE 120 98027 #054-04-1996 L1999 **PD** *020 †55

HILDEBRAND, David Alan. 22526 SE 64TH PL STE 120 98027 #018-03-1980 L1989 **PD NPM** *020 †55

HILSCHER, Stewart. ■ 98029 #035-08-1949 L1956 **OBG** *071 †30

HO, Leo E. ■ 98027 #041-02-1998 L2001 **PD** *020 †55

HOLESKI, Carolyn Jean. ■ 98075 #011-02-1988 L1991 **GE** *020 †20

HOSHIWARA, Isao. 22040 SE 40TH CT 98029 #054-04-1956 L1958 **OPH OTO** *071 †35

HOWELL, Milton M. ■ 98029 #035-45-1952 L1981 **GP** *071

HSIE, Tadd Taching. 450 NW GILMAN BLVD, STE 201 98027 #028-02-1991 L1998 **FM** *020 †18

HUANG, Roberta Felicia. 6520 226TH PL SE STE 120 98027 #035-19-1996 L2004 **OBG** *020 †30

HYMAN, Garrett Scott. 3707 PROVIDENCE POINT DR SE, STE G 98029 #033-06-1997 L2000 **PRS** *020 †60

IDJADI, Jeremy Alexander. 600 NW GILMAN BLVD, STE E 98027 #035-19-2000 L2006 **ORS** *020

IWANO, Joseph H. ■ 98029 #028-02-1950 L1957 **U** *071 †95

JACOBSON, Terry Lu. 710 NW JUNIPER ST STE 204 98027 #031-01-1995 L1998 **IM** *020 †20

JAYAKUMAR, Thinagara S. ■ 98029 #539-06-1988 L2007 **P CHP** *020 †75

JOHNSON, Rodney James. 450 NW GILMAN BLVD, STE 305 98027 #041-14-1982 L1983 **N CN** *071 †75

JONES, Robert F. ■ 98029 #048-12-1952 L1974 **GS** *071 †85

KAY, Kenneth Lew. 100 NE GILMAN BLVD 98027 #054-04-1988 L1990 **IM** *020 †20

KELLUM, Robert Eugene. 4212 182ND AVE SE 98027 #007-02-1955 L1969 **D** *071 †15

KIM, Helen Hyosoon. 6506 226TH PL SE, STE 102 98027 #024-07-1992 L1997 **GS** *020 †85

KIRSHNER, William Bruce. 100 NE GILMAN BLVD 98027 #054-04-1979 L1980 **FM** *020 †18

KOLWITZ, Ann Marie. 450 NW GILMAN BLVD, OVERLAKE OB GYN PC 98027 #038-40-1977 L1984 **OBG** *020 †30

KOMENDA, Gregory Andrew. 600 NW GILMAN BLVD, STE A 98027 #028-34-1989 L1997 **OSM GS** *020 †40

KOZLOWSKI, Paul Michael. 100 NE GILMAN BLVD 98027 #035-06-1993 L2000 **SCI** *020 †95

LAWLER, Michael Martin. 450 NW GILMAN BLVD, OVERLAKE OB GYN PC 98027 #007-02-1981 L1990 **OBG** *020 †30

LEONELLI, Susan Marie. ■ 98029 #016-11-2003 L2006 **IM OS** *020

LEYTON, Bryan Desmond. 450 NW GILMAN BLVD, STE 105 98027 #061-01-1965 L1972 **DR NM** *020 †80,28

LILLY, Joel David. 2005 NW SAMMAMISH RD, SEATTLE UROLOGICAL 98027 #036-01-1984 L1990 **U** *020 †95

LIN, Susanna W. 1455 11TH AVE NW 98027 #017-20-1999 L2006 **PD** *020 †55

LOPEZ PEREZ, Vincente. ■ 98075 #847-01-1961 L1974 **NTR PD** *040

MALLADI, Niriksha. ■ 98029 #061-01-2002 L2005 **PM** *012

MANDELL, Randy Brian. 1455 11TH AVE NW 98027 #056-05-1990 L1998 **IM** *020 †20

MANDT, Peter Richard. 600 NW GILMAN BLVD, STE E 98027 #054-04-1980 L1986 **ORS** *020 †40

MAPLETHORPE, Samantha M. 3707 PROVIDENCE POINT DR SE, STE G 98029 #021-01-2000 L2002 **FM** *020 †18

MARCOLINA, Susan Teresa. ■ 98027 #035-15-1984 L1999 **IM IMG** *062 †20

MARESCA, Theresa Marie. ■ 98027 #035-46-1984 L1985 **FM BBK** *020 †18

MARIS, Robert West. ■ 98029 #040-02-1945 L1951 **ORS** *071 †40

MARKS, William Matthew. 2005 NW SAMMAMISH RD B150, RADIA MEDICAL IMAGING 98027 #041-01-1974 L1975 **DR** *020 †80

MARQUARDT, Carolyn Ann. 3707 PROVIDENCE POINT DR SE, STE G 98029 #025-01-1993 L1999 **PM** *012

MC INTYRE, David Jos. ■ 98027 #054-04-1959 L1962 **OPH** *071 †35

MC QUEEN, Samuel. ■ 98029 #047-06-1961 L1990 **PTH** *071 †50

MENG, Yuan-Yuan. ■ 98029 #243-69-1984 L1998 **IM** *100

MICHALAK, Victor Roman. 295 NE GILMAN BLVD, STE 101 98027 #035-20-1983 L1987 **D CS** *020 †15 ‡

MILNE, John Stewart. 530 WILDERNESS PEAK DR NW 98027 #056-06-2000 L2003 **EM** *100 †16

MOONKA, Ravi. 100 NE GILMAN BLVD 98027 #041-01-1990 L1990 **GS** *020 †85

MOSBY, Jill Cathleen. ■ 98027 #056-06-2001 L2004 **IM** *020

MULLEN, John Steele. 2005 NW SAMMAMISH RD, SEATTLE UROLOGICAL 98027 #054-04-1993 L2000 **U** *020 †95

MULLIGAN, Lisa Marie. 175 1ST PL NW, STE C 98027 #025-07-1988 L1999 **OTO** *020 †45

NAGASAWA, Sharyn Kaye. 450 NW GILMAN BLVD STE 202 98027 #054-04-1984 L1987 **IM** *020 †20

NELSON, Leslie Gordon. ■ 98029 #054-04-1960 L1964 **OS PD** *071 †55

NIXON, Shawn Elliott. 2005 NW SAMMAMISH RD 98027 #054-04-1982 L1983 **FM** *020 †18

NORRIS, H Thomas. ■ 98029 #005-06-1959 L1967 **PTH** *071 †50

OLSON, Warren P. ■ 98027 #056-05-1953 L1955 **P OS** *100

OTTO, Desiree Lynn. 450 NW GILMAN BLVD, OVERLAKE OB GYN PC 98027 #054-04-1997 L2000 **OBG** *020 †30

PALEY, Jonathan Ira. 450 NW GILMAN BLVD, OVERLAKE OB GYN PC 98027 #035-45-1991 L1997 **OBG** *020 †30

PARRETT, Vernon Marshall. 98027 #005-12-1948 L1948 **IM** *071 †20

PLOSS, Robert E. ■ 98027 #035-06-1951 L1952 **GP AN** *071 †05

PROW, Harold Wayne, Jr. 450 NW GILMAN BLVD, STE 105 98027 #048-04-1995 L2001 **RNR** *020 †80

PRUESS, Kim Elizabeth. 450 NW GILMAN BLVD, STE 301A 98027 #024-07-1996 L2000 **IM** *020 †20

PURDON, Michael A J. 2005 NW SAMMAMISH RD, BLDG B 98027 #067-01-1992 L1999 **FM** *020 †18

RAINE, Mark. 204 MOUNTAIN PARK BLVD SW, C-101 98027 #016-45-1982 L1993 **GS EM** *020 †18

RAMIREZ, Joaquin Julian. ■ 98029 #042-01-1959 L1960 **IM GE** *071 †20

RANDOLPH, Ernest Le Roy. ■ 98029 #054-04-1956 L1957 **GP ADM** *071

RATCLIFFE, Steven Severns. 600 NW GILMAN BLVD, STE A 98027 #017-20-1977 L1978 **ORS** *050 †40

READ-WILLIAMS, Patricia G. 1455 11TH AVE NW 98027 #030-05-1984 L1986 **FM** *020 †18

REHMAN, Azra. 1455 11TH AVE NW 98027 #704-09-1984 L1997 **IM** *020 †20

RIABOVA, Katerina G. 4409 160TH AVE SE 98027 #913-15-1983 L2002 **CHP** *020

ROBON, Matthew Joseph. ■ 98027 #038-40-2001 L2007 **ORS** *020

ROMEYA, Ahmed Abdelfattah. 4127 243RD LN SE 98029 #957-01-1989 L2003 **TS** *012 †20,85

ROUILLARD, Victoria Mann. 450 NW GILMAN BLVD, STE 301A 98027 #005-14-1990 L1994 **IM** *020 †20

RUUD, Rebecca Tristan. 710 NW JUNIPER ST STE 204, MEDICAL ARTS OF ISSAQUAH 98027 #054-04-1993 L1995 **IM** *020 †20

SAILER, Michael Joachim. 600 NW GILMAN BLVD, STE E 98027 #054-04-1987 L1990 **OSM** *020 †40

SCHEMBRE, Drew Blackham. 100 NE GILMAN BLVD 98027 #033-05-1988 L1998 **GE OS** *020 †20

SCHRIER, Kimberly Merle. 100 NE GILMAN BLVD 98027 #005-19-1997 L2001 **PD** *020 †55

SEFI, Richard Rowley. ■ 98027 #352-09-1955 L1959 **FM** *071 †18

SEIDNER, Todd Jason. 2005 NW SAMMAMISH RD 98027 #005-14-1992 L1997 **OSM** *020 †40

SHAW, Dana Shafer. ■ 98027 #035-06-1989 L1993 **P** *020 †75

SHAW, David Preston. 470 FRONT ST N 98027 #035-06-1989 L1993 **P** *020 †75

SHIPLEY, Eric Robert. 6520 226TH PL SE STE 150, OVERLAKE MEDICAL CLINIC UR 98027 #049-01-1997 L2000 **EM** *020 †16

SILE-LAKE, Connie Gale. ■ 98075 #040-02-1983 L1984 **GS** *020

SJOBERG, Sandra Jean. 450 NW GILMAN BLVD STE 201 98027 #040-02-2001 L2004 **PD** *020 †55

SLUTSKY, Morley. 4580 KLAHANIE DR SE, # 125 98029 #062-01-1992 L1998 **OM** *020 †70 ‡

SMITH, Candace Leigh. 18724 SE 65TH PL, THE BELLEVUE CLINIC 98027 #005-02-1979 L1980 **IM** *020 †20

SMOOTS, Daniel William. 450 NW GILMAN BLVD, STE 105 98027 #054-04-1996 L1998 **DR** *020 †80

SNEIDERS, Ann Elisabeth. 100 NE GILMAN BLVD 98027 #026-04-1990 L1996 **PD** *020 †55 ‡

SPENCE, Jennifer Adams. 3707 PROVIDENCE PONT DR SE, STE G 98029 #020-02-2000 L2002 **FM** *020 †18

SUMMERS, Heidi Schneider. 5837 221ST PL SE 98027 #054-04-2002 L2005 **P** *020

TALEBAN, Sasha. ■ 98029 #054-04-2006 **IM** *012

TAMASAN, Ionel. ■ 98027 #781-03-1988 L2004 **IM** *020 †20

TAYLOR, Elizabeth Lehmann. 450 NW GILMAN BLVD STE 201 98027 #054-04-1972 L1974 **FM** *020 †18

TAYLOR, Kay Howard. 450 NW GILMAN BLVD, STE 205 98027 #054-04-1987 L1989 **FM** *020 †18

THAYER, John Lewis. 600 NW GILMAN BLVD, STE E 98027 #054-04-1977 L1978 **ORS** *020 †40

TOM, Karen Betty. 110 BIG BEAR PL NW 98027 #048-13-1975 L1975 **EM** *020 †16

UTLEY, Rodney Erwin. ■ 98027 #005-02-1977 L1981 **CD IM** *020 †20

VAN COEVORDEN, Reinier Z. 1490 NW GILMAN BLVD 98027 #305-01-1990 L1993 **GP** *020

VAN KESSEL, Katherine Ann. 450 NW GILMAN BLVD, OVERLAKE OB GYN PC 98027 #005-02-1996 L1998 **OBG** *020 †30

VIRA, Nasima K. 100 NE GILMAN BLVD 98027 #704-02-1987 L2000 **IM** *020 †20

VOLODKEVICH, Peter. ■ 98075 #913-17-1939 L1957 **PTH FOP** *071 †50

WAGNER, James Russell. ■ 98027 #030-06-1964 L1969 **GE IM** *071 †20

WARRICK, Delilah Koizumi. 1455 11TH AVE NW 98027 #021-06-1997 L1999 **FM** *020 †18

WATSON, James David. 450 NW GILMAN BLVD STE 302 98027 #041-07-1977 L1999 **CD** *020 †20

WEDGWOOD, Jeffrey Galton. 450 NW GILMAN BLVD STE 202 98027 #054-04-1980 L1984 **IM** *071 †20

WHEELER, William Stephen. PO BOX 7018, SPACELABS HELATHCARE 98027 #005-14-1975 L1976 **CD** *020 †20

WHITMER, John H. ■ 98029 #040-02-1950 L1970 **P** *071

WILBERT, Donald Eugene. ■ 98029 #038-41-1967 L1984 **P** *071 †75

WOHLMAN, Robert A. 450 NW GILMAN BLVD 98027 #028-34-1981 L1984 **GE IM** *020 †20

WU, Cecilia Weikei. ■ 98029 #054-04-2008 *012

YEE, James F. 450 NW GILMAN BLVD STE 301 98027 #056-06-1991 L1994 **FM** *020 †18 ‡

YOLER, Katharine Amon. 450 NW GILMAN BLVD, STE 105 98027 #054-04-1995 L1999 **DR** *020 †80

YOUNG, Timothy Geo. 450 NW GILMAN BLVD STE 303 98027 #352-07-1953 L1960 **P** *075 †75

KALAMA — COWLITZ

BLIDE, Richard Wayne. ■ 98625 #035-03-1955 L1969 **IM PM** *020

DI CRISTINA, Peter Whitin. ■ 98625 #422-01-2003 L2007 **FM** *020

KELSO — COWLITZ

BURKEY, John Newark. 700 LINCOLN ST, STE 100 98626 #038-41-1943 L1949 **R** *072 †80

COLVIN, Richard Ray. ■ 98626 #005-14-1961 L1964 **AN** *071 †05

EHRLICH, Robert Eugene. 700 LINCOLN ST 98626 #019-02-1972 L1976 **DR** *020 †80

GIBB, Tyler Douglass. 700 LINCOLN ST 98626 #054-04-1991 L1991 **DR** *020 †80

HICKS, Stanley Michael. 700 LINCOLN ST 98626 #040-02-1980 L1992 **DR** *020 †80

LUM, Wen Sun. ■ 98626 #060-02-2002 L2005 **IM** *020 †20

MC COY, Matthew Scott. 701 VINE ST, COWLITZ 2 FIRE & RESCUE 98626 #041-12-2000 L2003 **EM** *020 †16

SONG, Bonnie Hayoon. 607 CRAWFORD ST 98626 #005-12-2000 L2006 **AN** *100 †05

VEIGA, John. ■ 98626 #024-05-1991 L2002 **OPH** *020 †35

WILSON, Duane Charles. 700 LINCOLN ST, STE 100 98626 #005-12-1982 L1985 **R DR** *020 †80

WRIGHT, David Clinton. 700 LINCOLN ST 98626 #040-02-1982 L1985 **DR RNR** *020 †80

KENMORE — KING

ALLEN, Paul Leonard. 5531 NE 182ND ST 98028 #005-12-1962 L1965 **FM** *071

ARNOLD, Sara Jane. 6610 NE 181ST ST STE 2 98028 #036-01-1980 L1986 **GPM FM** *020 †18

AZIZ, Samir W.. ■ 98028 #915-03-1987 L2004 **PYG** *100

BLOOMSTROM, Albert Duane. ■ 98028 #054-04-1955 L1958 **AN** *071 †05

BRENTLINGER, Paula E. 6016 NE BOTHELL WAY, HEALTH CENTER 98028 #005-19-1983 L1984 **FM** *020 †18

BUSHNELL, Theodore Elliot. ■ 98028 #005-02-1999 L2004 **N** *100 †75

CHIN, Thomas Matt. 6016 NE BOTHELL WAY STE G, HEALTH CENTER 98028 #051-04-1991 L2002 **FM** *020 †18

COMTE, Charles Frederic. ■ 98028 #024-05-1963 L1965 **AN** *020 †05

CURTIS, Milton Leo. 18208 66TH AVE NE, STE 200 98028 #054-04-1979 L1980 **FM** *020 †18

EGGERTSEN, Sam Child. 6016 NE BOTHELL WAY, BOTHELL-KENMORE COMMUNITY 98028 #054-04-1976 L1977 **FM** *020 †18

KEERBS, Amanda Jane. 6016 NE BOTHELL WAY, HEALTH CENTER 98028 #005-14-1997 L2000 **FM** *020 †18

KJERULF, Terrell Dan. 18558 64TH AVE NE 98028 #054-04-1968 L1969 **NS** *020 †25

LEFTENANT, S Gordon. ■ 98028 #035-08-1980 L2002 **AN** *020 †05

MENDREY, Barbara S. 6443 NE 181ST ST 98028 #040-02-1976 L1996 **FM** *074 †18

MICHELBRINK, Lisa J. 18208 66TH AVE NE, STE 200 98028 #016-11-2001 L2003 **FM** *020 †18

ROWELL, Jonathan Carlyle. ■ 98028 #045-01-2003 L2005 **AN** *012

SIMPSON, Robert R. 18119 65TH AVE NE 98028 #017-20-1951 L1966 **GP GS** *020

KENNEWICK — BENTON

ABU KHIERAN, Emad Ibrahim. 320 W 10TH AVE 99336 #528-04-1989 L2001 **IM** *020 †20

ADAMS, David Larry. 4911 W CANAL DR 99336 #054-04-1969 L1970 **D A** *020

AHART, Sharon Louise. 815 S AUBURN ST 99336 #649-14-1980 L1994 **PD** *020

AL-HAWAMDEH, Mahmoud N. 320 W 10TH AVE STE 200 99336 #575-02-1993 L1999 **IM** *020 †20

ALTO, Angelita Quijano. 923 S AUBURN ST 99336 #748-01-1960 L1977 **PD PA** *071 †55

ANG, Ellen Tan. 521 N YOUNG ST 99336 #748-01-1998 L2004 **IM** *020 †20

ARIF, Fareed Ahmed. 510 N COLORADO ST, STE A 99336 #704-01-1996 L2004 **NEP** *020 †20

AXFORD, Robert V. ■ 99337 #005-12-1949 L1949 **EM** *071

BENAVIDES HIM, Oscar J. ■ 99336 #715-01-1990 L2005 **PD** *020 †55

BRINDLE, Jennifer Ruth. 320 W 10TH AVE, COLUMBIA FAMILY MEDICINE 99336 #068-01-1993 L1995 **FM** *020 †18

BURGDORFF, Janel Ann. 911 S WASHINGTON ST, STE B 99336 #005-12-1978 L1980 **PD** *020

CABANILLA, Leonardo M. 903 S AUBURN ST 99336 #748-07-1958 L1972 **GP IM** *020

CADWELL, John A. 1021 N KELLOGG ST 99336 #054-04-1976 L1977 **PM** *062

CAIN, Arthur Myles. 320 W 10TH AVE 99336 #054-04-1979 L1995 **FM** *020 †20

CANCADO, Paulo J. 216 W 10TH AVE STE 304 99336 #187-06-1990 L1996 **N** *020 †75

CARLOCK, Frederick J. 413 S ROOSEVELT ST 99336 #025-07-1981 L1984 **AN** *020 †05

CARRIER, Valerie E. ■ 99338 #305-01-1990 L1999 **AN** *020 †05

CASTILLO, Jesus Bautista. 925 S AUBURN ST 99336 #748-01-1959 L1977 **OBG** *071 †30

CHAUDHRY, Yasmin A.. 320 W 10TH AVE # 202 PO 99336 #704-01-2000 L2003 **FM** *020 †18

CHAVLA, Naeem Tariq. 216 W 10TH AVE, STE 306 99336 #704-04-1982 L2006 **U** *020 †95

CHEN, Mark T K. 8920 W CANYON AVE 99336 #028-78-1985, ▲ L1986 **AN** *020 †05

CHENAL RODRIQUEZ, Mario E. 7350 W DESCHUTES AVE, COLUMBIA BASIN HEMATOLOGY 99336 #429-01-1989 L2002 **HO** *020 †20

CHENG, Stephen. 4002 S JEAN ST 99337 #040-02-1993 L2002 **EM** *020

CHIANG, Ven-Chung. 602 N COLORADO ST STE D 99336 #187-04-1985 L1995 **NEP IM** *020 †20

CLAR DE JESUS, Teresita A. 521 N YOUNG ST 99336 #748-01-1993 L1999 **IM** *020 †20

COLER, Roderick Seymour. 811 S AUBURN ST 99336 #035-09-1954 L1958 **IM** *072

COOPER, Walter Thos, III. 2108 W ENTIAT AVE, THE CHAPLAINCY 99336 #054-04-1978 L1982 **FM** *020 †20

CUMMINGS, Michael Rowell. 203 W 8TH AVE, STE 100 99336 #045-01-1972 L1983 **ATP CLP** *020 †50

DATTA, Saumyajit. 4303 W 27TH AVE STE H, KGH PHYSICIAN CLINICS 99338 #495-79-1989 L1999 **FPG** *020 †18

DE LEON, Elma Tirol. 921 S AUBURN ST STE A 99336 #748-08-1966 L1979 **OBG** *020 †30

DE LOS REYES, Cynthia M. 923 S AUBURN ST 99336 #748-02-1985 L1997 **PD** *020 †55

DREISBACH, Leonard A, Jr. 320 W 10TH AVE, STE 100 99336 #005-19-1977 L1998 **OBG** *020 †30

DUNN, Garry Kimball. 7221 W DESCHUTES AVE, STE A 99336 #048-04-1989 L1993 **DR** *020 †80

EISLER, Toomas. 216 W 10TH AVE, STE 303 99336 #671-01-1968 L1979 **N OS** *020 †75

ELLO, Glenn Navasero. 521 N YOUNG ST, KGH MEDICAL MALL 99336 #748-02-1987 L2004 **PD** *020 †55

ELLO, Maria Aleli Tabio. 521 N YOUNG ST, KGH MEDICAL MALL 99336 #748-02-1989 L2005 **IM** *100

FERRIS, M Scott. 100204 E CLOVER RD 99338 #748-09-1981 L1986 **FM OM** *020

FLESHER, Mark Daniel. 7201 W GRANDRIDGE BLVD 99336 #028-34-1990 L1995 **OBG** *020

FONG, Randall Scott. 911 S WASHINGTON ST 99336 #056-06-1990 L1995 **OTO** *020 †45
FORREST, Susan Leslie. 4303 W 27TH AVE STE D, BIOSH 99338 #028-34-1983 L1988 **OM** *020 †70
FOSS, Fred Martin. 216 W 10TH AVE STE 306 99336 #016-42-1978 L1984 **U** *020 †95
FRANANO, Frank Nicholas. 900 S AUBURN ST 99336 #028-02-1994 L2002 **VIR** *020 †80
FREUND, Jack Danl. ■ 99336 #040-02-1943 L1944 **GP** *072
FRIEDLINE, John Allen. 8911 W GRANDRIDGE BLVD, STE B 99336 #041-02-1980 L1998 **PTH EM** *020 †50,18
GABA, Payal. 521 N YOUNG ST 99336 #496-07-1999 L2004 **FM** *020 †18
GABELMAN, Omer Philip. ■ 99336 #016-76-1948, ▲ L1968 **GP** *071
GIEVER, Richard Jos. 7350 W DESCHUTES AVE, STE A 99336 #054-04-1978 L1982 **RO** *020 †80
GOMEZ, Sophie. 8412 W GAGE BLVD, STE B 99336 #308-07-1983 L1994 **END IM** *020
GUEVARA, Ivan Siri Perez. 721 S AUBURN ST, STE A 99336 #748-10-1992 L2001 **PD** *020 †55
GUEVARA, Maria Nerissa. 521 N YOUNG ST 99336 #748-10-1992 L2004 **PD** *020 †55
GUEVARA, Sean P Jr. 320 W 10TH AVE, STE 202 99336 #748-10-1992 L2005 **PD** *020 †55
GUTIERREZ, Rinah Irene C. 903 S AUBURN ST, RINAH GUTIERREZ, MD PLLC 99336 #748-10-1992 L2001 **CHP** *020 †75
HANF, Robert Wm. ■ 99337 #040-02-1946 L1948 **R** *071 †80
HAYDEN, Dennis L. ■ 99338 #018-75-1978, ▲ L1980 **PTH** *020 †50
HIPOLITO, Cheryl Perez. ■ 99337 #748-02-2003 L2007 **FM** *100 †18
HOWELL, Craig Leon. 900 S AUBURN ST, KENNEWICK EMERGENCY 99336 #054-04-1984 L1985 **GP** *020
HUNT, Alan Neil. 7525 W DESCHUTES PL STE 1A, FAMILY MEDICINE 99336 #040-02-1979 L1986 **FM EM** *020 †18
INTRAVARTOLO, John, Jr. ■ 99338 #010-02-1968 L1972 **IM NM** *020 †20,28
JECHA, Larry Donald. 7102 W OKANOGAN PL 99336 #019-02-1966 L1988 **PHP AM** *030 †70
KACZYNSKI, Eligiusz. 2529 W FALLS AVE 99336 #759-06-1966 L1978 **OPH** *020 †35
KADLEC, James F. 900 S AUBURN ST, KENNEWICK GEN HOSP 99336 #020-02-1977 L1981 **DR** *020 †80
KLIPPER, William Scott. 8232 W GRANDRIDGE BLVD 99336 #060-01-1967 L1975 **PUD IM** *020 †20
KOHAN, Wayne Michael. 320 W 10TH AVE, STE 202 99336 #038-40-1984 L1987 **FM** *020 †18
KRAMER, Robert James. ■ 99337 #054-04-1953 L1954 **IM ON** *071 †20
KUFFEL, Cornelius F. 807 S AUBURN ST 99336 #054-04-1953 L1955 **R** *071 †80
LEAKE, Wilson Walker. ■ 99337 #048-02-1956 L1959 **AN** *071
LEWIS, Loren L. 28609 S CLODFELTER RD, OCCHEALTH SERVICES PLLC 99338 #031-01-1987 L2003 **OM FM** *020 †18,70
LILAGAN, Meneleo Trinidad. 901 S AUBURN ST 99336 #748-10-1976 L2001 **FM** *020 †18
LING, Stanley. 4309 W 27TH PL, STE 300 99338 #305-01-1991 L1993 **IM** *020 †20
MAC FARLAN, Mark Francis. 521 N YOUNG ST 99336 #048-04-1989 L2000 **FM** *020 †18
MADARANG, Ernesto D. 919 S AUBURN ST 99336 #748-08-1961 L1976 **IM HO** *071 †20
MADSEN, Paul Andrew. 3321 W KENNEWICK AVE # 210 99336 #649-33-1981 L1982 **GP** *020
MAHER, Peter Donald, IV. 602 N COLORADO ST STE D 99336 #010-01-1986 L1997 **GE IM** *020 †20
MALONEY, Walter Hugh. ■ 99338 #041-13-1972 L1977 **IM** *020 †20
MARQUARDT, Richard Gordon. ■ 99337 #054-04-1972 L1975 **ON IM** *071 †20
MC KEOWN, Charles W. 3321 W KENNEWICK AVE, STE 230 99336 #054-04-1973 L1981 **IM** *020
MEYER, John Wm. 7221 W DESCHUTES AVE, STE A 99336 #038-41-1966 L1971 **R AM** *020 †80
MILLS, Albert Vern. 552 N COLORADO ST 99336 #024-05-1946 L1947 **GP** *071
MORCUENDE, Maria Angeles. 7103 W GRANDRIDGE BLVD, STE C 99336 #847-13-1994 L2001 **P** *020 †75
MORRISON, David Stuart. 216 W 10TH AVE STE 300 99336 #021-01-1992 L1996 **OBG** *020 †30
NAZAR, Qayyum. 721 S AUBURN ST STE A 99336 #704-04-1989 L2000 **MPD** *020 †20,55
NEWMAN, James Allan. 900 S AUBURN ST, KENNEWICK EMERGENCY 99336 #654-01-1988 L1993 **EM** *020 †16
NEWMAN, Mary C. 1410 N PITTSBURG ST, ENDOCINE, METABOLISM & MED 99336 #654-01-1990 L2001 **IM** *020 †20
O'CONNOR, Caridad E. ■ 99338 #748-02-1946 L1957 **N P** *071
ONUORAH, Obioma Nnamdi. 510 N COLORADO ST STE A 99336 #690-04-1991 L2004 **NEP IM** *020 †20
PALMER, Marvin Gilman. 2427 W FALLS AVE, KENNEWICK EYE CLINIC INC 99336 #060-01-1954 L1960 **OPH** *020 †35
PENLEY, Michael Wm. 7221 W DESCHUTES AVE, STE A 99336 #016-02-1974 L1975 **DR** *020 †80 ‡
PERSHALL, Kenneth Q. ■ 99338 #040-02-1951 L1952 **GP GS** *071
PHILIP, Suresh. 7525 W DESCHUTES PL 99336 #690-07-1987 L2003 **GE** *020
PILLAI, Gnana Ranji. 320 W 10TH AVE, STE 200 99336 #220-01-1976 L1982 **IM** *020 †20
PODHAISKY, Gary Michael. 4309 W 27TH PL, STE 202 99338 #030-05-1994 L2007 **PD** *020 †55
RADO, Thomas Alexander. 7350 W DESCHUTES AVE, COLUMBIA BASIN HEMATOLOGY 99336 #004-01-1977 L1995 **HEM ON** *040 †20
RAPOSAS, Stella Camilon. 721 S AUBURN ST 99336 #748-02-1984 L2006 **PD** *020 †55
REDDY, Vedamurthy G. 900 S AUBURN ST 99336 #496-01-1971 L1981 **AN** *020 †05
REGE, Sheila Dattatraya. 7350 W DESCHUTES AVE, STE A 99336 #005-14-1989 L1997 **RO NM** *020 †28,80
RICH, Robert Dale. 102504 E TRIPPLE VISTA DR 99338 #041-02-1966 L1973 **DR NM** *020 †80
ROACH, John Michael. 811 S AUBURN ST 99336 #054-04-1973 L1975 **GE IM** *020 †20
SAHAI, Animesh. 905 S AUBURN ST 99336 #496-08-1989 L2005 **U** *020
SAHAI, Madhu. 7211 W DESCHUTES AVE, STE B 99336 #496-08-1989 L2006 **IM IMG** *020 †20
SALISBURY, Robert L. 320 W 10TH AVE, STE 102 99336 #034-01-1975 L2001 **OBG** *020 †30
SCHROFF, Gregory Paul. 320 W 10TH AVE STE 102 99336 #019-02-1988 L1991 **OBG** *020 †30
SCHWISOW, Donavon. ■ 99338 #005-12-1952 L1958 **FM** *071 †18
SCULLY, James Michael. 900 S AUBURN ST 99336 #005-15-1968 L1996 **GS VS** *020 †55,85
SIMMONS, Wm James, Jr. 5219 W CLEARWATER AVE 99336 #047-07-1966 L1970 **GP** *020 †16
SMITH, Herbert Matthew. 401 W 1ST AVE 99336 #054-04-1977 L1980 **FM** *020 †18
STEELE, Michael Eugene. 4309 W 27TH PL, STE 301 99338 #654-01-2003 L2007 **FM** *020 †18
SUNG, Charles C. 713 N DELAWARE ST 99336 #041-07-1992 L1998 **OPH** *020 †35
TACHOPOULOU, Olympia A. 510 N COLORADO ST STE A 99336 #418-02-1994 L2002 **ID** *020 †20
TAN, Thomas. 7103 W GRANDRIDGE BLVD, STE D 99336 #748-08-1980 L1999 **PCC** *020 †20
TATUNAY, Helen Santos. 8108 W GRANDRIDGE BLVD 99336 #748-12-1986 L2007 **PD** *020
THIEL, Arthur Edward. 900 S AUBURN ST 99336 #005-12-1979 L1985 **ORS HS** *020 †40
THIEL, Shelley Colleen. 911 S WASHINGTON ST, STE A 99336 #005-12-1981 L1984 **OTO HNS** *020 †45
TOBAR, Jorge. 4506 W 20TH AVE 99338 #308-03-1984 L2007 **PUD IM** *020 †20
TREGER, Donald M. ■ 99337 #019-02-1946 L1954 **GS GP** *071
TRIKALSARANSUKH, S. 7114 W HOOD PL 99336 #891-04-1980 L1993 **GE IM** *020 †20
TUAZON, Luzcel Guzman. 7221 W DESCHUTES AVE, STE C 99336 #748-02-1995 L2001 **IM** *020 †20
VASSA, Nalini. 510 N COLORADO ST, STE A 99336 #495-48-1967 L2004 **NEP** *020 †20
VATSIA, Gayathri R. 7516 W DESCHUTES PL 99336 #690-02-1979 L1984 **PD AI** *020
VILLANUEVA, Isagani E. 911 S AUBURN ST, STE B 99336 #748-01-1964 L1980 **OBG** *020
VONGTHAVARAVAT, Verapan. 7114 W HOOD PL 99336 #891-04-1991 L2005 **GE** *020 †20
WANNARACHUE, Nikom. 721 S AUBURN ST 99336 #891-02-1966 L1971 **PD PDE** *020 †55,03
WARD, Feyi. 7325 W DESCHUTES AVE, STE B21 99336 #065-10-1997 L1999 **IM** *020 †20
WEEKS, Harold Folger. ■ 99338 #040-02-1955 L1958 **FM EM** *071
WESTMAN, Charles W. ■ 99336 #026-04-1946 L1954 **PTH** *020
WOJNAS, Ronald Henry. 8108 W GRANDRIDGE BLVD 99336 #005-02-1964 L1970 **PD P** *020
YOU, Jean. 900 S AUBURN ST 99336 #243-64-1987 L2002 **PM** *020 †60
YU, Nelson C. 8232 W GRANDRIDGE BLVD 99336 #748-01-1989 L2005 **IM PCC** *020 †20
ZUROSKE, Glen Warren. 900 S AUBURN ST 99336 #054-04-1984 L1990 **CD IM** *020 †20

KENT - KING

ALLISON, Michael Douglas. 8009 S 180TH ST, STE 105 98032 #030-05-1977 L1979 **FM OM** *020 †70
ARNTZ, Craig Thos. 8009 S 180TH ST, STE 105 98032 #054-04-1981 L1983 **ORS GS** *020 †40
BARRETT, William Page. 8009 S 180TH ST, STE 105 98032 #005-06-1980 L1981 **ORS** *020 †40
BARTHEL, Traci G. 8009 S 180TH ST, STE 105 98032 #047-05-1995 L2001 **HS** *020 †40
BAUCKE, Robert Bruce. 222 STATE AVE N 98030 #016-02-1982 L1985 **IM** *020 †20
BRAN, Sergio Leonel. ■ 98032 #429-02-1987 **END** *100
BROWN, Dennis Bernard. 325 WASHINGTON AVE S 98032 #065-06-1977 L1987 **OPH** *020 †35
CARATAO, Efren R, Jr. 23643 104TH AVE SE, EAST HILL MEDICAL CLINIC 98031 #748-11-1979 L1990 *020
CERO, Susan Rose. 8009 S 180TH ST, STE 105 98032 #041-09-1988 L1992 **ORS** *020
CHAMBERLAIN, Dermot Peter. 17700 SE 272ND ST, MEDICAL PARK ANESTHESIA 98042 #917-30-1969 L1978 **AN** *020 †05
CHEN, Hilton Anthony. 222 STATE AVE N 98030 #054-04-1993 L1996 **FM** *020 †18
CHEN, Yiping. 17700 SE 272ND ST 98042 #243-54-1982 L2004 **CD** *020 †20
CHILCZUK, Benjamin Daniel. 8009 S 180TH ST, STE 105 98032 #132-01-1978 L1984 **OM OS** *020
CHOUDHARY, Ranu. 24604 104TH AVE SE, STE 202 98030 #495-54-1993 L1999 **IMG** *020 †20 ‡
CHRISTOFERSON, Holly Jill. 403 E MEEKER ST STE 30, CHCKC 98030 #054-04-2003 L2003 **FM** *020 †18
CHRISTOPHERSON, Chad R. 17700 SE 272ND ST 98042 #046-01-1993 L1999 **CD** *020 †20
CLARK, Theresa Ann. 613 W GOWE ST, KENT TEEN CLINIC 98032 #054-04-1997 L1999 **FM** *020 †18
CLINE, David Andrew. 13210 SE 240TH ST 98042 #016-01-1993 L1997 **MPD PD** *020 †20,55
CRAWBUCK-POPE, Ann F. 17700 SE 272ND ST, KENT MULTICARE CLINIC 98042 #054-04-1992 L1996 **AN** *020 †05
CRAWFORD, Rosemary A. 24031 104TH AVE SE 98030 #919-06-1968 L1980 **FM** *071
DANG, Derrick Allan. 24722 104TH AVE SE, STE 202 98030 #030-06-1983 L1985 **AN** *020 †05
DARROW, Phyllis Anastasia. ■ 98031 #007-02-1984 L1997 **EM** *020 †16
DE SELMS, Craig Alan. 13210 SE 240TH ST STE A1 98042 #040-02-1979 L1986 **FM** *020 †18
DESPREAUX, Michele Ann. 23213 PACIFIC HWY S 98032 #041-01-1992 L1996 **IM** *020 †20
DI MEGLIO, Giuseppina. 613 W GOWE ST, KENT TEEN CLINIC 98032 #063-01-1991 L1999 **PD AMI** *020 †55
DOMINIK, Janusz. 18230 E VALLEY HWY # 1, GREAT WALL MEDICAL DENTAL 98032 #539-02-1956 L1959 **IM PUD** *020
DU, Edward Lim. ■ 98030 #748-01-1962 L1973 **IM** *075
DURCH, Stephen Michael. 24920 104TH AVE SE, KENT PRIMARY CARE 98030 #054-04-1981 L1996 **FM** *020 †18
DY, Edward. 23213 PACIFIC HWY S 98032 #748-01-1991 L2007 **IM** *020 †20
EIDT, David Wm. 405 E SMITH ST 98030 #025-01-1970 L1990 **FM** *020 †18
EMERICK, Robert Scott. 17700 SE 272ND ST 98042 #035-01-1991 L2001 **CD** *020 †20
ENRICO, Alberto Cinco. ■ 98032 #748-01-1957 L1969 **FM IM** *071 †18
EPPER, Dale Edward. 222 STATE AVE N, KENT MULTICARE URGENT CARE 98030 #031-01-1987 L1990 **FM FPG** *020 †18
ERDMANN, Thomas C. 24920 104TH AVE SE 98030 #054-04-1991 L1993 **FM** *020 †18
FATTA, Ernest A. ■ 98031 #035-06-1963 L1990 **OM IM** *071
FAULKNER, D Joseph. 17700 SE 272ND ST 98042 #017-20-1982 L1987 **GS** *020 †85
GAUNT, Frank Peyton. 328 4TH AVE S, PEDIATRIC INTERIM CARE CEN 98032 #028-02-1972 L1975 **PD** *020 †55
GAUTHIER, Verlene Joyce. 8009 S 180TH ST, STE 105 98032 #054-04-1984 L1986 **RHU IM** *020 †20
GEERE, Linda Magdalgne. 10056 SE 240TH ST STE D 98031 #836-02-1977 L1988 **FM** *074
GENEMAN, Bonnie Jean. ■ 98032 #023-12-2007 **PD** *012
GILLSON, George Robert. 515 W HARRISON ST, TAHOMA CLINIC 98032 #060-02-1991 L1999 *020
GLOWITZ, Robert Jay. 21903 68TH AVE S 98032 #010-01-1971 L1972 **PTH** *020 †50
GRAHAM, Roger Winfield. 325 WASHINGTON AVE S # 6, P O BOX 34245 98032 #005-06-1977 L1983 **PTH** *020 †50
HARGRAVE, Mary Ellen. 325 W GOWE ST, VALLEY CITIES COUNSELING 98032 #021-06-1983 L2004 **P OS** *020 †75
HASANOGLU, Kaya Yalcin. 8009 S 180TH ST, STE 105 98032 #056-06-1993 L1995 **PM** *020 †60
HEFFNER, George Steiner. 403 E MEEKER ST, KENT COMMUNITY CLINIC 98030 #038-40-1975 L1978 **FM** *020 †18
HEI, Thomas Kou. 23213 PACIFIC HWY S 98032 #005-14-1995 L1997 **FM** *020 †18
HENDRICKSON, John, Jr. 8009 S 180TH ST, STE 105 98032 #011-03-1975 L1979 **ORS** *020 †40
HENRY, Melvin La Verne. 17700 SE 272ND ST 98042 #054-04-1964 L1969 **CD** *020 †20
HO, Kingman Kimwei. 24920 104TH AVE SE 98030 #033-06-1992 L1995 **IM** *020 †20
JONES, Ty Clayton. ■ 98042 #021-01-2008 *012
KALIDINDI, Vijay. 222 STATE AVE N, KENT MULTICARE CLINIC 98030 #495-21-1980 L1996 **PDC** *020 †55
KAY, Kenneth Geo. 12393 SE 201ST ST 98031 #054-04-1963 L1964 **ORS** *020 †40
KHAIT-PALANT, Olga V. 222 STATE AVE N 98030 #913-07-1978 L2000 **OBG** *020 †30
KIMBALL, Harry Raymond. ■ 98042 #028-02-1962 L1972 **IM ID** *030 †20
KISS, Eva Doreen. 23213 PACIFIC HWY S 98032 #026-04-1991 L2007 **PD** *020 †55

KRISHNAN, Uma M. 17700 SE 272ND ST 98042 #495-66-1994 L2002 **CD** *020 †20
KUHLMANN, Thomas Hans. 405 E SMITH ST 98030 #035-08-1992 L1996 **FM** *020 †18
KULAKIVSKY, Valentina. 1122 W JAMES ST STE 103 98032 #913-61-1976 L2000 **FM OM** *020 †18
LAMBA, Charanjit Kaur. 24703 38TH AVE S 98032 #496-09-1977 L1983 **FM** *020
LAPIN, Eugene Stewart. 17700 SE 272ND ST 98042 #007-02-1966 L1970 **CD IM** *020 †20
LAUINGER, Joseph Michael. 23213 PACIFIC HWY S 98032 #010-02-2000 L2003 **IM** *020 †20
LAUINGER, Nicole Katherin. 24920 104TH AVE SE 98030 #010-02-2000 L2003 **PD** *020 †55
LEE, Tobias Tongpo. 17700 SE 272ND ST 98042 #008-01-1998 L2005 **IC CD** *020 †20
LEV, Val A. 17700 SE 272ND ST 98042 #913-43-1984 L2004 **IC** *020 †20 ‡
LEVY, William Harris. 1851 CENTRAL PL S STE 123 98030 #016-11-1962 L1984 **P** *020 †75
LINDBERG, John Hjalmer. 6811 S 204TH ST, STE 300 98032 #016-06-1948 L1949 **IM NEP** *071 †20
LIPPMAN, Michael Robt. 17700 SE 272ND ST, # 125 98042 #054-04-1989 L1989 **IM OS** *020 †20
LITTLEWOOD, Peter. 403 E MEEKER ST, KING COUNTY COMM HLTH 98030 #917-20-1963 L1981 **GP** *020
MADEWELL, Lawrence John. 24920 104TH AVE SE, VMC KENT PRIMARY CARE 98030 #038-41-1997 L1999 **FM** *020 †18
MAGNUS, Vernon John. ■ 98042 #060-01-1959 L1964 **GS TS** *071 †85
MALHOTRA, Vinay. 17700 SE 272ND ST 98042 #495-73-1990 L2000 **CD** *020 †20
MARCUM, Erin Sue. ■ 98030 #054-04-2008 *012
MAURICE, Gordon Louis. ■ 98031 #040-02-1943 L1947 **CD PUD** *071
MICHAELIS, Ruth Joy. 403 E MEEKER ST, STE 200 98030 #016-45-1999 L2001 **FM** *020 †18
MINEHAN, David Michael. 222 STATE AVE N 98030 #054-04-1984 L1987 **OBG** *020 †30
MOMAH, Kingson Ikebude. 17700 SE 272ND ST 98042 #690-04-1985 L1996 **CD** *020 †20
MORAN, Genevie Tengco. 26004 104TH AVE SE, PENINSULA COMMUNITY HLTH S 98030 #748-02-1997 L2002 **IMG** *020 †20
MORTON, James Michael. 17700 SE 272ND ST 98042 #036-01-1967 L1973 **PD** *020 †55
MURRAY, Mitzi L. ■ 98032 #048-12-2006 L2007 **IM** *012
MYERS, Paul Bruce. 18000 72ND AVE S, STE 198 98032 #040-02-1976 L1980 **OBG** *020 †20
NACHT, Jeffrey Leslie. 17700 SE 272ND ST 98042 #061-01-1974 L1980 **ORS OSM** *020 †40
NAGLE, John Patrick. 17700 SE 272ND ST 98042 #054-04-1963 L1964 **CD IM** *071 †20
NGUYEN, Khuedung Lucy. 24920 104TH AVE SE 98030 #051-04-1997 L2000 **IM** *020 †20
NNOLI, Aisha. ■ 98089 #005-14-2007 L2008 *012
PARSONS, Eric Sheldon. 403 E MEEKER ST, STE 300 98030 #054-04-1998 L2000 **FM OBS** *020 †18 ‡
PHAM, Minh-Van. ■ 98031 #941-01-1973 L1984 **GP** *075
POPICH, Gregory Alan. 17700 SE 272ND ST 98042 #054-04-1972 L1976 **ORS** *020 †40
PROCHASKA, Deardra Eva. 23213 PACIFIC HWY S, UWPN 98032 #054-04-2000 L2003 **FM** *020 †18
PUGEDA, Jaime Guevara. 17700 SE 272ND ST 98042 #748-01-1992 L2003 **CD** *020 †20
RAINA, Rajesh. ■ 98042 #495-51-1991 L1995 **IM** *020 †20
RAINA, Rajesh. ■ 98042 #495-51-1989 L2005 **IM** *020 †20
RAMBERG, Marilyn. 17700 SE 272ND ST 98042 #005-19-1983 L1997 **IM DIA** *020 †20
RANNIGER, Dan Edward. 13210 SE 240TH ST 98042 #054-04-1957 L1958 **FM OS** *020
REA, Thomas David. 7064 S 220TH ST # 9, KING COUNTY MEDIC ONE 98032 #025-01-1992 L1992 **IM** *020 †20
REMINGTON, Mark Clement. 8009 S 180TH ST, STE 105 98032 #036-01-1986 L1986 **ORS** *020 †40
RICHARDSON, Catherine Ann. 21501 84TH AVE S, KENT DIALYSIS CENTER 98032 #019-02-1986 L1988 **NEP IM** *020 †20
ROME, Michael Peter. 17700 SE 272ND ST 98042 #019-02-1987 L1995 **CD** *020 †20
ROONEY, Walter George. 17700 SE 272ND ST, STE 200 98042 #038-41-1998 L2004 **OTO** *020
RUZECKI, Valentina Irene. 403 E MEEKER ST STE 200, COMM HLTH CTR OF KING CTY 98030 #038-41-1994 L2002 **PD** *020 †55
SARGENT, Robt Taylor, Jr. 222 STATE AVE N, MULTICARE CLINIC 98030 #023-12-1986 L1996 **FM** *020 †18
SHAW, John Warren. 17700 SE 272ND ST, MULTICARE CLINIC 98042 #025-01-1962 L1963 **FM** *020 †18
SHERIDAN, Alfred Irvin. ■ 98031 #016-06-1943 L1947 **GS** *071 †85
SHORR, Benjamin. ■ 98030 #016-43-1943 L1944 **IM CD** *071
SIMONS, Rebecca. 24920 104TH AVE SE 98030 #024-07-1998 L2000 **FM** *020 †18
SLOTKIN, Joseph Oliver L. 17700 SE 272ND ST 98042 #005-14-1981 L1994 **FM** *020 †18
SOBOIL, Richard Anthony E. 26004 104TH AVE SE 98030 #836-02-1966 L1998 **FM** *020
TANAKA, Steven Michael. 26004 104TH AVE SE 98030 #038-06-1982 L1989 **FM** *020 †18
TAN-JACOBSON, Cheryl. 17700 SE 272ND ST 98042 #005-12-1985 L1989 **PD** *020 †55
TE, Katharine Cua. 222 STATE AVE N 98030 #748-01-1976 L1984 **OBG** *020 †30
TERRY, Willa Michelle. 23213 PACIFIC HWY S 98032 #048-04-1989 L1990 **PD** *020 †55
THOMPSON, Jason Hoyt. 8009 S 180TH ST, STE 105 98032 #011-02-1999 L1999 **OSS ORS** *020 †40
TULLUS, Martin Shelton. 8009 S 180TH ST, STE 105 98032 #054-04-1976 L1977 **ORS** *020 †40
TWE, Sui Men. 10056 SE 240TH ST STE D 98031 #209-01-1959 L1978 **FM** *020
UEHARA, Curtis Tokue. 24031 104TH AVE SE 98030 #014-01-1979 L1982 **IM** *075
UHM, Do Sung. 24837 104TH AVE SE 98030 #583-02-1960 L1970 **OBG** *071 †30
ULLELAND, Christy Noreen. ■ 98064 #054-04-1967 L1970 **PD** *030 †55
VANCE, Robert Lee. 222 STATE AVE N, KENT MULTICARE CLINIC 98030 #019-02-1961 L1967 **PD** *071
VEITH, Robert Gordon. 8009 S 180TH ST, STE 105 98042 #054-04-1975 L1977 **ORS** *020 †40
VORA, Devendra K. 17700 SE 272ND ST 98042 #495-19-1980 L2002 **CD** *020 †20
WALKER, Nicola E. 17700 SE 272ND ST 98042 #054-14-1993 L1996 **FM OBS** *020 †20
WALLACE, Calvin P, Jr. 17700 SE 272ND ST 98042 #054-04-1983 L1987 **OBG EM** *020 †30
WARD, Needham Edgar. 17700 SE 272ND ST 98042 #040-02-1972 L1981 **CD** *020 †20
WHITTEN, Richard W. 6811 S 204TH ST, STE 300 98034 #016-06-1975 L1976 **IM CCM** *030 †20
WIN, Hla. ■ 98031 #209-01-1999 L2006 **END** *100 †20
YOUNG, Andrea June. 17700 SE 272ND ST 98042 #054-04-1999 L1999 **ORS** *020 †40
YOUNG, Craig Michael. 24020 132ND AVE SE 98042 #040-02-1978 L1982 **OPH** *020 †35 ‡
YOUNG, Robert Danl. ■ 98031 #005-12-1944 L1944 **GP** *020
ZENG, Ningxin. ■ 98032 #243-76-1982 L2005 **GE** *020 †20

KINGSTON — KITSAP

BRUCE, Ann Bridges. 10633 NE WEST KINGSTON RD 98346 #035-01-1989 L1995 **P** *020 ‡

COLLETTO, Kristan Ilene. 32014 LITTLE BOSTON RD NE 98346 #054-04-1996 L2000 **MPD** *020 †55,20
FABER, Byron Everett. ■ 98346 #005-12-1973 L1976 **DR NM** *071 †80
INGHAM, Robert Edwin. PO BOX 1200, UNIVERSITY OF WASHINGTON 98346 #035-20-1970 L1999 **CD** *020 †20
LUNGU, Adriana. 32014 LITTLE BOSTON RD NE 98346 #047-06-1991 L2006 **FM** *020 †18
MARCUSE, Edgar Korn. 33516 EGLON RD NE 98346 #005-11-1967 L1969 **PD PHP** *030 †55
NIVA, Roger Allen. ■ 98346 #054-04-1966 L1975 **OPH** *071 †35
PIFER, Gage Buchner. 25995 BARBER CUT OFF RD NE 98346 #005-06-1954 L1996 **ORS** *071
STEVENS, Donald Edward. 25989 BARBR CT OF NE #A3 98346 #054-04-1981 L1982 **IM** *020 †20
TANKSLEY, Gregory William. ■ 98346 #036-05-2004 L2007 **EM** *100
WUNDER, Willis Forrest. 23976 NEWELLHURST CT 98346 #051-04-1958 L1988 **R** *071 †80

KIRKLAND — KING

ADAMS, William Wright. 10200 NE 132ND ST, FAIRFAX HOSPITAL 98034 #048-04-1981 L2000 **P ADM** *020 †75
ADLERBERG, Howard Milton. ■ 98033 #016-42-1958 L1973 **EM** *071
AGARWAL, Pinky. 13030 121ST WAY NE STE 203, BOOTH GARDNER PARKINSONS C 98034 #495-32-1994 L2007 **IM N** *020 †75
ALEM, Astier M. 12911 120TH AVE NE STE E 98034 #040-02-1992 L1996 **NEP** *020 †20
ALLEGRA, Ludwig Armand. 3100 CARILLON PT 98033 #024-07-1978 L1980 **OTO FPS** *020 †45
ALTMAN, Gary. ■ 98034 #041-02-1973 L1976 **IM** *100
ANDERSON, Gill Earl. 13030 121ST WAY NE STE 202 98034 #040-02-1971 L1976 **OBG** *020 †30
ANONSEN, Cynthia Kay. 12040 NE 128TH ST 98034 #024-04-1979 L1981 **OTO HNS** *020 †45
ANOUS, Maher Mohamed. 5726 LAKE WASHNGTN BLVD NE, STE S1 98034 #915-02-1977 L1984 **PS GS** *020 †85,65
APPLETON, Warren Robt. 12040 NE 128TH ST, EVERGREEN HOSPITAL 98034 #025-07-1970 L1975 **EM GP** *020 †16
APRILL, Stephen Neal. 12911 120TH AVE NE, STE C50 98034 #016-11-1967 L1974 **IM** *020 †20
ARENDT, Kathryn Louise. 12303 NE 130TH LN STE 500, CENTER FOR WOMEN'S HEALTH 98034 #028-03-1990 L1994 **GYN** *020 †30
ARLOW, Seth M. 12040 NE 128TH ST 98034 #035-08-1972 L1973 **AN** *020 †05
ARMITANO REARDON, Erik R. 13107 121ST WAY NE 98034 #935-01-1996 L2004 **N PMM** *020 †75
ARORA, Rashmi Sagar. 207 8TH AVE W 98033 #495-12-1977 L1996 **PD** *020 †55
ARSHAD, Tahera. 12710 TOTEM LAKE BLVD NE, LAKESHORE CLINIC 98034 #704-02-1981 L1994 **IM** *020 †20
ASHWORTH, Susan Lorraine. 12333 NE 130TH LN STE 330 98034 #020-02-1983 L1989 **D** *020 †20,15
AVILES, Jennifer Marie. 6806 119TH AVE NE 98033 #026-08-2001 L2006 **EM** *020 †16
BACKLUND, William Milton. 12040 NE 128TH ST 98034 #048-04-1967 L1970 **ORS** *062
BADGER, David Smith. 12707 120TH AVE NE, STE 203 98034 #010-01-1987 L1991 **ORS** *020 †40
BAGDI, Phyllis. ■ 98083 #033-05-1960 L1964 **AN** *071 †05
BARTO, Deborah Ann. 13115 121ST WAY NE, # C 98034 #041-09-1974 L1977 **IM ON** *020 †20
BECK, Paul. 13115 121ST WAY NE 98034 #007-02-1961 L1986 **IMG END** *020 †20
BENTSEN, Chad Matthew. 12040 NE 128TH ST, MS#33 98034 #054-04-1997 L2000 **EM** *020 †16
BERMAN, Jeremy Seth. ■ 98033 #010-01-2007 L2007 **EM** *012
BERNER, Carl Frederick. 12040 NE 128TH ST 98034 #023-01-1961 L1962 **PS** *020 †85,65
BIBEAULT, Renee Marie. 11415 NE 128TH ST, STE 100 98034 #024-16-1996 L1998 **P** *020 †75
BILLETT, Kurt Randall. 12710 TOTEM LAKE BLVD NE 98034 #054-04-1984 L1985 **FM** *020 †18
BOLLIGER, Theodore T. ■ 98033 #038-06-1963 L1967 **R** *071 †80
BOSENBERG, Carola E. 12040 NE 128TH ST 98034 #033-06-1986 L1989 **CHP** *020 †75
BOUSE, Meagan K. 10413 NE 37TH CIR 98033 #539-06-2003 L2003 **IM** *020 †20
BOWEN, James D. 12333 NE 130TH LN, STE 225 98034 #023-07-1982 L1983 **N** *020 †75
BOWEN, Meath Maeve Misumi. 12040 NE 128TH ST MS 105, EVERGREEN HOSP MED CTR 98034 #054-04-2002 L2004 **IM** *020 †20
BRAMWELL, Steven Thos. 12707 120TH AVE NE STE 203 98034 #054-04-1971 L1972 **ORS OSM** *020 †40
BRENNER, Alan Steven. 12333 NE 130TH LN, STE 440 98034 #010-01-1976 L1978 **OTO** *020 †45
BRIMM, John Eugene. ■ 98033 #005-18-1974 L1975 **OS CLP** *050
BROWER, Scot Anthony. 11919 NE 128TH ST, PC 98034 #038-41-1974 L1979 **OPH** *020 †35
BROWN, Theodore Ross. 12333 NE 130TH LN, STE 225 98034 #024-01-1989 L1993 **PM** *020 †60
BRUMFIEL, Mary Neff. 13115 121ST WAY NE # C 98034 #026-08-1982 L1985 **OBG** *020 †30
BUEHRENS, Paul Eric. 12710 TOTEM LAKE BLVD NE 98034 #038-06-1978 L1981 **FM FPG** *020 †18
BURKS, Robert Scott. 10413 NE 37TH CIR 98033 #005-12-1991 L1993 **AN** *020 †05
CARDWELL, Maura Wheeler. 12333 NE 130TH LN STE 11 98034 #040-02-1985 L1989 **OBG** *020 †30
CASSIS, Anita Nellie. 12815 120TH AVE NE, STE E 98034 #054-04-1984 L1985 **U** *071 †95
CHAN, Christopher Yu Y. 12910 TOTEM LAKE BLVD NE, STE 101 98034 #060-01-1995 L1997 **FM** *020 †18
CHAN, Victor Po On. 10413 NE 37TH CIR 98033 #012-05-1987 L1989 **AN** *020 †20,05
CHANG, Ming Ta. ■ 98033 #385-04-1967 L1972 **IM** *071
CHAPUT, Debra Mary. 12710 TOTEM LAKE BLVD NE 98034 #065-09-1996 L1998 **FM** *020 †18
CHEN, Shirley. 12710 TOTEM LAKE BLVD NE, STE 101 98034 #005-01-1995 L2001 **FM** *020 †18
CHERECK, Edward Jos. ■ 98033 #016-06-1943 L1943 **OS GS** *071 †85
CHEUNG, Denice Yuchi. ■ 98033 #005-18-2000 L2002 **PD** *020
CHIEN, Angela Jauchyi. 12333 NE 130TH LN, STE 110 98034 #054-04-1995 L1999 **OBG** *020 †30
CHILDS, Kenneth Albert. 12910 TOTEM LAKE BLVD NE, STE 260 98034 #011-03-1971 L1978 **PD** *020 †55
CHUANG, Michael Deng-Jing. 12817 NE 126TH PL 98034 #244-06-1972 L1997 **GP** *020
CLINCH, Kelly Andrew. 12333 NE 130TH LN, STE 420 98034 #054-04-1994 L1997 **GS** *020 †85
COLE, Andrew James. 12911 120TH AVE NE, STE F160 98034 #051-01-1985 L1996 **PM PRS** *020 †60
COLIN, Julie Anne. 6611 NE 130TH LN 98034 #065-10-1990 L2004 *020 †18
COLLINS, A Thos. 13107 121ST WAY NE 98034 #035-45-1974 L1975 **N CHN** *020 †55,75 ‡
COLLINS, Kathryn Marin. 12911 120TH AVE NE, STE C50 98034 #025-01-1975 L1980 **PM** *020 †60

COLLINS, Terryl Rand. 8554 122ND AVE NE 98033 #016-02-1980 L1982 **PTH FM** *062 †50
COLQUHOUN, James Stuart, Jr. 12040 NE 128TH ST, MS-105 98034 #010-02-1996 L1999 **IM** *020 †20
COLSTON, Howard Lee, Jr. 10413 NE 37TH CIR 98033 #005-02-1985 L1986 **AN** *020 †05
CONDON, Joseph V. ■ 98033 #016-06-1946 L1946 **IM CD** *071 †20
CONKLIN, Jon Dennis. 12040 NE 128TH ST, RM C1-368 98034 #025-01-1966 L1974 **PTH** *020 †50
CONKLU, Ilhan. ■ 98034 #902-01-1958 L2007 **P** *071
CONNELLY, Steven Nesbit. 12040 NE 128TH ST 98034 #004-01-1986 L1992 **EM** *020 †16
COOPERRIDER, Peter A. 12911 120TH AVE NE, STE G100 98034 #025-01-1973 L1977 **D** *020 †15
CUFLEY, Gerald A. 11800 NE 128TH ST, STE 100 98034 #054-04-1970 L1977 **GE IM** *071 †20
CUPLIN, Stephen Raymond. 10413 NE 37TH CIR 98033 #054-04-1984 L1985 **AN** *020 †05
DAVID, Alexis Rene-Adkins. 12040 NE 128TH ST 98034 #025-01-2002 L2006 **FM** *020 †18
DAWSON, Steven Michael. 11410 NE 124TH ST # 631 98034 #028-02-1986 L1991 **OTO GS** *020 †45
DEANDREA, G A. 12303 NE 130TH LN STE 250 98034 #010-02-1985 L1989 **N SME** *020 †75
DECK, Andrew J. 11911 NE 132ND ST STE 200 98034 #005-19-1995 L1998 **U** *020 †95
DEPUYDT, Thomas Gerald. 11903 NE 128TH ST, STE A 98034 #025-12-1972 L1979 **ORS GPM** *020
DEV, Deepti. ■ 98033 #496-21-1997 L2006 **PDI** *100
DEVELLE, Stephanie R. 12815 76TH AVE NE, 12815 76 AVE NE 98034 #024-01-1998 L2001 **PD** *020 †55
DIACONU, Ioana M. 620 KIRKLAND WAY STE 200 98033 #781-02-1995 L2003 **P** *020
DI ANGI, Sandra Jean. 13014 120TH AVE NE 98034 #041-07-1978 L1983 **IM** *020 †20
DRY, Gavin. 13114 120TH AVE NE 98034 #061-01-1994 L1994 **PS** *020 †65
DUNBAR, Nancy Marie. ■ 98033 #054-04-2006 L2006 **PTH** *012
DUNDAS, Dennis Franklin. 13114 120TH AVE NE 98034 #005-06-1968 L1970 **PS GS** *020 †85,65
DUNN, Jeffrey Edward. 12333 NE 130TH LN STE 225, EVERGREEN NEURO INST 98034 #041-13-1989 L1990 **N** *020 †75
DYDELL, Jean. 12303 NE 130TH LN STE 450 98034 #019-02-1991 L2000 **OBG** *020 †30
EASTWOOD, Stacie Lynn. 11811 NE 128TH ST 98034 #054-04-1995 L1997 **DR** *020 †80
EBISU, John Saburo. 12333 NE 130TH LN, STE 420 98034 #014-01-1987 L1990 **GS VS** *020 †85
EDWARDS, Erin Kathleen. 12910 TOTEM LAKE BLVD NE, STE 101 98034 #054-04-1997 L1999 **IM** *020 †20
EICHNER, Manfred Harro. 12911 120TH AVE NE, STE F180 98034 #409-19-1980 L1983 **PD** *020
ENG, Sue C. 11800 NE 128TH ST 98034 #035-19-1996 L1999 **GE** *020 †20
EPLEY, K David. 11919 NE 128TH ST, PC 98034 #040-02-1993 L1998 **PO** *020 †35 ‡
ERLITZ, Marc D. 12040 NE 128TH ST 98034 #035-46-1972 L1973 **AN** *020 †05
EULBERG, Michael David. 12911 120TH NE #NE-G105 98034 #030-05-1977 L1984 **PUD IM** *020 †20
EVANS, Robert Blair. 11919 NE 128TH ST, PC 98034 #005-02-1976 L1980 **OPH OS** *020 †35
FARAGO, Denes Stephan. ■ 98033 #473-02-1940 L1968 **EM** *071
FAW, Kenneth Doyle. 12333 NE 130TH LN, STE 440 98034 #054-04-1976 L1982 **OTO HNS** *020 †45
FISH, Stephen Miles. ■ 98033 #054-04-1983 L1986 **FM** *020 †18
FONG, Brian Chi-Ming. 11911 NE 132ND ST, STE 200, EASTSIDE UROLOGY ASSOCIATE 98034 #065-01-1999 L2004 **U** *020 †95
FOY, Hjordis Mannbeck. ■ 98033 #858-02-1953 L1963 **PHP ID** *071 †70
FRANK, Michele B. 12303 NE 130TH LN STE 120 98034 #041-12-1993 L1997 **BBK IM** *020 †20
FURLONG, Richard Mark. 13014 120TH AVE NE 98034 #056-06-1986 L1988 **IM** *020 †20
GALAK, Robert Christopher. 13128 TOTEM LAKE BLVD NE, STE 206 98034 #035-09-1978 L1992 **P** *020 †75
GANG, Janet M. ■ 98034 #003-01-1978 L1997 **EM FM** *020 †18
GANT, Thomas David. 12040 NE 128TH ST 98034 #061-01-1966 L1979 **PS** *020 †65
GARBES, Archimedes D. 12040 NE 128TH ST, RM C1-368 98034 #748-02-1970 L1995 **PTH** *020 †50
GARCIA, Denise D. ■ 98033 #025-01-1999 L2006 **OPH** *020 †35
GARDNER, Jan Elaine. 10413 NE 37TH CIR 98033 #028-34-1998 L2004 **AN** *100 †05
GARRISON, Lisa Ann. ■ 98033 #054-04-2008 *012
GAVRILA, Alina. 11800 NE 128TH ST 98034 #781-01-1991 L1999 **GE** *020 †20
GERARD, James Paul. 12040 NE 128TH ST 33, EVERGREEN EMERG SVCS 98034 #067-01-1998 L2002 **EM** *020 †16
GETCHELL, William S. 12333 NE 130TH LN STE 320 98034 #005-18-1991 L2000 **CD** *020 †20
GIROUX, Monique Lillian. 13030 121ST WAY NE, STE 203 98034 #038-40-1992 L1998 **N** *020 †75
GOLDBERG, Russell S. 13014 120TH AVE NE 98034 #035-19-1978 L1983 **IM** *020 †20
GOLDMAN, Russel Wayne. 11911 NE 132ND ST, STE 100 98034 #836-02-1986 L1992 **FM** *020 †18
GONG, Bonnie. 12303 NE 130TH LN STE 230 98034 #050-02-1986 L1999 **OBG** *020 †30
GREEN, Lawrence Roscoe. 10230 NE POINTS DR, STE 530 98033 #038-43-1978 L1980 **FM** *020
GREENE, Thomas Rollin. 11800 NE 128TH ST STE 560, TOTEM LAKE FAMILY MEDICINE 98034 #054-04-1978 L1980 **FM** *020 †18
GRIFFIN, James Trenholme. ■ 98033 #054-04-1955 L1958 **RO NM** *072 †55,80,28
GRIFFITH, Alida Frances. 13030 121ST WAY NE, STE 203 98034 #024-16-1997 L2003 **N** *020 †75
GRIFFITH, Sandra K. 12040 NE 128TH ST 98034 #038-41-1975 L1978 **PD** *020 †55
GRIMES, William Thos. 12040 NE 128TH ST 98034 #036-05-1972 L1975 **IM** *071 ‡
GULKA, Mark Orest. 12910 TOTEM LAKE BLVD NE, STE 101 98034 #068-01-1992 L1994 **FM** *020 †18
HALL, Richard Eugene, Jr. 12911 120TH AVE NE, C-40 98034 #030-05-1989 L1996 **OSM** *020 †40
HALLORAN, John Lionel. 12040 NE 128TH ST 98034 #025-01-1965 L1968 **D** *071 †15
HAMILTON, Karen Jeanne. 12303 NE 130TH LN, STE 500 98034 #056-06-1993 L1997 **GYN CS** *020 †30
HANDLEY, Jack Kevin. 12040 NE 128TH ST 98034 #056-05-1990 L1998 **EM** *020 †16
HANSEN, E Kai. 12910 TOTEM LAKE BLVD NE, STE 100 98034 #041-09-1991 L1991 **IM** *020 †20
HAYNES, Robert Earl. 12333 NE 130TH LN, STE 320 98034 #038-41-1972 L1976 **CD IM** *020 †20
HEFFERNAN, John Timothy. 11919 NE 128TH ST, PC 98034 #054-04-1977 L1978 **OPH** *020 †35
HEFFRON, Charles Henry, Jr. 12303 NE 130TH LN STE 420 98034 #025-01-1971 L1981 **OBG** *020 †30
HEFFRON, John Patrick. 12303 NE 130TH LN, STE 420 98034 #054-04-1966 L1972 **OBG** *020 †30 ‡
HENNEMANN, Jack Gordon. ■ 98034 #005-12-1958 L1959 **GP** *071
HERRING, Stanley Alan. 11220 NE 53RD ST, SEATTLE SEAHAWKS 98033 #048-12-1979 L1981 **PM** *020 †60
HIBBERT, James Gerard. 12303 NE 130TH LN STE 530 98034 #054-04-1987 L1993 **CRS** *020 †85
HILL, Wayne Lyle. 8187 NE JUANITA DR 98034 #054-04-1965 L1966 **OBG** *020 †30
HOLLINGSWORTH, Kennan H. ■ 98083 #054-04-1960 L1966 **R** *071 †80
HOSKINS, Robert Graham. ■ 98033 #024-01-1953 L1961 **IM END** *062 †20
HUANG, Thomas Wen-Che. ■ 98034 #385-02-1962 L1969 **PTH** *020 †50
HUBBARD, Margaret Marian. 12040 NE 128TH ST 98034 #036-05-1986 L1993 **EM GS** *020 †16
HUGHES, Harold Vincent. ■ 98033 #065-05-1939 L1973 **OTO** *071 †05
HUGHES, Kathleen Ann. 13014 120TH AVE NE 98034 #056-06-1996 L1998 **IM** *071 †20
HUNGAR, Ann Alison. 12911 120TH AVE NE STE B10 98034 #010-01-1985 L1986 **FM** *020 †18
HUNTER, Krista Annette. 11919 NE 128TH ST, PC 98034 #005-12-2001 L2006 **OPH** *100 †35
HUNTER, Michael Andrew. 12040 NE 128TH ST, EVERGREEN HOSPITAL 98034 #008-01-1989 L1993 **RO** *020 †80
HYDE, Stephen G, II. 12303 NE 130TH LN, STE 420 98034 #030-06-1992 L2001 **OBG** *020 †30
IBRAHIM, Firoz A. 13128 TOTEM LAKE BLVD NE, STE 105 98034 #905-01-1972 L1992 **PD** *020 †55
ILIKA, Karen Lenette. 13030 121ST WAY NE STE 202 98034 #026-04-1982 L1985 **GYN** *020 †30
ISBELL, John Paul. 12303 NE 130TH LN STE 450 98034 #048-02-1977 L1988 **OBG EM** *020 †30
ISRAEL, Arthur Calvert. 11521 NE 128TH ST, STE 100 98034 #010-02-1974 L1976 **IM GP** *020 †20
JI, Hongxiu. 12040 NE 128TH ST, RM C1-368 98034 #243-16-1985 L2006 **PTH** *020 †50
JOHNSON, Christopher Lee. 12040 NE 128TH ST 98034 #054-04-1992 L1995 **PD** *020 †55
JOHNSON, Marion Cooper. 12333 NE 130TH LN STE 42 98034 #036-01-1990 L1993 **GS** *020 †85
JOHNSON, Miriam Diane. 12707 120TH AVE NE, STE 202 98034 #012-01-1984 L1987 **PSM PD** *020 †55
JUSTUS, Peter Gabor. 11800 NE 128TH ST 98034 #054-04-1974 L1983 **GE IM** *020 †20
KAMSON, Solomon. 12707 120TH AVE NE, STE 204 98034 #028-02-1982 L1984 **PME OS** *020 †05
KAPLAN, Gary Steven. 13014 120TH AVE NE 98034 #025-01-1978 L1979 **IM EM** *030 †20
KARIMI, Nassim Razzak. 12911 120TH AVE NE, STE F280 98034 #704-18-1983 L1991 **GE IM** *020 †20
KAUKONEN, Larisa Ann. 12040 NE 128TH ST, EVERGREEN HOSPITAL MED CEN 98034 #005-14-1987 L1990 **EM** *020 †16
KAUTH, James Philip. 515 STATE ST S 98033 #056-06-1961 L1964 **FM** *071 †18
KAZARAS, Michael P. 10126 NE 132ND ST STE A 98034 #035-46-1966 L1973 **PD** *020 †55
KELLEY, Robert Kenneth. 11800 NE 128TH ST STE 560 98034 #054-04-1989 L1991 **FM** *020 †18
KELLY, D Patrick. 11919 NE 128TH ST, PC 98034 #028-34-1996 L2000 **OPH** *020 †35
KENNEDY, Janet Louise. 12333 NE 130TH LN, STE 220 98034 #023-01-1978 L2004 **GYN REN** *020 †30
KENNER, William C, III. ■ 98033 #030-05-1952 L1956 **DR** *071 †80
KEYS, Shaunie Lutz. 12303 NE 130TH LN, STE 420 98034 #054-04-1994 L1998 **OBG** *020 †30
KILBURN, Howard Lee. 12040 NE 128TH ST 98034 #035-01-1962 L1964 **PD** *020 †55
KIM, David Youngho. 10413 NE 37TH CIR 98033 #005-15-1993 L1994 **AN** *020 †05
KIM, Edward. 12333 NE 130TH LN STE 320 98034 #083-01-1993 L2001 **CD** *020 †20
KIM, Susan Heesoo. 12815 120TH AVE NE, STE C 98034 #054-04-1995 L1999 **D** *020 †15
KINCAID, Michael Sean. 10413 NE 37TH CIR 98033 #048-13-2000 L2004 **AN** *100 †05
KLASSEN, Cathlyn S. 11800 NE 128TH ST STE 560, TOTEM LAKE FAMILY MEDICINE 98034 #003-01-1992 L1995 **FM** *020 †18
KLINE, Carolyn Roberta. 12040 NE 128TH ST, MFM EVERGREEN HOSPITAL 98034 #005-11-1990 L1994 **OBG MFM** *020 †30
KLOS, Julian Wolodymyr. 10413 NE 37TH CIR 98033 #041-14-1995 L1999 **APM** *020 †05
KNIGHT, Reginald Quentin. 12333 NE 130TH LN, ORTHOPAEDICS 98034 #035-15-1980 L1991 **ORS** *020 †40
KNIGHT, Ronald William. 312 5TH AVE, UNIT 4 98033 #005-06-1970 L1979 **TS GS** *071 †85,90
KNUTSON, James Alan. 830 6TH ST S 98033 #054-04-1990 L1996 **CHP** *020 †75
KOHLBERG, Irving Joel. 10200 NE 132ND ST 98034 #056-05-1963 L1968 **CHP P** *071 †55 ‡
KOHN, Aimee D. 12303 NE 130TH LN, STE 120 98034 #005-11-1999 L2001 **HEM** *100 †20
KOPP, Stanley Albert. 12911 120TH AVE NE, STE C50 98034 #007-02-1981 L1987 **ORS GS** *020 †40
KOVACICH, John Craig. 10413 NE 37TH CIR 98033 #054-04-2000 L2004 **AN** *100 †05
KOWALEWSKA, Jolanta. ■ 98034 #759-03-1995 L2003 **PTH** *020
KUPFERMAN, Susan Paulette. 6725 116TH AVE NE, STE 100 98033 #024-05-1996 L2001 **GYN** *020 †30
LAI, Yen Tsun. ■ 98034 #047-05-2000 L2003 **IMG** *100 †20
LANE, Jeffrey Alan. ■ 98034 #041-09-1974 L1977 **FM NTR** *071
LANTZ, Dan Mitchell. 12815 120TH AVE NE, STE C 98034 #054-04-1981 L1983 **D DMP** *020 †15
LANZER, William Linwood. 12333 NE 130TH LN, ORTHOPAEDICS 98034 #028-02-1977 L1984 **ORS** *050 †40
LAOHAPRASIT, Varun. 13107 121ST WAY NE 98034 #891-01-1978 L1986 **NS** *020 †25
LAUKAITIS, Steven Jos. 625 4TH AVE, STE 301 98033 #028-34-1979 L1990 **OPH PS** *020 †35
LAWRENCE, Dana Ann. ■ 98034 #035-01-1968 L1971 **AN** *071 †05
LAZORITZ, Martin. ■ 98033 #051-04-1971 L2007 **CHP P** *020 †75
LEE, June Lauren. 10413 NE 37TH CIR 98033 #054-04-1999 L2003 **AN** *020 †05
LEE, Steve Namhoon. 10413 NE 37TH CIR 98033 #032-01-1995 L1999 **AN** *020 †05
LEIDER, Allan Richard. ■ 98034 #026-04-1946 L1952 **P** *071 †75
LEVIN, Arnold I. 11800 NE 128TH ST 98034 #001-02-1974 L1988 **GE IM** *020 †20
LI, Liwei. 11410 NE 124TH ST # 148 98034 #243-25-1982 *100
LIDDELL, Robert Michael. 11811 NE 128TH ST STE 202 98034 #035-45-1984 L1985 **DR** *020 †80
LIKOSKY, Anne. 12333 NE 130TH LN, STE 330 98034 #003-01-1995 L1999 **D** *020 †15
LIKOSKY, David Jack. 12040 NE 128TH ST, MS 105 98034 #050-02-1994 L1996 **IM N** *020 †20,75
LINDEMEYER, Robert Irving. 12710 TOTEM LAKE BLVD NE, LAKESHORE CLINIC 98034 #028-02-1958 L1961 **IM** *071 †20
LIPSKY, Richard Kent. 11521 NE 128TH ST, STE 100 98034 #056-05-1970 L1975 **IM IMG** *020 †20 ‡
LOH, Johnson E-Zye. 12040 NE 128TH ST, MS-105 98034 #008-01-1993 L1996 **IM** *020 †20
LONERGAN, Matthew. 12303 NE 130TH LN, STE 120 98034 #024-01-1994 L1996 **ON** *020 †20
LUND, James Allen. 12040 NE 128TH ST 98034 #028-03-1991 L1993 **IM** *020 †20
MAIDAN, Rubin Richard. 12333 NE 130TH LN, STE 320 98034 #018-03-1979 L1985 **CD IM** *020 †20

■ = Address Information Privacy Protected

MARINKOVICH, Frank F. 11821 NE 128TH ST, STE D 98034 #654-01-1988 L1991 **IM** *020 †20
MARSHALL, Nancy A. 12040 NE 128TH ST, MS-105 98034 #016-42-2000 L2002 **IM** *100 †20
MARTY, Raymond. ■ 98033 #869-05-1959 L1970 **NM RO** *071 †80,28
MARXEN, Victoria Lynn. 11521 NE 128TH ST, STE 100 98034 #054-04-1987 L1987 **IM** *020 †20
MASON, Ronald Eugene. 11800 NE 128TH ST 98034 #001-02-1986 L2003 **GE** *020 †20
MAYEDA, Paul Kenneth. 12710 TOTEM LAKE BLVD NE, LAKESHORE CLINIC 98034 #005-14-1986 L1989 **FM** *020 †18
MC CARRON, James Patrick. 11919 NE 128TH ST, PC 98034 #539-02-1970 L1975 **GS GE** *020 †85
MC CARTY, Kevin Edward. 11800 NE 128TH ST, STE 560 98034 #054-04-1985 L1985 **FM** *020 †18
MC CORMACK, Anne Patricia. 12040 NE 128TH ST 98034 #054-04-1990 L1995 **ORS** *020 †40
MC CORMACK, John Leydon. ■ 98033 #041-02-1948 L1949 **U** *071 †95
MC FALL, Teri Lynn. 10413 NE 37TH CIR 98033 #049-01-1986 L1993 **AN** *020 †05
MC MILLAN, Sarah E. 13114 120TH AVE NE 98034 #025-12-2001 L2005 **PS** *020 †65
MELTZER, Catherine Moran. 13014 120TH AVE NE 98034 #024-01-1987 L1992 **PD** *020 †55
MHYRE, James Gregory. 12333 NE 130TH LN, STE 420 98034 #054-04-1973 L1980 **GS VS** *020 †85
MILAM, Phillip Edward. 12040 NE 128TH ST 98034 #048-04-1990 L2000 **FM** *020 †18
MINHAS, Avinder Singh. 13123 121ST WAY NE, STE D 98034 #495-03-1975 L2003 **IM** *020
MIXON, Jerry Nelson. 9757 NE JUANITA DR, STE 200 98034 #049-01-1976 L1986 **OS** *030 †18
MIYAUCHI, Dale Yoshi. 11800 NE 128TH ST 98034 #054-04-1983 L1984 **FM** *020 †18
MOE, Jennifer Diane. 7318 120TH AVE NE 98033 #054-04-2005 L2005 **EM** *012
MOE, Kristen Sean. ■ 98034 #054-04-1989 L1992 **OTO** *020 †45
MOE, Martha Christine. ■ 98034 #166-03-2002 L2003 **OBG** *020
MOHR, Benno Joseph. 12040 NE 128TH ST, MS-105 98034 #054-04-1997 L1999 **IM** *020 †20
MORELL, Patrick Wm. 12303 NE 130TH LN, STE 420 98034 #030-05-1975 L1991 **OBG** *020 †30
MORRISON, Laurel E. 13014 120TH AVE NE 98034 #054-04-1995 L1997 **FM** *020 †18
MUELLER, Travis H. 515 STATE ST S 98033 #028-34-1949 L1955 **FM** *071 †18
MUSTAFA, Syed Jamal. 10126 NE 132ND ST, STE C 98034 #704-22-1985 L1996 **CHP** *020
NACHT, Larry Elliott. 12710 TOTEM LAKE BLVD NE 98034 #026-04-1968 L1971 **FM** *020 †18
NAFICY, Saman. 12911 120TH AVE NE, STE G100 98034 #054-04-1992 L1999 **FPS** *020 †45
NAINI, Ali J. 13107 121ST WAY NE 98034 #024-01-1983 L1996 **NS** *020 †25
NAZEMI, Tanya Marie. 11911 NE 132ND ST, STE 200 98034 #048-02-2000 L2006 **U** *100 ‡
NEAL, Craig Eric. 13131 120TH AVE NE STE A 98034 #021-05-1997 L2000 **GS** *020
NEIMAN, Richard Alan. 11911 NE 132ND ST, STE 100 98034 #010-01-1978 L1985 **RHU IM** *020 †20
NELSON, Daniel Eric. 13123 121ST WAY NE STE D 98034 #005-06-1985 L1989 **AN** *020 †05
NELSON, Susan P. 219 LAKE ST S STE B 98033 #005-14-1988 L1990 **AN** *020 †05
NEU, Bruce John. 13114 120TH AVE NE 98034 #005-15-1968 L1969 **PS** *020 †65
NEWMAN, Mark Alan. 10413 NE 37TH CIR 98033 #019-02-1990 L1992 **AN IM** *020 †05
NODELL, Cynthia Gail. 13014 120TH AVE NE 98034 #016-01-1988 L1990 **DR** *020 †80
NOREHAD, Ernest Artin. 12815 120TH AVE NE, STE E 98034 #016-02-1962 L1968 **U** *020 †95
O'CALLAGHAN, James Joseph. 12040 NE 128TH ST, MAILSTOP 101 98034 #024-05-1999 L2002 **PD** *020 †55
O'CONNOR, Edmund Joseph. 12710 TOTEM LAKE BLVD NE, LAKESHORE CLINIC 98034 #035-09-1964 L1970 **IM** *071
OH, Kyle. 11811 NE 128TH ST STE 200 98034 #016-01-1988 L1992 **PM** *020 †60
OH, Kyu Jin. 11811 NE 128TH ST 98034 #016-01-1985 L1992 **GS VS** *020 †85
OKAMOTO, James Ken. 12910 TOTEM LAKE BLVD NE, STE 260 98034 #030-05-1992 L1995 **FM** *020 †18
OLSOY, Rolf Donald. 10413 NE 37TH CIR 98033 #054-04-1986 L1990 **AN** *020 †05
OPSAHL, Michael Scott. 12333 NE 130TH LN STE 220 98034 #045-01-1978 L2004 **REN OBG** *020 †30
OSETO, Matthew Christian. 12303 NE 130TH LN, STE 220 98034 #037-01-2002 L2007 **ORS** *020
PADGETT, Ryan Glenn. 12040 NE 128TH ST 98034 #054-04-2001 L2004 **EM** *020 †16
PALAZZO, Ettore Giovanni. 11818 HOLMES POINT DR NE 98034 #054-04-1998 L2001 **IM** *020 †20
PAPLOW, David Steven. 13014 120TH AVE NE 98034 #038-06-1977 L1982 **FM** *020 †18
PARISH, Ruth Ann. 13030 121ST WAY NE, STE 100 98034 #038-06-1977 L1982 **PD EM** *020 †55
PARK, Raymond. 12303 NE 130TH LN STE 325, EVERGREEN NEUROLOGY CLINIC 98034 #016-42-1995 L1997 **N** *020 †75
PARSONS, Philip James. 12040 NE 128TH ST 98034 #054-04-1975 L1978 **EM FM** *020 †16
PEARCE, Jeffrey Erle. 13107 121ST WAY NE 98034 #026-04-1978 L1984 **NS** *020 †25
PEARSON, Kathryn Anne. 12910 TOTEM LAKE BLVD NE, STE 101 98034 #024-07-1998 L2001 **IM** *020 †20
PERR, Irwin N. ■ 98033 #041-02-1950 L1951 **P LM** *071 †75
PHEIFER, Terrence Albert. 12303 NE 130TH LN, STE 420 98034 #028-02-1970 L1971 **OBG** *020 †30
PILCHER, Charles Alan. 12040 NE 128TH ST 98034 #054-04-1969 L1970 **EM FM** *071 †16
PINCZOWER, Gail Robin. 10413 NE 37TH CIR 98033 #005-15-1987 L1991 **AN** *020 †05
PITTENGER, Kim Richard. 13014 120TH AVE NE 98034 #038-41-1979 L1985 **FM** *020 †18
PLAYER, Glen Shirley. ■ 98033 #040-02-1943 L1944 **GP GS** *020
PONTO, Kathryn Louise. 13030 121ST WAY NE STE 202 98034 #016-02-1985 L1988 **GYN** *020 †30
PORTELANCE, Douglas Alan. 12333 NE 130TH LN, STE 310 98034 #054-04-1984 L1987 **IM** *020 †20
POTAMPA, Whitton Mark. 11919 NE 128TH ST, PC 98034 #054-04-1984 L1985 **OPH** *020 †35
PRECIADO-PARTIDA, K. 12040 NE 128TH ST 98034 #005-02-1981 L1992 **OBG FM** *020 †30
PRETLOW, Robert Ashton. 5406 LAK WSHNGTN NE #K 98033 #051-01-1971 L1978 **PD** *020 †55
PRICE, J Scott. 12911 120TH AVE NE, STE H210 98034 #054-04-1997 L2004 **OSS ORS** *020 †40
PRITCHETT, James W. 12333 NE 130TH LN, ORTHOPAEDICS 98034 #054-04-1979 L1981 **ORS** *020 †40
RAD, Ionel Crinisor. PO BOX 285 98083 #040-02-2004 L2007 **AN GS** *012
RADLO, Carol Maxine. 12910 TOTEM LAKE BLVD NE, STE 101 98034 #035-48-1981 L1982 **FM** *020 †18
RALSTON, Lewis Atley. ■ 98033 #054-04-1960 L1967 **OPH** *071 †35
REID, Robert Allen. 12911 120TH AVE NE, STE C50 98034 #007-02-1967 L2001 **IM** *020 †20
REMINGTON, Bradley Louis. 12303 NE 130TH LN STE 350 98034 #025-01-1982 L1991 **PS HS** *020 †65
RICE, Donald E. 620 KIRKLAND WAY, STE 200 98033 #030-05-1953 L1957 **P AM** *020
RICE, Donald Ervin. 620 KIRKLAND WAY STE 200 98033 #023-01-1969 L1973 **P** *020 †75
RIEDO, Francis X. 11911 NE 132ND ST, STE 100 98034 #023-07-1981 L1991 **ID IM** *020 †20
RITZEN, Alex August. 12040 NE 128TH ST 98034 #060-01-1957 L1966 **PTH FOP** *071 †50
ROBERTS, Neil Erland. 12333 NE 130TH LN, ORTHOPAEDICS 98034 #054-04-1992 L1993 **ORS OSM** *020 †40
ROBERTSON, Lorraine L R. 12303 NE 130TH LN, STE 230 98034 #054-04-1983 L1986 **OBS GYN** *020 †30
RODRIGUES, Derek Matthew. 12333 NE 130TH LN STE 320 98034 #917-29-1982 L1990 **CD IM** *020 †20
RODRIGUEZ, Raphael N. 10413 NE 37TH CIR 98033 #047-07-1986 L1990 **AN PME** *020 †05
ROGERS, Heidi Trandum. 13014 120TH AVE NE 98034 #054-04-1996 L1998 **FM** *020 †18
ROH, Jeffrey Seung. 12333 NE 130TH LN, ORTHOPAEDICS 98034 #056-06-1998 L2005 **OSS** *020 †40
ROLFE, Bruce Arthur. 12303 NE 130TH LN STE 220 98034 #040-02-1984 L1991 **ORS OSM** *020 †40
ROSSMAN, Allen M. 13122 120TH AVE NE 98034 #023-07-1970 L1977 **OPH** *020 †35
RUBIN, Jeremy Bennett. ■ 98034 #028-02-1982 L1984 **DR** *071 †80
RUSSELL, Dawn. 12303 NE 130TH LN STE 420 98034 #016-02-1997 L2001 **OBG** *020 †30
RUTHERFORD, Susan E. 12040 NE 128TH ST MS 36 98034 #054-04-1978 L1981 **MFM OBG** *020 †30
SANDSTROM, Paul Earland. 12710 TOTEM LAKE BLVD NE, LAKESHORE CLINIC 98034 #056-05-1970 L1971 **IM PUD** *020 †20
SANDVIK, David G. 13128 TOTM LK BLVD NE #104 98034 #154-07-1977 L1983 **P** *020 †75
SASAKI, Steven Susumu. 10413 NE 37TH CIR 98033 #005-18-1986 L1990 **AN** *050 †05
SAYYAH, Fardad John. ■ 98033 #048-13-1997 L1999 **IM** *100
SCHACH, Barbara Gayle. 12333 NE 130TH LN, STE 310 98034 #038-06-1983 L1989 **IM PLM** *020 †20
SCHEYER, William James. 12707 120TH AVE NE, STE 100 98034 #054-04-1957 L1959 **PSM** *072
SCHIEBEL, Steven Eugene. 13030 121ST WAY NE, STE 100 98034 #048-04-1995 L1998 **PD** *020 †55
SCHNEIDER, James Stephen. 12333 NE 130TH LN, STE 320 98034 #032-01-1975 L1980 **CD IM** *020 †20
SER, Peter. 12040 NE 128TH ST 98034 #005-02-1998 L2001 **IM** *020 †20
SHARMA, Pratima J. 12333 NE 130TH LN STE 310 98034 #495-01-1993 L2000 **IM** *020 †20
SHOUP, William Bradford. 11220 NE 53RD ST, SEATTLE SEAHAWKS 98033 #004-01-1984 L1987 **FM FSM** *020 †18
SHUMAN, William Phelps. 12040 NE 128TH ST, EVERGREEN HOSPITAL MEDICAL 98034 #035-15-1973 L1979 **DR** *020 †80
SHUMATE, Jennifer K. 12303 NE 130TH LN, STE 230 98034 #035-09-2003 L2007 **OBG** *020
SINGER, Robert Steven. 13107 121ST WAY NE 98034 #035-20-1969 L1970 **N** *020 †75
SINGHAL, Sukriti. 218 MAIN ST, # 486 98033 #495-11-1997 L2004 **CCM** *012
SKRYPZAK, Mary Elizabeth. ■ 98034 #041-09-1988 L1992 **OBG** *020 †30
SKUCAS, Andrius Petras. 10413 NE 37TH CIR 98033 #035-45-1998 L2001 **AN** *020 †20,05
SLOAN, Joanna Beata. 12303 NE 130TH LN, STE 330 98034 #016-02-1986 L1991 **D DMP** *020 †15
SLOANE, Thomas Robin. 11800 NE 128TH ST 98034 #021-01-1986 L1993 **GE** *020 †20
SMITH, Connie Jo. 11521 NE 128TH ST, STE 100 98034 #054-04-1984 L1985 **IM FPG** *020 †20
SMITH, David Macdonald. 11919 NE 128TH ST, EYE ASSOCIATES NORTHWEST 98034 #025-01-1959 L1965 **OPH** *071 †35
SMOOTS, Elizabeth Susan. 12040 NE 128TH ST 98034 #003-01-1982 L1985 **FM** *020 †18
SOOD, Narender. 13110 120TH AVE NE 98034 #495-45-1974 L1982 **U** *020 †95
SOOD, Rekha. ■ 98034 #495-45-1974 L1979 **AN** *020 †05
SPANIER, David Edward. 12911 120TH AVE NE, STE F160 98034 #038-41-1998 L2001 **PM** *020 †20,60
STAPLES, Russell Leroy. 12303 NE 130TH LN, STE 120 98034 #038-41-1978 L1991 **IM** *020 †20
STATES, James Henry, II. 13501 100TH AVE NE # 5221, BELLEVUE, WA 98004, MAILIN 98034 #041-13-1971 L1972 **ADL FM** *020 †18
STAVIG, Darrell Elwood. 12040 NE 128TH ST 98034 #054-04-1956 L1957 **FM** *071
STEMMERMAN, Debra Stavang. 12303 NE 130TH LN, STE 420 98034 #037-01-1989 L1992 **OBG** *020 †30
STIBBINS, Thomas Ray. 10413 NE 37TH CIR 98033 #017-20-1990 L2001 **AN** *020 †05
STROTHER, Michael Sean. 12911 120TH AVE NE, STE G100 98034 #021-06-1997 L1999 **D DS** *020 †15
SU, Henry. 12040 NE 128TH ST MS 1, EVERGREEN HEALTHCARE 98034 #005-18-1995 L1997 **IM** *020 †20
SUHR, Yun. 13014 120TH AVE NE 98034 #036-07-1991 L2000 **IM** *020 †20
SWANSON, Mark Andrew. 12040 NE 128TH ST 98034 #030-06-1972 L1973 **EM** *020 †16
SWENSON, Dana Andrea. 12910 TOTEM LAKE BLVD NE, STE 101 98034 #026-04-1991 L1991 **IM** *020 †20
TAFT, David Allan. 11821 NE 128TH ST, STE A 98034 #018-03-1959 L1969 **GS** *030 †85
TAKEMURA, Ken Kenneth. 12303 NE 130TH LN STE 220, KNEEFOOTANKLE CENTER, PLLC 98034 #016-42-1994 L2002 **PM** *020 †60
TATTONI, Diana S. 433 STATE ST S, STE 1 98033 #935-01-1964 L1970 **PD END** *020
TAYLOR, Eric Wm. 12040 NE 128TH ST, EVERGREEN RAD ONCOLOGY 98034 #054-04-1978 L1979 **RO** *020 †80
THIELE, Ray Adolph. 12815 120TH AVE NE 98034 #028-02-1956 L1958 **OBG** *071 †30
THOMASON, Susan Bess. 11800 NE 128TH ST, STE 560 98034 #016-06-1991 L1993 **FM** *020 †18
TOKARCHEK, Fred. ■ 98034 #041-09-1964 L1968 **ORS** *071 †40
TOMLIN, Jeffrey James. 10413 NE 37TH CIR 98033 #054-04-1986 L1988 **AN** *020 †05
TOMPKINS, Richard Leo. ■ 98034 #016-02-1961 L2000 **PD** *030 †55
TOWBIN, Michael Anthony. 12333 NE 130TH LN, STE 420 98034 #005-02-1983 L1987 **GS VS** *020 †85
TREMAIN, Katherine E Lane. ■ 98033 #054-04-1958 L1964 **PM** *020 †60
TROIANO, Barbara Joan. 12333 NE 130TH LN, STE 310 98034 #024-07-1979 L1984 **IM** *020 †20
TSANG, S Theresa. 12303 NE 130TH LN STE 230 98034 #016-11-1987 L1991 **OBG** *020 †30
TSUANG, Mary Wen. 12333 NE 130TH LN, STE 110 98034 #024-07-1995 L2000 **OBG** *020 †30
TSUANG, Min-Min. ■ 98034 #385-03-1960 L1980 **P OS** *020
TURNER, Joseph Edwin. 12303 NE 130TH LN 98034 #054-04-1982 L1986 **OBG GYN** *020 †30
TWEITO, Timothy Harry. 11919 NE 128TH ST, PC 98034 #019-02-2000 L2006 **OPH** *020 †35
ULVILA, John Matt. 12710 TOTEM LAKE BLVD NE, LAKESHORE CLINIC 98034 #028-02-1966 L1969 **IM NEP** *020 †20
UMMAT, Samira. ■ 98033 #496-07-1988 L2007 **PM** *071
UMMAT, Sunil K. 3100 CARILLON PT 98033 #064-01-1986 L2006 **OTO** *020 †45
UTTER, William V. 12040 NE 128TH ST 98034 #054-15-1969 **GP OS** *072
VALENTA, Lubomir Jan-V. PO BOX 3282 98083 #286-02-1956 L1972 **END IM** *071 †20

■ = Address Information Privacy Protected

VAN HAELST-PISANI, Carol. 12303 NE 130TH LN, STE 120 98034 #165-04-1982 L1992 ON IM *020 †20

VEITH, Ryan Richard. 10413 NE 37TH CIR 98033 #054-04-2003 L2003 AN *100

VESSELLE, Loren Jill. 13014 120TH AVE NE 98034 #038-06-1993 L1997 OPH *020 †35

VILLANUEVA, Diana Lynn. 12303 NE 130TH LN, STE 500 98034 #054-04-1986 L1991 OBG *071 †30

VIMONT, Thomas Richard. 5030 112TH AVE NE 98033 #028-34-1972 L1973 DR *020 †80

VINOPAL, Evelyn Struck. 12910 TOTEM LAKE BLVD NE 98034 #001-02-1987 L1987 IM *020 †20

VOSS, Julie Evelyn. 3100 CARILLON PT 98033 #005-15-1992 L1996 D DS *020 †15

VOSSLER, Mark Robt. 12333 NE 130TH LN, STE 320 98034 #035-45-1989 L2002 CD IM *020 †20

WAHL, David Von. 11911 NE 132ND ST STE 200 98034 #054-04-1969 L1970 U *020 †95

WALCZAK, Magdalena M. 12040 NE 128TH ST 98034 #759-09-1987 L1998 FM *020 †18

WALKER, Elisabeth C. ■ 98033 #007-02-1995 L1999 AN *020 †05

WALKER, Jo Marie. 11800 NE 128TH ST, STE 560 98034 #048-02-1989 L1989 FM *020 †18

WALTMAN, Dennis Danl. 11919 NE 128TH ST, PC 98034 #054-04-1969 L1976 OPH *020 †35

WALUND, Dean Curtis. 10413 NE 37TH CIR 98033 #054-04-1984 L1985 AN PD *020 †05,55

WALUND, Lori Carol. 13014 120TH AVE NE 98034 #054-04-1990 L1990 IM *020 †20

WANG, Hao. 12815 120TH AVE NE, STE C 98034 #005-02-1998 L2002 D *020 †15

WANG, Josephine Sophie. 12333 NE 130TH LN STE 110 98034 #035-48-1995 L1999 OBG *020 †30

WANI, Roohi Hassan. 12710 TOTEM LAKE BLVD NE 98034 #495-51-1998 L2003 IM *020 †20

WATTS, Lois S Hale. 12040 NE 128TH ST 98034 #036-07-1957 L1961 PD OPH *071 †55

WEBB, D Robert, Jr. 12911 120TH AVE NE # F260 98034 #038-06-1964 L1972 AI IM *020 †03,20

WEBSTER, Wade West. 12040 NE 128TH ST 98034 #035-03-1986 L1993 EM *020 †16

WEEKS, Diana. 10413 NE 37TH CIR 98033 #056-06-1984 L1986 AN *020 †05

WEINBERG, Sarah Kibbee. 12040 NE 128TH ST 98034 #054-04-1977 L1978 PD OS *071 †55

WELLS, Karen Vanauken. 12303 NE 130TH LN STE 500 98034 #005-12-1993 L1997 OBG *020 †30

WEST, John Michael. 12034 NE 130TH LN, EASTSIDE EAR NOSE & THROAT 98034 #028-03-1967 L1973 OTO GP *071 †45

WHARTON, Marcia Marie. 12710 TOTEM LAKE BLVD NE, LAKESHORE CLINIC PLLC 98034 #005-19-1989 L1993 FM *020 †18

WIETECHA, Tomasz Adam. ■ 98034 #759-07-1993 *100

WILK, Lynne Anne. 11411 NE 124TH ST STE 190 98034 #035-46-1970 L1990 P *020 †75

WILLIAMS, Emily Annwyllyd. ■ 98033 #054-04-2004 L2004 PS *012

WINN, Bryan Jon. 625 4TH AVE, STE 301 98033 #035-01-2003 L2007 OPH *100

WITTMAN, Mary Beth. 12303 NE 130TH LN STE 45 98034 #005-18-1994 L1998 OBG *020

WU, Chao-Ching. 12710 TOTEM LAKE BLVD NE, LAKESHORE CLINIC 98034 #056-06-1993 L1998 IM PD *020 †20,55

WYMAN, Rachael Ann. 12333 NE 130TH LN, STE 320 98034 #054-04-2000 L2007 CD *020 †20

YEH, Ronald Wenchung. 11800 NE 128TH ST 98034 #005-11-2000 L2005 GE *020 †20

YEN, Tony. 12040 NE 128TH ST 98034 #035-20-1994 L1996 IM *020 †20

YOON, Jeong Hoon. 11911 NE 132ND ST STE 200, EASTSIDE UROLOGY ASSOCIATE 98034 #008-01-1999 L2003 U *020 †95

YU, Harry Hsiaosung. 12333 NE 130TH LN STE 320 98034 #016-06-1995 L2002 CD *020 †20

ZABRISKIE, Vinette. 12303 NE 130TH LN STE 500 98034 #003-01-1978 L1982 OBG *071 †30

LA CONNER – SKAGIT

APTER, Robert Lynn. 5A BEACH DR 98257 #007-02-1974 L1975 EM *020 †16

BEACH, William Brown, Jr. ■ 98257 #016-02-1946 L1948 P CHP *071 †75

CLURE, Harold Raymond. 17400 RESERVATION RD, SWINOMISH HEALTH OFFICE 98257 #025-01-1962 L1964 FM OS *071 †18

CONGER, George Dean. ■ 98257 #017-20-1964 L1999 R *071 †80

GRATTON, Christopher A. ■ 98257 #005-14-1972 L1976 PTH *062 †50

GRAY, Norman Cunningham. ■ 98257 #067-01-1962 L1969 P *071

HILL, Jeffrey W. 539 OLALLIE WAY 98257 #054-04-1977 L2004 AN *020 †05

HUNTER, Joe E. PO BOX 1620 98257 #054-04-1953 L1954 GP *071

HYATT, Claris. ■ 98257 #054-04-1953 L1955 PHP *071

KRUEGER, James Davies. ■ 98257 #040-02-1957 L1956 OM IM *071

LA VIOLETTE, Rodney M. ■ 98257 #054-04-1955 L1957 FM *071 †18

PEARL, Janice Marie. ■ 98257 #023-07-1963 L1975 EM ETX *020 †16 ‡

THAIDIGSMAN, James Henry. 224 SKAGIT WAY 98257 #041-13-1957 L1969 OBG *071 †30

LACEY – THURSTON

ADARMES, Demitri A. PO BOX 5277 98509 #011-02-1995 L2005 IM *020 †20,60

ALDERMAN, Shawn Michael. ■ 98516 #023-12-2003 L2004 FM *020 †18

ALEXANIAN, Joann. ■ 98513 #056-06-1985 L1989 AN *020 †05

ARCHER, Bryan Matthew. ■ 98516 #352-07-1954 L1960 IMG FM *071 †18

AVALOS, Corinna. ■ 98516 #010-03-2005 L2007 IM *012

BADGER, Virginia Mae. ■ 98503 #041-07-1961 L1957 ORS PM *071 †40

BRATCHER, Carla E. ■ 98503 #041-01-1979 L1984 OBG *071 †30

BRIGDEN, Robert Bruce. ■ 98503 #005-15-1964 L1965 AN *071 †05

BRYAN, Angela Christine. ■ 98503 #051-04-2006 L2007 PD *012

CASE, Ronald Lee. 4705 8TH AVE NE 98516 #005-12-1969 L1970 A FM *020 †18

CATES, Edward David. 130 MARVIN RD SE STE 100, SEAMAR HEALTH CARE CENTER 98503 #054-04-1998 L2000 FM *020 †18

CHAN, Angela Izumi. 3928 PACIFIC AVE SE 98503 #005-12-1983 L1986 IM *020 †20

CORSON, Constance. 700 SLEATER KINNEY RD SE, STE B189 98503 #025-01-1983 L2005 P *020 †75

CUENCA, Peter John. 7756 SAWGRASS LN SE 98503 #010-02-1998 L1999 EM *100 †16

CUNNINGHAM, Bethany S. ■ 98503 #041-15-2008 *012

DOMAGALSKI, Jason Erek. ■ 98503 #056-06-2005 L2007 FP *012

DUFFY, Maribeth Theresa. 3928 PACIFIC AVE SE 98503 #010-01-1992 L1999 FM *020 †18

EGGEN, Robert Ralph. ■ 98516 #060-01-1954 L1969 PTH *071 †50

ESTRADA, Sarah Marie. ■ 98516 #016-11-2007 *012

FAIRBROOK, David Lynn. 4044 15TH AVE SE, STE A 98503 #054-04-1969 L1973 IM IMG *020 †20

FETT, James Derrill. ■ 98503 #026-04-1960 L1995 IM OS *020 †20

GADBAW, James Lewis. ■ 98513 #056-05-1970 L1975 OBG *020 †30

GARRETT, Wayne E. 6634 MILANO CT SE 98513 #041-01-1952 L1957 GS *071 †85

GERACI, Jane Marie. 8645 MARTIN WAY E 98516 #056-06-1986 L2006 IM *020 †20

GOODNOW, Robert Weston. ■ 98513 #005-06-1952 L1985 PTH FM *071 †50

GORTON, Steven John. 4525 3RD AVE SE STE 200 98503 #035-45-1973 L1982 ON IM *020 †20

GRIFFITH, Harry Steven. 4525 3RD AVE SE, # 200 98503 #054-04-1985 L1991 IM HO *020 †20

HARPER, Lonnie. 4525 3RD AVE SE, # 200 98503 #021-01-1967 L1974 ON IM *020 †20

HARRIS, Stanley Craig. ■ 98513 #054-04-1970 L1983 GS *072 †85

HARTMAN, Joseph Robt. 4525 3RD AVE SE, # 100 98503 #041-01-1987 L1989 RO *020 †80

HAVLAK, Dirk Francis. 5130 CORPORATE CENTR CT SE 98503 #048-04-1980 L1983

HECHT, Maximilian William. ■ 98513 #016-11-2006 L2008 OBG *012

HORTON, David Farrar. 4525 3RD AVE SE, # 100 98503 #005-14-1984 L1989 RO *020 †80

HUARD, Bernadette Louise. 4422 6TH AVE SE, BEHAVIORAL HEALTH 98503 #054-04-1981 L1982 P *020 †75

HUDDLESTON, Robert Thos. ■ 98503 #030-06-1954 L1955 FM EM *071

JANCICH, Sophy Ann. 4525 3RD AVE SE, STE 200 98503 #021-06-1997 L2006 ON *100 †20

JANSEN, Edward Lee. 8645 MARTIN WAY E 98516 #056-06-1985 L1988 IM *020 †20

JOHNSON, Cris Edward. 5130 CORPORATE CENTR CT SE 98503 #054-04-1995 L1997 FM *020 †18

KORPAL, Rowena Jo-Ann. ■ 98513 #748-01-1991 *100

KRAUSS, Ronald Chas. 5602 RUDDELL RD SE 98503 #016-43-1974 L1978 GP *020

LECHNER, James John. 4525 3RD AVE SE, # 200 98503 #005-14-1982 L1987 HEM ON *020 †20

LERAAS, John Albert. 8617 MARTIN WAY E, STE 101 98516 #054-04-1972 L1974 FM *020

LINKS, Susan Virginia. 3928 PACIFIC AVE SE 98503 #054-04-1993 L1997 IM *020 †20

LYNCH, James Alphonsus. ■ 98503 #539-05-1984 L1998 *020

MENDELSSOHN, Alan Norton. 1401 MARVIN RD NE 98516 #025-01-1960 L1992 CRS *071 †10

MILLER, Nathaniel Robert. ■ 98513 #049-01-2006 L2008 OBG *012

NCAYIYANA, Danl J Mandla. ■ 98509 #660-02-1969 L1973 OBG *020 †30

NUNN, Janet Lynn. 4160 6TH AVE SE STE 204 98503 #039-01-1987 L1991 P *020 †75

O'DEA, James Edward. ■ 98503 #040-02-1965 L1994 PD *020

OLSON, Jennifer Lynn. 4422 6TH AVE SE, BEHAVIORAL HEALTH 98503 #054-04-1998 L2004 P *020 †75

OTT, Carl Richard. 8645 MARTIN WAY E 98516 #054-04-1983 L1984 IM *020 †20

PAUL, Vincent James. ■ 98513 #019-02-2006 L2008 DR *012

PEREZ, Coryell Jade. ■ 98516 #051-04-2006 L2008 OBG *012

PERREAULT, Michael David. ■ 98513 #054-04-2006 EM *012

PHILLIPS, Karen Marie. ■ 98516 #048-13-1997 L1998 OMF *012

PLAYSTEAD, Jennifer Anne. 5130 CORPORATE CENTR CT SE 98503 #014-01-1998 L2000 FM *020 †18

PROFANT, Gene Richard. ■ 98516 #008-01-1963 L2001 IM CD *071 ‡

RAFFERTY, Thomas Francis. 5130 CORPORATE CENTR CT SE 98503 #016-45-1975 L1980 FM *020 †18

RAYMOND, James Fred. 4525 3RD AVE SE, STE 100 98503 #054-04-1993 L1995 RO *020 †80

READ, Robert Mendel. ■ 98503 #045-01-1956 L1956 OBG *071 †30

ROBERTSON, Paul Alexander. 4525 3RD AVE SE, # 200 98503 #049-01-1983 L1989 ON HEM *020 †20

RUDD, Jay C. 345 COLLEGE ST SE, CLARUS EYE SURGICAL 98503 #041-02-1995 L2000 OPH *020 †35

SAPP, Jason Elliott. ■ 98516 #023-12-2005 L2006 IM *012

SAWTELL, James Herbert. ■ 98503 #019-02-1941 L1952 GYN NTR *071 †30

SCHOLES, Gary Neal. 345 COLLEGE ST SE, CLARUS EYE SURGICAL 98503 #056-06-1986 L1991 OPH *020 †35

SESSIONS, Daniel Cole. ■ 98516 #023-12-2004 L2006 OBG *012

SHANNON, Michael Hugh. 8645 MARTIN WAY E, PROVIDENCE ENDOCRINOLOGY 98516 #005-18-2001 L2003 END IMG *020 †20

SHIVELEY, Matthew James. ■ 98503 #051-01-2002 L2003 AN *020 †05

SMITH, Donald Sanford, Jr. ■ 98503 #025-01-1961 L1962 IM *071

SOKOLOFF, Julia Lamont. 130 MARVIN RD SE, SEA MAR CHC 98503 #005-02-1991 L1991 FM *020 †18

STONE, Jason Robert. ■ 98513 #016-45-2007 EM *012

SYLWESTER, Patricia R. 3928 PACIFIC AVE SE 98503 #047-05-1984 L1986 GP *020

THOMPSON, James A. ■ 98503 #023-12-1953 L1958 IM OS *071

TOLLEFSON, David F J. ■ 98513 #056-05-1978 L1991 VS GS *020 †85

TRAN, Lien Mong. 1202 SLEATER KINNEY RD SE 98503 #941-01-1964 L1984 GP IM *020 ‡

TRUXAL, Anthony Robt. 345 COLLEGE ST SE, CLARUS EYE SURGICAL 98503 #041-13-1980 L1987 OPH OS *020 †35

VANDENBERG, Robert D. 4044 15TH AVE SE 98503 #051-04-1977 L1991 FM FPG *020 †18

VUTLA, Pragathy. 413 LILLY RD NE, PROVIDENCE ST PETER HOSP 98506 #496-21-2000 L2005 IM *020 †20

WEATHERS, Bruce Kent. ■ 98516 #051-01-1995 L1997 GS *020

WERNER, Haleigh K. 4525 3RD AVE SE, RADIANTCARE RADIATION ONCO 98503 #054-04-1995 L2004 RO *100 †20,80

WRIGHT, June Durig. ■ 98503 #040-02-1955 L1957 GP *071

WRIGHT, Peter Wm. ■ 98503 #040-02-1955 L1957 GP *071

YE, Zhou. 4525 3RD AVE SE STE 200 98503 #243-75-1987 L2004 IM *020 †20

YOUNG, Ricardo Montalbo. ■ 98516 #025-12-1998 L2000 GS *020 †85

LAKE FOREST PARK – KING

BOYCE, Thomas Richard. 20131 44TH AVE NE 98155 #054-04-1969 L1974 ORS HS *062 †40

BRYAN, Eunice Elizabeth. ■ 98155 #038-06-1937 L1949 PD *071 †55

CHEUNG, Ronald Seyuen. ■ 98155 #054-04-2006 L2006 PD *012

CHHIN, Leticia Esguerra. ■ 98155 #748-01-1968 L1982 PTH *020

ELLINGER, Daniel J. ■ 98155 #054-04-1953 L1954 ORS *071

GEIL, Carol Cullum. ■ 98155 #005-11-1965 L1968 PD *040 †55

GEIL, James Henry. ■ 98155 #038-06-1968 L1968 IM *071 †20

GOLD, Raelene Joy. ■ 98155 #054-04-1964 L1988 P PYA *071 †75

GRUENEWALD, David Allan. ■ 98155 #016-02-1983 L1984 IMG IM *020 †20

HOLLINGSWORTH, Lyman B. ■ 98155 #036-06-1936 L1993 IM AS *020

HUTCHINSON, John Forbes. 17191 BOTHELL WAY NE 98155 #024-01-1973 L1974 PUD IM *050 †20

KAWABORI, Isamu. 3822 NE 151ST ST 98155 #054-04-1966 L1969 PDC PD *020 †55

KREITER, Laurie Cushing. 17191 BOTHELL WAY NE, LAKE FOREST PARK MEDICAL 98155 #054-04-1993 L1996 FM *020 †18

LUU, Jenyung. 15730 BEACH DR NE 98155 #054-04-1990 L1992 **EM** *020 †16
MC GEE, Steven Roy. ■ 98155 #028-02-1980 L1980 **IM** *020 †20
MILLER, Karen Lynne. 17191 BOTHELL WAY NE 98155 #054-04-1993 L1995 **IM** *020 †20
NESSELHOF, William, Jr. ■ 98155 #047-06-1959 L1964 **P** *071
NEWTON, Leslie Stanz. 17191 BOTHELL WAY NE, LAKE FOREST PARK MEDICAL 98155
    #035-01-1972 L1973 **FM** *020 †18
NG, Amoy Aik-Woo. 17191 BOTHELL WAY NE, LAKE FOREST PARK MEDICAL 98155
    #005-12-1974 L1978 **FM** *020 †20
PARLE, Suzanna Marie. ■ 98155 #035-45-2008 *012
PARROT, Carol Antoinette. 19431 46TH AVE NE, DEPT OF ANESTHESIA 98155
    #056-06-1980 L1984 **AN** *020 †05
REID, Jean Patricia. ■ 98155 #016-06-1993 L1995 **FM** *020 †18
SALAMA, Youssef Attalla. ■ 98155 #330-03-1954 L1971 **PD END** *071 †55
SHEN, Fu-Hsiung. ■ 98155 #385-02-1965 L1973 **NEP IM** *020 †20
SHNEIDMAN, Danita Ann. ■ 98155 #048-13-1974 L1977 **FM** *020 †50
SURTEES-CARLSON, Mary N. ■ 98155 #041-13-1947 L1949 **FM OS** *071
SWANSON, Richard Allan. ■ 98155 #016-06-1973 L1974 **FM** *100
TSUCHIYA, Karen Doris. ■ 98155 #025-01-1990 L1990 **PTH** *020 †50
TUCKER, James Louis. ■ 98155 #035-20-1944 L1951 **PD OS** *071 †55
VAN BELLE, Johanna H P C. ■ 98155 #065-01-1961 L1975 **GP** *020
WATTS, Leland Forester. ■ 98155 #041-12-1956 L1960 **OPH OS** *020

LAKE STEVENS – SNOHOMISH

BURGOYNE, Ben Ross. ■ 98258 #040-02-1948 L1951 **FPG AN** *071
CRITCHFIELD, Thomas W. ■ 98258 #019-02-1944 L1954 **OBG** *071 †30
HATCHER, Mary Lou. 8910 VERNON RD, THE EVERETT CLINIC 98258 #054-04-1984 L1987
    FM *020 †18
HINTON, Robert L. 9408 N DAVIES RD 98258 #054-15-1969 **FM** *020 †18
IGUCHI, Robert Kenneth. 9811 CHAPEL HILL RD, SNOHOMISH COUNTY FPD #8 98258
    #054-04-1979 L1985 **EM** *020 †20
JACOBS, Edward Allen. 8910 VERNON RD 98258 #024-07-1965 L1991 **PD** *020 †55 ‡
KLEM, Robert James, Jr. 8910 VERNON RD, EVERETT CLINIC 98258 #016-45-1990 L1990
    FM *020 †18
LANK, John. 8910 VERNON RD 98258 #051-07-1991 L2000 **IM** *020 †20
RANHEIM, Philip Dale. 9407 4TH ST NE 98258 #054-04-1976 L1977 **FM** *020 †18
THOMPSON, Douglas Wm. ■ 98258 #054-04-1958 L1961 **PD** *071 †55
VASIL, George Wm. 8910 VERNON RD, STE 202 98258 #007-02-1984 L1987 **FM** *020 †18

LAKE TAPPS – PIERCE

BALL, James John. 1903 CHANNEL RD E 98391 #023-01-1955 L1983 **DIA IM** *072 †28,20
DAY, Lila Maureen. 3920 W TAPPS DR E, LAKE TAPPS FAMILY MEDICINE 98391
    #422-01-1994 L1998 **FM** *020 †18
ENDEN, James Abney. ■ 98391 #054-04-1962 L1964 **GYN** *071 †30
LAM, Tinh Chau. 3303 204TH AVENUE CT E 98391 #051-07-1983 L1986 **AN** *020 †05
MYERS, Gerald Burdette. 916 184TH AVENUE CT E 98391 #005-12-1967 L1972 **OBG** *071
RUUSKA, Paul Elmer. 3106 SUMNER TAPPS HWY E, STE A 98391 #040-02-1940 L1946
    ORS *072 †40
WEBER, Donald Conrad. 3920 W TAPPS DR E 98391 #054-04-1964 L1965 **FM** *020

LAKEBAY – PIERCE

ROES, William Frederick. 15610 89TH ST CT KP N 98349 #028-02-1978 L1979 **FM** *020 †18

LAKEWOOD – PIERCE

AFRASSIABI, Ali. 4810 112TH ST SW, NW MEDICAL BILLING 98499 #054-04-1990 L1996
    AN PME *020 †05
AHLERS, Bryson V. 6212 75TH ST W, POB 110577 98499 #005-12-1968 L1971
    GP PHP *020 †18
ALI, Jameel. 11315 BRIDGEPORT WAY SW 98499 #010-02-2005 *100
ANDRADE, William Pierre. 11307 BRIDGEPORT WAY SW, STE 200 98499 #054-04-1973 L1984
    A IM *020 †20,03
AREF, Amir Mohammad. ■ 98499 #056-05-1996 L1999 **IM** *020 †20
ARROYO, Julian Sanchez. 7308 BRIDGEPORT WAY W, STE 201 98499 #030-06-1991 L1997
    ORS *020 †40
BACA, Carlos Eduardo. ■ 98498 #737-01-1979 *100
BAK, John B. 11307 BRIDGEPORT WAY SW, STE 217 98499 #010-02-1994 L2005 **U** *020 †95
BARCHIESI, R Christopher. 9332 BRIDGEPORT WAY SW 98499 #045-01-1979 L1982 **GP** *020
BARONDEAU, Jesse Jay. ■ 98499 #046-01-2005 L2007 **PD** *012
BATEY, George Roscoe. ■ 98498 #047-06-1956 L1957 **GP OS** *075
BAUTISTA, Manuel F. 9115 BRIDGEPORT WAY SW 98499 #748-01-1965 L1989 **P** *020
BAXTER, Sean Thomas. 11315 BRIDGEPORT WAY SW 98499 #056-06-2004 L2007 **EM** *020
BEDE, William Brandt. 7308 BRIDGEPORT WAY W, STE 201 98499 #067-01-1970 L1972
    ORS *020 †40
BEDNARCZYK, Richard Henry. ■ 98498 #025-01-1976 L2000 **FM** *020 †18
BENSON, David R. 5920 100TH ST SW, STE 8 98499 #019-02-1987 L1990 **OPH** *020 †35
BENVENISTE, Ronald Jos. 7424 BRIDGEPORT WAY W, STE 305 98499 #054-04-1967 L1968
    OTO *020 †45
BHAGIA, Poonam. ■ 98498 #496-07-1998 L2005 **IMG** *100
BORLAND, Andrew Chas. 9601 STEILACOOM BLVD SW, FT STEILACOOM WA 98498 98498
    #005-12-1972 L1977 **P CHP** *030
BRAUN, Kevin Eugene. 5920 100TH ST SW STE 31, KEVIN E. BRAUN MD, PLLC 98499
    #024-07-1993 L1999 **FM OBS** *020 †18
BROWN, Gregory Allen. 11315 BRIDGEPORT WAY SW 98499 #038-06-1978 L1981
    EM GP *020 †16
BROWN, James Howard. 11307 BRIDGEPORT WAY SW, STE 200 98499 #005-02-1974
    PTH *020
BROWN, James Stuart. 11307 BRIDGEPORT WAY SW 98499 #040-02-1974 L1991
    AI IM *020 †18,20,03

BURTNER, Jennifer Jennine. 11315 BRIDGEPORT WAY SW 98499 #019-02-1995 L2005
    EM *020 †16
CALDWELL, Robert Louis. 4905 108TH ST SW 98499 #021-01-1974 L1994 **IM** *020 †20
CAMP, Richard Allen. ■ 98498 #016-06-1965 L1981 **HS ORS** *071 †40
CARLISLE, Lynda Lee. 8805 STEILACOOM BLVD SW, CHILD STUDY & TREATMENT CE 98498
    #012-01-1985 L1987 **P** *020 †75
CHAN, Alfred Hongleung. 6323 111TH ST SW 98499 #244-03-1972 L1982 **HO IM** *020 †20
CHANG, Emery Jintoh. 6210 75TH ST W, STE B100 98499 #024-05-1994 L2000 **GS** *020 †85
CHEN, Peter. 11315 BRIDGEPORT WAY SW, STE 301 98499 #048-04-1994 L2002 **PCC** *020 †20
CHO, David Sang June. 11315 BRIDGEPORT WAY SW, ST CLARE HOSPITAL 98499
    #012-05-1991 L1995 **AN** *020 †20
CHUNG, Jay Won. ■ 98498 #583-08-1973 L1983 **CHP** *020 †75
CHUNG, Nancy Marie. 11315 BRIDGEPORT WAY SW 98499 #025-07-1999 L2007 **EM** *020 †16
CLIFT, Stephen Douglas. 6103 MT TACOMA DR SW 98499 #012-05-1978 L1988 **PS** *020 †65
COHEN, Larry Scott. 11315 BRIDGEPORT WAY SW 98499 #016-11-1988 L1990 **EM** *020 †16
COLEN, John. ■ 98499 #660-03-1950 L1955 **AI IM** *072 †03
COOK, Stephen Gerard. 10510 GRAVELLY LAKE DR SW 98499 #005-02-1997 L2000
    FM *020 †18
COOPER, Ronald Heywood. ■ 98499 #005-18-1972 L1998 **IM** *020 †20
CORAY, Spencer Allen. 7308 BRIDGEPORT WAY W, STE 201 98499 #030-06-1998 L2004
    ORS *020 †40
COWAN, Ian David. 11315 BRIDGEPORT WAY SW, ST. CLARE HOSPITAL 98499
    #039-01-1985 L1995 **FM** *020 †18
CRAWFORD, David Anthony. ■ 98498 #038-40-2007 **ORS** *012
CRIDER, Anja B. 11307 BRIDGEPORT WAY SW, STE 320 98499 #024-07-1992 L1993
    OBG *020 †30
CRUZ, Cristina. ■ 98499 #042-02-2006 L2007 **N** *012
DAVIS, Shirley Diane. ■ 98498 #036-01-1979 L1980 **IM** *020 †20
DAWSON, Rachel Diane. 9332 BRIDGEPORT WAY SW 98499 #048-14-1987 L1990 **FM** *020 †18
DEYO, Glenn A. 11311 BRIDGEPORT WAY SW, STE 108 98499 #048-14-1982 L1989
    GS *020 †85
DURAS, Steven Geo. 11311 BRIDGEPORT WAY SW, STE 307 98499 #010-01-1976 L1981
    GS *020 †85
EARLY, James Francis. ■ 98499 #035-03-1955 L1961 **IM** *020 †20
EDGOOSE, Jennifer Y C. 10510 GRAVELLY LAKE DR SW 98499 #035-01-1996 L1998
    FM *020 †18 ‡
EHLERS, William Albert. 9601 STEILACOOM BLVD SW, (CENTER FOR FORENSIC SERVI 98498
    #016-02-1968 L1972 **P CHP** *020
EKLAND, David Alexander. 6103 MOUNT TACOMA DR SW 98499 #025-01-1966 L1971
    PS *020 †85,65
FARAGHER, Jeffrey Paul. 11315 BRIDGEPORT WAY SW 98499 #035-45-2002 L2006
    EM *020 †16
FLINK, Susie Marie. 11315 BRIDGEPORT WAY SW 98499 #025-07-2005 L2005 **EM** *012
FRIEDRICK, Stephen Edmund. 11315 BRIDGEPORT WAY SW 98499 #041-12-1996 L1999
    EM *020 †16
GARRETT, John Michael. 6103 MT TACOMA DR SW 98499 #017-20-1973 L1973 **OPH** *020 †35
GE, Zheng. 5919 LAKEWOOD TOWNE CENTER, BLVD SW #A 98499 #243-16-1987 L2000
    NEP *020 †20
GIST, Steven Brooks. 55 LAGOON LANE NORTH SW, AMERICAN LAKE VA HOSPITAL 98498
    #028-34-1980 L1981 **IM** *020 †20
GOLDFLIES, Myles Ellis. 6103 MT TACOMA DR SW 98499 #016-42-1978 L2006 **PS HS** *020 †65
GORE, Robert Taylor, Jr. 7206 MEADOW PARK RD W, GYNECOLOGY P.S. 98499
    #005-02-1969 L1975 **GYN** *020 †20
HAMILTON, Raymond Darrell. 9601 STEILACOOM BLVD SW 98498 #010-01-1966 L1979
    P *071 ‡
HARRIS, Charles Scott. 9601 STEILACOOM BLVD SW, WESTERN STATE HOSPITAL 98498
    #005-19-2000 L2005 **PYG** *020 †75
HARRISON, Benjamin Paul. 11315 BRIDGEPORT WAY SW 98499 #048-13-1991 L2003
    EM *020 †16
HARVEY, John Patrick. 12401 VINE MAPLE DR SW, NEONATOLOGIST 98499
    #023-12-1997 L2007 **NPM** *100 †55
HENRY, Christopher P. 11315 BRIDGEPORT WAY SW 98499 #003-01-1994 L2001 **EM** *020 †16
HILDEBRAND, Paul Wm. 11315 BRIDGEPORT WAY SW 98499 #011-02-1968 L1985
    EM *020 †16
HIRZ, Dale Lee. 7308 BRIDGEPORT WAY W, STE 201 98499 #018-03-1964 L1971 **ORS** *020 †40
HOFFMEISTER, Richard A. 5605 100TH ST SW 98499 #007-02-1958 L1974 **ORS** *071 †40
HUNT, Aaron James. 9601 STEILACOOM BLVD SW, THE WASHINGTON INSTITUTE 98498
    #028-34-2003 L2007 **PFP** *012
IBRAHIM, Zafar Yab. ■ 98497 #704-02-1981 L1997 **P** *020
JENSEN, Robert William. 11315 BRIDGEPORT WAY SW 98499 #050-02-2001 L2004
    EM *020 †16
KAELEY, Gurjit Singh. 11311 BRIDGEPORT WAY SW, STE 214 98499 #917-25-1990 L1998
    RHU IM *020 †20
KELLY, Michael John. 7525 CUSTER RD W 98499 #038-41-1975 L1989 **FM** *020 †18 ‡
KENEVAN, Robert John. 9315 GRAVELLY LAKE DR SW, STE 103 98499 #026-04-1975 L1976
    PS OTO *020 †45,65
KENNEL, David Robt. 5900 100TH ST SW STE 31, 5920-100TH ST SW #31 98499
    #025-01-1979 L1982 **FM** *020 †18
KIM, Dennis. 11306 BRIDGEPORT WAY SW, UNITB 98499 #005-12-1995 L2002 **IM** *020 †20
KIM, Kevin Taewoo. 6001 100TH ST SW 98499 #024-07-2002 L2003 **HO** *012 †20
KING, Rickey Duwane. 11315 BRIDGEPORT WAY SW 98499 #006-08-1985 L2001
    EM OM *020 †16
KLEIN, Ira Steven. 9601 STEILACOOM BLVD SW 98498 #025-07-1971 L1979 **P** *020
KLEIN, Robert. 8909 GRAVELLY LAKE DR SW 98499 #660-03-1956 L1958 **FM EM** *020 †18
KRISHNASWAMY, Titte S. ■ 98496 #495-53-1964 L1981 **CD IM** *020 †20
KWON, Andrew Ohjoon. 8820 59TH AVE SW 98499 #013-01-1991 L1997 **FM** *020 †18
LANCE, Michael David. 9601 STEILACOOM BLVD SW 98498 #010-01-2003 L2007 **P** *020
LARSON, Michael J. 11315 BRIDGEPORT WAY SW 98499 #028-34-1996 L2000 **EM** *020 †16
LARSON, Wayne Elmer. 6210 75TH ST W STE A200 98499 #018-03-1975 L1978 **FM** *050 †18
LA SALLE, Gerard Vincent. 11315 BRIDGEPORT WAY SW 98499 #035-20-1973 L1979
    EM OS *020 †16
LEE, Donald Doohee. 11311 BRIDGEPORT WAY SW, STE 100 98499 #056-05-1993 L1999
    IM *020 †20
LEE, James Choaming. 11315 BRIDGEPORT WAY SW 98499 #005-15-1995 L1998 **IM** *020 †20
LEE, Young Ho. 8725 S TACOMA WAY 98499 #583-12-1983 L1992 **EM IM** *020 †20
LEISENRING, Sarah E. 9601 STEILACOOM BLVD SW, WESTERN STATE HOSPITAL 98498
    #007-02-1997 L2001 **PFP** *020 †75

LEVINE, Andrew Richard. 7424 BRIDGEPORT WAY W, MEDICAL IMAGING NORTHWEST 98499 #035-09-1979 L1983 **DR NM** *020 †80

LIN, Tom Yih-Chao. 11311 BRIDGEPORT WAY SW, STE 311 98499 #244-04-1997 L2007 **GS** *020

LITEANU, Donald Brent. 9601 STEILACOOM BLVD SW, WESTERN STATE HOSPITAL 98498 #165-01-1978 L1983 **IM PTH** *020 †20

LO, Fredric Thomas. 11315 BRIDGEPORT WAY SW 98499 #025-07-1979 L1989 **EM** *020 †20,16

LONGLEY, Erin Joy. 10510 GRAVELLY LAKE DR SW 98499 #005-06-2000 L2004 **FM** *020 †18

MANETTI, Carlo C. ■ 98496 #957-03-1963 L1971 **AN** *071 †05

MATEO, Godofredo Layug. ■ 98499 #748-01-1958 L1972 **IMG FM** *071

MAYER, Harold. 11311 BRIDGEPORT WAY SW, STE 304 98499 #060-01-1957 L1965 **IM** *074

MC CLUSKEY, Heather. 4909 108TH ST SW 98499 #027-01-1986 L1990 **AN** *020 †05

MC GINNIS, Kelly Ann. 4909 108TH ST SW 98499 #030-05-1986 L1988 **AN** *020 †05

MC GOWEN, Gerry Ann Wentz. 8925 LAKE STEILCM PT RD SW 98498 #021-01-1965 L1971 **GP OS** *071

MC GOWEN, John Henry, III. 5900 100TH ST SW 98499 #021-01-1965 L1971 **D** *071 †15

MESSICK, Peter Carson. 11315 BRIDGEPORT WAY SW 98499 #036-01-2003 L2007 **EM** *100 †16

MEZGER, Barbara Sherry. 11315 BRIDGEPORT WAY SW 98499 #025-07-2000 L2004 **EM** *020 †16

MOHLER, George Thos. ■ 98499 #035-01-1944 L1962 **GP** *071 †18

MORRISON, Michele Debra. 9601 STEILACOOM BLVD SW, WESTERN STATE HOSPITAL 98498 #016-01-1987 L2004 **FM** *020 †18

NAFICY, Kamran. 9601 STEILACOOM BLVD SW, WESTERN STATE HOSP 98498 #517-05-1976 L1986 **CHP P** *020

NG, Angus Yatman. 11315 BRIDGEPORT WAY SW 98499 #026-04-1986 L1989 **EM** *020 †16

NYREEN, Mark Roland. 7424 BRIDGEPORT WAY W, STE 302 98499 #028-34-1984 L1985 **TS VS** *020 †90,85

OLSEN, Ambre Lane. 11307 BRIDGEPORT WAY SW, STE 220 98499 #054-04-1991 L2004 **OBG** *020 †30

OLSEN, Lisa Jane. ■ 98498 #035-03-1998 L2001 **FM** *020 †18

PANZER, Timothy Shawn. 10510 GRAVELLY LAKE DR SW 98499 #054-04-1999 L2001 **FM** *020 †18

PASION, Rolando Cruz. 9601 STEILACOOM BLVD SW, WESTERN STATE HOSP MAILSTO 98498 #748-01-1979 L1987 **P PYG** *030

PAYMASTER, Zaal Homi. ■ 98498 #025-07-2007 *012

PIATOK, Charles Michael. 11315 BRIDGEPORT WAY SW 98499 #054-04-1991 L1993 **AN** *020 †05

PONRAJ, Edson Gerry. 11315 BRIDGEPORT WAY SW 98499 #005-12-2001 L2004 **EM** *020 †16

POWELL, William Shaw, Jr. 11315 BRIDGEPORT WAY SW 98499 #014-01-1985 L1993 **EM** *020 †20,16

REKOW, Alisa Gertrude. 6103 MT TACOMA DR SW 98499 #041-07-1982 L2004 **PS** *020 †65

RICHARDSON, Margaret G. ■ 98498 #036-07-1983 L1984 **PTH** *020 †50

RUSSELL, John Norman. 9601 STEILACOOM BLVD SW, # 16-300 98498 #061-01-1992 L2004 **PFP** *100 †75 ‡

RYNES, Richard Isidor. 11311 BRIDGEPORT WAY SW, STE 214 98499 #041-01-1965 L1997 **RHU IM** *020 †20

SAEED, Mohammad Afzal. 7308 BRIDGEPORT WAY W, ELECTRODIAGNOSIS & REHAB 98499 #704-02-1970 L1981 **PM OS** *020 †60 ‡

SAMUJH, Kamla Devi. 7424 BRIDGEPORT WAY W 98499 #368-01-1976 L1992 **PD** *020 †55

SASHKO, John Robt. 11311 BRIDGEPORT WAY SW, STE 100 98499 #041-13-1988 L1995 **FM** *020 †18

SHERMAN, Lawrence Duane. 11315 BRIDGEPORT WAY SW 98499 #054-04-1979 L1982 **EM** *020 †16

SILER, Thomas T, Jr. 10510 GRAVELLY LAKE DR SW 98499 #047-06-1984 L1995 **IM** *020 †20

SMITH, Robert Keith. ■ 98498 #016-11-1964 L1970 **OBG** *020 †30

SMITH, Stephen Whitlock. 8103 STEILACOOM BLVD SW 98498 #010-01-1980 L2000 **EM IM** *071 †20,16 ‡

SOLLIE, Stanley Carol. ■ 98499 #026-04-1957 L1979 **OPH** *071 †35

SONG, Donald H S. 11311 BRIDGEPORT WAY SW, STE 302 98499 #005-12-1982 L1989 **OBG GP** *020 †30

SONOBE, Bethany Eriko. ■ 98499 #039-01-2007 **IM** *012

SORENSEN, Gregory Wm. ■ 98499 #005-02-1968 L1987 **D** *071 †15

STENE, Danny Owen. 11315 BRIDGEPORT WAY SW 98499 #035-15-1992 L2001 **EM PA** *020 †16

STROMBERG, Murray G, II. 9332 BRIDGEPORT WAY SW 98499 #049-01-1968 L1974 **OBG** *020 †30

TEENY, Steven Michael. 7308 BRIDGEPORT WAY W, STE 201 98499 #054-04-1984 L1989 **GS ORS** *020 †40

TENEYCK, Lisa Dawn. 11315 BRIDGEPORT WAY SW 98499 #028-02-2004 L2007 **EM** *020

THOMAS, Alan Blair. 7308 BRIDGEPORT WAY W, STE 201 98499 #005-12-1995 L2000 **ORS** *020 †40

THOMPSON, Daniel Wayne. 9332 BRIDGEPORT WAY SW, LAKEWOOD MULITCARE CLINIC 98499 #040-02-1973 L1999 **FM** *020 †18

TITOVA, Dina Ch.. 11311 BRIDGEPORT WAY SW, STE 214 98499 #913-82-1989 L2007 **RHU** *020 †20

TODD, Larry. ■ 98499 #005-14-1980 L2003 **AN** *020

UY, Alice Lisa. ■ 98498 #010-02-2006 L2008 **IM** *012

VANIVER, Karen Beth. 6103 MT TACOMA DR SW 98499 #041-01-1986 L2005 **PS** *020 †85,65

VAN PUTTEN, Robert Alan. 9601 STEILACOOM BLVD SW, WESTERN STATE HOSPITAL 98498 #033-06-1978 L1986 **P** *020 †75

VIDRINE, Lawrence Robt. 11307 BRIDGEPORT WAY SW, STE 217 98499 #048-02-1972 L1984 **U** *020 †95

VU, Linh Ngoc. 5202 100TH ST SW 98499 #306-01-1995 L1999 **FM** *020 †18

WALKER, Louis Edmund. ■ 98498 #048-04-1973 L1973 **PS HS** *020 †65

WARD, Lysa S. 11315 BRIDGEPORT WAY SW 98499 #048-12-1992 L2001 **EM** *020 †16

WEISSINGER, Keith A. 7424 BRIDGEPORT WAY W, STE 203 98499 #048-04-1990 L1993 **PD** *020 †55

WHANG, Young Jin. ■ 98498 #422-01-2002 L2002 **IM** *020

WHITE, Matthew. 5920 100TH ST SW, STE 30 98499 #041-02-1967 L1974 **FM** *020 †18 ‡

WILLIAMS, Douglas Kenya. 4909 108TH ST SW 98499 #041-02-1986 L1991 **AN** *020 †05

WILLIAMS, Edward. 6210 75TH ST W STE B100 98499 #024-07-1978 L1986 **OBG** *020 †30

WILSON, James Allan. 5920 100TH ST SW STE 26A 98499 #021-01-1981 L1989 **FM OBS** *020 †18

WINEMILLER, Jay Howard. 11307 BRIDGEPORT WAY SW, STE 217 98499 #054-04-1965 L1974 **U** *020 †95

WONG, Douglas Louis. ■ 98499 #038-06-1983 L1987 **AN** *020 †05

WOOD, Nathanael Richard. 11315 BRIDGEPORT WAY SW 98499 #035-03-2004 L2007 **EM** *020

YEARLEY, Anita Marie. 11315 BRIDGEPORT WAY SW 98499 #030-05-1990 L1998 **EM** *020 †16

YU, Allen Hsin-Bow. 11311 BRIDGEPORT WAY SW, STE 203 98499 #244-02-1978 L1991 **VS** *020 †85

LANGLEY – ISLAND

ALLDERDICE, John Douglas. 3495 BABY ISLAND RD 98260 #048-04-1969 L1975 **EM FM** *020 †16,18

ARVIDSON, Annemarie. ■ 98260 #024-05-1980 L1990 **P** *020 †75

ARVIDSON, Rolf. ■ 98260 #024-01-1953 L1958 **P** *020

BENNETT, Peter G. ■ 98260 #041-01-1952 L1983 **P CHP** *020

FITZPATRICK, Maureen M. ■ 98260 #025-12-1991 L1995 **PTH** *100

HURLOCKER, Julie J. PO BOX 137, 114 2ND ST 98260 #054-04-1979 L1985 **FM** *020 †18

MAC GREGOR, Betsy Adair. ■ 98260 #035-47-1977 **PD** *020 †55

MILLER, Abraham Herbert. ■ 98260 #041-01-1954 L1990 **OM** *071 †20

NOVEMBER, Harry John. ■ 98260 #005-16-1962 L1975 **FM** *071

OZANNE, Roy Douglas. ■ 98260 #056-05-1975 L2005 **OS** *050

SMITH, Robert Bernard. ■ 98260 #035-08-1965 L1966 **PS** *062 †85,65

WHITTEMORE, Stanley L, Jr. PO BOX 137, 114 2ND ST 98260 #016-01-1976 L1979 **FM** *020 †18

ZIMMERMAN, Pearl Grace. ■ 98260 #005-12-1994 L2000 **GPM** *020 †70

LEAVENWORTH – CHELAN

BUTRUILLE, Tony William. 817 COMMERCIAL ST 98826 #040-02-1997 L2002 **FM** *020 †18

DELIDUKA, John Robt. 817 COMMERCIAL ST 98826 #036-01-1982 L1985 **FM** *020 †18

DETWILER, Floy D. 817 COMMERCIAL ST 98826 #019-02-1978 L1999 **FM** *020 †18

HAFERMANN, Maury Daniel. 817 COMMERCIAL ST, CASCADE MEDICAL CENTER 98826 #054-04-1996 L1999 **FM** *020 †18

KOENIG, John Jos. ■ 98826 #028-34-1955 L1957 **GP** *071

PALMER, Bradley Jorgen. 11610 ALPEN VIEW DR 98826 #054-04-1978 L1979 **AN** *020

RICHARDSON, Geoffrey Dana. 817 COMMERCIAL ST, CASCADE MEDICAL CENTER 98826 #054-04-1996 L1998 **FM** *020 †18

ROWE, Ann-Elizabeth. 9880 EAGLE CREEK RD 98826 #026-08-2000 L2003 **EM** *100

SPEER, Marvin E, Jr. ■ 98826 #016-06-1935 L1938 **GP** *071

WEDDLE, Joseph Leland. 817 COMMERCIAL ST 98826 #016-06-1965 L1971 **PM PMM** *020

LIBERTY LAKE – SPOKANE

ABBOTTS, Bruce. 2207 N MOLTER RD, VALLEY YOUNG PEOPLES 99019 #007-02-1986 L1991 **PD** *020 †55

DAME, Hubert Alton. ■ 99019 #005-12-1964 L1965 **FM EM** *071 †85

FREEMAN, Richard Carlos. 2207 N MOLTER RD, STE 101 99019 #561-17-1974 L1977 **EM** *020

GRAUKE, Luke Jonathan. ■ 99019 #054-04-2007 **TY** *012

MESSER, Michelle. 2207 N MOLTER RD, VALLEY YOUNG PEOPLES 99019 #035-03-1992 L1998 **CCP** *020 †55

ROBERTS, Ann Michelle. 2207 N MOLTER RD, VALLEY YOUNG PEOPLES 99019 #033-06-1999 L2004 **PD** *020 †55

SANTIAGO, Anthony John. 2207 N MOLTER RD 99019 #035-03-1998 L2004 **N** *020 †75

STORMO GIPSON, Maj Greer. 2207 N MOLTER RD, VALLEY YOUNG PEOPLES 99019 #032-01-1982 L1997 **PD** *020 †55

STRUEBIN, Marla Kay. 2207 N MOLTER RD, VALLEY YOUNG PEOPLES 99019 #028-03-1984 L1991 **PD** *020 †55

TOEWS, Warren Henry. ■ 99019 #054-04-1971 L1972 **PDC PD** *071 †55

WIRTHLIN, Jeffrey Allen. ■ 99019 #001-02-1999 L2007 **P** *100 †75

LILLIWAUP – MASON

MONTGOMERY, Merlin Walter. ■ 98555 #030-05-1969 L1971 **NM** *020

LONG BEACH – PACIFIC

MC DONNELL, Jessop Mark. ■ 98631 #048-13-1981 L1987 **ORS OMO** *020 †40

OAKES, Robert John. ■ 98631 #039-01-1942 L1943 **FM** *071

LONGBRANCH – PIERCE

CUBBERLEY, David A. ■ 98351 #005-06-1949 L1985 **IM AM** *071 †20

LONGVIEW – COWLITZ

AARON, Shawn Justin. 1615 DELAWARE ST, FAMILY PRACTICE 98632 #005-19-1993 L1996 **FM** *020 †18

ABELL, Nancy Sue. 971 11TH AVE 98632 #005-19-1986 L1991 **PD** *020 †55

ABIDI, Maheen Zehra. 1615 DELAWARE ST, ST.JOHNS MEDICAL CENTER 98632 #704-02-1998 L2007 **ID** *100

AKHAVAN-SARAF, Homayoun. 790 14TH AVE 98632 #517-05-1985 L1997 **OBG** *020 †30

ARNSDORF, Robert Edward. 1615 DELAWARE ST 98632 #005-19-1993 L1998 **PM** *020 †60

AXELROD, Robert Charles. 600 BROADWAY ST, PSYCHIATRY 98632 #048-04-1999 L2003 **P** *020 †75

BAGHERI, Sholeh. 1615 DELAWARE ST 98632 #035-08-1996 L2007 **PCC** *100 †20

BALASU, Anca. 600 BROADWAY ST 98632 #781-01-1995 L2005 **CHP** *020 †75

BARD, Jennifer Lyn. 1230 7TH AVE, KAISER PERMANENTE 98632 #035-03-1995 L1998 **FM** *020 †18

BARONE, Jay Gino. 1614 E KESSLER BLVD 98632 #019-02-1987 L1997 **P PA** *020

BARTLETT, Michael Lee. 1615 DELAWARE ST, FAMILY PRACTICE 98632 #035-03-1995 L1998 **FM** *020 †18

BARTOLOME, Dale Iris. 3905 PENNSYLVANIA ST 98632 #014-01-1980 L1983 **PD** *020 †55

WASHINGTON

LONGVIEW

BEAVER, Roderick William. 1615 DELAWARE ST 98632 #010-02-1999 L2002 **EM** *020 †16

BECKER, Rebecca Lee. 1706 WASHINGTON WAY, KIRKPATRICK FAMILY CARE 98632 #038-43-1990 L1995 **IM** *020 †20

BELL, Sara Elizabeth. 1230 7TH AVE, KAISER PERMANENTE - LONGVI 98632 #040-02-1999 L2006 **PD** *020 †55

BERINSTEIN, Todd Harry. 1801 1ST AVE, STE 3A 98632 #005-06-1989 L1996 **OTO FPS** *072 †45

BERNARDEZ, Domingo B. 1614 E KESSLER BLVD 98632 #748-01-1955 L1967 **GP GS** *071

BITTNER, Cordon Douglas. 1615 DELAWARE ST 98632 #040-02-1975 L1978 **FM** *020 †18

BLACK, David Michael. 625 9TH AVE STE 210 98632 #021-01-1979 L1986 **ORS HS** *020 †40

BLACK, Kathryn L Bushart. 1614 E KESSLER BLVD 98632 #021-01-1979 L1986 **AN** *062 †05

BLACKSTONE, Bruce Gragg. 1615 DELAWARE ST STE G1 98632 #054-04-1978 L1983 **ORS** *020 †40

BLAIR, Philip W. 2736 TERRY AVE 98632 #011-02-1978 L1996 **FM** *020 †18

BOGIN, Vladimir Igorevich. 1706 WASHINGTON WAY 98632 #913-99-1995 L2001 **IM** *020 †20

BOHLING, Bryan Anthony. 971 11TH AVE 98632 #040-02-2000 L2005 **PD** *020 †55 ‡

BOUCHER, John Wm. 1230 7TH AVE 98632 #054-04-1983 L1984 **FM** *020 †18

BOUDREAUX, Denise Jean. 1660 DELAWARE ST 98632 #048-16-2002 L2006 **OBG** *020

BOYLON, James Lindsay. 1106 DOUGLAS ST STE F 98632 #054-04-1965 L1972 **D** *020 †15

BOYLON, Teresita Guerrero. 1106 DOUGLAS ST STE F 98632 #748-11-1964 L1970 **AN OS** *020 †05

BRENC, Paul Fredric. 1230 7TH AVE, KAISER-PERMANENTE/LONGVIEW 98632 #024-16-1987 L1990 **FM** *020 †18

BRIGMAN, Lance Dee. 1004 FIR ST 98632 #030-06-1973 L1974 **FM** *020 †18

BROWN, Michael Abe. 1615 DELAWARE ST 98632 #039-01-1981 L1988 **ORS** *020 †40

BURAK, Norman Louis. 1230 7TH AVE, LONGVIEW PERMANENTE 98632 #051-01-1967 L1998 **EM OPH** *020 †35,16

BURGER, Bradford Wm. 1614 E KESSLER BLVD, ANESTHESIA DEPT 98632 #018-03-1987 L1991 **AN** *020 †05

CABRALES, Steven Xavier. 1615 DELAWARE ST, STE 200 98632 #035-20-1988 L1992 **GS TS** *020 †85

CAMPBELL, Mark Doran. 1615 DELAWARE ST STE G1 98632 #035-03-1995 L2001 **ORS** *020 †40

CARROLL, Michael Peter. 1230 7TH AVE 98632 #039-01-1981 L1989 **FM EM** *020 †18

CAVENS, Phyllis M. 971 11TH AVE 98632 #040-02-1965 L1971 **PD** *071 †55

CAVENS, Travis Ray. 971 11TH AVE 98632 #040-02-1965 L1971 **PD** *071 †55

CHANG, Po-Shen. 1230 7TH AVE, LONGVIEW-KELSO 98632 #028-34-1994 L1997 **FM** *020 †18 ‡

CHESLEY, Chad Cordell. 625 9TH AVE, STE 120 98632 #028-34-1994 L2003 **U** *020 †95

CLARK, Marion Alfred. ■ 98632 #038-06-1947 L1950 **U** *071

CLARKE, William Robt. 1405 DELAWARE ST 98632 #005-14-1970 L2000 **OM AM** *020 †70

CLAWSON, Joseph Paul. 215 NEWT ESTATES RD 98632 #007-02-1957 L1969 **OTO GS** *020 †85,45 ‡

COLLINS, Christopher Joel. 1615 DELAWARE ST 98632 #048-14-2004 L2007 **FM** *020 †18

COPELAND, Stuart Randall. 971 11TH AVE 98632 #047-06-1992 L1999 **PD** *020 †55

COTTERELL, Louis Wm. 1615 DELAWARE ST, NEPHROLOGY 98632 #030-06-1984 L1988 **NEP IM** *020 †20

CRIDER, James Toliver. 1615 DELAWARE ST 98632 #004-01-1983 L1997 **FM** *020 †18

CUNDIFF, David R. 1057 12TH AVE 98632 #041-01-1980 L2000 **PHP FM** *020 †70

CURRIN, Julie Celeste. 784 14TH AVE 98632 #043-01-2004 L2007 **PD** *020 †55

DAVENPORT, Dennis Denby. 1614 E KESSLER BLVD 98632 #012-05-1946 L1949 **D** *071

DAVENPORT, William Danl. ■ 98632 #054-04-1972 L1974 **FM** *020

DAVIS, Jeffrey Rich. 1801 1ST AVE STE 3A, THE NW 98632 #048-04-1995 L2000 **OTO** *020 †45

DAVIS, Joseph Leslie. 1230 7TH AVE 98632 #054-04-1979 L1981 **FM OS** *030 †18

DE'AK, William Ralph. ■ 98632 #005-06-1965 L1978 **FM PD** *071 †55

DICKSON, Julie Anne. 600 BROADWAY ST 98632 #030-06-2002 L2006 **P** *020 †75

DICRISTINA, Marlene L. 1230 7TH AVE 98632 #451-01-2000 L2007 **FM** *020

DING, Mai. 2337 TRILLIUM HTS 98632 #243-44-1982 L2001 **AN** *020 †05

DONNELLY, James Patrick. 1615 DELAWARE ST 98632 #040-02-1955 L1957 **GP** *071

DOWNEY, Robin Lee. 820 11TH AVE, LOWER COLUMBIA HEAD & NECK 98632 #040-02-1982 L1988 **OTO** *020 †45

DUNCKEL, Phyllis Theresa. 1615 DELAWARE ST, FAMILY PRACTICE 98632 #024-07-1991 L1993 **FM** *020 †18

ELTON, William Johnson. 1217 14TH AVE 98632 #041-01-1960 L1966 **PTH NM** *020 †50,28

EVANS, Lisa Marie. 1615 DELAWARE ST, FAMILY PRACTICE 98632 #054-04-2002 L2004 **FM** *020 †18

EY, John Leigh. 971 11TH AVE 98632 #028-02-1964 L2004 **PD** *020 †55

FLEEGE, Herbert Wm. 15 COUNTRY CLUB DR 98632 #030-06-1974 L1979 **AN** *020 †05

FORD, Dennis Mitchell. 1615 DELAWARE ST 98632 #011-02-1984 L1991 **EM IM** *020 †20,16

FORTE, Mario Dino. 1615 DELAWARE ST, STE 200 98632 #054-04-1986 L1990 **GS** *020 †85

FORTNER, George Sherman. 1615 DELAWARE ST, STE 200 98632 #025-01-1977 L1978 **VS GS** *020 †85

FRANZEN, Robert Earl. 1614 E KESSLER BLVD 98632 #028-34-1974 L1979 **EM IM** *020 †20,16

FUESLER, Donald A. 1614 E KESSLER BLVD 98632 #030-05-1951 L1952 **GP** *071

GARNER, Frank A. ■ 98632 #041-09-1974 L2004 **P** *074

GEE, Glenn Ying. ■ 98632 #005-02-1976 L1980 **IM NEP** *020 †20

GEKAS, Lee Ann. 1230 7TH AVE, KAISER PERMANENTE 98632 #025-01-1984 L1988 **FM** *020 †18

GERRITY, Dianne Theresa. 1230 7TH AVE 98632 #028-34-1998 L2005 **PD** *020 †55

GIBSON, John Martin. ■ 98632 #041-13-2004 L2007 **EM** *100

GILLEN, Martin Lawrence. 1615 DELAWARE ST 98632 #025-07-1982 L1987 **EM** *020 †16

GO, George W. 1615 DELAWARE ST 98632 #040-02-1985 L1993 **EM** *020 †20,16

GREDZENS, Aris. 790 14TH AVE 98632 #035-19-1979 L1982 **OBG** *020 †30

GRUBBS, John M. 1230 7TH AVE, MOD F 98632 #048-14-1991 L1999 **FM** *020 †18

GURRAD, Peggy Ellen. 1230 7TH AVE 98632 #005-12-1985 L1989 **IM** *020 †20

HAFNER, Paul G. ■ 98632 #040-02-1941 L1952 **ORS** *071 †40

HALE, Bert Michael. 1052 DOUGLAS ST 98632 #039-01-1975 L1978 **FM** *020 †18

HAMILL, John William. 1615 DELAWARE ST, FAMILY PRACTICE 98632 #020-12-1993 L2001 **MPD PD** *020 †20,55

HANSON, Byron Wm. 1230 7TH AVE 98632 #054-04-1976 L1979 **FM** *020 †18

HARNISH, Erin K. 784 14TH AVE 98632 #017-20-1994 L1997 **PD** *020 †55

HARPOLE, Vern Wm. 1230 7TH AVE, DEPT. OF OCCUPATIONAL MEDI 98632 #040-02-1974 L1994 **FM OM** *020 †18

HENDERSON, Philip H, Jr. 790 14TH AVE 98632 #040-02-1948 L1950 **GYN** *071 †30

HENDERSON, Philip H, III. 790 14TH AVE 98632 #021-01-1976 L1980 **OBG** *020 †30

HICKEY, Thomas Anthony. 1230 7TH AVE, KAISER PERMANENTE LONGVIEW 98632 #016-01-1984 L1990 **FM** *020 †18

HODGE, Heidi Lynn. ■ 98632 #047-06-1993 L1996 **FM** *020 †18

HOPTOWIT, Sophie Michelle. 1055 9TH AVE, STE A 98632 #026-04-1996 L1998 **GS** *020

HOYT, Brian Thomas. 1615 DELAWARE ST, ST JOHN'S MEDICAL CENTER 98632 #040-02-1996 L1999 **EM** *020 †16

HUFFMAN, David Iolas. 1801 1ST AVE, STE 3A 98632 #038-40-1961 L1978 **OTO PS** *071 †45

HUGHEY, Robert Scott. 1615 DELAWARE ST 98632 #017-20-1994 L1998 **IM** *072 †20

HULBERT, James Ernest. 600 TRIANGLE CTR STE 40 98632 #056-06-1966 L1970 **OPH** *020 †35

IEROKOMOS, Alexander P. 820 11TH AVE 98632 #041-01-1978 L1984 **OTO HNS** *020 †45

ISREB, Majd Abdelkader. 1615 DELAWARE ST, ST JOHN MED CTR 98632 #875-01-1994 L2007 **NEP IM** *020 †20

JAIN, Sanjeev. 788 14TH AVE 98632 #056-05-1990 L2001 **AI IM** *020 †20,03

JOLLY, Cynthia Sue. 1614 E KESSLER BLVD 98632 #038-40-1984 L1991 **PS HS** *020 †65

JONES, Julie Lynn. ■ 98632 #033-06-2006 L2006 **IM** *012

JONES, Myles Channing. ■ 98632 #054-04-1959 L1969 **GS** *071 †85

JONES, Robert Andrew. ■ 98632 #033-06-2006 L2007 **EM** *012

KATO, Karen Sachiko. 1615 DELAWARE ST 98632 #028-34-1980 L1983 **PD** *020 †55

KEITH, Virgil Anderson. ■ 98632 #030-05-1966 L1975 **AN** *020

KELLY, Timothy Lawrence. 1615 DELAWARE ST 98632 #305-01-1997 L2003 **APM** *020

KHURTSIDZE, Gregory. 1706 WASHINGTON WAY, KIRKPATRICK FAMILY CARE 98632 #913-23-1995 L2003 **IM** *020 †20

KIEL, Steve John. 1230 7TH AVE 98632 #025-12-1986 L1992 **PYG P** *020 †75

KIM, Choong Ryul. 1615 DELAWARE ST 98632 #051-07-1988 L1993 **RO** *020 †80

KIM, Helen Hyunkee. 1217 14TH AVE 98632 #005-12-1982 L1989 **PTH NM** *020 †50,28

KIRKPATRICK, Donald Mark. 1614 E KESSLER BLVD 98632 #028-02-1986 L1990 **GE** *020 †20

KIRKPATRICK, Neal R. 1706 WASHINGTON WAY, KIRKPATRICK FAM CARE 98632 #056-05-1943 L1949 **IM** *020 †20 ‡

KIRKPATRICK, Richard Alan. 1706 WASHINGTON WAY, KIRKPATRICK FAMILY CARE 98632 #054-04-1972 L1976 **IM CD** *020 †20 ‡

KIRKPATRICK, Wendell C. 1706 WASHINGTON WAY 98632 #028-02-1951 L1953 **FM** *071 †18

KIRMAN, Eileen Ann. 1615 DELAWARE ST, ANESTHESIOLOGY 98632 #025-01-1978 L1980 **AN** *020 †05

KRANZ, Marc. 1615 DELAWARE ST, 4201 ST ANTOINE 98632 #040-02-2003 L2006 **EM** *020 †16

KRETZLER, Jon Edward. 1615 DELAWARE ST 98632 #041-01-1987 L1993 **ORS** *020 †40

KUBITZ, Michael Lee. 784 14TH AVE 98632 #040-02-1979 L1995 **PD** *020 †55

KUBITZ, Rebecca Lynn. 1057 12TH AVE 98632 #040-02-1980 L1995 **GYN** *020 †30

LA CHANCE, Steven Louis. 1801 1ST AVE STE 1A 98632 #016-06-1980 L1988 **U** *020 †95

LARSON, Charles J. ■ 98632 #016-11-1968 L1975 **ORS PM** *071 †40

LARSON, Larry Paul. 1230 7TH AVE 98632 #037-01-1977 L1999 **FM** *020 †18

LASKIEWICZ, Theresa K. 1230 7TH AVE, DEPT OF INDUSTRIAL MEDICIN 98632 #041-14-1985 L1994 **IM** *020 †20

LASSEN, Patrick Mark. 625 9TH AVE STE 120 98632 #040-02-1990 L1999 **U** *020 †95

LEININGER, Kirk Wiltse. 923 FIR ST 98632 #049-01-1997 L2001 **PM** *020 †60

LESLIE, Theodore Lee. 1615 DELAWARE ST, ST JOHN MEDICAL CENTER 98632 #005-06-1988 L1996 **EM** *020 †16

LIBBY, Jocelyn Dianne. 971 11TH AVE 98632 #056-05-2002 L2005 **PD** *020 †55

LIBERATORE, Holly Corrine. 1615 DELAWARE ST 98632 #028-34-2000 L2003 **EM** *020 †16

LINNELL, Daryl William, Jr. 784 14TH AVE 98632 #040-02-1981 L1984 **PD** *020 †55

LITTELL, Ned Giles, Jr. ■ 98632 #005-12-1984 L1989 **P** *075

LITTLE, Thomas Edward. REYNOLDS METALS CO 98632 #030-06-1960 L1961 **OM** *071

LUCKE, Wayne Chas. 1614 E KESSLER BLVD 98632 #040-02-1975 L1980 **EM** *020 †16

LUDWICZAK, Mary Helen. 1660 DELAWARE ST 98632 #016-42-1991 L1995 **OBG** *020 †30

LUH, Albert Hungpei. 1230 7TH AVE 98632 #036-01-1987 L1990 **FM** *020 †18

LUMPKIN, Elizabeth Noel. 1615 DELAWARE ST 98632 #028-03-1995 L1999 **AN** *020 †05 ‡

MAGINN, Patrick Chas. 1801 1ST AVE STE 1A 98632 #056-05-1975 L1981 **U GS** *071 †95

MATLOCK, Gordon Alford. 1615 DELAWARE ST STE 100, BOX 2400 98632 #026-04-1974 L1979 **GE IM** *020 †20 ‡

MCCOY, Anne-Marie B. 1615 DELAWARE ST, FAMILY PRACTICE 98632 #041-12-2000 L2003 **FM** *020 †18

MCNELLIS, Michael I. 1615 DELAWARE ST, BOX 3002 98632 #539-02-1990 L1993 **PCC IM** *020 †20

MC RAE, Laird Donald. ■ 98632 #016-06-1955 L1958 **FM** *071 †18

MEJO, Robert Walter. 600 BROADWAY ST, PEACE HEALTH 98632 #036-07-1962 L1967 **P** *071 †75

MELGAR, Gerardo R. 1057 12TH AVE, 12 SOUTH 8TH ST 98632 #748-02-1991 L1996 **IM** *020 †20

MONTGOMERY, Thomas Scott. 783 COMMERCE AVE, STE 10 98632 #054-04-1977 L1979 **AN** *075 †05

MOOREHEAD, Morrill T. 1217 14TH AVE 98632 #005-12-1984 L2004 **PTH** *020 †50

MORGAN, Christopher John. 1015 OCEAN BEACH HWY, LONGVIEW 98632 #025-01-1976 L2002 **DR EM** *020 †80

MORGAN, William L. ■ 98632 #039-01-1953 L1958 **AN** *071 †05

MORRISON, Susan Laurie. 1615 DELAWARE ST, STE 200 98632 #067-01-1993 L2003 **GS VS** *020 †85

MOSESON, Dane Leonard. 1615 DELAWARE ST, STE 200 98632 #023-01-1972 L1980 **GS SO** *020 †85

MURARI, Vivek Jagat. 1706 WASHINGTON WAY, KIRKPATRICK FAMILY CARE 98632 #495-22-1988 L2004 **IM** *020

MYERS, Kathleen Mc Cartan. ■ 98632 #040-02-1990 L1993 **EM** *020 †16

MYERS, Stanley Alan. 625 9TH AVE STE 120, LONGVIEW UROLOGY PLLC 98632 #040-02-1990 L1997 **U** *020 †95

NAILLON, Michael Joseph. 1615 DELAWARE ST 98632 #040-02-2003 L2006 **IM** *020 †20

NAKASHIMA, James Jimi. 1615 DELAWARE ST, IN MOTION CLINIC 98632 #030-06-1982 L1998 **RHU IM** *020 †20

NAQIB-OSMAN, Laila A. 1217 14TH AVE, LOWER COLUMBIA PATHOLGISTS 98632 #584-01-1985 L2003 **PTH** *020 †50

NASH, Teresa Lee. 748 14TH AVE, INTERNAL MEDICINE B 98632 #041-14-1983 L1990 **IM** *071 †20

NAU, Richard Carl. ■ 98632 #041-12-1966 L1969 **PTH** *071 †50

NELSON, William Robt. 1614 E KESSLER BLVD 98632 #048-13-1970 L1973 **FM** *020 †18

NEVILLE, Lawrence Harvey. 1615 DELAWARE ST, PEACE HEALTH - NEUROLOGY C 98632 #040-02-2000 L2005 **N** *020 †75 ‡

NOEL, Ray Allan. 1230 7TH AVE 98632 #036-05-1969 L1974 **PME ADM** *020 †18

NORQUIST, Stanley Roy. 1614 E KESSLER BLVD 98632 #026-04-1952 L1952 **FM** *071

NORRIS, Mary Elizabeth. 1615 DELAWARE ST 98632 #050-02-1972 L2006 **IM GE** *020 †20
OFSTUN, Milford Stanley. 900 FIR ST STE 1J 98632 #026-05-1956 L1958 **GS TS** *071 †85,90
OSMAN, Hasan Gamal. 1217 14TH AVE, LOWER COLUMBIA PATHOLOGIST 98632 #915-02-1988 L2003 **NM** *020 †28
PENCE, Thomas Victor. 1615 DELAWARE ST 98632 #026-04-1974 L1999 **NEP IM** *020 †20
PENNER, Gary Elliott. 1615 DELAWARE ST 98632 #047-05-1972 L1978 **EM** *020 †16
PETERSON, Patricia J. 748 14TH AVE, INTERNAL MEDICINE B 98632 #049-01-1976 L1979 **IM** *020 †20
PHILLIPS, Todd Anthony. 625 9TH AVE, STE 210 98632 #005-12-1994 L1999 **AN** *020 †05
POLO, Guillermo Castro. ■ 98632 #737-01-1956 L1962 **GP OBG** *071
POTSCHKA, Gretchen Marie. 1615 DELAWARE ST, PEACEHEALTH MEDICAL GROUP 98632 #005-12-1999 L2003 **MPD** *020 †20,55
RAFANO, Cesar P. 921 14TH AVE 98632 #748-02-1981 L1995 **P ADP** *020 †75
RANDALL, Timothy Allen. 1615 DELAWARE ST, FAMILY PRACTICE 98632 #037-01-1990 L1993 **FM** *020 †18
REARDON, Julie Ann. 1615 DELAWARE ST, FP TEAM A 98632 #008-02-1995 L1998 **FM** *020 †18
REIS, Mark Thos. 1615 DELAWARE ST, P O BOX 3002 98632 #016-06-1986 L1994 **ORS OSM** *020 †40
REISNER, James Gordon. 1057 12TH AVE 98632 #030-05-1962 L1967 **OBG** *071 †30
RICHARDS, John E, Jr. 605 BROADWAY ST 98632 #032-01-1974 L1977 **IM EM** *020 †20
ROBERTSON, Bertram C. ■ 98632 #005-12-1951 L1972 **ORS** *071
ROBISON, Horace C, Jr. 339 TRIANGLE CTR 98632 #051-01-1964 L1970 **OPH** *071 †35
ROSENFELD, Richard Neil. 1230 7TH AVE, KAISER PERM 98632 #847-06-1974 L1995 **IM IMG** *020 †20
SACKS, Matthew Jay. 1615 DELAWARE ST 98632 #035-15-1975 L2002 **ON IM** *020 †20
SADOFF, Leonard. 1614 E KESSLER BLVD 98632 #026-04-1954 L1998 **IM ON** *020 †20
SALOUM, Maher H.. 1615 DELAWARE ST 98632 #875-01-1999 L2004 **IM** *020
SANDSTROM, Robert Edward. 1217 14TH AVE 98632 #054-04-1971 L1978 **D DMP** *020 †50
SANTO DOMINGO, Noel E. 1615 DELAWARE ST, CARDIOLOGY PULM & CRIT 98632 #005-19-1991 L1999 **CD IM** *020 †20
SAPIRSTEIN, Mark Michael. 1106 DOUGLAS ST STE D 98632 #036-05-1970 L1977 **GS** *020 †85
SAXER, Jennifer Louise. 784 14TH AVE 98632 #056-05-1998 L2001 **PD** *020 †55
SCHATZEL, Kathleen L. ■ 98632 #030-06-1984 L1992 **PD** *071 †55
SCHILB, Richard Allan. 1615 DELAWARE ST, DEPT ANES ST JOHN MED CTR 98632 #039-01-1984 L1999 **AN** *020 †05
SCHNEIDER, Paul Albert. 1615 DELAWARE ST 98632 #025-01-1984 L1988 **EM FM** *020 †16
SCHOSTAL, Clifford J. 1615 DELAWARE ST, NEUROLOGY 98632 #036-07-1970 L1980 **N** *020 †75
SHAW, John Christopher. 1230 7TH AVE 98632 #003-01-2000 L2004 **MPD** *020 †55,20 ‡
SHERFY, Hilde V W. ■ 98632 #407-16-1949 L1971 **FM EM** *020
SIMONS, Anthony John. 1615 DELAWARE ST, STE 200 98632 #016-42-1988 L1997 **GS CRS** *020 †85,10
SMART, Dean Ralph. 820 11TH AVE 98632 #040-02-1966 L1980 **OTO HNS** *030 †45
SMEENK, Anne Mette K. 971 11TH AVE 98632 #037-01-1986 L1991 **PD** *020 †55
SMITH, Edward Eugene. 1614 25TH AVE 98632 #039-01-1959 L1963 **IM CD** *020
SQUIRES, Natalie Annmarie. 1615 DELAWARE ST 98632 #016-06-2001 L2007 **OFA** *020
STAHL, William Oliver. 1405 DELAWARE ST, OCCUPATIONAL MEDICINE 98632 #040-02-1970 L1990 **GP OM** *020
STARR, Harold Gene. ■ 98632 #048-02-1960 L1962 **GP** *071
STOLERMAN, Irina A. ■ 98632 #913-06-1995 L2001 **IM** *020 †20
STONE, Kenneth Irwin. 1615 DELAWARE ST 98632 #005-12-1976 L1980 **EM** *020 †16
STONE, Marcia Marie. ■ 98632 #005-12-1976 L1980 **GP** *020
STONEKING, Kim Warren. 1615 DELAWARE ST 98632 #048-14-2004 L2007 **FM** *020
STUBER, Paul Jos. 852 COMMERCE AVE 98632 #041-13-1975 L1976 **EM** *020
SUH, Jason Jangwon. 1615 DELAWARE ST 98632 #054-04-1994 L1997 **IM** *020 †20
TABIBI, Reza. 1615 DELAWARE ST 98632 #517-01-1990 L2007 **FM IMG** *020 †18
THOMAS, Harold Andrew, Jr. 1615 DELAWARE ST 98632 #011-02-1976 L1980 **EM** *020 †20,16
THOMPSON, Lori Sue. 1230 7TH AVE 98632 #056-06-1994 L1996 **IM** *020 †20
THORSON, Mark Russell. 748 14TH AVE, INTERNAL MEDICINE B 98632 #054-04-1974 L1976 **IM** *020 †20
TOLBY, Blaine Evan. 971 11TH AVE 98632 #040-02-1975 L1983 **PD OS** *020 †55
TOSSBERG, Thomas Elderkin. 1801 1ST AVE, LONGVIEW UROLOGY CLINIC 98632 #007-02-1963 L1968 **U** *071 †95
TREDENNICK, Trevor Doyle. 1615 DELAWARE ST 98632 #035-01-2000 L2004 **EM** *020 †16
TREYVE, Edward Leon. 1801 1ST AVE STE 3A, ENT CLINIC OF THE NW 98632 #040-02-1976 L1977 **OTO** *020 †45
TRIMBERGER, Daniel Lee, II. 1615 DELAWARE ST 98632 #056-05-2001 L2004 **EM** *020 †16
TURNER, William Taylor. 625 9TH AVE STE 210 98632 #009-04-1983 L1988 **ORS OSM** *020 †40
URMAN, Steven Maxwell. 1015 OCEAN BEACH HWY, LONGVIEW 98632 #040-02-1985 L1999 **DR** *020 †80
VRTISKA, Timothy Francis. 600 TRIANGLE CTR, STE 400 98632 #040-02-1976 L1980 **OPH** *020 †35
WAGNER, John Richard. 1230 7TH AVE 98632 #018-03-1955 L1985 **FM AM** *071
WANG, Min-Guang. 1217 14TH AVE 98632 #243-16-1983 L2006 **PTH HMP** *020 †50
WANG, Xin. 1615 DELAWARE ST, FAMILY PRACTICE 98632 #243-52-1987 L2005 **FM** *020 †18
WESTERFIELD, John F. ■ 98632 #033-06-1991 L1999 **AN** *020 †05
WESTRUP, David Wm. 1230 7TH AVE 98632 #005-15-1983 L1986 **FM** *020 †18
WHELAN, Douglas M. 790 14TH AVE 98632 #005-02-1981 L1989 **OBG** *020 †20
WILFLEY, Faith A. 784 14TH AVE 98632 #056-06-1998 L2006 **PD** *020 †55
WILFLEY, William Anthony, Jr. 1615 DELAWARE ST 98632 #030-06-2000 L2005 **GS** *020 †85
WILSON, Everett Elden. ■ 98632 #005-12-1955 L1956 **AN** *072
WOLGAMOTT, Gregory Alan. 1660 DELAWARE ST 98632 #054-04-1988 L1994 **OBG** *020 †30
WU, Kenneth Randy. 971 11TH AVE 98632 #033-05-2002 L2005 **PD** *020 †55
YILDIRIM, Zafer. 1615 DELAWARE ST 98632 #002-05-1989 L2003 **HO** *020 †20
ZEILENGA, Donald Wm. 1615 DELAWARE ST, CARDIOLOGY PULM & CRIT 98632 #016-11-1967 L1976 **CD IM** *020 †20

LOPEZ ISLAND – SAN JUAN

BRESLOW, Susan A. ■ 98261 #041-01-1967 L1975 **PHP P** *071 †80
DENGLER, George Wolfgang. ■ 98261 #035-19-1955 L1961 **FM** *020 †18
GOODNER, Charles Jos. 2787 LOPEZ SOUND RD 98261 #049-01-1955 L1963 **DIA END** *071 †20
HOFFMAN, Gerhard Heinz. ■ 98261 #054-04-1956 L1958 **R** *071 †80

JANEWAY, Charles Mc Kown. 95 EAGLES ROOST LN 98261 #035-45-1964 L1968 **GE IM** *020 †20
OGSTON, William Duncan. ■ 98261 #803-01-1955 L1976 **P** *071 †75
PHILLIPS, Theodore Jay. ACROSS FROM ISLANDERS BANK, LOPEZ ROAD NORTH 98261 #023-07-1959 L1971 **FM** *071 †18
SIMPSON, David Patten. 98261 #067-01-1957 L1965 **NEP IM** *072 †20
WILSON, Robert Arthur. 2228 FISHERMAN BAY RD, SAN JUAN COUNTY FIRE DIST 98261 #019-02-1992 L1992 **FM** *020 †18
YANG, George. ■ 98261 #016-42-1963 L1967 **NS** *072

LUMMI ISLAND – WHATCOM

BETHUNE, John Edmund. ■ 98262 #064-01-1953 L1983 **IM END** *071 †20
BROWNLEE, Robt T Winston. ■ 98262 #067-01-1959 L2001 **ON** *020

LYLE – KLICKITAT

BRUCKNER, John Mark. ■ 98635 #007-02-1968 L1973 **FM OS** *020 †18

LYNDEN – WHATCOM

ALEXANDER, Steven Jos. 1610 GROVER ST, STE D1 98264 #054-04-1978 L1979 **FM** *020 †18
ARIZ, Charles. 1610 GROVER ST, BLDG C 98264 #010-02-1995 L2006 **DR** *020 †80
ASHLEY, David Geo. 1610 GROVER ST, BLDG C 98264 #005-12-1982 L1990 **DR** *020 †80
BACKER, Laura Kay. 1610 GROVER ST, BLDG C 98264 #017-20-1993 L1997 **DR** *020 †80
BECKMAN, Laura Marie. ■ 98264 #054-04-2007 *012
BEHRNDT, Valerie J. 1610 GROVER ST, BLDG C 98264 #007-02-1992 L1999 **DR** *020 †80
BOSSOLT, Kathryn Ann. 1610 GROVER ST, BLDG C 98264 #050-02-1996 L2000 **DR** *020 †80
BRUCE, Steven John. 1610 GROVER ST, STE C6 98264 #016-11-1979 L1985 **ORS** *020 †40
BUETOW, Peter Christopher. 1610 GROVER ST, BLDG C 98264 #035-01-1986 L2002 **DR** *020 †80
BURDEN, Margaret Helen. 1610 GROVER ST 98264 #025-12-1986 L1990 **FM** *020 †18
CAHALAN, David Daskam. 1610 GROVER ST, BLDG C 98264 #025-07-1990 L1999 **VIR** *020 †20,80
CALDWELL, Robin Wayne. 1610 GROVER ST 98264 #005-12-1988 L1991 **FM** *020 †18
CARPENTER, Kenneth Dan. 1610 GROVER ST, BLDG C 98264 #054-04-1989 L1990 **DR** *020 †80
CRABO, Lars Gustaf. 1610 GROVER ST, BLDG C 98264 #024-01-1986 L1991 **DR NM** *020 †80
DICKSON, David Perry. 500 FRONT ST 98264 #018-03-1982 L1996 **FM GP** *020 †18
FRANKLIN, Jonathan Turner. 1610 GROVER ST, BLDG C 98264 #012-05-1978 L1980 **DR N** *062 †80
HARTWELL, Larry James. 1610 GROVER ST 98264 #028-34-1987 L1990 **FM** *020 †18
HODGE, George Gustave. 1610 GROVER ST, STE C6 98264 #056-05-1965 L1971 **ORS** *020 †40
HUGHES, Robert Milton. 1610 GROVER ST, BLDG C 98264 #056-06-1998 L2004 **RNR** *020 †80
JENSEN, Dag Andre. 1610 GROVER ST, BLDG C 98264 #005-12-1985 L1990 **DR VIR** *020 †80
KELLY, Richard Brawley. 1610 GROVER ST, BLDG C 98264 #030-06-1983 L1987 **DR** *020 †80
KIENZLE, Gregory Deke. 1610 GROVER ST, BLDG C 98264 #026-08-1977 L2002 **R** *020 †80
KITTLESON, Arthur C. ■ 98264 #025-01-1954 L1955 **R** *071 †80
KUKES, Wilbur Leroy. 1610 GROVER ST 98264 #008-01-1966 L1974 **ORS GS** *071 †40 ‡
MEESTER, Walter Danl. ■ 98264 #056-06-1966 L1983 **OM PTX** *071
MICHEL, Steven John. 1610 GROVER ST, BLDG C 98264 #056-06-2000 L2006 **GS** *020 †80
PEDERSON, Bruce Marlin. 1610 GROVER ST, STE D 98264 #026-04-1974 L1975 **FM** *020 †18
PETERSEN, Lyle Dana. 1610 GROVER ST 98264 #026-04-1974 L1975 **FM** *020 †18
PRATT, William David. 469 W BADGER RD, 469 W BADGER ROAD 98264 #005-14-1961 L1999 **FM** *020 †18
RABBANI, Gita Rahnema. 1610 GROVER ST, BLDG C 98264 #026-08-2000 L2000 **AR** *020 †80
SERVID, Lester Paul. ■ 98264 #005-11-1947 L1948 **FM** *071
STOANE, Jason Marsh. 1610 GROVER ST, BLDG C 98264 #035-08-1992 L1998 **RNR** *020 †80
STRAWN, Dale Ardene. ■ 98264 #005-12-1945 L1946 **GP AS** *071
STUDLEY, Matthew Thomas. 1610 GROVER ST, BLDG C 98264 #024-07-1999 L1999 **DR** *020 †80
THORPE, William James. ■ 98264 #028-34-1955 L1995 **PTH NM** *071 †50,28
WOO, Ronald Y G. 1610 GROVER ST, STE C6 98264 #054-04-1977 L1982 **ORS** *020 †40

LYNNWOOD – SNOHOMISH

AL-GHANIM, Hamed Abdulraz. ■ 98037 #528-06-1995 L2004 **FM** *020 †18
ALVIRA, Mariano M. ■ 98037 #847-04-1968 L1974 **ATP CLP** *071 †50
AN, Jennifer Sook. 14930 23RD PL W 98087 #016-42-2008 *012
ARANI, Keerthi N. ■ 98036 #054-04-2008 *012
ASHLING, Kerri Ann. 20200 54TH AVE W, LYNNWOOD MEDICAL CTR 98036 #043-01-1993 L1997 **FM** *020 †18
BERNARDEZ-FU, Robert. ■ 98087 #748-02-1972 L1976 **PM** *020 †60
BLADE, Kristie Lynn. 19116 33RD AVE W, MAILSTOP: A-NO 98036 #045-01-2001 L2003 **IM** *020
BORISH, Stanley David. 19526 64TH AVE W 98036 #048-04-1975 L1976 **OS** *020 †16
BSEIKRI, Mustafa Rashid. ■ 98037 #054-04-2008 *012
BURTON, Ryan Mark. ■ 98087 #054-04-2005 L2005 **AN** *012
BUSCH, Naomi Faye. 19401 40TH AVE W, STE 100 98036 #024-07-2001 L2001 **FM** *020 †18
CANTOR, Jeffrey Biron. 19401 40TH AVE W 98036 #005-18-1989 L1989 **FM** *020 †18
CHILDS, Ruth E. 20200 54TH AVE W 98036 #054-04-1985 L1989 **FM** *020 †18
CHU, Samuel I. 4629 168TH ST SW 98037 #583-02-1983 L1994 **MPD IM** *020 †55,20
CODAY, Arthur, Jr. 19720 68TH AVE W, STE B 98036 #024-01-1993 L1999 **GS** *020
COSTELLO, Paul Christian. 4111 194TH ST SW, CHC-SC LYNNWOOD MEDICAL CL 98036 #035-48-1991 L2000 **FM** *020 †18
ESPINOSA, Karla Marie. ■ 98036 #054-04-1984 L1985 **FM** *020 †18
FREEMAN, Ruth Ann. 19401 40TH AVE W 98036 #010-03-1992 L1998 **IM** *020 †20
FREIER, James Curtis. 20200 54TH AVE W 98036 #025-01-1971 L1972 **FM** *020 †18
GARCIA, Alfa Bormate. 19109 36TH AVE W, STE 109 98036 #748-01-1972 L1985 **AN** *020
GILLETTE, Jimy Edgar. 19116 33RD AVE W 98036 #014-01-1995 L2004 **IM** *020 †20
HALM, Timothy Ann. 19401 40TH AVE W 98036 #034-01-1973 L1976 **FM** *020 †18
HASTINGS, Denise Ann. 20200 54TH AVE W 98036 #025-12-1988 L1992 **IM** *020 †20

HERNANDEZ, Sonia Edith. 4111 194TH ST SW 98036 #005-06-1999 L2001 **FM IM** *020 †18
HIBBERT, Karen Evalene. 19401 40TH AVE W 98036 #054-04-1996 L1998 **IM** *020 †20
HOLLAND, Sundy Rae. 18631 ALDERWOOD MALL PKWY, STE 304 98037 #041-09-1994 L1996 **IM** *020 †20
HUGHES, Grant Cassidy. ■ 98037 #040-02-2001 L2004 **RHU** *100 †20
JIANG, Shan. ■ 98037 #243-21-1988 L2003 **FM** *020 †18
KHURANA, Shelly Kiron. 19116 33RD AVE W 98036 #028-46-1999 L2002 **IM PD** *020 †55,20 ‡
KILGORE, Joshua Edson. ■ 98036 #035-09-2007 L2007 **OBG** *012
KIRKHAM, Lindsay Jack, Jr. ■ 98037 #028-02-1946 L1946 **PHP IM** *071
KLOSS, Herbert. 19109 36TH AVE W, STE 109 98036 #041-14-1977 L1979 **AN IM** *020 †05
KUTSY, Tatyana. 4320 196TH ST SW, STE D 98036 #913-39-1983 L1995 **IM** *020 †20
LAPOINTE, Jennifer Raye. ■ 98037 #037-01-2007 L2007 **PTH** *012
LELAND, Harold Benj. 20200 54TH AVE W 98036 #054-04-1964 L1967 **FM** *020 †18
MACON, James David. 20200 54TH AVE W 98036 #005-19-1979 L1982 **PD** *020 †55
MERKLE, Vernon James. ■ 98036 #030-05-1948 L1957 **OBG** *074 †30
MERRILL, Jeffrey Robt. 7627 196TH ST SW, STE 208 98036 #054-04-1992 L1992 **FM** *020 †18
MONTES, Paul G. 20200 54TH AVE W 98036 #054-04-1978 L1979 **FM** *074 †18
MUMM, Alan Homer. 4208 198TH ST SW, STE 106 98036 #027-01-1969 L1995 **GPM GP** *020 †70
MUTISO, Tolani Barbara. ■ 98036 #577-01-1997 L2004 **FM** *020 †18
NAKONECHNY, Donald Saml. 6825 216TH ST SW, STE E 98036 #028-34-1971 L1972 **PTH FOP** *020 †50
NEWMAN, Jeffrey Stephen. 98087 #035-46-2002 L2002 **D** *100 †15
PAMINTUAN, Helen Padolina. ■ 98037 #748-01-1957 L1986 **P GP** *071
PAYNE, Otis Edd. 19520 66TH AVE W 98036 #045-01-1965 L1969 **P CHP** *020 †75
PESHECK, Paul Edward. 21702 LOCUST WAY 98036 #026-04-1977 L1978 **AN** *020 †05
PHAN, Daniel V. 6508 196TH ST SW 98036 #030-05-1989 L1995 **IM** *020
PIPER, Natalia A. 1504 151ST SW SW 98087 #913-95-1995 L2003 **AN** *020 †20,05
ROACH, Chinda Hopkins. 4111 194TH ST SW, CHC - SC LYNNWOOD MEDICAL 98036 #036-01-1992 L2000 **FM** *020 †18
SALMON, James Alan. 19520 66TH AVE W 98036 #040-02-1978 L1982 **P N** *020 †75
SOSSONG, Norman D. ■ 98036 #016-02-1975 L1976 **IM** *040
TAYLOR-SMITH, Paul John. 6825 216TH ST SW, STE E 98036 #836-01-1973 L1982 **PTH** *020 †50
THORSON, Alix Champin. 4320 196TH ST SW STE D, US HEALTHWORKS 98036 #007-02-1998 L2001 **EM** *020 †16
VILLAVICENCIO, Elisabeth. ■ 98037 #016-06-2002 L2005 **PHO** *012 †55
VOGEL, Arthur Marc. 6825 216TH ST SW, STE E 98036 #035-19-1975 L1976 **ATP** *020 †50
WALL, Eva Margaret. 4028 SERENE WAY 98087 #010-01-1993 L2003 **CCS** *020 †85
WEGERMANN, Alan Kirk. 20200 54TH AVE W 98036 #018-03-1974 L1980 **FM EM** *020 †18
WHANG, Susan Haiyoung. ■ 98087 #035-03-2006 L2006 **GS** *012
WHELAN, Michael F. 19625 68TH AVE W 98036 #028-34-1992 L1998 **PS FPS** *020 †65
WHITE, Almut Oettich. 20200 54TH AVE W 98036 #025-12-1983 L1987 **FM** *020 †18
WIGREN, Carl Walter. ■ 98087 #054-04-2001 L2001 **PTH** *100
WORTHAM, Donald Gene. 19109 36TH AVE W STE 109 98036 #039-01-1981 L1982 **FPS D** *020 †45

MALOTT – OKANOGAN

NAILS, Michael Jos. PO BOX 423 98829 #654-01-1981 L2006 **GP** *071

MANCHESTER – KITSAP

NELSON, Ralph Arthur. ■ 98353 #024-05-1965 L1969 **NO OTO** *071 †45
SHAW, Spencer Wm. ■ 98353 #054-04-1958 L1961 **FM ADM** *020

MANSON – CHELAN

DAME, John Benjamin. ■ 98831 #049-01-2004 L2006 **FM** *100 †18
DANKE, William Ernest. PO BOX 466, 333 WILLOW POINT RD 98831 #054-04-1972 L1973 **FM IMG** *020 †18

MAPLE VALLEY – KING

ALSAGER, Dale E. 20241 269TH AVE SE 98038 #028-79-1994, ▲ L1995 **OMM FM** *020
ANDERSON, Duane Alan. 25528 SE 224TH ST 98038 #016-42-1995 L1998 **EM** *020 †16
DAVIES, Stacy J. 22216 SE 272ND ST 98038 #060-01-1988 L1995 **FM** *020 †18
FUNK, Catrina Martha C. 23919 225TH WAY SE, STE B 98038 #039-01-1998 L2007 **OBG** *020 †30
GARCHA, Devinder Kaur. ■ 98038 #041-15-2007 L2007 **IM** *012
HASHEM, Ahmad. ■ 98038 #875-01-1990 *100
JANGALA, Chester Edmond. 26907 MAPLE VALLEY HWY, BLACK DIAMOND RD SE 98038 #054-04-1983 L1986 **FM** *020
KATTAR, Mireille. ■ 98038 #605-02-1991 L1998 **PTH** *020 †50
PAN, Roxanne Suitze. 23919 225TH WAY SE 98038 #005-14-2000 L2004 **PD** *020 †55 ‡
ROWBOTTOM, Samuel Wilby. ■ 98038 #016-43-1945 L1947 **FM OPH** *071 †18
SWEIGER, David Wm. 23846 SE KENT KANGLEY RD 98038 #028-03-1981 L1984 **FM** *020 †18
SWEIGER, James Howard. 23846 SE KENT KANGLEY RD 98038 #028-02-1948 L1999 **GP OS** *072

MARYSVILLE – SNOHOMISH

ANDREONI, Michael John. 11603 STATE AVE, STE G 98271 #054-04-1984 L1987 **IM** *020 †20
ANDREWS, Don Bruce. 4420 76TH ST NE, THE EVERETT CLINIC 98270 #005-19-1985 L1986 **IM** *020 †20
ANHOLM, Anne Cherie. 4420 76TH ST NE, THE EVERTT CLINIC 98270 #054-04-1989 L1989 **OBG** *020 †30
ATAL-BARRIO, Alka. 4420 76TH ST NE 98270 #005-11-1989 L1994 **PD** *020 †55
BAER, Carol Lynn. 4420 76TH ST NE 98270 #054-04-1984 L1985 **PD** *020 †55
BASTA, Robert Danl. 4420 76TH ST NE 98270 #040-02-1971 L1994 **FM** *020 †18

BEARD, Christopher Mathew. 4420 76TH ST NE 98270 #005-06-1999 L2002 *020 †18
CLARK, Harold Gene. 4404 80TH ST NE 98270 #054-04-1985 L1988 **FM** *020 †18
DABESTANI, Ardeshir Adi. 98271 #054-04-2007 L2007 **IM** *012
DE LA CRUZ, Eileen. 4420 76TH ST NE 98270 #016-06-1992 L1996 **IM** *020 †20
DUGAW, John Edward, Jr. 4420 76TH ST NE 98270 #030-06-1971 L1977 **FM FPG** *020 †18
DUPREE, David Warren. 4420 76TH ST NE 98270 #021-05-1984 L1990 **EM IM** *020 †16
ERSKINE, Evangeline Viola. 9710 STATE AVE 98270 #005-14-1992 L1993 **FM** *020 †18
FELTNER, Roland V. 4420 76TH ST NE, EVERETT CLINIC 98270 #038-41-1984 L1987 **FM** *020 †18
GAN, Evangeline Cua. 11603 STATE AVE, PROVIDENCE PHYSICIAN GROUP 98271 #748-01-1992 L1998 **MPD IM** *020 †20,55
GLEIN, Robert W. 4404 80TH ST NE 98270 #028-34-1953 L1955 **GP** *071
GUTIERREZ-RIVAS, Maria. 9710 STATE AVE 98270 #341-03-1996 L2003 **FM** *100
HO, Santosa. 1602 4TH ST 98270 #306-01-1984 L1994 **IM GP** *020
HOLLAND, Mark Christopher. 4404 80TH ST NE 98270 #005-19-1982 L1985 **FM** *020 †18
JARAMILLO, Pepito Mencero. 98270 #748-07-1957 *071
JENKS, Michael John C. 4420 76TH ST NE 98270 #005-12-1976 L1980 **IM** *071 †20
KAMMEYER, Ann Carol. 1416 8TH ST STE 1 98270 #030-06-1977 L1981 **FM** *020 †18
KANG, Seayong. 4420 76TH ST NE 98270 #583-03-1988 L2006 **IM** *020 †20
KEITHLEY, Lisa. 4420 76TH ST NE 98270 #041-09-1997 L2004 **FM** *020 †18
LABIB, Labib Albert. 11603 STATE AVE, STE G 98271 #915-02-1967 L1986 **IM** *020 †20
LARTER, William Edward. 4420 76TH ST NE 98270 #054-04-1971 L1977 **PD ID** *020 †55
MATA, Jose Matthew. 9710 STATE AVE 98270 #005-02-2002 L2006 **FM** *100 †18
MC CLINCY, Michael Sean. 4420 76TH ST NE, THE EVERETT CLINIC 98270 #023-12-1994 L2006 **FM** *020 †18
MC CRAE, Spencer Chas. ■ 98271 #035-09-1943 **ORS** *071 †40
MINA, Christopher Louis. 98271 #045-01-1991 L1996 **AN** *020 †20
NUESCA, Joyce Ramos. 9710 STATE AVE 98270 #748-10-1998 L2005 **FM** *020 †18
O'KINSELLA, Stacey E. 4420 76TH ST NE 98270 #056-06-1993 L1999 **FM** *020 †18
POIRIER-MC NEILL, Steven. 4420 76TH ST NE 98270 #036-01-1990 L1990 **FM** *020 †18
REHRL, Matthew D. 4420 76TH ST NE, THE EVERETT CLINIC 98270 #048-04-1993 L1993 **FM** *020 †18
SAINI, Mandeep Singh. 4420 76TH ST NE, EVERETT CLINIC 98270 #056-06-2002 L2002 **IM** *020 †18
SANDERS, Greg Stephen. 9710 STATE AVE 98270 #005-06-1989 L1989 **FM** *020 †18
SICOTTE, Jules Edgard. ■ 98271 #067-03-1957 L1969 **P** *071
SMITH, Philip Oliver. 4404 80TH ST NE 98270 #005-14-1977 L1980 **FM** *020 †18
STEADMAN, Zakiya Aisha. 4420 76TH ST NE 98270 #041-13-2001 L2005 **FM** *020 †18
SWANKE, William Roy. 15414 SMOKEY POINT BLVD 98271 #041-13-1968 L1991 **P** *020 †75
TERRY, Richard Newman. 4420 76TH ST NE, THE EVERETT CLINIC 98270 #035-06-1977 L1981 **IM IMG** *020 †20
THORDARSON, Nancy Orcutt. 4420 76TH ST NE 98270 #054-04-1986 L1988 **PD** *020 †55
VAN MIEGHEM, John Paul. ■ 98270 #054-04-2008 *012
WANG, Johanna. 4420 76TH ST NE 98270 #035-19-1997 L1999 **IM** *020 †20
YATES, Fred Thos. 1630 GROVE ST, TRADITIONS MEDICAL CLINIC 98270 #005-15-1975 L1987 **FM NPM** *020

MAZAMA – OKANOGAN

GODE, Richard Oliver. ■ 98833 #067-01-1960 L1966 **P CHP** *071 †55,75
LA VECK, Gerald D. ■ 98833 #054-04-1951 L1952 **PD PHP** *071 †55

MCCHORD AIR FORCE BASE – PIERCE

ANDRUS, John Richard. 690 BARNES BLVD, ATTN: CREDENTIAL OFFICE 98438 #023-12-1993 L1996 **GPM** *020 †18,70
BROWN, Roy C. 690 BARNES BLVD, ATTN CREDENTIAL OFFICE 98438 #048-02-1977 L1998 **OM GP** *030 †70
GERBER, Richard Jason. 690 BARNES BLVD, 62ND MDG 98438 #018-03-2000 L2001 **PD** *020 †55
KOESTER, Rita Lynn. 690 A ST, ATTN: CREDENTIAL OFFICE 98438 #019-02-1984 L1988 **PD** *020 †55
LAMMERS, Jonathon Vincent. 160 G ST STE 204, 62D MEDICAL GROUP 98438 #023-12-1999 L2000 **FM** *020 †18
LE VASSEUR, John Gregory. 690 A ST, 62 MDG/SGQ 98438 #023-12-1990 L1992 **D** *020 †15
NORTH, April Michelle. 690 A ST, 62 MDG/SGQ 98438 #025-12-1997 L2004 **FM** *020 †18
RAY, Maggie Lee Corbett. ■ 98439 #045-01-2001 L2007 **OBG** *020 †30
SPENCE, Timothy A. 690 BARNES BLVD, MCCORD AFB WA 98438 #048-04-2002 L2004 **PD** *020

MCCLEARY – GRAYS HARBOR

ANDREWS, Shawn Michelle. 322 S BIRCH ST 98557 #054-04-1994 L1996 **FM** *020 †18 ‡
MACKE, Edward Ronald. 322 S BIRCH ST 98557 #054-04-1974 L1977 **FM** *020 †18
OGILVIE, Patrick David. 322 S BIRCH ST 98557 #005-12-1994 L1994 **FM** *020 †18

MCKENNA – PIERCE

ALI, Karriem Hakim. PO BOX 49 98558 #005-11-1988 L1994 **PA ILI** *050 ‡
SANDBERG, Jon Drew. ■ 98558 #016-11-1964 L1970 **IM** *071

MEAD – SPOKANE

AMEND, Dexter Roland. ■ 99021 #040-02-1947 L1949 **U FOP** *071 †95
FERNAU, Walter August, Jr. ■ 99021 #028-02-1948 L1951 **PD** *071
JANSEN, Elizabeth Marie. ■ 99021 #038-40-2004 L2007 **FM** *020 †18
PENNOCK, John Chas. ■ 99021 #039-01-1984 L1991 **FM** *071
SHERMAN, Joseph Wm. 4206 E DAY MT SPOKANE RD 99021 #017-20-1984 L1987 **FM** *020
SMITH, John W. ■ 99021 #005-12-1951 L1952 **OS GP** *071

MEDICAL LAKE – SPOKANE

AKPAMGBO, Jane-Frances. 725 N STANLEY ST STE A, JA MEDICAL CTR PS 99022 #690-06-1991 L2003 **FM** *020 †18

BASNILLO, Jaime Yamut. MAPLE ST 99022 #748-09-1974 L1984 **P N** *020

BRANSTETTER, Vanessa Rain. ■ 99022 #031-01-2002 L2005 **EM** *020 †16

DACANAY, Evangeline V. MAPLE ST 99022 #748-01-1978 L1991 **P PYG** *020 †75

GOLDEN, Michael Saml. ■ 99022 #005-14-1968 L1974 **CD** *071 †20

GWINN, Douglas Ralph. 317 N BROAD ST 99022 #028-03-1980 L1993 **FM** *020 †18

HOPPS, Christopher Robin. PO BOX A 99022 #016-02-1966 L1979 **P** *020 †75

KOBARA, Thomas Yoji. ■ 99022 #016-06-1966 L1967 **DMP FM** *071 †50 ‡

LARIOSA, Marietta Lacaya. MAPLE ST 99022 #748-11-1976 L1992 **P PYG** *030 †75

MAMERTO, Blesilda Adolfo. ■ 99022 #748-08-1980 L1984 **IMG** *020

MONTENEGRO, Maria Lydia S. LAKELAND VILLAGE 99022 #748-01-1972 L1983 **P GP** *020 ‡

NELSON, Averly Henry. EASTERN STATE HOSPITAL 99022 #054-04-1970 L1972 **P IM** *020 †75

ROTCHFORD, John Gibbons. MAPLE ST 99022 #056-06-1945 L1948 **P IMG** *071 †30

SIMANGAN, Dodds Rosales. MAPLE ST 99022 #748-08-1980 L1984 **P** *020

MEDINA – KING

ANDERSON, Daniel H. ■ 98039 #056-06-1955 L1956 **OS P** *030 †75

BIDGOOD, Michael Carl. ■ 98039 #054-04-1971 L1972 **ORS** *020 †40

BOZARTH, Xiuhua Liang. ■ 98039 #243-72-1990 *071

GANNAN, Robert Michael. 2607 EVERGREEN PT RD 98039 #035-45-1973 L1978 **GE IM** *020 †20

HONG, Inpow. ■ 98039 #047-05-1967 L1979 **P** *020 †75

JONES, Hugh Warren. ■ 98039 #004-01-1938 L1941 **PTH** *071 †50

KROPP, Robert John. ■ 98039 #054-04-1965 L1966 **PS** *020 †65

MADHANI, Dhanwant J. 2614 EVERGREEN PT RD 98039 #495-01-1960 L1971 **ORS** *062 †40

MANNING, Jean Rainey. ■ 98039 #021-01-1980 L1995 **OPH** *071 †35

NGUYEN, Thuy Quynh. ■ 98039 #054-04-1994 L1996 **FM** *020 †18 ‡

PARK, Jin Soo. ■ 98039 #583-02-1962 L1972 **VS GS** *071 †85

PRICE, Christine Hervey. ■ 98039 #054-04-2002 L2002 **AN** *100

ROGERS, Richard Crosby. ■ 98039 #024-01-1960 L1969 **TS** *071 †85,90

ROZGAY, Clarence E. ■ 98039 #030-06-1949 L1950 **PD** *071 †55

SEELEY, James Albert. ■ 98039 #010-01-1960 L1965 **ORS** *071 †40

MERCER ISLAND – KING

ABRAMS, Ronald Earl. 7683 SE 27TH ST # 367 98040 #054-04-1969 L1970 **AN** *020 †05

ADDISON, John Hamilton. 7707 SE 27TH ST, STE 104 98040 #054-04-1979 L1980 **IM IMG** *020 †20

AIRUT, Carole. ■ 98040 #010-02-1994 *100

ALLISON, Kimberly H. ■ 98040 #035-09-2001 L2004 **PTH** *020 †50

AMIRI, Golriz. ■ 98040 #517-06-1976 L2003 **FM** *100

ANDERSEN, Stig Budtz. ■ 98040 #025-01-1957 L1960 **OBG** *071 †30

ARONSON, Charles Erwin. ■ 98040 #054-04-1967 L1968 **OPH** *020 †35

ARVANITIDIS, Alexander N. ■ 98040 #418-02-1964 L1985 **IM** *020 †20

ASMUTH, Michele. 5820 W MERCER WAY 98040 #051-04-1978 L1981 **FM** *020 †18 ‡

AUYONG, David Benjamin. ■ 98040 #054-04-2002 L2007 **AN** *100 †05

BAGAI, Shelly N. ■ 98040 #054-04-2006 L2006 **OPH** *012

BARON, Frank. 8435 SE 68TH ST STE 118, ISLAND DERM 98040 #041-01-1975 L1976 **D IM** *020 †20,15

BAVENDAM, Frederick A, Jr. ■ 98040 #041-01-1937 L1939 **R NM** *071 †80,28

BEATTIE, Kathryn Dolecek. ■ 98040 #036-01-1992 L2007 **PD** *020 †55

BENITEZ, Elias Ramon. 3239 74TH AVE SE 98040 #007-02-2004 L2005 **IM** *020 †20

BENNETT, Gregory Earl. ■ 98040 #054-04-1986 L1990 **EM** *020 †16

BERNSTEIN, Aaron. ■ 98040 #803-09-1942 L1952 **AN OS** *071

BLOUNT, Patricia. 6163 93RD AVE SE 98040 #012-01-1985 L1986 **GE IM** *020 †20

BRAND, Patricia Nancy. 4445 FOREST AVE SE 98040 #917-30-1978 L1980 **AN** *020 †05

BREDA, Uri Wilhelm. ■ 98040 #154-07-1963 L1966 **GS** *071 †85

BROOKE, Marvin M. 7707 SE 27TH ST, STE 104 98040 #012-05-1975 L1976 **PM** *020 †60

BRYAN, Vincent Edward. 9655 SE 36TH ST, STE 110 98040 #016-06-1966 L1969 **NS GP** *050 †25

BUCK, Charles Edward. ■ 98040 #017-20-1947 L1954 **PTH** *071 †50

BUCKNER, Fillmore. ■ 98040 #054-04-1952 L1954 **LM OBG** *071 †30

CASSERD, Frederick. 3236 78TH AVE SE, STE 200 98040 #040-02-1950 L1954 **IM** *071

CECH, Amy L. ■ 98040 #048-12-2003 L2003 **GS** *012

CHANG, Chu-Ping. ■ 98040 #244-02-1974 L1977 **AN CCM** *030

CHEN, Jimmy Chihhsien. 9725 SE 36TH ST STE 212 98040 #041-09-1991 L1994 **P PYG** *020 †75

CHRISTENSEN, John R, II. ■ 98040 #018-03-1947 L1951 **OTO** *071 †45

COE, Robert C. ■ 98040 #024-01-1950 L1953 **GS TS** *071 †85,90

COLLINS, Joanna Rose. ■ 98040 #041-01-1992 L1998 **DR AR** *020 †80

CONNOLLY, Nicholas Charle. ■ 98040 #030-06-2005 L2007 **GS** *020

CORRIGAN, Shannon Taylor. ■ 98040 #054-04-1992 L2002 **EM** *020 †16

COSSETTE, Suzanne Kay. 7711 SE 27TH AVE, VIRGINA MASON MERCER ISLAN 98040 #026-04-1994 L1996 **IM** *020 †20

COURLAS, Sharon Dinneen. 3003 77TH AVE SE 98040 #051-07-1978 L1982 **OS IM** *030 †20

DAIFUKU, Richard. ■ 98040 #054-04-1983 L1995 **ID IM** *050 †20

DAIN, Deborah Susan. ■ 98040 #005-02-1978 L1996 **OBG** *020 †30

D'ANDREA, Francis Xavier. ■ 98040 #054-04-02-1969 L1990 **PD GP** *020 †55

DAVIS, Matthew Edward. ■ 98040 #048-12-2003 L2007 **SCI** *012

DEMOPULOS, Peter Andrew. ■ 98040 #005-11-1981 L1989 **CD** *020 †20

DER YUEN, Douglas. ■ 98040 #005-02-1964 L1972 **OBG** *071 †30

DINTZIS, Suzanne Martha. ■ 98040 #005-11-1993 L1997 **PTH** *020 †50

DORER, Russell Kenneth. ■ 98040 #054-04-1998 L2006 **HMP** *020 †50

DUNNER, David Louis. 7525 SE 24TH ST STE 400 98040 #028-02-1965 L1978 **P** *020 †75 ‡

EDMONDS, Sandra G B. ■ 98040 #051-01-1972 L1974 **EM** *020 †16

ELLNER, Julie. 2553 76TH AVE SE, ASSOCIATES, INC, P.S. 98040 #005-14-1990 L1993 **PD** *020 †55

ESCOBEDO, Eva Marie. 7705 W MERCER WAY 98040 #005-11-1985 L1992 **DR** *020 †80

EVANS, Elizabeth Moore. ■ 98040 #048-04-2000 L2006 **PD** *020 †55

FERSE, Richard Alan. ■ 98040 #054-04-1970 L1971 **EM** *020 †16

FLAKE, Charles Robt. 3003 ISLAND CREST WAY 98040 #054-04-1979 L1983 **OBG** *020 †30

FRANKLIN, Abby. 3236 78TH AVE SE STE 200 98040 #038-40-1948 L1954 **IM** *071 †20

FRANKLIN, Seth Bernard. 3236 78TH AVE SE, STE 200 98040 #054-04-1986 L1988 **IM** *020 †20

FRISCH, Jane E. ■ 98040 #028-02-1934 L1934 **OS PHP** *071

GARCIA, Faustino V. ■ 98040 #748-02-1952 L1964 **CLP PTH** *062 †50

GELFAND, Martin David. ■ 98040 #023-07-1962 L1969 **GE IM** *071 †20

GEORGE, Stephen A. ■ 98040 #064-01-1975 L1998 **FM** *071 †16,18

GIBBONS, Robert Philip. ■ 98040 #035-45-1961 L1962 **U** *071 †95

GINSBERG, Holly Michelle. ■ 98040 #041-01-1998 L2006 **PD** *020 †55

GLASS, Lee Steven. ■ 98040 #054-04-1983 L1985 **FOP** *050

GLASSY, Danette Swanson. 2553 76TH AVE SE, MERCER ISLAND PEDS ASSOCS 98040 #054-04-1986 L1988 **PD** *020 †55

GOTTESMAN, James Edward. 8288 MERRIMOUNT DR 98040 #005-02-1970 L1973 **U** *020 †95

GOTTFRIED-JAFFE, Clara. ■ 98040 #154-07-1937 OS *071

GREISMAN, Harvey Allan. ■ 98040 #024-01-1998 L2004 **HMP PTH** *050 †50

GRESCH, Elizabeth Evans. 7803 SE 27TH ST STE 2 98040 #005-02-1965 L1997 **OM IM** *020 †70

GRONHOVD, Robert Glen. ■ 98040 #187-11-1967 L1978 **ON GS** *020 †85

HARDY, Paul E. ■ 98040 #028-34-1951 L1956 **IM** *071 †20

HATHAWAY, Tanya Rosanne. 8435 SE 68TH ST, STE 118 98040 #054-04-2002 L2006 **D** *020 †15

HECKBERT, Susan Russell. ■ 98040 #038-06-1981 L1982 **OS GPM** *020 †20

HERAUD-LARRANAGA, Jose. 7707 SE 27TH ST, STE 104 98040 #737-01-1967 L2007 **IM** *100

HISKEN, Eric Carnot. ■ 98040 #028-02-1977 L1985 **IM GE** *020 †20

HOLMAN, Colin B. ■ 98040 #041-01-1943 L1944 **R** *071 †80

HOOD, Robert Frederic. ■ 98040 #007-02-1949 L1968 **N P** *071 †75

HOOVER, J Joanne. ■ 98040 #016-11-1960 L1968 **PHP GPM** *071

HORNSTEN, Tom Robert. ■ 98040 #038-06-1962 L1967 **CD** *071 †20 ‡

HSIEH, Julie Yuanju. ■ 98040 #048-04-2003 L2006 **FM** *020

HUGHES, Allison. 2835 82ND AVE SE STE 21, MERCER ISLAND DERMATOLOGY, 98040 #016-42-2001 L2005 **D** *020 †15

HUTTENLOCHER, John Todd. ■ 98040 #007-02-1975 L1993 **EM FM** *020 †18,16

IKAI, Sue Ann. 7707 SE 27TH ST, STE 104 98040 #422-01-1986 L1999 **IM** *020 †20

JAECKS, Eric Paul. 7687 85TH PL SE 98040 #054-04-1991 L1994 **IM** *020 †20

JIN, Catherine Ying. 7707 SE 27TH ST, STE 104 98040 #054-04-1999 L2003 **FPG FM** *020 †18

KARLSBERG, Dana Kathryn. ■ 98040 #054-04-2006 **FP** *012

KASK, Linda E. ■ 98040 #005-06-1964 L1971 **IM** *071

KLAR, Theodore Francis. ■ 98040 #957-03-1958 L1967 **AN** *020 †05

KORMAN, Helen Shirley. ■ 98040 #065-01-1977 L2002 **AN** *020 †05 ‡

KRUPP, Brent Michael. ■ 98040 #054-04-1998 L1998 **AN** *100

KUNDAHL, Paul Chas. ■ 98040 #023-01-1942 L1949 **AN** *071 †05

LABAND, Manfred Max. ■ 98040 #035-19-1954 L1959 **OBG** *071 †30

LACRAMPE, Marc Jeffrey. ■ 98040 #048-02-1989 L1999 **DR** *020 †80

LACY, William E. ■ 98040 #016-11-1950 L1952 **GP** *071

LAURNEN, Edwin Leslie. 3236 78TH AVE SE, WASHINGTON ORTHOPAEDIC SVC 98040 #007-02-1958 L1968 **ORS OSS** *071 †40

LEFFMAN, Henry. ■ 98040 #286-01-1935 L1958 **N** *071 †75

LEVITT, Ari Simon. 11 ELDORADO DR 98040 #054-04-1997 L2001 **FM** *020 †18

LINDNER, Diana Egle B. 7240 86TH AVE SE 98040 #132-01-1965 L1972 **PD END** *020 †55

LOEWENBERG, Gerda. ■ 98040 #407-33-1955 L1961 **GP** *020

LOGAN, Gordon A. ■ 98040 #035-01-1951 L1953 **CD** *071 †20

LUKE, John James. ■ 98040 #917-07-1980 L1992 *100

LUKIN-WILLIAMS, Cara L. ■ 98040 #016-02-1989 L2003 **AN** *020 †05

MANDELKORN, Theodore D. 2553 76TH AVE SE 98040 #041-12-1966 L1969 **PD** *020 †55

MANNIK, Mart. ■ 98040 #038-06-1954 L1959 **RHU IM** *071 †20

MANUEL, Alexander G. ■ 98040 #035-20-1927 L1949 **IM** *071

MARTIN, James Craven, Jr. 3236 78TH AVE SE, STE 200 98040 #038-40-1988 L1990 **IM** *020 †20

MASTER, Samir Pankaj. ■ 98040 #016-06-1993 L1993 **D** *100

MC COLLUM, Richard Geo. 4155 BOULEVARD PL 98040 #041-01-1961 L1969 **ORS** *071 †40

MC CONNELL, Fiona Aline. ■ 98040 #035-06-1993 L2005 **PD** *020 †55

MC NEELY, William F. ■ 98040 #024-01-1950 L1950 **IM CD** *071 †20

MILLER, Brady Garland. ■ 98040 #048-12-2003 L2006 **HO** *012 †20

MITTAL, Neeti. 7707 SE 27TH ST STE 104, MERCER ISLAND PRIMARY CARE 98040 #495-34-1991 L1999 **IM** *020 †20

MIYATA, Kenichi Timothy. ■ 98040 #056-06-2006 L2006 **GS** *012

MURBURG, M Michele. ■ 98040 #035-46-1978 L1983 **P** *050 †75

MURPHY, Margaret Jean. ■ 98040 #028-34-1985 L1986 **PD** *020 †55

NAFICY, Homayoun. ■ 98040 #517-01-1958 L1983 **OBG GS** *071 †30

NERKAR, Manisha Sandip. 7707 SE 27TH ST, STE 104 98040 #495-19-1992 L1999 **IM** *020 †20

NOTHSTEIN, Donald Lou. ■ 98040 #054-04-1954 L1956 **PTH** *071 †50

OGILVIE, James Thos. 3003 77TH AVE SE, FARMERS LIFE INSURANCE 98040 #024-01-1963 L1969 **IM OS** *030

OLSON, Hilding Harold. ■ 98040 #040-02-1943 L1944 **GS CRS** *072 †85

PASCUALY, Ofelia Marcella. ■ 98040 #264-04-1983 L1985 **P** *020 †75

PAULSON, Thomas Eli. 7527 SE 24TH ST, STE 200 98040 #056-06-1984 L1988 **FM** *020 †18

PERTOWSKI, Carol Ann. ■ 98040 #021-01-1986 L1986 **PHP IM** *062 †20

PETERSON, John Cleve, III. 7030 N MERCER WAY 98040 #018-03-1968 L1969 **IM FPG** *020 †20,18

PHAN, Stephanie Tuyetnga. 3236 78TH AVE SE, EYE CLINIC OF BELLEVUE AT 98040 #005-02-1997 L2006 **OPH** *020 †35

PHILLIPS, James W. ■ 98040 #005-11-1939 L1947 **OTO** *071

PONHOLD, Helmut. ■ 98040 #154-01-1967 L1970 **AN** *020 †05

PUGSLEY, Jeffrey Morgan. ■ 98040 #010-01-2005 L2005 **DR** *012

QUINN, Hal Cooper. 2553 76TH AVE SE 98040 #048-15-1983 L1984 **PD** *020 †55

RAPHAELY, Doron E. ■ 98040 #024-05-1989 L1991 **P** *020 †75

RATTAZZI, Teresa. ■ 98040 #561-10-1964 L1978 **NEP IM** *020 †20

REAGAN, Thomas Richard. 5220 W MERCER WAY 98040 #026-04-1965 L1970 **TS** *020 †85

REEVES, Faith. 3236 78TH AVE SE, STE 200 98040 #055-01-1984 L1987 **IM NM** *020 †20,28

REIMANN, Julie Dylan. ■ 98040 #054-04-11-2003 L2003 **DMP** *100 †50

RIZEN, Michael. 3236 78TH AVE SE, EYE CLINIC OF BELLEVUE AT 98040 #005-02-2001 L2006 **OPH** *100 †35

ROSENSTEIN, David Hillel. ■ 98040 #041-12-1960 L1961 **P** *071 †75

ROSOFF, Leonard, Jr. ■ 98040 #005-06-1968 L1976 **IM OS** *071 †20

SAYERS, Gwen Melanie. ■ 98040 #836-01-1972 L1979 **D** *020 †20

SCHER, Maryonda E. ■ 98040 #054-04-1954 L1956 **P** *071 †75
SCHOR, Robert Alan. ■ 98040 #005-02-1973 L1977 **NM DR** *071 †20,28
SCHREUDER, John Gerard. 2553 76TH AVE SE 98040 #054-04-1996 L1999 **PD** *020 †55
SCHUMACHER, Donald P. ■ 98040 #018-03-1952 L1956 **AN** *071 †05
SHETTY, Ritu Khanna. 4410 E MERCER WAY 98040 #495-77-1986 L2003 **FM FPG** *020 †18
SIMPSON, Robert Wm. ■ 98040 #005-11-1942 L1949 **IM** *071 †20
SKINNER, Alfred L. ■ 98040 #024-01-1951 L1954 **PD** *071 †55
SMITH, Arnold Lee. ■ 98040 #028-03-1964 L1978 **ID PD** *050 †55
SMITH, Julia Ravenscroft. 7711 SE 27TH ST 98040 #051-01-1977 L1978 **IM** *020 †20
SMITH, Mackenzie. ■ 98040 #054-04-1955 L1959 **PD** *020 †55
SOMERS, Gary D. ■ 98040 #026-04-1981 L1984 **IM EM** *020 †16
SPENCE, William F. ■ 98040 #035-09-1953 L1966 **PUD CCM** *020 †20
SPENCER, Suzanne Diane. 6240 79TH AVE SE 98040 #054-04-1976 L1977 **FM** *020 †18
SPROUL, John Marshall. ■ 98040 #016-06-1958 L1964 **IM PUD** *020
STEPAN, Donald Reynold, Jr. ■ 98040 #048-12-2003 L2004 **GS** *020 †20
STROH, James Leonard. 3236 78TH AVE SE, EYE CLINIC OF BELLEVUE AT 98040
  #028-34-1999 L2003 **OPH** *020 †35
STUEBER, Danielle. ■ 98040 #016-45-2005 L2006 **IM** *012
SWENSON, Edward W. ■ 98040 #030-05-1950 L1950 **IM PUD** *071
SYTMAN, Paul Bernard. 3236 78TH AVE SE, STE 200 98040 #054-04-1990 L1993 **IM** *020 †20
THOMAS, Ildiko Hegyvary. ■ 98040 #054-04-2004 L2004 **PD** *020 †55
THOMPSON, Alvin Jerome. ■ 98040 #010-03-1946 L1954 **GE IM** *071 †20
THORNING, David Rex. ■ 98040 #019-02-1965 L1972 **PTH** *020 †50 ‡
THORNTON, Richard Ernest. ■ 98040 #005-12-1960 L1967 **ORS** *020 †40
TOBIS, Fredric Marc. ■ 98040 #041-07-1975 L1980 **CD IM** *020 †20
TROMBOLD, James Carter. ■ 98040 #019-02-1962 L1968 **CD IM** *020 †20
TSANG, Hannah Chi-Wan. 3236 78TH AVE SE STE 201, MERCER ISLAND NEUROLOGY 98040
  #011-02-1988 L1988 **N** *020
VAN GELDER, Russell Neil. ■ 98040 #005-11-1994 L2007 **OPH** *020 †35
VINCENT, H Bartlett, Jr. ■ 98040 #035-19-1961 L1965 **CHP P** *071
WEISS-MILLER, Ruth E. 3236 78TH AVE SE, EYE CLINIC OF BELLEVUE AT 98040
  #048-14-1993 L1997 **OPH** *075 †35
WEXLER, Robert Michael. ■ 98040 #005-19-1975 L1983 **EM** *020 †16
WIEGERT, Henry Thos. ■ 98040 #054-04-1955 L1956 **OS FM** *071 †18
WINDER, Daniel Paul. 2825 68TH AVE SE 98040 #054-04-1987 L1991 **DR** *020 †28,80
WINTERSCHEID, Loren C. ■ 98040 #041-01-1954 L1956 **GS CD** *071 †85
WOLTER, David F. ■ 98040 #054-04-1952 L1954 **OBG AM** *071 †30
WOOD, Chancel. ■ 98040 #034-01-1988 L1995 **IM** *020 †20
WOOLLEY, Janice Whitehead. 2553 76TH AVE SE 98040 #017-20-1966 L1970 **PD** *020 †55
YAU, Karin Kaiwai. ■ 98040 #054-04-2007 *012
YOUNG, James A. ■ 98040 #018-75-1963, ▲ L1966 **OS GE** *071
YU, Jennifer Tong-Young. ■ 98040 #028-02-2002 L2006 **OPH** *020
ZAWADZKI, Ilan. 6163 93RD AVE SE 98040 #035-19-1983 L1984 **NEP IMG** *020 †20
ZEMPLENYI, Eva Gociar. 6188 92ND AVE SE 98040 #005-14-1983 L1987 **OPH IM** *020 †35

METALINE — PEND OREILLE

BOROZAN, Bronko. PO BOX 65, 407 PEND OREILLE BLVD 99152 #054-04-1961 L1967
  GYN *071 †30

MILL CREEK — SNOHOMISH

ANDERSON, Mark Townsend. 1025 153RD ST SE STE 200, MILL CREEK FAMILY
  PRACTICE 98012 #054-04-1981 L1982 **FM** *020 †18
BACON, William Warner. 1025 153RD ST SE, STE 200 98012 #054-04-1986 L1988 **FM** *020 †18
BALSON, Scott Andrew. ■ 98012 #054-04-1989 L1997 **OBG** *062 †30
BEGERT, Ann Klink. 1025 152ND ST SE STE 200, MILL CREEK FAMILY PRACTICE 98012
  #054-04-1983 L1986 **FM** *020 †18
BISSEY, Jeffrey D. 15418 MAIN ST, UNIT 200 98012 #048-04-1987 L1991 **PD** *020 †55
BRANDT, Antonio L. 2620 161ST SE SE 98012 #048-12-2001 L2005 **EM** *020 †16 ‡
BROGREN, Julie Kristine. 1025 153RD ST SE, STE 200 98012 #003-01-2001 L2003 **FM** *020 †18
CARLSON, Mark Alan. ■ 98012 #007-02-1984 L1987 **EM** *062 †18
DAVIDSON, Graham M. ■ 98012 #067-01-1978 L1980 *020
EL SONBATY, Atef Girgis. ■ 98012 #915-02-1957 L1978 **AN** *020 †05
FOUNTAIN, Charles William. ■ 98012 #067-01-1951 L1968 **P** *071
GEORGE, Justus Winfred. ■ 98012 #054-04-1962 L1962 **GS** *072 †85
HATHAWAY, Melissa Elaine. PO BOX 13503 98082 #054-04-2007 **PD** *012
HERRON, Kevin Richard. 1025 153RD ST SE, STE 200 98012 #005-06-1999 L2001
  FM *020 †18 ‡
KENNY, Richard Joseph. 1025 153RD ST SE, STE 100 98012 #054-04-2001 L2003
  OPH *020 †35
KOH, Jerry Sung. 4410 137TH ST SE 98012 #016-42-2003 L2003 **IM** *020 †20
KOSER, William James. ■ 98012 #005-02-1946 L1946 **GP IM** *071
LAKHANI, Rozina Ramzanali. 805 164TH ST SE STE 102 98012 #704-25-1993 L1999 **P** *020 †75
LEE, Jae Chan. ■ 98012 #583-06-1960 L1979 **OBG** *020
LOVE, Gerald Frank. ■ 98012 #054-04-1953 L1955 **AN** *071 †05
MEDINA SORIANO, Maria L. ■ 98012 #024-01-1980 L1983 **PD PHP** *020
MORGAN, Nancy Jean T. 805 164TH ST SE STE 100, GUARDIAN FAMILY CARE, PLLC 98012
  #054-04-1977 L1980 **FM** *020 †18
MORGAN, Robert Laurince. 805 164TH ST SE, STE 100 98012 #054-04-1977 L1980
  FM *020 †18
NISTOR, Corina. 1025 153RD ST SE, STE 200 98012 #781-01-1993 L2005 **FM** *020 †18
PALMER, William Salton. ■ 98012 #005-12-1956 L1960 **GP** *071
PATEL, Rohit Shantilal. ■ 98012 #495-76-1981 L1983 **GP** *020
PATTERSON, Elizabeth Ann. ■ 98012 #010-03-1961 L1967 **DR** *062 †80
PRICE, Matthew Guy. 1025 153RD ST SE, STE 200 98012 #011-03-2002 L2004 **FM** *020 †18
REINHARDT, Rachel C. 1025 153RD ST SE STE 100, CASCADE EYE M.D.S, PLLC 98012
  #054-04-2011 L2004 **OPH** *020 †35
SHLAFER, Stephen Jos. 15808 MILL CREEK BLVD, STE 201 98012 #858-05-1986 L1991
  PD *020 †55
SINN, Charles M, Jr. ■ 98012 #023-07-1949 L1949 **IM ON** *071 †20
SMOLUCH, Michelle Marie. 15418 MAIN ST STE 20, THE EVERETT CLINIC 98012
  #016-43-2001 L2004 **IM** *020

STEINBERG, Orly Pnina. 15808 MILL CREEK BLVD, STE 200 98012 #048-04-1996 L2000
  OBG *020 †30
STUKOVSKY, Stephen Stewar. 1025 153RD ST SE, STE 200 98012 #422-01-2004 L2004
  FM *020 †18
UMBREIT, Jay Nicholas. ■ 98082 #024-07-1979 L2007 **ON** *050 †20 ‡
VARENBRINK, Maria P. ■ 98012 #660-01-1955 L1962 *075
VOTH, Cornelius Isaac. ■ 98012 #068-01-1961 L1966 **AN OS** *071 †05
WALLS, Theresa Ann. ■ 98012 #041-13-1997 L2007 **PEM** *020 †55
WELCOME, Anna Maria. 15808 MILL CREEK BLVD, STE 200 98012 #036-08-2002 L2007
  OBG *020
WYGANT, Edgar Gerard. ■ 98012 #016-43-1948 L1986 **A IM** *071 †03
YORIOKA, Gerald Norio. 805 164TH ST SE, STE 100 98012 #054-04-1969 L1976
  FM FSM *020 †18
ZIMBUREAN, John Michael. 15418 MAIN ST, UNIT 301 98012 #048-12-1981 L1996 **P** *020 †75

MILTON — PIERCE

CASTILLO, Mariben Cristin. 2748 MILTON WAY, STE 101 98354 #748-01-1997 L2003
  IM *020 †20
SIGALA, Sharon Lee. 902B 15TH AVE 98354 #003-01-1991 L1998 **PD** *020 †55

MONROE — SNOHOMISH

ANGELO, Richard Loren. 14841 179TH AVE SE, STE 330 98272 #054-04-1980 L1986
  ORS *020 †40
BECERRIL, David Antonio. 375 BUTLER AVE 98272 #005-02-1982 L1984 **FM FSM** *020 †18
BENSEN, Randal Dale. 14701 179TH AVE SE 98272 #060-01-1980 L1987 **EM OS** *020 †16
BOONE, Paul Wendell, Jr. 14692 179TH AVE SE, STE 500 98272 #051-04-1993 L2001
  FM *020 †18 ‡
BROWN, Charles K. ■ 98272 #054-04-1952 L1953 **AN** *071 †05
CHAMPOUX, James Arthur. 14841 179TH AVE SE, STE 330 98272 #005-06-1978 L1984
  ORS *020 †18
CHEN, Stan Su-Tah. ■ 98272 #244-04-1990 L1997 **AN** *020 †20,05
CHIOU, Kenneth Yingwei. 14701 179TH AVE SE, DEPT. OF ANESTHESIOLOGY 98272
  #056-05-1991 L2008 **AN** *020 †20
COFFMAN, Wendy J. 14692 179TH AVE SE, PROVIDENCE PHYSICIANS GROU 98272
  #021-01-1994 L1997 **FM** *020 †18
CONNOLLY, Dominic. 14701 179TH AVE SE 98272 #047-05-1999 L2002 **EM** *020 †16
COURINGTON, Frederick W. ■ 98272 #011-03-1965 L1983 **AN P** *071 †75,05
DANKERS, Christian Antoni. ■ 98272 #041-01-2007 L2007 **IM** *012
DANKERS, Johannes H. 14692 179TH AVE SE, PROVIDENCE PHYSICIANS 98272
  #005-11-1975 L1976 **FM** *030 †18
DEHKORDI, Reza Hosseini. 14701 179TH AVE SE 98272 #054-04-1996 L1998 **IM** *020 †20
DE NEEF, Charles Peter. 14692 179TH AVE SE, STE 100 98272 #011-02-1981 L1985
  FM *040 †18
DOERNER, Diane. 14841 179TH AVE SE 98272 #023-01-1993 L1996 **IM** *020 †20
EICKERMAN, Michael Scott. 19030 LENTON PL SE PMB 60 98272 #054-04-1987 L1992
  GS VS *020 †85
FUCHS, Robin. 14841 179TH AVE SE, STE 330 98272 #041-14-1997 L2002 **OAR** *020 †40
GOTTSCH, Henry Philip. ■ 98272 #054-04-2006 L2006 **GS** *012
GOULD, Randall Kirkgard. 14692 179TH AVE SE, STE 500 98272 #054-04-1974 L1977
  FM *020 †18
GREEN, James Floyd. 14841 179TH AVE SE, STE 330 98272 #005-11-1972 L1980 **ORS** *020 †40
GREGUSH, Ronald Valerian. 14841 179TH AVE SE, STE 330 98272 #028-02-2001 L2007
  OSM *020
GULICK, Mickey Leland. 14701 179TH AVE SE 98272 #028-02-1958 L1979 **GP** *071 †18
HAGER, Nelson Allen. 14841 179TH AVE SE, STE 320 98272 #054-04-1989 L2003 **PM** *020 †60
HANDLEY, Shirley. 14701 179TH AVE SE 98272 #056-05-1990 L1993 **FM** *020 †18
HARNESS, Hayley Ann. ■ 98272 #054-04-2008 *012
HITCHCOCK, Lauri L. 14692 179TH AVE SE 98272 #048-02-1985 L1993 **FM** *020 †18
HOPKINS, Susanne E. 14701 179TH AVE SE 98272 #028-46-1989 L1993 **OBG** *020 †30
ITO, Siri Eiko. 14701 179TH AVE SE 98272 #056-06-1997 L1999 **IM** *020 †20
JAFAR, Syed Hadi. 14841 179TH AVE SE, STE 210 98272 #704-16-1987 L2001 **P** *020 †75
KAHN, Harry Aaron. 14841 179TH AVE SE, STE 220 98272 #041-02-1989 L1996
  CRS *020 †10,85
KIM, Ellen M. 14692 179TH AVE SE, STE 900 98272 #041-13-1999 L2006 **IM** *020 †20
LIN, Kenneth C. 14841 179TH AVE SE, STE 330 98272 #016-11-2001 L2007 **ORS** *020 †40
LOW, Jasmine Iming. 14692 179TH AVE SE STE 800, PROVIDENCE PHYSICIAN GROUP 98272
  #035-45-2002 L2007 **PD** *020 †55
MADANI, Badrossadat. 14701 179TH AVE SE, MONROE PEDIATRICS 98272
  #517-01-1973 L1993 **PD** *020 †55
MC ALLISTER, Craig M. 14841 179TH AVE SE, STE 330 98272 #054-04-1985 L1990
  ORS *020 †40
MC KIBBEN, Helena. ■ 98272 #023-07-1950 L1951 **FM ID** *071
MEINKE, Dana S. 14692 179TH AVE SE, STE 100 98272 #008-01-1997 L1999 **IM** *020 †20
MIN, Kyung E. 14701 179TH AVE SE 98272 #010-01-1997 L2001 **MPD** *020 †20,55
MOFFAT, Kristi Sue. 14692 179TH AVE SE STE 100 98272 #016-42-1998 L2000 **FM** *020 †18
MORRIS, Beena Lakshmanan. 14692 179TH AVE SE, STE 800 98272 #496-23-1991 L2001
  PD *020 †55
MOWRY, James Preston. 14755 179TH AVE SE STE 500 98272 #054-04-1968 L1975
  ORS *020 †40
MUNOZ, Robert Hartnell. 14692 179TH AVE SE, STE 100 98272 #005-02-1984 L1986
  FM *020 †18
NALTY, Deborah Marie. 14692 179TH AVE SE, PROVIDENCE PHYSICIANS GROU 98272
  #007-02-1988 L1990 **FM** *020 †18
NESHAT, Katayoun. 14701 179TH AVE SE, VALLEY GENERAL HOSPITAL 98272
  #054-04-1997 L1999 **IM** *020 †20
NORLAND, Kristofor D. 163 VILLAGE CT, MONROE FIRE DISTRICT 3 98272 #016-01-2001 L2005
  EM *020 †16
NORLING, Gregory John. 14841 179TH AVE SE, STE 330 98272 #054-04-1975 L1979
  ORS *020 †40
OKEMAH, John Lee. 14841 179TH AVE SE STE 201, SKY RIVER INTERNAL MEDICIN 98272
  #037-01-1997 L2006 **IM** *020

PACKIA RAJ, Llewellyn N. 14841 179TH AVE SE, STE 320 98272 #422-01-1998 L2001 **IM** *020 †20,60

PYNE, Robert Sharp. 14692 179TH AVE SE, STE 900 98272 #035-03-1991 L1993 **IM** *020 †20

REPNIK, James Edward. ■ 98272 #056-06-1971 L1974 **FM** *020

RYBARCZYK, Richard Mark. 14841 179TH AVE SE 98272 #041-02-1981 L1997 **OBG** *020 †30

SHEAHAN, James Allen. 14692 179TH AVE SE, STE 100 98272 #054-04-1978 L1979 **FM** *020 †18

STICKNEY, Jeffrey Lynn. 14841 179TH AVE SE, STE 330 98272 #054-04-1986 L1990 **ORS** *020 †40

STRUB, Charles Roland. 14841 179TH AVE SE 98272 #048-04-1965 L1966 **PHL FM** *020 †18

SWENSON, James Don. 14841 179TH AVE SE 98272 #010-01-1989 L1993 **ORS** *020 †40

THOT, William Manning. 14841 179TH AVE SE, STE 310 98272 #048-02-1983 L1992 **OBG** *020 †30

TRAVERSO, Adele L Vinton. 14701 179TH AVE SE 98272 #054-04-1985 L1985 **GS** *020 †85

VATHEUER, Hans Martin. 14692 179TH AVE SE, STE 100 98272 #054-04-1998 L2000 **FM** *020 †18

WEAR, Richard Floyd. 14701 179TH AVE SE 98272 #005-02-1981 L1982 **AN** *020 †05

MONTESANO – GRAYS HARBOR

DAVIS-MOORE, Betty N. ■ 98563 #040-02-1943 L1947 **P** *072

MOORE, James Alter. ■ 98563 #016-06-1944 L1947 **OS GP** *072

SCHIMPF, Robert Wm. ■ 98563 #051-04-1966 L1969 **PD** *072 †55

SHIN, Clara Chon. 112 E BROADWAY AVE 98563 #054-04-1995 L1997 **IM** *020 †20

SHIN, Yong Ki. 112 E BROADWAY AVE 98563 #054-04-1993 L1995 **IM** *020 †20

MORTON – LEWIS

ADAMS, Charles Duane. PO BOX 640 98356 #054-04-1966 L1970 **U AS** *071 †95

COOPER, Merrell Nelson. 531 ADAMS STREET 98356 #018-75-1990, ▲ L1993 **FM OMM** *020 †18

ELIZAGA, Daniel P. 531 ADAMS AV, MORTON MEDICAL CENTER 98356 #748-02-1962 L1969 **FM GS** *020 †18

ELIZAGA, Leticia L. 220 PLEASANT VIEW DR 98356 #748-02-1962 L1983 **GP** *074

FORD, Jeffrey Allan. PO BOX C, 521 ADAMS AV 98356 #060-01-1992 L2002 **FM** *020 †18

HANSEN, Mark Millard. PO BOX B 98356 #005-12-1994 L1997 **FM** *020 †18

KESIRY, Riad. ■ 98356 #875-01-1998 L2007 **IM** *020 †20

MOSES LAKE – GRANT

BEAUBIEN, Marta Ann. 840 E HILL AVE, MOSES LAKE CLINIC 98837 #054-04-1996 L1999 **PD** *020 †55

BODNAR, Eszter Maria. 801 E WHEELER RD 98837 #473-03-1988 L1997 **IM** *020 †20

BOND, Toby Brent. 840 E HILL AVE, MOSES LAKE CLINIC 98837 #054-04-2004 L2007 **PD** *020 †55

BRANDT, Anni. 840 E HILL AVE, RADIOLOGY DEPARTMENT 98837 #054-04-1986 L1991 **DR** *020 †80

BROSS, Jill A Dudik. 615 S DIVISION ST 98837 #055-01-1982 L1988 **PD EM** *020 †55

BROWN, Doyle Hayes. ■ 98837 #040-02-1973 L1991 **ORS** *020 †40

CANFIELD, Daniel W. 840 E HILL AVE, MOSES LAKE CLINIC 98837 #010-01-1984 L1989 **ORS** *020 †40

CARTER, Andrea Michelle. 1550 S PIONEER WAY, STE 180 98837 #056-05-1997 L2000 **FM** *020 †18

CURNEL, David Lee. 840 E HILL AVE 98837 #040-02-1977 L1980 **FM** *020 †18

DE LEON, Conrado. 1550 S PIONEER WAY, STE 180 98837 #649-02-1981 L1986 **MPD** *020

DONICH, George Michael. PO BOX 1059 98837 #030-06-1939 L1939 **FM AN** *020

EARL, David Thurn. 1550 S PIONEER WAY STE 200 98837 #005-12-1988 L1991 **IM DR** *020

EMMANS, Paul E. ■ 98837 #018-75-1944, ▲ L1947 **GP** *071

FLAHERTY, Lynne Colson. 801 E WHEELER RD 98837 #005-02-1984 L1989 **EM** *020 †85

GRAHAM, Evan Michael. 840 E HILL AVE 98837 #054-04-1980 L1984 **IM** *020 †20 ‡

HAKE, James Edward. 841 E HILL AVE 98837 #026-04-1977 L1980 **FM EM** *020 †18

HART, Kenneth Craig. 840 E HILL AVE 98837 #039-01-1985 L1998 **IM** *020

HEMMERLING, Cole Q. 1550 S PIONEER WAY, STE 150 98837 #068-01-1994 L1996 **FM** *020 †18

HENDEE, Jennifer Joy. 840 E HILL AVE, OPTHALMOLOGY MOSES LAKE 98837 #005-12-2003 L2007 **OPH** *020

HOOVER, Edgar Donald. 840 E HILL AVE 98837 #060-02-1982 L1994 **FM** *020

HOURIGAN, Richard Jos. 844 E HILL AVE, FAMILY MEDICINE ASSOCIATES 98837 #019-02-1988 L1991 **FM** *020 †18

HYLANDER, Robert David. 615 S DIVISION ST, STE B 98837 #039-01-1979 L1990 **AI PDA** *020,03

IRWIN, James Robt. 1550 S PIONEER WAY, STE 370 98837 #019-02-1967 L1972 **GS TRS** *020 †85

ISSA, Hamid. ■ 98837 #875-02-1982 L2002 **IM** *020 †20

JACKSON, Thomas Robinson. 840 E HILL AVE 98837 #054-04-1990 L1998 **FM** *020 †18

KEARNS, Dennis Patrick. 840 E HILL AVE 98837 #054-04-1981 L1984 **FM FPG** *020 †18

KUBO, Karl Christopher. 615 RIVIERA AVE 98837 #048-13-1982 L1989 **PD** *020 †55

KUBOSUMI, Marcus Ray. 840 E HILL AVE 98837 #049-01-1984 L1997 **IM DIA** *020 †20

KVAMME, Leiv. ■ 98837 #021-01-1954 L1956 **OS** *071

LANEY, Thomas Joachim. 1308 S PIONEER WAY 98837 #030-05-1985 L1987 **FPS** *020

LANG, Juergen. 801 E WHEELER RD 98837 #028-34-2004 L2007 **PD** *020

LAURSEN, Shawna Lea. 801 E WHEELER RD 98837 #054-04-1994 L1997 **FM** *020 †18

LINDBERG, Karen Marie. 840 E HILL AVE 98837 #056-06-2001 L2004 **PD** *020 †55

LYONS, James Edward. 840 E HILL AVE 98837 #028-34-1990 L1993 **OBG** *020 †20

MARTIN, Louis F. 1550 S PIONEER WAY, STE 370 98837 #043-01-1976 L1977 **AS GS** *020 †85

MATTHEWS, Marshall Davis. ■ 98837 #048-04-1962 L1977 **OBG** *071 †30

MILLER, David Mitchell. 11058 NELSON RD NE, GRANT COUNTY FIRE DISTRICT 98837 #047-06-1977 L1987 **IM** *020 †20

MILLIGAN, Matthew H. 840 E HILL AVE, MOSES LAKE CLINIC 98837 #005-12-1994 L2001 **FM** *020 †18

MONLUX, George W, Jr. 1550 S PIONEER WAY STE 270, SAMARITAN HEALTH CARE 98837 #054-04-1971 L1974 **PM OM** *020 †16,18

MURPHY, Terry Grace. 801 E WHEELER RD 98837 #007-02-1997 L2007 **EM** *020 †16

NELSON, Robert Carl. 840 E HILL AVE 98837 #007-02-1973 L1992 **U** *020 †95

NOONAN, Bruce Douglas. ■ 98837 #054-04-1971 L1972 **OPH** *071 †35 ‡

NOYES, Edward Mac Arthur. 801 E WHEELER RD 98837 #038-41-1975 L1978 **EM** *020 †16

NYE, Andre Marcus. 605 S COOLIDGE ST, HEALTH CENTER 98837 #035-03-1997 L2000 **FM** *020 †18 ‡

O'BYRNE, Stuart Abbott. 840 E HILL AVE 98837 #017-20-1970 L1977 **DR** *020 †80

PALUCH, Natalie Rose. ■ 98837 #028-34-2004 L2007 **PD** *020 †55

PISTER, James Danl. 1550 S PIONEER WAY, STE 180 98837 #054-04-1971 L1979 **R IM** *020 †80

ROBINSON, Julia Jean. 840 E HILL AVE 98837 #021-01-1979 L1984 **PD** *020 †55

RODEMEYER, Adine Elise. 840 E HILL AVE 98837 #026-04-2000 L2003 **IM** *020 †20

ROLFS, Allen Douglas. 840 E HILL AVE 98837 #054-04-1977 L1978 **GS GP** *020 †85

ROMANO, Grace M. 840 E HILL AVE 98837 #054-04-1990 L1997 **FM** *020 †18

ROTH, Bernhard Paul. 1022 W IVY AVE 98837 #041-12-1956 L1964 **OPH** *071 †35

ROTH, Brian Paul. 1022 W IVY AVE 98837 #054-04-1992 L1997 **OPH** *020 †35

RUBY, Robert Holmes. ■ 98837 #028-02-1945 L1948 **GS** *071

SCHWEIGERDT, Elizabeth L. 840 E HILL AVE 98837 #016-11-1967 L1968 **IM** *020

SICA, Richard Matthew. 1550 S PIONEER WAY STE 350 98837 #306-01-1993 L2000 **D DS** *020

SIMON, Jill Kathleen. 605 S COOLIDGE ST, HEALTH CENTER 98837 #060-01-1992 L1995 *020

SMITH, Kevin Kimberly. 402 N CRESTVIEW DR, SOLE PROPRIETOR 98837 #005-14-1985 L1985 **EM** *020

STEEVES, Daniel Carmen. 1550 S PIONEER WAY, STE 150 98837 #064-01-1982 L1995 *020

STEFFENS, Thomas Earl. 1550 S PIONEER WAY, PIONEER MEDICAL CENTER 98837 #016-76-1981, ▲ L1990 *020

STEWART-FRIESEN, Andrea T. 1550 S PIONEER WAY, STE 150 98837 #031-01-2001 L2004 **FM** *020 †18

TALBOT, Craig Ferguson. 1550 S PIONEER WAY, STE 180 98837 #005-15-1985 L2001 **FM** *020

TAYLOR, Lynn Edwin. 801 E WHEELER RD 98837 #048-15-1981 L2005 **EM** *020 †16

THORN, Thomas Allen. ■ 98837 #030-06-1991 L1992 **FM** *020 †18

THORPE, Michael Lee. 601 S PIONEER WAY, STE F-382 98837 #049-01-1998 L2003 **FM** *020

TOLSON, Dedra Renee. 801 E WHEELER RD 98837 #054-04-1996 L2000 **EM** *020 †16

ULNICK, Keith Mitchell. 840 E HILL AVE 98837 #005-76-1992, ▲ L2005 **OTO** *020 †45

VERHAGE, Larry Wm. 605 S COOLIDGE ST, MOSES LAKE COMMUNITY HEALT 98837 #016-11-1990 L1997 **FM** *020 †18

WARNER, Steven Ray. 840 E HILL AVE, MOSES LAKE CLINIC 98837 #054-04-1979 L1980 **FM** *020 †18

WHEATON, John Henry. 840 E HILL AVE, MOSES LAKE CLINIC 98837 #040-02-1981 L1997 **ORS** *020 †40

WONG, Michael Yuen-Yue. 1550 S PIONEER WAY, ASSOCIATION OF SAMARITAN P 98837 #041-13-1998 L2002 **OBG** *020 †30

WRIGHT, C Larry. ■ 98837 #018-03-1960 L1969 **OPH** *071 †35

YOUNG, James Wm. ■ 98837 #020-02-1945 L1946 **GYN OS** *020

MOSSYROCK – LEWIS

MC CURRY, Kevin W. 233 WILLIAMS ST 98564 #033-06-1990 L1993 **FM** *020 †18

MOUNT VERNON – SKAGIT

ABBOTT, Richard Jos. 2116 E SECTION ST, NORTH CASCADE FAMILY PHYSI 98274 #007-02-1976 L1979 **FM** *020 †18

AHRENS, Lori Anne Holme. 1320 E DIVISION ST, SKAGIT RADIOLOGY INC PS 98274 #007-02-1988 L1990 **VIR** *020 †80

ANDERSON, Marshall W. 1400 E KINCAID ST, CENTER INC 98274 #048-15-1985 L1999 **OM GP** *020 †70

ARMBRUST, Earl N, Jr. 1400 E KINCAID ST, SKAGIT VALLEY MEDICAL CTR 98274 #017-20-1958 L1981 **ORS** *071 †40

ARRANZA, Dante Jesus Duma. 1400 E KINCAID ST 98274 #748-10-1999 L2006 **IM** *020 †20

ASHBY, Melissa Elisabeth. 1400 E KINCAID ST, CENTER INC 98274 #054-04-1995 L1995 **FM** *020 †18

BACKLUND, Mark Haze. 1100 S 2ND ST, COMPASS HEALTH NORTH 98273 #030-05-1972 L1978 **P** *020

BAILEY, Kristi Lynn. 1805 E DIVISION ST 98274 #048-04-2002 L2006 **OPH** *020

BARR, Mark Robt. 2101 LITTLE MOUNTAIN LN 98274 #054-04-1982 L1983 **PD** *020 †55

BART, Michael Jay. 1500 CONTINENTAL PL 98273 #048-02-1982 L1991 **AN** *020 †05

BARTEL, Sheryl June. 1415 E KINCAID ST 98274 #040-02-1977 L1985 **AN** *071 †05

BAUMANN, David Theodore. ■ 98274 #040-02-1968 L2001 **OTO OS** *074 †45

BENSON, David Bakke. 2116 E SECTION ST, NORTH CASCADE FAMILY PHYSI 98274 #054-04-1999 L2001 **FM** *020 †18

BENSON, Jennifer Kooiker. 2116 E SECTION ST, NORTH CASCADE FAMILY 98274 #054-04-1999 L1999 **FM** *020 †18

BERG, Bradley Ross. 1400 E KINCAID ST, CENTER INC 98274 #035-45-1999 L2003 **PN** *020 †55

BERGHUIS, Paul A. 1415 E KINCAID ST 98274 #005-76-1987, ▲ L1992 **AN** *020 †05

BERLINER, Carl Matthew. 1400 E KINCAID ST, CENTER INC 98274 #008-02-1999 L2001 **FM** *020 †18

BIESECKER, James Leonard. 2021 E COLLEGE WAY, STE 210 98273 #036-05-1967 L1979 **PTH** *062 †50

BISHOP, Lyall Arthur. 1400 E KINCAID ST, CENTER INC 98274 #054-04-1967 L1968 **PD** *020 †55

BOND, John David. 1400 E KINCAID ST, CENTER INC 98274 #038-40-1973 L1981 **OTO** *020

BRADFORD, Winifred R S. ■ 98274 #030-05-1948 L1971 **IMG ID** *071

BROWN, John Stephen, Jr. 1805 E DIVISION ST 98274 #051-04-1970 L1973 **OPH** *020 †35

BROWNELL, Kirk Hamilton. 1415 E KINCAID ST 98274 #054-04-1995 L1997 **FM** *020 †18

BUCZEK, Judith K Craig. 1310 E DIVISION ST 98274 #007-02-1970 L1971 **PTH NM** *020 †50

BURKE, John T. 1320 E DIVISION ST 98274 #025-07-1978 L1983 **DR** *020 †80

BYNUM, Daniel C. 111 N 17TH ST, MOUNT VERNON WOMEN 98273 #005-12-1985 L1989 **OBG** *020 †30

CAMBRON, Laurence Delmen. 1415 E KINCAID ST 98274 #020-02-1995 L1999 **RNR** *020 †80

CAMMOCK, Earl E. 215 S 13TH ST 98274 #026-04-1953 L1956 **CRS GS** *071 †85 ‡

CARRERO, Rosanne D. 1400 E KINCAID ST, CENTER INC 98274 #033-05-1982 L1987 **EM** *020 †16

CHALMERS, Frances Talcott. 2101 LITTLE MOUNTAIN LN 98274 #038-06-1978 L1979 **PD** *020 †55

CHAPMAN, Donald Shelton. 2101 LITTLE MOUNTAIN LN 98274 #016-42-1994 L2002 PE *020 †55

CHARLES, Erin Elizabeth. 1400 E KINCAID ST, CENTER INC 98274 #054-04-2001 L2004 PD *020 †55

CHATTERLEY, Scott M. 2021 E COLLEGE WAY, STE 210 98273 #654-01-1986 L1991 PTH OS *020 †50

CHMEL, Michael Mathews. 1415 E KINCAID ST 98274 #026-04-1975 L1977 EM FM *020 †18,16

COFFEY, Robert Lewis. 1415 E KINCAID ST 98274 #028-34-1976 L1979 PUD IM *020 †20

COOK, J Alan. 723 S 1ST ST STE C 98273 #039-01-1965 L1981 P AM *020 †75 ‡

COOPER, Thomas Patrick. 1611 BUCK WAY 98273 #025-01-1970 L1973 U *071 †95

CORKERY, Landry Moore. 1415 E KINCAID ST 98274 #021-01-1969 L1972 EM *020 †16

CORNELIUS, Darrell R. 1311 E DIVISION ST 98274 #048-04-1973 L1980 U *020 †95

CRIE, John Stanley. 307 S 13TH ST, STE 300 98274 #048-12-1974 L2005 CD IM *020 †20 ‡

CROWELL, Nannette Estelle. 1415 E KINCAID ST 98274 #005-12-1980 L1984 OPH *020 †35

DALE, Christopher Robert. ■ 98274 #016-06-2000 L2001 IM *100 †20

DALE, Rebecca Claire. ■ 98274 #026-04-2000 L2007 OPH *020

DARVILL, Fred T, Jr. ■ 98274 #054-04-1951 L1952 IM *071 †20

DEC, Karen Susan. 1320 E DIVISION ST 98274 #035-45-1987 L1993 DR *020 †80

DELLI-BOVI, Jan. 1320 E DIVISION ST 98274 #008-02-1977 L1985 OBG *071 †30

DESAI, Muneer Janak. 1415 E KINCAID ST 98274 #048-02-1997 L2001 VIR *020 †80

DILLARD, Michael Robt. 1415 E KINCAID ST 98274 #054-04-1981 L1986 FM *020 †18

DIVITA, Joseph Frank. 1415 E KINCAID ST 98274 #028-34-1977 L1978 EM *020 †16

DOEPFNER, Paul Manfred. 1110 E MONTGOMERY ST 98274 #407-20-1985 L1995 AN *020 †05

DRUMMOND, Dike Curtis. 19244 NELSON RD 98274 #026-08-1984 L1987 FM *020 †18

DURAN, Michael Gordon. 1415 E KINCAID ST 98274 #041-01-1999 L2003 AN *100 †05

EISNER, Jerry Dennis. 1400 E KINCAID ST, CENTER INC 98274 #025-07-1972 L1975 D IM *020 †20 ‡

EMERY, Lynette Marie. 2116 E SECTION ST, NORTH CASCADES FAMILY PHYS 98274 #035-06-1995 L1997 FM *020 †18

ERBSTOESZER, John Wm. 1400 E KINCAID ST, CENTER INC 98274 #056-05-1971 L1972 FM *020 †18

ESTEP, Leslie Amenson. 2116 E SECTION ST, NORTH CASCADE FAMILY 98274 #054-04-1992 L1994 FM *020 †18

ESTEP, Roger Paul. 2116 E SECTION ST, NORTH CASCADE FAMILY 98274 #054-04-1992 L1994 FM *020 †18

EVERETT, Worth Weaver. 1415 E KINCAID ST 98274 #048-14-1997 L2007 EM *020 †16

FACKENTHALL, Joy. 1400 N LAVENTURE RD 98273 #054-04-1997 L1999 FM *020 †18

FELD, Jeffrey Ellis. 307 S 13TH ST, STE 300 98274 #023-01-1975 L1979 CD IM *020 †20

FOIST, Nadine Burrington. 125 N 18TH ST, STE A 98273 #016-11-1984 L1990 GYN *020 †30

FRANKLIN, Patricia Ann. 1400 E KINCAID ST 98274 #004-01-1994 L1999 GS *020 †85

GAITHER, Dennis Warren. 1100 S 2ND ST, COMPASS HEALTH SKAGIT 98273 #054-04-1979 L1982 P *020 †75

GAMSON, Jonathan Calder. 2116 E SECTION ST, NORTH CASCADE FAMILY 98274 #054-04-1995 L1998 FM *020 †18

GARNER, Cheryl Esen. 2101 LITTLE MOUNTAIN LN 98274 #035-03-2004 L2004 PD *020 †55

GERAGHTY, Barbara Ellen. 1400 E KINCAID ST, CENTER INC 98274 #054-04-1994 L1994 PD *020 †55

GILMER, Deborah Holland. 2101 LITTLE MOUNTAIN LN, SKAGIT PEDIATRICS 98274 #051-04-1983 L1991 PD FM *020 †18,55

GJERSET, George Frank. 1415 E KINCAID ST 98274 #005-18-1978 L1981 ON IM *050 †20

GOETTER, Elizabeth Carol. 1415 E KINCAID ST 98274 #054-04-1983 L1988 AN *020 †05

GOFORTH, Virgil Avery. 1400 E KINCAID ST, SKAGIT VALLEY MEDICAL CTR 98274 #048-04-1963 L1969 PS *071 †65

GOLDSTON, Herbert J, Jr. 1315 E DIVISION ST 98274 #041-01-1969 L1972 N *020 †75

GORDON, Richard Evans. 1400 E KINCAID ST 98274 #036-07-1973 L1978 ORS PD *020 †55,40

GRUENER, Johann Michael. 1400 E KINCAID ST 98274 #407-16-1954 L1961 P FM *071

GUBNER, Richard Edwin. 307 S 13TH ST, STE 300 98274 #035-09-1977 L1985 CD IC *020 †20

HAHN, Barbara Jean. 1400 E KINCAID ST 98274 #054-04-1990 L1999 FM *020 †18

HALSEY, John Stuart. 1400 E KINCAID ST, CENTER INC 98274 #041-13-1972 L1973 GE IM *020 †20

HANNA, Halim. 1400 E KINCAID ST, CENTER INC 98274 #875-01-1998 L2007 PCC *020

HANSOM, Janet Gail. 2116 E SECTION ST, NORTH CASCADE FAMILY 98274 #054-04-1989 L1989 FM *020 †18

HARRISON, Scott Douglas. 1320 E DIVISION ST 98274 #054-04-1987 L1990 DR *020 †80

HERNANDEZ, Ana Cecilia. 1400 N LA VENTURE RD, SEA-MAR HEALTH CENTER 98273 #054-04-1991 L1994 FM *020 †18

HINDERSTEIN, William N. 1400 E KINCAID ST, CENTER INC 98274 #024-07-1967 L2000 OBG MFM *020 †30 ‡

HINES, Wirt Anderson, III. 1600 CONTINENTAL PL, STE 101 98273 #049-01-2001 L2005 D *020 †15

HOEFT, David Frederick. 1415 E KINCAID ST, CENTER AT SVH 98274 #056-05-1983 L2004 IM GP *020 †20

HUANG, George Chiuchi. 1400 E KINCAID ST 98274 #025-07-1988 L1995 PS *020 †65

JAFARI-BOROUJERDI, M. 307 S 13TH ST STE 100, SKAGIT CANCER CARE CENTER 98274 #409-20-1995 L2007 HO *020 †20

JAUREGUI, Lorena O. 1400 N LA VENTURE RD 98273 #649-16-1988 L1995 FM *020 †18

JOHNSON, Mark Damone. 1320 E DIVISION ST 98274 #024-01-1995 L2001 NS *020

JOHNSON, Mark Leland. 1400 E KINCAID ST, CENTER INC 98274 #054-04-1973 L1975 GS *020 †85

JOHNSON, Maynard Lee. 1400 E KINCAID ST 98274 #040-02-1947 L1948 OBG GP *071

JOHNSON, Morris Glenn. 1400 E KINCAID ST, CENTER INC 98274 #051-01-1979 L1982 GS *020 †20,85

JOHNSON, Paul Dean. 819 S 13TH ST 98274 #054-04-1975 L1978 FM *020 †18

JOHNSON, Steven Hall. 2116 E SECTION ST 98274 #017-20-1973 L1976 FM *020 †18

JOHNSTON, Marian E. 125 N 18TH ST STE B 98273 #048-04-1994 L1998 APM *020 †05

KAPLAN, Diane Mae. 1400 N LAVENTURE RD 98273 #054-04-1986 L1995 FM *020 †18

KENDREGAN, Brian Albert. 1400 E KINCAID ST, CENTER INC 98274 #005-06-1975 L2006 PUD IM *020 †20

KENNEDY, Billy Don. 1415 E KINCAID ST 98274 #039-01-1958 L1967 AN *020 †05

KINCAID, Jesse Jennings. 1320 E DIVISION ST, SKAGIT RADIOLOGY, INC. P.S 98274 #054-04-2002 L2002 RNR *012 †80

KNUDSEN, John Conrad. 111 N 17TH ST 98273 #040-02-1974 L1978 OBG *020 †30

KOTAL, Charles Vladimir. 1415 E KINCAID ST, CENTER AT SVH 98274 #051-04-1995 L1997 IM *020 †20

KOTLARCZYK, Jaroslaw J. 1415 E KINCAID ST 98274 #759-01-1991 L1995 AN *020 †05

KUMAR, Ajith J. 1617 E DIVISION ST 98274 #495-09-1991 L1998 NEP IM *020 †20

KWAN, Sandra Mae. 1400 E KINCAID ST 98274 #028-03-1994 L1997 FM *020 †18

LANDESBERG, Jeffrey Eric. 2101 LITTLE MOUNTAIN LN 98274 #041-01-1997 L1999 PD *020 †55

LANDRETH, Duncan Thos. 307 S 13TH ST 98274 #040-02-1978 L1983 CD IM *020 †20

LANGNER, Sabine Monika. 1400 E KINCAID ST, CENTER INC 98274 #062-01-1993 L1998 FM *020 †18

LEIBRAND, Howard Lee. 1415 E KINCAID ST 98274 #010-01-1981 L1987 EM PHP *020 †18

LEVINE, Richard Scott. 2101 LITTLE MOUNTAIN LN 98274 #005-14-1991 L1993 PD *020 †55

LLEWELLYN, Fred Warde, III. ■ 98273 #005-14-1966 L1969 P *075 †75

LOGEN, Peter Danl. 1400 N LAVENTURE RD 98273 #054-04-1970 L1971 OBG *020 †30 ‡

LYONS, Patrick Michael. 1415 E KINCAID ST 98274 #023-12-1985 L2000 ORS OSM *020 †40

MAGUIRE, Richard X. 1415 E KINCAID ST 98274 #054-04-1951 L1952 GS GP *071

MENNELLA, Scott Francis. 1400 E KINCAID ST, CENTER INC 98274 #010-01-1981 L1985 FM PD *020 †18

MEYER, Anita Marie. 2116 E SECTION ST, NORTH CASCADE FAMILY 98274 #005-14-1993 L1993 FM *020 †18

MOHR, Armin Asmus Arnold. 1805 E DIVISION ST 98274 #060-01-1962 L1970 OPH *071 †35

MOISEY, Stanley Gordon. ■ 98274 #917-23-1959 L1969 P *071

MORRIS, Allen David. 1310 E DIVISION ST, SKAGIT PATHOLOGY INC 98274 #041-12-1984 L2002 PTH *020 †50

MORRIS, David C. 1315 E DIVISION ST 98274 #016-06-1983 L1989 N *020 †75

MULLER, Lucia Cecilia. 2116 E SECTION ST, NORTH CASCADE FAMILY 98274 #054-04-1998 L2000 FM *020 †18

NELSON, Larry Ralph. 809 S 15TH ST 98274 #054-04-1973 L1974 FM *020 †18

NORTH, Deborah A W. 1400 E KINCAID ST, CENTER INC 98274 #016-06-1978 L1980 IM *020 †20

OATES, Kenneth Marshall. 1500 CONTINENTAL PL, NW ORTHO SURGEONS 98273 #041-01-1990 L1999 ORS OSM *020 †40

OCHIAI, Tomoyuki. 1400 E KINCAID ST, CENTER INC 98274 #067-01-1994 L2000 GS *020 †18

OEFELEIN, Michael Gerard. 1311 E DIVISION ST 98274 #038-06-1990 L2004 U *020 †95

OLPIN, Michael Kearns. 1415 E KINCAID ST 98274 #054-04-1970 L1971 EM *020 †16

OSEA, Sharon Albia. 1400 E KINCAID ST, CENTER INC 98274 #748-10-1998 L2006 FM *020 †18

PARRY, Henry Donald. 1310 E DIVISION ST, SKAGIT VALLEY LAB 98274 #035-03-1964 L1966 PTH *020 †50

PETERSON, Laurence Robt. 1415 E KINCAID ST 98274 #016-02-1973 L1975 PTH PCP *071 †50

PFORTE, Henning. 1400 E KINCAID ST, CENTER INC 98274 #408-11-1996 L2002 FM *020 †18 ‡

PHILLIPS, John Houghton. 1415 E KINCAID ST DEPT IM 98274 #035-01-1954 L1962 HEM ON *071 †20

PLOUDRE, Jonathan Kaiser. 2116 E SECTION ST, NORTH CASCADE FAMILY 98274 #047-20-2002 L2003 FM *020 †18

PRINGLE, Barbara Hynes. 125 N 18TH ST STE A 98273 #007-02-1978 L1982 OBG *020 †30

PRINGLE, Robert Ward. 125 N 18TH ST, STE A 98273 #007-02-1978 L1982 OBG *020 †30

RAISH, Robert John. 1415 E KINCAID ST 98274 #028-02-1980 L1989 ON HEM *020 †20

RAK, Ellen Mary. 1400 N LAVENTURE RD 98273 #024-01-1988 L1990 FM *020 †18

RAMSBOTTOM, Mary T. 1400 E KINCAID ST, CENTER INC 98274 #067-01-1985 L1989 IM PHP *050 †20,70

RANDHAWA, Ranjiv Randall. 1400 E KINCAID ST, CENTER INC 98274 #759-18-2002 L2005 IM *020 †20

REPPLIER, Elizabeth Evans. 1400 E KINCAID ST, CENTER INC 98274 #007-02-1993 L1996 FM *020 †18 ‡

RICHESON, Ronald Jay. 2911 E COLLEGE WAY, SKAGIT EMS COUNCIL 98273 #054-04-1969 L1972 OS AM *071 †16

ROBBLEE, Nancy Durand. 2101 LITTLE MOUNTAIN LN 98274 #038-41-1978 L1978 PD *020 †55

ROBERTSON, Suzanne. 1400 E KINCAID ST, CENTER INC 98274 #061-01-1990 L1998 FM *020 †18 ‡

ROSEBERRY, J Michael. 1415 E KINCAID ST 98274 #035-09-1999 L2002 EM *020 †16

ROSENFELD, Robert Louis. 1400 E KINCAID ST, CENTER INC 98274 #047-05-1994 L2005 OBG *020 †30

ROWLAND, Sara Christine. 111 N 17TH ST 98273 #005-12-2000 L2004 OBG *020

SAARHEIM-RIGGS, Anne. 1400 E KINCAID ST, CENTER INC 98274 #040-02-1993 L1995 FM *020 †18

SANTOS, Jhoanna Mapili. 1400 E KINCAID ST, CENTER INC 98274 #748-02-2001 L2007 IM *020 †20

SCHUTZ, Eric. 1415 E KINCAID ST 98274 #005-11-1973 L1976 EM *020 †16

SHAN, Lin. 1400 N LAVENTURE RD, SEA MAR CLINIC 98273 #048-13-2000 L2005 FM *020 †18

SHERKAWY, Assem Botros. 1415 E KINCAID ST, CENTER AT SVH 98274 #915-03-1994 L2005 IM *100 †20

SHNEKER, Ayham F. 1415 E KINCAID ST, CENTER AT SVH 98274 #875-01-1999 L2002 IM *020 †20

SIAPCO, Clarence Dan. 2100 LITTLE MOUNTAIN LN 98274 #005-12-1999 L2002 OPH *020 †35

SIDBURY, James Buren, Jr. ■ 98273 #035-01-1947 L1951 OS PD *072 †55

SKINNER, Bruce Chas. 1400 E KINCAID ST, CENTER INC 98274 #020-02-1977 L1978 GS CD *020 †85

SLACK, Donald Loren. 1415 E KINCAID ST 98274 #054-04-1991 L1995 EM *020 †16

SLIND, Robert Ole. 1400 E KINCAID ST, SKAGIT VALLEY MEDICAL CENT 98274 #054-04-1970 L1971 IM PD *020 †20

SMITH, Andrea Bradford. 2101 LITTLE MOUNTAIN LN 98274 #001-02-1998 L2000 PD *020 †55

SPAK, Bradley Philip. 313 S 13TH ST 98274 #016-11-1979 L1980 AN *020 †05

STANLEY, William Fred. 1400 E KINCAID ST, CENTER INC 98274 #026-04-1971 L1980 FM *020 †18

STEWART, Richard Henry. 1730 E DIVISION ST 98274 #036-05-1970 L1978 OPH GP *020 †35

STEWART, Robert Bruce. 307 S 13TH ST, STE 300 98274 #054-04-1988 L1991 CD IM *020 †20

STUDLEY, Mark Allison. 1320 E DIVISION ST 98274 #016-06-1970 L1972 DR *020 †80

STUTZ, F Helmut. 1415 E KINCAID ST, NORTH PUGET ONCOLOGY 98274 #005-12-1966 L1975 ON HEM *071 †20

TAN, Chee Yeow. 110 N LAVENTURE RD, SEA MAR OB BYN CLINIC 98273 #065-06-2003 L2007 OBG *020

TAVES, Donald R. 117 N 1ST ST, STE 53 CARNATION BLD 98273 #054-04-1953 L1954 P *050

TAYLOR, Jennifer Susan. 2101 LITTLE MOUNTAIN LN 98274 #054-04-1992 L1992 PD *020 †55

THOMAS, Frank Ephraim. 1310 E DIVISION ST 98274 #040-02-1967 L1974 PTH *020 †50

THRELKELD, Charles Evan. ■ 98273 #025-07-1956 L1961 EM *071

TOMBERLIN, Marcus Guy. 1415 E KINCAID ST, CENTER AT SVH 98274 #036-05-1987 L2004 ID IM *020 †20

TORRES, Raul C. 1400 E KINCAID ST 98274 #737-01-1957 L1967 GS *071

TRAYLOR, Guilford H. 2116 E SECTION ST, NORTH CASCADE FAMILY 98274 #054-04-1992 L1992 FM *020 †18

TSITSIS, Tianna. 1415 E KINCAID ST, CENTER AT SVH 98274 #041-02-1995 L1998 **IM** *020 †20
UNGER, Randall Lamonte. 1415 E KINCAID ST 98274 #054-04-1990 L1993 **EM** *020 †16
VOEGTLIN, Joseph Walter. ■ 98274 #054-04-1954 L1955 **GS GP** *071
VOGEL, Daryl Givens. 2021 E COLLEGE WAY, STE 210 98273 #054-04-1988 L1990 **PTH** *020 †50
VOTAVA, Jennie Marie. 2101 LITTLE MOUNTAIN LN 98274 #024-01-2001 L2004 **PD** *100 †55
WADWA, Kalyan Singh. 1400 E KINCAID ST 98274 #409-20-1983 L2000 **GE IM** *020
WAKELIN, Donald Edwin. 1400 E KINCAID ST, CENTER INC 98274 #539-02-2001 L2007 **GE** *020
WALKER, Duff Hil. 1320 E DIVISION ST 98274 #007-02-1967 L1971 **DR NM** *020 †80,28
WASHBURN, Margaret C. 1320 E DIVISION ST 98274 #005-12-1967 L1969 **DR** *020 †80
WEBB, Cathy K. 1400 E KINCAID ST, CENTER INC 98274 #054-04-2001 L2005 **PD** *020 †55
WELK, Kevin Donald. 1400 E KINCAID ST 98274 #039-01-1997 L1999 **RHU** *020 †20
WEST, Richard Moorby. 1400 E KINCAID ST, SKAGIT VALLEY MEDICAL CTR 98274 #017-20-1967 L1991 **ORS** *071 †40
WHEELIS, Roger Ferguson. 1310 E DIVISION ST, SKAGIT VALLEY LABS 98274 #005-06-1968 L1970 **PTH** *020 †50
WHITE, Donna Marie. 1400 E KINCAID ST, CENTER INC 98274 #054-04-1991 L1994 **PD** *020 †55
WHITLOCK, William James. 300 CLAREMONT PL 98274 #054-15-1964 **AN** *020
WINKES, Ben Mullin. 1400 N LAVENTURE RD, SEAMAR COMMUNITY HEALTH CL 98273 #054-04-1998 L2001 **FM** *020 †18
WINKES, L Sloane. 1400 N LAVENTURE RD 98273 #041-07-1998 L2001 **FM** *020 †18
WORLEY, Harry Ernest. ■ 98273 #056-05-1948 L1950 **OBG AS** *071
XUE, Feiyu. 1320 E DIVISION ST 98274 #032-01-1998 L2006 **NM** *020 †80,28
YINUG, Aloysius. 2116 E SECTION ST, NORTH CASCADE FAMILY 98274 #014-01-1997 L2002 **FM** *020 †18
ZWICK, Robert Harry. 1400 E KINCAID ST, CENTER INC 98274 #016-11-1969 L1982 **ORS** *020

MOUNTLAKE TERRACE — SNOHOMISH

BATES, Susan M. 6808 220TH ST SW, STE 100 98043 #035-06-1985 L1998 **DR** *020 †80
BAXTER, Richard Alan. 6100 219TH ST SW STE 290 98043 #005-18-1983 L1984 **PS GS** *020 †85,65
CASTIGLIA, John Louis. 7001 220TH ST SW, BLDG 4 MAIL STOP 414 98043 #038-43-1980 L1994 **OS DR** *030
CHAUHAN, Rakesh Tarun. 7001 220TH ST SW, MAILSTOP 414 98043 #024-07-1978 L1992 **FM** *030 †18
DAVIES, John Rendel. 6007 244TH ST SW, # B 98043 #054-04-1961 L1962 **FM** *071
DONG, Benhao. 6007 244TH ST SW, # B 98043 #243-16-1994 L2000 **IM** *020 †20
DOWNEY, James Robt. 6005 244TH ST SW, STE 111 98043 #024-07-1983 L1995 **U** *020 †95
DURKEE, Nathanial Jarrod. 6808 220TH ST SW, STE 100 98043 #025-07-1999 L2004 **DR** *020 †80
ERICSON, Wm Burton, Jr. 6100 219TH ST SW, STE 540 98043 #024-01-1983 L2004 **HS** *020 †40
GARBER, Malcolm. 6007 244TH ST SW, # B 98043 #020-02-1955 L1963 **PD** *071 †55
HALLOCK, Alexis. 6017 244TH ST SW, STE 74 98043 #030-06-1992 L1998 **P** *020 †75
JACOBY, Karny. 6005 244TH ST SW, STE 111 98043 #054-04-1986 L1992 **U** *020 †95
MAZZEO, Rocky Wm. 6007 244TH ST SW STE B, BALLINGER CLC 98043 #054-04-1988 L1990 **FM** *020 †18
MC CORKELL, Scott Jos. 6808 220TH ST SW STE 100, CENTER FOR DIAGNOSTIC IMAG 98043 #035-09-1976 L1977 **DR** *020 †80
SCHWARTZ, Alan Neil. 6808 220TH ST SW STE 100, CENTER FOR DIAGNOSTIC IMAG 98043 #035-47-1977 L1978 **DR PD** *020 †55,80
SHUSTOV, Andrei Rostislav. 4207 236TH ST SW, APT E302 98043 #913-13-1993 L2003 **HEM** *100 †20
SOLLEK, Mark G. 7001 220TH ST SW, BLDG 4 98043 #036-07-1968 L1972 **MDM IM** *030 †20
URRIOLA, Alina Maria. 6007 244TH ST SW, STE B 98043 #187-14-1983 L1998 **FM PHP** *020 †70,18 ‡
WALTERS, Susan J S. 6005 244TH ST SW, STE 111 98043 #028-34-1986 L1991 **U** *020 †95
WANG, Xiaowen. 98043 #243-32-1993 L2005 **ON** *100 †20
WEST, Peter Amory. 7001 220TH ST SW, MS 445 98043 #005-15-1969 L1971 **PD PHP** *020 †18
WRIGHT, Virgil G. 6702 220TH ST SW 98043 #407-34-1960 L1976 **AN** *075 †05

MUKILTEO — SNOHOMISH

BEIGHLE, Cheryl Lynn. 4410 106TH ST SW 98275 #054-04-1982 L1986 **PD** *020 †55
BROSS, Gerald Stuart. 4410 106TH ST SW 98275 #005-06-1978 L1995 **IM** *020 †20,16
BROWN, Ralph Dexter. 8024 53RD AVE W, UNIT F 98275 #016-06-1948 L1948 **IM** *020 †20
BUI, Thuy Dinh. ■ 98275 #396-27-1993 *100
BUMSTEAD, Katherine D. 4430 106TH ST SW, STE 102 98275 #065-05-1996 L1999 **FM** *020 †18
CABANOS, Naretta Bangloy. 11914 59TH AVE W 98275 #748-07-1961 *071
CARLSON, Mark Chas. 4410 106TH ST SW 98275 #026-04-1982 L1989 **FM** *020 †18
CISLER, Amanda Christina. ■ 98275 #048-04-2001 L2004 **IM** *020
COHEN, Mindy Sue. ■ 98275 #038-06-1992 L1995 **IM** *100
DAHLBERG, Stephen Frank. 4410 106TH ST SW 98275 #054-04-1987 L1989 **FM** *020 †18
DREYER, Sheryl Ann. 4410 106TH ST SW, THE EVERETT CLINIC 98275 #054-04-1988 L1990 **IM** *020 †20
DURCHMAN, Liisa Elina. ■ 98275 #054-04-2005 L2005 **P** *012
FORD, Elbert S C. ■ 98275 #047-05-1939 L1958 **PYA** *072
HAFFORD, Thomas Keith. 4430 106TH ST SW STE 102, HARBOUR POINTE FAMILY PRAC 98275 #025-07-1992 L1995 **FM** *020 †18
HAN, Jong Ha. ■ 98275 #583-02-1964 L1971 **PD** *071 †55
HOCHBERG, Howard Martin. ■ 98275 #035-06-1961 L1983 **OS CD** *071
JUDD, Brian Chas. ■ 98275 #008-01-1963 L1969 **AN** *071 †05
KINAHAN, Consuelo Aurea. ■ 98275 #061-01-1985 L1995 **FM EM** *020
KRAMER, June Elizabeth. 413 LINCOLN AVE, STE A 98275 #011-02-1973 L1987 **CHP P** *020 †75
LEE, Peter Kyubum. ■ 98275 #035-09-1996 L2004 **CCM** *020 †20
LEONARD, Mark Franklyn. 6011 CENTRAL DR 98275 #025-12-1987 L1990 **IM EM** *020 †20
LIU, Dongmei. 12024 WILMINGTON WAY 98275 #243-94-1976 L2002 **N** *020 †75
MA, Sandy. ■ 98275 #067-01-1992 L1998 **FM** *020 †18
MC KNIGHT, Robert Michael. 4410 106TH ST SW, THE EVERETT CLINIC 98275 #010-01-1983 L1994 **IM** *020 †20

MULDER, Matthew John. 4410 106TH ST SW 98275 #035-45-1995 L1997 **FM** *020 †18
MUSTO, Steven Wm. 5670 94TH PL SW 98275 #016-06-1984 L1997 **IM PUD** *020 †20
NOWBAR-NEKAHI, Negin A. ■ 98275 #054-04-2007 L2007 **IM** *012
OH, Kirstine Yungting. ■ 98275 #026-08-2001 L2001 **HMP** *100 †50
PARRISH, Rebecca Lynn. 4430 106TH ST SW, STE 102 98275 #035-03-1999 L2001 **FM** *020 †18
RENDALL, Heidi Strong. 8227 44TH AVE W, STE E 98275 #005-02-1979 L1981 **FM** *020
ROBBIE, Thomas Michael. 10710 MUKILTEO SPEEDWAY 98275 #024-07-1977 L1978 **FM** *020 †18,16
SHERMAN, Carolyn E. 4430 106TH ST SW, STE 102 98275 #041-09-1995 L2000 **MPD PD** *020 †20,55
SKIRM, Elizabeth Ann. 4410 106TH ST SW 98275 #054-04-1997 L2000 **IM** *020 †20
SNOW, Robert Howard. ■ 98275 #025-01-1942 L1965 **OBG** *071 †30
STEPHENS, Jack. 4410 106TH ST SW 98275 #051-07-1979 L1984 **PD** *020 †55
THORNGATE, Philip. ■ 98275 #036-08-1958 L1958 **IM** *071
WHITE, Lowell Elmond, Jr. ■ 98275 #054-04-1953 L1955 **NS OS** *071 †25
WISBECK, William Mason. 2075 MUKILTEO SPEEDWAY 98275 #054-04-1986 L1988 **RO** *020 †80
WONG, Ming Yin. ■ 98275 #385-03-1966 L1973 **GS** *020
YOSHIKAWA, Richard T. ■ 98275 #041-09-1943 L1946 **GP PD** *072 †18
YOUNGSTROM, George Brice. ■ 98275 #040-02-1945 L1951 **D A** *071
ZARET, Deborah Lynn. 4410 106TH ST SW, THE EVERETT CLINIC 98275 #025-01-1993 L1995 **PD** *020 †55

NACHES — YAKIMA

BAUER, Mark J. 102 E 2ND ST 98937 #025-07-1980 L1983 **IM** *020 †20
BOWMAN, Howard Randolph. ■ 98937 #054-04-1956 L1957 **FM** *071 †18

NAPAVINE — LEWIS

BIERLEY, John Robt. ■ 98565 #038-41-1934 L1935 **GS** *071 †85

NASELLE — PACIFIC

DURET, Edouard. 21 N VALLEY RD 98638 #440-01-1972 L1998 **GS EM** *020 †85
ENSMINGER, Mark Randall. 21 N VALLEY RD 98638 #054-04-1983 L1986 **FM** *020 †18
FABIANO, Albert Oscar. 21 N VALLEY RD 98638 #306-01-1987 L2003 **IM** *020 †20
KAY, William Norris. 21 N VALLEY RD 98638 #010-02-1997 L2001 **GS** *020 †85

NEAH BAY — CLALLAM

VAN EATON, Thomas Michael. ■ 98357 #054-04-1971 L1972 **GP** *020

NESPELEM — OKANOGAN

HALL, William John. PO BOX 71, COVLIVLLE INDIAN HEALTH CE 99155 #035-46-1984 L2006 **FM** *020 †18

NEWCASTLE — KING

CHANG, Pi-Lin. 14229 SE 83RD ST 98059 #056-06-1993 L1996 **PD** *020 †55
CRAMER, Pia Gemperli. 6920 COAL CREEK PKWY SE, COAL CREEK FAMILY MEDICINE 98059 #036-07-1988 L1992 **FM** *071 †18
ESKESEN, Staci Joanna. 7203 129TH AVE SE, STE 100 98056 #054-04-2003 L2003 **FM** *020 †18
GATIEN, Andrew Joseph. ■ 98059 #016-42-2000 L2003 **IM** *020 †20 ‡
HEILMAN, Richard B. ■ 98059 #056-05-1943 L1957 **OM ON** *071
JARAMILLO, Lorena. ■ 98056 #007-02-2002 L2006 **OBG** *100
LOMAS, Richard Wilson. 6947 COAL CREEK PKWY SE 98059 #038-06-1957 L1963 **OPH** *020 †35
MAC PHERSON, Geoffrey A. 7203 129TH AVE SE, STE 100 98056 #054-04-1968 L1970 **PD** *020 †55
MELO, Megan Jean. ■ 98056 #054-04-2007 L2007 **FP** *012
NICHOLSON, Vanessa Ann. 6920 COAL CREEK PKWY SE #1 98059 #016-43-1982 L1994 **FM** *020 †18
NISHIO, Isuta. ■ 98059 #572-55-1986 L2004 **APM** *020 †05 ‡
PARK, James Edward. 7203 129TH AVE SE # 100, VMC - NEWCASTLE PRIMARY CA 98056 #056-06-1998 L2000 **FM** *020 †18
PHILLIPS, Christopher B. 6947 COAL CREEK PKWY SE 98059 #039-01-1999 L2007 **OPH** *020 †35 ‡
POLLARA, Trisha Lee. 7203 129TH AVE SE, STE 100 98056 #005-12-2003 L2003 **FM** *020 †18
ROSA-BRAY, Marilyn. 7203 129TH AVE SE, STE 200 98056 #042-01-1997 L1999 **IM** *020 †20
SHEK, Byzan. 7203 129TH AVE SE, STE 200 98056 #030-06-1996 L1998 **IM** *020 †20
TAYLOR, Barbara Diane. 6947 COAL CREEK PKWY SE, STE 100 98059 #048-04-1985 L1986 **OBG** *020 †30

NEWMAN LAKE — SPOKANE

TAKAI, Robert J. 17824 N THOMPSON CREEK RD 99025 #054-04-1980 L1981 **DR** *020 †80

NEWPORT — PEND OREILLE

GASPAR, Mitchell. ■ 99156 #005-12-1953 L1953 **GP OS** *071
HOFFMEISTER, James A, III. 714 W PINE ST 99156 #047-06-1969 L2003 **GS** *030 †85
JASMAN, Lora Lee. ■ 99156 #054-04-1985 L2005 **IM** *020 †20 ‡
JONES, Geoffry Scott. 714 W PINE ST 99156 #054-04-1996 L1998 **FM** *020 †18
KERSTING, Clayton Wesley. 714 W PINE ST 99156 #005-19-1987 L1989 **FM** *020 †18

■ = Address Information Privacy Protected

KRAUS, Angelika Brigitte. 714 W PINE ST 99156 #665-01-1999 L2003 **FM** *020 †18
MATTIS, Richard Nathaniel. 714 PINE ST W 99156 #054-04-1997 L1999 **FM** *020 †18
MURRAY, David Kingman. 714 W PINE ST, NEWPORT COMMUNITY HOSP 99156 #038-06-1989 L2006 **GS** *020 †85
RADKE, Shannon Beth. 714 PINE ST W 99156 #026-04-1996 L1998 **FM** *020 †18
TAXTER, Max Edwin. ■ 99156 #039-01-1969 L1970 **GP** *071
WEIR, Andrew Peter. 117 S WASHINGTON AVE, NEWPORT AMBULANCE 99156 #040-02-1974 L1977 **FM** *071 †18

NINE MILE FALLS – SPOKANE

COLEMAN, Kenneth Hunt. ■ 99026 #005-12-1973 L1974 **EM FM** *020 †18
HARRINGTON, Earl George. ■ 99026 #005-17-1962 L1975 **GP GS** *020
LIMBER, Wayne S. ■ 99026 #050-02-1983 L1976 **IM GE** *071 †18
MC CULLY, Donald. PO BOX 246, 9 MILE RD 99026 #038-41-1972 L2001 **HEM PTH** *020 †50
PELLOW, Thomas O. ■ 99026 #005-12-1951 L1951 **GP OS** *071
POWELL, Bruce Duane. ■ 99026 #041-13-1955 L1959 **ORS** *071 †40
WHIPPLE, Katherine Joy. ■ 99026 #026-04-1998 L2004 **MPD** *100

NORDLAND – JEFFERSON

GEERLOFS, John Peter. ■ 98358 #033-05-1973 L1974 **EM** *020 †18
LASHER, Henry Edward. ■ 98358 #035-06-1967 L1968 **GP GS** *020

NORMANDY PARK – KING

FULWIDER, Kersten Ann. ■ 98166 #028-46-1991 L1996 **EM** *020 †16
GILLIES, Bruce Stuart. 210 SW 197TH PL 98166 #035-45-1984 L1989 **AN** *020 †05
LEE, Max M. 19711 1ST AVE S 98148 #244-06-1969 L1979 **IM** *020
MARTIN, Kenneth L. ■ 98166 #040-02-1950 L1956 **ORS** *071 †40
MC CULLY, John Thos. ■ 98166 #056-06-1956 L1967 **GYN** *071 †30
MEHAFFEY, Janet J Luschei. ■ 98166 #054-04-1955 L1956 **AN** *071
MOREIRA, Glaucia De Castr. 17837 1ST AVE S, PMB 292 98148 #187-09-1994 L2002 **AN** *020 †05
STANFORD, Marie T. 19401 EDGECLIFF DR SW 98166 #048-14-1989 L1992 **FM** *020 †18
WARWICK, Robert Barry. ■ 98166 #054-04-1973 L1975 **FM** *020 †18
WOLD, De Witt Edlay. ■ 98166 #054-04-1953 L1954 **DR** *071 †80

NORTH BEND – KING

GRANT, Harry Alfred, III. 7243 MOON VALLEY RD SE 98045 #005-11-1966 L1970 **DR** *020 †80
HASSE, Elwyn Ray. ■ 98045 #649-14-1962 L1963 **GP** *071 †18
LAWS, E Harold. ■ 98045 #017-20-1940 L1942 **IM** *071 †20
WINSHIP, Myron Jay. ■ 98045 #016-06-1966 L1976 **ID IM** *071 †20

OAK HARBOR – ISLAND

ADAMS, Charles F, Jr. 3475 N SARATOGA ST, NAVAL HOSPITAL OAK HARBOR 98278 #050-02-1984 L1989 **AM** *020 †05
ADAMS, Robert Jefferson. ■ 98277 #045-01-1979 L2003 **FM AM** *020 †18
ANDERSON, William Martin. 3475 N SARATOGA ST, NAVAL HOSPITAL 98278 #007-02-1981 L1988 **GS** *020 †85
APPLEGATE, William Rogers. ■ 98277 #038-41-1963 L1987 **ORS** *071 †40
BAKER, James Curtis. ■ 98277 #040-02-1978 L1968 **PTH FM** *020 †18
BARNES, Mary Quentin. 1051 NE 7TH AVE 98277 #051-01-1988 L1997 **PD** *020 †55
BARRETT, Nathan. ■ 98277 #035-08-1962 L1992 **ORS** *020 †40
BARTLEY, Tony Carroll. 275 SE CABOT DR STE B101 98277 #045-01-1972 L1985 **FM GP** *020 †18
BEATTY, Hugh Tyrrell. ■ 98277 #049-01-1968 L1985 **R GP** *071
BEGLEY, Vincent James. PO BOX 1068 98277 #035-09-1966 L1967 **GS** *071
BEUMER, John R. 275 SE CABOT DR, STE B102 98277 #038-41-1994 L2002 **PD** *020 †55
BIBBY, Christopher John. 275 SE CABOT DR STE B101, WHIDBEY COMMUNITY PHYS 98277 #054-04-1992 L1992 **FM** *020 †18
BOONE, John Leigh. 3475 N SARATOGA ST H, CODE 0905 98278 #018-03-1979 L1984 **OTO** *020 †45
BOUWENS, Ronda Dee. ■ 98277 #028-34-1998 L2000 **FM** *020 †18
BYLUND, Erik Roy. 3475 N SARATOGA ST, NAVY HOSPITAL 98278 #023-12-1997 L2007 **FM** *100 †18
CASE, Roger Sherman. 1791 NE 1ST AVE 98277 #038-40-1963 L1971 **FM PHP** *071 †18
CHINN, Colin Gregory. 3475 N SARATOGA ST, ATTN: CREDENTIAL OFFICE 98278 #051-04-1985 L1986 **GE IM** *030 †20
CRAWLEY, David Bruce. 3475 N SARATOGA ST 98278 #019-02-1971 L1972 **FM** *075
DEWEY, Thomas J, III. 3475 N SARATOGA ST, CODE 0906 98278 #021-05-1967 L1967 **ORS** *020 †40
DIVELBISS, Charles Levi. 316 SE PIONEER WAY, PMB 342 98277 #054-04-1957 L1959 **FM** *071 †18
DONALTY, Andrea Brunhart. 3475 N SARATOGA ST, ATTN CREDENTIALS OFFICE 98278 #010-01-1997 L1998 **PD** *020 †55
EGGERS, John Richard, Jr. 3475 N SARATOGA ST, NAVAL HOSPITAL OAK HARBOR 98278 #005-12-1985 L1992 **OBG** *020 †30
EHLERT, Anna Melissa. ■ 98277 #016-43-2001 L2008 *020 †20
ERIE, Norman Arndt. ■ 98277 #054-04-1955 L1959 **FM** *071 †18
FAIRFAX, George Taylor. ■ 98277 #054-04-1955 L1956 **OBG** *071 †30
FORT, Richard Allan. 3475 N SARATOGA ST 98278 #011-03-1977 L1986 **EM GP** *020 †16
FOX, Haigh Perrigo. 1300 NE GOLDIE ST, NORTH WHIDBEY COMMUNITY CL 98277 #054-04-1969 L1976 **FM** *020 †18
GEHRES, Mary Margaret. ■ 98277 #049-01-1958 L1965 **PD** *071 †55
GOETZ, Robert Lynwood. 665 SE PIONEER WAY 98277 #041-13-1953 L1959 **GP** *071
GOLDBERG, Marshall F. ■ 98277 #036-01-1973 L2005 **OBG PHP** *071 †30,70 ‡
GREEN, Ray Lyman. ■ 98277 #036-05-1972 L1972 **OBG** *020 †30

HANSEN, Frank Morris. 3475 N SARATOGA ST, NAVAL HOSP OAK HARBOR 98278 #054-04-1967 L1968 **DR NM** *020 †80,28
HOCKETT, Clyde Jay. ■ 98277 #040-02-1977 L1978 **P FM** *020 †18,75
HOPEN, Carina Cezar. 3475 N SARATOGA ST, ATTN: CREDENTIAL OFFICE 98278 #014-01-2000 L2006 **FM** *020 †18
HUEBNER, Chadley Ryan. 3475 N SARATOGA ST, NH OAK HARBOR WA 98278 #038-40-2000 L2001 **PD** *020 †55
JONES, William Bradley. ■ 98277 #054-04-1981 L1985 **DR OBG** *062 †80
KANJO, Zayan A. 231 SE BARRINGTON DR, STE 209 98277 #875-01-1983 L1990 **IM** *020
KLEIN, Chester Le Roy. ■ 98277 #019-02-1948 L1965 **IM AM** *071
KNAACK, Rudolph Herman. 275 SE CABOT DR, B101 98277 #054-04-1972 L1974 **FM** *020 †18
KUBISTY, Cheryl Ann. 830 SE IRELAND ST 98277 #035-06-1986 L1993 **IM PA** *020 †20
LANGROCK, Douglas G. 275 SE CABOT DR, STE B101 98277 #048-04-1987 L1990 **FM** *020 †18
LEDBETTER, Billy Ray, Jr. ■ 98277 #048-02-1993 L1994 **ID** *020
LEE, Terry Ann. 231 SE BARRINGTON DR, STE 208 98277 #005-06-1982 L1988 **OPH** *020 †35
LING, Shun Hung. 3475 N SARATOGA ST 98278 #005-06-1963 L1988 **OBG GP** *020 †30
LOEB, James Robt. ■ 98277 #028-34-1966 L1966 **OBG** *020 †30
LYCKSELL, Robert Lee. 231 SE BARRINGTON DR, STE 209 98277 #054-04-1979 L1982 **FM** *020 †18
MATTSON, Stephen D. 1242 ROSEMONT DR 98277 #023-12-1986 L2003 **EM** *020 †16
MAYS, Jane Ann. 275 SE CABOT DR, STE B102 98277 #047-05-1971 L1978 **PD** *020 †55
MC DANIEL, William James. 3475 N SARATOGA ST 98278 #039-01-1968 L1972 **ORS** *074 †40
MC DONALD, Herbert B. ■ 98277 #054-04-1963 L1989 **CD IM** *071 †20
MERRICK, Melanie Joyce. ■ 98277 #011-02-1993 L1994 **FM UM** *020 †18
MILLS, John Wm. ■ 98277 #016-45-1975 L1977 **AM FM** *020 †18,70
MORGAN, Vernon Dale. ■ 98277 #005-12-1982 L1983 **FM** *020 †18
MORLOCK, Noel Louis. ■ 98277 #054-04-1960 L1975 **GP OBG** *071
MOSOLINO, Laurie Beth. 3475 N SARATOGA ST, NAVAL HOSP 98278 #026-04-1981 L2002 **GS** *020 †85
MOTT, Lee Edward C. 3475 N SARATOGA ST, NAVAL HOSPITAL OAK HARBOR 98278 #001-02-1977 L1985 **DR** *071 †80
NELLERMOE, Carrol Wandell. 3348 GREEN RD 98277 #054-04-1953 L1957 **AN** *071
NELSON, Jeffrey Loren. ■ 98277 #026-08-1976 L1981 **P** *020
NIMMERRICHTER-BURGESS, Tra. 830 SE IRELAND ST 98277 #023-01-1988 L1993 **IM** *020 †20
OLSON, Bradley Douglas. 275 SE CABOT DR, STE B101 98277 #026-04-1996 L1999 **FM** *020 †18
OLSON, Russell James. 3475 N SARATOGA ST, NAVAL HOSPITAL 98278 #026-04-1982 L1983 **AM FM** *020 †18
PLAJA, Dennis John. 3475 N SARATOGA ST, CODE 0905 98278 #024-05-1983 L1988 **FM** *020 †18
RALSTON, Mark E. 1117 RAINIER CIR 98277 #035-20-1983 L1986 **PD PEM** *020 †55
RAMOS, Christopher G. 3475 N SARATOGA ST, CODE 0906 98278 #035-47-1981 L2000 **ORS** *020
RASMUSSEN, Clyde Mervyn. 3475 N SARATOGA ST, OAK HARBOR NAVAL HOSPITAL 98278 #005-02-1965 L1995 **PD** *020 †55
REAY, Donald Thos. ■ 98277 #049-01-1963 L1973 **FOP PTH** *071 †50
SANDERS, Jerald Gail. 275 SE CABOT DR, STE B101 98277 #054-04-1977 L1981 **FM** *020 †18
SCHMIDT, Rainer Siegfried. ■ 98277 #005-11-1962 L1981 **D** *071 †15
SILVETTI, Anthony N. 3475 N SARATOGA ST, NAVY HOSPITAL OAK HARBOR 98278 #016-11-1995 L1995 **OBG FM** *020 †18
SOLBERG, Gary E. 32785 SR 20 STE 2 98277 #016-06-1985 L1995 *020
SPARKS, Sidney Dana. 275 SE CABOT DR, STE B102 98277 #005-18-1988 L1995 **PD** *020 †55
ULLRICH, John Alan. 3475 N SARATOGA ST, NAVAL HOSPITAL OAK HARBOR 98278 #040-02-2001 L2003 **GS** *020 †85
WELDON, Dean Angela. 3475 N SARATOGA ST, ATTN: CREDENTIAL OFFICE 98278 #048-12-1980 L2006 **FM IM** *020 †18
WILLIAMS, Michael Eric. 3475 N SARATOGA ST, ATTN: CREDENTIAL OFFICE 98278 #023-12-1998 L1999 **FM** *020 †18
WILLIAMS, Wilfred Le Roy. ■ 98277 #010-01-1959 L1985 **GS** *071 †85
WOOLPERT, Keith Dellan. ■ 98277 #019-02-1957 L1991 **ORS** *072 †40
ZACOVIC, James Warren. NAS WHIDBEY ISLAND, NAVAL HOSPITAL 98278 #023-12-1988 L2000 **EM** *020 †16

OCEAN PARK – PACIFIC

JASTAK, Rocquelyn M Urgo. ■ 98640 #033-05-1962 L1993 **IM END** *072
METRA, Eugenia. ■ 98640 #594-01-1936 L1950 **P** *071
WAECHTER, Kenton Gifford. ■ 98640 #005-15-1964 L1965 **OBG** *071 †30

OCEAN SHORES – GRAYS HARBOR

BOUDWIN, James W. ■ 98569 #005-06-1949 L1958 **P IMG** *072 †75
HOLM, Alfred John. ■ 98569 #040-02-1999 L2003 **FM** *020

ODESSA – LINCOLN

GAHRINGER, John E, Jr. ■ 99159 #054-04-1951 L1952 **FM** *071 †18
POWELL, Linda Jayne. 502 E AMENDE ST 99159 #035-15-1989 L1992 **FM** *020 †18

OKANOGAN – OKANOGAN

CERPA-VALENZUELA, Mario E. PO BOX 1340, 716 1ST AVE S 98840 #231-01-1974 L1984 *020
CRANDELL, Blain Alan. 716 1ST AVE S 98840 #001-02-2001 L2004 **FM** *020 †18
DAVIS, Leon Thaddeus. PO BOX 1040 98840 #005-06-1974 L1978 **DR** *020 †80
MERRY, William Henry, III. ■ 98840 #005-06-1979 L1982 **GS** *020 †85

OLALLA – KITSAP

LEE, Marc Edward. ■ 98359 #054-04-1977 L1983 **FM EM** *071 †16,18
SCHNARE, David Peabody. ■ 98359 #035-09-1977 L1978 **GP** *020

■ = Address Information Privacy Protected

SNEAD, Thomas Arthur. ■ 98359 #023-12-1985 L1989 **GP** *020 †70

OLGA – SAN JUAN

DIXON, William Grant. ■ 98279 #019-02-1945 L1982 **GS TS** *020 †85
LANDER, Howard Hayes. ■ 98279 #016-06-1937 L1947 **NS** *075

OLYMPIA – THURSTON

ABDULKHADER, Joonis. 525 LILLY RD NE 98506 #495-80-2005 **FP** *012
ABEGG, Sharon Carol. 700 LILLY RD NE 98506 #041-09-1986 L1990 **P** *020 †75
ACHEBE, Ngozi Janet. 3900 CAPITOL MALL DR SW, CAPITAL MEDICAL CENTRE 98502 #690-04-1983 L2003 **RHU IM** *020 †20,18
AGTARAP, Laddie Anthony. 3525 ENSIGN RD NE, STE E 98506 #054-04-1992 L1996 **ORS** *020 †40
AHEARN, Marilyn Dienst. 700 LILLY RD NE 98506 #014-01-1989 L1994 **PD** *040 †55
ALBRECHT, Stephen Carl. 3622 ENSIGN RD NE, STE A 98506 #047-06-1981 L1982 **FM** *020 †18
ALLEN, Gregory C. 3624 ENSIGN RD NE, STE B 98506 #065-09-1983 L1988 **AN** *020 †05
ALLEN, Paul Jay. 2938 LIMITED LN NW, STE B 98502 #016-42-1986 L1990 **PM PRS** *020 †60
ALLISON, Stanley Chas. 420 LILLY RD NE 98506 #048-04-1965 L1978 **OPH DIA** *071 †35
ALLOTT, Leonard Sherwood. ■ 98501 #007-02-1956 L1960 **GP EM** *071
ANDERSON, Arthur Dean. 3525 ENSIGN RD NE STE A 98506 #054-04-1965 L1968 **U** *020 †95
ANDERSON, Gregory Cushing. ■ 98516 #038-41-1971 L1979 **PD GP** *020 †18
ANDERSON, Ryan Joseph. 3900 CAPITOL MALL DR SW, CAPITAL MEDICAL CENTER 98502 #054-04-1998 L2002 **AN** *020 †05
ANDRIACCHI, Frances C. 3624 ENSIGN RD NE # D 98506 #025-01-1978 L1982 **GYN** *020 †30
ANKENEY, Geoffrey Arthur. 525 LILLY RD NE 98506 #550-04-2005 L2006 **FP** *012
ANNEGERS, John Herman. ■ 98502 #016-06-1944 L1946 **OS** *071
ANTLES, Lee Allen. 406 YAUGER WAY SW STE A 98502 #005-12-1985 L1988 **IM** *020 †20
ANTOSH, Ivan J. ■ 98513 #048-13-2005 L2006 **ORS** *012
ARCOL, Delia Colcol. ■ 98502 #748-01-1962 *100
ASOMANING, Gilbert. ■ 98502 #412-01-1998 L2005 **IM** *100 †20
AVILA, Eduardo. 200 LILLY RD NE, STE C2 98506 #018-03-2000 L2002 **GS** *020 †85
BAIG, Mohammad Qasim. ■ 98507 #704-01-2000 L2006 **IM** *100 †20
BALFE, Michael Wm. 700 LILLY RD NE, GHC 98506 #040-02-1981 L1999 **FM** *020 †18
BALL, Janet Marie. 700 LILLY RD NE 98506 #005-19-1988 L1990 **FM** *020 †18
BALZ, James Beal. ■ 98501 #028-34-1972 L1972 **CRS GS** *071 †10,85
BARER, Lisa Marie S. 1920 BLACK LAKE BLVD SW, ABC PEDIATRICS 98512 #054-04-1998 L2000 **PD** *020 †55
BARTHA, Liliane. 942 CEDAR LAKE CT SE 98501 #067-02-1984 L1989 **EM GPM** *020
BARTHOLOMEW, Mary Strong. 700 LILLY RD NE, PUGET SOUND 98506 #054-04-1977 L1980 **FM** *020 †18
BARTON-HAAS, Lorraine. 3030 LIMITED LN NW, SEA MAR COMMUNITY HEALTH C 98502 #024-16-1983 L2006 **P** *020 †75
BAUER, John Mark. 500 LILLY RD NE, STE 120 98506 #040-02-1975 L1979 **D** *020 †15
BAUER, Kevin Douglas. ■ 98516 #035-09-2008 *012
BEARE, John Alan. DIV HEALTH MS LP 17 98504 #040-02-1960 L1962 **PHP** *030 †70
BELKO, Amy Zyra. 525 LILLY RD NE, STE 250 98506 #050-02-1991 L1991 **PD** *020 †55
BELL, Darrel James. 615 LILLY RD NE STE 200 98506 #030-06-2002 L2006 **OBG** *020
BELL, Gregory Dean. 525 LILLY RD NE, STE 210 98506 #054-04-1993 L1996 **N** *020 †75
BEPPU, William James. 3425 ENSIGN RD NE STE 100 98506 #005-11-1972 L1977 **AN** *020 †05
BERGER, Philip. 406 BLACK HILLS LN SW # A 98502 #018-75-1978, ▲ L1985 **CD IM** *020 †20
BHASKAR, Yashoda. 700 LILLY RD NE, PUGET SOUND, OLYMPIA MED C 98506 #495-89-1989 L2001 **IM** *020 †20
BLACK, Joel Waylon. 3920 CAPITOL MALL DR SW, STE 304 98502 #045-01-1967 L1974 **PUD PCC** *020 †20,03
BLACKMON, Kevin Paul. 3624 ENSIGN RD NE STE B 98506 #023-12-1991 L1999 **AN** *020 †05
BLACKNER, Gregary M. 403 BLACK HILLS LN SW # B 98502 #054-04-1986 L1989 **FM** *020 †18
BLANCO, Vivian L. 436 MCPHEE RD SW 98502 #054-04-1996 L1998 **FM** *020 †18
BODOIA, Rodger Dante. 215 LILLY RD NE 98506 #054-04-1985 L1987 **OPH** *020 †35
BONAUTO, David Keith. ■ 98501 #035-01-1993 L1996 **GPM** *020 †70,20
BONNER, Ian Daniel. 525 LILLY RD NE, RESIDENCY PROGRAM 98506 #054-04-2006 L2006 **FP** *012
BOWEN, Angela Joyce M. 3535 7TH AVE SW 98502 #054-04-1963 L1964 **END GYN** *071
BOYD, Michael R. 3622 ENSIGN RD NE, STE A 98506 #056-06-1972 L1975 **FM** *020 †18
BRACKEBUSCH, Mark Carl. 3900 CAPITOL MALL DR SW 98502 #040-02-1976 L1988 **AN** *020 †05
BRADFORD, Mark Wayne. 3624 ENSIGN RD NE BLDG D 98506 #025-01-1978 L1982 **IM END** *020 †20
BRANDT, Rebecca Christine. ■ 98502 #018-03-1979 L2006 **FM** *020 †18
BRANTNER, Richard Dayle. 413 LILLY RD NE 98506 #007-02-1989 L2001 **EM** *020 †16
BRAR, Harpreet Singh. 500 LILLY RD NE STE 204 98506 #306-01-1989 L1992 **GE** *020 †20
BRASETH, Arin Tait. 413 LILLY RD NE 98506 #011-03-1999 L2002 **EM** *020 †16
BRASHER, Ray Vernon, Jr. ■ 98516 #034-01-1974 L1983 **EM IM** *020
BRAY, George Alexander. 3435 MARTIN WAY E, STE H 98506 #016-02-1963 L1968 **AN PUD** *071 †05
BRAZIL, James Lawrence. 424 LILLY RD NE, STE A 98506 #040-02-1987 L1991 **D** *020 †15
BREMNER, James Douglas. 1021 4TH AVE W, JAMES D BREMNER MD INC PS 98502 #054-04-1956 L1958 **P** *071 †75
BRENNAN, William Patrick. 500 LILLY RD NE, STE 100 98506 #054-04-1980 L1985 **CD** *020 †20
BREWER, Larry La Verne. 525 LILLY RD NE 98506 #018-03-1962 L1963 **OBG** *071 †30
BROBERG, Lucille Rae. 3525 7TH AVE SW SW-MF1 98502 #068-01-1976 L1990 **PD** *020 †55
BROCK, Wesley Mason. DSHS-HA11 98504 #041-01-1945 L1946 **OS LM** *075
BROWN, Daniel Mark. 402 BLACK HILLS LN SW, STE A 98502 #048-13-1983 L2003 **U** *020 †95 ‡
BROWN, George J. ■ 98502 #024-05-1973 L2000 **GE IM** *030 †20
BROWN, Kristen Michelle. ■ 98501 #056-06-2002 L2007 **PD** *100
BROWN, Michael William. ■ 98501 #056-06-2002 L2007 **RO** *100
BROWN, Shelia Winifred B. 2126 CAPITOL WAY S 98501 #021-01-1976 L1980 **PD** *020 †55
BRUNTON, Robert Ira. 420 LILLY RD NE 98506 #054-04-1961 L1967 **OPH** *071 †35
BULATOVIC, Srdja. ■ 98502 #957-08-1983 L2004 **APM** *100 †05
BURTNER, Christopher Paul. 500 LILLY RD NE STE 203, MEMORIAL NEUROLOGY CLINIC 98506 #017-20-1998 L2003 **NEP** *020 †20
BURTNER, Melissa Garry. 615 LILLY RD NE STE 200, OLYMPIA OBSTETRICS & GYNEC 98506 #017-20-1998 L2003 **OBG** *020 †30
BUSER, Charles Nicholas. 3900 CAPITOL MALL DR SW 98502 #056-05-1975 L1976 **EM OM** *020
CADY, Francois Miguel. 413 LILLY RD NE 98506 #021-06-2001 L2007 **HMP** *100 †50
CALLAGHAN, Maureen Ann. 525 LILLY RD NE STE 210 98506 #005-14-1981 L1982 **N** *030 †75
CAMPOS, Frederick Anthony. 3425 ENSIGN RD NE STE 100 98506 #024-07-1973 L1978 **AN APM** *020 †05 ‡
CANNON, Virginia Ruth. 406 YAUGER WAY SW, STE A 98502 #016-11-1984 L1989 **NEP IM** *020 †20
CARNES, Roger Winfield. 413 LILLY RD NE 98506 #048-04-1969 L1973 **GYN OBG** *020 †30
CARPENTER, Clyde Toone. 3900 CAPITOL MALL DR SW 98502 #005-06-1986 L1994 **OSS** *020 †40
CARSLEY, Robert Thos. 3525 ENSIGN RD NE STE K 98506 #027-01-1970 L1975 **PD** *020 †55
CHAPPELL, George Lewis. 413 LILLY RD NE 98506 #005-14-1975 L1990 **P ADM** *020 †75
CHEN, Zachary H. 3624 ENSIGN RD NE, STE E 98506 #244-04-1980 L1985 **IM** *020 †20
CHENG, Fong-Kuei Frank. ■ 98516 #023-12-2007 **IM** *012
CHOE, Yun-Sun. 1212 HARRISON AVE NW 98502 #583-06-1991 L1998 **RHU IM** *020 †20
CHRISTENSEN, Reed Stanton. ■ 98516 #049-01-1985 L1986 **END IM** *020 †20
CLARK-NEITZEL, Charlotte. 3030 LIMITED LN NW 98502 #005-18-1989 L1990 **FM** *020 †18
COHEN, Mitchell Lewis. 525 LILLY RD NE 98506 #016-43-2001 L2003 **FM** *020 †18
COKER, John Wm. 3525 ENSIGN RD NE STE E 98506 #041-13-1964 L1966 **ORS** *020 †40
COLE, Robert Elmer. ■ 98502 #054-04-1957 L1959 **PHP** *071 †70
CONKLIN, William Lewis. 3624 ENSIGN RD NE STE B, OLYMPIA ANESTHESIA ASSOCIA 98506 #056-06-1994 L1998 **AN** *020 †05
CONNOLLY, Kevin Francis. 520 LILLY RD NE 98506 #005-02-1970 L1974 **N IM** *020 †20,75
CONRAD, Daniel Thos. 700 LILLY RD NE 98506 #005-14-1977 L1980 **FM** *020 †18
CONTE, William Robt. ■ 98501 #047-05-1945 L1965 **P** *072 †75
COOK, Stuart John. ■ 98506 #062-01-1952 L1972 **FM OS** *071 †18
COSLOW, Lee Ann. 700 LILLY RD NE 98506 #017-20-1983 L1989 **FM** *020 †18
COYNE, Carolyn Marie. ■ 98512 #021-05-1981 L2000 **FOP PTH** *020 †50
CRABS, Jack Marvin. 413 LILLY RD NE 98506 #054-04-1962 L1963 **IM** *020
CULLEN, John Patrick. ■ 98512 #007-02-1976 L1978 **FM** *020 †18
CUMINGS, Mark Douglas. 12137 DREAM ST SW 98512 #055-02-1995 L2003 **GE** *020 †20
DAKIN, Diane Elizabeth. 700 LILLY RD NE, GROUP HEALTH COOPERATIVE 98506 #005-02-1980 L1984 **FM** *020 †18
DAVIS, Catherine W C. 413 LILLY RD NE 98506 #005-14-1977 L1978 **PD** *020 †55
DAVIS, Melvin R. ■ 98501 #040-02-1949 L1950 **IM GP** *071 †20
DECKER, Raymond Mathew. ■ 98506 #028-34-1964 L1968 **OBG** *020 †30
DE GIVE, Henry Leon. 3525 ENSIGN RD NE 98506 #035-20-1972 L1980 **PD** *020 †55
DEITZ, David Michael. 3920 CAPITOL MALL DR SW, STE 203 98502 #036-01-1981 L1988 **VS GS** *020 †85
DESAI, Kirit Jayantilal. 700 LILLY RD NE, DEPT OF DERMATOLOGY 98506 #021-01-1964 L2002 **D** *020 †15
DEXTER, Mary J Buckley. ■ 98502 #025-01-1950 L1970 **P** *071 †75
DICKASON, Laurel Anne. 3920 CAPITOL MALL DR SW 98502 #051-04-1992 L1995 **OBG** *020 †30
DICKASON, Wayne Leroy. 413 LILLY RD NE 98506 #025-01-1965 L1974 **PS** *071 †65 ‡
DIEDERICH, Robert John. ■ 98506 #054-04-2004 L2007 **FP** *012
DIGHTMAN, Douglas A. ■ 98501 #054-04-2007 L2007 **FP** *012
DIGHTMAN, Lowell Richard. 525 LILLY RD NE 98506 #026-04-1974 L1982 **FM** *040 †18
DOOLITTLE, Gary Malcolm. 3425 ENSIGN RD NE, STE B 98506 #032-01-1987 L1991 **AN IM** *020 †05
DOUGHLY, Najla Mary. 700 LILLY RD NE, GROUP HEALTH COOPERATIVE 98506 #056-06-2001 L2003 **FM** *020 †18
DRYGAS, Henry F, Jr. 700 LILLY RD NE 98506 #038-40-1973 L1976 **OBG** *020 †30
EBALO, Evelyn Ebarle. 1920 BLACK LAKE BLVD SW, ABC PEDIATRICS 98512 #748-10-1983 L1991 **PD** *020 †55
EDSTAM, James Stephen. 700 LILLY RD NE 98506 #054-04-1976 L1977 **IMG IM** *020 †20
EDWARDS, Curtis John. 4310 FOXHALL DR NE 98516 #054-04-1985 L1991 **AM GS** *020 †85
EHLERS, William Arthur. 701 SLEATER KINNEY RD SE 98503 #030-05-1945 L1954 **FM** *071 †18
ELLEDGE, William Noel. 1925 BERRY ST NE 98506 #019-02-1968 L1971 **IM** *020 †20
ELLEN, Michael Robin. 128 LILLY RD NE, STE 205 98506 #010-02-1980 L1989 **U GS** *020 †95
EMMONS, William Frank. 205 LILLY RD NE STE B 98506 #060-01-1964 L1974 **NS N** *072 †25
ENSIGN, Leonard Harold. 413 LILLY RD NE 98506 #067-01-1956 L1959 **AN** *072
ENYEART, Dewayne Lee. 3425 ENSIGN RD NE STE 100 98506 #017-20-1970 L1980 **AN** *020 †05
ERICKSON, John Chas. ■ 98508 #016-06-1960 L1966 **OPH** *071
EVANS, Kirk Edward. ■ 98506 #054-04-1962 L1964 **OBG** *071 †30
EVERETT, Joel David. 3425 ENSIGN RD NE STE 100 98506 #054-04-1966 L1970 **AN** *020 †05
FAIOLA, Richard Louis. 3333 HARRISON AVE NW, HERITAGE FAMILY MEDICINE 98502 #005-12-1976 L1981 **FM** *020 †18
FARRER, John Hughes. 703 LILLY RD NE, STE 104 98506 #005-18-1979 L1988 **U** *020 †95
FAY, Gerald Jos. 525 LILLY RD NE 98506 #035-45-1975 L1980 **IM RHU** *020 †20
FAY, Sheila Grauer. 525 LILLY RD NE 98506 #035-46-1975 L1980 **GS VS** *020 †85
FEERO, Stanley Marlin. 413 LILLY RD NE 98506 #054-04-1976 L1977 **EM** *075 †20,16
FIDDA, Nisreen. 413 LILLY RD NE 98506 #875-01-1993 L2005 **PCP** *100 †50
FIELD, Ernest R, II. PO BOX 373 98507 #031-01-1983 L1984 **FM** *020
FIELDS, Mimi Louise. DEPT OF HEALTH ET21/7890 98504 #028-03-1978 L1988 **GPM PHP** *030 †70
FILL, Eileen K. ■ 98501 #040-02-1977 L1982 **DR** *020 †80
FILL, William Louis. ■ 98502 #016-11-1975 L1982 **DR** *020 †80
FINCH, Richard Marvin. 700 LILLY RD NE, GROUP HEALTH MEDICAL CENTE 98506 #005-02-1973 L1975 **FM** *020 †18
FLEMING, Craig. 700 LILLY RD NE, GROUP HEALTH COOPERATIVE 98506 #019-02-1982 L1995 **IM** *050 †20
FOCHT, Ferne Sabin. ■ 98502 #016-06-1946 L1951 **IM** *071
FOLEY, Arthur Lee, III. 3425 ENSIGN RD NE STE 300 98506 #025-12-1974 L1980 **PS HS** *020 †65
FONTANILLA, Larry Lorenzo, Jr. 413 LILLY RD NE 98506 #014-01-1999 L2004 **OS** *020 †20,16
FORAGE, John William. ■ 98501 #003-01-1995 L1998 **IM** *020 †20
FORREST, Gary Lane. 420 LILLY RD NE 98506 #054-04-1967 L1970 **OPH** *071 †35
FOSTER, Ralph H. 413 LILLY RD NE 98506 #016-06-1950 L1958 **GP** *071
FOX, Richard W. 413 LILLY RD NE 98506 #041-02-1961 L1962 **GS** *071 †85
FRANKLIN, Gary Michael. ■ 98501 #010-01-1969 L1988 **N PHP** *020 †75

FRANKLIN, Marcia Jane. 700 LILLY RD NE 98506 #005-12-1976 L1978 **FM GPM** *020 †18
FROST, Nathan Lee. ■ 98502 #016-43-2005 L2006 **ORS** *012
FUKUI-MINER, Karen. 525 LILLY RD NE STE 250 98506 #054-04-1987 L1990 **PD** *020 †55
FULLERTON, Monte William. ■ 98513 #016-11-1962 L1963 **PDS** *071 †85
FULLINGTON, Warren R. ■ 98512 #054-04-1956 L1964 **GYN** *071 †30
FUNKHOUSER, Robert David. ■ 98502 #017-20-1959 L1961 **FM** *071 †18
GACETTA, David John. 2103 59TH AVE NW 98502 #050-02-1981 L1985 **DR** *071 †80
GAGE, Marilyn. 500 LILLY RD NE, STE 100B 98506 #035-45-1982 L1991 **GYN MFM** *020 †30
GARDNER, Freda Eva. ■ 98502 #048-04-1976 L2005 **IM** *020 †20
GARRETT, William Millard. 413 LILLY RD NE 98506 #028-34-1980 L1981 **AN** *020 †05
GARRY, Benedict Michael. 700 LILLY RD NE, GROUP HLTH COOPERATIVE 98506 #010-02-1994 L2005 **FM** *020 †18
GAVIN, William Andrew. 500 LILLY RD NE, STE 100 98506 #016-06-1977 L1978 **CD IM** *020 †20
GENICH, Mark Henry. ■ 98502 #026-04-1971 L1973 **FM** *020 †18
GEVIRTZMAN, Louis. 700 LILLY RD NE 98506 #048-04-1986 L1991 **GS TS** *071 †85
GEYER, Dennis James. 413 LILLY RD NE, PROVIDENCE ST. PETER HOSPI 98506 #023-12-2000 L2007 **NS** *020
GHOSN, Maha Yehia. 413 LILLY RD NE, MAILSTOP LLH22 98506 #422-01-2003 L2007 **IMG** *020 †20
GIFFIN, Robert B. ■ 98501 #005-06-1949 L1972 **PHP PD** *071 †55
GILMER, Patricia A. 128 LILLY RD NE, STE 202 98506 #048-04-1984 L1991 **OTO HNS** *020 †45
GOBLE, Kathy Ann. 615 LILLY RD NE, STE 200 98506 #056-06-1994 L1998 **OBG** *020 †30
GOIN, Gary R. 412 BLACK HILLS LN SW 98502 #040-02-1982 L1985 **FM** *020 †18
GOLD, Jonathan Adam. 3900 CAPITOL MALL DR SW 98502 #016-43-1987 L1994 **OBG** *020 †30
GOLDEN, Thomas Wm. 3624 ENSIGN RD NE, STE B 98506 #039-01-1989 L1997 **AN** *020 †05
GOLDENBERG, Samuel. ■ 98507 #020-02-1943 L1946 **AN** *071 †05
GOMEZ, Mikel Ray. 405 BLACK HILLS LN SW # F 98502 #005-02-1974 L1975 **FM** *020
GRAY, Carroll Lee. ■ 98507 #036-01-1966 L1983 **P** *075
GREEN, Douglas O. 700 LILLY RD NE 98506 #016-11-1968 L1969 **P** *020 †75 ‡
GRIESMAN, Frederick A, II. 413 LILLY RD NE 98506 #005-12-1966 L1968 **GE IM** *020 †20
GRIFFITH, Chris Nolan. 3610 ENSIGN RD NE, SURGICAL ASSOCIATES 98506 #005-06-1979 L1985 **VS GS** *020 †85
GROMKO, Wm Anthony, Jr. 3928 PACIFIC AVE SE 98503 #030-06-1974 L1975 **FM** *020 †18
GROUS, Nicole Lee. 3920 CAPITOL MALL DR SW 98502 #041-09-1987 L1997 **HO** *020 †20
GUTMAN, Alan Josef. ■ 98508 #038-40-1958 L1958 **IM** *020
HAIRSTON, John Townes, III. 500 LILLY RD NE 98506 #048-12-1971 L1972 **GS** *020 †85
HALEY, Richard Kenneth. ■ 98507 #028-78-1960, ▲ L1960 **END** *071
HALL, Deborah Kay. 525 LILLY RD NE 98506 #027-01-1980 L1987 **PD** *074 †55
HALL, Robert Preston. ■ 98501 #016-02-1942 L1948 **OS** *071
HALPER, Jonathan. 3900 CAPITOL MALL DR SW 98502 #054-04-1985 L1986 **EM** *020 †18,16
HALPIN, Patrick Jos. 404 YAUGER WAY SW, STE 100 98502 #054-04-1976 L1980 **ORS** *020 †40
HAM, James Jin. ■ 98508 #016-42-2007 **EM** *012
HANNA, Lawrence James. 700 LILLY RD NE 98506 #019-02-1969 L1974 **PD** *071 †55
HANNUM, James Saville. 700 LILLY RD NE 98506 #025-01-1970 L1972 **OTO** *020 †45
HANSEN, Lucas David. 413 LILLY RD NE 98506 #054-04-2001 L2005 **EM** *020 †16
HARDING, Charles Richard. 3624 ENSIGN RD NE, STE B 98506 #005-02-1971 L1976 **AN** *020 †05
HARRIAGE, Scott Robinson. 700 LILLY RD NE 98506 #047-05-1977 L1981 **OBG** *020 †30
HARVEY, Beth Ellen. 3525 ENSIGN RD NE STE K, PEDIATRIC ASSOCIATES 98506 #028-46-1993 L1997 **PD** *020 †55
HAUGHTON, Kevin Mark. 525 LILLY RD NE 98506 #005-15-1986 L1995 **FM** *030 †18
HAWS, John Philip. 413 LILLY RD NE, ATTN MS DDH13 98506 #023-01-1962 L1976 **P** *020 †75 ‡
HAZELRIGG, Thomas Roy. 413 LILLY RD NE 98506 #036-07-1943 L1948 **GS GP** *071 †85
HEAP, Darien. 3920 CAPITOL MALL DR SW, OLYMPIA MULTISPECIALTY 98502 #028-34-1998 L2005 **GE** *020 †20
HECHT, Thomas William. 410 PROVIDENCE LN NE # 2 98506 #054-04-1995 L1999 **PM** *020 †60
HEIDAR, Helgi. 724 COLUMBIA ST NW, STE 100 98501 #005-12-1967 L1974 **OPH GP** *071 †35
HELPENSTELL, Thomas Scott. 3900 CAPITOL MALL DR SW 98502 #054-04-1985 L1986 **ORS OSM** *020 †40
HENEGAN, Richard N, Jr. 3920 CAPITOL MALL DR SW 98502 #048-13-1978 L1991 **OBG** *020 †30
HERMAN, Barry. 525 LILLY RD NE 98506 #035-15-1974 L2005 **OBG** *020 †30
HERRING, Michael David. 410 BLACK HILLS LN SW, STE B 98502 #040-02-1972 L1977 **IM RHU** *020 †20
HEYE, George Henry. DEPT HEALTH 98504 #030-06-1971 L1986 **PD** *030 †55
HIPP, Robert Sander. 3920 CAPITOL MALL DR SW 98502 #035-03-1966 L1972 **GS VS** *020 †85
HIRSCH, Evan Hillel. 525 LILLY RD NE PBP09, PROV ST PETER HOSP FMR 98506 #038-43-2003 L2004 **FM** *020 †18
HO, Lisa Ding-On. 525 LILLY RD NE 98506 #305-01-2006 L2006 **FP** *012
HOFFMAN, Edward Peter. ■ 98502 #036-07-1963 L1971 **NS** *071 †25 ‡
HOLLAND, John Paul. 9226 MILBURN LOOP SE, . 98513 #030-05-1977 L1983 **OM PTX** *020 †70
HOUGHTON, Eric Richard. ■ 98501 #040-02-1977 L1978 **FM** *020 †18
HOWARD, Jeffrey Paul. 413 LILLY RD NE 98506 #054-04-1982 L1984 **EM FM** *020 †18
HOWARD, Michael Alan. 700 LILLY RD NE 98506 #005-14-1972 L1978 **IM FM** *020 †20
HUBBARD, Megan Marie. 700 LILLY RD NE 98506 #005-18-1983 L1988 **PD** *020 †55
HUMMEL, Ralph Turner. 108 22ND AVE SW 98501 #023-01-1956 L1962 **P** *071
HUNNELL, Steven Troy. 3900 CAPITOL MALL DR SW 98502 #016-02-1999 L2003 **AN** *020 †05
HURD, Kathleen Margaret. 520 LILLY RD NE, BLDG 3 98506 #051-04-1989 L1992 **FM** *020 †18
HURLEY, William T, Jr. 4436 ELD LN NW, OLYMPIA EMERGENCY SERVICES 98502 #007-02-1985 L1986 **EM** *020 †16
HURST, Richard Edward. ■ 98516 #054-04-1967 L1970 **GS UM** *071 †85
HUSSEINI, Tina Maria. 4446 ELD LN NW 98502 #016-06-1991 L1998 **AN** *020 †05
IBRAHIM, Mohamed Said. 3624 ENSIGN RD NE STE B 98506 #915-02-1993 L2002 **AN** *020 †05
IRIYE, Annie Ikuko. ■ 98501 #016-42-1983 L1999 **OBG** *020 †30
IRWIN, Heather A. 700 LILLY RD NE, GROUP HEALTH COOPERATIVE 98506 #019-02-1979 L2002 **OBG** *020 †30
JADE, Klaus Bernhard. 205A LILLY RD NE STE 1 98506 #040-02-1968 L1990 **D IM** *020 †15,20
JAMES, David Robt. 3417 ENSIGN RD NE 98506 #007-02-1967 L1975 **R** *020 †80
JAVEL, Alan Francis. 2608 PACIFIC AVE SE STE F 98501 #033-05-1974 L1984 **P ADM** *020 †75
JENSEN, Frederick Arnold. 402 BLACK HILLS LN SW, STE D 98502 #040-02-1975 L1991 **RHU IM** *020 †20
JENSEN, Ray Edward. 128 LILLY RD NE, STE 202 98506 #023-12-1985 L1992 **OTO A** *020 †45
JIANG, Lin. 406 BLACK HILLS LN SW, STE D 98502 #243-32-1986 L2002 **PD** *020 †55
JOE, Rodney Wayne. 500 LILLY RD NE STE 204 98506 #049-01-1991 L1993 **GE** *020 †20
JOERES, Manfred Klaus. ■ 98507 #023-01-1963 L1966 **P** *020 †75
JOHNSON, Debra Armstrong. 3920 CAPITOL MALL DR SW 98502 #051-04-1988 L1999 **OBG** *020 †30
JOHNSON, Joanne Kathleen. 3624 ENSIGN RD NE STE B 98506 #005-18-1989 L1989 **AN** *020 †05
JOHNSON, Kelvie Ann. 525 LILLY RD NE 98506 #054-04-1982 L1987 **PD** *020 †55
JOHNSON, Leigh Denton. ■ 98506 #047-20-2006 L2008 **FP** *012
JOHNSON, Lisa Ann. 525 LILLY RD NE 98506 #051-01-1978 L1979 **FM** *020 †18
JOHNSON, Lowell Erik. 700 LILLY RD NE 98506 #026-04-1966 L1972 **A AI** *071 †20
JONES, Cristen Douglas. 413 LILLY RD NE 98506 #054-04-1990 L1998 **PTH** *020 †50
JULIN, James Gregg. 205 LILLY RD NE, OLYMPIA MULTISPECIALTY 98506 #028-34-1983 L1988 **CD** *075 †20
KABACY, George Elliott. 3900 CAPITOL MALL DR SW 98502 #005-06-1966 L1992 **GYN** *020 †30
KANG, Min Sok. 3920 CAPITOL MALL DR SW 98502 #038-40-1991 L1997 **HO** *020 †20
KANTHAWATANA, Sukanya. 500 LILLY RD NE STE 120, DERMATOLOGY & ALLERGYSPECI 98506 #891-03-1983 L1999 **AI** *020 †55,03
KARPEL, John T. 3525 ENSIGN RD NE STE K 98506 #028-03-1968 L1974 **PD** *020 †55
KATHER, Natalie. 1115 W BAY DR NW, STE 202 98502 #049-01-1996 L2007 **FM** *020 †18
KAUFMAN, Thomas Ira. 3900 CAPITOL MALL DR SW 98502 #007-02-1977 L1980 **EM** *020 †16
KECK, Charles Aikin. 413 LILLY RD NE 98506 #038-06-1962 L1967 **PD** *071 †55
KEEP, Albert Michael. 525 LILLY RD NE 98506 #422-01-2007 L2007 **FP** *012
KEHOE, John Edward. 2101 4TH AVE E, STE 200 98506 #036-05-1960 L1987 **P** *020
KELLEY, David Baker. 408 LILLY RD NE STE C 98506 #024-05-1960 L1978 **END DIA** *072
KENNEDY, Richard Pierce. 500 LILLY RD NE, STE 100 98506 #021-05-1983 L1996 **CD IM** *020 †20
KERSHISNIK, Erin Kathleen. 3703 ENSIGN RD NE STE 10A 98506 #041-07-1995 L1997 **FM** *020 †18
KESTING, Leo Wolfgang. 525 LILLY RD NE STE 210 98506 #054-04-1992 L2000 **N** *020 †75
KIM, Zoo Eung. ■ 98501 #583-02-1963 L1972 **PTH** *071 †50
KIRCHHEIM, Dieter. 413 LILLY RD NE 98506 #407-23-1951 L1962 **U** *020 †95
KISSICK, Hillary Allen. 525 LILLY RD NE, FAMILY PRACTICE RES 98506 #028-34-2001 L2003 **FM** *020
KISTLER, William A. 700 LILLY RD NE 98506 #041-09-1987 L1990 **FM** *020 †18
KLAASSEN, Anthony John. 700 LILLY RD NE 98506 #054-04-1981 L1985 **FM** *020 †18
KLEIN, Donald Richard. 3525 ENSIGN RD NE 98506 #005-15-1971 L1976 **DR** *020 †80 ‡
KLEIN, Eric John. 406 YAUGER WAY SW, STE A 98502 #054-04-1973 L1991 **IM** *020 †20
KNIGHT, Kendral Raymon. ■ 98506 #036-08-2007 **IM** *012
KNOUFF, Paul Michael. 525 LILLY RD NE 98506 #665-01-2007 L2007 **FP** *012
KNOWLTON, Carol Jeanne. 3000 LIMITED LN NW 98502 #048-02-1975 L1987 **AN** *020
KOCH, Richard S. 3000 LIMITED LN NW, # 150 98502 #041-77-1938, ▲ L1940 **FM PM** *071
KONDO, Yo. 525 LILLY RD NE 98506 #572-60-1998 L2006 **FP** *012
KOOIKER, John E. 418 CARPENTER RD SE, PINEL CLINIC STE 202 98503 #018-03-1945 L1980 **P** *020 †75
KOOIKER, Jon Christian. 525 LILLY RD NE, STE 210 98506 #017-20-1969 L1974 **N** *020 †75
KOUKOL, Dennis Chas. 120 STATE AVE NE, APT 222 98501 #056-06-1968 L1977 **CD** *071 †20
KOURI, Mary Elizabeth. 3900 CAPITOL MALL DR SW 98502 #054-04-2000 L2004 **AN** *020 †05
KRAMER, Sasha C. 500 LILLY RD NE, STE 120 98506 #041-15-1999 L2005 **D** *020 †18,15
KRANK, Kelvin Louis. 1400 FONES RD SE, APT 2-201 98501 #048-12-1980 L1983 **IM EM** *020 †20
KREBS, Clara Tatum. 525 LILLY RD NE PBP09, PROV ST PETER HOSP FAM MED 98506 #051-04-2005 L2005 **FP** *012
KRUG, James Arthur. 413 LILLY RD NE 98506 #038-41-1963 L1969 **GYN** *072 †30
KRUG, Richard Tang. 3610 ENSIGN RD NE 98506 #038-40-1994 L1999 **GS VS** *020 †85
KRUIDENIER, James Francis. 500 LILLY RD NE, STE 204 98506 #016-11-1977 L1982 **GE** *020 †20
LACLERGUE, Edward Gregory. 5130 CORPORATE CENTR CT SE 98503 #036-05-1971 L1975 **FM** *020 †18
LAMB, George Owen. 700 LILLY RD NE 98506 #054-04-1974 L1978 **IM IMG** *020 †20
LAMB, Joan. 3425 ENSIGN RD NE, STE 320 98506 #917-28-1964 L1978 **AN** *020
LAMPERT, Austin Chas. 3920 CAPITOL MALL DR SW, STE 308 98502 #038-41-1986 L1990 **IM** *020 †20
LANG, Robert Gilmer Ross. 3525 ENSIGN RD NE, STE J 98506 #065-06-1972 L1981 **NS EM** *020 †25
LARA, Terry Ellen. 3525 7TH AVE SW, MIDDLETON FOUNDATION, INC. 98502 #056-06-1989 L1989 **FM** *020 †18
LARSON, Larry Alan. ■ 98507 #016-02-1968 L1973 **AN** *071 †05
LARSON, Shelly Lea. 1316 DARCY LANE SE 98501 #665-01-2003 L2004 **N** *012
LAUMANS, Marius Lambert. 1408 STATE AVE NE, STE 108 98506 #409-33-2002 L2004 **FM** *020 †18
LAYTON, Mark Walter. 1212 HARRISON AVE NW 98502 #054-04-1982 L1987 **RHU** *020 †20
LEAHY, Robert Henry. ■ 98502 #035-45-1954 L1958 **IM** *071 †20
LEE, Kenneth P. 4324 MARTIN WAY E STE B 98516 #011-02-1990 L1997 **IM** *020 †20
LERNER, Sara Jo. 700 LILLY RD NE 98506 #054-04-1990 L1995 **P** *020 †75
LESTER, Robert Beverly. 406 BLACK HILLS LN SW, STE D 98502 #056-06-1984 L1987 **PD** *020 †55
LEYEN, Robert Wouters. 700 LILLY RD NE 98506 #047-06-1977 L1990 **ORS GS** *020 †40
LI, Qiang. 500 LILLY RD NE, STE 100 98506 #243-68-1987 L2006 **CD** *020 †20 ‡
LI, Zhongzeng. 525 LILLY RD NE, STE 210 98506 #243-32-1986 L2005 **N CN** *020 ‡
LILLEGARD, Donald Dean. 3624 ENSIGN RD NE STE B 98506 #007-02-1978 L1992 **AN** *020 †05
LIN, Julia. 700 LILLY RD NE, GROUP HEALTH OLYMPIA MEDIC 98506 #035-46-1998 L2007 **P PYG** *020 †75
LINCOLN, Bruce Edward. 413 LILLY RD NE 98506 #054-04-1983 L1986 **EM** *020 †16
LINDBERG, Stephen John. 3425 ENSIGN RD NE STE 100 98506 #054-04-1978 L1979 **AN EM** *020 †05
LINDGREN, Carl Andrew. 300 LILLY RD NE, STE A 98506 #056-05-1986 L1990 **PD** *020 †55
LIVINGSTONE, Donn Ashley. 128 LILLY RD NE, STE 202 98506 #061-01-1965 L1986 **OTO A** *020 †45
LUCKE, Lauren Howard. ■ 98502 #035-08-1952 L1953 **PHP** *071 †70
LUTEYN, Joyce. 3525 ENSIGN RD NE, STE E 98506 #054-04-1991 L1996 **FM** *020 †18
LUX, James J. 413 LILLY RD NE 98506 #035-45-1952 L1956 **IM CD** *071
LUX, Sarah A. 3425 ENSIGN RD NE, STE 220 98506 #054-04-1988 L1991 **IM** *020 †20
LYKINS, Stephen Douglas. 413 LILLY RD NE, DEPT OF PSYCHIATRY 98506 #038-40-1991 L1995 **P** *020 †75
LYNAM, Michael Anthony. 3525 ENSIGN RD NE STE R 98506 #048-04-1996 L1998 **FM OBS** *020 †18

■ = Address Information Privacy Protected

MAC INNES, Frederic C. 413 LILLY RD NE 98506 #064-01-1958 L1982 **PTH** *062 †50

MARLAN, Robert Scott. 111 MARKET ST NE, STE 355 98501 #038-41-1989 L1995 **OTO** *020 †45

MARTIN, Walburga Stephani. 525 LILLY RD NE, FAMILY MED RESIDENCY 98506 #004-01-2005 L2005 **FP** *012

MASON, Cole Vroman. 525 LILLY RD NE 98506 #005-14-1972 L1975 **PD** *020 †55

MASON, Jay Cort. ■ 98502 #056-06-1966 L1973 **P** *071 †75

MATLOCK, Michael Lee. 3525 ENSIGN RD NE STE O 98506 #054-04-1975 L1978 **IM ID** *020 †20

MC CABE, Marshall E, III. 3920 CAPITOL MALL DR SW, OLYMPIA MULTISPECIALTY 98502 #036-01-1978 L1985 **GE IM** *020 †20 ‡

MC CREA, Harold Jos. 413 LILLY RD NE 98506 #021-01-1944 L1947 **OTO OPH** *071 †45

MC DOWELL, James R. 525 LILLY RD NE, # 210 98506 #025-01-1970 L1973 **N CHN** *020 †75

MC FADDEN, Lee Alan. ■ 98512 #023-12-1994 L2006 **ORS** *020 †40

MC GEE, Michael David. ■ 98513 #041-13-1962 L1967 **OS PD** *071 †55

MCKAY, Mandi Jolene. ■ 98516 #003-01-2001 L2002 **IM** *020

MC KAY, Robert Trent. 1800 COOPER POINT RD SW, STE 9 98502 #003-01-2001 L2007 **ORS** *020

MC LEAN, Robert Bruce. ■ 98502 #054-04-1966 L1967 **FM AM** *071

MELTZER, Richard Chas. 700 LILLY RD NE, GROUP HLTH COOPERATIVE 98506 #050-02-1987 L1994 **GS** *020 †85

MENDEZ, Raul D. 413 LILLY RD NE, PSPH HOSPITALIST GROUP 98506 #748-19-1987 L2008 **IM** *020 †20

MERCHANT, Michael James. 400 LILLY RD NE BLDG 10, OLYMPIA PROFESSIONAL PARK 98506 #018-03-1965 L1973 **D DMP** *020 †15

MICHAELS, Sara Ann. 525 LILLY RD NE # B09, ROVIDENCE ST ETER HOS 98506 #010-01-1997 L1999 **FM** *020 †18

MICHEL, Jerry A. ■ 98512 #010-01-1996 L1998 **VIR** *020 †20,80

MICHELENA, Karen Kimbel. ■ 98501 #035-03-2001 L2004 **FM** *020 †18

MIKKELSEN, William James. 3417 ENSIGN RD NE 98506 #040-02-1957 L1963 **R** *071 †80

MILES, Ward C. 413 LILLY RD NE 98506 #041-01-1953 L1954 **GP** *071

MILHAM, Samuel. ■ 98502 #035-03-1958 L1968 **OM EP** *050 †70

MILLER, Margaret Schremp. 525 LILLY RD NE, ST PETER FAMILY MEDICINE 98506 #005-19-1984 L1990 **FM** *020 †18

MITCHELL, William James. 500 LILLY RD NE STE 204 98506 #035-01-1977 L1985 **GE IM** *020 †20

MOELLER, Raymond Anderson. 700 LILLY RD NE 98506 #005-14-1978 L1983 **FM** *030 †18

MOLINERO, Donald Peter. 700 LILLY RD NE, OF PUGET SOUND 98506 #054-04-1955 L1958 **CHP GS** *071

MONDRESS, Michael Gregory. 500 LILLY RD NE, MEMORIAL NEUROLOGY CLINIC 98506 #035-45-1998 L2005 **NEP** *020 †20

MONK, Benjamin F, Jr. 413 LILLY RD NE 98506 #048-04-1951 L1953 **GP AN** *071

MONSON, Lore Ann. ■ 98502 #054-04-1988 L1988 **AN** *020 †05

MOORE, Pamela Kim. 413 LILLY RD NE, MS:LLH22 98506 #056-06-1997 L2007 **PD** *020 †55

MORGAN, Karl Harris. ■ 98513 #041-12-1961 L1968 **R** *020 †80

MORUZZI, James Francis. 403 BLACK HILLS LN SW, OLYMPIA WOMEN'S HEALTH 98502 #035-08-1985 L1990 **OBS REN** *020 †30

MOSLIN, Pamela J. 521 UNION AVE SE STE 205 98501 #023-01-1987 L1996 **P** *074 †75

MUNSON, David Kelly. 2103 HARRISON AVE NW, # 2-181 98502 #028-46-1984 L1989 **EM** *020

MUNSON, Sally Elizabeth. 413 LILLY RD NE, DEPT OF PSYCHIATRY 98506 #054-04-1990 L1993 **P PYG** *020 †75

MURDOCH, Sara Jean. 3525 ENSIGN RD NE, PEDIATRIC ASSOCIATES 98506 #040-02-1987 L1991 **PD** *020 †55

MURPHY, James Patrick. 2014 BOUNDARY ST SE 98501 #011-02-1987 L1989 **AN** *020 †55,05

MYERS, Carl Blaine, Jr. 700 LILLY RD NE 98506 #021-01-1983 L2007 **OTO** *020 †45 ‡

NAMEROFF, Mark A. ■ 98513 #041-01-1965 **OS** *050

NASH, Sylvia Ruth. 1001 COOPER PT RD SW, STE 140-308 98502 #060-02-1978 L1984 **EM PD** *020 †16

NEAL, William Danl. 200 LILLY RD NE, STE C2 98506 #040-02-1981 L1998 **GS** *020 †85

NEILSON, John T. ■ 98513 #040-02-1984 L1985 **IM** *071 ‡

NEVITT, Courtney Macarl. 700 LILLY RD NE 98506 #016-01-1981 L1985 **IM OM** *020 †20,70

NEWELL-EGGERT, Margo K. 410 PROVIDENCE LN NE, BLDG 2 98506 #026-04-1986 L1992 **PM** *020 †60

NEWMANN, William Edward. 700 LILLY RD NE 2 98506 #038-06-1977 L1980 **FM** *020 †18

NGHIEM, Thieu Lenh. ■ 98506 #692-01-1952 L1977 **IM NTR** *075

NGUYEN, Vo Dang. 500 LILLY RD NE, MEMORIAL NEUROLOGY CLINIC 98506 #165-03-1978 L1991 **NEP** *020 †20

NIELSEN, Tore Kjell. 905 24TH WAY SW STE A1 98502 #054-04-1960 L1962 **P** *020 †75

NOEL, Clarisse E. 700 LILLY RD NE 98506 #040-02-1987 L2002 **FM** *020 †18

NORTON, Robert Steven. 3920 CAPITOL MALL DR SW, STE 201 98502 #040-02-1982 L1987 **GS** *020 †85

O'BYRNE, Barbara A Hoess. ■ 98516 #017-20-1969 L1978 **AN** *020 †05

OCHOA, Kevin Andrew. ■ 98502 #019-02-2001 L2007 **FM** *020 †18

O'CONNOR, Kathleen Ann. 6535 YOUNG RD NW 98502 #024-07-1992 L1998 **GPM** *020 †70

ODELL, J Michael. 413 LILLY RD NE 98506 #005-14-1979 L1980 **ATP CLP** *020 †55,50

O'LEARY, Linda Susan. 525 LILLY RD NE, STE 250 98506 #005-02-1984 L1985 **PD** *020 †55

O'MEARA, Thomas Francis. 3920 CAPITOL MALL DR SW, OLYMPIA MULTISPECIALTY 98502 #048-04-1975 L1980 **GE IM** *020 †20

O'NEILL, Robert Donald. 3900 CAPITOL MALL DR SW, CAPITAL MEDICAL CENTER 98502 #054-04-1970 L1974 **EM IM** *020 †20

OPAR, Susan Patricia. ■ 98513 #035-03-2004 L2005 **FM** *020 †18

OSBORN, Dustan C. 3920 CAPITOL MALL DR SW 98502 #064-01-1978 L1984 **ON IM** *020 †20

PACKER, Brent Charles. ■ 98512 #064-04-1994 L1996 **FM** *020

PALASI, Myrna Tumarao. ■ 98512 #748-17-1998 L2006 **FM** *020

PAPADOPOULOS, Patricia Jo. ■ 98501 #025-07-2004 L2005 **IM** *020 †20

PAPADOPOULOS, Yanni B. ■ 98501 #035-03-2001 L2003 **IM** *020

PARPALA, Wayne Milton. ■ 98516 #040-02-1956 L1960 **OBG** *071 †30

PARTLOW, Kenneth Lawrence. 615 LILLY RD NE 98506 #010-01-1973 L1978 **ORS** *050 †40

PATTEN, Randall Malcolm. 500 LILLY RD NE STE 160, NORTHWEST RADIOLOGY GROUP 98506 #005-18-1981 L1985 **DR** *020 †80

PAUDLER, Franklin Thos. 98506 #056-05-1967 L1976 **ORS** *020 †40

PEARSON, Roger Warren. ■ 98516 #054-04-1954 L1957 **D DMP** *020 †15

PECK, Dennis Frederick. 3900 CAPITOL MALL DR SW 98502 #010-01-1972 L1979 **PTH** *062

PECKLER, Mark Steven. 3525 ENSIGN RD NE, STE A 98506 #016-11-1976 L1981 **U** *020 †95

PELLICER, Joseph Francis. 413 LILLY RD NE MS04H07, OLYMPIA EMERGENCY SERVICES 98506 #054-04-1983 L1987 **FM** *020 †18

PENNER, Erik Elliot. 413 LILLY RD NE 98506 #047-05-1999 L2002 **EM** *020 †16

PERRIN, Laurence Ellis. ■ 98501 #005-06-1965 L1983 **GYN OS** *072 †30

PETERSEN, Dana Mark. 525 LILLY RD NE STE 250, OLYMPIA PEDIATRICS, PLLC 98506 #005-19-1980 L1987 **PD** *020 †55

PETERSON, John Melvin. 700 LILLY RD NE, GROUP HEALTH OLYMPIA 98506 #005-12-1976 L1980 **PD** *020 †55

PETERSON, Jon Tyson. 2960 LIMITED LN NW STE A, MEDICINE 98502 #048-78-1991, ▲ L1996 **FM** *020 †18 ‡

PETERSON, William Warren. 3525 ENSIGN RD NE, STE E 98506 #016-06-1982 L1990 **ORS** *020 †40

PHILLIPS, Timothy Michael. 3900 CAPITOL MALL DR SW, COLUMBIA CAPITAL MEDICAL C 98502 #054-04-1993 L1997 **AN** *020 †05

PLAEGER-BROCKWAY, Mariel. 700 LILLY RD NE, WEST OLYMPIAGROUP HEALTH 98506 #054-04-1985 L1986 **FM** *020 †18

PLANT, John Chas Douglas. 408 LILLY RD NE STE C 98506 #917-20-1959 L1979 **GS CRS** *071

PLUMLEY, Thomas Franklin. 3525 ENSIGN RD NE, STE B 98506 #054-04-1980 L1981 **DR** *020 †80

PORTER, Stacy Leigh. 215 LILLY RD NE, OLYMPIA EYE CLINIC 98506 #018-03-1997 L2000 **OPH** *020 †35

POUW, Tiong Hian. 403 BLACK HILLS LN SW, STE F 98502 #048-13-1983 L1990 **IM** *020 †20

POWELL, Douglas Frederic. ■ 98506 #036-05-2006 L2008 **IM** *012

POWER, James Lee. 500 LILLY RD NE, MEMORIAL CLNC LTD PS 98506 #054-04-1975 L1977 **OBG** *020 †30

PUNTENNEY, Robert E H. ■ 98502 #019-02-1950 L1952 **U** *071 †95

QUAN, Arlen. ■ 98508 #040-02-1957 L1969 **P** *071

QUINTON, Ronald Ray. 525 LILLY RD NE STE 200 98506 #021-01-1976 L1992 **TS GS** *020 †85,90

RAASTAD, Larisa Gennadyev. 525 LILLY RD NE, ST PETER HOSP 98506 #913-83-1984 L2004 **FM** *020

RANDOLPH, Gerald Guy. 406 YAUGER WAY SW, STE B 98502 #054-04-1961 L1969 **OTO OS** *030 †45

READE, Sarah Scott. 3901 48TH LN NE 98506 #025-12-1992 L1996 **IM GPM** *062 †20

REESE, Adele Bernadette N. 3645 SUNSET BEACH DR NW 98502 #051-04-1970 L1975 **P CHP** *020

REESE, Owen Glyndwr, Jr. 413 LILLY RD NE 98506 #005-02-1970 L1975 **NEP IM** *020 †20

REINKE, Curtis Dale. 405 BLACK HILLS LN SW # C, REINKE MEDICAL GROUP 98502 #305-01-1995 L1998 **IM** *012

REMIS, David Alan. 700 LILLY RD NE 98506 #062-01-1970 L1987 **D FM** *020

RENNIE, Gordon Friend. 700 LILLY RD NE, GROUP HEALTH COOPERATIVE 98506 #054-04-1977 L1978 **IM** *020 †20

REPPHUN, Andrea. ■ 98502 #028-46-1998 L2001 **FM** *020 †18

RETHERFORD, Franklin B. 525 LILLY RD NE 98506 #017-20-1977 L1980 **FM** *020 †18

REUS, James Leonard. 3425 ENSIGN RD NE, ENSIGN MEDICAL CENTER, STE 98506 #025-01-1977 L1979 **GS** *020 †85

REUS, Wm Frederick, III. 3425 ENSIGN RD NE STE 340 98506 #016-02-1980 L1991 **PS GS** *020 †85,65

RICE, Jack Caldwell. 700 LILLY RD NE 98506 #054-04-1971 L1974 **FM** *020 †18

RICHARDS, Julia Anne. 3920 CAPITOL MALL DR SW, STE 400 98502 #054-04-1990 L1994 **OBG** *020 †30

RICHERT, Charles Arlin. 3425 ENSIGN RD NE STE 360 98506 #005-12-1992 L1998 **PTH** *020 †50

RICHERT, Shauna Mc Lain. 500 LILLY RD NE, STE 120 98506 #005-12-1992 L1998 **D** *020 †20,15

RITCHIE, Rebecca Samantha. 525 LILLY RD NE 98506 #041-07-1987 L1990 **FM** *020 †18

ROBERTS, Travis Lee. ■ 98502 #054-04-2008 *012

ROBINSON, Kevin Dewey. 3610 ENSIGN RD NE, SURGICAL ASSOCIATES 98506 #054-04-1990 L1997 **VS** *020 †85

RODERICK, Laura Lee. 3900 CAPITOL MALL DR SW 98502 #016-06-1981 L1983 **AN** *071 †05

ROGERS, Don Allen. ■ 98502 #005-14-1971 L1974 **FM** *020 †18

ROGOZA, Michael Julian. 700 LILLY RD NE 98506 #054-04-1982 L1983 **FM** *020 †18

ROSER, Louis Alan. 3525 ENSIGN RD NE STE E 98506 #049-01-1965 L1967 **ORS** *020 †40

ROSSIGNOL, Anne C. ■ 98506 #050-02-1999 L2001 **IM** *020

RUHL, Ronald Alan. 500 LILLY RD NE STE 180 98506 #038-40-1970 L1975 **AI IM** *020 †20

RUSSELL, Robert Dean. 413 LILLY RD NE 98506 #060-01-1981 L1990 **OTO** *020

SAITO, Hideto. 525 LILLY RD NE PBP09, PROV ST PETER HOSP FAM MED 98506 #572-29-2004 L2005 **FP** *012

SALAMA, Samuel A. 617 8TH ST 98504 #915-03-1965 L1985 *020

SANDINE, Kurt R. 3306 WINDOLPH LOOP NW 98502 #016-43-1997 L2004 **FM AM** *020 †18

SANDVIG, Maria Margaret. 700 LILLY RD NE, GROUP HLTH 98506 #038-41-1992 L2002 **FM** *020 †18

SANTAMARINA, Luis F. 525 LILLY RD NE, OLYMPIA CARDIAC SURG 98506 #429-02-1985 L1999 **TS** *020 †85,90

SAWYER, Devin Richard. 525 LILLY RD NE 98506 #028-34-1995 L1998 **FM** *020 †18

SCHADT, Laurence Conrad. 3622 ENSIGN RD NE A 98506 #005-14-1977 L1988 **FM EM** *020 †16,18

SCHILLINGER, J Frederick. ■ 98506 #005-17-1962 L1975 **GP** *071

SCHOENING, David Henry. 500 LILLY RD NE STE 100 98506 #040-02-1972 L1977 **CD** *020 †20

SCHOLES, Timothy Alan. 700 LILLY RD NE, OLYMPIA MEDICAL CENTER 98506 #035-15-1988 L1991 **FM** *020 †18

SCHOONMAKER, Joseph H. 700 LILLY RD NE 98506 #007-02-1951 L1971 **GP GS** *020

SCHWEICH, Paula Jane. ■ 98516 #035-15-1980 L1989 **PD** *020 †55

SCOTT, Seth Edward. 700 LILLY RD NE, OLYMPIA MEDICAL CENTER 98506 #040-02-2001 L2004 **FM** *020 †18

SEAMAN, Richard Wm. ■ 98502 #054-04-1966 L1970 **OTO** *072 †45

SEARS, Cheri Denise. 615 LILLY RD NE STE 200, OLYMPIA OBSTETRICS & GYNEC 98506 #003-01-2000 L2003 **OBG** *020 †30

SEBESTA, James Alton. 6724 PRAIRIE RIDGE DR NE 98516 #023-12-1995 L2003 **GS** *020 †85

SEIFTER, Leonard Stuart. 300 LILLY RD NE STE C, EYE INSTITUTE OF OLYMPIA I 98506 #048-12-1981 L1985 **OPH IM** *020 †35

SEMONES, Karen Lea. 700 LILLY RD NE 98506 #654-01-2004 L2006 **FM** *020 †18

SHARANGPANI, Rajesh. 3900 CAPITOL MALL DR SW 98502 #495-73-1983 L2001 **AN** *020 †05

SHARANGPANI, Ritawari. 2617 12TH CT SW, STE B6 98502 #495-28-1992 L2003 **P** *020 †75

SHORT, Eugene H. ■ 98516 #026-04-1945 L1948 **GS OS** *020 †85

SILVERMAN, Bruce Alan. 500 LILLY RD NE, STE 204 98506 #016-01-1982 L1985 **GE IM** *020 †20

SIPHER, Bridget Kathleen. 525 LILLY RD NE, STE 250 98506 #054-04-2000 L2005 **PD** *020 †55

SMITH, Britt David. 700 LILLY RD NE, GROUP HEALTH COOPERATIVE 98506 #054-04-1981 L1983 **FM EM** *020 †18
SMITH, Bryan James. 413 LILLY RD NE, PROVIDENCE ST. PETER HOSPI 98506 #046-01-1993 L1999 **IM** *020 †20
SMITH, David Alexander. 700 LILLY RD NE, GROUP HEALTH OF PUGET SOUN 98506 #035-01-1986 L1990 **IM PD** *020 †20
SMITH, Deborah Anne. 413 LILLY RD NE, MS:DDH13 98506 #003-01-1985 L1989 **P** *020 †75
SMITH, Dennis E. 615 LILLY RD NE, STE 100 98506 #010-02-1976 L1979 **ORS** *020 †40
SMITH, Harton Singer. 205 LILLY RD NE, OLYMPIA MULTISPECIALTY 98506 #035-47-1980 L2003 **CD IC** *020 †20 ‡
SMITH, Kendra Kay. 700 LILLY RD NE, GROUP HEALTH 98506 #016-45-1987 L1990 **FM** *020 †18
SMITH, Mark William. 3900 CAPITOL MALL DR SW, CAPITAL MEDICAL CENTER 98502 #056-06-1997 L2002 **DR** *020 †05
SMITH, Ronald Paul. 525 LILLY RD NE, ST PETER FAMILY PRACTICE 98506 #027-01-1980 L1987 **DR** *071 †80
SMITH, Sherwood Paul. ■ 98502 #065-01-1965 L1972 **PS HS** *071 †65
SNOW, Stephen Wm. 404 YAUGER WAY SW, SUUITE 100 98502 #041-13-1985 L1986 **ORS** *020 †40
SON, Judith Ogan. 412 BLACK HILLS LN SW # A 98502 #748-11-1989 L1996 **IM** *020 †20
SON, Shane Allan Rizarri. 3030 LIMITED LN NW, SEAMAR COMMUNITY HEALTH CT 98502 #748-11-1988 L2002 **FM** *020
SORENSON, Laurie Thomas. 615 LILLY RD NE STE 200, OLYMPIA OBSTETRICS & GYNEC 98506 #037-01-1986 L1990 **OBG** *020 †30
SOURI, Bina Chhabra. 403 BLACK HILLS LN SW # C 98502 #495-03-1971 L1990 **OBG** *020 †30
SOURI, Mahadev Kuman. 1910 4TH AVE E, PMB 235 98506 #495-62-1967 L1987 **NS** *020
SPEE, Mark Adrian. 700 LILLY RD NE 98506 #025-07-1980 L1983 **FM** *020 †18
SPENCE, Kevin Johannas. 3900 CAPITOL MALL DR SW 98502 #030-05-1992 L1998 **AN** *020 †05
SPENCER, Alison J. 3030 LIMITED LN NW, SEAMAR COMMUNITY HEALTH CE 98502 #035-01-1995 L1998 **FM** *020 †18
SPIELHOLZ, Jesse B. ■ 98502 #035-08-1932 L1946 **GPM PHP** *071 †70
SPRAKE, William Glenn. 703 LILLY RD NE, STE 102 98506 #054-04-1982 L1986 **OBG** *020 †30
STANDAERT, Steven Michael. 3525 ENSIGN RD NE STE 02 98506 #054-04-1984 L1999 **ID** *020 †20
STEELE, Scott Russell. ■ 98513 #056-05-1998 L2007 **CRS** *020 †85,10
STEINWEG, Edward Wm. 525 LILLY RD NE, STE 250 98506 #016-11-1976 L1979 **PD** *020 †55
STEVICK, Clyde Andrew. 700 LILLY RD NE 98506 #005-11-1974 L1991 **VS** *020 †85
ST LOUIS, Elizabeth M. 6901 BAYVIEW DR NE 98506 #917-26-1966 L1979 **FM** *020
STOCKBRIDGE, Henry Lee. ■ 98512 #038-41-1984 L1988 **OM IM** *020 †20,70
STROM, Janice Lynne. ■ 98512 #020-02-1978 L1983 **IM IMG** *020 †20
STULL, Peter James. 413 LILLY RD NE 98506 #041-02-1995 L2003 **EM** *020 †16
SULLIVAN, Joan. 700 LILLY RD NE 98506 #010-01-1983 L1986 **ORS HS** *071 †40
SULLIVAN, Preston. 215 LILLY RD NE 98506 #032-01-1996 L2004 **OPH** *020 †35
SUNDELL, Ann Kristin. 700 LILLY RD NE 98506 #047-20-1999 L2004 **PD** *020 †55
SUNDERLAND, Paul Kenneth. 3804 4TH AVE NW 98502 #014-01-1997 L2003 **EM** *020 †16
SWAN, Jimmy. 205 LILLY RD NE, OLYMPIA MULTISPECIALTY 98506 #243-58-1983 L2005 **CD** *020 †20
SWENBY, Sandra Mae. 3436 MARY ELDER RD NE, EVALUATION & TREATMENT CEN 98506 #056-05-1976 L2007 **CHP P** *020 †75
TAYLOR, Andrew Robert. 3417 ENSIGN RD NE, S SOUND RADIOLOGY 98506 #056-06-1992 L1998 **DR** *020 †80
TAYLOR, Peter Charles. 3525 ENSIGN RD NE, STE R 98506 #051-01-1996 L1998 **FM** *020 †18
TERESHONOK, Nonna Olexand. 525 LILLY RD NE 98506 #913-10-1966 L2005 **FP** *012
THALER, Seth Mark. 500 LILLY RD NE, MEMORIAL NEUROLOGY CLINIC 98506 #035-19-1987 L1998 **NEP** *020 †20
THALHAMER, Stella Sinson. ■ 98502 #748-21-1989 L2004 **IM** *020 †20
THOMPSON, Charles Ray. ■ 98502 #047-05-1956 L1958 **OPH** *071 †35
THOMPSON, Michael Kent. 1001 COOPER POINT RD SW, STE 140 PMB 167 98502 #018-03-1976 L1996 **EM** *020 †16
THOMPSON, Robert Keith. ■ 98501 #054-04-1969 L1970 **FM OS** *071 †18
THREET, Richard Wm. 700 LILLY RD NE 98506 #039-01-1974 L1998 **OBG** *020 †30
TIBBITS, Scott Joseph. 3425 ENSIGN RD NE STE 22, PLLC 98506 #054-04-1990 L1993 **IM** *020 †20
TOMFORD, Robert Charles. 500 LILLY RD NE STE 203 98506 #038-06-1976 L1985 **NEP IM** *020 †20
TONNING, Per Helge. 413 LILLY RD NE 98506 #040-02-1964 L1969 **EM** *071
TOSOMEEN, Ann Heiling. 525 LILLY RD NE # PBP09, FAMILY PRACTICE RSDY PROGR 98506 #026-08-1997 L2000 **FM** *020 †18
TOUNEY, Kevin Howard. ■ 98502 #056-06-1998 L2001 **FM** *020 †18
TSIEN, Albert Yi. 700 LILLY RD NE, GROUP HLTH OLYMPIA MED CTR 98506 #016-11-1989 L2004 **AI IM** *020 †20,03
UPTON, Stephanie Jo. 525 LILLY RD NE PBP09, PROV ST PETER HOSP FAM MED 98506 #039-01-2005 L2005 **FP** *012
URMANSKI, Mark C. 3700 MARTIN WAY E STE 108 98506 #056-06-1968 L1970 **EM FM** *020
VANDEKIEFT, Gregg Kelvin. 525 LILLY RD NE 98506 #018-03-1987 L1990 **FM PLM** *040 †18
VANDEMAN, Philip R. 413 LILLY RD NE 98506 #038-40-1942 L1948 **OS CHP** *071 †55
VAN FLEET, Jessica Marie. ■ 98501 #054-04-2008 *012
VAUGHN, Jamie Rebecca. ■ 98513 #021-01-1999 L2007 **OTO** *020
VINEYARD, William R. ■ 98512 #028-02-1950 L1973 **D** *071 †15
VLECK, Jan Peter. 525 LILLY RD NE, PROVIDENCE ST PETER FAMILY 98506 #005-14-1978 L1981 **FM** *020 †18
VOGELGESANG, Ross E. 3624 ENSIGN RD NE STE B 98506 #048-13-1988 L1992 **AN** *020 †05
VOLKMANN, Donald Lee. 413 LILLY RD NE DEPT ANES 98506 #054-04-1973 L1975 **AN FM** *020 †18,05
VORHOFF, Gilbert H, Jr. 3425 ENSIGN RD NE STE 100 98506 #021-01-1981 L1982 **AN** *020 †05
VU, Dich Quoc. 3900 CAPITOL MALL DR SW 98502 #941-01-1969 L1981 **PD FM** *020 †55
WAGGONER, John William, III. 406 BLACK HILLS LN SW # A, OLYMPIA MULTI-SPECIALTY CL 98502 #040-02-1999 L2006 **IC** *020 †20
WAGNER, J Mark. 3624 ENSIGN RD NE STE B 98506 #054-04-1987 L1992 **AN PME** *020 †05
WAGNER, Kathryne A. 500 LILLY RD NE, STE 204 98506 #054-04-1987 L1992 **GE** *020 †20
WALES, Bryan Douglas. 3624 ENSIGN RD NE STE B 98506 #033-05-1988 L1992 **AN** *020 †05
WALKER, Keith Alan. ■ 98512 #018-03-1946 L1947 **ORS** *020 †40
WALKER, Steven Danl. 700 LILLY RD NE 98506 #038-43-1977 L1987 **EM IM** *020 †20
WANG, Yu. 413 LILLY RD NE, MS DDH09 98506 #040-02-2003 L2006 **EM** *020
WARD, Bryan Clark. 520 LILLY RD NE, BLDG 3 98506 #055-01-1988 L1991 **FM** *075 †18
WARD, David Mcvey. 3525 ENSIGN RD NE, STE A 98506 #021-05-1990 L1996 **U** *020 †95
WARK, Robert Scott. 500 LILLY RD NE, STE 100 98506 #054-04-1984 L1985 **ICE CD** *020 †20
WATANABE, Takenori. 525 LILLY RD NE, ST PETER HOSP 98506 #572-16-2003 L2004 **FM** *100 †18
WEHRLI, Craig John. 500 LILLY RD NE, STE 100 98506 #028-02-1979 L1980 **CD** *020 †20
WELLER, Glen Eugene. 700 LILLY RD NE 98506 #054-04-1979 L1982 **IM IMG** *020 †20
WELLOCK, Matthew Todd. 525 LILLY RD NE, ST PETER HOSP 98506 #665-02-2003 L2003 **FM** *020 †18
WELLS, Christine R. ■ 98501 #048-04-1986 L1991 **N** *062 †75
WENTWORTH, Mark Allen. 700 LILLY RD NE, GROUP HEALTH CORP OLYMPIA 98506 #024-05-1970 L2003 **FM EM** *020 †18
WEST, Lawrence. 700 LILLY RD NE 98506 #041-13-1968 L1971 **FM** *020 †18
WEST, Steven Chas. 413 LILLY RD NE 98506 #049-01-1977 L1981 **EM** *020 †16
WHARTON, Robert Stokes. 3425 ENSIGN RD NE, STE 320 98506 #041-01-1973 L1980 **AN** *071 †05
WHEAT, Gordon Warner. 700 LILLY RD NE, OLYMPIA MEDICAL CENTER 98506 #005-18-1983 L1988 **FM** *020 †18
WHITTEN, Rich. 3900 CAPITOL MALL DR SW 98502 #049-01-1982 L1984 **PTH** *030 †50
WIDROW, Robert Jon. 525 LILLY RD NE 98506 #054-04-2000 L2003 **IM** *020 †20
WIESE, Dean Scott. 403 BLACK HILLS LN SW # A 98502 #028-34-1977 L1993 **IM** *020 †20
WILCZYNSKA-OBERC, Karolina. 525 LILLY RD NE, PROV ST PETER HOSP FPR 98506 #759-01-2001 L2003 **FM** *020 †18
WILLIAMS, Jennifer King. 700 LILLY RD NE, GROUP HEALTH COOPERATIVE 98506 #054-04-1998 L2000 **FM** *020 †18
WILLIAMS, Richard Frank. 3425 ENSIGN RD NE, STE 220 98506 #024-01-1976 L1978 **IM** *020 †20
WILLIAMS, Ronald G. ■ 98502 #016-11-1966 L1993 **PD MDM** *030 †55,70
WILLIARD, William C, III. 3920 CAPITOL MALL DR SW, STE 201 98502 #041-09-1981 L1992 **GS** *020 †85
WILSON, John Wesley. ■ 98501 #023-01-1969 L1969 **EM IM** *020 †20,16
WILSON, Marjorie Montague. 3300 CARPENTER RD SE, VISTA VILLAGE 113E 98503 #016-02-1953 L1954 **GPM FM** *071
WOLFE, Christopher Lane. 500 LILLY RD NE, STE 100 98506 #025-07-1978 L1997 **CD IM** *050 †20
WOLFE, Cynthia Soghikian. 3900 CAPITOL MALL DR SW 98502 #012-05-1980 L1997 **EM FM** *020 †16,18
WOLTMAN, Todd Alan. 3920 CAPITOL MALL DR SW, STE 203 98502 #030-05-1998 L2003 **GS** *020 †85
WOOD, Franklin Hoover, Jr. ■ 98513 #023-12-1992 L1994 **PD** *020 †55
WOOD, Peter Brodie. 3525 ENSIGN RD NE, STE E 98506 #041-01-1989 L1989 **ORS** *020 †40 ‡
WREGGIT, John David. 700 LILLY RD NE, GROUP HEALTH COOPERATIVE O 98506 #025-01-1964 L1973 **CHP P** *020 †75
WU, Thomas Cheng Pong. 404 BLACK HILLS LN SW # C 98502 #054-04-1974 L1979 **GYN** *020 †30
WURSTER, Sarah Armstrong. 413 LILLY RD NE 98506 #028-46-1997 L2006 **EM** *020 †16
YAMAMOTO, Yoshihiro. 615 LILLY RD NE, STE 220 98506 #572-09-1985 L2005 **NS** *020 †25
YAPHOCKUN, Alexander Du. PO BOX 12389 98508 #748-11-1989 L1997 **PD** *020
YEE, Linda Kathleen. 3900 CAPITOL MALL DR SW 98502 #048-13-1992 L1998 **CCA** *020
YIM, Gary Yet Sung. 3417 ENSIGN RD NE 98506 #028-34-1967 L1973 **DR** *071 †80
YOUNG, James Wm. 3703 ENSIGN RD NE STE 10A 98506 #018-03-1960 L1967 **D** *071 †15
YU, Diana Tan. 412 LILLY RD NE, & SOCIAL SERVICES 98506 #054-04-1981 L1985 **PHP PD** *030 †55 ‡
ZECHMANN, Angela Joan. 8545 ISLAND VIEW CT NE 98506 #019-02-1988 L2000 **GPM** *020 †70
ZECHMANN, Jerome Henry. 3525 ENSIGN RD NE STE E 98506 #030-06-1963 L1970 **ORS** *071 †40
ZELIG, Craig Michael. ■ 98512 #023-12-1997 L1998 **OBG** *020 †30
ZHAO, Congzhi. ■ 98513 #056-06-2007 **N** *012
ZHU, Liqun. 525 LILLY RD NE 98506 #243-16-1984 L2006 **FP** *012
ZILMER, Mark Edward. 3621 ENSIGN RD NE 98506 #054-04-1973 L1975 **PS** *020 †65

OMAK – OKANOGAN

ANZALONE, Joseph. 810 JASMINE ST 98841 #035-09-1987 L1993 **IM** *020 †20
AVENA, Elizabeth S. 916 KOALA AVE 98841 #021-01-1999 L2001 **FM** *020 †18
BATES, Barbara Jean. 916 KOALA AVE 98841 #024-07-1978 L1984 **FM OBG** *020 †18
BONE, David James. 24 VALLEY VIEW RD 98841 #016-11-1957 L1958 **GP** *071 †18
BORDNER, Michael David. 916 KOALA AVE 98841 #010-01-1984 L1987 **FM** *020 †18
BRADFORD, David Anthony. 916 KOALA AVE 98841 #048-15-1985 L1988 **OBG** *020 †30
BRATRUDE, Amos Presily. 916 KOALA AVE 98841 #016-11-1955 L1959 **FM** *071 †18
BRECHT, Donald James. 529 JASMINE ST 98841 #040-02-1969 L1971 **FM** *071 †18
BRITT, James Michael. 717 OKOMA DR 98841 #028-34-1987 L1990 **OPH** *020 †35
BROWN, James Wm. 916 KOALA AVE 98841 #016-06-1964 L1970 **GE IM** *020 †20 ‡
CALL, Conley Ben. 717 OKOMA DR 98841 #028-34-2000 L2004 **OPH** *020 †35
COWAN, Lyle Jos. ■ 98841 #016-11-1957 L1959 **FM GYN** *071 †18
CRAIG, Bradley Robt. 529 JASMINE ST, MID VALLEY HOSPITAL 98841 #038-43-1982 L1987 **IM** *020 †20
CROMAR, Bradley Wayne. 916 KOALA AVE 98841 #049-01-1986 L1991 **IM AI** *020 †20,03
DURANTE, Cynthia P. 1007 KOALA AVE, OBHC AND MEDICAL CLINIC 98841 #031-01-1990 L1993 **FM** *020 †18
HELLESON, James Manley. 810 JASMINE ST 98841 #054-04-1976 L1979 **FM** *020 †18
JOLLY, Margaret Ann H. PO BOX 3819, 36 ALBRECHT LAKE RD RIV 98841 #024-01-1964 L1982 **P OS** *075
JUSTUS, Robert Eugene. 916 KOALA AVE 98841 #054-04-1981 L1982 **FM** *020 †18
KEGLEY, James Walser. 810 JASMINE ST 98841 #649-02-1958 L1961 **OS GP** *020
LEDGERWOOD, Greg Lee. 744 W RIDGE DR 98841 #054-04-1971 L1972 **FM A** *020 †18
LOVE, Joseph E. 916 KOALA AVE, OMAK CLINIC 98841 #040-02-1989 L1998 **DR** *020 †80
MALLORY, Cheryl Ann. 916 KOALA AVE 98841 #041-13-1993 L1999 **FM** *020 †18
MITCHELL, Andrew Clair. 810 JASMINE ST 98841 #038-41-1972 L1993 **EM FM** *020 †18,16
O'NEILL, Evonn Louise. ■ 98841 #056-06-1996 L1998 **FM** *020 †18
RAICHE, Miranda Mcintire. 529 JASMINE ST 98841 #041-15-2002 L2006 **FM** *020 †18
SCHNIBBE, Fred Chas. 810 JASMINE ST 98841 #005-12-1954 L1955 **FM** *071 †18
SHIELDS, Linda Peck. 916 KOALA AVE, OMAK CLINIC 98841 #055-01-1988 L2002 **FM** *020 †18
WEBER, Mark Edward. 916 KOALA AVE 98841 #049-01-1987 L1995 **DR** *020 †80

WESTON, Robert J. 916 KOALA AVE 98841 #054-04-2003 L2006 **FM** *020 †18
WHEELER, William W. 529 JASMINE ST 98841 #036-05-1982 L2007 **GS** *020 †85 ‡
YELLAND, Grace Vivona. 916 KOALA AVE, OMAK CLINIC 98841 #035-46-1987 L1991
    PD *020 †55
YELLAND, Joel Fuller. 916 KOALA AVE 98841 #035-46-1987 L1995 **FM** *020 †18
ZANG, Katherine Heiss. ■ 98841 #034-01-2001 L2004 **FM** *020

ONALASKA – LEWIS

ANDERSON, Charles Thos. ■ 98570 #041-13-1983 L2002 **GS** *020 †85
LEADBETTER, Mark Renton. 3222 CENTRALIA ALPHA RD 98570 #041-13-1974 L1991
    ORS *020
WEIL, Peter. ■ 98570 #154-07-1949 L1977 **GS TS** *071 †85,90

ORCAS – SAN JUAN

FLEMING, Timothy. ■ 98280 #038-41-1965 L1971 **CD** *020 †20
LAMB, Patrick Geo. E GRINDSTONE HARBOR ROAD 98280 #005-11-1976 L1994
    CHP P *020 †75
MAZZARELLA, Annette J. ■ 98280 #054-04-1976 L1978 **AN** *020
RYAN, Paul Robt. ■ 98280 #014-01-1977 L1981 **IM GP** *075 †20

OROVILLE – OKANOGAN

DI CROCE, Theresa Marie. 1617 MAIN ST, OROVILLE FAMILY MEDICINE C 98844
    #024-07-1984 L2004 **FM** *020 †18
DIENST, William Lewis, Jr. 1617 MAIN ST 98844 #054-04-1986 L1988 **FM** *020 †18

ORTING – PIERCE

MORCOS, Amira A. 214 WASHINGTON AVE N 98360 #915-04-1977 L1984 *020

OTHELLO – ADAMS

ANG, Dionisio Lim. 315 N 14TH AVE 99344 #748-10-1975 L1984 **GP OPH** *071
BUNCH, Randel Scot. 140 E MAIN ST, COLUMBIA BASIN HEALTH 99344 #305-01-1988 L1990
    FM *020 †18
BUNCH, Richard Paul. 140 E MAIN ST, COLUMBIA BASIN HEALTH 99344 #040-02-1961 L1962
    GP *020
DINGLASAN, Catherine Jane. ■ 99344 #748-10-2000 L2004 **FM** *020 †18
ELALI, Bashar. 140 E MAIN ST 99344 #875-01-1992 L2001 **FM** *020
FLOREZ, Julian Alberto. 140 E MAIN ST, COLUMBIA BASIN HEALTH 99344 #264-09-1994 L2003
    FM *100 †18 ‡
MIU, Hung Bong. 140 E MAIN ST, P O BOX 546 99344 #001-02-1994 L1998 **OBG** *020 †30
SCHULER, Christopher M. 140 E MAIN ST, COLUMBIA BASIN HEALTH 99344
    #040-02-1999 L2002 **FM** *020 †18
SEBESTA, Donald Gene. 255 N 13TH AVE 99344 #041-01-1963 L1968 **GS FM** *020 †85

OTIS ORCHARDS – SPOKANE

RICHARDSON, Larry Shay. ■ 99027 #056-06-2003 L2006 **EM** *020

OYSTERVILLE – PACIFIC

BEMILLER, David La Mar. PO BOX 128, 34409 J PL 98641 #036-07-1962 L1966 **OBG** *071 †30
NEWTON, Gwendolyn Gene. ■ 98641 #028-02-1955 L1956 **PD** *071 †55
NORMAN, Allen Carl. ■ 98641 #054-04-1958 L1960 **EM PA** *071

PACKWOOD – LEWIS

PRICE, Richard F. 115 TRAILS END 98361 #054-04-1961 L1964 **P ATP** *062 †50

PASCO – FRANKLIN

ACHARI, Narayana Krishna. 516 W MARGARET ST 99301 #495-24-1957 L1973 **NS** *071
ADAMIAN, Eli Adam. 520 N 4TH AVE, LADY OF LOURDES HEALTH CTR 99301
    #649-14-1977 L1983 **AN** *020
AHUJA, Dheeraj. 520 N 4TH AVE 99301 #496-09-1997 L2004 **PAN** *020 †05
BACHRACH, Ethan Allen. 520 N 4TH AVE 99301 #016-06-1995 L2005 **EM** *020 †16
BELL, John W. ■ 99301 #060-01-1974 L1984 **AN** *020 †05
BERRETTA, Jeanne S. 4403 W COURT ST, RIVERVIEW MEDICAL GROUP 99301
    #001-02-1979 L1996 **FM IMG** *071 †18
BRAUER, Albert David. 520 N 4TH AVE 99301 #040-02-1974 L1984 **EM** *020 †18
BROOKS, Victor Otto. 1525 W COURT ST 99301 #005-02-1984 L1987 **FM** *020 †18
BULKLEY, Peter Todd. 1200 N 14TH AVE, STE 265 99301 #016-06-1971 L1996 **U** *020 †95
BURGDORFF, Thomas Raymond. 9915 SANDIFUR PKWY 99301 #005-12-1974 L1980
    ORS *020 †40
CARL, Greg Allen. 1200 N 14TH AVE, STE 220 99301 #054-04-1980 L1984 **OTO** *020 †45
CARTER, Enrique D. 1200 N 14TH AVE 99301 #054-04-1973 L1975 **GE IM** *020
CAYETANO, Rolando Llanes. 531 W PARK ST STE 3 99301 #748-08-1972 L1991 **PD** *020
CHANG, Sophia Su-Fang. 516 W MARGARET ST, STE 6 99301 #244-01-1983 L1998
    RHU IM *020 †20
CHIOU, Yahn Kun. 1608 N ROAD 44, MIRAMAR HEALTH CENTER 99301 #244-02-1985 L2006
    FM *020 †18
CHOU, Henry Heung-Shan. 1200 N 14TH AVE, STE 285 99301 #462-01-1970 L1992
    PD *020 †55
CHOU, Valiant Wha-San. 1200 N 14TH AVE STE 255 99301 #244-01-1971 L1979 **OBG** *020 †30

DAVIS, Ronald E. 520 N 4TH AVE 99301 #016-01-1975 L1986 **FM EM** *020 †18
DE LOS SANTOS, Justiniano. ■ 99301 #748-01-1959 L1972 **FM** *071 †18
DIETSCH, Fernando. 520 N 4TH AVE 99301 #305-01-1996 L2002 **FM** *020 †18
DROESCH, John Thomas. ■ 99301 #054-04-2000 L2000 **GS** *020 †85
EVANS, Laurie Susan. ■ 99301 #028-03-1989 L1994 **GS** *020 †85
FIELD, Louis Wight. 7192 COLUMBIA RIVER RD 99301 #019-02-1954 L1961 **ORS** *071 †85
FISCHER, David Walther. 9915 SANDIFUR PKWY 99301 #005-12-1977 L1982 **ORS HS** *020 †40
FLORES, Sergio Javier. 515 W COURT ST 99301 #429-01-1987 L2004 **FM** *100 †18
HALES, Stanley Eugene. 1200 N 14TH AVE # 300 99301 #038-06-1976 L1982 **IM** *020 †20
HARN, Beverly Rae. 520 N 4TH AVE 99301 #040-02-1979 L1992 **EM FM** *020 †18
HENRIQUES, Cleve Bissette. 516 W MARGARET ST STE 11 99301 #649-02-1957 L1960
    FM OS *020 †18
HENRIQUES, John Christian. 516 W MARGARET ST STE 10 99301 #005-12-1969 L1971
    PD *020
HERNANDEZ MEJIA TORT, T A. 5908 BEDFORD ST 99301 #649-01-1982 L1996 **OBG** *020 †30
HIPOLITO, Mary Grace Pere. 1608 N ROAD 44 99301 #748-02-2000 L2007 **FM** *020 †18
HODGES, Kevin Eric. 520 N 4TH AVE 99301 #030-06-2003 L2006 **EM** *020 †16
HORSLEY, Jackson Stewart. 520 N 4TH AVE 99301 #038-41-1977 L1979 **EM** *020
HUBBARD, Bradley Brian. 520 N 4TH AVE 99301 #306-01-1984 L1992 **EM** *020 †18
ICAYAN, Elena Eustaquio. 520 N 4TH AVE 99301 #748-02-1953 L1973 **NM** *020 †28 ‡
JOHNSON, Mark Edward. 520 N 4TH AVE 99301 #016-01-1996 L2005 **EM** *020 †16
KAKUMBA, Kemunto P. 4403 W COURT ST, STE B 99301 #005-12-2000 L2004 **FM** *020 †18
KETTING, Effie Jean Potts. 515 W COURT ST, MICHEL ALEJANDRO MD 99301
    #005-12-1954 L1982 **OBG PTH** *020 †50
KOONCE, Christina Marie. 1200 N 14TH AVE STE 2 99301 #021-01-1994 L2001 **FM** *020 †18
LAMSENS, Stephen David. 520 N 4TH AVE 99301 #011-03-1995 L1999 **EM** *020 †16
LEVINGER, William Arthur. 520 N 4TH AVE 99301 #041-01-1982 L2002 **AN EM** *020 †05
MARKLE, Jeffrey Dayton. 1200 N 14TH AVE STE 300 99301 #054-04-1981 L1982 **IM** *020 †20
MARTIN, Janice J. 5304 N ROAD 68 99301 #068-01-1988 L1997 **FM** *020 †18
MAXWELL, David Timothy. 520 N 4TH AVE 99301 #005-12-2005 L2006 **EM** *012
MAYUGA, Enriqueta C. 531 W PARK ST STE 1 99301 #748-01-1962 L1969 **OBG** *020 †30 ‡
MAYUGA, Henrietta L. 520 N 4TH AVE 99301 #021-01-1993 L1997 **FM** *020 †18
MONTEILH, Alfred. 1200 N 14TH AVE STE 240 99301 #035-03-1973 L1980 **PS** *020 †65
MORRES, Clark Alton. 520 N 4TH AVE 99301 #023-12-1985 L1993 **FM** *020 †16
NAJERA, Alex B. 520 N 4TH AVE 99301 #056-06-1985 L1988 **IM** *020
NEWTON, Douglas Edward. 520 N 4TH AVE 99301 #005-12-1976 L1979 **EM GP** *020
PALANCA, Sergio Aquino. 527 W PARK ST STE 5 99301 #748-08-1960 L1979 **PD** *020 ‡
PALIT, Mark Kamal. 9915 SANDIFUR PKWY 99301 #016-11-1990 L2006 **ORS** *020 †40
PHIPPS, Heather L. 9915 SANDIFUR PKWY 99301 #038-75-1998, ▲ L2003 **ORS** *020
RACSA, Gertrudes Manaloto. 527 W PARK ST, STE 3 99301 #748-01-1968 L1978 **FM** *020
RACSA, Nemesio Arca. 520 N 4TH AVE 99301 #748-08-1968 L1976 **IM CD** *020 †20
RHO, Hee Kyu. 531 W PARK ST STE 4 99301 #583-01-1963 L1972 **OBG** *020 †30
RINT, Rolando T. 531 W PARK ST, STE 2 99301 #748-02-1961 L1979 **OS OBG** *020 †30
RIOJAS, Faustino, Jr. 707 W MARGARET ST 99301 #054-04-1990 L1993 **FM** *020 †18
ROSE, Ray Vincent. 520 N 4TH AVE 99301 #026-04-1946 L1950 **GS** *072 †85
SAMBASIVAN, Venkataraman. 1200 N 14TH AVE STE 295 99301 #495-66-1971 L1993
    CD IM *020 †20
SAUNDERS, David Starr. 516 W MARGARET ST STE 10 99301 #005-12-1976 L1992
    PD *020 †55
SHALLMAN, Richard Wm. 1200 N 14TH AVE STE 400 99301 #003-01-1982 L1987 **GS** *020 †85
SINGER, Reuben Amrit. 515 W COURT ST, COMMUNITY HEALTH CENTER LA 99301
    #308-03-1982 L1997 **PD** *020
STAEHELI, John Wm. 520 N 4TH AVE 99301 #030-06-1980 L1989 **ORS OTR** *020 †40
STRAHLE, John F. 9915 SANDIFUR PKWY, LOURDES OCCUP HLTH CTR. 99301
    #306-01-1983 L1990 **FM OM** *020 †18
TABER, Robert Lorin, Jr. 520 N 4TH AVE 99301 #019-02-1984 L1993 **EM** *020 †16
TAYLOR, Kevin Ralph. 4403 W COURT ST 99301 #054-04-1981 L1984 **FM** *020 †18
TRZCINSKI, William Karl. 1200 N 14TH AVE 99301 #033-05-1965 L1969 **PS OTO** *071 †45,65
UNDERHILL, Gary Thomas. 520 N 4TH AVE 99301 #005-12-1996 L1999 **FM** *020 †18
VAN HOUDT, Gerard A. 520 N 4TH AVE 99301 #054-04-1980 L2000 **FM** *020 †16,18
VARGAS, George Eladio. 515 W COURT ST, CHC LA CLINICA 99301 #308-04-1986 L1998
    END IM *020 †20
VAZ, Gladson M. 507 N 5TH AVE 99301 #496-15-1984 L1996 **PUD** *020 †20
WALKER-CONNER, Brenda E. 4403 W COURT ST, RIVERVIEW MEDICAL GREOUP 99301
    #047-07-1998 L2004 **FM** *020 †18
WILLIAMS, Lysle W, Jr. 5304 N ROAD 68 99301 #005-12-1971 L1989 **EM** *040 †16
YOUNG, Kipp Alan. 520 N 4TH AVE 99301 #028-03-1984 L1985 **EM OM** *020
ZIMMERMAN, Laurie Twila. 515 W COURT ST, LA CLINICA 99301 #023-01-1981 L1996
    P *020 †75

PESHASTIN – CHELAN

LONSDALE, Howard Chas. ■ 98847 #004-01-1960 L1960 **OTO GP** *072

POINT ROBERTS – WHATCOM

GHARAKHANIAN, Garen. ■ 98281 #704-02-1979 L1996 *020
HAMM, Leonard John Edward. ■ 98281 #062-01-1974 L2004 **EM** *062 †18,16
HOUBE, Jill Suzanne. ■ 98281 #024-01-1988 L1990 **PD** *020 †55
SHEY, Marianne I Tan. ■ 98281 #024-05-1967 L1968 **R** *075 †80
TAN, Min Hwa. ■ 98281 #572-12-1968 L1997 **AN** *020

POMEROY – GARFIELD

RICHARDSON, Doris Shirley. 808 COLUMBIA STREET 99347 #065-06-1955 L1963 **GP** *071

PORT ANGELES – CLALLAM

ADDISON, Danny Geo. 828 E 8TH ST 98362 #030-05-1977 L1978 **FM** *020 †18
ALLMAN, Robert M, Jr. 433 E 8TH ST 98362 #048-12-1953 L1960 **GS** *071 †85
ANDREW, Louise Briggs. 403 S LINCOLN ST, STE 4-51 98362 #036-07-1975 L2001
    EM LM *071 †20,16

AVERILL, Rex Thos. 1035 CAROLINE ST 98362 #026-04-1974 L1981 **U** *040 †95
BAKER, Margaret Mary. 832 GEORGIANA ST, CTR FOR BONES/JOINT SURG 98362 #010-02-1986 L1996 **ORS OSM** *020 †40
BAKER, Samuel Russell. ■ 98362 #054-04-1966 L1969 **ORS** *020 †40
BANGS, Margaret Elizabeth. 908 GEORGIANA ST 98362 #054-04-1983 L1987 **FM** *020 †18
BAUMAN, Randell Edward. 930 CAROLINE ST 98362 #030-05-1969 L2004 **OBG FM** *020 †30
BAY, Mildred Odicino. 902 CAROLINE ST, PENINSULA CHILDREN'S CLINI 98362 #005-14-2002 L2002 **PD** *020 †55
BENSEN, Carleen Tortello. 1035 CAROLINE ST 98362 #034-01-1987 L1992 **U** *020 †95
BERGES, Ulrich Peter. ■ 98362 #407-33-1961 L1970 **AN OS** *071
BERGMAN, Ronald James. ■ 98362 #039-01-1972 L1995 **GPM** *020 †50
BIRCH, Ann Mc Avoy Horn. ■ 98362 #023-07-1944 L1944 **ADM** *062 †55
BORRONE, Elizabeth Jane. 939 CAROLINE ST 98362 #065-09-1959 L1967 **PD FM** *020
BROWN, Roy Geo. ■ 98362 #030-06-1944 L1968 **IM CD** *071
BULLEN, Laura Kristine. 902 CAROLINE ST 98362 #035-19-2001 L2004 **PD** *020 †55
BUNDY, Charles Aanon. 1021 CAROLINE ST 98362 #026-04-1985 L1992 **GS** *020 †85
BUNDY, Pamela Jensen. 939 CAROLINE ST 98362 #026-04-1988 L1992 **AN PME** *020 †05
BUSH, Stephen Donald. 433 E 8TH ST, VIRGINIA MASON - PORT ANGE 98362 #016-43-1980 L2001 **OBS GYN** *020
BYERS, Le Roy Vernon. ■ 98362 #005-12-1978 L2007 **OPH** *020 †35
CAIN, James Mason. ■ 98362 #054-04-2001 L2005 **GS** *020 †85
CHAPMAN, Steven Holmes. 902 CAROLINE ST, PENIHSOLA CHILDRENS CLINIC 98362 #041-01-1993 L1995 **PD** *020 †55
CHEN, Jeffrey Lejay. 939 CAROLINE ST 98362 #028-46-1995 L2004 **IM** *020 †20
CHRISTIAN, Elizabeth E. 433 E 8TH ST 98362 #054-04-1986 L1991 **FM** *020 †18
CHURCHLEY, Steve James. 106 LAKE CRESENT RD, STORM KING RANGER STATION 98363 #054-04-1987 L1989 **FM** *020 †18
COLE, Kirk Alan. 939 CAROLINE ST, OLYMPIC MEDICAL CENTER 98362 #003-01-1997 L2003 **DR** *020
CRAVEN, Robert Wm. 315 E 8TH ST 98362 #003-01-1987 L1992 **OTO ALI** *020 †45
CREGG, Hugh Anthony, Jr. ■ 98362 #024-07-1945 L1990 **R** *071 †80
CRIST, Robert Saml. 433 E 8TH ST 98362 #030-06-1964 L1970 **IM** *020 †20
EISENSTADT, Mark Allen. 118 E 8TH ST, PENINSULA CROWN MENTAL HLT 98362 #035-08-1971 L1984 **P** *020 †75
EMERY, James Frank. ■ 98362 #049-01-1973 L2005 **CD IM** *020 †20
EPLER, Michael Alton. 433 E 8TH ST, VIRGINIA MASON PORT ANGELE 98362 #005-14-1982 L2003 **FM** *020 †18
EPSTEIN, Samuel Robert. 303 W 8TH ST, FAMILY MED OF PT ANGELES 98362 #054-04-1998 L2000 **FM OBS** *020 †18
ERICKSON, Peter James. ■ 98362 #026-04-1981 L1987 **FM** *020 †18
EVERETT, Harold Geo, Jr. 1205 E FRONT ST 98362 #056-06-1980 L1984 **OPH** *020 †35
FAIRSHTER, Jacob Jonah. 801 E FRONT ST 98362 #016-42-1941 L1947 **FM AM** *071
FERRELL, Susan Marie. 939 CAROLINE ST, SLEEP LAB 98362 #047-20-1993 L2005 **PTH** *020 †50
FINLEY, Alan Howard. ■ 98362 #067-01-1953 L1978 **PD PHP** *030 †55
FISCHER, Mark David. 923 GEORGIANA ST 98362 #040-02-1975 L1979 **IM PUD** *020 †20
FISHMAN, Michael Scot. 1102 E FRONT ST, PENINSULA RADIOLOGISTS 98362 #038-40-1987 L1992 **DR** *020 †80
FLOWERS, James Farrand. 1021 CAROLINE ST 98362 #048-14-1983 L1984 **GS** *020 †85
GACEK, Edward Michael. 111 EDIZ VW 98363 #010-01-1983 L1985 **IM** *020 †20
GANDARA, Juleann Cottini. 939 CAROLINE ST 98362 #054-04-1981 L1982 **R ON** *020
GARDNER, Gordon Doug. 939 CAROLINE ST 98362 #649-33-1979 L1982 **OBG** *020
GARDNER, Richard Marvin. 136 E 8TH ST 98362 #035-45-1955 L1965 **FM** *071 †20
GARLICK, Stanley Allen. 303 W 8TH ST 98362 #054-04-1976 L1977 **FM** *020 †18
GEREN, James Tennent. 1005 GEORGIANA ST 98362 #030-06-1994 L1997 **IM** *020 †20
GIPE, Robert Keith. 433 E 8TH ST 98362 #024-01-1994 L1996 **IM** *020 †20
GORDON, Lawrence A. 433 E 8TH ST 98362 #035-09-1984 L1990 **FM** *020 †18
GRIFFIN, Lee Martin. ■ 98363 #026-04-1955 L1956 **P N** *071
HAGELSTEIN, Arthur A. ■ 98362 #024-05-1945 L1958 **IM** *071 †20
HARRINGTON, Madeline M. 902 CAROLINE ST, PENINSULA CHILDREN'S CLINI 98362 #036-07-1977 L1984 **PD** *020 †55
HENNESSEY, Kathie S. 303 W 8TH ST 98362 #028-34-1984 L1986 **FM OBG** *020 †18
HENNESSEY, William F, Jr. 303 W 8TH ST 98362 #028-34-1985 L1986 **FM PD** *020 †18
HERZ, Guenther Frederick. ■ 98362 #407-10-1956 L1981 **R** *100 †80
HOBBS, William Nolan. 1005 GEORGIANA ST 98362 #054-04-1984 L1985 **IM** *020 †20
HOPFNER, Edward Anthony. ■ 98362 #005-76-1987, ▲ L2001 **AN FM** *020
HOWARTH, Stephen Thos. ■ 98362 #036-05-1974 L2004 **AN** *020 †05
HUDGINS, Daniel Webster. 433 E 8TH ST, OLYMPIC MED PHYS 98362 #011-02-1983 L1997 **FM FPG** *020 †18
KANG, Eunyoung. ■ 98363 #583-05-2002 L2007 **IM** *100 †20
KENNEDY, Robert Scott. 939 CAROLINE ST 98362 #054-04-1984 L1985 **FM** *030 †18
KINTNER, Quentin. ■ 98362 #017-20-1941 L1945 **IMG FM** *071
KINTNER, William Robt. 433 E 8TH ST 98362 #054-04-1978 L1979 **FM** *020 †18
KOSIEROWSKI, Richard Robt. 3430 E HIGHWAY 101, STE 25 98362 #033-06-1980 L1981 **ON HEM** *020 †20
KOTT, Betsy Lynne. 1205 E FRONT ST 98362 #041-07-1995 L1999 **OPH** *020 †35
LARSON, Loren Michael. ■ 98362 #040-02-2001 L2007 **ORS** *020
LEE, Fayzel. PO BOX 2409, 939 CAROLINE ST 98362 #060-01-1991 L2000 **AN** *020 †16,05
LEWIS, Peter Donald Rhys. 830 E 8TH ST 98362 #020-02-1978 L1979 **FM** *020 †18
LOCKE, Thomas H. 223 E 4TH ST 98362 #019-02-1975 L1979 **UM GPM** *030 †70
LUCAS, Michael James. 939 CAROLINE ST, OLYMPIC MEMORIAL HOSPITAL 98362 #054-04-1974 L1978 **AN** *020
MADSEN, Thomas Wm. 230 E 5TH ST 98362 #056-06-1943 L1944 **OS GP** *071
MANTOOTH, James Edward. 902 CAROLINE ST 98362 #039-01-1966 L1971 **PD GP** *020 †55
MARTIG, John F. ■ 98362 #005-76-1987, ▲ L2001 **AN FM** *020
MATHER, John Robt. 832 GEORGIANA ST 98362 #047-05-1968 L1975 **OTO FPS** *071 †45
MATTONI, John Arthur. ■ 98363 #038-40-1959 L1959 **OBG** *075 †30
MAXWELL, Michael Scott. 303 W 8TH ST 98362 #054-04-1988 L1990 **FM** *020 †18
MAYER, Ben H, Jr. ■ 98362 #019-02-1944 L1947 **AN** *071
MC COOL, Michael Finn. 433 E 8TH ST 98362 #054-04-1970 L1973 **GE** *075 †20
MC GOVERN, Regina May. 1112 CAROLINE ST 98362 #026-04-1994 L2000 **HS** *020 †40
MC VAUGH, Charles Champ. 433 E 8TH ST 98362 #017-20-1940 L1963 **DR** *071
MEAD, William Field. ■ 98362 #019-02-1954 L1955 **FM CD** *071 †18
METZLER, Charlotte Louise. ■ 98363 #034-01-1985 L1990 **D** *020 †15
MILES, John Wm. ■ 98363 #047-06-1954 L1954 **OTO NO** *071 †45

OAKES, Jerome Roger. 433 E 8TH ST 98362 #041-07-1998 L2001 **FM** *020 †18
OAKES, Roger Merrill. 433 E 8TH ST 98362 #054-04-1968 L1969 **FM FPG** *020 †18
PEDERSON, Paul Edward. 923 GEORGIANA ST, OMP KLAHHANE CLINIC 98362 #026-04-1986 L1990 **IM CD** *020 †20
PETERSON, Norman Frederic. 819 GEORGIANA ST, STE A 98362 #054-04-1969 L1970 **P** *020
PISCIOTTA, Benj Patrick. 1102 E FRONT ST 98362 #051-04-1977 L1983 **DR** *020 †80
QUISTGAARD, Jorgen. 939 CAROLINE ST 98362 #297-01-1957 L1962 **AN** *071 †05
REDLIN, Mark Steven. 816 E 8TH ST 98362 #037-01-1982 L1983 **FM** *020 †18
REZVANI, Laghaieh. 939 CAROLINE ST 98362 #517-04-1971 L1990 **R** *020 †80
ROWAN, Bruce Walter. 939 CAROLINE ST 98362 #054-04-1992 L1996 **FM EM** *075 †18
SCHUELER, Lawrence A, Jr. 621 E FRONT ST, CLINICARE 98362 #054-04-1952 L1953 **GP** *071
SCOTT, Robert Lester. 814 S PEABODY ST 98362 #025-07-1976 L1985 **FM** *020 †18
SHUBKIN, Catherine Dawn. 902 CAROLINE ST 98362 #010-01-1995 L2000 **PD** *020 †55
SIEMENS, John Lloyd. ■ 98362 #040-02-1948 L1950 **GP** *071
SPEES, Karl Eugene. 939 CAROLINE ST 98362 #047-06-1973 L1983 **EM FM** *071 †16,18
STEIGERWALD, Allan M. ■ 98363 #056-05-1967 L1968 **AN** *050 †05
STERN, Bernard B. ■ 98362 #054-04-1950 L1952 **GP** *071
SYMONDS, Frank Bruce. ■ 98362 #054-04-1956 L1961 **TS GS** *071 †85
TATRO, Sandra Jean. 228 W 12TH ST 98362 #034-01-1996 L2003 **GS** *020 †85
THORSON, Richard Dean. 939 CAROLINE ST 98362 #054-04-1959 L1966 **ORS** *062 †40
TORDINI, Arthur Louis. ■ 98362 #033-06-1979 L1983 **EM IM** *020 †20,16
TULLY, Thomas Wm. 939 CAROLINE ST, OLYMPIC MEDICAL CTR 98362 #016-43-1991 L1996 **EM IM** *020 †20
TURNER, Eugene Fay. 902 CAROLINE ST 98362 #054-04-1962 L1970 **PD GP** *020 †55
UDE, Marianne Joy. 939 CAROLINE ST 98362 #054-04-1980 L1981 **FM FPG** *020 †18
VAN CALCAR, Richard John. 939 CAROLINE ST 98362 #040-02-1969 L1972 **FM AM** *020 †18
VENZON, Dennis Eugene. ■ 98362 #028-02-1966 L1982 **PTH NM** *071 †50
WANG, Xinda D. 939 CAROLINE ST, OLYMPIC MED CTR 98362 #243-16-1983 L2004 **HO** *020 †20
WATKINS, Robt Preston, Jr. 939 CAROLINE ST 98362 #048-04-1967 L1970 **ORS** *020 †40
WEGMANN, John Douglas. 939 CAROLINE ST 98362 #056-05-1968 L1969 **PD** *020 †55
WEIDEN, Paul Lincoln. 939 CAROLINE ST 98362 #024-01-1967 L1971 **ON HEM** *050 †20
WEIGHTMAN, Mary Harbert. ■ 98363 #041-13-1961 L1962 **AN GP** *071 †05
WELLER, Jeffrey Charles. 902 CAROLINE ST, PENINSULA CHILDRENS CLINIC 98362 #023-07-1997 L1999 **PD** *020 †55
WELLER, Katrina C. 303 W 8TH ST 98362 #035-45-1998 L2000 **FM** *020 †18
WENDEL, Reed Arthur. ■ 98362 #016-02-1975 L1976 **GS VS** *071 †85
WHITNEY, Charles Ralph. ■ 98362 #005-11-1969 L1998 **OPH** *071 †35
WILSON, Steve Allen. ■ 98362 #018-03-1983 L1997 **FM** *020 †18
WINTERNITZ, Sarah Frances. 104 N LAUREL ST STE 101 98362 #024-07-1980 L1996 **P** *020 †75
WITHAM, Robert Rodney. 224 N WASHINGTON ST 98362 #040-02-1976 L1979 **IM ON** *020 †20 ‡
YERGAN, John. 2235 MONROE RD 98362 #035-01-1976 L1980 **IM** *030 †20
YOU, Chul-Hee. 433 E 8TH ST, VIRGINIA MASON MEDICAL CEN 98362 #583-02-1970 L2002 **GE IM** *020 †20
ZEY, John R. 136 E 8TH ST, PMB 134 98362 #748-11-1972 L1995 **EM** *020

PORT GAMBLE – KITSAP

GORDON, Glen Albert, Jr. ■ 98364 #030-06-1963 L1965 **OM OS** *020
WILCOX, Martin Waldo. ■ 98364 #019-02-1964 L1970 **GS AM** *020 †85

PORT HADLOCK – JEFFERSON

STAVNEY, L Stanton. ■ 98339 #054-04-1958 L1960 **GS TS** *020 †85,90
VANDEGRIFT, Paul Doughas. PO BOX 59 98339 #005-17-1962 L1975 *100

PORT LUDLOW – JEFFERSON

BEAN, Michael Arthur. 46 VILLAGE WAY # 165 98365 #007-02-1967 L1975 **OS ATP** *050 †50
CONRARDY, Peter Anthony. ■ 98365 #005-15-1969 L1971 **AN** *071 †05
DURHAM, Zoe Rei. 9522 OAK BAY RD, STE 400 98365 #054-04-1980 L1983 **PD** *020 †55
FROSOLONE, Chas Anthony. 51 CAMANO LN 98365 #056-06-1980 L2003 **GS TRS** *020 †85
GORDY, Tracy Ross. ■ 98365 #048-02-1961 L2000 **P PYG** *062 †75
HUDSON, Bruce H. ■ 98365 #024-01-1951 L1957 **PD** *071 †55
KRUEGER, J Carroll. ■ 98365 #028-34-1960 L1961 **ORS** *071 †40
MACDONALD, Constance. ■ 98365 #024-05-1960 L1963 **PD** *071
MARTIN, Shirley M Witham. ■ 98365 #041-01-1950 L1951 **AN OS** *071
MC DOUGALL, William J. ■ 98365 #035-15-1944 L1946 **GP OS** *071
PHILIPS, Peter Ashley. ■ 98365 #035-09-1963 L1989 **CD GS** *020 †85,90
RYAN, Kevin Gude. ■ 98365 #024-01-1959 L1994 **R NM** *071 †80,28
SHAMHART, Harry Wm. ■ 98365 #016-11-1948 L1949 **CRS GS** *071 †85
SMALL, Mary Lucile. ■ 98365 #005-12-1966 L1967 **OBG** *071 †30
VON SEGGERN, James Gates. ■ 98365 #054-04-1961 L1969 **U** *071 †95

PORT ORCHARD – KITSAP

ALBERICO, Paul Joseph. ■ 98366 #038-41-2007 **FP** *012
ANDERSON, Karen. 1141 BEACH DR E 98366 #054-04-1976 L1978 **IMG GPM** *030 †70
BATES, James Richard. 450 S KITSAP BLVD STE 2860 98366 #025-01-1981 L1982 **IM** *020 †20
BERNSTEIN, Gordon Allen. 7091 MUIRKIRK LN SW 98367 #018-03-1963 L1991 **R NM** *020 †80,28
BIALER, Allan Jeffrey. 1400 POTTERY AVE 98366 #038-41-1976 L1980 **FM** *020 †18
BOEHME, Robert Eugene. ■ 98366 #038-06-1948 L1949 **OM OS** *062
BONNEVIE, Regina Barbosa. 320 S KITSAP BLVD, PENINSULA COMMUNITY 98366 #010-01-1995 L1998 **IM** *020 †20
BOYER, Michael James. 450 S KITSAP BLVD, STE 2300 98366 #054-04-1973 L1975 **PD** *020 †55
BRAWLEY, Jessica Renae. ■ 98367 #051-04-2007 **FP** *012
BROWN, Debbie Ann. 450 S KITSAP BLVD, HARRISON URGENT CARE 98366 #036-01-1997 L2001 **FM** *020 †18

BUTLER, Michael John. 450 S KITSAP BLVD STE 2860 98366 #005-15-1975 L1979 FM IMG *020 †18

BYEON, Jai Jun. 320 S KITSAP BLVD 98366 #583-02-1985 L2004 FM *100 †18

CAMPBELL, James Anthony. 450 S KITSAP BLVD, SOUTH KITSAP HEALTHCARE CA 98366 #040-02-1967 L1991 PD *020 †55

CAVUOTI, Michael A. ■ 98366 #035-08-1933 GP *071

CHAMBERS, James Richard. ■ 98367 #054-04-1971 L1985 FM AM *020 †18

COGLEY, Catherine Elaine. 450 S KITSAP BLVD, STE 2300 98366 #048-02-1996 L2005 PD *020 †55

COOK, Michael Leroy. 450 S KITSAP BLVD, STE 1240 98366 #018-03-1984 L1990 DR *020 †80

CORRALES-DIAZ, John Jos. 450 S KITSAP BLVD, STE 2860 98366 #056-06-1981 L1984 PD *020 †55

CORRALL, Carmen James. 1951 MIRACLE MILE DR E 98366 #055-01-1976 L2003 EM PE *020 †55,16

COSTA, Derek Edward. 1400 POTTERY AVE 98366 #054-04-1985 L1986 FM *020 †18

CUNNINGHAM, David Melvin. ■ 98367 #040-02-2001 L2002 FM *020

DAELEY, Mark Anthony. ■ 98367 #028-34-1985 L1992 PD *020 †55

DAVIS, Mc William Henry. ■ 98366 #019-02-1964 L1973 IM GP *020

DELCAMPO, Pil-Chung Jenny. 1400 POTTERY AVE 98366 #040-02-2000 L2004 FM *020 †18

DOUDS, Howard Nesbit. 450 S KITSAP BLVD, STE 1240 98366 #041-12-1974 L1993 DR NM *020 †80,28

DUNLOP, John Sears. ■ 98367 #016-11-1955 L1956 OBG *072 †30

ENNIS, Gregory Mark. ■ 98367 #030-06-2003 L2005 FM *020 †18

FERINGA, Earl Robt. ■ 98366 #016-06-1957 L1993 N PTH *050 †75

FRANDSEN, Brad Russell. 450 S KITSAP BLVD, STE 1200 98366 #005-12-1983 L1992 FM OBS *020 †18

FREDRIKSON, Lynn C. ■ 98366 #016-06-1941 L1947 GP PHP *071

FREDRIKSON, Steven E. 1570 WOODRIDGE DR SE 98366 #010-02-1973 L1978 FM *020 †18

GJESDAL, Shane Matthew. ■ 98366 #019-02-1998 L1999 OBG *100 †30

GRAY, Kelly Marie. ■ 98366 #023-12-2006 L2007 FP *012

HARDAWAY, Christina. 450 S KITSAP BLVD, STE 2860 98366 #023-12-1994 L2005 D *020 †15

HEFTER, Thomas George. ■ 98367 #036-04-1981 L1988 P ID *020

HEISTAND, Kari Case. ■ 98366 #054-04-2002 L2003 P *020

HOEFLER, Matthew Francis. ■ 98366 #023-12-2007 FP *012

HOLSTEN, Kenneth Erwin. 7108 KILLEEN PL SW 98367 #005-02-1967 L1968 OPH *020 †35

IVERSEN, Martin Jens. 450 S KITSAP BLVD, STE 1600 98366 #422-01-1998 L2002 FM *020 †18 ‡

JOHNSON, Harry Richard. 7370 HAWKSTONE AVE SW 98367 #030-06-1974 L1980 ORS *071 †40

KRISHNANANTHAN, Ruben. 450 S KITSAP BLVD, STE 1240 98366 #143-02-1993 L2005 NM *100 †80,28

LEEN, Victor Hans. 450 S KITSAP BLVD, STE 1240 98366 #043-01-1988 L1994 DR *020 †80

LENZA, Gary Francis. ■ 98367 #016-11-1989 L1989 P *020

LUONG, Tai Hiep. 450 S KITSAP BLVD, STE 1240 98366 #039-01-1991 L1998 RNR *020 †80

MASTELLER, Malcolm Cary. ■ 98366 #016-42-2006 FP *012

MC CALL, Jennifer Gadeyne. ■ 98367 #010-02-2003 L2004 *100

MOUNTFORD, Paul Curtis. ■ 98366 #049-01-1965 L1969 FM *020 †18

NAMKUNG, Kenneth Kyun. 1400 POTTERY AVE 98366 #654-01-2003 L2005 FM *020 †18

POLYAKOV, Vladislav. 1400 POTTERY AVE, PORT ORCHARD MEDICAL CENTE 98366 #550-02-1999 L2002 FM *020 †18

RANKIN, Robert Reid. 450 S KITSAP BLVD, STE 1600 98366 #040-02-1974 L1979 FM GP *020 †18

RYAN, Mark. ■ 98366 #047-05-1975 L1979 PTH GS *020 †50

SEARLE, Alan J. 1400 POTTERY AVE 98366 #917-20-1973 L1982 FM *020 †16,18

SHILLING, Tamara L. 451 SW SEDGWICK RD, STE 110 98367 #022-75-2003, ▲ L2006 FM *020 †18

SHUTSKE, Matthew Gregory. 450 S KITSAP BLVD, STE 1240 98366 #033-05-2001 L2006 DR *020 †80

STACKHOUSE, David J. 1400 POTTERY AVE 98366 #048-14-1987 L1990 FM *020 †18

SUGIMOTO, Ginny E T. 1400 POTTERY AVE 98366 #054-04-1983 L1988 FM *020 †18

SUGIMOTO, Mark Masao. 1400 POTTERY AVE, PORT ORCHARD MED CTR 98366 #005-06-1984 L1988 FM *020 †18

TANAKA, Richard John. 1400 POTTERY AVE 98366 #016-42-1985 L1995 FM *020 †18

THIESSEN, Arthur D. ■ 98366 #016-11-1951 L1989 GP NTR *071 ‡

THOMAN, Mark Edward. ■ 98366 #028-03-1962 L1972 PDT *071 †55

TIUSECO, Kristine Andrea. 320 S KITSAP BLVD, PENINSULA COMMUNITY 98366 #748-02-2000 L2006 IMG *020 †20

WEISSMAN, Allan Norman. 1950 POTTERY AVE STE 20 98366 #054-04-1969 L1972 EM PD *020

YAPTINCHAY, Rosario C. ■ 98366 #748-02-1943 L1968 GP *072

ZAKA, Safoora. 450 S KITSAP BLVD, STE 2860 98366 #704-04-1999 L2006 IM *020 †20

PORT TOWNSEND – JEFFERSON

BARNETT, Andy Stuart. 834 SHERIDAN ST 98368 #036-07-2002 L2005 FM *020 †18

BARTL, Marion Anna. 1136 WATER ST, STE 110 98368 #054-04-1976 L1977 *020

BLOEMKER, William K. 1136 WATER ST, PORT TOWNSEND MEDICAL CLIN 98368 #017-20-1968 L1974 FM OBS *071 †18

BOGRAD, Gerald David. 2023 E SIMS WAY # 262 98368 #007-02-1968 L1969 P *020 †75

BRINGGOLD, Bradley Allen. 834 SHERIDAN ST 98368 #026-08-1976 L1996 FM *020 †18

BROWN, Cynthia Ann. ■ 98368 #048-02-1971 L1971 RO *020 †80

BUTTERFIELD, Robert S. 834 SHERIDAN ST, JEFFERSON GENERAL HOSPITAL 98368 #038-41-2000 L2004 MPD *020 †55,20

CARL, Jennifer Wynne. 1233 W SIMS WAY 98368 #054-04-1983 L1984 PM PRS *020 †60

CARLSON, Todd Jeffrey. 1010 SHERIDAN ST STE 101 98368 #026-04-1996 L1999 FM *020 †18

COLLIN, Jonathan. 911 TYLER ST 98368 #035-03-1975 L1977 GP GPM *020

COLLINS, Jeffrey Townes. ■ 98368 #039-01-1967 L2007 P *020

DAY, Carolyn J. 834 SHERIDAN ST, JEFFERSON HEALTHCARE 98368 #035-45-1998 L2002 MPD *020 †20,55

DICKERSON, Ben Roger. 834 SHERIDAN ST 98368 #054-04-1963 L1964 GP *071 †18

DRONKERT, Adrian. ■ 98368 #660-01-1950 L1954 IM PTH *071 †50,28,20

ELAM, Kenneth Craig. 834 SHERIDAN ST 98368 #010-01-1972 L1974 EM FM *020 †18,16

ERNEST, Karen Diane. 834 SHERIDAN ST, JEFFERSON GEN MED GRP 98368 #035-45-1987 L1998 IM PD *020 †20,55

FORBES, Gary Chas. 834 SHERIDAN ST 98368 #025-07-1990 L1998 MPD EM *020 †55,20

GREEN, David Lot. 527 SHERIDAN ST 98368 #017-20-1965 L1973 ORS *040 †40

GREENWALD, Alan Greg. 834 SHERIDAN ST 98368 #041-12-1977 L1979 ORS *020 †40

HARRIS, David Franklin. 1010 SHERIDAN ST STE 101 98368 #035-03-1999 L2002 FM *020 †18

HEINE, Carlton E. 834 SHERIDAN ST 98368 #040-02-2003 L2006 EM *020 †16

HUTTON, Jack Marvin. 1827 VAN NESS ST 98368 #048-12-1973 L1982 N *020 †75

JANSSEN, Claus Henner. 934 SHERIDAN ST 98368 #038-43-1990 L1993 FM *020 †18

KOLFF, Cornelis Albert. ■ 98368 #024-01-1971 L1976 GP PD *020 †55

KURATA, Douglas. 934 SHERIDAN ST 98368 #005-11-1977 L1980 FM *071 †18

KUZNETSOV, Dimitri David. 1274 7TH ST, STE B 98368 #035-19-1997 L2003 U *020 †95

LAMAS, Fernando Enrique. JEFFERSON GEN HOSPITAL 98368 #011-02-1980 L1988 DR *020 †80

LEVY, Bertram Jos. PO BOX 218, 1274 7TH ST 98368 #036-07-1968 L1975 U *071 †95

LINDELL, Maurice Ernest. ■ 98368 #041-01-1956 L1981 TS *071 †85,90

LYNN, Richard Rudd. 1136 WATER ST, STE 107 98368 #005-11-1973 L1974 IM GP *020 †20

MAGILL, Frank Bell. 834 SHERIDAN ST 98368 #035-45-1992 L2000 PD IM *020 †55,20

MARSTON, Nancy. 834 SHERIDAN ST 98368 #035-08-1982 L2004 IM *020 †20

MATTERN, Joseph John, III. 1010 SHERIDAN ST STE 101 98368 #041-15-2000 L2003 FM *020 †18

MAYHALL, William S T. ■ 98368 #048-02-1970 L1995 ORS HS *062 †40

MC GOVERN, Tristan M. 834 SHERIDAN ST 98368 #028-02-1991 L1999 ORS *020 †40

MC GRORY, Melanie. 1136 WATER ST STE 111 98368 #041-13-1987 L1989 FM *020 †18

MEADOWS, Richard Paul. 934 SHERIDAN ST 98368 #054-04-2000 L2006 FM *020 †18

MEDLICOTT, William Jay. ■ 98368 #054-04-1959 L1961 ORS *071 †40

MOSS, Richard Max. ■ 98368 #035-09-1972 L1973 *050

MUENS, Guenther E. 834 SHERIDAN ST 98368 #409-39-1987 L2006 IM *020 †20

MURPHY, Ruth Markmann. ■ 98368 #035-01-1948 L1953 P *071

NELSEN, Douglas Taylor. 834 SHERIDAN ST 98368 #054-04-1987 L1990 FM *020 †18

OTTAWAY, Katherine T. 934 SHERIDAN ST 98368 #051-04-1993 L1999 FM *020 †18

PARKMAN, Catherine A. ■ 98368 #040-02-1990 L1995 IM PD *020 †55,20

RAMOS, Ryan Francis Colla. 1010 SHERIDAN ST STE 2 98368 #748-01-1999 L2007 GS *020

RIENSTRA, Joseph Douwe. 242 MONROE ST 98368 #036-07-1969 L1971 GP NTR *020

ROOKSTOOL, Robert J. 834 SHERIDAN ST 98368 #055-01-1988 L1994 FM *020 †18

ROTCHFORD, James Kimber. 1334 LAWRENCE ST 98368 #054-04-1980 L1981 PME OS *020 †70

ROWE, John Cavanaugh. ■ 98368 #028-03-1970 L1971 FM *071 †18

SCHMIDT, Sarah Kay. 834 SHERIDAN ST, JEFFERSON GENERAL MEDICAL 98368 #016-43-2000 L2004 MPD *020 †55,20

SMITH-POLING, Sandra. 2112 LANDES ST 98368 #005-19-1976 L1977 IM GP *020 †20

STARKE, Lori Ann. 834 SHERIDAN ST 98368 #054-04-2004 L2007 EM *020

STOWE, Bruce Wallace. 1010 SHERIDAN ST, STE 202 98368 #007-02-1991 L1993 FM *020 †18

SUNDEEN, James Reinhold. ■ 98368 #005-02-1970 L1973 PTH *020 †50

SWEENEY, Lynne Marie. ■ 98368 #035-15-1988 *030

TACKER, Jack Ronald. ■ 98368 #039-01-1975 L1990 U *071

TATHAM, Elinor Jean. 1010 SHERIDAN ST STE 101 98368 #021-01-1991 L1995 FM *020 †18

THOMPSON, Linda Kay. ■ 98368 #026-04-1999 L2005 FM *020 †18

POULSBO – KITSAP

ANDERSEN, Brad Lawrence. 20730 BOND RD NE STE 205, NORTH KITSAP FAMILY PRACT 98370 #054-04-1994 L1996 FM *020 †18

ANDERSEN, Teresa Ann. 20730 BOND RD NE STE 205, NORTH KITSAP FAMILY PRACTI 98370 #054-04-1994 L2001 FM *020 †18

BRODIE, Jeffrey Henry. 19379 7TH AVE NE 98370 #040-02-1979 L2001 FM *020 †18

BROSTOFF, Laurence Martin. 23668 COBURG PL 98370 #005-06-1986 L1992 IM *020 †20

CARLTON, Bruce Eric. 19365 7TH AVE NE, STE 104 98370 #017-20-1973 L1978 IM *020 †20

CASE, Thomas Dale. 20696 BOND RD NE 98370 #040-02-1968 L1974 OPH *071 †35

CHUN, Andrea Akita. 19379 7TH AVE NE 98370 #040-02-1999 L2001 IM *100 †20

CHYMIY, Andrea L. 19379 7TH AVE NE 98370 #021-01-2000 L2002 FM *020 †18

COOPER, Richard Allen. ■ 98370 #016-42-1968 L1991 DR *020 †80

DEMSHKI, Andrew E, Jr. ■ 98370 #007-02-1944 L1944 OTO *071 †45

DEORDIO, John Edward. ■ 98370 #041-14-1996 L1997 EM *020 †16

FAULKNER, Sara Ellen. 19379 7TH AVE NE 98370 #016-01-1976 L1982 FM *020 †18

FREEDMAN, Toby. ■ 98370 #005-11-1948 L1988 IM AM *071 †20,70

HADLEY, Karl David. 19245 7TH AVE NE 98370 #054-04-1979 L1980 FM *020 †18

HART, Anna Kristina E. 4175 NE GUNDERSON RD 98370 #035-06-1989 L1992 OTO HNS *020 †45

HAWLEY, Wendy Zeeben. 20730 BOND RD NE STE 208 98370 #054-04-1993 L1993 PD *020 †55

HENNE, Manfred. 20700 BOND RD NE 98370 #409-38-1982 L1988 R *020 †80

HILLMAN, Steven Kirk. 911 NE LIBERTY RD, POULSBO FIRE DEPARTMENT 98370 #010-02-1978 L1985 EM *020 †18,16

HOFFMAN, Mark Charles. 20730 BOND RD NE, STE 205 98370 #054-04-1997 L2000 FM *020 †18

HOGNESS, David Franklin. 19379 7TH AVE NE, POULSBO MED CTR 98370 #054-04-1981 L1984 FM *020 †18

JACKSON, Melvin Lee. 20730 BOND RD NE, ROBERT V BETHEL DO 98370 #005-16-1962 L1991 FM GP *020 †18

JUNGKEIT, Michael Carl. 20730 BOND RD NE STE 104 98370 #005-19-1990 L1995 OTO *020 †45

KINA, George. 19245 7TH AVE NE 98370 #054-04-1969 L1976 FM *020 †18

LEHMANN, Peter Michael. 19245 7TH AVE NE 98370 #010-01-1990 L1996 FM *020 †18

LONG, Edwin Thomas, II. ■ 98370 #038-40-1996 L1998 GPM *012

MATTY, Marie Elaine. 19245 7TH AVE NE 98370 #054-04-2000 L2002 FM *020 †18

MC GUIRE, Terence F. ■ 98370 #030-06-1953 L1993 P AM *020 †75

MESSETT, Raleigh Clemens. ■ 98370 #054-04-1967 L1968 FM OS *071 †18

MORRISON, Kenneth James. ■ 98370 #061-01-1954 L1962 GP *071

MORTON, Karen Ann. ■ 98370 #035-45-1986 L1990 IM *075

OMORCHOE, David James. 20669 BOND RD NE STE 100 98370 #016-43-1987 L1992 OPH *020 †35

PLUMER, Michael Hart. 18550 NOLL RD NE 98370 #016-02-1970 L1982 AN *020 †05

POWER, Charles Wesley. 20730 BOND RD NE, NORTH KITSAP MEDICAL CENTE 98370 #004-01-1982 L1989 FM *020 †18

RASMUSSEN, Eric David. ■ 98370 #005-11-1990 L2005 IM *020 †20

REICHLEY, Stephen Chas. 19245 7TH AVE NE 98370 #038-40-1975 L1980 FM *020 †18
REINHART, Ronald Wm. 19365 7TH AVE NE, STE 102 98370 #017-20-1965 L1978 D IM *020 †20
SCHROFF, Charles Lee. ■ 98370 #019-02-1957 L1959 FM *071 †18
SHERMAN, Vance Eugene. 20215 NORRLAND LANE NE 98370 #007-02-1991 L1995 P *020 †75
SHLIFER, Susan Jalland. 19640 10TH AVE NE 98370 #010-02-1978 L1997 FM *020 †18
STANTON, Frank Anthony. 17300 VIKING WAY NW 98370 #005-06-1965 L1989 CHP P *062 †75
STRIDE, Garrick Lon. ■ 98370 #005-11-1999 L2000 EM AM *020 †16
SUDDUTH, Lynn Susanne. 17347 7TH AVE NE 98370 #028-34-1984 L1987 D *020 †55,15
SWANSON, Virginia E. 17791 FJORD DR NE, STE H-110 98370 #040-02-1985 L2002 PM *020 †60
SWARTZ, Linda Diane. 20730 BOND RD NE, STE 201 98370 #039-01-1986 L1990 N *020
TEGENFELDT, Edwin Gustaf. 19045 STATE HIGHWAY 305 NE, STE 180 98370 #026-04-1964 L1991 GP *020 †85
THOMAS, Eric Lawrence. ■ 98370 #051-07-1997 L2006 GS *020 †85
TOTH, William Vincent. 19379 7TH AVE NE, POULSBO MEDICAL CENTER 98370 #010-01-1979 L1983 FM *020 †18
TRACY, Patrick Lloyd. 19245 7TH AVE NE 98370 #054-04-1971 L1979 FM *020 †18
WONG, Jacqueline Wheeling. 20696 BOND RD NE 98370 #035-06-1990 L2001 OPH *020 †35
ZAMFIRESCU, Peter Leon. ■ 98370 #041-09-1984 L1997 PUD *020 †20

PROSSER – BENTON

ABACAN, Gloria Crese B. 740 MEMORIAL ST 99350 #748-01-1990 L2000 IM *020 †20
CLARK, James Abram, II. 723 MEMORIAL ST 99350 #005-15-1981 L1992 DR *020 †80
FIELD, Carl Burroughs. 821 MEMORIAL ST, STE 1 99350 #054-04-1977 L1978 FM *020 †18
LANE, Edward Michael. 821 MEMORIAL ST 99350 #028-34-1989 L1989 FM *020 †18
MAY, Clarence B, II. 723 MEMORIAL ST 99350 #054-04-1983 L1988 DR *020 †80
PRAKASH, Shimoga Ramaiah. ■ 99350 #495-99-1985 L2006 FM *020 †18
RANKIN, Timothy Day. 820 MEMORIAL ST 99350 #019-02-1991 L2005 ORS *020 †40
SCHREIBER, Paul E. 723 MEMORIAL ST 99350 #025-07-1969 L2001 GS *020 †85
SLATER, Wm Christopher. 820 MEMORIAL ST, STE 1 99350 #051-04-1978 L2005 OBG *020 †30
SONNICHSEN, Ben Wm. 821 MEMORIAL ST, VALLEY FAMILY MEDICINE 99350 #054-04-1975 L1979 FM *020 †18
SUNDERLAND, Steven John. 723 MEMORIAL ST 99350 #028-34-1984 L2006 R *020 †80
THOMAS, Richard Llewelyn. ■ 99350 #005-06-1963 L1964 PD GP *071
VINCI, Francesco. ■ 99350 #561-17-1996 L2004 IM *020
WATSON, Brooks, II. 723 MEMORIAL ST 99350 #016-11-1998 L2003 IM *020 †20
WELCH, Lon Sidney, Jr. 723 MEMORIAL ST 99350 #037-01-1995 L1999 DR *020 †80
YARGER, Richard John. 723 MEMORIAL ST 99350 #035-20-1974 L1981 GS VS *020 †85

PULLMAN – WHITMAN

ADAMS, Betty Kathleen. WSU STUDENT HLTH SERV 99164 #054-04-1956 L1957 GP P *071
ALTO, Merry Margaret. 1125 SE WASHINGTON ST 99163 #054-04-1990 L1990 EM *020
ARRIZABALAGA, Aria E. PO BOX 642302, 1125 WASHINGTON AVE 99164 #024-01-1998 L2006 FM *020 †18
BEIRNE, Sandra Denise. 1630 NE VALLEY RD # A-1 99163 #054-04-2005 PD *012
BERGMANN, Stephen Carl. 835 SE BISHOP BLVD, PULLMAN REGIONAL HOSPITAL 99163 #026-04-1972 L1973 PD *020 †55,16
BOWMAN, Bradley Paul. 835 SE BISHOP BLVD, STE 200 99163 #038-44-2002 L2005 FM *020 †18
BOWMAN, Jaime Kyilie. 825 SE BISHOP BLVD, STE 200 99163 #038-44-2002 L2005 FM *020 †18
BOYER, Lennis Kay. 1205 SE PROFESSINL ML BLVD, MALL BLVD 99163 #046-01-1984 L1990 PD *020 †55
BROWN, Larry Eldon. 139 N GRAND AVE, STE 3 99163 #016-43-1980 L1997 EM FM *020 †18,16
CAGGIANO, Richard Michael. 835 SE BISHOP BLVD, PULLMAN REGIONAL HOSPITAL 99163 #050-02-1978 L1998 EM IM *020 †20,16
CANNON, Lisa Marie. ■ 99163 #035-45-2008 *012
CONLEY, Becky Jo. 340 NE MAPLE ST 99163 #054-04-1991 L1995 P *020 †75
COX, Steven Joe. 1125 SE WASHINGTON ST 99163 #040-02-1972 L1973 GP UCM *020
DEAN, Stacey Richard. 1050 N GRAND AVE, GRAND AVENUE MEDICAL, P.S. 99163 #007-02-1975 L1979 IM *071
DUFFY, James Ora. ■ 99163 #017-20-1969 L1972 GP *071
EMTMAN, Richard A. 915 NE VALLEY RD, PULLMAN FAMILY MEDICINE 99163 #054-04-1981 L1982 FM *020 †18
FEARN, Linda Helen. WASHINGTON STATE UNIVERSIT, HEALTH AND WELLNESS SERVIC 99164 #054-04-1983 L1994 IM *020 †20 ‡
FREDERICKS, Sally Jo O. 1125 SE WASHINGTON ST 99163 #054-04-1959 L1961 P *071
GALICH, Richard. 825 SE BISHOP BLVD STE 6 99163 #016-43-1964 L1966 OTO FPS *020 †45
GEHEB, Karen Leona. 825 SE BISHOP BLVD, STE 200 99163 #048-02-1996 L1999 IM *020 †20
GILPATRICK, Thomas S. 1125 NW NYE ST 99163 #054-04-1953 L1959 GYN *071 †30
GUIDA, Kimberley Frances. 915 NE VALLEY RD, PULLMAN FAMILY MEDICINE 99163 #008-02-1995 L1997 FM *020 †18
HALL, Stephen Prince. 825 SE BISHOP BLVD, STE 200 99163 #028-34-1993 L1997 FM *020 †18
HAMMOND, Jennifer Smith. ■ 99163 #026-08-1977 L1988 AN GP *020 †05
HILL, Andrew B. 600 SE JAMAR ST 99163 #067-01-1986 GS *020 †85
HORSTKAMP, Aurora. ■ 99163 #056-05-1992 L1995 FM *020 †18
HUBERTY, John Richard. 1205 SE PROFESSINL ML BLVD 99163 #026-01-1964 L1972 GYN *020 †30
HUNT, Martha Kaye. 1125 NE WASHINGTON- POB 64, HEALTH WELLNESS SERVICE WS 99164 #016-45-1980 L1985 PD *020 †55
JACOBS, Cindy Ann. TERRACE PARK NO 52 99163 #054-04-1989 *100
KAPLAN, Elliott Abner. ■ 99163 #016-11-1943 L1945 IM *071 †20
KEIZUR, John Jay. 825 SE BISHOP BLVD STE 101 99163 #028-34-1987 L1996 U *020 †95
LEFF, Wenzel Albert. 1205 SE PROFESSINL ML BLVD 99163 #028-02-1959 L1965 IM *071
MARTINEZ, Fredy Edmundo. WASHINGTON STATE UNIV, PULLMAN MEMORIAL HOSPITAL 99164 #341-01-1967 L1977 GP N *071
MELINA, Carl Mark. 835 SE BISHOP BLVD 99163 #038-40-1976 L1986 EM FM *020 †18
MOODY, Timothy John. 825 SE BISHOP BLVD, STE 200 99163 #018-03-1983 L1987 GP *020 †70
MURPHY, Cornelius Michael. 1205 SE PROFESSINL ML BLVD 99163 #020-12-1968 L1979 GS *071 †85

PERINO, Lloyd Edwin. 825 SE BISHOP BLVD STE 200 99163 #016-02-1981 L1986 GE IM *020 †20
PHELPS, Harold Dean. ■ 99163 #048-12-1954 L1966 DR *072
RADAKOVICH, Jeffrey Brian. 1125 SE WASHINGTON ST, WSU HEALTH & WELLNESS SERV 99163 #048-04-1988 L1998 FM FSM *020 †18
RODRIQUEZ, Gerardo R. 835 SE BISHOP BLVD 99163 #048-02-1996 L1999 EM *020 †16
SATO, Kenneth K. 1045 N GRAND AVE 99163 #030-05-1953 L1957 FM *071
SHORT, Vicki L. 915 NE VALLEY RD, PULLMAN FAMILY MEDICINE 99163 #048-04-1988 L1998 FM *020 †18
SIMPSON, Dennis Leroy. 825 SE BISHOP BLVD, STE 200 99163 #019-02-1976 L1982 IM EM *020 †20
SPADY, Robert Neal. 825 SE BISHOP BLVD, STE 901 99163 #005-12-1985 L1995 IM *020 †20
SPENCER, David Neil. ■ 99163 #054-04-1970 L1971 FM *071 †18
STOIANOFF, John Roger. 1190 SE BISHOP BLVD 99163 #040-02-1971 L1987 GS *020 †85
STREHLER, Don Allen. ■ 99163 #041-09-1958 L1959 PD *071 †55
TINGSTAD, Edwin Michael. 825 SE BISHOP BLVD, STE 120 99163 #054-04-1993 L1999 ORS *020 †40
TRINH, Huong Ai. 1205 SE PROFESSINL ML BLVD, STE 102 99163 #048-02-1999 L2003 OBG *020
ULLRICH, Nathan Fe. 825 SE BISHOP BLVD STE 101 99163 #054-04-1999 L2005 U *020 †95
VAN EATON, Gloria. ■ 99163 #054-04-2008 *012
VISGER, Cherish Lynn. ■ 99163 #038-44-1998 L2000 PD *020
WRIGHT, Alfred Morgan. 1250 SE BISHOP BLVD, STE H 99163 #041-14-1976 L1989 PTH *020 †50
WRIGHT, Bruce Robt. WASHINGTON STATE UNIVERSIT, HEALTH AND WELLNESS CENTER 99164 #049-01-1990 L1994 P *020
YODER, Hubert Howard. ■ 99163 #869-01-1964 L1975 PTH CLP *020 †50

PUYALLUP – PIERCE

AARO, Kenith. 407 14TH AVE SE, GOOD SAMARITAN HOSP 98372 #035-46-1991 L1993 IM *020 †20
ACHETT, George Varkey. 1706 S MERIDIAN STE 120 98371 #016-11-2000 L2005 PD *020 †55
ADAMS, Wendall Wm. 3801 5TH ST SE, STE 120 98374 #038-06-1979 L1991 ORS *020 †40
AGUNBIADE, Sabrina T. 10217 125TH ST CT E, FL 3 98374 #054-04-1993 L1996 FM *020 †18
AHMED, Sheela Yadav. 702 23RD AVE SE 98372 #495-15-1988 L2007 IM *020 †20
ALLAN, Nicholas Norman. ■ 98371 #023-12-2006 L2008 EM *012
ALSTON, Robert Michael. 11019 CANYON RD E, STE A 98373 #054-04-1974 L1975 FM *020 †18
ANDERSEN, Clare Zeno. 11212 SUNRISE BLVD E 98374 #035-45-1974 L1984 DR GP *020 †80
ARANA-DOMONDON, Ladie C D. 800 S MERIDIAN, STE A 98371 #748-01-1984 L1996 * *020 †20
ARTHUR, Walter Martin. 110 W MEEKER 98371 #030-05-1962 L1963 GP OS *071
AUSTIN, George David. 407 14TH AVE SE 98372 #056-05-1980 L1981 PTH *020 †20,50
AVERSA, Marc Leo. 3908 10TH ST SE, STE 200 98374 #043-01-1996 L1998 FM *020 †18
BAHN, Elizabeth Louise. 407 14TH AVE SE, PHYSICIANS PLLC 98372 #056-05-2001 L2004 EM *020 †16
BALL, Vincent Lee. ■ 98373 #047-20-2005 L2006 EM *012
BANISTER, Holli Sue. 11019 CANYON RD E, STE A 98373 #051-07-2000 L2002 FM *020 †18
BENFANTI, Paul Lawrence. ■ 98373 #023-12-1990 L2001 ORS *020 †40
BENNETT, Randall Paul. 104 27TH AVE SE 98374 #038-40-1982 L1985 OTO HNS *020 †45
BERGMAN, Kenneth Sam. 400 15TH AVE SE, STE A 98372 #005-14-1990 L1992 RO *020 †80
BILLING, Paul Michael. 1706 S MERIDIAN STE 120 98371 #010-01-1974 L2004 EM *071
BJARKE, Erik Nels. 11212 SUNRISE BLVD E 98374 #005-12-1987 L1992 DR IM *020 †80
BLACKBURN, Darin Gene. 11102 SUNRISE BLVD E, STE 101 98374 #007-02-1999 L2001 FM OBS *020 †18
BLACKBURN, Michael G. 201 15TH AVE SW, STE C 98371 #016-01-1980 L1981 IM *020 †20
BLANKENSHIP, Barbara Ann. 11212 SUNRISE BLVD E 98374 #036-05-1995 L1999 DR *020 †80
BLANKENSHIP, Will O. 407 14TH AVE SE 98372 #048-14-2001 L2001 AN *020 †05
BOURDEAU, Lee Mason. 10209 136TH ST E 98374 #054-04-1972 L1974 EM *020
BRAR, Jaspreet S. 407 14TH AVE SE 98372 #048-15-1994 L1999 APM AN *020 †05
BREWER, Katherine H. 11102 SUNRISE BLVD E, STE 103 98374 #054-04-1996 L1999 FM *020 †18
BROOK, Michael Perry. 407 14TH AVE SE, PHYSICIANS PLLC 98372 #068-01-1984 L1990 EM *020 †16
BROWN, David Michael. 11803 101ST AVE E STE 10 98373 #016-42-1978 L1979 FM GPM *020 †18
BROWN, Michael Carlvan. 400 E PIONEER AVE, STE 204 98372 #035-01-1984 L1984 AN *020 †05
BRYANT, Mary Madeline. ■ 98374 #035-08-1977 L1996 PD *075
BRYSON, Scott A. 9921A 64TH AVENUE CT E, UNIVERSITY OF WASHINGTON S 98373 #048-13-2005 L2005 EM *012
BULLEY, Charles Kevin. 11019 CANYON RD E 98373 #054-04-1984 L1985 FM *020 †05,18
BULLEY, Wm Arthur, Jr. 324 E PIONEER AVE 98372 #054-04-1975 L1976 ORS GP *020 †40
CAMPBELL, Michael Scott. 11212 SUNRISE BLVD E 98374 #040-02-1967 L1969 R *020 †80 ‡
CARAS, William Emmanuel. 201 15TH AVE SW STE C, PUYALLUP PULMONARY CLINIC 98371 #048-14-1981 L1998 PUD IM *020 †18
CHIHOS, Tammy Jean. ■ 98375 #023-12-2005 L2007 OBG *012
CHITAIA, Nikoloz G. ■ 98375 #913-23-1994 L2004 END *020 †20
CHOI-CHINN, Katherine A. 11212 SUNRISE BLVD E 98374 #036-05-1994 L2001 DR *020 †80
CLARK, Howard Sherman. 407 14TH AVE SE 98372 #016-06-1979 L1981 AN *020 †05
COLVIN, Brenda B. ■ 98373 #028-34-1989 L1990 *020
COOLEY, Bruce Wm. 407 14TH AVE SE 98372 #054-04-1981 L1983 AN *020 †20,05
COWELL, Pamela De Graaf. 120 14TH AVE SE, STE C 98372 #012-05-1975 L1998 OBG *020 †30
CROWE, Mark Allen. 929 E MAIN, STE 210 98372 #048-02-1980 L2000 D *020 †55,15
CULL, Michael Douglas. 407 14TH AVE SE 98372 #143-03-1968 L1990 AN P *020 †75,05
CYR, Mary Eileen. 3850 S MERIDIAN 98373 #030-06-1992 L2007 FM *020 †18
DAHAN, Mazen. 120 14TH AVE SE STE A 98372 #875-02-1990 L2000 PD *020 †55
DAHLHAUSER, Keith Francis. 1703 S MERIDIAN STE 10 98371 #018-03-1990 L1994 OPH *020 †35
DANIEL, John Nirmal. 102 23RD AVE SE STE B 98372 #496-23-1993 L1999 FM *020 †18
DAVIDSON, David Alan. 11212 SUNRISE BLVD E 98374 #054-04-1989 L1998 DR *020 †80
DENTLER, Maureen Leclaire. 407 14TH AVE SE, PHYSICIANS PLLC 98372 #010-01-1986 L1991 EM *020 †16

■ = Address Information Privacy Protected

DE VERA, Alberto Caburian. ■ 98372 #748-02-1956 L1962 **PD** *071 †55

DE VITA, Edward Gregory. 205 15TH AVE SW STE C 98371 #041-07-1984 L1991 **N IM** *020 †75

DE VRIES, Donald Fred. 1011 E MAIN STE 302 98372 #025-07-1978 L1987 **NM END** *020 †20,28

DILLER, John Lewis. 610 S MERIDIAN 98371 #028-03-1969 L1974 **FM** *020

DOBBINS, Jill Marie. 11212 SUNRISE BLVD E 98374 #054-04-1991 L2000 **DR** *020 †80

DROUILLARD, Dennis Dean. 1703 S MERIDIAN STE 101, CASCADE EYE & SKIN CENTERS 98371 #041-14-1979 L1983 **OPH PS** *020 †35

DUENHOELTER, Johann H. 1706 S MERIDIAN STE 130 98371 #407-12-1963 L1979 **OBG** *071 †30

DULING, Reginald Douglas. 407 14TH AVE SE, PHYSICIANS PLLC 98372 #038-40-1995 L1998 **EM** *020 †16

DUNCAN, Stephen Fraser. 611 31ST AVE SW 98373 #017-20-1977 L1980 **FM** *020 †18

DURAN, Wayne Mark. 407 14TH AVE SE, GOOD SAMARITAN HOSP 98372 #054-04-1981 L1982 **EM FM** *020 †18,16

DURIS, Gerald Frederick. 800 S MERIDIAN STE A, PUYALLUP CLINIC, INC. 98371 #054-04-1973 L1989 **FM** *020 †18

EARNEST, Tim P. 1706 S MERIDIAN, STE 120 98371 #048-04-1993 L1995 **CHP P** *020 †75

EDSTROM, Kenneth Murray. 1420 4TH ST SE, STE B 98372 #005-12-1983 L1988 **OBG** *020 †30

EDWARDS, John Allen. ■ 98374 #023-12-1996 L2005 **FM** *020 †18

EGGE, Stephen Michael. 11019 CANYON RD E, STE A 98373 #054-04-1979 L1981 **FM** *020 †18

ELROD, Rachael Denise. 1703 S MERIDIAN, STE 101 98371 #054-04-1999 L2004 **OPH** *020 †35

ENE-STROESCU, Daniel C P. 11212 SUNRISE BLVD E, STE 201 98374 #781-01-1994 L2003 **IMG** *020 †20

ESTRADA, Joel Fausto K. 10217 125TH ST CT E, SEAMAR COMMUNITY HLTH CENT 98374 #748-01-1997 L2003 **IM** *020 †20 ‡

EUN, Paul H. 1420 4TH ST SE STE B 98372 #005-12-1983 L1994 **OBG** *020 †30

EVANS, Tanja Denise. 1706 S MERIDIAN STE 130, WOODCREEK PEDIATRICS 98371 #005-18-1999 L2004 **PD** *020 †55 ‡

FAJARDO, Renato Verano. 10209 136TH ST E 98374 #748-01-1977 L1993 **IM** *020

FATIMA, Tasbeeh. 325 E PIONEER AVE, BEHAVIORAL HEALTH 98372 #704-16-1995 L2000 **P** *020 †75

FEUCHT, Kenneth Allen. 1519 3RD ST SE, STE 230 98372 #040-02-1982 L1991 **SO GS** *020 †85

FOREST, Robert. 407 14TH AVE SE 98372 #067-06-1974 L2006 **AN** *020 †05

FOX, Barbara Jean. 1703 S MERIDIAN STE 101, CASCADE EYE & SKIN CENTERS 98371 #038-41-1979 L1980 **D** *020 †15

FOX, Leslie Passon. 1703 S MERIDIAN STE 101, CASCADE EYE & SKIN CENTERS 98371 #038-41-1978 L1979 **OPH** *020 †35

FRISTER, Sandra Janet. 1409 2ND ST SE 98372 #917-18-1968 L1976 **FM PD** *020

FROOD, Lawrence Raymond. 11212 SUNRISE BLVD E 98374 #005-12-1985 L1990 **DR VIR** *020 †80

GANDHI, Kevin Kishin. 618 S MERIDIAN STE B 98371 #016-43-1986 L1994 **UP U** *020 †95

GANT, Douglas Wm. 1824 MERIDIAN S 98371 #054-04-1974 L1978 **OBG** *020 †30

GENDRON, Blake Patrick. 407 14TH AVE SE, PHYSICIANS PLLC 98372 #023-12-1980 L1984 **EM** *020 †16

GERSTMANN, Paul E. 506 W PIONEER AVE 98371 #016-06-1952 L1953 **PD** *072 †55

GILDENHAR, Mark Richard. 2622 S MERIDIAN 98373 #038-41-1975 L1979 **OPH** *020 †35

GIVENS, Matthew David. ■ 98375 #021-05-2004 L2007 **DR** *012

GRAHAM, Martin Laren. 11212 SUNRISE BLVD E 98374 #005-02-1969 L1971 **DR** *020 †80 ‡

GRUBB, Mark Steven. 1706 MERIDIAN S, STE 130 98371 #021-06-1981 L1985 **PD** *020 †55

GRUBB, Nancy S. 3908 10TH ST SE 98374 #048-02-1990 L1990 **FM** *020 †18

GURAY, Eugenia Daileg. 800 S MERIDIAN, STE A 98371 #748-07-1985 L2003 **FM** *020 †18

GURSKI, Jennifer Lynn. ■ 98375 #021-01-2005 L2006 **U** *012

GUSTAFSON, Julie Aliina. 104 27TH AVE SE 98374 #054-04-1978 L1979 **OTO AI** *020 †45

HALL, Harriet A. ■ 98374 #054-04-1970 L1971 **FM AM** *071 †18

HAMMEN, Michael J. 407 14TH AVE SE 98372 #005-18-1991 L1993 **AN PME** *020 †05

HARPER, Thomas Warren. 407 14TH AVE SE 98372 #056-06-1994 L1998 **FM** *020 †18

HARRIS, Laurel Mermoud. 1703 S MERIDIAN STE 101, CASCADE EYE & SKIN CENTERS 98371 #012-05-1988 L1992 **OPH** *020 †35

HAVENSTRITE, Keith Austin. ■ 98374 #048-12-1994 L1995 **TS GS** *020 †85,90

HEATH, Sherburne W, Jr. 407 14TH AVE SE, GOOD SAMARITAN REHABILITAT 98372 #056-06-1945 L1947 **PM** *071 †60

HEGDE, Karkal Shwetha Sur. 16515 MERIDIAN E, STE 104A 98375 #495-98-2000 L2005 **IM** *020

HENDRIES, Jennie Gubbins. 1706 MERIDIAN S STE 120 98371 #017-20-1990 L1998 **PD** *020 †55

HERNANDEZ, Thomas Robert. 11102 SUNRISE BLVD E 98374 #005-11-1993 L1993 **PD** *020 †55

HIROTA, William Kozen. 424 29TH ST NE, TACOMA DIGESTIVE DISEASE 98372 #010-02-1990 L1999 **IM** *020 †20

HOGAN, Frances Alicia. 325 E PIONEER, HEALTHCARE 98372 #018-03-1983 L1989 **P CHP** *062

HOLLAND, Patrick Cline. 407 14TH AVE SE, GOOD SAMARITAN HOSPITAL DE 98372 #014-01-1999 L2002 **EM** *020 †16

HOPP, Duane Fredrick. 3801 5TH ST SE, STE 110 98374 #054-04-1967 L1970 **ORS** *020 †40

HUANG, Dur. 2223A S MERIDIAN 98371 #001-02-1988 L1990 **FM** *020 †18

HUANG, Lin. 1703 S MERIDIAN, STE 305 98371 #243-03-1989 L2001 **GE** *020 †20

HUGHES, William Allan. ■ 98374 #023-12-1984 L1985 **AN** *020 †05

HUNG, John C. 11212 SUNRISE BLVD E 98374 #056-06-2000 L2006 **OSM** *100

HURST, Jonathan James. 1703 S MERIDIAN, STE 305 98371 #054-04-1977 L1979 **GE** *020 †20

HUSARIK, Edward John. 1706 S MERIDIAN STE 120 98371 #054-04-1992 L1997 **PD** *020 †55

HUTNER, Edward Scott. 11212 SUNRISE BLVD E, STE 201 98374 #024-07-1974 L2005 **GS CCS** *020 †85

HUYNH, Linh Trang. 10116 116TH ST E STE 101 98373 #306-01-1995 L1999 **FM** *020 †18

HWANG, Chan S. 126 15TH ST SE 98372 #005-12-1994 L1998 **PM** *020 †60

INOUYE, Theodore Koichi. 201 15TH AVE SW, STE B 98371 #054-04-1980 L1985 **GS** *020 †85

INSALACO, Samuel Joseph. 407 14TH AVE SE 98372 #035-08-1974 L1980 **PTH** *020 †50

IP, Stanley S W. 1408 3RD ST SE, STE 100 98372 #065-01-1982 L1987 **GS CRS** *020 †85

IVERSON, Nichol Todd. 800 S MERIDIAN 98371 #054-04-1971 L1975 **IM** *020 †20

JACKSON, Michael H. 3908 10TH ST SE STE 200 98374 #019-02-1975 L1986 **FM** *071 †18

JACKSON, Stanley Martin. 105 27TH AVE SE 98374 #021-05-1973 L1976 **PS** *020 †45,65

JACOBSON, Charles David. 800 S MERIDIAN STE A 98371 #056-06-1972 L1973 **IM CCM** *020 †20

JIMENO, Victoria J. 1706 S MERIDIAN, STE 120 98371 #748-01-1984 L1995 **PD** *020 †55

JOHNSON, Erik Robert. ■ 98374 #023-12-2004 L2006 **PD** *020 †55

JOHNSON-COLT, Holly N. 1706 MERIDIAN S STE 120, WOODCREEK PEDIATRICS 98371 #032-01-1996 L1999 **PD** *020 †55

JOHNSTONE, Frederic Luke. 3801 5TH ST SE, STE 120 98374 #047-05-1982 L1986 **ORS GS** *020 †40

JOLLEY, Timothy Bernard. 1322 3RD ST SE STE 240 98372 #054-04-1971 L1976 **PD** *020

JOOSTEN, David John A. 11102 SUNRISE BLVD E STE 1 98374 #035-03-1996 L2001 **PD** *020 †55

JOSEFFER, Seth Serafin. 1519 3RD ST SE, STE 101 98372 #035-19-1999 L2005 **NS** *100

JUDISH, David Allen. 8012 112TH STRET CT E #120 98373 #047-06-1988 L1992 **PM** *020 †60

JUHLIN, Nancy Rae. 1609 S MERIDIAN, EAR NOSE THROAT AND 98371 #018-03-1985 L2003 **OTO** *020 †45

KALER, Robert Bruce. 3850 S MERIDIAN 98373 #011-02-1974 L1977 **FM OM** *020

KANG, Christopher Scott. 407 14TH AVE SE 98372 #016-06-1996 L2004 **EM** *020 †16 ‡

KARAKUS, Sule. 325 E PIONEER AVE 98372 #902-10-1985 L2003 **P** *020

KARR, Nancy Strehlow. 102 23RD AVE SE, STE A 98372 #054-04-1986 L1990 **RHU** *020 †20

KASE, Sidney. 8726 FRUITLAND AVE E 98371 #016-42-1950 L1956 **GP AS** *071

KELL, Jonathan Michael. 11212 SUNRISE BLVD E 98374 #056-05-2000 L2006 **DR** *020 †80

KEMMAN, John Frederick. 407 14TH AVE SE 98372 #016-11-1955 L1958 **FM** *071

KENNEDY, Thomas Patrick. 407 14TH AVE SE 98372 #054-04-1979 L1982 **AN CD** *020 †05

KHAN, Muhammad Bilal. 407 14TH AVE SE 98372 #704-04-1997 L2003 **IM** *020

KIERNEY, Philip Christian. 105 27TH AVE SE 98374 #005-14-1989 L1994 **PS** *020 †85,65

KIERUM, Calvin A, Jr. 1706 MERIDIAN S STE 120 98371 #048-13-1990 L1995 **PD** *020 †55

KIERUM, Stacie Reich. 1706 MERIDIAN S STE 120 98371 #048-13-1990 L1995 **PD** *020 †55

KIETZER, Glenn Julius. 10209 136TH ST E 98374 #054-04-1964 L1966 **OTO PS** *020 †45

KIM, Cholwoo Anthony. 1519 3RD ST SE STE 230 98372 #036-01-1993 L1999 **GS** *020 †85

KIM, Jessica Hee. 1703 S MERIDIAN, STE 101 98371 #023-01-1995 L2003 **D** *020 †15

KIMMEY, Michael Bryant. 424 29TH ST NE, TACOMA DIGESTIVE DISEASE 98372 #028-02-1979 L1980 **GE IM** *040 †20

KIMPEL, Thomas Guy. 1322 3RD ST SE STE 220 98372 #017-20-1983 L1987 **N** *020 †75

KING, Douglas Roy. 1519 3RD ST SE, STE 230 98372 #041-02-1984 L1985 **GS** *020 †85

KNOLL, Edward Jos. 800 S MERIDIAN, STE B 98371 #028-03-1971 L1977 **DR** *020 †80

KNOWLES, Jennifer Lynn. 3908 10TH ST SE, STE 200 98374 #054-04-1991 L1993 **FM** *020 †18

KOC, Sibel. 400 15TH AVE SE, STE D 98372 #902-07-1987 L1999 **HO** *020 †20

KODAMA, Brenda F. 1703 S MERIDIAN STE 101, CASCADE EYE & SKIN CENTERS 98371 #014-01-1986 L1993 **D IM** *020 †15

KOZMINSKI, Matthew. ■ 98374 #041-78-2005, ▲ L2006 **N** *012

KRABBE, Marjorie E. 16515 MERIDIAN E STE 100A 98375 #005-19-1994 L1996 **FM OBS** *020 †18

KRASNOKUTSKY, Michael V. 12623 MERIDIAN E STE A1, SOUND MEDICAL IMAGING 98373 #023-12-2000 L2002 **RNR** *100 †80

KREINBROOK, Suzanne Boyer. ■ 98374 #035-08-1964 L1965 **P** *071

KRONLUND, Scott Frederick. 407 14TH AVE SE 98372 #054-04-1983 L1986 **FM** *020 †18

KWON, Peter Soonki. 1701 3RD ST SE, STE 201 98372 #026-04-1994 L1999 **N** *020 †75

LAMBERT, Bret. 407 14TH AVE SE, PHYSICIANS PLLC 98372 #005-14-1984 L1992 **EM** *020 †16

LAUREN, Kenneth Boyd. 10209 136TH ST E 98374 #005-12-1972 L1973 **FM** *020

LAZARUS, Marlene Loris. 1408 3RD ST SE 98372 #016-01-1981 L1994 **CD IM** *020

LEE, Christine Jeesu. 407 14TH AVE SE 98372 #005-12-2003 L2007 **AN** *020

LIAO, Xinsheng. 1519 3RD ST SE STE 2 98372 #243-70-1984 L1998 **ON IM** *020 †20

LIESEMER, Eleane Beadle. ■ 98375 #023-12-2005 L2007 **PD** *012

LIESEMER, Kirk N. ■ 98375 #023-12-2005 L2007 **PD** *012

LINDBLAD, Randolph Myron. 2622 S MERIDIAN 98373 #016-06-1965 L1969 **OPH** *020 †35

LOGERFO, Peter Edward. 11025 CANYON RD E, STE A 98373 #054-04-1995 L1998 **FM** *020 †18

LOVEZZOLA, Michael Martin. ■ 98371 #024-07-1947 L1956 **GS** *071 †85

LURIE, Hugh James. 325 E PIONEER, SERVICES 98372 #008-01-1961 L1968 **P CHP** *020 †75

LUX, Peter Mark. 8012 112TH STREET CT E #12 98373 #016-01-2001 L2002 **PM** *020 †60

MA, Kelvin Kam-Wah. 201 15TH AVE SW STE D 98371 #067-01-1983 L1984 **N** *020 †75

MAHAJAN, Mohit Kumar. 11102 SUNRISE BLVD E, STE 102 98374 #496-26-1999 L2004 **FM** *100 †18

MAIORCA, John Patrick. 10209 136TH ST E 98374 #039-01-1976 L1998 **OPH** *020

MAJORS, James Travis. 1408 3RD ST SE, STE 150 98372 #045-01-1983 L2003 **OBG IM** *020 †30

MANN, Thomas Nelson. 702 23RD AVE SE 98372 #035-45-1983 L1991 **PUD IM** *020 †20

MANNING, Kathleen M. 1322 3RD ST SE STE 220 98372 #024-05-1996 L2004 **GS** *020 †85

MARSH, Robert Edward. 1519 3RD ST SE, STE 230 98372 #040-02-1995 L2001 **GS** *020 †85

MARSH, William Gardner. 11019 CANYON RD E, STE A 98373 #040-02-1972 L1978 **FM** *020 †18

MARTIN, Dan Henry. 11212 SUNRISE BLVD E 98374 #024-07-1979 L1989 **NR DR** *020 †80

MASI, Janice Iannone. ■ 98374 #726-01-1977 L1986 *075

MC ALEXANDER, Robert Alan. 120 14TH AVE SE 98372 #054-04-1958 L1959 **VS TS** *071 †85

MC ALLISTER, Debra Lynne. 1408 3RD ST SE, STE 200 98372 #028-34-1987 L1997 **OBG** *020 †30

MC DONALD, Maryanne B. 702 23RD AVE SE 98372 #016-43-1982 L1983 **NEP CCM** *020 †20

MC DONALD, Susan E. 3908 10TH ST SE, STE 200 98374 #054-04-1994 L1996 **FM** *020 †18

MC KAY, Patricia Ann. ■ 98374 #023-12-1999 L2006 **IM** *020 †20

MC PHEE, Megan Dow. ■ 98374 #051-07-2004 L2006 **OBG** *012

MEASE, Alan Dudley. ■ 98371 #028-03-1973 L1980 **NPM PD** *020 †55

MEBUST, Kimberly Anne. 1420 4TH ST SE, NEUROLOGY & NEUROSURGERY 98372 #008-02-1990 L1996 **N SME** *020 †75

MEDINA, Jorge Manuel. 11212 SUNRISE BLVD E 98374 #042-03-1996 L2006 **DR** *020 †80

MEMON, Aftab Ahmad. 407 14TH AVE SE, PHYSICIANS 98372 #704-02-1995 L2003 **IMG** *020

MEYERS, Glen Carl. 407 14TH AVE SE, INTERNAL MEDICINE ASSOC 98372 #005-14-1992 L2004 **IM** *020 †20

MICHAELSON, Julius, Jr. 1703 S MERIDIAN, STE 301 98371 #001-02-1977 L1994 **OBG** *020 †30

MIKKELSON, Michael Wm. 800 MERIDIAN ST S 98371 #056-06-1966 L1968 **R** *071 †80

MILLER, Seth Leland. ■ 98375 #016-42-2007 **GS** *012

MILLER, Warren Eugene. 11019 CANYON RD E, STE A 98373 #017-20-1976 L1979 **FM** *020 †18

MITCHELL, Jonathan C. 11102 SUNRISE BLVD E, STE 110 98374 #038-43-1998 L2002 **OBG** *020 †30

MOHIT, Abdi Alex. 205 15TH AVE SW, STE D 98371 #005-06-1999 L1999 **NS** *030

MOMAH, Dennis. 3850 MERIDIAN ST S 98373 #690-06-1982 L2000 **IM** *020 †20

MOORE, Daniel John. 400 15TH AVE SE, STE D 98372 #048-12-1998 L2005 **ON HEM** *020 †20

MORCOS, Peter Nabil. ■ 98371 #054-04-2007 L2007 **IM** *012

MORRIS, Ronald R. 407 14TH AVE SE 98372 #054-04-1980 L1983 **FM** *030 †18

MOSES, De Maurice. 336 2ND ST SE, THE CHILDREN'S CLINIC 98372 #038-06-1959 L1964 **PD AS** *071 †55

MOTT, Donald Harold. 407 14TH AVE SE 98372 #054-04-1966 L1973 **ORS** *030 †40

■ = Address Information Privacy Protected

MOUSSAN, Oussama Hanna. 1703 S MERIDIAN, STE 305 98371 #875-02-1982 L1995 **GE** *020 †50,20

MULHALL, Brian Patrick. 424 29TH ST NE, TACOMA DIGESTIVE DISEASE 98372 #028-34-1996 L1998 **GE** *020 †20

NAM, Charles Chan. 201 15TH AVE SW, STE A 98371 #054-04-1992 L1995 **IM** *020 †20

NEHLS, Daniel Gene. 205 15TH AVE SW, STE D 98371 #016-06-1980 L1993 **NS** *020 †25

NESSAN, Vernon Johnnie. 702 23RD AVE SE 98372 #039-01-1971 L1974 **PUD IM** *020 †20

NEUHALFEN, Elizabeth Ann. 407 14TH AVE SE 98372 #030-05-1984 L1997 **FM OBS** *020 †18

NGUYEN, Ngoc Xuan. 515 27TH AVE S 98374 #054-04-1999 L2002 **FM** *020 †18

NOH, Kyung Whan. 424 29TH ST NE, TACOMA DIGESTIVE DISEASE 98372 #033-05-2000 L2005 **GE** *020 †20

NOVIA, Michael Vincent. 515 27TH AVE SW 98371 #041-07-1980 L2001 **PS OTO** *020 †45,65

NUTTER, Paul Barnes. 8012 112TH STREET CT E, STE 120 98373 #054-04-1982 L1983 **PM** *020 †60

OBRYANT, Larry Kenneth. 407 14TH AVE SE 98372 #023-12-1989 L2000 **PTH** *020 †50

OH, Sangik. 424 29TH ST NE, TACOMA DIGESTIVE DISEASE 98372 #024-07-1995 L2004 **GE** *020 †20

OSBORNE, Robt Wesley, Jr. 220 15TH AVE SE, STE C 98372 #010-01-1975 L1981 **VS GS** *020 †85

OST, Kenneth Bryan. 407 14TH AVE SE 98372 #056-06-1986 L1992 **AN** *020 †05

OST, Michelle Hogan. 319 5TH ST SW 98371 #056-06-1986 L1992 **PD** *020 †55 ‡

OSTENSON, Lynn Carol. 407 14TH AVE SE, GOOD SAMARITAN HOSPITAL 98372 #054-04-1974 L1977 **IM** *020 †20

OUELLET, Lyne M. 407 14TH AVE SE, PHYSICIANS PLLC 98372 #067-03-1984 L1990 **EM** *020 †16

OVERFIELD, William Dale. 1701 3RD ST SE, STE 201 98372 #035-03-1971 L1972 **N** *020 †75

PEARSON, Alan David. 11212 SUNRISE BLVD E 98374 #023-12-1984 L2002 **DR** *020 †18,80

PEARSON, Michael Lane. 12904 94TH AVE E 98373 #010-01-1972 L1975 **PD** *020 †55

PENALVER, Ovidio Moises. 319 5TH ST SW 98371 #005-06-1975 L1975 **PD** *020 †55

PETERS, Werner H. 407 14TH AVE SE 98372 #016-43-1983 L1987 **AN** *020 †05

PETRIN, James Henri. 929 E MAIN, STE 210 98372 #054-04-1994 L1998 **D** *020 †15

PHILBRICK, Jack Howard. 1519 3RD ST SE, STE 210 98372 #048-12-1968 L1978 **U** *020 †95

PIENIAK, Stephen John. 407 14TH AVE SE, PHYSICIANS PLLC 98372 #038-40-1996 L1998 **EM** *020 †16

PILLAI, Sunanda. 407 14TH AVE SE 98372 #495-85-1987 L2000 **AN** *020 †05

PLASKON, Lora Ann. 407 14TH AVE SE 98372 #017-20-1995 L2000 **U** *020 †95

PLISKOW, Raymond Joel. 11212 SUNRISE BLVD E 98374 #025-01-1964 L1970 **DR VIR** *020 †80

POLLARD, William S, III. 1910 S MERIDIAN ST S 98371 #048-04-1980 L1987 **PD FM** *020 †55

POWERS, Joseph F. ■ 98374 #040-02-1953 L1979 **IM** *071

PRATT, Hugh Miles. 407 14TH AVE SE 98372 #041-12-2000 L2006 **AN** *020

PUIG, Christine M. 1609 S MERIDIAN, EAR NOSE THROAT AND 98371 #048-15-1993 L2000 **OTO FPS** *020 †45

PULLEN, Edward Allen. 3908 10TH ST SE, STE 200 98374 #024-07-1980 L1987 **FM** *020 †18

PUTTLER, Eric Geoffrey. ■ 98374 #023-12-1994 L2006 **ORS** *020 †40

PUZON, Romeo Sison. 10209 136TH ST E 98374 #748-01-1965 L1996 **PFP** *071

RANCE, Charles Wm. 11012 CANYON RD E, STE 8 98373 #035-20-1971 L1978 **OPH** *020 †35

RAUSCH, Michael William. 1703 S MERIDIAN, STE 101 98371 #007-02-1997 L2001 **OPH** *020 †35

REGALADO, Michael John. 407 14TH AVE SE, PHYSICIANS PLLC 98372 #005-11-1978 L1979 **IM** *020 †20,16

REINBOLD-CARTER, Alison J. 11212 SUNRISE BLVD E 98374 #005-06-1986 L1992 **DR IM** *020 †80

REINERTSON, Thomas E. 1703 S MERIDIAN, STE 305 98371 #025-12-1984 L1991 **GE IM** *020 †20,55

REITZUG, Heinrich C. 1706 MERIDIAN S STE 120 98371 #017-20-1972 L1978 **PD** *020 †55

RENN, John Stewart, II. 10317 122ND ST E, STE A 98374 #041-13-1964 L1968 **ORS OS** *071 †40

RINKER, William Robt. 407 14TH AVE SE 98372 #016-42-1975 L1979 **AN** *020 †05

ROBINSON, Nanette G. 400 15TH AVE SE, STE D 98372 #067-01-1990 L1993 **HEM** *020 †20

ROBSON, Douglas Ewart. 331 S MERIDIAN 98371 #005-14-1967 L1978 **FM** *020 †18

ROMIG, Bruce D. 520 14TH AVE SE 98372 #010-01-1971 L1975 **OBG** *020 †30

ROSE, Andrea Lee. 400 15TH AVE SE 98372 #024-07-1993 L1994 **IM** *020 †20

ROUSE, Robert M. 407 14TH AVE SE 98372 #024-07-1953 L1975 **GS AM** *071 †85

RUDOLPH, James Lawrence. 407 14TH AVE SE, GOOD SAMARITAN HOSPITAL 98372 #035-01-1993 L2001 **IM** *020

RUSSELL, Don R. 1910 MERIDIAN ST S STE A 98371 #018-75-1976, ▲ L1978 **PD NPM** *020 †55

RUSSELL, John Chas. 1519 3RD ST SE, STE 210 98372 #054-04-1982 L1990 **U** *020 †95

RYAN, Traci D. 1701 3RD ST SE, STE 201 98372 #048-04-1993 L2005 **N** *020 †75

SCHNEIDER, Oliver J. 407 14TH AVE SE 98372 #060-01-1977 L1994 **FM AN** *020

SERRA, Alexander Duane. 12623 MERIDIAN E, STE A1 98373 #035-20-1991 L1997 **DR** *020 †80

SHAH, Amol Jagdish. 407 14TH AVE SE, PHYSICIANS PLLC 98372 #041-07-1996 L2000 **EM** *020 †16

SHIELDS, Jerry Richard. 1703 S MERIDIAN STE 101, CASCADE EYE AND SKIN CENTE 98371 #012-01-1997 L2001 **OPH** *020 †35

SHIGEMITSU, Helen H. 11212 SUNRISE BLVD E 98374 #035-19-1999 L2005 **DR** *020 †80

SHIM, Uhngkyurob. 222 15TH AVE SE 98372 #054-04-1994 L2001 **DR** *020 †80

SHONNARD, Neal Herman. 3801 5TH ST SE, STE 120 98374 #031-01-1984 L1990 **ORS** *020 †40

SHOOK, David Earl. 11212 SUNRISE BLVD E 98374 #030-06-1998 L2004 **DR** *020 †80

SHORT, Matthew William. ■ 98374 #054-04-2000 L2001 **FM** *020 †18

SIMPER, Novae Bernadette. ■ 98372 #038-40-2005 L2006 **PTH** *012

SIPES, Bobbie Stephens. 407 14TH AVE SE, PHYSICIANS PLLC 98372 #049-01-1989 L1989 **EM** *020 †16

SMATHERS, Doug Henry. 16515 MERIDIAN E, STE 104A 98375 #047-07-1998 L2001 **FM** *020 †18

SMITH, Maureen Suzanne. 407 14TH AVE SE, PHYSICIANS PLLC 98372 #048-02-1997 L2000 **EM** *020 †16

SMITH, Stirling Howard. 1609 MERIDIAN S 98371 #025-01-1975 L1980 **OTO** *071

SNODGRASS, Cecil Eugene. 1409 2ND ST SE 98372 #054-04-1975 L1976 **EM** *020 †16

SONG, Sam Hwa. 1408 3RD ST SE, STE 200 98372 #054-04-1996 L2000 **OBG** *020 †30

SORUM, Randy Dean. 400 15TH AVE SE, STE A 98372 #046-01-1993 L1997 **RO** *020 †80

STEEDMAN, John Thos, Jr. 3801 5TH ST SE, STE 120 98374 #023-07-1989 L1997 **ORS** *020 †40

STEINITZ, Edgar Samuel. 324 E PIONEER, ELECTRODIAGNOSIS & REHAB 98372 #038-41-1978 L1979 **PM PMM** *030 †60 ‡

STEVENSON, Patrice Noel. 8012 112TH STREET CT E, STE 120 98373 #054-04-1982 L1984 **PM SCI** *020 †60

STONE, Laszlo Sztonak. 10209 136TH ST E 98374 #473-01-1975 L2004 **GP CN** *020

STOUT, Sean Stuart. 3908 10TH ST SE, STE 200 98374 #049-01-1996 L2003 **FM** *020 †18

STRAIT, Gail Burton. 1322 3RD ST SE, STE 330 CARDIAC STUDY CENT 98372 #054-04-1964 L1967 **CD IM** *071 †20

SYMONDS, James Kraft. 610 S MERIDIAN 98371 #054-04-1967 L1968 **GP** *071

TAGGART, Kevin William. 3908 10TH ST SE 98374 #005-14-1996 L1998 **FM** *020 †18

TANNER, Korina Schmidt. 3908 10TH ST SE, STE 200 98374 #030-06-1997 L1999 **FM** *020 †18

TAVAKOLI, Jahan. 407 14TH AVE SE 98372 #305-01-2002 L2006 **IM** *020 †20

TAYLOR, John Scott. 407 14TH AVE SE, C/O MEDICAL STAFF OFFICE 98372 #051-04-1996 L2007 **EM** *020 †16

TAYLOR, John Wm. 407 14TH AVE SE, PHYSICIANS PLLC 98372 #024-01-1970 L1971 **PD GPM** *020 †70,55

THOMAS, Retty Rachel. 11102 SUNRISE BLVD E, STE 102 98374 #305-01-2001 L2004 **IM** *020

THOMPSON, Andrew Mark. 16515 MERIDIAN E STE 100A, GSFM AT SOUTH HILL 98375 #004-01-1976 L1996 **OS FM** *020 †18

THURMAN, Michelle M. 16515 MERIDIAN E STE 104A 98375 #005-19-2000 L2003 **FM** *020 †18

TOMSKI, Mark Andrew. 205 15TH AVE SW STE B 98371 #056-06-1984 L1989 **PM PMM** *020 †60

TRICE, Kevin Kernan. 702 23RD AVE SE 98372 #020-02-2001 L2007 **PCC** *020 †20

TSOI, Andrew Man-Kuen. 10209 136TH ST E 98374 #054-04-1965 L1966 **GP** *030

TSUCHIDA, Amy Miyoko. 424 29TH ST NE, TACOMA DIGESTIVE DISEASE 98372 #023-12-1980 L1991 **GE IM** *020 †20

UTT, Terrill Robt. 11025 CANYON RD E, STE C 98373 #005-12-1980 L1985 **FM** *020 †18

VANBERGEYK, Anthony. 3801 5TH ST SE, STE 120 98374 #061-01-1996 L2005 **DR** *020

VAN PATTER, Viola S. ■ 98375 #030-06-1943 L1963 **CHP P** *071

VAUGHT, Charles Robt. ■ 98371 #030-06-1948 L1950 **OS GP** *071

VELEZ, Marilu Lourdes. 1706 MERIDIAN S, WOODCREEK PEDIATRICS 98371 #042-02-1997 L2006 **PD** *020 †55

VELMERE, Lolita Ingrida. ■ 98374 #913-16-1966 L1989 **P** *020

VINIARSKI, Angella Andrew. 1706 MERIDIAN S STE 120, WOODCREEK HEALTHCARE 98371 #913-36-1989 L2004 **PD** *020 †55

VINING, Suzanne S. 1706 S MERIDIAN STE 120 98371 #036-01-1999 L2002 **PD** *020 †55

WAFFLE, Clark Matthew. 407 14TH AVE SE, PHYSICIANS PLLC 98372 #054-04-1978 L1984 **EM IM** *020 †20,16

WAHEED, Umar. ■ 98372 #704-21-2001 L2004 **IM** *020 †20

WANG, Lester Po-Yang. 1519 3RD ST SE, STE 210 98372 #028-46-1988 L1998 **U** *020 †95

WANG, Zhuowei. 702 23RD AVE SE 98372 #243-58-1984 L2006 **NEP** *100 †20 ‡

WEISSMAN, Christopher Ala. ■ 98375 #041-13-2005 L2006 **FM** *020

WHITE, Lawrence Joseph. 2622 S MERIDIAN 98373 #056-05-1978 L1981 **OPH** *020 †35

WHITEMARSH, Bryan Donald. 16515 MERIDIAN E STE 104A, GOOD SAMARITAN FAMILY MEDI 98375 #054-04-2001 L2004 **FM** *020 †18

WIKLUND, Dan Algot. 929 E MAIN, STE 210 98372 #054-04-1974 L1980 **D IM** *020 †20,15

WINEGAR, Robert Chas. 12303 MERIDIAN E 98373 #016-43-1970 L1972 **ORS OS** *020 †40

WINKLE, Ronald Sylvester. 407 14TH AVE SE 98372 #010-03-1965 L1969 **PM** *071

WINKLER, Mary Katherine. 325 E PIONEER, SERVICES 98372 #016-43-1993 L1998 **PYG** *020 †75

WOHNS, Richard N W. 1519 3RD ST SE STE 101 98372 #008-01-1977 L1980 **NS** *020 †25

WONG, Carrie Charlene. 407 14TH AVE SE 98372 #041-09-1997 L2001 **OBG** *020 †30

WOODARD, Larry Odell. 407 14TH AVE SE, PHYSICIANS PLLC 98372 #039-01-1982 L1990 **EM** *020 †16

WRIGHT, Alvin J. 611 31ST AVE SW 98373 #019-02-1975 L1976 **FM** *020 †18 ‡

WRIGHT, Robert Chas. 1703 S MERIDIAN 98371 #054-04-1985 L1987 **GS** *020 †85

WYMAN, James John. 11212 SUNRISE BLVD E 98374 #033-05-1991 L1999 **ORS** *020 †40

YAO-TIU, Eveline Faith. ■ 98374 #016-02-1995 L1997 **FM** *020 †18,70

YI, Im S. 611 31ST AVE SW, GROUP HEALTH - PUYALLUP ME 98373 #422-01-1999 L2006 **FM** *020 †18

YOUNG, Christopher T. 3908 10TH ST SE 98374 #054-04-1991 L1997 **FM** *020 †18

YOUNGGREN, Bradley Nels. 407 14TH AVE SE, PHYSICIANS PLLC 98372 #023-12-1999 L2004 **EM** *020 †16 ‡

YOUNGGREN, Jennifer Beth. 407 14TH AVE SE, PHYSICIANS PLLC 98372 #051-01-1997 L2002 **GS** *020 †16

YUEN, Amy Elizabeth. 1706 S MERIDIAN, STE 120 98371 #051-04-2001 L2007 **MG** *100 †55,19

ZAIDI, Arshad Ali. 325 E PIONEER AVE, GOOD SAMARITAN BEHAVIORAL 98372 #704-16-1995 L2001 **P** *020 †75

ZBARASCHUK, R Ivan. 2709 E MAIN 98372 #005-12-1976 L1979 **U** *020 †95

ZHANG, Wenjun. 400 E PIONEER AVE STE 20 98372 #243-38-1985 L2002 **AN** *020 †05

QUINCY – GRANT

NASH, Edward Wilson. 908 10TH AVE SW, COMMUNITY HEALTH CLINIC 98848 #016-06-1945 L1946 **GP EM** *020

NEWKIRK, Wallace Allyn. 908 10TH AVE SW, QUINCY VALLEY MED CTR 98848 #166-02-2002 L2004 **FM** *020 †18

PLEYTE, John Jay. 908 10TH AVE SW, QUINCY HOSPITAL 98848 #034-01-1973 L1974 **EM FM** *030 †18

ROWE, Jennifer Stice. 908 10TH AVE SW 98848 #054-04-1993 L1993 **FM** *020

SHELLY, Robert Jon. 1450 1ST AVE SW, CENTER 98848 #035-45-1993 L2002 **MPD** *020 †20,55

STANSFIELD, James Arthur. 910 10TH AVE SW 98848 #010-01-1953 L1954 **GP** *071

TRANTOW, John Wm. 908 10TH AVE SW 98848 #054-04-1955 L1956 **FM** *071

VANCE, Byron Mark. 1450 1ST AVE SW, CENTER 98848 #028-34-1994 L1999 **FM** *020 †18

RAINIER – THURSTON

BEWLEY, Geoffrey A. ■ 98576 #352-03-1958 L1964 **AN** *071 †05

RAVENSDALE – KING

GLOVER, Agnes Enyonam. ■ 98051 #016-06-1993 L2004 **OBG** *020 †30

RAYMOND - PACIFIC

VON THIELE, H Horst. 410 2ND ST, RAYMOND CLINIC 98577 #407-21-1968 L1971 **FM** *071 †18

REDMOND - KING

ABDELHAI, Eltigani Musa. ■ 98052 #848-01-1992 L2003 **IM** *020 †20 ‡
AESCHLIMAN, Gregory Don. 8299 161ST AVE NE, STE 101 98052 #054-04-1979 L1984 **FM** *020 †18
ALLEN, Jill Kay. 2700 152ND AVE NE, GROUP HEALTH HOSPITAL 98052 #054-04-1979 L1980 **PD** *020 †55
ALWAY, Sophia Chamberlin. ■ 98052 #008-01-1941 L1942 **PD** *075
ANDERSON, Robert De Mar. ■ 98053 #054-04-1963 L1964 **P** *020 †75
ANDERSON, Thomas Robert. 8301 161ST AVE NE, STE 105 98052 #010-02-2002 L2005 **EM** *020 †16
ARGENYI, Esther Eva. 2700 152ND AVE NE 98052 #409-22-1984 L2001 **DR PTH** *020 †50,28,80
ATKINS, Robert Chad. 2700 152ND AVE NE, GROUP HEALTH HOSPITAL 98052 #028-34-1999 L2003 **PHO** *020 †55
ATWATER, Richard Denny. 2700 152ND AVE NE 98052 #054-04-1976 L1981 **ORS** *020 †40
AU, Kevin Kuen Wai. 2700 152ND AVE NE 98052 #462-01-1971 L1977 **GS VS** *020 †85
BAILEY, Desiray C. 2700 152ND AVE NE 98052 #030-05-1975 L1977 **AN** *030 †05
BAKER, Stephanie Ann. 15655 NE 85TH ST STE 2, INTEGRATED HEALTH CENTER 98052 #005-18-1996 L1998 **FM** *020 †18
BARASH, Ilona Anne. ■ 98053 #005-18-2007 **TY** *012
BARTHOLOMEW, Lydia. 8299 161ST AVE NE, STE 101 98052 #005-18-1983 L1986 **FM** *030 †18
BAYLES, Robert Hugh. 8299 161ST AVE NE STE 101 98052 #019-02-1984 L1988 **FM ADM** *020 †18
BENNETT, Patrick. 2700 152ND AVE NE 98052 #539-04-1954 L1959 **AN** *020 †05
BENWARD, Roy Edward. 15937 REDMOND WAY 98052 #040-02-1971 L1991 **FM** *020 †18
BITTNER, Nathan Hj. ■ 98052 #054-04-2003 L2003 **RO** *012
BLOOM, Allan I. ■ 98052 #005-02-1950 L1979 **FM OS** *071
BLOOMQUIST, Danica Mai. 2700 152ND AVE NE, EASTSIDE HOSP 98052 #035-09-1999 L2003 **OBG** *020 †30
BOCK, Steven N. 2700 152ND AVE NE, EAST SIDE HOSPITAL 98052 #035-19-1982 L1990 **GS** *020 †85
BOLNICK, Jennifer A. 2700 152ND AVE NE 98052 #005-19-1988 L1990 **FM** *020 †18
BOSLAND, Jon Howard. 3020 W LK SAMM PKWY NE 98052 #026-04-1963 L1968 **OPH** *071 †35
BROWN, James David. 8301 161ST AVE NE, STE 105 98052 #014-01-1986 L1986 **IM** *020 †20
BROWN, Jeffrey Wm. 16315 NE 87TH ST STE B6 98052 #005-19-1985 L1985 **FM FSM** *020 †18
BRUBAKER, Jill Hathaway. 8301 161ST AVE NE STE 202 98052 #024-01-1997 L2000 **PD** *020 †55
BUSCHER, David S. 8195 166TH AVE NE, STE 101 98052 #035-06-1972 L1978 **OS A** *020 †18
CANNING, Suzanne Ballew. 7810 BROWN ST STE 203 98052 #055-01-1981 L1998 **P** *020 †75
CAPWELL, Robin R. 15446 BEL RED RD 98052 #005-02-1979 L1987 **P** *020 †75
CARLSON, Edwin Jos. 12818 NE 106TH PLACE 98052 #054-04-1965 L1968 **FM GP** *020 †18
CARLYLE, Donald A. ■ 98052 #005-02-1948 L1960 **R** *071 †80
CARR, Franklin Dean. 2700 152ND AVE NE 98052 #016-11-1974 L1977 **FM** *020 †18
CARROLL, Janet Mellissa. 2700 152ND AVE NE 98052 #054-04-1986 L1990 **OPH** *020 †35
CHANG, Michael Shihchi. 2701 156TH AVE NE, DEPT OF RADIOLOGY 98052 #005-02-2000 L2004 **AR** *020 †80
CHATTRA, James A. 22635 NE MARKETPLACE DR, STE 120 98053 #035-01-1998 L2001 **PD** *020 †55
CHENG, David Ta Ling. ■ 98053 #825-01-1969 L2002 **CD IM** *020 †18,20
CHINN, Janet So. 2700 152ND AVE NE 98052 #054-04-1981 L1982 **GE IM** *020 †20
CHINN, Karri K. 8301 161ST AVE NE, STE 105 98052 #054-04-1988 L1991 **FM** *020 †18
CHOI, Tat Kuen. 2700 152ND AVE NE, GROUP HLTH COOP OF PUGET S 98052 #016-11-1970 L1989 **GS** *020 †85
CINCIRIPINI, Grace S. 2700 152ND AVE NE 98052 #035-19-1991 L1997 **OPH** *020 †35
CLARK, John Monte. 2700 152ND AVE NE, EASTSIDE HOSPITAL AND MEDI 98052 #016-02-1976 L1977 **ORS** *020 †40
COOK, Mark. 2700 152ND AVE NE, GROUP HEALTH OB/GYN 98052 #026-04-1993 L1997 **OBG** *020 †30
CORTEZ, Enrique. 2700 152ND AVE NE, SPECIALITY CENTER 98052 #270-01-1968 L1991 **OBG** *020 †30
CULLEN, Bruce Frederick. ■ 98053 #005-14-1966 L1972 **AN** *071 †05
CZARNECKI, Michael Frank. 15446 BEL RED RD 98052 #048-12-1978 L1984 **P** *020 †75
DAVIS, Bruce Van Arsdale. 2700 152ND AVE NE 98052 #054-04-1973 L1974 **FM** *020 †18
DE MAINE, James B. 2700 152ND AVE NE 98052 #041-01-1964 L1969 **PUD A** *030 †20
DHANDA, Benu S. ■ 98052 #495-03-1988 *100
DIANA, Louis Nicholas. ■ 98052 #035-09-1942 L1959 **OPH** *071 †35
DONALDSON, James Adrian. ■ 98052 #026-04-1954 L1965 **NO** *071 †45
DORNEY, Michael Eugene. 2700 152ND AVE NE, GROUP HEALTH EASTSIDE HOSP 98052 #038-06-1991 L1993 **CD** *020 †20
DRUMMOND, William Bayard. ■ 98053 #021-01-1962 L1967 **P** *071
DUDAS, Michael Shawn. 8301 161ST AVE NE, STE 204 98052 #041-12-1994 L1996 **PD** *020 †55
DUFFY, Joseph Geo. 2700 152ND AVE NE 98052 #024-05-1976 L1976 **DR** *020 †80
EATON, Marshall Henry. 2700 152ND AVE NE 98052 #054-04-1971 L1973 **FM** *020 †18
EKRAM, Tashfeen. ■ 98053 #025-01-2008 *012
EMERSON, Ruth Therese. 2701 156TH AVE NE, EASTSIDE PRIMARY CARE 98052 #054-04-1976 L1977 **FM** *020 †18
ESPOSITO, John Michael. ■ 98053 #561-01-1959 L1961 **OBG** *071 †30
ESTVOLD, Joellen. 22603 NE INGLEWOOD HILL RD 98074 #023-01-1984 L1988 **PD** *020 †55
EULBERG, Jeanne Marie. ■ 98052 #030-05-1977 L1984 **PD** *074
FAN, Ming. 2700 152ND AVE NE, DEPT. OF ANESTHESIOLOGY 98052 #243-29-1983 L2004 **AN** *020 †05 ‡
FEHER, Thomas Louis. 15446 BEL RED RD, STE B1 98052 #035-03-1964 L1970 **OS N** *050 †75
FESSENDEN, Ronald Eugene. 15937 REDMOND WAY 98052 #019-02-1970 L1982 **GP OM** *020
FINK, Lewis D. ■ 98052 #056-06-1949 L1951 **GP IMG** *071
FLETCHER, Paul Robt. 2700 152ND AVE NE 98052 #054-04-1980 L1984 **FM PHP** *030 †18
FLUGSTAD, Paul Morris. 2700 152ND AVE NE 98052 #030-06-1972 L1973 **AN** *020 †05
FOGELQUIST, Jan Elizabeth. ■ 98052 #035-01-1978 L1979 **P IM** *020 †20,75
FOWLER, Elizabeth Csilla. 2701 156TH AVE NE, EASTSIDE PRIMARY CARE 98052 #040-02-1979 L1979 **IM** *020 †20
FREEDMAN, Howard Lee. ■ 98052 #024-01-1973 L1978 **OPH** *071 †35
FURE, John Helge. 2700 152ND AVE NE 98052 #154-07-1975 L1983 **OBG** *020 †30
GAD, Alona. ■ 98053 #550-03-2001 L2003 **MG** *100
GATRELL, Harley. 16761 NE 79TH ST 98052 #054-15-1969 **GP** *020
GELGISSER, Jeffrey Harris. 2701 156TH AVE NE 98052 #035-09-1977 L1983 **FM EM** *020 †18
GELLER, J Hutter. 16260 NE 85TH ST, REDMOND MEDICAL CLINIC 98052 #024-05-1987 L1998 **FM** *020 †18
GEORGE, Michael D. 8301 161ST AVE NE, STE 202 98052 #035-15-1998 L2007 **PD** *020 †55
GIBBS, Warren. 2700 152ND AVE NE, PUGET SOUND, EASTSIDE HOSP 98052 #023-01-1982 L1983 **IM** *020 †20
GIRRES, Pamela Ann. 2701 156TH AVE NE, GROUP HEALTH COOPERATIVE 98052 #024-07-1997 L2001 **IM OM** *020 †20,70
GLOSTEN, Beth. ■ 98053 #054-04-1983 L1992 **AN** *020 †05
GOEPFERT, Richard Wallace. 2700 152ND AVE NE, 2700 152ND AVE NE 98052 #019-02-1967 L1972 **P** *020 ‡
GORAI, Ann Patricia. 2700 152ND AVE NE 98052 #054-04-1979 L1980 **ORS** *020 †40
GOUGH, Frances Marie. 15446 BEL RED RD STE B 98052 #054-04-1985 L1992 **IM** *020 †20
GREEN, Elmer Harold. 2701 156TH AVE NE, GROUP HEALTH MEDICAL CENTE 98052 #054-04-1966 L1967 **GP** *020
GREGORY, Jeffrey Kent. 2700 152ND AVE NE, GROUP HEALTH 98052 #023-07-1992 L1999 **OPH** *020 †35
GROSS, Richard L. ■ 98053 #018-03-1951 L1970 **IM** *071 †20
GUMPRECHT, Thomas Frank. 8301 161ST AVE NE 98052 #054-04-1975 L1976 **OTO IM** *020 †20,45
GUZAK, Steven Vincent, Jr. 16150 NE 85TH ST, STE 206 98052 #007-02-1963 L1973 **OPH** *020 †35
HAAS, Joel Edward. ■ 98053 #041-12-1967 L1976 **PP** *030 †50
HAMBY, Sharon Lynn. 8301 161ST AVE NE, STE 307 98052 #025-01-1984 L1988 **OPH** *071 †35
HANSEN, Robert Carl. ■ 98052 #048-13-2000 L2005 **IM** *020 †20 ‡
HANSON, Martin E. 2103 152ND AVE NE 98052 #016-02-1950 L1955 **FM** *071 †18
HAQ, Abid. 2700 152ND AVE NE, GROUP HEALTH COOPERATIVE 98052 #915-04-1984 L2005 **IM OM** *020 †20,70
HARNLY, Thomas Shepard. 2700 152ND AVE NE, GENERAL SURGERY DEPT GHC 98052 #041-01-1970 L1975 **GS** *020 †85
HARPER, Barbara Fisher. 2700 152ND AVE NE 98052 #048-12-1990 L1998 **IM** *020 †20
HART, Julian Deryl. 2700 152ND AVE NE 98052 #036-07-1964 L1980 **FM IM** *020 †20
HEMPLER, Sharon Kay. 8301 161ST AVE NE, STE 204 98052 #019-02-1974 L1977 **PD** *020 †55
HENG, Michelle Marianna. 2700 152ND AVE NE 98052 #036-07-1989 L1998 **PD** *020 †55
HERT, Richard Craig. 2700 152ND AVE NE 98052 #035-46-1986 L1988 **IM** *020 †20
HERZOG, Philip Franklin. 2701 156TH AVE NE, EASTSIDE HOSPITAL 98052 #035-09-1973 L1979 **PD PHO** *020 †55
HEYDT, Jennifer Lou. 8301 161ST AVE NE, STE 200 98052 #005-18-1997 L2003 **OTO** *020 †45
HIEMSTRA, Sybout. 2103 152ND AVE NE 98052 #660-04-1957 L1959 **FM** *071 †18
HIGHLEY, Robert Douglas. 2700 152ND AVE NE 98052 #016-11-1973 L1978 **CD PHP** *020 †20
HOBBS, Stuart Floyd. 2103 152ND AVE NE 98052 #039-01-1994 L1999 **FM FSM** *020 †18
HOLDREN, Cynthia C. 2700 152ND AVE NE 98052 #003-01-1978 L1981 **AN** *020 †05
HONG, Ming. 2700 152ND AVE NE, D118 98052 #243-03-1994 L2004 **N** *020 †75
HOPPER, Margaret P. ■ 98052 #054-04-1982 *071
HORVITZ, Eric. MICROSOFT RESEARCH 98052 #005-11-1994 **OS CCS** *050
HOU, Pen. 8301 161ST AVE NE, STE 308 98052 #243-47-1986 L2005 **FM** *020 †18
HSIA, Raymond Wuyang. 2700 152ND AVE NE 98052 #033-06-1987 L2001 **IM** *020,†20
HSU, Richard Wei-Yao. 2700 152ND AVE NE 98052 #048-12-1995 L2000 **OTO** *020 †45
HSUE, Mindy Lee. 8299 161ST AVE NE, STE 101 98052 #051-04-1998 L2001 **FM** *020 †18 ‡
HUI, Geoffrey Siukei. 2700 152ND AVE NE 98052 #016-06-1982 L1983 **AN** *020 †05
INNIS, Connie Ann. 2700 152ND AVE NE, EMB B1 RAD 98052 #003-01-1993 L1993 **DR** *020 †80
JAEGER, Brian Dean. 8301 161ST AVE NE STE 300 98052 #054-04-1991 L2006 **P** *020 †75
JENSEN, Dan Le Roy. 2700 152ND AVE NE, ATTN: EMERGENCY DEPARTMENT 98052 #054-04-1969 L1970 **EM AM** *020 †16
JENSEN, Denise Ann. 2700 152ND AVE NE, DEPT OF EMERGENCY MEDICINE 98052 #040-02-1986 L1989 **EM** *020 †16
JOHANSON, John Fredrik. 2103 152ND AVE NE 98052 #062-01-1952 L1964 **GP** *071
JOISHA, Ahalya Pramod. ■ 98052 #496-59-2001 L2006 **FP** *012
JONAS, Adam Harris. 2700 152ND AVE NE, DEPT OF IM, D221ESH 98052 #024-05-1992 L1992 **IM** *020 †20
JONES, Wallace Wilfred. 2700 152ND AVE NE # ORTH 98052 #005-11-1969 L1987 **HS ORS** *071 †40
JOSEPH, Jackline S. 2103 152ND AVE NE 98052 #915-02-1991 L1997 **IM** *020 †20
JULIAN, Carey. 2700 152ND AVE NE 98052 #054-04-1982 L1983 **FM** *020 †18
KARBOWSKI, Michael James. 2700 152ND AVE NE 98052 #016-02-1980 L1981 **AN** *020 †05
KASCHKO, John Harold. 2701 156TH AVE NE 98052 #054-04-1980 L1983 **IM** *020 †20
KELLER, Cynthia Marie. 8301 161ST AVE NE STE 204 98052 #016-43-1999 L2001 **PD** *020 †55
KELLEY, Alan Dewitt. 8301 161ST AVE NE, STE 308 98052 #035-19-1983 L1986 **FM** *020 †18
KELLY-HEDRICK, Heather M. 2700 152ND AVE NE 98052 #026-04-1991 L1993 **IM** *020 †20
KENT, Gerald Gershon. 2700 152ND AVE NE 98052 #005-15-1983 L1989 **GS** *020 †85
KIM, In Guk. 2700 152ND AVE NE 98052 #583-01-1961 L1983 **OTO** *020 †45
KIM, Paik Nyon. ■ 98053 #583-02-1958 L1973 **ON IM** *071 †20
KIRKMAN, Jacob Arthur. 2700 152ND AVE NE, DEPT OF EMERGENCY MEDICINE 98052 #036-05-1996 L2001 **EM** *020 †16 ‡
KNAUSS, Thomas Alvin. 2700 152ND AVE NE 98052 #005-14-1969 L1971 **CHN N** *071 †75
KNIGHT, Jonathan Lewis. 2700 152ND AVE NE 98052 #054-04-1971 L1975 **ORS OS** *020 †40
KORSAK, Christina Maria. ■ 98052 #065-01-1962 L2005 **P** *020 †75
KROUSE, Howard Alan. 2700 152ND AVE NE, EASTSIDE MEDICAL STAFF 98052 #054-04-1970 L1976 **AI IM** *020 †20,03
KUHL, Howard L. ■ 98052 #016-11-1950 L1988 **CRS GS** *071 †85
LAVIN, Sumi Josephine. 2800 152ND AVE NE, C-400 98052 #054-04-1989 L1993 **OBG** *020 †30
LAWLESS, Peter Albert. ■ 98053 #021-01-1968 L1972 **GS TS** *020 †85
LAWSON, W Maurice. ■ 98052 #016-06-1950 L1950 **FM** *071 †18
LEE, Ming Sing. ■ 98074 #244-02-1960 L1980 **GP GYN** *020
LENART, Thomas Duane. 17130 AVONDALE WAY 98052 #041-01-1994 L1999 **OPH PO** *020 †35
LEOU, Norman H. 2103 152ND AVE NE 98052 #004-01-1992 L1995 **IM** *020 †20
LEVINSON, Howard Michael. ■ 98053 #016-11-1961 L1971 **R** *020 †80
LINDQUIST, Thomas Donald. 2700 152ND AVE NE, GROUP HEALTH COOPERATIVE E 98052 #033-05-1981 L1982 **OPH** *020 †35
LINVILLE, George. 16149 REDMOND WAY, # 267 98052 #054-04-1972 L1975 **GS CD** *020 †85
LIOU, Iris Wanyun. ■ 98052 #054-04-2000 L2003 **GE** *012 †20

LOW, Edwin Siagaung. 6207 156TH AVE NE 98052 #056-05-1986 L2001 **PD** *020 †55
LYNCH, John I, Jr. 8301 161ST AVE NE, STE 204 98052 #051-04-1960 L1975 **PD** *071 †55
LYTLE, John Paul, Jr. 6729 204TH DR NE 98053 #025-01-1977 L1998 **RO** *020 †18,80
MANN, Winnie Lou. 14681 NE 95TH ST 98052 #026-04-1975 L1977 **GP** *020
MARSHALL, Ronald Paul A. 2701 156TH AVE NE, EASTSIDE MEDICAL CENTER 98052 #028-02-1970 L1975 **GP IM** *020 †20,18
MC AULEY, David Brian. ■ 98074 #041-13-1979 L1980 **OM OS** *050 †70
MC CANDLESS, Carol R. 19463 NE REDMOND RD 98053 #035-48-1978 L1979 **FM** *020 †18
MC CORMICK, John Kent. 8301 161ST AVE NE, STE 1 98052 #005-06-1979 L1985 **ORS** *020 †40
MC DERMOTT, Kimberly C. 16315 NE 87TH ST, STE B6 98052 #036-07-1991 L1994 **PD FM** *020 †55
MC DONALD, G Douglas. 8301 161ST AVE NE, STE 308 98052 #054-04-1982 L1985 **FM** *020 †18
MC GRATH, James Russel. ■ 98052 #016-02-1945 L1950 **PD** *071
MC GRATH, Peter W. 2700 152ND AVE NE, EASTSIDE GROUP HEALTH 98052 #054-04-1983 L1986 **CD IM** *020 †20,28
MC KENDRY, Elizabeth A. 15937 REDMOND WAY, US HEALTHWORKS 98052 #032-01-1985 L1991 **IM GPM** *020 †20
MC KIBBEN, Ernest C, Jr. ■ 98052 #010-01-1945 L1948 **FM** *071 †18
MC LEOD, Deane E. GROUP HEALTH HOSP 98052 #005-06-1949 L1952 **OBG** *020 †30
MC LEOD, Lesley Caroline. ■ 98052 #011-02-2003 L2007 **OBG** *100
MERCIER, John Randall. 2700 152ND AVE NE 98052 #016-06-1974 L1980 **EM OS** *020 †16
MIDDLETON, Arthur Gilman. 704 228TH AVE NE, PMB 693 98074 #061-01-1958 L1965 **PS** *071 †65
MOSS, Donald Jack. 17530 NE UNION HILL RD, STE 210 98052 #035-45-1968 L1994 **P ADL** *020
MUDGE, Barbara Jean. ■ 98052 #025-01-1969 L1970 **AN OBG** *071 †05
MUELLER, Jerome Wm. 2700 152ND AVE NE 98052 #025-01-1978 L1986 **EM** *020 †16
NAYAK, Narayan Pundarik. ■ 98052 #495-37-1967 L1974 **PD PHO** *020 †55
NEUZIL, Elizabeth K. 22603 NE INGLEWOOD HILL RD 98074 #047-05-1982 L1983 **PD** *020 †55
NIEBULSKI, Harvey I J. 2700 152ND AVE NE 98052 #035-45-1981 L1987 **DR** *020 †80
NIMLOS, John Edward. 2701 156TH AVE NE, GROUP HEALTH MEDICAL CENTE 98052 #026-04-1972 L1979 **OM** *020 †70,18
NOGUCHI, Patricia Shelton. ■ 98053 #054-04-2008 *012
NOHLE, Robert Carl. 2701 156TH AVE NE 98052 #054-04-1995 L1998 **PDC PD** *020 †55
NOMOTO, Kumiko Y. 2701 156TH AVE NE 98052 #026-04-1989 L1993 **FM** *020 †18
NORTHROP, Curtis Harold. 2700 152ND AVE NE 98052 #054-04-1966 L1967 **R** *020 †80
OEI, Tjwan Hong. ■ 98053 #506-01-1960 L1971 **FM** *071 †18
OISHI, Marisa Leiko. ■ 98052 #040-02-2007 **EM** *012
PARIS, Kathleen. ■ 98053 #041-09-1970 L1987 **PTH** *071 †50
PARTINGTON, Marshall T. 8309 165TH AVE NE STE 101, PARTINGTON PLASTIC SURG 98052 #035-20-1983 L1996 **GS** *020 †85,65
PEPE, Harry N, III. 8301 161ST AVE NE, STE 105 98052 #011-04-1984 L1989 **FM** *020 †18
PETRICH, John Michael. 8301 161ST AVE NE STE 300, REDMOND MEDICAL CENTER 98052 #005-14-1969 L1970 **P** *020 †75 ‡
PIEL, Jennifer Lynn. ■ 98052 #005-06-2007 L2007 **P** *012
PILECKI, Krystyna I. 8301 161ST AVE NE, STE 105 98052 #016-43-1984 L1986 **GP** *020
PINCZOWER, Eric F. 8301 161ST AVE NE, STE 200 98052 #005-15-1986 L1991 **OTO** *020 †45
POLLACK, Ari H. 8301 161ST AVE NE, STE 204 98052 #021-01-2002 L2002 **PD** *020 †55
POLSDORFER, J Ricker. 15127 NE 24TH ST, STE 364 98052 #005-14-1968 L1991 **FM** *020 †18
POTTER, Donald Eugene. 2701 156TH AVE NE, GROUP HEALTH COOPERATIVE-E 98052 #019-02-1974 L1992 **FM** *020 †18
PRATT, Robert Lee. ■ 98052 #050-02-1955 L1958 **NR** *071
PUTTER, Howard Neil. 2700 152ND AVE NE 98052 #030-06-1975 L1983 **ORS** *020 †40
RANDECKER, Harold H, Jr. 7520 196TH AVE NE 98053 #056-05-1969 L1975 **TS VS** *020 †85,90
REEVES, Gary Michael. 2700 152ND AVE NE 98052 #054-04-1991 L1994 **DR** *020 †80
RITSO, Olga. ■ 98052 #407-04-1948 **OPH** *071 †35
ROBBINS, James Robt. 8301 161ST AVE NE STE 102 98052 #040-02-1972 L1980 **ORS OSM** *020 †40
ROBERT, Ghislaine. 22500 NE MARKETPLACE DR, STE 206A 98053 #067-02-1982 L2003 **FSM** *020
ROBERTS, John Michael. ■ 98052 #048-04-2008 *012
ROGGE, Timothy Alan. ■ 98052 #023-07-1972 L1973 **P** *030 †75
ROOT, Daniel Christopher. 2701 156TH AVE NE 98052 #041-13-1999 L2003 **D** *100 †15
SACKETT, Clarice E. 2700 152ND AVE NE 98052 #014-01-1979 L1980 **IM** *020 †20
SAMANTA, Diptendu. 2700 152ND AVE NE 98052 #056-06-1995 L1999 **AN** *020 †05
SANDBLOM, Robert Edward. 2700 152ND AVE NE, EMBD 0GL 98052 #054-04-1976 L1980 **PUD** *020 †20
SARGUR, Mukund. ■ 98052 #495-33-1974 L1982 **HO HEM** *020 †20
SCHMIDT, William Russell. ■ 98053 #049-01-1961 L1963 **N** *071
SCHMULAND, Dennis Paul. 8299 161ST AVE NE, FAMILY MEDICINE OF REDMOND 98052 #054-04-1981 L1982 **FM** *030 †18
SCHNEBLE, William Jos. 8105 166TH AVE NE STE 202 98052 #056-06-1964 L1970 **FM IM** *020
SCHROEDER, Elizabeth Lynn. ■ 98053 #038-41-1993 L1995 **OBG** *020 †30
SCHROEDER, Franz Michael. 2532 265TH AVE NE, F. M. SCHROEDER MD PS 98053 #018-03-1970 L1982 **DR** *020 †80
SEKIJIMA, Sally V. 2700 152ND AVE NE, EAST SIDE HOSPITAL 98052 #054-04-1978 L1982 **OBG** *020 †30
SHERRY, Robert Arnold. 2700 152ND AVE NE 98052 #054-04-1955 L1956 **FM** *072 †18
SHIN, Kyung Joon. ■ 98053 #583-01-1951 L1974 **P** *020 †75
SHORT, Steven Owen. 2700 152ND AVE NE 98052 #005-14-1980 L1981 **OTO** *020 †45
SIMONOWITZ, David Alan. ■ 98053 #016-02-1970 L1973 **GS** *071 †85
SINGH, Divya. 2700 152ND AVE NE, CLUSTER C300 98052 #035-45-1994 L2005 **ORS HS** *020 †40
SINKEY, Mark Alan. 2700 152ND AVE NE 98052 #040-02-1979 L1986 **AN GS** *020 †05
SMITH, Jos Ignatius, Jr. ■ 98073 #028-34-1967 L2004 **PTH FM** *020 †50,18
SMITH, Stephen Lee. 2700 152ND AVE NE 98052 #026-04-1970 L1976 **IMG IM** *020 †20
SPARLING, Gerald Danforth. 2700 152ND AVE NE 98052 #004-01-1953 L1961 **DR** *071 †80
SPRINGMEYER, Steven Chase. 6675 185TH AVE NE 98052 #049-01-1974 L1975 **PUD CCM** *050 †20
STARR, Steven Elwin. 2701 152ND AVE NE 98052 #038-40-1971 L1973 **FM OS** *071 †18
STARRETT, Jack Richard. ■ 98052 #028-34-1947 L1948 **AM R** *071
STERN, Carol Sue. 17130 AVONDALE WAY, STE 114 98052 #035-19-1967 L1985 **D** *071
STOLL, Howard Walter. 2700 152ND AVE NE 98052 #035-15-1965 L1969 **U** *020 †95
STORCK, Susan E Brooks. 2700 152ND AVE NE 98052 #038-43-1981 L1989 **OBG** *020 †30
STRATER, William Thompson. 20009 NE 42ND ST, TIMBERLINE PARK 98074 #050-02-1982 L1985 **FM** *020 †18
SU, Susana F. 2700 152ND AVE NE 98052 #041-02-1992 L1995 **AN** *020 †05
SUBRAMANIAM, Priyadarshini. ■ 98052 #495-16-1997 **PM** *100
SULTAN, Sandra Jean. 2700 152ND AVE NE 98052 #025-07-1971 L1978 **OBG** *020 †30
SWANSON, Stephen Louis. 2700 152ND AVE NE 98052 #054-04-1970 L1971 **EM** *020 †16
TAY, Aye-Aye Lwin. ■ 98053 #209-01-1969 **AN** *075
THOM, Darrow Jay. 2700 152ND AVE NE, GHC-BHS 98052 #024-07-1981 L1989 **P** *020 †75
TOMICH, James Geo, Jr. 2700 152ND AVE NE 98052 #030-06-1980 L1981 **DR OS** *030 †80
TOUBBEH, Michael I. 2700 152ND AVE NE 98052 #034-01-1985 L1993 **OTO HNS** *020 †45
TUBBESING, Thomas Jay. 2700 152ND AVE NE 98052 #018-03-1978 L1983 **OPH** *020 †35 ‡
TUBBS, Loren Edward. 2700 152ND AVE NE 98052 #054-04-1979 L1982 **EM IM** *020 †20,16
TURNBULL, Lawrence F. ■ 98052 #016-06-1946 L1946 **AN** *071 †05
URBACH, John Robt. ■ 98052 #041-01-1947 L1990 **IM CD** *030 †20
VAN OSTRAND, James R. 2700 152ND AVE NE 98052 #035-20-1959 L1966 **OBG** *071 †30
VON VARENDORFF, Edeltraud. 7110 143RD PL NE 98052 #836-01-1970 *100
WADDINGTON, Neil Howard. 2700 152ND AVE NE, EMERGENCY DEPARTMENT EMB A 98052 #054-04-1981 L1986 **EM** *020 †16
WALKER, Stephen James. ■ 98053 #016-02-1975 L1981 **ORS** *071 †40
WALKER, Susannah. ■ 98053 #016-02-1975 L1981 **A** *071 †55,03
WALTER, John Richard. 2700 152ND AVE NE 98052 #038-40-1974 L1977 **EM** *020 †16
WANG, Bennet Minguang. 2700 152ND AVE NE, EMB-LL 98052 #008-01-1990 L1994 **CCM** *020 †20
WEAVER, Norman Dean. 2701 156TH AVE NE 98052 #040-02-1964 L1965 **GP** *020 †18
WEISS, Michael David. ■ 98052 #035-46-1991 L2001 **N** *020 †75
WELCH, Dan Alan. 15436 BEL RED RD STE 100 98052 #025-01-1978 L1979 **PM PRS** *020 †60
WEN, Julie Elizabeth. 22635 NE MARKETPLACE DR, UNIV OF WASHINGTON, SCH OF 98053 #005-18-2002 L2002 **PD** *020 †55
WERY, Frans Leopold T. 2700 152ND AVE NE 98052 #660-03-1951 L1956 **EM** *071
WHATLEY, Joseph Spalding. 2700 152ND AVE NE 98052 #017-20-1992 L1997 **ORS** *020 †40
WHITE, Beverly J Hixson. ■ 98053 #054-04-1963 L1968 **CCG CG** *062 †55,19
WHORTON, Adrian Meade. 8450 161ST AVE NE 98052 #054-04-1997 L2000 **EM** *020 †16
WICKS, Gina Landicho. 16701 CLEVELAND ST, STE 210 98052 #054-04-1984 L1985 **FM** *020 †18
WINKELMANN, Michael J. 2700 152ND AVE NE, GROUP HEALTH EASTSIDE HOSP 98052 #028-03-1986 L1991 **EM** *020 †16
WONGSURAWAT, Vaew Jon. 2700 152ND AVE NE, GRP HLTH EASTSIDE HOSP 98052 #047-05-1998 L2000 **GE** *020 †20
WORSHAM, Jerry Carl. 2700 152ND AVE NE, GROUP HLTH COOPERATIVE OF 98052 #035-03-1962 L1971 **OTO** *071 †45
YAM, John Ivan Chung-Wah. 2103 152ND AVE NE 98052 #462-01-1968 L1973 **PD N** *020 †55,18 ‡
YLVISAKER, J Thomas. 2700 152ND AVE NE 98052 #026-04-1970 L1972 **GE IM** *020 †20
YON, Sabrina Manyee. 8301 161ST AVE NE, STE 308 98052 #035-09-1998 L2001 **FM** *020 †18
YOO, Catherine Taekyong. 2701 156TH AVE NE 98052 #422-01-1997 L2001 **IM** *020 †20
YU, Julianna Tzuya. ■ 98073 #016-06-2001 L2003 **EM** *020 †16
YUAN, Ruiyong. 2700 152ND AVE NE, GROUP HEALTH EASTSIDE HOSP 98052 #243-95-1989 L2004 **CD IM** *020 †20
ZARGHAMI, Marjan. ■ 98052 #054-04-2006 L2007 **OBG** *012
ZEIDMAN, Lawrence. 2701 156TH AVE NE 98052 #654-01-1981 L1984 **IM** *020 †20
ZHANG, Yuan. 2700 152ND AVE NE 98052 #243-03-1989 L1999 **IM** *020 †20
ZIBELLI, Louis R. 2700 152ND AVE NE 98052 #035-06-1973 L1978 **CD IM** *020 †20
ZIMMERMANN, Donald L. 2014 179TH CT NE 98052 #068-01-1990 L1995 **APM** *020

RENTON – KING

AALAMI, Oliver Oppers. 400 S 43RD ST, DIVISION OF VASCULAR SURGE 98055 #024-05-1998 L2007 **VS** *020 †85
AHMED, Shiraz. 601 S CARR RD STE 100 98055 #495-99-1990 L1997 **IMG** *020 †20
AJUDIA, Dhiren N. 148 PARK AVE N 98057 #495-48-1982 L1985 **GP** *020
ALLA, Haritha Reddy. 4011 TALBOT RD S, STE 500 98055 #495-21-1996 L2003 **CD** *020 †20
ALLEN, Ginger Ann. 3915 TALBOT RD S, STE 401 98055 #054-04-2000 L2002 **FM** *020 †18
ALLEN, Ira Steven. 400 S 43RD ST 98055 #023-01-1985 L1991 **PTH** *020 †50
ALPEROVICH, Claudio G. 4033 TALBOT RD S, STE 560 98055 #035-45-1988 L2003 **GS TRS** *020 †85
ALTMAN, Leonard Chas. 1412 SW 43RD ST, ALLERGY CENTER PS 98057 #024-01-1969 L1970 **AI** *020 †20,03
AMORY, Josephine Harris. 400 S 43RD ST 98055 #005-02-1997 L2000 **OBG** *020
ANAND, Ashish. ■ 98055 #496-09-1996 L2003 **OAR** *020
ANDERSON, Michael Remsen. 4011 TALBOT RD S # 22 98055 #054-04-1973 L1975 **PD** *020 †55
ARLEIN, Wes Jonathan. 4300 TALBOT RD S, STE 315 98055 #035-01-1991 L1999 **GS** *020 †85
ATTAWAY, Nola Jean. 1412 SW 43RD ST, ALLERGY CENTER PS 98057 #048-02-1985 L1998 **AI PD** *020 †55,03
AVALON, Phillip Girard. ■ 98059 #016-11-1953 L1954 **FM** *071
BALL, John Hurst, Jr. 4509 TALBOT RD S STE 103 98055 #030-05-1964 L1971 **END IM** *020
BALOUSEK, Peter Andrew. 3915 TALBOT RD S, STE 104 98055 #025-01-1990 L1997 **NS** *020 †25
BALSER, Emily Katherine. 4033 TALBOT RD S, STE 570 98055 #030-06-2003 L2003 **FM** *020 †18
BARBOUR, Kelly Renee. 200 S 2ND ST 98057 #028-03-2001 L2003 **FM** *020 †18 ‡
BARKER, David Teter. 17930 TALBOT RD S 98055 #017-20-1968 L1978 **PS** *020 †65
BASNYAT, Pushpanjali. ■ 98055 #495-42-1994 L2007 **IM** *020 †20
BECKER, Jonathan Wingate. 1412 SW 43RD ST, ALLERGY CENTER PS 98057 #054-04-1987 L1990 **AI PD** *020 †03,55
BENJAMIN, Brent David. 400 S 43RD ST 98055 #026-04-1983 L1987 **PTH** *020 †50
BERGER, Carmen Maria. 4011 TALBOT RD S, STE 460 98055 #047-05-1995 L1997 **D** *020 †20,15
BERGQUIST, Avanti R B. ■ 98056 #020-02-2007 L2007 **P** *012
BJARKE, Chris Brent. 275 BRONSON WAY NE 98056 #005-06-1990 L1993 **FM** *020 †18
BLOCK, Terence Alan. 4011 TALBOT RD S # S-500 98055 #038-40-1971 L1974 **CD IM** *020 †20
BONDI, John Leslie. 3915 TALBOT RD S STE 401, VALLEY MEDICAL CENTER 98055 #041-09-1968 L1972 **IM ON** *040 †20

■ = Address Information Privacy Protected

BOYER, Suzanne Audrey. 4033 TALBOT RD S, STE 500 98055 #028-02-1996 L1999 PCC SME *020 †20

BRAZG, Ronald Leonard. 723 SW 10TH ST STE 10 98057 #836-01-1980 L1990 END IM *020 †20

BREWER, Craig Marvin. 315 MORRIS AVE S 98057 #010-01-1967 L1968 GP *020 ‡

BRIGGS, Kenneth Auburn. 4361 TALBOT RD S STE 102 98055 #021-05-1966 L1971 ORS *020 †40

BRISCOE, Patricia Ann. 17930 TALBOT RD S 98055 #047-05-1986 L1993 GS *020 †65

BRITELL, Jonathan Clyde. 3915 TALBOT RD S, STE 300 98055 #035-03-1973 L1985 ON HEM *020 †20

BROCK, Brigit Victoria. 400 S 43RD ST 98055 #054-04-1991 L1993 OBG *020 †30

BROCKENBROUGH, Andrew T. 4033 TALBOT RD S, STE 430 98055 #047-05-1998 L2000 NEP *100 L1999

BROERS, Marianne T. 4361 TALBOT RD S, STE 112 98055 #660-03-1990 L1992 FM *020 †18

BROWN, Dennis Foster. 1412 SW 43RD ST, STE 209 98057 #010-02-1975 L1982 OBG *020 †30

BROWN, Paul Curtis. 4300 TALBOT RD S, STE 104 98055 #028-46-1979 L1980 CRS GS *020 †85,10

BUCK, Cameron Ross. 400 S 43RD ST 98055 #047-05-1995 L1999 EM *020 †16

BUELL, Guy Vaughn. 4011 TALBOT RD S STE 440 98055 #012-05-1969 L1978 U *020 †95

BURGGRAAF, B Joseph. ■ 98059 #007-02-2007 L2007 GS *012

BURKE, Michael F. 1412 SW 43RD ST, STE 201 98057 #030-06-1979 L1983 GS VS *020 †85

BUTCHER, Mary Elizabeth. 451 DUVALL AVE NE 98059 #016-01-1980 L1981 GP *020

BUTLER, Charles William. 4033 TALBOT RD S, STE 570 98055 #054-04-2002 L2004 FM *020 †18

CALEY, David Wm. 4300 TALBOT RD S 98055 #051-01-1974 L1976 FM EM *071 †16

CANCRO, Robert Harding. 4011 TALBOT RD S STE 300 98055 #035-15-1970 L1971 ORS *020 †40

CAPLAN, Charles Henry. 4033 TALBOT RD S # 2 98055 #023-07-1970 L1971 OTO *020 †45

CARLSON, Duane Gregory. 4011 TALBOT RD S, STE 460 98055 #011-02-1975 L1976 GE IM *020 †20

CARLTON, Janice Carol. 3915 TALBOT RD S, STE 401 98055 #054-04-1983 L1983 FM *040 †18

CERVENKA, Frank John. 275 BRONSON WAY NE 98056 #054-04-1979 L1983 IM *020 †20

CHANG, Wallace Han-Jen. 17930 TALBOT RD S 98055 #036-07-1963 L1982 PS *071 †85,65 ‡

CHANNELL, Lori Denise. 4011 TALBOT RD S, STE 430 98055 #055-01-1996 L2000 OBG *020 †30

CHEN, Gilbert Shih. ■ 98058 #054-04-2003 L2003 EM *020 †16

CHEN, Jenny. 955 POWELL AVE SW, STE A 98057 #012-05-1999 L2003 FM *020 †18

CHEN, Jian. ■ 98059 #243-45-1983 L1999 PTH *100

CHEN, Wynne. 4033 TALBOT RD S, STE 500 98055 #035-48-1995 L2005 PCC *020 †20

CHEREWATENKO, Vern S. 4300 TALBOT RD S STE 200, HEALTHMAX, INCORPORATED 98055 #054-04-1986 L1988 FM OBS *020 †18

CHIKOS, Paul Martin, Jr. 400 S 43RD ST 98055 #055-01-1966 L1971 DR *071 †80

CHOI, Bokgi. 400 S 43RD ST 98055 #035-19-1988 L2001 AN *020 †05

CHOUDHURY, Rajib. 4011 TALBOT RD S, STE 500 98055 #495-78-1986 L2003 CD IM *020 †20

CHRISTOPHER, David Martz. 4011 TALBOT RD S STE 220 98055 #054-04-1979 L1982 PD *020 †55

CIEREBIEJ, Albert. 1601 LIND AVE SW 98057 #010-01-1956 L1960 AM OM *020 †70

CINCIRIPINI, Denise Robin. 4011 TALBOT RD S, STE 460 98055 #035-47-1993 L1998 IM *020 †20

COHEN, Ronald K. 4445 TALBOT RD S, VALLEY MEDICAL CENTER 98055 #028-03-1983 L1987 P MDM *020 †75

COLE, Kelly Duncan. 4011 TALBOT RD S, STE 430 98055 #055-01-1996 L2002 OBG *020 †30

CONSTANTIN, Flavia. 1412 SW 43RD ST, STE 209 98057 #781-01-1999 L2000 FM *100 †18

COOPER, Stephanie G. 4011 TALBOT RD S STE 500, VALLEY INTERNAL MEDICINE,I 98055 #005-02-1991 L1995 CD IC *020 †20

CORBIN, Shannon Lynn. 4445 TALBOT RD S 98055 #054-04-1999 L1999 P *020 †75

CORREA, Francisco Javier. ■ 98058 #737-01-1951 L1969 IMG IM *071

CUI, Ying. 3915 TALBOT RD S, STE 300 98055 #243-47-1988 L2000 HEM *020 †20

DAHLIN, Dennis Ray. 400 S 43RD ST 98055 #054-04-1969 L1971 IM *020 †20

DEAK, Andrew. 4509 TALBOT RD S, STE 101 98055 #004-01-1963 L1970 D *020 †15

DEL RIO, Graciela. 4011 TALBOT RD S, MELVIN L MORSE MD 98055 #005-19-1982 L1988 CCM PD *074 †55

DEL ROSARIO, Eduardo DI R. ■ 98058 #748-01-1964 *100

DE PAEPE, Jessica Lynn. 400 S 43RD ST, PHYSICIANS 98055 #049-01-1996 L2000 EM *020 †16

DION, Mary Lillian. 400 S 43RD ST 98055 #054-04-1979 L1981 AN *020 †05

DIRE, Christopher Anthony. 4011 TALBOT RD S, STE 460 98055 #016-43-1997 L2000 GE IM *020 †20

DISTELHORST, James Stuart. 400 S 43RD ST 98055 #024-01-1979 L1980 FM FPG *030 †18

DOUGLAS, Robert Martin. PO BOX 50010, 400 S 43RD ST 98058 #054-04-1991 L2003 RO *020 †80

DUNNE, John Edward. 1400 TALBOT RD S STE 203 98055 #016-06-1970 L1975 CHP P *020 †75

EBY, Amy Beth. 4011 TALBOT RD S STE 500 98055 #017-20-1997 L2000 IM *020 †20

EVERETT, Elise Grace. 400 S 43RD ST 98055 #054-04-1999 L1999 GO *020

FARACI, Andrew Jerome. 400 S 43RD ST 98055 #030-05-2001 L2002 AN *020 †05

FASSLER, Eric Neal. 1412 SW 43RD ST 98057 #003-01-1984 L1988 OBG *020 †30

FITHIAN, Robert Arthur. 400 S 43RD ST 98055 #054-04-1955 L1956 FM *072

FRARY, Lynn Reginald. 17620 SPRINGBROOK S, UROLOGICAL SURGEONS INC PS 98055 #030-05-1964 L1972 U GP *071 †95

FRIEDMAN, Daniel Baker. 4033 TALBOT RD S, STE 200 98055 #048-04-1996 L1999 PD *020 †55

FUJISAKI, Craig Ken. 4509 TALBOT RD S, STE 200 98055 #007-02-1978 L1979 D *020 †18,15

FUNG, Frank P. 4033 TALBOT RD S STE 430 98055 #038-06-1995 L1997 NEP *020 †20

FURUKAWA, Clifton Tokuji. 1412 SW 43RD ST, ALLERGY CENTER PS 98057 #035-45-1970 L1971 AI *020 †55,03

GALLAGHER, John Michael. 400 S 43RD ST 98055 #036-01-1963 L1967 P *030 †75

GAMON, Wilfred Antone. ■ 98055 #016-06-1943 L1946 GP *071

GAMPONIA, Grace Bacsa. 4033 TALBOT RD S, STE 570 98055 #748-10-1986 L1997 FM *020 †18

GATES, Trina Michelle. ■ 98056 #048-13-2003 L2004 FM *020

GERMAN, Gary Howard. 4011 TALBOT RD S, STE 220 98055 #028-46-1980 L1983 PD *020 †55

GIULIANO, Thomas Nicholas. 400 S 43RD ST 98055 #005-02-1986 L1989 AN *020 †05

GOLDMAN, Daniel Aaron. ■ 98055 #048-04-1979 L1979 PHP EP *062

GONZALEZ, Rachael E. 601 S CARR RD STE 100 98055 #005-18-1990 L1996 FM *020 †18

GORENBERG, David Matthew. 400 S 43RD ST 98055 #005-18-1996 L2003 OBG *020 †30

GORTON, Marquand M. 17900 TALBOT RD S 98055 #011-02-1977 L1980 IM *074 †20

GRAVES, Daniel Leahy. 17900 TALBOT RD S, STE 101 98055 #054-04-1977 L1979 IM *020 †20

GREGET, Martin Robt. 401 S 43RD ST STE 200 98055 #054-04-1979 L1988 OTO HNS *020 †45

GUERRA, Margarita Maria. 4361 TALBOT RD S, STE 103 98055 #042-02-1998 L2006 PD *020 †55

GUILBERT, Davis Alan. ■ 98059 #049-01-2000 L2007 RNR *020 †80

HANAFY, Hanafy Mohammad A. 4033 TALBOT RD S STE 560, WASH BAR & WT LOSS CTR 98055 #915-03-1978 L2007 GS *020 †85

HANLON, Kathleen Jo. 4011 TALBOT RD S, STE 430 98055 #028-03-1983 L1987 OBG *020 †30

HANSEN, Eric Theodore. 4033 TALBOT RD S, STE 270 98055 #054-04-1990 L2001 ORS GP *020 †40

HARDING, James Alfred. 400 S 43RD ST 98055 #050-02-1983 L1991 MFM OBG *020 †18,30

HASELMAN, Timothy. ■ 98058 #048-02-1994 L1995 GP *071

HASTREITER, Dawn Marie. 16804 166TH PL SE, UNIV OF WASH SCHOOL OF 98058 #024-01-2002 L2003 *100

HAWLEY, Tina Marie. 601 S CARR RD STE 100 98055 #054-04-1998 L2002 FM *020 †18

HAYNES, Jamie Lynn. 400 S 43RD ST, VALLEY MEDICAL CENTER 98055 #048-15-2004 L2004 FM *100 †18

HEIDE, Aaron Carl. 3915 TALBOT RD S, STE 104 98055 #054-04-1998 L2001 N *020 †75

HEINZEN, Molly Talcott. 4011 TALBOT RD S STE 430, UNIVERSITY OF CHICAGO 98055 #036-08-2003 L2007 OBG *020

HELLER, Stephen Alan. 1412 SW 43RD ST 98057 #035-19-1965 L1972 OBG *071 †30

HEMMEN, Gia Lynn. 400 S 43RD ST, VMC HIGHLANDS PRIMARY CARE 98055 #054-04-1995 L1997 FM *020 †18

HENDRICKSON, John M. 4033 TALBOT RD S, STE 270 98055 #026-04-1959 L1959 ORS *071 †80

HERMAN, Daniel John. 3915 TALBOT RD S 98055 #054-04-1988 L1999 FM *040 †18

HERSMAN, John Allan. 3915 TALBOT RD S # 30, STE 300 98055 #026-04-1972 L1973 ON IM *020 †20

HODGERS, John Henry. 1412 SW 43RD ST 98057 #040-02-1967 L1974 OBG D *020

HOLMAN, Andrew James. 4300 TALBOT RD S STE 1 98055 #028-03-1987 L1990 IM *020 †20

HOLMES, Maria Chernykh. 17722 TALBOT RD S 98055 #913-72-1989 L1999 OBG *020 †30

HOOCK, Jennifer Lynn. 3915 TALBOT RD S, STE 401 98055 #036-07-1989 L1990 FM *020 †18

HORI, Michael K. 4011 TALBOT RD S, STE 460 98055 #054-04-1983 L1984 IM ID *020 †20

HU, Daniel C. 4033 TALBOT RD S, STE 430 98055 #036-08-1997 L2004 NEP *020 †20

HUANG, Fredrick Scott. 4011 TALBOT RD S, STE 300 98055 #011-03-1996 L2001 ORS *020 †40

HUBBARD, Donald Dale. 17900 TALBOT RD S STE 101 98055 #028-02-1965 L1970 ORS OS *072 †40

HUEBNER, Jeffrey Albert. 200 S 2ND ST 98057 #056-06-2001 L2002 FM *020 †18

HUNG, Glen Por-Yuan. 400 S 43RD ST 98055 #385-02-1956 L1975 GYN GP *071 †20

HUTTER, Jonathan James. 17930 TALBOT RD S 98055 #024-01-1998 L2002 PS *020 †65

INGBER, Richard Geoffrey. 3915 TALBOT RD S, STE 300 98055 #008-01-1991 L1993 HEM *020 †20

ISACKSON, De Ann Wendy. 340 MORRIS AVE S, OFFICE OF LINDA L. HANSEN 98057 #030-06-1990 L1995 AN *020

ISNER, Robert Jos. 400 S 43RD ST 98055 #054-04-1988 L1988 AN *020 †05

JOHNSON, Michelle Marie. 1412 SW 43RD ST, STE 201 98057 #054-04-1994 L1998 GS *020 †85

JONES, Michael D. 1601 LIND AVE SW, AVIATION MEDICINE DIVISION 98057 #049-01-1981 L1983 AM *030

JONES, Peter Gaylord. 4011 TALBOT RD S STE 210 98055 #054-04-1981 L1985 OPH *020 †35

JOOS, Paul Norman. 4011 TALBOT RD S, VALLEY EYE & LASER CENTER 98055 #030-06-1973 L1978 OPH *072

JORDAN, Marcia Crozier. 1412 SW 43RD ST STE 200 98057 #054-04-1991 L1993 FM *020 †18

JOSHI, Amit Mukesh. 400 S 43RD ST 98055 #496-38-1993 L2007 IMG IM *020 †20 ‡

KADEG, Larry John. 400 S 43RD ST 98055 #054-04-1982 L1983 FM *020 †18

KAGEYAMA, Nicole Prevo. 1412 SW 43RD ST, STE 205 98057 #014-01-1998 L2006 D DMP *020 †15

KAIYALA, Anne Eve K. PO BOX 50010, 400 S 43RD 98058 #016-06-2001 L2004 EM *020 †16

KAMINSKI, Mike Jos. 14410 SE PETROVITSKY RD 98058 #037-01-1979 L1980 FM *020 †18

KANE, Ronald Matthew. 14410 SE PETROVITSKY RD, RD # 104 98058 #062-01-1993 L1997 FM *020 †18

KAPLAN, Barnett Morris. 1400 TALBOT RD S, STE 330 98055 #024-05-1971 L1976 P PYA *020 †75

KATO, Gary Hiroshi. 17900 TALBOT RD S, STE 102 98055 #054-04-1984 L1985 FM *020 †18

KAYNE, Allan Lee. 14037 SE 159TH PL 98058 #035-20-1973 L1982 D *020 †15

KEEGAN, Patricia. 4011 TALBOT RD S, STE 430 98055 #021-01-1986 L1989 OBG *020 †30

KELSBERG, Gary Alan. 3915 TALBOT RD S, STE 401 98055 #005-02-1980 L1982 FM FPG *040 †18

KENNEDY, Michael Sullivan. 1412 SW 43RD ST, ALLERGY CENTER PS 98057 #034-01-1974 L1975 AI IM *020 †20,03

KLAFF, Leslie J. 723 SW 10TH ST STE 1 98057 #836-01-1971 L1984 IM END *071 †20

KLASSEN, Lawrence Allen. 275 BRONSON WAY NE 98056 #006-16-1978 L1981 FM *020 †18

KLOKEID, Darla. 1412 SW 43RD ST, STE 200 98057 #005-12-1998 L2000 FM *020 †18

KLONOWSKA, Malgorzata Ewa. ■ 98057 #759-01-2001 L2007 N *100

KOMAROW, Julie Ann. 400 S 43RD ST 98055 #054-04-1983 L1984 FM OBS *020 †18

KOSHY, Saramma. 275 BRONSON WAY NE 98056 #495-27-1954 L1970 FM *071 †18

KRAEMER, Diana Lynn. 3915 TALBOT RD S, STE 104 98055 #005-14-1986 L1992 NS *020 †25

KRAMER, C Michael. 4011 TALBOT RD S, STE 460 98055 #054-04-1977 L1980 GE IM *020 †20

KUMASAKA, Brian Hisao. 4011 TALBOT RD S, STE 460 98055 #054-04-1988 L1990 D *020 †15

LAKE, Melvin Harold. 17722 SPRINGBROOK RD 98055 #005-12-1967 L1973 OBG *071 †30

LAMBRECHT, James Douglas. 3915 TALBOT RD S, STE 309 VMC CLINIC BILLING 98055 #016-43-1974 L1977 FM *020 †18,16

LASLEY, Mary Valdrighi. 1412 SW 43RD ST, ALLERGY CENTER PS 98057 #030-05-1990 L1996 AI PD *020 †03,55

LAU, Wayne Ming. 4011 TALBOT RD S, STE 420 98055 #024-07-1991 L1996 GS *020 †85

LAWRENCE, Augustine Hicks. 1412 SW 43RD ST, STE 200 98057 #024-16-1993 L1999 OBG DMP *020 †30

LEE, Dan T. 98056 #583-02-1963 L1968 AN *071

LEE, Michael Edward. 275 BRONSON WAY NE 98056 #005-02-1986 L1990 OPH *020 †35

LEW, Arthur, Jr. 400 S 43RD ST 98055 #016-11-1999 L2004 FM *020 †18

LIN, Yu Yu Jeff. 400 S 43RD ST 98055 #654-01-2007 FP *012

LOMBARDI, Susan Harris. 4033 TALBOT RD S STE 430 98055 #048-02-1993 L2002 NEP *020 †20

LORCH, Gerald Steven. 4011 TALBOT RD S, STE 460 98055 #024-07-1969 L1970 CD IM *020 †20

■ = Address Information Privacy Protected

LU, Christine. ■ 98059 #035-19-2005 L2005 **N** *012
LUNA, Wuaca Kareem. 3600 LIND AVE SW, STE 170 98057 #054-04-1999 L2001 **FSM** *020 †18
LUTHY, David Adair. 400 S 43RD ST 98055 #016-06-1973 L1974 **OBG MFM** *020 †30
LWAI, San. 400 S 43RD ST 98055 #209-01-1962 L1968 **CD IM** *020
MAC FARLANE, Robt Eugene. 900 SW 16TH ST STE 320, PO BOX 374 98057 #067-01-1961 L1967 **NM DR** *020 †80
MADDOX, Sonja Pierrette. 601 S CARR RD STE 100 98055 #054-04-1999 L2001 **FM** *020 †18
MAGI, Martin. 400 S 43RD ST 98055 #040-02-1958 L1968 **OTO HNS** *071 †45
MANN, Amardeep Kaur. ■ 98056 #496-20-1998 L2002 **IM** *020 †20
MARTIN, Michael. 4011 TALBOT RD S, STE 460 98055 #003-01-1975 L1993 **IM** *040 †20
MASLEN, Curtis Reed. 400 S 43RD ST 98055 #019-02-1985 L1986 **AN** *020 †05
MAURER, Gregory Gerard. 400 S 43RD ST 98055 #028-34-1987 L1992 **AN** *020 †05
MAXWELL, Mary Christine. 400 S 43RD ST 98055 #055-01-1980 L1984 **EM** *020 †16
MAXWELL, Thomas Edward. 4033 TALBOT RD S STE 230 98055 #028-34-1955 L1963 **OTO** *020 †45
MAYENO, John Kenneth. 17900 TALBOT RD S STE 102 98055 #054-04-1984 L1986 **FM** *020 †18
MC CLEAN, Steven Peter. 4033 TALBOT RD S, STE 540 98055 #030-06-1984 L1989 **A** *020 †20,03
MC FALL, Tori Ann. 4011 TALBOT RD S, STE 420 98055 #049-01-1986 L1991 **GS** *020 †85
MC GORAN, Craig Michael. 17900 TALBOT RD S STE 102 98055 #054-04-1996 L1998 **FM** *020 †18
MC LENNAN, Dorcas Ann. 1412 SW 43RD ST, WOMEN'S & FAMILY HEALTH SP 98057 #054-04-1986 L1988 **OBG** *020 †30
MEDINA, Phillip Alan. 4361 TALBOT RD S, STE 102 98055 #005-18-1982 L1991 **ORS** *020 †40
MEHTA, Uday Kantilal. 451 DUVALL AVE NE, STE 120 98059 #495-17-1983 L1992 **FM** *020 †18
MELBER, Daniel. 3915 TALBOT RD S, STE 104 98055 #016-11-1970 L1971 **N** *020 †75
MENDONCA, Brandi A. 3915 TALBOT RD S, STE 401 98055 #043-01-2003 L2003 **FM** *020 †18
MILLER, Howard Bernard. 920 N 1ST ST 98057 #036-05-1971 L1973 **FM** *020 †18
MILLER, Michael Glen. 4011 TALBOT RD S, STE 220 98055 #025-01-1986 L1988 **ORS** *020 †40
MILLIRON, Tara Jolene. 400 S 43RD ST 98055 #005-12-2005 L2006 **FP** *012
MITCHELL, Donald Waldo. 4011 TALBOT RD S, STE 500 98055 #024-01-1964 L1970 **IM PUD** *071 †20
MOCKOVAK, Michael Emeric. 900 SW 16TH ST, STE 200 98057 #008-01-1988 L2001 **OPH** *020 †35
MOLINA, Robert Edward. 451 DUVALL AVE NE 98059 #056-06-1991 L1997 **FM** *020 †18
MONPONBANUA, Aileen H. 601 S CARR RD, STE 100 98055 #035-09-2000 L2002 **FM** *020 †18
MONSON, Mikael Christian. 4011 TALBOT RD S, STE 210 98055 #054-04-1989 L1996 **OPH** *020 †35
MONTAG, Maurice Jos. 400 S 43RD ST, VALLEY GENERAL HOSP MEDIC 98055 #018-03-1977 L1977 **EM** *020 †16
MOOR, Thomas. 330 SW 43RD ST, STE K PMB 328 98057 #154-07-1958 L1967 **GYN** *020 †30
MOORE, William Le. 4011 TALBOT RD S, STE 220 98055 #048-02-1999 L2003 **PD** *020 †55
MORKOS, Ashraf A. 400 S 43RD ST, NEONATOLOGY 98055 #915-03-1987 L2005 **NPM** *100 †55
MORLIN, Gregory Leonard. ■ 98058 #028-03-2002 L2005 **ID** *012
MORSE, Melvin Lee. 4011 TALBOT RD S STE 220 98055 #010-01-1980 L1982 **PD** *020 †55
NAIBERT, David Keith, Jr. ■ 98056 #054-04-1987 L1989 **FM** *075
NAKABAYASHI, Kemi. 601 S CARR RD, STE 100 98055 #038-06-1988 L1990 **IM** *020 †20
NARDELLA, John Paul. 400 S 43RD ST 98055 #036-08-2002 L2003 **AN** *020 †05
NEHER, Jon Oscar. 3915 TALBOT RD S, STE 401 98055 #055-18-1984 L1985 **FM** *020 †18
NELSEN, Michele K. 400 S 43RD ST, VMC FAIRWOOD PRIMARY CARE 98055 #054-04-1995 L1997 **FM** *020 †18
NEMANICH, John W. 4011 TALBOT RD S, STE 460 98055 #016-11-1981 L1985 **CD IM** *020 †20
NGUYEN, Manh Minhkhac. 400 S 43RD ST, VALLEY ANESTHESIA ASSOCIAT 98055 #018-03-1995 L1999 **APM** *020 †05
NILSON, Karen L. 3600 LIND AVE SW, STE 170 98057 #054-04-1976 L1978 **IM** *030 †20,70
NUGENT, Carl Graul. 275 BRONSON WAY NE 98056 #007-02-1957 L1958 **GP** *020
NUNEZ, Stefanie. 4033 TALBOT RD S, STE 500 98055 #005-18-1996 L1999 **PCC** *020 †20
OAKES, Evan Merrill. 955 POWELL AVE SW, STE A 98057 #041-07-1996 L1998 **FM** *020 †18
OLSEN, Amy Marie. 4033 TALBOT RD S, STE 570 98055 #054-04-2001 L2003 **FM** *020 †18
OLSON, Naomi Kathleen. 1412 SW 43RD ST 98057 #026-04-1988 L1990 **OBG** *020 †30
O'NEILL, Daniel Patrick. 4011 TALBOT RD S, STE 460 98055 #024-01-1967 L1973 **GE IM** *020 †20
OTSU, Ichiro. 400 S 43RD ST 98055 #572-33-1981 L2000 **AN PME** *020 †05
PAEK, Robert. 400 S 43RD ST, DEPT OF ANESTHESIOLOGY 98055 #010-01-1995 L2001 **AN** *020 †05
PAINTER, Kimberly Lynn. 955 POWELL AVE SW 98057 #025-07-2001 L2006 **FM** *100 †18
PARK, William Young. 4033 TALBOT RD S, STE 500 98055 #025-01-1995 L1998 **PCC** *020 †20
PATULOT, Connie C. 4033 TALBOT RD S, STE 2 98055 #748-01-1974 L1981 **PD** *020
PAYNE, Jaime Joy. 400 S 43RD ST 98055 #422-01-2007 L2007 **FP** *012
PEARCE, William Alexander. 4011 TALBOT RD S, FIFTH FLOOR 98055 #010-01-1984 L1986 **GE IM** *020 †20
PEDROZA, Antonio. 3915 TALBOT RD S, STE 401 98055 #005-02-1986 L1988 **FM OBS** *040 †18
PENNINGTON, Paul. 400 S 43RD ST 98055 #040-02-1971 L1975 **FM** *020 †18 ‡
PEPPER, Ellendee. 4011 TALBOT RD S STE 460 98055 #016-11-1981 L1985 **D** *020 †15
PHILLIPS, Llewellyn, II. 4509 TALBOT RD S, STE 101 98055 #036-01-1965 L1973 **D** *020 †15
PHILP, Sarah B. 200 S 2ND ST 98057 #036-01-1997 L1999 **FM** *020 †18
PLASKON, Brian Joseph. 4033 TALBOT RD S, STE 540 98055 #017-20-1993 L1996 **GS** *020 †85
PLATAS, Angelina Alicia. 601 S CARR RD STE 100, PACIFIC MEDICAL CENTER REN 98055 #054-04-1999 L2002 **IMG** *020 †20
POSCH, Reinhold Anton. 275 BRONSON WAY NE 98056 #048-13-1983 L1986 **FM** *020 †18
POSTMA, Sidney Wm. 400 S 43RD ST 98055 #007-02-1978 L1980 **AN** *020 †05
QUIJADA, Vilma Elizabeth. 4033 TALBOT RD S STE 430 98055 #715-01-1977 L1996 **NEP IM** *020 †20
RAMOS, Jose Ramon. 400 S 43RD ST 98055 #319-03-1966 L1978 **GS** *020
RAO, A Mallikarjuna. 400 S 43RD ST 98055 #495-21-1961 L1971 **GS VS** *020 †85
REDDY, Shailaja N M. 601 S CARR RD, STE 100 98055 #496-39-1995 L2002 **IM** *020 †20
REED, David Craig. 400 S 43RD ST 98055 #017-20-1984 L1986 **U EM** *020 †95
REHNGREN, Joel Philip. 15 S GRADY WAY, STE 525 98057 #005-12-1956 L1960 **P IMG** *071
REIGEL, David Geo. 275 BRONSON WAY NE 98056 #039-01-1961 L1968 **PD** *020 †55
REISNER, Dale Paton. 400 S 43RD ST 98055 #054-04-1982 L1990 **MFM OBG** *020 †30
REYRAO, Rowena Lilibel P. 19243 98TH PL S 98055 #748-02-1992 L2000 **FM** *020 †18 ‡
RICE, James Phillip. 17722 TALBOT RD S 98055 #005-18-1981 L1990 **OBG** *020 †30
RICHEY, Mack David. 17930 TALBOT RD S 98055 #016-11-1963 L1970 **PS** *071 †85,65
RICHTER, Monica W. 4011 TALBOT RD S STE 220 98055 #005-18-1984 L1992 **PD** *020 †55
RIDDLE, Robby Clark. 4033 TALBOT RD S, STE 570 98055 #023-12-1995 L2002 **FM AM** *020 †18
RISA, Steve Lars. 3915 TALBOT RD S 98055 #054-04-1983 L1984 **OTO** *020 †45
ROSELLINI, Doris Harkson. 17900 TALBOT RD S, STE 102 98055 #005-19-1990 L1992 **FM** *020 †18
ROSELLINI, Gerald Philip. 3915 TALBOT RD S STE 401 98055 #005-15-1983 L1989 **FM** *020 †18
RUDISILL, Heather M. 3915 TALBOT RD S, STE 401 98055 #030-06-1999 L2001 **FM** *020 †18
RUOFF, David Philip. 4361 TALBOT RD S, STE 102 98055 #017-20-1981 L1987 **ORS** *020 †40
RUSSO, James Mariano, Jr. 4011 TALBOT RD S # 30 98055 #041-02-1968 L1970 **ORS** *071 †40
SACKS, Elliot Marc. 400 S 43RD ST 98055 #005-06-1975 L1991 **DR FM** *020 †80,18
SAMAVEDI, Vandita Saxena. 14410 SE PETROVITSKY RD 98058 #495-27-1993 L2002 **IM** *020 †20
SANDS, Andy Junior. 17600 TALBOT RD S, STE 7 98055 #028-03-1976 L1981 **P** *020 †75
SANTOS, David Q. 1412 SW 43RD ST STE 110, NORTHWEST HEAD & NECK SUR 98057 #021-01-1987 L1993 **OTO** *020 †45
SAREWITZ, Stephen John. 400 S 43RD ST, DEPT OF PATHLGY 98055 #035-01-1975 L1980 **PTH** *020 †50
SAUNDERS, Rebecca. 1412 SW 43RD ST, STE 200 98057 #060-01-1992 L1996 **FM** *020 †18
SCHNEBLE, Cynthia Lynn. 3600 LIND AVE SW, STE 170 98057 #038-45-1983 L1991 **AM** *020
SHEREEN, Tina. 200 S 2ND ST, RENTON COMMUNITY HEALTH CE 98057 #054-04-2001 L2004 **FM** *100 †18
SHIN, Chang B. 4300 TALBOT RD S, STE 303 98055 #048-13-1992 L1999 **N** *020
SMITH, Andrew Onstad. 400 S 43RD ST 98055 #054-04-1997 L2000 **AN** *020 †05
SMITH, Heidi Sue. 400 S 43RD ST 98055 #054-04-1982 L1983 **AN** *020 †05
SMITH, James Robt. 17910 TALBOT RD S, RENTON MEDICAL IMAGING 98055 #038-06-1956 L1977 **OBG NPM** *040
SNOW, Lawrence Wayne. 17910 TALBOT RD S 98055 #054-04-1971 L1973 **ORS OSM** *020 †40
SOLIS, Maurice Luto. ■ 98058 #005-06-2005 L2005 **DR** *012
SORENSEN, Tanya Kristi. 400 S 43RD ST 98055 #054-04-1985 L1986 **OBG MFM** *020 †30
SPIES, Russell Lee. 400 S 43RD ST 98055 #048-13-1985 L1988 **EM** *020 †16
SPRENGER, Jay Davis. 1412 SW 43RD ST, ALLERGY CENTER PS 98057 #035-03-1974 L1975 **AI IM** *030 †20,03
STEWART, Barry Craig. 14410 SE PETROVITSKY RD 98058 #010-01-1973 L1977 **GYN** *020 †30
STUMPP, Dennis Allan. 400 S 43RD ST 98055 #038-43-1980 L1990 **OM AM** *020 †70
STURMAN, Melvin Jerald. 17930 TALBOT RD S 98055 #054-04-1959 L1968 **PS HS** *071 †65
SUBRAMANIAM, Satish. 3600 LIND AVE SW STE 170, OCCUPATIONAL HEALTH SERVIC 98057 #495-94-1991 L1995 **OM** *020 †18
SUMMERFIELD, Steven L. 4361 TALBOT RD S STE 102 98055 #028-34-1989 L2000 **ORS** *020 †40
SUSSMAN, Allen Michael. 723 SW 10TH ST STE 1 98057 #035-09-1974 L1977 **END IM** *020 †20
SWORDS, Eamonn G. 4445 TALBOT RD S 98055 #539-04-1981 L1993 **P** *020 †75
TAGAVILLA, Anthony Froma. 17722 TALBOT RD S, VALLEY WOMEN'S CLINIC 98055 #166-03-2003 L2007 **OBG** *020
TALLEY, Dan Mark. 4011 TALBOT RD S, STE 500 98055 #056-06-1994 L2002 **PCC** *020 †20
TAN, Ling Han. 148 PARK AVE N 98057 #035-08-1980 L1985 **FM** *020 †18
TATUM, Ashley M Jerath. 1412 SW 43RD ST, ALLERGY CENTER PS 98057 #016-06-1995 L2001 **AI** *020 †20,03
TAYLOR, Christopher S. 1601 LIND AVE SW 98057 #034-01-1978 L1979 **FM PHP** *020
TEDRICK, Charles Arthur. 4300 TALBOT RD S 98055 #047-06-1966 L1969 **GS** *020 †85
THAI, Don Q. 400 S 43RD ST 98055 #054-04-1993 L1993 **PD N** *020 †75
THOMAS, Frank James, Jr. 4011 TALBOT RD S, STE 460 98055 #048-04-1979 L1981 **IM GE** *020 †20
THOMPSON, Robert Lawrence. 4033 TALBOT RD S, STE 570 98055 #017-20-1981 L1984 **FM** *020 †18
THOMPSON, Thomas E. 400 S 43RD ST 98055 #048-14-1994 L1998 **AN** *020 †05
THOROUGHGOOD, Veronica. 400 S 43RD ST 98055 #132-01-1984 L2002 **PCP** *020 †50
THULINE, Horace Crockett. ■ 98058 #054-04-1953 L1954 **OS** *071
TILLES, Stephen Andrew. 1412 SW 43RD ST, ALLERGY CENTER PS 98057 #005-18-1990 L2000 **AI** *020 †20,03
TIPTON, Nancy. 4300 TALBOT RD S STE 403, DBA CEDAR RIVER CLINICS-RE 98055 #016-42-1980 L1981 **OBG** *020 †30
TKACHEV, Arkadiy Borisovi. 601 S CARR RD, STE 100 98055 #913-05-1990 L2006 **FM** *100 †18
TOULOUSE, Dominick Robt. 4011 TALBOT RD S # 46 98055 #028-34-1980 L1983 **IM** *020 †20
TRAVAGLINI, John, Jr. 400 S 43RD ST 98055 #024-16-1981 L1982 **RO** *020 †80
TSE, Chun Hing. ■ 98059 #462-01-1977 L2004 **SP** *100
TUEFFERS, Paul M. 400 S 43RD ST 98055 #869-07-1957 L1958 **FM** *020
TWEED, Gerald Vernell. 4300 TALBOT RD S, STE 315 98055 #018-03-1964 L1968 **OBG** *020 †30
UNGER, Trisha Adrienne. 4011 TALBOT RD S 98055 #054-04-1996 L2002 **GS** *020 †85
VALDEPENAS, Edwin Babaran. 950 UNION AVE NE 98059 #748-01-1976 L1983 **GP FM** *075
VANDER HEYDEN, John L. 400 S 43RD ST 98055 #056-05-1975 L1979 **OBG OS** *020 †30
VERBRUGGHE, Johan Gilbert. ■ 98056 #165-02-1975 L1980 **GS** *020 †85
VILLARIASA, Belinda C. ■ 98058 #748-11-1969 L1987 *100
VIRANT, Frank S. 1412 SW 43RD ST, ALLERGY CENTER PS 98057 #028-34-1980 L1981 **AI PDA** *020 †55,03
VOSSLER, David Gregg. 400 S 43RD ST 98055 #041-02-1983 L1987 **N CN** *020 †75
VUONG, Monica Bui Dinh. 4532 NE 10TH ST 98059 #054-04-1999 L2004 **OPH** *020
WAHAN, Serv. ■ 98059 #041-15-2003 L2007 *100
WALKER, John Chas. 1412 SW 43RD ST, ALLERGY CENTER PS 98057 #023-12-1986 L2002 **AI** *020 †55,03
WALL, Richard Joseph, Jr. 4033 TALBOT RD S, STE 500 98055 #010-02-1998 L2003 **PCC** *020 †20
WALLACE, Teresa Louise. 3915 TALBOT RD S, STE 401 98055 #035-09-1986 L1988 **FM** *040 †18
WATERMAN, Eric T. 4033 TALBOT RD S STE 230, MED ARTS CTR 98055 #035-03-1987 L1992 **OTO** *020 †45
WEBB, Alison Louise. 4011 TALBOT RD S, STE 430 98055 #038-06-1994 L1998 **OBG** *072 †30
WEISS, Michael Elliot. 1412 SW 43RD ST, ALLERGY CENTER PS 98057 #035-48-1981 L1989 **AI IM** *020 †20,03
WILLIAMS, Paul Victor. 1412 SW 43RD ST, ALLERGY CENTER PS 98057 #054-04-1975 L1978 **AI PDA** *020 †55,03
WISEMAN, Linda. 4033 TALBOT RD S, STE 2 98055 #048-14-1986 L1991 **PD** *020 †55
WRIGHT, Jonathan Vincent. 801 SW 16TH ST, STE 121 98057 #025-01-1969 L1970 **FM** *020
WU, Minjing. 4445 TALBOT RD S 98055 #243-21-1988 L2001 **P** *020 †75
XUEREB, Rodrick John. 400 S 43RD ST 98055 #025-07-1985 L1986 **AN** *020 †05

■ = Address Information Privacy Protected

YAU, Pin-Yi. 4300 TALBOT RD S, STE 313 98055 #385-02-1966 L1970 **OBG** *071 †30
YOUNG, William Gregory, Jr. ■ 98058 #016-42-2008 *012
YOUNG, Ze'Ev. 920 N 1ST ST 98057 #035-46-1979 L1980 **FM** *030 †18 ‡
YU, Yahua. 3915 TALBOT RD S, STE 104 98055 #243-52-1987 L1998 **IM** *020 †75
YULE, Geoffrey James. 4300 TALBOT RD S STE 105 98055 #028-03-1991 L1997 **PS** *020 †65
ZAMORA, Ivan Antonio. 4011 TALBOT RD S # S-420 98055 #682-01-1971 L1978 **GS TS** *072
ZHAI, Zhimin. 4011 TALBOT RD S, SOUTH, SUITE 460 98055 #243-16-1987 L2001
    MPD *020 †20
ZHAO, Joy Yan. 3915 TALBOT RD S, STE 104 98055 #243-69-1991 L2004 **N CN** *020 †75 ‡
ZUMWALT, Theresa. 4300 TALBOT RD S STE 403, DBA CEDAR RIVER CLINICS-RE 98055
    #016-11-1971 L1998 **GYN OS** *020 †30

REPUBLIC – FERRY

ALRASHEDY, Farhad H. 10 ROS CIR 99166 #528-01-1974 L1984 **PN IM** *020
JULIAN, John Dee, Jr. 10 ROS CIR 99166 #012-01-1975 L1997 **GP** *020
KLEIN, Mary Lou Anderson. PO BOX 1020 99166 #005-12-1963 L1975 **GP FM** *071
SCHAAF, Karen Grey. 10 ROS CIR 99166 #054-04-1983 L1987 **FM** *020 †18
STEVENSON, Noel Wm. 470 THORNTON DR 99166 #143-05-1959 L1967 **EM FM** *071

RICHLAND – BENTON

ABED, Madar. 900 STEVENS DR, STE 101 99352 #187-04-1993 L2003 **CD** *020 †20
ABED, Nashwa. 2076 NEWHAVEN LOOP 99352 #875-01-1987 L1998 **HMP** *020 †50
ACHARYA, Naveen. 900 STEVENS DR, STE 101 99352 #035-09-2000 L2005 **CD** *020 †20
ALBERTINI, Michael F. 925 STEVENS DR STE 2B 99352 #003-01-1976 L1979 **PD** *020 †55
ALTAYAR, Sabah. 550 GAGE BLVD, PHYSICIANS IMMEDIATE CARE 99352 #902-10-1974 L1989
    FM *020 †18
AMBRADCHALELA, Esteban. 969 STEVENS DR, STE 1C 99352 #264-02-1990 L2000 **GS** *020
AMES, Geoffrey Stillman. 750 SWIFT BLVD STE 1 99352 #654-01-1986 L1989 **FM D** *020
ANDERT, Sara Elizabeth. 915 GOETHALS DR, ANDER FAMILY MED 99352 #040-02-1998 L2003
    FM *020 †18
ATWOOD, Barbara Lee. 925 STEVENS DR, STE 2D 99352 #054-04-1985 L1986 **IM** *020 †20
AYRES, Bruce Wallace. 800 SWIFT BLVD, STE 320 99352 #016-42-1990 L2004 **GS** *020 †85
BALDWIN, Timothy E. 1825 LESLIE RD 99352 #048-12-1983 L1984 **AN CCM** *020 †05
BANTAYAN, Rafael Pastrana. ■ 99354 #748-01-1974 *100
BATAYOLA, Charles E. 560 GAGE BLVD, STE 206 99352 #005-76-2000, ▲ L2003 **FM** *020 †18
BATOL, Miriam L. 660 GEORGE WASHINGTON WAY, STE 5-F 99352 #748-01-1982 L1992
    NPM PD *020 †55
BEESON, Donna Lynn. 888 SWIFT BLVD, ST LUKES INTERNAL MED 99352 #018-75-1997,
    ▲ L2007 **IM** *020 †20
BEISWENGER, Scott. 888 SWIFT BLVD 99352 #048-14-2002 L2002 **IM** *020 †20
BISGAARD, Carl Frederick. 750 SWIFT BLVD STE 5 99352 #297-01-1941 L1969 **GP** *020
BISGARD, Carl V, Jr. 1075 JADWIN AVE 99352 #024-01-1965 L1967 **AN N** *020 †05
BLANCHARD, Jeremy Robt. 888 SWIFT BLVD, KADLEC MEDICAL CENTER 99352
    #034-01-1991 L2002 **CCM** *020 †20
BOONPONGMANEE, Somprak. 780 SWIFT BLVD STE 280, TRI-CITIES DIGESTIVE HEALT 99352
    #891-02-1991 L2003 **GE** *020 †20
BORDERS, Rosa Maria. 1334 JADWIN AVE 99354 #649-01-1981 L1991 **GPM** *020 †70
BOWERS, Fredrick Jos. 945 GOETHALS DR, STE 210 99352 #048-02-1980 L1987
    GS CRS *020 †85,10
BRITTAIN, Dwane Theodore. 953 STEVENS DR, STE C 99352 #039-01-1984 L2000
    DR *020 †80,18
BUCHER, James I, Jr. 888 SWIFT BLVD 99352 #016-11-1987 L2002 **AN** *020 †05
CABEZAS, David Alexander. ■ 99352 #319-01-1992 L2003 **FM** *020
CAHN, Herbert Lewis. ■ 99354 #803-09-1942 L1951 **PHP OTO** *071 †45
CALCAGNI, John Alan. 1947 HARRIS AVE 99352 #050-02-1964 L1993 **OM AM** *071 †70
CALKIN, Cynthia Victoria. 915 GOETHALS DR 99352 #064-01-1993 L1995 **FM** *020 †18
CASEY, Richard William. ■ 99352 #024-07-1998 L2007 **DR** *020 †80
CHANDLER, Mary. ■ 99354 #036-07-1987 L1993 **OBG** *020 †30
CHARITY, Lynette Delcine. 1096 GOETHALS DR, TRICITIES REG SURG CTR 99352
    #024-07-1978 L1983 **AN** *020 †05
CHASE, Robert Ellis. ■ 99354 #016-11-1943 L1948 **GYN OS** *071
CHAU, Wing Chee. 943 STEVENS DR 99352 #023-01-1989 L1993 **PM** *020 †60
CHORLEY, Gordon Ewart. ■ 99352 #917-20-1950 L1963 **AN** *020
CHUA, Jimmy Dy. 888 SWIFT BLVD 99352 #748-01-1983 L2001 **ID IM** *020 †20
COKER, Martin Jeffrey. 550 GAGE BLVD, PHYSICIANS IMMEDIATE CARE 99352
    #030-05-1993 L1993 **FM** *020 †18
COLE, Frank Everett. 780 SWIFT BLVD STE 290 99352 #035-06-1975 L1978 **IM** *020 †20
COOK, Sherilyn Johnston. 560 GAGE BLVD, STE 203 99352 #054-04-1990 L1992
    FM OBS *020 †18
COOPER, Holly Sue. 888 SWIFT BLVD 99352 #005-12-1999 L2003 **EM** *020 †16
CORDERO, Juan Abner, Jr. 833 SWIFT BLVD 99352 #041-13-1993 L2007 **TS** *020 †85,90
CRABTREE, Glynda Gaye. 888 SWIFT BLVD 99352 #005-06-1995 L2001 **EM** *020 †16
CUELLO, Alcides. 471 WILLIAMS BLVD, MEDICAL CENTRAL SERVICE CO 99354
    #649-02-1960 L1967 **GYN** *072 †30
DAWSON, Brian Jefferson. 888 SWIFT BLVD 99352 #054-04-2000 L2003 **EM** *020 †16
DEITZ, Michael Eric. 475 BRADLEY BLVD 99352 #033-05-1974 L1984 **OPH EM** *020 †35
DERAY, Arnulfo Talamayan. 1050 GILMORE ST STE C, KADLEC CLINIC 99352
    #748-01-1998 L2007 **IMG** *020 †20
DERNBACH, Frances Harris. 925 STEVENS DR, STE 3A 99352 #005-18-1987 L1993
    PD *020 †18
DICKEN, Donald George. 888 SWIFT BLVD 99352 #026-04-1987 L1991 **PM** *020 †60
DICKERMAN, David Lyell. 985 GOETHALS DR 99352 #033-06-1992 L1998 **AN** *020 †05
DIETERT, Scott Edward. ■ 99354 #028-02-1962 L1968 **EP PTH** *050 †50
DILLON, Thomas Lee. 780 SWIFT BLVD STE 320 99352 #054-07-1974 L1981 **P** *020 †75
DOWLING, Elizabeth Ann. ■ 99354 #007-02-2004 L2007 **IM** *020 †20
DUBROW, Marc Edward. 888 SWIFT BLVD 99352 #041-07-1995 L2006 **EM** *030 †16
DUEY, Michael Allan. 888 SWIFT BLVD, KADLEC MEDICAL CENTER 99352 #007-02-1992 L2003
    AN *020 †05
DYE, Daniel Mark. 303 BRADLEY BLVD, STE 108 99352 #028-02-1986 L1990 **P** *020 †75
EGLI, Kenneth James. 888 SWIFT BLVD 99352 #665-01-1999 L2002 **EM** *020 †16
ELLNER, Harold J. 888 SWIFT BLVD 99352 #035-20-1953 L1960 **U** *071 †95

EVERETT, Kristin Marie. 945 GOETHALS DR STE 30 99352 #041-13-1996 L1999 **FM** *020 †18
EWER, Stephen Norton. 900 STEVENS DR STE 101, INLAND CARDIOLOGY ASSOCIAT 99352
    #031-01-1989 L1996 **CD IM** *020 †20
FARRAR, Jon R D. 1155 JADWIN AVE 99352 #038-44-1986 L1993 **CD IM** *020 †20
FAWCETT, Brian Peck. 1979 SNYDER ST, STE 150 99354 #055-02-1982 L2007 **GPM** *020 †70
FEENEY, Craig M. 953 STEVENS DR, STE C 99352 #012-05-1977 L1983 **DR EM** *020 †80
FEWEL, Matthew Evan. 833 SWIFT BLVD 99352 #005-06-1998 L2005 **NS** *020
FISHER, John A. 888 SWIFT BLVD, DEPT OF ANESTHESIOLOGY 99352 #060-01-1989 L1994
    AN *100 †05
FITZSIMON, Denise. 800 SWIFT BLVD, STE 300 99352 #048-16-1984 L2006 **PD** *020 †55
FORSYTHE, Markus L. 888 SWIFT BLVD 99352 #040-02-1993 L1996 **EM** *020 †16
FOX, Earl Ross. 1075 JADWIN AVE 99352 #054-04-1981 L1982 **GS TS** *020
FOX, John Steven. 112 COLUMBIA POINT DR, STE 101 99352 #027-01-1981 L1985
    GYN *020 †30
FRANCO, Robert. ■ 99354 #040-02-1940 L1942 **GS TS** *071 †85
FREEMAN, Stuart Vincent. 953 STEVENS DR STE B 99352 #041-01-1972 L1977 **IM** *020 †20
FREY, Gerald Chas. 355 ROCKWOOD DR 99352 #056-05-1971 L1976 **PD** *020 †55
GAMBER, Herbert Hampton. ■ 99352 #018-03-1958 L1976 **ORS LM** *071 †40
GEMBS, Eduardo Augusto. 112 COLUMBIA POINT DR, UPLAND EDGE MEDICAL GROUP 99352
    #737-10-1997 L2003 **FM** *020 †18
GEORGE, Richard Louis. 800 SWIFT BLVD, STE 200 99352 #054-04-1986 L1990 **IM** *020 †20
GO, Grace Tan. ■ 99352 #748-01-1986 L1998 **PD** *020
GOMEZ-ENGLER, Hugo. PO BOX 549, 1155 JADWIN AVE 99352 #132-04-1967 L1998
    TS CD *020 †85,90
GONZALEZ ACOSTA, Nestor A. ■ 99352 #264-04-1989 L2003 **FM** *020
GRANTHAM, Dale Courtney. 888 SWIFT BLVD 99352 #021-01-1979 L2002
    EM GPM *020 †18,16
GRUNVALD, Eugenio Roberto. 953 STEVENS DR, STE C 99352 #924-01-1970 L1979
    GE IM *020 †20
HADDADIN, Hassan Atef. 800 SWIFT BLVD, STE 200 99352 #408-08-1994 L2003
    PCC SME *020 †20
HADEED, Anthony. 888 SWIFT BLVD 99352 #875-01-1972 L1988 **NPM PD** *020 †55
HAGER, Christopher. 888 SWIFT BLVD, KADLEC MEDICAL CENTER-LAB 99352
    #045-01-1984 L2001 **PTH GS** *020 †50
HALES, Walter John. 821 SWIFT BLVD 99352 #035-45-1976 L1993 **ORS HS** *020 †40
HALVORSEN, Philip Roy. 969 STEVENS DR STE 3A 99352 #020-02-1979 L1988
    OBG MFM *020 †30
HAMMERSMITH, Scott M. 953 STEVENS DR, STE C 99352 #005-06-1990 L1992
    DR NM *020 †80
HAMNER, Albert Patton, Jr. 800 SWIFT BLVD, STE 200 99352 #048-02-1970 L1988
    PUD IM *020 †20
HAMNER, Amelia D O. 800 SWIFT BLVD STE 200 99352 #048-02-1971 L1990 **IM** *020 †20
HANNAN, Elhami Nozad. 888 SWIFT BLVD, KADLEC MEDICAL CTR 99352 #902-07-1994 L2003
    IM *020 †20
HARRISON, Devin Andrew. 475 BRADLEY BLVD, COLUMBIA RVR EYE CTR 99352
    #028-34-1989 L1994 **OPH** *020 †35
HASHMI, Farrukh Husnain. 1175 CARONDELET DR, LOURDES COUNSELING CENTER 99354
    #704-02-1984 L2000 **P** *020
HAZEL, James Robt. 821 SWIFT BLVD 99352 #040-02-1984 L1989 **ORS** *020 †40
HEAP, Adrian James. 1201 JADWIN AVE STE 104 99352 #352-05-1963 L1977 **GS OS** *020 †85
HIGGS, Owen Milo. 821 SWIFT BLVD, TRI CITY ORTHO CLINIC 99352 #049-01-1986 L2002
    ORS GS *020 †40
HINER, Jerry Leroy. 1445 SPAULDING PARK, SPAULDING BUSINESS PARK 99352
    #649-14-1971 L1979 **FM** *020 †18 ‡
HOITINK, Mark Allen. 705 GAGE BLVD STE 200, SUITE 200 99352 #017-20-1991 L1994
    FM *020 †18
HOLM, Jan. 825 JADWIN AVE, STE 250 99352 #869-07-1966 L1973 **IM** *020
HOPP, Robert Blaine. 560 GAGE BLVD, STE 102 99352 #056-06-1982 L1987 **D** *020 †15
HOWERTON, Randall Dean. 945 GOETHALS DR, ASSOCIATED PHYSICIANS FOR 99352
    #039-01-1989 L2007 **OBG** *020 †30
HSIEH, Gordon Henry. 875 SWIFT BLVD 99352 #018-75-1985, ▲ L1988 **ORS** *020 †18,40
HUANG, Huey-Ju Lin. 750 SWIFT BLVD STE 7 99352 #385-02-1967 L1977 **FM** *020
HUNSAKER, Steven Donald. 888 SWIFT BLVD, KADLEC MEDICAL CENTER 99352
    #040-02-1999 L2006 **IM** *020
HYMAN, Brian Kingston. 888 SWIFT BLVD 99352 #919-05-1964 L1988 **AN** *020
ILLIG, Karl Max. ■ 99354 #407-02-1938 L1966 **OPH** *071
ISAACSON, Erick B. 945 GOETHALS DR, STE 300 99352 #054-04-1978 L1981 **FM** *020 †18
JAMALI, Iyad N. 900 STEVENS DR, STE 101 99352 #875-01-1985 L1998 **CD IM** *020 †20
JARVIS, Carl William. 2033 HOXIE AVE 99354 #064-01-1993 L1995 **FM** *020 †18
KALICHMAN, William David. 560 GAGE BLVD STE 110 99352 #033-06-1990 L2006 **IM** *020 †20
KAMO, Gregory. 1096 GOETHALS DR, TRI CITY REG SURG CTR 99352 #005-12-1993 L1997
    AN *020
KASTHURI, Saravanan. 953 STEVENS DR, STE C 99352 #495-94-1992 L2000 **DR VIR** *020 †80
KATES, Richard Bernard. 969 STEVENS DR STE 3A 99352 #047-05-1965 L1980
    OBS MFM *020 †30
KAYSER, Henry Charles, III. ■ 99354 #038-40-1962 L1979 **OBG** *071 †30
KHANDHAR, Anuj Jayant. ■ 99354 #041-15-2008 *012
KHAWANDI, Wassim Abdallah. 309 BRADLEY BLVD # 4056 99352 #605-01-1998 L2004
    NEP *020 †20
KILDOW, John Oliver. 3080 GEORGE WASHINGTON WAY, H1-04 99352 #028-02-1948 L1949
    OM OS *072 †85
KINCAID, Steven Jon. 750 SWIFT BLVD, STE 22 99352 #007-02-1975 L1993 **GS** *020 †20
KLOKEID, Brian Grant. 888 SWIFT BLVD 99352 #005-12-1997 L2000 **EM** *020 †16
KLOTH, Robin Leigh. ■ 99352 #056-05-1997 L1997 **AN** *020 †05
KNIGHT, Joan Karene. 2612 QUARTERHORSE WAY 99352 #054-04-1994 L1998 **EM** *020 †16
KONTOGIANIS, Christopher. 888 SWIFT BLVD 99352 #035-19-1987 L1996 **ORS** *020 †40
KOSKINEN, Sean C. 888 SWIFT BLVD, DEPARTMENT OF RADIOLOGY 99352
    #023-01-1997 L2004 **DR** *020 †80
KRAUSE, Chas Edward, II. 750 SWIFT BLVD STE 17 99352 #040-02-1980 L1983 **FM** *020 †18
LAM, Mathias Martin. ■ 99352 #067-01-1968 L1974 **GE IM** *071 †20
LAWRENCE, Matthew C. 945 GOETHALS DR STE 300 99352 #054-04-1997 L1999 **FM** *020 †18
LE, Trieu Thuy. ■ 99354 #054-04-2007 L2007 **FP** *012
LEEDY, James Edward. 1215 GEORGE WASHINGTON WAY 99352 #040-02-1979 L1982
    FM *020 †18
LEES, John Kinler. ■ 99352 #028-34-1990 L1992 **FM** *020 †18
LIH, Bjorn. ■ 99352 #008-01-1941 L1947 **CRS** *072 †85

LOERA, Jose Luis. 1000 GEORGE WASHINGTON WAY, RICHLAND FIRE DEPARTMENT 99352 #056-06-1982 L1985 **FM** *020 †18

LONG, Richard Wm. 750 SWIFT BLVD, STE 5 99352 #054-04-1983 L1989 **PTH** *020 †50

LOYND, Graham Francis. 888 SWIFT BLVD 99352 #056-05-1969 L1978 **OBG** *020 †30

LUCKEY, Robert Carney. 471 WILLIAMS BLVD STE 4 99354 #005-02-1955 L1962 **PS GS** *071

MAHONY, Thomas Danl. 888 SWIFT BLVD 99352 #539-03-1956 L1964 **NM ATP** *071 †50,28

MALIK, Asif Usman. ■ 99352 #704-21-1996 L2006 **IM** *020 †20

MALONE, John Dudley. 902 BATTELLE BLVD, PACIFIC NW NATL LAB 99354 #038-40-1978 L2007 **ID IM** *050 †20

MANAWADU, Bingumal R. 1075 JADWIN AVE, V5 MEDICAL CTR 99352 #220-01-1964 L1981 **AN** *020 †05

MARCELO, Jesus Norberto. 1445 SPAULDING PARK, SPAULDING BUSINESS PARK 99352 #748-08-1991 L2001 **IMG** *020 †20

MARGULIES, Robert Allan. 888 SWIFT BLVD 99352 #033-05-1969 L1994 **EM AM** *020 †70,16

MARINOV, Hristo D. 2744 WILLOWBROOK AVE 99352 #198-03-1992 L2004 **AN** *020 †05

MARSHALL, Robert James. 925 STEVENS DR, STE 3C 99352 #016-11-1977 L1993 **D GP** *020 †15

MATHESON, John Robert. 888 SWIFT BLVD 99352 #049-01-1999 L2002 **EM** *020 †16

MATTA, Shakti Kumar. 712 SWIFT BLVD, STE 4 99352 #495-45-1988 L1998 **PD** *020 †55

MATTA, Tania Milad. 800 SWIFT BLVD STE 300 99352 #605-02-1990 L2007 **PD** *020 †55

MC CARTNEY, Richard Alan. 1608 HAINS AVE 99354 #040-02-1976 L1981 **GS** *071 †85

MC COY, Jon Thos. ■ 99352 #040-02-1976 L1979 **AN** *020

MC DONALD, Harry Pelot. ■ 99352 #047-07-1946 L1946 **GP** *071

MC DONALD, Palmer Bowling. ■ 99352 #041-13-1990 L1992 *100

MEADER, Willard Lingel. ■ 99352 #041-13-1958 **AM OM** *071 †70

MEDICA, John Francis. 1110 GILMORE ST 99352 #040-02-1991 L1998 **U** *020 †95

MEGNA, Lucien T. 705 GAGE BLVD STE 200 99352 #422-01-1987 L1996 **FM FSM** *020 †18

MELDER, Indrek. ■ 99352 #473-01-1977 L2001 **GS** *020 †70

MERKLEY, David Lee. 945 GOETHALS DR STE 300, THREE RIVERS FMLY MED PSC 99352 #049-01-1984 L1991 **FM** *020 †18

MERRELL, Mark Reid. 821 SWIFT BLVD 99352 #049-01-1990 L1996 **ORS** *020 †40

MERRIFIELD, Margaret K. 2400 STEVENS DR, SUITE-C 99354 #068-01-1981 L1993 **FM** *020

MILLS, Myron Leo. 1979 SNYDER ST 99354 #005-12-1972 L2005 **OM EM** *020 †16,70

MULHOLLAND, Mark Edward. 945 GOETHALS DR, ASSOCIATED PHYSICIANS FOR 99352 #038-40-1993 L1999 **OBG** *020 †30

MUSHEN, Robert Linton. 948 STEVENS DR, RICHLAND EYE CLINIC 99352 #040-02-1968 L1976 **OPH** *071 †35

NAJJAR, Fadi. ■ 99352 #875-01-1995 L2004 **NEP** *020 †20

NAND, Cheta. 1175 CARONDELET DR, LOURDES COUNSELING CENTER 99354 #368-01-1987 L2000 **ADP** *020 †75

NEFF, Douglas Lee. 1075 JADWIN AVE 99352 #035-09-1974 L1980 **ON HEM** *020 †20

NEMRI, Ghassan Solaiman. 1075 JADWIN AVE, APAC GROUPE, CENTERS FOR P 99352 #913-32-1979 L2007 **APM** *020 †10

NICHOLS, Robert David. 1175 CARONDELET DR 99354 #021-01-1961 L1980 **P GYN** *075 †30,75

NICHOLSON, Robin Wm. 888 SWIFT BLVD 99352 #040-02-1986 L1989 **EM** *020 †16

NIENDORFF, Cynthia M. 1096 GOETHALS DR, TRI CITY REGIONAL SURGERY 99352 #028-34-2000 L2004 **AN** *020 †05

NIENDORFF, Daniel F. 2571 AILERON LN 99354 #028-34-1998 L2004 **CCM** *020 †20

ORO, Joseph Peter. 12 COLUMBIA POINT DR, STE 103 99352 #305-01-1999 L2004 **FM** *020

ORTOLANO, Alexander M. ■ 99352 #054-04-2000 L2004 **OBG** *020 †30 ‡

PADAYATTY, Maylin Joseph. 888 SWIFT BLVD, KADLEC MEDICAL CENTER 99352 #495-37-1996 L2004 **IM** *020 †20

PATCHETT, Margaret Ann. 1096 GOETHALS DR, CENTER LLC 99352 #005-12-1987 L1993 **AN** *020 †05

PATTILLO, Michael Joseph. 945 GOETHALS DR STE 300 99352 #028-34-1998 L2002 **MPD** *020 †20,55

PE, Benjamin David. 1175 CARONDELET DR 99354 #016-11-1988 L1990 **CHP P** *020 †75

PERRY, John Christian. 800 SWIFT BLVD STE 280 99352 #049-01-1984 L1988 **OBG** *020 †30

PERRY, Johnathan Richard. 875 SWIFT BLVD 99352 #028-02-1989 L1996 **ORS OSM** *020 †40

PETTEE, Richard A. 888 SWIFT BLVD 99352 #030-05-1951 L1956 **ORS** *071 †40

PIRYANI, Suresh. 888 SWIFT BLVD, KADLEC MEDICAL CENTER 99352 #704-08-1982 L2004 **IM** *020 †20

PRIDGEN, Kelly Dean. 888 SWIFT BLVD 99352 #023-12-1989 L2002 **EM** *020 †16

QIU, Wei Wayne. 221 WELLSIAN WAY, STE 102 99352 #243-03-1988 L2001 **AN** *020 †05

RABENBERG, Jack R. 1075 JADWIN AVE 99352 #036-07-1949 L1961 **DR** *020

RAEKES, Julie Anne. 945 GOETHALS DR STE 300 99352 #030-06-1994 L1998 **MPD PD** *020 †20,55

RAMESH, Muthulakshmi. 1950 KEENE RD BLDG J 99352 #495-59-1975 L2001 **IM** *020 †20

RANA, Richie. ■ 99352 #041-15-2003 L2005 **IM** *100 †20

RAPPORT, Samuel. 750 GEORGE WASHINGTON WAY, STE 5 99352 #019-02-1954 L1989 **P** *030 †75

RAVAGE, Christopher Kevin. 925 STEVENS DR STE 2C, COLUMBIA BASIN CARDIOLOGY 99352 #030-06-1988 L1994 **CD** *020 †20

RAWLINS, Neil Whitney. 945 GOETHALS DR, ASSOCIATED PHYSICIANS FOR 99352 #049-01-1984 L1985 **OBG** *020 †30

REDDY, Anita. ■ 99352 #894-01-2000 L2005 **FM** *100 †18

REQUARD, Charles Kenneth. 953 STEVENS DR, STE C 99352 #051-07-1976 L1982 **DR NM** *020 †80

ROBINSON, Wendell Emerson. 750 SWIFT BLVD STE 13 99352 #649-01-1965 L1970 **CD IM** *020

ROLLER, Alfred Scarsi. 888 SWIFT BLVD 99352 #040-02-1981 L1983 **EM** *020 †16

ROSENBERG, Carrie Elizabe. ■ 99352 #030-06-2003 L2006 **AN** *020

SALINAS, Joseph Philip. 560 GAGE BLVD, STE 101 99352 #033-05-1990 L1999 **IM** *020 †20

SAMSELL, John Theodore. ■ 99354 #055-01-1971 L1979 **ORS** *071 †40

SARGEANT, Kevin Paul. 750 SWIFT BLVD STE 5 99352 #005-12-1987 L1994 **PTH** *020 †50

SCHILBACH, Christhart S. 1175 CARONDELET DR, LOURDES COUNSELING CENTER 99354 #028-02-1968 L1969 **P CHP** *020

SCHWARTZ, Ronald Evan. 925 STEVENS DR, STE 1A 99352 #010-02-1988 L1997 **OTO** *020 †45

SCOVAZZO, Mary Lynn. 875 SWIFT BLVD, NORTHWEST ORTHOPAEDIC ASSO 99352 #041-12-1982 L2002 **ORS OS** *020 †40

SEDA, Peter Eugene. 969 STEVENS DR STE 2A 99352 #030-05-1973 L1974 **CD IM** *020 †20

SEN, Anjan Kumar. 780 SWIFT BLVD STE 169 99352 #054-04-1957 L1967 **NS PMM** *020 †20

SEVERANCE, James Maurice. 888 SWIFT BLVD 99352 #007-02-1967 L1969 **EM FM** *020 †16

SHARMA, Vimal. 712 SWIFT BLVD STE 8 99352 #368-01-1981 L1994 **IM FM** *020 †20

SIZEMORE, Kenton L. 945 GOETHALS DR STE 200 99352 #049-01-1986 L1989 **OBG** *020 †30

SMITH, Frank John. 888 SWIFT BLVD, KADLEC MEDICAL CENTER 99352 #005-12-1976 L1979 **EM IM** *020 †16

SMITH, Larry Douglas. 945 GOETHALS DR, STE 200 99352 #051-07-1996 L2004 **OBG** *020 †30

SMITH, Stephen L. 550 GAGE BLVD, PHYSICIANS IMMEDIATE CARE 99352 #054-04-1980 L1981 **FM A** *020

SOMICH, Geraldine C. ■ 99352 #035-06-1952 L1958 **IM** *071

SPANN, William Jos, Jr. ■ 99352 #047-05-1978 L1994 **IM** *020

SRINIVASAN, Shantanu. ■ 99352 #496-39-1999 L2007 **AN** *020 †05

STAGER, James F. 1516 JADWIN AVE 99354 #016-06-1962 L1969 **PD FM** *071 †55,18

STALEY, Brian Esmond. 888 SWIFT BLVD, KADLEC MEDICAL CENTER 99352 #049-01-1996 L1996 **PTH** *020 †50

STRINGER, Penney Claire. 4960 RAU ST 99352 #010-02-1996 L2000 **FM** *020 †18

STRONG, James Ashley, Jr. 1075 JADWIN AVE, V-5 MEDICAL CENTER 99352 #048-04-1968 L2000 **AN** *020

SWINT, Margery Jean. 2426 ALEXANDER AVE 99354 #025-01-1961 L1979 **OM OS** *071

SZVETECZ, Matthew James. 888 SWIFT BLVD 99352 #041-09-1996 L1999 **IM** *020 †20

TABBARA, Saad Mohd Malih. 900 STEVENS DR, STE 101 99352 #605-01-1997 L2004 **IC** *020 †20 ‡

TEMPLE, Edward Houston. 471 WILLIAMS BLVD STE 2 99354 #048-04-1974 L1980 **GYN** *020 †30

THOMAS, Winifred Nancy. 888 SWIFT BLVD, KADLEC MEDICAL CENTER 99352 #038-40-2002 L2006 **PD** *100 †55

THRELKELD, Russell Dean. 640 JADWIN AVE STE G 99352 #649-02-1960 L1960 **IM** *075

TROTTA, Thomas Chas. 780 SWIFT BLVD, STE 370 99352 #040-02-1980 L1985 **GS** *030 †85

TRUITT, Carol Ann. ■ 99354 #041-09-1969 L1979 **PD** *071 †55

TURNER, Kevin Craig. 945 GOETHALS DR, ASSOCIATED PHYSICIANS FOR 99352 #054-04-1986 L1989 **OBG** *020 †30

VAUGHN, James Daniel. 560 GAGE BLVD, STE 206 99352 #054-04-1993 L1997 **FM** *020 †18

VONGTHAVARAVAT, Varaphon. ■ 99352 #891-01-1991 L1996 **IM** *020 †20

WADDILL, William Baxter. 953 STEVENS DR, STE C 99352 #036-08-1983 L2003 **DR** *020 †80

WADHWA, Surender Kumar. 780 SWIFT BLVD STE 200, RICHLAND MEDICAL CTR 99352 #495-45-1970 L1978 **CD IM** *020 †20

WADSWORTH, Donald Earl. ■ 99352 #040-02-1964 L1978 **DR** *071 †80

WAHL, Melvin Merle. 875 SWIFT BLVD 99352 #054-04-2001 L2001 **ORS** *100

WANG, Lawrence A. ■ 99354 #024-05-2003 *100

WASHINGTON, Clarence Danl. 780 SWIFT BLVD STE 190 99352 #010-03-1971 L1975 **N IM** *020 †75

WEIGHALL, Steven L. 953 STEVENS DR STE A, COLUMBIA BASIN IMAGING 99352 #049-01-1976 L1984 **DR** *040 †80

WELTER, Vincent Edward. 945 GOETHALS DR, STE 200 99352 #041-09-1996 L2000 **OBG** *020 †30

WILDER, William Hamlin. 1075 JADWIN AVE 99352 #054-04-1968 L1974 **OTO** *071 †55,45

WILKINSON, Thornton Thos. 780 SWIFT BLVD STE 160 99352 #040-02-1980 L2002 **NS** *020 †25

WILSON, Bruce Edward. 915 GOETHALS DR 99352 #054-04-1984 L1985 **END IM** *020 †20

WONG, Gene Kiang. 1215 GEORGE WASHINGTON WAY, STE 1 99352 #054-04-1976 L1979 **FM GYN** *020 †18

YANG, Hoyeol. 98 COLUMBIA POINT DR 99352 #583-06-1986 L1998 **GE IM** *020 †20

YANG, I-Yen. 1110 GOETHALS DR 99352 #385-02-1966 L1973 **A HEM** *020 †20,03

YEP, Ronald. 888 SWIFT BLVD 99352 #005-02-1967 L1988 **AN** *071 †05

ZHANG, Hui Juan. 221 WELLSIAN WAY STE 101 99352 #243-03-1988 L2001 **N** *020 †75

ZIRKLE, Lewis Greer, Jr. 875 SWIFT BLVD 99352 #036-07-1966 L1972 **ORS** *020 †40

ZIRKLE, Sara Kay Shilling. 925 STEVENS DR, STE 2 99352 #036-07-1965 L1973 **PD ADL** *020 †55

ZOLESSI, Leonel. 888 SWIFT BLVD 99352 #924-01-1974 L2002 **OBG MFM** *020 †30

RIDGEFIELD — CLARK

BROOKSBY, Craig Gerald. ■ 98642 #041-14-2007 L2007 **TY** *012

BROWNING, Dale Richard. ■ 98642 #005-17-1962 *071

CARLEO, James Paul. ■ 98642 #035-45-1998 L2006 **OBG** *020 †30

DREW, Josephine E. 8507 S 5TH ST STE 113, RIDGEFIELD FAMILY MED 98642 #014-01-1995 L1995 **FM** *020 †18

HARRISON, Mary T. ■ 98642 #041-01-1950 L1964 **PD GPM** *071

HOOPER, David Gordon. ■ 98642 #040-02-1967 L1969 **FM AM** *020 †18

MILLER, Craig Jos. ■ 98642 #040-02-1968 L1974 **DR** *071 †80

PEARSON, Derald Gaynard. ■ 98642 #054-04-1964 L1979 **IM** *071 †20

PEARSON, Patricia S W. ■ 98642 #016-43-1966 L1979 **GP** *071

RITZVILLE — ADAMS

BAUMANN, Otto Vernon. 216 E MAIN AVE 99169 #016-11-1954 L1956 **GP GS** *071

ECKLEY, Valerie Kay. 903 S ADAMS ST 99169 #054-04-1991 L1993 **FM** *020 †18

GERSH, Robert Harold. 903 S ADAMS ST 99169 #007-02-1975 L1980 **IM HEM** *020 †20

JARDEE, James Joseph. ■ 99169 #010-01-1962 L1966 **IM GP** *072

SACKMANN, Charles Martin. 903 S ADAMS ST 99169 #054-04-1987 L1990 **FM** *020 †18

ROCHESTER — THURSTON

CASERTA, Jennifer J. 18313 PAULSON ST SW, NORTHWEST PEDIATRIC 98579 #054-04-2001 L2004 **PD** *020 †55

FALOON, Michael David. ■ 98579 #051-07-1990 L1992 **FM** *020 †18

HU, Peter Ping. 4811 181ST LN SW, PROVIDENCE CENTRALIA HOSPI 98579 #049-01-1998 L2004 **DR** *020 †20

LO, Lily Limai. 18313 PAULSON ST SW, NORTHWEST PEDIATRIC 98579 #048-04-1992 L2000 **PD** *020 †55

MEKA, Srinivasa Rao. 18313 PAULSON ST SW STE A 98579 #495-11-2001 L2006 **FM** *020 †18

MILLER, James Mc Calmont. 18313 PAULSON ST SW, NORTHWEST PEDIATRIC 98579 #035-20-1964 L1992 **PD** *020 †55

POLLEY, Jennifer P. 18313 PAULSON ST SW, NORTHWEST PEDIATRIC 98579 #035-45-1984 L1990 **PD** *020 †55

■ = Address Information Privacy Protected

TSO, Jemima Huang. 18313 PAULSON ST SW, NORTHWEST PEDIATRIC 98579 #748-08-1983 L1991 **PD** *020 †55

WILEY, Joe W. 18313 PAULSON ST SW, NORTHWEST PEDIATRIC 98579 #020-12-1983 L1995 **PD** *075 †55

ROY – PIERCE

REED, Richard David. ■ 98580 #023-12-2000 L2002 **HO** *020 †20

ROYAL CITY – GRANT

DURANO, Sancho Derecho. 123 EVERGREEN ST W 99357 #748-07-1958 L1983 *071

SAMMAMISH – KING

AHUJA, Sukhdeep Kaur. ■ 98074 #496-39-1998 **P** *012

BEERS, Jeffrey Bryan. 1304 229TH PL NE 98074 #038-45-1985 L1993 **FM** *050

BRUNNER, Stephanie Lynn. 22603 NE INGLEWOOD HILL RD, SAMMAMISH, STE 100 98074 #054-04-2000 L2003 **PD** *100 †55

BURNSIDE, Monica Alex. 22603 NE INGLEWOOD HILL RD, # 100 98074 #054-04-2000 L2003 **PD** *020 †55

CHACKO, Leena. 22850 NE 8TH ST, STE 103 98074 #495-04-1992 L2006 **FM** *020 †18

CHEN, Luann Lawton. 22707 SE 29TH ST 98075 #054-04-1983 L1989 **FM** *020 †18

CHIANG, Tzu Sung. 98074 #012-01-1975 L1980 **GYN** *071 †30

CLAUDSON, Thomas Michael. 22603 NE INGLEWOOD HILL RD, STE 100 98074 #054-04-1995 L1998 **PD** *020 †55

DONG, Zhao Ming. 98075 #243-85-1983 L2004 **PTH** *100

GABORIAU, Henri. 22840 NE 8TH ST STE 103, SAMMAMISH CTR FOR FACIAL S 98074 #021-01-1994 L1999 **OTO FPS** *020 †45

GAN, Emilia Francoise. ■ 98074 #024-16-1998 **FM** *100

GEORGE, Evan. ■ 98075 #054-04-1986 L1991 **DMP** *020 †50 ‡

HOU, David. 2022 235TH PL NE 98074 #243-95-1983 L2002 **APM** *100 †18,05

IYER, Sujata Lakshmanan. ■ 98074 #496-38-1992 L1999 **PD** *020 †55

KIHICZAK, Luba. 22850 NE 8TH ST, STE 103 98074 #038-06-1976 L1976 **GS** *016

KOUSNETZ, Irving. ■ 98074 #016-11-1946 L1957 **CD IM** *071 †20

LUX, Glenn Alan. 22717 SE 29TH ST 98075 #035-45-1972 L1974 **PD IM** *020 †55 ‡

MADHAVAN, Lekha Sethu. ■ 98075 #495-31-1999 L2004 **IM** *020 †20

MC KEE, William Yeadon. 22850 NE 8TH ST, STE 103 98074 #045-01-1974 L1993 **FM** *020 †18

O'NEILL, Tracie Markay. 22717 SE 29TH ST 98075 #005-06-1991 L1993 **PD** *020 †55

ROSKIN, Robert Edward. 22717 SE 29TH ST, PEDIATRIC ASSOCIATES 98075 #041-01-1994 L1997 **PD** *020 †55

RYAN, Kathrine Silbernage. 22717 SE 29TH ST 98075 #005-02-1995 L1998 **PD** *020 †55

SINGH, Ravi Surendra. 22850 NE 8TH ST, STE 103 98074 #654-01-1998 L2002 **FM** *020 †18

STEWART, Donald Thos. 3854 E LK SAMM PKWY NE 98074 #054-04-1980 L1981 **FM DIA** *020 †18

TARDELL, Richard Heard. ■ 98074 #036-01-1985 L1986 **FM** *020 †18

VANKIREDDY, Haritha. ■ 98074 #495-11-1996 L2001 **FPG** *100 †18

VASANTHARAJAN, G. ■ 98075 #495-04-1967 L2004 **EM** *072 †16

WANG, Jen Fang. ■ 98075 #244-02-1955 L1998 **AN** *071

SEABECK – KITSAP

ARKLESS, Richard. PO BOX 790 98380 #041-01-1962 L1964 **DR** *072 †80

FAHLBERG, Vera Isabel. 2615 NELLITA RD NW 98380 #017-20-1959 L1988 **CHP PD** *040

GERLA, Dawn Catherine. ■ 98380 #054-04-2002 *100

HANSEN, Robert Wm. 12740 SEABECK HWY NW 98380 #056-06-1965 L1970 **OPH** *071 †35

KIRK, Jessica Lynn. ■ 98380 #008-01-2007 L2007 *012

WINSLOW, Jeffrey. ■ 98380 #051-01-1984 L1993 **EM** *020 †16

SEATAC – KING

CLIFTON, Elizabeth A. ■ 98188 #054-04-1978 L1979 **GP** *071

GREEN, Bert. 19540 INTERNATIONAL BLVD, STE 103 98188 #041-07-1974 L1978 **CD IM** *020 †20

OLAGESHIN, Sherifat Abiol. ■ 98188 #024-05-2005 L2007 *100

ROSCHEN, F Paul. ■ 98188 #026-04-1967 L1969 *075

SIFFER, Alan Norman. ■ 98188 #054-04-1973 **AN** *100

SKINNER, Suzanne Florence. 4040 S 188TH ST, STE 201 98188 #035-15-1993 L1995 **FM** *020 †18

WARING, William Michael. 2230 S 161ST ST, UNITED AIRLINES MED DEPT 98158 #051-04-1971 L1975 **OM AM** *020 †70 ‡

SEATTLE – KING

AACHEN-WINANS, James M. 2505 2ND AVE, STE 715 98121 #005-06-1980 L2005 **OTO FPS** *020 †45

AARABI, Shahram. PO BOX 356410, UNIV OF WASHINGTON 98195 #035-19-2007 L2007 **GS** *012

AARONSON, Barry Alan. 925 SENECA ST 98101 #010-01-1991 L1997 **IM** *020 †20

ABBASI, Siddique Akbar. 1959 NE PACIFIC, BOX 356340 98195 #028-34-2005 L2005 **IM** *012

ABBOTT, Arthur Travis. 125 16TH AVE E CSB-4, GROUP HEALTH/CAPITOL HILL 98112 #024-01-1971 L1977 **FM** *020 †18

ABBOTT, Chad Michael. ■ 98119 #021-01-2007 L2007 **FP** *012

ABDALLAH, Paul Sam. 1229 MADISON ST, STE 1500 98104 #005-02-1969 L1973 **IM ID** *020 †20

ABE, Denise Valentina. 2208 NW MARKET ST STE 410 98107 #005-06-1983 L1984 **IM** *020 †20

ABERLE, John H. 801 BROADWAY STE 1000 98122 #041-13-1952 L1954 **ORS** *071 †40

ABKOWITZ, Janis Lynne. 1959 NE PACIFIC ST, BOX 357710 98195 #024-01-1977 L1980 **HEM ON** *050 †20

ABOOD, Joseph Albert. ■ 98115 #038-40-2004 L2005 **AN** *012

ABOULAFIA, David Michael. 1100 9TH AVE G1-MSO, VIRGINIA MASON MEDICAL CEN 98101 #025-01-1983 L1990 **ON HEM** *020 †20

ABRAHAM, Senait Yohannes. 9650 15TH AVE SW STE 100 98106 #366-01-1990 L2002 **PD** *020 †20

ABRAHAM, Sumam Marion. 2505 2ND AVE, STE 200 98121 #495-37-1995 L1998 **FM** *020 †18

ABRAMOWITZ, Kelvyn. 747 BROADWAY 98122 #836-02-1974 L1988 **AN** *020 †05

ABRAMSON, Rachel Beth. 1730 MINOR AVE STE 1400 98101 #016-42-1995 L2001 **P** *020 †75

ABRASS, Christine Kreger. 1660 S COLUMBIAN WAY # 111 98108 #038-06-1973 L1985 **NEP IM** *030 †20

ABRASS, Itamar B. 325 9TH AVE # 359755 98104 #005-02-1966 L1984 **IMG END** *050 †20

ABSON, Kim Gittere. 1145 BROADWAY, THE POLYCLINIC 98122 #054-04-1986 L1991 **D IM** *020 †15

ACHENBACH, Chad Jeremy. ■ 98121 #016-06-2002 L2006 **ID** *012 †20

ACIERNO, Stephanie P. 1959 NE PACIFIC ST, GME PROGRAMS, BOX 356340 98195 #001-02-1999 L2004 **PDS** *012 †85

ACKERMAN, Peter. 1100 9TH AVE, VA MASON MED CTR B2-AN 98101 #035-09-1994 L1998 **APM** *020 †05

ACKLEY, Stanford Heaston. ■ 98103 #035-01-2003 L2007 **PEM** *012 †55

ACOSTA, David Al. 1959 NE PACIFIC ST, BOX 357430 98195 #005-15-1979 L1989 **FM** *030 †18

ADAM, Margaret Rode. 1100 9TH AVE 98101 #008-02-1990 L1997 **IM** *020 †20

ADAMS, Christine Marie. 6300 9TH AVE NE, STE 300 98115 #005-04-1981 L1982 **FM** *020 †18

ADAMS, Kay Elaine. 1229 MADISON ST, STE 1440 98104 #031-01-1980 L1981 **AN** *071 †05

ADAMS, Kristina Maria. 4245 ROOSEVELT WAY NE, STE 354775 98105 #026-08-1998 L2001 **OBG** *050

ADAMS, Neil Darius. ■ 98155 #054-04-1957 L1958 **GP** *030

ADAMSON, Richard Todd. 4020 E MADISON ST STE 210 98112 #047-05-1980 L1981 **P** *020 †75

ADDIS, Howard Michael. ■ 98102 #016-42-1968 L1969 **GS** *075

ADLER, Amanda Ingham. ■ 98119 #036-01-1988 L1989 **IM** *020 †20

ADLER, Katherine Jane. ■ 98107 #038-43-2003 L2003 **IM** *100

ADLER, Richard S. 1700 7TH AVE, STE 210 98101 #035-03-1983 L1996 **P OS** *020 †75

ADLER, Steven Jay. 1100 9TH AVE G1-MSO, VIRGINIA MASON MEDICAL CEN 98101 #028-02-1980 L1987 **DR** *020 †80

ADRA, Jimmy Shady. ■ 98102 #019-02-2006 L2006 **AN** *012

AFAN, Isagani Alvarez. 6044 MLK JR WAY S STE 104, SOUTHGATE MEDICAL CLINIC P 98118 #748-01-1959 L1983 **GP** *071

AFFOLTER, William T. 125 16TH AVE E 98112 #035-15-1969 L1970 **GP FM** *020 †18

AFRIDI, Seema Jaleel. ■ 98125 #016-45-2007 L2007 **PD** *012

AFZALI, Anita. ■ 98126 #054-04-2006 L2006 **IM** *012

AGARWAL, Ulka. 1959 NE PACIFIC ST BOX 356, UNIVERSITY OF WASHINGTON P 98195 #016-42-2004 L2005 **P** *012

AGNEW, Matthew Lawrence. 1959 NE PACIFIC ST, BOX 356410 98195 #041-12-2001 L2004 **GS** *012

AGOFF, Nicholas Sergay. 1100 9TH AVE 98101 #016-06-1996 L1999 **PTH** *020 †50

AGOSTI, Jan Marie. 1201 AMGEN CT W 98119 #005-18-1980 L1981 **ID A** *050 †20,03

AGOSTINI, Rosemary. 904 7TH AVE 98104 #035-09-1981 L1987 **FM OSM** *020 †18

AGRESS, Richard Lawrence. 1101 MADISON ST, STE 900 98104 #036-01-1978 L1979 **OBG** *020 †30

AHAD, Sajida. ■ 98115 #704-25-1998 L2006 **OBG GS** *100 †85

AHL, Kathrin Leanne. 600 BROADWAY, STE 170 98122 #005-02-1997 L2001 **DR** *020 †80

AHMAD, Suhail. 2150 N 107TH ST STE 160 98133 #495-67-1968 L1978 **NEP** *020

AHMAD, Vimlesh. ■ 98119 #495-67-1970 L1983 **GP AN** *020

AHMED, Sharmila. 1101 MADISON ST STE 301, PACIFIC MEDICAL CENTER/ONC 98104 #067-01-1997 L2006 **HO** *100 †20

AHRENHOLZ, Nicole Angela. ■ 98144 #040-02-2006 L2006 **IM** *012

AHRENS, Mario Enrique. 521 WALL ST 98121 #132-01-1958 L1983 **GS TRS** *020 †85

AHRENS, Sarah Elizabeth. 325 9TH AVE BOX 359702, HARBORVIEW MEDICAL CENTER 98104 #005-02-2002 L2002 **IM** *012

AIGNER, B Robt. 509 OLIVE WAY, MED DENTAL BLDG STE 1230 98101 #028-34-1952 L1953 **N** *062 †75

AIKAWA, Keiko. 1536 N 115TH ST, SWEDISH PROF HEALTH SERVIC 98133 #038-06-1996 L1998 **CD** *020 †20

AINSWORTH, Carla Renee. 550 16TH AVE, STE 100 98122 #028-02-1999 L2002 **FM** *020 †18

AITKEN, Moira Lesley. 1959 NE PACIFIC ST, MSC 359300 98195 #919-03-1978 L1983 **PUD** *050 †20

AJAM, Kamal Sami. 325 9TH AVE, PO BOX 359780 98104 #048-14-2000 L2005 **IM** *100 †20

AKHTAR, Saadia Ruby. 1959 NE PACIFIC ST RM C21, CAMPUS BOX 356340 98195 #025-01-1995 L2000 **PCC** *020 †20,55

AKINBAMI, Carolyn Omonike. 4400 37TH AVE S 98118 #054-04-1998 L2001 **PD** *020 †55

ALAVES, Maria. ■ 98109 #847-12-1982 L1990 **RHU** *020

ALBERDA, Bernard Jay. 10330 MERIDIAN AVE N, NORTH SEATTLE PEDIATRICS 98133 #049-01-1964 L1970 **PD OS** *020 †55

ALBERT, Alexa Elizabeth. 5129 NE 41ST ST, PSYCHIATRY RESIDENCY 98105 #024-01-1999 L2000 **PD** *020

ALBERT, Jesselle E. 4800 SAND POINT WAY NE #B-, CHILDRENS HOSP & REGIONAL 98105 #051-04-1999 L2005 **CCP** *012 †55

ALBERT, Tyler Jonathon. ■ 98105 #054-04-2008 *012

ALBERTS, Robert. ■ 98103 #660-03-1954 L1958 **P PHP** *020

ALBERTSON, Tina Marie. 4500 SAND POINT WAY NE 98105 #005-11-1999 L2002 **PHO** *020 †55

ALBRO, Peter Carey. 550 16TH AVE, STE 400 98122 #035-01-1970 L1973 **CD IM** *020 †20

ALDAPE, Hector Cantu. 2111 N NORTHGATE WAY, PATHOLOGY CONSULTANTS 98133 #649-02-1956 L1960 **PTH** *071 †50

ALDEA, Gabriel-Sorin. 1959 NE PACIFIC ST, U WA BOX 356310 DEPT CD 98195 #035-01-1981 L1998 **CD VS** *020 †85,90

ALEXANDER, Elizabeth M. 10740 MERIDIAN AVE N, STE 101 98133 #054-04-1980 L1982 **P** *020 †18,75

ALEXANDER, Eric Paul. UNIV OF WASHINGTON, DEPT OF REHAB MED 98195 #035-15-2004 L2006 **PM** *012

ALEXANDER, Jacob. 1959 NE PACIFIC ST 98195 #495-31-1998 **IM** *012

ALEXANDRESCU, Irina Ruxan. 1959 NE PACIFIC ST, UNIV OF WA SCH MED 98195 #781-01-1992 L2006 **NEP** *012 †20

ALI, Humera. 550 16TH AVE, STE 400 98122 #065-01-1990 L1998 **CD** *020 †20

ALKINDI, Salam Salem. FRED HUTCHINSON CANCER RES 98109 #539-03-1993 L2002 *100

ALLAN, Christopher H. 325 9TH AVE, BOX 359798 98195 #016-06-1992 L1998 **HS** *020 †40

ALLAN, Susan M. 98122 #024-01-1981 L2007 **PHP** *030 †70

ALLEN, Brady Lee. ■ 98102 #048-12-1979 L2007 **IM** *071 †20

ALLEN, Gregory J. 125 16TH AVE E, GROUP HEALTH FAMILY PRACTI 98112 #005-19-1976 L1977 **FM** *020 †18

ALLEN, Gregory James. 9730 3RD AVE NE, STE 202 98115 #028-02-1980 L1986 **DR** *020 †80
ALLEN, Hugh Willison. 1100 9TH AVE M6-AC, VIRGINIA MASON MEDICAL CEN 98101 #005-06-1988 L1992 **AN** *020 †05
ALLEN, John Douglas. 925 SENECA ST 98101 #024-01-1955 L1961 **IM PUD** *071 †20
ALLEN, Margaret Dale. ■ 98119 #005-18-1974 L1985 **TS** *050 †85,90
ALLEN, Matthew Ward. 7554 15TH AVE NW, BALLARD PEDIATRIC CLINIC 98117 #054-04-1998 L2000 **PD** *020 †55
ALLEN, Victoria Elizabeth. 1200 12TH AVE S 98144 #005-18-1989 L1992 **IM** *020 †20
ALLENDER, Brian Martin. ■ 98122 #038-06-2003 L2003 **P** *020
ALLISON, George H. 2271 NE 51ST ST 98115 #008-01-1945 L1949 **PYA** *020 †75
ALMARAZ, Lewis Benny. 420 MELROSE AVE E 98102 #005-19-1975 L1987 **CHN N** *020 †75
ALMOND, Madeline Camille. ■ 98102 #012-05-2005 L2005 **OPH** *012
ALMQUIST, Edward Eugene. 600 BROADWAY STE 440 98122 #054-04-1961 L1966 **HS** *071 †40
ALMQUIST, Howard Theodore. 1101 MADISON ST, STE 600 98104 #054-04-1966 L1977 **OPH** *071 †35
ALPERS, Charles Edward. 325 9TH AVE 98104 #035-45-1978 L1986 **ATP GP** *020 †50
ALTEMEIER, William Arthur. 1959 NE PACIFIC ST, BB-1253 HSB, BOX 356522 98195 #047-05-1992 L1992 **CCM** *020 †20
ALTHOUSE, Lesley. 1100 9TH AVE G1-MSO, VIRGINIA MASON MEDICAL CEN 98101 #917-09-1979 L1985 **IMG IM** *020 †20
ALTMAN, Jeff. 325 9TH AVE 98104 #024-07-1966 L1974 **FM ADL** *020 †18
ALVAREZ, Ann Margarette S. ■ 98116 #748-08-1991 L2005 **IM** *020 †20
ALVORD, Ellsworth C, Jr. 325 9TH AVE, HARBORVIEW MEDICAL CENTER 98104 #035-20-1946 L1961 **NP** *072
ALWOOD, Ashley Colleen. ■ 98199 #054-04-2008 *012
AMANN, Sean Michael. 1959 E ACIFI C STREET BOX, UW SCHOOL OF MEDICINE GME 98195 #016-42-2005 L2005 **ORS** *012
AMBROSE, Heidi Coryell. 1959 NE PACIFIC ST, BOX 356340 98195 #054-04-2001 L2001 **HS** *020
AMBROSIO, Renato. PO BOX 356485, UNIV OF WASHINGTON 98195 #187-78-1995 L2000 **OPH** *100
AMIN, Bijal Dilip. PO BOX 356340, GRADUATE MEDICAL EDUCATION 98195 #010-01-2003 L2003 **PTH** *012
AMIS, Benjamin. ■ 98122 #048-12-2007 L2007 **ORS** *012
AMORY, John Kenneth. 4245 ROOSEVELT WAY NE, STE 354775 98105 #005-02-1994 L1997 **IM** *020 †20
AMSLER, Lee Cameron. 125 16TH AVE E, CARDIO GROUP HLTH 98112 #010-02-1979 L1980 **CD IM** *020 †20
AMY, Bruce Melville. 200 15TH AVE E 98112 #054-04-1962 L1965 **OBG** *071 †30
ANAWALT, Bradley David. 1660 S COLUMBIAN WAY, GIMC (M111), SVAMC 98108 #005-19-1989 L1991 **END** *020 †20
ANAWALT, Kirsten L. ■ 98126 #054-04-1996 L1999 **IM** *071 †20
ANAYA SAENZ, Daniel Alfre. PO BOX 356410, UNIV OF WASHINGTON 98195 #264-04-1997 L2001 **GS** *100
ANDARSIO, Carlos Orestes. 2600 SW HOLDEN ST 98126 #654-01-1988 L1992 **IM** *020 †75
ANDERSEN, Arne Jerome. 125 16TH AVE E 98112 #054-04-1978 L1979 **FM** *020 †18
ANDERSEN, Beth Arkady. 1101 MADISON ST STE 800, SPD PEDIATRICS 98104 #054-04-1993 L1993 **UP** *020 †95
ANDERSEN, Christopher Mar. 1959 NE PACIFIC ST, U OF W HS AFFAIRS BOX 3563 98195 #035-01-2004 L2004 **IM** *020 †20
ANDERSEN, Kathleen Lisa. 4026 NE 55TH ST, # E251 98105 #054-04-1980 L1981 **P** *020
ANDERSEN, Roger Carl. 4702 42ND AVE SW 98118 #649-14-1978 L1983 **OBG OS** *020 †30
ANDERSON, Arthur Eric. ■ 98116 #016-01-1990 L2005 **CCM** *012
ANDERSON, Benjamin Olney. 1959 NE PACIFIC ST, MSC 359300 98195 #035-46-1985 L1994 **ON** *020 †85
ANDERSON, Britt Arick. 1930 POST ALY 98101 #054-04-2000 L2002 **IM** *100 †20
ANDERSON, Christine Marce. ■ 98101 #030-05-2004 L2004 **AN** *012
ANDERSON, Corrie Thaddeus. 4800 SAND POINT WAY NE, DEPT OF ANESTHESIOLOGY W9 98105 #005-11-1982 L2001 **PAN PME** *020 †05
ANDERSON, David W. 1201 3RD AVE, C/O GRINA MELLON 98101 #038-41-1949 L1957 **ORS** *071 †40
ANDERSON, Dennis R. 1601 5TH AVE STE 830, ELLIOTT BAY MEDICAL GROUP 98101 #056-06-1978 L1979 **EM FM** *020 †18,16
ANDERSON, James Larry. ■ 98116 #065-01-1959 **GP** *020
ANDERSON, James Lewis. ■ 98116 #054-04-1960 L1961 **FM** *071
ANDERSON, Jonathan Christ. BOX 356340, 1959 NE PACIFIC ST C212 98185 #054-04-2005 L2006 **AN** *012
ANDERSON, Ken Norman. 7210 ROOSEVELT WAY NE 98115 #054-04-1986 L1988 **FM** *020 †18
ANDERSON, Kenneth Norman. 801 BROADWAY, STE 730 98122 #054-04-1958 L1959 **U IM** *071 †95
ANDERSON, Kristin Joanne. ■ 98112 #024-07-2007 L2007 **FP** *012
ANDERSON, Larry D, Jr. PO BOX 19024, FHCRC, 1100 FAIRVIEW AVE N 98109 #048-14-2000 L2003 **ON** *100 †20
ANDERSON, Maxine Karen. 2100 WESTERN AVE 98121 #005-02-1967 L1971 **PYA CHP** *020 †75
ANDERSON, Nancy Ann. 4800 SAND POINT WAY NE, EMERGENCY DEPT 98105 #035-01-1980 L1987 **PD** *100 †55
ANDERSON, Shane Selassie. 1001 SW KLICKITAT WAY 98134 #026-04-1996 L2000 **PTH** *020 †50
ANDERSON, Shirley A Cooke. ■ 98116 #054-04-1955 L1956 **PD PHP** *071 †55
ANDERSON, Steen. 1959 NE PACIFIC ST 98195 #297-01-1979 L1983 **AN** *100
ANDERSON, Steven John. 3216 NE 45TH ST, STE 304 98105 #054-04-1980 L1983 **PSM PD** *020 †50
ANDREWS, Kirsten Marie. 509 OLIVE WAY, STE 900 98101 #043-01-2004 L2004 **FM** *020 †18
ANDREWS, Robert Goff. 1100 FAIRVIEW AVE N, FRED HUTCHINSON CANCER RES 98109 #026-04-1976 L1979 **PHO HEM** *050 †55
ANDREWS, Robert Torrance. 1959 NE PACIFIC ST #357115, UNIVERSITY OF WASHINGTON 98195 #005-18-1990 L2003 **DR VIR** *020 †80
ANDREWS, Shirley. 550 N 115TH ST STE 212, D/B/A SALISH WOMEN'T HEALTH 98133 #005-18-1988 L1993 **OBG** *020 †30
ANG, Darwin Noel. 325 9TH AVE BOX 3597 98104 #011-03-2001 L2006 **CCS** *012 †85
ANGEL, Brian Victor. 1400 6TH AVE 98101 #054-04-1993 **FM** *100
ANG-LEE, Kathleen Anne. ■ 98177 #016-02-2002 L2004 **ADP** *020
ANKOV, Donald Harry. ■ 98144 #017-20-1970 L1980 **PD** *020 †55
ANSELL, Julian S. 1660 S COLUMBIAN WAY 98108 #024-07-1951 L1960 **U** *071 †95
ANTEZANA, Marcos A. 1145 BROADWAY 98122 #054-04-1999 L2003 **D** *020 †15

ANTHES, Tara Birgitta. UNIV OF WASHINGTON MED CTR, DIAGNOSTIC RADIOLOGY BOX 98195 #054-04-2003 L2005 **DR** *012
ANTIA, Neville Minoo. 747 BROADWAY 98122 #661-02-2005 L2005 **FP** *012
ANTONSEN, John Edward. ■ 98115 #061-01-1989 L1994 **NEP** *100
ANWAR, Faten. PO BOX 77391 98177 #915-03-1985 L1998 **HMP PTH** *020 †50 ‡
AOUKAR, Pierre Sayed. 1408 12TH AVE, UNIT 307 98122 #035-06-2003 L2006 **CD** *012 †20
AOYAMA, David Tadashi. 1801 NW MARKET ST STE 309 98107 #054-04-1977 L1979 **IM** *020 †20
APODACA, Aaron Anthony. 925 SENECA ST #1930 98101 #034-01-2000 L2003 **IM** *020 †20
APPELBAUM, Frederick Ray. 1124 COLUMBIA ST, STE M126 98104 #024-07-1972 L1978 **ON** *050 †20
APPELL, Jeffrey Cyrus. 9800 4TH AVE NE 98115 #035-48-1980 L1983 **FM** *020 †18
APPIAH-KUSI, Joe. ■ 98103 #286-02-1973 **PHP GPM** *062
APPLETON, William Geo, Jr. 1550 N 115TH ST 98133 #024-01-1961 L1966 **IM** *071
A/RAHMAN, Enass Awad. ■ 98105 #848-01-1994 **GPM** *012
ARAND, Gloria Anne. 1101 MADISON ST, STE 301 98104 #023-07-1997 L2000 **PD** *020 †55
ARBABI, Saman. 325 9TH AVE, SURGERY DEPT BOX 359796 98104 #005-19-1992 L1995 **CCS** *020 †85
ARCEGA, Nathaniel E B. 5414 BARNES AVE NW, SWEDISH PHYSICIANS SUMMIT 98107 #748-02-1967 L1979 **CD** *020 †20
ARCERITO, Massimo. 1959 NE PACIFIC ST 98195 #561-04-1990 L2007 **GS** *012
ARDAKANI, Navid Arefi. ■ 98122 #016-42-1998 L2003 **DR** *020 †28,80
ARGENYI, Zsolt Balazs. 4225 ROOSEVELT WAY NE, STE 354697 98105 #473-01-1978 L2001 **D DMP** *020 †50,15
ARIAS, Elizabeth Marie. PO BOX 356340, UNIVERSAY OF WASHINGTON GR 98195 #056-05-2003 L2003 **IM** *020 †20
ARIEL, Leo. ■ 98122 #407-10-1953 L1959 **GS OBS** *071
ARMSTRONG, Theodore M. ■ 98194 #025-01-1943 L1947 **OM** *071 †85
ARNER, Arthur James. 320 WESTLAKE AVE N, STE 100 98109 #005-12-1965 L1968 **FM** *020 †18
ARNOLD, Richard W. 2505 2ND AVE, STE 200 98121 #016-06-1978 L1985 **IM** *020 †20
ARNTZEN, Kelli Renae. 4740 44TH AVE SW, STE 200 98116 #028-34-1986 L1990 **D** *020 †15
ARREOLA-RISA, Carlos. UNIV WA DEPT SURG 98195 #649-02-1985 *100
ARRIGONI, James. ■ 98177 #030-06-1980 L1983 **IM** *020 †20
ARTERBURN, David Eric. 1730 MINOR AVE, STE 1600 98101 #020-12-1997 L2001 **IM** *020 †20
ARTMAN, Lee Eric. 125 16TH AVE E 98112 #048-02-1973 L1980 **GO OBG** *020 †30
ARTRU, Alan Arthur. UNIV WASH MED SCHOOL, DEPT ANESTH%356540 98195 #056-06-1975 L1980 **AN** *030 †05
ARYAL, Prashanti. 7015 6TH AVE NW, UNIV OF WASHINGTON - G.M. 98117 #016-11-2003 L2003 **OBG** *020
ASAKURA, Kenji. 1959 NE PACIFIC ST C, CAMPUS BOX 356340 98195 #023-07-1998 L2005 **IM** *012
ASHENBURG, Carole Ann. 4800 SAND POINT WAY NE 98105 #035-45-1981 L1986 **PD** *040 †55
ASHLEIGH, E Alexandra. 1660 S COLUMBIAN WAY, 116 MHC 98108 #005-02-1985 L1986 **P** *020 †75
ASHLEY, Jennifer Renee. 1100 9TH AVE G1-MSO 98101 #016-43-1999 L2002 **IM** *020 †20 ‡
ASIF, Irfan Mohammed. 1959 NE PACIFIC ST, DEPT FM 98195 #038-41-2007 L2007 **FP** *012
ASPESBERRO, Francois. 4800 SAND POINT WAY NE, AND REGION 98105 #165-07-1994 L1999 **PD** *020 †55
ASSEFI, Nassim Parthia. 325 9TH AVE, MAILBOX 359780 98104 #054-04-1997 L2000 **IM** *020 †20
ASTION, Michael Lee. 1959 NE PACIFIC ST, MSC 359300 98195 #041-01-1989 L1993 **CLP** *020 †50
ATKINS, Harold Lawrence. ■ 98107 #065-09-1983 L1987 **HEM IM** *020 †20
ATKINSON, Monica Wendy. 2755 56TH AVE SW 98116 #048-04-1988 L1997 **OBG** *020 †20
ATKINSON, Nathan D. 1959 NE PACIFIC ST, RM C212 98195 #035-01-2006 L2006 **FP** *012
ATREYA, Chloe Evelyn. ■ 98122 #008-01-2005 L2005 **IM** *012
ATTAMAN, Jason Gene. 1200 12TH AVE S, DETROIT MEDICAL CENTER 98144 #016-76-2002, ▲ L2007 **APM** *020 †60
AUER, Nancy Jane. 747 BROADWAY, SWEDISH MED CTR 98122 #047-06-1975 L1980 **EM NS** *030 †16
AULD, Merritt Kevin. 900 TERRY AVE, STE 100 98104 #046-01-1979 L1986 **ORS** *020 †40
AUSK, Karlee Hall. ■ 98115 #054-04-2005 L2005 **IM** *012
AUSTIN, Kristen Ann. 1229 MADISON ST STE 1450 98104 #051-04-1998 L2002 **OBG** *020 †30
AUSTIN, Stephanie C. ■ 98112 #012-05-1995 L1995 *100
AVANSINO, Jeffrey Ronald. 4800 SAND POINT WAY NE, M/S W-7729 P.O. BOX 5371 98105 #031-01-1999 L2002 **PDS** *012 †85
AVASARE, Sonal Sudhir. ■ 98115 #054-04-2006 **PD** *012
AVELLINO, Anthony Michael. 4800 SAND POINT WAY NE 98105 #035-01-1992 L1996 **NS** *020 †25
AVERY, David Hartford. 325 9TH AVE, DEPT OF PSYCHIATRY 98104 #028-02-1972 L1980 **P** *020 †75
AVIN, Ilan David. PO BOX 356340, UW SCHOOL OF MED GME PROGR 98195 #051-04-2003 L2003 **GS** *012
AVRIETT, Donald Carlson. 9800 4TH AVE NE 98115 #025-07-1973 L1974 **FM** *020 †18
AYE, Ralph Williams. 1221 MADISON ST STE 400 98104 #041-12-1977 L1980 **GS TS** *020 †85
AYRE, William Henry. ■ 98115 #005-18-1987 L1988 **OM** *020
AZOSE, Albert Allan. 600 BROADWAY, STE 170 98104 #054-04-1977 L1980 **DR NR** *075 †80
BABINEAU, Sarah Megan. 1401 MADISON ST STE 100 98104 #043-01-2002 L2004 **FPG** *100 †18
BABINGTON, James Roy. ■ 98103 #054-04-2006 L2006 **PM** *012
BABINGTON, Katherine Kath. 12014 10TH AVE NW 98177 #054-04-2004 L2004 **P** *012
BACCHI, Carlos Eduardo. 551 N 34TH ST, STE 100 98103 #187-49-1979 *100
BACIEWICZ, Peter Anthony. 550 16TH AVE, STE 400 98122 #035-19-1983 L1986 **CD IC** *020 †20
BACK, Anthony Lee. 825 EASTLAKE AVE E, P O BOX 19023 98109 #024-01-1984 L1985 **ON IM** *050 †20
BACKOUS, Douglas Duane. 1100 9TH AVE 98101 #054-04-1989 L1997 **OTO** *020 †45
BACKUS, Frank Ira. 1660 S COLUMBIAN WAY, VA HOSPITAL 98108 #054-04-1962 L1965 **P PYG** *071 †75
BACON, Rosalind Clair. 325 9TH AVE 98104 #917-07-1988 L1997 *020
BADARU, Angelika. 1400 6TH AVE 98101 #690-02-1991 L2006 **PDE** *100 †55
BADEN, Harris P. 4800 SAND POINT WAY NE, CHILDREN HOSP MEDICAL 98105 #048-02-1989 L1992 **CCP** *020 †55
BADIOZAMANI, Kasra Ray. 1100 9TH AVE M6-AC, VIRGINIA MASON MEDICAL CEN 98101 #054-04-1995 L2001 **RO** *020 †80

BADURA, Richard John, Jr. 3626 NE 45TH ST STE 300 98105 #030-05-1979 L1980 NPM PD *020 †55

BAER, Adrian D. ■ 98105 #028-34-1943 L1947 PM N *075

BAERNSTEIN, Amy. 325 9TH AVE, BOX 359702 98104 #035-20-1993 L1995 IM *020 †20

BAETEN, Jared Murray. ■ 98116 #054-04-2003 L2006 ID *012 †20

BAGGETT, Molly Katherine. 1401 MADISON ST STE 100 98104 #025-12-1998 L2000 FM *020 †18

BAGGETT, Travis Paul. 1959 NE PACIFIC ST, 542171247 98195 #048-04-2004 L2004 IM *012 †20

BAGLEY, Chas Miller, Jr. 1560 N 115TH ST, STE G16 98133 #024-01-1967 L1970 ON *020 †20

BAGLI, Darius Jehan. 4800 SAND POINT WAY NE 98105 #067-01-1984 L1993 U *020 †95

BAHARIE, Brent Sema. 1606 3RD AVE N 98109 #005-06-1987 L2001 AN *020 †05

BAHIRAEI, Frohar. 925 SENECA ST # 1930, GRAD MED EDUC/H8-GME 98101 #001-02-2004 L2004 GS *012

BAI, Diane Yun. 1101 MADISON ST STE 400, PACIFIC MEDICAL CENTERS 98104 #048-12-2000 L2007 GE *020 †20

BAILES, Daniel Adam. ■ 98103 #056-06-1996 L1998 AN *020 †05

BAILEY, Eileen Kathryn. 1100 9TH AVE C8-G1M 98101 #030-06-1998 L2001 IM *020 †20

BAILEY, Katherine M. 4800 SAND POINT WAY NE, P O BOX 5371 98105 #061-01-1998 L2003 PAN *100

BAILEY, Lillian Amanda. 500 17TH AVE 98122 #060-01-1976 L1976 GS *100

BAILEY-TREGENZA, Bridget. 1959 NE PACIFIC ST, BOX 356340 98195 #025-76-2004, ▲ L2005 AN *012

BAIN, Robert C. ■ 98112 #016-06-1950 L1956 IM *071 †20

BAINS, O'Neil Singh. 1100 9TH AVE C1-MSO, VIRGINIA MASON MED CENTER 98101 #035-06-1996 L2002 IM SME *020 †20

BAIRD, Jane Elizabeth. 6020 35TH AVE SW 98126 #054-04-1987 L1989 FM *020 †18

BAKARI, Janna Patterson. 1959 NE PACIFIC ST, BOX356340 98195 #001-02-2004 L2004 NPM *012 †55

BAKER, Bonnie Virginia. ■ 98102 #035-45-2006 L2006 IM *012

BAKER, Carmen Kimberly. ■ 98117 #040-02-1995 L1997 GS *020 †85

BAKER, David Andrew. 325 9TH AVE, HARBORVIEW EM 98104 #054-04-1998 L2000 EM *100 †20

BAKER, Helen Thomas. ■ 98177 #023-07-1951 L1957 PD PHP *071 †55

BAKER, Tyler Jeremy. ■ 98133 #054-04-2008 *012

BAKER, William Blake. 515 MINOR AVE 98104 #054-04-1953 L1957 D PTH *071 †15

BAKKER, Adam Jess. ■ 98104 #026-04-2007 ORS *012

BAKTHAVATSALAM, Ramasamy. 1959 NE PACIFIC ST, BOX 356410 98195 #495-04-1984 L2001 *020

BALAKRISHNAN, Karthik. 1959 NE PACIFIC ST BOX 356, UW SCHOOL OF MEDICINE GME 98195 #023-07-2005 L2005 OTO *012

BALAKRISHNAN, Malini. 3400 CALIFORNIA AVE SW, STE 300 98116 #024-05-1992 L1994 IM *020 †20

BALDINI, Daniel J. 6529 NE WINDERMERE RD C 98105 #051-04-1977 L1980 AN EM *020 †16,05

BALDWIN, Gregory Todd. ■ 98125 #007-02-2005 L2005 IM *100

BALDWIN, Laura-Mae. 4245 ROOSEVELT WAY NE, STE 354775 98105 #005-06-1980 L1981 FM *050 †18

BALL, Adrianne Margaret M. 1120 CHERRY ST, STE 400 98104 #065-05-1994 L1999 NEP *020 †20

BALL, Jacquelyn Marie. 325 9TH AVE, UNIV OF WASHBOX 359911 98104 #054-04-1999 L2003 P *020

BALLARD, Diane Marie. 325 9TH AVE 98104 #054-04-1985 L1985 FM *020 †18

BALLARD, Paul Alfred C. 1550 N 115TH ST 98133 #028-03-1968 L1969 FM IM *020 †18

BALLARD, Phillip Ault, Jr. 1229 MADISON ST STE 820 98104 #019-02-1966 L1971 N P *020 †75

BALLARD, Robert Wayne. 1101 MADISON ST STE 301, PACMED CLINICS - MADISON 98104 #048-02-1975 L1976 OTO *020 †45

BALOGUN, Anifat Olaseni. 6800 E GREEN LAKE WAY N 98115 #041-09-1992 L2000 OTO PDO *020 †45

BALTZ, Timothy Jos. 1600 E JOHN ST 98112 #017-20-1980 L1983 AN *020 †05

BAMFORD, Nigel Simon. 4800 SAND POINT WAY NE, CHILDRENS HOSP & MED CTR 98105 #049-01-1992 L2002 CHN PD *020 †75,55

BAMSHAD, Michael Jos. PO BOX 356320, 1959 NE PACIFIC STREET HS 98195 #028-46-1989 L2005 PD *020 †55,19

BANDLA, Preetam. 550 17TH AVE, STE A30 98122 #495-99-1998 L2006 PDP *020 †55

BANG, Dae Hee. 1229 MADISON ST, STE 900 98104 #028-02-2002 L2002 DR *020 †80

BANKESLY, Osama. 2600 SW HOLDEN ST, HIGHLINE WEST SEATTLE MHC 98126 #875-02-1989 L2005 P *020

BANSMER, Charlotte A M. 2427 42ND AVE E 98112 #035-08-1945 L1948 PD IMG *075 †55

BAR, Meirav. 6327 SAND POINT WAY NE 98115 #550-01-1997 L2002 ON *100

BARAN, Francine Marie. ■ 98105 #041-15-2001 L2006 OPH PO *035

BARBIER, Suzanne E. 3216 NE 45TH PL, STE 100 98105 #010-02-1980 L1984 GYN *020 †30

BARCLAY, Lindsay Rachel. ■ 98103 #054-04-2008 *012

BARDY, Gust Harry. 7900 E GREEN LAKE DR N, STE 300 98103 #016-06-1977 L1983 CD IM *050 †20

BAREI, David Paul. 325 9TH AVE, DEPT OF ORTHOPEDIC SURGERY 98104 #065-09-1991 L1999 ORS *020 †40

BARFOD, Birte Elizabeth. ■ 98115 #054-04-1986 GPM *100

BARKER, Edward Allan. 13751 LAKE CITY WAY NE, STE 300 98125 #054-04-1964 L1969 ATP *020 †20

BARKER, Lisa Marie. 4800 SAND POINT WAY NE G-0, CHILDREN'S HOSP & REGIONA 98105 #054-04-2006 L2006 PD *012

BARNEBEY, Howard S. 901 BOREN AVE STE 1030 98104 #038-40-1977 L1985 OPH OS *020 †35

BARNES, Lee Francis. 10330 MERIDIAN AVE N # 150 98133 #041-13-1970 L1973 AN *020 †05

BARNES, Penelope Darell. U. WASH SCHOOL MEDICINE, DIV.INFECTIOUS DISEASES 98195 #917-28-1992 L2003 ID *100

BARNES, Robert Franklyn. 1660 S COLUMBIAN WAY, SEATTLE VA MEDICAL CENTER 98108 #049-01-1973 L1976 P *030 †75

BARNES, Robert Hardy, Jr. 98101 #051-04-1943 L1947 IM *071

BARNES, Sanford C. 4225 ROOSEVELT WAY NE, STE 354697 98105 #054-04-1966 L1968 D IM *020 †15

BARNETT, Anthony Scott. 1601 5TH AVE STE 830 98101 #005-06-1999 L2001 FM *020 †18

BARNETT, Claire M. 4500 9TH AVE NE STE 32 98105 #043-01-1988 L1990 FM *020 †18

BARNETT, Julia Ann. ■ 98101 #021-01-2007 L2007 GS *012

BARNETT, Todd Allen. 1221 MADISON ST, STE 1225 98104 #016-06-1987 L1993 RO *020 †80

BARNETTE, Leslie J. 10700 MERIDIAN AVE N # 100, QUALIS HEALTH 98133 #054-04-1975 L1976 FM OS *071 †18

BARNHART, Glenn R. 1600 E JEFFERSON ST 11 98122 #051-04-1977 L2007 GS CD *020 †85,90

BARNHART, Scott. 2324 EASTLAKE AVE E, STE 500 98102 #010-01-1979 L1980 GPM *020 †20,70

BARR, Darlene. 801 BROADWAY STE 300, FIRST HILL SURGEONS 98122 #001-02-1985 L1991 GS *085

BARR, David Holbrook. 10564 5TH AVE NE, P C 98125 #005-02-1974 L1976 OPH *020 †35

BARR, Karen Patricia. 1959 NE PACIFIC ST, BOX 358280 98195 #038-44-1993 L2002 PM *020 †60

BARRECA, Marco. 1959 NE PACIFIC ST, MSC 359300 98195 #561-17-1994 L2000 GS *020

BARRINGER, Charles C. 1959 NE PACIFIC ST 98195 #041-02-1946 PTH *075 †50

BARRY, Darcy Renee. 1959 NE PACIFIC ST, MSC 359300 98195 #056-06-1993 L1997 OBG *020

BARRY, Todd Skipper. PO BOX 356100, UNIV WASHINGTON DEPT PTH 98195 #036-07-1995 L1995 PTH *020 †50

BARTELS, Mary Garber. 1600 E OLIVE ST 98122 #036-01-1983 L1986 CHP *020 †75

BARTIMUS, Holly Ann. ■ 98102 #054-04-2006 L2006 GS *012

BARTLE, Pauline Louise. 1959 NE PACIFIC ST, PSYCHIATRY RESIDENCY PRGM 98195 #054-04-2006 L2006 P *012

BASHEIN, Gerard. 3518 FREMONT AVE N # 3 98103 #034-01-1974 L1975 AN *020 †05

BASINSKI, James Robert. 1959 NE PACIFIC ST BOX 356, UNIVERSITY OF WASHINGTON P 98195 #041-12-2005 L2005 P *012

BASSEN, Cecile R. 4033 E MADISON ST STE 202 98112 #036-07-1976 L2002 PYA P *020 †75

BASSETT, Mikelle Danne. ■ 98115 #054-04-2005 L2005 PD *012

BASSINGTHWAIGHTE, James B. PO BOX 357962, DEPT BIOENGINEERING 98195 #065-01-1955 L1958 OS *050

BASU, Soumit Kumar. 1959 NE PACIFIC ST, UNIV OF WA SCH MED 98195 #033-06-2004 L2007 HO *012

BATCHELDER, Andrew Graham. 1959 NE PACIFIC ST 98195 #028-02-1989 L1989 FM *020 †18

BATJER, John Danner. 747 BROADWAY 98122 #054-04-1968 L1973 PTH *020 †50

BATRA, Manbir S. 1100 9TH AVE 98101 #495-45-1963 L1978 AN PME *020 ‡

BATRA, Maneesh. 1959 NE PACIFIC ST RR542, DEPT OF PEDIATRICS BOX 356 98195 #005-11-2000 L2003 NPM *100 †55

BATTU, Madhu Bindu. ■ 98144 #025-01-2006 L2007 RO *012

BAUER, Jeremy Paul. 1959 NE PACIFIC ST, UW SCHOOL OF MEDICINE GME 98195 #041-15-2005 L2005 ORS *012

BAUERMEISTER, Don Eugene. 1100 9TH AVE C1-MSO, VIRGINIA MASON MEDICAL CEN 98101 #005-06-1962 L1969 PTH *020 †50

BAUMEISTER, Susanne Hilde. 4800 SAND POINT WAY NE, REGIONAL M 98105 #409-16-2004 L2006 PD *012

BAUMGAERTEL, Susan J. 1145 BROADWAY, THE POLYCLINIC 98122 #054-04-1993 L1995 IM *020 †20

BAUMGARTEN, Alexander. ■ 98115 #143-03-1959 L1972 ILI *020

BAVISOTTO, Linda Marie. 1959 NE PACIFIC ST 98195 #056-05-1981 L1986 HO IM *050 †20

BAXTER, Robin L. 1001 4TH AVE STE 3200 98154 #054-04-1974 L1978 P *020

BAY, Rebecca Ida. 7749 57TH AVE NE 98115 #054-04-1991 L1991 P *012 †70

BAYFIELD, Sofia T. 925 SENECA ST 98101 #061-01-1996 L2001 FM *020 †18

BAYLES, Stephen Wesley. 1100 9TH AVE 98101 #012-05-1994 L2003 OTO *020 †45

BAYS, Holly Dione. 905 SPRUCE ST STE 300, HEALTH 98104 #054-04-1996 L1998 FM *020 †18

BEACH, Kirk Watson. PO BOX 356410, DEPT SURGERY 98195 #054-04-1976 OS CD *050

BEARD, John Mark. 4245 ROOSEVELT WAY NE, STE 354775 98105 #028-03-1986 L1988 FM OBS *020 †18

BEATTY, John David. 1221 MADISON ST, STE 400 98104 #065-01-1970 L2003 SO GS *020 †85

BEATY, Christopher Dean. 1550 N 115TH ST, MAILSTOP A-500 98133 #050-02-1983 L1984 PUD IM *020 †20

BEAUBIEN, Joanne Louise. 2208 NW MARKET ST STE 410 98107 #054-04-1990 L2000 PD IM *020 †55,20

BEAUCHAMP, Norman Jos. 1959 NE PACIFIC ST, UWMC BOX 357115 98195 #025-12-1990 L2003 RNR *030 †80

BEAUDRY, David Charles. PO BOX 900, 1100 9TH AVENUE M6-AC 98111 #054-04-1980 L1984 OPH *020 †35

BECK, Anita Elizabeth. ■ 98103 #028-02-1997 L1999 PD *020 †55,19

BECK, George Robin. 1111 S ATLANTIC ST 98134 #054-04-1969 L1970 FM PD *040 †55

BECK, Randi Marie. 125 16TH AVE E, CSB-3 98112 #016-43-1987 L1991 PM OS *020 †60

BECKE, Julia Helene. PO BOX 356421, UNIV OF WASHINGTON 98195 #024-07-2005 L2006 IM *012

BECKER, Jane Leslie. ■ 98115 #010-03-1986 L1989 IM AMI *020 †20

BECKER, Kyra Jo. 325 9TH AVE, BOX 359775 98104 #036-07-1989 L1996 N *050 †75

BECKER, Nicole Rachel. 4800 SAND POINT WAY NE 98105 #041-01-1989 L1993 PN *020 †55

BECKER, Pamela Sue. 1959 NE PACIFIC ST, BOX 357710 98195 #024-01-1986 L2003 HEM *050 †20

BECKER, Robert Edward. PO BOX 3707 98124 #016-06-1956 L1966 AM OTO *020

BECKMANN, M Lee. 1600 E JOHN ST, DEPT NEPHROLOGY 98112 #010-01-1978 L2000 NEP IM *020 †20

BECKSTROM, Andrew Carl. 4800 SAND POINT WAY NE, AND REGION 98105 #038-41-2005 L2005 PD *012

BEDA, Rachel Marie. ■ 98112 #054-04-2001 L2003 IM *020

BEDALOV, Antonio. 825 EASTLAKE AVE E 98109 #957-01-1989 L1996 HEM *020 †20

BEDARD, Charles Kent. 901 BOREN AVE, STE 1776 98104 #003-01-1973 L1978 GE IM *020 †20

BEEGLE, Robert George. 1200 12TH AVE S 98144 #025-01-1962 L1969 CLP PTH *071 †50

BEER, Cecilia Victoria. 1100 9TH AVE G1-MSO, VIRGINIA MASON MEDICAL CEN 98101 #050-02-1992 L1995 IM *020 †20

BEHNIA, Fatemeh. 1959 NE PACIFIC ST 98195 #517-01-1988 L2007 NM *012

BEHR, James Paul. ■ 98103 #035-45-2004 L2005 PM *012

BEHRENS, Christopher B. 325 9TH AVE, MAILSTOP 359930 98104 #005-02-1996 L2000 FM *020 †18

BEINGESSNER, Daphne. 325 9TH AVE BX 359798, DEPT OF ORTHOPEDICS 98104 #065-06-1997 L2003 *020 †40

BEITZ, Laurie Owen. 1959 NE PACIFIC ST, RR RM 306 BOX 356320 98195 #036-01-1990 L2000 PD *020 †55

BELCHER, David Chris. 7210 ROOSEVELT WAY NE 98115 #041-01-1989 L1991 FM *020 †18

BELCHER, Donald W. 1001 4TH AVE, STE 420 98154 #054-04-1991 L1992 *075 †20

BELENKY, David Arnold. 3626 NE 45TH ST STE 300, PEDIATRIX MEDICAL GROUP 98105 #035-46-1969 L1973 NPM *071 †55

BELFIE, David James. 904 7TH AVE, SI-SM 98104 #054-04-1993 L1998 ORS *020 †40

BELL, Bridgit Sheldon. ■ 98102 #016-02-2002 L2005 PCC *012 †20

BELL, Kathleen Reilly. 4000 15TH AVE NE 98195 #041-13-1981 L1982 **PM** *040 †60

BELL, Ryan Corbett. 1959 NE PACIFIC ST, PSYCHIATRY RESIDENCY 98195 #035-45-2004 L2004 **P** *012

BELL, Shaquita Lynn. 4800 SAND POINT WAY NE G-0, CHILDREN'S HOSPITAL & REGI 98105 #026-04-2006 L2006 **PD** *012

BELLABARBA, Carlo. 325 9TH AVE, HMC-ORTHOPAEDICS BOX 35979 98104 #067-01-1992 L1999 **ORS OTR** *020 †40

BELLAMY, James Caylor. 325 9TH AVE 98104 #018-03-1956 L1968 **PTH** *071 †50 ‡

BELLAVIA, John Frank. 325 9TH AVE, DEPT OF PSYCH & BEHAV SCIE 98104 #035-08-1990 L1997 **P PYG** *020 †75

BELZ, Michael Kenneth. 1100 9TH AVE C1-MSO, VIRGINIA MASON MEDICAL CEN 98101 #019-02-1987 L1997 **CD** *020 †20

BEMIS, Brock. ■ 98103 #054-04-2008 *012

BENAVENTE, Marissa June. 8313 AURORA AVE N 98103 #016-11-1985 L1998 **FM NTR** *020 †18

BENAVIDES, Claude. 1600 E JOHN ST 98112 #025-07-1957 L1998 **GS** *020 †85

BENCA, Paul J. 1100 9TH AVE C1-MSO, VIRGINIA MASON MEDICAL CEN 98101 #016-06-1982 L1987 **ORS** *020 †40

BENDA, Peter Matthias. 1001 SW KLICKITAT WAY 98134 #054-04-1997 L2001 **PTH** *020 †50

BENDER, Arthur James. 1100 9TH AVE C8-GIM, VIRGINIA MASON MEDICAL CEN 98101 #054-04-1974 L1975 **IM** *020 †20

BENDER, Michael A. 2101 E YESLER WAY, STE 100 98122 #054-04-1990 L1993 **PHO** *020 †55

BENDER, Rachel Ann. ■ 98103 #054-04-2008 *012

BENDITT, Joshua Oliver. 1959 NE PACIFIC ST, OF PULMONARY MED BOX 35652 98195 #054-04-1982 L1993 **PUD IM** *020 †20

BENIRSCHKE, Stephen Kurt. 325 9TH AVE, BOX 359798 98104 #038-06-1979 L1985 **ORS** *030 †40

BENKERS, Tara Lyn. 1959 NE PACIFIC ST, BOX 356340 98195 #007-02-2007 L2007 **IM** *012

BENNET, Joseph Klarik. 1145 BROADWAY 98122 #012-05-1993 L1997 **IM** *020 †20

BENNETT, Forrest Curtiss. 1959 NE PACIFIC ST, CHDD,BOX 357920 UNIV OF WA 98195 #026-04-1970 L1976 **PD** *020 †55

BENNETT, John Robt. 210 NE 91ST ST, EPMG - NW 98115 #028-03-1978 L1983 **EM GP** *020 †16

BENNETT, Lisa Marie. 1925 2ND AVE W, UNIVERSITY OF WASHINGTON 98119 #054-04-2002 L2002 **PM** *100 †60

BENNETT, Siiri Nylund. ■ 98103 #054-04-1988 L2005 **GPM PHP** *020

BENNETT, Tellen Demeke. 4800 SAND POINT WAY NE, DIV OF CRTCL CARE CHILDS 98105 #023-07-2001 L2004 **CCP** *012 †55

BENNETT, William R Murray. ■ 98102 #061-01-1992 L1995 **P** *020 †75

BENOIT, Michelle Felice. ■ 98116 #028-34-1999 L2002 **OBG** *020

BENSINGER, Richard E. 1221 MADISON ST STE 1200 98104 #023-07-1969 L1977 **OPH PS** *020 †35

BENSINGER, William Ira. 1100 FAIRVIEW AVE N, D5 390 98109 #016-06-1973 L1976 **ON IM** *050 †20

BENSON, Crystal Mae. 1959 NE PACIFIC ST, BOX 356340 98195 #054-04-2004 L2004 **PD** *100 †55

BENSON, Edward Albert. 125 16TH AVE E 98112 #054-04-1975 L1976 **END IM** *020 †20

BENSON, James Wood, Jr. 1100 9TH AVE C1-MSO, VIRGINIA MASON MEDICAL CEN 98101 #024-01-1970 L1976 **END IM** *020 †20

BENSON, Janice Carol. 1600 E JOHN ST 98112 #041-07-1974 L1975 **FM** *020 †18

BENSON, John Edward. UNIV OF WASHINGTON, DEPT OF REHAB MED 98195 #056-06-2007 L2007 **PM** *012

BENSON, Robert Louis. ■ 98105 #054-04-1958 L1960 **P** *071 †03

BENTHAM, Wayne Davidleroy. 1959 NE PACIFIC ST, BOX 356560 98195 #010-03-1997 L2001 **P** *020 †75

BENVENISTE, Sara Elaine. ■ 98103 #054-04-2006 L2006 **FP** *012

BENZ, Paul Clarence. 747 BROADWAY 98122 #003-01-1980 L1983 **AN** *020 †05

BERCOVITZ, Rachel Sara. ■ 98115 #016-11-2005 L2005 **PD** *012

BERENSON, Les Meyer. ■ 98103 #021-01-1980 L1981 **IM** *020 †20

BERENSON, Ronald Jay. 825 EASTLAKE AVE E, CANCER RESEARCH CENTER 98109 #008-01-1979 L1984 **ON** *050 †20

BERG, Alfred Oren. 1959 NE PACIFIC ST, BOX 356390 98195 #028-02-1974 L1977 **FM GPM** *030 †70,18

BERG, Daniel. 4225 ROOSEVELT WAY NE, BOX 354697 98105 #065-01-1985 L1997 **D** *020 †15 ‡

BERG, Janet Marie. 901 BOREN AVE STE 1020 98104 #028-03-1977 L1978 **P** *075 †75

BERG, William Ellis. 515 MINOR AVE, STE 200 98104 #005-18-1995 L2000 **N** *020 †75

BERGER, Douglas Bradley. ■ 98112 #035-01-2006 L2006 **IM** *012

BERGER, Richard Eugene. 1959 NE PACIFIC ST, MS BOX 356510 98195 #016-02-1973 L1976 **U** *020 †95

BERGERON, Chris Mark. 300 QUEEN ANNE AVE N, # 177 98109 #005-15-2002 L2007 **OTO FPS** *100 ‡

BERGMAN, Abraham Baer. 325 9TH AVE, BOX 359774 98104 #038-06-1958 L1963 **PD GPM** *040 †55

BERGMAN, Sarah Eva. ■ 98103 #054-04-2008 *012

BERKSON, Joseph Koller. 9750 3RD AVE NE STE 3 98115 #016-11-1973 L1976 **FM** *020 †18

BERMAN, Henry Stephen. 4800 SAND POINT WAY NE 98105 #035-19-1965 L1981 **ADL PD** *071 †55 ‡

BERNACKI, Gwen Marie. ■ 98102 #035-06-2007 L2007 **IM** *012

BERNARDS, Christopher M. 1100 9TH AVE 98101 #040-02-1984 L1987 **AN** *020 †05

BERNHART, Kristin Pirkola. ■ 98115 #041-15-2005 L2005 **P** *012

BERNSTEIN, Crystal Lee. 501 N 34TH ST, STE 101 98103 #036-07-1996 L2002 **GE** *020 †20

BERNSTEIN, Gerald. 11011 MERIDIAN AVE N, STE 102 98133 #016-11-1962 L1966 **D DMP** *020 †15

BERNSTEIN, Irwin David. 4800 SAND POINT WAY N.E, CHILDREN'S ORTHOPEDIC HOSP 98195 #035-19-1967 L1973 **PHO PD** *050 †55

BERNSTEIN, Robert Mark. 1411 4TH AVE STE 1508, SEATTLE PREVENTIVE MEDICIN 98101 #036-01-1990 L1992 **FM** *020 †18

BERRINGTON, William R, III. 1959 NE PACIFIC ST, BOX 356523 98195 #001-02-2000 L2003 **ID** *012 †20

BERSIN, Robert Merle. 1730 MINOR AVE, STE 1010 98101 #005-14-1981 L2005 **IM CD** *020 †20

BERSON, Gabriel. 1100 9TH AVE G1-MSO, VIRGINIA MASON MEDICAL CEN 98101 #035-46-1999 L2002 **MG** *020 †15

BERTOZZI, Peter E, Jr. 1001 SW KLICKITAT WAY 98134 #041-01-1971 L1975 **PTH PHP** *020 †50

BESHLIAN, Kevin Michael. 1100 9TH AVE 98101 #051-01-1982 L1983 **PS** *072 †85,65

BESHLIAN, Sarah. ■ 98112 #016-06-1986 L1988 **HS ORS** *020 †40

BEST, Jennifer Ann. ■ 98199 #016-06-2000 L2003 **IM** *020 †20

BESTE, Lauren Anne. ■ 98103 #023-07-2004 L2007 **IM** *100 †20

BESWICK, Frances Jane. 2317 E WARD ST 98112 #917-24-1969 L1977 **AN** *040

BETTS, Richard Arthur. ■ 98101 #024-01-1943 L1949 **R** *071 †80

BEZRUCHKA, Stephen. ■ 98116 #005-11-1973 L1978 **EM PHP** *020 †16

BHAMA, Prabhat Kumar. NECK SURG, DEPT OF OTO/HEAD & 98195 #025-01-2006 L2006 **OTO** *012

BHANANKER, Sanjay Madhav. 4800 SAND POINT WAY NE 98105 #496-15-1989 L2002 *020

BHANDARI, Anuja. 1959 NE PACIFIC ST BOX 356, DEPT OPHTHALMOLOGY 98195 #495-27-1988 L2000 **OPH** *020 †35

BHARANI, Nipali Anil. 1959 NE PACIFIC ST BOX 35, UNIV OF WA SCHOOL OF MEDIC 98195 #048-04-1999 L2003 **P** *100 †75

BHARGAVA, Puneet. ■ 98125 #495-35-1999 L2006 **PDR** *012

BHATTACHARYA, Renuka. 1101 MADISON ST, PACMED MADISON 98104 #051-01-1997 L2000 **GE** *020 †20

BHATTACHARYA, Vishwanath. 1600 E JEFFERSON ST 98122 #495-73-1985 L1998 **VS** *100

BHOGAL, Neeta. 521 WALL ST, DEPT FM 98121 #495-29-2003 L2005 **FP** *012

BHRANY, Amit Dave. 1959 NE PACIFIC ST, BOX 356515 98195 #024-05-2001 L2001 **OTO** *100

BHUGRA, Hardeep Singh. 1959 NE PACIFIC ST 98195 #539-06-2005 L2005 **IM** *012

BHUTTA, Omar Jamal. ■ 98115 #041-12-2005 L2005 **PD** *012

BIANCO, James. ■ 98146 #035-47-1983 L1987 **ON IM** *020 †20

BIBACK, Sheldon Martin. 1550 N 115TH ST 98133 #065-01-1948 L1955 **OBG** *020 †30

BICK, Susan Arlene. 3223 1ST AVE S, STE C 98134 #054-04-1987 L1990 **GPM** *020

BICKNELL, Ryan T. 1959 NE PACIFIC ST, UNIV OF WA SCH OF MED 98195 #065-10-2000 L2006 *020

BIEHL, Thomas Robt. 1100 9TH AVE 98101 #005-18-1987 L1990 **GS SO** *020 †85

BIELY, George Gordon. ■ 98119 #061-01-1958 L1965 **P** *071 †75

BIERMAN, Charles Warren. 4540 SAND POINT WAY NE, STE 200 98105 #024-01-1947 L1951 **PDA** *071 †55,03

BIGOS, Stanley James. 325 9TH AVE BOX 359798, UNIVERSITY OF WASHINGTON 98104 #028-03-1975 L1980 **ORS** *020 †40

BIGOSINSKI, Krystian Wojc. 550 16TH AVE STE 100, PROVIDENCE FAMILY MEDININE 98122 #016-11-2005 L2005 **FP** *012

BILES, Andrew Richard, Jr. 200 16TH AVE E 98112 #021-05-1963 L1971 **PD** *071 †55

BILLINGHAM, Richard P. 1100 MADISON ST # 500 98104 #035-45-1971 L1974 **CRS** *020 †85,10

BILLINGS, Martha E. 747 BROADWAY 98122 #005-02-2002 L2006 **PCC** *012 †20

BIN, Steven Sun. 747 BROADWAY, PROVIDER SERVICES 98122 #016-02-1999 L2005 **PD** *020 †55

BINSWANGER, Ingrid A. UNIVERSITY OF WASHINGTON, RWJ CSP BOX 357183 98195 #005-02-2000 L2003 **IM** *100 †20

BIRCHFIELD, George R. 1560 N 115TH ST, STE G16 98133 #054-04-1985 L1991 **HO ON** *020 †20

BIRCHFIELD, Richard Irvin. 925 SENECA ST 98101 #054-04-1953 L1959 **N** *071 †75

BIRD, Thomas Dwight. 1660 S COLUMBIAN WAY 98108 #035-20-1968 L1970 **N MG** *020 †75 ‡

BIRGFELD, Craig Brendon. 4800 SAND POINT WAY NE, DIVISION OF PLASTIC SURGER 98105 #051-04-2000 L2006 **PS** *100

BIRKBY, Craig Steven. 1229 MADISON ST, STE 1090 98104 #018-03-1982 L1988 **D DS** *020 †15

BIRKELAND, Ivar W, Jr. 1600 E JEFFERSON ST, ORTHOPEDICS INTRNTL LTD PS 98122 #054-04-1959 L1960 **ORS** *071 †40

BIRNBAUM, Matthew Robert. ■ 98119 #036-05-2006 L2007 **AN** *012

BIROCHAK, Edward, Jr. 509 OLIVE WAY STE 847 98101 #041-09-1981 L1986 **P** *020 †75 ‡

BISHOP, Julianne Kristine. 4800 SAND POINT WAY NE, CUMG P O BOX 50010 98105 #019-02-2001 L2004 **PD** *020 †55

BISHOP, Lori Rene. 1959 NE PACIFIC ST 98195 #054-04-1989 L1990 **IM** *020

BISHOP, Michael Joshua. 1660 S COLUMBIAN WAY, DEPT OF ANES/S112ANES 98108 #005-18-1974 L1980 **AN CCM** *040 †20,05

BISHOP, Rachel Anne. 9800 4TH AVE NE, NORTHGATE MEDICAL CENTER 98115 #917-05-1991 L2004 **FM** *020 †18

BITTLE, Michelle Marie. 325 9TH AVE MS 359728 98104 #016-11-1997 L2000 **DR** *020 †80

BJORNERUD, Jon Erling. 747 BROADWAY 98122 #561-01-1995 L2002 **PAN** *020 †05

BLACK, Arthur Robbins. ■ 98198 #054-15-1964 **OM GP** *074

BLACKHAM, Dana. 9776 HOLMAN RD NW STE 108 98117 #054-04-1978 L1981 **OBG** *020 †30

BLACKLEY, Molly Purnell. 1959 NE PACIFIC ST, U OF W-HS AFFAIRS BOX 3563 98195 #036-01-2004 L2004 **IM** *100 †20

BLACKMAN, Andrew Joseph. ■ 98104 #054-04-2008 *012

BLACKMORE, Christopher C. 1959 NE PACIFIC ST, MSC 359300 98195 #035-45-1990 L1995 **DR** *050 †80

BLAGG, Christopher Robin. 700 BROADWAY, NORTHWEST KIDNEY CTRS 98122 #352-05-1954 L1967 **NEP IM** *050

BLAIR, Paul Henry B. 1600 E JEFFERSON ST # 101 98122 #539-01-1982 L1993 *020

BLAISDELL, Gregory Yates. ■ 98103 #041-14-2007 L2007 **ORS** *012

BLAKE-INADA, Louis M. 600 UNIVERSITY ST, STE 1200 98101 #038-06-1983 L2000 **CD** *020 †28,20

BLASKI, Mindy L. 3216 NE 45TH PL, STE 106 98105 #035-06-1977 L1980 **FM FPG** *020 †18

BLASKO, John Chas. 1221 MADISON ST, STE 1225 98104 #023-01-1969 L1977 **RO** *020 †80

BLATT, Joseph Aaron. 1959 NE PACIFIC ST 98195 #016-42-2000 L2003 **ICE** *012 †20

BLAU, Carl Anthony. 1959 NE PACIFIC ST, BOX 357710 98195 #038-40-1986 L1989 **ON IM** *020 †20

BLEAKLEY, Marie. 1959 NE PACIFIC ST 98195 #143-11-1994 L2002 **PHO** *100

BLEAKLY, Nicole Teresa. ■ 98115 #054-04-2008 *012

BLEDSOE, Julia Marie. 4245 ROOSEVELT WAY NE, STE 354775 98105 #054-04-1990 L1992 **PD** *020 †55

BLESSING, Matthew Scott. ■ 98103 #025-12-2005 L2005 **PD** *012

BLISH, Catherine Anne. PO BOX 356523, INFECTIOUS DISEASES, 1959 98195 #054-04-2001 L2003 **ID** *100

BLISS, Erika Barni. 509 OLIVE WAY STE 1607, QLIANCE MEDICAL GROUP OF W 98101 #005-18-2000 L2004 **FP** *012

BLISS, Garrison. 509 OLIVE WAY, STE 1607 98101 #049-01-1977 L1978 **IM** *020 †20 ‡

BLITZ, Maurice. 1101 MADISON ST, STE 850 98104 #061-01-1999 **TS** *012

BLOCK, Susanna. 600 UNIVERSITY ST 98101 #025-12-1998 L2002 **PD** *020 †55

BLOOM, Myron Earl. 300 ELLIOTT AVE W STE 300 98119 #048-13-1973 L1978 **FM MDM** *020 †18

BLOOM, Olga. ■ 98136 #539-03-1941 L1959 **P** *071

BLUE, Alfred Isaiah. 901 BOREN AVE, STE 1776 98104 #004-01-1955 L1961 **PS ORS** *020 †40,65 ‡

BLUME, Heidi Kirsten. 4800 SAND PONT WAY NE 5D-4, DIV OF CHILD NEUROLOGY 98105 #024-01-1997 L2000 **CHN** *020 †75,55

BLUMFIELD, Einat. 1959 NE PACIFIC ST 98195 #550-03-1992 L2004 **PDR** *100

BOATENG, Abena Emily. ■ 98115 #048-04-2007 L2007 **PD** *012

BODDEN, Alison Angela. ■ 98144 #950-01-1960 L1968 **AN PD** *071 †05

BODEAU, Valerie Susan. 8459 42ND AVE SW 98136 #017-20-1998 L2004 **SCI** *100 †60 ‡

BOECKH, Michael J. 1100 FAIRVIEW AVE N, FRED HUTCHINSON CANCER CTR 98109 #409-33-1985 L1993 ■ *050

BOEKER, Allen John. 861 POPLAR PL S 98144 #056-05-1963 L1969 **DR** *020 †80

BOENIG, Halvard Bjoern. 1100 FAIRVIEW AVE N 98109 #409-25-1997 L2006 *100

BOETTCHER, William Geo. 1221 MADISON ST, STE 1012 98104 #054-04-1963 L1965 **ORS** *071 †40

BOHANNON, Charles Thomas. 2645 W NEWTON ST 98199 #054-04-1995 L1998 **EM** *020 †16

BOHART, Zachary Winter. ■ 98103 #024-05-2005 L2006 **PM** *012

BOHLING, Sandra Dawn. ■ 98105 #049-01-2005 L2005 **PTH** *012

BOHMKE, Karen Lynn. 1101 MADISON ST STE 1150 98104 #005-19-1980 L1981 **OBG** *020 †30

BOHORFOUSH, Anthony G, III. 501 N 34TH ST, STE 101 98103 #030-06-1981 L1988 **GE IM** *020 †20

BOISEN, Elliott Gordon. ■ 98109 #030-05-1958 L1959 **FM AM** *071 †18

BOKAN, John Anthony. 1660 S COLUMBIAN WAY 98108 #034-01-1975 L1978 **P** *020 †75

BOLEN, Jennifer D. 1100 9TH AVE 98101 #054-04-1976 L1976 **P** *020 †75

BOLEN, John Wm. 1100 9TH AVE C1-MSO, VIRGINIA MASON MEDICAL CEN 98101 #054-04-1975 L1977 **PTH** *020 †50

BOLENDER, Nicole F. 2324 EASTLAKE AVE E, STE 500 98102 #869-05-1968 L1978 **R** *020 †80

BOLLINGER, Charles Wm. ■ 98199 #035-03-1965 L1969 **OM AN** *020 †05

BOLLYKY, Paul L. ROOM 136, BOX 355330, UW -HEALTH SCIENCES ANNEX 98195 #024-01-2001 L2004 **ID** *100

BOLTE, Mary Ann P. 1600 E OLIVE ST 98122 #054-04-1985 L1986 **P NUP** *020 †75

BOMSZTYK, Karol. 815 MERCER ST, BOX 358050 98109 #035-45-1977 L1983 **IM NEP** *050 †20

BONDURANT, George Timothy. ■ 98116 #020-02-1995 L1999 **P** *020 †75

BONE, Margaret Wassermann. 2611 NE 125TH ST, STE 206 98125 #054-04-1984 L1985 **P** *020 †18,75

BONURA, Pia A. ■ 98144 #033-06-2007 L2007 **PD** *012

BOONVISUDHI, Kitima. 1600 E JOHN ST 98112 #041-12-1994 L2000 **GS** *020 †85

BOORMAN, Eric Markley. ■ 98136 #011-04-1999 L2003 **PAN** *020 †05

BOORMAN, Richard Stuart. 1959 NE PACIFIC ST, MSC 359300 98195 #060-02-1994 L2000 **ORS** *100

BORGHESANI, Paul Roger. 1959 NE PACIFIC ST, BOX 356560 98195 #024-01-2001 L2004 **P** *100

BORINSTEIN, Scott C. 4800 SAND POINT WAY NE, M.S. B-6553 98105 #051-04-2002 L2002 **PHO** *012 †55

BORISOVSKAYA, Anna. ■ 98115 #054-04-2005 L2005 **P** *012

BORK, Sarah E. 747 BROADWAY, ADULT HOSP PROG 98122 #028-02-2003 L2003 **IM** *020 †20

BORMAN, Patricia Lynn. 1401 MADISON ST STE 100 98104 #010-01-1986 L1988 **FM FPG** *040 †18

BORN, Donald Edward. 1959 NE PACIFIC ST, BOX 359791 98195 #051-01-1987 L1992 **NP** *050 †50

BORNSTEIN, Larry S. 500 17TH AVE 98122 #035-19-1978 L1980 **P IM** *020 †75

BORNSTEIN, Paul. PO BOX 357350, BIOCHEMISTRY 98195 #035-19-1958 L1968 **OS IM** *050

BOROWIEC, James C. 4800 SAND POINT WAY NE, CHILDRENS HOSPITAL MEDICAL 98105 #054-04-2001 L2001 **PAN** *100 †05

BORROMEO, Marivic Vargas. 308 W HALLADAY ST 98119 #054-04-1990 L1992 **FM** *020 †18

BORROW, James Whitaker. 1001 BOYLSTON AVE 98104 #054-04-1971 L1973 **DR FM** *020 †80

BORSON, Soo. 1959 NE PACIFIC ST, MSC 359300 98195 #005-11-1969 L1975 **IMG P** *050 †75

BOSENBERG, Adrian T. 4800 SAND POINT WAY NE 98105 #836-02-1973 L1984 **AN** *020

BOSLEY, Laurence A. 1959 NE PACIFIC ST, BOX 356560 98195 #060-01-1992 L2002 **ADP** *100 †75 ‡

BOTTONE, Anthony Andrew. 4616 25TH AVE NE 394 98105 #035-08-1966 L1979 **P CHP** *020 †75

BOUDOUSQUIE, Alan Curtis. 1229 MADISON ST 98104 #040-02-1986 L1995 **PTH** *020 †50

BOUDREAUX, Marie Kowalski. 125 16TH AVE E, CAPITAL HILL CAMPUS, S. B 98112 #054-04-1978 L1979 **PM** *020

BOULDIN, Anthony Alva. 4800 SAND POINT WAY NE, DEPT OF NEUROLOGY 5D-4 98105 #020-02-1997 L2003 **CHN** *020 †55,75

BOURDEAU, Robert Vincent. ■ 98103 #016-06-1945 L1948 **GS** *071 †85

BOUSTEAD, Shannon Adam. ■ 98109 #048-12-2007 L2007 **FP** *012

BOUZIS, Ashley Rae. 1959 NE PACIFIC ST, PSYCHIATRY RESIDENCY PRGM 98195 #054-04-2007 L2007 **P** *012

BOWDEN, Douglas M. PO BOX 357330, DEPT PSYCH/BEHAV SCI 98195 #005-11-1965 L1970 **P** *050

BOWDEN, Raleigh Anne. 825 EASTLAKE AVE E, CANCER RESEARCH CENTER 98109 #054-04-1978 L1983 **ID ON** *020 †55

BOWDLE, Thomas Andrew. RM AA117C, DEPT. OF ANESTHESIOLOGY 98195 #054-04-1980 L1981 **AN PA** *020 †05

BOWE, David West. 1221 MADISON ST, STE 910 98104 #054-04-1996 L2000 **PD** *020 †55

BOWER, Laura Ann. ■ 98103 #005-06-2007 L2007 **OBG** *012

BOWERS, James Scott. 1530 N 115TH ST STE 104 98133 #054-04-1991 L1995 **IM IMG** *020 †20

BOWERSOX, D Ward. 500 17TH AVE 98122 #018-03-1968 L1969 **IM PUD** *030 †20

BOWLES, Terra Marie. 6020 35TH AVE SW 98126 #049-01-1997 L2000 **FM** *020 †18

BOYAN, William Loyola. 10631 8TH AVE NE 98125 #035-01-1995 L2005 **PCC** *020 †20

BOYD, Andrew John. ■ 98117 #034-01-1987 L1995 **EM** *020 †16

BOYD, Michael Edward. 1101 MADISON ST, STE 301 98104 #041-01-1976 L1981 **IM END** *020 †20

BOYDSTON, Lauren Anne. 1959 NE PACIFIC ST, PSYCHIATRY RESIDENCY 98195 #047-05-2004 L2004 **P** *012

BOYES, John Allan. 600 BROADWAY, STE 170 98122 #056-05-1969 L1971 **IM** *020 †80

BOYKO, Edward John. 1660 S COLUMBIAN WAY, VA PUGET SOUND S-152E 98108 #041-12-1979 L1982 **PHP IM** *050 †20,70

BOZZO, Thomas E. ■ 98103 #035-01-2005 L2005 **IM** *012

BRADEN, Jennifer Brennan. 999 3RD AVE STE 900, PUBLIC HEALTH SEATTLE/KING 98104 #056-06-1998 L2000 **P** *100 †70

BRADEN, John Philip. 11545 15TH AVE NE, STE 205 98125 #054-04-1962 L1965 **PD** *071 †55

BRADLEY, Bruce E, Jr. 747 BROADWAY #051-01-1962 L1970 **ORS** *071 †40

BRADLEY, Dewayne Thomas. 1100 9TH AVE 98104 #038-06-1998 L2004 **OTO FPS** *020 †45

BRADLEY, Emily B. 11011 MERIDIAN AVE N, STE 200 98133 #025-01-1999 L2004 **U** *020 †95

BRADLEY, Katharine A. 1660 S COLUMBIAN WAY, VA PUGET SOUND HEALTH CARE 98108 #005-11-1987 L1990 **IM** *020 †20

BRADLEY, Steven Michael. ■ 98107 #056-06-2003 L2003 **CD** *012 †20

BRADY, Jennifer Kathryn. ■ 98121 #054-04-2008 *012

BRAILE, Margaret Edith. 4800 SAND POINT WAY NE 98105 #054-04-1988 L1990 **PD** *020 †55

BRAKKE, Rachel Anne. 1959 NE PACIFIC ST, GME OFFICE BOX 356340 98195 #048-02-2005 L2006 **PM** *012

BRAKSTAD, Mark Thos. 1560 N 115TH ST, STE 102 98133 #054-04-1983 L1991 **GS PD** *020 †55,85

BRAMHALL, John Shepherd. 325 9TH AVE BOX 359724, ANESTHESIOLOGY DIVISION 98104 #005-18-1991 L1995 **AN** *020 †05

BRANCH, Kelley Robert. 1959 NE PACIFIC ST, BOX 356422 98195 #041-02-1998 L2001 **CD** *020 †20

BRANCHAUD, Ann Marie. ■ 98115 #054-04-1998 L2001 **P** *020

BRAND, Margaret Elizabeth. ■ 98116 #917-07-1943 L1977 **OPH** *071

BRANDABUR, John Jos. 1100 9TH AVE M6-AC, VIRGINIA MASON MEDICAL CEN 98101 #038-41-1984 L1985 **GE IM** *020 †20

BRANDENFELS, Emily Jill. ■ 98103 #005-02-1992 L1993 **IM** *020 †20

BRANDFORD, Harold G. 10330 MERIDIAN AVE N # 24 98133 #035-20-1976 L1979 **AN** *020 †05

BRANDLING-BENNETT, A D. ■ 98125 #024-01-1969 L1972 **PHP IM** *020 †20

BRANDON, Peter. 1801 NW MARKET ST STE 100 98107 #054-04-1989 L1989 **OBG** *020 †30

BRANDT, David Elmer. 310 15TH AVE E 98112 #018-03-1966 L1971 **OPH** *020 †35

BRANNEN, George Elsdon. 1959 NE PACIFIC ST, BOX 356510 98195 #016-06-1969 L1975 **U ON** *020 †95 ‡

BRANSFORD, Richard J. 1959 NE PACIFIC ST BOX 356, UNIVERSITY OF WASHINGTON 98195 #047-05-1996 L2001 **ORS** *020 †40

BRATT, Cheryl Lynn. 10330 MERIDIAN AVE N, NORTH SEATTLE PEDIATRICS 98133 #016-01-1997 L2000 **PD** *020 †55

BRAWER, Michael Kenneth. 1570 N 115TH ST, STE 15 98133 #005-14-1980 L1989 **U** *020 †95

BREDEWEG, Ryan Patrick. 925 SENECA ST # 1930, DEPT RAD 98101 #025-07-2006 L2006 **DR** *012

BREDFELDT, James Edward. 1100 9TH AVE, BOX 900 98101 #019-02-1974 L1988 **GE HEP** *020 †20 ‡

BREE, Robert Leonard. 1107 NE 45TH ST STE 440, UNIV OF WASH. DEPT OF RADI 98105 #025-01-1968 L2001 **DR AR** *020 †80

BREHMER, Lon B. 8720 14TH AVE S 98108 #649-10-1989 L1993 **FM** *074 †18

BREITNER, John Carl S. 1660 S COLUMBIAN WAY, VA PUGET SOUND HEALTH CARE 98108 #041-01-1970 L2004 **P PHP** *050 †70,75

BREMNER, William John. 1959 NE PACIFIC ST, UNIV WA BOX 356420 98195 #054-04-1969 L1978 **END IM** *030 †20

BRENNER, Carolyn Jill. 1959 NE PACIFIC ST, BOX 356560 98195 #050-02-2005 L2005 **P** *012

BRENTNALL, Teresa Averill. 1959 NE PACIFIC ST, MSC 359300 98195 #054-04-1987 L1991 **GE** *020 †20

BREUNER, Cora Collette. 4800 SAND POINT WAY NE 98105 #041-02-1982 L1990 **PD ADL** *040 †55

BREUNER, R Jos. 2124 4TH AVE, PUBLIC HEALTH CENTER 98121 #005-18-1987 L1990 **FM** *020 †18

BREWER, David Kent. COHMC-RADIOLOGY, BOX C-5371 98105 #024-01-1972 L1974 **PDR** *020 †80

BRIDENBAUGH, Lloyd D. 1118 9TH AVE 98101 #030-05-1947 L1952 **AN** *071 †05

BRIDGE, Janis Dee. 1959 NE PACIFIC ST 98195 #054-04-1994 L1997 **IM** *020 †20

BRIDGES, Ann Marjorie. 1145 BROADWAY, THE POLYCLINIC 98122 #016-06-1986 L1990 **OBG** *020 †30

BRIGHAM, Lance Natale. 901 BOREN AVE, STE 1776 98104 #054-04-1972 L1976 **ORS** *020 †40

BRINKLEY, John Robt. 500 UNION ST, STE 505 98101 #056-05-1973 L1975 **P** *020 †75

BRITELL, Catherine Sue. 4508 W RUFFNER ST 98199 #005-06-1973 L1986 **PM GP** *020 †60

BRITTIN, Jeffery Richards. 4744 41ST AVE SW, STE 106 98116 #005-15-1992 L1994 **FM** *020 †18

BRKANAC, Zoran. 1216 26TH AVE E 98112 #957-01-1993 L1999 **CHP** *020 †75

BROADMAN, Kathleen Louise. 4800 SAND POINT WAY NE, REGIONAL M 98105 #003-01-2006 L2006 **PD** *012

BROCK, Erin Michelle. ■ 98107 #005-02-2007 L2007 **FP** *012

BROCKENBROUGH, Edwin C. 1550 N 115TH ST 98133 #023-07-1956 L1964 **VS TS** *030 †85,90

BROCKETTE, Shelia Marlene. 325 9TH AVE, BOX 359929 98104 #047-06-1997 L2002 **ID** *020 †20

BROCKMAN, Roberta. 600 BROADWAY STE 440, SEATTLE HAND SURG GRP 98122 #035-20-1981 L1993 **HS ORS** *020 †40

BRODIE, Rosemary Eliot. ■ 98125 #016-06-1952 L1976 **PM** *071 †60

BRODKIN, Carl Andrew. 325 9TH AVE, BOX 395739 98104 #007-02-1983 L1989 **OM** *020 †20,70

BRODKIN, Kayla I. 1660 S COLUMBIAN WAY 182B 98108 #035-48-1982 L1989 **IM IMG** *020 †20

BRODT, Erik Ryan. ■ 98115 #026-04-2006 L2006 **FP** *012

BROGAN, Thomas Vincent. 4800 SAND POINT WAY NE 98105 #005-19-1990 L1993 **CCP** *020 †55

BROGHAMMER, Carrie Wienek. ■ 98104 #018-03-2002 L2007 **OBG** *100

BROGHAMMER, Joshua Alan. ■ 98104 #018-03-2002 L2007 **U** *020

BROLLEY, Maria. ■ 98118 #016-11-1950 L1978 **P** *071

BROMBERG-NEWELL, Shirley. 1001 4TH AVE STE 420 98154 #034-01-1978 L1984 **IMG** *020 †20

BRONNER, Jason Patrick. PO BOX 356340, U OF W HOUSESTAFF AFFAIRS 98195 #054-04-2001 L2001 **IM** *100 †20

BROOK, David Alan. 5409 BARNES AVE NW, EMERGENCY DEPARTMENT 98107 #025-01-1974 L1987 **EM** *020 †16

BROUDY, David Robt. 515 MINOR AVE, STE 300 98104 #041-12-1979 L1982 **IM CD** *020 †20

BROUDY, Virginia C. 325 9TH AVE, HARBORVIEW MED CTR 98104 #005-02-1980 L1985 **HEM IM** *030 †20

BROUGHTON, Tom Wheatley. 4026 NE 55TH ST STE B 98105 #054-04-1963 L1978 **P CHP** *020

BROUSSARD, Elizabeth K. 1959 NE PACIFIC ST, BOX 356424 98195 #035-20-2000 L2003 **GE** *100 †20

BROWN, Barron Chas. 7210 ROOSEVELT WAY NE 98115 #048-12-1990 L1993 **FM** *020 †18

BROWN, Bruce Gregory. 2815 EASTLAKE AVE E, STE 200 98102 #023-07-1969 L1981 **CD IM** *020

BROWN, Christopher B. ■ 98119 #065-09-1981 L1986 **HEM** *020

BROWN, Jack Ross. 521 WALL ST 98121 #025-01-1955 L1965 **P** *020 †75

BROWN, Jack W. 1401 MADISON ST 98104 #016-06-1950 L1950 **FM GP** *071 †18

BROWN, Jamin Scott. ■ 98108 #041-01-2004 L2004 **OPH** *012

BROWN, Julie C. 4800 SAND POINT WAY NE, BOX 5371/CH-04 98105 #067-01-1991 L1997 **PD** *020 †55

BROWN, Katherine Olivia. 509 OLIVE WAY, STE 900 98101 #041-01-1990 L1994 FM OS *020 †18

BROWN, Keith Ashley. 821 2ND AVE, STE 300 98104 #005-18-1983 L1987 **CHP** *020 †75

BROWN, Keri Li Momi Kiyot. ■ 98101 #030-06-2003 L2007 **OBG** *020

BROWN, Matthew Eric. 925 SENECA ST # 1930, GRAD MED EDU H8-GMC 98101 #012-05-2004 L2004 **DR** *012

BROWN, Maureen O'Reilly. 1401 MADISON ST STE 100 98104 #016-02-1981 L1994 **PHP** *020 †70,18

BROWN, Michael Lloyd. 100 W HARRISON ST, SOUTH TWR #560 98119 #187-30-1983 L1984 EM FM *020

BROWN, Norman Kingsbury. 1101 MADISON ST, STE 301 98104 #024-01-1956 L1961 IM ID *020 †20

BROWN, Paul Barton. 1229 MADISON ST STE 1460 98104 #016-02-1975 L1977 RHU IM *020 †20

BROWN, Rodney A. ■ 98121 #054-04-1952 L1953 **AN** *071 †05

BROWN, Thomas Allan. ■ 98125 #038-06-1963 L1970 **TS GS** *071 †85

BROWN, Zane Arthur. 1959 NE PACIFIC ST, BOX 356460 98195 #041-13-1966 L1977 OS DIA *020 †30

BROWN-CHANG, Janelle V. 2505 2ND AVE, STE 200 98121 #024-01-2002 L2002 **GE** *012 †20

BROWNE, Charles M. 9730 3RD AVE NE STE 200 98115 #005-14-1995 L1997 **OBG** *020 †30

BROWNING, Neil Graham. 1600 E JEFFERSON ST # 101 98122 #836-01-1980 L1994 *020

BROWNING, Sally. 201 16TH AVE E, GROUP HEALTH HOSPITAL 98112 #024-05-1981 L1985 DR PDR *020 †80

BROWNSTEIN, Alice Baldwin. ■ 98122 #016-02-1998 L2000 **IM** *020 †20

BROWNSTEIN, Dena Ruth. 4800 SAND POINT WAY NE, P O BOX C5371 98105 #054-04-1982 L1983 EM *020 †55

BROYLES, Frances E. 1229 MADISON ST, STE 1500 98104 #011-03-1984 L1990 IM *020 †20

BRUCK, David Allan. ■ 98144 #539-06-2002 L2002 **AN** *100 †05

BRUETT, Anna Lynn. ■ 98105 #054-04-2008 *012

BRUNETTE, Kenneth Wade. 515 MINOR AVE, MINOR & JAMES MEDICAL RADY 98104 #056-05-1962 L1967 **DR** *071 †80

BRUNNER, Debbie Kelley. 10416 5TH AVE NE, PACMED CLINICS - NORTHGATE 98125 #005-15-1995 L1997 FM *020 †18

BRUNSVOLD, Nancy Jane. 1145 BROADWAY 98122 #026-04-1991 L1993 IM *020 †20

BRUNZELL, John Dale. DEPARTMENT OF MEDICINE;356 98195 #054-04-1963 L1964 END NTR *050 †20

BRYAN, James Kyle. 1101 MADISON ST, STE 301 98104 #021-05-1986 L1990 ON HEM *020 †20

BRYAN, Shannon Lo. 747 BROADWAY, SWEDISH ADULT HOSPITALISTS 98122 #024-07-1996 L1999 IM *020 †20

BRYANT, Carrie Ann. ■ 98103 #040-02-2002 L2005 **IM** *020 †20

BRYANT, Sophia Suzanne. 1100 FAIRVIEW AVE N MS D3, FH CANCER RESEARCH CENTER 98109 #025-01-1997 L1999 ON *020 †20

BRYSON, Christopher L. 1660 S COLUMBIAN WAY, SEATTLE VA MED CTR S-111-G 98108 #048-12-1997 L2000 IM *020 †20

BRYSON, Staci. ■ 98125 #028-02-2007 L2007 **PTH** *012

BUB, Jennifer Lynn. 11011 MERIDIAN AVE N, STE 102 98133 #007-02-1998 L2003 D DS *020 †15

BUBAK, Paul John. 1145 BROADWAY 98122 #026-04-1975 L1988 **PS GS** *071 †85,65

BUCCI, Anne Marie. 747 BROADWAY 98122 #056-06-1985 L1986 AN *020 †05

BUCHANAN, Claire Louise. 1600 E JEFFERSON ST, STE 305 98122 #016-02-1998 L2005 GS *020 †85

BUCHER, Joy Brooke. PO BOX 356421, UNIV OF WASHINGTON 98195 #005-02-2006 L2006 IM *012

BUCHHOLZ, David Wayne. 2211 QUEEN ANNE AVE N 98109 #016-11-1986 L1989 **PD** *020 †55

BUCHINSKI, Anne Louise. 2271 NE 51ST ST 98105 #035-47-1983 L1986 **P CHP** *020 †75

BUCHMAN, Joseph Gilbert. ■ 98104 #035-19-1957 L2004 **CD IM** *020 †20

BUCHTER, Carol Michaelson. 1959 NE PACIFIC ST, DIV OF CARDIOLOGY, BOX 356 98195 #038-06-1978 L2001 IM CD *020 †20

BUCHWALD, Dedra Stefanie. 325 9TH AVE BOX 359780, HARBORVIEW MEDICAL CTR 98104 #005-18-1981 L1986 IM *050 †20

BUCKINGHAM, Richard E, Jr. 747 BROADWAY 98122 #017-20-1967 L1973 **AN** *075 †05

BUCKLER, Joshua Michael. ■ 98103 #025-01-2001 L2005 **CD** *012 †20

BUCKLEY, Michael James. ■ 98121 #028-34-1937 L1938 **IM** *071

BUCKLEY, Peter F. 2324 EASTLAKE AVE E 98102 #917-20-1968 L1977 **AN** *040

BUCKMILLER, John Farley. 1100 9TH AVE BOX G1-MSO, VIRGINIA MASON MEDICAL CEN 98101 #035-45-1980 L1986 HS ORS *020 †40

BUCKNER, Clarence Dean. 2324 EASTLAKE AVE E, STE 200 98102 #025-01-1961 L1963 ON OS *030 †20

BUCKNER, Frederick S. 1959 NE PACIFIC ST, BOX 357185 98195 #054-04-1988 L1992 ID *020 †20

BUCKNER, Jane Hoyt. 1201 9TH AVE, IN-RC 98101 #023-07-1987 L1992 **RHU IM** *020 †20

BUENVENIDA, Philip N. 4508 S ORCAS ST 98118 #748-01-1972 L1985 FM OM *020

BUI, Quynh Thanh. 8529A STONE AVE N 98103 #041-14-1999 L2001 FM *020 †18

BULGER, Eileen Metzger. 325 9TH AVE BOX 359796, DEPARTMENT OF SURGERY 98104 #035-20-1992 L1992 **CCS** *020 †85

BUNDESMANN, Michael M. ■ 98116 #025-12-2003 L2007 **PCC** *012 †20

BUNDY, Christopher C. 601 UNION ST, STE 1704 98101 #054-04-1998 L2001 **P** *020 †75

BUNN, Jack Calvin. 1405 NW 85TH ST 98117 #024-01-1966 L1972 **OPH** *071 †35

BUNTING, Kea Michelle. 9635 17TH AVE SW 98106 #041-13-2001 L2006 **FM** *100 †18

BURDICK, Robert Eugene. 1801 NW MARKET ST 98107 #054-04-1964 L1968 IM *071 †20

BURDICK, Theresa Agnes. 801 BROADWAY STE 707 98122 #028-34-1976 L1977 **OBG** *020

BURDICK, Thomas Ray. ■ 98136 #041-07-1996 L2000 **DR** *020 †80

BURGOYNE, John Daines. 515 MINOR AVE, STE 200 98104 #049-01-1986 L1997 **OTO** *020 †45

BURKE, Alson Kerry. ■ 98103 #054-04-2008 *012

BURKE, Bennett Curtis. 747 BROADWAY, SWEDISH ADULT HOSPITALISTS 98122 #038-41-2002 L2005 IM *020 †20

BURKE, Brian Patrick. 325 9TH AVE BOX 359739, HARBORVIEW MED CTR 98104 #020-02-1996 L2002 **OM** *020 †20

BURKE, Simpson S. ■ 98125 #024-01-1941 L1942 **OS AN** *071 †05

BURKE, Wylie Gilman. 1959 NE PACIFIC ST, BOX 357120 98195 #054-04-1978 L1979 IM OS *020 †20

BURKHARDT, Linda Darnell. 1001 SW KLICKITAT WAY 98134 #036-05-1989 L2002 PTH *020 †50

BURKLAND, Martin G. ■ 98116 #054-04-1950 L1951 **GP** *071

BURKMAN, James Montgomery. 747 BROADWAY 98122 #041-01-1997 L2002 **AN** *020 †05

BURMAN, Marcia Lynn. 1660 S COLUMBIAN WAY, STE 15 98108 #028-34-1993 L1997 IM *020 †20

BURMER, Glenna Christeen. ■ 98115 #054-04-1983 L1985 *020

BURNELL, James M. 515 MINOR AVE, STE 200 98104 #015-11-1949 L1951 **IM NEP** *020 †20

BURNETT, Leland Le Roy. 1100 9TH AVE # M6-AC, VIRGINIA MASON MED CTR 98101 #054-04-1959 L1960 **DR** *071 †80

BURNETT, Teri. 2800 E MADISON ST STE 301 98112 #001-02-1992 L1994 **PS** *020

BURNHAM, Sylvia Carole. ■ 98177 #061-01-1965 L1972 **AN** *020 †05

BURNS, Jane Louise. 4800 SAND POINT WAY NE 98105 #054-04-1978 L1979 **ID PD** *050 †55

BURNS, John F, Jr. 1145 BROADWAY, THE POLYCLINIC 98122 #010-02-1967 L1975 ORS *020 †40

BURNS, Mark Wilton, III. 1101 MADISON ST, STE 800 98104 #054-04-1979 L1981 **PD** *071 †95

BURNS, Robert Milton. ■ 98144 #054-04-1956 L1959 **PD** *071

BURNS, Stephen P, Jr. 1660 S COLUMBIAN WAY, SCI (128) VA PUGET SOUND 98108 #043-01-1992 L1996 **PM SCI** *020 †60

BURNSIDE, Lee David. 1100 9TH AVE, MAIL STOP C8-GIM 98101 #016-01-1993 L1996 IM *020 †20

BURROUGHS, Lauri Michelle. 4800 SAND POINT WAY NE, MAIL STOP 6D-1 98105 #056-05-1998 L2001 **PHO** *020 †55

BURROWS, Steven Kei. 200 15TH AVE E, CWB100 98112 #008-02-1998 L2000 FM *020 †18

BURT, Jacqueline A. 200 15TH AVE E, GROUP HEALTH COOPERATIVE 98112 #061-01-1966 L1967 **GP** *020 †18

BURT, Robert Keltie. 2001 E MADISON ST 98122 #919-05-1949 L1977 **GYN** *071

BUSCH, Joshua Louis. 325 9TH AVE, BOX 359702 98104 #035-01-2003 L2003 IM *100 †20

BUSCH, Maria Anne. HARBORVIEW MEDICAL CENTER, PIONEER SQUARE CLINIC 98104 #005-02-1995 L1998 IM *020 †20

BUSH, Roger Wade. 1100 9TH AVE 98101 #005-02-1980 L1981 IM *020 †20

BUSH, William Henry. 1959 NE PACIFIC ST, DEPT RADIOLOGY-BOX 357115 98195 #040-02-1967 L1970 **DR** *020 †80

BUSHYHEAD, James B, III. 515 MINOR AVE, STE 300 98104 #028-02-1971 L1973 IM *020 †20

BUTLER, John Ben. 2324 EASTLAKE AVE E, STE 500 98102 #035-19-1975 L1979 **PUD** *050

BUTLER, Stephen Harris. 1959 NE PACIFIC ST 98195 #065-01-1966 L1971 **OS AN** *040 †05

BUTLER, William Kerr. 521 WALL ST ACC-2, ATTN: STAFFING SERVICES 98121 #038-40-1973 L1998 **AI** *020 †55,03

BUTY, Steven Gerald. 801 BROADWAY STE 707 98122 #054-04-1980 L1981 **OBG** *020 †30

BUTZ, Roger Henry. PO BOX 34690, SAFECO LIFE/MED 98124 #016-06-1962 L1965 **GPM PHP** *071 †70 ‡

BUTZLAFF, Martin E. ■ 98117 #409-44-1990 L1995 **IM** *100

BUYCO, Alicia Deocampo. 1001 SW KLICKITAT WAY, STE 205 98134 #748-01-1955 L1968 **PTH OS** *071 †50

BYERS, Peter Howard. 1959 NE PACIFIC ST, BOX 357470 98195 #038-06-1969 L1976 CG CMG *050 †20,19

BYON, John Chonghan. 1959 NE PACIFIC ST RM C, CAMPUS BOX 356340 98195 #021-01-2002 L2002 HO *012 †20

BYRD, David Roland. 1959 NE PACIFIC ST, BOX 356410 98195 #021-01-1982 L1983 GS SO *071 †85

CABOU, Aurelie Rachel. ■ 98107 #041-01-2007 L2007 **FP** *012

CABRERA, Felix Tudela. ■ 98133 #054-04-2008 *012

CADERA, Werner. 10330 MERIDIAN AVE N, STE 370 98133 #065-10-1975 L1992 **OPH** *050 †35

CAHN, Martin Chas. 3601 FREMONT AVE N STE 309 98103 #024-07-1979 L1982 FM *020 †18

CAINE, William Thomas. 1959 NE PACIFIC ST, BOX 35310 98195 #049-01-1993 L2003 **TS GS** *012 †85,90

CAIRNS, Michael Raymond. 515 MINOR AVE 98104 #041-02-1981 L1989 **ID** *020 †20

CALARCO, Michael Paul. ■ 98104 #067-01-2006 L2007 **AN** *012

CALDEIRO, Ryan Mark. 1426 HARVARD AVE, # 254 98122 #038-06-2004 L2004 **P** *012

CALDERON, Alvin S. 925 SENECA ST # 1930 98101 #016-11-2000 L2003 IM *020 †20

CALDWELL, Christine. 4245 ROOSEVELT WAY NE, STE 354775 98105 #048-04-1975 L1984 **PD ADL** *020 †55

CALDWELL, James H, Jr. 1660 S COLUMBIAN WAY 98108 #028-03-1970 L1971 CD *020 †20

CALDWELL, Russell Bruce. 4225 ROOSEVELT WAY NE, STE 354697 98105 #030-06-1975 L1977 **D IM** *020 †15

CALHOUN, Kristine E. 1959 NE PACIFIC ST, CAMPUS BOX 356410 98195 #054-04-1998 L2005 GS *020 †85

CALHOUN, Robert E Lee. 747 BROADWAY 98122 #023-07-1960 L1961 **U** *071 †95

CALL, Adrian Parker. 10330 MERIDIAN AVE N, SEATTLE ARTHRITIS CLINIC 98133 #054-04-1982 L1983 **FM OBS** *020 †18

CALLAHAN, Megan Barbara. 1101 MADISON ST STE 1150 98104 #008-02-2003 L2007 **OBG** *020

CALLAHAN, Steven Kent. 125 16TH AVE E 98112 #050-02-1976 L1984 **ON** *020 †20

CALLEN, Amy Melissa. 1200 12TH AVE S 98144 #023-07-1999 L2001 **PD** *020 †55

CALLISON, Robert Donald. 901 BOREN AVE, STE 650 98104 #041-13-1943 L1944 **GP OS** *071

CAMERON, David Macintosh. 12360 LAKE CITY WAY NE, STE 200 98125 #019-02-1985 L1991 **IM IMG** *020 †20

CAMMARANO, Ann Ayers. 4800 SAND POINT WAY NE 98105 #047-05-1963 L1965 **PD** *071 †55

CAMPBELL, Alfred Gellhorn. UNIV OF WASHINGTON, DEPT OF REHAB MED 98195 #041-01-2005 L2005 **PM** *012

CAMPBELL, Cynthia Grant. 1600 E JEFFERSON ST, STE 620 98122 #038-41-1982 L1983 **PM** *020 †60

CAMPBELL, Mary Susanna. ■ 98144 #035-01-2000 L2004 **ID** *100 †20

CANDY, Ardis J. 2324 EASTLAKE AVE E, STE 500 98102 #056-05-1950 L1954 **P** *072

CANER, John Edward Z. 520 36TH AVE E, SEATTLE WA 98112 98112 #024-01-1956 L1961 **IM RHU** *071

CANNIFF, Kathryn Maura. ■ 98102 #047-05-2007 L2007 **IM** *012

CANNING, Christopher Adam. 201 16TH AVE E, MAIN BUILDING, CMB AA16, R 98112 #049-01-2001 L2006 **RO** *020 †80

CANNON, Todd Allen. ■ 98125 #054-04-2004 L2004 **AN** *012

CANTINI, Evan Miller. 1530 N 115TH ST, NORTHWEST PHYSIATRY 98133 #038-45-1980 L1982 **PM** *020 †60

CANTOR, David Asher. 925 SENECA ST, MEDICAL CENTER 98101 #036-07-2006 L2006 **AN** *012

CAPALLA, Ma Cecilia C C. ■ 98125 #748-14-1982 *100

CAPELL, Peter Terrance. 1959 NE PACIFIC ST, BOX 356426 98195 #035-45-1968 L1971 END IM *020 †20

CAPLAN, Robert Alex. 1100 9TH AVE 98101 #008-01-1977 L1981 **AN IM** *050 †20,05

CAPP, Philip Kenneth. 1463 E REPUBLICAN ST 98112 #010-01-2005 L2008 **P** *100

CAPUTO, P John. 901 BOREN AVE 98104 #028-34-1947 L1948 **GS TS** *072 †85

CARD, Allison Sara. 1959 NE PACIFIC ST, RESIDENCY TRAINING 98195 #054-04-2006 L2006 **P** *012

CAREW, Heather Theresa. ■ 98103 #054-04-2008 *012
CAREY, Brian Jos. 523 PINE ST, STE 200 98101 #021-01-1989 L1993 **OPH** *020 †35
CAREY, Thomas Francis. 5116 25TH AVE NE 98105 #054-04-1954 L1958 **OPH** *071 †35
CAREY, Timothy Patrick. 5116 25TH AVE NE, VILLAGE 98105 #028-34-1985 L1986
OPH PS *075 †35
CARITHERS, Robert L, Jr. 1959 NE PACIFIC ST, BOX 356174 98195 #041-01-1969 L1990
GE IM *050 †20
CARKIN, Julie Lyn. 10330 MERIDIAN AVE N, STE 250 98133 #024-05-1987 L1989 **RHU** *020 †20
CARLBOM, David John. 325 9TH AVE, EMERGENCY SERVICES BOX 359 98104
#054-04-1997 L2000 **PCC** *020 †20
CARLE, Mariann. ■ 98105 #056-06-1992 L1998 **FM** *020 †18
CARLETON, Brittany Szucs. ■ 98115 #012-05-2005 L2007 **FP** *012
CARLETON, Scott H. 1200 12TH AVE S 98144 #012-05-1978 L1985 **DR EM** *020 †80
CARLIN, Jeffrey Steven. 1100 9TH AVE, DIV OF RHEUMATOLOGY-VMMC 98101
#035-19-1975 L1978 **RHU IM** *020 †20
CARLISLE, Russell James. 500 17TH AVE, SWEDISH HEALTH SERVICES 98122
#005-14-1993 **EM IM** *020 †20,16
CARLON, Michael Jos. 1600 E JOHN ST 98112 #007-02-1973 L1986 **PTH IM** *020 †20,50
CARLSON, Cheryl Ann. 1959 NE PACIFIC ST, U OF W-HS AFFAIRS BOX 3563 98195
#054-04-2004 L2004 **HO** *012
CARLSON, Coldevin Bruce. 1145 BROADWAY 98122 #048-04-1959 L1966 **N CHN** *071 †55,75
CARLSON, Melvin Richard. 2501 N 45TH ST 98103 #054-04-1970 L1975 **OPH** *020 †35
CARLSON, Molly Jo. 509 OLIVE WAY, STE 900 98101 #054-04-2002 L2005 **END** *020 †20
CARLSON, Whitney Lynn. 325 9TH AVE, BOX 359911 98104 #018-03-1999 L2003
P PYG *020 †75
CARLSTEN, Christopher R. ■ 98144 #005-11-2000 L2002 **PCC** *100 †20,70
CARLYLE, Wendy Goldberg. 1100 9TH AVE 98101 #011-03-1990 L1991 **AN** *05
CARNEY, Pamela Stavely. 1101 MADISON ST, STE 1500 98104 #016-43-1990 L1997
OBG *020 †30
CARO-BRUCE, Emily. 1629 N 45TH ST 98103 #043-01-2006 **FP** *012
CAROLLO, Thomas C, Jr. 1959 NE PACIFIC ST BO 98195 #012-05-2000 L2006 **P** *012
CARPENTER, Paul Andrew. 1100 FAIRVIEW AVE N, FHCC BOX 358080 D5-290 98109
#143-03-1985 L2001 **PHO** *012
CARPENTER, Robert D. UNIVERSITY OF WASHINGTON, PAIN CENTER RC-95 98195
#671-01-1982 L1993 **APM** *020
CARR, Jennifer Mae. 1959 NE PACIFIC ST, RESIDENCY TRAINING 98195 #018-03-2006 L2006
P *012
CARR, Laurie Lynn. 1100 FAIRVIEW AVE N, C/O LISA ANDERSON 98109 #018-03-2000 L2003
ON *100 †20
CARR, Robert Brannon. PO BOX 3571, UNIV OF WASHINGTON 98124 #028-46-2006 L2007
DR *012
CARRANZA, Leslie. ■ 98103 #026-04-2006 L2006 **OBG** *012
CARRIER, Johanne. ■ 98105 #067-06-1993 L2000 **PAN** *100
CARROLL, Brant Franklin. 5300 17TH AVE NW 98107 #005-06-1991 L1998 **OPH** *020 †35
CARROLL, Herbert B. ■ 98116 #028-34-1945 L1946 **PD** *071 †55
CARSON, Simon Armour A. 1600 E JEFFERSON ST, PACIFIC VASCULAR INC 98122
#539-06-1954 L1960 **AN OS** *105
CARTER, Damien Wilson. ■ 98122 #016-11-2006 L2006 **GS** *012
CARTER, Edward Russo. 4800 SAND POINT WAY NE, CHILDREN'S HOSPITAL 98105
#047-05-1981 L1993 **PD PDP** *020 †55
CARTER, Nancy. 1420 5TH AVE STE 375, GHC DOWNTOWN MED CTR 98101
#035-46-1978 L1981 **FM OS** *020 †18
CARTER, Richard. 2271 NE 51ST ST 98105 #010-03-1976 L1977 **P PYA** *020 †75
CARTER, Stephen Jos. 2324 EASTLAKE AVE E, STE 500 98102 #054-04-1968 L1973
DR PDR *050 †80 ‡
CARY, Margaret Sheppard. ■ 98122 #040-02-2006 L2006 **P** *012
CASABONA-ROBERSON, Susan. 515 MINOR AVE 98104 #051-04-1979 L1982 **IM** *020 †20
CASEY, Robert Louis. ■ 98177 #039-01-1963 L1967 **P OS** *071
CASHMAN, Katherine Govier. ■ 98125 #056-06-2005 L2005 **AN** *012
CASHMAN, Margaret Anne. 2302 24TH AVE E, STE B 98112 #035-47-1977 L1986
CHP P *020 †75
CASPER, Corey. 1100 FAIRVIEW AVE N, MAILSTOP D3-100 98109 #035-20-1997 L2000
ID *050 †20
CASSIS, Farah. ■ 98115 #035-08-1999 L2007 **ICE** *100 †55
CASSIUS, David Andrew. ■ 98101 #047-07-1991 L1999 **PM IM** *020 †60
CASSMAN, Robert Michael. 515 MINOR AVE, STE 300 98104 #030-05-1986 L1994
IM *020 †50,20
CASTOR, Mei Lin. 425 QUEEN ANNE AVE N 98109 #012-05-1993 L2005 **GPM** *020 †18,70
CASTRO, Expedita Lumbao. 901 BOREN AVE, STE 1800 98104 #748-01-1954 L1968
IM GP *020
CASTRO, Miriam Imelda. ■ 98102 #054-04-2008 *012
CASTROFRENZEL, Karla Jose. 4800 SAND POINT WAY NE, MAILSTOP 9G-1 98105
#048-14-2000 L2001 **PAN** *100 †05
CATTAMANCHI, Ashok. 1959 NE PACIFIC ST, BOX 35 98195 #016-11-2003 L2003 **ID** *012 †20
CAWLEY, Peter Joseph. 1959 NE PACIFIC ST, BOX 356422 98195 #010-02-2000 L2004
CD *100 †20
CAWSE-LUCAS, Jeanne Marie. 550 16TH AVE STE 100, PROVIDENCE FAMILY MEDICINE 98122
#024-16-2006 L2006 **FP** *012
CAYLOR, Lisa Marie. 801 BROADWAY STE 901 98122 #035-45-1990 L1998 **N** *020 †20,75
CE CERE, Laura M. 712 N MOTOR PL, APT 3 98103 #048-12-2002 L2002 **PCC** *012
CELIX, Juanita Marie. 98117 #041-01-2004 L2004 **NS** *012
CELUM, Connie Locke. 325 9TH AVE 98104 #005-02-1984 L1987 **ID IM** *020 †20
CENTERWALL, Brandon S. 2139 7TH AVE W 98119 #066-18-1979 L1985 **P** *071 †70
CEPRIANO, Tresa Rose. 1959 NE PACIFIC ST, CAMPUS BOX 356540 98195 #054-04-2001 L2006
AN *012
CERVERA, Janina Hanushka. ■ 98122 #056-05-2005 L2005 **IM** *012
CHABAL, Charles. 1959 NE PACIFIC ST, MSC 359300 98195 #041-12-1982 L1985
AN PME *020 †05
CHABLI, Caroline Marie. ■ 98112 #010-02-1998 L2005 **ORS** *100
CHABRA, Shilpi. 1959 NE PACIFIC ST RR542, PO BOX 356320 98195 #495-96-1986 L2003
NPM *020 †55
CHADWICK, Heathcliff S. 1959 NE PACIFIC ST, MSC 359300 98195 #040-02-1976 L1980
AN *05
CHAE, Kyungai Mireille. 1229 MADISON ST STE 500, NORDSTROM TOWER 98104
#026-04-1995 L2004 **D DMP** *020 †55,15
CHAI, Sanders K. 521 WALL ST, GROUP HEALTH COOPERATIVE 98121 #035-03-1992 L1997
GPM OM *020 †55,70

CHAIT, Alan. 1959 NE PACIFIC ST, BOX 356426 98195 #836-02-1967 L1977 **END NTR** *050
CHAKRAVARTI, Aparna. 825 EASTLAKE AVE E G6-800, SEATTLE CANCER CARE ALLIAN 98109
#016-11-2002 L2006 **HO** *012
CHALLA, Harigovinda Reddy. 1959 NE PACIFIC ST 98195 #495-58-1997 **PDR** *012
CHAM, Aileen Renee. 550 16TH AVE STE 100, SWEDISH FAMILY MED 98122
#035-09-2007 L2007 **FP** *012
CHAMBERLAIN, Aaron Mark. ■ 98125 #005-02-2006 L2006 **ORS** *012
CHAMBERLAIN, Marc Chas. 825 EASTLAKE AVE E, MAIL STOP G-6800 98109
#035-01-1977 L2007 **N CHN** *020 †55,75
CHAMBERS, Allyson Heath. ■ 98109 #034-01-2006 L2007 **FP** *012
CHAMPOUX, Ann N. 1100 9TH AVE C1-MSO, VIRGINIA MASON MEDICAL CEN 98101
#005-06-1978 L1984 **PD** *020 †55
CHAN, Elaine Soling. ■ 98105 #028-02-2007 L2007 **PTH** *012
CHAN, Elizabeth. 1959 NE PACIFIC ST, BOX 356422 98195 #033-06-2002 L2006 **CD** *012 †20
CHAN, Gregory Kwok-Kay. 515 MINOR AVE, STE 200 98104 #056-06-1966 L1971 **OS** *020 †45
CHAN, Leighton. 1959 NE PACIFIC ST, BOX 356490 98195 #005-14-1990 L1992 **PM** *020 †60
CHAN, Molina Mowah. 1401 MADISON ST STE 100, RESIDENCY - 98104
#005-14-2007 L2007 *012
CHAN, Sau Yun. UNIV OF WA SCHOOL MED, HOUSESTAFF AFFAIRS SC64 98195
#243-38-1960 L1960 *012
CHAN, Steven T. ■ 98115 #043-01-2004 L2004 **PM** *012
CHAN, Vincent Thomas. 1959 NE PACIFIC ST #356340, UW SCHOOL OF MEDICINE 98195
#005-02-2002 L2002 **OTO** *012
CHAN, Ying Chih. ■ 98115 #462-01-1966 **OS** *100
CHANCE, Phillip Frazier. 1959 NE PACIFIC ST, BOX 356320 98195 #047-06-1978 L1997
OS N *050 †19
CHANDLER, Wayne Leslie. U WA-DEPT LAB MED-SB-10 98195 #028-34-1982 L1983
CLP *050 †50
CHANDRA, Arti. 600 UNIVERSITY ST # 12 98101 #016-43-1992 L1992 **FM** *020 †18
CHANG, Alice May. ■ 98122 #028-46-2003 L2006 **NEP** *012 †20
CHANG, Andrew Tien. 747 BROADWAY 98122 #056-06-1994 L1997 **AN IM** *020 †20,05
CHANG, Benjamin. ■ 98104 #028-79-2003, ▲ L2007 **PAN** *012
CHANG, David Chi. 1001 BROADWAY, STE 215 98122 #017-20-1995 L2006 **IM** *020 †20
CHANG, Denise. ■ 98101 #018-03-2007 L2007 **P** *012
CHANG, Dong Wook. 10631 8TH AVE NE 98125 #005-14-2000 L2004 **PCC** *100 †20
CHANG, Henry Shihhung. 9730 3RD AVE NE, STE 210 98115 #016-06-1992 L1999
OTO HNS *020 †45
CHANG, Jason Jerjia. ■ 98109 #020-12-2007 L2007 **GS** *012
CHANG, Jenq-Yue. 10212 5TH AVE NE STE 100 98125 #244-02-1976 L1990 **D** *020 †15
CHANG, Jesse Limmon. 1101 MADISON ST STE 30 98104 #035-19-2000 L2006 **PCC** *020 †20
CHANG, Lily Christine. 1100 9TH AVE, VIRGINIA MASON MEDICAL CEN 98101
#024-07-1996 L1998 **GS** *020 †85
CHANG, Tina. 325 9TH AVE, EMERGENCY MEDICINE DEPT 98104 #025-01-1996 L1998
IM *020 †20
CHANGAMIRE, Freeman Ticha. 1959 NE PACIFIC ST 98195 #775-01-2000 L2007 **FP** *012
CHANSKY, Howard Alan. 1660 S COLUMBIAN WAY, MAILSTOP ORT112 98108
#041-01-1987 L1992 **ORS** *020 †40
CHAO, C Tien-Bao. 1025 NE 73RD ST 98115 #035-01-1989 L1999 **GS** *020 †85
CHAO, Janna. 2505 2ND AVE, STE 200 98121 #054-04-1992 L1992 **FM** *020 †18
CHAPLIN, David M. 1229 MADISON ST STE 1600 98104 #917-01-1961 L1972 **ORS** *020 †40
CHAPMAN, A Zerne. 3400 CALIFORNIA AVE SW, STE 201 98116 #016-11-1943 L1960
IM *071 †20
CHAPMAN, Arthur Wellesley. 1401 MADISON ST, SWEDISH FAMILY MEDICINE 98104
#054-04-2005 L2005 **FP** *012
CHAPMAN, Ellen Edith. 10330 MERIDIAN AVE N, SEATTLE ARTHRITIS CLINIC 98133
#041-07-1985 L1985 **FM** *071 †18
CHAPMAN, Jens Robt. 4245 ROOSEVELT WAY NE, STE 354775 98105 #409-42-1983 L1990
OTR OSS *020 †40
CHAPMAN, John Timothy. 1570 N 115TH ST STE 14 98133 #010-01-1955 L1958 **N PD** *071 †55
CHAPMAN, Katharine H. 1214 E HAMLIN ST 98102 #016-01-1927 **OPH** *071 †35
CHAPMAN, Kyle W. 1530 N 115TH ST, MED ARTS BLDG RM 201 98133 #016-06-1951 L1952
GS *072 †85
CHAPMAN, Pamela Statler. 1959 NE PACIFIC ST, UNIVERSITY OF WASHINGTON 98195
#649-14-2000 L2005 **NPM** *100
CHAPMAN, Phillip Howe. 1101 MADISON ST STE 1400 98104 #054-04-1987 L1992 **U** *020 †95
CHAPMAN, Warren H. PO BOX 356510, DEPT UROLOGY 98195 #016-02-1952 L1957
U *071 †95
CHARD, Ronald Leslie. 4800 SAND POINT WAY NE 98105 #054-04-1963 L1965 **PHO ON** *071
CHARLTON, John Edmond. 2324 EASTLAKE AVE E, STE 500 98102 #917-04-1965 L1978
AN *040
CHARRON, Paul Daniel. 1101 MADISON ST STE 500, NORTHWEST COLON AND RECTAL 98104
#038-44-2002 L2007 **CRS** *012 †85
CHATAL, Catherine. 6800 E GREEN LAKE WAY N 98115 #050-02-1992 L1999 **PS** *020 †65
CHATARD, Peter R N, Jr. 1550 N 115TH ST 98133 #035-45-1960 L1967 **PS OTO** *020 †45,65
CHATILO, Alexandr I. 1530 N 115TH ST, NORTHWEST PHYSIATRY 98133 #913-09-1981 L2001
PM *020
CHATRIAN, Gian Emilio. 2324 EASTLAKE AVE E, STE 500 98102 #561-10-1951 L1989 **N** *050
CHATURVEDI, Abhishek. 1959 NE PACIFIC ST 98195 #496-02-1999 L2007 **AR** *012
CHATURVEDI, Apeksha. 1959 NE PACIFIC ST 98195 #495-30-1999 L2007 **AR** *012
CHAU, Vincent. 900 TERRY AVE, FOURTH FLOOR 98104 #016-02-1993 L1997 **AN** *05
CHAUNCEY, Thomas Reeve. 1959 NE PACIFIC ST 98195 #016-01-1985 L1986
ON HEM *020 †20
CHAVELLE, Anna Henderson. 6800 E GREEN LAKE WAY N 98115 #054-04-1957 L1958
FM *071 †18
CHAVEZ, Christina Diane. 4020 E MADISON ST, STE 240 98112 #048-13-1978 L1979 **P** *020
CHEBLI, Joseph Elie. 1570 N 115TH ST STE 5 98133 #035-48-1995 L2004 **GS** *020 †85
CHEEMA, Mohinder Singh. 1550 N 115TH ST 98133 #495-03-1969 L1974 **FM FPG** *020 †18
CHEEVER, Martin Alexander. 825 EASTLAKE AVE E G4-812, SCCA 98109 #025-01-1970 L1972
ON *050 †20
CHEN, Allen Tang. ■ 98105 #016-01-2002 L2007 **VIR** *012 †80
CHEN, Ann J. 1959 NE PACIFIC ST, CAMPUS BOX 356522 98195 #016-42-2002 L2005
PCC *012 †20
CHEN, Benson. ■ 98109 #016-42-2001 L2006 **OPH** *020
CHEN, Ching-Yu. ■ 98133 #244-02-1973 L1981 *020
CHEN, Ellen Huichin. 550 17TH AVE 98122 #056-06-1992 L2007 **IC** *020 †20
CHEN, Eric Yenpo. 1100 FAIRVIEW AVE N, MAILSTOP D3-190 98109 #056-05-1999 L2002
ON *100 †20

CHEN, Frederick Ming. 1959 NE PACIFIC ST 98195 #005-02-1996 L1998 **FM** *020 †18

CHEN, Gina Huiying. 550 17TH AVE 98122 #056-05-1995 L2006 **PCC** *020 †20

CHEN, Henry Jud-Lae. 1145 BROADWAY, THE POLYCLINIC 98122 #060-01-1987 L2002 **AI** *020 †20,03

CHEN, Herbert Weishing. 600 BROADWAY, STE 170 98122 #016-06-2000 L2005 **DR** *100 †80

CHEN, I-Jen. 10317 GREENWOOD AVE N #202 98133 #244-05-1977 L1985 **IM IMG** *020

CHEN, James Chongchu. 4800 SAND POINT WAY NE 98105 #054-04-1983 L1989 **NS** *020 †25

CHEN, Janet K. 747 BROADWAY 98122 #035-05-2002 L2006 **AN** *100 †05

CHEN, Jarvis Chung. 1959 NE PACIFIC ST, DEPT OF RADIOLOGY 98195 #036-07-2002 L2007 **VIR** *012 †80

CHEN, Jay. 1029 BELMONT AVE E 98102 #035-15-2003 L2005 **CD** *012 †20

CHEN, Maida Lynn. 4800 SAND POINT WAY NE, BOX A-5937 98105 #016-06-1998 L2005 **PDP** *020

CHEN, Michael Anthony. 325 9TH AVE, BOX 359748 98104 #025-01-1999 L2002 **CD** *100 †20

CHEN, Mien-Chi. 1145 BROADWAY 98122 #054-04-1993 L1999 **OTO** *020 †45

CHEN, Naixi. 122 16TH AVE E, WELLNESS CENTER 98112 #243-65-1986 L2001 **HO** *020 †20

CHEN, Philip Peihai. 1959 NE PACIFIC ST, BOX 356485 98195 #008-01-1991 L1996 **OPH** *020 †35

CHEN, Stephen Shau-Tsi. 1145 BROADWAY 98122 #244-02-1958 L1980 **P PYG** *071 †75

CHEN, Sutin. ■ 98105 #047-05-2008 *012

CHEN, Szuyu Jenny. ■ 98102 #054-04-2008 *012

CHEN, Ty C. 1600 E JOHN ST 98112 #035-03-1992 L1999 **AN** *020 †05

CHEN, Xiaoming. 1959 NE PACIFIC ST, BOX 357115 98195 #023-07-1997 L2004 **DR** *020 †80

CHENEY, Frederick W, Jr. 325 9TH AVE 98104 #024-07-1960 L1964 **AN** *030 †05

CHENG, Aaron M. ■ 98105 #024-01-2000 L2007 **TS** *012 †85

CHENG, Edith Yeetak. 1959N NE PACIFIC ST, DEPT OF OB/GYN BOX 356460 98195 #054-04-1987 L1990 **MFM MG** *020 †30,19

CHENG, Jennifer Kay Jean. 1959 NE PACIFIC ST RM C212, SCHOOL OF MEDICINE 98195 #028-46-2001 L2004 **CHP** *020

CHENG, Raymond. ■ 98122 #035-15-2003 L2003 **IM** *020 †20

CHENG-HAKIMIAN, Andrea Li. 325 9TH AVE, BOX 359745 98104 #028-02-1999 L2004 **IM** *020 †75

CHENTOW, Stephen Jerold. 3626 NE 45TH ST STE 300 98105 #035-45-1970 L1971 **PD** *020 †55

CHERIAN, Sindhu. ■ 98121 #012-05-2000 L2005 **HMP** *100

CHESNUT, Chas Haile, III. 4245 ROOSEVELT WAY NE, STE 354775 98105 #011-03-1966 L1970 **NM IM** *050

CHEW, Lisa Deanne. 325 9TH AVE, BOX 359780 98104 #005-02-1993 L1993 **IM** *020 †20

CHI, Ruchien. 1660 S COLUMBIAN WAY S-182 98108 #047-05-1998 L2000 **IMG** *020 †20

CHIANG, Seine. 4245 ROOSEVELT WAY NE, STE 354775 98105 #040-02-1990 L2006 **OBG** *020 †30

CHIEN, Andy Jauann. 1959 NE PACIFIC ST BOX 35 98195 #016-06-1999 L1999 **D** *020 †15

CHIEN, Jason Wen. 325 9TH AVE, UW BOX 359762 98104 #033-05-1994 L1999 **PCC** *020 †20

CHILCOTE, Heather Catheri. ■ 98102 #054-04-2008 *012

CHIN, Curtiss B. 201 16TH AVE E 98112 #244-05-1984 L1990 **FM** *020 †18

CHIN, George N. 10564 5TH AVE NE STE 102 98125 #748-08-1968 L1977 **OPH ID** *071 †35

CHINN, Hubert Dean. 120 NE NORTHGATE WAY # 436 98125 #021-01-1955 L1962 **D** *020 †15

CHINN, Jonathan. 1551 NW 54TH ST 98107 #054-04-1968 L1969 **OTO** *020 †45

CHINNAPONGSE, Robert B. 1101 MADISON ST STE 400, PACIFIC MEDICAL CTR 98104 #056-06-1994 L1998 **PM PME** *020 †60

CHIOU, Lisa Ann. 1959 NE PACIFIC ST, U OF W-HS AFFAIRS BOX 3563 98195 #054-04-2004 L2004 **IM** *020 †20

CHIU, Diane S. 1100 9TH AVE 98101 #054-04-1997 L2004 **D** *020 †15

CHIU, Harvey Kenn. 1959 NE PACIFIC ST C508, CAMPUS BOX 356426 98195 #036-05-1996 L2002 **PDE** *012 †20,55

CHIU, Lynn Leigh. NECK SURG, DEPT OF OTO/HEAD & 98195 #005-15-2005 L2005 **OTO** *012

CHIU-CHENG, Annie S. 1660 S COLUMBIAN WAY, S-117-RCS 98108 #035-19-1998 L2002 **PM** *020 †60

CHO, Denise Enock. 1560 N 115TH ST STE 109 98133 #041-13-1982 L1988 **OBG** *020 †30

CHOE, John Hyuk. 325 9TH AVE BOX 359780, HARBORVIEW MEDICAL CENTER 98104 #035-19-1997 L2000 **IM** *020 †20

CHOI, Jack Chak Sang. 4744 41ST AVE SW STE 101 98116 #061-01-1982 L2001 **FM** *020 †18

CHOI, Paul Hanbae. 1959 NE PACIFIC ST BOX 356, UNIVERSITY OF WASHINGTON 98195 #005-11-2004 L2005 **P** *012

CHOI, Peter. PO BOX 356340, UW SCHOOL OF MED GME PROGR 98195 #016-43-2003 L2003 **OTO** *012

CHONG, Dennis Khin-Heung. 701 5TH AVE STE 1900 98104 #060-02-1988 L1999 **PM FM** *030 †60

CHOPRA, Gopal Krishan. 500 17TH AVE, SWEDISH MED CTR 98122 #143-02-1989 L2004 **NS** *020

CHOROSTECKI, Eugene Jos. ■ 98115 #065-01-1960 L1966 **U** *071 †95

CHOU, David. 1959 NE PACIFIC ST NW120, UWMC, BOX 357110 98195 #041-12-1974 L1998 **CLP** *030 †50

CHOU, Jeffrey. 325 9TH AVE 98104 #041-12-2004 L2004 **HO** *012 †20

CHOUEITER, Nadine Fakhri. 1959 NE PACIFIC ST, DEPT OF PEDS CARDIOLOGY 98195 #605-01-2003 L2007 **PDC** *012 †55

CHOW, Eric Jessen. ■ 98103 #005-02-2001 L2004 **PHO** *100 †55

CHOW, Linda Ann. 515 MINOR AVE, STE 200 98104 #054-04-1990 L1993 **IM** *020 †20

CHOWDHARY, Abhineet. 1959 NE PACIFIC ST, BOX 356340 98195 #038-40-2003 L2003 **NS** *012

CHOY, Elizabeth Suenghae. 1101 MADISON ST STE 900 98104 #054-04-1984 L1986 **OPH** *020 †20

CHRISINGER, Eric Wayne. 11545 15TH AVE NE STE 205, NORTHWEST PEDIATRICS, PLLC 98125 #054-04-1984 L1985 **PD** *020 †55

CHRISTAKIS, Dimitri A. 1959 NE PACIFIC ST, MSC 359300 98195 #041-01-1993 L1995 **PD** *020 †55

CHRISTAL, Aric Adrian. 1959 NE PACIFIC ST BOX 356, UW SCHOOL OF MEDICINE GME 98195 #054-04-2005 L2005 **ORS** *012

CHRISTIE, David Parker. 325 9TH AVE DEPT OF, UNIVERSITY OF WASHINGTON 98104 #030-15-1944 L1951 **DR** *020 †80

CHRISTIE, Dennis Lee. 4800 SAND POINT WAY NE, DIV GAST NUTRITION 98105 #016-06-1968 L1969 **PD** *020 †20

CHRISTIE, Pandora Elisa. 901 BOREN AVE, STE 1730 98104 #917-25-1982 L2000 **A** *020

CHU, Felix Way-Keon. 11011 MERIDIAN AVE N, STE 200 98133 #028-34-1981 L1989 **OTO HNS** *020 †45

CHU, Joseph. 1124 COLUMBIA ST 98104 #010-02-1975 L1977 **GO PHP** *050

CHU, Lawrence. 1550 N 115TH ST 98133 #016-06-1984 L1987 **EM** *030 †16

CHU, Vy Xuan. ■ 98102 #054-04-2004 L2004 **IM** *020 †20

CHUANG, Elaine Lucille. 1959 NE PACIFIC ST, DEPT OF OPHTHALMOLOGY 98195 #048-13-1979 L1980 **OPH** *020 †35

CHUANG, Peter I. 125 16TH AVE E, CSB-2 FLOOR, PULMONARY CLI 98112 #048-04-1987 L1991 **CCM PUD** *020

CHUE, Ben Manfai. 122 16TH AVE 98112 #005-02-1991 L1993 **ON IM** *020 †20

CHUN, Alan J. 416 MAYNARD AVE S 98104 #014-01-1976 L1992 **FM** *074 †18

CHUN, Carrie Dianne. 1959 NE PACIFIC ST, BOX 356522 98195 #054-04-2001 L2005 **PCC** *012 †20

CHUN, Terrence Ung Hoong. 4800 SAND POINT WAY NE, CHILDREN'S HEART CENTER, 4 98105 #041-09-1997 L2004 **PDC** *020 †55

CHUNCHU, Kavitha. ■ 98125 #051-04-2006 L2006 **FP** *012

CHUNG, Andrew Hyunchan. 747 BROADWAY 98122 #054-04-2000 L2004 **AN** *020 †05

CHUNG, Hui-San. 1959 NE PACIFIC ST 98195 #025-07-2003 L2006 **CD** *012 †20

CHUNG, Jeanie Lee. ■ 98105 #054-04-2008 *012

CHUNG, Michael Hoonbae. 1959 NE PACIFIC ST, BOX 356523 98195 #016-02-1998 L2001 **ID** *100 †20

CHUNG, Thomas Taifung. 1600 E JEFFERSON ST, STE A1 98122 #025-01-1996 L2000 **PM** *020

CHUNG, Youngme Christina. ■ 98125 #054-04-2008 *012

CHURCH, Lili Lucile. 4245 ROOSEVELT WAY NE, STE 354775 98105 #018-03-1985 L1986 **FM** *020 †18

CIECHANOWSKI, Paul Simon. 4225 ROOSEVELT WAY NE 98105 #067-01-1991 L1994 **P** *020 †75

CILNIS, Juris Uldis. ■ 98125 #040-02-1960 L1963 **IM** *071 †20

CLARK, Barbara Louise. 2910 E MADISON ST STE 211 98112 #054-04-1993 L1995 **FM** *020 †18

CLARK, Clancy Jake. ■ 98125 #038-40-2004 L2004 **GS** *012

CLARK, Herbert Royal. 2409 N 45TH ST 98103 #054-04-01-1982 L1983 **ORS** *020 †40

CLARK, Hugh. 1229 MADISON ST STE 1500, MINOR & JAMES MEDICAL, PLL 98104 #035-01-1961 L1968 **IM IMG** *071 †20

CLARK, Joan Annette. 4800 SAND POINT WAY NE 98105 #028-02-1974 L1984 **PUD IM** *050 †20

CLARK, Linda Jean. 1550 N 115TH ST 98133 #005-02-1980 L1981 **FM OBS** *020 †18 ‡

CLARK, Michael Stuart. 325 9TH AVE 98104 #018-03-1997 L2001 **P** *050

CLARK, Owen Edward. ■ 98125 #054-04-1967 L1973 **P** *020 †75

CLARK, Roy D, Jr. 509 OLIVE WAY, STE 1419 98101 #019-02-1969 L1978 **P PFP** *020 †20,75 ‡

CLARK, Stephen Kent. 600 BROADWAY, STE 260 98122 #054-04-1973 L1976 **OTO HNS** *020 †45

CLARKE, Edmund R, Jr. 223 TAYLOR AVE N 98109 #007-02-1943 L1950 **PUD ON** *071

CLARKE, Jessica Anne. PO BOX 356560, 1959 NE PACIFIC ST 98195 #005-19-1988 L2007 **P** *012

CLARREN, Sterling Keith. 4800 SAND POINT WAY NE, P O BOX C5371 98105 #026-04-1973 L1975 **PD** *050 †55

CLAVETTE SHUHART, M. 325 9TH AVE # 359773, HARBORVIEW MED CTR 98104 #032-01-1988 L1991 **GE** *020 †20

CLAWSON, David Roger. 1600 E JEFFERSON ST, STE A4 98122 #020-12-1985 L1986 **PM** *030 †60

CLAWSON, Robert Stebbins. 2409 N 45TH ST 98103 #021-05-1966 L1974 **ORS** *020 †40

CLAYTON, Patricia Lynn. 509 19TH AVE E 98112 #025-01-1977 L1978 **FM** *020

CLAYTON, W Franklin. 509 OLIVE WAY, STE 620 98101 #005-12-1976 L1992 **ORS** *030

CLEMENTS, Margaret Helen. ■ 98136 #054-04-1978 L1979 **PD** *020 †55

CLEMENTS, Randolph. ■ 98105 #048-02-1949 L1956 **GE IM** *071 †20

CLICK, Eleanor Suchada. 1959 NE PACIFIC ST, BOX 356340 98195 #005-11-2003 L2003 **PD** *100 †55

CLIFTON, James Frederick. 1800 WESTLAKE AVE N, STE 206 98109 #054-04-1968 L1978 **CD IM** *030

CLINE, Kelley Lynn. ■ 98117 #422-01-2001 L2007 **RNR** *012 †80

CLINTON, Jeremiah Malachi. 1959 NE PACIFIC ST, BOX 356340 98195 #054-04-2002 L2002 **ORS** *100

CLOUD, Renee Apple. 1949 NE PACIFIC ST, BOX 356560 98195 #054-04-2003 L2004 **P** *100

CLOWES, Alexander W. 325 9TH AVE 98104 #054-04-1972 L1980 **VS** *050 †85

CLOWRY, Margaret E. 10416 5TH AVE NE, PACIFIC MEDICAL CLINICS 98125 #056-06-1987 L1990 **IM** *020 †20

CLURMAN, Bruce Edward. 1100 FAIRVIEW AVE N # D1-1 98109 #035-20-1989 L1991 **ON IM** *020 †20

COATES, Daniel Evan. ■ 98103 #016-02-2003 L2003 **IM** *020 †20

COATSWORTH, James Jos. 925 SENECA ST 98101 #035-20-1963 L1966 **N** *071 †75

COBB, Leonard Arthur. 325 9TH AVE # 359748 98104 #026-04-1952 L1957 **CD IM** *020 †20

COFFEY, Maitreya Sonmey. 4800 SAND POINT WAY NE, STE G0061 98105 #016-02-2001 L2004 **PD** *020 †55

COGHLAN, James Correll. 1530 N 115TH ST STE 303 98133 #054-04-1979 L1980 **GP FM** *020 ‡

COHEN, Gordon Alan. 4800 SAND POINT WAY NE, CHILDREN'S HOSP & REG MED 98105 #021-01-1989 L1996 **TS** *020 †85,90

COHEN, Mitchell Lee. 515 MINOR AVE, STE 200 98104 #005-06-1981 L1991 **GE IM** *020 †20

COHEN, Phillip Alan. 7817 12TH AVE NE 98115 #028-03-1968 L1973 **P CHP** *020 †55

COHEN, Seth Alexander. 130 NICKERSON ST STE 204 98109 #016-06-1981 L1985 **P LM** *020 †75

COHEN, Wendy Anne. 325 9TH AVE DEPT RAD 98104 #024-01-1975 L1987 **RNR R** *020 †80

COIT, Henry Gwinnell, Jr. 4616 25TH AVE NE, STE 618 98105 #005-18-1986 L1988 **PD OS** *020 †55

COLBERT, Robert Richard. 925 SENECA ST 98101 #005-18-1995 L1998 **IM** *020 †20

COLBY, Donn Jos. 1600 E JOHN ST 98112 #035-48-1989 L1989 **IM** *020 †20

COLE, B Sharon. 2201 6TH AVE, C/O BENSON & MCLAUGHLIN 98121 #054-04-1979 L1981 **RO** *020 †80 ‡

COLE, Bonnie Lynnelizabe. ■ 98199 #049-01-2005 L2005 **PTH** *012

COLE, Joanna Lynn. ■ 98117 #005-12-2007 **IM** *012

COLE, Robin Elizabeth. 1229 MADISON ST, STE 1500 98104 #054-04-1983 L1984 **OBG** *020 †30

COLEMAN, Brian Doyle. 325 9TH AVE 98104 #016-42-1978 L1980 **P** *020 †75

COLEMAN, Brian Howard. 4800 SAND POINT WAY NE, AND REGION 98105 #011-03-1999 L2003 **PEM** *100 †55

COLEMAN, Larissa Elaine. 925 SENECA ST # 1930, OFF OF HOUSESTAFF AFFAIRS 98101 #054-04-2004 L2004 **GS** *020

COLEMAN, Mario Tarell. ■ 98118 #039-01-2002 L2005 **CHN** *012

COLEMAN, Regina Felicia. ■ 98122 #016-11-2007 *012

COLEN, Teran Wilson. 1959 NE PACIFIC ST, BOX 356340 98195 #024-01-2003 L2004 **DR** *012

■ = Address Information Privacy Protected

COLER, Clark Seymour. 747 BROADWAY 98122 #035-09-1986 L1991 **IM** *020 †20
COLFELT, Robert Harold. 5606 14TH AVE NW 98107 #054-04-1959 L1961 **N** *020 †75
COLLEY, Peter Sturgis. 1959 NE PACIFIC ST 98195 #050-02-1967 L1973 **AN** *071 †05
COLLIER, Ann Cornwall. 325 9TH AVE, BOX 359929 98104 #032-01-1978 L1979 **ID IM** *050 †20
COLLINS, Bonnie Sue. 3532 SW 112TH ST, DEPT OF MEDICINE 98146 #005-15-1986 L1988 **NEP** *020 †20
COLLINS, Carol Jean. ■ 98115 #038-40-1991 L1997 **U** *020
COLLINS, Steven James. 1100 FAIRVIEW AVE N, PO BOX 19024 98109 #035-01-1973 L1980 **IM ON** *050 †20 ‡
COLLYMORE, Victor Alvin. 201 16TH AVE E, GROUP HEALTH 98112 #035-01-1981 L2003 **IM** *020 †20
COLTRERA, Marc Dante. 1959 NE PACIFIC ST, DEPT OF OTO-HNS, BOX 35651 98195 #008-01-1981 L1986 **OTO** *020 †45
COLVEN, Roy Mitchell. 325 9TH AVE BOX 359763, DEPT OF MEDICINE/DERMATOLO 98104 #054-04-1987 L1989 **D IM** *020 †20,15
COMBS, Heidi Lynn. 325 9TH AVE, BOX 359896 98104 #054-04-2000 L2001 **P** *100 †75
COMBS, Patrick Duffy. PO BOX 356410, UNIV OF WASHINGTON 98195 #016-11-2003 L2003 **GS** *012
COMBS, Sara Ann. ■ 98103 #054-04-2008 *012
COMPTON, Nicholas Lee. 1959 NE PACIFIC ST RM C2, CAMPUS BOX 356340 98195 #054-04-2002 L2004 **D** *012 †20
CONAGHAN, Lisa Anne. 1550 N 115TH ST 98133 #016-01-1994 L1998 **OBG** *020 †30
CONCANNON, Leah Grace. UNIV OF WASHINGTON, DEPT OF REHAB MED 98195 #016-11-2006 L2007 **PM** *012
CONE, Patricia Anne. 1100 9TH AVE C1-MSO, VIRGINIA MASON MEDICAL CEN 98101 #019-02-1993 L1997 **AN** *020 †05
CONKLIN, Edward R. 1601 5TH AVE STE 830, ELLIOTT BAY MEDICAL GROUP 98101 #024-07-1990 L1994 **FM** *020 †18
CONN, Ruth Aileen. 1100 9TH AVE C1-MSO, VIRGINIA MASON MEDICAL CEN 98101 #014-01-1984 L1985 **PD** *020 †55
CONNELL, Anita Johnson. 1229 MADISON ST 98104 #054-04-1976 L1976 **OBG** *020
CONNELL, Frederick Alan. 1104 35TH AVE 98122 #035-19-1972 L1976 **PHP PD** *050 †55
CONNELL, Sandra Kay. 1106 36TH AVE 98122 #016-06-1970 L1980 **PYA P** *020
CONNOLLY, Janice Mary. 747 BROADWAY 98122 #010-01-1985 L1994 **IM IMG** *020 †20
CONNOLLY, Lynn Elizabeth. ■ 98103 #005-02-2000 L2004 **ID** *100
CONRAD, Ernest Upshur, III. 4245 ROOSEVELT WAY NE, STE 354775 98105 #051-01-1979 L1986 **OMO** *040 †40
CONRAD, Paul De Witt. 747 BROADWAY 98122 #038-40-1975 L1988 **PD** *020 †55
CONSTANS, Darcy Wells. ■ 98122 #034-01-2007 **FP** *012
CONTI, Neal Raymond. 1100 9TH AVE 98101 #035-48-1995 L1999 **DR** *020 †80
CONWAY, Jack Steven. 601 UNION ST, STE 1704 98101 #030-05-1983 L1984 **P** *020 †75
COOK, Daniel Larue. ■ 98103 #054-04-1977 **D** *100
COOK, Jill Andrea. 4800 SAND POINT WAY NE G-0, CHILDREN'S HOSPITAL & REG 98105 #028-34-2006 L2006 **PD** *012
COOK, Rodney Malcolm W. 200 16TH AVE E 98112 #025-01-1956 L1965 **GS** *071 †85
COOKE, Colin Roy. 325 9TH AVE, BOX 359762 98104 #038-40-2000 L2003 **PCC** *100 †20
COOKE, Daniel Lewis. 1959 NE PACIFIC ST, BOX 356340 98195 #012-05-2004 L2005 **DR** *012
COOKE, Erin A. ■ 98101 #048-04-2005 L2005 **DR** *012
COOKSON, Andrea Nell. ■ 98122 #007-02-1970 L1976 **EM P** *075 †75
COOKSON, Brad T. 1959 NE PACIFIC ST, MSC 359300 98195 #028-02-1991 L1993 **PTH** *020 †50
COOMBS, John Bennett. 1959 NE PACIFIC ST, UW MEDICAL CTR BOX 356340 98195 #035-20-1972 L1974 **FM PD** *030 †55,18
COOMBS, Robert Wm. 325 9TH AVE, BOX 359690 98104 #064-01-1981 L1985 **ID IM** *050
COOPER, Emily L. 400 N 34TH ST, STE 300 98103 #654-01-1987 L1997 **FM FSM** *020 †18
COOPER, Eric Scott. ■ 98117 #011-02-1996 L2005 **EM** *020 †16
COOPER, Jeremy Ormond. 325 9TH AVE 98104 #671-02-1980 L1988 **AN** *020 †05
COOPER, Mindy Ann. 1100 9TH AVE M6-AC, VIRGINIA MASON MEDICAL CEN 98101 #010-01-1987 L1994 **NEP** *020 †20
COOPER, Stephanie Michele. 823 22ND AVE 98122 #054-04-2002 L2002 *020 †16
COPASS, Michael Keys, II. 325 9TH AVE, NEUROLOGY DEPT/BOX 359702 98104 #016-06-1964 L1973 **N EM** *020
COPELAND, James Rutledge. ■ 98102 #051-04-1995 L1999 **CCM** *020 †20
COPP, Daniel Harrison. ■ 98105 #054-04-2007 L2007 **FP** *012
COPPEANS, Christopher Wil. ■ 98112 #012-01-2007 L2007 **FP** *012
CORDES, Mark Alan. 747 BROADWAY 98122 #047-05-1999 L2004 **AN** *020 †05
CORDOVA, Marc Alfred. 1145 BROADWAY 98122 #028-34-1977 L1980 **IM** *020 †20
CORDY, Carol Jean. 1401 MADISON ST, STE 100 98104 #054-04-1983 L1984 **FM** *020 †18
COREY, Lawrence. 1100 FAIRVIEW AVE N #D3-100, FRED HTCHNSN CNCR RSCH CTR 98109 #025-01-1971 L1975 **ID IM** *050 †20
CORINTH, Claudia A D. UNIV OF WASHINGTON 98195 #409-10-1993 L1999 **PTH** *100
CORMAN, John Mayer. 1100 9TH AVE 98101 #048-04-1992 L1998 **U** *020 †95
CORNEJO, Carol Jane. 325 9TH AVE, BOX 359796 98104 #005-02-1991 L1991 **GS** *020 †85
CORNIA, Paul Bryan. 1660 S COLUMBIAN WAY, CARE SYSTEM, S-111(MAILSTO 98108 #038-06-1996 L1998 **IM** *020 †20
CORREA, Roy Jay. 1100 9TH AVE 98101 #025-01-1956 L1957 **U** *071 †95
CORSON, Adam Hunter. ■ 98102 #017-20-2006 L2006 **IM** *012
CORSON, Marshall Ayer. 325 9TH AVE, BOX 359748 98104 #048-04-1981 L1994 **CD IM** *050 †20
CORUH, Basak. ■ 98199 #051-04-2006 L2006 **IM** *012
CORWIN, David Jos. 1124 COLUMBIA ST, STE 200 98104 #025-01-1978 L1979 **PTH CLP** *020 †50
CORYELL, Robert Jason. 4800 SAND POINT WAY NE, REGIONAL M 98105 #040-02-2006 L2006 **PD** *012
COTTER, Elizabeth W. 1221 MADISON ST, STE 520 98104 #020-12-1989 L2006 **DR** *020 †80 ‡
COUNTER, Steven Frank. 11011 MERIDIAN AVE N, STE 200 98133 #056-06-1994 L1996 **GS** *020 †85
COUNTS, Richard Barton. 921 TERRY AVE 98104 #028-02-1967 L1974 **IM** *020 †20
COUNTS, Sandra Jo Karm. 747 BROADWAY 98122 #028-02-1967 L1971 **ADM PMM** *020 †55
COURSEN, Jennifer Preston. 747 BROADWAY 98122 #036-01-1986 L1990 **AN** *020 †05
COVELER, Andrew Lawrence. 815 MERCER ST, BOX 358050 98109 #016-06-2002 L2003 **HO** *012 †20
COWAN, Charles Allan. 4800 SAND POINT WAY NE, DIV OF GENETIC & DEV MED 98105 #016-42-1968 L1972 **PD OS** *020 †55
COWEN, Sheldon Jay. 515 MINOR AVE STE 160 98104 #025-01-1982 L1988 **OPH** *020 †35
COWLEY, Deborah Suzanne. 4245 ROOSEVELT WAY NE, STE 354775 98105 #041-01-1980 L1981 **P** *050 †75
COX, Inge E. 325 9TH AVE, PO BOX 359739 98104 #409-10-1974 L2005 **OM** *020 †18
COX, W Welby. 117 31ST AVE E 98112 #028-03-1970 L1973 **ON HEM** *020 †20
COY, David Laughlin. 1107 NE 45TH ST STE 440, UWMC DEPT. OF RADIOLOGY 98105 #054-04-2000 L2004 **AR** *100 †80
CRANE, Deborah Ann. ■ 98103 #021-01-2005 L2005 **PM** *012
CRANE, Heidi Mc Laughlin. 325 9TH AVE, MS 359931 98104 #054-04-1998 L2001 **ID** *020 †20
CRANE, Robert Douglas. 1100 9TH AVE 98101 #054-04-1978 L1979 **DR** *020 †80
CRANMER, Lisa Marie. ■ 98115 #023-07-2007 L2007 **PD** *012
CRAWFORD, Daniel Joseph. ■ 98144 #054-04-2004 L2004 **CHP** *012
CREE, Andrew Kenneth. 325 9TH AVE BOX 359, HARBORVIEW MEDICAL CENTER 98104 #143-03-1990 L1999 *100
CREELMAN, Steven Arthur. 300 LENORA ST # 146, ELLIOTT MEDICAL GROUP 98121 #054-04-1984 L1987 **FM** *020 †18
CREUTZFELDT, Claire Johan. 1959 NE PACIFIC ST, U OF W-HS AFFAIRS BOX 3563 98195 #409-16-2003 L2004 **N** *012
CREVENSTEN, Henry Daniel. GRADUATE MEDICAL ED BOX 35, UNIVERSITY OF WASHINGTON 98195 #054-04-2003 L2003 **IM** *100 †20
CRILL, Wayne Elmo. UNIV OF WASHINGTON, DEPT PHYSIOLOGY BOX 357290 98195 #054-04-1962 L1967 **N** *040 †75
CRISERA, Arthur Alfred. 747 BROADWAY 98122 #030-06-1967 L1972 **AN** *020 †05
CRITTENDEN, Robert Andrew. 325 9TH AVE, DEPT FAM MED MSC 359781 98104 #054-04-1976 L1977 **FM** *062 †18
CROCKER, John Albert. 9800 4TH AVE NE 98115 #038-06-1979 L1980 **FM** *020 †18
CROICU, Carmen A. 1959 NE PACIFIC ST, BOX 356560 98195 #781-01-1993 L2004 **P** *020 †75
CROUTHAMEL, Matthew Rober. ■ 98125 #054-04-2004 L2004 **GS** *012
CROWLEY, Lauren Abram. ■ 98102 #054-04-2007 *012
CRULL, Matthew Robert. ■ 98103 #054-04-2008 *012
CRUTCHER, James Page, Jr. 900 TERRY AVE, STE 100 98104 #054-04-1984 L1986 **ORS** *020 †40
CRYST, Cyrus. 1100 9TH AVE C1-MSO, VIRGINIA MASON MEDICAL CEN 98101 #016-02-1984 L1985 **NEP IM** *020 †20
CULLEN, Mark Seth. 747 BROADWAY 98122 #051-01-1983 L1987 **AN** *020 †05
CULLISON, Saml Wilkinson. 550 16TH AVE STE 100, PROVIDENCE FMLY MED CTR 98122 #028-03-1975 L1976 **FM FPG** *040 †18
CULP, Stephen Hembree. 1959 NE PACIFIC ST, BOX 359300 98195 #051-04-2002 L2002 **U** *012
CULVER, Bruce Henry. 1959 NE PACIFIC ST, BOX 356522 98195 #054-04-1969 L1972 **PUD CCM** *030 †20
CULVER, John Patrick. 325 9TH AVE, QLTY IMP BOX 359731 98104 #054-04-1978 *020
CUMMINGS, David Eustace. 1660 S COLUMBIAN WAY, SYSTEM (S-111-ENDO) 98108 #024-01-1987 L1989 **END** *050 †20
CUMMINGS, Felicia. 1100 9TH AVE 98101 #024-01-1987 L1987 **DR** *075 †80
CUMMINS, Richard Oliver. 1606 39TH AVE 98122 #038-06-1972 L1977 **EM IM** *020 †20,16
CUNNINGHAM, James Robt. 122 16TH AVE E, 2ND FL 98112 #038-41-1978 L2001 **ON HEM** *020 †20
CUNNINGHAM, Michael L. 4800 SAND POINT WAY NE 98105 #050-02-1988 L1988 **PD** *020 †55
CURIEL, Mary Elizabeth. 1401 MADISON ST, STE 100 98104 #040-02-1993 L1996 **FM** *020 †18
CURLIN, Marcel Etienne. 5102 47TH AVE NE # M 98105 #040-02-1995 L1998 **ID** *020 †20
CURRIN, Douglas Ross. ■ 98103 #054-04-1960 L1969 **PTH** *071 †50,28
CURRIN, Erin-Siobha Ross. ■ 98115 #054-04-2008 *012
CURRY, Christine Erin. ■ 98112 #056-05-2007 L2007 **P** *012
CURTIS, Jared Randall. 1959 NE PACIFIC ST BOX 359, BOX 359762 98195 #023-07-1988 L1990 **PCC IM** *050 †20
CURTIS, Peter. ■ 98115 #917-23-1962 L1976 **FM** *030 †18
CURTIS, Thomas Bruce. 1100 9TH AVE 98101 #056-06-1979 L1984 **PM PME** *020 †60
CURTIS, William Spencer. 363 LYNN ST 98109 #008-01-1989 L1992 **AN** *020 †05
CUSCHIERI, Joseph. 325 9TH AVE 98104 #025-07-1994 L2000 **GS TRS** *020 †85
CZAJA, Jaclyn Ann. ■ 98109 #025-01-2007 L2007 **PD** *012
CZARTOSKI, Todd Jay. 747 BROADWAY, INFECTIOUS DISEASES 98122 #038-40-1999 L2002 **ID** *100 †75
CZERNIECKI, Jos Michael. 1959 NE PACIFIC ST, MSC 359300 98195 #061-01-1981 L1983 **PM** *020 †60
DABELL, David W. 1100 9TH AVE 98101 #049-01-1981 L1999 **EM** *030 †16
DABHI, Vikramsinh M. 3426 WALLINGFORD AVE N # 3 98103 #048-12-1998 L2001 **ON** *100 †20
DACEY, Sara Ruth. 9800 4TH AVE NE 98115 #005-02-1988 L1990 **FM** *020 †18
DACHS, Samuel. ■ 98119 #016-42-1959 L1987 **PTH BBK** *071 †50
DAGADAKIS, Christos S. 325 9TH AVE BOX 359896 98104 #054-04-1974 L1976 **P A** *040 †75
DAGER, Stephen Roger. 1100 NE 45TH ST STE 555, DEPT OF RADIOLOGY 98105 #030-05-1978 L1980 **P** *050 †75
DAGGETT, Lorin Reid. 500 17TH AVE 98122 #023-07-1971 L1978 **P** *074 †75
DAHL, Allen W. 1601 5TH AVE, STE 2400 98101 #054-04-1957 L1958 **GP** *071
DAHL, Genia Kay. 8821 15TH AVE NE 98115 #035-09-2005 L2005 **IM** *012
DAHLEN, Debra Dee. 825 EASTLAKE AVE E, SEATTLE CANCER CARE ALLIAN 98109 #041-12-1992 L1992 **HEM** *020 †20
DAHLEN, James Howard. 1550 N 115TH ST 98133 #056-05-1961 L1963 **FM** *071
DAIL, David H. 1100 9TH AVE - C1-MSO, VIRGINIA MASON MEDICAL CEN 98101 #056-06-1968 L1979 **PTH** *020 †50
DAINES, Brian Keith. UNIV OF WASHINGTON MED CTR, DEPT OF ORTHOPAEDICS BOX 3 98195 #035-01-2006 L2006 **ORS** *012
DAKIN, Karen Affa. 925 SENECA ST, DEPT MED 98101 #054-04-1997 *100
DALAN, Aaron Matthew. 1959 NE PACIFIC ST, BOX 356340 98195 #054-04-2004 L2004 **PD** *020 †55
DALE, David Chandler. 4245 ROOSEVELT WAY NE, STE 354775 98105 #024-01-1966 L1971 **IM HEM** *040 †20
DALES, Mark Curtis. 1101 MADISON ST, STE 800 98104 #031-01-1982 L1989 **OP** *020 †40
DALLEY, Robert Wallace. 1959 NE PACIFIC ST, MSC 359300 98195 #049-01-1982 L1987 **DR IM** *020 †80
DALY, Kevin Pelham. 1959 NE PACIFIC ST RM C2, BOX 356340 98195 #012-01-2002 L2007 **VIR** *012 †80
DALY, Timothy Paul. 2409 N 45TH ST 98103 #023-01-1970 L1977 **ORS** *020 †40
DAMMAN, Christopher James. 1959 NE PACIFIC ST, DEPT IM 98195 #035-01-2006 L2006 **IM** *012
DAMROW, Kimberly Sue. 206 3RD AVE S 98104 #054-04-1980 L1980 **IM** *020 †20
DANDALA, Kalyan Reddy. 1959 NE PACIFIC ST BO 98195 #654-01-2003 L2007 **ADP** *012
DANDEKAR, Ajai Arvind. PO BOX 356421, INT MED DEPT 98195 #018-03-2005 L2005 **IM** *012
DANG, Michele Lynn. 2107 ELLIOTT AVE STE 202 98121 #021-05-1997 L2000 **P** *020 †75
DANG, Tobias. 1730 MINOR AVE STE 1400, METROPOLITAN PARK EAST 98101 #409-16-1996 L2002 **P** *020 †75

■ = Address Information Privacy Protected

D'ANGELI, Marisa Anne. 4800 SAND POINT WAY NE 98105 #005-19-1992 L1995 **PD** *020 †55
DANGOR, Ayoub A. 325 9TH AVE 98104 #068-01-1992 L1997 **AN** *100
DANIEL, Anna Gustanna. 1101 MADISON ST, STE 950 98104 #024-01-1981 L1982 **OBG** *020 †30
DANIEL, Brett Victor. 10416 5TH AVE NE 98125 #054-04-2002 L2004 **FM** *020 †18
DANIELL, William E. 325 9TH AVE 98104 #024-07-1979 L1984 **OM IM** *050 †20,70
DANIELSON, Benjamin S. 2101 E YESLER WAY, STE 100 98122 #054-04-1992 L1995 **PD** *020 †55
DANIELSON, Kirk Damien. ■ 98105 #040-02-2003 L2003 **PM** *100
DANIELSSON, Per Erik. 600 UNIVERSITY ST, STE 1200 98101 #054-04-1992 L1995 **IM EM** *020 †10
DANNHAUER, Allan Ray. 1120 CHERRY ST 98104 #016-11-1954 L1958 **P PYA** *071
DARBY, Emily Lynne. 1145 BROADWAY 98122 #054-04-2001 L2003 **ID** *020
DARLING, Stephen Elliott. 1959 NE PACIFIC ST, BOX 356340 98195 #014-01-2004 L2004 **DR** *012 †55
DARROUGH, Forrest M, Jr. 4026 NE 55TH ST STE B 98105 #039-01-1963 L1969 **P** *071
DASSEL, Steven Walter. 4575 SAND POINT WAY NE, STE 108 98105 #054-04-1965 L1967 **PD** *020 †55
DATTAN, Christopher Locke. 1730 MINOR AVE, STE 1400 98101 #016-43-1977 L1990 **P** *020 †75
DAURIA, Colin Kenneth. ■ 98112 #035-06-2006 L2006 **P** *012
DAVENPORT, Cricket Hewitt. 310 15TH AVE E 98112 #025-01-1974 L1976 **OBG** *020 †30
DAVIDSON, Bruce Lawrence. 1952 10TH AVE W 98119 #041-13-1977 L1999 **PCC OS** *020 †20 ‡
DAVIDSON, Joan. ■ 98115 #054-04-1950 L1955 **CHP P** *020 †75
DAVIDSON, Robert Craig. 1959 NE PACIFIC ST, MSC 359300 98195 #054-04-1953 L1957 **NEP IM** *071 †20
DAVIES, Julian Kent. 4245 ROOSEVELT WAY NE, STE 354775 98105 #005-02-2000 L2003 **PD** *020 †55
DAVIES, Matthew Donald. 1229 MADISON ST, STE 1500 98104 #016-11-1994 L2003 **IM** *020 †20
DAVIS, Arielle Patricia. ■ 98103 #035-01-2006 L2006 **IM** *012
DAVIS, Christopher Chas. 550 36TH AVE E 98112 #143-02-1965 L1974 **TS** *020 †85,90
DAVIS, Connie Lee. 1959 NE PACIFIC ST, BOX 356174 98195 #054-04-1980 L1987 **NEP IM** *020 †20
DAVIS, Erick Malone. 7048 22ND AVE NW, THE STUDIO BUILDING 98117 #054-04-1977 L1978 **P MDM** *030 †70
DAVIS, Frederick Bryant. ■ 98115 #048-04-1964 L1968 **PYA P** *020
DAVIS, Greg Eldon. 1959 NE PACIFIC ST #356330, UW SCHOOL OF MEDICINE 98195 #054-04-2000 L2000 **OTO** *020
DAVIS, Maia Johannaloui. GRADUATE MEDICAL ED BOX 35, UNIVERSITY OF WASHINGTON 98195 #054-04-2003 L2003 **IM** *020 †20
DAVIS, Michael Pennington. 4800 SAND POINT WAY NE 98105 #051-04-1992 L1999 **CCP** *020 †55
DAVIS, Nora Elizabeth Ann. 4800 SAND POINT WAY NE, BOX # C-5371 98105 #065-06-1965 L1969 **PD** *020 †55
DAVIS, Richard Edgar. 1100 9TH AVE G1-MSO, VIRGINIA MASON MEDICAL CEN 98101 #054-04-1997 L1999 **IM** *020 †20
DAVIS, Romalee Ann. 1800 NW MARKET STE 208 98107 #005-12-1981 L1986 **P PYA** *020
DAVISON, Sari Lisa. 3121 E MADISON ST, STE 204 98112 #054-04-1991 L1996 **IM** *020 †20
DAWSON, Henk Iwan. 1600 E JEFFERSON ST, STE A1 98122 #011-02-1975 L1976 **PM** *071
DAWSON, Katie Edna. 925 SENECA ST # 1930, GRAD MED EDUC/H8-GME 98101 #054-04-2006 L2006 **GS** *012
DAWSON, Patricia L. 1600 E JEFFERSON ST # 305, CENTER JEFFERSON TOWER 98122 #033-05-1977 L1979 **GS SO** *020 †85
DAWSON, Therese Mary. 1660 S COLUMBIAN WAY, SYSTEM SEATTLE DIVISION 98108 #143-04-1986 L1996 **IM** *020 †20
DAY, Robert Winsor. 98112 #016-02-1956 L1970 **GPM PHP** *072 †70
DEAL, Thomas J. 5343 TALLMAN AVE NW 98107 #011-02-1977 L1978 **FM ADM** *020
DEAN, James Paul. 1100 FAIRVIEW AVE N, FHCRC-MED ONC D4-100 98109 #018-03-2000 L2003 **ON** *100 †20 ‡
DEAN, Larry Stephen. 1959 NE PACIFIC ST, CARDIOLOGY, BOX 356115 98195 #001-02-1980 L1991 **CD IM** *040 †20
DEAN, Thomas Charles. 925 SENECA ST, # H8-GME 98101 #023-01-2003 L2003 **AN** *012
DEANS, Amy Margaret. 2208 NW MARKET STE 410 98107 #054-04-2000 L2002 **IM** *020 †20
DE BELL, Megan Alicia. 2101 E YESLER WAY # 150 98122 #003-01-2002 L2004 **FM** *020 †18
DEBIEC, Katherine E. 1959 NE PACIFIC ST # C-2, BOX 356340 98195 #054-04-2005 L2005 **OBG** *012
DEBLEY, Jason Scott. 4800 SAND POINT WAY NE, REGIONAL ME 98105 #016-06-1995 L2000 **PDP** *020 †55 ‡
DEBOER, Ian Harm. 1959 NE PACIFIC ST, BOX 356521 98195 #040-02-1999 L2002 **NEP** *100 †20
DEBOOY, Jonathan David. PO BOX 356421, UNIV OF WASHINGTON 98195 #005-12-2007 L2007 **IM** *012
DE BRUYN, Guy. 1100 FAIRVIEW AVE N J3-100 98109 #836-01-1994 L2004 **ID** *020 †20
DECKELMAN, Mary Carmel. 100 23RD AVE S, CATHOLIC COMMUNITY SERVICE 98144 #023-01-1989 L1999 **CHP** *020 †75
DE CLARO, Romeo Angelo Mo. 1959 NE PACIFIC ST, CAMPUS BOX 357710 98195 #748-02-1998 L2003 **HEM** *020 †20 ‡
DE CLERCQ, Lucas Danl. MADISON & WEST 98122 #836-01-1957 L1981 **OTO** *072 †45
DE COOK, Timothy H. 550 16TH AVE, STE 405 98122 #018-03-1976 L1980 **AN** *020
DEE, Katherine Elizabeth. 9730 3RD AVE NE, STE 202 98115 #408-01-1994 L1998 **DR** *020 †80
DEEG, Hans Joachim. 1100 FAIRVIEW AVE N, D1-100 98109 #042-02-1973 L1976 **ON HEM** *050 †20
DEEM, Steven Arthur. 325 9TH AVE, BOX 359724 98104 #016-45-1984 L1992 **AN IM** *020 †20,05
DEETER, Kristina Heer. 1959 NE PACIFIC ST, DEPT PCC 98195 #035-09-1998 L2006 **CCP** *012 †55
DEETER, Matthew James. ■ 98105 #035-09-1998 L2007 **GS** *020 †85
DEHART, Cor. 1001 4TH AVE 98154 #660-01-1955 L1992 **P CHP** *030 †75
DEHART, Cornelius. 1959 NE PACIFIC ST RM C2, UNIV OF WASH SCH OF MEDICI 98195 #422-01-2002 L2003 **P** *020
DEISHER, Robert Wm. UNIV WASH SCH MED WJ 10 98105 #028-02-1944 L1949 **ADL AI** *071 †55
DELANEY, Colleen S. 1100 FAIRVIEW AVE N, RM D2-373 98109 #024-01-1996 L2001 **PHO** *020 †55

DELANEY, Joseph H. 9730 3RD AVE NE, STE 202 98115 #054-04-1974 L1975 **DR** *020 †80
DE LA OSSA, Juan Carlos. 1145 BROADWAY, THE POLYCLINIC 98122 #016-02-1993 L2000 **GS** *020 †85
DE LA TORRE, Sarah Helen. 1101 MADISON ST, STE 950 98104 #034-01-1999 L2001 **OBG** *020 †30
DEL BECCARO, Kathryn E H. 7554 15TH AVE NW, BALLARD PEDIATRIC CLINIC 98117 #054-04-1983 L1983 **PD** *020 †55
DEL BECCARO, Mark Andrew. 4800 SAND POINT WAY NE, NE MS-B5520 98105 #054-04-1985 L1985 **PEM PD** *020 †55
DELGADO, Erica Collins. 1550 N 115TH ST, NORTHWEST HOSPITAL AND MED 98133 #016-02-2005 L2005 **IM** *012
DELIGANIS, Anastasia V. 1959 NE PACIFIC ST, MSC 359300 98195 #054-04-1994 L1997 **DR** *020 †80
DELLIT, Timothy Harold. 325 9TH AVE BOX 359930, HARBORVIEW MEDICAL CENTER 98104 #035-20-1997 L2001 **ID** *100 †20
DEMARS, Adam David. ■ 98115 #054-04-2008 *012
DE MARTINI, Wendy Burton. 1959 NE PACIFIC ST, BOX 357115 98195 #051-04-1997 L2003 **RNR** *100 †20
DE MENEZES, Marcio A S. 550 17TH AVE 5TH FL 98122 #187-09-1984 L1996 **CHN** *020 †75
DEMERS, Eric Jon. 3626 NE 45TH ST, STE 300 98105 #054-04-1998 L2001 **NPM** *100 †55
DE MERS, Shaune Marie. 1959 NE PACIFIC ST, BOX 356340 98195 #054-04-2000 L2000 **PYM** *012
DEMOPULOS, Gregory A. 1420 5TH AVE, STE 2600 98101 #005-11-1988 L1996 **HS** *020 †20
DENEVAN, Paula Bunkers. 1560 N 115TH ST, STE 102 98133 #030-05-2001 L2001 **GS** *020 †85
DENNEY, John Donovan. ■ 98199 #035-20-1966 L1968 **NM OS** *071 †28,20
DENNISTON, George C, Jr. 2442 NW MARKET ST # 42 98107 #041-01-1959 L1963 **GYN GPM** *020 †70
DENNO, Donna Marie. 325 9TH AVE MS 359774, HARBORVIEW MEDICAL CENTER 98104 #025-01-1991 L1993 **PD** *020 †55
DEPASO, William J. 1100 9TH AVE M6-AC, VIRGINIA MASON MEDICAL CTR 98101 #016-02-1981 L1982 **PUD CCM** *020 †20
DE PINNA, Germano A. 2324 EASTLAKE AVE E, STE 500 98102 #462-01-1954 L1965 **AN PD** *071 †05
DE PINTO, Mario Giovanni. 325 9TH AVE 98104 #561-17-1985 L2002 **AN PME** *020
DEPPEN, Krisanna Lee. ■ 98117 #038-44-2004 L2007 **FM** *100 †18
DERIUGIN, Tatiana. 521 WALL ST, M/C ACC-2 98121 #422-01-1998 L2002 **AN** *020 †05
DERLETH, Mark David. ■ 98102 #024-05-2006 L2006 **IM** *012
DERR, Jeffrey James. 1959 NE PACIFIC ST, GME OFFICE BOX 356340 98195 #026-04-1995 L2004 **PM** *012 †10
DERRICK, Peter Huntington. ■ 98119 #041-15-2006 L2006 **AN** *012
DE RUITER, Cynthia Jane. 325 9TH AVE, HARBORVIEW MEDICAL CENTER 98104 #016-02-2001 L2004 **PCC** *100 †20
DESAI, Amish Jawahar. 600 UNIVERSITY ST, STE 1200 98101 #422-01-1998 L2005 **IC** *100 †20
DESAI, Shilpa Patel. 1101 MADISON ST, STE 301 98104 #038-40-1999 L2006 **OBG** *020 †30
DESANO, Alison Giovanna. 1959 NE PACIFIC ST # C, BOX 356340 98195 #054-04-2004 L2005 **OBG** *012
DESGRANGES, Patrick Zana. PO BOX 356421, UNIV OF WASHINGTON 98195 #024-07-2007 L2007 **IM** *012
DE SOUZA, Maria De Fatima. 1550 N 115TH ST 98133 #495-25-1973 L1978 **PTH** *020 †50
DESYATNIKOVA, Stella S. 509 OLIVE WAY STE 1430 98101 #054-04-1997 L2002 **OTO FPS** *020 †45
DETERING, Barbara Joan. 200 15TH AVE E # 2 98112 #054-04-1989 L1992 **FM** *020 †18
DETTER, James Cox. 1959 NE PACIFIC ST 98195 #019-02-1962 L1968 **HEM IM** *020 †20
DEUBNER, Heike. ■ 98112 #054-04-1991 L1993 **PTH** *020 †50
DEVERS, Allison Lee. 6020 35TH AVE SW 98126 #050-02-2003 L2005 *020 †18
DEWHURST, Timothy Andrew. 550 16TH AVE, STE 400 98122 #060-01-1986 L1989 **CD IC** *020 †20
DEWITT, Dawn Elise. 1959 NE PACIFIC ST, BOX 354760 98195 #024-01-1990 L1992 **IM** *040 †20
DEYSINE, Gaston Roque. 1100 9TH AVE G1-MSO, VIRGINIA MASON MEDICAL CEN 98101 #035-08-1988 L1993 **ORS** *020 †40
DHANIREDDY, Shireesha. CAMPUS BOX 358050, UW MEDICINE - SOUTH LAKE U 98195 #010-02-1999 L2001 **ID** *100 †20
DICHEK, A K Helen L. 1959 NE PACIFIC ST, UNIV OF WASH BOX 356320 98195 #165-04-1980 L2000 **PDE REN** *020 †55
DICHEK, David Anthony. 1959 NE PACIFIC ST 98195 #005-14-1984 L2001 **CD IM** *050 †20
DICK, Sarah Elizabeth. ■ 98164 #024-01-1995 L1997 **D** *020 †20,15
DICKSON, John Flint. 1229 MADISON ST, STE 1410 98104 #048-01-1969 L1970 **RHU IM** *020 †20
DICKSON, Robert Pickett. ■ 98105 #036-07-2007 L2007 **IM** *012
DIDDEE, Seema. 4245 ROOSEVELT WAY NE, STE 354775 98105 #495-78-1999 L2003 **FM** *020 †18
DIDDLE, John Wesley. ■ 98103 #047-06-2005 L2005 **PD** *012
DIEDE, Scott John. 920 E LYNN ST, UNIV. OF WA. 98102 #016-02-2003 L2003 **PHO** *012 †55
DIEHL, Delfred Laurie. 310 15TH AVE E GNB-5, GROUP HEALTH COOPERATIVE 98112 #065-01-1984 L1989 **OPH** *071 †35
DIEKEMA, Douglas Scott. 4800 SAND POINT WAY NE, EMER SVCS/CH 04 98105 #036-01-1985 L1990 **PEM PD** *020 †55
DIETZ, Andrew Charles. 98122 #026-04-2005 L2008 **PD** *012
DI FURIA, Giulio. ■ 98121 #561-01-1951 L1958 **P** *030
DI GENNARO, Jane L. 4800 SAND POINT WAY NE, MS W8866 98105 #021-05-2000 L2004 **CCP** *012 †55
DIGHE, Manjiri Kiran. 1959 NE PACIFIC ST, P O BOX 357115 98195 #495-01-1998 L2002 *020
DI JULIO, Marc A. 3178 NE 81ST ST 98115 #010-02-1981 L1983 **EM** *020 †16
DIMER, Jane Ann. 310 15TH AVE E # CNB2 98112 #016-06-1988 L1998 **OBG OBS** *020 †30
DIMOND, Richard Allan. 325 9TH AVE 98104 #018-03-1966 L1967 **ORS** *020 †40
DIMUGNO, Leanne Helen. 1145 BROADWAY 98122 #041-09-1995 L2001 **GS** *020 †85
DING, Alice Hueyching. 500 17TH AVE 98122 #054-04-1993 L1995 **IM** *020 †20
DINGACCI, Richard Michael. 4744 41ST AVE SW, STE 101 98116 #031-01-1983 L1989 **FM** *020 †18
DINGES, Warren Lewis. ■ 98122 #048-12-2003 L2005 **ID** *012 †20
DINNO, Nuhad D. 2324 EASTLAKE AVE E, STE 500 98102 #528-01-1961 L1981 **PD** *071 †55
DINSIO, Kyl Jane. ■ 98112 #038-06-2006 L2006 **P** *012
DION, Francis Richard. 1100 9TH AVE, VIRGINIA MASON CLINIC 98101 #026-04-1955 L1961 **PD** *071 †20
DIORIO, Mary Ellen. 2611 NE 125TH ST STE 225 98125 #010-01-1990 L1997 **CHP** *020 †75
DIPBOYE, Larry Keith, Jr. 1100 9TH AVE 98101 #016-11-1994 L1999 **IM** *020 †20

DIPERNA, Costanzo Aldo. 1959 NE PACIFIC ST, UWMC 98195 #035-47-1998 L2003 **TS** *100 †85,90

DISIS, Mary Lenora. 1959 NE PACIFIC ST, MSC 359300 98195 #030-05-1986 L1990 **ON** *020 †20

DISTAD, Barbara Jane. 1959 NE PACIFIC ST, BOX 356465 98195 #038-43-1994 L1998 **N** *020

DIZON, Teresita R. ■ 98118 #748-01-1960 *074

DJANG, David Winston. 1229 MADISON ST STE 1150, SEATTLE NUCLEAR MED/ULTRAS 98104 #048-12-1998 L2000 **NM** *020 †28

DJANG, Eleanor Y. 1229 MADISON ST STE 1150, SEATTLE NUCLEAR MED/ULTRAS 98104 #048-12-1998 L2003 **DR** *020

DO, Tuoc Huu. 1400 S JACKSON ST STE 24, RAINIER OCC MEDICALCENTER 98144 #941-01-1972 L1982 **OM EM** *020

DOAN, Roscius Newell. ■ 98125 #038-06-1965 L1971 **PD PHP** *030 †55

DOBBS, Lary Shannon. 747 BROADWAY 98122 #054-04-1960 L1963 **AN PD** *020 †55,05

DOBIE, Dorcas Jean. 1959 NE PACIFIC ST 98195 #025-01-1984 L1985 **P PYG** *040 †75

DOBIE, Sharon Ann. 4245 ROOSEVELT WAY NE, STE 354775 98105 #005-02-1979 L1983 **FM** *020 †18 ‡

DOBYNS, Richard Jos. 5316 RAINIER AVE S 98118 #036-05-1989 L1989 **FM** *020 †18

DOCES, John Gust. 550 16TH AVE, STE 400 98122 #054-04-1969 L1970 **CD IM** *020 †20

DOCTER, Jack Merton. 4800 SAND POINT WAY NE 98105 #035-01-1941 L1942 **PD PUD** *071 †55

DODDS, Jodi Anderson. ■ 98144 #045-01-2005 L2005 **N** *012

DODDS, Steven Jeffrey. 3626 NE 45TH ST, STE 300 98105 #039-05-1989 L2000 **ID PD** *020 †55

DODGE, Wayne Thos. 1600 E JOHN ST, CEB-100W 98112 #035-45-1976 L1979 **FM OS** *020 †18

DOEDERLEIN, Susan Marie. 6300 9TH AVE NE STE 200 98115 #016-43-1984 L1987 **FM** *020 †18

DOESCHER, Mark Philip. 2212 QUEEN ANNE AVE N 98109 #005-02-1989 L1994 **FM** *020 †70,18

DOHERTY, Daniel Andrew. 4800 SAND POINT WAY NE, CHRMC BOX A7938 UW BOX 359 98105 #005-02-1998 L2000 **PD** *020 †55

DOHERTY, Michael John. 550 17TH AVE 5TH FL, SWEDISH PHYSICIAN DIVISION 98122 #024-07-1997 L1999 **CN** *020 †75

DOMBROWSKI, Julia Cook. ■ 98115 #036-07-2004 L2007 **ID** *012 †20

DOMINGUEZ, Arturo R. BOX356340 1959 NE PACIFIC, UNIV OF WASH GRAD MED EDUC 98195 #048-12-2005 L2005 **IM** *012

DOMINITZ, Jason Alan. 1660 S COLUMBIAN WAY, 111 S GASTRO 98108 #023-01-1991 L1997 **GE IM** *020 †20

DOMINO, Karen Barbara. 325 9TH AVE, HARBORVIEW MED CTR-ANESTH 98104 #025-01-1978 L1985 **AN** *020 †05

DON, Creighton Wright. ■ 98108 #005-02-2001 L2004 **CD** *012

DONALDSON, Jake David. ■ 98122 #054-04-2008 *012

DONALDSON, Lauren Mary. ■ 98144 #061-01-1994 L1994 **FM** *100

DONE, Stephen Lawrence. 4800 SAND POINT WAY NE, CHRMC DEPT OF RAD CH-69 98105 #049-01-1970 L1989 **DR PD** *040 †55,80

DONEY, Kristine Craig. 1100 FAIRVIEW AVE N 98109 #025-01-1972 L1978 **HEM ON** *050 †20

DONG, David Edwin. 1560 N 115TH ST STE G16, PUGET SOUND CANCER CTR 98133 #049-01-1986 L1990 **ON IM** *020 †20

DONNELLAN, Rory Basil Ber. NEUROPATHOLOGY, BOX 359791, HARBORVIEW MEDICAL CENTER 98195 #836-02-1994 L2003 **NP** *020

DONOHUE, Kimberly R. ■ 98107 #028-34-2007 L2007 **FP** *012

DONOHUE, Lawrence Ray. 1800 9TH AVE, MAIL STOP S 515 98101 #056-06-1964 L1970 **OBG** *030 †30

DONOHUE, Megan Moore. ■ 98112 #024-16-2006 L2006 **IM** *012

DOOLEY, Annemarie C. 1100 OLIVE WAY, STE 1400 98101 #005-19-2001 L2003 **NEP** *100

DORAN, Daniel James. ■ 98109 #007-02-2004 L2004 **AN** *012

DORDONI, Betina Graciela. 10416 5TH AVE NE 98125 #132-01-1968 L1976 **IM PHP** *020

DORN, Elizabeth Magassy. ■ 98102 #054-04-1995 L2001 **EM** *020 †16

DOROSHOW, Carol Ann. 12317 15TH AVE NE, APT 103 98125 #041-02-1977 L1983 **PD** *020 †55

DOTEN, Ian Christopher. 747 BROADWAY 98122 #025-07-1999 L2002 **EM** *020 †16

DOUGLAS, James Gordon. 1959 NE PACIFIC ST BOX 356, UNIV OF WASH MEDICAL CENTER 98195 #038-06-1980 L1981 **RO PHO** *020 †55,80

DOUGLAS, Smith W, III. 200 16TH AVE E 98112 #054-04-1965 L1973 **ON HEM** *020 †20

DOUGLASS, J Kirk. 11545 15TH AVE NE 98125 #054-04-1957 L1958 **PD** *071 †55

DOW, Sara Powell. 521 WALL ST, GROUP HEALTH COOPERATIVE 98121 #041-01-2003 L2003 **PD** *020 †55

DOWNER, Philip. 2409 N 45TH ST 98103 #063-01-1995 L2002 **ORS** *020 †40

DOWNEY, Daniel Lee. 1536 N 115TH ST STE 105 98133 #054-04-1983 L1984 **PS GS** *040 †85,65

DOWNS, Joseph Caspar M. ■ 98122 #024-07-1954 L1967 **IMG GP** *071 †18

DRAGOVICH, Jerry J. 5410 CALIFORNIA AVE SW 98136 #056-06-1945 L1946 **AI OTO** *071 †45

DRAPER, Franklin Montague. ■ 98105 #024-01-1954 L1958 **P** *020 †75

DRAZNIN, Michelle. 4225 ROOSEVELT WAY NE, WASHINGTON DERMATOLOGY 98105 #007-02-2001 L2006 **PRD** *020 †15

DREIS, David Fenton. 1100 9TH AVE 98101 #026-04-1978 L1979 **PUD IM** *020 †20

DREISBACH, Robt Hastings. PO BOX 357234, DEPT EH ADMIN 98195 #016-02-1942 L1943 **GPM** *071

DRENNAN, Fred Miller. 1100 9TH AVE G1-MSO, VIRGINIA MASON MEDICAL CEN 98101 #008-01-1982 L1985 **GE IM** *020 †20

DRESANG, Steven Edward. 1629 N 45TH ST 98103 #008-01-1996 L1998 **FM** *020 †18

DRESCHER, Charles Wm. 1101 MADISON ST STE 1500, PACIFIC GYNECOLOGY SPEC, P 98104 #025-01-1982 L1989 **GO GYN** *020 †30

DRESDEN, Graham Mears. 4245 ROOSEVELT WAY NE #354 98105 #041-02-2004 L2004 **FM** *020 †18

DREZNER, Jonathan Adam. 4245 ROOSEVELT WAY NE, BOX 354775 98105 #005-14-1996 L1998 **FM** *020 †18

DRIANO, Andrea Nicole. 4800 SAND POINT WAY NE, BOX 359300 98105 #054-04-1998 L2001 **PD** *020 †55

DRISCOLL, Richard H, Jr. 515 MINOR AVE STE 200 98104 #041-01-1972 L1986 **GE IM** *020 †20

DROCTON, Peter. ■ 98109 #005-14-2005 L2007 **IM** *012

DRUCKER, David Neal. 1530 N 115TH ST STE 105 98133 #035-45-1984 L1988 **OPH OS** *020 †35

DRUCKER, Mariann Julie. 600 BROADWAY, STE 170 98122 #035-45-1986 L1988 **DR** *020 †80

D'SOUZA, Maria Frances. ■ 98122 #028-46-2005 L2005 **IM** *012

DUBINSKY, Theodore Jay. ■ 98117 #023-01-1983 L1984 **DR IM** *062 †80

DUBLIN, Sascha. 1660 S COLUMBIAN WAY, VA PUGET SOUND HEALTH CARE 98108 #054-04-2001 L2004 **IM** *100

DUBOIS, Philip David. 1101 MADISON ST, STE 301 98104 #017-20-1966 L1973 **OBG** *020 †30

DUCHIN, Jeffrey Scott. 401 5TH AVE, STE 3 98104 #033-06-1985 L1995 **ID EP** *020 †20

DUCKERT, Larry Gene. 1959 NE PACIFIC ST BOX 356, SCHOOL OF MEDICINE 98195 #026-04-1973 L1978 **OTO GS** *020 †45

DUDGIKAR, Darshana. 521 WALL ST, DEPT FM 98121 #496-20-2002 L2006 **FP** *012

DUDLEY, Donald Larry. 3245 FAIRVIEW AVE E, STE 200 98102 #054-04-1964 L1972 **OS PM** *075

DUDLEY, Morton Dickenson. 600 BROADWAY, STE 170 98122 #051-01-1980 L1984 **DR** *020 †80

DUDLEY, Stephen Thomas. 10330 MERIDIAN AVE N, SEATTLE ARTHRITIS CLINIC 98133 #054-04-1994 L1996 **FM** *020 †18

DUESTERHOEFT, Sara Mae. ■ 98103 #026-04-2002 L2002 **HMP** *012 †50

DUFFY, Patrick Emmet. ■ 98119 #036-07-1986 L1988 **IM** *020 †20

DUFFY, Sheila Ann. 515 MINOR AVE STE 210 98104 #003-01-2002 L2007 **N** *020

DUGDALE, David Clark. PO BOX 354410, UNIV OF WASHINGTON 98195 #041-01-1982 L1983 **IM** *020 †20

DUGOWSON, Carin E. 4245 ROOSEVELT WAY NE, BOX 354740 98105 #016-11-1976 L1977 **RHU IM** *030 †20

DUKE, Rebecca Susan. 1600 E JEFFERSON ST # 510 98122 #026-04-1997 L1997 **FM** *020 †18

DUNBAR, Peter J. 325 9TH AVE 98104 #919-01-1978 L1984 **AN PMM** *030 †05

DUNBAR, Robert Paul, Jr. ■ 98101 #010-02-1993 L2002 **ORS** *020 †40

DUNDORE, Diana Elaine. 1801 NW MARKET ST STE 307 98107 #041-12-1974 L1976 **PM** *020 †60

DUNN, Andrew Kalman. 925 SENECA ST 98101 #054-04-1983 L1984 **IM** *020 †20

DUNN, Catherine Lynn. ■ 98103 #035-09-1975 L1977 **CHP** *020 †75

DUNN, John Ernest. 801 BROADWAY, SEATTLE ORTHOPEDIC & FRACT 98122 #016-06-1963 L1969 **ORS** *071 †40

DUNNING, Steven Bruce. 1200 12TH AVE S, PACIFIC MEDICAL CENTER 98144 #005-11-1979 L1980 **IM** *020 †20

DUNPHY, Barry Emons. ■ 98125 #054-04-1960 L1962 **OM** *020 †70

DUNSMOOR, Rebecca Frances. 1959 NE PACIFIC ST, BOX 356460 98195 #041-01-2001 L2005 **OBG** *100 †30

DUONG, Duong Minh. 620 S JACKSON ST 98104 #941-01-1975 L1979 **GP IM** *020 †20

DURFEE, Marcia Ann. 408 W COMSTOCK ST 98119 #054-04-1979 L1980 **OBG** *020 †30

DURTSCHI, Martin Bouska. 1600 E JEFFERSON ST, STE 603 98122 #054-04-1977 L1978 **GS** *020 †85

DURVASULA, Raghu Venkata. 1959 NE PACIFIC ST, BOX 356521 98195 #067-01-1996 L2000 **NEP** *050 †20

DWIGHT, Megan Mc Gilvray. 1959 NE PACIFIC ST, BOX 356560 98195 #038-41-1992 L1996 **P** *020 †75

DWORZNIK, Katherine Ann. ■ 98133 #038-40-2006 L2006 **IM** *012

DWYER, David Carroll. 600 BROADWAY, STE 170 98122 #067-01-1978 L1985 **DR** *020 †80

DY, Maria Luisa Tudtud. 4508 S ORCAS ST 98118 #748-11-1978 L2004 **FM** *020

DYER, Rachael Marie. ■ 98104 #017-20-2007 L2007 **FP** *012

DYESS, Cynthia Lee. 925 11TH AVE E 98102 #008-01-1986 L1989 **P PYA** *020

DYM, Andrew Martin. 10416 5TH AVE NE 98125 #041-12-1987 L1990 **IM** *020 †20

DZIERSK, Jorg. 1959 NE PACIFIC ST #356540, UNIVERSITY OF WASHINGTON 98195 #409-16-1988 L2002 **FM** *020

EACKER, Anne Marie. 4245 ROOSEVELT WAY NE, GENERAL INTERNAL MEDICINE 98105 #054-04-1997 L1999 **IM** *020 †20

EARLY, Ronald Gayle. 2505 2ND AVE STE 600 98121 #048-13-1975 L1976 **P** *040 †75

EARY, Janet Frances. 1959 NE PACIFIC ST, BOX 356113 98195 #025-12-1980 L1981 **NM** *020 †50,28

EASTERLING, Thomas R, III. 1959 NE PACIFIC ST, BOX 356460 98195 #036-01-1981 L1985 **OBG** *020 †30

EASTWOOD, Katherine L. ■ 98115 #040-02-2001 L2005 **OBG** *100

EATHER, Kenneth Frederick. ■ 98199 #041-01-1945 L1949 **AN** *071 †05

EATON, Keith David. 825 EASTLAKE AVE E, SCCA- BOX 358081 MS G4-830 98109 #005-18-1998 L2000 **ON** *020 †20

EATON, Peggy Jo. 2101 E YESLER WAY STE 150 98122 #054-04-1982 L1983 **IM** *020 †20

EBEL, Beth Ellen. 325 9TH AVE, BOX 359960 98104 #024-01-1996 L1999 **PD** *050 †55

EBY, Kerry Jo. 325 9TH AVE, HARBORVIEW MEDICAL CENTER 98104 #054-04-2001 L2003 **IM** *020

EBY, Peter Reist. 1107 NE 45TH ST, STE 440 98105 #047-05-1999 L2003 **DR** *020 †80

ECKERT, Linda Faye. 325 9TH AVE, BOX 359865 98104 #005-18-1987 L1992 **OBG ID** *020 †30

EDDY, Allison Audrey. 4800 SAND POINT WAY NE 98105 #065-10-1975 L1997 **PN CLP** *050 †55

EDDY, Melissa Jane. ■ 98112 #036-01-1979 L1982 **AN** *020 †05

EDDY, Roger Coe. ■ 98101 #054-04-1959 L1961 **PYA P** *020 ‡

EDLEFSEN, Kerstin Lara. ■ 98115 #054-04-2002 L2002 **SP** *100 †50

EDLUND, Leah Marie. 1959 NE PACIFIC ST, BOX 356340 98195 #054-04-2006 L2006 **P** *012

EDMONDS, Albert Wm. 747 BROADWAY 98122 #051-01-1973 L1974 **AN** *020 †05

EDMONSON, Paul Frederick. 1550 N 115TH ST, PATHOLOGY A-220 98133 #026-08-1997 L2000 **PTH** *062 †50

EDRICH, Vanessa Beth. 1550 N 115TH ST 98133 #005-14-1983 L1986 **FM** *020 †18

EDWARDS, Catherine Whitte. ■ 98125 #054-04-2005 L2005 **FP** *012

EDWARDS, James Anthon. ■ 98117 #031-01-2003 L2003 **PS** *012

EDWARDS, Kay Kohara. ■ 98125 #021-05-1943 L1943 **PHP** *071

EDWARDS, Lynn Kohara. 319 NICKERSON ST, # 415 98109 #054-04-1980 L1981 **FM** *072 †18

EDWARDS, Oliver Lee. ■ 98122 #048-02-2007 L2007 **TY** *012

EDWARDS, William Thos. 325 9TH AVE, MS 359724 98104 #024-16-1975 L1990 **PME AN** *020 †05

EDWARDSON, Matthew Allen. PO BOX 356465, DEPT OF NEUROLOGY 98195 #016-06-2005 L2005 **N** *012

EFFMANN, Eric Leonard. 4800 SAND POINT WAY NE, CHILDRENS HOSP & REG MED 98105 #017-20-1967 L1991 **PDR DR** *020 †80

EFIRD, Alex Christopher. 515 MINOR AVE, STE 300 98104 #005-06-1999 L2002 **IM** *020 †20

EGAAS, Susan Ann. ■ 98115 #054-04-1985 L1986 **EM IM** *020 †20,16

EGAN, Melinda Ferguson. 747 BROADWAY STE 731, SWEDISH MED CTR FIRST HILL 98122 #010-01-2007 L2007 **GS** *012

EGGERT, John Francis. 125 16TH AVE E, CENTRAL SPECIALTY CENTER 98112 #396-02-1983 L1998 **RHU IM** *020 †20

EHLE, Albert Lawrence. ■ 98109 #054-04-1967 L1973 **N** *062 †75

EHLEN, Catherine Anne. ■ 98109 #026-04-2006 L2007 **IM** *012

EHLENBACH, William Joseph. ■ 98122 #056-05-2002 L2006 **PCC** *012 †20

EHRLICH, Alan Jos. ■ 98126 #035-15-1972 L1992 **EM** *020 †16

EHRLICH, Ari Raine. 521 WALL ST DEPT FAM 98121 #038-06-1997 L1999 **FM** *020 †18

EINSTEIN, Albert B, Jr. 1221 MADISON ST STE 1110, SWEDISH CANCER INSTITUTE 98104 #035-20-1967 L1972 **ON IM** *030 †20

■ = Address Information Privacy Protected

EINTRACHT, Jason Fred. 1100 9TH AVE 98101 #048-13-2002 L2002 **IM** *020 †20

EISENBERG, Brian. 1100 9TH AVE M6-AC, VIRGINIA MASON MEDICAL CEN 98101 #041-13-1981 L1991 **NM** *020 †80,28

EISENBERG, Matthew Adam. 4800 SAND POINT WAY NE, CHILDREN'S HOSP & REG MED 98105 #005-02-1987 L1996 **PD** *062 †55

EISENBERG, Mickey Stewart. 401 5TH AVE STE 1200 98104 #038-06-1971 L1973 **EM IM** *050 †20

EISNER, Jessica Deborah. 1959 NE PACIFIC ST, DEPT OF PATHOLOGY BOX 3561 98195 #005-18-1996 L1998 **PTH** *020

EISSES, Michael James. 4800 SAND POINT WAY NE 98105 #054-04-1995 L1999 **PAN AN** *020 †05

EK, Marit. 1959 NE PACIFIC ST 98195 #836-02-1959 L1970 **ATP PCP** *020 †50

EKSIOGLU, Ayse Secil. 1959 NE PACI ST BX 357115, UNIV WA DEPT RAD 98195 #902-03-1995 L2003 *020

EKSTEEN, Eduard Celliers. 4800 SAND PT WAY NE NE/6E-, CHILDRENS HOSPITAL / OTO-H 98105 #836-04-1985 L2003 *100

ELANDER, Chelsea Dawn. 4800 SAND POINT WAY NE, REGIONAL M 98105 #024-01-2006 L2006 **PD** *012

ELDRED, Christianne. 7554 15TH AVE NW, BALLARD PEDIATRIC CLINIC 98117 #054-04-1995 L1998 **PD** *020 †55

EL GAFY, Hossein Kamal El. 325 9TH AVE BOX 359798, HARBORVIEW MEDICAL CENTER 98104 #915-04-1985 L2005 *020

ELGEE, Neil J. 1229 MADISON ST, STE 1500 98104 #035-45-1950 L1953 **END IM** *071 †20

ELKIN, William Paul. ■ 98107 #039-01-1935 L1941 **R** *071 †80

ELKON, Margaret Lipton. ■ 98144 #035-46-1991 *100

ELLENBOGEN, Richard G. 325 9TH AVE 359766, HARBORVIEW MED CTR 98104 #043-01-1983 L1997 **NS** *020 †25

ELLINGTON, Elizabeth Joy. ■ 98112 #054-04-2006 L2006 **OBG** *012

ELLIOTT, Kathryn Jane. ■ 98112 #060-02-1985 L1990 **N** *020 †75

ELLIOTT, Kevin Corry. 1001 BROADWAY STE 316 98122 #041-01-1980 L1983 **IM** *020

ELLIOTT, Michael Alan. 1100 9TH AVE G1-MSO, VIRGINIA MASON MEDICAL CEN 98101 #010-01-1990 L1996 **N** *020 †75

ELLIS, Erin D. 1221 MADISON ST, 2ND FLOOR ARNOLD BUILDING 98104 #023-07-1985 L1991 **ON IM** *020 †20

ELLIS, Georgiana F. 1959 NE PACIFIC ST, MSC 359300 98195 #054-04-1982 L1983 **ON IM** *020 †20

ELLIS, William John. 1959 NE PACIFIC ST, BOX 356510 98195 #023-07-1985 L1991 **U SO** *020 †95

ELLSBURY, Kathleen Elise. 1959 NE PACIFIC ST, BOX 356390 98195 #023-07-1977 L1982 **FM** *030 †18

ELMORE, Joann Grace. 325 9TH AVE 98104 #005-11-1987 L1996 **IM EP** *020 †20

ELORANTA, Sharon Irene. ■ 98125 #010-02-1986 L1989 **PD** *020 †55

ELTRINGHAM, James Robt. 1225 MADISON ST 98104 #025-01-1960 L1985 **RO** *071 †80

ELWOOD, Thomas. 4800 SAND POINT WAY NE 98105 #064-01-1987 L1997 **PD AN** *020

EMANUEL, Irvin. PO BOX 357236, UNIV OF WASHINGTON 98195 #035-45-1960 L1966 **GPM PD** *071

EMANUEL, Margaux Raelynn. ■ 98102 #051-07-2006 L2006 **FP** *012

EMERSON, Bettina Meyerhof. PO BOX 5371, UNIV STATION 98105 #023-07-1943 L1947 **PD** *020 †55

EMERSON, Connie Leona. 1200 12TH AVE S, INLAND IMAGING ASSOCIATES, 98144 #065-06-1979 L2000 **DR** *020 †80

EMERSON, Gwendolyn Beth. 1959 NE PACIFIC ST BOX 356, UW SCHOOL OF MED GME PROGR 98195 #048-02-2005 L2005 **ORS** *012

EMERSON, Julia Childress. ■ 98115 #051-01-1981 **GPM PTH** *100

EMERY, Helen Margaret. ■ 98105 #143-01-1972 L1977 **PPR PD** *020 †55

EMMONS, Rebecca Alice. 1100 FAIRVIEW AVE N, N., D2-373 98109 #023-01-2003 L2006 **PHO** *012 †55

ENDICOTT, Raymond Donald. ■ 98102 #040-02-1961 L1964 **R** *071 †80

ENDOW, Curtis S. 1100 9TH AVE # M6-AC, VIRGINIA MASON MEDICAL CEN 98101 #035-01-1982 L1983 **IM** *020 †20

ENENBACH, Michael John. PO BOX 5371, M/S W3636 98105 #019-02-2000 L2007 **CHP** *012 †75 ‡

ENG, Calvin Alexander. ■ 98102 #024-05-2003 L2003 **AN** *012

ENG, David Yun. 747 BROADWAY 98122 #054-04-1974 L1976 **AN** *020 †05

ENG, Freida Anne. ■ 98118 #054-04-1999 L2001 **FM** *020 †18

ENG, Marlene. 1550 N 115TH ST 98133 #048-02-1958 L1963 **AN** *071 †05

ENGEL, David Steven. 4245 ROOSEVELT WAY NE, BOX 354775 98105 #005-02-2005 L2005 **FP** *012

ENGEL, Gregory Alexander. 550 16TH AVE, STE 400 98122 #048-01-1992 L2002 **FM** *020 †18

ENGEL, Juliette M. 1900 W NICKERSON ST, STE 116 98119 #054-04-1974 L1976 **R** *020 †80

ENGELBERG, Steven James. 2271 NE 51ST ST 98105 #025-01-1970 L1976 **P PYA** *020 †75

ENGLISH, Loellen Kay. 1101 MADISON ST STE 301, PAC MED CLINICS MADISON 98104 #033-05-1977 L1987 **IM** *020 †20

ENGLISH, Milton Tate, III. 1229 MADISON ST STE 1500, SEATTLE CARDIOLOGY 98104 #028-03-1969 L1970 **CD IC** *020 †20

ENGRAV, Loren Henry. 325 9TH AVE, BOX 359796 98104 #005-14-1969 L1977 **PS** *020 †85,65

ENSINCK, John Wm. 1959 NE PACIFIC ST, DEPT OF MED, BOX 356426 98195 #067-01-1956 L1961 **IM END** *050 †20

ENZMANN, Gary David. 1229 MADISON ST STE 1500, MINOR & JAMES, PLL 98104 #025-01-1976 L1977 **END IM** *020 †20

ERICKSON, Michael Shane. 611 12TH AVE S, STE 200 98144 #054-04-2000 L2000 **FM** *020 †18

ERICKSON, Robert Vernon. 747 BROADWAY 98122 #054-04-1956 L1959 **IM** *071 †20

ERIKSSON, Tracy Petersen. 1100 9TH AVE G1-MSO 98101 #051-01-1991 L2002 **OTO** *020 †45

ERJAVEC, Miklavz. 747 BROADWAY 98122 #064-01-1985 L1992 **APM** *020 †05

ERLANGER, Lisa. 550 16TH AVE STE 100 98122 #028-02-1995 L1995 **FM** *020 †18

ERLICH, Marta Shala. 1949 NE PACIFIC ST, OFC C315 98195 #054-04-2000 L2000 **PTH** *100

ERLICH, Victor Manuel. 1570 N 115TH ST STE 14 98133 #035-46-1985 L1989 **N** *020 †75

ESCHENBACH, David Arthur. 4245 ROOSEVELT WAY NE, STE 354775 98105 #056-05-1968 L1970 **OBG ID** *050 †30

ESCOURROU, Pierre Jean L. U WASHINGTON SJ 40 98105 #396-06-1979 L1980 **CD PUD** *050

ESHGHABADI, Mashalah. ■ 98125 #051-08-1976 **PTH** *100 †50

ESHLEMAN, Michael Kaye. 1959 NE PACIFIC ST, MSC 359300 98195 #008-01-1974 L1977 **OS** *020 †18

ESKANDARI, Farideh. PO BOX 900, 1100 NINTH AVE 98111 #517-05-1989 L2007 **END IM** *020 †20

ESKOLA-FEIG, Christine C. ■ 98107 #054-04-1976 L1976 **DR** *020 †80

ESKRIDGE, Joe Michael. 1959 NE PACIFIC ST, UWMC 98195 #020-02-1981 L1987 **DR** *020 †80

ESMAIL, Sophie. 4115 ROOSEVELT WAY NE #416 98105 #048-12-2008 *012

ESPARZA, Edward Manuel. 1959 NE PACIFIC ST, BOX 356340 98195 #028-02-2007 L2007 **IM** *012

ESPINOLA, John Mercier. 901 5TH AVE, STE 1500 98164 #024-07-1998 L2001 **IMG** *020 †20

ESSELMAN, Peter Carey. 325 9TH AVE, BOX 35940 98104 #054-04-1986 L1988 **PM** *020 †60

ETOH, Akiko. 4509 INTERLAKE AVE N 98103 #025-07-1997 *100

ETZEL, Jason Paul. PO BOX 356421, UNIV OF WASHINGTON 98195 #036-07-2005 L2005 **IM** *012

EUBANK, William Bryan. 1229 MADISON ST STE 900, SEATTLE RADIOLOGIST 98104 #021-01-1986 L1996 **DR** *040 †80

EUGENIO, Margaret Desiree. ■ 98103 #012-01-2005 L2005 **IM** *012

EULAU, Dana Wolinsky. 1229 MADISON ST 98104 #005-19-1993 L1998 **PTH** *020 †50

EULAU, Stephen Martin. 1221 MADISON ST, STE 1225 98104 #005-19-1993 L1997 **RO** *020 †80

EUSEBIO, Emmanuel J. 10416 5TH AVE NE, PACIFIC MEDICAL CLINICS 98125 #054-04-1990 L1992 **PD** *020 †55

EVANS, Andrew Richard. ■ 98121 #016-43-2002 L2007 **ORS** *100

EVANS, Ashley Toth. PO BOX 356421, UNIV OF WASHINGTON 98195 #040-02-2007 L2007 **IM** *012

EVANS, Charles A. PO BOX 357242, DEPT MICROBIOLOGY 98195 #026-04-1937 L1937 **ID** *071

EVANS, Ginger Ann. ■ 98103 #005-06-2007 L2007 **IM** *012

EVANS, Heather Leigh. ■ 98199 #035-45-1999 L2007 **CCS** *012 †85

EVANS, Jason Michael. 325 9TH AVE 359798 98104 #038-41-2002 L2007 **ORS** *020

EVANS, Kelly Nicole. 4800 SAND POINT WAY NE, AND REGION 98105 #005-06-2004 L2004 **PD** *012 †55

EVANS, Lauren Elizabeth. 2120 RAINIER AVE S, APT B 98144 #048-02-1981 L1986 **FM HNS** *020

EVANS, Michael Dean. 1600 E JOHN ST 98112 #054-04-1971 L1973 **FM AM** *020 †18

EVANS, Timothy Chas. 4245 ROOSEVELT WAY NE, GIMC 98105 #025-01-1974 L1980 **IM** *020 †20

EVANS, Yolanda Nicole. 4800 SAND POINT WAY NE, AND REGION 98105 #040-02-2005 L2005 **PD** *012

EVENSON, Mallorie Jean. ■ 98125 #054-04-2008 *012

EVERY, Nathan Robt. 1660 S COLUMBIAN WAY, SEATTLE VAMC HSRD #152 98108 #012-05-1988 L1990 **CD** *020 †20

EWINGS, Maria Kate. ■ 98122 #054-04-2006 L2006 **IM** *012

EXNER, Albert Jos. 1801 FAIRVIEW AVE E, NOAA MARINE OPERATIONS CEN 98102 #055-02-1983 L2003 **FM EM** *030 †18

EYER, Kenneth Moore. ■ 98104 #054-04-1956 L1957 **CD** *071 †20

EYTAN, Ted Aaron. 521 WALL ST ACC2 98121 #003-01-1995 L1997 **FM** *020 †18

FABIAN, Polly Tarleton. 8720 14TH AVE S 98108 #054-04-1982 L1983 **FM** *074 †18

FADER, Darrell Jonathan. 1801 NW MARKET ST, STE 107 98107 #028-02-1991 L2000 **D** *020 †15

FAGAN, Mark Stephan. PO BOX 1930 98111 #032-01-1986 L1986 **GP** *020

FAILOR, Richard Alan. 4225 ROOSEVELT WAY NE 98105 #035-47-1977 L1980 **IM END** *020 †20

FAITH, John Russell. 1600 E JOHN ST 98112 #017-20-1976 L1981 **OTO HNS** *020 †45

FALICOV, Alexis. 801 BROADWAY STE 1000 98122 #024-01-1999 L1999 **ORS** *020

FALK VAN ROOYEN, Inge. ■ 98112 #836-04-1992 L2001 *020

FALL, Gordon Francis F. 7715 24TH AVE NW 98117 #054-04-1963 L1965 **FM** *020 †18

FALLAHIAN, Amir Hosein. 1959 NE PACIFIC ST 98195 #517-08-1998 L2007 **AR** *012

FAMY, Christopher Scott. 550 16TH AVE, STE 100 98122 #054-04-2000 L2002 **P** *020 †18

FAN, Vincent Sh-Yeh. 1660 S COLUMBIAN WAY, HSR&D (152) 98108 #026-04-1995 L1997 **PCC** *020 †20 ‡

FANG, Ferric Chuwen. 1959 NE PACIFIC ST, UWMC- BOX 357242 98195 #024-01-1983 L2001 **ID** *020 †20

FANG, Liming Christine. 1959 NE PACIFIC ST, UNIVERSITY OF WASHINGTON 98195 #049-01-2005 L2006 **RO** *012

FANN, Gloria Mei. 550 16TH AVE, STE 100 98122 #054-04-2003 L2003 **FM** *020 †18

FANN, Jesse Ruey. UNIVERSITY OF WASHINGTON, SCI, BOX 356560 98195 #016-06-1989 L1990 **P** *020 †75

FARBER, Stuart J. 1959 NE PACIFIC ST, UWMC BOX 356390 98195 #054-04-1974 L1978 **FM PLM** *040 †18

FARIN, Federico M. ■ 98102 #005-19-1980 **PTH** *020

FARIVAR, Alexander Soheil. 1959 NE PACIFIC ST, BOX 356340 98195 #024-05-1999 L2002 **TS** *012 †85

FARJAH, Farhood. DEPT OF SURGERY, BOX 3564, UNIVERSITY OF WASHINGTON 98195 #040-02-2002 L2002 **GS** *012

FARMER, Sharon Lee. 1930 POST ALY 98101 #054-04-1980 L1981 **P** *020 †75

FARQUHAR, Carey. 325 9TH AVE, BOX 359909 98104 #024-01-1994 L1998 **ID** *020 †20

FARRA, Hassan. 4800 SAND POINT WAY NE, # 4G1 98105 #875-01-1996 L2004 **PDC** *020 †55

FARRELL, Donald Francis. 1959 NE PACIFIC ST, BOX 356115 98195 #010-01-1965 L1971 **N** *050 †75

FARRELL, Jeanette Marie. 1959 NE PACIFIC ST, BOX 356340 98195 #054-04-2001 L2003 **P** *020

FARRELL, Roy Geo. 200 15TH AVE E, GROUP HEALTH HOSPITAL 98112 #041-13-1972 L1973 **EM** *020 †16

FARRINGTON, Mary Lisa. 1100 9TH AVE 98101 #017-20-1987 L1990 **AI** *020 †55,03

FARRIS, Reid William. ■ 98112 #037-01-2005 L2005 **PD** *012

FARROKHI, Farrokh Reza. 1100 9TH AVE 98101 #048-04-1998 L2003 **NS** *012

FARROKHI, Virginia E. ■ 98112 #048-13-2001 L2003 **VS** *012 †85

FARWELL, Jacqueline Ruth. 2324 EASTLAKE AVE E, STE 500 98102 #005-02-1972 L1979 **CHN CN** *020

FATHI, Daniel Jay. 1629 N 45TH ST 98103 #054-04-1993 L1995 **FM** *020 †18

FAUCHER, Kimberly Rae. 1101 MADISON ST STE 301, PACIFIC MEDICAL CLINICS 98104 #023-12-1989 L1998 **OBG** *020 †30

FAUST, Alfred Francis. ■ 98109 #033-05-1998 L2003 **ORS** *020 †40

FECHNER, Patricia Yvonne. 4800 SAND POINT WAY NE, CHILDREN'S HOSPITAL & REGI 98105 #016-06-1986 L2006 **PDE** *012

FEFER, Alexander. 1959 NE PACIFIC ST, BOX 356527 98195 #005-11-1964 L1969 **ON IM** *050

FEHSENFELD, Drew Mathew. ■ 98115 #048-13-2003 L2003 **ORS** *012

FEIGENBAUM, Alyson Leigh. 1629 N 45TH ST 98103 #033-06-2007 **FP** *012

FEIGL, Eric Otto. UNIV OF WASHINGTON, PHYSIOLOGY 357290 98195 #026-04-1958 L1970 **OS CD** *050

FEIN, Warren Lewis. 2208 NW MARKET ST STE 410 98107 #054-04-1985 L1988 **IM** *020 †20

FEINBLOOM, Richard I. ■ 98116 #041-01-1960 L1961 **FM PD** *020 †55,18

FEINSTEIN, James Aaron. ■ 98115 #041-01-2007 L2007 **PD** *012

FELDMAN, Eric M. 201 16TH AVE E 98112 #056-06-1978 L1982 **ON HEM** *020 †20

■ = Address Information Privacy Protected

FELDMAN, Gary Ross. 1221 MADISON ST STE 1116 98104 #054-04-1977 L1979 **FPS HNS** *020

FELDMAN, Kenneth Wayne. 2101 E YESLER WAY, STE 100 98122 #056-05-1970 L1971 **PD** *020 †55

FELDMAN, Robert Keith. 600 BROADWAY, STE 170 98122 #011-03-1979 L1988 **DR** *020 †80

FELICIANO, Beejay Amurao. ■ 98119 #005-19-2004 L2004 **GS** *012

FELKER, Bradford Laird. 1660 S COLUMBIAN WAY, DEPARTMENT OF VETERANS AFF 98108 #051-01-1987 L1997 **P** *020 †20,75

FELLNER, Billie Jane. UNIVERSITY OF WASHINGTON, HALL HEALTH CENTER, BOX 35 98195 #041-14-1978 L1979 **FM** *020 †18

FELLNER, Carl Heinz. ■ 98102 #869-05-1952 L1972 **P** *071

FELLOWS, Christopher Lee. 1100 9TH AVE C1-MSO, VIRGINIA MASON MEDICAL CEN 98101 #040-02-1980 L1983 **CD IM** *020 †20

FENG, Jing. ■ 98105 #008-01-2005 L2006 **D** *012

FENICHEL, Robert Ross. ■ 98118 #024-01-1976 L1977 **EM** *050 †16

FENNER, Ray Harrison. 600 BROADWAY, EXIGERA CORP 98122 #035-15-1962 L1969 **ORS IM** *071 †40

FENNESSY, Sean Diarmuid. 747 BROADWAY 98122 #539-03-1999 L2005 **IM** *020 †20

FENSKE, Marla Rae. 1100 9TH AVE 98101 #054-04-1985 L1990 **PTH PCP** *020 †50

FENSTERMACHER, Marc James. 9730 3RD AVE NE, STE 202 98115 #048-02-1982 L2005 **DR** *020 †80

FER, Mehmet Fatih. 1600 E JEFFERSON ST STE A4 98122 #902-05-1974 L1986 **ON IM** *050 †20

FERGUSON, Laura C. 1660 S COLUMBIAN WAY, SEATTLE VAMC MHC-116 98108 #054-04-1998 L2000 **ADP** *020

FERGUSON, Mark R. 1959 NE PACIFIC ST, BOX 35 98195 #025-01-2003 L2004 **DR** *012

FERGUSON, William Duany. ■ 98115 #041-02-1967 L1972 **P CHP** *020 †75

FERGUSSON, Raymond C. ■ 98125 #035-09-1945 L1949 *071

FERNANDEZ, Ceferino Ame. 7909 RAINIER AVE S 98118 #748-08-1972 L1984 **GP GS** *020

FERO, Matthew Luke. 1100 FAIRVIEW AVE N, FRED HUTCHINSON CANCER RES 98109 #005-15-1990 L1993 **ON** *050 †20

FERRI, Raymond Thomas. 4800 SAND POINT WAY NE, NEUROLOGY RM B-5552 98105 #041-07-1995 L2003 **CHN** *020 †55,75

FERRUCCI, Cynthia Grace. 2505 2ND AVE, STE 200 98121 #035-03-1981 L1984 **IM** *020 †20

FETHERSTON, Debra S. 1100 9TH AVE 98101 #024-05-1986 L1991 **IM IMG** *020 †20

FEYMA, Timothy John. 1959 NE PACIFIC ST C21, UW BOX 356340 98195 #056-05-2004 L2006 **CHN** *012

FIALA, Suzanne Jana. 4744 41ST AVE SW, STE 102 98116 #054-04-1991 L1994 **FM** *020 †18

FIALKOW, Michael F. ■ 98119 #054-04-1997 L1999 **OBG** *020 †30

FIELD, Leslie Ann. ■ 98102 #025-07-2007 L2007 **PD** *012

FIFE, Laura Elizabeth. 1959 NE PACIFIC ST, BOX 356123 98195 #049-01-1979 L1983 **EM IM** *020 †20,16

FIGGE, David C. 325 9TH AVE 98104 #016-06-1950 L1952 **GO GYN** *040 †30

FIGLEY, Melvin Morgan. 2324 EASTLAKE AVE E, STE 500 98102 #024-01-1944 L1958 **R** *071 †80

FIGUEREDO, Edgar Jose. 325 9TH AVE, 1959 NE PACIFIC ST 98104 #264-18-1988 L2001 **CCS** *012 †85 ‡

FIHN, Stephan Dittler. 1660 S COLUMBIAN WAY, VA PUGET SOUND HEALTH CARE 98108 #028-34-1977 L1978 **IM** *050 †20

FILLIPO, Drew Craig. 10330 MERIDIAN AVE N, NORTH SEATTLE PEDIATRICS 98133 #036-01-1989 L1992 **PD** *020 †55

FINA, John Jos. 2033 6TH AVE, STE 1011 98121 #035-06-1974 L1996 **IM OS** *071 †20 ‡

FINCH, Clement A. 2324 EASTLAKE AVE E, STE 500 98102 #035-45-1941 L1950 **HEM** *071 †20

FINCH, Derel. 1560 N 115TH ST, STE 110 98133 #054-04-1995 L1998 **PCC** *020 †20

FINE, Alan Lewis. 125 16TH AVE E, GROUP HEALTH MEDICAL CENTE 98112 #035-45-1973 L1977 **IM** *020 †20

FINE, Gabriel Chaim. ■ 98112 #054-04-2008 *012

FINE, James Stephen. UNIV OF WASHINGTON, DEPT OF LAB MED BOX 357110 98195 #026-04-1972 L1986 **CLP OS** *030 †50

FINE, Meredith A Blehert. 1600 E OLIVE ST 98122 #026-04-1972 L1978 **P IM** *020 †20,75

FINEMAN, Robert Michael. ■ 98118 #035-08-1972 L1991 **MG PD** *040 †55,19

FINESMITH, Tina Helene. 1801 NW MARKET ST, STE 405 98107 #041-02-1987 L1994 **D IM** *020 †15

FINK, Kenneth Stuart. 2201 6TH AVE S M 40, CENTERS FOR MEDICARE AND M 98134 #041-01-1996 L1998 **FM GPM** *050 †70,18

FINKEL, Gerald Chas. 325 9TH AVE 98104 #024-01-1959 L1993 **PTH** *071 †50

FINKELSTEIN, Claudia A. 325 9TH AVE BOX 359892, ADULT MEDICINE CLINIC 98104 #067-01-1996 L2000 **IM** *020 †20

FINLAY, Judy Win. 4800 SAND POINT WAY NE 98105 #016-06-1977 L1978 **PD** *075 †55

FINLEY, Randall James. 1959 NE PACIFIC ST, RM RR-215 98195 #035-46-2000 L2007 **DR** *100 †80

FINN, Laura Susan. 4800 SAND POINT WAY NE, REGIONAL MEDICAL CENTER 98105 #041-14-1989 L1997 **PTH** *020 †50

FIRESTONE, Jordan Aaron. 325 9TH AVE 98104 #007-02-1995 L1997 **GPM** *020 †75,70

FISCHER, Eckhard Otto. ■ 98177 #407-05-1955 L1964 **HS** *071 †85

FISCHER, Rebecca Corinne. 7326 47TH AVE NE 98115 #054-04-2000 L2003 **P** *020

FISCHER-WYBREGT, Susanna. ■ 98177 #660-03-1959 L1965 **PD** *074

FISHBEIN, Daniel Philip. 1959 NE PACIFIC ST, BOX 356422 98195 #035-46-1980 L1981 **IM CD** *020 †20

FISHEL, Mark Adam. 1660 S COLUMBIAN WAY G, S 182 98108 #010-02-1996 L2000 **N** *020 †75

FISHER, Carlotto Anzette. ■ 98115 #054-04-2008 *012

FISHER, Christopher J. 1959 NE PACIFIC ST 98195 #143-07-1989 L1998 *100

FISHER, Frank Edmund. ■ 98115 #051-01-1974 L1976 **OS IM** *020 †20

FISHER, Nancy Louise. 4800 SAND POINT WAY NE 98105 #048-04-1976 L1978 **MG PD** *030 †55,19

FISHER, Peter. ■ 98121 #041-01-1948 L1954 **IM GP** *020 †20

FISHER, Warren Leo. ■ 98105 #054-04-1990 L1993 **EM** *020 †16

FITZGERALD, Allison Anne. 1629 N 45TH ST, 45TH ST CLINIC 98103 #008-02-1989 L1992 **FM** *020 †18

FITZGERALD, Kimberly Ann. 900 TERRY AVE 4TH FL, COLUMBUS PAVILION 98104 #030-06-1993 L1997 **AN** *020 †05

FITZGIBBON, Dermot R. 1959 NE PACIFIC ST BOX 356, UNIVERSITY OF WASHINGTON 98195 #539-02-1983 L1992 **AN** *020 †05

FITZHARRIS, John Thomas. 1221 MADISON ST, C/O ABBY DONOVAN 98104 #028-34-1998 L2007 **HO** *020 †20

FITZSIMMONS, Kari Denae. 747 BROADWAY 98122 #054-04-2003 L2006 **EM** *020 †16

FITZTHUM, Jeffery Edward. 1530 N 115TH ST, NORTHWEST PHYSIATRY 98133 #040-02-1989 L2000 **PM PMM** *020 †60

FIX, Oren Kadouri. 1959 NE PACIFIC ST, BOX 356174 98195 #035-06-1999 L2006 **GE** *100 †20

FLACCO, Michael Paul. 500 17TH AVE 98122 #041-02-1975 L1979 **AN** *020 †05

FLECKMAN, Philip Howard. 4225 ROOSEVELT WAY NE, STE 354697 98105 #028-02-1973 L1982 **D** *050 †15

FLEET, Jacob Riley. 1560 N 115TH ST STE 106 98133 #054-04-2000 L2003 **IM** *020 †20

FLEET, Wendell Patrick. 325 9TH AVE, # 359764 98104 #030-06-1965 L1969 **IM NEP** *020 †20

FLEISHMAN, Rachel Amy. 4800 SAND POINT WAY NE, AND REGION 98105 #035-46-2005 L2005 **PD** *012

FLEISIG, Ani J. 1959 NE PACIFIC ST, DEPARTMENT FO 98195 #035-06-2000 L2004 **GS** *020 †85

FLEMING, John Lawerance. 6300 9TH AVE NE 98105 #005-12-1969 L1970 **FM** *020 †20

FLEMING, Sara Anne. 550 16TH AVE STE 100 98122 #028-02-2002 L2004 **FM** *020 †18

FLEMING, Thomas C. ■ 98116 #035-01-1967 L1996 **ORS** *072 †40

FLETCHER, Grant Selmer. ■ 98102 #036-01-2002 L2006 **IM** *100 †20

FLIGNER, Corinne Lina. 1959 NE PACIFIC ST, UWMC BOX 356100 98195 #034-01-1976 L1977 **ATP FOP** *020 †50

FLORENCE, Lisa Savage. 1101 MADISON ST, STE 200 98104 #054-04-1985 L1994 **TTS GS** *020 †85

FLORENCE, Michael Glenn. 1600 E JEFFERSON ST, STE 603 98122 #012-05-1975 L1976 **GS VS** *020 †85

FLORER, Robert Emerson. ■ 98116 #020-02-1941 L1946 **GS** *071 †85

FLOURNOY, Mary Catherine. 1959 NE PACIFIC ST, PSYCHIATRY RESIDENCY PRGM 98195 #016-43-2007 L2007 **P** *012

FLOWERS, Gerald. ■ 98177 #352-10-1951 L1960 **AN** *071 †05

FLOWERS, Mary Evelyn D. 1959 NE PACIFIC ST # 35808, UNIVERSITY OF WASHINGTON M 98195 #187-16-1977 L1990 **HEM ON** *020

FLOWERS, Nicole Tamara. 5423 S HUDSON ST 98118 #005-11-1996 L1999 **PD** *020 †55

FLOYD, Anneliese Herseth. 1629 N 45TH ST 98103 #054-04-2005 L2005 **FP** *012

FLOYD, James Song. ■ 98122 #036-07-2005 L2005 **IM** *012

FLUGSTAD, Daniel Lloyd. 925 SENECA ST 98104 #054-04-1980 L1981 **ORS** *020 †40

FLUHRER, Patricia Lee. 98136 #005-19-1984 L1985 **IM** *020 †20

FLUVOG, Philip Ernest. 3339 CASCADIA AVE S 98144 #054-04-1955 L1956 **TS GS** *071

FLYNN, Jerald Paul, Jr. ■ 98168 #054-04-1989 *020

FLYNN, Joseph Thomas. 4800 SAND POINT WAY NE, CHILDREN'S HOSPITAL AND RE 98105 #035-15-1987 L2007 **PN PD** *020 †55

FOFIE, Anita Estelle Afua. ■ 98121 #016-06-2007 L2007 **GS** *012

FOGERTY, Richard Alan. 1801 NW MARKET ST STE 309 98107 #018-03-1974 L1977 **IM** *020 †20

FOLGER, Carol Anne. 9800 4TH AVE NE, NORTHGATE CLINIC 98115 #045-01-1987 L1990 **FM** *020 †20

FOLTZ, Gregory Dean. 550 17TH AVE 5TH FL, SEATTLE NEURO INSTITUTE SP 98122 #028-02-1995 L1995 **NS** *020

FOLTZ, Luba Mishelle. 1101 MADISON ST, STE 950 98104 #054-04-2000 L2004 **OBG** *020 ‡

FONG, Abraham Park. ■ 98121 #041-14-2004 L2007 **PHO** *012 †55

FONG, Walter C. 10416 5TH AVE NE 98125 #016-11-1980 L1987 **IM** *020 †20

FONG, Willis Ming. 521 WALL ST 98121 #041-13-1944 L1952 **PD PDA** *071 †55

FOOTE, Nancy Louise. ■ 98118 #007-02-1976 L1977 **FM** *020 †18

FORAL, Jonathan Michael. 1107 NE 45TH ST # 4, UNIV OF WASH,DEPT OF RADIO 98105 #030-05-2001 L2006 **DR** *020 †20

FORD, Kerry King. 93 S JACKSON ST, # 65753 98104 #048-02-1976 L1976 **DR** *020 †80

FORD, Robert Stephen. 747 BROADWAY 98122 #048-12-1981 L1995 **EM** *020 †16

FORD, William Pendleton. ■ 98116 #054-04-1958 L1962 **IM** *071 †20

FORDYCE, Christine J. 9800 4TH AVE NE 98115 #001-06-1985 L1986 **FM** *020 †18

FORGETTE, Margaret Mary. 1600 E JEFFERSON ST, STE 620 98122 #054-04-1984 L1987 **PM** *020 †60

FOROUZANNIA, Arman. ■ 98122 #025-07-2004 L2004 **DR** *012

FORSLUND, Timothy Matthew. 4120 STONE WAY N 98103 #054-04-1994 L1996 **P** *020 †75

FOSTER, Dante Mariachase. ■ 98117 #024-01-2006 L2006 **GS** *012

FOSTER, Jennifer Haunani. ■ 98103 #014-01-2007 L2007 **PD** *012

FOTINOS, Charissa. 999 3RD AVE, STE 900 98104 #016-11-1988 L1990 **FM** *020 †18

FOTOOHI, Mehran. 925 SENECA ST # H8-GME, VIRGINIA MASON MED CTR 98101 #016-42-1995 L1998 **VIR** *020 †80

FOUKE, Bernard Irwin, Jr. 1100 9TH AVE 98101 #004-01-1974 L1980 **EM** *020 †16

FOURNARAKIS, Bill Mike. 1101 MADISON ST, STE 800 98104 #054-04-2001 L2003 **PD** *020 †55

FOUSER, Laurie Sue. 1101 MADISON ST, STE 800 98104 #030-05-1979 L1980 **PN PD** *020 †55

FOUTY, Robert Almond. 13751 LAKE CITY WAY NE, STE 300 98125 #054-04-1956 L1957 **PTH** *020 †50

FOWLER, Kory Blaine. 5300 TALLMAN AVE NW 98107 #040-02-1995 L1998 **IM** *020 †20

FOWLER, Lawrence Joseph. 2409 N 45TH ST 98103 #048-14-1977 L2004 **AN** *020 †05

FOX, Katrina Virginia. 4245 ROOSEVELT WAY NE, STE 354775 98105 #051-04-2003 L2003 **OBG** *100

FOX, Lindsay Louise. ■ 98102 #025-12-2007 L2007 **PD** *012

FOX-DEWHURST, Rebecca D. 726 BROADWAY, STE 305 98122 #012-05-1989 L1989 **PUD IM** *071 †20

FOY, Hugh Martin. 325 9TH AVE, DEPT OF SURGERY 2A-16 98104 #030-05-1978 L1979 **GS** *020 †85

FRANCIS, David Oliver. 1959 NE PACIFIC ST, UW SCHOOL OF MED GME PROGR 98195 #035-45-2004 L2004 **OTO** *012

FRANCIS, Emily Marie. ■ 98105 #054-04-2005 L2005 **AN** *012

FRANCIS, Robert Rankin. 1221 MADISON ST, VITREORETINAL ASSOCIATES 98104 #054-04-1984 L1985 **OPH** *020 †35

FRANCK, Alice Marie. 4400 37TH AVE S 98118 #041-13-2002 L2004 **FM** *020 †18

FRANCK, Kevin Matthew. 1959 NE PACIFIC ST, UNIV OF WA SCH MED 98195 #305-01-2007 L2007 **AN** *012

FRANCO, Amparo Armi B L. 11508 5TH AVE NE 98125 #748-01-1977 L1980 **IM** *020

FRANK, Arnold Jay. 1401 MADISON ST, STE 100 98104 #054-15-1964 **P** *071 †75

FRANK, Daniel S. 1001 BROADWAY, STE 309 98122 #036-01-1987 L1990 **EM IM** *020 †20

FRANK, Danielle. ■ 98116 #025-07-2001 L2004 **IM** *020

FRANK, David. 1100 9TH AVE C1-MSO, VIRGINIA MASON CLINIC 98101 #016-43-1985 L1986 **EM IM** *020 †20

FRANK, George Ivor. 1536 N 115TH ST, SUMMIT CARDIOLOGY 98133 #008-01-1973 L1974 **CD IM** *020 †20

FRANK, Leonard Robt. 1959 NE PACIFIC ST, MSC 359300 98195 #035-03-1988 L1997 **IM** *020 †16,20

FRANKLIN, David Bencion. 3400 CALIFORNIA AVE SW, STE 200 98116 #010-01-1980 L1981 **PD** *020 †55

FRANKLIN, Jonathan Louis. 2409 N 45TH ST 98103 #054-04-1983 L1984 **ORS** *020 †40

■ = Address Information Privacy Protected

FRANKWICK, Dawn Marie. 10330 MERIDIAN AVE N, STE 300 98133 #056-06-1983 L1988 **OBG** *020 †30

FRAZER, Timothy Wayne. 1426 HARVARD AVE 98122 #020-02-1982 L1987 **P CHP** *020 †75

FREDERICK, John Thomas. 325 9TH AVE BOX 359911, HARBORVIEW MEDICAL CENTER 98104 #017-20-1996 L1998 **P** *020 †75

FREDERICK, Mary Melissa. GRADUATE MEDICAL ED BOX 35, UNIVERSITY OF WASHINGTON 98195 #054-04-2002 L2003 **FM** *020 †20

FREDRICKS, David Neal. 1100 FAIRVIEW AVE N D3-100, BOX 19024 98109 #038-06-1990 L2001 **ID** *020 †20

FREDRICKSON, Sherman R. 2114 W BERTONA ST 98199 #025-01-1977 L1978 **IM** *020 †20

FREEBORN, Mark A. 325 9TH AVE, BOX 359798 98104 #025-01-2003 L2003 **ORS** *012

FREEDMAN, Edward Wm. UNIVERSITY HOSP, DEPT PSYCH 98105 #033-05-1970 L1972 **P PD** *020

FREEDMAN, Lawrence Z. ■ 98104 #024-07-1944 L1946 **P PYA** *071 †75

FREEDMAN, Steven J. ■ 98109 #005-11-1986 *100

FREEMAN, Erica Renee. ■ 98103 #028-02-2005 L2005 **PD** *012

FREEMAN, Lynne Michelle. 1600 E JOHN ST 98112 #054-04-1990 L1992 **IM** *020 †20

FREEMAN, Rosario V. 4245 ROOSEVELT WAY NE, STE 354775 98105 #016-43-1995 L2001 **CD** *020 †20

FREENY, Patrick Clinton. 1959 NE PACIFIC ST, UNIV OF WASH, BOX 357115 98195 #039-01-1968 L1975 **DR GS** *020 †80

FREIDIN, Morris. ■ 98105 #005-06-1943 L1943 **GS** *071

FREITAS, Anne Elizabeth. 1229 MADISON ST STE 1150 98104 #025-07-1986 L1989 **DR** *020 †80

FRENCH, Charles Edward. 3626 NE 45TH ST, STE 300 98105 #054-04-1975 L1977 **NPM PD** *071 †55

FRENCH, James Wm. 4800 SAND POINT WAY NE 98105 #025-01-1963 L1983 **PDC PD** *071 †55

FRENKEL, Lisa Marie. 4800 SAND POINT WAY NE, # W-8851 98105 #019-02-1981 L1994 **PD ID** *020 †55

FREUND, Felix G. UNIV WA DEPT ANES RN10 98105 #132-01-1948 L1962 **AN** *071 †05

FREUND, Peter Ronald. 1959 NE PACIFIC ST, UNIV OF WASHINGTON MED CEN 98195 #035-01-1975 L1976 **AN** *020 †05

FRIEDLY, Janna Lee. UNIV OF WASHINGTON, DEPT OF REHAB MED 98195 #040-02-2001 L2001 **PM** *100 †60

FRIEDMAN, Andrew Scott. 1100 9TH AVE G1-MSO, VIRGINIA MASON MEDICAL CEN 98101 #025-01-1991 L1993 **PM** *020 †60

FRIEDMAN, Debra Lynn. 1100 FAIRVIEW AVE N, STE D5-280 98109 #033-06-1991 L1998 **PHO PD** *020 †55

FRIEDMAN, Jamie Blake. ■ 98115 #065-10-1981 L1983 **IM ON** *020 †20

FRIEDMAN, Jay Max. 1560 N 115TH ST, PACIFIC RETINA SPEC #G-10 98133 #047-06-1982 L1992 **OPH** *020 †20,35

FRIEDMANN, Daniel Theodor. 1801 NW MARKET ST, BALLARD MEDICAL PLZ STE 3 98107 #054-04-1981 L1983 **FM** *020 †18

FRIEDRICH, Jason Michael. ■ 98115 #040-02-2006 L2006 **PM** *012

FRIEDRICH, Jeffrey Barton. 325 9TH AVE, BOX 359796 98104 #048-14-2000 L2003 **HS** *100

FRIEDSTAT, Jonathan Seth. 1959 NE PACIFIC ST, BOX 356340 98195 #016-11-2006 L2006 **GS** *012

FRIEND, William Garrick. 1221 MADISON ST, COLON & RECTAL CLINIC 98104 #035-01-1964 L1970 **CRS** *071 †10,85

FRIGON, Chantal. 4800 SAND POINT WAY NE #067-06-1994 L1999 **PAN** *100

FRITZ, James Kenneth. 1600 E JOHN ST 98112 #054-04-1976 L1977 **CD** *050 †20

FRITZ, Mark Paul. 747 BROADWAY 98122 #025-12-1985 L1992 **AN CCM** *020 †05

FRITZSCHE, Ulrich. 1530 N 115TH ST STE 301 98133 #407-16-1965 L1972 **OBG** *020 †20

FROESE, Daniel Paul. 1221 MADISON ST STE 1220 98104 #917-13-1984 L1986 **CRS GS** *020 †85,10

FROHLICH, Mark Walter. 3005 1ST AVE 98121 #024-01-1990 L2002 **IM ON** *050 †20

FROHN, Ross Hedlund. 1550 N 115TH ST, NORTHWEST HOSPITAL 98133 #021-01-2003 L2004 **AN** *020

FROINES, Eric John. 200 15TH AVE E CMB-3, DEPT OF SURGERY 98112 #054-04-1986 L1991 **GS** *020 †85

FROLUND, Ernest Lauritz. 747 BROADWAY 98122 #005-17-1962 L1975 **GP AN** *071

FROMM, Jonathan Raymond. 1959 NE PACIFIC ST, UNIV OF WA MEDICAL CENTER 98195 #018-03-1997 L2002 **HMP** *020 †50

FROWNFELTER, Milah Blinka. 1145 BROADWAY 98122 #054-04-2003 L2003 **IM** *020 †20

FU, Anita. 5254 UNIVERSITY WAY NE 98105 #748-02-1975 L1980 **IM** *020

FU, Belinda. 4245 ROOSEVELT WAY NE, BOX 354775 98105 #005-02-2001 L2003 **FM** *020 †18

FUHS, Stephen Earl. 600 BROADWAY, SEATTLE HAND SURGERY 98122 #056-05-1974 L1980 **HS ORS** *020 †40

FUJIMOTO, Michael Ken. PO BOX 356340, UNIVERSITY OF WASHINGTON G 98195 #054-04-2005 L2005 **IM** *012

FUKUDA, Yuko. ■ 98105 #041-15-2003 L2003 **P** *100

FUKURA, Robert Takeshi. 1100 9TH AVE G1-MSO, VIRGINIA MASON MEDICAL CEN 98101 #054-04-1981 L1982 **PD** *020 †55

FULLERTON, Melissa Jean. ■ 98102 #051-01-2008 *012

FULLMER, Joseph Miller. ■ 98125 #026-04-2006 L2006 **NP** *012

FUNDIS, Linda Kay. 550 16TH AVE, STE 400 98122 #031-01-1988 L1991 **AN** *020 †05

FURMANCZYK, Paul. 4203 BROOKLYN AVE NE #308A 98105 #054-04-2005 L2005 **PTH** *012

FURST, Michael L. 216 1ST AVE S, STE 333 98104 #054-04-1986 L1991 **P** *020 †75

FUSARO, Aldo J. 325 9TH AVE, PO BOX 359792 98104 #018-75-1991, ▲ L2005 **FOP** *020 †50

FUTRAN, Neal D. 1959 NE PACIFIC ST, BOX 356515 98195 #035-08-1987 L1995 **OTO HNS** *020 †45

GAASERUD, Annelise Marjol. 125 16TH AVE E 98112 #550-04-2004 L2005 **FP** *012

GABANEK, Darlene Hedy. 100 W HARRISON ST, S TOWER SUITE 330 98119 #054-04-1990 L1994 **P** *020

GABIKIAN, Patrik. 1959 NE PACIFIC ST, BOX 356340 98195 #023-07-2002 L2002 **NS** *012

GABRIO, Wesley F. 509 OLIVE WAY, THE SPORTS MEDICINE CLINIC 98101 #028-02-1950 L1951 **GYN OS** *072 †30

GADGIL, Aneal Sitaram. ■ 98121 #495-37-1998 L2001 **PCC** *100 †20

GADI, Vijayakrish K. 1959 NE PACIFIC ST, BOX 356340 98195 #001-02-2000 L2002 **ON** *100 †20

GAINES, John Elliott. 1560 N 115TH ST, STE 109 98133 #035-01-1967 L1977 **OBG** *020 †30

GALAGAN, Katherine A S. 1100 9TH AVE 98101 #054-04-1980 L1984 **PTH PCP** *020 †50

GALE, James Lyman. DEPT OF EPIDEMIOLOGY SC-36, UNIVERSITY OF WASHINGTON 98195 #035-01-1961 L1968 **OS ID** *071

GALLAFENT, James Hampton. PO BOX 356421, UNIV OF WASHINGTON 98195 #054-04-2006 L2006 **IM** *012

GALLAGHER, Emily Rose. 1959 NE PACIFIC ST C212, UNIV OF WA, SOM 98195 #040-02-2007 L2007 **PD** *012

GALLAGHER, Thomas Henry. 4245 ROOSEVELT WAY NE, STE 354775 98105 #024-01-1990 L2002 **IM** *050 †20

GALLANIS, John Thos. 500 17TH AVE 98122 #028-34-1976 L1980 **IM** *020

GALLO, Kacie Mckenna. ■ 98133 #054-04-2006 L2006 **FP** *012

GALVEZ, Eva Marie. 8720 14TH AVE S 98108 #054-04-2004 L2004 **FM** *020 †18

GAMBLE, Katherine Lawder. 1401 MADISON ST, FIRST HILL 98104 #023-01-2004 L2007 **FM** *020 †18

GAMBLE, Susan Rebecca. ■ 98144 #054-04-2008 *012

GAN, Rong. ■ 98144 #016-11-2002 L2006 **AN** *012

GAN, Sandra Colleen. 515 MINOR AVE STE 300 98104 #005-11-1989 L1995 **CD IM** *020 †20

GANDHI, Mehul Vasantray. PO BOX 356421, UNIV OF WASHINGTON 98195 #016-11-2006 L2006 **IM** *012

GANGOPADHYAY, Kunal. 1959 NE PACIFIC ST, BOX 356515 98195 #495-02-1992 L2004 **AN** *012

GANTT, Soren Matthew. 4800 SAND POINT WAY NE 8G, & REGIONAL 98105 #035-19-2001 L2003 **PDI** *100 †55

GARBRICK, Lisa Marie. 500 17TH AVE, E.R. DEPARTMENT 98122 #054-04-1990 L1994 **EM** *020 †16

GARCIA, Chris Fuentes. PO BOX 356340, UNIV OF WA SCH OF MED 98195 #054-04-2000 *100

GARCIA, Jorge Mf. 5300 TALLMAN AVE NW 98107 #005-02-1983 L1985 **FM** *020 †18

GARCIA, Patricia Jannet. 325 9TH AVE # 359909 98104 #737-06-1988 L1994 **ID IM** *100 †20

GARCIA, Rochelle Lorraine. 325 9TH AVE 98104 #054-04-1989 L1989 **PTH** *020 †50

GARDELLA, Carolyn Marie. 1959 NE PACIFIC ST, MSC 359300 98195 #035-48-1995 L1997 **OBG** *020 †30

GARDELLA, Dean. ■ 98199 #031-01-2006 **DR** *012

GARDEN, Gwenn Anne. 1959 NE PACIFIC ST, BOX 356465 98195 #054-04-1994 L2000 **N** *020 †75

GARDEY, Takla Elizabeth. 3400 CALIFORNIA AVE SW 98116 #021-01-1993 L1997 **FM** *020 †18

GARDINER, Lorin D. 325 9TH AVE, BOX 359896 98104 #836-02-1991 L1997 **P** *020 †75

GARDNER, Bruce. 1915 QUEEN ANNE AVE N, QUEEN ANNE FAMILY MED 98109 #054-04-1982 L1983 **FM** *020 †18

GARDNER, Gregory Chas. 1959 NE PACIFIC ST, BOX 356428 98195 #048-04-1984 L1989 **RHU IM** *020 †20

GARDNER, Michael James. 325 9TH AVE BOX 359798, HARBORVIEW MEDICAL CENTER 98104 #041-15-2001 L2007 **ORS** *020

GARG, Ruchi. ■ 98115 #011-02-2001 L2005 **OBG** *100 †30

GARG, Tanu. 320 WESTLAKE AVE N, STE 100 98109 #495-45-2003 L2004 **FM** *100 †18

GARLITZ, Cristopher Jon. ■ 98102 #041-02-1999 L2005 **U** *100 †95

GARNETT, Daniel Jos. 1801 NW MARKET ST, STE 401 98107 #035-01-1967 L1973 **GS TS** *020 †85

GARR, Jeffrey Lee. 900 TERRY AVE, STE 100 98104 #047-05-1994 L2000 **OSS** *020 †40

GARR, K Elizabeth. 1229 MADISON ST STE 1600, ORTHOPEDIC PHYSICIAN ASSOC 98104 #021-01-1994 L1996 **APM AN** *020 †05 ‡

GARRISON, James Millard. 200 16TH AVE E 98112 #024-07-1958 L1968 **LM OBG** *072 †30

GARRISON, Leslie. 51 UNIVERSITY ST 98101 #035-48-1981 L1989 **OS PD** *050 †55

GARRITANO, Joanna C. 1100 9TH AVE 98101 #016-43-1999 L2004 **EM** *020 †16

GARTMAN, David Miner. 1600 E JEFFERSON ST, STE 110 98122 #021-05-1980 L1986 **CD TS** *020 †85,90

GARTON, Kyle Justin. 4225 ROOSEVELT WAY NE, STE 354697 98105 #054-04-2004 L2004 **D** *012

GARTON, Rachel Avery. 125 16TH AVE E, GROUP HLTH CNTRL-DERMTLGY 98112 #054-04-1999 L2003 **D** *020 †15

GARVIN, Kanishka W.. ■ 98101 #001-02-2007 L2007 *012

GARY, Megan Catherine. 1959 NE PACIFIC ST BOX 356, UNIV OF WASHINGTON 98195 #016-43-1999 L2007 **P** *012

GASPARICH, James Peter. 1221 MADISON ST, SEATTLE UROLOGICAL 98104 #016-02-1979 L1981 **U** *020 †95

GASS, Michael Arthur. 1100 9TH AVE 98101 #025-07-1954 L1963 **R OS** *020 †80

GASSNER, Holger Guenther. 1959 NE PACIFIC ST C212, UNIV OF WASHINGTON BOX 356 98195 #409-04-1998 L2006 **OTO** *100 †45

GAST, Paul William. 201 16TH AVE E, GROUP HEALTH COOPERATIVE 98112 #016-43-1997 L1999 **FM** *020 †18

GASTER, Barak. 4245 ROOSEVELT WAY NE, BOX 354760 98105 #005-02-1993 L1995 **IM** *020 †20

GATEWOOD, Medley Okeefe. 1959 NE PACIFIC ST, BOX 356123 98195 #016-02-2001 L2005 **EM** *020 †16

GAUVIN, France. 4800 SAND POINT WAY NE, CHILDRENS HOSP & MED CTR 98105 #067-02-1993 L1998 **CCP** *100 †55

GAYDOS-GABRIEL, Juliann E. 2849 EASTLAKE AVE E, UNIT 421 98102 #043-01-2008 *012

GAYMAN, John Parker. 925 SENECA ST 98101 #005-11-1979 L1980 **FM FSM** *020 †18

GAYNOR, Christopher Harry. 6300 9TH AVE NE, STE 300 98115 #024-07-1993 L1993 **FM** *040 †18

GEBALLE, Adam Philip. 1100 FAIRVIEW AVE N, RESEARCH CENTER 98109 #036-07-1978 L1987 **ID IM** *050 †20

GEE, Susanne Loraine. 4744 41ST AVE SW, STE 104 98116 #010-01-1995 L1998 **D DS** *020

GEGGEL, Harry Steven. 1100 9TH AVE G1-MSO 98101 #028-02-1978 L1984 **OPH** *020 †35

GEIDUSCHEK, Jeremy Mark. 4800 SAND POINT WAY NE, CHLDRNS HOSP & MED CTR 98105 #047-05-1983 L1984 **AN PD** *020 †55,05

GEIMAN, Benjamin John. 747 BROADWAY 98122 #054-04-1995 L1999 **AN** *020 †20,05

GELFENBEYN, Mikhail. 1959 NE PACIFIC ST BOX 356, UW SCHOOL OF MED GME PROGR 98195 #913-99-1978 L2003 **NS** *012

GELLER, Arthur Sigmund. 521 WALL ST 98121 #035-01-1962 L1968 **R** *071 †80

GELMAN, Michael Aaron. 1959 NE PACIFIC ST, BOX 356340 98195 #056-05-2005 L2005 **IM** *020

GELPI, Armand P. ■ 98136 #005-02-1949 L1949 **IM** *071 †20

GEMAR, Kjersti Anne. ■ 98119 #054-04-2007 L2007 **P** *012

GEMES, David Lamar. 521 WALL ST 98121 #005-02-1973 L1975 **AN** *020 †05

GEMPERLINE, Patrick L. 8720 14TH AVE S 98108 #049-01-1986 L1988 **FM** *020 †18

GENDO, Karna. 325 9TH AVE, HARBORVIEW MEDICAL CENTER 98104 #005-19-1995 L1998 **IM** *020,03

GENSCH, Erin Marie. 1107 NE 45TH ST # 44, UNIV OF WASH,DEPT OF RADIO 98105 #005-02-2002 L2002 **DR** *020

GENSINI PAEZ, Francisco J. PO BOX 356410, UNIV OF WASHINGTON 98195 #264-05-1990 L2003 **TS** *012

GENTRY, Rex Nathan. 121 LAKESIDE AVE, STE 100 98122 #017-20-1974 L1978 **P** *030

GEORGE, David Paul. 1959 NE PACIFIC ST 98195 #040-02-1975 L1996 **OPH GP** *071 †35

GEORGES, George Earl. 1100 FAIRVIEW AVE N D1-100 98109 #005-02-1990 L1994 ON *050 †20

GERAGHTY, Patricia Rausch. ■ 98104 #005-11-2002 L2003 MSR *020 †80

GERBER, Frederic H. 1229 MADISON ST, STE 900 98104 #036-07-1965 L1971 DR NM *072 †80,28

GERBINO, Anthony Jos. 1100 9TH AVE G1-MSO, VIRGINIA MASON MEDICAL CEN 98101 #005-14-1992 L1992 PCC *020 †20

GERBINO, Ingrid Fuss. 1100 9TH AVE G1-MSO, VIRGINIA MASON MEDICAL CEN 98101 #005-14-1992 L1992 IM *020 †20

GERCHMAN, Fernando. 1660 S COLUMBIAN WAY 98108 #187-02-1997 L2006 IM END *050

GERDES, Patrick Victor. ■ 98105 #054-04-2001 L2005 AN *020

GERNSHEIMER, Terry B. 921 TERRY AVE 98104 #035-48-1979 L1982 IM HEM *040 †20

GERTLER, Robert Andrew. 1600 E JOHN ST 98112 #038-06-1978 L1980 AN *020 †05

GERTON, Brooke Kaiulani. ■ 98105 #051-01-2004 L2004 N *012

GETTELMAN, Rebecca. 1959 NE PACIFIC ST, U OF W-HS AFFAIRS BOX 3563 98195 #005-18-2004 L2004 IM *100 †20

GEY, George Otto, Jr. MS 1W-91, THE BOEING CO 98124 #352-03-1964 L1971 OM CD *071 ‡

GEYER, Jeffrey Russell. 4800 SAND PT WAY NE, MS B-6553 CHILDS HOSP & MD 98105 #025-07-1977 L1984 PD PHO *020 †55

GEYMAN, John Payne. SCHOOL OF MEDICINE, UNIV OF WASHINGTON HQ-30 98195 #005-02-1960 L1977 FM *071 †18

GHARIB, Sina Aliasghar. 1959 NE PACIFIC ST 98195 #024-01-1996 L1999 PCC *100 †20

GHODKE, Basavaraj Vishnu. 1959 NE PACIFIC ST, UNIV OF WA SCH OF MED 98195 #495-01-1991 L2002 *020

GHODS, Massroor. 1730 MINOR AVE STE 1010, SEATTLE CARDIOLOGY CLINIC 98101 #517-08-1983 L1990 CD IM *020 †20

GIANUTSOS, Louis Paul. 550 16TH AVE STE 100, PROVIDENCE 98122 #005-14-1993 L1995 FM *020 †20

GIBBONS, Edward Francis. 1100 9TH AVE 98101 #016-02-1978 L1985 CD *020 †20

GIBBONS, Eileen A Jr. 1325 4TH AVE, STE 1240 98101 #054-04-1994 L1996 FM *020 †18

GIBBONS, Mary S. 325 9TH AVE 98104 #041-02-1985 L1986 FM *020 †18

GIBBS, Jeffrey Spencer. 1101 MADISON ST, STE 301 98104 #056-06-1988 L2004 CD *020 †20

GIBLETT, Eloise R. ■ 98115 #041-02-1951 L1952 BBK HEM *071

GIBRAN, Nicole Simone. 325 9TH AVE 98104 #024-05-1985 L1990 GS *020 †85

GIBSON, Jack Lonnie. ■ 98125 #004-01-1953 L1968 OBG *040 †30

GIBSON, John Conrad. 747 BROADWAY 98122 #067-01-1961 L1967 NS *020 †25

GIBSON, Ronald. CH-68, 4800 SAND POINT WAY NE 98105 #028-02-1982 L1983 PD NPM *050 †55

GIBSON, Scot N. ■ 98122 #005-19-2005 L2005 P *012

GIBSON, William M. ■ 98136 #067-01-1950 L1965 OS PM *020 †55

GIEDT, Cassandra. 550 16TH AVE STE 100 98122 #054-04-1992 L1994 FM *020 †18

GIEDT, Walvin Roland. ■ 98177 #016-01-1937 L1944 PTH PHP *071 †70

GIESEL, Ann Elizabeth. 4800 SAND POINT WAY NE, CHILDREN'S HOSPITAL MED CE 98105 #020-02-1985 L1986 PD ADL *012

GIFFORD, Joseph Michael. 6026 28TH AVE NE 98115 #005-18-1980 L1981 IM *020 †16

GILBERT, David Anthony. 1145 BROADWAY 98122 #016-02-1973 L1974 GE IM *020 †20

GILBERT, Erin Wian. 1959 NE PACIFIC ST BOX 356, UW SCHOOL OF MEDICINE GME 98195 #021-05-2005 L2005 GS *012

GILBERT, Mark John. 1124 COLUMBIA ST, MAILSTOP M758 98104 #018-03-1986 L1990 ON *020 †20

GILBERT, Michael Jeffery. 2225 E MILLER ST 98112 #038-41-2001 L2006 PDI *012 †55

GILL, Edward A, Jr. 1959 NE PACIFIC ST, BOX 359748 98195 #054-04-1984 L1985 CD *020 †20

GILL, Sharon Kathleen. ■ 98103 #008-01-2005 L2005 IM *012

GILL, Wendy Parkinson. ■ 98103 #005-11-2001 L2005 ID *012

GILLESPIE, Hamilton Sawye. 325 9TH AVE, HARBORVIEW MED CTR 98104 #054-04-2004 L2004 IM *020 †20

GILLESPY, Marjorie P. ■ 98177 #041-02-1980 L1990 FM *020 †18

GILLESPY, Thurman, III. 600 BROADWAY, STE 170 98122 #041-02-1980 L1990 DR *040 †80

GILLETTE, Thomas E. 1101 MADISON ST, PC 98104 #035-06-1973 L1980 OPH *020 †35

GILLIAM, Lisa Katherine. 4800 ROOSEVELT WAY NE 98105 #036-07-1999 L2001 END *100 †20

GILLIGAN, Diana Mary. 921 TERRY AVE, PUGET SOUND BLOOD CTR 98104 #035-46-1985 L2000 ON *020 †20

GILMAN, Naomi Kim. ■ 98105 #054-04-2008 *012

GILMER, Brian Brandon. ■ 98103 #048-02-2008 *012

GILMORE, Ari Alexander. ■ 98103 #054-04-2005 L2005 FP *012

GILMORE, Christina Marie. 325 9TH AVE BOX 359780, HARBORVIEW MEDICAL CENTER 98104 #054-04-2003 L2003 IM *100 †20

GILMORE, Timothy Michael. 600 E JOHN ST 98112 #054-04-1981 L1982 OM FM *020 †70,18

GIMBRERE, Kathreen. 325 9TH AVE, UNIVERSITY OF WASHINGTON 98104 #035-20-1990 L1994 P *020

GINSBERG, Arthur Henry. 10740 MERIDIAN AVE N, STE 107 98133 #067-01-1969 L1970 N IM *020 †20,75

GINSBERG, Steven. 201 16TH AVE E, GROUP HEALTH PERMANENTE 98112 #035-08-1984 L1998 ON IM *050 †20

GLADDEN, Debra R. ■ 98118 #005-12-1989 L1990 IM *020 †20

GLADSTONE, Laura Jean. 515 MINOR AVE, STE 200 98104 #028-02-1999 L2005 CRS *100 †85,10

GLANCEY, Kelley Kennedy. 7210 ROOSEVELT WAY NE 98115 #010-01-2002 L2002 FM *020 †18

GLASNER, Steven Duane. 200 15TH AVE E 98112 #037-01-1987 L1991 PTH *020 †50

GLASS, Ian Amos. 4800 SAND POINT WAY NE, CH-65 98105 #671-01-1979 L2000 MG *020 †19

GLASS, Joseph Patrick. UNIV OF WASHINGTON, SURGICAL PATHOLOGY FELLOWS 98195 #035-15-1996 L2007 SP *012 †18,50

GLAUBER, Dennis T. 4000 AURORA AVE N 98103 #836-01-1949 L1978 AN *071

GLAVAN, Bradford Joseph. 1959 NE PACIFIC ST, BOX 356421 98195 #041-01-2003 L2003 PCC *012 †20

GLEASON, Christine. UNIV OF WASHINGTON, DEPT PEDS BOX 356320 98195 #035-45-1979 L1997 PD NPM *050 †20

GLEASON, Terrence Hughes. 200 15TH AVE E DEPT PTH 98112 #005-02-1963 L1968 CLP GP *020 †50

GLEASON, Timothy Peter. 600 BROADWAY, STE 170 98122 #035-45-1989 L1994 DR *020 †80

GLEESON, Francis Gerald. 3207 NE 125TH ST 98125 #054-04-1958 L1959 FM OS *020

GLENN, Lucille Wallenberg. 1100 9TH AVE 98101 #067-01-1981 L1984 DR *020 †80

GLENN, Michael Gerard. 1100 9TH AVE, VIRGINIA MASON MED CTR 98101 #005-02-1981 L1986 HNS OTO *030 †45

GLENNY, Robb Wm. 1959 NE PACIFIC ST, BOX 356522 98195 #051-01-1984 L1987 PUD IM *020 †20

GLESER, Malcolm Anthony. 401 2ND AVE S STE 200 98104 #035-46-1968 L1970 *062

GLEW, Gwen M. 4800 SAND POINT WAY NE, BOX 5371 98105 #023-07-1996 L1999 DBP *012 †55

GLICKERMAN, David J. ■ 98125 #035-03-1983 L1989 DR *020 †80

GLICKMAN, Kenneth Irving. 200 16TH AVE E 98112 #054-04-1961 L1967 PD *071 †55

GLOBERMAN, Stacy Ivan. 9800 4TH AVE NE 98115 #005-02-1985 L1987 FM *020 †20

GLOMSET, John A. WASH U REG PRIM RESCH CTR 98105 #858-03-1960 OS *050

GLOSTER, Robert Carey. 700 MINOR AVE 98104 #010-01-1974 L1975 EM IM *040 †20,16

GLOVER, Dianne Michele. 1101 MADISON ST, STE 800 98104 #034-01-1978 L1981 PD ID *020 †55

GLOYD, Park Willis. 2409 N 45TH ST 98103 #041-01-1948 L1949 ORS *071 †40

GLOYD, Stephen Stewart. ■ 98107 #016-02-1973 L2003 PHP FM *040 †18

GLUCK, Michael. 1100 9TH AVE 98101 #005-14-1981 L1982 GE IM *020 †20

GMUR, Frances Wyman. 1221 MADISON ST, STE 910 98104 #035-46-1989 L2001 PD *020 †55

GODWIN, Joseph David, II. 325 9TH AVE 98104 #005-11-1971 L1986 DR *020 †80

GOFF, Barbara Ann. 1959 NE PACIFIC ST, UWMC- BOX 356460 98195 #041-01-1986 L1992 OBG *020 †20

GOFFE, Bernard Saul. 1730 MINOR AVE STE 1000 98101 #054-04-1962 L1963 D DMP *020 †15

GOFORTH, Mabel Louise. ■ 98105 #048-02-1939 L1946 OBG *071 †30

GOGLIN, W Henry. ■ 98103 #011-02-1961 L1965 R NM *071

GOITEIN, Lara. ■ 98136 #024-01-1998 L2002 DR *012 †20

GOLAN, Ralph Theodore. 7522 20TH AVE NE 98115 #035-03-1975 L1976 GPM *020

GOLD, Mitchell Howard. 3005 1ST AVE 98121 #016-01-1993 L1993 U *100

GOLD, Philip Jordan. 1221 MADISON ST 98104 #011-02-1991 L1993 ON *020 †20

GOLDBERG, Sheldon Zackery. 515 MINOR AVE, STE 170 98104 #035-19-1978 L1988 HEM ON *020 †30

GOLDBERG, Stefan Vincent. 325 9TH AVE BOX 359776, SEATTLE KING COUNTY 98104 #007-02-1981 L1987 PUD IM *020 †20

GOLDBERG, Steven Lewis. 1959 NE PACIFIC ST, BOX 356155 98195 #019-02-1984 L1985 CD IM *020 †20

GOLDEN, Alana Shira. ■ 98105 #035-46-2005 L2005 CHN *012

GOLDEN, Jane Borkowski. 1560 N 115TH ST, STE G16 98133 #023-07-1994 L1996 ON *020 †20

GOLDEN, Matthew Robert. 325 9TH AVE BOX 359777, HARBORVIEW MEDICAL CENTER 98104 #023-07-1994 L1996 ID *020 †20

GOLDHAMMER, Philip. PO BOX 34697 98124 #007-02-1969 L1991 FM *071 †18

GOLDIN, Adam Bradley. 4800 SAND POINT WAY NE, CHILDRENS HOSPTIAL OF WISC 98105 #016-01-1997 L2001 PDS *100 †15

GOLDMAN, Allan J. 1229 MADISON ST STE 14 98104 #010-02-1974 L1979 AN *020 †05

GOLDMAN, Stephen Leon. 1229 MADISON ST STE 1410 98104 #056-06-1971 L1972 CRS GS *020 †10,85

GOLDSTEIN, Barry. 1660 S COLUMBIAN WAY, SCI&D SHG 128NAT 98108 #005-14-1986 L1990 PM *020 †60

GOLDSTEIN, Erika Ann. 325 9TH AVE BOX 359780, ADULT MEDICINE CLINIC 98104 #035-45-1981 L1982 GPM IM *020 †20

GOLDSTEIN, Lynn Carol. 1001 SW KLICKITAT WAY, STE 205 98134 #024-05-1979 L1982 PTH *020 †50

GOLDSTEIN, Robert. ■ 98118 #024-01-1937 L1937 IM HEM *071 †20

GOLDSTEIN, Robert Bruce. 1550 N 115TH ST, SURGICAL SVCS B-250 98133 #550-03-1997 L2001 AN *020 †05

GOLER, Karl Andrew. 125 16TH AVE E, NEUROSURGERY DEPARTMENT 98112 #038-06-1977 L1991 NS OS *020 †25

GOLOMBEK, Alison A. 400 LAKESIDE AVE S, APT 101 98144 #038-40-2002 L2002 CHP *050

GOMEZ, Oscar Gilberto. 4800 SAND POINT WAY NE, MEDICAL CENTER, SUITE 8G-1 98105 #264-01-1987 L2004 PDI *100 †20

GONCHAR, Marc David. 1145 BROADWAY, THE POLYCLINIC 98122 #035-47-1998 L2001 IM *020 †20

GONZALEZ, Elia Raquel. 1959 NE PACIFIC ST, BOX 356560 98195 #649-14-2002 L2006 P *012

GONZALEZ, Luz Maria. 4800 SAND POINT WAY NE G-0, CHILDREN'S HOSPITAL & REGI 98105 #054-04-2006 L2006 PD *012

GONZALEZ, Ruben. ■ 98117 #054-04-2008 *012

GONZALEZ-DILAN, Daniel. 1321 E OLIVE ST 98122 #054-04-1978 L1980 EM OM *020 †18,16

GOODE, Robert C. 550 17TH AVE STE 110, SWEDISH EXECUTIVE HEALTH C 98122 #048-04-1992 L1995 FM *020 †18 ‡

GOODELL, Brian Wayne. 747 BROADWAY 98122 #054-04-1966 L1971 IM ON *030 †20

GOODFRIED, Richard Mark. 747 BROADWAY 98122 #001-02-1995 L1998 EM *020 †16

GOODKIN, Robert. 325 9TH AVE, MAIL BOX 359766 98104 #016-42-1964 L1987 NS *072 †25

GOODMAN, Gary E. 1221 MADISON ST 2ND FL, SWEDISH CANCER INSTITUTE 98104 #016-11-1974 L1981 ON *050 †20

GOODMAN, Richard Bruce. 1660 S COLUMBIAN WAY, V A PUGET SOUND HLTH CARE 98108 #039-01-1982 L1986 PUD IM *020 †20

GOODMAN, Steven Robt. 6523 CALIFORNIA AVE SW, PMB 334 98136 #035-06-1984 L1986 PM OS *020 †60

GOODWIN, Mary Alice. 1959 NE PACIFIC ST RM C212, STAF AFFAIRS.GME BOX 35634 98195 #005-15-2001 L2001 CCP *100 †55

GOPAL, Ajay Kumar. 825 EASTLAKE AVE E, RM 6802 98109 #012-05-1993 L1997 ON *020 †20

GOPALANI, Sameer. 1229 MADISON ST STE 750 98104 #041-02-1997 L2001 OBG *020 †30

GORAI, Arthur S. 1420 5TH AVE, STE 375 98101 #054-04-1959 L1960 GP *020 †18

GORDEN, Jed Abraham. 515 MINOR AVE 98104 #047-05-1997 L1999 PCC *040 †20

GORDON, James Miller. 1570 N 115TH ST STE 14 98133 #038-06-1982 L1996 N *020 †75

GORGOS, Linda Marie. ■ 98144 #023-07-1995 L2006 ID *012

GORMAN, Annalisa Karen. 1229 MADISON ST STE 1480 98104 #054-04-1998 L2003 D *020 †15

GORMAN, Jennifer Diane. 1100 9TH AVE C1-MSO, VIRGINIA MASON MEDICAL CEN 98101 #054-04-1995 L2002 RHU IM *020 †20

GORMAN, Michael Robt. 1600 E JOHN ST 98112 #036-07-1978 L1983 OPH GS *020 †35

GORTNER, David Allen. 1100 9TH AVE C1-MSO, VIRGINIA MASON MEDICAL CEN 98101 #026-04-1967 L1975 IM *020 †20

GOSPE, Sidney Maloch, Jr. 4800 SAND POINT WAY NE, CHILDRENS HOSP 98105 #036-07-1981 L2000 CHN PD *012 †55 ‡

GOSS, Christopher Hooper. 1959 NE PACIFIC ST, CAMPUS BOX 356522 98195 #007-02-1992 L1997 PCC *020 †20

GOSS, J Richard. 325 9TH AVE, HARBORVIEW 98104 #040-02-1987 L1993 IM *020 †20

GOSWAMI, Gaurav K. PO BOX 354807, 1107 NE 45TH STREET SUIT 98195 #495-01-1987 L2004 VIR *020 †80

GOTCSIK, Marah Elizabeth. 1959 NE PACIFIC ST C2, UNIVERSITY OF WASH 98195 #041-01-2007 L2007 PD *012

GOTSHALL, Robert Allison. 200 16TH AVE E 98112 #005-02-1961 L1971 **N IM** *020 †20,75
GOTTHEIL, Edward. UNIVERSITY OF WA, NO 356560 98195 #048-12-1955 L2002 **P** *072 †75
GOTTHEIL, Ellen Frances. 4020 E MADISON ST STE 325 98112 #005-11-1982 L1989 **P** *020 †75
GOTTLIEB, Geoffrey S. 1959 NE PACIFIC ST, BOX 358070 98195 #016-42-1995 L1998 **ID** *020 †20
GOTTLIEB, Greg. 9661 46TH AVE SW 98136 #005-18-1979 L1985 **AN PD** *040 †05
GOTTLIEB, Jourdan Russell. 1600 E JEFFERSON ST, STE 501 98122 #038-06-1976 L1985 **PS GS** *020 †85,65
GOULART, Bernardo Haddock. 1959 NE PACIFIC ST 98195 #187-03-1997 L2005 **HO** *012
GOULD, Ryan Kierkegaard. ■ 98160 #021-01-2006 L2007 *012
GOULD, William Stuart. 11726 5TH AVE NE, C/O SHIRLEY BUDISELICK 98125 #041-01-1981 L1982 **FM** *020
GOWN, Allen Michael. 551 N 34TH ST, STE 100 98103 #035-46-1975 L1979 **PTH** *050 †50
GRABER, John Danl. 1100 9TH AVE M6-AC, VIRGINIA MASON MEDICAL CEN 98101 #023-07-1967 L1974 **CD IM** *020 †20
GRABOWSKI, Richard Barry. 1229 MADISON ST, STE 1290 98104 #035-03-1998 L2004 **D** *020 †15
GRADY, Christina Tewksbur. ■ 98144 #054-04-2008 *012
GRADY, Richard Welker. 4800 SAND POINT WAY NE 98105 #025-01-1990 L1996 **UP** *020 †95
GRAFF, Gary B. 4739 UNIVERSITY WAY NE # 1 98105 #016-06-1986 L1990 **FM** *020 †18
GRAHAM, C Benjamin. 1959 NE PACIFIC ST 98195 #054-04-1958 L1959 **PDR R** *071 †80
GRAHAM, Elinor Ann. 325 9TH AVE, HMC DEPT PEDS 2A-53 98104 #035-45-1970 L1980 **PD** *020 †55
GRAHAM, Susan Marie. HEALTH SCIENCES ANNEX #R13, DAID, U WASHINGTON 98195 #067-01-2000 L2003 *100 †20 ‡
GRAJALES-ZWEIGLE, M. ■ 98115 #649-01-1975 L1992 **EM** *020
GRALOW, Julie Ruth. 825 EASTLAKE AVE E, MAIL STOP G-3200 98109 #005-06-1988 L1992 **ON** *020 †20
GRANDE, Lucinda Alpert. 1959 NE PACIFIC ST, U OF W-HS AFFAIRS BOX 3563 98195 #054-04-2004 L2004 **AN** *100
GRANT, Brian L. 1200 6TH AVE, #1800 PARK PL 98101 #025-12-1978 L1978 **P** *030 †75
GRAUNKE, Kathleen Elsie. 6800 E GREEN LAKE WAY N, GREENLAKE PRIMARY CARE 98115 #056-05-1977 L1990 **PD** *020 †55
GRAVATT, Andrea R. 1509 44TH AVE SW 98116 #041-12-1979 L2001 **PD OS** *020 †55
GRAVENKEMPER, Chas Forest. ■ 98112 #038-41-1959 L1965 **IM** *071 †20
GRAVETT, Michael Glen. 1959 NE PACIFIC ST, DEPT OB 98195 #005-14-1977 L1978 **MFM ID** *020 †30
GRAY, Fredianne. ■ 98105 #054-04-2000 L2000 **P** *100
GRAY, Heidi Joy. ■ 98119 #005-14-1997 L1999 **OBG** *020 †30
GRAY, Kristen Anne. ■ 98115 #034-01-2008 *012
GRAYSTON, J Thos. PO BOX 357236, EPIDEMIOLOGY 98195 #016-02-1948 L1961 **GPM IM** *050 †20,70
GREANEY, Ann Margaret. 600 UNIVERSITY ST, STE 1200 98101 #051-01-1992 L1992 **FM** *020 †18
GREAVES, Richard F. ■ 98102 #005-11-1952 L1952 **AN** *071 †05
GREEN, Benjamin Michael. 1601 5TH AVE STE 830 98101 #033-06-2004 L2007 **FM** *020 †18
GREEN, Beverly Beth. 1730 MINOR AVE, STE 1600 98101 #038-43-1976 L1982 **FM PHP** *020 †18
GREEN, Damian Jonathan. ■ 98115 #038-40-2000 L2004 **ON** *100 †20
GREEN, Douglas Erwin. ■ 98112 #050-02-1991 L2007 **DR** *020 †80
GREEN, John Robt, III. 3950 MONTLAKE BLVD RM 148, UWMC- BOX 354060 98195 #038-41-1991 L2002 **OSM ORS** *020 †40
GREEN, Thomas C. 1101 MADISON ST STE 1400 98104 #033-06-1979 L1985 **U** *020 †95
GREEN, Thomas Morrison. 1100 9TH AVE, VIRGINIA MASON CLNC X6-ORT 98101 #054-04-1969 L1970 **ORS** *020 †40
GREENBAUM, Carla J. 4225 ROOSEVELT WAY NE 98105 #043-01-1981 L1982 **END IM** *020 †18
GREENBAUM, Marianne Clare. 1229 MADISON ST, STE 1150 98104 #016-42-1994 L1999 **DR** *020 †80
GREENBERG, Deborah Lynn. 4245 ROOSEVELT WAY NE, STE 354775 98105 #028-02-1990 L1993 **IM** *020 †20
GREENBERG, Jordan Wm. ■ 98112 #024-07-1985 L2006 **CCP** *020 †55
GREENBERG, Philip Dennis. 1959 NE PACIFIC ST BOX 356, UNIVERSITY OF WASHINGTON 98195 #035-08-1971 L1976 **IG ON** *050 †20
GREENE, Courtney C. PO BOX 356340, GRADUATE MEDICAL EDUCATION 98195 #048-13-2003 L2003 **IM** *020 †20
GREENE, Harry Leon, Jr. 2601 4TH AVE 98121 #023-07-1969 L1979 **CD** *020 †20
GREENE, Martin Lee. 515 MINOR AVE, STE 200 98104 #024-01-1965 L1969 **GE IM** *020 †20
GREENE, Steven Louis. 200 15TH AVE E, GROUP HLTH CORPERATIVE DER 98112 #036-01-1980 L1984 **D** *020 †15 ‡
GREENLEE, Theodore K. 1959 NE PACIFIC ST, UWMC- BOX 358280 98195 #016-06-1959 L1962 **ORS** *020 †40
GREER, Benjamin Edward. 1959 NE PACIFIC ST, UWMC BOX 356460 98195 #041-01-1966 L1980 **GO** *040 †30
GREER, Cynthia. 4020 E MADISON ST STE 240 98112 #007-02-1978 L1980 **P** *020 †75
GREER, Hilton Thos, Jr. 1959 NE PACIFIC ST, UWMC- BOX 356390 98195 #027-01-1974 L1978 **FM** *020 †18
GREER, Michael Edward. 509 OLIVE WAY STE 1349 98101 #041-09-1976 L1982 **OBG EM** *020 †30
GREER, Pamela Renee. 509 OLIVE WAY, STE 1349 98101 #041-09-1976 L1982 **DR** *072
GREFENSON, Leslie. 206 3RD AVE S, PIONEER SQUARE CLN 98104 #054-04-1992 L1995 **IM** *020 †20
GREGG, Mary Grace. 747 BROADWAY 98122 #028-02-1980 L1987 **TS GS** *020 †85,90
GREINER, William Evans. 600 BROADWAY, STE 170 98122 #035-03-1977 L1978 **DR FM** *020 †80
GREKIN, Paul Martin. 1700 AIRPORT WAY S 98134 #025-01-1984 L1985 **P ADP** *020 †20
GRENLEY, Robert Michael. 600 BROADWAY, STE 320 98122 #054-04-1980 L1981 **PS** *020 †65
GRETCH, David Richard. 1959 NE PACIFIC ST, MSC 359300 98195 #018-03-1990 L1993 **PTH** *020 †50
GREVES, Helene Marie. ■ 98103 #041-01-2003 L2003 **PD** *100 †55
GRICE, Jeffrey L. 1600 E JOHN ST 98112 #048-15-1993 L1996 **OBG** *020 †30
GRIEP, Robert John. 1229 MADISON ST 98104 #048-02-1958 L1971 **NM IM** *020 †28,20
GRIFFIN, Thomas Ward. UNIVERSITY HOSPITAL, UNIVERSITY OF WASHINGTON 98195 #030-05-1970 L1973 **RO** *020 †80
GRIFFITHS, Richard Craig. 600 BROADWAY STE 460, AMBULATORY SURGERY CENTER 98122 #010-01-1972 L1981 **AN** *020 †05
GRIGG, Aaron Wells. ■ 98105 #048-04-2007 L2007 **PD** *012

GRIGG, Eliot B. ■ 98116 #010-01-2007 L2007 **AN** *012
GRIGGS, Paul B. 1100 9TH AVE 98101 #028-46-1985 L1990 **OPH** *020 †35 ‡
GRIM, Jonathan Ezra. ■ 98117 #001-02-1999 L2002 **ON** *100 †20
GRIM, Linda Fues. 10330 MERIDIAN AVE N, NORTH SEATTLE PEDIATRICS 98133 #001-02-1996 L1999 **PD** *020 †55
GRIMLEY, Jaime Lynn. 925 SENECA ST, DEPT OF DIAG RAD 98101 #025-01-2005 L2006 **DR** *012
GRIMLUND, Birgit Heidrun. 9800 4TH AVE NE, NORTHGATE GROUP HEALTH CTR 98115 #054-04-1994 L1996 **FM** *020 †18
GRIMM, Erin Elyse. ■ 98103 #018-03-2004 L2005 **PTH** *012
GRIMM, Huber K. ■ 98125 #028-34-1949 L1950 **FM GS** *071
GRIMSRUD, Emily Geneva. ■ 98102 #054-04-2008 L2008 *012
GROMKO, Linda Jo. 200 W MERCER ST STE 104 98119 #054-04-1984 L1985 **FM** *020 †18
GROO, Stephen Conrad. 1001 SW KLICKITAT WAY, STE 205 98134 #010-01-1986 L1998 **PTH** *020 †50
GROSS, Abigail Louise. 550 16TH AVE STE 100 98122 #054-04-2002 L2002 **FM** *020 †18
GROSS, Joel Alan. 325 9TH AVE BOX 359728, HARBORVIEW MED CTR 98104 #005-19-1994 L2001 **DR** *020 †80
GROSS, Kenneth M. 1145 BROADWAY 98122 #035-48-1976 L1982 **END** *020 †20
GROSSMAN, David Campbell. 1730 MINOR AVE, STE 1600 98101 #005-14-1982 L1988 **PD PHP** *030 †55
GROTE, Peter N. 4464 FREMONT AVE N, STE 103 98103 #035-03-1991 L1993 **FM** *020 †18
GROUDINE, Mark Terry. 1959 NE PACIFIC ST, UWMC BOX 356043 98195 #041-01-1975 L1980 **R** *020
GROVER, Sheena. 1101 MADISON ST STE 200, HEADACHE AND PAIN MANAGEME 98104 #495-08-1989 L2000 **N** *020 †75
GRUBE, Matthew. ■ 98102 #005-12-2007 L2007 **TY** *012
GRUBER, William Anthony. 10330 MERIDIAN AVE N, STE 250 98133 #028-34-1970 L1974 **ORS** *071 †40
GRUEN, Russell Lindsay. 1959 NE PACIFIC ST, UNIV OF WASHINGTON/HARBORV 98195 #143-02-1992 L2005 *100
GRUNDY, Robert Duncan. ■ 98112 #803-03-1970 L1972 **EM IM** *020 †20,16
GRUSS, Joseph Selwyn. 325 9TH AVE, ZA-16 98104 #836-01-1969 L1990 *020
GUDE, Jose Antonio. 600 UNIVERSITY ST, STE 1200 98101 #021-05-1993 L2000 **HOS** *020 †20
GUERRA, Juan Julio. 600 UNIVERSITY ST, STE 1200 98101 #005-11-1997 L1999 **FM** *020 †18
GUERRA, Sierra P. 600 UNIVERSITY ST, STE 1200 98101 #005-11-1998 L2001 **FM** *020 †18
GUGEL, Anja Patricia. 747 BROADWAY, SWEDISH MED CTR 98122 #409-05-2000 L2004 **FM** *020
GUINEE, Donald G, Jr. 1100 9TH AVE, DEPT OF PATHOLOGY C6-PTH 98101 #021-01-1986 L1998 **PTH** *020 †50
GUNBY, Thomas Clarke. 1100 9TH AVE, MS C8-GIM 98101 #054-04-1980 L1985 **IM** *050 †20
GUNDLE, Michael J. 2910 E MADISON ST 98112 #019-02-1970 L1987 **P PYA** *020 †75
GUNN, Martin Lee David. 1107 NE 45TH ST, STE 440 98105 #671-02-1995 L2002 *020
GUNTHER, Daniel Farrell. 4800 SAND POINT WAY NE, MAIL STOP - M 1-3 98105 #005-19-1992 L1998 **PDE** *020 †20
GUNTHEROTH, Warren G. PO BOX 356320, UNIVERSITY OF WASHINGTON 98195 #024-01-1952 L1958 **PDC PD** *020 †20
GUO, Shunhua. ■ 98105 #243-97-1992 **NEP** *100
GUPTA, Neel Kamal. ■ 98121 #005-19-2006 L2006 **IM** *012
GUSE, Sabrina Elsie. ■ 98103 #056-05-2005 L2005 **PD** *012
GUSTAFSON, Eric Albert. 1959 NE PACIFIC ST, BOX 346340 98195 #008-01-2004 L2004 **PD** *012 †55
GUSTAFSON, Harold C. 1717 NW MARKET ST, MARKET STREET CLINIC 98107 #054-15-1969 **FM** *071
GUSTIN, Allen Nathaniel. ■ 98121 #045-01-1996 L2007 **CCA** *040 †05
GUTIERREZ, Robert Lee. 1959 NE PACIFIC ST, BOX 356340 98195 #054-04-2001 L2001 **DR** *100 †80
GUTMAN, Jonathan Aaron. ■ 98105 #035-19-2002 L2006 **HO** *012 †20
GUYER, Robert Edward. 4959 NE LAURELCREST LN 98105 #054-04-1962 L1964 **GP** *020
GUYTON, Sigrid Pakula. 1145 BROADWAY, THE POLYCLINIC 98122 #024-01-1976 L1991 **GS AS** *020 †18
GWINN, Ryder Patten. 600 UNIVERSITY ST STE 1200, SWEDISH PHYSICIAN DIVISION 98101 #005-14-1996 L2004 **NS** *020
GYURKOCZA, Boglarka. ■ 98121 #473-01-1999 L2006 **HO** *100 †20
HA, Richard Sunghun. UNIV OF WASHINGTON MED CTR, DEPT OF RADIOLOGY BOX 3571 98195 #054-04-2005 L2005 **DR** *012
HABERKERN, Charles Martin. 4800 SAND POINT WAY NE, DEPT OF ANESTHESIOLOGY 98105 #035-01-1974 L1976 **PD AN** *020 †55,05
HACKMAN, Robert Cordell. 1124 COLUMBIA ST 98104 #005-11-1971 L1977 **PTH ID** *050 †50
HACKWORTH, Jeremy Robert. 925 SENECA ST, MEDICAL CENTER 98101 #028-34-2001 L2007 **PMM** *012
HADDAD, George Edmond. 747 BROADWAY, SWEDISH MEDICAL CENTER 98122 #035-06-1994 L2001 **IM** *020 †20
HADLAND, Brandon Kenneth. 4800 SAND POINT WAY NE, REGIONAL M 98105 #028-02-2006 L2006 **PD** *012
HAECK, Phillip Carl. 901 BOREN AVE STE 1650 98104 #025-12-1980 L1983 **PS** *020 †65
HAFERMANN, Mark David. 4000 15TH AVE NE 98105 #026-04-1959 L1960 **RO** *071 †80
HAGEMAN, Joseph Wm. 10030 15TH AVE SW 98146 #006-11-1955 L1956 **GP** *071
HAGEN, Christopher B. 2006 14TH AVE W 98119 #054-04-2003 L2004 **AN** *100
HAGEN, Jennifer Elizabeth. ■ 98121 #038-06-2008 *012
HAGEN, John M V. 1600 BELL PLAZA RM 403 98101 #035-45-1950 L1953 **OM IM** *071
HAGGITT, Rodger Christian. 1959 NE PACIFIC ST, MSC 359300 98195 #047-06-1967 L1984 **PTH** *050 †50
HAGIWARA, Shotaro. ■ 98121 #572-22-1990 L2001 *100
HAGMAN, Melissa Mae. 1959 NE PACIFIC ST, BOX 356429 98195 #054-04-1999 L2001 **IM PLM** *020 †20
HAGOPIAN, William Arthur. 4225 ROOSEVELT WAY NE 98105 #016-02-1987 L1989 **END IM** *020 †20
HAGUE, Andrew. 1959 NE PACIFIC ST, HSB C212 98195 #067-01-2004 L2004 **AN** *012
HAHN, Si Houn. 4800 SAND PT WAY NE A6901, UNIVERSITY OF WASHINGTON 98105 #583-03-1983 L2006 **IMG** *020 †18
HAINING, Robert Gerard. 1570 N 115TH ST STE 11 98133 #005-11-1956 L1964 **IMG OS** *020
HAKIMI, Kevin Nima. UNIV OF WASHINGTON, DEPT OF REHAB MED 98195 #025-07-2000 L2004 **PM** *020 †60
HAKIMIAN, Shahin. 325 9TH AVE BOX 359745, HARBORVIEW MED CTR 98104 #028-02-2000 L2004 **N** *020 †75

■ = Address Information Privacy Protected

HAKKI, Morgan Basil. 1100 FAIRVIEW AVE N, MS-D3100 98109 #041-13-1997 L2000 ID *020 †20

HAKOMORI, Senitiroh. 201 ELLIOTT AVE W, STE 305 98119 #572-10-1950 OS *050

HALAMAY, Kate Elizabeth. 4800 SAND POINT WAY NE, REGIONAL M 98105 #041-01-2006 L2006 PD *012

HALAR, Eugen. 1959 NE PACIFIC ST BOX 3, UNIVERSITY OF WASHISHINGTO 98195 #957-01-1959 L1970 PM *072 †60

HALARNAKAR, Vasant G. 1600 E OLIVE ST 98122 #495-01-1983 L1991 P *020

HALBACH, Susan Margaret. 4800 SAND POINT WAY NE, MAILSTOP A7931 98105 #016-02-2004 L2004 PN *012 †55

HALE, C Gordon. 500 17TH AVE 98122 #005-12-1959 L1961 CD IM *071

HALE, Chas Harrison, Jr. ■ 98102 #039-01-1961 L1967 P PFP *062 †75

HALL, Akiko Eileen. ■ 98125 #005-02-2007 L2007 PD *012

HALL, Dale Gordon. 747 BROADWAY 98122 #007-02-1967 L1969 TS PDS *020 †85,90

HALL, David Connolly, III. 564 NE RAVENNA BLVD, PUGET SOUND 98115 #054-04-1978 L1979 CHP P *020

HALL, Judith L Goslin. 4800 SAND POINT WAY NE 98105 #054-04-1966 L1972 PD END *040 †55,19

HALL, Kathryn Colby. ■ 98102 #054-04-1988 L2004 P *020 †75

HALL, Margaret Langan. 1536 N 115TH ST, SUMMIT CARDIOLOGY 98133 #054-04-1982 L1983 CD IM *020 †20

HALL, Mcclure Huntington. 1221 MADISON ST, STE 520 98104 #051-01-1963 L1969 R *071 †80

HALL, Robert Alan. 1100 9TH AVE C1-MSO, VIRGINIA MASON MEDICAL CEN 98101 #051-01-1987 L1994 TS *020 †85,90

HALL, Steven Michael. 747 BROADWAY 98122 #049-01-1982 L1987 OS *020 †18

HALL, Yoshio N. 1660 S COLUMBIAN WAY, BUILDING 100, RDU S111 98108 #048-04-1999 L2007 IM *100 †20

HALLAHAN, Andrew R. 4800 SAND POINT WAY NE, DEPT HEM-ONC 98105 #143-03-1991 L2001 PHO *020

HALLAM, Danial Kelly. 325 9TH AVE, BOX 359728 98104 #005-11-1989 L2000 RNR *020 †80

HALLDORSON, Jeffrey Burke. 1959 NE PACIFIC ST, BOX 356174 98195 #025-01-1992 L2003 GS *020 †85

HALLEY, Carolyn Swope. ■ 98144 #054-04-2004 L2004 FM *020 †18

HALLINGBYE, Thor Martinse. ■ 98105 #054-04-2008 L2008 P *020

HALLSTRAND, Janie G. 4800 SAND POINT WAY NE, CHILDRENS REG MED CTR 98105 #050-02-1993 L1997 PD *020 †55

HALLSTRAND, Teal Sterling. 1959 NE PACIFIC ST, PO BOX 356522 98195 #054-04-1993 L1997 PCC *020 †20

HALPERIN, Abigail C. 1600 E JEFFERSON ST, MEDALIA UPTOWN 98122 #035-46-1983 L1984 FM *074 †18

HALPERN, Jeffrey Stein. 925 SENECA ST 98101 #047-06-1991 L1993 IM *020 †20

HALSELL, John Tucker. 1229 MADISON STE 900 98104 #048-02-1957 L1972 R GS *071 †85,80

HALTER, Rebecca Jean. 2600 SW HOLDEN ST 98126 #049-01-2001 L2003 FM *020 †18

HAMBLIN, Mark Wm. 1660 S COLUMBIAN WAY, GRECC 182B 98108 #005-18-1982 L1990 P *020 †75

HAMILTON, Francis Norman. 201 16TH AVE E 98112 #054-04-1966 L1971 AN *020 †05

HAMILTON, Glen Willard. 2324 EASTLAKE AVE E, STE 500 98102 #054-04-1965 L1967 NM CD *020 †20,28

HAMILTON, Steven Reel. 600 BROADWAY, STE 170 98122 #005-15-1986 L1991 N *020 †75

HAMLAT, Christian Abdenno. ■ 98103 #005-18-2004 L2004 GS *012

HAMLIN, Nason Peabody. 1959 NE PACIFIC ST, BOX 356119 98195 #024-01-1972 L1995 IM *020 †20

HAMLIN, William B. 1229 MADISON ST, STE 500 98104 #048-12-1961 L1966 CLP PTH *071 †50

HAMM, John Edward. 515 MINOR AVE, STE 220 98104 #040-02-1972 L1974 P PFP *020 †75

HAMMAR, Ned Jacob. 550 16TH AVE STE 100, PROVIDENCE FAMILY MEDICINE 98122 #023-07-2005 L2005 FP *012

HAMMER, Charles John. 1100 9TH AVE # M6-AC, VIRGINIA MASON MED CTR 98101 #023-01-1954 L1960 D *071 †15

HAMMOND, Margaret C. 1660 S COLUMBIAN WAY # 117 98108 #056-06-1979 L1980 PM *020 †60

HAMMOND, William P. 515 MINOR AVE STE 170, MINOR & JAMES MEDICAL, PLL 98104 #024-07-1972 L1973 HO ON *020 †20

HAMOR, Kathi Lynn. ■ 98117 #005-15-2007 L2007 PTH *012

HAMPSON, Neil Bradley. 1100 9TH AVE 98101 #054-04-1981 L1988 UM P *020 †20

HAMRICK, Marcie Renee. 6300 9TH AVE NE, STE 300 98115 #048-04-1999 L1999 FM *020 †18

HAN, Kyung Hi. 1145 BROADWAY 98122 #001-02-1992 L1995 GE *020 †20

HANASH, Samir Maroun. 1212 ALOHA ST, MS-C849 98109 #065-01-1972 L1978 HEM PD *050 †55

HANDLEY, Matthew Ross. 460 N 42ND ST 98103 #005-19-1984 L1986 FM *020 †18

HANDSFIELD, H Hunter. 1100 DEXTER AVE N, STE 400 98109 #035-01-1968 L1970 PHP ID *050 †20

HANEL, Douglas Paul. 325 9TH AVE, BOX 359798 98104 #028-34-1977 L1992 HS *040 †40

HANEVOLD, Coral Dawn. 4800 SAND POINT WAY NE, MAILSTOP A-7931 98105 #012-01-1982 L2007 PN NEP *020 †55

HANEY, Leland Forest. 98104 #010-01-1962 L1966 DR *071

HANKES, Lynn Robt. 720 OLIVE WAY STE 1010 98101 #010-02-1964 L1993 ADM U *071 †95

HANNA, Jocelyn Denise. 1401 MADISON ST STE 100, MEDICINE RESIDE 98104 #036-01-2006 L2007 P *012

HANNA, Rabi. ■ 98115 #875-02-2002 L2007 PHO *012 †55

HANNIBAL, Mark Charles. 4800 SAND PT WAY NE, MEDICAL GENETICS M2-9 98105 #025-01-1994 L1999 MG *020 †19,55

HANNIFAN, Kathleen Anne. 4800 SAND POINT WAY NE, CHILDREN'S HOSP & REG MED 98105 #054-04-2006 L2006 PD *012

HANNON, Elena Maria. 1101 MADISON ST, STE 900 98104 #007-02-1995 L1999 OBG *020 †30

HANRAHAN, Kelley Ann. 1229 MADISON ST, STE 1500 98104 #017-20-1994 L1998 OBG *020 †30

HANSCOM, David Alfred. 1600 E JEFFERSON ST, ORTHOPAEDICS 98122 #005-12-1979 L1980 ORS *020 †40

HANSEN, Scott Matthew. 1131 N 94TH ST A 98103 #056-06-2004 L2004 P *012

HANSEN, Sigvard T, Jr. 325 9TH AVE DEPT ORTHO, BOX 359798 98104 #054-04-1961 L1967 OFA OTR *040 †40

HANSEN, Thomas Nanastad. PO BOX 5371, MS T-0111 98105 #048-04-1973 L2006 NPM PD *050 †55

HANSING, Charles Earl. 747 BROADWAY 98122 #041-01-1965 L1971 CD IM *071 †20

HANSON, Craig Curtis. 9730 3RD AVE NE, STE 202 98115 #018-03-1978 L1979 DR VIR *020 †80

HANSON, Daniel Jos. 1100 9TH AVE G1-MSO, VIRGINIA MASON MEDICAL CEN 98101 #046-01-1991 L1993 IM *020 †20

HANSON, James Danl. 3207 NE 125TH ST 98125 #016-06-1970 L1972 IM *020 †20

HANSON, James Marshal. 1221 MADISON ST STE 400 98104 #056-05-1971 L1972 GS VS *020 †85

HANSON, Matthew Perry. ■ 98115 #054-04-2003 L2005 IM *100 †20

HANSON, Vivien Webb. ■ 98199 #054-04-1958 L1959 FM PHP *040 †18

HAO, Zales Ong. ■ 98118 #748-09-1971 P *020

HARBINE, Kasey Lee. 1959 NE PACIFIC ST RM C2, CAMPUS BOX 356340 98195 #054-04-2002 L2002 IM *020 †20

HARDER, Eric Michael. 1145 BROADWAY 98122 #028-02-1972 L1979 GE IM *020 †20

HARDY, John Sherman, Jr. 4540 SAND POINT WAY NE, STE 200 98105 #005-06-1968 L1998 A IG *020 †20,03

HARGISS, James Leonard. 1602 43RD AVE E # 21B 98112 #028-34-1945 L1948 OPH *040 †35

HARIDAS, Rajesh Parsotam. ■ 98115 #836-05-1985 L1992 AN *100

HARLAN, John Marshall. 325 9TH AVE, HARBORVIEW MEDICAL CENTER 98104 #016-02-1973 L1976 HEM ON *050 †20

HARLEY, John Duncan. 1660 S COLUMBIAN WAY 98108 #028-02-1966 L1969 DR *020 †80

HARLIN, Vivian E J Krause. ■ 98133 #040-02-1950 L1951 GPM GP *071

HARMON, Kimberly Garrison. 1959 NE PACIFIC ST, MSC 359300 98195 #017-20-1993 L1997 ISM *020 †18

HARP, Larry Wayne. U OF WA SCH OF MED 98105 #054-04-1979 *020

HARPER, Amy Elwell. 201 16TH AVE E 98112 #005-06-1997 L2003 GS *020 †85

HARRAST, Mark Anthony. 1959 NE PACIFIC ST, UNIV OF WASH BOX 356490 98195 #016-06-1996 L2001 PRS PM *020 †60

HARRELL, Barbara Blain. 1101 MADISON ST 98104 #054-04-1981 L1982 OBG *020 †30

HARRINGTON, Robert Deasy. 357190, UNIV OF WASHINGTON, T-148A HEALTH SCIENCES BLD 98195 #024-07-1983 L1989 ID IM *040 †20

HARRIS, Albert Basil. UNIV.OF WAS.MC/1959 NE PAC, DEPT OF NEURO SURG RI-20 98195 #001-02-1954 L1967 NS *071 †25

HARRIS, Bradley Rennie. 1145 BROADWAY 98122 #035-45-1976 L1977 IM *020 †20

HARRIS, Geoffrey Webb. 1560 N 115TH ST, STE 207 98133 #054-04-1979 L1982 IM *020 †20

HARRIS, George Christian. 8420 DAYTON AVE N 98103 #028-34-1962 L1967 P OS *020 †75

HARRIS, Jeffrey Randall. 1107 NE 45TH ST, STE 200 98105 #048-12-1978 L1984 PHP IM *030 †20,70

HARRIS, John R, Jr. 747 BROADWAY 98122 #051-04-1985 L1985 EM *020 †20

HARRIS, Kalynne. PO BOX 356421, UNIV OF WASHINGTON 98195 #054-04-2007 L2007 IM *012

HARRIS, Kathryn Alice. 1560 N 115TH ST STE 207 98133 #054-04-1979 L1982 IM *020 †20

HARRIS, Richard Rudolph. 118 17TH AVE E # 1 98112 #007-02-1994 L1996 FM *020 †18

HARRIS, Sheryl Lezada. 925 SENECA ST 98101 #010-03-1996 L1998 FM *020 †18

HARRIS, Tyler James. PO BOX 356421, UNIV OF WASHINGTON 98195 #054-04-2007 L2007 IM *012

HARRIS, William Proctor. 325 9TH AVE BOX 359702, HARBORVIEW MEDICAL CENTER 98104 #035-01-2001 L2001 HO *012 †20

HARRISON, David Arnold. ■ 98105 #005-19-2003 L2007 PYM *012

HARRUFF, Richard Chas. 325 9TH AVE, MAIL STOP MS 359792 98104 #017-20-1976 L1993 PTH *040 †50

HARRY, Eric Douglas. 4800 SAND POINT WAY NE, P O 5371 98105 #040-02-1999 L2002 CCP *020 †55

HART, Laura Jeannine. 4800 SAND POINT WAY NE 98105 #038-06-1987 L1997 U GS *020 †95

HART, Michael Jude. 1221 MADISON ST STE 1411 98104 #008-01-1971 L1978 GS *020 †85

HARTLEY, Carol Astrid. 925 SENECA ST 98101 #040-02-1993 L1993 IM *020 †20

HARTMAN, Abigail Riblet. ■ 98112 #035-45-2002 *100

HARTMANN, Eric Geo Gordon. 747 BROADWAY 98122 #067-01-1973 L1983 EM *030 †16

HARTQUIST, Glenn Alan. ■ 98115 #026-04-1958 L1960 FM *071 †18

HARTZOG, Grady R, III. 1100 9TH AVE C1-MSO, VIRGINIA MASON MEDICAL CEN 98101 #011-03-1982 L1996 DR *020 †80

HARVEY, Anna Marie. 701 N 36TH ST, STE 410 98103 #048-13-1987 L1990 P *020 †75

HARVEY, David Allen. 4464 FREMONT AVE N, STE 103 98103 #054-04-1993 L1993 FM *020 †18

HARVEY, Susan Meinholtz. 1101 MADISON ST, STE 950 98104 #054-04-1987 L1989 OBG *020 †30

HASCHE-KLUENDER, H. 747 BROADWAY 98122 #025-01-1970 L1971 AN *020 †05 ‡

HASELEY, David Richard. 1229 MADISON ST, STE 1150 98104 #035-01-1989 L1998 NM *020 †80,28

HASELEY, Leah Ann. 325 9TH AVE, BOX 359764 98104 #035-01-1990 L1998 NEP *020 †20

HASELKORN, Jodie Kangas. 1660 S COLUMBIAN WAY, RCS 117 98108 #021-05-1985 L1986 PM PHP *020 †60

HASHIMOTO, Beverly Emiko. 1100 9TH AVE G1-MSO, VIRGINIA MASON MED CENTER 98101 #005-11-1978 L1985 DR *020 †80

HASHISAKI, Geraldine Ann. 1133 17TH AVE E 98112 #054-04-1971 L1974 FM *020 †18

HASHITATE, Mari Mary. ■ 98125 #041-01-1999 L2002 PHO *100 †55

HASKEY, Robert Stanley. 1800 9TH AVE, MS S515 98101 #019-02-1970 L1976 GS *030 †85

HASNAIN, Saif. ■ 98102 #054-04-2008 *012

HASSELBRACK, Robert. 10740 MERIDIAN AVE N, STE G3 98133 #005-12-1963 L1964 PTH *020 †50

HASSELQUIST, Mary Beth. 200 15TH AVE E CNB-2, GROUP HEALTH COOPERATIVE 98112 #026-08-1980 L1989 OBG *020 †30

HASTETTER, Nikolaus Josef. ■ 98104 #407-16-1951 L1961 GP *075

HATFIELD, Kevin Stewart. 509 OLIVE WAY, STE 900 98101 #038-06-1999 L2001 FM *020 †18

HATSUKAMI, Thomas Susumu. 1660 S COLUMBIAN WAY, SPC 112 VA PUGET SOUND HCS 98108 #005-14-1982 L1983 VS *040 †85

HATTORI, Naoya. 1959 NE PACIFIC ST 98195 #572-01-1990 L2007 NM *012

HAUGO, Adam John. ■ 98103 #035-01-2006 L2006 IM *012

HAULMAN, Norma Jean. HALL HLTH 10 CARE CENTER, UNIV OF WA 98195 #005-18-1980 L1981 EM PD *020 †55,16

HAUPTMANN, Ellen Mary. 1100 9TH AVE 98101 #028-46-1985 L1991 DR *020 †80

HAUTMAN, Barbara Ann. 1229 MADISON ST, STE 1210 98104 #654-01-1984 L1987 AN *020

HAVEN, Grant Gilbert. 901 BOREN AVE STE 1910 98104 #028-03-1989 L1989 P *020 †75

HAWKINS, Douglas Scott. 4800 SAND POINT WAY NE, MC-CH29 98105 #024-01-1990 L1992 PHO *020 †55

HAWKINS, Joshua David. ■ 98109 #035-09-2007 L2007 GS *012

HAWN, Thomas Richard. 1959 NE PACIFIC ST, UWMC, BOX 356523 98198 #023-07-1995 L1997 ID *020 †20

HAYASHI, Steven Akira. 1100 9TH AVE C1-MSO, VIRGINIA MASON MEDICAL CEN 98101 #035-19-1983 L1995 IM *040 †20

HAYDEN, Michael Norman. 515 MINOR AVE 98104 #036-07-1995 L2003 **IM** *020 †20
HAYDEN, Patricia Wills. ■ 98112 #035-45-1953 L1958 **PD NM** *071 †55,28
HAYES, Austin George. ■ 98109 #035-01-2007 L2007 **GS** *012
HAYES, Frances Ann. 1201 AMGEN CT W 98119 #060-01-1968 L1997 **PHO HEM** *050 †55
HAYES, Jennifer Eleanorca. ■ 98102 #005-18-2004 L2005 **AN** *012
HAYES, Mary Ann Grace. ■ 98125 #065-01-1962 L1963 **P CHP** *071
HAYES, Maxine D. 4800 SAND POINT WAY NE 98105 #035-06-1973 L1985 **PHP PD** *030 †55
HAYES, Rutherford Platt. 2505 2ND AVE STE 200 98121 #054-04-1989 L1989 **IM** *020 †20
HAYKIN, Martin D. 901 BOREN AVE, STE 1020 98104 #030-06-1962 L1965 **P** *071 †75
HAYMON, Ava Carroll. 1401 MADISON ST 100, SWEDISH FAMILY MEDICINE 98104 #024-07-1999 L2002 **FM** *020 †18
HAYNES, Allan Louis, III. UNIVERSITY OF WASHINGTON, DEPT OF SURGERY BOX #35641 98195 #048-15-2000 L2004 **GS** *100 †85
HAYNOR, David Robt. UNIV OF WASHINGTON, BOX 35, DEPT OF RADIOLOGY 98195 #024-01-1979 L1980 **DR GS** *020 †80
HAYS, Ross Mc Gandy. 4800 SAND POINT WAY NE, CHILDREN'S HOSPITAL 98105 #054-04-1978 L1983 **PM PD** *020 †60,55
HAYWARD, Kristen Nicole. 4800 SAND POINT WAY NE, MS R5420 98105 #005-02-2001 L2004 **PPR** *012 †55
HAZZARD, William Russell. 1660 S COLUMBIAN WAY, S-182-GEC GERIATRICS & EXT 98108 #035-20-1962 L1965 **IM IMG** *030 †20
HEADSTROM, Peggy Drucker. 1145 BROADWAY 98122 #054-04-1999 L2001 **GE** *020 †20
HEALD, Alison Evans. 325 9TH AVE 98104 #041-01-1986 L2000 **ID** *020 †20
HEALEY, Patrick James. 4800 SAND POINT WAY NE, CHILDRENS HOSP/REG MED 98105 #024-05-1987 L1993 **PDS TTS** *020 †85
HEALEY, William Vincent. 901 BOREN AVE STE 1910 98104 #048-04-1986 L1988 **P** *020 †75
HEATH, Carl Herbert. 747 BROADWAY 98122 #054-04-1992 L1992 **AN** *020 †05
HEATH, Michelle L. 2325 MINOR AVE E 98102 #054-04-1999 L2001 **D** *020 †20,15
HEBNER, Claire Marie. 4005 WALLINGFORD AVE N 98103 #054-04-1996 L1999 **PD** *020 †55
HECKER, Bernice Ruth. ■ 98102 #054-04-1975 L1976 **AN** *040 †05
HEDEEN, Ashley Nancy. ■ 98133 #048-02-1982 L1985 **GPM** *020 †55
HEDEMARK, Michael David. ■ 98115 #054-04-2005 L2005 **IM** *012
HEFTY, Thomas Roy. 1100 9TH AVE G1-MSO, VIRGINIA MASON MEDICAL CEN 98101 #056-05-1976 L1992 **U OS** *020 †95
HEGSTROM, Robert Marvin. 901 BOREN AVE, STE 1020 98104 #054-04-1955 L1959 **NEP IM** *071 †20
HEGYVARY, Csaba. 901 BOREN AVE STE 1020, CABRINI MEDICAL TOWER MED 98104 #473-01-1962 L1986 **P CD** *020 †75
HEIDRICH, Fred Edmund, III. 1600 E JOHN ST 98112 #005-11-1976 L1977 **FM FPG** *020 †18
HEIKE, Carrie Lyn. U OF W BOX 356320, ATTN; BETTE HORISHIGE 98195 #054-04-2000 L2003 **PD** *100 †55
HEILBRUNN, Ken Steven. 901 BOREN AVE STE 1920 98104 #054-04-1970 L1974 **PTH FM** *020 †80
HEILBRUNN, Ruth. ■ 98112 #869-02-1937 L1951 **P** *072
HEIMBACH, David Milton. 325 9TH AVE BOX 359796, HARBORVIEW MEDICAL CENTER 98104 #035-20-1964 L1974 **GS** *020 †85
HEINBERG, Eric Max. 747 BROADWAY STE 731, SWEDISH MED CTR FIRST HILL 98122 #021-01-1998 L2006 **GS** *012 †30
HEINECKE, Jay Walter. 1959 NE PACIFIC ST, UWMC- BOX 356426 98195 #028-02-1981 L1982 **END IM** *020 †20
HEINEN, Corinne Sue. 2505 2ND AVE, STE 200 98121 #018-03-1989 L1990 **FM** *020 †18
HEISTAND, Justin Daniel. ■ 98177 #054-04-2008 *012
HEITRITTER, Shannon Marie. 1145 BROADWAY, THE POLYCLINIC 98122 #024-01-2000 L2005 **END** *020 †20
HELGERSON, Steven Dale. 601 BELMONT AVE E, F 11 98102 #054-04-1973 L1975 **PHP EP** *062 †70
HELLER, Jacob Leo. 1100 9TH AVE 98101 #035-19-1973 L1974 **EM IM** *020 †20,16
HELLER, Lori Beth. 747 BROADWAY 98122 #054-04-1993 L1993 **AN** *020 †20,05
HELLER, Thomas Allen. 1200 12TH AVE S 98144 #016-11-1974 L1980 **IM IMG** *020 †20
HELLSTROM, Karl Erik L. 3005 1ST AVE 98121 #858-02-1964 **OS** *050
HELMAN, James Diller. 1100 9TH AVE C1-MSO, VIRGINIA MASON MEDICAL CEN 98101 #011-02-1983 L1994 **AN PME** *040 †05
HELMERS, Laurilyn Dee. 4800 SAND POINT WAY NE, CHILDRENS HOSPITAL REG MED 98105 #018-03-1991 L2005 **AN** *020 †05
HELSELL, J Spencer. 1959 NE PACIFIC ST, BOX 356340 98195 #054-04-2001 L2001 **CHP** *020
HENDERSON, Jenifer Lee. 600 BROADWAY, STE 280 98122 #005-06-1992 L1999 **OTO** *020 †45
HENDERSON, Maureen M. 1959 NE PACIFIC ST 98195 #352-04-1949 L1970 **GPM PHP** *050
HENDERSON, William Reed. 815 MERCER ST RM 254, ASTHMA & INFLAMMATION CENT 98109 #005-02-1973 L1978 **A** *020 †20,03
HENDON, Natalie Marie. ■ 98133 #025-01-2007 L2007 **IM** *012
HENDRICKSON, Helen E. 2033 MINOR AVE E, STE 2 98102 #048-04-1986 L1988 **P** *020 †75
HENDRICKSON, Nyle Allan. ■ 98104 #003-01-2007 L2007 **GS** *012
HENDRIE, Paul Curtis. 1959 NE PACIFIC ST, DIVISION OF HEMATOLOGY 357 98195 #017-20-1995 L1998 **HEM** *020 †20
HENLEY, Elaine Dimitman. 325 9TH AVE 98104 #005-02-1951 L1955 **END IM** *071 †20
HENLEY, Michael Bradford. 325 9TH AVE 6EC21, HMC BOX 359798 98104 #054-04-1979 L1987 **ORS OTR** *040 †40
HENRY, Amy Jo. 4800 SAND POINT WAY NE 98105 #054-04-1996 L1998 **P** *020 †75
HENRY, John Robt. ■ 98134 #047-07-1944 L1956 **GS OS** *020
HENRY, Rohan Kevin. ■ 98115 #566-01-2000 L2007 **PDE** *012 †55
HENTZ, Tracy Anne. 4800 SAND POINT WAY NE, CHILDREN'S HOSPITAL 98105 #041-13-2001 L2004 **PHO** *020
HERMAN, Albert Ellis. ■ 98105 #030-05-1953 L1953 **P** *075
HERMAN, Clifford Morris. 2324 EASTLAKE AVE E, STE 500 98102 #050-02-1959 L1977 **GS TRS** *071 †85
HERR, Robert Douglas. 1600 E JOHN ST 98112 #028-02-1984 L2000 **EM** *030 †20,16
HERRERA, Carmen M. 1959 NE PACIFIC ST, BOX 356320 98195 #231-01-1990 L2006 **NPM PD** *050 †55
HERSHBERG, Robert Mark. 1700 7TH AVE, STE 1900 98101 #005-14-1992 L1992 **MG GS** *020 †19
HERSTEIN, Paul Robt. 200 15TH AVE E, #CMB-AA-11 98112 #005-11-1974 L1989 **RO** *020 †80
HERTZ, Peter. 11011 MERIDIAN AVE N, STE 104 98133 #035-06-1995 L1998 **OMF** *020
HERTZIG, Jeremy Stewart. 1959 NE PACIFIC ST, UNIV WA SCH MED 98195 #050-02-2004 L2007 **CCP** *012
HERZ, Susanne P. 1959 NE PACIFIC ST, BOX 356340 98195 #005-11-2003 L2003 **PD** *100 †55
HESCH, Donald Jos. ■ 98115 #054-04-1956 L1957 **DR** *071 †80
HESS, Darren Michael. ■ 98115 #041-01-2006 L2006 **GS** *012
HESSLEIN, Peter Stone. 1101 MADISON ST, STE 800 98104 #048-04-1976 L2004 **PDC PD** *020 †55
HETHERINGTON, Kelly A. ■ 98117 #048-13-2003 L2007 **AI** *012 †55
HEUGEL, Judson Ryan. ■ 98112 #040-02-2008 *012
HEVNER, Robert Francis. 325 9TH AVE, PATHOLOGY BOX 359791 98104 #056-06-1992 L2001 **NP** *020 †50
HEYN, Julie P. 1536 N 115TH ST, SUMMIT CARDIOLOGY 98133 #054-04-1992 L1992 **CD** *020 †20
HEYREND, Noel B. ■ 98134 #016-02-1950 L1951 **FM** *071 †18
HICKMAN, Robert Othello. 825 EASTLAKE AVE E, SEATTLE CANCER CARE ALLIAN 98109 #023-01-1957 L1959 **PN** *020 †55
HICKOK, Lee Richard. 1101 MADISON ST, STE 1050 98104 #054-04-1984 L1986 **OBG REN** *020 †30
HICKS, John D. 1229 MADISON ST, STE 1480 98104 #054-04-1952 L1956 **OPH** *071 †35
HICKS, Raegan Javon. ■ 98119 #024-05-2005 L2005 **AN** *012
HIGANO, Celestia Savoye. 825 EASTLAKE AVE E, SCCA (G4-830) 98109 #024-16-1979 L1982 **ON HEM** *020 †20
HIGGINBOTHAM, Bruce Wayne. 1229 MADISON ST STE 1050, SEATTLE NUCLEAR MEDICINE/U 98104 #047-20-1984 L2004 **NM** *020 †28
HIGGINS, Michael Herbert. ■ 98103 #054-04-1962 L1969 **U** *030 †95
HIGGINS, Timothy Taylor. 747 BROADWAY 98122 #035-20-1983 L1987 **AN OS** *020 †05
HIGGS, Roger Byron. 10564 5TH AVE NE, STE 201 98125 #028-03-1974 L1980 **FM OM** *020 †18
HILDEBRAND, Alice G. ■ 98101 #030-05-1936 L1942 **IM** *075 †20
HILGENBERG, Sarah Lynn. ■ 98103 #005-11-2007 L2007 **PD** *012
HILGERS, Herbert Max. 10330 MERIDIAN AVE N # 210 98133 #019-02-1963 L1965 **PD** *071
HILL, Carter Degen. 300 ELLIOTT AVE W, MEDICAL DEPT 98119 #026-04-1975 L1976 **EM IM** *020 †20,16
HILL, James Andrew. 1959 NE PACIFIC ST, BOX 356340 98195 #054-04-2003 L2003 **DR** *012
HILL, Joselyn Sarah. 925 SENECA ST, MEDICAL CENTER 98101 #054-04-2005 L2006 **AN** *012
HILL, Mark E. 1100 9TH AVE, VIRGINA MASON MED CTR 98101 #049-01-1989 L1989 **CD** *020 †85,90
HILL, Matthew Walter. 747 BROADWAY 98122 #028-02-2000 L2004 **AN** *020 †05
HILLEL, Allen David. 1660 S COLUMBIAN WAY, VA MEDICAL CTR 98108 #005-11-1976 L1984 **OTO** *020 †45
HILLIER, David Alfred. 1600 E JOHN ST 98112 #028-02-1992 L1999 **DR** *020 †80,28
HILLSON, Jan Leslie. 2446 WARREN AVE N 98109 #005-11-1980 L1981 **RHU IM** *020 †20
HILT, Robert John. 4800 SAND POINT WAY NE, M/S W3636, PO BOX 5371 98105 #035-45-1996 L1999 **CHP** *100 †55,75
HINDS, John Patrick. 501 N 34TH ST, STE 101 98103 #918-01-1977 L1988 **GE IM** *020 †20
HINGORANI, Sangeeta Ram. 4800 SAND PT WAY NE CH-46, CHILDREN'S HOSPITAL/NEPHRO 98105 #035-46-1993 L1996 **PN** *020 †55
HINGORANI, Sunil Ram. ■ 98115 #008-01-1994 L2006 **HO** *020
HINKE, Richard Marvin. 1100 9TH AVE 98101 #056-05-1992 L1997 **DR** *020 †80
HINKLE, Molli E. 1959 NE PACIFIC ST, BOX 356340 98195 #038-45-1997 L2002 **P CHP** *020 †75
HINSON, Roger Mack. 747 BROADWAY 98122 #010-01-1989 L2002 **NPM** *020 †55
HINTON, Jennie Louise. 325 9TH AVE 98104 #003-01-1976 L1977 **P** *071
HINTON, Walter Ladson, III. 1618 E ALOHA ST, W LADSON HINTON MD 98112 #028-02-1961 L1989 **PYA** *020 †75
HIPPS, Linda Joy. 825 E LAKE AVE E, SEATTLE CANCER CARE ALLIAN 98109 #165-04-1983 L2007 **GYN** *020 †30
HIPPS, Sarah Watts. ■ 98112 #025-01-1999 L2001 **AN** *100
HIRANO, Lianne Aya. ■ 98117 #008-01-2005 L2005 **IM** *012
HIRAYAMA, Kimo Chikami. 720 8TH AVE S, STE 100 98104 #041-12-1986 L1988 **FM** *020 †18
HIRSCH, Irl. 4225 ROOSEVELT WAY NE 98105 #028-03-1984 L1990 **DIA IM** *020 †20
HIRSCH, Jack Henry. 1229 MADISON ST STE 1150 98104 #010-01-1970 L1973 **NM** *020 †80
HIRSCHMANN, Jan Victor. 1660 S COLUMBIAN WAY, MEDICAL SVC 111 98108 #054-04-1970 L1976 **IM ID** *020 †20
HIRUY, Hiwot. 4800 SAND POINT WAY NE, AND REGION 98105 #023-07-2005 L2005 **PD** *012
HITTI, Jane Evelyn. 1959 NE PACIFIC ST, BOX 356460 98195 #050-02-1989 L1993 **ID** *020 †30
HO, John Chia Wen. ■ 98103 #043-01-1985 **VIR** *100
HO, John Wah. 3525 BAGLEY AVE N, JOHN HO, MD 98103 #008-02-1995 L2003 **VIR R** *020 †80
HO, Lawrence Anhtuan. ■ 98115 #038-44-2007 L2007 **IM** *012
HO, Mary Ting. 2324 EASTLAKE AVE E, STE 500 98102 #024-01-1976 L1984 **EM IM** *020 †20,16
HO, Phoenix Anhdung. ■ 98115 #038-44-2003 L2006 **PHO** *012 †55
HO, William C. 747 BROADWAY 98122 #462-01-1962 L1965 **FM** *020 †18
HOAG, Robert D. 1001 SW KLICKITAT WAY #205 98134 #025-01-1959 L1969 **PTH** *071 †50
HOANG, Katherine. 4744 41ST AVE SW STE 101 98116 #942-01-1996 L2004 **FM** *020 †18
HOANG, Tuyen Van. 600 BROADWAY, STE 170 98122 #005-02-1991 L2000 **DR** *020 †80
HOBBS, Jenny Bichsel. ■ 98117 #035-45-2006 L2006 **IM** *012
HOBBS, William Edward, II. 1959 NE PACIFIC ST, UNIV OF WASH HEM DIV 98195 #041-12-2002 L2002 **HO ON** *012 †20
HOCKENBERY, David Mark. 1100 FAIRVIEW AVE N, MAILSTOP D2-190 98109 #028-02-1982 L1992 **GE IM** *020 †20
HODAPP, Julie Ann. 1100 9TH AVE 98101 #026-04-2001 L2001 **PM** *020 †60
HODDE, Naomi Hannah. ■ 98112 #041-13-2002 L2002 **IM** *020 †20
HODEL, Lara Leah. 5300 TALLMAN AVE NW, 5 SOUTH 98107 #054-04-1997 L2004 **FM** *020 †18
HODGE, Charles Hunter. 1550 N 115TH ST 98133 #016-42-1997 L2001 **EM** *020 †16
HODGE, Janet Miles. 507 N 49TH ST, POST OFFICE BOX 31967 98103 #054-04-1963 L1965 **IMG GP** *020
HODGES, Wallace Robt. 515 MINOR AVE 98104 #025-01-1970 L1976 **IM IMG** *020 †20
HODSON, William Alan. ROOM RR 451 HLTH SCIENCES, DEPT OF PEDIATRICS BOX 356 98195 #062-01-1959 L1967 **PD NPM** *040 †55
HOERR, Mark Reeves. 500 17TH AVE, HOSPITALIST 98122 #038-06-1984 L1985 **P** *020 †75
HOFF, Laura Heather. ■ 98112 #056-05-2007 L2007 **OBG** *012
HOFF, Robert Allen. ■ 98105 #054-04-1973 L1974 **DR PDR** *071 †80
HOFFER, Fredric Alan. 4800 SAND POINT WAY NE, CHILDREN'S HOSPITAL & REGI 98105 #018-03-1975 L2006 **DR PD** *020 †55,80
HOFFERT, Marvin Jay. 1530 N 115TH ST STE 207 98133 #008-01-1974 L1997 **OS N** *020 †75
HOFFMAN, Lucas Raphael. 4800 SAND POINT WAY NE, WAY, A-5937 98105 #005-02-1998 L2001 **PDP** *100 †55
HOFFMAN, Noah Gabriel. PATHOLOGY RES PROGRAM, UNIV OF WASHINGTON BOX 356 98195 #036-01-2005 L2005 **PTH** *012
HOFFMAN, Shane Philip. 4800 SAND POINT WAY NE 98105 #035-48-1983 L1999 **PEM PD** *020 †55

■ = Address Information Privacy Protected

HOFFMANN, Sarah Ruth. ■ 98122 #005-02-1989 L1991 **IM** *020 †20

HOGG, Robert Thos. 2208 NW MARKET ST STE 410 98107 #027-01-1986 L1988 **FM** *020 †18

HOHN, Peter James. 4413 38TH AVE NE 98105 #005-14-1983 L1986 **FM** *020 †18

HOINESS, Marty Harold. 1100 9TH AVE G1-MSO, VIRGINIA MASON MEDICAL CEN 98101 #054-04-1995 L1997 **P** *020 †75

HOLCENBERG, John Stanley. PO BOX 5371, 4800 SAND POINT WAY NE 98105 #054-04-1961 L1967 **PA ON** *050 †20

HOLDEMAN, Terra Celeste. 2442 NW MARKET ST 98107 #048-02-2005 L2006 **GS** *100

HOLDER, Larry Russell. 1100 9TH AVE 98101 #048-02-1986 L1991 **DR** *020 †80

HOLDER, Walter Dalton, Jr. 1145 BROADWAY 98122 #036-01-1971 L2003 **GS** *020 †85

HOLEN, Anna Louise. 325 9TH AVE, PO BOX 359797 98104 #017-20-2001 L2001 **P** *100 †75

HOLLAND, Lawrence E. 1229 MADISON ST, STE 1600 98104 #005-14-1981 L1982 **ORS** *020 †40

HOLLAND-POPE, Kim Ionia. 5316 RAINIER AVE S 98118 #024-05-1980 L1980 **FM** *020 †18

HOLLON, Matthew Frederick. 4245 ROOSEVELT WAY NE, U OF WA MC BOX 354760 98105 #054-04-1994 L1996 **IM PHP** *012

HOLLOW, Walter Boyd. 9800 4TH AVE NE 98115 #054-04-1975 L1977 **FM PYA** *020 †18

HOLM, Vanja Adele. 4800 SAND POINT WAY NE 98105 #858-01-1954 L1956 **PD** *071 †55

HOLMAN, Hilton Matthew. ■ 98109 #048-02-2005 L2005 **AN** *012

HOLMBERG, Leona Ann. 1124 COLUMBIA ST 98104 #011-02-1986 L1989 **ON** *050 †20

HOLMBERG, Timothy Josiah. PO BOX 356421, UNIV OF WASHINGTON 98195 #054-04-2007 L2007 **IM** *012

HOLMES, John Richard. 1100 9TH AVE G1-MSO, VIRGINIA MASON MEDICAL CEN 98101 #054-04-1978 L1979 **CD** *020 †20

HOLMES, King Kennard. 325 9TH AVE # 359931 98104 #035-20-1963 L1967 **ID IM** *050 †20

HOLMES, Mark David. 325 9TH AVE BOX 359745, HARBORVIEW MEDICAL CENTER 98104 #038-40-1977 L1990 **N CN** *020 †75

HOLMES, Rebecca Simmons. ■ 98177 #008-01-2003 L2003 **FM** *062

HOLT, Gregory Earl. ■ 98103 #016-43-2002 L2006 **PCC** *012

HOLT, Rose Marie. 600 BROADWAY, STE 170 98122 #049-01-1987 L1990 **DR RNR** *020 †80

HOLZAPFEL, Marie Kristine. ■ 98105 #054-04-2008 *012

HOM, Denis Jae. 4700 36TH AVE SW 98126 #026-04-1977 L1978 **IM** *020 †20

HOM, Douglas Leong. 4700 36TH AVE SW, DOUGLAS L HOM MD 98126 #026-04-1974 L1985 **IM** *020 †20

HOMER, Joanna Rachel. ■ 98115 #917-09-1998 L2003 **AN** *100 †05

HOMYAK, Michelle. 4742 42ND AVE SW # 485 98116 #005-06-1992 L2002 **AN** *020 †05

HONARI, David. 125 16TH AVE E CSB-3, GROUP HEALTH 98112 #056-06-1995 L2001 **ORS OSM** *020 †40

HONG, Borah Justina. ■ 98115 #041-12-2007 L2007 **PD** *012

HONG, Chieu Vi. ■ 98104 #028-02-2006 L2006 **GS** *012

HONG, Kenneth. 623 S WELLER ST 98104 #244-06-1973 L1978 **IM** *020 ‡

HONGLADAROM, Thaworn. 1100 9TH AVE 98101 #054-04-1964 L1967 **PM** *020 †60

HOOD, Beth Renae. ■ 98101 #030-05-2007 **GS** *012

HOOD, Leroy Edward. 1441 N 34TH ST 98103 #023-07-1964 **OS** *075

HOOD, William Boyd. 325 9TH AVE 98104 #024-01-1958 L1999 **CD** *050 †20

HOOFNAGLE, Andrew Norbert. RESIDENCY PROGRAM, PATHOLOGY 98195 #007-02-2004 L2004 **PTH** *100 †50

HOOK, Robert Matthew. 1550 N 115TH ST 98133 #056-05-1977 L1982 **EM** *020 †16

HOOKS, Margaret Ann. 1959 NE PACIFIC ST 98195 #035-08-1996 L1998 **CCA** *020 †20,05

HOOVER, Khristina Jewel. ■ 98121 #045-01-2005 L2005 *100

HOOVER, Ulista Nmi. 1959 NE PACIFIC ST, RESIDENCY TRAINING 98195 #040-02-2005 L2005 **P** *012

HOPENBECK, James Richard. 216 JAMES ST 98104 #005-15-1989 L1989 **P** *020 †75

HOPKINS, Rodney J. 9730 3RD AVE NE, STE 202 98115 #030-06-1979 L1980 **DR** *020 †80

HOPPER, Richard A. 4800 SAND POINT WAY NE, CLDS HOSP&RMC POB5371CH-78 98105 #063-01-1993 L2001 **PS** *020

HORAN, Kathleen Lesley. 2001 S STEVENS ST 98144 #048-12-1998 L2003 **PCC** *020 †20

HORAN, Mary Patricia. 1560 N 115TH ST, STE 106 98133 #050-02-1984 L1986 **PUD IM** *020 †20

HORMEL, Scott Edward. 900 TERRY AVE, STE 100 98104 #054-04-1990 L1990 **OSM** *020 †40

HORN, Stephanie M. ■ 98103 #043-01-2001 L2006 **PE** *100 †16

HORNE, David John. 10631 8TH AVE NE 98125 #005-02-2000 L2005 **PCC** *012

HORNE, Michael John. 600 1ST AVE, STE 306A 98104 #143-03-1969 L1999 **P** *040 †75

HORST, Thomas Eugene. 1600 E JOHN ST 98112 #054-04-1978 L1982 **FM** *020 †18

HORSTMAN, Joseph Arthur. 1959 NE PACIFIC ST, U OF W-HS AFFAIRS BOX 3563 98195 #048-04-2004 L2004 **IM** *012 †20

HORTON, John Michael. 4033 E MADISON ST, STE 105 98112 #054-04-1972 L1986 **P PYA** *020 †75

HORTON, Marc Douglas. 600 UNIVERSITY ST, STE 1200 98101 #054-04-1987 L1989 **GS** *020 †85

HORTON, Matthew. 1229 MADISON ST 98104 #035-03-1992 L2001 **PTH** *020 †50

HORVATH, Karen. 1959 NE PACIFIC ST, BOX 356410 98195 #035-09-1990 L1998 **GS CCS** *020 †85

HORWITCH, Carrie Ann. 1100 9TH AVE 98101 #003-01-1987 L1990 **IM** *020 †20

HORWITZ, Marshall Scott. UNIV OF WASH SCH OF MED, DIV MED GENETICS BX 357720 98195 #054-04-1990 L1992 **IM MG** *050 †20,19

HOSHI, Tetsuya. PO BOX 356340, 1959 NE PACIFIC ST 98195 #572-74-1992 L2003 **RHU** *100 †18

HOSODA, Setsuko. 550 16TH AVE STE 100, PROVIDENCE CAMPUS 98122 #025-01-1995 L1996 **FM** *020 †18

HOSTETTER, Lucy Seiple. 925 SENECA ST, MEDICAL CENTER 98101 #005-14-2006 L2006 **AN** *012

HOTCHKIN, David Lee. 1959 NE PACIFIC ST, BOX 356421 98195 #054-04-2002 L2004 **PCC** *012 †20

HOTT, Sue Merle. 3400 CALIFORNIA AVE SW, STE 200 98116 #035-48-1979 L1984 **PD** *075 †55

HOUCK, Peter Michael. ■ 98115 #054-04-1981 L1984 **GPM FM** *020 †18

HOUGH, Brian Stuart. PO BOX 84026, 747 BROADWAY 98124 #048-12-1991 L1996 **IM** *020 †20

HOUK, Robert Louis. 1600 E OLIVE ST 98122 #054-04-1963 L1969 **P** *020

HOUMARD, Brenda Sue. 4245 ROOSEVELT WAY NE, STE 354775 98105 #038-40-1994 L1998 **OBG** *020 †30

HOUSER, Marc Alan. 1600 E JOHN ST 98112 #017-20-1988 L1990 **FM** *020 †18

HOUSTON, Stephen Carter. 1560 N 115TH ST, STE 209 98133 #005-14-1993 L2000 **NS GS** *020 †25

HOVSEPIAN, Rafi. 925 SENECA ST 98101 #039-05-1988 L1991 **IM** *020 †20,85

HOWARD, Donald Raymond. 1229 MADISON ST STE 500 98104 #035-03-1973 L1985 **PTH** *020 †50

HOWARD, Ileana Michelle. ■ 98168 #024-01-2004 L2005 **PM** *012

HOWARD, James L. 325 9TH AVE BOX 359798, HARBORVIEW MEDICAL CENTER 98104 #060-02-2000 L2005 *100

HOWE, Catherine Qing. 1959 NE PACIFIC ST, PSYCHIATRY RESIDENCY TRAIN 98195 #243-03-1997 L2006 **P** *012

HOWE, Christopher Ray. ■ 98115 #037-01-2003 L2003 **ORS** *012

HOWE, John Frantz. 200 15TH AVE E 98112 #038-06-1971 L1972 **NS N** *071 †25

HOWISEY, Robert Leigh. 1560 N 115TH ST STE 102 98133 #010-01-1975 L1976 **GS VS** *071 †85

HOWLETT, John Patrick. 1959 NE PACIFIC ST, BOX 356195 98195 #005-02-2003 L2003 **ORS** *012

HOYT, Jeanna Marie. 10564 5TH AVE NE, P C 98125 #054-04-1992 L1996 **OPH** *020 †35

HSI, Richard Alexander. 1100 9TH AVE G1-MSO, VIRGINIA MASON MEDICAL CEN 98101 #025-01-1991 L1999 **RO** *020 †20,80

HSIA, Danny Weiming. 1959 NE PACIFIC ST, DIV OF PED PULMONOLOGY 98195 #035-09-2001 L2005 **PDP** *012 †55

HSIANG, John Keung. 1100 9TH AVE M6-AC, VIRGINIA MASON MEDICAL CEN 98101 #016-02-1988 L1997 **NS** *020 †25

HSIAO, Ray Chihjui. CAMPUS BOX 356340, UNIVERSITY OF WA SCHOOL OF 98195 #016-06-2000 L2004 **ADP** *020 ‡

HSIE, Sing Tje. 2838 MT SAINT HELENS PL S 98144 #028-34-1991 L2007 **FM** *020 †18

HSU, Evelyn Kanyu. 9233 17TH AVE NE 98115 #005-02-2003 L2003 **PG** *012 †55

HSU, Florence Chialing. 1100 9TH AVE G1-MSO, VIRGINIA MASON MEDICAL CEN 98101 #038-06-1996 L1998 **RHU** *020 †20

HSU, Jim Chun-Jen. 1551 NW 54TH ST 98107 #035-45-1999 L2005 **OSM** *020 †40

HSU, Raymond Kungyung. ■ 98102 #016-06-2005 L2005 **IM** *012

HSU, Wendy. 1959 NE PACIFIC ST, BOX 357115 98195 #041-01-2000 L2000 **AR** *020 †80

HU, James. 1229 MADISON ST, STE 830 98104 #035-46-1976 L1980 **D DS** *020 †15

HU, Shu-Ching. 325 9TH AVE, # 3597 98104 #244-02-1993 L2001 **N** *100

HUANG, Agnes Shenvie. 600 BROADWAY STE 100, SEATTLE OPHTHALMOLOGY 98122 #005-19-1990 L1999 **OPH** *020 †35 ‡

HUANG, Joe Chinsun. PO BOX 356421, UNIVERSITY OF WASHINGTON 98195 #050-02-2007 L2007 **IM** *012

HUANG, Kimberly Kathleen. ■ 98136 #035-20-1996 L1997 **IM** *020 †20

HUANG, Maria Chen. 4800 SAND POINT WAY NE, REGIONAL M 98105 #038-06-2006 L2006 **PD** *012

HUANG, Martin Hsiang Shui. 4800 SAND POINT WAY NE, CHILDREN'S HOSP MED CTR 98105 #825-01-1985 L1994 *100

HUANG, May Yimei. 1221 MADISON ST STE 1410 98104 #036-01-1987 L1999 **NO** *020 †45

HUANG, Minnie V. 2309 NE 94TH ST 98115 #048-02-1995 L1998 **IM** *020 †20

HUANG, Paul Po-Wen. 550 17TH AVE, STE 630 98122 #016-06-1992 L1999 **CD IC** *020 †20

HUANG, Xiaoxue. ■ 98105 #028-02-2007 L2007 **IM** *012

HUANG, Xuewei. ■ 98115 #036-07-2000 L2003 **IM** *100 †20

HUBACKER, Allan Stuart. ■ 98115 #025-01-1954 L1955 **GYN EM** *020 †30

HUBERT, Kristin Elizabeth. 1959 NE PACIFIC ST, BOX 356340 98195 #024-07-2003 L2005 **NPM** *012 †55

HUBKA, Michal. ■ 98122 #054-04-2005 L2005 **GS** *012

HUDSON, Dean G. ■ 98115 #035-20-1950 L1951 **IM** *071

HUDSON, Leonard D. 325 9TH AVE, BOX 359762 98104 #054-04-1964 L1969 **CCM IM** *050 †20

HUDSON, Reuben Guy. 1101 MADISON ST, STE 800 98104 #017-20-1998 L2007 **UP** *020 †95

HUDSON, Ryan Christopher. 4245 ROOSEVELT WAY NE, BOX 354775 98105 #038-06-2004 L2004 **FM** *020 †18

HUEBSCH, Lothar Bernd. UNIV OF WASH SCH OF MED 98105 #065-09-1975 L1978 **IM** *100 †20

HUEHNERGARTH, Kier Vorse. 1959 NE PACIFIC ST BOX 356, UNIVERSITY OF WASHINGTON 98195 #035-03-2002 **CD** *012 †20

HUETSCH, John Christian. PO BOX 356421, UNIV OF WASHINGTON 98195 #028-02-2007 L2007 **IM** *012

HUFBAUER, Sarah Beth. 550 16TH AVE, STE 100 98122 #005-15-1991 L1993 **FM** *020 †18

HUFF, William Lee. 200 15TH AVE E, GROUP HEALTH CARE URGENT 98112 #005-02-1986 L1992 **FM** *020 †18

HUFFINE, Chas Walter, Jr. 3123 FAIRVIEW AVE E 98102 #054-04-1968 L1973 **CHP P** *020

HUGHES, Charles Geo. 12610 DES MOINES MEM DR S 98168 #054-15-1964 **GP** *072

HUGHES, Elizabeth C W. 1101 MADISON ST, PACIFIC MED CTR 98104 #051-01-1994 L2004 **D** *020 †15

HUGHES, Grady Maxson. 1600 E JEFFERSON ST, STE 202 98122 #054-04-1982 L1986 **OPH** *020 †35

HUIZAR, Isham Aleiandro. ■ 98177 #649-13-1997 L2005 **PCC** *100 †20

HUIZENGA, Hugh Fletcher. 4319 EASTERN AVE N 98103 #028-02-1991 L1991 **IM** *020 †20

HULVERSHORN, Justin Wayne. ■ 98109 #041-01-2006 *012

HUME, Clifford Robert. UNIV OF WASHINGTON, DEPT OF OTO 98195 #035-20-1996 L2002 **OTO NO** *020 †45

HUMMEL, Philip Jeffrey. 2505 2ND AVE, STE 200 98121 #054-04-1976 L1978 **GPM IM** *020 †20

HUMSI, Juliette Ann. 925 SENECA ST # 1930, DIV OF ANESTHESIOLOGY 98101 #051-01-2006 L2007 **AN** *012

HUNDEMER, Gregory Louis. ■ 98102 #047-05-2007 L2007 **IM** *012

HUNDER, Naomi Noelle. ■ 98115 #041-02-1998 L2001 **ON** *020 †20

HUNG, Chi Fung. PO BOX 356340, UNIVERSITY OF WASHINGTON G 98195 #005-18-2005 L2005 **IM** *012

HUNT, Ben Martin. 747 BROADWAY STE 731, SWEDISH MED CTR FIRST HILL 98122 #005-02-2006 L2006 **GS** *012

HUNT, David Danl. 1959 NE PACIFIC ST, BOX 356340 98195 #035-20-1973 L1977 **P** *030 †75

HUNT, Sheri Ann. 4033 E MADISON ST STE 108, THE N W CLINIC 98112 #056-06-1990 L1995 **CHP** *020

HUNT, Stephen Carl. ■ 98103 #039-01-1977 L1978 **GPM** *020

HUNTER, Charles Jos. 1229 MADISON ST 98104 #025-01-1986 L1999 **DMP** *020 †20,50

HUNTER, Robert Eaton. 98118 #045-01-1959 L1969 **PD HEM** *071 †55

HUNTINGTON, David C. 9800 4TH AVE NE 98115 #041-09-1977 L1983 **FM FPG** *020 †18

HUNTINGTON, Jane Hoskins. 1959 NE PACIFIC ST, BOX 359781 98195 #054-04-1994 L1996 **FM** *020 †18

HURST, Keith Andrew. 720 OLIVE WAY STE 300, COMMUNITY HEALTH PLAN 98101 #054-04-1990 L1990 **FM** *030 †18

HURST, Stanley Leon. 4225 ROOSEVELT WAY NE, DERM CENTER 4TH FLOOR 98195 #017-20-1973 L1978 **D** *020 †18,15

HURT, Christopher Jason. 1959 NE PACIFIC ST, BOX 356 98195 #023-07-2003 L2004 **DR** *012

HUSEBY, Jon Sigurd. 1145 BROADWAY 98122 #010-01-1970 L1972 **IM** *020 †20

HUSSAIN, Sadaf. ■ 98126 #306-01-1996 L2006 **FM** *020 †18

HUSS-FRECHETTE, Ellen E. ■ 98117 #054-04-2004 L2004 **IM** *020

HUTCHINSON, Elizabeth Chr. ■ 98105 #054-04-2004 L2004 **FM** *020 †18

HUTCHINSON, Anne Victoria. 1959 NE PACIFIC ST, BOX 356320 98195 #028-02-1985 L1999 **PD** *020 †55,19

HUTCHISON, Margaret L. 801 BROADWAY, STE 623 98122 #054-04-1989 L1993 **OBG** *020 †30

HUTCHISON, Walter Wm. ■ 98103 #040-02-1963 L1966 **GP** *074

HUYNH, Paul Trong. 1959 NE PACIFIC ST 98195 #941-01-1963 L1985 **GP** *075

HUYNH, Vananh Thi. 1959 NE PACIFIC ST BOX 356, UNIV OF WASHINGTON UROLOGY 98195 #016-02-2005 L2005 **U** *012

HUZYK, Peter. 1600 E JOHN ST 98112 #008-02-1981 L1985 **DR** *020 †80

HWANG, Harry Chanhwe. ■ 98107 #041-01-1995 L1999 **SP** *020

HWANG, Lucy Chen. 2505 2ND AVE, STE 200 98121 #024-05-2000 L2002 **FM** *020 †18 ‡

HWANG, Michael Dingjay. 1959 NE PACIFIC ST BOX 356, UW SCHOOL OF MEDICINE GME 98195 #016-02-2005 L2005 **ORS** *012

HWANG, Wayne She. 1100 9TH AVE X3-CAR, VIRGINIA MASON MEDICAL CEN 98101 #017-20-1996 L2003 **CD** *020 †20

HWANG, Yao Chung. ■ 98105 #385-02-1961 L1969 **P** *071

HYDE, Martha Lynn. 600 UNIVERSITY ST, STE 1200 98101 #051-01-1986 L1989 **IM** *020 †20

HYSLOP, Ann Elizabeth. 1959 NE PACIFIC ST, BOX 356340 98195 #048-14-2005 L2007 **CHN** *012

IFFT, Robin Dawn. 1100 9TH AVE C1-MSO, VIRGINIA MASON MEDICAL CEN 98101 #036-05-1988 L1996 **PD** *020 †55

IMAHARA, Scott Downs. 1959 NE PACIFIC ST, BOX 356340 98195 #010-02-2000 L2003 **PS** *012

INCARDONA, John P. ■ 98105 #038-06-1996 L1996 *100

INGLIS, Andrew F, Jr. 4800 SAND POINT WAY NE, OTOLARYNGOLOGY-HNS /W7729 98105 #041-07-1981 L1982 **OTO** *020 †45

INGRAHAM, Michael Douglas. 1100 9TH AVE C1-MSO, VIRGINIA MASON MEDICAL CEN 98101 #056-06-1995 L1998 **IM** *020 †20

INMAN, Christi Joy. 4800 SAND POINT WAY NE 98105 #041-15-2003 L2006 **PPR** *012 55

INNES, Jay Badgley. 4319 STONE WAY N 98103 #051-01-1985 L1988 **P** *020 †75

INOUE, Yoshio. 1959 NE PACIFIC ST, UNIV WA MED CTR 98195 #023-01-2003 L2006 **HO** *012 †20

INOUYE, Ruby A. ■ 98118 #041-07-1948 L1949 **FM** *071

IOANNOU, George Nicou. 1959 NE PACIFIC ST RM C2, CAMPUS BOX 356340 98195 #917-09-1996 L2000 **GE** *020 †20

IQBAL, Rumi. ■ 98112 #043-01-2005 L2006 **FP** *012

IRANI, Shayan Sarosh. 1100 9TH AVE G1-MSO, TEMPLE UNIVERSITY HOSPITAL 98101 #496-38-2000 L2007 **GE** *020 †20

IRETON, Robt Christopher. 1530 N 115TH ST, STE 205 98133 #054-04-1979 L1980 **U ON** *020 †95

IRIZARRY, Fernando. 2211 QUEEN ANNE AVE N, QUEEN ANNE CLINIC 98109 #016-11-1997 L2005 **FM GPM** *020 †18

IRVING, Gordon A. 1101 MADISON ST STE 200, SWEDISH PAIN HEADACHE CTR 98104 #917-04-1973 L1998 **PME AN** *020 †05

IRWIN, Brandith Gail. 1101 MADISON ST, STE 1490 98104 #054-04-1984 L1985 **D IM** *020 †20,15

ISACSON, Christina. 1100 9TH AVE 98101 #018-03-1990 L2000 **PTH** *020 †50

ISHAK, Gisele Elias. 1959 NE PACIFIC ST, UNIV OF WA SCH OF MED 98195 #605-03-2000 L2005 **PDR** *012

ISHIKI, Dean Mitsuo. 515 MINOR AVE STE 220, FIRST HILL MEDICAL BUILDIN 98104 #048-04-1968 L1980 **P** *020 †75

ISIK, F Frank. 1145 BROADWAY 98122 #035-47-1985 L1990 **PS** *020 †85,65

ISLER, John Tracy. 1530 N 115TH ST, STE 201 98133 #035-48-1978 L1979 **CRS** *020 †10

ISSARACHAI, Surasit. ■ 98108 #891-02-1993 L1998 **HEM** *020 †20

ITO, Melanie Sadae. 4400 37TH AVE S, COLUMBIA HEALTH CTR 98118 #054-04-1988 L1991 **PD** *020 †55

IVANOVA, Iskra Ivanova. 4800 SAND POINT WAY NE, MAILSTOP W9824 98105 #198-01-1998 L2007 **PAN** *012

IVERSON, Carrold Keister. 4120 STONE WAY N 98103 #008-01-1951 L1958 **P** *071

IYER, Ramesh Subramaniam. C-212 HEALTH SCIENCES CENT, OFFICE OF GRADUATE MEDICAL 98195 #035-19-2005 L2005 **DR** *012

JACK, Christopher Stephen. 925 SENECA ST # 1930, DEPT MED 98101 #005-06-2005 L2007 **IM** *012

JACK, Gregory Martin. 1010 BOYLSTON AVE, SEATTLE EYE PHYSICIANS 98104 #041-02-1981 L1982 **OPH OS** *071

JACK, Marious Kim. 1101 BOYLSTON AVE, # A 98101 #054-04-1957 L1958 **OPH** *071 †35

JACK, Richard Douglas. ■ 98122 #067-01-1962 **GP OS** *020

JACKSON, Allen Willis. 2409 N 45TH ST 98103 #010-01-1969 L1974 **ORS TRS** *020 †40

JACKSON, Benjamin Kyle. ■ 98122 #036-01-2005 L2005 **PD** *012

JACKSON, Carol A. ■ 98105 #005-02-1984 L1990 **FM** *020 †18

JACKSON, J Carey. 325 9TH AVE # 359780 98104 #025-12-1986 L1990 **IM** *020

JACKSON, Jo Ann. 4245 ROOSEVELT WAY NE, STE 354775 98105 #025-12-1979 L1982 **FM OBG** *020 †18

JACKSON, John Craig. 4800 SAND POINT WAY NE, INFANT ICU ADMIN 4G-2 98105 #047-05-1979 L1980 **NPM PD** *020 †55

JACKSON, Lisa Anne. 1730 MINOR AVE STE 1600 98101 #051-01-1988 L1990 **PHP IM** *050 †70,20

JACKSON, Sara Lisle. 325 9TH AVE, # 359854 98104 #020-02-1995 L1998 **IM** *020 †20

JACKSON, Shari Marie. 9730 3RD AVE NE, STE 202 98115 #054-04-2000 L2006 **RNR** *100 †80

JACOB, Shevin Thomas. ■ 98107 #040-02-2004 L2007 **IM** *100 †20

JACOBS, Andrew David. 1100 9TH AVE M6-AC, VIRGINIA MASON MEDICAL CEN 98101 #917-30-1977 L1993 **HO HEM** *020 †20

JACOBS, Laurence Perry. 2840 EASTLAKE AVE E 98102 #035-08-1959 L1961 **P** *075

JACOBS, Stephen Michael. 747 BROADWAY 98122 #054-04-1999 L2004 **AN** *020 †05

JACOBS, Timothy William. 1100 9TH AVE 98101 #836-02-1986 L2002 **PCP** *020 †50

JACOBSON, Avrum Israel. 1959 NE PACIFIC ST, BOX 356510 98195 #067-01-1996 L2002 **U** *020

JACOBSON, Elizabeth Noell. 1959 NE PACIFIC ST, BOX 356340 98195 #026-08-2004 L2004 **PD** *020 †55

JACOBSON, Julie Ann. 1752 NW MARKET ST 98107 #011-04-1994 L2000 **FM** *050 †18

JACOBSON, Lawrence Edward. 4800 SAND POINT WAY NE 98105 #025-01-1979 L1985 **AN** *020 †05

JAFFE, Craig Daniel. ■ 98117 #054-04-2001 L2003 **P ADP** *020

JAFFE, Kenneth Marc. 4800 SAND POINT WAY NE, CHILDREN'S HOSPITAL 98105 #024-01-1975 L1976 **PM PD** *020 †55,60

JAFFE, Robert David. 500 17TH AVE 98122 #025-12-1979 L1980 **FM PHP** *071 †18

JAFFERANY, Mohammad. 4800 SAND POINT WAY NE, REGIONAL M 98105 #704-16-1984 L2006 **CHP** *012

JAMES, Jennifer J. 140 4TH AVE N, STE 170 98109 #050-02-1994 L1999 **PM** *020 †60

JAMES, John Alexander. ■ 98199 #803-03-1947 L1981 **PD PN** *071 †55

JAMES, Karen Clifford. 1401 MADISON ST STE 100 98104 #054-04-1999 L2001 **FM** *040 †18

JAN-AMADI, Arash. 1959 NE PACIFIC ST, BOX 356485 98195 #035-15-1996 L2001 **OPH** *020 †35

JANES, Robert Grant, Jr. 5000 30TH AVE NE STE 105 98105 #007-02-1966 L1973 **PYA P** *020 †09

JANSON, Vida J. 1836 WESTLAKE AVE N, UW CHILD PSYCHIATRY PROGRA 98109 #067-01-1999 L2004 **CHP** *020

JANSSEN, Traci W. 1100 9TH AVE 98101 #021-01-1993 L1996 **AN** *020 †05

JAPHA, Irene Ruth. 4700 42ND AVE SW, STE 210 98116 #016-01-1979 L1984 **FM** *074 †18

JARDINE, David Stuart. 4800 SAND POINT WAY NE, BOX C5371 98105 #023-07-1980 L1987 **AN CCP** *050 †55

JARRIS, Raymond F, Jr. 3223 1ST AVE S 98134 #024-05-1982 L1983 **EM FM** *030 †18

JARVIK, Gail Pairitz. 1959 NE PACIFIC ST, BOX 357720 98195 #018-03-1987 L1991 **IM** *020 †20,19

JARVIK, Jeffrey Gil. 1959 NE PACIFIC ST, BOX 357115 98195 #005-18-1987 L1992 **RNR DR** *020 †80

JARVIS, David Bradford. ■ 98115 #054-04-1962 L1964 **P CHP** *020

JASPAN, Heather Beryl. ■ 98103 #021-01-1999 L1999 **PD** *020 †55

JASPAN, Jacqueline. 2910 E MADISON ST STE 204 98112 #836-01-1972 L1999 **P** *020

JAUCIAN, Jennifer Rose. 600 UNIVERSITY ST STE 1200, SWEDISH PHYSICIANS-HCFW 98101 #056-05-1997 L2001 **OBG** *020 †30

JAYADEV, Suman. UNIV OF WASH, BOX 3566340 98195 #035-09-2000 L2004 **N** *020 †75

JAYARAJ, Arjun. PO BOX 356340, UNIV OF WASHINGTON 98195 #495-44-2000 L2007 **GS** *012

JEANNET, Pierre-Yves. NEUROLOGY DEPT/BOX 356465, UNIV OF WASHINGTON 98195 #869-04-1992 L1998 **CHN** *100

JEANNETTE, Michelle. 1145 BROADWAY, THE POLYCLINIC 98122 #024-16-1990 L1998 **IM** *020 †20

JEFFERSON, Jonathan A. 1959 NE PACIFIC ST, BOX 356521 98195 #918-01-1989 L2003 **NEP** *020

JEFFRIES, Howard Elliot. 4800 SAND POINT WAY NE, REG MED CTR STE 9G-1 98105 #021-01-1996 L2003 **CCP** *020 †55

JELACIC, Jill Katherine. ■ 98125 #054-04-2004 L2004 **AN** *012

JELACIC, Srdjan. ■ 98115 #054-04-2006 L2006 **AN** *012

JENKIN, Renata M. 1100 9TH AVE 98101 #065-10-1989 L1999 **D** *020

JENNINGS, Terese Leslie. 3626 NE 45TH ST STE 300, PEDIATRIX MEDICAL GROUP 98105 #016-11-1986 L2002 **NPM** *050 †55

JENSE, Ryan Joseph. ■ 98112 #054-04-2002 L2003 **AN** *100

JENSEN, Aaron Ross. 1959 NE PACIFIC ST, BOX 356340 98195 #041-13-2004 L2004 **GS** *012

JENSEN, Carl Frank. 1660 S COLUMBIAN WAY #116A 98108 #047-05-1978 L1979 **P** *020 †75

JENSEN, Ole Jorgen, Jr. ■ 98104 #067-01-1939 L1946 **LM U** *071 †95

JENSEN, Ray S, Jr. 9730 3RD AVE NE, STE 202 98115 #048-04-1990 L1995 **VIR R** *020 †80

JERNBERG, Elizabeth T. 1530 N 115TH ST 98133 #054-04-1977 L1990 **RHU** *020 †20

JERNBERG, Timothy Scott. 200 15TH AVE E, 235 DEPT. ANESTHESIOLOGY 98112 #054-04-1985 L1988 **AN** *020 †05

JEROME, Jennifer Marie. ■ 98107 #038-06-2003 L2006 **PD** *020 †55

JEROME, Keith Robert. 1100 FAIRVIEW AVE N, FHCR 98109 #036-07-1993 L1998 **PTH** *020 †50

JEWELER, Gary Frederick. 800 5TH AVE STE 4100 98104 #051-01-1992 L1992 **FM** *062

JEWELL, Patrick Donald. WASHINGTON MEDIC, UNIVERSITY OF 98195 #054-04-2005 L2005 **RO** *012

JIMENEZ, Miguel Francisco. 8720 14TH AVE S 98108 #737-03-1989 L2004 **FM** *100

JIMENEZ, Nathalia. 4800 SAND POINT WAY NE, MAILSTOP CH-05 98105 #264-04-1994 L2002 **PAN** *020

JIMENEZ, Richard Alan. 10330 MERIDIAN AVE N, SEATTLE ARTHRITIS CLINIC 98133 #038-43-1974 L1977 **RHU** *020 †20

JIMENEZ CELI, Julio. 8720 14TH AVE S 98108 #737-03-1993 L1999 **FM** *020 †18

JIMENEZ-CELI, Ramos R. 8720 14TH AVE S 98108 #737-03-1982 L1990 **FM** *020 †18

JINGUJI, Thomas Martin. 4800 SAND POINT WAY NE, CH30 98105 #054-04-1993 L1995 **PD** *020 †55

JOBE, Kathleen Ann. 1959 NE PACIFIC ST, BOX 356123 98195 #007-02-1986 L1988 **EM IM** *020 †20,16

JOHANNSEN, Tracy Ann. 1101 MADISON ST STE 1150 98104 #054-04-1982 L1983 **OBG** *020 †30

JOHN, C Kunjappan. 2701 CALIFORNIA AVE SW, APT 235 98116 #495-27-1960 L1973 **U** *071 †95

JOHN, David Watson. PO BOX 3707 98124 #035-45-1961 L1971 **P** *020

JOHN, Grace Chiramukuth. 325 9TH AVE, BOX 359909 98104 #025-01-1987 L1992 **ID PD** *050 †20,55

JOHN, Gregory G. 1145 BROADWAY 98122 #040-02-1952 L1954 **IM CD** *071

JOHN, Gregory Martin. 1145 BROADWAY 98122 #054-04-1978 L1981 **IM** *020 †20

JOHNSEN, Jill Marie. 921 TERRY AVE, PUGET SOUND BLOOD CTR 98104 #038-06-1998 L2008 **IM HO** *050 †20 ‡

JOHNSON, Allan Fred. 4575 SAND POINT WAY NE, SAND POINT INTERNISTS 98105 #038-06-1954 L1960 **IM** *071 †20

JOHNSON, Allen Lee. 1145 BROADWAY 98122 #056-05-1992 L1992 **IM** *020 †20

JOHNSON, Andrew Steven. 925 SENECA ST 98101 #065-06-1993 L1999 **ID IM** *050 †20

JOHNSON, Bruce Gatlin. ■ 98104 #045-04-2003 L2007 **PMM** *012

JOHNSON, Charles Richard. 509 OLIVE WAY, 1334 MEDICAL DENTAL BLDG 98101 #005-12-1958 L1963 **P** *020 †75

JOHNSON, Cynthia Bird. 1801 NW MARKET ST, STE 203 98107 #054-04-1976 L1977 **FM** *020 †18

JOHNSON, Dexter Withrow. 747 BROADWAY 98122 #054-04-1958 L1959 **DR RO** *071 †80

JOHNSON, Douglas Dean. 1221 MADISON ST STE 1110 98104 #020-12-1970 L1977 **CD TS** *071 †85,90

JOHNSON, E William. ■ 98116 #014-01-2003 L2003 **U** *012

JOHNSON, Geo Theodore, III. 1100 9TH AVE 98101 #026-04-1975 L1976 **EM** *020 †20,16

JOHNSON, Germaine Richard. ■ 98115 #041-01-2003 L2005 **DR** *012

JOHNSON, Harold Reed. 625 38TH AVE 98122 #047-06-1958 L1965 **P** *020 †75

JOHNSON, Janet Ann. 1959 NE PACIFIC ST, MSC 359300 98195 #014-01-1985 L1990 **DR NM** *020 †80

JOHNSON, Katherine C. 1101 MADISON ST STE 950, 1101 MADISON 950 98104 #020-02-1993 L1995 **OBG** *020 †30

■ = Address Information Privacy Protected

JOHNSON, Kay Marie. ■ 98118 #026-04-1991 L1993 **IM** *020 †20

JOHNSON, Kristen Randi. 11011 MERIDIAN AVE N, STE 200 98133 #026-08-2003 L2006 **FM** *020 †18

JOHNSON, Laura C. 1959 NE PACIFIC ST RM C, CAMPUS BOX 356340 98195 #005-15-2002 L2004 **IM** *020 †20

JOHNSON, Lloyd Philip. 801 BROADWAY, STE 901 98122 #054-04-1956 L1960 **GS TS** *071 †85

JOHNSON, Mark Andrew. 1629 N 45TH ST, 45TH STREET CLINIC 98103 #056-06-2001 L2003 **FM** *020 †18

JOHNSON, Martha Claire. 1660 S COLUMBIAN WAY, ANESTHESIOLOGY, VAMC, 98108 #032-01-1989 L1989 **GS** *020 †05

JOHNSON, Martin Mc Dermid. 801 BROADWAY, STE 925 98122 #035-01-1971 L1978 **P** *020 †75

JOHNSON, Maureen M. 201 16TH AVE E, CMB-D133 98112 #030-06-1975 L1979 **IM OM** *020 †20,70

JOHNSON, Quentin L. 1111 E MADISON ST # 406 98122 #016-11-1955 L1977 **AN** *020

JOHNSON, Reiko Kayashima. 4245 ROOSEVELT WAY NE, BOX 354775 98105 #014-01-2003 L2003 **FM** *100 †18

JOHNSON, Rick Lane. 901 BOREN AVE, STE 1500 98104 #054-04-1961 L1964 **AI IM** *071 †03,20

JOHNSON, Shannon Jean. ■ 98116 #054-04-1999 L2001 **FM** *020 †18

JOHNSON, Stephen Leonard. 2324 EASTLAKE AVE E, STE 500 98102 #054-04-1964 L1971 **IM CD** *020 †20

JOHNSON, Sylvia Christine. 125 16TH AVE E CSB-3 98112 #038-06-1970 L1980 **D IM** *020 †20,15

JOHNSON, Timothy Stuart. ■ 98115 #054-04-2008 *012

JOHNSON, Tinsley Coble. ■ 98112 #054-04-1994 L1997 **IM** *020 †20

JOHNSON, Victor Paul. ■ 98119 #028-34-1957 L1957 **R** *071 †80

JOHNSON, Brian Duncan. 1959 NE PACIFIC ST, MSC 359300 98195 #005-18-1990 L1992 **PD** *020 †55

JOHNSTON, Charles Mark. ■ 98103 #054-04-1974 L1977 **P** *050

JOHNSTON, Christine M. 600 BROADWAY, STE 400 98122 #026-04-2001 L2004 **ID** *100

JOHNSTON, Craig Joseph. 4704 NE 47TH ST 98105 #054-04-2002 L2006 **AN** *020 †05

JOHNSTON, Kirkwood Alexan. PO BOX 356428, 1959 NE PACIFIC 98195 #539-02-2003 L2006 **RHU** *012 †20

JOHNSTON, Leland Mann. 2271 NE 51ST ST, BLAKELEY PSYCHIATRIC BLDG 98105 #012-05-1978 L1979 **P CHP** *020 †75

JOHNSTON, Matthew Alexand. ■ 98144 #019-02-2005 L2005 **GS** *012

JOHNSTON, Troy Alan. 4800 SAND POINT WAY NE, CENTER 98105 #051-01-1991 L1999 **PDC** *020 †55

JOHNSTON, Wm Frederick. 1550 N 115TH ST 98133 #054-04-1974 L1977 **EM** *020 †16

JOHNSTONE, Murray Alan. 1221 MADISON ST STE 1124 98104 #028-02-1967 L1968 **OPH** *020 †35

JOKI, James Allen. 1570 N 115TH ST STE 9 98133 #048-02-1975 L1978 **OBG** *020 †30

JOKINEN, Chris Howard. 1959 NE PACIFIC ST BOX 35, UNIVERSITY OF WASHINGTON M 98195 #026-04-2004 L2004 **PTH** *012

JOLLEY, Sarah Elizabeth. ■ 98104 #021-05-2007 L2007 **IM** *012

JOLLY, Philip Clayton. 1100 9TH AVE M6-AC, VIRGINIA MASON MEDICAL CEN 98101 #047-05-1959 L1967 **TS GS** *071 †85,90

JOLY, Jean R. 1959 NE PACIFIC 98195 #067-02-1974 **GPM** *020

JONES, Antoine Dante. ■ 98112 #023-01-2001 L2007 **PMM** *100 †60

JONES, Helena B. 200 16TH AVE E 98112 #024-07-1981 L1984 **PUD IM** *020 †20

JONES, Jodie Elizabeth. PO BOX 356340, GRADUATE MEDICAL EDUCATION 98195 #056-06-2003 L2003 **AN** *020

JONES, Karen Jean. 1229 MADISON ST, STE 1450 98104 #040-02-1984 L1988 **OBG** *020 †30

JONES, Muriel Ellenor. 1600 E JOHN ST 98112 #051-04-1969 L1970 **FM** *071 †18

JONES, Rebecca Marie. 1959 NE PACIFIC ST, MSC 359300 98195 #035-48-1979 L1980 **P** *020 †75

JONES, Thomas Kenny. 4800 SAND POINT WAY NE 98105 #041-02-1978 L1979 **PDC PD** *020 †55

JONESCHILD, Elizabeth S. 600 BROADWAY, SEATTLE HAND SURGERY 98122 #036-07-1997 L2003 **HS** *020 †40

JONOV, Craig R. 509 OLIVE WAY STE 1454 98101 #041-07-1994 L2003 **OMF CS** *020

JOOS, Timothy James. 4400 37TH AVE S 98118 #026-04-1993 L2003 **MPD GPM** *020 †70,55,20

JORDAN, Carolyn Diana. 2401 4TH AVE, STE 900 98121 #040-02-1991 L2002 **PCP** *020 †20

JORDAN, Lisbeth. 1560 N 115TH ST STE 212 98133 #026-08-1994 L1998 **OBG** *020 †30

JOSEPH, Frederic Barry. 9800 4TH AVE NE, STE 202 98115 #012-05-1989 L2001 **VIR** *020 †80

JOSEPH, Prathap J. UNIV OF WASHINGTON, DEPT OF REHAB MED 98195 #048-14-2006 L2006 **PM** *012

JOSEPH, Raymond Samuel, Jr. 1100 9TH AVE 98101 #048-16-1999 L2003 **AN** *020 †05

JOSEPHSON, Neil Cary. 921 TERRY AVE RM 3014, PUGET SOUND BLOOD CENTER 98104 #035-01-1988 L1994 **HEM** *020 †20

JOYNER, Byron David. 1959 NE PACIFIC ST, MSC 359300 98195 #024-01-1988 L1998 **UP** *020 †95

JUAREZ, Ida. PO BOX 356421, UNIV OF WASHINGTON 98195 #048-14-2007 L2007 **IM** *012

JUDELMAN, Julian Joe. 747 BROADWAY 98122 #836-01-1973 L1981 **AN** *020 †05

JUDGE, Karen Olson. 1229 MADISON ST, STE 1450 98104 #005-06-1997 L2001 **OBG** *020 †30

JUDGE, Luke Milburn. ■ 98103 #054-04-2008 *012

JUJ, Harbir Kaur. 4800 SAND POINT WAY NE, REGIONAL M 98105 #040-02-2006 L2006 **PD** *012

JUNG, Charles Fenelon. 1600 E JOHN ST 98112 #056-05-1980 L1985 **ORS** *020 †40

JUNG, Lily. 550 17TH AVE, 5TH FL 98122 #016-06-1986 L1988 **N** *020 †75

JUNO, Philip. 747 BROADWAY 98122 #143-02-1966 L1974 **AN** *020

JURKOVICH, Gregory Jerome. 325 9TH AVE, DEPT SURG 98104 #026-04-1978 L1988 **TRS GS** *020 †85

JUUL, Sandra E. 1959 NE PACIFIC ST, DEPT OF PEDIATRICS RR-439 98195 #054-04-1981 L1982 **NPM** *050 †55

JUULDAM, Tina Evonne. 1959 NE PACIFIC ST RM C1, CAMPUS BOX 356350 98195 #005-02-2002 L2004 **IM** *100

KAARMA, Erik Edward. ■ 98125 #016-11-1982 L1984 **OM GPM** *030 †20

KABASHIMA, Kenji. PO BOX 356421, MED RESIDENCY PGM 98195 #572-01-1996 L1997 **IM** *100

KADEL, Nancy Jennifer. 1959 NE PACIFIC ST, ORTHOPAEDIC DEPT., BOX 356 98195 #054-04-1988 L1997 **ORS** *020 †40

KADERA, Richard Warren. 925 SENECA ST 98101 #007-02-1995 L1999 **IM** *020 †20

KAHN, Sima Delilah. 3111 S DOSE TER, GROUP HEALTH COOP 98144 #005-18-1983 L1987 **OBG** *020 †30

KAHN, Steven Emanuel. 1959 NE PACIFIC ST, UWMC BOX 358280 98195 #836-02-1978 L1986 **END IM** *050 †20

KAHN, Stuart Jonathan. 1124 COLUMBIA ST STE 600, IDRI 98104 #033-05-1985 L1986 **PD IG** *020 †55

KAHSAI, Yordanos Tewolde. 925 SENECA ST G2-GHC, VIRGINIA MASON MEDICAL CEN 98101 #005-15-1998 L2002 **IM** *020

KAISER, Jeffrey Paul. 1959 NE PACIFIC ST, BOX 356560 98195 #036-01-2000 L2000 **CHP** *100 ‡

KAKAR, Suzette Rene. 1550 N 115TH ST 98133 #017-20-1977 L1979 **PHP GP** *074

KALBFLEISCH, Kristine Ann. 1959 NE PACIFIC ST C21, PO BOX 356340 98195 #056-06-2004 L2005 **EM** *020

KALFF, Karin. 1550 N 115TH ST 98133 #033-05-1978 L1981 **AN PD** *020 †05

KALINA, Robert Edward. OPHTH BOX 356485, UW MEDICAL CENTER 98195 #026-04-1960 L1967 **OPH** *020 †35

KALISH, Grace Mariko. 1959 NE PACIFIC ST, BOX 356340 98195 #008-01-2004 L2004 **DR** *012

KALNOSKI, Michael Howard. 1001 SW KLICKITAT WAY 98134 #028-34-1997 L2001 **HMP** *020 †50

KALUS, Andrea Anita. 4225 ROOSEVELT WAY NE, STE 354697 98105 #054-04-1999 L2002 **D** *100 †20,15

KALUS, Robert Michael. 325 9TH AVE, UWMC BOX 359702 98104 #008-01-1998 L2001 **IM** *020 †20

KAMINSKI, Anna Wildy. 4500 9TH AVE NE, STE 324 98105 #005-02-1990 L1990 **FM** *020 †18

KAMITSUKA, Michael David. 747 BROADWAY 98122 #028-03-1982 L1984 **NPM PD** *020 †55

KAMM, Ralph Frederick. 801 BROADWAY, STE 617 98122 #054-04-1961 L1966 **NS** *071 †25

KANDALAFT, Patricia Lynn. 551 N 34TH ST STE 100, PHENOPATH LABORATORIES 98103 #028-46-1986 L1993 **PTH** *020 †20

KANG, Hyoung-Min. 1959 NE PACIFIC ST, BOX 356 98195 #583-10-1986 L1999 **BBK** *100

KANG, Robert Suk. ■ 98103 #035-46-2004 L2004 **OTO** *012

KANTER, Evan David. 1660 S COLUMBIAN WAY, SYSTEM SEATTLE 116 MHC 98108 #056-05-1994 L1998 **P** *020 †75

KANTER, Robert Alan. 1530 N 115TH ST STE 208 98133 #016-02-1973 L1976 **END IM** *020 †20

KAO, Steve Jangfu. 1100 9TH AVE G1-MSO 98101 #035-08-1996 L2000 **IM** *020 †20

KAO, Sue-Chin. 3609 NE 41ST ST 98105 #385-02-1965 *100

KAPANJIE, Robert. 1530 N 115TH ST, STE 302 98133 #018-75-1963, ▲ L1968 **IM FM** *071

KAPLAN, Charles. ■ 98115 #065-01-1937 L1947 **PD** *071 †55

KAPLAN, Henry Geo. 1221 MADISON ST, STE 1225 98104 #035-45-1972 L1973 **ON HEM** *020 †20

KAPLAN, Judith E. 2271 NE 51ST ST 98105 #054-04-1983 L1985 **P** *020 †75

KAPUR, Raj Paul. 4800 SAND POINT WAY NE, CHLDNS HSP MED CTR DPT LAB 98105 #005-06-1988 L1990 **PTH** *020 †50

KAPUR, Vishesh Kishore. 1959 NE PACIFIC ST, MSC 359300 98195 #008-01-1989 L1993 **CCM** *020 †20

KARANDIKAR, Mahesh. 325 9TH AVE, HARBORVIEW MED CTR 98104 #048-12-2004 L2004 **NS** *012

KARBOWSKI, Mariola Beata. ■ 98119 #035-06-2005 L2005 **GS** *012

KARCH, Robert Wm. ■ 98112 #017-20-1955 L1956 **AN** *071

KARGI, Atil Yilmaz. 1959 NE PACIFIC ST, BOX 356426 98195 #902-20-2000 L2005 **END** *012 †20

KARL, Helen Weist. 4800 SAND POINT WAY NE, CHILDRENS HOSP & MED CTR 98105 #051-04-1976 L1990 **AN** *040 †05

KARMALI, Zahra Aminmohame. 550 16TH AVE, STE 100 98122 #054-04-2004 L2004 **FM** *020 †18

KARMARKAR, Sonali Sanjeev. 1959 NE PACIFIC ST 98195 #496-38-1997 L2006 **AN** *012

KARP, Laurence Edward. ■ 98199 #035-19-1963 L1970 **OBG OS** *020 †30,19

KARPANIAN, Hagop Varant. ■ 98102 #056-06-2004 L2005 **AN** *012

KARR, Catherine Jean. 4245 ROOSEVELT WAY NE, STE 354775 98105 #054-04-1999 L2002 **PD EP** *050 †55

KARRAS, Bryant Thomas. SUITE 200, 1107 NE 45TH ST 98195 #056-05-1995 L2003 **IM** *020

KARSAN, Aly. ■ 98103 #065-05-1986 **HMP** *020

KARTON, Mitchell Alan. 1221 MADISON 98104 #005-19-1979 L1980 **END IM** *020 †20

KASER, Karen Suzanne. 4744 41ST AVE SW, STE 101 98116 #048-13-1976 L1977 **GP** *020

KASSAB, Frederick Demeer. 9800 4TH AVE NE 98115 #025-07-1985 L1988 **PD** *020 †55

KASSAB, Paul Georges. ■ 98125 #605-01-1993 L2007 **IM** *020

KASSEBAUM, Jeremy David. 1959 NE PACIFIC ST, BOX 356340 98195 #023-07-2004 L2004 **PD** *020 †55

KATES, David Martin. ■ 98112 #061-01-1987 L1993 **NEP** *100

KATO, Patricia Ellen. 9800 4TH AVE NE 98115 #005-02-1987 L1989 **FM** *020 †18

KATON, Wayne Jay. 1959 NE PACIFIC ST, DEPT PSYCHIATRY, BOX 35656 98195 #040-02-1976 L1977 **P** *020 †75

KATSMAN, Alvin. 910 BOYLSTON AVE 98104 #030-05-1948 L1951 **IM** *071

KATZENELLENBOGEN, Rachel. 4800 SAND PONT WAY NE 2M-4, CHILDS HOSP & REG MED CTR 98105 #023-07-1999 L2002 **ADL** *050 †55

KAUFF, David Manuel. 2505 2ND AVE STE 200, UNIV WA PHYSICIAN 98121 #035-45-1990 L1992 **IM** *020 †20

KAUFFMAN, Elizabeth Nell. ■ 98106 #054-04-1985 L1986 *074

KAUFFMAN, Ellen Jenny. 1221 MADISON ST 98104 #054-04-1978 L1979 **OBG** *020 †30

KAUFFMAN, Mary J P. ■ 98102 #023-01-1996 L2001 **FM** *020 †18

KAUFMAN, Jedediah Abel. 600 UNIVERSITY ST # 120, SWEDISH PHYSICIAN DIVISION 98101 #026-04-1999 L2003 **GS** *020 †85

KAUFMAN, Joel D. 4245 ROOSEVELT WAY NE, STE 354775 98105 #025-01-1986 L1988 **IM OM** *050 †70,20

KAUFMAN, Marla Suzanne. 1959 NE PACIFIC ST, GME OFFICE BOX 356340 98195 #041-15-2002 L2002 **PMM** *020 †60

KAWAGUCHI, T Paul. ■ 98144 #056-06-1955 L1972 **PTH** *071 †50

KAWAMOTO, Cathy Yumiko. 5316 RAINIER AVE S, GROUP HEALTH COOP 98118 #054-04-2000 L2002 **FM** *020 †18

KAWATA, Jean Karen. 747 BROADWAY 98122 #038-06-1984 L1985 **AN** *020 †05

KAYES, Lucille Marie. 1959 NE PACIFIC ST 98195 #028-03-1989 **OS** *100

KAZ, Andrew Michael. 1959 NE PACIFIC ST, UNIVERSITY OF WASHINGTON S 98195 #036-07-1999 L2003 **GE** *100 †20

KAZEMI, Assadullah. 4515 MARTN LTHR KNG JR S, PROVIDENCE ELDER PLACE 98108 #495-53-1985 L1993 **FPG IMG** *020 †20

KAZMIER, Katie Marie. 4800 SAND POINT WAY NE, AND REGION 98105 #028-34-2005 L2005 **PD** *012

KEAM, Jennifer Choi. ■ 98122 #040-02-2003 L2006 **RO** *012

KEARNEY, David J. 1959 NE PACIFIC ST, BOX 356424 98195 #028-46-1989 L1996 **GE** *020 †20

KEATING, Gordon Westlie. ■ 98102 #005-11-1967 L1971 **P CHP** *020

KECK, Carleton Allen. 600 BROADWAY, SEATTLE HAND SURGERY 98122 #017-20-1981 L1982 **HS ORS** *020 †40

■ = Address Information Privacy Protected

KEEBLE, Tanya. 1959 NE PACIFIC ST, DEPT OF PSYCHIATRY BOX 356 98195 #917-30-1998 L2004 **P** *020
KEEBLER, Craig Arthur. 801 BROADWAY, STE 730 98122 #041-13-1976 L1983 **OBG END** *020 †30
KEECH, John Charles. 1959 NE PACIFIC ST, BOX 356340 98195 #016-43-2004 L2004 **GS** *012
KEEL, Sioban Bridget. 1522 17TH AVE E 98112 #026-04-1999 L2002 **HEM** *100 †20
KEELER, George Eldridge. ■ 98109 #048-02-1958 L2005 **EM OS** *020 †18
KEEN, Misbah Kabir. 4245 ROOSEVELT WAY NE, STE 354775 98105 #495-51-1993 L2002 **FM** *020 †18
KEENAN, Lynn Mary. 1600 E JOHN ST 98112 #041-02-1987 L2001 **PUD** *020 †20
KEENE, John Edward. 1101 MADISON ST STE 1400 98104 #054-04-1961 L1965 **U** *020 †95
KEETER, Laura Elizabeth. ■ 98102 #036-01-2002 L2007 **IM** *100 †20
KEHOE, Jessica Alaine. 1401 MADISON ST STE 100, SWEDISH FAMILY MEDICINE 98104 #054-04-2005 L2005 **FP** *012
KEIFER, Matthew C. 325 9TH AVE BOX 359739, HARBORVIEW MEDICAL CENTER 98104 #016-11-1982 L1983 **OM IM** *050 †20,70
KELLER, Timothy Williams. 515 MINOR AVE, STE 220 98104 #038-06-1966 L1980 **P OS** *020 †75
KELLY, Jennifer Andrea. 201 16TH AVE E, GHC RADIOLOGY 98112 #016-45-1997 L2003 **DR** *020 †80
KELLY, Kathleen Ann. 1959 NE PACIFIC ST, RADIATION ONCOLOGY 98195 #018-03-1975 L2006 **RO IM** *020 †20,80
KELLY, Kristen Lynn. 1959 NE PACIFIC ST, DEPT OF FAMILY MEDICINE 98195 #005-02-2006 L2006 **FP** *012
KELLY, Michael Robt. 515 MINOR AVE 98104 #030-06-1969 L1971 **NEP IM** *020 †20
KELLY, Rosemary Helena. 1521 34TH AVE 98122 #026-04-1992 L2000 **P** *020 †75
KELLY, Scott Mason. 747 BROADWAY 98122 #054-04-1984 L1985 **AN** *020 †05
KELLY, Thorpe Maurice. 1801 NW MARKET ST STE 202 98107 #035-01-1955 L1960 **OBG** *020 †30
KELLY, William Saml. 9423 CALIFORNIA AVE SW, VA PUGET SOUND HEALTHCARE 98136 #012-01-1973 L1996 **P** *020 †05,75
KELSO, Gail Marie. 10330 MERIDIAN AVE N, NORTH SEATTLE PEDIATRICS 98133 #054-04-2001 L2005 **PD** *020 †55
KEMPE, Kelly. ■ 98102 #054-04-2008 *012
KENDRICK, Elizabeth Ann. 1959 NE PACIFIC ST, BOX 356521 98195 #005-06-1985 L1994 **NEP** *020 †20
KENNEDY, David James. ■ 98117 #011-03-2004 L2005 **PM** *012
KENNEDY, Diana King. 1101 MADISON ST, STE 301 98104 #054-04-1977 L1980 **IM** *071 †20
KENNEDY, Jesse Ward. ■ 98102 #035-45-1959 L1961 **CD IM** *071 †20
KENNEDY, Michael Elmer. 925 SENECA ST 98101 #054-04-1969 L1971 **AN** *071 †05
KENNEDY, Ruth C Johnson. 515 MINOR AVE, STE 200 98104 #054-04-1965 L1970 **D** *020
KENNELLY, John Mc Rae, Jr. ■ 98148 #010-01-1948 L1956 **U** *071 †95
KENNING, Ian Gregory. 801 26TH AVE E 98112 #018-03-2006 L2006 **FP** *012
KENT, Christopher D. 1959 NE PACIFIC ST, UNIVERSITY OF WASHINGTON 98195 #065-05-1988 L2005 **AN** *100 †05
KENT, Marcia D. 4701 SW ADMIRAL WAY # 25 98116 #025-12-1997 L2000 **PFP** *020 †75
KENYON, Christi Marian. 515 MINOR AVE, STE 300 98104 #054-04-1984 L1985 **RHU IM** *020 †20
KEOGH, Bart P. 600 BROADWAY, STE 170 98122 #041-01-1997 L2001 **DR** *100 †80
KERKERING, Katrina Marie. ■ 98122 #054-04-2006 *012
KERN, Donald Eric. 1145 BROADWAY, STE 2K 98122 #054-04-1990 L1992 **D DS** *020 †15
KERSEY, David Leonard. ■ 98122 #051-01-1987 L1995 **P** *020 †75
KERTESZ, Cynthia Tamar. 4245 ROOSEVELT WAY NE 98105 #016-06-1992 L1992 **PD** *020 †55
KESSLER, Stacy Miho. ■ 98115 #054-04-2008 *012
KESTENBAUM, Bryan Robert. 1959 NE PACIFIC ST, NEPHROLOGY, BB126S HSB 98195 #024-16-1995 L1999 **NEP** *020 †20
KETCHUM, Eric. PO BOX 356421, UNIV OF WASHINGTON 98195 #005-11-2007 L2007 **IM** *012
KETTE, Robert William. 200 16TH AVE E 98112 #038-40-1962 L1963 **PD** *071
KETTLER, Jason Harris. ■ 98121 #055-01-1998 L2006 **ID** *020 †55,20
KEUNG, Bonnie Mayhung. ■ 98109 #016-01-2007 L2007 **IM** *012
KEYS, Kari Anne. ■ 98119 #005-02-2006 L2006 **GS** *012
KEYSER, Charles Keith. 1229 MADISON ST STE 900 98104 #038-06-1981 L1986 **DR** *020 †80
KHACHATRYAN, Gohar A. ■ 98138 #054-04-2005 L2006 **AN** *012
KHALFAYAN, Elias Edward. 900 TERRY AVE, STE 100 98104 #028-34-1984 L1995 **ORS** *020 †40
KHALIGHI, Mehraneh. UNIV OF WASH, BOX 3566340 98195 #054-04-2000 L2003 **IM** *100 †20
KHANFAROOQI, Waqqar Bin. 900 TERRY AVE, STE 100 98104 #005-11-2000 L2000 **ORS** *020
KHATRI, Minesh. PO BOX 356421, UNIV OF WASHINGTON 98195 #036-07-2007 L2007 **IM** *012
KHORASANI, Leila. ■ 98121 #016-02-2003 L2003 **NS** *012
KHOT, Sandeep Prakash. 1959 NE PACIFIC ST RM C212, CAMPUS BOX 356340 98195 #021-01-2002 L2002 **N** *100 †75
KIDD, John Robt. ■ 98103 #054-04-1991 L1994 **AN** *020 †55,05
KIDD, Reiley. 1660 S COLUMBIAN WAY, WAY S-113RAD 98108 #048-04-1971 L1975 **DR** *020 †80
KIEFER, David Stanley. 3635 DENSMORE AVE N, COLLEGE OF MEDICINE 98103 #056-05-1997 L1999 **FM** *020 †18
KIEM, Hans-Peter. 825 EASTLAKE AVE E, FHCR 98109 #407-19-1987 L1993 **ON** *020 †20
KIERAS, David Michael. 1100 9TH AVE C1-MSO, VIRGINIA MASON MEDICAL CEN 98101 #025-01-1985 L1986 **ORS OSM** *020 †40
KIERNEY, Carl Everett. ■ 98109 #033-05-1964 L1968 **D** *071 †15
KIEU, Kimquy Thi. F-350 H S BLDG SC-30 98195 #005-18-1983 L2001 **GPM** *020 †70
KIFLE, Yemiserach. 4800 SAND POINT WAY NE, MED CTR, CH-68 PULMONARY 98105 #366-01-1976 L1998 **PDP** *020 †55
KILLEY, Benjamin James. ■ 98115 #016-45-2003 L2007 **EM** *020
KILLIAN, Robert Kent. 901 BOREN AVE, STE 705 98104 #049-01-1993 L1996 **FM** *020 †18
KILLIEN, F Christian. 201 16TH AVE E 98112 #054-04-1967 L1968 **DR** *020 †80
KIM, Brian. 4245 ROOSEVELT WAY NE, BOX 354775 98105 #039-01-1986 L2005 **ON HEM** *020 †20
KIM, Brian Sangwoo. PO BOX 356421, UNIV OF WASHINGTON 98195 #054-04-2007 L2007 **IM** *012
KIM, Brian Yong. ■ 98102 #035-20-2004 L2004 **FM** *020
KIM, David Keesu. 1229 MADISON ST STE 900, SEATTLE RADIOLOGISTS, APC 98104 #026-08-1999 L1999 **RNR** *012 †80
KIM, David Kernhoe. 4800 SAND POINT WAY NE, MAILSTOP W9824 98105 #036-05-2002 L2006 **PAN** *100 †05
KIM, Do Kyun. 125 15TH AVE E, GROUP HEALTH CENTRAL 98112 #016-02-1989 L1992 **NS** *020 †25
KIM, Francis. 325 9TH AVE 98104 #005-02-1990 L1993 **CD** *020 †20
KIM, Ham Hwi. ■ 98115 #583-03-1973 L1981 **ADL** *020
KIM, Hojoong Mike. ■ 98195 #016-11-2002 L2003 **N** *100 †75
KIM, Hyang Nina. 325 9TH AVE, 2W CLINICS 98104 #005-02-1999 L2001 **ID** *100 †20
KIM, James Inbok. 4245 ROOSEVELT WAY NE, BOX 354775 98105 #005-12-2005 L2005 **FP** *012
KIM, James Suyoung. ■ 98103 #005-14-2005 L2006 **IM** *100
KIM, Janice Nam. 1959 NE PACIFIC ST, BOX # 356043 98195 #016-42-2001 L2006 **RO** *100
KIM, Jason. 4616 25TH AVE NE # 437 98105 #038-43-2002 L2004 **AN** *100
KIM, Jerry Hyun. 4800 SAND POINT WAY NE, # W-9824 98105 #041-02-2002 L2006 **PAN** *100 †05
KIM, Jinna Diane. 8444 RAINIER AVE S 98118 #043-01-1996 L1998 **FM** *020 †18
KIM, Karl Hyun. 125 16TH AVE E, GROUP HEALTH COOPERATIVE 98112 #041-02-1998 L2004 **GE** *020 †20
KIM, Kihan. ■ 98122 #023-01-2003 L2007 **CCP** *012 †55
KIM, Man Ki. 925 SENECA ST 98101 #005-14-1982 L1990 **OPH** *020 †35
KIM, Naehwa. ■ 98101 #034-01-2007 L2007 **GS** *012
KIM, Patricia Mitori. 551 N 34TH ST STE 100, PHENOPATH LABORATORIES PLL 98103 #056-06-2002 L2006 **SP** *100
KIM, Stephen Sangwan. 4800 SAND POINT WAY NE, DEPT OF SURGERY MS W-7729 98105 #051-01-1994 L2001 **PDS GS** *020 †85
KIM, Steve Hoonsang. 1536 N 115TH ST, STE 300 98133 #025-01-1997 L2003 **OPH** *020 †35
KIMBALL, Ann Marie. 1959 NE PACIFIC ST, MSC 359300 98195 #054-04-1976 L1978 **GPM** *020 †70
KIM-DEOBALD, Jessie. 1530 N 115TH ST, STE 301 98133 #054-04-1990 L1992 **GE** *020 †20
KIMELMAN, Judith Mara. 1101 MADISON ST, STE 950 98104 #005-11-1989 L1989 **OBG** *020 †30
KIMMEL, Robt Raymond, Jr. 1100 FAIRVIEW AVE N, RESEARCH CTR, ROOM C2-023 98109 #028-34-1979 L1983 **IM END** *020 †20
KIM-MILLER, Sally H. ■ 98102 #035-20-1977 L1984 **OPH** *071 †35
KINDER, Eric Anthony. 9730 3RD AVE NE, STE 202 98115 #005-02-1997 L2002 **RNR** *020 †80
KINDER, Russell Robert. ■ 98104 #016-42-2007 L2007 **TY** *012
KING, Bryan Harry. 4800 SAND POINT WAY NE, SEATTLE CHILDREN'S HOSPITA 98105 #056-06-1983 L2005 **CHP** *020 †75
KING, Harold Eugene. 747 BROADWAY 98122 #054-04-1955 L1957 **IM** *071 †20
KING, Jane Elizabeth. 2101 E YESLER WAY 98122 #005-02-1993 L1993 **FM** *020 †18
KING, Janet Chiawen. 7532 20TH AVE NE 98115 #035-09-2001 L2003 **GE** *012
KING, Jason Charles. 1959 NE PACIFIC ST, BOX 356340 98195 #010-02-2004 L2004 **ORS** *012
KING, Lloyd Thos, Jr. 747 BROADWAY 98122 #018-03-1960 L1961 **GS TS** *071 †85,90
KING, Philip J. 2208 NW MARKET ST 98107 #054-04-1952 L1953 **GP** *071
KING, Robert Christopher. 1959 NE PACIFIC ST, MSC 359300 98195 #041-01-1993 L1993 **TS** *100 †85,90
KING, Stephen Haim. 1959 NE PACIFIC ST, BOX 356340 98195 #005-15-2001 L2002 **U** *012
KING, Thomas Steele. 1145 BROADWAY 98122 #054-04-1992 L1994 **IM** *020 †20
KINNISH, William Homer. 600 UNIVERSITY ST, STE 1200 98101 #054-04-1970 L1971 **FM** *020 †18
KINTNER, Mary Jo. 2450 33RD AVE W, STE 100 98199 #054-04-1984 L1987 **FM** *020 †18
KINYOUN, James Lovgren. 1959 NE PACIFIC ST, MSC 359300 98195 #030-05-1971 L1978 **OPH** *020 †35
KIRBY, Anna Catherine. ■ 98105 #054-04-2007 **OBG** *012
KIRBY, Philip Keeling. 325 9TH AVE BOX 359763, HARBORVIEW MED CTR 98104 #054-04-1978 L1979 **D IM** *020 †20,15
KIRBY, Richard Murray. 900 TERRY AVE, STE 100 98104 #054-04-1977 L1978 **ORS** *020 †40
KIRKPATRICK, John Nelson. 1100 9TH AVE 98101 #054-04-1973 L1976 **IM** *020 †20
KIRSCH, Edward Barry. ■ 98177 #005-02-1971 L1978 **P** *020
KIRSCHNER, Heidi M. ■ 98115 #154-07-1937 L1957 **GPM GP** *071
KIRSCHNER, Marc Alan. 1570 N 115TH ST STE 14 98133 #038-06-1982 L1997 **N IM** *020 †75
KIRTLAND, Steven Howard. 1100 9TH AVE 98101 #005-18-1986 L1988 **IM** *020 †20
KIRZ, Howard Lutz. 200 15TH AVE E, GROUP HEALTH HOSPITAL 98112 #016-02-1967 L1968 **EM OS** *071 †18,16
KITA, Mariko. 1100 9TH AVE, MX-X7-NEU 98101 #016-06-1994 L2000 **N** *020 †75
KITAHARA, Masaki. ■ 98105 #572-03-1987 L1991 **APM** *020
KITAHATA, Mari Massey. 325 9TH AVE, DEPT CFAR 98104 #041-01-1987 L1991 **IM** *020 †20
KITANO, Yuka. 925 SENECA ST # 1930 98101 #572-01-1996 **IM** *012
KITCHELL, Carolyn Claar. 7006 BRIGHTON LN S 98118 #051-01-1982 L1986 **CLP ATP** *074 †50
KITCHELL, Margaret Anne. 1410 E PINE ST, UNIT 312 98122 #028-02-1974 L1975 **P** *020 †75
KITCHELL, Robert Webster. 1221 MADISON ST 98104 #051-01-1982 L1986 **IM** *020 †20
KIVIAT, Leah Naomi. 1959 NE PACIFIC ST, BOX 356340 98195 #054-04-2003 L2003 **DR** *012
KIVIAT, Mark David. 515 MINOR AVE, STE 240 98104 #035-15-1964 L1969 **U** *020 †95
KIVIAT, Nancy Carol. 2324 EASTLAKE AVE E, STE 500 98102 #054-04-1975 L1976 **PTH** *030 †50
KIYASU, Elizabeth Kisako. 1959 NE PACIFIC ST, BOX 359753 98195 #012-05-1993 L1993 **IMG** *020 †20
KIYONAGA, Glen Kazuteru. 2902 BEACON AVE S 98144 #054-04-1976 L1977 **FM** *020 †18
KJOS, Bent Olav. 600 BROADWAY, STE 170 98122 #005-18-1979 L1990 **DR OS** *020 †80
KLAFF, Lindy Sara. 1959 NE PACIFIC ST RM C212, CAMPUS BOX 356340 98195 #054-04-2002 L2004 **PCC** *012 †20
KLAUSNER, Richard Danl. ■ 98177 #036-07-1976 L1978 **IM** *100
KLEBANOFF, Seymour J. 1959 NE PACIFIC ST, BOX 357185 98195 #065-01-1951 L1976 **ID IG** *050
KLEIN, Daniel Ethan. 1425 WESTERN AVE APT 303 98101 #010-01-1981 L1988 **P** *020 †75
KLEIN, Deborah Ellen. 1001 4TH AVE STE 420 98154 #054-04-1990 L1992 **FM** *020 †18
KLEIN, Eileen Joy. 4800 SAND PT WAY NE # 5D-1, CHILDRENS HOSP & MED CTR 98105 #023-07-1988 L1988 **PE** *020 †55
KLEIN, Matthew Brady. 325 9TH AVE, UNIVERSITY OF WASH./ BOX 3 98104 #008-01-1997 L2003 **GS** *020 †65
KLEIN, Steven Lewis. 1560 N 115TH ST STE 209 98133 #047-05-1984 L1993 **NS GS** *020 †25
KLETTER, Gad B. 1101 MADISON ST STE 800, SWEDISH PED SPECLTY CLC 98104 #550-02-1983 L1995 **PDE PD** *050 †55
KLINE, James Sanborn. ■ 98136 #032-01-1975 L1979 **EM** *020 †16
KLINGHARDT, Dietrich K. 1315 MADISON ST # 4 98104 #409-05-1979 L1984 *020
KLUGE, Wolfgang Fritz. 1560 N 115TH ST, SUMMIT CARDIOLOGY 98133 #407-16-1961 L1967 **CD IM** *071 †20
KNAPP, Calvin Horace, Jr. 515 MINOR AVE, STE 200 98104 #054-04-1981 L1990 **OTO PS** *020 †45
KNAUP, Stephen Andrew. 747 BROADWAY 98122 #028-34-1977 L1978 **AN** *020 †05
KNEELAND, Kerry Anne. 747 BROADWAY 98122 #021-01-1990 L1994 **OS AN** *020

■ = Address Information Privacy Protected

KNICKERBOCKER, Heidi Jo. 1801 NW MARKET ST, STE 100 98107 #054-04-1988 L1988 **OBG** *020 †30

KNIERIM, Richard Harlin. 1229 MADISON ST 98104 #005-12-1970 L1972 **PTH DMP** *020 †50

KNIGHT, Christopher L. 4245 ROOSEVELT WAY NE, STE 354775 98105 #054-04-1996 L1999 **IM** *020 †20

KNIGHT, Jeffrey Clarence. 925 SENECA ST H8-GME, VIRGINIA MASON MEDICAL CEN 98101 #054-04-2004 L2004 **IM** *012 †20

KNIGHT, Joseph Eric. 9800 4TH AVE NE 98115 #054-04-1974 L1977 **FM** *020 †18

KNIGHT, Richard Benjamin. ■ 98122 #054-04-2008 *012

KNIPPERS, Johnny Dewitt, Jr. ■ 98115 #056-06-2006 L2007 **OPH** *012

KNOPES, Keith Danl. 1100 9TH AVE 98101 #005-11-1981 L1986 **AN PA** *020 †05

KNOPP, Robert Henry. 325 9TH AVE, # 359720 98104 #035-20-1964 L1974 **END IM** *050 †20

KNUDSON, Richard Arnold. ■ 98125 #020-02-1945 L1958 **GP** *071

KNUDSON, Robert Wendell. ■ 98102 #054-04-1971 L1977 **PD** *020 †55

KNUTSON, Tristan Leif. ■ 98144 #023-12-2005 L2006 **EM** *012 †18

KO, Andrew Lin. 325 9TH AVE, # 359766 98104 #016-11-2005 L2005 **NS** *012

KO, Cynthia Wunping. 1959 NE PACIFIC ST, BOX 356424 98195 #005-11-1991 L1994 **GE IM** *050 †20

KO, Dennis Chunyone. ■ 98125 #005-11-2005 *100

KO, Eugene. 2902 BEACON AVE S 98144 #054-04-1953 L1954 **FM** *071

KOALA, Diana Kay. 1101 MADISON ST, STE 950 98104 #054-04-1994 L1999 **OBG** *020 †30

KOBER, Margo Marie. 515 MINOR AVE 98104 #054-04-1992 L1992 **IM** *020 †20

KOCAREK, Catherine Marie. 7563 CALIFORNIA AVE SW 98136 #038-40-1996 L2000 **IM** *020 †20

KOCH, Johannes. 11027 MERIDIAN AVE N # 100, SEATTLE GASTROENTEROLOGY 98133 #021-01-1987 L2001 **GE** *020 †20

KOCH-LEIBMANN, Angelika T. 1959 NE PACIFIC ST 98195 #409-21-1999 L2005 **IM** *012

KOCSIS, Agnes B. ■ 98103 #473-01-1995 L2000 **CHP** *020

KODE, Shubhada Kalidas. 1100 9TH AVE G1-MSO, VIRGINIA MASON MEDICAL CEN 98101 #495-22-1980 L1983 **P ADP** *020 †75

KODISH, Ian Michael. 1959 NE PACIFIC ST BOX 35, UNIV OF WASHINGTON PSYCHIA 98195 #016-11-2004 L2004 **CHP** *012

KODNER, Daniel Aaron. 6707 35TH PL S 98118 #056-05-1994 L1998 **P** *020 †75

KOEHLER, Richard P. 1100 9TH AVE, MAILSTOP C6-GS 98101 #041-12-1999 L2006 **GS** *020 †85,90

KOELLE, David Martin. 1959 NE PACIFIC ST, MAIL STOP 358117 98195 #054-04-1985 L1988 **ID IM** *050 †20

KOENIG, Elizabeth Louise. 1959 NE PACIFIC ST # 3565, RESIDENCY TRAINING PROG 98195 #054-04-1995 L1997 **P** *020 †75

KOEPSELL, Thomas Dickey. UNIV OF WASH, EPIDEMIOLOGY BOX 357236 98195 #024-01-1972 L1974 **EP IM** *050 †20

KOERKER, Richard Mortson. 2324 EASTLAKE AVE E, STE 500 98102 #025-01-1970 L1974 **N OS** *071 †75

KOFLER, Thomas John. 1221 MADISON ST, SEATTLE RADIOLOGISTS APC 98104 #056-06-1973 L1974 **DR** *020 †80

KOGUT, Kevin T. 747 BROADWAY 98122 #035-45-1994 L1997 **AN** *020 †05

KOGUT, Matthew Jay. 1959 NE PACIFIC ST, BOX 356340 98195 #038-40-2004 L2004 **DR** *012

KOH, Eun-Mi. UNIV OF WASHINGTON 98195 #583-02-1984 L1993 **RHU** *020

KOH, Wui Jin. 1959 NE PACIFIC ST # 35604, UNIV WA MC DEPT RAD ONC 98195 #005-12-1984 L1986 **RO** *020 †80

KOHEN, Ruth. 1660 S COLUMBIAN WAY, SEATTLE VA GRECC 182B 98108 #409-39-1986 L1992 **P PYG** *050 †75

KOHL, Shane Kevin. UNIV OF WASHINGTON, SURGICAL PATHOLOGY FELLOWS 98195 #030-05-2003 L2007 **SP** *012 †50

KOHLER, Ted Raney. 1660 S COLUMBIAN WAY 98108 #024-01-1976 L1978 **VS** *040 †85

KOHLS, Shannah Marie. 1401 MADISON ST STE 100, MEDICINE RESIDE 98104 #038-41-2006 L2006 **FP** *012

KOHMETSCHER, Mark Allen. 600 UNIVERSITY ST, STE 1200 98101 #018-03-1996 L1999 **IM** *020 †20

KOHN, Samuel Maurice. 4800 SAND POINT WAY NE, REGIONAL M 98105 #036-01-2006 L2006 **PD** *012

KOHR, Jennifer Ruth. 1959 NE PACIFIC ST, BOX 356340 98195 #005-02-2005 L2005 **DR** *012

KOJNOK, Eva. 515 MINOR AVE, STE 300 98104 #035-45-1994 L1997 **IM** *020 †20

KOLDEN, Rolf Julius. 815 35TH AVE 98122 #038-06-1976 L1987 **P PD** *020 †75

KOLLER, Martina Mary. 6300 9TH AVE NE, STE 200 98115 #033-06-1987 L1990 **FM** *020 †18

KOLLMANN, Tobias Reinhard. 1959 NE PACIFIC ST, CAMPUS BOX 356340 98195 #035-46-1998 L2003 **PDI** *020 †55

KONG, Crystal Gailrose. ■ 98125 #025-01-2007 L2007 **FP** *012

KONIKOW, Joel C. 1801 NW MARKET ST STE 209 98107 #025-07-1972 L1974 **FM IM** *020 †18

KOO, Anthony Bonyoung. ■ 98103 #016-01-2007 L2007 **AN** *012

KOOY, Todd Lane. 1107 NE 45TH ST # 44, UNIV OF WASH,DEPT OF RADIO 98105 #054-04-2001 L2001 **VIR** *100 †80

KOPPULA, Bhasker Rao. 1959 NE PACIFIC ST 98195 #495-21-1996 L2005 **NM** *012

KORBONITS, Charles Wm. 3763 W COMMODORE WAY 98199 #041-02-1973 L1975 **EM** *020 †16

KORNRICH, Rachel Marie. ■ 98105 #040-02-2006 L2006 **FP** *012

KOSCHMANN, Carl Johannes. ■ 98103 #056-05-2007 L2007 **PD** *012

KOSHY, Reena Anna. 6020 35TH AVE SW, HIGH POINT CLINIC 98126 #016-01-1993 L1995 **FM** *020 †18

KOST, Amanda Rhea. 4245 ROOSEVELT WAY NE, BOX 354775 98105 #035-06-2005 L2005 **FP** *012

KOSTER, John Frederick. 506 2ND AVE, STE 1200 98104 #034-01-1976 L1978 **OS IM** *030 †20

KOVACS, Kathryn Ann. 1100 9TH AVE C1-MSO, VIRGINIA MASON MEDICAL CEN 98101 #050-02-2000 L2000 **IM** *100

KOVAR, Michael Allan. 550 16TH AVE, STE 100 98122 #010-01-1983 L1987 **FM** *075 †18

KOVAR, Richard David. 500 19TH AVE E, COUNTRY DOCTOR COMM HLTH 98112 #010-01-1980 L1984 **FM** *020 †18

KOVICH, Heather Clare. 4245 ROOSEVELT WAY NE, BOX 354775 98105 #041-13-2005 L2005 **FP** *012

KOWAL, Mark Timothy. 747 BROADWAY STE 731, SWEDISH MED CTR FIRST HILL 98122 #007-02-2006 L2006 **GS** *012

KOWALS, Stephanie Gail. 3123 FAIRVIEW AVE E, LAKE UNION PSYCHIATRIC GRO 98102 #054-04-1990 L1991 **P** *020 †75

KOWDLEY, Krishnamurt V. 1100 9TH AVE G1-MSO, UWMC-BOX 356424 98101 #035-47-1985 L1993 **IM GE** *050 †20

KOZAREK, Richard Anthony. 747 BROADWAY 98122 #056-05-1973 L1983 **GE IM** *020 †20

KRABILL, Kimberly Ann. 1101 MADISON ST STE 800 98104 #026-04-1981 L1999 **PDC** *020 †55

KRAEMER, Doris Maria. FRED HUTCHINSON CANCER RES 98109 #409-15-1993 L2003 *020

KRAFT, George Howard. 1959 NE PACIFIC ST, BOX 356490 98195 #038-40-1963 L1970 **PM SCI** *020 †60

KRAFT, Vara. 7715 24TH AVE NW, OLYMPIC MEDICAL CENTER 98117 #021-01-1992 L1992 **IM** *020 †20

KRAJINA, Alexander A. 1560 N 115TH ST, STE 207 98133 #021-05-1986 L1989 **IM** *020 †20

KRAMAR, Piroska Olga. 1101 MADISON ST STE 700, PACIFIC MEDICAL CENTER 98104 #030-06-1964 L1970 **OPH** *071 †35

KRAMER, Dawna Jacobsen. 1100 9TH AVE G1-MSO, VIRGINIA MASON MEDICAL CEN 98101 #054-04-1983 L1984 **DR** *020 †80

KRANE, Bjorn Britton. 1570 N 115TH ST STE 14 98133 #040-02-2000 L2005 **CN** *020 †75

KRASHIN, Daniel Lawrence. 4532 47TH AVE NE 98105 #025-01-1994 L2002 **P** *020 †75

KRATZ, Rodney Jon. 1530 N 115TH ST, STE 201 98133 #017-20-1997 L2002 **GS** *020 †85,10

KRAUS, Eric Edward. 925 SENECA ST 98101 #026-04-1991 L1991 **N** *020 †75

KRAUSE, Robin Ernest. 2505 2ND AVE, STE 200 98121 #005-11-1996 L1998 **IM** *020 †20

KRAUSS, Ruth Helen. 310 15TH AVE 98122 #035-19-1965 L1968 **GYN** *030 †30

KREBS, Edwin Gerhard. PO BOX 357750, DEPT PHARMACOLOGY 98195 #028-02-1943 L1950 **OS** *071

KREGENOW, David Allan. 1100 9TH AVE 98101 #041-01-1995 L1997 **PCC** *020 †20

KREHBIEL, Alice Ann. 509 OLIVE WAY, STE 900 98101 #054-04-1984 L1987 **FM** *020 †18

KREISS, Joan Kathryn. 325 9TH AVE 98104 #028-02-1978 L1985 **ID IM** *020 †20

KREJCI, Sonja Maria. 509 OLIVE WAY, STE 900 98101 #054-04-1987 L1995 **D** *020 †55,15

KREM, Maxwell Masters. ■ 98105 #028-02-2004 L2007 **HO** *012 †20

KREMBS, Alexander Wm. 747 BROADWAY 98122 #056-06-1969 L1974 **AN** *020 †05

KREMER, Richard Merle. ■ 98133 #025-01-1964 L1972 **GS VS** *071 †85

KRESS, Catherine Maria. ■ 98103 #054-04-2008 *012

KRETSCHMER, Klaus-Peter. ■ 98118 #407-16-1959 L1966 **GS TS** *071 †85

KRETZLER, Harry H, Jr. ■ 98115 #041-01-1951 L1953 **ORS** *071 †40

KREVAT, Seth Andrew. 1100 9TH AVE C1-MSO, VIRGINIA MASON MEDICAL CEN 98101 #010-02-2000 L2003 **IM** *020 †20

KRIEG, James Christopher. 325 9TH AVE BOX 359798, HARBORVIEW MEDICAL CENTER 98104 #033-05-1990 L1995 **ORS** *020 †40

KRIEGER, Eric. 1959 NE PACIFIC ST, BOX 356422 98195 #035-47-2002 L2006 **CD** *012 †20

KRIEGER, James Warren. 401 5TH AVE, STE 1300 98104 #005-02-1984 L1986 **PHP IM** *050 †20

KRIEGER, John Newton. 1660 S COLUMBIAN WAY, VA PUGET SOUND 112UR 98108 #035-20-1974 L1982 **U ID** *050 †95

KRISHNA, P Hari. 1959 NE PACIFIC ST, UNIV OF WASHINGTON 98195 #495-14-1999 L2006 *100

KRISHNAMURTHY, Shoba. 1101 MADISON ST, STE 301 98104 #495-33-1974 L1981 **GE IM** *020 †20

KRISHNAN, Ranjini Murali. 1959 NE PACIFIC ST BOX 35, U OF WASHINGTON, CARDIOLOG 98195 #495-59-1999 L2003 **CD** *012 †20 ‡

KRITZER, Gordon Lee. 1100 9TH AVE G1-MSO, VIRGINIA MASON MEDICAL CEN 98101 #005-18-1980 L1992 **CD IM** *020 †20

KROBER, Marvin Smith. 200 16TH AVE E 98112 #038-06-1968 L1998 **PD ID** *020 †55

KROHN, Aaron John. PO BOX 356421, UNIV OF WASHINGTON 98195 #054-04-2006 L2006 **IM** *012

KROLL, Heather Roma. 4300 AURORA AVE N, STE 100 98103 #054-04-1994 L1998 **PM PMM** *020 †60

KROLL, Robin. 3216 NE 45TH PL, STE 100 98105 #041-07-1981 L1986 **GYN** *020 †30

KRONMAN, Matthew P. 1959 NE PACIFIC ST, BOX 356340 98195 #008-01-2003 L2003 **PD** *020 †55

KROSS, Erin Kathryn. BB-1253 HSC, UWMC DIVISION OF PULMONARY 98195 #018-03-2002 L2005 **PCC** *012 †20

KRUEGER, Philip John. 4245 ROOSEVELT WAY NE, STE 354775 98105 #005-02-2002 L2007 **ORS** *100

KRUGER, Jaco. 3216 NE 45TH PL, STE 200 98105 #836-06-1993 L2003 **FM** *020 †18

KRYMAN, Jonathon. ■ 98117 #038-45-2003 L2003 **AN** *020

KRYNICKI, Paul Francis. 1145 BROADWAY 98122 #025-01-1966 L1969 **IM RO** *020

KUAN, James Kenneth. 1101 MADISON ST, STE 1400 98104 #068-01-1999 L2005 **U TRS** *020

KUBESH, Claudine Mae. 325 9TH AVE 98104 #026-04-2003 L2003 **IM** *100 †20

KUBLIN, James Gerard. 1100 FAIRVIEW AVE N, LE 5034 98109 #010-02-1988 L2005 **GPM** *020 †70

KUCHINAD, Daisy Thomman. 1100 9TH AVE, VIRGINIA MASON MEDICAL CEN 98101 #016-45-1987 L2006 **IM** *020 †20

KUDENCHUK, Peter James. UNIV OF WASHINGTON, CARDIOLOGY BOX 356422 98195 #054-04-1979 L1980 **ICE CD** *020 †20

KUECHLE, Melanie Kidd. 1959 NE PACIFIC ST, BOX 356524 98195 #048-04-1989 L1995 **D** *020 †15

KUEHL, Laurel Marie. 1300 SPRING ST, STE 500 98104 #054-04-1996 L1998 **FM** *020 †18

KUHARIC, Henry Anton. 747 BROADWAY 98122 #054-04-1954 L1960 **IM PUD** *071 †20

KUHLMAN-WOOD, Kate Ashli. ■ 98101 #047-20-2007 L2007 **GS** *012

KUHR, Christian Senesac. 1959 NE PACIFIC ST, BOX 356174 98195 #054-04-1988 L1993 **U** *020 †95

KULANDER, Bruce Gregory. 1229 MADISON ST 98104 #054-04-1962 L1964 **PTH** *020 †50

KULGREN, Rebecca Anne. ■ 98115 #054-04-2004 L2005 **OBG** *012

KULIN, Pamela Ann. 4740 44TH AVE SW, # 200 98116 #054-04-1979 L1980 **D IM** *020 †20,15

KUMAR, Anjuli. 4800 SAND POINT WAY NE, AND REGION 98105 #035-20-2003 L2006 **AI** *012

KUMAR, Rashmi Prem. 1959 NE PACIFIC ST, U OF W-HS AFFAIRS BOX 3563 98195 #054-04-2003 L2004 **IM** *100 †20

KUMAR, Tushar Mahi. ■ 98177 #054-04-2008 *012

KUMASAKA, Kenneth Haruo. 3400 CALIFORNIA AVE SW, STE 200 98116 #035-01-1988 L1991 **PD** *020 †55 ‡

KUMASAKA, Yukio. 5421 CALIFORNIA AVE SW 98136 #054-04-1955 L1959 **PD PDA** *071

KUNDU, Anjana. 4800 SAND POINT WAY NE, CHILDREN'S HOSPITAL DEPT O 98105 #495-69-1991 L2003 **AN** *020 †80,05

KUNIYOSHI, Catherine J. 1959 NE PACIFIC ST BOX 356, UNIVERSITY OF WA SCH OF ME 98195 #005-06-2001 L2001 **CHP** *020

KUNIYOSHI, Jon Shinzen. 1959 NE PACIFIC ST, GRADUATE MED ED BOX 356340 98195 #005-06-2001 L2001 **CHP** *100

KUNJAPPAN, Vimala E. 2701 CALIFORNIA AVE SW, STE 235 98116 #495-27-1960 L1973 **AN** *020 †05

KUNKLER, James Robt. 1100 9TH AVE M6-AC, VIRGINIA MASON MEDICAL CEN 98101 #007-02-1975 L1977 **FM OM** *020 †18

KUNTZ, Christopher Alan. 1101 MADISON ST STE 301, PACMED CLINICS - MADISON 98104 #005-02-1993 L1997 **OPH** *020 †35

■ = Address Information Privacy Protected

KUO, Cho-Chou. PO BOX 357238, UNIV WA STE SC38 98195 #385-02-1959 L1974 **GPM** *050
KURACHI, Akiko Lynne. 1801 NW MARKET ST STE 2 98107 #025-01-2003 L2003 **OBG** *020
KURATANI, John David. 4800 SAND POINT WAY NE, CHILDREN'S HOSP REG CTR B 98105 #021-01-1990 L1999 **CN N** *020 †75
KURIBAYASHI, Aya. 1401 MADISON ST STE 100, MEDICINE RESIDE 98104 #024-01-2004 L2004 **FM** *020 †18
KURTZ, Christopher Eric. UNIV OF WASHINGTON, DIVISION OF CARDIOLOGY BOX 98195 #026-08-2004 L2007 **CD** *012 †20
KURTZ, John Mosser. 747 SUMMIT AVE E 98102 #005-02-1973 L1979 **RO** *100 †80
KUSSICK, Steven James. 1959 NE PACIFIC ST 98195 #054-04-1994 L1997 **PTH** *100 †50
KUSZLER, Patricia Carol. ■ 98115 #026-08-1978 L1979 **EM** *030
KUVER, Rahul Pradyumna. 1959 NE PACIFIC ST, UWMC- BOX 356424 98195 #054-04-1989 L1989 **GE IM** *050 †20
KVIDERA, Dennis Jay. 515 MINOR AVE, STE 200 98104 #018-03-1976 L1977 **ORS** *020 †40
KWAN, Herman C. 1101 MADISON ST, STE 1400 98104 #061-01-2001 L2006 **U** *100
KWAN-GETT, Taosheng C. 401 5TH AVE, STE 1300 98104 #024-01-1991 L1991 **PD** *020 †55
KWEON, Christopher Yang. ■ 98102 #054-04-2008 *012
KWOK, Louisa Vanfung. PO BOX 356340, UNIVERSITY OF WASHINGTON G 98195 #054-04-2005 L2005 **N** *012
KWON, Sung. UNIV OF WASHINGTON, DEPT OF SURGERY #356410 98195 #016-11-2007 L2007 **GS** *012
KWON, Yong Seok. 1959 NE PACIFIC ST, GME PROGRAMS, BOX 356340 98195 #054-04-2005 L2005 **GS** *012
KYLLO, Jeffrey Eldon. 1145 BROADWAY, THE POLYCLINIC 98122 #028-34-1981 L1982 **PS GS** *020 †85,65
LABELLA, Angelena Maria. ■ 98109 #035-48-2005 L2005 **IM** *012
LACAMBRA, John Chambliss. 1100 9TH AVE G1-MSO, SWEDISH HEALTH SERVICES 98101 #011-04-1989 L1992 **EM** *020 †16
LACAMBRA, Mark Luis. 7715 24TH AVE NW 98117 #054-04-2001 L2003 **FM** *020 †18
LACAS, Alethea D. 1401 MADISON ST STE 100, SWEDISH MED CTR-SEATTLE 98104 #064-01-2002 L2003 **FPG** *012 †18
LACEY, Benjamin William. 1959 NE PACIFIC ST, GME OFFICE BOX 356340 98195 #018-03-2005 L2005 **PM** *012
LACKERMANN, Ellen Marie. 1200 12TH AVE S, PACIFIC MEDICAL CLINIC 98144 #018-03-1984 L1986 **FM** *020 †18
LACY, John Matthew. 1959 NE PACIFIC ST 98195 #016-43-1999 L2001 **NP** *100
LAFFERTY, William Ernest. 600 BROADWAY, STE 400 98122 #019-02-1978 L1983 **A ID** *020 †20
LA FLAMME, Michael Alan. 1959 NE PACIFIC ST 98195 #012-05-1999 L2002 **PTH** *020 †50
LAGALBO, Regina Kathleen. 1560 N 115TH ST, STE 212 98133 #056-05-1999 L2003 **OBG** *020 †30
LAGERBERG, Eugene Vernon. ■ 98115 #054-04-1958 L1959 **OBG** *071 †30
LAGERBERG, Steven James. ■ 98101 #030-05-1971 L1972 **FM** *020 †18
LAHAD, Amnon. 4245 ROOSEVELT WAY NE, FAMILY MEDICINE CLINIC UW 98195 #550-01-1988 L1993 **UM** *020 †70
LAKSHMINARAYAN, Sambasiva. 4435 BEACON AVE S 98108 #495-36-1965 L1975 **PUD IM** *020
LAM, Arthur M. 325 9TH AVE 98104 #065-06-1974 L1987 **AN** *020 †05
LAM, Daniel Yuguan. PO BOX 356421, UNIV OF WASHINGTON 98195 #024-07-2007 L2007 **IM** *012
LAM, Deborah Lapyan. 4343 ROOSEVELT WAY NE #501 98105 #016-06-2002 L2004 **OPH** *020
LAM, Derek Jeremy. PO BOX 356340, UW SCHOOL OF MED GME PROGR 98195 #054-04-2003 L2003 **OTO** *012
LAM, Sing. 10317 GREENWOOD AVE N, UNIT 201 98133 #143-07-1984 L1991 **GE IM** *020 †20
LAMBERT, Mary Jane. 1600 E JOHN ST 98112 #035-19-1984 L1988 **IM IMG** *020 †20
LAMEY, Jack Ritchie. 1959 NE PACIFIC ST, BOX 356460 98195 #054-04-1965 L1966 **OBG** *020 †30
LAMMERT, Joyce Kathleen. 1100 9TH AVE 98101 #036-01-1985 L1986 **AI IM** *030 †20,03
LAMOLA, Steven Anthony. 1959 NE PACIFIC ST, U OF W-HS AFFAIRS BOX 3563 98195 #005-02-2004 L2004 **IM** *100
LANDIS, Daniel Marc. 1560 N 115TH ST STE G16, SWEDISH CANCER INST/NW HOS 98133 #054-04-2001 L2001 **RO** *020 †80
LANDO, Courtney Anne. 1601 5TH AVE STE 830, ELLIOT BAY MEDICAL GROUP 98101 #054-04-2001 L2004 **FM** *100
LANDON, John W. 1241 E OLIVE ST 98122 #028-34-1975 L1978 **IM** *020
LANE, Fenton John. 1550 N 115TH ST 98133 #025-01-1945 L1953 **IM DIA** *071
LANE, James J, Jr. 1145 BROADWAY, THE POLYCLINIC 98122 #054-04-1955 L1958 **IM RHU** *071
LANE, Pamela Elizabeth. 4800 SAND POINT WAY NE, CHILDREN'S HOSPITAL AND RE 98105 #054-04-1993 L1993 **PD** *020 †55
LANE, Robert Ferguson. 1560 N 115TH ST 98133 #054-04-1973 L1978 **HO** *020 †20
LANE, Robyn Nordstrom. ■ 98122 #026-08-2004 L2004 **FM** *020 †18
LANG, Mara Y. 1959 NE PACIFIC ST, CAMPUS BOX 356426 98195 #043-01-2002 L2002 **END** *012 †20
LANGDALE, Lorrie Aileen. 1660 S COLUMBIAN WAY, VA PUGET SOUND HEALTH CARE 98108 #054-04-1979 L1985 **GS CCM** *020 †85
LANGE, Brian Cole. 801 BROADWAY, STE 522 98122 #054-04-1984 L1985 **VS GS** *020 †85
LANGE, Paul Henry. 1959 NE PACIFIC ST, BOX 356510 98195 #028-02-1967 L1988 **U ON** *050 †95
LANGE, Steven Henry. 4700 42ND AVE SW, STE 210 98116 #030-06-1981 L1988 **FM** *040 †18
LANGER, Erna Elisabeth. ■ 98117 #407-23-1963 L1971 **D** *071 †15
LANG-FURR, Mary Barnhardt. ■ 98107 #018-03-2006 L2006 **P** *012
LANGMAN, Alan Wayne. 9714 3RD AVE NE STE 100, PUGET SOUND HEARING & BALA 98115 #041-09-1982 L1990 **OTO** *020 †45
LANKA, Prasad Venkata Lak. 1959 NE PACIFIC ST, UNIV OF WASHINGTON 98195 #495-58-1989 L2006 *100
LANS, Kenneth Nathan. ■ 98125 #025-01-1979 L1982 **GP OM** *020
LAO, Oliver Bennett. 1959 NE PACIFIC ST, UNIVERSTY OF WASHINGTON 98195 #047-05-2004 L2004 **GS** *012
LARAMORE, George Ernest. 1959 NE PACIFIC ST, BOX 356043 98195 #011-02-1976 L1977 **RO** *020 †80
LARRABEE, Wayne Fox, Jr. 600 BROADWAY STE 280 98122 #021-01-1971 L1979 **FPS** *020 †45
LARSON, Amy Allison. 925 SENECA ST, # H8-GME 98101 #005-02-1999 L1999 *100
LARSON, Anne Marie. 1959 NE PACIFIC ST, BOX 356174 98195 #054-04-1991 L1993 **HEP GE** *020 †20
LARSON, Bruce Davin. 1101 MADISON ST, STE 1260 98104 #048-04-2001 L2005 **P** *020
LARSON, Eric Berg. 4245 ROOSEVELT WAY NE, STE 354775 98105 #024-01-1973 L1975 **IM PHP** *020 †20

LARSON, Lance Crawford. 1100 9TH AVE C1-MSO, VIRGINIA MASON MEDICAL CEN 98101 #016-43-1990 L1992 **IM** *020 †20
LARSON, Ritchie Allen. 747 BROADWAY 98122 #016-02-1992 L1992 **AN** *020 †05
LARSON, Roger V. 3950 MONTLAKE BLVD NE, BANK OF AMERICA ARENA #148 98195 #049-01-1973 L1982 **OSM ORS** *020 †40
LARSON, Timothy Leigh. 600 BROADWAY, STE 170 98122 #054-04-1983 L1983 **DR** *062 †80
LASPADA, Albert Russell. 1959 NE PACIFIC ST, MSC 359300 98195 #041-01-1993 L1993 **PTH** *020 †50,19
LASSER, Suzanne. 533 18TH AVE E, GROUP HEALTH DOWTOWN MED C 98112 #043-01-1993 L1996 **IM** *020 †20
LATENDRESSE, Thomas Roy. 4800 SAND POINT WAY NE, MAILSTOP W9824 98105 #028-34-1992 L2003 **PAN** *012 †18
LAU, Randy Kar Ming. ■ 98115 #014-01-2006 L2006 **DR** *012
LAUVSTAD, Walter Armin. ■ 98117 #018-03-1958 L1959 **ORS PM** *071 †40,60
LAVINE, Stephen Roderick. 200 15TH AVE E, CMB 235, DEPT ANESTHESIA 98112 #036-01-1997 L1999 **AN** *012
LAVITT, David Scott. 747 BROADWAY 98122 #016-42-1984 L1987 **AN** *020 †05
LAVY, Eric Timothy. 1959 NE PACIFIC ST, BOX 356560 98195 #054-04-2005 L2006 **P** *012
LAW, Casey S. 4245 ROOSEVELT WAY NE, BOX 354775 98105 #018-03-2005 L2005 **FP** *012
LAW, Therese. 600 BROADWAY, STE 230 98122 #019-02-1977 L1980 **IM** *020 †20
LAW, Yuk Ming. 4800 SAND POINT WAY NE, G-0050 98105 #005-14-1987 L2006 **PD** *020 †55
LAWES, Karen Leigh. 1601 5TH AVE STE 830 98101 #050-02-1993 L1993 **FM** *020 †18
LAWLER, Sean S. 1101 MADISON ST, STE 800 98104 #043-01-1994 L1998 **PD** *020 †55
LAWLOR, Kean Brendan. 3216 NE 45TH PL STE 203 98105 #028-46-1989 L1993 **D** *020 †15
LAWRENCE, Anne Alexandra. ■ 98115 #026-04-1974 L1977 **OS** *062 †05
LAWRENCE, Christopher A. 2915 E MADISON ST, STE 305 98112 #005-18-1979 L1983 **N** *020 †75
LAWRENCE, Stewart L. 3626 NE 45TH ST STE 300, WASHINGTON ADMIN OFFICE 98105 #035-47-1982 L2002 **NPM PD** *020 †55
LAWSON, Barry Michael. 3626 NE 45TH ST STE 300 98105 #422-01-1981 L1986 **PD NPM** *020 †55
LAXMANAN, Balaji. ■ 98117 #025-01-2007 L2007 **IM** *012
LAY, Mark Wm. ■ 98103 #038-06-1984 L1985 **FM** *075 †18
LAYA, Mary Beth. 4245 ROOSEVELT WAY NE, STE 354775 98105 #030-06-1982 L1993 **IM OS** *020 †12
LAYTON, Richard Howard. 600 UNIVERSITY ST STE 1200 98101 #054-04-1954 L1955 **FM GS** *040 †18
LAZACHEK, Gary Walter. 600 1ST AVE 98104 #056-06-1968 L1978 **LM OPH** *075
LAZAR, Daniel Anthony. 1560 N 115TH ST STE 209, NEUROSURGICAL CONSULTANTS 98133 #054-04-1998 L1998 **NS** *020
LAZAROUS, Patsy Crystal. 325 9TH AVE BOX 359755, HARBORVIEW MEDICAL CENTER 98104 #495-37-1996 L2003 **IMG** *020 †20
LA ZERTE, Gordon Douglas. 1959 NE PACIFIC ST, MSC 359300 98195 #024-07-1948 L1949 **PTH NM** *071 †50,28
LE, Dang Khang. ■ 98118 #054-04-2007 L2007 **AN** *012
LE, Ian L. 325 9TH AVE, BOX 359798 98104 #060-01-2000 L2005 **OFA** *100
LE, Quan Phuoc. 4069 RAINIER AVE S STE A 98118 #941-01-1973 L1984 **GP** *020
LE, Thieng Dinh. 1416 SW ROXBURY ST 98106 #941-02-1969 L1983 *020
LE, Thomas. ■ 98105 #054-04-2008 *012
LEAF, Frederick Arvid. 1145 BROADWAY, POLYCLINIC 98122 #054-04-1982 L1984 **D** *020 †15
LEAHY, Jennifer Martin. 515 MINOR AVE, STE 200 98104 #054-04-2003 L2003 **IM** *020 †20
LEAR, William. ■ 98105 #065-01-1998 L2007 **PRD** *012
LEAVITT, Anne Melinda. 1959 NE PACIFIC ST, BOX 357920 98195 #038-06-1980 L1983 **PD** *050 †55
LE BLANC, Johanne. 201 16TH AVE E, GROUP HEALTH CENTRAL HOSPI 98112 #067-03-1985 L1992 **DR** *020 †80
LEBSOCK, Christopher Vinc. ■ 98103 #054-04-2008 *012
LECA, Nicolae. 1959 NE PACIFIC ST, BOX 356521 98195 #781-01-1997 L2005 **NEP** *020 †20
LECHNER, David John. 2515 SW TRENTON ST, STE 201 98106 #035-45-1973 L1975 **OPH** *020 †35
LEDBETTER, Daniel James. 4800 SAND POINT WAY NE 98105 #011-03-1981 L1982 **PDS TS** *020 †85
LEDDY, Laura Sigismund. ■ 98115 #051-01-2007 L2007 **GS** *012
LEE, Alice Meisze. ■ 98103 #054-04-1999 L2003 **IM** *020 †20
LEE, Angie Kar Yin. 925 SENECA ST # 1930 98101 #143-03-2004 L2005 **IM** *012
LEE, Betty Tung. 747 BROADWAY 98122 #024-01-1994 L1999 **AN** *020 †05
LEE, Blair Stephen. 200 16TH AVE E 98112 #005-14-1988 L1999 **AN MDM** *030 †05
LEE, Carabeth. 125 16TH AVE E, GROUP HEALTH COOPERATIVE 98112 #017-20-1995 L2000 **ORS** *020 †40
LEE, Catherine Marie. 325 9TH AVE, HARBORVIEW BOX 359762 98104 #005-02-1996 L1999 **PCC** *020 †20
LEE, Catherine Terri. 4033 E MADISON ST, STE 109 98112 #041-01-1984 L1991 **P CHP** *020 †75 ‡
LEE, Charles Jongwoo. 1145 BROADWAY, STATION 1-F 98122 #041-02-1999 L2006 **PCC PUD** *020 †20
LEE, Chong Chia. 700 9TH AVE, # 359766 98104 #016-02-2001 L2001 **NS** *012
LEE, Christine Anne. 600 UNIVERSITY ST, STE 1200 98101 #010-01-1993 L1997 **GS** *020 †85
LEE, Christine Garyee. 1959 NE PACIFIC ST, BOX 346340 98195 #045-01-2003 L2006 **END** *012 †20
LEE, Christopher Ryan. ■ 98115 #054-04-2003 L2003 **AN** *040
LEE, Douglas. 98107 #035-01-1990 **GS** *071
LEE, Douglas. ■ 98107 #061-01-1969 L1975 **OPH** *071 †35
LEE, Douglas J. 1560 N 115TH ST, STE G16 98133 #583-01-1963 L1972 **P** *020
LEE, Douglas Jonathan. 1560 N 115TH ST, STE G16 98133 #008-01-1981 L1985 **IM ON** *020 †20
LEE, Edmond Siuwo. 747 BROADWAY 98122 #054-04-2002 L2003 **AN** *020 †05
LEE, Edward. 1959 NE PACIFIC ST, BOX 356340 98195 #036-07-2002 L2002 **DR** *020
LEE, Elton Robert. 1145 BROADWAY 98122 #024-07-1993 L1997 **IM** *020 †20
LEE, Frederick Sang. ■ 98121 #035-48-1995 L1998 **GPM** *020
LEE, Gerald William. 325 9TH AVE BOX 359702, HARBORVIEW MEDICAL CENTER 98104 #016-42-2001 L2004 **IM EM** *020 †20
LEE, Gisoo. 1959 NE PACIFIC ST 98195 #026-04-2002 L2002 **OTO** *012
LEE, Jason Kwanggu. 1145 BROADWAY 98122 #005-11-1996 L2006 **VS** *020 †85
LEE, Jay Chang-Hyun. ■ 98103 #060-02-1994 **U** *100
LEE, Jean Hwa. 1107 NE 45TH ST STE 440, DEPARTMENT OF RADIOLOGY 98105 #583-03-1996 L2005 **NM** *100 †28

■ = Address Information Privacy Protected

LEE, Jeffrey Peter. 8444 RAINIER AVE S, RAINIER BEACH CLINIC 98118 #024-01-1986 L1988 FM *020 †18

LEE, John. 10560 5TH AVE NE 98125 #054-04-1957 L1960 DR *020 †80

LEE, John Alexander Hugh. UN WA DEPT EPIDE SC 36 98122 #803-03-1949 PHP *071

LEE, Kyung Min. 125 16TH AVE E CSB-1060, CAPITOL HILL FAMILY HEALTH 98112 #054-04-2001 L2003 FM *020 †18

LEE, Lorrie Anne. 325 9TH AVE 98104 #055-01-1989 L1995 AN *020 †05

LEE, Marie Emily. 1100 9TH AVE 98101 #012-05-1977 L1984 R NR *020 †80

LEE, Mary Soojung. ■ 98119 #016-06-2005 L2006 AN *012

LEE, Matthias Ky-Suh. 1100 9TH AVE G1-MSO, VIRGINIA MASON MEDICAL CEN 98101 #035-06-1996 L2003 P *020 †75

LEE, Michael Borhwa. ■ 98103 #054-04-2003 L2003 ORS *012

LEE, Michael Kufren. ■ 98177 #025-01-1996 L2002 AN *020 †05

LEE, Michele Denise. ■ 98115 #054-05-12-2004 L2005 FM *012

LEE, Minako Yoshioka. ■ 98115 #572-18-1963 L1975 HEM *050 †50

LEE, Ming Jong. ■ 98115 #385-02-1963 L1975 PTH *071 †50

LEE, Miriam Ellen. ■ 98103 #054-04-2006 L2006 AN *012

LEE, Myungja. 1100 9TH AVE C1-MSO, VIRGINIA MASON MEDICAL CEN 98101 #040-02-1989 L2003 IM *020 †20

LEE, Naomi. PO BOX 356340, GRADUATE MEDICAL EDUCATION 98195 #054-04-2003 L2003 IM *100 †20

LEE, Norma Jean. 550 16TH AVE 98122 #005-15-1988 L1990 AN *071 †05

LEE, Scott David. 1959 NE PACIFIC ST, MSC 359300 98195 #041-02-1994 L1997 GE *020 †20

LEE, Shoo K. 98199 #825-01-1980 L1995 NPM PHP *050 †55

LEE, Stanley Weilun. 1145 BROADWAY, THE POLYCLINIC 98122 #038-06-1995 L1997 GE IM *020 †20

LEE, Stephanie Joi. 1100 FAIRVIEW AVE N, D5-290 98109 #005-11-1990 L2005 HO *020 †20

LEE, Sum Ping. 1660 S COLUMBIAN WAY, DEPT OF MEDICINE (111-G1) 98108 #462-01-1970 L1986 IM GE *020 †20

LEE, Sylvia Mina. GRADUATE MEDICAL ED BOX 35, UNIVERSITY OF WASHINGTON 98195 #036-01-2003 L2003 HO *012 †20

LEE, Terry Git. 2815 EASTLAKE AVE E 98102 #026-04-1987 L1989 CHP P *020 †75

LEE, Timothy J. 1660 S COLUMBIAN WAY 98108 #005-14-1986 L1990 IM EM *020 †20

LEE, Tyler Yangmao. ■ 98121 #047-05-2006 L2006 IM *012

LEE, Young Joo. ■ 98144 #583-06-1958 GS IM *020

LEGNER, Victor Joseph. ■ 98115 #016-01-1997 L2000 IMG *020 †20

LEHMAN, Constance Dobbins. 825 EASTLAKE AVE E, SCCA BOX G-3200 98109 #008-01-1990 L1990 DR *020 †80

LEHMAN, Robert Michael. 1545 NW 57TH ST UNIT 522 98107 #024-07-1978 L1989 ADL PD *050 †55

LEHMANN, Kenneth Grant. 1959 NE PACIFIC ST, MSC 359300 98195 #005-18-1979 L1991 CD IM *020 †20

LEHMANN, Ronald Paul. 600 UNIVERSITY ST, STE 1200 98101 #054-04-1994 L2001 IM *020 †20

LEHNERT, Bruce Edwin. 1959 NE PACIFIC ST 98195 #034-01-2005 L2006 DR *012

LEHR, Hans-Anton. ■ 98177 #409-41-1987 L1996 PTH *020 †50

LEIGH, Martha Jeanne. 600 UNIVERSITY ST STE 120 98101 #054-04-1990 L1994 IM *020 †20

LEININGER, Christopher J. 550 17TH AVE, STE 110 98122 #035-19-1975 L1976 FM MDM *030 †18

LEINONEN, Martin Jos. ■ 98107 #054-04-1971 L1972 FM *020 †18

LEITH, Jordan Michael. 1959 NE PACIFIC ST, BOX 356500 98195 #061-01-1994 L1999 ORS *020

LEMAIRE, Jane Bertha. 1959 NE PACIFIC ST RM 76 98195 #065-09-1986 L1986 IM *020 †20

LEMERE, Frederick. ■ 98177 #030-05-1932 L1937 P *071 †75

LEMIRE, Ronald John. 4800 SAND POINT WAY NE, P O BOX 5371 98105 #054-04-1962 L1963 PD *030 †55

LEMLEY, William Scott. 1229 MADISON ST, STE 900 98104 #054-04-1999 L2004 DR *020 †80

LEMOS, Bianca Catherine. ■ 98105 #041-12-2005 L2005 IM *100

LEMOS, John Paul. ■ 98105 #054-04-2008 *012

LENDVAY, Thomas. 1959 NE PACIFIC ST, BOX 356510 98195 #041-13-1999 L2004 UP *100 †95

LENNARD, Dorothy E Camp. ■ 98105 #048-12-1970 L1974 EM FM *071 †16,18

LENTZ, Gretchen Mary. 1959 NE PACIFIC ST 98195 #054-04-1986 L1989 GYN U *020 †30

LEONARD, Erica Victoria. ■ 98102 #041-12-2008 *012

LEONCIO, Ferritha Aquino. 1401 MADISON ST STE 100, MEDICINE RESIDE 98104 #054-04-2006 L2006 FP *012

LEON GUERRERO, Angela L. 1959 NE PACIFIC ST, BOX 356560 98195 #048-12-2001 L2005 PYG *100

LEPPIG, Kathleen Ann. 201 1ST AVE S, GROUP HEALTH COOPERATIVE 98104 #038-06-1986 L1989 PD *020 †55,19

LESHEN, Zachary Joemarana. ■ 98106 #016-06-2005 L2005 IM *012

LESKO, Sarah Ellen. 2101 E YESLER WAY, STE 150 98122 #041-01-1998 L2003 FM *020 †18

LESSLER, Daniel Stephan. 325 9TH AVE, HARBORVIEW MEDICAL CENTER 98104 #005-11-1986 L1990 IM *050 †20

LEUNG, Eric Gregory. ■ 98112 #048-13-1996 L2001 NPM *020 †55

LEUNG, Jessica Yinwan. 1959 NE PACIFIC ST, BOX 356340 98195 #024-01-2004 L2005 DR *012

LEUNG, Kenneth Yuk Kan. 900 TERRY AVE 98104 #462-01-1971 L1980 ORS *020 †40

LEVASSEUR, Sarah Marie. 98104 #035-03-2007 GS *012

LEVERENZ, James Bruce. 1660 S COLUMBIAN WAY, VA-PSHCS 98108 #054-04-1985 L1992 N NP *050 †75

LEVERSEE, John Holzheid. U WA DEPT FAM PRAC RF 30 98195 #026-04-1952 L1952 FM *040 †18

LEVERSEE, Robert Owen. ■ 98136 #054-04-1998 *100

LEVIN, Ronald Wm. 4033 E MADISON ST 98112 #016-11-1971 L1976 PYA P *020 †20

LEVINE, Henry Max. ■ 98115 #054-04-1981 *100

LEVINE, Howard Jay. 902 14TH AVE 98122 #035-09-1973 L1982 OBG *020

LEVINE, Robert Paul. 1101 MADISON ST, STE 1150 98104 #054-04-1980 L1984 OBG *020 †30

LEVINTHAL, B Richard. 515 MINOR AVE STE 140 98104 #035-19-1959 L1963 OTO HNS *071 †45

LEVISON, Andrew Victor. PO BOX 50010 98105 #917-28-1986 L1997 *100

LEVITAN, Diane Elaine. 1959 NE PACIFIC ST BOX 35, UNIV OF WA MEDICAL CENTER 98195 #005-18-2000 L2003 IM *100 †20

LEVITT, David M. 1530 N 115TH ST, STE 207 98133 #041-09-1989 L1992 IM *020

LEVITT, Gilbert W. 521 WALL ST 98121 #035-45-1962 L1971 OTO *075 †45

LEVITT, Keith Neil. 1501 QUEEN ANNE AVE N 98109 #305-01-1981 L1998 PM *020 †05

LEVITT, Michael Robert. ■ 98104 #016-43-2007 L2007 GS *012

LEVITT, Rhonda Lynn. 500 17TH AVE 98122 #005-02-1979 L1980 PD GP *020 †55

LEVY, Adam Edward. 1959 NE PACIFIC ST, MSC 359300 98195 #038-41-1990 L1990 GS *020

LEVY, Michelle Heather. 2450 33RD AVE W STE 100, MAGNOLIA 98199 #065-10-1998 L2000 FM *020 †18

LEVY, Mitchell Rod. 1959 NE PACIFIC ST, BOX 354694 98195 #010-01-1996 L1998 P *020 †75

LEVY, Phillip Monroe. 1959 NE PACIFIC ST 98195 #869-04-1980 L1983 IM *020

LEVY, Sanford. 550 16TH AVE, STE 405 98122 #005-02-1976 L1978 AN *020 †05,18

LEVY, Wayne Cecil. 1959 NE PACIFIC ST, BOX 356422 98195 #005-12-1985 L1985 CD IM *020 †20

LEVY-LAHAD, Ephrat. ■ 98115 #550-01-1988 L1993 MG *020 †19

LEW, Janice Cecilia. 747 BROADWAY 98122 #005-14-1991 L1997 PD *020 †05

LEWIN, Mark Brent. 4800 SAND POINT WAY NE, CHILDRENS HOSPITAL 98105 #005-06-1991 L2001 PDC *020 †55

LEWIS, Alison Jeannette. 1600 E JOHN ST 98112 #016-43-1988 L1991 FM *020 †18

LEWIS, Anna Roach. 747 BROADWAY, SWEDISH MED CTR 98122 #050-02-2000 L2002 FM *020

LEWIS, Brent Ian. 1600 E JOHN ST 98112 #005-06-1984 L1990 OTO *020 †20

LEWIS, Charlotte Wood. 4800 SAND POINT WAY NE, CHRMC CRANIOFACIAL CENTER 98105 #005-02-1994 L1998 PD *020 †55

LEWIS, David Arthur. 1600 E JOHN ST 98112 #005-19-1986 L1999 PUD *020 †20

LEWIS, David Howard. 1959 NE PACIFIC ST 98195 #051-04-1985 L1986 NM IM *020 †20,28

LEWIS, Donald. ■ 98112 #016-06-1951 L1953 PD OS *071 †55

LEWIS, Frederick Gary. 1221 MADISON ST, COLON & RECTAL CLINIC 98104 #065-05-1959 L1961 CRS *071 †85,10

LEWIS, Gregory Patrick. 1100 9TH AVE 98101 #040-02-1978 L1982 OS DR *020 †80

LEWIS, Howard Stites. 550 16TH AVE, STE 402 98122 #054-04-1983 L1983 CD IM *020 †20

LEWIS, Merry Alician. 98112 #054-04-2006 L2006 OBG *012

LEWIS, Rayburn Stanley. 550 16TH AVE STE 100 98122 #054-04-1978 L1980 IM *020 †20

LEWIS, Robert Allen. ■ 98115 #035-45-1971 L1974 IM *030 †55,03

LEWIS, Robert Donald. ■ 98112 #035-01-1964 L1973 GS TS *071 †55

LEWIS, Steven Thos. 11027 MERIDIAN AVE N STE 1 98133 #005-14-1973 L1978 GE IM *020 †20

LHEWA, Dekey Yangzom. ■ 98115 #054-04-2007 L2007 IM *012

LI, Dun Dorothy. ■ 98118 #054-04-2006 L2006 AN *012

LI, Ellen Jennifer. ■ 98122 #048-02-1998 L2003 PYG *100 †75

LI, Ge. 1660 S COLUMBIAN WAY, PSHCS 116 MIRECC 98108 #243-39-1983 L2001 PYG *020

LI, Henry Yeh. 1145 BROADWAY 98122 #005-11-1996 L1998 HO *020 †20

LI, Wei-I. 1600 E JEFFERSON ST 98122 #023-07-1965 L1975 TS GS *020 †85,90

LI, Xi Susan. 1959 NE PACIFIC ST, RM C212, CAMPUS BOX 356340 98195 #054-04-2002 L2002 IM *100 †20

LIAO, Darwin James. 523 PINE ST, STE 200 98101 #021-01-1994 OPH *020

LIAO, Jay Justin. ■ 98101 #025-01-2002 L2007 *100

LIAO, Ray Poonjui. 1959 NE PACIFIC ST # 35654, UNIVERSITY OF WASHINGTON 98195 #016-11-1998 L2004 AN *020

LIAU, Derek Wenyu. 1959 NE PACIFIC ST, BOX 356340 98195 #054-04-2004 AN *012

LIAW, Gene S J. 662A S JACKSON ST, EVERGREEN FAMILY CLINIC 98104 #244-05-1973 L1985 GP *020

LICHTENSTEIN, Joel Edward. 1959 NE PACIFIC ST, BOX 375115 98195 #038-40-1972 L1999 DR *020 †80,28

LIDDELL, Marti Hyatt. 1145 BROADWAY 98122 #051-01-1984 L1987 IM *020 †20

LIEBERMAN, James Robert. 747 BROADWAY 98122 #054-04-1996 L2000 PD *020 †05

LIEBERMAN, Joshua M. ■ 98115 #056-06-1982 L1993 IM *020

LIEBERMANN, Jerrold David. ■ 98112 #035-48-1982 CD IM *050

LIEPPMAN, Robert Eric. 1229 MADISON ST, STE 1500 98104 #048-02-1974 L1976 OBG *020 †30

LIEU, Binh Kien. 1959 NE PACIFIC ST, U OF W HS AFFAIRS BOX 3563 98195 #024-07-2004 L2004 IM *020 †20

LIEU, Tuan My. 4739 1/2 RAINIER AVE S 98118 #941-01-1969 L1983 GP *020

LIGHTBODY, Peter. 521 WALL ST ACC-3 98121 #065-05-1993 L2000 FM *020

LIGON, John Vance. ■ 98109 #040-02-1973 GP *020 †18

LIKOSKY, William Harris. 515 MINOR AVE 98104 #050-02-1966 L2000 N IM *020 †75

LILES, Wayne Conrad, Jr. 1959 NE PACIFIC ST BOX 357, UNIVERSITY OF WASHINGTON 98195 #054-04-1987 L1990 ID IM *050 †20

LILLARD, Sydney R. PO BOX 356410, UNIV OF WASHINGTON 98195 #048-13-2001 L2001 GS *100 †85

LILLEHEI, Nancy Gay. ■ 98103 #026-04-1986 L1991 AN GS *020 †05

LIM, Paul Chuwn. ■ 98102 #054-04-2004 L2004 PM *012

LIMAYE, Ajit Prakash. 1959 NE PACIFIC ST, BOX 357110 98195 #054-04-1992 L1994 IM *020 †20

LIN, Daniel Wei. 1959 NE PACIFIC ST, BOX 356510 98195 #047-05-1994 L1997 U *050 †95

LIN, David Tat-Chi. ■ 98105 #067-01-1983 L1996 OPH *020 †35

LIN, Elizabeth Hiok-Bun. 6529C NE WINDERMERE RD 98105 #005-11-1979 L1980 FM *050 †18

LIN, Eugene Clement. 1100 9TH AVE G1-MSO, VIRGINIA MASON MEDICAL CEN 98101 #016-06-1992 L2001 DR *020 †80,28

LIN, Karen. 10330 MERIDIAN AVE N 98133 #010-02-2001 L2005 OTO *020 †45

LIN, Otto Schiuehtzan. 1100 9TH AVE, (MG-AC) 98101 #024-01-1994 L2001 IM GE *020 †20

LINDELL, Ashley Caye. 7035 BEACH DR SW 98136 #025-01-2001 L2003 FM *020

LINDEMAN, Roger Chas. 1100 9TH AVE 98101 #025-07-1960 L1968 NO OTO *071 †45

LINDEN, Hannah Margaret. ■ 98109 #024-16-1989 L1993 HEM *020 †20

LINDENBAUM, Jeffrey E. 9800 4TH AVE NE 98115 #035-06-1966 L1973 PD ADL *020 †55

LINDENTHALER, Evelyn. 900 TERRY AVE 4TH FL, COLUMBUS PAVILION 98104 #061-01-1989 L1992 AN *020 †20

LINDER, Heather Elizabeth. ■ 98106 #041-14-2006 L2006 FP *012

LINDNER, Armando. VET ADMIN HOSP 98108 #132-01-1964 L1970 NEP *020 †20

LINDSAY, Jessica Ann. 4800 SAND POINT WAY NE, CHILDRENS HOSP & REG MED C 98105 #035-46-2006 L2006 PD *012

LINDSAY, Philip Gaylord. 1101 MADISON ST STE 1260 98104 #005-12-1963 L1970 P IM *020 †20,75

LINDSEY, Joshua David. ■ 98116 #056-05-2007 L2007 ORS *012

LINENBERGER, Michael Lee. 825 E LAKE AVE E, MAIL STOP G6-800 98109 #019-02-1982 L1986 HEM IM *020 †20

LING, Mabel C S. 4800 SAND POINT WAY NE, MEDICAL CTR, ANEST. DETP C 98105 #462-01-1971 L1980 AN *020 †05

LINGAPPA, Jairam Rao. 901 BOREN AVE STE 1300, UW/PIP 98104 #005-02-1991 L1993 PD *020 †55

LINGAPPA, Jaisri Rao. ■ 98112 #024-16-1987 L1988 IM *020 †20

LINKER, David Thor. 1959 NE PACIFIC ST, MSC 359300 98195 #005-11-1976 L1977 CD PDC *050 †20,55

LINKS, Ann Christina. 1959 NE PACIFIC ST, BOX 356340 98195 #054-04-2004 L2004 **ORS** *012

LINN, Margaret Ruth. 600 BROADWAY, STE 170 98122 #047-05-1984 L1990 **DR** *020 †80

LINNAU, Ken Floris. 1959 NE PACIFIC ST, BOX 356 98195 #154-07-1996 L2003 **DR** *012

LION, Katherine Casey. ■ 98105 #005-02-2007 L2007 **PD** *012

LIONBERGER, Jack Michael. PO BOX 19024, 1100 FAIRVIEW AVE N 98109 #030-05-2001 L2005 **ON** *100

LIPKE, Anne Butler. ■ 98103 #051-04-2002 L2006 **PCC** *012 †20

LIPKIN, Edward Walter. 1959 NE PACIFIC ST, BOX 356426 98195 #038-01-1978 L1982 **END IM** *040 †20

LIPPMAN, Michael Jeffrey. 10501 MERIDIAN AVE N STE C 98133 #035-06-1977 L1978 **FM** *020 †18

LIPSKI, Gregory Lee. ■ 98105 #054-04-2008 *012

LIPSKY, Benjamin Alan. 1660 S COLUMBIAN WAY #111M 98108 #035-20-1973 L1974 **IM ID** *020 †20

LISCHNER, David Ho. 126 NW CANAL ST STE 310, CANAL CENTRE 98107 #054-04-1998 L2000 **P** *020

LISS, Hillary Karen. 325 9TH AVE, PO BOX 359780 98104 #023-01-1997 L1999 **IM** *020 †20

LITCH, James Anthony. ■ 98115 #025-01-1992 L1992 **FM** *020 †18

LITTLE, James Wendell. 1660 S COLUMBIAN WAY, SCI SERVICE (S-128) 98108 #016-02-1977 L1979 **PM** *020 †60

LITTLE, Malaika Love. 4800 SAND POINT WAY NE, AND REGION 98105 #050-02-2005 L2005 **PD** *012

LITWIN, Josh Peter. 1501 QUEEN ANNE AVE N, REGENERATION 98109 #016-42-2000 L2004 **OPH** *020 †35

LIU, Chi. 600 UNIVERSITY ST, STE 1200 98101 #243-16-1985 L2004 **ON** *020

LIU, Clive Maopang. 1730 MINOR AVE STE 1000 98101 #035-19-1998 L2004 **D** *020 †15

LIU, Daniel Zhidi. ■ 98144 #028-02-2006 L2006 **GS** *012

LIU, David Chengchung. 925 SENECA ST # 1930, GRADUATE MED EDU H8-GME 98101 #010-01-2005 L2005 **AN** *012

LIU, Eric Tse-Chun. 1200 12TH AVE S 98144 #028-46-1990 L1992 **IM** *020 †20

LIU, Esther Fanglin. 600 UNIVERSITY ST, STE 1200 98101 #040-02-1991 L1994 **FM** *020 †18

LIU, Franklin. 1959 NE PACIFIC ST, BOX 356340 98195 #035-01-2004 L2004 **DR** *012

LIU, Lenna L. 2101 E YESLER WAY, STE 100 98122 #041-01-1992 L1992 **PD** *020 †55

LIVIAKIS, Lea Renee. GRADUATE MEDICAL ED BOX 35, UNIVERSITY OF WASHINGTON 98195 #005-19-2003 L2003 **IM** *100 †20

LIVINGSTON, Brian James. 747 BROADWAY 98122 #035-09-2001 L2005 **EM** *100 †16

LIVINGSTONE, De Anna Sue. ■ 98112 #017-20-1980 L1983 **PD OS** *075 †55

LIVINGSTONE, Simon Benjam. ■ 98115 #034-01-2008 *012

LIYANARACHCHI, Thanuja Ud. 125 16TH AVE, GHC FAMILY PRACTICE RESIDE 98122 #220-01-1999 L2004 **FM** *020 †18

LO, Harry Chun-Sung. 7101 MARTN LTHR KNG JR S, STE 217 98118 #385-03-1962 L1967 **FM PTH** *020 †50

LO, Serena Hoy Yun. ■ 98115 #014-01-2006 L2006 **IM** *012

LOBER, William Barry. 2409 N 45TH ST 98103 #005-02-1994 L1997 **EM** *020 †16

LOCKWOOD, Reed Reuel. ■ 98125 #054-04-1971 L1973 **D IM** *075 †20,15

LOEB, Keith Randy. PO BOX 356100, UNIV WA MED CTR DEPT PATH 98195 #056-06-1995 L1999 **HMP** *100 †50

LOEB, Lawrence Arthur. 1959 NE PACIFIC ST, DEPT OF PATHOLOGY, 357705 98195 #035-19-1961 L1978 **OS PTH** *050

LOEBEL, Jean Pierre. 2324 EASTLAKE AVE E, STE 500 98102 #836-01-1970 L1978 **PYG** *062 †75

LOEKEN, Janiese Ann. 1730 MINOR AVE STE 1400 98101 #054-04-1977 L1978 **P** *020 †75

LOESER, John David. UOFW BOX 356470, DEPT OF NEUROLOGICAL SURG 98195 #035-19-1961 L1964 **NS NSP** *020 †25

LOGALBO, Matthew James. 1629 N 45TH ST 98103 #024-16-2006 L2006 **FP** *012

LOGAR, Christine Marie. 325 9TH AVE, RENAL CLINIC 98104 #038-40-1999 L2003 **NEP** *020 †20

LO GERFO, James Paul. 325 9TH AVE 98104 #035-45-1968 L1971 **IMG PHP** *020 †20

LOGERFO, Sung Eun. 1959 NE PACIFIC ST, BOX 356340 98195 #054-04-2002 L2002 **RNR** *012 †80

LOGSETTY, Sarvesh. 325 9TH AVE, MAILBOX 359796 98104 #060-01-1990 L1998 **GS** *020 †85

LOHMANN, Donna Jean. 1730 MINOR AVE, STE 1400 98101 #005-02-1992 L1998 **P** *020 †75

LOHSE, Grant Richardson. ■ 98112 #016-06-2007 L2007 **ORS** *012

LOISELLE, Christopher Roy. 1959 NE PACIFIC ST, BOX 356043 98195 #023-07-2006 L2007 **RO** *012

LOLLO, Loreto. 1959 NE PACIFIC ST 98195 #561-17-1987 L1996 **AN** *020 †05,18

LOMBARDI, Thomas Louis. ■ 98119 #005-06-2007 L2007 **IM** *012

LOMBILLO, Vivian Aurora. PO BOX 356524, UWMC DERMATOLOGY DIVISION 98195 #008-01-2002 L2003 **D** *100

LONDBORG, Peter Delwyn. 901 BOREN AVE STE 1800 98104 #026-04-1979 L1979 **P** *050 †75

LONG, Layron Omar. 1959 NE PACIFIC ST, BOX 359300 98195 #047-07-2000 L2005 **U** *020

LONGNION, Alison Diane. 4800 SAND POINT WAY NE, CHILDREN'S HOSP & REG MED 98105 #054-04-2006 L2006 **PD** *012

LONGO, Marie-Christine. 1221 MADISON ST STE 910, POLYCLINIC PEDIATRICS 98104 #035-06-1992 L1999 **PD** *020 †55

LONGO, Michael Jos. 1100 9TH AVE C1-MSO, VIRGINIA MASON MEDICAL CEN 98101 #035-06-1992 L1994 **CD** *020 †20

LONGSTRETH, Wm Thacher, Jr. 325 9TH AVE 98104 #041-01-1975 L1976 **N** *020 †20,75

LOO, Yolanda Lai. 1959 NE PACIFIC ST, PSYCHIATRY RESIDENCY PRGM 98195 #036-05-2007 L2007 **P** *012

LOOMIS, Sharon. 1959 NE PACIFIC ST, UNIV HOSP DET REHAB MED 98195 #054-04-1984 L1986 **PM** *020 †60

LOPEZ, Jose A. 921 TERRY AVE, PUGET SOUND BLOOD CENTER 98104 #034-01-1981 L1982 **HEM IM** *020 †20

LORD, James Daniel. ■ 98102 #054-04-2001 L2003 **GE** *012

LORD, Julie Ann. 1959 NE PACIFIC ST BOX 35, UNIV OF WASHINGTON MED CEN 98195 #005-11-1996 L2000 **P** *020 †75

LORD, Sandra M. 634 11TH AVE E 98102 #054-04-1996 L1998 **IM** *020 †20

LOREN, David Jonathan. 1959 NE PACIFIC ST, DEPT OF PEDIATRICS - BOX 3 98195 #016-01-1997 L2004 **PD** *020 †55

LORENTZ, Wendy Moch. 1959 NE PACIFIC ST # C-21, BOX 356340 98195 #054-04-2005 L2005 **OBG** *012

LORENZ, Wolfgang Anton. ■ 98118 #409-33-1977 L1985 **P** *020

LORTON, William Lewis. ■ 98115 #016-02-1947 L1949 **P** *071 †75

LOSH, David Paul. 4245 ROOSEVELT WAY NE, STE 354775 98105 #019-02-1974 L1992 **FM FPG** *040 †18

LOUDON, Robert Guthrie. ■ 98118 #803-03-1947 L1971 **PUD IM** *040

LOUIE, Brian Edward. 1101 MADISON ST, STE 850 98104 #065-01-1996 L2005 **TS** *020

LOVING, Vilert Alon. 1959 NE PACIFIC ST, BLDG C212 98195 #041-01-2004 L2005 **DR** *012

LOW, Donald Edward. 1100 9TH AVE C1-MSO, VIRGINIA MASON MEDICAL CEN 98101 #065-05-1981 L1986 **TS GS** *020 †85

LOWDERMILK, Mark Douglas. 1229 MADISON ST, STE 1450 98104 #049-01-1994 L1996 **OBG** *072 †30

LOWE, Marc Allen. 1600 E JOHN ST 98112 #030-05-1984 L1987 **U** *020 †95

LOWRY, Jennifer. 4800 SAND POINT WAY NE 98105 #005-76-2003, ▲ L2006 **CHP** *012

LOWRY, John Charles. 4800 SAND POINT WAY NE 98105 #005-76-2003, ▲ L2006 **CHP** *012

LOZANO, Paula. 1730 MINOR AVE STE 1600, CENTER FOR HLTH STUDIES 98101 #024-01-1989 L1989 **PD** *020 †55

LU, Ann Shihlong. 550 16TH AVE, SWEDISH FAMILY MEDICINE 98122 #054-04-2004 L2004 **FP** *012

LU, Caroline D Wan. 5209 55TH AVE NE, NW ANESTHESIOLOGISTS 98105 #143-02-1985 L1991 **AN** *020 †05

LU, Cheng-En. ■ 98105 #242-17-1949 L1957 **OTO** *071 †45

LU, Jennie W. ■ 98105 #242-17-1948 L1964 **P** *071

LU, Joseph. 1530 N 115TH ST, STE 307 98133 #026-04-1980 L1991 **AN GS** *020 †05

LU, Kimberly Kweimei. 325 9TH AVE, BOX 359796 98104 #024-01-1999 L2002 **PS** *020 †65

LU, Mei. 720 8TH AVE S, STE 100 98104 #243-64-1982 L2003 **FM** *020 †18

LU, Miranda. 1629 N 45TH ST 98103 #005-02-2004 L2004 **FM** *020 †18

LU, Thomas Shen Chuan. 1959 NE PACIFIC ST, BOX 356500 98195 #061-01-1999 L2005 **HS** *100

LUBECK, Norma A. 747 BROADWAY 98122 #005-76-1996, ▲ L1997 **AN** *020 †05 ‡

LUBINSKI, Lissa Kate. ■ 98102 #026-04-2007 L2007 **FP** *012

LUCAS, Sylvia Maria. 1959 NE PACIFIC ST, BOX 356169 98195 #054-04-1988 L1992 **N** *020 †75

LUCAS, Timothy Harris, Jr. 1959 NE PACIFIC ST, BOX 356340 98195 #011-03-2001 L2001 **NS** *012

LUCERO, Vince Maxim. 747 BROADWAY 98122 #007-02-1980 L1981 **AN PD** *020 †55,05

LUCHI, Jean Marie. 620 15TH AVE E 98112 #048-14-1983 L1986 **PD** *020 †55

LUCKMAN, Yehudit. 1959 NE PACIFIC ST, UWMC BOX 354807 98195 #550-04-1992 L2004 *020

LUDLAM, William Henry. 500 17TH AVE, STE 500 98122 #035-46-1995 L2007 **END** *020

LUDWIG, Cora Megan. ■ 98115 #054-04-2008 *012

LUDWIG, William Richard. 1200 12TH AVE S, PACIFIC MEDICAL CENTER 98144 #025-01-1974 L1975 **IM** *030 †20

LUECK, Thomas Robt. 1600 E JOHN ST 98112 #056-05-1974 L1975 **AN** *020 †05

LUFBURROW, Elizabeth. 9730 3RD AVE NE STE 206 98115 #038-06-1985 L1986 **P** *020 †75

LUFT, John Herman. ■ 98109 #054-04-1953 **IM** *072

LUGO, Denise Michelle. 1100 9TH AVE G1-MSO, VIRGINIA MASON MEDICAL CEN 98101 #005-02-1998 L2002 **OPH** *020 †35

LUK, Andrew James. 1660 S COLUMBIAN WAY A11, VA PUGET SOUND HEALTH CARE 98108 #038-06-1988 L1997 **AI** *020 †03,20

LUKE, Dahlia Ann. ■ 98133 #040-02-2006 L2006 **IM** *012

LUKS, Andrew Mark. 325 9TH AVE, STE 10EG25 98104 #005-18-2000 L2002 **PCC** *100 †20

LUM, Donald Munbun. 310 15TH AVE E CNB5 98112 #023-07-1982 L1988 **OPH** *020 †35

LUNDGREN, Rachel Sasha. ■ 98146 #034-01-2003 L2003 **GS** *012

LUSTER, Linda. ■ 98177 #016-11-1974 L1979 **P CHP** *012

LUU, Paul. 5420 RAINIER AVE S 98118 #005-14-1989 L1995 **HS PS** *020 †65

LUU, Robert. ■ 98103 #005-02-2004 L2005 **AN** *012

LY, Kiet Anh. ■ 98125 #010-02-1995 L1999 **GPM** *100

LYNCH, John Buckley. 3518 FREMONT AVE N 98103 #054-04-2002 L2005 **ID** *012 †20

LYNCH, Joseph Randall. 1959 NE PACIFIC ST, BOX 356500 98195 #040-02-2002 L2002 **ORS** *100

LYNCH, Maureen Kim. 1600 E JEFFERSON ST, STE 603 98122 #054-04-1983 L1985 **GS** *020 †85

LYNGE, Dana Christian. 1959 NE PACIFIC ST, BOX 358280 98195 #067-01-1985 L1991 **GS** *020 †85

LYNN, Anne Marie. 4800 SAND POINT WAY NE 98105 #005-11-1975 L1976 **AN CCP** *040 †55,05

LYONS, Matthew Lawrence. 1959 NE PACIFIC ST 98195 #054-04-2007 L2007 **ORS** *012

LYONS, Richard Bernard. 2201 6TH AVE, ROOM 710, M/S RX-20 98121 #040-02-1960 L1975 **FM OM** *072

MABUNGA, Rogelio Flores. 7131 MARTN LTHR KNG JR S 98118 #748-10-1964 L1980 **GP** *075

MACAULAY, Kathryn E. ■ 98115 #021-01-1988 L1994 **DR** *020

MAC CAMY, Edwin Thos. ■ 98133 #016-06-1940 L1944 **GYN** *071 †30

MAC DOUGALL, Nora Lindsay. 200 15TH AVE E 98112 #054-04-1983 L1985 **PTH** *020 †50

MAC GILLIVRAY, Robin G. ■ 98125 #836-02-1972 L1985 **AN** *050

MACKIE, Kenneth Paul. 1959 NE PACIFIC ST RM RN10 98195 #008-01-1984 L1987 **AN** *050 †05

MACKOFF, Leslie. 4800 SAND POINT WAY NE 98105 #054-04-1953 L1955 **PD** *071 †55

MACKOWIAK, Benjamin. ■ 98125 #035-19-2004 L2007 **PD** *012

MAC LEAN, James Barry. 925 SENECA ST 98101 #054-04-1962 L1967 **N IM** *020 †75

MAC LENNAN, Benjamin D. 1600 E JEFFERSON ST, STE 400 98122 #018-03-2002 L2007 **ORS** *020

MAC LURG, Brian Jason. 1120 CHERRY ST STE 240 98104 #054-04-1983 L1987 **P OS** *020 †75

MAC MAHON, Ross G. 24 ROY ST, # 447 98109 #539-02-1972 L1999 **U** *100 †95

MAC MILLAN, Margaret Anne. 4800 SAND POINT WAY NE, CHILDREN'S HEART CENTER 98105 #035-45-2000 L2000 **PDC** *100 †55

MACNAB, Aimie Urton. ■ 98126 #051-04-2005 L2005 **IM** *012

MAC NEAL, Nancy Jean. ■ 98116 #016-11-1983 L1984 **IM ID** *020 †20

MADDELA, Daniel Edwards. 2600 SW HOLDEN ST 98126 #018-03-1992 L1992 **P** *020 †75

MADRIAGA, Lorelei T. ■ 98108 #748-08-1975 L1985 *075

MADSEN, Berit L. 1100 9TH AVE C1-MSO, VIRGINIA MASON MEDICAL CEN 98101 #005-11-1989 L1993 **RO** *020 †80

MADSEN, Nicolas Leth. ■ 98122 #054-04-2005 L2005 **PD** *012

MADTES, David Keith. 1100 FAIRVIEW AVE N, RESEARCH CENTER 98109 #041-12-1979 L1983 **PUD CCM** *050 †20

MADWED, Karin Tina. 9800 4TH AVE NE 98115 #005-18-1986 L1986 **FM** *020 †18

MADWED, Michael Paul. 320 NW 113TH PL 98177 #035-09-1982 L1985 **FM ADL** *040 †18

MAEDA, Christopher Y. 1200 12TH AVE S, PACIFIC MEDICAL CENTERS 98144 #056-06-2001 L2003 **FSM** *020 †18

MAENZA, Janine Ruth. 901 BOREN AVE STE 600 98104 #035-01-1990 L1999 **ID** *020 †20

MAESER, Sherwin M. 901 BOREN AVE STE 600 98104 #049-01-1944 L1958 **U** *071 †95

MAESTAS, Ramoncita R. 550 16TH AVE STE 100 98122 #054-04-1983 L1984 **FM** *020 †18

MAGDALENO, Mark Edward. 8210 ASHWORTH AVE N 98103 #003-01-1994 L2004 **MPD** *020 †55

MAGRUDER, Levin F, Jr. N W MARKET & BARNES 98107 #021-05-1956 L1974 **N P** *071 †75
MAHER, Dennis Patrick. 10330 MERIDIAN AVE N, NORTHWEST HAND SPECIALISTS 98133 #048-14-1979 L1991 **HS PS** *071 †65
MAHER, Vincent M Gerard. 325 9TH AVE 98104 #539-05-1981 L1994 **CD** *020
MAHESHWARI, Rajshri. ■ 98109 #048-04-2004 L2004 **ORS** *012
MAHMOED, Mohamed Nizar N. 1600 E JOHN ST 98112 #065-01-1988 L1999 **ORS** *020 †40 ‡
MAHONEY, Anne Margaret. 1100 9TH AVE 98101 #019-02-1998 L2001 **PCC** *020 †20
MAHONEY, Charles Patrick. 4800 SAND POINT WAY NE, CHILDREN'S HOSP, CH.92. 98105 #007-02-1955 L1960 **END PD** *071 †55
MAHONY, Barry S. 1229 MADISON ST, STE 1150 98104 #007-02-1979 L1986 **DR** *020 †80
MAI, Jeffrey Chingkwei. 1959 NE PACIFIC ST, UW SCHOOL OF MEDICINE GME 98195 #041-12-2005 L2005 **NS** *012
MAIER, Ronald Vitt. 325 9TH AVE, SURGERY 359796 98104 #036-07-1973 L1975 **GS CCS** *020 †85
MAILMAN, Eric David. 747 BROADWAY 98122 #023-01-1992 L1997 **EM** *020 †16
MAITRE, Sarah Katherine. ■ 98122 #040-02-2007 L2007 *012
MAJOR, Daniel Edward. 1959 NE PACIFIC ST 98195 #005-18-2003 L2004 **N** *020
MAK, Ceayee. 1959 NE PACIFIC ST, RM C-212 98195 #035-09-2002 L2007 **AR** *012 †80
MAKI, Jeffrey Harold. 1660 S COLUMBIAN WAY, 114 98108 #036-07-1991 L1991 **DR** *020 †80
MAKIELSKI, Kathleen H. 1145 BROADWAY 98122 #025-01-1978 L1985 **OTO HNS** *020 †45
MAKISHIMA, Sandra Eiko. ■ 98125 #010-01-1988 L1990 **AN** *020
MAKOVSKI, Mikhail V. 4719 9TH AVE NE 98105 #913-99-1986 L2001 **GPM** *020
MALETIC, Kathleen Marie. ■ 98102 #023-07-1987 L1998 **ID** *020 †20
MALHOTRA, Uma. 1959 NE PACIFIC ST, BOX 358080 98195 #495-36-1985 L1995 **ID** *020 †20
MALIK, Rubeela. 125 16TH AVE E 98112 #704-01-1982 L1992 **GE IM** *020 †20
MALIK, Sundeep. 747 BROADWAY 98122 #056-06-1999 L2003 **AN** *020 †05
MALLAREDDY, Madhavi. 1959 NE PACIFIC ST, UNIV OF WASHINGTON MED CTR 98195 #495-21-1997 L2007 **NEP** *012 †20
MALLICK, Kim Shannon. 1221 MADISON ST STE 1218 98104 #016-11-1983 L1989 **OPH OS** *020 †35
MALLIRIS, Ourania B. 7554 15TH AVE NW, BALLARD PEDIATRIC CLINIC 98117 #024-01-1978 L1979 **PD** *020 †55
MALLON, Daniel Perry. ■ 98105 #017-20-2007 L2007 **PD** *012
MALONE, Beth Anne. 10560 5TH AVE NE 98125 #039-01-1988 L1990 **AN** *020 †05
MALONEY, David Geo. 1959 NE PACIFIC ST, MSC 359300 98195 #005-11-1985 L1994 **ON IM** *020 †20
MANANGAN, Nicanor Rodrigo. 1420 TERRY AVE UNIT 1503 98101 #748-09-1981 L1982 **DR NM** *020
MANCHANDA, Vivek. 1107 NE 45TH ST STE 440, DEPARTMENT OF RADIOLOGY 98105 #496-09-1994 L2004 **NM** *020 †18,28
MANDEL, Dan Aviel. 1959 NE PACIFIC ST, BOX 356428 98195 #550-02-2002 L2005 **RHU** *020 †20
MANDEL, Michael R. 4033 E MADISON ST 98112 #005-14-1974 L1976 **P** *020
MANDELL, Katherine Ann. 112 10TH AVE 98122 #021-01-2003 L2003 **GS** *012
MANDELL, Samuel Pierce. 1959 NE PACIFIC ST, US SCHOOL OF MEDICINE GME 98195 #024-16-2005 L2005 **GS** *012
MANGHAM, Charles A, Jr. 801 BROADWAY, STE 830 98122 #051-01-1970 L1973 **NO** *020 †45
MANGHAM, Chas Adley, Sr. 4033 E MADISON ST 98112 #051-01-1942 L1949 **PYA** *020 †75
MANGIONE-SMITH, Rita Mary. 6200 NE 74TH ST STE 210, CHILD HEALTH INSTITUTE 98115 #025-07-1991 L2005 **PD** *020 †55
MANHAS, Dev Raj. 1600 E JEFFERSON ST, STE 110 98122 #495-03-1959 L1971 **TS VS** *020 †85,90
MANICONE, Anne Marie. MED, PULMONARY & CRITICAL CARE 98195 #035-20-1998 L2001 **PCC** *020 †20
MANKEY, Martin Geo. 1229 MADISON ST STE 1600, ORTHOPAEDIC PHYSICIANS INC 98104 #016-42-1984 L1987 **ORS** *020 †40
MANKOFF, David A. 1959 NE PACIFIC ST, BOX 356113 98195 #041-01-1988 L1990 **NM** *020 †20,28
MANLEY, Thomas John. 4800 SAND POINT WAY NE, DEPARTMENT OF HEMATOLOGY 98105 #056-05-1996 L1999 **PD** *020 †55
MANN, Frederick Archibald. 600 BROADWAY, STE 170 98122 #017-20-1975 L1992 **DR** *020 †20,80
MANN, Gary Neil. 1959 NE PACIFIC ST, BOX 356410 98195 #836-01-1989 L2000 **GS** *020 †85
MANNING, Kristin Ann. 1229 MADISON ST, STE 900 98104 #003-01-1995 L1998 **DR** *020 †80
MANNING, Scott Clark. 4800 SAND POINT WAY NE, W-7729 98105 #021-01-1980 L1995 **OTO PDO** *020 †45
MANNING, Thomas. 1959 NE PACIFIC ST, DEPT OF NEURO SURGERY 98195 #016-02-2000 L2000 **NS** *020
MANOS, Peter James. 1100 9TH AVE 98101 #025-01-1979 L1982 **P** *020 †75
MANS, Else. ■ 98115 #660-03-1960 L1964 **P** *071
MANSFIELD, Peter Bicknell. 500 17TH AVE, PROVIDENCE MEDICAL CENTER 98122 #024-01-1962 L1970 **TS PDS** *030 †85,90
MANSY, Alexander Wm. 200 15TH AVE E 98112 #054-04-1954 L1955 **R** *071 †80
MANTEI, Kristin Marie. ■ 98112 #054-04-2001 L2002 **HMP** *020
MAO, Constance. 325 9TH AVE 98104 #005-06-1988 L1990 **OBG** *020 †30
MAO, Jennie. 1101 MADISON ST, STE 301 98104 #025-01-1991 L1995 **OBG** *020 †30
MAR, David F. 747 BROADWAY 98122 #028-34-1993 L2001 **FM OBG** *020 †18
MAR, Kelvin Get. PO BOX 16546 98116 #028-34-1998 L2004 **EM** *020 †16
MARASINGHE, Thejana Kapil. 320 WESTLAKE AVE N, STE 100 98109 #220-01-2003 L2006 **FP** *012
MARAVILLA, Kenneth R. 325 9TH AVE 98104 #035-08-1970 L1986 **RNR NS** *020 †80
MARCHIONDA, Paula Jeane. ■ 98112 #003-01-2007 L2007 **FP** *012
MARCHIONNE, Anna Maria. 5513 NE 65TH ST 98115 #045-01-1992 L2001 **AN** *020 †05
MARCONDES, Antonio Mario. 825 E LAKE AVE E, FRED HUTCHINSON CANCE RESE 98109 #187-50-2000 L2005 *100
MARCUS, Sarah Rose. 1959 NE PACIFIC ST, BOX 356460 98195 #016-06-1995 L1999 **OBG** *020 †30
MARDER, Carrie Page. ■ 98109 #005-14-2006 L2007 **DR** *012
MARGLIN, Stephen Irving. 825 EASTLAKE AVE E, G2-2099300 98109 #008-01-1968 L1980 **DR ON** *040 †80
MARGO, Eduardo Saul. 1560 N 115TH ST STE 106, NORTHWEST HOSPITAL 98133 #048-12-1996 L1998 **IM** *020 †20
MARGOLIS, Milton Theodore. MASON CLINIC 98101 #024-07-1960 L1972 **DR** *071 †80
MARING, Thomas S. 509 OLIVE WAY, STE 750 98101 #005-14-1993 L1996 **OMF CS** *020
MARK, Angela Noelle. ■ 98125 #023-07-2005 L2005 **N** *012
MARK, Karen Elizabeth. 600 BROADWAY STE 400 98122 #005-02-1998 L2003 **ID** *020 †20
MARKOWITZ, Stephen. 900 TERRY AVE FL 4, $ 98104 #836-01-1983 L1992 **AN** *020 †05
MARKS, Richard Edward. 1001 BROADWAY, STE 200 98122 #005-02-1972 L1975 **N** *020 †75
MARKS, Sidney. ■ 98112 #016-11-1942 L1951 **PHP PTH** *071 †50
MARKS, William Henry. 1101 MADISON ST STE 200 98104 #016-43-1977 L1993 **TTS GS** *020 †85
MARON, Howard Glenn. 1101 MADISON ST STE 1501 98104 #005-14-1977 L1978 **IM** *020 †20
MARON, Jonathan Steven. 747 BROADWAY 98122 #012-05-1990 L1994 **APM** *020 †05
MARQUARDT, Deborah Lane. 1959 NE PACIFIC ST, BOX 356340 98195 #005-12-2002 L2002 **GS** *020 †85
MARQUEZ, Joseph Charles. 1145 BROADWAY 98122 #016-06-1999 L2004 **U** *020 †95
MARRA, Christina. 325 9TH AVE, DEPT NEUR 98104 #040-02-1984 L1985 **N ID** *020 †75
MARRAZZO, Jeanne Marisa. 325 9TH AVE, HARBORVIEW MED CTR #359931 98104 #041-02-1988 L1992 **ID** *020 †20
MARRIOTT, Daniel Francis. 1145 BROADWAY, THE POLYCLINIC 98122 #054-04-1966 L1969 **IM** *020
MARRS, Jessie Michele. ■ 98144 #054-04-2004 L2004 **OBG** *012
MARSHALL, Caroline Belle. 1959 NE PACIFIC ST BOX 35, U OF WASHINGTON MEDICAL CE 98195 #048-04-1999 L2002 **NEP** *100 †20
MARSHALL, Lorna A. 1101 MADISON ST STE 1050, PACIFIC NW FERTILITY AND I 98104 #016-06-1979 L1983 **REN GYN** *020 †30
MARSHALL, Maureen. 1145 BROADWAY, POLYCLINIC 98122 #031-01-1989 L1989 **END IM** *020 †20
MARSHALL, Susan Gayle. 4800 SAND POINT WAY NE, CHILDREN"S HOSP MEDICAL CN 98105 #005-14-1980 L1981 **PDP PD** *050 †55
MARSHALL, Victor M. ■ 98101 #048-02-1938 L1938 **OPH** *071 †35
MARTEL, Elaine P. 4400 37TH AVE S 98118 #054-04-1991 L1992 **PD** *020 †55
MARTIN, Carolyn. 1101 MADISON ST, STE 950 98104 #054-04-1990 L1997 **OBG MFM** *020 †30
MARTIN, Daniel Benjamin. 919 N 81ST ST 98103 #008-01-1995 L1999 **HEM HO** *020 †20
MARTIN, David Andrew. 1959 NE PACIFIC ST 356428, UNIVERSITY OF WASHINGTON 98195 #035-45-1998 L2002 **RHU** *020 †20
MARTIN, David K. 4800 SAND POINT WAY NE 98105 #051-04-1981 L1991 **PD PHO** *050 †55
MARTIN, David Reid. 8521 15TH AVE NE 98115 #024-01-1983 L1986 **OS FM** *020 †18
MARTIN, Gary Victor. 1660 S COLUMBIAN WAY, CARDIOLOGY 111C 98108 #003-01-1980 L1984 **CD IM** *020 †20
MARTIN, George M. UNIV WA SCH MED/PATH 98105 #054-04-1953 L1956 **PTH OS** *050 †50,19
MARTIN, Lynn Douglas. 4800 SAND POINT WAY NE 98105 #054-04-1982 L1993 **PAN CCP** *040 †55,05
MARTIN, Paul Jos. 825 EASTLAKE AVE E 98109 #041-01-1974 L1978 **ON IM** *050 †20
MARTIN, Richard Allen, Jr. ■ 98104 #028-46-1976 L1978 **EM GP** *020 †16
MARTIN, Thomas Geo. 1959 NE PACIFIC ST, BOX 356330 98195 #041-14-1977 L1996 **PTX EM** *050 †70,16
MARTIN, Thomas R. 1660 S COLUMBIAN WAY #111B 98108 #041-01-1973 L1974 **IM** *020 †20
MARTIN, Thomas Wayne. 1001 SW KLICKITAT WAY 98134 #028-34-1983 L1993 **ATP HMP** *020 †50
MARTIN, Troy Michael. ■ 98103 #054-04-1999 L1999 **ID** *100
MARTIN, Wayne Evans. 1229 MADISON ST STE 1440 98104 #048-12-1958 L1965 **AN** *071 †05
MARTINEAU, Paul. ■ 98109 #067-01-2000 L2006 **HS** *100
MARTINEZ, Ryan Jeffrey. 747 BROADWAY, # 734 98122 #038-40-2001 L2004 **GS** *020 †85
MARTINEZ, Shay Marie. ■ 98126 #035-45-2005 L2005 **IM** *012
MARTINEZ LEMKE, Tania Luc. ■ 98145 #025-01-2005 L2005 **FP** *012
MARTINI, Shahm. 901 BOREN AVE, STE 1020 98104 #875-02-1990 L2003 **P** *020 †75
MARTINIS, Andrew John. 801 BROADWAY 98122 #054-04-1954 L1955 **TS** *072 †85,90
MARTINS, Renato. 825 EASTLAKE AVE E, MS G-4830 98109 #187-03-1992 L2003 **IM** *020 †20
MARZBANI, Edmond Ardeshir. PO BOX 356421, UNIV OF WASHINGTON 98195 #036-01-2007 L2007 **IM** *012
MASCHER, Marcella Theresi. 1959 NE PACIFIC ST, DIV N 98195 #649-01-1999 L2005 **NPM** *012 †55
MASHINO, Yoko. 600 UNIVERSITY ST, STE 1200 98101 #572-31-1993 L1999 **IM** *020 †20
MASONIS, Susan Lee. 521 WALL ST ACC-2, GROUP HEALTH COOPERATIVE 98121 #041-02-2001 L2005 **IM** *020
MASSAGLI, Teresa Luisa. 4800 SAND POINT WAY NE 98105 #008-01-1982 L1985 **PM PD** *020 †55,60
MASSARWEH, Nader Nabile. ■ 98115 #021-01-2005 L2005 **GS** *012
MASSEY, Philip Gray. 1101 MADISON ST, STE 301 98104 #047-05-1996 L2000 **CD** *020 †20
MASTEN, Sue Ann. 10453 MAPLEWOOD PL SW 98146 #054-04-1987 L1989 **IM** *020 †20
MASUDA, David Lee. ■ 98117 #037-01-1980 L1981 **DR** *020 †80
MATE, Timothy Philip. 1221 MADISON ST, STE 1225 98104 #030-06-1977 L1978 **RO IM** *020 †80
MATESAN, Manuela-Cristina. PO BOX 356421, UNIV OF WASHINGTON 98195 #781-04-1996 L2007 **IM** *012
MATHES, David Woodbridge. ■ 98144 #021-01-1996 L2006 **PS** *100 †85,65
MATHEW, George. 121 VINE ST, UNIT 1503 98121 #418-01-1987 L1996 **IM ON** *020 †20
MATHEWS, Christopher Mark. 720 OLIVE WAY STE 300 98101 #014-01-1982 L1983 **IM** *020 †20
MATHEY, Bruce Chas. 2311 MCGILVRA BLVD E, . 98112 #016-11-1989 L1992 **HEM** *020 †20
MATHIASEN, Patrick Leroy. 1570 N 115TH ST, STE 14 98133 #026-04-1985 L1988 **P** *020 †75
MATIN, Michelle Lee. 11011 MERIDIAN AVE N, STE 200 98133 #054-04-1993 L1995 **FM** *020 †18
MATSEN, Frederick A, III. 4245 ROOSEVELT WAY NE, STE 354775 98105 #048-04-1968 L1971 **ORS** *020 †40
MATSUMOTO, Alvin Mitsu. VA MED CTR GRECC 182B 98108 #054-04-1975 L1977 **IMG END** *050 †20
MATSUMOTO, Shinichi. 1959 NE PACIFIC ST, BOX 356174 98195 #572-30-1988 L2001 *100
MATTHEWS, Dana Christine. 4800 SAND POINT WAY NE, CHILDREN'S HOSP & MED CTR 98105 #054-04-1981 L1984 **PHO** *050 †55
MATUTE-BELLO, Gustavo. 815 MERCER STREET, BOX 358 98195 #935-07-1988 L1994 **IM PCC** *050 †20
MAUNEY, Marc. P S BOX 34245 98124 #034-01-1980 L1984 **PTH** *050 †50
MAURER, Scott Henry. 1959 NE PACIFIC ST, BOX 356340 98195 #040-02-2004 L2004 **PHO** *012 †55
MAWJEE, Shamsa Zindani. 521 WALL ST, GROUP HEALTH PERMENANTE 98121 #704-06-1988 L2005 **FM** *020 †18
MAXIM, Peter Edward. 2324 EASTLAKE AVE E, STE 500 98102 #008-01-1966 L1973 **P** *050 †75
MAXIMIN, Phamila R. ■ 98121 #495-31-1958 L1974 **IM PHP** *071 †18
MAXIN, Michael. 1600 E JOHN ST 98112 #016-42-1994 L1998 **DR** *020 †80
MAXYM, Maya. ■ 98125 #008-01-2007 L2007 **PD** *012

■ = Address Information Privacy Protected

MAY, David Joseph. ■ 98103 #038-41-2005 L2005 **FP** *012

MAY, Eugene Frank. 600 BROADWAY, STE 170 98122 #016-02-1987 L1995 **N** *020 †75

MAY, Karl Jos, Jr. ■ 98177 #054-04-1957 L1958 **GS CD** *071 †85,90

MAY, Mary Patricia. 4800 SAND POINT WAY NE 98105 #024-07-1986 L1997 **PD** *020 †55

MAYADEV, Jyoti Shyam. WASHINGTON MEDIC, UNIVERSITY OF 98195 #038-06-2004 L2006 **RO** *012

MAYBERG, Marc Robt. 1600 E JEFFERSON ST, STE 205 98122 #026-08-1978 L1985 **NS VS** *020 †25

MAYEDA, Kenneth Eugene. 2902 BEACON AVE S 98144 #054-04-1973 L1976 **FM** *020 †18

MAYER, Charles Jacob. 4245 ROOSEVELT WAY NE, UW FAMILY MEDICINE CLINCI 98105 #010-03-1991 L1993 **FM** *020 †18

MAYHILL, Monica Lynn. 402 20TH AVE # 1 98122 #055-02-2003 L2003 **FM** *020 †18

MAYNARD, James Edwin. 1455 NW LEARY WAY 98107 #067-01-1959 L1964 **GPM** *050 †70

MAYO, Michael Edward. 1959 NE PACIFIC ST, UNIVERSITY OF WASHINGTON 98195 #917-21-1962 L1975 **U GS** *020 †95

MAYO, Monique Antoinette. ■ 98105 #054-04-2008 *012

MAYOCK, Dennis Edward. UNIVERSITY OF WASHINGTON, PEDIATRICS, BOX 356320 98195 #038-40-1975 L1978 **NPM PD** *050 †55

MAZEIKA, Gandis Gediminas. 10564 5TH AVE NE STE 205 98125 #005-19-1993 L2000 **P N** *020 †75

MAZOR, Robert Lee. 4800 SAND POINT WAY NE, DIV OF CRITICAL CARE B 452 98105 #016-11-1995 L2004 **PDC** *100 †15

MAZRIM, Brian Scott. ■ 98118 #028-34-1996 L2001 **FOP** *020

MAZUREK, Mark Eugene. ■ 98105 #054-04-2006 *012

MAZZARELLA, John Anthony. 1560 N 115TH ST, STE 201 98133 #035-20-1958 L1964 **CD IM** *071

MAZZONCINI, Joey Primo. 6700 ROOSEVLT WAY NE #A114 98115 #054-04-2005 L2006 **EM** *012

MC ADAM, Michael Kevin. 900 TERRY AVE, STE 100 98104 #048-13-1999 L1999 **ORS** *020 †40

MC AFEE, Timothy A. 999 3RD AVE, STE 2100 98104 #005-02-1986 L1986 **ADM PHP** *030 †18 ‡

MC ALLISTER, Clarence O. 1915 QUEEN ANNE AVE N 98109 #054-04-1957 L1958 **FM** *071 †18

MC ARTHUR, James Roderick. PO BOX 357430, DEPT MEDICINE 98195 #024-01-1956 L1973 **IM HEM** *071 †20

MC AULIFFE, William. 325 9TH AVE 98104 #143-06-1985 L1993 **RNR** *100

MC BRINN, Damon Edmund. 2211 QUEEN ANNE AVE N 98109 #035-03-1997 L1999 **FM** *020 †18

MC CABE, Edward F. ■ 98105 #056-06-1943 L1947 **GP GS** *071

MCCABE, Mark Owen. ■ 98102 #016-02-2007 L2007 **IM** *012

MC CAFFERTY, Alexandra F. ■ 98115 #054-04-1994 L1994 **FM** *100

MCCARREN, Megan Colleen. ■ 98102 #054-04-2007 L2007 **IM** *012

MC CARTHY, Elizabeth R. 1200 12TH AVE S 98144 #005-02-1991 L1994 **FM** *020 †18

MC CARTHY, Michael Benet. ■ 98125 #024-05-1983 L1984 **IM** *020 †20

MCCLASKEY, Daniel Oshaugn. PO BOX 356421, UNIV OF WASHINGTON 98195 #054-04-2007 L2007 **IM** *012

MC CLEAN, John Patrick. 500 17TH AVE 98122 #030-06-1947 L1948 **OPH OTO** *071 †45

MC CLELLAN, Jon M. 13925 PAR PL NE 98125 #025-01-1984 L1985 **P** *020 †75

MC CLELLAND, Raymond S. 325 9TH AVE, UNIV OF WASH BOX 359909 98104 #054-04-1995 L1998 **ID** *020 †20

MC CLOSKEY, Lon Wm. ■ 98115 #020-02-1971 L1987 **GPM OS** *020

MC CLUNG, Mark Richard. 2025 1ST AVE STE 760 98121 #048-12-1983 L1995 **P** *062 †75

MC CONNELL, Gwenyth Katy. 1959 NE PACIFIC ST 98195 #054-04-1991 L1993 **P** *020 †75

MC CONNELL, Robert Gerald. ■ 98133 #054-06-1967 L1973 **ORS HS** *040 †40

MCCORMICK, Kinsey Ann. ■ 98105 #054-04-2008 *012

MC CORMICK, Susan Erin. 1100 9TH AVE C1-MSO, VIRGINIA MASON MEDICAL CEN 98101 #010-01-1988 L1997 **GE** *020 †20

MC CORMICK, Wayne C. 325 9TH AVE BOX 359755, MEDICINE GERIATRICS ZA-87 98104 #028-02-1983 L1987 **IM IMG** *020 †20,70

MC CORNACK, E Bruce. 1600 E JEFFERSON ST, STE 600 98122 #005-06-1958 L1963 **ORS** *071 †40

MCCOURTIE, Anton Stuart. SURGERY #356410, DEPARTMENT OF 98195 #917-01-1999 L2006 **GS** *012

MC COY, Candice. 1201 AMGEN CT W 98119 #005-02-1989 L1992 **ON** *050 †20

MC COY, Kathleen Ann. 10416 5TH AVE NE, PACIFIC MEDICAL CENTER 98125 #054-04-1984 L1985 **IM** *075 †20

MC CREERY, Joseph Michael. 7817 12TH AVE NE 98115 #048-13-1980 L1983 **P FM** *020 †75,18

MC CULLOCH, David K. 4009 31ST AVE W 98199 #919-03-1977 L1987 **IM** *020 †20

MC CULLOUGH, Brendan John. ■ 98103 #054-04-2007 L2007 **GS** *012

MC CULLOUGH, Richard Paul. 515 MINOR AVE, STE 110 98104 #030-06-1958 L1964 **ORS** *071 †40

MCCUTCHEN, Yuli Son. ■ 98115 #054-04-2007 L2007 **IM** *012

MC DAVID, Joshua Dent. 6227 21ST AVE NE 98115 #036-01-1988 L1995 **P** *020 †75

MC DERMOTT, James A. ■ 98119 #016-11-1963 L1966 **P GP** *071

MC DERMOTT, John Edward. 1600 E JEFFERSON ST, STE 400 98122 #030-05-1960 L1971 **ORS** *020 †40

MC DERMOTT, Tiffany Marie. 1101 MADISON ST, STE 900 98104 #033-05-1993 L1997 **OBG** *020 †30

MC DONAGH, Deirdre P. 1229 MADISON ST 98104 #036-07-1991 L1998 **PCP** *020 †50

MC DONALD, George Bernard. 1100 FAIRVIEW AVE N #D2-19, FRED HUTCHINSON CANCER RES 98109 #028-02-1967 L1968 **GE IM** *020 †20

MC DONALD, Pamela H. 3216 NE 45TH PL, STE 200 98105 #054-04-1977 L1978 **FM** *020 †18

MC DONALD, Roger Koefod. ■ 98109 #026-04-1946 L1982 **P** *071 †20

MC DONALD, Ruth Ann. 4800 SAND POINT WAY NE 98105 #026-04-1987 L1989 **PN PD** *020 †55

MC DONNELL, Julia Hannan. 4800 SAND POINT WAY NE 98105 #028-34-1983 L1997 **PD** *020 †55

MC DONOUGH, Karen Ann. 1959 NE PACIFIC ST, UWMC- BOX 356429 98195 #056-05-1993 L1995 **IM** *020 †20

MC EACHRANE-GROSS, F. 6553 CALIFORNIA AVE SW, NEWSTART HEALTHCARE 98136 #308-07-1983 L1993 **FM** *020 †70,18

MC ELRATH, Margaret J. 325 9TH AVE 98104 #045-01-1980 L1989 **IM** *020 †20

MCELROY, Courtney Erin. ■ 98102 #054-04-2008 *012

MC ELROY, Donald M. ■ 98199 #028-02-1941 L1946 **GP** *071

MC EVOY, Joseph P. 1600 E JOHN ST 98112 #024-05-1973 L1978 **U** *020 †95

MC EVOY, Joseph Peter. 200 15TH AVE E 98112 #026-04-1943 L1954 **U** *071 †35

MC GINTY, Molly Rose. 125 16TH AVE E, GROUP HEALTH COOP 98112 #040-02-2003 L2003 **FM** *020 †18

MC GONIGLE, Dee Jos. ■ 98105 #028-34-1955 L1964 **GS** *071 †85

MCGONIGLE, Kathryn F. 1560 N 115TH ST, MOB SUITE 101 98133 #028-34-1984 L2001 **GO OBG** *020 †30

MC GOODWIN, Michael C. ■ 98115 #048-04-1969 L1973 **DR NM** *075 †80,28 ‡

MCGOODWIN, Wendy Loraine. ■ 98115 #054-04-2004 L2004 **IM** *020 †20

MC GUIRE, John Kennedy. 4800 SAND POINT WAY NE, CHILDREN'S HOSPITAL & REG 98105 #016-06-1993 L2004 **CCP** *020 †55

MC HUGH, James Anthony. 1600 E JEFFERSON ST STE 51 98122 #054-04-1974 L1977 **FM** *020 †18

MC INTOSH, Robert E, Jr. 1101 MADISON ST STE 1500 98104 #047-06-1966 L1976 **OBG** *020 †30

MC INTYRE, Lisa. 325 9TH AVE, HARBORVIEW MEDICAL CENTER 98104 #054-04-1995 L1995 **TRS CCS** *020 †85

MC INTYRE, Scott Talley. 3216 NE 45TH PL, STE 200 98105 #054-04-1982 L1983 **FM** *020 †18

MC KAY, Hunter Albert. 1145 BROADWAY 98122 #007-02-1970 L1972 **U AM** *020 †95 ‡

MC KEE, Ann Lynn. 125 16TH AVE E, CSB 4 98112 #054-04-1981 L1982 **FM** *020 †18

MC KILLOP, Brian Richard. 1101 MADISON ST, PC 98104 #054-04-1976 L1977 **OPH** *020 †35

MC KINNEY, Martha Louise. 4800 SAND POINT WAY NE, P O BOX 5371 98105 #036-05-1992 L2000 **PDP** *020 †55 ‡

MC KONE, Edward Francis. 1253 HLTH SCIENCES BLDG 35, PULMONARY & CRITICAL CARE 98195 #539-03-1993 L2002 **PCC** *020

MC LANAHAN, David Jos. ■ 98136 #041-13-1967 L1976 **GS** *071 †85

MCLAREN, Kimberly Dawn. 4225 ROOSEVELT WAY NE, STE 306 98105 #048-14-2000 L2004 **P** *020 †75 ‡

MC LAUGHLIN, John Francis. 4800 SAND POINT WAY NE, CHILD HOSP REG MED CTR 98105 #016-06-1970 L1971 **PD** *020 †55

MC LEAN, Edward Barnard. 1221 MADISON ST STE 1420 98104 #049-01-1966 L1972 **OPH** *071 †35

MCLEAN, Katherine Ann. 1959 NE PACIFIC ST # C-, BOX 356340 98195 #016-02-2006 L2006 **OBG** *020

MC LEANRIGGS, Heather Joy. ■ 98112 #008-01-1992 *100

MCLEMORE, Leslie Carruthe. ■ 98115 #028-34-2006 L2006 **OBG** *012

MC MAHON, Edward M. 7554 15TH AVE NW, BALLARD PEDIATRIC CLINIC 98117 #036-07-1972 L1973 **PD** *020 †55

MC MAHON, Kerry Maureen. 1959 NE PACIFIC ST BOX 35 98195 #054-04-2003 L2007 **OBG** *100

MC MAHON, Ross Leslie. 24 ROY ST, # 447 98109 #065-05-1994 L2006 **GS** *020 †85

MCMENAMIN, Drew Scott. PO BOX 357115, 1959 NE PACIFIC RR-215 98195 #143-05-1999 L2007 *100

MC MILLAN, Daniel Eugene. 550 16TH AVE STE 100, MEDICINE CLI 98122 #040-02-2001 L2003 **FM** *020

MC MULLEN, Wm Russell. 1959 NE PACIFIC ST, BOX 356123 98195 #038-41-1978 L1979 **EM IM** *040 †20

MC MURRAY, James Edward. 1229 MADISON ST, STE 1440 98104 #048-02-1963 L1974 **AN** *071 †05

MC NABB, Vannee R. 3654 W COMMODORE WAY 3700 98199 #891-01-1959 L1969 **AN OBG** *020

MCNALLEY, Thomas Edward. ■ 98117 #018-03-2004 L2005 **PM** *012

MC NAMARA, Kevin Raymond. ■ 98116 #010-01-1986 L1991 **ORS** *020

MC NEELY, Marguerite J. 4245 ROOSEVELT WAY NE, STE 354775 98105 #054-04-1988 L1990 **IM** *020 †20

MC NUTT, Michael Allen. 747 BROADWAY 98122 #026-04-1981 L1982 **PTH** *020 †50

MC PHILLIPS, Heather Anne. 4245 ROOSEVELT WAY NE, STE 354775 98105 #016-02-1994 L1998 **PD** *020 †55

MC QUINN, Wm Chas, Jr. 201 16TH AVE E, GROUP HEALTH SURGERY CMB-3 98112 #027-01-1980 L1997 **VS GS** *020 †85

MCTIERNAN, Anne M. 1100 FAIRVIEW AVE N, MS M4-B402 98109 #035-09-1989 L1989 **IM OS** *050 †20

MEASE, Philip Judson. 1101 MADISON ST STE 1000 98104 #005-11-1977 L1978 **IM RHU** *020 †20

MECKLENBURG, Robert Scott. 1100 9TH AVE 98101 #016-06-1969 L1973 **END IM** *071 †20

MECKLER, Ken Alan. 1001 SW KLICKITAT WAY 98134 #024-07-1994 L1998 **PTH** *020 †50

MEDFORD, Richelle N. ■ 98105 #023-01-2007 L2007 **OBG** *012

MEDVERD, Jonathan Russell. 1660 S COLUMBIAN WAY S-11, VA PUGET SOUND HEALTH CARE 98108 #035-19-1995 L1997 **DR** *020 †80

MEDWELL, Steven Jos. 515 MINOR AVE STE 300, 515 MINOR AVE #230 98104 #017-20-1973 L1976 **CRS GS** *020 †85,10

MEEHAN, Jeffrey R. 1145 BROADWAY 98122 #048-04-1987 L1990 **IM** *020 †20

MEEHAN, John James, Jr. 4800 SAND POINT WAY NE W7, U OF I HOSPITALS & CLINICS 98105 #018-03-1993 L2007 **PDS** *020 †85

MEEHAN, Tammy Denise. 1221 MADISON ST STE 910, DEPT OF PEDATRICS 98104 #018-03-1993 L2007 **PD** *020 †75

MEEKINS, Gregg David. 1660 S COLUMBIAN WAY, NEURO 127 98108 #021-01-1993 L1997 **N** *020 †75

MEEKINS, John Allen. 5334 TALLMAN AVE NW 98107 #035-09-1956 L1965 **PTH** *071 †50

MEFFORD, Heather Christy. 1959 NE PACIFIC ST, BOX 356349 98195 #054-04-2003 L2003 **PD** *020 †19,55

MEHLUM, David Lee. 125 16TH AVE E, OTOLARYNGOLOGY DEPT 98112 #048-12-1976 L1982 **OTO HNS** *020 †45

MEHRA, Atul K. 1959 NE PACIFIC ST # 3565, HEALTH SCIENCES CENTER BB1 98195 #060-01-1989 L1999 **PYG** *020

MEHTA, Alka. 7323 BOWLYN PL S 98118 #051-01-1991 L1994 **PD** *020 †55

MEHTA, Ami Dharmesh. 4800 SAND POINT WAY NE, REGIONAL M 98105 #024-07-2006 L2006 **PD** *012

MEHTA, Khushboo. 521 WALL ST, DEPT FM 98121 #496-07-2004 L2006 **FP** *012

MEHTA, Vivek Krishan. 1221 MADISON ST STE 1225 98104 #054-04-1996 L2001 **RO** *020 †80

MEHTER, Hashim Moosa. ■ 98133 #038-40-2007 L2007 **IM** *012

MEI, Johnny Yong Yi. ■ 98112 #550-04-2003 L2007 **IM** *100 †20

MEIER, Cynthia Andrea. PO BOX 356421, UNIVERSITY OF WASHINGTON 98195 #050-02-2005 L2005 **IM** *012

MEIER, Robert Michael. 1221 MADISON ST, STE 1225 98104 #005-14-1985 L1997 **RO** *020 †80

MEISSNER, Eric Gerhard. PO BOX 356421, UNIV OF WASHINGTON 98195 #036-01-2007 L2007 **IM** *012

MEISSNER, Mark Harmon. 1959 NE PACIFIC STREET, DEPT OF SURGERY BOX 356410 98104 #007-02-1985 L1986 **VS GS** *020 †85

MEISSNER, Nancy Ann. ■ 98125 #007-02-1985 L1986 **IM** *020

MELMAN, Kenneth Newport. 1120 CHERRY ST, STE 240 98104 #028-02-1979 L1979 **P IM** *020 †75

MELSON, Stephen John. 10330 MERIDIAN AVE N STE 3 98133 #018-03-1968 L1974 **P** *020 †75

MELVILLE, Jennifer Lynn. 1959 NE PACIFIC ST, UNIV OF WASH OB/GYN 98195 #005-14-1995 L1997 **OBG** *050 †30

MELVIN, Ann Jorns. 4800 SAND POINT WAY NE 98105 #021-01-1986 L1988 **PD ID** *050 †55

MELVIN, Michael Arthur. 747 BROADWAY 98122 #016-43-1974 L1985 **AN** *020 †05

MELZER, Sanford Morris. 4800 SAND POINT WAY NE, # T0111 98105 #035-47-1982 L1989 **PD** *020 †55

MENA, Hilda. 8720 14TH AVE S 98108 #054-04-2001 L2004 **FM** *020 †18

MENDEZ, Eduardo. ■ 98115 #023-01-1999 L1999 **OTO** *100 †45

MENDIRATTA, Viksa. 4245 ROOSEVELT WAY NE, STE 354775 98105 #038-40-1994 L1998 **OBG** *020 †30

MENES, Keith Caesar. ■ 98101 #005-12-2003 L2003 **GS** *012

MENES, Kevin Caesar. ■ 98101 #005-12-2005 L2005 **EM** *012

MENGERT, Terry John. 1959 NE PACIFIC ST, MSC 359300 98195 #054-04-1984 L1985 **IM** *020 †20,16

MENON, Manoj P. 1959 NE PACIFIC ST RM C2, CAMPUS BOX 356340 98195 #036-01-2002 L2004 **IM** *020 †20

MENSHER, John Howard. 1101 MADISON ST STE 900, POLYCLINIC OPTHAMOLOGY SEC 98104 #035-09-1967 L1979 **OPH** *020 †35

MENZIES, Barbara Excell. 1660 S COLUMBIAN WAY, WAY (111-ID) 98108 #047-05-1988 L2000 **ID** *020 †20

MERAGLIA, Tami Simmone. 125 16TH AVE 98122 #665-01-2004 L2004 **FM** *100

MERATI, Albert Lincoln. ■ 98105 #054-04-1991 L2007 **OTO** *020 †45

MERATI, Jay K. ■ 98105 #517-06-1961 L1969 **AN OS** *020 †05

MERCKER, Janis Maryan G. 1229 MADISON ST, STE 900 98104 #054-04-1976 L1978 **DR PDR** *020 †80

MEREDITH, Charles Wesley. 1959 NE PACIFIC ST RM C2, UNIVERSITY OF WASHINGTON 98195 #056-05-2001 L2001 **ADP** *020 †30

MEREL, Susan Eva. ■ 98115 #016-02-2005 L2005 **IM** *012

MERENDINO, K Alvin. ■ 98177 #008-01-1940 L1949 **GS TS** *071 †85,90

MERKLE, Donald Warren. 507 3RD AVE # 520 98104 #040-02-1947 L1948 **IM** *100 †20

MERRIAM, Geo Rennell, III. 1959 NE PACIFIC ST, MSC 359300 98195 #024-01-1976 L1989 **END IM** *050 †20

MERRIFIELD, Eric Sabbaton. ■ 98112 #023-07-1956 L1963 **IM PUD** *071 †20

MERRILL, Joseph Owen. ■ 98122 #008-01-1990 L1996 **IM** *020 †20

MERRIMAN, Tiffany Mixon. ■ 98115 #021-05-1998 L1998 **IM** *100

MERRITT, Andrew Laurance. ■ 98122 #005-06-2007 L2007 **ORS** *012

MERRITT, John L, II. 4800 SAND POINT WAY NE, MS B-6594 98105 #005-12-1999 L2007 **CBG MG** *020 †55,19

MERRY, Heather Elizabeth. 1959 NE PACIFIC ST #356340 98195 #054-04-2002 L2002 **GS** *012

MERRYFIELD, Lloyd W. ■ 98177 #024-01-1950 L1953 **IM** *072

MERTZ, James L. ■ 98115 #035-20-1952 L2003 **PD** *071 †55 ‡

MERTZ, Robert Harold. ■ 98115 #035-19-1998 L2002 **NPM** *020 †55

MESHER, Richard Alan. 200 15TH AVE E 98112 #054-04-1979 L1980 **N** *020 †75

MESHINCHI, Soheil. 1959 NE PACIFIC ST, MSC 359300 98195 #025-07-1994 L1998 **PHO** *020 †20

MESINA, Lupe Na. 550 16TH AVE STE 100, PROVIDENCE FAMILY MEDICINE 98122 #054-04-2005 L2005 **FP** *012

MESSE, Mark Thos. 1101 MADISON ST STE 950 98104 #035-19-1973 L1975 **OBG** *071 †30

MESSERLI, Brandon J. 98107 #038-75-2007, ▲ L2007 **PM** *012

METCALFE, Donald Gordon. PO BOX 900 98111 #060-01-1979 L1985 **U** *020 †95

METZ, James Benson. 4800 SAND POINT WAY NE, REGIONAL M 98105 #050-02-2006 L2006 **PD** *012

MEULBROEK, Harvey John. ■ 98115 #056-05-1956 L1987 **A IM** *071

MEYER, Jennifer Lynne. ■ 98117 #011-02-2000 L2002 **PD** *020 †55

MEYER, Kenneth Wm. 1229 MADISON ST STE 1440, PHYSICIANS ANESTHESIA SERV 98104 #030-06-1970 L1973 **AN** *020 †05

MEYER, Marcus Andreas. 2525 SW TRENTON ST STE 101, HIGHLINE EYE CLINIC 98106 #028-34-1990 L2000 **OPH** *020 †35

MEYER, Vincent S, Jr. ■ 98109 #005-02-1970 L1971 **AN** *020 †05

MEYERS, Jennifer Lynne. 4800 SAND POINT WAY NE, MAIL CODE W-9824 98105 #041-14-2001 L2007 **PAN** *100

MEZISTRANO, Joseph S. ■ 98118 #054-04-1960 L1963 **ORS** *071 †40

MICEK, Mark Albert. 1930 POST ALY, PIKE MARKET MEDICAL CLINIC 98101 #016-06-1994 L1996 **IM** *020 †20

MICHAEL, Joshua B. 1100 9TH AVE C1-MSO, VIRGINIA MASON MEDICAL CEN 98101 #054-04-2002 L2006 **EM** *020 †20

MICHALOWSKI, Piotr. 1660 S COLUMBIAN WAY, VA PUGET SOUND HEALTHCARE 98108 #759-03-1980 L1998 **AN** *020 †05

MICHIELS, Erica Ann. 1959 NE PACIFIC ST, BOX 356340 98195 #025-12-2004 L2004 **PD** *012 †55

MIELCAREK, Marco Bernd. 1600 29TH AVE 98122 #409-33-1986 L2000 **ON** *020 †20

MIGEON, Mary Bascom. 4245 ROOSEVELT WAY NE, STE 354775 98105 #054-04-1993 L1995 **IM** *020 †20

MIGITA, Darren Shigeo. 4800 SAND POINT WAY NE 98105 #038-06-1996 L1999 **PD** *020 †55

MIGITA, Russell Takeo. 4800 SAND POINT WAY NE, EMERGENCY SERVICES, B-5520 98105 #005-18-1995 L1998 **PEM** *100 †55

MIGNONE, John Luigi. ■ 98104 #036-07-2006 L2006 **IM** *012

MIHALOV, Linda S. 1100 9TH AVE 98101 #016-11-1980 L1981 **GYN** *020 †30

MIKSZEWSKI, Jerold. 1200 12TH AVE S, PACMED CLINICS BEACON HILL 98144 #010-02-1975 L2006 **N** *020 †75

MIKYSA, Bridget Nicole. UNIV OF WASHINGTON MED CTR, DEPT OF RADIOLOGY BOX 3571 98195 #047-05-2001 L2002 **DR** *100

MILDER, Michael Stuart. 1221 MADISON ST, 2ND FL 98104 #028-02-1970 L1972 **ON HEM** *020 †28,20

MILES, Andrew Nicholas. 325 9TH AVE BOX 35924 98104 #143-06-1991 L2000 *100

MILES, Wandra Kaye. 1221 MADISON ST, STE 1520 98104 #041-07-1991 L1999 **PS** *020 †65

MILLER, Catherine L. ■ 98125 #048-13-1993 L2004 **IM** *100

MILLER, Claire R. 10030 15TH AVE SW 98146 #035-15-1950 L1965 **PD PDA** *071

MILLER, Daniel Guthrie. ■ 98115 #054-04-1996 L1999 **MG** *020 †19,55

MILLER, Daniel Stephen. 3800 S MYRTLE ST, HOLLY PARK MED CLINIC 98118 #005-18-1980 L1984 **GPM FM** *020 †18

MILLER, Donald Wesley, Jr. 801 BROADWAY, STE 300 98122 #024-01-1965 L1974 **TS** *020 †85,90

MILLER, Earl Vonnidore. 2324 EASTLAKE AVE E, STE 500 98102 #047-07-1947 L1959 **U** *020 †95

MILLER, Elizabeth Anne. 1959 NE PACIFIC ST, BOX 356510 98195 #028-02-1994 L2001 **U** *020 †95

MILLER, George Andrew, Jr. 200 15TH AVE E 98112 #035-20-1977 L1984 **DR OS** *020 †80

MILLER, James Heath. 1101 MADISON ST STE 1150 98104 #036-05-1993 L1995 **OBG** *020 †30

MILLER, Jane Louise. 1959 NE PACIFIC ST, BOX 356510 98195 #039-01-1985 L1985 **U** *020 †95

MILLER, Joan Ellen. 1516 2ND AVE STE 303 98101 #054-04-1990 L1992 **IM** *062 †20

MILLER, John Wm. 325 9TH AVE # 359745, HARBORVIEW MED CTR 98104 #016-11-1977 L1999 **N CN** *020 †75

MILLER, Leslie. 1801 NW MARKET ST, STE 100 98107 #054-04-1990 L1990 **OBG** *020 †30

MILLER, Mark H. 1550 N 115TH ST 98133 #035-46-1974 L1975 **IM EM** *020 †20,16

MILLER, Richard Alan. 1660 S COLUMBIAN WAY, VAPSHCS 111-ID 98108 #024-01-1977 L1980 **ID IM** *020 †20

MILLER, Samuel Irving, II. 1959 NE PACIFIC ST, UWMC BOX 357710 98195 #048-04-1979 L1996 **IM** *020 †20

MILLER, Susan Marie. 600 UNIVERSITY ST, STE 1200 98101 #054-04-1994 L1998 **PD** *020 †55

MILLER, Walter Taylor. 1207 PUBLIC SAFETY BLDG 98104 #803-01-1946 L1956 **PUD** *020

MILLER, Zachary Adam. PO BOX 356465, DEPT OF NEUROLOGY 98195 #041-12-2004 L2005 **N** *012

MILLER, Zachary Ian. 125 16TH AVE E, GROUP HELATH, INFECTIOUS D 98112 #035-01-1971 L1975 **ID PD** *020 †55

MILLICAN, Jean Madeleine. 901 BOREN AVE, STE 1776 98104 #010-02-1978 L1979 **N** *062 †75

MILLICAN, Mary F Kennedy. ■ 98112 #047-06-1948 L2004 **P PYA** *020

MILLIGAN, Donald Robt. PO BOX 5371, 4800 SAND POINT WAY NE 98105 #056-06-1983 L2002 **PD** *020 †55

MILLS, Edward Henry. 1120 CHERRY ST STE 220 98104 #005-11-1955 L1959 **ORS** *020 †40

MILLS, Richard Pence. 1221 MADISON ST, STE 1124 98104 #040-01-1968 L1970 **OPH** *020 †35

MILNE, Scott Thomas. ■ 98144 #040-02-1994 L1998 **EM** *020 †16

MILSTEIN, Jerrold M. 4800 SAND POINT WAY NE 98105 #026-04-1964 L1977 **CHN** *071 †55,75

MILTUN, David Clyde. ■ 98118 #025-12-1997 L1997 *100

MIN, David Byung. ■ 98103 #016-43-2006 L2006 **IM** *012

MINAMI, Elina. 1959 NE PACIFIC ST, BOX 356422 98195 #010-01-1995 L1999 **CD** *020 †20

MINELLA, Alexander C. 1100 FAIRVIEW AVE N D2-100, FRED HUTCHINSON CANCER RES 98109 #047-05-1998 L2000 **HO IM** *050 †20

MINIEL, Nicholas Joseph. UNIV OF WASHINGTON, DEPT OF SURGERY #356410 98195 #005-14-2007 L2007 **GS** *012

MINOSHIMA, Satoshi. 1959 NE PACIFIC ST, MSC 359300 98195 #572-05-1987 L2000 **NM** *020 †28

MINOTTI, Dominick A. 4540 SAND POINT WAY NE, NORTHWEST ASTHMA & ALLERGY 98105 #010-02-1971 L1976 **AI IM** *071 †20,18,03

MINZEL, Jerry Chas. 1145 BROADWAY 98122 #054-04-1967 L1969 **U** *071 †95

MIRONOV, Vitali G. 600 UNIVERSITY ST, STE 1200 98101 #913-64-1994 L2001 **IM** *020 †20

MIRZA, Amer Jawad. 325 9TH AVE BOX 359798, HARBORVIEW MEDICAL CENTER 98104 #040-02-2001 L2006 **ORS** *020

MIRZA, Sohail Kassim. 325 9TH AVE BOX 359798, DEPT OF OTHOPAEDICS 98104 #007-02-1989 L1993 **ORS** *020 †40

MISCH, Elizabeth Ann. 1959 NE PACIFIC ST, DEPT OF INFECT DISEASE 98195 #023-07-2003 L2003 **ID** *100 †20

MISHRA, Rajashree. 1959 NE PACIFIC ST, UNIV OF WA SCH OF MED 98195 #495-53-1989 L2003 **GS** *100

MITCHELL, Caroline M. 1959 NE PACIFIC ST # C-, BOX 356340 98195 #024-01-2002 L2002 **OBG** *100

MITCHELL, David Arthur. 1100 FAIRVIEW AVE N, MAILSTOP C3-168 98109 #067-01-1985 L1992 **PHO** *050 †55

MITCHELL, Frank K, III. 6800 E GREEN LAKE WAY N, STE 200 98115 #011-03-1969 L1973 **IM** *020 †20

MITCHELL, Steven Randall. 1801 NW MARKET ST STE 311 98107 #001-06-1981 L1982 **P** *020 †75

MITSUMORI, Lee Masato. 1959 NE PACIFIC ST, UWMC- BOX 357115 98195 #014-01-1996 L2002 **DR** *020 †80

MIYA, Leslie Yoshiko. ■ 98103 #038-06-1991 L1996 **IM** *020 †20

MIYAGAWA, Tadashi. ■ 98115 #572-22-1993 L2005 *100

MIYAKOSHI, Asako. ■ 98115 #572-79-1997 L2006 **RNR** *100 †80

MIYANO, John Andrew. 600 BROADWAY, SEATTLE HAND SURGERY 98122 #016-06-1990 L1996 **ORS** *020 †40

MOCK, Charles Newman. 1959 NE PACIFIC ST, BOX 359796 98195 #043-01-1980 L1992 **GS** *020 †85

MOE, David Christopher. 1107 NE 45TH ST STE 440, UNIV OF WASH DEPT OF RADIO 98105 #056-06-2000 L2006 **PDR** *100 †80

MOE, Roger Edmund. 1959 NE PACIFIC ST, MSC 359300 98195 #054-04-1959 L1961 **GS RO** *071 †85

MOELLER, Kristy Lynn. ■ 98115 #054-04-2006 L2006 **OPH** *012

MOEN, John Alan. 1001 4TH AVE, STE 420 98154 #035-09-1985 L1986 **IM** *020 †20

MOHAI, Peter. 515 MINOR AVE, STE 300 98104 #012-05-1975 L1976 **IM RHU** *020 †20

MOHAMED, Abdirahman Dirie. 1455 NW LEARY WAY 98107 #016-11-1995 L1998 **FM** *062 †18

MOHANDESON, Michael M. 10564 5TH AVE NE STE 301 98125 #016-06-1973 L1978 **OPH** *020 †35 ‡

MOHATT, Justin William. 130 NICKERSON ST STE 204 98109 #054-04-2000 L2005 **CHP** *100 †75

MOHR, Brandt Charles. ■ 98105 #054-04-2002 L2003 **DR** *012

MOHR, Lisa Ann. 2450 33RD AVE W STE 100 98199 #054-04-2002 L2002 **FM** *020 †18

MOHRI, Hitoshi. 1959 NE PACIFIC ST, DEPT SURG 98195 #572-10-1955 **TS GS** *050

MOINPOUR, Yass. 1101 MADISON ST, STE 301 98104 #048-12-1995 L1998 **PD** *055 †55

MOKADAM, Nahush Ashok. 1959 NE PACIFIC ST, BOX 356310 98195 #041-01-1998 L2005 **TS** *100 †20

MOKHA, Arvinder Singh. 1145 BROADWAY, STE 900 98122 #023-01-1995 L2002 **AI** *020 †20,03

MOLNAR, Robert Balazs. 325 9TH AVE, BOX 359798 98104 #143-07-1995 L2003 *071

MOLONEY, Francis Benedict. 550 17TH AVE, STE 630 98122 #143-05-1975 L1981 **PS** *020

MONDZAC, William Simmons. 747 BROADWAY 98122 #010-02-1991 L1993 **AN** *020 †05

MONNAT, Raymond Jos, Jr. 1959 NE PACIFIC ST, MSC 359300 98195 #016-02-1976 L1977 **PTH** *020 †50

MONROE, Robert Bruce. 200 16TH AVE E 98112 #016-06-1957 L1960 **FM** *071 †18

MONTANA, Robert Charles, III. ■ 98122 #048-02-2002 L2006 **EM** *020 †16

MONTES, Agustin. HARBORVW MED CTR, DEPT MED 98104 #847-04-1968 **IM** *075

MONTEZA, Franco. 8720 14TH AVE S, 8720 14TH AVE SOUTH 98108 #737-03-1989 L1999 **FM** *020 †18

MONTGOMERY, Alan Bruce. 2025 1ST AVE, CORUS PHARMA, STE 800 98121 #054-04-1979 L1980 **PUD IM** *050 †20
MONTGOMERY, Duncan O. 521 WALL ST 98121 #048-02-1947 L1965 **GS OS** *100 †85
MONTGOMERY, Susan Kathlee. ■ 98103 #054-04-2008 *012
MONTOYA, Jennifer A. 4800 SAND POINT WAY NE G00, CHILDREN'S HOSP & REGIONAL 98105 #043-01-2005 L2005 **PD** *012
MOO, Jeffrey Bard. 1600 E JEFFERSON ST, STE A1 98122 #048-12-1988 L1990 **PM** *020 †60
MOOKHERJEE, Somnath. ■ 98105 #054-04-2004 L2005 **IM** *100 †20
MOON, Edward Sanghyun. PO BOX 356500, UNIV OF WASHINGTON 98195 #038-41-2006 L2006 **ORS** *012
MOONEY, James John. 4800 SAND POINT WAY NE, DEPT OF ANESTHESIA 98105 #024-05-2001 L2007 **PAN** *100
MOORE, Daniel Chas. 1100 9TH AVE 98101 #016-06-1944 L1948 **AN** *071 †05
MOORE, David Walter. 1221 MADISON ST STE 1523 98104 #017-20-1979 L1982 **OTO SO** *020 †45
MOORE, Donald Earl. ■ 98105 #038-06-1967 L1977 **END GYN** *071 †30
MOORE, Eugene Field. ■ 98133 #054-04-1953 L1954 **FM** *020 †18
MOORE, Eva Michele. 4800 SAND POINT WAY NE 98105 #023-07-2004 L2004 **PD** *020 †55
MOORE, Julene Rae. UNIV OF WASHINGTON, SURGICAL PATHOLOGY FELLOWS 98195 #034-01-2002 L2007 **SP** *012 †50
MOORE, Michael Geoffrey. ■ 98105 #005-14-2002 L2007 **GS** *100
MOORE, Patrick Michael. 1560 N 115TH ST, STE 102 98133 #051-04-1990 L1995 **GS CRS** *020 †85,10
MOORE, Richard J. ■ 98115 #065-01-1952 L1958 **P** *071 †75
MOORE, Tess Tiffany. ■ 98102 #054-04-2006 L2006 **FP** *012
MOORES, Madison D. ■ 98107 #040-02-1952 L1953 **GP** *071
MOORMAN, Alec Jay. ■ 98103 #016-06-2005 L2005 **IM** *012
MORA, Marc Walter. 1600 E JOHN ST 98112 #005-02-1990 L1995 **IM** *020 †20
MORACA, Robert Joseph. 925 SENECA ST, MAIL STOP H8 GME 98101 #041-12-2000 L2002 **TS** *012 †85
MORALES, Bonapart Lainez. 1959 NE PACIFIC ST, DEPT OF OPHTHALMOLOGY 98195 #748-01-1993 L2002 *100
MORANTES, Connie Maria. 1660 S COLUMBIAN WAY 98108 #005-14-1990 L1990 **IM** *020 †20
MORENO, Katherine Ione. ■ 98115 #043-01-2006 L2006 **GS** *012
MORGAN, Alan. 4800 SAND POINT WAY NE 98105 #352-02-1957 L1969 **PDS GS** *020
MORGAN, Dennis E. ■ 98125 #063-01-1980 L1987 *100
MORGAN, Gail N. 1100 9TH AVE 98101 #010-03-1980 L1987 **DR** *020 †80
MORGAN, Jacqueline G. ■ 98116 #021-05-1965 L1965 **PHP** *071 †70
MORGAN, John David. 801 BROADWAY, STE 901 98122 #038-40-1991 L1998 **CHN** *020 †55,75
MORGAN, John Douglas. ■ 98168 #054-04-1986 L1989 **PDA PD** *020 †55
MORGAN, Richard Henry. 509 OLIVE WAY 98101 #007-02-2000 L2002 **FM** *020 †18
MORGAN, Thomas Edward, Jr. ■ 98115 #036-07-1954 L1964 **IM PUD** *071 †20
MORGAN, Todd Matthew. P O BOX 35340 1959 NE PACI, US SCHOOL OF MED GME PROGR 98195 #024-01-2003 L2003 **U** *012
MORGENROTH, David Crespi. ■ 98102 #035-08-2003 L2004 **PM** *100
MORISHIMA, Chihiro. 325 9TH AVE, UW BOX 359690 98104 #028-02-1988 L1991 **PPR** *050 †55
MORISHIMA, Michael Shoji. 1100 9TH AVE G1-MSO 98101 #054-04-1974 L1975 **DR** *020 †80
MORISHIMA-NELSON, Judith. 720 8TH AVE S STE 200, ASIAN COUNSELING AND REFER 98104 #054-04-1989 L1993 **P** *020 †75
MORISON, Ian M. ■ 98115 #671-01-1984 L1989 **CLP** *020 †50
MORNINGSTAR, Douglas A. 747 BROADWAY 98122 #054-04-1959 L1961 **PTH** *071 †50
MORRAY, Brian Harrod. ■ 98103 #035-45-2008 *012
MORRIS, Amy Elizabeth. ■ 98105 #054-04-2001 L2001 **PCC** *012
MORRIS, Carl G. 4245 ROOSEVELT WAY NE, UW FMC RESIDENCY 98105 #024-01-1994 L1994 **FM** *020 †18
MORRIS, Gabrielle. 1151 DENNY WAY 98109 #050-02-1993 L2001 **GPM OM** *020 ‡
MORRIS, John Paul. 4744 41ST AVE SW STE 101, HIGHLINE MEDICAL GROUP 98116 #048-13-1975 L1977 **FM** *020 †18
MORRIS, Joseph Newton. 1600 E JOHN ST 98112 #051-01-1972 L1977 **ORS** *020 †40
MORRIS, Leslie Janine. 4800 SAND POINT WAY NE, MED C 98105 #012-01-1997 L2006 **CHP** *012
MORRIS, Lucien E. ■ 98194 #038-06-1943 L1955 **AN** *071 †05
MORRISON, Alexandra M. 1100 9TH AVE G1-MSO, VIRGINIA MASON MEDICAL CEN 98101 #017-20-2001 L2003 **IM** *020
MORRISON, Crystal Aque. ■ 98115 #025-07-1994 **PD** *100
MORRISON, Elizabeth Dana. 1959 NE PACIFIC ST, UWMC- BOX 356424 98195 #032-01-1994 L1997 **GE** *020 †20
MORRISON, Laura Katherine. 1959 NE PACIFIC ST, DEPT RAD 98195 #016-11-2006 L2007 **DR** *012
MOSCA, Vincent Stephen. 4800 SAND POINT WAY NE, PO BOX 5371/W5801 98105 #035-45-1978 L1985 **OP** *020 †40
MOSCATO, Eve Elisa. MAILSTOP BOX 356340, GRADUATE MEDICAL EDUCATION 98195 #035-06-2004 L2005 **OPH** *012
MOSCOVITZ, Mark Jason. 1801 NW MARKET ST, STE 308 98107 #016-42-1997 L2000 **FM** *020 †18
MOSHIRI, Maryam. 1107 NE 45TH ST, STE 440 98105 #035-08-1995 L2005 **DR** *020 †80
MOSIER, Michael James. 325 9TH AVE, MEDICAL DIRECTOR'S OFFICE, 98104 #028-34-2003 L2003 **GS** *012
MOSKOWITZ, Samuel Mark. 4800 SAND POINT WAY NE, CHILDREN'S HOSP & REG MED 98105 #024-01-1994 L1997 **PDP** *020 †55
MOSS, Albert Adam. 1959 NE PACIFIC ST, RADIOLOGY BOX 357115 98195 #035-15-1967 L1984 **DR** *020 †80
MOSS, Gregory Brian. 515 MINOR AVE STE 300, MINOR & JAMES MEDICAL, PLL 98104 #010-01-1984 L1989 **ID EM** *020 †20
MOSS, Nicholas James. ■ 98102 #005-15-2006 L2006 **IM** *012
MOSTAGHEL, Elahe Anna. 1100 FAIRVIEW AVE N, MS D4-100 98109 #036-07-2000 L2003 **ON** *100 †20
MOTTET, Norman K. 1959 NE PACIFIC ST 98195 #008-01-1952 L1959 **ATP** *040 †50
MOTULSKY, Arno Gunther. 1959 NE PACIFIC ST, UWMC BOX 356423 98195 #016-11-1947 L1954 **MG IM** *050 †20,19
MOWERY, Carol Ann. 1101 MADISON ST, STE 800 98104 #054-04-1979 L1984 **ORS** *020 †40
MOZAFFARIAN, Gholamali. 1221 MADISON ST STE 918 98104 #517-01-1966 L1979 **IM END** *020
MOZAFFARIAN, Neelufar. 1959 NE PACIFIC ST, BOX 356428 98195 #035-46-2001 L2004 **RHU** *100 †20
MRUGALA, Maciej Michal. ■ 98103 #759-03-1995 L2006 **N ON** *100 †75
MUBALLE, Kadhaya David. 1959 NE PACIFIC ST 98195 #577-01-1994 L2004 *020
MUCZYNSKI, Kimberly Ann. 1959 NE PACIFIC ST, BOX 356521 98195 #054-04-1984 L1986 **NEP IM** *020 †20
MUDUMBAI, Raghu. 325 9TH AVE 98104 #035-08-1994 L2000 **OPH** *020 †35
MUEHLING, Jeffrey Brandon. 1550 N 115TH ST, NORTHWEST HOSPITAL AND MED 98133 #054-04-2002 L2006 **AN** *020 †05
MUELLER, Elliott Louis. 925 SENECA ST, MEDICAL CENTER 98101 #024-07-2006 L2006 **DR** *012
MUELLER, Roland Fritz. ■ 98133 #005-02-1966 L1980 **PTH** *071 †50
MUETINGNELSEN, Peter Fran. 925 SENECA ST, MEDICAL CENTER 98101 #038-40-2005 L2006 **AN** *012
MUGAISI, Hesed Namundera. 521 WALL ST, DEPT FM 98121 #577-01-1998 L2005 **FP** *012
MUHM, James Michael. 2324 EASTLAKE AVE E, STE 500 98102 #005-19-1974 L1979 **OM IM** *030 †20,70
MUIRHEAD, Richard J, Jr. UNIV WASH, PHYS 351560 98195 #023-01-1975 L1976 **GP** *075
MUKHERJEE, Paramita Asish. 1959 NE PACIFIC ST 98195 #496-44-1997 L2007 **IM** *012
MULDER, Gordon Byrns. 801 BROADWAY STE 617 98122 #016-11-1957 L1966 **NS** *071
MULIA, Antonius Gusti. 1145 BROADWAY, THE POLYCLINIC 98122 #024-07-1990 L2001 **IM** *020 †20
MULKERIN, Lawrence E. 1959 NE PACIFIC ST, U OF WASH CANCER CTR-RADIO 98195 #041-12-1962 L1979 **RO DR** *020 †80
MULLARKEY, Michael F. 1145 BROADWAY, POLYCLINIC STATION 3B 98122 #024-05-1970 L1976 **AI IM** *071 †20,03
MULLEN, Dennis Lee. 521 WALL ST 98121 #048-04-1972 L1977 **PTH** *050 †50
MULLEN, Marr Parker. 1600 E JEFFERSON ST # 400 98122 #054-04-1955 L1956 **OAR** *071 †40
MULLER, Bart. 10416 5TH AVE NE 98125 #660-01-1967 L1971 **P** *020 †75
MULLIGAN, Thomas G. 2515 SW TRENTON ST, STE 201 98106 #067-01-1989 L1992 **OPH** *020 †35
MULLIGAN, William Patrick. 2515 SW TRENTON ST # 201 98106 #067-01-1956 L1957 **OPH** *020 †35
MULLINS, Christiane D. 1959 NE PACIFIC ST, BOX 356340 98195 #048-13-2005 L2006 **DR** *012
MULLINS, John Richard. ■ 98105 #028-34-1945 L1954 **N IM** *071 †75,20
MULLOY, Daniel Patrick. ■ 98109 #051-01-2007 L2007 **GS** *012
MULROY, Michael F, II. 925 SENECA ST 98101 #035-20-1969 L1971 **AN** *040 †05
MUNGY, Maria Christine. 4800 SAND POINT WAY NE 98105 #016-11-1995 L1998 **PD** *020 †55
MUNI, Nimish Haresh. ■ 98105 #054-04-2007 L2007 **IM** *012
MUNOZ, Luis Daniel. UNIV OF WASHINGTON, DIVISION OF CARDIOLOGY BOX 98195 #024-01-2004 L2007 **CD** *012 †20
MUNSEN, Richard S. 1221 MADISON ST STE 1002 98104 #018-03-1972 L1975 **OPH OS** *071 †35
MUNSON, Sarah F. 7554 15TH AVE NW 98117 #005-18-1995 L1998 **PD** *020 †55
MUNTZ, Howard Gordon. 1560 N 115TH ST STE 101, WOMEN'S CANCER CARE OF SEA 98133 #024-01-1984 L1992 **GO GYN** *020 †30
MUPAS, Thelma F P. ■ 98168 #748-08-1965 L1981 **PTH** *020
MURAKAMI, Craig Stuart. 4800 SAND POINT WAY NE 98105 #054-04-1983 L1989 **FPS OTO** *020 †45
MURAMOTO, Allen. 1101 MADISON ST, STE 301 98104 #054-04-1973 L1974 **PUD IM** *020 †20
MURINOVA, Natalia. 1959 NE PACIFIC ST, UNIVERSITY OF WASHINGTON 98195 #286-03-1991 L2004 **N** *020 †20,75
MURPHY, Cynthia Ruth. ■ 98116 #021-05-2002 L2007 **N** *100
MURPHY, James L, Jr. 201 16TH AVE E, DEPT ANESTH. CENTRAL MED B 98112 #054-04-1986 L1990 **AN** *020 †05
MURPHY, Janet. 2324 EASTLAKE AVE E, STE 500 98102 #352-08-1967 L1969 **NPM PD** *071 †55
MURPHY, Joe David. ■ 98177 #054-04-2005 L2006 **AN** *012
MURPHY, Lawrence Cullum. 550 17TH AVE, FIFTH FLOOR 98122 #054-04-1983 L1986 **N** *020 †75
MURPHY, Teresa Ann. 1930 POST ALY 98101 #005-02-1989 L1989 **IM** *020 †20
MURRAY, Arthur Anthony. 1550 N 115TH ST 98133 #048-12-1948 L1956 **P** *071 †75
MURRAY, Hugh Creighton. 411 W MERCER ST 98119 #024-07-1963 L1964 **P** *030 †75
MURRAY, John Augustus, Jr. 1530 N 115TH ST, STE 110 98133 #048-04-1961 L1964 **CD IM** *020 †20
MURRAY, Julia Harby. 411 W MERCER ST 98119 #054-04-1982 L1984 **CHP** *020 †75
MURRAY, Karen Field. 4800 SAND POINT WAY NE 98105 #023-07-1990 L1990 **PD** *020 †55
MURRAY, Kevin F. 550 16TH AVE, STE 100 98122 #054-04-1978 L1979 **FM** *020 †18
MURRAY, Peter Churnside. ■ 98118 #352-04-1955 L1964 **AN** *071
MURRAY, Robert Wm. 1145 BROADWAY 98122 #056-06-1975 L1985 **END IM** *020 †20
MURRAY, Suzanne Buek. 1959 NE PACIFIC ST, MSC 359300 98195 #041-13-1997 L2001 **PYG** *020 †75
MURRY, Charles Emerson. 815 MERCER ST RM 454, CNT CARDIOVASCLR BIOGY 98109 #036-07-1989 L1989 **PTH** *050 †50
MUSHER, Benjamin Leon. 8033 CORLISS AVE N 98103 #048-04-2000 L2003 **HO** *012 †20
MUSYOKI, Francis. ■ 98115 #067-01-2003 **DR** *012
MUTTI, Martha Jane. PO BOX 34245 98124 #016-02-1970 L1971 **PTH** *020 †50
MYER, Ralph Edwin. 8720 14TH AVE S, SEA MAR COMMUNITY HLTH CEN 98108 #042-01-1972 L1974 **FM OBG** *020 †18
MYERS, David Arthur. 4800 SAND POINT WAY NE, MAIL STOP MI-5 98105 #047-05-1997 L2006 **PN** *012 †55
MYERS, Jed Anthony. 4026 NE 55TH ST STE A 98105 #038-06-1981 L1983 **P** *020 †75
MYERS, Ronald Allen. 346 26TH AVE 98122 #011-02-1982 L1989 **AN** *020 †05
MYERSON, David Henry. 1100 FAIRVIEW AVE N 98109 #035-46-1979 L1983 **ATP** *020 †50
MYINT, Erane K. 1100 9TH AVE C1-MSO, VIRGINIA MASON MEDICAL CEN 98101 #041-12-1996 L2000 **IM** *020 †20
MYINT, Michael. 1145 BROADWAY 98122 #041-02-1996 L2000 **ID EP** *020 †20
MYRE, Laura E. 4515 MARTN LTHR KNG JR S 98108 #048-12-1984 L2002 **FM** *020 †18
MYSLIWIEC, Angela Elaine. ■ 98121 #023-12-1996 L1998 **HO** *020 †20
NADLER, Samuel Todd. GRADUATE MEDICAL ED BOX 35, UNIVERSITY OF WASHINGTON 98195 #056-05-2003 L2003 **PCC** *012 †20
NAGLE, Kyle Britton. 1959 NE PACIFIC ST RM C21, HOUS/STAF AFFRS. GME BX356 98195 #056-05-2002 L2002 **PD** *020 †55
NAIK, Vibhuti. ■ 98109 #035-08-2001 L2004 **PD** *020
NAIMAN, Theodore Samuel. 1100 9TH AVE C1-MSO, VIRGINIA MASON MEDICAL CEN 98101 #005-12-1997 L2000 **FM** *020 †18
NAIR, M Nathan. 1959 NE PACIFIC ST, RM C212 98195 #035-01-2002 L2002 **NS** *012
NARITA, Masahiro. 325 9TH AVE, CAMPUS BOX 359776 98104 #572-20-1988 L2002 **PCC IM** *030 †20
NASH, Richard Anthony. 1100 FAIRVIEW AVE N, D1-100 98109 #062-01-1977 L1989 *100

NASH, Robert Wm. 1221 MADISON ST, VITREORETINAL ASSOCIATES 98104 #012-05-1988 L1996 **OPH IM** *020 †35

NASON, Laura Katherine. ■ 98103 #024-01-2007 L2007 **TY** *012

NATARAJAN, Sabareesh Kuma. PO BOX 356340 98195 #495-42-2000 L2007 *100

NATHAN, Joshua Max. 1959 NE PACIFIC ST # C-21, BOX 356340 98195 #010-01-2004 L2004 **OBG** *012

NATHAN, Robert Otto. 1959 NE PACIFIC ST BOX 35 98195 #039-01-1977 L1982 **DR** *020 †80

NATHENS, Avery B. 325 9TH AVE 98104 #065-05-1990 L1998 **CCS** *085

NAUMANN, Christopher R. ■ 98103 #048-04-2003 L2007 **GE** *012 †20

NAUMANN, Heather Leah. ■ 98103 #048-04-2003 L2007 **PAN** *012

NAVA BAHENA, Ruben Guadal. 1959 NE PACIFIC ST 98195 #649-05-2000 L2007 **GS** *012

NAYLOR, Gordon Schueller. 1100 9TH AVE C1-MSO, VIRGINIA MASON MEDICAL CEN 98101 #023-12-1983 L1993 **PD** *020 †55

NAYLOR, John Grant. PO BOX 356340, 1959 NE PACIFIC ST L212 98195 #021-01-2003 L2003 **AN** *020

NDUAGUBA, Chiazoka Onyeka. ■ 98125 #054-04-2008 *012

NEAGOE, Gabriela. ■ 98115 #781-01-1997 L2006 **GPM** *100 †70

NEAL, Joseph Moore. 1100 9TH AVE 98101 #055-01-1978 L1978 **AN EM** *040 †16,05

NEBORSKY, Rebecca Kate. 1959 NE PACIFIC ST, DEPT OF FAMILY MEDICINE 98195 #041-02-2006 L2006 **FP** *012

NEDVED, James Frances. 1145 BROADWAY, SWEDISH ADULT HOSPITALISTS 98122 #054-04-1996 L1999 **IM** *020 †20

NEFF, John Michael. 1100 OLIVE WAY STE 500, METROPOLITAN PAUL WEST 98101 #024-01-1960 L1981 **PD ID** *050 †55

NEFF, Margaret Jane. 325 9TH AVE, BOX 359762 98104 #005-11-1993 L1997 **PCC** *020 †20

NEIDERS, Tina. ■ 98144 #041-07-1996 L2000 **EM** *020 †16

NEIGHBOR, William Edward, Jr. 4245 ROOSEVELT WAY NE, STE 354775 98105 #054-04-1979 L1983 **FM** *040 †18

NEIMAN, Paul Eric. 2324 EASTLAKE AVE E, STE 500 98102 #054-04-1964 L1970 **ON** *071 †20

NELP, Wil Borchers. 1959 NE PACIFIC ST, UNIVERSITY OF WASHINGTON M 98195 #023-07-1955 L1963 **NM IM** *020 †20,28

NELSON, Aimee Elizabeth. ■ 98119 #016-43-2000 L2004 **OBG** *020

NELSON, Brian Robt. 1100 9TH AVE BOX 900 98101 #028-34-1981 L1982 **OPH** *071 †35

NELSON, Charles Anthony. ■ 98125 #054-04-2008 *012

NELSON, Judith Lee. 1100 FAIRVIEW AVE N, FHCR 98109 #005-19-1977 L1981 **RHU IM** *040 †20

NELSON, Karin Marie. ■ 98177 #026-04-1995 L2001 **IM** *050 †20

NELSON, Peter Stanley. 1100 FAIRVIEW AVE N, MS D4-100 98109 #019-02-1986 L1993 **ON** *020 †20

NELSON, Wallace. 747 BROADWAY 98122 #054-04-1952 L1955 **NS** *071 †25

NEME, Santiago. 1959 NE PACIFIC ST 98195 #132-05-2002 L2005 **IM** *012

NEMECEK, Andrew Nicholas. 1959 NE PACIFIC ST RMC21, H/STAFF AFFRS CAMPUS BX 35 98195 #038-06-1998 L1998 **NS** *100

NEMUTH, Marcus Graham. 1660 S COLUMBIAN WAY, SEATTLE VETERANS HOSPITAL 98108 #051-04-1981 L1983 **P** *020

NENE, Parag Anand. 1100 9TH AVE MS H8-25, PO BOX 900 98101 #041-12-2001 L2005 **IM** *020 †20

NEPOM, Barbara Snyder. 2324 EASTLAKE AVE E, STE 500 98102 #054-04-1978 L1982 **OS PD** *071

NEPPE, Vernon Michael. 6300 9TH AVE NE, STE 353 98115 #836-01-1973 L1986 **NUP PFP** *075

NERAAS, Kathryn Ann. 2611 NE 125TH ST STE 245 98125 #054-04-1990 L1990 **P** *020 †75

NETT, Matthew Hardin. UNIV OF WASHINGTON MED CTR, DEPT OF RADIOLOGY BOX 3571 98104 #017-20-2006 L2006 **DR** *012

NEUFELD, Michael D. 1959 NE PACIFIC ST, BOX 356320 98195 #048-13-1993 L1999 **NPM** *020 †55

NEUMAIER, John F. 325 9TH AVE, BOX # 359911 98104 #054-04-1990 L1990 **P** *020 †75

NEUMEISTER, William Herbe. PO BOX 91059 98111 #054-04-1966 L1969 **PD** *030 †55

NEUPERT, Jerrol Ross. 1101 MADISON ST, PC 98104 #054-04-1971 L1977 **OPH** *020 †35 ‡

NEUZIL, Daniel Florian. 1100 9TH AVE 98101 #054-04-1987 L1998 **VS GS** *020 †85

NEVINS, Michael Lee. 1600 E JOHN ST 98112 #024-16-1994 L2000 **PCC** *020 †20

NEWALL, Joseph. ■ 98121 #803-03-1947 **RO** *071

NEWBERGER, Jennifer Franc. ■ 98144 #003-01-2008 *012

NEWELL, David Warren. 325 9TH AVE, BOX 359766 98104 #038-06-1982 L1983 **NS** *050 †25

NEWELL, Laura Fugal. ■ 98103 #005-19-2004 L2007 **HO** *012 †20

NEWMAN, Brenda Leann. 4225 ROOSEVELT WAY NE, STE 354697 98105 #040-02-2002 L2006 **D** *020 †15

NEWMAN, Jeffrey Edward. 1959 NE PACIFIC ST RM C212, CAMPUS BOX 356340 98195 #027-01-1969 L1970 **FM** *020 †18

NEWTON, Christopher Robin. ■ 98122 #010-01-1997 L2007 **PDS** *100 †85

NEWTON, Dana Spencer. ■ 98105 #005-11-1956 L1967 **OPH** *071 †35

NEWTON, Jennifer Marie. ■ 98117 #054-04-2008 *012

NEWTON, Saint Elmo. 2409 N 45TH ST 98103 #047-06-1958 L1964 **ORS** *020 †40

NEY, John Peter. ■ 98112 #021-01-2000 L2002 **N** *020 †75

NGHIEM, Paul Xuantuan. 815 MERCER ST, UNIVERSITY OF WASHINGTON D 98109 #005-11-1994 L2005 **D** *050 †15

NGO, Anh-Vu Huynh. ■ 98125 #056-06-2008 *012

NGO, Danh Minh. 515 MINOR AVE, STE 200 98104 #012-05-2001 L2007 **NEP** *020

NGO, Lam Quynh Thi. 9635 17TH AVE SW 98106 #048-04-1985 L1988 **FM** *020 †18

NGUYEN, Aikhue Thi. 3815 S OTHELLO ST, 2ND FL 98118 #047-20-2002 L2002 **FM** *020 †18

NGUYEN, Anh Hong. 1400 S JACKSON ST, STE 24 98144 #941-01-1977 L1986 **IM** *020

NGUYEN, Catherine Mary. ■ 98105 #016-11-2006 **PTH** *020

NGUYEN, Dewey Dinh. 1959 NE PACIFIC ST RM C2, CAMPUS BOX 356340 98195 #007-02-2002 L2002 **IM** *100 †20

NGUYEN, Diem Dang. ■ 98118 #941-01-1965 L1977 **GP** *071

NGUYEN, Donald Huu. 9714 3RD AVE NE, STE 203 98115 #056-05-1984 L1990 **UP U** *020 †95

NGUYEN, Hong-Nhung Thi. 7322 18TH AVE SW 98106 #665-01-2004 L2008 **FM** *100

NGUYEN, Loc H.. ■ 98102 #305-01-2003 L2007 **AN** *020

NGUYEN, Minh Van. 9431 17TH AVE SW 98106 #941-01-1967 L1983 **GP** *020

NGUYEN, Nguyen-Lan Duc. EDUCATION BOX 356340 NE P, UNIV OF WASHINGTON GRADUAT 98195 #054-04-2005 L2005 **IM** *012

NGUYEN, Son Van. 7101 MARTN LTHR KNG JR S, STE 217 98118 #054-04-1993 L1996 **IM** *020

NGUYEN, Theresa Thuy. ■ 98106 #035-09-2005 L2005 **IM** *012

NGUYEN, Tuong Tu. 1101 MADISON ST, PC 98104 #023-07-1995 L2000 **OPH** *020 †35

NGUYEN, Vong Hy. 1120 E TERRACE ST, FIRST HEALTHCARE 98122 #941-01-1968 L1981 **P GP** *071

NGUYEN-VERMILLION, Annie. ■ 98115 #056-05-2004 L2007 **NPM** *012 †55

NI, Karen. ■ 98119 #005-18-2007 L2007 **P** *012

NICANDRI, Gregg Thomas. ■ 98103 #051-04-2003 L2003 **ORS** *012

NICHOL, Graham. 325 9TH AVE, MAILSTOP 359727 98104 #065-06-1988 L2004 *020

NICHOL, Walter Paul. 1660 S COLUMBIAN WAY, VA MED CTR 11C 98108 #036-07-1976 L1990 **IM IMG** *030 †20

NICHOLS, Dennis Darrel. 1959 NE PACIFIC ST, DEPT OF SURGERY #356410 98195 #023-12-1991 L1996 **TS** *020 †85,90

NICHOLS, Jos Carrol, Jr. 999 3RD AVE, STE 1700 98104 #003-01-1974 L1979 **ORS** *030 †40

NICHOLS, Kaaren Andrea. ■ 98102 #054-04-1979 L1981 **FM** *071

NICHOLS, Samuel Jaccard. 1229 MADISON ST STE 900 98104 #048-04-1968 L1969 **DR** *020 †80

NICHOLS, William Ward. 1550 N 115TH ST B250 98133 #036-01-1987 L1991 **AN PME** *020 †05

NICHOLSON, Bradley L. 747 BROADWAY, SWEDISH HOSPITAL MEDICAL C 98122 #007-02-1996 L1999 **EM** *020 †20,16

NICOLAZZI, Sharon Ann. 1229 MADISON ST, STE 1090 98104 #056-05-1985 L1989 **D** *020 †15

NICOSIA, Roberto. 1660 S COLUMBIAN WAY, DEPT OF V.A. PS HEALTH CAR 98108 #561-17-1976 L1999 **PTH** *020 †50

NIELSEN, Katie Ruth. ■ 98115 #018-03-2006 L2006 **PD** *012

NIELSEN, Robert L. ■ 98115 #024-01-1951 L1953 **IM END** *071 †20

NIEMSIRI, Vipavee. 4800 SAND POINT WAY NE, ENDOCRINE DIV 98105 #891-05-1996 L2002 *020

NIETSCH, Hubertus. 1101 MADISON ST STE 301, PACMED CLINICS - MADISON 98104 #409-16-1994 L1999 **GE** *020 †20

NIGRINI, Elisabeth. 1959 NE PACIFIC ST # C-21, BOX 356340 98195 #041-12-2005 L2005 **OBG** *012

NILES, Clarence. 5220 CALIFORNIA AVE SW 98136 #054-04-1981 L1984 **FM** *020 †18

NILES, Nancy Louise. 1530 N 115TH ST, STE 208 98133 #035-45-1978 L1979 **END IM** *020 †20

NINAN, Anita Susan. 10416 5TH AVE NE 98125 #025-12-2001 L2005 **OBG** *020

NITSCHE, Bruce Alan. 1100 9TH AVE G1-MSO, VIRGINIA MASON MEDICAL CEN 98101 #005-06-1980 L1981 **IM** *020

NIX, Kristi Anne. 810 NE 60TH ST 98115 #016-02-2000 L2003 **PD** *020 †55

NIXON, Jason Neal. UNIV OF WASHINGTON MED CTR, DEPT OF RADIOLOGY BOX 3571 98195 #016-42-2006 L2007 **DR** *012

NJEGOVAN, Mary Elizabeth. ■ 98115 #050-02-1993 L1996 **PM** *020 †60

NOH, Induk. ■ 98121 #583-11-1979 L1985 **P** *020

NOKES, Rosalain Jean. 521 WALL ST 98121 #054-04-1965 L1966 **NEP IM** *071 †20

NOLAN, Charles Murphy. 2324 EASTLAKE AVE E, STE 500 98102 #004-01-1969 L1980 **IM** *062 †20

NOLL, Elizabeth Anne. 701 N 36TH ST STE 410 98103 #054-04-1989 L1991 **P** *020 †75

NOONAN, Edward John. 550 17TH AVE STE 110 98122 #054-04-1982 L1983 **PUD ID** *020 †20

NORA, Peter Colin. 1100 9TH AVE M6-AC, VIRGINIA MASON MEDICAL CEN 98101 #021-01-1991 L1998 **NS** *020 †25

NORASETTHADA, Lalita. 1959 NE PACIFIC ST RM K13, UNIV MED CTR 98195 #891-03-1997 L2003 **HEM** *020

NORDEN, Michael James. 13210 BITTER PL N 98133 #005-11-1981 L1985 **P** *020 †75

NORDSTROM LANE, Brian D. ■ 98122 #026-08-2004 L2004 **IM** *020 †20

NORIEGA, Miguel, Jr. 1959 NE PACIFIC ST 98195 #005-06-1999 L1999 **IM** *100

NORK, Sean Edward. 325 9TH AVE, BOX 359798 98104 #005-18-1992 L1997 **ORS** *020 †40

NORLAND, Emily. ■ 98115 #018-03-2004 L2004 **OBG** *012

NORMAN, Lee Alan. 3826 42ND AVE NE 98105 #026-04-1978 L1985 **FM EM** *040 †18

NORQUIST, Barbara Marie. 1959 NE PACIFIC ST # C-, BOX 356340 98195 #054-04-2004 L2004 **OBG** *012

NORQUIST, Scott Wallace. 1550 N 115TH ST 98133 #012-05-1979 L1980 **AN** *020 †05

NORRIS, Thomas Elmore. 1959 NE PACIFIC ST STE A30, HSB STE A300 UW BOX 3563 98195 #048-02-1973 L1986 **FM IMG** *040 †18

NORTH, Crystal Marie. ■ 98115 #054-04-2008 *012

NORTHWAY-MEYER, Robert. ■ 98105 #035-09-1944 L1948 **AN** *100 †05

NORTON, Charles Eric. ■ 98122 #024-01-1956 L1962 **P** *050 †75

NORUM, Robert Anthony. 1145 BROADWAY 98122 #023-07-1968 L1993 **D OS** *020 †19,20,15

NORWOOD, Thomas Hyatt. PO BOX 357470, UNIVERSITY OF WASHINGTON 98195 #023-01-1968 L1970 **PTH** *050 †19

NOV, Asher Amazia. 200 15TH AVE E 98112 #550-02-1973 L1978 **DR R** *020 †80

NOVACK, Alvin H. 146 N CANAL ST 98103 #041-13-1958 L1979 **PD GPM** *040 †55

NOVACK, Alvin J. 1221 MADISON ST, STE 1523 98104 #054-04-1952 L1957 **HNS FPS** *020 †45

NOVAIS, Jaime. 515 MINOR AVE STE 300, MINOR & JAMES MEDICAL 98104 #187-09-1985 L1991 **IM IMG** *020 †20

NOVAK, L Charles. 325 9TH AVE, ANESTHESIOLOGY, BOX 359724 98104 #007-02-1968 L1973 **AN** *020 †05

NULU, Shanti. ■ 98119 #048-04-2006 L2007 **IM** *012

NUMRYCH, Thomas. 4575 SAND POINT WAY NE, STE 108 98105 #016-11-1994 L1994 **PD** *020 †55

NUNN, Chris Carter. 747 BROADWAY 98122 #054-04-2001 L2002 **AN** *020 †05

NUSSBAUM, Berl Edward. ■ 98115 #035-46-1970 L1976 **OS CLP** *050 †50

NUSSBAUM, Charles Enzer. 1100 9TH AVE G1-MSO, VIRGINIA MASON MEDICAL CEN 98101 #035-45-1984 L1990 **NS** *020 †20

NWOKO, Nkeiruka Clementin. 925 SENECA ST # 1930, DEPT OF INTERNAL MEDICINE 98101 #017-20-2006 L2006 **IM** *012

NYLANDER, Nicola Rosalind. 509 OLIVE WAY, STE 900 98101 #023-07-1989 L1989 **D** *020 †15

NYSOE, Tara Evans. ■ 98115 #054-04-2003 L2003 **IM** *020 †20

NYWEIDE-WHITE, Kristin C. 1100 9TH AVE, MAILSTOP G1-MSO 98101 #047-05-2003 L2003 **PD** *020 †55

OAKES, Patricia Kathleen. DEPARTMENT OF NEUROLOGY, UNIV OF WASHINGTON MED CTR 98195 #025-01-2002 L2002 **N** *100

OAKLEY, John Christopher. ■ 98125 #054-04-2001 L2001 **CN** *020 †75

OBEK, Can. 1959 NE PACIFIC ST, BOX 356510 98195 #902-07-1989 L2003 **U** *100

OBERLE, Mark Wm. PO BOX 357230, UNIVERSITY OF WASHINGTON 98195 #023-07-1974 L1993 **PHP** *070

OBIAYA, Patrick Chukwuma. ■ 98103 #038-06-1974 L1978 **OTO GS** *020

O'BRIEN, Edward Redmond. 1959 NE PACIFIC ST 98195 #065-09-1985 L1991 **CD** *050 †20

O'BRIEN, Kevin Douglas. 1959 NE PACIFIC ST, UWMC- BOX 356422 98195 #054-04-1984 L1984 **CD IM** *020 †20

O'BRIEN, Thomas Patrick. ■ 98107 #028-34-1966 L1981 **CHP P** *071

O'BYRNE, John Martin. 325 9TH AVE 98104 #539-04-1986 L1996 **ORS** *100

O'CALLAGHAN, Mark Gerard. 9730 3RD AVE NE, STE 202 98115 #143-05-1993 L2006 RNR *100 †80

O'CARROLL, Patrick Fionan. ■ 98105 #539-02-1973 ORS *100

O'CARROLL, Patrick Wm. 4525 NE 41ST ST, DHHS 98105 #023-07-1983 L2005 PHP *050 †70

OCHI, Rex Ford. 1145 BROADWAY 98122 #054-04-1980 L1981 NEP IM *020 †20

OCHS, Hans Dieter. 1959 NE PACIFIC ST, BOX 356320 98195 #407-05-1961 L1971 IG PD *050 †55,03

OCHS, Ulrike Isabel. 925 SENECA ST 98101 #016-06-1988 L1988 D PD *020 †55,15

OCHS, Ute Hanna. ■ 98105 #407-05-1961 L1972 PD OS *071 †55

O'CONNOR, Kim Marie. 4245 ROOSEVELT WAY NE, STE 354775 98105 #054-04-1999 L2002 IM *020 †20

ODLAND, Peter Brierley. 1229 MADISON ST STE 1480 98104 #016-42-1984 L1989 DS *020 †15

ODOM, Audrey Ragan. 1959 NE PACIFIC ST, BOX 356340 98195 #036-07-2003 L2003 PDI *012

O'DONNELL, Brendan Rhodes. 1959 NE PACIFIC ST, BOX 356044 98195 #005-19-1998 L2004 AN *020 †05

O'DONNELL, Paul V. 1100 FAIRVIEW AVE N, FHCRC BOX 358080 D5-290 98109 #023-07-1992 L2001 ON *020 †20

OEHLER, Vivian Gudrun. 325 9TH AVE, HARBORVIEW MEDICAL CENTER 98104 #038-06-1997 L1999 HEM *020 †20

OELSCHLAGER, Anne-Marie A. 4245 ROOSEVELT WAY NE, STE 354775 98105 #047-05-1997 L2000 OBG *020 †30

OELSCHLAGER, Brant Kurt. 1959 NE PACIFIC ST, BOX 356410 98195 #036-01-1995 L1999 GS *020 †85

OFARRELL, Cathleen M. ■ 98177 #005-19-1991 L1991 FM *050 †18

O'GRADY, Lilla Ruth. 4800 SAND POINT WAY NE 98105 #026-04-1970 L1973 PUD PD *074 †55

OH, Michelle Young. 201 16TH AVE 98122 #054-04-1994 L1998 DR *020 †80,28

OH, Young Suk. 515 MINOR AVE STE 200, MINOR & JAMES MEDICAL PLLC 98104 #048-12-2000 L2007 GE *100 †2 ‡

O'HARA-HAWN, Maryann L. 747 BROADWAY 98122 #023-07-1994 L1997 FM *020 †18

O'HARE, Ann Margaret. ■ 98119 #051-01-1996 L2007 NEP *020 †20

OHASHI, Masahiro. ■ 98115 #572-37-1969 L1977 PM *100 †60

OHKI, Takao. 710 6TH AVE S, # 1137 98104 #572-37-1987 L1998 VS GS *020

OHM, Winfried Wilhelm. 550 16TH AVE, STE 203 98122 #407-25-1966 L1975 AN *020 †05

OJEMANN, George Alvin. UNIVERSITY HOSP NEURO SURG 98105 #018-03-1959 L1962 NS *040 †20

OJEMANN, Jeffrey. 4800 SAND POINT WAY NE, BOX G-0035 98105 #028-02-1992 L1999 NSP NS *050 †25

OJEMANN, Linda M. 325 9TH AVE, HARBORVIEW HOSP 98104 #016-11-1960 L1966 N OS *071 †75

OKAMURA, Daryl Miyoshi. 4800 SAND POINT WAY NE, MEDICAL CENTER 98105 #014-01-1998 L2001 PN *050 †55

OKANE, John William, Jr. 1959 NE PACIFIC ST, BOX 354060 98195 #050-02-1993 L1993 FM FSM *020 †18

O'KEEFE, Grant Edward. 325 9TH AVE, BOX 359796 98104 #060-01-1988 L1994 GS *020 †85

O'KEEFFE, Kevin Michael. 98112 #010-02-1969 L1979 OM EM *062 †16,18,70

O'KELLY, Colleen Meghan. ■ 98103 #031-01-2007 L2007 GS *012

OKIMOTO, Joseph Tsutomu. 5410 CALIFORNIA AVE SW 98136 #024-01-1963 L1969 P GPM *020 †70,75

OKORN, Dobrina Marie. 600 UNIVERSITY ST, STE 1200 98101 #040-02-1999 L2001 FM *020 †20

OLDHAM, Fred B. 501 ELLIOTT AVE W, # 400 98119 #039-01-1968 L1969 HO IM *050

O'LEARY-STICKNEY, K M. 1145 BROADWAY 98122 #054-04-1986 L1990 OTO *020 †45

OLERUD, John Everett. 4225 ROOSEVELT WAY NE, STE 354697 98105 #054-04-1971 L1976 D IM *040 †20,15

OLIVAR, Stephen John. ■ 98122 #016-01-1997 L2001 AN *020 †05

OLIVEIRA, Andrew Borgesde. 413 PINE ST, STE 200 98101 #005-02-1984 L1985 FM MDM *030 †18

OLIVER, Lynn Marie. 4245 ROOSEVELT WAY NE, STE 354775 98105 #054-04-1983 L1984 FM *020 †18

OLLIFFE, Jeffrey Fred. 1120 CHERRY ST, STE 320 98104 #031-01-1981 L1986 FM *020 †18

OLMSTED, Richard W. ■ 98119 #024-01-1944 L1948 CHP PD *020 †55

OLSEN, John Vester. 550 17TH AVE, STE 630 98122 #035-19-1980 L1981 CD IM *020 †20

OLSEN, Robert Barrington. 1101 MADISON ST STE 1290 98104 #054-04-1971 L1978 P IM *020 †20,75

OLSEN, Stephen Barry. 1600 E JOHN ST 98112 #048-04-1984 L1999 VS *020 †85

OLSON, Alicia Nicole. ■ 98103 #054-04-2008 *012

OLSON, James Lynn. 6645 57TH AVE NE 98115 #018-03-1971 L1973 FM *020 †18

OLSON, James Michael. 4800 SAND POINT WAY NE, STE CH30 98105 #025-01-1991 L1994 PHO *020 †55

OLSON, Jared Dean. ■ 98103 #016-02-2008 *012

OLSON, Jeanne Marie. 4744 41ST AVE SW STE 101 98116 #017-20-1993 L1998 FM *020 †18

OLSON, Joan Elaine. 10330 MERIDIAN AVE N, SEATTLE ARTHRITIS CLINIC 98133 #035-15-1995 L1998 IM *020 †20

OLSON, John Chas. 1529 MED DENT BLDG 98101 #016-06-1974 L1975 P PYA *020 †75

OLSON, Rachel Anne. ■ 98103 #054-04-2008 *012

OLSON, Sonja Irene. 1629 N 45TH ST 98103 #054-04-2005 L2005 FP *012

OLSON, Soren Lance. ■ 98109 #054-04-2004 L2004 ORS *012

O'MAHONY, Darragh Shane. 4245 ROOSEVELT WAY NE, BOX 354760 98105 #054-04-2004 L2005 IM *012

O'MAHONY, Lila N. ■ 98115 #054-04-2004 L2005 PD *012

OMDAL, David Gordon. 600 BROADWAY, STE 170 98122 #041-13-1991 L2000 VIR *020 †80

OMEARA, Megan Marie. ■ 98125 #003-01-2005 L2005 IM *012

OMORO, Sophia Aomo. 1959 NE PACIFIC ST #356340, UW SCHOOL OF MEDICINE 98195 #021-01-2002 L2002 OTO *012

O'NEIL, Meghan Lee. 1959 NE PACIFIC ST, BOX 356560 98195 #005-14-2006 L2006 P *012

O'NEIL, Nancy Anne. 1101 MADISON ST STE 1150 98104 #016-06-1978 L1982 OBG *020 †30

O'NEILL, Bruce Charlton. 1145 BROADWAY 98122 #038-41-1989 L1992 NEP *020 †20

O'NEILL, Darby Erin. 1959 NE PACIFIC ST RM C, CAMPUS BOX 356340 98195 #028-02-2002 L2002 GE *012 †20

O'NEILL, Mary Kathleen. 1501 3RD AVE STE 201, UNIFORM MEDICAL PLZ 98101 #054-04-1984 L1985 PM PMM *030 †60

ONG, Brandon Nelson. ■ 98108 #035-46-2002 L2004 IM *020 †20

ONG, Nancy A. ■ 98125 #506-04-1973 *075

OPEL, Douglas John. 4800 SAND POINT WAY NE 98105 #016-02-2002 L2002 PD *100 †55

OPPENHEIM, Gary Evan. 1730 MINOR AVE, STE 1010 98101 #041-01-1981 L1990 CD IM *020 †20

ORALLO, Maria Origenes. ■ 98125 #748-01-1953 L1962 AN *071

ORBINO, Bella Labuanan. 6044 MLK JR WAY S STE 104, SOUTHGATE MED CLINIC 98118 #748-13-1988 *100

ORCUTT, James Craig. 1959 NE PACIFIC ST 98195 #007-02-1977 L1978 OPH *020 †35

ORENCIA, Melanie Sandoval. ■ 98126 #748-16-1989 L2007 FM *020 †18

ORENSTEIN, Herbert Norman. 901 BOREN AVE STE 702 98104 #005-06-1972 L1973 P *020 †75

ORESKOVICH, Michael Robt. 720 OLIVE WAY STE 1010 98101 #054-04-1974 L1975 ADP P *020 †85,75

O'RIORDAN, Colm Patrick. 901 BOREN AVE, STE 1776 98104 #539-06-1964 L2001 ORS *020 †40

ORME, Burton M. 925 SENECA ST 98101 #028-02-1962 L1969 IM N *071 †20

OROZCO, John Henry. 8720 14TH AVE S 98108 #005-14-1963 L1976 EM *071 †16

OROZCO, Johnnie Jose. 1100 FAIRVIEW AVE N, APT C1-015 98109 #054-04-2006 IM *012

ORR, Rosemary Jean. 4566 NE 89TH ST, MEDICAL CENTER/ANESTHESIOL 98115 #539-01-1967 L1971 AN PD *020 †55,05

ORSBORN, Mack Talmage. 1660 S COLUMBIAN WAY, VETERAN'S HOSPITAL 98108 #054-04-1987 L1991 IM *020

ORTEGA, Jose R. 825 EASTLAKE AVE E, SEATTLE CANCER CARE 98109 #187-50-2000 L2007 *100

ORTIZ, Justin Redding. 1959 NE PACIFIC ST, U OF WASH BOX 356522 98195 #005-02-2002 L2007 PCC *012 †20

ORTIZ-CHIVERS, Frank. ■ 98139 #031-01-1996 L2000 AN *020 †05

OSBORN, Justin Eugene. 2505 2ND AVE, UWPN-BELLTOWN STE 200 98121 #051-01-1989 L1989 FM *020 †18

OSBORN, Tristan Richard. ■ 98115 #054-04-2007 L2007 IM *012

OSBUN, Joshua William. UNIV OF WASHINGTON, DEPT OF SURGERY #356410 98195 #048-12-2007 L2007 GS *012

OSORIO MANOTAS, Roberto E. 1959 NE PACIFIC ST 98195 #264-02-2002 L2007 GS *012

OSTEN, Barbara Elizabeth. 1550 N 115TH ST 98133 #054-04-1953 L1955 FM GP *071 †18

OSTROW, Jonathan Herbert. ■ 98133 #035-46-1962 L1964 IM PUD *020 †20 ‡

O'SULLIVAN, Gabrielle A. 8720 14TH AVE S 98108 #054-04-2000 L2003 FM *020 †18

OSWALD, Lisa Lynn. 1200 12TH AVE S, PACIFIC MEDICAL CENTER 98144 #026-04-2001 L2004 IM *020

OTERO, Henry Orlando. 1100 9TH AVE G1-MSO, VIRGINIA MASON MEDICAL CEN 98101 #025-12-1989 L1994 ON *020 †20

OTJEN, Jeffrey Parke. ■ 98103 #048-04-2005 L2005 PD *012

OTT, Susan Marie. 4245 ROOSEVELT WAY NE, STE 354775 98105 #054-04-1974 L1979 NM *050 †18,20

OTTO, Catherine Mary. 1959 NE PACIFIC ST, BOX 356422 98195 #054-04-1979 L1982 CD IM *020 †20

OTTO, Randolph Kevin. 4800 SAND POINT WAY NE, CHILDREN'S HOSPITAL & REGI 98105 #025-01-1985 L1990 PDR DR *020 †80

OU, Chau-Su. 10330 MERIDIAN AVE N, STE 372 98133 #244-06-1974 L1982 OBG *020 †30

OU, Henry Chihyuan. 4800 SAND POINT WAY NE, CHILDRENS HOSP & REG MC 98105 #028-02-1998 L2004 OTO *020

OVERMAN, Steven Scott. 10330 MERIDIAN AVE N, STE 250 98133 #001-02-1975 L1977 RHU IM *020 †18

OVERSTREET, Frederica. 2101 E YESLER WAY STE 200, CENTER 98122 #054-04-1996 L1999 FM *020 †18

OWEN-MAJOROWICZ, Mary. 1930 POST ALY 98101 #054-04-1985 L1986 IM *020 †20

OWENS, Brian David. 1100 9TH AVE, VIRGINIA MASON CLNC B2-AN 98101 #041-13-1977 L1988 AN CCA *040 †20,05

OWENS, David Scott. 1959 NE PACIFIC ST BOX 35, U OF WASHINGTON, CARDIOLOG 98195 #028-02-1998 L2005 CD *012 †20

OXORN, Donald Charles. 1959 NE PACIFIC ST, BOX 356540 98195 #067-01-1978 L1997 AN *020 †05

OYER, Deborah Jean. 1001 BROADWAY STE 320 98122 #024-01-1987 L1989 FM *020 †18

PAAUW, Douglas Stephen. 4245 ROOSEVELT WAY NE, STE 354775 98105 #025-01-1985 L1986 IM *020 †20

PABICH, Wendy Leah. ■ 98103 #054-04-2004 L2004 AN *012

PACE, James Lee. 1959 NE PACIFIC ST BOX 356, UW SCHOOL OF MEDICINE GME 98195 #024-05-2005 L2005 ORS *012

PADEN, Grady Ralph. 1660 S COLUMBIAN WAY, S-111 GIMC 98108 #054-04-1986 L1988 IM *020 †20

PAEK, Bettina W. 1959 NE PACIFIC ST RM BB66, BOX 356460 98195 #409-16-1994 L2004 OBG *020

PAGALIAUAN, Genevieve L. 4245 ROOSEVELT WAY NE, STE 354775 98105 #054-04-2000 L2002 IM *020 †20

PAGE, Richard L. 1959 NE PACIFIC ST 98195 #036-07-1984 L2002 ICE CD *020 †20

PAGE, Stephanie Theresa. 1959 NE PACIFIC ST C, CAMPUS BOX 356340 98195 #054-04-1999 L2002 END M *100 †20

PAGEL, John Michael. 1100 FAIRVIEW AVE N, FRED HUTCHINSON CANCER RES 98109 #024-05-1996 L1999 ON *020 †20

PAGON, Roberta Anderson. 4800 SAND POINT WAY NE, CHILDREN'S HOSP & MED CTR 98105 #024-01-1972 L1975 MG PD *050 †55,19

PAIGE, Keith Thos. 1100 9TH AVE G1-MSO, VIRGINIA MASON MEDICAL CEN 98101 #024-01-1989 L1989 PS *020 †65,85

PAIK, Hui Jung. 1100 9TH AVE G1-MSO, VIRGINIA MASON MEDICAL CEN 98101 #016-11-1993 L2001 IM *020 †20

PAIK, Kiwan. 1570 N 115TH ST, STE 16 98133 #583-03-1972 L1984 PD GP *020 †20

PAINE, Robert Morse. ■ 98119 #035-01-1946 L1951 CD IM *071 †20

PALADIN, Angelisa Marie. 4800 SAND POINT WAY NE 98105 #016-42-1994 L1998 DR *020 †80

PALANATI, Mamatha. 125 16TH AVE E CSB160 98112 #495-70-1991 L2001 FM *020

PALANCA-WESSELS, Maria C. 1100 FAIRVIEW AVE N, MAILSTOP D3-190 98109 #054-04-2001 L2003 HO *012 †20

PALASKAS, Constantine W. 515 MINOR AVE, STE 200 98104 #047-05-1983 L1985 NO OTO *020 †45

PALERMO, Joseph J. 10564 5TH AVE NE 98125 #024-15-1942 L1943 D OS *020

PALKEN, Morton. 10330 MERIDIAN AVE N 98125 #024-07-1946 L1954 U *071 †95

PALMER, Gayle Herzog. 600 UNIVERSITY ST, STE 1200 98101 #005-06-1968 L1991 GP OS *020 †18

PALMER, Jerry Philip. 1660 S COLUMBIAN WAY, VA CTR RM 111 98108 #035-15-1970 L1975 DIA END *050 †20

PALO, Theodore Albert. 801 BROADWAY STE 628, HEALTH BUILDING 98122 #025-01-1971 L1976 OBG FM *020 †18,30

PAN, Lihua. 1959 NE PACIFIC ST, C/O SEATTLE CANCER CARE 98195 #243-52-1995 L2006 HO *012 †20

PANERIO-LANGER, Joseph La. ■ 98115 #030-05-2006 L2006 IM *012

PANG, Jenny W. 200 16TH AVE E 98112 #023-07-1992 L1997 PHO *050 †55,20

PANIAGUA, Miguel. 325 9TH AVE, BOX 359755 98104 #016-11-1998 L2000 IMG *020 †20

PANITCH, Martha. 7724 35TH AVE NE, P O BOX 51188 98115 #005-06-1987 L1992 IM CCM *020 †20

PANKOVICH, Martha Bonnie. 4800 SAND POINT WAY NE 98105 #847-11-1999 L2005 PAN *100 †05

PAPAC, Jesse Martin. 2124 4TH AVE 98121 #054-04-2005 L2007 FP *012

PAPATHANASIOU, James. 1101 MADISON ST 98104 #041-12-1998 L2002 IM *020 †20

PAPPAS, George Peter. 515 MINOR AVE STE 300, MINOR & JAMES MEDICAL, PLL 98104 #016-06-1988 L1992 CCM *020 †70,20

PAPROCKI, Thaddeus R. 600 BROADWAY, STE 170 98122 #035-20-1976 L1978 NR R *020 †80

PARADA, Gregory. ■ 98106 #054-04-2006 L2006 FP *012

PARAMSOTHY, Pathmaja. 1959 NE PACIFIC ST, BOX # 356422 98195 #034-01-1998 L2002 CD *100 †20

PARDEE, Neely Eugene. 1100 9TH AVE # M6-AC, VIRGINIA MASON MEDICAL CLI 98101 #026-04-1954 L1959 IM PUD *071 †20

PAREDES, Valentine L. 500 17TH AVE, UW SCHOOL OF MED GME PROGR 98122 #005-02-1996 L2003 EM *020 †18,16

PARETSKY, Eve. 4245 ROOSEVELT WAY NE, BOX 354775 98105 #016-02-2003 L2003 FM *020 †18

PARIKH, Jay R. 1221 MADISON ST STE 520 98104 #065-09-1990 L2000 R *020 †80

PARIMI, Chinnaya. ■ 98144 #495-65-2003 L2006 GS *012

PARIMI, Soumya. 925 SENECA ST # 1930 98101 #495-65-2003 L2005 IM *012

PARIMON, Tanyalak. ■ 98103 #748-13-1993 L2002 IM *100 †20

PARIS, Carolyn Anne. 4800 SAND PONT WAY NE 5D-1 98105 #035-20-1991 L1994 PD *020 †55

PARISI, Marguerite T. 4800 SAND POINT WAY NE, CHILDREN'S HOSP & REG MED 98105 #035-08-1977 L2001 PDR NR *020 †55,80

PARISI, Melissa Ann. 1959 NE PACIFIC ST, DEPT OF PEDS-BOX 356320 98195 #005-11-1994 L1997 MG PD *050 †19,55

PARK, David R. 1959 NE PACIFIC ST BOX 359, BOX 359762 98195 #050-02-1988 L1990 CCM IM *020 †20

PARK, James Oh. 1959 NE PACIFIC ST, BOX 356410 98195 #041-01-1998 L2007 GS *100 †85 ‡

PARK, Julie R. 4800 SAND POINT WAY NE, MAILSTOP B6553 98105 #050-02-1988 L1988 PHO *020 †55

PARK, Kathleen Jung. H220 HLTH SCIENCES BOX 357, 1959 NE PACIFIC ST 98195 #038-06-1999 L2001 PD *020 †55

PARK, Paul Craig. 747 BROADWAY 98122 #010-02-1993 L2000 AN *020 †05

PARK, Robert Scott, II. 1959 NE PACIFIC ST C, CAMPUS BOX 356340 98195 #005-18-1999 L1999 FM *100

PARK, Sangtae. 1959 NE PACIFIC ST, HSB BB-1115, BOX 356510 98195 #005-02-1999 L2006 U *100 †95

PARK, Steven Ilkwon. 1959 NE PACIFIC ST RM C, MED.CAMPUS BX 356340 98195 #005-19-2002 L2002 HO *012 †20

PARKER, Andrew J. 1100 VIRGINIA ST, STE 215 98101 #061-01-1981 L1985 OM PHP *030 †70

PARKER, Charles Russell. ■ 98106 #035-20-1945 L1954 P *071

PARKER, Colleen Jean. 600 BROADWAY, STE 170 98122 #836-01-1984 L1992 DR *020 †80

PARKER, Gregory James. 1401 MADISON ST STE 100, MEDICINE RESIDE 98104 #018-03-2006 L2006 FP *012

PARKER, James Adam. 1730 MINOR AVE STE 1400 98101 #054-04-1980 L1981 CHP *020 †35,75 ‡

PARKER, John Talmadge. 9730 3RD AVE NE, STE 210 98115 #016-11-1983 L1990 OTO *020 †45

PARKER, Melanie Jean. 1959 NE PACIFIC ST, BOX 356340 98195 #035-09-2006 L2006 FP *012

PARKER, Molly Beth. 1629 N 45TH ST 98103 #054-04-2003 L2003 FM *020 †18

PARKER, Richard Malcolm. 801 BROADWAY STE 912 98122 #024-01-1962 L1971 U UP *071 †95

PARKER-JOHNSON, Rebecca A. ■ 98102 #041-15-2007 L2007 GS *012

PARKS, David Lloyd. ■ 98125 #054-04-2003 L2003 GS *012

PARNELL, Shawn Elizabeth. 1107 NE 45TH ST # 44, UNIV OF WASH,DEPT OF RADIO 98105 #051-07-2001 L2002 PDR *100 †80

PARRA, Juan David. 1959 NE PACIFIC ST, DEPT OF GENERAL SURGERY 98195 #264-04-2000 L2004 GS *012

PARTLOW, Liza Katherine. ■ 98112 #016-06-2007 L2007 P *012

PARVATHANENI, Upendra. 1959 NE PACIFIC ST #356043 98195 #496-28-1993 L2006 RO *100

PASCARELLI, Erica Suzanne. 925 SENECA ST # 1930 98101 #005-06-2000 L2000 IM *020 †20

PASETTE, Arthur Lee. 1959 NE PACIFIC ST, BOX 356429 98195 #005-06-1965 L1971 GE IM *071 †20

PASIC, Jagoda. 325 9TH AVE, BOX 359896 98104 #957-08-1978 L1999 P *020 †75

PASS, Bertram R. 1200 12TH AVE S 98144 #054-04-1953 L1955 FM *071 †18

PASS, Harry David. 1305 4TH AVE, STE 216 98101 #020-02-1940 L1941 FM *072 †18

PASSLOFF, Ellen Simone. 11545 15TH AVE NE STE 205 98125 #041-01-1990 L1990 PD *020 †55

PASTERNAK, Derick Peter. 10264 RICHWOOD AVE NW 98177 #024-01-1967 L1998 MDM IM *030 †20

PASTOR, Claire Judith. 325 9TH AVE, MEDICAL CENTER BOX 359945 98104 #021-05-1996 L1998 P *020 †75

PASTOR, Linda Maureen. 1229 MADISON ST STE 1150 98104 #054-04-1986 L1991 DR *020 †80

PATCHEN, Glenn Allen. 9730 4TH AVE NE, BREAST DIAGNOSTIC CENTER 98115 #005-12-1961 L1963 GYN *071 †30

PATEL, Jigish S. 925 SENECA ST # 1930, GRADUATE MED EDU H8-GME 98101 #012-01-2003 L2004 DR *012

PATEL, Niraj Pramukh. 1101 MADISON ST, STE 700 98104 #025-01-1994 L2001 OPH IM *020 †35

PATEL, Pallavi M. 125 16TH AVE E 98112 #016-06-1991 L2001 IM GE *020 †20

PATEL, Shilpen Ajit. 753 HARVARD AVE E # B 98102 #048-02-2001 L2006 RO *100 †80

PATEL, Shreya Jayendra. 4800 SAND POINT WAY NE, REGIONAL M 98105 #048-13-2006 L2006 PD *012

PATEL, Smita. 600 BROADWAY, STE 170 98122 #016-43-1990 L2002 DR *020 †80

PATEL, Uresh. 600 BROADWAY, STE 170 98122 #917-24-1987 L2002 RNR DR *020 †80

PATON, Richard Reid. PO BOX 900 98111 #054-04-1954 L1959 NEP IM *071 †20

PATT, Joshua Charles. 325 9TH AVE, BOX 359798 98104 #021-01-2000 L2005 ORS *100

PATTERSON, James Richard. ■ 98112 #038-40-1957 L1962 IM *071

PATTERSON, Kathleen. 4800 SAND POINT WAY NE 98105 #018-03-1976 L1992 ATP PD *020 †50

PATTERSON, Laird Gunn. 1100 9TH AVE M6-AC, VIRGINIA MASON MEDICAL CTR 98101 #024-01-1968 L1976 N *020 †20,75

PATTERSON, Susan D. 1100 9TH AVE 98101 #005-02-1971 L1976 PTH *020 †50

PATTISON, Julie Ann. 1100 9TH AVE G1-MSO, VIRGINIA MASON MEDICAL CTR 98101 #048-02-1984 L1989 IM *020 †20

PATTON, Harry Dickson. ■ 98122 #008-01-1946 OS *071

PATTON, Kristen Kimberly. 1959 NE PACIFIC ST, CAMPUS BOX 356422 98195 #040-02-1995 L2004 ICE *020 †20

PATTON, Richard George. 1550 N 115TH ST 98133 #030-05-1969 L1970 PTH *020 †50

PAUK, John S. 1145 BROADWAY, THE POLY CLINIC 98122 #036-07-1993 L1995 ID *020 †20

PAUL, Christine Elizabeth. 521 WALL ST, DEPT FP 98121 #061-01-2007 FP *012

PAUL, Greg Jerome. 747 BROADWAY 98122 #030-05-1990 L1991 AN *020 †05

PAUL, Lael Georgene. 1100 9TH AVE 98101 #030-05-1991 L1993 IM *020 †20

PAULL, Daniel Leonard. 1100 9TH AVE 98101 #024-07-1978 L1985 TS *020 †85,90

PAULOVICH, Amanda Grace. 1100 FAIRVIEW AVE N, BOX 19024 98109 #054-04-1998 L2004 HO *020 †20

PAULSEN, Charles Alvin. 3528 W HOWE ST, UNIV OF WA SCH OF MED 98199 #040-02-1952 L1958 END *050

PAULSEN, Harold Jay. 2201 6TH AVE MS RX-21, FEDERAL OCCUPATIONAL HLTH 98121 #007-02-1977 L1986 PHP OM *062 †70

PAUWELS, Judith A. 4245 ROOSEVELT WAY NE, STE 354775 98105 #056-05-1983 L1994 FM EM *040 †18

PAVLIN, Dorothy Janet. 1959 NE PACIFIC ST, DEPARTMENT OF ANESTHESIA 98195 #062-01-1969 L1974 AN *020

PAVLIN, Edward Geo. 325 9TH AVE, HARBORVIEW MED CTR ZA-14 98104 #062-01-1968 L1973 AN *020

PAVLISCAK, Jill Kathleen. 550 16TH AVE STE 100, MEDICINE CLI 98122 #040-02-2001 L2003 FM *020

PAXSON, Chauncey G, Jr. 747 BROADWAY 98122 #041-02-1950 L1957 IM *071 †20

PAYAWAL, Jonathan Haber. ■ 98122 #005-15-2004 L2005 AN *012

PAYNE, Thomas Howard. 4245 ROOSEVELT WAY NE, STE 354775 98105 #054-04-1980 L1989 IM *020 †20

PEALE, Franklin Vale, Jr. PO BOX 357290, DEPT PATHOLOGY 98195 #035-45-1990 L1993 PTH *020 †50

PEARLMAN, Alan Stuart. 1959 NE PACIFIC ST, UNIV OF WA BOX 356422 98195 #024-01-1970 L1978 CD IM *040 †20

PEARLMAN, Robert A. 1660 S COLUMBIAN WAY, GRECC (IGP-182-S) 98108 #024-05-1975 L1977 IMG IM *062 †20

PECK, Angela Jean. 4800 SAND POINT WAY NE, MEDICAL CENTER, 8G-1 98105 #047-05-1999 L2001 PDI *100 †55

PECK, Annette Pavlova. 1001 SW KLICKITAT WAY #205, PUGET SOUND INSTITUTE OF P 98134 #040-02-1998 L2002 PCP *020

PECKINPAUGH, Jeffrey Laws. ■ 98105 #054-04-2007 L2007 TY *012

PEDEGANA, Larry Russell. 1600 E JEFFERSON ST STE 4, ORTHOPAEDICS 98122 #060-01-1968 L1971 ORS *020 †40

PEIRCE, Kenneth Read. 200 16TH AVE E 98112 #038-06-1969 L1971 NS *071

PELEKIS, Vaira Inta. 1229 MADISON ST STE 500 98104 #869-04-1964 L1973 PTH *071 †50

PELLEGRINI, Carlos A. 1959 NE PACIFIC ST, BOX 356410 98195 #132-04-1971 L1993 GS GE *020 †85

PELLERIN, Richard Albert. 4100 SW ADMIRAL WAY 98116 #025-01-1974 L1975 GP *020

PELZEL, Robert Burry. ■ 98119 #024-01-1954 L1958 IM *030

PEMBERTON, Jane Marshall. 1550 N 115TH ST 98133 #030-05-1985 L1989 FM *020 †18

PENALOZA, Dorothy Ann. 1100 9TH AVE, VIRGINIA MASON MEDICAL CEN 98101 #040-02-2004 L2005 AN *012

PENDERGRASS, Thomas Wayne. 1959 NE PACIFIC ST 98195 #047-06-1971 L1975 PHO PD *020 †55

PENG, Holly Wenho. 521 WALL ST, GROUP HEALTH PERM 98121 #003-01-1997 L2000 FM *020 †18

PENG, John Yenjei. 1100 9TH AVE G1-MSO, VIRGINIA MASON MEDICAL CEN 98101 #035-03-1997 L1999 IM *020 †20

PENN, Justin David. ■ 98102 #054-04-2008 *012

PENUELAS, Anita Fanjul. 1801 NW MARKET ST, STE 203 98107 #054-04-1994 L1996 FM *020 †18

PEPIN, Christopher John. 1145 BROADWAY 98122 #054-04-1996 L1999 IM *020 †20

PEPIN, Craig James. 1145 BROADWAY 98122 #054-04-1995 L1997 IM *020 †20

PERALES BURGOS, Norma Lil. 550 16TH AVE E STE 100 98112 #176-03-2002 L2004 *100 †18

PERBECK, Leif. 801 BROADWAY STE 915 98122 #858-02-1972 L1997 *100

PEREIRA, Peter Kevin. 6020 35TH AVE SW 98126 #054-04-1987 L1989 FM *020 †18

PERERA, David Rhoads. 1600 E JOHN ST 98112 #035-01-1966 L1971 GE IM *020 †18

PEREZ, Christine Marie. 1959 NE PACIFIC ST, U OF W-HS AFFAIRS BOX 3563 98195 #041-01-2004 L2004 IM *012

PEREZ, Julian Cecilio. ■ 98115 #054-04-2004 L2004 FM *020 †18

PEREZ-ACOSTA, Romelia. 3808 S ANGELINE ST 98118 #308-01-1982 L1995 CHP *020 †75

PEREZ-REYES, Nuria. 1229 MADISON ST 98104 #038-06-1987 L1989 PCP ATP *020 †50

PERGAM, Steven Aaron. ■ 98122 #030-05-1998 L2005 ID *012 †20

PERIMAN, Laura Marie. 1959 NE PACIFIC ST 98195 #054-04-1997 L2001 OPH *071 †35

PERINE, Peter Loring. 325 9TH AVE 98104 #019-02-1966 L1970 GPM IM *020 †20

PERKIN, Gordon Wesley. 4 NICKERSON ST 98109 #065-01-1959 L1965 OS FM *030

PERKINS, James Dennis. 1959 NE PACIFIC ST #356410, DEPT OF SURGERY 98195 #004-01-1979 L1989 AS *020 †85

PERKINS, Jessica Driggs. 1959 NE PACIFIC ST, BOX 356320 98195 #041-02-2003 L2006 NPM *012 †55

PERKINS, Jonathan A. 4800 SAND POINT WAY NE, CHILDREN'S HOSP MEDICAL CE 98105 #018-75-1987, ▲ L1994 PDO *020 †45

PERKINSON, Diana T. 515 MINOR AVE, STE 300 98104 #001-02-1979 L1980 NEP IM *020 †20

PERLMUTTER, Roger Matthew. UNIV OF WASHINGTON, DIV OF MEDICAL GENETICS SL 98195 #028-02-1979 L1984 IG IM *020

PERMUT, Lester Cal. 4800 SAND POINT WAY NE 98105 #024-05-1983 L2002 PCS CD *020 †85,90

PERRIN, Alison Lytle. 1560 N 115TH ST, STE 102 98133 #054-04-1993 L1997 GS VS *020 †85

PERRONE, Juan Manuel Mart. 1959 NE PACIFIC ST, BOX 356340 98195 #132-07-1997 L2005 GS *020

PERRY, Robert L. 12610 DES MOINES MEM DR S, STE 206 98168 #054-15-1964 GP *020

PERSER, Karen Nicole. 1959 NE PACIFIC ST, GME PROGRAMS/ BOX 356340 98195 #048-14-2004 L2004 ORS *012

PERSOHN, Linda Kay. 1600 E JEFFERSON ST, STE 300 98122 #048-02-1978 L1999 **R** *071 †80

PERSON, Jettie Margaret. 1530 N 115TH ST STE 104 98133 #054-04-1983 L1985 **D** *020 †15

PESANDO, John Michael. ■ 98102 #035-46-1974 L1983 **ON IM** *050 †20

PESKIND, Elaine Roslyn. 1660 S COLUMBIAN WAY, VA PUGET SOUND S116-6EAST 98108 #054-04-1986 L1988 **PYG** *020 †75

PETERS, Mary Lee Evans. 901 BOREN AVE, STE 1650 98104 #051-04-1977 L1988 **PS GS** *020 †65

PETERS, Michael James. 600 BROADWAY, STE 170 98122 #054-04-1983 L1984 **DR** *020 †80

PETERS, Wm Anthony, III. 1101 MADISON ST STE 1500 98104 #051-01-1974 L1983 **GYN GO** *020 †30

PETERSDORF, Effie Wang. 1100 FAIRVIEW AVE N, FRED HUTCHINSON CANCER RES 98109 #067-01-1982 L1982 **ON** *050

PETERSDORF, Robert G. 1959 NE PACIFIC ST, MSC 359300 98195 #008-01-1952 L1960 **IM ID** *072 †20

PETERSDORF, Stephen H. 825 EASTLAKE AVE E 98109 #043-01-1983 L1984 **HEM ON** *020 †20

PETERSEN, John Louis. 550 17TH AVE, STE 630 98122 #054-04-1964 L1969 **CD IM** *020 †20

PETERSEN, Walter Connell. ■ 98112 #054-04-1955 L1959 **OPH** *075 †35

PETERSON, Charles Alfred. 2409 N 45TH ST 98103 #035-20-1967 L1974 **ORS** *020 †40

PETERSON, Charles Alfred, II. 2409 N 45TH ST 98103 #054-04-1990 L1996 **ORS OSM** *020 †40

PETERSON, Donald Grant. 747 BROADWAY 98122 #028-34-1974 L1975 **AN** *020 †05

PETERSON, Donald Richard. U WA SCH PUB HLTH COMM ME 98195 #040-02-1947 L1955 **OS PHP** *071 †70

PETERSON, Eric Cecala. 1959 NE PACIFIC ST, GME PROGRAMS, BOX 356340 98195 #025-01-2005 L2005 **NS** *012

PETERSON, Gene Nels. 1959 NE PACIFIC ST 98195 #016-02-1982 L1983 **AN** *030 †05

PETERSON, Ingrid Marie. 1100 9TH AVE M6-AC, VIRGINIA MASON MEDICAL CEN 98101 #005-11-1978 L1986 **DR** *040 †80

PETERSON, Janice Lynn. ■ 98116 #054-04-1975 L1978 **PM OS** *075 †60

PETERSON, Jeff Regan. 10330 MERIDIAN AVE N, SEATTLE ARTHRITIS CLINIC 98133 #054-04-1997 L1999 **RHU** *020 †20

PETERSON, Karen Linnea. 600 UNIVERSITY ST, STE 1200 98101 #018-03-1991 L1998 **OTO** *020 †45

PETERSON, Keith Duane. 1551 NW 54TH ST STE 200 98107 #054-15-1969 **OS GP** *020

PETERSON, Mitchell Jay. 11011 MERIDIAN AVE N, STE 200 98133 #054-04-1991 L1991 **FM** *020 †18 ‡

PETERSON, Wilbur Robt. 4800 SAND POINT WAY NE 98105 #054-04-1959 L1961 **PD CHN** *020 †55

PETERSON-BUCKLEY, Sheri L. ■ 98178 #047-07-2000 L2003 **FM** *020

PETRESCU, Oana M. 550 17TH AVE 98122 #035-03-2001 L2007 **CD** *100

PETRICCA, Sarah Elise. ■ 98117 #012-05-2008 *012

PETRIE, Eric Cameron. 1660 S COLUMBIAN WAY, MC S-182 GRECC VAMC 98108 #054-04-1985 L1990 **P** *020 †75

PETROV, Roman Vladimirovi. 1600 E JEFFERSON ST, STE 101 98122 #913-99-1996 L2004 **GS** *020

PETRUK, Lyudmila Ivanovna. 1959 NE PACIFIC ST RM C2, CAMPUS BOX 356340 98195 #054-04-2002 L2002 **N** *020

PETTIS, Samuel R. 1570 N 115TH ST STE 10 98133 #010-03-1978 L1979 **NEP IM** *050 †20

PETTRONE, Sarah Katherine. ■ 98121 #051-01-2002 L2007 **HSO** *012

PETTY, Charles Neuman. UNIV OF WASH BOX 354410, HALL HLTH PRIMARY CARE CTR 98195 #049-01-1977 L1978 **OBG IM** *020 †20,30

PFEIFFER, Joshua David. ■ 98109 #054-04-2008 *012

PHAM, Hien. ■ 98118 #054-04-2006 L2006 **IM** *012

PHAM, Hien Xuan. 1200 S JACKSON ST STE 27 98144 #941-01-1975 L1984 **GP** *020

PHAM, Huong Thanh. 1100 9TH AVE, VIRGINIA MASON PBOX 900 98101 #023-01-1992 L2000 **RO** *020 †80

PHAM, Mai Thanh. ■ 98115 #039-01-2000 L2007 **VS** *020 †85

PHAM, Phat Phu. 1101 MADISON ST, STE 800 98104 #054-04-1999 L2006 **PD** *020 †55

PHAM, Uyenvy Vu. ■ 98144 #040-02-2007 **FP** *012

PHAN, Binhan Phuong. 10631 8TH AVE NE 98125 #025-01-2002 L2004 **CD** *012 †20

PHELAN, Elizabeth Anne. 325 9TH AVE, BOX 359755 98104 #024-07-1992 L1996 **IM IMG** *020 †20

PHELAN, Patrick Joseph. ■ 98112 #012-05-2007 L2007 **GS** *012

PHELPS, Janice Keller. 7TH & OLIVE WAY 98101 #016-06-1957 L1959 **NTR OS** *020

PHILIP, Mary. ■ 98103 #016-02-2004 L2006 **HO** *012 †20

PHILLIPS, Edyth D Yeates. 4800 SAND POINT WAY NE 98105 #005-12-1961 L1964 **P CHP** *020

PHILLIPS, Grace Sian. 4800 SAND POINT WAY NE, CHRMC RADIOLOGY 5C-1 98105 #023-07-1997 L2002 **PDR** *020 †80

PHILLIPS, Nicole Nida. ■ 98109 #038-40-2002 L2004 **SME** *012

PHILLIPS, Stephen Gregory. 1229 MADISON ST, SOUND EYE AND LASER, P.S. 98104 #035-46-1982 L1986 **OPH** *020 †35

PHILLIPS, Thomas Edward. 325 9TH AVE, MED HARBORVIEW MED CTR 98104 #028-02-1977 L1978 **IMG IM** *020 †20

PHILLIPS, William Robt. 1233 NE 88TH ST 98115 #054-04-1975 L1976 **FM GPM** *050 †70,18

PHINNEY, Alexi Jordan. 1100 9TH AVE, VIRGINIA MASON MEDICAL CEN 98101 #026-08-1997 L2000 **R** *020 †80

PHIPPS, Warren Theodore. ■ 98102 #024-01-2002 L2006 **ID** *012 †20

PICHLER, Raimund H. UNIV OF WASHINGTON, DEPT OF MEDICINE 98195 #154-07-1993 L2000 **NEP** *020 †20

PICKETT-GIES, Cheryl Ann. 1959 NE PACIFIC ST, UNIV OF WASHINGTON BOX 356 98195 #007-02-1988 L1999 **END IM** *050 †20

PICOZZI, Vincent Jos, Jr. 1100 9TH AVE M6-AC, VIRGINIA MEDICAL CENTER 98101 #005-11-1978 L1985 **HEM IM** *050 †20

PIEKARSKI, Irene M. 3216 NE 45TH PL, STE 100 98105 #005-02-1968 L1988 **GP EM** *020 †16 ‡

PIEPKORN, Michael Wm. 4225 ROOSEVELT WAY NE, STE 354697 98105 #026-04-1973 L1975 **D PTH** *020 †50,15

PIERCE, John Hutchins. 1600 E JEFFERSON ST, STE 600 98122 #054-04-1965 L1971 **ORS** *071 †40

PIERSON, David John. 325 9TH AVE 98104 #023-07-1969 L1976 **PUD CCM** *040 †20

PIERSON, William Edward. 2324 EASTLAKE AVE E, STE 500 98102 #016-06-1960 L1963 **PDA PUD** *075 †55,03

PIHOKER, Catherine. 4800 SAND POINT WAY NE, CHLMC PED ENDO MI-3 98105 #041-02-1984 L1997 **PDE PD** *020 †55

PIKER, Mark Khaem. 1959 NE PACIFIC ST, BOX 356465 98195 #003-01-2002 L2002 **N** *100

PILLAI, Manoj M. 1101 FAIRVIEW AVE N D4-10, CANCER RESEARC 98109 #495-36-1998 L2002 **ON** *100 †20

PILLOW, Randolph P. 1100 9TH AVE 98101 #051-01-1944 L1949 **IM** *071 †20

PILMER, Gregory M. ■ 98102 #005-14-2005 L2005 **IM** *012

PINDER, Mary Colleen. 1100 9TH AVE, C2- HEM 98101 #005-11-2002 L2007 **ON** *012 †20

PINEDA, Christinema Castr. ■ 98144 #054-04-2005 L2005 **IM** *012

PINEDA, Dinelle Maria. 550 16TH AVE STE 100, PROVIDENCE FAMILY MEDICINE 98122 #039-01-2005 L2005 **FP** *012

PINSKY, Linda Ellen. 4245 ROOSEVELT WAY NE, UNIV OF WASHINGTON 98105 #054-04-1989 L1989 **IM** *020 †20

PINTO MARQUES, Pedro Migu. 1959 NE PACIFIC ST, BOX 356424 98195 #770-02-1997 L2005 *100

PIOUS, Donald Adrian. UNIV-WASH SCH MED, DEPT PED 98105 #041-01-1956 L1964 **PD** *050 †55

PIPAVATH, Sudhakar Naik J. 1107 NE 45TH ST STE 44, UW DEPARTMENT OF RADIOLOGY 98105 #495-36-1997 L2004 **RNR** *100

PIPER, August Thos, Jr. 901 BOREN AVE, STE 1010 98104 #010-03-1969 L1972 **P IM** *020 †20

PIROUZKAR, Behrouz. 1530 N 115TH ST STE 110 98133 #040-02-1989 L1999 **EM** *020

PITLUK, Jessica Danielle. ■ 98122 #003-01-2007 L2007 **FP** *012

PITTIER, Ann Catherine. WASHINGTON MEDIC, UNIVERSITY OF 98195 #539-03-2002 L2004 **RO** *012 †20

PITTLE, Lester Bertram. 1930 POST ALY 98101 #051-01-1972 L1975 **IM PHP** *020 †20

PIZER, Ellen Sarah. 1229 MADISON ST 98104 #048-12-1991 L2002 **PTH** *020 †50

PIZZUTE, Christine. 201 16TH AVE E, CAPITOL HILL MAIN BLDG 98112 #010-02-2000 L2007 **GE** *100 †20

PLACE, John Richard. PO BOX 354410, UNIVERSITY OF WASHINGTON 98195 #035-45-1987 L1996 **OBG** *020 †30

PLANT, Barry James. ■ 98122 #539-02-1996 L2005 **PCC** *100

PLATTNER, Philip Brent. 1660 S COLUMBIAN WAY, 136 C&P 98108 #048-13-1973 L1977 **P PYA** *075 †75

PLISKOWSKI, Teresa Jane. ■ 98102 #035-15-2004 L2004 **FM** *100 †18

PLOPLYS, Emilia Ann. 325 9TH AVE, BOX 359796 98104 #016-02-2002 L2002 **PS** *012

PLORDE, James Jos. 98105 #026-04-1959 L1964 **IM OS** *071 †20

PLOSS, Janet E. 9800 4TH AVE NE, NORTHGATE MEDICAL CENTER 98115 #035-46-1984 L2000 **IM OM** *020 †70

PLOTKIN, Elizabeth Ann. 10416 5TH AVE NE 98125 #008-01-1986 L1988 **IM** *020 †20

PLUT, Harry Geo, Jr. 1801 NW MARKET ST, STE 201 98107 #030-06-1963 L1965 **IM PUD** *071 †20

PLYMATE, Stephen Rex. 325 9TH AVE, BOX 359625 98104 #030-05-1968 L1980 **END IM** *050 †20

PODELL, Michael Scott. 747 BROADWAY 98122 #048-13-1995 L1999 **AN** *020 †05

PODEMSKI, Benjamin. 125 16TH AVE E, BLDG CSB-3 98112 #040-02-1973 L1998 **N** *020 †20,75

POESCHLA, Brian Doering. 325 9TH AVE 98104 #012-05-1986 L2002 **P** *020 †75

POHLMANN, Sarah K. 10330 MERIDIAN AVE N # 230 98133 #054-04-1997 L2000 **IM** *020 †20

POLAKOFF, Robert Ira. 1932 1ST AVE, STE 604 98101 #012-05-1994 L1994 **PYG** *020 †75

POLLACK, Louis David. ■ 98125 #010-01-1976 L1977 **PD** *020 †55

POLLARD, Jason C. 747 BROADWAY 98122 #035-01-2000 L2001 **PAN** *020 †05

POLLEY, Robert Francis L. 4800 SAND POINT WAY NE 98105 #028-34-1945 L1949 **PD** *071 †55

POLLOCK, Julia Elizabeth. 1100 9TH AVE 98101 #047-20-1986 L1990 **AN** *020 †05

POLLOCK, Preston Scott. 515 MINOR AVE, STE 300 98104 #005-14-1971 L1976 **RHU IM** *020 †50,20

POLYAK, Christina Stephan. ■ 98117 #023-01-2007 L2007 **IM** *012

POMEROY, Fletcher Janes. 1200 HARVARD AVE 98122 #024-01-1954 L1961 **N** *071

POND, Kyle Kirkpatrick. 4245 ROOSEVELT WAY NE 98105 #036-07-2000 L2000 **CD** *020 †20

PONG, David. 600 UNIVERSITY ST, STE 1200 98101 #050-02-1997 L2001 **IM** *020 †20

PONG, Ryan Peter James. ■ 98119 #005-12-2003 L2003 **AN** *020

POOLE, Jeanne Engstrom. 1959 NE PACIFIC ST, BOX 356422 98195 #054-04-1980 L1981 **ICE CD** *020 †20

POOLOS, Nicholas Pete. 325 9TH AVE, BOX 359745 98104 #005-11-1991 L2001 **N** *050 †75

POPE, Charles Edward. 1959 NE PACIFIC ST, BOX 356424 98195 #038-06-1957 L1965 **GE IM** *050 †20

POPPEMA, Suzanne Therese. 1001 BROADWAY, STE 320 98122 #024-01-1974 L1975 **FM** *071 †18

PORTER, Brian Story. ■ 98103 #032-01-2007 L2007 **IM** *012

PORTER, Bruce Arnold. 1001 BOYLSTON AVE 98104 #005-19-1974 L1984 **DR** *050 †80

PORTER, Christopher R. 1100 9TH AVE G1-MSO, VIRGINIA MASON MEDICAL CEN 98101 #016-01-1990 L2002 **U** *020 †95

PORTER, James Roscoe, Jr. 1101 MADISON ST, STE 1400 98104 #038-43-1990 L1992 **U GS** *020 †95

PORTER, Michael Patrick. 1959 NE PACIFIC ST, BOX 356510 98195 #018-03-1997 L1999 **U** *020 †20

PORTER, Peggy Lee. 1959 NE PACIFIC ST, MSC 359300 98195 #034-01-1987 L1991 **PTH** *020 †50

PORTMAN, Michael Allan. 4800 SAND POINT WAY NE 98105 #038-41-1980 L1992 **PDC** *071 †55

PORTUESE, William Anthony. 1101 MADISON ST STE 1280, SURGERY CENTER 98104 #039-01-1985 L1991 98103 #054-04-1990 L1990 **IM** *020 †20

POTIGAILO, Valeria L. NECK SURG, DEPT OF OTO/HEAD & 98195 #023-07-2006 L2006 **OTO** *012

POTTINGER, Paul Stuart. ■ 98122 #008-01-1998 L2002 **ID** *100 †20

POTTS, Catherine Joan. 1100 9TH AVE G1-MSO 98101 #054-04-1990 L1990 **IM** *020 †20

POUW, Lian-Tien. 4800 SAND POINT WAY NE 98105 #048-13-1983 L1986 **PD** *020 †55

POWELL, Clermont Smith. 1229 MADISON ST STE 500 98104 #041-02-1948 L1958 **PTH OS** *071 †50

POWELL, Heidi Sara. 4245 ROOSEVELT WAY NE, STE 354775 98105 #040-02-1986 L1990 **IM** *020 †20

POZOS, Tamara Christine. 1959 NE PACIFIC ST, BOX 357242 98105 #005-11-1998 L2002 **PDI** *100 †55

PRABHU, Somnath Jagannath. ■ 98103 #026-04-2008 *012

PRAY, Lauren Elizabeth. 1101 MADISON ST STE 1 98104 #038-06-2003 L2007 **OBG** *020

PRECHT, Andrew Felix. 1101 MADISON ST STE 200 98104 #759-07-1991 L2003 **TTS HEP** *020

PRECHT, Lisa M. ■ 98144 #005-19-2002 L2004 **GS** *012

PRESS, Joshua Z. UW SCHOOL OF MEDICINE, 356400 98195 #060-01-2001 L2007 **OBG** *020

PRESS, Oliver Wm. 1100 FAIRVIEW AVE N, MS D3-190 HUTCHINSON CNC 98109 #054-04-1979 L1982 **ON IM** *050 †20

PRESS, Shoshanna Adine. 126 NW CANAL ST 98107 #054-04-1998 L2002 **P** *020 †75

PRESSLEY, Zakiya Mandisa. 1959 NE PACIFIC ST, BOX 356340 98195 #054-04-2003 L2003 **PD** *100 †55

■ = Address Information Privacy Protected

PRESSMAN, Nicole Marie. ■ 98107 #054-04-2008 *012

PREVITI, Michael Charles. ■ 98104 #024-16-2006 L2006 **IM** *012

PRICE, Amanda Lee. 4245 ROOSEVELT WAY NE, BOX 354775 98105 #048-12-2003 L2003 **FM** *020 †18

PRICE, Susan Loucette. ■ 98118 #051-01-1980 L1982 **AN** *050 †05

PRICE, Tammira Dae. 1100 9TH AVE 98101 #035-20-1994 L1996 **IM** *020 †20

PRICE, Thomas Harrison. 921 TERRY AVE, PUGET SOUND BLOOD CENTER 98104 #023-07-1966 L1976 **BBK HEM** *030 †20

PRIEST, James Rush. ■ 98103 #005-11-2008 *012

PRIMROSE, David Craig. 1100 9TH AVE G1-MSO, VIRGINIA MASON MEDICAL CEN 98101 #026-04-1982 L1989 **NS** *020 †25

PRINCE, C Edward. ■ 98105 #054-04-1955 L1956 **OBG** *071 †30

PRINCE, James Wm. 403 DEWEY PL E 98112 #012-05-1981 L1982 **P** *020 †75

PRITCHARD, Colin C. RESIDENCY PROGRAM, PATHOLOGY 98195 #054-04-2007 L2007 **PTH** *012

PRITCHETT, Thomas Rand. 1100 9TH AVE C7-URO, VIRGINIA MASON MEDICAL CEN 98101 #005-14-1980 L1981 **U GS** *020 †95

PROANO, Pablo Roberto. 1229 MADISON ST, STE 1210 98104 #054-04-1981 L1982 **P** *020 †75

PROBSTFIELD, Jeffrey Lynn. 2815 EASTLAKE AVE E, STE 200 98102 #054-04-1967 L1994 **PA IM** *050 †20

PROCTOR, Monja Lea. 1101 MADISON ST, STE 800 98104 #048-12-1993 L2003 **GS** *020 †85

PRUEITT, John Leon. 3626 NE 45TH ST STE 300 98105 #005-15-1970 L1972 **NPM** *030 †55

PRUTHI, Sumit. 1107 NE 45TH ST, STE 440 98105 #495-01-1998 L2006 *100

PRUTKIN, Jordan Matthew. 1959 NE PACIFIC ST BOX 356, UNIVERSITY OF WASHINGTON 98195 #008-01-2002 L2005 **CD** *012 †20

PSATY, Bruce Mark. 325 9TH AVE, HARBORVIEW MEDICAL CENTER 98104 #017-20-1981 L1984 **IM** *020 †20

PUDDY, Walter E, Jr. 925 SENECA ST 98101 #005-02-1948 L1953 **P PYG** *071 †75

PUGLIESE, Matthew S. 747 BROADWAY, SWEDISH MEDICAL CENTER 98122 #038-41-2003 L2003 **GS** *012

PUJARI, Astrid Marie. 1370 STEWART ST, PUJARI CENTER 98109 #024-07-1998 L2001 **IM** *020 †20

PULLING, Michele Carolyn. 1959 NE PACIFIC ST, BOX 356421 98195 #035-45-2003 L2003 **GE** *012 †20

PULSE, Ronda Lin. ■ 98107 #054-04-2005 L2005 **AN** *012

PUNTENNEY, Mary Elsie. ■ 98136 #041-07-1960 L1961 **EM** *071

PUTNAM, William Shields. 501 N 34TH ST, STE 101 98103 #036-07-1980 L1990 **GE IM** *020 †20

PUTSCH, Robt Waldemar, III. 270 S HANFORD ST 98134 #024-07-1984 L1990 **IM OS** *020

PUZ, David Vincent. 550 16TH AVE, STE 405 98122 #054-04-1972 L1974 **AN** *020 †05

PYLMAN, John Allen. ■ 98103 #010-01-2008 *012

PYNE, Gordon Earl. 1564 ALKI AVE SW 98116 #054-04-1953 L1959 **PD** *071 †55

QUAN, Helen Kuan. 6517 35TH AVE SW 98126 #748-08-1974 L1982 **GP** *020

QUAN, Linda. 4800 SAND PNT NE #C5371 98105 #054-04-1971 L1972 **PD DMP** *030 †55,16

QUANG, Tony. ■ 98142 #041-15-2002 L2002 **RO** *100

QUIGLEY, Terence Michael. 1560 N 115TH ST, STE 102 98133 #024-05-1976 L1988 **VS GS** *020 †85

QUINNAN, Laura Rose. ■ 98199 #024-07-2005 L2005 **IM** *012

QUINT, Howard John. ■ 98115 #016-06-1986 L1992 *062 †95

QUIROGA, Elina. 1959 NE PACIFIC ST, UW SCHOOL OF MEDICINE GME 98195 #132-01-1999 L2005 **GS** *012

RABAK, David W. ■ 98101 #005-02-1949 L1950 **FM AM** *071 †18

RACKLEY, Jeremy David. ■ 98103 #012-01-2003 L2003 **AN** *100

RADANT, Allen David. ■ 98109 #005-19-1985 L1987 **P** *020 †75

RADICH, Jerald Patrick. 1100 FAIRVIEW AVE N D-4-1, RESEARCH CENTER 98109 #005-19-1983 L1984 **IM HO** *050 †20

RADIN, Laura Ann. 1001 4TH AVE, STE 420 98154 #054-04-1994 L1996 **FM** *020 †18

RAETZ, Jaqueline G. 4245 ROOSEVELT WAY NE, STE 354775 98105 #036-07-2001 L2003 **FPG** *020 †18

RAFF, Michael Leonard. 4800 SAND POINT WAY NE, M2-9 98105 #067-01-1991 L1994 **IM** *020 †20,19

RAGAZ, Anna. ■ 98144 #286-03-1966 L1985 **D DMP** *020 †15

RAGEN, Patrick A. 1100 9TH AVE 98101 #016-01-1952 L1957 **IM HEM** *071 †20

RAGHU, Ganesh. 1959 NE PACIFIC ST, MEDICAL CENTER-BOX 356522 98195 #495-09-1974 L1981 **IM END** *020 †20

RAGHU, Prema Kumari. 10330 MERIDIAN AVE N # 220 98133 #495-09-1973 L1981 **IM DIA** *020

RAGNARSSON, Gunnar Bjarni. 1101 FAIRVIEW AVE N, CANCER RESEARC 98109 #484-01-1998 L2002 **HO** *012 †20

RAHIM, Khawla A. 1959 NE PACIFIC ST, RM C212-HOUSE STAFF GME-BX 98195 #528-01-1986 L1999 **PD** *020 †55 ‡

RAHMAN, Saad. ■ 98105 #704-09-1993 L2005 **IM** *020 †20

RAINES-HEPPLE, Robert Pie. ■ 98115 #005-19-2006 L2007 **DR** *012

RAINEY, Petrie Morrison. 1959 NE PACIFIC ST, BOX 357110 98195 #036-01-1980 L2000 **CLP PA** *040 †50

RAINS, Derek David. ■ 98115 #054-04-2006 L2006 **ORS** *012

RAISIS, James Emanuel. 801 BROADWAY, STE 617 98122 #007-02-1970 L1976 **NS** *020 †25

RAJAN, Jayant Varada. ■ 98103 #035-45-2003 L2003 **ID** *012 †20

RAJENDRAN, Joseph G. 1959 NE PACIFIC ST, MSC 359300 98195 #495-42-1974 L1995 **NM** *020 †28

RAJIAH, Prabhakar. 1959 NE PACIFIC ST 98195 #495-04-1997 L2007 **AR** *012

RAJVANSHI, Arti. 1145 BROADWAY 98122 #495-55-1990 L1998 **IM** *020 †20

RAJVANSHI, Pankaj. 1101 MADISON ST STE 400, PACMED CLINICS - MADISON 98104 #495-55-1986 L1998 **GE HEP** *020 †20

RAKER, Edmond John. 1100 9TH AVE G1-MSO, VIRGINIA MASON MEDICAL CEN 98101 #024-01-1974 L1982 **VS GS** *020 †85

RAKITA, Robert Michlin. 1100 9TH AVE 98101 #038-06-1983 L1984 **ID** *020 †20

RALPH, David De Witt. 1959 NE PACIFIC ST, BOX 356522 98195 #005-11-1972 L1975 **PUD CCM** *012

RALSTON, James Douglas. 1730 MINOR AVE STE 1600, CENTER FOR HEALTH STUDIES 98101 #054-04-1994 L1996 **IM** *020 †20

RAMAKRISHNA, Rohan. 325 9TH AVE, HARBORVIEW MED CTR 98104 #041-01-2006 L2006 **NS** *012

RAMAKRISHNAN, Aravind. 1101 FAIRVIEW AVE N, CANCER RESEARC 98109 #033-06-2001 L2004 **ON** *100

RAMAKRISHNAN, Lalita R. 1959 NE PACIFIC ST, BOX 357242 98195 #495-23-1981 L2001 **IM** *020 †20

RAMAN, Eric Raghavan. 500 17TH AVE 98122 #054-04-1995 L1998 **IM** *020 †20

RAMENOFSKY, David Hyman. ■ 98115 #056-06-2007 L2007 **IM** *012

RAMERS, Christian Boyd. ■ 98126 #005-18-2003 L2007 **ID** *012 †55

RAMOS, Louis Ealdama. 747 BROADWAY 98122 #035-45-1999 L2002 **IM** *020 †20

RAMPERSAD, Sally E. 4800 SAND POINT WAY NE, NE W9824 98105 #917-14-1986 L2003 **AN** *100 †05

RAMSEY, Ann Elizabeth. ■ 98112 #024-01-2005 L2005 **PD** *012

RAMSEY, Bonnie. 1100 OLIVE WAY STE 500, CHILD HOSP REG MED CTR 98101 #024-01-1976 L1978 **PD PDP** *050 †55

RAMSEY, Donald Hunton. 8637 FAUNTLEROY WAY SW 98136 #005-02-1975 L1977 **AN GS** *040 †20

RAMSEY, Paul Glenn. 1959 NE PACIFIC ST, BOX 356350 98195 #024-01-1975 L1978 **IM ID** *030 †20

RAMSEY, Scott David. 4245 ROOSEVELT WAY NE, STE 354775 98105 #018-03-1990 L1990 **IM** *050 †20

RAND, Richard Pierce. UNIVERSITY OF WASHINGTON, UNIVERSITY OF WA PLAS SURG 98195 #025-01-1981 L1990 **PS** *020 †65,85

RANDHAWA, Sandeep. ■ 98115 #495-08-1998 L2007 **OPH** *012

RANGUELOV, Rostislav D. ■ 98115 #198-01-1995 L2003 **PTH** *020 †50

RANK, Joseph Paul. 1124 COLUMBIA ST, STE 200 98104 #054-04-1990 L1991 **PTH** *020 †50

RANSOM, Bruce Robt. 1959 NE PACIFIC ST, DEPT OF NEURO BOX 356465 98195 #028-02-1972 L1996 **N** *050 †75

RAO, Ashwin Laxminaraya. 4245 ROOSEVELT WAY NE, BOX 354775 98105 #038-06-2003 L2003 **FSM** *012 †18

RAO, Sujata. 825 EASTLAKE AVE E, MS G-4830 98109 #035-06-1984 L1992 **ON** *020 †20

RAPHAELI, Tal Ron. ■ 98146 #048-02-2006 L2006 **GS** *012

RAPP, David Elliot. 1100 9TH AVE, STOP G1-MSO 98101 #010-01-2001 L2007 **U** *020

RAPP, Suzanne Ellen. 1959 NE PACIFIC ST, BOX 356044 98195 #054-04-1981 L1982 **AN** *020 †05

RAPPAPORT, Harold Lee. 5606 14TH AVE NW 98107 #024-07-1981 L1987 **N P** *020 †75

RAPPORT, Richard L II. 1600 E JOHN ST 98112 #025-01-1969 L1973 **NS** *020 †25

RARDEN, Xandra Ellen. 1401 MADISON ST, STE 200 98104 #005-18-2003 L2003 **FM** *100 †18

RASCHKO, Paula K. 700 BROADWAY, DIV OF NEONATOLOGY 98122 #016-43-1975 L1987 **NPM PDC** *020 †55

RASIC, Philip John. 1229 MADISON ST STE 1040 98104 #024-05-1962 L1968 **OPH** *071 †35

RASKE, Molly Elizabeth. 1959 NE PACIFIC ST RM C212, CAMPUS BOX 356340 98195 #038-40-2001 L2003 **PDR** *012 †80

RASKIND, Murray A. 1660 S COLUMBIAN WAY # S-1 98108 #035-01-1968 L1970 **P** *050 †75

RASKIND, Wendy Herlihy. 1959 NE PACIFIC ST, MED CTR BOX 35-7720 98195 #054-04-1978 L1979 **MG IM** *050 †20

RATZLIFF, Anna M. ■ 98125 #005-15-2005 L2005 **P** *012

RAU, Natalie. 925 SENECA ST # 1930 98101 #409-06-2005 **IM** *012

RAUGI, Gregory John. 1660 S COLUMBIAN WAY, DERMTLGY-111D VA MED CTR 98108 #036-07-1975 L1979 **D** *040 †15

RAUSCHE, Melanie. 1660 S COLUMBIAN WAY, VAMC SEATTLE 98108 #038-40-2004 L2006 **FM** *100 †18

RAVE, Lelach. 4800 SAND POINT WAY NE, CHILDRENS HOSP & REG MED C 98105 #028-02-1999 L2004 **PD** *020 †55

RAVENHOLT, Reimert T. 3156 E LAURELHURST DR NE 98105 #026-04-1952 L1954 **EP IM** *071 †70

RAVINDRAN, Bipin K. UNIV OF WASHINGTON, DIVISION OF CARDIOLOGY BOX 98195 #041-02-2001 L2005 **CD** *012 †20

RAVITS, John Meyer. 1100 9TH AVE 98101 #026-08-1979 L1985 **N RO** *020 †75

RAY-FRIELE, Eleanor L. 1229 MADISON ST, STE 1450 98104 #054-04-1987 L1993 **OBG IM** *020 †30

RAYMER, Patricia Annelle. 509 OLIVE WAY, STE 900 98101 #054-04-1989 L1989 **FM** *020 †18

READ, Alexandra Elizabeth. 11027 MERIDIAN AVE N 98133 #038-06-1983 L1991 **GE IM** *020 †20

READE, Carleton W, Jr. ■ 98102 #025-01-1946 L1948 **R** *071 †55,80

REAGAN, Krista Maelynette. ■ 98102 #054-04-2008 L2008 *012

REAGAN, Tara Christine. UWMC 1959 NE PACIFIC STREE, DEPT OF ANESTHESIA BOX 356 98195 #010-02-2002 L2002 **AN** *020 †18

REARDON, Cynthia E. 10308 RAINIER AVE S 98178 #054-04-1984 L1986 **P** *012 †05

REBELES, Fidel Carrillo. UNIV HOSPITAL, DEPT OF RADIOLOGY/BOX 3571 98195 #024-01-2000 L2000 **DR** *100 †50

REDDING, Gregory James. 4800 SAND POINT WAY NE, PULMNRY DIV CHLDRNS HOSP 98105 #005-11-1974 L1980 **PD PUD** *050 †55

REDDY, Rishindra Mamidi. 1959 NE PACIFIC ST, UNIVERSITY OF WASHINGTON 98195 #016-06-2000 L2007 **TS** *012 †85 ‡

REDDY, Vijaya Kaditam. ■ 98144 #028-46-2004 L2007 **NEP** *012

REDFERN, Michael J. ■ 98199 #836-02-1966 L1977 **AN** *020

REDPATH, Allison Carrie. ■ 98105 #038-06-2004 L2007 **PN** *012 †55

REED, Emily-Rae. ■ 98112 #016-43-2004 L2007 **FM** *100

REED, May Jennifer. 325 9TH AVE 98104 #024-01-1986 L1989 **IM IMG** *050 †20

REED, Robyn Cathleen. ■ 98103 #036-07-2004 L2004 **PP** *012

REED, Steven Lee. 6669 NE WINDERMERE RD # G 98115 #054-04-1982 L1983 **HS OS** *020 †40

REED, Susan Dalton. 325 9TH AVE, DEPT OBGYN 98104 #005-11-1986 L1990 **OBG** *020 †30

REESE, Harry S. 5220 CALIFORNIA AVE SW, STE A 98136 #047-07-1972 L1989 **ORS OS** *020 †40

REESE, Thomas Vyn, Jr. 1101 MADISON ST, STE 301 98104 #005-02-1975 L1979 **IM** *020 †20

REICHENBACH, Dennis Dale. HARBORVW MED CTR, DPT PTH 98104 #054-04-1958 L1959 **ATP** *071 †50

REICHERT, Albert. 620 15TH AVE E 98112 #024-05-1961 L1964 **PD OS** *071

REICHERT, Drew David. ■ 98117 #041-01-1997 L1999 **PD** *020 †55

REID, Brian Jay. 1124 COLUMBIA ST - CL-015, FRED HUTCHINSON CANCER CTR 98104 #054-04-1980 L1982 **IM** *020 †20

REID, Jennifer Robin. 4800 SAND POINT WAY NE 98105 #054-04-1998 L2001 **PEM** *020 †55

REID, Robert John. 1730 MINOR AVE, STE 1600 98101 #060-01-1986 L2003 **PHP GP** *050 †70

REIF, Mary Ellen. 515 MINOR AVE, STE 200 98104 #018-03-1978 L1979 **N** *020 †75

REIFEL, Edward. 1100 9TH AVE, VIRGINIA MASON CLINIC 98101 #025-01-1956 L1964 **NS** *071 †25

REILLY, Dominic Francis. 1959 NE PACIFIC ST, UNIV OF WASH 98195 #054-04-1988 L1990 **IM** *020 †20

REILLY, Philip Andrew. 8720 14TH AVE S 98108 #005-02-1996 L1999 **FM** *020 †18 ‡

REIMEL, Beth Ann. PO BOX 356340, UW SCH OF MED GME PROGRAM 98195 #041-13-2002 L2002 **GS** *100 †85

REINER, Alexander Paul. 1959 NE PACIFIC ST, BOX 358080 98195 #023-07-1984 L1988 **IM PTH** *020 †20

■ = Address Information Privacy Protected

REINERTSON, Jodie Shub. 901 BOREN AVE, STE 1900 98104 #422-01-1982 L1991 **DR** *020

REISMAN, Mark. 801 BROADWAY, STE 808 98122 #550-02-1985 L1994 **IM CD** *020 †20

REISS, Paul Herbert. 200 15TH AVE E 98112 #038-06-1979 L1984 **ORS** *020 †40

REITER, Jack Martin. 1404 E YESLER WAY, STE 201 98122 #041-12-1968 L1969 **CHP P** *075

REITZ, Jennifer Nicole. ■ 98122 #046-01-2004 L2004 **GS** *012

REITZ, Megan Susanne. 1629 N 45TH ST 98103 #005-11-2002 L2004 **FM** *020 †18

REMINGTON, Jared William. 1959 NE PACIFIC ST, U OF W-HS AFFAIRS BOX 3563 98195 #054-04-2004 L2004 **IM** *100 †20

REMINGTON, John Michael. 747 BROADWAY 98122 #054-04-1969 L1970 **AN** *020 †05

REMPEL, Marcus Theodore. 8444 RAINIER AVE S 98118 #005-18-1983 L1984 **FM** *020 †18

REOUX, Joseph Paul. 1660 S COLUMBIAN WAY, VAPSHCS-116 ATC 98108 #048-14-1985 L1996 **ADP** *020 †75

RESNICK, Arthur D. 327 NW 113TH PL 98177 #024-01-1979 L1980 **CD IM** *020 †20

RESOL, Juan H. ■ 98121 #748-01-1958 L1975 **GP GS** *075

REUSSER, Pierre David. 324 LAKESIDE AVE S APT 206 98144 #869-01-1979 L1989 **ID** *100

REUTER, David Gene. 4800 SAND POINT WAY NE, SEATTLE CHILD HOS 98105 #017-20-1994 L1997 **PD** *050 †55

REYES, Maria Regina. 1959 NE PACIFIC ST, BOX 356490 98195 #041-14-1992 L1996 **PM** *020 †60

REYSIO-CRUZ, Marcelino Ga. 1959 NE PACIFIC ST, UNIV OF WA BOX 357920 98195 #748-02-1993 L2003 *020

REZVANI, Andrew R. ■ 98107 #041-13-2001 L2004 **ON** *100 †20

RHIM, Edwin Yongsoo. 1100 9TH AVE 98101 #054-04-1997 L1999 **D** *020 †20,15

RHIM, Jonathan Arch. 125 16TH AVE E, GROUP HEALTH 98112 #010-01-1989 L1997 **ATP DMP** *050 †50

RHO, Robert Woochul. 1959 NE PACIFIC ST, BOX 356422 98195 #005-12-1992 L2002 **ICE** *020 †20

RHOADES, Dorothy Alison. 925 SENECA ST, G2-GHC-VMMC 98101 #005-02-1989 L1997 **IM EP** *020 †20

RHOADS, Caroline Shipley. 325 9TH AVE BOX 359780 98104 #041-01-1989 L1989 **IM** *020 †20

RHODES-ZOROUFY, Darius S. 550 17TH AVE, STE A30 98122 #041-09-1993 L2005 **IM SME** *020

RICE, Andrew Lauren. ■ 98117 #054-04-1989 L1993 **AN** *020 †05

RICE, Damaris E Suttle. 2271 NE 51ST ST 98105 #030-05-1952 L1956 **PYA** *071

RICE, Glen Griffith. 747 BROADWAY 98122 #040-02-1942 L1950 **OBG** *071 †30

RICE, Hope Marie. 600 UNIVERSITY ST, STE 1200 98101 #056-05-1983 L1986 **FM** *020 †18

RICE, Kimball W. 600 BROADWAY, STE 170 98122 #036-07-1984 L1990 **R** *071 †80

RICHARD, Robert Edwin. 1959 NE PACIFIC ST 98195 #035-48-1992 L1996 **HEM HO** *050 †20

RICHARDS, Gail E. 4800 SAND POINT WAY NE, WAY NE/CH-65 98105 #016-06-1970 L2000 **PDE PD** *020 †55

RICHARDSON, Laura Paul. 6200 NE 74TH ST STE 210, CHILD HEALTH INSTITUTE 98115 #025-01-1994 L1998 **ADL** *020 †20,55

RICHARDSON, Londe Apolphe. ■ 98199 #008-01-1978 L1979 **DR IM** *020 †20,80,28

RICHARDSON, Michael L. 1959 NE PACIFIC ST 98195 #048-04-1975 L1982 **DR** *020 †80

RICHARDSON, Randal C. 4800 SAND POINT WAY NE, REGIONAL M 98105 #043-01-2003 L2005 **CHN** *012

RICHEY, Luther Merritt. ■ 98105 #036-01-2007 L2007 **IM** *012

RICHTER, Andrew Otto. 1401 MADISON ST STE 100 98104 #024-07-2004 L2004 **P** *020 †18

RICHTER, Evelyn Birkeland. 6533 SEAVIEW AVE NW 98117 #035-01-1958 L1967 **D** *071

RICHTER, Mary Alexandria. 901 BOREN AVE STE 1530 98104 #017-20-1966 L1971 **IM** *020 †20

RICKETT, Howard Wm. 98105 #040-02-1941 L1948 **ORS** *071 †40

RIDDELL, Duncan Alexander. 9730 3RD AVE NE, STE 210 98115 #061-01-1985 L1992 **OTO** *020 †45

RIDDELL, Kim Minard. 125 16TH AVE E 98112 #011-03-1985 L1986 **PTH** *020 †50

RIDDELL, Stanley Ralph. 1100 FAIRVIEW AVE N, N -D3-100 98109 #062-01-1979 L1986 **ON IM** *050

RIDZON, Renee. PO BOX 23350 98102 #028-34-1986 L2003 **IM ID** *050 †20

RIEDESEL, Greta Valentine. ■ 98133 #054-04-2008 *012

RIEGELS, Nicholas Andreas. ■ 98115 #005-19-2003 L2005 **PAN** *012

RIEHLE, Kimberly Jean. 1959 NE PACIFIC ST, BOX 356340 98195 #012-05-2001 L2001 **GS** *012

RIEKE, Alyson Pierce. ■ 98112 #026-04-1963 L1967 **FM** *020 †18

RIES, Richard Kirkland. 325 9TH AVE # 359911 98104 #016-06-1975 L1976 **P** *020 †75

RIFAAT, Hassan Shafik. VIRGINIA MASON HOSP, DEPT ROTAT 98101 #051-01-1988 *100

RIGGINS, Robert C K. 925 SENECA ST 98101 #035-01-1961 L1970 **CD IM** *071 †20

RIGGS, Micky Ray. 512 NEWTON ST 98109 #008-01-1992 L2000 **P** *100

RILEY, John Winchell, III. 1801 NW MARKET ST STE 212 98107 #035-20-1962 L1968 **IM N** *071 †20

RILEY, Robert Francis. ■ 98105 #051-01-2008 *012

RILEY, Robert Jos. 6521 CALIFORNIA AVE SW 98136 #054-15-1964 **FM** *071

RINGO, Shelley Rae. ■ 98144 #054-04-2004 L2004 **FM** *100 †18

RINGOLD, Sarah. ■ 98103 #024-01-2001 L2004 **PPR** *012 †55

RINN, Kristine Josephine. 1221 MADISON ST, 2ND FL ARNOLD BLDG 98104 #054-04-1992 L1992 **ON** *020 †20

RIORDAN, Robert Henry. UNITED AIRLINE SEA TAC 98158 #040-02-1958 L1989 **AM GPM** *071

RISING, Doane Motsinger. 1932 1ST AVE, STE 600A 98101 #054-04-1994 L1996 **P PYA** *020 †75

RISK, Michael Christopher. ■ 98103 #016-11-2003 L2003 **U** *012

RISSE, Kathy Akers. 1100 9TH AVE G1-MSO, VIRGINIA MASON MEDICAL CEN 98101 #054-04-1997 L1999 **PD** *020 †50

RITTENBERG, Steven Wade. 600 UNIVERSITY ST, STE 1200 98101 #005-15-1993 L1993 **IM** *020 †20

RIVARA, Frederick Peter. 325 9TH AVE BOX 359960 98104 #041-01-1974 L1978 **PD** *040 †55

RIVERO, Maria Delosange. ■ 98103 #016-02-1991 L1996 **DR** *100 †80

RIVIN, Beth Ellen. 4800 SAND POINT WAY NE 98105 #036-08-1982 L1994 **PD GPM** *020 †55

RIVKIN, Saul Eugene. 1221 MADISON ST 2ND FL, ARNOLD PAVILION 98104 #054-04-1964 L1965 **ON** *020 †20

RIX, Donald Blake. 2201 3RD AVE, APT 1704 98121 #065-06-1957 L1979 **PTH** *030

RIX, Emily Parker. 747 BROADWAY, BETH ISRAEL DEACONESS MEDI 98122 #012-05-2004 L2007 **IM** *100 ‡

ROACH, Jared Carter. 1441 N 34TH ST, INSTITUTE FOR SYSTEM BIO 98103 #054-04-1999 L2001 IM *050

ROAN, Florence. ■ 98112 #012-05-2003 L2007 **ID** *012 †20

ROBACHINSKI, Chester Mark. 818 12TH AVE 98122 #041-13-1987 L1990 **P** *020

ROBBINS, Frances. 509 OLIVE WAY, STE 1233-35 98101 #028-02-1955 L1958 **P AN** *071 †05,75

ROBERTS, Arthur. ■ 98125 #035-09-1955 L1984 **AN** *071 †05

ROBERTS, James Michael. 1124 COLUMBIA ST 98104 #035-01-1984 L1984 **OS** *100

ROBERTS, Jessie Marie. ■ 98103 #026-04-2007 L2007 **FP** *012

ROBERTS, Joan. 4800 SAND POINT WAY NE, MEDICAL CENTER 98105 #031-01-1992 L1992 **CCP** *020 †55

ROBERTS, John Warren. 1100 9TH AVE 98101 #040-02-1987 L2000 **N** *020 †75

ROBERTS, Lloyd Andrew. 1959 NE PACIFIC ST, UNIVERSITY OF WASHINGTON M 98195 #035-47-1991 L1994 **IM** *020 †20

ROBERTS, Paul Parker. 747 BROADWAY 98122 #005-11-1982 L1986 **P** *020 †20,75

ROBERTS, Zachary Vaughn. ■ 98101 #039-01-2002 L2007 **ORS** *100

ROBERTSON, Cassandra. 1959 NE PACIFIC ST, BOX 356500 98195 #060-02-1996 L2003 **HS** *020

ROBERTSON, H Thomas. 1959 NE PACIFIC ST, UNIV HOSP-BOX 356522 98195 #024-01-1968 L1970 **PUD CCM** *040 †20

ROBERTSON, John Wilbur. 900 TERRY AVE, STE 100 98104 #048-13-1974 L1981 **FM GPM** *020

ROBERTSON, Roderick Paul. 720 BROADWAY 98122 #030-06-1964 L1970 **DIA END** *050 †20,75

ROBERTSON, William O. 155 NE 100TH ST STE 400, WASHINGTON POISON CENTER 98125 #035-45-1949 L1963 **PD PDT** *071 †55

ROBILIO, Peter Andrew. PO BOX 356460, 1550 NE PACIFIC ST 98195 #005-19-2002 L2006 **OBG** *100

ROBINSON, David Hallock. 1100 9TH AVE G1-MSO, VIRGINIA MASON MED CTR 98101 #054-04-1991 L1991 **DR** *020 †80

ROBINSON, David Mc Kinney. 1100 9TH AVE G1-MSO, VIRGINIA MASON MEDICAL CEN 98101 #028-34-1983 L1984 **AI IM** *020 †20,03

ROBINSON, Douglas P. 2910 E MADISON ST 98112 #049-01-1976 L1977 **P** *075 †75

ROBINSON, James Patrick. 4245 ROOSEVELT WAY NE, STE 354775 98105 #005-14-1978 L1979 **PM PME** *050 †60

ROBINSON, John C. ■ 98105 #025-01-1946 L1953 **IM OS** *071 †20

ROBINSON, Lawrence Allan. ■ 98115 #054-04-1972 L1973 **EM** *020

ROBINSON, Lawrence R. 325 9TH AVE, HARBORVIEW MED CTR 98104 #048-04-1982 L1989 **PM** *020 †60

ROBINSON, Lillian Harris. ■ 98103 #021-01-1942 L1943 **P PYA** *071 †75

ROBINSON, Raymond Paul. 1100 9TH AVE G1-MSO, VIRGINIA MASON MEDICAL CEN 98101 #035-01-1975 L1981 **ORS** *020 †20

ROBLES, David Thomas. UNIV OF WASHINGTON MED CTR, DIV OF DERMATOLOGY BOX 356 98195 #005-06-2004 L2005 **D** *012

ROCKHILL, Carol Mary. 1959 NE PACIFIC ST, BOX 365650 98195 #016-11-2000 L2002 **CHP** *100 †75

ROCKHILL, Jason King. 1959 NE PACIFIC ST BOX 356, UWMC CANCER CENTER 98195 #016-11-1998 L2002 **RO** *100 †80

ROCKWELL, James C. 801 BROADWAY STE 927 98122 #010-01-1981 L1985 **OTO FPS** *020 †45

RODLER, Eve Therese. 825 EASTLAKE AVE E G3-63, BOX 19 98109 #010-01-1997 L2007 **HO** *020 †20

RODRIGUES, Patricia A. 10330 MERIDIAN AVE N, STE 200 98133 #043-01-1988 L1994 **OBG** *020 †30

RODRIGUEZ, Amy Erin. ■ 98165 #054-04-2007 L2007 **FP** *012

RODRIQUEZ, Arthur Alfred. 1660 S COLUMBIAN WAY, REHABILITATION MEDICINE SR 98108 #056-05-1972 L1997 **PM** *040 †60

ROE, Elaine Bolling. 600 UNIVERSITY ST, STE 1200 98101 #021-01-2000 L2003 **FM** *020 †18

ROEDEL, Eric John. ■ 98122 #054-04-2002 L2002 **FM** *020 †18

ROEDEL, Robert Francois. 747 BROADWAY 98122 #056-06-1946 L1947 **R** *071 †80

ROESEL, David John. 325 9TH AVE, DEPT 359702 98104 #005-11-1996 L1999 **IM** *020 †20

ROETMAN, Karen Jo. 1100 9TH AVE 98101 #018-03-1985 L1991 **APM** *020 †05

ROGERS, James Virgil, III. 1229 MADISON ST, STE 1150 98104 #012-05-1975 L1976 **DR** *020 †80

ROGERS, Keith Lindsay. 1660 S COLUMBIAN WAY, MENTAL HEALTH 116 MHC 98108 #018-03-1982 L1992 **P** *050 †75

ROGERS, Sarah Elizabeth. ■ 98103 #036-01-2006 L2006 **IM** *012

ROGERS, Shawn Erica. 9730 3RD AVE NE, STE 210 98115 #030-06-1994 L1999 **OTO** *020 †45

ROGERS, Terry Reid. ■ 98177 #035-20-1966 L1967 **ADM PUD** *100 †80

ROGERSON, Lynne. 1001 SW KLICKITAT WAY #205, PATHOLOGY 98134 #045-01-1989 L1993 **PTH** *020 †50

ROGGE, Janet Louise. 509 OLIVE WAY STE 1259 98101 #054-04-1974 L1975 **D** *020 †15

ROGGE, Leland Edgar. 2409 N 45TH ST, FIRST HILL ORTHOPEADIC CTR 98103 #028-02-1966 L1967 **ORS** *020 †40

ROHRMANN, Chas Albert, Jr. 1959 NE PACIFIC ST, MSC 359300 98195 #054-04-1966 L1971 **DR** *020 †80

ROLING, Gerald Thos. ■ 98199 #056-06-1960 L1979 **IM GE** *072 †20

ROLLER, Mark Franklin. 200 15TH AVE E, DIV OF UROLOGY 98112 #054-04-1969 L1970 **U** *071 †95

ROMANO, Robert Leonard. 1600 E JEFFERSON ST, JEFFERSON MEDICAL TOWER 98122 #028-34-1948 L1949 **ORS** *071 †40

ROMBOUTS, Otto Ralf. 4000 AURORA AVE N # NO-103 98103 #660-03-1957 L1961 **AN PUD** *071

ROMEO, Pasquale Matthew. 2 NICKERSON ST STE 304 98109 #561-10-1965 L2000 **P** *020 †75

ROMERO, Colin Anthony. 10501 MERIDIAN AVE N, NORTH PUBLIC HEALTH CENTER 98133 #010-03-1971 L1977 **FM PHP** *020 †18

ROMERO-DELGADO, Oscar. 1120 CHERRY ST STE 240 98104 #264-05-1966 L1983 **P PYA** *020 †75

ROMM, Sharon. 325 9TH AVE, HARBORVIEW MED CTR 98104 #024-05-1972 L1996 **P** *020 †65,75

RONGITSCH, Jessica Ann. 1930 POST ALY 98101 #026-04-1998 L2001 **IM** *020 †20

ROOS, Carlton Friedrich. ■ 98103 #047-05-1986 L1996 **DR** *020 †80

ROPER, Embra Arthur. 1145 BROADWAY 98122 #012-01-1981 L1991 **PUD IM** *020 †20

ROPER, Martha H. 1455 NW LEARY WAY, # PATH 98107 #035-19-1980 L1981 **IM** *020 †20

RORABACK, Jenny Heidi. ■ 98115 #054-04-2007 L2007 **IM** *012

ROSE, Andrew Brent. ■ 98107 #054-04-2008 *012

ROSE, Caroline Rose. 1200 12TH AVE S 98144 #025-01-1998 L2000 **FM** *020 †18

ROSE, Mary Hodgson. 500 17TH AVE 98122 #005-11-1969 L1978 **AI FM** *020 †18

ROSEN, Eric Laurence. 1107 NE 45TH ST, STE 440 98105 #005-02-1991 L2005 **DR** *020 †80

ROSEN, Gary David. 1801 NW MARKET ST, STE 203 98107 #035-19-1975 L1976 **FM** *020 †18

ROSEN, Henry. 1959 NE PACIFIC ST 98195 #035-45-1972 L1973 **ID IM** *050 †20

ROSEN, Sheldon Neil. 125 16TH AVE E, CSB 2 - 2ND FLOOR 98112 #038-06-1967 L1970 **GE** *020 †20

ROSENBAUM, David Michael. 4800 SAND POINT WAY NE, DEPT OF RADIOLOGY 5C-1 98105 #035-46-1977 L1983 **PDR DR** *020 †80

ROSENBERG, Abby R. ■ 98115 #005-11-2006 L2006 **PD** *012

ROSENBLATT, Roger Alan. 1959 NE PACIFIC ST, BOX 354696 98195 #024-01-1971 L1972 **FM PHP** *040 †18

ROSENFELD, Margaret. 4800 SAND POINT WAY NE #024-01-1988 L1990 **PDP** *020 †55

ROSENSTOCK, Linda. 325 9TH AVE, UNIVERSITY OF WASHINGTON, 98104 #023-07-1977 L1978 **OM IM** *020 †20,70

ROSENTHAL, Norman Ronald. 1100 9TH AVE, VIRGINIA MASON MEDICAL CEN 98101 #041-02-1978 L1987 **END IM** *020 †20

ROSHAL, Mikhail Z. PATHOLOGY RES PROGRAM, UNIV OF WASHINGTON BOX 356 98195 #035-45-2005 L2005 **PTH** *012

ROSHANRAVAN, Baback. ■ 98115 #016-06-2005 L2005 **IM** *012

ROSIN, Richard A. 901 BOREN AVE, STE 702 98104 #917-14-1988 L1999 **P** *020 †75

ROSINSKI, Steven Lawrence. PO BOX 356421, UNIV OF WASHINGTON 98195 #007-02-2005 L2006 **IM** *012

ROSS, Andrew Scott. 1100 9TH AVE STOP G1, UNIV OF CHICAGO HOSPITALS 98101 #035-47-2000 L2007 **GE** *100 †02

ROSS, Anita Erin. 521 WALL ST 98121 #054-04-1983 L1984 **FM** *020 †18

ROSS, Brian Kent. 4714 UNIVERSITY VIEW PL NE 98105 #054-04-1983 L1984 **AN** *020 †05

ROSS, Donald Jay. 2271 NE 51ST ST 98105 #048-13-1974 L1983 **P PYA** *020 †75

ROSS, Vernon Frank. 521 WALL ST 98121 #027-01-1965 L1968 **GP FM** *020 †18,16

ROSSE, Cornelius. PO BOX 357420, BIOLOGICAL STRUCTURE 98195 #917-02-1964 **OS** *030

ROSSI, Ralph A. 1145 BROADWAY 98122 #005-18-1991 L1993 **IM EP** *020 †20

ROSTAD, Steven Wayne. 550 17TH AVE, STE 300 98122 #054-04-1983 L1987 **ATP NP** *020 †50

ROTER, Bradley Scott. 500 19TH AVE E, CLINIC 98112 #028-02-1986 L1989 **FM** *020 †18

ROTH, Christian L.. 4800 SAND POINT WAY NE 98105 #409-10-1990 L2006 **END** *100

ROTH, Gerald James. 1660 S COLUMBIAN WAY, SEATTLE VAMC 111 MED 98108 #024-01-1967 L1968 **HEM OS** *050 †20

ROTH, Gilbert Jos. ■ 98112 #016-43-1955 L1956 **ATP DMP** *071 †50

ROTH, Gregory. 1959 NE PACIFIC ST RM C2, CAMPUS BOX 356340 98195 #043-01-2002 L2002 **IM** *020 †20

ROTHBLATT, Alan Barry. 1100 9TH AVE C1-MSO, VIRGINIA MASON MEDICAL CEN 98101 #005-18-1983 L1987 **OBG** *020 †30

ROTHENBERG, Michael Bruce. ■ 98105 #038-06-1954 L1967 **CHP** *071 †75

ROTHENFLUCH, Michael Dean. ■ 98103 #030-06-2007 L2007 **P** *012

ROTHMIER, Justin Dale. 1551 NW 54TH ST, THE SPORT MEDICINE CLINIC 98107 #054-04-2002 L2005 **FM** *020 †18

ROTKIS, Walter Molden. 1221 MADISON ST STE 1420 98104 #016-11-1972 L1978 **OPH IM** *020 †20,35

ROUTT, Milton L, Jr. 325 9TH AVE, BOX 359798 98104 #048-02-1983 L1988 **ORS TS** *020 †40

ROWBERG, Alan Hardy. 2324 EASTLAKE AVE E, STE 500 98102 #054-04-1970 L1982 **OS** *050

ROWINSKY, Peter Alexander. ■ 98102 #041-01-2007 L2007 **PD** *012

ROWLAND, John Paul. 1600 E JOHN ST 98112 #917-10-1977 L1992 **OTO** *020 †45

ROXBY, Alison Christina. ■ 98107 #054-01-2003 L2006 **ID** *012 †20

ROY, Millie Snigdha. ■ 98102 #024-16-2004 L2007 **IM** *100 †20

ROYAL, Philip Wayne. 1100 9TH AVE 98101 #036-01-1989 L2000 **IM** *020 †20

ROY-BYRNE, Peter. 325 9TH AVE, BOX 359911 98104 #024-07-1978 L1986 **P** *050 †75

ROYS, David Shannon. 901 BOREN AVE STE 200 98104 #054-04-1964 L1968 **P** *020 †75

ROYS, Harvey Curtis, Jr. ■ 98119 #039-01-1943 L1947 **D** *071 †15

RUBENFELD, Gordon David. 325 9TH AVE, # 10EH25 98104 #041-02-1987 L1991 **IM** *020 †20

RUBENS, Craig Edward. 1900 9TH AVE 8TH FL, CHILDRENS HOSP & MED CENTE 98101 #054-04-1982 L1983 **ID PD** *050 †55

RUBENS, Daniel David. 4800 SAND POINT WAY NE, ANESTHESIOLOGY/ CH-05. 98105 #143-07-1992 L1999 **AN** *020

RUBENS, Loretta Van. 100 W HARRISON ST, STE 330, S TOWER 98119 #008-01-1984 L1985 **P PYA** *020 †75

RUBENSTEIN, Carrie Beth. 1401 MADISON ST, STE 100 98104 #033-06-2002 L2004 **FPG** *100 †18

RUBENSTEIN, Simeon Asher. 1600 E JOHN ST 98112 #016-11-1967 L1972 **CD IM** *030 †20

RUBIN, Cyrus E. 2324 EASTLAKE AVE E, STE 500 98102 #024-01-1945 L1954 **GE** *072 †20

RUBIN, William David. 2228 40TH AVE E 98112 #028-02-1988 L1993 **ON** *020 †20

RUBIN, William David. 98112 #054-04-1981 L1993 **PS** *071 †65

RUBINSON, Lewis. 325 9TH AVE, CAMPUS BOX 359762 98104 #016-06-1997 L2006 **PCC** *100 †20

RUBY, Jeanette Elizabeth. ■ 98112 #016-42-1978 L1990 **FM** *020 †18

RUDD, Thomas Geo. ■ 98102 #025-01-1963 L1969 **DR NM** *020 †20,28,80

RUDDY, Ginger Rae. 1200 12TH AVE S 98144 #048-04-2001 L2001 **FM** *020

RUDNICK, Sarah Lenore. 521 WALL ST 98121 #016-43-2001 L2004 **FM** *020 †55

RUDOLF, Gregory David. 550 16TH AVE, STE 100 98122 #041-02-2000 L2002 **FM** *020 †18

RUDOLPH, Rebecca Evonne. 1660 S COLUMBIAN WAY, 5-111-PCC 98108 #054-04-1992 L1995 **IM** *020 †20

RUDOLPH, Robert Herman. 1100 9TH AVE 98101 #041-01-1962 L1966 **ON IM** *071 †20

RUHLMAN, Scott David. PO BOX 356340, 1959 N E PACIFIC ST 98195 #038-43-2004 L2004 **ORS** *012

RULYAK, Stephen James. 1959 NE PACIFIC ST, BOX 356424 98195 #041-01-1997 L2000 **GE** *020 †20

RUNCHEY, Shauna Suzanne. ■ 98118 #026-04-2003 L2003 **IM** *100 †20

RUPKE, Tracy Dawn. 325 9TH AVE BOX 359798, HARBORVIEW MEDICAL CENTER 98104 #065-05-2001 L2007 **ORS** *020

RUPP, Stephen Mitchell. 1100 9TH AVE G1-MSO 98101 #025-01-1978 L1986 **AN** *020 †05

RUSSELL, David Wm. 1959 NE PACIFIC ST, BOX 357720 98195 #035-20-1989 L1992 **HEM** *020 †20

RUSSELL, Kenneth John. 1959 NE PACIFIC ST, UNIV OF WASH 98195 #024-01-1979 L1985 **RO** *050 †80

RUSSELL, Mai Theresa. 1200 12TH AVE S, INLAND IMAGING ASSOCIATES, 98144 #028-34-2001 L2002 **RNR** *020 †80

RUSSELL, Nina Devol. 1959 NE PACIFIC ST, MSC 359300 98195 #038-06-1993 L2000 **IM** *020 †20

RUSSELL-TRONOLONE, Penny. ■ 98121 #010-02-1977 L2004 **ADL** *020 †55

RUSSO, Anthony John. 325 9TH AVE BOX 359798, HARBORVIEW MEDICAL CENTER 98104 #010-01-1998 L2006 **ORS** *020

RUSTON, Delaney Constance. 4245 ROOSEVELT WAY NE, BOX 354760 98105 #005-11-1995 L2003 **IM** *020

RUTHRAUFF, Michael. 5000 30TH AVE NE, STE 105 98105 #021-01-1978 L1988 **P** *020 †75

RUTLEDGE, Joe Cathey. 4800 SAND PNT NE #C5371 98105 #047-05-1976 L1977 **PTH PP** *020 †50

RUTTER, Carolyn Jill. 1959 NE PACIFIC ST, GME C212 OX-356340 98195 #056-06-2002 L2002 **IM** *100

RUVALCABA, Alberto. ■ 98103 #054-04-2008 *012

RYAN, Alisse Michele. 1100 9TH AVE, (MAIL STOP: G1-MSO) 98101 #054-04-1998 L2001 **IM** *020 †20

RYAN, John Austin, Jr. 1100 9TH AVE, MASON CLNC 98101 #025-01-1969 L1977 **GS CRS** *020 †85

RYAN, Michael Jos. 325 9TH AVE, BOX 359764 98104 #025-01-1986 L1989 **NEP** *020 †20

RYAN, Robert John. 521 WALL ST 98121 #028-34-1962 L1968 **OBG** *071 †30

RYNEARSON, Edward King. 1118 9TH AVE 98101 #038-06-1965 L1971 **P** *020 †75

SABATH, Daniel Eliot. 1959 NE PACIFIC ST, MSC 359300 98195 #041-01-1989 L1991 **PTH** *020 †50

SABATH, Diana Hausman. 1959 NE PACIFIC ST, RM -10 98195 #041-01-1989 L1991 **HEM** *020 †20

SACHS, Bernice Cohen. 1730 MINOR AVE, METROPOLITAN PARK II 98101 #025-01-1942 L1949 **P** *072

SACHTER, Elaine Faith. 1100 9TH AVE 98101 #040-02-1985 L1989 **IM** *020 †20

SACK, John Thomas. 600 BROADWAY, SEATTLE HAND SURGERY 98122 #041-02-1966 L1968 **HS ORS** *020 †40

SACKS, Lili Ann. 515 MINOR AVE STE 300, MINOR & JAMES MEDICAL PLLC 98104 #016-02-1990 L1990 **IM** *020 †20

SAFRIN, Maurice J H. ■ 98125 #035-09-1953 L1995 **IM** *071 †20

SAHI, Gurinder Pal. 10330 MERIDIAN AVE N, STE 230 98133 #495-29-1987 L1998 **IM** *020 †20

SAHIN, Hakan. 1959 NE PACIFIC ST, BOX 357115 98195 #902-03-1997 L2002 *100

SAILER, Joachim F. 200 16TH AVE E 98112 #407-10-1955 L1962 **DR** *020 †80

SAINI, Monica Harvant. ■ 98109 #016-01-2001 L2007 **DR** *020 †80

SAINT CLAIR, Mary M. 8313 AURORA AVE N 98103 #054-04-1986 L1988 **FM OS** *020

SAITTA, Joseph Chas. 1101 MADISON ST STE 301, PACMED CLINICS 98104 #005-06-1983 L1985 **IM END** *020 †20

SAKATA, Vicki Lynn. 600 UNIVERSITY ST, STE 1200 98101 #007-02-1989 L1989 **PD EM** *020 †55,16

SAKOWITZ, Oliver Werner. 1959 NE PACIFIC ST RM C212, UNIV OF WASHINGTON SOM 98195 #409-36-1996 L2001 *100

SALAMA, Samy Mikhail. 5300 TALLMAN AVE NW, SWEDISH MEDICAL CENTER 98107 #915-03-1958 L1975 **AN** *020 †05

SALAZAR, Lupe G. 815 MERCER ST, BOX 358050 98109 #026-04-1996 L1999 **HEM** *020 †20

SALAZAR, Marco Antonio. 1959 NE PACIFIC ST BOX 35, WASHINGTON UROLO 98195 #008-01-2004 L2004 **U** *012

SALE, George Edgar. 825 EASTLAKE AVE E # G1309 98109 #005-11-1968 L1974 **PTH HEM** *020 †50

SALEM, Leon. 1959 NE PACIFIC ST, DEPT OF GENERAL SURGERY 98195 #550-01-1995 L2004 **GS** *100

SALERNO, Carol L. 10330 MERIDIAN AVE N, STE 200 98133 #005-18-1999 L2003 **OBG** *020 †30

SALERNO, Jack Christian. 4800 SAND POINT WAY NE, MAIL STOP W-4841 98105 #005-18-1996 L2003 **PDC** *020 †55

SALIMAN, Joshua Adam. 1145 BROADWAY 98122 #007-02-1999 L2003 **PCC** *020 †20

SALIMAN, Laurel Hanck. 1101 MADISON ST, STE 800 98104 #007-02-1997 L2003 **OP** *020 †40

SALINAS, Francis Victor. 1100 9TH AVE G1-MSO, VIRGINIA MASON MEDICAL CEN 98101 #016-11-1992 L1992 **AN** *020 †20,05

SALTONSTALL, Kent. 325 9TH AVE 98104 #035-01-1968 L1975 **ORS** *062 †40

SALUJA, Sunil Kumar. 3626 NE 45TH ST, STE 300 98105 #041-01-1995 L1998 **NPM** *050 †55

SALZER, Charles Eugene. 1001 SW KLICKITAT WAY, STE 205 98134 #038-40-1960 L1964 **PTH** *071 †50

SAMAVEDI, Sundara Rajan. 10416 5TH AVE NE 98125 #495-36-1995 L2002 **IM** *020 †20

SAMII, Ali. 1959 NE PACIFIC ST, MSC 359300 98195 #067-01-1989 L1998 **N** *020 †75

SAMII, Ali Mehraban. 1959 NE PACIFIC ST, DEPT OF NEUROLOGY 359775 98195 #041-13-1965 L1967 **TS** *020 †85,90

SAMMER, Marla B K. 1959 NE PACIFIC ST, BOX 356340 98195 #012-05-2003 L2004 **DR** *012

SAMPATACOS, Nels Evan. ■ 98121 #003-01-2007 L2007 **ORS** *012

SAMSON, Anna Lissa. PO BOX 356421, UNIV OF WASHINGTON 98195 #040-02-2006 L2006 **IM** *012

SAMSON, Gregory Teodel. ■ 98146 #035-08-1992 L1996 **P** *020

SAMSON, Werner Edgar. 1959 NE PACIFIC ST, BOX 356171 98195 #054-04-1953 L1954 **CD** *040 †20

SANDE, Merle Alden. 325 9TH AVE, BOX 359931 98104 #054-04-1965 L2005 **ID IM** *030 †20

SANDERS, Benjamin Lee. 500 5TH AVE 6W, JAIL HEALTH SVCS 98104 #038-41-1994 L2001 **FM** *020 †18 ‡

SANDERS, Don Brunell. ■ 98105 #016-06-2003 L2006 **PDP** *012 †55

SANDERS, Jean E Mc Kinnie. 1100 FAIRVIEW AVE N D5-280, HUTCHINSON CANCER RES CTR 98109 #018-03-1970 L1976 **PHO PD** *020 †55

SANDERSON, Scott Richard. ■ 98105 #054-04-2008 *012

SANDISON, Taylor Gordon. 7342 18TH AVE NW, UNIVERSITY OF WASHINGTON 98117 #054-04-2001 L2005 **ID** *012 †20

SANDLER, Andrew Seth. 1191 2ND AVE, STE 1000 98101 #035-47-1990 L1997 **ON** *020 †20

SANDLER, Netanya Golda. GRADUATE MEDICAL ED BOX 35, UNIVERSITY OF WASHINGTON 98195 #048-04-2003 L2003 **ID** *012 †20

SANDMAIER, Brenda M. 1100 FAIRVIEW AVE N, FHCR 98109 #060-02-1983 L1985 **ON HEM** *050 †20

SANDMAN, Beth Mac Gregor. 1600 E OLIVE ST 98122 #056-06-1986 L1988 **P** *020 †75

SANDNES, Diana Lee. ■ 98115 #054-04-2006 L2007 **AN** *012

SANDS, Julie Rae. 521 WALL ST A, GROUP HEALTH 98121 #007-02-1990 L1994 **IM** *020 †20

SANDSTROM, Claire Kalsch. ■ 98115 #036-07-2006 L2007 **DR** *012

SANETO, Russell P. 4800 SAND POINT WAY NE, CHILDREN'S HOSP & REG MED 98105 #018-75-1994, ▲ L2001 **CN CHN** *020 †75,55

SANFORD, Christopher A. BOX354410, HALL HEALTH UNIV OF WASHIN 98195 #005-18-1985 L1990 **FM EM** *020 †18

SANFORD, Robert Leslie. 515 MINOR AVE STE 200 98104 #016-02-1975 L1976 **GE IM** *020 †20

SANGEORZAN, Bruce Jos. 325 9TH AVE, ORTHO ZA-48 98104 #025-07-1981 L1986 **ORS** *020 †40

SAN JUAN, Victoria Louise. 1660 S COLUMBIAN WAY 98108 #035-47-1991 L1991 **IM** *020 †20

SANO, Yuko. 4800 SAND POINT WAY NE, MAILSTOP W9824 98105 #016-02-2002 L2006 **PAN** *100 †05

SANTIESTEBAN, Jos Angel. ■ 98121 #308-07-1981 L1985 **IM** *020

SANTOS, Felipe. 1959 NE PACIFIC ST 356340, UW SCHOOL OF MEDICINE 98195 #035-20-2002 L2002 **OTO** *012

SAPERSTEIN, David Alan. 1221 MADISON ST, STE 1002 98104 #041-14-1987 L2000 **OPH** *020 †35

SARANTINOS, George A. 747 BROADWAY 98122 #038-44-1989 L1993 **AN** *020 †05

SARATHY, Priya. 900 TERRY AVE, SEATTLE SURGERY CENTER 98104 #495-59-1992 L2000 **AN** *020 †05

SARGENT, Paul R. ■ 98136 #054-15-1964 L1966 **GP** *071

SARJEANT-TUGGY, Peggy. 1100 9TH AVE # M6-AC, VIRGINIA MASON MEDICAL CTR 98101 #048-04-1987 L1989 **PD** *020 †55

SARMAH, Anita. 1959 NE PACIFIC ST, BOX 356540 98195 #917-08-1991 L2001 **AN** *100

SASAKI, April Katsuko. ■ 98112 #014-01-1976 L1992 **GP** *020 †16

SASSO, Eric Harry. ■ 98105 #005-18-1980 L1984 **RHU IM** *050 †20

SATAVA, Richard M, Jr. 1959 NE PACIFIC ST #356410, UNIVERSITY OF WASHINGTON 98195 #041-09-1968 L2002 **GS AM** *020

SATHYANARAYANA, Sheela. 325 9TH AVE, DEPARTMENT OF PEDIATRICS 98104 #005-06-2002 L2002 **PD** *020 †55

SATO, Holly Reimeinikk. ■ 98107 #054-04-2008 *012

SAUER, Tatum Majel. 747 BROADWAY STE 731, SWEDISH MED CTR FIRST HILL 98122 #054-04-2006 L2006 **AN** *012

SAUNDERS, David Richard. 1959 NE PACIFIC ST, BOX 356424 98195 #067-01-1957 L1966 **GE** *040

SAUNDERS, Robert Clarence. 10330 MERIDIAN AVE N, SEATTLE ARTHRITIS CLINIC 98133 #010-01-1967 L1985 **IM CD** *020

SAUNTRY, John Philip. ■ 98115 #054-04-1951 L1955 **GS TS** *071 †85

SAUTER, Hansjoerg. ■ 98177 #407-16-1953 L1959 **IM** *071 †20

SAUVAGE, Lester Rosaire. 528 18TH AVE 98122 #028-34-1948 L1951 **TS GS** *071 †85,90

SAUVAGE, Lester Rosaire. 515 MINOR AVE 98104 #028-34-1983 L1990 **IMG IM** *020 †20

SAWIN, Robert Stanford. 4800 SAND POINT WAY NE, CHILDREN'S HOSPITAL MED CT 98105 #041-12-1982 L1987 **PDS** *020 †85

SAWYER, Tom K. 700 BROADWAY, NORTHWEST KIDNEY CENTER 98122 #047-05-1962 L1967 **NEP** *030

SAXBERG, Bror V H. ■ 98105 #024-01-1990 *100

SAXON, Andrew J. 1660 S COLUMBIAN WAY, MS 116 ATC 98108 #024-07-1977 L1978 **P OS** *020 †75

SAYLOR, Kent Douglas. 4800 SAND POINT WAY NE, CH-30 98105 #005-11-1994 L1996 **PD** *020 †55

SAYSON, Kirsten Joy. ■ 98115 #054-04-2008 *012

SCANGA, Andrew Ernest. ■ 98101 #036-01-2002 L2005 **GE** *012 †20

SCARBOROUGH, Thomas E. ■ 98109 #038-41-2003 L2006 **AI** *012 †55

SCARDAPANE, Jos Nicholas. 1101 MADISON ST, SWEDISH FAMILY MEDICINE 98104 #035-08-1964 L1966 **FM FPG** *071 †18

SCEARCE, Timothy Andrew. 201 16TH AVE E CMBO-640, GROUP HEALTH COOPERATIVE 98112 #010-02-1988 L1990 **N** *020 †75

SCHALLER, Robert Thos, Jr. 4800 SAND POINT WAY NE, BOX C-5371 98105 #024-01-1960 L1965 **PDS GS** *040 †85

SCHARENBERG, Andrew Mark. 4800 SAND POINT WAY NE 98105 #036-01-1990 L2000 **PD** *050 †55

SCHEELE, Leonard Andrew. 325 9TH AVE 98104 #010-02-1980 L1984 **P N** *020

SCHEER, Diane Lee. ■ 98115 #041-02-2008 *012

SCHEFFER, Jonathan L. ■ 98116 #005-19-1997 L2005 **FM** *020 †18

SCHELL, Barbara Jean. 601 N 34TH ST, STE C 98103 #017-20-1988 L1996 **OS D** *020 †15

SCHENDEL, Eric Gordon. 1550 N 115TH ST 98133 #048-04-1976 L1981 **EM FM** *020 †75,18

SCHENKMAN, Kenneth Aron. 4800 SAND POINT WAY NE, CHILDREN'S HOSPITAL B-9524 98105 #017-20-1986 L1990 **AN** *020 †55

SCHEPP, Sara Kay. ■ 98107 #054-04-2006 L2006 **IM** *012

SCHEVE, Carolyn Johanna. 1926 FAIRVIEW AVE E # 305 98102 #054-04-1983 L1987 **GP** *020

SCHEVE, Dawn Annjeanette. 1229 MADISON ST, STE 1500 98104 #054-04-1998 L2002 **OBG** *020 †30

SCHIFF, Melissa Ann. 2001 E MADISON ST 98122 #025-01-1987 L1999 **OBG** *020 †30

SCHIFF, Stanley R. 1570 N 115TH ST, STE 16 98133 #035-46-1980 L1988 **N** *020 †75

SCHIMMELBUSCH, Werner H. 4033 E MADISON ST, STE 204 98112 #054-04-1962 L1964 **PYA CHP** *020

SCHINZINGER, Barbara Anne. 1600 E JOHN ST 98112 #005-18-1987 L1989 **FM** *020 †18

SCHLAGEL, Helen Jones. ■ 98117 #019-02-1953 L1956 **OM GP** *075

SCHLANSKY, Barry Lee. PO BOX 356421, UNIV OF WASHINGTON 98195 #041-02-2006 L2006 **IM** *012

SCHLENKER, Christine M. 1959 NE PACIFIC ST, UNIV OF WA SCH MED 98195 #047-05-2002 L2006 **GE** *012 †20

SCHLENKER, James David, Jr. ■ 98112 #041-01-1999 L1999 **HSO** *012 †85

SCHLENKER, Robert Eric. 1959 NE PACIFIC ST, BOX 356340 98195 #016-43-2003 L2007 **PS** *012

SCHLEYER, Anneliese M. 325 9TH AVE, BOX 359780 98104 #054-04-1999 L2001 **IM** *020 †20

SCHMALE, Gregory Arthur. 4800 SAND PONT WAY NE W580 98105 #054-04-1994 L2000 **ORS** *020 †40

SCHMECHEL, Stephen C. 325 9TH AVE, PATHOLOGY BOX 359791 98104 #026-04-1997 L1998 **PCP** *100 †50

SCHMER, Gottfried. UNIV WASH DEPT LAB MED, SB 10 98115 #154-07-1956 L1988 **HEM CLP** *071

SCHMIDEK, Alexandra K. 1100 9TH AVE, VIRGINIA MASON MEDICAL CEN 98101 #032-01-2000 L2006 **PS** *100 †65

SCHMIDT, Elizabeth K. 1650 NE 115TH ST 98125 #054-04-1980 L1982 **PTH** *020 †50

SCHMIDT, Rodney Alan. 1959 NE PACIFIC ST, MSC 359300 98195 #054-04-1984 L1985 **ATP** *020 †50

SCHMIEDL, Udo Paul. 600 BROADWAY, STE 170 98122 #409-10-1982 L1989 **R** *020 †80

SCHMIT, Alison Lea. ■ 98105 #036-07-2007 L2007 **PD** *012

SCHMIT, Berndt Philip. 4510 SW HEMLOCK WAY 98136 #024-07-1991 L1998 **R** *020 †80

SCHMITT, Nicole Cherie. ■ 98144 #028-02-2006 L2006 **OTO** *012

SCHMITT, Susan Close. 3213 EASTLAKE AVE E APT A 98102 #041-09-1994 L1995 **PM** *020 †60

SCHMITZ, Tracy Lee. 4800 SAND POINT WAY NE 98105 #024-07-1999 L2001 **PD** *020 †55

SCHNAKE, Carol Mila. 6901 SAND POINT WAY NE, CHRMC C/O MEDICAL STAFF OF 98115 #016-11-1980 L1987 **PD** *020

SCHNAPP, Lynn Meryl. 325 9TH AVE, BOX 359640 98104 #041-01-1986 L2000 **PUD IM** *020 †20

SCHNEEWEISS, Ronald. 356390, UNIVERSITY OF WASHINGTON 98195 #836-02-1964 L1978 **FM** *040 †18

SCHNEIDER, Alina Nicole. ■ 98122 #038-06-2005 L2006 **P** *012

SCHNEIDER, Danielle Susan. 9730 3RD AVE NE, STE 206 98115 #005-18-1992 L1998 **P CHP** *020 †20

SCHNEIDER, Jon Dawse. 901 BOREN AVE, STE 1910 98104 #056-05-1988 L1990 **FM** *020 †75

SCHNEIDER, Neil Frederick. 861 POPLAR PL S 98144 #025-07-1969 L1975 **R IMG** *020 †80

SCHOENECKER, Kelly Ann. ■ 98125 #054-04-2005 L2005 **PTH** *012

SCHOETTLE, Ulrich C. 3123 FAIRVIEW AVE E 98102 #005-14-1974 L1978 **CHP P** *020 †75

SCHOLNICK, Joshua David. 515 MINOR AVE, STE 300 98104 #036-07-2000 L2004 **CD** *020 †20

SCHOLTE, Jan Aart. ■ 98105 #660-03-1953 L1964 **AN** *020

SCHOLTEN, Roger Carl. 3400 CALIFORNIA AVE SW, STE 200 98116 #016-01-1989 L1994 **PD** *020 †55

SCHORR, Nina L. 2910 E MADISON ST, # 302 98112 #035-45-1972 L1999 **P PYA** *020 †20,75

SCHOUTEN, Jeffrey Thos. ■ 98118 #035-08-1977 L1991 **GS** *074 †85

SCHROEDL, Gregory Patrick. 1550 N 115TH ST 98133 #054-04-1974 L1979 **EM** *020 †16

SCHUBACH, William Harley. 1660 S COLUMBIAN WAY, S-111-ONC VAPSHCS 98108 #035-01-1974 L1975 **IM** *020 †20

SCHUETTE, Nancy Suzanne. 1221 MADISON ST, STE 910 98104 #054-04-1976 L1980 **PD** *020 †55

SCHUFFLER, Michael David. PO BOX 356424, 1959 NE PACIFIC ST 98195 #016-11-1966 L1970 **GE IM** *020 †20

SCHULTE, Cecilia Ann. ■ 98122 #054-04-1987 L1990 **IM** *020 †20

SCHULTE, Scott John. 1959 NE PACIFIC ST, MSC 359300 98195 #054-04-1979 L1980 **R** *020 †80

SCHULTKE, Elisabeth. 1959 NE PACIFIC ST, UNIV OF WASH MEDICAL CENTE 98195 #408-31-1991 L1999 **PTH** *100

SCHULTZ, Amy Hirshfeld. 4800 SAND PT WAY NE G0035, CHILDRENS HOSP/REG MED CTR 98105 #041-01-1996 L2005 **PDC** *020 †55

SCHUMANN, Francis J. 1150 16TH AVE E 98112 #041-01-1981 L1988 **U GS** *020 †95

SCHUR, Ellen Anne. 325 9TH AVE, BOX 359780 98104 #005-11-1999 L2001 **IM** *020 †20

SCHUSTER, Gary Richard. 600 BROADWAY, STE 270 98122 #016-02-1979 L1981 **IM ISM** *020 †20

SCHUSTER, Joseph Arnold. 747 BROADWAY 98122 #054-04-1964 L1966 **IM ADM** *071 †20

SCHUTTE, David Dennis. 600 UNIVERSITY ST, STE 1200 98101 #012-05-2000 L2005 **IM** *020 †20

SCHWAEGLER, Paul Edward. 1600 E JEFFERSON ST, ORTHOPAEDICS 98122 #028-34-1984 L1990 **ORS** *020 †40

SCHWARTZ, Barbara. ■ 98122 #005-18-1980 L2003 **OBG** *020 †30

SCHWARTZ, Lawrence H. 1120 CHERRY ST STE 240 98104 #036-07-1949 L1953 **PYA P** *020 †75

SCHWARTZ, Margot Anne. 1100 9TH AVE 98101 #023-07-1991 L1993 **ID IM** *020 †20

SCHWARTZ, Matthew Aaron. ■ 98115 #054-04-2006 L2007 **AN** *012

SCHWARTZ, Michael Warren. 325 9TH AVE 359757, HARBORVIEW MEDICAL CENTER 98104 #016-01-1983 L1984 **END** *050 †20

SCHWARTZ, Stephen Mark. PO BOX 357335, DEPT PATH 98195 #024-05-1967 **PTH** *020

SCHWARTZBAUER, Karen Lynn. 925 SENECA ST, VMMC G2-GHC 98101 #026-04-1992 L1992 **IM** *020 †20

SCHWARZ, Milton Dorian. 413 PINE ST, STE 400 98101 #035-15-1968 L1970 **PD** *020 †55

SCHWEID, Abraham I. 200 16TH AVE E 98112 #035-20-1953 L1963 **PTH** *071 †50

SCHWID, Howard Alan. 1660 S COLUMBIAN WAY 98108 #056-05-1982 L1986 **AN** *020 †05

SCHWINN, Debra Anne. PO BOX 356540, UNIVERSITY OF WASHINGTON 98195 #005-11-1983 L2007 **AN** *050 †05

SCOTT, Alison Hodges. 1959 NE PACIFIC ST, BOX 356340 98195 #054-04-2003 L2003 **PD** *020 †20

SCOTT, Bart Lee. ■ 98122 #001-06-1996 L1999 **ON** *020 †20

SCOTT, Clifford Ronald. 1959 NE PACIFIC ST, BOX 356320 98195 #054-04-1959 L1964 **PD OS** *040 †55,19

SCOTT, Douglas Victor. ■ 98195 #060-01-1988 L1995 **NM** *100 †80,28

SCOTT, Jeffrey Robert. ■ 98105 #054-04-2003 L2003 **PS** *012

SCOTT, John Douglas. ■ 98144 #019-02-1988 L2002 **ID** *020 †20

SCOTT, Michael J, Jr. 509 OLIVE WAY, STE 817 98101 #030-06-1946 L1949 **D** *020 †15

SCOTT, Patricia Mcjennett. 4800 SAND POINT WAY NE 98105 #010-02-1998 L2002 **PD** *020 †55

SCOTT, Robert Harold. 1401 MADISON ST, SWEDISH FAMILY MEDICINE 98104 #035-45-1979 L1980 **FM** *071 †18

SCOTT, Steven G. 2201 6TH AVE, STE 1001 98121 #019-02-1986 L2001 **OM** *030 †70

SCOTT, Thomas Putnam. 1629 N 45TH ST, HEALTH CENTERS-45TH STREET 98103 #007-02-1989 L1991 **FM** *020 †18

SCRANTON, Pierce Edward. 1600 E JEFFERSON ST # 400 98122 #038-41-1972 L1979 **ORS** *020 †40

SCRIBNER, Robert Rollin. 1660 S COLUMBIAN WAY, HEALTH CARE SYSTEM-SEATTLE 98108 #010-02-1971 L1975 **P FM** *020 †75,18

SCURLOCK, James Edward. 3824 E HIGHLAND DR, 3824 EAST HIGHLAND DRIVE 98112 #048-12-1970 L1971 **AN** *020 †05

SEALE, Robert Holt. 3516 E UNION ST 98122 #028-02-1972 L1975 **EM** *020 †16

SECHENA, Ruth C. 12208 GREENWOOD AVE N 98133 #016-11-1979 L1980 **OM** *062 †70

SEEBERGER, Teri Marie. ■ 98122 #054-04-2008 *012

SEEWALDT, Victoria Louise. 1959 NE PACIFIC ST, MSC 359300 98195 #005-19-1989 L1989 **ON** *020 †20

SEIFFERT, Armin Kurt. 521 WALL ST 98121 #025-01-1964 L1968 **N** *071 †75

SEILER, Douglas Paul. ■ 98116 #021-01-2002 L2003 **RNR** *012 †80

SEKARAN, Nalini Thavi. ■ 98105 #035-47-1990 L1997 **CHN** *100

SEKARAN, Nishant Krishna. ■ 98102 #047-05-2006 L2006 **IM** *012

SEKHAR, Laligam N. 325 9TH AVE, NEUROSURGERY BOX 359924 98104 #495-04-1974 L2004 **NS N** *020 †25

SEKIJIMA, John Haruto. 1101 MADISON ST, STE 400 98104 #054-04-1983 L1986 **GE IM** *020 †20

SELIGMAN, Gerald Marvin. 1600 E JOHN ST 98112 #065-01-1964 L1977 **ORS** *020 †40

SELLORS, John William. 325 9TH AVE, HARBORVIEW MEDICAL CENTER 98104 #065-10-1972 L2001 **OBG** *020

SELLS, Jill Marie. 4616 25TH AVE NE # 710 98105 #054-04-1993 L1995 **PD** *062 †55

SEMENTI, Olivia Michael. 1959 NE PACIFIC ST # C-, BOX 356340 98195 #054-04-2005 L2005 **OBG** *012

SEMPER, Thomas Frederick. 818 12TH AVE 98122 #030-06-1995 L1999 **CHP** *020 †75

SENTER, Carlin Hurst. ■ 98112 #005-14-2004 L2005 **IM** *012

SEO, Benjamin Genesuk. ■ 98103 #036-01-2005 L2005 **EM** *012

SEPKUTY, Jehuda P. 600 UNIVERSITY ST 1200 98101 #550-02-1990 L2007 **N** *020 †75

SEROUSSI, Richard Emanuel. 3213 EASTLAKE AVE E # A1, SEATTLE SPINE & REHAB MED 98102 #038-06-1991 L1993 **PM** *020 †60

SERU, Vinita. 10330 MERIDIAN AVE N, NORTH SEATTLE PEDIATRICS 98133 #035-47-1995 L1998 **PD** *020 †55

SETHI, Rajiv Kumar. ■ 98105 #024-01-2001 L2007 **ORS** *020

SETHI, Tanmeet Kaur. 1401 MADISON ST, STE 100 98104 #016-01-1997 L1999 **FM** *020 †18

SETIA, Sabeena. ■ 98102 #054-04-2004 L2006 **IM** *100 †20

SETIAWAN, Christopher Tan. ■ 98125 #048-04-2006 **AN** *012

SEWELL, Hobart H, Jr. 6201 15TH AVE NW 98107 #047-06-1965 L1965 **P** *020 †75

SEYL, Peter Sanders. ■ 98115 #016-06-1969 L1971 **FM GP** *020 †18

SEYMOUR, Christopher Warr. 2651 NW 57TH ST B 98107 #041-01-2004 L2007 **PCC** *012 †20

SEYMOUR, Laura Jeanine. 1959 NE PACIFIC ST, BOX 356340 98195 #054-04-2006 L2006 **P** *012

SHADLEN, Michael N. 1959 NE PACIFIC ST, MSC 359300 98195 #043-01-1988 L1996 **N** *020

SHAFFER, Anita Marie. 1145 BROADWAY 98122 #026-04-1975 L1976 **IM** *020 †20

SHAFII, Taraneh. 325 9TH AVE BOX 359777, AIDS AND STD RESEARCH 98104 #020-02-1996 L2000 **ADL** *020 †55

SHAH, Chirag Ashok. ■ 98109 #017-20-2002 L2002 **OBG** *100

SHAH, Javeed Ali. ■ 98122 #016-02-2005 L2005 **IM** *012

SHALHUB, Sherene. ■ 98112 #011-04-2003 L2003 **GS** *012

SHALIGRAM, Abhijit Sadashi. SURGERY #356410, DEPARTMENT OF 98195 #495-83-2001 L2006 **GS** *012

SHALIT, Peter. 1120 CHERRY ST, STE 320 98104 #054-04-1985 L1986 **IM** *020 †20

SHAMSELDIN, Joseph Ali. 550 16TH AVE STE 100 98122 #054-04-1973 L1974 **FM** *020 †18

SHAMSELDIN, Michael Sam. 7210 ROOSEVELT WAY NE, SWEDISH PHYSICIANS LLC 98115 #054-04-1992 L1992 **FM** *020 †18

SHAMSELDIN, Shannon Sam. 7210 ROOSEVELT WAY NE 98115 #016-43-1991 L1991 **FM** *020 †18

SHANAHAN, Michael F. 2817 S MCCLELLAN ST 98144 #030-06-1951 L1952 **GP** *071

SHANDRO, Jamie Rae. 325 9TH AVE, CAMPUS BOX 359702 98104 #054-04-2003 L2006 **EM** *100 †16

SHANKLAND, Stuart James. 1959 NE PACIFIC ST, MSC 359300 98195 #836-02-1983 L1994 **IM** *020 †20

SHAPIRO, Joel Allen. 2409 N 45TH ST 98103 #035-06-1995 L2001 **ORS** *020 †40

SHARAR, Samuel Randolph. 325 9TH AVE 98104 #054-04-1983 L1984 **AN CCM** *020 †05

SHARMA, Umang. 4245 ROOSEVELT WAY NE, BOX 354775 98105 #028-02-2003 L2003 **FM** *020 †18

SHARP, Christopher Dewey. ■ 98121 #021-06-2008 *012

SHARP, Gregory Nathan. 1145 BROADWAY 98122 #054-04-2004 L2004 **IM** *020 †20

SHASTEEN, Nancy Margaret. 1145 BROADWAY, POLYCLINIC STE 2Q 98122 #054-04-1989 L1989 **RHU** *012

SHASTRI, R Arunkumar. ■ 98115 #495-35-1973 L1985 *100

SHAUL, William Lawrence. 5316 RAINIER AVE S, GROUP HEALTH COOP 98118 #041-14-1973 L1975 **GPM PHP** *020 †18

SHAW, Allison Joy. ■ 98116 #041-15-2003 L2003 **HMP** *012 †50

SHAW, Cheng-Mei. 325 9TH AVE, BOX 359791 98104 #385-02-1950 L1965 **NP** *071 †25

SHAW, Dennis Webster. 4800 SAND POINT WAY NE, DEPT OF RADIOLOGY 98105 #054-04-1983 L1984 **PDR RNR** *020 †80

SHAW, James Mc Gowan. 1550 N 115TH ST 98133 #803-05-1943 L1956 **GP AS** *071

SHAW, Steven Michael. 501 N 34TH ST, STE 101 98103 #038-06-1995 L1998 **GE** *020 †20

SHAW-CLARK, Barbara Lee. ■ 98125 #028-02-1962 L1964 **PHO PD** *071 †55

SHEARER, Diana Nadia. 1516 2ND AVE STE 303, DETERMINATION SERVICES 98101 #836-02-1971 L1976 **PHP** *012

SHECKTER, Carol B. 4026 NE 55TH ST 98105 #065-10-1982 L1983 **END IM** *020 †20

SHEEHAN, Florence Huang. 2324 EASTLAKE AVE E, STE 500 98102 #016-02-1975 L1980 **CD** *050 †20

SHEEHY, James Gerard. ■ 98109 #803-09-1949 L1959 **AN** *071

SHEETS, Pamela Kay. 1145 BROADWAY 98122 #025-12-1982 L1982 **RHU IM** *040 †20

SHEFFIELD, John Van Loon. 325 9TH AVE # 359782, HARBORVIEW MED CTR 98104 #024-01-1989 L1992 **IM** *020 †20

SHEFVELAND, John Ronald. 200 16TH AVE E 98112 #026-04-1957 L1962 **FM IMG** *072 †18

SHELDON, Albert M, III. 2271 NE 51ST ST 98105 #038-06-1975 L2002 **P FM** *020 †75

SHEN, Tong. 1959 NE PACIFIC ST, DEPT OF PSYCH 98195 #243-45-1991 L2004 **CHP** *012

SHEN, Tueng. 1959 NE PACIFIC ST, BOX 356485 98195 #024-01-1997 L2002 **IM** *020

SHENDURE, Jay Ashok. ■ 98115 #024-01-2007 *012

SHENG, Alexander Xiaoren. UNIV OF WASHINGTON, DEPT OF REHAB MED 98195 #016-01-2006 L2007 **PM** *012

SHENOI, Jaideep. ■ 98115 #495-52-1996 L2007 **HO** *012

SHENOI, Susan. ■ 98115 #496-38-1998 L2007 **PD** *020 †55

SHENOY, Uma A. 1600 E JOHN ST 98112 #495-33-1976 L1985 **ATP PCP** *020 †50

SHEPARD, Phillip Bruce. ■ 98108 #025-01-1968 L1969 **FM** *075 †18

SHEPARD, Thomas H. 4800 SAND POINT WAY NE 98105 #035-45-1948 L1955 **PD** *050 †55

SHEPHARD, Elena Marie. 4800 SAND PT WAY NE BOX 5, CHILDRENS HOSPITAL & REGIO 98105 #067-01-2002 L2005 **PEM** *012 †55

SHERENSKY, Robert Thos. ■ 98102 #035-45-1966 L1967 **TS GS** *020 †85

SHERER, David M. 200 15TH AVE E 98112 #035-06-1969 L1974 **OBG CLP** *071 †50

SHERIDAN, Meghan Kelly. 1221 MADISON ST, STE 910 98104 #054-04-2004 L2007 **PD** *020 †55

SHERMAN, Daniel Adam. 550 16TH AVE STE 300 98122 #023-07-1972 L1975 **P** *020 †75 ‡

SHERMAN, Joseph Patrick. 1526 31ST AVE 98122 #051-04-1985 L2000 **PD** *020 †55

SHERMAN, Paul Edward. 1600 E JOHN ST 98112 #023-07-1989 L1989 **PD** *020 †55

SHERMAN, Roberta Ruth. 509 OLIVE WAY, STE 900 98101 #054-04-1981 L1982 **FM** *020 †18

SHERRARD, Donald James. 1660 S COLUMBIAN WAY 98108 #054-04-1960 L1968 **NEP IM** *050 †20

SHERRIS, John Chas. ■ 98195 #917-26-1944 L1964 **OS** *071

SHERRY, Davonna Rozell. 1101 MADISON ST STE 301, PACIFIC MEDICAL CENTER 98104 #054-04-1994 L1997 **FM** *020 †18

SHEWCHUK, Jason Ronald. 1959 NE PACIFIC ST RR215, DEPT OF RADIOLOGY, BOX 357 98195 #062-01-1998 L2003 **DR** *100 †80

SHIBATA, Dean Kazuo. 1959 NE PACIFIC ST, UWMC RADIOLOGY, BOX 357115 98195 #005-11-1989 L1990 **RNR** *020 †80

SHIBUYA, Grant Isamu. 747 BROADWAY 98122 #054-04-1984 L1990 **AN PD** *020 †55,05

SHIELDS, Andrew Thos. 1959 NE PACIFIC ST, UNIV OF WASHINGTON MEDICAL 98195 #054-04-1985 L1986 **NM** *020 †28

SHIGAKI, Alison Lynn. 3815 S OTHELLO ST 2ND FL 98118 #056-06-1994 L1994 **FM** *020 †18

SHIMAMURA, Akiko. 4800 SAND POINT WAY NE, CHILDREN'S HOSPITAL 98105 #035-45-1991 L2007 **PHO PD** *050 †55

SHIOTA, Merrilynne Gail. 1801 NW MARKET ST STE 207 98107 #001-02-1988 L1990 **IM** *020 †20

SHIRK, Tracey Bernard. 747 BROADWAY 98122 #038-43-1988 L1997 **EM** *020 †16

SHIVARAM, Giridhar Mysore. 747 BROADWAY STE 731, SWEDISH MED CTR FIRST HILL 98122 #005-11-2007 L2007 **GS** *012

SHNORHAVORIAN, Margaret. ■ 98115 #005-02-2000 L2005 **UP** *100

SHOCKLEY, Paula B. 2611 NE 125TH ST, STE 201 98125 #048-12-1988 L1988 **P** *020 †75

SHOPE, Anna Rose. ■ 98177 #054-04-2007 L2007 **OBG** *012

SHORES, Molly Mc Donough. 1660 S COLUMBIAN WAY, MS 182B 98108 #054-04-1987 L1989 **P** *020 †75

SHORR, Rachel Brinn. 550 16TH AVE STE 100, PROVIDENCE FAMILY MEDICINE 98122 #550-04-2005 L2005 **FP** *012

SHORR, Stuart S. 747 BROADWAY 98122 #008-01-1970 L1974 **PD** *020 †55

SHORS, Andrew Richard. 125 16TH AVE E, 3RD FLOOR, S BLDG 98112 #054-04-2000 L2004 **D** *020 †15

SHORT, Denis Stafford. 1200 12TH AVE S 98144 #054-04-1961 L1981 **P GP** *072

SHORT, Floyd Alvin. 801 BROADWAY, STE 725 98122 #035-45-1959 L1966 **CD** *071 †20

SHOWELL, Patrizia A. 1145 BROADWAY, POLY CLINIC -ADMIN 98122 #021-01-1993 L2000 **IM** *020 †20

SHOWMAN, Emily Susan. ■ 98105 #054-04-2007 L2007 **PD** *012

SHUGERMAN, Richard Philip. 4800 SAND POINT WAY NE 98105 #001-02-1984 L1985 **PD PEM** *040 †55

SHUHART, Christopher Robt. 600 UNIVERSITY ST, STE 1200 98101 #032-01-1987 L1991 **IM** *020 †18

SHULER, Michael Simms. ■ 98121 #023-07-2002 L2007 **HSO** *012

SHULL, Frederick Whitney. ■ 98115 #035-45-1944 L1948 **OBG** *075

SHULMAN, Harold. ■ 98109 #016-42-1965 L1972 **R** *020

SHULMAN, Howard Michael. 1124 COLUMBIA ST 98104 #005-14-1971 L1973 **PTH** *020 †50

SHURTLEFF, David Bertrand. UNIV OF WASHINGTON, DEPT OF PEDS RD 20 98195 #024-07-1955 L1958 **PD PM** *071 †55

SHUSHAN, Denise V. 4800 SAND POINT WAY NE 98105 #005-02-1998 L2000 **PD** *020 †55

SHUSTERMAN, Dennis J. 325 9TH AVE, BOX 359739 98104 #005-19-1978 L1985 **FM OM** *020 †70,18

SHVIDLER, Joseph. ■ 98101 #041-14-2002 L2007 **OTO** *020

SHWETZ, Mary Helen. 2271 NE 51ST ST 98105 #016-11-1979 L1981 **P PYA** *020 †75

SHY, Kirkwood K. 4245 ROOSEVELT WAY NE, STE 354775 98105 #025-07-1973 L1975 **OBG** *020 †30

SHYU, Siegfried. ■ 98116 #036-05-1997 L2004 **AN** *020 †05

SICURO, Paul Lewis. 1100 9TH AVE 98101 #054-04-1989 L1991 **DR** *020 †80

SIDDIQUE, Asma. 925 SENECA ST # 1930 98101 #024-21-1994 L2007 **IM** *012

SIDDIQUI, Afreen. 4245 ROOSEVELT WAY NE, PAIN CENTER UWMC ROOSEVELT 98105 #704-25-1993 L2000 **AN** *020 †05

SIDHU, Manrita Kaur. 1229 MADISON ST, STE 900 98104 #041-07-1988 L1995 **PDR VIR** *020 †80

SIE, Kathleen C Y. 4800 SAND POINT WAY NE, REGIONAL MEDICAL CENTER 98105 #025-01-1984 L1995 **PDO** *020 †45

SIECKE, Neil Warren. 600 UNIVERSITY ST STE 1200, SWEDISH PHYSICIAN DIVISION 98101 #035-19-1998 L2006 **CD** *020 †20

SIEGAL, Justin Aaron. 1100 9TH AVE, MAILSTOP C5XR VMMC RAD 98101 #028-34-2000 L2003 **RNR** *020 †20

SIEGEL, Martin Stuart. 1145 BROADWAY 98122 #038-06-1972 L1978 **ID IM** *020 †20

SIEG-ROSS, Martin Paul. 4744 41ST AVE SW STE 102, THE HEALING ARTS PARTNERSH 98116 #017-20-1988 L1995 **FM** *062 †18

SIEW, David D. 1959 NE PACIFIC ST RM C2, CAMPUS BOX 356340 98195 #016-02-2002 L2004 **IM** *020 †20

SIGLEY, Margaret Ellen S. 6852 34TH AVE NE 98115 #005-14-1968 L1972 **PD** *020 †55

SIGLEY, Robert Danl. ■ 98199 #005-14-1968 L1972 **GS** *071 †85

SIIMO, Helju. PO BOX 34245, PUGET SOUND INSTITUTE OF P 98124 #062-01-1958 L1960 **PTH** *062 †50

SIKKEMA, Wesley Wm. 1200 12TH AVE S 98144 #025-01-1957 L1969 **GS TS** *071 †85

SIKORA, Agata Katharina. 1145 BROADWAY, THE POLYCLINIC 98122 #054-04-1996 L1998 **IM** *020 †20

SILBERGELD, Daniel Lance. 1959 NE PACIFIC ST, MSC 359300 98195 #038-41-1984 L1986 **NS** *020 †25

SILBERGELD, Janet Joy. 1959 NE PACIFIC ST 98195 #038-40-1989 L1989 **DR** *020 †80

SILVA, William Jos. 3400 CALIFORNIA AVE SW 98116 #035-45-1978 L1984 **EM** *020 †20

SILVER, Lloyd Hutchins. ■ 98102 #005-12-1938 L1938 **A NTR** *071

SILVERMAN, Donald Ray. 1600 E JEFFERSON ST, STE A1 98122 #030-05-1957 L1961 **PM** *071 †60

SILVERSTEIN, Bruce Derryl. 2324 EASTLAKE AVE E, STE 500 98102 #047-05-1975 L1978 **GE IM** *072 †20

SILVERSTEIN, Fred Eli. 601 UNION ST, STE 3300 98101 #035-01-1967 L1969 **GE OS** *020 †20

SILVERSTEIN, Michael. 1959 NE PACIFIC ST RM C212, GRAD OF EDUC,BX 356340 98195 #024-01-1998 L2001 **PD** *020 †20

SIM, Hong Gee. 1959 NE PACIFIC ST, DEPT OF UROLOGY, UNI OF WA 98195 #825-01-1994 L2005 *100

SIM, Jae Hoon. ■ 98112 #041-02-1995 L1997 **FM** *020 †18 ‡

SIMKIN, Peter Anthony. 4000 15TH AVE NE 98195 #041-01-1961 L1967 **RHU IM** *050

SIMMONS, James Russell. 1100 9TH AVE G1-MSO, VIRGINIA MASON MEDICAL CEN 98101 #021-01-1969 L1973 **IM** *020 †20

SIMMONS, Lavone Elizabeth. 1959 NE PACIFIC ST # C-2, BOX 356340 98195 #050-02-2004 L2005 **OBG** *012

SIMON, Ednea Aparecida. 4800 SAND POINT WAY NE, CHILDREN'S HOSP/NEURO B-55 98105 #187-30-1983 L2004 **PD** *020 †75

SIMON, Gregory Edward. 4426B FRANCIS AVE N 98103 #036-01-1982 L1983 **P IM** *050 †20,75

SIMON, Nancy Ellen. 4245 ROOSEVELT WAY NE, STE 354775 98105 #051-01-1994 L1997 **IM** *020 †20

SIMONOWITZ, Barbara J. 1229 MADISON ST, STE 1440 98104 #016-43-1976 L1978 **AN** *071 †05

SIMONSEN, Jane Marie. UNIV OF WA, HALL HEALTH GS-10 98105 #003-01-1977 L1984 **FM** *062 †18

SIMRELL, Charles Raymond. 1550 N 115TH ST 98133 #011-03-1978 L1992 **PTH HMP** *020 †50

SIN, Kunthearith. ■ 98125 #054-04-2004 L2004 **IM** *020 †20

SINANAN, Mika Narad. 1959 NE PACIFIC ST, BOX 356410 98195 #023-07-1980 L1981 **AS GS** *020 †20

SINCLAIR, John D. 155 NE 100TH ST, STE 402 98125 #065-01-1962 L1997 *020

SINCLAIR, Robt Bruce Ian. ■ 98116 #065-01-1966 L1980 **AN** *020 †05

SINFUEGO, Andrew S. 201 16TH AVE E, MAILSTOP CNB -480 98112 #748-01-1991 L2000 **PD** *020

SING, Amy Pratt. ■ 98117 #005-11-1987 L1990 **PHO PD** *020 †55

SINGER, Jack W. 501 ELLIOTT AVE W 98119 #035-08-1968 L1972 **ON IM** *050 †20

■ = Address Information Privacy Protected

SINGH, Devika. ■ 98122 #035-45-2003 L2003 **ID** *012 †20
SINGH, Nalini. 1660 S COLUMBIAN WAY, PUGET SOUND HEALTHCARE SYS 98108 #005-02-1995 L2002 **END** *020 †20
SINGH, Pradeep Kumar. 1959 NE PACIFIC ST, CAMPUS BOX 357242 98195 #016-06-1989 L2006 **PCC** *020 †20
SINGH, Sudershan Jaswant. ■ 98125 #054-04-2008 *012
SINGH, Suraj. ■ 98101 #035-09-2001 L2006 **RO** *100
SINGH, Virtaj. UNIV OF WASHINGTON, DEPT OF REHAB MED 98195 #048-04-2006 L2006 **PM** *012
SINGLER, Ronald Francis. 4744 41ST AVE SW 98116 #020-12-1972 L1978 **FM P** *030 †18 ‡
SINHA, Abhishek. ■ 98119 #008-01-2003 L2007 **CD** *012 †20
SINTON, Toby Isaac. ■ 98102 #041-12-2006 L2006 **IM** *012
SIRC, Evan Michael. ■ 98112 #026-04-2007 L2007 **TY** *012
SIRES, Bryan Stewart. 1959 NE PACIFIC ST, BOX 356485 98195 #016-06-1990 L1990 **OPH** *020 †35
SISCOVICK, David Stuart. 325 9TH AVE BOX 359780, HARBORVIEW MEDICAL CENTER 98104 #023-01-1976 L1977 **IM PHP** *050 †20
SKARPIDI, Evangelia. PATHOLOGY BOX 356100, UNIV OF WASHINGTON 98195 #418-01-1992 L2000 **PTH** *100 †19,50
SKEELS, Vernon H. ■ 98103 #016-06-1950 L1951 **IM** *072
SKEITH, Maurice D. 747 BROADWAY 98122 #030-05-1960 L1961 **RHU IM** *071 †20
SKERRETT, Shawn J. 325 9TH AVE, BOX 359640 98104 #035-19-1978 L1983 **PUD ID** *050 †20
SKINNER, Gwendolyn Louise. ■ 98103 #054-04-2005 L2005 **IM** *012
SKIRKO, Jonathan Robert. ■ 98199 #054-04-2007 L2007 **OTO** *012
SKOLNICK, Jeffrey Stuart. 726 BROADWAY 98122 #305-01-1984 L1988 **P** *020 †75
SKUBI, Kazimer Bogar. ■ 98103 #016-01-1940 L1944 **IM** *071 †20
SLABAUGH, Mark Anthony. ■ 98105 #054-04-2004 L2005 **OPH** *012
SLACK, David Patrick. UNIV OF WASHINGTON, DEPT OF REHAB MED 98195 #041-15-2002 L2003 **PM** *020 †60
SLACK, Stephen Francis. 1801 NW MARKET ST, STE 100 98107 #028-02-1984 L1985 **OBG** *020 †30
SLADE, Ian Robert. ■ 98108 #054-04-2008 *012
SLATER, Paula Lynne. 2107 ELLIOTT AVE STE 202 98121 #049-01-1999 L2001 **P** *020 †75
SLATORE, Christopher G. ■ 98115 #054-04-2001 L2004 **PCC** *012
SLEE, Teresa Ann. 2324 EASTLAKE AVE E 98102 #054-04-1983 L1983 **AN** *040 †05
SLICHTER, Sherrill Jeane. 921 TERRY AVE 98104 #010-01-1963 L1968 **BBK HEM** *050 †20
SLOAN, Dean Clair. ■ 98105 #030-05-1959 L1960 **AN** *071 †05
SLOAN, Kevin Lawrence. SEATTLE VAMC 98108 #016-02-1986 L1991 **P ADP** *020 †75
SLOAN, William Hugh. 747 BROADWAY 98122 #040-02-1945 L1946 **GP OM** *072
SMALL, Barbara Elaine. 4800 SAND POINT WAY NE, MS B6553 98105 #048-12-1985 L2004 **PHO OS** *020 †55 ‡
SMART, Brian Frederick. ■ 98102 #041-15-2006 L2007 **P** *012
SMART, Craig Stephen. 601 UNION ST STE 1704 98101 #045-01-1984 L1985 **P** *020 †75
SMERSH, Thomas C. ■ 98125 #026-04-1949 L1956 **OTO** *071 †45
SMITH, Allen Mc Nair. 2460 WESTLAKE AVE N 98109 #049-01-1977 L1978 **IM** *020
SMITH, Allison Marie. 521 WALL ST 98121 #051-04-1988 L2004 **DR** *020 †80
SMITH, Bruce Cameron. 125 16TH AVE E, CEB 301 98112 #054-04-1984 L1985 **IMG PLM** *030 †20
SMITH, Catherine E. 7210 ROOSEVELT WAY NE 98115 #048-04-2000 L2002 **FM** *020 †18 ‡
SMITH, Christopher Hazard. 1101 MADISON ST STE 301, PACIFIC MEDICAL CENTER 98104 #024-01-1989 L1989 **IM** *020 †20
SMITH, Craig Harlan. 1100 OLIVE WAY STE 150 98101 #054-04-1975 L1976 **N OPH** *020 †75
SMITH, Donald Clyde. 1101 MADISON ST STE 1500 98104 #054-04-1962 L1967 **GYN OBG** *020 †30
SMITH, Donna Lee. 4575 SAND POINT WAY NE 98105 #040-02-1985 L1985 **PD** *020 †55
SMITH, Douglas Geo. 325 9TH AVE BOX 359798 98104 #016-02-1984 L1988 **ORS TRS** *020 †40
SMITH, Dustin Jared. ■ 98102 #054-04-2008 L2008 *012
SMITH, Frederick Benj. 550 16TH AVE STE 100 98122 #033-06-1979 L1980 **FM** *020 †18
SMITH, Gretchen Jeanne. ■ 98105 #054-04-2007 L2007 **TY** *012
SMITH, Ian Alexanders. ■ 98117 #041-02-1999 L2003 **PCC** *020 †20
SMITH, Ian Michael. 1100 9TH AVE G1-MSO 98101 #025-01-2004 L2006 **OTO** *012
SMITH, James Bernard. 1600 E JEFFERSON ST, STE 600 98122 #030-06-1956 L1958 **ORS** *071 †40
SMITH, James Callan. 1600 E JEFFERSON ST, STE 101 98122 #016-43-1965 L1971 **TS** *071 †85,90
SMITH, Joanne R. ■ 98112 #038-40-1951 L1951 **AN** *071 †05
SMITH, Jodi Marie. 4800 SAND POINT WAY NE 98105 #067-01-1995 L1999 **PN** *020 †55
SMITH, John Martin. ■ 98103 #001-02-1968 L1970 **OS GYN** *020 †30
SMITH, Kelly David. 1959 NE PACIFIC ST, MSC 359300 98195 #018-03-1996 L2000 **PTH** *020 †50
SMITH, Kevin Leon. 125 16TH AVE E 98112 #016-45-1990 L1995 **ORS OSM** *040 †40
SMITH, Kurt Stucki. ■ 98121 #041-14-1986 L2000 **AN** *020 †05
SMITH, Leah. ■ 98115 #054-04-2004 L2004 **IM** *012 †20
SMITH, Lincoln Samuel. 4800 SAND POINT WAY NE, 4D-1 98105 #056-05-1999 L2003 **PD** *100 †55
SMITH, Mark Scott. 1959 NE PACIFIC ST, MSC 359300 98195 #051-01-1969 L1970 **ADL PD** *040 †55
SMITH, Michael Rust. 1101 MADISON ST STE 1500 98104 #054-04-1962 L1965 **GO GYN** *020 †30
SMITH, Nathan James. 4800 SAND POINT WAY NE 98105 #056-05-1945 L1965 **PD IM** *030 †55
SMITH, Neale Daine. ■ 98115 #054-04-1973 L1981 **CD** *071 †20
SMITH, Paul Allen. 1100 9TH AVE 98101 #054-04-1980 L1984 **IM** *020 †20
SMITH, Robert H. ■ 98115 #054-04-1950 L1951 **AN** *071 †05
SMITH, Sherilyn. 4800 SAND POINT WAY NE, MAILSTOP 8G-1 98105 #048-04-1989 L1994 **PD** *050 †55
SMITH, Steven Paul. 200 15TH AVE E, GROUP HEALTH OF PUGET SOUN 98112 #005-14-1980 L1984 **OPH** *020 †35
SMITH, Tanya Tinette. 1001 4TH AVE STE 420, SWEDISH PHYSICIANS 98154 #054-04-1997 L1999 **FM** *020 †18
SMITH, Thomas James. 1221 MADISON ST STE 1415 98104 #034-01-1976 L1978 **IM** *020 †20
SMITH, Timothy James. 747 BROADWAY 98122 #034-01-1976 L1980 **IM** *020 †20
SMITH, William Thayer. ■ 98103 #025-01-1938 L1939 **PHP** *071
SMITHERMAN, Matthew Langs. ■ 98102 #054-04-2005 L2005 **IM** *012
SMOYER, Larie Honey. 1215 4TH AVE, STE 1925 98161 #054-04-1996 L2000 **OBG** *020
SMYTH, Cynthia Marie. 515 MINOR AVE STE 300, MINOR & JAMES MEDICAL, PLL 98104 #041-02-1993 L1995 **IM** *020 †20
SNAPP, Nancy Joy. 720 8TH AVE S STE 100 98104 #054-04-1980 L1982 **GPM FM** *020 †18
SNEE, Karen Lynne. 1600 E JOHN ST 98112 #051-01-1989 L1994 **AN** *020 †05
SNELL, Julie Elizabeth. ■ 98112 #047-05-1997 L2000 **PD** *100 †55,05
SNOWDEN, Mark Brian. 325 9TH AVE 98104 #054-04-1990 L1990 **P** *050 †75
SNYDER, Benjamin David. ■ 98112 #023-01-2004 L2005 **PM** *012
SNYDER, Christin Nancy. 1959 NE PACIFIC ST, BOX 356426 98195 #040-02-2004 L2007 **END** *012 †20
SNYDER, D'Annette. ■ 98105 #040-02-1950 L1954 **PD** *071
SNYDER, Eleanor N. ■ 98102 #005-11-1950 L1960 **PD PHP** *071 †55
SNYDER, Garth Russell. ■ 98125 #035-45-2006 *012
SNYDER, Michael L. 1600 E OLIVE ST 98122 #016-06-1978 L1989 **P PYG** *020 †75
SNYDER, Richard. 1600 E JOHN ST 98112 #005-11-1987 L1990 **AN** *020 †05
SODERSTROM, Richard M. 1946 HARVARD AVE E 98102 #016-06-1959 L1961 **GYN** *071 †30
SOHN, Elliott Harry. ■ 98121 #054-04-2003 L2003 **OPH** *100
SOLA, Anders E. 1959 NE PACIFIC ST 98195 #054-04-1950 L1951 **PM OS** *071
SOLACK, Sandra Darlene. 10330 MERIDIAN AVE N, SEATTLE ARTHRITIS CLINIC 98133 #054-04-1987 L1989 **FM** *020 †18
SOLAN, Janet Shimada. 1530 N 115TH ST STE 307 98133 #054-04-1992 L1992 **P** *020
SOLAN, William Jos. 1530 N 115TH ST, STE 307 98133 #054-04-1987 L1990 **P** *020 †75
SOLARI, Patrick Barry. 4800 SAND POINT WAY NE, REGIONAL M 98105 #028-34-2003 L2006 **PEM** *012 †16
SOLAZZI, Richard Wm. 1229 MADISON ST STE 1440 98104 #054-04-1980 L1981 **AN** *020 †05
SOLOMON, Andrew Edward. ■ 98119 #005-02-2003 L2004 **AN** *020
SOLOMON, Andrew Keith. 10330 MERIDIAN AVE N, STE 250 98133 #550-02-1985 L1991 **RHU** *020 †20
SOLOMON, Robert Eric. ■ 98199 #018-03-1989 L1989 **AN** *020 †05
SOMA, Vijaya Lakshmi. ■ 98109 #035-48-2005 L2005 **PD** *012
SONG, Guobin. 1100 9TH AVE 98101 #243-46-1988 L2003 **RO** *020 †80
SONNEN, Joshua Aaron. ■ 98118 #005-06-2002 L2005 **NP** *100 †50
SONTROP, Maria Anna. 3216 NE 45TH PL, STE 200 98105 #660-04-1995 L2000 **FM** *020 †18
SOONTORNVACHRIN, Mark Sul. ■ 98199 #005-06-2005 L2006 **OPH** *012
SORENSEN, Gregory Kent. 1101 MADISON ST, STE 800 98104 #030-05-1978 L1979 **AN PD** *020 †55,05
SORENSEN, Lyle Steven. 1100 9TH AVE 98101 #054-04-1988 L1988 **ORS SO** *020 †40
SORENSEN, Mathew Don. ■ 98103 #007-02-2004 L2004 **U** *012
SORIANO, Brian Daniel. 4800 SAND POINT WAY NE, G-0035 98105 #038-43-1996 L2007 **PDC** *020 †20,55
SORIANO, Scarlet. ■ 98122 #041-01-2007 L2007 **FP** *012
SORROR, Mohamed Lotfy. 825 EASTLAKE AVE E 98109 #915-05-1993 L2005 *100
SORSBY, Stephen C. 1100 VIRGINIA ST, STE 215 98101 #004-01-1983 L1995 **OM** *030 †18,70
SOTOODEHNIA, Nona. 325 9TH AVE BOX 359748, HARBORVIEW MEDICAL CENTER 98104 #024-01-1996 L1999 **CD** *020 †20
SOUDERS, Jennifer Ellyn. 1660 S COLUMBIAN WAY, S-112-A 98108 #016-02-1988 L1992 **AN CCM** *020 †05
SOULAKVELIDZE, Irakli. 1100 9TH AVE, MAILSTOP C5APC 5TH FLOOR B 98101 #913-23-1979 L2001 **APM** *020 †05
SOUNG, Michael Chunling. 1959 NE PACIFIC ST #356340, UNIV OF WA GRAD MED ED 98195 #016-06-2003 L2003 **IM** *100 †20
SOUSA, Manuela M. 747 BROADWAY 98122 #496-15-1991 L2002 **PAN** *020 †05
SOUTER, Karen Jane. ■ 98115 #917-31-1985 L2002 **AN** *020
SOUTH, Allen Gregg. 1229 MADISON ST, STE 610 98104 #016-06-1966 L1973 **OBG** *020 †30
SOWDER, Lisa Lynn. 901 BOREN AVE, SUITE 1650 CABRINI MEDICAL 98104 #054-04-1983 L1990 **PS GS** *020 †85,65
SOYODE, Olufemi Oluseun. 4800 SAND POINT WAY NE, REGIONAL MED 98105 #690-02-2000 L2006 **CHN** *012 †55
SPACH, David Henry. 325 9TH AVE # 359930 98104 #036-07-1986 L1988 **ID** *020 †20
SPADONI, Leon Richard. 325 9TH AVE 98104 #054-04-1957 L1962 **REN** *072 †30
SPAIN, William Jonathen. 1660 S COLUMBIAN WAY, NEUROLOGY SECTION 127 98108 #035-01-1977 L1978 **N** *020 †75
SPARKS, John Wm. 925 SENECA ST G2-GHC, VIRGINIA MASON MEDICAL CEN 98101 #038-06-1992 L1992 **IM** *075 †20
SPARKS, Patricia Jo. 9594 1ST AVE NE, DMB #410 98115 #049-01-1975 L1984 **OM IM** *030 †70,20
SPECHT, Jennifer Marie. 825 EASTLAKE AVE E G3-200, SEATTLE CANCER CARE ALLC 98109 #054-04-1999 L2002 **ON** *020 †20
SPECK, Sarah Marshall. 500 17TH AVE, STE 100 98122 #016-11-1977 L1978 **IM CD** *020 †20
SPECTOR, Gary Brian. 1221 MADISON ST, STE 910 98104 #025-01-1973 L1978 **PD IM** *020 †55
SPEICHER, James Edward. ■ 98115 #019-02-2006 L2006 **GS** *012
SPENCE, Alexander Morton. 1959 NE PACIFIC ST, UNIV OF WASH MED CTR 98195 #016-02-1965 L1974 **N NP** *040 †75
SPITTERS, Christopher E. 1637 N 53RD ST 98103 #005-11-1989 L1991 **GPM** *020 †70
SPOERL, Otto Heinrich. 1730 MINOR AVE STE 1400 98101 #407-04-1957 L1963 **P** *071 †75
SPOONEMORE, Kerrie Joell. 1101 MADISON ST STE 700 98104 #054-04-2001 L2001 **D** *020
SPRINGER, David Alan. 4005 WALLINGFORD AVE N 98103 #038-06-1969 L1972 **GPM PHP** *020 †55
SPRINGER, Wilbur J, Jr. 3400 CALIFORNIA AVE SW 98116 #024-01-1961 L1967 **IM** *020
SQUIRE, James Michael. 5343 TALLMAN AVE NW, STE 203 98107 #038-06-1969 L1980 **GP ADM** *020 †55
SRINIVAS, Nivedita Suvarn. 4800 SAND POINT WAY NE, REGIONAL M 98105 #005-02-2006 L2006 **PD** *012
SRINIVASAN, Jayashree. 801 BROADWAY STE 617, NEUROSURGICAL CONSULTANTS 98122 #035-01-1990 L1991 **NS** *020 †25
STACK, Fe' Cabuso. 500 5TH AVE - 6W, HEALTH & REHAB SERVICES 98104 #748-01-1955 L1988 **P** *071
STACK, Robert Erwin. 1118 9TH AVE 98101 #041-01-1957 L1965 **HS ORS** *071 †40
STACKHOUSE, Frank Alan. 325 9TH AVE 98104 #025-12-1983 L1993 **MPD IM** *020 †20,55
STADIUS, Michael Lauri. 1660 S COLUMBIAN WAY, VA MEDICAL CENTER 98108 #040-02-1978 L1982 **CD** *050 †20
STAFFORD, Michele Monique. ■ 98103 #028-79-2007, ▲ L2007 *012
STAFIE, Daniela Cristina. 1959 NE PACIFIC ST BOX 356, UW SCHOOL OF MEDICINE GME 98195 #781-02-2000 L2005 **GS** *020
STAGE, David Elliott. 1100 9TH AVE 98101 #024-01-1965 L1969 **RHU IM** *071 †20
STAGMAN, Robert Gary. 200 16TH AVE E 98112 #016-02-1962 L1970 **OTO** *071 †45
STAHELI, Lynn Taylor. 4800 SAND POINT WAY NE, CHILDREN'S HOSPITAL, CH-59 98105 #049-01-1959 L1964 **ORS** *071 †40
STAHL, Justin Hugh. 1100 9TH AVE G1-MSO, VIRGINIA MASON MEDICAL CEN 98101 #041-14-2000 L2005 **CN** *020 †75

9288

■ = Address Information Privacy Protected

STAIGER, Thomas Owen. 4245 ROOSEVELT WAY NE, STE 354775 98105 #054-04-1985 L1986 **EM IM** *020 †20
STALL, Luke Edward. ■ 98122 #038-06-2004 L2005 **DR** *012
STAMATOYANNOPOULOS, Geo. UNIVERSITY OF WASHINGTON, UNIV WA PHYS MEDL GENETICS 98195 #418-01-1958 **OS** *050 †19
STAMATOYANNOPOULOS, John. ■ 98122 #054-04-1995 **HO** *100 †20
STAMATOYANNOPOULOS, T. 1959 NE PACIFIC ST RM 1, BOX 357710 98195 #418-01-1961 L1975 **HEM IM** *050
STAMBOR, Daniel Chas. 747 BROADWAY 98122 #038-40-1981 L1999 **IM CD** *020 †20
STAMM, Stanley J. 4800 SAND POINT WAY NE 98105 #028-34-1952 L1954 **PDC PD** *072 †55
STAMM, Walter Edward. 1959 NE PACIFIC ST, DISEASES 98195 #024-01-1971 L1972 **ID IM** *050 †20
STANDAERT, Christopher J. 325 9TH AVE, BOX 359721 98104 #024-01-1992 L1999 **PM** *020 †60 ‡
STANEK, Dawn Marie. ■ 98107 #054-04-2008 *012
STANESCU, Arta Luana. 1959 NE PACIFIC ST 98195 #781-01-1994 L2006 **AR** *012
STANGER, Michael Terence. ■ 98112 #035-19-2007 L2007 **P** *012
STANGLER, Ronnie Sue. ■ 98101 #035-08-1971 L1975 **P OS** *020 †75
STANLEY, Carol Ann. 125 16TH AVE E, CSB 4 98112 #005-19-1979 L1980 **FM** *020 †18
STANLEY, Robt Boswell, Jr. 325 9TH AVE # 359894, HARBORVIEW MEDICAL CTR 98104 #036-07-1976 L1993 **HNS** *040 †45
STANLEY, William Jeffrey. 600 UNIVERSITY ST, STE 1200 98101 #041-12-1987 L1998 **CD** *020 †20
STANSFIELD, Stephen James. ■ 98107 #010-01-1977 L1979 **FM** *071 †18
STAPLES, Shannon Dawn. 335 16TH AVE E UNIT A 98112 #045-01-1998 L2001 **PD** *020 †55
STAPLETON, Ann Elizabeth. 1959 NE PACIFIC ST 98195 #035-46-1984 L1987 **ID IM** *050 †20
STAPLETON, Fielding B. 4800 SAND POINT WAY NE, DEPT PD 98105 #019-02-1972 L1996 **PD PN** *030 †55
STARKEBAUM, Gordon Alan. 1660 S COLUMBIAN WAY, VA PUGET SOUND HEALTH CARE 98108 #035-01-1970 L1971 **RHU IM** *030 †20
STARKEBAUM, Mary Kathryn. 6800 E GREEN LAKE WAY N 98115 #054-04-1978 L1979 **IM** *020 †20
STARNES, Benjamin Mason. 600 UNIVERSITY ST, STE 1200 98101 #012-22-1998 L2007 **PD** *020 †55
STAUDINGER, Benjamin John. 1959 NE PACIFIC ST, U OF W-HS AFFAIRS BOX 3563 98195 #054-04-2004 L2004 **IM** *012 †20
STAUNTON, Catherine E. 622 11TH AVE E, KIN COUNTY DEPART OF HEALT 98102 #035-20-1991 L1993 **PD** *020 †55
STAVER, Jonathan Harrison. ■ 98117 #054-04-2005 L2005 **AN** *012
ST CLAIR, Torri. ■ 98144 #010-03-2003 L2003 **AN** *100
STEAD, George John. 1770 NW 58TH ST STE 124 98107 #028-34-1954 L1961 **R** *071 †80
STEEGE, Timothy Douglas. 801 BROADWAY STE 617 98122 #005-11-1979 L1980 **NS** *020 †25
STEELE, Jeffrey James. 7554 15TH AVE NW 98117 #028-34-1968 L1971 **PD** *020 †55
STEFANOVIC, Ksenija B. 1100 9TH AVE C1-MSO, VIRGINIA MASON MEDICAL CEN 98101 #957-02-1978 L2001 **IM** *020 †20
STEIERT, Jerry Carl. 901 BOREN AVE STE 1800, SUMMIT RESEARCH NETWORK 98104 #054-04-1968 L1969 **P** *050 †75
STEIGER, Scott Jeffrey. ■ 98107 #028-02-2005 L2005 **IM** *012
STEIN, August Lawrence. ■ 98105 #054-04-2008 *012
STEIN, Diane T C. 4026 NE 55TH ST STE E200 98105 #026-04-1968 L1971 **P CHP** *020 †75
STEINBACH, Gideon. 1959 NE PACIFIC ST, BOX 356424 98195 #035-46-1981 L2000 **IM GE** *020 †20
STEINBERG, Kenneth P. 325 9TH AVE, CAMPUS BOX 359762 98104 #035-09-1985 L1989 **PCC IM** *050 †20
STEKLER, Joanne Donna. 325 9TH AVE, BOX 359930 98104 #036-07-1997 L2000 **ID** *100 †20
STEMPIEN, April Caroline. 1959 NE PACIFIC ST, BOX 356422 98195 #008-02-1990 L1994 **CD** *020 †20
STENCHEVER, Morton Albert. 130 NICKERSON ST, STE 211 98109 #035-06-1956 L1977 **OBG** *040 †30
STEPAK, Paul Howard. ■ 98103 #005-02-1982 L1995 **OM** *075
STEPHENSON-FAMY, Alyssa B. ■ 98117 #054-04-2004 L2004 **OBG** *012
STERN, Eric James. 325 9TH AVE 98104 #033-05-1985 L1992 **DR** *020 †80
STERN, Ryan Edward. 1959 NE PACIFIC ST 356340, UW SCHOOL OF MEDICINE 98195 #035-19-2001 L2001 **OTO** *020
STEVENS, Alexander R, Jr. 747 BROADWAY 98122 #035-20-1946 L1950 **ON HEM** *071 †20
STEVENS, Anne Marguerite. ■ 98109 #048-04-1995 L1997 **PPR** *020 †55
STEVENS, Bryn. 9800 4TH AVE NE 98115 #048-12-1987 L1989 **PD** *020 †55
STEVENS, Gary Scott. 1801 NW MARKET ST, STE 308 98107 #054-04-1976 L1977 **FM** *020 †18
STEVENS, Nancy Gray. 1959 NE PACIFIC ST, BOX 356390 98195 #054-04-1979 L1982 **HS PHP** *020 †18
STEVENSON, Bruce Eric. 1100 9TH AVE 98101 #016-11-1969 L1970 **EM** *071 †20,16
STEVENSON, James Geoffrey. 4800 SAND POINT WAY NE, CHLDRNS HOSP W4841 98105 #048-04-1970 L1974 **PDC PD** *020 †55
STEVENSON, Rae Lee. ■ 98105 #054-04-2008 *012
STEVER, Robert Chandler. ■ 98126 #041-01-1961 L1965 **GP** *020
STEWART, Douglas Keith. 1959 NE PACIFIC ST, UNIVERSITY HOSPITAL RP 20 98195 #024-01-1965 L1968 **CD** *020 †20
STEWART, Forrest Marc. 825 EASTLAKE AVE E, G4-100 98109 #017-20-1977 L2000 **IM HEM** *020 †20
STEWART, Glenn Rutledge. ■ 98101 #021-01-1983 L1986 **RO** *020 †80
STEWART, Michael Berkley. PO BOX 9089 98109 #023-01-1975 L1978 **ON HEM** *050 †20
STEWART, Patricia Stott. 1124 COLUMBIA ST 98104 #055-01-1969 L1973 **EM** *020 †20
STEWART, Wm Crawford, Jr. 515 MINOR AVE 98104 #055-01-1965 L1973 **IM PUD** *020 †20
STICHMAN, Jennifer Ruth. ■ 98115 #054-04-2008 *012
STIENS, Steven Andrew. 1660 S COLUMBIAN WAY, SCI 128 VA PUGET SOUND HEA 98108 #038-41-1986 L1993 **PM** *020 †60
STILLWAGGON, Jenny Elizab. ■ 98107 #024-01-2007 L2007 **PD** *012
STIMSON, John Boyd. 1145 BROADWAY 98122 #054-04-1981 L1982 **IM** *020 †20
STIPP, Charles Grant. ■ 98105 #019-02-1943 L1949 **OBG OS** *071 †30
STIREWALT, Derek Lynn. 1959 NE PACIFIC ST, BOX 358080 98195 #036-01-1992 L1996 **ON** *020 †20
STIRTON, Malcolm Scott. ■ 98136 #005-11-1972 L1976 **PTH** *071 †50
STITES, Ryan Deane. 1959 NE PACIFIC ST 98195 #539-04-2005 L2005 **AN** *012
STITHAM, Sean O'Brien. ■ 98103 #050-02-1981 L1995 **IM** *020 †20
STITZEL, Maria Ramos. ■ 98117 #016-06-2006 L2007 **PTH** *012
STIVELMAN, John Cooper. 700 BROADWAY, NORTHWEST KIDNEY CENTERS 98122 #041-01-1978 L1999 **NEP IM** *030 †20
STOBBE, Gary Allen. 515 MINOR AVE, STE 200 98104 #035-03-1989 L1993 **N** *020 †75
STODDARD, Cynthia Padden. ■ 98103 #054-04-1998 L2002 **P** *020 †75
STOILOVA, Zornitza Stoilo. ■ 98103 #016-06-2004 L2004 **N** *012
STOLOV, Walter Chas. 1959 NE PACIFIC ST, MSC BOX 356490 98195 #026-04-1956 L1960 **PM** *020 †60
STOLZ, Jeffrey Whitcomb. 1101 MADISON ST, STE 800 98104 #036-01-1988 L1998 **NPM** *020 †55
STOLZ, Sarah Ellen. 801 BROADWAY, INSTITUTE HEATH BLDG STE#7 98122 #038-06-1985 L1989 **SME** *020 †75
STONE, E Franklin. ■ 98115 #041-02-1954 L1963 **PD OS** *020 †55
STONE, Giancarlo Clyde. 1600 E JOHN ST 98112 #561-11-1979 L1985 **RHU IM** *020 †20
STONE, Jessica Margaret. 1959 NE PACIFIC ST RM C2, GRAD. MEDICAL BOX 356340 98195 #054-04-1995 L1999 **P** *020
STONE, Kimberly P. 4800 SAND POINT WAY NE, MAILSTOP B-5520 98105 #005-02-2001 L2005 **PEM** *100 †55
STONE, Miriam Lee. 747 BROADWAY 98122 #054-04-1987 L1995 **AN** *020 †05
STONINGTON, David Tailer. 125 16TH AVE E 98112 #007-02-1970 L1973 **FM** *020 †18
STORCK, Michael Guy. ■ 98105 #038-43-1980 L1989 **P CHP** *020 †75
STOREK, Jan. 1100 FAIRVIW AVE N #D1-100 98109 #286-13-1984 L1992 **IM HO** *050 †20
STOREY, Donald Duncan. 600 UNIVERSITY ST, STE 1400 98101 #040-02-1972 L1976 **PUD CCM** *020 †20
STORY, Brian Thomas. PO BOX 356421, UNIV OF WASHINGTON 98195 #054-04-2007 L2007 **IM** *012
STOUT, David Michael. 747 BROADWAY 98122 #019-02-1983 L1984 **AN OS** *020 †05
STOUT, James Walden. 6200 NE 74TH ST, STE 210 98115 #036-05-1986 L1989 **PD** *020 †55
STOVER DALTON, Susan A. ■ 98115 #054-04-1985 L1986 **IM** *020 †20
ST PIERRE, Jos Raoul, Jr. 200 15TH AVE E CHF-313, GROUP HEALTH COOPERATIVE 98112 #024-05-1969 L1970 **GS VS** *020 †85
STRACENER, Janice Carol. 600 BROADWAY, STE 170 98122 #023-12-1988 L1991 **DR** *040 †80
STRAHILEVITZ, Aharona. PO BOX 25008 98165 #550-01-1961 L1981 **CHP P** *071 †75
STRAHILEVITZ, Meir. 4501 NE 106TH ST, BOX 25008 98125 #550-01-1963 L1969 **P** *020 †75
STRALEY, Hugh Larrington. 320 WESTLAKE AVE N, STE 100 98109 #054-04-1968 L1973 **ON HEM** *020 †20
STRAND, Glenn T. 901 BOREN AVE STE 707 98104 #054-04-1952 L1954 **P** *071 †75
STRANDBERG, Eric John. 1151 DENNY WAY 98109 #054-04-1980 L1983 **FM** *020 †18
STRATE, Lisa Lynn. 325 9TH AVE, BOX 359773 98104 #005-02-1995 L2006 **GE IM** *050 †20
STRATIL, Peter Gabriel. 1959 NE PACIFIC ST, BOX 356340 98195 #016-02-2005 L2006 **DR** *012
STRATIS, Christina Antoni. ■ 98115 #054-04-2008 *012
STRATTON, John Russell. 1660 S COLUMBIAN WAY #111C 98108 #008-01-1973 L1976 **CD IM** *050 †20
STRAUSS, Susan Gail. 4800 SAND POINT WAY NE, P O BOX C-5371 98105 #016-42-1984 L1987 **AN** *020 †05
STREIDL, John Ryan. 11011 MERIDIAN AVE N, STE 200 98133 #028-34-1997 L2001 **D** *020 †15
STRICK, Lara Beth. 901 BOREN AVE, STE 1300 98104 #041-01-1999 L2001 **ID** *100 †20
STRICKLAND, Elizabeth Ann. 1100 9TH AVE 98101 #054-04-1982 L1983 **OBG** *020 †30
STRIEGL, Amanda Michele. 4800 SAND POINT WAY NE, MAIL STOP A-5937 98105 #007-02-2004 L2004 **PDP** *012 †55
STRIGEL, Roberta Marie. 1959 NE PACIFIC ST, UNIV OF WASHINGTON 98195 #056-05-2004 L2005 **DR** *012
STROMATT, Scott C. 501 ELLIOTT AVE W, STE 400 98119 #016-02-1983 L1984 **IM OM** *050 †20
STROTE, Jared Nathan. 1959 NE PACIFIC ST, BOX 356123 98195 #024-01-1999 L2002 **EM** *020 †16
STROTE, Justin Aribenjami. ■ 98199 #025-01-2001 L2003 **IC** *012
STROUD, Julie Ann. 1401 MADISON ST STE 100, SWEDISH MED CTR-SEATTLE 98104 #905-02-2003 L2003 **FM** *100 †18
STRUMWASSER, Todd Alan. 747 BROADWAY 98122 #005-06-1981 L1982 **AN** *020 †05
STRUTYNSKA-LONGAWA, Marta. ■ 98115 #759-01-1993 L2000 **AN** *020 †05
STUART, Michael Emmett. 6831 31ST AVE NE 98115 #054-04-1971 L1972 **FM OS** *030 †18
STUART, Scott Robert. ■ 98103 #054-04-2001 L2004 **IM** *100
STURMAN, Robert M. PO BOX 3004 98114 #035-19-1949 L1993 **OPH** *071 †35
SU, Catherine T. ■ 98102 #385-02-1962 L1969 **IM** *071
SUBRAMANIAN, Savitha. 1959 NE PACIFIC ST, CAMPUS BOX 356426 98195 #495-16-1997 L2004 **END** *020 †20
SUBRAMANIAN, Shoba Lakshm. ■ 98105 #065-01-2003 L2007 **END** *012 †20
SUCHDEV, Parminder Singh. ■ 98105 #016-06-2002 L2004 **PD** *100 †55
SUCHOSKI, Jos Francis, Jr. 5421 CALIFORNIA AVE SW, CHILDREN'S CLINIC INC PS 98136 #054-04-1965 L1966 **PD** *071 †55
SUEDA, Lilaann Akie. 1100 9TH AVE 98101 #014-01-1995 L1999 **AN** *020 †05
SUEDA, Odette Tamiko. 4400 37TH AVE S, COLUMBIA HEALTH CENTER 98118 #014-01-1982 L1983 **PD** *020 †55
SUGAR, Naomi F. 1401 E JEFFERSON ST # 400 98122 #056-06-1979 L1982 **PD** *020 †55
SUGARMAN, Jonathan Reuel. 10700 MERIDIAN AVE N, STE 100 98133 #035-46-1981 L1982 **FM PHP** *030 †70,18
SUGG, Nancy Kathleen. 325 9TH AVE MS 359945, HARBORVIEW MEDICAL CENTER 98104 #023-01-1983 L1984 **IM** *020 †20
SULLIVAN, Jeffrey Hugh. 125 16TH AVE E, GROUP HEALTH 98112 #026-04-1991 L1999 **PCC** *020 †20
SULLIVAN, Kent Nugent. 1530 N 115TH ST 98133 #017-20-1960 L1969 **PUD CCM** *020
SULLIVAN, Mark Danl. 4245 ROOSEVELT WAY NE, STE 354775 98105 #047-05-1984 L1985 **P** *020 †75
SULLIVAN, Mark David. ■ 98103 #054-04-2003 L2003 **IM** *100 †20
SULLIVAN, Mary Ann. 2111 N NORTHGATE WAY 98133 #054-04-1966 L1976 **IM** *020
SULTANA, Razia. 1959 NE PACIFIC ST, UNIV OF WA SCH OF MED 98195 #704-20-1985 L2007 **P** *012
SUMI, Shuzo Mark. 2324 EASTLAKE AVE E, STE 500 98102 #065-01-1956 L1967 **N NP** *071 †75
SUMMERFIELD, Jill Anne. 3400 CALIFORNIA AVE SW, STE 300 98116 #054-04-1985 L1986 **IM** *020 †20
SUMMERS, Krista Jane. 550 16TH AVE STE 100, SWEDISH FAMILY MED 98122 #023-01-2006 L2007 **FP** *012
SUN, Gilbert Dong Feng. 747 BROADWAY, SWEDISH ADULT HOSPITALISTS 98122 #825-01-1999 L2005 **IM** *020 †20
SUN, Jen Chih. 1425 BROADWAY, PMB 418 98122 #047-07-1998 L2002 **AN** *020
SUN, Lucille Chin-Yun. ■ 98109 #242-09-1944 L1958 **PTH** *071 †50
SUN, Wensi. 10564 5TH AVE NE STE 102 98125 #243-29-1983 L2001 **OPH** *020 †35
SUNDARARAJAN, Lavanya. ■ 98103 #495-04-1998 L2005 **ON** *100
SUNG, Jeffrey Chenning. 126 NW CANAL ST, STE 310 98107 #016-06-1998 L2001 **P** *020 †75

SURAWICZ, Christina M. 325 9TH AVE, HARBORVIEW MEDICAL CENTER 98104 #020-12-1973 L1974 **GE** *020 †20

SURI, Pradeep. 1660 S COLUMBIAN WAY, VA PUGET SOUND HLTH CARE 98108 #025-01-2002 L2002 **PM** *100

SUSKIND, David Lewinter. PO BOX 5371, CHILDRENS HOSP OF SEATTLE 98105 #021-05-1997 L2003 **PG** *100 †55

SUSLOVA, Olga Ernestovna. 1959 NE PACIFIC ST, BOX 356560 98195 #913-05-1985 L2003 **P** *100 †75

SUSNOW, Nathan Jeremy. ■ 98102 #048-12-2004 L2007 **GE** *012 †20

SUSSMAN, Amy Nicole. 1959 NE PACIFIC ST, BOX 356521 98195 #003-01-2001 L2004 **NEP** *012

SUTCLIFFE, Erin C. 325 9TH AVE, BOX 359780 98104 #016-02-2000 L2003 **IM** *020 †20

SUTCLIFFE, Richard Toby. 1229 MADISON ST STE 1190 98104 #061-01-1978 L1983 **OPH PS** *071

SUTPHEN, Lucy Rusk. 1100 9TH AVE 98101 #023-07-1985 L1988 **IM** *030 †20

SUTTON, Eliza Leeds. 4245 ROOSEVELT WAY NE, STE 354775 98105 #024-01-1990 L1990 **IM** *020 †20

SUTTON, Paul Randolph. 4245 ROOSEVELT WAY NE, STE 354775 98105 #016-02-1994 L1998 **IM** *020 †20

SUVER, Daniel William. PO BOX 356410, UNIV OF WASHINGTON 98195 #054-04-2004 L2004 **GS** *012

SUWANVANICHKIJ, Voravit. ■ 98122 #023-07-2000 L2003 **IM** *100 †20

SUYDAM, Christine Naomi. ■ 98105 #047-05-1992 L1992 **CHP** *020

SUYEHIRA, Janice Gayle. 125 16TH AVE E, GROUP HEALTH COOPERATIVE O 98112 #054-04-1975 L1976 **FM** *020 †18

SVIRCEV, Jelena Natascha. 1660 S COLUMBIAN WAY, SCI 128 98108 #056-05-2001 L2005 **SCI** *100 †60

SVIRI, Gill Ephraim. 1959 NE PACIFIC ST BOX 356, UW SCHOOL OF MED GME PROGR 98195 #550-03-1996 L2002 *100

SWAFFORD, Thomas D. 509 OLIVE WAY, STE 555 98101 #048-02-1951 L1962 **D** *020 †15

SWAN, David Anthony. ■ 98115 #005-06-1963 L1964 **CD IM** *071 †20

SWANSON, Jonathan Ogden. UNIV OF WASHINGTON MED CTR, DIAGNOSTIC RADIOLOGY BOX 98195 #041-01-2003 L2003 **DR** *012

SWANSON, Mary Nielsen. ■ 98115 #054-04-2005 L2005 **FP** *012

SWANSON, Phillip Dean. UNIV WASH SCH MED MED NEUR 98105 #023-07-1958 L1965 **N** *050 †75

SWANSON, Thomas Nestor. 1101 MADISON ST, STE 800 98104 #051-04-1985 L1988 **ID PD** *020 †55

SWARNY, Bruce Robt. 1959 NE PACIFIC ST, PSYCHIATRY RESIDENCY PRGM 98195 #038-41-1990 L2007 **P** *012 †18

SWARTZ, Mia Addison. 1959 NE PACIFIC ST BOX 3, WASHINGTON UROLO 98195 #005-12-2001 L2001 **U** *100

SWEENEY, Terrence J. 3626 NE 45TH ST STE 300 98105 #054-04-1980 L1985 **NPM PD** *020 †55

SWEETSER, Marianne T. PO BOX 356320, UNIV OF WASHINGTON SCH OF 98195 #028-02-1990 L1993 **IG PLI** *050 †03,55

SWENSEN, Ron Edward. UNIVERSITY OF WASHINGTON, DEPT OF OB-GYN BOX 356460 98195 #005-12-1984 L2003 **GO OBG** *020 †30

SWENSON, Cara Alane. 1959 NE PACIFIC ST, DEPT OF NEPHROLOGY 98195 #054-04-2003 L2003 **NEP** *012 †20

SWENSON, Erik Richard. 1660 S COLUMBIAN WAY, S-111-PULM 98108 #005-18-1979 L1984 **PUD IM** *020 †20

SWINDALL, Jennifer Lynn. ■ 98115 #048-02-2007 L2007 **IM** *012

SWINGLE, Jad Damon. 550 16TH AVE, STE 400 98122 #016-43-2000 L2007 **ICE** *100 †20

SWISHER, Elizabeth Mary. 1959 NE PACIFIC ST, BOX 356460 98195 #005-18-1992 L1992 **OBG** *020 †30

SY, Jesus Balbin. 2535 BEACON AVE S 98144 #748-08-1981 L1985 **GP** *020

SYBERT, Virginia Phyllis. 125 16TH AVE E CSB3, GROUP HEALTH COOPERATIVE 98112 #035-06-1974 L1978 **MG D** *020 †55,19

SYLVESTER, Carrie E. 1600 E OLIVE ST 98122 #054-04-1970 L1972 **CHP PD** *020 †55,75

SYLVESTER, John Edward. 1101 MADISON ST, STE 1101 98104 #005-14-1984 L1988 **RO** *020 †80

SYMONS, Jordan Matthew. 4800 SAND POINT WAY NE, DIV OF PED NEPH M1-5 98105 #035-01-1992 L1999 **PD** *020 †55

SYROVY, Eva O. ■ 98155 #286-02-1955 L1971 **PD** *020

SYROVY, George. 1959 NE PACIFIC ST 98195 #286-02-1955 L1971 **AN** *020

SYTMAN, Alexander Ludwik. 550 17TH AVE 98122 #054-04-1963 L1964 **CD IC** *020 †20

SZALAY, Andrew George. 7210 ROOSEVELT WAY NE 98115 #030-06-1998 L2000 **FM** *020 †18

SZYSZKO, Amy Lidia. ■ 98103 #033-06-1998 L2007 **EM** *020 †16

TA, Kent Thien. 515 MINOR AVE, STE 200 98104 #008-01-1997 L2002 **RHU** *020 †20

TAAGEN, Sam Rand. 1530 N 115TH ST, STE 104 98133 #056-05-1995 L2002 **IM** *020 †20

TAFEN WANDJI, Marcel Kleb. 1959 NE PACIFIC ST 98195 #913-65-2000 L2006 **GS** *012

TAHERI, Mohammad Reza. ■ 98146 #056-06-2004 L2005 **DR** *012

TAI, Oliver Shuon. 1959 NE PACIFIC ST, MEDICINE, BOX 356521 98195 #036-07-2000 L2003 **CCM** *012 †20

TAIRA, Al Vincent. ■ 98102 #005-11-2005 L2006 **RO** *012

TAIT, Jonathan Francis. 1959 NE PACIFIC ST, MSC 359300 98195 #028-02-1983 L1984 **CLP CMG** *050 †50,19

TAITSMAN, Lisa A. 325 9TH AVE BOX 359798, MED CTR/DEPT OF ORTHOPEDIC 98104 #043-01-1994 L2001 **ORS** *020 †40

TAKAHASHI, Traci Ann. 1660 S COLUMBIAN WAY, HSR&D VA PUGET SOUND MS152 98108 #005-18-1995 L1995 **IM** *020 †20

TAKAKI, Mark Thomas Takeo. 1107 NE 45TH ST # 44, UNIV OF WASH,DEPT OF RADIO 98105 #014-01-2001 L2001 **AR** *020 †80

TAKAKI, W Richard. 200 16TH AVE E 98112 #010-01-1964 L1965 **FM GP** *071 †18

TAKAMIYA, Robert Kiyomi. 1101 MADISON ST, STE 1101 98104 #035-19-1999 L2004 **RO** *020 †80

TAKARO, Timothy K. 4225 ROOSEVELT WAY NE, STE 98105 #036-01-1985 L1993 **OM** *020 †70

TAKASUGI, Julie Emiko. 1959 NE PACIFIC ST, MSC 359300 98195 #005-14-1982 L1988 **DR** *020 †80

TAKAYAMA, Thomas K. 1959 NE PACIFIC ST BOX 356, UNIVERSITY OF WASHINGTON 98195 #024-07-1985 L1989 **U** *040 †95

TAKESHITA, Junko. ■ 98102 #028-02-2007 L2007 **IM** *012

TAKI, James Alan. 1001 4TH AVE STE 420 98154 #054-04-1983 L1984 **FM FPG** *020 †18

TALBOT, Peter Allan. 500 17TH AVE 98122 #056-05-1971 L1976 **PD FM** *020 †55

TALL, Lisa Carol. 200 16TH AVE E 98112 #054-04-1985 L1990 **IM** *020 †20

TALLEY, Angela Kathleen. UNIV WA MED CTR ANNEX #4, BOX 355330 98195 #035-47-2001 L2004 **ID** *012 †20

TALLEY-ROSTOV, Audrey Ros. 10330 MERIDIAN AVE N, STE 370 98133 #028-02-1988 L1993 **OPH** *020 †35

TALNER, Lee Bland. 325 9TH AVE 98104 #008-01-1963 L1993 **DR** *040 †80

TAM, Roland Kam. ■ 98103 #035-46-2005 L2006 **AN** *012

TAMADDON, Houman. ■ 98109 #035-45-1997 L2000 **AN** *020 †05

TAMBURINE, Francis. 1321 35TH AVE S 98144 #050-02-1986 L1998 **AN** *020 †05

TAMIMI, Hisham K. 1959 NE PACIFIC ST, UWMC BOX 356460 98195 #330-02-1969 L1977 **GO OBG** *020 †30

TAMMISETTI, Varaha Satya. 1107 NE 45TH ST, STE 440 98105 #495-11-1998 L2005 **AR** *012

TAMURA, Glen Sho. 4800 SAND POINT WAY NE 98105 #005-11-1987 L1990 **PD** *050 †55

TAN, Dave Benedicto. ■ 98115 #748-02-1981 L1988 **NEP IM** *020 †55

TAN, Sharon Nuval. 1401 MADISON ST, STE 100 98104 #748-10-1998 L2006 **FP** *012

TAN, Swee Lian. 1145 BROADWAY, THE POLYCLINIC 98122 #024-01-1988 L2004 **VS GS** *020 †85

TANIGUCHI, Darik Kono. 1145 BROADWAY 98122 #054-04-1988 L1990 **GE** *020 †20

TANK, Robert Eugene. 7006 BRIGHTON LN S 98118 #035-03-1966 L1973 **PTH** *071 †50

TANNER, Christina Elena. 4245 ROOSEVELT WAY NE, STE 354775 98105 #064-01-1987 L1992 **FM** *020 †18

TANNOUS, Beatrice. 10330 MERIDIAN AVE N, STE 210 98133 #018-03-2001 L2006 **PD** *100 †55

TAPLIN, Stephen Hunt. 200 15TH AVE E CX5, FAMILY PRACTICE 98112 #005-19-1978 L1983 **GPM PHP** *020 †18

TAPP, Jesse W, Jr. ■ 98115 #016-02-1955 L1976 **GPM FM** *071 †70,18

TAPSCOTT, Stephen Justice. 1100 FAIRVIEW AVE N, FRED HUTCHINSON CNCR RESCH 98109 #041-01-1982 L1986 **N** *050 †75

TARADAY, Julie Kay. 1401 MADISON ST STE 100 98104 #054-04-2002 L2004 **FM** *020 †18

TARAS, Angie Rosanne. ■ 98109 #054-06-2005 L2006 **GS** *012

TARCZY-HORNOCH, Peter Z. 1959 NE PACIFIC ST, 356320 RR542 HSB 98195 #005-11-1989 L1992 **NPM** *050 †55

TARICA, Samuel H. 747 BROADWAY 98122 #054-04-1952 L1953 **PD A** *071 †55

TARNOFF, Stephen Leslie. 521 WALL ST 98121 #005-06-1978 L1979 **FM FPG** *030 †18

TASCH, Michael Andrew. 1959 NE PACIFIC ST, PO BOX 356521 98195 #054-04-2000 L2004 **NEP** *012

TAUBEN, David J. 515 MINOR AVE STE 300, MINOR & JAMES MEDICAL PLLC 98104 #024-07-1979 L1980 **IM GP** *020 †20

TAURO, Andrew John. UNIV OF WASHINGTON MED CTR, DIVISION OF NUCLEAR MED 98195 #143-02-1989 L1999 *100

TAUTVYDAS, Rasa Monika. 500 17TH AVE 98122 #026-04-1995 L1997 **IM** *020 †20

TAYLOR, Brianne Nicole. ■ 98115 #054-04-2008 *012

TAYLOR, Grant Edwin. 747 BROADWAY, PROVINDENCE CAMPUS 98122 #007-02-2004 L2004 **FPG** *012 †18

TAYLOR, James A, Jr. 4245 ROOSEVELT WAY NE, STE 354775 98105 #036-01-1980 L1987 **PD** *020 †20

TAYLOR, James Vinton. ■ 98102 #061-01-1954 L1961 **EM AN** *071 †05,16

TAYLOR, Jason Alan. 1959 NE PACIFIC ST, BOX 357710 98195 #005-15-2000 L2003 **HEM** *100

TAYLOR, Lynne Patricia. 1100 9TH AVE, MAILSTOP X7N 98101 #028-02-1982 L1988 **N ON** *020 †75

TAYLOR, Paul W. ■ 98115 #035-45-1953 L1973 **OBG** *071 †30

TAYLOR, Susannah Irene. 2808 BROADWAY E 98102 #054-04-1986 L1986 **IM OBG** *020 †20

TAYLOR, Thomas Raymond. 1959 NE PACIFIC ST, FAMILY MEDICINE-BOX 354696 98195 #803-05-1957 L1981 **FM** *030 †18

TAZUMA, Laurie Midori. 4020 E MADISON ST STE 240 98112 #054-04-1978 L1980 **P** *020 †75

TEKLEMICHAEL, Dawit Neray. ■ 98115 #054-04-2008 *012

TEKLU, Bayu. ■ 98122 #605-01-1965 L1973 **PUD** *050 †20

TE KOLSTE, Katherine Anne. 747 BROADWAY 98122 #017-20-1976 L1980 **PD** *020 †55

TELZROW, Robert Wm. 7554 15TH AVE NW, BALLARD PEDIATRIC CLINIC 98117 #038-40-1968 L1974 **PD GS** *020 †55

TEMPEST, David Peter. 1600 E JEFFERSON ST, STE 620 98122 #040-02-1979 L1980 **PM** *020 †60

TEMPLETON, Adam Webster. 544 N 73RD ST 98103 #032-01-2007 **IM** *012

TENCKHOFF, Eleonore. 4800 SAND PT WAY NE 98105 #917-20-1952 L1976 **PDC** *040

TENCKHOFF, Heinrich A M. ■ 98105 #407-22-1955 L1966 **NEP IM** *071

TENG, Leland. 1100 9TH AVE C1-MSO, VIRGINIA MASON MEDICAL CEN 98101 #048-12-1983 L1984 **IM** *020 †20

TEPLY, Joseph Frank. 1600 E JEFFERSON ST, STE 110 98122 #038-40-1976 L1992 **TS VS** *020 †85,90

TERASAKI, Genji. 1822B 23RD AVE 98122 #038-06-2001 L2003 **IM** *020

TERASAKI, Rodney Dale. 1200 12TH AVE S 98144 #021-01-1983 L1984 **IM** *020 †20

TERHAAR, Paula Ann. 125 16TH AVE E 98112 #054-04-1981 L1982 **FM** *020 †18

TERMAN, Gregory Wm. 1959 NE PACIFIC ST, BOX 356540 98195 #011-02-1987 L1989 **AN PME** *050 †05

TESCHNER, Robert Erwin. ■ 98127 #054-04-1974 L1976 **FPG P** *075

TESH, Donald Wayne. 1221 MADISON ST, STE 1220 98104 #054-04-1967 L1968 **RO** *071 †80

TEWARI, Muneesh. 1100 FAIRVIEW AVE N, MAILSTOP D4-100 98109 #025-01-1997 L2007 **HO** *020 †20

TEWARI, Suman Lata. 4527B NE 55TH ST 98105 #025-07-1998 L2005 **OBG** *020 †30

TEWODROS, Abel. ■ 98115 #054-04-1995 L1998 **EM** *020 †16

THACH, Tien Thuy. PO BOX 95613 98145 #054-04-2006 L2006 **IM** *012

THAKAR, Monica Sharad. 4800 SAND POINT WAY NE 6D1, CHILDREN'S HOSPITAL & REGI 98105 #045-01-2001 L2004 **PHO** *020 †55

THAKE, Mary Elizabeth. ■ 98105 #016-45-2007 L2007 **OBG** *012

THAKRAR, Pooja Dhiren. 747 BROADWAY STE 731, SWEDISH MED CTR FIRST HILL 98122 #048-12-2007 L2007 **GS** *012

THAKUR, Sarvesh Smiley. 747 BROADWAY 98122 #068-01-1990 L1998 **NEP OS** *020 †20

THALER, Joshua Paul. GRADUATE MEDICAL ED BOX 35, UNIVERSITY OF WASHINGTON 98195 #005-18-2003 L2003 **END** *012 †20

THANDRA, Vamshi R. ■ 98122 #025-07-2005 L2006 **IM** *012

THAPA, Mahesh Man. 1107 NE 45TH ST, UNIV OF WASH,DEPT OF RADIO 98105 #005-06-2000 L2001 **PDR** *100 †80

THAYER, Christopher W. 125 16TH AVE E, GRP HLTH CHS BLDG 98112 #005-14-1997 L2004 **FM** *100 †18

THEISEN, Michael Patrick. 1550 N 115TH ST, SURGICAL SERVICES 98133 #054-04-1979 L1980 **AN** *020 †05

THEISS, Monica Strope. 325 9TH AVE, PO BOX 359911 98104 #054-04-1999 L2005 **P** *100 †75

THEOBALD, Michael Ashton. ■ 98177 #054-04-1968 L1969 **GS** *100 †85

THIELKE, Stephen Michael. 7527 12TH AVE NE 98115 #054-04-2001 L2003 **PYG** *100

THIEME, William Terrance. 1801 NW MARKET ST, STE 403 98107 #028-02-1961 L1966 **ORS** *020 †40

THILO, Jane L. 509 OLIVE WAY, 3RD FL 98101 #036-05-1978 L1984 **AN OS** *030 †05

THIRLBY, Richard Coller. 1100 9TH AVE, VA MASON MED CTR POB 900 98101 #025-01-1978 L1987 **GS GE** *020 †85

THISTLETHWAITE, Julie Mar. 1629 N 45TH ST 98103 #038-41-2007 L2007 **FP** *012

THOMAS, Chad Baldo. ■ 98115 #016-11-2006 L2006 **OBG** *012

THOMAS, David Bartlett. 1124 COLUMBIA ST 98104 #054-04-1963 L1965 **OS GPM** *050

THOMAS, Edward D. 1124 COLUMBIA ST 98104 #024-01-1946 L1963 **IM** *071 †20

THOMAS, George I. 1600 E JEFFERSON ST, STE 110 98122 #023-07-1949 L1953 **TS CD** *020 †85,90

THOMAS, Herbert C, Jr. 747 BROADWAY 98122 #007-02-1967 L1970 **OTO PDO** *020 †45

THOMAS, John Bradley. 4413 38TH AVE NE 98105 #054-04-1977 L1979 **FM** *020 †18

THOMAS, Kathy Jo. 415 N 85TH ST 98103 #041-01-1996 L1998 **FM** *020 †18

THOMAS, Kenneth Charles. 1229 MADISON ST, STE 1600 98104 #065-05-1997 L2001 **ORS** *100

THOMAS, Lisa Ann. 7210 ROOSEVELT WAY NE 98115 #005-02-1993 L1993 **FM** *020 †18

THOMAS, Tracy Danielle. 1959 NE PACIFIC ST C212, STAFF AFFAIRS BOX 356395 98195 #036-01-2002 L2002 **PD** *100 †55

THOMMAN, Sanju. 1401 MADISON ST, STE 100 98104 #016-11-1998 L2000 **FM** *020 †18

THOMPSON, Arthur R, III. 921 TERRY AVE, PUGET SOUND BLOOD CENTER 98104 #054-04-1981 L1974 **HEM IM** *050 †20

THOMPSON, Callie Marie. ■ 98144 #047-07-2008 *012

THOMPSON, Catherine S. 1100 9TH AVE 98101 #048-14-1979 L1991 **NEP IM** *020 †20

THOMPSON, Chas Edward, Jr. 1660 S COLUMBIAN WAY 98108 #010-01-1972 L1974 **P** *020 †75

THOMPSON, Chris Raymond. ■ 98144 #054-04-2000 L2002 **FM** *020 †18

THOMPSON, D Britzmann. 1229 MADISON ST STE 1290, NORTHWEST SKIN SPECIALISTS 98104 #054-04-1990 L1993 **D IM** *020 †15

THOMPSON, Doris V Harrell. 10030 15TH AVE SW 98146 #025-01-1958 L1978 **PD PHP** *071 †55

THOMPSON, Jeffery Noel. 401 2ND AVE S STE 400, MILLIMAN & ROBERTSON 98104 #030-05-1987 L1993 **OM IM** *030 †20,70

THOMPSON, Jennifer Christ. ■ 98112 #005-14-2004 L2004 **IM** *100 †20

THOMPSON, John Ainslie. 1959 NE PACIFIC ST, UWMC BOX 358081 G4-830 98195 #001-02-1979 L1980 **ON HEM** *020 †20

THOMPSON, John Shands. 98115 #035-08-1947 L1948 **P AM** *072

THOMPSON, Lester Walker. 310 15TH AVE E, GROUP HEATLH COOP 98112 #017-20-1968 L1975 **U** *020 †75

THOMPSON, Nathan Robert. ■ 98136 #054-04-2005 L2005 **FP** *012

THOMPSON, Rachel Ellen. 325 9TH AVE, HARBORVIEW MEDICAL CENTER 98104 #054-04-2000 L2002 **IM** *100 †20

THOMPSON, Robert Gail, Jr. 509 OLIVE WAY STE 1138 98101 #054-04-1971 L1972 **CD IM** *020 †20

THOMPSON, Robert Leonard. 1600 E JOHN ST 98112 #051-01-1972 L1973 **ID IM** *020 †20

THOMPSON, Robert Sharpe. 1730 MINOR AVE STE 1600 98101 #023-07-1965 L1971 **PD GPM** *050 †55

THOMPSON, Sara Allison. ■ 98112 #054-04-2008 *012

THOMPSON, Sara Ducharme. 125 16TH AVE E CSB4 98112 #054-04-1979 L1982 **FM** *020 †18

THOMSON, Blythe. 4800 SAND POINT WAY NE, MS B6553 98105 #038-40-1992 L1995 **PHO** *020 †55

THORNE, Frank Leadley. 1229 MADISON ST, STE 790 98104 #041-01-1957 L1968 **PS HS** *071 †65

THORNER, Brooke Joann. 2910 E MADISON ST, # 209 98112 #050-02-1978 L1982 **P PFP** *020 †75

THORNTON, Sean David. 1229 MADISON ST 98104 #054-04-1990 L1992 **PTH** *020 †50

THOTTINGAL, Paul A. ■ 98102 #062-01-1995 **IM ID** *100 †20

THRONSON, Lauren Renata. PO BOX 356421, UNIV OF WASHINGTON 98195 #024-01-2005 L2005 **IM** *012

THUC, Nguyen Huu. ■ 98136 #941-01-1970 **IM** *071 †20

THYERLEI, Dinah. 1959 NE PACIFIC ST 98195 #409-05-2000 L2006 **IM** *020

TIBLE, Prudencio Galvez. 5023 S BARTON PL 98118 #748-08-1979 L1984 **GPM FM** *062

TICKMAN, Ronald J. 1229 MADISON ST 98104 #012-05-1984 L1990 **PTH** *020 †50

TIEDER, Joel Stanford. ■ 98105 #012-01-1999 L2002 **PD** *020 †55

TILGHMAN, Stephen Ian. 747 BROADWAY 98122 #014-01-1997 L2004 **EM** *020 †16

TING, Andrew. 801 BROADWAY, STE 300 98122 #067-01-1990 L1990 **GS** *020 †85

TIRSCHWELL, David L. 325 9TH AVE 98104 #035-20-1991 L1993 **N** *020 †75

TISDALE, Patrick David. ■ 98119 #010-02-1958 L1982 **PD** *071 †55

TISHKEVICH, Natalia. 515 MINOR AVE, STE 200 98104 #913-64-1996 L2003 **RHU** *100 †20

TOBE, Robert. ■ 98105 #025-01-1955 L1962 **IM ON** *072 †20

TOBIAS, Stephen Schrom. 153 34TH AVE E, 153 34TH AVENUE 98112 #048-04-1974 L1976 **GP** *020

TOBIN, Richard W. 11027 MERIDIAN AVE N, N STE #100 98133 #048-12-1987 L1991 **GE** *020 †20

TODARO, George Jos, Jr. 3005 1ST AVE 98121 #035-19-1963 **PTH IG** *050

TODARO, Jane Wendy Lehv. 515 MINOR AVE, STE 200 98104 #035-19-1965 L1983 **GE PD** *020 †55

TODD, Mark Overton. 1100 9TH AVE 98101 #021-01-1981 L1982 **IM** *075

TOKESHI, Jay Ryan Seiko. 925 SENECA ST, MEDICAL CENTER 98101 #014-01-2006 L2006 **AN** *012

TOLMAN, J Samuel. 1560 N 115TH ST, STE G16 98133 #033-05-2000 L2007 **IM** *020 †20 ‡

TOMBERG, Michael F. 509 OLIVE WAY, STE 900 98101 #032-01-1997 L1999 **FM** *020 †18

TONCRAY, Kristina Ai. 4031 AURORA AVE N STE 402 98103 #028-02-2005 L2005 **PD** *012

TONELLI, Mark R. 1959 NE PACIFIC ST, DEPT OF PULMONARY MEDICINE 98195 #007-02-1989 L1993 **CCM PUD** *020 †20

TONELLI, Melinda Merlie. 1560 N 115TH ST STE 106 98133 #054-04-1998 L2002 **IM** *020 †20

TONG, Daphne Y K. 1600 E JOHN ST 98112 #462-01-1971 L1975 **RO** *071 †80

TONNING, Ove Arvid Haakon. ■ 98111 #040-02-1958 L1963 **FM** *071

TOOLEY, John Wm. ■ 98118 #030-06-1954 L1955 **GP** *020

TOOMEY, Eugene Pepper. 900 TERRY AVE, STE 100 98104 #037-01-1981 L1990 **ORS** *020 †40

TOOMEY, Hugh Edward. 1229 MADISON ST STE 1600 98104 #005-14-1963 L1964 **ORS** *071 †40

TOOMEY, Sean David. 1229 MADISON ST STE 1600 98104 #016-43-1994 L2000 **ORS** *020 †40

TOPINKA, Walter Anton. 14031 AMBOURN BLVD S W 98166 #038-40-1952 L1955 **OPH** *071 †35

TORELLI, Peter Richard. 1801 NW MARKET ST STE 302 98107 #054-04-1968 L1969 **IM GE** *020 †20

TORGERSON, Erik Lang. 1101 MADISON ST STE 1400 98104 #048-04-1994 L2000 **U** *020 †95

TORGERSON, Troy Robert. 307 WESTLAKE AVE N, STE 300 98109 #047-05-1998 L2000 **PPR** *020 †15

TORNOW, Alexander Paul. ■ 98101 #048-04-2005 L2005 **DR** *012

TORREZ, Rachel Marie. 1801 NW MARKET ST, STE 212 98107 #054-04-1998 L2000 **FM** *020 †18

TOSTENRUD, Robert Paul. ■ 98115 #054-04-2005 L2005 **AN** *012

TOUBOUL, Omri Haim. 1229 MADISON ST STE 820 98104 #005-06-1991 L1992 **IM** *020 †20

TOULEGENOV, Erlan Sericzh. 1959 NE PACIFIC ST RM C, CAMPUS BOX 356340 98195 #913-29-1996 L2002 **AN** *012

TOWER, Robert Neill. HSB-RR801, 1959 NE PACIFIC ST. 98195 #048-12-1999 L2005 **OPH FPS** *020 †35

TOWERS, Tamara. 600 UNIVERSITY ST, STE 1200 98101 #054-04-1994 L1994 **FM** *020 †18

TOWNES, David Andrew. 1959 NE PACIFIC ST, UNIV OF WASHINGTON 98195 #024-16-1993 L2001 **EM** *020 †16

TOWNSEND, Oren Geo. 1145 BROADWAY, THE POLY CLINIC 98122 #017-20-1992 L1999 **IM** *020 †20

TOZER, Kathleen Rene. UNIV OF WASHINGTON MED CTR, DIAGNOSTIC RADIOLOGY BOX 98195 #017-20-2000 L2000 **DR** *012

TRACY, Dean Ellison. 1550 N 115TH ST 98133 #054-15-1964 **GP** *072

TRAN, Don Thieu. PO BOX 356340, UW SCHOOL OF MED GME PROGR 98195 #035-46-2002 L2002 **DMP** *012 †50

TRAN, Ky Van. 4203 RAINIER AVE S STE C 98118 #941-02-1971 L1986 **FM** *020

TRAN, Lan T. 1229 MADISON ST STE 750, SWEDISH MEDICAL CENTER FIR 98104 #048-12-1999 L2003 **OBG** *020

TRAN, Linh V. 1550 N 115TH ST 98133 #048-13-1995 L1999 **AN** *020 †05

TRAN, Nam Thanh. ■ 98119 #054-04-1996 L1999 **VS** *100 †85

TRAN, Nguyetanh Thi. PO BOX 356428, DIVISION OF RHEUMATOLOGY 98195 #047-06-2004 L2007 **RHU** *012 †20

TRAN, Thao Ngoc. 4540 SAND POINT WAY NE 98105 #023-01-2000 L2004 **AI** *020 †20,03

TRANSUE, Emily Reagle. 1145 BROADWAY 98122 #032-01-1996 L1998 **IM** *020 †20

TRAUB, Oren. PO BOX 356340, U OF W HOUSESTAFF AFFAIRS 98195 #054-04-2001 L2003 **IM** *012

TRAVERSO, L William. 1100 9TH AVE G1-MSO, VIRGINIA MASON MEDICAL CEN 98101 #005-14-1973 L1984 **GS** *020 †85

TRAVIS, Dane Scott. 5343 TALLMAN AVE NW STE 20 98107 #005-19-1993 L1996 **FM** *020 †18

TREDWAY, Trent Lane. ■ 98101 #016-01-1997 L2004 **NS** *020

TREGER, Calvin L. 1145 BROADWAY 98122 #035-06-1967 L1970 **D IM** *071 †20,15

TREGILLUS, Leslie Claire. 3400 CALIFORNIA AVE SW, STE 300 98116 #054-04-1984 L1985 **FM** *020 †18

TRENCE, Dace Lilliana. 4225 ROOSEVELT WAY NE 98105 #026-04-1977 L1997 **IM END** *020 †20

TRIBBLE, Stacy. 1145 BROADWAY, POLYCLINIC 98122 #054-04-1996 L1999 **IM** *020 †20

TRIDGELL, Angela Chua. ■ 98105 #026-04-2005 L2005 **PD** *012

TRIER, William Cronin. ■ 98101 #035-09-1947 L1985 **PS** *071 †85,65

TRIMINGHAM, Laura A. ■ 98119 #024-07-2000 *100

TRIMIS, Kris Ann. 925 SENECA ST 98101 #019-02-1986 L1988 **IM** *020 †20

TRIMMER, Karen Rae. 900 TERRY AVE 4TH FL 98104 #051-01-1979 L1990 **AN** *020 †05

TRIVEDI, Raksha V. 1560 N 115TH ST, STE 108 98133 #495-76-1972 L1978 **OBG** *020 †30

TRONOLONE, Michael John. 1145 BROADWAY 98122 #010-02-1977 L2003 **MDM IM** *030 †20,03

TROWBRIDGE, Catherine H. 1145 BROADWAY 98122 #010-02-1994 L2000 **END** *020 †20

TROYER, Eric Jon. 900 UNIVERSITY ST, HORIZON HOUSE CLINIC 98101 #051-04-1998 L2000 **FPG FM** *020 †18

TRUE, David Dwight. 1101 MADISON ST, STE 301 98104 #005-15-1991 L1991 **IM** *020 †20

TRUE, Lawrence Dashiell. 1959 NE PACIFIC ST, MSC 359300 98195 #021-01-1971 L1972 **ATP PHP** *020 †50

TRUMBLE, Thomas Earl. 4245 ROOSEVELT WAY NE, STE 354775 98105 #008-01-1979 L1989 **ORS HS** *020 †40

TRUSCOTT, Al Mckenzie. 320 WESTLAKE AVE N, STE 100 98109 #005-06-1974 L1979 **OBG** *030 †30

TRUXILLO, Terrence Michae. ■ 98101 #021-05-2004 L2004 **AN** *012

TSAI, Charlotte Leslie. ■ 98199 #035-09-2001 L2005 **D** *020 †15

TSAI, Elaine Chin-San. 1660 S COLUMBIAN WAY, VA PSHCS 152E 98108 #048-04-1988 L1991 **END IM** *020 †20

TSAI, James Chungtien. 1959 NE PACIFIC ST, U OF W-HS AFFAIRS BOX 3563 98195 #048-04-2004 L2004 **IM** *020 †20

TSCHIRHART, John Howard. 1101 MADISON ST STE 701 98104 #025-01-1993 L1995 **GS** *020

TSEN, Joseph Wenchin. 12510 33RD AVE NE STE A 98125 #244-05-1968 L1981 **FM AN** *020

TSENG, Kwo-Hwa. ■ 98122 #385-02-1963 L1973 **P** *020 †75

TSUANG, Debby Wen. 1660 S COLUMBIAN WAY, S-116 98108 #018-03-1988 L1992 **PYG P** *050 †75

TSUJI, Wayne Hiroharu. 1101 MADISON ST STE 400, PACIFIC MEDICAL CLINICS 98104 #005-02-1974 L1980 **RHU IM** *020 †20

TU, Anh Dang. 1145 BROADWAY 98122 #054-04-1991 L1995 **IM** *020

TU, Shinping. 1660 S COLUMBIAN WAY, GENERAL INTERN MED SECTION 98108 #038-41-1989 L1993 **IM** *020 †20

TUBBS, Eric Paul. ■ 98103 #054-04-2007 L2007 **FP** *012

TUBRIDY, Frank Jos. 509 OLIVE WAY 98101 #035-01-1971 L1974 **FM** *020 †18

TUCKER, Eben Ezra. 1959 NE PACIFIC ST BOX 359, UNIVERSITY OF WASHINGTON 98195 #025-01-1976 L2003 **CD IM** *020 †20

TUCKER, Gary Jay. 1959 NE PACIFIC ST, BOX 356560 98195 #038-06-1960 L1985 **P** *071 †75

TUCKER, Kenneth Richard. 515 MINOR AVE, STE 140 98104 #054-04-1965 L1972 **PS** *071 †65

TUGGY, Michael Leonard. 1401 MADISON ST, STE 100 98104 #048-04-1987 L1989 **FM FSM** *040 †18

TULLY, Hannah More. 4800 SAND POINT WAY NE G-0, CHILDREN'S HOSPITAL & REGI 98105 #036-07-2006 L2006 **PD** *012

TUMBER, Perm-Paul S. 4245 ROOSEVELT WAY NE, BOX 354750 98105 #068-01-1991 L1997 **APM** *100

TUNG, Bruce Y. 1959 NE PACIFIC ST, UWMC BOX 356424 98195 #016-02-1992 L1992 **GE** *020 †20

TUPPER, Bradley James. 747 BROADWAY 98122 #041-01-1982 L1990 **AN** *020 †05

TUPPER, James W. ■ 98105 #041-01-1953 L1957 **ORS** *071 †40

TURCK, Marvin. 325 9TH AVE, BOX 359931 98104 #016-11-1959 L1962 **IM ID** *030 †20

TURCOTTE, Lucie Marie. ■ 98103 #026-04-2007 L2007 **PD** *012

TURELLA, Andrew Francis. PO BOX 356540, UNIVERSITY OF WASHINGTON D 98195 #054-04-2004 L2004 **AN** *012

TURK-GONZALES, Melissa A. 1100 9TH AVE 98101 #050-02-1999 L1999 **PM** *020 †60

TURKMEN-SOYGUR, Isil. 1959 NE PACIFIC ST 98195 #902-03-1995 L2001 **RNR** *100

TURNER, Jennifer Kathleen. ■ 98115 #054-04-2001 L2004 **PPR** *020 †55

TUTTLE, Anne Erin. 1100 9TH AVE C1-MSO, VIRGINIA MASON MEDICAL CEN 98101 #028-02-1998 L2001 *020 †20

TWIGGS, Gary Allen. 3626 NE 45TH ST STE 300 98105 #005-14-1981 L1982 **NPM PD** *020 †55

TYKODI, Gunjan Lal. 1600 E JOHN ST 98112 #039-01-1995 L2000 **END** *020 †20

TYKODI, Scott Simon. 1100 FAIRVIEW AVE N BOX D3, BOX 19024 98109 #028-02-1997 L2000 **ON** *020 †20

TYSHLER, Leanna. 1145 BROADWAY 98122 #054-04-1998 L2001 **NEP** *020 †20

TYTUS, John S. ■ 98112 #038-40-1947 L1958 **NS** *071 †25

UDENYI, Nkechinyere Nneka. 401 5TH AVE STE 1300 98104 #690-04-1997 L2006 **FM** *100 †18

UFFMAN, Joshua Christian. 747 BROADWAY 98122 #017-20-1999 L2004 **PAN** *020 †05 ‡

UHLIR, Jane Kehoe. 1101 MADISON ST STE 1500, 1ST HILL CAMPUS 98104 #054-04-1978 L1979 **GYN** *020 †30

ULDALL, Karina Kai. 901 BOREN AVE STE 1100 98104 #028-03-1987 L1989 **P** *020 †75

ULRICH, Delmont Marion. 500 17TH AVE 98112 #026-04-1944 L1947 **IM** *020 †20

UMAN, Howard Michael. 1401 MADISON ST, # 100 98104 #010-01-1973 L1977 **PD** *020 †55

UNDERBRINK, Michael P. 1959 NE PACIFIC ST BB1165, UNIVERSITY OF WASHINGTON 98195 #048-14-1999 L2004 **OTO** *020 †45

UNDERHILL, Hunter Reeve. PO BOX 356340, 1959 NE PACIFIC ST 98195 #036-05-2001 L2001 **NS** *100

UNGER, Jennifer Anna. 4245 ROOSEVELT WAY NE, STE 354775 98105 #008-02-2003 L2005 **OBG** *100

UNUTZER, Juergen. UNIV OF WASHINGTON MED SCH, DEPT OF PSYCHIATRY BOX 356 98195 #047-05-1990 L1994 **P** *030 †75

UPPAL, Anita Sohi. 10330 MERIDIAN AVE N # 230, SAND POINT INTERNISTS 98133 #495-43-1989 L1999 **IM ID** *020 †20

UPPAL, Maninderdip Singh. 747 BROADWAY 98122 #035-15-1992 L1998 **AN CD** *020 †05

UPTON, Melissa Perry. 1959 NE PACIFIC ST, BOX 356100 98195 #016-06-1978 L2001 **ATP PCP** *020 †50

URDAHL, Kevin Bradley. 4800 SAND POINT WAY NE 98105 #026-04-1995 L2003 **PDI** *020 †55

URE, Noah Silver. ■ 98118 #026-04-2004 L2004 **FM** *100 †18

URITSKIY, Igor Borisovich. ■ 98125 #016-42-2006 L2006 **IM** *012

URIU, Stanley Asao. ■ 98109 #016-02-1958 L1959 **OPH IM** *071 †25

URY, Andrew Gray. 2033 6TH AVE STE 707 98121 #005-11-1978 L1979 **FM** *020 †18

USO, Londres Riessen. ■ 98103 #041-01-2006 L2006 **AN** *012

UTZSCHNEIDER, Kristina M. 1660 S COLUMBIAN WAY 151, VA PUGET SOUND HEALTH CARE 98108 #024-01-1993 L1995 **END** *100 †20

VAKAR-LOPEZ, Funda. ■ 98144 #902-10-1988 L2006 **SP** *020 †50

VALIANTE, Taufik A. PO BOX 356470, DEPT OF NEUROSURGERY 98195 #065-01-1997 L2002 *100

VALLIERES, Eric. 1959 NE PACIFIC ST, MSC 359300 98195 #067-04-1982 L1996 **TS** *072

VALPEY, Raymond Winfield. 901 BOREN AVE, STE 1776 98104 #005-06-1974 L1975 **N SME** *020 †75

VALREY, Marvin Keith. 1959 NE PACIFIC ST, MSC 359300 98195 #054-04-1996 L2000 **EM** *020 †16

VAN CITTERS, Robert Lee. 2324 EASTLAKE AVE E, STE 500 98102 #019-02-1953 L1976 **IM OS** *075

VANCLEVE, William Carlyle. ■ 98103 #016-02-2006 L2006 **PD** *012

VANDENBELT, Russell A. 901 BOREN AVE, STE 1776 98104 #005-19-1980 L1981 **P GP** *020 †75

VAN DER MEULEN, Pieter W. 9800 4TH AVE NE 98115 #660-03-1961 L1965 **GP OBG** *071 †18

VAN EATON, Erik Gentry. PO BOX 356340, 1959 NE PACIFIC ST 98195 #054-04-2001 L2004 **GS** *012

VANHEE, Victor Christian. 1959 NE PACIFIC ST RM C, CAMPUS BOX 356340 98195 #019-02-2002 L2002 **OM** *020 †20,70

VANKIRKBARR, Kristine Kay. ■ 98106 #054-04-2008 *012

VAN LIEW, David Allen. ■ 98105 #049-01-1961 L1963 **P** *071 †75

VAN NIEL, Cornelius W. 8720 14TH AVE S 98108 #041-01-1996 L1999 **PD** *020 †55

VAN NIMWEGEN, Donald. 200 15TH AVE E, GROUP HEALTH HOSPITAL 98112 #067-01-1966 L1972 **AN** *020 †05

VAN NORMAN, Gail Ann. 943 19TH AVE E 98112 #054-04-1981 L1982 **AN IM** *020 †20,05

VAN STELLE, Roger Donald. ■ 98112 #056-05-1977 L1983 **OS** *020

VANSTON, Sarah Ann. 1401 MADISON ST # 100, MEDICINE RESIDE 98104 #025-01-2005 L2005 **FP** *012

VAN VOORHIS, Wesley C. ■ 98195 #035-20-1984 L1986 **ID** *050 †20

VAN WESEP, Gerard L. ■ 98119 #025-01-1971 L1999 **OPH** *071 †35

VANWYK, Jill Renae. 125 16TH AVE E 98112 #018-03-2002 L2004 **FM** *100 †18

VARGAS BENDEZU, Claudia P. 747 BROADWAY, SWEDISH MED CTR 98122 #132-02-2003 L2005 **FM** *100

VARLEY, Christopher K. 4800 SAND POINT WAY NE, DEPT PSYCH 98105 #054-04-1973 L1977 **CHP P** *040 †75

VARNI, Jill R Franklin. ■ 98105 #023-01-1975 L1979 **OBG** *071 †30

VARY, James Corydon. ■ 98105 #054-04-2005 L2005 **D** *012

VASAVADA, Reena Kamendu. 1229 MADISON ST STE 1450, HEALTHCARE FOR WOMEN 98104 #016-11-1999 L2006 **OBG** *020 †30

VASAVADA, Zubin Balendu. 4245 ROOSEVELT WAY NE, BOX 354775 98105 #023-07-2005 L2005 **FP** *012

VASKO, John Ralph, Jr. 1770 NW 58TH ST STE 124 98107 #035-08-1960 L1967 **R** *071 †80

VASQUEZ, Nora Linda. ■ 98115 #054-04-2008 *012

VASSALL, John Henry. 747 BROADWAY, A FLOOR WEST 98122 #054-04-1978 L1984 **IM** *020 †20

VATH, Brian Eugene. 1229 MADISON ST, STE 1210 98104 #054-04-2000 L2002 **P** *020 †18

VATH, Julie Scherrer. 925 SENECA ST 98101 #054-04-2000 L2004 **AN** *020 †05

VATH, Raymond Eugene. 1229 MADISON ST, STE 1210 98104 #054-04-1965 L1966 **P** *020

VAUGHAN, David John. 4800 SAND POINT WAY NE, CHILDRENS HOSP MED CTR 98105 #539-04-1992 L1998 **PDP** *100

VAUGHAN, Matthew M. 1959 NE PACIFIC ST, MSC 359300 98195 #917-10-1991 L2001 **DR** *012

VAUGHAN, Michael Ronald. 1959 NE PACIFIC ST, BOX 356521 98195 #010-02-1999 L2001 **NEP** *100 †20

VAUGHT, Meridale Amy. ■ 98117 #048-04-2004 L2004 **IM** *012 †20

VAVILALA, Monica Shanta. 325 9TH AVE BOX 359724, DEPT OF ANESTHESIOLOGY 98104 #048-14-1991 L1994 **AN** *020 †05,55

VAZ, Louise Elaine. ■ 98115 #047-05-2007 L2007 **PD** *012

VAZQUEZ, Benjamin Guiller. ■ 98102 #054-04-2007 L2007 **IM** *012

VAZQUEZ, Frederick. 1229 MADISON ST STE 1440, P A S 98104 #649-14-1971 L1978 **AN** *020

VEAL, Curtis Franklin. 6090 UPLAND TER S 5 98118 #012-01-1981 L1982 **PUD CCM** *030 †20

VEDAL, Sverre. 4225 ROOSEVELT WAY NE, STE 100 98105 #007-02-1976 L2005 **PUD IM** *020 †20

VEDDER, Nicholas Blair. 325 9TH AVE, BOX 359796 98104 #038-06-1981 L1982 **PS HS** *020 †65,85

VEDOVATTI, Philip Anthony. 1959 NE PACIFIC ST, P O BOX 356119 98195 #054-04-1993 L1996 **IM** *020 †20

VEERAMACHANENI, Srivalli. ■ 98116 #496-24-2001 L2006 **IM** *100 †20

VEGA, Fernando Domingo. 6300 9TH AVE NE STE 200 98115 #054-04-1978 L1981 **FM** *020 †18

VEITENGRUBER, Jason Paul. 325 9TH AVE # 359896 98104 #054-04-2000 L2000 **P** *020 †75 ‡

VEITH, Richard Charles. 1959 NE PACIFIC ST, BOX 356560 98195 #054-04-1973 L1974 **IMG P** *030 †75

VELAN, Tomas. 1959 NE PACIFIC ST, U OF W-HS AFFAIRS BOX 3563 98195 #286-13-1996 L2004 **AN** *020 †20

VELASCO, Roberto A, Jr. 6044 M L KING JR WAY S, STE 104 98118 #748-07-1973 L1984 **GP** *020

VELEZ-CUTURA, Dennis A. PO BOX 84026, 1600 E JEFFERSON 98124 #042-03-1998 L1999 **NS** *100

VELJOVICH, Dan Steven. 1101 MADISON ST STE 1500, PACIFIC GYNECOLOGY SPECIAL 98104 #051-01-1994 L2001 **GO** *020 †30

VEMULAKONDA, Vijaya M. ■ 98105 #027-01-2000 L2006 **UP** *012

VENDRELL, Michael Jos. 1001 BOYLSTON AVE, FIRST HILL DIAG IMAGING 98104 #048-12-1976 L2006 **DR PYA** *020 †80

VENKATESWARAN, Raji. 8444 RAINIER AVE S, RAINIER BEACH MED CLINIC 98118 #025-01-1996 L1998 **FM** *020 †18

VER ELLEN, Patricia Anne. ■ 98116 #054-04-1988 L1992 **P** *020 †75

VERHALEN, Jon Peter. ■ 98119 #024-01-2002 L2002 **PS** *012

VERHEY, Joseph Wm. 1100 UNIVERSITY ST 98101 #054-04-1958 L1962 **P** *020 †75

VERHULST, Johan Maria F. 4225 ROOSEVELT WAY NE, STE 306 98105 #165-04-1964 L1978 **P** *040 †75

VERMEULEN, Sandra Suzanne. 1560 N 115TH ST, NORTHWEST HOSPITAL 98133 #005-12-1983 L1986 **RO** *020 †80

VERNIE, Rudolf. ■ 98136 #660-03-1954 L1959 **PD** *071 †55

VERRIER, Edward Donald. 1959 NE PACIFIC ST #356310, UNIVERSITY OF WASHINGTON 98195 #024-07-1974 L1989 **TS VS** *020 †85,90

VERRILLI, John Loftus. 515 MINOR AVE, STE 300 98104 #035-01-1973 L1974 **IM** *020 †20

VESSELAGO, Michael Geo. 1550 N 115TH ST 98133 #041-01-1965 L1968 **IM NTR** *020

VESSELLE, Hubert. 1959 NE PACIFIC ST, BOX 356113 98195 #038-06-1991 L1997 **DR NR** *020 †80

VETTO, Roy R. 521 WALL ST 98121 #041-02-1951 L1954 **GS CD** *071 †85,90

VETZNER, Jorielle Rebecca. 1801 NW MARKET ST, STE 203 98107 #038-06-1999 L2001 **FM** *020 †18

VIARENGO, Claire Marie. 1959 NE PACIFIC ST, BOX 356540 98195 #041-01-1978 L1981 **AN** *020 †05

VIDGER, Donald Leonard. 1229 MADISON ST, STE 1440 98104 #016-42-1982 L1998 **AN PME** *020 †05

VIERNES, Darwin Cortina. ■ 98119 #005-14-2007 L2007 *012

VIG, Elizabeth K. 325 9TH AVE 98104 #035-19-1993 L1996 **IMG** *020 †20

VIJAY, Anupama Varma. 4800 SAND POINT WAY NE G-0, CHILDREN'S HOSPITAL & REGI 98105 #050-02-2006 L2006 **PD** *012

VILELA, Marcelo Duarte. 325 9TH AVE, BOX 359766 98104 #187-06-1995 L2005 **NS** *100

VILLA, Marie Luz. 325 9TH AVE BOX 359753, HARBORVIEW MEDICAL CENTER 98104 #005-11-1986 L1994 **IM** *020 †20

VILLACRES, Enrique Carlos. 325 9TH AVE, BOX 359896 98104 #056-06-1981 L1982 **P** *050 †75

VILLARD, Mark Antone. ■ 98116 #005-06-1969 L2002 **OBG** *072 †30

VINCENT, E Chris. 1401 MADISON ST # 100, SWEDISH FAMILY MEDICINE 98104 #005-14-1983 L1986 **FM** *020 †20

VINCENT, James Maxwell. 1101 MADISON ST STE 1501, MD2 98104 #012-05-1980 L1981 **PUD** *020 †20

VINCENT, Jennifer G. 1401 MADISON ST, STE 100 98104 #005-14-1983 L1986 **CHP P** *040 †75

VIRGIN, Jeffrey Bob. ■ 98112 #038-06-1988 L1991 **PTH** *020 †50

VISKONTAS, Darius G. 325 9TH AVE, DEPT OF ORTHOPAEDICS & SPO 98104 #065-09-2000 L2006 **ORS** *100

VISWANATHAN, Mohan N. ■ 98105 #005-02-1999 L2007 **ICE** *020 †20

VITIELLO, Eugene German. 505 E DENNY WAY APT 508 98122 #665-02-2006 L2008 *100

VITOLS, Mintauts Mickey. ■ 98103 #036-01-1956 L1980 **P** *071 †75

VLCEK, Brien Wayne. 801 BROADWAY STE 711 98122 #056-06-1979 L1981 **N** *020 †75

VO, Dong Thi. ■ 98106 #054-04-2005 L2005 **IM** *012

VO, Nghia Nhan. 4800 SAND POINT WAY NE, DEPT OF RADIOLOGY 98105 #056-06-1999 L2005 **VIR PDR** *020 †80

VOEGTLIN, Karl F. 1229 MADISON ST 98104 #016-06-1960 L1965 **GE IM** *071 †20

VOGELZANG, Janet Helen. ■ 98103 #038-06-1989 L1989 **IM** *020 †20

VOGELZANG, Philip Jay. 600 BROADWAY, STE 170 98122 #054-04-1984 L1992 **DR IM** *020 †80

VOLLKOMMER, Mara Wells. 4800 SAND POINT WAY NE, REGIONAL M 98105 #036-01-2006 L2008 **PD** *012

VONALVENSLEBEN, Johannes. ■ 98125 #054-04-2007 L2007 **PD** *012

VON BEHRENS, Wieland E. 3638 50TH AVE NE 98105 #143-01-1966 **HEM OS** *050

VON GELDERN, Gloria Heide. 1959 NE PACIFIC ST 98195 #408-14-2004 L2007 **IM** *012

VON PREYSS-FRIEDMAN, S. 325 9TH AVE 98104 #409-16-1982 L1987 **IMG IM** *075 †20

VONTVER, Louis Andrew. 1959 NE PACIFIC ST, BOX 356460 98195 #026-04-1960 L1964 **OBG ID** *030 †30

VOORHEES, Richard L. ■ 98112 #040-02-1953 L1966 **OTO** *071 †45

VOORSANGER, Matthew A. 550 17TH AVE STE 450, MINOR & JAMES MEDICAL PLLC 98122 #028-34-1992 L2007 **CD** *020 †20

VRACKO, Rudolf. 1660 S COLUMBIAN WAY 98108 #407-16-1955 L1960 **PTH** *030 †50

VU, Mark Philip. ■ 98112 #061-01-2001 L2008 **AN** *100

VU, Thanhdanae Nghiem. 10330 MERIDIAN AVE N, STE 200 98133 #035-09-1997 L2001 **OBG** *020 †30

VU, Thu Baotrung. 4800 SAND POINT WAY NE, REGIONAL M 98105 #021-05-2006 L2006 **PD** *012

VUKY, Jacqueline. 1100 9TH AVE G1-MSO, VIRGINIA MASON MEDICAL CEN 98101 #040-02-1995 L2001 **HO** *020 †20

VUONG, Thao Thanh. 1200 S JACKSON ST STE 24 98144 #941-01-1974 L1987 **GP PTH** *020

WAGENAAR, Flory Ella. ■ 98115 #660-01-1950 L1954 **AN** *071 †05

WAGENAAR, Philip. ■ 98115 #016-11-1953 L1956 **OPH** *071 †35

WAGER, Susan. ■ 98136 #035-48-1979 L1985 **IM** *020 †20

WAGHMARE, Alpana Amalkant. ■ 98105 #054-04-2007 **PD** *012

WAGHRAY, Arpan. ■ 98104 #496-01-2001 L2007 **P** *020

WAGNER, Amy Jacqueline. 607 E HARRISON ST, APT 401 98102 #056-06-2001 L2002 **GS** *012

WAGNER, Edward H. 200 15TH AVE E 98112 #035-06-1965 L1984 **IM FM** *050 †20

WAGNER, Lara Reid. ■ 98112 #054-04-2003 L2003 **EM** *020 †16

WAGNER, Mark David. 10330 MERIDIAN AVE N, SPORTS MEDICINE CLINIC 98133 #011-04-1982 L1985 **FM FSM** *020 †18

WAGNER, Theodore Anstey. 4245 ROOSEVELT WAY NE, STE 354775 98105 #041-13-1968 L1970 **ORS GS** *020 †40

WAGNER, Thor Andrew. ■ 98112 #041-13-2000 L2005 **PDI** *012 †55

WAGNER, William Francis. 600 BROADWAY, SEATTLE HAND SURGERY 98122 #017-20-1991 L1997 **HS** *071 †40

WAGONER, Richard Ryan. 415 1ST AVE N, PO BOX 90312 98109 #054-04-1984 L1985 **IM** *020 †20

WAHBEH, Ghassan. 4800 SAND POINT WAY NE 5P1, C/O PEDIATRIC GASTRO UW CH 98105 #575-01-1996 L2004 **PG** *020 †55

WAHL, Christopher John. B OF A ARENA RM 148, 3950 MONTLAKE BLVD 98195 #008-01-1996 L2004 **ORS** *020

WAHL, William H. ■ 98122 #016-43-1959 L1965 **IM GE** *074 †20

WAIBLINGER, Brian Eugene. ■ 98122 #054-04-1996 L1999 **P** *020

WAINER, Joseph Kenneth. 2323 N 65TH ST 98103 #010-03-2000 L2004 **P** *100

WAINSTEIN, Luis. 747 BROADWAY 98122 #132-01-1960 L1972 **IM** *062 †20

WAJDA, Jeffery. 1550 N 115TH ST, NORTHWEST HOSPITAL AND MED 98133 #016-76-1989, ▲ L1993 **EM CCM** *030 †16

WAKO, Elizabeth. ■ 98105 #049-01-2003 L2003 **AN** *012

WALD, Anna. 600 BROADWAY, STE 400 98122 #035-47-1985 L1989 **ID** *020 †20

WALDHAUSEN, John H. 4800 SAND POINT WAY NE, CHLDS HOSP MED CTR W7729 98105 #041-14-1986 L1992 **PDS** *020 †85

WALDSCHMIDT, Brian Michae. ■ 98115 #054-04-2008 *012

WALES, Lee Robt. ■ 98144 #026-04-1968 L1978 **DR** *020 †80

WALHOUT, Janelle Rengel. 4400 37TH AVE S 98118 #026-04-1986 L1988 **FM** *020 †18

WALIKE, Joseph Wm. 1117 MINOR AVE 98101 #005-02-1961 L1968 **FPS HNS** *071 †45

WALKER, Benjamin Joseph. ■ 98102 #056-05-2004 L2005 **AN** *012

WALKER, Edward Anthony. 1959 NE PACIFIC ST, BOX 356330 98195 #054-04-1984 L1984 **P** *020 †75

WALKER, Kym. 1959 NE PACIFIC ST, BOX 356460 98195 #035-45-2003 L2003 **OBG** *020

WALKER, Melanie S. ■ 98104 #048-02-1998 L2001 **N** *020

WALKER, Sandra Clement. 1120 CHERRY ST STE 240 98104 #054-04-1993 L1993 **P** *020 †75

WALKER, Scott Andrew. 1107 NE 45TH ST # 44, UNIV OF WASH,DEPT OF RADIO 98105 #016-11-2001 L2006 **RNR** *020 †80

WALKER, Stuart A. 2324 EASTLAKE AVE E, STE 500 98102 #671-02-1979 L1985 *020

WALKER, William Otis, Jr. 4800 SAND POINT WAY NE, MS A7398 CLDS HOSP 98105 #021-01-1979 L1997 **OS PD** *020 †55

WALKER LEWIS, Gale Louise. ■ 98102 #054-04-1984 L1991 **FM** *020 †18

WALLACE, Carol Ann. 4800 SAND POINT WAY NE 98105 #025-01-1973 L1975 **RHU PD** *020 †55

WALLACE, James Findlay. 1959 NE PACIFIC ST 98195 #028-02-1961 L1966 **IM ID** *030 †20

WALLACE, Stephanie Ellen. 4800 SAND POINT WAY NE, M2-9 98105 #005-14-1999 L2004 **PD** *020 †55,19

WALLACH, Robert Wm. 1600 E JOHN ST 98112 #035-15-1973 L1977 **IM** *020 †20

WALLEN, Herschel Dean. 1100 FAIRVIEW AVE N, D3-100 98109 #025-01-1999 L2001 **ON** *050 †20

WALLER, Sarah Anne. ■ 98112 #021-01-2004 L2005 **OBG** *012

WALLIS, Wayne Jack. 1201 AMGEN CT W 98119 #034-01-1978 L1981 **RHU IM** *020 †20

WALLNER, Kent Emerson. 1660 S COLUMBIAN WAY, DEPT OF VA # 174 98108 #038-40-1982 L1997 **RO** *020 †80

WALSH, Cathleen Marie. PO BOX 16587 98116 #036-07-1981 L1983 **P** *100

WALSH, James Steven. 5300 TALLMAN AVE NW, SWEDISH MEDIC AL CENTER - 98107 #035-08-1992 L1995 **FM** *020 †18

WALSON, Judd L. 325 9TH AVE, # 359909 98104 #024-07-2000 L2004 **ID** *100

WALTER, Eric Charles. ■ 98103 #054-04-2002 L2006 **PCC** *012 †20,55

WALTER, Roland Bruno. 1100 FAIRVIEW AVE N, # D2-373 98109 #869-07-1996 L2005 **HO** *012

WALTERS, Sarahanne Margrj. PO BOX 356421, UNIV OF WASHINGTON 98195 #005-18-2007 L2007 **IM** *012

WANAGAT, Jonathan Matthew. 1959 NE PACIFIC ST RM C2, CAMPUS BOX 356340 98195 #056-05-2002 L2002 **IMG** *100 †20

WANDER, Pandora Lucrezia. ■ 98101 #054-04-2008 *012

WANDERER, Michael Jos. 122 16TH AVE E 98112 #054-04-1972 L1973 **FM** *040 †18

WANG, Andy Hueiming. 6842 39TH AVE NE 98115 #054-04-1997 L1999 **FM** *020 †18

WANG, Chia Chen. 325 9TH AVE, BIX 359-908 98104 #016-06-1990 L1994 **ID** *020 †20

WANG, Constance. 1001 4TH AVE STE 420 98154 #054-04-1988 L1991 **IM** *020 †20

WANG, Dennis Oliver. 1959 NE PACIFIC ST RM C2, CAMPUS BOX 356340 98195 #016-06-2000 L2003 **RNR** *012 †80

WANG, Eric Chunchieh. ■ 98105 #005-14-2002 L2004 **DR** *012

WANG, Grace Mu-En. 4400 37TH AVE S 98118 #035-20-1982 L1997 **FM** *020 †18

WANG, Karen Hsingyi. 5714 SW SPOKANE ST, KAREN WANG 98116 #025-01-1993 L1997 **IM** *020 †20

WANG, Keith Yu-Chih. 1229 MADISON ST STE 1150 98104 #011-02-1982 L1983 **DR** *020 †80

WANG, Kevin Shawshing. 1401 MADISON ST STE 100 98104 #025-07-2004 L2007 **OBS** *012 †18

WANG, Leilei. 1100 9TH AVE 98101 #041-12-1990 L1990 **PM** *020 †60

WANG, Lilian Chiao. UNIV OF WASHINGTON MED CTR, DIAGNOSTIC RADIOLOGY BOX 98195 #028-02-2003 L2004 **DR** *012

WANG, Lucy Yihui. 1660 S COLUMBIAN WAY, S-116-6E 98108 #041-14-2002 L2002 **P** *100 †75

WANG, Nan Ping. 1229 MADISON ST STE 500 98104 #244-04-1985 L1992 **PTH** *020 †50

WANG, Roger. 1550 N 115TH ST A-150 98133 #016-06-1994 L1998 **EM** *020 †16

WANG, San-Pin. PO BOX 357238, DEPT PATHOBIOLOGY 98195 #572-20-1944 **IG PHP** *050

WANG, Wei. 1959 NE PACIFIC ST, U OF W-HS AFFAIRS BOX 3563 98195 #243-03-1997 L2004 **IM** *100 †20

WANG, Xiaotong. ■ 98199 #243-72-1990 L2007 **SP** *012 †50

WANG, Zhiqian. ■ 98115 #243-47-1993 L2007 **RHU** *012

WANGLER, Valory Elizabeth. ■ 98122 #048-04-2006 L2006 **FP** *012

WARD, Nicholas Geoffroy. 325 9TH AVE # 359896, HARBORVIEW MED CTR 98104 #035-20-1973 L1975 **P** *071 †75

WARE, Elisabeth Prince. 10416 5TH AVE NE, PACMED CLINICS - NORTHGATE 98125 #024-16-1995 L1999 **MPD PD** *020 †20,55

WARNER, Valentina R. 8444 RAINIER AVE S 98118 #054-04-1995 L1998 **FM** *020 †18

WARREN, Billy Hoyt. 1959 NE PACIFIC ST, BOX 357115 98195 #048-04-1968 L1972 **DR OS** *020 †80

WARREN, Edus H, III. 1100 FAIRVIEW AVE N D3-100, CLIN RESRCH DIV POB 19024 98109 #024-01-1991 L1993 **ON IM** *050 †20

WARREN, Sam Anthony. 325 9TH AVE, MAILSTOP 359702 98104 #005-11-1999 L2002 **IM** *020 †20

WARTH, David Chas. 1536 N 115TH ST, SUMMIT CARDIOLOGY 98133 #054-04-1979 L1984 **AS EM** *020 †20

WARWICK, Susan Elizabeth. 310 15TH AVE E CCN-2, GROUP HEALTH COOPERATIVE O 98112 #010-01-1988 L1991 **OBG** *020 †30

WASHINGTON, Deborah Leigh. 747 BROADWAY 98122 #005-02-1995 L1997 **IM** *020 †20

WASSERHEIT, Judith Nina. 325 9TH AVE, BOX 359931 98104 #024-01-1978 L1982 **ID IM** *030 †20

WASSERMAN, Peter B. 1145 BROADWAY 98122 #035-19-1967 L1972 **IM HEM** *020 †20

WASSERMANN, Joel Mark. 747 BROADWAY 98122 #043-01-1992 L1992 **EM** *071 †18,16

WASZAK, Stephen James. 1530 N 115TH ST 98133 #025-01-1975 L1976 **GYN** *020 †30

WATANABE, Jill Midori. 325 9TH AVE 98104 #023-07-1990 L1998 **IM** *020 †20

WATERMAN, Sara. 1200 12TH AVE S, PAC MED CLINICS- BEACON HI 98144 #054-04-1996 L1998 **FM** *020 †18

WATKINS, Richard Neal. 200 15TH AVE E, GROUP HEALTH HOSPITAL 98112 #020-12-1970 L1973 **EM FM** *020 †16

WATKINS, Sandra Lee. 4800 SAND PNT NE #NE-C5371 98105 #048-14-1981 L1982 **PN PD** *020 †55

WATKINS, Timothy Ryan. ■ 98107 #038-40-2000 L2004 **PCC** *100 ‡

WATSON, James Calvert, Jr. 1145 BROADWAY 98122 #005-02-1986 L1993 **VS** *020 †85

WATSON, Margaret Ann. 2101 E YESLER WAY, ODESSA BROWN CHILDREN'S CL 98122 #054-04-1986 L1990 **PD** *020 †55

WATSON, Nathaniel F. 325 9TH AVE BOX 359803, HARBORVIEW MEDICAL CENTER 98104 #036-01-1996 L2000 **N** *020 †75

WATSON, Ronald Owen. 600 UNIVERSITY ST, STE 1200 98101 #001-02-1983 L1983 **IM** *020 †20

WATT, J Michael. 2409 N 45TH ST 98103 #005-11-1985 L1990 **ORS** *020 †40

WATTS, Mary. 1959 NE PACIFIC ST, MSC 359300 98195 #056-06-1980 L1984 **IM** *020 †20

WAY, Singsing Y. 1959 NE PACIFIC ST, BOX 357650 98195 #035-46-1999 L2001 **PDI** *050 †55

WAYMACK, Carol Louise. 11011 MERIDIAN AVE N # 200, POLYCLINIC FAMILY MEDICINE 98133 #054-04-1987 L1989 **FM** *020 †18

WAYS, Martha Helen. 10416 5TH AVE NE, PACIFIC MEDICAL CENTER 98125 #005-19-1990 L1990 **IM** *020 †20

WAYS, Peter. ■ 98112 #035-01-1953 L1962 **IM** *062

WEAVER, Edward Malcolm. 1660 S COLUMBIAN WAY, VA PSHCS 112-OTO 98108 #008-01-1993 L1998 **OTO SME** *020 †45

WEAVER, Lois Jean. 701 5TH AVE, SUITE 2900/ M/S 105 98104 #016-02-1970 L1973 **IM PUD** *020 †20

WEBB, Todd M. ■ 98136 #035-45-1997 **FM** *100

WEBER, Edward Lawrence. 1225 MADISON ST 98104 #041-01-1961 L1965 **ON IM** *071 †20

WEBER, James Karl. 1801 NW MARKET ST, STE 301 98107 #035-01-1974 L1977 **GS VS** *020 †85

WEBER, Scott David. 1601 5TH AVE, STE 830 98101 #056-05-1986 L2001 **FM** *020 †18

WEBSTER, Bruce Allan. 747 BROADWAY 98122 #024-16-1996 L2000 **EM** *020 †16

WEBSTER, Wayne Arthur. 6020 35TH AVE SW 98126 #016-01-1994 L2001 **FM** *020 †18

WECHKIN, Hope Ann. 6300 9TH AVE NE, STE 200 98115 #054-04-1997 L1999 **FM** *020 †18

WECHTER, Debra Gerry. 1100 9TH AVE 98101 #005-19-1980 L1983 **GS** *040 †85

WEEMS, Charles Ellis. 500 17TH AVE 98122 #035-01-1959 L1968 **GS TS** *071 †85

WEGLEY, Steven Jack. 501 N 34TH ST, STE 101 98103 #054-04-1981 L1984 **GE IM** *020 †20

WEIGEL, Wade Anthony. 1100 9TH AVE G1-MSO, DEPT OF ANESTHESIOLOGY 98101 #056-06-1998 L1998 **AN** *020 †05

WEIGLE, David Scott. 325 9TH AVE 98104 #024-01-1978 L1981 **END IM** *050 †20

WEIL, Alexis Cherie. 325 9TH AVE, BOX 359702 98104 #012-05-1998 L2000 **IM** *020 †20

WEIL, Wayne Mitchell. 2409 N 45TH ST, STE 403 98103 #035-19-1999 L2004 **HS** *020 †40

WEINBERGER, Edward. 4800 SAND POINT WAY NE 98105 #024-01-1979 L1980 **DR PD** *020 †80

WEINGEIST, Aaron Perera. 2515 SW TRENTON ST STE 201, WEST SEATTLE HIGHLINE 98106 #018-03-1993 L1993 **OPH** *020 †35

WEINSTEIN, Jill Morros. 509 OLIVE WAY, STE 900 98101 #016-06-2002 L2006 **D** *100 †15

WEINSTEIN, Jonathan R. 1959 NE PACIFIC ST, RR 650 98195 #005-15-1998 L2002 **N** *020 †75

WEINSTEIN, Michael Simon. 1100 9TH AVE 98101 #054-04-1983 L1984 **PM** *020 †60

WEINSTEIN, Stuart Mark. 325 9TH AVE, # 359721 98104 #035-09-1983 L1984 **PM** *020 †60

WEISBERG, Herbert. 200 16TH AVE E 98112 #869-05-1959 L1983 **GE IM** *020 †20

WEISS, Avery Harold. 4800 SAND POINT WAY NE, CHLDRNS HOSP & REG MED CTR 98105 #011-02-1974 L1991 **OPH PO** *020 †35

WEISS, David Brian. 325 9TH AVE BOX 359798, HARBORVIEW MEDICAL CENTER 98104 #010-02-1996 L2004 **ORS** *020 †40

WEISS, Mary Bethany. 550 16TH AVE, STE 100 98122 #054-04-1988 L1990 **FM** *020 †18

WEISS, Nina Tal. 201 16TH AVE E, GRP HLTH URGENT CARE 98112 #024-07-1995 L2001 **FM** *020 †18

WEISS-FLUM, Tracey. 310 15TH AVE E, 2ND 98112 #011-02-1990 L2000 **OBG** *020 †30

WEISSMAN, Hazel Faye. ■ 98122 #035-19-1964 L2007 **P** *020 †75

WEISSMAN, Jerry. ■ 98122 #035-46-1964 L1965 **OPH** *071 †35 ‡

WEISSMAN, Scott Jeffrey. 4800 SAND POINT WAY NE 98105 #005-15-1997 L2000 **PDI** *050 †55

WEISSMAN, Wayne David. 1221 MADISON ST, SEATTLE UROLOGICAL 98104 #018-03-1974 L1980 **U** *020 †95

WEITKAMP, Gretchen Ann. 550 16TH AVE, STE 100 98122 #054-04-1991 L1993 **FM** *020 †18

WELCH, Alison Corinne. ■ 98122 #051-01-2006 L2007 **PM** *012

WELCH, Marshall Porter. 325 9TH AVE # 359764, HARBORVIEW MED CTR 98104 #048-12-1983 L1989 **D IM** *020 †20,15

WELCH, Philip David. 10338 BEDFORD CT NW 98177 #054-04-1978 L1981 **OBG** *020 †30

WELDIN, Joshua David. 1959 NE PACIFIC ST C212, STAFF AFFAIRS BOX 356340 98195 #054-04-2002 L2002 **PD** *020 †55

WELK, Richard Andrew. 1145 BROADWAY 98122 #025-01-1981 L1987 **PS** *020 †85,65

WELLINGTON, David Pasho. 1221 MADISON ST 98104 #017-20-1962 L1968 **OPH** *071

WELLINGTON, Marie F. 325 9TH AVE BOX 359755, HARBORVIEW MEDICAL CENTER 98104 #043-01-1983 L1995 **IM IMG** *020 †20

■ = Address Information Privacy Protected

WELLS, Craig Garrett. 1221 MADISON ST STE 1002, VITREORETINAL ASSOC 98104 #040-02-1979 L1980 **OPH** *020 †35

WELLS, Denise Ann. 1959 NE PACIFIC ST 98195 #054-04-1985 L1987 **CLP** *020 †50

WELLS, Sean Michael. 1101 MADISON ST STE 400, PACIFIC MEDICAL CLINICS 98104 #024-07-1994 L1994 **GS** *020 †85

WELLS, Stanley Dale. 1959 NE PACIFIC ST BOX 35, DEPT OF RADIOLOGY 98195 #019-02-1969 L2007 **DR** *071 †80

WELTI, Douglas Wakefield. ■ 98112 #049-01-1952 L1954 **FM** *071

WEMPLE, Mary Ann. 1200 12TH AVE S, PACIFIC MEDICAL CLINICS 98144 #025-01-1995 L1997 **RHU** *020 †20

WEMPLE, Matthew Lawrence. 601 SUMMIT AVE E, APT 402 98102 #025-07-2003 L2003 **IM** *100 †20

WEN, Marco Nee. 1600 E JEFFERSON ST, ORTHOPAEDICS 98122 #025-01-1991 L1993 **PM** *020 †60

WENDER, Regina. 1959 NE PACIFIC ST, UNIV WASH MED CTR 98195 #054-04-2002 L2002 **AN** *100 †05

WENER, Mark Howard. 1959 NE PACIFIC ST, BOX 357110 98195 #028-02-1974 L1980 **RHU CLP** *020 †20

WENNBERG, Richard P. 1959 NE PACIFIC ST, UNIV OF WASH BOX 356320 98195 #054-04-1962 L1968 **NPM PD** *050 †55

WENTWORTH, Kelly Lee. ■ 98109 #008-02-2008 **IM** *012

WEPPNER, William Guy. 1959 NE PACIFIC ST, CAMPUS BOX 356429 98195 #054-04-2002 L2004 **IM** *020 †20

WERBLIN, Joshua Paul. ■ 98102 #021-01-2001 L2006 **CHP** *012

WERESCH, Joseph Martin. 1101 MADISON ST, STE 301 98104 #016-45-1980 L2005 **ON IM** *020 †20

WERNER, Michael David. PO BOX 354410, UNIVERSITY OF WASHINGTON 98195 #054-04-1995 L2002 **FM** *020 †18

WERRBACH, Jon Harper. 325 9TH AVE 98104 #056-05-1959 L1961 **DIA END** *071 †20

WESCH, Jessica Ann. 1401 MADISON ST, STE 100 98104 #054-04-2001 L2004 **FM** *020 †18

WESOL, Adrianne Bernice. 310 15TH AVE E, CNB-2 98112 #040-02-1994 L1998 **OBG** *020 †30

WESSELLS, Hunter Buchanan. 325 9TH AVE, HARBORVIEW MEDICAL CENTER 98104 #010-02-1988 L2001 **U** *020 †95

WEST, Heather Fraser. 6019 28TH AVE NE 98115 #007-02-2000 L2002 **HO** *100 †20

WEST, Howard Lawrence. 1221 MADISON ST, MED ONCOLOGY 2ND FL 98104 #024-01-1996 L1998 **ON IM** *020 †20

WEST, Paula Ann. 1151 DENNY WAY 98109 #005-18-1992 L1992 **FM** *020 †18

WEST, Shawn H D. 1801 NW MARKET ST, STE 308 98107 #054-04-1995 L1997 **FM** *020 †18

WEST, Timothy Eoin. 1959 NE PACIFIC ST, BOX 356522 98195 #051-04-1999 L2003 **PCC** *100 †20

WESTBROOK, Megan Alysa. 4118 WALLINGFORD AVE N 98103 #021-01-2007 **PD** *012

WESTCOTT, Roger Jeffrey. 1229 MADISON ST, STE 1500 98104 #034-01-1971 L1972 **CD IM** *020 †20

WESTENDARP, Zander. 1122 E PIKE ST, PMB 911 98122 #048-12-1977 L1998 **IM PA** *020 †16

WESTLEY, Michael Earl. PO BOX 900, 1100 9TH AVENUE M6AC 98111 #041-14-1973 L2002 **IM CCM** *030 †20

WETSTONE, Susan Catherine. ■ 98103 #054-04-2002 L2002 **AN** *020 †05

WEYAND, James G M, Jr. 2920 FUHRMAN AVE E, HOUSEBOAT A 98102 #038-06-1966 L1969 **OBG** *020 †30

WEYANT, Maxine Jane. 1600 E JEFFERSON ST # 98122 #025-01-1991 L1993 #018-03-1986 L1988 **FSM FM** *020 †18

WEYMULLER, Ernest A, Jr. 1959 NE PACIFIC ST, MSC 356515 98195 #024-01-1966 L1978 **OTO HNS** *040 †45

WEYRAUCH, Karl Frederick. ■ 98105 #035-20-1980 L1985 **FM** *020 †18

WHANG, Thomas Kyuho. 201 16TH AVE CMB-3, GROUP HEALTH COOP 98122 #035-15-1988 L2002 **VS** *020 †85

WHEELER, Cathrine Jenkins. 1100 9TH AVE C8-GIM 98101 #054-04-2002 L2002 **IM** *020 †20

WHEELER, Chad Kennedy. 1959 NE PACIFIC ST BOX 356, UW SCHOOL OF MED GME PROGR 98195 #011-04-2004 L2004 **PS** *012

WHEELER, Heather Kalani. PO BOX 356410, UNIV OF WASHINGTON 98195 #003-01-2007 L2007 **GS** *012

WHEELER, Kathryn Mcelroy. ■ 98133 #041-12-2005 L2006 **PD** *012

WHEELER, Margaret Ann. 1100 9TH AVE G1-MSO 98101 #054-04-1981 L1985 **PD** *020 †55

WHEELER, Stephanie Grace. 1660 S COLUMBIAN WAY, S-111-GIMC 98108 #054-04-1993 L1993 **IM** *020 †20

WHEELING, Kim Yeasoon. 14419 GREENWOOD AVE N331 98133 #054-04-1987 L1992 **IM** *020 †20

WHEREAT, Eliz Eliason. ■ 98103 #041-01-1952 L1953 **IM** *071

WHIMBEY, Estella E. ■ 98112 #035-20-1978 L2001 **ID IM** *020 †20

WHINSTON, Melicent Ames. 720 OLIVE WAY, STE 300 98101 #038-41-1981 L1994 **FM** *020 †18

WHIPPLE, Mark Eliot. 1959 NE PACIFIC ST, BOX 356515 98195 #054-04-1991 L2001 **OTO** *020 †45

WHIPPLE, Robin Green. 1229 MADISON ST STE 1290 98104 #054-04-1991 L2001 **D** *020 †15

WHITE, Andrew Austin. 1660 S COLUMBIAN WAY, S-111-PCC, SEATTLE VAMC 98108 #047-05-2004 L2004 **IM** *012

WHITE, Asher Abbott, Jr. 310 15TH AVE E 98112 #054-04-1963 L1965 **OBG** *020 †30

WHITE, Cynthia Diane. 1801 NW MARKET ST, STE 100 98107 #014-01-1996 L2000 **OBG** *020 †30

WHITE, David Abbott. 1145 BROADWAY, POLY CLINIC 98122 #008-01-1982 L1983 **HO IM** *020 †20

WHITE, Esther Ann. 9800 4TH AVE NE 98115 #054-04-1997 L1999 **FM** *020 †18

WHITE, Harlan R. 1600 E OLIVE ST 98122 #016-11-1977 L1998 **GPM P** *020

WHITE, John Jos. ■ 98133 #067-01-1957 L1957 **PDS TS** *85,90

WHITE, Kelly Ross. 509 OLIVE WAY, STE 900 98101 #007-02-1987 L1994 **FM** *020 †18

WHITE, Klane Keele. 4800 SAND POINT WAY NE, M/C: W-7706 98105 #010-01-1997 L2006 **OP** *100

WHITE, Mary Katherine. 1959 NE PACIFIC ST, UNIV OF WA 98195 #036-01-1993 L2007 **P** *012

WHITE, Nancy Kelley. 1801 NW MARKET ST, STE 212 98107 #054-04-1977 L1978 **FM** *020 †18

WHITE, Nicole Brie. 1570 N 115TH ST, STE 5 98133 #054-01-1999 L2004 **GS** *020 †85

WHITE, Nicole Marie. ■ 98125 #054-04-2008 *012

WHITING, Sam Herrick. 825 EASTLAKE AVE E, MAILSTOP G4-830 98109 #054-04-1999 L2001 **ON** *020 †20

WHITTAKER, Lori Anne. 1809 7TH AVE, STE 1212 98101 #067-01-1989 L1995 **FM** *062 †18

WHITTEN, Bireen L. 6212 39TH AVE NE 98115 #045-01-2001 L2007 **IM** *020

WHITTEN, Camelia Giroir. 9730 3RD AVE NE, STE 202 98115 #048-02-1985 L2006 **DR** *020 †80

WIATER, Brett Peter. PO BOX 356500, UNIV OF WASHINGTON 98195 #025-07-2006 L2006 **ORS** *012

WICHER, John Brian. 1660 S COLUMBIAN WAY 111- 98108 #054-04-1987 L1989 **IM** *020 †20

WICHOLAS, Bertrand Lee. PO BOX 356340, 1959 NE PACIFIC STREET RM 98195 #008-01-2003 L2003 **P** *100

WIEBUSCH, Abigail Kathlee. ■ 98136 #048-12-2006 L2006 **GS** *012

WIEGAND, Virginia Harriet. ■ 98126 #011-03-1989 L1990 **IM** *100

WIERUSZ, Mary Mei-Li. 1401 MADISON ST, STE 100 98104 #054-04-2005 L2005 **FP** *012

WIESELERBUYER, Karen Mari. UNIV OF WASHINGTON MED CTR, DEPT OF RADIOLOGY BOX 3571 98195 #054-04-2006 L2006 **DR** *012

WIEST, Francine C. 1660 S COLUMBIAN WAY, MAILSTOP 152 98108 #035-01-1998 L2001 **IM** *020 †20

WIEST, Stephen Michael. ■ 98117 #054-04-2007 L2007 **IM** *012

WIGGINS, Kendra Lyn. ■ 98103 #054-04-2008 *012

WILBER, Ellen Marie. 1101 MADISON ST STE 900, THE POLYCLINIC OBGYN 98104 #054-04-1992 L1992 **OBG** *020 †30

WILBURN, Robert Lyle. 1100 9TH AVE G1-MSO, VIRGINIA MASON MEDICAL CTR 98101 #030-05-1970 L1971 **NEP IM** *020 †20

WILCOX, Cynthia Lynn. 10416 5TH AVE NE, PACMED CLINICS 98125 #016-01-1994 L1996 **FM** *020 †18

WILCOX, Jason James. ■ 98133 #047-06-2004 L2004 **ORS** *012

WILCOX, Robert Todd. 925 SENECA ST H8-ME 98101 #007-02-1996 L2000 **GS** *020 †85

WILDERMUTH, Orliss. ■ 98103 #038-41-1943 L1947 **RO ON** *071 †80

WILENSKY, Alan Jos. 325 9TH AVE, BOX 359745 98104 #065-01-1967 L1976 **N PA** *020

WILEY, Carol E. 1100 9TH AVE 98101 #048-04-1986 L1988 **AN** *020 †20,05

WILKERSON, Amy Nicole. 1401 MADISON ST STE 100, MEDICINE RESIDE 98104 #040-02-2006 L2006 **FP** *012

WILKINS, Victoria Lynn. 4800 SAND POINT WAY NE, AND REGION 98105 #005-19-2004 L2005 **PD** *100 †55

WILKINSON, Daniel V, Jr. 1536 N 115TH ST, SUMMIT CARDIOLOGY 98133 #041-09-1980 L1987 **CD IM** *020 †20

WILKINSON, Rhonwyn S. ■ 98117 #041-09-1980 L1983 **AN IM** *020 †05

WILKUS, Robert J. 2324 EASTLAKE AVE E, STE 500 98102 #016-43-1962 L1963 **OS N** *020 †75

WILLEMS, James Patrick. 550 16TH AVE, STE 400 98122 #051-01-1995 L1997 **CD** *020 †20

WILLETT, Tracy. 1200 12TH AVE S 98144 #054-04-1988 L1990 **FM** *020 †18

WILLIAMS, Chase Christian. ■ 98115 #054-04-2008 *012

WILLIAMS, Courtney R A. 3815 S OTHELLO ST 2ND FL 98118 #007-02-1997 L1999 **FM** *020 †18

WILLIAMS, Deborah Merrill. ■ 98105 #005-11-2004 L2005 **AN** *012

WILLIAMS, Jay Blake. 900 TERRY AVE, STE 100 98104 #035-01-1997 L2003 **ORS** *020 †40 ‡

WILLIAMS, Jill Annette. 1100 9TH AVE 98101 #036-08-1994 L2002 **PM** *072 †60

WILLIAMS, Kurt. 325 9TH AVE 98104 #060-02-1980 **ID** *020

WILLIAMS, Lisa Howard. 2300 E ROY ST 98195 #001-02-2001 L2003 **D** *100 †20,15

WILLIAMS, Michael Dennis. ■ 98101 #036-01-2002 L2002 **END** *012 †20

WILLIAMS, Ocean. ■ 98118 #035-03-2004 L2004 **FM** *020 †18

WILLIAMS, Paul Frederick. 515 MINOR AVE, STE 200 98104 #054-04-1982 L1986 **ORS OSM** *020 †40

WILLIAMS, Teresa Chapman. 1959 NE PACIFIC ST, CAMPUS BOX 357115 98195 #028-02-2000 L2000 **PDR** *100 †80

WILLIAMS, Virginia. 2324 EASTLAKE AVE E, STE 500 98102 #021-01-1973 L1975 **AN PD** *075 †55,05

WILLIAMS, Wm Marion, III. 1122 E PIKE ST STE 125 98122 #045-01-1978 L1989 **PTH** *020 †50

WILLIAMSON-KIRKLAND, Thos. 925 SENECA ST 98101 #054-04-1971 L1973 **PM PMM** *020 †60

WILLIS, Brita Marie. ■ 98119 #030-06-2005 L2005 **IM** *012

WILLIS, Susan Hayes. 3123 FAIRVIEW AVE E, LAKE UNION PSYCHIATRIC GRO 98102 #008-02-1984 L1990 **CHP** *020 †20

WILLKENS, Robt Frederick. 325 9TH AVE 98104 #035-45-1954 L1955 **RHU IM** *020 †20

WILLSON, Howard. 747 BROADWAY 98122 #016-11-1998 L2004 **EM** *020 †16

WILLSON, Richard Atwood. 325 9TH AVE 98104 #026-04-1962 L1973 **HEP IM** *020 †20

WILSKE, Kendell Colleen. 1100 9TH AVE 98101 #056-06-1993 L1997 **D** *020 †15

WILSKE, Kenneth Ray. 1100 9TH AVE C1-MSO, VIRGINIA MASON MEDICAL CEN 98101 #054-04-1959 L1961 **RHU IM** *020 †20

WILSON, Anthony John. 325 9TH AVE, BOX 359728 98104 #671-01-1972 L1994 **DR** *020

WILSON, Charles Lee. ■ 98105 #054-04-1977 L1978 **FM OBS** *020 †18

WILSON, Christopher Bruce. 1959 NE PACIFIC ST, BOX 357650 98195 #005-14-1972 L1979 **ID PD** *050 †55

WILSON, Christopher P. 1820 12TH AVE STE 5 98122 #048-02-2000 L2000 **P** *020

WILSON, Clyde Hallam. 3223 1ST AVE S 98134 #008-02-1979 L1993 **OM IM** *020 †20

WILSON, David Q. PO BOX 9282 98109 #005-06-1951 L1977 **ORS** *062 †40

WILSON, John T, Jr. PO BOX 357234, DEPT EH ADMIN 98195 #035-01-1950 L1996 **OM IM** *030 †70

WILSON, Lawrence Geo. 325 9TH AVE, DEPT OF PSYCHIATRY, BOX 35 98104 #019-02-1966 L1970 **P PFP** *020 †75 ‡

WILSON, Mark Aaron. 1959 NE PACIFIC ST, BOX 356340 98195 #054-04-2004 L2004 **DR** *012

WILSON, Michael Edwin. U WASH SCH MED, DEPT ANES 98195 #917-05-1960 L1973 **AN** *020

WILSON, William John. 2409 N 45TH ST 98103 #010-01-1980 L1983 **ORS** *020 †40

WILSON, William S. ■ 98133 #035-08-1950 L1957 **IM** *071

WINCH, Roberta Lyn. 1201 TERRY AVE, ROBERTA WINCH MD 98101 #054-04-1989 L1992 **PD** *020 †55

WINER, Bernard Aaron. ■ 98136 #019-02-1961 L1961 **EM FM** *071 †30,18

WINFIELD, Kirby Franklin. 600 BROADWAY, STE 170 98122 #035-03-1970 L1971 **DR** *020 †80 ‡

WING, Diane Christine. ■ 98104 #054-04-2003 L2004 **AN** *100

WINGERSON, Dane Kurt. 1660 S COLUMBIAN WAY, 116-MHC 98108 #054-04-1987 L1989 **P** *050 †75

WINGFIELD, Emily Jane. 1959 NE PACIFIC ST, BOX 356560 98195 #005-02-2004 L2005 **P** *012

WINKLER, Daniel Cornell. 747 BROADWAY 98122 #054-04-1974 L1975 **AN** *071 †05

WINQUIST, Robert Alan. 900 TERRY AVE, STE 100 98104 #054-04-1969 L1970 **ORS** *020 †40

WINROW, Robert Michael. 1959 NE PACIFIC ST, BOX 356340 98195 #038-40-2002 L2005 **NEP** *100 †20

WINSLOW, Richard Sears. 325 9TH AVE, HARBORVIEW BOX 359797 98104 #054-04-1976 L1978 **P** *020 †75

WINTERBAUER, Richard Hill. 1100 9TH AVE # M6-AC, VIRGINIA MASON MEDICAL CEN 98101 #023-07-1962 L1965 **PUD IM** *071 †20

WIPF, Joyce Elaine G. 1959 NE PACIFIC ST 98195 #026-04-1984 L1985 **IM** *020 †20

WIRSING, Deborah Lynne. ■ 98115 #012-01-2008 **IM** *012

WISCHMAN, Charles Leo. 521 WALL ST 98121 #025-01-1961 L1968 **IM GE** *071

WISEMAN, Merrell Thames. 320 WESTLAKE AVE N, STE 100 98109 #001-02-1985 L1987 **PD** *020 †55

WISSE, Brent Eugene. 1959 NE PACIFIC ST, BOX 359757 98195 #067-01-1995 L1999 **END** *020 †20

WITHERSPOON, Robt Philip. 1100 FAIRVIEW AVE N, STE D5280 98109 #048-04-1970 L1971 **ON IM** *050 †20

WITTNER, Brandi Rose. 515 MINOR AVE, STE 210 98104 #019-02-1999 L2005 **N** *020 †75

WITZ, Aaron Michael. 747 BROADWAY 98122 #054-04-1997 L2000 **PD** *020 †55

WOHL, Jodie Carol. 1550 N 115TH ST 98133 #035-01-1985 L1986 **FM OBG** *020 †18

WOHLAUER, Max Valentin. PO BOX 356410, UNIV OF WASHINGTON 98195 #035-03-2007 L2007 **GS** *012

WOJTKOWSKI, Thea Agnes. 1145 BROADWAY 98122 #054-04-1999 L2004 **ORS** *020

WOLF, Christopher Frank. 1959 NE PACIFIC ST, GME PROGRAMS, BOX 356340 98195 #041-02-2005 L2005 **ORS** *012

WOLF, Patrick Stephen. PO BOX 356410, UNIV OF WASHINGTON 98195 #056-06-2003 L2003 **GS** *012

WOLFE, Michael John. 1101 MADISON ST, STE 301 98104 #054-04-1998 L2006 **OTO** *020 †45

WOLIN, Melissa Suzanne. ■ 98119 #028-46-1999 L2003 **FM** *020 †18

WOLNER-HANSSEN, Pal. 2324 EASTLAKE AVE E, STE 500 98102 #869-01-1974 L1984 **GYN OBS** *050

WOMACK, William Martin. 2923 E HARRISON ST 98112 #051-01-1961 L1964 **CHP P** *040 †75

WONDERLY, Richard Karl. 1200 12TH AVE S 98144 #005-12-1974 L1980 **U** *020 †95

WONG, Alan. ■ 98117 #041-15-2000 L2006 **END** *020 †20

WONG, Brian Dennis. 500 17TH AVE # C34008 98122 #005-02-1978 L1979 **FM** *030 †18

WONG, Christopher Jurn. 4245 ROOSEVELT WAY NE, UNIV OF WASHINGTON MED CTR 98105 #005-11-2001 L2003 **IM** *020

WONG, Emily Yen. 4245 ROOSEVELT WAY NE, STE 354775 98105 #054-04-1990 L1995 **IM** *020 †20

WONG, Eugene. 4742 42ND AVE SW, # 563 98116 #061-01-1982 L1985 **N** *020 †75

WONG, Henry Chiu. 1101 MADISON ST, STE 700 98104 #016-01-1983 L2004 **U** *020 †95

WONG, Jimmie C. UNIV HOSPITAL, DEPT OF RADIOLOGY/BOX 3571 98195 #036-07-2000 L2000 **DR** *100 †80

WONG, Leslie Pak. 515 MINOR AVE, STE 200 98104 #048-12-1998 L2003 **NEP** *020 †20

WONG, Matthew. 901 BOREN AVE STE 711 98104 #005-06-1967 L1968 **NO** *020 †45

WONG, Roman. 801 BROADWAY, STE 522 98122 #023-01-1978 L1979 **VS GS** *020 †85

WONG, Trisha Erin. ■ 98102 #030-06-2003 L2006 **PHO** *012 †55

WOO, Joan Susie. 1959 NE PACIFIC ST, CAMPUS BOX 356422 98195 #036-07-2002 L2004 **CD** *012 †20

WOO, William. 2208 NW MARKET ST STE 410 98107 #034-01-1983 L1984 **IM** *020 †20

WOOD, Brent Lee. 1959 NE PACIFIC ST, BOX 357110 98195 #005-12-1990 L1990 **PTH HMP** *020 †50

WOOD, Brian Russell. PO BOX 356421, UNIV OF WASHINGTON 98195 #054-04-2007 L2007 **IM** *012

WOOD, Douglas Earl. 2001 WESTERN AVE, STE 710 98121 #024-01-1983 L1991 **TS** *020 †85,90

WOOD, Francis Clark, Jr. UNIVERSITY OF WASHINGTON, UNIV WA PHYS ENDOCRINOLOGY 98195 #024-01-1954 L1961 **END IM** *072 †20

WOOD, Jeffrey Carleton. 1600 E JOHN ST 98112 #024-05-1984 L1991 **GS** *020

WOOD, Matthew Douglas. ■ 98116 #012-01-2004 L2004 **AN** *012

WOOD, Robert Wm. 400 YESLER WAY, STE 300 98104 #035-45-1970 L1976 **IM** *030 †20

WOOD, Sue Moses. 2150 N 107TH ST STE 200 98133 #048-02-1965 L1970 **P CHP** *071

WOOD, Thomas H. 747 BROADWAY 98122 #054-04-1973 L1974 **FM** *020 †18

WOOD, Wende Jean. 1420 5TH AVE, STE 375 98101 #010-01-1981 L1989 **IM** *020 †20

WOODCOCK, Rachel Ann. ■ 98103 #016-43-2006 L2006 **FP** *012

WOODFORD, Diane Ethel. 1101 MADISON ST STE 1050, PACIFIC NORTHWEST FERTILIT 98104 #035-03-1999 L2006 **OBG** *020 †30

WOODLAND, Robin Victor. 747 BROADWAY 98122 #005-15-1982 L1983 **AN** *020 †05

WOODRUFF, Anthony Joseph. 2410 3RD AVE W 98119 #004-01-2002 L2007 **U** *100

WOODRUM, David Ennis. 356320, UNIVERSITY OF WASHINGTON/P 98195 #016-11-1965 L1971 **NPM PUD** *030 †55

WOODS, Laurel Tani. 125 16TH AVE E CSB-4 98112 #005-14-1997 L2000 **FM** *020 †18 ‡

WOODS, Ronald Kent. 747 BROADWAY 98122 #016-11-1993 L1993 **TS PDS** *020

WOODWARD, George Anthony. 4800 SAND POINT WAY NE, CHILDS HOSP & REG MED CTR 98105 #041-13-1983 L2003 **PD PEM** *030 †55

WOODWARD, Joseph Folsom. 1959 NE PACIFIC ST, BOX 356340 98195 #054-04-2004 L2004 **GS** *012

WOODWARD, Madeline Lee. 2111 N NORTHGATE WAY, STE 201 98133 #034-01-1989 L1998 **PTH** *020 †50

WOOLFREY, Ann Elizabeth. 1100 FAIRVIEW AVE N, FRED-HUTCHINSON CANCER RES 98109 #026-04-1984 L1989 **PHO PD** *020 †20,55

WOOTEN, Karen Michelle. ■ 98117 #036-05-1998 L1999 **PM** *020 †60

WORSHAM, Nancy Green. 500 17TH AVE 98122 #035-03-1963 L1972 **PM** *020 †60

WORTH, Jillian E. 1100 9TH AVE G1-MSO, VIRGINIA MASON MEDICAL CEN 98101 #550-02-1998 L2001 **FM** *020 †18

WORTHINGTON, Philip. 1959 NE PACIFIC ST 98195 #917-06-1956 L1980 **FPS** *020

WOTHERS, Deborah L. ■ 98102 #041-01-1981 L1983 **P** *020

WOYNA, Susan Johanna. 2003 WESTERN AVE STE 340 98121 #054-04-1992 L1992 **P** *020 †75

WRAY, Linda Michelle M. 901 BOREN AVE, STE 1776 98104 #016-06-1977 L1978 **N** *020 †75 ‡

WRIGHT, Abbie Catherine. 2301 NE BLAKELEY ST, APT 37 98105 #054-04-2008 *012

WRIGHT, Alison Packwood. ■ 98144 #054-04-2006 L2006 **IM** *012

WRIGHT, Ian Howard. 747 BROADWAY 98122 #917-20-1980 L1992 **AN CCA** *020 †05

WRIGHT, Jeffrey Alan. 4245 ROOSEVELT WAY NE, PD CARE CTR MS 354780 98105 #028-46-1978 L1988 **PD** *040 †55

WRIGHT, Jennifer Joanmill. ■ 98103 #054-04-2005 L2005 **IM** *012

WRIGHT, Jessica A. 1959 NE PACIFIC ST, RM C212 98195 #035-01-2000 L2003 **PHO** *100 †55

WRIGHT, John Luther. 747 SUMMIT AVE E, SWEDISH HOSP 98102 #041-09-1956 L1964 **END IM** *071 †20

WRIGHT, Jonathan Lawrence. ■ 98133 #054-04-2001 L2001 **GS** *100

WRIGHT, Lanita M S. ■ 98107 #041-13-1962 L1963 **CHP** *071

WRIGHT, Paige Leanne. 4800 SAND POINT WAY NE, MS 85520 98105 #017-20-1996 L2002 **PD PEM** *020 †55

WRIGHT, Patricia Jane. 10416 5TH AVE NE, PACMED CLINIC 98125 #048-02-1996 L2005 **FM** *020 †18

WRIGHT, Raymond Dayne, Jr. 325 9TH AVE BOX 359798 98104 #038-06-2002 L2007 **ORS** *100

WRIGHT, Robert Grantham. 325 9TH AVE 98104 #035-45-1954 L1959 **P** *071 †75

WU, Amie Chifang. ■ 98105 #005-19-2005 L2005 **PD** *012

WU, Christopher Christian. ■ 98102 #045-01-2004 L2004 **AN** *012

WU, Dan Yinyuan. 1660 S COLUMBIAN WAY, MEDICAL ONCOLOGY 98108 #005-12-1991 L1993 **ON** *020 †20

WU, David Shih. 1200 12TH AVE S 98144 #048-04-2001 L2004 **IM** *020 ‡

WU, Janice Jiashyuan. ■ 98102 #025-01-2006 L2007 **AN** *012

WU, Jennifer Nanmae. ■ 98146 #005-02-2003 *100

WU, Jimmy Shuoh-Yiing. 1959 NE PACIFIC ST, UNIV OF WASHINGTON MED CTR 98195 #016-42-2004 L2007 **NEP** *012 †20

WU, Michael Chaohwa. 1959 NE PACIFIC ST, BOX 356485 98195 #048-12-1998 L2004 **IM** *020 †35

WU, Peter Changchung. 1660 S COLUMBIAN WAY S-1 98108 #041-02-1993 L2005 **GS** *020 †85

WU, Thomas Hsinlung. ■ 98103 #024-07-2003 L2007 **EM** *020

WURFEL, Mark Matsuo. 1959 NE PACIFIC ST, PULMONARY & CRITICAL CARE 98195 #035-20-1997 L1997 **PCC** *020 †20

WYCKOFF, Tom Lawrence. ■ 98105 #054-04-1974 L1976 **PM** *071 †60

WYLER, Allen Raymer. 801 BROADWAY, STE 901 98122 #054-04-1969 L1970 **NS** *020 †25

WYNN, John David. 1120 CHERRY ST STE 240 98104 #016-11-1983 L1990 **P IM** *020 †20,75

XU, Min. 4800 SAND POINT WAY NE 98105 #243-47-1986 L2002 **PTH** *020 †50

XUE, Run. 600 UNIVERSITY ST, STE 1200 98101 #243-45-1988 L1998 **IM** *020 †20 ‡

YAGER, Elaine M. 1550 N 115TH ST 98133 #054-04-1990 L1992 **AN** *020 †05

YAKOVLEVITCH, Marko. 1536 N 115TH ST 98133 #008-01-1990 L1990 **CD IM** *020 †20

YAMADA, Tadataka. ■ 98102 #035-19-1971 L1972 **GE IM** *050 †20

YAMAGUCHI, Ikuyo. 4800 SAND POINT WAY NE, DIV OF NEPHROLOGY A-7931 98105 #572-07-1987 L2003 **PN** *100 †55

YANAY, Ofer. 4800 SAND POINT WAY NE, PEDIATRIC CRITICAL CARE UN 98105 #550-01-1993 L1998 **CCP** *100

YANG, Benduan. 1145 BROADWAY 98122 #243-70-1986 L2001 **N** *020 †75

YANG, Claire Cheng. 1959 NE PACIFIC ST, DEPT OF UROLOGY, BOX 35651 98195 #047-05-1988 L1993 **N** *020 †95

YANG, Dorothy. 1221 MADISON ST, STE 1018 98104 #035-09-1975 L1980 **D** *020 †15

YANG, Louis Jufang. ■ 98121 #016-42-2007 L2007 **TY** *012

YANG, Maria Chaoming. ■ 98122 #005-19-2004 L2004 **P** *012

YANG, See-Young. 600 BROADWAY, STE 200 98122 #056-06-2000 L2005 **OTO** *020 †45

YANG, Steve Lihsing. 1229 MADISON ST, STE 900 98104 #035-08-1998 L2005 **DR** *020 †80

YANG, Thomas Siewhon. 1101 MADISON ST, STE 200 98104 #024-07-1995 L2000 **AN** *020

YANG, Tong. 325 9TH AVE, HARBORVIEW MED CTR 98104 #008-01-2006 L2006 **NS** *012

YANG, Tze Yi Steve. UNIV OF WA MED EDUC 98195 #825-01-1994 L2003 **CCM** *100

YARI, Sachiko Jean. ■ 98108 #054-04-2005 L2005 **P** *012

YASHRUTI, Salah Hadi. 1970 HARVARD AVE E, E 1 98102 #869-05-1959 L1964 **GS GP** *071

YASSA, Naguib Helmy. PO BOX 356100, DEPT PATHOLOGY 98195 #915-03-1976 L1997 **PTH** *100 †50

YASUDA, Kyle Etsuo. 4800 SAND POINT WAY NE 98105 #054-04-1980 L1981 **PD** *020 †55

YASZAY, Burt. UNIVERSITY OF WASHINGTON, DEPT OF ORTHOPAEDICS & SPO 98195 #005-11-2001 L2001 **OSS** *100

YAU, Edwin J. ■ 98115 #048-04-2003 L2003 **DR** *012

YEARGIN, Kimberlee Ann. 4902 SW HUDSON ST 98116 #054-04-2000 L2004 **EM** *020 †16

YEATMAN, Carter Fitzhugh. UW SCHOOL OF MED, DIVISION OF NUCLEAR MED 98195 #051-04-2003 L2006 **NM** *012

YEE, Cassian Ka Shing. 825 E LAKE AVE E 98109 #062-01-1986 L1991 **ON IM** *020 †20

YEE, Christopher Kelly. 169 25TH AVE 98122 #016-02-2002 L2004 **FM** *100 †18

YEE, David Thomas. 12750 LAKE CITY WAY NE 98125 #020-02-1992 L2004 **OPH** *100

YEE, Norbert Keat-S'Eng. 1200 12TH AVE S, INLAND IMAGING BEACON HILL 98144 #143-07-1996 L2004 **RNR NM** *020 †80,28

YEH, Iwei. 1959 NE PACIFIC ST, DERMATOLOGY BB1353 98195 #005-11-2006 L2007 **D** *012

YEOH, Tiong Keat. 550 17TH AVE, STE 580 98122 #825-01-1979 L2001 **CD** *020 †20

YEOMANS, Charlotte Heathe. ■ 98105 #054-04-2004 L2004 **IM** *012

YETMAN, Thomas James. 1200 12TH AVE S, QTRS 6/7 98144 #010-01-1983 L1984 **OBG** *020 †30

YEUNG, Raymond S W. 1959 NE PACIFIC ST, BOX 356410 98195 #065-01-1982 L1997 **OS GS** *020 †85

YI, Chung Hwan. UNIV OF WASHINGTON, DEPT OF RADIOLOGY BOX 3571 98195 #005-12-2002 L2007 **RNR** *012 †80

YI, Sang Pong. 1229 MADISON ST STE 1440 98104 #036-07-2001 L2005 **AN** *020 †05

YONEKAWA, Karyn Etsuko. 4800 SAND POINT WAY NE, DIV OF PED NEPH, BOX 5371/ 98105 #041-12-1998 L2002 **PN** *100 †55

YOO, Bryan Young. ■ 98121 #005-18-2007 L2007 **IM** *012

YOO, Jane. PO BOX 356340, U OF W HOUSESTAFF AFFAIRS 98195 #028-02-2001 L2001 **D** *012

YOO, Sirius Kunwha. 1959 NE PACIFIC ST, BOX 356340 98195 #025-01-2003 L2003 **OTO** *012

YOO, Susan Sooyun. PO BOX 84026, 747 BROADWAY 98124 #023-01-2000 L2004 **IM** *020 †20

YOON, Jeanie Christina. PO BOX 356421, UNIV OF WASHINGTON 98195 #024-01-2007 L2007 **IM** *012

YOSHIDA, Douglas Kurt. 1601 5TH AVE, STE 2100 98101 #028-34-1982 L1984 **EM LM** *020

YOSHIMI, Anzai. 1959 NE PACIFIC ST, MSC 359300 98195 #572-05-1986 L2000 **RNR** *020 †80

YOSHIOKA, Minori. 925 SENECA ST # 1930, VIRGINIA MASON MED CTR 98101 #572-09-1999 L2004 **IM** *020 †20

YOUN, Kristi S M. ■ 98101 #014-01-2003 L2003 **DR** *012

YOUNG, Alison Zuyung. 1100 9TH AVE C1-MSO, VIRGINIA MASON MEDICAL CEN 98101 #035-20-2001 L2006 **D DMP** *020 †15

YOUNG, Allison Amelia. ■ 98125 #024-01-2007 L2007 **PD** *012

YOUNG, Audrey Julie. ■ 98112 #054-04-1998 L2001 **ORS** *020 †20

YOUNG, Bessie Ann. 1600 29TH AVE 98122 #054-04-1987 L1989 **NEP** *020 †20

YOUNG, Eva. 1229 MADISON ST STE 1600, ORTHOPEDIC PHYSICIAN ASSOC 98104 #021-01-2001 L2002 **PM** *020 †60

YOUNG, John Jos. 550 17TH AVE, 6TH FL 98122 #038-40-1992 L2006 **CD** *020 †20

YOUNG, Philip Aunkuo. 701 PIKE ST, STE 1025 98101 #021-01-1999 L2005 **OTO** *100 †45

YOUNGBLOOD, Garland Gail. ■ 98103 #001-02-2005 L2005 **PD** *012

YOUNGER, Jon Paul. 1145 BROADWAY, THE POLYCLINIC 98122 #008-01-1983 L1988 **IMG IM** *020 †20

YOUSSEF, Samuel John. 747 BROADWAY STE 731, GENERAL SURGERY RESIDENCY 98122 #905-02-2004 L2005 **GS** *012

YU, Cong. 1101 MADISON ST STE 200, SWEDISH PAIN CENTER 98104 #243-16-1984 L2002 **APM AN** *020 †05

YU, David Tzehsia. 1100 9TH AVE, MAILSTOP: X7 PMR 98101 #036-05-1992 L1993 **PM** *020 †60

YU, Evan Yawen. 825 EASTLAKE AVE E, MAILSTOP G4-830 98109 #054-04-1998 L2004 **HO** *020 †20

YUE, Agnes Kau-Wah. 1801 NW MARKET ST STE 410 98107 #041-07-1974 L1979 **OTO** *020 †45

■ = Address Information Privacy Protected

YUE, Gigli Oh. 9800 4TH AVE NE 98115 #825-01-1970 L1980 **FM** *020 †18 ‡
YUEN, John Bowkeongk. 1101 MADISON ST, STE 400 98104 #038-06-1990 L2001 **AI** *020 †03,20
YUKAWA, Michi. 325 9TH AVE BOX 359755, HARBORVIEW MED CTR 98104 #043-01-1989 L1998 **IMG** *020 †20
YUNG, Delphine. 4800 SAND POINT WAY NE, CHILDREN'S HOSPITAL & REGI 98105 #005-11-1997 L2004 **PD** *020 †55
YUODELIS-FLORES, C. 325 9TH AVE BOX 359896 98104 #054-04-1985 L1986 **P** *020 †75
YUSKAITIS, Matthew P. 2450 33RD AVE W STE 100, SWEDISH PHY-MAGNOLIA 98199 #032-01-1991 L1993 **FM** *020 †18
ZABETIAN, Cyrus Parse. ■ 98118 #011-02-1994 L1997 **N** *020 †75
ZAFAR, Shahzad. ■ 98133 #704-01-1997 L2006 **CRS** *020 †85
ZAGER, Richard Allen. 325 9TH AVE 98104 #016-06-1969 L1973 **IM NEP** *050 †20
ZAGOREOS, Nikolaos. 1959 NE PACIFIC ST 98195 #473-03-1995 L2004 **HS** *100
ZAHARIADIS, George. 1959 NE PACIFIC ST, CAMPUS BOX 356523 98195 #065-01-1997 L1999 **ID** *020 †20
ZANOLLI, Gerard M. 5236 CALIFORNIA AVE SW, STE B 98136 #047-20-1992 L1997 **P CHP** *020 †75
ZANTOP, Veronika Marianne. 1959 NE PACIFIC ST RM C, GRADUATE MED ED BOX 35634 98195 #005-02-2000 L2003 **P** *012 †18
ZATOCHILL, Donald Lee. 1600 E JOHN ST 98112 #026-04-1973 L1975 **AN** *020 †05
ZATZICK, Douglas Farber. 325 9TH AVE # 359911 98104 #005-18-1989 L2000 **P** *050 †75
ZAVALETA, Jeffrey Reese. 4800 SAND POINT WAY NE, MAILSTOP W9824 98105 #048-12-2002 L2006 **PAN** *100 †05
ZBARASCHUK, Lisa Elaine. 126 NW CANAL ST STE 31 98107 #005-12-1998 L2001 **P** *020 †75
ZEBALA, John Anthony, Jr. 1959 NE PACIFIC ST 98195 #035-20-1993 L1993 **PTH** *020
ZEHNDER, Ryan Joseph. ■ 98105 #054-04-2007 L2007 **PM** *012
ZEICHNER, Lindsay Rose. ■ 98107 #054-04-2008 *012
ZELIKOVIC, Israel. 4800 SAND POINT WAY NE 98105 #550-02-1974 L1990 **PN PD** *020 †55
ZEMCUZNIKOV, Nicolas. 2713 9TH AVE W 98119 #407-19-1948 L1976 **P** *071 †75
ZENG, Ying. ■ 98133 #025-01-2007 L2007 **AN** *012
ZENG, Yun. 510 7TH AVE S 98104 #243-98-1986 L1999 **FM** *020 †18
ZEPEDA, Oscar Rene. 325 9TH AVE BOX 3597, HARBORVIEW MEDICAL CENTER 98104 #054-04-2003 L2003 **IM** *100 †20
ZERNGAST, Wendy Wilkinson. 1550 N 115TH ST 98133 #054-04-2000 L2004 **AN** *100 †05
ZERR, Danielle Marie. 4800 SAND POINT WAY NE, CHILDREN'S HOSPITAL, R5441 98105 #041-13-1993 L1995 **PDI ID** *050 †55
ZERZAN, Judy Teresa. 1660 S COLUMBIAN WAY, SEATTLE VA 98108 #040-02-1998 L2004 **IM** *100 †20
ZHAI, Li. 303 23RD AVE S, APT 311 98144 #243-14-1982 *100
ZHANG, Kristine Yang. 5901 ROOSEVELT WAY NE #307 98105 #026-04-2002 L2002 **GE** *012 †20
ZHANG, Yue Hua. 1959 NE PACIFIC ST 98195 #243-48-1982 L2007 **PCP** *012
ZHAO, Richard Weiguo. 5300 TALLMAN AVE NW 98107 #243-29-1983 L2000 **IM** *020 †20
ZHOU, Hong. 4908 32ND AVE NE 98105 #054-04-2005 L2005 **IM** *012
ZHU, Liqing. PATHOLOGY FELLOWS, GI & HEPATIC 98195 #243-03-1990 L2006 **SP** *012
ZHU, Yong. PO BOX 356428, DIV OF RHEUMATOLOGY 98195 #243-58-1985 L2006 **RHU** *012 †20
ZIA, Jasmine Kaitse. ■ 98101 #054-04-2006 L2006 **IM** *012
ZIEVE, David Alan. 600 UNIVERSITY ST, STE 1200 98101 #038-43-1980 L1984 **EM** *020 †18
ZIEVERS, Paul Christopher. 747 BROADWAY 98122 #056-06-1979 L1982 **AN** *020 †05
ZIMMERMAN, Jerry John. 4800 SAND POINT WAY NE, RM W-8866 98105 #056-05-1979 L1998 **PD CCP** *020 †55
ZIMMERMAN, Marni Ann. 1101 MADISON ST STE 301, PACIFIC MEDICAL CENTER 98104 #005-18-1993 L1993 **IM** *020 †20
ZIMMERMAN, Zachary F. ■ 98104 #011-02-2007 L2007 *012
ZIMNEY, Edward Lawrence. 315 5TH AVE S, STE 700 98104 #035-15-1975 L1994 **IM HEM** *040 †50
ZINNER, Samuel Hamilton. UNIV OF WASHINGTON, CHDD-BOX 357920 98195 #005-18-1994 L2002 **PD** *020 †55
ZIVIN, Adam Henry. 550 17TH AVE, STE 580 98122 #040-02-1991 L1998 **CD ICE** *020 †20
ZIVIN, Julie Robertson. 325 9TH AVE BOX 359780, HARBORVIEW MEDICAL CENTER 98104 #026-04-1995 L1999 **NEP** *020 †20
ZLOMISLIC, Vinko. ■ 98107 #025-12-2005 L2005 **ORS** *012
ZOLLARS, Laurel Elise. ■ 98103 #008-01-1980 L2000 **R DR** *020 †80
ZOLLMAN, Ted Mc Kinley. 1600 E JEFFERSON ST, STE 202 98122 #054-04-1995 L1999 **OPH** *020 †35
ZONIES, David Hal. 325 9TH AVE 98104 #041-02-2002 L2007 **CCS CCS** *012
ZOOK, Paula Deanna. 4225 ROOSEVELT WAY NE, STE 354697 98105 #054-04-1999 L1999 **D** *020 †15
ZORN, Richard Allen. 900 TERRY AVE, STE 100 98104 #054-04-1972 L1975 **ORS** *020 †40
ZORN, Sherri Lynn. 1221 MADISON ST, STE 910 98104 #005-14-1992 L1998 **PD** *020 †55
ZOROTOVICH, Rodney Anton. 550 16TH AVE STE 405 98122 #054-04-1974 L1975 **AN** *020 †05
ZUCKER, David Samuel. 1101 MADISON ST STE 200, OUTPATIENT REHABILITATION 98104 #005-11-1989 L1994 **PM** *020 †60
ZUMSTEG, Jennifer Michell. UNIV OF WASHINGTON, DEPT OF REHAB MED 98195 #016-02-2005 L2005 **PM** *012
ZUNT, Joseph Raymond. 325 9TH AVE, NEUROLOGY MAILSTOP 359775 98104 #026-04-1991 L1993 **ID** *020 †75

SEATTLE — KITSAP

CARLSON, Dennis Gordon. ■ 98110 #054-04-1955 L1956 **PHP GP** *030
HOLT, Brantley, Jr. ■ 98110 #024-01-1943 L1946 **GS** *071 †85

SEDRO WOOLLEY — SKAGIT

ALDRICH, Stephen Mc Cague. 1971 HIGHWAY 20 98284 #010-01-1971 L1974 **FM PD** *020 †18
BACHENBERG, Kenneth L. 2000 HOSPITAL DR 98284 #030-06-1979 L1988 **AN CCA** *020 †05,05
BISSELL, Peggy M. 1990 HOSPITAL DR, CENTER INC 98284 #024-16-1983 L2003 **IM** *020 †20
BLACKBURN, Terri Walker. 2000 HOSPITAL DR 98284 #021-05-1990 L1999 **AN** *020 †05
CAMPBELL, Robert Todd. 2000 HOSPITAL DR 98284 #054-04-1998 L2002 **AN** *020 †05

DECK, Joseph Jerome. 2000 HOSPITAL DR 98284 #030-06-1989 L1989 **AN** *020 †05
DIETRICH, Rowland Dean. 1990 HOSPITAL DR, STE 100 98284 #005-12-1965 L1970 **GP** *071 †18
DILLON, Peter John. 2000 HOSPITAL DR 98284 #050-02-1977 L1978 **AN IM** *020 †20,05
EGGEN, James Robt. 2000 HOSPITAL DR 98284 #016-42-1948 L1988 **AN** *020 †05
ESPINOSA, John Lloyd. 1971 HIGHWAY 20 98284 #016-43-1967 L1969 **NM IM** *020 †28
FAWELL, Thomas Wesley. 2000 HOSPITAL DR 98284 #036-05-1995 L1999 **AN** *020 †05
FINE, Nora Schoenfelder. 2000 HOSPITAL DR 98284 #026-04-1988 L1992 **AN** *020 †05
FISH, Jonathan Wayne. 1990 HOSPITAL DR, DIETRICH & SMITH CLINIC 98284 #005-12-1998 L2001 **FM** *020 †18
GONTER, Aaron Fredric. 2000 HOSPITAL DR 98284 #054-04-2000 L2004 **PD** *020 †05
HARLOCK, Denis Alexander. 830 BALL ST, SEDRO-WOOLEY FAMILY MEDICI 98284 #065-06-1978 L2002 **FM** *072 ‡
HEGG, Theodore D. 1971 HIGHWAY 20 98284 #054-04-1970 L1975 **CD IM** *020 †20
HERBIG, Peter Karl. 2000 HOSPITAL DR 98284 #005-18-1991 L1995 **AN** *020 †05
HERRINGTON, David Dyton. 2000 HOSPITAL DR, UNITED GENERAL HOSPITAL 98284 #054-04-1969 L1970 **OS** *020
HINK, Maryann. 1990 HOSPITAL DR, CENTER INC 98284 #056-06-1997 L1999 **IM** *020 †20
HITT, Donald Ira. 20847 ROCKY RIDGE LN 98284 #010-03-1965 L1986 **FM** *071
HOUGHTON, Henry S, II. ■ 98284 #054-04-1965 L1966 **EM OS** *020 †16
HUNTER, Karen Stanley. 1990 HOSPITAL DR, SKAGIT VALLEY MEDICAL CENT 98284 #047-06-1985 L2006 **GS** *020 †85
HYMES, Alan Chas. ■ 98284 #054-04-1956 L1987 **TS GS** *020 †85,90
JAMES, Wilbert Daniel. 25959 COMMUNITY PLAZA WAY, SWINOMISH INDIAN HEALTH CL 98284 #054-04-1996 L1998 **FM** *020 †18
KANTOROWITZ, David A. 2000 HOSPITAL DR 98284 #054-02-1983 L1989 **RO** *020 †80
KRETSCHMER, Hildegard T. ■ 98284 #407-15-1953 L1963 **P IM** *071
LEUM, Linda Lorraine. 2000 HOSPITAL DR 98284 #024-01-1987 L1990 **AN** *020 †05
LUTHER, Steven Wm. 830 BALL ST, SEDRO WOOLLEY FAMILY MED 98284 #054-04-1972 L1973 **FM** *020 †18
MARTIN, Teackle W. 1990 HOSPITAL DR, CENTER INC 98284 #016-02-1972 L1975 **IM** *020 †20
METZGER, Chris Allen. 2000 HOSPITAL DR 98284 #654-01-2000 L2003 **AN** *020 †05
MICKELWAIT, John Semmes. 1971 HIGHWAY 20 98284 #054-04-1966 L1974 **D GP** *020
MOAT, Chelle Lynne. ■ 98284 #054-04-1986 L1989 **IM** *020 †20
MOUAT, Amy Kathleen. 2000 HOSPITAL DR 98284 #054-04-2001 L2001 **AN** *020 †05
MUFF, Nicholas Saml. 2000 HOSPITAL DR 98284 #005-12-1972 L1976 **RO** *020 †80
NEWELL, Christopher Doty. 2000 HOSPITAL DR 98284 #028-02-1990 L2004 **AN** *020 †05
PFEIFFER, Peter Richard. 2000 HOSPITAL DR 98284 #305-01-2001 L2004 **AN** *020
ROMANO, Rico Vincent Magb. 1990 HOSPITAL DR, STE 200 98284 #748-02-2001 L2006 **IM** *020 †20
ROSE, Frederick Albert. ■ 98284 #038-06-1936 L1977 **R IM** *071 †20,80
SCHROETER, John Erik. 1971 HIGHWAY 20 98284 #005-19-1997 L2001 **AN** *020 †05
SHETABI, Houshang. 2000 HOSPITAL DR 98284 #517-01-1965 L1979 **ON HEM** *020 †20
SMITH, Vanoy Henry. 1990 HOSPITAL DR, STE 100 98284 #005-12-1970 L1971 **FM** *020 †18
SPILKER, Chris William. 2000 HOSPITAL DR 98284 #030-05-1999 L1999 **AN** *020 †05
STICKLE, Herbert Edwin. 1990 HOSPITAL DR, DIETRICH & SMITH CLINIC 98284 #005-12-1993 L1996 **FM** *020 †18
SULLIVAN, Shaun Paul. 2000 HOSPITAL DR 98284 #054-04-1981 L1982 **AN** *020 †05
TELFER, Peter Alan. 2000 HOSPITAL DR 98284 #143-02-1974 L1981 **AN** *020 †05
THOMAS, Charles Forrest. 1916 HOSPITAL DR 98284 #005-02-1957 L1980 **ORS** *071 †40
VON FELDT, Matthew James. 2000 HOSPITAL DR 98284 #056-06-1997 L1998 **AN** *020 †05
WALTERS, Lawrence Cooper. 2000 HOSPITAL DR 98284 #016-42-1995 L1998 **AN** *020 †05

SELAH — YAKIMA

BETHEL, Ross William. 202 W NACHES AVE 98942 #054-04-1997 L1999 **FM** *020 †18
COX, William T. 9 E 1ST AVE STE 4 98942 #033-75-1983, ▲ L1984 **GP** *020
CROSE, Robert F. STATE OF WA, YAKIMA VALLEY SCHOOL 98942 #005-02-1945 L1951 **PD** *071 †55
DE MOND, William Bradford. ■ 98942 #041-01-1946 L1953 **IM** *071 †20
FIGGS, Fred Gerald. ■ 98942 #019-02-1967 L1970 **PD** *071 †55
HOOVER, Galen Hayes. ■ 98942 #054-04-1954 L1955 **ORS HS** *071 †40
MARKIN, Karl Edward. ■ 98942 #035-15-1955 L1978 **OBG OBS** *020 †30
MARSH, Glyn Everett Alex. ■ 98942 #005-12-2002 L2006 **PM** *100
THYSELL, Frederick Jarl. ■ 98942 #041-09-1984 L1987 **EM** *020 †16
ZINGERMAN, James Peter. 202 W NACHES AVE 98942 #039-05-1987 L1990 **FM** *020 †18 ‡

SEQUIM — CLALLAM

AMSTUTZ, Kenneth N. ■ 98382 #025-01-1944 L1946 **IM A** *071 †20
BARTON, Matthew. 244 HOLGERSON RD 98382 #055-01-1979 L1996 **AN PME** *020 †05
BEDFORD, Fred Grinnell. ■ 98382 #026-04-1956 L1979 **AN** *071 †05
BERMAN, Stanton S. 103 W CEDAR ST 98382 #016-11-1957 L1975 **FM** *071
BERTUCIO, Clare Scott. 844 N 5TH AVE, OLYMPIC MEDICAL CANCER CEN 98382 #026-08-1993 L2000 **RO** *020 †80
BOISSEVAIN, Andre Robt. 160 JOSLIN RD 98382 #041-02-1963 L1996 **FM** *071 †18
BROWN, Lida Crockett. ■ 98382 #041-07-1948 L1958 **P OS** *071
BRYANT, David Gordon. ■ 98382 #035-09-1960 L1961 **ORS** *071 †40
BURDICK, Penny Ilene. 777 N 5TH AVE, JAMESTOWN FAMILY HEALTH CL 98382 #048-02-1977 L1987 **FM OS** *020 †18
BURKHARDT, John Henry. 777 N 5TH AVE, JAMESTOWN FAMILY HEALTH CL 98382 #048-04-1968 L1979 **OBG** *020 †20
CATELLI, William Frank. ■ 98382 #005-12-1975 L1979 **EM FM** *071
COLLINS, William Lynn. 994 N MINSTREL RD 98382 #027-01-1966 L1969 **AN** *071 †05
CORLEY, Rebecca Sue. 840 N 5TH AVE, # 1500 98382 #054-04-1983 L1989 **PUD IM** *020 †20
CRIM, Michael Walter. 777 N 5TH AVE, SEQUIM MEDICAL PLAZA 98382 #054-04-1983 L1988 **FM** *020 †18
CUNNINGHAM, Paul Richard. 777 N 5TH AVE 98382 #054-04-1999 L2001 **FM** *020 †18
FAILONI, Daniel David. ■ 98382 #038-40-1965 L1965 **PTH HMP** *071 †50
FIELD, Michael Warren. 795 N 5TH AVE 98382 #047-06-1970 L1983 **OPH** *020 †35
FINMAN, Joel Robert. 777 N 5TH AVE 98382 #003-01-1988 L1991 **FM** *020 †18
FOX, Gertrude. ■ 98382 #016-02-1937 L1972 **OS PUD** *071
FOXLEE, Richard Heath. 844 N 5TH AVE, OLYMPIC MEDICAL CANCER CEN 98382 #025-12-1982 L1990 **RO ON** *020 †80

FRANKEL, Donna Lucas. 540 W HENDRICKSON RD 98382 #023-01-1977 L1980 PM PME *020 †20,60

GARDNER, William James. ■ 98382 #005-12-1944 L1945 GP *071

GLENNY, William R. ■ 98382 #026-04-1953 L1953 PTH *020 †50

GOLDING, Thomas Alexander. ■ 98382 #067-01-1943 L1957 PUD IM *071

GUTHRIE, Timothy Kenton. ■ 98382 #005-12-1983 L2003 FM *030 †18

HARRIS, Alvin Jared. ■ 98382 #016-11-1951 L1977 ORS *071 †40

HAYCOX, Claire Louise. 565 EUREKA WAY 98382 #054-04-1993 L1997 D *020 †15

HEGGE, Donald Wayne. ■ 98382 #054-04-1963 L1970 U *071 †95

HENRIKSEN, Gary Lee. 362 GREYWOLF RD 98382 #010-01-1974 L1975 AM GP *020 †70

HILL, Eldon Fred. ■ 98382 #056-05-1947 L1948 OBG *071 †30

HILL, Robert Lee. ■ 98382 #017-20-1947 L1955 IM CD *071 †20

HOQUE, Paul Murray. 540 W HENDRICKSON RD, SHERWOOD MED CTR 98382 #005-19-1976 L1977 FM *020 †18

HUMPHREY, James Leslie. ■ 98382 #054-04-1980 L1981 FM PME *062 †18

KAILIN, Eloise Whittlesey. 771 OLD BLYN HWY 98382 #010-01-1943 L1971 A *071 †03

KIM, Kookmin M. ■ 98382 #583-02-1960 L1972 PTH *050 †50

KITTLE, Esther Laura. 540 W HENDRICKSON RD, SHERWOOD MEDICAL GROUP 98382 #005-12-1994 L2006 FM *020 †18

KNUDSEN, Richard Paul. ■ 98382 #038-41-1978 L1984 CHN PD *020 †55,75

KOWITZ, Alan Scott. 840 N 5TH AVE, STE 1500 98382 #050-02-1989 L1989 U *020 †95

KUMMET, Thomas Dale. 844 N 5TH AVE, OLYMPIC MED CANCER CTR 98382 #026-04-1978 L2006 HEM *050 †20

LEE, Wilma Faythe. ■ 98382 #005-15-1965 L1966 FM PD *020

LEIBOLD, Edwin Francis. ■ 98382 #056-06-1942 L1947 FM *071

LITTLEJOHN, Robert E. 149B MEDSKER RD 98382 #035-20-1943 L1948 GP GS *071

LYLES, Ann Louise. 720 E WASHINGTON ST ■ 98382 #005-19-1990 L2000 P *020 †75

LYNCH, Thomas A. ■ 98382 #054-04-1950 L1958 R *071 †80

MAC ROBBIE, D Stuart. ■ 98382 #024-07-1950 L1991 P *071 †75

MASANGKAY, Alfonso V. ■ 98382 #748-01-1981 L2006 PTH *020 †50

NELSON, Otto Bryan. PO BOX 201 98382 #030-05-1963 L1963 CD FM *071 †18

NIEMEYER, Agnieszka B. ■ 98382 #005-12-1999 L2007 D *020

NOVAK, Joseph Charles. 777 N 5TH AVE, SQUIM SAME DAY SURG 98382 #016-11-1962 L1971 ORS *030 †40

OLSEN, Kari Devick. 777 N 5TH AVE 98382 #046-01-1979 L1981 FM *020 †18

OLSEN, Roger Dean. 777 N 5TH AVE 98382 #046-01-1977 L1982 FM *020 †18

ORREN, Jerry Mac. ■ 98382 #048-04-1965 L2002 OBG *071 †30

PADDOCK, Leland Eugene. 1751 RESERVOIR RD 98382 #005-12-1947 L1950 GP *071

PEARL, Don Chester. ■ 98382 #024-01-1958 L1964 GS TS *071 †85

PFAFF, John P. ■ 98382 #016-06-1950 L1953 PTH FOP *071 †50

PHILIPP, Louis D. ■ 98382 #056-05-1953 L1954 GS *071 †85

PHILLIPS, C Albert, Jr. 9732 OLD OLYMPIC HWY 98382 #054-04-1960 L1966 P *020

PULLARA, Joseph Michael. 777 N 5TH AVE 98382 #050-02-2000 L2003 FM *020 †18

RADEY, Charles Robt. ■ 98382 #025-12-1983 L1995 *020

REITER, Samantha Faye. 777 N 5TH AVE STE 100 98382 #041-15-2000 L2003 IM *020 †20

ROBERTS, James Shelton. ■ 98382 #028-02-1969 L1974 OS IM *030

ROYALTEY, Harold H. ■ 98382 #024-01-1952 L1953 PHP *071 †70

SMITH, Charles Robt. 736F MARINE DR 98382 #040-02-1948 L1949 OM GP *075

SULLIVAN, Charles Douglas. 777 N 5TH AVE 98382 #054-04-1976 L1981 FM *020 †18

THAYER, Larry Robt. ■ 98382 #005-12-1971 L1972 AN FM *020

THOMPSON, Paul Benhart. 675 N 5TH AVE 98382 #040-02-1973 L1977 D *020 †18,15 ‡

TSAI, Paulus Darcy. 500 W FIR ST, STE A 98382 #041-02-1994 L2004 OTO *020 †45

URNES, Kara Kurtz. 840 N 5TH AVE, OLYMPIC MEDICAL PHYSICIAN 98382 #049-01-1990 L1990 CD *020 †20

WATTS, Charlotte. ■ 98382 #048-12-1971 L1990 FM *020

WEBER, Asma. 800 N 5TH AVE, STE 101 98382 #051-07-1996 L2001 FM *020 †18

WEBER, Carl G, II. 800 N 5TH AVE, STE 101 98382 #051-07-1995 L2002 IM *020 †20

WELCH, Richard Douglas. ■ 98382 #021-01-1959 L1964 PM PD *071 †55,70

WHITTIER, Lucille S Scott. ■ 98382 #024-05-1952 L1954 OS *100

ZETTAS, James Paul. ■ 98382 #016-11-1955 L1992 ORS *020 †40

ZUZARTE, Josephine C. 265 SIMPSON RD 98382 #577-01-1975 L2003 PTH PCP *020 †50

SHAW ISLAND – SAN JUAN

DEANE, Philip G. ■ 98286 #008-01-1952 L1955 PD *071 †55

MOODY, John Lindsay. DRIFTWOOD DR 98286 #056-06-1955 L1978 P *020 †75

WEDGWOOD, Ralph Josiah P. ■ 98286 #024-01-1947 L1962 IG PD *072 †55

SHELTON – MASON

AL ALOU, Saad. 247 PROFESSIONAL WAY, OAKLAND PEDIATRICS 98584 #308-11-1995 L2004 PD *020 ‡

ALBERT, Leonard Harvey. 2026 OLYMPIC HWY N 98584 #016-02-1976 L1977 PA IM *075 †20,05

BARNARD, Michael Dana. 421 N 3RD ST 98584 #007-02-1972 L1990 ORS *020 †40

BELVILLE, Roy Glendon. 901 MOUNTAIN VIEW DR 98584 #025-01-2001 L2004 EM *020 †16

BOZICH, Christine Marie. 939 MOUNTAIN VIEW DR, STE 100 98584 #005-12-1993 L1996 FM *020 †18

BREZEL, Bruce Saml. 1667 N 13TH ST A 98584 #041-01-1983 L1989 GS CRS *075 †85

BUTLER, John V. 939 MOUNTAIN VIEW DR, STE 100 98584 #010-02-1975 L1976 FM PHP *020 †18

CORLEY, Mark R. 2300 KATI CT STE C 98584 #048-02-1983 L1987 OPH *075 †35

DAVIS, Bonnie. 939 MOUNTAIN VIEW DR, STE 100 98584 #005-12-1999 L2003 FM *020 †18

DAVIS, Bonnie J Morrison. 939 MOUNTAIN VIEW DR, STE 100 98584 #035-47-1973 L1974 PA END *050 †20

DAVIS, John Mc Henry. ■ 98584 #048-04-1964 L1971 OBG *071 †30

FORMAN, Burnett B. ■ 98584 #017-20-1938 L1939 GP GS *071

GRAINGER, Kevin J. 939 MOUNTAIN VIEW DR, STE 100 98584 #665-01-2001 L2004 OBG FM *020 †18

GUSHEE, Dean Ernest. 901 MOUNTAIN VIEW DR 98584 #049-01-1986 L1993 EM *020 †16

HENDRYX, Rebecca Kristine. 237 PROFESSIONAL WAY, MADSEN FAMILY HEALTH CENTE 98584 #049-01-2003 L2006 FM *020 †18

HOFFMAN, Joe. 2019 JEFFERSON ST, MASON COUNTY MEDIC ONE 98584 #054-04-1992 L1997 EM *020 †16

JAQUES, Norman A. ■ 98584 #352-07-1956 L1980 GP *071

JINDAL, Anurag. 901 MOUNTAIN VIEW DR, MASON GENERAL HOSPITAL 98584 #495-69-1989 L2004 EM *020 †16

KARATEPE, Meltem. ■ 98584 #902-10-1996 L2006 PD *020

MAC DONOUGH, Harold J. ■ 98584 #660-01-1957 L1959 R *100

MANTHIRAM, Vanni Chendu. 1710 N 13TH LOOP RD 98584 #025-07-1999 L2006 GS *020 †85

MIHALCEA, Ana Maria. ■ 98584 #409-39-1999 L2006 IM *100 †20

MILLARD, Allen Lamont, III. 939 MOUNTAIN VIEW DR, STE 100 98584 #056-06-1986 L1988 FM *020 †18

MILLER, Donald Rex. 219 PROFESSIONAL WAY 98584 #017-20-1984 L1989 U *020 †95

MILLER, Robert Raymond. ■ 98584 #030-06-1960 L1963 PD *071 †55

OGLE, Samuel Garrett. 1710 N 13TH LOOP RD 98584 #051-04-1968 L1994 GS *020 †85

RUPPERT, Karl Donald. 901 MOUNTAIN VIEW DR 98584 #021-01-1957 L1968 GS OS *071

SCHLAUDERAFF, Mark Luther. 237 PROFESSIONAL WAY 98584 #026-04-1980 L1981 IM *020 †20

SEBBY, Kenneth Randolph. 939 MOUNTAIN VIEW DR, STE 130 98584 #030-05-1972 L1994 ORS *020 †40

SINE, Eugene Raymond. 90 SE KLAH CHE MIN DR, SQUAXIN ISLAND HEALTH CENT 98584 #016-01-1980 L1981 GP *020

THOMAS, Michael G E. 221 PROFESSIONAL WAY 98584 #016-42-1991 L1991 ORS *020 †40

THURSTON, Duska Joy. 247 PROFESSIONAL WAY 98584 #050-02-1993 L1999 PD *020 †55

TOWNSEND, Katherine Irwin. ■ 98584 #041-14-1979 L1980 P *075 †75

TRUCKSESS, Mark Edward. ■ 98584 #007-02-1966 L1971 FM PHP *071 †18

VELIKOVA, Diana Evgenieva. 237 PROFESSIONAL WAY 98584 #198-03-1996 L2003 IM *020 †20

WEBER, Tim James. 939 MOUNTAIN VIEW DR, STE 100 98584 #019-02-1974 L1975 FM *020 †18

WILSON, Doris J Hunter. 939 MOUNTAIN VIEW DR, STE 100 98584 #054-04-1951 L1965 GP *020

WU, Johnny. PO BOX 900, 2321 W DAYTON AIRPORT RD 98584 #422-01-1998 L2006 IM *020 †20 ‡

XIE, Meimin. 939 MOUNTAIN VIEW DR, STE 120 98584 #243-47-1995 L2006 GE *020

SHORELINE – KING

AFLATOONI, Iraj. 1207 N 200TH ST 98133 #517-07-1965 L1984 GS VS *020

AHMEDULLAH, Hoor Bano. ■ 98133 #495-21-1957 FM GP *062

ALANIS, Lindsy Jo. 825 NE 179TH ST 98155 #054-04-2006 L2006 IM *012

AL-KHATTI, Adil Al-Shaikh. ■ 98133 #797-01-1978 L1984 HEM IM *020 †20

ALLEN, Camilla Trine. ■ 98133 #045-01-2004 L2004 SP *012

APGOOD, Elmer Rand. ■ 98177 #004-01-1960 L1968 R *071

BACON, William Dudson. 1207 N 200TH ST 98133 #041-02-1956 L1964 OPH *071

BALLO, James Lawrence. ■ 98177 #054-04-1968 L1975 U *020 †95

BERNHARDT, Jeremia Dougla. ■ 98133 #010-01-2006 L2006 FP *012

BURGWALD, Elroy Geo. ■ 98177 #016-11-1945 L1953 GS *071 †85

CAMERON, Tracy Lynn. ■ 98177 #054-04-1993 L1999 FM *020 †18

CAMITTA, David R. 1355 N 205TH ST 98133 #063-01-1999 L2005 IM *020 †20

CAMPBELL, Michael James. ■ 98155 #005-19-2007 L2007 GS *012

CHU, Cong-Qiu. ■ 98133 #243-92-1983 L2004 RHU *100

CLARK, Jonna Derbenwick. ■ 98177 #040-02-2003 L2003 PD *055

COBB, Oliver Ellsworth. 1207 N 200TH ST STE 211 98133 #035-01-1956 L1965 U *071 †95

COHN, William Morton. ■ 98133 #035-19-1958 L1970 NS *071 †25

CONRAD, Suzanne Haddow. ■ 98177 #035-19-1956 L1973 OS OBG *050

COOK, Adrian Robt. ■ 98177 #803-02-1958 L1963 P *072 †75

DASH, Aditya. 17299 15TH AVE NW 98177 #054-04-1992 L2000 AN *012

DAVIDSON, Giana Marie. ■ 98133 #054-04-2006 L2006 GS *012

DAVIES, Catherine Lorrain. ■ 98155 #041-02-2006 L2007 P *012

DU PREE, Leonard Rene. 1355 N 205TH ST 98133 #054-04-1977 L1987 FM *020 †18

EACHEMPATI, Rama Gopal. 1207 N 200TH ST, STE 216 98133 #495-11-1957 L1992 END IM *020 †28,20

ERNST, Jeffrey Clark. 357 NW RICHMOND BEACH RD 98177 #054-04-1997 L2000 PD *020 †55

FALKENBERG, Giselle Lynn. 357 NW RICHMOND BEACH RD 98177 #024-05-1987 L1990 PD PHP *020 †55

FISCHNALLER, Joseph E. ■ 98177 #016-06-1943 L1947 IM PHP *071 †20

FORD, Linda Catherine. 18016 9TH AVE NE 98155 #054-04-1995 L1997 CHP *020 †75

FORNEY, William Ray. 355 NW RICHMOND BEACH RD 98177 #038-41-1956 L1964 PD *071 †55

FOSBACK, Stephanie Marie. ■ 98155 #054-04-2006 L2006 IM *012

FOSSACECA, Christopher Ro. ■ 98133 #038-06-2006 L2006 AN *012

GHADIANIPOUR, Haidar Ali. ■ 98155 #517-01-1968 OBG *100

GOINEY, Robert Charles. 829 NW 165TH PL 98177 #054-04-1979 L1980 DR *020 †80

GOLDOFT, Marcia J. 1610 NE 150TH ST, STE K17-9 98155 #038-06-1981 L1995 IM *075 †70

GREEN, William Larimore. ■ 98177 #024-01-1954 L1969 END IM *071 †20

GRUVER, Jean Marie. 1355 N 205TH ST 98133 #054-04-1987 L1991 PD *020 †55

GULATI, Reena Kaur. 1610 NE 150TH ST MS K17-9, COMMUNICABLE DISEASE EPI 98155 #040-02-2002 L2003 IM *100 †20

GUYTON, Steven Wm. ■ 98177 #024-01-1975 L1986 TS GS *020 †85,90

HAGEDORN, Joel Steven. 355 NW RICHMOND BEACH RD 98177 #016-02-1973 L1988 IM *020 †20

HANCOCK, William Eugene. ■ 98177 #054-04-1967 L1970 OPH *020 †35

HAUCK, Robert Chas. 355 NW RICHMOND BEACH RD 98177 #026-04-1964 L1966 PD *020 †55

HICKOK, Ruth Ilona Kokko. 15230 15TH AVE NE 98155 #040-02-1949 L1963 IM *071 †20

HOGNESS, John Rusten. ■ 98133 #016-02-1946 L1951 IM *071 †20

HONDL, Edeltraud A. ■ 98177 #056-06-1968 L1970 P CHP *071 †75

HUDGINGS, Laura Heath. 1355 N 205TH ST 98133 #048-13-2000 L2002 FM *020 †18

HYDE, Susan Mary. 1355 N 205TH ST 98133 #054-04-1984 L1987 PD *020 †55

JACKSON, David Bruce. 355 NW RICHMOND BEACH RD 98177 #054-04-1985 L1988 IM *020 †20

JAFFY, Matthew Brian. 1355 N 205TH ST 98133 #054-04-2000 L2004 FM *020 †18

JENKINS, Claire Southern. 1355 N 205TH ST 98133 #036-05-1998 L2004 FM *020 †12

JENSEN, Eric Hougaard. 1306 N 175TH ST 98133 #024-01-1960 L1963 GP AM *020

JHAVERI, Varun Marron. 357 NW RICHMOND BEACH RD 98177 #016-01-2000 L2003 PD *020 †55

KATSURA, Shigeaki. ■ 98155 #572-10-1948 L1966 **GP IM** *071

KIM, Bong Sup. 15208 AURORA AVE N 98133 #583-02-1983 L1986 **RHU IM** *020

KIM, Hang Sig. 1207 N 200TH ST STE 105 98133 #583-10-1976 L1991 **N** *020

KIMM, Soon Hi. 1207 N 200TH ST, STE 215 98133 #583-03-1973 L1984 **IM** *020

KNOWLTON-ATKINSON, Susan. PO BOX 55805 98155 #054-04-2002 L2002 **GS** *020

KOBAYASHI, John Mitsutaro. 1610 NE 150TH ST 98155 #005-11-1975 L1982 **PHP FM** *030 †18

LEE, Benjamin Buck. ■ 98133 #023-01-1953 L1970 **AN** *071 †05

LEE, Jennifer Marie. ■ 98155 #030-06-2007 **GS** *012

LICHTY, Lloyd Real. ■ 98133 #054-04-1956 L1958 **GP** *071

LIEM, Brian Cheeho. ■ 98177 #035-19-2008 *012

LIOU, Leeloung. ■ 98155 #025-01-2003 L2003 **N** *100

LOFY, Kathryn Hilary. 1610 NE 150TH ST, WASHINGTON ST DEPT OF HLTH 98155 #005-14-1998 L2004 **PD** *020 †55

LOPERENA OROPEZA, Gabriela. ■ 98133 #649-31-2001 L2007 **END** *012 †20

LUNDEEN, Jessica Mae. ■ 98133 #054-14-2004 L2004 **N** *012

LUU, Minh Triet. 19091 11TH AVE NW 98177 #035-19-1999 L2004 **IM** *020 †20

MATTSON, Julianne. 1355 N 205TH ST 98133 #051-01-1994 L1994 **FM** *020 †18

MC CULLOUGH, Laura Ann. ■ 98155 #028-34-1998 L2004 **CHN** *020 †75

MILLAR, Daniel. 14731 AURORA AVE N, CARE PLUS MEDICAL CENTER 98133 #016-06-1982 L1985 **FM OS** *020

MILMAN, Irina D. 1207 N 200TH ST STE 102 98133 #913-50-1989 L2003 **MPD** *020 †20,55

MITCHELL, Kara J. ■ 98177 #054-04-2002 L2005 **IM** *020 †20

MITCHELL, Steven Harold. 2306 NW 192ND PL 98177 #054-04-2002 L2005 **EM** *020 †16

MOORE, Nola Mae. 1207 N 200TH ST 98133 #056-05-1958 L1961 **FM** *071 †18

MURTI, Gudrun G M. 15230 15TH AVE NE, FIRCREST R H C 98155 #858-05-1968 L1996 **PD** *071 †55 ‡

OH, Shenton Min Yueh. 19930 BALLINGER WAY NE 98155 #825-01-1970 L1980 **AN MDM** *020

OKAMOTO, Deems. 14731 AURORA AVE N 98133 #005-06-1971 L1976 **FM** *020 †16,18

O'KANE, Elizabeth. 1355 N 205TH ST 98133 #050-02-1994 L1996 **FM** *020 †18

OKOS, Anthony John. 15230 15TH AVE NE, FIRCREST RHC/HARBORVIEW ME 98155 #418-01-1966 L1986 *020

OSBORNE, Lester Francis. ■ 98133 #020-02-1939 L1941 **GP** *071 ‡

PATNI, Yaquta. 1355 N 205TH ST 98133 #496-44-1998 L2005 **IMG** *020 †18

PIAZZA, Franco Miguel. ■ 98177 #737-06-1982 L1984 **PDP PD** *050 †55

PURINGTON, Susan Dee. ■ 98133 #054-04-1986 L1988 **FM** *020 †18

QAZI, Khajista. ■ 98133 #704-02-1985 L1999 **PEM** *020 †55

RABINOVICH, N Regina. ■ 98177 #016-45-1982 L1989 **OS PD** *030 †55

RABINOVITCH, Peter Saml. 18125 14TH AVE NW 98177 #054-04-1979 L1983 **P** *050

REESE, Anne Harriet. 357 NW RICHMOND BEACH RD 98177 #005-11-2000 L2000 **PD** *020 †55 ‡

REILLY, Lynn. 355 NW RICHMOND BEACH RD 98177 #035-03-1994 L2002 **IM** *020 †20

REMINGTON, John Paul. ■ 98155 #026-04-1943 L1946 **FM** *071

RICE, Glen Velman. 1206 NW 199TH PL, AURORA PHYSICIANS INC PS 98177 #049-01-1964 L1966 **GP** *071

SANAI, Sassan. 1207 N 200TH ST STE 210 98133 #869-04-1962 L1966 **CD IM** *020 †20

SCHNALL, Bill Stuart. 355 NW RICHMOND BEACH RD 98177 #035-20-1971 L1973 **PD PDA** *020

SILVA, Diana Bartolata. ■ 98133 #748-01-1989 *100

SIMPSON, Sarah Roskam. 1355 N 205TH ST 98133 #016-01-1981 L1996 **IM EM** *020 †20

SINGH, Asha. 15230 15TH AVE NE 98155 #495-18-1970 L1983 **GP OS** *030

SMITH, Robert Laber. ■ 98177 #036-07-1957 L1965 **OBG AM** *071 †30

TAVAKKOL, Zarry. ■ 98155 #025-01-2004 L2004 **GS** *100

TRUONG, Hoang Van. 1355 N 205TH ST 98133 #054-04-1994 L1994 **FM** *020 †18

VAN WINKLE, Jason Warren. ■ 98133 #054-04-2008 *012

VYHMEISTER, Edwin Dwight. 19930 BALLINGER WAY NE 98155 #005-12-1982 L1988 **HS ORS** *020 †85

WAHL, Harley Clair. 357 NW RICHMOND BEACH RD 98177 #056-05-1963 L1966 **PD** *071 †55

WALLACE, John Gordon. 17515 N PARK PL N 98133 #065-06-1955 L1964 **OS P** *020

WALSH, Melissa Cecilia. 357 NW RICHMOND BEACH RD 98177 #035-45-2004 L2004 **PD** *020 †55

WEBER, Patricia Ann. 15230 15TH AVE NE 98155 #020-12-1980 L1984 **PD GP** *020

ZUFALL, Kathryn Amy. 18211 RIDGEFIELD RD NW 98177 #024-01-1976 L1976 **IM** *020 †20

SILVER CREEK – LEWIS

MC CURRY, William Raymond. ■ 98585 #025-07-1961 L1965 **FM** *020 †18

SHERMAN, Harry Jos. ■ 98585 #021-01-1963 L1994 **OS PD** *071

SILVERDALE – KITSAP

AL-AGBA, Niran Saad. 9615 LEVIN RD NW, STE 101 98383 #054-04-1999 L2001 **PD** *020 †55 ‡

AL-AGBA, Saad Khalil M. 9615 LEVIN RD NW STE 101 98383 #528-01-1960 L1970 **PD END** *020 †55

ALBERTS, Monica Sue. ■ 98383 #010-01-1999 L1999 **HS ORS** *020

ALVESTAD-MC INTYRE, Anita. 9750 LEVIN RD NW 98383 #054-04-1992 L1996 **OBS GYN** *020 †30

ANDERSEN, Brock Arben. ■ 98315 #041-15-2004 L2005 **GS** *100

BADILLO, Jessie C. 12199 RIDGEPOINT CIR NW 98383 #748-01-1979 L1997 **PD** *074 †55

BAYS, Patrick Norman. 2414 NW MYHRE RD, SILVERDALE ORTHOPAEDICS 98383 #028-79-1984, ▲ L1991 **ORS** *020

BIRD, Martha A. 9230 BAYSHORE DR NW 98383 #020-12-1982 L1992 **CHP** *075 †75

BLISS, Donald Gordon. 4409 NW ANDERSON HILL RD 98383 #054-04-1977 L1979 **ORS OAR** *020 †18,40

BLITZ-SEIBERT, Alisa J. 10452 SILVERDALE WAY NW, SILVERDALE MEDICAL CENTER 98383 #023-12-1992 L2006 **FM** *020 †18

BOHANNON, Nancy Jones. 9750 LEVIN RD NW 98383 #054-04-1991 L1993 **OBG** *020 †18

BORJA, Catherine Anne. ■ 98383 #016-06-2002 L2005 **OBG** *020

BRESAW, Lois Stansbery. 9750 LEVIN RD NW 98383 #018-03-1982 L1987 **OBG** *020 †30

BRION, Arnel Mangubat. 9576 RIDGETOP BLVD NW, STE L101 98383 #748-02-1982 L1988 **PM OS** *020 †20,60

BRIONES, Edgar Torres. 2600 NW RANDALL WAY, STE 111 98383 #748-10-1978 L1983 **OM** *020

BRONOLD, Melody A. 9951 MICKELBERRY RD NW, STE 101 98383 #025-01-2000 L2007 **PD** *020 †55

BROOKS, Courtenay Nicole. 1780 NW MYHRE RD, STE 2120 98383 #010-02-2000 L2003 **FM** *020 †18

BUNO, Irene J. 2200 NW MYHRE RD 98383 #007-02-1993 L1998 **D** *020 †15 ‡

CARLSON, Glen Robt. ■ 98383 #054-04-1992 L1997 **EM** *020 †16

CARR, Christopher. ■ 98383 #041-01-1997 L2007 **GS** *100 †85

CARTER, Sharon Maureen. ■ 98383 #917-03-1973 L1983 **P PYG** *071 †75

CHAN, Kimberly Mingyee. 9800 LEVIN RD NW STE 204 98383 #035-47-2000 L2006 **GS** *100

CHOW, Jenny. 1780 NW MYHRE RD 98383 #028-02-1996 L1999 **PD** *020 †55

CHRISTEN, Glen Stanley. 1780 NW MYHRE RD 98383 #006-06-1986 L1990 **OBG** *020 †30

CHRISTENSEN, Mahlon Frank. 10049 KITSAP MALL BLVD NW, STE 302 98383 #049-01-1967 L1986 **D** *071 †15

CHU, Lee Wah. 10452 SILVERDALE WAY NW 98383 #016-11-1976 L1979 **FM** *020 †18

CHUN, Terry. ■ 98383 #005-06-2000 L2006 **RNR** *020 †80

CHUN, Ty. 9800 LEVIN RD NW, STE 204 98383 #014-01-1986 L1991 **GS** *020 †85

CIANI, Peter Victor. 10513 SILVERDALE WAY NW 98383 #035-15-1977 L1979 **FM** *072 †18

CLEMEN, James Thos. 2200 NW MYHRE RD 98383 #046-01-1982 L1991 **GS** *020 †85

COLE, Eric Albert. 9800 LEVIN RD NW, STE 101 98383 #051-04-1994 L1999 **OPH** *020 †35

COLKITT, Michelle. 10513 SILVERDALE WAY NW 98383 #023-12-1983 L1993 **GP** *020

CRAWFORD, David Michael. 7111 SEALION RD, SDS-5 MEDICAL DEPT 98315 #051-07-2003 L2004 **GP** *020

CRESCENZI, Victoria T. ■ 98383 #035-09-1989 L2007 **PD** *020 †55

CROLEY, Thomas Frank. ■ 98383 #028-02-1968 L1974 **AN** *100 †05

DAVIS, Robert Lloyd. ■ 98315 #016-06-1948 L1948 **EM GS** *071 †85

DIAMOND, Daniel E. 9398 RIDGETOP BLVD NW 98383 #054-04-1983 L1986 **FM OBS** *020 †18

DIONNE, Ralph Ronald. 9951 MICKELBERRY RD NW, STE 101 98383 #033-05-1973 L1976 **PD** *020 †55

DULAY, Rolando Padua. ■ 98383 #748-07-1962 L1988 **OM GP** *020

EIDINGER, David. 10049 KITSAP MALL BLVD NW 98383 #035-01-1959 L1985 **A ON** *020 †03

ERICHSEN, Christian Ann. 1780 NW MYHRE RD, STE 1220 98383 #048-16-2000 L2006 **DR NM** *100 †80

ESCUTIN, Evelyn Ong. 9951 MICKELBERRY RD NW, STE 101 98383 #748-01-1988 L2001 **PD** *020 †55

ESSER, Gillian Greer. 3343 NW BYRON ST STE A 98383 #005-06-1993 L1997 **OBG** *020 †30

FABERT, Kenneth Ralph. 10452 SILVERDALE WAY NW 98383 #036-05-1979 L2001 **FM EM** *020 †18

FECHNER, Kenneth Michael. ■ 98383 #026-04-2005 L2008 **P** *012

FLEISCHHAUER, G G, Jr. 9800 LEVIN RD NW, STE 204 98383 #016-11-1980 L1985 **GS** *020 †85

GARDNER, Todd Anthony. ■ 98383 #023-12-2000 L2002 **FP** *012

GARVIN, Todd Jeffrey. 9398 RIDGETOP BLVD NW 98383 #008-01-1980 L1992 **U** *020 †95

GORMAN, Larry Michael. ■ 98383 #054-04-1967 L1991 **ORS** *020 †40

HAPP, Carolyn Marie. 2200 NW MYHRE RD, THE DOCTORS CLINIC SALMON 98383 #041-09-1996 L2006 **DR** *020 †80

HARKINS, Hugh Harrison. ■ 98383 #041-12-1959 L1973 **IM** *071

HARRIS, George H. ■ 98383 #035-01-1950 L1956 **DR** *071

HARRIS, James Frederick. ■ 98383 #035-45-1998 L2007 **ORS** *020

HAWKES, Nathan Christophe. ■ 98383 #023-12-2005 L2006 *020

HEBARD, Kathy. 9750 LEVIN RD NW 98383 #054-04-1999 L2001 **OBG** *020 †30

HEINE, Geary Allan. 9395 LINDER WAY NW STE 202, SUITE 202 98383 #037-01-1985 L1989 **P** *020

HINTLIAN, Nancy S. ■ 98383 #654-01-1987 **OBG** *071

HUNT, Phillip Dean. ■ 98383 #028-03-1968 L1989 **UM PD** *020 †55,16

JOHNSON, Donald Robt. 12494 MT WORTHNGTN LOOP NW 98383 #019-02-1974 L2002 **PD** *020 †55

JOHNSRUDE, Theodore E. 9398 RIDGETOP BLVD NW 98383 #068-01-1966 L1982 **U** *071 †95

KAUR, Raveen. 1780 NW MYHRE RD # 122, ADVANCED MEDICAL IMAGING 98383 #495-03-1992 L2002 **DR** *020 †80

KENNEDY, Timothy Robt. 1780 NW MYHRE RD 98383 #030-06-1987 L1990 **OBG** *020 †30

KESSLER, David Jos. 2200 NW MYHRE RD 98383 #054-04-1981 L1987 **OTO HNS** *020 †45

KLUSSMANN, Kurt Gernot. 2200 NW MYHRE RD 98383 #051-04-1988 L1992 **OPH** *020 †35

KOSKELLA, Kenneth Ray. 4409 NW ANDERSON HILL RD 98383 #028-02-1973 L1999 **ORS** *020 †40

KROOK, Linda Susan. ■ 98383 #035-09-1978 L1983 **END IM** *020 †20

LA PLANT, Don Gerard. 10452 SILVERDALE WAY NW, GRP HEALTH COOPERATIVE 98383 #054-04-1981 L1986 **FM** *020 †18

LARSEN, Mark Aaby. 2916 NW BUCKLIN HILL RD, # 139 98383 #016-06-1972 L1991 **EM IM** *020 †20,16

LARSON, Christine Halina. 9951 MICKELBERRY RD NW, STE 101 98383 #016-11-1980 L1985 **PD** *020 †55

LEE, Uyen Truong. 1780 NW MYHRE RD 98383 #028-34-1994 L1997 **PD** *020 †55

LEVISOHN, Dianne Rae. 2200 NW MYHRE RD 98383 #028-02-1985 L1992 **D** *020 †15

LEWIS, Fred Richard. ■ 98383 #040-02-1948 L1949 **PM ORS** *071 †40,95

LIN, James. 10049 KITSAP MALL BLVD NW, STE 109 98383 #012-22-1995 L2006 **OBG** *020 †30

LOGUE, Michael James. 10452 SILVERDALE WAY NW, GROUP HEALTH COOPERATIVE 98383 #040-02-1977 L1999 **FM** *020 †20

MATSENBAUGH, David Paul. 10513 SILVERDALE WAY NW 98383 #039-01-1972 L1980 **DR** *020 †80

MC MILLAN, Julie Amber. 1780 NW MYHRE RD 98383 #005-06-1996 L2002 **OBG** *020 †30

MERIFIELD, Christopher D. 9800 LEVIN RD NW, STE 201 98383 #019-02-1987 L2001 **APM** *020 †05

METZMAN, Michael S. 9951 MICKELBERRY RD NW, STE 201 98383 #011-02-1991 L1991 **D** *020 †15

MILLER, Brian Keith. 10452 SILVERDALE WAY NW, GROUP HEALTH COOPERATIVE-S 98383 #054-04-1981 L1984 **FM** *020 †18

MILLER, David Owen. 10452 SILVERDALE WAY NW 98383 #016-01-1982 L1987 **FM** *020 †18

MILLIK, Filiz. 9951 MICKELBERRY RD NW 98383 #902-05-1991 L2002 **PD AI** *020 †55,03

MOELLER, Randall James. 9398 RIDGETOP BLVD NW 98383 #025-01-1971 L1983 **U** *020 †95

MOORE, Richard John. 10452 SILVERDALE WAY NW 98383 #048-04-1970 L1987 **EM** *020 †16

MOURNING, David Michael. 2200 NW MYHRE RD 98383 #051-01-1998 L2004 **ORS** *020 †40

NAKAHARA, Hank Hidenobu. 9951 MICKELBERRY RD NW, STE 101 98383 #572-07-1968 L1994 **PD** *020 †55

NAVARRO, Godofredo L, Jr. ■ 98383 #748-01-1966 L1980 **GS** *030

NELSON, Richard Arnold. ■ 98383 #039-01-1966 L1974 **OM GPM** *071 †70

NEWKIRK, Jay Harrison. 9398 RIDGETOP BLVD NW, THE DOCTOR'S CLINIC 98383 #054-04-1970 L1971 **GE IMG** *071 †20

OLCH, Christopher Lovejoy. 2200 NW MYHRE RD 98383 #023-12-1987 L1998 **HS** *020 †40

■ = Address Information Privacy Protected

PATNODE, Diane Lynn. 10452 SILVERDALE WAY NW 98383 #054-04-1990 L1990 **FM** *020 †18
PETERSON, Daniel Reuben. 10900 OLD FRONTIER RD NW 98383 #030-06-1972 L1981 **PD GP** *020 †55
PIERCE, Carol Ann. 9398 RIDGETOP BLVD NW, THE DOCTOR'S CLINIC 98383 #040-02-1980 L1983 **FM** *071 †18
POHL, Aaron Christopher. ■ 98383 #007-02-1994 L1996 **OS** *020
PRETZER, Mary Margaret H. ■ 98383 #016-02-1973 L1977 **END IM** *020 †20
QUIMBY, Jennifer C. 9750 LEVIN RD NW 98383 #054-04-1998 L2002 **OBG** *020 †30
RANDALL, Craig Joseph. ■ 98383 #012-01-1999 L2001 **GS** *020
RANKIN, Christopher Colin. 2200 NW MYHRE RD 98383 #048-04-1995 L2001 **ORS** *020 †40
RANKIN, Melissa Lo. 1780 NW MYHRE RD STE 2120 98383 #016-42-1995 L2001 **OBG** *020
RASMUSSEN, Eric Allen. 10049 KITSAP MALL BLVD NW 98383 #025-01-1970 L1975 **OTO** *071 †45
REIMER, Susan Lee. 9951 MICKELBERY RD NW #101 98383 #023-01-1977 L1980 **PD** *020 †55
RENNER, Richard John. 10452 SILVERDALE WAY NW 98383 #025-12-1980 L1989 **PD** *071 †55
RICE, Preston Andrew. 2200 NW MYHRE RD 98383 #035-45-1984 L1990 **OTO GS** *020 †45
RICO, Alexander Glen. 2200 NW MYHRE RD 98383 #054-04-1982 L1989 **OPH** *020 †35
ROBERTS, Dustin James. 2916 NW BUCKLIN HILL RD, # 282 98383 #023-12-2004 L2005 *100
ROOT, Spencer Scott. 2200 NW MYHRE RD 98383 #023-12-1985 L1999 **GE** *020 †20
SCHNEIDER, Steven Richard. 10452 SILVERDALE WAY NW 98383 #023-12-1983 L1993 **FM** *020 †18
SCHNEIDERMAN, Todd Evan. 1780 NW MYHRE RD STE 2140 98383 #005-18-1990 L1996 **OPH** *020 †35
SERBOUSEK, Stanley A. 9615 LEVIN RD NW, THE DOCTORS CLINIC 98383 #030-05-1959 L1965 **PD** *071 †55
SHAW, Lein-Chun. 10513 SILVERDALE WAY NW, STE 109 98383 #385-02-1965 L1977 **PD** *020 †55
SMITH, Sandra Jean. ■ 98383 #054-04-1982 L1983 **OBG IM** *020
SOLZE, James Wesley, III. 1780 NW MYHRE RD, STE 1220 98383 #001-06-2001 L2006 **DR** *020 †80
SPENCER, Craig Randall. ■ 98383 #023-12-1996 L2005 **U** *100 †95
SPINAK, David Jeremy. 9800 LEVIN RD NW STE 203 98383 #023-01-1999 L2005 **OPH** *040 †35
STUART, Barbara Anna S. 10452 SILVERDALE WAY NW 98383 #041-01-1981 L1985 **GP GPM** *020 †70
SUDDUTH, Bob Herdman. 2200 NW MYHRE RD 98383 #028-34-1984 L1988 **IM** *020 †20
SUFFIS, Marc Ira. 4409 NW ANDERSON HILL RD, DOCTORS CLINIC PROMPT CARE 98383 #048-13-1978 L1981 **EM** *020 †16
SYMONDS, Timothy Robt. 10452 SILVERDALE WAY NW 98383 #030-06-1977 L1981 **FM** *020 †18
THOMSEN, Ingela. 9398 RIDGETOP BLVD NW 98383 #054-04-1994 L1997 **FM** *020 †18
THOMSEN, Russel John. ■ 98383 #005-12-1968 L1974 **OBG** *020 †30
TOLLES, Steffan Ross. 1780 NW MYHRE RD, STE 2360 98383 #054-04-1983 L1984 **FM OBS** *020 †18
TRESCOTT, Claire E. 10452 SILVERDALE WAY NW 98383 #025-07-1976 L1978 **GP** *020
TRUONG, Oanh Hoang. 9398 RIDGETOP BLVD NW 98383 #054-04-1996 L1998 **FM** *020 †18
VAN BUECKEN, Kent Paul. 2200 NW MYHRE RD 98383 #056-05-1980 L1989 **ORS** *020 †40
VEATCH, William Meeks. 10513 SILVERDALE WAY NW, STE 101 98383 #040-02-1961 L1968 **DR NM** *071 †80
VOEGTLEN, Russell B, Jr. 9951 MICKELBERRY RD NW, STE 101 98383 #038-41-1976 L1979 **PD** *020 †55
VONDRAN, Janet Elise. 3473 NW LOWELL ST, STE 100 98383 #047-20-1987 L1995 **P** *020 †75
WALCOTT, William Oliver. 10452 SILVERDALE WAY NW 98383 #008-02-1974 L1992 **OBS GYN** *020 †30,18
WATSON, Michael J. ■ 98383 #048-15-2001 L2003 **FM** *020 †18
WATTERS, Bradley Jay. 4409 NW ANDERSON HILL RD, WESTSOUND ORTHOPAEDICS, PS 98383 #054-04-1985 L1990 **ORS OS** *020 †40
WICKS, Brian Peter. 2200 NW MYHRE RD 98383 #035-15-1984 L1990 **ORS HS** *020 †40
WILDER, Thomas Carroll, Jr. 10452 SILVERDALE WAY NW, GHC SILVERDALE MED CTR 98383 #054-04-1966 L1971 **ORS OFA** *020 †40
WOODS, David Andrew. ■ 98383 #016-42-1986 L1994 **OPH** *020 †35
ZAPATA, Jorge Orlando. 9750 LEVIN RD NW 98383 #737-01-1971 L1978 **OBG** *020 †30
ZARNECKI, Matthew. 1780 NW MYHRE RD, STE 1250 98383 #759-10-1974 L1984 **OBG** *020 †30

SKOKOMISH — MASON

HOSFORD, Peggy Ann. 100 N TRIBAL CENTER RD, SKOKOMISH HEALTH SERVICES 98584 #005-11-1976 L1976 **FM** *020 †18

SNOHOMISH — SNOHOMISH

ALLER, Leeon F, Jr. ■ 98290 #041-01-1951 L1953 **FM PD** *071 †18
ALTMANN, Irene G Maria. 401 2ND ST 98290 #409-16-1992 L2001 **PCC** *020 †20
ANDERSON, John Olaf. ■ 98290 #005-15-1962 L1975 **FM D** *071 †18
AUSTIN-ROMBERGER, A M. ■ 98290 #041-13-1947 L1950 **IM DIA** *071
BISHOP, Jonathan Edward. 629 AVENUE D 98290 #040-02-1971 L1976 **FM FPG** *020 †18
BROWN, Ronald Lee. 8010 180TH ST SE, SNOHOMISH COUNTY FD 7 98296 #012-05-1992 L1997 **EM** *020 †16
CORPUZ, Virginia. ■ 98296 #748-16-1990 L2006 **P** *100
DUBIN, Max. ■ 98296 #050-02-1943 L1964 **OS GP** *071 †85
FINN, Samuel James. 8010 180TH ST SE, SNOHOMISH COUNTY FIRE DIST 98296 #038-41-1978 L1979 **EM** *020 †16
FRYMIRE, John Arthur. ■ 98290 #016-11-1946 L1973 **GS GP** *071
GENSTLER, Curtis Cornell. ■ 98290 #005-12-1978 L1979 **GP** *100
GERRISH, Winslow Bradlee. 629 AVENUE D 98290 #054-04-1969 L1972 **FM** *020 †18
GIUSTOZZI, Anna Maria. 18122 HIGHWAY 9 STE B, CLEARVIEW MEDICAL CENTER 98296 #561-15-1979 L1997 **FM** *040
GRACE-FILISKY, Chance D. ■ 98290 #035-09-1997 L1997 **TS** *100
HANSEN, Sarah Marie. 98290 #016-01-2001 L2005 **EM** *020 †16
HERTZOG, Kristian Erik. ■ 98290 #005-12-1987 L1991 **AN PD** *075 †05
HERTZOG, Roxanne Ellen. ■ 98290 #005-12-1991 L1995 **AN** *020 †05
IHLE, Loren John. 401 2ND ST 98290 #054-04-1986 L1989 **FM** *020 †18
JACOBSON, Steven Carl. 401 2ND ST, SNOHOMISH OFFICE 98290 #054-04-1987 L1989 **FM** *020 †18

JANZEN, Carl Victor. 1830 BICKFORD AVE, STE 211 98290 #060-01-1994 L2005 *020 †18
JENKINS, Janet Patricia. 1830 BICKFORD AVE STE 211, MEDALIA SNOHOMISH 98290 #065-10-1976 L1998 **GP** *020
JOHNSTON, Brenda A. 401 2ND ST 98290 #067-01-1985 L1997 **OBG** *020 †30
KIRKENDOLL, Whitney Paige. 401 2ND ST 98290 #021-05-1995 L2004 **FM** *020 †18
KORNELL, Albert Karl. ■ 98290 #030-06-1956 L1957 **R** *071 †80
KUBO, Midori. ■ 98296 #054-04-2008 *012
LARSON, James Raymond. 13409 106TH DR SE 98296 #056-06-1985 L1989 **AN** *020 †05
LE, Hieu T. ■ 98296 #306-01-2000 L2004 **AN** *020
LEE, Tszying. ■ 98290 #016-11-2005 L2007 **IM** *012
LENNARD, Edwin Stanley. ■ 98296 #048-12-1968 L1974 **GS ID** *071 †85
LEWIS, Diana Patricia. 629 AVENUE D, SNOHOMISH FAMILY MEDICAL C 98290 #132-02-1994 L2006 **FM** *020 †18
MATIAS, Susana Jane. 1830 BICKFORD AVE 98290 #054-04-2000 L2003 **FM** *020 †18
NELSON, Melvin Hilding. 629 AVENUE D 98290 #054-04-1956 L1959 **FM** *071 †18
ORMEROD, Leslie David. ■ 98290 #917-20-1969 L1983 **OPH** *071 †35
PERSSON, Torbjorn E. ■ 98290 #858-03-1983 L1994 **FM** *020 †18
REIS, Susan Marie. 1212 10TH ST STE A 98290 #038-40-1981 L1987 **FM** *020 †18
ROMMEN, Idar. 629 AVENUE D 98290 #054-04-1982 L1983 **FM** *020 †18
SALAZAR, Miriam C. 401 2ND ST 98290 #054-04-1990 L1995 **IM** *020 †20
SALYER, Ival Lee. 629 AVENUE D 98290 #025-01-1972 L1978 **FM** *020 †18
SCHEELE, Drew Fredrick. 201 SW LK ROESIGER RD 98290 #010-01-1980 L1989 **AN CCA** *020 †05,16
SHER, Stephen Gary. 401 2ND ST, THE EVERETT CLINIC 98290 #016-42-1971 L1981 **PD** *020 †55
SITTIPUNT, Chanchai. ■ 98296 #891-01-1989 L1996 **PCC** *020
THIBERT, Mark Alan. ■ 98296 #054-04-2000 L2000 **IM** *020
TROTTER, William Douglas. 629 AVENUE D 98290 #054-04-1978 L1984 **FM** *020 †18
TUOHY, Cedric Edward Mero. 1320 7TH ST 98290 #067-01-1953 L1955 **GP GS** *071
VAN VALKENBURGH, Robert E. ■ 98290 #054-04-1971 L1982 **AN** *020 †05
VEATCH, La Vonne. 401 2ND ST, EVERETT CLINIC AT SNOHOMIS 98290 #024-07-1973 L2001 **IM** *020 †20
WEAKLAND, Melissa Ruthe. 401 2ND ST, THE EVERETT CLINIC 98290 #054-04-2001 L2004 **FM** *100 †18
YATES, Dewey Jerome. ■ 98290 #045-01-1967 L1975 **OBG** *020 †30

SNOQUALMIE — KING

ANDERSEN, Richard Thos. PO BOX 2013 98065 #028-34-1957 L1958 **GP** *071
BURSTEN, Colleen Sue. ■ 98065 #008-01-1981 L1982 **P IM** *020 †20,75
DOERFLER, Maurice Lee. 120 RIVER ST, SNOQUALMIE VALLEY CLINIC 98065 #030-06-1972 L1974 **FM** *020 †18
EDDINGS, Ralph Hueston. 9450 ETHAN WADE WAY SE # A 98065 #054-04-1956 L1957 **FM** *020 †18
GRAUMAN, David W. 6422 DENNY PEAK DR SE 98065 #005-12-1959 L1962 **GS** *020 †85
JOHNSON, Alan Keith. 35022 SE KINSEY ST, SNOQUALMIE RIDGE MEDICAL 98065 #054-04-1982 L1983 **FM** *020 †18
KEENE, Christopher Dirk. ■ 98065 #026-04-2005 L2005 **NP** *012
KRAMP, David Gerard. ■ 98065 #028-34-1962 L1969 **IM RHU** *071 †20
LAMBE, Mary Elizabeth. 9575 ETHAN WADE WAY SE 98065 #025-01-1980 L1984 **FM** *020 †18
OWENS, James Wyche Manier. 33010 SE 99TH ST, ECHO GLEN CHILDREN'S CENTE 98065 #035-15-1960 L1965 **ADL PD** *020 †55
SCHURCH, Janitzia. 7829 CENTER BLVD SE # 156 98065 #042-01-1995 L2005 **IM** *020
SHROFF, Ashok B. 1505 MEADOWBROOK WAY SE, SNDQUALMIE VALLEY HOSPITAL 98065 #495-73-1976 L1992 **AN** *020 †05
SPIEGEL, Ronald Martin. 35022 SE KINSEY ST, SNOQUALMIE RIDGE MEDICAL 98065 #041-02-1996 L2002 **PD** *020 †18
TINUBU-KARCH, S Iyabo. 9575 ETHAN WADE WAY SE 98065 #422-01-1991 L1996 **IM HOS** *020
WHITTALL, Jeffrey Jarvis. 9575 ETHAN WADE WAY SE, DBA SNOQUALMIE VALLEY HOSP 98065 #039-01-1998 L2007 **MPD** *020 †20,55

SNOQUALMIE PASS — KITTITAS

BRIGGS, Richard Marvin. ■ 98068 #035-01-1954 L1968 **GYN** *020 †30
HANSEN, Earl Edward. PO BOX 101 98068 #049-01-1966 L1993 **FM** *071

SOAP LAKE — GRANT

AZAB, Salah Eldin. ■ 98851 #915-02-1954 L1979 **FM GS** *071

SOUTH BEND — PACIFIC

HING, Frank Andrew. 810 ALDER ST 98586 #566-01-1977 L1983 **FM FPG** *020
MILLER, Richard Ray. ■ 98586 #038-40-1938 L1939 **GP** *071
PNIEWSKI, Stanislaw. ALDER & CEDAR STS 98586 #759-04-1971 L2000 **R** *050 †80
STROLE, Jan Erik. ALDER & CEDAR STS 98586 #858-04-1973 L1992 **OBG** *075

SOUTHWORTH — KITSAP

UTZ, Gregory Chas. PO BOX 236 98386 #010-02-1986 L1992 **ID** *020 †20

SPANAWAY — PIERCE

BROUNTS, Lionel Richard. ■ 98387 #056-05-2005 L2007 **GS** *012
CHAMBERS, Todd Lawrence. 134 188TH ST S, COMMUNITY HEALTH CARE 98387 #039-01-2000 L2002 **FM** *020 †18
DENINA, Judith Santos. 1806 150TH ST S 98387 #748-24-1992 L2002 **FM** *020 †18.
HARMON, Christine Louise. 225 176TH ST S 98387 #007-02-1984 L1988 **FM** *075 †18
JONES, Elisa Dulcinea. ■ 98387 #023-12-2005 L2007 **PD** *012

KIM, Jeong Hoon. 144 169TH ST S STE A 98387 #005-12-1995 L1998 **IM** *020 †20

MOORE, Dan Cockrill. ■ 98387 #036-07-1969 L1975 **PDE ADL** *071 †55

SARNER, Robin M. 225 176TH ST S, MULTICARE SPANAWAY 98387 #041-02-1995 L2001 **FM** *020 †18

SOFFE, Pierre John. 225 176TH ST S 98387 #054-04-1996 L1999 **FM** *020

TONDER, Kathryn Megan. 134 188TH ST S 98387 #005-18-2002 L2004 **FM** *020 †18

WILSON, Christopher Edwar. ■ 98387 #051-07-2008 *012

SPOKANE – SPOKANE

ABOU-HARB, Jamil. 101 W 8TH AVE, STE 100L-1 99204 #654-01-2000 L2006 **PD** *100 †55 ‡

ABRAMS, Edward Wm. ■ 99203 #040-02-1937 L1946 **IM OS** *071 †20

ACOSTA, Reinaldo. 101 W 8TH AVE, WOMEN'S HEALTH CENTER 99204 #264-04-1993 L2005 **OBG** *020 †30

ADAMS, John Anthony. 530 S COWLEY ST STE 180 99202 #027-01-1971 L1980 **PS** *020 †85,65

ADAMS, Warren James. 801 W 5TH AVE 99204 #024-01-1974 L1979 **ORS** *020 †40

AGARWAL, Sanjay Kumar. 910 W 5TH AVE, STE 500 99204 #496-39-1995 L2006 **PCC SME** *020 †20

AGER, Jeffrey Dwight. 400 E 5TH AVE, ROCKWOOD CLINIC, PS 99202 #028-34-1987 L1990 **DR IM** *020 †80

AHLSTROM, Karen Kay. 9922 N NEVADA ST 99218 #003-01-1996 L2001 **OTO** *020 †45

AHMAD, Saima Mumtaz. 101 W 8TH AVE 99204 #704-21-1994 L2001 **IM** *040

AHMED, Amna Tahir. 212 E CENTRAL AVE STE 240, HEART CLINICS NORTHWEST 99208 #704-25-1993 L2005 **CD** *020 †20

ALAEDDINI, Jamshid. 9631 N NEVADA ST, STE 302 99218 #517-08-1989 L2006 **ICE** *020 †20

ALEXIANU, Daniela Carmen. 104 W 5TH AVE STE 230E 99204 #781-01-1989 L2001 **AN** *020 †05

ALEXIANU, Mihai Dan. 801 W 5TH AVE 99204 #781-01-1989 L2001 **U** *020 †95

ALFORD, Philip Patrick. 4815 N ASSEMBLY ST, DEPT OF SURGERY 99205 #011-02-1984 L1986 **GS CCS** *020 †85

ALICIC, Radica. 104 W 5TH AVE 99204 #957-08-1987 L2001 **IM** *020 †20

ALLEN, Terence Beckington. ■ 99208 #005-02-1976 L1997 **GP FOP** *020 †50

AL NAHLAWI, Hasna. 101 W 8TH AVE, INLAND EMPIRE HP SERV ASSO 99204 #875-01-2000 L2005 **FM** *100

ALSCHIBAJA, Thinathin. 101 W 8TH AVE 99204 #407-16-1948 L1981 **PTH** *071 †50

ALYEA, Alan Dale. 220 E ROWAN AVE, STE 100 99207 #054-04-1980 L1987 **ORS** *020 †40

ANDERSON, Charles C. 101 W 8TH AVE 4300 99204 #048-04-1993 L2002 **PDC** *020 †55

ANDERSON, Christopher G. 601 W 5TH AVE STE 400 99204 #056-05-2001 L2006 **ORS** *020

ANDERSON, Edward Wesley. ■ 99203 #005-06-1963 L1964 **FM** *074 †18

ANDERSON, Eric Robert. 400 E 5TH AVE, ROCKWOOD CLINIC 99202 #040-02-2000 L2005 **FM** *020 †18

ANDERSON, James Milton. ■ 99223 #005-12-1968 L1969 **FM** *072 †18

ANDERSON, Jared Michael. ■ 99203 #038-40-2007 **FP** *012

ANDERSON, Kristina H H. 220 E ROWAN AVE STE 330 99207 #054-04-1996 L1999 **FM** *020 †18

ANDERSON, Kurt Allen. 785 E HOLLAND AVE, ORTHOPAEDIC SPECIALTY CLIN 99218 #003-01-2001 L2007 **HS** *020

ANDERSON-JENKINS, Jill L. 800 W 5TH AVE 99204 #054-04-1988 L1990 **EM FM** *020 †18

ANDRONIC, Cristian. 105 W 8TH AVE, STE 6020 99204 #781-01-1992 L2004 **OBG** *020 †30

ANDRONIC, Roxana Gabriela. 104 W 5TH AVE STE 250E, ANESTHESIA ASSOCIATES, PS 99204 #781-01-1992 L2004 **AN** *020 †05

ANGEID-BACKMAN, Elin. 5715 N LIDGERWOOD ST, INLAND IMAGING 99208 #016-02-1988 L2004 **DR** *020 †80

ANGELL, Ethan Macy. 3919 N MAPLE ST 99205 #040-02-2001 L2004 **FM** *020 †18

ANTONIUK, Nelson. 2713 N ARGONNE RD 99212 #041-13-1995 L2002 **FM** *020 †18

APPEL, Anthony John. 101 W 8TH AVE, SACRED HEART HOSP EMERG RM 99204 #054-04-1967 L1970 **EM** *071 †16

APPEL, Ronald James. 101 W 8TH AVE, BOX 2555 99204 #054-04-1993 L1996 **EM** *020 †16

ARGUINCHONA, Henry B. 101 W 8TH AVE 99204 #030-06-1961 L1966 **PTH NM** *020 †50,28

ARGUINCHONA, Henry Louis. 2910 E 57TH AVE, STE 5 99223 #054-04-1988 L1988 **ID** *020 †20

ARMSTRONG, Heather Marie. 322 W NORTH RIVER DR, RIVERFRONT MEDICAL CENTER 99201 #028-34-1999 L2001 **FM** *020 †18

ARNETT, Robert Leuty. 5715 N LIDGERWOOD ST, INLAND IMAGING 99208 #031-01-1995 L2002 **DR** *020 †80

ARRIENDA, Minerva. ■ 99223 #748-07-1976 L1997 **P** *020

ARTHURS, James Richard. 3919 N MAPLE ST 99205 #054-04-1968 L1975 **PHP FM** *020 †70

ARVIN, Kara Lynn. 105 W 8TH AVE # 336C 99204 #028-02-1996 L2006 **NPM** *020 †55

ASHBY, Howard Bennett. 105 W 8TH AVE, STE 6055 99204 #018-03-1974 L1982 **CHP P** *020 †75

ASHLEY, Susan Lynn. 400 E 5TH AVE 99202 #048-14-1989 L1989 **FM** *020 †18

ATTWOOD, Wayne Le Roy. 820 S MCCLELLAN ST STE 314 99204 #019-02-1959 L1963 **IM** *071 †20

ATWAL, Sandeep. 101 W 8TH AVE 99204 #495-29-2005 L2007 **IM** *012

ATWOOD, Jesse William. 101 W 8TH AVE, SACRED HEART MEDICAL CENTE 99204 #028-34-1995 L2003 **PD** *020 †55

AUFFANT, Roberto A. 911 W 5TH AVE, SHRINERS HOSPITAL 99204 #935-03-1973 L1979 **AN CCA** *020 †05

BACHHUBER, Nicholas A. 235 E ROWAN AVE, STE 102 99207 #056-06-1966 L1973 **OBG** *071 †30

BAGBY, George W. 105 W 8TH AVE 99204 #041-13-1946 L1956 **ORS** *072 †40

BAILEY, Hal Lee, Jr. 3010 S SOUTHEAST BLVD 99223 #005-12-1991 L1994 **FM** *020 †18

BAILEY, Jodi Lynn. 525 S COWLEY ST, INLAND IMAGING ASSOC 99202 #005-12-1989 L1997 **DR** *020 †80

BAIRD, Glen Olsen. 911 W 5TH AVE, SPOKANE 99204 #049-01-1993 L1999 **ORS** *020 †40

BAKKER, Cornelis B. ■ 99201 #660-04-1952 L1955 **P** *071 †75

BALE, Richard H. 404 W 15TH AVE 99203 #020-02-1969 L1970 **FM** *020 †18

BALMFORTH, Gregory John. 5715 N LIDGERWOOD ST, INLAND IMAGING 99208 #016-43-2001 L2006 **DR** *100 †80

BARE, David Howard. 3919 N MAPLE ST 99205 #054-04-1975 L1978 **FM** *020 †18

BARNES, Richard Barry. 104 W 5TH AVE STE 200W 99204 #040-02-1974 L1978 **FM OS** *040 †18

BARNETT, Sol. 105 W 8TH AVE STE 7050, GASTROENTEROLOGY 99204 #038-41-1961 L2000 **IM GE** *020 †20

BARRONG, Shawn Dale. 105 W 8TH AVE, STE 6020 99204 #054-04-1993 L1996 **OBG** *020 †30

BARROW, Craig Ridges. 785 E HOLLAND AVE, ATTN: MARSHA PINAT 99218 #005-12-1997 L2003 **ORS** *020 †40

BARRY, Jane Wallis. 801 S STEVENS ST, INLAND IMAGING 99204 #038-06-1973 L1980 **R CD** *020 †80

BARSOTTI, Michael R. 35 W 8TH AVE STE 440 99204 #028-34-1986 L1997 **NPM** *020 †55

BASSETT, Mark Robt. 400 E 5TH AVE 99202 #054-04-1977 L1982 **OTO** *020 †45

BATES, Daniel Matthew. 910 W 5TH AVE, STE 550 99204 #025-01-1973 L1978 **GS** *020 †85

BATKOFF, Braden Wm. 318 E ROWAN AVE, STE 240 99207 #048-14-1989 L1992 **CD** *020 †20

BAUER, Mark Douglas. 101 W 8TH AVE, SACRED HEART EMEG DEPT 99204 #005-12-1986 L1991 **EM** *020 †16

BAUM, Carl Alan. 601 S DIVISION ST, SPOKANE PSYCHIATRIC CLINIC 99202 #036-01-1974 L1980 **P FM** *020 †18,75

BAUMGARTNER, Scott Walter. 104 W 5TH AVE STE 240, ASSOCIATED INTERNISTS PS 99204 #054-04-1975 L1985 **RHU IM** *050 †20

BAX, Timothy William. 318 E ROWAN AVE, STE 227 99207 #040-02-1992 L1998 **GS TRS** *020 †85

BAXTER, Chadwick Franklin. 101 W 8TH AVE 99204 #038-06-1954 L1962 **PDS** *075 †85

BEALE, Paul Allen. 400 E 5TH AVE 99202 #038-40-1964 L1970 **R** *071 †80

BEAULAURIER, Patrick T. 104 W 5TH AVE, STE 250 99204 #054-04-1985 L1985 **AN IM** *020 †20,05

BECKER, Bruce Erhart. 105 W 8TH AVE STE 200, PHYSICAL MEDICINE & REHABI 99204 #021-01-1969 L1974 **PM** *030 †60

BECKER, Paul Wm. 5901 N LIDGERWOOD ST, STE 118 99208 #028-03-1967 L1975 **D** *071 †15

BECKNER, Ronda Marie. 910 W 5TH AVE STE 600 99204 #040-02-1996 L1998 **FM** *020 †18

BEJJANI, Bassem Abdu. 120 N PINE ST STE 242C, SIGNATURE GENOMIC LABORATO 99202 #605-01-1987 L2003 **CG PD** *020 †55,19

BELENKY, Gregory Lucas. 412 E SPOKANE FALLS BLVD, SLEEP AND PERFORMANCE RESE 99202 #005-11-1971 L2006 **P** *050 †75

BELL, Gary Vernon. 5715 N LIDGERWOOD ST, INLAND IMAGING 99208 #054-04-1978 L1979 **RNR R** *020 †80 ‡

BELL, Laurie Virginia. ■ 99224 #048-14-1978 L1987 **GS** *071 †85

BENDER, Berdine Shelia. 801 W 5TH AVE 99204 #016-42-1978 L1983 **IM** *020 †20

BENDER, William Ira. 105 W 8TH AVE, STE 1000 99204 #016-42-1978 L1983 **N** *020 †75

BENEDETTI, Robert Geo. 235 E ROWAN AVE, STE 209 99207 #054-04-1977 L1986 **NEP IM** *030 †20

BENEDETTO, Jette. 400 E 5TH AVE, FAMILY MED DEPT 99202 #297-01-1989 L1995 **FM** *020 †18

BENNETT, William L. 107 S DIVISION ST, SPOKANE COMM MENTAL HEALTH 99202 #016-11-1981 L1993 **P** *020 †75

BENNETT, William Robert. 122 W 7TH AVE, STE 310 99204 #020-02-1978 L1986 **CD** *020 †20

BENSON, Judy Ann. 101 W 8TH AVE, 101 WEST EIGHTH AVE. (SHMC 99204 #030-05-1983 L1984 **IM IMG** *040 †20

BEREN, Richard Anthony. 5715 N LIDGERWOOD ST, INLAND IMAGING 99208 #048-04-1975 L1983 **DR** *020 †80

BERG, Michael Paul. 421 W RIVERSIDE AVE # 280 99201 #054-04-1966 L1973 **OPH** *020 †35

BERGMAN, Melanie Kim. 601 S SHERMAN ST 99202 #051-04-1994 L2002 **OBG GO** *020 †30

BERGUM, Mary Frances. 3154 E 29TH AVE 99223 #054-04-2001 L2003 **FM** *020 †18

BERING, Stacie Cherniack. 801 W 5TH AVE, STE 422 99204 #048-04-1978 L1982 **OBG PLM** *020 †30

BERNDT, Thomas Edward. ■ 99224 #005-15-1972 L1977 **FM A** *020 †18

BHAT, Ishwar Praveen. 5715 N LIDGERWOOD ST, INLAND IMAGING 99208 #495-37-1992 L2005 **DR** *020 †80

BIGGS, Dennis W, Jr. ■ 99208 #036-05-1948 L1974 **NM IM** *071 †28,20

BINDLER, Julian. 711 S COWLEY ST 99202 #035-20-1971 L1974 **AN** *020 †05

BINGHAM, James Moyer. 322 W NORTH RIVER DR 99201 #054-04-1981 L1982 **FM FSM** *020 †18

BIRRER, Bret Michael. ■ 99223 #054-04-2008 *012

BISHOP, Timothy Charles. 101 W 8TH AVE 99204 #003-01-1995 L2001 **CD** *020 †20

BISWELL, Flora Corkery. ■ 99203 #040-02-1935 L1942 **OS** *071

BLISS, Lisa Stranc. 105 W 8TH AVE, STE 1000 99204 #016-06-1999 L2003 **PM** *020 †60

BLYKOWSKI-MAY, Monica. 9001 N COUNTRY HOMES BLVD 99218 #054-04-1995 L1997 **FM** *020 †18

BOCEK, Zdenek. 105 W 8TH AVE STE 7050, ROCKWOOD CLINIC 99204 #869-07-1978 L2001 **GE IM** *020 †20

BODENSTEIN, Carl Jay. 105 W 8TH AVE, STE 336C 99204 #035-06-1978 L1983 **NPM PD** *020 †55

BODINE, Birgit J. 104 W 5TH AVE STE 200W 99204 #409-10-1997 L2005 **IM** *020

BOGAROSH, Christopher L. 6002 N LIDGERWOOD ST 99208 #039-01-1974 L1975 **FM FPG** *020

BOND, Travis Scott. ■ 99202 #030-06-2007 **TY** *012

BOND, William Chas. ■ 99203 #035-20-1973 L1978 **N** *020

BONE, Craig Melvin. 220 E ROWAN AVE, STE 100 99207 #054-04-1990 L2000 **ORS** *020 †40

BONNEAU, Robert Allen. 5901 N MAYFAIR ST 99208 #056-06-1967 L1974 **OTO GP** *020 †45

BONVALLET, James Cecil. 220 E ROWAN AVE, STE 230 99207 #017-20-1959 L1969 **TS CD** *020 †85,90

BOSSHARDT, James Scott. PO BOX 2555 99220 #034-01-1990 **AN** *100

BOT, David Douglas. 105 W 8TH AVE, STE 6055 99204 #037-01-1980 L1984 **P** *020 †75

BOUBEL, Thomas Richard. 104 W 5TH AVE STE 230E 99204 #040-02-1981 L1984 **AN** *020 †05

BOULET, Andrew James. 122 W 7TH AVE STE 310 99204 #048-12-1984 L1991 **CD IM** *020 †20

BOUMA, Bruce Alan. 235 E ROWAN AVE STE 204, N SPOKANE SURGEONS PS 99207 #025-01-1973 L1982 **GS VS** *020 †85

BOVITZ, Sara Harkness. ■ 99203 #054-04-2003 L2003 **IM** *100 †20

BOWMAN, Sarah Love. ■ 99203 #010-01-2006 L2008 **AN** *012

BOWTON, Eric Jason. 12 E 5TH AVE, STE 202 99202 #054-04-1989 L1990 **ORS** *020 †40

BRADDY, Michelle Rae. 104 W 5TH AVE, STE 200W 99204 #028-46-2004 L2007 **FM** *020 †18

BRADLEY, Deborah Lynne. 123 W FRANCIS AVE, ORAL SURGERY PLUS 99205 #005-14-1996 L1999 *020

BRADLEY, Scot Llewellyn. 400 E 5TH AVE 99202 #024-07-1973 L1979 **PUD IM** *020 †20 ‡

BRADLEY, William Franklin. 400 E 5TH AVE, ROCKWOOD CLINIC 99202 #028-34-1975 L1978 **EM FM** *020 †18

BRASCH, James Vincent. 212 E CENTRAL AVE STE 34 99208 #054-04-1984 L1988 **OBG** *020 †30

BRAY, Robert Francis. 104 W 5TH AVE, STE 200W 99204 #005-15-1981 L1982 **FM** *040 †18

BRAY, William Hugh. 510 S COWLEY ST 99202 #030-06-1981 L1982 **OPH** *020 †35

BREMNER DEXTER, Sandra J. 906 W 2ND AVE STE 600 99201 #054-04-1992 L1992 **CHP P** *020 †75

BREWSTER, Robert Conover. 601 W 5TH AVE STE 400 99204 #019-02-1968 L1975 **ORS** *020 †40

■ = Address Information Privacy Protected

BRICKNER, Charles David. 400 E 5TH AVE 99202 #041-14-1992 L2001 **PD** *020 †55
BRIGHT, Richard Andrew. 105 W 8TH AVE, STE 7070 99204 #001-02-1993 L1998 **GS** *020 †85
BRINK, Francis Marion. ■ 99223 #060-01-1940 L1941 **ORS** *071 †40
BRINKMAN, James Frederick. 530 S COWLEY ST 99202 #019-02-1964 L1971 **PS HS** *071 †85,65
BRISBOIS, Robert Steven. 508 W 6TH AVE, STE 500 99204 #040-02-1972 L1980 **OBG** *020 †30
BRITT, Charles Wm, Jr. 42 E ROWAN AVE, STE B 99207 #048-02-1976 L1998 **OS N** *020 †75
BROCKMANN, Rupert Otto. 2525 E 29TH AVE, STE 10B-357 99223 #007-02-1961 L1967 **OTO** *071 †45
BRONDOS, Charles Edward. 715 S COWLEY ST, STE 224 99202 #016-11-1968 L1974 **N** *020 †75
BRONSON, William E. 105 W 8TH AVE, STE 200 99204 #054-04-1986 L1992 **OSS PD** *020 †40
BROOKING, Fredrick Todd. 800 W 5TH AVE, DEACONESS MEDICAL CENTER/ 99204 #665-01-2003 L2003 **FM** *020 †18
BROOKS, Lowell M. ■ 99203 #020-02-1943 L1949 **AN** *071 †05
BROW, Edward Peter. 322 W NORTH RIVER DR 99201 #005-15-1980 L1986 **EM FM** *020 †18
BROWER, Jayson Scott. 212 E CENTRAL AVE, STE 245 99208 #028-34-1999 L2005 **VIR** *020 †80
BROWN, Lynn A. 5633 N LIDGERWOOD ST, HOLY FAMILY HOSPITAL 99208 #048-15-1993 L2006 **EM** *020 †16
BROWN, William Loren. 4815 N ASSEMBLY ST, C/O SPOKANE VAMC MS116 99205 #040-02-1991 L2004 **P** *020 †75
BROWN, William R, Jr. 9631 N NEVADA ST, STE 100 99218 #054-04-1962 L1963 **GP** *020
BROWNLEE, William Arthur. 1715 E ESTATES RD 99224 #055-01-1970 L1971 **ORS GP** *071 †40
BRUNJES, Carl Frederick. ■ 99203 #035-01-1961 L1967 **ORS LM** *071 †40
BRUNKAN, Richard Sanville. 5715 N LIDGERWOOD ST, INLAND IMAGING 99208 #056-06-1999 L2005 **R** *020 †80
BRUTOCAO, Daniel Paul. 101 W 8TH AVE, SACRED HEART MED CTR 99204 #016-43-1986 L1989 **PD** *020 †55
BRUYA, Timothy Edward. 104 W 5TH AVE STE 400W 99204 #054-04-1974 L1979 **PUD IM** *020 †20
BUDENHOLZER, Brian Robt. 4102 S REGAL ST, STE 101 99223 #005-06-1980 L1986 **FM** *020 †18
BUFORD, Malcolm Lavern, Jr. 610 S SHERMAN ST STE 201, ROCKWOOD CLINIC NEPHROLOGY 99202 #039-01-1999 L2005 **IM** *100 †20
BULLOCK, Forrest A. ■ 99204 #049-01-1998 L2001 **AN** *020
BUNCH, David C, Jr. 101 W 8TH AVE 99204 #021-05-1945 L1955 **IM A** *071 †20
BUNN, Jeffrey David. 9922 N NEVADA ST 99218 #005-12-1996 L2002 **OTO** *020 †45
BUNN, Tamalyn Jo. ■ 99223 #005-12-1998 L2002 **PD** *074 †55
BURG, Pamela Garza. 101 W 8TH AVE STE 4300 99204 #048-02-1991 L2000 **PDC** *020 †55
BURGAN, Jeffrey Dwight. 104 W 5TH AVE STE 230 99204 #031-01-1988 L1992 **AN** *020 †05
BURNETT, Robert John, III. 910 W 5TH AVE, STE 380 99204 #038-41-1991 L1998 **GS CD** *020 †90,85
BURNS, Amy Giblin. ■ 99203 #019-02-2003 L2003 **P** *012
BUTLER, Jeffrey Bragg. 105 W 8TH AVE STE 6080, ARTHRITIS NORTHWEST 99204 #024-07-1985 L1991 **RHU IM** *020 †20
BYAZROVA, Eteri S. 122 W 7TH AVE, STE 310 99204 #913-23-1995 L2006 **ICE** *020 †20
BYRD, Leroy James. 406 E ROWAN AVE STE 200 99207 #056-06-1964 L1970 **IM** *020 †20
BYRD, Richard Bourne. 400 E 5TH AVE 99202 #028-34-1954 L1980 **PUD CCM** *020 †20
CAIN, Orlan Randy. 5901 N LIDGERWOOD ST, STE 18B 99208 #038-41-1966 L1972 **FM** *075 †18
CALKINS, Mary E. ■ 99201 #040-02-1950 L1952 **GP GS** *071
CAMBARERI, John Jos. 104 W 5TH AVE STE 230E 99204 #054-04-1986 L1999 **AN PME** *020 †05
CAMMACK, Daniel Forbert. 105 W 8TH AVE STE 7010, ROCKWOOD CLINIC ASC 99204 #040-02-1974 L1975 **GS TS** *020 †85
CAMP, Jakob Obie. 105 W 8TH AVE STE 450E, SACRED HEART PSYCHIATRIC C 99204 #027-01-1985 L2005 **P** *020 †75
CAMPBELL, Gabriel Antonio. ■ 99205 #046-01-2002 L2003 **FM** *020
CANNON, Jean Suzanne. 3904 S SHERMAN ST 99203 #665-01-2001 L2004 **IM** *100
CANTLON, Gary Eugene. 9922 N NEVADA ST 99218 #030-05-1973 L1981 **OTO** *020 †45
CAREY, Alexandra Sarah. ■ 99203 #010-03-1998 L2001 **PD** *020 †55
CAREY, Colleen Ruth. 910 W 5TH AVE STE 570 99204 #041-07-1974 L1980 **END** *020 †20
CARLILL, Roland J. 6701 N COUNTRY HOMES BLVD 99208 #005-12-1955 L1956 **GP GS** *071
CARLSON, Christel Ann. 104 W 5TH AVE STE 230E 99204 #011-03-1981 L1985 **AN CCM** *020 †05
CARLSON, Scott Eric. 400 E 5TH AVE 99202 #007-02-1984 L1988 **N OS** *020 †75
CARLSON, Stephen Alan. 104 W 5TH AVE, STE 230E 99204 #021-01-1979 L1993 **AN** *020 †05
CARSON, Richard W. 235 E ROWAN AVE, STE 209 99207 #012-01-1979 L1996 **NEP IM** *020 †20
CARTER, Jimmy Keith. 104 W 5TH AVE STE 250E 99204 #060-02-1992 L2004 *020
CASHION, Medford. ■ 99224 #048-04-1973 L1973 **EM** *020 †16
CASKEY, Paul Martin. 800 W 5TH AVE 99204 #056-05-1980 L1991 **OP PD** *020 †40
CASTER, Mark Parsons. ■ 99208 #016-06-1972 L1986 **IM GE** *020 †20
CASTLEBERRY, Victor Earl. ■ 99224 #048-02-1955 L1958 **IM CD** *071 †20
CASTRO, Jerome Gerard. 800 W 5TH AVE 99204 #028-46-1989 L1989 **IM** *020
CAVALIERI, Stuart Aran. 122 W 7TH AVE STE 240, ROCKWOOD CLINIC CARDIOLOGY 99204 #016-02-1988 L1999 **CD** *020 †20
CAVANAGH, Charles R, Jr. ■ 99203 #008-01-1947 L1956 **GS** *071 †85
CECIL, Karlene Anne. 2910 E 57TH AVE, STE 5 99223 #054-04-1985 L1985 **IM** *020
CHALEM, Mark L. 105 W 8TH AVE, STE 6055 99204 #043-01-1976 L1979 **P** *020 †75
CHAPMAN, Wallace John. 322 W NORTH RIVER DR, RIVERFRONT MEDICAL CENTER 99201 #005-14-1959 L1991 **EM** *020
CHARBONNEAU, Gabriel Dane. 104 W 5TH AVE STE 200 99204 #049-01-2004 L2004 **FM** *020
CHARYK, Joseph John. 3104 S REGAL ST 99223 #010-02-1978 L1983 **FM** *040 †18
CHAUDHRY, Arvind. 318 E ROWAN AVE, STE 220 99207 #495-08-1989 L1999 **HEM** *020 †20
CHENG, Vera Hingfung. 601 W 5TH AVE, 5TH FL 99204 #023-01-1990 L1992 **AN** *020 †05
CHESLEY, Jason Michael. ■ 99205 #056-06-2006 **DR** *012
CHESTNUT, J. 322 W NORTH RIVER DR 99201 #054-04-1980 L1981 **NTR ID** *020 †20
CHESTNUT, Timothy Michael. 801 W 5TH AVE STE 504 99204 #054-04-1981 L1982 **PUD CCM** *020 †20
CHILSON, Donald Arthur. 122 W 7TH AVE STE 310 99204 #005-12-1976 L1985 **OS CD** *020 †20
CHIU, Mary Anna. 5633 N LIDGERWOOD ST, HOLY FAMILY HOSPITAL EMERG 99208 #025-01-1991 L1993 **EM** *020 †16
CHOI, Joe Ung. 819 E 35TH AVE 99203 #583-02-1968 L2005 **IM ON** *020 †20
CHOW, Nelson. 801 W 5TH AVE STE 415 99204 #067-01-1995 L2001 **NEP** *020 †20
CHOW, Ward Kevin. 820 S MCCLELLAN ST STE 500 99204 #054-04-1987 L1990 **IM IMG** *020 †20
CHRISTENSEN, Janice D. 800 W 5TH AVE 99204 #003-01-1990 L2001 **CD** *020 †20
CHURCH, Erin Anne. 3016 E 57TH AVE, STE 27 99223 #054-04-1997 L1999 **FM** *020 †18
CILYO, Cynthia Lou. 101 W 8TH AVE 99204 #016-06-1979 L1986 **OPH** *020 †35
CLARK, Edward Leroy. PO BOX 3048 99220 #010-03-1963 L1969 **GP** *075
CLARK, John Robt. 42 E ROWAN AVE, STE B 99207 #054-04-1973 L1978 **N** *020 †75
CLEVELAND, Philip Dana. 104 W 5TH AVE, STE 340W 99204 #054-04-1966 L1967 **FM** *040 †18
CLIFFE, Anne Mary. 101 W 8TH AVE 99204 #352-02-1962 L1985 **GP** *075
CLODE, Jeffrey Bennett. 820 S MCCLELLAN ST, STE 500 99204 #038-06-1972 L1975 **IM** *020 †20
CLYDE, Jon Courtney. 910 W 5TH AVE, STE 550 99204 #049-01-1985 L1990 **GS** *020 †85
COBLE, Walter Ross. 322 W NORTH RIVER DR 99201 #048-15-1979 L1986 **AM FM** *020 †18
COCCHIARELLA, Ronald Jay. 801 W 5TH AVE, STE 205 99204 #007-02-1974 L1979 **DR NM** *020 †80
COFFIN, Susan Ivie. 6120 N MAYFAIR ST 99208 #003-01-1989 L1992 **IM** *020 †20
COHEN, Arnold Norman. 801 W 5TH AVE, SPOKANE DIGESTIVE DISEASE 99204 #024-01-1975 L1980 **GE IM** *020 †20
COHEN, David Nemser. 235 E ROWAN AVE STE 107 99207 #035-20-1964 L1975 **OPH N** *020 †35
COLEMAN, William Sanford. 910 W 5TH AVE, STE 380 99204 #028-02-1974 L1981 **TS VS** *020 †85,90
COLLINS, Jeffrey B. 101 W 8TH AVE 99204 #016-11-1981 L1982 **IM** *030 †20
COLLINS, John Marvin. 123 E INDIANA AVE, STE 102 99207 #048-04-1969 L1970 **FPG FM** *071 †18
COLQUHOUN, James Chas. 5515 S CUSTER RD 99223 #068-01-1969 L1975 **CRS PRO** *020
COLVIN, Kyle Lyn. 400 E 5TH AVE 99202 #028-34-1989 L2002 **DR** *020 †80
COLWELL, Charles Michael. 715 S COWLEY ST, STE 228 99202 #026-04-1971 L1992 **FM EM** *020 †18
CONATY, James Francis. 901 W 5TH AVE, ASSOCIATED ORTHO SPEC P S 99204 #028-34-1964 L1971 **ORS HS** *071 †40
CONNELLY, Jan Stuart. 5901 N MAYFAIR ST STE 101 99208 #040-02-1976 L1981 **OTO** *020 †45
CONNOR, Patrick James. 105 W 8TH AVE, STE 120C 99204 #051-04-1986 L1986 **EM** *020 †16
CONOVALCIUC, Pavel. 4001 N COOK ST 99207 #913-50-1998 L2005 **FM OBS** *020 †18
CONSIGLIO, Anya Darice. 406 E ROWAN AVE, STE 200 99207 #005-06-2002 L2007 **IM** *020 †20
COOKE, Dennis Brian. 122 W 7TH AVE, STE 310 99204 #028-02-1976 L1982 **CD** *020 †20
COOKE, Nelson Roger. 800 W 5TH AVE 99204 #008-01-1969 L1975 **N** *020 †75
COOMES, Thomas Randall. 101 W 8TH AVE 99204 #030-06-1994 L1999 **EM** *020 †16
COOPER, Robert Lawrence. 530 S COWLEY ST, STE 100 99202 #007-02-1977 L1990 **PS GS** *020 †85,65
COPLEY, John Smith. ■ 99203 #030-05-1961 L1963 **OM GP** *071
COPPIN, Christophe M. ■ 99223 #024-07-1993 *100
COPSEY, Harvey G. 101 W 8TH AVE 99204 #030-05-1941 L1948 **N IM** *071 †20
CORAM, Frank John. ■ 99224 #010-01-1955 L1958 **GP** *071
CORBETT, Robert K, Jr. 9631 N NEVADA ST STE 304, HEALTHY FOCUS FAMILY MEDIC 99218 #016-01-1994 L1996 **FM** *020 †18
CORBETT, Robert Kendall. 235 E ROWAN AVE STE 202 99207 #054-04-1960 L1966 **U** *071 †95
CORELL, William Frank. 3424 S GRAND BLVD 99203 #005-11-1974 L1979 **FM** *020 †18
COSSETTE, Irby V. ■ 99208 #067-01-1967 L1975 **PTH** *020 †50
COSTELLO, Lauri Martha. 2709 W BOONE AVE 99201 #005-19-1985 L1986 **FM** *020 †18
COTTER, Thomas Leo. 104 W 5TH AVE STE 250E, ANESTHESIA ASSOCIATES PS 99204 #030-06-1991 L2003 **AN** *020 †18,05
COULSTON, Daniel Robt. 801 W 5TH AVE # 504, STE 504B 99204 #054-04-1979 L1980 **IM CCM** *020 †20
COVER, Gregory Chas. 101 W 8TH AVE, SHMC EMERGENCY DEPT 99204 #030-05-1981 L1986 **EM FM** *020 †18,16
COWMEY, Philip Brendon. ■ 99223 #054-04-2007 **TY** *012
COX, Lylanya. 120 W MISSION AVE 99201 #054-04-1998 L2001 **FM** *020 †18
COX, Svetlana F. 2709 W BOONE AVE 99201 #913-83-1988 L2000 **IM** *020 †20
CRAIG, Arthur B. ■ 99223 #023-07-1951 L1954 **IM PUD** *071
CRAIG, Gary Leslie. 105 W 8TH AVE, ARTHRITIS NORTHWEST 99204 #065-10-1976 L1992 **RHU** *020
CRAIG, Joan Groschupf. 101 W 8TH AVE 99204 #023-07-1951 L1957 **ON HO** *071
CRECELIUS, Lyle Edmund. 104 W 5TH AVE 99204 #040-02-1962 L1969 **R** *071 †80
CREEL, Douglas Michael. 101 W 8TH AVE 99204 #028-34-1988 L1988 **IM** *020 †20
CROSBY, Paul Nathan. 101 W 8TH AVE, OB WAMI SACRED HEART MED C 99204 #037-01-1981 L1985 **OBG** *020 †30
CROSS, Robert Lawrence. ■ 99223 #065-09-1955 L2002 **GS** *071 †85
CROTTY, Nancy Anne K. 704 E SHARP, HEALTH CLINIC 99258 #010-01-1974 L1978 **IM** *020 †20
CRUM, Timothy Earl. 9001 N COUNTRY HOMES BLVD, ROCKWOOD CLINIC NORTH 99218 #030-06-1985 L1991 **PD** *020 †55 ‡
CRUZ, Michael Joseph. 9922 N NEVADA ST 99218 #056-06-1995 L2000 **OTO** *020 †45
CUBBERLEY, Don Alan. 525 S COWLEY ST, INLAND IMAGING ASSOCIATES, 99202 #040-02-1978 L1987 **DR** *020 †80
CUMMINS, Randy C. 400 E 5TH AVE, ROCKWOOD CLINIC PS 99202 #048-12-1986 L1990 **FM** *020 †18
CUNNINGHAM, Michael H. 510 S COWLEY ST 99202 #004-01-1974 L1979 **OPH** *020 †35
CUNNINGHAM-HARTWIG, Roxie. 101 W 8TH AVE 99204 #054-04-2003 L2003 **FM** *020 †18
CURNOW, Alfred John. 800 W 5TH AVE, DEACONESS MED CTR-SPOKANE 99204 #005-12-2007 **TY** *012
CURTIS, Phillip Wayne, Jr. 5715 N LIDGERWOOD ST, INLAND IMAGING 99208 #054-04-1987 L1990 **NR** *020 †80
DANIELSON, Alan Roger. 601 W 5TH AVE STE 400 99204 #005-14-1968 L1974 **OAR** *020 †40
DANLY, Diane Louise. 1809 S GLENROSE RD 99223 #054-04-1987 L1989 **FM** *020 †18
DAVIS, Andrew Garth. 4815 N ASSEMBLY ST, V.A. MEDICAL CENTER 99205 #041-01-1966 L1985 **U** *020 †95
DAVIS, John Steven. 5715 N LIDGERWOOD ST, INLAND IMAGING 99208 #040-02-1982 L1987 **DR** *020 †80
DAVIS, Joseph Anton. 212 E CENTRAL AVE, STE 245 99208 #019-02-1997 L2003 **VS** *020 †85
DAVIS, Joseph William. ■ 99204 #010-02-2006 **IM** *012
DAVIS, Stuart Arthur. 101 W 8TH AVE 99204 #056-06-1956 L1957 **OS GP** *071
DAY, Steven Edwin. 427 S BERNARD ST, SPOKENE EYE CLC 99204 #036-07-1993 L1998 **OPH** *020 †35
DE ALWIS, Tanuja Marion. 101 W 8TH AVE 99204 #550-04-2007 L2007 **FP** *012
DEAN, David Scott. 9001 N COUNTRY HOMES BLVD, ROCKWOOD CLINIC, PS 99218 #041-12-1994 L1996 **FM** *020 †18
DECKER, Gordon Wm. 801 W 5TH AVE, STE 109 99204 #005-14-1974 L1975 **FM** *020 †18

■ = Address Information Privacy Protected
9301

DE FELICE, Randal Philip. 5633 N LIDGERWOOD ST 99208 #016-43-1985 L1988
EM FM *020 †18

DEHAL, Himdip Kaur. 101 W 8TH AVE, INLAND EMPIRE HP SERV ASSO 99204
#305-01-2006 L2006 FP *012

DE LA FUENTE, George Robt. ■ 99208 #016-06-1962 L1967 EM *071

DELICH, Philip Chas. 105 W 8TH AVE STE 7050 99204 #005-06-1984 L2001 IM *020 †20

DEMAKAS, John James. 801 W 5TH AVE, STE 210 99204 #030-06-1973 L1984 NS *020 †25

DEMORY, Anthony Charles. 801 W 5TH AVE STE 509, NORTHWEST RENAL SERVICES 99204
#016-02-1987 L2006 NEP IM *020 †20

DE NIRO, Elizabeth Anne. 501 S BERNARD ST 99204 #007-02-1975 L1981 FM *020 †18

DENTLER, Bruce Howard. 1010 W ROSEWOOD AVE 99208 #017-20-1973 L1974
FM FPG *020 †18

DERBY, Lynn Deeann. 235 E ROWAN AVE STE 206 99207 #026-04-1990 L1996 PS *020 †65

DETAR, Michael Wm. 800 W 5TH AVE 99204 #031-01-1989 L1994 PTH *020 †50

DE WOOD, Marcus A. 820 S MCCLELLAN ST, STE 226 99204 #030-06-1974 L1976
IM CD *020 †20

D'HULST, Daniel Matthew. 104 W 5TH AVE, STE 250E 99204 #056-06-2000 L2004
AN *020 †05 ‡

D'HULST, Sarah Elizabeth. 400 E 5TH AVE 99202 #056-06-2000 L2004 PD *020 †55 ‡

DICKSON, Robert Cameron. ■ 99203 #035-06-1958 L1959 AN *071 †05

DIDIER, Mark Earnest. 9001 N COUNTRY HOMES BLVD 99218 #023-12-1990 L1992
FM *020 †18

DIONNE, Daniel Joseph. 820 S MCCLELLAN ST, STE 314 99204 #010-01-1987 L1989
IM *020

DIRKERS, Jerome David. 5901 N LIDGERWOOD ST, STE 119 99208 #036-07-1965 L2006
IM *020

DITTMAN, William A. 101 W 8TH AVE, SACRED HEART MEDICAL CTR 99204
#056-05-1953 L1959 HEM IM *071 †20

DITTMAN, Wm Albert, Jr. ■ 99203 #054-04-1981 L1982 HEM ON *050 †20

DIXON, Steven Lewis. 59 E QUEEN STE 102 99207 #049-01-1979 L1991 D DMP *020 †15

DIXSON, Michael Dean. 46 E ROWAN AVE, SPOKANE DIGESTIVE DISEASE 99207
#016-11-1972 L1978 GE IM *020 †20

DO, Dang Hoang. 101 W 8TH AVE 99204 #104-01-2006 L2007 FP *012

DODD, Gentry Charles. ■ 99203 #017-20-2007 L2008 TY *012

DODGE, Michael Eldon. 508 W 6TH AVE 99204 #028-02-1968 L1976 PD NPM *020 †55

DOMARADZKI-NARKIEWICZ, M. 140 S ARTHUR ST, STE 690 99202 #759-01-1978 L1993
P *020

DOUBEK, Michael F. 4815 N ASSEMBLY ST 99205 #028-34-1983 L1987 EM IM *020 †20

DOYLE, James Thos. 105 W 8TH AVE, STE 6050 99204 #028-34-1982 L1991 GE IM *020 †20

DRAIN, Kerry Lynn. 508 W 6TH AVE STE 700, SPOKANE ALLORGY & ASTHMA C 99204
#016-06-1996 L2002 AI *020 †20,55,03

DRISCOLL, John Francis. 820 S MCCLELLAN ST, STE 314 99204 #016-43-1959 L1961
IM CD *071 †20

DRISCOLL, Thomas Andrew. TAF-C9 99204 #054-04-1962 L1965 DR R *020 †80

DUBA, David Robt. 715 S COWLEY STE 228 99204 #054-04-1988 L1993 PM GP *020 †60

DUBIEL, William John. 400 E 5TH AVE, ROCKWOOD CLINIC 99202 #023-01-1992 L2002
DR *020 †80

DUNCAN, Brien Mark. 101 W 8TH AVE 99204 #030-06-1985 L1994 EM *020 †16

DUNLAP, James Nelson. 601 W 5TH AVE, STE 400 99204 #021-01-1989 L1997
ORS OFA *020 †40

DUNLAP, James P. ■ 99223 #016-11-1951 L1952 ORS *071 †40

DUNN, James Michael. 101 W 8TH AVE, PO BOX 2555 99204 #030-06-2007 TY *012

DURCAN, Fiona J. 208 W 5TH AVE 99204 #048-04-1982 L2001 OPH *020 †35

DURNFORD, Robert Kenneth. 105 W 8TH AVE, SPOKANE DIGESTIVE DISEASE 99204
#005-12-1992 L2001 GE *020 †20

DUTTA, Sanjit Kumar. 801 W 5TH AVE STE 416, PHYSICIANS CLINIC OF SPOKA 99204
#160-10-1988 L2003 IMG *020 †20

EASTBURN, Lawrence S A. 507 S WASHINGTON ST, STE 170 99204 #665-01-1997 L1999
FM *020 †18

EASTWOOD, Robert Allen. 53507 RIDGEVIEW DR 99206 #040-02-1965 L1975 EM FM *020

EASWARAN, Geetha. ■ 99202 #495-66-1999 L2007 IM *012

EATON, Michael Lawrence. 400 E 5TH AVE 99202 #019-02-1971 L1972 DR *020 †80 ‡

EDENFIELD, Diana L. 101 W 8TH AVE # 300 99204 #014-01-1980 L1999 OBG *020 †30

EDENS, Mark Steven. 525 S COWLEY 99202 #056-06-1989 L1997 DR *020 †80

EDMINSTER, Scott Clinton. 800 W 5TH AVE 99204 #003-01-1977 L1983 EM *020 †16

EDWARDS, John H. 4815 N ASSEMBLY ST 99205 #016-01-1980 L1981 P MDM *020 †75

EGGER, David Wayne. 105 W 8TH AVE # 336C 99204 #040-02-1996 L2002 NPM *020 †55

EKEN, Elizabeth Bramell. 101 W 8TH AVE 99204 #041-09-1947 L1976 P N *071 †75

EKLUND, Diane K. ■ 99206 #003-01-1988 L2001 BBK CLP *020 †50

ELKHARWILY, Alaa Elsayed. ■ 99204 #915-07-1998 L2007 IM *012

ELLINGSEN, Bruce Alfred. 2525 E 29TH AVE, STE 10B 99223 #054-04-1965 L1970
OPH *071 †35

ELLINGSEN, Donald Alvin. ■ 99223 #054-04-1963 L1964 OPH *071 †35

ELLINGSEN, Donald Eugene. 601 W 5TH AVE STE 400 99204 #048-02-1988 L1993
ORS *020 †40

ELLINGSEN, Tammy Darby. 910 W 5TH AVE STE 60 99204 #054-04-1988 L1993 FM *020 †18

ELLSWORTH, Waverly J, Jr. 801 W 5TH AVE STE 404 99204 #035-06-1949 L1958
TS CD *071 †85,90

ELMER, James Benson. 104 W 5TH AVE STE 400W 99204 #048-12-1977 L1980
PUD IM *020 †20

ELMER, Jeffrey Chas. 104 W 5TH AVE STE 400W 99204 #048-13-1982 L1987
CCM PUD *020 †20

ELSTON, Richard E. ■ 99208 #030-05-1950 L1954 GS *071 †85

EMCH, A Willard, Jr. 906 W 2ND AVE STE 600 99201 #047-05-1994 L2000 CHP †75

ENGAR, Colby Scott. ■ 99223 #056-06-2008 *012

ENGLISH, Michael Lynott. ■ 99203 #049-01-2008 *012

ENLOW, Brett Eugene. 5633 N LIDGERWOOD ST 99208 #010-01-1998 L2002 EM *020 †16

ERICK, Laureli Rose. 104 W 5TH AVE, STE 230E 99204 #005-12-1985 L1998 AN *020 †05

ERICKSON, Vincent John. 104 W 5TH AVE, STE 230E 99204 #012-05-1985 L1989 AN *020 †05

ESCANDON, Gilbert Richard. 800 W 5TH AVE, DEACONESS MEDICAL CENTER 99204
#056-05-1990 L1992 IM *020 †20

EUGSTER, George Stanley. 122 W 7TH AVE STE 310 99204 #026-04-1967 L1974
CD IM *071 †24

EVERETT, John Paul. 212 E CENTRAL AVE, STE 240 99204 #054-04-1987 L1995
CD IM *020 †20

EWERT, Todd Richard. 5633 N LIDGERWOOD ST, HOLY FAM EMGY CTR EMGY PHY 99208
#016-01-1988 L2006 EM *020 †16

FAIRBANKS, Robert Kenneth. 910 W 5TH AVE, STE 102 99204 #021-01-1992 L1999
RO *020 †80

FAIRCHILD, Thos Nickerson. 801 W 5TH AVE 99204 #035-15-1977 L1979 U *020 †95

FALLON, Michael John. 911 W 5TH AVE, SHRINERS CHILDRENS HOSPITA 99204
#054-04-1988 L2003 AN *020 †05

FALOON, William Wassell. 400 E 5TH AVE 99202 #024-01-1944 L1945 GE IM *071 †20

FALOON, Wm Wassell, Jr. 400 E 5TH AVE, ROCKWOOD CLINIC, P.S. 99202 #035-15-1981 L1989
ORS *020 †40

FARAH MUSA, Abdeen Rihan. ■ 99223 #848-01-1996 L2006 IM *012

FARNER, Robert Murray. 400 E 5TH AVE, ROCKWOOD CLINIC 99202 #016-01-1985 L1989
DR *020 †80

FEALK, Stuart Jay. 104 W 5TH AVE STE 230E 99204 #025-01-1978 L1982 AN *020 †05

FELD, Andrew Dean. 105 W 8TH AVE, STE 7050 99204 #012-05-1976 L1977 GE IM *020 †20

FELGENHAUER, Judy Linn. 800 W 5TH AVE 99204 #054-04-1986 L1992 PHO *020 †55

FERN, Peter Earl. 105 W 8TH AVE, STE 6020 99204 #040-02-1977 L1985 OBG *020 †30

FERNAU, Walter August, III. 400 E 5TH AVE 99202 #054-04-1980 L2003 FM *020 †18

FERNISH, Ted Robt. ■ 99223 #869-02-1960 L1988 U *071

FERRARO, Angelo Stephen. 122 W 7TH AVE STE 310, HEART CLINICS NORTHWEST 99204
#010-02-1982 L1993 CD *020 †20

FERRIES, Michael Carson. 104 W 5TH AVE, STE 230E 99204 #040-02-1988 L1992 AN *020 †05

FINCHER, Roger Donald. 801 W 5TH AVE, STE 525 99204 #037-01-1976 L1981 U *020 †95

FINE, Kurt Pettis. 212 E CENTRAL AVE STE 34 99208 #010-02-1995 L1999 OBG *020 †30

FISCHER, James Donald. 800 W 5TH AVE, DEACONESS MEDICAL CENTER 99204
#060-01-1970 L2002 PDS *050

FITTERER, Joseph Duncan. 105 W 8TH AVE, STE 6050 99204 #054-04-1971 L1976 IM *020 †20

FITTERER, Sally Aiken. 5901 N LIDGERWOOD ST # 24B, SPOKANE MEDICAL EXAMINER 99208
#054-04-1982 L1983 FOP PTH *062 †50

FLETCHER, Lee Francis. 5715 N LIDGERWOOD ST, INLAND IMAGING ASSOCIATES, 99208
#041-13-1977 L1983 DR RNR *020 †80

FLOURA, Kamaljit Singh. 3815 E SUMAC DR 99223 #495-46-1975 L1989 P GS *020

FLOYD, John Forrest. 801 W 5TH AVE, STE 415 99204 #041-12-1980 L1981 IM IMG *020 †20

FLUME, John Bernard. 5633 N LIDGERWOOD ST 99208 #048-12-1960 L1965 PTH *020 †50

FOGLESONG, Jillian Rae. 99207 #036-05-2007 L2007 FP *012

FORNWALT, Sandra Lee. 101 W 8TH AVE, MATERNAL AND FETAL MEDICIN 99204
#041-07-1983 L1985 OBG *020 †30

FORSNES, Evan Victor. 101 W 8TH AVE STE 1100, SACRED HEART WOMEN'S CENTE 99204
#054-04-1993 L2006 OBG *020 †30

FOSTER, Sherwin Stephen. ■ 99203 #422-01-1994 L2007 NEP IM *020 †20

FRANCIS, Michael Reed. ■ 99203 #028-79-2006, ▲ IM *012

FRAZIER, James Stuart. 105 W 8TH AVE, STE 7035 99204 #054-04-1986 L1994 P *071 †75

FREGEAU, David Raymond. 101 W 8TH AVE 99204 #005-19-1991 L1993 PD *020 †55

FREUEN, Patrick Francis. 235 E ROWAN AVE, STE 102 99207 #030-06-1971 L1977
OBG *020 †30

FRIEND, Christopher John. 525 S COWLEY ST, INLAND IMAGING ASSOCIATES, 99202
#041-12-2001 L2007 DR *020 †80

FRY, Cecilia Lu. 101 W 8TH AVE, ASSOCIATES 99204 #054-04-1990 L1996 CCP *020 †55

FUHS, Bryan Edward. 910 W 5TH AVE, STE 300 99204 #054-04-1984 L1991 CD IM *020 †20

FULLER, Morris Everett. ■ 99203 #035-15-1943 L1990 GS *072

FULLMER, Daniel Richards. 400 E 5TH AVE, ROCKWOOD CLINIC, P.S. 99202
#049-01-1996 L2007 DR *020 †80

FULTON, Robert Joel. 5715 N LIDGERWOOD ST, INLAND IMAGING 99208 #030-05-1971 L1974
DR CD *020 †80

GADDY, James Burrel. 910 W 5TH AVE STE 600 99204 #048-02-1975 L1976 FM *020 †18

GAMBLE, David Gregory. ■ 99203 #067-01-1993 L1997 ID *020 †20

GANJI, Homayoon. 105 W 8TH AVE STE 550 99204 #005-15-1962 L1972 TS VS *071 †85,90

GARABEDIAN, Carl Puzant. 101 W 8TH AVE # 4300 99204 #056-06-1995 L2000 PDC *020 †55

GARABEDIAN, Hrair. 101 W 8TH AVE, # 4300 99204 #605-01-1967 L1971 PDC NPM *020 †55

GARDNER, Timothy John. 6120 N MAYFAIR ST, STE 101 99208 #030-06-1976 L1982
IM *020 †20

GARDUNO, Tamara. 3016 E 57TH AVE, STE 24 99223 #005-15-1996 L1996 IM *020 †20

GARMAN, Edward Leo. 5715 N LIDGERWOOD ST, INLAND IMAGING 99208 #018-03-1969 L1973
PDR R *071 †80

GARMAN, Edward Todd, Jr. 801 W 5TH AVE, STE 421 99204 #030-06-1994 L1997 IM *020 †20

GARMAN, Sean William. 801 W 5TH AVE STE 407 99204 #030-06-1994 L1995 IM *020 †20

GARVIN, Lawrence Thaddeus. W 801 5TH-412 99204 #016-43-1962 L1963 OBG *071 †30

GASCOIGNE, Richard H, Jr. 5629 N LIDGERWOOD ST # 150 99208 #025-07-1999 L2003
FM *020 †18

GATES, Gerald Lee. 801 W 5TH AVE, STE 405 99204 #051-04-1970 L1974 GS *020 †85

GAVELIN, Robin J. 104 W 5TH AVE STE 230E 99204 #060-01-1981 L1989 AN PME *020 †05

GENUNG, Sharon Rose. 911 W 5TH AVE 99204 #004-01-1984 L1990 PD *020 †55

GERAGHTY, Madeleine C. 400 E 5TH AVE, ROCKWOOD CLINIC 99202 #005-02-1999 L2005
N *020 †75

GERBER, Henry Wallace. 800 W 5TH AVE 99204 #018-03-1961 L1969 NS *071 †25

GERDING, James John. 1419 E PARK LN 99203 #026-04-1970 L1975 AN *020 †05

GERMAN, Monica Maria. 9001 N COUNTRY HOMES BLVD, ROCKWOOD CLINIC, P.S. 99218
#781-01-1990 L2003 PD *020 †55 ‡

GIDDINGS, Neil Arthur. 105 W 8TH AVE, STE 1000 99204 #038-43-1982 L1993 NO *020 †45

GILBERT, Mary Lynn. 800 W 5TH AVE 99204 #054-04-1996 L1998 FM *020 †18

GILLESPIE, Hal Graveley. 107 S DIVISION ST, SPOKANE MENTAL HEALTH 99202
#045-01-1964 L2006 P GP *020 †75 ‡

GILLUM, Michael David. 104 W 5TH AVE STE 400W 99204 #054-04-1983 L1988 ID IM *020 †20

GIN, Florence Mae. 105 W 8TH AVE STE 1000, INLAND IMAGING ASSOCIATES, 99204
#017-20-1991 L2001 DR *020 †80

GIPSTEIN, Brian N. ■ 99203 #035-08-1967 L1974 CHP P *071

GIRVIN, George W. 105 W 8TH AVE STE 7060 99204 #007-02-1951 L1954 GS CD *020 †85

GITHAIGA, Andrew Ndirangu. ■ 99208 #577-01-1997 L2006 PCC *020 †20

GLASS, Peter Martin. 105 W 8TH AVE, STE 450E 99204 #035-01-1966 L1967 AN *020 †05

GOFF, James Satterlee. 105 W 8TH AVE STE 6010 99204 #054-04-1989 L2002 GE IM *020 †20

GOINS, Chad Robert. 842 S COWLEY ST, STE 1 99202 #054-04-1998 L2002 OPH *020 †35

GOLDBERG, Harold Robt. 104 W 5TH AVE, STE 1000 99204 #035-03-1977 L1988 CD *040 †20

GOLDMAN, Lorne Eric. 910 W 5TH AVE STE 3, SPOKANE CARDIOLOGY P.S.C 99204
#067-01-1994 L2001 IC *020 †20

GOLLHOFER, John Gordon. 105 W 8TH AVE STE 7040, ROCKWOOD CLINIC, PS 99204
#028-02-1972 L1989 OBG *020 †30

GOODELL, Steven Earl. 105 W 8TH AVE, SPOKANE DIGESTIVE DISEASE 99204
#049-01-1976 L1979 GE IM *020 †20

GOODMAN, Francis J. 6002 N LIDGERWOOD ST, LIDGERWOOD HLTH CARE CTR 99208 #008-02-1979 L1982 **FM** *020 †18

GOODMAN, Gary Julius. 910 W 5TH AVE STE 300 99204 #054-04-1968 L1970 **CD IM** *020 †20

GOODWIN, Christopher L. 120 W MISSION AVE 99201 #043-01-1991 L1994 **FM** *020 †18

GORE, Debra Rose. 101 W 8TH AVE 99204 #034-01-2000 L2002 **FM** *020 †18

GOTHBERG, Loren August. ■ 99223 #024-01-1948 L1954 **IM NEP** *071

GOTTLIEB, Klaus. 12128 N DIVISION ST, # 164 99218 #409-02-1987 L1998 **GE IM** *020 †20

GOTTLIEB, Monika A. ■ 99206 #017-20-1997 L1999 **IM** *020 †20

GOULD, Barry Kenneth. 400 E 5TH AVE, ROCKWOOD CLINIC, PS 99202 #010-01-1965 L1973 **END IM** *020 †20

GOULD, Edward Paul. 101 W 8TH AVE 99204 #019-02-1970 L1987 **OS GS** *020 †85

GOWER, Richard Glen. 823 W 7TH AVE, MARYCLIFF ALLERGY SPEC 99204 #007-02-1972 L1977 **AI IM** *020 †20,03

GOYANKO-BORROMEO, Imelda. ■ 99223 #748-23-1977 L1997 **P** *020

GRABLE, George Stanley. 525 S COWLEY ST, INLAND IMAGING ASSOCIATES, 99202 #005-12-1974 L1981 **DR** *020 †80

GRAHAM, Janice Loreen. 6002 N LIDGERWOOD ST 99208 #054-04-1984 L1985 **FM** *020 †18

GRAHAM, Jeffery James. ■ 99202 #038-41-1966 L1972 **PD CHN** *030 †55

GRAHAM, John Clinton. 6002 N LIDGERWOOD ST, LIDGERWOOD HEALTH CARE CEN 99208 #054-04-1984 L1985 **NEP IM** *020 †20

GRAINGER, David Wm. 105 W 8TH AVE, STE 6060 99204 #035-01-1959 L1967 **ORS** *071 †40

GRANDINETTI, Kimberly Ann. 101 W 8TH AVE STE 100L-1, SACRED HEART CHILDREN'S 99204 #016-43-1999 L2006 **PD** *020 †55

GREELEY, David Roger. 507 S WASHINGTON ST, STE 101 99204 #054-04-1989 L1993 **N** *020 †75

GREEN, Harry C, Jr. ■ 99203 #020-02-1949 L1968 **CRS GS** *071 †85

GREEN, James Clifford. 105 W 8TH AVE, STE 408 99204 #016-11-1965 L1976 **P** *020 †75

GREEN, Todd Robt. 6120 N MAYFAIR ST, STE 101 99208 #028-34-1985 L1990 **PUD IM** *020 †20

GREER, Alexander Pearson. ■ 99203 #041-01-1955 L1957 **IM PUD** *071 †20

GRETEBECK, Ronda Jean. 35 W 8TH AVE STE 440 99204 #056-05-1983 L1999 **PD NPM** *020 †55

GRIFFING, Katherine Louis. 101 W 8TH AVE, BOX 2555 99204 #409-23-2000 L2002 **IM** *020 †20

GRIFFITH, Jon Lance. 101 W 8TH AVE, STE LL3 99204 #048-12-1981 L1982 **RO IM** *020 †20,80

GRIGG, Andersen. ■ 99201 #003-75-2007, ▲ **TY** *012

GRIM, Tamara B. 400 E 5TH AVE 99202 #040-02-1993 L2000 **FM** *020 †18

GRISMER, Joseph Francis. VET ADMIN HOSP 99208 #030-06-1960 L1961 **P** *071

GROENIG, David C. ■ 99223 #026-04-1950 L1957 **OBG** *071 †30

GROEPPER, Jay Richard. 104 W 5TH AVE, STE 230E 99204 #054-04-1975 L1976 **AN** *020 †05

GROSSMANN, Andrew E, III. ■ 99223 #019-02-1969 L1975 **IM GE** *071 †20

GROZA, Petru. 610 S SHERMAN ST, STE 201 99202 #781-01-1992 L2006 **NEP** *020 †20

GRUBB, David George. 105 W 8TH AVE STE 6055 99204 #005-02-1972 L1980 **P** *020 †75

GRUBB, Paul Nicholas. 400 E 5TH AVE 99202 #054-04-1982 L1989 **PD** *020 †55

GRUBER, David Powell. 105 W 8TH AVE STE 200 99204 #040-02-1992 L1999 **NS** *020 †25

GRUBER, Michael Ruetger. 104 W 5TH AVE, STE 230E 99204 #025-01-1975 L1976 **AN** *020 †05

GULARTE, Gary Gant. 5633 N LIDGERWOOD ST 99208 #005-14-1991 L1994 **EM** *020 †16

GUTHRIE, Carol Ruth. 105 W 8TH AVE, STE 650 SPOKANE BREAST CTR 99204 #005-14-1986 L1994 **SO** *020 †85

HABEL, Dan Wm. ■ 99203 #025-01-1959 L1967 **OTO** *020 †45

HAGAN, Cornelius E, Jr. ■ 99203 #051-04-1935 L1947 **OTO** *071 †45

HAGN, Emily Elisabeth. ■ 99202 #049-01-2006 **TY** *012

HAHN, Cynthia Ann. 5901 N LIDGERWOOD ST, MICRONEUROSURGERY & SPINE 99208 #016-01-1983 L1993 **NS NSP** *020 †25

HAHN, John Francis, Jr. 104 W 5TH AVE, STE 250E 99204 #040-02-1980 L1983 **AN** *020 †05

HALPERN, Lloyd Michael. 104 W 5TH AVE STE 230E 99204 #038-40-1985 L1991 **AN GS** *020 †05

HALVORSON, Thomas Lee. 400 E 5TH AVE 99202 #021-01-1988 L1999 **ORS OSM** *020 †40

HAMACHER, Edward N. ■ 99203 #010-02-1943 L1947 **PS** *071

HAMADEH, Zaher. ■ 99223 #875-01-2002 L2006 **IM** *020 †20

HAMMOND, Lawrence Alan. 104 W 5TH AVE, STE 200W 99204 #024-01-1984 L1987 **IM** *020 †20

HANCOCK, Priscilla J. 35 W 8TH AVE STE 440, NW NEONATOLOGY ASSOC 99204 #011-02-1978 L1983 **NPM PD** *020 †55

HANDY, Robert Blaise. 5715 N LIDGERWOOD ST, INLAND IMAGING 99208 #048-12-1989 L1989 **RNR** *020 †80

HANF, Tiffany Starr. 101 W 8TH AVE 99204 #654-01-2004 L2004 **IM** *020 †20

HANSEN, James Ernest. 101 W 8TH AVE, PO BOX 2555 99204 #005-14-2004 **TY** *012

HANSEN, Michelle M. 5633 N LIDGERWOOD ST 99208 #048-02-1983 L1997 **AN** *020 †05

HANSEN, Thomas Jay. 9222 N NEWPORT HWY 99218 #054-04-1962 L1963 **GP** *071

HANSON, Roger Wm. 814 W 17TH AVE 99203 #054-04-1979 L1988 **FM AM** *020 †18

HARDER, Louise Ann. 104 W 5TH AVE, STE 400W 99204 #060-01-1992 L2000 **IM** *020 †20

HARDIE, Monica Jane. 101 W 8TH AVE, SACRED HEART MED CTR 99204 #054-04-1994 L1997 **IM** *020 †20

HARDY, Ronald Davenport. 235 E ROWAN AVE STE 102 99207 #049-01-1997 L2004 **OBG** *020 †18,30

HARPER, Deborah Joy. 322 W NORTH RIVER DR 99201 #016-11-1980 L1985 **PD** *020 †55

HARR, Craig Allyn. 5715 N LIDGERWOOD ST, INLAND IMAGING 99208 #048-16-2001 L2007 **RNR** *100 †80

HARTMAN, Jeffrey Everard. 104 W 5TH AVE, STE 140W 99204 #040-02-1978 L1978 **DIA END** *020 †20

HARVEY, Arthur L. ■ 99224 #062-01-1946 L1950 **GYN** *071 †30

HASSING, Jeanne Marie. 105 W 8TH AVE STE 660, PEDIATRIC ENDOCRINOLOGY 99204 #030-05-1983 L2001 **PDE PD** *020 †55

HATHEWAY, John Alden. 105 W 8TH AVE, STE 200 99204 #010-02-1993 L2007 **APM** *020 †05

HAUCK, Terrance L. 101 W CASCADE WAY, STE 103 99208 #048-13-1996 L2000 **GS** *020

HAVEKOST, Clinton Trevor. 3016 E 57TH AVE, STE 27 99223 #005-18-1995 L1997 **FM** *020 †18

HAVIN, Derrick Ray. 235 E ROWAN AVE, STE 102 99207 #028-34-1999 L2006 **OBG** *020

HEATON, William Edward. 105 W 8TH AVE STE 707, ROCKWOOD CLINIC UROLOGY 99204 #028-34-1990 L2002 **U** *020 †95

HEDEQUIST, Robert Douglas. 5629 N LIDGERWOOD ST STE 1 99208 #030-06-1960 L1961 **OBG** *071 †30

HEGEDUS, Stephen A. ■ 99208 #473-01-1937 L1958 **ON GS** *071 †85

HEICK, Meredith Ann. 820 S MCCLELLAN ST, STE 200 99204 #003-01-1976 L1981 **RHU** *020 †20

HELLER, Heidi Maria. 4815 N ASSEMBLY ST, VAMC 99205 #018-03-1990 L1994 **N** *020 †75

HEMPSTEAD, Richard H. ■ 99223 #025-01-1944 L1952 **U OS** *071 †95

HENDERSON, Curtis D. 610 S SHERMAN ST, STE 208 99202 #048-04-1988 L1996 **D** *020 †15

HENDRICKSON, Alan Verne. 400 E 5TH AVE, ROCKWOOD CLINIC INC 99202 #056-05-1967 L1977 **PD GE** *020 †55

HENKE, Charles P. ■ 99208 #016-06-1945 L1952 **OS** *071 †85

HENKEL, Brett Eric. 101 W 8TH AVE, INLAND EMPIRE HP SERV ASSO 99204 #143-11-2002 L2005 **FP** *012

HENSLEY, Gerald Ross. 122 W 7TH AVE, HEART CLINICS NORTHWEST 99204 #023-07-1965 L1972 **CD IM** *071 †20

HENZLER, David Michael. 42 E ROWAN AVE STE B 99207 #019-02-1991 L1998 **N** *020 †75

HERDENER, Richard Sherman. 820 S MCCLELLAN ST, STE 426 99204 #054-04-1976 L1986 **D EM** *020 †15

HERNANDEZ, Eric James. 101 W 8TH AVE, INLAND EMPIRE HOSP 99204 #025-01-2007 L2007 **FP** *012

HERSCHEL, Kenelm Winslow. ■ 99208 #048-12-1979 L2005 **AN** *020 †05

HERSHEY, John E. 5904 N DIVISION ST 99208 #035-45-1949 L1953 **FM GS** *020 †85

HESKETT, Robert Glynn. ■ 99203 #024-01-1941 L1949 **PD** *071 †55

HESTDALEN, Rodney Finn. ■ 99203 #005-12-1996 L2001 **AN** *020 †05

HEUSNER, John Edmund. 104 W 5TH AVE STE 230E 99204 #038-41-1987 L1994 **AN** *020 †05

HIGGINS, D Curran. ■ 99203 #016-43-1953 L1954 **IMG P** *071 †85

HILL, Robert Dean. 122 W 7TH AVE STE 310, THE HEART INSTITUTE OF SPO 99204 #016-42-1980 L1987 **IM CD** *020 †20

HILTON, Jeffrey Lee. 105 W 8TH AVE, STE 6020 99204 #018-03-2002 L2006 **OBG** *020

HINNEN, Michael Lynn. 639 N RIVERPOINT BLVD, 9 WEST 99202 #025-01-1968 L1975 **CD** *071 †20

HIRSCH, Howard Mark. 5715 N LIDGERWOOD ST, INLAND IMAGING 99208 #023-01-1970 L1975 **R** *020 †80

HIRSCHAUER, Jeffrey S. 105 W 8TH AVE, STE 200, SACRED HEART DOCTORS BUILD 99204 #017-20-1974 L1989 **NS** *020 †25

HISS, Glen Alan. 105 W 8TH AVE, STE 6020 99204 #035-03-1977 L1986 **OBG** *020 †30

HO, Caroline L. 5715 N LIDGERWOOD ST, INLAND IMAGING 99208 #038-44-2001 L2007 **DR** *020 †80

HO, Elizabeth Chia. 800 W 5TH AVE 99204 #035-47-1997 L2001 **IM** *020 †20

HOEFER, Megan Annette. ■ 99203 #030-06-1995 L1999 **IM** *020 †20

HOEFER, Scott Brennan. 5715 N LIDGERWOOD ST, INLAND IMAGING 99208 #030-06-1994 L1999 **DR** *020 †80

HOFFMANN, John Finley. 217 W CATALDO AVE 99201 #048-04-1983 L2001 **OTO GS** *020 †45

HOGSETT, Smith F, Sr. 711 S COWLEY ST 99202 #041-12-1938 L1946 **OPH** *071 †35

HOLBERT, D Vernon. 910 W 5TH AVE, STE 380 99204 #035-03-1976 L1984 **CD** *020 †85,90

HOLBERT, Daniel Vernon. ■ 99203 #035-03-2006 **DR** *012

HOLBROOK, Ryan Frederick. 601 S SHERMAN ST 99202 #016-06-1986 L1995 **SO GS** *020 †85

HOLLENBAUGH, Cindy Kay. 235 E ROWAN AVE, STE 117 99207 #054-04-1992 L1996 **PD** *020 †55

HOLLON, Clyde Frederick. 801 W 5TH AVE 99204 #028-34-1967 L1973 **U** *020 †95

HOLLOWAY, Jonathan A. 126 N WASHINGTON ST, THE EYE CARE TEAM 99201 #054-04-1956 L1961 **OPH** *071 †35

HOLMES, Edwin Ruthven, III. 501 N RIVERPOINT BLVD #302, INLAND IMAGING 99202 #047-06-1968 L1979 **NM IM** *020 †28

HOLMQUIST, Gunnar Ervin. 322 W NORTH RIVER DR, GROUP HEALTH COOPERATIVE 99201 #005-06-1984 L1985 **FM** *020 †18

HOLTE, Halford Brian. 5715 N LIDGERWOOD ST, INLAND IMAGING 99208 #054-04-1975 L1977 **DR** *020 †80

HONG, Steven Woo Tae. 801 W 5TH AVE, SPOKANE DIGESTIVE DISEASE 99204 #005-06-1986 L1991 **GE** *020 †20

HOPKINS, Bruce G. 105 W 8TH AVE, STE 6060 99204 #018-03-1970 L1971 **OBG** *020 †30

HORLACHER, Lowell Eugene. 5633 N LIDGERWOOD ST 99208 #060-01-1959 L1961 **FM** *071 †18

HORN, Paul Conrad. 235 E ROWAN AVE, STE 117 99207 #054-04-1992 L1998 **ORS** *020 †40

HORN, Peter John. 5715 N LIDGERWOOD ST, INLAND IMAGING 99208 #017-20-1963 L1964 **R** *071 †80

HORNE, Landon Tyler. 400 E 5TH AVE, ROCKWOOD CLINIC, P.S. 99202 #051-01-1994 L2002 **ORS** *020 †40

HORNING, Sandra Wicks. 101 W 8TH AVE PO, SACRED HEART MEDICAL CENTE 99204 #021-01-1979 L1981 **PD** *020 †55

HOSMER, Jamie Brent. 800 W 5TH AVE, DEACONESS MED CTR-SPOKANE 99204 #007-02-2006 **TY** *012

HOTCHKISS, Laura Anne. 801 W 5TH AVE, STE 205 99204 #043-01-1987 L2005 **DR** *020 †80

HOUGLUM, Karl Peter. 105 W 8TH AVE, SPOKANE DIGESTIVE DISEASE 99204 #054-04-1984 L1998 **IM** *020 †20

HOWARD, Don Scott. 104 W 5TH AVE, STE 400W 99204 #056-06-1990 L1999 **CCM** *020 †20

HOWARD, John Dale. 5901 N LIDGERWOOD ST, OFFICE OF THE MEDICAL EXAM 99208 #054-04-1982 L1983 **FOP** *020 †50

HOWLAND, Richard Charles. ■ 99208 #038-40-1962 L1969 **ORS** *020 †40

HOWLETT, Andrew Thomas. 601 W 5TH AVE STE 4, NORTHWEST ORTHOPAEDIC SPEC 99204 #054-04-1998 L2003 **ORS** *020 †40

HSU, Benjamin. 605 E HOLLAND AVE, STE 218 99218 #005-11-1986 L1996 **D** *020 †20,15

HUANG, Po Sheng. PO BOX 2555, CENTER, GHP-HOSPITALIST SV 99220 #016-06-1992 L2003 **IM** *020 †20

HUBBARD, Benjamin Clegg. 101 W 8TH AVE 99204 #028-79-2005, ▲ L2005 **FP** *012

HUBER, Philip Roy. 800 W 5TH AVE 99204 #049-01-1996 L2003 **CD** *020 †20

HUGHES, Vincent Patrick. 220 E WELLESLEY AVE 99207 #038-40-1952 L1973 **R** *072 †80

HULL, Thomas Richard. 5904 N DIVISION ST 99208 #007-02-1979 L1986 **EM** *020

HUMPHREYS, Pat Language. ■ 99218 #836-02-1964 L1973 **GP** *072

HURLEY, E David. 104 W 5TH AVE STE 390E 99204 #054-04-1994 L1997 **FM** *020 †18

HURLEY, John Herrmann. 105 W 8TH AVE 99204 #016-43-1955 L1963 **ORS** *071 †40

HURLEY, Sean David. 406 E ROWAN AVE, STE 200 99207 #068-01-1992 L1996 **IM** *020 †20

HUSKY, Daniel Louis. 104 W 5TH AVE STE 390E 99204 #039-01-1977 L1978 **FM** *030 †18

HUTCHINSON, Julia Mumma. 101 W 8TH AVE 99204 #054-04-1990 L1992 **IM** *020 †20

HUTSINPILLER, Molly. 101 W 8TH AVE 99204 #049-01-1992 L1996 **EM** *020 †16

IANNUZZI, Debra Mary. 1330 N WASHINGTON ST #2080, SPOKANE DISBLTY DET SERV 99201 #041-12-1985 L2003 **PD PDP** *020 †55

ICENOGLE, Deborah Ann. 1101 W COLLEGE AVE, SPOKANE COUNTY HEALTH DIST 99201 #034-01-1978 L1991 **PD** *074 †55

ICENOGLE, Timothy Bock. 105 W 8TH AVE STE 532, TRANSPLANT SURGEONS, PS 99204 #034-01-1979 L1989 **CD TTS** *020 †85,90

ILG, Ron Craig. 35 W 8TH AVE STE 440 99204 #040-02-1994 L2003 **NPM** *020 †55

INAHARA, Gerald T. 104 W 5TH AVE, STE 230E 99204 #040-02-1983 L1987 **AN** *020 †05

■ = Address Information Privacy Protected

IRWIN, Hampton Wm. 801 W 5TH AVE, HAMPTON W IRWIN MD PS 99204 #025-01-1955 L1961 GYN *071 †30

ISPIRESCU, Jeffrey Sorin. ■ 99220 #005-12-1999 L2007 AN PME *020 †05

ISSEN, Sima Gail. 4815 N ASSEMBLY ST, SPOKANE VA MED CTR 99205 #016-06-1982 L1987 IM *020 †20

JACCARD, John Thaddeus. 131 S DIVISION ST 99202 #051-04-1979 L1999 P CHP *020 †75

JACOBSON, Bert P. ■ 99223 #041-02-1944 L1946 GP OBG *071

JACOBSON, Randall Kenneth. 427 S BERNARD ST, SPOKANE EYE CLINIC, PS 99204 #028-34-1994 L1999 OPH *020 †35

JAMES, Norman John. 235 E ROWAN AVE, HOLY FAMILY MEDICAL BLDG # 99207 #016-02-1964 L1973 PS HS *020 †85,65 ‡

JAMISON, Nicole M. ■ 99223 #048-14-2001 L2002 IM *100

JANOUT, Karen Ellingsen. ■ 99203 #030-06-2001 L2006 OPH *020

JANOUT, Marek. 6002 N MAYFAIR ST, FL 2 99208 #030-06-1999 L2005 CD *100 †20

JANOUT, Martin. ■ 99203 #030-06-2001 L2007 HS *020

JEMMETT, Michael Edward. 800 W 5TH AVE 99204 #049-01-2000 L2003 EM *020 †16

JENSEN, Richard Allan, Jr. 101 W 8TH AVE STE 4300 99204 #005-12-1987 L2003 PDC *020 †55

JOHNSON, Andrea Kathleen. 400 E 5TH AVE, ROCKWOOD CLINIC 99202 #054-04-1998 L2000 FM *020 †18

JOHNSON, Byron Everett. 101 W 8TH AVE 99204 #056-05-1965 L1966 AN *020 †05

JOHNSON, Darcy Taylor. 400 E 5TH AVE 99202 #005-14-1983 L1983 IM *020 †20

JOHNSON, David Michael. 2210 W NORTH FIVE MILE RD 99208 #041-02-1987 L1994 FM *020 †18

JOHNSON, Eric Stuart. 104 W 5TH AVE, STE 230E 99204 #054-04-1976 L1977 AN *020 †05

JOHNSON, Jay R. ■ 99208 #028-34-1953 L1954 U *071 †95

JOHNSON, Jeff L. 400 E 5TH AVE 99202 #048-02-1993 L1997 IM *020 †20

JOHNSON, Mark Alan. 800 W 5TH AVE 99204 #054-04-1977 L1978 IM *020 †20

JOHNSON, Robert S. 101 W 8TH AVE 99204 #016-06-1947 L1953 RHU IM *071 †20

JOHNSON, Stephen Gregory. 820 S MCCLELLAN ST, STE LL10 99204 #054-04-1976 L1979 IM *020 †20

JOHNSTON, Dagmar. 400 E 5TH AVE, ROCKWOOD CLINIC 99202 #286-11-2000 L2003 FM *020 †18

JONES, James Gregory. 800 W 5TH AVE 99204 #054-04-1982 L1982 EM FM *020 †18

JONES, Jason Herrin. 208 W 5TH AVE 99204 #038-40-1995 L2000 OPH *020 †35

JONES, Jeffrey Dwight. 5633 N LIDGERWOOD ST, HOLY FAMILY HOSPITAL, 99208 #054-04-1990 L1998 IM GE *020 †20

JONES, John Edward. 800 W 5TH AVE 99204 #036-01-1997 L2000 EM *020 †16

JONES, Kari L. 101 W 8TH AVE, SACRED HEART CHILDREN'S HO 99204 #040-02-1998 L2006 PD *020 †55

JONES, Millard Ernest. 715 S COWLEY ST 99202 #040-02-1946 L1953 N *071

JONES, Phillip Eugene. 9631 N NEVADA ST, STE 302 99218 #012-05-1978 L1991 CD IM *020 †20

JONES, Thomas Henry. 104 W 5TH AVE, SPOKANE ONCOLOGY HEMATLGY 99204 #030-06-1954 L1958 FM *071 †18

JOSHI, Shaun Kumar. 5633 N LIDGERWOOD ST 99208 #062-01-1992 L1999 NEP *020 †20

JOY, James Vincent, III. 104 W 5TH AVE, STE 230E 99204 #035-01-1990 L1993 AN *020 †05

JUDD, Corey Derek. 5715 N LIDGERWOOD ST, INLAND IMAGING 99208 #028-34-2001 L2004 DR *020 †80

JUDD, Michael A. 525 S COWLEY ST, INLAND IMAGING 99202 #035-06-1964 L1970 VS GS *071 †85

JUDGE, Terrance Patrick. 910 W 5TH AVE, SPOKANE CARDIOLOGY PSC 99204 #054-04-1962 L1968 CD *071 †20

JUVILER, Adam Herz. 318 E ROWAN AVE, STE 227 99207 #051-01-1999 L2005 GS *100 †85,10

KACZMARK, Julie Rachelle. 101 W 8TH AVE, INLAND IMAGING ASSOCIATES 99204 #028-34-2000 L2006 PDR *020 †80

KADEL, Keith Arthur. 212 E CENTRAL AVE STE 240, HEART CLINICS NORTHWEST 99208 #041-14-1983 L1991 CD IM *020 †20

KANESHIGE, Gary Donald. 104 W 5TH AVE # 250, ANESTHESIA ASSOCIATES P.S. 99204 #016-42-1996 L2003 AN *020 †05

KANTER, Roy A. 5901 N LIDGERWOOD ST # 25B 99208 #048-02-1981 L2003 N P *020 †75

KAPSTAFER, Kennard Jos. 235 E ROWAN AVE, STE 117 99207 #030-06-1961 L1965 PD PDA *020

KARP, Jeffrey W. 801 W 5TH AVE, STE 619 99204 #028-02-1981 L1990 PS OS *020 †65

KASS, Thomas Joseph. 104 W 5TH AVE STE 230E 99204 #056-06-1987 L1991 AN *020 †05

KAVANAUGH, Kevin Matthew. 122 W 7TH AVE STE 310 99204 #046-01-1983 L1994 CD *020 †20

KAWAKAMI, Kari Lehua. 107 S DIVISION ST 99202 #014-01-2001 L2001 CHP *020

KAYA, Hakan. 601 S SHERMAN ST, CANCER CARE NORTHWEST 99202 #902-03-1993 L2001 HO *020 †20

KEARNEY, Thomas Anthony. ■ 99223 #024-07-1975 L1981 FM *071 †18

KEBLAWI, Samir Said. 400 E 5TH AVE 99202 #051-07-1992 L1996 PD *020 †55

KELLEY, Kal. 104 W 5TH AVE STE 200W, HOSPITAL SERVICE 99204 #048-12-2006 L2006 FP *012

KELLOGG, Glenn Kieth. 104 W 5TH AVE STE 250E 99204 #031-01-1986 L1990 AN *020 †05

KELSCH, Walter Daryl. 800 W 5TH AVE 99204 #054-04-1955 L1956 AN *071 †05

KENDALL, Robert W. 101 W 8TH AVE 99204 #040-02-1953 L1963 TS *071 †85,90

KENNEDY, Criswell Allen. 1100 W MALLON AVE, SPOKANE COUNTY JAIL 99260 #060-01-1978 L1979 GP *020

KENNEY, Howard Mark. 105 W 8TH AVE STE 6080, ARTHRITIS NORTHWEST 99204 #049-01-1977 L1983 RHU IM *020 †20

KERNERMAN, Steven M. 508 W 6TH AVE STE 700 99204 #018-75-1986, ▲ L1992 AI IM *020 †20,03

KERR, Robert Bruce. 101 W 8TH AVE 99204 #054-04-1982 L1985 EM IM *020 †20,16

KERSTEN, Tycho Erwin. 601 W 5TH AVE STE 400 99204 #026-04-1995 L2001 OSM *020 †40

KESTELL, Michael Francis. 105 W 8TH AVE, SPOKANE DIGESTIVE DISEASE 99204 #054-04-1985 L1986 GE IM *020 †20

KESTER, Eugene Francis. 1330 N WASHINGTON ST # 208, & HLT SERV DIS DET. DETERM 99201 #023-01-1967 L1978 P *020 †75

KEY, Jerry Lynn. 218 N BERNARD ST 99201 #054-04-1965 L1967 AN *020 †05

KEYES, Ted Wm. 2525 E 29TH AVE STE 10B 99223 #049-01-1980 L1999 ON GP *020 †20

KEYES, William David. 5715 N LIDGERWOOD ST, INLAND IMAGING 99208 #046-01-1980 L1991 RNR R *020 †80

KHAN, Karla Elizabeth. 235 E ROWAN AVE, STE 102 99207 #040-01-1995 L1999 OBG *020

KINCAID, Joseph P. 1402 S GRAND BLVD 99203 #054-04-1989 L1992 PD *020 †55

KING, Margaret Webb. 400 E 5TH AVE 99202 #026-04-1985 L1997 IM *020 †20

KIRKPATRICK, Sarah K. 101 W 8TH AVE 99204 #056-05-1998 L2001 IM *020 †20

KIRSCH, Michael David. 5715 N LIDGERWOOD ST, INLAND IMAGING 99208 #016-06-1987 L1993 DR *020 †80

KISHIYAMA, Christopher M. ■ 99203 #007-02-2000 L2007 PDE *020 †55 ‡

KLEAVELAND, Richard N. ■ 99203 #024-01-1951 L1956 VS GS *071 †85

KLIM, John Nathaniel. 400 E 5TH AVE 99202 #005-12-1984 L1991 IM *020 †20

KLOCK, Lawrence E, Jr. ■ 99203 #054-04-1968 L1969 PUD IM *071 †20

KNIGHT, Jesse Rogoza. ■ 99203 #054-04-2004 L2006 DR *012

KNOX, Gary Marshall. 3016 E 57TH AVE, STE 27 99223 #040-02-1980 L1981 FM *020 †18

KODY, Michael Henry. 601 W 5TH AVE STE 400 99204 #051-01-1984 L1991 ORS *020 †40

KOHLMEIER, Lynn-Anne. 601 W 5TH AVE STE 570, SPOKANE, PLLC 99204 #005-11-1988 L1999 IM *020 †20

KOHLMEIER, Pamela Sue. 101 W 8TH AVE, SPOKANE EMERGENCY PHYSICIA 99204 #030-05-1995 L2006 EM *020 †16

KOOY, Jamie Lee. 3016 E 57TH AVE, STE 27 99223 #054-04-1997 L1999 FM *020 †18

KORDASH, Terance Raymond. 823 W 7TH AVE 99204 #016-43-1970 L1971 A IM *020 †20,03

KRAEMER, Kenneth Gerald. 400 E 5TH AVE 99202 #025-01-1970 L1974 ON IM *020 †20

KRAEMER, Michael Jerome. 508 W 6TH AVE STE 30 99204 #054-04-1977 L1978 A AI *050 †55,03

KREJCI, Christopher Scott. 5715 N LIDGERWOOD ST, INLAND IMAGING 99208 #049-01-1998 L2002 DR RNR *020 †80

KROEGER, Robert Henry. 4815 N ASSEMBLY ST 99205 #040-02-1958 L1962 IM *020 †20

KRUEGER, Ronald Lee. 220 E ROWAN AVE, DOCTORS CLINIC 99207 #409-05-1981 L1983 EM GP *020

KUEHL, Tiffany Anne. 800 W 5TH AVE, DEACONESS EMERGENCY PHYSIC 99204 #023-07-2001 L2004 EM *020 †16

KUWIK, Robert A. 4815 N ASSEMBLY ST, BHS 116 - SPOKANE VAMC 99205 #035-06-1972 L2000 P PYG *020 †75

KWASMAN, Michael Alan. 318 E ROWAN AVE, STE 240 99207 #035-06-1984 L1993 CD IM *020 †20

KWIK, Raymond Siong Hie. 104 W 5TH AVE STE 250E, ANESTHESIA ASSOCIATES, PS 99204 #917-29-1969 L1987 AN *020 †05

LADICH-ROGERS, David G. 104 W 5TH AVE, STE 230E 99204 #005-18-1985 L1989 AN *020 †05

LAGERQUIST, Lynn G, Jr. 400 E 5TH AVE 99202 #008-01-1969 L1999 IM OS *020 †20

LALANI, Tasneem A K. 5715 N LIDGERWOOD ST, INLAND IMAGING 99208 #060-01-1993 L2000 DR *020 †80

LAMB, Larry Kent. 801 W 5TH AVE STE 104 99204 #049-01-1988 L1992 PM *020 †60

LAMBERT, Richard James. 104 W 5TH AVE STE 400W 99204 #005-19-1980 L1981 PUD IM *040 †20

LAMOREAUX, Wayne Tenney. 910 W 5TH AVE STE 102 99204 #049-01-2000 L2005 RO *020 †80

LANEY, Steven Richard. 322 W NORTH RIVER DR 99201 #010-01-1974 L1977 FM *020 †18

LANG, Christopher John. 220 E ROWAN AVE, STE 100 99207 #012-01-1994 L2004 ORS *020 †40

LANGSTRAAT, Ruth Elaine. ■ 99204 #018-03-1976 L1985 IM *020 †20

LANTSBERGER, Paula Ann. 323 E 2ND AVE, OCCUPATIONAL MEDICINE 99202 #046-01-1985 L1986 OM *020 †70

LA ROWE, Peter Clark. 205 DEACONESS MEDICAL BG, X-RAY MOBILE 99204 #036-01-1964 L1971 DR NR *020 †80

LARSEN, Paul Richard. 104 W 5TH AVE STE 200W, FAMILY MEDICINE SPOKANE 99204 #030-06-1997 L1999 FM *020 †18

LARSON, Daniel Kurtis. 104 W 5TH AVE STE 230E 99204 #056-06-1979 L1985 AN *020 †05

LARSON, Gordon Eric. 104 W 5TH AVE, STE 390E 99204 #018-03-1968 L1972 OPH *071 †35

LARSON, Leif John. 3016 E 57TH AVE, STE 24 99223 #014-01-1984 L1991 GP OM *020

LA SALLE, Andre J. 105 W 8TH AVE, STE 7070 99204 #054-04-2007 L1983 VS GS *020 †85

LASALLE, Gretchen Wright. 3016 E 57TH AVE STE 27 99223 #021-01-2007 L2007 FM *020 †18

LA SALLE, Sean Paul. 105 W 8TH AVE, STE 6080 99204 #021-01-2001 L2007 RHU *020

LASELLE, Brooks Thomas. ■ 99223 #016-06-2004 L2005 EM *020

LA SELLE, Thomas Clement. 400 E 5TH AVE 99202 #026-04-1972 L1977 IM IMG *020 †20

LATTIN, Daniel E. 5901 N LIDGERWOOD ST # 117 99208 #049-01-1978 L1982 OPH *020 †35

LAUDENBACH, Charles W. 400 E 5TH AVE 99202 #026-04-1983 L1996 IM *020 †20

LAUGEN, Robert Henry. 601 S SHERMAN ST 99202 #030-05-1972 L1978 ON HEM *020 †20

LAURIER, Lisanne G. 400 E 5TH AVE 99202 #065-10-1984 L2003 IM END *020 †20

LAWLESS, Isaac J. ■ 99206 #039-01-1969 L1970 P *071 †75

LAXTON-SWANSON, Judy. 104 W 5TH AVE STE 200W 99204 #054-04-1984 L1985 IM *020 †20

LAYTON, Matthew Eric. 107 S DIVISION ST 99202 #019-02-1990 L1993 P *020 †75

LEACH, Jordan Ross. 4815 N ASSEMBLY ST, VA MED CTR 99205 #054-04-1995 L1995 IM *020 †20

LEACHMAN, Michael Reid. 6419 N MONROE ST 99208 #048-13-1994 L2000 OPH *020 †35

LEACHMAN, Wallace Reid. 5901 N LIDGERWOOD ST, STE 224 99208 #048-02-1961 L1973 ORS *071 †40

LECLAIRE, Jerry Edward. 427 S BERNARD ST, SPOKANE EYE CLINIC 99204 #024-01-1980 L1985 OPH *020 †35

LEE, Catherine Andrea. 400 E 5TH AVE, ROCKWOOD CLINIC 99202 #038-40-1997 L2002 RHU IM *020 †20

LEE, Christopher Melvin. 910 W 5TH AVE, STE 102 99204 #028-34-2001 L2006 RO *020 †80

LEE, Gary Wing. 101 W 8TH AVE, SACRED HEART MED CTR 99204 #054-04-1984 L1990 PD *020 †55

LEE, Hi Young. 17 E EMPIRE AVE 99207 #583-01-1965 L1969 FM GS *020 †18

LEE, Jonathan Joongsub. 1028 W 5TH AVE 99204 #056-05-1998 L2001 PD *020 †55

LEE, Sun Myung. 17 E EMPIRE AVE 99207 #583-01-1965 L1973 GP *020

LEFCORT, Diane W. 820 S MCCLELLAN ST, STE 314 99204 #012-01-1999 L2001 IM *020 †20

LEHMANN, Arnold L. ■ 99203 #062-01-1944 L1946 GP GS *072 †85

LEHRER, Sanford Lawrence. 910 W 5TH AVE 99204 #035-08-1963 L1989 P *020

LEIMGRUBER, Pierre Paul. 101 W 8TH AVE 99204 #869-07-1977 L1985 CD IM *020 †20

LEMBERGER, Michael John. 400 E 5TH AVE 99202 #056-06-1976 L1981 EM *020 †16

LEMOINE, Christina Jow. ■ 99208 #035-09-2007 TY *012

LEONARD, Jack Jeffrey. 910 W 5TH AVE STE 380 99204 #054-04-1971 L1980 TS CD *020 †85,90

LESSMEIER, Timothy Jon. 122 W 7TH AVE, STE 310 99204 #018-03-1985 L1986 ICE CD *020 †20

LESTER, Edward Leroy. 911 W 5TH AVE, SHRINERS HOSP FOR CRIPPLED 99204 #054-04-1960 L1965 ORS OP *071 †40

LEWIS, Kevin Leon. 5633 N LIDGERWOOD ST, ANESTHLGY 99208 #023-12-1989 L2001 AN *020 †05

LEWIS, Stephen Francis. 400 E 5TH AVE 99202 #041-12-1989 L2001 IM *020 †20

LEWIS, Terri H. 5715 N LIDGERWOOD ST, INLAND IMAGING 99208 #045-04-1992 L1997 PDR *020 †80

LILES, Jeffery Lewis. PO BOX 2555, 101 W 8TH AVE 99220 #016-01-1998 L2003 **IM** *020 †20
LIN, Henry H. 601 W 5TH AVE, STE 400 99204 #016-11-1987 L1993 **HS ORS** *020 †40
LIN, Paul Hsufeng. 910 W 5TH AVE, STE 550 99204 #016-06-1987 L1991 **GS** *020 †85
LING, Benjamin Chihhung. 105 W 8TH AVE, STE 200 99204 #038-40-1997 L2004 **NS** *020
LINSCOTT, Luke Luther. ■ 99223 #049-01-2007 L2008 **TY** *012
LINTMAER, Ingrid. 101 W 8TH AVE 99204 #781-01-1998 L2007 **IM** *012
LIU, David Ming-Teh. 212 E CENTRAL AVE, STE 245 99208 #065-01-1998 L2007 **R VIR** *020 †80
LLOYD DAVIES, Stephen E. 5904 N DIVISION ST 99208 #054-04-1986 L1994 **FM** *020 †18
LOCHNER, Jerrel Ray. 406 E ROWAN AVE STE 200 99207 #034-01-1974 L1977 **IM** *071
LOCKWOOD, William Bryce. 400 E 5TH AVE, ROCKWOOD CLINIC 99202 #025-01-1987 L1992 **EM** *020 †16
LOEFFLER, Joyce Ann. 105 W 8TH AVE STE 7070, ROCKWOOD CLINIC 99204 #007-02-1991 L2001 **U** *020 †95
LOGAN, Arch H, Jr. ■ 99205 #016-01-1942 L1950 **IM GE** *071 †20
LOGSDON-POKORNY, Valerie. ■ 99203 #011-03-1984 L2005 **OBG** *071 †30
LONG, Kendra Beth. 1803 W MAXWELL AVE, NATIVE HLTH OF SPOKANE 99201 #054-04-2001 L2003 **FM** *020 †18
LOVELL, Tim P. 400 E 5TH AVE 99202 #005-14-1985 L1986 **OAR** *020 †40
LOWELL, Roy S. ■ 99203 #040-02-1944 L1947 **GS** *071
LUBBE, Dieter F. 910 W 5TH AVE, STE 300 99204 #836-02-1989 L2004 **CD** *020 †20
LUBER, Stephen Robt. 400 E 5TH AVE 99202 #005-02-1975 L1988 **PD A** *020 †55
LUDINGTON-HEUSNER, Judith. 407 E 2ND AVE STE 200A, OCCUPATIONAL MEDICINE, NW 99202 #038-41-1987 L1994 **OM** *020 †70
LUEDERS, Jonathan Warren. 101 W 8TH AVE, SACRED HEART MEDICAL CENTE 99204 #026-04-1991 L1995 **EM** *020 †16
LUERA, Natalia Anna. ■ 99223 #054-04-2006 L2006 **FP** *012
LUNA, Gregory Kevin. 212 E CENTRAL AVE, STE 245 99208 #007-02-1978 L1980 **GS VS** *020 †85
LUND, Kirk Allen. 910 W 5TH AVE, STE 700 99204 #049-01-1982 L1996 **ON IM** *050 †20
LUND, Richard Elwood. 5715 N LIDGERWOOD ST, INLAND IMAGING 99208 #026-04-1966 L1970 **DR** *071 †80
LUNOE, Peter Chesnut. 101 W 8TH AVE, PO BOX 2555 99204 #054-04-2007 **TY** *012
LURUS, Angelo G. 5805 E 21ST AVE 99223 #010-01-1957 L1965 **R** *020 †80
LUTHER, Ralph D. MEDICAL CENTER BG, SPOKANE PANEL EVALUATIONS 99204 #041-13-1942 L1951 **ORS** *071 †40
LUTZ, Robert B, Jr. 3016 E 57TH AVE, STE 24 99223 #041-13-1988 L2004 **FM** *020 †18
LYNCH, Patrick S, Jr. 601 W 5TH AVE STE 400 99204 #054-04-1988 L1990 **ORS** *020 †40
MACCINI, David Michael. 46 E ROWAN AVE, SPOKANE DIGESTIVE DISEASE 99207 #050-02-1982 L1984 **GE IM** *020 †20
MAC DONALD, Gregory Paul. 101 W 8TH AVE, STE 4200 99204 #025-01-1983 L1999 **CHN PD** *020 †55,75
MACDUFF, Douglas Kim. 105 W 8TH AVE, STE 450E 99204 #054-04-1969 L1970 **AN** *071 †05
MACFARLANE, Mark Phillip. 400 E 5TH AVE 99202 #005-19-1989 L1997 **GS SO** *020 †85
MACIAS, Angelica. 101 W 8TH AVE, DEPT OF FAMILY MEDICINE 99204 #054-04-2006 L2006 **FP** *012
MACKAY, Alan Blair. 842 S COWLEY ST, STE 4 99202 #050-02-1961 L1968 **OPH** *071 †35
MACKAY, Alexander R. 711 S COWLEY ST, STE 210 99202 #024-01-1975 L1981 **NS** *020 †25
MACKENZIE, Gordon Keith. 715 S COWLEY ST, STE 228 99202 #054-04-1973 L1977 **PM FM** *020 †18,60
MADDOX, J Alan. 220 E ROWAN AVE STE 330 99207 #047-20-1994 L1997 **FM** *020 †18 ‡
MAHER, Stephen Campbell. 208 W 5TH AVE 99204 #010-01-1976 L1981 **OPH** *020 †35
MAIXNER, Robert Paul. 235 E ROWAN AVE, STE 117 99207 #030-05-1972 L1976 **PD** *020 †55
MALDONADO, Anastacia B. 400 E 5TH AVE, ROCKWOOD CLINIC, PS 99202 #308-02-1990 L2005 **RHU** *020 †20
MALIREDDI, Krishna Mohan. 801 W 5TH AVE, STE 309 99204 #495-11-1992 L2002 **NEP** *020 †20
MALLO, Rebecca Dawn. ■ 99202 #054-04-2006 **IM** *012
MALNAR, Stanley James. 101 W 8TH AVE, SACRED HEART MED CTR 99204 #054-04-1981 L1984 **FM OBS** *020 †18
MALONE, David Shawn. 9922 N NEVADA ST 99218 #040-02-1992 L1998 **OTO** *020 †45
MANSON, Timothy Patrick. 2713 N ARGONNE RD 99212 #028-03-1992 L1999 **FM** *020 †18
MANZ, Michael Paul. 807 W 7TH AVE 99204 #048-04-1973 L1980 **CHP** *020 †75
MAPLE, Jeffrey Eugene. 7719 N FOX POINT DR 99208 #039-01-1995 L1997 **FM AM** *020 †18
MARGRAF, Robert Alan. 1001 W 2ND AVE, COMMUNITY HEALTH ASSOC OF 99201 #040-02-2003 L2006 **FM** *020 †18
MARINEAU, William Pierre. ■ 99223 #016-06-1953 L1966 **FM OBG** *071 †18
MARINO, Christina A. 820 S MCCLELLAN ST, STE 426 99204 #005-18-1981 L1997 **PHP D** *020 †15
MARQUIS, Scott Philip. 101 W 8TH AVE, SACRED HEART MEDICAL CENTE 99204 #040-02-2002 L2005 **EM** *020 †16
MARR, Thomas Arthur. 400 E 5TH AVE, ROCKWOOD CLINIC PS 99202 #026-04-1953 L1957 **IM** *071 †20
MARTIN, Deborah J. 4815 N ASSEMBLY ST 99205 #054-04-1993 L1995 **IM** *020
MARTIN, Franklin H. 800 W 5TH AVE 99204 #026-04-1969 L1979 **PTH OS** *071 †50
MARTIN, Judith Ann. 604 W 6TH AVE 99204 #033-06-1979 L2000 **CG PD** *020 †19,55
MARTIN, Thomas Richard. 7222 S HATCH RD 99224 #038-40-1966 L1971 **AN** *071
MARTINEZ PEREZ, Juan Carl. 104 W 5TH AVE STE 200W, INLAND EMPIRE HOSPITAL SER 99204 #264-06-1995 L2006 **FP** *012
MARTON POPOVICI, Monica. ■ 99202 #781-05-1998 L2006 **IM** *012
MARTZ, Robert Dean. 105 W 8TH AVE STE 200, SUITE 200 99204 #038-06-1984 L1990 **NS** *020 †25
MATHIA, Kelley Gross. 105 W 8TH AVE, STE 6060 99204 #028-34-1993 L1997 **OBG** *020 †30
MATSON, Mark Alan. 400 E 5TH AVE 99202 #026-04-1986 L2003 **NEP IM** *020 †20
MATSUMOTO, Gary Hiromi. 104 W 5TH AVE, STE 7060 99204 #054-04-1970 L1979 **GS VS** *071 †85
MATTOX, Troy Edward. 5633 N LIDGERWOOD ST, HOLY FAMILY HOSPITAL 99208 #049-01-2004 L2007 **EM** *020
MAUGHAN, Brent Sjoberg. 910 W 5TH AVE, STE 560 99204 #040-02-1980 L1984 **OBG** *020 †30
MAUGHAN, Timothy Dee. 101 W 8TH AVE 99204 #054-04-1999 L2005 **ID** *020 †20,55
MAVIOGLU, Hilmi. 4815 N ASSEMBLY ST 99205 #902-01-1952 L1963 **HEM ON** *071 †20
MAXWELL, Keegan Lawrence. ■ 99203 #054-04-2001 L2007 **U** *020
MC ALLISTER, James. 318 E ROWAN AVE 99207 #018-03-1953 L1956 **IM** *071 ‡
MC CABE, Kenneth James. 5715 N LIDGERWOOD ST, INLAND IMAGING 99208 #007-02-1999 L2005 **RNR** *020 †80
MC CAFFREE, Floyd Martin. 601 W 5TH AVE STE 301 99204 #030-05-1972 L1978 **OBG** *020 †30
MCCARTHY, Diane W. 101 W 8TH AVE, # 100-L1 99204 #021-05-1989 L2000 **PDS CCP** *020 †85
MC CARTHY, Michael Mc Cue. 800 W 5TH AVE, FL 5N 99204 #054-04-1976 L1981 **AI PUD** *020 †55,03
MC CLELLAN, David L. 5633 N LIDGERWOOD ST 99208 #018-03-1955 L1958 **FM FPG** *071
MC CLELLAN, David Scott. 101 W 8TH AVE 99204 #023-12-1982 L1984 **EM GP** *020 †16
MC CORQUODALE, Douglas L. ■ 99203 #038-06-1947 L1947 **P** *071 †75
MC CRADY, Andrea Mercer. 322 W NORTH RIVER DR 99201 #067-01-1980 L1982 **FM** *020 †18
MC CROREY, Steven Trevor. 120 W MISSION AVE 99201 #030-06-1996 L1999 **FM** *020 †18
MC HUGH, James Wm. ■ 99208 #038-06-1977 L1983 **PUD IM** *020 †20
MC KENNA, John Ignatius. 235 E ROWAN AVE STE 102 99207 #054-04-1990 L1994 **OBG** *020 †30
MC KENNA, John Jos. 235 E ROWAN AVE, STE 102 99207 #056-06-1961 L1965 **OBG** *071 †30
MC MANUS, Joseph Bradley. 5901 N LIDGERWOOD ST, STE 220 99208 #041-13-1976 L1989 **PD EM** *020 †55
MCNEILL, James I. 534 E SPOKANE FALLS BLVD, STE 200 99202 #005-12-1972 L1993 **OPH** *020 †35 ‡
MC NEVIN, Michael Shane. 910 W 5TH AVE, STE 550 99204 #025-07-1994 L2002 **CRS** *020 †85,10
MC VEY, Kevin. 400 E 5TH AVE 99202 #010-01-1979 L1986 **OTO FPS** *020 †45
MEEKIN, Francis Arne. 5633 N LIDGERWOOD ST, HOLY FAMILY HOSPITAL 99208 #056-06-1958 L1963 **RO R** *071 †80
MEIGHAN, Jacob W. 525 S COWLEY ST 99202 #056-06-1962 L1964 **R** *020 †80 ‡
MELINE, Lewis John. 910 W 5TH AVE, STE 510 99204 #049-01-1996 L2002 **OBG** *020
MELLEMA, James Dale. ■ 99223 #005-18-1990 L1993 **CCP** *020 †55
MELLEMA, Rita Heinzinger. 800 W 5TH AVE 99204 #005-02-1990 L1993 **EM** *020 †16
MEMON, H Sara. 4815 N ASSEMBLY ST, VA MEDICAL CENTER 99205 #517-08-1982 L1991 **IM** *020 †20
MERCHEN, Lee Ann. 918 W 23RD AVE 99203 #038-45-2000 L2004 **IM** *020
MERG, Anders Richard. 910 W 5TH AVE, STE 550 99204 #056-05-1996 L2001 **GS** *020 †85
MERKELEY, Ward Donald. 5633 N LIDGERWOOD ST 99208 #049-01-1980 L1981 **FM EM** *020 †16
MERRILL, Kevin Douglas. 800 W 5TH AVE, DEACONESS MED CTR-SPOKANE 99204 #005-14-2004 L2006 **OPH** *012
MESSINGER, J Robin Lee. 601 W 5TH AVE, STE 301 99204 #048-16-2001 L2005 **OBG** *020 †30
MEYER, Kathleen Lynn. 711 S COWLEY ST, STE 230 99202 #040-02-1981 L1989 **NS** *020 †25
MEYER, Marynell Hoag. 105 W 8TH AVE, STE 6060 99204 #005-12-1977 L1978 **OBG** *020 †30
MEYER, Timothy James. 322 W NORTH RIVER DR 99201 #056-05-1974 L1979 **FM** *020 †18
MICHELS, Joseph T, Jr. 400 E 5TH AVE, ROCKWOOD CLINIC 99202 #016-06-1979 L1989 **IM** *020 †20
MIELKE, Brendan Allen. 235 E ROWAN AVE, STE 209 99207 #048-12-1992 L2001 **NEP** *020 †20
MIELKE, Clarence H, Jr. 310 N RIVERPOINT BLVD, BOX J 99202 #020-02-1963 L1988 **HEM** *030 †20
MIETHKE, Marion Claire. 4815 N ASSEMBLY ST, 6TH FL 99205 #018-03-1984 L1989 **D** *020 †15
MIHALICK, Trent D. 5633 N LIDGERWOOD ST, RADIATION ONCOLOGY DEPARTM 99208 #036-05-1987 L2005 **RO IM** *020 †20,80
MIKKELSEN, David Jos. 801 W 5TH AVE 99204 #016-06-1984 L1990 **U** *020 †95
MILLER, Andrew B. 104 W 5TH AVE STE 230E 99204 #012-01-1999 L2003 **AN** *020 †05
MILLER, Evan Thomas. ■ 99204 #017-20-2008 *012
MILLER, Gilbert Thos. 101 W 8TH AVE, SACRED HEART MED CTR 99204 #054-04-1964 L1965 **OS** *030 †45
MILLER, Gregory Scotford. 104 W 5TH AVE STE 230E 99204 #049-01-1983 L1987 **AN** *020 †05
MILLER, Patrick Thomas. 104 W 5TH AVE STE 230E 99204 #030-06-1996 L2001 **AN** *020 †05
MILLER, Raymond Arthur. 801 W 5TH AVE, STE 518 99204 #054-04-1968 L1969 **U** *071 †95
MILLER, Richard Cramer. ■ 99223 #024-01-1941 L1948 **HS GS** *071 †85
MILLIGAN, Robert Cathie. 212 E CENTRAL AVE STE 34, ASSOCIATES FOR WOMEN'S HEA 99208 #010-02-1995 L2006 **OBG** *020 †30
MILNER, Gilbert Cecil. ■ 99204 #048-12-1965 L1985 **CHP P** *020 †75
MILSOW, Larry. 520 S COWLEY ST 99202 #020-12-1979 L1983 **OPH** *020 †35
MINANA, Mitchell Frank. 104 W 5TH AVE, STE 230E 99204 #028-03-1984 L1991 **AN** *020 †05
MINTEN, Nancy Lee. 800 W 5TH AVE 99204 #054-04-1992 L1993 **FM** *020 †18
MOBERLY, Merle Laidley. 525 S COWLEY ST 99202 #035-45-1958 L1965 **DR NM** *071 †80
MOHANAKUMAR, Meera. 104 W 5TH AVE 99204 #220-04-1993 L2002 **FM** *020 †18
MOISE, Vivian Marie. 511 S PINE ST, # D 99202 #005-02-1982 L1986 **PM** *020 †60
MOLANDER, Kevin Jon. 2713 N ARGONNE RD 99212 #005-12-2002 L2006 **FM** *020 †18
MOMANY, George Marshall. 104 W 5TH AVE, STE 230E 99204 #025-01-1985 L1989 **AN PMM** *020 †05
MOMENI, Fereshteh. 101 W 8TH AVE, SACRED HEART MEDICAL CENTE 99204 #517-01-1981 L1997 **P** *020
MONDAL, Kenneth Mark. 510 S COWLEY ST, ROCKWOOD CLINIC EYECENTER 99202 #041-01-1975 L1992 **OPH** *020 †35
MONKMAN, George Robb. 400 E 5TH AVE 99202 #060-01-1970 L1984 **ORS** *020 †40
MONTAGUE, Christopher Jon. PO BOX 3405, INCYTE PATHOLOGY 99220 #026-04-1993 L1998 **SP** *020 †50
MONTANA, Margaret Anne. 801 W 5TH AVE, STE 205 99204 #028-02-1978 L1984 **DR NRN** *020 †80
MONTGOMERY, Anne Marie. 104 W 5TH AVE STE 200W, FAM MED SPOKANE 99204 #026-08-1986 L1994 **FM OBS** *040 †18
MOON, Renata M Stoszek. 101 W 8TH AVE, SACRED HEART CHILDREN'S HO 99204 #028-02-1993 L2004 **PD** *020 †55 ‡
MOORE, Harold Guy. 104 W 5TH AVE, STE 200W 99204 #005-12-1989 L1989 **FM** *020 †18
MOORE, Michael Ryan. 400 E 5TH AVE 99202 #054-04-1985 L1990 **GS** *020 †85
MOORE, Pauline Kurachi. ■ 99203 #007-02-1953 L1954 **OS** *071
MOORMAN, Daniel Robert. 5901 N LIDGERWOOD ST, STE 220 99208 #054-04-2004 L2007 **PD** *020
MORAN, Julie Anne. 5633 N LIDGERWOOD ST 99208 #041-12-1995 L1998 **FM** *020 †18
MORGAN, David Granville. 105 W 8TH AVE, STE 7035 99204 #048-13-1973 L1979 **PD** *020 †55
MORIMOTO, Pamela Kaiulani. 105 W 8TH AVE, STE 7030 99204 #014-01-1996 L1998 **PS HS** *020
MORNIN, Elizabeth Douglas. 400 E 5TH AVE 99202 #054-04-1985 L1985 **IM** *020 †20
MORRIS, Astrid Dorothee. 400 E 5TH AVE 99202 #409-21-1991 L2002 **RO** *020 †80
MORRISON, Philip Stephen. 711 S COWLEY ST STE 310 99202 #028-02-1964 L1970 **PM** *071 †60
MORTON, Frank Jos. 9631 N NEVADA ST, STE 101 99218 #056-06-1955 L1956 **GP** *071 †18
MORTON, Keith Allen. 406 E ROWAN AVE STE 200 99207 #005-12-1999 L2002 **IM** *020 †20
MOSS, Robert Edward. 4815 N ASSEMBLY ST, SPOKANE VAMC 99205 #010-02-1977 L2000 **PUD CCM** *020 †20

■ = Address Information Privacy Protected

9305

MOULTON, John Porter. 6406 W RUTTER PKWY 99208 #054-04-1974 L1977 **P** *020 †75
MOUSER, Lowell Thos. ROCKWOOD CLINIC 99204 #055-01-1963 L1972 **CD IM** *071 †20
MOYER, John Arthur. 101 W 8TH AVE 99204 #016-11-1947 L1955 **OBG** *071
MROCH, Henry. 400 E 5TH AVE 99202 #005-15-1993 L1995 **NEP** *020 †20
MUIR, Linda Varrella. 105 W 8TH AVE STE 160, SACRED HEART DOCTORS BUILD 99204 #005-02-1990 L2004 **PD** *020 †55
MULLEN, James P. ■ 99223 #030-06-1982 L1985 **FM** *020 †18
MULLER, Jan Herbert. 1001 W 2ND AVE 99201 #409-36-1996 L2002 **FM** *020 †18
MULVIHILL, Robert Leonard. 400 E 5TH AVE 99202 #048-02-1995 L2001 **P** *012 †35
MULVIHILL, Sue-Ann E. 107 S DIVISION ST 99202 #048-02-1996 L2000 **P** *020 †75
MURPHY, Brian David. 101 W 8TH AVE 99204 #005-06-2000 L2004 **AN** *020 †05
MURPHY, John Jos. 5715 N LIDGERWOOD ST, INLAND IMAGING 99208 #030-06-1960 L1967 **R RO** *020 †80
MURPHY, William Schaefer. 9631 N NEVADA ST, STE 302 99218 #040-02-1977 L1982 **CD IM** *020 †20
MURRAY, Daniel James. 212 E CENTRAL AVE, STE 245 99208 #028-34-1985 L1986 **DR** *020 †80
MURRAY, Stephen Paul. 212 E CENTRAL AVE, STE 245 99208 #039-05-1984 L1997 **GS** *020 †85
MUSA, John Louis. 235 E ROWAN AVE, STE 209 99207 #016-01-1993 L2001 **IM** *020 †20
MYERS, Paul Edward. 105 W 8TH AVE STE 7070, SACRED HEART DOCTORS BUILD 99204 #038-40-1984 L1990 **GS** *020 †85
NACHREINER, Ryan Dean. 5715 N LIDGERWOOD ST, INLAND IMAGING 99208 #005-12-1997 L2007 **VS** *020 †85
NAIL, Gregory Chas. 910 W 5TH AVE STE 600 99204 #054-04-1973 L1974 **FM** *075 †18
NAIR, Giju. 105 W 8TH AVE STE 707 99204 #038-44-1995 L2002 **U** *020 †95
NALL, John Stephen. 9222 N NEWPORT HWY 99218 #005-06-1977 L1997 **FM** *020 †18
NAMJOSHI, Kavita S. 1030 E 29TH AVE, MED. SCHOOL ASSO. NORTH 99203 #495-28-1995 L2006 **IM** *020 †20
NANIA, James Mark. 800 W 5TH AVE 99204 #016-43-1976 L1979 **EM** *020 †16
NAYLOR, John Kimball. 910 W 5TH AVE STE 500 99204 #054-04-1988 L1990 **PCC IM** *020 †20
NDIRANGU, Magdaline Wambu. ■ 99208 #577-01-1997 L2007 **FM** *020 †18
NEGRETTI, Raymond M A. 6008 N MAYFAIR ST, THE DOCTORS' CLINIC 99208 #041-09-1950 L1953 **GP** *071
NELSON, Bradford A. 105 W 8TH AVE, STE 7070 99204 #054-04-2001 L2006 **U** *020 †95
NELSON, Brent Darrell. 9001 N COUNTRY HOMES BLVD, ROCKWOOD CLINIC NORTH 99218 #051-04-1988 L1991 **FM** *020 †18
NELSON, Charles H. ■ 99224 #026-04-1951 L1977 **GP GS** *071 †85
NELSON, Peter Norman. 5633 N LIDGERWOOD ST 99208 #054-04-1981 L1982 **EM** *020 †16
NESSA, Yarun. ■ 99202 #160-02-1999 L2006 **IM** *012
NEVEN, Darin Eugene. 101 W 8TH AVE, SACRED HEART MEDICAL CENTE 99204 #018-03-1998 L2005 **EM** *020 †16
NEWBERRY, Jerry Eugene. 104 W 5TH AVE, STE 230E 99204 #048-02-1972 L1975 **AN** *071
NEWKIRK, Gary Ray. 104 W 5TH AVE, FAMILY MED SPOKANE # 200W 99204 #005-18-1978 L1979 **FM** *040 †18
NEWMAN, Corliss Luise. 910 W 5TH AVE, STE 700 99204 #054-04-1993 L2004 **HO** *020 †20
NGUYEN, Kimdung Thi. ■ 99223 #305-01-1999 L2006 **IM** *020 †20
NICKEL, Barbara Jan. ■ 99201 #033-06-2008 *012
NICKOLOFF, Jonathan M. 318 E ROWAN AVE, STE 227 99207 #030-06-2000 L2004 **TS** *020 †85
NIGHTINGALE, Daniel Ray. PO BOX 3405 99220 #021-05-2000 L2005 **PTH** *100 †50
NISCO, Steven J. 910 W 5TH AVE, STE 380 99204 #005-11-1988 L1999 **TS CD** *020 †85,90
NOBLE, Mary Miriam. 104 W 5TH AVE, STE 200 99204 #065-10-1977 L1979 **IM** *020 †20
NOLAND, Gary Lester. 4815 N ASSEMBLY ST, VETERANS AFFAIRS MEDICAL C 99205 #040-02-1975 L1979 **FM** *030 †18
NORMAN, Cindy Rae. ■ 99204 #021-06-1983 L1988 **IM** *075
NOTSKE, Robert Norman. 800 W 5TH AVE 99204 #054-04-1965 L1969 **CD IM** *020 †20
NOVAN, George. 101 W 8TH AVE, INTERNAL MED RES SPOKANE 99204 #005-14-1973 L1990 **IM ID** *040 †20
NUMATA, Robert Alan. 400 E 5TH AVE, ROCKWOOD CLINIC, PS 99202 #054-04-1973 L1975 **FM** *071 †18
NUNES, Geoffrey Carle. 104 W 5TH AVE, ASSOCIATED SURGEONS PS 99204 #005-02-1965 L1973 **GS** *071 †85
NYE, Christina Nelson. 105 W 8TH AVE, STE 512 99204 #038-40-1994 L1999 **OPH PO** *020 †35
NYE, Scott Walker. 910 W 5TH AVE, STE 550 99204 #038-40-1994 L1999 **GS** *020 †85
OAKLEY, Anne Dennison. 104 W 5TH AVE, STE 230E 99204 #036-01-1986 L1992 **AN IM** *020 †05
OAKLEY, Russell Neal. 820 S MCCLELLAN ST, STE 300 99204 #041-14-1984 L1992 **ORS GS** *020 †40
O'CONNOR, Jeffrey Robt. 2709 W BOONE AVE 99201 #003-01-1975 L1980 **FM** *020 †18
OGDEN, Philip Douglas. 5633 N LIDGERWOOD ST, HOLY FAMILY HOSPITAL 99208 #054-04-1985 L2005 **AN** *020 †05
OJDROVIC, Jovan. 101 W 8TH AVE, SACRED HEART MEDICAL CENTE 99204 #056-06-1978 L1982 **EM** *020 †16
O'KEEFE, Neil John. 9922 N NEVADA ST 99218 #040-02-1966 L1969 **OTO HNS** *020 †45
OLDS, Michael Jos. 217 W CATALDO AVE 99201 #054-04-1989 L1996 **OTO HNS** *020 †45
OLIVA, Alfonso. 530 S COWLEY ST 99202 #016-11-1982 L1994 **PS HS** *020 †85,65
OLMSTED, Gerald Wm. 105 W 8TH AVE STE 550 99204 #040-02-1966 L1974 **PS HS** *020 †65
OLSON, Alan Christopher. 5901 N LIDGERWOOD ST, STE 126 99208 #049-01-1979 L1982 **PD** *020 †55
OLSON, Craig Arthur. 4511 S MADELIA ST 99223 #054-04-1971 L1972 **EM** *020 †18
OLSON, Kirt Stephen. 105 W 8TH AVE STE 7070, ROCKWOOD CLINIC, P.S. 99204 #049-01-1982 L1998 **GS** *020 †85
OLSON, Lance Edwin. ■ 99203 #024-01-1971 L1976 **OPH** *071 †35
OLSON, Mark Chas. 800 W 5TH AVE 99204 #054-04-1969 L1973 **ORS** *020 †40
O'MEARA-BRINK, Margaret W. 2707 E. DEERWOOD COURT 99223 #060-01-1943 L1955 **OBG** *071
ORME, Eric Charles. 122 W 7TH AVE, STE 310 99204 #049-01-1979 L1989 **CD IM** *020 †20
O'ROURKE, Patricia Ceceli. 10117 N DIVISION ST, STE 3 99218 #025-12-1980 L1988 **GP PTH** *020
ORTIZ, Ronald Leslie. 406 E ROWAN AVE, STE 200 99207 #005-18-1984 L2003 **IM** *020 †20
OSBORN, John Jay. 423 W 1ST AVE, STE 240 99201 #054-04-1983 L1984 **IM** *020 †20
OSEBOLD, William Russell. 601 W 5TH AVE, STE 400 99204 #005-14-1972 L1980 **ORS** *071 †40 ‡
OSKIN, Terri Ann. 6120 N MAYFAIR ST 99208 #020-02-1992 L1999 **IM** *020 †20
OSMUN, Paul. 220 E ROWAN AVE, DOCTORS CLINIC 99207 #028-79-2003, ▲ L2006 **FM** *020 †18
OSTEN, Thomas John. ■ 99224 #018-03-1969 L1970 **FM** *071
OTT, David Alan. 800 W 5TH AVE, WOUND & HYPERBARIC CTR 99204 #030-05-1975 L1976 **EM FM** *020 †18,16
OTTE, Wade R. 104 W 5TH AVE, STE 230E 99204 #048-13-1988 L1992 **AN** *020 †05
OTTO, Frank Eric. 104 W 5TH AVE, STE 200W 99204 #005-14-1983 L1984 **FM** *040 †18
PADMARAJU, Chandrasekhar. ■ 99223 #495-65-2001 L2007 **IM** *020 †20
PADRTA, Brian John. 9631 N NEVADA ST STE 304 99218 #056-06-1989 L1995 **ORS** *020 †40
PAGCATIPUNAN, Maria. 6120 N MAYFAIR ST 99208 #016-01-1999 L2006 **END** *100 †20
PAKPREO, Ponrat. 101 W 8TH AVE STE 100L-1, SACRED HEART CHILDRENS HOS 99204 #056-05-1999 L2006 **PD ADL** *100 †55
PALMER, Penny Marilyn. 1027 W 20TH AVE 99203 #047-05-1983 L1999 **P** *020 †75
PALPANT, Samuel David. 2709 W BOONE AVE 99201 #041-13-1974 L1985 **IM ID** *040 †20
PALUKURU, Ajitha Reddy. 101 W 8TH AVE BOX 2555, INTERNAL MEDICINE RESIDENC 99204 #495-70-1999 L2004 **IM** *020 †20
PARISOT, Michael Albert. 820 S MCCLELLAN ST, STE 500 99204 #010-02-1982 L1989 **IM IMG** *020 †20
PARKER, Alden Russell. ■ 99204 #025-01-1955 L1961 **D** *071 †15
PARKER, Danielle Erin. 800 W 5TH AVE 99204 #049-01-2001 L2006 **EM** *020
PARKER, Edward Haig, Jr. ■ 99212 #005-06-1964 L1985 **DR AM** *071 †70,80
PARKER, Robert Patrick. ■ 99203 #030-06-1948 L1953 **IM** *071 †20
PARTOLL, Linda Marie. 105 W 8TH AVE STE 6020 99204 #016-11-1987 L1993 **GYN** *020 †30
PARTOVI, Parviz. PO BOX 28217 99228 #517-01-1961 L1972 **GS VS** *071 †85 ‡
PARVIZ, Maryam. 601 S SHERMAN ST 99202 #056-06-1994 L2003 **GS** *020 †85
PATTERSON, Eugene Barto. 801 W 5TH AVE, STE 422 99204 #010-01-1975 L1977 **P ADP** *020 †75
PAULSON, Eric Randolph. 801 W 5TH AVE STE 109, DEACONESS OFFICE BLDG 99204 #026-04-1946 L1948 **FM** *071
PAULSON, Paul Sherman. 4815 N ASSEMBLY ST, VA MEDICAL CENTER #114 99205 #026-04-1956 L1957 **DR** *071 †80
PEARSALL, Deborah Jean. ■ 99203 #016-01-2005 L2005 **FP** *012
PEDERSEN-GLOVER, Elaine K. 5633 N LIDGERWOOD ST 99208 #056-05-1949 L1958 **IM** *020 †20
PEFFER, Alina Ivanovna. ■ 99223 #913-07-1992 L2004 **IM** *020 †20
PELLOW, Thomas Ray. 212 E CENTRAL AVE, STE 245 99208 #005-12-1977 L1984 **VS GS** *020 †85
PENASKOVIC, Stephen G. 101 W 8TH AVE, EMERG DEPT 99204 #016-42-1985 L1994 **EM** *020 †16
PERRY, James D. 601 W 5TH AVE STE 400 99204 #007-02-1979 L1986 **ORS** *020 †40
PERRY, Melvin Gerald, Jr. 800 W 5TH AVE 99204 #021-05-1995 L2002 **CCP** *020 †55
PETERDY, Geraldine Anne. PO BOX 3405 99220 #539-02-1994 L2003 **DMP ATP** *062 †50
PETERS, J Wm. 3016 E 57TH AVE, STE 27 99223 #054-04-1973 L1974 **FM** *020 †18
PETERSEN, Eric John. ■ 99210 #048-12-2006 L2006 **FP** *012
PETERSON, Arnold G. 820 S MCCLELLAN ST, STE 300 99204 #054-04-1970 L1974 **ORS** *020 †40
PETERSON, John Gerald. 101 W 8TH AVE 99204 #005-11-1992 L1992 **IC** *020 †20
PETERSON, Lucy Elizabeth. 105 W 8TH AVE, STE 500 99204 #036-07-1980 L1993 **PS IM** *020 †65
PETERSON, Neal Joshua. 510 S COWLEY ST, ROCKWOOD CLINIC EYE CENTER 99202 #048-14-2003 L2007 **OPH** *020
PETRUZZELLO, Edward J, Jr. 605 E HOLLAND AVE STE 100, CANCER CARE NW 99218 #035-09-1971 L1981 **RO GP** *071 †80
PFEFFER, Robert David. 910 W 5TH AVE, STE 700 99204 #054-04-1986 L1986 **RO ON** *020 †80
PHAM, Truc Thanh. ■ 99223 #005-18-2002 L2007 **HMP** *100 †50
PHANEUF, Joseph Danl. 5633 N LIDGERWOOD ST 99208 #016-42-1987 L1998 **IM IMG** *020 †20
PHELPS, Justin A. ■ 99217 #035-06-1947 L1982 **GS** *020 †85
PHILLIPS, Daniel Gordon. 801 W 5TH AVE STE 515 99204 #012-01-1968 L1973 **OBG** *020 †30
PHILLIPS, Roswell W. ■ 99218 #035-01-1944 L1960 **IM** *071 †20
PIPER, Clinton Albert. ■ 99219 #024-01-1947 L1959 **EM CD** *071 †85,90
PIPER, Paul Edward. 220 E ROWAN AVE, DOCTORS CLINIC 99207 #019-02-1970 L1973 **GP** *020
PIRWITZ, Mark J. 910 W 5TH AVE, STE 300 99204 #048-12-1989 L2005 **CD** *020 †20
PISTON, Robert. 6002 N LIDGERWOOD ST 99208 #047-05-1975 L1990 **PD** *020 †55
PLASTINO, John Patrick. 316 W BOONE AVE STE 669 99201 #049-01-1964 L1965 **FM ISM** *020
POCHIS, William Terry. 4815 N ASSEMBLY ST, SPOKANE VA MEDICAL CENTER 99205 #016-11-1984 L1994 **ICE CD** *020 †20
POKORNY, Alan T. 217 W CATALDO AVE 99201 #054-04-1989 L2004 **OTO** *020 †45
POKORNY, Richard L. ■ 99203 #019-02-1950 L1956 **AN** *071 †05
PONCHER, Randy A. 3919 N MAPLE ST, 6614 S TOMAKER LN SPOKANE 99205 #016-11-1969 L2004 **PD** *040 †55
POPE, Bradley Wm. 5615 W SUNSET HWY 99224 #054-04-1980 L1983 **FM** *030 †18
POPP, Dale Devere. ■ 99208 #018-03-1947 L1954 **ORS** *071 †40
PORTER, Rex Clayton. 104 W 5TH AVE, STE 230E 99204 #005-14-1983 L1987 **AN** *020 †05
POTYK, Darryl Keith. 101 W 8TH AVE 99204 #005-06-1986 L1994 **IM** *020 †20
POWELL, Timothy Wayne. 400 E 5TH AVE, ROCKWOOD CLINIC 99202 #036-05-1994 L2000 **N** *020 †75
PRATT, William Abbett. 105 W 8TH AVE, STE 450 99204 #030-05-1956 L1957 **AN** *071 †05
PRENTISS, Alan Robt. ■ 99208 #056-06-1984 L1985 **IM** *020 †20
PRIANO, Lawrence Leland. ■ 99205 #048-02-1974 L1974 **CD AN** *020 †05
PURDY, Alan Dale. 124 E ROWAN AVE, STE 102 99207 #040-02-1976 L1979 **FM** *020 †18
PURSLEY, Ryan Michael. ■ 99203 #019-02-2004 L2007 **EM** *020
PURUCKHERR, Michael. 220 E ROWAN AVE STE 230 99207 #409-15-1995 L2004 **PCC SME** *020 †20
QUEEN, Cari Jean. 400 E 5TH AVE 99202 #054-04-1994 L1995 **IM** *020 †20
QUERUBIN-ATONSON, Melanie. 1315 N DIVISION ST, NORTHWEST MEDICAL REHAB., 99202 #913-09-1991 L2002 **PM** *020 †60
QUINN, John R. 9103 N DIVISION ST 99218 #030-06-1953 L1955 **GP GS** *020
QUISANO, Melissa Ann. ■ 99203 #005-12-2006 L2006 **FP** *012
RAABE, Rodney Dean. 212 E CENTRAL AVE, STE 245 99208 #040-02-1979 L1984 **DR VIR** *020 †80
RADEMACHER, John Jos. 5715 N LIDGERWOOD ST, INLAND IMAGING 99208 #025-07-1966 L1999 **DR** *020 †80
RAINES, Alyssa Dalton. 101 W 8TH AVE 99204 #016-45-2004 L2007 **EM** *020
RANDOLPH, Daniel Lee. 9631 N NEVADA ST STE 304 99218 #004-01-1991 L1994 **FM** *020 †18
RANLETT, Robert Darrel. 210 W CATALDO AVE, INLAND NORTHWEST BLOOD CTR 99201 #035-46-1976 L2005 **BBK CLP** *020 †20,50
RANSON, Nicholas Todd. 208 W 5TH AVE 99204 #028-03-1999 L2003 **OPH** *020 †35

RASMUSSEN, Reed Charles. 4815 N ASSEMBLY ST 99205 #016-02-1970 L1991 **FM OS** *020 †18
RATCLIFF, Brad J. 101 W 8TH AVE, INLAND IMAGING ASSOCIATES 99204 #008-01-1990 L1998 **DR** *020 †80
RATCLIFF, Robin Deborah. 5715 N LIDGERWOOD ST, INLAND IMAGING 99208 #008-01-1990 L1998 **DR** *020 †80
RAVASIA, Debra. 9425 N NEVADA ST, STE 300 99218 #068-01-1994 L2005 **OBG** *020 †30 ‡
RAVASIA, Sajid. 101 W 8TH AVE, DEPT OF PSYCHIATRY 99204 #068-01-1993 L2005 *020 †75
RAWLINS, Mathew Claude. 105 W 8TH AVE, STE 7070 99204 #054-04-1997 L2000 **GS** *020 †85
REAM, Marilyn Doris. 324 W GIBBS RD 99224 #005-02-1980 L1981 **FM** *020 †18
REDFIELD, William Jay. ■ 99224 #054-04-1962 L1970 **D** *020 †15
REDMAN, D Scott. 820 S MCCLELLAN ST, STE 300 99204 #007-02-1978 L1983 **ORS** *020 †40
REED, Terry Alan. 525 S COWLEY ST 99202 #048-04-1969 L1976 **DR PDR** *071 †80
REED, Thomas Harold. 400 E 5TH AVE, ROCKWOOD CLINICS PS 99202 #054-04-1963 L1967 **D** *071 †15
REED, William Franklin. 4112 S GREYSTONE LN 99223 #054-04-1999 L2001 **IM** *020 †20
REGGIN, James Douglas. 101 W 8TH AVE STE 4200 99204 #068-01-1977 L2004 **N** *020 †75
REHMANN, Greg Jude. 42 E ROWAN AVE STE A, NORTHSIDE FAMILY PRACTICE 99207 #050-02-1996 L1999 **FM** *020 †18
REILLY, M Kathleen. 212 E CENTRAL AVE, STE 245 99208 #016-43-1975 L1994 **VS EM** *020 †85
REISIG, A Henry, Jr. 122 W 7TH AVE STE 310 99204 #025-01-1967 L1972 **CD** *071 †20
REISMAN, Edward Jay. 6002 N LIDGERWOOD ST 99208 #005-14-1983 L1987 **FM** *020 †18
REMEDIOS, Peter Anthony. 5715 N LIDGERWOOD ST, INLAND IMAGING 99208 #005-18-1982 L1998 **DR** *020 †80
REMPEL, Terrence Dell. 323 E 2ND AVE, OCCUPATIONAL MEDICINE 99202 #005-12-1985 L1986 **OM IM** *020 †20,70
REODICA, Aurora Ng. ■ 99223 #748-01-1959 *100
REODICA, Romeo E. ■ 99223 #748-01-1957 L1972 **P** *030
REUTER, Jason M. 105 W 8TH AVE STE 6060, SPOKANE OBSTETRICS AND GYN 99204 #030-06-2001 L2005 **OBG** *020 †30
REYNOLDS, Ann R. ■ 99208 #049-01-1977 L1983 **IM** *071 †20
REYNOLDS, Brandon Robert. 910 W 5TH AVE, STE 380 99204 #010-02-1991 L1991 **TS** *020 †85,90
REYNOLDS, Brian Thomas. 800 W 5TH AVE 99204 #054-04-2000 L2003 **EM** *100 †16
REYNOLDS, Frank Asa. 1402 S GRAND BLVD 99203 #056-05-1960 L1968 **PD HEM** *020 †55
REYNOLDS, Jay Bryan. 601 W 5TH AVE STE 500 99204 #049-01-1977 L1980 **AN** *020 †05
RHEE, Benjamin Jeehyun. 910 W 5TH AVE, STE 300 99204 #016-11-1997 L2004 **ICE** *020 †20
RICE, George Himes. 104 W 5TH AVE 99204 #040-02-1964 L1968 **OBG OS** *071 †30
RICE, Kristi Anne. 235 E ROWAN AVE, STE 117 99207 #056-06-1996 L1999 **PD** *020 †55
RICHARDS, Shawn Charles. ■ 99223 #028-34-2007 **TY** *012
RICHARDSON, George F. ■ 99203 #045-01-1982 L1988 **FM EM** *074 †18
RICHARDSON, Thomas E. 400 E 5TH AVE 99202 #007-02-1978 L1980 **R OS** *020 †80
RIDER, Russell David. 104 W 5TH AVE, STE 230E 99204 #005-12-1989 L1990 **AN** *020 †05
RIETZE, Julie Theresa. 910 W 5TH AVE, STE 600 99204 #048-14-1999 L2003 **FM** *020 †18
RIETZE, Stacey Alan. 104 W 5TH AVE, STE 230E 99204 #048-14-1999 L2003 **AN** *020 †05 ‡
RIFFEL, Gordon Wm. ■ 99223 #005-12-1955 L1956 **GP GS** *071
RIGGS, Randall Stuart. 1314 S GRAND BLVD, STE 2 99202 #025-07-1973 L1974 **PYA P** *020 †50,75
RING, Michael Elroy. 122 W 7TH AVE, STE 310 99204 #047-05-1982 L1990 **IC CD** *020 †20
RIVERS, Richard James. 4815 N ASSEMBLY ST 99205 #035-06-1972 L1974 **IM** *020 †20
ROBERTS, Chuck N. 5633 N LIDGERWOOD ST 99208 #038-41-1989 L1998 **EM GS** *020 †16
ROBINS, Edwin Dwight. 508 W 6TH AVE STE 500 99204 #005-12-1986 L1998 **OBG** *020 †30
ROBINSON, Kirsten Beth. 322 W NORTH RIVER DR, GROUP HEALTH PERMANENTE 99201 #054-04-1999 L2001 **FM** *020 †18
ROBINSON, Robert Stanley. 6202 S SMITH LN 99223 #021-05-1970 L1976 **OPH** *020 †35
ROBNETT, Ausey H. ■ 99210 #016-06-1942 L1954 **PHP GS** *071 †85
ROBY, Alyson Gale. 3919 N MAPLE ST, OF SPOKANE 99205 #005-02-1985 L2000 **FM** *020 †18
ROCHOLL, Christian W. 4821 W HAYDEN LN 99208 #035-06-1997 L2005 **PEM** *020 †55
ROCKWELL, Edward Geo, Jr. 920 W RIVERSIDE AVE, SPOKANE MEPS RM 240 99201 #025-01-1960 L1968 **GS** *030 †85
RODGERS, Thomas Albert. 107 S DIVISION ST 99202 #007-02-1967 L1968 **P** *020 †75
RODKEY, George Wm. 101 W 8TH AVE 99204 #025-07-1948 L1949 **PUD IM** *071
ROGERS, John L. ■ 99223 #030-06-1953 L1987 **FM** *071
ROJAS, Sylvia Beatriz. 42 E ROWAN AVE, STE B 99207 #054-04-2000 L2002 **N** *100 †20
ROLLER, Carrie Ann. 217 W CATALDO AVE 99201 #010-02-1997 L2007 **OTO** *020 †45
ROMANO, John Parker. 525 S COWLEY ST, INLAND IMAGING ASSOCIATES 99202 #054-04-1990 L1996 **DR** *020 †80
ROOP, Jonathan Crane. ■ 99202 #008-02-2002 L2007 **IM** *100 †20
ROSALES, Joseph Grant. 318 E ROWAN AVE, STE 220 99207 #005-14-1999 L2006 **HO** *020 †20
ROSE, Robert Jess. 9405 N NEWPORT HWY 99218 #055-01-1974 L1979 **GS** *020 †85
ROTH, William Terrence. 101 W 8TH AVE 99204 #005-12-1993 L1997 **FM** *020 †18
ROUNDY, Russell Carlyle. 101 W 8TH AVE 99204 #040-02-1975 L1976 **EM** *020 †18,16
ROWBOTHAM, Kirk L. 820 S MCCLELLAN ST, STE 200 99204 #054-04-1989 L1989 **IM** *020 †20
ROWLES, John Richard. 910 W 5TH AVE, STE 380 99204 #010-02-1988 L2000 **TS** *020 †85,90
ROZARIO, Nirmala J. 4815 N ASSEMBLY ST, SPOKANE VAMED CTR 99205 #308-11-1985 L1987 **FM FPG** *020 †18 ‡
RUBENS, Norman Lester. 5109 W NORTHWEST BLVD, C/O DAVID RUBENS 99205 #040-02-1952 L1956 **GP GS** *071
RUBIN, Diane L. 920 W RIVERSIDE AVE, STE 240 99201 #010-03-1981 L1991 **END** *020 †20
RUBIO RODRIGUEZ, G. 4815 N ASSEMBLY ST 99205 #649-01-1968 L1975 **END IM** *020 †20
RULON, John Thos. 217 W CATALDO AVE, SPOKANE EAR NOSE THROAT 99201 #067-01-1955 L1964 **OTO** *071 †45
RUSH, Joseph Michael. 801 W 5TH AVE, DEACONESS MED BLDG#507 99204 #030-05-1964 L1969 **U** *071 †95
RUSSELL, David Arlo. 5715 N LIDGERWOOD ST, INLAND IMAGING 99208 #036-05-1967 L1993 **DR AM** *020 †80
RUTHERFORD, Robert E. 235 E ROWAN AVE STE 117 99207 #054-04-1968 L1970 **ORS** *071 †40
RYAN, Jacquelyn Ann. 4815 N ASSEMBLY ST, VETERANS AFFAIRS MEDICAL C 99205 #017-20-1986 L2001 **ICE CD** *020 †20
RYAN, Michael Bliss. 101 W CASCADE WAY 99208 #047-05-1974 L1987 **FM** *020 †18
RYAN, Michael Edward. 5901 N LIDGERWOOD ST 99208 #048-02-1970 L1982 **D** *020 †15
SACHDEV, Yogendra K. 4815 N ASSEMBLY ST 99205 #495-54-1972 **P** *100
SAGERSON, Robert Patrick. ■ 99223 #041-01-1940 L1947 **DR** *071 †80
SAHM, Roger Alan. 800 W 5TH AVE BX 248 99204 #047-05-1988 L1988 *020
SAMS, David Christopher. 400 E 5TH AVE 99202 #054-04-1992 L1992 **FM** *020 †18
SANCHEZ, Bardomiano. 5633 N LIDGERWOOD ST, HOLY FAMILY HOSP 99208 #043-01-1985 L1997 **IM** *020 †20
SANDERS, Trent Allen. 5715 N LIDGERWOOD ST, INLAND IMAGING 99208 #039-01-1998 L2001 **DR** *020 †80
SANDLER, David. 105 W 8TH AVE STE 532 99204 #913-01-1976 L1992 **TTS** *020
SANTOS, Igmidio Ambrocio. ■ 99223 #748-01-1965 L1986 **P** *030
SARUBBI, Marc Peter. 3327 S TEKOA ST 99203 #035-15-1996 L1998 **P** *020 †75
SASICH, Randy Louis. 801 W 5TH AVE, STE 504 99204 #010-02-1998 L2005 **PCC** *100 †20
SATTERFIELD, Thomas A. 104 W 5TH AVE STE 230E, PHYSICIANS ANESTHESIA GROU 99204 #048-12-2001 L2005 **PAN** *020 †05
SATTERFIELD, Traci. 601 W 5TH AVE STE 301, OB/GYN ASSOCIATES OF SPOKA 99204 #030-06-1997 L2005 **OBG** *020 †30
SAUE, Gregory Lee. 2709 W BOONE AVE 99201 #041-13-1973 L1978 **RHU IM** *020 †20
SAXEY, Roderick. 525 S COWLEY ST 99202 #010-01-1980 L1993 **DR** *020 †80
SAYRES, William Gosnell. 322 W NORTH RIVER DR 99201 #035-45-1983 L1990 **FM** *020 †18
SCHAAF, Thomas Paul. 5615 W SUNSET HWY 99224 #005-14-1983 L1992 **FM** *020 †18
SCHADE, Scott Herbert. 105 W 8TH AVE STE 7040, ROCKWOOD CLINIC, P.S. 99204 #016-11-1976 L1989 **OBG** *020 †30
SCHAFFER, Daniel Jos. 322 W NORTH RIVER DR 99201 #035-06-1970 L1979 **GP OBG** *020
SCHAFFNER, Vann E. 800 W 5TH AVE, DEACONESS MED CTR 99204 #048-12-1984 L2006 **PTH** *020 †50
SCHARFFENBERG, John A. ■ 99204 #005-12-1948 L1948 **NTR** *071
SCHAUNAMAN, Gwen Michele. ■ 99203 #046-01-2007 **TY** *012
SCHEMMEL, Mark Thos. 105 W 8TH AVE, STE 6060 99204 #016-43-1992 L1996 **OBG** *020 †30
SCHEMMEL, Thomas George. ■ 99223 #018-03-1962 L1966 **P** *071 †75
SCHERER, Arthur Thos. 4815 N ASSEMBLY ST 99205 #038-40-1965 L1991 **RHU IM** *020 †20
SCHIMPF, Mariah Rene. 120 W MISSION AVE 99201 #054-04-1995 L1997 **FM** *020 †18
SCHLECHTER, William G. 3811 W RUTTER PKWY 99208 #041-02-1975 L1984 **PUD IM** *020 †20
SCHLEPP, Gregory Ellis. 105 W 8TH AVE STE 6 99204 #028-34-1983 L1986 **GE** *020 †20
SCHMITZ, Roger Wm. 19 E QUEEN AVE 99207 #016-43-1956 L1957 **GYN** *071 †30
SCHMUTZ, Donald Andrew. 101 W 8TH AVE, LL3 99204 #035-20-1963 L1972 **RO R** *071 †80
SCHNEIDER, George Willard. 5633 N LIDGERWOOD ST 99208 #040-02-1955 L1963 **PTH BBK** *071 †50
SCHREOTER, Rosemary Elsie. 322 W NORTH RIVER DR 99201 #056-05-1983 L1994 **FM** *020 †18
SCHROCK, Lawrence George. 910 W 5TH AVE, STE 550 99204 #056-06-1967 L1974 **GS** *020 †85
SCHULTE, William Eugene. 5715 N LIDGERWOOD ST, INLAND IMAGING 99208 #018-03-1985 L1993 **DR** *020 †80
SCHWARTZ, Robert Kenneth. 711 S COWLEY ST, ST LUKES REHABILITATION IN 99202 #041-14-1986 L2004 **PM** *020 †60
SCHWINTEK, Jason Richard. 4815 N ASSEMBLY ST 99205 #005-12-1999 L2001 **IM** *020 †20
SCOTT, Amaryllis J. 785 E HOLLAND AVE 99218 #035-09-1990 L1997 **ORS** *020 †40
SCOTT, David Forrest. 785 E HOLLAND AVE, ORTHOPAEDIC SPECIALITY CLI 99218 #024-07-1990 L1997 **ORS** *020 †40
SCOTTOLINI, Alfred Guido. ■ 99208 #041-02-1954 L1997 **PTH OS** *071 †50
SEARS, Stephen Robt. 123 W CASCADE WAY STE A, ONE PLUS LLC 99208 #051-01-1972 L1982 **ORS** *020 †40
SEELY, Allen Ross. 2709 W BOONE AVE 99201 #005-14-1990 L1993 **FM** *020 †18
SEIBOLD, Cameron James. 212 E CENTRAL AVE, STE 245 99208 #054-04-1994 L2000 **VIR** *020 †80
SELINGER, Samuel Lee. 910 W 5TH AVE, STE 380 99204 #023-07-1969 L1978 **TS** *071 †85,90
SEMOGAS, Vytas Peter. 801 W 5TH AVE STE 205 99204 #067-01-1975 L1997 **DR** *020 †80
SEPPA, Mark Timothy. 322 W NORTH RIVER DR 99201 #054-04-1972 L1976 **PD** *020 †55
SEPPI, Brian J. 820 S MCCLELLAN ST STE 500 99204 #049-01-1990 L1993 **IM** *020 †20
SESHAM, Sirisha. 801 W 5TH AVE, STE 301 99204 #495-21-2000 L2006 **IM** *020 †20
SESTERO, Bridget Conahan. 525 S COWLEY ST, INLAND IMAGING ASSOCIATES, 99202 #030-06-1999 L2000 **DR** *012
SEXTON, Carol Norris. 1403 S GRAND BLVD 99203 #021-06-1980 L1981 **P** *012
SEXTON, Robert Lyman. 322 W NORTH RIVER DR 99201 #010-01-1974 L1980 **P** *020 †75
SHAHAN, Jared Ty. 104 W 5TH AVE STE 200W, HOSPITAL SERVICE 99204 #048-15-2005 L2005 **FP** *012
SHANBOUR, Jody M. 400 E 5TH AVE 99202 #030-06-2001 L2004 **IM** *020
SHANEWISE, Robert P. 910 W 5TH AVE, ASSOCIATED ORTHO SPEC P S 99204 #035-45-1950 L1955 **ORS** *071 †40
SHANKS, William Michael. 601 W 5TH AVE 99204 #056-06-1963 L1964 **ORS** *062 †40
SHAPIRO, Ronald. 35 W 8TH AVE, STE 440 99204 #836-02-1972 L1984 **NPM** *020 †55
SHATZ, Arnold Irwin. 5633 N LIDGERWOOD ST 99208 #041-13-1969 L2002 **U** *020 †95
SHAW, James Steven. 5633 N LIDGERWOOD ST 99208 #032-01-1973 L1977 **FM** *020 †18
SHAW, Wilson W, Jr. ■ 99202 #035-06-1951 L1981 **VS TS** *071 †85,90
SHEA, Caroline Jill. 105 W 8TH AVE STE 512, OPHTHALMOLOGY 99204 #016-06-1992 L2003 **OPH** *020 †35
SHEN, Yu Lisa. ■ 99223 #054-04-2008 *012
SHEPARD, Fredric Alan. ■ 99223 #051-07-1978 L1983 **FM** *020 †18
SHEPHERD, Paula Jean. 5715 N LIDGERWOOD ST, INLAND IMAGING 99208 #035-45-1997 L2002 **DR** *020 †80
SHIELDS, John Paul. 801 W 5TH AVE 99204 #054-04-1954 L1961 **CD** *071 †20
SHIPOWICK, David Glen. 3010 S SOUTHEAST BLVD 99223 #005-12-1990 L1993 **FM** *020 †18
SHUSTER, John Kline. 601 W 5TH AVE STE 400, NORTHWEST ORTHOPAEDIC & FR 99204 #016-02-1991 L1998 **ORS** *020 †40
SICILIA, Michael Peter. 5633 N LIDGERWOOD ST 99208 #005-12-1991 L1998 **EM** *020 †16
SIGG, Daniel Michel. ■ 99223 #005-14-1999 L2006 **NM** *100 †28
SIGMAN, Robert Karl. 800 W 5TH AVE FL 2 99204 #041-12-1972 L2006 **MFM** *020 †30
SIKORA, Michael James. 6002 N LIDGERWOOD ST 99208 #060-01-1993 L1998 **FM** *020 †18
SILHA, Paula Maria. ■ 99203 #054-04-1997 L1999 **FM** *020 †18
SILVERSTEIN, Pamela. 910 W 5TH AVE STE 510 99204 #048-04-1974 L1981 **OBG IM** *020 †30
SILVERSTEIN, Steven V. 801 W 5TH AVE STE 404 99204 #048-04-1974 L1981 **U** *020 †95
SIM, Daniel Clamor. 9222 N NEWPORT HWY 99218 #748-08-1976 L2006 **FM** *020 †18 ‡
SIM, Joel Clamor. ■ 99201 #748-08-1964 L1977 **DR R** *020 †80
SIMANGAN, Preciosa Puache. ■ 99223 #748-08-1978 L1983 **P** *030
SINCLAIR, William James. 407 W RIVERSIDE AVE 99201 #062-01-1943 L1950 **GS** *020 †85
SIWEK, Leland Graham. 910 W 5TH AVE, STE 380 99204 #024-01-1978 L1988 **TS CD** *020 †85,90
SKOOG, Erik D. 427 S BERNARD ST, SPOKANE EYE CLINIC 99204 #035-06-1995 L2002 **OPH** *020 †35

■ = Address Information Privacy Protected

SKREI, Richard Paul. 6002 N LIDGERWOOD ST, LIDGERWOOD HLTH CARE CTR 99208 #038-43-1987 L1994 **FM** *020 †18
SLICHTER, Gene Terry. 9631 N NEVADA ST, STE 101 99218 #030-05-1954 L1956 **CD GS** *071
SLOBODOW, Jerzy. 5432 S QUAIL RIDGE CT 99223 #759-09-1951 L1970 **P GYN** *071
SMALL, Dennis Joseph. 800 W 5TH AVE 99204 #031-01-1996 L1999 **PTH** *020 †50
SMART, Ellen Francis. 104 W 5TH AVE STE 200W, 5TH & BROWNE MEDICAL CENTE 99204 #040-02-2002 L2002 **FM** *020 †18
SMETANA, Lori Sayers. 601 W 5TH AVE STE 301 99204 #039-01-1992 L1996 **OBG** *020 †30
SMIT, Barbara Ann. 208 W 5TH AVE 99204 #054-04-1995 L1999 **OPH** *020 †35
SMITH, Barry Malcolm. ■ 99223 #055-01-1963 L1971 **GP** *071
SMITH, Esther Yu. 101 W 8TH AVE, DEPT OF INT MED 99204 #003-01-2006 L2006 **FP** *012
SMITH, Gilbert Archer. 801 W 5TH AVE, STE 518 99204 #054-04-1964 L1969 **OBG** *071 †30
SMITH, Justin Pieter. 5715 N LIDGERWOOD ST, INLAND IMAGING 99208 #054-04-1982 L1984 **DR NM** *020 †28,80
SMITH, Nanette. 322 W NORTH RIVER DR 99201 #054-04-1978 L1979 **FM** *020 †18
SMITH, Paul Quentin. ■ 99223 #047-06-1981 L1992 **OPH IM** *020 †20,35
SMITH, Ronald Peter. ■ 99223 #040-02-1959 L1967 **PTH** *071 †50
SNOW, Jeffery Michael. 208 W 5TH AVE 99204 #030-05-1973 L1974 **OPH PO** *020 †35 ‡
SNOW, Tasca D. ■ 99208 #048-16-1992 L1998 **P** *020 †75
SOHN, Eric Allan. 5011 W LOWELL AVE STE 100 99208 #031-01-1996 L1999 **FM** *020 †18 ‡
SOHN, Steven Youngjin. 5715 N LIDGERWOOD ST, INLAND IMAGING 99208 #054-04-1998 L2004 **R RNR** *020 †80
SONNELAND, John E. 169 S STEVENS ST 99201 #016-06-1949 L1956 **GS GE** *062 †85
SORENSEN, Eric Christian. 421 W RIVERSIDE AVE, 280 PAULSEN BLDG 99201 #016-11-1968 L1974 **OPH** *020 †35
SOUSLEY, Melissa. 6002 N LIDGERWOOD ST 99208 #007-02-1976 L1977 **FM** *020 †18
STAGAMAN, David Jos. 122 W 7TH AVE, STE 240 99204 #038-41-1983 L1990 **CD IM** *020 †20
STAHLY, Walter Rex. 2005 E 29TH AVE 99203 #054-04-1978 L1979 **FM** *020 †18
STAINBROOK, Ruth Elizabet. ■ 99204 #661-04-2006 L2007 **IM** *012
STAMM, Bryan Kenneth. 104 W 5TH AVE, STE 200W 99204 #008-02-1984 L1990 **FM EM** *020 †18
STANEK, Karen Ann. 1315 N DIVISION ST 99202 #027-01-1988 L1993 **PM** *020 †60
STANG, Howard David. 605 E HOLLAND AVE 99218 #010-01-1973 L1983 **HEM ON** *020 †20
STARKO, Michael J. 101 W 8TH AVE 99204 #060-01-1983 L1988 **OS** *020
STARR, Nancy Trauba. 315 W 9TH AVE 99204 #049-01-1985 L1994 **U GS** *020 †95
STAUDINGER, Suzanne H S. 101 W 8TH AVE 99204 #054-04-1982 L1982 **FM FPG** *020 †18
STEADMAN, Robert K. 801 W 5TH AVE, STE 212 99204 #166-03-2002 **OMF** *020 ‡
STEPAN, Crenguta. 101 W 8TH AVE 99204 #781-01-2002 **IM** *012
STEPHENS, Michael James. 910 W 5TH AVE, STE 600 99204 #054-04-1994 L1996 **FM** *020 †18
STERNE, Gregory Michael. 5715 N LIDGERWOOD ST, INLAND IMAGING 99208 #054-04-1999 L2004 **DR** *020 †80
STEVENSON, Jon Todd. 105 W 8TH AVE, STE 6080 99204 #054-04-1977 L1982 **RHU** *020 †20
STIER, Alton R. PO BOX 2687 99220 #040-02-1952 L1955 **PTH NM** *071 †50,28
STIER, Robert Arleth. 823 W 7TH AVE 99204 #040-02-1945 L1946 **AI IM** *062 †20,03
STIFTER, William Francis. 122 W 7TH AVE, STE 310 99204 #010-02-1974 L1979 **CD** *020 †20
STONESTREET, Cong Ying. 12128 N DIVISION ST 99218 #243-16-1988 L2006 **PUD** *020
STOOP, Daniel Howard. 5901 N LIDGERWOOD ST, STE 18B 99208 #054-04-1992 L1994 **FM** *020 †18
STRANDNESS, Erik Lee. 35 W 8TH AVE STE 440 99204 #030-06-1986 L1996 **PD** *020 †55
STRONGIN, I Scott. 322 W NORTH RIVER DR, RIVERFRONT MEDICAL CENTER 99201 #016-06-1990 L1997 **FM** *020 †18
STROUP, Edwin Leroy. 5633 N LIDGERWOOD ST 99208 #041-09-1979 L1980 **EM IM** *020 †20,16
STUCKY, Craig Bennett. 400 E 5TH AVE 99202 #030-05-1973 L1979 **PD** *074 †55
STUCKY, Eric D. 212 E CENTRAL AVE STE 240, HEART CLINICS NORTHWEST 99208 #019-02-1975 L1979 **CD** *020 †20
SULLIVAN, David E. ■ 99203 #040-02-1940 L1947 **PS** *071 †65
SUMMERS, Laurie. 5925 W EXCELL AVE 99208 #019-02-1986 L1992 **FM OBG** *020 †18
SUNDBERG, Carol L. ■ 99203 #016-06-1943 L1949 **IM CD** *071
SUTHERLAND, Kenneth Ian. ■ 99204 #040-02-1960 L1967 **CD** *071 †20
SWANBECK, C Robt. ■ 99224 #035-15-1954 L1992 **AN GP** *071 †05
SWANSON, Dawn Martha. 104 W 5TH AVE 99204 #661-02-2003 L2004 **FM** *020 †18
SWEENY, Kevin David. 400 E 5TH AVE 99202 #054-04-1982 L1990 **FM** *020 †18
SYMINGTON, Kenneth Earl. 212 E CENTRAL AVE, STE 245 99208 #038-41-1982 L2002 **DR** *020 †80
TALLEY, Melinda Rhea. ■ 99201 #046-01-2004 L2006 **DR** *012
TANAS, Munirzakary Raja. ■ 99218 #054-04-2004 L2004 **SP** *100 †50
TAYLOR, Amber Laurel. ■ 99205 #143-11-2005 **IM** *012
TEEL, Gordon Stanley. 525 S COWLEY ST, INLAND IMAGING ASSOCIATES, 99202 #054-04-1990 L1996 **R** *020 †80
TENNICAN, Patrick O. 105 W 8TH AVE STE 350 99204 #054-04-1965 L1970 **ID IM** *020 †20
TERRELL, Gregory Scott. ■ 99209 #016-11-1986 L2005 **EM GS** *020
TEWEL, Susan Jane. 235 E ROWAN AVE STE 210 99207 #007-02-1979 L1983 **GYN** *020 †30
TFAILI, Amer Said. 800 W 5TH AVE, EMPIRE HEALTH 99204 #605-01-2000 L2006 **IM** *020 †20
THAI, Camtu Minh. 9001 N COUNTRY HOMES BLVD, ROCKWOOD CLINIC NORTH 99218 #054-04-1998 L2000 **FM** *020 †18
THEW, Stephen Thomas. 122 W 7TH AVE STE 310 99204 #030-05-1995 L2005 **IC CD** *020 †20
THIEL, Shirley Owens. 4815 N ASSEMBLY ST 99205 #005-12-1953 L1953 **GP** *071
THOMAS, Steven Oren. 6208 N COLTON ST 99208 #040-02-1976 L1977 **UCM GP** *020
THOMPSON, Marshall W. 101 W 8TH AVE, SACRED HEART MEDICAL CENTE 99204 #048-12-1962 L1963 **EM** *020 †18
THOMPSON, Matthew A. 1402 S GRAND BLVD 99203 #054-04-2000 L2004 **PN** *020 †55 ‡
THOMPSON, Susan Jean. 104 W 5TH AVE STE 230E 99204 #054-04-1991 L1995 **AN** *020 †05
THORBURN, Kim Marie. 123 E INDIANA AVE STE 100P, BOX 7340 99207 #005-02-1976 L1997 **IM** *030 †20
THORNE, David Adams. 212 E CENTRAL AVE, STE 245 99208 #049-01-1984 L1989 **DR NM** *062 †80
THORNE, Paul C. 101 W 8TH AVE, # 100-L1 99204 #064-01-1992 L2002 **GS PDS** *020 †85
THYKESON, Karen Ann. 101 W 8TH AVE 99204 #054-04-1988 L1990 **IM** *020 †20
TING, Helen Yu. ■ 99203 #748-01-1971 L1994 **GP PD** *020
TOBIN, Thomas Roger. 800 W 5TH AVE 99204 #035-03-2001 L2004 **EM** *020 †16
TOCHTERMAN, Jody Marie. 101 W 8TH AVE, STE 1100 99204 #048-12-2001 L2007 **OBG** *020 †30
TOHMEH, Antoine Ghassan. 785 E HOLLAND AVE 99218 #605-01-1983 L1998 **ORS GS** *020 †40
TOMEO, Elizabeth Ann. 5901 N LIDGERWOOD ST, STE 217 99208 #010-01-1978 L1981 **PD** *020 †55
TOMPKINS, Bryan Justin. 911 W 5TH AVE 99204 #007-02-2001 L2007 **OP** *100
TORIBARA, Ted Yoshio. 910 W 5TH AVE STE 680, EDUCATION BUILDING 99204 #054-04-1970 L1971 **GP** *020 †18
TRAIL, Jeffery Allen. 42 E ROWAN AVE STE A 99207 #047-05-1985 L1989 **FM** *020 †18
TRAN, John Ton Tu. 107 S DIVISION ST, SPOKANE MENTAL HEALTH 99202 #028-34-1995 L1999 **PYG** *020 †75
TRELOAR, Richard Paul. 601 W 5TH AVE STE 400 99204 #005-15-1970 L1975 **ORS** *020 †40
TROBAUGH-LOTRARIO, Angela. PO BOX 2555 99220 #016-06-1998 L2005 **PHO** *020 †55
TROIANO, Jennifer Ann. 1001 W 2ND AVE 99201 #024-07-1997 L2001 **MPD** *020 †20,55
TRYTKO, Rodney Lee. 104 W 5TH AVE, STE 250E 99204 #011-03-1983 L1988 **AN** *020 †05
TUBBS, William Curl. 525 S COWLEY ST, STE 322 99202 #040-02-1958 L1964 **R** *071 †80
TULLIS, Christopher Alan. 5633 N LIDGERWOOD ST 99208 #028-34-1996 L1999 **EM** *020 †16
TURNER, Daniel Gleaton. 525 S COWLEY ST, INLAND IMAGING 99202 #012-01-1999 L2004 **DR** *020 †80
TUTTLE, Katherine Rose. 104 W 5TH AVE, STE 350E 99204 #016-06-1982 L1991 **NEP IM** *050 †20
TWIGG, Dennis Thos. 2525 E 29TH AVE STE 10-B- 99223 #005-18-1984 L1991 **P** *020 †75
UHDER, Kerstin Alice. 101 W 8TH AVE 99204 #409-23-1994 **IM** *012
UHRON, Steven Mark. 101 W 8TH AVE, EMERGENCY DEPT. 99204 #028-34-1979 L1980 **EM** *020 †16
UMBDENSTOCK, Renee Bradle. 101 W 8TH AVE, PO BOX 2555 99204 #054-04-2007 **TY** *012
UNIS, Alan Stephen. 101 W 8TH AVE, SACRED HEART MED CTR 99204 #041-12-1976 L1987 **CHP P** *020 †75
URSIC, Eric. ■ 99223 #011-03-2007 **TY** *012
VAID, Vedbrat Shivnath. 508 W 6TH AVE STE 410 99204 #495-28-1954 L1969 **N** *020
VANDERBOSCH, Leonard John. 1003 E TRENT AVE, STE 150 99202 #017-20-1965 L1968 **GP** *020
VANDERWILDE, Russell S. 601 W 5TH AVE STE 400 99204 #054-04-1987 L1993 **ORS OSM** *020 †40
VAN GEMERT, John Victor. 208 W 5TH AVE 99204 #056-05-1971 L1972 **OPH GP** *071 †35
VAN GERPEN, Royce Ferol. 323 E 2ND AVE, OCCUPATIONAL MEDICINE 99202 #018-03-1971 L1974 **OM GP** *020 †16,70
VAN HEUVELEN, Gary. 101 W 8TH AVE, STE LL3 99204 #037-01-1979 L1983 **RO** *020 †80
VANKIRK, Christian Sommer. ■ 99207 #007-02-2005 L2007 **DR** *012
VANOS, David Neil. 5633 N LIDGERWOOD ST, HOLY FAMILY HOSPITAL 99208 #030-06-1985 L1991 **AN** *020 †05
VAN VEEN, Francis L. ■ 99217 #040-02-1946 L1965 **IMG IM** *071
VARGA, Mark Robt. 715 S COWLEY ST STE 228 99202 #010-01-1987 L1998 **PM** *020 †60
VASSEY, Navid Vahdat. 101 W 8TH AVE 99204 #104-01-2007 **IM** *012
VEENSTRA, Timothy Rolf. ■ 99208 #034-01-1994 L2006 **EM** *020 †16
VENTERS, Wayne Burnette. 400 E 5TH AVE, ROCKWOOD CLINIC PS 99202 #036-01-1964 L2001 **ORS** *020 †40
VERHOOGEN, Alex R. 105 W 8TH AVE, STE 454E 99204 #005-15-1968 L1969 **ORS** *020 †40
VINCENT, Ronald Lee. 105 W 8TH AVE STE 124 99204 #048-12-1963 L1971 **NS** *062 †25 ‡
VIREN, Fred Kenneth. 521 S BERNARD ST 99204 #010-01-1955 L1962 **IM END** *040 †20
VISHWANATH, Mandya. 910 W 5TH AVE, STE 380 99204 #495-21-1977 L1989 **TS CD** *020 †85,90
VOLK, Randall. 5633 N LIDGERWOOD ST 99208 #016-42-1987 L1991 **EM** *020 †16
VOLYN, Glen Paul. 2713 N ARGONNE RD 99212 #005-12-1988 L1991 **FM** *020 †18
VOLZ, Vicki Ann. 101 W 8TH AVE, STE 4200 99204 #028-03-1975 L1982 **PD CHP** *020 †55
VON LINTEL, Philip Herman. 101 W 8TH AVE, SACRED HEART MED CTR ED D 99204 #026-04-1969 L1970 **EM** *020
WAGGONER, L Douglas, Jr. 122 W 7TH AVE, STE 310 99204 #041-02-1997 L1999 **CD** *020 †20
WALCHAK, Frank Robt. 235 E ROWAN AVE STE 206, HOLY FAMILY MEDICAL BLDG 99207 #041-02-1968 L1976 **PS HS** *020 †65
WALKER, Janet Margaret. 322 W NORTH RIVER DR, RIVERFRONT MED CTR 99201 #028-02-1982 L2005 **FM** *020 †18 ‡
WALKER, Richard Ward. 5633 N LIDGERWOOD ST, HOLY FAMILY HOSPITAL 99208 #018-03-1977 L1980 **EM** *020 †20,16
WALKER, Robert Norman. 105 W 8TH AVE STE 6020 99204 #028-03-1965 L1971 **GYN** *071 †30
WALTERSKIRCHEN, Mark Jose. 801 W 5TH AVE STE 404 99204 #054-04-1991 L2007 **U** *020 †95
WARD, Richard J. 405 E SINTO AVE 99202 #028-34-1949 L1950 **AN** *071 †05
WATANABE, Arthur S. 528 E SPOKANE FALLS BLVD, STE 14 99202 #038-41-1985 L1989 **PME R** *020 †80
WATANABE, James Michio. ■ 99208 #054-04-1956 L1957 **PTH** *071 †50
WATKINS, Jack B. 105 W 8TH AVE STE 6080 99204 #040-02-1951 L1956 **ORS** *071 †40
WATLING, David Lee. 104 W 5TH AVE STE 250E 99204 #028-02-1988 L1990 **AN** *020 †05
WATSON, Blake Andrew. ■ 99208 #048-02-2008 *012
WEBB, Kathleen Suzanne. 35 W 8TH AVE STE 440, PEDIATRIX MEDICAL GROUP 99204 #054-04-1986 L1999 **NPM PD** *020 †55
WEBER, Charles Holten. ■ 99203 #010-02-2008 *012
WEIGAND, Robert Geo. 525 S COWLEY ST 99202 #030-06-1961 L1963 **R** *071 †80
WEIGEL, William Leroy. 105 W 8TH AVE, STE 200 99204 #030-05-1976 L1996 **APM** *020 †05
WEITZMAN, Peter Louis. 5633 N LIDGERWOOD ST 99208 #005-14-1989 L1992 **IM** *020 †20
WELTY, Elizabeth Main. 800 W 5TH AVE 99204 #035-20-1941 L1948 **IM** *071 †20
WENDLING, Lyle Reinhold. 101 W 8TH AVE 99204 #056-05-1968 L1975 **DR RNR** *020 †80
WERSCHLER, William Philip. 104 W 5TH AVE, STE 330 99204 #010-01-1985 L1989 **D DS** *020 †15
WEST, Sadie Marie. ■ 99204 #054-04-2008 *012
WHALEN, John Thos. ■ 99205 #028-34-1943 L1969 **GP EM** *020
WHISENANT, Michael Neil. 910 W 5TH AVE, STE 300 99204 #045-01-1980 L2006 **CD** *020 †20
WHITACRE, Matthew Scott. 101 W 8TH AVE 99204 #422-01-2007 L2007 **FP** *012
WHITE, Jeffrey R. 6002 N LIDGERWOOD ST 99208 #039-05-1985 L1987 **FM** *020 †18
WHITE, Travis Edward. 235 E ROWAN AVE 99207 #039-01-1962 L1967 **ORS OS** *020 †40
WHITING, John Craig. 105 W 8TH AVE, STE 7070 99204 #007-02-1978 L1983 **U** *020 †95
WHITMAN, Mark Christopher. 5633 N LIDGERWOOD ST 99208 #035-09-1998 L2001 **EM** *020 †16
WICKERSHAM, Nicholas W. ■ 99203 #054-04-2003 L2005 **DR** *012
WICKRE, Curtis Gordon. 235 E ROWAN AVE, STE 209 99207 #040-02-1977 L1982 **NEP IM** *020 †20
WIGERT, Robert Dean. 801 W 5TH AVE 99204 #030-05-1982 L1983 **IM** *020 †20
WILCOX, Howard Gordon. CHIEF OF STAFF 11, SPOKANE VA MEDICAL CTR 99205 #016-11-1961 L1985 **NEP IM** *030 †20

■ = Address Information Privacy Protected

WILHELM, James Paul. 105 W 8TH AVE STE 100, INLAND IMAGING ASSOCIATES, 99204 #028-02-1973 L1974 **DR** *020 †80

WILKENS, Keith Leslie. 3010 S SOUTHEAST BLVD 99223 #005-12-1982 L1985 **FM** *020 †18

WILLIAMS, James Lynch. 901 W 5TH AVE, ASSOCIATED ORTHO SPEC P S 99204 #036-01-1964 L1970 **ORS** *071 †40

WILLIAMS, Jeffery Allen. 105 W 8TH AVE, STE 6060 99204 #055-01-2000 L2005 **OBG** *020

WILLIAMS, Michael Paul. 122 W 7TH AVE, STE 310 99204 #031-01-1993 L1995 **CD** *020 †20

WILLIAMSON, Mark Edward. PO BOX 2555 99220 #023-07-1964 L1981 **CLP PTH** *071 †50,28

WILSON, David Phillip. 104 W 5TH AVE STE 200, 5TH AND BROWN 99204 #030-06-1977 L2007 **EM FM** *020 †16,20

WILSON, Leo. ■ 99203 #035-19-1929 **GYN** *071 †30

WINTER, Gregory Reinhold. 4815 N ASSEMBLY ST 99205 #034-01-1985 L2002 **P PYG** *030 †75

WIRTHLIN, Robert Samuel. 427 S BERNARD ST, SPOKANE EYE CLINIC 99204 #025-01-2000 L2006 **OPH** *020 †35

WITTENKELLER, Jay Lee. 910 W 5TH AVE, STE 700 99204 #016-45-1990 L1996 **ON** *020 †20

WIWATOWSKI, Laurence John. ■ 99218 #040-02-1964 L1970 **D** *071 †15

WOHLEN, Karen Ann. 801 W 5TH AVE, STE 309 99204 #032-01-1986 L1990 **OBG** *020 †30

WOLF, Steven J. 104 W 5TH AVE STE 230E 99204 #056-06-1976 L1982 **AN** *020 †05

WOLFE, Charles Robt. 323 E 2ND AVE, STE 102 99202 #030-05-1956 L1960 **OM** *020

WONG, Yung-Tsing. ■ 99223 #242-07-1948 L1956 **PD** *072

WOODKE, Donald Duane. 4407 N DIVISION ST STE 919 99207 #026-04-1961 L1966 **P** *071 †75

WOODRUFF, Roger Dean. 3010 S SOUTHEAST BLVD, SPOKANE, PS 99223 #005-12-1981 L1987 **FM** *040 †18

WORRALL, Neil Kevin. 910 W 5TH AVE, STE 380 99204 #028-02-1991 L2000 **TS VS** *020 †85,90

WRAY, William Andrew. 5901 N LIDGERWOOD ST # 118 99208 #047-06-1987 L1993 **D** *020 †15

WRIGHT, Bruce Claud. 10111 N COMANCHE DR 99208 #054-04-1960 L1962 **R** *020 †80

WU, Michael Patwai. ■ 99223 #038-06-2004 L2004 **P** *012

WU, Sherry Man. 400 E 5TH AVE, ROCKWOOD CLINIC, PS 99202 #005-14-1999 L2006 **RHU** *100 †20

WUKELIC, Michael Steven. 400 E 5TH AVE 99202 #038-40-1985 L1986 **IM** *020 †20

WURST, John Mason. 105 W 8TH AVE, STE 1000 99204 #051-01-1988 L1992 **N** *020 †75

WYMORE, Michael James. 101 W 8TH AVE, SACRED HEART MEDICAL CENTE 99204 #018-03-1981 L1987 **EM** *020 †16

WYSHAM, Carol Hatch. 400 E 5TH AVE 99202 #018-03-1980 L1992 **END IM** *020 †20

WYSHAM, Douglas Graham. 400 E 5TH AVE, # C13 99202 #036-01-1980 L1992 **CD** *020 †20

YANG, Daniel Ta-Cheng. 406 E ROWAN AVE, STE 200 99207 #056-06-1995 L2003 **IM** *020 †20

YUEN, Carey. 11616 N ASHLEY LN, HOSPITAL SPECIALISTS PLLC 99218 #028-34-1990 L2006 **IM** *020 †20

YUNUSOV, Murad Yusufkhano. 101 W 8TH AVE 99204 #913-21-1980 L2007 **IM** *012

ZELLMAN, Hershel Meyer. 801 W 5TH AVE, STE 109 99204 #005-15-1975 L1977 **FM** *020 †18

ZIELINSKI, Xavier John. 5715 N LIDGERWOOD ST, INLAND IMAGING ASSOCIATES, 99208 #045-01-1980 L1988 **DR** *020 †80

ZIMMER, Roy W, Jr. 104 W 5TH AVE # 200 99204 #056-05-1953 L1962 **GS** *071 †85

ZOBELL, Royce Lynn. 525 S COWLEY ST 99202 #049-01-1975 L1988 **DR** *062 †80

ZUGEC, Mirko. 525 S BERNARD ST, ZUGEC MEDICAL CLINICS, PS 99204 #957-01-1985 L1999 **IM** *020 †20

ZURCHER, Robert Lewis. 5633 N LIDGERWOOD ST, EMERGENCY CENTER 99208 #040-02-1985 L1988 **EM** *020 †16

ZYLAK, Christopher M. 212 E CENTRAL AVE, STE 245 99208 #065-05-1996 L2002 **VIR** *020 †80

SPOKANE VALLEY – SPOKANE

AHMAD, Rana N. 1414 N HOUK RD, STE 104 99216 #704-21-1988 L1997 **GS SO** *020 †85

ALCARAZ, Veronique T. 14402 E SPRAGUE AVE 99216 #003-01-1990 L1995 **IM PD** *020 †55,20

ALLERDING, Thomas James. 11604 E INDIANA RD 99206 #038-40-1976 L1983 **PTH** *020 †50

AMUNDSON, Bruce Arnold. ■ 99206 #026-04-1965 L1979 **FM** *050 †18

ANDERSON, Amy J. 14408 E SPRAGUE AVE 99216 #040-02-2000 L2003 **FM** *020 †18

ANDERSON, William E. ■ 99216 #041-13-1949 L1951 **GP** *071

BACKER, Amy Martha. 13103 E MANSFIELD AVE 99216 #050-02-1994 L2002 **PTH** *020

BASSLER, Thomas Joseph. 13103 E MANSFIELD AVE 99216 #051-04-1989 L1997 **PTH PCP** *020 †50

BERG, Tracy Ann. 12615 E MISSION AVE, STE 109 99216 #023-01-1989 L1995 **GS VS** *020 †85

BEYERSDORF, Steven Ray. 1414 N HOUK RD, STE 104 99216 #054-04-1982 L1987 **GS CRS** *020 †85

BONACUM, Glenn Gerard. 12525 E MISSION AVE # 107 99216 #019-02-1976 L1982 **ORS** *020 †40

BRIDGE, Sharon Ann. 9621 E SPRAGUE AVE 99206 #054-04-1983 L1984 **FM** *030 †18

BROPHY, Michael Caran. 12409 E MISSION AVE 99216 #028-34-1978 L1988 **GE IM** *020 †20

BROWN, Duncan Robert. 1415 N HOUK RD 99216 #060-01-1964 L1995 *020

CEDERBLOM, Conlyn John. ■ 99214 #051-01-1961 L1961 **GP** *071

CHESTER, Andrew E. 1215 N MCDONALD RD, SPOKANE INTERNAL MEDICINE 99216 #048-02-1994 L2000 **IM** *020 †20

COFF, Philip Matthew. 12401 E SINTO AVE, VALLEY GASTROENTEROLOGY, P 99216 #041-09-1977 L2007 **GE IM** *020 †20 ‡

CRAIG, Paul Martin. 12401 E SINTO AVE 99216 #023-07-1985 L1992 **HEP IM** *020 †20

CRYAN, David Michael. 1807 N HUTCHINSON RD 99212 #005-14-1961 L1978 **D** *071 †15

CVANCARA, Joseph L. 1807 N HUTCHINSON RD 99212 #023-12-1992 L2002 **OS D** *020 †15

DARLING, Stephen Jeffrey. 13103 E MANSFIELD AVE 99216 #040-02-1980 L1992 **PTH** *030 †50

DERBY, Alfred James. ■ 99037 #054-04-1959 L1968 **OBG** *071 †30

DIBBLE, T Daniel. 1117 N EVERGREEN RD, SPINE TEAM SPOKANE 99216 #054-04-1991 L2003 **PME AN** *020 †05

DINSA-CHESTER, Kawaljit K. 12410 E SINTO AVE STE 101, ROCKWOOD CLINIC VALLEY ONC 99216 #060-01-1991 L2000 **IM ON** *020 †20

DOERING, Gregory Jon. 1215 N MCDONALD RD, SPOKANE INTERNAL MEDICINE 99216 #308-03-1981 L1983 **IM** *020

DOMINEY, Andrea Mead. 1807 N HUTCHINSON RD, ADVANCED DERMATOLOGY & SKI 99212 #048-04-1985 L1994 **D** *020 †15

DUNN, Paul Thompson. 1807 N HUTCHINSON RD 99212 #056-06-1991 L1999 **D** *020 †15

ECKERT, Darin Paul. 14408 E SPRAGUE AVE, ROCKWOOD CLINIC - VALLEY 99216 #054-04-1998 L2000 **FM** *020 †18

FAIRCHILD, Thomas Hayes. 1414 N HOUK RD 99216 #017-20-1979 L1979 **OTO OM** *020 †45

FANDEL-PENNINGS, Terese. 11604 E INDIANA RD 99206 #026-04-1988 L1994 **PTH IM** *020 †50

FISCHER, David Walther. 1215 N MCDONALD RD, STE 101 99216 #005-12-2004 L2006 **IM** *012

FRIESEN, Susan Grace. 14402 E SPRAGUE AVE 99216 #019-02-1988 L1991 **FM** *020 †18

GAPEN, Christopher James. 14408 E SPRAGUE AVE, ROCKWOOD CLINIC, PS 99216 #018-03-1997 L2002 **PD** *020 †55 ‡

GIBB, Paul Douglass. 1215 N MCDONALD RD, SPOKANE INTERNAL MEDICINE 99216 #054-04-1970 L1976 **IM** *020 †20

GOLDEN, Robert John. 12615 E MISSION AVE, STE 303 99216 #051-01-1978 L1983 **U** *020 †95

GRAY, William Lewis. 1414 N VERCLER RD STE 5 99216 #062-01-1974 L1977 **FM AM** *020 ‡

GREENE, Wm Hutton, Jr. 14402 E SPRAGUE AVE 99216 #005-14-1970 L1976 **PD** *020 †55

GROSEN, Elizabeth Ann. 12615 E MISSION AVE, STE 200 99216 #054-04-1984 L2000 **GO** *020 †30

GUDGEL, Kenneth Eugene. ■ 99216 #018-03-1948 L1949 **FM** *071 †18

HANDER, Robert W. 12120 E MISSION AVE STE 2 99206 #033-05-1977 L1981 **OPH** *020 †35

HARRISON, Linda Sator. 12615 E MISSION AVE, STE 108 99216 #005-15-1988 L1991 **FM** *020 †18

HART, Cheryle Joyce. 505 N ARGONNE RD BLDG C 99212 #037-01-1980 L1987 **GYN** *020 †30

HARTMAN, Robert Green. 1415 N HOUK RD STE A, VALLEY OBSTETRICS & 99216 #037-01-1980 L1984 **OBG** *020 †30

HATCH, Larry Keith. 11604 E INDIANA RD 99206 #030-06-1963 L1969 **PTH NM** *062 †28

HATHAWAY, Carol Lee. 1415 N HOUK RD STE B 99216 #014-01-1984 L1991 **PS** *020 †85,65

HAYES, Elizabeth Ann. 15425 E MISSION AVE 99037 #005-19-1994 L1997 **FM** *020 †18

HEDLUND, Robert Kent. 12420 E MISSION AVE, INLAND IMAGING ASSOCIATES, 99216 #051-04-1975 L1979 **DR FM** *020 †18,80

HENNEBERY, Michael Owen. 1414 N HOUK RD 99216 #016-06-1971 L1974 **U** *020 †95

HJERMSTAD, Brent Martin. 13103 E MANSFIELD AVE 99216 #003-01-1977 L1996 **PTH** *020 †50

HOAK, David Chas. 13103 E MANSFIELD AVE, INCYTE PATHOLOGY 99216 #016-06-1980 L1983 **PTH** *020 †50

HOGSETT, Smith Fuller. 1414 N HOUK RD STE 103 99216 #054-04-1968 L1969 **OPH** *071 †35

HOLLENBAUGH, Darren C. 1215 N MCDONALD RD, STE 202 99216 #054-04-1989 L1991 **CD IM** *020 †20

HUSTRULID, Robert Iver. 1215 N MCDONALD RD STE 10 99216 #026-04-1968 L1971 **IM** *020 †20

JACOBSON, Charles Marvin. ■ 99206 #005-15-1962 L1994 **GP** *071

JANES, Merle Edward. 1414 N VERCLER RD STE 3 99216 #649-14-1978 L1989 **PM** *020 †60

JECKLE, Milan Andrew. 1005 N PINES RD, STE 230 99206 #056-06-1964 L1965 **FM** *020 †18

JONES, Ottiwell Wood, III. 12525 E MISSION AVE, SPOKANE EYE CLINIC PS 99216 #005-02-1958 L1963 **OPH** *071 †35

JOY, Lori Beth Frank. 1415 N HOUK RD STE A 99216 #054-04-1993 L1995 **OBG** *020 †30

JULIAN, Geoffrey Garrison. 1414 N HOUK RD, STE 208 99216 #016-43-1994 L1999 **OTO** *020 †45

KATZ, Guy Edward. 1215 N MCDONALD RD, STE 202 99216 #021-01-1981 L1990 **CD IM** *020 †20

KEEVE, Jonathan Philip. 12410 E SINTO AVE, STE 201 99216 #032-01-1981 L1986 **ORS OS** *020 †40

KERKERING, Michael C. 1215 N MCDONALD RD, SPOKANE INTERNAL MEDICINE 99216 #054-04-1994 L1996 **IM** *020 †20

LANG, Melanie Sue. 12109 E BROADWAY AVE, STE C 99206 #011-03-1996 L2000 **OS FPS** *020

LARSON, John Ferrin. 112 N UNIVERSITY RD, STE 106 99206 #060-01-1976 L1977 **GS GP** *020

LAUDER, Cecilia Marie. 12509 E MISSION AVE, VALLEY FAM PHYSICIANS 99216 #039-01-2002 L2004 **FM** *020 †18

LEAVITT, Eric Bryan. 1414 N HOUK RD, STE 208 99216 #010-02-1987 L1992 **OTO** *020 †45

LEE, Matthew R. ■ 99212 #037-01-2005 L2007 **DR** *012

LEHMAN, Susan Kaye. 1414 N VERCLER RD, STE 5 99216 #035-75-1997, ▲ L2000 **FM** *020

LINDHOLM, George Richard. 13103 E MANSFIELD AVE 99216 #054-04-1976 L1977 **PTH FOP** *062 †50

LITTLE, David Wayne. 13102 E MISSION AVE 99216 #054-04-1990 L1990 **FM** *020 †18

LITTLE HIDEG, Alisa M. 14402 E SPRAGUE AVE 99216 #005-12-1995 L1997 **FM** *020 †18

LUDKA, Tiffany Marie. ■ 99212 #054-04-2008 *012

MAINER, Michael Jacks. 12606 E MISSION AVE, VALLEY HOSPITAL 99216 #048-02-1973 L1976 **FM EM** *020 †18,16

MARTINCIC, Danko. 12615 E MISSION AVE, STE 200 99216 #957-01-1988 L2006 **HO** *020 †20

MARTINEZ, Felix, Jr. 13103 E MANSFIELD AVE, P O BOX 3405 99216 #007-02-1980 L1987 **PTH CLP** *020 †50

MC CLELLAND, G Bruce. 1414 N HOUK RD, STE 208 99216 #056-06-1967 L1972 **OTO A** *020 †45

MIKI, Seiko Christine. ■ 99016 #048-04-1993 L1998 **DR** *020 †80

MILLER, Carl Don. 13102 E MISSION AVE 99216 #030-05-1958 L1959 **FM** *071

MITCHELL, Robin Lee. 13102 E MISSION AVE 99216 #040-02-1979 L1982 **FM** *020 ‡

MOERSHEL, David Wm. 14402 E SPRAGUE AVE 99216 #018-03-1975 L1979 **PD** *020 †55

MOLINE, Stephanie Rose. 12615 E MISSION AVE, STE 200 99216 #047-05-1994 L2002 **GS** *020 †85

MONROE, Philip Le Roy. 1414 N VERCLER RD STE 2 99216 #018-03-1970 L1974 **FM** *020 †18

MOON, Christopher James. 14408 E SPRAGUE AVE 99216 #028-02-1993 L2005 **PD** *020 †55 ‡

MORNIN, Dan, Jr. 13103 E MANSFIELD AVE 99216 #054-04-1985 L1986 **PTH** *020 †50

MORRISON, Paul D. ■ 99206 #047-07-1989 L1993 **P IM** *020 †20 ‡

MUELLER, Mark Edward. 12606 E MISSION AVE 99216 #005-15-1981 L1992 **EM IM** *020 †20 ‡

NELSON, Dale Alan. 1215 N MCDONALD RD, SPOKANE INTERNAL MEDICINE 99216 #056-05-1976 L1979 **IM EM** *020 †20

NORDEEN, Steven James. 14408 E SPRAGUE AVE, VALLEY ROCKWOOD CLINIC 99216 #018-03-2000 L2006 **FM** *020 †18

NORQUIST, Douglas Geo. 12410 E SINTO AVE, STE 201 99216 #005-06-1975 L1977 **ORS** *020 †40

NUMATA, James Alvin. 12509 E MISSION AVE, VALLEY FAM PHYSICIANS 99216 #054-04-1978 L1979 **FM** *020 †18

OBERMILLER, Leo E, Jr. 12610 E MIRABEAU PKWY, STE 100 99216 #054-04-1979 L1981 **NEP IM** *020 †20

OCCHINO, Amy Rose. ■ 99206 #038-44-1994 L2002 **OBG** *020 †30

ORENSTEIN, Beth June. 14408 E SPRAGUE AVE, VALLEY ROCKWOOD CLINIC 99216 #026-04-1984 L1987 **FM** *020 †18

OSTRANDER, Daniel New. 13102 E MISSION AVE 99216 #054-04-1974 L1978 **FM** *020 †18

PARKER, Richard Francis. 1215 N MCDONALD RD, STE 101 99216 #005-12-1983 L1983 **IM** *020 †20

PARSONS, Abby Kay. ■ 99212 #054-04-2008 *012

PEARCE, Patrick Zim. 14408 E SPRAGUE AVE, VALLEY ROCKWOOD CLINIC 99216 #054-04-1980 L1981 **FSM OS** *020 †18

PERSON, Jefferson Taylor. ■ 99216 #040-02-1947 L1948 **GP** *071

PIERCE, Ellen Stella. ■ 99216 #054-04-1993 L1996 **ATP** *040

■ = Address Information Privacy Protected

POPPEL, Clinton Scott. 12401 E SINTO AVE 99216 #010-02-1988 L1999 **IM** *020 †20
PRATT, Sherrill L V. ■ 99206 #030-05-1953 L1957 **OS** *075
PREIKSAITIS, Harold G. 12409 E MISSION AVE, ROCKWOOD CLINIC VALLEY GAS 99216 #067-01-1983 L2003 **IM GE** *020 †20
PRENGER, Thomas Frederick. 13102 E MISSION AVE 99216 #028-03-1976 L1991 **FM** *020 †18
PUGH, Steven Lynn. 1420 N MULLAN RD, STE 100 99206 #028-03-1996 L1996 **N** *020
REES, John Wm, Jr. 12606 E MISSION AVE 99216 #048-13-1977 L1980 **AN** *020 †05
RICHES, Wayne G. 13103 E MANSFIELD AVE 99216 #054-04-1977 L1982 **PTH OS** *020 †50
RIGGS, Robert J. 14402 E SPRAGUE AVE 99216 #040-02-1984 L1992 **FM** *020 †18
RINALDI, Peter Dominic. 12509 E MISSION AVE, VALLEY FAM PHYSICIANS 99216 #054-04-1973 L1975 **FM** *020 †18
RITCHEY, Timothy James. 14402 E SPRAGUE AVE 99216 #054-04-1974 L1977 **FM** *020 †18
ROBINSON, Joel Clair. 12606 E MISSION AVE 99216 #028-34-1998 L2006 **AN** *020 †05
RUARK, Glen Wilton. 1215 N MCDONALD RD, SPOKANE INTERNAL MEDICINE 99216 #054-04-1969 L1972 **IM** *071 †20
RYAN, Thomas Michael. 11017 E SPRAGUE AVE 99206 #054-04-1965 L1994 **D DS** *020 †15 ‡
SANWICK, Steven Michael. 12410 E SINTO AVE, STE 201 99216 #054-04-1969 L1973 **ORS** *020 †40
SEARS, Joel Kent. 1807 N HUTCHINSON RD 99212 #018-03-1985 L1991 **D** *020 †15
SESTERO, Anthony Michael. 1414 N HOUK RD, STE 102 99216 #030-06-1998 L2004 **HS** *020 †40
SESTERO, John David. 1215 N MCDONALD RD, SPOKANE INTERNAL MEDICINE 99216 #030-06-1994 L1998 **IM** *020 †20
SESTERO, Robert Francis. 12509 E MISSION AVE, STE 201 99216 #030-06-1972 L1975 **OBG** *020 †30
SIMMERMAN, Brian Lane. 1414 N VERCLER RD, STE 1 99216 #040-02-1997 L2000 **PD** *020 †55
SIMMERMAN, Tamara. 1414 N VERCLER RD, STE 1 99216 #040-02-1997 L2000 **PD** *020 †55
SINHA, Renu. 1414 N HOUK RD, STE 200 99216 #038-40-1989 L2001 **GS CCS** *020 †85
SKIDMORE, Allen Royal. 13102 E MISSION AVE 99216 #054-04-1999 L2006 **FM** *020 †18
SLICK, William Clifford. 5813 E 4TH AVE 99212 #039-01-1969 L1992 **GP OS** *030
SMENTEK, Craig Michael. 1415 N HOUK RD, VALLEY OBSTETRICS & 99216 #016-06-1982 L1990 **OBG** *020 †30
SNOW, Rita Mae. 1512 N VERCLER RD 99216 #054-04-1985 L1989 **IM** *020 †20
STADLER, Frank, III. 1414 N HOUK RD, STE 200 99216 #041-13-1963 L1974 **GS PUD** *071 †85
STALEY, Norman Elmer. 1414 N VERCLER RD STE 4 99216 #061-01-1959 L1960 **FM** *071
STAPLETON, Ross Brenton. 14402 E SPRAGUE AVE 99216 #054-04-1967 L1970 **FM** *020 †18
STOVALL, William Steven. 12509 E MISSION AVE, STE 201 99216 #012-01-1980 L1985 **OBG** *020 †30
STREAM, Glen Richard. 14408 E SPRAGUE AVE 99216 #054-04-1982 L1983 **FM** *030 †18
STURBAUM, Christopher W. 1414 N HOUK RD, STE 103 99216 #036-01-1992 L1997 **OPH OS** *020 †35
SUDARSANAM, Hardhi Priya. 12509 E MISSION AVE, VALLEY FAM PHYSICIANS 99216 #495-22-1998 **FM** *020 †18
TEDESCO, Joseph Alexander. 12122 E CATALDO AVE 99206 #021-01-1957 L1968 **OPH** *071 †35
THIEL, Francis A. 12606 E MISSION AVE 99216 #005-12-1953 L1953 **FM** *071
THORNTON, Donald Alan. ■ 99206 #422-01-2003 L2007 **AN** *020
THRASHER, William Curtis. ■ 99206 #012-05-1972 L1974 **GS** *020
VANDER WILDE, Alexander. ■ 99212 #660-01-1956 L1959 **FM** *071 †18
WANDSCHNEIDER, Gary Thoma. 13102 E MISSION AVE 99216 #056-05-1971 L1972 **FM** *020 †18
WARD, Staci Michelle. 1807 N HUTCHINSON RD 99212 #048-04-1998 L2004 **D** *020 †15 ‡
WARDZALA, Alexandra M. 13103 E MANSFIELD AVE 99216 #028-34-1985 L1990 **ATP** *020 †50
WATTS, James Harvey. 12509 E MISSION AVE # 201 99216 #021-01-1972 L1973 **OBG** *020 †30
WEAVER, Lewis Clay. 13102 E MISSION AVE, SPOKANE VALLEY FAMILY MEDI 99216 #054-04-1993 L1996 **FM** *020 †18
WEAVER, Victoria Shore. 1512 N VERCLER RD STE 2 99216 #054-04-1993 L1996 **IM** *020 †20
WESCHE, David Henry. 12606 E MISSION AVE 99216 #040-02-1966 L1976 **VS GS** *071 †85
WICKENKAMP, Carolyn Kay. 15425 E MISSION AVE, HEALTH SOUTH 99037 #005-19-1982 L1996 **FM** *020 †18
WOOLF, Philip Dee. 13102 E MISSION AVE 99216 #060-01-1977 L1978 **GP** *020
YARBER, Christopher D. 12606 E MISSION AVE 99216 #005-76-2002, ▲ L2006 **AN** *020 †05
YATES, Brian Todd. 1215 N MCDONALD RD, SPOKANE INTERNAL MEDICINE 99216 #054-04-1990 L1996 **IM** *020 †20
YELKOVAN, Cem. 12606 E MISSION AVE 99216 #902-03-1994 L2002 **EM IM** *020 †20
ZHANG, Manchun. 13103 E MANSFIELD AVE 99216 #243-16-1985 L2004 **DMP PTH** *020

STANWOOD – ISLAND

AGER, Ernest Arthur. ■ 98282 #026-04-1952 L1956 **PM N** *071 †60
CAVELL, Richard Jos. ■ 98282 #024-05-1961 L1988 **OTO** *072 †45
COOPER, Pamela Emelie. ■ 98282 #352-01-1951 L1970 **FM IMG** *071 †18
REMINGTON, Frederick K. ■ 98282 #030-05-1951 L1952 **GP** *071
TATE, Dale Richard. ■ 98282 #649-19-1978 L1982 **IM** *020

STANWOOD – SNOHOMISH

ANDERSON, Rupert F, Jr. ■ 98292 #035-01-1946 L1949 **GS** *071 †85
BARRIO, Gabriel Wm. 7205 265TH ST NW 98292 #005-11-1989 L1994 **PD** *020 †55
BRESKO, Corrine Louise. 9631 269TH ST NW, CENTER INC 98292 #048-13-2002 L2002 **FM** *020 †18
CLARK, Patrick Andrew. 9631 269TH ST NW, CENTER INC 98292 #018-03-1983 L1986 **FM** *020 †18
CLAY, Kevin Randle. 7205 265TH ST NW, THE EVERETT CLINIC 98292 #005-12-1984 L1996 **FM** *020 †18
COLOMBO, Mark Richard. 7205 265TH ST NW 98292 #054-04-1991 L1993 **FM** *020 †18
DIGMAN, Robert Howard, Jr. 7205 265TH ST NW 98292 #031-01-1990 L1993 **FM** *020 †18
FRITCH, Thomas Edward. ■ 98292 #005-06-1972 L1990 **FM** *071 †18
GARO, Glenn Michael. 9631 269TH ST NW, CENTER INC 98292 #014-01-2003 L2006 **IM** *020 †20
GRIERSON, James Bryan. 9631 269TH ST NW, CENTER INC 98292 #054-04-2001 L2004 **FM** *020

HOEKSEMA, Carol Lynn. 9631 269TH ST NW, SKAGIT VALLEY MEDICAL CENT 98292 #018-03-1983 L1985 **FM** *020 †18
HOLT, Albert C. ■ 98292 #007-02-1949 L1950 **GS OM** *071 †85
JACKSON, Donald Pearce. ■ 98292 #025-01-1954 L1966 **P** *020
KERN, Michael Lee. ■ 98292 #024-01-1966 L1968 **P GP** *020
KHAN, Talat. 9631 269TH ST NW, CENTER INC 98292 #704-16-1998 L2006 **PD** *020
LASSINGER, Brett Cameron. 7205 265TH ST NW, THE EVERETT CLINIC OF STAN 98292 #054-04-1993 L1996 **PD** *020 †55
MARTONICK, Michael. 7205 265TH ST NW 98292 #028-34-1974 L1977 **IM** *020 †20 ‡
RONNING, Arvid Ivar. ■ 98292 #054-04-1963 L1966 **GP P** *071
ROSSI, Alan Hartzell. 7205 265TH ST NW, THE EVERETT CLINIC 98292 #005-02-1964 L1990 **FM GP** *020 †18
STROMBERG, Don Darold. 6618 PIONEER HWY 98292 #054-04-1966 L1974 **AN** *071 †05
TAMARIN, Sara Judith. 7205 265TH ST NW, THE EVERETT CLINIC 98292 #035-45-2002 L2005 **PD** *020 †55
WILCOX, Johnna Kay. 9631 269TH ST NW, CENTER INC 98292 #028-46-1988 L2000 **FM** *020 †18

STEILACOOM – PIERCE

ADAMS, Douglas Robert. ■ 98388 #023-12-2007 **ORS** *012
BATIG, Timothy Scott. ■ 98388 #023-12-2005 L2007 **OBG** *012
BRAWAND, Kurt. ■ 98388 #869-02-1953 L1957 **P** *071 †75
BROWNLEE, Wm Henry, Jr. ■ 98388 #021-01-1948 L1954 **GP** *071
BURT, Robert Raymond. ■ 98388 #040-02-1944 L1947 **GS** *071 †85
CHAN, Wing L. ■ 98388 #462-01-1959 L1978 **IM GE** *071
CHEAH, Keong-Chye. ■ 98388 #004-01-1967 L1971 **P IMG** *020 †75
COBB, David Scott. ■ 98388 #025-01-1999 L2005 **FM** *020 †18
COWGILL, Herbert F. 105 CHINOOK LN # H 98388 #038-41-1943 L1971 **DR** *071 †80
EVANS, Eric S. ■ 98388 #005-15-1962 L1975 **FM PHP** *071
FRANKLIN, Jillian Michell. ■ 98388 #023-12-2008 *012
HAASE, Patricia. ■ 98388 #016-11-1979 L1988 **IM ADM** *030 †20
HAROLD, Dawn Marie. ■ 98388 #047-20-2006 L2008 **GS** *012
HEATH, Michael Anthony. ■ 98388 #048-14-1982 **AM** *012
HEINER, Jason Daniel. ■ 98388 #050-02-2006 **EM** *012
HIGGINS, Christopher Chih. ■ 98388 #023-12-2004 **AN** *012
HILL, George Blanchard. ■ 98388 #061-01-1961 L1965 **FM** *020 †18
ICASIANO, Melodie Marie. 1602 NISQUALLY ST 98388 #041-02-1999 L2003 **OBG** *020 †30
IVERSEN, Mary Ellen. ■ 98388 #054-04-1973 L1974 **GP EM** *020
JACKSON, Leslie Wilgus. ■ 98388 #010-09-1991 L1993 **RHU IM** *020 †20
JACKSON, Roger Keith. ■ 98388 #017-20-1978 L1993 **P** *020 †75
KILZIEH, Nael. ■ 98388 #875-02-1984 L1992 **P** *020 †75
KOLINA, John Stephen. ■ 98388 #017-20-1957 L1992 **NM IM** *071 †28
LASELLE, Priti Arun. ■ 98388 #016-06-2004 L2007 **PD** *020 †55
LEE, Kenneth Yun. ■ 98388 #056-06-2001 L2005 **AN** *020 †05
LITTLE, Dustin John. ■ 98388 #054-04-2007 **IM** *012
MC GUIRE, James Richard. ■ 98388 #056-05-1975 L1975 **P** *020 †18
PATES, Jason Andrew. ■ 98388 #023-12-2000 L2002 **OBG** *020
PERKINS, Robert Mark. ■ 98388 #041-12-2000 L2001 **NEP** *100 †20
PRZASNYSKI, Edward Joseph. 86 TATOOSH PL 98388 #028-03-1973 L1978 **END IM** *071 †20
ROBERGE, Joseph Lewis. ■ 98388 #005-15-1962 L1992 **AM FM** *071 †18,70
SIMPSON, Carroll S. ■ 98388 #028-03-1962 L1970 **CD IM** *072 †20
SPARLING, David L. ■ 98388 #035-03-1948 L1960 **PD** *071 †55
STAYTON, Conrad L, Jr. ■ 98388 #028-02-1969 L1979 **PD** *020 †55
TURNER, Guthrie L, Jr. PO BOX 88950 98388 #010-03-1953 L1981 **AM IM** *071 †70
VIRTUE, Clarence Mc Curdy. ■ 98388 #035-45-1956 L1978 **A P** *071 †55,03
WHEELER, Bruce Ross. 1301 NISQUALLY ST 98388 #021-01-1976 L1985 **HS ORS** *020 †40
ZOLTANI, John Gregory. 215 WILKES ST STE 202, PACIFIC NORTHWEST NEUROLOG 98388 #016-11-1980 L1990 **N** *020 †75

STEVENSON – SKAMANIA

BULOTA, William Reed. ■ 98648 #041-12-1974 L1983 **AN** *020
LABERGE, Roy Allen. PO BOX 338, 253 SW FIRST 98648 #054-04-1993 L1993 **FM** *020 †18
ROSENTHAL, Robert Lahn. ■ 98648 #025-01-1973 L1977 **EM FM** *020 †18,16

SULTAN – SNOHOMISH

BAKER-HALL, Victoria Ann. 615 W STEVENS AVE 98294 #054-04-1985 L1986 **FM** *020 †18
HOLE, Benjamin Visscher. ■ 98294 #005-11-1964 L1987 **FM R** *071 †80
ROBERTS, C Evans. ■ 98294 #035-01-1957 L1961 **OS** *020 †20

SUMAS – WHATCOM

CLAYPOOL, David Ronald. PO BOX 782 98295 #016-06-1967 L1972 **GP GYN** *020
SMITH, Keith Andrew. ■ 98295 #004-01-1984 L1984 **AN** *020 †05
WHITE, James Wilson. PO BOX 1079 98295 #005-12-1964 L1965 **CD NTR** *020

SUMNER – PIERCE

BILJAN, William Emil. 5814 GRAHAM AVE STE 100 98390 #026-04-1969 L1978 **FM P** *020
CAMP, Douglas Allan. 1518 MAIN ST 98390 #054-04-1996 L1998 **FM** *020 †18
CHAVAN, Preeti Vijaykumar. 1110 FRYAR AVE 98390 #495-98-2001 L2004 **FM** *020 †18
CORLISS, Robert Wm. 5814 GRAHAM AVE STE 100 98390 #056-06-1992 L1995 **IM** *020 †20
DAGAN, Benigno-Waldo A. 1518 MAIN ST 98390 #748-08-1990 L1998 **IM** *020 †20
DUFFY, James Patrick. 5814 GRAHAM AVE STE 100 98390 #018-03-1946 L1951 **GP** *071
GRAYSON, Sharon Beth. 1110 FRYAR AVE 98390 #035-03-2002 L2004 **FM** *020 †18
GRIGGS, David Norman. 1518 MAIN ST 98390 #005-14-1969 L1990 **GP** *020
KANDA, John Masayoshi. ■ 98390 #028-34-1954 L1956 **FM** *071
KHAN, Asif Rashid. 1518 MAIN ST 98390 #704-25-2000 L2005 **ID** *100 †20

LEITZ, Fred John. 5814 GRAHAM AVE STE 100 98390 #054-04-1974 L1976 **FM** *020 †18
MOLEN, David Glenn. 16202 64TH ST E, STE 105 98390 #026-08-2003 L2005 **OMF** *020

SUNNYSIDE – YAKIMA

BUSH, Robert Dickerson. 1016 TACOMA AVE 98944 #038-41-1976 L1983 **FM EM** *020 †18
CHAND, Krishna. 1017 TACOMA AVE 98944 #025-07-1983 L1990 **GS** *020 †85
EASTON, Karen Lyn. 1016 TACOMA AVE 98944 #065-01-1992 L1995 **FM** *020 †18
ELERDING, Steven Curtis. 500 S 11TH ST 98944 #005-15-1974 L1980 **GS SO** *020 †85
GRONSKI, Henry Wm. 718 FRANKLIN AVE 98944 #054-04-1967 L1969 **OTO AM** *020 †45 ‡
HALMA, Harlan Dean. 1016 TACOMA AVE 98944 #025-12-1991 L1994 **FM** *020 †18
KIM, Saekyu Robt. 500 S 11TH ST 98944 #047-06-1977 L2003 **U** *020
KIRK, Richard Alex. 1016 TACOMA AVE 98944 #054-04-1959 L1960 **GP** *071 †18
MADEJ, Anna Zofia. 1000 E EDISON AVE, VALLEY INTERNAL MEDICINE 98944 #759-01-2000 L2003 **IM** *020 †20
MANJUNATH, Kavitha Vani. 1614 E EDISON AVE, STE A 98944 #495-98-1983 L1999 **FM** *020 †18
MEININGER, Marc Gregory. 720 FRANKLIN AVE 98944 #048-04-1973 L1994 **OBG** *020 †30
NEALEN, Anne Marguerite. 1614 E EDISON AVE STE F 98944 #056-06-1972 L1980 **PD** *020 †55
ROACH, Richard Wayne. 1016 TACOMA AVE 98944 #030-06-1954 L1957 **FM GP** *071 †18
SHIELS, Hugh. 1413 E EDISON AVE 98944 #055-06-1970 L1976 **ORS** *020 †40
SKINNER, Glenn S. 812 MILLER AVE 98944 #041-13-1962 L1975 **FM** *071 †18
SMITH, Coke Rogers. 1000 E EDISON AVE 98944 #038-41-1976 L1982 **IM** *020 †20
WRUNG, Douglas Edward. 720 FRANKLIN AVE 98944 #025-01-1972 L1989 **FM** *020

TACOMA – PIERCE

ABBI, Monica. 521 MARTIN LTHR KNG JR WAY, JR WAY 98405 #495-36-1990 L2006 **OBG** *020
ABDEL-RAHMAN, Khaled A. 1123 PACIFIC AVE 98402 #915-04-1988 L2003 **CCM** *020 †20
ABOLINS, Andrew Robt. 3611 S D ST, STE 4 98418 #054-04-1982 L1985 **FM** *020
ADAM, Yaseen Bashir. ■ 98402 #875-02-1999 L2006 **IM** *020 †20
ADAMS, Kristin Joelle. 1708 YAKIMA AVE 98405 #054-04-1983 L1984 **IM** *075 †20
ADDISON, Clyde R. 3124 S 19TH ST, STE 200 98405 #005-15-1991 L2007 **FM** *020 †18
AFAQ, Tauseef. 1709 DOCK ST, SOUND INPATIENT PHYSICIANS 98402 #704-21-1996 L2002 **IM** *020 †20
AHMAD, Naila. 1708 YAKIMA AVE, STE 110 98405 #704-05-1992 L1996 **FM** *020 †18
AHMAD, Naila Bushra. 1708 YAKIMA AVE STE 110 98405 #038-45-1998 L2001 **RHU** *020 †20
AINBINDER, Darryl Jay. 9040 REID ST A, ATTN: CREDENTIAL OFFICE 98431 #043-01-1987 L1988 **OPH** *020 †35
AKAMATSU, Toshio. 3580 PACIFIC AVE 98418 #026-04-1959 L1962 **AN PME** *071 †05
ALENICK, Leonard Bennett. 5920 100TH ST SW, STE 33 98499 #023-07-1965 L1968 **OPH** *020 †35
ALGER, John Richard. ■ 98467 #016-06-1953 L1960 **EM** *071 †85,65
ALI, Fizzah Musfirah. 1717 S J ST 98405 #704-06-1988 L2000 **IM** *020 †20
ALINEA, Mario Guzman, Jr. 1901 S UNION AVE STE A203 98405 #748-01-1991 L1997 **FM OM** *020 †18
ALLAN, Thos Noel Kingsley. AMERICAN LAKE RAD 114 98493 #917-04-1956 L1975 **DR** *020 †80
ALLCHIN, Carol Louise. 11315 BRIDGEPORT WAY SW 98499 #010-01-1981 L1993 **IM PUD** *020 †20
ALLEN, Alfred Marston. ■ 98403 #005-02-1963 L1986 **OM PHP** *071 †70
ALLEN, Jason William. 3402 S 18TH ST, TRA MEDICAL IMAGING 98405 #010-02-2000 L2007 **NRN** *100 †75,80
ALLISON, Jon Craig. 9040 REID ST A, MADIGAN AMC 98431 #033-05-1988 L1995 **IM** *020 †20
AL-MATEEN, Majeed. 311 S L ST, # 2W-NEURO 98405 #005-19-1979 L1998 **CHN PD** *020 †55,75
ALVORD, Rex Martin, Jr. 901 N YAKIMA AVE 98403 #023-12-1985 L1997 **AN** *020
AMOROSO, Paul Joseph. 9040 FITZSIMMONS DR, MADIGAN ARMY MED CTR 98431 #023-12-1985 L1986 **AM EP** *050 †70
ANDERSEN, Charles Abe. 9040 FITZSIMMONS DR A 98431 #049-01-1968 L1970 **VS GS** *020 †85
ANDERSON, Charles Le Roy. 11315 BRIDGEPORT WAY SW 98499 #054-04-1962 L1972 **CHP P** *071
ANDERSON, Gerald Wilfred. 3315 S 23RD ST, STE 200 98405 #056-05-1971 L1976 **GS** *020 †85
ANDERSON, Robert Wm. OLD MADIGAN, BUILDING 9913A 98431 #054-04-1960 L1975 **OS IM** *030
ANDERSON, Ronald Gene. 316 MARTIN LTHR KNG JR WAY, STE 201 98405 #021-01-1967 L1972 **U** *020 †95
ANDRESS, Dennis Ladd. AMERICAN LAKE RESEARCH 15 98493 #039-01-1978 L1982 **NEP IM** *020 †20
ANDREW, John Scott. 11315 BRIDGEPORT WAY SW 98499 #051-01-1983 L1988 **EM FM** *020 †18
ANG, Jessy Edgardo. 2411 S 19TH ST 98405 #748-01-1974 L1980 **P** *020 †75
ANGWAFO, Nimae Ngumnaah. ■ 98402 #010-03-2005 L2007 *100
ANNEST, Leonidas. 1717 S J ST 98405 #020-02-1944 L1946 **GS TRS** *071 †85
ANNEST, Lon Sutherland. 2423 N 31ST ST 98407 #056-06-1974 L1975 **TS** *071 †85,90
ANWAR, Mian Hanif. 11315 BRIDGEPORT WAY SW 98499 #704-01-1958 L1968 **AN** *062 †05 ‡
APA, Theodore. ■ 98444 #016-11-1953 L1954 **PTH** *071 †50
ARBUCK, Marina. 1624 S I ST, NORTHWEST MEDICAL 98405 #913-64-1982 L2003 **ID** *020 †20
ARNETT, Gavin Wayne. DEPT OF RADIOLOGY, MADIGAN ARMY MED CTR 98431 #023-12-2006 L2007 **DR** *012
ARNETTE, Gregory Edwin. 1901 S UNION AVE STE A226 98405 #038-43-1978 L1981 **IM** *072
ARNTSON, Eric William. 1901 S UNION AVE 98405 #040-02-1989 L1993 **PTH** *020 †50
ARRINGTON, Edward D. 9040A REID ST, ATTN: CREDENTIAL OFFICE 98431 #023-12-1988 L2001 **ORS OSM** *020 †40
ASPLIN, Iain Robert. 314 MARTIN LTHR KNG JR WAY, STE 9 98405 #036-07-2001 L2004 **CCP** *020 †55
ATTIG, Douglas Lee. 2102 N PEARL ST STE 300 98406 #018-03-1975 L1976 **FM** *020 †18
AULAKH, S Singh. 9601 STEILACOOM BLVD SW, C-8 98499 #046-13-1981 L1983 **P** *020
AYALA, Leticia Maria. 521 MARTIN LTHR KNG JR WAY, JR WAY 98405 #054-04-2006 L2006 **FP** *012
AYARS, Deborah Jeanne. 1901 S UNION AVE STE B1010 98405 #021-01-1980 L1989 **PD** *020 †55

AYER, Julian Winfred. 316 MARTIN LTHR KNG JR WAY, STE 212 98405 #016-01-2000 L2004 **PD** *020 †55
AZAROW, Kenneth Scott. MADIGEN ARMY MEDICAL CENTE, GENERAL SURGERY SERVICE 98431 #023-12-1987 L1996 **PDS** *020 †85
BACON, Jonathan P. 209 MARTIN LTHR KNG JR WAY 98405 #051-04-1977 L1984 **ORS** *020 †40
BAER, Duncan Theodore. 2202 S CEDAR ST, STE 100 98405 #054-04-1957 L1963 **OPH** *071 †35
BAGHDADI, M Tarek. 1802 YAKIMA AVE STE 300 98405 #539-06-1980 L1989 **OBG** *020 †30
BAHMILLER, Jonathan C. 2115 S 56TH ST 98409 #011-02-1975 L1978 **OPH** *020
BAHN, Cordell Hunt. 1802 YAKIMA AVE 98405 #035-45-1962 L1972 **TS** *071 †85,90
BAILEY, Daniel Robt. 515 S M ST, STE 201 98405 #030-06-1971 L1976 **AN GP** *020 †05
BAIRD, Robert Willie. 2633 PACIFIC AVE, STE 204 98402 #054-04-1972 L1976 **AN** *020 †05 ‡
BAKER, Thomas Matthew. 1624 S I ST, NORTHWEST MEDICAL 98405 #016-43-1976 L1982 **ON HEM** *020 †20
BALDERRAMA, Miguel Angel. 910 TACOMA AVE S, PIERCE COUNTY SHERIFF DEPT 98402 #649-23-1985 L1996 **FM** *020 †18
BALDWIN, Katisha Denise. MADIGAN ARMY MED CTR, DEPT OF EMERGENCY MED 98431 #030-20-2007 **EM** *012
BALES, James David. MADIGAN ARMY MED CTR, ATTN MCHJ-MIM 98431 #004-01-1971 L1981 **IM ID** *020 †20,70 ‡
BALINGIT, Antonio Guinto. 9040 REID ST A, ATTN CREDENTIAL OFFICE 98431 #748-01-1972 L1982 **NM** *020 †28
BANTHANAVASI, Shahina. 1709 DOCK ST 98402 #495-59-2000 L2003 **IM** *020 †20
BARGREN, John Herbert. 1112 6TH AVE, STE 300 98405 #056-05-1967 L1969 **ORS OSM** *020 †40
BARNETT, Paul R. 2209 E 32ND ST 98404 #048-13-1986 L1993 **FM** *020 †18
BARNWELL, Robert Michael. ■ 98405 #023-12-2008 *012
BARRAZA, Evelyn Maria. MADIGAN ARMY MED CTR, ATTN MCHJ-PV 98431 #021-01-1982 L1983 **PHP** *030 †70
BARRETT, John Patrick. COMMANDER, MADIGAN ARMY MED CTR 98431 #023-12-1995 L1997 **GPM** *012 †18
BARRON, Thomas Sherwood. ■ 98496 #016-11-1943 L1947 **ORS** *020 †40
BARRONIAN, Richard F. 315 S MARTIN LUTHER KING J 98405 #024-07-1950 L1954 **IM** *071 †20
BASA, Ranjy Concha. ■ 98403 #748-02-1991 L1995 **IM** *020 †20
BATEMAN, Michael Johansen. 1812 S J ST STE 102 98405 #028-03-1991 L1994 **FM FSM** *020 †18
BATSON, Jack Miller. 2209 E 32ND ST 98404 #047-05-1958 L1958 **IM** *071 †20
BATTS, Keith Forrester. 1717 S J ST 98405 #051-04-1988 L1998 **EM TRS** *030 †16
BAUR, Ernst W. ■ 98448 #407-16-1946 L1959 **IM** *071
BAYRAKCI, Cemil. ■ 98407 #902-01-1955 L1969 **PD HEM** *071 †55
BECK, Ronald Julius. ■ 98499 #016-11-1959 L1964 **OPH** *071
BECKER, Leslie Andrew. 209 MARTIN LTHR KNG JR WAY 98405 #054-04-1980 L1983 **FM** *020 †18
BECKER, William Gary. 2302 S UNION AVE STE B18 98405 #023-07-1966 L1971 **AI PD** *071 †55,03
BECKERMAN, Nathan Samuel. ■ 98406 #038-41-2006 L2007 **EM** *012
BEEKLEY, Alec Carl. "MCHJ-SGY DEPT OF SURGERY 98431 #038-06-1996 L1998 **GS** *020 †85
BEHRENS, Melinda Louise. DEPT OF PEDIATRICS, MADIGAN ARMY MED CTR 98431 #003-01-1992 L1998 **PD** *020 †55
BELDOWICZ, Brian Christop. ■ 98405 #016-43-2004 L2006 **GS** *012
BELIC, Lanie Wong. 3209 S 23RD ST STE 340, DIGESTIVE HEALTH SPECIALIS 98405 #005-06-1974 L1977 **GE IM** *020 †20
BELL, Chas Michael Andrew. 3633 PACIFIC AVE, STE 204 98418 #917-22-1963 L1970 **AN** *020
BELL, Robert C. ■ 98445 #054-04-1916 L1918 **FM** *071 †18
BELL, Teresa Dawn. 2522 N PROCTOR ST, PMB 42 98406 #048-13-1988 L2000 **GS CCS** *020 †85
BELTS, Richard Paul. FORT LEWIS 98431 #040-02-1970 L1991 **OBG** *075 †30
BENJAMIN, Gary Gordon. 2202 S CEDAR ST, STE 200 98405 #056-06-1992 L1996 **GS** *020 †80
BENJAMIN, Sabrina Ann. 316 MARTIN LTHR KNG JR WAY, INTERNAL MEDICINE 98405 #023-12-1981 L1987 **IM** *020 †20
BENKO, Rebecca Lynn. 521 MARTIN LTHR KNG JR WAY, TACOMA FAMILY MEDICINE 98405 #025-12-1993 L1994 **FM** *020 †18
BERMAN, Steven Carl. 1717 S J ST 98405 #016-43-1965 L1977 **PD** *020 †55
BERNARD, Mary Theresa. 9040A REID ST, ATTN MC HJ QCR 98431 #026-04-1998 L2002 **AN** *020 †05
BERNARDO, Johann Don V. 1708 YAKIMA AVE STE 110 98405 #748-02-1995 L1999 **IM** *020 †20 ‡
BERNS, Robert Milton. 1708 YAKIMA AVE, STE 110 98405 #005-06-1976 L2000 **FM** *020 †18
BERTRAM, Kenneth Alvin. FORT LEWIS 98431 #026-04-1985 L1987 **HO IM** *020 †20
BETTERIDGE, Loren Bryce. 3733 S THOMPSON AVE 98418 #054-04-1988 L1990 **FM** *020 †18
BHALERAO, Prachi Pramod. 1709 DOCK ST 98402 #495-83-1998 L2003 **IM** *020 †20
BHANOT, Bhavana. 1709 DOCK ST 98402 #496-07-2000 L2006 **IM** *100 †20
BIANCHI, Elizabeth Ann. 3702 S FIFE ST, STE K # 44 98409 #011-03-1995 L1997 **FM** *020 †18
BICKLING, Rachel Lynn. 521 MARTIN LTHR KNG JR WAY, C/O BARBARA YORK 98405 #035-03-2002 L2005 **FM OBS** *040 †18
BILLINGSLEY, James G. 901 FAWCETT AVE 98402 #039-01-1955 L1965 **AM PUD** *020
BILLINGSLEY, Jerome Lane. 9040A REID STREET, ATTN: CREDENTIAL OFFICE 98431 #027-01-1973 L1975 **GS** *020 †28
BILNOSKI, William. 1802 YAKIMA AVE, STE 307 98405 #054-04-1979 L1984 **CD IM** *020 †20
BINGCANG, Peter Pangan. ■ 98422 #748-08-1979 L1984 **P** *020
BISCHOFF, G W. 315 S MARTIN LUTHER KING J 98405 #660-03-1953 L1959 **GP** *020
BISSONNETTE, Gerald W. ■ 98444 #061-01-1954 L1956 **P** *071
BITSEFF, Edward Louis, Jr. 1901 S UNION AVE, STE B5010 98405 #028-34-1980 L1987 **PS** *020 †65
BLACKETT, W Ben. 4366 N LEXINGTON ST 98407 #025-01-1958 L1966 **NS LM** *062 †25
BLAIR, John M, Jr. 1515 M L KING JR WAY 98405 #016-02-1989 L1997 **OSS ORS** *020 †40
BLAKE, Jeffrey Steven. ■ 98403 #032-01-1999 L2003 **PEM** *100 †55
BLANKENSHIP, James Milton. S 19TH & UNION STS 98405 #030-05-1955 L1958 **FM** *071
BLANKENSHIP, Robert Brice. 9040 REID ST A, MADIGAN AMC 98431 #038-41-1997 L1999 **EM** *020 †16
BLEAU, Brian L. 1112 6TH AVE 98405 #060-01-1983 L1998 **GE IM** *071 †20
BLEIWEISS, Milton Sanford. 3402 S 18TH ST, ADMINISTRATIVE OFFICE 98405 #028-02-1967 L1974 **DR** *071 †80 ‡
BLISS, Clinton Lee. 9600 VETERANS DRIVE, VA : A111-PC L. RODRIGUEZ 98493 #005-14-1989 L1990 **OS** *020 †18

BLOOM, Erete Sofina. 315 MARTIN LTHR KNG JR WAY 98405 #054-04-1998 L2001 **PD** *020 †55
BLOOM, Matthew Noel. 209 MARTIN LTHR KNG JR WAY, GROUP HEALTH COOPERATIVE 98405 #035-46-1987 L1997 **NM** *020 †80,28
BLOUSTINE, Stanley Aaron. DEPT OF SURGERY, MADIGAN ARMY MED CTR 98431 #020-12-1967 L1979 **PS** *020 †45,65 ‡
BLUMAN, Eric Michael. 9040 REID ST A, MAMC ORTHOPAEDICS 98431 #035-06-1998 L2005 **OFA OTR** *020 †40
BODEN, John Heber. MADIGAN ARMY MED CTR, ATTN: MCHJ-SOU 98431 #023-12-2004 L2005 **OPH** *012
BODILY, Kenton Chas. 1802 YAKIMA AVE, STE 204 98405 #040-02-1971 L1979 **VS** *020 †85
BOLT, Jodie Lynn. MADIGAN ARMY MED CTR, NEUROLOGY SVC FT LEWIS 98431 #023-12-1988 **CHN N** *020 †75
BOLT, Stephen Laurence. 9040A REID ST, ATTN: CREDENTIAL OFFICE 98431 #023-12-1988 L1990 **AN PME** *020 †05
BONSACK, Bruce Allen. 9600 VETERANS DR SW 98493 #028-34-1994 L1997 **IM** *020 †20
BOSCH, Wouter James. 2420 S UNION AVE STE 300 98405 #028-03-1961 L1968 **ORS** *071 †40
BOSSIO, Adrienne Eve. 315 MARTIN LTHR KNG JR WAY 98405 #041-09-1995 L2002 **IM** *020 †20
BOUMA, Jess Weston. 316 MARTIN LTHR KNG JR WAY, STE 101 98405 #054-04-1996 L1999 **FM** *020 †18
BOURDEAU, Emory J. 2202 S CEDAR ST, STE 200 98405 #030-06-1969 L1970 **DR** *071 †80
BOUTERSE, Phillip M. 3633 PACIFIC AVE STE 204, TACOMA ANESTHESIA ASSOCIAT 98418 #056-06-1990 L1997 **AN** *020 †05
BOUTRY, Donald Alan. 314 MARTIN LTHR KNG JR WAY, STE 104 98405 #005-15-1984 L1988 **OBG** *020 †30
BOVILLE, Brian Mitchell. 314 M L KING JR WAY STE 9, PEDIATRIX MEDICAL GROUP 98405 #056-05-1999 L2005 **CCP** *012
BOWDEN, David Karl. 9601 STEILACOOM BLVD SW, WESTERN STATE HOSPITAL 98498 #422-01-1998 L2004 **P NDN** *020
BOWE, Richard Geo. 2202 S CEDAR ST, STE 100 98405 #054-04-1964 L1971 **OPH** *020 †35
BOYD, Harold Eugene. 315 MARTIN LTHR KNG JR WAY, TACOMA GENERAL HOSPITAL 98405 #054-04-1976 L1982 **EM FM** *020 †18,16
BOYLE, Loueen Jo. AMERICAN LAKE VA 98493 #054-04-1976 L1978 **IM** *020 †20
BRACHVOGEL, Max Wm. 1901 S UNION AVE 98405 #067-01-1957 L1959 **OPH** *071 †35
BRAMMER, Shelby Richard. MADIGAN AMC 98431 #023-07-1968 L1986 **END IM** *071 †20
BRAND, William Wayne. 1708 YAKIMA AVE, STE 110 98405 #019-02-1969 L1978 **IM** *020 †20
BRAUN, Loranee Edwards. ■ 98431 #023-12-1997 L1999 **PD** *020 †55
BRICKA, Imants. 9900 VETERANS DR SW 98493 #407-25-1949 L1960 **P** *071
BROOKS, Joseph Patrick. ■ 98407 #041-02-1999 L2001 **RO** *020 †80
BROOKS, Sheldon. ■ 98431 #649-14-1978 **AN** *062
BROWN, Jay Albert. 2624 S 38TH ST 98409 #017-20-1978 L1989 **OM FM** *050 †18,70
BROWN, Linda Louise. 9040 REID ST A, MADIGAN ARMY MED CTR 98431 #023-12-1994 L1996 **ALI** *020 †03,20
BROWN, Peter Giddon. 915 6TH AVE, STE 200 98405 #010-02-1995 L2001 **NS** *020 †25
BROWN, Stanton R. ■ 98498 #041-09-1962 L1963 **NM PTH** *071 †50,28
BROWN, Thomas Kiefer. 11315 BRIDGEPORT WAY SW 98499 #016-11-1965 L1974 **OBG END** *071 †30
BRUNELLE, David. 315 MARTIN LTHR KNG JR WAY, MULTICARE MED CTR 98405 #050-02-1992 L1992 **PD** *020 †55
BUCHANAN, Bruce Douglas. 9600 VETERANS DR SW, VA PSHCS, AM. LAKE DIV. 98493 #056-06-1969 L1970 **PUD IM** *020 †20
BUENAVENTURA, Julio F. 9601 STEILACOOM BLVD SW 98498 #748-01-1959 L1967 **IM** *020
BUNPLOOG, June. 2420 S UNION AVE STE 100, MULTICARE MEDICAL GROUP 98405 #016-01-2002 L2005 **IMG** *020 †20
BURKEBILE, David La Verne. 1530 S UNION AVE, STE 13 98405 #035-03-1963 L1969 **P PD** *020
BURNS, Norman Harry. 419 S L ST, STE 101 98405 #016-01-2000 L2007 **GS** *020 †85
BUSCHMAN, Dennis Le Roy. 209 MARTIN LTHR KNG JR WAY, TSC-RAD 98405 #019-02-1968 L1975 **DR GP** *020 †80
BUTTORFF, Douglas Petrie. ■ 98466 #016-06-1944 L1947 **GYN** *071 †30
BUTTORFF, James Douglas. 1802 YAKIMA AVE, STE 204 98405 #035-03-1975 L1981 **VS GS** *020 †85
CAIN, Gregory Howard. 1530 S UNION AVE, UNION AVENUE PEDIATRICS 98405 #054-04-1980 L1983 **PD** *020 †55
CALLAHAN, Kevin E. 315 MARTIN LTHR KNG JR WAY, JR WAY 98405 #654-01-1990 L1996 **IM** *020 †16
CALLIS, William Garey, III. COMMANDER, MADIGAN ARMY MED CTR 98431 #023-12-2006 **GPM** *012
CAMERON, David Adams. 101 E 26TH ST, COMMUNITY HEALTH CARE 98421 #054-04-1999 L2001 **FM** *020 †18
CAMMARANO, Clare Lydia. 314 MARTIN LTHR KNG JR WAY, STE 104 98405 #010-02-1989 L1998 **OBG** *020 †30
CAMMARANO, William B, III. 314 MARTIN LTHR KNG JR WAY, STE 104 98405 #010-02-1989 L1998 **AN CCA** *020 †20,05
CAMP, Harry Wallace, Jr. 315 S K ST 98405 #038-41-1945 L1952 **OPH** *071
CANNON, Michele Marie. 1530 S UNION AVE, STE 1 98405 #038-06-1995 L2000 **PD** *020 †55
CANNON, Peter John S. 314 S K ST STE 302, TACOMA ANESTHESIA ASSOCS I 98405 #917-25-1955 L1965 **AN** *071 †05
CARMEL, Willard J, Jr. ■ 98499 #035-19-1945 L1951 **IM** *071 †20
CARTER, Elizabeth J M H. 209 MARTIN LTHR KNG JR WAY 98405 #050-02-1970 L1973 **DR** *020 †80
CARTER, Preston Leroy. 2007 GARDINER LOOP 98431 #050-02-1970 L1973 **GS** *020 †85
CARTER, Tony. 9040 REID ST A, MCHJ-QCR 98431 #019-02-1977 L1983 **GS** *020 †85
CARTWRIGHT, Victoria W. 9040 REID ST A, MCHJ-QCR, FORT LEWIS 98431 #023-12-1995 L1997 **PPR** *020 †50
CASHIN, Brian Vincent. MADIGAN ARMY MED CTR, DEPT OF EMERGENCY MED 98431 #005-15-2007 **EM** *012
CASON, Rochelle Lyvette. DEPARTMENT OF PEDIATRICS, MADIGAN ARMY MEDICAL CENT 98431 #047-07-2002 **PD** *020
CEFALU, James Bal. 209 MARTIN LTHR KNG JR WAY 98405 #005-18-1983 L1989 **DR** *020 †80
CHALETT, Jonathan M. 409 S J ST 98405 #008-02-1983 L1990 **OS PD** *020 †55
CHAMPEAUX, Anne Louise. FORT LEWIS, MADIGAN ARMY MED CTR 98431 #056-05-1996 L1997 **PTH** *040 †50
CHAMUSCO, Roger Frank D. 209 MARTIN LTHR KNG JR WAY, JR. WAY 98405 #187-03-1970 L1980 **CD IM** *020
CHAPPELL, John Stanley. 311 S L ST, # 3W-SURG 98405 #836-01-1959 L2000 **GS PDS** *020

CHARBONNEL, Thomas Shumpe. 1530 S UNION AVE, UNION AVENUE PEDIATRICS 98405 #007-02-1969 L1991 **PD ADL** *020 †55
CHARETTE, John David. 9040A REID ST, ATTN: CREDENTIAL OFFICE 98431 #023-12-1988 L1997 **EM** *020 †16
CHEN, Angela Hueyhwa. 1709 DOCK ST 98402 #054-04-1999 L2004 **IM** *020 †20
CHEN, Dali. 1628 S MILDRED ST, STE 104 98465 #243-47-1983 L1997 **IM END** *020 †20
CHEN, David Paul. 315 MARTIN LTHR KNG JR WAY 98405 #005-12-1990 L1995 **IM** *020 †20
CHEN, Min-Chun. 1003 S 5TH ST # 3L 98405 #244-04-1981 L1992 **ON HEM** *020 †20
CHENG, Stanley Geacie. 2202 S CEDAR ST, STE 200 98405 #035-19-1998 L2002 **DR** *020 †80
CHIKANCHI, Alexander. 9601 STEILACOOM BLVD SW, WESTERN STATE HOSPITAL 98498 #649-14-1977 L1984 **OM FM** *020
CHIN, Raymond N. 521 MARTIN LTHR KNG JR WAY, TACOMA FAMILY MEDICINE 98405 #040-02-2005 L2006 **FP** *012
CHINN, Gary G. 1019 PACIFIC AVE STE 1600 98402 #054-04-1983 L1984 **AN** *020 †05
CHINN, Michael Kwanlee. 9040 FITZSIMMONS DR 98431 #035-09-1994 **OBG** *020 †30
CHLUDZINSKI, Paula Marie. 3124 N 19TH ST, STE 240 98406 #031-01-1995 L2004 **IM** *020 †20
CHO, Eugene Syn. 419 S L ST, STE 101 98405 #016-06-1990 L2004 **GS** *075 †85
CHOI, Youl. 11311 BRIDGEPORT WAY SW, STE 201 98499 #583-06-1970 L1989 **OBG** *020 †30
CHOTINER, Darren Michael. 1123 PACIFIC AVE, SOUND INPATIENT PHYSICIANS 98402 #031-01-2005 L2005 **FP** *012
CHOW, Gregory Edmund. 9040A REID ST, ATTN: CREDENTIAL OFFICE 98431 #016-01-1988 L1999 **OBG** *020 †20
CHOWDHRY, Iftikhar Ahmad. 316 MARTIN LTHR KNG JR WAY, INTERNAL MEDICINE 98405 #704-21-1990 L2002 **RHU** *020 †20
CHUNG, Kam-Hung. 1802 YAKIMA AVE, STE 307 98405 #462-01-1965 L1979 **CD IM** *020 †20
CIERI, Martin Vincent. 1708 YAKIMA AVE, STE 110 98405 #023-01-1994 L1997 **PDI PD** *020 †55
CLABOTS, Joseph Paul. 7424 BRIDGEPORT WAY W, STE 307 98499 #028-02-1977 L1986 **TS GS** *020 †85,90
CLABOTS, Maria Teresa. 7424 BRIDGEPORT WAY W, STE 307 98499 #019-02-1979 L1986 **PD END** *020 †55
CLAGETT, Cynthia Lucile. 9040 REID ST A, MADIGAN AMC 98431 #023-12-1992 L1995 **PUD** *020 †20
CLAPPER, John Franklin. 1628 S MILDRED ST, STE 101 98465 #054-04-1975 L1978 **PD** *020 †55
CLARK, Allen Magruder. 502 S M ST, STE 200 98405 #041-02-1966 L1987 **PTH GP** *020 †50
CLARK, Annette. ■ 98465 #054-04-1985 *074
CLARK, David Graham. 1802 YAKIMA AVE STE 307, STE 307 98405 #035-45-1972 L1979 **CD** *020 †20
CLARK, Gary West. 9040A REID ST, ATTN: CREDENTIAL OFFICE 98431 #023-12-1988 L1989 **FM** *040 †18
CLARK, Lynne Patricia. 6002 WESTGATE BLVD, STE 150 98406 #051-07-1987 L1998 **GS** *020 †85
CLAYPOOL, Elsie Tytla. ■ 98407 #041-07-1951 L1984 **PD PM** *071 †55
CLEMONS, Jeffrey Linn. MADIGAN ARMY MEDICAL CTR, DEPT OF OB-GYN 98431 #035-19-1991 L1993 **OBG** *020 †30
CLERC, Daniel Todd. 705 S 9TH ST STE 102 98405 #028-34-1998 L2003 **FM** *020 †18
CLINGAN, Thos Akroyd, III. MADIGAN ARMY MED CTR, DEV PED CLN 98431 #011-02-1977 L1984 **PD** *020 †55
CLOUD, Robert Sidney. ■ 98498 #039-01-1959 L1980 **RHU IM** *071
COE, Darlene Renarita. 7424 BRIDGEPORT WAY W, STE 203 98499 #056-06-1989 L2002 **PD** *020 †55
COHEN, Leslie Ann. 1717 S J ST 98405 #050-02-2001 L2004 **EM** *020 †16
COLES, Maha Dibee. 1812 S J ST STE 102, PRIMARY CARE NW 98405 #030-06-1999 L2002 **FM** *020 †18 ‡
COLMAN, Lauren Kenneth. 1003 S 5TH ST 98405 #054-04-1975 L1978 **ON HEM** *020 †20
COLT, Ross Edwin. 9040A REID STREET, ATTN: CREDENTIAL OFFICE 98431 #032-01-1994 L1996 **FM** *020 †18
CONGER, Michael Robt. 209 MARTIN LTHR KNG JR WAY 98405 #054-04-1969 L1973 **U** *020 †95
CONNOLLY, Margaret E. ■ 98406 #054-04-1964 L1976 **PS OTO** *071 †45,65
CONNORS, Amy Beth. 9040 REID ST A, MADIGAN AMC 98431 #038-40-1995 L1997 **PD** *020 †55
COOK, Elizabeth Flora. 1624 S I ST STE 202 98405 #041-02-1991 L1997 **PM OSM** *020 †60
COOK, James Edward. 9040 JACKSON AVE 98431 #005-06-1988 L2006 **GPM GP** *030 †70
COOPER, Robert Lowell. 316 MARTIN LTHR KNG JR WAY, STE 212 98405 #033-05-1998 L1998 **PD PME** *020 †60
CORTHELL, Lisa Lia. 4301 S PINE ST, STE 301 98409 #054-04-1985 L1989 **P** *020 †75
COSGROVE, Anne Elizabeth. 2111 S 90TH ST, TACOMA SOUTH MEDICAL CLINI 98444 #024-16-1986 L1998 **PD** *020 †20,55
COTE, Cynthia Louise. 1708 YAKIMA AVE, ST JOSEPH MEDICAL CLINIC 98405 #041-13-1987 L1998 **FM** *020 †18
COVE, Jos A. 1515 MARTN LTHR KNG JR WAY 98405 #660-04-1986 L2001 **ORS** *020 †40
CRABB, William John. 315 M L KING JR WAY 98405 #040-02-1978 L1986 **EM** *020 †16
CRABILL, Robert Philander. ■ 98499 #040-02-1948 L1949 **FM AM** *071
CRAVEN, Philip Cheney. 1624 S I ST STE 405 98405 #023-07-1969 L1984 **ID IM** *020 †20 ‡
CRAWFORD, James Vincent. ATTN: MCHJ-SET, MAMC 98431 #023-12-1998 L2006 **OTO** *020 †45
CREEL, Naomi Beth. ■ 98407 #021-01-1999 L2000 **D** *020 †15
CRUZ, Marco Orlando Lauri. ■ 98409 #748-10-2001 L2007 **IM** *020 †20
CRUZ-URIBE, Federico Paul. 3629 S D ST STOP 0, TACOMA PIERCE CO HEALTH DE 98418 #056-05-1978 L1993 *020
CUADRADO, Daniel Geraldo. MADIGAN ARMY MED CTR, GENERAL SURGERY SERVICE 98431 #023-01-2002 L2004 **GS** *012
CUEVAS, Eduardo Samaniego. 1901 S UNION AVE, STE A114 98405 #748-08-1983 L1991 **IM** *020 †20
CUNNINGHAM, Brian Patrick. ■ 98402 #054-04-2008 *012
CURL, Charles Wayne. ■ 98407 #036-05-1965 L1968 **GYN** *020 †30
CUSHNER, Howard Marc. MADIGAN AMC WA, ATTN:CREDENTIAL OFFICE 98431 #023-01-1977 L1977 **NEP IM** *020 †20
DABE, Irwin Berkshire. 209 MARTIN LTHR KNG JR WAY, GROUP HEALTH CO-OP - ONCOLO 98405 #021-05-1969 L1989 **ON HEM** *020 †20
DAGG, Steven Edward. 1720 E 44TH ST 98404 #021-01-1993 L1995 **FM** *020 †18
DANIELS, Colin Yuri. 9040 REID ST, MADIGAN ARMY MED CTR 98431 #023-12-1997 L2003 **OS** *020 †75
DANIELS, Heather Sue. 1530 S UNION AVE, UNION AVENUE PEDIATRICS 98405 #040-02-1976 L1986 **PD** *020 †55

DANIELS, Jasmine Tho Phan. 9040 REID ST, MADIGAN ARMY MED CTR 98431 #023-12-1997 L2004 **IM** *020 †20

DARBY, Paul Sumner. 1930 PORT OF TACOMA RD, FRANCISCAN OCCUPATIONAL HE 98421 #010-02-1993 L2001 **OM** *020 †70

DASHIELL, Donald Allen. 1802 YAKIMA AVE, STE 100 98405 #038-44-1985 L1989 **AN** *020 †05

DAVIDSON, Douglas T, III. 209 MARTIN LTHR KNG JR WAY 98405 #041-01-1970 L1972 **ORS** *020 †40

DAVIDSON, Howard. 9040A REID ST, ATTN: CREDENTIAL OFFICE 98431 #021-01-1975 L1989 **ON HEM** *020 †20

DAVIS, Beth Gyauch. 9040A REID ST, ATTN: CREDENTIAL OFFICE 98431 #051-01-1986 L1989 **PD** *040 †55

DAVIS, Henry Matthew. 315 M L KING JR WAY, A5-IPSH 98405 #031-01-1999 L2001 **FM** *020 †18

DAVIS, Jason L. 9040 FITZSIMMONS DR, MADIGAN ARMY MEDICAL CENTE 98431 #048-13-1998 L2006 **CD** *020 †20

DEAN, Margaret D. 9601 STEILACOOM BLVD SW, WESTERN STATE HOSPITAL 98498 #043-01-1995 L1999 **PFP** *062 †75

DEAN, William Matthew. 314 MARTIN LTHR KNG JR WAY, STE 103 98405 #030-05-1972 L1974 **U** *020 †95

DECASTRO, Brian John. ■ 98431 #035-15-2002 L2003 **U** *012

DEEM, Clark W. 4717 S 19TH ST, STE 101 98405 #028-02-1968 L1972 **OPH** *020 †35

DEEM, Shirley Ruth Klemp. 9601 STEILACOOM BLVD SW 98498 #028-02-1970 L1973 **FM** *020 †18

DE GUZMAN, Fernando F, Jr. 3716 PACIFIC AVE 98418 #748-01-1972 L1984 *020

DEHLINGER, Richard T. 3124 S 19TH ST, STE C240 98405 #005-06-1980 L1990 **IM** *020 †20

DELAMARTER, Kristine Mari. 521 MARTIN LTHR KNG JR WAY 98405 #041-13-2004 L2004 **FM** *020 †18

DELCAMPO, Jaime L, Jr. 315 MARTIN LTHR KNG JR WAY, TACOMA EMERG CARE PHYS 98405 #040-02-2000 L2004 **EM** *020 †16

DE LEON, Felino Bautista. 3716 PACIFIC AVE, STE D 98418 #748-07-1976 L1984 **GP** *020

DELLAGIUSTINA, David Alan. 9040A REID STREET, ATTN: CREDENTIAL OFFICE 98431 #023-12-1991 L1993 **EM** *020 †16

DELLA-GIUSTINA, Karen L. 9040A REID STREET, ATTN: CREDENTIAL OFFICE 98431 #023-12-1991 L1993 **PD** *020 †55

DELL'AGLIO, Mark Jos. 1112 6TH AVE STE 200 98405 #041-09-1985 L1986 **GE IM** *020 †20

DELL ISOLA, Lawrence R. 1709 DOCK ST, SOUND INPATIENT PHYSICIANS 98402 #038-06-1975 L1997 **IM IMG** *020 †20

DELYANIS, George Peter. ■ 98465 #035-03-1966 L1970 **N** *071 †75

DEMARS, Sean Michael. MEDICAL CENTER, MADIGAN ARMY 98431 #051-01-2003 L2004 **OTO** *012

DEMIRJIAN, Keith Edward. 1812 S J ST, STE 102 98405 #001-06-1978 L1981 **FM FPG** *020 †18

DEMPSTER, David Warren. 1708 YAKIMA AVE, STE 107 98405 #054-04-1999 L2001 **NEP** *100 †20

DENNEHY, Rita Marie. ■ 98408 #025-12-1987 **DR** *020

DENNY, Mark Allen. ATTN: MCHJ-EM (MARK DENNY, COMMANDER - MADIGAN AMC 98431 #038-40-1999 L2003 **EM** *020

DEOL, Ajit Singh. 315 MARTIN LTHR KNG JR WAY, MS 315-J1-TRM 98405 #496-01-1985 L2000 **CCS TRS** *020 †85

DESERTSPRING, David N. 1601 S UNION AVE, ALLENMORE ANESTH ASSOC 98405 #016-11-1985 L2007 **AN APM** *020 †05

DEUTSCH, David L. ■ 98499 #016-11-1943 L1969 **GE IM** *071 †20

DEUTSCH, Drew H. 3402 S 18TH ST, TRA MEDICAL IMAGING 98405 #016-11-1981 L1988 **DR IM** *020,80

DEVINE, John Glenden. 9040 REID ST, MADIGAN AMC 98431 #023-12-1994 L2002 **ORS** *020 †20

DICKINSON, Cordelia Case. 521 MARTIN LTHR KNG JR WAY, TACOMA FAMILY MEDICINE 98405 #054-04-2003 L2003 **FM** *100 †18

DIEHL, Alissa Lynn. 521 MARTIN LTHR KNG JR WAY, JR WAY 98405 #056-06-2003 L2005 **FM** *020

DIERWECHTER, Leaza Miya. 3124 S 19TH ST, STE 220 98405 #008-01-1995 L2001 **GS** *020 †85

DIETRICH, Kenneth A, II. 314 MARTN LTHR KNG JR #9, PEDIATRIX CRITICAL CARE 98405 #021-05-1982 L1990 **PD** *020 †55

DILWORTH, Raymond David. 1812 S J ST, STE 102 98405 #024-05-1965 L1978 **FM OS** *020 †18

DITTMER, Stephanie Suzann. 521 MARTIN LTHR KNG JR WAY, TACOMA FAMILY MEDICINE 98405 #005-15-2005 L2005 **FP** *012

DODGE, Byron Maurice. 2217 N 30TH ST # 102 98403 #010-01-1958 L1965 **OPH** *071

DOEL, Michael Lewis. 314 S K ST STE 302 98405 #917-26-1951 L1966 **AN** *071 †05

DOHNALEK, Donna Marie. FORT LEWIS 98431 #054-05-1978 L1981 **DR** *020 †80

DONATO, Todd Owen. 3633 PACIFIC AVE, STE 204 98418 #054-04-1995 L1999 **AN** *020 †05

DONG, Kathleen J. 620 N C ST 98403 #043-01-1985 L2002 **P** *020 †75

DONION, Stacey Ann. 209 M L KING JR WAY 98405 #054-04-2001 L2001 **ORS** *020

DONLEY, Patrick Jos. 3609 S 19TH ST 98405 #038-40-1969 L1982 **P ADP** *020 †75

DONNER, Charles Steven. 2202 S CEDAR ST, STE 330 98405 #409-10-1988 L1999 **GE IM** *020 †20

DOREY, Lee Roy. 1901 S UNION AVE 98405 #005-14-1967 L1978 **ORS** *075 †40 ‡

DORMAN, Cynthia Beth. 3315 S 23RD ST, STE 200 98405 #005-14-1984 L1995 **IM** *072 †20

DOUGLAS, Thomas E. ■ 98402 #041-02-1948 L1953 **OM IM** *020

DOWD, Michael Thos. 2202 S CEDAR ST, STE 200 98405 #016-02-1992 L1992 **DR** *020 †80

DOYLE, Michael Edward. 9040A REID STREET, ATTN: CREDENTIAL OFFICE 98431 #023-12-1992 L1994 **P** *020 †75

DRESSEL, Marshall V. 9040 REID ST A, MADIGAN AMC 98431 #051-04-1978 L2004 **PD** *020 †55

DUDLEY, Paul Sherman. 3209 S 23RD ST 98405 #012-05-2000 L2007 **OBG** *100 †30

DUKE, William Sterling. MEDICAL CENTER, MADIGAN ARMY 98431 #021-05-2003 L2004 **OTO** *012

DUMITRASCU, Diana. 1501 TACOMA AVE S UNIT 203 98402 #422-01-1994 L2004 **IM** *020 †20

DUNAWAY, Peter M. 9040 REID ST A, MADIGAN AMC WA 98431 #047-06-1996 L1998 **GE** *020 †20

DURALDE, Yolanda Ampuero. 1112 S 5TH ST 98405 #012-05-1981 L1987 **FM** *020 †18

DURAN, Maria Cristina H. 1123 PACIFIC AVE 98402 #748-01-1992 L1998 **IMG** *020 †20

DURTSCHI, Hyrum. HQ MEDICAL EDUATION, MADIGAN ARMY MED CTR 98431 #028-79-2005, ▲ L2006 **FP** *012

DY, Benjamin O. 4314 E PORTLAND AVE STE 7, PORTLAND AVE FAMILY CLINIC 98404 #748-08-1965 L1988 **UCM FM** *020

DYKSTRA, Aaron Douglas. ■ 98402 #046-01-2005 L2006 **ORS** *012

DZURILLA, Marta. 9040 FITZSIMMONS DR, MADIGAN ARMY MEDICAL CENTE 98431 #039-01-1994 L2002 **IM** *020 †20

EAMAN, Elizabeth. ■ 98402 #025-01-2007 L2007 **FP** *012

EDWARDS, Cynthia Wilson. 1901 S UNION AVE, STE B7005 98405 #028-02-1980 L1980 **FM** *020 †18

EGGEBROTEN, Wm Ernest. 9040A REID STREET, ATTN: CREDENTIAL OFFICE 98431 #041-02-1977 L1987 **GS** *020 †85

EHRET, Frederick W. 2202 S CEDAR ST, STE 100 98405 #024-05-1995 L2000 **PS** *020 †65

EIDAL, Christen Evans. 315 MARTIN LTHR KNG JR WAY, MULTICARE INPATIENT SVC 98405 #040-02-1974 L1975 **IM** *020 †20

EIGNER, David Joseph. ■ 98407 #023-12-2001 L2002 **PD** *020

ELAM, Erik Anthony. 2202 S CEDAR ST, STE 200 98405 #016-43-1986 L1998 **DR** *020 †80

ELDER, Stephen Jos. 3633 PACIFIC AVE STE 204, TACOMA ANESTHESIA ASSOCIAT 98418 #054-04-1985 L1990 **AN** *020 †05

ELDER, Thomas Ramsey. 13308 15TH AVE S, COURT E 98444 #803-02-1952 L1964 **PTH CLP** *071 †50

ELLIS, Juliana. 9040A REID ST, ATTN: CREDENTIAL OFFICE 98431 #030-06-1981 L1986 **P** *020 †75

ELMER, Lloyd Chas. 1901 S UNION AVE STE B2003, ALLENMORE MEDICAL CENTER 98405 #021-01-1964 L1969 **D** *071 †15

ELONKA, Dennis Robt. 209 MARTIN LTHR KNG JR WAY 98405 #040-02-1975 L1991 **OTO** *020 †45

ENQUIST, Robert Wm. 9040A REID ST, ATTN: CREDENTIAL OFFICE 98431 #054-04-1970 L1973 **IM PUD** *020 †20

ERWIN, Stanton A. 316 MARTN LTHR KNG JR #305 98405 #039-01-1979 L1991 **OTO** *020 †45

ESTROFF, David. 9040A REID ST, ATTN: CREDENTIAL OFFICE 98431 #041-09-1976 L1987 **PD** *020 †55

ETTLINGER, Robert Emil. 1901 S CEDAR ST STE 201 98405 #035-15-1972 L1978 **RHU IM** *020 †20 ‡

ETZKORN, Eugene Thos. MADIGAN ARMY MED CTR, INTERNAL MED 98431 #035-09-1977 L1996 **IM ID** *020 †20

EVANS, Robert Lewis. 1717 S J ST, SAINT JOSEPH MEDICAL CENTE 98405 #054-04-1972 L1997 **OS PD** *020 †20

FAHMY, Jana Lynn. 2202 S CEDAR ST, STE 200 98405 #005-12-1987 L2000 **PDR** *020 †80

FAHY, Edward Robert. 1530 S UNION AVE, UNION AVENUE PEDIATRICS 98405 #025-12-1977 L1992 **PD** *020 †55

FAIRCLOTH, Ruth Sonya. DEPT OF PEDIATRICS, MADIGAN ARMY MED CTR 98431 #023-12-2006 L2007 **PD** *012

FALZGRAF, Sharon. VA MED CTR AMERICAN LAKE 98493 #847-04-1977 L1986 **IMG** *030 †20

FANNIN, Lilia Ancheta. 9040 JACKSON AVE 98431 #023-12-1989 L2000 **OPH** *020 †35

FARABAUGH, Philip Thomas. 1623 E J ST STE 4 98421 #023-12-1997 L1997 **FM** *020 †18

FARAH, Marina S. 1709 DOCK ST 98402 #913-62-1994 L2002 **IM** *020 †20

FARZAD, Said. 9601 STEILACOOM BLVD SW 98498 #517-01-1976 L2000 **P CHP** *020

FAUCETTE, Kelly. 9040 REID ST A, MADIGAN ARMY MED CTR 98431 #023-12-1984 L1988 **PD PHO** *020 †55

FERGUSON, Robert M. ■ 98407 #016-11-1950 L1951 **FM OS** *071 †18

FERRER, Thomas John. 315 MARTIN LTHR KNG JR WAY, MS:315-J1-TRM 98405 #028-02-1991 L2004 **TRS GS** *020 †85

FIELDS, Angela Clark. 2202 S CEDAR ST, STE 330 98405 #036-01-1997 L2003 **PTH** *020 †50

FIFE, Walter Danl. 1717 S J ST 98405 #021-05-1967 L1974 **ORS LM** *072 †40

FINLEY, Loren Curtis. 1812 S J ST, STE 230 98405 #040-02-1981 L1986 **OBG** *020 †30

FINNERTY, Robert U. 1802 YAKIMA AVE, STE 205 98405 #010-02-1976 L1981 **U** *020 †95

FITZ, James Dudley. 315 MARTIN LTHR KNG JR WAY, TACOMA GENERAL HOSPITAL 98405 #005-02-1976 L1982 **IM** *020 †20

FITZGERALD, Boyce Ray, III. 209 MARTIN LTHR KNG JR WAY 98405 #030-06-1970 L1975 **FM PD** *020 †18

FLACK, Robert Duane. 9505 S STEELE ST 98444 #048-02-1977 L1984 **FM** *020 †18

FLAGG, Stephanie Darcell. 209 MARTIN LTHR KNG JR WAY 98405 #010-01-1979 L1989 **R** *020 †80

FLAHERTY, Michael John. 315 S K ST, MULTICARE MEDICAL CENTER 98405 #005-18-1985 L1986 **PTH** *020 †50

FLETCHER, Ronald Mark. 209 MARTIN LTHR KNG JR WAY, GHP DEPT OF RAD 98405 #054-04-1984 L1986 **DR VIR** *020 †80

FLOOD, John Aston. 7424 BRIDGEPORT WAY W, NO 103 98499 #054-04-1962 L1972 **R NM** *071 †80

FLORENCE, Robert Wm. ■ 98406 #039-01-1941 L1942 **ORS** *071 †40

FLYNN, Diane. 9040A REID ST, ATTN: CREDENTIAL OFFICE 98431 #041-02-1988 L2006 **FM** *020 †18

FONG, Andrew Eliot. MADIGAN AMC 98431 #035-46-2002 L2006 **DR** *020 †80

FORTE, Anthony Jos. 1802 YAKIMA AVE, STE 100 98405 #054-04-1985 L1986 **AN** *020 †05

FOSS, James Michael. 13410 PACIFIC AVE S 98444 #054-04-1975 L1978 **FM EM** *020 †18

FOSTER, Andrew Joseph. 9040 REID ST A, ATTN: CREDENTIAL OFFICE 98431 #023-12-1999 L2001 **AN** *020 †05

FOSTER, Mary K. 9600 VETERANS DRIVE, VA PUGET SOUND/AMERICAN LA 98493 #056-06-1982 L1987 **P** *020 †75

FREDERICKSEN, Roy Edward. ■ 98498 #030-05-1953 L1954 **FM** *071

FRIEND, Lore Ruth. ■ 98407 #040-02-1990 L2001 **GS** *020 †20

FRY, James Arthur. 316 MARTIN LTHR KNG JR WAY, STE 314 98405 #035-20-1971 L1976 **IM** *020 †20

FULCHER, James Kelso. 1717 S J ST 98405 #005-14-1972 L1980 **EM IM** *020 †20,16

FYNTRILAKIS, Anastasia. 1708 YAKIMA AVE, STE 110 98405 #024-05-1997 L2000 **FM** *020 †18

GABRE-KIDAN, Tesfai. VET ADMIN HOSP, DEPT MED 98493 #366-01-1968 L1976 **ID IM** *020 †20

GABRIELE, Mary Elizabeth. PO BOX 5013 98415 #041-15-2004 L2007 **FM** *100 †18

GABRIEL LOUTH, Mary C. MADIGAN ARMY MED CTR, DEPT OF PEDIATRICS 98431 #011-03-1999 L2000 **DBP** *012 †55

GAGE, Bruce Carlson. 9601 STEILACOOM BLVD SW, THE WASHINGTON INST 98498 #054-04-1983 L1990 **PFP P** *030 †75

GAINES, Margaret F. 950 PACIFIC AVE STE 800, GRP HLTH HM HLTH & HOSPICE 98402 #034-01-1984 L1988 **IMG PLM** *012

GALBRAITH, Charles J. ■ 98406 #028-34-1952 L1957 **GS** *071 †85

GALBRAITH, Dawn Elizabeth. MADIGAN ARMY MED CTR, DEPT OF PEDIATRICS 98431 #004-01-1995 L2002 **DBP** *012 †55

GALLEVO, Remi Verlene. 315 MARTIN LTHR KNG JR WAY 98405 #748-19-1990 L2007 **FM** *020 †18

GALLUCCI, John. 1003 S 5TH ST, DEPT OF RAD/ONCLGY 98405 #056-06-1959 L1988 **RO** *020 †80

GALVON, Dennis J. 7440 PACIFIC AVE 98408 #060-02-1979 L2002 *020

GARCIA, Jose Antonio, Jr. 223 N K ST 98403 #041-01-1969 L1971 **GYN** *020 †30

GAUGER, David Wm. 209 MARTIN LTHR KNG JR WAY 98405 #018-03-1979 L1986 **GS** *020 †85

GEORGE, Roger Kay. OPHTHALMOLOGY SERVICE, MADIGAN ARMY MED CTR 98431 #023-12-1986 L2006 **OPH** *020 †35

GERNON, William Hall. ■ 98499 #016-02-1963 L1977 **OTO FPS** *071 †45

GHIDELLA, Sean David. 9040 A REID STREET; MCHJ-Q, ATTN: CREDENTIAL OFFICE 98431 #010-02-1989 L2002 **HS** *100 †40

GHUMAN, Mandeep Singh. 521 MARTIN LTHR KNG JR WAY, TACOMA FAMILY MEDICINE 98405 #038-41-2006 L2006 **FP** *012

GIACOPPE, George N. 9040A REID STREET, ATTN: CREDENTIAL OFFICE 98431 #023-12-1986 L1999 **PUD OS** *020

GIAMANCO, Nicole Michelle. DEPT OF PEDIATRICS, MADIGAN ARMY MED CTR 98431 #028-34-2006 L2008 **PD** *012

GIBSON, Carl A. ENDOCRINE CLINIC, MADIGAN ARMY MEDICAL CENTE 98431 #001-02-1987 L1988 **END IM** *020 †20

GILL, Alan Robt. 521 MARTIN LTHR KNG JR WAY, JR WAY 98405 #025-01-1987 L2000 **FM** *040 †18 ‡

GILL, Amarbir Kaur. 9505 S STEELE ST, TACOMA SOUTH MEDICAL CENTE 98444 #495-03-1995 L2007 **FM** *020 †18

GILMAN, George C. 1112 6TH AVE STE 300 98405 #016-06-1952 L1960 **ORS** *071 †40

GINSBERG, Daniel C. 3124 S 19TH ST, STE C140 98405 #023-12-1986 L1996 **IM** *020 †20

GLANCE, Shayna Dianne. ■ 98409 #028-46-2007 **GS** *012

GLEVA, George Frank. 1717 S J ST 98405 #054-04-1994 L1999 **IM** *020 †20

GLEYZER, Roman. 9601 STEILACOOM BLVD SW, WESTERN STATE HOSPITAL 98498 #913-01-1980 L1997 **P PFP** *020 †75

GODA, Fatime Orsolya. 1709 DOCK ST 98402 #473-03-1993 L2002 **IM** *020 †20

GOLDEN, Richard Allen. VA PUG SOUND HEALTH CARE 98493 #051-01-1968 L1986 **P PYG** *020 †75

GOLDSMITH, Martin A. 316 MARTIN L KING JR WAY, WAY 212 98405 #035-03-1975 L1992 **PD** *020 †55

GOLSTON, Alan Geo. 209 S K ST 98405 #021-05-1982 L1988 **CD** *020 †20

GONZALEZ-VIZOSO, Rafael A. 1717 S J ST 98405 #024-01-1990 L1996 **EM** *020 †16

GOODENBERGER, Ann Louise. 9040 REID ST A, MADIGAN ARMY MED CTR 98431 #018-03-1979 L1986 **IM** *020 †20

GOODIN, John Oliver. 2202 S CEDAR ST, STE 100 98405 #012-01-1971 L1984 **OPH GP** *020 †35

GOODSON, David Nigel M. 3633 PACIFIC AVE, STE 204 98418 #352-03-1953 L1958 **AN** *071 †05

GORDON, Michael Jeffrey. 1802 YAKIMA AVE, STE 100 98405 #035-46-1967 L1978 **AN** *071 †05

GORTNER, Jean Kay. 317 S MARTIN LUTHER KING J 98405 #054-04-1977 L1978 **PD** *020 †55

GOSWAMI, Sushanta Kumar. 1717 S J ST, MEDICAL STAFF OFFICE 98405 #495-13-1987 L1999 **IM** *020 †20

GRAEVE, Allen Henry. 314 MARTIN LTHR KNG JR WAY, MULTICARE CARDIOTHORACIC S 98405 #036-06-1977 L2003 **TS** *020 †90,85

GRAF, Ronald Jonathan. 1901 S CEDAR ST STE 205 98405 #035-03-1971 L1973 **END IM** *020 †20

GRAFF, Ronald Mark. 209 MARTIN LTHR KNG JR WAY 98405 #046-01-1982 L1986 **GS** *020 †85

GRAHAM, Donald Arthur. 1901 S UNION AVE 98405 #025-01-1955 L1960 **OPH** *071 †35

GRAHAM, Kenneth D, Jr. 315 S MARTIN LUTHER KING J 98405 #010-01-1956 L1961 **GP** *071 †18

GRASSBAUGH, Jason A. ■ 98403 #032-01-2003 L2004 **ORS** *012

GRAZKO, Marybeth A. MADIGAN ARMY MED CTR, ATTN MCHJ-MNR 98471 #010-02-1990 L2003 **N** *020 †75

GREENE, James Hayes. 209 MARTIN LTHR KNG JR WAY 98405 #028-46-1987 L1991 **OBG** *020 †30

GREYDANUS, Wesley Kent. 1802 YAKIMA AVE, STE 100 98405 #056-06-1984 L1987 **AN** *020 †05

GRIECO, Basil John. 209 MARTIN LTHR KNG JR WAY 98405 #054-04-1983 L1989 **DR** *020 †80

GRIES, Delores Mary. 9040 REID ST A, MADIGAN AMC 98431 #023-12-1993 L1994 **NPM** *020 †55

GRIFFITH, James S, Jr. 2201 S 19TH ST STE 205 98405 #040-02-1970 L1979 **N** *020 †75

GRIFFITH, Thomas G. 3515 S 15TH ST, STE 101 98405 #054-04-1973 L1979 **PS HS** *020 †40,65

GRUZENSKY, William Dean. 2915 S ALDER ST 98409 #005-12-1982 L1999 **OPH** *020 †35

GUILFOIL, Erna Fluth. ■ 98405 #035-08-1943 L1948 **AN** *071

GUIRGUIS-BLAKE, Janelle. 521 MARTIN LTHR KNG JR WAY, TACOMA FAMILY MEDICINE 98405 #043-01-1999 L2005 **FM** *020 †18

GULLER, Barbara. ■ 98446 #869-07-1957 L1982 **PDC CD** *071 †55

GUTIERREZ, Antonio. ■ 98497 #264-01-1972 L1979 **P CHP** *020

GUTIERREZ, Jaime Gabriel. ■ 98446 #264-12-2000 L2003 **GS** *100

HABERLIN, Polly Johnston. 315 MARTIN LTHR KNG JR WAY, MAIL STOP AS-IPHS 98405 #054-04-1994 L1997 **IM** *020 †20

HALLIGAN, John Brendan. MADIGAN ARMY MED CTR, RADIATION ONCOLOGY SERVICE 98431 #023-12-1989 L1993 **RO** *020 †80

HALVERSEN, Gary Vaughan. MADIGAN ARMY MEDICAL CENTE, MCHJ-R ATTN: MAJ HALVERSE 98431 #010-01-2000 L2002 **DR** *020 †80

HAMELE, Mitchell Thomas. DEPT OF PEDIATRICS, MADIGAN ARMY MED CTR 98431 #023-12-2006 L2008 **PD** *012

HAMILL, Lisa V. 2420 S UNION AVE, STE 100 98405 #016-43-1991 L1998 **IM** *020 †20

HAMILL, Nicholas James. 1901 S UNION AVE STE B2010 98405 #016-43-1991 L1998 **OTO** *020 †45

HAMLIN, Nonila O Vilches. ■ 98499 #748-07-1963 L1989 **CHP P** *020

HAMMOND, Deborah Singer. VA PSHCS AMERICAN LAKE 98493 #005-18-1976 L1987 **FM PLM** *020 †18

HAMMOND, Kenric Wm. VA PUGET SOUND, 116M AMERICAN LAKE DIV 98493 #005-18-1974 L1988 **P** *020 †75

HAN, Soon Ja. ■ 98404 #583-08-1966 *075

HANNIGAN, Neil Ross. 1624 S I ST STE 200 98405 #065-10-1996 L2002 *100 †20

HANSEN, Elizabeth Ann. 9040A REID ST, ATTN: CREDENTIAL OFFICE 98431 #023-12-1982 L1997 **OPH** *020 †35 ‡

HANSEN, K Royce. 12723 GRAVELLY DR SW 98499 #010-01-1964 L1967 **AN GS** *071

HARDIN, Ellen Marie. 209 MARTIN LTHR KNG JR WAY, JR WAY 98405 #028-46-1981 L2002 **IM** *020 †20

HARMON, Kirk Thos. 1930 PORT OF TACOMA RD 98421 #035-20-1984 L1988 **OM IM** *020 †20

HARPER, George Richard. ■ 98403 #028-02-1964 L1973 **ORS HS** *071 †40

HARRELSON, Orvis A. ■ 98403 #028-02-1953 L1955 **OM OS** *030

HARRIS, Christopher John. 209 MARTIN LTHR KNG JR WAY 98405 #034-01-1976 L1984 **U** *020 †95

HARRIS, Mark Winfred. 6418 EASTSIDE DR NE 98422 #017-20-1980 L1999 **EM OS** *020 †16

HARROUN, Douglas Venable. 3611 S D ST 98418 #025-07-1977 L1991 **IM** *020 †20

HARROWE, David Joel. 3629 S D ST, 3800 W. CHANDLER BLVD. 98418 #030-06-1973 L1985 **PHP PTH** *062 †50,70

HART, Wesley Leroy. 3633 PACIFIC AVE STE 20, SUITE 201 98418 #005-12-1987 L1991 **AN IM** *020 †05

HARTNETT, Douglas Rowland. 3633 PACIFIC AVE, STE 204 98418 #054-04-1998 L2003 **AN** *100 †05

HARVEY, Richard Adrian. 1717 S J ST 98405 #005-06-1971 L1992 **EM** *020 †16

HASERT, Elizabeth Nuhn. MADIGAN ARMY MED CTR, DEPT OF PEDS 98431 #023-12-1985 L1988 **PD** *020 †55

HASLUND, Benjamin Albert. 209 MARTIN LTHR KNG JR WAY 98405 #008-01-1994 L1996 **GS** *020 †85

HASSIG, Walter Mark. 3209 S 23RD ST, STE 340 98405 #025-12-1986 L1999 **GE IM** *020 †20

HAWKINS, Richard Scott. 1901 S UNION AVE, STE 7005 98405 #040-02-1973 L1974 **FM** *020 †18

HAYAMI, Marvin Yoshikazu. 9040A REID STREET, ATTN: CREDENTIAL OFFICE 98431 #054-04-1977 L1983 **IMG** *020 †20

HAYS, Leonard Le Roy. MADIGAN ARMY MED CTR 98431 #040-02-1962 L1964 **OTO HNS** *020 †45

HAZELRIGG, James Edward. ■ 98422 #030-05-1954 L1955 **FM** *071 †18

HE, Yajuan. 1802 YAKIMA AVE STE 208 98405 #243-16-1987 L2002 **NEP** *020 †20

HEDRICH, Olaf. 1802 YAKIMA AVE STE 307, TUFTS-NEW ENGLAND MEDICAL 98405 #836-01-1996 L2007 **ICE** *020 †20

HEILBRUNN, Mark Ronald. 7440 PACIFIC AVE 98408 #054-04-1965 L1966 **GP PTH** *020 †50

HEITHAUS, Angela G. 4215 49TH AVE NE 98422 #010-01-1993 L1997 **IM** *020

HELLER, Daniel Noah. 3402 S 18TH ST 98405 #005-11-1992 L2001 **DR** *020 †80

HELLYER, David Tirrell. 8201 6TH AVE, APT 53 98406 #016-02-1944 L1946 **PD** *071 †55

HENDERSON, Charles Gerry. ATTN MCHJ SU UROLOGY, CDR MADIGAN AMC 98431 #001-06-1993 L1994 **U** *050 †95 ‡

HENDRICKSON, Melinda Anne. ■ 98403 #041-01-1989 L1998 **NPM** *020 †55

HENDRIX, Maecenas B, III. 1112 6TH AVE, STE 300 98405 #027-01-1976 L1978 **ORS OSM** *020 †40

HENNINGER, Tonya Michelle. 1123 PACIFIC AVE 98402 #026-04-2003 L2003 **IM** *100 †20

HENSCHEL, Eugene Victor. 2420 S UNION AVE 98405 #028-03-1982 L1992 **PTH** *020 †50

HERMAN, Eric Daniel. 521 M L KING JR WAY, TACOMA FAMILY MEDICINE 98405 #054-04-2001 L2004 **FM** *020 †18

HICKS, Raquel Victoria. 9040 REID ST # A, ATTN: CREDENTIAL OFFICE 98431 #737-06-1967 L1973 **RHU PD** *020 †55

HICKS, Russell Donald. 9040 REID ST # A, ATTN: DEPT OF PSYCH 98431 #005-06-1967 L1969 **P ADL** *020 †55

HILBY, Coral Lee. 315 S MARTIN LUTHER KING J 98405 #054-04-1985 L1988 **FM** *020 †18 ‡

HILGER, John Rothrock. 1901 S UNION AVE STE B7008 98405 #067-01-1957 L1968 **PS OTO** *020 †45

HILL, John Chas. 1802 YAKIMA AVE, STE 302 98405 #040-02-1964 L1966 **CD IM** *071 †20

HILL, Kent R. 9601 STEILACOOM BLVD SW, MAIL CODE 18305 98498 #049-01-1990 L1993 **P CHP** *020 †75

HILLIS, Stephen Boyd. 1812 S J ST, STE 102 98405 #005-12-1992 L1996 **FM** *020 †18

HILL-LEN, Mary Katherine. ■ 98407 #016-42-1985 L1996 **GE PD** *020 †55

HILTON, Edwin Bruce. 2201 S 19TH ST 98405 #041-02-1973 L1979 **PM** *071 †60

HIPP, Barbara Lynne. 314 MARTIN LTHR KNG JR WAY, STE 9 98405 #047-05-1993 L2003 **CCP** *020 †55

HIRSIG, Michael Charles. 2710 YAKIMA AVE, RURAL/METRO AMBULANCE 98409 #016-42-1996 L2005 **EM** *020 †16

HITCHCOCK, Christina P. 521 MARTIN LTHR KNG JR WAY, MULTICARE OB-GYN ASSOC 98405 #016-42-1993 L2001 **OBG** *020 †30 ‡

HO, James Ping. 11225 PACIFIC AVE S 98444 #038-43-1982 L1990 **FM** *020 †18

HO, Phoebe Fei. 3711 SOUTH D ST 98418 #005-06-1993 L2000 **OBG** *020 †30

HOAGLAND-SCHER, John E. 209 MARTIN LTHR KNG JR WAY, GROUP HEALTH COOPERATIVE 98405 #024-05-1984 L1985 **FM** *020 †18

HOAGLAND-SCHER, Mary C. 209 MARTIN L KING JR WAY, GROUP HEALTH URGENT CARE 98405 #024-01-1983 L1984 **FM** *020 †18

HOBBS, Curtis Jean. 9040A REID ST, ATTN: CREDENTIAL OFFICE 98431 #023-12-1985 L1987 **END IM** *020 †20

HODGES, George Farmin. 315 MARTIN LTHR KNG JR WAY, DEPT OF LAB MED 98405 #010-01-1984 L1985 **PTH HMP** *020 †50

HOFFMAN, Monica Ann. ■ 98433 #026-04-2006 L2008 **IM** *012

HOGUE, Jacob Scott. ■ 98406 #023-12-2005 L2007 **PD** *012

HOHMAN, Marc Hale. MADIGAN ARMY MED CTR, OTOLARYNGOLOGY HNS 98431 #032-01-2006 L2008 **OTO** *012

HOLDERMAN, William Henry. 3209 S 23RD ST STE 200, DIGESTIVE HEALTH SPECIALIS 98405 #016-42-1987 L1993 **GE** *020 †20

HOLLAND, Randall Morgan. 311 S L ST, # 3W-SURG 98405 #054-04-1986 L1993 **GS PDS** *020 †85

HOLLENBECK, David Dee. 9601 STEILACOOM BLVD SW 98498 #005-12-1965 L1971 **P** *020

HOLTTUM, John Robt. 3315 S 23RD ST STE 102 98405 #054-04-1988 L1994 **CHP P** *020 †75

HOLTZ, Russell Rene. 1802 YAKIMA AVE, STE 100 98405 #030-06-1983 L1988 **AN** *020 †05

HORI, Kiyoaky. ■ 98406 #040-02-1956 L1959 **AN** *071 †05

HORN, Kimberly Krystina. 3633 PACIFIC AVE, STE 204 98418 #014-01-1978 L1981 **AN** *020 †05

HOTCHKISS, John Henry. ■ 98405 #005-12-2007 **TY** *012

HOUGH, David Wood. 9040A REID ST, ATTN: CREDENTIAL OFFICE 98431 #023-12-1987 L1992 **P PA** *020 †75

HOUGLUM, Oris Burton. 314 MARTIN LTHR KNG JR WAY, STE 403 98405 #054-04-1957 L1965 **OBG** *071 †30

HOWARD, James Dale. 5909 ORCHARD ST W 98467 #048-12-1968 L1975 **P** *020 †75

HOWEILER, Bradley Scott. 1717 S J ST 98405 #016-01-1989 L1993 **EM** *020 †16

HRIVNAK, Jacqueline Anne. 311 S L ST, # 2W-NEURO 98405 #041-12-1992 L2002 **CHN PD** *020 †55,75

HSIAO, Amber Fong. 209 MARTIN LTHR KNG JR WAY 98405 #016-06-1996 L2003 **DR** *020 †80

HSU, Yung-Chih Lilly. 3633 PACIFIC AVE STE 204, TACOMA ANESTHESIA ASSOCIAT 98418 #048-13-1999 L2006 **PAN** *020 †05

HUBBELL, Charles Gadue. 1901 S UNION AVE STE A229 98405 #050-02-1973 L1975 **D AM** *020 †15

HUDDLESTONE, John Robt. 915 6TH AVE, NEUROLOGY & NEUROSURGERY 98405 #025-01-1971 L1981 **N** *020 †75

HUGI, Maria R. 9040 JACKSON AVE 98431 #061-01-1979 L1991 **EM** *020 †16

HUILLET, Adam Lee. MADIGAN ARMY MED CTR, DEPT OF PEDIATRICS 98431 #023-12-2002 L2002 **DBP** *012 †55

HUNTER, David H. 209 MARTIN LTHR KNG JR WAY 98405 #010-01-1981 L1982 **OBG** *020 †30

HURT, Thomas Lynn. ■ 98405 #055-01-1983 L1988 **CCM EM** *020 †55 ‡

HUTCHINSON, Brendon Barry. 1708 YAKIMA AVE, STE 110 98405 #028-34-1995 L1998 **FM** *020 †18

HWANG, Andrew Sutaeg. 2201 S 19TH ST STE 201 98405 #583-02-1971 L1990 **P** *020 †75

IMKAMP, Evert-Jan Marinus. 9200 VETERANS DRIVE, AMERICAN LAKE VA 98493 #660-03-1980 L1987 **DR** *020 †18,80

INOUYE, Paul Toshio. 315 MARTIN LTHR KNG JR WAY, TACOMB GENERAL HOSPITAL 98405 #010-01-1990 L2002 **CCS** *020 †85

IONESCU, Andrei Manuel. 316 MARTIN LTHR KNG JR WAY, INTERNAL MEDICINE 98405 #781-01-1998 L2002 **IM** *020 †20

IREGUI, Manuel G. 1102 S I ST 98405 #264-10-1991 L2002 **PCC SME** *020

IRIGOYEN, Richard Gregory. ■ 98403 #056-06-2000 L2004 **AN** *020 †05

IRISH, Thomas Judson, Jr. 9040 JACKSON AVE 98431 #018-03-1962 L1972 *062 †85,65 ‡

IRVIN, Thomas Lee. 9040 REID ST # A, ATTN: CREDENTIAL OFFICE 98431 #030-06-1981 L1985 **RHU IM** *020 †20

IRWIN, Jennifer Ann. ■ 98403 #025-12-1989 L2005 **P** *020

IRWIN, Robert Gordon. 9040A REID STREET, ATTN: CREDENTIAL OFFICE 98431 #048-13-1991 L2004 **PHO** *020 †55

ISAAC, Johnson. ■ 98433 #495-37-1992 L1997 **NPM** *100 †55

IVANOV, Roumen Kirilov. 1709 DOCK ST, SIP, PLLC 98402 #198-01-1986 L2002 **IM** *020 †20

IVERSON, Julie Marie. 3711 PACIFIC AVE STE 200, ALL WOMENS HEALTH 98418 #026-08-1991 L1995 **OBG** *020 †30

IYENGAR, Jaisimha. 1901 S UNION AVE STE A301, CTR 98405 #495-09-1984 L1998 **APM** *020 †05

JACKSON, William Bert. 2202 S CEDAR ST, STE 200 98405 #036-05-1964 L1970 **R NM** *100,28

JACOB, Jason Sandford. 3402 S 18TH ST, JACKSON MEMORIAL HOSPITAL 98405 #028-02-2000 L2007 **DR** *020 †28,80

JACOBS, Jeffrey Michael. 2522 N PROCTOR ST # 38 98406 #011-02-1990 L1998 **AI** *020 †03,55

JAFRI, Afzaal Imam. 9601 STEILACOOM BLVD SW, WESTERN STATE HOSPITAL 98498 #704-16-1989 L1998 **P** *020

JAIN, Lizaantoin Garcia. ■ 98402 #026-04-2007 L2007 **FP** *012

JAIN, Vivek. 9600 VETERANS DR, AMER LAKE DIV A-116 MHC 98493 #495-05-1997 L2007 **P** *020 †75

JANK, Julie Michelle. ■ 98402 #028-46-2007 **FP** *012

JARVIS, Michael John. ■ 98406 #054-04-1967 L1970 **PM** *071

JASPER, Joseph F. 1628 S MILDRED ST STE 105 98465 #038-41-1981 L1982 **AN PME** *020 †18,05

JENNER, Carrie Larson. 1708 YAKIMA AVE, STE 110 98405 #010-02-1994 L1996 **PD** *020 †55

JENSEN, Robert Dean. ■ 98464 #030-05-1979 L2002 **PTH** *020 †20

JESIC, Lucy T Brooks. 9601 STEILACOOM BLVD SW, WESTERN STATE HOSPITAL 98498 #748-07-1965 L1983 **PM** *071

JIN, Jonathan Yong-Jin. 11311 BRIDGEPT WAY SW #204 98499 #583-09-1988 L1992 **IM** *020 †20

JOHNSON, Ralph Allen. 708 BROADWAY, STE 400 98402 #041-01-1956 L1961 **MDM GS** *071 †85

JOHNSON, William Michael. 3124 S 19TH ST, STE 220 98405 #019-02-1998 L2003 *020 †85

JOHNSTON, George Gilbert. 1802 YAKIMA AVE, STE 102 98405 #047-06-1969 L1981 **CD TS** *020 †85,90

JOHNSTON, Harold B. ■ 98406 #048-02-1949 L1952 **P N** *071 †75

JOHNSTON, Karen Louise. 9600 VETERANS DR SW, ALVA A116-MHC 98493 #054-04-1991 L1993 **P** *020 †75

JOHNSTON-KITAZAWA, M. 2209 E 32ND ST 98404 #041-14-1978 L1981 **FM** *020 †18 ‡

JONES, Thomas Kenneth, Jr. 314 S K ST STE 11, TACOMA RADIATION CENTER 98405 #023-07-1959 L1981 **RO** *071 †80

JORDAN, Glenn Davis. 315 S K ST BOX 5299 98405 #051-01-1982 L1988 **NPM PD** *020 †55

JORGENSEN, Jacqueline R. 1901 S UNION AVE 98405 #007-02-1957 L1974 **AI** *071 †55,03

JOSEPH, Andre C, Jr. 1708 YAKIMA AVE STE 40 98405 #005-14-1985 L1991 **GS** *020 †85

JUAREZ, Juan Francisco. 1112 S CUSHMAN 98405 #014-01-1977 L1979 **PD** *020

JUNG, Frank Martin. 1802 YAKIMA AVE 98405 #028-02-1975 L1979 **OBG** *020 †30

KABANI, Faried Gulam Ali. 9600 VETERANS DR SW, DIV 98493 #704-02-1988 L1999 **IM** *020 †20

KAHLSTROM, Richard Allen. 316 MARTIN LTHR KNG JR WAY, STE 401 98405 #054-04-1990 L1992 **IM** *020 †20

KALLAS, Robin Haber. 317 MARTIN LTHR KNG JR WAY 98405 #016-06-1989 L2004 **PD** *020 †55

KALLSEN, Robert A. ■ 98407 #026-04-1945 L1955 **IM** *071

KARL, Robert D, Jr. 209 M L KING JR WAY 98405 #054-06-1972 L1984 **DR NM** *020 †80

KARNIK, Nitin M. 514 S 13TH ST 98402 #495-37-1980 L1985 **P** *020 †75

KARRO, Jason Francis. 3633 PACIFIC AVE, STE 204 98418 #054-04-2000 L2004 **AN** *100 †05

KASPER, Mark James. 1708 YAKIMA AVE, ST JOSEPH MEDICAL CLINIC 98405 #054-04-1982 L1997 **IM** *074 †20

KASSNER, Adam Wayne. 1717 S J ST 98405 #054-04-1992 L1995 **IM** *020 †20

KASUBHAI, Saifuddin M. 1624 S I ST, NORTHWEST MEDICAL 98405 #495-01-1988 L2001 **ON** *020 †20

KATSMAN, Ralph Jay. 1802 YAKIMA AVE, STE 201 98405 #054-04-1986 L1993 **GE** *020 †20

KAUFMAN, Laura Rachel. 9505 S STEELE ST 98444 #038-41-2000 L2005 **GPM** *020 †18,70

KAUR, Harpreet. 9601 STEILACOOM BLVD SW, WESTERN STATE HOSPITAL 98498 #496-15-1998 L2004 **IM** *020

KELLEY, James Lewis. 2202 S CEDAR ST STE 310 98405 #040-02-1970 L1991 **PTH** *020 †50

KELLY, Kevin Michael. MADIGAN ARMY MED CTR 98431 #038-40-2003 L2005 **FM** *020 †18

KENNEDY, John August. 1624 S I ST, STE 303 98405 #010-02-1962 L1963 **NEP CD** *020 †20

KENNEDY, Kevin S. 1818 S UNION AVE, STE 2C 98405 #016-76-1982, ▲ L1990 **OTO FPS** *020 †45

KEPPLER, William Charles. MADIGAN ARMY MED CTR, ATTN: CREDENTIAL OFFICE 98431 #023-12-1997 L1999 **P** *020 †75 ‡

KESKEY, Thomas Scott. 3402 S 18TH ST, ADMINISTRATIVE OFFICE 98405 #056-06-1987 L1990 **DR VIR** *020 †80

KEW, Rosalind Elizabeth. PO BOX 5299 98405 #919-05-2004 L2006 **FP** *012

KEWALRAMANI, Jacquelin. 3633 PACIFIC AVE, STE 204 98418 #018-03-1986 L1989 **AN** *020 †05,18

KHALIGHI, Mehrdad. 9601 STEILACOOM BLVD SW, WESTERN STATE HOSPITAL 98498 #308-11-1984 L2004 **IMG** *020 †18

KHAN, Shireen Enette. 2202 S CEDAR ST, STE 200 98405 #028-02-1993 L1998 **DR** *020 †80

KIESEL, Eric L. 3619 PACIFIC AVE 98418 #021-05-1982 L1984 **FOP** *020 †50

KIESLING, Victor John. 1901 S UNION AVE STE A221 98405 #040-02-1973 L1998 **U** *020 †95

KIHARA, Todd K. 1802 YAKIMA AVE STE 204 98405 #023-01-1992 L1999 **VS GS** *020 †85

KILBORN, Kenneth Stanley. 5920 100TH ST SW 98499 #040-02-1957 L1963 **OPH** *071 †35

KILGORE, David Bruce. 521 MARTIN LTHR KNG JR WAY, JR WAY 98405 #005-06-1985 L1988 **FM PLM** *030 †18

KIM, Chong Chol. 128 131ST ST S 98444 #583-12-1979 L1993 *020

KIM, Daniel Shinil. 521 MARTIN LTHR KNG JR WAY, TACOMA FAMILY MEDICINE 98405 #016-06-2004 L2005 **FP** *012

KIM, Francis Youngjin. 316 MARTIN LTHR KNG JR WAY, STE 312 98405 #016-02-1992 L2001 **U GS** *020 †95

KIM, Paul Joong. 314 MARTIN LTHR KNG JR WAY, STE 303 98405 #016-11-1999 L2005 **PDC** *020 †55

KIM, Sung Hyun. ■ 98406 #583-06-1966 L1976 **GP PTH** *071 †50 ‡

KIMBALL, Catherine Anne. ATTN: MCHJ-P, MAMC DEPT OF PEDIATRICS 98431 #023-12-1999 L2001 **PD** *020 †55

KING, Diana Marie. 4215 49TH AVE NE 98422 #054-04-1993 L1993 **FM** *020 †18

KING, James J. 9040 REID ST # A 98431 #035-46-1979 L2003 **CD IM** *020 †20

KINNEY, James Bedford, Jr. 9040 REID ST A, MADIGAN ARMY MED CTR 98431 #039-01-1970 L1987 **PDC PD** *020 †55

KINNEY, Kurt Gary. ■ 98431 #023-12-1997 L2007 **IC** *020 †20

KIRKEGAARD, Lance Wells. 1717 S J ST, INPATIENT SERVICES 98405 #048-14-1978 L1989 **IM CCM** *020 †20

KIROV, Borislav Tzenov. 1717 S J ST, ST JOSEPH MEDICAL CENTER 98405 #198-01-1992 L2004 **IM** *020 †20 ‡

KITCHIN, Jonathan. 9040 REID ST A, ATTN CREDENTIAL OFFICE 98431 #048-13-2001 L2008 **AN** *100 †15

KITLEY, Charles Aaron. DEPT OF RADIOLOGY, MADIGAN ARMY MED CTR 98431 #023-12-2006 L2007 **DR** *012

KJORSTAD, Randy Jon. ■ 98406 #037-01-2003 L2005 **GS** *012

KLARNET, Jay P. 1003 S 5TH ST 3RD FL 98405 #035-06-1980 L1983 **ON IM** *020 †20

KLATT, Gordon Roy. 1307 S 11TH ST 98405 #026-04-1968 L1977 **CRS GS** *020 †85,10

KNODEL, Arthur Raymond. 316 MARTIN LTHR KNG JR WAY, STE 401 98405 #054-04-1977 L1982 **PUD IM** *020 †20

KNOPF, Keith Ronald. 209 MARTIN LTHR KNG JR WAY 98405 #018-03-1954 L1991 **FM** *071 †18

KNUDSON, Richard Palmer. 315 S K ST 98405 #040-02-1972 L1975 **PD** *020 †55

KOBLENZ, Lillian Helen. 311 S L ST, CMCC 98405 #005-18-1986 L1998 **PD** *020 †55

KODAMA, Christopher Allan. PO BOX 5299, 737 S FAWCETT MS H2PHY 98415 #035-46-1999 L2003 **PD** *020 †55

KODAMA, Steven Makoto. 1717 S J ST 98405 #041-02-1999 L2003 **EM** *020

KODE, Shaila B. MADIGAN ARMY MED CTR, DEPT OF INTERNAL MED 98431 #495-01-1973 L1978 **GP PD** *020 †20

KOMOROUS, James Michael. 1901 S UNION AVE, STE B2003 98405 #054-04-1973 L1977 **D DMP** *020 †15

KOONTZ, Clyde Harry. 316 MARTIN LTHR KNG JR WAY, STE 401 98405 #054-04-1971 L1975 **PUD IM** *020 †20

KOPSTEIN, Andrew Berk. 2202 S CEDAR ST, STE 100 98405 #026-04-1995 L1999 **OPH** *020 †35

KOTHENBEUTEL, Robt Lewis. 1401 MARTN LTHR KNG JR #A, DBA CEDAR RIVER CLINICS-TA 98405 #018-03-1969 L1971 **GYN** *020

KOTT, Brian Richard. 3402 S 18TH ST, ATTN: SUZANNE 98405 #041-07-1998 L2003 **RNR** *020

KOUKLIS, Norma V. 3609 S 19TH ST 98405 #048-02-1970 L1971 **P PYG** *020

KOVANDA, Carol J. 314 MARTIN LTHR KNG JR WAY, STE 104 98405 #016-11-1979 L1983 **OBG** *020 †20

KOZMINSKI, Tonya Nicole. 9040 JACKSON AVE 98431 #041-78-2002, ▲ L2002 **FM** *020 †18

KOZNARSKY, Michael Joseph. ■ 98498 #023-12-2001 L2004 **PM** *100

KRAJCER, Anthony M. ■ 98407 #048-14-2003 L2007 **RHU** *012 †20

KREGENOW, Lily. 316 MARTIN LTHR KNG JR WAY, STE 212 98405 #041-15-1999 L2007 **PD** *020 †55

KRICK, George Howard. 1901 S CEDAR ST STE 201 98405 #025-01-1971 L1976 **RHU** *020 †20

KRIEGSMAN, William Edwin. 521 MARTIN LTHR KNG JR WAY, JR WAY 98405 #054-04-2002 L2004 **FM OBS** *040 †18

KRILICH, Chad Blaise. 1102 S I ST 98405 #024-07-2001 L2001 **FM** *020 †18 ‡

KRISHNA, Samakshi. 1717 S J ST, FRANCISCAN INPATIENT SERVI 98405 #495-05-1995 L2003 **IM** *020 †20

KRUEGER, Ray Harry. 9505 S STEELE ST, TACOMA SOUTH GRP HLTH 98444 #054-04-1980 L1982 **FM FPG** *020 †18

KRUMINS, Peter Egil. 2420 S UNION AVE, STE 300 98405 #054-04-1988 L1994 **ORS OSM** *020 †40

KUIZON, Delia Dilag. 1709 DOCK ST, SOUND INPATIENT PHYSICIANS 98402 #748-02-1995 L2003 **IM** *020 †20

KUMAR, Shashi B. 9040A REID STREET, ATTN: CREDENTIAL OFFICE 98431 #495-74-1969 L1979 **PM** *020 †60

KUMKE, Kevin Michael. MADIGAN ARMY MED CTR, PULMONARY AND CRITICAL 98431 #016-43-1988 L1990 **PUD CCM** *020 †20

KUNDRA, Ajay. 1709 DOCK ST, SOUTH SOUND INPATIENT PHYS 98402 #496-43-1999 L2005 **IM** *020 †20

KUNZ, Geo Gilbert R, Jr. ■ 98403 #041-13-1942 L1943 **GP** *071

LACSINA, Emmanuel Q. 3629 S D ST 98418 #748-08-1963 L1984 **PTH** *062 †50

LAGEN, Thomas Hardy. 4920 WA TAU GA AVE NE 98422 #028-34-1997 L2001 **FM UCM** *020 †20

LAI, David C. 1901 S UNION AVE, ALLENMORE HOSPITAL 98405 #035-03-1994 L1998 **AN** *020 †05

LAMBERT, Drew Thos. 209 MARTIN LTHR KNG JR WAY 98405 #011-02-1986 L1989 **DR** *020 †80

LAMPE, Thomas Heyl. POC 116A, VETERANS ADMIN MED CTR AME 98493 #017-20-1977 L1979 **P PYG** *020 †75

LANG, Christine E. ■ 98433 #023-12-1998 L1999 **GPM** *012 †18

LANGLOIS, Joseph Claude. 209 MARTIN LTHR KNG JR WAY 98405 #056-05-1974 L1975 **D IM** *020 20,15

LANGWORTHY, David Paul. 3633 PACIFIC AVE, STE 204 98418 #005-12-1985 L1992 **AN** *020 †05

LANTZ, Calvin Roy, Jr. 315 S MARTIN LUTHER KING J 98405 #016-06-1945 L1951 **IM** *071 †20
LARHS, Anthony Emil. 2202 S CEDAR ST, STE 200 98405 #065-01-1993 L2000 **NM** *020 †80,28
LARSEN, John Andrew. 1901 S UNION AVE, ALLENMORE HOSPTIAL 98405 #016-01-1986 L2004 **AN** *020 †05
LARSEN, Rosanne Marie. 9505 S STEELE ST 98444 #054-04-1986 L1988 **FM OBG** *020 †18
LARSON, Todd Duane. 1708 YAKIMA AVE, STE 110 98405 #047-05-1992 L1997 **FM** *020 †20
LARSON, Vernon Oscar. 7424 BRIDGEPORT WAY W, STE 103 98499 #054-04-1956 L1961 **R** *071 †80
LATTU, Alison Lea. MEDICAL CENTER, MADIGAN ARMY 98431 #048-16-2002 L2004 **OBG** *020 †30
LAU, Theodore Ka Shun. 1802 YAKIMA AVE STE 307 98405 #067-01-1996 L2002 **IC CD** *020 †20
LAW, David Edward. 314 MARTIN LTHR KNG JR WAY, STE 101 98405 #409-33-1978 L1983 **IM** *020
LAWSON, Ian Bruce. 1550 S UNION AVE, STE 210 98405 #061-01-1986 L1997 **ORS** *020 †40
LAZAR, Anthony Stephen. 3402 S 18TH ST, ADMINISTRATIVE OFFICE 98405 #017-20-1968 L1974 **DR NM** *071 †80
LE, Thu Van. 1212 S 11TH ST, STE 39 98405 #941-01-1973 L1983 **GP** *020
LECKY, John Halton. 1717 S J ST 98405 #041-01-1968 L1988 **AN** *020 †05
LE DOUX, Edward J. 316 MARTIN L KING JR WAY, STE 401 98405 #040-02-1983 L1988 **IM PCC** *020 †20
LEE, Ann Miehyung. 316 MARTIN LTHR KNG JR WAY, STE 401 98405 #035-19-1994 L2002 **PCC** *020 †20
LEE, Curtis Alan. 9040A REID STREET, ATTN: CREDENTIAL OFFICE 98431 #037-01-1994 L2000 **EM** *020 †16
LEE, David Emerson. 1717 S J ST, STAFF OFFICE 98405 #028-34-1972 L1976 **PUD CCM** *020 †20
LEE, Hyung Bae. ■ 98498 #583-12-1973 L1992 **EM** *020 †16
LEE, James Russell. 9040 JACKSON AVENUE 98431 #049-01-2001 L2006 **AN** *020
LEE, Kok Wai. 9601 STEILACOOM BLVD SW 98498 #244-03-1971 L1981 **P ADP** *020 ‡
LEE, Ling. 101 E 26TH ST 98421 #825-01-1990 L2002 **FM** *020 †18
LEE, Mary Ann. 521 M L KING JR WAY, 4TH FL 98405 #048-13-1983 L1987 **OBG** *020 †30
LEE, Moo Keun. 9115 S TACOMA WAY, STE 105 98499 #583-03-1979 L1985 **GP** *020 ‡
LEE, Peter Shaopei. 1112 S CUSHMAN AVE, SEA MAR COMMUNITY HEALTHCE 98405 #035-08-1996 L2002 **FM** *020 †18
LEE, Roger Bing. 1717 S J ST 98405 #041-09-1968 L1980 **GO OBG** *020 †30
LEE, William Sy. 1901 S UNION AVE, # 2005 98405 #748-11-1977 L1991 **IM CD** *020 †20
LENIHAN, John Philip, Jr. 314 MARTIN LTHR KNG JR WAY, STE 104 98405 #048-04-1973 L1982 **GYN** *020 †30
LEON, Enrique Conrad. 1720 E 44TH ST 98404 #010-03-1996 L1998 **FM** *020 †18
LEONG, Gregory Bruce. 9601 STEILACOOM BLVD SW 98498 #005-15-1975 L1987 **P PFP** *062 †75
LESH, Phillip Craig. 3402 S 18TH ST, ADMINISTRATIVE OFFICE 98405 #005-14-1978 L1986 **R** *020 †80
LESPERANCE, Richard Nelso, Jr. ■ 98446 #023-12-2006 L2007 **GS** *012
LESTER, Paul Anthony. 1717 S J ST 98405 #016-43-1990 L1996 **IM** *020 †20
LEUSNER, Charles Raymond. 3402 S 18TH ST 98405 #054-04-1994 L2007 **VIR** *020 †80
LEVANT, Jonathan Alan. 1901 S UNION AVE STE B4006 98405 #035-19-1968 L1973 **GE IM** *020 †20
LEWIS, Edmund Emil. 3402 S 18TH ST 98405 #035-15-1963 L1969 **R** *071 †80
LEWIS, Neville Allen. 1624 S I ST, STE 301 98405 #038-41-1977 L1986 **ORS HS** *020 †40
LEYSE, Robert Merwin. ■ 98406 #028-02-1954 L1958 **GS TS** *071 †85,90
LIEN, Elizabeth Anne. 1624 S I ST, NORTHWEST MEDICAL 98405 #030-06-1993 L2002 **ID** *020 †20
LIM, Sonia. 9900 VETERANS DR SW 98493 #748-08-1978 L1993 **P** *072 †75
LIM, Sook Kyung. 9601 STEILACOOM BLVD SW, WESTERN STATE HOSPITAL 98498 #583-03-1958 L1983 **PTH CLP** *030
LIN, Angel Tsuiping. 521 MARTIN LTHR KNG JR WAY, TACOMA FAMILY MEDICINE 98405 #038-41-2006 L2006 **FP** *012
LIN, Yann G. 315 MARTIN L KING JR WAY, MULTICARE HEALTH SYSTEM 98405 #035-15-1995 L2001 **FM** *020 †18 ‡
LINDSEY, Ernest J. ■ 98445 #047-07-1986 L1987 **IM** *020 †20
LINEHAN, Colin Andrew. 9040A REID ST, ATTN: CREDENTIAL OFFICE 98431 #021-01-1998 L2003 **FM** *020 †18
LING, Richard K. ATTN: MCHJ-M-APC, MADIGAN ARMY MEDICAL CENTE 98431 #016-06-1989 L1991 **IM** *020 †20
LINK, Peter Chas. 209 MARTIN LTHR KNG JR WAY 98405 #056-05-1985 L1991 **U GS** *020 †95
LITSKY, Steven H. 2702 S 42ND ST STE 310, NORTHWEST CTR 98409 #550-02-1993 L1999 **PM** *020 †60
LIU, Sam Sungyuan. 3402 S 18TH ST, RADIOLOGY SERVICES 98405 #041-01-1992 L2005 **DR NM** *020 †80,28
LIU, Yan. 521 MARTIN LTHR KNG JR WAY, TACOMA FAMILY MEDICINE 98405 #243-72-1993 L2006 **FP** *012
LIVINGSTON, Robert Robb. 2202 S CEDAR ST, STE 200 98405 #041-01-1976 L1977 **R** *020 †80
LLERA, Jorge Luis. 1717 S J ST 98405 #017-20-1978 L1983 **EM** *020 †16 ‡
LOCKER, Olivia Shea. MEDICAL CENTER, MADIGAN ARMY 98431 #012-05-2004 L2006 **FM** *100
LONGAWA, Grzegorz Andrzej. 9601 STEILACOOM BLVD SW 98498 #759-01-1991 L1995 **P** *020 †75
LOO, Abraham. ■ 98445 #035-08-2006 L2007 **PTH** *012
LOOMIS, Carlton Adam. DEPT OF PEDIATRICS, MADIGAN ARMY MED CTR 98431 #007-02-2006 L2008 **PD** *012
LOOMIS, Donald Andrew. 2517 N WASHINGTON ST 98406 #054-04-1981 L1982 **FM** *020 †18
LORD, Timothy D. 3633 PACIFIC AVE, STE 204 98418 #007-02-1992 L1995 **AN PAN** *020 †05 ‡
LOUIE, Douglas Heung. 12157 PACIFIC AVE S 98444 #054-04-1985 L1987 **FM PHP** *020 †18
LOUIE, Ronald Richard. 311 S L ST, MARY BRIDGE CHILDRENS HOSP 98405 #038-43-1980 L1984 **PHO PD** *020 †55 ‡
LOUISSE, Marco Cornelis. 11225 PACIFIC AVE S 98444 #016-02-1999 L2002 **FM** *020 †18
LOUSTEAU, Leslie Lyons. ■ 98466 #010-02-2005 L2006 **OBG** *012
LOVY, Michael Robt. 1310 S UNION AVE 98405 #025-01-1975 L1982 **RHU IM** *020 †20
LU, Tingi Tim. 317 MARTIN LTHR KNG JR WAY, A6-6KMS 98405 #051-04-1997 L2000 **PD** *020 †55
LUBER, John Michael. 1812 S J ST STE 21, NORTHWEST CARDIOVASCULAR A 98405 #021-01-1973 L1998 **TS CD** *020 †85,90
LUDVIGSON, Mark Allan. 419 S L ST, MOUNT RAINIER SURGICAL ASS 98405 #026-04-1983 L1988 **GS PDS** *020 †85
LUDWIG, Mary Jo. 521 MARTIN LTHR KNG JR WAY 98405 #007-02-1991 L1993 **FM** *020 †18
LYMAN, Richard Bishop. 209 MARTIN LTHR KNG JR WAY 98405 #035-03-1970 L1983 **OTO A** *020 †45
LYNAM, Laura Marie. 915 6TH AVE STE 200, MULTICARE MEDICAL GROUP 98405 #018-03-2001 L2006 **CN** *020
LYNDE, Grant Charles. 2539 FREMONT ST 98406 #041-12-1998 L2002 **AN** *020 †05
LYONS, Michael F, II. 1717 S J ST 98405 #023-12-1982 L1986 **GE IM** *020 †20
LYUS, Richard John. 1401 MARTIN LTHR KNG JR WAY, STE A 98405 #917-24-2005 L2005 **FP** *012
MACK, Maria Jacoba. 1717 S J ST, ST JOSEPH MED CTR 98405 #050-02-1980 L1984 **AN** *020 †05
MACKINNON, Brad Robert. 521 MARTIN LTHR KNG JR WAY, TACOMA FAMILY MEDICINE 98405 #050-02-2007 L2007 **FP** *012
MAC LEOD, Douglas Anthony. 502 S M ST 98405 #035-01-1968 L1975 **OPH A** *020 †35
MADDALOSSO, Michele. ■ 98498 #561-11-1954 L1967 **GP OS** *071
MAEHREN, Johnette Barnes. 314 MARTIN LTHR KNG JR WAY, STE 401 98405 #028-78-1984, ▲ L1994 **OBG** *020
MAGELSSEN, David John. MADIGAN ARMY MED CTR, DEPARTMENT OB/GYN 98431 #007-02-1974 L1978 **OBG** *020 †30
MAH, Roger Wm. 9601 STEILACOOM BLVD SW 98498 #005-14-1971 L1989 **P EM** *020 †75
MAKARI, George Sadek. 311 S L ST 98405 #915-02-1980 L1990 **CHN** *020 †75,55
MAKARI, Nevine Fahmy N. ■ 98407 #915-02-1984 L1990 *020
MAKI, Henry Edwin. ■ 98403 #025-01-1948 L1952 **R** *071 †80
MAKOWSKI, Renee Lynn. MADIGAN ARMY MED CTR, OTOLARYNGOLOGY HNS 98431 #047-05-2007 **OTO** *012
MALIK, Muneeb Sharif. 1123 PACIFIC AVE 98402 #704-22-1996 L2002 **IM HOS** *020 †20
MALO, Leslie Smith. 316 MARTN LTHR KNG JR #309, PEDIATRIC SPECIALTY CARE 98405 #035-45-1979 L1986 **PDS** *020 †85
MANCUSO, Joseph J, Jr. ■ 98403 #011-02-1977 L1987 **OBG AN** *071 †30,05
MANOS, Theodore Andrew. 2440 S STEELE ST UNIT 208 98405 #054-04-1983 L1986 **AN** *020 †05
MANOSO, Mark William. 9040 REID ST, ORTHOPEDIC SERVICE 98431 #023-07-1997 L2005 **ORS** *020 †40
MANZO, Andrea Renate. 2202 S CEDAR ST, STE 200 98405 #047-06-1995 L2004 **DR** *020 †80
MAPES, Randall Craig. 209 MARTIN LTHR KNG JR WAY, GROUP HEALTH PERMANENTE, T 98405 #028-34-1985 L1996 **OSM** *020 †40
MARIANI, Mark Richard. 3209 S 23RD ST STE 100 98405 #054-04-2002 L2006 **FM** *020 †18
MARLATT, Darwin A. 1717 S J ST 98405 #030-06-1951 L1952 **GP** *071
MARSH, Gregory B. 1802 YAKIMA AVE, STE 100 98405 #054-04-1988 L1992 **AN** *020 †20,05
MARSH, Peter K. 1624 S I ST, NORTHWEST MEDICAL 98405 #041-02-1976 L1981 **ID IM** *020 †20
MARSHALL, Heather Anne. ■ 98407 #040-02-2000 L2003 **EM** *020 †16
MARTIN, Gregory John. COMMANDER, MADIGAN ARMY MED CTR 98431 #007-02-1997 L1998 **GPM** *012 †70
MARTIN, Joseph Dix. 1213 S 11TH ST 98405 #067-01-1957 L1962 **D** *062
MARTIN, Michael John. 1515 MARTN LTHR KNG JR WAY 98405 #025-07-1986 L1993 **OSS ORS** *020 †40
MARTIN, Thomas Jacob. 1708 YAKIMA AVE, STE 107 98405 #038-06-1977 L1991 **NEP** *020 †20
MARTIN, William Harman. 419 S L ST, STE 101 98405 #016-11-1967 L1976 **GS** *071 †85
MASON, James Clifford. 209 MARTIN LTHR KNG JR WAY 98405 #010-03-1979 L1982 **U** *020 †95
MASTRAS, Dean George. 1802 YAKIMA AVE, STE 103 98405 #050-02-1989 L1990 **RO** *020 †80
MATHEWS, Paul Thos. 3633 PACIFIC AVE STE 204 98418 #005-12-1987 L1991 **AN** *020 †05
MATTHEWS, Hollie Lu. 521 MARTIN LTHR KNG JR WAY, JR WAY 98405 #054-04-2004 L2006 **FP** *012
MATTHYS-OLLODART, Susanne. 1530 S UNION AVE, UNION AVENUE PEDIATRICS 98405 #869-07-1991 L1997 **PD** *020 †55
MATTSON, Steven Lee. ■ 98403 #051-01-2003 L2003 **AN** *020
MATZENAUER, Ales. 7511 CUSTER RD W 98499 #286-05-1978 L1989 **IM** *020 †20
MAURER, Donald Ervin. 315 MARTIN LTHR KNG JR WAY, TACOMA GENERAL HOSPITAL 98405 #004-01-1976 L1981 **EM** *020 †16
MAYO, Keith Allan. 316 MARTIN LTHR KNG JR WAY, STE 201 98405 #054-04-1978 L1979 **ORS** *020 †40
MAZZOLI, Robert Alan. MADIGAN AMC HSHJ SOU 98431 #023-12-1982 L1997 **OPH** *020 †35
MC BRIDE, Glenn Geo. 5340 N BRISTOL ST 98407 #016-06-1940 L1941 **GP** *071
MC BRIDE, Robert Garth. 315 S MARTIN LUTHER KING J 98405 #060-01-1966 L1975 **IM** *020
MC CARTHY, Joseph C, Jr. 9040 REID ST A, MADIGAN AMC WA 98431 #054-04-1968 L1969 **FM IM** *020 †20,55,18
MC CLELLAN, Donald Ray. MADIGAN ARMY MEDICAL CTR, DEPT OF PEDIATRICS 98431 #023-12-1988 L1990 **PD PDE** *020 †55
MC CLOSKEY, John Patrick. 314 MARTIN LTHR KNG JR WAY, STE 303 98405 #005-02-1983 L1983 **PDC** *020 †55
MC CLURE, George B. MCHJ-QCR, 9040A REID STREET 98431 #051-07-1983 L1995 **OBG FM** *020 †30
MC CLURKAN, James Michael. 1901 S UNION AVE STE B1010 98405 #021-01-1965 L1978 **PD ADL** *020 †55
MCCOLGIN, Ila Cheree. DEPT OF PEDIATRICS, MADIGAN ARMY MED CTR 98431 #023-12-2007 **PD** *012
MC COWEN, Karl David. 1628 S MILDRED ST, STE 104 98465 #048-04-1971 L1979 **END PDE** *020 †20 ‡
MC CRAVEY, Martha Alice. ■ 98406 #047-06-1975 L1985 **CCM PD** *020 †55
MC CROSKEY, Robert Donald. 1624 S I ST, NORTHWEST MEDICAL 98405 #054-04-1983 L1991 **HEM IM** *020 †20
MC CUNE, David Edwin. 9040A REID STREET, ATTN: CREDENTIAL OFFICE 98431 #048-04-1992 L2000 **HO** *020 †20
MC DERMOTT, Glenn David. MADIGAN ARMY MED CTR, ATTN: MCHJ-PV-OH 98431 #054-04-1988 L1990 **AM GP** *020 †70
MC DONOUGH, John Richard. 1901 S UNION AVE 98405 #030-06-1954 L1955 **CD IM** *071 †70,20
MC DONOUGH, Michael John. 1802 YAKIMA AVE, STE 103 98405 #028-34-1990 L1995 **RO** *020 †80
MC ENIRY, David Winters. 1624 S I ST, NORTHWEST MEDICAL 98405 #051-01-1977 L1988 **IM ID** *020 †20
MCGRANE, Owen Lane. ■ 98405 #010-01-2007 **N** *012
MC GREAL, Robert Dana. S 19TH & UNION STS 98405 #054-04-1957 L1958 **FM A** *071 †18
MC GROARTY, Raymond James. ■ 98403 #041-02-1964 L1969 **PD OS** *071 †55
MC ILMAIL, Daniel Paul. ■ 98407 #030-06-1993 L1999 **EM** *020 †16

■ = Address Information Privacy Protected

MC ILROY, William. 315 S MARTIN LUTHER KING J 98405 #054-04-1957 L1958 **OBG** *071 †30
MC KELVEY, John Jay, III. 9600 VETERANS DR SW, MS: A-111-CARD 98493 #041-13-1969 L1977 **CD IM** *020 †20
MC KINNEY, Elizabeth T. 314 MARTIN LTHR KNG JR WAY, STE 402 98405 #028-02-1989 L2003 **OBG** *020 †30
MCLAUGHLIN, Carol Theresa. DEPARTMENT OF RADIOLOGY, MADIGAN ARMY MEDICAL CENTE 98431 #038-40-2003 L2004 **DR** *012
MC LEES, Robert Zack. 502 S M ST, # 200 98405 #051-04-1971 L1975 **GYN OS** *020 †30
MC NAIR, John Timothy. 9116 LAKE STEILCM PT RD SW 98498 #016-45-1975 L1978 **OM EM** *020 †16
MC NAUGHTON, Marse L. 3733 S THOMPSON AVE 98418 #060-01-1976 L1977 **FM** *020
MC NERTHNEY, Mary C F. ■ 98401 #030-06-1932 L1932 **OS** *071
MC PHEE, Wm Archibald, Jr. ■ 98465 #028-34-1947 L1948 **GP** *071
MEAS, Hay S. 3716 PACIFIC AVE STE H 98418 #215-01-1971 L1992 **OBG GP** *020
MEISBURGER, John Edward. 1802 YAKIMA AVE, STE 100 98405 #040-02-1983 L1987 **AN** *020 †05
MENON, Vidya Prabhak. 1717 S J ST, FRANCISCAN INPATIENT SRV 98405 #496-38-1991 L2000 **IM** *020 †20
MERCHANT, Emily Elizabeth. ■ 98405 #017-20-2006 L2008 **EM** *012
MERGENER, Klaus. 3209 S 23RD ST, STE 340 98405 #409-10-1989 L2001 **GE IM** *020 †20
MESKE, Lorette Irene. 1717 S J ST, MS A-1 TRAUMA 98405 #016-06-1982 L2000 **IM** *075 †20
MEYER, John Gary. MCHJ-OM BLD 9040, MADIGAN ARMY MEDICAL CENTE 98431 #040-02-1971 L1979 **GS OM** *020 †20
MEYER, Michael Scott. 9040 JACKSON AVE 98431 #023-12-1995 L2003 **TS GS** *020 †85,90
MEYER, Paula Ann. 5702 N 26TH ST 98407 #007-02-1980 L1985 **FM** *020 †18
MEYERS, Mitchell Scott. MADIGAN ARMY MED CTR, PREVENTIVE MED SERV 98431 #031-01-1994 L1996 **GPM** *070
MIAN, Atif Munawar. 1717 S J ST 98405 #704-25-1992 L1998 **IM** *020 †20
MICHEL, Terrel Jos. 2440 S STEELE ST # 30 98405 #021-05-1972 L1979 **OBG GO** *020 †30
MICHELS, Benjamin Richard. 521 MARTIN LTHR KNG JR WAY, TACOMA FAMILY MEDICINE 98405 #018-03-2007 L2007 **FP** *012
MICHELS, Thomas C. 9040 REID ST 98431 #041-01-1979 L1998 **FM FPG** *020 †18
MIHALI, Alexander Karl. 1901 S UNION AVE, STE B7005 98405 #056-06-1971 L1976 **IM** *020 †20
MILLER, Christopher R. 1901 S UNION AVE, STE B7005 98405 #018-03-1971 L1973 **FM** *020 †18
MILLER, James Francis, Jr. 209 MARTIN L KING JR WAY 98405 #054-04-1981 L1999 **ORS GS** *020 †40
MILLER, John Bernard. 521 MARTIN LTHR KNG JR WAY, TACOMA FAMILY MEDICINE 98405 #054-04-2000 L2002 **FM** *020 †18
MILLER, Joseph Perretty. 9040 JACKSON AVE 98431 #023-12-1989 L1999 **AN** *020 †05
MILLIK, Mehmet. 2302 S UNION AVE BLDG B 98405 #902-05-1992 L2002 **IM** *020 †20
MINAGAWA, Arthur Wataru. 3633 PACIFIC AVE, STE 204 98418 #005-12-1988 L1992 **AN** *020 †05
MINORE, Joseph Francis. 1709 DOCK ST, SOUND INPATIENT PHYSICIANS 98402 #035-19-1989 L2006 **NEP** *020 †20
MINTER, Thomas Jos. 1717 S J ST 98405 #005-02-1983 L1991 **EM** *020 †16
MISKOVSKY, Thomas James. 1112 6TH AVE, STE 300 98405 #025-01-1963 L1968 **ORS** *071 †40
MITCHELL, David Bruce. ■ 98403 #007-02-1991 L2005 **DR** *020 †80
MODARELLI, Robert Orestes. 1624 S I ST 98405 #033-05-1968 L1974 **U** *020 †95
MOFFETT, Peter Matthew. MADIGAN ARMY MED CTR, DEPT OF EMERGENCY MED 98431 #041-02-2007 **EM** *012
MOFFITT, Donald Ray. 9040A REID STREET, ATTN: CREDENTIAL OFFICE 98431 #007-02-1974 L1978 **PDP PD** *020 †55
MOGRI, Shera Basrai. 101 E 26TH ST STE 100, COMM HEALTH CARE ADM OFF 98421 #495-22-1969 L2000 **FM** *020 †18
MOLLOY, Thomas Alexis. ■ 98405 #032-01-1981 L1993 **TS** *020 †85,90
MOORE, Jane A. 6002 WESTGATE BLVD STE 160, 6002 N. WESTGATE BLVD STE 98406 #039-01-1976 L1983 **FM UCM** *020 ‡
MOORE, Kimberly Lynn. 1717 S J ST 98405 #038-40-1996 L2003 **EM** *020 †16
MORAVEK, Carlos Enrique. 1901 S UNION AVE STE B701 98405 #054-04-1993 L1997 **PM** *020 †60
MORELOCK, Michael Dennis. 209 MARTIN LTHR KNG JR WAY, JR WAY 98405 #030-06-1979 L1999 **OTO** *020 †45
MORGAN, James Curtis. 1708 YAKIMA AVE STE 60 98405 #005-19-1972 L1973 **FM** *020 †18
MORGAN, Lori Jean. 315 MARTIN LTHR KNG JR WAY, MS: 315-J1-TRM 98405 #054-04-1989 L2000 **CCS GS** *020 †20
MORHAIME, Jacquelyn Leigh. 3619 PACIFIC AVE 98418 #035-20-2000 L2007 **SP** *020
MORRIS, Joseph Thos, III. FT LEWIS MED CTR, DEPT OF MED-MADIGAN ARMY 98431 #016-06-1984 L1985 **ID IM** *020 †20
MORRIS, William Jos. 915 6TH AVE, STE 2 98405 #010-02-1977 L1989 **NS NSP** *020 †25
MORRISON, Royce Alan. 3815 PACIFIC AVE 98418 #005-11-1973 L1975 **IM IMG** *020 †20
MORRISON, William Harry. 9601 STEILACOOM BLVD SW 98498 #054-04-1967 L1968 **FM** *020
MOSIER, Andrew D. MADIGAN ARMY MED CTR, GRAD MED EDU 98431 #038-75-2007, ▲ **TY** *012
MOURAVEV, Rostilav. ■ 98422 #913-05-1988 L2004 **IM** *100
MUELLER, Stanley Adolph. ■ 98406 #010-01-1956 L1963 **ORS** *071 †40
MULCAHY, Michael Joseph. ■ 98402 #038-41-2004 L2007 **GS** *012
MULLEN, Bernard Neil. 9040 JACKSON AVE 98431 #048-13-1974 L1987 **EM PEM** *030 †55,16
MULLIGAN, John Carlton. 315 S K ST 98405 #041-12-1970 L1971 **NPM** *020 †55
MUMTAZ, Munawar. 3611 S D ST 98418 #704-06-1977 L1985 **FM** *020 †18
MUNARETTO, Joseph Anthony. 9040A REID ST, ATTN: CREDENTIAL OFFICE 98431 #023-12-1995 L1997 **PCP** *020 †50
MUNOZ, David Raul. 314 MARTIN LTHR KNG JR WAY, INTERNAL MEDICINE 98405 #024-01-1978 L1979 **IMG IM** *020 †20
MURAYWID, Mohammed Maher. 1717 S J ST, FRANCISCAN IN-PATIENT TEAM 98405 #875-01-1999 L2005 **IM** *020 †20
MURPHY, Mark Thos. 3124 S 19TH ST STE 200 98405 #030-06-1990 L1998 **FM** *020 †18
MYHRE, Selma Ann. 14016 A ST S 98444 #049-01-1965 L1968 **PTH PD** *071
MYSLIWIEC, Vincent. MADIGAN ARMY MEDICAL CTR, PULMONARY DEPT 98431 #023-12-1996 **PCC** *100 †20
NADARAJAH, Senthilraj. 315 MARTIN LTHR KNG JR WAY, MS:315-M3-ISN 98405 #220-04-1992 L2002 **IM** *020 †20
NAEEM, Mohammad. DEPT OF RADIOLOGY, MADIGAN ARMY MED CTR 98431 #704-01-1995 L2006 **DR AR** *020 †80

NANDY, Mousumi. 1709 DOCK ST, SOUND INPATIENT PHYSICIANS 98402 #495-74-1989 L2005 **IM** *020 †20
NAPOLITANO, Peter G. 9040A REID STREET, ATTN: CREDENTIAL OFFICE 98431 #016-43-1989 L1996 **OBG MFM** *020 †30
NATTER, Lonny Ray. MADIGAN ARMY MEDICAL CENTE, DEPT OF PSYCHIATRY 98431 #028-02-1984 L1988 **P** *020 †75
NEFF, Timothy Wayne. 222 N J ST 98403 #019-02-1986 L1995 **OBG** *020 †30
NEIGHBOR, Ralph Martin. 3611 S D ST, STE 7 98418 #019-02-1972 L1984 **OBG** *020 †30
NELSON, Dayne Matthew. ■ 98431 #023-12-2004 L2006 **U** *012
NELSON, James Wm. 9040A REID ST, MADIGAN AMC, ANESTHESIA (D 98431 #040-02-1986 L1992 **AN PME** *020 †05
NELSON, Karen Marie. 314 MARTIN LTHR KNG JR WAY, STE 400 98405 #016-06-1988 L1996 **OBG** *020 †30
NELSON, Mark Lewis. 9040 JACKSON AVE 98431 #023-12-1993 L2003 **OPH** *020 †35
NELSON, Paul Stewart. 9040 JACKSON AVE 98431 #005-12-1983 L1993 **AN LM** *020 †05
NEVAROV, James Allan. 3633 PACIFIC AVE, STE 204 98418 #005-12-1999 L2003 **AN** *020 †05
NEVISSI, Guity P. 9900 VETERANS DR SW 98493 #517-01-1968 L1978 **PM** *020 †60
NEWMAN, Robert Jay. MADIGAN ARMY MEDICAL CTR, DEPT PEDIATRICS 98431 #056-06-1980 L2005 **PD PDE** *020 †55
NEWTON, Frank Jos. ■ 98407 #023-12-1992 L2006 **FM** *020 †18
NGAI, Bernard Chokwan. ■ 98493 #048-13-1982 L1983 **END IM** *020 †20
NGUYEN, Dangtuong V. 1206 S 11TH ST, STE 4 98405 #305-01-2004 L2006 **FM** *020 †18
NGUYEN, Dung Xuan. 3817 YAKIMA AVE 98418 #941-01-1971 L1986 **GP** *020
NGUYEN, Khanh Dinh. 4215 49TH AVE NE 98422 #054-04-1995 L1997 **FM** *020 †18
NGUYEN, Khoa Van. 315 MARTIN LTHR KNG JR WAY, MS 315-M5-ISH 98405 #035-46-1996 L1999 **IM** *020 †20
NGUYEN, Thanh Huu. 9601 STEILACOOM BLVD SW 98498 #942-01-1975 L1997 **IM** *020 †20
NIAMATALI, Gavind Habib. 316 MARTIN LTHR KNG JR WAY, INTERNAL MEDICINE 98405 #539-05-2001 L2006 **IM** *100 †20
NICKEL, Gary Wayne. 222 N J ST, STE A 98403 #036-05-1977 L1978 **OBG** *020 †30
NIELSEN, Judith Dyrell. 209 MARTIN LTHR KNG JR WAY, JR WAY 98405 #031-01-1985 L1989 **IM FM** *020 †20
NIELSEN, Ronald Deen. 1149 MARKET ST 98402 #005-12-1981 L1989 **IM PLM** *020 †20
NILSEN, Karen Wright. ■ 98407 #030-06-1995 L1998 **PD** *020 †55
NORBECK, John Chas. FORT LEWIS 98431 #046-01-1977 L1993 **U UP** *020 †95
NORDESTGAARD, Aksel G. 1802 YAKIMA AVE STE 204, CASCADE VASCULAR ASSOCIATE 98405 #297-01-1983 L1991 **VS GS** *020 †85
NORMAN, Kurt Andrew. 209 MARTIN LTHR KNG JR WAY, TACOMA MED CENTER 98405 #016-11-1997 L2006 **HEM ON** *020 †20
NUCCIO, Maureen Ann M. 1717 S J ST, ATTN:KAREN PATTERSON 98405 #028-34-1970 L1973 **PUD IM** *020 †20
NUCCIO, Paul J. 9900 VETERANS DR SW 98493 #035-08-1970 L1973 **IM** *020 †20
NUNN, Robert R. ■ 98407 #048-04-1953 L1980 **PYA P** *071 †75
NYLAND, Sarah Virginia. 209 MARTIN LTHR KNG JR WAY 98405 #054-04-1999 L2001 **FM** *020 †18
O'BRIEN, Kerry Lynne. MEDICAL CENTER, MADIGAN ARMY 98431 #024-05-2002 **PTH** *020 †50
O'CONNELL, Shelmar Ruth. 315 MARTIN LTHR KNG JR WAY, TACOMA GENERAL HOSPITAL 98405 #007-02-1985 L1988 **IM** *020
ODENTHAL, Allison A. 3124 S 19TH ST, STE 200 98405 #010-01-1985 L1995 **FM** *020 †18
OH, George Duckjoo. 1624 S I ST, RM 309 98405 #583-01-1961 L1970 **OBG** *071 †30
OH, Hyung Suk. 209 MARTIN LTHR KNG JR WAY 98405 #583-01-1983 L1988 **FM** *020 †18
O'HALLORAN, Patricia M. ■ 98407 #034-01-1994 L2003 IM *020 †20
OHME, Richard Kenneth. 1901 S UNION AVE, STE A221 98405 #030-05-1964 L1967 **U** *071 †95
OJEABURU, Jeremiah V. 3209 S 23RD ST, STE 340 98405 #690-01-1988 L2002 **GE IM** *020 †20
OJHA, Ambrish Kumar. 316 MARTIN LTHR KNG JR WAY, INTERNAL MEDICINE 98405 #495-15-1998 L2004 **ID** *020 †20
O'KEEFE, Anthony Jos. 314 S K ST STE 302 98405 #539-02-1955 L1962 **AN** *020 †05
OLARIU, Mihaela Elena. 1123 PACIFIC AVE 98402 #781-03-1996 L2003 **IM** *100 †20
OLIVIER, Richard Marcel. 209 MARTIN LTHR KNG JR WAY 98405 #021-05-1974 L1983 **IM** *020 †20
OLTMAN, Mason Woolridge. 316 MARTIN LTHR KNG JR WAY, STE 212 98405 #035-09-2002 L2005 **PD** *020 †55
ONYALI, Kenneth Obidigbo. 315 MARTIN LTHR KNG JR WAY, A5-1PSH MAILSTOP 98405 #690-04-1985 L2001 **IM** *020 †20
OPPLIGER, Ina Rose. 209 MARTIN LTHR KNG JR WAY, GROUP HEALTH MEDICAL CENTE 98405 #019-02-1980 L1985 **RHU IM** *020 †20
ORAVETZ, Jan. 3611 S D ST S-22 98418 #286-03-1955 L1975 **AN GP** *071 †05
ORMAZABAL, Amaya. 2202 S CEDAR ST, STE 200 98405 #048-12-2000 L2000 **PDR** *020 †80
ORTEGA, Oscar Montejo. 4314 E PORTLAND AVE, STE 7 98404 #748-11-1973 L1985 **FPG** *020
OSGOOD, John Christopher. 209 MARTIN LTHR KNG JR WAY 98405 #023-12-1984 L1994 **ORS** *020 †40
OSTERICHER, Robert. 209 S K ST, TACOMA SPECIALTY CENTER 98405 #010-02-1982 L1992 **U GS** *020 †95
OVERMAN, Richard Hinson. ■ 98466 #005-11-1954 L1954 **OS** *071
OVERSTREET, Debora W. 1708 YAKIMA AVE, STE 110 98405 #054-04-1992 L1996 **PD** *020 †55
OZOLIN, Arthur Juris. 2420 S UNION AVE STE 300 98405 #038-40-1964 L1971 **ORS** *020 †40
PACE, Steven Albert. 315 MARTIN LTHR KNG JR WAY, TACOMA GENERAL HOSPITAL 98405 #054-04-1978 L1979 **EM ETX** *020 †16
PADEN, Lindsay Bernard. ■ 98431 #005-12-1976 L2004 **P CHP** *071 †75
PAGE, Doris Adams. 1901 S UNION AVE STE B3003 98405 #007-02-1982 L1989 **FM GP** *020
PALMQUEST, Margaret Aslin. 9900 VETERANS DR SW 98493 #035-47-1982 L1983 **EM FM** *020 †20
PALY, David A. 1802 YAKIMA AVE, STE 100 98405 #008-01-1981 L1982 **AN** *020 †05
PANDHI, Anshul. ■ 98407 #495-45-1993 L2005 **RHU** *020 †20
PARK, Gary Steven. 314 MARTIN LTHR KNG JR #9, PEDIATRIX CRITICAL CARE 98405 #040-02-1984 L1990 **CCP PD** *020 †55
PARK-HWANG, Esther M. 521 MARTIN LTHR KNG JR WAY 98405 #005-12-1993 L1998 **OBG** *020 †30
PASCHALL, John Alan. 314 MARTIN LTHR KNG JR #9, PEDIATRIC SPECIALTY CARE 98405 #051-04-1983 L1993 **CCP PD** *020 †55
PASTERNAK, Keith Charles. 216 PUYALLUP AVE 98421 #011-04-1995 L1998 **IM** *020 †20
PATTISON, Bradley Dowd. 1802 YAKIMA AVE, STE 100 98405 #054-04-1982 L1989 **AN GS** *020 †05
PAXSON, Charles Speakman. DEPT OF MEDICINIE, VA PUGET SOUND PHCS 98493 #041-01-1970 L1973 **RHU IM** *020 †20
PEARSON, Don Cary. ■ 98499 #016-11-1959 L1964 **OPH** *071 †35

PEARSON, Erik Disney. ■ 98418 #023-12-2004 L2005 *100

PECK, Dennis Wayne. 5702 N 26TH ST, CARE 98407 #025-01-1982 L1985 **FM** *020 †18

PEIXOTTO, John Harvey. 2202 S CEDAR ST, STE 200 98405 #050-02-1978 L1989 **DR PD** *020 †55,80

PERERA, Neil Gamini. ■ 98402 #038-41-2007 **EM** *012

PETERSON, Andrew Charles. ATTN: MCHJ-SOU, MADIGAN ARMY MEDICAL CENTE 98431 #032-01-1995 L2000 **U** *95

PETERSON, Cecily Karen. 9040 FITZSIMMONS DR, FORT LEWIS 98431 #032-01-1995 L1997 **IM** *020 †20

PETERSON, Kris Allen. 9040A REID STREET, ATTN: CREDENTIAL OFFICE 98431 #023-12-1991 L1993 **P** *020 †75

PETERSON, Rosemary Pedraz. 9040A REID STREET, ATTN: CREDENTIAL OFFICE 98431 #023-12-1993 L2004 **CD** *020 †20

PETTY, Christopher Neuman. 1307 S 11TH ST 98405 #049-01-2000 L2004 **CRS** *020 †85,10

PHAM, Joseph Tuan. 2202 S CEDAR ST, STE 100 98405 #040-02-1991 L1996 **OPH** *020 †35

PHAN, Hung Xuan. 9601 STEILACOOM BLVD SW, WESTERN STATE HOSP G M U 98498 #941-01-1981 L1991 **EM** *020 †20

PHILLIP, Douglas Fredrick. 9040A REID STREET, ATTN: CREDENTIAL OFFICE 98431 #054-04-1979 L1985 **GPM FM** *071 †70,18

PHILLIPS, Vincent Fabian. 3611 S D ST, STE 4 98418 #035-48-1975 L1992 **IM HEM** *020 †20

PHILP, James Robt. 3611 S D ST, STE 4 98418 #005-02-1958 L1971 **D PTH** *020 †50,15

PIENKOS, Brian Lee. ■ 98405 #051-07-2004 L2007 **ORS** *012

PIER, Bruce Duane. ■ 98405 #023-12-2008 *012

PIERCE, Brian Thomas. 9040 REID ST # A, ATTN: CREDENTIAL OFFICE 98431 #024-07-1994 L1996 **OBG** *020 †30

PIERI, Marytheres Ann. MADIGAN ARMY MED CTR, OTOLARYNGOLOGY HNS 98431 #023-12-2007 **OTO** *012

PIM, Kenneth Lee. 2420 S UNION AVE STE 330 98405 #054-04-1963 L1964 **FM** *071 †18

PINCUS, Simon H. 9040 REID ST A, MADIGAN AMC 98431 #023-12-1987 L2005 **P** *020 †75

PITT, Deborah June. 315 S MARTIN LUTHER KING J 98405 #917-24-1972 L1979 **FM** *020 †20

PLISKOW, Vita Sari. 1901 S UNION AVE 98405 #061-01-1967 L1971 **AN PUD** *020 †05

PLONSKY, Carl. 1530 S UNION AVE, UNION AVENUE PEDIATRICS 98405 #010-02-1968 L1979 **PD CHP** *020 †55

PLYMATE, Lisa Catherine. 9040 REID ST A, MADIGAN AMC 98431 #016-01-1974 L1978 **END IM** *050 †20

PORTER, Clifford Allen. 419 S L ST, STE 101 98405 #023-12-1986 L1998 **GS** *020 †85

PORTER, Nicole Ann. 3633 PACIFIC AVE STE 204, TACOMA ANESTHESIA ASSOCIAT 98418 #054-04-2000 L2000 **AN** *020 †05

POSADAS, Manuel P, Jr. 3716 PACIFIC AVE, STE F 98418 #748-01-1972 L1984 *020

POSS, James Matthew. ■ 98405 #031-01-2004 L2006 **OTO** *012

POWELL, Jennifer Michelle. MEDICAL CENTER, MADIGAN ARMY 98431 #038-41-2003 L2004 **U** *012

PRAGER, Sarah Ward. 1401 MARTN LTHR KNG JR WAY, STE A 98405 #048-12-2000 L2006 **OBG** *020 †30 ‡

PRATT, Dave Van Doren. 1901 S CEDAR ST, CEDAR MEDICAL CENTER 98405 #005-06-1989 L1997 **FPS PS** *012

PRATT, David Frederic. 2202 S CEDAR ST STE 300 98405 #010-01-1986 L1999 **PS** *020 †85,65

PREDMORE, Susan Sylvia. 1102 S I ST, COMMUNITY HEALTH CARE 98405 #054-04-1986 L1989 **OBG GP** *040 †30

PRESCOTT, Stanford T, Jr. 1901 S UNION AVE 98405 #049-01-1990 L1991 **AN** *020 †05

PREWITT, Charles Delbert. 1901 S UNION AVE STE B2009 98405 #054-04-1962 L1964 **OTO** *020 †45

PRIEBE, William Michael. 11315 BRIDGEPORT WAY SW 98499 #025-07-1974 L1980 **GE** *020 †20

PUNTEL, Robert Anthony. MCHJ-P, PEDIATRICS MADIGAN AMC 98431 #023-12-1989 L1998 **PDC** *020 †55

QUIROZ, Armando Jesus. 1112 S CUSHMAN AVE 98405 #054-04-1996 L1998 **FM** *020 †18

QURAISHI, Abdul. ■ 98466 #409-12-1972 L1999 **FM** *020

RAFOTH, Thomas Jay. 3402 S 18TH ST, TACOMA RADIOLOGICAL ASSOCI 98405 #016-11-1973 L1978 **DR** *020 †80

RAGHUNATH, Nagavedu D. 5909 ORCHARD ST W 98467 #495-04-1980 L1991 **P** *020

RAJACICH, Nicholas. 311 N L ST 98403 #023-07-1982 L1990 **OP ORS** *020 †40

RAMOS, Nelly Calantoc. ■ 98422 #748-10-1967 L1981 **P** *020

RAMOS, Rufino. ■ 98422 #748-09-1964 L1979 **P** *020

RAMUSACK, Raymond Geo. 1802 YAKIMA AVE, STE 100 98405 #017-20-1983 L1990 **APM** *020 †20,05

RANEY, Brendan Eugene. 3 ROSEMONT WAY, STE 201 98406 #005-06-1978 L2004 **IM** *030 †20

RAO, Jerome Paul. 1901 S UNION AVE, STE A206 98405 #561-17-1975 L1981 **U** *020 †95

RAWIE, Eric Wilhelm. DEPT OF RADIOLOGY, MADIGAN ARMY MED CTR 98431 #023-12-2002 L2004 **DR** *012

RAWLINGS, James Scott. 315 S MARTIN LUTHER KING J 98405 #047-05-1973 L1995 **NPM PD** *020 †55

RAYMOND, William Romain. MADIGAN ARMY MED CTR 98431 #010-03-1985 L1992 **OPH** *020 †35

RAYNOR, Lynne Catherine. MADIGAN ARMY MED CTR 98431 #024-05-2002 L2004 **DBP** *012

READ, John Alexander. 1717 S J ST 12THF, ST JOSEPHS HOSPITAL 98405 #005-14-1972 L1986 **MFM OBG** *050 †30

READY, Laurence Brian. 1901 S UNION AVE STE A-2, ALLENMORE HOSPITAL MS19U-A 98405 #068-01-1967 L1978 **AN** *020

REAGAN, Brian Wm. PO BOX 2197 98401 #054-04-1970 L1985 **EM** *020 †16

REALICA, Ross. 1530 S UNION AVE, NORTH PAVILION STE #5 98405 #748-02-1990 L1999 **PS** *020 †85,65

REDDY, Kaditam V. 915 6TH AVE, STE 101 98405 #043-01-1998 L2005 **N** *100

REDDY, Nallathimmayyagari. 1717 S J ST, ST JOSEPH MEDICAL CENTER 98405 #495-70-1974 L2001 **IM HOS** *020 †20

REECE, William Brent. 9040 REID ST A, MCHJ-QGR 98431 #023-12-1987 L1997 **RO IM** *020 †20,80

REED, James Stewart. 3209 S 23RD ST, STE 300 98405 #036-01-1972 L1987 **GE IM** *071 †20

REGIMBAL, Joseph Wm. 316 MARTIN LTHR KNG JR WAY, INTERNAL MEDICINE 98405 #054-04-1981 L1982 **IMG IM** *020 †20

REID, Dennis Gerard. 2111 S 90TH ST 98444 #038-06-1991 L1998 **PD** *020 †55

REILLEY, Sandra Faye. 3615 PACIFIC AVE 98418 #054-04-1985 L1986 **OBG OS** *050 †30

REINEMAN, Diane Louise. 1901 S UNION AVE STE A233, ALLENMORE MEDICAL CENTER 98405 #016-11-1988 L1992 **IM PD** *020 †55

REPLOGLE, John Randall. MCHJ-IMC, INTERNAL MEDICINE CLINIC 98431 #012-05-1976 L1982 **IM OM** *020 †20

RETAILLIAU, Henry F. 3124 N 19TH ST, STE 240 98406 #054-04-1974 L1978 **IM ID** *020 †70,20

REYNOLDS, Angie Marie. 521 MARTIN LTHR KNG JR WAY, TACOMA FAMILY MEDICINE 98405 #054-04-2004 L2004 **FM** *100 †18

RHONE, Sorin S. 9601 STEILACOOM BLVD SW, WESTERN STATE HOSPITAL 98498 #561-01-1950 L1967 **GS OBG** *071

RIBEIRO, Moacyr. 1624 S I ST, NORTHWEST MEDICAL 98405 #187-06-1987 L1992 **ON IM** *020 †20

RICHARDSON, Yolanda James. 209 MARTIN LTHR KNG JR WAY 98405 #033-05-1984 L1989 **OBG** *020 †30

RICKER, David Hamilton. 316 MARTIN L KING JR WAY, STE 212 98405 #003-01-1984 L1991 **PDP PD** *020 †55

RIEKE, John Whitelaw. 1003 S 5TH ST, L1 98405 #040-02-1982 L1987 **RO IM** *040 †20,80

RIES, Gerald Edward, Jr. 2209 E 32ND ST 98404 #030-06-1991 L1995 **FM** *020 †18

RITSON, Jonathan Lee. 2200 N 30TH ST, STE 201 98403 #045-01-1985 L1987 **PM** *020 †60

RITTER, Kenneth J. 1302 N I ST 98403 #054-04-1958 L1959 **GS** *020 †85

RIVERA, Rostom D. 7800 PACIFIC AVE 98408 #748-04-1964 L1968 **FM** *020 †18

RIVERO, Luis Raul. 9040A REID STREET, ATTN: CREDENTIAL OFFICE 98431 #042-03-1994 L1998 **AM** *020 †20

RIZZO, Tanya Renee. 1709 DOCK ST, SOUTH INPATIENT PHYSICIANS 98402 #038-45-2001 L2005 **MPD** *020 †20

ROBERGE, Eric Achille. DEPARTMENT OF RADIOLOGY, MADIGAN ARMY MEDICAL CENTE 98431 #041-02-2001 L2002 **DR** *012

ROBINETTE, Joseph Arnold. 502 S M ST # 200 98405 #018-03-1971 L1974 **GYN OBS** *020 †30

ROBINSON, Jeffrey Richard. 3633 PACIFIC AVE STE 204, TACOMA ANES ASSOC 98418 #054-04-1998 L2002 **AN** *020 †05

ROBINSON-TERRY, Jill D. 2326 BROWNS POINT BLVD 98422 #005-18-1976 L2004 **OS** *020 †80

ROBNETT, Gary Boyd. ■ 98499 #028-03-1965 L1974 **R** *071 †80

RODRIGUEZ, Deborah Ann. 316 MARTIN LTHR KNG JR WAY, STE 212 98405 #048-04-1992 L2000 **PD** *020 †55

ROGERS, Derek John. MADIGAN ARMY MED CTR, OTOLARYNGOLOGY HNS 98431 #023-12-2006 L2007 **OTO** *012

ROHNER, William Leonardo. ■ 98403 #018-03-1956 L1960 **R** *020 †80

ROMNEY, Craig Thos. 1310 S UNION AVE STE 22 98405 #040-02-1975 L1982 **IM** *020 †20

RONE, Craig Alan. 316 MARTIN LTHR KNG JR WAY, STE 305 98405 #054-04-1977 L1978 **OTO** *020 †45

ROOKS, John James, Jr. 7424 BRIDGPRT WAY W #W-305 98499 #011-02-1968 L1989 **OTO** *020 †45

ROOS, James Michael. 521 MARTIN LTHR KNG JR WAY, TACOMA FAMILY MEDICINE 98405 #026-08-2002 L2004 **FM** *100 †18

ROSE, Donald Richard. 3402 S 18TH ST, ADMINISTRATIVE OFFICE 98405 #007-02-1974 L1979 **NM DR** *050 †80,28

ROSE, John Creighton. 5410 N 44TH ST 98407 #014-01-1991 L1994 **CHP P** *020 †75

ROSEN, Irene Michele. MADIGAN ARMY MEDICAL CTR, DEPT OF FAMILY MEDICINE 98431 #023-12-1999 L2007 **FM** *020 †18 ‡

ROSEN, Joel D. ■ 98431 #550-02-1982 L1982 **PN** *020 †55

ROSENTHAL, Jill Robin. 209 M L KING JR WAY, GHC DERM 98405 #024-01-1985 L2005 **D** *020 †15

ROSS, Nathan Stuart. 1628 S MILDRED ST STE 104, ENDOCRUINE CONSULTANTS NW 98465 #043-01-1979 L2001 **IM** *020 †20

ROTH, Bernard Johannes. MCHJ-EDME, MADIGAN ARMY MED CTR 98431 #024-16-1985 L1986 **PCC IM** *040 †20

ROTH, Rob Roy. 315 M L KING JR WAY 98405 #007-02-1974 L1981 **PTH** *020 †50

ROUSSEL, Paula L. 3124 N 19TH ST, # 200 98405 #041-14-1979 L1994 **FM** *020

ROWLANDS, John Hamilton. 316 MARTIN LTHR KNG JR WAY, STE 401 98405 #054-04-1976 L1982 **PUD IM** *020 †20

ROYAL, Beth Lynn. 521 MARTIN LTHR KNG JR WAY, TACOMA FAMILY MED 98405 #005-12-2007 L2007 **FP** *012

RUDD, Anthony Dale. 1717 S J ST 98405 #056-06-2002 L2005 **EM** *020 †16

RUE, Kirk Erwin. 3633 PACIFIC AVE, STE 204 98418 #005-12-1975 L1978 **AN** *020 †05

RUIZ-MOLLESTON, Joy P. 3716 PACIFIC AVE STE G 98418 #748-01-1977 L1987 **GPM ADM** *020

RUIZ PAREDES, Daniel. 9601 STEILACOOM BLVD SW 98498 #649-14-1984 L1996 **P** *020

RUSINKO, Joseph Brion. 315 MARTIN LTHR KNG JR WAY, TACOMA GENERAL HOSPITAL 98405 #021-01-1983 L1995 **EM** *020 †16

RUSSELL, Michael Douglas. 3633 PACIFIC AVE, STE 204 98418 #054-04-1990 L1990 **AN** *020 †05

RUSSELL, Patricia Jean. 2420 S UNION AVE 98405 #054-04-1993 L1993 **FM** *020 †18

RUTBERG, Samara Amaris. ■ 98407 #023-12-1999 L2001 **CD** *020 †20

RYAN, Stephen Carme, Jr. ■ 98407 #040-02-2001 L2007 **PCC** *020

RYTTING, Aimee Michelle. DEPT OF RADIOLOGY, MADIGAN ARMY MED CTR 98431 #010-01-2004 **DR** *012

SABETI, Mohebat. ■ 98467 #517-04-1976 L1990 **P IMG** *020 †75

SACKS, Jay Gilbert. 1901 S UNION AVE STE A103 98405 #048-13-1974 L1975 **FM** *020

SALAM, Tariq. 1901 S CEDAR ST, STE 301 98405 #011-04-1996 L2003 **ICE CD** *020 †20

SALLOUM, Maan Geo. 8215 64TH STREET CT W 98467 #915-02-1973 L1978 **AN** *020 †05

SALO, Susan Joyce. 1708 YAKIMA AVE, 1ST FL 98405 #054-04-1975 L1978 **FM** *020 †18

SAM, Joseph William. 3402 S 18TH ST, TRA MEDICAL IMAGING 98405 #035-46-1996 L2007 **DR NM** *020 †80,28

SAMS, Richard Woodville. MADIGAN AMC, ATTN: CREDENTIAL OFFICE 98431 #024-05-1995 L1996 **FM** *020 †18

SAND, Bonnie Jean. 209 MARTIN LTHR KNG JR WAY, TACOMA SPECIALTY CLINIC 98405 #005-19-1987 L1998 **IM** *020 †20

SANDALL, Corie Lynn. 1708 YAKIMA AVE, STE 110 98405 #023-01-1999 L2005 **IM** *020 †20

SANDERS, Brenda. 1628 S MILDRED ST, STE 101 98465 #016-11-2003 L2006 **PD** *020 †55

SANDERS, Kevin Eugene. 314 MARTIN LTHR KNG JR WAY, TACOMA RADIATION ONCOLOGY 98405 #016-11-2001 L2006 **RO** *020 †80

SANDS, Robert Edward. 3609 S 19TH ST 98405 #054-04-1972 L1976 **P CHP** *020 †75

SANFORD, Elizabeth Grace. 6002 WESTGATE BLVD, STE 230 98406 #048-02-1982 L1985 **OBG** *020 †30

SARGENT, Robert Taylor. 9601 STEILACOOM BLVD SW, WESTERN STATE HOSPITAL 98498 #017-20-1955 L1965 **P** *020

SARNAT, Andrew James. ■ 98403 #016-06-1976 L1977 **AN** *020 †20

SARNER, Carol. 6002 WESTGATE BLVD STE 230 98406 #005-15-1989 L1999 **OBG** *020 †30

SARRAM, Mahmood. 7424 BRIDGEPORT WAY W 98499 #407-05-1957 L1962 **OBG** *071 †30

SATO, Ray Yoshiro. 315 MARTN LTHR KNG JR 20-N, PEDIATRIX MED GRP 98405 #016-06-1990 L1996 **NPM** *020 †55

SAVAGE, Christopher M. 4225 N STEVENS ST 98407 #003-01-2000 L2004 **AN** *020 †05
SAVAGE, William Lee. ■ 98446 #039-01-1957 L1957 **OM** *030
SCHAAF, Daniel John. 4530 E F ST 98404 #016-11-1961 L1969 **AN** *020 †05
SCHACHTER, David Todd. FT LEWIS CARDIOLOGY SERVIC, MADIGAN ARMY MEDICAL CENTE 98431 #024-07-1987 L1996 **CD IC** *020 †20
SCHILT, Stephen Neal. ■ 98406 #005-12-1976 L1983 **P CHP** *020 †75
SCHMITT, Christopher John. 9505 S STEELE ST 98444 #028-34-1978 L1985 **FM** *020 †18
SCHMITZ, Bradley John. 1901 S UNION AVE, ALLENMORE INTL MED 98405 #056-05-1983 L1996 **IM** *020 †20
SCHNEIDER, Richard Leigh. 3609 S 19TH ST 98405 #041-09-1969 L1989 **P CHP** *020 †75
SCHNELLER, Daniel James. 1924 S CEDAR ST 98405 #028-34-1987 L1990 **PD** *020 †55
SCHNELLER, James Lewis. 1924 S CEDAR ST 98405 #028-34-1959 L1968 **PD PDA** *020 †55
SCHOEN, Eric Alan. 209 MARTIN LTHR KNG JR WAY, JR WAY 98405 #041-13-1990 L2004 **RHU** *020 †20
SCHOENFELDER, Kevin Peter. 1515 MARTN LTHR KNG JR WAY 98405 #026-04-1979 L1980 **ORS** *020 †40
SCHOENIKE, Sumner Lee. 7424 BRIDGEPORT WAY W, STE 203 98499 #048-04-1974 L1986 **PD PHP** *020 †55
SCHOEPPNER, Harald Lothar. 3209 S 23RD ST, STE 340 98405 #409-20-1987 L1997 **GE** *020 †20
SCHOLL, Dennis Gerald. 2202 S CEDAR ST, STE 200 98405 #056-05-1973 L1976 **R** *020 †80
SCHOPP, James Jos. 3124 S 19TH ST, STE 220 98405 #016-11-1986 L1991 **GS** *020 †85
SCHRENK, David. 3633 PACIFIC AVE STE 204, INC PS 98418 #005-12-1988 L1992 **AN** *020 †05
SCHROEDER, Richard Leo. 521 MARTIN LTHR KNG JR WAY 98405 #048-04-1971 L1996 **OBG** *020 †30
SCHUAL-BERKE, Sharon Kay. 1717 S J ST 98405 #035-09-1979 L1985 **CD IM** *071 †20
SCHUBERT, Ronald. 5702 N 26TH ST 98407 #306-01-1984 L2000 **FM** *020 †18
SCHUBERT, Timothy Thos. 3209 S 23RD ST, STE 340 98405 #005-11-1973 L1992 **GE IM** *020 †20
SCHULZE, Paula Lea. PO BOX 5467, 521 S K ST 98415 #048-02-1983 L1984 **FM** *071 †18
SCHUMER, David Saul. 4215 49TH AVE NE 98422 #025-12-1985 L1989 **FM** *020 †18
SCHWARTZ, Lawrence Edward. 1624 S I ST, NORTHWEST MEDICAL 98405 #038-43-1986 L1992 **IM PD** *020 †20,55
SCIARRONE, Daria. 3124 S 19TH ST, STE 240 98405 #051-04-2000 L2004 **FM** *020 †18
SCOTT, Beverly Rice. 9040A REID ST, MCHJ-QCR 98431 #038-06-1985 L1986 **N** *020 †75
SEAHOLM, Norman A. 4215 49TH AVE NE 98422 #054-04-1997 L2001 **FM** *020 †18
SEAMAN, John Merrill. 209 MARTIN LTHR KNG JR WAY 98405 #005-19-1975 L1993 **RHU IM** *020 †20
SEAVELLO, Julia Frances. 1019 PACIFIC AVE STE 1600 98402 #005-11-1994 L1998 **AN** *020 †05
SECAIRA, Roberto A. 1802 YAKIMA AVE STE 307 98405 #429-02-1992 L2000 **IC** *020 †20
SEMANCIK, Gregory John. 9040 JACKSON AVE 98431 #023-12-1989 L1992 **PG PD** *020 †55
SENECAL, Francis Mark. 1624 S I ST STE 102, NORTHWEST MED SPECIALTIES 98405 #017-20-1977 L1978 **ON HEM** *020 †20
SERRANO, Culbert. 316 MARTIN LTHR KNG JR WAY, STE 304 98405 #748-02-1995 L2004 **IM** *020 †20
SETTLE, C Stephen. 2201 S 19TH ST STE 104 98405 #038-41-1976 L1978 **PM PME** *020 †60
SHANLEY, Elizabeth Carol. DEPT OF FAMILY PRACTICE, MADIGAN ARMY MED CTR 98431 #023-12-1995 L1997 **IMG** *020 †18
SHARPE, Louis Jedediah. 521 MARTIN LTHR KNG JR WAY, TACOMA FAMILY MEDICINE 98405 #038-45-2001 L2003 **FM** *020
SHAUKAT, Muhammad I. 9040A REID STREET 98431 #704-02-1969 L1977 **IM OS** *100 †05
SHELTON, Alan Edward. 2209 E 32ND ST 98404 #040-02-1981 L1984 **FM** *020 †18
SHIBATA, Kenneth Hisakazu. 1708 YAKIMA AVE STE 110 98405 #054-04-1977 L1980 **IM** *020 †20
SHIELDS, William Kenneth. 2914 S ALDER ST 98409 #054-04-1983 L1988 **OPH** *020 †35
SHIN, Peter Changhag. 1802 YAKIMA AVE, STE 306 98405 #038-44-1991 L2001 **NS** *072 †25
SHINOBU, Marian C. 209 MARTIN LTHR KNG JR WAY, JR WAY 98405 #054-04-1977 L2001 **EM IM** *020 †20,16
SHIRBACHEH, Mansour V. 1708 YAKIMA AVE, STE 115 98405 #035-06-1993 L2002 **PS** *020 †65
SHIVELEY, Sherrod Palm. 1717 S J ST, ST JOSEPHS MED CTR 98405 #040-02-2000 L2003 **IM** *020 †20
SHREWSBURY, Donald Wm. 1901 S UNION AVE # 2010 98405 #026-04-1975 L1981 **OTO HNS** *020 †45
SHULMAN, Alan Jay. 315 MARTIN LTHR KNG JR WAY 98405 #054-04-1993 L1994 **FM** *020 †18
SIEGEL, David Allen. 17520 22ND AVE E, CENTRAL PIERCE FIRE & RESC 98445 #023-12-1992 L1999 **EM** *020 †16
SIEGEMUND, Ronald Dieter. 2111 S 90TH ST 1ST FL, MEDALIA HEALTHCARE 98444 #005-18-1992 L1998 **PD** *020 †55
SILAS, Victoria Mcclellan. 311 S L ST 98405 #024-16-1991 L2001 **OP ORS** *020 †40
SIM, Stephen Hyonkyu. ■ 98422 #054-04-1999 L2002 **IM** *020 †20
SIMMER, John Jerome. 9040 REID ST A, MADIGAN AMC 98431 #026-04-1989 L1990 **OTO** *040 †45
SIMONSON, Mary Kristine. 4041 RUSTON WAY STE 202 98402 #046-01-1982 L1983 **P** *020 †75
SIMS, Robert Brownell. 1624 S I ST, STE 405 98405 #040-02-1983 L1989 **HEM ON** *020 †20
SINGH, Cecilia B. 7914 99TH AVE SW 98498 #496-07-1953 L1985 **FM P** *071
SINGH, Surinderjit. 701 N STADIUM WAY 98403 #495-08-1969 L1978 **PM OS** *020 †60
SINGH, Tejinderpal. 1717 S J ST 98405 #035-47-1990 L1994 **IM** *020 †20
SKRINAR, Kathleen G. 3611 S D ST 98418 #030-06-1956 **OS** *071
SLADEK, Wayne Alan. 209 MARTIN LTHR KNG JR WAY 98405 #005-12-1981 L1989 **AI PD** *020 †55,03
SMITH, Arthur Mc Danel. 2201 S 19TH ST STE 205 98405 #004-01-1961 L1970 **N** *020
SMITH, David Scott. 209 MARTIN LTHR KNG JR WAY, GROUP HEALTH TACOMA MED CE 98405 #056-06-1976 L1986 **ORS** *020 †40
SMITH, Donald Vincent. 9040 REID ST A, ATTN: CREDENTIAL OFFICE 98431 #003-01-1983 L1994 **DR** *020 †80
SMITH, Gerald Bruce. 209 MARTIN LTHR KNG JR WAY 98405 #054-04-1973 L1979 **FM** *020 †18
SMITH, Jeffrey Lee. 14916 WASHINGTON AVE SW 98498 #054-04-1992 L1994 **FM** *020 †18
SMITH, Paul Brown, Jr. ■ 98407 #005-11-1957 L1963 **OPH** *071 †35
SMITH, Paula Lynn. 209 MARTIN LTHR KNG JR WAY 98405 #041-09-1982 L1989 **OBG** *020 †30
SMITH, Steven Richard. 9040 REID ST A, ATTN:CREDENTIAL OFFICE 98431 #054-04-1979 L1997 **OM PHP** *020 †70
SMITH, Wendel Julio. 1802 YAKIMA AVE, STE 102 98405 #016-01-1988 L1998 **TS** *020 †85,90
SMOLEN, Harry G, Jr. 2201 S 19TH ST STE 104 98405 #040-02-1983 L2006 **PM** *020 †60
SMOLEY, Brian Alan. 9040A REID ST, MCHJ-QCR 98431 #026-04-1997 L1998 **FM** *020 †18
SMOOT, Kyle Eugene. 209 MARTIN LTHR KNG JR WAY 98405 #038-41-2000 L2004 **N** *020 †75
SMOOTS, John Stephen. 1708 YAKIMA AVE, STE 110 98405 #003-01-1984 L1987 **IM** *020 †20
SNODGRASS, Lanny Lloyd. AMERICAN LAKE VAMC, 9900 VETERAN DR. BLDG 61 98493 #649-33-1980 L1988 **P ADP** *020 †75
SNOWDEN, Stacey Lynne. 521 MARTIN LTHR KNG JR WAY, TACOMA FAMILY MEDICINE 98405 #005-12-2005 L2006 **FP** *012
SOBBA, Walter L. ■ 98406 #030-06-1951 L1952 **FM** *071
SOMAN, Michael Philip. 950 PACIFIC AVE, STE 900 98402 #005-19-1978 L1982 **FM GPM** *020 †18
SONNEBORN, Miranda Rose. ■ 98407 #051-04-2008 *012
SORENSEN, Douglas M. 9040A REID STREET, ATTN: CREDENTIAL OFFICE 98431 #023-12-1992 L2000 **OTO** *020 †45
SOROKOVSKA, Daniela Jorda. 521 MARTIN LTHR KNG JR WAY, TACOMA FAMILY MEDICINE 98405 #913-15-1992 L2005 **FP** *012
SORONEN, Michael David. 314 MARTN LTHR KNG JR #11 98405 #025-01-1969 L1973 **R RO** *020 †80
SPAIN-REMY, Claire Leona. PO BOX 5299, MS 1501-2-MMG 98415 #036-07-1985 L1987 **OBG** *030 †30
SPAULDING, Richard Knapp. 1530 S UNION AVE, STE 5 N PAVILION/ 98405 #041-13-1971 L1978 **FM** *071 †18
SPEER, Sabine Ellen. 3633 PACIFIC AVE, STE 204 98418 #001-02-1978 L1979 **AN** *020 †05
STANGL, Frank Fredrick. ■ 98406 #007-02-1948 L1948 **OBG GS** *071 †30
STANGL, James Alan. 9040 JACKSON AVE 98431 #016-06-1992 L1993 **AN** *020 †05
STANTON-ANDERSON, Mary. 209 MARTIN LTHR KNG JR WAY, WAY 98405 #005-14-1979 L1984 **OBG** *020 †30
STARNES, Benjamin Ware. 9040 REID ST, MADIGAN ARMY MED CTR 98431 #041-02-1992 L2005 **GS** *020 †85
STARR, Hillary Brooke. ■ 98422 #005-12-2006 L2006 **FP** *012
STARR, Kirk Newell. 316 MARTIN LTHR KNG JR WAY, STE 212 98405 #012-05-1971 L1975 **PD** *020 †55
STATSON, Andrew N. 1901 S CEDAR ST STE 204 98405 #396-06-1962 L1973 **OBG** *071 †30
STEBNER, Frederick C. 9040A REID STREET, ATTN: CREDENTIAL OFFICE 98431 #051-01-1964 L1964 **NM** *020 †80,28
STEFANELLI, Christopher B. 314 MARTIN LTHR KNG JR WAY, STE 303 98405 #030-06-1997 L2003 **PDC** *020 †55
STEFANELLI, Tammara Susan. 2517 N WASHINGTON ST 98406 #030-06-1997 L1999 **FM** *020 †18
STEGMAN, Roger J. 9040 LAUDER LOOP RD, INTERNAL MED CLNC 98431 #024-07-1973 L1977 **ON IM** *020 †20
STEINWENDER, Helmut A. 9601 STEILACOOM BLVD SW, W27-19 98498 #154-07-1981 L1992 **P** *020 †75
STEPHAN, Mark Jos. MADIGAN MED CTR, DEPT PED 98431 #007-02-1971 L1977 **PD** *020 †55
STEPHENSON, Roberta Sue. 311 S L ST, M/S B1-CC 98405 #035-09-1990 L1996 **PDC** *020 †55
STEUDEL, Wolfgang Theodor. ATTN HCHJ-MCD, MADIGAN ARMY MED CTR 98431 #005-12-1966 L1969 **CD IC** *020 †20
STEWART, James M. ■ 98466 #061-01-1975 *100
STEWART, William Marsden. 1802 YAKIMA AVE, STE 100 98405 #049-01-1987 L1991 **AN** *020 †05
ST HILAIRE, Roland James. 3209 S 23RD ST, STE 340 98405 #012-05-1975 L1976 **GE IM** *020 †20
STOVER, William Henry. 718 FAWCETT AVE 98402 #023-07-1973 L1997 **MDM PD** *030 †55
STOWELL, Virginia Anne. 3124 S 19TH ST, STE 220 98405 #016-01-1987 L1989 **GS** *020 †85
STRACENER, Carl Edward. FORT LEWIS 98431 #021-05-1956 L1971 **PD** *071 †55
STRINGFELLOW, Steve C. 3124 S 19TH ST, STE 240 98405 #001-02-1984 L1985 **IM** *020 †20
STUART, Paula Leigh. 209 MARTIN LTHR KNG JR WAY, GROUP HEALTH, DPT OF RADIO 98405 #040-02-1984 L1985 **DR** *020 †80
STUBBS, William Richard. 315 MARTIN LTHR KNG JR WAY, MULTICARE 98405 #004-01-1971 L1994 **MDM FM** *030 †18
STUBENRAUCH, Phillip E. FORT LEWIS 98431 #056-05-1959 L1964 **FM AM** *071
STUEN, Marcus Rodway. ■ 98406 #056-06-1946 L1949 **P** *071 †75
STUTTERHEIM, John Karel A. 316 S K ST # ST406 98405 #660-01-1957 L1963 **FM** *071
SU, William Wei-Shin. 209 MARTIN LTHR KNG JR WAY 98405 #244-01-1982 L1992 **OBG FM** *020 †18,30
SUGIYAMA, William M. ■ 98498 #038-06-1949 L1956 **GS OS** *071
SULLIVAN, Jerry J. 9505 S STEELE ST 98444 #030-06-1977 L1978 **FM** *020 †18
SULLIVAN, Mary Theresa. ■ 98498 #048-12-1957 L1959 **AN** *020 †05
SULLIVAN, Rebecca Ann. 3629 S D ST MS 091 98418 #030-06-1975 L1979 **MDM FM** *030 †18
SUN, Howard. 2202 S CEDAR ST, STE 200 98405 #016-11-1993 L2000 **VIR R** *020 †80
SURESH, Anand. 3402 S 18TH ST 98405 #028-34-2001 L2004 **DR** *020 †80
SWANSON, Ana Denise. 521 MARTIN LTHR KNG JR WAY, TACOMA FAMILY MEDICINE 98405 #054-04-2006 L2006 **FP** *012
SWINEHART, Paul A, Jr. 3633 PACIFIC AVE, STE 204 98418 #030-06-1979 L1980 **AN** *020 †05
SZIGETI, Christine Lynn. 9040 REID ST # A, ATTN: CREDENTIAL OFFICE 98431 #023-12-1990 L1999 **AN** *020 †05
SZIGETI, Julius, II. 1708 YAKIMA AVE, STE 110 98405 #038-06-1986 L1998 **OBG** *020 †30
TAN, Darryl Dean. 7424 BRIDGEPORT WAY W, PEDIATRIC ASSOC LAKEWOOD 98499 #005-12-1982 L1990 **PD** *020 †55
TANBARA, A George. 1717 S J ST 98405 #026-04-1952 L1952 **PD** *020 †55
TANG, Keith Ching. 1206 S 11TH ST STE 4 98405 #166-02-2002 L2004 **FM** *020 †18
TANZ, Henry Alan. 209 MARTIN LTHR KNG JR WAY 98405 #005-14-1974 L1979 **ORS** *020 †40
TAPP, Andre. AMERICAN LAKE (116A), VETERANS AFFAIRS MEDICAL C 98493 #165-01-1977 L1994 **P** *020 †75
TART, Gary Conley. 1628 S MILDRED ST, STE 101 98465 #040-02-1981 L1998 **PD** *020 †55
TAUBMAN, Gary Richard. 1802 YAKIMA AVE, STE 201 98405 #040-02-1980 L1985 **GE IM** *020 †20
TAUSCH, Timothy James. MADIGAN ARMY MED CTR, DEPT OF SURGERY 98431 #038-06-2007 **GS** *012
TAYLOR, James Robt. 316 M L KING JR WAY # 40 98405 #005-02-1982 L1982 **PUD CCM** *020 †20
TAYLOR, Muriel King. 9900 VETERANS DR SW 98493 #035-20-1962 L1968 **P CHP** *071 †75
TAYLOR, Ronald Glenn. 2121 S 19TH ST, 2121 SO 19TH ST 98405 #036-05-1968 L1970 **GS EM** *020 †85
TEAGUE, Nathaniel Scott. COMMANDER, MADIGAN ARMY MED CTR 98431 #021-01-2006 L2006 **GPM** *012
TEER, Bethany Noelle. MADIGAN ARMY MED CTR, DEPT OF FAMILY MED 98431 #048-12-2007 **FP** *012
TEMERLIN, Steven M. 1717 S J ST 98405 #039-01-1979 L2005 **EM** *020 †20,16
TEREM, Theresa Marie. 419 S L ST, STE 101 98405 #016-43-1981 L1987 **CRS GS** *020 †10,85
TERRY, Melissa Virginia. HQ MEDICAL EDUATION 98431 #028-03-2000 L2002 **OBG** *020

■ = Address Information Privacy Protected

THEMELIS, Nicholas James. 11601 PACIFIC AVE S, PACIFIC PEDIATRICS 98444 #040-02-1985 L1988 **PD** *020 †55

THIESSEN, Abram Robt. ■ 98407 #062-01-1970 L1976 **ON HEM** *072 †20

THOMAS, Ali Manning. 209 MARTIN LTHR KNG JR WAY 98405 #025-01-2002 L2007 **IM** *100 †20

THOMAS, William Jos, Jr. 316 MARTIN LTHR KNG JR WAY, STE 212 98405 #041-02-1972 L1993 **PHO PD** *020 †55

THOMPSON, W Frederick. 1550 S UNION AVE STE 210 98405 #012-05-1985 L1995 **ORS** *020 †40

THORPE, Robert Jacob. 1708 YAKIMA AVE, STE 110 98405 #039-01-1979 L1997 **FM AM** *072 †18

TIMONEN, Robert Martin. 1019 PACIFIC AVE STE 1600 98402 #054-04-1978 L1979 **AN** *020 †05

TIO-MATOS, Iris M. ■ 98406 #042-01-1987 L1993 **IMG IM** *020 †20

TIU, Alvin Yuhico. MCHJ-QCR, 9040 A REID STRE, ATTN: CREDENTIAL OFFICE 98431 #016-02-1995 L2007 **FM** *020 †18

TOBIN, Richard Scott. 2202 S CEDAR ST, STE 200 98405 #054-04-1981 L1986 **R** *020 †80

TOMKINS, Michael James. 311 S L ST, MARY BRIDGE CHILDREN'S HEA 98405 #917-20-1988 L1997 **PD** *020 †55

TOMPKINS, Jeremy Robert. 3633 PACIFIC AVE, TACOMA ANESTHESIA ASSOCIAT 98418 #056-06-2000 L2004 **AN** *020 †05

TORNOW, John Jos. 1501 MARKET ST STE 200 98402 #010-01-1975 L1998 **FM** *030 †18

TORRES, Mark Francis. MADIGAN ARMY MEDICAL CTR, OPHTHALMOLOGY SERVICE 98431 #034-01-1990 L2004 **OPH AM** *040 †35

TOTH, Eileen Rose. 1901 S UNION AVE, STE B7005 98405 #024-01-1972 L1975 **IM GP** *020 †20

TRAN, Khai Anh. 2202 S CEDAR ST, STE 200 98405 #032-01-1992 L1995 **DR** *020 †80

TRIPPEL, Donald L. 1901 S CEDAR ST STE 103 98405 #054-04-1980 L1981 **PDC** *020 †55

TUELL, Stanley Wayne. ■ 98403 #016-06-1944 L1944 **GS** *071 †85

TUOHY, Craig D. 1708 YAKIMA AVE 98405 #067-01-1987 L1992 **GE** *020 †20

TURELLA, Giorgio S. MCHJ-QCR, 9040A REID ST 98431 #561-13-1967 L1980 **N** *020 †75

TUTIHASI, Mimi Azalea. 1708 YAKIMA AVE STE 110, ST JOSEPH MED CLNC 98405 #035-45-1977 L1993 **PD** *020 †55

URIBE, Paul Shane. MADIGAN AMC, ATTN: CREDENTIAL OFFICE 98431 #023-12-2001 L2003 *100 †50

USMAN, Junaid Quadir. 1717 S J ST, FRANCISCAN INPATIENT TEAM 98405 #496-32-1998 L2004 **GPM** *100

UYPITCHING, Nicholas R. ■ 98499 #748-10-1972 **GS** *020

VACCARO, John Anthony. 1901 S UNION AVE STE A221, ALLENMORE MED CTR 98405 #035-15-1976 L1991 **ON U** *020 †95

VAIDYA, Omma Go. 521 MARTIN LTHR KNG JR WAY, MULTICARE OB/GYN ASSOCIATE 98405 #025-12-2001 L2005 **OBG** *020 †30

VANCE, Philip A. 1708 YAKIMA AVE STE 50 98405 #028-03-1980 L1985 **FM** *020 †18

VANDENHOVEN, Michele D. 3633 PACIFIC AVE STE 204, INC PS 98418 #005-12-1992 L1998 **AN** *020 †05

VAN DOOREN, Hugo. ■ 98407 #660-01-1952 L1954 **P PYA** *072 †75

VAN DUKER, Bradford Scott. 515 S M ST, STE 201 98405 #041-13-1988 L1992 **AN** *020 †05

VAN WAGENEN, Peter B. 209 MARTIN LTHR KNG JR WAY 98405 #005-11-1974 L1979 **GS** *020 †85

VEGA, Danielle Anne. 1708 YAKIMA AVE, STE 202 98405 #035-47-1998 L2004 **MG** *100

VEGH, Arthur Benjamin. 1901 S UNION AVE, STE B6010 98405 #054-04-1983 L1989 **AI OS** *020 †20,03

VENTURA, Veronica Lee. 314 MARTIN LTHR KNG JR WAY, STE 104 98405 #021-01-1996 L2003 **OBG** *020 †30

VENUTO, Gail Carreau. 1812 S J ST, STE 120 98405 #010-01-1987 L1999 **OBG** *020 †30

VERCIO, Raymond Lawrence. 1802 YAKIMA AVE, STE 100 98405 #005-12-1984 L1988 **AN** *020 †20

VETTER, David Paul. ■ 98445 #023-12-1994 L1996 **IM** *020 †20

VIER, Michael William. 1717 S J ST, FRANCISCAN INPATIENT TEAM 98405 #038-41-1996 L1998 **IM** *020 †20

VINCENT, Damon T. 1717 S J ST 98405 #028-02-2004 L2007 **EM** *012

VISKOVICH, Borko Bartuo. 11315 BRIDGEPORT WAY SW 98499 #957-01-1961 L1981 **AN** *075

VITIKAINEN, Kari Juhani. 1802 YAKIMA AVE, STE 102 98405 #035-15-1965 L1976 **TS** *020 †85,90

VORA, Swati D. 2201 S 19TH ST STE 205, PEDIATRICS NEUROLOGY ASSOC 98405 #495-98-1985 L2002 **CHN** *020 †75

VOZENILEK, Z Jos. ■ 98403 #869-05-1949 L1956 **OBG** *071 †30 ‡

WACHTEL, Robert Franklin. 315 MARTIN LTHR KNG JR WAY, TACOMA GENERAL HOSPITAL 98405 #024-05-1975 L1976 **EM** *020 †18

WADA, Sumiho. 515 S M ST, STE 201 98405 #572-16-1958 L1965 **AN** *071 †05

WADSWORTH, Troy W. 1821 DOCK ST, UNIT 502 98402 #048-15-2000 L2007 **HO** *020

WAGONER, John D. 1717 S J ST 98405 #654-01-1991 L1995 **IM** *020 †20

WAGONFELD, James Bart. 3209 S 23RD ST, STE 340 98405 #016-42-1970 L1978 **GE IM** *020 †20

WALKLEY, Edward Ingersoll. 311 S L ST 98405 #024-01-1970 L1975 **PD EM** *020 †55

WALSH, Jean Margaret. 209 MARTIN LTHR KNG JR WAY, JR WAY 98405 #003-01-1978 L1996 **ORS EM** *020 †40

WALTMAN, Richard Elliott. 1901 S UNION AVE 98405 #035-46-1975 L1981 **FM IMG** *020 †18

WAMBAUGH, Geo Wilmar, Jr. 209 MARTIN LTHR KNG JR WAY 98405 #023-01-1969 L1980 **N IM** *020 †75

WANG, Herbert Lim. 314 MARTN LTHR KNG JR #11 98405 #005-19-1995 L2004 **RO** *020 †80

WANG, Hui. 2201 S 19TH ST # 1 98405 #243-79-1982 L2005 **PM PMM** *020

WANG, Ken Sandor. ■ 98403 #041-01-2006 L2006 **P** *012

WANWIG, John Danl. 1901 S UNION AVE STE A305 98405 #054-01-1971 L1972 **P IM** *020 ‡

WARNER, Allan Maxwell. 1000 TOWN CTR NE STE 180 98422 #005-06-1955 L1994 **P** *072 †75

WARWICK, Wendy Irene. 3633 PACIFIC AVE STE 204, TACOMA ANESTHESIA ASSOC 98418 #054-04-2001 L2001 **AN** *020 †05

WATERMEYER, Deryck S. 1802 YAKIMA AVE, STE 100 98405 #836-01-1984 L1990 **PME AN** *020

WATRIN, Kerry Gene. 521 MARTIN LTHR KNG JR WAY, TACOMA FAMILY MEDICINE 98405 #054-04-1980 L1981 **FM** *040 †18

WEARN, Joseph Henry. 1717 S J ST 98405 #041-01-1964 L1970 **PD** *020 †55

WEATHERBY, Charles Melvin. 1812 S J ST, STE 102 98405 #054-04-1978 L1981 **FM** *020 †18

WEDMORE, Ian Shamus. 9040 REID ST A, DEM 98431 #035-09-1990 L1995 **EM** *020 †16

WEEKS, Alexandra Louise. 3008 N NARROWS DR, UNIT G301 98407 #041-01-2002 L2005 **EM** *100 †16

WEEKS, David Champ. 3124 S 19TH ST, BLDG C 98405 #045-01-1999 L2005 **U** *020 †95

WEIS, George Andrew. 2202 S CEDAR ST 98405 #017-20-1970 L1973 **DR** *020 †80

WELED, Barry Jerome. 316 MARTIN LTHR KNG JR WAY, STE 401 98405 #054-04-1972 L1975 **PUD CCM** *020 †20

WENZELL, Daniel Mark. COMMANDER MADIGAN ARMY MED 98431 #040-02-1999 L2001 **AN PME** *020 †05

WERSCHKUL, John Douglas. 9040A REID STREET, ATTN: CREDENTIAL OFC; MCHJ 98431 #040-02-1969 L1977 **NS** *020 †25

WESSBECHER, Francis W. 2202 S CEDAR ST, STE 200 98405 #023-07-1984 L1989 **DR** *020 †80

WEST, Shawn R. ■ 98409 #028-46-2007 **TY** *012

WETTLAUFER, John Nichols. 1624 S I ST, STE 204 98405 #010-02-1958 L1974 **U** *020 †95

WHALEN, Danl Anthony, Jr. 515 S M ST STE 201, INC PS 98405 #016-06-1974 L1977 **AN** *020 †05

WHALEY, Sidney F, Jr. 314 MARTIN LTHR KNG JR WAY, JR WAY 98405 #041-01-1963 L1969 **D IM** *020 †20,15

WHITNEY, Allene Marie. 1720 E 44TH ST 98404 #034-01-2002 L2004 **FM** *020 †18

WHITNEY, Robert Byron. 7424 BRIDGEPORT WAY W 98499 #008-01-1959 L1965 **DR RO** *071 †80

WHITTAKER, Paul E. MADIGAN ARMY MED CTR, MCHJ-PA 98431 #023-01-1980 L1998 **FM** *030 †18

WICKS, Merrill James. 315 S MARTIN LUTHER KING J 98405 #041-13-1946 L1947 **PTH** *072 †50

WIESE, G Michael. 1112 6TH AVE STE 302 98405 #010-02-1967 L1972 **NS** *020 †25

WIESEN, Andrew Richard. 9040 REID ST A, ATTN: CREDENTIAL OFFICE 98431 #056-05-1991 L1992 **GPM IM** *020 †70,20

WIGBOLDY, Jay Foster. ■ 98431 #017-20-1997 L2007 **DR** *020 †80

WILHYDE, David Edward. ■ 98403 #054-04-1960 L1962 **ATP PTH** *071 †50 ‡

WILLHAM, Bruce Edward. 315 M L KING JR WAY 98405 #017-20-1978 L1985 **NPM PD** *020 †55

WILLIAMES, Lee David. MADIGAN ARMY MED CTR, DEPT OF PEDIATRICS 98431 #010-02-1996 L1997 **DBP** *012 †55

WILLIAMS, Ann Roberson. 2721 N WASHINGTON ST 98407 #054-04-1981 L1982 **ON IM** *020 †20

WILLIAMS, Nelson J, Jr. 8818 PACIFIC AVE, STE C 98444 #016-45-1980 L1989 **CHP** *020

WILLIAMSON, Nicole Ayanna. ■ 98405 #024-07-2006 L2008 **IM** *012

WILSON, Bruce Alan. 209 MARTIN LTHR KNG JR WAY 98405 #054-04-1993 L1996 **IM** *020 †20

WILSON, James L. 1901 S UNION AVE, STE B7005 98405 #016-06-1948 L1949 **IM** *071

WILSON, James Mason, Jr. 1901 S UNION AVE, ALLENMORE HOSPITAL 98405 #035-45-1975 L1980 **IM** *020 †20

WILSON, Michael Jeffrey. 1802 YAKIMA AVE, ST. JOSEPH MEDICAL PAVILIO 98405 #026-04-1985 L2002 **CD** *020 †20

WILSON, Robert Mc Clain. 9040A REID STREET, ATTN: CREDENTIAL OFFICE 98431 #007-02-1968 L1981 **PS GS** *071 †85,65

WINTER, Kristie Janine. 9040A REID STREET, ATTN: CREDENTIAL OFFICE 98431 #016-42-1993 L1995 **ID** *020 †20

WOLF, Charles Jos. 1717 S J ST 98405 #041-13-1976 L1977 **FM EM** *020 †18

WOOD, Alan Bridges. 209 MARTIN LTHR KNG JR WAY 98405 #024-01-1975 L1985 **ORS IM** *020 †20,40

WOOD-COOK, Judith. 1802 YAKIMA AVE, CASCADE VASC ASSOC 98405 #041-01-1996 L2003 **VS** *020 †85

WOODMAN, Troy J. 2202 S CEDAR ST, STE 300 98405 #048-04-1995 L2000 **OPH** *020 †35

WOODRUFF, Mary Ann Apa. 316 MARTIN L KING JR WAY, STE 212 98405 #054-04-1983 L1989 **PD** *020 †55

WOOLARD, Deborah Jean. 317 MARTIN LTHR KNG JR WAY, MULTICARE HEALTH SYSTEM 98405 #051-04-1982 L1998 **PEM PD** *020 †55

WOOLERY, Wilhelm Edward. 317 MARTIN LTHR KNG JR WAY 98405 #010-01-1998 L2007 **PD** *020 †55

WU, Robert. 1901 S UNION AVE, ALLENMORE HOSPITAL 98405 #051-04-1987 L1995 **AN PME** *020 †05

WURST, Tod Evans. 2202 S CEDAR ST, STE 200 98405 #008-02-1986 L1992 **DR** *020 †80

WYMAN-CLEMONS, Jennifer G. FT. LEWIS, MADIGAN ARMY MEDICAL CENTE 98431 #024-16-1986 L2003 **AI IM** *020 †20,03

WYSONG, Melissa Suzanne. 521 MARTIN LTHR KNG JR WAY, TACOMA FAMILY MEDICINE 98405 #005-12-2005 L2006 **FP** *012

XU, Rending. 315 MARTIN LTHR KNG JR WAY, MS 315-M5-ISH 98405 #243-70-1992 L2004 **IM** *020 †20

XU, Weidong. ■ 98406 #243-95-1975 L1999 **IM** *020 †20

YAMAMOTO, Kazunori. VA PUGET SOUND HLTH CARE, DEPT OF MED 98493 #024-07-1986 L1997 **GE** *020 †20

YEATMAN, Gentry Wayne. FORT LEWIS 98431 #027-01-1972 L1981 **P PD** *071 †55

YEE, Lorrin Kwockchong. 1624 S I ST STE 305, PLLC 98405 #005-14-1984 L2000 **ON IM** *050 †20

YEH, Hsushi. 1311 S UNION AVE, STE 101 98405 #038-40-1974 L1979 **OPH** *020 †35

YODER, Carl Cecil. 9040 REID ST A, ATTN CREDENTIAL OFFICE 98431 #039-01-1984 L2006 **CHN PD** *020 †75,55

YOEST, Stephen Michael. 9040A REID STREET, ATTN: CREDENTIAL OFFICE 98431 #023-12-1989 L1992 **RNR** *020 †80

YOON, Justin Kyungho. 2202 S CEDAR ST, STE 200 98405 #051-04-1996 L1999 **DR** *020

YOUNGBERG, Rush Alexander. 9040 REID ST # A, ATTN: CREDENTIAL OFFICE 98431 #005-02-1969 L1973 **R** *020 †80 ‡

YUHASZ, Mark Steven. 2202 S CEDAR ST, STE 200 98405 #041-01-1983 L1988 **DR** *020 †80

YUWONO, Melawati. 311 S L ST, 2ND FLOOR GI CLINIC 98405 #409-38-1983 L1999 **PG** *020 †55

ZACHARIAH, Daisy S. ■ 98422 #825-01-1971 L1979 **GP OBG** *020

ZARAGOZA, Rogelio Soria. AMERICAN LAKE DIVISION, SYSTEM 98493 #748-10-1982 L1991 **P** *020 †75

ZATZKIN, Jay Bogart. 1003 S 5TH ST 98405 #020-02-1974 L1994 **ON HEM** *071 †20 ‡

ZEMMERS, Robert Maris. 9900 VETERANS DR SW 98493 #026-04-1964 L1970 **P** *020

ZENGER, David Charles. 9040 REID ST, MADIGAN ARMY MED CTR 98431 #023-12-1994 L1996 **AN** *020 †05

ZHONG, Fang. 2702 S 42ND ST STE 310 98409 #243-52-1990 L2001 **PM** *020

ZHU, Yu. 915 6TH AVE, NEUROLOGY & NEUROSURGERY 98405 #243-78-1982 L2002 **N** *020 †20

ZILBERSTEIN, Arthur Kevin. 9040 JACKSON AVE 98431 #005-18-1994 L1995 **AN** *020 †05

ZIRINSKY, Kenneth. 209 M L KING JR WAY, TACOMA SPECIALTY CENTER, G 98405 #035-19-1978 L1990 **R** *020 †80

ZOPF, Katherine Susanne. 11225 PACIFIC AVE S 98444 #035-45-2001 L2003 **FM** *020

TAHOLAH – GRAYS HARBOR

SOLIS, Teresa Ann. PO BOX 219 98587 #025-12-1982 L1997 **FM** *020 †18

■ = Address Information Privacy Protected

TAHUYA – MASON

WEST, Raymond Owen. ■ 98588 #005-12-1952 L1979 **FM PHP** *072 †70,18

TEKOA – WHITMAN

BARNES, John Canute. N. 115 CROSBY, TEKOA MEDICAL CLINIC 99033 #049-01-1952 L1959 **IM P** *071

MC CONNELL, Graham S. TEKOA MEDICAL CLINIC 99033 #040-02-1942 L1947 **FOP IMG** *072

TENINO – THURSTON

CAVENDISH, Jean Fleming M. 22216 THOMPSN CRK RD SE #3 98589 #919-05-1961 L1978 **P** *020

CRABBE, Richard Arthur. 14440 TILLEY RD S 98589 #412-01-1976 L2000 **CHP** *020 †75

JUMP, Leyton Endicott. 273 SUSSEX AVE E 98589 #040-02-1975 L1985 **GP** *020

THORP – KITTITAS

RENTFRO, Richard A, Jr. ■ 98946 #005-12-1972 L1973 **ORS EM** *020

TONASKET – OKANOGAN

BOLZ, Justina Marie. 17 S WESTERN AVE 98855 #054-04-2000 L2003 **FM** *020 †18

HENZE, Walter Arthur. 17 S WESTERN AVE 98855 #023-07-1973 L1975 **FM** *071 †18

LEE, Robin Guinocor. 203 S WESTERN AVE 98855 #748-11-1976 L1984 **AN PME** *020

MCCARTHY, John Francis. 17 S WESTERN AVE, NORTH VALLEY MEDICINE 98855 #054-04-1990 L1990 **FM** *020 †18

STANGLAND, David Grant. 17 S WESTERN AVE 98855 #005-19-1976 L1977 **FM** *020 †18

WELTON, Richard Craig. 106 S WHITCOMB AVE, FAMILY HEALTH CENTERS 98855 #061-01-1979 L1996 **FM EM** *020 †18

WILCOX, Ute Marianne. 203 S WESTERN AVE 98855 #409-23-1985 L1997 **FM EM** *020 †18

WILSON, Douglas Lee. 17 S WESTERN AVE 98855 #054-04-2001 L2004 **FM** *020 †18

TOPPENISH – YAKIMA

BARRY, Geoffrey Graham. 502 W 4TH AVE, HOSPITALIST OFFICE 98948 #041-13-2001 L2007 **FM** *020 †18

BROWN, Robert Jos. 502 W 4TH AVE 98948 #016-11-1966 L2006 **IM CD** *020 †20

DANIELS, David Carroll. 401 BUSTER RD 98948 #041-01-1980 L1981 **FM** *020 †18

DAVIS, Kathleen Kingsford. 518 W 1ST AVE 98948 #010-01-1977 L1996 **IM** *020 †20

EFFLER, Dean Frederick. 401 BUSTER RD 98948 #043-01-1975 L1982 **OS PD** *030 †55

FARLEY, Mark C. 518 W 1ST AVE 98948 #040-02-1985 L1989 **IM PD** *020,55

GAENSBAUER, James T. 518 W 1ST AVE, FARM WORKERS CLINIC 98948 #047-05-1999 L2003 **PD** *020 †55

GARGAS, Donald Chester. 518 W 1ST AVE 98948 #016-06-1968 L1973 **PD GP** *020 †55

HEISEY, Kyle Landis. 518 W 1ST AVE 98948 #041-14-1988 L1991 **FM** *020 †18

HERNANDEZ, Patricia A. 518 W 1ST AVE 98948 #030-05-1987 L1991 **OBG** *020 †30

HOCSON, Danial Lloyd. 401 BUSTER RD 98948 #054-04-1993 L1993 **FM** *020 †18

IOVINO, Yvana. 518 W 1ST AVE 98948 #035-08-1980 L1992 **OBG** *020 †30

KLIEWER, Peter James. 518 W 1ST AVE 98948 #028-02-1987 L1989 **IM** *020 †20

KRUSE, Donn Gilbert. 401 BUSTER RD 98948 #054-04-1982 L1982 **FM** *020 †18

LEACOCK-CHAU, Natasha. 518 W 1ST AVE 98948 #028-02-1997 L2000 **PD** *020 †55

MAITLAND, Lindsay. 518 W 1ST AVE 98948 #038-41-1992 L1992 **PD** *020 †55

MONAHAN, Paul Matthew. 518 W 1ST AVE 98948 #030-06-1965 L1970 **IM GP** *020 †20

MORAN, John Kevin. 502 W 4TH AVE, TOPPENISH COMMUNITY HOSPIT 98948 #028-34-1984 L1990 **IM** *020 †20

PEASE, Christina Lyne. 504 W 4TH AVE 98948 #048-04-2001 L2004 **PD** *020 †55

QUAEMPTS, Rex Matthew. 401 BUSTER RD 98948 #054-04-1992 L1992 **FM** *020 †18

RAMOS-DIAZ, Mirna Isabel. 518 W 1ST AVE 98948 #011-02-1990 L1998 **PD** *020 †55

REMINGTON, Chas Lewis E. PO BOX 190 98948 #026-04-1968 L1973 **GP** *020

RICKING, Julie Annette. 518 W 1ST AVE 98948 #041-07-1971 L1977 **IM PUD** *020 †20

RONISH, Ross Henry. 518 W 1ST AVE, YAKIMA VALLEY FARM WORKERS 98948 #028-02-1982 L1990 **OM** *030 †70

RUE, Janis Marie. 518 W 1ST AVE, YAKIMA VALLEY FARM WORKERS 98948 #040-02-1985 L1989 **OBG** *020 †30

SAUERWEIN, Mark Frederick. 518 W 1ST AVE, CLINIC, P.O. BOX 190 98948 #040-02-1982 L1986 **FM** *020 †18

SEAMAN, Matthew Edwin. 502 W 4TH AVE 98948 #047-05-1982 L1989 **EM IM** *020 †20,16

SEYMOUR, George N. 502 W 4TH AVE 98948 #040-02-1983 L1984 **EM** *020

SHEARER, Douglas Wm. 504 W 4TH AVE 98948 #054-04-1971 L1974 **FM OBS** *020

SHEARER, Raymond Orville. 505 W 4TH AVE 98948 #005-12-1962 L1963 **FM** *071 †18

SMITH, Frank L. 516 W 4TH AVE, ASSOCIATES 98948 #024-01-1972 L2001 **GS EM** *020 †85

SULE, Joseph Alex. 503 W 4TH AVE 98948 #005-12-1972 L1973 **GP** *020

ULLOM, Brian B. 518 W 1ST AVE 98948 #048-15-1992 L1995 **PD** *020 †55

WALSH, Kevin Counts. 518 W 1ST AVE 98948 #054-04-1982 L1992 **FM** *020 †18

TOUCHET – WALLA WALLA

CAUDILL, Timothy Grant. 1277 WOODWARD CANYON RD 99360 #031-01-1990 L1994 **AN** *020 †05

RAY, Evert Stanley. 345 SHORT RD 99360 #005-12-1959 L1973 **AN** *020 †05

RICE, Robert Houston. 1277 WOODWARD CANYON RD 99360 #023-12-1987 L1998 **AN** *020 †05

SCHLICKER, Kurt Jos. 1277 WOODWARD CANYON RD 99360 #054-04-1988 L1993 **AN** *020 †55,05

TRACYTON – KITSAP

CHEN, Pai Nan. ■ 98393 #385-01-1962 L1978 **GS** *071 †85

HUTCHINSON, Heidi Lilia. ■ 98393 #054-04-1991 L1995 **FM** *071 †18

TUKWILA – KING

AGER, Leanne Zimmer. 13030 MILITARY RD S, STE 200 98168 #054-04-1985 L1987 **GP EM** *075

APPEL, Samuel David. 12844 MILITARY RD S 98168 #025-12-1975 L2007 **P PYG** *020 †75

BALLARD, Jack Duane. 12844 MILITARY RD S 98168 #039-01-1943 L1946 **GS** *071 †85

BARNES, Patricia Jane. 16040 CHRISTENSEN RD, RIVERVIEW PLAZA BLDG 1 98188 #010-01-1971 L1974 **P CHP** *020 †75

BLANTON, Ronald Keith. 13030 MILITARY RD S, STE 208 98168 #040-02-1986 L1990 **PM** *020 †60

CHINN, Wilbur. 14463 MILITARY RD S 98168 #054-15-1964 **GP** *020

CORBETT, James Thos. ■ 98188 #028-34-1947 L1953 **P** *071 †75

DESHPANDE, Aarti Rahul. 200 ANDOVER PARK E, STE 8 US HEALTHWORKS 98188 #496-46-1996 L2003 **FM** *020 †18 ‡

EPSTEIN, H Stephen. 13030 MILITARY RD S, A WOMEN'S WELLNESS CENTER 98168 #054-04-1968 L1969 **OBG** *071

FLORES, Maria S. 13030 MILITARY RD S, STE 210 98168 #035-15-1998 L2000 **FM** *020 †18

FORSTER, Charles Jos. 14220 INTERURBAN AVE, S #140 98168 #036-01-1989 L1991 **FM** *020 †18

GREGORY, Peter Campbell. 14220 INTERURBAN AVE S, STE A107-110 98168 #051-04-1997 L2004 **NEP** *020

HARRIS, Stanley Eugene. 12844 MILITARY RD S 98168 #054-04-1962 L1963 **GP OBG** *071 †18

HILDEBRANDT, Nancy Beyer. 12844 MILITARY RD S 98168 #025-12-1976 L1988 **OBG** *075 †30

HSIUNG, Robert Lu. ■ 98168 #035-46-2002 L2002 **CCA** *012 †05

HUMPHREY, David Richard. 12844 MILITARY RD S 98168 #065-01-1978 L1980 **GP** *020

HUYNH, Ngoc Le. 13100 MILITARY RD S STE 2 98168 #665-02-2001 L2006 **FM** *100 †18

KAY, Edmond. 13030 MILITARY RD S, STE 210 98168 #005-02-1980 L1981 **FM UM** *020 †18

LAWTON, Steven Robert. 13030 MILITARY RD S, STE 210 98168 #016-06-1994 L1998 **FM** *020 †18

LAZZARETTI, John J. 6720 FORT DENT WAY, VIRGINIA MASON STE 110 98188 #054-04-1982 L1984 **OM PHP** *020 †70

LEVEAUX, Mark Frederick. 12400 E MARGINAL WAY S, GROUP HLTH COOPERATIVE 98168 #050-02-1979 L1990 **P** *020 †75

LEYDEN, Keith Henry. 12400 E MARGINAL WAY S 98168 #051-01-1986 L1988 **IM** *020 †20

LOK, Calvin Yungsing. 13030 MILITARY RD S, HIGHLINE REHABILITATION 98168 #048-13-1988 L1992 **PM** *020 †60

MANGUBAT, E Antonio. 16400 SOUTHCENTER PKWY, STE 101 98188 #054-04-1979 L1994 **CS GS** *020 †16

MOLIN, Judith Lynn. 6720 FORT DENT WAY, STE 110 98188 #003-01-1994 L1998 **FM FSM** *020 †18

MOLSEE, Melissa Marie. ■ 98168 #054-04-2007 L2007 **IM** *012

MORAN, John Regis. 12844 MILITARY RD S 98168 #054-04-1953 L1954 **GS PA** *020

NAGEL, Charles La Dell. 13030 MILITARY RD S, STE 202 98168 #016-06-1960 L1961 **P** *020

NAYAN, Alvin Sanchez. 13030 MILITARY RD S, STE 100 98168 #748-24-1988 L2001 **OM** *020 †70

O'BARA, Kenneth John. 6720 FORT DENT WAY, STE 110 98188 #025-01-1976 L1980 **EM OM** *030 †16

PATAMIA, Thomas Anthony. 12844 MILITARY RD S, HIGHLINE MEDICAL CENTER/SP 98168 #010-02-1998 L2003 **PYG** *020 †75

PATTON, Laura. 12400 E MARGINAL WAY S 98168 #054-04-1979 L1980 **FM** *020 †18

PIETRZYK, Maria Elzbieta. 16040 CHRISTENSEN RD, ROAD #212 98188 #759-03-1963 L1976 **PCH** *050

PURDY, Donald Dana. 12844 MILITARY RD S 98168 #054-04-1953 L1954 **FM** *071 †18

RAMALEY, Shawn Robt. 17780 SOUTHCENTER PKWY 98188 #054-04-1987 L1992 **FM** *020 †18

RATCLIFFE, Arthur R. 13100 MILITARY RD S, STE 1 98168 #054-04-1957 L1960 **ORS** *071

SCHLIITER, Jena. 200 ANDOVER PARK E, STE 6 98188 #067-01-1990 L1995 **PM GP** *020 †60

SINTON, Richard Ian Rae. 12844 MILITARY RD S 98168 #917-03-1959 L1981 **AN** *020

SIVERLING, Robt La Verne. 12844 MILITARY RD S 98168 #054-04-1953 L1955 **GP** *071

SLIGHTAM, John David. 13030 MILITARY RD S STE 20 98168 #038-40-1980 L1991 **P** *020 †75

THOMPSON, Woodrow Cuff. 15439 53RD AVE S 98188 #047-06-1977 L1985 **AN** *020 †05

TOPIWALA, Hansa. 12844 MILITARY RD S 98168 #495-01-1961 L1971 **OBG** *071 †30

TURNER, David Lutz. 2801 S 128TH ST 98168 #054-04-1960 L1961 **FM** *071 †18

VU, Andy-Linh Hung. 13100 MILITARY RD S, STE 2 98168 #308-13-1998 L2003 **FM** *020 †18 ‡

VU, Lawrence Luan-Dinh. 13100 MILITARY RD S, STE 2 98168 #308-13-1998 L2003 **FM** *020 †18 ‡

WAESCHE, Jeffrey Morrow. 6720 FORT DENT WAY, STE 140 98188 #054-04-1972 L1975 **OBG** *020 †30

WELLER, Richard Davis. 7755 E MARGINAL WAY S, THE BOEING COMPANY 98108 #005-18-1974 L1985 **IM OM** *020 †20

WINSKY, Robt Leonard, Jr. 13030 MILITARY RD S, STE 202 98168 #019-02-1978 L2006 **P** *020 †75 ‡

WONG, Kent Tse-Yin. 12844 MILITARY RD S 98168 #024-01-1983 L1985 **AN** *020 †05

WU, Louis Shih Hsun. 5428 S 150TH ST 98188 #028-34-1972 L1999 **AN** *020

ZIETAK, Aleksandra Maria. 13030 MILITARY RD S, STE 208 98168 #759-03-1978 L1983 **OM** *020 †60

TULALIP – SNOHOMISH

ALAYNICK, Susan Porter. ■ 98271 #048-13-1970 L1974 **PTH** *071 †50

ALEXANDER, Lise Kalliah. 7520 TOTEM BEACH RD 98271 #054-04-2003 L2004 **FM** *020 †18

BAGGETT, Mony Mehrotra. 3528 MISSION BEACH RD 98271 #041-14-1998 L2001 **EM** *020 †16

FOLKEMER, Marion Lois. 7520 TOTEM BEACH RD 98271 #049-01-2001 L2004 **PD** *020 †55

HAMMOND, Charles A. ■ 98271 #054-04-1952 L1954 **GP** *071

MADLER, Marianne Theresa. 7520 TOTEM BEACH RD, TULALIP TRIBES HEALTH CLIN 98271 #041-07-1980 L2000 **FM** *020 †18

MAIMON, Martin. 7520 TOTEM BEACH RD 98271 #054-04-1996 L2000 **MPD** *020 †20,55

MINOR, Ralph Hugh. ■ 98271 #054-04-1954 L1956 **OPH** *071 †35

MORRIS, Gerald Lee. 8825 34TH AVE NE, STE L152 98271 #030-05-1964 L1964 **PTH** *071 †50

NGUYEN, Dat H. 7520 TOTEM BEACH RD 98271 #942-01-1970 L1996 **FM** *020 †18

ORDONEZ, Priscilla A. 419 118TH ST NE, LOCUM TENENS 98271 #748-01-1962 L2002 **GP IM** *020

REID, Maxine Leslie. ■ 98271 #060-02-1975 L1978 **AN** *020 †05
STURGIS, Charles David. ■ 98271 #019-02-1992 L2007 **PCP ATP** *020 †50
SULLIVAN, Daniel Edward. 3528 MISSION BEACH RD 98271 #054-04-1982 L1986 **IM EM** *020 †20,16

TUMWATER – THURSTON

AITKEN, Gloria Stone. ■ 98512 #035-19-1948 L1998 **AN** *071 ‡
ALLEN, Gregory William. ■ 98501 #005-12-2002 L2007 **RO** *100
BAUMAN, Roxanne Lee. 1625 MOTTMAN RD SW, STE A 98512 #017-20-1985 L1986 **AN** *020 †20,05
BORUCHOW, Irwin Bernard. 310 ISRAEL RD SE, MEDICAL COMMISSION 98501 #010-02-1962 L1981 **TS** *020 †85,90
DUNCAN, Thomas J. 150 DENNIS ST SW 98501 #004-01-1996 L2001 **FM** *020 †18
FINO, Gina Marie. ■ 98511 #008-02-1992 L1998 **FOP PTH** *062 †50
FLEMING, Paul L. 3010 BUSH MT CT SW 98512 #028-34-1990 L1993 **EM** *020 †16
HARRIS, W Kirk. 6981 LITTLEROCK RD SW, STE 101 98512 #048-16-1988 L1991 **FM** *020 †18 ‡
HEUERMANN, Laurie Li. 1625 MOTTMAN RD SW, STE B 98512 #007-02-1983 L1986 **AN** *020 †05
HUSSEINI, Ghalib Arthur. 1625 MOTTMAN RD SW, STE A 98512 #016-11-1992 L1998 **ORS HS** *020 †40 ‡
LARSON, Amy Jeannette. ■ 98512 #028-34-1996 L2000 **EM** *020 †16
MARAPAO, Conrado M, Jr. ■ 98512 #748-02-1963 L1995 **GP** *020
PARKER, Michael Richard. 150 DENNIS ST SW, STE A 98501 #035-19-1984 L1987 **FM** *020 †18
PRITCHARD, Jack Stuart. ■ 98501 #016-06-1947 L1947 **GPM IM** *072
SANTOYO-PEREZ, Michelle M. ■ 98501 #035-46-2007 **OBG** *012
SILVERSTEIN, Michael A. 7273 LINDERSON WAY SW 98501 #005-11-1971 L1990 **OM PHP** *062 †70
STERN, Marc Francis. ■ 98501 #035-06-1982 L2002 **IM** *030 †20
TOBIAS, Angela Lynn. ■ 98512 #048-04-2003 L2006 **FM** *100 †18
VASEK, Constance Dolby. ■ 98501 #040-02-1985 L1990 **FM** *020 †18
WHITNEY, Cynthia Able. 150 DENNIS ST SW, TUMWATER FAMILY PRACTICE C 98501 #016-42-1995 L1998 **FM** *020 †20
WILHELM, Monica Anne. 150 DENNIS ST SW 98501 #054-04-1997 L1999 **FM** *020 †18
WU, Ching Yuan. ■ 98512 #244-04-1969 L1975 **IM** *020
YUNG, Edward Vance. ■ 98501 #040-02-1956 L1968 **OS PHP** *071 †70
ZECHMANN, Jerome Peter. 1625 MOTTMAN RD SW, STE A 98512 #019-02-1988 L1993 **ORS** *020 †40

TWISP – OKANOGAN

HOWELL, Roy Keith. ■ 98856 #005-02-1964 L1965 **DR NM** *071 †80

UNDERWOOD – SKAMANIA

SCANNELL, Gianna. ■ 98651 #561-11-1974 L2004 **GS** *020 †85

UNION – MASON

DYER, James Stephen. ■ 98592 #041-02-1966 L1974 **FM** *071 †18
SCHUMACHER, William Henry. E1471 WEBB HILL RD 98592 #030-05-1958 L1962 **FM** *072 †18

UNION GAP – YAKIMA

EDGERLY, Richard Duane. 1420 AHTANUM RIDGE DR 98903 #054-04-1994 L1996 **FM** *020 †18
MACKI, Victoria Lynn. 2 E VALLEY MALL BLVD 98903 #025-07-1983 L1996 **FM** *020 †18
REYNOLDS, Jeffrey M. 2 E VALLEY MALL BLVD 98903 #011-02-1979 L1982 **FM PTH** *020 †50
RIES, Lincoln. ■ 98903 #016-06-1942 L1946 **GP GS** *071 †85
ROBERTSON, Wm Egbert, II. 2 E VALLEY MALL BLVD 98903 #028-34-1964 L1973 **GP OS** *020 †20
STOHL, Rudolph Melvin. 3304 MAIN ST 98903 #005-15-1962 L1975 **GP** *020
TAYLOR, Steve Erwin. 1420 AHTANUM RIDGE DR, AHTANUM RIDGE FAMILY MEDIC 98903 #054-04-1992 L1994 **FM** *020 †18
TRUHLER, Terrence Don. 2 E VALLEY MALL BLVD 98903 #026-04-1970 L1974 **GP** *020
VICKERS, Joseph Lee. 1420 AHTANUM RIDGE DR 98903 #054-04-1993 L1995 **FM** *020 †18
WHITTLESEY, Craig Douglas. 1420 AHTANUM RIDGE DR 98903 #054-04-1993 L1996 **FM** *020 †18

UNIVERSITY PLACE – PIERCE

AASHEIM, Glen Harlow. 1905 BRIDGEPORT WAY W, STE 202 98466 #054-04-1968 L1973 **OBG** *020 †30
ALLISON, Don Henry. ■ 98467 #048-02-2003 L2006 **FM** *100 †18
ANCHETA, Jonnette Miguel. 6824 19TH ST W, # 154 98466 #038-40-1989 L1992 **PD** *020 †55
BERRY, Brian John. 7210 40TH ST W STE 100 98466 #054-04-1982 L1986 **PD** *020 †55
BHASIN, Deepshikha. ■ 98467 #495-43-2002 L2007 **IMG** *020 †20
BISHOP, Lori Lynn. ■ 98466 #018-03-1988 L1989 **OBG** *071 †30
BOWDEN, Thomas Leonard. ■ 98466 #803-03-1950 L1968 **GP** *071
BOYD, Jason David. ■ 98467 #023-12-2004 L2005 *100
BRAMMER, Gregory Ray. 3631 74TH AVE W UNIT B, PROT DISTRICT 3 98466 #054-04-1995 L1999 **EM** *020 †16
BRAZINA, Bruce Danl. ■ 98467 #041-09-1974 L1977 **IM** *020 †20
BRIEJER, Kristin Gayle. 4320 BRIDGEPORT WAY W 98466 #054-04-1996 L1998 **FM** *020 †18
BROMAN, Roy Dallas. ■ 98466 #061-01-1962 L1971 **FM EM** *071 †18
BROOKS, Mark Franklin. 7210 40TH ST W STE 100, UNIVERSITY PLACE MEDICAL C 98466 #027-01-1978 L1994 **FM** *020 †18
BURNEY, Richard Owen. ■ 98466 #023-12-1997 L1999 **OBG REN** *020 †30
CARRIM, Osman Omar. 7501 29TH ST W 98466 #654-01-1983 L1986 **IM** *020 †20
CHAN, Chung Chun. 3526 OLYMPIC BLVD W 98466 #462-01-1962 L1973 **GS VS** *062

DE VITA, Jocelyn Vallarta. 4310 BRIDGEPORT WAY W, STE A 98466 #016-43-1986 L1991 **PD** *020 †55,20
DODGE, Erin Eileen. 4230 BRIDGEPORT WAY W 98466 #054-04-1996 L1999 **FM** *020 †18
EDMOND, Charles V, Jr. ■ 98466 #048-12-1985 L1992 **OTO** *020 †45
EHRHART, John David. ■ 98466 #040-02-1967 L1973 **AN** *071 †05
EPISTOLA, Rosa F. ■ 98467 #748-07-1978 L1984 **P PYG** *020 †75
ERICKSON, Kristin Elise. ■ 98466 #054-04-2000 L2005 **GPM** *020 †70
FINDLAY, Robert Frank. 5225 CIRQUE DR W, CASCADE EYE & SKIN CENTERS 98467 #028-02-1979 L1987 **D DMP** *020
FRIEDMAN, Jason Albert. ■ 98467 #023-12-1996 L1997 **N** *020 †75
GIRVIN, Robert Wm. 4310 BRIDGEPORT WAY W # A 98466 #035-19-1982 L1983 **IM** *020 †20
GLEYZER, Elena Alex. 4119 BEECHWOOD DR W 98466 #913-01-1980 L1997 **FM** *020 †18
GOSCH, Norman Albert. 3509 SOUNDVIEW DR W 98466 #030-05-1962 L1985 **FM** *020 †18
HESS, George Harry. ■ 98466 #056-05-1936 L1956 **GP** *071
HYDES, Jennifer R. ■ 98466 #040-14-2000 L2006 **GPM** *012
IREGUI, Juan. 2901 BRIDGEPORT WAY W 98466 #264-10-1993 L2006 **IM PLM** *020 †20
JACKSON, George Frazier. 5909 ORCHARD ST W 98467 #005-14-1995 L2001 **P** *020 †75
JOHNSON, Michael Ward. 7210 40TH ST W, STE 100 98466 #023-12-1991 L2000 **FM** *020 †18
KELLY, Christina Marie. ■ 98467 #038-40-2003 L2003 **FM** *020 †18
LIU, Binqiu. ■ 98466 #243-54-1982 L2005 **AN** *100
LIU, Yajun. 5511 78TH AVENUE CT W 98467 #243-92-1982 L1999 **IM** *020 †20
LUU, Vinh Duc. ■ 98466 #025-12-1986 L2007 **CD** *020 †20
MERCED, Jorge Marquez. 6824 19TH ST W # 169 98466 #748-01-1975 L1982 **AN** *020 ‡
MUNSON, Patrick Daniel. ■ 98467 #028-02-2006 L2008 **OPH** *012
NOWOGROSKI, James Alan. ■ 98467 #054-04-1971 L1972 **OM FM** *020
OLEJAR, Michael. 2603 BRIDGEPORT WAY W, STE E 98466 #038-40-1963 L1965 **IM** *071 †20
PACIO, Glenn Amante. 5320 ORCHARD ST W 98467 #748-02-1994 L1999 **IM ID** *020 †20
PARK, John Chongki. 3019 SOUNDVIEW DR W, PARKS MEDICAL CLINIC 98466 #583-16-1984 L1985 **GP** *020
PATTERSON, Jeffrey David. 6824 19TH ST W 98466 #012-05-1973 L1982 **ORS** *020 †40
PATTISON, Marilyn Elsie. 2901 BRIDGEPORT WAY W, FRANCISCAN HOSPICE 98466 #054-04-1982 L1989 **PLM IM** *020 †20
PEREZ, William Jos. ■ 98467 #054-04-1987 L1987 **AN** *020 †05
PHAM, Thanh Vincent. 7210 40TH ST W 98466 #028-34-1997 L2000 **IM** *020 †20
RAMSAY, Jennifer Stratton. ■ 98467 #045-01-1999 L2001 **PTH** *020 †50
SCHULTZ, Nancy Joan. ■ 98467 #007-02-1976 L1978 **PD** *020 †55
SEBESTA, Michael Joseph. ■ 98466 #023-12-1996 L1997 **U** *020 †95
SEVER, Buel Laud. ■ 98466 #016-02-1943 L1944 **GP** *071
STEPHENS, Dewey D. ■ 98466 #018-75-1964, ▲ L1965 **GP OS** *071
STUTE, William D. ■ 98466 #016-05-1962 L1975 **OM** *071
TESORO, Olmedo A R. 6427 61ST ST W 98467 #748-01-1994 L2004 **APM** *020 †05
WILLIAMS, Jerry Lee. 7411 27TH ST W, OLYMPIA MED CENT 98466 #018-03-1964 L1966 **GP** *071
WILSON, Karen Lynn. ■ 98467 #023-12-2005 L2007 **OBG** *012
XIE, Baiyan. ■ 98467 #243-70-1983 L2004 **IM** *020
YANG, Keyi. ■ 98466 #243-45-1982 L2001 **N** *040 †75 ‡
YOKOYAMA, Cheryl Mitsuko. 2603 BRIDGEPORT WAY W # F 98466 #005-02-1983 L1987 **OPH OS** *020 †35

VALLEYFORD – SPOKANE

NAPIER, Ian C. 14404 SOUTH DUNN RD 99036 #352-11-1953 L1957 **AN** *071 †05 ‡

VANCOUVER – CLARK

ACOSTA, Rigoberto. 2211 NE 139TH ST, DEPARTMENT OF MEDICAL AFFA 98686 #042-01-2003 L2007 **IM** *020 †20
ADSIT, Elaine Ramsey. 12607 SE MILL PLAIN BLVD 98684 #003-01-1989 L1996 **OBG** *020 †30
AHEARN, Jane L. 406C SE 131ST AVE, STE 304 98683 #040-02-1985 L1992 **OBG** *020 †30
AKHTER, Ayesha. 501 SE 172ND AVE 98684 #496-12-1994 L2001 **IM** *020 †20
ALBERTS, Michael Stuart. 2211 SE MILL PLAIN BLVD 98661 #040-02-1994 L1999 **GS** *020 †85
ALEXANDER, Allan Richard. 7101 NE 137TH AVE 98682 #033-05-1974 L1977 **FM** *020 †18
ALLEN, Beverley Elaine. 16420 SE MCGILLIVRAY BLVD, STE 103 98683 #023-01-1989 L2000 **CHP P** *020 †75
ALLEN, George Solomon. 8614 E MILL PLAIN BLVD # 3 98664 #875-01-1994 L2003 **AI IM** *020 †20,03
ALLMON, Thomas Craig. 12607 SE MILL PLAIN BLVD, CASCADE PARK MEDICAL OFFIC 98684 #038-40-1975 L1994 **FM** *020 †18
AMBUR, Sumanth. 2211 NE 139TH ST, EMERGENCY DEPARTMENT 98686 #051-07-2001 L2005 **EM** *020 †16
AMEUDA, Patrick Moses. PO BOX 1600 98668 #913-12-1997 L2003 **FM** *100 †18
ANDERSON, Mark Richard. 2525 NE 139TH ST 98686 #005-06-1978 L1991 **EM** *020 †16
ANDERSON, Philemon Lynn. 1405 SE 164TH AVE, STE 102 98683 #005-12-1988 L1997 **OTO AI** *020 †45
ANDERSON, Sharon Joy. PO BOX 1600, SOUTHWEST WASHIN 98668 #056-05-2007 L2007 **FP** *012
ANDISON, Bruce James. 2101 NE 139TH ST, THE WOMENS CLINIC OF 98686 #143-02-1980 L1983 **OBG GO** *020
ANDRES, Valentino W, Jr. ■ 98668 #028-34-1967 L1967 **P** *020 †75
ANGEL, Aaron L. 2211 E MILL PLAIN BLVD 98661 #048-13-1985 L1997 **CD** *020 †20
ARNOTT, Gordon Mackenzie. 1319 NE 134TH ST, STE 105 98685 #005-12-1988 L1988 **FM** *020 †18
ARROYO, Christopher S. 505 NE 87TH AVE, UROLOGY CLINIC OF 98664 #054-04-1987 L1994 **U** *020 †95
ASLAM, Muhammad. ■ 98686 #704-01-1961 L1968 **IM GE** *071 †20
AUSTIN, Jennifer M. 501 SE 172ND AVE 98684 #021-01-1997 L2000 **PD** *020 †55
AVRAMOV, Valentin Y. 6926 E FOURTH PLAIN BLVD 98661 #913-97-1972 L2002 **CHP** *020
AXTELL, Ricky Jay. 100 E 33RD ST 98663 #054-04-2004 L2004 **FM** *100 †18
BACIOCCO, Juliet Ann. 14406 NE 20TH AVE 98686 #010-02-1999 L2002 **PD** *020 †55
BACKMAN-POHLE, Jennifer L. 501 SE 172ND AVE 98684 #005-77-2003, ▲ L2006 **FM** *020
BADER, Gerald Francis. 2525 NE 139TH ST 98686 #030-06-1966 L1971 **PD** *020 †55
BAKER, Hinton Jos. ■ 98683 #035-01-1945 **FM** *020
BAKER, Megan C. 501 SE 172ND AVE 98684 #047-05-1997 L2000 **PD** *020 †55

BAKER, Steven Edward. 100 E 33RD ST 98663 #011-02-1987 L1993 FM *020 †18

BAME, Marvin Lawrence. 700 NE 87TH AVE 98664 #038-40-1974 L1979 OBG *020

BARNHART, Amy Kathleen. 2211 NE 139TH ST, LEGACY SALMON CREEK HOSPIT 98686 #654-01-2001 L2005 MPD *020 †55

BARTELS, Sande. 203 SE PARK PLAZA DR STE 1 98684 #050-02-1996 L2002 OTO *020 †45

BARTH, G Dean. ■ 98664 #024-04-1954 L1955 IMG EM *071

BARTON, John Selby, Jr. 700 NE 87TH AVE 98664 #010-01-1974 L1977 FM *074 †18

BASCH, Corinne Vivian. 100 E 33RD ST 98663 #023-07-1990 L1992 FM NTR *020 †18

BATSON, Jack Miller, Jr. 407 NE 87TH AVE 98664 #047-05-1982 L1986 FM *020 †18

BAXTER, Louise Marie. 2211 NE 139TH ST, NORTHWEST NEWBORN 98686 #054-04-1986 L1988 NPM *020 †55

BEALL, Samuel T. ■ 98683 #020-02-1950 L1954 IM *071 †20

BECKER, Jennifer Louise. 2525 NE 139TH ST 98686 #035-20-1991 L2006 PD *020 †55

BECKSTROM, Dwight Lee. 700 NE 87TH AVE 98664 #056-06-1976 L1979 IM *020 †20

BEDROSSIAN, Robert Haig. ■ 98685 #041-13-1947 L1957 OPH *071 †35

BELKIN, Rod Ira. 3250 SE 164TH AVE, STE 108 98683 #016-11-1979 L1988 DR *020 †80

BELL, J Bruce. ■ 98664 #035-20-1963 L1967 N *071 †75

BELL, Marty Craig. 400 NE MOTHER JOSEPH PL 98664 #010-02-1984 L1985 EM *030 †16

BENIKOVA, Yanina M. 700 NE 87TH AVE, THE VANCOUVER CLINIC 98664 #913-05-1988 L1999 FM *020 †18

BENZ, Donald J. 140 SE 164TH AVE, STE 201 98684 #068-01-1975 L1978 FM *020 ‡

BERGEN, Harold Geo. ■ 98660 #035-01-1939 L1940 OBS *071

BERMAN, Jonathan Dayton. 6926 NE FOURTH PLAIN BLVD 98661 #005-18-1973 L1993 P ADP *030 †20

BERNHEIMER, Richard A, Jr. 505 NE 87TH AVE STE 100, VANCOUVER EYE CARE 98664 #005-19-1993 L1998 OPH *020 †35

BERNSTEIN, Keith Aaron. 13215 SE MILL PLAIN BLVD, STE C8 98684 #005-14-1990 L2004 R RNR *020 †80

BERNSTEIN, Michael James. 3400 MAIN ST 98663 #017-20-1983 L1994 P PYG *020 †75

BERRIOS, Jorge C. 700 NE 87TH AVE 98664 #054-04-1997 L2007 PCC *100 †20

BESSAS, Peter James. 13115 NE 4TH ST STE 230, PARK PLACE MEDICAL CENTER 98684 #040-02-2000 L2002 FM *100

BICE, Christopher Paul. 505 NE 87TH AVE, THE WOMENS CLINIC OF 98664 #024-07-1970 L1977 OBG *020 †30

BIGALKE, Mark Alan. 400 NE MOTHER JOSEPH PL 98664 #056-05-1986 L1991 AN *020 †05

BISGARD, Lisa Ann. 14406 NE 20TH AVE 98686 #007-02-1998 L2002 PD *020 †55

BISHOP, David Kent. 2101 NE 139TH ST, THE WOMENS CLINIC OF 98686 #021-01-1987 L1991 OBG *020 †30

BISHOP, William Alden. 505 NE 87TH AVE STE 260 98664 #040-02-1957 L1961 OBG *071 †30

BLACK, David John. 2211 E MILL PLAIN BLVD 98661 #008-02-1986 L1998 PD *020 †55

BLIZARD, Eugene Barie. 400 NE MOTHER JOSEPH PL 98664 #041-02-1959 L1972 PTH *071 †50

BLOCH, Robert David. 16821 SE MCGILLIVRAY BLVD 98683 #016-42-1991 L1998 DR VIR *020 †80

BOGATY, Gene Vincent. ■ 98661 #041-01-1957 L1977 PTH NM *071 †50

BOKHARI, Syed Amin-Ur-Ras. 700 NE 87TH AVE 98664 #704-02-1994 L2007 IM *020

BONDURANT, James H. 12607 SE MILL PLAIN BLVD, NORTHWEST PERMANENTE 98684 #020-02-1956 L1995 IM *071 †70,20

BONG, David Andrew. 2525 NE 139TH ST 98686 #056-05-1973 L1976 RHU IM *020 †20

BONNER, Candace Noreen. 400 NE MOTHER JOSEPH PL, SW WASHINGTON MED CTR 98664 #014-01-1977 L1990 IM EM *020 †20,16

BORLAND, Duncan B. 505 NE 87TH AVE STE 460, VANCOUVER NEUROLOGY 98664 #018-75-1979, ▲ L2002 N *020 †75

BORUS, Todd. 2121 NE 139TH ST, STE 300 98686 #035-47-2000 L2006 ORS *020

BOSTON, David Ronald. 200 NE MOTHER JOSEPH PL, STE 330 98664 #016-06-1987 L1992 CD *020 †20

BRADFORD, Richard Maxwell. 400 NE MOTHER JOSEPH PL, SOUTHWEST WASHINGTON MEDIC 98664 #005-19-1993 L1998 IM *020 †20

BRADLEY, Robert Ellison. 505 NE 87TH AVE STE 160 98664 #067-01-1962 L1977 GP *071

BRADLEY, Susan Gail. 600 NE 92ND AVE, SOUTHWEST WASHINGTON MED C 98664 #040-02-1994 L1994 IM END *020 †20

BRAR, Manjit Inder Singh. 3100 MAIN ST 98663 #495-29-1960 L1974 PS *020 †85,65

BRAUN, Marcus Paul. 210 SE 136TH AVE 98684 #054-04-1986 L1995 IM *020 †20

BREVARD, Ryan Andrew. 2211 NE 139TH ST, EMERGENCY DEPARTMENT 98686 #056-06-2000 L2005 EM *020 †16

BRICE, Larry Thos. 700 NE 87TH AVE 98664 #040-02-1964 L1968 END IM *020

BRINKMAN, William Joseph. 16821 SE MCGILLIVRAY BLVD 98683 #016-11-1999 L2003 RNR *020 †80

BROOKING, Emil Wilson. 400 NE MOTHER JOSEPH PL 98664 #016-06-1943 L1943 GP *071

BROUNS, Matthew Chas. 210 SE 136TH AVE 98684 #056-06-1984 L1990 ON HEM *020 †20

BROWN, Arlin Edward. 7600 NE 41ST ST, ONE PARK PLACE, STE 310 98662 #025-01-1969 L1993 P *020 †75

BROWN, John Ollis. 14406 NE 20TH AVE 98686 #008-01-1973 L1984 GS TS *020 †85

BRYANT, M Lamar. 2525 NE 139TH ST 98686 #027-01-1999 L2005 GE *020 †20

BUCERZAN, Adrian Sorin. 501 SE 172ND AVE 98684 #781-03-1992 L2005 PUD CCM *020 †20

BUCHER, Sharon Ann. 505 NE 87TH AVE, EVERGREEN PEDIATRIC 98664 #035-06-1981 L1984 PD *020 †55

BUDESA, Marie Juliette. 100 E 33RD ST, STE 100 98663 #654-01-2006 L2007 FP *012

BUNTEN, Carol Elizabeth. 2525 NE 139TH ST 98686 #008-01-1984 L2004 OBG *020

BURGER, Leslie Morton. 1601 E FOURTH PLAIN BLVD, BLDG A5 98661 #035-15-1967 L1968 IM ID *030 †20

BURLINGAME, Robert Kelley. 100 E 13TH ST STE 101 98660 #030-05-1971 L1989 P *020 †75

BURRIS, Otis Franklin. 8716 E MILL PLAIN BLVD 98664 #039-01-1955 L1962 GS *071 †85

BUTZER, Mark Anthony. 2211 E MILL PLAIN BLVD, DEPT PD 98661 #056-06-1961 L1967 PD *020 †55

CAGLE, Leslie Ann. 505 NE 87TH AVE STE 301 98664 #048-14-1983 L1989 GS *020 †85

CAMPBELL, John Myers. ■ 98683 #018-03-1944 L1945 GP *071

CAMPBELL, Michael Jack. 12607 SE MILL PLAIN BLVD, KAISER PERMANENTE 98684 #058-18-1981 L2002 P *020 †55,75

CAMPBELL, Robert Bryce. 505 NE 87TH AVE STE 260 98664 #040-02-1960 L1966 PD *071 †30

CANNAN, Charles Ross. 2525 NE 139TH ST 98686 #836-02-1986 L2002 CD *020 †20

CANON, Todd A. 2525 NE 139TH ST, STE 260 98686 #048-13-1998 L2001 FM *020 †18

CANTRELL, Richard F. ■ 98661 #018-75-1952, ▲ L1957 *071

CARDER, Elizabeth Ann. 6100 NE FOURTH PLAIN BLVD 98661 #034-01-1995 L2003 OBG *020

CARLIN, Michele Lynn. 100 E 33RD ST 98663 #011-02-1999 L2002 FM *020 †18

CARLSON, Cynthia Ann. 16703 SE MCGILLIVRAY BLVD, FISHER'S LANDING MEDICAL O 98683 #054-04-1989 L1989 FM *020 †18

CARP, Harvey Mitchell. 400 NE MOTHER JOSEPH PL 98664 #011-02-1984 L1997 AN *020 †05

CARROLL, Meta Loren. 2211 NE 139TH ST, EMERGENCY DEPT 98686 #016-06-1990 L2005 EM PEM *020 †16

CARTER, Charles Bo Dine. 3200 MAIN ST, VANCOUVER EYE CARE PS 98663 #040-02-1960 L1965 OPH *071 †35

CARULLI, Nicholas Frank. 304 N LIESER RD 98664 #040-02-1987 L1999 IM *020 †20

CASEBEER, Jon Eric. 7101 NE 137TH AVE, NORTHWEST KAISER PERMANENT 98682 #040-02-1990 L1993 FM *020 †20

CASIMO, Matthew Anthony. 700 NE 87TH AVE 98664 #050-02-1984 L1989 GE IM *020 †20

CASON, Mary Patricia. ■ 98666 #005-12-1983 L1987 P *020 †55

CHADDERDON, Scott Matthew. 400 NE MOTHER JOSEPH PL 98664 #041-02-2002 L2005 CD *012 †20

CHANDLER, Rebecca Ellen. 700 NE 87TH AVE, THE VANCOUVER CLINIC 98664 #012-05-1998 L2003 ID *100 †20

CHANDRAN, Rekha. ■ 98683 #495-31-1997 L2007 IM *100 †20

CHANG, Joe S. 505 NE 87TH AVE, THE WOMENS CLINIC OF 98664 #048-12-1999 L2004 OBG *040 †30

CHANG, Ming-Jei. 2525 NE 139TH ST 98686 #243-47-1984 L2003 CD *020 †20

CHANG, Sarah Anne. 700 NE 87TH AVE 98664 #048-12-2002 L2004 IM *100 †20

CHAO, Nicole Tien. 700 NE 87TH AVE 98664 #016-06-2002 L2006 PD *020 †55

CHAPLAIN, Edward John. 16811 SE MCGILLIVRAY BLVD, STE 101 98683 #040-02-2002 L2005 FM *020 †18

CHAPMAN, Jay Norman. 17720 SE MILL PLAIN BLVD 98683 #038-43-1986 L1991 OPH PD *020 †35

CHAPMAN, Jean A. ■ 98664 #019-02-1959 L1983 OM FPG *071

CHASTENEY, Edward A, IV. 2211 E MILL PLAIN BLVD 98661 #041-02-1987 L1988 IM *020 †20

CHAU, Patrick Kin Yee. 9901 NE 7TH AVE, STE C120 98685 #039-05-1988 L1992 CHP P *020 †75

CHELDELIN, Lawrence V. 2211 NE 139TH ST, NORTHWEST NEWBORN 98686 #040-02-1972 L1998 NPM *020 †55

CHEN, Frances Yeh. 700 NE 87TH AVE 98664 #040-02-1987 L1990 IM *020 †20

CHEN, Timothy Richard. 2525 NE 139TH ST 98686 #041-09-1995 L1999 OBG *020 †30

CHENG, Shu Feng. ■ 98683 #385-02-1957 L1968 U *071 †95

CHERNELL, Eugene. ■ 98683 #035-19-1959 P CHP *071

CHOW, Alexander Chiajen. 700 NE 87TH AVE, THE VANCOUVER CLINIC 98664 #011-03-1991 L2005 IM *020 †20

CHOW, Selina Laiming. ■ 98683 #023-01-2005 L2005 IM *100

CHOWDHURY, Jasmine Sonya. 700 NE 87TH AVE, THE VANCOUVER CLINIC 98664 #005-06-2001 L2007 IMG *020

CHRISMAN, Jeremy J. 700 NE 87TH AVE 98664 #005-76-2003, ▲ L2007 *100

CHUBINSKAYA, Yekaterina. 400 NE MOTHER JOSEPH PL, SWMC INPATIENT PHYSICIANS 98664 #913-01-1994 L2004 END *100

CHUN, Michael Sam Nin. ■ 98664 #040-02-1966 L1972 AN *071 †05

CHUNG, Kelli Hyunchung. 2211 E MILL PLAIN BLVD 98661 #035-45-1998 L2005 GS *020 †85

CLARK, Calvin Clayton. 700 NE 87TH AVE 98664 #024-07-1963 L1965 PD *055 †55

CLARY, William F, Jr. ■ 98683 #047-06-1950 L1950 P *075 †75

CLAUD, Jonathan Thomas. 2211 NE 139TH ST, C/O EMERGENCY DEPARTMENT 98686 #016-11-2002 L2007 EM *100 †16

CLAYTON, Theresa Louise. 17720 SE MILL PLAIN BLVD 98683 #035-09-1981 L1991 OPH *020 †35

CLEAVER, Truman Grant. 400 NE MOTHER JOSEPH PL, PO BOX 1600 98664 #040-02-1974 L1975 EM *020 †16

CLELAND, Laurie Anne. 505 NE 87TH AVE STE LL50, VANCOUVER RADIOLOGISTS 98664 #040-02-1987 L1998 DR *020 †80

COALE, Edward Hodge, Jr. 2121 NE 139TH ST, STE 300 98686 #025-07-1986 L1992 ORS †40

COALE, Martha. 501 SE 172ND AVE 98684 #037-01-1990 L1995 DR *020

COHEN, Howard Stephen. 2211 NE 139TH ST, NORTHWEST NEWBORN 98686 #016-11-1973 L2004 NPM PD *020 †55

COLVEN, Cynthia Woodson. 1412 NE 134TH ST, STE 260 98685 #051-01-1991 L1995 FM *074 †18

COLVILLE, Mark Richard. 2121 NE 139TH ST, STE 300 98686 #025-01-1980 L1995 ORS OS *020 †40

COMER, Carolyn Roe. 16821 SE MCGILLIVRAY BLVD, STE 110 98683 #001-06-1979 L2001 AI PD *020 †03,55

COMPERE, Sally Jean. 12205 NW 10TH AVE 98685 #008-01-1991 L2002 AN *020 †05

CONNELL, Gregory Allen. 400 NE MOTHER JOSEPH PL, SOUTHWEST WASHINGTON MED. 98664 #051-01-2000 L2003 AN *020 †05 ‡

COOPER, Guy Michael. 100 E 33RD ST 98663 #005-06-1986 L1989 FM *020 †18

COOPER, Michael David. 2525 NE 139TH ST 98686 #040-02-1992 L1999 CD *020 †20

COPPOCK, Michael Andrew. 700 NE 87TH AVE 98664 #060-02-1983 L1988 IM *020 †20

CORRIGAN, William James. ■ 98665 #040-02-1942 L1956 OS U *071

COSTA, Emily Jill. 12607 SE MILL PLAIN BLVD, KAISER PERMANENTE 98684 #041-12-1997 L2000 PD *020 †55

COWGILL, Sarah Macy. 2211 E MILL PLAIN BLVD, 2 COLUMBIA DR 98661 #041-14-2000 L2000 GS *020 †85

CRARY, Jay Lyall. 2121 NE 139TH ST, STE 300 98686 #005-11-1993 L1999 ORS OFA *020 †40

CRARY, Lyall Sturgeon, Jr. 505 NE 87TH AVE STE 200 98664 #008-01-1959 L1967 U *071 †95

CRAVEN, Timothy John. 12607 SE MILL PLAIN BLVD 98684 #040-02-1977 L1986 OM *020 †70,18

CREWS, Stanley Lloyd. 12306 SE MILL PLAIN BLVD, STE 100 98684 #011-02-1984 L1987 OPH *020 †35

CRISAN, Crina Otilia. 501 SE 172ND AVE 98684 #781-03-1996 L2003 FM *020 †18

CRITCHFIELD, Jessica B. 700 NE 87TH AVE 98664 #054-04-2001 L2004 IM *020

CROWELL, Sharon A. 501 SE 172ND AVE STE 130 98684 #048-13-1983 L1993 IM *020 †20

CULHANE, Thomas Edward. 19120 SE 34TH ST, STE 201 98683 #040-02-1979 L2000 FM MDM *030 †18

CUNEO, Susan Dana. 505 NE 87TH AVE, EVERGREEN PEDIATRIC 98664 #021-01-1991 L1994 PD *020 †55

CYMOREK, Jaroslaw Henryk. 2525 NE 139TH ST 98686 #759-07-1988 L2001 GE *020 †20

CYRAN, Stanley Josef, III. 2525 NE 139TH ST 98686 #020-02-1986 L2001 D IM *020 †15

DALLY, Paul David. 505 NE 87TH AVE STE 301, PACIFIC SURGICAL SPECIALIS 98664 #054-04-1982 L1987 GS VS *020 †85

DANIELS, Antonio Andrew. 2211 E MILL PLAIN BLVD 98661 #007-02-1980 L1983 FM *020 †18

DARR, Marilyn Sue. 100 E 33RD ST 98663 #028-46-1985 L1989 **FM** *020 †18

DATLOFF, Joel H. 505 NE 87TH AVE, STE 303 98664 #048-12-1982 L1986 **D DMP** *020 †15

DAVIS, Laura Jane Barbara. 14508 NE 20TH AVE, STE 200 98686 #048-12-1999 L2004 **AI** *020 †20,03

DAVIS, Nadia Ali. 7101 NE 137TH AVE 98682 #797-03-1991 L2001 **IM** *100

DAVIS, Robert Bruce. 2525 NE 139TH ST 98686 #041-09-1977 L2006 **IM** *020 ‡

DAVIS, Susan Jean. 11808 NE FOURTH PLAIN RD, STE A 98682 #040-02-1987 L1990 **FM** *020 †18

DAY, Steven Arthur. 2525 NE 139TH ST 98686 #026-04-2002 L2007 **CN** *100 †75

DECHET, George John. 505 NE 87TH AVE, UROLOGY CLINIC OF 98664 #041-01-1966 L1974 **U** *020 †95

DECKER, Michael R. 700 NE 87TH AVE, UCI ENDOCRINOLOGY DEPARTME 98664 #005-12-1999 L2008 **END** *020 †20

DEMERELL, Daniel Gerard. 2415 NE 134TH ST, STE 107 98686 #003-01-1999 L2005 **AI** *020 †55,03

DEMLOW, Anita Joy. 400 NE MOTHER JOSEPH PL 98664 #040-02-1990 L1997 **UCM EM** *020 †16

DEMLOW, Thomas Andrew. 505 NE 87TH AVE, STE LL50 98664 #039-05-1985 L1997 **DR** *020 †80

DENHAM, Becky Kay. 400 NE MOTHER JOSEPH PL 98664 #020-02-1979 L1985 **EM IM** *020 †20,16

DENNY, Justin Evans. 1601 E FOURTH PLAIN BLVD, CLARK COUNTY HEALTH DEPART 98661 #051-07-1998 L2004 **GPM** *020 †18,70

DE RENNE, Aidan Honus. 505 NE 87TH AVE, EVERGREEN PEDIATRIC 98664 #041-07-1996 L1999 **PD** *020 †55

DICK, H Lenox H. ■ 98683 #041-02-1944 L1987 **IM** *071

DIETRICH, Marlene Emilie. 505 NE 87TH AVE STE 460 98664 #016-02-1983 L1998 **N CN** *020 †75

DIETRICH, Thomas Simeon. 200 NE MOTHER JOSEPH PL, STE 1200 98664 #025-07-1963 L1971 **NS** *062 †25

DIRKX, James Michael. 400 NE MOTHER JOSEPH PL 98664 #005-19-1998 L2001 **EM** *020 †16

DISHER, Leslie Michelle. 200 NE MOTHER JOSEPH PL, STE 330 98664 #028-78-2002, ▲ L2007 **GS** *020 †85

DIXON, David Lee. 6108 NE HIGHWAY 99, STE 108 98665 #040-02-1965 L1966 **FM** *020 †18

DJERGAIAN, Robert Steven. 200 NE MOTHER JOSEPH PL, REBOUND REHAB MEDICINE 98664 #041-02-1979 L1993 **PM** *030 †60

DO, Son. 2101 NE 139TH ST STE 265 98686 #305-01-1997 L2003 **GE** *020 †20

DOBROW, Richard Bein. ■ 98661 #024-01-1962 L1969 **HO IM** *020 †20

DODGE, Cyril Sheldon. 700 NE 87TH AVE 98664 #036-01-1975 L1976 **IM** *020 †20

DOMASH, Michael Dennis. 2215 BROADWAY ST 98663 #016-06-1974 L1979 **P** *020 †75

DONG, Steven P. 2211 E MILL PLAIN BLVD 98661 #048-13-1985 L1988 **IM** *020 †20

DOORANI, Tariq. 505 NE 87TH AVE STE 460, VANCOUVER NEUROLOGISTS, PS 98664 #704-02-1992 L2002 **N** *020

DOUGLASS, Robert Earl. 203 SE PARK PLAZA DR, STE 140 98684 #025-07-1982 L1992 **GS** *020 †85

DOYLE, Allen Edward. 406 SE 131ST AVE # A-104 98683 #005-12-1986 L1989 **IM** *020 †20

DRAPER, Wendy Allyn. 700 NE 87TH AVE, THE VANCOUVER CLINIC 98664 #040-02-1994 L2000 **OBG** *020 †30

DRESHER, Charles Sevareid. 400 NE MOTHER JOSEPH PL 98664 #030-05-1959 L1967 **ORS** *071 †40

DRONKOWSKI, Carl Wm. 700 NE 87TH AVE 98664 #025-07-1980 L2005 **IM** *020 †20

DRYDEN, John David. ■ 98664 #040-02-1988 L1990 **PM** *020 †60

DUEWEL, Helen Irene. 7101 NE 137TH AVE 98682 #005-12-1979 L1992 **IM** *020 †20

DUNCAN, Allison Michelle. 2525 NE 139TH ST 98686 #056-06-1999 L2003 **OBG** *020 †30

DUNCAN, Elmore Edward. 14406 NE 20TH AVE, KAISER PERMANENTE, DEPT PS 98686 #054-04-1958 L1997 **P** *071 †75

DYEHOUSE, Thomas More. 1000 SE TECH CENTER DR 98683 #038-41-1997 L2000 **FM** *020 †18

DYKSTRA, Jonathan James. 16811 SE MCGILLIVRAY BLVD, STE 101 98683 #025-07-1995 L1998 **FM** *020 †18

EBBING, Devon E. 501 SE 172ND AVE 98684 #016-01-2002 L2006 **PD** *020 †55

EIGNER, Frank Davenport. 8906 NW LAKESHORE AVE, FRANK D EIGNER 98665 #040-02-1975 L1985 **FM** *020 †18

EISENFELD, Peter Mark. 700 NE 87TH AVE 98664 #025-01-1978 L1981 **PD** *020 †55

EMDEN, Ronnie-Gail. 700 NE 87TH AVE 98664 #010-02-1978 L1983 **OBG** *020 †30

ERHART, Bruce Allin. 12607 SE MILL PLAIN BLVD 98684 #005-12-1994 L2003 **OBG** *020 †30

ERHART, Veronica Stasa. 6100 NE FOURTH PLAIN BLVD, SW WASH MD CTR/HLTHY STEPS 98661 #005-15-1995 L2003 **PD** *020 †55

ERICH, Jonathan Geo. 2211 NE 139TH ST, FAMILY BIRTH CTR-LSCH 98686 #005-12-1982 L1998 **OBG** *020 †30

EUSSEN, Megan Elaine. 505 NE 87TH AVE, EVERGREEN PEDIATRIC 98664 #028-46-1987 L1995 **PD** *020 †55

EVEN, Aaron. 1916 SE IMAGE RD 98664 #016-11-1996 L2000 **AN** *020 †05

FARBER, Michael Scott. 505 NE 87TH AVE, THE WOMENS CLINIC OF 98664 #041-01-1995 L1999 **OBG** *020 †30

FAUST, Robert Blakeslee. 306 E 34TH ST 98663 #030-05-1958 L1971 **OTO** *071 †45

FAVOUR, Kenneth Daniel. 700 NE 87TH AVE 98664 #056-05-1997 L2000 **IM** *020 †20

FELICIANO, Adoracion. ■ 98661 #748-08-1958 L1970 **AM GP** *071

FELICIANO, Macario G. ■ 98661 #748-08-1958 L1970 **AN GP** *071

FELL, Sean Chambers. 3250 SE 164TH AVE, STE 108 98683 #005-02-1990 L2001 **DR** *020 †80

FERDOWS, Mehdi Shahab. 814 NE 87TH AVE 98664 #048-13-1993 L2002 **GE IM** *020 †20

FERNANDEZ, Elizabeth A. ■ 98683 #748-07-1966 L1983 **P** *020

FEUER, Scott Irwin. 7101 NE 137TH AVE 98682 #035-08-1977 L1981 **FM** *020 †18

FINLEY, Christopher John. 400 NE MOTHER JOSEPH PL 98664 #040-02-1988 L1992 **EM** *020 †16

FISCHER, Kevin D. ■ 98665 #040-02-2007 L2007 **IM** *012

FISHER, Jerry Jos. 4421 NE ST JOHNS RD 98661 #040-02-1966 L1968 **FM OS** *072 †18

FISHER, Robert Hill. 501 SE 172ND AVE 98684 #067-01-1969 L1969 **PUD IM** *020 †20

FLEISS, Jason Ash. 12607 SE MILL PLAIN BLVD 98684 #422-01-1996 L1999 **GPM** *020 †70

FLYNN, Mikiko. 14406 NE 20TH AVE 98686 #005-19-1981 L1998 **OPH** *020 †35

FORD, Jeffrey Edward. 14406 NE 20TH AVE 98686 #028-34-1991 L1995 **FM** *020 †18

FORSYTHE, Barbara Ann. 406C SE 131ST AVE STE 304, PLLC 98683 #003-01-1982 L1986 **OBG** *020 †30

FOSTER, Claudia Jean. 700 NE 87TH AVE 98664 #005-12-1979 L1983 **FM FSM** *020 †18

FOSTER, Maryann Ellis. 12607 SE MILL PLAIN BLVD 98684 #047-05-1986 L1994 **OBG** *020 †30

FOURTOUNIS, Panagiotis D. 14406 NE 20TH AVE 98686 #418-01-1988 L2005 **IM NEP** *020 †20

FOWLER, John Christian. 700 NE 87TH AVE 98664 #836-02-1976 L1983 **PUD IM** *020 †20

FOX, Colleen Lynn. 505 NE 87TH AVE, THE WOMENS CLINIC OF 98664 #041-13-1994 L1998 **OBG** *020 †30

FRALEY, Christopher Lance. 700 NE 87TH AVE 98664 #038-40-1999 L2006 **PCC** *020 †20

FRANCO, Kathleen Marie. 12607 SE MILL PLAIN BLVD 98684 #054-04-1984 L1988 **IM** *020 †20

FREDRIKSSON, Linnea. 3250 SE 164TH AVE, STE 108 98683 #035-03-1987 L1993 **DR** *020 †80

FREI, Yvonne Irma. 700 NE 87TH AVE 98664 #008-01-1989 L1993 **OBG** *020 †30

FREIDBERG, Stanton Lee. ■ 98661 #038-06-1960 L1966 **CD IM** *071 †20

FREITAG, Breton Charles. 2211 NE 139TH ST, NORTHWEST NEWBORN 98686 #040-02-1996 L2005 **NPM PD** *020 †55

FRIESEN, Jason Harlow. 16821 SE MCGILLIVRAY BLVD, STE 110 98683 #035-03-1999 L2005 **AI** *020 †55,03

FUCHS, Axel K. 12607 SE MILL PLAIN BLVD 98684 #409-25-1974 L1997 **OBG** *020 †30

FUCHS, Charles Elliott. 505 NE 87TH AVE, EVERGREEN PEDIATRIC 98664 #005-02-1977 L1981 **PD** *020 †55

FURIN, Mark John. 203 SE PARK PLAZA DR, STE 140 98684 #041-14-1985 L2000 **OTO HNS** *020 †45

FURLONG, Lee. 700 NE 87TH AVE 98664 #036-01-1987 L1990 **IM** *020 †20

GABRIEL, Allen. 505 NE 87TH AVE, STE 250 98664 #031-01-2001 L2003 **PS** *020

GAGNON, Patrick James. ■ 98683 #010-02-2005 L2005 **RO** *012

GALEN, William P. 210 SE 136TH AVE 98684 #040-02-1948 L1951 **ON IM** *071 †20

GAMBEE, L Phaon. ■ 98664 #030-06-1957 L1957 **ORS** *072 †40

GAMBEE, Matthew Jude. 200 NE MOTHER JOSEPH PL, STE 210 98664 #030-06-1983 L1991 **PM** *020 †60

GARDNER, Patricia Ann. 6926 NE FOURTH PLAIN BLVD 98661 #017-20-1987 L2001 **P** *020 †75

GARRETT, Kristin Kay. 2211 NE 139TH ST, LEGACY SALMON CRK-HOSP OFC 98686 #034-01-2002 L2005 **IM** *020 †20

GEARY, Louise Margaret. 13912 NE 20TH AVE, STE H206 98686 #539-02-1978 L1990 **FM** *100

GHOFRANI, Mohiedean. 3400 MAIN ST, MEMORIAL HEALTH 98663 #517-08-1998 L2006 **PTH PCP** *020 †20

GIENAPP, Todd W. 700 NE 87TH AVE, MEDICAL COLLEGE OF WISCONS 98664 #028-79-1998, ▲ L1999 **PCC** *012 †20

GILBERT, Jennifer Catheri. ■ 98682 #001-02-2008 *012

GILLETTE, Darren Lee. 2211 NE 139TH ST, LEGACY SALMON CREEK HOSP E 98686 #017-20-1994 L2005 **OS PD** *020 †16

GILLILAND, Michael W. ■ 98683 #005-12-1997 L2003 **APM** *020 †05

GINSBERG, Jill Sydney. 12607 SE MILL PLAIN BLVD, CASCADE PARK MEDICAL OFFIC 98684 #005-02-1986 L1989 **FM** *020 †18

GLASS, David Eugene. ■ 98665 #065-01-1957 L1958 **N P** *071 †75

GLASS, Graham David. 222 NE PARK PLAZA DR # 100 98684 #005-06-1996 L1999 **IM** *020 †20

GLORIA, Alexander Flores. 14201 NE 20TH AVE, STE 1102 98686 #020-12-1997 L2000 **FM** *020 †18

GOEI, Monica Mingtie. 1601 E 4TH PLAIN BLVD, VANCOUVER VA MEDICAL CENTE 98661 #048-02-1991 L2003 **IM** *020 †20

GOLUBAN, Ernest Louis. ■ 98682 #025-07-1968 L1991 **GP** *020 †16

GOODMAN, Tom Arthur. 400 NE MOTHER JOSEPH PL 98664 #040-02-1975 L1981 **DR** *071 †80

GOODWIN, Robert Wagner. 7701 NE HIGHWAY 99, STE F 98665 #017-20-1972 L1980 **EM** *020 †16

GORDON, Janet Irene. 7017 NE HIGHWAY 99 STE 202 98665 #038-40-1974 L1979 **OPH** *020 †35

GORECKI, Daniel Marek. 400 NE MOTHER JOSEPH PL 98664 #056-06-1993 L1997 **EM** *020 †16

GORITSKI, William Jos. 400 NE MOTHER JOSEPH PL, SOUTHWEST WA MED CTR ANGS 98664 #032-01-1988 L1992 **AN** *020 †05

GOTKOWITZ, Carrie Jeankay. 210 SE 136TH AVE 98684 #043-01-1988 L1993 **RO** *020 †80

GOWEN, Paul Curtis. 2911 SE VILLAGE LOOP 98683 #040-02-1995 L2001 **IM** *020 †20

GOWLEE, Guillermo. 14406 NE 20TH AVE 98686 #005-12-1988 L1994 **IM** *020 †20

GRAHAM, Lisa Dobyns. 6100 NE FOURTH PLAIN BLVD, HEALTHY STEPS CLINIC 98661 #010-01-1994 L1997 **PD** *020 †55

GRAHAM, Richard Perry. 2211 E MILL PLAIN BLVD, VANCOUVER MEDICAL OFFICE 98661 #010-01-1994 L1997 **IM** *020 †20

GRAHAM, Ronald Milton. 200 NE MOTHER JOSEPH PL #2 98664 #010-01-1961 L1964 **GS** *020 †85

GRAMSTAD, Gregory Dean. 2121 NE 139TH ST, STE 300 98686 #056-06-1999 L2005 **ORS** *020 †40

GRANT, James David. 400 NE MOTHER JOSEPH PL 98664 #003-01-1990 L1999 **AN** *020 †05

GRAY, Cynthia Dee. 615 SE CHKALOV DR 98683 #005-12-1984 L1991 **PS** *020 †65

GREANEY, Stephen Joseph. 501 SE 172ND AVE 98684 #028-03-1999 L2002 **FM** *020 †18

GREEN, Richard K, Jr. 14411 NE 20TH AVE, STE 103 98686 #016-11-1989 L1996 **PS HS** *020 †65

GREENHILL, Andrew Howard. 2525 NE 139TH ST, STE 210 DEPT OF ALLERGY 98686 #008-01-1972 L2007 **A RHU** *020 †55,03

GREVES, John Hans, III. 2525 NE 139TH ST 98686 #017-20-1972 L1973 **CD IM** *020 †20

GRIGGS, Chauncey Theodore. 8614 E MILL PLAIN BLVD, COLUMBIA SURGICAL 98664 #026-04-1996 L2001 **GS** *020 †85

GROSSMAN, Anne Elizabeth. ■ 98682 #038-41-1993 L1998 **IM** *020 †20

GRUDZIEN, Zbigniew M. 3606 MAIN ST STE 105 98663 #759-01-1985 L2000 **AN** *020 †05

GUENZBURGER, Todd N. 2211 NE 139TH ST, LEGACY SALMON CREEK HOSPIT 98686 #067-01-1989 L2005 **IM** *020 †20

GUILLERY, Edward Nigel. 2211 NE 139TH ST, LEGACY SALMON CREEK HOSPIT 98686 #016-02-1987 L2005 **PN** *020 †55

GUNGOR, Yamac. 2101 NE 139TH ST, CASCADE HEART PS 98686 #035-01-1997 L2002 **CD** *020 †20

GUO, Fuhua Holly. 8614 E MILL PLAIN BLVD, STE 310 98664 #243-16-1985 L2001 **IM** *020 †20 ‡

GURDIAN, Silvio Jose. 17720 SE MILL PLAIN BLVD 98683 #027-01-1996 L2001 **OPH** *020 †35

GUZEK, James Paul. 2205 NE 129TH ST 98686 #041-09-1974 L2003 **OPH** *020 †35

GUZMAN, Noel J, Jr. 222 NE PARK PLAZA DR # 100, NORTHWEST MEDICAL ASSOC PS 98684 #005-19-1994 L1996 **FM** *020 †20

HAGEN, David John. 400 NE MOTHER JOSEPH PL 98664 #054-04-1995 L1986 **FM** *020 †18

HALL, Joseph Andrew, Jr. ■ 98661 #062-01-1944 L1948 **OS IM** *071

HALLAS, Gregory J. 2525 NE 139TH ST 98686 #030-06-1985 L1989 **IM** *020 †20

HALVORSON, Derek Scott. 400 NE MOTHER JOSEPH PL 98664 #026-04-2001 L2004 **EM** *020 †16

HANDEL, Daniel Aaron. ■ 98685 #016-06-2002 L2002 **EM** *100 †16

HANFILETI, Peter S. ■ 98684 #035-06-1991 L1994 **GP** *020 †55

HANLEY, Jason Daniel. 400 NE MOTHER JOSEPH PL 98664 #016-43-2000 L2003 **EM** *020 †16

HANNA, Rafik Malak. ■ 98664 #915-04-1983 L1987 **PTH ATP** *020 †50
HANSEN, Jeffrey Jon. 2215 BROADWAY ST 98663 #026-04-1994 L1999 **P** *020 †75 ‡
HARPER, Shaun David. 2101 NE 139TH ST, CASCADE HEART PS 98686 #038-40-1996 L2002 **CD** *020 †20
HARWOOD, Brian Phillip. 700 NE 87TH AVE 98664 #040-02-1975 L1980 **PUD** *020 †20
HASSAN, Sammy James. 2211 NE 139TH ST RM 2C117, SURGICAL SERVICES, ANESTHE 98686 #054-04-1992 L2005 **AN** *020 †05
HASSETT, Joseph Michael. 650 N DEVINE RD, STE B 98661 #033-06-1977 L1996 **AI ALI** *020 †20,03
HATCHER-ROSS, Kevin Stuar. 700 NE 87TH AVE 98664 #023-07-2004 L2007 **PD** *100 †55
HAUGEN, Robert Cameron. 14406 NE 20TH AVE 98686 #040-02-1993 L1997 **OBG** *020 †30
HAYES, Thomas David. 2121 NE 139TH ST, STE 300 98686 #021-01-1966 L1975 **ORS** *020 †40
HAYS, David Lee. 2525 NE 139TH ST, STE 260 98686 #012-05-1998 L2002 **FM** *020 †18
HE, Xingyue. 700 NE 87TH AVE 98664 #243-68-1984 L2005 **HO** *020 †20
HEDRICK, John William. 1319 NE 134TH ST STE 107, WASHINGTON 98685 #021-05-1994 L2001 **FM** *020 †18
HEE, Vernon Ge Kin. 700 NE 87TH AVE 98664 #014-01-1980 L1988 **GE IM** *020 †20
HEHN, Robert Jacob. 814 NE 87TH AVE 98664 #040-02-1967 L1972 **U GS** *020 †95
HEID, James Jos. 2525 NE 139TH ST, STE 260 98686 #005-19-1992 L2000 **FM OBS** *020 †18
HEIDSIEK, Lynne Clarke. 14406 NE 20TH AVE 98686 #005-15-1981 L1990 **FM** *020 †18
HELGASON, Paul Norman. ■ 98664 #056-06-1993 L1994 **IM** *020 †20
HELM, Frederic Carl. ■ 98665 #016-11-1965 L1971 **AN OM** *072 †05
HERD, Melvin Dale. 700 NE 87TH AVE 98664 #028-34-1999 L2006 **FM** *020 †18
HERSH, Craig Stephen. 14406 NE 20TH AVE 98686 #028-34-1988 L1991 **D** *020 †15
HERZBERG, William Steven. 505 NE 87TH AVE, STE 460 98664 #005-11-1989 L1994 **CN SME** *020 †75
HERZIG, William Nelson. 2525 NE 139TH ST 98686 #010-01-1989 L1993 **OBG** *020 †30
HESTON, Leonard Lancaster. ■ 98661 #040-02-1961 L1990 **P** *071
HICKS, Shauna Michelle. 12607 SE MILL PLAIN BLVD 98684 #005-19-2003 L2007 **OBG** *020
HIGGINS, Allison Laurel. 505 NE 87TH AVE, THE WOMENS CLINIC OF 98664 #048-04-1991 L1995 **OBG** *020 †30
HIGHKIN, Daniel J. 700 NE 87TH AVE 98664 #005-02-1984 L1988 **IM** *020 †20
HILDEBRAND, Teresa Anne. 1000 SE TECH CENTER DR, STE 120 98683 #049-01-1991 L1993 **FM** *020 †18
HITCHCOCK, Jeremy John. ■ 98662 #048-16-2005 L2005 **FP** *012
HO, Hon Lung. ■ 98665 #040-02-2007 L2007 **P** *012
HOFFELT, Stephen C. 400 NE MOTHER JOSEPH PL, SOUTHWEST WASHINGTON MEDIC 98664 #007-02-1998 L2005 **RO** *100 †80
HOFFMAN, Rebecca Ruth. 1319 NE 134TH ST, STE 105 98685 #041-02-1997 L2000 **FM VS** *020 †18 ‡
HOGNESS, Christopher Gore. 100 E 33RD ST 98663 #005-02-1986 L1995 **IM** *020 †20,18
HOKANSON, Carolyn Sue. 12607 SE MILL PLAIN BLVD 98684 #025-07-1976 L1977 **FM** *020 †18
HOLBROOK, Lisa Kay. 14201 NE 20TH AVE, STE 1102 98686 #017-20-1997 L2001 **FM** *020 †18
HOLMES, William Wayne. 700 NE 87TH AVE 98664 #019-02-1944 L1947 **GYN OBS** *071
HOLTER, Howard E. ■ 98663 #028-34-1953 L1972 **FM** *071
HOSKINS, Gregory C. 400 NE MOTHER JOSEPH PL 98664 #020-12-1998 L2004 **EM** *020 †16
HOSSEINION, Eva. 100 E 33RD ST, STE 100 98663 #286-04-2003 L2006 **FP** *012
HSU, Frank Kueyung. 8614 E MILL PLAIN BLVD 20 98664 #025-01-1992 L2004 **DR** *020 †80
HSU, Michael Chiashao. ■ 98665 #036-07-2002 L2002 **PM** *100 †60
HSU, Wei-Tzy. ■ 98665 #385-04-1967 L1973 **OBG** *020 †30
HU, Chester Chi Tak. 2211 NE 139TH ST 98686 #034-01-1993 L2000 **AN EM** *020
HUANG, Carber Ching-Ho. 2101 NE 139TH ST STE 250, LEGACY COLUMBIA VASCULAR A 98686 #048-12-1995 L2005 **VS** *020 †85
HUANG, Virginia Shaushen. 14411 NE 20TH AVE 98686 #008-01-1985 L2005 **PS** *020 †65
HUTCHINSON, Doris Ellen. 14508 NE 20TH AVE, STE 300 98686 #040-02-1982 L1989 **OBG** *020 †30
HUTCHINSON, Kathleen M. 505 NE 87TH AVE, EVERGREEN PEDIATRIC 98664 #040-02-1987 L1990 **PD** *020 †55
HUTFILZ, Rebecca Lynn. 2211 NE 139TH ST, LEGACY SALMON CREEK HOSPIT 98686 #041-14-1998 L2005 *020 †55
HUYNH, Van Khanh. 700 NE 87TH AVE 98664 #024-07-1997 L2007 **IM** *020 †20
JACKSON, Christopher F. 200 NE MOTHER JOSEPH PL #3 98664 #068-01-1974 L1982 **GS** *020 †85
JACKSON, Ricky Lee. 5512 NE 107TH AVE 98662 #005-12-1979 L1981 **FM EM** *020 †18
JACOB, Shalini Mary. 400 NE MOTHER JOSEPH PL 98664 #495-27-1976 L1998 **IM** *020 †20
JACOBSEN, Paul Lind. 505 NE 87TH AVE STE 460 98664 #051-04-1985 L1989 **N** *020 †75
JAIN, Kiren Mehra. 13215 SE MILL PLAIN BLVD, STE C8-901 98684 #028-34-1992 L2001 **DR** *020 †80
JAMIESON, Andrew David. ■ 98664 #001-02-1972 L1973 **OBG** *071 †30 ‡
JAMSHIDI, Maryann. 2525 NE 139TH ST, THE VANCOUVER CLINIC INC 98686 #034-01-1998 L2003 **CD** *020 †20
JANCHAR, Timothy Adam. 2211 NE 139TH ST, EMERGENCY DEPARTMENT 98686 #010-02-1999 L2002 **EM** *020 †16
JENKINS, Thomas Moore. 2211 NE 139TH ST, LEGACY MFM 98686 #040-02-1994 L2005 **OBG** *020 †30
JENSEN, Brad W. 400 NE MOTHER JOSEPH PL 98664 #030-06-1979 L1992 **PTH IM** *020 †20,50
JOHN, Benjamin Travis. 2525 NE 139TH ST 98686 #051-04-1998 L2006 **ICE** *020 †20
JOHNS, Gordon Everett. 2205 NE 129TH ST 98686 #005-12-1973 L1993 **OPH** *020 †35 ‡
JOHNSON, Bruce Carl. 748 SE FAIRWINDS LOOP 98661 #016-42-1978 L1991 **P PA** *020 †75
JOHNSON, Paul W. 700 NE 87TH AVE 98664 #020-75-2002, ▲ L2006 **FSM** *020 †20
JONES, Alan Victor. 222 NE PARK PLAZA DR # 100 98684 #030-05-1983 L1986 **IM** *020 †20
JONES, Nila Gardner. 100 E 33RD ST, STE 206 98663 #040-02-1998 L2001 **FM** *020 †18
JORDHEN, Laura Pompel. 501 SE 172ND AVE 98684 #040-02-2001 L2004 **FM** *020 †18
JUNKER, John Arthur. 505 NE 87TH AVE, VANCOUVER RADIOLOGISTS PC 98664 #039-01-1966 L1970 **DR** *071 †80
JURA, J Brittian. 501 SE 172ND AVE 98684 #028-46-1998 L2004 **PCC** *020 †20
JUSTER, Jeanette Ilene. 400 NE MOTHER JOSEPH PL 98664 #005-02-1975 L1978 **EM FM** *020 †18,16
KAEMPF, Joseph Wm. 2211 NE 139TH ST, NORTHWEST NEWBORN 98686 #040-02-1983 L1997 **NPM PD** *020 †55
KAISER, John Erlin. 2525 NE 139TH ST, STE 260 98686 #056-05-1982 L1985 **FM** *020 †18
KARMY-JONES, Riyad C. 200 NE MOTHER JOSEPH PL, STE 300 98664 #060-01-1983 L1997 **GS TRS** *020 †85,90
KARPLUS, Theresa Marie. 2525 NE 139TH ST 98686 #024-07-1992 L1992 **RHU** *020 †20
KASCH, Erich Courtney. ■ 98664 #040-02-1996 *062
KATTERHAGEN, Christine M. 14411 NE 20TH AVE 98686 #016-42-1992 L1997 **GS** *020 †85
KAZMIEROWSKI, John Albert. 417 SE 164TH AVE, STE 300 98684 #016-11-1971 L1972 **D A** *020 †20,03,15
KEARNEY, Jason Francis. 400 NE MOTHER JOSEPH PL 98664 #012-01-1994 L2000 **EM** *020 †16
KEITH, Lynn M. ■ 98683 #023-12-1987 L1989 **IM** *100
KELLY, Nicole Christine. 400 NE MOTHER JOSEPH PL 98664 #005-06-1999 L2002 **EM** *020 †16
KENNEDY, Stephen Campbell. 615 SE CHKALOV DR STE 14 98683 #020-12-1970 L1979 **PS HS** *020
KEOWN, Paul Manchester. 17720 SE MILL PLAIN BLVD 98683 #040-02-1979 L1983 **OPH** *020 †35
KHAN, Sameer Hamid. 1325 SE TECH CENTER DR, STE 110 98683 #056-06-2000 L2006 **OPH** *100 †35
KHAN, Uzma Anwar. 2525 NE 139TH ST 98686 #704-02-1991 L2004 **RHU** *020 †20
KHAW, Jamie S. 8614 E MILL PLAIN BLVD, STE 201 98664 #035-03-2000 L2007 **GS** *020
KHEITER, Ahmed. 400 NE MOTHER JOSEPH PL 98664 #422-01-2001 L2004 **IM** *100 †20
KHOO, Eng-Lock. ■ 98683 #572-05-1965 L1973 **IM CD** *020
KILGORE, Erik James. 3250 SE 164TH AVE, STE 108 98683 #047-05-1993 L1998 **DR NM** *020 †80,28
KILWAY, James Bernard, II. 8614 E MILL PLAIN BLVD, COLUMBIA SURGICAL 98664 #041-09-1996 L2001 **GS AS** *020 †85
KIM, Edward Dongpil. 2525 NE 139TH ST 98686 #005-12-2001 L2006 **SCI** *100 †60
KIM, Lawrence Young. 12607 SE MILL PLAIN BLVD, CONTRA COSTA REGIONAL MEDI 98684 #583-01-1961 L1992 **P** *020 †75
KIM, Michael C. 17720 SE MILL PLAIN BLVD 98683 #028-02-1995 L2000 **OPH** *020 †35
KIM, Stephen S. 222 NE PARK PLAZA DR # 100, NORTHWEST MEDICAL ASSOCIAT 98684 #583-01-1992 L1996 **IM** *020 †20 ‡
KLINGENMAIER, C Herman. 600 NE 92ND AVE 98664 #041-01-1964 L1975 **AN PUD** *020 †05
KNOWLES, Richard Derrick. 3200 SE 164TH AVE, STE 101 98683 #654-01-2001 L2003 **FM** *020
KOEHLER, John Adam, III. ■ 98683 #038-40-2006 L2006 **FP** *012
KOLBEINSSON, Magnus Eric. 200 NE MOTHER JOSEPH PL, STE 330 98664 #484-01-1977 L2002 **GS** *020 †85
KOLIBABA, Kathryn Stegen. 2501 NE 134TH ST STE 100 98686 #040-02-1990 L1996 **HO** *020 †20
KORMANYOS, Stephen Wm. 400 NE MOTHER JOSEPH PL 98664 #054-04-1991 L2003 **IM** *020 †20
KOSCINSKA, Maria Anna. 100 E 33RD ST STE 206 98663 #759-03-1988 L2001 **IM** *020 †20
KOVARIC, Thomas Richard. 2525 NE 139TH ST 98686 #028-34-1975 L1980 **CD IM** *020 †20
KOZINSKA, Malgorzata I. 200 NE MOTHER JOSEPH PL, STE 400 98664 #016-01-1999 L2006 **IC** *020 †20
KRALL, Michael Adam. 14406 NE 20TH AVE, KAISER PERMANENTE SALMON C 98686 #040-02-1980 L1997 **FM OS** *020 †18
KRANZPILLER, Susan E. 1000 SE TECH CENTER DR #12 98683 #409-10-1999 L2002 **FM** *020 †18
KREMEN, Michal. 2211 NE 139TH ST, SALMON CREEK LEGACY HOSPIT 98686 #286-11-2000 L2004 **IM** *020 †20
KRETSCHMAR, Paul Otto. 700 NE 87TH AVE 98664 #016-11-1954 L1960 **IM OM** *020 †20,70
KROB, Herbert Alexander. 2525 NE 139TH ST 98686 #036-05-2002 L2007 **N** *100 †75
KRUGER, Janine Kathryn. 700 NE 87TH AVE 98664 #056-06-1998 L2005 **OBG** *020 †30
KUBICZ, Gina Diane. ■ 98661 #040-02-2008 *012
KUBINIEC, Richard Thos. 11801 NE 65TH ST # A 98662 #028-34-1992 L1997 **OBG** *020 †30
KUMAR, Bharat Bhushan. ■ 98683 #495-15-1950 L1961 **P PD** *071 †55
KURYLA, Karen Ann. 12607 SE MILL PLAIN BLVD, CASCADE PARK MEDICAL OFFIC 98684 #035-06-1986 L1991 **FM** *020 †18
KYPER, Robert James. 1040 SE COLUMBIA RIDGE DR 98664 #041-15-2001 L2005 **AN** *020 †05
LADERAS, Manuela G. ■ 98684 #748-08-1963 L1973 **IM** *071
LADERAS, Rosalina. 304 N LIESER RD 98664 #748-01-1965 L1973 **IM** *071
LADERAS, Teofilo G, Jr. 400 NE MOTHER JOSEPH PL 98664 #748-02-1961 L1971 **AN** *020 †05
LAM, Nhung Tuyet. 400 NE MOTHER JOSEPH PL 98664 #035-45-1997 L2004 **AN** *020 †05
LAMBERTON, Dale Francis. 2211 E MILL PLAIN BLVD 98661 #005-12-1988 L2006 **CD** *020 †20
LANGE, Andrea Kathryn. 8614 E MILL PLAIN BLVD, COLUMBIA SURGICAL 98664 #041-02-1995 L2001 **CRS** *020 †85,10
LAROSA-PEDROSO, Juan-Carlo. ■ 98661 #275-01-1994 **GP** *020
LARRABEE, Paige B. 2211 NE 139TH ST, NORTHWEST NEWBORN 98686 #010-01-1998 L2004 **NPM** *020 †55
LASATER, John Allard. 7101 NE 137TH AVE 98682 #040-02-1974 L1996 **PD** *020 †55
LAVELLE, Michael Thos. 2102 NE 139TH ST, STE 360 98686 #016-43-1966 L1973 **CD IM** *071 †20
LAYCOE, Bryan Harold. 2121 NE 139TH ST, STE 300 98686 #040-02-1972 L1979 **ORS** *020 †40
LE, Hoang Nhut. 200 NE MOTHER JOSEPH PL, STE 1200 98664 #035-45-1997 L2004 **NS** *020
LEANING, Katharine E. 2211 NE 139TH ST, LEGACY SALIMON CREEK HOSP 98686 #024-05-1999 L2005 **PD** *020 †55
LEE, Larry Kay. 700 NE 87TH AVE 98664 #005-14-1984 L1997 **IM** *020 †20
LEE, Won Sok. 2121 NE 139TH ST, LEGACY SALMON CREEK HOSPIT 98686 #040-02-1994 L1998 **RO** *020 †80
LELAND, Elise Leaf. 5500 NE 109TH CT STE E, ORCHARDS FAMILY MEDICINE I 98662 #054-04-2002 L2002 **FM** *020 †18
LESTER, Melvin Arthur. 6100 NE FOURTH PLAIN BLVD, HLTHY STEPS WOMENS & CHILD 98661 #010-01-1956 L1992 **OBG** *071 †18,30
LEVY, Stuart Bayliss. 2211 E MILL PLAIN BLVD 98661 #038-41-1974 L1980 **FM** *020 †18
LEW, Robyn Michelle. 2525 NE 139TH ST 98686 #005-02-2001 L2005 **OBG** *020 †30
LEWALLEN, Patrick Kane. 2211 NE 139TH ST, NORTHWEST NEWBORN 98686 #017-20-1980 L1989 **PD NPM** *020 †55
LEWISKI, Michael S. 505 NE 87TH AVE, VANCOUVER RADIOLOGISTS PC 98664 #062-01-1955 L1956 **R NM** *071 †80,28
LHEWA, Tsering Lhoden. ■ 98684 #054-04-2008 *012
LI, Helen Chang Shan. 12607 SE MILL PLAIN BLVD, KAISER CLINIC 98684 #005-11-1967 L1997 **PD IM** *050 †55
LIANG, Griffith Enchia. 700 NE 87TH AVE 98664 #028-02-1997 L2004 **PCC** *020 †20
LIEM, Caleb. 6100 NE FOURTH PLAIN BLVD 98661 #005-12-1970 L1993 **GYN** *020
LIM, Bum Sub. 6527 NE HIGHWAY 99 98665 #583-10-1965 L1974 **GP** *071
LIN, George Ting. 2211 NE 139TH ST, LEGACY SALMON CREEK HOSPIT 98686 #016-02-2002 L2005 **EM** *020 †16
LIN, Margaret Michi. 12607 SE MILL PLAIN BLVD, CASCADE PARK MEDICAL OFFIC 98684 #040-02-1995 L2002 **CHP** *020 †75
LIN, Mike Geng-Li. 14406 NE 20TH AVE 98686 #056-06-1995 L2001 **IM** *020 †20

LINDGREN, John C. 6926 NE FOURTH PLAIN BLVD, COLUMBIA RIVER MENTAL HEAL 98661 #051-01-1992 L2004 **P** *020 †75

LINDGREN, Kelvin Allister. 3506 MAIN ST 98663 #005-12-1959 L1985 **OTO** *020 †45

LINTS, Rasjad Kenton. 14406 NE 20TH AVE 98686 #054-04-1990 L1993 **PD** *020 †55

LIPP, Edward Birkin, Jr. 2121 NE 139TH ST, STE 300 98686 #041-02-1960 L1993 **ORS HS** *020 †40

LISS, Michaelann L. 700 NE 87TH AVE, THE VANCOUVER CLINIC 98664 #041-77-2000, ▲ L2006 **HO** *020

LIU, Joyce Christine. 12607 SE MILL PLAIN BLVD 98684 #035-15-1991 L1994 **PD** *020 †55

LIU, Michael C. 100 E 33RD ST STE 100 98663 #026-08-1994 L2001 **FM** *020 †18

LIU, Nancy Yufang. 2525 NE 139TH ST 98686 #016-06-2000 L2001 **OTO** *020 †45

LIVAUDAIS, West, Jr. 100 E 33RD ST 98663 #047-06-1970 L1994 **GS TRS** *030 †85

LLOYD, David J. 400 NE MOTHER JOSEPH PL 98664 #065-06-1974 L1999 **EM** *020 †16

LONG, Jack Edmond. 100 E 33RD ST 98664 #038-41-1986 L1991 **IM END** *020 †16

LONGO, Julia Claire. PO BOX 1600, SW WASHINGTON MED CTR 98668 #005-18-1986 L1999 **PTH GYN** *020 †50

LOOK, Regan Mon. 210 SE 136TH AVE 98684 #035-19-1991 L1997 **HO** *020 †20

LOTTIG, Kristin Anne. 14406 NE 20TH AVE 98686 #038-40-1997 L2006 **PD** *020 †55

LOWDER, Anne. 400 NE MOTHER JOSEPH PL 98664 #049-01-1998 L2001 **FM** *020 †18

LU, Di. ■ 98665 #243-45-1983 L2002 **PTH GYN** *020 †50

LU, Steven T. 400 NE MOTHER JOSEPH PL 98664 #243-58-1986 L2001 **IM** *020 †20

LUCKWITZ, John Wallace. 400 NE MOTHER JOSEPH PL 98664 #038-44-1992 L2003 **AN PME** *020 †05

LUDWIG, Linda B. ■ 98686 #025-12-1976 L1979 **ID PD** *020 †55

LUNDEEN, Robert Taylor. ■ 98683 #016-11-1953 L1954 **FM** *071

LUU, Huong T. 12004 NE 4TH PLAIN RD, STE G 98682 #409-16-1987 L1993 **FM** *020 †18

LY, Jessica. 2525 NE 139TH ST, THE VANCOUVER CLINIC, INC 98664 #016-43-1996 L2000 **IM PD** *020 †20,55

LYONS, Jennifer Michelle. 501 SE 172ND AVE 98684 #041-07-1998 L2004 **PD** *020 †55

MAC DONELL, Janet R. 14406 NE 20TH AVE 98686 #026-04-1995 L1998 **PD** *020 †55

MAH, Theresa Ng. 501 SE 172ND AVE 98684 #028-78-2002, ▲ L2006 **D** *100

MAHNKE, Jennifer Lynn. 700 NE 87TH AVE 98664 #038-06-1995 L2000 **OBG** *020 †30

MAILHOT, Mark Francis. 501 SE 172ND AVE, THE VANCOUVER CLINIC INC 98684 #041-12-1997 L2007 **IM** *020 †70,20

MALETZKY, Barry Michael. ■ 98664 #035-08-1967 L1968 **P** *071

MANSOORI, Noor Agha. 2211 NE 139TH ST, LEGACY SALMON CREEK HOSPIT 98686 #003-01-2001 L2005 **AN** *100 †05

MARANZE, Harriette P. 2211 E MILL PLAIN BLVD 98661 #038-41-1975 L1980 **FM** *020 †18

MARION, Jos Anthony, Jr. 7101 NE 137TH AVE 98682 #030-06-1985 L2000 **FM** *020 †18

MARKHAM, Michael James. 200 NE MOTHER JOSEPH PL, STE 210 98664 #040-02-1973 L1987 **NS** *071 †25

MARMION, Patrick James. 13215 SE MILL PLAIN BLVD, STE C8 # 144 98684 #016-11-1975 L2004 **OBG PHP** *020 †70,30

MARONEY, John Walker, Jr. 14406 NE 20TH AVE 98686 #041-02-1986 L1991 **IMG** *020 †18

MARRINER, Ellsworth Fred. ■ 98684 #035-06-1948 L1973 **OM GPM** *071

MARSH, Loyal Douglas. 406 SE 131ST AVE, STE A101 98683 #040-02-1985 L1994 **EM** *020 †16

MARTENS, Henrik. ■ 98660 #297-01-1967 L1973 **D** *071 †15

MARTIN, Mark Alan. 200 NE MOTHER JOSEPH PL, PLACE #410 98664 #017-20-1990 L1997 **TS** *020 †85,90

MARTINSON, Lindsey. 12607 SE MILL PLAIN BLVD 98684 #056-06-1980 L1993 **OM FM** *020 †70,18

MASON, Lawrence Carroll. 700 NE 87TH AVE 98664 #040-02-1967 L1974 **PD** *020 †55

MASSON, Douglas Bruce. 505 NE 87TH AVE, UROLOGY CLINIC OF 98664 #054-04-1991 L1997 **U** *020 †95

MATOUS, Steven K. 505 NE 87TH AVE STE 301 98664 #048-04-1990 L1996 **GS** *020 †85

MATTHEWS, Kerry Anne. 12607 SE MILL PLAIN BLVD, KAISER CASCADE PARK 98684 #005-15-1990 L1994 **FM** *020 †18

MC AFEE, James Martin. 505 NE 87TH AVE STE LL50 98664 #040-02-1983 L1990 **DR OS** *020 †80

MC ANINCH, Edward M. 400 NE MOTHER JOSEPH PL 98664 #041-02-1952 L1953 **FM** *072 †18

MC AULIFFE, Kathleen. 400 NE MOTHER JOSEPH PL 98664 #054-04-1979 L1989 **FM** *020 †18

MC BRIDE, William Steven. 700 NE 87TH AVE 98664 #025-01-1985 L1995 **PCC IM** *020 †20

MC CLEARY, Robert Edward. 400 NE MOTHER JOSEPH PL 98664 #041-01-1973 L1980 **PD** *020 †16

MC CLUGGAGE, Clare M. 14406 NE 20TH AVE 98686 #028-03-1982 L2006 **FM** *020 †18

MC CREIGHT, Wm Horner. 1319 NE 134TH ST, STE 107 98685 #041-01-1976 L1977 **FM** *020 †18

MC DONALD, Jeffrey Howard. 400 NE MOTHER JOSEPH PL 98664 #040-02-1991 L1994 **EM** *020 †16

MC DONALD, Jennifer Ann. 100 E 33RD ST STE 206, HUDSONS BAY MED GRP 98663 #054-04-1977 L1985 **IM** *020 †20

MC DONALD, John V. 2211 NE 139TH ST, NORTHWEST NEWBORN 98686 #056-05-1979 L1988 **NPM PD** *030 †55

MC DOUGALL, Donald John. ■ 98661 #016-06-1953 L1954 **P GP** *071

MC FARLAND, Joseph Roy. 200 NE MOTHER JOSEPH PL, STE 1200 98664 #040-02-1967 L1975 **ORS** *020 †40

MCFARLANE, Mhairi Ann. 7410 DELAWARE LN 98664 #919-05-1997 L2000 **FM** *020

MC GAREY, William Carl. 203 SE PARK PLAZA DR # 140 98684 #011-02-1974 L2000 **ORS** *020 †40

MC GOUGH, Benji Harrison. 2121 NE 139TH ST, STE 300 98686 #004-01-1957 L1968 **ORS** *020 †40

MC GUINESS, Phillip A. 700 NE 87TH AVE 98664 #021-05-1979 L1982 **PD** *020 †55

MC GUIRE, Laura Ann. ■ 98661 #051-07-2003 L2007 **OBG** *020

MCNALLY, Cynthia. 2101 NE 139TH ST, THE WOMENS CLINIC OF 98686 #051-01-1995 L2002 **OBG** *020 †30

MEITZ, Kevin P. 2525 NE 139TH ST 98686 #028-78-2001, ▲ L2007 **GE** *020

MELTON, Russell Wayne. 700 NE 87TH AVE 98664 #054-04-1961 L1971 **GYN** *071 †30

MENDEL-HARTVIG, Janet. 3250 SE 164TH AVE, STE 108 98683 #040-02-1997 L2005 **DR** *020 †80

METZDORFF, Mark T. 200 NE MOTHER JOSEPH PL, PLACE, #410 98664 #056-05-1980 L1991 **TS** *020 †90,85

METZGER, Jens Newyl. 2525 NE 139TH ST 98686 #054-04-1997 L2000 **IM** *020 †20

METZGER, Laurie Kawabata. 700 NE 87TH AVE, THE VANCOUVER CLINIC 98664 #054-04-1997 L2000 **PD** *020 †55

MICHAELS, Arthur H. ■ 98664 #418-01-1953 L1963 **OBG** *020 †30

MILLER, Cathleen Jackson. 2211 E MILL PLAIN BLVD, VANCOUVER MED OFFICES 98661 #005-02-1988 L2006 **N** *020 †75

MILLER, Darrell Michael. 406 SE 131ST AVE, STE A101 98683 #040-02-1968 L1976 **EM** *020

MILLER, Stephen Michael. 501 SE 172ND AVE, STE250 98684 #028-34-1992 L1995 **PD** *020 †55

MIRAMONTES, Teresa. 2525 NE 139TH ST 98686 #054-04-2001 L2004 **FM** *020 †18

MISCHEL, Rebecca Eve. 2211 NE 139TH ST, NORTHWEST NEWBORN 98686 #005-02-1991 L1997 **PD NPM** *020 †18

MITCHELL, Cameron David. 400 NE MOTHER JOSEPH PL 98664 #040-02-1999 L2002 **EM** *020 †16

MITCHELL, Jennifer Kron. 16811 SE MCGILLIVRAY BLVD, STE 101 98683 #040-02-1999 L2002 **FM** *020 †18

MITCHELL, Michael. 203 SE PARK PLAZA DR, STE 140 98684 #048-12-1989 L2001 **OTO** *020 †45

MITCHELL, Michael Alton. 203 SE PARK PLAZA DR, STE 140 98684 #005-14-1987 L1988 **EM** *020

MIZUTANI, Patricia Ann. 3250 SE 164TH AVE, STE 108 98683 #010-01-1986 L1998 **R** *040 †80

MODHA, Ashok. 200 NE MOTHER JOSEPH PL, STE 110 98664 #062-01-1997 L2004 **NS** *020 †25

MOLLENHOLT, Peter Jan. 400 NE MOTHER JOSEPH PL, SOUTHWEST WASHINGTON MED C 98664 #858-01-1977 L2003 *020

MOLLERUS, Robert James. 700 NE 87TH AVE 98664 #056-06-1962 L1967 **GS** *071 †85

MOLLOY, Molly Kelly. 14406 NE 20TH AVE 98686 #005-19-2001 L2004 **PD** *020 †55

MOREAU, Louis G. 200 NE MOTHER JSPH PL #330 98664 #024-07-1999 L2005 **TS** *020 †85

MOREHART, Mark Alan. 2211 NE 139TH ST 98686 #048-12-1983 L2007 **AN PME** *020 †05

MORFORD, Gregory Leroy. 2211 NE 139TH ST 98684 #041-09-1984 L2001 **FM** *020

MORGAN, Elizabeth. 700 NE 87TH AVE, VANCOUVER CLINIC 98664 #040-02-1997 L2001 **OBG** *020

MORICH, Michael Dieter. 13215 SE MILL PLAIN BLVD, STE C8-901 98684 #040-02-1999 L2005 **DR** *020 †80

MORRISON, Donald T. ■ 98685 #021-01-1950 L1956 **PTH** *071 †50

MORRISON, Lisa Jo. 501 SE 172ND AVE 98684 #005-02-1982 L1985 **PD** *030 †55

MORRISROE, Dennis Edward. 100 E 33RD ST, FAMILY MEDICINE OF SOUTHWE 98663 #040-02-2007 L2007 **FP** *012

MORTIMER, Dale Burton. 10000 NE 7TH AVE, STE 385 98685 #040-02-1985 L1991 **N P** *020 †75

MOSSMAN, Frank David. ■ 98662 #030-05-1940 L1948 **OPH OTO** *071

MOYNIHAN, Daniel J. 2211 NE 139TH ST 98686 #005-15-1987 L1992 **FM** *020 †18

MUCHOWSKI, Karen E. 2525 NE 139TH ST, STE 260 98686 #005-19-1996 L2002 **FM** *020 †18

MULLER, David James. 12607 SE MILL PLAIN BLVD 98684 #005-14-1986 L1990 **FM** *020 †18

MURPHY, David Lee. 2211 NE 139TH ST, NORTHWEST NEWBORN 98686 #005-12-1980 L1998 **PD** *071

MURPHY, Janet Ann. 400 NE MOTHER JOSEPH PL 98664 #040-02-1991 L1998 **AN** *020 †05

MUSGRAVE, Douglas Stone. 2121 NE 139TH ST, STE 300 98686 #036-07-1997 L2003 **HS ORS** *020 †40

MUZIK, Elizabeth Anne. ■ 98664 #054-04-2006 L2006 **FP** *012

MYERS, Douglas Randall. 8614 E MILL PLAIN BLVD, STE 100 98664 #040-02-1978 L1984 **OTO** *020 †45 ‡

NADAL, Natalya Nikolayevn. 700 NE 87TH AVE 98664 #913-72-1999 L2003 **PD** *020

NELSON, Donald Wm. ■ 98685 #056-06-1946 L1947 **OBG AM** *071 †30

NELSON, Howard Andre. 700 NE 87TH AVE 98664 #040-02-1994 L2006 **VIR** *020 †80

NELSON, Lyle Wilfred. 3215 SE 192ND AVE STE 112, CASCADE ORAL SURGERY 98683 #030-05-1987 L1989 **HNS FPS** *020

NELSON, Martha. 2211 NE 139TH ST, NORTHWEST NEWBORN 98686 #025-12-1990 L2005 **NPM** *020 †55

NELSON, Rebecca Lynne. 2525 NE 139TH ST 98686 #051-01-1999 L2003 **PD** *020 †55

NEWELL, Donald Edward. 1405 SE 164TH AVE, STE 102 98683 #040-02-1981 L1990 **OTO A** *020 †45

NEWMAN, Alan Philip. 2121 NE 139TH ST, STE 300 98686 #028-02-1977 L1997 **ORS OSM** *020 †40

NEWMAN, Daniel I. 315 E EVERGREEN BLVD 98660 #035-08-1981 L1997 **PMM IM** *020 †20

NEWMAN, Valerie. 2211 NE 139TH ST, NORTHWEST NEWBORN 98686 #035-15-1991 L1991 **NPM** *020 †20

NG, James Jeremy. 700 NE 87TH AVE, THE VANCOUVER CLINIC 98664 #040-02-1994 L2000 **IM** *020 †20

NGO, Vu Viet. 14406 NE 20TH AVE 98686 #942-01-1986 L2004 **IM** *020 †20

NICACIO, Jamie. ■ 98684 #041-09-1996 L2000 **PM** *020 †60

NICHOLLS, Stephen Chas. 200 NE MOTHER JOSEPH PL 98664 #671-02-1974 L1986 **VS** *020 †85

NICOSKI, Ricky Anthony. 14201 NE 20TH AVE, URGENT MEDICAL CENTER 98686 #026-04-1982 L1993 **FM** *020 †18

NOONAN, Michael Jos. 16821 SE MCGILLIVRAY BLVD, STE 110 98683 #030-05-1964 L1980 **AI PD** *050 †55,03

NOPACHAI, Supranee Amy. 2501 NE 134TH ST, STE 200 98686 #016-45-1998 L2002 **MPD** *020 †20,55

NOVACK, Craig Martin. 2211 NE 139TH ST, NORTHWEST NEWBORN 98686 #054-04-1989 L1995 **PD NPM** *020 †55 ‡

NUNEZ-FINLEY, Armida E. 400 NE MOTHER JOSEPH PL 98664 #051-07-1993 L1996 **EM** *020 †16

NUSSER, John Andrew. 7410 DELAWARE LN 98664 #054-04-2000 L2003 **FM** *020 †18

OATES, Martin John. 100 E 33RD ST 98663 #056-06-2003 L2003 **FM** *030 †18

ORCHARD, Susan Marie. 505 NE 87TH AVE, STE 303 98664 #040-02-1981 L1995 **D** *020 †15

ORR, Christina L. 700 NE 87TH AVE 98664 #046-01-1996 L2003 **END** *020 †20

OSBORN, Marjory G Thomas. ■ 98683 #025-01-1946 L1947 **P** *071

OSMUNDSEN, Lynn R. 200 NE MOTHER JOSEPH PL, STE 330 98664 #024-07-1990 L1994 **OBG** *020 †30

O'TOOLE, Michael John. 2211 E MILL PLAIN BLVD 98661 #054-04-1996 L2004 **GS** *020 †85

OTT, Frederick David. 14406 NE 20TH AVE, KAISER PERMANENTE 98686 #025-01-1988 L1998 **D** *020 †15

OWEN, James Griffith. 700 NE 87TH AVE 98664 #028-02-1943 L1949 **GS** *020 †85

OWENS, Susan Zulke. 1000 SE TECH CENTER DR 98683 #016-11-1990 L1994 **FM** *020 †18

OZGUR, Hasan Tuna. 3250 SE 164TH AVE, VANCOUVER RADIOLOGISTS PC 98683 #902-05-1991 L1999 **RNR** *020 †20

PALISSON, Rosie Villagome. 12607 SE MILL PLAIN BLVD, KAISER PERMANENTE 98684 #014-01-1994 L2007 **IM** *020 †20

PALMER, Lowell E, Jr. 400 NE MOTHER JOSEPH PL 98664 #016-42-1993 L1996 **IM** *020 †20

PANG, Maynard Kung Lee. 14406 NE 20TH AVE, SALMON CREEK MEDICAL OFFIC 98686 #024-07-1996 L2001 **IM** *020 †20

PARADIS, Jean Michael. 400 NE MOTHER JOSEPH PL, MEDICAL CENTER 98664 #016-42-1996 L1999 **AN** *020 †05

PARK, Harry C S. 400 NE MOTHER JOSEPH PL 98664 #649-02-1959 L1960 **FM OS** *071

PARK, Yon Joo. 3250 SE 164TH AVE, STE 108 98683 #040-02-2002 L2007 **DR** *020 †80

PARKER, Aaron Butch. 400 NE MOTHER JOSEPH PL 98664 #051-01-1998 L2002 **AN** *020 †05 ‡

PARKINSON, Edward C. ■ 98662 #040-02-1943 L1956 **FM** *071

PATEL, Sandip Shashikant. 400 NE MOTHER JOSEPH PL 98664 #422-01-1998 L2005 **IM** *020 †20

PATTERSON, Emily Lynne. 14406 NE 20TH AVE, KAISER PERMANENTE-SALMON C 98686 #003-01-2000 L2005 **OPH** *100 †35

PATTERSON, James Randolph. ■ 98683 #035-01-1968 L1974 **PUD IM** *071 †20

PAVLICK, Theodore Jos. ■ 98685 #038-41-1956 L1956 **OPH** *071 †35

PEACHEY, Paul Eugene. 2211 E MILL PLAIN BLVD 98661 #003-01-1975 L1985 **FM** *020 †18

PEREIRA, Natasha Michele. 2525 NE 139TH ST 98686 #041-01-1999 L2004 **PD** *075 †55

PERLSTEIN, Abraham P. 6926 NE FOURTH PLAIN BLVD 98661 #035-19-1953 L1994 **P PYG** *075

PETER, David Chas. 12503 SE MILL PLAIN BLVD 98684 #305-01-1982 L1989 **P** *075

PETERS, Mark Anthony. 3305 MAIN ST, STE 100 98663 #056-06-1979 L1987 **OPH OS** *020 †35

PETERSON, Donny Juvenal. 200 NE MOTHER JOSEPH PL, STE 330 98664 #026-04-2002 L2002 **GS** *020 †85

PFAFF, David Arthur. 100 E 33RD ST, STE 206 98663 #028-03-1966 L1973 **GE IM** *020 †20

PHAM, Lan Ngoc. 100 E 33RD ST STE 206, HUDSONS BAY MED GRP 98663 #048-04-1996 L1999 **IM** *020 †20

PHAM, Tu Truong. 400 NE MOTHER JOSEPH PL 98664 #048-12-2002 L2005 **IM** *020 †20

PHILLIPSON, Beverley E. 800 NE TENNEY RD STE 110, PMB 107 98685 #040-02-1976 L1978 **END NTR** *071

PLAMP, Charles E, III. 700 NE 87TH AVE 98664 #020-12-1973 L1975 **NEP IM** *020 †20

PLANT, Sandford Byers. 700 NE 87TH AVE 98664 #040-02-1989 L1992 **IM PLM** *020 †20

PLAUT, Melanie Margaret. 12607 SE MILL PLAIN BLVD 98684 #041-01-1980 L1988 **OBG** *020 †20

PLETSCH, Theodore Danl. 8113 NE WARD RD 98682 #005-11-1956 L1973 **OBG GPM** *071 †30

PLISKA, Stephen Edward. 406 SE 131ST AVE, STE A101 98683 #040-02-1970 L1972 **EM** *020 †20

POLEHNA, Pavel. 700 NE 87TH AVE 98664 #286-13-1993 L2006 **FM** *020

PRATT, Kelley Dean. 2211 NE 139TH ST, EMERGENCY DEPT. 98686 #054-04-2002 L2005 **EM** *020 †16

PREMER, Danna Marie. 2211 NE 139TH ST, NORTHWEST NEWBORN 98686 #026-04-1992 L2001 **NPM** *020 †55

PRETCHER, Joy Lin. 3400 MAIN ST, MEMORIAL HEALTH 98663 #041-01-1997 L2004 **OBG** *020 †30

PRITEL, Philip Alex. ■ 98664 #005-12-1943 L1943 **OS GS** *071 †85

PROANO, Augusto. 8614 E MILL PLAIN BLVD, PSYCHIATRIC SERVICES GROUP 98664 #319-01-1952 L1959 **P PYG** *071 †75

PROANO, Fernando Diego. 11808 NE FOURTH PLAIN RD, URGENT MEDICAL CENTER 98682 #054-04-1979 L1981 **OM** *020 †70,18

PROVOST, Pierre Eusebe. 400 NE MOTHER JOSEPH PL 98664 #024-05-1987 L1992 **AN** *020 †05

QIAN, Zheng. 501 SE 172ND AVE, THE VANCOUVER CLINIC, INC 98684 #038-06-2000 L2006 **D DS** *100 †15

QUINTERO, Mauricio. 12607 SE MILL PLAIN BLVD, CASCADE PARK MEDICAL OFFIC 98684 #264-04-1991 L2004 **IM** *020 †20,18

QUINTOS, Robert F. 2525 NE 139TH ST 98686 #048-14-1997 L2005 **CD** *020 †20

RAGHURAM, Akhil. 400 NE MOTHER JOSEPH PL, SOUTHWEST WASHINGTON MEDIC 98664 #496-34-1999 L2005 **IM** *020 †20

RAGSDALE, Edgar Knapp. 2121 NE 139TH ST, STE 300 98686 #007-02-1972 L1978 **ORS OS** *020 †40

RAMIREZ, Ana T. 14406 NE 20TH AVE 98686 #040-02-1998 L2001 **IM** *020 †20

RANDOLPH, Kamala Joy. 2525 NE 139TH ST, THE VANCOUVER CLINIC 98686 #016-11-2003 L2007 **MPD** *020 †20,55

RAO, Anita G. 13215 SE MILL PLAIN BLVD, STE C8-505 98684 #016-06-1996 L2002 **ORS** *020 †40

RAPP, Charles Edward. 505 NE 87TH AVE, EVERGREEN PEDIATRIC 98664 #041-13-1998 L2001 **PD** *020 †55

RASKY, Adam Louis. 3400 MAIN ST, MEMORIAL HEALTH 98663 #065-01-1995 L2002 **OPH** *020 †35

RASTALL, John Robt. 700 NE 87TH AVE 98664 #036-01-1978 L1983 **N IM** *020 †20

RAVI, Haritha. 700 NE 87TH AVE 98664 #495-65-1994 L2001 **NEP** *020 †20

REED, Frank Andrew. 400 NE MOTHER JOSEPH PL 98664 #040-02-1995 L2000 **EM** *020 †16

REES, Sean Mikell. 400 NE MOTHER JOSEPH PL 98664 #040-02-1994 L1998 **EM** *020 †16

REID, John Warren. 2101 NE 139TH ST, CASCADE HEART PS 98686 #040-02-1974 L1980 **CD IM** *020 †20

REIS, Thomas Chas. 700 NE 87TH AVE 98664 #030-06-1969 L1975 **IM** *020 †20

REISS, James Arthur. 2101 NE 139TH ST, CASCADE HEART PS 98686 #054-04-1995 L1997 **CD ICE** *020 †20

RENTFRO, Joelle Edna. ■ 98684 #005-12-1941 L1942 **OS** *020

RETTMANN, Jonathan Allyn. 2211 E MILL PLAIN BLVD 98661 #040-02-1997 L2004 **PCC** *020 †20

REUTHER, James Louis. 400 NE MOTHER JOSEPH PL 98664 #035-06-1999 L2003 **P** *020 †75

REZNICK, Andrew David. 700 NE 87TH AVE 98664 #035-45-2002 L2007 **NEP** *020 †20

RHODES, Barry Booker. 200 NE MOTHER JOSEPH PL, STE 110 98664 #039-01-2003 L2007 **FSM** *020 †18

RICE, David Scott. 12607 SE MILL PLAIN BLVD 98684 #039-01-1993 L1997 **OBG** *020 †30

RICHARDS, Stephanie Jane. 7701 NE HIGHWAY 99, STE F 98665 #065-09-1995 L2000 **FM** *020 †18

RIVERA, Juan Antonio. 2525 NE 139TH ST 98686 #042-03-1983 L1987 **PD** *020 †55

ROBERTS, Alden Warren. 2211 E MILL PLAIN BLVD 98661 #021-05-1976 L1989 **GS** *020 †85

ROBERTS, Donald Wm. 2121 NE 139TH ST, STE 300 98686 #005-11-1980 L1986 **ORS** *020 †40

ROBERTS, James Phillip. 16811 SE MCGILLIVRAY BLVD, STE 101 98683 #036-01-1995 L2002 **MPD** *020 †20,55

ROBERTSON, Douglas James. 2211 NE 139TH ST 98686 #005-12-1998 L2003 **IM** *020 ‡

ROBINSON, Elena. 505 NE 87TH AVE STE 460, VANCOUVER NEUROLOGISTS 98664 #054-04-1998 L2003 **APM** *100 †75

ROCKOFF, Steven Bruce. 7101 NE 137TH AVE 98682 #038-06-1977 L1988 **FM** *020 †18

RODGERS, Michelle Leigh. ■ 98685 #004-01-2000 L2005 **AR** *020 †80

RODRIGUEZ, Gilbert M. 12800 NE SALMON CREEK AVE, B-107 98686 #007-02-1965 L1989 **AN CCM** *020

ROKOSZ, Norman Carl. 200 NE MOTHER JOSEPH PL, STE 210 98664 #016-42-1993 L2000 **NS** *020 †25

ROSE, Lawrence Hayes. 16821 SE MCGILLIVRAY BLVD 98683 #010-02-1988 L2005 **DR** *020 †80

ROSS, Timothy T. 400 NE MOTHER JOSEPH PL 98664 #025-12-1979 L1982 **IMG IM** *020

RUBANO, Christopher. 200 NE MOTHER JOSEPH PL, STE 330 98664 #005-12-1999 L2005 **GS** *020 †85

RUBENSTEIN, Joel Allen. 3250 SE 164TH AVE, STE 108 98683 #016-43-1974 L2000 **R** *075 †80

RUIZ, David Rene. 100 E 33RD ST, STE 100 98663 #054-04-1977 L1978 **FM** *040 †18

RUNDLE, John Platt. 3200 MAIN ST 98663 #040-02-1962 L1967 **OPH** *020 †35

RUSSELL, June Marilyn. 406 SE 131ST AVE, STE 108 98683 #054-04-1980 L1983 **PD** *020 †55

RUTHERFORD, Kelly Dee. 2211 E MILL PLAIN BLVD 98661 #040-02-1977 L1980 **FM** *020 †18

RYAN, Minhuey Chen. 700 NE 87TH AVE 98664 #026-04-2003 L2006 **FM** *020 †18

RYTTING, Richard Mason. 700 NE 87TH AVE 98664 #010-01-1970 L2001 **IM GP** *030 †20

SABAHI, Ramin. 700 NE 87TH AVE 98664 #517-01-1990 L2007 **RHU** *100 †20

SACAMANO, Joseph S. 200 NE MOTHER JOSEPH PL, STE 1200 98664 #028-03-1963 L1971 **ORS** *071 †40

SAHLSTROM, Gary Bernard. 505 NE 87TH AVE LL50 98664 #040-02-1974 L1979 **DR** *020 †80

SALE, Edward Julian. 16811 SE MCGILLIVRAY BLVD 98683 #040-02-1974 L1977 **FM** *020 †18

SALVADORI, Gabriele V. 100 E 33RD ST 98663 #561-03-1990 L2002 **FM** *020 †18

SANCHEZ, Damion Paul. 400 NE MOTHER JOSEPH PL, SOUTHWEST WASHINGTON MEDIC 98664 #034-01-2001 L2001 **AN** *020 †05

SANER, Deborah Lynn. 2101 NE 139TH ST, THE WOMENS CLINIC OF 98686 #016-45-1995 L2000 **OBG** *020 †30

SANGPATSON, Paurin. 12607 SE MILL PLAIN BLVD 98684 #056-06-1996 L2001 **PD** *020 †55

SANTIANO, Flordelys. 1319 NE 134TH ST STE 105 98685 #748-01-1985 L1996 **FM** *020 †18

SANTIANO, Rene B. 1319 NE 134TH ST STE 105, SALMON CREEK FAMILY PRACTI 98685 #748-01-1985 L1996 **FM** *020 †18

SAUNDERS, Gregory Rogers. 16811 SE MCGILLIVRAY BLVD, FAMILY PHYSICIANS GROUP PS 98683 #054-04-1995 L1998 **FM** *020 †18

SAUSER, Donald Duane. 16821 SE MCGILLIVRAY BLVD 98683 #005-12-1971 L2004 **DR** *020 †80

SAWHNEY, Shruti. ■ 98683 #496-23-1998 L2007 **IM** *100

SAYESS, Polina Yur'Yevna. 8716 E MILL PLAIN BLVD, P O BOX 1600 98664 #913-10-2000 L2005 **FP** *012

SCARBOROUGH, James Porter. 200 NE MOTHER JOSEPH PL, STE 330 98664 #001-02-1970 L1978 **GS OBG** *020 †85

SCHILLER, Nicholas K. 400 NE MOTHER JOSEPH PL, COLUMBIA ANESTHESIA GROUP 98664 #040-02-1991 L1995 **AN** *020 †05

SCHILLING, Lumen B. PO BOX 1224 98666 #748-02-1958 L1965 **AN** *071

SCHMIDT, Nicole M. 2211 NE 139TH ST, NORTHWEST NEWBORN 98686 #048-16-1997 L2003 **PD** *020 †55

SCHNEIDER, Scott B. 210 SE 136TH AVE 98684 #005-14-1991 L1996 **RO** *020 †80

SCHREIBER, Ellen Selden. ■ 98662 #025-01-1986 L2002 **AN** *020 †05

SCHREINER, Andrew Michael. ■ 98664 #028-34-2000 L2007 **PCP** *100 †50

SCHROEDER, John W. 3250 SE 164TH AVE, STE 108 98683 #040-02-1987 L1991 **DR** *020 †80

SCHULTZ, Jess Morgan. 2101 NE 139TH ST, STE 260 98686 #040-02-1998 L2006 **TS** *100 †85

SCHULTZ, Robert Wm. 11613 SE 7TH ST 98683 #005-12-1945 L1945 **AN** *071

SEEKAMP, Alfred Henry, III. 2525 NE 139TH ST 98686 #035-01-1991 L1996 **OBG** *020 †30

SEITZ, Kristen Michelle. 2211 NE 139TH ST, DEPARTMENT OF CHILDREN'S S 98686 #040-02-1998 L2006 **PD** *020 †55

SEMENYUK, Lesya. 400 NE MOTHER JOSEPH PL 98664 #913-86-1986 L2004 **IM** *020 †20

SERGEJEV, Ivan P. ■ 98660 #143-03-1969 L2005 **AN** *020 †05

SHAMBAUGH, Craig E. 8070 E MILL PLAIN BLVD, STE 316 98664 #040-02-1981 L1985 **OBG** *020 †20

SHANNO, George Bailey. 200 NE MOTHER JOSEPH PL, STE 210 98664 #047-05-1995 L2002 **NS** *020 †25

SHAO, Spencer Hsiao-Yang. 210 SE 136TH AVE 98684 #036-07-1992 L2002 **HO** *020 †20

SHARMAN, Martha Elizabeth. ■ 98661 #048-04-1977 L1980 **GP** *020

SHAW, Lian Richard. 2101 NE 139TH ST, CASCADE HEART PS 98686 #040-02-1997 L2003 **CD** *020 †20

SHAWLER, William Gerald. 2211 NE 139TH ST, EMERGENCY DEPART 98686 #005-12-2002 L2005 **EM** *100

SHEA, Roger Paul, III. 400 NE MOTHER JOSEPH PL 98664 #024-07-1978 L1981 **EM** *020 †16

SHELBY, James Keith. 700 NE 87TH AVE, THE VANCOUVER CLINIC 98664 #047-06-1994 L2007 **DR** *020 †80

SHELEPOVA, Tatiana Lvovna. 7410 DELAWARE LN 98664 #913-81-1996 L2003 **IMG** *020 †20

SHEPARD, Mary Alice. 7101 NE 137TH AVE 98682 #005-02-1978 L1986 **IM IMG** *020 †20

SHEPPERT, Andrew David. 2525 NE 139TH ST 98686 #036-05-1999 L2004 **OTO** *020 †45

SHLAER, William Jos. 505 NE 87TH AVE 98664 #034-01-1976 L1980 **DR** *071 †80

SHOTWELL, Janet Helen. 400 NE MOTHER JOSEPH PL 98664 #054-04-1997 L2001 **EM** *020 †16

SHRESTHA, Salona. ■ 98661 #495-38-2000 L2007 **IM** *100 †20

SHUEY, Richard Michael. 6926 NE FOURTH PLAIN BLVD, COLUMBIA RIVER MENTAL HEAL 98661 #016-43-1992 L2007 **CHP** *075

SIDDIQUI, Subeeh Ahmed. PO BOX 5157, COLUMBIA ANESTHESIA GROUP 98668 #048-16-2003 L2007 **AN** *020

SIEGAL, Francine M. 400 NE MOTHER JOSEPH PL 98664 #023-07-1967 L1995 **P** *020 †75

SIMEONE, Alan Arthur. 200 NE MOTHER JOSEPH PL, STE 300 98664 #051-07-1993 L2007 **CCS** *020 †85,90

SIMON, Miklos. 210 SE 136TH AVE, CANCER CARE OF MAINE 98664 #473-01-1993 L2007 **ON HO** *020 †20

SLAPPER, Debra Diane. 8512 NE SUNNYSIDE DR 98662 #040-02-1981 L2004 **EM** *020 †16

SLAYTON-MILAM, Suzanne D. 14508 NE 20TH AVE, STE 300 98686 #021-06-1989 L2003 **OBG** *020 †30

SLOVIC, Steven Brent. 200 NE MOTHER JOSEPH PL #3 98664 #008-01-1988 L1993 **GS** *020 †85

SMITH, David Allen. 210 SE 136TH AVE, NORTHWEST CANCER SPECIALIS 98684 #054-04-1987 L1994 **HEM ON** *020 †20

SMITH, Jacquelin Kathleen. 2525 NE 139TH ST 98686 #004-01-1987 L1992 **PD PDE** *020 †55

SOBECK, John Anthony. 12607 SE MILL PLAIN BLVD 98684 #054-04-1989 L1990 **OBG** *020 †30

SODEN, Jennifer Lynn. 505 NE 87TH AVE, EVERGREEN PEDIATRIC 98664 #040-02-1999 L2002 **PD** *020 †55

SOELLING, John L. 100 E 33RD ST, STE 206 98663 #035-09-1946 L1953 **GE IM** *020 †20

SOLTI, Magdolna. 210 SE 136TH AVE 98684 #473-02-1992 L2004 **HO IM** *020 †20

SOUTHERLAND, Lucy Claire. 4521 NW 122ND ST 98685 #065-05-1986 L2002 **AN** *020

SOUTHERLAND, Stephen R. 2121 NE 139TH ST, STE 300 98686 #061-01-1988 L1997 **OSM** *020 †40

SPARLING, Edward Arthur. 2121 NE 139TH ST, STE 300 98686 #005-19-1992 L1998 **ORS** *020 †40

SPARLING, Marcia Jo. 2525 NE 139TH ST 98686 #060-02-1983 L1989 **RHU** *020 †20

SPEAKER, Jill Ann. 2501 NE 134TH ST, STE 200 98686 #048-04-1998 L2002 **MPD** *020 †20,55

SPOHR, Megan Louise. 2525 NE 139TH ST 98686 #019-02-1998 L2006 **MPD** *020 †20,55

SRINIVASAN, Renganathan. 2525 NE 139TH ST 98686 #016-11-2002 L2007 **AI** *100 †20,03

STAGEBERG, Jeffrey Erick. 400 NE MOTHER JOSEPH PL 98664 #056-06-1998 L2001 **EM** *020 †16

STARK, Geraldine Marie. 400 NE MOTHER JOSEPH PL 98664 #040-02-1987 L1990 **EM** *020 †16

STEIN, Michael Thomas. 700 NE 87TH AVE 98664 #023-12-1994 L2007 **ID** *100 †20

STEINBERG, Lewis Mark. 505 NE 87TH AVE, STE 320 98664 #023-01-1983 L1998 **ON HEM** *020 †20

STEINGART, Karen. 2000 FORT VANCOUVER WAY 98663 #035-19-1975 L1986 **PHP OS** *030 †70

STEPANIAK, Rebecca Kathle. 2525 NE 139TH ST 98686 #001-02-1999 L2006 **PD** *020 †55

STICH, Peter Cornell. 400 NE MOTHER JOSEPH PL 98664 #041-07-1984 L1987 **EM** *020 †16

STIRLING, John. 700 NE 87TH AVE 98664 #025-01-1976 L1979 **PD** *020 †55

ST JOHN, Philip Don. 501 SE 172ND AVE 98684 #025-07-1993 L1996 **FM** *020 †18

STOLER, Eric Michael. 1916 SE IMAGE RD 98664 #005-02-1985 L1989 **AN PD** *020 †55,05

STONE, David Anthony. 400 NE MOTHER JOSEPH PL 98664 #056-06-1992 L1999 **IM** *020 †20

STORM-DICKERSON, Toni L. 505 NE 87TH AVE, STE 301 98664 #018-03-1998 L2003 **GS** *020 †85

STRATTON, Leon Berle. 600 NE 92ND AVE 98664 #040-02-1978 L1982 **PTH** *020 †50

STRONG, Bradley Wright. 2903 NW 128TH ST 98685 #019-02-1988 L2001 **P** *020 †18,75

STRONG, Janet Lynne. PO BOX 2339 98668 #007-02-1973 L2005 **GS** *020 †85

STROUSE, Catherine M. 7101 NE 137TH AVE, ORCHARDS MEDICAL OFFICE 98682 #040-02-1987 L1991 **FM** *020 †18

STRUXNESS, Leslie Anne. 1498 SE TECH CENTER PL, STE 100 98683 #040-02-1981 L1985 **OBG** *020 †30

STUDER, Joshua William. 400 NE MOTHER JOSEPH PL 98664 #016-42-2002 L2005 **IM** *100 †20

STUMP, Jack. 400 NE MOTHER JOSEPH PL 98664 #040-02-1989 L1999 **EM** *020 †16

SUBOCZ, Michael Edward. 2101 NE 139TH ST, CASCADE HEART PS 98686 #025-01-1978 L1984 **CD** *020 †20

SUGARMAN, Stanley Micah. 222 NE PARK PLAZA DR # 100 98684 #016-06-1983 L1986 **IM** *020 †20

SUGIYAMA, Ronald Kingo. 2205 NE 129TH ST 98686 #040-02-1978 L1986 **OPH** *020 †35

SUI, Carolyn H. 501 SE 172ND AVE 98684 #048-12-2000 L2003 **IM** *020 †20 ‡

SUN, Johnny Weiting. 2211 NE 139TH ST, LEGACY SALMON CREEK HOSPIT 98686 #005-18-2000 L2005 **PD** *020 †55

SUNSHINE, Jeffrey Allen. 200 NE MOTHER JSPH PL #300, PHYSICIANS PAVILLION 98664 #041-02-1979 L1985 **GS** *030 †85

SUNSHINE, Kathleen Mae. ■ 98664 #041-02-1979 L1993 **PTH** *020 †50

SUPPLITT, George Wm. 501 SE 172ND AVE STE 21 98684 #016-11-1987 L1990 **FM** *020 †18

SWAN, John Robt. 16811 SE MCGILLIVRAY BLVD, STE 101 98683 #021-01-1982 L1985 **FM** *020 †18

SWARTZ, Conrad Melton. 12911 NW 25TH CT, SIU SCHOOL OF MEDICINE 98685 #026-04-1974 L2007 **P PYG** *020 †75

SWENSON, Robert David. 2525 NE 139TH ST 98686 #005-06-1981 L1984 **CD IM** *050 †20

SWENTON, David Edward. 501 SE 172ND AVE 98684 #035-75-2002, ▲ L2006 **IM** *020

SYLTEBO, Thomas Frederick. 2211 E MILL PLAIN BLVD 98661 #054-04-1977 L1983 **FM** *020 †18

TAYLOR, Michelle Dione. 2211 NE 139TH ST, LEGACY SALMON CREEK HOSPIT 98686 #016-02-1999 L2006 **GS** *100 †85

TELFORD, Barbara Jane. 2211 NE 139TH ST, EMERGENCY DEPARTMENT 98686 #040-02-1980 L1984 **GS** *020 †16

TENOLD, Robert Eldon. ■ 98664 #040-02-1978 L1986 **AN IM** *020 †20,05

TENOLD, Susan Roberts. 17720 SE MILL PLAIN BLVD 98683 #040-02-1978 L1983 **OPH** *020 †35

TERRILL, Mitchell N. 2525 NE 139TH ST, THE VANCOUVER CLINIC, INC 98686 #045-04-1997 L2005 **DR** *020 †80

THALBERG, Steven Alan. 14406 NE 20TH AVE 98686 #028-34-1982 L1985 **OBG** *020 †30 ‡

THOMING, Christopher S. 2211 NE 139TH ST, EMERGENCY DEPART 98686 #040-02-1986 L2004 **UCM** *020

THOMPSON, Craig Franklin. 2105 NE 129TH ST, STE 107 98686 #003-01-1982 L1988 **GPM** *020 †18,70

THOMPSON, Donald Murray. 505 NE 87TH AVE, EVERGREEN PEDIATRIC 98664 #049-01-1972 L1979 **PD RHU** *020 †55

THOMPSON, Douglas Andrew. 3400 MAIN ST 98663 #040-02-1967 L1973 **AN** *020 †05

THORNTON, Robert Donald. 7701 NE HIGHWAY 99, STE F 98665 #040-02-1968 L1972 **EM** *020

THRELKELD, Judson E. 16821 SE MCGILLIVRAY BLVD 98683 #048-02-1994 L1997 **VIR** *020 †80

TIGANUS, Diana Minerva. PO BOX 1600 98668 #781-04-1999 L2006 **FP** *012

TILSON, Donald Heath. 2211 E MILL PLAIN BLVD 98661 #028-02-1955 L1969 **ORS OM** *020 †70,40

TOM, William Koon Chou. ■ 98664 #007-02-1966 L1973 **OBG** *020 †30

TRAN, Duy Quang. 2525 NE 139TH ST 98686 #048-15-2002 L2006 **FM** *020 †18

TRASK, Sara Joan. 400 NE MOTHER JOSEPH PL 98664 #056-06-1989 L2003 **FM** *020 †18

TROTTER, Bonnie Kay. 12607 SE MILL PLAIN BLVD, CASCADE PARK MEDICAL OFFIC 98684 #048-04-2002 L2003 **FM** *020 †18

TRUEWORTHY, Stacey Ann. 12607 SE MILL PLAIN BLVD 98684 #019-02-2001 L2006 **OBG** *020

TSE, Elaine Y. 8000 NE 58TH AVE, NEW HEIGHTS CLINIC 98665 #048-04-1988 L2002 **IM** *020

TSEN, Ann Elizabeth. 7913 NE 58TH AVE 98665 #040-02-1987 L2000 **IM** *020 †20

UBA, Angela Ijeoma. 7410 DELAWARE LN 98664 #690-07-1985 L2006 **FM** *020

UDARBE, Clayton Tomaneng. 11808 NE FOURTH PLAIN RD, URGENT MEDICAL CENTER 98682 #748-01-1981 L1988 **FM** *020

UHLAND, Hugo. ■ 98683 #030-05-1961 L1961 **IM IMG** *071 †20

URIBE, Jorge I. 600 NE 92ND AVE, SOUTHW WASHINGTON HOSPS 98664 #264-03-1965 L1979 **AN GP** *020 †05

VAN TILBURG, Christopher. PO BOX 64109 98666 #054-04-1994 L1998 **FM OS** *020 †18

VAUGHN, Katherine F. 700 NE 87TH AVE 98664 #017-20-1986 L1989 **PD** *020 †55 ‡

VAUGHN, Stephanie S. 7101 NE 137TH AVE 98682 #005-15-1991 L1996 **FM** *020 †18

VAZQUEZ, Jaime Amilcar. 7600 NE 41ST ST STE 310 98662 #042-01-1973 L2002 **P** *020 †75

VERNIER, Karen Ann. 3400 MAIN ST, MEMORIAL HEALTH CENTER 98663 #025-12-1999 L2005 **P** *020

VIGELAND, Geo Norman, Jr. 3200 MAIN ST 98663 #040-02-1967 L1969 **OPH** *071 †35

VIGELAND, Karen Marie. 505 NE 87TH AVE, STE 303 98664 #040-02-1976 L1979 **D** *020 †15 ‡

VILHAUER, Allison Laurel. 2525 NE 139TH ST 98686 #040-02-1996 L1999 **IM** *020 †20

VINCENT, R Andrew. 2211 NE 139TH ST, LEGACY SALMON CREEK HOSPIT 98686 #847-08-1982 L1998 **OBG ATP** *020 †30 ‡

VINSON, Jonathan Levin. 16811 SE MCGILLIVRAY BLVD, STE 100 98683 #012-05-1999 L2005 **FM** *020 †18

VIRGIN, Robin Worrell. 16811 SE MCGILLIVRAY BLVD, STE 101 98683 #040-02-1995 L1997 **FM** *020 †18 ‡

VOLDENGEN, Donna Louise. 12607 SE MILL PLAIN BLVD, CASCADE PARK MEDICAL CENTE 98684 #040-02-1998 L2001 **PD** *020 †55

VOLFORD, Katalin. 222 NE PARK PLAZA DR # 100 98684 #473-02-1989 L1998 **IM** *020 †20

WABER, Horst Alex. ■ 98663 #407-21-1957 L1961 **AN** *071 †05

WACHENHEIM, Daniel Edwin. 12607 SE MILL PLAIN BLVD 98684 #040-02-1997 L2001 **IM** *020 †20

WAEHNELDT, Niels R. ■ 98661 #407-12-1952 L1971 **AN** *071 †05

WAGENHOFFER, Andrew J. ■ 98682 #030-06-1997 *100

WAGNER, Clifford Wm. 9120 NE VANCOUVER MAL LOOP, STE 230 98662 #005-12-1971 L1972 **EM FM** *020 †18

WAIKHOM, Bandana. ■ 98682 #038-44-1992 L2004 **OPH** *075 †35

WANG, Can. 16811 SE MCGILLIVRAY BLVD, STE 101 98683 #243-47-1982 L1999 **FM** *020 †18 ‡

WANG, Charles E. 14406 NE 20TH AVE, DEPT OF RADIOLOGY 98686 #024-07-1997 L2004 **DR** *020 †80

WANG, Spencer Eshen. 501 SE 172ND AVE 98684 #024-07-1998 L2005 **DR** *020 †80

WARFEL, Thomas Edward. 16821 SE MCGILLIVRAY BLVD 98683 #041-12-1997 L2004 **DR** *020 †80

WATERS, Robert Nelson. 12607 SE MILL PLAIN BLVD, CASCADE PARK MEDICAL OFFIC 98684 #005-12-1974 L1981 **P** *020 †75

WEAVER, Gerald Geo. ■ 98662 #028-02-1958 L1958 **GS** *071 †85

WEAVER, Kathleen A Milne. 8716 E MILL PLAIN BLVD 98664 #040-02-1967 L2007 **IM PMM** *030 †20

WEAVER, Margaret E. 505 NE 87TH AVE, THE WOMENS CLINIC OF 98664 #041-13-1999 L2003 **OBG** *020

WEAVER, Simon Abram. 400 NE MOTHER JOSEPH PL 98664 #040-02-1999 L2002 **EM** *020 †16

WEBB, Duane David. 700 NE 87TH AVE 98664 #035-48-1974 L2006 **GE IM** *020 †20

WEILAND, Allan Jay. 14406 NE 20TH AVE 98686 #016-06-1972 L1978 **OS OBG** *030 †30

WEINSTEIN, Jessica Robin. 2211 NE 139TH ST, INTERNAL MEDICINE HOSPITAL 98686 #016-45-2003 L2006 **NEP** *012 †20

WEISS, Valerie Elizabeth. 700 NE 87TH AVE 98664 #007-02-2001 L2004 **PD** *020 †55

WESTERMEYER, Matthew Lee. 2211 NE 139TH ST, EMERGENCY DEPARTMENT 98686 #005-12-2003 L2006 **EM** *100 †16

WHITE, Jeanie Diane. 16703 SE MCGILLIVRAY BLVD 98683 #021-05-1995 L2005 **FM** *020 †18

WHITTAM, Karli. 1000 SE TECH CENTER DR 98683 #061-01-1991 L1997 **FM** *020 †18

WICKHAM, Dennis James. 900 W 13TH ST, P O BOX 5000 98660 #040-02-1981 L1996 **FOP PTH** *062 †50

WIEBE, George E. 315 SE STONE MILL DR, STE 210 98684 #060-01-1966 L1980 **N IM** *020

WIENS, Joy Elsbeth. 505 NE 87TH AVE, THE WOMENS CLINIC OF 98664 #032-01-1996 L1998 **OBG** *020 †30

WILCOX, Lee Arturo. 400 NE MOTHER JOSEPH PL 98664 #024-07-1991 L1995 **AN** *020 †05

WILKE, Tanya Marie. ■ 98664 #021-05-2006 L2006 **FP** *012

WILKINS, John Paul. 2211 E MILL PLAIN BLVD 98661 #007-02-1991 L1998 **PUD** *020 †20

WILL, Brian Ralph. 8100 NE PARKWAY DR, STE 125 98662 #005-12-1985 L1989 **OPH** *020 †35

WILL, Virginia Kay. ■ 98662 #018-03-1986 L2005 **EM** *071 †16

WILLIAMS, Karen R. 406A NE 131ST AVE, STE 109 98684 #011-02-1986 L1998 **IM** *020 †20

WILLIAMS, Sally E. 700 NE 87TH AVE 98664 #038-41-1990 L1994 **ID** *020 †20

WILLIAMS, Terry Randall. 12607 SE MILL PLAIN BLVD 98684 #040-02-1982 L1985 **FM** *020 †18

WILLIAMS, Theopolis C. 7101 NE 137TH AVE 98682 #010-03-1983 L1988 **FM** *020 †18

WILLIAMS, Tracy G. 2525 NE 139TH ST 98686 #028-34-1987 L1994 **PD IM** *020 †20,55

WILMINGTON, Michael R. 14406 NE 20TH AVE 98686 #048-14-1991 L1997 **PD** *020 †55

WILSON, Adam Spach. 1405 SE 164TH AVE STE 102, HEAD AND NECK SURGERY CLIN 98683 #036-01-1990 L1996 **OTO** *020 †45

WIRA, Raymund Leopold. ■ 98664 #025-12-1988 L2002 **RNR DR** *020 †80

WISLER, Kathleen Rae. 8815 E MILL PLAIN BLVD 98664 #028-34-1990 L1994 **P** *020 †75

WITTWER, Lynn Keith. 400 NE MOTHER JOSEPH PL 98664 #040-02-1968 L1977 **EM FM** *030 †18,16

WOBIG, Elo K. 400 NE MOTHER JOSEPH PL 98664 #005-18-1994 L1997 **EM** *020 †16

WOLL, Theodore Scott. 2121 NE 139TH ST, STE 300 98686 #005-06-1981 L1983 **OAR** *020 †40

WON, Paul Kihun. 2211 E MILL PLAIN BLVD, KAISER PERMANENTE 98661 #005-12-1991 L1999 **FM PHP** *020 †18,70

WONG, Kirk Landon. 2121 NE 139TH ST, STE 300 98686 #005-12-1995 L2001 **HS** *020 †40

WOOD, Marilyn M. 400 NE MOTHER JOSEPH PL 98664 #061-01-1969 L1974 **AN** *020

WOODEN, Patricia H. 16811 SE MCGILLIVRAY BLVD, STE 100 98683 #040-02-1998 L2001 **FM** *020 †18

WORKMAN, Carol J. 1405 SE 164TH AVE, STE 101 98683 #040-02-1986 L1994 **IM** *020

WORKMAN, Michael Lee. 1405 SE 164TH AVE 98683 #026-04-1986 L1993 **PS** *020 †65 ‡

WRIGHT, Olivia Rae. 100 E 33RD ST 98663 #020-12-1990 L2002 **FM** *020 †18

WYLIE, Regan Beth. 2211 NE 139TH ST, LEGACY SALMON CREEK HOSPIT 98686 #041-07-1997 L2001 **EM** *020 †16

YAMASHITA, Shellie Kim. 2211 NE 139TH ST 98686 #014-01-2002 L2005 **ID** *012 †20

YAN, Tom Dejian. 2211 E MILL PLAIN BLVD 98661 #035-48-2000 L2006 **PCC** *020 †20

YANG, Ya-Yun. 501 SE 172ND AVE 98684 #243-47-1984 L2004 **IM** *020 †20

YBALLE, Liza Sedillo. 1601 E FOURTH PLAIN BLVD, BLDG D-7 98661 #016-43-1995 L1997 **IM** *020 †20

YEHUDAI, Loran. 200 NE MOTHER JOSEPH PL, STE 330 98664 #012-05-1999 L2007 **IC** *100 †20

YOUNG, David Allen. 14406 NE 20TH AVE 98686 #005-12-1990 L1993 **IM** *020 †20

YOUNG, Michael Patrick. 8716 E MILL PLAIN BLVD 98664 #028-34-1977 L1980 **FM** *020 †18

YOUNG, Thomas G S. ■ 98661 #803-05-1946 L1976 **OS** *071

ZAKRZEWSKI, Leanne Marie. ■ 98683 #010-02-2008 *012

ZAWACKI, Amie Jennifer. PO BOX 1600 98668 #665-01-2005 L2005 **FP** *012

ZEVELY, John Bernard. ■ 98661 #040-02-1952 L1953 **AN** *071 †05

ZHOU, Fan. PO BOX 1600, DEPT OF PATHOLOGY 98668 #243-94-1984 L2007 **HMP** *020 †50

ZINSMEISTER, Stephen Carl. 505 NE 87TH AVE STE 460 98664 #038-40-1967 L1971 **CHN N** *071 †55,75

9328

■ = Address Information Privacy Protected

ZUKOWSKI, Matthew Henry. 12607 SE MILL PLAIN BLVD 98684 #025-01-1975 L1995 **IM** *020 †20

ZWART, Jon Edward. 2525 NE 139TH ST 98686 #005-12-2002 L2007 **OTO** *020

VASHON – KING

ALTAMORE, Rita Ann. PO BOX 2749 98070 #024-05-1977 L1978 **PHP FM** *040 †70,18

BAER, Karen J. ■ 98070 #065-01-1964 L1965 **ADL PD** *020 †55

BROWNE, C Hughes. 13623 SW POHL RD 98070 #011-02-1958 L1976 **GP P** *020

EMMONS, Richard Wm. ■ 98070 #041-01-1957 L1958 **PHP GPM** *071 †70

FARRELL, Kim Cornelison. 10030 SW 210TH ST 98070 #026-04-1996 L1998 **FM** *020 †18

FULTON, Gail Lynn. ■ 98070 #054-04-1988 L1990 **FM** *020 †18

GROSSKOPF, Barry. ■ 98070 #011-02-1970 L1971 **P** *020 †75

KAPPELMAN, Michael Porter. 10030 SW 210TH ST 98070 #028-02-1980 L1981 **FM FPG** *020 †18

KOCH, Gary Alan. 10030 SW 210TH ST 98070 #028-02-1977 L1978 **FM FPG** *020 †18

LEEDE, William E. ■ 98070 #040-02-1937 L1938 **IM** *071 †20

MAGNUSON, Chad Raymond. 10030 SW 210TH ST 98070 #016-11-1991 L1999 **FM** *020 †18

MORGAN, John A. ■ 98070 #018-03-1950 L1951 **R RO** *071 †80

NELSON, Elizabeth F. ■ 98070 #041-07-1973 L1974 **IM** *071 †20

SIMONS, Ronald C. ■ 98070 #028-02-1960 L1966 **P** *020 †75

STENEKER, Sjardo Siardus. 17917 VASHON HWY SW 98070 #660-05-1991 L1992 **FM** *020 †18

TORREY, Charles Wray. ■ 98070 #005-02-1973 L2004 **P** *020

VALLARTA, Leopoldo T. ■ 98070 #748-01-1958 L1968 **OTO** *020 †45

WALKER, Mary Ellen. PO BOX 389 98070 #054-04-1978 L1982 **FM PHP** *020 †18

WEISPFENNING, Charles Geo. 17639 100TH AVE SW 98070 #054-04-1972 L1974 **FM** *020 †18

WOOD, Barbara Ann. ■ 98070 #005-02-1972 L1978 **R** *071 †80

VAUGHN – PIERCE

TRAYNOR, Joseph Edward. ■ 98394 #028-34-1955 L1956 **GP** *071

VERADALE – SPOKANE

BELKNAP, Donald E. ■ 99037 #028-34-1953 L1955 **FM GS** *071 †18

WAITSBURG – WALLA WALLA

HEVEL, S Roger. 815 ORCHARD ST 99361 #040-02-1949 L1953 **FM AN** *071 †18

WALDRON – SAN JUAN

COOK, William Bell, Jr. ■ 98297 #041-01-1955 L1957 **P CHP** *020

REED, Delbert. ■ 98297 #030-05-1938 L1938 **OS GP** *071

ROACH, John Jared. 100 N BEACH 98297 #024-01-1959 L1968 **GS HS** *020 †85

WALLA WALLA – WALLA WALLA

ABBOTT, Martin Keith. 1025 S 2ND AVE, WALLA WALLA GEN HOSP 99362 #005-12-1989 L1996 **AN** *020 †05

ACEVEDO, Carlos F. 77 WAINWRIGHT DR 99362 #847-08-1969 L1972 **P AM** *020

ADAMS, John B. ■ 99362 #056-06-1950 **EM** *071

ASHBY, William Edward. 1103 S 2ND AVE B 99362 #005-12-1968 L1973 **IM** *020 †20

ASHLEY, Donald Keith. 1111 S 2ND AVE, BLUE MOUNTAIN MEDICAL GROU 99362 #005-12-1977 L1993 **PD EP** *020 †55

ASHLEY, Shirley Hynson. 1111 S 2ND AVE, BLUE MOUNTAIN MED GRP 99362 #005-12-1978 L1993 **PD** *020 †55

AVBEL, Allan Francis. ■ 99362 #041-07-1976 L1978 **DR IM** *020 †20,80

BAKER, Delwyn Richard. PO BOX 67 99362 #054-04-1977 L1980 **IM** *020 †20

BALL, Eric Martin. 55 W TIETAN ST 99362 #054-04-1984 L1987 **IM** *020 †20

BARBOSA, Joilo Cesar. 401 W POPLAR ST 99362 #005-12-1993 L2004 **EM** *020 †16

BARGA, Bruce Edward. 401 W POPLAR ST, ADMINISTRATION 99362 #028-02-1984 L1986 **IM** *020 †20

BARGA, Jack Lee. 401 W POPLAR ST 99362 #010-01-1956 L1968 **OTO** *071 †45

BARILA, Timothy Geo. ■ 99362 #010-01-1950 L1969 **GPM OM** *071 †05

BARRY, Timothy Danl. 320 W WILLOW ST 99362 #040-02-1976 L1980 **OBG** *020 †30

BAUER, Carl Leroy. ■ 99362 #005-12-1961 L1962 **GE IM** *071 †20

BAUGHER, John Oliver. ■ 99362 #016-02-1941 L1949 **IM** *071

BEIRNE, James Anthony. 55 W TIETAN ST 99362 #048-04-1973 L1979 **IM NM** *020 †20,28

BEITO, George Norman, Jr. 401 W POPLAR ST 99362 #054-04-1981 L1982 **GS TS** *020 †85

BERGSTROM, Theodore John. 55 W TIETAN ST 99362 #040-02-1982 L1985 **PD** *020 †55

BERNSTEIN, Michael Scott. 55 W TIETAN ST 99362 #038-06-1983 L1984 **PCC SME** *020 †20

BERRETTA, Edward S. 380 CHASE AVE 99362 #035-03-1974 L1996 **FM EM** *020 †18

BILLINGSLEY, Robert A. 401 W POPLAR ST, EMERGENCY DEPT-ST MARYS MC 99362 #054-04-2002 L2002 **EM** *020 †16

BINGHAM, Korth Elwood. ■ 99362 #007-02-1964 L1971 **R RO** *071 †80

BLACKWELDER, John Timothy. 20 E POPLAR ST STE 202 99362 #005-12-1973 L1983 **R DR** *040 †80

BOLDUC, Jennifer. 55 W TIETAN ST 99362 #050-02-1996 L2003 **PD** *020 †55

BOLDUC, Thomas George. 55 W TIETAN ST 99362 #050-02-1996 L2003 **PD** *020 †55

BOLTON, Glenn Cassius. 1111 S 2ND AVE 99362 #005-12-1940 L1941 **GS** *071

BOND, John W L. 1610 PENNY LN 99362 #025-01-1946 L1955 **OPH** *071 †35

BOND, Robert Martin. 310 W POPLAR ST BOX 1753, WALLA WALLA CTY HLTH DP 99362 #028-02-1945 L1975 **PHP** *020

BRELAND, William Michael. 401 W POPLAR ST 99362 #048-02-1985 L1997 **PM N** *020 †60

BRONSTEIN, Seymour M. 401 W POPLAR ST 99362 #036-07-1992 L2007 **HO** *020 †20

BROOKS, Peter Thacher. 342 CATHERINE ST 99362 #035-01-1942 L1949 **GS** *071 †85

BROWN, Edward David. 401 W POPLAR ST, ADMINISTRATION 99362 #051-01-1987 L2002 **IM** *020 †20

BROWN, Lori Alborn. 380 CHASE AVE, ADMINISTRATION 99362 #005-11-1987 L2002 **IM** *020 †20

BROWN, Michael L. 401 W POPLAR ST, ST MARY MED CTR 99362 #007-02-1987 L1991 **RO PMM** *020 †80

BRUCE, Marc Brian. ■ 99362 #054-04-2002 L2005 **DR** *020 †80

CAMP, Perry Ernest. 301 W POPLAR ST, STE 220 99362 #040-02-1974 L1976 **NS** *020 †25

CARDELL, Jose Emilio. 1111 WOODLAWN ST, P O BOX 1601 99362 #008-01-1963 L1980 **P PTH** *020 †75

CARMODY, Robert William. 55 W TIETAN ST 99362 #028-34-1979 L1982 **FM FPG** *020 †18

CAUDILL, Robert Grant. ■ 99362 #054-04-1964 L1966 **IM** *020 †20 ‡

CHAIDARUN, Sushela. 55 W TIETAN ST 99362 #891-01-1988 L2003 **END** *020 †20 ‡

COLEMAN, Jamie Marie. 1610 PENNY LN 99362 #054-04-1988 L1992 **OPH** *020 †35

COLLINS, Raquel M. 301 W POPLAR ST, STE 50 99362 #048-14-1997 L2003 **GS** *020 †85

CONDER, John P. 401 W POPLAR ST 99362 #028-02-1962 L1965 **ON IM** *071

CORVINO, Jos Michael, Jr. ■ 99362 #038-06-1970 L1977 **P** *020 †75

COSMA, Mihaela. 55 W TIETAN ST 99362 #781-05-1992 L2007 **END** *020 †20

CRABTREE, Gary Mc Clendon. ■ 99362 #025-01-1981 L1984 **OTO HNS** *020 †45

CRAIGG, Gerald B. 1111 S 2ND AVE 99362 #005-12-1996 L2005 **IM** *020 †20 ‡

CUMMINGS, Lou Anne. 310 W POPLAR ST, DEPARTMENT 99362 #005-12-1976 L1995 **PHP** *062 †20

DAVIDSON, Timothy Arthur. 401 W POPLAR ST, ST MARY MEDICAL CTR 99362 #040-02-1992 L1995 **PCC** *020 †20

DAVIS, Frederic. ■ 99362 #040-02-1941 L1949 **PTH** *071 †50

DIDELIUS, Donald Paul. ■ 99362 #067-01-1962 L1980 **ORS** *020 †40

DIETRICH, Terry James. 401 W POPLAR ST, ADMINISTRATION 99362 #005-12-1971 L1990 **ORS** *020 †40

DIETZMAN, Dale Edward. ■ 99362 #048-04-1968 L1972 **PD ID** *020 †55

DOAN, Thuy Anh. 1634 PLAZA WAY 99362 #054-04-2008 *012

DUFFY, Sean Thomas. 1120 W ROSE ST 99362 #051-01-1994 L1996 **FM** *020 †18

DUNHAM, Douglas David. 380 CHASE AVE, SAINT MARY MEDICAL CENTER 99362 #054-04-1999 L2001 **FM** *020 †18

EARLE, Regina Margaret. 401 W POPLAR ST, ST MARY'S MEDICAL CENTER 99362 #016-42-1982 L2002 **EM** *020 †16

EBERHARDT, Kirsten B. 320 W WILLOW ST 99362 #409-39-1991 L1993 **OBG** *020 †30

ECKHARDT, Karl Robt. 1025 S 2ND AVE 99362 #023-07-1969 L1992 **AN** *020 †05

EDWARDS, James Jos. 401 W POPLAR ST, ADMINISTRATION 99362 #005-12-1973 L1982 **EM** *020 †16,18

EHLERS, Carmen Alicia. 1125 S 2ND AVE, STE B 99362 #132-04-1993 L2005 **FM** *020 †18

FALCON, Jennings Carl, II. 301 W POPLAR ST, STE 230 99362 #018-03-1978 L1987 **N SME** *071 †75

FELT, Richard Wayne. 1025 S 2ND AVE 99362 #040-02-1980 L1983 **IM PUD** *020 †20 ‡

FETROE, Dale Thayne. 1017 S 2ND AVE STE 2 99362 #005-12-1978 L1981 **FM** *020 †18 ‡

FIELD, Frederick Ian. 1017 S 2ND AVE STE 3 99362 #005-12-1980 L1990 **VS GS** *050 †85

FLAMMANG, Jeannette S. 1120 W ROSE ST 99362 #056-06-2003 L2003 **FM** *020 †18

FLECK, Ronald W. 209 W POPLAR ST 99362 #649-14-1970 L1982 **GP** *020

FLEMING, Robert Dale. 77 WAINWRIGHT DR, VETERANS ADMINISTRATION ME 99362 #649-14-1980 L1986 **IM EM** *020 †20

FOSTER, Karen Emily. 401 W POPLAR ST 99362 #023-07-1998 L2001 **END** *100 †20

GARDNER, Jon Bryson. 401 W POPLAR ST, ADMINISTRATION 99362 #054-04-1994 L1996 **IM** *020 †20

GEHLING, Guy Frank. 301 W POPLAR ST, STE 220 99362 #040-02-1976 L1982 **NS** *020

GEROW, Elwyn C. ■ 99362 #005-12-1936 L1936 **GS GP** *071

GIBBS, Benjamin F, Jr. ■ 99362 #005-02-1961 L1962 **VS** *071 †85

GILLESPIE, Michael Wade. 228 W BIRCH ST 99362 #048-04-1967 L1975 **ORS** *020 †40

GRINSTEAD, Dan Scott. 55 W TIETAN ST 99362 #019-02-1974 L2005 **IM** *020 †20 ‡

GRYLER, Erik Christopher. 55 W TIETAN ST 99362 #005-02-1995 L2000 **ORS** *020 †40

GUNSHEFSKI, Linda Anne. 299 W TIETAN ST 99362 #033-06-1988 L1996 **OPH** *020 †35

HALL, Christopher P. 89 W TIETAN ST 99362 #040-02-1997 L2001 **PD** *020 †55

HAMPSON, David Franklin. 380 CHASE AVE 99362 #045-04-1986 L1989 **FM** *020 †18

HANSON, Robert Leroy. 1025 S 2ND AVE 99362 #025-07-1970 L1977 **DR EM** *020 †80

HARRI, James Ely. 301 W POPLAR ST STE 210, MEDICAL ARTS CLINIC 99362 #054-04-1977 L1983 **GE** *020 †20

HEDINE, Duane R. 55 W TIETAN ST 99362 #026-04-1953 L1962 **U** *020 †95

HENDERSON, Karen Waller. 55 W TIETAN ST 99362 #005-12-1980 L2006 **PD** *062 †55

HENDERSON, Richard Lyle. 380 CHASE AVE, ST MARY PHYS GRP 99362 #005-12-1979 L2006 **ORS** *020 †40

HERBERT, George Nelson. ■ 99362 #035-06-1947 L1950 **PHP** *020 †05

HOEHN, John Byron. 1111 S 2ND AVE 99362 #005-12-1971 L1986 **FM D** *020

HOGENSON, Clifford D. ■ 99362 #056-05-1941 L1945 **OPH OTO** *071 †35

HOLM, Cindy Louise. 345 BOYER AVE, WHITMAN COLLEGE 99362 #054-04-1986 L1996 **P** *020 †75

HOWARD, Theodore C. ■ 99362 #005-12-1951 L1951 **FM** *071 †18

HUGHES, Timna Lastine. 1017 S 2ND AVE STE 4 99362 #005-12-1987 L2006 **OBG** *020 †30

HUTSON, Scott Bradley. 1017 S 2ND AVE 99362 #005-12-1977 L1982 **ORS OSM** *020 †40

HUTTON, David Alan. 401 W POPLAR ST, ADMINISTRATION 99362 #005-12-1989 L1997 **U** *020 †95

ISAACS, Kenneth Howard Z. 301 W POPLAR ST STE 230 99362 #041-07-1977 L1981 **N** *020 †75

JAMES, Charles W. 55 W TIETAN ST 99362 #054-04-1994 L1999 **GS** *020 †85

JAUHIAINEN, Eric Jon. 55 W TIETAN ST 99362 #040-02-1992 L1997 **IM** *020 †20

JOHNSON, James Melvin. 55 W TIETAN ST 99362 #054-04-1967 L1970 **GP** *071 †20

JOHNSON, Robert Arnold. 362 S 3RD AVE 99362 #054-04-1969 L1983 **CD** *040 †20

JONES, Aaron Bruce. 401 W POPLAR ST 99362 #041-12-2001 L2004 **EM** *020 †16

KAMINSKY, Daniel F. 320 W WILLOW ST, WOMEN'S CLINIC 99362 #048-02-1994 L2000 **OBG** *020 †18,30

KARMY, Regina Elsa. 1103 S 2ND AVE, # B 99362 #005-12-1974 L1982 **OBG** *020 †30

KEENAN, Hugh Carter. ■ 99362 #056-06-1944 L1947 **GS** *071 †85

KELLOGG, Barry Lynn. ■ 99362 #005-12-1966 L1975 **FM** *020 †18

KEYES, Ralph Sayward. ■ 99362 #067-01-1937 L1943 **P** *071

KILZER, Helen Margaret. 301 W POPLAR ST STE 110 99362 #028-02-1983 L1994 **IM** *020 †20 ‡

KIM, Kyongchol. 1111 S 2ND AVE 99362 #583-06-1993 L2002 **IMG GE** *020 †20

KIRBY, Alison Esther. 55 W TIETAN ST 99362 #016-45-1988 L1991 **PD** *020 †55

KIRTLEY, Samuel Wm. 55 W TIETAN ST 99362 #017-20-1976 L2005 **FM** *020 †18

KRIZAN, Kelly Joe. ■ 99362 #024-07-1978 L1986 **DR FM** *020 †18,80

KUECHENMEISTER, Mark E. 299 W TIETAN ST 99362 #026-04-1969 L1973 **OPH** *071 †35

LAIDLAW, Melvern Ellis. 77 WAINWRIGHT DR 99362 #023-07-1954 L1956 **IM A** *071
LA PIER, Rachel Carlene. 401 W POPLAR ST, ADMINISTRATION 99362 #038-41-1996 L1999 **FM** *020 †18
LARSON, Lauri Renee. 380 CHASE AVE, ST MARY PHYSICIAN GRP 99362 #005-12-2001 L2004 **FM PLM** *020 †18
LIEBRAND, Esther Groom. ■ 99362 #005-12-1953 L1954 **PD** *071
LONG, William Ernest. ■ 99362 #048-04-1937 L1953 **GS TS** *071 †85
LOSEY, Jimmie D. 1025 S 2ND AVE 99362 #005-12-1953 L1955 **GP AM** *071
LY, Hoa Hong. ■ 99362 #941-01-1965 L1984 **DR NM** *071 †60
MAROLDO, Thomas Vincent. 209 W POPLAR ST 99362 #035-01-1975 L1996 **DR CD** *020 †20,80
MARSH, Glyn Everett. 301 W POPLAR ST STE 201 99362 #005-12-1974 L1985 **OTO GP** *020 †45
MARTONICK, Gregory Jos. 320 W WILLOW ST STE 6 99362 #056-06-1974 L1980 **AI IM** *020 †20,03
MC ILVAINE, Patricia M. 55 W TIETAN ST 99362 #049-01-1984 L2002 **IM** *020 †20
MC LAIN, Paul Larimer, Jr. 380 CHASE AVE, ST MARY URGENT CARE 99362 #041-01-1967 L1971 **FM IMG** *072 †18
MC QUARRIE, Galen S. 77 WAINWRIGHT DR 99362 #026-04-1967 L1968 **IM ON** *020 †20
MEEKER, David Ware. 320 W WILLOW ST 99362 #021-01-1964 L1972 **PTH** *020 †50
MEYER, Joseph F. 401 W POPLAR ST, ADMINISTRATION 99362 #040-02-1986 L1989 **IM** *020 †20
MEYERS, James Leroy. 320 W WILLOW ST 99362 #041-09-1963 L1970 **OBG** *071 †30
MILLER, Byron Ronald. 401 W POPLAR ST, ST MARY MEDICAL CENTER 99362 #007-02-1976 L1977 **OPH** *020 †35 ‡
MILLER, Daniel Byron. 401 W POPLAR ST, EMERGENCY DEPARTMENT 99362 #054-04-1991 L1994 **EM** *020 †16
MILLER, Jordan Emmanuel. PO BOX 2697 99362 #047-06-1958 L1966 **PS** *071 †65
MILLIGAN, Deyan Z. 1025 S 2ND AVE 99362 #243-47-1983 L1995 **AN** *020 †05
MOORE, C Barton. 1111 S 2ND AVE 99362 #007-02-1978 L1981 **FM** *020 †18
MORGAN, Philip Reeves. 320 W WILLOW ST 99362 #047-05-1974 L1979 **OTO FPS** *020 †45
MORRIS, Robert Earle. 1111 S 2ND AVE 99362 #005-12-1983 L1984 **DR IM** *020 †80
MUZZALL, Hugh Arthur. ■ 99362 #054-04-1956 L1965 **GS** *071 †85
NELSEN, Carl Edwin. ■ 99362 #018-03-1960 L1970 **PD NEP** *071 †55
NEWBOLD, Robson Sims. 77 WAINWRIGHT DR 99362 #005-12-1944 L1944 **GS GP** *072 †85,90
NEWBOLD, Scott Gregory. 1017 S 2ND AVE, STE 3 99362 #005-12-1978 L1991 **GS** *020 †85
NEWHOUSE, Franklin Claude. 55 W TIETAN ST, WALLA WALLA CLINIC 99362 #054-04-1986 L1996 **FM** *020 †18
O'CONNOR, Carolyn Anne. 380 CHASE AVE 99362 #040-02-1994 L1997 **FM** *020 †18
O'NEIL, Cornelia P S. ■ 99362 #021-05-1941 L1942 **AN** *071
OPARA, James Uzoma. 1120 W ROSE ST 99362 #690-04-1981 L1996 **FM** *020 †18
ORGUL, Onder. 301 W POPLAR ST, STE 100 99362 #902-05-1991 L2002 **NEP** *020 †20
PALMER, Robert Lester. PO BOX 1477 99362 #028-02-1964 L1988 ■ *071
PALOTAS, Geza John. 117 E ROSE ST 99362 #056-06-1974 L1978 **AN** *020
PARKER, Paul Edward. 380 CHASE AVE 99362 #054-04-1984 L1985 **IM** *020 †20
PARNICKY, Michael W. 77 WAINWRIGHT DR 99362 #040-02-1984 L1992 **IM** *020 †20
PETERSON, Alan P. 320 W WILLOW ST 99362 #024-05-1974 L1977 **PTH** *020 †50
PFLUGRAD, Randall Wayne. 380 CHASE AVE 99362 #005-12-1981 L1982 **IM** *020 †20
PLATTER, Howard Laurence. 1025 S 2ND AVE 99362 #054-04-1968 L1969 **FM FPG** *062 †18
POYEN, Sarah B. 55 W TIETAN ST 99362 #010-01-1996 L1999 **PD** *020 †55
QUACKENBUSH, Robert Craig. 401 W POPLAR ST, ST MARY MED CTR 99362 #028-02-1992 L2001 **HO IM** *020 †20 ‡
RABINDRANATH, Kolady N. ■ 99362 #495-11-1947 **P** *071
RAMPTON, Ralph Richard. 55 W TIETAN ST, WALLA WALLA CLINIC 99362 #038-41-1966 L1972 **CD IM** *071 †20
RANDOLPH, Albert M, II. 1111 S 2ND AVE 99362 #005-12-1971 L1992 **FM** *020 †18
RASCH, Cynthia L. 401 W POPLAR ST, ST MARY MEDICAL CTR 99362 #054-04-1991 L1994 **IM** *020 †20
REESE, Lawrence W. ■ 99362 #005-12-1951 L1951 **PTH** *071 †50
REIBER, Gary Lynn. 401 W POPLAR ST 99362 #005-12-1978 L1991 **AN** *020 †05
RICH, Brian Winston. 1111 S 2ND AVE 99362 #005-12-1989 L1997 **DR** *075 †80
RICK, Calvin John. 1111 S 2ND AVE 99362 #005-12-1979 L1991 **PD GP** *020 †55
RITTENBACH, Jon Vernon. ■ 99362 #005-12-2001 L2007 **PTH** *020 †50
RODRIGUEZ, Benjamin. 1120 W ROSE ST 99362 #035-20-1976 L1987 **IM OS** *020 †20
ROSE, Julie Kay. 401 W POPLAR ST 99362 #005-18-1984 L1986 **ON HEM** *071 †20
ROSER, Donald Max. 55 W TIETAN ST, WALLA WALLA CLINIC 99362 #054-04-1957 L1958 **OBG** *071 †30
ROTH, Daniel Geo. 55 W TIETAN ST 99362 #023-07-1965 L1980 **IM OS** *020 †20
ROWBERG, Donald Louis. 77 WAINWRIGHT DR 99362 #054-04-1979 L1982 **IM** *020 †20
RUGGERI, Robert Wm. 55 W TIETAN ST, WALLA WALLA CLINIC 99362 #024-05-1963 L1975 **ORS OSM** *071 †40
SAMEH, Abbas Ali. 320 W WILLOW ST 99362 #517-06-1957 L1968 **PTH CLP** *020 †50
SCHAEFFER, Robert Houck. 55 W TIETAN ST 99362 #040-02-1945 L1946 **PD PDA** *020 †55
SCHMITZ, Joanne Mary. 55 W TIETAN ST 99362 #056-06-1994 L1998 **DR** *020 †80
SCHOLAR, Luisa Sofia X. 55 W TIETAN ST 99362 #694-14-1977 L1996 **FM** *020
SCHWENKE, Quentin G R. ■ 99362 #054-04-1953 L1954 **GP** *071
SHANNON, John Paul. 301 W POPLAR ST STE 50 99362 #056-05-1971 L1976 **GS AM** *020 †85
SHINKLE, Debra Sue. 1120 W ROSE ST, FAMILY MEDICAL CENTER 99362 #049-01-1993 L2000 **FM** *020 †18
SHOEMAKER, David W. 401 W POPLAR ST, RADIOLOGY DEPARTMENT 99362 #016-42-1984 L1992 **DR** *020
SIMON, Richard De Loe. 401 W POPLAR ST, ADMINISTRATION 99362 #016-02-1944 L1961 **PD** *071 †55
SISLOW, John Gerard. 55 W TIETAN ST 99362 #016-02-1983 L1984 **U** *020 †95
SKAARUP, Theodore P. ■ 99362 #005-06-1990 L1999 **AN** *020 †05
SMITH, Donald Alexander. 1848 HIGHLAND RD 99362 #005-12-1943 L1961 **ORS AN** *072 †40
SMITH, Shawn Michael. 55 W TIETAN ST 99362 #049-01-2003 L2007 **N** *020
STEIN, Edwin, Jr. 345 BOYER AVE 99362 #038-06-1969 **OS P** *071
STILES, Jeffrey Craig. 55 W TIETAN ST 99362 #016-01-1982 L1998 **D** *020 †18,15
STRATTON, Yvonne Eloise. 401 W POPLAR ST 99362 #005-12-1975 L1993 **OBG** *071 †30
SWANSON, David L, Jr. ■ 99362 #005-02-1960 L1961 **FM** *071 †18
TAYLOR, Dee Ann. 1111 S 2ND AVE 99362 #005-12-1998 L2002 **FM** *020 †18
THOMPSON, Susan Elizabeth. 55 W TIETAN ST 99362 #040-02-1984 L1987 **IM** *020 †20
TOKAR, Ronald L. 299 W TIETAN ST 99362 #054-04-1971 L1975 **OPH** *020 †35
TOMS, Jeremy Brian. 1025 S 2ND AVE 99362 #005-12-2001 L2005 **AN** *020

TURNER, Ronald Michael. ■ 99362 #748-09-1980 L1982 **P** *074
UTT, Theodore P. ■ 99362 #005-12-1953 L1954 **P** *071
UYEDA, Marianne Yoko. 401 W POPLAR ST 99362 #025-01-1987 L1991 **P** *020
VAN SLYKE, Patricia Ann. 380 CHASE AVE, CHASE MEDICAL COMPLEX/URGE 99362 #028-46-1995 L2005 **FM** *020 †18
VAN YSERLOO, Ronald John. 401 W POPLAR ST, ST MARY COMMUNITY HOSP 99362 #056-06-1972 L1976 **AN** *071 †05
VARNELL, Daniel Dale. 1520 KELLEY PL, DEPARTMENT OF HUMAN SERVIC 99362 #005-12-2002 L2006 **P** *020 †75
VAUGHN, Ann Marie. 1120 W ROSE ST 99362 #049-01-1996 L1999 **FM** *020 †18
VIAVANT, Peter. 1120 W ROSE ST 99362 #049-01-1986 L1993 **FM PHP** *020 †18
WARING, George Robt. 401 W POPLAR ST, ADMINISTRATION 99362 #016-11-1974 L1993 **EM FM** *020 †18
WHITAKER, Malcolm Arthur. ■ 99362 #023-12-1992 L2006 **DR** *020 †80
WHITNEY, Nathaniel Lemson. 221 HARRIER HILL RD 99362 #005-12-2008 *012
WILCOX, Michael John. 55 W TIETAN ST 99362 #040-02-1992 L1996 **IM** *020 †20
WILKINSON, Richard S. ■ 99362 #005-12-1975 L1977 **GP** *020
WILLARD, Kirk Ellsworth. 380 CHASE AVE 99362 #005-12-1989 L1999 **ORS** *020 †40
WONGSUWAN, Suwong. 401 W POPLAR ST, CARDIOLOGY DEPT 99362 #891-07-1986 L2001 **CD** *020 †20
WOOLEVER, David Paul. 1125B S 2ND AVE 99362 #005-12-1983 L1997 **IM** *020 †20
WREN, Joseph Edward. 1111 S 2ND AVE 99362 #005-12-1992 L2005 **PD** *020 †55
WUEST, Julie. 55 W TIETAN ST 99362 #035-09-1991 L1998 **FM** *020 †18
WUJEK, Joseph John. 320 W WILLOW ST 99362 #047-05-1986 L1993 **OBG** *020 †30
YU, Ronny Y. 1103 S 2ND AVE # A 99362 #748-01-1978 L1986 **IM CD** *020 †20
YURCHAK, Edward Franklin. PO BOX 227A, E 3 99362 #030-06-1971 L1976 **PUD IM** *071 †20
YUSTE, Bessie Chen. ■ 99362 #748-01-1978 L1986 **FM** *020
ZAWATZKY, Lawrence S. 55 W TIETAN ST 99362 #023-07-1970 L1971 **GE IM** *020 †20

WAPATO – YAKIMA

ARAGON, Perry Reas. 114 W 3RD ST 98951 #748-09-1967 L1985 **GP** *075
DOORNINK, Glenn Marion. 431 E PARKER HEIGHTS RD #A 98951 #054-04-1953 L1954 **FM** *071 †18
MAC LEOD, Margaret Anne. 620 W 1ST ST 98951 #005-02-1980 L2006 **FM EM** *020 †18

WASHOUGAL – CLARK

BROWN, Robert Mc Dannell. ■ 98671 #040-02-1959 L1970 **EM** *075
DYCK, Abram Antone. ■ 98671 #040-02-1952 L1953 **GP** *071
THIEMAN, Donald Edward. ■ 98671 #016-06-1973 L1992 **MDM FM** *030 †18
TOM, Jacob Joseph. ■ 98671 #048-04-1994 L2001 **DR** *020 †80

WENATCHEE – CHELAN

ABBOTT, Michael Lee. 25 N WENATCHEE AVE, STE 210A 98801 #028-34-1979 L1982 **FM** *020 †18
AGUILU, Steven Danl. 1215 S MILLER ST 98801 #003-01-1981 L1982 **FM** *020 †18
ALEXANDER, Robert D. 820 N CHELAN AVE 98801 #054-04-1970 L1976 **OBG** *020 †30
ALLEN, Frank Fosdick. 1300 FULLER ST 98801 #024-07-1948 L1958 **U** *071 †95
APPLEGATE, John Robt. 19 S BUCHANAN AVE 98801 #054-04-1967 L1968 **AN** *020 †05
BAGULEY, Christine R. 19 S BUCHANAN AVE 98801 #021-01-1972 L1978 **AN** *020 †05
BALDWIN, William Grove. ■ 98801 #040-06-1947 L1950 **OTO** *020 †18
BALLINGER, Paul Jerome. 820 N CHELAN AVE, WENATCHEE VALLEY CLINIC 98801 #040-02-1986 L1993 **GE IM** *020 †20
BARBER, Brent Allen. 933 RED APPLE RD, STE B 98801 #054-04-1990 L1995 **ID** *020 †20
BARNWELL, Timothy Glenn. 19 S BUCHANAN AVE 98801 #030-05-1990 L1992 **AN** *020 †05
BASFORD, Alice Blanche. ■ 98801 #025-01-1961 L1967 **AN** *040 †05
BASKIN, Morrisa. 820 N CHELAN AVE, WENATCHEE VALLEY CLINIC 98801 #005-06-1987 L1992 **D** *020 †15
BASSETT, Corinne Kay. 707 N EMERSON AVE, HAUG BUILDING 98801 #054-04-1984 L1988 **FM** *020 †18
BASSETT, Gerald Alan. 175 E PENNY RD, STE C 98801 #028-34-1981 L1982 **GE IM** *020 †20
BATANOIU, Mircea S. 820 N CHELAN AVE 98801 #781-01-1995 L2000 **IM** *020 †20
BAUER, Peter Wm. 1215 S MILLER ST 98801 #041-01-1979 L1995 **FM** *020 †18
BAUMEISTER, Brenda Depew. 820 N CHELAN AVE 98801 #054-04-1990 L1997 **CCP** *020 †55
BENNION, Richard Soren. 820 N CHELAN AVE 98801 #016-06-1976 L1987 **OPH** *020 †35
BERGMAN, Roy Thos, II. 526 N CHELAN AVE, STE B 98801 #016-06-1985 L1992 **VS GS** *020 †85
BHIDE, Vasuder N. 820 N CHELAN AVE 98801 #495-45-1990 L1998 **RNR** *020 †80
BOCKENSTEDT, Fred P. 820 N CHELAN AVE 98801 #018-03-1967 L1973 **R** *020 †80
BRICKER, Charles Richard. 820 N CHELAN AVE 98801 #017-20-1979 L1992 **IM** *020 †20
BRIDGE, Danielle Marie. 820 N CHELAN AVE, PREVEA CLINIC 98801 #025-12-1994 L1998 **OBG** *020 †30
BRIDGE, Ross Edward. 1215 S MILLER ST, PREVEA CLINIC-HOWARD 98801 #025-12-1994 L1998 **FM** *020 †18
BROBERG, Mark Allen. 520 N CHELAN AVE 98801 #028-34-1980 L1985 **ORS** *020 †40
BROWNLEE, Richard Craig. 520 N CHELAN AVE 98801 #054-04-1980 L1985 **ORS** *020 †40
BULGER, Kyran Noel. 820 N CHELAN AVE 98801 #539-03-1982 L1991 **ON HEM** *020
BUTLER, Malcolm Andrew. 600 ORONDO AVE STE 1, HEALTH 98801 #054-04-1989 L1993 **FM** *020 †18
BYRD, James Chadwick. 820 N CHELAN AVE 98801 #030-05-2002 L2007 **RHU** *100 †20
CAHILL, Deborah Lynne. 820 N CHELAN AVE 98801 #054-04-1982 L1984 **OBG** *020 †30
CARLSON, Thomas Patrick. 820 N CHELAN AVE 98801 #003-01-1999 L2004 **RO** *020 †80
CARMACK, Edwin Blount. 820 N CHELAN AVE, ST MARY'S HOSPITAL 98801 #054-04-2002 L2007 **IM** *100 †20
CHVILICEK, Jeffrey Paul. 19 S BUCHANAN AVE 98801 #030-06-1989 L1996 **AN** *020 †05
CLARK, Travis Matthew. 820 N CHELAN AVE, WENATCHEE VALLEY MEDICAL C 98801 #047-05-1999 L2004 **U** *020 †95
CLARKE, Jeffery Stephen. 820 N CHELAN AVE 98801 #028-34-1983 L1986 **IM** *020 †20
COLLINS, Francis J. 600 ORONDO AVE, STE 7 98801 #539-04-1971 L1980 **OS PHP** *020
COLPITTS, John Frederick. 19 S BUCHANAN AVE 98801 #036-01-1974 L1980 **AN** *020 †05

■ = Address Information Privacy Protected

COOK, David Andrew. 933 RED APPLE RD, COLUMBIA PEDIATRICS 98801 #056-06-1983 L1986 PD *020 †55

COOK, James Robt. 820 N CHELAN AVE 98801 #003-01-1982 L1990 IM *020 †20

COWGILL, Faith Merrill. 1300 FULLER ST 98801 #038-06-1990 L1994 EM *016

CRABTREE, Rodney Lynn. 820 N CHELAN AVE, WENATCHEE VALLEY MEDICAL C 98801 #047-06-1986 L2007 IM *020 †20

CRANE, John Alexander. 1201 S MILLER ST 98801 #007-02-1986 L1997 EM *020 †16

CRAWFORD, Edward W. ■ 98801 #067-01-1952 L1961 AN *071 †05

CRAWFORD, Jerry D. 933 RED APPLE RD, COLUMBIA PEDIATRICS 98801 #049-01-1983 L1986 PD *020 †55

CUNNINGHAM, Ian Robert. 820 N CHELAN AVE 98801 #065-09-1982 L1989 DR VIR *020 †80

CUNNINGHAM, John Melvin. 820 N CHELAN AVE 98801 #039-01-1974 L1996 FM EM *020 †18

DAHL, James Andrew. 820 N CHELAN AVE 98801 #023-12-1988 L1998 ORS GS *020 †40

DAINES, Clark Rainey. 820 N CHELAN AVE 98801 #054-04-1994 L2005 PTH *020 †50

DAINES, Michael Conrad. 820 N CHELAN AVE 98801 #054-04-1987 L1997 PTH *020 †50

DANFORTH, Howard Bacon. 1300 FULLER ST 98801 #054-04-1958 L1959 OTO *071 †45

DANIEL, David Lawrence. 820 N CHELAN AVE 98801 #054-04-1986 L1992 IM PUD *020 †20

DANT, Eric Duane. 2033 S METHOW ST 98801 #005-12-1990 L1993 FM *020 †18

DEAL, Edson Fred. 520 N CHELAN AVE, WENATCHEE ORTHOPAEDICS 98801 #054-04-1965 L1966 ORS *071 †40

DE PERSIO, Edward John. 820 N CHELAN AVE, WENATCHEE VALLEY CLINIC 98801 #047-06-1965 L1981 RO *020 †80

DESIRE, Marie-Carmel. 701 N MILLER ST, COLUMBIA VALLEY BEHAVIOR 98801 #847-02-1981 L2004 P *020

DICKSON, Richard Abram. 820 N CHELAN AVE, WENATCHEE VALLEY CLINIC 98801 #068-01-1969 L1980 N IM *020 †20,75

DIETZMAN, Daniel Burton. 820 N CHELAN AVE, WENATCHEE VALLEY MEDICAL C 98801 #054-04-1995 L2003 D *020 †15

DILLON, Thomas Patrick. 820 N CHELAN AVE 98801 #007-02-1993 L1998 FM *020 †18

DOMINGUEZ, Jonathan Edgar. 820 N CHELAN AVE, WENATCHEE VALLEY CLINIC 98801 #025-07-1986 L1999 GE IM *020 †20

DRACH, Frederick Stewart. 820 N CHELAN AVE, INFECTIOUS DISEASE DEPARTM 98801 #024-07-1979 L1987 ID IM *020 †20,16

EBERHEART, Louise Kimiyo. ■ 98801 #028-34-1994 L1996 IM *020 †20

EICHLER, Andrew G. 707 N EMERSON AVE, HAUG BUILDING 98801 #005-76-1984, ▲ L1986 FM *020 †18

ETTINGER, Thomas Boldin. 1300 FULLER ST, CENTRAL WASHINGTON HOSPITA 98801 #040-02-1981 L1982 EM *020 †16

FADICH, Michael Jeffrey. 1215 S MILLER ST 98801 #067-01-1992 L1995 FM *020 †18

FARRAR, Edward L, III. 520 N CHELAN AVE 98801 #012-01-1978 L1979 ORS *020 †40

FEINMAN, Gail Ruth. 820 N CHELAN AVE 98801 #007-02-2001 L2004 IM *020 †20

FIEDLER, Stephen Eric. 820 N CHELAN AVE 98801 #005-12-1982 L1988 FM *020 †18

FREED, Stuart Dean. 820 N CHELAN AVE 98801 #054-04-1984 L1985 FSM FM *020 †18

GARRISON, Mitchell Allen. 820 N CHELAN AVE 98801 #024-05-1995 L2006 HO *020 †20

GARVER, Craig Mapes. 820 N CHELAN AVE, WENATCHEE VALLEY CLINIC 98801 #007-02-1977 L1986 N *020 †75

GIBBONS, Gerald Everett. ALCOA/WENATCHEE WORKS 98807 #035-45-1957 L1959 OM GS *071 †85

GIBBONS, Wallace S. 820 N CHELAN AVE, WENATCHEE VALLEY CLINIC 98801 #035-45-1985 L1987 U *020 †95

GILL, John Wendell. 820 N CHELAN AVE 98801 #054-04-1972 L1977 IM IMG *020 †20

GORHAM, Jay Richard. 820 N CHELAN AVE 98801 #010-01-1977 L1980 CD *020 †20

GOTTHOLD, William Eugene. 820 N CHELAN AVE, WENATCHEE VALLEY CLINIC 98801 #021-01-1969 L1978 EM MDM *030 †16

GROSDIDIER, Jonathan L. 820 N CHELAN AVE 98801 #046-01-1992 L1997 GS *020 †85

GROSDIDIER, Shannon Rae. 820 N CHELAN AVE, DEPT OF NEUROLOGY, WENATCH 98801 #046-01-2004 N *020 †75 ‡

GROSSE, Scott Edward. 820 N CHELAN AVE 98801 #054-04-1992 L1992 PM *020 †60

HALGREN, Thomas Howard. 820 N CHELAN AVE 98801 #056-06-1968 L1974 OBG *071 †30

HANNON, Gary Thomson. 820 N CHELAN AVE BOX 489, WENATCHEE VALLEY CLINIC 98801 #060-01-1957 L1966 PTH CLP *071 †50

HARDEN, Hal D. 330 KING ST, STE 5 98801 #005-12-1963 L1978 FM *072 †18

HARMS, Geoffrey Lowell. 820 N CHELAN AVE 98801 #054-04-1982 L2000 CD IM *020 †20

HAVLICEK, Russell Kevin. 820 N CHELAN AVE 98801 #030-06-1993 L1996 IM *020 †20

HIGGINS, Alfred Clinton. 820 N CHELAN AVE 98801 #010-02-1977 L1994 NS *020 †25

HILL, James Rowland. ■ 98801 #016-02-1960 L1967 DR RO *072 †80

HOLCOMB, James Louis. 933 RED APPLE RD, STE 100 98801 #027-01-1964 L1981 OTO A *071 †45

HOLDEN, Peter Kent. 820 N CHELAN AVE 98801 #056-05-1972 L1980 PHP *020 †55

HORNBY, Shauna Lynn. 933 RED APPLE RD STE C 98801 #005-12-2003 L2006 PD *020 †55

HORTON, Cindy D. 600 ORONDO AVE, STE 1 98801 #028-46-1991 L1994 FM *020 †18

HOUGHLAND, David Jerome. 820 N CHELAN AVE 98801 #054-04-1979 L1985 IM *020 †20

HOUGHLAND, John Eric. ■ 98801 #054-04-2007 L2007 EM *012

HOXSEY, Robert John. ■ 98801 #056-06-1947 L1948 IM OS *071

HSU, Rita Jiann. 820 N CHELAN AVE 98801 #005-19-1985 L1989 OBG *020 †30

HUFMAN, Stephen Lee. 820 N CHELAN AVE 98801 #049-01-1977 L1989 FM FSM *020 †18

JAECKS, David Martin. 1201 S MILLER ST 98801 #056-05-1964 L1967 IM NEP *071 †20

JAHAN, Mumtaz. 600 ORONDO AVE STE 1, CVCH 98801 #160-02-1972 L2002 FM *020 †18

JAN, Wesley Howard. 820 N CHELAN AVE, WENATCHEE VALLEY MEDICAL C 98801 #005-11-1974 L2001 NEP IM *020 †20

JANSSEN, Erwin T. 600 ORONDO AVE, STE 1 98801 #018-03-1962 L1963 CHP P *071 †75 ‡

JANSSEN, Julie A. 1201 S MILLER ST 98801 #019-02-1987 L1991 P PYG *020 †75

JANTZEN, James Wm. 820 N CHELAN AVE 98801 #017-20-1983 L1987 PD *020 †55

JARECKI, John Patrick. 19 S BUCHANAN AVE 98801 #040-02-1997 L2001 AN *020 †05

JARECKI, Mary Catherine. 820 N CHELAN AVE 98801 #040-02-1999 L2002 IM *020 †20

JENKINS, John Thos. 933 RED APPLE RD, STE D 98801 #023-07-1955 L1967 R NM *071 †80

JOHNSON, James Brockbank. 246 N MISSION ST 98801 #056-06-1972 L1973 FM OM *020 †18,70

JONES, Kenneth Michael. 526 N CHELAN AVE, STE A 98801 #016-43-1981 L1991 PS GPM *020 †65

KASTER, Steven Richard. 820 N CHELAN AVE, WENATCHEE VALLEY CLINIC 98801 #005-06-1987 L1992 FM *020 †18

KELLEY, Shawn Charlotte. 820 N CHELAN AVE 98801 #056-05-1995 L1999 IM *020 †20

KERR, Daniel Jos. 820 N CHELAN AVE 98801 #026-04-1986 L1992 PTH *020 †50

KERR, Randall Hastingsel. 19 S BUCHANAN AVE 98801 #005-12-2001 L2005 AN *100 †05

KEYSER, Andrea Ashleigh. 600 ORONDO AVE, STE 1 98801 #054-04-1990 L1992 IM *020 †20

KEYSER, Peter Francis. 933 RED APPLE RD STE C, 933 RED APPLE RD 98801 #005-18-1989 L1989 PD *020 †55

KJOBECH, Carl Henry. 820 N CHELAN AVE 98801 #016-06-1963 L1969 HEM IM *071 †20

KNECHT, Ben Harrold. 820 N CHELAN AVE 98801 #018-03-1964 L1972 GS *071 †85 ‡

KNOX, Stephen Bismark. 820 N CHELAN AVE 98801 #054-04-1981 L1982 GS *020 †85

KOLDE, David Arthur. 1215 S MILLER ST 98801 #041-09-1996 L2002 FM *020 †18 ‡

KRAFT, Warren J. PO BOX 489 98807 #016-06-1946 L1950 PD OS *071 †55

KRAKOWKA, George Frank. 820 N CHELAN AVE, WENATCHEE VALLEY CLINIC 98801 #016-02-1945 L1952 IM DIA *071 †20

KSANDER, Lori Christine. 600 ORONDO AVE STE 1, COLUMBIA VALLEY COMM HEALT 98801 #007-02-1993 L1998 FM *020 †18

KUNZ, Craig Raymond. 820 N CHELAN AVE 98801 #040-02-1997 L2004 PCC *020 †20

KUNZ, Keary Parker. 520 N CHELAN AVE 98801 #054-04-1981 L1982 OSM ORS *020

LAMMERT, Albert Chas. ■ 98801 #038-06-1948 L1948 OBG *071 †30

LEE, Byron Wayne. 820 N CHELAN AVE 98801 #021-05-1970 L1976 D *020 †15

LEE, James Jong. ■ 98801 #583-01-1993 L1997 IM FM *020 †20

LEE, Laurence Martyn. 820 N CHELAN AVE, WENATCHEE VALLEY CLINIC 98801 #061-01-1977 L1993 U *020 †95

LEVITSKY, David B. 820 N CHELAN AVE 98801 #005-02-1988 L1989 R *020 †80

LEWIS, Evelyn R. ■ 98801 #352-05-1947 L1947 FOP *071 †50

LIPTON, Aaron Howard. 1300 FULLER ST 98801 #056-06-1957 L1995 PTH FOP *071 †50

LOCATELLI, James F. 19 S BUCHANAN AVE 98801 #054-04-1998 L2002 AN *020 †05

LONG, Toby Wayne. 933 RED APPLE RD, STE B 98801 #040-02-1992 L1996 IM *020 †20

LUDWICK, Arthur L. 1300 FULLER ST 98801 #019-02-1936 L1946 FM GS *071 †18

LYNN, Richard Milton. 246 N MISSION ST, WORK CARE PLLC 98801 #048-13-1973 L1974 FM *020 †18

MACK, Ralph James. 820 N CHELAN AVE 98801 #038-41-1979 L1986 CD IM *020 †20

MAJIDIAN-LYNCH, Mina. ■ 98801 #028-34-1993 L1995 IM *071

MALHI, Sareena. 820 N CHELAN AVE 98801 #495-03-1996 L2004 HO *020 †20

MANHART, John Danl. ■ 98801 #067-01-1955 L1964 OBG *071 †30

MARINELLI, C Thos. 820 N CHELAN AVE, WENATCHEE VALLEY MEDICAL C 98801 #011-04-1980 L2001 PUD IM *020 †20

MATTERN, Kathy Leigh. 19 S BUCHANAN AVE 98801 #054-04-1981 L1982 AN *020 †05

MC BRIDE, Chad Rylan. 600 ORONDO AVE, STE 1 98801 #034-01-2002 L2003 FM *020 †18

MEAD, Carl Owen. 820 N CHELAN AVE, WENATCHEE VALLEY CLINIC 98801 #023-07-1965 L1972 NS *071 †25

MEAD, Philip Joel. 820 N CHELAN AVE 98801 #018-03-1970 L1979 OBG GP *030 †30

MILNES, Philip Dennis. 820 N CHELAN AVE 98801 #039-05-1989 L1993 PD PDC *020 †55

MITCHELL, John Scott. 820 N CHELAN AVE, WENATCHEE VLY MED CTR 98801 #028-34-1981 L2007 IM *020 †20

MIZGALA, Liane M. 933 RED APPLE RD STE D 98801 #067-01-1985 L1997 OBG *020 †30

MONDA, Jeffrey Mark. 820 N CHELAN AVE, WENATCHEE VALLEY CLINIC 98801 #054-04-1990 L1996 U *020 †95

MONSON, Jeffrey Thomas. 820 N CHELAN AVE, WENATCHEE VALLEY CLINIC 98801 #028-34-1997 L1999 GS *020 †85

MORPER, Jack Gregory. 933 RED APPLE RD STE B 98801 #028-34-1981 L1988 IM *020 †20

MOSELEY, Randal Chas. 1201 S MILLER ST 98801 #054-04-1981 L1999 IM *020 †20

MOVIUS, Earnest A. 601 OKANOGAN AVE, # PCU 120 98801 #040-02-1941 L1942 OBG OS *071 †30

MUNGER, Richard Stockton. ■ 98801 #028-34-1947 L1948 PHP N *071 †60

MURPHY, Donald Ray. 820 N CHELAN AVE 98801 #039-01-1983 L1987 OS *020

MURRAY, Ann Laurie. 820 N CHELAN AVE 98801 #016-43-1995 L2002 IM *020 †20

MURRAY, James John. 820 N CHELAN AVE, WVMC ATTN: LISA GUEST 98801 #016-43-1994 L2005 IM *020 †20

MURRAY, William Alexander. 820 N CHELAN AVE, WENATCHEE VALLEY CLINIC 98801 #054-04-1989 L1989 CD *020 †20

MYER, Everett Burr. ■ 98801 #005-12-1941 L1942 GP *071

NAWROCKI, Pola Louise. ■ 98801 #409-15-1975 L1984 *100

NEWMAN, Walter Sterling. 933 RED APPLE RD STE C 98801 #021-01-1969 L1974 PD *020 †55

NEWTON, John Richard. 820 N CHELAN AVE, WENATCHEE VALLEY CLINIC 98801 #038-06-1971 L1973 IM RHU *020 †20

NIMMAGADDA, Lokanadha B. 504 ORONDO AVE, STE A 98801 #495-58-1975 L2003 CHP P *020

NOTTER, David Taylor. 820 N CHELAN AVE, P O BOX 489 98801 #054-04-1971 L1978 ON IM *020 †20

O'DEA, Timothy Owen. 19 S BUCHANAN AVE 98801 #054-04-1979 L1999 AN PME *020 †05

OGBURN, Robert Murdock. 820 N CHELAN AVE, WENATCHEE VALLEY CLINIC 98801 #048-04-1970 L1971 GE IM *020 †20

OLSON, Eric Joseph. 600 ORONDO AVE, STE 1 98801 #054-04-1992 L1992 FM *020 †18

ORTIZ, Patricia. 707 N EMERSON AVE 98801 #054-04-1979 L1980 FM *020 †18

ORTIZ, Samuel Martin. 933 RED APPLE RD, STE B 98801 #649-46-1995 L2005 IM EM *020 †20 ‡

OSGOOD, Thomas Bradbury. 933 RED APPLE RD, STE 100 98801 #056-06-1993 L1997 OPH *020 †35

OTRUBA, Zdenek. 19 S BUCHANAN AVE 98801 #065-01-1986 L2000 AN *020 †05

PATTON, Timothy John. 933 RED APPLE RD, STE 100 98801 #028-02-1979 L1984 OTO *020 †45

PAUGH, Donald Richard, Jr. 820 N CHELAN AVE, WENARHEE VALLY MED CTR 98801 #054-04-1984 L1990 OTO *020 †45

PETERSEN, Lisa Jo. 933 RED APPLE RD, WOMENS HEALTHCARE CLINIC 98801 #016-45-1989 L1994 FM *020 †18 ‡

PETERSON, Dale Thos. 820 N CHELAN AVE, WENATCHEE VALLEY CLINIC 98801 #016-06-1964 L1971 U *020 †95

PHILLIPS, Simone D. 820 N CHELAN AVE, WENATCHEE VALLEY MEDICAL C 98801 #047-06-1997 L2002 IM *020 †20

PITTS, Kevin Scott. 820 N CHELAN AVE 98801 #039-01-1986 L1990 OBG *020 †30

PRASAD, Andy Karayalar R. 820 N CHELAN AVE 98801 #495-16-1990 L2004 NEP *100 †20

PRIMM, Richard Kirby. 820 N CHELAN AVE, WENATCHEE VALLEY CLINIC 98801 #036-01-1970 L1984 CD IM *020 †20

RAPPE, Gerald Alan. ■ 98801 #040-02-1970 L1972 PTH *071 †50

REEDER, David Carl. 19 S BUCHANAN AVE 98801 #054-04-2003 L2007 AN *020

REGISTER, John Thomas. 820 N CHELAN AVE 98801 #038-40-1995 L2000 RO *050 †80

ROBERTSON, Mandy D Hender. 820 N CHELAN AVE, DEPT HEM/ONC 98801 #011-03-1999 L2001 HO IM *020 †20

ROMPALA, John Felix. 19 S BUCHANAN AVE 98801 #026-08-1999 L2003 **AN** *020 †05
ROSS, Tom Lee. 707 N EMERSON AVE, HAUG BUILDING 98801 #005-14-1971 L1976 **FM** *020 †18
ROSSI, Michael Joseph. 1201 S MILLER ST 98801 #005-15-1996 L2003 **ORS OSM** *020 †40
ROWLES, Billie Lamb. 933 RED APPLE RD, WASHINGTON HOSP 98801 #037-01-1984 L2000 **OBG** *020 †30
RUBIN, Allen David. 820 N CHELAN AVE, WENATCHEE VALLEY MEDICAL C 98801 #045-01-1991 L2001 **VS** *012 †85,90
RUCKMAN, Arthur Lewis. 820 N CHELAN AVE 98801 #021-06-1978 L1983 **EM** *020
RUTHERFORD, Peter Douglas. 820 N CHELAN AVE 98801 #054-04-1982 L1990 **IM** *020 †20 ‡
SCHATZ, Linda Kay. 19 S BUCHANAN AVE 98801 #040-02-1986 L1990 **AN** *020 †05
SCHIEFELBEIN, Richard A. ■ 98801 #005-02-1969 L1973 **PTH** *020 †50
SCHROEDER, Carl Robt. 1300 FULLER ST 98801 #025-01-1959 L1961 **AN** *071
SCHULZ, John Chas. 820 N CHELAN AVE, WENATCHEE VALLEY CLINIC 98801 #055-01-1986 L1991 **OPH** *020 †35
SCULL, Eliot Wadsworth. 600 ORONDO AVE 98801 #067-01-1967 L1973 **OPH** *071 †35
SCULL, Grant Schofield. 600 ORONDO AVE, STE 1 98801 #054-04-1998 L2000 **FM** *020 †18
SEE, Carolina Que. 820 N CHELAN AVE 98801 #748-01-1997 L2006 **PCC** *020 †20 ‡
SEGUIN, Sharon. 820 N CHELAN AVE, WENATCHEE VALLEY CLINIC 98801 #016-43-1989 L2000 **D** *020 †20,15 ‡
SHAW, Gillian Sutcliffe. 820 N CHELAN AVE 98801 #065-09-1983 L1989 **FM** *020 †18
SHERMER, Kenneth. 600 ORONDO AVE STE 1, HEALTH 98801 #001-06-1996 L1998 **FM** *020 †18
SHIPMAN, Mark Wm. 820 N CHELAN AVE 98801 #041-07-1977 L1978 **AN** *020 †16
SLAPNICKA, Petr. 820 N CHELAN AVE, WENATCHEE VALLEY MEDICAL C 98801 #286-04-1985 L1998 **IM** *020 †20
SMITH, Alan Chris. 820 N CHELAN AVE, WENATCHEE VALLEY CLINIC 98801 #054-04-1980 L1981 **GE IM** *020 †20
SMITH, Julie Christian. 820 N CHELAN AVE 98801 #049-01-1993 L1999 **HO** *020 †20
SMITH, William Vaughn. ■ 98801 #048-04-1954 L1956 **ORS** *071 †40
SOBBA-HIGLEY, Anne E. 707 N EMERSON AVE 98801 #030-06-1990 L1996 **OTO** *020 †45
SOROM, Galen R. 820 N CHELAN AVE 98801 #054-04-2001 L2005 **IM** *020 †20
SOROM, Jeb Andrew. 19 S BUCHANAN AVE 98801 #054-04-2001 L2005 **AN** *020 †05
SOROM, Terry Allen. ■ 98801 #026-04-1966 L1972 **OPH** *071 †35
SPARKS, Daniel Robert. 820 N CHELAN AVE 98801 #001-01-1994 L2000 **GS** *020 †85
STAHLER, Christopher, Jr. 820 N CHELAN AVE, WENATCHEE VALLEY CLINIC 98801 #035-20-1960 L1966 **GS CD** *072 †85,90
STARKWEATHER, Roger James. 304 N CHELAN AVE 98801 #010-01-1971 L1978 **ORS OSM** *020 †40
STOJOWSKI, Alfred J. 1300 FULLER ST 98801 #035-01-1944 L1953 **GS TS** *071 †85
STONE, Lisa Marie. 820 N CHELAN AVE 98801 #036-07-1988 L1990 **END IM** *020 †20
STRAND, Linda Louise. 933 RED APPLE RD, STE D 98801 #023-12-1981 L1992 **DR** *020 †80
STRAUS, Michelle Naomi. 820 N CHELAN AVE, WENATCHEE VALLEY MEDICAL C 98801 #016-11-1988 L2002 **IM** *020 †20
STROMING, Scott Lynn. 1201 S MILLER ST, CENTRAL WASHINGTON HOSP 98801 #010-02-1990 L1994 **EM** *020 †16
SUBLETTE, Matthew Lewis. ■ 98801 #020-02-2003 L2007 **OBG** *020
SWETT, Henry Arthur. 820 N CHELAN AVE, WENATCHEE VALLEY CLINIC 98801 #033-05-1970 L1998 **DR** *020 †80
THOMAS, John Gerard. 19 S BUCHANAN AVE 98801 #039-05-1985 L1992 **AN** *020 †05
THORSON, Eric Peter. 820 N CHELAN AVE 98801 #016-01-1983 L1989 **ORS HS** *020 †40
TIMOTHY, Stephania Kay. 820 N CHELAN AVE, WENATCHEE VALLEY MEDICAL C 98801 #039-01-1997 L2006 **GS** *020 †85
TIMOTHY, William Scott. 820 N CHELAN AVE, WENATCHEE VALLEY MEDICAL C 98801 #039-01-1997 L2007 **PM** *020 †60
TORNABENE, Joseph Andrew. 820 N CHELAN AVE 98801 #043-01-1988 L2000 **N** *020 †75
TOTH, Andrew Leonard, Jr. 707 N EMERSON AVE, WENATCHEE FAMILY PRACTICE 98801 #005-12-1996 L1998 **FM** *020 †18
TROPPER, Jean. 820 N CHELAN AVE, WENATCHEE VALLEY CLINIC 98801 #067-06-1985 L1997 **NS** *020
TUSZYNSKI, Thomas Raymond. 820 N CHELAN AVE 98801 #023-07-1985 L1990 **TS GS** *020 †90,85
UTLEY, Dennis Doyle. 820 N CHELAN AVE 98801 #001-02-1974 L1983 **OBG** *020 †30
VADERAH, Sanjeev. 820 N CHELAN AVE 98801 #496-09-1987 L1997 **CD** *020 †20
VALAAS, Peter Whitcomb. 820 N CHELAN AVE 98801 #054-04-1980 L1981 **AN** *020 †05
VAN LOBEN SELS, Elisabeth. 820 N CHELAN AVE, WENATCHEE VALLEY MEDICAL C 98801 #054-04-1996 L1999 **IM** *020 †20
VEJVODA, Hank James. 820 N CHELAN AVE, CWH WENATCHEE ORTHOPAEDICS 98801 #016-45-1998 L2002 **ORS** *020 †40
VOLKMANN, Roger Jos. 820 N CHELAN AVE 98801 #026-04-1984 L1989 **ORS** *020 †40
VOORHIES, Stephen F. 707 N EMERSON AVE, HAUG BUILDING 98801 #016-42-1979 L1993 **FM** *020 †18
VOTH, Brian Russell. 19 S BUCHANAN AVE 98801 #054-04-1992 L1996 **AN** *020 †05
WALLING, Erin Michel. 820 N CHELAN AVE 98801 #005-15-1998 L2004 **GS** *020 †85
WARD, Peter Michael. 820 N CHELAN AVE, WENATCHEE VALLEY MEDICAL C 98801 #041-12-1995 L2001 **NS** *020 †25
WEBER, David Lee. 820 N CHELAN AVE, WENATCHEE VALLEY MED CLNC 98801 #018-03-1968 L1975 **OS** *030 †80
WEBER, David Lee, Jr. 820 N CHELAN AVE, RADIOLOGY DEPT 98801 #005-12-2000 L2004 **DR** *020 †80
WEBER, Susan Annette Leff. 820 N CHELAN AVE, WENATCHEE VALLEY CLINIC 98801 #018-03-1968 L1975 **GP FM** *020
WELLS, Rodney Nelson. 820 N CHELAN AVE 98801 #028-34-1991 L1995 **OBG** *020 †30 ‡
WENDT, Patrick Jos. 820 N CHELAN AVE 98801 #046-01-1977 L1981 **DR** *062 †80
WESTERLUND, Susan Hanna. 820 N CHELAN AVE 98801 #054-04-1980 L1981 **FM** *020 †18
WHITEHEAD, Myron Eugene. 820 N CHELAN AVE 98801 #040-02-1976 L1991 **PTH** *020 †50
WICHETA, William Edmond. 933 RED APPLE RD STE 100 98801 #048-12-1982 L1988 **OPH EM** *020 †35
WIGGUM, David Chas. 19 S BUCHANAN AVE 98801 #054-04-1983 L1986 **AN** *020 †05
WILLIS, Carter Pratt. 19 S BUCHANAN AVE 98801 #011-03-1986 L1992 **AN** *020 †05
WITHAM, Deborah M. 19 S BUCHANAN AVE 98801 #016-42-1989 L2000 **AN** *020 †05
WOODS, Renee L. 1325 PRINCETON AVE 98801 #048-12-1987 L2000 **OBG** *020 †30 ‡

WENATCHEE – DOUGLAS

O'DONNELL, Theodore F. 100 HIGHLINE DR 98802 #005-15-1973 L1991 **FM EM** *020 †18

WEST RICHLAND – BENTON

BAXTER, Nancy Ballenas. 3605 E LATTIN RD 99353 #035-09-1988 L1997 **PD** *020 †55
BRITT-MARINOV, Amy Helen. 4001 KENNEDY RD, STE 7 99353 #003-01-1997 L2007 **FM** *020 †18
SMITH, Sidney Bernard. ■ 99353 #042-02-1998 L2006 **D** *020 †15
TUDOR, Charles C. ■ 99353 #035-09-1930 L1946 **OM PHP** *071 †70

WESTPORT – GRAYS HARBOR

HOUTZ, Dudley Wm. ■ 98595 #019-02-1955 L1956 **OS** *071
UHLIG, Bennett Ellsworth. ■ 98595 #019-02-1963 **CRS GS** *071 †85,10

WHITE SALMON – KLICKITAT

BOYER, Warren J. ■ 98672 #021-05-1951 L1951 **IM** *071 †20
CAMPBELL, Douglas Thobro. ■ 98672 #040-02-1970 L1971 **PHP EM** *050 †16
FITZ SIMMONS, Raymond J. PO BOX 1519 98672 #054-04-1976 L1982 **FM** *020 †18 ‡
GIMENEZ, Alice Susan. PO BOX 1519 98672 #054-04-1993 L1993 **FM** *020 †18
GOZDOWSKI, James Matthew. ■ 98672 #024-07-1969 L1974 **AN GS** *020 †05
GUYER, Betsy Hauge. 85 PALOS VERDE, P O BOX 619 98672 #040-02-1981 L1996 **R RNR** *020 †80
JANNEY, James G. 211 SKYLINE DR 98672 #054-04-1973 L1974 **FM** *071 †18
OLSON, Lloyd Clarence. ■ 98672 #024-01-1961 L1976 **PDI PD** *071 †55
WITHERRITE, Liette Caryl. ■ 98672 #016-06-2002 L2006 **FM** *020 †18
WITHERRITE, Troy Robert. ■ 98672 #056-06-2002 L2006 **GS** *100 †18
YAMAZAKI, James Nobuo. ■ 98672 #056-06-1943 L1950 **PD** *071 †55
ZUCK, Gregory Dean. 211 SKYLINE DR 98672 #028-34-1981 L1984 **GP** *020 †18

WINLOCK – LEWIS

ELLIS, David Abraham. 100 CEDAR CREST DR, PO BOX 567 98596 #005-12-1976 L1991 **FM** *020
HOHMANN, Betty Jo. ■ 98596 #041-07-1959 L1961 **ORS** *071

WINTHROP – OKANOGAN

DIAMOND, Ann. 1116 HWY 20 98862 #005-02-1993 L1995 **FM** *020 †18
FISHER, Stephen Lee. PO BOX 1156, 360 WISTER WAY 98862 #005-14-1978 L2006 **IM** *020 †16
GLICK, R Victor. ■ 98862 #051-04-1974 L1991 **AN** *020 †05
SCHREINER, Elizabeth Jean. ■ 98862 #036-07-1980 L1991 **AN** *071 †05
WIMBERGER, Herbert C. PO BOX 326 98862 #154-07-1953 L1962 **P CHP** *071
WINSOR, Joan Mary Marson. ■ 98862 #005-06-1967 L1989 **AN** *071 †05

WOODINVILLE – KING

ANDERSON, Whitney E. 17000 140TH AVE NE, UNIT 102 98072 #041-02-2001 L2004 **PD** *020 †55
BANGA, Baljit Kaur. 22511 NE 165TH CT 98077 #495-48-1997 L2003 **IM** *020
BARRON, Lauren Renee. ■ 98072 #011-02-1979 L1980 **EM** *020 †16
BARTHEL, Steven William. 17000 140TH AVE NE, BELLEVUE EAR NOSE & 98072 #047-05-1995 L2001 **OTO HNS** *020 †45
BECHTEL, Robert Kurt. 17131 163RD AVE NE, PACIFIC ANESTHESIA 98072 #038-45-1989 L1993 **AN PME** *020 †05
BELL, Glenn Wm. ■ 98072 #049-01-1946 L1947 **GP GS** *071
BERNER, Jonathan Eric. 18500 156TH AVE NE, STE 201 98072 #005-14-1993 L1996 **P** *020 †75
BILGER, Marie Louise. 17000 140TH AVE NE # 102 98072 #005-19-1992 L2001 **PD** *020 †55
BURNER, Timothy Gene. 17638 140TH AVE NE, UWPN WOODINVILLE 98072 #054-04-1986 L1988 **FM** *020 †18
CHATHAM, David Michael. 17000 140TH AVE NE, UNIT 101 98072 #023-01-1989 L1992 **FM** *020 †18
CHLEBOWSKI, Taryn C. 17638 140TH AVE NE 98072 #056-06-2003 L2007 **MPD** *020 †20,55
COUSER, William Griffith. 16050 169TH AVE NE 98072 #024-01-1965 L1982 **NEP IM** *050 †20
CUMMINGS, Barbara C. 17000 140TH AVE NE, UNIT 102 98072 #040-02-1985 L1986 **PD** *020 †55
DEBELAK, Danielle Bergan. 17638 140TH AVE NE 98072 #054-04-2002 L2004 **FM** *020 †18
DEL TORO, Iris M. ■ 98077 #042-01-1971 L1978 **P** *020 †18
DEVNEY, Robert Bernard. 18500 156TH AVE NE STE 201 98072 #026-04-1978 L1982 **CHP P** *020 †75
DY, Grace. 17000 140TH AVE NE, UNIT 101 98072 #005-15-1996 L1999 **EM** *020 †16
EDWARDS, Sally Saran. 17311 135TH AVE NE, STE A700 98072 #054-04-1988 L1990 **FM** *020 †18
EMMONS, Stephen Wilson. 17638 140TH AVE NE 98072 #041-13-1997 L2000 **IM** *020 †18
ESCALONA, Eduardo S. 15330 162ND AVE NE 98072 #231-01-1948 L1973 **AN** *071
FACKELMAN, J Robert. 17000 140TH AVE NE, UNIT 101 98072 #030-05-1968 L1987 **EM IM** *020 †20
GAREIS, Louis C. ■ 98077 #023-01-1938 L1969 **OBG** *071 †30
GEISE, Robert Edward. 23117 77TH AVE SE 98072 #051-04-1995 L1999 **ID IM** *020 †20
GLASS, Stephen Tolman. 17924 140TH AVE NE STE 200 98072 #050-02-1974 L1976 **CHN N** *020 †55,75
GRESS, Jeffrey Paul. ■ 98072 #010-02-1986 L1998 **CD IM** *020 †20
HANSON, Kevin Michael. ■ 98072 #054-04-1998 L2001 **EM** *012
HARPER, Larry Robt. 17000 140TH AVE NE, UNIT 101 98072 #019-02-1974 L1976 **FM** *020 †18
HARTMAN, Matthew. ■ 98077 #016-11-2006 L2006 **IM** *012
HASBUN-MARCOS, Alberto. ■ 98072 #341-01-1982 L1986 **IM IMG** *071
JAP, Tjien Bo. ■ 98072 #506-01-1963 L1988 **DR NM** *071 †80,28
JOHNSON, Dwight Winnette. ■ 98077 #005-12-1956 L1964 **OS** *071
JOHNSON, Larry Don. 17000 140TH AVE NE # 101 98072 #054-04-1998 L1980 **FM EM** *020 †18
KANESHIRO, Neil Kazuyuki. 17000 140TH AVE NE, UNIT 102 98072 #014-01-1992 L1992 **PD PE** *020 †55

KASMAN, Deborah Lynn. 17311 135TH AVE NE, STE A700 98072 #036-01-1985 L1986 **FM** *020 †18

KNOX, Kristen Kay. 17311 135TH AVE NE, STE A700 98072 #005-14-1987 L1989 **FM** *020 †18

KOH, David Anthony. 17000 140TH AVE NE, UNIT 102 98072 #024-05-1987 L1991 **PD** *020 †55

LEE, Samson. 17000 140TH AVE NE, UNIT 205 98072 #036-07-1999 L1999 **OTO FPS** *020 †45 ‡

LIPTON, Judith Eve. 17000 140TH AVE NE, WOODINVILLE PEDIATRICS 98072 #036-01-1974 L1976 **P ADL** *072 †75

LOMOTAN, Christine A. 17000 140TH AVE NE, UNIT 101 98072 #748-10-1986 L1992 **FM** *020 †18

MARLOWE, Sarah Swider. 17638 140TH AVE NE 98072 #041-07-1987 L1994 **FM** *020 †18

MAUSETH, Richard Scott. 17000 140TH AVE NE, UNIT 102 98072 #038-41-1973 L1977 **PDE PD** *020 †55

MAYFIELD, Jennifer Alice. 21609 57TH AVE SE 98072 #005-12-1977 L1978 **PHP FM** *050 †70,18

MAYNARD, Robert E. 13317 NE 175TH ST STE U, EYE CLINIC-NORTHSHORE 98072 #035-06-1953 L1958 **OPH** *071 †35

MILLER, Jill Truex. 17000 140TH AVE NE # 102, WOODINVILLE PEDIATRICS 98072 #054-04-1992 L1992 **PD** *020 †55

MITRA, Srobona. ■ 98072 #495-39-2001 L2006 **FP** *012

NAKAHARA, Joseph Kenji. 17000 140TH AVE NE, UNIT 102 98072 #014-01-1988 L1990 **PD** *020 †55

NGUYEN, Brigitte N. 17000 140TH AVE NE, WOODINVILE PEDIATRICS 98072 #035-46-1991 L2001 **PD** *020 †55

PISANI, Richard Jos. 14421 WOODINVL RDMND RD NE 98072 #021-01-1982 L1992 **PUD IM** *020 †20

RAEES, Basma. ■ 98072 #704-01-2000 L2005 **PD** *020

RAMCHANDANI, Geeta Sushil. 17000 140TH AVE NE, SUITE101 98072 #496-36-1995 L2002 **FM** *020 †18

RIEGEL, Daniel J. 17000 140TH AVE NE # 101 98072 #026-04-1986 L1989 **FM** *020 †18

SACKETT, Andrew Paul. ■ 98072 #025-01-1941 L1942 **PHP OS** *071 †15

SAVAGE, Brandon Richard. ■ 98072 #005-18-1997 L1999 **IM** *020 †20

SEELY, Daniel Randolph. 17000 140TH AVE NE, BELLEVUE EAR NOSE & 98072 #048-04-1987 L1989 **OTO HNS** *020 †45

SHEFFIELD, Pamela. 17638 140TH AVE NE 98072 #054-04-1993 L1993 **FM** *020 †18

SLIMAN, Gregory Alan. 17000 140TH AVE NE, UNIT 102 98072 #023-07-1988 L1990 **PN** *020 †55

SLOCUM, John Payne. PO BOX 2031 98072 #016-11-1956 L1959 **FM** *071

SOBOTA, Holly Marie. ■ 98072 #010-01-2005 L2006 **PD** *012

SOMOGYI, Emil Laszlo. ■ 98077 #473-01-1952 L1960 **AN** *071 †05

STEVENS, Virginia T. 14024 NE 181ST ST, STE 201 98072 #048-14-1983 L1992 **IM** *020 †20

STOCKDALE, Kristi Marie. 14143 171ST AVE NE 98072 #054-04-1988 L1991 **IM** *020 †20

STUHRING, Glen Thos. 17000 140TH AVE NE, UNIT 101 98072 #054-04-1978 L1982 **FM** *020 †20

TOBIASAN, Parthenia Fanny. ■ 98077 #021-01-1990 L2000 **FM** *020 †18

TRAUTMAN, John-Paul. 17638 140TH AVE NE 98072 #007-02-1994 L1994 **FM** *020 †18

WEBB, Timothy Stanwood. 16332 NE 198TH ST 98072 #054-04-1993 L1996 **FM** *020 †18

WEINBERG, Mitchell Bruce. 17000 140TH AVE NE, UNIT 102 98072 #038-06-1981 L1982 **PD PDA** *020 †55

WHITAKER, John Steven. ■ 98072 #017-20-1983 L1984 **EM** *020

YOUNKIN, Robert Ray. 17000 140TH AVE NE, UNIT 101 98072 #007-02-1972 L1978 **FM** *020 †18

ZBIRUN, Oleg Nefalimovic. ■ 98072 #054-04-2008 *012

ZUNDEL, Roger Scott. 17000 140TH AVE NE, BELLEVUE EAR NOSE & 98072 #049-01-1991 L1996 **OTO** *020 †45

WOODLAND – COWLITZ

JOHNSON, Ellis W. 527 2ND ST, PEARSON MEDICAL CLINIC 98674 #040-02-1984 L1986 **IM** *020 †20

PEARSON, R C John. 527 2ND ST, PEARSON MEDICAL CLINIC 98674 #054-15-1964 L1972 **GP** *071

ROBERTS, Cecil Lawrence. ■ 98674 #028-34-1971 L1972 **OS** *020

WOODWAY – SNOHOMISH

HAHN, Yung Hee Kim. ■ 98020 #583-08-1963 **PTH** *074

KIRBY, Barbara Dole. ■ 98020 #054-04-1974 L1978 **ID IM** *040 †20

LEVIN, Wendy Jo. 10920 S DEER DR 98020 #422-01-1998 L2001 **HEM** *020 †20

SNYDER, Kim Morris. ■ 98020 #048-04-1973 L1979 **ID IM** *020 †20

YACOLT – CLARK

SARGENT, Barbara Clark. ■ 98675 #048-04-1955 L1961 **AN** *020

SARGENT, Dwayne Lee. ■ 98675 #048-04-1955 L1960 **U** *071 †95

SCRIVENS, Bruce Floyd. ■ 98675 #005-02-1960 L1961 **PD PN** *071 †55

YAKIMA – YAKIMA

AALPOEL, Justin Arthur. 110 S 9TH AVE 98902 #016-02-1945 L1946 **TS** *071 †85,90

ABBENHAUS, James Iver. 307 S 12TH AVE STE 12 98902 #007-02-1964 L1970 **OTO PS** *020 †45

ABRAHA, Surafeal Ghedamu. 602 E NOB HILL BLVD 98901 #366-02-1999 L2005 **IM** *020 †20

ADKISON, John Warrell. 1211 N 16TH AVE 98902 #054-04-1973 L1978 **ORS HS** *020 †40

AL-BUSTAMI, Omar Mahmoud. 611 N 39TH AVE 98902 #575-01-1997 L2005 **IM** *100 †20 ‡

ALLEN, Albert Robt. 98901 #016-11-1943 L1950 **PUD IM** *071

ALLEN, Loxi Marian. ■ 98902 #040-02-1968 L1969 **AN PMM** *071 †05

AMES, Jay David. ■ 98902 #054-04-1974 L1977 **FM** *020 †16

ANDERSON, Molly W. 504 N 40TH AVE 98908 #035-19-1994 L1996 **FM** *020 †18

ANGULO ZERECEDA, David An. 303 HOLTON AVE 98902 #737-11-1999 L2006 **PCC** *020 †20

ASGHAR, Amjad Shakeel. 1111 W SPRUCE ST STE 26 98902 #704-09-1975 *100

ATTAWAY, Tommy J. 302 S 10TH AVE 98902 #048-02-1986 L1998 **GE** *020 †20

ATWOOD, Robert George. ■ 98902 #056-05-1962 L1971 **PHP GPM** *075

AVERY, James Keith. 229 S 2ND AVE, YAKIMA OPERATIONS 98902 #054-04-1971 L1972 **EM FM** *020 †18,16

BALL, Bruce Le Roy. 110 S 9TH AVE 98902 #030-06-1978 L1979 **FM** *020 †18

BALLEW, Donald Harrison. ■ 98902 #067-01-1955 L1959 **CD IM** *071 †20

BAPAT, Ashutosh Vishnu. 406 S 30TH AVE, STE 201 98902 #496-39-1997 L2004 **CD** *020 †20

BARANY, John Stephen. 303 HOLTON AVE STE 1 98902 #054-04-1971 L1974 **PUD IM** *071 †20

BARG, Neil Larry. 303 HOLTON AVE STE 1 98902 #041-13-1979 L1997 **ID IM** *040 †20

BARTLETT, Jeffrey Donald. 314 S 11TH AVE STE A, YAKIMA PEDIATRIC ASSOC INC 98902 #054-04-1982 L1983 **PD** *020 †55

BENEDETTI, Thomas Jos. 2811 TIETON DR 98902 #054-04-1973 L1979 **MFM OBG** *050 †30

BENSON, Eric Philip. 5512 DOUGLAS DR 98908 #917-29-1955 L1967 **DR RO** *071 †80

BERGGREN, Ralph Eugene. ■ 98908 #016-06-1959 L1960 **FM** *071 †18

BERKO, Robert Simon. 110 S 9TH AVE 98902 #041-12-1981 L2001 **AN** *020 †05

BERMAN, Mark Steven. 406 S 30TH AVE, STE 201 98902 #040-02-1987 L1995 **CD** *020 †20

BERNFELD, Barry David. 3003 TIETON DR, STE 300 98902 #028-02-1977 L1984 **GS VS** *020 †85

BHASKARAN, Sunny John G. 402 S 12TH AVE 98902 #495-16-1992 L2001 **FM** *020 †18

BIRGE, James Robt. 6 BURNING TREE DR 98902 #041-01-1972 L2002 **IM** *071 †20

BLACK, Vicki Lynn Allen. 1806 W LINCOLN AVE 98902 #016-43-1974 L1977 **FM** *020 †18

BOBBA, Swapna Jyothi. 1806 W LINCOLN AVE, FAMILY MED 98902 #495-57-1996 L2005 **FP** *012

BOBOVSKY, Joseph Michael. 732 SUMMITVIEW AVE # 576 98902 #025-07-1980 L1985 **AN EM** *020 †05,16

BOCEK, Max M. 1111 W SPRUCE ST 98902 #040-02-1950 L1955 **ORS** *071 †40

BOCEK-LILLEY, Nicola. 504 N 40TH AVE 98908 #028-34-1975 L1976 **FM** *020 †18

BORNFLETH, Leslie R. 10600 ESTES RD 98908 #026-04-1962 L1975 **NS** *020 †25

BOS, Gary Dale. 1470 N 16TH AVE 98902 #016-02-1978 L2006 **ORS** *020 †40

BOUCHER, John K. 111 S 11TH AVE, STE 223 98902 #051-01-1969 L1978 **GS** *020 †85

BOYD, Richard Barclay. 1111 W SPRUCE ST, STE 30 98902 #010-01-1973 L1978 **IM FM** *020

BOYD, Thomas Edwin. 808 N 39TH AVE 98902 #048-12-1979 L1985 **ON HEM** *020 †20

BOYKIN, John Lanham. 315 HOLTON AVE, STE 100 98902 #017-20-1967 L1975 **NEP IM** *020 †20

BRACCHI, Roger Lewis. 1806 W LINCOLN AVE 98902 #040-02-1975 L1976 **FM** *020 †18

BRADY, Albert Michael. 3911 CASTLEVALE RD, STE 201 98902 #005-14-1970 L2005 **ON IM** *030 †20

BRANDT, Cornelis Diedrich. 1015 S 40TH AVE STE 12 98908 #660-01-1955 L1957 **GP** *020

BRASSEUR, Victor Bernard. ■ 98908 #016-06-1962 L1968 **R** *071 †80

BREMJIT, Vani. 2501 BUSINESS LN 98901 #220-01-1983 L1996 **FM** *020 †18

BREWER, Gayle Franklin. 110 S 9TH AVE 98902 #005-14-1966 L1970 **NM IM** *030 †20,28

BROWN, David Lee. ■ 98902 #018-03-1977 L1980 **EM** *020 †16

BROWN, Timothy Edwin. 302 S 10TH AVE 98902 #051-01-1977 L1981 **GE IM** *020 †05

BRUNDIDGE, Phyllis Kaye. 4001 SUMMITVIEW AVE #5-323 98908 #028-02-1987 L2005 **AN** *020 †05

BRYAN, Albert Harold. 401 S 12TH AVE, CENTRAL WA EYE PHYSICIAN & 98902 #018-03-1964 L1970 **OPH** *071 †35

BURKE, Edmund Leroy. 110 S 9TH AVE 98902 #005-12-1957 L1958 **GP** *020

CAPATI, Marciano Baul, Jr. 1806 W LINCOLN AVE, FAMILY MED 98902 #748-08-2001 L2007 **FP** *012

CARHART, Isaac Whitfield. 314 S 11TH AVE 98902 #028-02-1962 L1972 **DR R** *071 †80

CARLSON, Kathryn Lynne. 2205 W LINCOLN AVE 98902 #028-02-2004 L2007 **EM** *012 †55

CATE, Sara Irene. 1117 TIETON DR 98902 #054-04-1988 L1990 **FM** *075 †18

CATTON, Christopher K. 2811 TIETON DR 98902 #054-04-1989 L1989 **IM** *020 †20

CELERIAN, Maria Cecelia R. 1806 W LINCOLN AVE, DEPT OF FAMILY MED 98902 #748-14-1991 L2007 **FP** *012

CHAN, Wai Sun. 1806 W LINCOLN AVE, DEPT OF FAMILY MED 98902 #462-01-1987 L2007 **FP** *012

CHIRITESCU, Alina A. 102 S NACHES AVE 98901 #781-08-1996 L2000 **PD** *020 †55

CHIRITESCU, Cristian V. 2811 TIETON DR 98902 #781-08-1995 L2000 **PD** *020 †55

CHRISTOPHER, Katina R. 504 N 40TH AVE 98908 #028-78-2004, ▲ L2007 **FM** *020

CHUA, Chester Sim. ■ 98901 #748-01-2001 L2007 **IM** *020 †20

CLEARY, Sean Fulton. 808 N 39TH AVE 98902 #051-04-1990 L1995 **RO** *020 †80

CLIPPINGER, Mark Steven. 1806 W LINCOLN AVE 98902 #046-01-1983 L1988 **EM OM** *020 †18 ‡

COFFIN, Stanley. ■ 98902 #054-04-1963 L1955 **FM** *072

COHEN, Betty Ann. 206 S 11TH AVE # 48, CENTRAL WA OCCUPATIONAL ME 98902 #036-01-1985 L2004 **GPM** *020 †20,70

COJOCARU, Odheth Maria. 402 S 12TH AVE, CORNERSTONE MEDICAL CLINIC 98902 #781-01-1998 L2005 **IM** *100 †20

CONROY, Robert John. 3003 TIETON DR STE 300 98902 #036-05-1992 L1997 **GS** *020 †85

COON, Douglas Earl. 110 S 9TH AVE, DEPT OF EMERGENCY 98902 #005-12-1986 L1993 **EM** *020 †16

COOPER, Robert Kay. 406 S 30TH AVE, STE 202 98902 #054-04-1975 L1977 **AN** *020 †05

CORPRON, Douglas Ogden. 504 N 40TH AVE 98908 #054-04-1956 L1958 **FM** *071 †18

CRAFTS, Ryan Mcarthur. 504 N 40TH AVE 98908 #001-06-2000 L2002 **FM** *020 †18

CROOK, Amy Jo. 406 S 30TH AVE, STE 202 98902 #025-01-1997 L2001 **AN** *020 †05

CROOK, Michael Edward. 314 S 11TH AVE STE A 98902 #025-01-1997 L2001 **PD** *020 †55

DART, Leroy Harris. 2811 TIETON DR 98902 #005-02-1954 L1974 **NS PTH** *020 †50,25

DAVENPORT, Nathaniel Acob. 1806 W LINCOLN AVE, CENTRAL WASHINGTON FAMILY 98902 #054-04-2002 L2004 **FM** *100 †20

DAVIES, Robyn Kaye. 1806 W LINCOLN AVE 98902 #422-01-2005 L2005 **FP** *012

DAVISON, Cheryl A. PO BOX 9338 98909 #025-12-1986 L2003 **RO** *020 †80

DEGENFELDER, Paul S. 111 S 11TH AVE STE 320, CENTRAL WASH ORTHO SURG 98902 #035-09-1999 L2005 **ORS OSM** *020 †40

DERAMO, Mark Anthony. 1806 W LINCOLN AVE, CENTRAL WASH FAMILY MEDICI 98902 #010-02-1997 L2000 **FM** *020 †20

DESHPANDE, Abhijit G. 1460 N 16TH AVE STE B 98902 #495-01-1988 L1996 **IM SME** *020 †20

DESHPANDE, Prajakta Abhij. 110 S 9TH AVE 98902 #496-38-1993 L2001 **FM** *020 †18 ‡

DEW, Robert Ralph. 110 S 9TH AVE 98902 #038-06-1943 L1970 **PD PHP** *071 †55

DINESCU, Cristian L. 402 S 12TH AVE 98902 #781-01-1989 L2001 **IM** *020 †20

DODGE, James Theodore. 2811 TIETON DR 98902 #054-04-1962 L1964 **IM NM** *020 †28

DONALDSON, Wallace Alvin. 110 S 9TH AVE 98902 #016-06-1961 L1964 **FM** *020

DONLEY, Constance A S. ■ 98902 #038-40-1972 L1995 **IM** *020 †20

DOORNINK, Daniel Glenn. 402 S 12TH AVE 98902 #054-04-1987 L1990 **IM** *020 †20

DOORNINK, David Wm. 402 S 12TH AVE 98902 #054-04-1979 L1980 **IM** *020 †20

DRENGUIS, William Richard. 406 S 30TH AVE, STE 202 98902 #054-04-1978 L1982 **AN** *020 †20,05

DUFAULT, Anna Thompson. 3003 TIETON DR STE 240 98902 #054-04-2002 L2006 **OBG** *020
DULEK, Daniel Ervin. 602 E NOB HILL BLVD 98901 #028-02-2004 L2007 **PD** *020 †55
ECKLUND, Kirk T. 506 N 40TH AVE, STE 201 98908 #040-02-1984 L1995 **D** *020 †15
EDGAR, Craig William. 2801 TIETON DR, YAKIMA VALLEY MEMORIAL HOS 98902 #038-41-1999 L2003 **EM** *020 †16
EDWARDS, Amy Susanne. ■ 98903 #025-01-2001 L2007 **P** *100
EGAN, James Russell. ■ 98902 #018-03-1964 L1970 **OTO PS** *071 †45
EGLIN, Thomas Leroy. 2811 TIETON DR 98902 #012-05-1982 L1991 **EM** *020 †16
EHLERS, Richard Eugene, Jr. 3403 POWERHOUSE RD 98902 #001-02-1976 L1986 **OPH** *020 †55,35
EIDER, Wendy Roberta. 3902 CREEKSIDE LOOP, STE 120 98902 #028-02-1976 L1984 **RHU** *020 †20
ELLIOTT, William John. ■ 98908 #016-42-1979 L1981 **PA IM** *020 †20
ELLISON, Gerald Henry. 402 S 12TH AVE 98902 #005-12-1966 L1975 **FM** *020 †18
EL REFAIE, Moataz Abdel M. 918 E MEAD AVE 98903 #915-04-1991 L2004 **CHP** *020 †75
ENGELHARDT, Elizabeth Lee. 2811 TIETON DR, YAKIMA MEMORIAL HOSPITAL 98902 #028-02-1980 L1996 **NPM PD** *020 †55
ESCARCHA, Loraine Arambur. 102 S NACHES AVE 98901 #748-29-1987 L2005 **PD** *020 †55
FELDMANN, William Coulter. 314 S 11TH AVE, STE B 98902 #048-04-1989 L2001 **DR** *020 †80
FELIX, Hector Rene. 406 S 30TH AVE, STE 202 98902 #003-01-1985 L1992 **AN IM** *020 †05
FERRIN, Lance Jos. 5 S 14TH AVE 98902 #023-07-1987 L2003 **IM** *020 †20
FIGGS, George Wayne. ■ 98901 #019-02-1967 L1982 **OBG GS** *071 †30
FISCHER, Mary Frances. 111 S 11TH AVE, STE 220 98902 #016-43-1990 L2001 **AN PD** *020 †05,55
FOLEY, Kevin Patrick. 406 S 30TH AVE STE 201 98902 #016-02-1971 L1981 **CD IM** *020 †20
FORREST, William Morgan. 311 S 10TH AVE 98902 #054-04-1970 L1971 **OPH** *020 †35
FRANCE, Donald Geo. 406 S 30TH AVE, STE 202 98902 #030-06-1975 L1977 **AN** *020 †05
FUNK, Katherine. 306 HOLTON AVE 98902 #007-02-1980 L1983 **FM** *020 †18
GARCIA, Jose Luis. 1806 W LINCOLN AVE 98902 #275-04-1992 L2005 **FP** *012
GARFEIN, George Saml. 1015 S 40TH AVE, GEORGE S GARFEIN MD INC PS 98908 #035-15-1971 L1972 **GP** *072
GASKILL, Dennis Marvin. 111 S 11TH AVE, STE 124 98902 #005-12-1985 L1992 **U** *020 †95
GILMORE, Peter Clift. 111 S 11TH AVE, STE 321 98902 #010-03-1976 L1980 **N** *020 †75
GLADSON, Marina. 2811 TIETON DR 98902 #495-20-1984 L2003 **FM** *020 †18
GLENSKI, William Jan. 314 S 11TH AVE, STE B 98902 #026-08-1992 L2000 **VIR** *020 †80
GOECKLER, John Edward. ■ 98908 #041-02-1947 L1954 **ORS** *072 †40
GONDO, Roy Eiji. 306 S 12TH AVE STE 2 98902 #026-08-1992 L1997 **FM SME** *020 †18
GOSHIKE, Deepika Srinivas. 1806 W LINCOLN AVE, FAMILY MED 98902 #495-21-2002 L2006 **FP** *012
GOTTLIEB, Cornelius M. 2811 TIETON DR 98902 #660-01-1951 L1958 **NS** *071 †25
GOTTLIEB, Steven Errol. 602 E NOB HILL BLVD, YAKIMA VALLEY FARM WORKERS 98901 #024-01-1978 L1992 **PD PHP** *020 †55
GOULD, Debra Ann. 1806 W LINCOLN AVE 98902 #035-06-1987 L1990 **FM** *020 †18
GOUVEIA, Joseph Paul. 314 S 11TH AVE, STE B 98902 #003-01-1974 L1980 **DR** *020 †80
GREENBERG, Geoffrey M. 406 S 30TH AVE, STE 204 98902 #005-14-1978 L1979 **SME** *020 †20
GREENE, Robert Neal. 1211 N 16TH AVE 98902 #067-01-1990 L2006 *020 †40
GRIFFITHS, Gene Laren. ■ 98908 #028-34-1991 L2007 **ORS** *020 †40
GROSS, Rick D. 307 S 12TH AVE, YAKIMA MED CENTER 98902 #048-13-1990 L2007 **OTO FPS** *020 †45
GROW, Thomas Cogswell. 307 S 12TH AVE, STE 7 98902 #048-12-1969 L1974 **ORS** *020 †40
GRYTE, Glenn A. ■ 98901 #005-12-1953 L1979 **OBG** *020 †30
GUNN, Jack Matthew. 110 S 9TH AVE 98902 #039-01-1985 L2001 **AN** *020 †05
HA, Tony. 808 N 39TH AVE 98902 #583-10-1988 L1995 **HEM** *020 †20
HANSEN, Ross Draper. ■ 98902 #021-01-2005 L2005 **GS** *100
HARDY, Frank M, Jr. 412 S 12TH AVE 98902 #010-01-1945 L1946 **P** *071
HARRINGTON, John F. 3003 TIETON DR, STE 230 98902 #028-34-1953 L1954 **OBG** *020 †30
HARRINGTON, Kevin Michael. 3003 TIETON DR STE 230 98902 #054-04-1978 L1982 **OBG** *020 †30
HARRISON, Howard Francis. 2811 TIETON DR, MEMORIAL HOSPITAL 98902 #040-02-1973 L1997 **P FM** *020 †18,75
HARRISON, Karen M. 315 HOLTON AVE, STE 100 98902 #054-04-1987 L1989 **NEP IM** *020 †20
HART, Elmer E. ■ 98908 #005-12-1953 L1954 **GP** *072
HARTHCOCK, Kerry Alfred. 314 S 11TH AVE STE A, YAKIMA PEDIATRIC ASSOCIATE 98902 #048-14-1981 L1988 **PD NPM** *020 †55
HARTMAN, Bonnie. 1460 N 16TH AVE 98902 #016-01-1994 L1997 **CHP** *020 †75
HARVESON, Peter Kenneth. 602 E NOB HILL BLVD 98901 #041-13-1974 L1975 **FM** *020 †18
HARVEY, Judith Kathryn. 2811 TIETON DR 98902 #017-20-2000 L2002 **END OBS** *020 †18
HAUGE, Christopher W. 3003 TIETON DR STE 310 98902 #008-01-1964 L1973 **PS GS** *020 †85,65 ‡
HAUKE, Michael James. 2811 TIETON DR 98902 #017-20-1989 L2000 **EM** *020 †16
HAVEN, James Jay. 1211 N 16TH AVE 98902 #041-13-1964 L1971 **ORS** *020 †40
HEFLICK, Scott Kevin. 6201 SUMMITVIEW AVE, STE 106 98908 #054-04-1993 L1995 **FM** *020 †18
HEINZEN, Joel Chas. 110 S 9TH AVE 98902 #054-04-1974 L1975 **EM FM** *020 †18,16
HEMSTAD, Jan Ragnvald. ■ 98908 #054-04-1987 L1988 **AN** *020 †05
HENDERSON, John Michael. 314 S 11TH AVE, STE B 98902 #019-02-1977 L1982 **DR** *020 †80
HENDERSON, Marjorie Lynn. 110 S 9TH AVE, YAKIMA REGIONAL HOSPITAL 98902 #054-04-1980 L1981 **PM IM** *020 †20,60
HENDERSON, Phyllis Jo. ■ 98908 #005-12-1984 L1989 **P ADP** *020 †75
HENRETIG, Robert David. 314 S 11TH AVE, STE B 98902 #005-11-1968 L1977 **DR OS** *020 †80
HERR, Brent Leroy. 732 SUMMITVIEW AVE # 621, CENTRAL WA HOSPITALISTS 98902 #025-12-1993 L2006 **FM** *020 †18
HIBBS, Jonathan Russell. ■ 98902 #041-13-1984 L1985 **ID OS** *050 †20
HILL, A Sherman. 316 HOLTON AVE 98902 #038-06-1957 L1965 **IM OS** *071 †20
HILL, Donald Gary. 102 S NACHES AVE 98901 #025-07-1976 L1990 **FM** *020 †18
HOPP, Richard Hansen. 3999 ENGLEWOOD AVE, STE 101 98902 #028-34-1986 L1990 **OPH** *020 †35
HOROWITZ, Jay Lenard. 111 S 11TH AVE STE 220 98902 #021-05-1974 L1992 **AN** *020 †05
HOTCHKO, George J. 3003 TIETON DR, STE 320 98902 #039-01-1976 L1984 **IM** *020 †20
HOWRY, Cherie Lee Butts. ■ 98902 #054-04-1957 L1958 **PD OS** *030 †55
HWANG, John J. 1211 N 16TH AVE 98902 #023-07-1992 L1998 **ORS HS** *020 †40
IQBAL, Jawad. ■ 98908 #704-01-1993 L2004 **IM** *020 †20
ISAACS, Nancy Winifred. 210 S 11TH AVE 98902 #704-06-1955 L1986 **PM** *071
JABILE, James Jonathan Pa. 102 S NACHES AVE 98901 #748-02-1999 L2004 **PD** *020 †55
JACH, Michael Edward. 602 E NOB HILL BLVD, WORKERS CLINIC 98901 #056-05-1992 L1993 **FM** *020 †18
JACKSON, Caryn Lynette. 602 E NOB HILL BLVD 98901 #010-03-2002 L2005 **IM** *020
JENNINGS, Jeffrey Leon. 402 S 4TH AVE 98902 #036-05-1984 L1994 **P IMG** *020 †75
JEREZA, Daniel Valentin C. 2811 TIETON DR 98902 #748-14-1991 L2004 **FM** *020 †18
JOECKEL, Sara H. 1701 CREEKSIDE LOOP # 120, CREEKSIDE BUSINESS PARK 98902 #025-07-1992 L1998 **D** *020 †15
JOHNS, Jonathan Paul. 3003 TIETON DR, STE 200 98902 #041-12-1998 L2004 **OBG** *020 †30
JOHNSON, Robert Emery. 2811 TIETON DR, DEPT EM 98902 #041-15-1999 L2002 **EM** *020 †16
JONES, Portia Dian. 1806 W LINCOLN AVE 98902 #026-04-1988 L2005 **FM AMF** *040 †18
JONES, Vicky Eileen. 808 N 39TH AVE 98902 #018-03-1983 L2002 **HEM ON** *020 †20
JORGENSEN, Maria Janice. 808 N 39TH AVE 98902 #024-07-1989 L1989 **HEM IM** *020 †20
JOY, Mark Walter. 732 SUMMITVIEW AVE # 621, CENTRAL WA HOSPITALISTS 98902 #040-02-1993 L2006 **FM** *020 †18
JUSTICE, Wade Wm. 314 S 11TH AVE BS, YAKIMA VALLEY RAD P.C. 98902 #003-01-1989 L1996 **DR** *020 †80
KANU, Ernest Oji. 602 E NOB HILL BLVD 98901 #690-07-1985 L2004 **IM** *020 ‡
KAPLAN, Jeffrey Stewart. 504 N 40TH AVE 98908 #041-01-1986 L1989 **FM** *020 †18
KATZ, Ross Alan. 406 S 30TH AVE, STE 202 98902 #005-06-1982 L1983 **AN** *020 †05
KENNEDY, Thomas Campbell. 1211 N 16TH AVE 98902 #028-02-1984 L1990 **ORS OSM** *020 †40
KERNS, Thomas Franklin. 215 S 11TH AVE, STE E 98902 #025-01-1954 L1960 **OPH** *071
KERR, Elton Robt. 3911 CASTLEVALE RD STE 301, CASCADE WOMENS HEALTHCARE 98902 #005-12-1976 L2005 **OBG U** *020 †30
KHANWANI, Suneeta. 1806 W LINCOLN AVE 98902 #704-18-1996 L2007 **FM** *100
KIM, Anatole Sung. 406 S 30TH AVE, STE 201 98902 #043-01-1984 L2002 **NM** *020 †20,28
KIM, Elizabeth Akiyama. ■ 98908 #025-01-1989 L1990 **PTH** *020 †50
KINI, Jayanth. 2811 TIETON DR 98902 #495-59-1973 L2000 **PTH** *020 †50
KIRSCHNER, Nora Brigitta. 402 S 12TH AVE, CORNERSTONE MEDICAL CLINIC 98902 #010-02-1988 L2005 **IM** *020 †20
KISALA, John Michael. 3003 TIETON DR, STE 300 98902 #016-11-1981 L2004 **CCM** *020 †85
KITE, Robert Bruce. 1470 N 16TH AVE 98902 #060-01-1997 L1999 *020
KOKENGE, Roy Francis. ■ 98908 #054-04-1960 L1963 **N** *071 †75
KRAUTH, Robert James. 504 N 40TH AVE 98908 #003-01-1998 L2000 **FM** *020 †18
KRISHNAMANI, Kavitha. 1806 W LINCOLN AVE 98902 #495-04-2001 L2007 **FM** *100 †18
KRUEGER, David Wm. 406 S 30TH AVE STE 201 98902 #054-04-1984 L1986 **CD** *020 †20
KWOK, Clark Tuan. 1806 W LINCOLN AVE, DEPT OF FAMILY MED 98902 #654-01-2006 L2007 **FP** *012
KWON, Daniel Myung. 1470 N 16TH AVE, DESERT PAIN CARE 98902 #005-12-2001 L2002 **PM PMM** *020 †60
LABES, Silvia. 402 S 12TH AVE 98902 #781-01-1995 L2000 **IM** *020 †20
LAGUERRE-SIMON, Kerby. 1806 W LINCOLN AVE, CENTRAL WASHINGTON 98902 #665-02-2007 *100
LAM, Teresa Hongchen. 1806 W LINCOLN AVE 98902 #243-76-1993 L2006 **FP** *012
LANG, Gary Carl. 314 S 11TH AVE STE A, YAKIMA PEDIATRIC ASSOC INC 98902 #035-03-1971 L1990 **PD** *020 †55
LANGE, Jan E. 1020 S 40TH AVE STE C 98908 #539-06-1977 L1978 **FM** *020 †18
LARSON, Kristin Ileen. 1020 S 40TH AVE, STE C 98908 #041-14-2001 L2003 **FM** *020 †18
LASCAR, Gabriel. 402 S 12TH AVE 98902 #781-01-1995 L2000 **IM** *020 †20
LASCAR, Laurentia D. 402 S 12TH AVE 98902 #781-01-1997 L2004 **IM** *020 †20
LASCAR, Mihai. 402 S 12TH AVE 98902 #781-01-1998 L2004 **IM** *020 †20
LAUFER, Andres. ■ 98903 #935-01-2002 L2007 **IM** *020
LEMP, Rolf Wm. ■ 98908 #041-02-1963 L2002 **P FM** *020 †18
LEWIS, Karsten Conley. 808 N 39TH AVE 98902 #054-04-1961 L1968 **IM** *071
LI, Abel W. 311 S 10TH AVE 98902 #048-14-1993 L2000 **OPH** *020 †35
LICHT, Jeffrey Hamilton. 315 HOLTON AVE, STE 100 98902 #016-11-1973 L1984 **NEP IM** *020 †20
LIEBE, Diane Elizabeth. 3801 KERN WAY, CHILDRENS VILLAGE 98902 #035-15-1988 L1991 **PD** *020 †55
LINDGREN, David Aaron. 1806 W LINCOLN AVE, DEPT OF FAMILY MEDICINE 98902 #422-01-2007 L2007 **FP** *012
LINDSTROM, James Edward. 1111 W SPRUCE ST STE 32 98902 #054-04-1981 L1986 **FM** *020 †18
LIU, George Su. 1211 N 16TH AVE, ORTHOPEDICS NORTHWEST 98902 #024-01-1995 L2003 **ORS** *020 †40
LIVINGSTON, Mark Wesley. 2811 TIETON DR, YAKIMA VALLEY MEMORIAL HOS 98902 #031-01-1998 L2001 **EM** *020 †16
LOVERN, Walter Jackson. 111 S 11TH AVE STE 120 98902 #040-02-1970 L1975 **U** *020 †95
LOZANO, Manuel Leonardo. 111 S 11TH AVE, STE 223 98902 #018-03-2001 L2006 **GS** *020
LYOU-KIM, Chung Hi. 402 S 4TH AVE 98902 #583-03-1952 L2003 **P** *020 †75 ‡
LYPCHUK, Lauren Carol. 504 N 40TH AVE, FAMILY MEDICINE OF YAKIMA 98908 #061-01-1992 L1994 **FM** *020 †18
MAIER, Russell Glenn. 1806 W LINCOLN AVE, CNTRL WASHINGTON FMLY MED 98902 #054-04-1988 L1989 **FM** *040 †18
MAIOCCO, Mark Anthony. 2501 BUSINESS LN 98901 #054-04-1994 L1997 **FM** *020 †18
MANDZUIK, Michael John. 2811 TIETON DR 98902 #550-04-2004 L2005 **FP** *012
MAPLES, Michael Wm. 1806 W LINCOLN AVE 98902 #054-04-1980 L1981 **FM** *020 †18
MARLEY, David E, Jr. 314 S 11TH AVE 98902 #001-02-1966 L1976 **R** *020 †80
MARQUEZ, Lydia D. ■ 98908 #748-01-1968 L1982 **P** *020
MARTINEZ ROCHA, Rosa M. 1111 W SPRUCE ST STE 26 98902 #649-03-1975 L1993 **IM IMG** *020
MASI, Jose Domingo. 1120 W SPRUCE ST 98902 #726-01-1974 L1986 **PTH** *020 †50
MATHER, Robert W. ■ 98908 #041-13-1945 L1953 **OPH** *071 †35
MATUS, Ismael Arturo. 303 HOLTON AVE 98902 #270-02-1997 L2005 **PCC** *020 †20
MC CARTNEY, Harold Hugh. 1120 W SPRUCE ST 98902 #028-34-1971 L1979 **PTH** *020 †50
MC CONNELL, Edward B, Jr. ■ 98903 #041-01-1982 L1988 **IM** *020 †20
MC DONNELL, Thomas Robt. ■ 98901 #025-07-1964 L1968 **FM** *071
MC FARLANE, Claude Lee. 110 S 9TH AVE 98902 #054-04-1963 L1977 **OM EM** *071 †70,16
MC GALLIARD, Lesley Jane. 2811 TIETON DR 98902 #054-04-1977 L1979 **FM OBS** *020 †18
MC LAUGHLIN, Chester S. 622 S 36TH AVE 98902 #041-09-1960 L1979 **ORS** *020 †40
MC LAUGHLIN, Ralph Thos. 406 S 30TH AVE, STE 201 98902 #030-06-1987 L1993 **CD** *020 †20
MELHORN, Timothy Lewis. 402 S 12TH AVE 98902 #054-04-1974 L1977 **IM PUD** *020 †20
MENASHE, Phillip Isaac. 303 HOLTON AVE 98902 #054-04-1980 L1981 **PUD CCM** *030 †20
MERRELL, Raymond Weldon. 111 S 11TH AVE STE 120 98902 #041-02-1974 L1980 **U** *020 †95
MILLER, Erik Chas. 2811 TIETON DR, YAKIMA MEMORIAL HOSPITAL 98902 #054-04-1991 L1993 **EM** *020 †16
MILLER, Steven Chas. 2811 TIETON DR 98902 #030-05-1977 L1979 **GS** *075

■ = Address Information Privacy Protected

MOLFINO, Chie Morooka. 1806 W LINCOLN AVE 98902 #572-21-1993 L2005 **FM** *100
MONAHAN, Sarah Kathleen. 210 S 11TH AVE 98902 #054-04-1992 L1996 **OBG** *020 †30
MONICK, Duane Allen. 406 S 30TH AVE STE 201 98902 #018-03-1972 L1976 **CD IM** *020 †20
MONTGOMERY, Frederick A. 306 S 12TH AVE 98902 #030-06-1965 L1966 **P ADM** *020 †75
MORRISON, Douglas Andrew. 406 S 30TH AVE, YAKIMA HEART CTR 98902 #041-12-1973 L1978 **CD IM** *040 †20
MOSS, Norman Wm. 215 S 11TH AVE STE D 98902 #054-04-1958 L1962 **FM AM** *020 †18
MUEHLECK, Stephen D. 1120 W SPRUCE ST 98902 #040-02-1979 L1983 **PTH** *062 †50
MURPHY, Michael John. 1005 W WALNUT ST, STE 101 98902 #054-04-1967 L1973 **OTO A** *020 †45
MURRAY, Michele Lynn. ■ 98908 #026-04-1983 L1990 **DR** *020 †80
NAIDEN, Norman John. 2205 W LINCOLN AVE, FAMILY HEALTH NETWORK 98902 #054-04-1971 L1973 **OBG** *020 †30
NATHE, Tyler Joseph. ■ 98908 #054-04-2006 L2007 **ORS** *012
NESLAND, Robert Stanley. 206 S 11TH AVE STE 48, CWOM 98902 #054-04-1965 L1966 **EM OM** *020 †16
NEVIL, Keven John. 3003 TIETON DR STE 200, HEALTH PLLC 98902 #305-01-1998 L2003 **OBG** *020 †30
NEWSTEAD, Robert Richard. 206 S 11TH AVE # 48 98902 #016-43-1963 L1971 **U** *071 †95
NWOGU, Esther Nnenna. 1806 W LINCOLN AVE, DEPT OF FAMILY MEDICINE 98902 #690-12-1999 L2007 **FP** *012
O'BRIEN, Patrick Ralph. ■ 98902 #036-01-1995 L2004 **DR** *020 †80
O'DONNELL, Shawn Michael. 2205 W LINCOLN AVE 98902 #539-03-1992 L1998 **FM** *020 †18
OLDEN, Carl Raymond. 311 S 72ND AVE, PACIFIC CREST FAMILY MEDIC 98908 #054-04-1981 L1984 **FM FPG** *020 †18
OLSON, David Grant. 206 S 11TH AVE, STE 48 98902 #026-04-1971 L1976 **EM OM** *020 †16
ONG, Gilbert Ko. ■ 98903 #748-01-1997 L2006 **GE** *020 †20
ONSTAD, John Wynn. 110 S 9TH AVE 98902 #054-04-1971 L1975 **PTH** *020 †50
ORTIZ, Robert Andrew. 406 S 30TH AVE, STE 201 98902 #005-14-1987 L1997 **IM CD** *020 †20
ORVALD, Thomas Owen. 1005 W WALNUT ST STE 203 98902 #041-09-1960 L1977 **TS** *020 †85,90
ORVALD, Todd Busse. 1211 N 16TH AVE 98902 #041-02-1971 L1981 **ORS OS** *020 †40
OSAMA, Fauzia Khalida. 611 N 39TH AVE, QUALITY CARE MEDICAL CLINI 98902 #495-77-1991 L2006 **IM** *020 †20
OVERAND, Patrick Timothy. 110 S 9TH AVE, YAKIMA REGIONAL MEDICAL CT 98902 #040-02-1982 L1986 **AN** *020 †05
PADAVICH, Craig Anthony. 406 S 30TH AVE, STE 202 98902 #054-04-1983 L1984 **AN** *030 †05
PADILLA, Robert Brian. 8302 SCENIC DR 98908 #049-01-1998 L2001 **EM** *020 †16
PAK, Daniel. 8702 MIDVALE RD 98908 #010-02-1991 L2005 **DR** *020 †80
PALESCH, Raymond John. 213 S 11TH AVE 98902 #016-43-1969 L1976 **ORS** *020 †40
PALMATIER, Theodore Harry. 409 S 12TH AVE, YAKIMA WORKER CARE, PLLC 98902 #020-02-1970 L1971 **OM** *020 †18,16
PAN, Sheau-Fang. 1806 W LINCOLN AVE, CENTRAL WA FAMILY MEDICINE 98902 #035-08-2006 L2006 **FP** *012
PANDOLFI, Gonzalo. 3909 CREEKSIDE LOOP STE 13 98902 #649-14-1998 L2005 **IM** *020 †20
PATTERSON, Alan Eugene. ■ 98908 #038-40-1963 L1970 **ORS** *020 †40
PEARSON, Stephen James. 1806 W LINCOLN AVE 98902 #008-01-1983 L1989 **PD** *020 †55
PEDROSA, Jocelyn. 102 S NACHES AVE 98901 #748-02-1991 L1995 **PD** *020 †55
PEHLKE, D Michael. 1111 W SPRUCE ST STE 24, YAKIMA DERM/SKIN SURG CTR 98902 #036-07-1972 L1976 **D PHL** *020 †20,15
PELLICER, Joseph Geo. 602 E NOB HILL BLVD 98901 #016-43-1955 L1968 **GP** *071 †18
PELLICER, Mary Clare. 732 SUMMITVIEW AVE, # 566 98902 #054-04-1987 L1990 **OS** *030 †18
PERRY, Thomas Linwood. ■ 98908 #051-01-1967 L1969 **D** *020 †15
PETERSON, Carl Victor. 406 S 30TH AVE, STE 202 98902 #054-04-1990 L1993 **AN** *020 †20,05
PETERSON, Daniel Robt. 302 S 10TH AVE, STE 202 98902 #040-02-1977 L1980 **IM** *020 †20
PETZINGER, George L. 918 E MEAD AVE, YAKIMA VALLEY FARMWORKERS 98903 #028-34-1995 L2000 **CHP** *020 †75
PHAM, By Jayduy. 102 S NACHES AVE 98901 #054-04-2000 L2002 **FM** *020 †18
PIERSON, Roy Saml. 1470 N 16TH AVE 98902 #023-12-1983 L2005 **ORS** *020 †40
PLACE, John Shandon. 3907 CREEKSIDE LOOP, STE 100 98902 #048-04-1965 L1971 **ORS** *020 †40
POLAGE, David Louis. 314 S 11TH AVE STE A, YAKIMA PEDIATRIC ASSO INC 98902 #028-02-1966 L1972 **PD** *071 †55
POMMER, David Arthur. 402 S 12TH AVE 98902 #054-04-2000 L2003 **FM** *020 †18 ‡
PREACHER, Abner B, Jr. 406 S 30TH AVE, STE 201 98902 #045-01-1967 L1975 **CD** *020 †20
PRESSLEY, Richard La Marr. 215 S 11TH AVE, STE A 98902 #036-01-1963 L1994 **NS** *071 †25
QUAVE, Brett Tyler. 1470 N 16TH AVE, 16TH AVENUE STATION 98902 #005-12-1999 L2007 **APM** *020 †05
RAMAKRISHNAN, Amarnath V. 3909 CREEKSIDE LOOP STE 12 98902 #496-23-1994 L2003 **GE** *020 †20
RANA, Ankur Madhukar. 1806 W LINCOLN AVE, CENTRAL WASHINGTON 98902 #913-12-2001 *100
REINMUTH, Karl Scott. 2811 TIETON DR 98902 #054-04-1997 L2000 **FM** *020 †18
REINSTEIN, Lila May. 602 E NOB HILL BLVD, YAKIMA VALLEY FARM WORKERS 98901 #040-02-1988 L1991 **OBG** *020
RIVERO, Jacobo Alejandro. 1806 W LINCOLN AVE, CENTRAL WASH. FAMILY MEDIC 98902 #649-40-1985 L1995 **FM** *020 †18
ROBERTSON, Julia K. 2501 BUSINESS LN, PROVIDENCE TER HTS MED CLN 98901 #048-14-1984 L1993 **FM** *020 †18
ROBINSON, Justin Andrew. 111 S 11TH AVE, STE 223 98902 #054-04-1980 L1988 **VS GS** *020 †85
ROBINSON, William Wayne. 1111 W YAKIMA AVE 98902 #005-12-1960 L1972 **FM** *020 †18
RODENBERGER, Philip Drew. 402 S 4TH AVE 98902 #041-01-1970 L2005 **P** *030 †75
ROESLER, Stephen Paul. 111 S 11TH AVE 98902 #005-12-1982 L2006 **ORS** *020 †40
ROMNEY, Douglas. 2811 TIETON DR 98902 #035-45-1950 L1958 **GS CD** *071 †85
ROULSTON, George S. ■ 98901 #018-75-1954, ▲ L1955 **GP CD** *071
ROUX, Richard Douglas. 1211 N 16TH AVE 98902 #005-18-1983 L1990 **ORS** *020 †40
ROWLES, Roger Barrett. 3003 TIETON DR STE 240 98902 #054-04-1972 L1979 **OBG** *020 †30
ROZELLE, Brent Crocker. 1111 W SPRUCE ST, STE 32 98902 #049-01-1971 L1981 **GS AN** *020 †05
RUDD, Theodore Hubert. 3911 CASTLEVALE RD, STE 301 98902 #054-04-1963 L1965 **OBG** *020 †30
RUDE, J Donald. ■ 98901 #040-02-1954 L1958 **GS GP** *071 †85
RYDER, Amanda Gail. 110 S 9TH AVE 98902 #032-01-1995 L1998 **FM** *020 †18
SABRY, Fady Fayez. 102 S NACHES AVE 98901 #915-09-1980 L2006 **IM** *020 †20
SACKMANN, Richard Ruben. 2811 TIETON DR 98902 #040-02-1947 L1948 **AN** *071 †05
SAWYER, Gregory Dean. 2811 TIETON DR, PSYCH 1 NORTH 98902 #005-06-1980 L1988 **P PYA** *030 †75
SCHEFTER, Robert Paul, Jr. 1005 W WALNUT ST STE 101 98902 #030-06-1979 L1984 **OTO A** *020 †45
SCHMELZER, Christopher R. ■ 98902 #056-06-2001 L2007 **EM** *020 †16
SCHNADER, Dagmar Anne. 2205 W LINCOLN AVE, LINCOLN AVENUE MEDICAL CEN 98902 #028-34-1984 L1990 **PD** *020 †55
SCHULTZ, Jonathan. 2811 TIETON DR 98902 #043-01-1978 L1991 **EM FM** *020 †18
SCHWAEGLER, Lester John. 111 S 11TH AVE STE 223 98902 #028-34-1957 L1964 **GS** *071 †85
SCOTVOLD, Marvin Jos. 111 N PEAR AVE 98908 #054-04-1963 L1966 **D PD** *020 †55,15
SELTZER, Shalom Danl. 622 S 36TH AVE 98902 #010-01-1972 L2005 **ORS** *020 †40
SHAH, Vivek Kanubhai. 102 S NACHES AVE 98901 #496-41-1993 L2001 **IM** *020 †20
SHARMA, Baljit K. 602 N 39TH AVE, STE 200 98902 #495-73-1977 L1994 **TS VS** *020 †85,90
SHARPE, Victor Vivian, III. 402 S 12TH AVE 98902 #011-02-1979 L1988 **IM** *020 †20
SHAUL, Stephen Richard. 1111 W SPRUCE ST STE 28 98902 #035-20-1969 L1970 **RHU IM** *020 †20
SHIVELY, Marilee. ■ 98902 #040-02-1981 L1988 **PD** *075 †55
SHIVELY, Norman Paul. 111 S 11TH AVE, STE 120 98902 #040-02-1981 L1988 **U** *020 †95
SHOEMAKER, Stacy D. 1470 N 16TH AVE, SPINECARE MEDICAL GROUP 98902 #067-01-1997 L1999 **PM** *020 †60
SIMMONS, Jamie Elizabeth. 2811 TIETON DR, PSYCHIATRIC SERVICES 98902 #005-12-1998 L2002 **P** *020 †75
SIMMS, Roy James, Jr. 314 S 11TH AVE, STE A 98902 #001-02-1977 L1978 **PD** *020 †55
SINGEL, Soren A. 111 S 11TH AVE, STE 321 98902 #409-33-1993 L2005 **NS** *020
SINGH, Pragati. ■ 98908 #496-07-1996 L2007 **IMG** *020 †20
SKARIN, Robert Mark. 2811 TIETON DR 98902 #036-07-1974 L1977 **NPM PD** *020 †55
SKINNER, H Harlow, Jr. ■ 98908 #038-06-1945 L1951 **GS CRS** *071 †85
SLOOP, Jay. 307 S 12TH AVE, BONNY ALKOFER ARNP 98902 #005-12-1960 L1965 **OBG** *072 †30
SLOOP, Raymond Richard. 307 S 12TH AVE STE 16 98902 #005-12-1986 L1991 **N IM** *020 †75
SMALLEY, Katherine Ann. 1806 W LINCOLN AVE 98902 #047-06-2001 L2001 **IM** *100
SMIGAJ, Diana. 3911 CASTLEVALE RD, STE 301 98902 #048-02-1989 L1995 **OBG** *020 †30
SNYDER, Mark A. 602 N 39TH AVE, STE 200 98902 #016-02-1960 L1970 **TS** *020 †85,90
SNYDER, Raymond Paul. 1211 N 16TH AVE 98902 #048-04-1986 L1988 **FM FSM** *020 †18
SOHREN, Laura Ann. ■ 98908 #028-02-2004 L2007 **EM** *100
SONG, Kit M. 3801 KERN WAY 98902 #018-03-1985 L1995 **ORS GS** *020 †40
SPIEGEL, Richard Kerr. 406 S 30TH AVE STE 201 98902 #018-03-1976 L1981 **CD IM** *020 †20 ‡
SPRINGEL, Ronald David. ■ 98902 #041-02-1978 L1986 **OM ADM** *075
STASIUK, Jan M. 406 S 30TH AVE, STE 202 98902 #047-05-1989 L1997 **AN** *020 †05
STEPANEK, David C. 314 S 11TH AVE, STE B 98902 #016-11-1976 L1981 **DR** *020 †80
STODDARD, Rodney Garret. 111 S 11TH AVE, YAKIMA AMBULATORY SURGERY 98902 #030-06-1988 L1991 **AN** *020 †05
SWARTZ, Bernard Louis. 3003 TIETON DR, STE 330 98902 #038-41-1973 L2003 **PS** *020 †65
SZIEBERT, Leslie Andrew. 2003 EVERGREEN CT 98902 #048-02-1984 L1989 **P** *020 †75
TANWANI, Tekchand. 111 S 11TH AVE, STE 223 98902 #704-16-1986 L1997 **CCS** *020 †85
TARIQUE, Ahmed. 611 N 39TH AVE, QUALITY CARE MEDICAL CLINI 98902 #496-16-1991 L2005 **IM** *020
TAYLOR, Michael Alan. 506 N 40TH AVE, STE 100 98908 #017-20-1961 L1963 **OPH** *020 †35
TOMPKINS, Paul Arthur. 402 S 12TH AVE 98902 #039-05-1990 L2001 **MPD PD** *020 †55,20
TREECE, Gary Lee. 209 S 12TH AVE 98902 #005-15-1971 L1985 **END IM** *020 †20
TUFAIL, Fawad Aslam. 611 N 39TH AVE, QUALITY CARE MEDICAL CLINI 98902 #704-20-1994 L2003 **IM** *020
TWISS, Richard Davis. 406 S 30TH AVE STE 201 98902 #054-04-1960 L1966 **CD IM** *020 †20
UBER, Ralph Leroy. ■ 98908 #041-13-1945 L1950 **IM OS** *071
UDELL, Mindy A. 1806 W LINCOLN AVE, CENTRAL WA FAMILY MEDICINE 98902 #054-04-2006 L2006 **FP** *012
UHLMAN, Mark Scott. 111 S 11TH AVE STE 120, YAKIMA UROLOGY ASSOCIATES, 98902 #018-03-1981 L1985 **U** *020 †95
ULLOM, Josephine Hemphill. ■ 98902 #048-14-1986 L1996 **IM** *074 †20
URRUTIA, Luis Ernesto. 3800 SUMMITVIEW AVE, ATTENTION: CREDENTIALING 98902 #270-02-1995 L2004 **CCM** *020 †20
UWAOMA, Ugochukwu E. 602 E NOB HILL BLVD, CLINIC 98901 #690-04-1992 L2000 **IM** *020 †20 ‡
VALENCIA, Saul. 1806 W LINCOLN AVE, CENTRAL WA FAMILY MEDICINE 98902 #054-04-2006 L2006 **FP** *012
VARNAVAS, Gus Geo. 3003 TIETON DR, STE 210 98902 #023-12-1990 L2007 **NS** *020 †25
VATHESATOGKIT, Pratan. 303 HOLTON AVE STE 1 98902 #891-04-1996 L2003 **PCC** *020 †20
VIELBIG, Roger E. 406 S 30TH AVE STE 201 98902 #035-08-1973 L1982 **CD IM** *020 †20
VLAHAKIS, George John, Jr. 1460 N 16TH AVE STE G 98902 #056-05-1970 L1975 **P** *020 †75
VON STUBBE, Wm Frederick. 808 N 39TH AVE 98902 #054-04-1965 L1969 **ON IM** *020 †20
VORENKAMP, Richard James. 5 S 14TH AVE 98902 #025-01-1960 L1967 **OPH** *071 †35
WAARVICK, Kim Jonathan. 504 N 40TH AVE 98908 #054-04-2002 L2002 **FM** *020 †18
WABER, Patrick Richard. 1020 S 40TH AVE STE A, APPLE VALLEY FAMILY MEDICI 98908 #030-06-1994 L1996 **FM** *020 †18
WALKER, Jeffrey Scott. 3003 TIETON DR, STE 210 98902 #048-14-1979 L2006 **NS** *020 †25
WAMBUZI, Selemani Ernest. 2811 TIETON DR 98902 #965-01-2000 **FM** *100
WELTY, James. ■ 98901 #055-01-2007 **TY** *012
WEY, John Jos. 402 S 4TH AVE, MENTAL HEALTH 98902 #038-45-1986 L1989 **CHP P** *020 †75
WILLIAMS, Charles Donald. 402 E YAKIMA AVE STE 330 98901 #054-04-1973 L1974 **CHP P** *020 †75
WILLIAMS, David Wilson. 2811 TIETON DR 98902 #040-02-1952 L1956 **GE IM** *071
WILLIAMS, Donald K. 111 S 11TH AVE STE 223 98902 #016-06-1952 L1953 **GS** *072 †85
WILLIAMS, Robt Mac Learn. 302 S 10TH AVE 98902 #005-18-1980 L1987 **GE** *020 †20
WILSON, William Gauld. 2811 TIETON DR, YAKIMA VALLEY MEMORIAL HOS 98902 #067-01-1986 L1986 **EM** *020
WISELEY, Thomas Gordon. 1120 W SPRUCE ST 98902 #030-06-1976 L1980 **PTH** *030 †50
WOLF, John Arthur, Jr. 110 S 9TH AVE, PROVIDENCE MED CTR REHAB 98902 #054-04-1961 L1963 **U** *072 †95
WON, Alvina. 111 S 11TH AVE STE 22 98902 #005-18-1997 L2006 **GS TS** *020
WOOD, David L. ■ 98902 #048-02-1989 L1991 **FM** *075
WREDE-SEAMAN, Linda D. 2811 TIETON DR 98902 #020-12-1981 L1989 **FM** *020 †16,18
WRIGHT, Gregory Alan. ■ 98908 #023-12-1993 L2007 **DR** *100 †80
YEVERINO-FLORES, Jaime G. 5808 SUMMITVIEW AVE # 55 98908 #649-14-1982 L1994 **IM** *020 †20
YOUNG, Peter Russell, Jr. 3003 TIETON DR, STE 300 98902 #036-01-1992 L2000 **GS** *020 †85

YOUNGSTROM, Carl Evert. ■ 98908 #067-01-1971 L1975 **GS** *071 †85
ZAKHARY, Rafat Reed. 1460 N 16TH AVE STE G 98902 #915-03-1979 L1990 **CHP P** *020
ZAKY, Maged Monir. 209 S 12TH AVE, CENTRAL WA INTERNAL MEDICI 98902 #915-03-1984 L2004 **IM** *020 ‡
ZIMMERMAN, James E. 3170 NACHES HEIGHTS RD # 3 98908 #040-02-1945 L1946 **GP** *071
ZULAUF, David R. 314 S 11TH AVE STE B 98902 #054-04-1983 L1988 **DR VIR** *020 †80

YARROW POINT – KING

ANDERSON, Arthur Melvin. ■ 98004 #054-04-1954 L1957 **CD AM** *071 †20
CHUNG, Gakyung. ■ 98004 #024-01-1991 L2005 **GS** *020 †85
FREEMAN, Melvin Irwin. ■ 98004 #054-04-1960 L1969 **OPH** *071 †35 ‡
ROBINS, Anthony John. 4241 92ND AVE NE 98004 #054-04-1985 L1992 **ORS GS** *071 †40
WHITING, Adolph M. 9040 POINTS DR NE 98004 #026-04-1946 L1952 **P** *072 †75

YELM – THURSTON

ANANDASAKARAN, Rathidevi. ■ 98597 #220-02-1971 L1999 **AN EM** *020
AROCHO, Milagros I. ■ 98597 #042-03-1988 L2006 **OBG** *020

BUNN, Tamara Camis. 202 CULLENS ST NW, YELM FAMILY MEDICINE 98597 #005-12-1999 L2002 **FM** *020 †18
CRANTON, Elmer Mitchell. 503 1ST ST S, STE 1 98597 #024-01-1964 L1989 **FM A** *020 †18
DORHAUER, Cheri Marie. 202 CULLENS ST NW, YELM FAMILY MEDICINE 98597 #030-06-2002 L2004 **FM** *020 †18
KEAY, Brian Donald. 313 W YELM AVE 98597 #025-07-1977 L1991 **PUD IM** *020 †20
LINDSAY, Laura Marie. 202 CULLENS ST NW, YELM FAMILY MEDICINE 98597 #054-04-1999 L2002 **FM** *020 †18
MARCUM, Rodd Everett. ■ 98597 #023-12-2002 L2004 **IM** *020 †20
MYE, George Lai. ■ 98597 #035-06-1955 L1990 **GS** *071 †85
OWEN, Grace Miele. ■ 98597 #054-04-1982 L1988 **PD** *071 †55
PENN, William Jared. 202 CULLENS ST NW, YELM FAMILY MEDICINE 98597 #016-42-1978 L1982 **FM ORS** *020 †16 ‡
SESSOMS, Rose Marie. ■ 98597 #008-01-1975 L1992 **OM FM** *020 †18
SMITH, Jewel Nadine. ■ 98597 #030-06-1975 L2002 **OBG** *020

ZILLAH – YAKIMA

FORTIN, Anna Lynn. ■ 98953 #054-04-2008 *012
HOFFMEISTER, Rex Todd. ■ 98953 #030-05-1955 L1962 **RHU IM** *071 †20
JAMES, Freburn L. ■ 98953 #005-12-1949 L1970 **PTH** *072 †50 ‡
SHEARER, Frank Wm. ■ 98953 #005-12-1933 L1933 **IMG** *071

ALBRIGHT – PRESTON

NESTOR, Jennings Elliott. ■ 26519 #055-01-2008 *012

ALDERSON – GREENBRIER

GLASER, Marilyn Knoll. PO BOX 680 24910 #041-07-1983 L1987 FM *020 ‡

ALLOY – FAYETTE

STANLEY, Vernon Ray. ROUTE 60 E, VALLEY EMER MED SERVICE 25002 #051-01-1974 L1975 EM *020

APPLE GROVE – MASON

MC GINNIS, Michael Jon. 329 MOSS RD, BOX 5 25502 #055-01-1969 L1975 GP *020

AURORA – PRESTON

FOY, Andrew Miles. ■ 26705 #055-01-2002 L2005 FM *020 †18

BAKER – HARDY

RISING, James L. PO BOX 97 26801 #016-11-1990 L2001 UCM AM *020

BARBOURSVILLE – CABELL

BAILES, James R, Jr. 659 CENTRAL AVE 25504 #055-02-1990 L1994 PD *020 †55
BANNISTER, Tammy Lynn. 659 CENTRAL AVE 25504 #055-02-1994 L1996 FM *020 †18
BOUKHEMIS, Rabah. 659 CENTRAL AVE 25504 #125-03-1977 L1990 PM GP *020
CONSTANTINO, Francisco A. 5960 US ROUTE 60 E 25504 #748-01-1963 L1975 GP GS *020
DIAZ, Antonio R, Jr. 5960 US ROUTE 60 E, STE 2 25504 #748-01-1973 L1992 P *020
DUNDERVILL, Robert Frank. 2 CHATEAU GROVE LN 25504 #051-04-1990 L1995 OPH *020 †35
GIBBS, Michael Warren. 100 MEADOW POINTE 25504 #055-02-1989 L1990 FM FSM *040 †18
GROSS, Donald Andrew. ■ 25504 #665-01-2000 L2005 AN *020 ‡
HADDOX, Theodore Prescott. 659 CENTRAL AVE 25504 #055-01-1969 L1978 OBG *020 †30
HADI-SADEGH, Hossein. 659 CENTRAL AVE 25504 #517-01-1965 L1976 TS CD *020 †85,90
HARRIS, Matthew Wayne. 4 CHATEAU LN 25504 #025-07-1987 L1992 IM PD *020 †20,55
HATFIELD, R Mark. 2 CHATEAU GROVE LN 25504 #055-02-1983 L1984 OPH *020 †35
HAYAT, Murtaza. 723 MERRITT ST 25504 #704-02-1999 L2006 IM *020 †20
HOLMES, Allen Jason. ■ 25504 #055-02-2003 L2006 EM *020 †16
HUGHES, Jamie Leigh. ■ 25504 #055-01-1994 L1996 PTH PCP *020 †50
HUNT, David John. 2 CHATEAU GROVE LN 25504 #055-02-1995 L2000 OPH *020
JONES, James William. ■ 25504 #055-02-2005 L2005 AN *012
KHAN, Mehr Amjad. ■ 25504 #704-02-2002 L2007 IMG *100
KHOKAR, Amira Idrees. ■ 25504 #055-01-2006 PD *012
LEPPLA, David Chas. 659 CENTRAL AVE 25504 #007-02-1979 L1985 PTH *071 †50
LOVEJOY, Uel Clinton. ■ 25504 #051-04-1937 L1938 GP *071
MARCUZZI, Mary Lynn. 100 MEADOW POINTE 25504 #055-02-1997 L1998 FM *020 †18
MARPLE, William Kessler. ■ 25504 #038-41-1945 L1950 OTO OPH *071
MULLINS, George Roy. ■ 25504 #023-01-1942 L1946 OPH *071
NAIR, Dilip. 659 CENTRAL AVE 25504 #008-02-1992 L1993 FM *040 †18
NAIR, Laurie Bennett. 659 CENTRAL AVE 25504 #008-02-1992 L1993 FM *020 †18
NEWBERRY, Michael Shane. ■ 25504 #055-02-2008 *012
NUTTER, Stephen Bryan. ■ 25504 #055-02-1996 L1997 GS *020
O HANLON, Kathleen Marie. 659 CENTRAL AVE 25504 #055-02-1986 L1987 FM *020 †18
PETRANY, Stephen Michael. 659 CENTRAL AVE 25504 #010-02-1980 L1983 FM *040 †18
POSKITT, Thomas Richard. 659 CENTRAL AVE 25504 #024-07-1970 L1988 HEM ON *030 †20
RATCLIFF, Bruce Alan. 659 CENTRAL AVE 25504 #051-01-1966 L1968 OBG OS *020 †30
SABER, Kathy Lynn. 6475 FARMDALE RD, SABER MEDICAL OFFICE INC 25504 #055-02-1994 L1996 FM *020 †18
SAXE, Timothy Gerhart. 1 CHATEAU LN 25504 #055-01-1977 L1978 IM *020 †20
SHAW, Jeffrey Lee. 6007 US ROUTE 60 E, STE 203 25504 #055-02-1997 L2002 AI *020 †55,03
STINES, Jackie Ray, Jr. ■ 25504 #055-02-2005 PD *012
TOUCHON, Robert Chas. 6007 US ROUTE 60 E, CUMBERLAND CARDIOLOGY, PSC 25504 #028-34-1965 L1982 CD *040
VARLEY, Michael Patrick. 2 CHATEAU GROVE LN 25504 #038-06-1983 L1991 OPH *020 †35
WINGER, Cynthia A. 659 CENTRAL AVE 25504 #055-01-1983 L1984 FM *040 †18
YOUNG, Roderick Allen, II. 3012 CHAMPION DR, P O BOX 1164 25504 #055-02-1995 L1996 OM *020 †18

BARRACKVILLE – MARION

MAGUNIA, Shivji Lalji. PO BOX 809, 210 PIKE ST 26559 #495-23-1971 L1975 IM *071 †20

BEAVER – RALEIGH

BILLIPS, Ronald Wayne. PO BOX 479 25813 #104-01-2005 L2005 FP *012
DABABNAH, Mousa Ibrahim Y. PO BOX 247, BEAVER MED CLINIC 25813 #875-01-1969 L1976 FM *020 †18
MC MILLEN, J Wayne. ■ 25813 #051-01-1978 L1980 EM GP *020 †16
PATEL, Narendrakumar M. PO BOX 2028 25813 #495-23-1966 L1975 IM CCM *020 †20

BECKLEY – RALEIGH

ABRAHAM, Joshy. 179 WOODLAND DR 25801 #495-31-1966 L1975 CD IM *020 †20

ABRAHAM, Mariamma V. 405 CARRIAGE DR 25801 #495-31-1968 L1974 OBG *020 †30
AHMED, Mohammed Jamil. 227 PRINCE ST 25801 #704-01-1950 L1966 PTH *020 †50
AKBAR, Shazia. 250 STANAFORD RD, BECKLEY PEDIATRIC ASSOC LH 25801 #704-16-1991 L1997 PD *020 †55
AKSOY, Yasar. 103 BECKLEY PLZ 25801 #902-03-1963 L1987 GP AN *020
AMIR, Ali Afsar. ■ 25801 #495-21-1989 L1997 P *020
AMJAD, Hassan. 306 STANAFORD RD 25801 #704-01-1970 L1977 HEM IM *020 †20
AMJAD, Quartel-Ayne. ■ 25801 #055-02-2007 L2007 IM *012
ANAND, Ajay. 306 STANAFORD RD 25801 #495-69-1986 L2003 CD IM *020 †20
ANTHONY, Bryce Chadwick. 301 SUNSET DR, RALEIGH ANESTHESIA ASSN 25801 #010-03-1944 L1991 AN *071 †05
AUJLA, Sukhdev Singh. 250 STANAFORD RD 25801 #495-03-1965 L2006 IM *020 †20
BANKS, Ugoala Chikezie Wu. 250 STANAFORD RD, ARH SOUTHERN WEST VIRGINIA 25801 #654-01-1982 L2006 CD *020
BARGHOUTHI, Thair. 306 CARRIAGE DR 25801 #875-01-1978 L1991 IM CD *020 †20
BAZI, Tony M. 250 STANAFORD RD, SOUTHERN WV CLINIC 25801 #605-01-1984 L1990 OBG *020 †30
BEHNAM, Anis Matta. 250 STANAFORD RD, SOUTHERN WV CLINIC 25801 #330-01-1951 L1969 U *072 †95
BELLA, Cecilia B. 1710 HARPER RD 25801 #748-01-1965 L1985 PTH *020 †50
BEMBALKAR, Shrikant L. 252 RURAL ACRES DR 25801 #496-38-1967 L1973 IM PUD *020 †20
BERRYMAN, John David. 200 VETERANS AVE, BECKLEY VA HOSPITAL 25801 #051-01-1967 L2007 OBG U *020 †30 ‡
BHALODI, Ashokkumar V. 407 CARRIAGE DR 25801 #495-48-1972 L1986 U *020 †95
BLAINE, David Allan. 84 BROOKSHIRE LN 25801 #036-05-1991 L2005 OTO *020 †45
BODNER, Neal Mitchell. 1710 HARPER RD, RALIEGH GENERAL HOSPITAL 25801 #035-47-1984 L2006 AN *020 †05
BOSE, Mikkilineni S. 419 CARRIAGE DR 25801 #495-50-1972 L1980 GS GP *020 †85
BOU-ABBOUD, Charles Fouad. 58 BROOKSHIRE LN 25801 #605-01-1985 L1990 GE IM *020 †20
BOUSTANI, Maria Rizkalhah. 421 CARRIAGE DR 25801 #605-01-1988 L1995 IM PUD *020 †20
CATTERSON, Eileen C. 1710 HARPER RD 25801 #041-07-1974 L1977 PD *071 †55
CHADWICK, Donald R. PO BOX 1229 25802 #024-01-1949 L1970 PHP *030
CHATTHA, Ashraf Ali. 379 STANAFORD RD, MED-SURG GROUP INC 25801 #704-01-1996 L2003 IM *020 †20
CHHABRA, Amarinder P. 306 STANAFORD RD, C/O ADMIN OFFICE/BECKLEY 25801 #495-08-1988 L1995 IM *020 †20
CINTRON, Deborah Ruth. 200 VETERANS AVE 25801 #033-05-1985 L2007 EM IM *020 †20
CORBIN, Anna Katherine. 1710 HARPER RD, DEPT OF EMERGENCY 25801 #051-01-2001 L2004 EM *020
CORRO, Prudencio C. 251 STANAFORD RD 25801 #748-08-1963 L1972 OTO A *020 †45
COVEY, Anneva L French. ■ 25801 #036-07-1944 L1952 PD *071
CRANDALL, David Bruce. 200 VETERANS AVE 25801 #036-11-1967 L1974 GS *030 †85
CRUZ, Halberto Gomez. ■ 25801 #748-02-1969 L1979 DR *020
DANIEL, Charles R, Jr. 1710 HARPER RD, RALEIGH GENERAL HOSPITAL 25801 #055-01-1982 L1983 R *020 †80
DANIEL, Charles Richard. 275 DRY HILL RD 25801 #051-04-1956 L1957 R *071 †80
DANIEL, Doff D, Jr. 125 1/2 MAIN ST STE 301 25801 #051-01-1948 L1949 IM *020
DANIEL, John Morton. 2233 S KANAWHA ST 25801 #041-02-1956 L1957 IM OS *020 †18 ‡
DASARO, Anthony Peter. ■ 25801 #654-01-1996 L1999 IM *020
DAVE, Chaitanya V. 200 VETERANS AVE 25801 #654-01-1987 L1996 HO IM *020 †20
DHALIWAL, Sanjit Kaur. 306 STANAFORD RD, ATTN: SCHUMAN 25801 #035-48-1996 L2004 EM *020 †16
DICKENSON, Stacey D. 252 RURAL ACRES DR 25801 #020-12-1992 L1999 PD *020 †55
DOCTRY, Nathan Elliott. 250 STANAFORD RD, LEE REGIONAL MEDICAL CENTE 25801 #033-05-1979 L2007 ORS *020
DY, Antonio Teng. 1710 HARPER RD 25801 #748-10-1971 L1980 PTH *020 †50
DY, Johnny T. 2401 S KANAWHA ST STE 102, JOHNNY DY MD 25801 #748-02-1967 L1974 N *020 †75
EL-HARAKE, Mayez. 275 DRY HILL RD 25801 #528-01-1981 L1994 HO IM *020 †20
ELSARRAG, Zaki. 1710 HARPER RD, RALIEGH HOSPITAL 25801 #849-01-1988 L1994 IM *020 †20
EVANS, Carlotta Ray. 410 CARRIAGE DR 25801 #055-02-1988 L1989 OBG *020 †30
FAHEEM, Ahmed Daver. 1014 JOHNSTOWN RD 25801 #495-77-1971 L1981 P *020 †75
FARID, Touraj. 1844 HARPER RD, GASTEROENTEROLOGY OF S WV 25801 #517-01-1965 L1984 IM GE *020 †20
FOX, Lewis Nevin. 1710 HARPER RD 25801 #051-04-1954 L1955 FM *071
FRANCIS, Shoukry Latif. 407 CARRIAGE DR 25801 #330-02-1952 L1972 OS *071 †95
GAFFAR, Anila. 200 VETERANS AVE, VA HOSPITAL 25801 #704-16-1992 L1998 IM *020 †20
GAJENDRAGADKAR, Subhash V. 209 WOODLAWN AVE 25801 #495-28-1969 L1981 IM NEP *075
GALAL, Galal Z. 275 DRY HILL RD 25801 #915-04-1974 L1992 GS *020
GARDNER, James Anderson. 250 STANAFORD RD, SOUTHERN WV CLINIC 25801 #803-05-1954 L1964 GS *071
GOGO, Prospero Barquero. 425 STANAFORD RD, THE CHILDRENS CLINIC 25801 #748-09-1962 L1974 PD *071 †55
GOLDEN, Joseph Ivan. 306 STANAFORD RD 25801 #008-02-1975 L1979 FM FPG *020 †18
GORDINHO, Jose Jorge. 310 GEORGE ST, ALLEGHANY MEDICAL SVCS PC 25801 #649-14-1980 L1989 NEP IM *020
GOSIENE, Henry Pagan. 22 MALLARD CT 25801 #748-07-1966 L1976 OPH *020
GRAVELY, Lewis Wm. 413 CARRIAGE DR 25801 #051-04-1972 L1978 OPH *020 †35
GREEN, Samuel Marvin. 1038 N EISENHOWER DR, NO 333 25801 #654-01-1986 L1987 GPM A *075
GUADALUPI, Pietro. 250 STANAFORD RD 25801 #561-03-1984 L2001 TS *020 †90,85
HADDADIN, Ramzi Nimer. 379 STANAFORD RD, MED-SURG GROUP INC 25801 #575-02-1993 L2002 IM *020 †20
HARVEY, Harold E, II. 214 PROFESSIONAL PARK 25801 #422-01-1988 L1992 IM A *020
HARVEY, Harold Edward. 214 PROFESSIONAL PARK 25801 #036-07-1943 L1947 A IM *071
HASAN, Mohammad Khalid. 24 MALLARD CT 25801 #495-67-1967 L1976 P IMG *020 †75
HASAN, Omar Khalid. ■ 25801 #055-01-2001 L2004 OS *100 †20,75
HASSAN, Surayia Tehsin. 224 PROFESSIONAL PARK 25801 #704-06-1965 L1976 IM *020 †20
HAUGHT, John Michael. 2401 S KANAWHA ST 25801 #055-01-1978 L1979 GE *020 †20
HOOPER, Anne C Dodge. ■ 25801 #028-02-1952 L1972 PTH FOP *062 †50
HOOPER, William D. ■ 25802 #028-02-1952 L1972 GS *071 †85
IMBING, Fausto Domingo. 306 STANAFORD RD 25801 #748-14-1987 L1997 PTH *020 †50

ISAAC, Elias Hanna. 1828 HARPER RD 25801 #875-01-1970 L1975 **GS** *020 †85
IYER, Shivkumar L. 101 S EISENHOWER DR, FMRS HEALTH SYSTEMS INC 25801 #495-89-1988 L1996 **P** *020 †75
JAFARY, Hassan A. 451 STANAFORD RD, STANAFORD MED CLNC 25801 #704-21-1986 L1995 **IM** *020 †20
JAFARY, Hassan Arshad. ■ 25801 #308-12-1989 L2008 **P** *012
JAMES-HART, Tyshaun M. 250 STANAFORD RD, HEALTHSCOPE 25801 #055-02-1989 L2004 **GS** *020 †85
JEREZA, Ramon Casa, Jr. 200 RALEIGH AVE 25801 #748-10-1964 L1972 **IM HEM** *020 †20
JOHNSON, John Henry, III. 250 STANAFORD RD, BECKLEY PEDIATRIC ASSOCIAT 25801 #055-02-1994 L1997 **PD** *020 †55
JOHNSON, Wallace D, Jr. 306 STANAFORD RD 25801 #020-02-1965 L1985 **GE IM** *071 †20
KABBARA, Wadih Mohamad Wa. 250 STANAFORD RD, STE 102 25801 #913-96-1999 L2006 **IM** *020 †20
KARAM, Jebran G. 1836 HARPER RD 25801 #875-02-1982 L1992 **CD** *020 †20
KEATING, Laura Graybeal. 921 NEVILLE ST, STE 200 25801 #045-01-1998 L2002 **IM** *020 †20
KHALIL, Marcia Bohn. 410 CARRIAGE DR 25801 #055-01-1976 L1977 **OBG** *020 †30
KHANNA, Rajiv. 275 DRY HILL RD, RALEIGH REGIONAL CANCER CT 25801 #495-53-1986 L1995 **IM HEM** *020 †20
KHIAMI, Ahmad. 110 PROFESSIONAL PARK 25801 #875-01-1986 L1994 **PD** *020 †55
KILLMER, Scott Matthew. 230 GEORGE ST STE 2 25801 #055-01-1991 L1992 **GS** *020 †85
KIM, Hak Lim. FRONT & TEEL STS 25801 #583-02-1956 L1971 **U** *071
KLINGENSMITH, Walter E. ■ 25801 #024-01-1954 L1961 **GS TS** *071 †85,90
KOH, Sukjung Gerald. 1710 HARPER RD 25801 #583-04-1966 L1993 **PTH HMP** *020 †50
LACANILAO, Ramon L. 250 STANAFORD RD 25801 #748-02-1990 L2006 **PD** *020 †55
LANDIS, Andrew E, Jr. 417 CARRIAGE DR 25801 #051-01-1970 L1977 **ORS** *020 †40
LAO, Dominador Yti. 2233 S KANAWHA ST 25801 #748-08-1974 L1981 **GS GP** *020
LARSON, Carl Sven. 454 CRANBERRY DR 25801 #016-43-1974 L1980 **ON IM** *020 †20
LEE, Jung Kuk. 200 VETERANS AVE, BECKLEY VA HOSP 25801 #583-06-1975 L1985 **IM** *020 †20
LEE, Stephen To June. 250 STANAFORD RD 25801 #056-06-1955 L1957 **GS TS** *071 †85
LEVIN, Barry Alan. 379 STANAFORD RD, MED-SURG GROUP INC 25801 #016-42-1974 L1996 **ORS** *020 †40
LEWIS, James Stuart. 306 STANAFORD RD, MESA BECKLET AMALACHIAN RE 25801 #055-01-1982 L1983 **IM EM** *020 †20
LINDLEY, Juddson D I. 410 CARRIAGE DR 25801 #055-01-1995 L1999 **OBG** *020 †30
LINTALA, Alan Mathew. 63 TIMBER RIDGE DR 25801 #055-01-1991 L1995 **DR** *020 †80
LIU, Edward Ting. 300 STANAFORD RD 25801 #748-02-1958 L1975 **OPH** *071 †35
LOVEGROVE, George Edward. 4130 ROBERT C BYRD DR 25801 #055-01-1978 L1979 **IM D** *020 †20
LUCERO, Carlos Estanislao. 403 CARRIAGE DR 25801 #132-09-1966 L1975 **NPM PD** *020 †55
LUCKTONG, Boonlua. 200 VETERANS AVE 25801 #891-02-1963 L1974 **GS** *075
MAIOLO, Joseph Anthony. 252 RURAL ACRES DR 25801 #051-04-1961 L1967 **IM** *020 †20
MALONZO, Raul Yu. 252 RURAL ACRES DR 25801 #748-01-1966 L1983 **PD GP** *020
MAOUAD, Michel I. 2401 S KANAWHA ST, BECKLEY MED ARTS 25801 #605-01-1959 L1987 **OTO FPS** *071 †45
MARAMBA, Lamberto Cendana. 200 RALEIGH AVE 25801 #748-08-1962 L1974 **CD IM** *020
MARTIN, James Tyrone. 201 WOODCREST DR 25801 #047-07-1973 L1980 **FM PD** *020
MC CORD, Larry Patrick. 275 DRY HILL RD 25801 #012-01-1974 L1982 **RO** *020 †80
MC FARLANE, Anthony A. 1830 HARPER RD 25801 #023-07-1990 L1999 **CD IM** *020 †20
MC KELVEY, Mary Elizabeth. ■ 25801 #041-01-1983 L1989 **IM** *020 †20
MC LEAN, William David. ■ 25801 #051-04-1954 L1955 **D A** *071 †15
MEADOWS, Owen Curtis, Jr. 410 CARRIAGE DR 25801 #051-01-1960 L1963 **OBG OS** *071 †30
MEHTA, Rasiklal B. ■ 25801 #495-33-1962 L1971 **IM CD** *040
MILANO, Amabile. 2401 S KANAWHA ST 25801 #055-01-1977 L1979 **DS** *020 †85,65
MILLER, John Chas. 207 SUNSET DR, STE A 25801 #051-04-1978 L1987 **GS** *020 †85
MOHAN, Petaiah. 194 CARRIAGE DR 25801 #495-09-1968 L1995 **NPM PD** *020 †55
MOHAN, Saraswathi. 194 CARRIAGE DR 25801 #495-09-1977 L1995 **PD** *020
MOTLEY, Ronald Clark. ■ 25802 #010-03-1983 L1984 **U** *020 †95
MOUROT, Susan Griffin. 1710 HARPER RD, DEPT OF EMERGENCY 25801 #004-01-1984 L2002 **FM** *020 †18
MULLINS, Bandy Bill. 404 CARRIAGE DR 25801 #055-01-2002 L2006 **GS** *020 †85
MULLINS, Norma Jean. 3771 ROBERT C BYRD DR 25801 #055-01-1975 L1978 **PUD IM** *020 †20
MUNOZ, Oscar F. 1002 NEVILLE ST 25801 #748-01-1969 L1978 **IM PA** *020
MURAGALI, Chandrashekhar. 1710 HARPER RD 25801 #495-23-1962 L1980 **IM** *071 †20
NAZER, Husam Mohammad I. 1710 HARPER RD 25801 #915-04-1972 L1982 **GE IM** *020 †20
OAR, Paul Arthur. 1007 S OAKWOOD AVE, BECKLEY HOSPITAL INC 25801 #064-01-1981 L1995 **GP** *020
ORPHANOS, George. 76 TIMBER RIDGE DR 25801 #418-01-1965 L1973 **ORS** *020 †40
OVERMILLER, Carl Lee. 200 VETERANS AVE 25801 #041-02-1986 L1994 **EM GS** *020 †85
OYCO, Jose L. 415 CARRIAGE DR, PROFESSIONAL ASSOC MED 25801 #748-08-1957 L1971 **IM GE** *020
PAINE, Albert J, Jr. 84 BROOKSHIRE LN 25801 #055-01-1981 L1982 **OTO FPS** *020 †45
PAINE, Albert James. 84 BROOKSHIRE LN 25801 #051-04-1945 L1951 **OTO** *020 †45
PARMAR, Vinod Bachubhai. 306 STANAFORD RD 25801 #495-48-1976 L1985 **AN** *020
PARSI, Rouzbeh Kamkar. 379 STANAFORD RD, MED-SURG GROUP INC 25801 #011-02-1969 L1988 **GS VS** *071 †85
PATEL, Bharat Govindbhai. 306 STANAFORD RD, PO BOX 941 25801 #495-76-1976 L1996 **DR** *020 †80
PATEL, Manubhai Nagjibhai. 250 STANAFORD RD 25801 #917-08-1977 L1987 **DR** *020 †80
PATEL, Nainesh M. 207 SUNSET DR, BECKLEY GASTROENTEROLOGY, 25801 #495-48-1986 L1999 **GE** *020 †20
PATEL, Rajesh Vitthal. 1710 HARPER RD 25801 #016-06-1998 L2005 **ORS** *020 †40
PATEL, Rohiniben N. 200 VETERANS AVE 25801 #495-23-1967 L1975 **PTH** *020 †50
PATEL, Sheila. 1710 HARPER RD, DEPARTMENT OF EMERGENCY ME 25801 #051-04-1996 L2001 **IM EM** *020 †20
PATNAIK, Dhirendranath. 331 S EISENHOWER DR 25801 #495-13-1963 L1976 **GS VS** *020 †85
PECORARO, Salvatore A. 3771 ROBERT C BYRD DR 25801 #561-17-1970 L1978 **CD IM** *020
PEREZ, Inocencio Perez. ■ 25801 #748-01-1954 L1972 **GP EM** *071
PITSENBARGER, Kelly M. 314 GEORGE ST 25801 #055-02-1983 L1984 **FM** *020 †18
POROWSKI, Janusz W. 1710 HARPER RD 25801 #067-02-1983 L1995 **EM** *020
PULLIAM, Robert Parker. 410 CARRIAGE DR, ASSOCIATES OB/GYN 25801 #036-05-1962 L1967 **OBG** *020 †30
PURANIK, Prakash R. 250 STANAFORD RD, ORTHOPEDIC STE 25801 #495-73-1970 L1995 **ORS** *020
PURANIK, Vidya Prakash. 250 STANAFORD RD STE 1 25801 #495-56-1973 L1995 **GYN** *020
RAHIM, Mustafa. 321 S EISENHOWER DR 25801 #704-02-1988 L1995 **IM** *020 †20
RAINEY, David Mark. 410 CARRIAGE DR, ASSOCIATES IN OB/GYN 25801 #020-12-1994 L1996 **OBG** *020 †30
RAMAS, Mario Cui. 417 CARRIAGE DR 25801 #748-11-1963 L1974 **ORS** *020
RAMAS, Mercedes Epifania. 1710 HARPER RD 25801 #055-01-1996 L2000 **DR** *020 †80
RASHEED, Syed. 20 MALLARD CT, WOODCREST ADDITION 25801 #704-08-1962 L1975 **IM END** *020 †20
RASHEED, Zarina. 306 STANAFORD RD 25801 #704-02-1965 L1974 **PTH** *020 †50
RASMUSSEN, Donald L. 421 CARRIAGE DR 25801 #049-01-1952 L1963 **PUD IM** *020 †20
REESMAN, Shawn Dewayne. 303 1/2 PRINCE ST, RALEIGH RADIOLOGY INC 25801 #055-02-1996 L1997 **DR** *020 †80
RESLEY, Todd Cornelius. 410 CARRIAGE DR 25801 #048-13-1987 L1989 **OBG** *020 †30
RICHMOND, Richard Dale. 2401 S KANAWHA ST, STE 106 25801 #055-01-1963 L1964 **OPH** *072 †35
RODRIGUEZ CAYRO, Narciso. 1902 HARPER RD, ANESTHESIA DEPT 25801 #308-03-1981 L1984 **AN** *020
ROHANI, Meredith. 101 SIDNEY ST 25801 #517-01-1957 L1966 **GS** *020
ROSAS, Angel L. 410 CARRIAGE DR 25801 #042-01-1986 L1991 **OBG** *020 †30
RUBIO, Epimaco Origen. 321 DRY HILL RD, MEDICAL WEIGHT LOSS CLINIC 25801 #748-01-1955 L1993 **AN** *020
RYAN, Patrick Thomas. 404 CARRIAGE DR 25801 #055-01-2004 L2006 **MPD** *012
SADAT, Taoufik Anwar. 22 MALLARD CT 25801 #055-02-1996 L2001 **OPH IM** *020
SAFIULLAH, Syed. 1014 JOHNSTOWN RD 25801 #495-57-1990 L1998 **P** *020 †75
SAHADEVAN, Velayudhan. 155 DRY HILL RD 25801 #154-07-1963 L1983 **RO** *020
SAIKALI, Wassim S. 421 CARRIAGE DR 25801 #605-01-1988 L1993 **RHU IM** *020 †20
SAINT-GERARD, Henriot. 321 DRY HILL RD, GRAHAM ENTERPRISES 25801 #440-01-1972 L1996 **AN** *020
SALMASSI, Jafar Z. 306 STANAFORD RD, BARH HOSPITAL 25801 #517-01-1981 L1993 **NEP** *020 †20
SALON, Ely Jean. 200 RALEIGH AVE 25801 #055-01-1993 L1995 **IM** *020 †20
SALON, Iligino F. 200 RALEIGH AVE 25801 #748-01-1955 L1972 **IM FM** *071 †18
SCARING, William Anthony. 1710 HARPER RD 25801 #028-34-1964 L1979 **OBG** *020 †30
SEANGIO, Catherine R. 1710 HARPER RD 25801 #748-01-1996 L2002 **FM** *020 †18
SETLIFF, Henry Lee. 1710 HARPER RD 25801 #055-01-1983 L1986 **DR** *020 †80
SHAH, Ramesh Chamanlal. 200 VETERANS AVE, VA MEDICAL CENTER 25801 #495-37-1967 L1982 **P CHP** *020 †75
SHAMBLIN, David Carol. 2233 S KANAWHA ST 25801 #055-01-1976 L1984 **ORS** *020
SHAMMAA, Ammar. 410 CARRIAGE DR, HUTZEL HOSPITAL, OBGYN DEP 25801 #875-02-1992 L2007 **OBG** *020
SHARMA, Aditya. 101 S EISENHOWER DR 25801 #495-05-1997 L2005 **P CHP** *020 †75
SHIMM, David Stuart. 275 DRY HILL RD, RALEIGH REGIONAL CANCER CE 25801 #036-07-1977 L2002 **RO IM** *020 †20,80
SIDDIQI, Syed M Z A. 93 HICKORY DR 25801 #704-09-1966 L1979 **GE IM** *020 †20
SIEGEL, Norman Lang. 410 CARRIAGE DR 25801 #748-08-1980 L1991 **OBG** *020 †30
SILK, Adnan. 1902 HARPER RD 25801 #875-01-1967 L1975 **NS** *020 †25
SINGH, Jay Pal. ■ 25801 #055-02-2006 **IM** *012
SINGH, Jogindar. 200 VETERANS AVE # 3-B 25801 #495-03-1953 L1977 **GS** *020 †85
SINGH, Rajendra Pratap. 201 WOODCREST DR 25801 #495-12-1963 L1975 **GS** *020 †85
SINGH, Sunita. 101 S EISENHOWER DR, FMRS INC 25801 #495-05-1996 L2006 **P** *020 †75
SOBHAN, Mohammad Abdus. 252 RURAL ACRES DR 25801 #160-02-1967 L1978 **FM** *020 †18 ‡
SOLARI, Teddy Wayne. 230 GEORGE ST STE 4 25801 #055-02-1986 L1988 **PD** *020 †55
STUART, David Livingstone. 250 STANAFORD RD 25801 #010-03-2000 L2007 **GS** *020
SUBBARAYA, Hiriyannappa. 169 GEORGE ST 25801 #495-19-1962 L1974 **CD IM** *020 †20
SULEIMAN, Ali Ahmad. 242 GEORGE ST 25801 #575-01-1984 L1992 **IM** *020 †20
TAMAYO, Raul H. 306 STANAFORD RD, BECKLEY ARH HOSPITAL 25801 #748-08-1967 L1976 **EM FM** *020 †18
TAYLOR, Norman Wayne. 410 CARRIAGE DR 25801 #023-01-1970 L1977 **OBG** *071 †30
THOMAS, Suresh P. 179 WOODLAND DR, STE 202 25801 #495-31-1981 L2000 **IM** *020 †20
TOLENTINO, Wilfredo F. 365 HARPER PARK DR, CURE CLINIC 25801 #748-08-1968 L1994 **NS** *020
TUMMALA, Krishnarao. 200 VETERANS AVE 25801 #495-58-1980 L1993 **IM** *020 †20
TZYSTUCK, Fred Patrick, II. ■ 25801 #055-02-2001 L2004 **EM** *020
UDDIN, Firoz. 200 VETERANS AVE, VETERANS ADMINISTRATION 25801 #160-02-1978 L2003 **AN IM** *020
VALIVETI, Rajendra Prasad. 200 VETERANS AVE, BECKLEY VA MEDICAL CENTER 25801 #495-58-1973 L1983 **DR IM** *020
VAUGHT, Barry Keith. 3155 ROBERT C BYRD DR 25801 #055-01-2001 L2005 **IM** *100 †75
VILLANUEVA, Cirilo Zafra. 1007 S OAKWOOD AVE 25801 #748-09-1961 L1977 **AN** *020
VILLANUEVA, Emma Calderon. 105 S EISENHOWER DR 25801 #748-09-1965 L1979 *020 ‡
VILLANUEVA, Ida Zafra. 252 RURAL ACRES DR 25801 #748-11-1971 L1979 **GP** *020
WALLACE, Richard Austin. 211 SUNSET DR 25801 #055-01-1977 L1978 **OTO** *020 †45
WASYLYK, Irene M. 224 PROFESSIONAL PARK 25801 #665-01-1999 L2005 **IM** *020 †20
WEBB, Michael Terry. 410 CARRIAGE DR 25801 #035-01-1973 L1978 **OBG** *020 †30
WEBB, Nancy Jeanne R. 410 CARRIAGE DR 25801 #035-01-1973 L1978 **OBG** *071 †30
WEBER, Charles M. 306 STANAFORD RD 25801 #010-02-1951 L1987 **R NM** *020 †28
WHANG, Hoon Kyou. 200 VETERANS AVE 25801 #583-02-1968 L1978 **PM** *020 †60
WHELAN, Francis Jos. 129 MAIN ST, STE 406, P.O. BOX 7249 25801 #018-03-1966 L1984 **P GP** *020 †75
WHITFIELD, Stephen Brett. 1007 S OAKWOOD AVE 25801 #041-01-1998 L2003 **ORS** *100 †40
WHYTE, Brian Roland. 240 GEORGE ST 25801 #041-13-1987 L2007 **VS GS** *020 †85
WISMAN, Richard Camp. 379 STANAFORD RD 25801 #055-01-1980 L1981 **FM FPG** *020 †18
WOLFE, Roy Roger, Jr. 410 CARRIAGE DR 25801 #055-01-1993 L2001 **OBG** *020 †30
YATES, James Ernest. 252 RURAL ACRES DR 25801 #038-45-1986 L1987 **FM AM** *020
YATES, Roy James. 252 RURAL ACRES DR 25801 #051-04-1959 L1961 **IM** *020
YEE, Robert C. 120 PROFESSIONAL PARK, STANAFORD RD 25801 #748-01-1969 L1978 **GP** *020
YOUNG, Harry Wetzel, Jr. 200 VETERANS AVE 25801 #055-75-1991, ▲ L1992 **IM PHP** *020
ZAHIR, Syed Abdul. 179 WOODLAND DR STE 1 25801 #495-30-1962 L1972 **ORS HS** *020 †40
ZINZUWADIA, Bella N. 1902 HARPER RD, STE E 25801 #495-22-1990 L1999 **IM** *020 †20
ZINZUWADIA, Nayan K. ■ 25801 #495-76-1986 L1999 **AN** *020

BELINGTON – BARBOUR

BYRD, Walter Redding, Jr. 1410 CRIM AVE 26250 #048-13-1975 L1996 **P** *020 †75

CHANDRAN, Bala Narayan. 1410 CRIM AVE 26250 #495-17-1961 L1975 **GP AN** *020 ‡
HENDERSON, John P, II. 210 N STURMER ST, BELINGTON COMMUNITY 26250
  #055-01-1992 L1993 **FM** *020 †18
HIGH, Carl Stephen. 210 N STURMER ST, BELINGTON COMMUNITY 26250 #041-14-1979 L1982
  FM A *020 †18

BELLE – KANAWHA

DAGHER, Ghassan Yusuf. 2700 E DUPONT AVE 25015 #605-01-1975 L1979 **OPH** *020 †35
GAMPONIA, Melissa Jose. 1 WARRIOR WAY, STE 103 25015 #055-01-1991 L1992
  FM PHP *020 †18

BENWOOD – MARSHALL

SOKOS, Mathew Gus. 4850 EOFF ST 26031 #055-02-1989 L1992 **FM** *020 †18
VEMURI, Dwarka N. 4850 EOFF ST, REAR 26031 #495-65-1980 L1993 **IM** *075

BERKELEY SPRINGS – MORGAN

BAER, Carlton Philip. 104 GAYLE DR, BERKELEY SPRINGS MEDICAL A 25411
  #051-04-1990 L1993 **FM** *071 †18
BAER, Karen Ann. 226 GAYLE DR 25411 #051-04-1989 L1993 **OPH** *071 †35
BERENS, Andrew Jos. 236 N WASHINGTON ST 25411 #055-01-1990 L1991 **FM** *020 †18
BERMAN, Edward S. 109 WAR MEMORIAL DR, MORGAN CNTY WAR MEMORIAL H 25411
  #034-01-1980 L2000 **EM** *020 †16
COOK, Jeffrey Trent. 109 WAR MEMORIAL DR 25411 #048-02-1979 L1980 **EM FM** *020 †16,18
DRESSLER, William Conrad. 83 WAR MEMORIAL DR, CITY URGENT CARE 25411
  #055-01-1971 L1977 **FM** *020 †18
GAYLE, Michael E. 226 GAYLE DR 25411 #051-04-1977 L1982 **FM** *071 †18
HASHEM, Joseph F. 226 GAYLE DR 25411 #875-01-1984 L1990 **IM** *020 †20
LAKEW, Elias. 109 WAR MEMORIAL DR, MORGAN COUNTY WAR MEMORIAL 25411
  #366-01-1987 L2001 **IM UCM** *030 †20
LEVEY, Jules Frank. 109 WAR MEMORIAL DR, WAR MEMORIAL HOSPITAL 25411
  #025-07-1970 L2006 **GS EM** *020 †85
MANN, Brian Thompson. 226 GAYLE DR 25411 #064-01-1972 L1995 **FM** *100 †18
MIIKE, Lawrence Hiroshi. ■ 25411 #005-02-1966 **OS** *075
QUARANTILLO, Edward P, Jr. 81 WAR MEMORIAL DR 25411 #010-02-1961 L1974 **GS** *071 †85
QUARANTILLO, Edward Paul. 81 WAR MEMORIAL DR 25411 #055-01-1988 L1994 **FM** *020 †18
QUARANTILLO, Pamela L. 81 WAR MEMORIAL DR, PED & FAM PHYS OF MORGANCO 25411
  #036-08-1990 L1994 **PD** *020 †55
RENIE, William Andrew. 109 WAR MEMORIAL DR, ATTN: ADMINISTRATION 25411
  #028-02-1978 L1981 **EM IM** *020 †20,16
RICHTER, Kimber Creager. ■ 25411 #038-41-1979 L1980 **IM** *030

BLUEFIELD – MERCER

AGARWAL, Anil B. 1333 SOUTHVIEW DR 24701 #495-19-1965 L1976 **IM CD** *020 †20
AHMAD, Syed Mahmood. 500 CHERRY ST 24701 #704-01-1976 L1985 **RHU IM** *020 †20
AHMED, Muhammad Shamim. 1027 FREDERICK ST 24701 #704-02-1986 L2001 **HO** *020 †20
AMIN, Mayank S. 512 CHERRY ST, BLDG I 24701 #007-02-1995 L1998 **IM** *020 †20
ANTOUN, Basim W. 1333 SOUTHVIEW DR, ST. LUKE'S HOSPITAL-RADIOL 24701
  #605-01-1984 L1993 **DR** *020 †80
ASBURY, Carol M. 3720 COAL HERITAGE RD, BLUEWELL FAMILY CLINIC 24701
  #038-44-1991 L1994 **FM** *020 †18
ASCUE, Joseph T. 1333 SOUTHVIEW DR, ST LUKES HOSPITAL 24701 #051-07-1984 L1985
  GPM *020
BEIN, Norman Nathan. 1331 SOUTHVIEW DR, ST LUKE'S HOSPITAL 24701 #041-09-1970 L2002
  GS *020 †85
BHAGAT, Rasikbhai M. 500 CHERRY ST, BLUFIELD REGIONAL MEDICAL 24701
  #495-23-1970 L1976 **EM** *020 †16
BHASIN, Ram Pal. 1333 SOUTHVIEW DR 24701 #495-47-1964 L1974 **GP GS** *020
BLAYDES, James E, Jr. 1333 SOUTHVIEW DR 24701 #041-01-1954 L1955 **OPH** *071 †35
BLAYDES, Stephen Hill. 1109 W CUMBERLAND RD 24701 #051-01-1989 L1994 **OPH** *020 †35
BUENAFE, Waldro Barbero. 1333 SOUTHVIEW DR 24701 #748-07-1971 L1982 **GP** *020
CABRAL, Mariano T. 500 CHERRY ST 24701 #748-08-1965 L1974 **AN** *071
CAPPIELLO, Enrico John. 1333 SOUTHVIEW DR 24701 #010-02-1970 L1984 **DR NM** *020 †80
CARDONA, Mario Soto. 1331 SOUTHVIEW DR, STE 1 24701 #264-04-1959 L1972 **IM PCC** *020
CHANDEL, Ashutosh. 504 CHERRY ST 24701 #495-20-1984 L1993 **CD IM** *020 †20
CHOUDHARI, Vimal Babubhai. 500 CHERRY ST, BLUEFIELD REG MED CTR 24701
  #495-76-1997 L2005 **AN** *100 †05
CORTELLESI, Thomas Brian. 510 CHERRY ST, STE 308 24701 #055-75-1991, ▲ L1999
  IM *020 †20
DUREMDES, Gene Bermejo. 500 CHERRY ST 24701 #055-01-1988 L1990 **GS** *020 †85
EDWARDS, Robert Wilson. 1333 SOUTHVIEW DR 24701 #055-01-1996 L1998 **OBG** *020 †30
ELLIOTT, Wm Martin, II. 500 CHERRY ST, BLUEFIELD REGIONAL MEDICAL 24701
  #051-04-1980 L1983 **EM** *020 †18
ESPANOL, Jose Solanor. 500 CHERRY ST 24701 #748-11-1973 L1979 **FM AN** *020
FELSINGER, Katja. 512 CHERRY ST, BLDG I 24701 #409-23-1993 L2001 **END** *020 †20
FRAZER, Teresa. 510 CHERRY ST STE 2 24701 #017-20-1975 L1998 **PDE PD** *050 †55
GUPTA, G Sri Rama. 504 CHERRY ST 24701 #495-09-1960 L1971 **IM** *071
HAHN, Kathleen Wycklendt. 324 NORTH ST 24701 #056-01-1978 L1984 **AN** *020 †05
HAJJAR, Mohamed Salim. 510 CHERRY ST 24701 #875-01-1959 L1972 **OBG** *071 †30
HEGSTROM, Michael T. 512 CHERRY ST BLDG I 24701 #001-02-1996 L2004 **GS** *020 †85
HILES, Charles H, Jr. 500 CHERRY ST, BLUEFIELD REGIONAL MED 24701 #051-07-1983 L2007
  IM *020
HYACINTHE, Jean Michel F. 500 CHERRY ST 24701 #440-01-1973 L1997 **PS** *020
JAIN, Pushpa Rani. 500 CHERRY ST, DEPT RADIATION ONCOLOGY 24701 #495-19-1962 L1980
  RO *020 †80
JAVIER, Domingo G. 1701 JEFFERSON ST 24701 #748-01-1965 L1975 **GP GS** *020
KANAWATI, Mohammad Yasier. 510 CHERRY ST, STE 305 24701 #875-01-1966 L1981
  OPH *035

KHAN, Nasir A. 500 CHERRY ST 24701 #704-16-1982 L1991 **PTH PCP** *062 †50
KIRKPATRICK, Cassandra M. 500 CHERRY ST, BLUEFIELD REGIONAL MEDICAL 24701
  #038-40-1992 L2000 **EM** *020 †16
KISTNER, Mary Louise T. 1027 FREDERICK ST 24701 #041-01-1977 L1985 **HO HEM** *071 †20
KONGKASUWAN, Suradech. PO BOX 873 24701 #891-02-1962 L1974 **PD GP** *020 †55
KRISHNAN, Radha K. 615 FREDERICK ST 24701 #495-04-1964 L1975 **PUD IM** *020 †20
KUPPUSAMI, Muthusamy. 1331 SOUTHVIEW DR 24701 #495-04-1963 L1972 *062 †85
KURAGUNTLA, Paul Raj. 1333 SOUTHVIEW DR, ST LUKES HOSP DEPT ANES 24701
  #495-50-1976 L1989 **AN GS** *020
LARKIN, David Jos. 500 CHERRY ST 24701 #055-01-1977 L1978 **AN** *020 †05
LASKER, Bruce Lawrence. 510 CHERRY ST STE 102 24701 #047-06-1971 L1976 **OBG** *020 †30
LITZ, Edward Mann. 490 CHERRY ST STE A 24701 #051-04-1966 L1973 **ORS** *020 †40
LLADO-MARTINEZ, Juan. 510 CHERRY ST STE 302 24701 #042-01-1975 L1996 **U GP** *020
MALAMISURA, Michael A. 500 CHERRY ST 24701 #055-01-1978 L1979 **GE IM** *020 †20
MATHEW, Thomas. 324 NORTH ST STE 2 24701 #495-44-1965 L1972 **AN** *020 †05 ‡
MC RAE, Henry Grady. ■ 24701 #048-02-1954 L1964 **PD** *071
MESHEL, Jack Chas. 510 CHERRY ST, BLDG A 24701 #010-03-1967 L2002 **CD IM** *020
MILNER, Lee Byer. 500 CHERRY ST 24701 #024-07-1966 L1981 **DR** *020 †80
MISAK, Steve Jos. 510 CHERRY ST 24701 #060-01-1955 L1967 **U** *071 †95
MORHOUS, Eugene J. ■ 24701 #035-06-1945 L1951 **IM** *071 †20
MULL, Richard Theodore. 1333 SOUTHVIEW DR 24701 #012-01-1981 L1988 **DR NR** *020 †80
NAJJAR, Sakib Muslih. 1331 SOUTHVIEW DR, STE 10 24701 #605-01-1965 L1992
  CD IM *071 †20
OFIR, Erez Abraham. 500 CHERRY ST 24701 #055-15-1988 L1992 **AN** *020 †05
OLMSTED, Charles Morgan. 500 CHERRY ST 24701 #004-01-1969 L1982 **RO** *020 †80
ONGLATCO, John D. 500 CHERRY ST, BLUEFIELD REGIONAL MEDICAL 24701
  #748-14-1992 L2001 **AN** *020 †05
PARKER, Kenneth John M. 500 CHERRY ST 24701 #065-06-1987 L1992 **AN** *020 †05
PHADE, Vijaykumar. 500 CHERRY ST 24701 #495-97-1970 L1981 **GS VS** *020 †85
POLAVARAPU, Padmaja Pam. 1333 SOUTHVIEW DR 24701 #495-50-1987 L1993 **IM** *020 †20
POOLOS, Stephen Patrick. 500 CHERRY ST, BLUESHIELD REG MED CTR 24701
  #036-05-1974 L1982 **PTH** *020 †50
PRUETT, Charles D. ■ 24701 #036-07-1951 L1953 **IM NM** *071
PUJARI, Bhasker Rao. 1331 SOUTHVIEW DR, STE 2 24701 #495-21-1959 L1975 **U** *020 †95 ‡
PULLINS, Dennis Ivan. 810 PARKWAY AVE 24701 #055-01-1979 L1983 **PTH** *020 †50
QAZI, Nadeem G. 1279 STADIUM DR 24701 #704-21-1990 L1998 **NM** *020 †28,20
RANA, Izhar Ahmad. 1333 SOUTHVIEW DR 24701 #704-01-1974 L1981 **GS** *020 †85
RANA, Riaz Akhtar. 488 CHERRY ST BLDG E, SUITE 1 24701 #704-01-1964 L1973
  GS GP *020 †85
RANA, Tahir Iqbal. 500 CHERRY ST 24701 #704-01-1984 L2000 **N** *020 †75
RAVAL, Jugalkishor T. ■ 24701 #495-89-1976 L2008 **N** *020
RICHARDSON, Thomas Edward. 3008 E CUMBERLAND RD 24701 #055-01-1964 L1965
  PD *071 †55
RUCKMAN, Carol Nyberg. ■ 24701 #011-03-1976 L2007 **EM PD** *020 †55
SAMPSON, John E. 500 CHERRY ST, BLUEFIELD REGIONAL MEDICAL 24701
  #064-01-1987 L1997 **EM** *030 †18 ‡
SARNO, Riel Escasa. 1333 SOUTHVIEW DR, ST LUKES HOSP 24701 #748-10-1986 L1994
  EM *020 †18
SCHOR, Joel Anthony. 1027 FREDERICK ST 24701 #016-11-1981 L1987 **ON HEM** *020 †20 ‡
SEKKARIE, Mohamed Abdul K. 510 CHERRY ST, BLDG A 24701 #875-01-1981 L1990
  NEP PA *020 †20
SIDDIQI, Sumaiya Waseem. 510 CHERRY ST, STE 306 24701 #704-01-1991 L2007
  NEP *100 †20
TAYLOR, John Brookins. 510 CHERRY ST 24701 #051-01-1954 L1960 **IM** *020
TEPOEL, Louis Dean. 1333 SOUTHVIEW DR, ST. LUKES HOSPITAL 24701 #007-02-1977 L1988
  EM FM *020 †18
TOLER, Merton Causey. 500 CHERRY ST 24701 #027-01-1974 L1991 **FM EM** *020
VARDAN, Sandeep. 496 CHERRY ST 24701 #024-05-1990 L1998 **CD IM** *020 †20
VIDOT, Milagros Mercedes. 512 CHERRY ST, BLDG I 24701 #041-07-1998 L2002 **FM** *020 †18
WIDES, Kathleen Ellen. 500 CHERRY ST 24701 #016-43-1982 L1987 **EM** *020 †20

BOWDEN – RANDOLPH

BARROWS, Barry Van. ■ 26254 #055-01-1981 L1982 **FM** *020 †16,18

BRADLEY – RALEIGH

KINCAID, Christopher Euge. PO BOX 124 25818 #055-01-2007 **FP** *012
VILLANUEVA, Manuel Bunoan. FAMILY CLINIC 25818 #748-01-1963 L1979 **FM** *020 †18

BRANCHLAND – LINCOLN

BELGRAVE, Claire. 25 LINCOLN PLZ 25506 #566-01-1977 L2006 **CHP** *020
BOWEN, Jon Robert. ■ 25506 #055-01-2005 L2007 **FP** *012
RAZAVIPOUR, Nika. 25 LINCOLN PLZ 25506 #847-19-1994 L2004 **PYG** *020

BRIDGEPORT – HARRISON

ADENIYI, Olatokunbo Modup. ■ 26330 #690-01-1994 L2004 **MPD** *020 †55,20
BAILEY, James D, Jr. 1370 JOHNSON AVE 26330 #055-01-1992 L1993 **FM** *020 †18
BARCINAS, Gaspar Z. 103 DOCTORS DR 26330 #748-10-1963 L1974 **GP GS** *020 †18
BOWERS, Robert John, II. 1370 JOHNSON AVE 26330 #055-01-1992 L1993 **FM** *020 †18
BYRNE, Richard Harvey. 9B CHENOWETH DR 26330 #010-02-1980 L2005 **U** *020 †95
COGAR, Janet Elaine. 900 LODGEVILLE RD 26330 #055-01-1983 L1986 **PD** *020 †55
COLVIN, David Forrest. 1160 JOHNSON AVE STE 105, PSYCH ASSOCS 26330
  #055-01-1974 L1975 **P** *020 †75
DEE, Sally Ong. 153 W MAIN ST 26330 #748-02-1993 L2003 **AI** *020 †20,03
DOUKAS, William Carlton. ■ 26330 #023-12-1988 L2007 **ORS** *020 †40
FARIS, David Allen. 2 CHENOWETH DR STE B 26330 #055-01-1984 L1990 **OPH** *020 †35
FRYER, Karyn L. 11 CHENOWETH DR, P O BOX 390 26330 #055-75-2002, ▲ L2004 **PD** *020
GOCKE, John Thos. ■ 26330 #041-02-1942 L1943 **OPH OS** *071 †35

■ = Address Information Privacy Protected

GRECO, Robert. ■ 26330 #051-04-1948 L1949 **OBG** *071 †30
GUIRGUIS, Nabil. 166 THOMPSON DR 26330 #915-04-1987 L2003 **NEP** *020 †20
HAQ, Syed Nadeemul. 170 THOMPSON DR 26330 #704-02-1991 L1999 **END** *020
HAQUE, Naveed U. ■ 26330 #704-02-1990 L1994 **RHU IM** *020 †20
HARMAN, Haeley E. 1511 JOHNSON AVE, # 104 26330 #055-75-1998, ▲ L1999 **FM** *020 †18 ‡
HARRON, Raymond Anthony. PO BOX 400 26330 #035-09-1957 L1961 **R NM** *071 †80,28
HESS, David Elwood. 215 W MAIN ST 26330 #055-01-1991 L1993 **FM** *020 †18
HESS, David Rae. 215 W MAIN ST 26330 #055-01-1965 L1966 **FM OS** *020
HESS, Michael Raymond. 1511 JOHNSON AVE 26330 #055-01-1998 L1999 **FM** *020 †18
JONES, Cathy S. 900 LODGEVILLE RD 26330 #055-01-1982 L1985 **PD EM** *020 †55
KING, Richard Wade. 902 LODGEVILLE RD 26330 #654-01-1990 L1993 **OBG** *020 †30
LIEBIG, Carl Warren. 106 DOCTORS DR 26330 #055-01-1981 L1982 **FM** *020 †18
LINGER, Harry Teter. ■ 26330 #051-04-1946 L1953 **OPH** *071 †35
MC CLURE, Simon. 1160 JOHNSON AVE, STE 105 26330 #067-01-1986 L1992 **P** *020 †75
MEDINA, Teodoro G. 2 CHENOWETH DR STE A 26330 #748-01-1967 L1981 **IM GE** *020
MENZEL, Charlotte Emilie. ■ 26330 #067-01-1986 L1996 **FM** *020 †18
MIELE, Vincent John, Jr. 215 RUFFED GROUSE DR, UNITED HOSPITAL 26330
  #055-01-2001 L2002 **NS** *020
MILAN, Edita P. 153 W MAIN ST, EXEMPLAR MED GRP 26330 #748-10-1962 L1994 **PD GP** *020
MILLER, Susan H W. 140 W MAIN ST 26330 #041-07-1973 L1982 **GP** *020
MITCHELL, Bradley David. 900 LODGEVILLE RD 26330 #055-02-2000 L2003 **PD** *020 †55
MOMEN, Jennifer Jill. 11 CHENOWETH DR, STE A 26330 #035-06-1991 L1996 **PD** *020 †55
MOMEN, Joseph Mard. 11 CHENOWETH DR 26330 #517-01-1972 L1979 **PD NPM** *020 †55
MOREHEAD, Raymond August. ■ 26330 #016-11-1976 L1977 **CRS** *075 †85
MURRAY, Frances Blake. 1370 JOHNSON AVE STE 201 26330 #055-01-1989 L1990
  FM *040 †18 ‡
NELSON, Kelly Raphael. 1370 JOHNSON AVE, MEDBROOK MED CTR 26330
  #001-02-1986 L1987 **FM** *020 †18
PALMER, Louis Carroll. 105 DOCTORS DR 26330 #055-01-1967 L1968 **D** *020 †15 ‡
PARAMJIT, Chumber. ■ 26330 #495-03-1988 L2005 **P** *100 †75
POLICANO, Brian C. 11 CHENOWETH DR STE A 26330 #055-01-2000 L2003 **PD** *020 †55
RANDOLPH, Edward Burl. ■ 26330 #023-01-1944 L1946 **U** *071 †95
RATINO, John Manfred. ■ 26330 #023-01-1964 L1987 **PS** *020 †65
RUPPERT, John Michael. ■ 26330 #023-07-1990 *100
STODDARD, Kelley Erin Hol. 902 LODGEVILLE RD 26330 #011-02-2001 L2005 **OBG** *020
TARIQ, Mohammad. 7 CHENOWETH DR, STE 4 26330 #704-01-1996 L2006 **CCM** *020
THIMMAPPA, B G. 2 CHENOWETH DR 26330 #495-09-1966 L1972 **IM HEM** *020 †20
THIMMAPPA, Brinda. ■ 26330 #043-01-2002 L2003 **PS** *012
THOMAS, Jill Ashley. ■ 26330 #055-01-2007 **FP** *012
TOYE, Frederic Jerome. ■ 26330 #041-02-1964 L1985 **NS** *071 †25
WILKINSON, Amos Wesley. 1370 JOHNSON AVE, P O BOX 238 26330 #055-01-1981 L1982
  OPH *020 †35
WILLIAMSON, Walter E, Jr. ■ 26330 #048-04-1956 L1968 **GS VS** *071 †85
WOOFTER, Dominick Ryan. ■ 26330 #055-01-2001 L2004 **FM** *020 †18

BRUCETON MILLS — PRESTON

CLARK, Thomas Saml. ■ 26525 #055-01-1975 L1976 **OM** *071
TINNIN, Louis Watson. RR 1 BOX 215E, LAKE O WOODS 26525 #016-02-1961 L1979 **P** *020 †75

BUCKEYE — POCAHONTAS

SORIANO ULLOA, Luis E. RR 2 BOX 54G 24924 #308-01-1975 L1980 **FM** *020 ‡

BUCKHANNON — UPSHUR

ALMOND, Araceli V Ganan. ■ 26201 #748-08-1967 L1975 **PD** *020
ALMOND, Greenbrier D R. 27 S KANAWHA ST 26201 #055-01-1974 L1974 **P FM** *020 †75 ‡
ATTIA, Safwat Mikhael. 104 E MAIN ST 26201 #055-01-1978 L1993 **CHP** *020 †75
BLACK, Jerry Nelson. 10 AMALIA DR 26201 #011-02-1976 L1980 **OPH** *020 †35
CHAMBERLAIN, Robert L. ■ 26201 #051-04-1945 L1946 **FM** *071
COTTON, April Elaine. 11 N LOCUST ST, BUCHANNON MEDICAL CARE 26201
  #016-45-1996 L1997 **FM** *020 †18
FAILINGER, Conard F, III. 1 AMALIA DR 26201 #047-05-1980 L1990 **CD IM** *020 †20
FARRY, Kimberly Marie. 56 E MAIN ST, ASSOCS FOR WOMEN HLTH PLLC 26201
  #041-13-1991 L1996 **OBG** *020 †30
GALEY, John Patrick. 10 AMALIA DR STE B1 26201 #065-01-1981 L1992 **ORS** *020 †40
HARTMAN, I Franklin, II. PO BOX 669, 4 HARTMAN PLZ 26201 #023-01-1964 L1971 **GS GP** *020
HARTZOG, Joseph Michael. 1 AMALIA DR 26201 #055-01-1993 L1994 **FM** *020 †16
HAYNES, Herbert C. PO BOX 817 26201 #035-01-1952 L1980 **P** *071 †75
HILDRETH-WHITEHAIR, Aimee. ■ 26201 #055-01-2004 L2008 **FP** *012
KHAN, Ali A. 2 HARTMAN PLZ 26201 #704-01-1988 L1994 **NEP** *020 †20
KIRCHDOERFER, Elaine Jean. 1 AMALIA DR 26201 #041-14-1987 L1992 **FM** *020 †18
KIRK, Michael David. 1 AMALIA DR 26201 #041-14-1987 L1992 **FM** *020 †18
LATIF, Murshid Abdel. RR 2 BOX 110A 26201 #575-01-1984 L1993 **OBG MFM** *020 †30
LEWIS, William Darrell. 10 AMALIA DR, STE B1 26201 #055-01-1999 L2001 **FM** *020 †18
LONG, Susan E. 10 AMALIA DR, GROUP DBA UPSHUR MEDICAL 26201 #050-02-1992 L1997
  GS *020 †85
MATHIAS, John Allen, Jr. 10 AMALIA DR, GROUP DBA UPSHUR MEDICAL 26201
  #055-01-1970 L1975 **FM IMG** *020 †18
MITCHELL, Clyde Paul. 10 AMALIA DR, GROUP DBA UPSHUR MEDICAL 26201
  #041-12-1978 L1985 **FM FPG** *020 †18 ‡
O'LOUGHLIN, Gerard Joseph. 10 AMALIA DR, GROUP DBA UPSHUR MEDICAL 26201
  #055-75-1988, ▲ L1989 **FM OBS** *020 †18
PEARSON, Amy Hamilton. 93 W MAIN ST, MY DOCTOR'S OFFICE, INC 26201
  #055-02-1995 L1996 **FM** *020 †18 ‡
PEARSON, Ronald Bradburnv. 10 AMALIA DR, STE B1 26201 #055-02-1995 L2000 **GS** *020
RAMIREZ, Rigoberto T. ■ 26201 #649-01-1953 L1965 **GS GP** *071
REED, Joseph Blount. 1 AMALIA DR 26201 #055-01-1962 L1964 **FM** *020 †18
ROLLINS, John Michael. 10 AMALIA DR, GROUP DBA UPSHUR MEDICAL 26201
  #055-01-1978 L1989 **OBG** *020 †30
RUSMISELL, James A, Jr. ■ 26201 #041-13-1941 L1942 **GP R** *071

SEMBELLO, William James. 10 AMALIA DR, STE B1 26201 #055-01-1973 L1974
  IM IMG *071 †20
SMITH, Stephen Michael. 11 N LOCUST ST 26201 #055-01-1977 L1978 **IM** *020 †20
TALKINGTON, Andrew Alan. 11 N LOCUST ST, BUCKHANNON MEDICAL CARE 26201
  #055-01-1992 L1993 **FM** *020 †18
WIEST, Jeanie A. 20 MOUNT VISTA DR 26201 #020-12-1968 L1973 **PD CHP** *020

BUNKER HILL — BERKELEY

GRODE, David Lloyd. ■ 25413 #036-07-1967 L1974 **R** *020 †80

CABINS — GRANT

COOLEY, S Dallas. ■ 26855 #038-41-1961 L1989 **OBG** *071 †30
WHETSELL, David L. ■ 26855 #055-01-1985 L1986 **EM GPM** *020

CAIRO — RITCHIE

MATHIAS, Phillip Benj. ■ 26337 #055-01-1966 L1967 **OTO A** *071 †45

CALDWELL — GREENBRIER

BALLOU, Hosea Chas. ■ 24925 #026-04-1940 L1948 **IM** *071

CAMDEN — LEWIS

FAHEY, John James, Jr. CHURCHVILLE 26338 #038-40-1971 *071

CAMDEN ON GAULEY — WEBSTER

TRENBATH, Richard S. 10003 WEBSTER RD, CAMDEN-ON-GAULEY MEDICAL C 26208
  #010-01-1978 L1981 **FM FPG** *020 †18

CAMERON — MARSHALL

BARKI, Kelly. RR 4 BOX 19, WILSON DRIVE 26033 #041-77-2000, ▲ L2003 **IM** *020 †20

CHAPMANVILLE — LOGAN

BAISAS, Domingo Calingo. ■ 25508 #748-01-1953 L1970 **GP OS** *071
BAISAS, Roger Calingo. PO BOX 1229, RT 10 MAIN STREET 25508 #748-01-1950 L1991
  NS *020 †25
BASU, Dilip Kumar. 55 HUBERT HILL RD, SPECIALISTS PLLC 25508 #495-38-1960 L1974
  CD *020 †20
CABE, Ellen Mary. 22 AIRPORT RD RR2, CHAPMANVILLE PEDIATRICS 25508
  #048-15-1999 L2005 **PD** *020 †55
IYER, Ramakrishnan S. 55 HUBERT HILL RD, SPECIALISTS PLLC 25508 #495-23-1973 L1982
  CD IM *020 †20
LEE, Marciano Belderol. 55 HUBERT HILL RD, SPECIALISTS PLLC 25508 #748-19-1985 L1995
  CD *020 †20
NARASIMHAN, Srinivasan. 55 HUBERT HILL RD, SPECIALISTS PLLC 25508 #495-59-1980 L1996
  CD *020 †20
PACIS, Flora Flores. PO BOX 41 25508 #748-01-1963 L1974 **PD OS** *020
RACADAG, Alex Presbitero. HC 74 BOX 3012, SUNSHINE CIRCLE 25508 #748-01-1981 L1997
  PTH *020 †50
RANAVAYA, Mohammed I. 100 CONSTITUTIONAL AVE 25508 #704-02-1979 L1986
  OM EM *020 †70
SALEH, Samer Abdelwahab. ■ 25508 #915-03-1995 L2003 **PCC** *020 †20

CHARLES TOWN — JEFFERSON

ACEVEDO, Yliana Margarita. ■ 25414 #935-01-1995 L2007 **FM** *020
ARUMUGANATHAN, T. 127 E 2ND AVE 25414 #220-02-1976 L1993 **OBG** *020 †30
BONYAK, Edward Vincent. 201 N GEORGE ST, STE 103 25414 #041-14-1989 L2002
  CD *020 †20
FISHER, Johanna Greer. ■ 25414 #055-01-2005 L2007 **FP** *012
HARRIS, Barton Aldis. ■ 25414 #035-09-1954 L1957 **IM** *071 †20
JARROTT, David Michael. ■ 25414 #021-01-1972 L1972 **NS GP** *020 †25
MAHESWARAN, Vettivelu. ■ 25414 #495-37-1963 L1976 **OBG** *071 †30
NASHED, Trisha Bansal. 201 N GEORGE ST, STE 103 25414 #011-02-1997 L2003 **CD** *020 †20
RACZKOWSKI, Wanda Teresa. 84 SOMERSET BLVD, SOMERSET VILLAGE 25414
  #041-02-1980 L1986 **FM** *020 †18
RITTELMEYER, James T. 201 N GEORGE ST, STE 103 25414 #010-02-1978 L1994 **CD** *020 †20
STEELEY, Gwen Scott. ■ 25414 #803-05-1957 L1963 **OBG** *072 †30
WILLIAMS, Fred Andrew, Jr. 1003 WESTSIDE LN 25414 #051-04-1978 L1980 **EM** *020 †16
ZUCKER, Robert S. ■ 25414 #036-01-1985 L2003 **IM PM** *071 †60

CHARLESTON — KANAWHA

ABBAS, Raja Sohail. 3200 MACCORKLE AVE SE 25304 #704-20-2000 L2006 **OS** *071
ABDUL-JALIL, Majester N. ■ 25314 #055-02-2002 L2006 **MPD** *020
ABNER, Kellee. 4605 MACCORKLE AVE SW 25309 #055-01-1992 L1998 **AN PMM** *020 †05
ABOUSHAAR, Yusr. 11950 MACCORKLE AVE, CHESAPEAKE PEDIATRICS, INC 25315
  #875-01-1989 L1995 **PD** *020 †55
ABRAMOWITZ, David. 4605 MACCORKLE AVE SW, KANAWHA VALLEY 25309
  #048-02-1980 L1985 **DR** *020 †80

ABU-HALIMAH, Shadi Jabr. ■ 25304 #575-01-2000 **GS** *012
ABU RAHMA, Ali F. 1201 WASHINGTON ST E, STE 108 25301 #915-03-1970 L1975 **VS GS** *020 †85
ADI, Adla. 121 WASHINGTON ST W 25302 #495-04-1962 L1970 **FM** *020 ‡
ADKINS, Clark David. 100 TRACY WAY 25311 #055-02-1989 L1994 **ORS HS** *020 †40
AGARWAL, Bharat Das. ■ 25314 #495-05-1965 L1977 **FM** *071 †18
AGARWAL, Chaitanya Kumar. 11950 MACCORKLE AVE 25315 #495-49-1960 L1977 **GP** *020 †35
AGARWAL, Samir. 3110 MACCORKLE AVE SE, CHARLESTON AREA MEDICAL CE 25304 #055-01-2000 L2002 **CCS** *100 †85 ‡
AHMED, Nazia. 3200 MACCORKLE AVE SE, CHARLESTON AREA MEDICAL CT 25304 #704-25-1993 L2004 **IM** *020 †20
AKKACH, Kamal. ■ 25304 #473-01-1986 L2007 **MPD** *100 †20
AL-ASADI, Lo'Ay Mahmoud. 3100 MACCORKLE AVE 25304 #875-01-1985 L1992 **PCC PUD** *020
AL-ASBAHI, Riad S. 4605 MACCORKLE AVE SW, KANAWHA VALLEY 25309 #875-01-1971 L1979 **R** *020 †80
ALLARA, R David. 310 35TH ST SE, STE 11 25304 #055-01-1987 L1987 **OPH** *020
ALLEN, Leonard Franklin. 1215 VIRGINIA ST E 25301 #021-06-1993 L1996 **OMF FPS** *020
AMIN, Ahmad Zamael. ■ 25314 #036-01-2008 *012
AMORES, Constantino Y. 415 MORRIS ST STE 400, GENERAL MED PAVILION 25301 #748-01-1960 L1974 **NS** *020 †25
AMORES, Diana Suson. 333 LAIDLEY ST, DEPT RADIO 25301 #748-11-1963 **R** *020
ANSELMO, Mario T. 3200 MACCORKLE AVE SE, DEPT OF PATHOLOGY 25304 #748-01-1971 L1991 **PTH** *020 †50
ANTON, John Jos. 3416 MACCORKLE AVE SE 25304 #055-02-1992 L1998 **DR** *020 †80
ANTON, Michael Eugene. 1120 KANAWHA BLVD E, ASSOCIATED RADIOLOGISTS IN 25301 #055-02-1999 L2004 **DR** *020 †80
ARCEO, Constantino C. 830 PENNSYLVANIA AVE, STE 110 25302 #748-01-1963 L1973 **OBG** *071 †30
ARCEO-FREDERICK, Liza A. 3508 STAUNTON AVE SE, STE 300 25304 #055-02-1993 L1994 **AN** *005
ARIF, Jawad. 3200 MACCORKLE AVE SE 25304 #704-16-1999 **P** *012
ARMBRUST, Frederick H. 415 MORRIS ST 25301 #016-06-1971 L1992 **NS** *020 †25
ARTZ, Steven Albert. 4522 MACCORKLE AVE SE, STE 3 25304 #035-15-1962 L1967 **NM END** *040 †28,20
ASHHAB, Hazem A. 4701 MACCORKLE AVE SE 25304 #575-01-1988 L2001 **GE** *020 †20
ASHRAF, Syed Saud. 333 LAIDLEY ST, P O BOX 471 25301 #704-25-1998 L2002 **IM** *020 †20
AYOUBI, Mark B. 310 35TH ST SE STE 21 25304 #875-01-1970 L1974 **PD** *020 †55
AZIZ, Fatima Zehra. 3100 MACCORKLE AVE SE 25304 #704-25-1998 L2003 **IM** *020 †20
BABAR, Tania Bushra. 25311 #055-01-2006 L2007 *012
BABAR, Zarpash. 25311 #055-01-2005 L2006 **IM** *012
BACHWITT, Paul. 10 COURTNEY DR 25304 #051-04-1973 L1979 **OTR OAR** *020 †40
BAEK, James Jongmin. 4605 MACCORKLE AVE SW, KANAWHA VALLEY 25309 #038-06-1990 L1996 **DR** *020 †80
BAILEY, Bonnie Jean. 800 PENNSYLVANIA AVE, WOMEN AND CHILDRENS HOSPITAL 25302 #055-01-1996 L1999 **PD** *020 †55
BAILEY, Justin Dale. ■ 25304 #055-01-1999 L2001 **MPD** *020 †20
BAILEY, Thomas David. 419 BROOKS ST 25301 #055-01-1992 L1993 **IM** *020 †20
BAISDEN, April Michele. ■ 25314 #055-02-2004 **MP** *012
BAKER, Nicholas. ■ 25304 #055-01-2008 *012
BALIKAI, Shilpa. ■ 25302 #055-75-2007, ▲ L2012 *012
BALMASEDA, Mario T, Jr. 501 MORRIS ST, CAMC GENERAL DIV MED REHAB 25301 #748-02-1972 L1989 **PM** *020 †60
BANDAK, Abdalla Z. 4920 MACCORKLE AVE SE, BANDAK PLASTIC SURGERY 25304 #575-01-1983 L2005 **PS FPS** *020 †85,65
BANGANI, Prakash Chandra. 100 TRACY WAY 25311 #495-20-1964 L1972 **ORS** *020 †40
BARRETA, Telly Mendoza. 3200 MACCORKLE AVE SE, CHARLESTON AREA MED CTR 25304 #748-02-1969 L1994 **PTH** *020 †50
BATES, Mark Cline. 3110 MACCORKLE AVE SE 25304 #055-01-1986 L1987 **CD** *020 †20
BEARDSLEY, Andrew Richard. ■ 25304 #055-01-2008 *012
BEASLEY, Amy Burdette. ■ 25304 #055-01-2000 **PD** *100
BEASLEY, Michael Scott. 1306 KANAWHA BLVD E 25301 #055-01-2001 L2006 **OTO** *020 †45 ‡
BELLAPRAVALU, Sameer. 3200 MACCORKLE AVE SE 25304 #495-57-2002 **MP** *012
BENSENHAVER, Jessica Mile. ■ 25314 #055-02-2006 **GS** *012
BERRY, Bruce Lyle. 215 VIRGINIA ST W # 217 25302 #055-01-1972 L1974 **GYN** *071 †30
BHANOT, Veena Kumari. ■ 25314 #495-29-1972 L1981 **P** *020 †75
BHIRUD, Nilina R. 8618 MACCORKLE AVE 25315 #495-83-1980 L1984 **IM** *020 †20
BIANCO, Sabatino. 415 MORRIS ST STE 4, GENERAL MEDICAL PAVILLION 25301 #561-31-1995 L2005 **NS** *020 ‡
BISWAS, Kanoj Kumar. ■ 25314 #495-39-1959 L1973 **OBG** *020 †30
BIXLER, Danae. 350 CAPITOL ST RM 125, SURVELLANCE & DISEASE CONT 25301 #020-02-1983 L2000 **IM** *020 †20
BLOOM, Beth Erin. ■ 25314 #055-01-2007 **PD** *012
BOIKO, Iouri. 619 VIRGINIA ST W, OFFICE OF THE CHIEF MEDICA 25302 #913-47-1983 L2006 **FOP ATP** *062 †50 ‡
BOLAND, James Pius. 3110 MCCORKLE AVE SE 25304 #041-02-1956 L1976 **GS VS** *040 †90,85
BOONSUE, Elizabeth R. 3200 MACCORKLE AVE SE 25304 #055-01-1987 L1990 **IM** *020 †20
BORS, Kathleen Patricia. 1201 WASHINGTON ST E # 108, FAM MED CTR OF CHARLESTON 25301 #055-01-1987 L1990 **FM** *040 †18
BOSLEY, Miranda Lynn. ■ 25314 #055-01-2004 **GS** *100
BOURBIA, Abdelhamid. 830 PENNSYLVANIA AVE, PEDIATRIX MEDICAL GROUP, P 25302 #125-01-1988 L2005 **PD NPM** *020 †55
BOUSTANY, M M. 434 DIVISION ST, STE 1 25309 #875-01-1970 L1975 **GS VS** *020 †85
BOWDEN, Roy Thomas. 3701 MACCORKLE AVE SE, CHARLESTON INT MED INC 25304 #055-75-1997, ▲ L1998 **IM** *020 †20
BOWMAN, Kristin Daveen. ■ 25302 #055-75-2006, ▲ **IM** *012
BOWMAN, Richard Graham. 4605 MACCORKLE AVE SW, THE CENTER FOR PAIN 25309 #055-01-1987 L2000 **PM** *020 †60
BOWN, Paul Christian. 3100 MACCORKLE AVE, STE 602 25304 #048-15-1996 L2001 **GS** *020 †85
BRACERO, Luis A. 800 PENNSYLVANIA AVE, WOMEN AND CHLDRNS HOSP 25302 #035-47-1978 L2005 **OBG MFM** *020 †30
BRAUN, Nohl Arthur, Jr. 1418 MACCORKLE AVE SW, STE A 25303 #055-02-1993 L1995 **CHP GP** *020 †75
BREEDING, Lisa Michaelle. 331 LAIDLEY ST 25301 #055-01-1993 L1995 **OBG** *020 †30

BREHM, John G, Jr. 3001 CHESTERFIELD AVE, MEDICAL DIRECTOR WVMI 25304 #041-01-1970 L2001 **IM MDM** *030 †20
BROWN, James Walter. 4315 MACCORKLE AVE SE 25304 #055-02-1998 L2000 **FM** *020 †18
BUCKLEY, Marla Shea. ■ 25314 #055-01-2004 L2006 **IM** *020 †20
BURDETTE, John Ahearn. 3200 MACCORKLE AVE SE, CHARLESTON AREA MEDICAL CT 25304 #055-01-1983 L1984 **IM** *020
BURDETTE, Michelle Rene. 1097 FLEDDERJOHN RD, STE 1 25314 #055-02-1990 L1992 **FM** *020 †18 ‡
BUSCH, Gina Rae. 9 COURTNEY DR, SEDGELY OFFICE PARK 25304 #055-01-1982 L1983 **GYN** *020 †30
BUSH, Stephen H. 830 PENNSYLVANIA AVE # 304 25302 #055-01-1982 L1983 **OBG** *020 †30
BUSH, Stephen Harold, II. ■ 25304 #055-01-2008 *012
BYRD, John Wm. 3200 MACCORKLE AVE SE 25304 #055-01-1968 L1969 **RHU** *020 †20
CAFONCELLI, Antonio R. ■ 25304 #132-01-1961 L1981 **CD TS** *071 †85,90
CALHOUN, Byron Craig. ■ 25302 #018-03-1983 L2006 **OBS MFM** *020 †30 ‡
CAMPBELL, James Robert, II. 3110 MACCORKLE AVE SE 25304 #055-02-2003 L2006 **IM** *100 †20
CAMPBELL, John Erwin. ■ 25314 #055-02-2003 L2007 **IM** *100 †20
CANTRELL, Carrie Marie. ■ 25309 #055-01-2008 *012
CAPINPIN, Alberto G. 3200 MACCORKLE AVE SE 25304 #748-01-1953 L1964 **PS** *071
CAPITO, Richard Anthony. 1097 FLEDDERJOHN RD, ASHTON MEDICAL 25314 #055-01-1980 L1981 **EM OM** *020 †20,16
CARDOSO, Norbert Joe. 501 MORRIS ST 25301 #577-01-1975 L2000 **AN** *020
CARPER, Marshall J. 3200 MACCORKLE AVE SE 25304 #051-04-1952 L1953 **FM** *071 †18
CARROLL, Samuel Everett. 25309 #055-02-1997 L1998 **FM** *020 †18
CARTER, William Henkel. 3110 MACCORKLE AVE SE 25304 #051-01-1963 L1970 **CD IM** *020 †20
CASINGAL, Philip La Pena. 800 PENNSYLVANIA AVE 25302 #055-02-1992 L1999 **AN** *020 †05
CASSIS, Nick, Jr. 418 MORRIS ST, STE 300 25301 #055-01-1976 L1977 **END IM** *020 †20
CASSIS, Stephen Paul. 301 49TH ST SE STE A 25304 #055-01-1978 L1982 **OPH** *020 †35
CASTILLO, Alvin Renato. 800 PENNSYLVANIA AVE 25302 #055-02-2002 L2006 **AN** *020
CAUDILL, James White. 331 LAIDLEY ST, STE 102 25301 #055-01-1980 L1981 **OPH** *020 †35
CAVENDER, A Jean Plunkett. 3200 MACCORKLE AVE SE 25304 #051-04-1952 L1953 **GP** *071 †18
CAVENDER, Susan L. 1115 LEE ST E 25301 #055-01-1984 L1985 **FM** *020 †18
CENDANA, Elena H. ■ 25304 #748-01-1959 **IM ON** *071
CENDANA, Graciano E, Jr. 3200 MACCORKLE AVE SE 25304 #748-01-1958 L1971 **ATP CLP** *020 †50
CHAFFIN, David Garvin, Jr. 500 POPLAR ST, STE 202 25309 #023-07-1984 L1994 **OBG** *020 †30
CHALLA, Kishore Kumar. 428 DIVISION ST, STE 2 25309 #495-21-1962 L1989 **CD IM** *020 †20
CHAMBERS, John Turner. PO BOX 10 25321 #038-06-1947 L1951 **GYN** *071 †30
CHANCEY, Michael Howard. 4602 MACCORKLE AVE SE 25304 #055-01-1980 L1983 **GP** *020
CHANEY, Malcolm Lindsay. 1201 WASHINGTON ST E, STE 201 25301 #055-01-1978 L1979 **FM** *020 †18
CHANEY, Matthew Thomas. ■ 25314 #055-01-2005 L2005 **DR** *012
CHANG, Ho-Huang. 3200 MACCORKLE AVE SE 25304 #244-01-1968 L1975 **PTH PCP** *020 †50 ‡
CHAPMAN, John Ludwig. RR 4 BOX 50 25312 #023-01-1979 L1980 **EM** *020 †20,85,90
CHAUVENET, Allen Russell. 830 PENNSYLVANIA AVE 25302 #011-03-1978 L2007 **PHO PD** *020 †55
CHIANG, Myra Lee. 830 PENNSYLVANIA AVE, STE 104 25302 #748-10-1979 L1988 **PN PD** *020 †55
CLARK, James Paul, II. 3411 NOYES AVE STE A 25304 #055-02-1991 L1993 **AI** *020 †20,03
CLARK, Mary H Hoback. 500 QUARRIER ST STE 500, DISABILITY DETER SECT 25301 #055-01-1976 L1976 **CHP P** *030
CLARKE, Gregory Dresel. 3110 MACCORKLE AVE SE 25304 #055-01-1989 L1990 **IM PD** *020 †20,55
CLAY, Ricky Perry. 3200 MACCORKLE AVE SE, CHARLESTON AREA MED CTR 25304 #001-02-2007 **GS** *012
CO, Jeannie Po. 3200 MACCORKLE AVE SE, CHARLESTON AREA MED CTR 25304 #748-02-2004 **MPD** *012
COCHRAN, Robert Carter. 1201 WASHINGTON ST E, STE 108 25301 #024-05-1960 L1983 **GS** *040 †85
COHEN, Justin David. 3100 MACCORKLE AVE, STE 101 25304 #016-01-1981 L1998 **ON IM** *020 †20
COLLINS, Michael Allan. ■ 25304 #055-75-2002, ▲ L2003 **NEP** *012 †20
CONNER, Timothy Allen. 3416 MACCORKLE AVE SE 25304 #055-01-1988 L1989 **R** *020 †80
COOLEY, Frederick Morton. ■ 25304 #055-01-1962 L1963 **OS** *072 †18
COOMBE, Raymond Paul. 800 PENNSYLVANIA AVE 25302 #041-02-1989 L1993 **AN PME** *020 †05
COPELAND, Stacey Ellen. 9 COURTNEY DR 25304 #028-46-1993 L1994 **GS** *020 †85
CORDELL, Ronald Eugene. 3416 MACCORKLE AVE SE 25304 #047-06-1975 L1981 **DR VIR** *020 †80 ‡
COTTRILL, Casey Brooke. ■ 25303 #055-01-2008 *012
COUSINS, Geoffrey Ramon. 2345 CHESTERFIELD AVE, STE 304 25304 #025-01-1998 L2005 **TS** *100 †85,90
COVELLI, Michael Anthony. 2345 CHESTERFIELD AVE, STE 307 25304 #055-01-1993 L1994 **GS** *020 †85
COWEN, Richard Leslie. ■ 25314 #038-41-1962 L1976 **R** *071 †80
CRIGGER, William D. ■ 25314 #041-13-1950 L1951 **FM FPG** *071 †18
CRISALLI, Robert James. 3100 MACCORKLE AVE SE, STE 503 25304 #012-05-1972 L1977 **PUD IM** *020 †20
CRISLIP, Seth Montgomery. ■ 25314 #055-01-2008 *012
CROSS, Kimberly Sue. 501 MORRIS ST 25301 #055-01-1997 L1999 **PD IM** *020 †20,55
CROTTY, Glenn, Jr. 1201 WASHINGTON ST E, STE 108 25301 #055-01-1976 L1976 **END IM** *030 †20
CROW, Robert Jos. 415 MORRIS ST 25301 #001-02-1987 L1997 **NS** *020 †25
CRUZ, Julia Margarita. 3110 MACCORKLE AVE SE, BOWMAN GRAY SCHOOL OF MED 25304 #011-03-1978 L2008 **HO IM** *062 †20
CULPEPPER, John Wesley, Jr. 210 BROOKS ST, STE 200 25301 #012-01-1998 L2005 **PS** *020 †65
CUNNINGHAM, Jan Howard. 830 PENNSYLVANIA AVE, STE 405 25302 #055-01-1973 L1974 **GYN** *020 †30
CURNUTTE, Larry Douglas. 4501 MACCORKLE AVE SW, STE 200 25309 #055-01-1965 L1966 **GYN OS** *020 †30
CURRY, Wyson, Jr. 123 WASHINGTON ST W 25302 #051-04-1946 L1948 **IM GP** *074

CURTIS, Clinton Edward. 3200 MACCORKLE AVE SE 25304 #055-02-1997 L1999 **IM** *020 †20
DAIA, Euripedes Antonio. 800 PENNSYLVANIA AVE 25302 #187-28-1968 L1995 **AN** *020 †05
DALABIH, Abdallah Riad. ■ 25304 #902-07-2004 L2006 **PD** *012
DALRYMPLE, Joanne Lee. 4605 MACCORKLE AVE SW, C/O THOMAS MEM HOSP 25309 #005-12-1990 L1998 **IM** *020 †20
DAMERON, Jeffrey Craig. 1120 KANAWHA BLVD E, P O BOX 11137 25301 #055-02-1996 L1997 **DR** *020 †80
DANS, Nestor Felipe. 2345 CHESTERFIELD AVE, STE 203 25304 #021-01-1985 L2000 **TS VS** *020 †85,90
DARNELL, Timothy A. ■ 25302 #055-75-2006, ▲ **IM** *012
DAVALOS, Julio Gustave. 11 COURTNEY DR 25304 #055-01-2000 L2004 **U** *020 †95
DAVE, Darshankumar A. 3100 MACCORKLE AVE SE, STE 802 25304 #495-89-1990 L2003 **N CN** *020
DAWSON, George Stephen. 500 DONNALLY ST, ASSOCIATES OF CHARLESTON 25301 #055-02-1997 L1999 **OTO** *020 †45
DEAN, Alan Michael. 3508 STAUNTON AVE SE 25304 #047-05-1998 L2002 **AN** *020 †05
DEAN, Rodney Douglas. 432 DIVISION ST 25309 #055-01-1973 L1977 **U** *020 †95
DEARDORFF, William Alva. ■ 25314 #051-04-1956 L1957 **R NM** *071 †80,28
DEER, Timothy Ray. 4605 MACCORKLE AVE SW, THE CENTER FOR PAIN 25309 #055-01-1990 L1994 **PMM AN** *020 †05
DEFADE, Brian. ■ 25314 #055-75-2004, ▲ L2005 **GS** *100
DELGRA, Cecilio Galvez, Jr. ■ 25309 #055-01-1999 *100
DELGRA, Cecilio V. 800 PENNSYLVANIA AVE 25302 #748-11-1962 L1983 **AN** *020 ‡
DELGRA, Lemwel Galvez. 800 PENNSYLVANIA AVE 25302 #055-01-1992 L1998 **AN** *020 †05
DEL ROSARIO, M Concepcion. ■ 25314 #748-14-1989 L2005 **PD** *020
DELUCA, John Anthony. 1201 WASHINGTON ST E, STE 108 25301 #055-01-1989 L1993 **GS** *020 †85
DEPOND, Robert Todd. 400 COURT ST STE 100 25301 #055-01-1990 L1992 **GYN** *020 †30
DERAKHSHAN, Iraj. 415 MORRIS ST STE 401 25301 #517-01-1968 L1996 **N** *050 †75
DEWITT, Michael S. 506 CHESTNUT ST 25309 #055-75-1989, ▲ L1990 **FM** *020 †18
DICKEY, Thomas Oscar, III. 501 MORRIS ST 25301 #055-01-1978 L1979 **P CHP** *020 †75
DICKMAN, Daniel Jos. 1201 WASHINGTON ST E, STE 108 25301 #055-01-1988 L1991 **FM** *020 †18
DIETZ, Paul Dale. 830 PENNSYLVANIA AVE, STE 304 25302 #055-01-1998 L2002 **OBG** *040 †30
DIN, Farid Ud. 3200 MACCORKLE AVE SE, CHARLESTON AREA MED CTR 25304 #704-25-2000 L2007 **GS** *100
DOUGLASS, Thomas Richard. 800 PENNSYLVANIA AVE 25302 #055-01-1979 L1980 **AN** *020 †05
DOWNHAM, Lisa Elaine. 1201 WASHINGTON ST E, STE 208 25301 #055-01-1996 L1998 **MPD CCM** *020 †20,55
DUDZINSKI, Cezary Dariusz. 3200 MACCORKLE AVE SE 25304 #759-06-1990 **P** *012
DULING, Walter E. ■ 25304 #041-02-1953 L1955 **FM** *075 †18
DUMM, Kelli Jo. 400 COURT ST STE 200 25301 #055-01-2001 L2003 **MPD** *020 †20
DUNCAN, Harry Earl, Jr. 4701 MACCORKLE AVE SE 25304 #055-01-1974 L1975 **GE IM** *020 †20
DYER, Benjamin Whited. ■ 25304 #055-02-2004 **GS** *012
EADS, Kristen Price. 3200 MACCORKLE AVE SE, DEPT OF SURGERY 25304 #055-02-2003 **GS** *012
ECKERD, John Marcus. 830 PENNSYLVANIA AVE, STE 104 25302 #036-05-1969 L1987 **PDC** *040 †55
EDE, David Elias. 415 MORRIS ST, STE 104 25301 #011-02-1990 L1997 **ORS** *020 †40
EGGLESTON, Kevin Lee. 3200 MACCORKLE AVE SE, WVU CAMC CLINIC A 25304 #055-01-2001 L2003 **PCC** *020
EGGLESTON, Robert Michael. 400 COURT ST, STE 200 25301 #055-01-1997 L1998 **MPD** *020 †20
EGNOR, James Kesley. 4602 MACCORKLE AVE SE 25304 #055-01-1971 L1971 **IM** *020
ELDER, Katrina Rae. 1201 WASHINGTON ST E, STE 108 25301 #055-01-2005 L2007 **FP** *012
EL-GAMMAL, Ahmed Mahmoud. ■ 25302 #915-02-1993 L2001 **ID** *020
ELGHUL, Ashraf Mohamed. 3200 MACCORKLE AVE SE 25304 #613-02-1996 L2006 **IM** *020
ELHABYAN, Abdulkarim. 3110 MACCORKLE AVE SE, INTERNAL MEDICINE DEPT,R30 25304 #875-02-1991 L2006 **IM** *020 †20
ELKSNIS, Stephen Mark. 3416 MACCORKLE AVE SE 25304 #023-01-1988 L1989 **NR** *020 †80
ELLIOTT, Sandra Young. 3501 MACCORKLE AVE SE, # 202 25304 #055-02-1987 L1989 **ID IM** *020 †20
ESTALILLA, Oscar Cinco. 3200 MACCORKLE AVE SE, DEPT OF PATHOLOGY-CAMC 25304 #748-19-1984 L2000 **PTH** *020 †50
EWING, Kimberly Faye. 800 PENNSYLVANIA AVE, WOMENS & CHILDREN'S EMER D 25302 #055-02-1986 L1989 **PD** *020 †55
FAMULARCANO, Earl Michael. 3200 MACCORKLE AVE SE 25304 #748-07-1999 L2007 **FM** *020
FANNING, Robin Leeann. 4602 MACCORKLE AVE SE, PROVIDERS INC 25304 #055-01-1993 L1996 **PD** *020 †55
FARINASH, Lloyd Joseph. 3100 MACCORKLE AVE SE, STE B1 25304 #055-01-2001 L2006 **RO** *020 †80
FARMER, Donald Edward. 3100 MACCORKLE AVE SE, STE 810 25304 #055-01-1965 L1974 **D** *020
FARRA, Sami Al. 415 MORRIS ST STE 205 25301 #875-01-1970 L1980 **U** *020
FARRIS, Joseph H, II. 3200 MACCORKLE AVE SE, CAMC-MEMORIAL PAT ACCESS 25304 #055-01-1981 L1982 **IM** *020 †20
FATHY, Harry H. 415 MORRIS ST STE 407 25301 #517-03-1962 L1984 **ORS** *020 †40
FAW, Mary Elizabeth. 2335 CHESTERFIELD AVE, STE 302 25304 #055-02-1998 L2001 **END** *020 †20
FELSEN, James D. ■ 25312 #035-06-1966 L2000 **PHP GPM** *071 †70
FETSAK, Andriy. 3200 MACCORKLE AVE SE 25304 #913-17-1996 L2007 **IM** *020 †20
FIDLER, Michael O'Neil. 100 TRACY WAY 25311 #051-01-1974 L1980 **ORS HS** *020 †40
FIGUEROA, Edmundo E. 415 MORRIS ST, STE 301 25301 #748-01-1968 L1976 **TS VS** *020 †85,90
FORERO, Jaime. 13 SAINT CHARLES PL, 1575 SMITH ROAD 25314 #264-01-1960 L1975 **EM ORS** *071
FORTNER, Thomas Edward. 3100 MACCORKLE AVE SE, STE 202 25304 #055-01-1970 L1970 **GP** *075
FOSTER, Daniel Stevenson. 333 LAIDLEY ST 25301 #005-11-1974 L1979 **GS VS** *071 †85
FOX, Melissa Dawn. 830 PENNSYLVANIA AVE, STE 104 25302 #055-02-2004 L2007 **PD** *100 †55
FRAIL, Carol Johnson. 830 PENNSYLVANIA AVE 25302 #055-01-1984 L1987 **PD** *020 †55
FRAME, James Norman. 3200 MACCORKLE AVE SE, CANCER CENTER ADMIN 25304 #055-01-1981 L1982 **ON HEM** *020 †20
FRANCKE, Paul Frederick. 1201 WASHINGTON ST E # 203 25301 #055-01-1979 L1980 **OPH** *020 †35
FRANCO, Manuel Perez. 1097 FLEDDERJOHN RD, STE 1 25314 #748-01-1970 L1979 **EM GP** *020 †16
FRAZER, Jason Allen. 3200 MACCORKLE AVE SE, DEPT OF INTERNAL MEDICINE 25304 #055-01-2004 L2008 **MPD** *012
GARMANY, Farah H. 3100 MACCORKLE AVE SE, STE 808 25304 #422-01-1990 L1997 **PDC** *020 †55
GARMANY, Firooz. 3100 MACCORKLE AVE SE, STE 808 25304 #305-01-1991 L1997 **IM PD** *020
GATELEY, Kerry Wix. 108 LEE ST E, KANAWHA CHARLES HLTH DEPT 25301 #047-06-1985 L2003 **PHP GPM** *030 †70
GATELEY, Laura Turney. 1111 FLEDDERJOHN RD, BOX 112 25314 #047-06-1985 L2003 **FM** *074 †18
GAZIANO, Dominic. 3100 MACCORKLE AVE SE, STE 404 25304 #051-04-1962 L1966 **PUD IM** *020 †20
GEORGES, Talal. 3200 MACCORKLE AVE SE 25304 #665-01-2000 **FM** *100
GERONILLA, Dante Rizal. 800 PENNSYLVANIA AVE 25302 #748-01-1968 L1983 **AN GP** *020 †18,05
GHIZ, Robert Leroy. 3200 MACCORKLE AVE SE 25304 #016-06-1963 L1970 **ORS** *020 †40
GHODASARA, Dilip P. 4 SHAMBLIN PL 25314 #495-48-1984 L1995 **IM** *020 †20
GLOGOWSKI, Karen Ann. 104 ALEX LN 25304 #055-01-1999 L2000 **FM** *020 †18
GO, Rosalind Lee. ■ 25314 #748-01-1961 L1974 **IM** *062
GOAD, John Lee. 2930 CHESTERFIELD AVE 25304 #055-01-1987 L1988 **CD** *020 †20
GOEL, Ashutosh. 3200 MACCORKLE AVE SE 25304 #495-36-1994 L2006 **FM** *020 †18
GOGINENI, Ravindra K. 4605 MACCORKLE AVE SW, KANAWHA VALLEY 25309 #495-65-1974 L1981 **DR** *020 †80 ‡
GOINS, Michael Roy. 500 DONNALLY ST, ASSOCIATES OF CHARLESTON 25301 #055-01-2000 L2005 **OTO** *020 †45
GOLDBERG, Todd Harley. 3110 MACCORKLE AVE SE, WVU PHY CHARLESTON 25304 #035-19-1984 L2007 **IMG IM** *020 †20 ‡
GOLDFARB, Glenn Robt. 2345 CHESTERFIELD AVE, STE 303 25304 #055-01-1982 L1987 **N** *020 †75
GOMEZ, A Rafael. 3500 STAUNTON AVE SE 25304 #036-05-1961 L1969 **IM HEM** *030
GRAY, David Benoni. 3200 MACCORKLE AVE SE 25304 #023-01-1943 L1947 **GS OS** *071 †85
GREEN, Gordon James. 419 BROOKS ST, DEPARTMENT OF EMERG MED 25301 #061-01-1992 L1998 **PD** *020
GREISMAN, Bernard. 830 PENNSYLVANIA AVE, STE 304 25302 #065-09-1967 L2000 **OBG** *040 ‡
GREY, Edward Jos. 3100 MACCORKLE AVE SE, STE 806 25304 #055-02-1992 L1994 **PUD** *020 †20
GRIFFIN, Stacie M. ■ 25304 #055-01-2008 *012
GRIFFITH, Brian Keith. 1306 KANAWHA BLVD E, EYE, EAR CLINIC PHYSICIANS 25301 #055-01-1999 L2003 **OPH** *020 †35
GRIFFITH, James. 3200 MACCORKLE AVE SE, CHARLESTON AREA MEDICAL CT 25304 #055-01-1985 L1987 **P IM** *040 †75,20
GRUBB, Stephen Ray. 3110 MACCORKLE AVE SE 25304 #051-04-1969 L1977 **END IM** *020 †20
GUHA, Somes Chandra. 419 BROOKS ST, STE 108 25301 #495-39-1972 L2002 **FM** *020 †18
GUO, Wei-Xing. 3508 STAUNTON AVE SE 25304 #243-58-1983 L2002 **AN** *020 †05
GUY, Charles David. PO BOX 1393 25325 #055-01-1980 L1982 **P** *020
GUYER, Greta. 2345 CHESTERFIELD AVE #204 25304 #055-02-1990 L1992 **END** *020 †20
HABIB, Joseph Hasan. ■ 25314 #055-01-2005 **GS** *012
HADDY, Julie Ann. 2345 CHESTERFIELD AVE, STE 301 25304 #055-01-2001 L2003 **NEP** *020
HAIDAR, Zeina Nadim. 888 OAKWOOD RD STE 110 25314 #605-02-1994 L1998 **PD** *020 †55
HAIDER, Adnan. 3200 MACCORKLE AVE SE 25304 #704-02-2003 **IM** *012
HAIKAL, Nabila Abdel-Aziz. 619 VIRGINIA ST W, OFFICE OF THE CHIEF MEDICA 25302 #605-01-1983 L2004 **PTH** *020 †50
HALL, Carl Bemis. ■ 25304 #051-04-1940 L1941 **FM** *071
HALL, Michael David. 1201 WASHINGTON ST E, STE 208 25301 #039-01-1983 L1984 **GS VS** *020 †85
HALL, Phillip. 4300 MACCORKLE AVE SE 25304 #055-01-1988 L1989 **ADM** *020 †18 ‡
HALL, Rodney Lee. 4605 MACCORKLE AVE SW 25309 #055-01-1972 L1972 **AN** *020 †05
HALL, William David, Jr. 800 PENNSYLVANIA AVE 25302 #055-02-2002 L2006 **AN** *020
HALLAK, Omar Kamel. 331 LAIDLEY ST STE 402, CHARLESTON CARDIOVASCULAR 25301 #875-01-1984 L1999 **CD IC** *020 †20
HALLEY, Michael Willford. ■ 25311 #055-01-1986 L1987 **FM EM** *020 †18
HAMRICK, George Vincent. ■ 25314 #023-01-1948 L1959 **OPH** *071 †35
HAMRICK, Roland Edward. 1117 LEE ST E 25301 #055-01-1979 L1979 **GS VS** *020 †85
HANING, Hedda A Litowitz. 4605 MACCORKLE AVE SW 25309 #038-06-1968 L1995 **AN PD** *020 †55,05
HANING, Ray Vernon, Jr. ■ 25314 #038-06-1968 L1968 **OBG** *075 †30
HANLON, Charin Lee. 3200 MACCORKLE AVE SE 25304 #055-01-1999 L2000 **IM P** *040 †20,75
HANNAH, John Walton. 400 DIVISION ST, STE 6 25309 #055-01-1989 L1994 **U** *020 †95
HANSBARGER, Echols Alcott. PO BOX 2548 25329 #051-04-1956 L1974 **PTH** *071 †50
HANSBARGER, Luther Clark. 3110 MACCORKLE AVE SE, WVU SCHOOL OF MEDICINE 25304 #051-04-1957 L1972 **PD** *020 †55
HARISH, Gorli. 4803 MACCORKLE AVE SE 25304 #495-99-1971 L1975 **OBG** *020 †30
HARLESS-MEHTA, Sheryl L. 333 LAIDLEY ST 25301 #055-02-1995 L1997 **FM** *020 †18
HARLOW, Gene Wm. 1418 MACCORKLE AVE SW, STE A 25303 #020-02-1963 L1964 **GP** *071
HARMON, Michael B. 3100 MACCORKLE AVE SE, STE B1 25304 #055-01-1985 L1986 **RO** *020 †80
HARRIS, William Lee. 3100 MACCORKLE AVE SE, STE 307 25304 #055-01-1974 L1975 **FM FPG** *020 †18
HASAN, Sulaiman Bashir. 2335 CHESTERFIELD AVE, STE 300 25304 #704-02-1980 L1996 **TS CD** *020 †90,85
HAWKINS, Richard Allen. 5003 VENABLE AVE # A 25304 #055-01-1969 L1970 **D** *020 †15
HAYAT, Faisal. 3110 MACCORKLE AVE SE 25304 #704-09-1999 L2007 **IM** *012
HAYES, John David. 3110 MACCORKLE AVE SE 25304 #055-01-2003 **GS** *012
HAYES, Thomas Morton. 301 QUARRIER ST, KANAWHA VALLEY RADS INC 25301 #048-02-1967 L1974 **DR NM** *020 †80
HENDERSON, James M. 3200 MACCORKLE AVE SE 25304 #023-01-1998 L2001 **OS** *020
HENRY, Bradley Dean. 600 MORRIS ST, STE 102 25301 #055-02-1991 L1994 **IM** *020 †20
HENRY, Debra L. 4605 MACCORKLE AVE SW 25309 #055-01-1986 L1987 **EM FM** *020 †18
HENSON, Samuel Lee. 1520 WASHINGTON ST E, WEST VIRGINIA HEALTH RIGHT 25311 #055-01-1966 L1967 **PTH FM** *020 †50 ‡
HERNANDEZ, Antonio Garin. ■ 25304 #748-01-1931 L1978 **GP** *071
HERNANDEZ, Jaime E. 3110 MACCORKLE AVE SE, WVU HELATH SCIENCES CENTER 25304 #429-01-1981 L1990 **ID** *020 †20
HEROLD, William Sawyers. ■ 25311 #051-04-1947 L1948 **PHP AN** *071

HEYWOOD, Elijah Reed. 501 MORRIS ST 25301 #049-01-1968 L1991 **OBG** *040 †30

HEYWOOD, Samuel Greg. 1003 OAKHURST DR 25314 #005-12-1996 L1999 **OBG** *020 †30

HIJAZI, Najla. 419 BROOKS ST, DEPT OF EMERGENCY MEDICINE 25301 #605-01-1992 L1997 **PD** *020 †55

HILL, Randall James. 830 PENNSYLVANIA AVE, STE 301 25302 #051-01-1983 L1984 **OBG** *020 †30

HIX, Charity Vika. 1306 KANAWHA BLVD E, EYE & EAR CLINIC PHYSICIAN 25301 #018-03-2000 L2002 **OPH** *020 †35

HOFELDT, Matthew John. 3100 MACCORKLE AVE, WVU - DEPT OF SURGERY, C/O 25304 #055-01-2002 L2005 **GS** *020

HOGUE, Gavin Neil. 102 PATRICK STREET PLZ, PHYSICAL EXAMS INC 25312 #055-01-1983 L1987 **OM PD** *020

HOH, William Gerard. 301 RHL, STE 201 25309 #041-12-1992 L2001 **OM** *020 †70

HORSFORD, Nichole M. 300 56TH ST SE 25304 #422-01-1998 L2003 **P** *100

HORSMAN, Thomas Allen. 501 MORRIS ST 25301 #055-01-1974 L1975 **IM ID** *020 †20

HORSWELL, Bruce Brian. 415 MORRIS ST, FACIAL SURGERY STE 309 25301 #008-02-1991 L2001 **FPS** *020

HOSSINO, Hatem Mahmoud. 415 MORRIS ST STE 101 25301 #915-08-1970 L1976 **GS** *020 †85

HOSTLER, John Andrew. ■ 25311 #055-01-1978 L1980 **NPM PD** *020

HOWARD, Thomas Wm, II. 100 TRACY WAY 25311 #055-01-1978 L1979 **RHU IM** *020 †20

HOYLMAN, Vera Louise. 310 35TH ST SE STE 21 25304 #055-01-1973 L1974 **PD** *020 †55

HUANG, Tzong-Wen E. 3200 MACCORKLE AVE SE, DEPT PATH CHARLESTON MED 25304 #244-02-1980 L1997 **NP ATP** *020 †50

HUMPHREYS, David John. 5130 MACCORKLE AVE SE 25304 #040-02-1975 L1986 **P** *020 †75

HUNTER, Francis Scott. 830 PENNSYLVANIA AVE, STE 408 25302 #055-02-1981 L1984 **OBG** *020 †30

HUNTER, Paul Brian. 830 PENNSYLVANIA AVE, STE 402 25302 #055-01-1995 L1999 **OBG** *020 †30

HUTTON, John Patrick. 1418 MACCORKLE AVE SW, STE A 25303 #055-01-1974 L1974 **P IM** *020 †75

IBRAHIM BACHA, Ghali. 11950 MACCORKLE AVE STE B 25315 #875-02-1993 L1998 **IM** *020 †20

IQBAL, Syed Zafar. 3200 MACCORKLE AVE SE, CHARLESTON AREA MED CTR 25304 #704-22-1992 *100

ISTFAN, Michael Alan. 500 DONNALLY ST, BLDG B 25301 #055-02-1984 L1985 **RHU IM** *020 †20

ISTFAN, Sharon L. 800 PENNSYLVANIA AVE, CHILDREN'S MEDICINE CTR 25302 #055-01-1993 L1996 **PD** *020 †55

JACKSON, Harry Arden. ■ 25314 #051-04-1955 L1956 **IM** *072 †20

JACKSON, Robert B. 400 DIVISION ST, STE 1 25309 #055-01-1987 L1995 **OPH** *020 †35

JACKSON, Theodore A. 415 MORRIS ST, STE 200 25301 #055-01-1982 L1983 **PS HS** *020 †65

JACKSON, Utaiwan S. 4819B PENN AVE 25302 #891-03-1970 L1974 **GP** *071

JAGANNATH, Thopsie V. 5314 MACCORKLE AVE SE 25304 #495-33-1981 L1990 **IM** *020 †20

JAIN, Neha. ■ 25301 #496-04-2005 L2006 **P** *012

JAIN, Sunil Kumar. 3200 MACCORKLE AVE SE 25304 #495-93-1987 **IM** *012

JANICKI, Thomas Jos. ■ 25314 #051-04-1961 L1962 **FM** *071 †18

JARRELL, Joseph. 3456 PIEDMONT RD 25306 #055-01-1992 L1997 **IMG PD** *020

JAYARAM, Davangere M. 830 PENNSYLVANIA AVE, STE 406 25302 #495-99-1971 L1977 **OS** *020 †55

JAYARAM, Geeta Davangere. 4403 44TH ST SE, MEYER4 181 25304 #495-35-1974 L1981 **PD** *020 †55

JEFFREY, Jamie Latham. 800 PENNSYLVANIA AVE, WOMEN & CHILDREN'S HOSPITA 25302 #055-02-1992 L1995 **PD** *020 †55

JEFFREY, William Randolph. 500 DONNALLY ST STE 203 25301 #055-02-1991 L1995 **IM** *020 †20

JELIC, Tomislav. ■ 25304 #957-01-1975 L1994 **PTH** *020 †50

JENKINS, Janet A. GENERAL DIVISION, CHARLESTON AREA MED CTR 25325 #055-02-1988 L1992 **PM** *020 †60

JESSE, Jane Marie. 3200 MACCORKLE AVE SE 25304 #665-02-2003 L2008 **P** *012

JOHN, Molly. 3110 MACCORKLE AVE SE, WVU PHYSICIANS OF CHARLEST 25304 #495-31-1979 L1992 **IM** *020 †20

JOHNSON, William Michael. 401 DIVISION ST, STE 205 25309 #055-01-1992 L1999 **FM** *020 †18

JOHNSTON, Robert Brian. 1201 WASHINGTON ST E, STE 201 25303 #055-01-2002 L2003 **FM** *020 †18

JONES, Ronald S. 830 PENNSYLVANIA AVE # 305 25302 #051-04-1977 L1978 **OBG** *020 †30

JOSHI, Aniket A. 830 PENNSYLVANIA AVE SU, PEDIATRIX MEDICAL GROUP 25302 #495-28-1988 L2003 **CCP** *020 †55

JOSHI, Sarita. 830 PENNSYLVANIA AVE, STE 104 MEDICAL STAFF BLDG 25302 #495-28-1988 L2003 **PHO** *040 †55

JOYCE, Joseph Lee. 1417 NOTTINGHAM RD 25314 #055-02-1997 L2002 **OS** *020 †20,16

JUBELIRER, Steven James. 3100 MACCORKLE AVE, STE 101 25304 #038-41-1974 L1980 **HO IM** *020 †20

JUSTICE, John David. 5600 MACCORKLE AVE SE 25304 #055-01-1993 L1998 **P** *062 †75

KAHWASH, Ziad. 436 DIVISION ST 25309 #875-01-1987 L1993 **END IM** *020 †20

KAPLAN, James Anthony. ■ 25314 #045-01-1984 L1997 **PTH** *020 †50

KASEM, Hoda. 1201 WASHINGTON ST E, STE 108 25301 #875-01-1995 **FP** *012

KASLOVSKY, Robert Allen. 830 PENNSYLVANIA AVE, STE 103 25302 #035-03-1981 L2005 **PDP PD** *020 †55

KASTURI, Vellore Gundurao. 3200 MACCORKLE AVE SE, CHARLESTON AREA MED CTR 25304 #495-35-1989 L2008 **OBG** *012

KATRIB, Karim Abdul. 400 DIVISION ST, STE 11 25309 #875-01-1976 L1984 **OTO** *020 †45

KAZMI, Samina. 415 MORRIS ST STE 403, MEDICAL STAFF BUILLDING 25301 #704-16-1988 L2002 **NEP CN** *020 †75

KELLY, Lawrence Bennett. 415 MORRIS ST STE 306 25301 #055-01-1979 L1980 **P ADP** *020 †75

KERNS, Fred Timothy. 3100 MACCORKLE AVE, STE 604 25304 #055-01-1977 L1978 **ID IM** *020 †20

KESSLER, Michaela Elaine. 3200 MACCORKLE AVE SE 25304 #055-75-2003, ▲ L2005 **OBG** *012

KHALID, Ahmed A. 3100 MACCORKLE AVE SE, STE 101 25304 #704-20-1988 L2004 **HO** *020 †20

KHAN, Aftab Ali. ■ 25304 #496-27-1997 **P** *100

KHAN, Ahmad Aftab. 2335 CHESTERFIELD AVE, STE 300 25304 #035-09-1999 L2007 **TS** *020

KHAN, Jamal Hameed. 2335 CHESTERFIELD AVE, STE 300 25304 #704-01-1961 L1972 **TS GS** *071 †85,90

KHAN, Mohammad Zafrullah. 2335 CHESTERFIELD AVE, STE 300 25304 #704-01-1961 L1974 **TS VS** *020 †85,90

KHAN, Muhammad Atif. 3200 MACCORKLE AVE SE 25304 #704-02-2003 **PD** *012

KHAN, Noma. 3200 MACCORKLE AVE SE 25304 #704-16-1996 **IM** *012

KHAN, Parveen. 3200 MACCORKLE AVE SE 25304 #704-17-1988 L2007 **OBG** *012

KHAN, Raheel Rasheed. 830 PENNSYLVANIA AVE, STE 104 25302 #704-02-1983 L1993 **PD PDI** *040 †55

KHAN, Roohi Majeed. 1701 5TH AVE STE 5 25312 #704-02-1998 L2004 **IM** *020 †20

KHAN, Sofia Salim. 4501 MACCORKLE AVE SE 25304 #704-16-1988 L1997 **PD** *020 †55

KHAN, Yusuf Hameed. 511 BROOKS ST, DEPT OF EMERGENCY MEDICINE 25301 #305-01-2001 L2005 **FM** *020

KIM, Christopher Konkyo. 4605 MACCORKLE AVE SW, THE CENTER FOR PAIN 25309 #051-04-1993 L1999 **APM** *020 †05

KIM, Jay Ja-Eark. 2335 CHESTERFIELD AVE, STE 300 25304 #583-02-1975 L1995 **TS VS** *020 †85,90

KINDER, Jack Lee, Jr. 600 MORRIS ST, STE 102 25301 #055-02-1991 L1994 **IM** *020 †20

KING, Russell Frederick. 3416 MACCORKLE AVE SE 25304 #055-01-1991 L1993 **DR** *020 †80

KIRATISEAVEE, Siwat. 208 MACCORKLE AVE SE 25314 #891-01-1997 L2007 **AI** *020 †20,03

KISNER, Amy Horsman. 4602 MACCORKLE AVE SE 25304 #055-01-1997 L1998 **MPD** *020 †55,20

KISTER, Nathanial Lloyd. ■ 25312 #055-01-2008 *012

KLAPPROTH, Karl L. 3200 MACCORKLE AVE SE 25304 #407-23-1959 L1973 **PTH ORS** *020

KLIMEK, Deborah Lynn. 24 MACCORKLE AVE SW, STE 203 25303 #026-04-1997 L2003 **PO OPH** *020 †35

KNEBEL, Richard. 800 PENNSYLVANIA AVE 25302 #041-77-1988, ▲ L2002 **AN** *020 †05

KOIKE, Jun. 830 PENNSYLVANIA AVE 25302 #305-01-2004 L2008 **OBG** *012

KOMMOR, Martin Jay. 501 MORRIS ST 4, WVU DEPT BEHAVIORAL MED 25301 #020-02-1972 L1975 **P** *030 †75

KORESHI, Muhammad Kashif. 3200 MACCORKLE AVE SE 25304 #704-16-1998 **FM** *100

KOVALENKO, Tetyana Olexan. 3200 MACCORKLE AVE SE 25304 #913-10-1997 **PD** *012

KOWALSKI, Tadeus Edward. 3200 MACCORKLE AVE SE 25304 #654-01-2006 **MP** *012

KRESA-REAHL, Kiren. 415 MORRIS ST STE 100, STE 100 25301 #010-02-1991 L1996 **N** *020 †75

KRISHNATHAS, Ananthan. 333 LAIDLEY ST, DEPT OF HOSP MED ST FRANCS 25301 #220-04-1989 L2004 **IM** *020

KSHIRSAGAR, Arundhati V. 1562 NOTTINGHAM RD 25314 #496-38-1966 L1979 **OBG** *020 †30

KSHIRSAGAR, Vasudeo H. ■ 25314 #495-21-1960 L1979 **PTH** *062 †50

KUSMINSKY, Roberto E. 1201 WASHINGTON ST E, STE 108 25301 #132-01-1967 L1977 **CRS GS** *020 †10,85

LABUS, Lester. 500 DONNALLY ST STE 203 25301 #055-01-1983 L1984 **FM FPG** *020 †18

LAGMAN, Manuel David. 333 LAIDLEY ST 25301 #748-01-1993 L1994 **FM** *071

LANSANG, Ramon Salalila. 501 MORRIS ST, CAMC/GENERAL DIVISION 25301 #748-16-1993 L2002 **PM** *020 †60

LAO, Michael Ramos. 830 PENNSYLVANIA AVE, STE 304 25302 #748-11-2000 L2005 **OBG** *020

LAWTON, William E, Jr. ST FRANCIS MEDICAL BLDG 25301 #051-01-1949 L1950 **GS OS** *071 †85

LE, Tai Anh. 3200 MACCORKLE AVE SE 25304 #104-01-2004 **FM** *100

LEADBETTER, Robert Lewin. 1805 ALPHA RD 25304 #051-04-1959 L1960 **OM VS** *071 †85

LEE, Alberto C. ■ 25314 #748-01-1961 L1970 **IM** *071

LEE, Brandon David. 331 LAIDLEY ST STE 102 25301 #055-01-2002 L2006 **OPH** *020

LEE, Hans. 415 MORRIS ST STE 200 25301 #583-02-1965 L1972 **PS HS** *020 †85,65 ‡

LEE, Kee Chin. 2335 CHESTERFIELD AVE, STE 300 25304 #583-02-1972 L1985 **TS GS** *020 †85,90

LEEF, Johnsey Lee, Jr. 1440 ALEXANDRIA PL 25314 #055-01-1968 L1973 **DR NM** *020 †80,28

LEEF, Johnsey Lee, III. 3416 MACCORKLE AVE SE 25304 #055-01-1998 L2003 **DR** *020 †80

LEFEVRE, Medard L. 3200 MACCORKLE AVE SE 25304 #055-01-1984 L1987 **IM** *020

LEGESSE, Benalfew Tesfaye. 501 MORRIS ST 4W 25301 #366-01-1999 L2007 **MP** *012

LEGG, Paul Stephen. 100 TRACY WAY, NORTHGATE BUSINESS PARK 25311 #055-01-1991 L1996 **ORS** *020 †40

LERFALD, Sidney Clark. 415 MORRIS ST, STE 306 25301 #055-01-1975 L1976 **P** *020 †75

LEVIEN, Joel Arnold. 3110 MACCORKLE AVE SE, WVU DEPARTMENT OF MEDICINE 25304 #011-02-1974 L2003 **GE IM** *050 †20

LEWIS, Richard Allen. 4004 MACCORKLE AVE SE 25304 #020-02-1945 L1946 **GP** *072

LEWIS, Sandra Jean. 4004 MACCORKLE AVE, STE 1A 25304 #055-02-1994 L1997 **FM** *020 †18

LEWIS, Stephen Alan. 3100 MACCORKLE AVE, STE 709 25304 #055-01-1975 L1988 **CD IM** *020 †20

LIFE, David Michael. 4602 MACCORKLE AVE SE 25304 #055-01-1991 L1993 **FM EM** *020 †18

LILLY, Donald Ray. 2930 CHESTERFIELD AVE 25304 #055-01-1980 L1985 **CD IM** *020 †20

LILLY, Josiah Kenneth, III. 4407 MACCORKLE AVE SE, 1ST FL 25304 #055-01-1971 L1977 **PME AN** *020 †05

LIM, Arturo Yap. 415 MORRIS ST, STE 209 25301 #748-10-1979 L1988 **GS VS** *020 †85

LIM, Mely Ong Co. 8 COURTNEY DR 25304 #748-10-1980 L1990 **FM** *020 †18

LIM, Raymond A. 500 QUARRIER ST, STE 500 25301 #748-01-1961 L1971 **IM CD** *020

LIM, Rogelio T. 331 LAIDLEY ST, STE 407 25301 #748-01-1964 L1972 **IM CD** *020

LIM, Romeo Y. ■ 25314 #748-02-1962 L1973 **OTO** *071 †45

LINDSAY, Richard David. 915 EDGEWOOD DR 25302 #055-01-1974 L1974 **LM** *020

LINGER, Robert Thos. 3100 MACCORKLE AVE SE #311 25304 #055-01-1979 L1980 **FM FPG** *020 †18

LINGER, Robert Thos, Sr. 3100 MACCORKLE AVE SE 25304 #024-01-1948 L1956 **OS GS** *071 †85

LOHAN, James Andrew. 3100 MACCORKLE AVE SE 25304 #055-01-1999 L2003 **CRS GS** *020 †85,10

LOIMIL, Luis Alberto. 3510 MACCORKLE AVE SE 25304 #132-01-1965 L1974 **ORS** *020 †40

LOUGH, David Richard. 500 DONNALLY ST, ASSOCIATES OF CHARLESTON 25301 #055-01-1991 L1994 **OTO** *020 †45

LOUGH, Erik Greg. 3200 MACCORKLE AVE SE, CHARLESTON AREA MED CTR 25304 #055-01-2007 **GS** *012

LOWERY, James Wesley, Jr. 830 PENNSYLVANIA AVE, STE 406 25302 #055-02-1987 L1988 **NPM** *020 †55

LUCAS, Lesli Marie. ■ 25302 #055-01-2008 *012

LUCENTE, Frank Charles. 1201 WASHINGTON ST E, STE 108 25301 #055-01-1985 L1987 **GS TRS** *020

LUKOWSKI, Peter Jos. 500 DONNALLY ST, STE 100 25301 #055-01-1978 L1986 **ORS** *020 †40

LY, Tchuoc-Poin. 830 PENNSYLVANIA AVE # 400 25302 #385-02-1967 L1977 **PDC** *020 †55

LYNCH, Joann Eudora. 3100 MACCORKLE AVE SE, STE 205 25304 #038-40-1997 L2005 **ICE** *020 †20

MAGEE, Alfred John. ■ 25304 #035-08-1944 L1955 **OPH** *071 †35 ‡
MAHMOUD, Hamada El-Shazly. 619 VIRGINIA ST W, OFFICE OF THE CHIEF MEDICA 25302 #915-04-1977 L1999 **PTH** *020
MAJESTRO, Tony Colerio. 415 MORRIS ST, STE 104 25301 #055-01-1966 L1967 **ORS** *020 †40
MALAS, Amer Muheideen. 331 LAIDLEY ST, ST FRANCIS HOSP 25301 #605-01-1984 L1995 **IM** *020 †20
MALI, Cyrus Jamshed. 3100 MACCORKLE AVE, STE 500 25304 #704-02-1971 L1976 **U** *020 †95
MALI, Daryoush Jamshed. ■ 25314 #409-05-1966 L1975 **GP PD** *071
MALIK, Farhan Firasat. ■ 25304 #055-01-2008 *012
MALIK, Firasat Sarwar. 2335 CHESTERFIELD AVE, STE 300 25304 #704-01-1972 L1985 **TS** *020 †85,90
MALOOF, Jane. 4605 MACCORKLE AVE SW, KANAWHA VALLEY 25309 #143-03-1990 L1997 **DR** *020 †80
MANGANO, William Edward. 3200 MACCORKLE AVE SE, MEMORIAL DIVISION 25304 #036-01-1992 L1998 **PTH** *020 †50
MANGUS, Jimmie Lee. ■ 25304 #051-04-1959 L1960 **FM OS** *071 †18
MANTZ, Eric Paul. 1201 WASHINGTON ST E, STE 108 25301 #055-01-1972 L1972 **GS VS** *040 †85
MARAIKAYER, Ahmed Mustafa. 6515C MACCORKLE AVE SE 25304 #495-04-1958 L1980 **GP** *020
MARKEY, John B. 415 MORRIS ST STE 105 25301 #051-04-1954 L1955 **GS GYN** *071
MARTIN, Diana Joyce. ■ 25309 #055-02-1991 L1995 **GPM** *020 †20
MARTIN, Kathleen June. 800 PENNSYLVANIA AVE 25302 #055-01-2005 L2008 **PD** *012
MARTINEZ, Frederick Carl. 11 COURTNEY DR 25304 #005-02-1978 L1998 **U UP** *020 †95
MASOOD, Shahana. 3200 MACCORKLE AVE SE 25304 #704-06-2000 L2008 **IM** *012
MATULIS, Steven Robt. 4701 MACCORKLE AVE SE 25304 #055-01-1985 L1986 **GE IM** *020 †20
MATULIS, Wannetta Sue. 3100 MACCORKLE AVE SE, STE 509 25304 #055-01-1985 L1986 **ID IM** *020 †20
MATUNDAN, Isabel Alcazar. 4524 MACCORKLE AVE SW 25309 #748-01-1961 L1978 **PD** *071
MATUSIC, Joseph H. 830 PENNSYLVANIA AVE 25302 #055-01-1989 L1991 **PD** *020 †55
MAXSON, David Russell. 4605 MACCORKLE AVE SW 25309 #055-01-1990 L1994 **AN** *020 †05
MAXSON, Ward Willis. 830 PENNSYLVANIA AVE # 108 25302 #025-01-1961 L1969 **OBG** *071 †30
MAXWELL, Damian Randolph. 3110 MACCORKLE AVE SE 25304 #566-01-2000 L2006 **GS** *100 †85
MAXWELL, Stefan Randolph. 830 PENNSYLVANIA AVE, STE 406 25302 #566-01-1977 L1990 **NPM PD** *020 †55
MC CAIN, James Bryson. 1120 KANAWHA BLVD E, ASSOCIATED RADIOLOGISTS IN 25301 #055-02-2002 L2006 **RNR** *012 †80
MC CLANAHAN, Rose Hamlett. 501 MORRIS ST 25301 #004-01-1943 L1944 **GP P** *071
MC CLUNG, Reginald Jay. 331 LAIDLEY ST, STE 205 25301 #055-02-1983 L1984 **FM** *020 †18
MC CORMICK, Candace Ann. 800 PENNSYLVANIA AVE 25302 #055-01-1981 L1982 **AN PD** *020 †55,05
MC CORMICK, Steven Lin. 2930 CHESTERFIELD AVE 25304 #055-01-1981 L1982 **CD** *020 †20
MC COWAN, Ronald Jeffrey. 505 CAPITOL ST 25301 #005-12-1980 L1989 **ICE CD** *020 †20
MC JUNKIN, Brittain. 3110 MACCORKLE AVE SE, WVU HEALTH SCI CTR 25304 #055-01-1973 L1978 **GE** *040 †20
MC JUNKIN, James Enoch. 800 PENNSYLVANIA AVE 25302 #055-01-1977 L1987 **CCP** *020 †55
MC JUNKIN, Mary Han. 1120 KANAWHA BLVD E, P O 11137 25301 #055-01-1977 L1987 **DR PDR** *020 †80
MC LAURIN, Donald Ray. 1215 VIRGINIA ST E, DRS BLACK JACKFERT YATES & 25301 #021-05-1992 L1995 **GS** *100
MC NEIL, Kenneth Francis. 100 PEYTON WAY, STE 200 25309 #055-02-1986 L1990 **AN PMM** *020 †05
MC ROBIE-MARTIN, Shelda A. 3110 MACCORKLE AVE SE, CHARLESTON DIVISION 25304 #055-01-1996 L1998 **IM** *020 †20
MEGA, John Francis. 1120 KANAWHA BLVD E, PO 11137 25301 #055-01-1993 L1995 **DR** *020 †80
MEGHA, Nayana Rohit. 4605 MACCORKLE AVE SW 25309 #495-89-1971 L1987 **AN** *020 †05
MEMON, Hafsa Umar. 3200 MACCORKLE AVE SE 25304 #704-25-2005 L2008 **OBG** *012
MIAN, Farhat S. 2335 CHESTERFIELD AVE, STE 203 25304 #704-21-1985 L1993 **PTH** *020 †50
MIAN, Muhammad Shahbaz. 2335 CHESTERFIELD AVE, STE 203 25304 #704-01-1980 L1993 **CD IM** *020 †20
MILLER, Karen Kay. 707 CHESTNUT ST 25309 #055-02-2003 L2005 **FM** *020 †18
MILLER, Scott Edward. 3100 MACCORKLE AVE SE, STE 610 25304 #055-02-1986 L1987 **CD IM** *020 †20
MILROY, Stephen K. 3100 MACCORKLE AVE SE, STE 809 25304 #055-01-1973 L1973 **D** *020 †15
MIMNAGH, Kathleen M. 3100 MCCORKLE AVE SE, CAMC-MEMORIAL ADM 25304 #035-48-1987 L1992 **IM** *020 †20
MINARDI, Lawrence Matthew. 500 DONNALLY ST 25301 #055-01-1977 L1978 **OPH** *020 †35 ‡
MINENKO-MCDANIEL, Olga Sv. 3200 MACCORKLE AVE SE 25304 #913-05-1998 **MPD** *012
MIRZA, Saqib Nisar. ■ 25304 #704-01-1993 **IM** *100
MITCHELL, Barry Michael. 3110 MACCORKLE AVE SE, WVU CHARLESTON, DEPARTMEN 25304 #055-01-2005 L2007 **MPD** *012
MOLINA, Manuel Evencio. 415 MORRIS ST, STE 104 25301 #055-02-1987 L1993 **ORS** *020 †40
MONINGI, Venkata Ramana. 3200 MACCORKLE AVE SE, CAME HOSPITALIST 25304 #496-05-1981 L2006 **IM** *020 †20
MONTGOMERY, Emily Anne. 800 PENNSYLVANIA AVE, WOMEN AND CHILDREN'S HOSPI 25302 #055-01-1994 L1997 **OBG** *012 †18
MOODY, Melissa Ann. 3200 MACCORKLE AVE SE, MED/PSYCH PROGRAM 25304 #055-01-2006 **MP** *012
MOORE, Donald Halstead. 1097 FLEDDERJOHN RD, STE 1 25314 #055-01-1981 L1982 **EM FM** *020 †16,18
MOORE, Justin Ross. 3200 MACCORKLE AVE SE 25304 #661-04-2005 **IM** *012
MORGAN, Barbara Jean Uber. ■ 25314 #055-01-1972 L1972 **N CHN** *020
MORGAN, William C, Jr. ■ 25314 #051-01-1948 L1954 **OTO** *071 †45
MORRIS, Ira Alan. 4924 MACCORKLE AVE SE 25304 #024-01-1967 L1995 **IM** *020
MOUSA, Luay. 3110 MACCORKLE AVE SE 25304 #875-01-2004 **IM** *012
MOUSATTAT, Alaa. ■ 25314 #875-03-1999 L2006 **IM** *020 †20
MOUSATTAT, Youmna. 3200 MACCORKLE AVE SE 25304 #875-02-1999 **PD** *012
MOUSHMOUSH, Bassam. 331 LAIDLEY ST STE 402 25301 #875-01-1982 L1991 **CD IM** *020 †20
MOXNESS, Margaret Ann. ■ 25311 #038-41-1979 L1980 **CHP** *020 †75
MUKKAMALA, Prasadarao. 1 UNION SQ STE 3 25302 #495-58-1968 L1979 **EM PM** *020 †60
MURPHY, Patricia Ann. 1545 LOUDEN HEIGHTS RD 25314 #748-12-1981 L1998 **OTO A** *020
MURTHY, Kris Gan. 5303 MACCORKLE AVE SE 25304 #308-11-1986 L1993 **N** *020
MURTHY, Srinivas. 4605 MACCORKLE AVE SW 25309 #495-99-1987 L1995 **AN** *020 †05
MUTO, Deidra Fawn. PO BOX 471, 333 LAIDLEY ST 25322 #055-01-1998 L2004 **PTH** *100
MUTO, Frank Allan. 1120 KANAWHA BLVD E 25301 #055-01-1998 L2003 **DR** *020 †80
NAEGELE, Scott Alan. 830 PENNSYLVANIA AVE # 108 25302 #051-04-1990 L1992 **OBG** *020 †30
NAHLA, Adnan M. 3200 MACCORKLE AVE SE, MEDICAL STAFF OFFICE CENTE 25304 #613-02-1991 L2002 **IMG** *020 †20
NAIR, Ambika Kumari. 101 DEE DR STE 103, WEST VIRGINIA BOARD OF MED 25311 #496-29-1989 L2007 **N** *012
NAIR, Lionel Joseph. 331 LAIDLEY ST, STE 310 25301 #495-09-1963 L1972 **U** *071 †95
NAMAY, David Lee. 3411 NOYES AVE, STE B 25304 #055-01-1975 L1978 **CD IM** *020 †20
NAMAY, Kevan Andrews. 3411 NOYES AVE, STE B 25304 #055-01-1977 L1980 **IM** *075 †20
NARAYAN, Rathi. 3110 MACCORKLE AVE SE 25304 #495-99-1990 L2004 **GE** *100 †20
NASIR, Amana Nighat. ■ 25314 #704-25-1998 L2003 **PD** *100 †55
NAVARRO, Maria Luna Tan. 331 LAIDLEY ST 25301 #748-11-1971 L1978 **CD IM** *020
NAZHA, Hani. 3200 MACCORKLE AVE SE 25304 #875-01-2004 **MP** *012
NEAL, Matthew Ross. ■ 25301 #055-01-2007 **IM** *012
NEASE, Sarah Moore. 3100 MACCORKLE AVE, STE 709 25304 #055-01-1988 L1991 **CD** *020 †20
NELLHAUS, Kurt Myron. 501 MORRIS ST 25301 #422-01-1981 L1988 **PUD CCM** *020 †20
NELSON, Timothy Wm. 800 PENNSYLVANIA AVE 25302 #055-01-1986 L1990 **AN** *020 †05
NEWBROUGH, Mark Allen. 3110 MACCORKLE AVE SE 25304 #055-01-1985 L1986 **FPG IM** *040 †20
NICHOLAS, Jane Elizabeth. 800 PENNSYLVANIA AVE, CHILDREN'S MEDICINE CENTER 25302 #055-01-1998 L2002 **PD** *040 †55
NICHOLS, Phillip Todd. 500 DONNALLY ST, ASSOCIATES OF CHARLESTON 25301 #055-01-1994 L1997 **OTO** *020 †45
NICHOLS, Roger Phillip. 500 DONNALLY ST 25301 #055-01-1969 L1970 **OTO HNS** *071 †45
NIKFAR, Nahid. ■ 25311 #517-01-1971 L1978 **IM** *020
NOORANI, P A. 830 PENNSYLVANIA AVE, WV HEALTH SCIENCE CTR, SUI 25302 #704-08-1967 L2006 **CHN PD** *020 †55,75
NUCUM, Araceli Sison. ■ 25309 #748-11-1964 L1985 *075
NUNLEY, Michael Gray. 1201 WASHINGTON ST E # 203 25301 #055-01-1984 L1991 **OPH** *020 †35
OBALANLEGE, Adeniyi Monzo. 3200 MACCORKLE AVE SE 25304 #690-08-1997 L2004 **IM** *020 †20
OBENZA, Ebenezer. 6087 SISSONVILLE DR, PHYSICIAN HEALTH CARE CLIN 25312 #748-11-1976 L1984 **GP** *020
O'CONNOR, Sara Eubank. 1306 KANAWHA BLVD E, CHARLESTON, INC. 25301 #055-01-1998 L2002 **OPH** *020 †35
O'HARA, Brendan Linus. 419 BROOKS ST, DEPT. OF EMERGENCY MEDICIN 25301 #001-02-1974 L2001 **EM FM** *020 †16
OLIVER, Ross Saml. 4701 MACCORKLE AVE SE 25304 #055-01-1983 L1984 **U** *020 †95
OSBORNE, John Edward. ■ 25303 #055-01-1965 L1966 **OM PHP** *075 †70
OTELLIN, Alexander Vladim. ■ 25314 #913-69-1989 L2006 **P** *020
OVINGTON, Robert C. 3100 MACCORKLE AVE SE 25304 #030-05-1951 L1959 **P** *072
PANGER, Michael R. 800 PENNSYLVANIA AVE 25302 #055-01-1989 L1990 **AN PME** *020 †05
PARRY, Aaron Rockney, II. ■ 25313 #055-02-2008 *012
PARSONS, Debra Lynn Hall. 4502 MACCORKLE AVE SE, STE B 25304 #055-02-1993 L1995 **PD** *020 †55
PARSONS, Nolan Chas, Jr. 331 LAIDLEY ST STE 403 25301 #055-01-1971 L1974 **D** *020 †15
PATALINJUG, Marilou B. 14 PRESIDIO POINTE 25313 #748-02-1987 L2003 **PFP** *020 †75
PATEL, Mahendrakumar M. 401 DIVISION ST STE 106 25309 #495-23-1970 L1976 **PUD SME** *020 †20
PATEL, Taral Arun. 3200 MACCORKLE AVE SE 25304 #654-01-2005 **IM** *012
PATTON, David Jamison. 1003 OAKHURST DR 25314 #055-01-1994 L1997 **OBG** *020 †30
PAUL, Anil Varghese. ■ 25339 #495-37-1992 L1999 **P** *100
PAYNE, William Neil. 3200 MACCORKLE AVE SE 25304 #055-01-1978 L1979 **EM** *020 †16
PEARCY, Thompson Embleton. 830 PENNSYLVANIA AVE, STE 110 25302 #055-01-1975 L1976 **OBG** *020 †30
PEROS, Kristen Lea. 3200 MACCORKLE AVE SE 25304 #055-01-2005 L2007 **IM** *012
PERSILY, Eric M. 800 PENNSYLVANIA AVE 25302 #011-02-1989 L1993 **AN** *020 †05
PETTIT, James J, II. 2930 CHESTERFIELD AVE 25304 #055-01-1985 L1988 **IM** *020 †20
PFISTER, Alfred Karl. 3110 MACCORKLE AVE SE 25304 #010-01-1962 L1969 **IM** *072 †20
PIERSON, John Patrick. 100 TRACY WAY 25311 #017-20-2001 L2006 **ORS** *020
PLANTS, Brian Allen. 3100 MACCORKLE AVE SE, STE B1 25304 #055-01-1999 L2004 **RO** *020 †80 ‡
PLATA, Milton Julio. 3200 MACCORKLE AVE SE 25304 #737-05-1977 L1984 **PTH PCP** *020 †50
PLYMALE, W Jos. 3200 MACCORKLE AVE SE 25304 #055-01-1980 L1981 **U** *075 †95
POLANCO, Lisbette. 4501 MACCORKLE AVE SE 25304 #649-14-1996 L2006 **PD** *020
POLAND, Thomas W. 3508 STAUNTON AVE SE 25304 #055-01-1976 L1977 **AN** *020 †05
POLICARPIO, Dionisio E. 209 WASHINGTON ST W 25302 #748-08-1964 L1978 **GS GP** *020
POLLARD, Robert Emmet. 1306 KANAWHA BLVD E, CHARLESTON, INC. 25301 #010-02-1984 L1993 **OTO PDO** *020 †45
POLLOCK, Frederic Harry. 415 MORRIS ST STE 201, GENERAL MEDICAL PAVILION 25301 #016-11-1974 L1990 **ORS** *020 †40
PORTILLO, Augusto Luis. 830 PENNSYLVANIA AVE, STE 403 25302 #737-01-1957 L1970 **PS HS** *072
PORTUGAL, Salvador C. 400 DIVISION ST, STE 9 25309 #748-02-1972 L1983 **OTO** *020
POTTERFIELD, Thomas G. 3200 MACCORKLE AVE SE 25304 #051-04-1946 L1950 **PD** *071 †55
POULOS, Despina Melissa. 3200 MACCORKLE AVE SE 25304 #104-01-2007 **GS** *012
POWELL, Melissa Ann. 1201 WASHINGTON ST E, STE 208 25301 #020-12-1990 L1991 **GS CCS** *020 †85
PRIDDY, Jeffrey Glenn. 511 MORRIS ST 25301 #055-01-1986 L1987 **P** *020 †75
PRUDICH, Daniel Brent. ■ 25314 #055-02-1983 L1985 **EM IM** *020 †20,55
PULIDO, Fred Taguba, Jr. 1213 VIRGINIA ST E, 3RD FL 25301 #748-02-1962 L1975 **PS** *020
PULLIN, George A. 419 BROOKS ST, DEPT EM 25301 #060-01-1990 L1993 **IM** *020 †20
PUZZUOLI, Gina Michelle. 511 MORRIS ST 25301 #055-01-1976 L1976 **P** *020 †75
QOUSSOUS, Ashraf Numan Sa. 3200 MACCORKLE AVE SE, CHARLESTON AREA MED CTR 25304 #575-02-2002 **PD** *100
QURESHI, Faraz. 511 MORRIS ST 25301 #704-02-1991 L2001 **CHP ADP** *020 †75
RADER, Danny Allan. ■ 25314 #055-02-1985 L1986 **EM** *020 †18
RAGO, Vincent Eric. 800 PENNSYLVANIA AVE 25302 #055-01-2001 L2005 **AN** *020 †05
RAHMAN, Asif. 2345 CHESTERFIELD AVE, STE 301 25304 #495-77-1976 L1983 **NEP IM** *020 †20

■ = Address Information Privacy Protected

RAJA, Premkumar. 3100 MACCORKLE AVE SE, STE B1 25304 #055-01-1996 L2003 **RO** *020 †80
RAJARATNAM, Arunthathie. 800 PENNSYLVANIA AVE 25302 #220-01-1970 L1977 **AN** *020 †05
RAMESH, H S. 400 COURT ST STE 203, PHYS MED & REHAB ASSOCS 25301
 #495-35-1977 L1994 **PMM PM** *020 †60
RANSON, David Ward. 401 DIVISION ST, STE 303 25309 #055-01-1981 L1982 **GS** *020 †85
RASHID, Humayun. 2335 CHESTERFIELD AVE, STE 300 25304 #704-01-1967 L1979
 TS GS *020 †85,90
RATNANI, Mohammad Salim. 3100 MACCORKLE AVE SE, STE 811 25304 #704-02-1983 L1996
 TS *020 †85,90
REAHL, Harry L, IV. 415 MORRIS ST, STE 100 25301 #010-02-1991 L1996 **N** *020 †75
REDDY, Palle. 800 PENNSYLVANIA AVE 25302 #495-62-1972 L1983 **AN** *020 †05 ‡
REDDY, Uha. ■ 25314 #010-01-2007 L2007 **IM** *012
REDDY, Uma P. 888 OAKWOOD RD STE 110 25314 #495-62-1973 L1983 **PD** *020 †55
REED, Charles David. 1206 KANAWHA BLVD E, STE 201 25301 #055-01-1990 L1993
 EM IM *020 †16,55,20
REHMAN, Khawaja Ateeq. 3200 MACCORKLE AVE SE, ATTN: SHARON ORNDORFF 25304
 #495-35-1998 L2004 **IM** *020
REIFSTECK, John Ernest. 3416 MACCORKLE AVE SE 25304 #004-01-1979 L1987
 VIR R *020 †80
REMOLONA, Helen Rose R. 3508 STAUNTON AVE SE 25304 #748-10-1982 L1998 **AN** *020
REMOLONA, Nathan Mendiola. 800 PENNSYLVANIA AVE 25302 #748-10-1982 L1990
 AN *020 †05
REVERCOMB, William C, Jr. ■ 25314 #035-01-1951 L1957 **IM** *071 †20
REYES FERNANDEZ, Bernardo. 3200 MACCORKLE AVE SE 25304 #035-03-1999 **IM** *012
REYES-PULIDO, Brenda E. ■ 25314 #748-01-1962 L1974 **PD OS** *020 †55
REYNOLDS, Diana Putman. ■ 25302 #035-09-1987 L1991 **PD** *020 †55
REYNOLDS, Gorman Joel. 424 DIVISION ST STE 1, UNIVERSITY OF KY 25309
 #020-12-2001 L2007 **GE** *020 †20
REYNOLDS, Harry Richard. 3100 MACCORKLE AVE SE #302 25304 #055-01-1982 L1986
 D *020 †15
REYNOLDS, Kristina Joi. ■ 25304 #055-02-2005 **PD** *012
RHODES, Terence Duane. ■ 25304 #055-01-2006 **IM** *012
RICHMOND, Bryan Kelly. 3110 MACCORKLE AVE SE 25304 #055-01-1993 L1994 **GS** *020 †85
RIDENOUR, Glenn Allen. 3100 MACCORKLE AVE SE, STE 604 25304 #055-01-1998 L2006
 PDI *020 †20,55
ROBERTSON, Jana Rene. ■ 25314 #048-15-2005 L2005 **PD** *012
ROMAINE, Robert Howard. 1201 WASHINGTON ST E STE 1, DEPT OF FAMILY MED 25301
 #055-01-2006 **FP** *012
RONCAGLIONE, Carl J. ■ 25301 #051-04-1951 L1956 **OS** *071 †40
RONEN, Leon. 4602 MACCORKLE AVE SE 25304 #035-06-1993 L1999 **FM** *020 †18
ROSENCRANCE, James G. 3110 MACCORKLE AVE SE 25304 #055-02-1988 L1989 **IM** *020 †20
ROSSI, Kimberly Ann. 3100 MACCORKLE AVE SE, STE 201 25304 #055-01-1994 L2002
 D *020 †15
ROSSI, Samuel Christopher. ■ 25314 #055-01-1999 L2004 **GS** *020 †85
ROSSMAN, William Byron. ■ 25304 #017-20-1938 L1946 **P N** *071 †75
ROTHBERG, Sara Roshanna. 2345 CHESTERFIELD AVE, STE 300 25304 #847-11-1981 L1984
 IM *020 †20
RUBIN, Philip Morris. 1021 QUARRIER ST STE 311 25301 #051-04-1958 L1959 **FM FPG** *020
SAAD, Beena. PO BOX 1547 25326 #704-16-1997 L2003 **P** *012
SADEHH, Abdulmalek Mhd. A. 3200 MACCORKLE AVE SE 25304 #575-02-2004 **MP** *012
SAFLEY, Travis Lawson. 3200 MACCORKLE AVE SE, CHARLESTON AREA MED CTR 25304
 #027-01-2007 **GS** *012
SAHLOUL, Raghda Gassan. 3100 MACCORKLE AVE SE, STE 606 25304 #875-01-1993 L2002
 END *020 †20
SAKKAL, Ahmed Moudar. 331 LAIDLEY ST STE 406, CHARLESTON HEART CLINIC 25301
 #875-02-1977 L1991 **CD IM** *020 †20
SAKKAL, Amal F. 331 LAIDLEY ST, STE 406 25301 #875-02-1985 L1997 **IM** *020 †20
SALDANHA, Francis Maxim. 4701 MACCORKLE AVE SE 25304 #495-16-1975 L1981
 AN PME *020 †05 ‡
SALE, William Goodridge. 100 TRACY WAY 25311 #051-01-1966 L1980 **ORS** *020 †40
SALMAN, Faiza. 3200 MACCORKLE AVE SE 25304 #704-02-1998 **FP** *012
SALUTILLO, Victor P. 5392 BIG TYLER RD 25313 #748-09-1967 L1982 **FM** *020
SAMPATH, Ramanathan. 3100 MACCORKLE AVE SE, STE 904 25304 #495-42-1972 L1981
 TS *020 †85,90
SANDHU, Ujjal Singh. 4408 MACCORKLE AVE SE 25304 #495-39-1965 L1971 **OBG** *072 †30
SANKARI, Bashir Riad. 1201 WASHINGTON ST E # 100, 1201 WASHINGTON ST E #100 25301
 #605-01-1981 L1991 **U** *020 †95
SANKARI, Samar Ryiad. 331 LAIDLEY ST STE 201, PROFFESSIONAL ENDOCRINOLOG 25301
 #605-01-1984 L1996 **IM** *020 †20
SANTOS, Rolando Ruiz. ■ 25304 #748-08-1982 L1995 **IM** *012
SANTROCK, David Alan. 7030 VALLEY BROOK DR, CAPITAL ORTHOPAEDICS 25312
 #055-01-1967 L1968 **ORS** *020 †40
SANTROCK, Paul Richard. 5480 BIG TYLER RD 25313 #017-20-1955 L1956 **FM** *072 †18
SARKER, Chitta Ranjan. 3100 MACCORKLE AVE SE, STE 101 25304 #704-12-1968 L2000
 HEM IMG *020 †20
SAVILLE, Paul David. 500 DONNALLY ST # B-303 25301 #352-07-1949 L1974 **RHU** *071
SAWYER, Phyllis Ruth. ■ 25314 #045-01-1983 L1997 **PTH** *020 †50
SCHADE, Charles Price. 3001 CHESTERFIELD 25304 #048-04-1972 L1996 **PHP** *050 †70
SCHIANO, Michael Anthony. 1 COURTNEY DR, WV OBG ASSOC 25304 #035-09-1979 L1995
 GO *020 †30
SCHICK, Alexandra Isabell. 3200 MACCORKLE AVE SE 25304 #166-04-2006 **P** *012
SCHLARB, Christopher A. 3416 MACCORKLE AVE SE 25304 #055-01-1991 L1996 **DR** *020 †80
SCHMIDT, John Henry, III. 415 MORRIS ST 25301 #007-02-1979 L1982 **NS** *020 †25
SEIDLER, David E. 3200 MACCORKLE AVE SE, C/O DEPT EMER MED 25304
 #016-11-1980 L1983 **EM** *020 †16
SEIDLER, Donald Leon. 4602 MACCORKLE AVE SE, HEALTHPLUS URGENT CARE 25304
 #038-40-1993 L2005 **FM EM** *020 †18
SELINGER, Harold. 3100 MACCORKLE AVE SE, STE 709 25304 #035-08-1953 L1962
 CD IM *072 †20
SERRATO, Jose. 3100 MACCORKLE AVE SE, STE 909 25304 #264-01-1961 L1971 **U** *020 †95
SHABIH, Khan A. 2345 CHESTERFIELD AVE, STE 301 25304 #704-02-1989 L2003 **NEP** *020 †20
SHAFFER, Matthew James. 331 LAIDLEY ST STE 601 25301 #055-01-2004 L2007 **FM** *100
SHAFI, Muhammad. 333 LAIDLEY ST, ST FRANCIS HOSP 25301 #704-01-1966 L1975
 AN *020 †05
SHAH, Jayesh Babulal. 830 PENNSYLVANIA AVE # 406, CHARLESTON AREA MED CTR 25302
 #495-22-1980 L1993 **PD NPM** *020 †55

SHAH, Nilay Arvind. 1201 WASHINGTON ST E, STE 108 25301 #665-02-2007 **FP** *012
SHAIKH, Khurram Rafi. 3200 MACCORKLE AVE SE 25304 #704-16-1997 **P** *012
SHAMIM, Qurrat Ul Ain. 3200 MACCORKLE AVE SE 25304 #704-02-2002 **IM** *012
SHAMS, Seyed Ali. 501 MORRIS ST 25301 #154-07-1996 L1999 **IM** *020 †20
SHANMUGHAM, N T. 333 LAIDLEY ST 25301 #495-04-1963 L1973 **U GS** *071 †95
SHAUKAT, Salman. 3200 MACCORKLE AVE SE 25304 #704-20-1999 **IM** *012
SHEIKH, Nasim Ahmad. 4502 MACCORKLE AVE SW 25309 #704-01-1981 L1994 **AI** *020 †20,03
SHEPHERD, James B, Jr. PO BOX 4352 25364 #055-01-1968 L1969 **FM** *071
SHIBATA, Shigefumi. 501 MORRIS ST # GENERAL- 25301 #572-49-1988 **CHP** *012
SHIM, Chull. 3200 MACCORKLE AVE SE 25304 #583-10-1970 L1981 **PTH NP** *020 †50
SHIN, Robert Bongchul. 3100 MACCORKLE AVE STE 202 25304 #054-04-1995 L2003
 GS *020 †85
SIBLEY, Richard Henry. 333 LAIDLEY ST 25301 #055-01-1967 L1976 **ORS HS** *071 †40
SIDHU, Kanwar Ajit Singh. 3200 MACCORKLE AVE SE 25304 #495-03-1995 **P** *012
SIEGEL, Eric. ■ 25304 #305-01-2006 **OBG** *012
SIMPKINS, Rodney Michael. 1012 KANAWHA BLVD E, STE 400 25301 #055-01-1986 L1988
 FM EM *020
SINGH, Atul. 3110 MACCORKLE AVE SE 25304 #025-76-1995, ▲ L2005 **IM OBG** *020 †20
SINGH, Sarabjit K.. ■ 25304 #496-43-1996 L2008 **MP** *012
SISSOKO, Moussa. 3200 MACCORKLE AVE SE 25304 #422-01-2007 **IM** *012
SITLER, Michael Glenn. 503 BROOKS ST, DEPT OF EMERG MED 25301 #055-01-1998 L1999
 MPD *020 †20,55
SIVAPRAKASAM, Michael J. 800 PENNSYLVANIA AVE 25302 #220-01-1990 L2004 **AN** *020 †05
SKAFF, Kimberly Lynn. 4502 MACCORKLE AVE SE # A 25304 #055-01-1982 L1983 **D** *020 †15
SKAFF, Leeann. 4922 MACCORKLE AVE SE 25304 #055-01-1985 L1986 **IM END** *020
SKAFF, Paul Alexander, II. 800 PENNSYLVANIA AVE 25302 #055-01-1986 L1990 **AN** *020 †05
SKAFF, Sam. 4501 MACCORKLE AVE SE 25304 #875-01-1988 L1996 **PD** *020 †55
SKINNER, Mary S. 3607 KANAWHA BLVD E 25306 #021-05-1955 L1956 **PHP PD** *030
SLAYTON, Donna Jean. 800 PENNSYLVANIA AVE 25302 #055-02-1986 L1990 **AN PME** *020 †05
SLEMP, Catherine C. 505 CAPITOL ST, STE 200 25301 #036-07-1989 L1994
 PHP FM *062 †70,18
SMITH, Daniel Lee. 4602 MACCORKLE AVE SE 25304 #055-01-1983 L1984 **FM EM** *020 †18
SMITH, James Brandon. ■ 25304 #055-02-2007 **GS** *012
SMITH, James Tucker. 3416 MACCORKLE AVE SE 25304 #019-02-1965 L1972 **DR** *020 †80 ‡
SMITH, Jennifer Marie. 1120 KANAWHA BLVD E, PO BX 11137 25301 #051-01-1998 L2004
 DR *020 †80
SMITH, Ralph Silas, Jr. 1215 QUARRIER ST 25301 #016-06-1966 L1974 **P CHP** *020 †75 ‡
SMITH, Robert. 4605 MACCORKLE AVE SW, KANAWHA VALLEY 25309 #035-08-1979 L1987
 DR NM *020 †80,28
SMITH, Robert Lewis. ■ 25314 #035-46-1981 L1982 **IM** *020 †20
SMYTHE, Gai Louise. 4813 MACCORKLE AVE SE, ALPHA CARE CORPORATION 25304
 #055-02-1997 L2001 **GP** *020
SNIDER, Allan Jeffrey. 800 PENNSYLVANIA AVE 25302 #035-46-1979 L1999 **AN** *020 †05
SONDIKE, Stephen Barry. 830 PENNSYLVANIA AVE, STE 104 25302 #035-08-1994 L2005
 ADL *020 †55
SOUTHERN, Steven C. 12 COURTNEY DR 25304 #055-02-1991 L1995 **OBG** *020 †30
SPANGLER, Elizabeth Lee. 501 MORRIS ST, OFFICE OF MEDICAL AFFAIRS 25301
 #055-02-1986 L1987 **MDM IM** *030 †20
SPARKS, Tiffany Olivia. ■ 25304 #704-01-2005 **P** *012
SPENCER, James Thos., Jr. 500 DONNALLY ST, EAR NOSE & THROAT ASSOCS 25301
 #041-02-1944 L1948 **OTO A** *071 †45
SPORCK, Frederick Thos. 500 DONNALLY ST, ASSOCIATES OF CHARLESTON 25301
 #055-01-1972 L1972 **OTO** *020 †45
STA. MARIA, Maria Sheila. 3200 MACCORKLE AVE SE 25304 #748-01-1991 **OBG** *012
STANTON, Howard James. 4315 MACCORKLE AVE SE 25304 #055-01-1979 L1979
 CD IM *020 †20
STEAD, Jeffrey Allan. 1201 WASHINGTON ST E, STE 103 25301 #041-09-1978 L1984
 PTH *020 †50
STEPHENS, Mark Kerry. 4602 MACCORKLE AVE SE 25304 #055-02-1983 L1984 **IM** *020 †20
STEPHENS, Rodney Lee. 331 LAIDLEY ST, STE 204 25301 #021-01-1970 L1976 **GYN** *020 †30
STEWART, William Andrew. 4415 MACCORKLE AVE SE, STE 304 25304 #055-01-1988 L1989
 PS *020 †65
STICKLER, Daniel Lee, II. 600 TRACY WAY, NORTHGATE BUSINESS PARK 25311
 #055-01-1993 L1999 **GS** *020 †85
STOCK, Rodolfo Karl. 4216 MACCORKLE AVE SW, MED-PLUS 25309 #737-01-1956 L1965
 GP GS *075
STOLTZFUS, Patricia B. 1201 WASHINGTON ST E, STE 103 25301 #051-04-1988 L1994
 DR *020 †80
STONE, Patrick Alan. 3110 MACCORKLE AVE SE, CHARLESTON DIVISION 25304
 #055-02-1999 L2004 **VS** *100 †85
STOUGHTON, Wade Blair. 1201 WASHINGTON ST E, STE 108 25301 #055-01-1971 L1978
 U *071 †95
STOUT, Robert Christopher. 3200 MACCORKLE AVE SE, WVU PHYSICIANS 25304
 #051-04-1983 L1988 **EM** *020 †16
STRICKLAND, Samuel Asher. 1306 KANAWHA BLVD E, EYE & EAR CLINIC PHYS INC 25301
 #055-01-1966 L1972 **OPH** *020 †35
SULLESTA, Rene Octaviano. 1313 QUARRIER ST, STE A 25301 #748-01-1967 L1983
 U GS *020 †95
SUSON, Eduardo Madarang. 830 PENNSYLVANIA AVE, STE 102 25302 #748-11-1964 L1976
 PDS GS *071 †85
SWAIN, Randall Alan. 4602 MACCORKLE AVE SE 25304 #055-01-1987 L1990 **FM FSM** *020 †18
SWISHER, Sally Hanna. 331 LAIDLEY ST STE 307 25301 #055-01-1973 L1980 **N** *020 †75
TALLAKSEN, Robert James. 3200 MACCORKLE AVE SE, WVU PHYSICIANS 25304
 #036-01-1976 L1983 **DR** *020 †80
TANGUILIG, Ernesto R. 3200 MACCORKLE AVE SE 25304 #748-02-1960 L1975 **N** *071 †80
TARAKJI, Muhib Shukri. 418 GREENWAY AVE 25309 #605-01-1973 L1978 **OPH PO** *020 †35
TARANTINO, Heather N. 3200 MACCORKLE AVE SE, OUTPATIENT CLINIC 25304
 #055-01-2003 L2005 **IM** *020 †20
TARRY, William Fred. 501 MORRIS ST, WVU PHYSICIANS 25301 #041-14-1977 L1981
 U PDS *020 †95
TATE, Jessica Amelia. ■ 25304 #055-01-2008 *012
TAUPRADIST, Parinya. ■ 25314 #891-01-1960 L1972 **GS GP** *071
TAYLOR, Mary Belle. 3200 MAC CORKLE AV SE PATH 25304 #055-01-1971 L1971
 BBK PTH *030 †50
TAYLOR, Paula Flanagan. 1001 KENNAWA DR, KANAWHA HOSPICE CARE INC 25304
 #055-02-1996 L1999 **MPD** *020 †20

TELERON, Amylynn Abenoja. ■ 25304 #055-01-2008 *012
TEODORO, Julio D, Jr. 415 MORRIS ST STE 400 25301 #748-08-1961 L1975 **N** *071 †75
TETER, Donald Fred. 4522 MACCORKLE AVE SE, STE 5 25304 #055-01-1977 L1978
OM *030 †70,18
THAKKAR, Jashvanthal K. 331 LAIDLEY ST STE 208 25301 #495-22-1982 L1993
CD IM *020 †20
THAKKER, Chandrani Ganpat. 800 PENNSYLVANIA AVE 25302 #495-22-1973 L1982
PD *020 †55
THALHEIMER, Liza Opper. ■ 25304 #055-01-2008 *012
THAXTON, Jeffrey Norman. 120 CORNWALL LN 25314 #055-02-1992 L1994 **PS** *020 †65
THISTLETHWAITE, Daniel B. 4825 MACCORKLE AVE SW 25309 #055-01-1987 L1988
P *020 †75
THISTLETHWAITE, Timothy. 4825 MACCORKLE AVE SW 25309 #055-01-1991 L1993 **P** *020 †75
THOMAS, Daniel Randolph. 800 PENNSYLVANIA AVE 25302 #046-01-2000 L2004 **AN** *020 †05
THOMAS, David Wayne. 830 PENNSYLVANIA AVE, STE 402 25302 #055-01-1978 L1979
OBG *030 †30
THOMAS, John Willis. ■ 25314 #050-02-1978 L1980 **IM EM** *075
THOMPSON, Cheryl Ann. 1201 WASHINGTON ST E, STE 108 25301 #665-02-2006 **FP** *012
THORNE, Olga Petrovna. 3200 MACCORKLE AVE SE 25304 #913-53-1996 **OBG** *012
THRUSH, Lawrence B, Jr. 3411 NOYES AVE STE A 25304 #055-01-1970 L1979
AI PDA *020 †20,03
TIERNEY, Letitia Elaine. ■ 25304 #055-01-2006 **MPD** *012
TILEY, Edward Henry, III. 4701 MACCORKLE AVE SE 25304 #055-01-1979 L1981
GS VS *020 †85
TINNEY, Melissa Jugo. ■ 25314 #055-01-2002 L2005 **PM** *020
TODD, Jean E. 1418 MACCORKLE AVE SW, STE A 25303 #067-01-1953 L1972 **PTH** *020 †50
TOMA, George Edward. 331 LAIDLEY ST STE 102 25301 #038-40-1968 L1975 **OPH** *071 †35
TOMCHIN, Shayna Beth. ■ 25313 #055-01-2004 L2005 **PTH** *012 †50
TOMLINSON, William Paul. ■ 25312 #055-01-2006 **MPD** *012
TORRES, Ascension M. 830 PENNSYLVANIA AVE # 104, WVU PHYSICIANS 25302
#038-41-1982 L1993 **PDS GS** *020 †54
TORRES, Reynaldo Bautista. 3200 MACCORKLE AVE SE 25304 #748-10-1999 **IM** *100
TRAMMELL, Shirley Willis. 1201 WASHINGTON ST E, STE 108 25301 #021-01-1970 L1978
GS *85
TREADWAY, Christy Lynn. 3200 MACCORKLE AVE SE, MEMORIAL HOSPITAL 25304
#055-01-2000 L2002 **OS** *100 †20 ‡
TRUPO, Frank J, Jr. 331 LAIDLEY ST, STE 510 25301 #055-01-1984 L1985 **PS HS** *020 †65
TURLEY, John Austin. 800 PENNSYLVANIA AVE, WVU PHYSICIANS 25302 #055-02-1994 L1995
FM *020 †18
TURNER, Chad Christopher. 7133 SISSONVILLE DR, CABIN CREEK HEALTH SYSTEMS 25320
#055-02-2002 L2005 **FM** *020 †18
UDALL, John Nicholas, Jr. 830 PENNSYLVANIA AVE, STE 103 25302 #041-13-1969 L2005
PD NTR *020 †55
UMSTOT, Richard K, Jr. 1201 WASHINGTON ST E, STE 108 25301 #055-01-1985 L1987
GS *020 †85
UPTON, Sue A. 830 PENNSYLVANIA AVE 25302 #055-01-1992 L1995 **PD** *020 †55
URFY, Mian Zain Ul Sajade. 3200 MACCORKLE AVE SE 25304 #704-25-2005 **IM** *012
UY-ARCEO, Elizabeth. 830 PENNSYLVANIA AVE # 200 25302 #748-01-1963 L1973 **PD** *020 †55
VAGHELA, Vishal Naresh. ■ 25311 #055-01-2008 *012
VALENZUELA, Roberto C. 100 PEYTON WAY STE 200 25309 #017-20-1986 L1988
AN PME *020 †05
VANIKAR, Dipti. ■ 25304 #496-07-2003 **FP** *012
VAUGHAN, John Wm. 50 RIVER WALK MALL 25303 #055-01-1963 L1964 **GP** *020
VAUGHAN, Nathan Andrew. ■ 25304 #055-01-1981 L1982 **CD IM** *020 †20
VELASQUEZ, Alfredo C. 333 LAIDLEY ST 25301 #748-01-1956 L1970 **NS** *020
VERMA, Happy. 5052 BENNINGTON DR 25313 #495-30-1974 L1980 **PD** *020
VERMA, Purushottam Lal. 830 PENNSYLVANIA AVE # 201 25302 #495-19-1960 L1971
PD PDA *020 †55 ‡
VERMA, Sarojni Devi. ■ 25304 #495-05-1960 **P OBG** *074
VIDAL, Melchor Fernandez. PO BOX 4535 25364 #748-08-1971 L1983 **GP** *020
VIDAL, Melvin Theodore. 1313 QUARRIER ST 25301 #055-01-1996 L1999 **IM** *020 †20
VILLAPENA, Geraldine Deli. ■ 25304 #748-10-1993 **FP** *012
VOELKER, Joseph Lee. 1201 WASHINGTON ST E, STE 108 25301 #017-20-1981 L1991
NS GS *020 †25
VOLTIN, Russell I. 4825 MACCORKLE AVE SW 25309 #055-01-1988 L1989 **P** *020 †75
WALKER, Matthew Phillip. 415 MORRIS ST 25301 #055-01-1997 L2003 **OSS** *020 †40
WALKER, Robert Leo, Jr. 4701 MACCORKLE AVE SE 25304 #047-07-1977 L1981 **AN** *020
WALKER, Rozelle Jenee. 3200 MACCORKLE AVE SE 25304 #055-01-1984 L1987
CHP P *020 †75
WALLACE, Wm Taylor, Jr. STATE CAPITOL BLDG 3 #519, DEPT OF HEALTH & HUMAN
RES 25305 #050-02-1961 L1991 **PHP GPM** *030 †70
WARREN, Carolyn Coppinger. 1001 KENNAWA DR 25311 #038-06-1971 L1974
IM PLM *020 †18,20
WARREN, Stafford Gay. 400 DIVISION ST, STE 3 25309 #035-45-1969 L1974 **CD IM** *020 †20
WARWICK, Tanya Catherine. 3110 MACCORKLE AVE SE, WVU DEPT OF INTERNAL
MEDIC 25304 #055-02-2000 L2004 **N** *100 †75
WEISE, Charles Commodore. 5600 MACCORKLE AVE SE, STE 10 25304 #041-01-1955 L1961
P PFP *020 †75
WEISSE, Martin Edward. 1201 WASHINGTON ST E, STE 103 25301 #048-14-1984 L1993
PD ID *040 †55
WERSHBA, Martin Stuart. ■ 25301 #010-02-1969 L1975 **DR** *071 †80
WESTFALL, Sue Ann. ■ 25306 #055-01-1991 L1992 **FM** *020 †18
WESTMORELAND, Robert T. 800 PENNSYLVANIA AVE 25302 #036-01-1968 L1979 **AN** *020 †05
WESTON, W Donald. 3110 MACCORKLE AVE SE, RM 3031 25304 #005-06-1958 L1969
P CHP *071
WHALEY, Lewis Allen. 3100 MACCORKLE AVE SE 25304 #041-77-1980, ▲ L1982
RO FM *020 †80
WHEATLEY, Edward Ronald. ■ 25314 #055-01-1968 L1977 **DR** *071 †80
WHITE, Joe J, Jr. 4701 MACCORKLE AVE SE 25304 #055-01-1983 L1983 **GE IM** *020 †20
WHITEMAN, Charles Richard. 3200 MACCORKLE AVE SE, WVU PHYSICIANS 25304
#055-01-1985 L1988 **EM** *020 †16
WILLIAMS, Caroline A. 100 TRACY WAY 25311 #055-01-1985 L1988 **FM** *020 †18
WILLIS, John Alan. 1120 KANAWHA BLVD E 25301 #055-01-1986 L1989 **DR** *020 †80
WINKLER, Charles P, Jr. 400 COURT ST, STE 300 25301 #051-04-1984 L1988 **OBG** *020 †30
WINKLER, Moseley Hubbard. 1306 KANAWHA BLVD E 25301 #051-04-1955 L1957
OPH *071 †35

WIRTS, Amy B. 4602 MACCORKLE AVE SE 25304 #055-01-1996 L1998 **IM** *020 †20
WISE, David Paul. 415 MORRIS ST STE 309, FACIAL SURGERY CENTER 25301
#030-05-1993 L1996 **OS FPS** *020
WITHROW, Curtis Lee. 415 MORRIS ST STE 400, GENERAL MED PAVILION 25301
#041-09-1957 L1961 **N** *020
WITSBERGER, Todd Andrew. 1201 WASHINGTON ST E, STE 108 25301 #055-01-1987 L1991
GS *020 †55
WOOD, Daniel J. 415 MORRIS ST 25301 #055-01-1989 L1991 **PS** *020 †85,65
WRIGHT, Edward Eugene. 3200 MACCORKLE AVE SE 25304 #055-01-1978 L1979
FM *020 †18,16
WRIGHT, Glen Alan. 501 MORRIS ST 4, W V UNIVERSITY, DEPT OF BE 25301
#055-01-1988 L1991 **P IM** *040 †20,75
WRIGHT, Kenneth Carr. 501 MORRIS ST, CHARLESTON AREA MEDICAL CE 25301
#025-01-1980 L1987 **PM SCI** *020 †60
WYNER, Lawrence Michael. 1204 WASHINGTON ST E, STE 100 25301 #036-01-1983 L1991
U TTS *020 †95
YASAR, Uzay. 1201 WASHINGTON ST E, STE 105 25301 #035-08-1996 L2005 **U** *020 †95
YOSUICO, Arnold Timothy D. 800 PENNSYLVANIA AVE 25302 #748-01-1983 L1997 **AN** *020 †05
YOUNG, John Adam, III. 501 MORRIS ST, WVU PHYSICIANS 25301 #055-01-1988 L1990
P *020 †75
YOUNG, Nicholas Ryan. 3110 MACCORKLE AVE SE, WVU BUILDING 25304 #055-01-2004 L2005
MPD *020
YOUSAF, Mohammad Babar. 428 DIVISION ST, STE 2A 25309 #704-02-1982 L1989 **IM** *020 †20
ZAIDI, Syed Ali Faraz Raz. 3200 MACCORKLE AVE SE 25304 #704-02-2003 **FP** *012
ZALDIVAR, George Luis Leo. 3100 MACCORKLE AVE SE, STE 404 25304 #055-01-1971 L1974
PUD SME *020 †20
ZAMORA, Pelagio P. ■ 25313 #748-10-1969 L1985 **GP** *071
ZANGENEH, Fereydoun. 830 PENNSYLVANIA AVE, STE 104 25302 #517-01-1960 L1983
PDE PD *020 †55
ZARROUF, Fahd Aziz. 101 29TH ST SE, APT 11 25304 #875-01-2001 L2006 **MP** *012
ZEKAN, Steve Michael. 1208 KANAWHA BLVD E 25301 #055-01-1975 L1979 **GS VS** *020 †85
ZUNIGA, Jonathan. 4607 MACCORKLE AVE SW, STE 206 25309 #748-08-1986 L2001
NEP *020 †20

CHARLTON HEIGHTS – FAYETTE

BAUTISTA, Ariston R. ■ 25040 #748-01-1953 L1966 **GP OM** *071

CHESTER – HANCOCK

KUBICKI, Krzysztof Jerzy. 111 1ST ST, LIFECARE MEDICAL ASSOCIATE 26034
#759-03-1983 L1993 **IM** *020 †20

CLARKSBURG – HARRISON

ABRAHAM, Rajan. 1 MED CENTER DR, ONCOLOGY SECTION 26301 #496-11-1978 L1987
ON HEM *020 †20
AHMED, Jamil. 4 HOSPITAL PLZ, STE 106 26301 #704-20-1986 L2003 **PUD** *020 †20
ALCANTARA, Frederick Mana. 1 HOSPITAL PLZ, P O BOX 2308 26301 #422-01-2003 L2007
FM *020
ANGOTTI, John David. 4 HOSPITAL PLZ, STE 100 26301 #055-01-1986 L1989 **IM** *020 †20
ANGOTTI, Michael Thos. 4 HOSPITAL PLZ, STE 100 26301 #055-01-1983 L1986 **IM** *020 †20
ARGIRO, Thomas Robt. MED CTR DR VA HOSP RM 373 26301 #051-04-1954 L1956 **PTH** *071
ARNETT, Charles Lee. 1 HOSPITAL PLZ 26301 #041-09-1965 L1975 **FM PD** *040 †18
AZAR, John Jurjis. 300 DAVISSON RUN RD, STE 302 26301 #605-01-1985 L1993
ON IM *020 †20
BADIK, Jill Kristen. PO BOX 1680, UNITED HOSP CTR 26302 #016-76-2007, ▲ **FP** *012
BATALLA, Gamaliel E P. 300 DAVISSON RUN RD, STE 103 26301 #748-02-1993 L2002
PME *020 †05
BELLOTTE, John Anthony. 3 HOSPITAL PLZ STE 106, BOX 1680 26301 #055-01-1972 L1972
PUD IM *020 †20
BISHOP, Harry Arthur. 3 HOSPITAL PLZ 26301 #005-02-1954 L1981 **R NM** *020 †80,28
BOND, Brian Kenneth. ■ 26301 #055-01-2005 L2005 **OBG** *012
BRAGER, Paul Mitchell. 300 DAVISSON RUN RD 26301 #008-01-1980 L1986 **HEM ON** *020 †20
BRAGG, Dana Eugene. 4 HOSPITAL PLZ, STE 304 26301 #055-01-1985 L1988 **FM** *020
BRYANT, James Lee, II. 125 N 6TH ST 26301 #055-01-1963 L1964 **OTO A** *020 †45
BURGESS, Kimberly Ann. 300 DAVISSON RUN RD, STE 101A 26301 #055-02-1992 L1993
ORS FSM *020 †18
BURTNER, Charles David. 4 HOSPITAL PLZ, UNITED HOSPITAL CENTER 26301
#051-04-1985 L1986 **DR RNR** *020 †80
CHAN, Sokhom. 1 MED CENTER DR 26301 #215-01-1973 L1997 **P FM** *020
CHANGLANI, Mahesh. 4 HOSPITAL PLZ, STE 210 26301 #496-38-1984 L1993
CD CCM *020 †20
CHINNIS, Ann Short. 3 HOSPITAL PLZ 26301 #051-07-1981 L1991 **EM** *020 †16
CHISHOLM, Lionel Donald J. 1 MED CENTER DR 26301 #065-01-1959 L1993 **OPH** *020
CHUA, Windell Tan. 1 MED CENTER DR 26301 #748-08-1968 L1976 **CD IM** *020 †20
CHURCH, David Harlan. 4 HOSPITAL PLZ, STE 210 26301 #051-04-1979 L1986 **CD IM** *020 †20
CONLEY, Francis W. ONE MEDICAL DRIVE 26301 #018-03-1943 L1975 **IM** *020 †20
COONLEY, Craig Jos. 300 DAVISSON RUN RD, SUTIE 304 26301 #035-01-1977 L1990
ON HEM *020 †20
CORDER, William Thomas. 399 EMILY DR, MOUNTAIN STATE MEDICAL SPE 26301
#055-01-1985 L1986 **AI** *020 †55,03
CORNWELL, Creel Sayre, Jr. 399 EMILY DR, SPECIALITES 26301 #055-01-1969 L1971
IM CD *020 †20
CUNANAN, Rolando Fernande. PO BOX 1680 26302 #748-31-2003 **FP** *012
DAGHER, Ibrahim Khalil. ■ 26301 #605-01-1951 L1977 **GS** *020 †85,90
DATTA, Chinmay Kumar. 215 CANDLELIGHT DR 26301 #495-32-1962 L1977
PTH BBK *020 ‡
DAVIS, Paul D. 3 HOSPITAL PLZ 26301 #055-01-1981 L1987 **FM EM** *020 †18
DE LA MATA, Ruby Nieves. 3 HOSPITAL PLZ 26301 #748-01-1964 L1976 **PTH** *020
DE MARCO, James J. 4 HOSPITAL PLZ, STE 205 26301 #305-01-1986 L1993 **NEP** *020 †20
DEMBY, Alan Mark. 300 DAVISSON RUN RD, STE 307 26301 #011-02-1981 L2005 **U** *020 †95

DODSON, Jeffrey Alan. 399 EMILY DR 26301 #055-01-2001 L2005 **D** *020 †15
DOUGLAS, Richard Allen. 4 HOSPITAL PLZ, STE 103 26301 #016-06-1983 L1999
   NS OSS *020 †25
DWIVEDI, Isha. PO BOX 2308, 1 HOSPITAL PLZ 26302 #055-01-2002 L2004 **FM** *020 †18
FISCHER, Carl Rudolph, III. 300 DAVISSON RUN RD, STE 201A 26301 #041-09-1972 L1989
   GS *020 †85
FRANCO, Wilma Tolero. LAB SER 113 VA MED CTR 26301 #748-02-1972 L1982
   PTH CLP *020 †50 ‡
FRANZ, Charles Bradley. 399 EMILY DR, SPECIALITES 26301 #055-01-1989 L1990 **D** *020 †15
FREDRICK, George Theodore. 1 HOSPITAL PLZ, FAMILY MEDICINE CENTER 26301
   #020-12-1979 L1980 **FM** *072 †18
FUNG, Saravut Srifueng. 211 S CHESTNUT ST 26301 #891-01-1966 L1974 **OPH** *020 †35
GABRIELE, Frederick John. 4 HOSPITAL PLZ, UNITED HOSPITAL CENTER 26301
   #055-01-1989 L1991 **RNR** *020 †80
GASATAYA, Julian Delina. 3 HOSPITAL PLZ 26301 #748-01-1956 L1964 **AS GP** *071
GENIN, James Alan. 3 HOSPITAL PLZ 26301 #055-01-1972 L1978 **OPH** *020 †35 ‡
GENIN, Jason Alan. ■ 26301 #055-75-2007, ▲ *012
GINJUPALLI, S. 3 HOSPITAL PLZ 26301 #495-50-1961 L1978 **IM** *020
GOODWIN, Andrew Wirt, II. 4 HOSPITAL PLZ, UNITED HOSPITAL CENTER 26301
   #025-01-1957 L1962 **DR NM** *071 †80,28
GOODYEAR, Suzanna. 916 W PIKE ST, HEALTH ACCESS INC 26301 L1991
   FM *071 †18
GORDON, Paul Edwin. 3088 WASHINGTON AVE., HARRISON COUNTY CLARKSBURG 26301
   #051-04-1948 L1949 **GS** *071
GROSSMAN, David Mark. 1 MED CENTER DR, LOUIS A JOHNSON VA MEDICAL 26301
   #035-09-1983 L1987 **IM END** *040 †20
GUPTA, Pradeep Mohan. 1 MED CENTER DR, LOUIS A JOHNSON MED CTR 26301
   #495-69-1978 L1998 **IM CD** *020 †20
HANCOX, John Gibson. 399 EMILY DR, MOUNTAIN STATE DERMATOLOGY 26301
   #055-01-2001 L2006 **PRD** *020 †15
HANUMARA, Devika. ■ 26301 #496-01-2000 L2005 **FP** *012
HESS, Elizabeth Harrison. 1 HOSPITAL PLZ 26301 #055-01-1997 L1998 **FM** *040 †18
HESS, Robert Dale. 1 HOSPITAL PLZ 26301 #051-04-1958 L1959 **FM** *040 †18
HETZER, Timothy Bruce. 4 HOSPITAL PLZ, UNITED HOSPITAL CENTER 26301
   #055-01-1977 L1978 **DR NR** *020 †80
JACKSON, Jeffrey B. 399 EMILY DR, SPECIALITES 26301 #055-01-1989 L1991 **D** *020 †20,15
JACKSON, Sidney Boggess. 1 MED CENTER DR 26301 #055-01-1977 L1978 **FM** *020 †18
JAIN, Prasoon. 1 MED CENTER DR, LOUIS A JOHNSON VA MED CTR 26301
   #495-45-1985 L1997 **PCC** *020 †20
JANI, Dilip Shankerlal. ONE MEDICAL DRIVE 26301 #495-17-1957 L1982 **IM PUD** *071 †20
JOSEPH, Nancy Lea. 1 MED CENTER DR, FAMILY MEDICINE 26301 #055-02-1985 L1986
   FM *040 †18
KAFKA, Shelly Pearl. 300 DAVISSON RUN RD, STE 201B 26301 #047-05-1988 L2005
   RHU *020 †20
KASSIS, Joseph. 600 DAVISSON RUN RD, SUUITE 201 26301 #875-01-1970 L1979 **U** *020 †95
KAUFMANN, Richard James. 1 MED CENTER DR 26301 #654-01-1981 L1983 **GS** *020 †85
KEESEE, Sean Thomas. 4 HOSPITAL PLZ STE 100 26301 #055-01-2002 L2005 **IM** *020 †20
KENNEDY, Thomas James. 4 HOSPITAL PLZ, STE 308 26301 #028-34-1971 L2001
   PS HS *020 †85,65
KUNG, Markus K. ONE VETERANS DR, VA HOSPITAL 26301 #869-04-1970 L1987 **IM** *020 †20
KURAPATI, Surekha. 1 MED CENTER DR, VAMC 26301 #495-21-1975 L1994 **P** *020
LABATIA, Sherif Youssef. PO BOX 1680, UNITED HOSP CTR 26302 #915-02-2000 L2007
   FM *020 †18
LAPLANTE, Jon Schrae. 4 HOSPITAL PLZ, UNITED HOSPITAL CENTER 26301
   #055-01-1990 L1994 **DR** *020 †80
LAPUZ-DE LA PENA, Erlinda. 1 MED CENTER DR 26301 #748-01-1957 L1971 **OS PTH** *071 †50
LEFEBURE, Charles Armand. 4 HOSPITAL PLZ STE 203, PHYSICIANS OFFICE BLDG 26301
   #065-09-1970 L1975 **ORS** *020 †40
LEHKI, Robert. 3 HOSPITAL PLZ, UHC EMERGENCY DEPT 26301 #025-07-1993 L2005
   EM *020 †16
LEON, John Anthony. 4 HOSPITAL PLZ, UNITED HOSPITAL CENTER 26301 #055-01-1984 L1985
   DR *020 †80
LINGER, Elbert Leon. 3 HOSPITAL PLZ 26301 #041-13-1953 L1954 **AN** *071 †05
LOPEZ, Amante. ANESTHESIA DEPARTMENT, UNITED HOSPITAL CENTER 26301
   #748-08-1976 L1990 **AN** *071 †05
LOPEZ, Florencia Cancio. 3 HOSPITAL PLZ 26301 #748-01-1960 L1976 **OBG** *071
LOPEZ, Gerardo Cancio. 4 HOSPITAL PLZ, STE 210 26301 #055-01-1992 L1993 **CD** *020 †20
MACE, Kevin James. 4 HOSPITAL PLZ, DEPT OF EMERGENCY MEDICINE 26301
   #055-01-2001 L2004 **EM** *020
MADDEN, Jeffrey Wayne. 300 DAVISSON RUN RD, STE 201A 26301 #038-43-1996 L2001
   GS *020 †85
MASSOUD, Abdel-Fatah S M. 1 MED CENTER DR 26301 #915-04-1978 L1991 **P FM** *020
MC CAMMON, Julie Kathryn. 300 DAVISSON RUN RD, STE 303B 26301 #051-01-1979 L1988
   OBG *020 †30
MC KINNEY, Douglas Edgar. 1 MED CENTER DR, LOUIS A JOHNSON VAMC 26301
   #055-01-1967 L1976 **U** *020 †95
MENDOZA, Catalino B, Jr. ■ 26301 #748-07-1955 L1968 **GS GE** *071 †85
MENEZ, Maria Rosario. 1 MED CENTER DR, LA JOHNSON VA MED CTR 26301
   #748-10-1977 L1992 **IM FM** *020 †20
MESAROS, Laura Kronquist. ■ 26302 #025-01-1942 L1952 **IM CD** *071
MIGAIOLO, Joseph Raphael. 4 HOSPITAL PLZ, UNITED HOSPITAL CENTER 26301
   #055-01-1992 L1996 **DR** *020 †80
MILLER-CANFIELD, Patricia. ■ 26301 #020-02-1988 L2002 **PTH** *020 †50
MORRISON, Kristian Matthe. ■ 26301 #055-01-2006 L2008 **FP** *012
MORTELL, Edward J. VETERANS ADMIN MED CTR 26301 #056-05-1943 L1943 **P** *020 †75
NARANJO, Carlos Alberto. 300 DAVISSON RUN RD 26301 #319-01-1965 L1973 **U** *071 †95
NASHED, Mazen. 200 ROUTE 98 W ST, STE 107 26301 #875-02-1981 L1998 **IM** *020 †20
NAVADA, Shivshankar U. 4 HOSPITAL PLZ STE 110 26301 #495-37-1977 L1990 **N** *020 †75
NEWMAN, Jonathan Gabriel. 3 HOSPITAL PLZ 26301 #055-01-1995 L1997 **EM** *020 †16
NOON, Saima Nazli. ■ 26301 #704-21-1997 L2008 **FP** *012
NORTON, Amy Beth. 399 EMILY DR, SPECIALITES 26301 #055-01-2002 L2004 **D** *020 †15
ORTENZIO, Louis F, Jr. 104 E MAIN ST, STE 2D 26301 #023-01-1979 L1980 **FM FPG** *020 †18
PHAM, Thanh-Ha Thi. 4 HOSPITAL PLZ, STE 06 26301 #308-13-1999 L2005 **IM** *020
PICKHOLTZ, Paul Sanford. 300 DAVISSON RUN RD, STE 302 26301 #038-41-1970 L2008
   GE IM *020 †20
PRICE, Rebecca A. 3 HOSPITAL PLZ 26301 #055-01-1989 L1992 **GS** *020

RABANAL, Aristotle A. 3 HOSPITAL PLZ 26301 #748-01-1961 L1974 **GP GS** *020 †85
RADCLIFFE, Eric John. 1 HOSPITAL PLZ # 2308 26301 #055-01-1989 L1992 **FM** *040 †18
RAHIMIAN, Ali. 300 DAVISSON RUN RD, STE 203 26301 #517-01-1968 L1978 **OBG** *020 †30
RAJJOUB, Salam H. 300 DAVISSON RUN RD, STE 303A 26301 #875-02-1990 L2001
   PCC SME *020 †20
RAVAL, Dipa Kanubhai. PO BOX 1680, UNITED HOSP CTR 26302 #665-01-2005 L2008 **FP** *012
REDDY, Sathyanarayan M. 4 HOSPITAL PLZ, STE 210 26301 #495-21-1981 L1991
   CD IM *020 †20
RUBI, Dionisio Jose. 1 MED CENTER DR 26301 #023-01-1999 L1999 **IM** *020 †20 ‡
RUSH, Sandra Ingram. 6 HOSPITAL PLZ 26301 #055-02-1997 L1999 **FM** *020
SANG-LUK, Elena. 1 MED CENTER DR, LOUIS A JOHNSON VAMC 26301 #308-02-1986 L1994
   ID *020 †20
SCHAFFNER, Liza Gail. 6 HOSPITAL PLZ 26301 #016-42-2001 L2006 **PYG** *020
SHAFFER, Linda Lee. ■ 26302 #055-01-1967 L1984 **EM** *020 †16
SHEHL, George Wm. 1 MED CENTER DR, PCCM 11 26301 #055-01-1977 L1980 **CD IM** *020 †20
SHUMAN, Victoria L. 1 HOSPITAL PLZ, BOX 2308 26301 #055-75-1996, ▲ L1997 **FM** *020 †18
SICKLES, Doyle Russell. 3 HOSPITAL PLZ 26301 #055-01-1979 L1980 **ORS** *020 †40
SKAR, Sandra Leslie. 1 MED CENTER DR 26301 #055-02-1997 L1999 **P** *020
SNIDER, Glenn Russell, Jr. 1 MED CENTER DR, LOUIS A JOHNSON DVAMC 26301
   #055-01-1980 L1981 **IM IMG** *030 †20
SNYDER, Thomas Malcolm. ■ 26301 #016-01-1942 L1948 **IM** *071
SOOD, Vineet Kumar. ■ 26301 #496-01-2000 **FP** *012
SUBBAREDDY, Kurapati. 1 MED CENTER DR, VA MEDICAL CTR 26301 #495-50-1967 L1986
   AN *020
SUDHARTO, Ratih Bulan Tre. 1 HOSPITAL PLZ, BOX 2308 26301 #506-23-2002 L2007
   FM *100 †18
SUTTON, Cheryl R E. 4 HOSPITAL PLZ, DOCTOR'S OFFICE BLDG STE 1 26301
   #016-11-1974 L1988 **PD** *020
THAGIRISA, Sivaparvati. 1 MED CENTER DR, LOUIS A. JOHNSON VA MC 26301
   #495-70-1976 L1987 **FM** *020 †18
THOMPSON, James Alpha. 300 DAVISSON RUN RD 26301 #051-04-1947 L1950 **IM** *072
URBAN, Donald Gordon. ■ 26302 #041-02-1968 L1984 **GP** *075 †18
VILLARREAL, Victor Vidal. 4 HOSPITAL PLZ 26301 #024-01-1982 L1989 **GS** *020 †85
WAXMAN, David Lee. 600 DAVISSON RUN RD, STE 102 26301 #023-01-1982 L1985
   ORS *020 †40
WEDEMEYER, Gerald Thos. 3 HOSPITAL PLZ, DAVISSON RUN RD 26301 #018-03-1980 L1991
   PTH HMP *020 †50
WESTFALL, Lora Lynn. 1 MED CENTER DR, LOUIS A JOHNSON VA MEDICAL 26301
   #055-01-1994 L1996 **IM** *020 †20
WHITE, Janis Page. 3 HOSPITAL PLZ 26301 #055-01-1975 L1981 **PTH** *071 †50
WILLARD, Deborah Ann. 4 HOSPITAL PLZ, UNITED HOSPITAL CENTER 26301
   #055-01-1978 L1979 **R NR** *020 †80
WILSON, Victoria Vasanthi. PO BOX 1680, UNITED HOSP CTR 26302 #495-37-1997 **FP** *012
WOOD, Brian Lee. 300 DAVISSON RUN RD, REGIONAL EYE ASSOCIATES 26301
   #055-01-2001 L2005 **OPH** *020 †35

CLAY – CLAY

JAMIE, Shahrooz Saheb. PO BOX 10, 43 MAIN ST 25043 #517-01-1970 L1975 **GP** *020
JONES, Christine Lynn. PO BOX 147, 125 CENTER ST 25043 #055-02-2002 L2004 **FM** *020 †18
KHAN, Muhammed Aslam. 125 CENTER ST, CLAY PRIMARY HEALTH CARE 25043
   #704-25-1994 L2001 **IM** *020 †20
PRABHAKAR, Balakrishna R. 125 CENTER ST, CLAY PRIMARY HEALTH CARE 25043
   #495-94-1989 L1999 **MPD** *020 †20,55
WEHRHEIM, Heidi Maria. 125 CENTER ST, PRIMARY CARE SYSTEMS, INC. 25043
   #038-45-2000 L2003 **FM** *100 †18

CLENDENIN – KANAWHA

ORE, Robert Martin. ■ 25045 #055-02-2008 *012

CORE – MONONGALIA

HORAN, Charlene F. 1929 MASON DIXON HWY 26541 #023-01-1978 L1979 **IM** *020 †20

CRAB ORCHARD – RALEIGH

BLANDO, Generoso Bona. PO BOX 1610, 1315 ROBERT C BYRD DR 25827
   #748-07-1960 L1985 **FM** *071
LIRIO, Apolonio Ebron. ■ 25827 #748-10-1970 L1979 **U** *020 †95
LIRIO, Mariza A. BOX 1170 RTE 16 25827 #748-10-1971 L1979 **PM** *020 †60

CRAIGSVILLE – NICHOLAS

RODEBAUGH, Jeffrey Mark. PO BOX 492 26205 #055-01-2007 **FP** *012

CROSS LANES – KANAWHA

AUDITOR, Jose Y. 45 PRESIDIO POINTE 25313 #748-11-1972 L1979 **FM** *020
CASTRO, Fortunato D. ■ 25313 #748-07-1966 L1985 **GS** *020
PARIKSHAK, Narendra. 117 GOFF MOUNTAIN RD 25313 #495-22-1982 L1995 **IM** *020 †20
RAMSEY, William Nathaniel. ■ 25313 #055-02-2008 *012
SABET, Minu D. ■ 25313 #902-03-1966 **PTH** *100
SABET, Zia. ■ 25313 #902-03-1969 L1995 **PTH FOP** *020
SHETH, Ashish P. 117 GOFF MOUNTAIN RD 25313 #496-30-1991 L1997 **IM** *020 †20
STONESTREET, Gregory C. 5480 BIG TYLER RD 25313 #055-01-1981 L1982 **FM** *020 †18
VIRADIA, Arvind Z. 117 GOFF MOUNTAIN RD 25313 #495-89-1982 L1987 **PHL IMG** *020 †20

CULLODEN – CABELL

COLE, Jacqueline N. 1023 JANE DR, BOX 979 25510 #055-02-1998 L1999 **FM** *020 †18

GUBERMAN, Bruce Allen. ■ 25510 #023-07-1974 L1982 **IM** *020 †20

DANIELS – RALEIGH

CRUZ, Ricardo C. ■ 25832 #748-07-1960 *100
DIMLICH, Stephen Henry. ■ 25832 #038-06-1962 L1962 **U OS** *071 †95
ETTEHADIEH, Seid A. 1 PAVILION DR 25832 #517-04-1966 L1980 **PD** *020 †55
FERRARACCIO, Ponziano P. 1 PAVILION DR 25832 #051-04-1976 L1979 **FM EM** *020
GUTTA, Mohandas Gandhi. ■ 25832 #495-37-1965 L1976 **GS SO** *071 †85
HANKS, Carl Eugene, Jr. 1 PAVILION DR 25832 #051-01-1985 L1986 **FM** *020 †18
HONRADO, Cordell Rivera. 1 PAVILION DR 25832 #748-11-1965 L1978 **IM** *030
KELLY, Michael Anthony. 1 PAVILION DR 25832 #064-01-1981 L1983 **EM FM** *030 †16
MENDOZA, Ciriaco Ada. ■ 25832 #748-07-1970 L1984 **EM IMG** *020
NANDA, Rajesh. 1004 LAKE DR 25832 #495-01-1991 L2001 **GS EM** *020
PADGETT, Shanis Anay. ■ 25832 #055-01-2000 L2003 **AN** *020 †05
ROMANI, Livio. ■ 25832 #561-17-1989 L2004 **GS** *020 †85
ROMERO, Jose Maria S. 1 PAVILION DR 25832 #748-01-1975 L1984 **EM** *020
SANTOS, Yolanda A. 106 HAWTHORN LN 25832 #748-01-1966 L1982 **FM** *020
SLACK, Richard Lee. 1 PAVILION DR 25832 #010-01-1954 L1959 **GP** *071 †85
STEWART, Edward E, Jr. 1 PAVILION DR 25832 #055-01-1987 L1988 **PD** *020

DANVILLE – BOONE

KESARI, Sriramloo. 163 PRICHARD RD, 163 PRICHARD ROAD 25053 #495-21-1974 L1979 **GP EM** *020
THORNTON, Ted D. 376 KENMORE DR, PROCESS STRATEGIES 25053 #055-01-1985 L1986 **P** *020 †75

DAVIS – TUCKER

LOGAR, John Michael. ■ 26260 #055-01-2001 L2003 **EM** *100 †16
MAZZELLA, Vincent James. HC 70, BOX 571 26260 #055-01-1969 L1971 **EM FM** *020 †40

DAWES – KANAWHA

SHAALAN, M Bashar. PO BOX 70, CABIN CREEK HEALTH CENTER 25054 #875-02-1989 L2002 *020 †20

DELBARTON – MINGO

CARRILLO, Oscar Paclibon. MINGO MED ASSOCS INC 25670 #748-01-1961 L1981 **AN** *075

DELLSLOW – MONONGALIA

AZUMAH, Michael Wuni. ■ 26531 #308-12-1985 **GP** *020

DUNBAR – KANAWHA

ALJOUDI, Haytham M.I.. ■ 25064 #575-01-2001 L2007 **IM** *020 †20
CHINUNTDET, Prabhohn. ■ 25064 #891-01-1959 L1970 **GS GP** *071
CHONGSWATDI, Natavoot Nic. ■ 25064 #055-02-2005 **FP** *012
CHUNG, Jennifer Young. ■ 25064 #041-15-2007 **IM** *012
KURYLA, Paul Timothy. 1100 GROSSCUP AVE 25064 #055-02-1987 L1988 **FM** *020 †18
LADD, Jennifer Jeanette. ■ 25064 #055-75-2007, ▲ **IM** *012
LILLY, John Preston, Jr. 1100 GROSSCUP AVE 25064 #055-01-1986 L1987 **IM** *020 †20
LILLY, Jonathan Paul. 1100 GROSSCUP AVE 25064 #055-01-1989 L1990 **FM** *020 †18
MALISKA, Jerry A. ■ 25064 #847-04-1963 L1970 **GP EM** *071
MANZOOR, Kamran. ■ 25064 #704-04-2000 L2007 **IM** *100 †20
MERRIFIELD, John Vincent. 1100 GROSSCUP AVE 25064 #055-01-1968 L1969 **OS** *071 †18
NEASE, Victor Ferris. 1020 GROSSCUP AVE 25064 #055-02-1985 L1987 **P** *020 †75
PARTOVIFAR, Mahmood. 210 11TH ST 25064 #517-01-1973 L1979 **FM** *020
SOYLU, Danis. ■ 25064 #902-03-1957 **P** *074
UPTON, Matthew Bradford. 1100 GROSSCUP AVE 25064 #055-01-1992 L1995 **IM** *020 †20

ELIZABETH – WIRT

AVULA, Lakshmi R. PO BOX 609 26143 #495-59-1992 L1997 **IM** *020 †20
PATEL, Janak Raman. 1301 ELIZABETH PIKE 26143 #012-01-1991 L1993 **FM** *020 †18

ELKINS – RANDOLPH

ALICEA-ROLON, Juan A. 213 MAIN ST 26241 #308-03-1982 L2002 **CD IM** *020
ANGER, Eric Ray. 1123 S DAVIS AVE 26241 #055-01-2000 L2002 **FM** *020 †18 ‡
ARNETT, Jerome Cayton, Jr. 1200 HARRISON AVE 26241 #055-01-1967 L1968 **PUD IM** *020 †20
AUBLE, Debra Marie. ■ 26241 #047-05-1988 L1991 **FM** *020 †18
BOBES, Susan Unruh. 1 REED ST 26241 #007-02-1993 L1997 **EM** *020 †16
BOYD, Mary Simon. 911 GORMAN AVE, STE 302 26241 #055-01-1979 L1980 **PD** *020 †55
BUCHER, Samuel Jacob. REED AND GORMAN AVES 26241 #041-13-1943 L1946 **GP** *071
CASHELL, Alan Wallace. REED ST & GORMAN AVE, DAVID MEMORIAL HOSP 26241 #010-01-1978 L1992 **PTH HMP** *020 †50
CHUA, Catherine Miranda. ■ 26241 #055-75-2001, ▲ L2002 **FM** *020 †18 ‡
CHUA, Domingo Tan. 1092 HARRISON AVE 26241 #748-01-1962 L1972 **U** *020 †95
CHUNG, Soon Ok. RR 1 BOX 330E 26241 #583-03-1958 L1982 *020
CHUNG, Yack-Hoon. CHENOWETH CK RD 26241 #583-02-1953 L1975 **AN OS** *071
COX, Kevin Wayne. 635 ROBERT E LEE AVE 26241 #035-03-1988 L1998 **OPH** *020 †35
CROSS, Jenny Lynn. 903 GORMAN AVE 26241 #047-07-2002 L2004 **OTO** *100

CUPP, Matthew Adam. 911 GORMAN AVE, STE 301 26241 #055-01-1994 L1995 **FM** *020 †18
CURRENCE, David Jay. 909 GORMAN AVE, STE 4 26241 #055-01-1994 L1995 **FM** *020 †18 ‡
DARROUX, Edmund S. PO BOX 150 26241 #566-01-1971 L1996 **OBG PD** *020 †55,30
DE COURTEN, Jos Francois. ■ 26241 #869-04-1971 L1978 **OBG** *020 †30
DOLATA, Wojciech. 801 HARRISON AVE 26241 #759-04-1986 L2006 **HO** *100 †20
DOWNS, Matthew Paige. 911 GORMAN AVE, STE 304 26241 #055-02-2001 L2004 **PD** *020 †55
DURGIN, Jeffrey Durham. 911 GORMAN AVE, STE 103 26241 #048-13-2001 L2006 **GS** *020 †85
FAHIM, Mohamed Mohamed. 812 GORMAN AVE, DAVIS MEM HOS PAIN MNGMN 26241 #915-02-1982 L2002 **APM AN** *020 †05
FEDDER, Leo Michael. DAVIS MEMORIAL HOSPITAL 26241 #055-01-1981 L1983 **EM** *020 †18,16
FLEMING, Donald Ray, Jr. 810 HARRISON AVE 26241 #020-02-1986 L1987 **HO** *020 †20
GAINER, James Ward. 1123 S DAVIS AVE 26241 #055-01-1992 L1994 **FM** *020 †18
GOERLICH, Berthold H. ■ 26241 #407-19-1953 L1965 **DR** *071 †80
GOW, Robert Campbell. 119 BARRON AVE 26241 #041-12-1946 L1961 **GP PD** *071 †55
HUMMER, Joel Thos. 19 MAIN ST 26241 #055-02-1991 L1992 **FM** *020 †18
HUMMER, Terry E. 19 MAIN ST 26241 #055-02-1990 L1991 **FM** *020 †18
HUTTON, Eugene E, Jr. ■ 26241 #051-04-1946 L1948 **OPH OTO** *071
KHAN, Farukh Ahmed. 1 PLEASANT AVE, STE 1 26241 #495-09-1974 L1979 **EM FM** *020 †16
KIRCHNER, Lorrie Ann. ■ 26241 #055-02-2001 L2004 **PD** *020
KUO, Jern Jon. 224 BRUCE ST 26241 #244-02-1967 L1977 **OTO** *071
LANGFORD, Matthew Alan. ■ 26241 #041-13-2006 L2007 *012
LOBBAN, John Howard. 213 MAIN ST 26241 #055-01-1988 L1989 **CD IM** *020 †20
LYONS, Morgan Hertzog, Jr. 213 MAIN ST 26241 #055-01-1978 L1979 **CD IM** *020 †20
MAURER, Margitta Regina. ■ 26241 #041-07-1970 L1971 **GS** *020
MEMON, Khalid-U-Zaman. 725 YOKUM ST 26241 #704-16-1988 L2003 **P** *071
MORALES, Ramon Antonio. ■ 26241 #308-02-1976 L1981 **OBG** *020 †30
NORONHA, Joseph A H. ■ 26241 #495-09-1966 L1973 **GS TS** *071 †85
PAVLOVICH, Lucas John, Jr. 1502 HARRISON AVE 26241 #051-01-1989 L1996 **OSM** *020 †40
PICCIRILLO, Richard E. 62 BARNARD AVE 26241 #055-01-1972 L1973 **IM** *020 †20
PONDO, Jaroslaw S. 62 BARNARD AVE 26241 #759-11-1989 L2002 **PUD** *020 †20
RAHMAN, Muhammad Mujibur. 119 MAIN ST STE 2 26241 #160-02-1972 L2003 **CN N** *020 †75
RATNAKAR, Nitesh. 911 GORMAN AVE, STE 303 26241 #495-45-1998 L2006 **GE** *020 †20 ‡
RHEE, Joung Wye. MAIN & BERNARD STS 26241 #583-02-1965 L1975 **PD PG** *020 †55
ROBERTS, Peter Rudolph. PO BOX 1999 26241 #055-01-1974 L1977 **IM** *020 †20
ROBERTS, Samuel Kump. 1200 HARRISON AVE, STE 121 26241 #055-01-1975 L1976 **FM OBS** *020 †18
ROSE, Robert Allen. 911 GORMAN AVE, STE 203 26241 #016-11-1973 L1980 **GS** *020 †85
SANTRA, Nityananda. 911 GORMAN AVE STE 20 26241 #495-38-1966 L1973 **GS GP** *020 †85
SCOTT, Mary Ann. 801 GORMAN AVE, ATTN: SHIRLEY DANIELS 26241 #016-43-1990 L2002 **OBG** *020 †30 ‡
SEARS, Timothy Scott. 1 REED ST 26241 #055-01-1991 L1994 **EM** *020 †18
TAVOLACCI, Joseph Anthony. 1200 HARRISON AVE, STE G-16 26241 #561-01-1970 L1978 **OPH** *020 †18
THOMPSON, Archie Carey. ■ 26241 #051-04-1945 L1946 **IM** *071 †20
THOMPSON, Caren Lee. 630 ROBERT E LEE AVE 26241 #055-75-2000, ▲ L2002 **FM** *020 †18 ‡
TONEY, Steven Roy. 1123 S DAVIS AVE 26241 #055-01-1993 L1995 **FM** *020 †18
TOPPING, Richard Edmund. 1502 HARRISON AVE 26241 #051-01-1989 L1996 **ORS** *020 †40
VALENTINE, Hannah Ariel. ■ 26241 #055-01-2008 *012
VEACH, John Sanford. PO BOX 1484, DAVIS MEMORIAL HOSPITAL 26241 #055-01-1977 L1978 **EM** *020 †16

ELKVIEW – KANAWHA

HADDOX, Craig Dewitt. ■ 25071 #055-02-2003 L2006 **AN** *100
HANSEN, David Allan. ■ 25071 #028-34-1985 L1995 **PTH CLP** *020 †50
SHAFER, Cheryl Renae. 5004 ELK RIVER RD S 25071 #055-02-1992 L1997 **IM** *020 †20
SRIDHARAN, Balakrishnan. ■ 25071 #495-33-1972 L1997 **AN IM** *020 †20

ELM GROVE – OHIO

MEJIA, Fredeswinda Galang. 3 KRUGER ST 26003 #748-08-1971 L1981 **PD** *020

FAIRMONT – MARION

ABDALLA, Fouad Hassan. 700 VILLAGE DR 26554 #330-03-1956 L1973 **R NR** *071 †80
AHMAD, Saeed. 1000 BROOKSIDE DR 26554 #704-04-1965 L1976 **CD NEP** *020
ALAPPAT, Paul Antony. 1325 LOCUST AVE, CONSULTANTS ASSOCIATES 26554 #495-35-1984 L1999 **CD IM** *020 †20
AMEREDES, Harry Theodore. 700 VILLAGE DR 26554 #055-01-2000 L2005 **DR** *100 †80
ANDERSON, Warren Thorsten. 1325 LOCUST AVE 26554 #041-13-1967 L1977 **CD IM** *020 †20
ANG, Peter Lee. 5 ERWIN LN, STE B 26554 #748-02-1985 L1992 **IM IMG** *020 †20
ARJA, Mohamad. 110 GASTON AVE 26554 #561-24-1992 L1998 **IM** *020 †20
AZZOUZ, Mouhannad. 1325 LOCUST AVE, 3RD FL 26554 #875-02-1995 L2001 **CN OS** *020 †20,75
BARNETT, Steven Michael. 700 VILLAGE DR, DAVIS MEMORIAL HOSP 26554 #023-01-1978 L1982 **DR** *020 †80
BAXTER, Allison G. ■ 26554 #016-11-1952 L1980 **GP** *071
BHATTACHARYYA, Ardhendu. 1325 LOCUST AVE 26554 #495-39-1955 L1974 **GP** *020
BLACKSBERG, Ilene Rae. 1322 LOCUST AVE 26554 #422-01-1982 L1990 **IM OS** *075
BLUM, Jonathan Christophe. ■ 26554 #055-01-2008 *012
BONASSO, Patrick Corkrean. 1703 LOCUST AVE 26554 #055-02-1981 L1982 **OBG ID** *020 †30
BUCHANAN, Laura Susan. ■ 26554 #055-01-2005 L2007 **GS** *012
CADOGAN, Eusebio. 1 PHYSICIANS PLZ 26554 #726-01-1960 L1973 **OPH** *071
CHIDESTER, Candace. 1840 LOCUST AVE 26554 #055-01-1978 L1980 **FM** *020 †16
CHUA, Philip Joseph. 1314 LINCOLN WAY 26554 #055-75-1999, ▲ L2002 **IM** *020 †18 ‡
CIAROLLA, David A. 1228 COUNTRY CLUB RD, STE 300 26554 #041-09-1987 L1994 **GE IM** *020 †20
CLARKE, Kevin Michael. 48 V I P WAY 26554 #055-02-1987 L1988 **IM P** *020
CLOWDIS, William G. ■ 26554 #051-07-1990 L1991 **OBG GYN** *071 †30
COURTNEY, Derek Dana. ■ 26554 #055-01-2006 **NS** *012
CUNANAN, Roberto A. 1322 LOCUST AVE, FAIRMONT CLINIC 26554 #748-01-1966 L1976 **R** *020

DARISTOTLE, Joedy Louis. 1712 LOCUST AVE 26554 #055-02-1985 L1986 **OTO GS** *020 †45
DEVABHAKTHUNI, Babu R. 312 10TH ST 26554 #495-50-1971 L1978 **PD A** *020 †55
DEVABHAKTHUNI, Pramoda K G. 1031 MORGANTOWN AVE 26554 #496-07-1980 L1988 **IM** *020 †20
DEVABHAKTHUNI, Prasad V D. 1325 LOCUST AVE STE 35 26554 #495-50-1981 L1988 **PUD CCM** *020 †20
DORCHAK, Joseph John. 700 VILLAGE DR 26554 #038-41-2000 L2005 **NR** *020 †80
DUVERT, Joseph Hugo. ■ 26554 #661-01-1990 L1996 **PUD** *020 †20
EDGERTON, Peter John. 1325 LOCUST AVE 26554 #035-09-1977 L1999 **U** *020 †95
FLOWER, Lisa Moore. 100 VILLAGE DR, STE 200 26554 #055-01-2000 L2003 **FM** *020 †18 ‡
FRANK, Charles Edward. 1708 LOCUST AVE 26554 #020-02-1990 L1995 **GS VS** *020 †85
FRANKLIN, Grant Lafayette. 1343 LOCUST AVE 26554 #038-43-1994 L1998 **U** *020 †95
FRANZ, Agnes Marie. 1322 LOCUST AVE, INC 26554 #016-11-1977 L1982 **PD** *020 †18,55
GOODWIN, Claudia Ann. 700 VILLAGE DR, RADIOLOGICAL PHYSICIAN 26554 #055-01-1974 L1976 **DR NR** *020 †80 ‡
GOTSES, Paul Spiro. ■ 26554 #051-04-1945 L1946 **GS AS** *071
GRANT, Michael Allen. 1708 LOCUST AVE, SURGICAL ASSOCIATES 26554 #055-01-1972 L1977 **GS VS** *071 †85
HACKNEY, Mark A. 700 VILLAGE DR 26554 #055-01-1999 L2002 **DR** *020 †80
HAISLIP, Charles Edward. 1325 LOCUST AVE 26554 #055-01-1966 L1967 **OTO** *020 †45 ‡
HALL, Trevelyn F, Jr. 1712 LOCUST AVE 26554 #055-01-1965 L1966 **OTO** *071 †45
HALLBERG, John Andrew. 1325 LOCUST AVE 26554 #021-01-1982 L2007 **ORS** *020 †40
HAMILTON, Robert B. ■ 26554 #041-13-1943 L1951 **GP GS** *071
HILSBOS, Kenneth. 403 VIRGINIA AVE STE 202, HILSBOS FAMILY CARE PLLC 26554 #055-01-1990 L1993 **FM** *020 †18
HILTZ, Deborah Jane. 1322 LOCUST AVE 26554 #041-02-1977 L1995 **PD** *020 †55
HIRSCH, William Louis, Jr. 700 VILLAGE DR, RADIOLOGICAL PHYSICIAN ASS 26554 #041-12-1981 L1993 **R** *020 †80
HOFFMAN, Elissa Jane. 3 CROSSWINDS DR 26554 #035-46-1984 L1994 **CHP P** *020 †75
HOGAN, Michael Thos. 700 VILLAGE DR 26554 #035-03-1967 L1974 **R** *020 †80,28
HOOGLAND, Yvonne T. 1325 LOCUST AVE, FAIRMONT GENERAL HOSPITAL 26554 #264-01-1984 L2008 **RHU IM** *020
HORNER, Philip H. 1031 MORGANTOWN AVE 26554 #055-01-1982 L1983 **FM** *020 †18 ‡
JORDAN, Mary. ■ 26554 #028-02-1943 L1951 **PHP PD** *071
KAMAL, Maliha Ahmed. 1322 LOCUST AVE 26554 #704-25-1996 L2005 **IM** *020 †20
KATRAGADDA, Sitha Rama S. 1325 LOCUST AVE, FAIRMONT GENERAL HOSPITAL 26554 #495-58-1972 L1982 **AN** *020 †05
KATRAGADDA, Sudha Rani. 606 FAIRMONT AVE 26554 #495-50-1975 L1984 **IM** *020 †20
KLINE, Deloris Irene. RR 9, BOX 494 26554 #038-40-1966 L1972 **GS** *020 †85 ‡
KOAY, Jack S. 19 OAKWOOD RD 26554 #385-02-1964 L1972 **ORS HS** *020
KOAY, Thomas Caping. 700 VILLAGE DR 26554 #055-01-1998 L2003 **DR** *020 †80
KOPPEL, Donald M. 1322 LOCUST AVE 26554 #016-11-1949 L1958 **IM HEM** *020 †20 ‡
KUZBARI, Samer. 1228 COUNTRY CLUB ST 6 26554 #875-01-1989 L1998 **IM** *020 †20
LAU, Stephen Chor Kin. ■ 26554 #462-01-1969 L1991 **VS TS** *020 †85,90
LEE, Chi Meen. 1322 LOCUST AVE 26554 #583-04-1962 L1973 **U** *071 †95
LINDSAY, John David, Jr. 1221 GREENBRIER RD, FOREST HILL 26554 #041-13-1947 L1953 **EM OM** *072 †20
LOGAN, Jonathan Roy. 1325 LOCUST AVE, FAIRMONT GENERAL HOSPITAL 26554 #051-04-2000 L2001 **FM** *020 †18 ‡
LOPEZ, Gerardo M. 1325 LOCUST AVE 26554 #748-01-1960 L1976 **R** *020
LUKETICH, Dale Jos. 401 GUFFEY ST, MARION HEALTH CARE HOSPITA 26554 #055-01-1974 L1975 **FM** *020
MALLAMO, Franklin Wm. ■ 26554 #051-04-1945 L1946 **IM** *071 †20
MANUEL, Mervin Punzalan. 1322 LOCUST AVE 26554 #748-01-1992 L2006 **PD** *020 †55 ‡
MARTIN, Damon. 6 TIGER TRL 26554 #055-01-1982 L1983 **CCM IM** *071
MC KINLEY, Nancy Ellen. 1325 LOCUST AVE, STE 201 26554 #026-04-1986 L1991 **ORS OSM** *020 †40
MCLELLAN, David M. 1078 LOCUST AVE, STE 102 26554 #027-01-1977 L1982 **GS VS** *020 †85
MENEZ, Eugenio Aldea. 1714 LOCUST AVE 26554 #748-10-1977 L1992 **IM** *020 †20
MIHELIC, Charles Jos. 1325 LOCUST AVE 26554 #028-46-1980 L1994 **EM FM** *020 †16
MILLER, Thomas Bradley. 1912 LOCUST AVE, MARION MEDICAL ASSOCIATES 26554 #055-01-2004 L2006 **IM** *020
MILLER, Thomas Stuart. 1912 LOCUST AVE 26554 #055-01-1974 L1975 **IM CD** *020
MISENHELDER, Jason Andrew. 1325 LOCUST AVE, FAIRMONT GENERAL HOSPITAL 26554 #055-01-2003 L2005 **FM** *020 †18
MULPURU, Sree Krishna. 312 10TH ST 26554 #495-50-1967 L1978 **PD** *020 †55
PADRO, Silvina Beatriz. 1322 LOCUST AVE 26554 #132-01-1988 L2003 **IM** *020 †20
PATEL, Govind M. 1844 LOCUST AVE 26554 #495-22-1973 L1983 **IM A** *020 †20
PATEL, Pravinchandra I. 1322 LOCUST AVE, INC 26554 #495-23-1968 L1974 **IM** *020 †20
PETRIDOU, Sevastiani. 1322 LOCUST AVE, INC 26554 #665-01-2002 L2006 **FM** *020 †18
PROUTY, Tyler James. 1703 LOCUST AVE 26554 #055-01-2003 L2006 **OBG** *020
PUMPHREY, Jennifer A. 100 VILLAGE DR STE 301 26554 #055-01-1998 L2002 **PD** *020 †55
RAMSAY, Sarah Jane. ■ 26554 #055-01-1997 L1999 **EM** *020 †16
RIZZO, John Anthony. ■ 26554 #055-01-1965 L1966 **OBG** *020
ROIDAD, Mohammad. 1614 LOCUST AVE 26554 #704-09-1971 L1980 **GE IM** *020 †20
ROSIELLO, David Carl. 1325 LOCUST AVE 26554 #033-05-1991 L1995 **DR** *020 †80
SANTMYIRE-ROSENBERGER, Bet. 100 VILLAGE DR, STE 201 26554 #055-01-2001 L2003 **D** *020 †15 ‡
SCHROERING, Michael S. 1322 LOCUST AVE, INC 26554 #020-12-1975 L1984 **FM FPG** *020 †18
SCHWAB, Larry. 1 PHYSICIANS PLZ, REGIONAL EYE ASSOCIATES 26554 #055-01-1966 L1967 **OPH** *062 †35
SHERLOCK, Kathryn Lee. 312 10TH ST, PEDIATRIC PARTNERS, PLLC 26554 #055-01-2005 L2007 **PD** *012
SIMPSON, Richard Alan. 1325 LOCUST AVE 26554 #041-09-1975 L1990 **IM** *020 †20
STADTMILLER, Richard J. 1325 LOCUST AVE 26554 #024-01-1974 L1992 **OS FM** *020 †18
STEELE, Thomas Wesley. 312 10TH ST 26554 #055-01-1991 L1994 **PD** *020 †55
SULEIMAN, Raed M Tayseer. 300 2ND ST, MARION COUNTY HEALTH DEPAR 26554 #584-01-1991 L2000 **PCC** *020
TADROS, Hany Maher. ■ 26554 #048-14-1999 L2007 **HS** *100 ‡
TASKIN, Ilhan Baki. ■ 26554 #902-03-1955 L1973 **AN** *071 †05
THAGIRISA, Anjaneyulu. 1325 LOCUST AVE 26554 #495-70-1974 L1982 **IM** *020 †20
THOMPSON, Robt Clayton, Jr. RR 8 BOX 18E 26554 #055-01-1975 L1976 **EM** *020 †16
THRUSH, Peter Kent. 1708 LOCUST AVE, STE 101 26554 #055-01-1973 L1974 **ORS** *020 †40
THRUSH, Walter P. 700 VILLAGE DR, RADIOLOGICAL PHYSICIAN ASS 26554 #055-01-1986 L1987 **NR** *020 †80

TSAI, Peeng Jau. 1408 COUNTRY CLUB RD 26554 #385-02-1962 L1974 **PD NPM** *071 †55
TURNER, Tommy. 1840 LOCUST AVE 26554 #055-01-1968 L1976 **OBG** *075 †30
TWIGG, Shari Jean. ■ 26554 #055-01-2007 **OBG** *012
VALLS, Jason John. ■ 26554 #021-05-2001 L2004 **FM** *020 †18
VILLAVICENCIO, Jose. 1325 LOCUST AVE, EMERGENCY DEPARTMENT 26554 #748-02-1987 L1994 **IM** *020 †20
VOGT, Joel Alan. 28 OAKWOOD RD, FAIRMONT PHYSICIANS 26554 #048-16-1981 L2007 **P** *020 †75
WALKER, Wm Nelson, Jr. ■ 26554 #051-04-1947 L1949 **AN PUD** *071 †05
WANG, Shen K. 1345 LOCUST AVE 26554 #024-01-1957 L1959 **ORS** *071 †40
ZITO, Dominick S. 5 ERWIN LN 26554 #561-04-1983 L1993 **IM OM** *020 †20

FALLING WATERS – BERKELEY

MURPHY, Ian Douglas. ■ 25419 #041-09-1943 L1943 **ORS TRS** *071 †40
RYDLAND, Danine Anne. 6225 WILLIAMSPORT PIKE 25419 #011-02-1980 L1984 **GYN** *020 †30

FAYETTEVILLE – FAYETTE

ASHBY, Diane Elizabeth. 207 W MAPLE AVE, MED-SURG GROUP INC 25840 #034-01-1989 L1993 **EM** *020 †16
BATEMAN, Robert Odell. RR 3 BOX 458C, HERITAGE MEDICAL ASSOCIATE 25840 #047-06-1962 L1990 **ORS** *071
COOK, Lewis Anderson. RR 3 BOX 4A, WEST MAPLE AVE 25840 #055-01-1973 L1973 **FM** *020 †18
RUSHIN, Jeanne Marie. ■ 25840 #051-07-1981 L1986 **PTH** *020 †50
STAGGERS, Margaret Anne. ■ 25840 #055-01-1969 L1970 **EM FM** *020 †16,18
WHITE, Mark Douglas. RR 3 BOX 458E 25840 #055-01-1982 L1985 **FM EM** *020 †18

FOLLANSBEE – BROOKE

BERNARDO, Jose Francisco. 138 ROCKDALE RD 26037 #737-06-1984 L2005 **NEP IM** *020 †20
FRITZ, Bryan Jeffrey. ■ 26037 #021-01-2005 L2005 **AN** *012
SAIEED, Saieed Hizkeal. 1421 MAIN ST 26037 #915-05-1984 L1999 **IM** *020 †20

FORT GAY – WAYNE

HANSEN, Zachary Henrylee. 3329 BRIDGE ST 25514 #055-02-2004 L2005 **FM** *020 †18
JACKSON, Paul Edward. ■ 25514 #305-01-2000 L2005 **IM** *020

FRANKFORD – GREENBRIER

CAVALLARO, Joseph Wm. ■ 24938 #023-01-1955 L1959 **PUD OTO** *071 †45

FRANKLIN – PENDLETON

HARTMAN, Heidi. ■ 26807 #055-75-2007, ▲ L2007 *012
SEEGAR, John K. 305 N MAIN ST 26807 #055-01-1984 L1987 **PD** *020 †55

GASSAWAY – BRAXTON

BORDONADA, Jose Delfin. 100 HOYLMAN DR, C/O BRAXTON CO. MEM HOSP 26624 #748-10-1964 L1981 **GS GP** *075
GIVEN, W Douglas. 617 RIVER ST 26624 #055-02-1983 L1984 **FM** *020 †18 ‡
KENT, Roy Denvall. 710 ELK ST 26624 #010-01-1964 L1997 **EM FM** *071
PIGOTT, Darla Kay. 626 ELK ST, ELK MEMORIAL CLC 26624 #055-01-1999 L2000 **FM** *020 †18

GERRARDSTOWN – BERKELEY

DE SOTO, Joseph A. ■ 25420 #010-03-2005 **HO** *040

GLEN DALE – MARSHALL

BATICH, John Wm. 426 8TH ST, STE 303 26038 #033-05-1987 L2005 **OBG** *020
BAYSAL, Erdogan Yasar. 800 WHEELING AVE 26038 #902-10-1957 L1970 **IM CD** *071
BURKHART, Michael Warren. 800 WHEELING AVE, REYNOLDS MEM HOSP 26038 #055-01-1980 L1984 **EM FM** *020 †16
CHIU, Edward Kin Yip. 800 WHEELING AVE 26038 #068-01-1988 L2002 **CD IM** *020
DAGUE, Gerald Arnold. 800 WHEELING AVE, REYNOLDS MEM HOSP 26038 #055-02-2000 L2002 **EM FM** *020 †18
DICKEY, Thomas Oscar, Jr. ■ 26038 #038-40-1945 L1950 **PHP EM** *071 †18,16
DIETTINGER, Frank Geo. 800 WHEELING AVE, REYNOLDS MEMORIAL HOSPITAL 26038 #561-01-1974 L1998 **DR** *020 †80
DOLGOVSKIJ, Michail. ■ 26038 #407-07-1950 L1957 **FM** *030
HESS, David Frederick. 407 WHEELING AVE 26038 #055-01-1998 L2002 **MPD** *020 †20,55
HESS, Michelle L. 407 WHEELING AVE, GLEN DALE MED & PEDIATRICS 26038 #055-01-1998 L2002 **PD** *020 †55
JIMENEZ, Carlos C. 1000 WHEELING AVE 26038 #748-01-1964 L1974 **IM END** *020
JONES, Wendell Everett. 800 WHEELING AVE 26038 #041-01-1964 L1992 **R** *071 †80
KLINE, Kenneth K. 426 8TH ST, STE 203 26038 #055-02-1982 L1983 **FM FPG** *020 †18
KUREISHY, Zaveen Ahmad. 426 8TH ST STE 102 26038 #704-02-1988 L1998 **IM** *020 †20
MAYSONET, Jesus Manuel. 800 WHEELING AVE 26038 #042-02-1994 L1999 **AN** *020 †05
MEHROTRA, Sunila. 426 8TH ST STE 101, MARSHALL CTY PROF BLDG 26038 #495-45-1976 L1982 **PD** *020 †55
NALLY, David Michael. 426 8TH ST 26038 #055-01-1973 L1975 **EM GP** *020
NEIBERG, Howard. 800 WHEELING AVE 26038 #041-12-1968 L1984 **DR** *020 †80
OSHEA, Heather Ann. 1307 WHEELING AVE, STE A 26038 #055-01-2000 L2001 **FM** *020

ROBERTSON, Fred Shaune. 800 WHEELING AVE, REYNOLDS MEM HOSP 26038 #055-01-1980 L1997 **EM** *020 †16

SALUDES, Melvin T. 426 8TH ST STE 305, MARSHALL CTY. PROF. CENTER 26038 #748-18-1991 L1994 **PUD** *020 †20

TEMPLETON, John, Jr. 800 WHEELING AVE 26038 #055-01-1977 L1978 **FM** *020 †18

TRUSTY, Daryl Ashley. ■ 26038 #055-75-2006, ▲ L2007 *012

VENTOSA, Jose J, Jr. 400 3RD ST 26038 #748-01-1964 L1974 **PD ADL** *020 †55

VILLAVERDE, Manuel Abaro. 800 WHEELING AVE 26038 #748-01-1956 L1972 **PTH** *020 †50

WAYT, Michael Timothy. 1307 WHEELING AVE STE A 26038 #055-01-1994 L1995 **FM** *020 †18

WINIKOFF, Stephen Edward. 800 WHEELING AVE, REYNOLDS MEMORIAL HOSPITAL 26038 #035-01-1997 L2007 **GS** *020 †85

GLENVILLE – GILMER

MIMS, Gregory Schuyler, II. ■ 26351 #005-12-1997 L1999 **FM** *020 †18

NICHOLS, Carl Edwin. 101 COLLEGE ST, GILMER COUNTY URGENT CARE 26351 #055-01-1968 L1969 **GP GYN** *020 †30

GRAFTON – TAYLOR

BENDER, David Brian. 500 MARKET ST 26354 #041-02-1987 L1990 **FM** *020 †18

CRAIG, Michael David. 207 W MAIN 26354 #055-01-2000 L2002 **HO** *020 †20

CRAIG, Nancy Lee. 207 W MAIN ST 26354 #055-02-1986 L1987 **EM FM** *075 †18

DAVENPORT, Gary Bruce. 500 MARKET ST, GRAFTON CITY HOSPITAL 26354 #038-45-2000 L2003 **IM** *020 †20

DICKEY, William T, III. 500 MARKET ST 26354 #048-15-1997 L2001 **EM** *020 †16

LONG, Shawn Edward. 401 N PIKE ST 26354 #055-01-2000 L2001 **FM** *020 †18 ‡

MC NEER, Michael Dennis. 501 N PIKE ST 26354 #055-01-1969 L1970 **P ADM** *020 †75

RADER, Edwin Lee. 725 N PIKE ST 26354 #055-01-1985 L1987 **FM** *020 †18

SANTIBANEZ, Samuel. 500 MARKET ST 26354 #748-01-1955 L1973 **GP GS** *071

VILLARAZA, Christopher Z. 500 MARKET ST 26354 #748-10-1973 L1977 **GP** *020

WENTZEL, Peter Volkmar. 725 N PIKE ST, MEDICAL CENTER OF TAYLOR C 26354 #422-01-2002 L2006 **FM** *100 †18

WINFRED, Rajeev Isaac. 725 N PIKE ST, PRESTON TAYLOR COMM HLTH 26354 #422-01-1995 L1999 **MPD** *020,55

WITKOWSKI, Mark Thos. 725 N PIKE ST 26354 #041-09-1989 L1992 **FM** *020 †18

WOODFORD, James Wm. 500 MARKET ST, AFF OF GRAFTON CITY HOSPIN 26354 #055-01-1966 L1973 **GS** *020 †85

GRANTSVILLE – CALHOUN

AYA-AY, Juanito. 186 HOSPITAL DR, MINNIE HAMILTON HLTH SYS 26147 #748-01-1966 L1972 **IM IMG** *071

BALASUBRAMONY, Suresh. 186 HOSPITAL DR 26147 #495-31-1991 L2002 **IM** *020 †20

CINCO, Alfonso Piczon, III. 186 HOSPITAL DR 26147 #748-01-1980 L1991 **IM** *020

HANDE, Vishwanath. 186 HOSPITAL DR 26147 #495-04-1983 L1996 **PCC** *020 †20

HARRAH, John Dae. 186 HOSPITAL DR, MINNIE HAMILTON HEALTH SYS 26147 #051-01-1964 L1970 **TS FM** *020 †85,90

KEVAK, Rudolph Michael D. 186 HOSPITAL DR 26147 #308-08-1983 L1996 **IM** *020

MURPHY, Jonathan B. 186 HOSPITAL DR 26147 #055-01-1985 L1987 **MPD PTX** *020 †20,55

GREEN BANK – POCAHONTAS

BURGESS, Clyde Albert. NORTH FORK RD 24944 #038-41-1961 L1962 **FM EM** *071 †18

OHLE, Elpenor Rudolf. ■ 24944 #024-01-1941 L1943 **GP OS** *071

HAMLIN – LINCOLN

ELKINS, Gregory Allen. 412 MARKET ST 25523 #055-02-1988 L1989 **FM** *020 †18

GILLISPIE, Deborah Harper. 7400 LYNN AVE, LINCOLN PRIMARY CARE CTR 25523 #055-02-1991 L1992 **FM** *020 †18

HERNANDEZ, Leopoldo. ■ 25523 #649-02-1953 L1960 **GP** *075

LAHNOVYCH, Victor. 7400 LYNN AVE 25523 #041-15-2004 L2007 **FM** *100

MC KAY, George Leo. 7400 LYNN AVE 25523 #055-02-1992 L1993 **IM** *020 †20

MILAM, Kevin Mitchell. 7400 LYNN AVE 25523 #055-02-2002 L2004 **FM** *020 †18

STOLL, Syam Babu. 7400 LYNN AVE, LINCOLN PRIMARY CARE CENTE 25523 #055-02-2001 L2004 **GP** *020

WRIGHT, Susan Lilly. 7400 LYNN AVE 25523 #055-01-1980 L1982 **PD** *020

HARPERS FERRY – JEFFERSON

ALVAREZ, Maria Victoria. 31 TAYLOR ST 25425 #306-01-2001 L2005 **N** *100 †75

BALTIERRA, David Alonso. ■ 25425 #025-01-1993 L2001 **FM** *020 †18

BENTLEY, Shannon Kristeen. 31 TAYLOR ST 25425 #038-45-1997 L2006 **FM** *020 †18

BRENNAN, Robert J. ■ 25425 #010-01-1952 L1956 **OBG** *071

BUDI, Lakshmi. ■ 25425 #495-11-1991 **FP** *012

CANNARELLA, Rosemarie E. 171 TAYLOR ST, BOLIVAR MEDICAL CENTER 25425 #055-01-1979 L1980 **FM** *030 †18

CASABAR, Vivian Cefre. 31 TAYLOR ST, HARPERS FERRY FAMILY MEDIC 25425 #748-10-1998 L2006 **FM** *020 †18

CUCUZZELLA, Mark Thos. 31 TAYLOR ST, BOLIVAR MEDICAL CENTER 25425 #051-01-1992 L2005 **FM** *020 †18

DE VINE, Timothy Michael. 171 TAYLOR ST, HARPERS FERRY FAMILY MEDIC 25425 #055-01-2005 **FP** *012

FLEMING, G Alexander. ■ 25425 #012-05-1977 L1980 **END EM** *030 †20

FREAS, Carol Diane. 31 TAYLOR ST, UHA HARPERS FERRY 25425 #020-12-1976 L1990 **CHP P** *075

HACK, Dallas Christian. ■ 25425 #005-12-1975 L1986 **PHP GP** *040 †70

HOLT, Jane E. ■ 25425 #055-75-2007, ▲ **FP** *012

JANUS, Jennifer Cox. 171 TAYLOR ST, HARPERSFERRY FAMILY MEDICI 25425 #023-01-2002 L2006 **MPD** *020 †55,20 ‡

MACISAAC, Gregory Francis. 31 TAYLOR ST, UHA HARPERS FERRY 25425 #064-01-1986 L1994 **GP FM** *020 †18

MACIUNAS, Kristina A. 31 TAYLOR ST, RESIDENCE PROGRAM 25425 #055-01-1992 L1993 **FM** *020 †18

MESKE, Allen Edward. ■ 25425 #038-40-1990 L2006 **EM** *020 †16

MOERSCHEL, Sarah K. 171 TAYLOR ST 25425 #016-43-1997 L2004 **PD** *020 †55

MORGAN, Scott Ingles. 31 TAYLOR ST, RURAL FAMILY MEDICINE RESI 25425 #021-05-1979 L1992 **FM** *100

NAU, Konrad Chas. 31 TAYLOR ST, UHA HARPERS FERRY 25425 #055-01-1979 L1980 **FM IMG** *040 †18

PEETE, Maricceo Davonchea. 31 TAYLOR ST 25425 #305-01-2002 **FM** *020

RAJAH, Suganthi Varatha. 31 TAYLOR ST, HAPERS FERREY FAMILY MED 25425 #496-23-1991 **FP** *012

SCHILDT, Travis Alleneuge. ■ 25425 #055-01-2006 L2008 **FP** *012

STOEBIG, Quirispina Lagar. ■ 25425 #748-19-2001 **FP** *012

TABUENA, Philomela Martir. 31 TAYLOR ST, HARPERS FERRY FAMILY MED 25425 #748-10-1997 **IM** *012

WANG, Ye. 31 TAYLOR ST, HARPERS FERRY FAMILY MEDIC 25425 #243-16-1985 L2006 **FM** *100 †18

HARRISVILLE – RITCHIE

BUTT, Saad Ullah. 135 S PENN AVE 26362 #704-21-1987 L1996 **IM** *020 †20

EDORA, Floresita. 135 S PENN AVE, RITCHIE CTY PRIMARY-PO 373 26362 #748-08-1968 L1980 **GP PHP** *020

HATFIELD, Asel P. ■ 26362 #051-04-1952 L1953 **GP PHP** *072

HARTS – LINCOLN

KESSINGER, Linda Louise. 22 FLEMING DR 25524 #055-01-1988 L1989 **FM** *020 †18

HEDGESVILLE – BERKELEY

HORNICK, Frederick Walter. ■ 25427 #016-02-1965 L1969 **OBG** *071 †30

PHARES, Robert William. 3790 HEDGESVILLE RD, STE H 25427 #055-01-2000 L2003 **FM** *020 †18

HIGH VIEW – HAMPSHIRE

MC CANN, William John. PO BOX 10 26808 #005-11-1943 L1943 **OBG OS** *071 †30

HILLSBORO – POCAHONTAS

GIFFORD, Bonnie Dupper. HC 64 BOX 167 24946 #038-40-1979 L2003 **OM IM** *020 †20

VALENCIA, Jenaro Antonio. DENMAR STATE HOSP 24946 #264-02-1957 **OS** *075

HINTON – SUMMERS

ANAND, Seema K. ■ 25951 #495-92-1989 L1994 **IM** *020 †20

DAY, Stanley Tyler. 197 PLEASANT ST 25951 #055-01-1980 L1982 **FM** *020 †18

HENDERSON, Andrew H, Jr. ■ 25951 #038-41-1950 L1951 **IM** *071

KHAN, Waheed A. PO BOX 940, TERRACE STREET 25951 #704-21-1985 L1995 **IM** *020 †20

RAJGURU, Hanmant Laxman. PO BOX 940 25951 #495-28-1963 L1972 **DR NM** *071 †28

SATOW, Symon. ■ 25951 #038-06-1953 L1993 **GS GP** *071 †85

SEATON, Ronald S. ■ 25951 #023-07-1949 L1994 **GS** *071 †85

SHAMMAA, Sahib Kadhum. 319 2ND AVE 25951 #528-01-1955 L1976 **FM GP** *020 †55

HOLDEN – LOGAN

CARBONEL, Rely C. PO BOX Y2, HOLDEN CLN 25625 #748-08-1966 L1978 **GP** *020

PRITCHARD, Joseph. PO BOX X 25625 #748-11-1969 L1981 *075

HOMETOWN – PUTNAM

CRAWFORD, Dudley Deshon. ■ 25109 #024-05-1987 L1991 **FM** *020 †18

HUNTINGTON – CABELL

ABADIR, Farouk Helmy. 1340 HAL GREER BLVD 25701 #915-05-1976 L1990 **AN** *020

ABDELGABER, Ahmed Mohamed. 5170 US ROUTE 60 25705 #915-03-1994 L2006 **FM** *020 †18

ABDU, Mohammed Mustapha. 1600 MEDICAL CENTER DR, DEPT OF INT MED 25701 #366-01-1997 **IM** *012

ABRAHAM, Charles. 1231 6TH AVE 25701 #055-01-1968 L1969 **OTO A** *062 †45 ‡

ABRAHAM, Nazem. 1321 HAL GREER BLVD 25701 #055-01-1964 L1965 **D** *020 †15

ABRENICA, Nelio Sangalang. 1340 HAL GREER BLVD 25701 #748-01-1973 L1978 **GS** *020 †16

ABU SULTANEH, Samer Moham. ■ 25705 #575-02-2003 **PD** *012

ACUNA, Andreia Moraes. 1600 MEDICAL CENTER DR, STE 3400 DEPT OF OB/GYN 25701 #187-41-2000 **OBG** *012

ADAMS, Frederick David. 5694 US ROUTE 60, INC 25705 #055-02-1983 L1984 **AN** *020 †05

ADAMS, Samuel Lee. 307 5TH AVE 25701 #020-12-1999 L2001 **FM** *020 †18

ADDISON, Jeffery Floyd. 5170 US ROUTE 60 E, HUNTINGTON INT MED GP 25705 #045-01-1980 Ł1989 **NEP IM** *020 †20

AGAHTEHRANI, Abdolreza. 5170 US ROUTE 60 25705 #041-13-1998 L2007 **IC** *100 †20

AGRAWAL, Lalit Saran. ■ 25701 #495-49-1962 L1975 **FM** *020 †18

AHMAD, Aslam Moeed. 1600 MEDICAL CENTER DR, STE G500 25701 #704-02-1984 L1993 CD PTH *020 †20

AHMAD, Ijaz. 2828 1ST AVE STE 202 25702 #704-01-1969 L1980 N *020 †75

AHMAD, Mohammed Suleiman. 1600 MEDICAL CENTER DR, STE 3400 25701 #575-02-2002 IM *012

AHMAD, Naushaba. 2900 1ST AVE, ASSOCIATED PATH HUNTINGTON 25702 #704-20-1987 L2003 PTH DMP *062 †50

AHMED, Monjur. 1249 15TH ST, UNIVERSITY PHYSICIANS & SU 25701 #160-01-1983 L2002 GE *020 †20

AKERS, Paul Dexter. 5170 US ROUTE 60 25705 #055-02-1997 L2003 DR *020 †80

AKOGHLANIAN, Shoghik. 1600 MEDICAL CENTER DR, STE 3500 25701 #875-01-2004 PD *012

ALBERICO, Anthony Michael. 1600 MEDICAL CENTER DR, STE G500 25701 #041-13-1981 L2007 NS *020 †25

ALBRECHT, Amy Lynn. 1600 MEDICAL CENTER DR, STE 1400 25701 #038-45-2003 L2004 FM *100 †18

ALKHANKAN, Fadi Walid. 1801 6TH AVE 25703 #875-02-2000 L2008 PUD *012 †20

ALLAN, Benjamin Lee. 2866 1ST AVE, STE 501 25702 #055-02-2003 L2006 FM *020 †18

ALMAHASNEH, Firas Suleima. 1801 6TH AVE 25703 #575-02-2002 IM *012

ALMANSARI, Abdulqawi A. ■ 25705 #797-02-1992 L1998 END *100 †20

ALNAS, Majd. ■ 25705 #875-01-2000 L2008 PUD *012 †20

AL NIMRI, Omar Mousa. 1801 6TH AVE 25703 #575-02-2003 IM *012

ALTAYEH, Abdullah. 1600 MEDICAL CENTER DR, STE 3400 25701 #422-01-2002 L2007 PUD *012 †20

ANAND, Sumit. 1230 6TH AVE, DEPT OF ADMINISTRATION 25701 #917-21-1992 L2003 CHP *100 †75

ANDERSON, Marsha S. 5170 US ROUTE 60 25705 #055-02-1988 L1994 DR *020 †80

ARVANITIS, Michael James. 5170 US ROUTE 60 25705 #038-43-1995 L2006 VIR *020 †80

ARYA, Sirous. 1600 MEDICAL CENTER DR 25701 #517-03-1962 L1972 GS VS *020 †85

ASSALEY, Joseph Phillip. 2900 1ST AVE 25702 #055-02-1988 L1992 OBG *020 †30

ATARO, Peter Rajoro. 1600 MEDICAL CENTER DR, STE 3400 DEPT OF IM 25701 #704-15-1996 IM *012

AWILI, Mustafa Hassanalar. 1249 15TH ST, MU DEPT OF INTERNAL MED 25701 #613-02-1998 IM *012

BAIRU, Samuel Haileab. 1600 MEDICAL CENTER DR, STE 3400 DEPT OF IM 25701 #366-01-1992 IM *012

BAKSI, Mitali. ■ 25705 #055-02-1991 L1996 PTH *020 †50

BALDERA, Alfred. 1340 HAL GREER BLVD 25701 #024-05-1977 L1978 FM EM *020 †18

BALDONADO, Adoracion S. HUNTINGTON STATE HOSP 25705 #748-07-1969 L1976 *020

BALLESTER, Oscar F. 1400 HAL GREER BLVD, LSU SCIENCES CENTER 25701 #132-02-1971 L2007 HEM ON *020 †20

BAREBO, Ronald Ernie. 5170 US ROUTE 60 25705 #055-02-1991 L1995 N *020 †75

BARYUN, Esam Nuri. 2828 1ST AVE, STE 200 25702 #613-02-1998 L2003 ICE *012 †20 ‡

BAUR, Jack H. 1340 HAL GREER BLVD 25701 #038-41-1948 L1955 HEM IM *071 †20

BAXTER, Franklin Ross. ■ 25705 #012-01-2005 OBG *012

BEAM, William Randy. 5170 US ROUTE 60 E, HIMG 25705 #041-13-1984 L1993 PUD IM *020 †20

BEARD, Kip Randall. 612 6TH AVE, TRISTATE OCCPTNL MED 25701 #017-20-1995 L1998 IM *062 ‡

BEAVER, Bonnie Lou. 1600 MEDICAL CENTER DR, STE 2500 25701 #038-40-1979 L1995 PDS TRS *020 †85

BECKER, James Bernard. 1600 MEDICAL CENTER DR, STE 1500 25701 #055-02-1993 L1994 FM *020 †18

BELAY, Sileshi Admassu. 1600 MEDICAL CENTER DR, STE 3400 DEPT OF IM 25701 #366-03-1992 IM *012

BELL, Naaman Lee. 2900 1ST AVE 25702 #055-02-1998 L2000 MPD EM *020 †20

BENHAMED, Nesreen A. 1600 MEDICAL CENTER DR, STE G500 25701 #613-02-1989 L2001 IM *020 †20

BENNETT, Amanda Katharine. 307 5TH AVE 25702 #055-02-2003 L2004 FM *020 †18

BENNETT, Ashley William. ■ 25705 #055-02-2005 L2007 GS *012

BENNETT, Lori Kay. 1340 HAL GREER BLVD, CABELL HUNTINGTON HOSPITAL 25701 #041-13-1981 L1982 EM *020 †16

BENTON, Roland E. 2900 1ST AVE 25702 #654-01-1996 L1999 IM PD *020

BERHANE, Medhanie Chichi. ■ 25705 #036-08-2003 L2007 GS *012

BINDER, James Thos. 1600 MEDICAL CENTER DR, STE 2500 25701 #041-12-1977 L1983 CHP *020 †55,75

BLAKE, Rodger Alan. 5170 US ROUTE 60 25705 #023-07-1986 L1992 DR R *020 †80

BLOM, Dina. 1508 6TH AVE, EYE CARE INC 25701 #051-07-1995 L2004 OPH *020 †35

BLOM, Paul Henry. 5170 US ROUTE 60 25705 #012-01-1994 L2004 VIR *020 †80

BODALA, Prathima. 3375 US ROUTE 60, PRESTERA CENTER FOR MHS 25705 #495-50-1997 L2006 P *100 †75

BOOTH, Richard Osborne, Jr. 401 10TH ST, STE 410 25701 #055-02-1998 L2001 OBG *020 †30

BORA, Narendra Kumar. 1530 NORWAY AVE, HUNTINGTON STATE HOSPITAL 25705 #495-18-1959 L1980 P *071

BOWER, Brian Edward. 307 5TH AVE 25702 #055-02-1998 L2002 OBG *020 †30

BOWMAN, Sara Catherine. ■ 25705 #055-01-1997 L2000 IM *020 †20

BRANAM, Christopher O. 2900 1ST AVE 25702 #041-12-1990 L1994 FM *020 †20

BRILEY, Dennis Patrick. 2828 1ST AVE, STE 300 25702 #917-07-1979 L1992 N IM *020 †20,75

BRIZENDINE, Paul Thos. 533 4TH AVE 25701 #028-03-1965 L1980 EM GS *030 †18,16

BROWN, Linda Gail. 1001 10TH AVE 25701 #055-02-1993 L1995 PTH *020 †50

BRUMFIELD, Steven Scott. 2866 1ST AVE, STE 501 25702 #055-02-1999 L2002 OBG *020 †30

BUCKHOLTZ, Anita Holly. ■ 25705 #045-01-1979 L1980 IM *100

BURDICK, Hoyt Jeffery. 1340 HAL GREER BLVD 25701 #027-01-1980 L1985 PCC *030 †20

BUTCHER, Amanda Lee. ■ 25701 #055-02-2008 *012

CAMPBELL, Yolanda Yvonne. 1600 MEDICAL CENTER DR, STE 4500 25701 #055-02-2004 L2008 OBG *012

CANSINO, Silvestre Perez. 1249 15TH ST, STE 4000 25701 #748-08-1971 L1993 CD IM *050 †20

CARAWAY, David Lee. 2900 1ST AVE 25702 #051-01-1992 L1996 AN *020 †05

CARICO, Gregory Alan. 5170 US ROUTE 60 25705 #055-02-1989 L1990 FM *020 †18

CARPENTER, Anne Betts. 1340 HAL GREER BLVD 25701 #055-02-1993 L1995 PCP *020 †50

CASERTA, Larry Allen. 5187 US ROUTE 60 25705 #055-01-1973 L1974 OBG *020

CHAFIN, James Brett. 1616 13TH AVE, STE 100 25701 #055-01-1992 L1995 PDO *100 †45

CHAMBERLAIN, Allan Scott. 2866 1ST AVE, STE 501 25702 #038-41-1983 L1986 OBG *020 †30

CHANDRAN, Prathap G. 2828 1ST AVE, STE 304 25701 #495-31-1963 L1985 TS *020 †20

CHANDRASEKARAN, Jay. 553 WASHINGTON AVE 25701 #495-16-1983 L1999 PM PMM *020 †60

CHANEY, Gregory Donald. 2628 5TH AVE 25702 #055-02-1990 L1991 IM *020

CHARLES, Paul Mitchell. 1340 HAL GREER BLVD 25701 #055-02-1988 L1991 FM EM *020 †18

CHAUDHRY, Sarmad Munir. 1249 15TH ST, 2ND FLOOR BYRD CLINIC CENT 25701 #704-24-1997 IM *012

CHERTOW, Bruce Sherwin. 1600 MEDICAL CENTER DR, STE G500 25701 #016-11-1965 L1978 END NM *020 †28,20

CHIDESTER, Andrew David. ■ 25705 #055-02-2008 *012

CHILDERS, Robert Steve. 5170 US ROUTE 60 25705 #055-01-1985 L1988 FM *071 †18

CHIRICO, Peter Anthony. 5170 US ROUTE 60 25705 #033-06-1986 L1991 DR *040 †80

CHOUDHRY, Ihtisham. 1249 15TH ST STE 2, INTERNAL MEDI 25701 #704-01-2004 IM *012

CHOUDHRY, Ihtisham. 1249 15TH ST STE 20, MU DEPARTMENT OF INTERNAL 25701 #704-01-2004 IM *012

CHOUINARD, Sarah Bolen. 305 12TH AVE 25701 #055-02-1998 L1999 FM *020 †18

CHOWDHURY, Nepal C. 2828 1ST AVE, STE 200 25702 #160-10-1987 L2007 GS *020 †85,90

CHRISTIAN, Homer Lee. 1230 6TH AVE 25701 #055-01-1970 L1972 GP *020

CLARK, Carolyn Edwards. 1124 19TH ST 25701 #055-01-1979 L1983 OBG *020 †30

CLEMENTS, Charles Wesley. 1600 MEDICAL CENTER DR, STE 1500 25701 #055-02-1997 L1998 FM OM *020 †18

COCHRANE, J Alan. 5170 US ROUTE 60 25705 #918-01-1973 L1979 DR VIR *020 †80

COCKE, William Marvin, Jr. 1600 MEDICAL CENTER DR, STE 2500 25701 #048-04-1960 L1986 PS *020 †65

COCKERHAM, Christopher Al. 5170 US ROUTE 60 E 25705 #665-02-2002 L2005 IM *020 †20

COFFMAN, Shawn Wayne. 5170 US ROUTE 60 25705 #055-02-1987 L1988 IM *020 †20

COMPTON, Ricky Jack. 5170 US ROUTE 60 25705 #055-02-1994 L1999 DR *020 †80

CONAWAY, Kevin James. 1600 MEDICAL CENTER DR, STE 4500 25701 #055-02-1991 L1995 OBG *020 †30

CONJURA, Ann. ■ 25705 #023-07-1984 L1998 IM HEM *074 †20

COOK, David Wellington. 1300 3RD AVE 25701 #050-02-1979 L1984 OPH *020 †35

COOK, Samantha Linn. ■ 25701 #055-02-2007 PD *012

COOPER, Shannon Kathleen. 1600 MEDICAL CENTER DR, STE 1500 25701 #055-02-2004 L2006 FM *100 †18

COPLEY, Mary Stevens. 528 RIDGEWOOD RD 25701 #055-02-1990 L1991 FM *020 †18

CORN, George Brian. 1340 HAL GREER BLVD, HOSPITAL 25701 #055-02-1998 L2001 FM *020 †18

CORNELL, John Edwin. 1600 MEDICAL CENTER DR, STE 1500 25701 #055-02-1999 L2001 FM *020

COUCH, Amos Paul. 1001 10TH AVE, UNIV PATH SVCS 25701 #034-01-1983 L2006 PTH DMP *020 †50

COUCHOT, Michael David. 3135 16TH STREET RD, STE 20 25701 #020-02-1998 L1999 *020

COWELL, Daniel David. 1600 MEDICAL CENTER DR, DEPT PSYCH/BEHAVORIAL MED 25701 #033-05-1960 L1994 P *020 †75 ‡

COYNER, John Legion, Jr. ■ 25701 #055-02-2007 *012

CRAIG, Paul W, II. 2828 1ST AVE, STE 401 25702 #012-01-1983 L1995 OM LM *020 †70

CRAYTHORNE, Colin M. 2828 1ST AVE STE 400 25702 #539-01-1960 L1973 ORS LM *071 †40

CREMEANS, Gary David, II. 1600 MEDICAL CENTER DR, STE 1500 25701 #055-02-1996 L1997 FM *020 †18

CRUZ, Pablo. ■ 25701 #649-26-1985 L1994 *020

CURE, Robert Joseph. 5170 US ROUTE 60 25705 #055-02-1998 L2003 DR *020 †80

CUZZOURT, Jeremy Clifton. 5170 US ROUTE 60 25705 #012-22-2001 L2006 *020 †45

CYRUS, Melody S. 723 9TH AVE 25701 #055-02-1996 L1998 PD *020 †55

DAMRON, Timothy Andrew. 5170 US ROUTE 60 E, HIMG 25705 #055-02-1986 L1987 CD *020 †20

DANIELS, James David. 5170 US ROUTE 60 25705 #051-04-1966 L1972 ON IM *020 †20

DANNALS, Thomas Edward. 5170 US ROUTE 60 25705 #035-45-1984 L1987 FM *020 †18

DARRAT, Yousef Hadi. 1249 15TH ST STE 2, INTERNAL MEDI 25701 #613-02-2002 IM *012

DAVID, Kirk Jamieson. ■ 25701 #035-01-1944 L1953 GS *071 †85

DAVIS, John Dylan. ■ 25701 #055-02-2008 *012

DAWLEY, Brenda Lee. 1600 MEDICAL CENTER DR, STE 4500 25701 #011-02-1990 L1998 OBG *020 †30

DAY, James Bruce. 1600 MEDICAL CENTER DR, STE 2500 25701 #016-11-2000 L2006 ORS *012 ‡

DAY, Maurice Jerome, Jr. 2828 1ST AVE, STE 400 25702 #004-01-1989 L1996 NS *020 †25

DE EULIS, Timothy Guiney. 2866 1ST AVE STE 501, UNITED HEALTH PROFESSIONAL 25702 #055-01-1976 L1999 GO GYN *020 †30

DEL CHECCOLO, Richard L. 2900 1ST AVE, ST MARYS HOSPITAL 25702 #055-01-1981 L1982 EM IM *071 †20,16

DENNING, David Alan. 2561 3RD AVE 25703 #055-01-1977 L1982 GS *020 †85

DENNISON, William Brian. 5170 US ROUTE 60 25705 #055-01-1983 L1991 RHU IM *020 †20

DEVARAJ, Kiran Shashi. 1600 MEDICAL CENTER DR, STE B500 25701 #917-05-1993 L2001 P *020 †75

DEWESE, Christopher Lee. 1600 MEDICAL CENTER DR, STE 3500 25701 #055-02-1997 L2000 PD *020 †55

DHANJAL, Ashu. 1249 15TH ST STE 2, INTERNAL MEDI 25701 #496-07-2000 IM *012

DIAL, Larry Dale, Jr. 1600 MEDICAL CENTER DR, STE G500 25701 #055-02-1999 L2002 IM *020 †20

DIAZ, Salvador. ■ 25705 #649-03-1954 L1963 GS *020

DI CRISTOFARO, Sharon U. 2860 3RD AVE STE 30, WEE CARE PEDIATRICS GRP PL 25702 #055-02-1998 L2001 PD *020 †55

DIMARTINO, Peter Louis. ■ 25701 #011-02-2004 CD *012 †20

DI STEFANO, John Francis. 5170 US ROUTE 60 E, HUNTINGTON INTERNAL MED GR 25705 #016-43-1974 L1991 ON HEM *020 †20

DOLAN, Jenna Bree. 1600 MEDICAL CENTER DR, STE 3500 25701 #055-02-2004 L2007 PD *020 †55

DOMANICO, Renee Sue. 1600 MEDICAL CENTER DR, STE 3500 25701 #038-44-1988 L1994 NPM *020 †55

DOMINGUEZ, Fernando. ■ 25705 #649-01-1951 L1963 GS *020

DOUGHERTY, Thomas Herbert. 1001 10TH AVE 25701 #030-06-1985 L2006 BBK PTH *020 †50

DOUGLAS, Wade Gerard. 1600 MEDICAL CENTER DR, STE 2500 25701 #011-03-1995 L2005 GS *020 †85

DRANSFELD, Hans Gerhard. 5170 US ROUTE 60 25705 #055-01-1985 L1990 DR *020 †80

DRANSFELD, Hans Werner. 8 SUTHERLAND RD 25705 #407-15-1950 L1959 R *071 †80

DRANSFELD, Joseph Werner. 5170 US ROUTE 60 25705 #055-02-1991 L1997 DR *020 †80

DRISCOLL, Henry Keane. 1249 15TH ST 25701 #024-16-1981 L1987 END *020 †20 ‡

DULING, Leila Sakhai. ■ 25701 #055-02-2007 FP *012

DUNCAN, Laura Suzanne. 1249 15TH ST 25701 #055-02-2003 L2006 IM *020 †20

DUNLAP, Brian Stewart. 1600 MEDICAL CENTER DR, PEDS 25701 #055-02-2004 L2007 PD *100 †55

DUNWORTH, R Lawrence. 30 6TH AVE W STE 106 25701 #010-02-1960 L1967 **OPH** *071 †35
DURRENBERGER, Stephen D. 625 8TH ST 25701 #055-01-1995 L1999 **P** *020 †75
DURST, Paul Ray. 1340 HAL GREER BLVD 25701 #055-02-1984 L1998 **PTH** *020
EASTONE, John Anthony. 5170 US ROUTE 60 25705 #051-01-1995 L2005 **GE** *020 †20
EATON, Stephen Ray. 1801 6TH AVE 25701 #305-01-2005 **GS** *012
ECHOLS, William Jerry. 2860 3RD AVE STE 210 25702 #055-01-1964 L1970 **IM CD** *071 †20
ECHOLS-MARSHALL, Sandra. 5170 US ROUTE 60 25705 #055-02-1989 L1993 **D** *020 †15
EDWARDS, Benjamin Mitchel. 1600 MEDICAL CNTR DR #4500 25701 #055-01-1975 L1977
　OBG *040
EDWARDS, Charles Stephen. 1225 6TH AVE, CENTER 25701 #055-02-1987 L1992
　CHP P *020 †75
EDWARDS, Roy Alvin, Jr. 523 13TH ST 25701 #051-04-1948 L1949 **P** *071 †75
EL-AWADY, Mohammed Fawzi. 1530 NORWAY AVE, MILDRED MITCHELL-BATEMAN 25705
　#915-03-1995 L2004 **CHP** *020
ELBASH, Feras Ahmad. 1249 15TH ST, MEDICINE 25701 #055-01-2004 L2005 **IM** *100 †20
ELBASH, Salah Mohammad. ■ 25705 #055-01-2005 L2006 **IM** *012
ELHAMDANI, Mehiar Omar. 1249 15TH ST, STE 4000 25701 #613-02-1989 L1999 **CD** *100 †20
ELITSUR, Noeet. ■ 25701 #055-02-2008 **IM** *012
ELITSUR, Yoram. 1600 MEDICAL CENTER DR, STE 3500 25701 #550-01-1979 L1990
　PD GE *040 †55
ELKADRY, Ayman Hussein. 1249 15TH ST, UNIVERSITY PHYSICIANS INTE 25701 #913-35-1999
　END *012 †20
ESTACIO-SUAREZ, Maria C. 611 7TH AVE 25701 #748-01-1964 L1975 **GP** *075 †18
ETMAN, Yasser Mohamed Kam. 1600 MEDICAL CENTER DR, STE G500 25701
　#915-11-2000 L2008 **IM** *012
EVANS, Joseph Edward. 1600 MEDICAL CENTER DR, STE 3500 25701 #055-02-1982 L1986
　PD *020 †55
EWEN, Julia Lynn. ■ 25701 #055-01-1993 L1994 **IM** *020 †20
EY, Douglas Wm. ■ 25701 #051-04-1954 L1956 **GP** *071
FAHRMANN, Elke Renate. ■ 25701 #055-02-2007 **IM** *012
FAKHOURI, Nadia Adel. 6744 COUNTRY CLUB DR 25705 #575-01-1996 **IM** *100
FALTAOUS, Adel Aiad. 2561 3RD AVE 25703 #915-09-1977 L1994 **PS** *020 †65
FEASTER, Stephen James. 1600 MEDICAL CNTR DR #4500, UNIVERSITY OB GYN 25701
　#055-01-1971 L1971 **GYN OBG** *020 †30
FERGUSON, Paul Brent. ■ 25705 #055-02-2007 **MPD** *012
FERNANDEZ, Hortencia R N. 401 10TH ST STE 410 25701 #748-01-1960 L1978 **GP PD** *020
FIERY, Michael Allen. 1508 6TH AVE 25701 #055-01-1977 L1978 **OPH** *020 †35
FINK, Kenneth Martin. 1112 6TH AVE 25701 #055-01-1972 L1972 **P CHP** *020 †75
FLASKAS, Marina Yurievna. ■ 25701 #913-73-1996 L2004 **CD** *012
FORTUNATO, Andrea Lynne. ■ 25701 #055-02-2007 **OBG** *012
FOSTER, Earl James. 2828 1ST AVE STE 400 25702 #018-03-1974 L1980 **ORS HS** *020 †40 ‡
FRAME, Jerry Lee. 25705 #055-01-1984 L1986 **EM PD** *020
FRANCIS, Charles David. 1616 13TH AVE, STE 2B 25701 #055-01-1993 L1996 **OPH** *020 †35
FRANCKE, Paul, Jr. 1340 HAL GREER BLVD 25701 #016-02-1946 L1952 **R RO** *071 †80
FRANCO, Joseph Earl. ■ 25701 #011-02-1992 **OBG** *100
FRAZIER, Marie D. 1600 MEDICAL CENTER DR, STE 3500 25701 #055-02-2001 L2004
　CCP *020 †55
FRY, Russell Leslie, II. 1151 HAL GREER BLVD 25701 #055-02-2000 L2004 **OPH** *100 †35
FRYE, Hadassah Dae. 1600 MEDICAL CENTER DR, STE 1500 25701 #055-02-2003 L2005
　FM *100 †18
FULLER, Jeremy Dale. 1600 MEDICAL CENTER DR 25701 #055-02-2003 L2004 **FSM** *020 †18
GABORDI, Robert Charles. ■ 25701 #055-02-2008 *012
GABRIEL, Hosny S. 1340 HAL GREER BLVD, ANESTHESIA DEPARTMENT 25701
　#915-03-1968 L1985 **AN** *020 †16
GAGNEJA, Ashok. 1801 6TH AVE, MARSHALL UNIV SCH OF MED 25703 #495-03-1978 **IM** *100
GALVEZ, Rosalia Cenon. 1530 NORWAY AVE, MILDRED MITCHELL BATEMAN H 25705
　#748-01-1954 L1984 **P GP** *071
GARDNER, Glenn Pierce. 1600 MEDICAL CENTER DR, MU SCHOOL OF MEDICINE -SUR 25701
　#017-20-1986 L2004 **VS** *020 †85
GARMESTANI, Ali Asghar. 2900 1ST AVE 25701 #517-01-1960 L1970 **PS HS** *071 †85,65
GARZA GUERRA, Gilberto A. 2828 1ST AVE STE 303 25702 #649-02-1980 L1983 **IM** *020
GAYAM, Swapna. 1600 MEDICAL CENTER DR, DEPT OF INTERNAL MEDICINE 25701
　#495-73-2003 **IM** *012
GEBREGIORGIS, Yared Assef. 1801 6TH AVE, DEPT OF INTERNAL MED 25703 #366-01-1993
　END *012 †20
GEBREYES TEKLEYES, Fikadu. 1249 15TH ST STE 2000, UNIVERSITY PHYSICIANS INTE 25701
　#366-01-1996 L2004 **IM** *100
GHAREEB, Samia Kay. 1600 MEDICAL CENTER DR 25701 #055-02-2003 L2007 **FM** *100 †18
GIANGARRA, Charles Eugene. 1600 MEDICAL CENTER DR, STE 2500 25701
　#035-08-1981 L2004 **ORS OSM** *020 †40
GIBBS, Scott Robt. 1616 13TH AVE, STE 100 25701 #047-05-1992 L1999 **OTO** *020 †45 ‡
GILBERT, Gary Gene. 2585 3RD AVE 25703 #055-01-1963 L1964 **OBG U** *040 †30
GILKERSON, Christine Lynn. 1600 MEDICAL CENTER DR, STE G500 25701 #055-02-2001 L2002
　IM *020 †20
GILL, Muhammad Taimoor La. 1249 15TH ST 25701 #704-21-1997 L2007 **CD** *100 †20
GOEBEL, Lynne Janice. 1249 15TH ST, UNIVERSITY PHYSICIANS INTE 25701
　#041-07-1986 L1993 **IM IMG** *020 †20
GOETZ, James C. 5170 US ROUTE 60 25705 #038-43-1990 L1993 **IM** *020 †20
GOODING, Kellie King. 12 BRIGHTON WAY 25705 #055-01-1991 L1997 **DR** *020 †80
GOREJA, Mohd Arif J. 1249 15TH ST, UNIVERSITY PHYSICIANS & SU 25701
　#704-21-1991 L2004 **NEP** *020 †20 ‡
GRAHAM, Nancy Lynn. 1415 6TH AVE 25701 #055-02-1987 L1989 **P** *020 †75
GREER, Ronald Edward, II. ■ 25701 #055-02-2006 **FP** *012
GRESS, Todd William. 1249 15TH ST, UNIV. PHYSIGANS INTERAL ME 25701
　#055-02-1993 L1994 **IM EP** *020 †20
GRISWOLD, Doreen C. 1001 10TH AVE 25701 #038-44-1998 L2004 **HMP** *020 †50
GRUETTER, Darlene Yao. 2900 1ST AVE, LABORATORY 25702 #055-02-1987 L1992
　PTH *020 †20
GUIRGIS, Hany Zaky. 1249 15TH ST, STE 4000 25701 #915-02-1997 L2004 **CD** *012 †20
GUNNLAUGSSON, Skuli T. 5170 US ROUTE 60 25705 #484-01-1994 L2005 **IC** *020 †20
HABERLIN, William James, II. 1600 MEDICAL CENTER DR, STE 2500 25701 #654-01-2007
　GS *012
HABERMAN, Ronald Jay. 5170 US ROUTE 60 25705 #016-01-1984 L2007 **CD** *020 †20
HACKMAN, Michael Patrick. ■ 25701 #055-02-2008 *012
HADDOX, Joshua Alexander. 2900 1ST AVE, ST. MARY'S MEDICAL CENTER 25702
　#055-02-1998 L2001 **FM** *100 †18

HAGAN, Charles Henry, Jr. ■ 25701 #051-04-1945 L1946 **GP** *071
HAGAN, Larry Lynn. 1001 20TH ST 25703 #048-02-1975 L2006 **AI** *020 †55,03
HAIKAL, Lee Corey. 5170 US ROUTE 60 25705 #055-02-1994 L1999 **VIR** *020 †80
HAMMACK, Deron John. ■ 25703 #055-75-2007, ▲ **R** *012
HAMO, Abdrhman. 1600 MEDICAL CENTER DR, DEPT OF INTERNAL MEDICINE 25701
　#875-02-2001 **IM** *012
HAMOUDEH, Eyad Mustafa. ■ 25705 #575-02-2001 **IM** *012
HANNA, Ibrahim. 1600 MEDICAL CENTER DR, UNIV PHYS & SURGEON 25701
　#875-01-1996 L2004 **GS** *020 †85
HANSBARGER, John Travis. 2240 5TH AVE STE 221 25703 #055-02-1999 L2001 **FM** *020 †18
HARMAN, Larry G. ■ 25705 #055-02-2006 **FP** *012
HARPER, Glenn Anthony. 1600 MEDICAL CENTER DR, STE 1500 25701 #055-02-1995 L1996
　FM *020 †18
HARPER, Laurie Winchester. 5170 US ROUTE 60 E 25705 #041-14-1992 L1996
　IM PD *020 †55,20
HARRIS, Erika Marie. 1600 MEDICAL CENTER DR, STE 1500 25701 #055-02-2002 L2003
　FM *020 †18
HARRISON, Curtis Wayne, Jr. 1600 MEDICAL CENTER DR, STE 2500 25701
　#055-02-1998 L2003 **GS** *020 †85
HAYS, Jeremie Bryan. 1249 15TH ST STE 200, MU DEPT OF INTERNAL MED 25701
　#020-12-2007 **IM** *012
HEABERLIN, Brian Kent. 5170 US ROUTE 60 25705 #055-02-2001 L2006 *020 †45
HEFFERNAN, David M. 2900 1ST AVE 25702 #649-33-1983 L1986 **OBG** *071 †30
HEGG, Kyle Rice. 2828 1ST AVE STE 400 25702 #026-08-1979 L1984 **ORS OSM** *020 †40 ‡
HENDERSHOT, Tracy Lee. ■ 25701 #055-02-2008 **IM** *012
HENDRICKS, Gregory Scott. 1600 MEDICAL CENTER DR, STE 2500 25701 #055-02-2001 L2005
　FSM *020 †18
HENSON, Douglas Wilson. 1600 MEDICAL CENTER DR, STE 2500 25701 #055-02-1993 L1997
　GS *020 †85
HENSON, Scott Lee. 2860 3RD AVE STE 10 25702 #055-02-1985 L1987 **NS** *075
HEYDARIAN, Mahmood. 1600 MEDICAL CENTER DR, STE 3500 25701 #517-01-1964 L1975
　PDC PD *020 †55
HICKMAN, Crystal Marie. ■ 25701 #055-01-2007 **FP** *012
HIRSI, Awil Warsame. 1801 6TH AVE 25703 #561-17-2000 **IM** *012
HOFFMAN, Edna T Maura. ■ 25701 #051-04-1954 L1954 **OS FPG** *030
HOFFMAN, Karen Elizabeth. ■ 25705 #055-02-2003 *100
HOLBROOK, Thomas J. 1249 15TH ST, # 4000 25701 #047-05-1941 L1948 **NS** *020 †25
HOOD, Ellie Earles. ■ 25705 #055-02-2005 **OBG** *012
HOSSEINZADEH, Pooya. 1801 6TH AVE 25703 #517-06-2004 **GS** *012
HOTIANA, Mateen Munir. 1249 15TH ST 25701 #704-21-2002 L2007 **IM** *020 †20
HOWARD-CLAUDIO, Candace M. 5170 US ROUTE 60 25705 #041-02-2000 L2006 **DR** *100 †80
HRAFNKELSSON, Hannes. 1801 6TH AVE DEPT MED 25703 #484-01-1986 **IM** *100
HUDAK, Jason Anthony. 2866 1ST AVE, STE 501 25702 #055-02-2005 L2007 **FM** *020 †18
HUNT, John Aspinall. 1340 HAL GREER BLVD 25701 #836-01-1953 L1979 **GS OS** *071 †15
HURT, Buddy L. 2585 3RD AVE 25703 #055-75-1997, ▲ L2006 **FM** *020 †18
HUSSAIN, Syed Naveed. 1600 MEDICAL CENTER DR, STE G500 25701 #704-16-1999 L2003
　END *012 †20
HUSSAINI, Syeda Fatima Sh. 1600 MEDICAL CENTER DR, STE 3500 25701 #496-27-2001 L2006
　PG *012 †20
HUTCHISON, Larry Dale, Jr. ■ 25705 #055-02-2007 **GS** *012
HYDER, Muhammad Ali. 1530 NORWAY AVE, MMBH 25705 #704-02-1982 L2005 **P** *020 †75
IBANEZ, Cesar B, II. 2900 1ST AVE 25702 #748-01-1972 L1976 **EM FM** *020 †16
IBANEZ, Noel Desantos. ■ 25705 #055-01-2006 **MP** *012
IGBOELI, Ifeoma Jacquelin. ■ 25701 #055-02-2008 **GS** *012
IGNATIADIS, Panos. 2860 3RD AVE, STE 10 25702 #418-01-1969 L1980 **NS** *020 †25
JACOBS, Helene Renee. 910 4TH AVE, STE 302 25701 #051-07-1988 L1996 **CHP** *020 †75
JAIN, Rajendra Kumar. 2828 1ST AVE STE 204 25702 #495-20-1967 L1978 **OS** *020 †95
JAMES, Suresh Kumar. 1801 6TH AVE 25703 #495-04-1983 **IM** *100
JANUSZKIEWICZ, Saml Alvie. 1600 MEDICAL CENTER DR, STE 500 25701 #055-01-1981 L1983
　IM P *020 †75
JARRELL, Eugenia Marie. 2900 1ST AVE 25702 #055-02-2000 L2002 **FM** *020 †18
JAVIER, Marcos Morales. 1340 HAL GREER BLVD, DEPT OF ANESTHESIOLOGY 25701
　#055-02-1998 L2006 **AN** *020 †05
JENNINGS, Tucker Gisler. 5170 US ROUTE 60 25705 #055-01-1996 L2001 **GS** *020 †85
JENNINGS, William Mason, III. 2900 1ST AVE, JOSLIN DIABETES CENTER 25702
　#051-04-1967 L1975 **DIA IM** *030 †20
JEREZA, Gina. ■ 25701 #055-02-2005 **OBG** *012
JONES, Charlotte Teresa. 1600 MEDICAL CENTER DR, STE 3500 25701 #023-01-1994 L2001
　CHN *020 †55,75
JUDE, David Clyde. 1600 MEDICAL CENTER DR, STE 4500 25701 #055-02-1988 L1993
　OBG *020 †30
JUNG, Thomas Martin. 3 STONECREST DR, TRI STATE OTOLARYNGOLOGY 25701
　#018-03-1990 L1997 **OTO** *020 †20
KARZOUN, M.Eyad. 1249 15TH ST STE 2, INTERNAL MEDI 25701 #875-02-2004 **IM** *012
KEADLE, David Miller. 5170 US ROUTE 60 25705 #055-01-1996 L2002 **DR** *020 †80
KEBLAWI, Hisham Ahmed. 1600 MEDICAL CENTER DR, STE 4500 25701 #613-02-1988 L2006
　OBG *100
KEBREAB, Frezgi. 1801 6TH AVE 25703 #366-01-1998 **IM** *012
KELLY, Patricia Jean. 1600 MEDICAL CENTER DR, STE 3500 25701 #024-05-1977 L1978
　PD *020 †55
KHAN, Jahanzeb Masood. 2900 1ST AVE 6TH FL, ST MARY'S MED CTR, SLEEP C 25702
　#704-21-2000 L2007 **IM** *100 †20
KHANNA, Raj Kumar. 1600 MEDICAL CENTER DR, STE 2500 25701 #041-15-2000 L2000 *020
KHAWAJA, Imran Tausif. 1249 15TH ST 25701 #704-01-1985 L1994 **PUD CCM** *020 †20
KHEETAN, Reem Heidar Khal. 1801 6TH AVE 25703 #055-01-2005 **IM** *012
KHITAN, Zeid Jawdat. 1249 15TH ST, UNIVERSITY PHYSICIANS INTE 25701 #575-01-1992 L2000
　IM *020 †20
KILKENNY, Michael E. 2585 3RD AVE 25703 #055-02-1982 L1983 **FM GP** *020 †18
KIM, Melissa Aragones. ■ 25701 #055-02-2000 *100
KIMMEY, Gerrit Anthony. 5170 US ROUTE 60 25705 #045-01-1979 L1984 **IM** *020 †20
KING, Stacie Naylor. ■ 25701 #055-02-2000 *100
KING, Stephen Scott. ■ 25705 #055-02-2002 **GS** *012
KLEIN, Carol A. 1415 6TH AVE 25701 #055-01-1988 L1991 **CHP P** *020 †75
KNIGHT, Susan Lee. ■ 25701 #055-02-2007 **PD** *012
KOESTER, Alan Richard. 1600 MEDICAL CENTER DR, STE G500 25701 #016-45-1989 L1989
　ORS *020 †40

KOK, Boon Cheng. 2628 5TH AVE, TRI-STATE MEDICAL CENTER 25702 #422-01-1996 L2004 HO *100 †20

KOPP, William J. ■ 25701 #038-41-1950 L1953 PD *071 †55

KORONA, Michael V, Jr. 5170 US ROUTE 60 25705 #051-01-1988 L1995 DR VIR *020 †80

KORSTANJE, Marion C. 1508 6TH AVE 25701 #038-40-1955 L1961 OPH *075 †35

KRASNOW, Michael A. 5187 US ROUTE 60, STE 6 25705 #005-76-1985, ▲ L1990 OPH *020

KROENING, John Jos. 2 STONECREST DR 25701 #030-06-1969 L1981 EM *020

KUHL, Amber Lee. 2866 1ST AVE, STE 501 25702 #055-02-2000 L2004 OBG *020

KUMAR, Rashmi. 1656 13TH AVE 25701 #496-09-1977 L1982 P CHP *020 †75

KUMAR, Subhash. 1656 13TH AVE 25701 #495-69-1971 L1981 NEP IM *020 †20

KUMAR, Suresh Gopalakurup. 5170 US ROUTE 60 E 25705 #654-01-2001 L2005 CN *020 †20

KURCZYNSKI, Elizabeth K. 1600 MEDICAL CENTER DR, STE 3500 25701 #038-06-1968 L1997 PHO HEM *020 †55

KURTZ, Enid A. 3375 US ROUTE 60 E, PRESTERA CENTER FOR MENTAL 25705 #042-01-1974 L1997 P IM *020

LAHIRY, Subrat Kumar. 1600 MEDICAL CENTER DR, STE 2500 25701 #495-20-1965 L1978 GS END *020 †85

LAHR, Barbara Ann. ■ 25705 #018-03-1989 L1990 DR *020 †80

LAKHANI, Jay Rasiklal. ■ 25706 #055-02-2006 MPD *012

LAKHANI, Nalini Rasiklal. ■ 25701 #495-23-1969 L1981 *020

LAKHANI, Rasiklal Haridas. 1117 20TH ST 25703 #495-05-1960 L1975 FM *020 †18

LAMBERT, Robert Aaron. ■ 25705 #055-02-2008 *012

LAMBROS, Iralane Pippa. 1600 MEDICAL CENTER DR, STE 3500 25701 #045-04-1992 L1996 PD *020 †55

LATIF, Jawaid. 3375 US ROUTE 60 25705 #704-17-1986 L2004 P *020 †75

LAVERY, G William. 1448 10TH AVE STE 100, EBENEZER MED OUTRCH INC 25701 #016-11-1979 L1986 OPH *020 †20

LE, Francis Kiet. 1249 15TH ST STE 4000, MARSHALL UNIVERSITY DEPT O 25701 #045-01-1997 L2008 IC *020 †20

LEABERRY, Jeffrey Louis. 5694 US ROUTE 60, INC 25705 #055-02-1990 L1994 AN *020 †05

LECLERCQ, Toussaint. 1600 MEDICAL CENTER DR, STE G500 25701 #165-03-1966 L2007 NS *020 †25

LEE, Bong Hyun. 1530 NORWAY AVE 25705 #583-03-1992 L2005 P *020 †75

LEE, Lawrence David. 5699 US ROUTE 60 E 25705 #055-02-1994 L1999 AN *020 †05

LEE, Paul Samuel. ■ 25701 #055-02-1994 L1998 OBG *020 †30

LEE, Tae Hoon. 1600 MEDICAL CENTER DR SU 25701 #583-02-2002 IM *012

LEONARD, Eric Lawrence. 5170 US ROUTE 60 25705 #055-02-1997 L2002 DR *020 †80

LEPANTO, Philip Bliss. 5170 US ROUTE 60 25705 #020-02-1970 L1979 RO *020 †80

LEWIS, Donald R, Jr. 5170 US ROUTE 60 25705 #023-01-1985 L1997 DR NM *020 †28,80

LEWIS, James M. 1600 MEDICAL CENTER DR, STE 3500 25701 #035-06-1975 L1983 PD *020 †55

LEWIS, Myron Alan. 5170 US ROUTE 60 25705 #055-01-1994 L1995 FM *020 †18

LIESEN, James Gerard. 2828 1ST AVE, STE 305 25702 #016-76-1995, ▲ L2005 PD *020 †55

LILLY, Dale Blake. 2823 3RD AVE 25702 #055-02-1990 L1992 OPH *020 †35

LIMJOCO, Teresa I T. 1001 10TH AVE 25701 #748-02-1985 L1999 PTH *062 †50

LINDBERG, Cheri Yost. 1600 MEDICAL CENTER DR, STE B500 25701 #055-02-1996 L1997 P *020 †75

LINSENMEYER, Geo John, III. 2860 3RD AVE STE 2, ULTIMATE HEALTH SERVICES, 25702 #055-01-1977 L1979 CD *020 †20

LOBO, Jaldir. ■ 25705 #187-06-1952 L1966 NS *071 †25

LOCASCIO, Joseph Anthony. 5170 US ROUTE 60 E 25705 #051-01-1975 L1990 OPH *020 †35 ‡

LONG, Wen. ■ 25705 #243-74-1982 L2007 GS *020

LORENZANA, Alejandro. 5170 US ROUTE 60 25705 #429-02-1984 L2007 PUD *020 †20

LOUDIN, Sean. ■ 25705 #055-02-2005 PD *012

LUMAPAS, Arturo Ramirez. 1530 NORWAY AVE, M.M. BATEMAN HOSPITAL 25705 #748-01-1968 L1984 P *020

LUTZ, Tricia Ann. 1600 MEDICAL CENTER DR, STE 3500 25701 #055-02-1994 L1996 PD *020 †55

LYNCH, Joan Anne. 1001 20TH ST 25703 #055-02-1988 L1990 PD AI *020 †55

MAC FARLAND, Dawn Lee. 2674 5TH AVE, STE 2 25702 #055-02-1996 L1999 IM *020 †20

MACIAS, Daniel. 5170 US ROUTE 60 E 25705 #308-11-1984 L1992 IM END *020 †20

MADDOX, Chaundra Jo. 1340 HAL GREER BLVD 25701 #055-01-1995 L1999 PD *020 †55

MAILLOUX, Richard John. 5170 US ROUTE 60 25705 #033-06-1989 L1995 GE IM *020 †20

MANOHARAN, Arun. 1600 MEDICAL CENTER DR, STE 2500 25701 #496-23-2002 GS *012

MARCUM, Andrea Dale. ■ 25701 #055-02-2006 OBG *012

MARCUM, Patti Jo. 1115 20TH ST 25703 #055-02-2001 L2002 FM *100 †18 ‡

MARSHALL, Robert James. ■ 25701 #539-01-1952 L1976 CD IM *071

MARTIN, Joye Ann. 2010 CHERRY AVE 25701 #041-07-1977 L1980 IMG IM *020 †20

MARTIN, Malcolm Bruce. 508 10TH ST 25701 #051-04-1947 L1953 PD *071

MARU, Mehrette Mallede. 1600 MEDICAL CENTER DR, STE 3400 25701 #366-01-2002 L2007 CD *012 †20

MASHAQI, Saif Arsan. 1600 MEDICAL CENTER DR, DEPT OF INTERNAL MEDICINE 25701 #575-01-2002 IM *012

MASON, John Edward. ■ 25705 #055-02-2002 L2007 CD *012 †20

MASOOD, Shahid. 1530 NORWAY AVE, MILDRED MITCHELL-BATEMAN H 25705 #704-02-1979 L1997 P *020 †75

MATCHESWALLA, Shabbir Man. 1600 MEDICAL CENTER DR, DEPT MED 25701 #055-02-2007 IM *012

MATIN, Khan. 3375 US ROUTE 60 25705 #160-01-1970 L1980 P *020

MAZAGRI, Rida Suleiman. 2860 3RD AVE, CENTER INC 25702 #613-02-1987 L2003 *020 †25

MC CARTY, Sarah Ann. 1600 MEDICAL CENTER DR, INTERNAL MEDICAL, SUITE G5 25701 #050-02-1979 L1982 IM *020 †20

MC COMAS, Carl Frederick. 2860 3RD AVE STE 20 25702 #055-01-1979 L1980 N *020 †75

MC CORMICK, Chas Calvin. 1600 MEDICAL CENTER DR, STE 1500 25701 #055-02-1985 L1986 FM *020 †18

MC GINNIS, Lyle Beuhring. 1340 HAL GREER BLVD 25701 #051-01-1948 L1952 OTO *072 †45

MC GUFFIN, Aaron Michael. 1249 15TH ST 25701 #055-02-1999 L2001 MPD *020 †20,55

MC KAY, Chas Elford, Jr. 1340 16TH ST 25701 #051-01-1948 L1952 R *071 †80

MC KEAND, Christopher H. 1340 HAL GREER BLVD, CABELL HUNTINGTON HOSPITAL 25701 #055-02-2001 L2004 PD *100

MCKINNEY, Gerald. 1600 MEDICAL CENTER DR, STE 2500 25701 #016-11-1991 L2003 GS *020 †85

MCKINNEY, Shawn Avril. 1415 HAL GREER BLVD 25701 #012-21-1997 L2003 GS SO *020

MC KOWN, Chas Henry, Jr. 1600 MEDICAL CENTER DR, STE 3408 25701 #051-04-1960 L1961 R *030 †80

MCUNU, Arthur Ntando, Jr. 2866 1ST AVE, STE 402 25702 #010-03-1993 L2001 TS *020 †85,90

MC WHORTER, Richard E. 5170 US ROUTE 60 25705 #055-01-1978 L1982 DR *020 †80

MEADOWS, Charles Edward. 1600 MEDICAL CENTER DR, STE 6500 25701 #055-02-1998 L2001 IM *020 †20

MEKONNEN, Legesse Lemma. 1600 MEDICAL CENTER DR, DEPT OF INTERNAL MEDICINE 25701 #366-01-2000 IM *012

MESHESHA, Girma Alemu. 1801 6TH AVE, DEPT OF INTERNAL MED 25703 #366-01-1987 L2007 IM *100 †20

MICHAEL, Barbara Mae. ■ 25705 #055-02-2006 FP *012

MICHAIL, Eyob Estifanos. 1600 MEDICAL CENTER DR SU 25701 #366-01-1992 IM *012

MILLER, Bobby A, II. 919 6TH AVE 25701 #055-02-1984 L1985 PFP P *020 †75

MILLER, Bobby Lynn. 1600 MEDICAL CENTER DR, STE 3500 25701 #055-02-1997 L1998 NPM *020 †20,55

MILLER, Stephen Blaine. 5170 US ROUTE 60 E, STE 3600 25705 #055-02-1994 L1996 PS *020 †65

MIRANDA, Raymund Sipin. 1801 6TH AVE, MARSHALL UNIV SCH OF MED 25703 #748-21-1995 IM *100

MIRANDA, Sherrie Napier. 2915 3RD AVE 25702 #055-01-1991 L1992 PD *020 †55

MITCHELL, Scott Weston. 1600 MEDICAL CENTER DR, STE 1500 25701 #055-02-2002 L2003 FM *020 †18

MITCHELL-BATEMAN, Mildred. 1600 MEDICAL CENTER DR, STE B500 25701 #041-07-1946 L1947 P *020 †75

MOHAMMAD, Bilal. 1801 6TH AVE, MARSHALL UNIV OF SCH 25703 #704-02-1990 PD *020 †55

MOHIUDDIN, Zahur. 1530 NORWAY AVE, MILDRED MITCHELL-BATEMAN H 25705 #704-19-1985 L2004 P CHP *020

MOLINA, Rafael Evencio. 2585 3RD AVE 25703 #055-02-2000 L2005 OBG *020

MOLINA SABUCEDO, Rafael E. 1654 13TH AVE 25701 #275-01-1949 L1969 U *071 †95

MONDEREWICZ, Kathleen M. 612 6TH AVE, TRI STATE OCCUPATIONAL MED 25701 #041-13-1994 L2004 FM *020 †18

MONDLOCH, Michael Christo. ■ 25701 #055-02-2007 IM *012

MONTERO, Marianito Ruiz. ■ 25712 #748-07-1956 L1973 P PHP *020

MOOSAVI, Benjamin Lee. ■ 25701 #028-34-2004 L2007 GS *012

MORABITO, Rocco Anthony. 2860 3RD AVE STE 230 25702 #055-01-1976 L1977 U *020 †95

MORGAN, Charles Stephen. 2 STONECREST DR 25701 #055-01-1972 L1977 IM RHU *020 †20 ‡

MORGAN, Craig Michael. 1611 13TH AVE 25701 #047-05-1981 L1987 OPH *020 †35

MORGAN, James Hanly, III. 5170 US ROUTE 60 25705 #055-02-1988 L1993 GS *020 †85

MORGAN, John Robert, Jr. 5170 US ROUTE 60 E 25705 #055-02-1998 L1999 MPD *020

MOSES, Melin Jonathan. 2959 3RD AVE, MOSES FAMILY MEDICINE 25702 #005-12-1995 L1998 FM *020 †18

MUFSON, Maurice Albert. 1249 15TH ST, UNIVERSITY PHYSICIANS INTE 25701 #035-19-1957 L1976 IM ID *040

MULLEN, John Owen. 2828 1ST AVE STE 40, CENTER INC 25702 #018-03-1968 L1976 ORS *020 †40

MURPHY, Robert Scott. 2828 1ST AVE, STE 104 25702 #048-14-1999 OMF *020

MURTHY, Anupama Prashanth. 1600 MEDICAL CENTER DR, MARSHALL MEDICAL SCH 25701 #495-99-1995 PTH *100

NADAL, Francisco Javier. ■ 25705 #042-02-1993 L1998 IM *020

NADER, Raheem. 2585 3RD AVE 25703 #517-05-1966 L1976 GS *020 †85

NAEGELE, Jay Thomas. 1600 MEDICAL CENTER DR, STE 3500 25701 #055-02-1997 L2000 PD *020 †55

NAKKAR, Samer. 1600 MEDICAL CENTER DR SU 25701 #875-02-2006 IM *012

NAMBURI, Lukaji. 1801 6TH AVE, MARSHALL UNIV SCH OF MED 25703 #495-50-1993 PD *100

NARAYAN, Mysore G. 1340 HAL GREER BLVD 25701 #495-33-1971 L1980 IM PUD *020 †20

NATHANSON, Steve Harry. 2900 1ST AVE 25702 #422-01-1999 L2002 MPD *020

NAWAZ, Raja Atif. ■ 25701 #704-20-2002 L2007 CD *012 †20

NEAL, Mickey Jon. 1340 HAL GREER BLVD, CABELL HUNTINGTON HOSPITAL 25701 #055-01-1979 L1980 AN *020 †05

NEASE, Darren Blaine. 1600 MEDICAL CENTER DR 25701 #038-40-1994 L2004 GS *020 †85

NEGINHAL, Vivekanand Shan. 2828 1ST AVE, STE 400 25702 #495-98-1985 L2006 ORS OAR *020

NEITCH, Shirley M. 1249 15TH ST, UNIVERSITY PHYSICIANS INTE 25701 #051-04-1977 L1980 IMG IM *040 †20

NELSON, Earl Lynn. 1151 HAL GREER BLVD 25701 #020-12-1968 L2007 OPH *020

NERHOOD, Robert Clarke. 1600 MEDICAL CENTER DR, STE 4500 25701 #055-01-1969 L1970 OBG *030 †30

NEWFELD, Mark Lee. 2900 1ST AVE, STE 6019 25702 #048-12-1990 L1991 AN *020 †05

NEWMARK, Howard. 1340 HAL GREER BLVD, CABELL HUNTINGTON HOSPITAL 25701 #047-07-1970 L1984 TS *020

NICELER, Brock James. ■ 25701 #055-02-2006 L2007 FP *012

NIEN SHY, Yih-Dar. ■ 25701 #231-03-2001 L2007 GS *012

NINE, Bradley Allen. 2900 1ST AVE, ST. MARYS HOSPITAL 25702 #055-02-1988 L1989 IM *020 †20

NOUREDDINE, Nizar Darwich. ■ 25705 #055-02-2004 L2005 IM *020 †20

NUSAIR, Ahmad Rakad. ■ 25701 #575-02-1997 L2007 ID *100 †20

NUTT, Mitchell Eric. 2866 1ST AVE, STE 501 25702 #055-01-1990 L1991 OBG *020 †30

OAKES, Sally Lue Reggel. ■ 25701 #016-11-1968 L1973 OPH *062

OAKLEY, Gerald Joseph, Jr. 1600 MEDICAL CENTER DR, STE 4500 25701 #025-01-1983 L1997 GO *020 †30

OBEIDAT, Shadi Falah. 1801 6TH AVE 25703 #575-02-2003 IM *012

O'BRIEN, Patrick Joshua. ■ 25701 #055-02-2004 GS *012

OLEY, Gretchen E. 1600 MEDICAL CNTR DR #3400, STE 3400 25701 #055-02-1982 L1983 IM IMG *030 †20

OLIASHIRAZI, Alireza. 1600 MEDICAL CENTER DR 25701 #010-01-1992 L1997 ORS *020 †40

OSTWANI, Waseem. 1600 MEDICAL CENTER DR, DEPT OF PEDIATRICS 25701 #875-01-2005 PD *012

OTTAVIANO, Jorge Vicente. 3174 SUMNER AVE 25705 #726-01-1948 L1970 P *071

OTTAVIANO, Peter. 5170 US ROUTE 60 25705 #055-75-1987, ▲ L1988 IM OS *020 †20

OTTO, John Freeman, Jr. 1115 20TH ST 25703 #038-41-1948 L1957 IM END *071 †20

OTTO, Marilyn Marjorie. 5170 US ROUTE 60 25705 #038-43-1990 L1993 IM *020 †20

OZTURK, Ahmet Husamettin. 1623 13TH AVE, REGIONAL PAIN MANAGEMENT C 25701 #902-04-1977 L1988 PMM AN *020 †05

PACIOLES, Toni Orlino Her. 1600 MEDICAL CENTER DR, STE 3400 DEPT OF INTER MED 25701 #748-02-2004 IM *012

PARK, Kwang-Soo. 1600 MEDICAL CNTR DR #B500, DEPT OF PSY & BEH MED 25701 #583-19-1989 L2002 P PYG *020

PARKER, Jeffery Edward. 5170 US ROUTE 60 E, HUNTINGTON INTERNAL MEDICI 25705 #055-01-1998 L2006 **GS** *020 †85

PARKER, John Arthur, Jr. 1600 MEDICAL CENTER DR, STE 1500 25701 #051-01-1978 L2003 **FM** *040 †18

PARONG, Maria Paulina San. 1600 MEDICAL CENTER DR, DEPT OF INTERNAL MEDICINE 25701 #748-16-1996 **IM** *012

PARSEGHIAN, Shant Artur. 1600 MEDICAL CENTER DR, MARSHALL MED SCH 25701 #875-01-1998 L2006 **END** *100

PASQUALE, Julia Lynn. 1340 HAL GREER BLVD, CABELL HUNTINGTON HOSPITAL 25701 #055-02-2003 L2006 **EM** *020 †16

PATICK, David Lawrence. 5170 US ROUTE 60 25705 #001-06-1981 L1984 **IM** *020 †20

PATTERSON, Carol Lynn. 1600 MEDICAL CENTER DR, STE G500 25701 #055-02-2001 L2005 **MPD** *020 †20,55

PATTON, Ross M. 1600 MEDICAL CENTER DR, STE 1500 25701 #055-01-1976 L1977 **FM FSM** *020 †18

PAYNE, Bryan Rankin. 1600 MEDICAL CENTER DR, STE G500 25701 #020-02-1992 L2007 **NS** *020 †25

PAYNE, Mary Say. ■ 25701 #021-05-2002 L2008 **PD** *020

PECIREP, Dragan. ■ 25702 #935-01-1968 L1987 **TS** *020 †85

PENDLETON, Andrew L. 1600 MEDICAL CENTER DR, STE 3500 25701 #045-04-1989 L1995 **PHO** *020 †55

PETTY, Grant Douglas. 5170 US ROUTE 60 25705 #020-02-2001 L2007 **DR** *100 †80

PINO, Eduardo. 1600 MEDICAL CENTER DR, STE 3500 25701 #042-04-1983 L1986 **CCP** *020 †55

PINO, Isabel Maria. 1600 MEDICAL CENTER DR, STE 3500 25701 #308-03-1980 L1991 **PD IM** *020

PORRES, Edwin R. ■ 25701 #429-01-1975 L1981 **EM ID** *020 †20,16

PORTER, David Lee. 1001 10TH AVE 25701 #055-01-1975 L1981 **PTH EM** *020 †50

POULTON, Thomas Jon. 1600 MEDICAL CENTER DR, STE 3500 25701 #038-40-1975 L2007 **PD AN** *020 †05

POWELL, Jason Allen. ■ 25701 #055-02-2008 *012

PRABHAKARAN, Vinay. 1801 6TH AVE, MARSHALL UNIV SCH OF MED 25703 #495-73-1997 **IM** *100

PRICE, Donovan Thomas. ■ 25701 #055-02-2007 **FP** *012

PRITT, Audra L. ■ 25705 #055-01-2007 **PD** *012

QASSEM, Zaher. 1600 MEDICAL CENTER DR, DEPT MED 25701 #875-01-1998 L2007 **PUD** *012 †20

RAMOS, Ricardo Lorenzo. 1636 MCCOY RD, STE 301 25701 #649-14-1979 L1993 **AN** *020

RANKIN, Joy Dalyn. ■ 25701 #012-22-2005 **GS** *012

RASHID, Mitchell Nicholas. 1249 15TH ST, STE 4000 25701 #055-02-2000 L2002 **IC** *020 ‡

RATCLIFF, Gilbert A, Jr. 1600 MEDICAL CENTER DR, STE 3500 25701 #023-07-1963 L1966 **PD NPM** *020 †55

RAY, Jacqueline Renee. 1600 MEDICAL CENTER DR, STE 3500 25701 #055-02-1995 L1998 **PD** *020 †55

RELLAN, Dev Raj. 5170 US ROUTE 60 25705 #495-36-1960 L1973 **NEP IM** *020 †20

REYNOLDS, James M. 5221 US ROUTE 60 E, RADIOLOGY, INC. 25705 #012-01-1982 L2007 **FM** *020 †18

REYNOLDS, James Milton. 5170 US ROUTE 60 25705 #055-02-2001 L2003 **VIR** *100 †80

RICARD, Jose Israel. 1600 MEDICAL CENTER DR 25701 #275-01-1960 L1972 **FM FSM** *020

RICHARDSON, Bradley J. 2900 1ST AVE, ST. MARY'S MEDICAL CENTER 25702 #055-02-1993 L1995 **IMG HOS** *020 ‡

RICHTER, Frank. 1600 MEDICAL CENTER DR, STE 2500 25701 #408-34-1990 L2006 **U** *020 †95

RIPLEY, Gary Lemasters. 1115 20TH ST 25703 #051-04-1956 L1959 **FM** *071

RITCHIE, Adam Douglas. ■ 25701 #055-02-2007 **OBG** *012

RIVAS, Eduardo Alfredo. 1340 HAL GREER BLVD 25701 #176-03-1968 L1981 **AN** *020

RIVAS, Frank. 1302 4TH AVE 25701 #935-01-1964 L1979 **CD IM** *020 †20

ROBARTS, Tim David. 5170 US ROUTE 60 25705 #047-05-1989 L1992 **GS** *020 †85

ROBINSON, Dustin Edward. 1801 6TH AVE 25703 #654-01-2003 **GS** *012

ROHRBACH, Matthew Alan. 5170 US ROUTE 60 25705 #055-02-1984 L1990 **GE** *020 †20

ROISMAN, Tully Stephen. 1151 HAL GREER BLVD 25701 #011-02-1978 L1981 **OPH** *020 †35

ROSE, Vera Ann. 2900 1ST AVE, ONCOLOGY 25702 #047-20-1985 L1990 **HEM IM** *020 †20

ROSS, James Allen. 6 LORRIMEL DR 25705 #055-02-1996 L1999 **DR** *020 †80

RUMBAUGH, Christopher All. ■ 25705 #055-01-2006 **IM** *012

RUSHTON, Jill Elizabeth. ■ 25701 #005-12-2008 *012

RUSHTON, Thomas Coleman. 1249 15TH ST, STE 3000 25701 #011-04-1989 L1994 **ID IM** *020 †20

RUSSELL, Daniel Wynn. 5694 US ROUTE 60, INC 25705 #055-02-1990 L1994 **AN** *020 †05

SABLAY, Teodoro Longalong. 3375 US ROUTE 60 E 25705 #748-07-1967 L1992 **P** *020

SADEK, Mohamed Hafez. 14 BIRCH DR, MOHAMED SADEK, MD 25705 #915-04-1990 L1997 **N** *100 †20

SAKHAI, Hossein. 1340 HAL GREER BLVD 25701 #517-03-1956 L1969 **NS N** *071 †25

SALAMA, Mona Saad. 1600 MEDICAL CENTER DR, UNIV PHYSICIAN & SURGEON 25701 #915-07-1986 **GS** *100

SALEME, Mauricio Naim. 2828 1ST AVE STE 205 25702 #132-02-1971 L1977 **GS** *020

SALMAN, Ashar. 1249 15TH ST, STE 3000 25701 #704-01-1994 L2002 **PUD** *020 †20

SANTHANA KRISHNAN, S G. 1656 13TH AVE 25701 #495-31-1993 L2006 **NEP** *020 †20

SANTHANAM, Prasanna. 1801 6TH AVE 25703 #495-22-2001 **IM** *012

SAULLE, Dwight. ■ 25702 #055-02-2008 *012

SAUNDERS, Elizabeth Anne. ■ 25701 #055-02-2007 **MPD** *012

SAUNDERS, Susan Kathleen. ■ 25701 #055-02-2008 *012

SAVORY, Linda Jane. 1115 20TH ST 25703 #025-01-1977 L1978 **FM** *020 †18

SAVORY, Thomas Keyes. 1249 15TH ST, UNIVERSITY PHYSICIANS SURG 25701 #025-01-1975 L1978 **IM** *020

SCOTT, Jerry Wayne. 1600 MEDICAL CENTER DR, STE 1500 25701 #055-02-1995 L1996 **FM** *020 †18

SCOTT, Thomas Francis. 2828 1ST AVE STE 400 25702 #025-01-1958 L1961 **ORS** *072 †40

SEBERT, Stephen Lowell. 5170 US ROUTE 60 25705 #055-01-1977 L1978 **FM PHP** *020 †18

SEIFU, Mesfin Alemayehu. 1600 MEDICAL CENTER DR, STE G500 25701 #366-01-1998 L2005 **PCC** *012 †20

SETSER, Edward Ray. 2828 1ST AVE STE 200, HIGHLAWN MEDICAL BUILDING 25702 #036-08-1985 L1996 **GS** *020 †85,90

SHAFIQ, Rehman. 1600 MEDICAL CENTER DR, STE 3400 25701 #704-16-2000 **IM** *100

SHARMA, Sanjeev Simeon. 5170 US ROUTE 60 25705 #055-02-1993 L1997 **RO** *020 †80

SHARMA, Surendra Mohan. 2900 1ST AVE 25702 #495-03-1960 L1977 **IM N** *020 †20

SHAVER, Warren Mitchel. 1600 MEDICAL CENTER DR, STE 1500 25701 #055-02-1990 L1991 **FM FSM** *040 †18

SHEETS, Mirie Roanne. 1001 20TH ST 25703 #016-06-1997 L2004 **AI** *020 †20,03

SHEILS, John Paul. 1001 10TH AVE 25701 #051-04-1960 L1963 **PTH** *020 †50

SHEILS, William Sol. 5170 US ROUTE 60 E 25705 #051-04-1960 L1961 **IM CD** *071 †20

SHEILS, William Sol, Jr. 5170 US ROUTE 60 25705 #055-02-1983 L1984 **R** *020 †80

SHEPPE, Jack Ogden. 1340 HAL GREER BLVD 25701 #051-04-1957 L1958 **FM IM** *071

SHERIDAN, Mark Frederick. 3 STONECREST DR, TRI STATE OTOLARYNGOLOGY 25701 #055-02-1987 L1998 **OTO HNS** *020 †45

SHIELDS, Jessica. 1600 MEDICAL CENTER DR, STE 3500 25701 #055-02-2003 L2006 **PD** *100 †55

SHIREY, Carol Ann. 2240 5TH AVE, FAMILY MEDICAL CENTER & UR 25703 #055-01-1994 L2006 **IM** *020

SHORA, Waseem. 1600 MEDICAL CENTER DR, STE G500 25701 #875-01-1966 L1980 **GE IM** *020 †20

SHORT, John Patrick. 2900 1ST AVE, EMERGENCY DEPARTMENT 25702 #054-04-1990 L1991 **EM** *020 †16

SHOULDIS, Eric Daniel. 2860 3RD AVE STE 210, HUNTINGTON INTERNAL MEDICI 25702 #055-01-2000 L2003 **IM** *020 †20

SHY, David Grant. 2900 1ST AVE 25702 #055-75-1988, ▲ L1989 **AN** *020 †05

SIAS, Tina Hatfield. 1249 15TH ST, STE 4000 25701 #055-02-1992 L1995 **CD** *020 †20

SIDDIQI, Farooq Hussain. 2900 1ST AVE 25702 #495-21-1964 L1974 **PD** *020 †55

SIEGLER, Charles Morgan. 5170 US ROUTE 60 25705 #033-05-1991 L1997 **DR** *020 †80

SIGDEL, Saroj Kumar. ■ 25701 #305-01-1999 L2006 **PTH** *100

SIGURDARDOTTIR, Bryndis. 1600 MEDICAL CENTER DR, STE G500 25701 #484-01-1996 L2005 **ID** *020 †20

SIMPSON, Friday Geene. 2627 5TH AVE, DRS FRIDAYS 25702 #055-02-1991 L1992 **FM** *020 †18

SIMPSON, Matthew Earl. ■ 25701 #305-01-2003 L2008 **GS** *012

SINGH, Shailini. 1600 MEDICAL CENTER DR, STE 4500 25701 #496-07-1967 L2003 **MFM OBG** *020 †30

SKOLIK, Stephanie Ann. 1616 13TH AVE, STE 3B 25701 #055-02-1985 L1989 **OPH** *020 †35

SMITH, Chadwick Ray. 2900 1ST AVE 25702 #055-02-2000 L2003 **MPD** *020 †20,55

SMITH, Shannon Lea. ■ 25701 #055-02-2003 L2006 **PD** *100

SMITH, Stephen Chas. 5170 US ROUTE 60 E, 1399 HOSPITAL DRIVE 25705 #055-02-1981 L1984 **IM** *020 †20

SMITH, Tyson De Lloyd. ■ 25705 #047-06-1975 L1976 **MDM** *030 †50

SMOOT, Sunshine Michele. ■ 25705 #020-02-2006 **PD** *012

SNAVELY, Daniel Decker. 5170 US ROUTE 60 25705 #055-01-1994 L1997 **IM CD** *020 †20

SNODGRASS, Amanda Dawn. 723 9TH AVE, VALLEY HEALTH YOUTH & PEDI 25701 #055-02-2004 L2007 **PD** *020

SNYDER, Jason Andrew. ■ 25701 #055-02-2008 *012

SOLEYMANI, Kambiz. 1415 6TH AVE 25701 #847-19-1994 L2004 **P** *020

SOMMERVILLE, Troy Donald. 729 9TH AVE STE 11 25701 #055-01-1989 L1991 **IM** *020 †20

SPANGLER, Phillip Richard. 1600 MEDICAL CENTER DR, STE B500 25701 #055-02-2000 L2002 **P** *020

SPEARS, James F, II. 5170 US ROUTE 60 25705 #055-02-1987 L1988 **FM EM** *020 †18

SPINDEL, Michael Roy. 2860 3RD AVE, STE 220 25702 #012-05-1981 L1993 **PS** *020 †95

STEEL, Jack Ross. 2828 1ST AVE STE 400 25702 #055-01-1983 L1984 **ORS** *020 †40

STEELE, David Reid. 2 STONECREST DR 25701 #061-01-1977 L1981 **GP EM** *020

STEMPLE, Marie Ann. 5170 US ROUTE 60 25705 #055-01-1996 L1999 **IM** *020 †20

STEVENS, Phillip R. 3 STONECREST DR, TRI STATE OTOLARYNGOLOGY 25701 #055-01-1983 L1988 **OTO** *020 †45

STEVENS, Ralph Albert. 1249 15TH ST, STE 4000 25701 #055-01-1973 L1975 **CD IM** *020

STEVENS, Sarah L Cockrell. ■ 25705 #048-04-1936 L1941 **IM A** *072

STEVENSON, Mabel Margaret. 2900 1ST AVE 25702 #539-01-1952 L1973 **BBK CLP** *030 †50

STEVENSON, Richard Gregg. 19 KENSINGTON LN 25705 #055-01-1969 L1976 **CD IM** *030 †20

STEWART, Michael Addingto. 1801 6TH AVE 25703 #305-01-2004 **GS** *012

STONE, Bartlett Allen. 5694 US ROUTE 60, INC 25705 #055-02-1987 L1991 **AN** *020 †05

STRITZ, Stanislav. 2900 1ST AVE 25702 #286-03-1972 L1988 **AN** *020 †05

STROW, Misty Katherine. 1340 HAL GREER BLVD, DEPT OF EMERGENCY MEDICINE 25701 #055-02-2000 L2004 **PD** *020

STUDENY, Mark Allen. 1249 15TH ST, STE 4000 25701 #055-02-1986 L1990 **CD** *020 †20

STULTZ, Debra Jane. 2866 1ST AVE, STE 501 25702 #055-02-1989 L1991 **P CHP** *020 †75

STYER, Thomas B. 533 4TH AVE, WHITAKER NATIONAL CORP 25701 #055-02-1982 L1983 **EM PD** *020 †55

SZENDI-HORVATH, Imre. 1340 HAL GREER BLVD 25701 #473-02-1961 L1972 **ORS** *020

TACKETT, Chandos Dewayne. 5170 US ROUTE 60 25705 #055-02-1992 L1995 **FM** *020 †18

TADDESSE, Abay Tassew. 1600 MEDICAL CENTER DR, STE 3400 25701 #366-03-1997 **IM** *012

TAMMO, Sami. 1600 MEDICAL CENTER DR SU 25701 #875-02-2005 **IM** *012

TANG, Hua. 1600 MEDICAL CENTER DR, STE 3400 25701 #243-74-1983 **GS** *012

TAO, Stanley S. 2828 1ST AVE, STE 400 25702 #038-06-1995 L2001 **OSM** *020 †40

TAYLOR, I Ewen. ■ 25701 #051-04-1936 L1937 **GS CRS** *100

TIANO, John Theodore. ■ 25701 #055-02-2003 L2004 **CD** *012 †20

TONSKI, Ernest Richard. 2 STONECREST DR 25701 #055-01-1978 L1980 **EM** *020 †16

TOPPINS, Beth Ann. 1340 HAL GREER BLVD, DEPT OF EMERGENCY 25701 #055-02-2000 L2003 **FM** *020 †18

TOUMA, Joseph Bichara. 1616 13TH AVE STE 100 25701 #875-01-1962 L1973 **OTO** *020 †45

TOUMA, Omayma Tayar. 1600 MEDICAL CENTER DR, STE 1500 25701 #875-01-1966 L1973 **PD** *030 †55

TOUMA, Susan C. 2900 1ST AVE 25702 #055-01-1998 L2001 **D** *020 †15

TRAYLOR, Jack Richard, Jr. 1415 HAL GREER BLVD 25701 #055-01-1977 L1982 **GS** *020

TRIA-TIRONA, Ma Rosalia B. 1600 MEDICAL CENTER DR, STE G500 25701 #748-10-1981 L1992 **HEM ON** *020 †20

TRIPLETT, Terrence Wayne. 5170 US ROUTE 60 25705 #055-02-1986 L1989 **FM** *020 †18

TRUE, Jennifer Fay. 1600 MEDICAL CENTER DR, STE 3400 25701 #020-12-2006 **IM** *012

TURNER, Charles Edward. 5170 US ROUTE 60 25705 #055-01-1963 L1964 **GE IM** *020 †20

TURNER, Robert Ernest. 5170 US ROUTE 60 25705 #055-02-1981 L1984 **FM** *020 †18

TWEEL, Harry Karl. 1115 20TH ST 25703 #021-01-1962 L1970 **PUD IM** *030

UDDEMARRI, Sreevani. 1801 6TH AVE 25703 #495-58-1997 **IM** *100

VALLEJOS-ARCE, Javier. 2628 5TH AVE 25702 #737-01-1969 L1978 **OBG** *020 †30

VARNEY, Jamie Benjamin. ■ 25705 #020-02-2004 L2005 **FSM** *012 †18

VAUGHAN, Amy Anne. 1934 11TH AVE 25701 #055-02-1992 L1996 **D** *020 †15

VEERASWAMY, Manimekalai. 1301 HAL GREER BLVD, VALLEY HEALTH HUNTINGTON 25701 #495-42-1985 L1997 **MPD PD** *020 †55,20

VEGA, Elmer Teofilo. 2828 1ST AVE STE 301 25702 #176-03-1957 L1972 **AN** *071 †05

VILASAGAR, Nivedita. ■ 25701 #055-02-2008 *012

9354

■ = Address Information Privacy Protected

WALDECK, James Michael. 1600 MEDICAL CENTER DR, STE 3500 25701 #055-01-1982 L1984 **PD** *020 †55

WALDEN, John Beaumont. 1600 MEDICAL CENTER DR, STE 1500 25701 #055-01-1970 L1971 **FM** *030 †18

WALDEN, Martha Lee. 1600 MEDICAL CENTER DR, STE B500 25701 #020-02-1989 L1999 **P** *072 †75

WALDRON, Vincent David. ■ 25701 #023-01-1974 L1974 **ORS** *020 †40

WALKER, Robert Bruce. 1600 MEDICAL CENTER DR, STE 1500 25701 #011-03-1974 L1975 **FM** *020 †18,70

WALKER, William E. 2900 1ST AVE, ST MARY'S HOSP EM DEPT 25702 #055-01-1968 L1969 **EM** *020 †16

WALLACE, Janet Nease. 2703 3RD AVE 25702 #055-02-1992 L1993 **FM** *020 †18

WALLACE, William C. 1600 MEDICAL CENTER DR, STE 2500 25701 #055-02-2001 L2004 **FM** *020 †18

WALTERS, Torin Patrick. 5170 US ROUTE 60 25705 #055-01-1990 L1994 **DR** *020 †80

WATSON, James Keith. 5170 US ROUTE 60 25705 #020-12-2002 L2007 **DR** *020 †80

WEBB, Deleno H, III. 10 6TH AVE W STE 300 25701 #055-01-1971 L1971 **P PMM** *020

WEBB, Ralph Wyatt. 1249 15TH ST, UNIVERSITY PHYSICIANS INTE 25701 #055-01-1984 L1985 **IM RHU** *040 †20

WEHNER, Paulette Suzanne. 1249 15TH ST, STE 4000 25701 #055-02-1989 L1990 **CD** *020 †20

WEIMER, Mathew Benjamin. 1600 MEDICAL CENTER DR, STE 1500 25701 #038-43-2005 L2006 **FP** *012

WEINSWEIG, David Leslie. 2860 3RD AVE, STE 10 25702 #041-12-1985 L1992 **NS** *020 †25

WERTHAMMER, Joseph Wm. 1600 MEDICAL CENTER DR, STE 3500 25701 #055-01-1973 L1976 **PD NPM** *020 †55

WHITE, Margaret Ann. 1600 MEDICAL CENTER DR, STE 1500 25701 #012-01-2005 L2007 **FP** *012

WHITMORE, David John. 2585 3RD AVE 25703 #055-75-1997, ▲ L1998 **FM** *020 †18 ‡

WILCOX, Stephen Nelson. 2240 5TH AVE, FL 2 25703 #055-02-2001 L2002 **FM** *020 †18

WILGUS, Janna. 25703 #055-02-1989 L1990 **CD** *020

WILLIAMS, Anne Kathleensh. ■ 25701 #055-02-2008 *012

WILLIS, Erick James. ■ 25705 #055-02-2005 **PD** *012

WILSON, Matthew C. 1001 20TH ST 25703 #038-40-1978 L1982 **AI PDA** *020 †55,03 ‡

WILSON, Thomas Cabell. 641 6TH ST 25701 #051-04-1954 L1955 **EM** *020 †50

WIPPEL, Mark Eric. 1600 MEDICAL CENTER DR, STE 3500 25701 #055-02-1986 L1987 **PD** *020 †55

WOLDETENSAY, Solomon. 1600 MEDICAL CENTER DR, DEPT MED 25701 #665-01-2005 **IM** *012

WOLFE, Stephen Kenneth. 3 STONECREST DR 25701 #048-04-1971 L1977 **OTO HNS** *020 †45

WONG, Dominique M. 1340 HAL GREER BLVD, DEPT OF EMERGENCY MEDICINE 25701 #038-40-1995 L1997 **FM** *020 †18

WRIGHT, David Owen. 846 8TH AVE, CABELL COUNTY E.M.S. 25701 #055-01-1977 L1978 **EM IM** *020 †20,16

WROCZYNSKI, Brian F. ■ 25701 #055-01-1979 L1982 **EM FM** *020 †18

YAQUB, Nadia. 1600 MEDICAL CENTER DR, STE G500 25701 #704-06-1997 L2002 **END IM** *020 †20

YARBROUGH, Charles Logan. 1934 11TH AVE 25701 #051-04-1970 L1976 **D DMP** *020 †15

YATES, Walter Kinstler. ■ 25705 #051-04-1947 L1949 **IM** *071

YINGLING, Kevin Wesley. 1249 15TH ST, STE 2000 25701 #055-02-1985 L1990 **IM PA** *020 †20

YOUNG, Elaine Matthews. 1411 6TH AVE 25701 #055-02-1986 L1990 **D** *020 †15

YUDINA, Svetlana. ■ 25705 #913-11-1988 L2000 **GS** *020 †85

ZAMAN, Mumtaz U. 1249 15TH ST STE 3000, UNIVERSITY PHYSICIANS INTE 25701 #704-02-1991 L2005 **PCC** *020 †20

ZAPPACOSTA, Anne Marie. 1600 MEDICAL CENTER DR, STE B500 25701 #055-01-1996 L1998 **CHP P** *020

ZARRAGA, Cynthia Gonzales. 1600 MEDICAL CENTER DR 25701 #748-01-1983 L1989 **PUD** *020 †20

ZEID, Fuad Moh'D Ali. 1249 15TH ST 25701 #575-01-1984 L1992 **PCC IM** *020 †20

ZEID, Iyad M. ■ 25705 #575-01-1986 L1994 **PG** *100 †55

ZITTER, William Palmer. 1340 HAL GREER BLVD 25701 #038-40-1975 L1994 **EM** *071 †16

ZWAWI, Karima M. Shmila. 1600 MEDICAL CENTER DR, DEPT OF OB/GYN 25701 #613-02-1990 **OBG** *012

HUNTINGTON – WAYNE

ADKINS, Zachary Brooks. ■ 25704 #055-02-2006 **FP** *012

ALLOJU, Bhagya Lakshmi. 1542 SPRING VALLEY DR 25704 #495-50-1981 L2004 **FM** *100

BADIN, Shadi. 1540 SPRING VALLEY DR, VAMC-MEDICAL SERVICE 25704 #875-01-1997 L2005 **PUD** *020 †20 ‡

BENEKE, George Robert. 1540 SPRING VALLEY DR, VA MEDICAL CENTER #581 25704 #055-01-1976 L1978 **U GS** *020 †95

BHATTI, Farrukh Latif. 1540 SPRING VALLEY DR 25704 #704-24-1990 L2005 **P** *020 †75

BOWEN, Shane Allan. 7 OLD TRL 25704 #055-02-1993 L1995 **EM** *020 †16

BRAMMER, Christopher M. 1540 SPRING VALLEY DR, VA MEDICAL CENTER 25704 #038-44-1998 L1999 **PM SCI** *030 †60

BREAUX, Jeffery Bernard. 1540 SPRING VALLEY DR, VA. MEDICAL SERVICE (111) 25704 #409-16-1980 L1981 **IM** *020 †20

BROWN, Garry D. 1542 SPRING VALLEY DR 25704 #010-02-1977 L1983 **PTH** *075

CANTERBURY, Timothy David. 1540 SPRING VALLEY DR, VA MEDICAL CENTER 25704 #055-02-1984 L1985 **GS PD** *040 †85

CHATEL, John Chas. 1540 SPRING VALLEY DR 25704 #030-06-1965 L1966 **P** *020 †75

CID, Ernesto. 1540 SPRING VALLEY DR 25704 #847-04-1965 L1992 **OS U** *020

CID, Martha Alicia Galano. 1540 SPRING VALLEY DR, BLDG 6A 25704 #847-04-1964 L1992 **P PTH** *071

DALTON, William Carlos. 401 CAMDEN RD 25704 #055-02-1998 L2000 **FM** *020 ‡

DILLON, Joshua Lee. ■ 25704 #055-02-2007 **PD** *012

DUTHIE, James S. 1540 SPRING VALLEY DR, MEDICAL CENTER 25704 #495-27-1974 L1995 **IM** *020 †20

DYSON, Lillan Barber. 1540 SPRING VALLEY DR, VA MEDICAL CENTER 25704 #020-02-1979 L1980 **IM** *020 †20

EDWARDS, Diane. ■ 25704 #055-01-1990 L1999 **NP** *075

GALAPON, Philip Andrew. ■ 25704 #055-02-2008 *012

HARTMAN, Kristina Jan. 1540 SPRING VALLEY DR, VAMC-ER 25704 #028-03-1982 L1982 **FM EM** *020 †18

HAYES, James Robertalle. ■ 25704 #055-02-2008 *012

HELWANI, Hassan. 1540 SPRING VALLEY DR, DEPT. OF MEDICINE 25704 #875-01-1991 L2000 **IM** *020 †20

HOFFMAN, Robert V, Jr. ■ 25704 #024-01-1945 L1950 **PTH** *071 †50

HOLMES, Gregory Arthur. 2908 AUBURN RD 25704 #051-04-1991 L1999 **FM** *020 †18

JOHNSON, Karin Christine. ■ 25704 #055-02-2005 **PD** *012

JOSEPH, Sandra Jean. 1540 SPRING VALLEY DR 25704 #055-02-1981 L1982 **FM** *030 †18

JUSTICE, Jill Mc Clanahan. 1540 SPRING VALLEY DR, VA MEDICAL CENTER 25704 #055-01-1993 L1998 **DR** *020 †80

KOON, Richard Ethen. PO BOX 448, 1530 NORWAY AVE 25709 #036-07-1976 L1978 **P CHP** *075 †75

KUMAR, Arun. 1540 SPRING VALLEY DR #111 25704 #495-54-1995 L2004 **ON HEM** *020 †20

LAZARO, Lydia Legaspi. PO BOX 448 25709 #748-07-1953 **P** *020

LEIDY, John Wm, Jr. 1540 SPRING VALLEY DR, MEDICAL SERVICE, 581/111 25704 #054-04-1979 L1986 **END IM** *040 †20

MANIS, Richard Benedict. 1540 SPRING VALLEY DR, DEPT OF SURGERY 25704 #035-09-1969 L2000 **ORS** *020

MCCLOUD, Beth Megan. ■ 25704 #055-02-2008 *012

MEURER, Dennis Raymond. 1540 SPRING VALLEY DR 25704 #048-14-1984 L1998 **CCS** *020 †85

MODY, Jayshri Mukul. 1420 WASHINGTON AVE 25704 #495-23-1968 L1982 **AN** *020

MORITZ, Dennis Michael. 1540 SPRING VALLEY DR, SURGICAL CLINIC 25704 #016-11-1981 L1999 **TS** *020 †90,85

MORRIS, Matthew William. ■ 25704 #055-02-2008 *012

MOSS, Ned Samson. VETERANS ADMIN MED CTR 25704 #035-19-1955 L1979 **PTH OS** *020 †50

MOUFARREGE, Ghassan T. 1540 SPRING VALLEY DR, CHF/ANESTH-HUNTINGTON VAMC 25704 #605-01-1995 L2001 **AN PME** *020 †05

MULLIN, Richard Patrick, III. ■ 25704 #055-02-2007 **P** *012

MUNN, Nancy Jo. 1540 SPRING VALLEY DR 25704 #020-02-1978 L1983 **PUD IM** *040 †20

NARAYAN, Manjula. ■ 25704 #495-33-1970 L1980 **PM** *020 †60

NORTON, Nancy Bedient. 1542 SPRING VALLEY DR, DEPT OF PATH 25704 #055-02-1999 L2003 **IM** *040 †20

PELLECCHIA, Joseph A P. 1540 SPRING VALLEY DR 25704 #010-02-1960 L1968 **IM CD** *030 †20

PITZER, Keith Dwayne. ■ 25704 #036-05-2002 **PS** *012

PLYMALE, Mickey Franklin. ■ 25704 #055-02-2006 **ORS** *012

POLLARD, Amanda Christine. ■ 25704 #055-02-2008 *012

RAJAN, Narasanna. 1540 SPRING VALLEY DR 25704 #495-37-1962 L1973 **IM PUD** *020 †55,20

RAMAN, Sarat Chandra. 1540 SPRING VALLEY DR 25704 #055-02-2000 L2003 **FM** *020 †18

RAO, Nagaraja. 1540 SPRING VALLEY DR, VA MEDICAL CENTER 25704 #495-62-1975 L1994 **N CN** *020 †75

ROSS, Rhonda Scites. 1540 SPRING VALLEY DR, VA MEDICAL CENTER 25704 #055-02-1994 L1997 **IM** *020

SARKAR, Deepak Ranjan. 1540 SPRING VALLEY DR, VA MEDICAL CTR 25704 #495-67-1978 L2002 **AN** *020 †05

SHAREEF, Amirah Lachaune. ■ 25704 #055-02-2008 *012

SHARMA, Tara Chand. 1540 SPRING VALLEY DR 25704 #495-03-1960 L1972 **U UP** *020 †95

SINDHE, B N Subba Rao. 1540 SPRING VALLEY DR, VAMC 25704 #495-09-1962 L1972 **CD IM** *020 †20

SINGH, Ranvir. 1540 SPRING VALLEY DR 25704 #495-47-1992 L1997 **GE** *020 †20

SKEENS, William Michael. 1540 SPRING VALLEY DR 25704 #055-02-1987 L1988 **IM IMG** *020 †20

SMITH, Erica Lynn. ■ 25704 #055-02-2008 *012

SOLTIS, Lucia Irene. ■ 25704 #055-02-2008 *012

SULTANA, Afroza. 1540 SPRING VALLEY DR, VA MEDICAL CTR 25704 #160-05-1992 L2006 **IM** *020 †20

TEKA, Samson Tulu. 1540 SPRING VALLEY DR, VA MEDICAL CTR 25704 #408-14-1988 L2001 **IM** *020 †20

TRIEST, William E. 1540 SPRING VALLEY DR, VA MEDICAL CTR 25704 #023-07-1976 L1982 **PTH IG** *020 †50

WALKER, Ernest M, Jr. 1542 SPRING VALLEY DR, DEPARTMENT OF PATHOLOGY 25704 #045-01-1974 L1992 **PTH** *020 †50

WALKER, John Tracy. 1540 SPRING VALLEY DR 25704 #028-03-1980 L1986 **GS** *030 †85

WILSON, Stephen Lawrence. 1540 SPRING VALLEY DR, VA MED CTR DEPT SURG 25704 #012-01-1988 L1989 **GS** *020 †85

WOLFER, Rebecca Sue. 1540 SPRING VALLEY DR 25704 #028-02-1990 L2001 **TS** *020 †85,90

HURRICANE – PUTNAM

ALIFF, James Paul. 4000 OUT LOOK DR 25526 #051-04-1940 L1941 **IM OS** *071

BAILEY, Marsha Lee. 1203 HOSPITAL DR STE 1203, OCCUP & ENVIRON HLTH PLLC 25526 #055-02-1984 L1994 **OM** *020 †70

BARAZI, Hassan. ■ 25526 #055-02-2008 *012

BLAIR, Paul Alex. 3667 TEAYS VALLEY RD 25526 #055-01-1977 L1978 **OTO FPS** *020 †45

BOWMAN, Christopher E. 3752 TEAYS VALLEY RD, STE 2 25526 #055-01-1996 L1998 **MPD** *100

BUKOVINSKY, Charles. 3520 TEAYS VALLEY RD, STE 1 25526 #055-02-1987 L1988 **FM** *020 †18

BURKE, Lisa Gail. 1401 HOSPITAL DR, STE 101 25526 #055-02-1993 L1998 **OBG** *020 †30

BURKHOLDER, Garry Wayne. ■ 25526 #055-02-2004 **FP** *012

CAMPBELL, Stephen Douglas. 1400 HOSPITAL DR 25526 #055-02-2000 L2002 **IM** *020

CLARK, John Mirrell. 3860 TEAYS VALLEY RD, STE 4 25526 #055-01-2003 L2005 **IM** *020 †20

CRUZ, Lorna Rubiano. ■ 25526 #748-08-1983 L2006 **PTH** *020 †50

CUPIT, Dennis Marshall. ■ 25526 #055-02-1993 L1994 **FM** *020 †18

DICRISTOFARO, Sean C. 104 STATION PLACE WAY 25526 #055-02-1997 L1999 **FM** *020 †18

DUFFY, Scott Patrick. 62 STONERIDGE DR 25526 #055-02-1998 L2001 **CD** *100 †20

GREEN, Jami Elyse. ■ 25526 #055-02-2005 **FP** *012

HAFFAR, Mohammed Yaser. 1211 HOSPITAL DR, CARDIOVASCULAR CONSULTANTS 25526 #875-01-1984 L1990 **CD IM** *020 †20

HARRAH, Gregory Scott. 3857 TEAYS VALLEY RD, STE 1 25526 #055-02-1991 L1993 **FM** *020 †18

HARVEY, Hyla M. 35 CHASE DR 25526 #035-48-1991 L1992 **FM** *020 †18

HOLMES, Jeffrey Scott. 3752 TEAYS VALLEY RD, STE 1 25526 #055-02-1993 L1996 **IM** *020 †20

■ = Address Information Privacy Protected

HOWARD, Thomas William, III. ■ 25526 #055-01-2008 *012
KING, Devin Audric. 1204 HOSPITAL DR 25526 #055-02-1999 L2003 **OPH** *020 †35
KOTTAPALLI, Mahija. 1401 HOSPITAL DR STE 201 25526 #496-24-1996 L2003 **P** *020 †75
KURUCZ, Jane A. 3647 TEAYS VALLEY RD 25526 #055-01-1983 L1988 **GS OS** *020 †85
LAMBRECHTS, Marcel G. ■ 25526 #165-04-1953 L1961 **PD** *020
LAMP, Candina Ranee. ■ 25526 #055-02-2007 **OBG** *012
LEE, Daria L. 1400 HOSPITAL DR, EMERGENCY CONSULTANTS INC 25526 #055-02-1995 L2000 **FM** *020 †18
MAC CALLUM, John Patrick. 3855 TEAYS VALLEY RD 25526 #055-01-1974 L1975 **P CHP** *020 †75
MASILAMANI, Sanjay Stanle. ■ 25526 #055-02-2007 **P** *012
MOLANO, Wilfredo N. 2733 MAIN ST 25526 #748-08-1967 L1975 **FM** *020
MOLINA, Louis Rafael. 1206 HOSPITAL DR 25526 #055-02-1984 L1989 **U** *020 †95
NEVILLE, John Wallace, Jr. 3752 TEAYS VALLEY RD, STE 2 25526 #055-02-1993 L1994 **FM** *020 †18 ‡
NITARDY, William Arland. ■ 25526 #055-02-2006 **MPD** *012
PETERSON, Randall W. 3952 TEAYS VALLEY RD 25526 #055-01-1981 L1984 **FM** *020 †18 ‡
RATLIFF, David Summers. 3665 TEAYS VALLEY RD, STE 2500 25526 #055-02-1986 L1987 **GS** *020 †85
RESTREPO, Ana Lucia. ■ 25526 #264-16-1997 L2004 **FM** *100 †18
RESTREPO OCHOA, Alberto. ■ 25526 #264-03-1965 L1972 **P** *020 †75
ROMERO, Erdulfo Silan. ■ 25526 #748-07-1958 L1976 **FM GS** *020
SOBIESKI, Michael Wm. 1107 OLDE PINE DR, CHARLESTON PATHOLOGISTS AS 25526 #045-04-1991 L1999 **PTH IM** *020 †50
STA ANA, Enrique C, Jr. 1100 HOSPITAL DR 25526 #748-01-1969 L1978 **GP GS** *020
SZEGO, Gabriel Gabor. 3768 TEAYS VALLEY RD, FRESENIUS MED CARE OF HURR 25526 #396-04-1974 L1980 **NEP IM** *020 †20
THURSTON, Deborah Reed. ■ 25526 #055-02-2005 **PD** *012
TRUMP, Jeffrey Scott. 3006 MOUNT VERNON RD #1070 25526 #055-01-1992 L1993 **FM** *020 †18
WHITE, Ambryan Leigh. ■ 25526 #055-02-2005 **FP** *012
WILSON, Asbury Irwin. ■ 25526 #047-06-1954 L1954 **P** *071
ZHANG, Peilin. ■ 25526 #243-47-1987 L2001 **PTH** *020 †50

INWOOD — BERKELEY

HARDEN-MACK, Angela M. 102 HOOVER DR 25428 #025-07-1994 L2000 **IM PD** *020 †55,20
MICHAELS, Robert M. ■ 25428 #010-02-1972 L2007 **RHU IM** *020 †20
SPIESS, Christopher Micha. ■ 25428 #055-01-2008 *012

IVYDALE — CLAY

BOGGS, James Ernest. STAR ROUTE 4 BOX 128 25113 #023-01-1953 L1954 **GS** *071 †85

JANE LEW — LEWIS

LUZIETTI, Richard Paul. 533 HACKERS CREEK RD 26378 #008-02-2005 L2008 **GP** *020

KEARNEYSVILLE — JEFFERSON

CHAUDARY, Nauman Arif. ■ 25430 #704-22-1998 L2003 **PCC** *100 †20
ELBAAGE, Thar Yahya Yasir. ■ 25430 #528-01-1980 L2003 **PCC** *020 †20
GREENAN, James Howard. ■ 25430 #030-05-1967 L1968 **AN** *071

KENOVA — WAYNE

GIBSON, Joshua Dale. ■ 25530 #055-02-2007 **IM** *012

KERENS — RANDOLPH

NIELSEN, Melissa Matthews. RR 1 BOX 116 26276 #038-41-1993 L1996 **EM** *020 †16

KERMIT — MINGO

DAVIS, Cynthia Gail. ■ 25674 #055-02-2008 *012
ENDICOTT, James Wm. PO BOX 430 25674 #055-02-1983 L1985 **FM FPG** *020 †18
HENSLEY, Joshua Hode. ■ 25674 #055-02-2006 *012

KEYSER — MINERAL

BESS, Charles David. RR 3 BOX 3267 26726 #011-04-1991 L1993 **FM** *020 †18
BOKIL, Harshad S. 566 S MINERAL ST 26726 #495-96-1994 L2002 **IM** *020 †20
CHAPMAN, David Robt. ■ 26726 #055-01-1975 L1976 **GP** *020
DENNE, Nicolas Steven. ■ 26726 #055-01-2007 *012
HAHN, John Lee. 90 SOUTHERN DR 26726 #055-02-1983 L1984 **OBG FM** *030 †30
HAYWOOD, Anthony K. 167 S MINERAL ST 26726 #055-75-1994, ▲ L1995 **FM EM** *020 †18
HEALY, Paul T. 30 N MAIN ST 26726 #010-01-1953 L1954 **GP** *071
ITANI, Bilal Abdul-Hamid. 233 S MINERAL ST 26726 #605-01-1991 L1991 **PD** *020 †55
KHURANA, Inder Kumar. 537 S MINERAL ST 26726 #495-29-1971 L1979 **GS** *020 †85
LEFLER, Kenneth David. 167 S MINERAL ST, POTOMAC VALLEY HOSP EMERG 26726 #028-34-1977 L1991 **EM FM** *020 †18
LIEBIG, Carl A. 167 S MINERAL ST 26726 #038-41-1949 L1958 **GP EM** *071 †85
SAWEIKIS, Anthony Allen. 167 S MINERAL ST 26726 #055-01-1993 L1995 **FM** *020 †18
SHENOY, Suratkal Vaman. 167 S MINERAL ST 26726 #495-37-1974 L1981 **GS** *020 †85
SHROFF, Mahesh Babulal. 390 CARSKADON LN 26726 #495-17-1977 L1990 **IM PUD** *020 †20
STAGGERS, Phillip Gary. ■ 26726 #023-01-1955 L1959 **GP AN** *020
SYED, Aijaz A. 167 S MINERAL ST, POTOMAC VALLEY HOSPITAL 26726 #704-02-1986 L1993 **IM NEP** *020 †20

THOMAS, William Scott. RR 3 BOX 3152, BLACKBURN SQUARE 26726 #055-01-2001 L2004 **FM P** *020 †18,75
ZALZAL, Rabie Habib. 537 S MINERAL ST 26726 #605-01-1987 L1991 **IM GP** *020 †20

KINGWOOD — PRESTON

CLARKSON, Cynthia Clark. ■ 26537 #055-01-2004 L2006 **MPD** *012
CONLEY, Frederick Allen, II. 300 S PRICE ST 26537 #055-01-1976 L1977 **EM FM** *020 †18
DANI, Saryu Punamchand. 115 DAISY ST 26537 #495-46-1967 L1981 **OBG FM** *020
FORMAN, Bonnie Jo. 301 E MAIN ST 26537 #055-01-1996 L1998 **FM** *020 †18
GAMPONIA, Edgar Clarence. 300 S PRICE ST, REGIONAL EYE ASSOCIATES 26537 #055-01-1993 L1997 **OPH** *035
GHAMANDE, Shekhar Anant. 300 S PRICE ST, SPECIALIST CENTER A 26537 #496-38-1993 L2002 **PCC SME** *020
GUILFOOSE, John Alan. 301 S PRICE ST, MOUNTAINEER FAMILY CARE CE 26537 #041-15-2001 L2005 **ID** *012
HARNED, Max Allen. ■ 26537 #056-05-1980 L1981 **FM** *075 †18
HAYMOND, Thomas A. 300 S PRICE ST 26537 #024-01-1951 L1965 **IM ADM** *071 †20
HOFFMAN, Donald Lawrence. 300 S PRICE ST, PRESTON MEMORIAL HOSPITAL 26537 #035-46-1984 L1992 **N** *020 †75
HOLEHOUSE, James Michael. 300 S PRICE ST 26537 #308-07-1982 L1987 **OBG** *020 †30
KEEFE, John Jos. 301 S PRICE ST, STE NO2 26537 #016-43-1981 L1982 **FM** *020 †18
MEYERS, Dale M, Jr. 300 S PRICE ST, PRESTON MEMORIAL HOSP 26537 #023-01-1981 L1986 **EM** *020
MILLER, Lawrance Saml. ■ 26537 #051-01-1945 L1952 **ORS HS** *071 †40
MILLER, Timothy Chas. 301 S PRICE ST, STE 1 26537 #055-01-1979 L1981 **GS** *020 †85
PARSONS, Michael John. 411 MORGANTOWN ST, PESTON FAMILY HEALTH CENTE 26537 #045-01-1997 L1998 **FM** *020 †18
RAMBERG, Julia Elisabeth. 428 MORGANTOWN ST, TOTAL FAMILLY CARE 26537 #012-01-1998 L2000 **FM PD** *020 †18
SCHWARZENBERG, Bernice. 110 N PRICE ST 26537 #051-04-1984 L1987 **PD** *020 †55
SCHWARZENBERG, Michael R. 110 N PRICE ST 26537 #051-04-1984 L1987 **FM** *020 †18
SHETTY, Ram Mohan. 428 MORGANTOWN ST 26537 #012-01-1997 L2000 **FM** *020 †18
WATSON, David Alan. 300 S PRICE ST, PRESTON MEMORIAL HOSPITAL 26537 #055-02-1997 L1999 **FM** *020 †18
WOLFE, Lorn Augustin. 300 S PRICE ST 26537 #055-01-2001 L2004 **FM** *020 †18

LAVALETTE — WAYNE

DAVIS, Scott Edward. ■ 25535 #055-02-2006 **FP** *012
FRANKS, Adam Michael. 4600 ROUTE 152 25535 #055-02-1999 L2001 **FM** *020 †18
MC CANN, Kevin Scott. 4600 ROUTE 152 25535 #055-02-1995 L1996 **FM** *020 †18

LEWISBURG — GREENBRIER

BAKER, John Jay. 540 N JEFFERSON ST, BOX 7 24901 #025-07-1968 L1990 **ON HEM** *071 †20
BHUSAWANG, Yongyudh. ■ 24901 #891-01-1968 L1978 **PTH GP** *020 †50
BRODY, Arnold Jason. ■ 24901 #028-02-1947 L1956 **LM CD** *071 †20
CONLY, Samuel S, Jr. ■ 24901 #041-02-1944 L1947 **OS** *071
CORNELIUS, Jennifer Lynn. 400 N JEFFERSON ST 24901 #055-02-2000 L2002 **FM** *020 †18 ‡
CUNNINGHAM, Polley K Hale. ■ 24901 #055-01-1974 L1979 **RHU** *020 †20
DURHAM, Richard R. RR 2 BOX 171, GREENBRIER PULMONOLOGY 24901 #055-75-1988, ▲ L1989 **PUD IM** *020 †20
EDNACOT, Romeo Ruiz. ■ 24901 #748-01-1966 L1974 **PD** *020
FERRELL, Robert Morris. ■ 24901 #051-04-1938 L1939 **OPH** *071
HOLWICK, Jann Leigh. RR 2, BOX 171 24901 #005-14-1976 L1993 **GS** *020 †85
HONAINY, Hassan K. RR 2, BOX 171 24901 #605-01-1990 L1996 **IM NEP** *020 †20
ISSENBERG, Steven Allen. ■ 24901 #011-02-1966 L1989 **OTO** *020 †45
JEWELL, Noel Brian. 100 CHURCH ST, SENECA HEALTH SERVICES, IN 24901 #055-01-2001 L2007 **OS** *020 †20,75
KHAN, Atif. RR 2 BOX 171, VALLEY MEDICAL ASSOCIATES 24901 #067-01-1997 L2003 **GS** *020
KNUDSEN, Knud David. ■ 24901 #693-01-1950 L1980 **IM** *071
LI, Te-Cheng. ■ 24901 #244-05-1988 **FM** *100
MC CLUNG, Amanda Beth. ■ 24901 #055-02-2002 L2003 **GS** *020
MITCHELL, Helen Marr. 400 N JEFFERSON ST 24901 #035-03-1970 L1998 **PD FM** *020 †55
MODLIN, Robert Kent. ■ 24901 #008-01-1957 L1969 **IM** *071 †20
MOSSBURG, William Lee. FAIRVIEW ROAD 24901 #055-01-1969 L1970 **VS TS** *071 †85
MOUGHRABI, Bassel. 129 SENECA TRL, GAMBRO HEALTHCARE GREENBRI 24901 #875-01-1986 L2002 **EM NEP** *020 †20
OTHMAN, Joe O. RR 2, BOX 169 24901 #528-01-1973 L1988 **N** *020 †75
PENCE, Lorenzo L. 400 N LEE ST 24901 #055-75-1985, ▲ L1986 **FM GP** *040
RAGSDALE, Dorris Ann. RR 2, BOX 171 24901 #051-04-1979 L1982 **IM** *020
RICHARDS, Brian Gerard. 323 N JEFFERSON ST 24901 #055-01-1979 L1980 **IM** *020 †20
SCOTT, Robert Kenneth. 22 COLEMAN DR 24901 #055-01-1974 L1975 **OPH** *071
SHELTON, Charles H, III. 187 SKYLAR DR, GREENBRIER VLY CANCER CTR 24901 #001-06-1992 L1999 **RO** *020 †80
SHIREY, Robert Garland. 223 MAPLEWOOD AV 24901 #023-01-1955 L1956 **IM** *071
SMITH, Lynn Nicholson. RR 2 BOX 171 24901 #051-04-1978 L1982 **IM** *074 †20
SPEILMAN, Danl Edgar, Jr. RR 2 BOX 169C 24901 #048-13-1977 L1994 **PS OTO** *020 †45,65
TEJA, Kuldeep. 400 N LEE ST, WV SCHOOL OF OSTEOPATHIC M 24901 #495-03-1960 L1994 **PTH** *020 †50
TOMLIN, Matthew Blake. ■ 24901 #038-45-2007 L2007 **TY** *012
VON DOHLEN, Thomas Walter. 157 SKYLAR DR, THE HEART CENTER INC 24901 #055-01-1981 L1982 **CD IM** *020 †20
WALL, Haven Neill, Jr. RR 2 BOX 171C, GREYROCK PROFESSIONAL PARK 24901 #023-01-1969 L1979 **CD IM** *020 †20
WEIDMAN, Clare David. 171 DAVIS ST 24901 #025-12-1975 L1985 **ORS** *020 †40
WEINSTEIN, Chas Elliott. ■ 24901 #035-08-1954 L1982 **DR** *072 †80
WHITE, Christopher L. 152 DAWKINS DR, GREYROCK PROFESSIONAL PARK 24901 #041-77-1999, ▲ L2006 **OTO FPS** *020
YAEGER, John Julius. ■ 24901 #010-02-1944 L1952 **DR** *071 †80

LOGAN – LOGAN

AGAS, Ulysses D. 557 MAIN ST 25601 #748-11-1966 L1982 **GP PTH** *020

AHMED, Safique. 77 HOSPITAL DR, 3RD FLOOR KRUGER BUILDING 25601 #160-02-1977 L2000 **HO** *020 †20

BERES, Michael Brian. 20 HOSPITAL DR, LOGAN GENERAL HOSPITAL 25601 #055-02-1996 L2000 **OPH** *020

BOPPANA, Prasada R. 20 HOSPITAL DR 25601 #495-50-1970 L1980 **IM** *020

BRENDEMUEHL, Judith. 140 STOLLINGS AVE STE 5 25601 #011-04-1978 L1980 **GS** *020

CHANDER, Bhanot Subhash. 140 STOLLINGS AVE 25601 #495-29-1973 L1981 **U** *020 †95

CHILLAG, Erwin Rudolph. 13 WHITE ST 25601 #035-06-1943 L1948 **GP OS** *020

CISCO, Jodi Michelle. 77 HOSPITAL DR, STE 201 25601 #055-02-1997 L2002 **GS** *020 †85

DE LARA, Carlos F. 20 HOSPITAL DR 25601 #748-08-1963 L1974 **PTH CLP** *050

DONAHOE, Dorval Hendrix. ■ 25601 #055-01-1963 L1964 **FM** *020 †18

FARIDI, Ahmad Bilal. 167 STOLLINGS AVE 25601 #747-02-1998 L2006 **NEP** *100 †20

GANGI, Mohsin Tauqir. 77 HOSPITAL DR 25601 #919-01-1984 L2003 **IM** *020 †20 ‡

GONZALEZ, Fernando Luis. ■ 25601 #649-14-1996 L2003 **IM** *020

GOSIENGFIAO, Jaime P. 20 HOSPITAL DR 25601 #748-07-1966 L1985 **EM** *040

HAFFAR, Mohammad B. 20 HOSPITAL DR 25601 #875-01-1982 L1990 **GE IM** *020 †20

HANSEL, John Seybert. 13 1/2 WHITE ST 25601 #051-01-1956 L1991 **OTO** *075 †45

JOSEPH, Joby. 38 HOSPITAL DR, KINGER MED PLA STE 300 25601 #495-37-1978 L1988 **N** *020

KITIPHONGSPATTANA, K. 20 HOSPITAL DR 25601 #891-02-1969 L1980 **GS TS** *020 †85

KOPPIKAR, Mahesh M. 20 HOSPITAL DR, LOGAN GENERAL HOSPITAL 25601 #495-17-1967 L1983 **DR NM** *020 †28,80

KUKKILLAYA, Radhakrishna. 20 HOSPITAL DR, LOGAN GENERAL HOSPITAL 25601 #495-37-1990 L1996 **IM** *020 †20

LACKEY, Nicole. 20 HOSPITAL DR, LOGAN REGIONAL MCR 25601 #055-02-1999 L2003 **FM** *020 †18

LOYNAB, Noor Ahmed. 396 DINGESS ST, GUYAN VALLEY HOSPITAL 25601 #572-05-1970 L1981 **IM** *020

MANUEL, Ernesto Castro. 396 DINGESS ST, 396 DINGESS STREET 25601 #748-07-1965 L1985 *020 ‡

MARZOUK, Kamel Attef. 20 HOSPITAL DR, LOGAN REG MED CTR 25601 #915-03-1993 L2006 **PCC** *020

MENARD, Pierre Riviere C. 20 HOSPITAL DR, ANESTHESIA DEPT 25601 #440-01-1965 L1990 **AN** *020 †05

NNACHI, Okpani Martin. 60 HOSPITAL DR 25601 #690-04-1996 L2005 **PD** *020

PADMANABAN, Ramanathan. 20 HOSPITAL DR, LOGAN GENERAL HOSPITAL 25601 #495-42-1977 L1985 **ORS HS** *020

PELAEZ, Abelerd A. 13 WHITE ST 25601 #748-07-1959 L1972 **R IM** *075

PEREZ, Robert Eguaras. 20 HOSPITAL DR, MEDICAL OFFICE BUILDING 25601 #748-01-1972 L2002 **IM** *020 †20

RAJA, Desingu Subbaraja. 20 HOSPITAL DR 25601 #495-04-1963 L1975 **ORS** *020 †40

RAO, Sathischandra N. 38 HOSPITAL DR 25601 #496-01-1976 L1982 **IM** *020

ROJAS, Samuel P. 143 1/2 STOLLINGS AVE 25601 #748-09-1966 L1982 **PD FM** *020

ROOPANI, Ghazala Quddus. 167 STOLLINGS AVE, STE A 25601 #704-06-1979 L1992 **NEP IM** *020 †20

RUSHDEN, Raymond O. 140 STOLLINGS AVE STE 2 25601 #915-02-1975 L1978 **GS GE** *020

SALEM, Ziad. 20 HOSPITAL DR 25601 #422-01-1999 L2005 **GE** *020 †20

SUBRAMANIAM, Subramaniam. 20 HOSPITAL DR 25601 #495-17-1967 L1978 **R** *020 †80

TIVITMAHAISOON, Chanchai. 38 HOSPITAL DR 25601 #891-02-1968 L1978 **GS** *020 †85

TUANQUIN, Narciso Bugarin. 112 BRIDGE ST 25601 #748-08-1974 L1981 **IM** *020 †20

VELOSO, Rogelio Q. 20 HOSPITAL DR, LOGAN GENERAL HOSPITAL 25601 #748-07-1967 L1985 **FM** *020

LOST CREEK – HARRISON

BECKSTEAD, Laurinda Raye. ■ 26385 #049-01-1986 L1987 **FM** *020 †18

LONGENECKER, Jo Ann. RR 1 BOX 57A2 26385 #051-04-1987 L1988 **FM** *020 †18

MC WHORTER, John Henry. RR 3 BOX 942, DUCK CREEK ROAD 26385 #055-01-1974 L1975 **FM IM** *020 †18

MADISON – BOONE

ATKINS, Robert Burton. 467 MAIN ST, STE 2 25130 #055-01-1977 L1978 **FM** *020 †18

CHANAA, Ziad Amin. 701 MADISON AVE, BOONE MEMORIAL HOSPITAL 25130 #847-08-1974 L1998 **IM** *020 †20

DIAL, Walter Everett. 701 MADISON AVE 25130 #055-02-1996 L1997 **IM** *100

HENSLEY, Jennifer Ann. 701 MADISON AVE 25130 #055-02-1997 L1999 **FM** *020 †20

LONG, Wenqing. 340 STATE ST 25130 #243-62-1982 L1998 **IM** *020 †20

SAYRE, Amy Parker. 471 MAIN ST, WV FAMILY WELLNESS CTR 25130 #055-01-2002 L2005 **FM** *100 †18

STOLLINGS, Ron Douglas. 467 MAIN ST STE 200 25130 #055-01-1982 L1985 **IM IMG** *020 †20

YUTIAMCO, Ernesto Tan. 701 MADISON AVE 25130 #748-11-1965 L1982 **FM EM** *020

MAIDSVILLE – MONONGALIA

LEVOY, Laura Leanne. ■ 26541 #047-20-2004 L2006 **EM** *100

MAN – LOGAN

BELLAM, R M. 600 E MCDONALD AVE 25635 #495-50-1963 L1977 **GP EM** *020 †16

CABAUATAN, Livia Nuevas. 600 E MCDONALD AVE, COMMUNITY HEALTH FOUNDATIO 25635 #748-07-1962 L1985 **FM EM** *020 ‡

CHEVY, Suthipan. 600 E MCDONALD AVE, CHF OF MAN 25635 #891-03-1970 L1976 **OBG** *020

LAYOS, Rolando Ugalde. 700 E MCDONALD AVE 25635 #748-01-1962 L1985 **GP** *020

LIMTON, Tawee Ray. PO BOX 777 25635 #891-03-1966 L1977 **GS** *020

LONG, Thomas Porter. 700 E MCDONALD AVE 25635 #051-04-1954 L1957 **FM** *020

MOHAN, Usha. 211 MAIN ST 25635 #495-21-1968 L1977 **GP** *020

ORTIZ-PEREZ, Julio. PO BOX 485 25635 #275-01-1931 L1971 **OBG OS** *100

RALLOS, Enrico Virtucio. 600 E MCDONALD AVE 25635 #748-07-1965 L1972 **FM** *020

SRICHAI, Prakob. 600 E MCDONALD AVE, COMMUNITY HEALTH FNDTN MAN 25635 #891-02-1967 L1980 **GS GP** *075 †85

SUTTIRATANA, Pimpa M. 600 E MCDONALD AVE, MAN 25635 #891-02-1970 L1980 **OBG** *020

TORDILLA, Plaridel Palma. 600 E MCDONALD AVE, COMMUNITY HEALTH FNDTN MAN 25635 #748-01-1964 L1983 **FM PD** *020

VIGO PAREDES, Tomas E. 600 E MCDONALD AVE 25635 #042-04-1989 L1994 **GP** *020

WALTERS, Randall Wayne. 600 E MCDONALD AVE, COMMUNITY HEALTH FOUNDATIO 25635 #047-20-1997 L2006 **FM** *020 †18

MARLINTON – POCAHONTAS

BULLARD, James Wilson. ■ 24954 #041-01-1962 L1992 **PYA P** *071

FRANKLIN, Morton Jerome. ■ 24954 #035-08-1954 L1999 **EM IM** *071 †16

LEVEAUX, Guy David. 603 9TH ST, PMH MEDICAL PRACTICE 24954 #039-01-1970 L1974 **FM LM** *020

WALKUP, Harry Ernest, Jr. 103 8TH ST 24954 #055-01-1975 L1982 **FM** *075 †18

MARTINSBURG – BERKELEY

AGARWAL, Akhilesh N. 510 BUTLER AVE, VA MEDICAL CENTER 25405 #495-05-1970 L1997 **IM** *020 †20

AGBAYANI, Ernesto H. 2000 FOUNDATION WAY, CITY HOSP STE 2400 25401 #748-10-1984 L1999 **FM** *020 †18

AGNIR, Betty Y. ■ 25401 #748-01-1962 L1980 **AN** *071

AGNIR, Orlando Ines. ■ 25401 #748-08-1962 L1974 **CD IM** *071

AHMED, Kalim. 115 AIKENS CTR STE 1 25404 #704-16-1989 L2003 **PCC SME** *020 †20 ‡

AHMED, Sayeed. 105 TAVERN RD 25401 #495-65-1971 L1987 **CD IM** *020

ALENCHERRY, Johny Rao. 115 AIKENS CTR STE 1 25404 #495-52-1980 L1997 **PUD IM** *020 †20

AL MASHAT, Jafar. 235 S WATER ST, EASTRIDGE HEALTH SYSTEMS 25401 #528-01-1969 L1997 **P** *020 †20

ALVAREZ RIVERA, Marcos N. PO BOX 1146, SHENANDOAH VALLEY MED CTR 25402 #737-05-1969 L2001 **PD END** *020 †55

AMARILLO, Rizalito A. CHARLESTOWN ROAD 25401 #748-07-1955 L1969 **FM GP** *071 †18

AMBROZ, Alexander. 51 STREET OF DREAMS 25403 #957-05-1980 L1985 **GP** *020 †70

ANDERSON, Stacey Almeida. 2010 DOCTOR OATES DR, STE 106 25401 #033-05-2001 L2006 **OBG** *100

ARNETT, Edward Fike. 2000 PROFESSIONAL CT STE C 25401 #055-01-1973 L1974 **PD** *020 †55

BAKHTIAR, James Abol H. 235 S WATER ST 25401 #051-01-1963 L1998 **P** *020 †75

BENAVIDES, Aurelio. 1004 SUSHRUTA DR STE B 25401 #264-04-1967 L1975 **U** *020 †95

BENEGALRAO, Yogini. RR 9, VA MEDICAL CENTER 25404 #496-38-1980 L1995 **FM END** *020 †20

BENJAMIN, Eugene Elliot. 510 BUTLER AVE, DEPT OF NEUROLOGY 25405 #067-01-1978 L1980 **N CN** *020 †75

BIRD, Kevin. RR 9, VETERANS AFFAIRS MEDICAL C 25404 #495-27-1982 L1990 **ON IM** *020 †20

BLANCO, John Louis. 1002 TAVERN RD 25401 #035-03-1994 L2000 **DR** *020 †80

BLUNDELL, George Phelan. VA MED CTR 25401 #067-01-1948 L1961 **PTH** *071 †50

BOTROS, Emad Maher. 2010 DOCTOR OATES DR, STE 101 25401 #915-02-1988 L1998 **IM** *020 †20

BOWEN, Robert Evans. 2000 FOUNDATION WAY, STE 2400 25401 #016-11-1978 L1982 **PUD CCM** *020 †20

BOWERS, Timothy Keefe. 2008 PROFESSIONAL CT 25401 #055-01-1968 L1978 **IM ON** *020 †20

BROWN, James Edward. 2010 DOCTOR OATES DR, STE 106 25401 #047-07-1974 L1994 **OBG** *020 †30

CARRIER, James Marshall. 1004 SUSHRUTA DR, STE C 25401 #055-01-1978 L1979 **GS** *020 †85

CERVIERI, Christina Leigh. 510 BUTLER AVE, VAMC DPT OF ORTHOPEDICS 25405 #005-14-1998 L2008 **OSM** *020

CHANG, Joyce Ruixin. ■ 25401 #243-36-1983 L2002 **IM** *020 †20 ‡

CHENO, Anteneh H. 510 BUTLER AVE, MARTINSBURG VA MED CTR 25405 #366-02-1984 L1998 **IM** *020 †20

CHO, Kenneth Ok. VA MEDICAL CENTER, .RLES TOWN ROAD 25401 #583-02-1956 L1963 **ORS** *020 †40

CHOUDRY, Maksed Sultan. 510 BUTLER AVE, VA MEDICAL CENTER, 613-11E 25405 #160-02-1981 L1997 **FPG** *020 †20

COHEN, Edwin Eli. 510 BUTLER AVE, MARTINSBURG VA 25405 #041-02-1965 L1991 **GS** *071 †85 ‡

COURTNEY, John Wm. 510 BUTLER AVE, VA MEDICAL CENTER 25405 #539-04-1967 L1976 **AN** *020 †05

CRUDEN-PARHAM, Consuela. 99 TAVERN RD, SHENANDDOAH VLY MED SYS 25401 #305-01-2003 L2007 **OBG** *100

CRUZ, Sylvia Santos. 215 S LOUISIANA AVE, SYLVIA S CRUZ DO 25401 #028-79-1993, ▲ L1997 **OBG PME** *020

DANAI, Pajman Alexander. 115 AIKENS CTR 25404 #010-01-2000 L2007 **PCC** *020 †20

DELANOY, Anne Elizabeth. 99 TAVERN RD 25401 #051-04-2003 L2006 **FM** *020 †18

DEL GIORNO, Louis John. 2630 AIKENS CTR 25404 #561-08-1981 L1991 **FM** *075 †18

DIDDEN, David Gregory. 99 TAVERN RD 25401 #051-01-1999 L2004 **FM** *020 †18

DINH, Anthony Tung. RR 9, MARTINSBURG VA MEDICAL CTR 25404 #941-01-1967 L1983 **ID IM** *020 †20

DOYLE, John J. CHARLESTOWN RD 25401 #067-01-1951 L1952 *020

DRAKE, Holly Ann. ■ 25401 #055-01-2008 *012

DRAPER, John A. 309 MEDICAL CT 25401 #047-06-1976 L1984 **ORS** *020 †40

DUFFY, Richard N, III. RR 9 25404 #036-01-1976 L1976 **IM FM** *020 †20

DUFFY, Tressie. 101 MARCLEY DR 25401 #055-01-1996 L1999 **FM** *020 †18

DUMITRACHE, Angela. 99 TAVERN RD 25401 #781-01-1992 L2003 **CHP ADP** *020 †75

ELLIS, John Wesley. TAVERN & DRY RUN RDS 25401 #010-01-1985 L1991 **FM** *020 †18

ESTIGOY, Romulo J. 121 N COLLEGE ST 25401 #748-01-1959 L1979 **IM OS** *020

FISHKIN, David L. 2010 OATES DR, STE 103 25401 #035-08-1985 L1992 **GE IM** *020 †20

FLAX, Stephen Howard. 1008 WINCHESTER AVE 25401 #035-46-1985 L1999 **D** *020 †20,15

FLEMING, Martin Patrick. CITY HOSPITAL INC, DEPT OF RADIOLOGY 25401 #539-02-1962 L1979 **DR OS** *020 †80

FOGLE, Everett S. ■ 25401 #016-42-1943 L1952 **GP** *071
FOGLE, Jerry Allen. 2002 PROFESSIONAL CT 25401 #023-07-1974 L1983 **OPH** *020 †35
FUNK, Cathy Marie. 65 HEALTH CARE LN 25401 #055-01-1998 L1999 **IM** *020 †20
GAVIRIA, Diana M. 101 MARCLEY DR 25401 #038-06-1989 L1993 **FM** *074 †18
GEROMIN-AMBROZ, Clara. ■ 25403 #561-24-1980 L2006 **OM** *071 ‡
GERVACIO, Danilo Jose L. 94 OLD MILL RD 25401 #748-08-1980 L1994 **AN PME** *020 †05
GILL, Satinder Pal Singh. VET ADMIN HOSP MED CTR, DEPT NUCLEAR MED 25401 #495-36-1971 L1980 **NM IM** *020 †28
GLASSFORD, Justin Paul. ■ 25404 #055-01-2007 **FP** *012
GREENBERG, Michael David. RR 9, MARTINSBURG VA MEDICAL CEN 25404 #035-09-1988 L1989 **CD EM** *020
GREENSPOON, Laurence S. 510 BUTLER AVE, VA MEDICAL CLINIC TEAM 1 25405 #010-01-1981 L1987 **FM** *020 †18
GUNDAVDA, Hemant P. 99 TAVERN RD 25401 #495-01-1970 L2006 **PD** *020 †55
HABTE, Bethesaida Tafari. 510 BUTLER AVE, VA MEDICAL CENTER 25405 #366-03-1991 L2001 **IM** *020 †20
HAMILTON, Alan F. VET ADMIN MED CTR, DEPT MED 25401 #010-03-1971 L1976 **IM** *071
HAMILTON, Frank A. 1125 CIRCLE DR 25401 #051-04-1952 L1953 **FM** *020
HANNA, Daniel Attia. VET ADMIN CTR, DEPT OF SURGERY 25401 #330-02-1959 L1973 **PM GS** *020
HARDY, John Cullen. 2010 DOCTOR OATES DR, STE 101 25401 #021-01-1988 L2000 **IM** *020 †20
HARPOLD, Robert Morris. 65 HEALTH CARE LN, PANHANDLE MEDICAL ASSOCIAT 25401 #055-01-2001 L2004 **IM** *020 †20
HENDRICKS, D Ewell. TAVERN & DRY RUN RDS 25401 #051-04-1957 L1962 **GS** *020 †85
HILL, James Harvey, Jr. RR 9, VA HOSPITAL 25404 #008-01-1964 L1970 **P IM** *020 †20,75
HOE, George Li Shong. 510 BUTLER AVE, VAMC 25405 #209-01-1988 L1998 **IM** *020 †20
HOPKINS, Krista Lynn. 99 TAVERN RD, SHENANDOAH WOMENS HEALTH 25401 #055-01-2001 L2004 **OBG** *020
HUMMA, Gerard Theodore. CHARLESTOWN RD 25401 #041-13-1956 L1957 **GP IMG** *071
HURST, Erik Brian. ■ 25403 #055-02-2003 L2007 **D** *020 †15
IQBAL, Shaheen. 115 AIKENS CTR STE 1 25404 #704-02-1987 L1997 **PCC SME** *020 †20
JACQUES, Charles Halsey. 2500 FOUNDATION WAY, WVU HEALTH SCIENCE CENTER 25401 #025-12-1981 L1993 **FM** *030 †18
JALAZO, Jesse B. 1002 SUSHRUTA DR, MARTINSBURG INTERNAL 25401 #041-01-1979 L1985 **IM** *020 †20
JIMENEZ DUMIT, Hernando. ■ 25403 #264-01-1966 L1974 **PTH PCP** *020 †50 ‡
JOE, Caroline E. 315 PENDLETON DR, MARTINSBURG PEDIATRICS 25401 #561-14-1994 L2004 **PD** *020 †55
JONES, Dawn Reed. 99 TAVERN RD 25401 #005-11-1982 L2002 **IM** *020 †20
JONES, Matthew Philip. 2000 FOUNDATION WAY, MAINE GENERAL MEDICAL CENT 25401 #007-02-1989 L1992 **PD** *020 †55
JUNG, Hojoon. 1002 TAVERN RD 25401 #025-01-1997 L2003 **DR** *020 †80
JURAND, Joseph Anthony. 99 TAVERN RD 25401 #010-03-1975 L1993 **P** *020 †75
KAMATH, C Ramadas. 510 BUTLER AVE, VA MED CTR-SURG SVC 25405 #495-04-1959 L1998 **HNS OTO** *020 †45
KAPOOR, Mohit. 510 BUTLER AVE 25405 #496-09-1990 L1999 **NEP** *020 †20
KHAN, Shahnoor Ali. 2000 FOUNDATION WAY, STE 3500 25401 #496-27-1994 L2001 **FM** *020 †18
KHATTRI, Ashok. RR 9, MEDICAL CENTER 25404 #495-41-1977 L1997 **PUD** *020 †20
KIGGUNDU, Edward William. 2000 FOUNDATION WAY, SUITIE 1100 25401 #041-02-1996 L2005 **RO** *020 †80
KONGKANAND, Apichat. VA MED CT 25401 #572-05-1969 L1977 **U** *020 †95
KOSURI, Ramakrishna Raju. 309 MEDICAL CT, ROBINWOOD ORTHOPEDIC 25401 #495-50-1989 L2002 **PM** *020 †60
LA MONACA, Gianluca. 99 TAVERN RD 25401 #561-23-1990 L2001 **CHP** *020 †75
LANDES, Harold Brian. 1008 WINCHESTER AVE, DERMATOLOGY ASSOCIATES 25401 #038-06-1963 L1978 **D** *071
LARUSSO, Daryl Michael. 2500 HOSPITAL DRIVE, CITY HOSPITAL INC. 25401 #016-43-1985 L1988 **FM EM** *020 †18
LEMPERG, Rudolf Karl. ■ 25404 #154-01-1949 L1981 **ORS** *020
LEUNG, Albert Ki-Kin. 1001 SUSHRUTA DR 25401 #063-01-1979 L1994 **OBG** *020 †30
LOBATON, Cherry B. 1004 SUSHRUTA DR, STE D 25401 #748-13-1984 L1998 **FM** *020 †18
LOPEZ, Mary Ruth Motomal. 2010 DOCTOR OATES DR, STE 102 25401 #748-01-1986 L2006 **FM** *020 †18
LYNCH, Robert John. 311 MEDICAL CT 25401 #033-05-1976 L1983 **IM AM** *020
MAC QUEEN, Ian James. RR 9, VA MEDICAL CENTER 25404 #917-23-1950 L1981 **TRS ORS** *071
MALLEA, Jorge Martin. 510 BUTLER AVE, RM 4A146 25405 #737-05-1993 L2000 **PCC SME** *020 †20 ‡
MALLOTT, Stephen James. 99 TAVERN RD, P O B 1146 25401 #041-12-1978 L1986 **IM PHP** *020 †20
MARKOVIC, Peter R. RR 9, VA MEDICAL CENTER 25404 #957-02-1954 L1992 **DR** *020 †80
MATHIEU, Michael Eric. 1008 WINCHESTER AVE 25401 #010-03-1984 L2001 **D ID** *020 †20,15
MC CARTHY, Ryan Timothy. 1002 SUSHRUTA DR, MARTINSBURG INTERNAL 25401 #055-01-2002 L2005 **MPD** *020 †20
MC CUNE, William R. ■ 25401 #051-04-1946 L1947 **U** *071 †95
MCLAUGHLIN, Aaron Matthew. ■ 25404 #055-01-2008 *012
MC LAUGHLIN, William Henr. 2010 DOCTOR OATES DR, STE 101 25401 #041-12-1989 L1995 **CD** *020 †20
MC LELLAN, Sarah M. RR 9, VA MEDICAL CENTER 25404 #021-01-1981 L2007 **AN** *075 †05
MC QUEEN, Robert Clarkson. 1008 WINCHESTER AVE 25401 #041-09-1973 L1986 **AI IM** *020 †20,03
MEANY, Mark Edward. 510 BUTLER AVE, VAMC 25405 #038-40-1973 L1979 **EM** *071 †16
MEHTA, Prashant Hasmukh. 510 BUTLER AVE 25405 #495-52-1973 L1988 **U** *020
MENON, Satish K. 94 OLD MILL RD 25401 #055-75-1989, ▲ L1994 **AN PME** *020 †05
MISAILIDIS, Dimitri. 1002 TAVERN RD 25401 #418-02-1979 L1989 **DR IM** *020 †80
MOFFITT, John S. ■ 25404 #041-02-1949 L1953 **R OS** *071
MORAN, Robert E, III. 510 BUTLER AVE, VA MEDICAL CENTER, 613-11E 25405 #051-01-1984 L1988 **FM** *020 †18
MORGAN, John Doyle. VA MED CTR, DEPT MED SERV 25401 #028-02-1961 L1990 **PUD IM** *020 †20
MORIN, Garrison Vasile. 321 LUTZ AVE 25404 #023-12-1981 L2005 **OTO SMO** *071 †45 ‡
MORRIS, Linda Jane. ■ 25404 #035-06-1978 L1981 **IM** *030 †20
MORRIS, Samuel David. 101 MARCLEY DR 25401 #055-01-1980 L1981 **FM** *020 †18
MURPHY, Brian Patrick. 829 E MOLER AVE 25404 #055-01-1991 L1995 **AN** *075 †05
MURRAY, Ethelann. RR 9, VA MEDICAL CENTER - 160 25404 #035-01-1966 L1967 **IM HEM** *030 †20
NAIR, Ratna Leela. 510 BUTLER AVE, VA HOSP 25405 #495-65-1975 L2002 **IM** *020 †20
NAKAMURA, Monica Suzan. RR 9, VETERANS AFFAIRS MEDICAL C 25404 #054-04-1989 L1991 **ID** *020 †20
NEGERI, Aster. RR 9, VA MEDICAL CTR 25404 #366-01-1988 L1998 **IM** *020 †20
NGANGA, Jackson Maina. 99 TAVERN RD 25401 #577-01-1988 L2003 **CCP** *020 †55
NIETO, Ernesto. 510 BUTLER AVE, SURGEICAL SVC (112) 25405 #649-01-1966 L1977 **ORS** *020 †40 ‡
OWUNNA, Anthony Uchenna. 99 TAVERN RD 25401 #690-12-1992 L2000 **IM** *020 †20
PADMANABHA-RAO, V. 501 BUTLER AVE 25405 #495-09-1961 L1973 **GS TS** *020 †85
PALKOT, John Sylvester. TAVERN & DRY RUN RDS 25401 #055-01-1964 L1965 **FM PD** *071
PALOMO, Florecita Peralta. 510 BUTLER AVE, VA MED CTR 25405 #748-01-1969 L1978 **GP** *020
PALUMBO, Jessica Anne. 1006 TAVERN RD STE 100, FAST TRACK ANESTHESIA ASSO 25401 #041-13-1996 L2004 **AN** *020 †05
PARK, Chan Dong. 1002 SUSHRUTA DR, MARTINSBURG INTERNAL 25401 #035-46-1979 L1993 **IM** *020 †20
PARK, Jane C. 1002 SUSHRUTA DR, MARTINSBURG INTERNAL 25401 #055-01-1980 L1993 **IM** *020 †20
PAU, Rosanna Kwingshun. 172 WINSLOW DR 25404 #041-15-2000 L2004 **EM** *020 †16
PICKARD, Julia Patricia. 101 MARCLEY DR, BERKLEY FAMILY MEDICINE 25401 #010-01-1997 L2004 **FM** *020
PITTALUGA, Juan Manuel. 2010 DOCTOR OATES DR, STE 101 25401 #308-02-1983 L1992 **IM CD** *020 †20
PRAGANI, Babulal. CHARLESTOWN RD 25401 #495-01-1957 L1988 **GS** *071 †85
PRICE, H Donald. 315 PENDLETON DR 25401 #028-02-1974 L1988 **PD** *020 †55
PROMERSBERGER, Mark E. 2002 PROFESSIONAL CT 25401 #051-04-1991 L1998 **OPH** *020 †35
QUE, Chris Clinton Tan. 2010 DOCTOR OATES DR, STE 105 25401 #748-10-1993 L2001 **FPG** *012 †20
RAFAT, Ghulam Faruk. RR 9, VAMC 25404 #118-01-1962 L1973 **IM** *071
RAMANNA, Nanjappa. CHARLESTOWN ROAD 25401 #495-09-1960 L1975 **ORS** *071
RECHT, Keith Arnold. 1004 SUSHRUTA DR STE A 25401 #055-01-1975 L1977 **U** *020 †95
REESE, Daniel Burton. 2010 DOCTOR OATES DR, STE 101 25401 #051-01-1992 L1998 **CD** *020 †20
REIDY, Terrence Jos. 99 TAVERN RD, PO BOX 1146 25401 #016-43-1978 L1985 **IM HO** *020 †20
REISENWEBER, Harvey D. 101 MARCLEY DR 25401 #055-01-1965 L1970 **FM** *020 †18
RENZI, Randolph Hector. 2010 DOCTOR OATES DR 25401 #010-02-1982 L1995 **CD** *020 †20
REYNA, Roberto C. 65 HEALTH CARE LN 25401 #737-09-1991 L1998 **IM** *020 †20
REZAIAN, Michael M. 2010 OATES DR, STE 104 25401 #308-10-1985 L1990 **RHU PPR** *020 †20
RICE, Anthony Kieler, Jr. 101 MARCLEY DR 25401 #035-06-1998 L2004 **FM** *020 †18
ROSENBERG, Mervyn T. RR 3 BOX 185 25404 #836-01-1957 L1977 **GP** *020
RUDOLPH, Karen Jon. 1002 SUSHRUTA DR, MARTINSBURG INTERNAL 25401 #051-04-1979 L1985 **IM IMG** *020 †20
RYAN, Philip Jos. 2000 FOUNDATION WAY, STE 3100 25401 #017-20-1976 L2003 **DIA END** *020 †20
RYAN, Yasmin Carina. 510 BUTLER AVE, VAMC 25405 #550-02-2000 L2003 **IM** *020 †20 ‡
SABADO, Francisco D, Jr. 781 ROCK CLIFF DR 25401 #748-01-1965 L1975 **OTO AI** *020
SAID, Nicholas. ■ 25402 #055-01-2008 L2008 *012
SAID, Said Edward. 1008 TAVERN RD 25401 #915-02-1969 L1991 **ORS OM** *020 †40
SALUJA, Sanjay. 1002 TAVERN RD 25401 #495-53-1989 L2004 **DR** *020 †80
SETHI, Elisabeth M. 510 BUTLER AVE, VAMC (11G) 25405 #409-06-1983 L1985 **IMG IM** *020 †20
SHAMBLIN, Jack F, III. 94 OLD MILL RD 25401 #055-01-1990 L1994 **AN PME** *020 †05
SHAPIRO, Raymond Marc. 142 N QUEEN ST, STE 103 25401 #035-47-1987 L1995 **P** *020 †75
SLOANE, Yancey Alvin. ■ 25403 #010-03-1964 L1964 **U** *020 †95
SOE, Ma S. RR 9, VA MEDICAL CENTER 25404 #209-01-1989 L1996 **IM** *020 †20
SOMPALLI, Bala Prasad. RR 9, V.A. MED CEN, PSYCHIATRY D 25404 #495-58-1978 L1994 **N** *020
SPALT, Harry Alfred. 2010 OATES DR, STE 105 25401 #023-01-1963 L1985 **N** *071
SPEROW, Clifford. 105 S RALEIGH ST 25401 #051-04-1956 L1961 **ORS OSM** *071 †40
SPILSBURY, Paul Roscoe. 2010 DOCTOR OATES DR, STE 107 25401 #049-01-1968 L2000 **N CN** *020 †75
STACEY, Michael John. 2001 STREET OF DREAMS, FIRST PRIORITY 25401 #023-12-1990 L1994 **OS** *020
STATUM, Kasey Avis. 99 TAVERN RD 25401 #010-03-1999 L2005 **PD** *020
STEIN, Terry Robert. ■ 25404 #055-01-2008 *012
STILLWAGON, Paul Krehl. 1008 WINCHESTER AVE 25401 #051-01-1981 L1986 **AI PD** *020 †55,03
STRAUCH, Robert Salade. 2000 PROFESSIONAL CT, STE A 25401 #038-06-1968 L1977 **GS TS** *020 †85
STRUTHERS, Courtney H. 99 TAVERN RD 25401 #055-01-1993 L1997 **IM** *020 †20
SULICA, Lucian. RR 9, VA MEDICAL CENTER -160 25404 #781-03-1957 L1975 **IM** *071 †20
TAMARA, Antonio. ■ 25401 #264-04-1962 L1977 **PTH** *062 †50
TAN, Vigilio M. 219 S SPRING ST 25401 #748-01-1962 L1983 **OPH** *020
TEICHMAN, Peter Gerard. 215 S LOUISIANA AVE, HAHN MEDICAL PRACTICE, INC 25401 #025-12-1992 L1999 **FM** *020 †18
TOWNSEND, Clarence V. 125 E KING ST 25401 #051-04-1949 L1950 **IM CD** *071
TRAN, Ngoc Dung. 510 BUTLER AVE, VAMC 25405 #396-11-1971 L1974 **IM OM** *020
TRAWICK, Jamika W. 2000 PROFESSIONAL CT, STE C 25401 #012-21-2001 L2004 **PD** *020
VAGHEI, Reza. VA MED CTR 25401 #517-01-1958 L1978 **TS VS** *020 †85,90
VAN DONGEN, Philip Clark. ■ 25403 #035-08-1988 L1997 **EM** *020 †20
VANNOSTRAND, Keriann Mari. ■ 25401 #055-01-2008 *012
VARGA, Karoly. 2000 FOUNDATION WAY, STE 3200 25401 #473-01-1978 L2004 **N** *020 †75
VELTMAN, John Collett. 35 AIKENS CTR 25404 #051-04-1980 L1995 **EM UM** *020 †16
VOLCJAK, Edward Eugene. 94 OLD MILL RD 25401 #023-01-1968 L1981 **AN PME** *071 †05
VONGXAIBURANA, Marneerat. VA MED CTR, DEPT MED 25401 #891-01-1967 L1975 **IM** *020 †20
WAGNER, Trumer James, Jr. DRY RUN RUN, CITY HOSP, EMER DEPT 25402 #023-01-1992 L1995 **EM** *020 †16
WANGER, Helge Alexander. 99 TAVERN RD 25401 #055-01-1966 L1967 **OBG** *020 †30
WEAR, William Edward. 2000 PROFESSIONAL CT, STE C 25401 #001-06-1991 L2000 **PD** *020 †55
WELCH, Paul Gregory. 103 MARCLEY DR 25401 #023-12-1983 L2004 **NEP IM** *020 †20
WENZEL, Frederick George. 1008 WINCHESTER AVE, DERMATOLOGY ASSOCIATES 25401 #036-07-1993 L1997 **D** *020 †15

WHYTE, John Jeffrey. 855 CAPERTON BLVD, QUADMED 25403 #654-01-1999 L2003 **FM** *020 †18
WILLIAMSON, Brandt H. DRY RUN ROAD, CITY HOSPITAL 25401 #051-01-1992 L1995 **EM** *020 †16
WINFREY, Charles Jack. 510 BUTLER AVE, VA MED CTR 25405 #051-01-1972 L1982 **P** *020 †75
XIE, Jianming. VA MEDICAL CENTER, NHCU-B RM 108 25401 #243-33-1982 L1999 **IM IMG** *020 †20
YANES, Bahaa Aldin. RR 9, VAMC 25404 #875-01-1976 L1989 **PTH** *020 †50
YELLOTT, Chesley W. 99 TAVERN RD 25401 #024-07-1976 L2000 **FM** *020 †18
ZABAT-SANTOS, Gracia C. VA MED CTR 25401 #748-10-1975 L1979 **IM IMG** *020 †20

MASON — MASON

ROQUE, Edilberto Dalmacio. ■ 25260 #748-07-1956 L1985 *020
TAYENGCO, Robert G. 11 N 2ND ST 25260 #748-11-1990 L1997 **IM** *020 †20

MAYBEURY — MCDOWELL

BENDY, Robert Harold, Jr. MAYBEURY CLINIC 24861 #041-02-1961 L1991 **IM ID** *075

MCMECHEN — MARSHALL

BORBELY, Leslie J. ■ 26040 #473-04-1949 L1967 **P** *020

MEADOW BRIDGE — FAYETTE

GWINN, James Alexis. ■ 25976 #047-06-1963 L1979 **EM** *072
JONES, Curran Lyle. ■ 25976 #055-75-2001 ▲ L2004 **AN** *020 †05 ‡
SHAH, Rajnikant Chandulal. 1502 MEADOW BRIDGE RD 25976 #495-01-1971 L1977 **GS** *020 †85

MILL CREEK — RANDOLPH

RAHMAN, Aamer. PO BOX 247, 250 26280 #704-01-1993 L2000 **PCC** *012 †20

MILTON — CABELL

BAILEY, Shelley Rene. 1 HARBOUR WAY 25541 #055-02-2000 L2003 **FM** *020 †18 ‡
GRADY, Joseph Edward, II. ■ 25541 #017-20-1994 L1999 **IM** *020 †20
MCQUINN, Laura Emily. ■ 25541 #055-02-2008 *012
PAULEY, Amanda Nicole. ■ 25541 #055-02-2008 *012
REVELL, David. 308 E MAIN ST, GRANT MEDICAL CTR 25541 #050-02-1975 L1976 **FM** *020
RICHMOND, Lewis Cass, Jr. ■ 25541 #023-01-1953 L1954 **GP** *071
THACKER, Anthony Wayne. 1155 MAIN ST, POST OFFICE BOX 39 25541 #055-02-1990 L1993 **FM** *020 †18
THACKER, Teresa Rolfe. 1155 MAIN ST 25541 #055-02-1990 L1993 **FM** *020 †18

MINERAL WELLS — WOOD

TOWARNICKY, Marvin Jos. ■ 26150 #062-01-1955 L1956 **GP** *071

MONTGOMERY — FAYETTE

ACKLIN, Traci Elizabeth. 401 6TH AVE STE 100 25136 #055-01-1998 L2001 **PD** *020 †55
AGUILAR, Enrique. 6TH AV 25136 #649-01-1945 L1957 **GP GS** *071
ATASSI, Sammar. 401 6TH AVE 25136 #875-01-1989 L1993 **IM EM** *020 †20
BHIRUD, Ravindranath H. 401 6TH AVE 25136 #495-28-1974 L1984 **IM CD** *020 †20
BIRCKHEAD, Roland S. 401 6TH AVE 25136 #055-04-1952 L1953 **GP** *020
BOWE, Ronald Dee, III. 401 6TH AVE, MONTGOMERY MEDCORP 25136 #055-02-2001 L2002 **MPD** *100 †20,55
CASTILLO, Renato. 401 6TH AVE 25136 #748-01-1956 L1977 **EM** *071
DAVIS, Samuel R. 401 6TH AVE 25136 #055-02-1983 L1984 **DR GP** *020 ‡
DWYER, Kenneth Lee. 401 6TH AVE, RADIOLOGY DEPT 25136 #051-04-1966 L1983 **R NM** *020 †80,28
HABASH, Afif Salim. 401 6TH AVE 25136 #605-01-1971 L1976 **PD** *020 †55
JUGO, Felipe E. 401 6TH AVE, STE 304B 25136 #748-08-1963 L1975 **GP** *020
MIR, Saghir-Ur Rehman. 401 6TH AVE 25136 #704-01-1965 L1976 **ORS HS** *020 †40
MIRZA, Abdul Majid. 401 6TH AVE STE 204 25136 #704-01-1960 L1972 **IM END** *071
NOLASCO, Cornelio C. 406 6TH AVE STE D-30, 301 MONTGOMERY GENERAL 25136 #748-02-1957 L1973 **U** *071
PRIDDY, Myra Denise. 401 6TH AVE, MONTGOMERY GENERAL HOSPITA 25136 #055-02-1995 L1998 **FM** *020 †18
RAMIREZ, La Conmemoracion. 401 6TH AVE 25136 #748-01-1959 L1974 **PD HEM** *020 †55
RAMIREZ, Rolando C. 311 ADAMS ST 25136 #748-01-1959 L1976 **IM CD** *020
SANKARI, Mohammed. 401 6TH AVE, MONTGOMERY GENERAL HOSPITA 25136 #605-01-1982 L1994 **IM** *020 †20
SCARLATESCU, Sorin. 401 6TH AVE, STE 102 25136 #781-01-1998 L2002 **IM** *100 †20
TIMBAYAN, Adin L. 411 WASHINGTON ST 25136 #748-01-1970 L1978 **GS AS** *020
TIMBAYAN, Victoria Santos. 401 6TH AVE 25136 #748-01-1969 L1978 **AN** *020

MOOREFIELD — HARDY

ANANTHARAMAN, Priya. 8 LEE ST, MOOREFIELD CKD CLINIC 26836 #496-23-1998 L2003 **NEP** *020 †20
MASIH, Rajan B. 747 N MAIN ST, STE E 26836 #495-43-1990 L1997 **EM** *020 †20
MASIH, Ravi Bakhshish. 747 N MAIN ST, MOUNTAIN MEDICAL PC, PLLC 26836 #035-08-1994 L2001 **EM IM** *020 †20

REXRODE, Carmen Rebecca. 112 KUYKENDALL LN, CLINIC, INC 26836 #055-01-1988 L1992 **FM** *020 †18
RIGGLEMAN, Michael Paige. 112 KUYKENDALL LN 26836 #023-01-1985 L1991 **FM** *020 †18
SCHMITT, Susan Ann W. 8 LEE ST 26836 #056-05-1975 L1976 **FM** *020 †18

MORGANTOWN — MONONGALIA

ABDEL-AZIZ, Mohsen Hassan. ■ 26505 #915-04-1981 **AN** *100
ABORAYA, Ahmed Sayed. 930 CHESTNUT RIDGE RD, CHESTNUT RIDGE HOSPITAL 26505 #915-02-1977 L1994 **P** *040
ABOU-SAMRA, Muhammad N. 510 MEDICAL CENTER DR, MARY BABB RANDOLPH CTR 26505 #875-01-1989 L2000 **AN** *020 †05
ABRAHAM, Jame. 510 MEDICAL CENTER DR, MARY BABB RANDOLPH CTR 26505 #495-44-1991 L2000 **HO** *020 †20
ABRO, Masroor Anwar. ■ 26505 #704-08-2003 **IM** *012
ACHESON, Todd Munro. ■ 26505 #654-01-2007 **IM** *012
ADAMSKI, Thomas Robt. 510 MEDICAL CENTER DR, MARY BABB RANDOLPH CTR 26505 #055-01-1982 L1984 **FM** *020 †20,75
ADKINS, Farrell Christoph. 1600 UNIVERSITY AVE, DEPT OF SURGERY 26506 #055-01-2006 **GS** *012
AGARWAL, Shashi. MEDICAL CENTER DRIVE PEDS 26506 #495-49-1979 **PD** *100
AHMAD, Sameen. ■ 26508 #704-25-2005 **P** *100
AHMAD, Sharjeel. HEALTH SCIENCE CENTER, RM 2181 26506 #704-25-2002 L2007 **ID** *012 †20
AHMED, Nasir Uddin. ■ 26505 #160-02-1980 L2007 **PD** *100
ALAZZAZ, Abdulkader A. 510 MEDICAL CENTER DR, MARY BABB RANDOLPH CTR 26505 #797-03-1989 L1999 **DR** *020 †80
ALBERT, Melissa Ann. 930 CHESTNUT RIDGE RD, WEST VIRGINIA UNIV HOSPITA 26505 #055-01-2001 L2006 **P** *100
ALBRINK, Margaret J. WV UNIVERSITY, HEALTH SCIENCE CTR S MED 26505 #008-01-1946 L1961 **IM END** *071
AL-BUKEIRAT, Faisal A. ■ 26507 #575-01-1986 L1993 **GE HEP** *020 †20
ALDERMAN, Frank Wayne. 605 VALLEY VIEW DR 26505 #055-01-1997 L1998 **UCM** *020 †16
ALEXANDER, Allison Bahar. 1192 PINEVIEW DR 26505 #020-12-1995 L2003 **OBG** *020 †30
AL-HASANI, Nada Al-Kabir. ■ 26505 #055-01-2005 **IM** *100
ALLEN, Anna Margaret. PO BOX 9190, 3860 HEALTH SCIENCE S 26506 #055-01-2000 L2003 **OM** *020 †18
ALLEN, Dennis Wayne. 2171 LAKESIDE ESTS 26508 #055-01-1980 L1981 **AN** *020 †05
ALLEN, Joel V. 1200 J D ANDERSON DR 26505 #055-01-1971 L1971 **P MDM** *030 †75
ALLINDER, Maureen. 930 CHESTNUT RIDGE RD, CHESTNUT RIDGE HOSPITAL 26505 #020-12-1988 L1995 **P EM** *075
ALMEIDA, Nicole. MEDICAL CENTER DR 26506 #305-01-2006 **P** *012
ALMUBARAK, Mohammed. ■ 26505 #010-01-2003 L2005 **HO** *012 †20
ALTAHA, Ramin. ■ 26508 #409-21-1994 L2002 **HO** *020 †20
ALTIZER, Melanie Dawn. ■ 26504 #055-01-2002 L2006 **OBG** *012
AMIN, Ansuya A. 1200 J D ANDERSON DR 26505 #495-36-1968 L2001 **DR GP** *062 †80
ANDERSON, David Mark. 710 VENTURE DR 26508 #055-01-1990 L1991 **EM** *020 †16
ANIS, Amir. ■ 26505 #704-02-1993 L2005 **HO** *012 †20
ANSARI, Hossein. PO BOX 9180, MEDICAL CENTER DR 26506 #517-10-1997 **TY N** *012
APPLEWHITE, Douglas A. 255 SCOTT AVE 26508 #935-01-1974 L1990 **NS** *012
ARBOGAST, James Grey. 510 MEDICAL CENTER DR, MARY BABB RANDOLPH CTR 26505 #055-01-1976 L1977 **FM** *040 †18
ARCHINAL, Jeffrey Allen. PO BOX 9214, DEPARTMENT OF PEDIATRICS 26506 #038-44-2008 **PD** *012
ARDITO, Alison. ■ 26508 #047-06-2007 **PD** *012
ARMENI, Mark Anthony. 510 MEDICAL CENTER DR, MARY BABB RANDOLPH CTR 26505 #038-40-1988 L1994 **OTO** *020 †45
ARMISTEAD, Drury Lacy. ■ 26508 #051-04-1998 L2004 **D** *100 †20,15
ARMISTEAD, Niti Singh. 510 MEDICAL CENTER DR, MARY BABB RANDOLPH CTR 26505 #023-01-1993 L1998 **IM** *020 †20
ARSHAD, Amina. MEDICAL CENTER DR 26506 #704-25-2000 **IM** *100 †20
ARSHAD, Hassan. ■ 26505 #025-07-2005 L2007 **OTO** *012
ARTHURS, Charles Brian. 1197 VAN VOORHIS RD, WEDGEWOOD FAMILY PRACTICE 26505 #055-01-1985 L1986 **FM FPG** *020 †18
ASATO, Hiroaki. W VA UNIV HOSP, DEPT MED 26506 #572-07-1967 L1976 **CD IM** *020 †20
ASHCRAFT, Harold G. MEDICAL CTR DR - STADIUM D 26505 #055-01-1983 L1987 **CLP** *020 †50
ASHLEY, Jeffrey Vernon. 510 MEDICAL CENTER DR, MARY BABB RANDOLPH CTR 26505 #055-01-1985 L1986 **FM** *040 †18
ASHRAF, Mohammed. 200 WEDGEWOOD DR, STE 204 26505 #704-01-1970 L1979 **GO OBG** *020 †30
ATTAALLAH, Ahmed Fikry. ■ 26505 #915-02-1994 L2004 **AN** *020 †05
AUBER, Miklos Laszlo. WV UNIVERSITY, DEPT MED 26506 #473-01-1977 L1988 **ON IM** *020 †20
AYOUBI, Susan Renee. ■ 26505 #055-01-2008 *012
BAILEY, Nathanael Glen. ■ 26506 #055-01-2005 L2006 **PTH** *012
BAKER, Jeffrey C. ■ 26505 #048-14-2007 **OTO** *012
BAKER, Maurice Wynne. ■ 26505 #055-01-1990 **GPM** *100
BAKER, Vicki Vaughan. 1192 PINEVIEW DR 26505 #036-01-1980 L2005 **GO GYN** *020 †30
BAKHTAWAR, Humayun. MEDICAL CENTER DR, WV UNIV SCH MED 26506 #704-25-2003 **GS** *012
BALASKO, Bridgette Galye. ■ 26508 #055-01-2007 L2007 **P** *012
BALIAN, Arpy Arbi. ■ 26501 #875-02-1974 L1982 **PDC** *020 †55
BALTUSNIK, Peter Gregory. MEDICAL CENTER DR, WV UNIV SCH MED 26506 #055-01-2007 **GS** *012
BANVARD, Christine Adele. PO BOX 9247, ROBT C BYRD HSC WVU 26506 #055-01-1987 L1990 **PD ADL** *055
BARCLAY, Roger Stevenson. 200 WEDGEWOOD DR STE 102 26505 #023-01-1976 L1978 **IM** *020 †20,16
BASHIR, Shahida. ■ 26505 #704-25-2000 L2005 **PCC** *012 †20
BATTIN, John Alan. 1000 J D ANDERSON DR, STE 401 26505 #041-12-1993 L1996 **U** *020 †95
BEALL, Charles Lawrence. 300 WEDGEWOOD DR, MORGANTOWN INTERNAL MEDICI 26505 #055-01-1970 L1975 **ON HEM** *020
BEHNAM, Kamal Matta. 200 WEDGEWOOD DR STE 204 26505 #330-01-1957 L1973 **GYN** *020 †30

■ = Address Information Privacy Protected

BEHNAWA, Jawaid Ahmad. PO BOX 8059 26506 #104-01-2005 **MPD** *012

BEIMESCH, Claire Frances. ■ 26505 #020-12-2007 **ORS** *012

BELLOTTE, Heather E. ■ 26505 #055-01-2004 L2006 **DR** *012

BENNETT, Mark R. PO BOX 8255, 1 MEDICAL CENTER DR 26506 #055-01-1982 L1983 **AN** *020 †05

BENNETT, Todd Preston. 204 CEDARSTONE RD 26505 #055-02-1994 L1996 **EM** *020 †16

BENSON, Scott Michael. 1200 J D ANDERSON DR, MEMORIAL GENERAL EMEG DEPT 26505 #055-01-1998 L2000 **EM** *020 †16

BETO, Robert James, II. 300 WEDGEWOOD DR 26505 #055-01-1993 L1994 **CD** *020 †20

BEZOUSKA, Christine Ann. 1200 J D ANDERSON DR, ANESTHESIA SERVICES 26505 #035-06-1978 L1991 **AN CRS** *020 †85,10,05

BHARTI, Sanjay. 177 WINDWOOD DR 26505 #495-08-1987 L1998 **IM FM** *020 †20

BHATT, Asit Narendra. ■ 26505 #496-38-1980 L2006 **OBG** *100

BLAKE, Kendra Elizabeth. ■ 26508 #055-01-2008 *012

BLANKENSHIP, Kevin Jay. 215 DON KNOTTS BLVD, STE 130 26501 #055-01-1996 L1997 **EM** *020 †16

BLUM, Frederick Carl. EMERG MED DEPARTMENT, W VIRGINIA UNIV MED CTR 26505 #055-01-1981 L1998 **EM IM** *040 †20,55,16

BLUME, Thomas Edward. 1200 J D ANDERSON DR, ANESTHESIA SERVICES 26505 #055-01-1977 L1978 **EM FM** *020 †18,16

BODE, Eric Kenneth. ■ 26501 #030-06-2002 L2006 **NR** *012 †80

BOLING, Warren W. PO BOX 9183, ROBERT C. BYRD HEALTH SCIE 26506 #048-15-1991 L2002 **NS** *020 †25

BONNEY, Walter Allan. 1000 J D ANDERSON DR, STE 402 26505 #035-01-1954 L1966 **GYN** *071 †30

BOO, Sohyun. ■ 26505 #055-01-2005 L2007 **DR** *012

BOOTH, Hobson Gill. 1192 PINEVIEW DR 26505 #051-01-1977 L2001 **OBG** *020 †30 ‡

BORSHARD, Elizabeth. ■ 26505 #021-01-2007 **OTO** *012

BOWEN, Sarah Danielleev. ■ 26501 #055-01-2007 **OBG** *012

BOYCE, Brandon Mark. ■ 26508 #012-01-2005 L2006 **ORS** *012

BRADFORD, Geoffrey Eugene. ■ 26505 #041-14-1988 L1998 **OPH PO** *020 †35

BRAMER, Michelle Anne. ■ 26505 #035-15-2004 L2007 **ORS** *012

BRANT, Richard William. 1063 MAPLE DR STE 3A 26505 #055-01-2000 **PD** *062

BREETZ, Gary Allen. ■ 26505 #055-01-2006 L2008 **EM** *012

BREETZ, Karen Green. ■ 26505 #055-01-2005 L2007 **PD** *012

BRICK, James Emmerson. PO BOX 9156, 1 MEDICAL CENTER DR 26506 #055-01-1977 L1978 **RHU IM** *040 †20

BRICK, John Franklin. W V U HOSP, DEPT NEUROLOGY 26506 #055-01-1977 L1978 **N** *020 †75

BROOKS, Claudette Elise. 1 MEDICAL CENTER DR, WVU HSC BOX 9180 26505 #305-01-1996 L1999 **N** *020

BROWN, Patrick Alexander. ■ 26508 #055-01-2006 **IM** *100

BRUNNER, Matthew David. ■ 26508 #055-01-1996 L2000 **MPD** *040 †20,55

BRUNNER, Nancy E. ■ 26508 #055-01-1996 L2000 **PD** *040 †55

BRUNO, Christine Marie. PO BOX 9152, ROBERT C. BYRD HSC of WVU 26506 #055-01-2000 L2003 **FM** *020 †18

BURMAN, Robert Ward. ■ 26508 #025-01-2004 L2006 **DR** *012

BURNS, William Hugh. 4000 HAMPTON CTR, STE A 26505 #055-01-1992 L1997 **GS** *020 †85

BURRIESCI, Mark. PO BOX 9001A, WEST VIRGINIA UNIV SCH MED 26506 #422-01-2005 L2007 **EM** *012

BURTON, Dennis Morgan. 1200 J D ANDERSON DR, MONONGALIA GENERAL HOSPITA 26505 #055-02-1981 L1983 **DR** *020 †80 ‡

BYRON, Brandon Patrick. 1197 VAN VOORHIS RD 26505 #055-01-1996 L1999 **FM** *020 †18

CAMPBELL, Matthew Brent. PO BOX 9149, DEPT OF EMERGENCY MED 26506 #422-01-2006 **EM** *012

CAMPBELL, Michael Cory. ■ 26505 #041-02-2005 L2007 **FPP** *012

CAMPBELL, Michael Jos. ■ 26505 #016-11-1940 L1940 **PD** *071 †55

CANNON, Mary Louise. ■ 26505 #051-07-1988 L2001 **PDR** *020 †80

CAPELLE, Susan Christine. 3496 UNIVERSITY AVE 26505 #055-01-1991 L2000 **OBG** *020 †30

CARDENAS, Silvia Cecilia. PO BOX 9214, A MEDICAL CTR DR 26506 #737-06-1996 L2007 **PD** *012

CAREY, Kim Bryan. 900 FAIRMONT RD 26501 #055-01-1983 L1984 **FM** *020 †18

CARLISLE, Robert Thomas. ■ 26505 #020-02-1999 L2005 **FM** *020 †18

CARNEY, John Michael. ■ 26505 #041-15-2006 **AN** *012

CARPENTER, Jeffrey Scott. PO BOX 9235, MEDICAL CENTER DRIVE 26506 #055-01-1995 L2000 **RNR** *040 †80

CARSON, Larry Van. PO BOX 9183, DEPARTMENT OF NEUROSURGERY 26506 #012-01-1976 L1985 **NS PS** *020 †25,65

CASSIS, Adam Michael. ■ 26508 #055-01-2006 **OTO** *012

CASTELLAN, Robert Michael. 1095 WILLOWDALE RD, NIOSH-CDC 26505 #043-01-1975 L1978 **OM PUD** *050 †20,70

CASTILLO, Tony Joseph, Jr. ■ 26505 #055-01-2008 *012

CASTILLO, William Javier. PO BOX 9214, WVU DEPT OF PEDIATRICS 26506 #264-05-1987 L2002 **PDC** *020 †55

CATHER, Carl H, Jr. 1188 PINEVIEW DR 26505 #024-01-1952 L1959 **A OTO** *071 †45

CATHER, Glenna Anne. PO BOX 9247, WVU STUDENT HLTH SVC 26506 #055-01-1983 L1984 **FM** *020 †18

CHAFIN, Christopher Mark. 710 VENTURE DR 26508 #055-01-1997 L1998 **EM** *020 †16

CHANDRAN, Dilip Narayan. 301 SCOTT AVE, COMMUNITY MENTAL HEALT 26508 #055-01-1992 L1995 **P** *020 †75

CHANG, William Wei-Lien. WV UNIV MED CTR PATH 26506 #385-02-1958 L1979 **ATP** *071 †50

CHARLTON, Judie Fern. PO BOX 9193, RCBHSC 26506 #055-01-1985 L1986 **OPH** *020 †35

CHASE, N Bruce. ■ 26505 #036-07-1964 L1986 **AM GPM** *071 †70

CHEEMA, Muhammad Qasim. PO BOX 9001A 26506 #704-25-2003 **IM** *012

CHEN, Bruce Jengon. ■ 26501 #055-01-2006 **IM** *012

CHERIAN, John. ■ 26505 #055-01-2008 *012

CHIDECKEL, Elliott Wolf. W V U MEDICAL CENTER 26506 #023-01-1969 L1981 **END IM** *050 †20

CHINNAPONGSE, Sangsiddhi. WV UNIVERSITY, HEALTH SCIENCE CTR S PATH 26506 #891-02-1953 **GS OBG** *100

CHISHOLM, Dugald Donald, III. ■ 26508 #024-07-2007 **EM** *012

CHITNIS, Shubhangi Chandr. ■ 26508 #495-82-1993 L2006 **CHN** *020 †75

CHOBY, Susanne. ■ 26505 #055-01-2002 L2004 **MP** *100

CIANCIOLO, Thomas James. ■ 26505 #049-01-1987 L1988 **AN** *020

CIHLA, Allison Nicole. ■ 26508 #038-43-2007 **IM** *012

CLARK, Christy Ann. ■ 26505 #055-01-2008 *012

CLARK, Cristina Mirela. ■ 26505 #055-01-2008 *012

CLARK, Karen Elaine. 1 MED CTR DR, STUDENT HEALTH SERVICE 26506 #055-02-1989 L1990 **IM** *020 †20

CLAUSELL, Paul Lindorf. 930 CHESTNUT RIDGE RD, BM & P 26505 #055-01-1976 L1976 **P** *020 †75

CLEAVENGER, Ronald Lee. 1160 VAN VOORHIS RD 26505 #055-01-1978 L1979 **FM** *020 †18

CLUMP, David Anthony. ■ 26505 #055-01-2008 *012

COBEN, Jeffrey Hy. 1299 PINEVIEW DR, WHITE BIRCH TOWERS 4TH FLO 26506 #041-12-1984 L2004 **EM IM** *050 †20,16

COGER, Brenton Raval. ■ 26508 #047-06-2003 L2005 **NS** *012

COMBS, Amanda Kaye. 1600 UNIVERSITY AVE, DEPT OF FAMILY MEDICINE 26506 #055-01-2006 **FP** *012

CONN, Arthur Gerald. ■ 26508 #025-07-1976 L1981 **DR** *020 †80

COOK, Linda Lou. 1200 J D ANDERSON DR, MONONGALIA GENERAL HOSPITA 26505 #038-40-1979 L1985 **PTH PCP** *020 †50

COOPER, Melinda Nicole. ■ 26508 #055-01-2006 **MPD** *012

COREY, William Steven. ■ 26505 #055-01-2003 L2006 **ORS** *012

COST, Jamey Lynn. ■ 26508 #055-01-2005 L2007 **OTO** *012

COVEY, Thomas Harvey, Jr. 50 QUAIL RD 26508 #024-01-1961 L1971 **GS ORS** *071 †85

CRANKSHAW, Kathryn Alicia. PO BOX 9149, WEST VIRGINIA UNIV HOPS 26506 #422-01-2004 L2007 **IM** *012

CRISER, Andrew Lee. ■ 26508 #055-01-2003 L2005 **AN** *100

CROCCO, Todd Jeffrey. ■ 26505 #041-12-1995 L2001 **EM** *020 †16

CROSBY, Thomas Wm. 300 WEDGEWOOD DR 26505 #055-01-1970 L1970 **N** *020 †75

CROWELL, Edward B, Jr. WV U DEPT MED HEM/ON SER 26506 #016-02-1962 L1990 **IM HO** *040 †20

CRUZZAVALA, Jose Luis. 330 SCOTT AVE 26508 #649-19-1977 L1988 **TS GS** *020 †85,90

CUMMINGS, Kristin J. 1095 WILLOWDALE RD, MS 2800 26505 #023-07-2000 L2004 **GPM** *100 †20

CUNNINGHAM, Michael E. MEDICAL CTR DR - STADIUM D 26505 #055-01-1982 L1985 **R DR** *020 †80

CUPPETT, Courtney Dawn. ■ 26508 #055-01-2005 L2007 **OBG** *012

CURCI, Kristina Marie. 930 CHESTNUT RIDGE RD, CHESTNUT RIDGE HOSPITAL 26505 #055-01-1995 L1997 **OS P** *020 †75

CURRY, George Alexander. ■ 26508 #038-41-1944 L1946 **PUD IM** *071

CURRY, Sean Michael. ■ 26505 #020-12-2001 L2005 **EM** *020 †16

CURTIS, Robert James. 1200 J D ANDERSON DR 26505 #032-01-1978 L1978 **EM** *030 †16

CUTLIP, William David. 930 CHESTNUT RIDGE RD 26505 #055-01-1980 L1981 **N** *020 †75

CZINEGE, Ervin Illes. 1200 J D ANDERSON DR, MONONGALIA GENERAL HOSPITA 26505 #473-02-1981 L1999 **AN** *020 †05

DAI, Alper Ibrahim. ■ 26501 #902-07-1990 **PD** *100

DALTON, Justin Blake. 2960 POINT MARION RD 26505 #055-01-2008 *012

DANGELO, John James, Jr. MEDICAL CENTER DR, WV UNIV SCH MED 26506 #011-03-2007 **EM** *012

DAR, Imran Ahmed. ■ 26505 #055-01-2005 L2005 **IM** *012

DARBANDI, Kokab Christina. PO BOX 9214, DEPARTMENT OF PEDIATRICS 26506 #055-01-2007 **MPD** *012

DARMELIO, Matthew Philip. 200 ORTHOPEDIC WAY, MOUNTAINSTATE ORTHOPEDIC 26506 #055-01-1994 L1996 **ORS** *020 †40

DATTOLA, Richard Kennedy. WV UNIV M C DPT FAM PRAC 26506 #041-13-1983 L1985 **FM** *020 †18

DAVIS, Barry Christopher. ■ 26508 #047-06-2006 **ORS** *012

DAVIS, Christopher Chad. 1261 COLONIAL DR 26505 #035-01-2000 L2004 **AN** *100

DAVIS, Eric Howard. 3711 COLLINS FERRY RD, NYLAN PHARMACEUTICALS 26505 #055-01-1991 L1994 **P** *075

DAVIS, Erica Beth. ■ 26508 #055-02-2008 *012

DAVISSON, Laura Marie. ■ 26508 #055-01-1999 L2002 **IM** *020 †20

DAY, Kevin Allen. ■ 26505 #039-01-2003 L2006 **GS** *012

DEDHIA, Harakh V. W VA UNIV MED CTR G280 HSS 26506 #495-01-1971 L1979 **CCM PUD** *020 †20

DEHAVEN, Benjamin Aaron. ■ 26505 #055-01-2008 *012

DE LA GARZA, Vincent W. ■ 26508 #023-01-1976 L1992 **FPG FM** *020 †18

DER SARKISSIAN, David. PO BOX 9168, WEST VIRGINA UNIV HOSP 26506 #422-01-2004 **IM** *100

DESAI, Bharati Shirish. 930 CHESTNUT RIDGE RD 26505 #495-23-1968 L1982 **CHP P** *020 †75

DHOLAKIA, Rut Dinkar. ■ 26505 #496-36-2004 **N** *012

DI BARTOLOMEO, Anthony G. PO BOX 897, UNIVERSITY HELATH ASSOC 26507 #055-01-1967 L1975 **RHU IM** *020 †20

DIETZ, Matthew James. ■ 26508 #041-13-2006 L2007 **ORS** *012

DI GIOACCHINO, Rocco Jos. ■ 26505 #561-01-1968 L1986 **R** *020 †80

DILLIS, Charlotte. 930 CHESTNUT RIDGE RD, CHESTNUT RIDGE HOSPITAL 26505 #010-02-1981 L1990 **DR** *020 †80

DINAPOLI, Vincent Anthony. ■ 26505 #055-01-2008 *012

DITTY, Jack Foster. ■ 26508 #020-12-2002 L2004 **EM** *100 †16

DIVEKAR, Preeti Rajesh. 4601 HEALTH SERVICE NORTH 26506 #496-38-1996 L2007 **OBG** *012

DOD, Harvinder Singh. PO BOX 9157, WEST VIRGINIA UNIV 26506 #495-74-1996 L2004 **CD** *012 †20

DONOVAN, Anna Kate. ■ 26505 #055-01-2008 *012

DOUGHERTY, Joseph Thomas. ■ 26505 #055-01-2008 *012

DOUGLAS, Justin Wayne. ■ 26505 #055-01-2008 *012

DOWER, Joshua Michael. ■ 26508 #055-01-2004 L2006 **MPD** *012

DOYLE, Edward Jerome, Jr. 1160 VAN VOORHIS RD 26505 #010-01-1975 L1995 **OM FM** *030 †70,18

DOYLE, Gregory Alan. 930 CHESTNUT RIDGE RD, CHESTNUT RIDGE HOSPITAL 26505 #051-04-1978 L1988 **FM** *040 †18

DOYLE, Heather Marie. ■ 26505 #055-01-2008 *012

DRIVER, Richard P, Jr. 930 CHESTNUT RIDGE RD, CHESTNUT RIDGE HOSPITAL 26505 #045-04-1988 L1989 **AN** *020 †05

DUCATMAN, Alan Marc. 930 CHESTNUT RIDGE RD, CHESTNUT RIDGE HOSPITAL 26505 #025-07-1978 L1992 **OM IM** *040 †20,70

DURST, Christopher Robert. ■ 26505 #055-01-2007 L2008 **TY** *012

EDDY, Lori Ann. 930 CHESTNUT RIDGE RD, CHESTNUT RIDGE HOSPITAL 26505 #055-01-1998 L2001 **IM** *020 †20

ELLER, Richard Warren. 930 CHESTNUT RIDGE RD, CHESTNUT RIDGE HOSPITAL 26505 #055-01-1959 L1979 **AN** *071 †05

ELLIS, Brian David. 930 CHESTNUT RIDGE RD, CHESTNUT RIDGE HOSPITAL 26505 #041-13-1989 L1994 **OPH** *020 †35

ELLISON, Matthew Blair. 120 DONNA AVE 26505 #055-01-2004 L2006 **AN** *012

ELSWICK, Daniel Elliot. 930 CHESTNUT RIDGE RD, DEPT OF BEHAVIORAL MEDICIN 26505 #055-01-2001 L2004 **OS** *100 †20,75

ELY, Brian Arthur. 1600 UNIVERSITY AVE, DEPT OF PEDIATRICS 26506 #055-01-2006 **PD** *012

EMERY, Gwen Arens. 3958 EASTLAKE DR 26508 #036-07-1981 L2004 **FM** *020 †18

EPLING, James Andrew. ■ 26505 #055-01-2006 L2007 **DR** *012

ERICSON, Solveig Gronning. PO BOX 9162, WEST VIRGINIA UNIV MED CTR 26506 #024-05-1985 L1995 **ON HEM** *030 †20

ESAN, Olukemi Ayotunde. PO BOX 9203 26506 #690-01-1991 **PTH** *012

EVANS, Matthew Ryan. ■ 26505 #055-01-2006 L2007 **IM** *012

EVERLY, Vicki Lynn. ■ 26508 #055-01-1999 L2002 **EM** *020

FALLON, Kenneth Brian. ■ 26501 #021-05-1989 L2006 **NP** *020 †50

FANCY, Tanya. ■ 26508 #704-25-2001 **OTO** *012

FARAHMAND, Navid. ■ 26505 #005-18-2004 L2006 **AN** *012

FARIVAR-MOHSENI, Hesam. PO BOX 9251, UROLOGY DIVISION 26506 #065-01-1992 L2002 **U** *020 †95

FARRUGIA, David Joseph, Jr. ■ 26505 #035-06-2007 **IM** *012

FEATHERS, Christopher Cha. ■ 26508 #055-01-2006 L2007 **MPD** *012

FEGHALI, Joseph George. 2000 HAMPTON CTR, STE D 26505 #605-01-1981 L1986 **OPH** *020

FELTNER, Cynthia Kay. ■ 26501 #055-01-2002 L2006 **OS** *012

FERRARI, Norman D, III. 930 CHESTNUT RIDGE RD, CHESTNUT RIDGE HOSPITAL 26505 #055-01-1982 L1983 **PD ADL** *020 †20,55

FERREBEE, Michael Lee. 1200 J D ANDERSON DR, HOSPITAL ER 26505 #055-01-1988 L1995 **PD** *020 †55

FIDLER, Donald Carl. 1117 UNIVERSITY AVE, STE 505 26505 #036-01-1975 L1987 **P** *040 †75

FIKREMARIAM, Debebe. PO BOX 9001A 26506 #366-01-1992 **AN** *012

FINKEL, Mitchell Simon. 930 CHESTNUT RIDGE RD, CHESTNUT RIDGE HOSPITAL 26505 #023-01-1979 L1996 **CD IM** *050 †20

FINKENBINE, Ryan Dale. 930 CHESTNUT RIDGE RD 26505 #017-20-1992 L1999 **P PFP** *040 †75

FISHER, Melanie Ann. 930 CHESTNUT RIDGE RD, CHESTNUT RIDGE HOSPITAL 26505 #041-14-1977 L1980 **ID IM** *020 †20

FITZPATRICK, Karen M. PO BOX 9152, W VA DEPT OF FAMILY MED 26506 #055-01-1983 L1984 **FM** *020 †18

FOGARTY, David Chas. 165 SCOTT AVE, STE 206 26508 #055-01-1973 L1980 **PS HS** *071 †65

FOLEY, Mark Joseph. PO BOX 9238 26506 #539-02-2006 **GS** *012

FORE, David Charles. ■ 26508 #055-02-2001 L2004 **DR** *100 †80

FOSHEY, Michelle Lynn. ■ 26508 #011-04-2000 L2003 **FM** *062 †18 ‡

FRAME, Daniel S. 710 VENTURE DR 26508 #055-01-1986 L1987 **EM** *020 †16

FRANCE, John Chas. 1160 VAN VOORHIS RD 26505 #041-12-1986 L1995 **ORS** *020 †40

FRANCIS, Richard Mcmaster. ■ 26508 #055-01-2005 L2007 **OPH** *012

FRANKLIN, Grant L. ■ 26508 #047-07-1951 L1951 **GS** *071 †85

FREEMAN, Jessica Gale. ■ 26508 #051-07-2004 L2006 **GS** *012

FRICH, John Carl, Jr. MEDICAL CENTER DR, UNIV WV DEPT RAD/ONCO 26506 #010-01-1959 L1963 **RO DR** *020 †80

FRIEDMAN, Scott J. 235 HIGH ST, STE 225 26505 #055-01-1995 L1998 **FM** *020

FROST, James Lawrence. 2567 UNIVERSITY AVE # 3008 26505 #023-07-1957 L1977 **FOP ATP** *062 †50

FRYE, Benjamin Michael. ■ 26508 #055-01-2007 **ORS** *012

FULLMER, John Lee. 1212 VAN VOORHIS RD 26505 #055-01-1963 L1964 **FM OS** *071 †18

FULTON, Jonathan Reid. ■ 26505 #055-01-2004 **IM** *100

GADIKOTA, Kishore. PO BOX 9214 26506 #496-24-2003 **PD** *012

GAINER, Robert Brooks, II. 300 WEDGEWOOD DR, MORGANTOWN INTERNAL MED GR 26505 #055-01-1969 L1971 **IM ID** *071 †20

GAIS, Richard Domenick. 1197 VAN VOORHIS RD 26505 #055-01-1977 L1978 **FM** *020 †18

GAMBREL, Mary Jean. PO BOX 9001A 26506 #654-01-2004 L2006 **P** *012

GARNER, Susan Leah. 710 VENTURE DR 26508 #055-01-1998 L2000 **FM** *020 †18

GARRETT, Sheli Ruth. ■ 26508 #055-75-2006, ▲ L2007 **OBG** *012

GASKINS, Ronald De Voe. 1200 J D ANDERSON DR, ANESTHESIA SERVICES 26505 #045-01-1962 L1981 **GE IM** *071 †20

GEORGE, Kerri Lynn. 200 WEDGEWOOD DR, STE 201 26505 #055-02-2003 L2007 **OBG** *020

GERBO, Robert Michael. PO BOX 9190 26506 #055-01-1990 L1993 **FM** *020 †18

GHARIB, Rola Michelle. ■ 26505 #055-01-2005 L2006 **IM** *012

GHARIB, Wissam. PO BOX 9168, 1 MEDICAL CENTER DR 26506 #055-01-1998 L1999 **CD** *020 †20

GILBRIDE, Anne Katherine. ■ 26501 #030-06-2002 L2006 **PTH** *012

GILL, Arashdeep. MEDICAL CENTER DR 26506 #104-01-2005 **P** *012

GILL, Vikramjit Singh. 930 CHESTNUT RIDGE RD 26505 #495-29-1996 L2007 **P** *012

GINGOLD, Monique. 816 SOMERSET ST 26505 #055-01-1989 L1991 **CHN** *020 †75

GLOVER, Douglas Dennis. WVU SCH OF MED, DEPT OB/GYN 26506 #012-05-1961 L1962 **OBG ID** *071 †30

GLUSHKOV, Oleg Vasilyevic. ■ 26505 #913-06-1994 L2007 **FM** *020

GOCKE, Ryan Thomas. ■ 26505 #010-02-2004 L2006 **ORS** *012

GOEBEL, Stephan. PO BOX 9161, WVU DEPT OF MEDICINE 26506 #409-07-1991 L1997 **GE** *020 †20

GOETZ, David Wm. 1063 MAPLE DR, STE 1A 26505 #023-12-1981 L1997 **AI ALI** *020 †55,03 ‡

GOODYKOONTZ, Toni B. 930 CHESTNUT RIDGE RD, CHESTNUT RIDGE HOSPITAL 26505 #055-01-1988 L1989 **P** *020 †75

GRADDY, Logan Gabriel. ■ 26501 #011-04-2003 L2008 **P** *020

GRAEBER, Geoffrey Marc. 1200 J D ANDERSON DR 26505 #035-15-1971 L1989 **TS** *020 †85,90

GRAEBER, Janet Page E. WVU SCHOOL OF MEDICINE, DEPT OF PEDIATRICS 26506 #035-15-1972 L1989 **NPM PD** *050 †55

GRAF, David Frederick. WVU MED CTR, DEPT ANES 26506 #035-03-1972 L1977 **AN EM** *040 †05,16

GRANT, Maurice Rayshawn. ■ 26501 #017-20-1998 L2007 **SP** *020

GRAVES, Cynthia Frances. PO BOX 9238, WVUH 26506 #055-01-1989 L1994 **GS** *020 †85

GRAYSON, Stephanie Anne. ■ 26508 #041-13-2006 **PD** *012

GREEN, Francis Harry Y. 944 CHESTNUT RIDGE RD # OS 26505 #917-08-1968 L1978 **PTH** *050 †50

GREY, Carl Robert. ■ 26505 #055-01-2004 L2007 **IM** *012

GRISAFI, Frank Nicholas. ■ 26508 #041-02-2004 L2007 **ORS** *012

GRISAFI, Heather Shaw. ■ 26508 #041-02-2005 L2007 **DR** *012

GROSE, Brian Wade. ■ 26505 #055-01-2000 L2004 **AN** *100 †05

GROSS, Scott Wm. MEDICAL CENTER DRIVE PED 26506 #011-03-1988 **PD** *100

GROVES, Samuel Shawn. PO BOX 9157, WVU RCB HSC DEPT OF CARDIO 26506 #055-01-1999 L2000 **IC** *020 †20

GUALBERTO, Gary Crisanto. PO BOX 9180, MEDICAL CENTER DR 26506 #748-10-2005 **TY N** *012

GUDAUSKY, Todd Michael. 1 MEDICAL CENTER DRIVE, PEDIATRIC CARDIOLOGY 26506 #016-43-1999 L2006 **PDC IM** *020 †20,55

GUSTAFSON, Robert Allen. MEDICAL CTR DR - STADIUM D 26505 #055-01-1976 L1977 **TS GS** *020 †85,90

GUTIERREZ, Alvaro Rafael. WVU MED CTR DPT N 26506 #132-04-1977 L1984 **N** *020 †75

GUTMANN, Laurie. 1200 J D ANDERSON DR, ANESTHESIA SERVICES 26505 #055-01-1986 L1993 **N** *020 †75

GUTMANN, Ludwig. WV UNIVERSITY, HEALTH SCIENCE CTR S NEUR 26505 #031-01-1959 L1966 **N OS** *020 †75

GUZMAN PEREZ-CARRILLO, Glo. ■ 26505 #042-01-2004 L2006 **DR** *012

GYURE, Kymberly Anne. ■ 26508 #038-43-1992 L2005 **PTH NP** *020 †50

HACKETT, Anne E. WV UNIVERSITY 26506 #045-01-1983 L1984 **AN** *020 †05

HADIQUE, Sarah. ■ 26505 #704-25-2003 **IM** *012

HAHN, Joseph Mitchell. ■ 26505 #055-02-2002 L2004 **ORS** *012

HAILEMICHAEL, Eyassu. PO BOX 9235, WVU DEPT OF RADIOLOGY 26506 #366-02-1984 L2005 **PDR** *020

HALBRITTER, Kevin Ashley. MEDICAL CTR DR - STADIUM D 26505 #055-01-1985 L1987 **IM** *020 †20

HALES, Milton R. ■ 26501 #005-06-1944 L1970 **ATP** *071 †50

HALL, David Michael. 1000 J D ANDERSON DR, STE 401 26505 #055-01-1995 L2001 **U** *020 †95 ‡

HALL, Mary Jean. 400 DRUMMOND ST 26505 #055-01-1998 L2001 **D** *020 †15

HALL, William Lloyd. 400 DRUMMOND ST 26505 #055-01-1969 L1970 **D** *020 †15 ‡

HAMILTON, William Kent. 200 WEDGEWOOD DR STE 201, WMNS HLTHCARE MORGANTOWN 26505 #055-01-1979 L2003 **OBG** *020

HAMLIN, Brian R. ■ 26508 #048-12-1994 L2006 **OAR** *100 †40

HANOWELL, Jonathan Long. ■ 26501 #010-01-2007 **EM** *012

HARDY, Kenneth Franklin. 1311 PINEVIEW DR, WHITE BIRCH TOWERS II 26505 #055-01-1993 L1994 **D IM** *020 †15

HARMAN, Thomas Frederick. 1000 J D ANDERSON DR, STE 402 26505 #038-40-1988 L1992 **GYN** *020 †30

HARPER, Tiffany Leigh. ■ 26508 #055-01-2004 L2007 **PTH** *012

HARRIS, Darren Leonard. PO BOX 9203, WVU DEPT OF PATHOLOGY 26506 #055-02-1997 L2002 **PTH** *100

HARRISON, H Summers. 900 FAIRMONT RD 26501 #051-04-1958 L1959 **PD FM** *071 †55

HARRISON, Patricia June. MONONGALIA GEN HOSP FP 26505 #055-01-1976 L1977 **EM FM** *020 †16,18 ‡

HARSHBARGER, Todd Lee. 1279 RICHWOOD AVE 26505 #032-01-1995 L2004 **NS** *012

HARTEL, James Vincent. ■ 26501 #654-01-2005 **PTH** *012

HARTEL, Paul Herbert. PO BOX 9203, WV UNIV HOSP 26506 #654-01-2000 L2005 **PTH** *020 †50

HARTMAN-ADAMS, Holly B. 608 CHEAT RD 26508 #055-01-1994 L1995 **FM** *020 †18

HARVEY, Jessica Louise. ■ 26508 #055-75-2007, ▲ **IM** *012

HARVEY, Wade Vincent. PO BOX 9152, CLARK K SLEETH FAM 26506 #055-01-2006 L2007 **FP** *012

HASHMI, Mahreen. 1192 PINEVIEW DR 26505 #038-43-1992 L1996 **OBG** *020 †30

HASHMI, Syed Hamid. PO BOX 9238 26506 #704-25-1993 L2003 **CCS** *020 †85

HASSANI, Farzaneh. 1526 MILEGROUND RD 26505 #654-01-1987 L2000 **IM** *020 †20

HATFIELD, Ginger Patty. ■ 26508 #055-01-2005 L2006 **DR** *012

HAWTHORNE, Brian Wendell. 210 LAKEWOOD CTR, LAKESIDE FAM PRACT PLLC 26508 #035-15-1994 L1997 **FM** *020 †18

HAZARD, Hannah Wright. 1 MEDICAL CTR DR, HEALTH SCIENCES CTR 26506 #055-01-2001 L2005 **GS** *020 †85

HAZEY, Matthew Allyn. ■ 26505 #055-01-2007 **TY** *012

HEIRONIMUS, Terring W, III. WV UNIVERSITY, HEALTH SCIENCE CTR S 26506 #051-01-1955 L1956 **AN PUD** *020 †05

HEISKELL, Charles Andrew. 4000 HAMPTON CTR 26505 #016-06-1969 L1975 **GS VS** *020 †85 ‡

HELSLEY, James Doyle. 1200 J D ANDERSON DR 26505 #055-01-1977 L1980 **FM FPG** *040 †19

HEMBREE, Wanda Marie. 1063 MAPLE DR STE 2A 26505 #055-02-1990 L1991 **OBG** *020 †30

HENRICKSON, Roy Eric. ■ 26505 #050-02-1996 L1998 **AN** *020 †05

HERVEY, Sheleika Linette. ■ 26505 #036-07-2003 L2008 **TY** *012

HESS, Alan Ray. 300 WEDGEWOOD DR 26505 #055-01-1990 L1993 **IM** *020 †20

HILL, Cheryl Anne. 930 CHESTNUT RIDGE RD, CHESTNUT RIDGE HOSPITAL 26505 #055-01-2001 L2004 **PFP** *100 †75

HILVERS, Pamela Sue. ■ 26501 #055-01-2005 L2007 **PD** *012

HINERMAN, Raymond Albert, Jr. 1188 PINEVIEW DR 26505 #055-01-2000 L2005 **OTO** *100 †45

HIXENBAUGH, Heather Marie. ■ 26505 #055-01-2000 L2003 **MPD** *100 †55,20

HOCHBERG, Charles J. ■ 26505 #016-42-1967 L2007 **OBG** *020 †30

HODDER, Corbin. ■ 26508 #041-78-2005, ▲ L2006 **IM** *012

HODOUS, Thomas Knight. 1160 VAN VOORHIS RD 26505 #023-07-1971 L1976 **OM PUD** *050 †20,70

HOELDTKE, Robert Danl. ■ 26508 #035-20-1966 L1990 **IM** *050

HOFER, Jacob Heinz. ■ 26505 #055-01-2008 *012

HOFFMAN, Earl Theodore. WV UNIVERSITY, DEPT RAD 26506 #010-02-1961 L1980 **DR NM** *075 †80,28

HOGG, Jeffery Paul. 1200 J D ANDERSON DR 26505 #055-01-1983 L1988 **DR RNR** *040 †80

HONAKER, Matthew Jason. ■ 26508 #055-01-2005 L2007 **OBG** *012

HOODA, Deepak. PO BOX 9001A, DEPT OF INT MED 26506 #495-80-2001 **IM** *012

HORNSBY, Jo Ann Allen. 1160 VAN VOORHIS RD 26505 #045-01-1992 **RHU IM** *020 †20

HORVATH, Gabriella G. 3132 COLLINS FERRY RD, HHP INTERNAL MEDICINE PLLC 26505 #473-02-1982 L1998 **IM** *020 †20

HOSSAIN, Akm Mosharraf. 1354 HEADLEE AVE 26505 #160-02-1996 L2005 **HO** *012 †20

HOUSHMANDPOUR, Payman. PO BOX 9214 26506 #661-02-2007 **PD** *012

HOUSTON, Brian Delaney. 1199 VAN VOORHIS RD STE 5 26505 #055-01-1974 L1975 **RHU IM** *020 †20

HOWARD-MCNATT, Marissa M. PO BOX 9238, WEST VIRGINIA UNIVERSITY D 26506 #024-01-1995 L2004 **GS** *020 †85

HOWELL, Jodie E. ■ 26508 #055-01-2002 L2005 **FM** *020 †18

HOWELL, Stephen Moore. ■ 26508 #055-01-2003 L2005 **AN** *100

HRABOVSKY, Ellen E. WVU SCHOOL OF MEDICINE, DEPT OF SURGERY 26506 #047-05-1969 L1976 **PDS** *020 †20

HUBBARD, David Frederick. PO BOX 9196, ROBERT C BYRD HEALTH SCI C 26506 #055-02-1989 L1993 **OTR ORS** *020 †40

HUBBARD, Heather Jo. ■ 26508 #055-01-2006 L2008 **FP** *012
HUBER, Stanford James. 102 WINDWOOD DR 26505 #023-01-1971 L1975 **PME AN** *020 †18,05 ‡
HULSE, Ronald Stephen. ■ 26508 #305-01-2002 L2005 **CD** *012 †20
HUMMEL, Marybeth. WV UNIVERSITY, HEALTH SCIENCE CTR S PEDS 26505 #017-20-1981 L1986 **MG PD** *020 †9,55
HURST, Michael Kenneth. 1188 PINEVIEW DR 26505 #055-02-1988 L1989 **OTO** *020 †45
HUST, Kara Lynn. ■ 26505 #055-01-2008 *012
HYDER, Tara. ■ 26506 #065-01-2004 L2008 **MPD** *012
IAMMARINO, Richard M. PO BOX 9122 26506 #016-43-1953 L1979 **PTH** *071 †50
IANNETTI, Michael Patrick. ■ 26501 #055-01-2007 **IM** *012
IBRAHIM, Muhammad. ■ 26505 #704-09-1991 **N** *012
ISSA, Mayada. 129 CRESTVIEW DR, PRINCE GEORGES HOSPITAL 26505 #528-06-1993 L2007 **IM** *020 †20
ISSA, Mohammed Abdallah. MEDICAL CENTER DR 26506 #915-03-2004 **P** *012
JABBOUR, Nabil Milad. 1200 J D ANDERSON DR 26505 #605-01-1980 L1985 **OPH** *020
JACKSON, Emme Dustin. ■ 26505 #055-01-2006 **GS** *012
JAIN, Abnash Chander. WV UNIVERSITY, HEALTH SCIENCE CTR S 26506 #495-29-1959 L1973 **CD IM** *020 †20
JAIN, Sumesh. ■ 26505 #495-45-1996 **IM** *012
JAKUBEC, P John. 404 INGLEWOOD BLVD 26505 #041-12-1964 L1967 **PD** *020 †55 ‡
JALISI, Farrukh Mahfuz. 1 REGENCY CT 26505 #704-25-1994 L2000 **IC** *012 †20
JAMERSON, Scott Conrad. ■ 26508 #055-02-2004 L2006 **OPH** *012
JANOO, Jabin Tajdin K. 1192 PINEVIEW DR 26505 #704-25-1994 L2002 **OBG** *020 †30 ‡
JARRELL, Brett Eric. ■ 26505 #055-02-2001 L2003 **EM** *100 †16
JAWORSKI, Andrzej. 1265 PINEVIEW DR 26505 #759-06-1980 L1988 **PUD IM** *020 †20
JAYNES, Margaret E. ■ 26501 #055-01-1991 L1996 **CHN** *020 †75
JIN, Chuanfang. 730 TIMBERLINE 26505 #243-39-1982 L2001 **GPM** *020 †20,70
JOHN, Collin Christopher. ■ 26505 #055-01-2007 **MPD** *012
JOHNSON, Jerome Gordon. 200 WEDGEWOOD DR, ASSOCIATES INC 26505 #026-04-1965 L1967 **GS** *020 †85
JOHNSON, Mark Leo. 200 WEDGEWOOD DR, ASSOCIATES INC 26505 #026-04-1992 L1995 **GS** *020 †85
JOHNSON, Melissa Roedel. 364 PATTESON DR 26505 #051-07-2001 L2006 **DR** *020 †80
JOHNSTONE, Robert Edmund. MEDICAL CTR DR - STADIUM D 26505 #038-40-1970 L1991 **AN** *020 †05
JONES, David Smith. ■ 26505 #016-43-1945 **OS** *071
JONES, Evan A. 1160 VAN VOORHIS RD 26505 #055-01-1988 L1993 **PDE** *020 †55
JONES, Staci Lin. 608 CHEAT RD 26508 #055-01-1998 L2002 **PD** *020 †55
JORDAN MANZANO, Carlos. 930 CHESTNUT RIDGE RD 26505 #176-01-2000 **P** *012
JORET, Dale Marie. PO BOX 9186, WVU MEDICAL CTR 26506 #041-13-1975 L1990 **OBG** *071 †30
JU, Justina Yeehua. ■ 26505 #051-01-2004 L2007 **GE** *012
JUCKETT, Roy Gregory. 1160 VAN VOORHIS RD 26505 #041-14-1981 L1984 **FM** *020 †18
JULIEN, Terrence Darryl. ■ 26508 #010-03-1993 L2007 **NS** *100
JUNEJA, Sonia. 930 CHESTNUT RIDGE RD 26505 #495-95-2000 L2008 **P** *012
KAI-LEWIS, Emmanuel Harol. PO BOX 9193, 1 STADIUM DR 26506 #010-03-2006 **OPH** *012
KAMATH, Geetha S.. ■ 26505 #495-37-1993 L2004 **IM** *100
KANATE, Abraham Sebastian. PO BOX 9001A 26506 #495-52-2003 **IM** *012
KANDZARI, Stanley Jos. MEDICAL CENTER, WEST VIRGINIA UNIVERSITY 26506 #055-01-1963 L1964 **U** *020 †95
KANE, Elizabeth Dye. ■ 26505 #055-02-2006 **FPP** *012
KANJ, Ghassan Hani. 99 J D ANDERSON DR 26505 #605-01-1991 L1999 **PCC SME** *020 †20
KANWAL, Richard Singh. 1095 WILLOWDALE RD, DRDS FSB NIOSH 26505 #035-46-1989 L1990 **GPM** *050 †05,70
KARIM, Muhammad Sohaib. PO BOX 9001A 26506 #704-25-2003 **IM** *012
KARLSSON, Bengt Gunnar. ■ 26508 #858-02-1980 L2006 *100
KARNSAKUL, Wikrom. ■ 26505 #891-04-1992 L2004 **PG** *055
KASSAWAT, Muhannad. 930 CHESTNUT RIDGE RD 26505 #275-01-1992 **P** *012
KEEFOVER, Robert W. ■ 26501 #055-02-1982 L1985 **N P** *020 †75
KELLER, Frank G, Jr. WV UNIV HLTH SCIENCES CTR, DEPT OF PEDS 26506 #036-01-1986 L1993 **PHO** *020 †20,55
KELLEY, Arthur W. 1200 J D ANDERSON DR 26505 #041-12-1950 L1952 **FM** *071 †18
KERBY, Jessica Dawn. PO BOX 9001A, WEST VIRIGINA UNIV SCH OF 26506 #055-75-2006, ▲ **OBG** *012
KERR, Richard Stephen. 1224B PINEVIEW DR, RM B 26505 #055-01-1967 L1968 **OBG** *020 †30
KESSEL, James Weaver. 102 WINDWOOD DR 26505 #055-01-1971 L1975 **AN FM** *020
KHAKOO, Rashida Abbas. 1160 VAN VOORHIS RD 26505 #905-01-1969 L1977 **ID IM** *030 †20
KHAMARE, Chetan. PO BOX 9168, WV UNIV HOSP 26506 #305-01-2004 L2007 **IM** *100 †20
KHAN, Asad. PO BOX 9165, WVU DEPT NEPH 26506 #704-02-1990 L2005 **NEP IM** *100 †75,20
KHAN, Asad H. 930 CHESTNUT RIDGE RD 26505 #704-21-1988 L1995 **P PFP** *020
KHAN, Fida Ali. 1018 IRWIN ST, # 55 26505 #704-25-1997 L2004 **ID** *100 †20 ‡
KHAN, Mudussara Asad. ■ 26505 #055-01-2002 L2005 **HO** *012 †20
KHAN, Uzer Sher Dil. PO BOX 9238 26506 #704-25-2005 **GS** *012
KHANNA, Deepak. PO BOX 9157, 2203 HEALTH SCIENCES S 26506 #422-01-1997 L2005 **CD** *012 †20
KIMYAIASADI, Mithra. ■ 26508 #010-03-2006 L2008 **DR** *012
KINCAID, Christine R. WV U MED CTR, DEPT MED 26506 #055-01-1985 L1986 **IM** *020 †20,55
KINDER, Carl Lee. ■ 26505 #055-01-2003 **GS** *100
KING, Roger Edward. 4000 HAMPTON CTR, STE A 26505 #055-01-1964 L1965 **GS VS** *020 †85
KINNEY, David M. BASIC SCIENCE BLDG, WV UNIV DEPT OF FAM MED 26505 #055-01-1989 L1990 **EM** *020 †18
KLEMAN, Bradey Thomas. ■ 26508 #038-45-2004 L2007 **PD** *012
KLINE, Laura Mccaskill. ■ 26505 #055-01-2008 *012
KNIGHT, Jennifer C. ■ 26505 #055-01-2003 L2006 **GS** *012
KOHLI, Anjali. 1404 LAKESIDE VLG 26508 #422-01-1997 L2005 **IM** *020 †20
KOHLI, Arpan. ■ 26505 #055-01-2008 *012
KOLANKO, Vincent Paul. 1197 VAN VOORHIS RD 26505 #055-01-1983 L1984 **IM** *020 †20,55
KOLAR, Maria Munoz. MEDICAL CTR DR - STADIUM D 26505 #055-01-1988 L1992 **IM** *020 †20
KONNUR, Neelam. 224 PINEVIEW DR, STE E 26506 #495-44-1998 L2003 **PD** *020 †55
KOVACH, Angela Dawn. ■ 26508 #654-01-2001 L2004 **IM** *020 †20
KOVACH, Rodney Frederick. WVU MED CTR, DEPT DERM 26506 #055-01-1978 L1979 **D** *020 †15
KRANTZ, William Albert, II. 1200 J D ANDERSON DR 26505 #055-01-1996 L2001 **DR** *020 †80
KREISS, Kathleen. 1095 WILLOWDALE RD, DRDS STE H-2800 26505 #024-01-1975 L1977 **OM IM** *050 †20,70

KRIST, Gary Steven. 930 CHESTNUT RIDGE RD, CHESTNUT RIDGE HOSP 26505 #305-01-1992 L2001 **P** *100
KROLL, Jerry Stephen, Jr. PO BOX 782, 1 STADIUM DR 26507 #055-01-2005 L2008 **PD** *012
KRUSKA, Lindsay Anne. ■ 26505 #055-01-2008 *012
KUMAR, Sunita Tarun. PO BOX 9100A, DEPT O GENERAL SURGERY 26506 #495-74-1995 **GS** *100
KUMAR, Tarun. PO BOX 9238, 770 HSS 26506 #495-74-1995 L2008 *100
KUPEC, Justin Thomas. ■ 26505 #055-01-2004 L2006 **IM** *012 †20
KURIAN, Sobha. ■ 26505 #495-31-1990 L2000 **HO** *020 †20
KUTROVAC, Kyle Thomas. ■ 26505 #055-01-2008 *012
LABATIA, Ihab Youssef. 1160 VAN VOORHIS RD, SERVICES 26505 #915-04-1992 L2002 **SCI** *020 †60
LAFFERTY, Benjamin Randol. ■ 26505 #055-01-2004 L2006 **CHP** *012
LAKHANI, Paresh Vinodrai. ■ 26505 #055-01-2008 *012
LAMBERT, Matt Wade. ■ 26508 #055-02-1997 L1998 **EM** *020 †16
LANCASTER, Jeffrey David. ■ 26508 #055-01-2003 L2006 **MPD** *100 †55
LANDER, Owen Macliesh. ■ 26508 #035-48-2001 L2005 **EM** *020 †16
LA PLANTE, E Schrae. 200 WEDGEWOOD DR STE 104 26505 #026-04-1962 L1966 **GS TRS** *071 †85
LAPP, N Le Roy. WVU MED CTR G280 HSS MED 26506 #041-13-1961 L1966 **PUD** *071 †20
LARZO, Cristoforo Raymond. PO BOX 9193 26506 #055-01-2001 L2005 **OPH** *020 †35
LARZO, Melissa Rife. ■ 26505 #055-01-2000 L2003 **PD** *055
LAVENDER, Chad David. ■ 26505 #055-01-2008 *012
LAVOIE, Danielle. 364 PATTESON DR 26505 #422-01-2000 L2004 **CN** *100 †75
LAWRENCE, David Wayne. 1200 J D ANDERSON DR, MONONGALIA GENERAL HOSPITA 26505 #055-01-1995 L2000 **EM** *020 †16
LAYNE, Cathy Sue. ■ 26505 #055-02-2006 **P** *012
LAYNE, Richard David. MEDICAL CTR DR - STADIUM D 26505 #055-01-1980 L1982 **IM IMG** *020 †20
LAZOVIC, Gavrilo. 643 VALLEY VIEW DR 26505 #957-08-1983 L2004 **IM** *020 †20
LAZOVIC, Nina. PO BOX 9152, ROBERT C BYRD HLTH SCI CTR 26506 #957-08-1990 L2007 **FM** *100
LEE, Norman Kaching. 1200 J D ANDERSON DR 26505 #035-09-1994 L1999 **DR** *020 †80
LEMLEY, J A. ■ 26505 #035-15-2003 L2006 **ORS** *012
LERFALD, Nathan Meyer. PO BOX 9156, DEPT. OF INTERNAL MEDICINE 26506 #055-01-1997 L2000 **IM** *020 †20
LEYS, Monique J. ■ 26505 #165-04-1982 L1995 **OPH** *020 †35
LI, Lap-Yang Joseph. 404 INGLEWOOD BLVD, MONONGALIA PD & YOUTH ASSO 26505 #016-42-1994 L1998 **MPD PD** *020 †20,55
LIBELL, David Peter. ■ 26505 #041-13-1995 L2000 **N** *020 †75
LILLING, Menachem. WV UNIVERSITY, HEALTH SCIENCE CTR S 26506 #550-01-1973 L1983 **ORS** *020
LINBERG, John Vincent. MEDICAL CTR DR - STADIUM D 26505 #035-19-1971 L1983 **OPH** *020 †35
LINDSAY, Hugh Alexander. 1200 J D ANDERSON DR 26505 #055-01-1973 L1975 **FM** *020 †18
LINDSEY, Brock Anthony. ■ 26508 #038-41-2004 L2005 **ORS** *012
LINK, Jodi Ann. ■ 26508 #055-01-2006 L2008 **PD** *012
LIRIO, Eric Alvarez. ■ 26505 #055-01-2005 L2007 **IM** *012
LIVENGOOD, Ryan Hershey. ■ 26505 #055-01-2004 L2006 **PTH** *012
LLAUDES, Maximo Kevin. ■ 26506 #305-01-2003 **PTH** *012
LONG, Mary Ann. ■ 26508 #055-01-2001 L2003 **FM** *020 †18
LOOS, Matthew Stephen. ■ 26505 #007-02-2003 L2006 **GS** *012
LOWERS, Ryan Douglas. ■ 26505 #055-01-2005 L2007 **FP** *012
LOYA, Melissa Dawn. 344 INDEPENDENCE HLS 26505 #055-01-2006 **FP** *012
LUDMER, Philip Ross. ■ 26501 #495-09-1999 L2007 **PAN** *020 †05
LUTFI, Riad. PO BOX 8059, DEPT OF PEDATRICS 26506 #875-01-2003 **PD** *012
LYNCH, David A. ■ 26505 #055-01-1975 L1975 **DR PDR** *071 †80
LYNCH, John David. 200 ORTHOPEDIC WAY, MOUNTAINSTATE ORTHOPEDIC 26505 #055-01-1989 L1992 **PM** *020 †60
LYNCH, Susan Reese. SCIENCE CENTER, 9214 ROBERT C BYRD HEALTH 26505 #055-01-1990 L1994 **NPM PD** *020 †55
LYONS, John David. ■ 26508 #055-01-1971 L1978 **PTH GP** *071
MACE, Andrew Harold, Jr. 1200 J D ANDERSON DR 26505 #055-01-1979 L1980 **R** *020 †80
MACE, Kelly Marie. 211 CANYON VLG 26508 #055-01-1997 L1998 **FM** *020 †18
MAC KAY, Karen. 4095 HEALTH SCIENCES N, W VIRGINIA SCHOOL OF MED 26506 #049-01-1981 L1993 **IM** *020 †20
MAERTZ, Nathan Allan. ■ 26505 #056-05-2005 L2007 **DR** *012
MAHIN, Edwin J. WV UNIV MED CTR PATH 26506 #517-01-1972 L1978 **BBK CLP** *030 †50
MAIERS, Kane Alexander. ■ 26508 #055-01-2008 *012
MAJUMDER, Indira. 1189 PINEVIEW DR, STE E 26505 #495-13-1966 L1976 **PD** *020
MALONE, Patricia Thomson. ■ 26505 #055-01-2003 L2006 **PD** *020 †55
MALONE, Paul Frederick. 1188 PINEVIEW DR 26505 #055-01-1967 L1974 **OTO** *020 †45
MANIVANNAN, Shanthi. PO BOX 9160, DEPT OF MEDICINE 26506 #495-04-1988 L1998 **IM** *020 †20
MAOUAD, Michele. 1189 PINEVIEW DR, STE G2 26505 #055-01-1999 L2003 **D** *020 †15
MARANO, Gary David. MEDICAL CTR DR - STADIUM D 26505 #055-01-1976 L1977 **DR NR** *040 †80
MARCUCCI, Anthony David. 608 CHEAT RD, WVU CHEAT LAKE PHYSICIANS 26508 #055-01-1994 L1995 **FM** *020 †18
MARRA, Kevin York. ■ 26505 #055-01-2008 *012
MARSHALL, Ian Wm. WV UNIVERSITY, HEALTH SCIENCE CTR S 26506 #055-01-1989 L1993 **NR** *020
MARSHALL, Thomas Christop. ■ 26505 #055-01-2008 *012
MARTIN, Christopher John. 3858 HEALTH SCIENCE CTR S 26506 #063-01-1994 L1999 **OM** *020 †70
MARTIN, Daniel Allen. ■ 26505 #017-20-2002 L2007 **DR** *012
MARTIN, James Douglas. WV UNIVERSITY, HEALTH SCIENCE CTR S NEURO 26506 #047-05-1959 L1965 **N** *071 †75
MARTIN, Luke Weldon. ■ 26505 #036-08-2005 L2007 **GS** *012
MASHAT, Sammy Jafar. ■ 26505 #055-01-2008 *012
MASSINOPLE, David Samuel. ■ 26505 #055-01-2002 L2004 **CD** *012 †20
MATHELIER, Hansie Marie. ■ 26505 #023-07-2005 **IM** *012
MCALLISTER, Michael Von. ■ 26505 #030-06-2007 **TY** *012
MC CLELLAN, William T. ■ 26508 #055-01-2001 L2004 **HS** *020
MCCONNELL, Paul Stout. ■ 26505 #055-01-2006 **OPH** *012

MC DEVIT, Lindsay Kristin. ■ 26508 #041-12-2004 L2007 **FM** *020 †18
MCDONNELL, Andrew J. 364 PATTESON DR, BOX 297 26505 #035-03-1986 L2006 **DR** *020 †80
MC DONOUGH, Edward Barry. ■ 26508 #016-43-1999 L2007 **OSM ORS** *020 †40
MC DOWELL, Donald England. W VIRGINIA UNIV MEDIC, DEPT OF SURG 26506 #041-13-1947 L1974 **VS TS** *071 †90,85
MC GINNIS, Kevin Thomas. 1322 PINEVIEW DR STE 2, CENTER FOR REPRODUCTIVE ME 26505 #020-12-1993 L2006 **OBG REN** *020 †30
MC KNIGHT, John Allen. 300 WEDGEWOOD DR, MORGANTOWN INTERNAL MEDICI 26505 #055-01-1994 L1996 **CD** *020 †20
MEADE, Barbara Jean. ■ 26508 #055-01-2008 *012
MEDINA, Amando R. 918 CHESTNUT RIDGE RD, PRIORITY ONE MEDICAL ASSOC 26505 #748-01-1965 L1994 **PTH GP** *020 †50
MEDROSO, Melanie Anne. ■ 26505 #306-01-2003 **FP** *012
MEHLMAN, Tracey Renea. ■ 26505 #055-01-2008 *012
MELO, Marco Eleno Faria. ■ 26505 #187-06-1985 L2004 **OM** *012
MENGUITO, Roberto Gauddah. PO BOX 9001A, WEST VRIGINIA UNIV SCH OF 26506 #748-10-1994 **P** *012
MERENDA, Daniel James. ■ 26508 #055-01-2003 L2005 **OTO** *012
MERRILL, James Jay. 300 WEDGEWOOD DR 26505 #054-04-1986 L2008 **ICE CD** *020 †20 ‡
MERZOUK, Maria D. 1192 PINEVIEW DR 26505 #055-75-2001, ▲ L2006 **OBG** *020
MILLER, Gary James. ■ 26505 #055-01-2004 L2006 **OPH** *012
MILLER, Steven C. 1195 PINEVIEW DR, STE ONE 26505 #055-01-1976 L1977 **ORS** *020 †40
MILTENBERGER, Edward J. ■ 26508 #055-01-2006 L2008 **P** *012
MINARDI, Joseph J. ■ 26508 #055-01-2003 L2004 **EM** *012
MINHAS, Khalid Mahmood. ■ 26505 #913-03-1999 **IM** *012
MIRANDA, Max Claire. ■ 26505 #014-01-2004 L2007 **GE** *012 †20
MIRZA, Muhammad Azim. 1200 J D ANDERSON DR 26505 #704-02-1996 L2006 **HO** *012 †20
MISHRA, Anand Donald. ■ 26508 #055-01-2003 L2006 **CD** *012
MOFFETT, Kathryn. MEDICAL CTR DR - STADIUM D 26505 #041-14-1988 L1998 **PD PDI** *020 †55
MOGRI, Idrees. ■ 26505 #704-16-2001 L2007 **PCC** *012 †20
MOHTASHAM, Lida. ■ 26505 #517-08-1992 L2007 **PD** *012
MOLA, Sara Jann. ■ 26508 #055-01-2005 L2007 **PD** *012
MONGOLD, Bradley Wayne. ■ 26508 #055-01-2003 L2005 **EM** *020 †16
MONGOLD, Derek Skeet. ■ 26505 #055-01-2005 L2007 **FPP** *012
MONSEAU, Aaron Joel. ■ 26505 #055-01-2007 **EM** *012
MONSEAU, Ronna Louise. 215 DON KNOTTS BLVD, STE 130 26501 #055-01-1996 L1997 **EM** *020 †16
MONSEAU, Vincent Edward. 215 DON KNOTTS BLVD, STE 130 26501 #055-01-1996 L1997 **EM** *020 †16
MONTELEONE, Gaetano Peter. ■ 26508 #041-02-1990 L2004 **FM** *020 †18
MONTJOY, Carol Ann. PO BOX 9166, WEST VIRGINIA UNIV SCH OF 26506 #038-41-2000 L2007 **PCC** *012 †20
MOORE, Kristen Nicole. PO BOX 9214, DEPARTMENT OF PEDIATRICS 26506 #055-01-2007 **MPD** *012
MOORE, Renee Saggio. WV UNIVERSITY, HEALTH SCIENCE CTR S PEDS 26506 #055-01-1985 L1989 **PD** *020 †55
MOOREHEAD, Benjamin David. 943 MAPLE DR, WVU SPORTS MED CTR - LL 26505 #017-20-2002 L2006 **IM ISM** *020 †20
MORABITO, Rocco Anthony, Jr. ■ 26505 #055-01-2006 L2007 **U** *012
MORAN, Walter Harrison. WV UNIVERSITY, HEALTH SCIENCE CTR S GS 26505 #024-01-1955 L1960 **GS EM** *071 †85
MORELAND, Jason Allen. ■ 26508 #055-01-2003 L2005 **CD** *012 †20
MORGAN, David Michael. 930 CHESTNUT RIDGE RD, CHESTNUT RIDGE HOSPITAL 26505 #055-01-1975 L1977 **P** *071
MORGAN, David Zackquill. ■ 26505 #051-04-1952 L1953 **IMG IM** *071 †20
MORGAN, Edwin James. ■ 26508 #041-12-1964 L1967 **IM PUD** *071 †20
MORGAN, Winfield S, III. ■ 26505 #041-13-1945 L1975 **PTH** *071 †50
MORISE, Anthony Peter. WEST VA UNIV RM 2209 HSC 26506 #050-02-1975 L1980 **CD** *040 †20
MORTON, Dana R.. ■ 26505 #654-01-1995 L2002 **P** *012
MOSS, Alvin Howard. PO BOX 9022 26506 #041-01-1975 L1983 **NEP PLM** *050 †20
MOSTAFAVIFAR, Ahmad Mehra. ■ 26505 #055-01-2008 *012
MOVASSAGHI, Babak. PO BOX 9100A 26506 #305-01-2006 **N** *012
MUDRY, Ronald Alan, Jr. ■ 26508 #055-01-2001 L2004 **PCC** *100
MULDOON, Mary Elizabeth. ■ 26505 #055-02-2007 **MPD** *012
MULLETT, Charles Jacob. ■ 26508 #055-01-1993 L1999 **CCP** *020 †55
MULLETT, David Stewart. 1600 UNIVERSITY AVE, DEPT OF MED/PEDS 26506 #055-01-2006 **MPD** *012
MULLETT, Martha Dilley. WV UNIVERSITY, HEALTH SCIENCE CTR S PEDS 26505 #055-01-1972 L1974 **NPM PD** *020 †55
MULLINS, Jeffrey Kyle. ■ 26508 #055-01-2008 *012
MUNOZ-POSADA, Emmanuel. 918 CHESTNUT RIDGE RD, STE 9 26505 #341-01-1966 L1981 **GP IMG** *020
MUNTASSER, Siham. ■ 26508 #561-19-1989 L2003 **P CHP** *020 †75
MURRAY, Gordon Franklin. 330 SCOTT AVE 26508 #025-01-1963 L1985 **TS GS** *071 †90,85
MUTH, James Nelson. PO BOX 9001A, WEST VIRGINIA UNIV SCH OF 26506 #422-01-2005 **IM** *012
MYERBERG, David Zell. ■ 26501 #035-01-1973 L1978 **PD NPM** *071 †55
NAIR, Christopher Raj. ■ 26505 #055-01-2003 **GS** *100
NAJMUDDIN, Asif Anwarali. 953 IRWIN ST, APT 2 26505 #704-25-2005 **IM** *012
NAMSUPAK, James S. ■ 26505 #055-01-2008 *012
NANCE, Christopher Scott. ■ 26508 #036-05-1999 L2005 **CN N** *100 †75
NANDA, Sharmila Harikrish. ■ 26505 #495-16-1990 L2003 **PD** *100 †55
NAQVI, Samrina. PO BOX 9152, ROBERT C BYRD HLTH SCI CTR 26506 #704-02-1998 **FM** *100
NAVARRO, Arsenio Ponce. 1200 J D ANDERSON DR 26505 #748-08-1970 L1977 **DR GS** *020
NAZIM, Muhammad Haris. ■ 26505 #704-25-2003 **GS** *012
NEAL, Bijal Patel. WEST VA UNIV HOSPS, MEDICAL CENTER DR 26506 #665-01-2002 L2005 **AN** *100
NEAL, William Albert. 2315 LAKESIDE ESTS, WVU HLTH SCIENCES CTR 26508 #055-01-1966 L1974 **PDC PD** *030 †55
NEELY, Elizabeth Ann J. 404 INGLEWOOD BLVD 26505 #055-01-1979 L1984 **PD** *074 †55
NEELY, Jeffrey Lynn. MEDICAL CTR DR - STADIUM D 26505 #055-01-1983 L1984 **IM** *020
NELMS, Timothy Daye. 1200 J D ANDERSON DR 26505 #037-01-1985 L1989 **EM PD** *020 †55
NEWMAN, Jeremy Herschel. ■ 26508 #007-02-2005 L2007 **EM** *012 ‡
NGUYEN, Anna Oanh. MEDICAL CENTER DR, WV UNIV SCH MED 26506 #056-06-2007 **PD** *012

NGUYEN, Thuanphuong. 1200 J D ANDERSON DR 26505 #010-02-1989 L1995 **DR** *020 †80
NIELD, Linda Susan. WV UNIVERSTIY, HEALTH SCIENCE CTR S 26506 #032-01-1990 L1993 **PD** *040 †55
NILFOROUSHAN, Mostafa. ■ 26505 #517-01-1967 L1975 **IM** *020
NUGENT, George R. W VA UNIV MED CTR, DEPT NS 26506 #038-41-1953 L1961 **NS** *072 †25
NULPH, Laura Lea. ■ 26508 #055-01-2005 L2007 **FP** *012
NUSS, Michelle Ann. PO BOX 9160, RCB HSC 26506 #055-01-1992 L1994 **IM P** *020 †20,75
OATES, Gary Edward. ■ 26505 #055-01-2005 L2007 **EM** *012
OGERSHOK, Paul Richard. ■ 26508 #055-01-1994 L1997 **AI** *100 †20,55,03
O'KEEFE, Joann Audia. 300 WEDGEWOOD DR 26505 #055-01-1981 L1982 **IM GE** *020 †20
O'KEEFE, Michael Vincent. 300 WEDGEWOOD DR, MORGANTOWN INT MEDICINE GR 26505 #055-01-1975 L1976 **CD IM** *050 †20
OLIVERIO, Brock Joseph. ■ 26508 #055-01-2004 L2007 **PTH** *012
OLIVERIO, Matthew Aaron. ■ 26505 #055-01-2005 **OTO** *012
OLNESS, Erik John. ■ 26505 #055-01-2007 **AN** *012
O'MALLEY, Gregg Michael. 200 ORTHOPEDIC WAY, MOUNTAINSTATE ORTHOPEDIC 26505 #041-12-1980 L1985 **ORS HS** *012 †40
OMAR, Hossai. ■ 26508 #055-01-1997 **GS** *100
ONDER, Alimirza. ■ 26505 #902-01-1997 L2006 **PN** *100 †55
ONDER, Songul. ■ 26505 #902-01-1997 **IM** *012
OPALINSKI, Yvonne. MEDICAL CENTER DRIVE 26506 #065-01-1990 **OPH** *100
ORJUELA, Alvaro Hernando. PO BOX 9214 26506 #264-04-1995 **PD** *012
ORPHANOS, John Russell. ■ 26505 #055-01-2004 L2006 **NS** *012
ORTEL, R Wade. WVU SCH MED, DEPT MED 26506 #023-01-1958 L1977 **RHU** *020
OSMAN, Salman Salahuddin. 1600 UNIVERSITY AVE, DEPT OF INTERNAL MEDICINE 26506 #704-01-2004 **IM** *012
OSTRINSKY, Yevgeniy. ■ 26508 #035-08-2003 L2006 **GE** *012 †20
OVERBECK, Henry West. ■ 26508 #016-06-1956 L1989 **IM OS** *020 †20
OXLEY, Kevin Scott. ■ 26505 #055-01-2003 L2005 **OTO** *012
PAINE, Ward Jackson. 1526 MILEGROUND RD 26505 #055-01-1999 L2001 **IM** *020 †20
PALADE, Adriana Elena. PO BOX 9180, WEST VA UNIV HLTH SCI CTR 26506 #781-01-1995 L2002 **N CN** *020 †75
PALLIE, Erika Anne. 608 CHEAT RD 26508 #055-01-1995 L1997 **FM** *020 †18
PALMER, Hugh C, Jr. 26506 #051-01-1992 L1994 **IM** *020 †20
PALMER, Ingrid Vivian. ■ 26505 #028-34-2006 L2007 **OBG** *012
PALMER, Jan Elwin. W VIRGINIA U HSP FAM PRAC 26506 #035-15-1977 L1978 **FM** *020 †18
PARKER, John Eugene. 1 STADIUM DR, PULMONARY & CRITICAL MED 26506 #025-07-1976 L1985 **PUD IM** *050 †20
PAULSON, Debra Jo. MEDICAL CTR DR - STADIUM D 26505 #026-04-1983 L1991 **EM PD** *020 †16
PAWAR, Gauri Vikram. PO BOX 9180, DEPT OF NEUROLOAY WV UNIV. 26506 #495-82-1991 L1999 **N CN** *020 †75
PAWLOWSKI, Edward John. ■ 26505 #759-01-2002 L2007 **PD** *100
PAYNE, Chris S. MEDICAL CENTER DR, WV UNIV SCH MED 26506 #012-22-2007 **AN** *012
PAYNE, Rita Kay. 1000 J D ANDERSON DR, STE 402 26505 #048-02-1980 L1982 **GYN** *020
PEARSON, Richard John C. WVU HEALTH SCIENCES CTR, COMMUNITY MEDICINE 26506 #352-03-1954 L1977 **GPM FM** *071
PEDAPATI, Sashi Kiran. PO BOX 9001A 26506 #495-11-2003 **IM** *012
PELLEGRINO, Bethany Sue. ■ 26508 #055-01-1999 L2002 **NEP** *100 †20
PELLEGRINO, Ronald James. ■ 26508 #055-01-1999 L2002 **IM** *020 †20
PERKINS, Kathaleen Claire. MEDICAL CTR DR - STADIUM D 26505 #035-03-1954 L1990 **ADL** *071 †55
PETRI, Justin Daniel. 301 SCOTT AVE, VALLEY MENTAL HEALTH 26508 #055-01-2005 L2007 **P** *012
PETSONK, Edward Lee. 1095 WILLOWDALE RD 26505 #067-01-1973 L1980 **PUD IM** *050 †20 ‡
PETTIT, Wm Francis, Jr. 930 CHESTNUT RIDGE RD 26505 #016-11-1969 L2001 **P ADM** *020 †75 ‡
PEYKANU, James Arash. 930 CHESTNUT RIDGE RD 26505 #030-06-2003 L2006 **P** *012
PHELPS, Kelly Dawn. 1 MEDICAL CENTER DR, DEPT OF EMERGENCY MED 26506 #012-01-2006 **EM** *012
PIEDIMONTE, Giovanni. ■ 26508 #561-17-1986 L2006 **PDP PD** *020 †55
PIHLBLAD, Matthew Simon. ■ 26505 #055-01-2008 *012
PILNEY, Jeffry Jos. SURGERY BOX 9238, WEST VIRGINIA UNIV DEPT OF 26506 #038-45-1991 L1996 **GS TRS** *071 †85
POLAK, Mark Jos. PHYSICIAN OFFICE CENTER, RENEE MOORE MD 26505 #055-01-1982 L1983 **PD NPM** *020 †55
POLING, Mark Alan. ■ 26505 #055-01-2005 L2007 **IM** *012
POLLARD, Scott Elliott. 930 CHESTNUT RIDGE RD 26505 #048-02-1980 L1982 **P** *020 †75
POPOVICH, Teppe. 99 J D ANDERSON DR, AMERIRAD 26505 #021-05-1999 L2004 **RNR** *020 †80
POSEY, Jodie Lynn. ■ 26505 #055-01-2008 *012
POSSEHN, Jessica Linn. ■ 26504 #055-01-2008 *012
POST, William Richard. 2195 CHEAT RD STE 2 26508 #041-07-1986 L1987 **OSM ORS** *020 †40
POWELL, Eddie Nelson, II. ■ 26505 #036-08-2002 L2004 **ORS** *100
POWERS, Roxann Lucinda. MEDICAL CTR DR - STADIUM D 26505 #055-01-1976 L1977 **D FM** *040 †20,15
PRASAD, Soumya. 608 CHEAT RD, WVU-CHEAT LAKE PHYSICIANS 26508 #035-08-2001 L2004 **PD** *100 †55
PRATHER, Cynthia Erin. 930 CHESTNUT RIDGE RD, CHESTNUT RIDGE HOSPITAL 26505 #055-01-1995 L1997 **P** *100
PRESCOTT, John E. PO BOX 9100, 1040 H S S 26506 #010-02-1981 L1990 **EM** *030 †16
PRUD'HOMME, Bonhomme Jos. ■ 26508 #048-01-1989 L1995 **HS** *100 †40
PRYPUTNIEWICZ, David M. ■ 26508 #047-20-2002 L2004 **NS** *012
PUCKETT, Frankie Allen. ■ 26505 #055-02-2002 L2007 **TS** *012
PULLER, Leon Saul. ■ 26505 #030-06-1947 L1948 **IM** *071
QAISER, Rabia. PO BOX 9100A 26504 #704-25-2004 **IM** *012
QUIGLEY, Brian Patrick. 930 CHESTNUT RIDGE RD, CHESTNUT RIDGE HOSP 26505 #054-04-2001 L2006 **PFP** *100 †75
QURESHI, Hammad Nasir. MEDICAL CENTER DR, WV UNIV SCH OF MED 26506 #704-01-2004 L2006 **IM** *012
QURESHI, Wasif Aleem. 163 MEADOW RIDGE TOWNHOMES 26505 #704-25-1998 L2003 **IC** *020 †20 ‡
RAHMAN, Rubayat Naila. ■ 26505 #160-02-1997 **IM** *012
RAI, Alia Ansaar. ■ 26508 #704-25-1994 **ADL** *100 †55
RAI, Ansaar Tariq. 1200 J D ANDERSON DR 26505 #704-25-1994 L2002 **DR** *020 †80

RAJU, Leela Vadrevu. ■ 26505 #055-02-2003 L2005 **IM** *100
RAJU, Vadrevu K. 3140 COLLINS FERRY RD 26505 #495-11-1966 L1977 **OPH** *020 †35 ‡
RAMADAN, Hassan H. 1188 PINEVIEW DR 26505 #605-01-1982 L1991 **OTO PDO** *020 †45
RAMSEY, William Dale. 190 HART FIELD RD, NOROP 26505 #055-01-1984 L1987 **EM** *030 †16
RANA, Muhammad Ali Asghar. WV UNIV SCH MED, MEDICAL CENTER DR 26506 #704-25-2003 L2007 **GS** *012
RAO, Katikineni Murali K. 1095 WILLOWDALE RD, BOX 2015 26505 #495-65-1968 L1976 **CLP** *050 †50
RASHID, Paul Ferris. ■ 26505 #055-02-2006 L2008 **P** *012
RASMUSSEN, Norval Leroy. 1526 MILEGROUND RD 26505 #055-01-1977 L1978 **GP GYN** *020
RASSEKH, Christopher H. ■ 26508 #018-03-1986 L1999 **OTO HNS** *020 †45
RAVIENDRAN, Raveen Thekke. PO BOX 8059, DEPT OF MED/PEDS 26506 #305-01-2005 **MPD** *012
REECE, Josephine Louise. PO BOX 9214, DEPARTMENT OF PEDIATRICS 26506 #055-01-2008 **IM PD** *012
REHMAN, Raheela. PO BOX 9001A, DEPT OF INTERNAL MED 26506 #704-25-1998 L2007 **NEP** *012 †20
REMICK, Scot Clifton. 1801 HEALTH SCIENCES SOUTH, MARY BABB RANDOLPH CAN CT 26506 #035-09-1982 L2007 **ON** *012
RENN, Joseph John, III. 99 J D ANDERSON DR 26505 #055-01-1964 L1969 **PUD IM** *020 †20
RENZELLI, Anthony James. ■ 26505 #055-01-2003 L2005 **CD** *012
REYNOLDS, Shelley Breanne. ■ 26505 #055-01-2008 *012
REZAEE, Fariba. ■ 26505 #517-06-1998 L2007 **PD** *100 †55
RICHARDS, Joelyn. WV UNIVERSITY, HEALTH SCIENCE CTR S NEPH 26506 #026-04-1984 L1989 **NEP IM** *020 †20
RIGGS, Betty Sue. ■ 26508 #020-02-1979 L1981 **EM** *050 †16
RIGGS, Jack Edward. 1160 VAN VOORHIS RD 26505 #035-45-1976 L1981 **N IM** *020 †20,75
RINGUS, Vytautas Matas. ■ 26505 #016-11-2004 L2006 **ORS** *012
ROBERTS, Scott Christian. ■ 26508 #055-01-2007 **ORS** *012
ROBERTS, Thomas Darius. 819 RIVERVIEW DR, STE 840 26505 #055-01-1979 L1980 **DR VIR** *020 †80
ROBINSON, Nalini Pillai. 608 CHEAT RD 26508 #055-01-1995 L1998 **PD** *100 †55
ROBINSON, Richard O. W VA UNIV MED CTR 26506 #917-25-1967 L1977 *100
ROCHLANI, Maya. ■ 26505 #495-01-1964 L1983 **PTH** *020 †50
ROCHLANI, Satyabhlashi P. W VA UNIV MED CTR PATH 26506 #495-04-1955 L1974 **PTH** *071 †50
ROGERS, Aimee Elise. MEDICAL CENTER DR, WV UNIV SCH MED 26506 #020-02-2007 **GS** *012
ROGERS, John Stafford, II. 1160 VAN VOORHIS RD 26505 #010-01-1970 L1975 **IM HEM** *040
ROIDAD, Nasira. ■ 26505 #055-01-2006 L2008 **MPD** *012
ROSE, William Darrell. DEPT OF EMERGENCY MEDICINE, WVU HOSPITAL PO BOX 9149 26506 #055-01-1983 L1986 **EM** *020 †16
ROSEN, Charles L. ■ 26508 #035-19-1994 L2001 **NS** *020
ROSEN, David Alan. MEDICAL CTR DR - STADIUM D 26505 #051-07-1980 L1992 **AN CCM** *020 †05
ROWAN, Shon Patrick. ■ 26508 #055-01-2004 L2006 **OBG** *012
RUDOLPH-WATSON, Lisa Ann. PO BOX 9247, ROBERT C. BYRD HEALTH SCI 26506 #055-01-1992 L1994 **P** *020 †75
RUSSELL, Christopher Davi. ■ 26508 #055-01-2005 L2007 **IM** *012
RYU, Jaiyoung. WV UNIVERSITY, HEALTH SCIENCE CTR S OSM 26506 #583-10-1977 L1992 **HS ORS** *020 †40
SAAD, Ayman Abd El Momen. ■ 26505 #915-04-1994 L2005 **HO** *012 †20
SAFDER, Sara. ■ 26505 #055-02-2006 L2008 **DR** *012
SALAHUDDIN, Nawal. MEDICAL CENTER DR, WEST VIRGINIA UNIV HOSPS 26506 #704-25-1990 L1998 **PCC** *100 †20
SALEEM, Mark. ■ 26501 #041-13-1999 L2006 **GS** *100 †18,85
SAMORA, Walter Paul. ■ 26505 #055-01-2004 L2006 **ORS** *012
SANTOS, Angelo Noel. ■ 26505 #055-01-2004 L2004 **CCS** *100
SARWARI, Arif R. PO BOX 9163, DEPARTMENT OF MEDICINE 26506 #704-25-1990 L1994 **ID** *020 †20
SAUNDERS, Darrell Francis. 300 WEDGEWOOD DR 26505 #055-01-1974 L1975 **ON IM** *020 †20
SAUNDERS, Susan Elizabeth. ■ 26505 #055-01-2005 L2007 **U** *012
SAVIDGE, Todd Owen. 215 DON KNOTTS BLVD, STE 130 26501 #038-43-1989 L1995 **FM** *020 †18
SAWYER, Kevin James. ■ 26505 #010-02-2003 L2006 **DR** *012
SCHEMM, Jessica M. 930 CHESTNUT RIDGE RD 26505 #030-06-2003 L2006 **PFP** *012
SCHIEBEL, Franklin G. 484 LAWNVIEW DR, BYRD HSES 26505 #649-14-1971 L1981 **CCM NS** *020
SCHMIDT, Matrina J. ■ 26505 #038-43-2001 L2004 **PTH** *100
SCHMIDT, Rebecca Jane. PO BOX 9165, SECTION OF NEPHROLOGY 26506 #018-75-1985, ▲ L1993 **NEP IM** *020 †20
SCHMIDT, Stanley Burnett. WV UNIVERSITY 26506 #051-01-1979 L1985 **CD ICE** *062 †20
SCHREIMAN, Judith Stark. 101 STADIUM DR, WVUH MAMMOGRAM 26506 #025-12-1980 L1992 **DR** *020 †80
SCHWARTZ, Terry Lynn. PO BOX 9193, WEST VA INST 26506 #055-01-1982 L1985 **OPH PO** *020 †35
SCOTT, Anna Marie. ■ 26505 #055-01-2007 **EM** *012
SCOTT, George Wesley. PO BOX 9001A, DEPT OF NEUROLOGY 26506 #306-01-2004 L2008 **N** *012
SCOTT, Janna Elaine. ■ 26508 #055-01-2004 L2006 **MPD** *012
SEDNEY, Cara Lynn. ■ 26505 #055-01-2007 **GS** *012
SEFTICK, Gregory Eric. MEDICAL CENTER DR, WV UNIV SCH MED 26506 #026-04-2007 **EM** *012
SELBY, Joseph Barry. HEALTH SCIENCE CENTER, DEPT OF FAMILY MEDICINE 26505 #055-01-1990 L1993 **FM P** *020 †18,75
SEYNNAEVE, Katrijn. ■ 26501 #055-01-2006 L2007 **P** *012
SHAFFER, Marcus Doddridge. ■ 26508 #055-01-2008 *012
SHAFQUAT, Azam. WV UNIVERSITY, HEALTH SCIENCE CTR S MED 26506 #704-25-1989 L1996 **CD** *100 †20
SHAHAB, Sohrab. PO BOX 9200, 222 HEALTH SCIENCES CTR S 26506 #051-07-2004 L2006 **OTO** *012
SHAHZAD, Farooq. MEDICAL CENTER DR 26506 #704-25-2001 L2006 **GS** *012
SHAMMA'A, John Michel. W VIRGINIA U MC, DEPT MED 26506 #012-05-1978 L1984 **GE IM** *020 †20
SHAMSI, Rohma. ■ 26505 #704-02-1999 L2008 **IM** *012
SHAMS MOORKANI, Minoo. WV UNIV MED SCH, MEDICAL CENTER DR 26506 #517-06-1999 **N** *012

SHANNON, Claude Kennard. 1160 VAN VOORHIS RD 26505 #055-01-1979 L1980 **FM EM** *050 †18
SHARMA, Luna. PO BOX 9214, DEPT OF PEDIATRICS 26506 #495-02-2001 L2007 **PDI** *012 †55
SHARMA, Manish. MEDICAL CENTER DR 26506 #305-01-2003 L2006 **HO** *012 †20
SHEK, Gilberto Hernan. ■ 26505 #264-05-1994 **OBG** *012
SHENOY, Santosh G. ■ 26505 #496-09-1991 L2006 **GS** *100 †20
SHERRY, James Hoy. ■ 26508 #055-01-1987 L1999 **N** *020 †75
SHOCKCOR, William Thos. 1160 VAN VOORHIS RD 26505 #050-02-1982 L1984 **IM IMG** *020 †20
SHOWALTER, Kelly Renee. ■ 26505 #055-01-2005 L2007 **PD** *012
SHUHAIBER, Jeffrey Jabra. ■ 26505 #917-19-1998 L1999 **TS GS** *020 †85,90
SHULTZ, Ryan William. ■ 26505 #055-01-2006 **OPH** *012
SIAVASHI, Ali. MEDICAL CENTER DR 26506 #305-01-2006 **P** *012
SIKORA, Rosanna Dawn. DEPT OF EMERGENCY MEDICINE, WEST VA SCHOOL OF MEDICINE 26506 #055-01-1982 L1983 **EM PD** *040 †20,55,16
SIMMONS, Matthew Edward. ■ 26508 #055-01-2006 **IM** *012
SINCLAIR, Jeffrey Byron. 1200 J D ANDERSON DR 26505 #055-01-1984 L1985 **EM FM** *020 †18
SINE, Wilbur Zinn. 1197 VAN VOORHIS RD 26505 #055-01-1973 L1973 **FM** *020 †75,18
SIRIKONDA, Naga Srinivas. PO BOX 9214 26506 #496-24-2005 *100
SIVAK-CALLCOTT, Jennifer. ■ 26505 #038-40-1996 L2001 **OPH** *020 †35
SMITH, Andria Lee. ■ 26505 #055-01-2008 *012
SMITH, Eleanor Alice. MEDICAL CENTER DR, WV UNIV SCH MED 26506 #055-01-2007 **PD** *012
SMITH, Jimmie Kirkland. ■ 26505 #027-01-2006 **PTH** *012
SMITH, Lee Bryan. MEDICAL CTR DR - STADIUM D 26505 #055-02-1982 L1983 **EM LM** *020
SMITH, Matthew Scott. ■ 26501 #055-01-2007 **MN** *012
SMITH, Richard Lee, II. ■ 26505 #055-01-2001 L2004 **CD** *020 †20
SMITH, Robert Thomas, Jr. ■ 26505 #051-04-2002 L2006 **ORS** *100
SMITH, Tamara Susan. ■ 26505 #051-04-2001 L2004 **IM** *100
SMOTHERS, Daniel Patrick. ■ 26505 #055-01-2005 L2008 **DR** *012
SNIDER, Geo Everett, Jr. 1188 PINEVIEW DR 26505 #055-01-1974 L1975 **OTO** *020 †45
SOMESHWAR, Jean. ■ 26505 #028-34-1994 L2003 **PD** *020 †55
SOMESHWAR, Shiv Prasad. ■ 26505 #496-09-1985 L2002 **PD** *020 †55
SOTOMAYOR, Talia Bettina. ■ 26504 #737-09-1988 L2006 **PD PUD** *020 ‡
SPARKS, Stephen Scott. PO BOX 9238, WVU DEPT OF UROLOGY 26506 #048-04-2003 L2006 **U** *012
SPENCER, Richard Alan. 1200 J D ANDERSON DR 26505 #055-01-1986 L1989 **FM** *020 †18
SRICHOMKUAN, Aree. WV UNIV MED CTR RADIO DPT 26506 #891-02-1969 **R** *100 †80
STANLEY, Jonathan Edmund. ■ 26505 #055-75-2007, ▲ **IM** *012
STARCHER, Larry Victor, II. 215 DON KNOTTS BLVD, STE 130 26501 #055-01-1999 L2002 **FM** *020 †18
STARK, Linda J. MEDICAL CTR DR - STADIUM D 26505 #055-01-1988 L1989 **IM** *020 †20
STEEVES, Stacey Wade. MEDICAL CENTER DR 26506 #654-01-2001 **N** *012
STEFAN, Angela. PO BOX 9214, DEPARTMENT OF PEDIATRICS 26506 #781-01-1989 L2007 **PHO** *100 †55 ‡
STEMPLE, Larry Jack. 200 ORTHOPEDIC WAY, MNTN STATE ORTHO ASSOC 26505 #055-01-1965 L1966 **ORS** *020 †40
STEPHENS, Kathryn Jane. ■ 26505 #055-01-2007 L2007 *012
STEVENS, Roy James. 400 INGLEWOOD BLVD 26505 #055-01-1963 L1968 **OBG OS** *020 †30
STEVENS, Scott Kenneth. ■ 26508 #028-34-2004 L2007 **OPH** *012
STEVENSON, James Marcus. 930 CHESTNUT RIDGE RD, CHESTNUT RIDGE HOSP 26505 #055-01-1970 L1970 **P** *030 †75
STEVENSON, Sarah E. ■ 26508 #055-01-2001 L2002 **R** *020
STEWART, Russell Raymond. 1200 J D ANDERSON DR, ANESTHESIA DEPARTMENT 26505 #041-12-1981 L2003 **AN** *020
STEWART, Staci Kay. 1192 PINEVIEW DR 26505 #055-01-1997 L2001 **OBG** *020 †30 ‡
STITELY, Michael Lynn. 1192 PINEVIEW DR 26505 #041-12-1994 L2004 **OBG** *020 †30
STOLL, David Allen. 200 ORTHOPEDIC WAY, MOUNTAINSTATE ORTHOPEDIC 26505 #018-03-1971 L1974 **ORS OSM** *020 †40
STOVER, Garrett Wayne. ■ 26505 #055-01-2007 **TY** *012
STUCHELL, Bryan Keith. 215 DON KNOTTS BLVD, STE 100 26501 #055-01-1998 L1999 **EM** *020
SULLIVAN, Carl Rollynn. 930 CHESTNUT RIDGE RD, CHESTNUT RIDGE HOSPITAL 26505 #055-01-1980 L1981 **P** *020 †20,75
SULLIVAN, Pamela. 930 CHESTNUT RIDGE RD, CHESTNUT RIDGE HOSPITAL 26505 #055-01-1978 L1979 **P** *020 †75
SUMNER, Calvin Russell. 930 CHESTNUT RIDGE RD, CHESTNUT RIDGE HOSPITAL 26505 #010-01-1981 L1986 **P CHP** *030 †75
SUNDARAM, Uma. ■ 26508 #038-43-1983 L2004 **GE** *020 †20
SWEARINGEN, Phillip Van. 200 WEDGEWOOD DR, ASSOCIATES INC 26505 #021-05-1972 L1984 **GE** *020 †20
SWEDARSKY, Robert Hutcher. 1200 J D ANDERSON DR, DEPT OF PATHLGY 26506 #010-02-1974 L1995 **PTH PCP** *020 †50
SZE, Eddie Hung Mow. 1117 UNIVERSITY AVE, STE 409 26505 #422-01-1982 L2005 **OBG** *020 †30
TADROS, Allison. ■ 26508 #055-01-1999 L2002 **EM** *020 †16
TAKAMORI, Masaharu. W VA UNIV MED CTR, DEPT N 26506 #572-08-1958 **N** *020
TALLMAN, Todd Edward. 4000 HAMPTON CTR STE A, ASSOCIATES, INC. 26505 #055-01-1992 L1997 **GS** *020 †85
TALUG, Can. ■ 26505 #038-44-2004 L2006 **U** *012
TANVEER, Khan Meraj. ■ 26505 #704-02-2000 L2007 **FM** *020
TAYLOR, Edwin Tom. MEDICAL CENTER DR 26506 #913-22-1993 L2003 **PD** *100 †55
TAYLOR, Sarah Elizabeth. ■ 26505 #055-01-2008 *012
TAZEN, Sirinan. PO BOX 9180, MEDICAL CENTER DR 26506 #305-01-2006 **TY N** *012
TEBA, Catalina Villanna. ■ 26508 #055-01-2006 **IM** *012
TERCAN, Erdogan. 1200 J D ANDERSON DR 26506 #902-03-1964 L1974 **AN PUD** *100 †05
TERRELL, Andrew Michael. ■ 26501 #017-20-2007 **OTO** *012
THAMMASITBOON, Satid. PO BOX 9214, ROBERT C. BYRD HEALTH SCIE 26506 #891-07-1995 L2004 **CCP** *012
TILLOTSON, Roger Decker. ■ 26508 #035-08-2001 L2005 **EM** *100 †16
TINGLER, David Charles. ■ 26508 #055-01-2003 L2005 **CD** *012 †20
TOFFLE, Roger Chas. 1192 PINEVIEW DR 26505 #026-04-1974 L1984 **OBG REN** *020 †30
TOLER, Jeremy Michael. ■ 26505 #055-01-2008 **TY** *012
TONDAPU, Sumanth Reddy. PO BOX 9214 26506 #495-11-2004 **MPD** *012
TONG, Shiu Yu F. ■ 26505 #407-30-1939 L1965 **P GP** *071

TOSSON, Hanan Mahmoud. PO BOX 9214, 1 MEDICAL CENTER DR 26506 #915-02-1983 L2007 PDE *055

TRAUBERT, John Wm. 800 J D ANDERSON DR 26505 #038-40-1965 L1967 FM *071 †18

TROISCHT, Megan Judith. PO BOX 9214, 1 STADIUM DR 26506 #051-01-2000 L2004 PD *020 †55

TRUMBULL, Diane Welch. 930 CHESTNUT RIDGE RD, CHESTNUT RIDGE HOSPITAL 26505 #036-01-1975 L1983 CHP P *020 †75

TUEL, David. WV UNIVERSITY, HEALTH SCIENCE CTR S 26506 #055-01-1988 L1990 ORS *020 †12

TYRE, Loraine L. 608 CHEAT RD 26508 #055-01-1972 L1974 OBG *020 †30

TYSZKO, Sean Michael. ■ 26505 #023-01-2003 L2005 DR *012

UDUGAMPOLA, Bianca Priyad. PO BOX 9168, WEST VIRGINIA UNIV HOSP 26506 #305-01-2004 L2007 IM *020

ULLRICH, Irma Hilda. 209 POPLAR DR 26505 #026-04-1969 L1974 END IM *040 †20

UNGER, Merv Wayne Todd. PO BOX 9001A 26506 #305-01-2005 AN *012

URBAN, Vanessa Angelina. ■ 26508 #016-43-2001 L2005 P *020

VAGLIENTI, Richard Martin. 1075 VAN VOORHIS RD, STE 150 26505 #055-01-1986 L1987 AN *020 †05

VALINA, Mary Rose Belen. PO BOX 9214 26506 #894-01-2002 *100

VANDERSLOOT, Paul. 1188 PINEVIEW DR 26505 #060-01-1997 L2003 OTO *020

VANHOOSE, Timothy Aaron. ■ 26505 #055-01-2008 N *012

VANIN, John Romildo. 930 CHESTNUT RIDGE RD, CHESTNUT RIDGE HOSPITAL 26505 #055-01-1977 L1978 P FM *020 †75,18

VAN RIPER, Louise E. 200 WEDGEWOOD DR, STE 201 26505 #055-01-1966 L1967 OBG *020 †30

VASILAKIS, Christ. 200 ORTHOPEDIC WAY 26505 #055-01-1992 L1994 ORS *020 †40

VASUDEVAN, Arvind. 930 CHESTNUT RIDGE RD 26505 #055-01-2003 L2005 PYN *012

VAUGHAN, Richard Alan. PO BOX 9238, WV UNIV DEPT SURG 26506 #055-01-1979 L1984 GS *020 †85

VAUGHN, Kavara Susan. ■ 26508 #055-01-2008 *012

VEDULA, Giridhar Venkata. ■ 26505 #055-01-2003 L2006 GS *012

VESELICKY, Kenneth Andrew. ■ 26505 #055-01-1997 L2000 R NR *020 †80

VIRANI, Shamsuddin. ■ 26505 #704-25-2002 IM *012

VOELLINGER, Mark Thomas. ■ 26508 #055-01-2007 IM *012

VOHRA, Rakesh Kumar. HSCS ROOM 2203, WEST VIRGINIA HOSPITALS 26508 #495-43-1988 L1997 CD IM *020 †20

VOLESKY, Patrick Joseph. ■ 26505 #040-02-2001 L2006 AN *100 †05

WADE, William Alexander. ■ 26505 #055-01-2004 L2006 PCC *012 †20

WALD, Donald Marvin. UNIVERSITY HOSP RAD DEPT 26505 #019-02-1945 L1982 R NM *040 †80,28

WALKER, Robert Michael. 1200 J D ANDERSON DR 26505 #021-06-1981 L2002 DR *020 †80

WALKER, Thomas Nelson. 1200 J D ANDERSON DR, MONONGALIA GENERAL HOSPITA 26505 #055-02-1990 L1994 AN *020 †05

WALLING, Barry David. ■ 26505 #055-02-2005 L2007 EM *012

WALLING, Terri Lynn. ■ 26505 #055-02-2006 IM *012

WALSH, Cynthia Leah. 1322 PINEVIEW DR 26505 #055-01-1992 L1996 OBG *020 †30

WANG, Hung-Shu. ■ 26501 #385-02-1959 GS *020

WARD, John J. ■ 26501 #021-06-1981 L2008 ON ORS *020 †40

WARD, Stephen Edward. ■ 26505 #055-01-2006 IM *012

WARDAK, Mohammed Omar. WV UNIVERSITY, HEALTH SCIENCE CTR S GASTR 26505 #118-01-1962 L1980 GE IM *020

WARDEN, Bradford Edgar. 300 WEDGEWOOD DR 26505 #055-01-1994 L1996 CD *020 †20

WARDEN, Mary Davidson. PO BOX 9160, HSC NORTH 26506 #055-01-1998 L2001 IM *020 †20

WARNER, Daniel Jeffrey. ■ 26508 #055-01-2006 ORS *012

WEAVER, Bryan Douglas. MEDICAL CTR DR - STADIUM D 26505 #055-01-1993 L1995 OS *020

WEIMER, Tracy Lee. ■ 26508 #055-02-2000 L2002 CN *100 †20,75

WEISSMAN, David Neil. 1095 WILLOWDALE RD, CDC-N105H-ASB MAILSTOP L-4 26505 #016-06-1978 L1992 PUD AI *050 †20,03

WELCH, Jon Eric. PO BOX 9214, I MEDICAL CENTER DR 26506 #021-06-1997 L2003 MPD *020

WETMORE, Stephen Jeffrey. 1188 PINEVIEW DR 26505 #025-01-1971 L1988 NO OTO *020 †45

WHITE, Carol Ann. 1200 J D ANDERSON DR 26505 #055-01-1999 L2000 EM *020 †16

WHITE, Charles W, III. WV UNIVERSITY, HEALTH SCIENCE CTR S IM 26506 #055-01-1990 IM *100

WHITMAN, John Michael. ■ 26508 #055-02-2005 EM *012

WILEY, Lee Avery. 17 NORDIC DR, W. VA. UNIV./DEPT. OF OPHT 26505 #041-12-1983 L1999 OPH *020 †35

WILKINSON, Ronald Lynn. 2 WATERFRONT PL, STE 1403 26501 #055-01-1968 L1970 OTO *020 †45

WILKS, David Hunt. PO BOX 8255, 1 MEDICAL CENTER DR 26506 #041-12-1976 L2006 AN *020 †05

WILLIAMS, Dorian J. 763 CHESTNUT RIDGE RD 26505 #055-01-1989 L1991 FM *020 †18

WILLIAMS, Harold James. ■ 26508 #027-01-1985 L2003 PTH *020 †50

WILLIAMS, Jeffrey Marion. ■ 26505 #055-01-2006 L2008 D *012

WILLIAMS, Jeremy Scott. 1600 UNIVERSITY AVE, DEPT OF FAMILY MEDICINE 26506 #055-01-2006 L2008 FP *012

WILLIAMS, Patricia W. 1193B PINEVIEW DR STE 6 26505 #055-01-1975 L1976 P *020 †75

WILLIAMS, Vickie Lynn. PO BOX 9235, 1 MEDICAL CENTER DR 26506 #055-01-1985 L1986 DR *020 †80

WILLOUGHBY, Channing Dale. ■ 26508 #045-01-2006 L2008 AN *012

WILSON, Anna-Marie Laura. MEDICAL CENTER DR 26506 #495-62-1994 OBG *020

WILSON, Colin Alexander. MEDICAL CENTER DR, WV UNIV SCH MED 26506 #020-12-2007 AN *012

WILSON, David L. ■ 26508 #055-01-2006 FP *012

WITARSA, Meijianti. ■ 26508 #409-24-1979 L1990 PTH *020 †50

WITHERSTY, David James. 930 CHESTNUT RIDGE RD, CHESTNUT RIDGE HOSPITAL 26505 #055-01-1970 L1970 P *071 †75

WOLEN, John Jason. 4000 HAMPTON CTR, STE A 26505 #055-02-2001 L2007 GS *020 †85

WONSETTLER, Dana M. 1200 J D ANDERSON DR, MONONGALIA GENERAL HOSPITA 26505 #055-01-1999 L2004 FM *020 †50

WOOD, Lisa Anne. 511 BURROUGHS ST, STE 101 26505 #055-01-2003 L2006 PD *020 †55

WOSHNER, Raymond Alan. MEDICAL CENTER DR, WV UNIV SCH MED 26506 #041-07-1998 L2007 PTH *012 †18

YADWADKAR, Kaustubh Subha. ■ 26505 #055-01-2008 *012

YAKOOB, Mohammad Yawar. PO BOX 9001A 26506 #704-25-2001 IM *100

YAN, Xiaohua. PO BOX 9001A 26506 #243-24-1983 FP *012

YARBROUGH, John Matthew. 301 SCOTT AVE 26508 #010-01-2004 L2006 P *100

YE, Huaqing. ■ 26505 #243-21-1984 L2006 GE *012 †20

YEDNOCK, Joel Bernard. ■ 26505 #055-01-2006 L2008 IM *012

YEPES, Cesar Bernardo. 100 N MAIN ST 26505 #264-17-1992 L2003 IC CD *020 †20

YIN, Jie. ■ 26505 #243-76-1986 L2007 N *012

YOSSUCK, Panitan. PO BOX 9214, WVU DEPT OF PEDIATRICS 26506 #891-07-1989 L2002 NPM *020 †55

YOST, Jeffrey Marshall. 1200 J D ANDERSON DR, MORGANTOWN 26505 #055-01-1967 L1971 R OS *020 †80

ZAHIR, Fatima. PO BOX 9238 26506 #704-25-2005 GS *012

ZASLAU, Stanley. PO BOX 9251, WVU SECTION OF UROLOGY 26506 #041-09-1994 L2001 GS U *020 †95

ZBOJNIEWICZ, Andy Michael. ■ 26508 #025-12-2003 L2006 DR *012

ZERVOS, Nick Logothetis. 200 ORTHOPEDIC WAY, MOUNTAINSTATE ORTHOPEDIC 26505 #055-01-1991 L1994 ORS *020 †40

ZHENG, Wanhong. ■ 26505 #243-16-1992 P *012

ZIA, Abid. 445 OAKLAND ST 26505 #306-01-1992 IM *100

ZIMMERMAN-KLIMA, Pamela. ■ 26508 #036-08-1999 L2006 VS *020 †85

ZISS, Bethany Ellen. MEDICAL CENTER DR, WV UNIV SCH MED 26506 #041-02-2007 PD *012

MOUNDSVILLE – MARSHALL

ANGULO, Edwin Borruel. 210 GRANT AVE 26041 #748-01-1969 L1976 AN OS *020

ANWAR, Mohammad Farooq. 1500 LAFAYETTE AVE 26041 #704-01-1960 L1971 OPH *020

CHIN, Victorino D. 1110 2ND ST 26041 #748-01-1965 L1974 GS *020

HO, Jesus. 1001 1ST ST 26041 #748-01-1965 L1974 IM FM *020

IRISARI, Oscar S. 119 JEFFERSON AVE 26041 #748-01-1965 L1977 OBG *071 †30

MASON, Trent Glen. 1001 3RD ST 26041 #055-01-1998 L2001 FM *020 †18

SISON, Elisa Miranda. 119 JEFFERSON AVE 26041 #748-01-1964 L1977 OBG *020

TAN, Romeo Bihag. 1601 3RD ST 26041 #748-09-1965 L1975 GS GP *020

TSACRIOS, Nicky Mike, Jr. ■ 26041 #011-03-1972 IM *100

VINCENT, Alfred James. 800 5TH ST 26041 #671-01-1954 L1970 OBG *071

WADE, Robert B. 1001 3RD ST 26041 #055-01-1991 L1997 FM *020 †18

MOUNT CLARE – HARRISON

DOBRANSKI, Stefan Andrew. ■ 26408 #665-02-2001 L2004 GS *100 †16

MOUNT HOPE – RALEIGH

AMJAD, Mohammad. 324 SHAWNEE CIR 25880 #308-11-1994 L2004 IM *020

MOUNT OLIVE – FAYETTE

WILLIAMSON, Larry Dean. 1 MOUNTAINSIDE WAY, MOUNT OLIVE CORRECTIONAL C 25185 #028-34-1994 L2003 FM *020

MULLENS – WYOMING

BARIT, Manuel Cortez. PO BOX 457 25882 #748-08-1973 L1982 GP *020

FORDHAM, George F. ■ 25882 #036-07-1944 L1947 IM LM *071

REECE, Rebecca Marie. ■ 25882 #055-01-2008 *012

NEW HAVEN – MASON

LIEVING, Wesley R. ■ 25265 #055-75-2004, ▲ L2006 IM *020 †20

NEW MARTINSVILLE – WETZEL

ADA, Jesse Ramirez. 3 E BENJAMIN DR, FIRST SETTLEMENT 26155 #005-14-1978 L1992 ORS *020 †40

BLUM, Donald Alan. 3 ADA DR STE 5 26155 #055-01-1974 L1974 FM OM *020 †18

COFFIELD, Elmond Le Moyne. 317 WHITTEN LN 26155 #051-04-1947 L1948 FM OM *071

DESHPANDE, Avinash S. 253 N STATE ROUTE 2 26155 #495-17-1989 L1999 PD *020 †55

DONADO-SUYAO, Rosario. 150 PADUCAH DR 26155 #748-01-1965 L1975 PD PHP *020 †55

EKANEM, Ibanga Michael. 100 PADUCAH DR 26155 #690-02-1990 L1999 PD *020 †55

EMCH, Edward Lee. 261 MONROE AVE 26155 #055-01-1977 L1978 FM EM *020 †18

GEORGE, David Spencer. 3 E BENJAMIN DR 26155 #038-40-1988 L1992 OPH *020 †35

HAWKINBERRY, Denzil W, II. ■ 26155 #055-01-2000 L2002 AN *020 †05 ‡

HENRY, John Sherman. 3 E BENJAMIN DR, FIRST SETTLEMENT 26155 #055-01-1995 L2000 ORS *020 †40

KING, John Robt, Jr. 3 E BENJAMIN DR 26155 #055-01-1977 L1978 FM EM *020 †18

KRIVCHENIA, Gregory B. 3 E BENJAMIN DR, FIRST SETTLEMENT 26155 #038-06-1954 L1962 ORS *071 †40

KRIVCHENIA, Gregory B, II. 3 E BENJAMIN DR, FIRST SETTLEMENT 26155 #038-41-1981 L1986 ORS *020 †40

LINDERT, David Jonathan. 3 E BENJAMIN DR 26155 #016-11-1968 L1975 U *020 †95

MARSHALL, Mary-Anne. 3 E BENJAMIN DR, WETZEL COUNTY HOSPITAL 26155 #063-01-1991 L1997 FM EM *020 †18

MILLER, Gary Wayne. 3 E BENJAMIN DR, FIRST SETTLEMENT 26155 #023-01-1970 L1971 ORS VS *020 †40

MOHAREB, Moheb M. ■ 26155 #915-02-1971 L2003 GS *020 †85

MOUNTBATTEN-WINDSOR, Hedy. 150 PADUCAH DR, # 1 26155 #748-10-1971 L1981 OBG *020

SCOTT, Richard Arnold. 3 E BENJAMIN DR 26155 #016-06-1968 L1981 PTH CLP *020 †50

SOVANI, Vinayak Krishna. 3 E BENJAMIN DR 26155 #495-83-1982 L2003 PTH *020 †50

STRICKLER, Scott Howard. 3 E BENJAMIN DR 26155 #055-01-1988 L1992 OPH *020 †35

SUYAO, Ricaredo Palisada. 190 E THISTLE CT, NEW MARTINSVILLE 26155 #748-10-1963 L1975 GP *020

■ = Address Information Privacy Protected

SWAMY, Hemalatha C. ■ 26155 #495-16-1970 L1997 **IM** *020 †20
TALLMAN, Terry Tyrone. 3 E BENJAMIN DR 26155 #055-01-1963 L1966 **FM** *071 †18
TANTOCO, Manuel R. 3 E BENJAMIN DR, WETZEL COUNTY HOSP 26155 #748-01-1964 L1988 **AN OS** *071
URVAL, Shashi Raj. 295 N STATE ROUTE 2 26155 #495-72-1993 L1999 **IM** *020 †20

NITRO – KANAWHA

HAIKAL, Elias Geo. 4114 1ST AVE 25143 #012-01-1973 L1977 **FM** *020
HOGSHEAD, George Wm. ■ 25143 #041-13-1944 L1947 **GP** *071
KWEI, Leon Shiulung. 24 LAKE LN 25143 #055-01-1986 L1989 **EM MPD** *55,20
LEE, Matthew Franklin. 642 CROSS LANES DR 25143 #055-01-1997 L2001 **EM** *020 †16
MODI, Jignesh Jashawant. 40 FAIRLAND DR 25143 #027-10-1994 L1999 **ID** *020 †20
MORELAND, Gregory Mark. 2206 22ND ST 25143 #055-02-1984 L1985 **FM** *020 †18
STEELE, James Lebrecht. ■ 25143 #051-04-1962 L1964 **EM** *071 †16
STEWART, John Anderson. 2401 24TH ST 25143 #041-09-1943 L1944 **FM OBG** *072

NORTHFORK – MCDOWELL

COFER, Harold Anthony. PO BOX 787 24868 #041-02-1978 L1981 **GP** *020
RAGO, Andres L. HC 52 BOX 135 24868 #748-08-1968 L1978 **GP GS** *020

NUTTER FORT – HARRISON

ADENIYI, John Adetunji. 200 ROUTE 98 W ST STE 1, ASSOCIATED SPECIALISTS, IN 26301 #690-01-1990 L2003 **VS GS** *085
GOODEN, Michael Allen. 200 ROUTE 98 W ST, STE 107 26301 #003-01-1996 L2006 **VS** *020 †85
KAZBAY, Kasim. 200 ROUTE 98 W ST, STE 107 26301 #902-04-1986 L2004 **GE** *020
LATEEF, Atiya Malik. 200 ROUTE 98 W ST STE 10, STE 103 26301 #704-25-1989 L1995 **IM** *020 †20
MOSSALLATI, Saad. 200 ROUTE 98 W ST, STE 107 26301 #875-01-1972 L1982 **CD VS** *020 †85
PONS, Roger Karl. 200 RT 98 W STE 105 26301 #308-01-1982 L1986 **CRS GS** *020 †85,10
RHODES, Maurice Clement. 200 ROUTE 98 W ST STE 401 26301 #051-04-1978 L1979 **FM** *020 †18
SALMAN, Muhammad. 200 ROUTE 98 W ST, STE 310 26301 #704-20-1986 L1999 **P** *020
WEINSTEIN, James David. 200 ROUTE 98 W ST STE 109, JAMES D. WEINSTEIN, M.D. 26301 #041-01-1964 L1982 **NS** *020 †25

OAK HILL – FAYETTE

ANWARULLAH, Mohammad. 435 MAIN ST W 25901 #160-03-1966 L1973 **GS** *020
ASHIR, Mohammad A. 435 MAIN ST W, OAKHILL PEDS 25901 #160-07-1988 L2001 **PD** *020
CONCEPCION, Roberto G. ■ 25901 #748-01-1962 L1974 **PD OS** *075
DOYLE, Daniel Barry. 430 MAIN ST W 25901 #024-01-1974 L1977 **FM GPM** *020 †18
EELLS, David Acevedo. 550C JONES AVE 25901 #005-11-1979 L1985 **GS EM** *020
ELLIOTT, Lisa Ann. 430 MAIN ST W 25901 #045-01-1984 L1987 **FM** *020 †18
GOSIEN, Oscar P. PO BOX 200 25901 #748-07-1964 L1980 **GP AN** *020
JAMSHIDI, Khossrow. 502 MAIN ST W 25901 #517-01-1959 L1994 **OTO** *071
LOOT, Jesse Laspinas. 430 MAIN ST 25901 #748-11-1971 L1978 **AN** *020
LOOT, Sarah Osorio. 430 MAIN ST 25901 #748-11-1971 L1978 **PD** *020 †55
LOVE, Brian Stephen. 430 MAIN ST W, ATTN: DR BRIAN LOVE 25901 #055-02-2003 L2006 **FM** *020
MADUCDOC, Serafino S, Jr. 320 JONES AVE 25901 #748-07-1963 L1977 **FM** *020
MAMINTA, Mauro U. 430 MAIN ST W 25901 #748-01-1961 L1976 **GP** *020
MURUGAPPAN, Alamelu. 502 MAIN ST W, MED-SURG GROUP, INC. 25901 #495-66-1993 L2000 **CN** *100 †75
NUNNARI, Diego. OAK HILL HOSP 25901 #561-01-1943 L1956 **GP ORS** *020
WHITE, Byrd. 422 23RD ST, MARY'S GARDEN 25901 #048-04-1941 L1972 **GS** *071 †85

OCEANA – WYOMING

BHAVSAR, Shashikant B. ■ 24870 #495-22-1969 L1977 **FM** *020 ‡

OLD FIELDS – HARDY

TAYLOR, Kathleen E Curtin. PO BOX 285 26845 #025-07-1973 L2002 **D** *020 †15

PARKERSBURG – WOOD

AMSBARY, Harry Lowell. 800 GARFIELD AVE 26101 #038-40-1973 L1977 **OPH** *071
ARMSTRONG, Orton Carl. 600 18TH ST, STE 404 26101 #055-01-1993 L1994 **MPD IM** *55,20
AUVIL, Loretto M Redd. 806 DIVISION ST 26101 #051-04-1957 L1959 **FM** *020
AVERY, David Wayne. 418 GRAND PARK DR STE 312 26105 #035-15-1979 L1980 **FM FSM** *020 †18 ‡
AVINGTON, Michael David. 600 18TH ST, STE 512 26101 #010-02-1966 L1973 **CD** *020 †20
BAGE, Seyoum Daffo. 600 18TH ST STE 212, SRYOUM BAGE MD 26101 #366-01-1993 L2004 **ID** *020 †20
BARNETT, Charles H. ■ 26104 #030-06-1949 L1950 **GP GS** *071
BEANE, David Joel. 4 ROSEMAR CIR, ROSEMAR MEDICAL 26104 #055-02-1999 L2000 **FM** *020 †18 ‡
BEANE, John Edward. 4 ROSEMAR CIR, ROSEMAR MEDICAL 26104 #055-01-1966 L1968 **FM** *020 ‡
BEANE, Michael Edward. 4 ROSEMAR CIR, ROSEMAR MEDICAL 26104 #055-02-1996 L1997 **FM** *020 †18
BERHANE, Miniya Kafel. 600 18TH ST STE 601 26101 #366-01-1991 L1998 **PD** *020 †55
BICE, Walter Bernard. 1019 GARFIELD AVE 26101 #055-01-1967 L1968 **FM** *020
BOGGS, Joseph Louis. 800 GARFIELD AVE 26101 #035-45-1969 L1976 **GS TRS** *085
BRAR, Gur Preet Singh. 600 18TH ST, STE 302 26101 #495-45-1972 L1978 **RHU IM** *020 †20

BROOKS, A Paul, Jr. 800 GARFIELD AVE 26101 #055-01-1966 L1967 **FM** *062
BROWN, Marion Sanderson. PO BOX 899 26102 #005-12-1942 L1947 **OBG** *071 †30
CABRAL, John David Y. 1824 MURDOCH AVE, ST JOSEPH'S HOSPITAL 26101 #024-05-1997 L2008 **AN** *020
CANSINO, Ophelia. 1481 ASHBY RIDGE RD 26104 #748-08-1968 L1976 **AN** *020
CAPEL, Terry Wm. 1019 GARFIELD AVE 26101 #055-01-1984 L1986 **FM** *020 †18
CARTWRIGHT, William E. 1907 ANN ST 26101 #055-01-1998 L1999 **FM** *020 †18
CASEY, Ronald Lee. 800 GARFIELD AVE, HOSPITALISTS MANAGEMENT GR 26101 #051-04-1996 L2003 **MPD** *020 †20
CAYTON, Wayne Boyd, Jr. 800 GARFIELD AVE, CAMDEN CLARK MEM HOSP 26101 #055-01-1977 L1982 **EM ESM** *020 †16
CHAMBERS, Craig A. 800 GARFIELD AVE, CAMDEN CLARK MEMORIAL HOSP 26101 #055-75-1999, ▲ L2000 **DR** *020 †80 ‡
CHANDRASEKHAR, S. 32 SOUTH LAKE DR 26101 #495-66-1987 L2005 **IM** *020 †20
CHEEMA, Muhammad Akhtar. 1824 MURDOCH AVE, DEPT OF PATHOLOGY 26101 #704-02-1982 L2002 **PCP** *020 †50
CHOI, Chang Hyuk. 418 GRAND PARK DR 26105 #583-08-1975 L1982 **IM** *075 †20
CONLEY, Yale David. 1122 MARKET ST 26101 #055-02-1987 L1988 **GS** *071 †85
COTTRELL, Dominic Joseph. 3211 DUDLEY AVE 26104 #055-01-1996 L1999 **AN** *020 †05
CRAMER, David Thomas. 1907 ANN ST 26101 #055-01-1982 L1983 **FM** *020 †18
CROOKS, Robert Dils. ■ 26104 #038-41-1947 L1953 **PD** *071 †55
CRUZ, Joy Spychalski. 600 18TH ST, STE 611 26101 #041-13-1997 L2001 **FM** *020 †18
DAS, Titu Dilip. 245 BROOKTREE DR 26101 #496-46-1995 L2002 **ID** *012 †20
DAVID, Corazon S. 1812 GARFIELD AVE 26101 #748-01-1957 **AN** *075
DICKERSON, Michael M. ■ 26101 #023-12-1983 L1997 **EM** *020 †16
DIP FIGUEROA, Allan. 800 GARFIELD AVE 26101 #649-14-1973 L1985 **EM GP** *020
DUESTERHOEFT, D'Ann E. 705 GARFIELD AVE STE 440 26101 #023-07-1987 L1998 **AN OS** *020 †05
DUGAN, Cindy Constantino. 2121 7TH ST 26101 #055-01-1995 L2000 **IM** *020 †75
DURNELL, Thomas Alan. 705 GARFIELD AVE, STE 360 26101 #055-01-1980 L1984 **OBG** *020 †30
DUSHKOFF, Robert B. 417 GRAND PARK DR STE 103 26105 #055-01-1985 L1986 **FM** *020 †18
EKE, Joseph Wayne, Jr. 800 GARFIELD AVE 26101 #017-20-1996 L2003 **DR** *020 †80
ESCANDON, Humberto. 3803 EMERSON AVE 26104 #264-01-1957 L1971 **NS** *071 †25
ESTRADA, Cristina Garde. 2910 EMERSON AVE 26104 #748-10-1969 L1990 **PD** *020
ESTRADA, Ruben Castro. 1824 MURDOCH AVE 26101 #748-10-1969 L1989 **AN** *020
FILOZOF, Peter Paul. 705 GARFIELD AVE STE 310 26101 #012-05-1994 L1998 **OBG** *020 †30
FRAME, Ronald David, II. 705 GARFIELD AVE STE 380 26101 #055-02-1996 L2000 **OPH** *020 †35
GEVAS, George. ■ 26104 #023-01-1953 L1957 **OBG** *071
GHODSI, Seyed Abdolreza. 1212 GARFIELD AVE, STE 300 26101 #018-03-1994 L2000 **NS** *020 †25
GILLESPIE, Frederick D. 1205 MARKET ST 26101 #051-01-1956 L1963 **OPH** *020 †35
GNEGY, David Alan. 600 18TH ST, STE 512 26101 #023-01-1989 L1995 **CD** *020 †20
GODDARD, John Allen. 600 18TH ST STE 512 26101 #055-01-1998 L2001 **CD** *020 †20
GODFREY, Larry James. 1824 MURDOCH AVE, ST. JOSEPH' S HOSPITAL - P 26101 #055-01-1978 L2007 **PTH** *020 †50
GODLEWSKI, Matthew J. ■ 26104 #759-03-1970 L1979 **NEP IM** *071
GOLD, Rammy Schmuel. 1212 GARFIELD AVE, STE 300 26101 #038-06-1988 L1996 **NS** *020 †25
GONDALIA, Bhailal G. 600 18TH ST, STE 111 26101 #495-22-1979 L1991 **IM** *020 †20
GUY, E Samuel. 3194 CORE RD 26104 #055-01-1978 L1979 **P IM** *020 †20,75
HANNA, Stephan Douglas. 1907 ANN ST 26101 #055-01-1980 L1983 **FM** *020 †18
HENSHAW, Raymond Edward, II. 600 18TH ST, STE 610 26101 #040-02-1977 L1993 **ORS** *020 †40
HENSLEY, William Michael. 800 GARFIELD AVE, HOSPITAL 26101 #024-01-1979 L1983 **DR** *020 †80
HERCEG, Robert Joseph. 800 GARFIELD AVE, CAMDEN CLARK MEM HOSP 26101 #016-02-1992 L1998 **PTH PCP** *020 †50
HERRIOTT, George Ephraim. 1600 MURDOCH AVE, STE 100 26101 #055-01-1994 L1997 **ORS** *020 †40
HONAKER, Charles Rodney. 801 GARFIELD AVE STE 100 26101 #055-01-1974 L1975 **GE IM** *020 †20
HOPKINS, Gail Eason. ■ 26104 #016-01-1981 L2004 **ORS** *020 †40
HOPKINS, Leah Gail. 3705 EMERSON AVE 26104 #016-43-1996 L2003 **IM** *020 †20
HOUFF, Stephen Louis. 800 GARFIELD AVE, CAMDEN CLARK MEM HOSP ATTN 26101 #023-01-1987 L2001 **GE** *020 †20
HOWES, Robt Winfield, Jr. ■ 26104 #051-04-1953 L1954 **FM** *071
HUNG, Cheng-Tong. 800 GARFIELD AVE 26101 #385-02-1961 L1974 **OBG AM** *071 †30
IRVIN, Heather Ann. 600 18TH ST, STE 201 26101 #055-01-2000 L2004 **OBG** *020
JACOB, Lily Ferrer. 2121 7TH ST, MEDICAL SERVICES DIVISION 26101 #748-08-1970 L1985 **GP** *020
JACOB, Remigio Ontalan. 800 GARFIELD AVE, CAMDEN-CLARK MEMORIAL HOSP 26101 #748-01-1968 L1979 **EM** *020
JOHN, Sabu. 600 18TH ST, STE 512 26101 #495-63-1991 L2005 **CD** *020 †20
JOHNS, Richard Edward, Jr. 1824 MURDOCH AVE 26101 #041-09-1978 L1981 **OPH** *020 †35 ‡
JONES, Archbold M, Jr. ■ 26101 #041-02-1959 L1960 **PD OS** *075 †55
JOSEPH, Bridget. 418 GRAND PARK DR 26105 #495-44-1982 L1992 **IM** *020 †20
KANU, Chikere Anthony. 1321 42ND ST 26104 #690-02-1990 L2004 **IM** *020 †20
KATRAPATI, Parvati. 2323 MURDOCH AVE, PMR CLINIC 26101 #495-75-1984 L2003 **IM** *020 †20
KELLEY, John Fredric. 2121 7TH ST 26101 #067-01-1958 L1968 **CHP P** *020 †75
KEMP, Judith Diane. 800 GARFIELD AVE 26101 #045-01-1983 L1987 **PTH** *020 †50
KHALIL, Ghassan Abou. 800 GARFIELD AVE 26101 #605-02-1961 L1972 **PS GS** *071 †85
KHAN, Abdul Q. 2323 MURDOCH AVE 26101 #704-08-1991 L2001 **IM** *020 †20
KHOSROVI, Houman. 1212 GARFIELD AVE, STE 300 26101 #055-01-1992 L1995 **NS** *020 †25
KITCHEN, Anthony Wayne. 800 GARFIELD AVE 26101 #048-44-1994 L1998 **EM** *020 †16
KRAUSE, Gregory E. 1905 ANN ST 26101 #028-02-1994 L2000 **OTO** *020 †45
KUMAR, Chandra Mohan. 418 GRAND PARK DR 26105 #495-36-1965 L1979 **AI PDA** *020 †55,03
KUNCHERIAH, Shibu. 936 MARKET ST 26101 #041-13-2002 L2004 **CHP** *020 †75
KUPPUSWAMY, Bairavasundara. 2610 CAMDEN AVE 26101 #495-99-1994 L2005 **IM** *020 †20
LANTZ, Donald Ross. ■ 26104 #051-04-1954 L1956 **OM EM** *071
LAWRENCE-BERREY, Robert E. ■ 26104 #054-04-1962 L1972 **PTH FOP** *075 †50
LAZER, Zane Patrick. 418 GRAND PARK DR STE 315, OHIO VALLEY EYE PHYSICIANS 26105 #051-01-1995 L1999 **OPH** *020 †35

LOAR, Charles Richard. 1212 GARFIELD AVE, STE 300 26101 #055-01-1970 L1972 **NS** *020 †25
LOWDEN, Eric Richard. 705 GARFIELD AVE, STE 420 26101 #038-43-1992 L1998 **OBG** *020 †30 ‡
LUNDBLAD, Daniel Miles. 19TH & MURDOCK AVE 26101 #041-09-1963 L1972 **PTH** *071 †50
MAMIDI, Satyanarayana M. 600 18TH ST, STE 512 26101 #496-05-1969 L1981 **IM CD** *020 †20
MANDERS, Scott Jeffrey. 600 18TH ST STE 512 26101 #005-02-1971 L2004 **CD** *020 †20
MARINAKIS, Harry Arthur. 1824 MURDOCH AVE, EMERGENCY DEPARTMENT 26101 #034-01-1998 L2001 **EM** *020 †16
MATCHESWALLA, Mansoor H. 800 GARFIELD AVE 26101 #495-01-1961 L1980 **PTH** *020 †50
MC CARTY, George E. 3 WESTERN HILLS DR, HEALTH SOUTH/WESTERN HILLS 26105 #051-04-1953 L1955 **OM** *071
MC COY, Lance Morgan. 2801 DUDLEY AVE # B 26101 #055-01-1989 L1997 **PYG P** *050 †75
MCELROY, John Jeffrey. 1600 MURDOCH AVE, STE 100 26101 #055-02-1992 L2002 **ORS** *020 †40
MC GRAW, Daniel Jos. 705 GARFIELD AVE, STE 460 26101 #023-07-1985 L1998 **GS VS** *020 †85
MICHELS, Donald Hastings. 1900 BLIZZARD DR 26101 #055-01-1978 L1979 **IM EM** *071 †20
MICHELS, Ronald Chas. 912 MARKET ST 26101 #055-01-1972 L1972 **END IM** *020 †20
MILLER, Christopher Todd. 600 18TH ST STE 404 26101 #055-01-1993 L1995 **CD** *012 †55,20
MILLER, Kenneth Thomas. 800 GARFIELD AVE 26101 #041-02-1993 L1997 **DR** *020 †80
MILLER, Russell Anthony. 1900 GARFIELD AVE STE C 26101 #566-01-1973 L1977 **PD** *020 †55
MODI, Hemant Chandulal. 600 18TH ST, STE 512 26101 #495-76-1979 L1989 **CD IM** *020 †20
MODIE, Paul G., Jr. 1122 MARKET ST 26101 #038-06-1962 L1970 **GS** *020 †85
MOINUDDEEN, Khaja. 1824 MURDOCH AVE 26101 #495-35-1988 L2004 **TS** *100 †85,90
MORALES, Alfonso. 1136 MARKET ST 26101 #649-02-1959 L1961 **FM GS** *020 †18
MOSES, Gregory J. 705 GARFIELD AVE 26101 #055-01-1990 L1996 **PTH** *020 †50
MOSES, Michael Solomon. 1512 36TH ST 26104 #055-01-1983 L1984 **IM** *020 †20
NORRIS, Joseph Peter. 3194 CORE RD, STE 1 26104 #041-09-1956 L1973 **P** *020
OCAMPO, Luis Horacio. 410 MARKET ST, INTERNAL MEDICINE 26101 #264-05-1964 L1971 **IM** *071
OLSON, Gabriella M. 1907 ANN ST 26101 #055-01-1997 L1999 **FM** *020 †18
ONESTINGHEL, John V. 1907 ANN ST 26101 #055-01-1990 L1994 **IM PD** *020
PAMFILIS, Stanley Manuel. 600 18TH ST, PARKERSBURG CARDIO ASSOCIA 26101 #023-01-1988 L1994 **CD** *020 †20
PANTELIDIS, Anastasios. 1824 MURDOCH AVE 26101 #055-01-1995 L1997 **AN PME** *020 †05
PATEL, Anilkumar J. 1824 MURDOCH AVE 26101 #495-48-1979 L1985 **AN** *020 †05
PATEL, Prakashchandra M. 600 18TH ST STE 101, PHYSICIAN'S OFFICE CENTER 26101 #495-99-1984 L1991 **PD** *020
PHILLIPS, John Robert. 1824 MURDOCH AVE 26101 #041-14-1994 L2001 **PDC** *020 †55
PIERSON, Bruce, Jr. 600 18TH ST STE 311 26101 #010-02-1968 L1975 **D** *020 †15
PIPPIN, William Doyle. 800 GARFIELD AVE 26101 #038-40-1990 L2004 **AN** *020 †05
PONCE, Francisco L. 600 18TH ST STE 213 26101 #748-02-1968 L1974 **U** *020
POWDERLY, Finbar Gerard. 800 GARFIELD AVE 26101 #539-04-1977 L1981 **FM** *020
POWER, Younger Lovelace. ■ 26104 #035-15-1962 L1973 **OM** *020
POWERS, Elizabeth Susan. 3 ROSEMAR CIR, STE D 26104 #055-01-1993 L1995 **IM** *020 †20
PRIETO JARAMILLO, Alfredo. 2021 35TH ST 26104 #264-06-1964 L1975 **OBG** *020
RAJAN, Dorai T. 2610 CAMDEN AVE 26101 #495-53-1971 L1974 **IM HEM** *020 †20
RALSTEN, John Neville. 1122 MARKET ST, LOWER LEVEL 26101 #055-01-1965 L1966 **R** *071 †80
RAMIREZ-TALAVERA, Perla F. PO BOX 4158 26104 #748-10-1964 L1973 **PD** *074 †55
RAZA, Syed Tasnim. 1824 MURDOCH AVE, STE 214 26101 #704-01-1970 L2005 **TS** *020 †85,90
REDDY, N Narayana. 2911 EMERSON AVE 26104 #495-70-1970 L1981 **IM PUD** *020 †20
RICHARDS, Steven Douglas. 1907 ANN ST 26101 #055-01-1999 L2002 **FM** *020 †18
RICHARDSON, Brian Keith. 800 GARFIELD AVE, ATTN: MEDICAL STAFF OFFIC 26101 #055-01-2002 L2005 **EM** *020 †16
RUDOLPH, Robert Lee, II. 705 GARFIELD AVE, STE 440 26101 #023-01-1980 L1981 **GS VS** *020 †85
RURAK, John Anthony. ■ 26104 #055-01-1968 L1972 **OBG FM** *075
RUSSELL, Gail. 600 18TH ST, STE 204 26101 #016-42-1993 L1995 **OBG** *020 †30
SABO, Alex Jos. ST JOSEPHS HOSP 26101 #055-01-1965 L1969 **PTH** *020 †50
SABO, Sandra Kovach. ■ 26104 #055-01-1965 L1967 **FM** *071 †18
SANCHEZ, Gilberto. 19TH ST AND MURDOCH AVE 26102 #264-05-1959 L1974 **CD IM** *071 †50
SANDFORD, John Lee. 104 LAKEVIEW CTR STE 307 26101 #039-01-1960 L1980 **EM GP** *071 †75
SANTER, Michael A, Jr. 600 18TH ST STE 202 26101 #010-02-1965 L1972 **CD IM** *020 †20
SCHWABE, Mario Rafael. 3194 CORE RD, STE 1 26104 #041-13-1966 L1986 **P** *020 †75
SEKAR, Chandra S. CANDEN CLARK MEM HOSP 26101 #495-53-1970 L1978 **RO** *020 †20
SESHAGIRI RAO, Kalapala. 2323 MURDOCH AVE 26101 #495-58-1976 L1992 **PM IM** *020 †60
SHAH, Mukund K. 1903 ANN ST 26101 #495-76-1970 L1984 **IM HO** *020
SHAH, Nikunj Manmohanbhai. 800 GARFIELD AVE 26101 #495-76-1972 L1979 **HEM ON** *050
SHANK, Terry Clark. 800 GARFIELD AVE 26101 #055-01-1992 L1993 **DR** *020 †80
SHANNON, Harry Lee, III. 418 GRAND PARK DR, STE 311 26105 #021-01-1968 L1975 **U OS** *071 †95
SHIFFLER, Joel David. 1230 GARFIELD AVE 26101 #305-01-1994 L2000 **FM** *020 †18
SHOCKLEY, Michael Curtis. 705 GARFIELD AVE, STE 400 26101 #039-01-1985 L1993 **OBG** *020 †30
SHRAMOWIAT, Michael. 1158 46TH ST 26105 #305-01-1985 L1993 **PM FM** *020 †60
SIERRA, Maida. 3194 CORE RD, STE 1 26104 #042-01-1983 L2007 **P** *030 †75
SIMS, Rutherford Clark. 1824 MURDOCH AVE 26101 #055-01-1967 L1968 **OBG** *071 †30
SMITH, Chester Donald, III. 800 GARFIELD AVE, INPATIENT MEDICAL SPECIALI 26101 #055-01-1999 L2002 **FM** *020 †18
SNYDER, Charles W. 3199 CORE RD 26104 #308-11-1986 L1998 **CHP** *020
SOBIERAJ, Krzysztof M. 705 GARFIELD AVE, STE 370 26101 #759-09-1980 L1996 **IM** *020 †20
SPYCHALSKI, James Norman. 600 18TH ST, STE 611 26101 #041-13-1998 L2001 **FM** *020 †18
STAEHELI, Bruce Wayne. 1824 MURDOCH AVE, 4M EMERGENCY SYSTEMS PARKE 26101 #054-04-1982 L2008 **EM** *020 †20,85
STROBL, Neil Robert. 5101 GLENBROOK DR, P O BOX 1066 26105 #055-01-1997 L1999 **DR** *020 †80
STROBL, Peter Wilhelm. 1824 MURDOCH AVE 26101 #055-01-1992 L1996 **DR** *020 †80
STROBL, Philip Harlow. 1824 MURDOCH AVE, DEPT OF RADIOLOGY 26101 #055-01-1992 L1996 **DR** *020 †80
STROBL, Wolfgang Wilhelm. 1824 MURDOCH AVE 26101 #028-34-1969 L1973 **DR PDR** *020 †80
TALAVERA, Joseph J. 2901 EMERSON AVE 26104 #748-08-1964 L1973 **U** *071 †95
TARRANT, Lawrence Wm. 600 18TH ST STE 310 26101 #025-01-1965 L1988 **PS** *020 †65

TOPPERCER, Laura Fajfer. 800 GARFIELD AVE 26101 #759-03-1970 L1979 **EM** *020
TUCKER, Gary Jackson, Jr. 1217 BLIZZARD DR 26101 #055-01-1994 L1995 **FM** *020 †18
TWITE, Anthony E. 1230 GARFIELD AVE 26101 #917-21-1967 L1978 **ORS** *071 †40
VAN DYKE, Paul Eugene. 1824 MURDOCH AVE 26101 #055-01-1975 L1976 **DR NR** *020 †80
VASAN, S. 800 GARFIELD AVE 26101 #495-09-1974 L1984 **N** *020 †80
VEGA, Carlos V. 3194 CORE RD, STE 1 26104 #042-01-1983 L1985 **IM P** *020 †75
VELOSO, Mary Lind D. 418 GRAND PARK DR 26105 #748-02-1990 L1996 **AI IM** *020 †20,03
WAGGONER, Keith Alan. 1824 MURDOCH AVE, EMERG DEPT 26101 #027-01-1987 L1995 **IM EM** *020 †20
WALKER, David Keith. 3194 CORE RD, STE 1 26104 #055-01-1972 L1973 **P** *020 †75
WANCHICK, Michael Allen. 600 18TH ST, STE 202 26101 #038-40-1968 L1974 **OPH** *020 †35
WHITAKER, Charles F, III. 600 18TH ST STE 304, OFFICE BUILDING 26101 #041-12-1970 L1971 **PD** *020 †55
WHITE, Curtis Desmond. 705 GARFIELD AVE STE 400 26101 #055-01-1975 L1976 **GO OBG** *020 †30
WOOFTER, Joseph Corder. 1110 20TH ST 26101 #051-04-1968 L1972 **D** *020 †15
WORTHINGTON, Edna Kathryn. 3194 CORE RD, STE 1 26104 #308-12-1984 L1995 **P** *020 †20
ZERRUDO, Cenon Degayo. 1710 1/2 MARKET ST 26101 #748-07-1953 L1999 **FM** *020 †55

PARSONS – TUCKER

MICHAEL, Guy H, Jr. RT 219 SOUTH 26287 #041-01-1949 L1951 **GP** *071
MOWE, Deborah Ann. 307 MAIN ST, TUCKER FAMILY CARE CLINIC 26287 #051-04-1986 L1997 **FM** *020 †18

PAW PAW – HAMPSHIRE

TORKELSON, Michael Robt. MOUNTAINEER COMM HEALTH CT 25434 #046-01-1992 L2004 **FM** *020 †18

PENNSBORO – RITCHIE

CALHOUN, Arthur Lewis. 304 MASONIC AVE 26415 #005-12-1972 L1977 **FM** *020
LE VOS, James Edward. 304 MASONIC AVE 26415 #005-12-1970 L1979 **GP** *020

PETERSBURG – GRANT

BENSENHAVER, Dewey F. HC 30 BOX 95, GRANT MEM HOSP DRIVE 26847 #055-01-1971 L1972 **FM** *020 †18
GOLDIZEN, Cristina Leigh. 10 VALLEY VIEW ST, STE 203 26847 #055-01-1992 L1994 **P** *020 †75
INDACOCHEA, Fernando J. ROUTE 55 WEST 26847 #737-06-1983 L1992 **PD PDI** *020 †55
KIM, James Jupyung. 10 VALLEY VIEW ST # 101 26847 #583-02-1968 L2003 **ORS** *020 †40
KITZMILLER, Melissa Dawn. ■ 26847 #055-01-1999 L2000 **FM** *020 †18
LEE, Joan Waichung. PO BOX 1019, 1 HOSPITAL DR 26847 #028-02-2001 L2004 **PD** *020 †55
LEMLEY, Heath Lane. 10 VALLEY VIEW ST, REGIONAL EYE ASSOCIATES 26847 #055-01-1994 L1997 **OPH** *020 †35
LESLIE, Bruce W. ROUTE 55 WEST 26847 #010-01-1982 L1985 **IM** *020 †20
MAKANI, Anil Kumar. ROUTE 55 WEST 26847 #495-41-1976 L1988 **GS GE** *020 †85
MAYLE, Mark Douglas. 10 VALLEY VIEW ST, REGIONAL EYE ASSOCIATES 26847 #055-01-1991 L1994 **OPH** *020 †35
POWELL, Stephen Randall. 10 VALLEY VIEW ST, REGIONAL EYE ASSOCIATES 26847 #055-01-1983 L1987 **OPH** *020 †35
ROGERS, Larry Calvin. ROUTE 55 WEST 26847 #055-01-1974 L1975 **FM** *020 †18
SMITH, Elizabeth Hynes. ROUTE 55 WEST 26847 #041-14-1983 L1991 **OBG** *020 †30
THOMPSON, Stephen C. GRANT MEMORIAL HOSPITAL 26847 #055-75-1989, ▲ L1992 **IM** *020 †20
VALLEY, Thomas Clifford. ■ 26847 #039-01-1997 L2006 **IM** *020 †20

PETERSTOWN – MONROE

MILLER, Stephen. ■ 24963 #055-75-1996, ▲ L1997 **FM** *020

PHILIPPI – BARBOUR

ARNETT, James Allen. RR 3 BOX 278A1, 123 SESAME ST 26416 #055-01-1981 L1982 **FM** *020 †18
FARNSWORTH, Mark Bryan. RR 4 BOX 315 26416 #041-07-1986 L1987 **FM** *020 †18
FRANYUTTI, Fulvio Rogelio. PO BOX 190 26416 #649-01-1960 L1972 **IM PTH** *020
HOLBERT, Cecil Todd. 3 HEALTHCARE DR, MYERS CLINIC 26416 #055-01-1999 L2000 **FM** *020 †18 ‡
KREIDER, Elvin Groff. 3 HEALTHCARE DR, MYERS CLINIC 26416 #041-13-1964 L1970 **A** *020 †55
MYERS, Mary Elizabeth. 112 WOODS ST 26416 #041-07-1952 L1954 **P OS** *071
POLING, Evangeline Myers. ■ 26416 #023-01-1950 L1952 **PD PHP** *071
SAN PABLO, William A. 112 WOODS ST 26416 #748-01-1958 L1979 **IM CD** *020

PIEDMONT – MINERAL

BESS, Robert Wm, Jr. 122 ASHFIELD ST 26750 #051-04-1958 L1959 **FM OM** *072

PINCH – KANAWHA

MORRIS, John Leonard. ■ 25156 #055-01-2002 L2006 **AN** *100 †05

PINEVILLE – WYOMING

DIWAN, Vaman Shripad. 335 WILLIAMSON AVE 1470 24874 #495-28-1957 L1976 **FM GS** *020

POINT PLEASANT – MASON

ABDEEN, M Anway Yahya. 2520 VALLEY DR, EMERGENCY DEPARTMENT 25550 #605-01-1991 L2001 **IM** *020 †20

AGRAWAL, Suresh Kumar. 2520 VALLEY DR, PLEASANT VALLEY HOSPITAL 25550 #495-20-1973 L1982 **DR** *020

ASRIAN, Artour George. 2520 VALLEY DR, PLEASANT VALLEY HOSPITAL 25550 #913-15-1983 L2005 **GS** *020 †85

AUSMUS, Craig. ■ 25550 #654-01-1989 L1995 **FM** *020 †18

AYERS, Harold E, Jr. 2520 VALLEY DR, STE 118 25550 #055-02-1984 L1988 **IM PD** *020 †20,55

BOSLEY, Lois J. 2605 JACKSON AVE 25550 #055-75-1990, ▲ L1991 **FM** *020 †18

CLARKE, Russell Paul, Jr. 2605 JACKSON AVE 25550 #028-34-1970 L2001 **ORS OS** *020 †40

CORBIN, Michael W. 2520 VALLEY DR, STE 215 25550 #010-02-1988 L1998 **OBG** *020 †30

DILLARD, Carrie Marie. 2414 JEFFERSON AVE, PVH MEDICAL OFFICE CENTER 25550 #055-02-2003 L2006 **FM** *100 †18

ENRICO-SIMON, Agnes A. 2420 JEFFERSON AVE 25550 #748-01-1988 L2001 **FM PD** *020 †18

FELDER, David Arthur, Jr. 2520 VALLEY DR, STE 211 25550 #023-01-1978 L1979 **ORS** *020

FRANCO, Manuel T. ■ 25550 #042-03-1980 L2008 **DR RNR** *075

HAWKINS, Randall Fleming. 2520 VALLEY DR, MED OFF BLDG STE 212 25550 #055-02-1987 L1990 **IM** *020 †20

HOLLEY, Robert Melvin. 2500 JEFFERSON AVE 25550 #049-01-1976 L1978 **FM AM** *020

JAMORA, Ismael O. 2520 VALLEY DR, PLEASANT VALLEY HOSPITAL 25550 #748-02-1966 L1974 **IM CD** *020

KOTTAPALLI, Ajay K. 2605 JACKSON AVE, HOLZER CLINIC OF WEST VIRG 25550 #495-65-1987 L1997 **IM OS** *020 †20

KRANZ, Eric. 1716 JEFFERSON BLVD 25550 #561-17-1977 L1983 *075

LARES, Nancy Beth. 2520 VALLEY DR 25550 #055-02-2004 L2006 **FM** *100 †18

LEVERT, Samuel Logan, Jr. 2605 JACKSON AVE, MASON CO BRANCH 25550 #021-05-1966 L1987 **N** *071 †75

LEWIS, Robert Lee, II. 2520 VALLEY DR, STE 13 25550 #055-01-1999 L2003 **N CN** *020 †75

LI, Joseph Y. 2605 JACKSON AVE, HOLZER CLINIC OF WV 25550 #748-15-1981 L1994 **PD** *020 †55

LINDER, Howard Eugene. 2605 JACKSON AVE, HOLZER CLINIC OF W.V. 25550 #038-41-1965 L1986 **PUD IM** *020 †20

LINKOUS, Cheryl Lynn. 2605 JACKSON AVE, HOLZER CLINIC OF W.V. 25550 #051-04-1973 L1975 **IM CD** *020 †20

MAGNUSSEN, James Robt. 2605 JACKSON AVE, HOLZER CLINIC OF WV 25550 #038-40-1972 L1982 **OTO HNS** *020 †45

MIZE, Marilyn Suzanne. 2605 JACKSON AVE, HOLZER CLINIC INC 25550 #038-41-1977 L1984 **CD IM** *020 †20

MORGAN, Breton Lee. ■ 25550 #055-01-1986 L1987 **GP IM** *020

NOLAN, Mark Warren. 2520 VALLEY DR STE 214 25550 #039-01-1986 L1997 **OBG** *020

OLIVAREZ-ORTEZA, Imelda. 2520 VALLEY DR STE 215 25550 #748-02-1982 L1990 **PD** *020 †55

ORTEZA, Ephraim Neal C. 2520 VALLEY DR, STE 215 25550 #748-10-1980 L1990 **PD** *020 †20

RODGERS, Daniel A. ■ 25550 #055-01-2008 *012

SEAMAN, Robert Wm. 2520 VALLEY DR 25550 #035-15-1975 L1998 **R** *020 †80

SERFONTEIN, Stephanus Joh. 2418 JEFFERSON AVE 25550 #836-03-1986 L2004 **IM** *100 †20 ‡

SHAH, Mahendrakumar C. 2520 VALLEY DR 25550 #495-23-1974 L1984 **IM GP** *020 †20

SIMON, Theresa S. 2520 VALLEY DR, PLEASANT VALLEY HOSPITAL 25550 #748-08-1995 L2007 **IM** *100

SOL, Benjamin Jatico. 2520 VALLEY DR STE 215, PLEASANT VALLEY HOSPITAL 25550 #748-09-1961 L1975 **OBG GP** *071

ST ONGE, Rick D. 2605 JACKSON AVE, HOLZER CLINIC OF WEST VIRG 25550 #068-01-1989 L1995 **OBG** *020 †30

STRAFFORD, J Craig. 2907 JACKSON AVE, T PLEASANT ORTHOPEDIC CENT 25550 #038-40-1972 L1987 **OBG MDM** *030 †30

SUBIK, Marc Anthony. 2605 JACKSON AVE, HOLZER CLINIC OF WV 25550 #035-15-1979 L1980 **GE IM** *020 †20

THOMPSON, Carl Winston. ■ 25550 #016-42-1948 L1949 **R** *071 †80

TZUK, Ori. 2410 JEFFERSON AVE 25550 #550-02-1992 L2008 **GE** *020 †20

VAIDYA, Shrikant. 2520 VALLEY DR STE 16 25550 #495-20-1971 L1984 **U GS** *020 †95

WADE, John A, Jr. 2520 VALLEY DR STE 112 25550 #055-01-1973 L1975 **OTO A** *020 †45

WILLOCK, Murray Scott. 2605 JACKSON AVE 25550 #038-41-1969 L1969 **GP** *020 †18

WILTZ, John Franklin. 2801 JACKSON AVE 25550 #017-20-1988 L1995 **PD** *020 †55

PRICHARD – WAYNE

MCCAGG, Jillian Miriah. ■ 25555 #055-02-2006 **GS** *012

PRINCETON – MERCER

AHMED, Afzal Uddin. 122 12TH STREET EXT 24740 #495-21-1971 L1982 **DR** *020 †80

AHMED, Taufiq Uddin. ■ 24740 #055-01-2005 **AN** *012

AL-ATTAR, Inas H. 34 NEW HOPE RD 24740 #605-01-1988 L1995 **PD PDI** *020 †55

AYCOTH, Edward D. 122 12TH STREET EXT 24740 #036-01-1969 L1978 **DR NM** *020

AZZO, Walid Hikmet. 122 12TH STREET EXT 24740 #011-02-1987 L1994 **ORS OTR** *020 †40 ‡

BELCHER, Darrell Cecil. 311 COURTHOUSE RD 24740 #055-01-1967 L1968 **ORS** *020 †40

BHASIN, Sunita Malhotra. 122 12TH STREET EXT 24740 #495-41-1966 L1991 **IM IMG** *020

BIRD, William C. 3997 BECKLEY RD 24740 #055-01-1983 L1984 **FM** *020 †18

BIZRI, Ahmad Ghassan. 200 12TH STREET EXT, BRIDGEWATER CLINIC 24740 #409-38-1983 L1997 **P** *020

BRANSON, Philip Jos. 311 COURTHOUSE RD 24740 #016-06-1982 L1987 **ORS** *020 †40

CARLSON, Clifford Hugh. 144 SPRINGHAVEN DR 24740 #035-20-1977 L1988 **PM** *020 †60

CRAFT, Gary Clifton. 3022 EADS MILL RD 24740 #055-01-1966 L1968 **GP** *020

DAR, Naasreen Riaz. 200 NEW HOPE RD, 6 QUAIL VALLEY MED CTR 24740 #704-06-1970 L1980 **P** *020

DELA ROSA, Romulo G. ■ 24740 #748-07-1974 L1985 **IM** *020

DUREMDES, Generoso D. 100 NEW HOPE RD, STE 106 24740 #748-08-1960 L1973 **GS PDS** *072 †85

DUREMDES, Janelle Bermejo. PRINCETON MED ARTS CLINIC 24740 #748-08-1960 L1974 **PD** *071 †55

ELLINGTON, Joe Carey, Jr. 144 UNDERCLIFF TER, ELLINGTON WOMEN'S HEALTH C 24740 #036-05-1991 L2002 **OBG** *020 †30

EPSTEIN, William Harris. 122 12TH STREET EXT 24740 #041-09-1967 L1976 **GS** *020 †85 ‡

FAULKNER, Pamela P. 904 HARRISON ST 24740 #055-75-1985, ▲ L1986 **FM** *020 †18

FOWLER, Daniel Troy. 122 12TH STREET EXT 24740 #047-06-1970 L1989 **DR** *020 †80

GABE, Charles E. 210 NEW HOPE RD 24740 #005-76-1982, ▲ L1989 **RO** *020

GARCIA, Servillano De V. 12TH STREET EM 24740 #748-01-1965 L1978 **EM GP** *020

GHABRA, Nabeel. 160 SPRINGHAVEN DR 24740 #875-02-1979 L1992 **NEP IM** *020 †20

GOLAMCO, Sandra Pe. 153 SPRINGHAVEN DR, MEDICAL REHABILITATION ASS 24740 #748-10-1994 L2004 **PM** *020

GONZALES-CHAMBERS, Rowena. 1 UNDERCLIFF TER 24740 #748-10-1980 L1990 **IM HEM** *020 †20

GREENBERG, Jeffrey Alan. 114 UNDERCLIFF TER 24740 #045-01-1978 L2003 **NS** *020 †25

GROTEN, David Lee. 122 12TH STREET EXT 24740 #007-02-1986 L1999 **DR GS** *020 †80

HASAN, Nusrath. 160 UNDERCLIFF TER, NEW HOPE PSYCHIATRIC ASSOC 24740 #495-21-1983 L1992 **P** *020 †75

HENSLEY, Loren. 407 12TH STREET EXT, BLUE RIDGE INTERNAL MED 24740 #025-76-1999, ▲ L2002 **IM** *020

HIRSCH, Harry. 122 12TH STREET EXT 24740 #165-08-1985 L1991 **GP IM** *020 †28

HOPKINS, Eric Shane. 201 12TH STREET EXT 24740 #055-02-1998 L1989 **GS** *020 †85

HUFFMAN, Jamette R. 403 12TH STREET EXT 24740 #055-75-1997, ▲ L2001 **OBG** *020

HUSSAIN, Farid Md. 3997 BECKLEY RD 24740 #160-05-1986 L2001 **PD** *020 †55

JONES, Robert March. MED ARTS CLN STE 19 24740 #041-09-1978 L1983 **OTO** *020 †45

KASSEM, Omar R. 122 12TH STREET EXT 24740 #047-06-1981 L2000 **FM** *020 †18

KHOKAR, Ghazala Qureshi. 200 NEW HOPE RD STE 3 24740 #704-06-1968 L1987 **PD** *020 †55

KHOKHAR, Muhammed Idrees. 200 NEW HOPE RD STE 3 24740 #704-01-1971 L1982 **ON IM** *020 †20

KOH, Yung Hie. 100 NEW HOPE RD, STE 5 24740 #583-02-1963 L1972 **PD** *020 †55

KROPAC, Robert Phillip. 311 COURTHOUSE RD 24740 #038-40-1969 L1995 **ORS OM** *020

LITTLE, Paul Michael, Jr. ■ 24740 #055-02-1994 L1996 **FM** *020 †18

LOHUIS, Nancy Ann. 904 HARRISON ST 24740 #065-01-1989 L1992 **FM** *020 †18

MENA, Ashraf. ■ 24740 #915-04-1984 L1999 **IM END** *020 †20

MERVA, William Andrew. 100 NEW HOPE RD STE 23 24740 #041-07-1982 L1985 **N** *020 †75

MIRABILE, Charles John. 100 NEW HOPE RD STE 204, PRINCETON MEDICAL ARTS CLI 24740 #055-01-1975 L1981 **IM IMG** *020 †20

MULLINS, David Arthur. 201 12TH STREET EXT 24740 #055-01-1996 L1997 **GS** *020 †85

MUZAFFER, Rahmet. 122 12TH STREET EXT 24740 #308-08-1984 L1994 **NPM** *020

MYERS, Thomas T, III. 34 NEW HOPE RD STE 1, DERM 1 PLLC 24740 #026-04-1962 L1963 **D OS** *071 †15

NERI, Florencio P, Jr. 702 STAFFORD DR 24740 #748-08-1969 L1978 **GP** *020

OLSON, Dana Otmar. 122 12TH STREET EXT 24740 #048-14-1973 L1987 **DR NM** *020 †28,80

PARDASANI, Gopal Manumal. ■ 24740 #495-19-1967 L1975 **PTH** *072 ‡

PATEL, Dilip Babubhai. 122 12TH STREET EXT 24740 #495-22-1973 L2006 **R** *020 †80

PATEL, Kamalesh P. 405 12TH STREET EXT 24740 #041-01-1987 L2002 **GE IM** *020 †20

PATEL, Vishnu Amaram. 1155 MERCER ST 24740 #495-89-1985 L1997 **PUD SME** *020 †20

PATHAK, Aruna Kishor. ■ 24740 #495-19-1968 L1979 *020

PATHAK, Kishor S. 122 12TH STREET EXT 24740 #495-19-1967 L1977 **DR** *020

PERVAIZ, Naeem. 200 NEW HOPE RD, STE 1 24740 #704-01-1970 L1978 **U** *020 †20

PIRACHA, Abdul Rashid. 100 NEW HOPE RD, STE 7 24740 #704-04-1964 L1972 **CD** *020 †20

PRESCOTT, Gordon F. 100 NEW HOPE RD, STE 7 24740 #024-07-1968 L1974 **CD** *020 †20

RAMADAN, Mohamed S. 100 NEW HOPE RD, STE 201 24740 #330-04-1964 L1984 **OBG** *020 †30

RANA, Anjum. PO BOX 5049 24740 #704-01-1982 L1993 **PD AI** *020 †03,55

RANA, Hamza. 3997 BECKLEY RD, BLUESTONE HEALTH CENTER 24740 #704-21-2000 L2005 **IM** *020 †20

RANA, Imtiaz Ahmad Khan A. ■ 24740 #704-01-1961 L1976 **DIA IM** *071 †20

RANA, Shahid Rashid. 200 NEW HOPE RD STE 4, QUAIL VALLEY MEDICAL CTR 24740 #704-01-1986 L1995 **IM** *020 †20

RAYEVSKY, Igor G. 122 12TH STREET EXT 24740 #913-06-1952 L2001 **RO** *071

RAZZAQ, Khalid. 122 12TH STREET EXT 24740 #704-01-1987 L1995 **N OS** *020 †75

SAFDER, Asma. 216 NEW HOPE RD 24740 #495-21-1973 L1977 **PD** *020 †55

SARNO, Macy Jimenez. 122 12TH STREET EXT, PRINCETON COMMUNITY HOSPIT 24740 #748-02-1991 L2000 **FM** *020 †18

SHAH, Mian-Wilayat. 100 NEW HOPE RD, STE 207 24740 #704-01-1961 L1974 **U GS** *020 †85,95

SHAHAN, Michael Ellsworth. 122 12TH STREET EXT 24740 #051-01-1972 L1985 **DR** *020 †80

SHELTON, Carl Randolph. 153 SPRINGHAVEN DR 24740 #041-13-1987 L1991 **PM PMM** *020 †60

SMITH, Lee Elliott. 100 NEW HOPE RD, MED ARTS CLNC STE 20 24740 #024-05-1978 L1983 **OTO** *020 †45

SMITH, Todd A. 617 MERCER ST 24740 #055-75-1997, ▲ L2000 **IM** *020

SPITZER, Mark Alexander. 2767 CLOVER DEW DAIRY RD, LOCUM TENANS 24740 #024-05-1986 L2001 **EM IM** *020 †20

VRINCEANU-HAMM, Alina. 200 12TH STREET EXT 24740 #781-01-1994 L2002 **P ADP** *020 †75

WHEELER, Miriam Ruth. TOTAL LIFR FPC 12TH ST 24740 #045-04-1985 L1988 **FM** *020 †18

WILLS, Danny Ray. 1501 W MAIN ST 24740 #055-01-1975 L1975 **FM** *020 †18

YADAV, Yoginder. 122 12TH STREET EXT 24740 #496-09-1996 L2001 **IM** *020 †20

YU, Min. ■ 24740 #243-21-1982 L2004 **PTH** *020

RAINELLE – GREENBRIER

COCCARO, Peter Joseph. 645 KANAWHA AVE 25962 #051-07-1994 L2005 **PD** *020 †55

JARVIS, Phillip Edward. 210 MAIN ST 25962 #038-40-1964 L1982 **IM NEP** *020

SINGAREDDY, Sanjay. 645 KANAWHA AVE 25962 #495-21-1991 L2005 **IM** *020 †20

RANSON – JEFFERSON

BOCCHINO, Vincent James. 300 S PRESTON ST 25438 #010-02-1982 L1985 **EM** *020 †16

BUENVENIDA, Rene P. 207 S PRESTON ST 25438 #748-10-1961 L1975 **PTH CLP** *020 †50

DAYAL, Vikram. 207 E 5TH AVE 25438 #495-73-1980 L1990 **MPD IM** *020 †55,20

DUGAN, Ellen Marie. 300 S PRESTON ST 25438 #010-02-1982 L1986 **EM** *020 †16

FAIR, Isabelle Evelyn C. 300 S PRESTON ST, JEFFERSON MEMORIAL 25438 #035-46-1967 L1982 **DR NM** *020 †80

FRICK, Mathis Peter. 300 S PRESTON ST 25438 #869-07-1970 L1993 **R NM** *030 †80,28
GROVE, Philip Sumner. 300 S PRESTON ST 25438 #010-02-1996 L2005 **ATP CLP** *020 †50
INGERSOLL, Eric Bennett. 201 S PRESTON ST STE B 25438 #010-02-1986 L1993 **ORS** *020
JONES, Robert Erin, III. 300 S PRESTON ST 25438 #055-02-1995 L1999 **MPD** *020 †20,55
JORDAN, Joseph Paul. 300 S PRESTON ST 25438 #016-42-1956 L2000 **FM** *100 †18 ‡
KLETTER, Jan Cary. 205 E 5TH AVE 25438 #033-05-1981 L2000 **GS AS** *020 †85
LANGLET, Jules Francis. 300 S PRESTON ST 25438 #023-07-1952 L1958 **GP** *071
MENON, K G Sreedhara. 201 E 5TH AVE 25438 #495-37-1962 L1974 **IM GE** *071
MERIWETHER, Wilhelm D. 300 S PRESTON ST, EMERGENCY DEPT. 25438 #036-07-1967 L1991 **EM PHP** *020 †20
MILLER, William Smith. 203 E 4TH AVE 25438 #055-01-1968 L1980 **FM** *020 †18
NAYAK, Sitaram Pangal. 207 S PRESTON ST # POB-10 25438 #495-37-1962 L1975 **ORS** *071 †40
PEAKE, Sharon Parks. 121 W 3RD AVE 25438 #047-06-1990 L1999 **IM** *020 †20
SHAKESPHERE, Alfret. 201 E 5TH AVE, STE 1 25438 #220-04-1987 L1997 **IM** *020 †20
SHAKESPHERE, Geetha. 201 E 5TH AVE, STE 1 25438 #220-04-1988 L1997 **IM** *020 †20
SINGH, Gagan Jit. 201 E 5TH AVE, STE 2 25438 #010-03-1997 L2002 **OPH** *020
SMITH, Marilyn Judy. 121 W 3RD AVE 25438 #055-01-1999 L2001 **FM** *020 †18
SWART, Stephany Suzann. 300 S PRESTON ST, JEFFERSON MEMORIAL 25438 #055-01-1998 L2002 **DR** *020 †80
TRACY, Lloyd Runnels. 300 S PRESTON ST 25438 #305-01-2000 L2003 **FM** *020 †18 ‡
VONGXAIBURANA, Ophas. 201 E 5TH AVE 25438 #891-01-1967 L1974 **GS GP** *020
WALKER, James Drew. 300 S PRESTON ST, JEFERSON MEMORIAL HOSPITAL 25438 #014-01-1981 L2007 **EM** *020 †16
WEBB, Robert Francis. 319 S PRESTON ST 25438 #055-01-1975 L1976 **IM ON** *020 †20
WILLIAMS, Leah Mildred. 300 S PRESTON ST 25438 #051-04-1947 L1948 **GP** *071

RAVENSWOOD – JACKSON

GANDEE, Durwood F. 1979 PROFESSIONAL CIR, RAVENSWOOD MEDICAL CENTER 26164 #055-02-1983 L1984 **FM** *020
MALIK, Arif Mahmood. 505 1/2 WASHINGTON ST 26164 #308-01-1991 L1999 **IM** *020 †20

RED JACKET – MINGO

CAMOMOT, Wigberto C. PO BOX 329, MAIN ST 25692 #748-11-1966 L1983 **GP AN** *071

REDSTAR – FAYETTE

MOASSER, Amir H. 502 MAIN ST W, MED-SURG GROUP INC 25901 #517-01-1981 L1994 **NEP** *020 †20

REEDSVILLE – PRESTON

WOLF, John Herman, Jr. ■ 26547 #036-05-1961 L1963 **A PD** *071

RENICK – GREENBRIER

MUSSELMAN, Laurence K. ■ 24966 #051-04-1956 L1957 **P** *071

RHODELL – RALEIGH

ROBERTS, Joanna M. PO BOX 158 25915 #035-06-1964 L1974 **IM** *020

RICHWOOD – NICHOLAS

CHANG, Hao. 25 OAKFORD AVE 26261 #244-01-1970 L1974 **GP** *020
DIAZ, Clemente. 75 AVENUE B 26261 #649-01-1959 L1970 **GS GP** *020
HARDWAY, Mark Jason. 75 AVENUE B 26261 #055-02-1998 L2000 **PD** *020 †55
MORAN, Edward John. 75 AVENUE B, RICHWOOD AREA COMMUNITY HO 26261 #055-02-2004 L2006 **MPD** *012
PARVIZ, Sheikh S. 75 AVENUE B, RIVERSIDE ADDITION 26261 #704-25-1995 L2002 **ID** *020 †20
WHITLOCK-MORALES, Autumn. 75 AVENUE B, RACH 26261 #055-02-2002 L2005 **MPD** *020 †55,20

RIDGELEY – MINERAL

MYERS, Mark Alan. RR 3 BOX 142, HUNT CLUB MEDICAL CLINIC 26753 #055-01-1982 L1983 **EM** *020 †18
STANSBURY, John Gaither. 11 HUNT CLUB PLZ, HUNT CLUB MED CLINIC 26753 #055-01-1973 L1987 **EM** *020 †16

RIPLEY – JACKSON

ALI, Ahmed. ■ 25271 #495-21-1956 L1970 **GS GYN** *071
BARNES, William Everett. PINELL ST 25271 #055-01-1966 L1968 **GS** *020 †85
BREITINGER, Ernst Robt. PINELL ST 25271 #033-06-1985 L1993 **FM** *075 †18
COKER, Donald Duane. PO BOX 587, PINNELL STREET 25271 #025-01-1969 L2005 **GS HNS** *020 †85
HAJI-MORAD, Ali. ■ 25271 #517-01-1955 L1967 **GS** *071
HUGHES, James Thos. PINELL ST 25271 #041-02-1960 L1965 **IM** *071 †20
JOSEF, Ernesto Jacinto. PINELL ST 25271 #748-01-1956 L1964 **GP** *071
KESARI, Sudhakar. 600 CHURCH ST S STE 2, JACKSON FAMILY CARE 25271 #496-01-1987 L1994 **IM** *020 †20
LA CARBONARA, Fredric E. PINELL ST 25271 #561-17-1978 L1987 **PTH** *020 †50
LARES, Todd Allan. 45 MOUNTAIN CREST LN 25271 #055-02-1996 L1997 **EM** *020
MC ELDOWNEY, Anthony Jos. ■ 25271 #038-41-1989 L2004 **ORS OSM** *020

MC INTOSH, Michael S. 122 PINNELL ST, JACKSON GENERAL HOSPITAL 25271 #055-01-1979 L1980 **EM** *020 †16 ‡
VONGSNAKORN, Prasid. 202 MAIN ST W 25271 #891-01-1963 L1973 **GS EM** *071 †85
YOUNIS, Mark Sharbel. 122 PINNELL ST 25271 #055-01-1989 L1992 **DR** *020 †80

ROMNEY – HAMPSHIRE

CHOWDHARY, Vijay Kumar. 549 CENTER AVE 26757 #308-11-1983 L1991 **IM** *020
GIRON, Nabal Burguillos. 549 CENTER AVE 26757 #748-02-1965 L1975 **IM GP** *020
GIRON, Zinnia Bacol. 205 E MAIN ST 26757 #748-01-1967 L1975 **IM** *020
HAHN, Jerry Mitchel. ROUTE 50 26757 #055-02-1986 L1987 **FM D** *020 †18
LEE, Irene Pua. 549 CENTER AVE, HAMPSHIRE MEMORIAL HOSPITA 26757 #748-01-1994 L1999 **IM** *020 †20
QURESHI, Abdul. 549 CENTER AVE, HAMPSHIRE MEMORIAL HOSPITA 26757 #704-17-1989 L1995 **IM** *020 †20
RAZZOOK, Salah Philip. 201 W GRAVEL LN 26757 #528-01-1971 L1983 **GS GE** *020 †85
SURATTANONT, Sadtha. 549 CENTER AVE 26757 #891-02-1964 L1975 **GP GS** *020
SZATMARY, Gabriella. 549 CENTER AVE 26757 #473-01-1992 L2000 **OS** *020 †75

RONCEVERTE – GREENBRIER

ADAM, George Franklin, Jr. 119 MAPLEWOOD AVE, AT FAIRLEA 24970 #016-45-1998 L2004 **U** *020 †95
AMAR, John Jason. 200 MAPLEWOOD AVE 24970 #039-01-1986 L1991 **GE** *020 †20
ARVAN, Yuri L. 200 MAPLEWOOD AVE, GREENBRIER PHYSICIANS INC 24970 #913-69-1984 L2004 **OPH** *020
BANKS, James W. 200 MAPLEWOOD AVE 24970 #004-01-1949 L1952 **ORS** *071
BENHAM, Ramsey A. 202 MAPLEWOOD AVE 24970 #528-01-1959 L1991 **IM CD** *020 †20
BOOKOUT, Craig Lewis. 202 MAPLEWOOD AVE 24970 #055-02-1983 L1985 **FM EM** *020 †18
CASTO, John Theron. 202 MAPLEWOOD AVE 24970 #055-01-1994 L1996 **AN** *020 †05
COLLINS, John Orvil. 100 TAYLOR LN 24970 #048-12-1993 L2004 **N** *020 †75
COOK, Irving Kenneth. 200 MAPLEWOOD AVE, GREENBRIER PHYSICIANS 24970 #051-01-1963 L1989 **DR NM** *020 †80
CORNETT, Edgar Stuart. 202 MAPLEWOOD AVE, GREENBRIER VALLEY MED CTR 24970 #055-01-1997 L1998 **AN** *020 †05
CRITES-SAMS, Debra. 122 MAPLEWOOD AVE 24970 #055-75-1987, ▲ L1988 **GP** *020
DUKART, William Stuart. 200 MAPLEWOOD AVE, GREENBRIER PHYSICIANS INC 24970 #024-07-1973 L1982 **PD GP** *020 †55
FLOWERS, Coy Alden. 200 MAPLEWOOD AVE, GREENBRIER PHYSICIANS INC 24970 #055-01-1998 L2000 **OBG** *020 †30
FORT, Kyle Fredrick. 119 MAPLEWOOD AVE, AT FAIRLEA 24970 #017-20-1978 L1983 **U** *020 †95
GIANTURCO, Anna Maria. 202 MAPLEWOOD AVE, GREENBRIER VALLEY MEDICAL 24970 #654-01-1997 L2003 **AN** *020
GOMEZ, Manuel Antonio. 202 MAPLEWOOD AVE 24970 #264-04-1969 L1975 **PTH PCP** *020 †50 ‡
HARRIS, Nathaniel Noble. 200 MAPLEWOOD AVE 24970 #020-02-1978 L1981 **FM** *071 †18 ‡
HENRY, Francis P. GREENBRIAR VALLEY HOSP 24970 #041-09-1947 L1980 **EM** *020 †30
HORNE, Francis G. ■ 24970 #036-07-1951 L1954 **AN** *071 †05
JONES, Ray Lee. 202 MAPLEWOOD AVE 24970 #055-75-1986, ▲ L1991 **GS** *020
KARRS, Thomas Michael. 103 DAVIS STUART RD 24970 #055-01-1984 L1985 **D** *020 †20,15
KOWALKOWSKI, Thos Stephen. 202 MAPLEWOOD AVE 24970 #041-09-1984 L1985 **U** *020 †95
LIGHT, Philip Nelson. 101 DAVIS STUART RD, EYE CENTER OF GREENBRIER 24970 #051-07-1988 L1993 **OPH** *020 †35
MORRISON, Katherine M. 200 MAPLEWOOD AVE 24970 #055-01-2003 L2007 **PD** *100
MOUCHIZADEH, Joseph. 119 MAPLEWOOD AVE, GREENBRIER VALLEYUROLOGY A 24970 #917-29-1979 L2002 **U** *020 †95
NICHOLAS, R S B. 202 MAPLEWOOD AVE, GREENBRIER VALLEY MEDICAL 24970 #957-07-1969 L1985 **DR IM** *020 †80
PETRARCA, Robert Allan. 202 MAPLEWOOD AVE, GREENBRIER VALLEY MEDICAL 24970 #055-75-2006, ▲ L2007 *012
PLYBON, Benjamin Lee. 200 MAPLEWOOD AVE 24970 #055-01-1964 L1966 **GS TS** *020 †85,90
ROSE, Colin Alexander. 202 MAPLEWOOD AVE 24970 #063-01-1977 L1994 **DR** *020 †80
ROSE, Heather Jayne. 202 MAPLEWOOD AVE 24970 #063-01-1989 L1994 **DR** *020 †80
SAYVETZ, Tom Andrew. 202 MAPLEWOOD AVE 24970 #023-07-1976 L1994 **PHP** *050 †70,16
SCOBBO, Ronald Roger. 202 MAPLEWOOD AVE 24970 #055-01-1971 L1972 **IM** *071 †20 ‡
SHIREY, Robert Arleigh. 17 RED OAKS SHOPPING CTR 24970 #055-01-1980 L1981 **IM** *020 †20
WHEELER, Robert Lee. 200 MAPLEWOOD AVE, GREENBRIER PHYSICIANS INC 24970 #011-03-1978 L1982 **OBG** *020 †30

SAINT ALBANS – KANAWHA

ABAYON-CASTRO, Ladislawa. 200 KANAWHA TER 25177 #748-09-1967 L1983 **PD** *020
ALLEN, Mark Wayne. 2333 MACCORKLE AVE, STE 102 25177 #055-01-1998 L1999 **FM** *020 †18
EDENS, Jerry Wayne. 12 KANAWHA TER 25177 #055-01-1976 L1976 **FM** *075 †18
GRAHAM, Anthony Wm. 509 4TH AVE 25177 #055-01-1972 L1972 **FM** *020 †18
LOPEZ, Carmelo Javier. ■ 25177 #748-01-1964 L1978 **FM EM** *071
MOORE, Iva Elaine. 221 4TH AVE 25177 #055-01-1988 L1989 **FPG** *020 †18
PATEL, Ajay Tirbhovan. 450 2ND ST 25177 #495-23-1987 L2001 **IM** *020 †20
SADORRA, Lagrimas Babiera. PO BOX 1326 25177 #748-09-1967 L1981 **GP ADM** *020
VAN WINKLE, Glenn F. ■ 25177 #051-04-1954 L1955 **OBG** *074

SAINT GEORGE – TUCKER

PAZ, Alvaro Nivardo. RR 1 BOX 208, ST. GEORGE MEDICAL CLINIC 26287 #176-03-1970 L1979 **FM** *071

SAINT MARYS – PLEASANTS

BYLER, David J. 201 LAFAYETTE ST 26170 #027-01-1983 L1986 **FM** *020 †18
DE JOSEF, Teresita P. 111 LAFAYETTE ST, STE 201 26170 #748-07-1967 L1980 **IM EM** *020

SALEM – HARRISON

CHONG, Charles Fernandez. ■ 26426 #005-19-1977 L1978 **GP** *020
DAVIS, Andrea Arlene. ■ 26426 #055-01-2007 L2007 **FP** *012
MIKOWSKI, Mary Caroline. PO BOX 392 26426 #051-01-1993 L1994 **FM** *020 †18
SAYRE, Robert Walter. ■ 26426 #409-23-1980 L1983 **IM** *020

SCARBRO – FAYETTE

KORESHI, Sabeen Kashif. RR 2 BOX 615A, NEW RIVER HEALTH ASSOCIATE 25917
#704-02-1998 L2006 **FM** *100 †18

SCHERR – MINERAL

KUNKEL, Allan Burt. HC 72 BOX 7006 26726 #065-09-1966 L1999 **IM ID** *071

SCOTT DEPOT – PUTNAM

AKINS, James Alan. 303A GREAT TEAYS BLVD 25560 #055-02-1994 L1999 **IM** *020
BASSO, Ana Cristina. 301 GREAT TEAYS BLVD STE 6, WOMEN CARE INC 25560
#187-76-1996 L2005 **OBG** *020 †30
CILIBERTI, Devin Mark. 301 GREAT TEAYS BLVD STE 6 25560 #055-01-1997 L1998
OBG *020 †30
ELMORE, Michael Scott. ■ 25560 #055-02-2003 **GS** *012
FERGUSON, Angela Beth. 301 GREAT TEAYS BLVD STE 6 25560 #055-02-1998 L2001
PD *020 †55
JENKINS, Mary Buffington. 301 GREAT TEAYS BLVD, STE 6 25560 #055-02-1993 L2002
FM *020 †18
LAMBERNEDIS, Ann Maree. 303 GREAT TEAYS BLVD, STE 101 25560 #055-02-1992 L1995
PD *020 †55
SHUFF, Charles Edward. ■ 25560 #055-02-1997 L2007 **OSS** *020 †40
STALLO, Pamela Evans. 303 GREAT TEAYS BLVD, STE 101 25560 #055-02-1989 L1992
PD *020 †55
WEBB, Christina Dawn. ■ 25560 #055-02-2006 L2007 **FP** *012

SHEPHERDSTOWN – JEFFERSON

ABBRECHT, Peter Herman. ■ 25443 #025-01-1962 L2001 **PUD IM** *020 †20
ALDIS, John W. ■ 25443 #019-02-1971 L2002 **FM PHP** *050 †18
CLAASEN, Frans George. ■ 25443 #660-03-1957 L1966 **IM** *071
DE BIASI, Roberta Lynn. ■ 25443 #051-01-1992 L1993 **PD ID** *050 †55
FREUND, Alvin. ■ 25443 #011-02-1966 L1996 **PD** *020
KEIGHLEY, John Francis H. ■ 25443 #352-03-1956 L1960 **PUD IM** *071 †20
KELLOGG, Jeffrey Douglas. 45 MADDEX DR 25443 #039-05-1985 L1988 **FM** *020 †18
NORTHRUP, Robert Smither. ■ 25443 #024-01-1964 L1979 **PHP IM** *062
PHILLIPS, Sarah Elizabeth. ■ 25443 #055-01-2008 *012
REGUERO, Wilfred. ■ 25443 #010-03-1966 L2004 **OBG** *071 †30
STARO, Francis Louis. 68 GREYSTONE DR 25443 #024-05-1970 L2006 **OTO PS** *020 †45
STINE, Oscar Cebren. 7633 FLOWING SPRINGS RD 25443 #010-01-1954 L1974
FM PHP *071 †55,18

SHINNSTON – HARRISON

DUBBERKE, Lance Dieter. 686 S PIKE ST, HARRISON COUNTY FAM. PRACT 26431
#039-05-1989 L1990 **FM** *020 †18
KALAYCIOGLU, Mehmet V. 686 S PIKE ST, HARRISON COUNTY FAM. PRACT 26431
#902-01-1950 L1963 **FPG FM** *071

SISTERSVILLE – TYLER

AHMAD, Saed Aftab. 314 S WELLS ST 26175 #704-25-1996 L2001 **MPD** *020 †20,55
BANTUG, Rogelio Orito. 314 S WELLS ST 26175 #748-11-1970 L1976 **GP** *020
BEANE, James Michael. 314 S WELLS ST, SISTERSVILLE GENERAL HOSPI 26175
#055-01-1977 L1978 **FM** *020
BOONE, Ralph H. 314 S WELLS ST 26175 #051-04-1951 L1953 **GP OM** *071
FAGUNDO, Ramon H. 314 S WELLS ST 26175 #270-01-1974 L1982 **EM PD** *020 †16
NICHOLS, Amanda Diane. 314 S WELLS ST 26175 #055-01-2001 L2004 **FM** *020 †18
NICHOLS, Gary Allen. 314 S WELLS ST 26175 #055-01-2001 L2004 **FM** *020 †18

SOPHIA – RALEIGH

JIMENEZ, Teodoro Dimaano. SOPHIA MEDICAL CLINIC 25921 #748-10-1970 L1978 **FM** *071

SOUTH CHARLESTON – KANAWHA

ABDU, Tarek M. 4605 MACCORKLE AVE SW, THOMAS MEMORIAL HOSP 25309
#915-04-1979 L1997 **NPM** *020 †55
AHMAD, Bali. 401 DIVISION ST, STE 202 25309 #875-02-1985 L2002 **GS** *020 †85
AL-HAJJ, Gabriel Emile. 400 DIVISION ST STE 7 25309 #605-01-1972 L1976 **GS VS** *020 †85
AYOOB, Rose Mary. ■ 25303 #055-01-2006 **PD** *012
BABAYEV, Marietta. 313 MACCORKLE AVE SW 25303 #035-08-1995 L2002 **PM PRS** *020 †60
BACCHUS, Melissa Nadine-N. 4607 MACCORKLE AVE SW, STE 204 25309 #566-01-2002 L2007
PD *020
BAROSSO, Carl. 500 POPLAR ST, STE 304 25309 #035-08-1987 L2008 **TS VS** *020 †85,90
BASTIN, Crystal Heatherma. 4607 MACCORKLE AVE SW, STE MP200 25309
#055-01-1999 L2001 **FM** *020 †18
BATTLE, Emily Hamrick. 424 DIVISION ST, STE 100 25309 #055-01-1993 L1994 **GE** *020 †20

BAUTISTA, Carmelita N. 4605 MACCORKLE AVE SW, THOMAS MEMORIAL HOSPITAL 25309
#748-10-1969 L1980 **GP FM** *020
BERNARDO, Elma Zapanta. 401 DIVISION ST STE 203 25309 #748-01-1960 L1980 **P** *020
BERNARDO, Ignacio Dizon. ■ 25309 #748-07-1960 L1983 **GP EM** *071
BINNS, Carl Brooks, Jr. 416 DIVISION ST, KANAWHA VALLEY RADIOLOGIST 25309
#041-02-1968 L1983 **DR** *071 †80
BUCKALEW, Christy Lynn. ■ 25303 #055-02-2007 **PD** *012
CHILDERS, Clark Edwin, Jr. 4607 MACCORKLE AVE SW, MP STE 204 25309
#055-02-1991 L1995 **PD** *020 †55
CINCO, Angel Ma. 4605 MACCORKLE AVE SW 25309 #748-11-1965 L1975 **PTH** *020 †50
COTES, Osterman. 500 POPLAR ST, STE 200 25309 #308-01-1969 L1974 **OBG** *020 †30
CRIGGER, Charles David. 4607 MACCORKLE AVE SW, STE MP406 25309 #041-13-1980 L1984
OTO HNS *020 †45
D'AGOSTINE, Ramona Ann. 4607 MACCORKLE AVE SW, STE 201 25309 #055-02-1995 L1999
OBG *020 †30
DEEL, John Tate. 500 POPLAR ST, STE 304 25309 #055-02-1999 L2007 **TS** *020
DE TEMPLE, Julie Ann. 538 3RD AVE SW 25309 #055-01-1998 L1999 **FM** *020 †18
DY, Rosendo Yu. 4605 MACCORKLE AVE SW 25309 #748-01-1964 L1983 **FM** *020
EL-KHATIB, Hussein E. 401 DIVISION ST STE 204 25309 #915-04-1985 L1994 **P PYM** *020 †75
ESPIRITU, Julian L, Jr. 24 MACCORKLE AVE SW, STE 201 25303 #748-02-1979 L1986
NEP IM *020 †20
FERNANDES, Joseph Edmund. 401 DIVISION ST STE 104 25309 #561-11-1965 L1981
ORS *020 †40
FOSTER, Bruce Alan. 400 DIVISION ST, STE 2 25309 #041-02-1977 L1978 **GP PLM** *020
FULKS, Richard Morrison. 4605 MACCORKLE AVE SW 25309 #024-01-1973 L1986
PTH *020 †35
GHANNAM, Mouwafak Amad. 4501 MACCORKLE AVE SW, STE 401 25309 #875-01-1966 L1976
OTO *020 †45
GOAD, Betty Amelia. 131 7TH AVE 25303 #020-02-1993 L1997 **OBG** *020 †30
GOLIATH, Gilbert. 424 DIVISION ST, STE 102 25309 #308-01-1982 L1989 **PD** *020 †55
GOODE, Christopher Scott. 4605 MACCORKLE AVE SW, EMP OF KNAWHA PLLC 25309
#055-02-2002 L2004 **EM** *100 †16
HARPER, Timothy G. 424 DIVISION ST STE 100 25309 #055-01-1976 L1977 **GE IM** *020 †20
HARRIS, Michael L. 4501 MACCORKLE AVE SW, STE 500 25309 #041-13-1989 L1993
OPH *020 †35
HAUPT, Bruce Fredric. 500 POPLAR ST STE 303 25309 #047-05-1990 L1995
ORS OTR *020 †40
HAYES, Richard Darrell. 312 6TH AVE SW STE 3 25303 #055-01-1974 L1975 **FM** *020 †18
HENSLEY, Elizabeth Kristi. 538 3RD AVE SW 25303 #055-02-1997 L1999 **FM** *020 †18 ‡
HIVELY, Jeffrey Wayne. 707 CHESTNUT ST 25309 #055-02-1993 L1994 **FM** *020 †18
HIVELY, Robert Lee. 500 POPLAR ST STE 300 25309 #055-01-1973 L1974 **GP** *020
HUGHES, Mark Andrew. 4607 MACCORKLE AVE SW, STE 305 25309 #047-06-1986 L1995
P *020 †75
JOGENEPALLY, Narender Rao. 401 DIVISION ST, STE 100 25309 #495-65-1986 L1997
HO *020 †20
JOHN, Kuruvilla. 401 DIVISION ST, STE 104 25309 #495-31-1981 L1990 **N CN** *020 †75
JOHNSON, Elizabeth Ann. ■ 25309 #055-01-2004 L2007 **MPD** *012
KALOU, Mohamad Samah. 500 POPLAR ST STE 20, MOUNTAINEER FAMILY MEDICIN 25309
#875-01-1996 L2006 **FM** *020 †18
KAYI, Mallinath. 401 DIVISION ST 25309 #495-99-1974 L1984 **IM PCC** *020 †20
KHAN, Moona Zia. 313 MCCORKLE AVE SW, HOLZER CLINIC 25303 #704-02-1992 L2003
FM *020 †18 ‡
KOWATLI, Emad A. 500 POPLAR ST STE 204 25309 #875-01-1983 L2000 **PCC SME** *020 †20
KYER, Paul Dean, III. 414 GREENWAY AVE, STE 100 25309 #055-01-1994 L1999 **GS** *020 †85
LAKHANI, Vinodrai B. 4840 KENTUCKY ST 25309 #495-01-1965 L1975 **FM IMG** *020
LAMB, Robert Vaughn, III. 24 MACCORKLE AVE SW, STE 201 25303 #036-07-1975 L1981
NEP IM *020 †20
LANTZ, Elizabeth Cary. 4607 MACCORKLE AVE SW, STE MP200 25309 #055-01-1998 L2001
IM *020 †20
LEWIS, Mary Lou. 24 MACCORKLE AVE SW 25303 #012-05-1965 L1971 **NEP IM** *020 †20
LUBY, Bernard Jos. 624 CHESTNUT ST 25309 #055-01-1980 L1981 **GYN OBG** *020 †30
MANI, John Henry. 400 DIVISION ST STE 6 25309 #055-01-1977 L1985 **U** *020 †95
MC CLELLAN, Elizabeth Ann. 414 GREENWAY AVE, STE 200 25309 #037-01-1997 L2005 **P** *100
MEARS, James Michael. 401 DIVISION ST STE 205 25309 #055-02-1988 L1989 **FM** *020 †18
MEHTA, Nimish Kunj. 203 SOUTHERN WOODS DR 25309 #055-02-1997 L1999 **PD** *020 †55
MICHAEL, Roger Lynn. ■ 25303 #045-01-1978 L1979 **OBG** *020
NASHERALNEAM, Muhammed S. 500 POPLAR ST, STE 201 25309 #875-02-1996 L2003 **N** *020
NUCUM, Magdaleno S. 4605 MAC CLARKE AVE SW 25309 #748-01-1966 L1980 *020 ‡
PATEL, Kiran Ranchhodbhai. 401 DIVISION ST, STE 306 25309 #495-37-1987 L1992
OBG *020 †30
PATEL, Leela K. 401 DIVISION ST, STE 306 25309 #495-37-1988 L1997 **FM** *020 †18
PETERSON, Richard Boyd. 401 DIVISION ST STE 100 25309 #040-01-1972 L1997 **IM** *020 †20
PISANO, Raul Valdes. 701 JEFFERSON RD 25309 #231-01-1947 L1977 **FOP PTH** *020 †50
POLLACK, James Albert. 4607 MACCORKLE AVE SW, STE 306 25309 #055-01-1991 L1993
GS *020 †85
RASHID, Nicole Mary. 4513 MACCORKLE AVE SW 25309 #055-02-2001 L2005 **OPH** *020 †35
RASHID, Richard Charles. 4513 MACCORKLE AVE SW 25309 #051-04-1962 L1963
OPH *020 †35
RAY, Tara Faun. 4607 MACCORKLE AVE SW, STE 305 25309 #055-75-2001, ▲ L2005 **P** *020 †75
RAZON, Benjamin De Mesa. 4605 MACCORKLE AVE SW 25309 #748-01-1954 L1971 **GP** *071
RECTENWALD, Robert Wm, II. 25 E COVENTRY WOODS 25309 #055-01-1975 L1976
AM IM *020 †20,70
RITTINGER, Thomas John. 1090 GREENLAND CIR, 4605 MACCORKLE AVENUE SW 25309
#055-02-1999 L2001 **FM** *020 †18
SHABB, Samir. 428 DIVISION ST 25309 #605-01-1953 L1960 **GS GYN** *071 †85
SHAH, Arvindkumar. 401 DIVISION ST STE 100 25309 #495-23-1976 L1983 **ON HEM** *020 †20
SHAMMA, Bassam Nicholas. 4607 MACCORKLE AVE SW, STE 301 25309 #605-01-1988 L1992
OBG *020 †30
SKAGGS, Christopher C. 707 CHESTNUT ST 25309 #055-02-1996 L1999 **IM** *020 †20
SOPHER, Irvin Murray. 701 JEFFERSON RD 25309 #023-01-1966 L1975 **FOP ATP** *020 †50
SOULSBY, David Leon. 610 CHESTNUT ST, ORTHOCLINIC PC INC 25309 #055-01-1982 L1983
ORS *020 †40
STEINVURZEL, Mark Daniel. 24 MACCORKLE AVE SW, STE 202 25303 #012-05-1996 L2003
OPH *020 †35
STICKLER, Alatheia. 4607 MACCORKLE AVE SW, STE 400MP 25309 #055-01-1995 L1997
PD *020 †55

SUBIT, Michael James. ■ 25303 #055-01-2006 **OBG** *012
TARAKJI, Hossam Saleh. 4605 MACCORKLE AVE SW 25309 #875-02-1992 L2001 **IM** *020 †20
TARAVATH, Sasidharan. 401 DIVISION ST, STE 206 25309 #495-73-1971 L1996 **CHN SME** *020 †75,55
THOMPSON, Jaime Layne. ■ 25309 #055-01-2003 L2006 **FM** *020
TICKLE, Amy Elizabeth. ■ 25303 #055-01-2005 L2008 **FP** *012
TULLY, Carl C. ■ 25309 #051-04-1947 L1948 **FM** *071 †18
WARREN, Randy Lee. 414 GREENWAY AVE, STE 200 25309 #055-02-2000 L2005 **P** *100
WAZIR, Badshah Jan. 428 DIVISION ST, STE 2A 25309 #704-08-1971 L1977 **CD IM** *020 †20
WILSON, George Butler. 60 RHL, MOUNTAINEER IMAGING 25309 #047-20-1988 L1993 **DR** *020 †80
WINNINGS, Melanie Anne. 4607 MACCORKLE AVE SW, STE 400 25309 #055-01-1997 L2002 **PD** *020 †55
ZANABLI, Abdulrahman. 500 POPLAR ST, CHARLESTON NEPHROLOGY, HYP 25309 #875-02-1993 L2007 **NEP** *020 †20
ZEKAN, Thomas James. 60 RHL, MOUNTAINEER IMAGING 25309 #055-01-1989 L1996 **DR** *020 †80

SPANISHBURG — MERCER

CAPPIELLO, Alexandra. ■ 25922 #023-07-2004 L2007 **PTH** *012

SPENCER — ROANE

AKALAL, Melanie Garcia. 146 WILLIAMS DR 25276 #748-02-1995 L2006 **PYG** *100 †75
AMBROSIO, Pedro N. ■ 25276 #748-02-1965 L1974 **IM GP** *071 †20
CHRISTIANSEN, Carroll D. 146 WILLIAMS DR 25276 #016-43-1980 L1981 **FM** *020 †18
CLANCY, Paul Jos. ■ 25276 #055-02-1991 L1995 **EM** *020 †16
CLETO, Emmanuel Mercado. 200 HOSPITAL DR, ROANE GENERAL HOSPITAL 25276 #748-02-1982 L1991 **DR** *020 †20,28,80
CORPUZ-AMBROSIO, Erlinda. 200 HOSPITAL DR 25276 #748-02-1965 L1974 **PD GP** *071 †55
COTTLE, Aaron Depue. ■ 25276 #010-01-1964 L1967 **FM GS** *075
DESOUZA, Alexandre S. 200 HOSPITAL DR, ROANE MEDICAL HOSP 25276 #187-24-1984 L1997 **PS GS** *020
FAMULARCANO, Precilla T. 146 WILLIAMS DR 25276 #748-07-1968 L1978 **FM** *020
GAMPONIA, Herminio L. ■ 25276 #748-07-1958 L1970 **GS FM** *071
HUSSAIN, Roshan A. 146 WILLIAMS DR 25276 #308-11-1992 L1996 **FM** *020 †18 ‡
KESSELL, Maria Lee. 200 HOSPITAL DR 25276 #055-02-1998 L1999 **FM** *020 †18
LO, Pedro Felipe. 200 HOSPITAL DR 25276 #748-01-1963 L1973 **GS AS** *020
MC MURRY, John Pelham. 200 HOSPITAL DR 25276 #020-02-1981 L2002 **OBG** *100 †30
NG, Hong Kin. 200 HOSPITAL DR, ROANE GENERAL HOSPITAL 25276 #041-02-1998 L2001 **GS MDM** *020
SEEN, Kenneth James. 200 HOSPITAL DR 25276 #023-01-1986 L1987 **FM** *020 †18
SITLER, Teresa Mc Clung. 200 HOSPITAL DR, ROANE GENERAL HOSPITAL 25276 #055-01-1999 L2001 **MPD** *020 †55,20
WATSON, Brent Edward. 200 HOSPITAL DR 25276 #055-01-1999 L2001 **IM MPD** *040 †20

SUMMERSVILLE — NICHOLAS

BYRD, Mark Andrew. 702 PROFESSIONAL PARK DR, GREENBRIAR PHYSICIANS INC 26651 #027-01-1993 L2003 **PUD** *020 †20
CARSON, William Raymond. 400 FAIRVIEW HEIGHTS RD, ACC SUITE 301 26651 #035-09-1990 L1995 **ORS** *020
CONLEY, Paul Joseph. 400 FAIRVIEW HEIGHTS RD, SUMMERSVILLE MEMORIAL HOSP 26651 #055-75-1997, ▲ L2000 **IM** *020 †20
DICKENSON, Joseph Kevin. 400 FAIRVIEW HEIGHTS RD 26651 #055-01-1992 L1999 **GS** *020 †85
EITEL, Douglas Ray. 1305 WEBSTER RD 26651 #018-03-1999 L2003 **P** *020 †75
FLEER, Robert Eric. 400 FAIRVIEW HEIGHTS RD 26651 #040-02-1974 L1975 **EM FM** *020 †18,16
GREENBERG, Bruce Kevin. 350 FAIRVIEW HEIGHTS RD 26651 #005-12-1986 L1993 **FM** *020 †18
GREENBERG, Sunita Phasge. 350 FAIRVIEW HEIGHTS RD, BOX F 26651 #005-12-1987 L1993 **FM** *020 †18
GROVES, Louis William, Jr. 480 HANNA FARM RD 26651 #055-01-1962 L1963 **FM GS** *020
JOO, Yong-Don. 818 ARBUCKLE RD 26651 #583-01-1960 L1971 **GS ORS** *020
KHORSHAD, Miraflor G. 415 MAIN ST 26651 #748-07-1969 L1982 **GP FM** *020
LASSERE, Michael Warren. 400 FAIRVIEW HEIGHTS RD, SUMMERSVILLE WOMENS HEALTH 26651 #021-05-1981 L1988 **OBG** *020 †30
MERIWETHER, David Farbod. 315 FAIRVIEW HEIGHTS RD 26651 #038-41-1980 L1986 **U** *020 †95
MORRIS, Stanley Thomas. 400 FAIRVIEW HEIGHTS RD, SUMMERSVILLE MEMORIAL HOS 26651 #055-01-1998 L1999 **FM** *020 †18
OLSON, Arthur Wesley. 400 FAIRVIEW HEIGHTS RD 26651 #005-12-1969 L1977 **FM** *062 †18
ORBETA, Buenaventura P. 800 NORTHSIDE DR, STE 26 26651 #748-08-1966 L1972 **R** *071
ROSTOCKI, Lukasz A. 400 FAIRVIEW HEIGHTS RD, # 201 26651 #759-12-1975 L2006 **OBG OCC** *020 †30
SALGADO, Purificacion. 400 FAIRVIEW HEIGHTS RD, # 302 26651 #748-10-1981 L1994 **PD** *020 †55
SHANK, Crischelle Lynn. 350 FAIRVIEW HEIGHTS RD 26651 #005-12-2004 L2007 **FM** *100 †18
SHANK, John Stephen. 350 FAIRVIEW HEIGHTS RD, BOX F 26651 #005-12-1970 L1978 **FM** *020 †18
SHORT, Yancy Scott. 400 FAIRVIEW HEIGHTS RD 26651 #055-01-1990 L1991 **GS** *020 †85
TAYLOR, Michael Eugene. 400 FAIRVIEW HEIGHTS RD, RURAL HEALTH CENTER 26651 #055-01-1980 L1981 **FM** *020 †18
TOMSHO, Mark Michael. 400 FAIRVIEW HEIGHTS RD, STE 302 26651 #041-01-1982 L1986 **PD** *020 †55
URICK, Lois Alana. 1305 WEBSTER RD 26651 #051-07-1997 L2001 **P** *020 †75
WANTZ, Margaret Suzanne. 350 FAIRVIEW HEIGHTS RD 26651 #005-12-1985 L1988 **FM** *020 †18
WANTZ, Mark Lynwood. 350 FAIRVIEW HEIGHTS RD, BOX F 26651 #005-12-1983 L1988 **FM** *020 †18

WILLIS, Bradley Steven. ■ 26651 #055-01-2006 **FP** *012
WURTH, Marvin J. 400 FAIRVIEW HEIGHTS RD, SUMMERSVILLE MEM HOSP 26651 #010-01-1984 L1987 **IM** *020 †20

SUTTON — BRAXTON

GOBUNSUY, Rodolfo S. ■ 26601 #748-10-1972 L1993 **IM** *075
SABIO, Arturo B. 196 RIVERVIEW DR 26601 #748-10-1972 L1977 **GS GP** *020 ‡
STALNAKER, Ralph Allen. 700 MEADOW LN 26601 #649-14-1976 L1982 **GP IM** *020

TERRA ALTA — PRESTON

GOOD, John Dryden. RR 1 BOX 223, SHAWNEE HILLS REHAB UNIT 26764 #062-01-1957 L1986 **GP OS** *071
LEWIS, Roger Allen. 603B W STATE AVE 26764 #055-01-1980 L1981 **FM** *020 †18
ROCHA, Hilton Da Cunha. ■ 26764 #187-13-1952 L1963 **GP IMG** *071

THORNTON — TAYLOR

NICHOLS, Nancy Lynn. RR 1 BOX 147MD, MOUNTAINEER FAMILY CARE CE 26440 #654-01-2001 L2006 **IM** *100
STOCKETT, Cheryl Lynn. RR 1 BOX 147MD 26440 #055-01-2001 L2004 **FM** *020 †18

TRIADELPHIA — OHIO

NUGENT, Milton E, Jr. ■ 26059 #016-01-1942 L1965 **OPH** *071 †35

UNION — MONROE

GELDERMAN, Albert Herman. PO BOX 500 24983 #023-07-1961 L1972 **GP PTH** *020
YATES, Barry Cordell. ■ 24983 #041-02-1965 L1976 **P** *020

UPPER TRACT — PENDLETON

EYE, Harry L. PO BOX 1280, US RTE 220 SOUTH 26866 #023-01-1953 L1956 **GP** *020
MALLOW, William Stanley. ■ 26866 #055-01-2000 L2002 **OM** *100

VALLEY GROVE — OHIO

ALBAUGH, Chad Allen. ■ 26060 #055-01-2007 **EM** *012

VARNEY — MINGO

MC DEVITT, Brian J. RR 52 BOX 279, VARNEY MED CTR 25696 #055-75-1995, ▲ L1998 **FM** *020

VIENNA — WOOD

ADKINS, Catherine Allman. 800 GRAND CENTRAL MALL 26105 #055-02-1997 L1998 **FM** *020 †18
ALVARADO, Benj Antonio. ■ 26105 #748-07-1957 L1969 **GP** *071
AZAR, Robert Wm. 1801 GRAND CENTRAL AVE 26105 #055-01-1972 L1972 **OTO** *020 †45
CARTER, James M. ■ 26105 #051-01-1953 L1965 **R** *071 †80
CHASE, Jeffrey Scott. 807 51ST ST 26105 #041-02-1968 L1975 **R** *020 †80
DAUPHIN, James Madison. 600 16TH ST 26105 #055-01-1975 L1982 **ORS** *020 †40
DUGAN, Patrick Parker. 800 GRAND CENTRAL MALL, STE 4 26105 #055-01-1995 L2000 **U** *020 †95
FABER, George Herman. ■ 26105 #055-01-1993 L2003 **PTH PCP** *062 †50
FERRELL, David Ralph. 1500 GRAND CENTRAL AVE, STE 115 26105 #055-01-1997 L1999 **FM** *020 †18
FLUHARTY, Kelly Colleen. 800 GRAND CENTRAL MALL, STE 4 26105 #055-01-1996 L1997 **FM** *020 †18
GARRETT, Bernard Ofa, Jr. 105 51ST ST 26105 #055-75-1980, ▲ L1981 **DR** *062 †80
GUSTKE, Robert Fred. 1504 GRAND CENTRAL AVE 26105 #055-01-1963 L1964 **GE IM** *020
HEAVNER, Robert Randal. 800 GRAND CENTRAL MALL, STE 4 26105 #055-01-1986 L1987 **FM** *020 †18
HERRMANN, Thomas Alfred. 800 GRAND CENTRAL AVE, STE 4 26105 #038-43-1989 L1990 **FM** *020 †18 ‡
HIGGS, Douglas Martin. ■ 26105 #055-01-2003 L2003 **EM** *012
HOVIS, Logan Wm. ■ 26105 #025-01-1942 L1943 **AN** *071
KAPLAN, Adam Jared. 800 GRAND CENTRAL MALL, STE 2 26105 #038-45-1989 L2004 **GS** *020 †85
KHEDRI, Mahrokh. ■ 26105 #496-11-1991 L2004 **IM** *071 †20
KOCH, John Kevin. 800 GRAND CENTRAL MALL, STE 2 26105 #055-01-1993 L1998 **GS** *020 †85
LIFSON, Barry Jay. 800 GRAND CENTRAL MALL, UROLOGY ASSOCIATES INC. 26105 #035-09-1990 L2003 **U** *020 †95
MENDOZA, David Catalino. 800 GRAND CENTRAL MALL, STE 4 26105 #055-01-1991 L1996 **U** *020 †95
MILHOAN, Stevan Jeffrey. 1504 GRAND CENTRAL AVE # A 26105 #055-02-1986 L1987 **IM PD** *020 †20,55
MILLER, Lisa Marie. 1105 9TH ST 26105 #041-02-1993 L1997 **D** *020 †15
MOSBERG, Stephen Randall. ■ 26105 #023-01-1979 L1980 **FM** *074 †18
NEWLAND, Dennis Eugene. 800 GRAND CENTRAL MALL, STE 4 26105 #038-40-1987 L1988 **FM** *020 †18
PARVEEN, Ruby Jamal. ■ 26105 #495-96-1993 L2005 **OS N** *020 †75
RITCHIE, Douglas F. 1500 GRAND CENTRAL AVE, STE 112 26105 #055-02-2002 L2004 **DR** *100
ROBERTS, Michael Don. 800 GRAND CENTRAL MALL, STE 2 26105 #055-01-1991 L1993 **GS** *020 †85

■ = Address Information Privacy Protected

SINGH, Anil K. 1504B GRAND CENTRAL AVE, DIGESTIVE CARE CENTER 26105 #495-15-1988 L2000 **GE IM** *020 †20
STOOKE, Kim Marie. 800 GRAND CENTRAL MALL, STE 4 26105 #055-01-1994 L1996 **FM** *020 †18
VANCE, Sharileda C. 800 GRAND CENTRAL MALL, STE 4 26105 #055-01-1994 L1996 **FM** *020 †18

WAR – MCDOWELL

MACATANGAY, Sergio Capuno. ■ 24892 #748-07-1973 L1982 **GP** *020

WARDENSVILLE – HARDY

FRIDLEY, James Owen. ■ 26851 #055-01-1967 L1968 **FM** *071 ‡
MATHIAS, James Dolan. ■ 26851 #051-04-1946 L1949 **GP** *071

WEBSTER SPRINGS – WEBSTER

BENNETT, Roger Paul. 121 POINT MOUNTAIN RD 26288 #055-01-1974 L1975 **FM** *020 †18
HUNTER, Jack Willison. 324 MILLER MOUNTAIN DR 26288 #045-01-1943 L1946 **GS OS** *071
MACE, Robert Morgan. 324 MILLER MOUNTAIN DR 26288 #055-01-1969 L1970 **FM** *020

WEIRTON – HANCOCK

ABU-HANTASH, Hadi Mahmoud. ■ 26062 #915-03-1981 L1991 **CD** *020 †20
AGGARWAL, Krishan Kumar. 3710 PENNSYLVANIA AVE, STE 2 26062 #495-55-1967 L1978 **IM** *020
AGGARWAL, Madhu. 3710 PENNSYLVANIA AVE, STE 2 26062 #495-30-1971 L1978 **OBG ICE** *020 †30
AGGARWAL, Neil Krishan. ■ 26062 #038-06-2004 **P** *012
AJAYI, Richard Olutoyin. 601 COLLIERS WAY, LEVEL 9 26062 #690-08-1990 L2002 **P** *020 †75
ALIMARIO, Lubin Cabrera. 601 COLLIERS WAY 26062 #748-07-1961 L1981 **AN PME** *071
ALIMARIO, Teresita E. 3722 PENNA AVE 26062 #041-01-1963 L1976 **P** *071 †75
ALVEZ, Laura D. 3209 WEST ST 26062 #748-11-1979 L1995 **NEP IM** *020 †20
BLAKE, Robert Eugene. 601 COLLIERS WAY 26062 #055-01-1994 L1996 **EM** *020 †16
BRANCAZIO, Lisa Ann. 601 COLLIERS WAY, WEIRTON MEDICAL CENTERLVL 26062 #055-01-1986 L2000 **ATP PCH** *020 †50
BRAVO, Keith Michael. 651 COLLIERS WAY, STE 502 26062 #005-15-1985 L1999 **IM PD** *020 †20,55
CAPITO, Charles Peter. 703 COLLIERS WAY 26062 #055-01-1978 L1979 **ORS OSM** *020 †40
CAPITO, John Emil. 2619 PENNSYLVANIA AVE # 1 26062 #308-03-1980 L1983 **IM** *020 †20
CASTALDO, Camille Joan. 651 COLLIERS WAY, STE 411 26062 #055-01-1994 L1995 **FM** *020 †18
CASTRO, Renato Camacho. ■ 26062 #748-07-1957 L1967 **IM** *020
CHAHAL-PUREWAL, Guneet. 651 COLLIERS WAY, WEIRTON MEDICAL CENTER 26062 #495-45-1994 L1999 **IM** *020
CHATTHA, Jaswinder. 485 COLLIERS WAY 26062 #495-29-1960 L1974 **P PCH** *020
CHUNG, Chung Wha. 601 COLLIERS WAY 26062 #583-06-1968 **GP** *100
CLARKE, John Stephen. ■ 26062 #011-02-1976 L1981 **EM** *030 †16
CORONEOS, Emmanouel. 485 COLLIERS WAY, STE A 26062 #418-02-1979 L2001 **IM NEP** *020
COWHER, Christopher J. 2416 PENNSYLVANIA AVE 26062 #055-01-1994 L1997 **IM** *020 †20
CRISAN, Viorica-Maria. 651 COLLIERS WAY STE 406 26062 #781-03-1989 L2001 **END IM** *020 †20
DIZON, Maria Angela. 601 COLLIERS WAY, WEIRTON MEDICAL CENTER 26062 #033-06-1991 L2000 **PTH** *020 †50
ENDRICH, Joseph Peter. 651 COLLIERS WAY, STE 501 26062 #308-03-1982 L1986 **IM** *020 †20
FOURNIER, Kelli Mc Donald. 3136 WEST ST 26062 #055-02-1997 L1999 **FM** *020 †18
GABRIEL, Hani Farid Aziz. 601 COLLIERS WAY 26062 #915-04-1992 L2002 **AN PME** *020 †05
GAHLOT, Luxmi. 601 COLLIERS WAY 26062 #495-55-1995 L2006 **APM** *100 †05
GRAY, Cynthia Allyson. 651 COLLIERS WAY, STE 201 26062 #041-12-1972 L2006 **OBG** *020 †30
GRECO, Ray Silvio. 2416 PENNSYLVANIA AVE 26062 #051-04-1947 L1948 **GP OS** *072 †18
GUPTA, Sanjay. 485 COLLIERS WAY, STE A 26062 #495-74-1988 L1997 **IM** *020 †20
GUPTA, Sanjay K. ■ 26062 #495-45-1988 L1997 **FM** *020
HAGINS, Tod. ■ 26062 #038-45-1995 L1996 **FM** *020 †18
HANSON, Gary Arnold. 2619 PENNSYLVANIA AVE 26062 #023-07-1975 L1981 **IM CD** *020 †20
HARRISON, Donna Michelle. 601 COLLIERS WAY, EMERGENCY DEPARTMENT 26062 #023-01-1993 L2005 **EM** *020 †16
ISLA, Roger. 651 COLLIERS WAY, STE 408 26062 #737-03-1968 L1974 **OTO PS** *020 †45
JOHN, Cherian. 651 COLLIERS WAY, STE K 26062 #496-38-1977 L1986 **CD IM** *020 †20
KHURANA, Amar N. 485 COLLIERS WAY STE E1 26062 #496-14-1980 L1990 **IM** *020 †20
KIM, Hee-Sun. 601 COLLIERS WAY, WEIRTON MEDICAL CENTER 26062 #028-46-1995 L1996 **FM** *020 †18
KOCHHAR, Brijinder Singh. 2950 PENNSYLVANIA AVE 26062 #495-29-1971 L1981 **PUD SME** *020 †20
KOCHHAR, Chan Preet Kaur. ■ 26062 #055-01-2007 L2007 **FP** *012
KOLLI, Ravindranath. 501 COLLIERS WAY, HEALTH WAYS 26062 #495-58-1982 L1992 **P ADP** *020 †75
KOSAR, George Stephen. 2416 PENNSYLVANIA AVE 26062 #041-12-1958 L1962 **OBG** *071 †30
LEE, Young Jie. 601 COLLIERS WAY, WEIRTON MEDICAL CENTER 26062 #583-06-1969 L1982 **DR** *020 †80
LICATA, Antonio Saml. 3032 WEST ST 26062 #055-01-1964 L1965 **GS AS** *071
LICATA, Samuel David. 701 COLLIERS WAY 26062 #055-01-1990 L1995 **GS** *020 †85
LUTHRA, Juginder Kumar. 314 PENCO RD 26062 #495-03-1966 L1976 **OPH** *020 †35
MAKAR, Jasbir Singh. 485 COLLIERS WAY STE A 26062 #495-03-1966 L1973 **CD IM** *020 †20
MALAYIL, Michael Thos. 501 COLLIERS WAY 26062 #495-37-1970 L2000 **P** *020 †75
MANDAC, Edmundo Reyes. 601 COLLIERS WAY, WEIRTON MEDICAL CENTER 26062 #014-01-1977 L1984 **IM EM** *020 †16
MC CABE, Lloyd B. MEDICAL DEPT WEIRTON STEEL 26062 #028-34-1949 L1977 **OM IM** *030
MILAN, Primo P. 601 COLLIERS WAY, WEIRTON MEDICAL CENTERLVL 26062 #748-10-1970 L1990 **DR** *020 †80

MITCHELL, John Marvin. 651 COLLIERS WAY, STE 511 26062 #038-44-1999 L2004 **GS** *020 †85
NANDRA, Charn Singh. 485 COLLIERS WAY, STE K 26062 #917-18-1976 L1996 **CD IM** *020 †20
NOLAN, Sean. 651 COLLIERS WAY, STE 413 26062 #539-05-1967 L1995 **END IM** *020 †20
O'KARMA, Kara Anne. 601 COLLIERS WAY, STE 201 26062 #055-75-2000, ▲ L2004 **OBG** *020 †30
PARIHAR, Hardev Singh. 485 COLLIERS WAY STE N 26062 #495-45-1976 L1984 **U** *020 †95
PETROLA, Frank Lewis. 3920 WASHINGTON ST 26062 #649-14-1970 L1973 **FM** *071
PLACCI, Carlos Alberto. 501 COLLIERS WAY 26062 #132-02-1959 L1991 **P PYG** *020 †75
PUREWAL, Aman S. 485 COLLIERS WAY, STE B 26062 #055-01-1993 L1999 **GE** *020 †20
PUREWAL, Gurdev Singh. 485 COLLIERS WAY, STE H 26062 #495-03-1962 L1977 **ORS** *020 †40
PUREWAL, Navdeep Singh. 601 COLLIERS WAY, WMC-LEVEL 9 26062 #665-01-2001 L2005 **P** *020
RICHMAN, Melanie. 601 COLLIERS WAY 26062 #027-01-1984 L2002 **EM** *020 †16
RODRIGUEZ, Norberto A. 501 COLLIERS WAY 26062 #132-02-1964 L1991 **CHP P** *020 †75 ‡
ROIG, Jorge William. 601 COLLIERS WAY 26062 #041-13-1997 L1999 **AN** *020 †05
SACHTER, Joseph Jonah. 601 COLLIERS WAY 26062 #035-08-1986 L2002 **EM** *020 †16
SCHULTZ, John Paul. 2619 PENNSYLVANIA AVE 26062 #055-01-1991 L1993 **FM** *020 †18
SHETTY, Atul S. 485 COLLIERS WAY, STE M 26062 #495-37-1992 L1999 **IM** *020
SINGH, Ranjeet Kaur. 3600 WEST ST STE 1, TRINITY HEALTH SYSTEM 26062 #495-03-1967 L1975 **PTH** *020 †50
SINGH, Sarjit. 3600 WEST ST 26062 #495-03-1962 L1975 **N** *020 †75
SINGH, Shalu. 3600 WEST ST, STE 1 26062 #495-29-1996 L2003 **N** *020 †75
SURAY, Anna Maria. 3045 PENNA AVE STE 3 26062 #055-02-1991 L1996 **PD ADL** *020 †55
TAMBOLI, Ardeshir T. 2814 PENNSYLVANIA AVE 26062 #495-28-1972 L1980 **AI PD** *020 †55
TAMBOLI, Jasmin Ardeshir. 2814 PENNA AVE 26062 #495-01-1970 L1992 **FM** *020
TAYAL, Harinarayan R. 485 COLLIERS WAY STE M 26062 #495-20-1963 L1972 **GE IM** *071 †20
TORRES, Carolina Manzano. ■ 26062 #748-01-1962 L1976 **AN** *020
TORRES, Luis Panopio. ■ 26062 #748-01-1961 L1985 *071
UJEVICH, M Mark. 601 COLLIERS WAY, WEIRTON MED CTR 26062 #010-01-1987 L1989 **R** *020
VASQUEZ, Carlos Leonel. 601 COLLIERS WAY, WEIRTON MEDICAL CENTERLVL 26062 #308-01-1961 L1970 **R** *071
VERTOSICK, Frank Thos, Jr. 601 COLLIERS WAY, WEIRTON MEDICAL CENTER 26062 #041-12-1981 L1995 **OS** *020 †20
VIDUCICH, Raymond Anthony. 601 COLLIERS WAY, WEIRTON MEDICAL CENTER 26062 #041-12-1991 L2000 **EM** *020 †16
YURKO, Anthony Andrew, Jr. RR 2 BOX 17 26062 #051-04-1961 L1962 **GS** *020

WELCH – MCDOWELL

ABDALLA, Maha Abdalla. 454 MCDOWELL ST, WELCH EMERGENCY HOSPITAL 24801 #848-03-1989 L1996 **PD** *020 †55
ADENUPE, Olumade Adebambo. 454 MCDOWELL ST, WELCH COMMUNITY HOSPITAL 24801 #690-08-1995 L2004 **PD** *020 †55
BOFILL, Rano Solidum. 454 MCDOWELL ST 24801 #748-01-1966 L1972 **DR FM** *020
DOLLYMORE, Maura Kathleen. 454 MCDOWELL ST 24801 #023-01-1981 L1984 **IM** *020 †20
DUMAPIT, Ruperto D, Jr. 922 VIRGINIA AVE 24801 #748-10-1977 L1984 **GP** *020
FLORES, Charito Tan. 17 MCDOWELL ST 24801 #748-09-1966 L1978 **GP** *020
GOPAL, Veeraraghavan. 454 MCDOWELL ST, WELCH COMMUNITY HOSPITAL 24801 #495-45-1990 L2001 **IM** *020 †20
GORRAFA, Aly Abdel M. 454 MCDOWELL ST 24801 #330-03-1957 L1997 **OBG OBS** *020 †30
HERLAND, Alexander Louis. 454 MCDOWELL ST, WEH 24801 #561-03-1951 L1984 **OBG** *071 †30
LEACOCK, Darrick Sidney. 950 MOUNT VIEW RD, STE 500 24801 #010-03-1974 L1992 **FM** *020
LEO, Sherwood Phillip. 454 MCDOWELL ST, WELCH COMMUNITY HOSPITAL 24801 #051-01-1994 L1996 **EM GS** *020
LUCERO, Mario Saniel. 454 MCDOWELL ST 24801 #748-09-1972 L1983 **GP** *020
POLLACCHI, Luis Enrique. ■ 24801 #132-01-1970 L1977 **GS** *100
SALIH, Salwa Mohamed. 454 MCDOWELL ST, WELCH EMERGENCY HOSPITAL 24801 #848-01-1988 L1996 **IM** *020 †20
SHARMA, Chandra Prakash. 454 MCDOWELL ST, C/O WELCH COMMUNITY HOSP 24801 #495-45-1963 L1975 **FM GS** *020 †18
SULTAN, Julito D. 454 MCDOWELL ST, WELCH COMMUNITY HOSPITAL 24801 #748-07-1963 L1985 **OBG GP** *020
TUMBOKON, Dennis Cipriano. 454 MCDOWELL ST, WELCH COMMUNITY HOSPITAL 24801 #748-10-1972 L1984 **OBG** *020
VEGA, Louis Agusture. ■ 24801 #649-02-1950 L1956 **PD** *071

WELLSBURG – BROOKE

CIPOLETTI, Patsy Paul, Jr. 1421 COMMERCE ST 26070 #055-01-1978 L1979 **GP** *020 ‡
DEPETRO, Joseph James, III. 69 8TH ST 26070 #041-12-1991 L1992 **FM** *020 †18
MARKS, Edward Robert, III. 1006 COMMERCE ST 26070 #055-02-1995 L1996 **FM** *020 †18 ‡
MC CREARY, Patricia Ann. ■ 26070 #016-06-1954 L1974 **IM** *071 †20
RODGERS, John T. 1439 WASHINGTON PIKE 26070 #041-12-1953 L1954 **GP OS** *020

WEST LOGAN – LOGAN

KANURI, Karunasree. 1115 2ND AVE, OLD RT 10 25601 #495-50-1995 L2005 **FM** *020 †18

WESTON – LEWIS

ABDALLAH, Ehab Salem. 936 SHARPE HOSPITAL RD 26452 #915-03-1995 L2004 **P** *020 †75
ABDULLA, Essa. RT 33 W 26452 #495-42-1967 L1980 **FM** *020
ABDULNABI, Yousef. 29 HOSPITAL PLZ STE E 26452 #875-01-1992 L1999 **CD IM** *020 †20
ADEL, Anoushirvan. 936 SHARPE HOSPITAL RD, W R SHARPE HOSP 26452 #517-09-1985 L1992 **P** *020 †75
ALMASE, Luis A. 233 CENTER AVE 26452 #748-02-1955 L1974 **GP GS** *072 †85
ALTAHA, Bahar. 936 SHARPE HOSPITAL RD, W SHARPE HOSPITAL 26452 #409-21-1998 L2004 **P** *100 †75 ‡
BORCHERT, Christopher A. 29 HOSPITAL PLZ STE F 26452 #055-01-1982 L1986 **ADL PD** *020 †55

CORMIER, Serge. 66 HOSPITAL PLZ, STE 103 26452 #067-02-1978 L1992 **OBG** *020 †30 ‡
CRUZ, Sotero Bautista, Jr. RR 3 BX 895 26452 #748-07-1957 L1985 **GP** *071
ESPINOZA, Felipe Vinicio. 230 HOSPITAL PLZ 26452 #047-05-1995 L2001 **R AR** *020 †80
FRANCE, Cheryl Ann. 936 SHARPE HOSPITAL RD, WILLIAM R. SHARPE HOSPITAL 26452 #033-06-1988 L1997 **P** *020 †75
GRANT, Catherine E. 25 GARTON PLZ 26452 #035-46-1986 L1987 **FM** *020 †18
GRUSPE, Arnold F. 474 MAIN AVE 26452 #748-01-1959 L1972 **U GS** *071
HUSARI, Ahmad W. 66 HOSPITAL PLZ, STE 104 26452 #605-01-1986 L1993 **CCM** *020 †20
KATINY, Antoine. 230 HOSPITAL PLZ 26452 #875-01-1984 L1993 **IM** *020 †20
KELLEY, William E. 230 HOSPITAL PLZ, STONEWALL JACKSON MEMORIAL 26452 #055-01-1985 L1986 **FM** *020
LA NASA, Salvatore. 29 HOSPITAL PLZ, STE B 26452 #561-12-1981 L2001 **GS** *020 †85
MAHMOUD, Khalid. 66 HOSPITAL PLZ, STE 104 26452 #704-20-1983 L1999 **IM** *020 †20
MALIK, Nitin. 936 SHARPE HOSPITAL RD, WM R SHARPE JR HOSPITAL 26452 #495-45-1996 L2000 **P** *020 †75
NAIM, Antoine Alberto. 66 HOSPITAL PLZ STE 10 26452 #605-01-1987 L2001 **OBG** *020 †30
NIZAMI, Kamal Ahmad. 936 SHARPE HOSPITAL RD, W R SHARPE JR HOSPITAL 26452 #704-02-1960 L1977 **GP IM** *020
OBLEADA, Lydia Pasamba. 936 SHARPE HOSPITAL RD, WILLIAM R. SHARPE,JR. HOSP 26452 #748-08-1967 L1991 **P CHP** *020
ORVIK, Bennett Duane. 25 GARTON PLZ 26452 #026-04-1976 L1978 **FM** *020 †18
PASCASIO, Porfirio R. 514 MAIN AVE 26452 #748-02-1961 L1974 **GS GP** *020
POULOS, Pete Nickitas. RT 33 W 26452 #418-01-1954 L1985 **GP GYN** *071
SABBAGH, Abdulmalek. 29 HOSPITAL PLZ, STE E 26452 #875-02-1983 L1993 **IM** *020 †20
SCATTAREGIA, Francis A. RR 4 26452 #561-01-1975 L1979 **IM** *020
SCHARF, Charles Selden. 37 ELIZABETH DR 26452 #041-09-1976 L1989 **P ADP** *020
SHREVES, Jennifer Ann. 230 HOSPITAL PLZ 26452 #055-01-1993 L1994 **IM EM** *020 †20
SIVAKUMARAN, M. 29 HOSPITAL PLZ STE A 26452 #495-16-1979 L1996 **PD PDI** *020 †55
SNEAD, Joseph Akin. 29 HOSPITAL PLZ, STE B 26452 #036-07-1966 L1984 **ORS** *020 †40
THOMAS, John Joseph. 66 HOSPITAL PLZ, # 102 26452 #038-40-1994 L2004 **GS TRS** *020 †85
TICE, Douglas Scott. 29 HOSPITAL PLZ, STE C 26452 #055-01-1990 L1992 **ORS** *020 †40
WYLLIE, John Wm, III. 244 CENTER AVE 26452 #028-34-1970 L2008 **OTO EM** *020 †45

WESTOVER – MONONGALIA

BOWLIN, David Alan. 900 FAIRMONT RD, WEDGEWOOD FAMILY PRACTICE 26501 #055-01-1997 L2001 **MPD** *020 †55
BOYD, Carole Brooks. ■ 26501 #025-07-1964 L1975 **PTH** *071 †50
BOYER, Treah Shea. ■ 26501 #055-01-2007 **FP** *012
DIXON, Brian Jeremy. 900 FAIRMONT RD 26501 #055-01-1999 L2000 **FM** *020 †18
LUCAS, Denise Coral. ■ 26501 #055-01-2007 **FP** *012
MARSHALEK, Patrick Joseph. ■ 26501 #055-01-2006 L2007 **P** *012
MITCHELL, William C. 900 FAIRMONT RD, 900 FAIRMONT ROAD 26501 #055-01-1994 L1995 **FM** *020 †18
SEDLMEYER, Troy Lynn. 900 FAIRMONT RD 26501 #055-01-2001 L2003 **FM** *020 †18

WHEELING – OHIO

ABALLAY, Richard Anthony. 203 S FRONT ST 26003 #035-46-2005 L2007 **FM** *100
ADAMOVICH, Edward, Jr. 1 MEDICAL PARK 26003 #038-40-1977 L1994 **PTH PCP** *020 †50
AGUIRRE, Alfredo A. 2000 EOFF ST, STE 704 26003 #737-06-1982 L1992 **P CHP** *020 †75
ALAHMAR, Ammar. 40 MEDICAL PARK, STE 406 26003 #875-02-2004 L2006 **FP** *012
ALKHOURI, Nabiel. 20 MEDICAL PARK, STE 202 26003 #875-03-1986 L1996 **HO** *020 †20
ALLEN, Kenneth Scott. 1 MEDICAL PARK, ANESTHESIOLOGISTS INC 26003 #055-01-1990 L1994 **AN** *020 †05
ALMARIO, Evangelina B. ■ 26003 #748-01-1971 L1978 **PTH** *020 †50
ALTMEYER, Robert Brann. 1131 NATIONAL RD 26003 #055-01-1975 L1978 **PUD IMG** *020 †20
ANDERSON, Chad David. ■ 26003 #055-01-2006 L2007 **EM** *012
ANDERSON, Charla Lynn. 2115 CHAPLINE ST, STE 101 26003 #055-01-1995 L1997 **FM** *020 †18 ‡
ARAGONES, Peter Carantes. 1 MEDICAL PARK 26003 #748-10-1964 L1973 **R** *020 †80
ARAUJO, Armando. 1 MEDICAL PARK 26003 #649-01-1972 L1982 **GP** *020
ARCHBOLD, Lori Lynn. 30 MEDICAL PARK, STE 200 26003 #055-01-1990 L1992 **PD** *020 †55
ASLI, Reza Parivash. 2000 EOFF ST 26003 #517-01-1961 L1970 **NS** *071
AULICK, Neal Finley, II. ■ 26003 #020-12-1995 L1996 **EM** *020 †16
AYAD, Amira Nabih. 40 MEDICAL PARK, MED PARK STE 105 26003 #915-03-2002 **FP** *012
BADOUR, Ashraf Soliman. ■ 26003 #915-02-1974 L1988 **N** *020 †75
BAILES, Julian E, Jr. 2000 EOFF ST 26003 #021-05-1982 L2000 **NS** *020 †25
BALA, Peter Zygmunt. 30 MEDICAL PARK, STE 219 26003 #067-01-1979 L1998 **OBG** *020 †30
BALZANO, Eric Roger. 1 MEDICAL PARK 26003 #038-43-1996 L2001 **DR** *020 †80
BANNAN, Raymond Anthony. 20 MEDICAL PARK, STE 105 26003 #038-40-1986 L1991 **OPH** *020 †35
BARBERIA, Regina Margaret. ■ 26003 #051-04-1948 L1950 **GP PD** *020
BARTON, William R. ■ 26003 #065-09-1951 L1964 **ORS OS** *071 †40
BASTUG, Erol. 42 BOXWOOD CIR, OAKMONT HILLS 26003 #902-03-1957 L1972 **DR** *071 †80
BATTAGLINO, John Jos. 20 MEDICAL PARK, STE 301 26003 #051-04-1955 L1962 **OBG** *020 †30 ‡
BELL, Ross O, Jr. ■ 26003 #041-01-1951 L1952 **PTH** *071 †50
BENNETT, Jack David. 2000 EOFF ST 26003 #038-43-1991 L2002 **PD** *020 †55
BENSON, Mark Leigh. 1 MEDICAL PARK 26003 #055-01-1989 L1992 **DR RNR** *020 †80
BERLOW, A Joseph. PO BOX 1060, 909 CENTRAL UNION BLDG 26003 #803-09-1952 L1961 **OTO OPH** *071
BLATT, Michael Wm. 10 MEDICAL PARK, STE 301 26003 #033-05-1975 L1980 **PUD** *020 †20
BLOSSER, Laura Rue. 30 MEDICAL PARK, STE 202 26003 #038-40-1989 L1992 **PD** *020 †55
BOBBALA, Govardhan Reddy. 1 MEDICAL PARK 26003 #495-21-2003 L2008 **FP** *012
BONITATIBUS, Patricia S. 2000 EOFF ST 26003 #055-01-1985 L1987 **FM** *075
BOWMAN, David Alan. 1 MEDICAL PARK 26003 #055-01-1978 L1979 **GE HEP** *020 †20
BRACKEN, Samuel Jos, Jr. 1 MEDICAL PARK 26003 #010-02-1964 L1969 **OBG OS** *020 †30
BUNNER, Julie Suzanne. 1 MEDICAL PARK 26003 #055-01-1997 L1999 **END** *020 †20
BURKLAND, Carl David. 620 NATIONAL RD, MEDEXPRESS URGENT CARE, PL 26003 #055-01-1980 L1981 **EM** *020 †16
BUSH, Marjorie Lynn. 40 MEDICAL PARK STE 200, MEDICAL PARK 26003 #055-01-1977 L1986 **PS HS** *020 †85,65
BYEON, Sang Jun. 1 MED PARK 26003 #583-09-1990 L2006 **FP** *012
CAO, Wenhui. 20 HOMESTEAD AVE, PETERSON REHAB HOSP 26003 #243-36-1992 L2006 **PM** *020 †60
CARLOS, Scott Anthony. 40 MEDICAL PARK, STE 400 26003 #025-01-1999 L2000 **FPG** *020 †18
CARUSO, Michael Jos. 21 12TH ST STE 404 26003 #010-02-1956 L1958 **IM** *071
CARUSO, Vincent James. 1 MEDICAL PARK 26003 #055-01-1991 L1997 **DR** *020 †80
CASTRO, Hernan Alejandro. 316 WASHINGTON AVE # 61 26003 #264-19-1993 L2001 **IM** *020
CATER, Maryann Nicolas. 1 MEDICAL PARK, ANESTHESIOLOGISTS INC 26003 #055-75-1988, ▲ L1989 **AN** *020 †05
CAVENEY, Robert Ackermann. 30 MEDICAL PARK STE 220 26003 #055-01-1976 L1981 **ORS** *020 †40
CHAUDHARY, Asmita. 40 MEDICAL PARK STE 406, FAMILY HEALTH CTR 26003 #495-15-2003 L2007 **FP** *012
CHEEMA, Tariq Javed. 1 MEDICAL PARK 26003 #704-20-2000 L2005 **PCC** *012 †18,20
COLEMAN, Catherine Carey. 30 MEDICAL PARK STE 230 26003 #020-12-1978 L1981 **OBG** *020 †30
COMERCI, James Louis. 7 E COVE AVE BOX 3019, STE A 26003 #055-01-1980 L1981 **FM** *020 †18
CORDER, Steven. 2121 EOFF ST 26003 #055-01-1985 L1987 **P** *020 †75
CROSS, Robert Louis. 1021 MOUNT DE CHANTAL RD, FACS 26003 #041-13-1976 L1983 **GS** *020 †85
CUI, Xue Liang. 40 MEDICAL PARK 26003 #243-64-1983 L2008 **FM** *020
DEGUZMAN, Gary Steven. 2115 CHAPLINE ST, STE 306 26003 #748-08-1988 L1999 **OBG** *020 †30
DODD, Larry Allen. 58 16TH ST 26003 #055-01-1968 L1970 **OTO** *020 †45
DOMAOAL, Ana Maria V. ■ 26003 #748-01-1968 L1978 **PTH** *020 †50
DOMAOAL, Antonio M. 2000 EOFF ST 26003 #748-01-1967 L1976 **AN OS** *020
DONZELLA, Joseph Guy. 40 MEDICAL PARK STE 505 26003 #055-75-2000, ▲ L2001 **FM** *020 †18 ‡
DORSEY, John Thos, III. 40 MEDICAL PARK STE 502 26003 #055-01-1981 L1987 **GE IM** *020 †20
DREWS, Marion Hencken, Jr. 58 16TH ST 26003 #045-01-1976 L1981 **NEP IM** *020 †20
DUDICH, John Edward. 1 MEDICAL PARK, ANESTHESIOLOGISTS INC 26003 #038-43-1989 L1994 **AN** *020 †05
DUNN, Bruce Eugene. 40 MEDICAL PARK, STE 300 26003 #035-20-1964 L2004 **CD** *020 †20
DURIG, James Christian. 20 MEDICAL PARK STE 201 26003 #055-01-1971 L1973 **U** *071 †95
EDGMON, Jeremy John. 30 MEDICAL PARK STE 215 26003 #055-01-2000 L2002 **FM** *020 †18
ENTRESS, Cheryl H Pixley. 58 16TH ST 26003 #041-12-1966 L1969 **FM** *020 †18
ESAKA, Emmanuel Jabea. MED PARK STE 105, WHEELING HOSP 26003 #561-01-1999 L2004 **OBG** *012
ESKINS, Christopher R. ■ 26003 #055-01-2001 L2004 **IC** *012
ETEMADI, Hassah. ■ 26003 #517-05-1967 L1976 **R** *020 †80
EVANS, Catherine J. 1079 NATIONAL RD 26003 #055-01-1991 L1992 **FM** *020 †18
FAHEY, Rebecca Lee. ■ 26003 #665-01-2007 *100
FAWCETT, Raphael Alan. ■ 26003 #041-01-1943 L1944 **OPH** *071 †35
FEDER, Arlene Joyce S. 10 MEDICAL PARK, STE 206 26003 #041-09-1975 L1981 **END IM** *020 †20
FEDER, Richard R. 1300 MARKET ST STE 404 26003 #035-09-1973 L1981 **PD** *020 †55
FORTUNATO, Michael A. 400 MEDICAL PARK 26003 #038-43-1985 L1986 **FM** *020 †18 ‡
FOX, Matthew Platt. 40 MEDICAL PARK, STE 401 26003 #008-02-1982 L1983 **EM FM** *020 †18
FRAME, Kelby Lee. 2000 EOFF ST, OHIO VALLEY MEDICAL CENTER 26003 #041-09-1996 L2001 **DR** *020 †80
FREED, John Douglas. ■ 26003 #055-01-1972 L1973 **OS** *020 †16
FRENN, Adel E. 2000 EOFF ST, 6 W 601 OVMC 26003 #654-01-1987 L1994 **CD** *020 †20
GANZER, Gary Albert. 58 16TH ST, THE WHEELING CLINIC 26003 #041-09-1981 L1983 **DMP FM** *020 †15
GAYDOSH, Michael A. ■ 26003 #051-04-1936 L1937 **GP** *071
GEARY, Richard C, Jr. 1038 MARKET ST 26003 #041-77-1980, ▲ L1986 **D** *020 †15
GEORGES, Angelo Nicholas. 40 MEDICAL PARK, STE 501 26003 #038-40-1985 L1988 **IM** *020
GHAPHERY, Alfred David. 601 NATIONAL RD 26003 #041-12-1959 L1960 **GS** *071 †85
GHAPHERY, David Alfred. 601 NATIONAL RD 26003 #055-01-1988 L1990 **GS** *020 †85
GHOBRIAL, Alber Lewis. 2101 JACOB ST, STE 501 26003 #915-04-1977 L1995 **P** *020
GIATRAKIS, John Stephens. ■ 26003 #418-01-1969 **AN EM** *071
GIUSTINI, Fernando. PRO CTR III MED PK STE 230 26003 #561-17-1956 L1962 **OBG** *020 †30
GOVINDAN, Srinivasan. 40 MEDICAL PARK, STE 304 26003 #495-04-1970 L1973 **SME N** *020
GRIFFITH, John Perry, Jr. 40 MEDICAL PARK, ORTHOPEDIC SURGERY INC 26003 #041-12-1943 L1958 **ORS** *071 †85
GROUX, Wayne Ellsworth. 40 MEDICAL PARK, STE 504 26003 #055-02-1983 L1984 **GYN** *020 †30 ‡
HARGRAVES, Ronald Wm. 2000 EOFF ST 26003 #023-12-1983 L2004 **NS** *020 †25
HERSHFIELD, Barton Kent. 1 MEDICAL PARK, WHEELING HOSPITAL ER 26003 #023-01-1979 L1989 **EM FM** *020 †18,16
HILES, Charles Hall. 58 16TH ST 26003 #041-12-1938 L1947 **IM** *071 †20
HILL, Lisa Caroline. 58 16TH ST, WHEELING CLINIC 26003 #665-01-1998 L2001 **FM** *020 †18
HOFREUTER, Donald H. 1 MEDICAL PARK 26003 #035-01-1958 L1960 **FM** *030 †18
HOLLOWAY, John Du Bois. 2115 CHAPLINE ST STE 305 26003 #055-01-1979 L1983 **IM VM** *020 †20
IKHLAQUE, Nadeem. 2101 JACOB ST STE 401, OHIO VALLEY MEDICAL CENTER 26003 #704-20-1992 L2006 **HO** *020 †20
IMPERIO, Ephraim Caparoz. MEDICAL PK ANES 26003 #748-07-1953 L1972 **AN** *020
JACOB, James A, Jr. ■ 26003 #035-01-1952 L1953 **IM** *071
JAMES, Frank P. 30 MEDICAL PARK STE 203 26003 #016-45-1996 L2004 **P CHP** *020 †75
JAVID, Roya Omid. 1038 MARKET ST 26003 #010-01-2000 L2007 **D** *020
JELLEN, Albert Valentin. 2097 NATIONAL RD 26003 #154-01-1963 L1975 **FM OS** *020
JIRAK, George Victor. 2115 CHAPLINE ST STE 206, VALLEY PROFESSIONAL BLDG 26003 #056-05-1981 L2001 **OBG** *020 †30
JONES, Robert Eugene. 1 PROFESSIONAL CTR, STE 108 26003 #055-01-1972 L1977 **TS CD** *020 †85
JOSEPH, Robert Lance. 1300 MARKET ST 26003 #055-01-1968 L1969 **OPH** *020 †35
JOSEPH, Wilda S Sarver. 1300 MARKET ST 26003 #038-06-1938 L1939 **GYN** *071
KENAMOND, Carter Alan. 1 MEDICAL PARK 26003 #055-01-2001 L2007 **RNR** *100 †80
KENAMOND, Thomas Gary. 58 16TH ST 26003 #055-01-1974 L1977 **NEP IM** *020 †20
KETTLER, Henry Louis. 1 MEDICAL PARK 26003 #055-01-1969 L1972 **N** *020 †75
KHALIL, Busaina Labib. 1 MEDICAL PARK, WHEELING HOSP 26003 #915-04-1976 L1997 **PTH** *020 †50

KHALIQUE, Moshin Riaz. 2000 EOFF ST, OVMC DEPT OF PSYCH 26003 #704-25-1995 L2006 P *100 †75

KHOURY, Rajai Tawfiq. 309 OAKMONT RD 26003 #605-01-1976 L1980 TS VS *020 †85,90

KING, John Herbert. 2000 EOFF ST, OVMC 26003 #055-01-1977 L1978 FM *020 †18 ‡

KITE, Carl James. 953 NATIONAL RD, # 127 26003 #055-01-1976 L1981 GS *071 †85

KITTS, Ellen Louise. 1305 NATIONAL RD, EASTER SEALS 26003 #017-20-1976 L1984 PM PD *020 †55,60

KLAY, John Whitaker. 40 MEDICAL PARK, STE 301 26003 #008-01-1972 L1994 CD VS *020 †90,85 ‡

KNIERIM, Timothy Henry. 40 MEDICAL PARK STE 400, FAMILY PRACTICE RESIDENCY 26003 #055-01-2001 L2004 FM *020 †18

KUMAR, Ashok Ranchand. 1 MEDICAL PARK, ANESTHESIOLOGISTS INC 26003 #495-94-1977 L1992 GS *020 †05

LATOS, Derrick Louis. 58 16TH ST 26003 #055-01-1972 L1976 NEP IM *020 †20

LECHNER, Jonathan David. 2000 EOFF ST, EAST BLD STE 603 26003 #010-02-1979 L1986 ORS *020 †40 ‡

LEE, Thomas Fukching. 2000 EOFF ST 26003 #038-40-1994 L2002 DR *020 †80

LEEPER, Harold Frank. 58 16TH ST 26003 #035-46-1985 L1991 OPH *020 †35

LOH, Gary. 1 MEDICAL PARK 26003 #041-02-1980 L1985 DR VIR *020 †80

MACAULAY, Brian W. 1 MEDICAL PARK 26003 #055-01-1985 L1986 FM FPG *040 †18 ‡

MARKER, Marnie Jo. 58 16TH ST STE 500, NEPHROLOGY ASSOCIATES, INC 26003 #055-01-1995 L2000 NEP *020 †20

MARONEY, Michael Joseph. 1 MEDICAL PARK 26003 #055-02-1994 L1999 RNR *020 †80

MAROON, Joseph C. 10 MEDICAL PARK 26003 #017-20-1965 L1976 NS *020 †25

MARRA, Dante Anthony. 10 MEDICAL PARK, 203 PROFESS CIR # 1 26003 #035-01-1992 L1997 ORS *020 †40

MC FARLAND, James Jos. 1021 MOUNT DE CHANTAL RD, WHEELING HEAR INSTITUTE 26003 #561-01-1976 L2005 TS VS *071 †85,90

MC MURRAY, John Thos. ■ 26003 #055-01-1963 L1964 R NM *071 †80

MEHRA, Suwan. 40 MED PARK, STE 406 26003 #495-37-2000 L2007 OBG *012 †18

MEHROTRA, Sushil K. 2101 JACOB ST STE 302 26003 #495-45-1976 L1982 ON IM *020 †20

MENDOZA, Jose. 2121 EOFF ST 26003 #275-01-1946 L1974 P *020

MERCER, William Carl. 58 16TH ST 3RD FL, WHG CLINIC 26003 #055-01-1979 L1979 FM FPG *020 †18

MERRICK, Gregory Stephen. 1 MEDICAL PARK, SCHIFFLER CANCER CENTER 26003 #055-01-1985 L1989 RO *020 †80

MILIK, Sherif Akladyous. 1 MED PARK 26003 #915-02-2002 L2005 FP *012

MILLER, Laura M. 30 MEDICAL PARK, STE 230 26003 #055-75-1999, ▲ L2000 FM *020 †18

MILLIT, Henry David. 1 MEDICAL PARK 26003 #038-40-1975 L1980 CD IM *020 †20

MILLS, Steven Christopher. 2101 JACOB ST, STE 602 26003 #654-01-1996 L2000 FM *020

MISSETT, Joseph Vincent. 40 MEDICAL PARK, STE 406 26003 #306-01-2004 L2005 FM *100

MODI, Shakuntala. 1025 MAIN ST STE 416 26003 #495-34-1964 L1977 P *020 †75

MONGA, Manish. 20 MEDICAL PARK, STE 202 26003 #495-45-1994 L2002 ON IM *020 †20

MOSMAN, David Alexander. 1 MEDICAL PARK, PEDIATRIC ASSOCIATES 26003 #051-04-1995 L2004 PD *020 †55

MUELLER, Karl Jos. 40 MEDICAL PARK STE 200, PROF CENTER IV 26003 #028-34-1986 L1996 PS HS *020 †65 ‡

MUKKAMALLA, Mahaveer. 40 MEDICAL PARK, MED PARK STE 105 26003 #495-50-2001 L2008 FP *012

MURTHY, Narayan B. ■ 26003 #495-04-1973 L1992 NM DR *020

NAEEM, Mohtashim. 2000 EOFF ST, OHIO VALLEY MED CTR 26003 #704-02-1995 L2005 PTH HMP *020 †50

NANNERS, Kenneth Charles. 1 MEDICAL PARK, ANESTHESIOLOGISTS INC 26003 #055-01-1994 L1997 AN *020 †05

NASSAR, Souheil J. 2000 EOFF ST, 601 W 26003 #875-01-1987 L1997 HMP *020 †50

NEIS, Thomas Ray. 1 MEDICAL PARK 26003 #019-02-1975 L1980 DR R *020 †80

NIESS, Dennis Richard. 20 MEDICAL PARK, STE 306 26003 #055-01-1980 L1981 FM FPG *020 †18

NOBLE, William Ellsworth. 2000 EOFF ST, STE 601 26003 #041-12-1972 L1977 CD IM *020 †20

NOBLE, William Lee. 1 MEDICAL PARK 26003 #055-01-1976 L1977 R *020 †80

NOCHE, Alexander Cabral. 40 MEDICAL PARK STE 406 26003 #748-02-2002 L2005 FP *012

OATES, James Alvin. 1 MEDICAL PARK 26003 #048-04-1956 L1976 EM *071

OLEXO, Robert E. 40 MEDICAL PARK STE 406 26003 #055-75-2001, ▲ L2002 FM *020

PAPADIMITRIOU, Basil Paul. 103 S PENN ST 26003 #418-01-1953 L1964 FM *020

PAPADIMITRIOU, Leigh Anne. 2000 EOFF ST STE 502 26003 #055-01-1992 L1994 GYN *030

PAPADIMITRIOU, Paul B. 2000 EOFF ST, 5TH FLOOR EAST BLDG 26003 #055-01-1990 L1992 P *020

PARMAR, Christobel Pamela. 2198 NATIONAL RD 26003 #495-08-1966 L1977 FM *071

PARMAR, Jaywant P. 2000 EOFF ST, DEPT PATHOLOGY 26003 #495-08-1963 L1972 PTH CLP *020 †50

PATEL, Kumar Raman. 2101 JACOB ST, STE 601 26003 #016-11-1996 L2001 AI *020 †20,03

PATEL, Tejal Bhanubhai. 40 MEDICAL PARK, MED PARK STE 105 26003 #495-23-2004 L2008 FP *012

PATEL, Vina B. ■ 26003 #495-33-1988 L1996 CHP *020 †75

PAYNE, Frederic James. 40 MEDICAL PARK, STE 301 26003 #065-01-1970 L1982 NS *071

PEREZ, Gilbert Basco. 40 MEDICAL PARK, STE 406 26003 #748-21-2006 L2008 FP *012

PICCIO, Catherine Alinea. 40 MEDICAL PARK STE 406, FAMILY HEALTH CTR 26003 #748-01-2001 L2007 FP *012

PIZARRO, Cesar Del R. 2115 CHAPLINE ST STE 201 26003 #748-08-1970 L1978 OBG *020 †30

PIZARRO, Evangeline C. 2115 CHAPLINE ST 26003 #748-08-1972 L1978 IM *020

POLACK, Edward Phillips. 40 MEDICAL PARK, STE 200 26003 #055-01-1971 L1979 PS *020 †85,65

POLLOCK, Jondavid. 1 MEDICAL PARK, SCHIFFLER CANCER CTR 26003 #024-05-1992 L2000 RO *020 †80

POSIN, Shawn Lee. 2000 EOFF ST, 601 W 26003 #055-01-1994 L1996 EM *020 †16

PRZYBYSZ, Thomas Michael. 10 MEDICAL PARK, STE 101 PROF CENTER 1 26003 #055-01-1979 L1982 ON HEM *020 †20

PRZYBYSZ, Thomas Michael. ■ 26003 #055-01-2006 L2006 IM *012

RAHBAR, Habibollah. ■ 26003 #025-01-2005 L2005 DR *012

RAO, Sheela R. 19 STONE GATE DR 26003 #496-24-1994 L2002 PD *020 †55

RAY, Raymond Daniel, II. 1 MEDICAL PARK 26003 #055-02-1993 L1994 GS *020

REAM, Thomas Scot. 1608 WARWOOD AVE 26003 #011-03-1987 L1989 FM *020 †18

REED, Janis English. 2101 JACOB ST, STE 402 26003 #055-01-1983 L1993 OPH *020 †35

REED, Robert Jeffrey, III. 2000 EOFF ST STE 702, OHIO VLY MED CTR 26003 #041-01-1956 L1962 GS GP *071 †85

REITER, Martin David. 2101 JACOB ST, STE 601 26003 #041-02-1945 L1954 A *071 †20,03

REYES, Romeo Campana. 2000 EOFF ST 26003 #748-01-1966 L1981 AN *020

RICHARDSON, Bryan A. 118 HERITAGE DR 26003 #038-43-1991 L2002 AN *020 †05

ROGERS, Joyce Baker. 30 MEDICAL PARK STE 230 26003 #001-02-1961 L1980 AN *075

RUBEEN, Shafia. 40 MEDICAL PARK, MED PARK STE 105 26003 #496-22-2004 L2008 FP *012

RUBEN, Alan Marshall. ■ 26003 #021-01-1967 L1977 D *071 †15 ‡

RUBEN, Geoffrey Lee. 1 MEDICAL PARK 26003 #055-01-1985 L1987 EM PD *020 †55

SALISBURY, Robert Saml. 1 STAMMS ACRES 26003 #055-01-1966 L1967 PTH *071 †50

SCHEINHOLTZ, Martin F. ■ 26003 #041-14-1977 L1978 AN *071 †05

SCHMITT, Bradley Adam. 40 MEDICAL PARK STE 406 26003 #055-01-2004 L2005 FM *020 †18

SCHMITT, Thomas Jos. 1817 WARWOOD AVE 26003 #165-01-1968 L1972 END IM *020

SECO, Fred. 2000 EOFF ST, OVMC 26003 #847-04-1978 L1982 GP EM *020 ‡

SEUNG, Hong II. ■ 26003 #583-02-1962 L1973 OTO *071 †45

SHAH, Shishir H. 107 AARONWOODS CT, (OGLEBAY PARK ESTATES) 26003 #495-22-1987 L1998 APM *020 †05

SHAH, Umer Sayeed. ■ 26003 #024-05-1990 L2003 TS *020

SHULTZ, Jeffrey Saville. 2000 EOFF ST, OHIO VALLEY MEDICAL CENTER 26003 #055-01-1967 L1968 IM END *020 †20

SIMBRA, Delfin Villa, Jr. 58 16TH ST, WHEELING CLINIC 26003 #748-08-1962 L1974 OPH *071

SLAYSMAN, Michael Lofland. 1 MEDICAL PARK 26003 #051-01-1977 L1986 DR IM *020 †80

SMALTZ, Virgil William. 1 MEDICAL PARK, WHEELING HOSPITAL ER 26003 #055-02-1993 L1994 EM *020 †16

SMITH, Beverly Jill. ■ 26003 #035-03-1976 L1979 GS *071 †85

SOBRAY, Janice Claire. 1 MEDICAL PARK, WHEELING HOSPITAL 26003 #055-01-1980 L1981 EM FM *020 †18

SOFKA, Sarah Helen. ■ 26003 #055-01-2008 *012

SON, Dong Soo. 1 MEDICAL PARK 26003 #583-31-2004 L2007 FP *012

SONNEFELD, Christian A. ■ 26003 #055-01-2002 L2005 N *020 †75

SOVANI, Santwana V. 2000 EOFF ST, OHIO VALLEY MEDICAL CENTER 26003 #495-19-1983 L2002 AN *020 †05

SRINIVASAN, Ram. ■ 26003 #495-94-1975 L1993 END IM *075

STAAB, Charles Henry, III. ■ 26003 #041-12-1977 L1977 PD *020 †55

STEGER, William Jos. ■ 26003 #023-01-1939 L1947 IM *071

STEIN, Vilja Kreek. 2238 EOFF ST 26003 #041-01-1963 L1978 CHP P *071 †75 ‡

STRAUCH, William Douglas. 96 12TH ST 26003 #055-01-1976 L1977 OPH *020 †35

SULTANA, Shamim. 1 MED PARK 26003 #496-21-2001 L2006 FP *012

SWAMY, Chandra Setunath. MED PK PROF CTR IV STE 507 26003 #495-45-1969 L1981 OBG *020 †30

TAUBENSLAG, Walter Neal. 20 MEDICAL PARK, STE 201 26003 #023-01-1978 L1985 U *020 †20,95

TELLERS, John Gregory. 40 MEDICAL PARK, STE 500 26003 #055-01-1974 L1975 N P *020 †75

TERRY, Richard Franklin. 111 PARK VIEW LN, STE 202 26003 #055-01-1973 L1973 CD IM *020 †20

THOMAS, Thomas L. ■ 26003 #056-06-1953 L1954 GP OS *071

TIMMS, Steve Ray. 58 16TH ST, WHEELING CLINIC 26003 #055-02-1990 L1994 N *020 †75

TIU, Christopher. 58 16TH ST, WHEELING CLINIC 26003 #055-01-1996 L2003 OTO *020 †45

TIU, Jeremy Jonathan. ■ 26003 #055-01-2002 L2005 OTO *100

TIU, Wilfredo Ang. 58 16TH ST, WHEELING CLINIC 26003 #748-01-1960 L1971 OTO *020 †45

TRAVAGLINO-PARDA, Rhonda. 40 MEDICAL PARK, STE 200 26003 #038-43-1985 L1998 PS *020 †65

TRIVEDI, Rupal Pravin. 40 MEDICAL PARK STE 406 26003 #496-25-1999 L2006 FP *012

UHL, Michelle Dianne. 10 MEDICAL PARK, STE 101 26003 #023-01-1977 L1984 ON IM *071 †20

URVAL, Krishna Raj. 2101 JACOB ST STE 601, OHIO VLY ASTHMA & ALLERGY 26003 #495-09-1979 L1991 AI PD *020 †03,55

VALENTINE, Albert M. 2000 EOFF ST 26003 #051-04-1951 L1952 CD IM *075 †20

VAN PELT, Byron Leslie. 20 MEDICAL PARK STE 303 26003 #055-01-1968 L1971 IM *020 †20

VASILAKIS-DONZELLA, Amy A. 30 MEDICAL PARK STE 221 26003 #055-75-2000, ▲ L2001 FM *020 †16

VASQUEZ, Carlos A. 2101 JACOB ST STE 302, VALLEY PROF CTR SOUTH 26003 #264-01-1966 L1975 HO IM *040 †20

VAWTER, Robert Lee. 30 MEDICAL PARK, PROF CTR 3 STE 101 26003 #748-12-1983 L1990 RHU *020

VAZQUEZ-CARRERO, Mirza. 2000 EOFF ST STE 70, CARE PLLC 26003 #042-02-1985 L2000 CHP *020

VOSS, Edward C, Jr. 58 16TH ST 26003 #035-06-1950 L1962 GS *072 †85

VUKELICH, Sam. MEDICAL PARK TOWER IV 302 26003 #041-12-1964 L1971 ORS *071

WACK, Thomas Geo, Jr. 616 FAIRMONT PIKE 26003 #055-01-1974 L1977 FM *020 †18

WADE, Alga Myrtle. ■ 26003 #047-07-1931 L1937 GS *020

WAHEED, Musaddiq. 40 MEDICAL PARK STE 406 26003 #704-20-2002 L2006 FP *012

WALMSLEY, Bruce Gordon. 30 RENAISSANCE WAY 26003 #064-01-1978 L1980 EM *071 †16

WEST, Max Lee. 1 MEDICAL PARK, WHEELING HOSP EMER DEPT 26003 #041-02-1981 L1983 FM *020 †18

WEYRICH, Randall Patrick. 2000 EOFF ST 26003 #055-01-1979 L1980 OTO FPS *020 †45

WILEY, Kim Steven. 2108 LUMBER AVE 26003 #055-01-1994 L1996 CRS *020 †85,10

WILSON, Daniel Wayne. 7 E COVE AVE 26003 #055-01-1983 L1984 FM FPG *020 †18

WRIGHT, William Harold. 1 MEDICAL PARK, ANESTHESIOLOGISTS INC 26003 #918-01-1970 L1984 AN OS *020 †05

WURTZBACHER, John Jos. 2000 EOFF ST, STE 601-W 26003 #055-01-1975 L1976 CD IM *020 †20

WYMER, Merrill Fayne. 2000 EOFF ST, OVMC RADIOLOGY DEPT 26003 #055-01-1965 L1966 R NM *071 †80,28

YASSINI-FARD, Hossein. 1132 NATIONAL RD 26003 #517-01-1961 L1970 FM PD *071 †18 ‡

YBANEZ-MORANO, Jessica R. 2101 JACOB ST, STE 201 26003 #055-01-1989 L1997 OBG *020 †30

YOUSEF, Michael Matias B. 1 MEDICAL PARK, WHEELING HOSP 26003 #915-03-1975 L2001 PTH *020 †50

YOUSSEF, Nazih Rizk. 1 MEDICAL PARK 26003 #915-04-1956 L1983 RO *071

ZALESKI, Robert John. 10 MEDICAL PARK, STE 203 26003 #055-01-1975 L1980 ORS *020

ZGUTA, Andrew. ■ 26003 #407-16-1949 L1960 AN *071

ZYZNEWSKY, Wladimir. 2115 CHAPLINE ST, STE 301 26003 #935-04-1971 L1981 N *020 †75

WHITE HALL – MARION

SPENCER, Frederick Arthur. 3 TYGART VALLEY MALL, OCC MED DPET FG HOSP 26554 #004-01-1961 L1966 FM FSM *071

WHITE SULPHUR SPRINGS – GREENBRIER

BALDWIN, Ernest Frank, III. 320 W MAIN ST 24986 #035-20-1979 L1984 **IM END** *020 †20
BARRETT, Milton Ralph, II. 320 W MAIN ST 24986 #004-01-1979 L2006 **DR** *020 †80
BROWN, Patrick Lee. 320 W MAIN ST 24986 #055-01-1972 L1972 **CD IM** *020 †20
CUNNINGHAM, Wm Norman. 320 W MAIN ST, GREENBRIER CLINIC 24986 #055-01-1974 L1979 **GE** *020 †20
DOTSON, Thomas Owen. 320 W MAIN ST 24986 #055-01-1964 L1965 **IM** *020
HARRIS, Melvin Wm. GREENBRIER VILLAGE, 327 CREEKSIDE COTTAGES 24986 #035-08-1943 L1986 **IM CD** *071 †20
JONES, Douglas Larkin. 320 W MAIN ST 24986 #047-05-1970 L1975 **IM END** *020 †20
KLINE, Richard Brash. 320 W MAIN ST 24986 #023-01-1972 L1979 **FM** *020 †55,16
MANN, Thomas Forrest. 320 W MAIN ST 24986 #055-01-1977 L1977 **IM** *020 †20
POPE, Herbert Lee. GREENBRIER CLINIC 24986 #047-06-1959 L1969 **R** *071 †80
ROMEO, Martha Suzanne. 320 W MAIN ST 24986 #055-01-1993 L1995 **IM** *020 †20
SPEIDEN, Lois Marian. 320 W MAIN ST 24986 #041-13-1966 L1983 **R** *071 †80
THOMPSON, George Robt. 320 W MAIN ST 24986 #041-13-1980 L1985 **IM** *020 †20

WHITESVILLE – RALEIGH

SANTIAGO, Loreto Santos. PO BOX 187 25209 #748-07-1955 L1979 **GP EM** *071

WIDEN – CLAY

QUAREQUIO-RODI, Francesco. ■ 25211 #561-10-1957 L1994 **GP P** *071

WILLIAMSBURG – GREENBRIER

HAWLEY, William David, Jr. PO BOX 10 24991 #055-01-1970 L1974 **GP** *020

WILLIAMSON – MINGO

ACOSTA, Armando M. 116 W 2ND AVE 25661 #308-03-1980 L1983 **EM GP** *020
ANGCO, Manual Martinez. 701 COLLEGE HL 25661 #748-07-1972 L1985 *020
ARANAS, Bonifacio B. 859 ALDERSON ST 25661 #748-11-1968 L1977 **GP EM** *020
BATAUSA, Jaime Calunia. 859 ALDERSON ST, WILLIAMSON MEM HOSP EMER D 25661 #748-11-1972 L1984 **EM GS** *020

CORTAS, George. 215 LOGAN ST STE 42 25661 #024-05-1991 L1997 **GE** *020 †20
FERNANDEZ, Alberto A, Jr. 859 ALDERSON ST 25661 #748-11-1971 L1979 **FM EM** *020
FRASER, Francis A. 701 COLLEGE HL STE 4, PROFESSIONAL 25661 #024-07-1984 L1990 **U** *020 †95
GOMEZ, Pastor Centeno. 859 ALDERSON ST 25661 #748-01-1946 L1968 **GP OS** *071
GUTHI, Jhansi Rani. 859 ALDERSON ST, WILLIAMSON MEMORIAL HOSP 25661 #495-11-1980 L2001 **AN** *020
HARIDAS, Shobha. 104 LOGAN ST 25661 #495-04-1984 L1999 **PD** *020 †55
HOFFMAN, James David. 215 LOGAN ST 25661 #055-02-1983 L1989 **FM PTH** *075
HOOVER, Katherine Anne. 35 W 3RD AVE 25661 #025-12-1975 L1978 **IM PD** *020 †20
KIM, Je Hyun. 859 ALDERSON ST BOX 1980 25661 #583-01-1956 L1986 **DR NM** *020 †28
MAHALINGASHETTY, Prakash. 183 E 2ND AVE 25661 #495-35-1970 L1998 **GS** *020 †85
PAJARILLO, Leo P. 701 COLLEGE HL 25661 #748-11-1968 L1978 **PD** *020
PARSLEY, Sybil R. ■ 25661 #055-75-2006, ▲ **IM** *012
SHAFER, Diane Elain. 114 W 2ND AVE 25661 #041-13-1976 L1980 **ORS EM** *074 ‡
SOUTHERN, Donald Eugene. PO BOX 729 25661 #055-01-1964 L1987 **PS** *020
TABLANTE, Liberty R, Jr. 859 ALDERSON ST 25661 #748-11-1968 L1980 **GS** *071 †85
TAMPOYA, Manolo Daligdig. 75 W 4TH AVE 25661 #748-08-1976 L1984 **FM** *020
THAMBI, Lilian. 859 ALDERSON ST 25661 #495-27-1955 L1983 **P** *020
VISINTINE, Aarolyn Marie. 859 ALDERSON ST 25661 #038-40-1963 L1987 **PD** *071
WINGFIELD, Thos Whetsell. 859 ALDERSON ST 25661 #023-01-1965 L2000 **AN** *020 †05 ‡

WILLIAMSTOWN – WOOD

FREED, Holly Janel. ■ 26187 #055-01-2003 L2006 **FM** *020 †18
HOLTGREWE, Michael Ray. 424 HIGHLAND AVE 26187 #030-05-1976 L1983 **FM** *020 †18
MARTINSEN, Cynthia D. 424 HIGHLAND AVE 26187 #055-75-1995, ▲ L1996 **FM OS** *020 †18
MONCMAN, Jeffrey Steven. 15 N PINE ST 26187 #055-01-1980 L1981 **DR** *020 †80

WINFIELD – PUTNAM

MABIE, Richard Harry. 3240 WINFIELD RD 25213 #056-06-1955 L1958 **PD** *071 †55
MORGAN, Michael Richard. 100 WESTLAND EST 25213 #047-20-2002 L2004 **ID** *012 †55,20
PHILLIPS, Joan Antolini. 16 BAYBERRY ST 25213 #055-01-1980 L1981 **PD** *071 †55
VON WULFFEN, Sara Walker. ■ 25213 #055-01-2003 L2007 **PD** *020 †55

WOLFE – MERCER

JOSE, Reynaldo D. HIGHWAY 102 24751 #748-07-1966 L1978 **FM EM** *020

ADELL – SHEBOYGAN

GRIMM, Suzanne Beth. W6199 INDIAN MOUND RD 53001 #018-03-1990 L1996 **P** *020

ALGOMA – KEWAUNEE

ANDERSON, Robert James. 1510 FREMONT ST 54201 #056-06-1995 L1996 **FM** *020 †18
HASSEL, Carla J. N8434 COUNTY RD S 54201 #018-75-1996, ▲ L1999 **FM OMM** *020
MARCH, Jack F. 413 4TH ST 54201 #028-02-1950 L1952 **CD GP** *075
PAPENDICK, David Ellis. 521 OHIO ST 54201 #005-12-1961 L1962 **GP GS** *071

ALTOONA – EAU CLAIRE

BLASER, Lon A. 2503 N HILLCREST PKWY, EAU CLAIRE 54720 #025-76-1986, ▲ L1987 **MDM RHU** *030 †20
LOKKESMOE, Kristin Shover. ■ 54720 #026-04-1991 L1994 **PD** *074 †55
SALLIS, Douglas Arnold. ■ 54720 #065-05-1955 L1958 **FM CD** *072 †18

AMERY – POLK

ARLT, Geoffrey John. ■ 54001 #026-04-1985 L1998 **OS N** *020 †75
ARNESON, Orrin Nathan. ■ 54001 #056-05-1956 L1957 **FM** *071
COE, Dylan. 225 SCHOLL ST, AMERY REGIONAL MEDICAL CTR 54001 #060-02-1988 L1995 **FM** *020 †18
DASLER, Herbert Alfons. ■ 54001 #056-05-1944 L1946 **GP GS** *071 †18
ELBING, Paul Frederic. ■ 54001 #056-05-1976 L1977 **FM** *020 †18
GALE-WYRICK, Kenneth L. 225 SCHOLL ST, AMERY REGIONAL MEDICAL CEN 54001 #007-02-1981 L1982 **FM** *020 †18
GLEICH, Walter Paul. 225 SCHOLL CT, METROPOLITAN UROLOGIC 54001 #025-01-1977 L1984 **U** *071 †95
GORRES, Geoffrey Hugh. 225 SCHOLL CT, AMERY REGIONAL MEDICAL CEN 54001 #026-04-1993 L1994 **FM** *020 †18
HENLEY, Robin K. 225 SCHOLL CT 54001 #018-75-2001, ▲ L2003 **FM** *020
JOHNSON, Craig Timothy. 225 SCHOLL CT, AMERY REGIONAL MEDICAL CTR 54001 #026-04-1981 L1982 **FM** *020 †18
KARLEN, Richard Glenn. 225 SCHOLL CT, MIDWEST ENT SPECIALISTS 54001 #026-04-1992 L2002 **OTO FPS** *020 †45
LONG, Linda Ann. 225 SCHOLL CT, AMERY REGIONAL MED CTR 54001 #055-01-1970 L1983 **CD IM** *020 †20
MARRA, Michael Thos G. ■ 54001 #050-02-1948 L1949 **GP** *071
MEISTERLING, Michael R. 225 SCHOLL CT 54001 #030-06-1998 L2004 **ORS** *020 †40
QUENAN, James Peter. 265 GRIFFIN ST E, AMERY REGIONAL MEDICAL CEN 54001 #056-06-1971 L1977 **GS FM** *020 †85
RADUEGE, William Edward. 225 SCHOLL CT 54001 #056-05-1966 L1967 **FM** *020 †18
RIMESTAD, Martin Lee. 225 SCHOLL ST, AMERY REGIONAL MEDICAL CEN 54001 #037-01-1979 L1982 **FM** *020 †18
ROBERTS, Susan Kathleen. ■ 54001 #034-01-1994 L1995 **FM** *020 †18
RYAN, Ann Marie. 265 GRIFFIN ST E, AMERY REGIONAL MED CTR 54001 #026-04-2001 L2004 **FM** *020
STRODTHOFF, Debra Ann. ■ 54001 #056-05-1983 L1984 **GP** *020 †18
SULLIVAN, James Henry. 225 SCHOLL CT 54001 #018-03-1990 L1994 **DR** *020 †80
TOLAN, Christopher John. 265 GRIFFIN ST E 54001 #026-04-1991 L1999 **FPS OTO** *020 †45
TULKKI, Barry Leonard. 265 GRIFFIN ST E, AMERY REGIONAL MEDICAL CEN 54001 #026-04-1979 L1980 **FM** *020 †18
VEAL, Jennifer Lynn. 225 SCHOLL CT 54001 #026-04-2003 L2006 **FM** *100
VERBEEK, Steven Allen. 265 GRIFFIN ST E, HEALTH PARTNERS-ARMC 54001 #026-04-2002 L2006 **OBG** *100
WHITE, John Carl. 225 SCHOLL CT 54001 #023-01-1993 L1996 **FM** *020 †18
WHITESELL, Frank Bean. ■ 54001 #010-02-1977 L1992 **GS** *020 †85
WHITESELL, Frank Bean, Jr. 225 SCHOLL CT, AMERY REGIONAL MEDICAL CEN 54001 #010-02-1941 L1945 **GS OS** *020
WHITLARK, Frederick Louis. 309 HARRIMAN AVE N 54001 #016-11-1946 L1949 **GP** *071

AMHERST – PORTAGE

MARKMAN, Lenard David. 272 CHRISTY ST 54406 #018-75-1985, ▲ L1990 **FM** *020
MARKMAN, Leslie Hoey. 272 CHRISTY ST 54406 #041-77-1985, ▲ L1990 **GP** *020

AMHERST JUNCTION – PORTAGE

BETINIS, John Irven. 1661 CARY RDG 54407 #005-06-1967 L1977 **GPM NTR** *020

ANTIGO – LANGLADE

BEATTIE, Bernard W. ■ 54409 #056-06-1953 L1954 **GP** *071
BOWMAN, Kenneth Lee. 112 E 5TH AVE 54409 #020-12-1980 L2001 **DR** *020 †80
BRUNZLICK, Larry Ray. 700 EDISON ST 54409 #056-05-1981 L1982 *020
BURKETT, Frank Ellis. 110 E 5TH AVE, ASPIRUS GENERAL CLINIC 54409 #016-06-1973 L2002 **GS SO** *085
CROMER, Robert W. 1111 LANGLADE RD 54409 #016-06-1952 L1954 **FM** *071
DEEP, Noel Nain. 110 E 5TH AVE 54409 #495-21-1995 L2000 **IM** *020 †20 ‡
DENNISON, Sylvia Jean. 110 E 5TH AVE 54409 #017-20-1983 L2002 **P ADM** *020 †75
FLOWERS, Kristine Ellen. 110 E 5TH AVE 54409 #056-05-1994 L1997 **FM** *020 †18
FOX, Theodore Conrad. 110 E 5TH AVE 54409 #056-05-1957 L1958 **FM** *072 †18
FRANK, Howard Wm, Jr. 112 E 5TH AVE, LANGLADE ORTHOPEDIC CLINIC 54409 #038-40-1977 L2001 **ORS** *020 †40
GARRITTY, John E. ■ 54409 #035-08-1949 L1952 **GP** *071
GIBSON, Donald Carroll. ■ 54409 #005-06-1959 L1986 **PTH** *050
GILBERTSON, Anna Grace. 110 E 5TH AVE 54409 #056-06-1998 L2003 **GS** *020 †85

HEGRANES, Gary Michael. 110 E 5TH AVE 54409 #016-43-1982 L1985 **FM** *020
HENDRICKSON, Robert L. ■ 54409 #056-05-1952 L1953 **GP** *071
HENDRICKSON, Todd R. 110 E 5TH AVE 54409 #056-05-1980 L1985 **GS** *020 †85
HEUSS, Charles Andrew. ■ 54409 #018-03-1972 L1974 **FM** *071 †18
KEENER, Robert Lewis. 112 E 5TH AVE 54409 #038-40-1956 L1972 **GP** *071
KNEELAND, Bart Robert. 110 E 5TH AVE, GENERAL CLNC ANTIGO 54409 #018-03-1997 L1998 **FM** *020 †18
MC KENNA, John Eugene. 112 E 5TH AVE 54409 #056-05-1957 L1959 **GP** *072 †18
MOERMOND, James Orlin. 110 E 5TH AVE, THE GENERAL CLINIC 54409 #018-03-1965 L1969 **FM OBG** *020 †18
MOORE, Michael Scott. 112 E 5TH AVE, LANGLADE MEMORIAL HOSPITAL 54409 #036-08-1998 L1999 **FM** *020 †18
MYERS, John R. 110 E 5TH AVE 54409 #056-06-1978 L1981 **IM** *020 †20
NORRBOM, Corina Jo. 110 E 5TH AVE, THE GENERAL CLILNC 54409 #028-02-1994 L1996 **FM** *020 †18 ‡
PERKINS, Rick Leon. 110 E 5TH AVE 54409 #028-03-1984 L1992 **OBG** *020 †30
PLAMANN, Ryan Arthur. ■ 54409 #056-05-2006 L2006 **PD** *012
QAMAR, Samina. 110 E 5TH AVE 54409 #704-20-1986 L2003 **FM** *020 †18
SENNHOLZ, Troy Donald. 110 E 5TH AVE 54409 #056-06-1996 L1999 **FM** *020 †18
SKOWRON, Ralph David. 112 E 5TH AVE, LANGLADE MEM HOSP 54409 #422-01-1982 L1992 **EM** *020
STARYNSKI, John Robt. 112 E 5TH AVE, MARSHFIELD CLINIC-LAKELAND 54409 #041-02-1980 L2006 **ORS** *020 †40
TURNBULL, James Michael. 110 E 5TH AVE 54409 #056-06-1984 L1987 **FM** *020 †18
WHEELER, Kristi Anne. 110 E 5TH AVE 54409 #041-09-1997 L1999 **FM** *020 †18

APPLETON – OUTAGAMIE

ACOSTA, Ernesto Lobrigo. 1818 N MEADE ST, MEDICAL OFFICE BLDG WEST 54911 #748-01-1976 L1982 **OBG** *020 †30
ADLER-FISCHER, Karen Ruth. 3329 N RICHMOND ST 54911 #056-05-1980 L1981 **FM** *020 †18
ALASWAD, Khaldoon. 1818 N MEADE ST, APPLETON CARDIOLOGY ASSOCI 54911 #875-01-1990 L1997 **IC** *020 †20
ALEXANDER, Avery Devlin. 250 N METRO DR 54913 #005-11-1985 L1989 **OPH** *020 †35
ALLEN, David Bruce. 1506 S ONEIDA ST 54915 #036-07-1980 L1982 **PD** *020 †55
ALLEN, Herbert Martin. 1531 S MADISON ST, FOX VALLEY PSYCHIATRIC 54915 #051-01-1970 L1974 **P** *020
ALLEN, Susan. 1506 S ONEIDA ST, DEPT. OF ANESTHESIOLOGY 54915 #012-05-1992 L2006 **AN** *105
ALLHISER, John Norman. 229 S MORRISON ST 54911 #056-06-1977 L1986 **FM** *071 †18
ANDERLA, David Brian. 2809 N PARK DRIVE LN, THEDACARE PHYSICIANS 54911 #056-05-1993 L1996 **FM** *020 †18
ANDERSON, Jack Craig. 820 E GRANT ST 54911 #056-05-1981 L1984 **IM** *020 †20
ANDERSON, Jack G. ■ 54911 #056-06-1951 L1955 **IM** *071 †20
ARNDT, Joseph Anthony. 1818 N MEADE ST, APPLETON MEDICAL CENTER 54911 #056-05-1996 L2000 **AN** *020 †05
AUSTIN, Mark Christopher. 1301 E NORTHLAND AVE STE A 54911 #026-04-1989 L1992 **OPH** *020 †35
AWE, Merici Ann. 229 S MORRISON ST 54911 #056-05-2006 L2007 **FP** *012
AYANRINO, Femi Bello. 1506 S ONEIDA ST 54915 #690-08-1992 L2004 **IM** *020 †20
BALLARD, Robert Blakeslee. 1818 N MEADE ST, FOX VALLEY SURGICAL 54911 #025-12-1991 L1999 **VS** *020 †85
BANKWALLA, Arnaz Adil. 3121 N RAMBLING ROSE DR 54914 #704-02-1986 L2003 **FM** *020 †18
BAR-LEV, Avi. 900 E GRANT ST 54911 #561-01-1982 L1993 **ON** *020 †20
BARTON, Wendy Jeanne. 2701 E ENTERPRISE AVE 54913 #056-06-1986 L1994 **PD** *020 †55
BASTASIC, Jeffrey Michael. ■ 54913 #056-06-2007 **FP** *012
BAUM, Karl Edward. 1506 S ONEIDA ST, AFFINITY MEDICAL GROUP 54915 #056-06-1993 L1994 **IM** *020 †20
BAUTISTA-SANTOS, Maria E. 3329 N RICHMOND ST 54911 #748-10-1988 L2000 **FM** *020 †18
BAX, Jan Chenette. 1506 S ONEIDA ST 54915 #017-20-1980 L1987 **HS ORS** *020 †40
BEISER, George David. 1818 N MEADE ST, APPLETON CARDIOLOGY 54911 #038-06-1963 L2004 **CD IM** *020 †20
BEJVAN, Stephen Michael. 229 S MORRISON ST 54911 #056-06-1992 L1997 **DR** *020 †80
BELGAM, Robert Alan. 900 E GRANT ST, RADIATION ONCOLOGY 54911 #035-03-1985 L1994 **RO GP** *020 †80
BERNAUER, Timothy Andrew. 229 S MORRISON ST 54911 #016-06-1994 L2003 **RNR** *020 †80
BETTAG, Matthew Edward. 1520 N MEADE ST, EAR NOSE & THROAT 54911 #016-42-1997 L2002 **OTO** *020 †45
BIRN, Christoffer Kaj. 1506 S ONEIDA ST, ST ELIZABETH HOS 5TH FL 54915 #034-01-2001 L2002 **PD** *020 †55
BONILLA, Pedro Jose. 229 S MORRISON ST 54911 #847-06-1997 L2003 **P** *100
BOREN, Clark Henry, Jr. 1818 N MEADE ST, FOX VALLEY SURGICAL 54911 #016-06-1973 L1979 **GS VS** *020 †85
BOULOS, Mona S. 1506 S ONEIDA ST, ST ELIZABETH HOSPITAL 54915 #915-04-1976 L1982 **PD** *020 †55
BRADY, Nicole Ann. N9642 COUNTY RD N 54915 #056-06-2000 L2001 **FM** *020 †18 ‡
BRAVICK, Donald Dean. 1506 S ONEIDA ST 54915 #016-02-1953 L1960 **U** *071 †95
BROOKS, David Jerome. 1818 N MEADE ST 54911 #056-06-1988 L1993 **ID** *020 †20
BRUCKER, Robert George. 229 S MORRISON ST 54911 #056-06-1979 L1986 **AS** *062 †80
BRUDER, Kenneth James. 1501 S MADISON ST 54915 #039-05-1987 L1994 **GS** *020 †85
BRYAN, Albert Rahr. 5 INNOVATION CT, THEDA CARE 54914 #067-01-1960 L1963 **PUD IM** *020
BUCHANAN, David Alden. 1818 N MEADE ST, APPLETON CARDIOLOGY 54911 #056-05-1981 L1987 **CD IM** *020 †20
BUDI, Joanne Friis. ■ 54915 #018-03-1985 L1990 **FM** *071 †18
BURROWS, Thomas Howard. 1506 S ONEIDA ST 54915 #023-07-1962 L1968 **OTO** *071 †45
BURWITZ, James Edward. 10 TRI PARK WAY, JOHN H BRADLEY VA CBOC 54914 #056-05-1978 L1979 **FM** *020 †18
BUSEMAN, Sandra Kay. 2009 S MEMORIAL DR 54915 #046-01-1996 L2007 **GPM PM** *030 †70
BUTITTA, John Michael. 1501 S MADISON ST 54915 #016-11-1975 L1979 **IM NTR** *020 †20
CANLAS, Richard Leonard. ■ 54915 #654-01-1988 L2001 **FSM** *020 †18
CARLSON, William James. 3329 N RICHMOND ST, AFFINITY MEDICAL GROUP 54911 #056-05-1976 L1980 **FM** *020 †18
CHANDLER, William Warren. ■ 54911 #056-06-1946 L1947 **GS** *071 †85

■ = Address Information Privacy Protected

CHELSKY, Mark Jos. 820 E GRANT ST 54911 #016-43-1988 L1994 **U** *020 †95
CHEN, Timothy Spencer. 2500 E ENTERPRISE AVE, UNIT C 54913 #017-20-1999 L2005 **DR** *020 †80
CHENG, Charles C. 1818 N MEADE ST, FOX VALLEY SURGICAL 54911 #005-06-1994 L2001 **SO GS** *020 †85
CHENG, Theresa Meiwan. 1506 S ONEIDA ST 54915 #056-06-1989 L1995 **NS** *020
CHERNEY, Jeffery James. 1818 N MEADE ST, STE 330 54911 #056-05-1986 L1992 **OBG GS** *020 †30
CHERNEY, Jon James. ■ 54913 #056-05-1989 L1990 **HS ORS** *020 †40
CHIEN, S H. 315 W WISCONSIN AVE 54911 #244-04-1969 L1973 **AN** *020
CIHLA, Michelle Laundrie. 121 E WATER ST, NO 207 54911 #056-05-1989 L1991 **D** *020 †15
CLINE, Richard Stanley. 1818 N MEADE ST 54911 #056-06-1954 L1955 **GYN** *071 †30
COMPETENTE, Estrella D. ■ 54911 #748-01-1968 L1977 **PD** *100
COMPETENTE, Perfecto C. 1506 S ONEIDA ST, ST ELIZABETH HOSPITAL 54915 #748-01-1968 L1976 **AN** *020
CONNOR, Ellen Lancon. 1506 S ONEIDA ST 54915 #021-06-1988 L1994 **PDE PD** *020 †55
CONSTANTINESCU, Daniela C. 1501 S MADISON ST 54915 #781-04-1993 L2003 **IM** *020 †20
CORBETT, Colleen Marie. 21 PARK PL, VALLEY EYE ASSOCIATES 54914 #056-06-1982 L1986 **OPH** *020 †35
CORDERO, Armenio C. 1506 S ONEIDA ST 54915 #748-01-1963 L1971 **PTH HEM** *020 †50
CRUZ, Stephen Tang. 3329 N RICHMOND ST 54911 #016-43-1993 L1999 **FM** *020 †18
DANFORD, Harold G. ■ 54915 #056-05-1952 L1953 **OS** *071 †20
DARLING, Raymon Earl. 47 PARK PL, STE 100 54914 #018-03-1980 L1984 **OBG** *020 †30
DAVE, Jagdish Sadashive. 411 S ELM ST 54911 #495-48-1967 L1992 **P IG** *020 †50
DE MURI, Brian Michael. 10 TRI PARK WAY 54914 #025-01-1994 L2000 **P** *020 †75
DERKSEN, Dirk Jon. 3916 N INTERTECH CT 54913 #026-04-1970 L1975 **FM** *020 †18
DERNLAN, Stephen Robt. 3916 N INTERTECH CT 54913 #056-05-1986 L1989 **IM** *020 †20
DESAI, Abhilash K. 444 N WESTHILL BLVD 54914 #496-38-1991 L2004 **PYG** *020 †75
DE WITT, David Charles. 5320 MICHAELS DR, NEUROSPINE CENTER OF WISCO 54913 #016-43-2000 L2001 **ORS** *100
DIAMOND, Carol Ann. 1506 S ONEIDA ST 54915 #016-42-1985 L1999 **PD** *020 †55
DOMASHEVSKY, Lubomyr. ■ 54913 #016-43-1994 L2004 **EM OS** *020 †16
DUMAS, Constantine Gus. 2009 S MEMORIAL DR, THEDACARE AT WORK 54915 #025-01-1996 L2008 **OM GPM** *020 †70
DUPPLER, David W. 1818 N MEADE ST, FOX VALLEY SURGICAL 54911 #056-05-1980 L1992 **GS** *020 †85
EBBEN, David Matthew. 3916 N INTERTECH CT 54913 #056-05-1979 L1982 **FM** *020 †18
EDWARDS, Jill Hogfeldt. 2701 E ENTERPRISE AVE 54913 #016-11-1990 L1992 **PEM PD** *020 †55
EDWARDS, John Anderson. 2701 E ENTERPRISE AVE 54913 #056-05-1994 L1997 **PD** *020 †55
EGGERT, David Alan. 2105 E ENTERPRISE AVE 54913 #056-05-1981 L1982 **ORS** *020 †40
EIBEN, Sonya Rae. 3916 N INTERTECH CT 54913 #018-03-1989 L1993 **IM** *020 †20
ENGSTROM, Denton Paul. ■ 54914 #026-04-1946 L1960 **P** *071 †75
ERICKSON, Eric Wayne. 820 E GRANT ST 54911 #056-05-2000 L2001 **ORS** *020
FABER, John Wm. 412 E LONGVIEW DR 54911 #016-06-1964 L1967 **D** *071 †15 ‡
FAUSTICH, Mark Wm. 1531 S MADISON ST, STE 350 54915 #025-01-1982 L1985 **OBG** *020 †30
FENLON, Charles Edward. 100 W LAWRENCE ST 54911 #018-03-1953 L1961 **OM FM** *020 †18
FENLON, John Wichman. 424 E WISCONSIN AVE STE 10 54911 #028-02-1962 L1973 **DR** *071 †80
FERNANDEZ, Pascual B. 1818 N MEADE ST 54911 #748-07-1954 L1968 **AN** *071
FERRANTE, Robert Jos. 1818 N MEADE ST STE N347 54911 #033-05-1990 L2002 **TS** *020 †85,90
FLANAGAN, Deidre Ann. 1501 S MADISON ST 54915 #016-45-1994 L1999 **GS VS** *020 †85
FLOOD, Michael. 820 E GRANT ST 54911 #041-13-1999 L2004 **IM** *020 †20
FLOOD, Michael Stafford L. 820 E GRANT ST, THEDACARE 54911 #561-01-1979 L1983 **PS HS** *020 †85,65
FORS, Tait Dennis. 820 E GRANT ST 54911 #056-05-2000 L2006 **U** *020 †95
FOX, Robert Sheldon. 3916 N INTERTECH CT 54913 #025-01-1980 L1983 **FM** *020 †18
FRANK, Jennifer Ewen. 229 S MORRISON ST 54911 #024-05-1999 L2006 **FM** *020 †18
FULLER, Stephen Craig. 3916 N INTERTECH CT 54913 #030-06-1985 L1986 **FM** *020 †18
GARRETT, Kevin Chas. 1818 N MEADE ST, APPLETON MEDICAL CENTER-AD 54911 #018-03-1980 L1985 **PUD CCM** *020 †20
GEALL, Michael Geo. 900 E GRANT ST 54911 #917-19-1962 L1977 **GE IM** *020 †20
GITTER, Michael Joseph. 1818 N MEADE ST, APPLETON CARDIOLOGY 54911 #056-05-1987 L1992 **CD IM** *020 †20
GOETHKE, Randy L. 1818 N MEADE ST 54911 #056-05-1998 L1999 **AN** *020
GOGGINS, Timothy F. 1531 S MADISON ST, STE 250 54915 #035-03-1997 L2004 **HO** *020 †20,55
GOLDSMITH, Robin Jean. 315 W WISCONSIN AVE 54911 #056-05-1991 L1997 **AN** *020 †05
GRANT, Douglas Henry. 3329 N RICHMOND ST 54911 #056-05-1975 L1979 **FM** *020 †18
GRAVES, Maury David. 3329 N RICHMOND ST 54911 #056-06-1962 L1963 **PD** *071 †55
GROMER, Rex Coleman. 1506 S ONEIDA ST 54915 #016-06-1967 L1974 **OTO** *071 †45
GROSS, Harold T. ■ 54911 #016-06-1939 L1948 **GP GS** *071
GRUNER, Dean Alan. 2009 S MEMORIAL DR, FAMILY DOCTORS, S.C. 54915 #026-04-1980 L1981 **FM** *030 †18
GUENTHER, Wm Carl, Jr. 900 E GRANT ST 54911 #018-03-1981 L1988 **IM ON** *020 †20
GUEVARA, Pedro Gildardo. 1506 S ONEIDA ST, ST ELIZABETH HOSPITAL 54915 #056-06-1998 L1999 **AN** *020 †05
GUTTORMSEN, Brian Neil. 1818 N MEADE ST, APPLETON CARDIOLOGY ASSOCI 54911 #056-06-2001 L2002 **IC** *012
HAGEN, Jonathan Eric. 3916 N INTERTECH CT 54913 #018-03-1986 L1987 **FM** *020 †18
HAGEN, Steven James. 3916 N INTERTECH CT 54913 #016-06-1992 L1996 **FM** *020 †18
HAGENS, Jerome Howard. 1341 N LAKE CT 54913 #056-06-1967 L1977 **ORS LM** *062 †40
HAINE, James Edward. 1501 S MADISON ST 54915 #056-05-1998 L2002 **IM** *020 †20
HALE, William H. ■ 54914 #016-06-1950 L1952 **FM EM** *071 †18
HALL, Marvin Lee. 1301 E NORTHLAND AVE, STE A 54911 #017-20-1975 L1979 **OPH** *020 †35
HALLETT, Mark Boren. 820 E GRANT ST 54911 #056-05-1987 L1993 **FM FSM** *020 †18
HAMEL, Hubert H. ■ 54915 #056-05-1952 L1953 **GS OS** *020
HANMIAH, Rajeshwar. ■ 54911 #062-01-1989 L1996 *020 †18
HARBICK, Kara H. 1301 E NORTHLAND AVE STE A 54911 #016-11-1997 L2002 **OPH** *020 †35
HARMS, Ronald Lloyd. 3500 E DESTINATION DR, STE 300 54915 #056-05-1971 L1972 **FM** *020 †18
HARRINGTON, Robert Wm. 1531 S MADISON ST 54915 #654-01-1979 L1993 **OBG FM** *020
HARRIS, John Sterling. ■ 54911 #025-01-1961 L1965 **OBG** *071 †30
HASH, Lee Wayne. 1531 S MADISON ST 54915 #018-03-1988 L2006 **ORS** *020 †40
HASSLER, Tania Marie. ■ 54913 #037-01-2000 L2003 **PD** *020
HAUSSERMAN, Robert Lee. 2105 E ENTERPRISE AVE 54913 #030-05-1970 L1975 **ORS** *030 †40
HEBL, Brian Alan. 229 S MORRISON ST 54911 #056-05-1988 L1994 **DR** *020 †80
HEINDEL, Kelli Kellbach. 2809 N PARK DRIVE LN 54911 #056-05-1990 L1991 **FM** *020 †18 ‡
HENDEL, Craig Stefan. 2809 N PARK DRIVE LN, THEDACARE PHYSICIANS 54911 #028-03-1983 L2007 **FM PLM** *020 †18
HENDRICKS, Archna. ■ 54913 #056-05-1994 L1995 **IMG** *020 †20
HENRY, Chasity Ann. 2701 E ENTERPRISE AVE 54913 #056-05-2003 L2006 **PD** *020 †55
HENSHAW, H Cullen. 1818 N MEADE ST 54911 #025-01-1966 L1970 **PTH** *020 †50
HERMINA, Mona Saad T. 1818 N MEADE ST 54911 #915-05-1978 L2000 **PTH** *020 †50
HEYERDAHL, Dan Lawrence. 3916 N INTERTECH CT 54913 #056-05-1978 L1979 **FM** *020 †18
HEYL, Bruce Anthony. 477 S NICOLET RD 54914 #028-34-1965 L1971 **P** *020 †75
HEYRMAN, Kurt Andrew. 1506 S ONEIDA ST, ST ELIZABETH HOSPITAL 54915 #056-06-1979 L1980 **PD** *020 †55
HO, Paul C. 229 S MORRISON ST 54911 #028-02-1994 L1995 **DR** *020 †80
HOMBURG, Nancy Jean. 3329 N RICHMOND ST 54911 #056-05-1974 L1975 **FM PLM** *020 †18
HUNT, Jennifer Ann. 2701 E ENTERPRISE AVE 54913 #056-06-1998 L2000 **PD** *020 †55
HUNTER, Gregory James. 1818 N MEADE ST, EMERGENCY ROOM 54911 #056-06-1990 L1991 **EM** *020 †18
HUSS, Richard Glenn. 229 S MORRISON ST 54911 #056-06-1979 L2006 **DR** *020 †80
HUTH, Glenn Richard. 1818 N MEADE ST, APPLETON CARDIOLOGY 54911 #056-06-1986 L1988 **IM** *020 †20
IGLAR, John Robt. 229 S MORRISON ST 54911 #056-06-1987 L1990 **DR** *020 †80
IHDE, Deborah Ann. 820 E GRANT ST 54911 #046-01-1997 L1998 **IM** *020 †20
ISKANDAR, Bermans Jamil. 1506 S ONEIDA ST 54915 #041-01-1989 L1997 **NS NSP** *020 †25
JAKUBOWSKI, Michael Leo. 2701 E ENTERPRISE AVE 54913 #016-06-1987 L2003 **PD** *020 †55
JANU, Peter George. 1506 S ONEIDA ST 54915 #056-05-1993 L1999 **GS** *020 †85
JARES, Joseph J, III. 1506 S ONEIDA ST 54915 #016-01-1986 L2000 **N** *020 †75
JOHNSON, Michael Anthony. 3916 N INTERTECH CT 54913 #017-20-1990 L1993 **IM** *020 †20
JOHNSON, Misty Lee. 1506 S ONEIDA ST 54915 #038-43-1993 L1994 **IM** *020 †20
JOHNSON, Richard Alan. 3329 N RICHMOND ST, AFFINITY MEDICAL GROUP 54911 #018-03-1985 L1986 **FM** *020 †18
JOHNSON, Samuel Buchanan. PO BOX 8031 54912 #056-05-1963 L1968 **AN** *071
JOHNSTON, Jessica Ruth. 229 S MORRISON ST 54911 #056-05-2006 L2007 **FP** *012
JONES, Ann Bislew. 2701 E ENTERPRISE AVE 54913 #056-05-1996 L1999 **PD** *020 †55
JOSEPH, Shanthi Antonette. 1501 S MADISON ST 54915 #495-52-1992 L1998 **IM** *020 †20
JUNTUNEN, Kristine Grace. 3916 N INTERTECH CT 54913 #056-06-1996 L1997 **IM** *020 †20
KAGEN, Charles Norman. 100 W LAWRENCE ST, STE 409 54911 #056-05-1980 L1982 **D** *020 †15
KAGEN, Steven Leslie. 100 W LAWRENCE ST STE 410 54911 #056-05-1976 L1979 **AI ALI** *020 †20,03
KALUGDAN, Joseph Richard. 229 S MORRISON ST 54911 #748-20-2001 **FP** *012
KEANE, Keith Mc Kinley. 2600 S HERITAGE WOODS DR, UNIT A-134 54915 #056-05-1943 L1947 **P CHP** *071 †75
KIESNOWSKI, Brian. 5605 WATERFORD LN 54913 #016-01-1992 L2000 **PS HS** *020 †65
KIM, Jin Sik. ■ 54915 #583-01-1971 L1979 **OBG** *071 †30
KIMBALL, Erin Betty. ■ 54914 #056-05-2007 **FP** *012
KINDE, Robert Richmond. 424 E WISCONSIN AVE, RADIOLOGY ASSOC OF APPLETO 54911 #025-01-1962 L1967 **R** *071 †80
KIRKPATRICK, John Edward. 4321 N BALLARD RD 54913 #056-06-1985 L1986 **IM** *020 †20
KLINGBEIL, Jeffrey Karl. 1818 N MEADE ST, FOX VALLEY SURGICAL 54911 #056-06-1990 L1991 **CRS GS** *020 †10,85
KNUDSON, Gregory Jos. 229 S MORRISON ST 54911 #037-01-1984 L1988 **DR R** *020 †80
KOELLERMEIER, Michelle. 900 E GRANT ST 54911 #035-09-1995 L2003 **OBG** *020 †30
KOEPER, David William. 2701 N ONEIDA ST, STE D 54911 #016-43-1997 L2000 **NEP** *020 †20
KORGER, John Norbert. 1506 S ONEIDA ST 54915 #056-06-1985 L1991 **CHP P** *020 †75
KRAINIK, Andre Matthew. 2701 E ENTERPRISE AVE 54913 #056-06-2002 L2005 **PD** *020 †55
KRIEGER, Westscot G. 1818 N MEADE ST 54911 #026-04-1979 L1984 **EM ESM** *020
KRONER, Travis L. 3916 N INTERTECH CT 54913 #056-06-1995 L1996 **FM** *020 †18
KRUEGER, Editha Agustin. ■ 54914 #016-43-1997 L2003 **RO** *020 †80
KRUEGER, Michael Alan. 3329 N RICHMOND ST 54911 #056-05-1980 L1981 **FM EM** *020 †18
KRYGER, John Vincent. 1506 S ONEIDA ST 54915 #056-05-1992 L1994 **UP U** *020 †95
KUPLIC, J David. 2105 E ENTERPRISE AVE, STE 111 54913 #028-02-1991 L1996 **ORS** *020 †40
KWASNY, William C. 1506 S ONEIDA ST, NEW ANESTHIOLOGY S.C. 54915 #056-06-1999 L2005 **AN** *020 †05
KWATERSKI, Mitchell F. 1520 N MEADE ST, EAR NOSE & THROAT 54911 #056-06-1964 L1968 **OTO** *020 †45
LARSEN, Timothy Craig. 1818 N MEADE ST 54911 #056-05-1999 L2002 **AN** *020 †05
LARSON, Kirsten Witzke. 3329 N RICHMOND ST 54911 #025-07-1998 L1999 **FM** *020 †18
LAUDERDALE, Bradley. 1611 S MADISON ST 54915 #035-01-1980 L1986 **PCC SME** *020 †20
LE CLOUX, David Roland. 1531 S MADISON ST 54915 #056-05-1971 L1973 **OBG** *020 †30
LEE, Linda Haekum. 229 S MORRISON ST, UW HEALTH FOX VALLEY 54911 #036-07-1998 L2005 **D** *020 †15
LEE, Teresa Hanson. 1501 S MADISON ST 54915 #056-05-1995 L1996 **IM** *020 †20
LENZ, David Jude. 1501 S MADISON ST, LASALLE CLINIC 54915 #056-06-1983 L1984 **IM** *020 †20
LEVEILLE, Leonard Ludovic. 4480 W SPENCER ST 54914 #065-09-1985 L1995 **FM** *020 †18
LIEBESKIND, Ann Marie. 1611 S MADISON ST 54915 #056-05-1998 L2002 **MPD** *020 †20,55
LINDO-DRUSCH, Nancy Jo. W3124 VAN ROY RD, FAMILY CARE OF THE FOX CIT 54915 #028-34-1980 L1986 **FM OS** *020 †18
LIVENGOOD, Larry Craig. 2555 NORTHERN RD 54914 #025-12-1982 L1988 **HS ORS** *020 †40
LOHRBACH, Brian Lee. 2105 E ENTERPRISE AVE 54913 #028-02-1996 L2002 **ORS** *020 †40
LUDWIG, Gary Keith. 1818 N MEADE ST 54911 #025-01-1972 L1988 **PTH FOP** *020 †50
LUMSDEN, Boyd Christopher. 2323 N CASALOMA DR, NE WISCONSIN 54913 #016-06-1998 L2001 **HS** *020 †40
LUND, Dennis Paul. 1506 S ONEIDA ST 54915 #024-01-1980 L1999 **PDS** *020 †85
LUTHER, Thomas W. 1506 S ONEIDA ST 54915 #056-05-1950 L1952 **D** *071 †15
MACRANDER, Stephanus J. 229 S MORRISON ST 54911 #016-11-1983 L1984 **DR** *020 †80
MAHINDRA, Ashish. 1611 S MADISON ST 54915 #759-06-2000 L2007 **IM PCC** *100 †20
MAJAHALME, Silja Kyllikki. 1818 N MEADE ST, APPLETON CARDIOLOGY 54911 #374-04-1984 L2002 *020
MAJID, Abdul H. 1818 N MEADE ST 54911 #495-09-1965 L1972 **N CN** *020 †75
MAKEEVER, Robert Mark. 3916 N INTERTECH CT 54913 #028-02-1987 L1994 **FM** *020 †18
MANNEBACH, Patrick C. 1818 N MEADE ST, APPLETON CARDIOLOGY ASSOCI 54911 #056-06-2000 L2002 **CD** *100 †20

MARIANO, Dionisio James. 1818 N MEADE ST, APPLETON CARDIOLOGY 54911 #026-08-1985 L1992 **ICE CD** *020 †20
MARNOCHA, Jesse Richard. ■ 54914 #056-06-2006 L2008 **IM** *012
MARQUIS, Stephen John. 1506 S ONEIDA ST 54915 #024-07-1982 L1992 **PD** *020 †55 ‡
MC CARTHY, David Michael. 4620 N KNOLLWOOD LN 54913 #056-05-1991 L1995 **AN** *020 †05
MCCORMICK, Joseph Patrick. 1531 S MADISON ST FL 4 54915 #056-06-1997 L2002 **ORS** *020 †40
MC CORMICK, Joseph Paul. 1531 S MADISON ST 54915 #010-01-1974 L1976 **GS TS** *020 †85
MC GOVERN, Anna Lynn. ■ 54913 #056-06-1998 L2000 **IM** *100
MC GOVERN, James Joseph. 1818 N MEADE ST, APPLETON MEDICAL CENTER 54911 #056-06-1998 L2004 **IM** *020 †20
MC INTIRE, Robert Ellis. 1531 S MADISON ST, AFFINITY MEDICAL GROUP 54915 #056-05-1986 L2002 **CHP** *020 †75
MC INTYRE, Steven James. 1818 N MEADE ST 54911 #041-14-1995 L1998 **EM** *020 †16
MC KEE, Charles Arthur. 3916 N INTERTECH CT 54913 #038-06-1972 L1977 **FM** *020 †18
MC NELIS, Teri Dee. 900 E GRANT ST 54911 #046-01-1998 L2006 **OBG** *020 †30
MC NUTT, Gail Mary. 10 TRI PARK WAY, APPLETON VETERAN ADMIN. CB 54914 #056-06-1985 L1986 **AI IM** *020 †20,03
MEJIA, Etienne Arturo. 277 ALTENHOFEN DR 54913 #021-01-1988 L1999 **OSM** *020 †40
MELICH, Paz Guidote. ■ 54911 #748-02-1940 L1972 **OBG** *071 †30
MEMMEN, James Edward. 3232 N BALLARD RD, STE 203 54911 #016-01-1981 L1988 **OPH** *020 †35
METZLER, Jeremy David. 229 S MORRISON ST 54911 #025-12-2006 L2007 **FP** *012
MEYER, Douglas R. 620 E LONGVIEW DR, PRIMARY CARE ASSOCIATES 54911 #010-02-1976 L1980 **OBG** *020 †30
MEYER, Douglas Raymond. 3916 N INTERTECH CT 54913 #056-05-1998 L1999 **FM** *020 †18
MEYER, Erica Rose. 1818 N MEADE ST, APPLETON EMERGENCY SERVICE 54911 #056-05-1996 L1997 **EM** *020 †16
MICH, Gerald Richard. ■ 54914 #056-06-1977 L1980 **FM** *071 †18
MIELKE, John Edward. 1818 N MEADE ST, APPLETON CARDIO ASSOC LTD 54911 #056-05-1958 L1959 **CD IM** *071 †20
MILDE, Michael Wayne. 229 S MORRISON ST 54911 #037-01-1977 L1981 **DR** *020 †80
MINORIK, Jay Michael. 2105 E ENTERPRISE AVE, STE 111 54913 #056-05-1996 L2002 **OSM ORS** *020 †40
MOLOGNE, Timothy Scott. 277 ALTENHOFEN DR 54913 #007-02-1988 L2003 **OSM** *020 †40
MOORE, William Downs, Jr. 1531 S MADISON ST, 4TH FLOOR ORTHOPEDICS 54915 #016-06-1976 L1981 **ORS** *020 †40
MOUAMMAR, Marwan Kameel. 1506 S ONEIDA ST, ST ELIZABETH HOSPITAL 54915 #875-01-1993 L2002 **PCC** *012 †20
MOUNAJJED, Meruan. 1506 S ONEIDA ST, ST. ELIZABETH HOSPITAL 54915 #875-01-1993 L2003 **IM** *020 †20
MUBASHER, Fazal. ■ 54915 #704-21-1993 L2007 **FM** *020 †18
MUELLER, Ross Albert. ■ 54911 #056-05-1967 L1970 **OPH** *071 †35
MUNSON, Nathan Daryl. ■ 54911 #026-08-2002 L2002 **RO** *020
MURPHY, James Edward. 424 E WISCONSIN AVE 54911 #056-05-1963 L1970 **R** *071 †80
NEWTON, Christine Ann. 2809 N PARK DRIVE LN 54911 #060-02-1987 L1995 **FM** *020
NICHOLS, Frank Edward. ■ 54913 #016-06-1964 L1967 **ORS** *071 †40
NICHOLS, George Philip. 1818 N MEADE ST 54911 #056-05-1948 L1949 **IM DIA** *020 †20
NOBLE, N Carter. 3329 N RICHMOND ST 54911 #056-05-1976 L1977 **FM** *020 †18
NOONAN, Kenneth John. 1506 S ONEIDA ST 54915 #018-03-1989 L2001 **ORS** *020 †40
NORDSTROM, Mary Elizabeth. 1506 S ONEIDA ST 54915 #056-06-1992 L1993 **PD** *020 †55
O'BRIEN, Patrick Danl. 1611 S MADISON ST 54915 #056-05-1985 L1986 **CD IM** *020 †20
OLVEY, Scott Preston. 2323 N CASALOMA DR, HAND & UPPER EXTREMITY CEN 54913 #056-06-1999 L2007 **HS** *020 †40
ORZEPOWSKI, Walter, Jr. 200 E WASHINGTON ST 54911 #056-05-1994 L1995 **AN** *020 †05
PADILLA, Arthur Ayade. 820 E GRANT ST, STE 335 54911 #748-15-1993 L2007 **AN** *020 †05
PAINTON, Todd E. 1818 N MEADE ST, APPLETON MEDICAL CENTER HO 54911 #048-04-1997 L2000 **IM** *020 †20
PANAGOPOULOS, Electra Lel. ■ 54911 #056-06-2006 L2006 **AN** *012
PANZER, Fred David. 229 S MORRISON ST 54911 #056-05-1983 L1986 **DR** *020 †80
PANZER, Michael Jos. 1531 S MADISON ST, FOX VALLEY PSYCHIATRIC 54915 #056-05-1987 L1992 **P** *020 †75
PATEL, Darshana. 3329 N RICHMOND ST 54911 #495-23-1992 L1999 **FM** *020 †18
PEPLINSKI, William James. ■ 54913 #017-20-1977 L1982 **OBG** *020
PETERSEN, George J. ■ 54915 #056-05-1952 L1953 **OBG** *071 †30
PETERSON, Lowell Frank. 1818 N MEADE ST, APPLETON CARDIOLOGY 54911 #056-05-1962 L1963 **CD IM** *020 †20
PODLUSKY, Peter Vladimir. 1506 S ONEIDA ST, ST ELIZABETH HOSP 54915 #748-01-1981 L1986 **PTH** *020 †50
POWLEY, Kent Winfield. 229 S MORRISON ST 54911 #025-12-1985 L1986 **DR** *020 †80
PRATO, Christopher Allen. 1531 S MADISON ST, AFFINITY ORTHO SPORTS MED 54915 #056-06-1997 L2002 **ORS** *020 †40
QUEROL, Gabriel Jesus. 1818 N MEADE ST STE 120 54911 #748-01-1952 L1960 **U** *071 †95
QURESHI, Atif Aziz. 2701 N ONEIDA ST, STE D 54911 #704-01-1991 L2004 **NEP** *020 †20
RAICHLE, Timothy Stephen. 1531 S MADISON ST 54915 #028-02-1999 L2000 **OBG** *020 †30
RALSTON, Deborah Joan. 3916 N INTERTECH CT 54913 #018-03-1991 L2000 **FM** *020 †18
RAMOS, Shiloh James. 10 TRI PARK WAY, APPLETON VA CLINIC 54914 #056-05-2001 L2002 **FM** *020 †18
RASMUSSEN, Carl Adrian. 1506 S ONEIDA ST RM 484 54915 #056-05-1982 L1987 **IM** *020 †20
RATTRAY, Trevor Anthony. 1818 N MEADE ST 54911 #566-01-1969 L1979 **TS** *020 †85,90
RAY, Michael Edward. 229 S MORRISON ST 54911 #025-01-1998 L2007 **RO** *020 †80
RAYSON, Thomas Chas. 1506 S ONEIDA ST, ST ELIZABETH HOSP DEPT PTH 54915 #045-04-1992 L1993 **PTH** *062 †50
REDDI, Padma Kanumuru. 10 TRI PARK WAY, FOX VALLEY CBOC 54914 #654-01-1998 L2001 **P** *020 †75
REEB-ALBA, Cathy Ann. 1531 S MADISON ST 54915 #056-06-1981 L1982 **OBG** *020 †30
REECE, Deeann Benson. 1501 S MADISON ST 54915 #018-03-1990 L1994 **OBG** *020
REED, Amanda Anne. 1000 S MIDPARK DR 54915 #056-06-2008 *012
REINKE, Ted O. 424 E WISCONSIN AVE 54911 #056-05-1975 L1978 **RO** *071 †80
RICHARDS, William Russell. 1818 N MEADE ST STE 210 54911 #028-02-1957 L1962 **ORS** *071 †40
RICHTER, James Robt. W3124 VAN ROY RD 54915 #028-02-1984 L1991 **FM OS** *020 †18
RIGHTER, Elisabeth Lynn. 229 S MORRISON ST, FOX VALLEY FAM MED RES 54911 #038-45-1989 L2007 **FM** *020 †18
RIGSTAD, Eugene Clifford. 1818 N MEADE ST, 2809 NORTH PARK DRIVE LANE 54911 #026-04-1986 L1987 **FM** *020 †18
RINK, Sharon L. 2701 E ENTERPRISE AVE 54913 #016-43-1991 L1995 **PD IM** *020 †20,55
RITZOW, David Chas. 2105 E ENTERPRISE AVE, STE 111 54913 #056-05-1992 L1998 **ORS** *020 †40
ROBERTS, Timothy Roland. 229 S MORRISON ST 54911 #056-05-2004 L2005 **FM** *020 †18
ROBINSON, John Dale. 1531 S MADISON ST 54915 #028-03-1977 L2005 **CHP OS** *020 †75
ROLAIN, Rick Allen. 1506 S ONEIDA ST 54915 #056-05-1991 L2001 **GS** *020 †05
RUBNER, Frederick James. 1506 S ONEIDA ST, ST. ELIZABETH HOSPITAL NIC 54915 #056-06-2000 L2002 **NPM** *100 †55
RUSIN, Wayne Jos. 1506 S ONEIDA ST 54915 #026-04-1979 L1990 **PD OS** *020 †55
SALMON, Douglas Dean. ■ 54911 #018-03-1971 L1972 **FM** *071
SALUD, Antonio De Villa. 315 W WISCONSIN AVE 54911 #748-08-1966 L1973 **AN** *071
SAMPICA, Gerald Joel. 10 TRI PARK WAY, VA CLINIC 54914 #056-06-1974 L1975 **FM** *020 †18
SANDLEBACK, Brad Lee. 1818 N MEADE ST, AMC-ED 54911 #048-14-1994 L2000 **EM** *020 †16
SARGENT, James Miller. 2105 E ENTERPRISE AVE, # 111 54913 #025-01-1961 L1965 **ORS HS** *072 †40
SAVAGE, Ellen Lee. 1818 N MEADE ST 54911 #056-06-1983 L1999 **GS** *020 †85
SAVAGE, Stephen George. 1818 N MEADE ST, MEDICAL OFC BLDG WEST 54911 #056-06-1980 L1984 **OBG** *020 †30
SCHACHT, Michelle Lynn. 229 S MORRISON ST 54911 #056-05-2004 L2005 **FM** *020 †18
SCHAEFER, Kent C, II. 1520 N MEADE ST, EAR NOSE & THROAT 54911 #056-06-1990 L1991 **OTO** *020 †45
SCHELBLE, Thomas Chas. 3329 N RICHMOND ST 54911 #056-06-1977 L1980 **FM** *020 †18
SCHERER, Mark John. 1501 S MADISON ST 54915 #056-05-1984 L1991 **GS PS** *020
SCHINABECK, Thomas John. 1818 N MEADE ST 54911 #056-05-1967 L1968 **PS** *071 †65
SCHLICHT, Douglas Anthony. 4239 HONEYWOOD CT 54913 #037-01-1994 L2003 **AN** *020 †05
SCHRANK, Melanie Jane. 229 S MORRISON ST 54911 #056-06-2005 L2006 **FP** *012
SCHREIBER, Brian Dean. 1531 S MADISON ST 54915 #035-06-1980 L1993 **NEP** *020 †20
SCHREIBER, Ronald Thos. 1501 S MADISON ST 54915 #041-13-1988 L1989 **IM** *020 †20
SCHROEDER, Norman John, II. 4321 N BALLARD RD 54919 #016-11-1975 L1978 **FM MDM** *030 †18
SCHROEDER, Wendy L. 229 S MORRISON ST, UW HEALTH FOX VALLEY FAMIL 54911 #018-75-2006, ▲ L2007 **FP** *012
SCHULTZ, Deborah Lynne. 229 S MORRISON ST 54911 #056-06-1992 L1993 **FM** *040 †18
SCUGLIK, Deborah Lee. 1531 S MADISON ST, STE 580 54915 #056-05-1997 L2005 **CHP ADP** *020 †75
SEEGER, Kimberly Joy. 1506 S ONEIDA ST, NICU ST ELIZABETH HOSPITAL 54915 #056-06-1996 L2002 **NPM** *020 †55
SENDELBACH-ELIZONDO, K M. 1818 N MEADE ST, APPLETON MEDICAL CENTER 54911 #016-11-1989 L1997 **HMP** *020 †50
SERVAIS, Amy Lynn. 3916 N INTERTECH CT 54913 #056-05-1995 L1996 **FM** *020 †18
SHELDON, Kari J. 2809 N PARK DRIVE LN 54911 #056-05-1996 L1997 **FM** *020 †18
SHERA, Gary Scott. 1493 W WESTCHESTER CT 54914 #018-03-1978 L1990 **FM OS** *030
SHILLINGLAW, John Andrew. 21 PARK PL 54914 #028-02-1968 L1972 **OPH** *020 †35
SIDDIQUI, Nadeem. 2700 E ENTERPRISE AVE, STE C 54913 #704-02-1990 L1993 **GE IM** *040 †20
SIMAYTIS, Christine J. 10 TRI PARK WAY, APPLETON VA OUTPATIENT CLI 54914 #045-01-1987 L2001 **IM** *020 †20
SKARPHOL, Darrell Peter. 200 E WASHINGTON ST 54911 #019-02-1963 L1971 **PTH** *071 †50
SLAUGHENHOUPT, Bruce L. 1506 S ONEIDA ST 54915 #008-02-1988 L2005 **UP GS** *020 †95
SLOVICK, Ronald Wiet. 1501 S MADISON ST 54915 #016-43-2000 L2002 **U** *020 †95
SMALL, Michael P. ■ 54915 #020-02-1962 L2000 **U PD** *071 †95
SMICK, James Francis. 4517 N KNOLLWOOD LN 54913 #016-11-1984 L1989 **DR** *020 †80
SMITH, Todd Benedict. 820 E GRANT ST, ORTHPEDICS PLUS 54911 #048-04-2000 L2001 **OSM** *020
SMULLEN, Paul Michael. ■ 54913 #056-06-2007 **FP** *012
SNOW, Patrick David. ■ 54915 #054-04-1977 L1984 **OS FM** *071 †18
SOMMERFELD, David Paul. ■ 54914 #056-05-2007 **FP** *012
SOVINE, David Louis. 1531 S MADISON ST 54915 #017-20-1972 L1977 **P OS** *020 †75
SOWIN, John Edward. 229 S MORRISON ST 54911 #016-11-1991 L1997 **R NM** *020 †80,28
SPEER, Tod Wheeler. 1506 S ONEIDA ST, UW CANCER CENTER ST ELIZA 54915 #017-20-1988 L2003 **RO** *020 †80
SPRINGER, Errol Ray. 2105 E ENTERPRISE AVE, STE 111 54913 #056-05-1982 L1983 **ORS** *020 †40
SREENARASIMHAIAH, S. 900 E GRANT ST 54911 #028-46-1997 L2007 **OBG** *020 †30
STAFFORD, Richard Byron. 1531 S MADISON ST, FOX VALLEY PSYCHIATRIC 54915 #056-05-1961 L1962 **P** *071 †75
STAMBAUGH, Norman F, Jr. 301 E FLORIDA AVE 54911 #012-05-1950 L1954 **OPH** *071 †35
STANIS, George R. 1501 S MADISON ST 54915 #016-01-1975 L1980 **GS GE** *020 †85
STASTNY, Mary Jo. 1501 S MADISON ST 54915 #056-06-1984 L1985 **IM** *020 †20
STEINLAGE, John Paul. 4480 W SPENCER ST, THEDACARE PHYSICIANS 54914 #026-04-1995 L1996 **FM** *020 †18
STRICKLAND, Leslie E. 229 S MORRISON ST 54911 #048-16-2006 L2007 **FP** *012
SULLIVAN, Robert Dennis. 1195 N CASALOMA DR 54913 #018-03-1971 L1974 **OPH GP** *020 †35
SUMNICHT, Paul Henry. ■ 54914 #056-05-1982 L1983 **FM** *020 †18
SWANSON, John D, Jr. 900 E GRANT ST, FVHO 54911 #018-03-1982 L1991 **ON HEM** *020 †20
SYVERUD, James Carter. 21 PARK PL 54914 #056-05-1968 L1970 **OPH AM** *020 †35
SZADKOWSKI, Sylvester A. 401 S ELM ST, OUTAGAMIE COUNTY HUMAN SER 54911 #759-03-1964 L1980 **P** *020 †75
TALEON, Orlando Angelo Li. 820 E GRANT ST 54911 #748-10-1993 L2005 **IMG** *020 †20
TATLOCK, Thomas Ward. 1531 S MADISON ST STE 550 54915 #019-02-1974 L1978 **P** *071
TOIVONEN, David Alan. 2325 N CASALOMA DR, P O BOX 7700 54913 #056-06-1989 L1990 **HS** *020 †40
TORRES, Iris Nereida. ■ 54911 #649-14-2000 L2007 **FP** *012
TOUSSAINT, John Steven. 1818 N MEADE ST 54911 #018-03-1982 L1985 **IM** *030 †20
TURK, Norma Kay. 1818 N MEADE ST, HOSPITALIST SERVICE 54911 #056-05-1997 L2002 **IM** *020 †20
TURLAPATI, Ramamohan V. 900 E GRANT ST, DR RAM 54911 #495-50-1971 L1988 **CD IM** *020 †20
TURLAPATI, Suhasini. 820 E GRANT ST 54911 #495-50-1975 L1983 **GE IM** *020 †20
UTRIE, Paul Cassian. 820 E GRANT ST 54911 #056-05-1992 L1997 **RHU** *020 †20
VACCA, Brian Domenic. 820 E GRANT ST, THEDACARE ORTHOPEDICS PLUS 54911 #016-43-2003 L2007 **PM** *020
VANDENBERG, Steven James. 1520 N MEADE ST, EAR NOSE & THROAT 54911 #056-05-1993 L1994 **OTO** *020 †45

VAN LIESHOUT, Francis X. 1506 S ONEIDA ST 54915 #056-06-1955 L1956 **GP** *020

VEREGGE, Paul A. 3329 N RICHMOND ST 54911 #056-05-1986 L2000 **FM** *020

VILLAMAGNA, Andrew Peter, Jr. 229 S MORRISON ST 54911 #051-04-2006 L2007 **FP** *012

VLACH, Robert Elmer. 820 E GRANT ST, VALLEY UROLOGIC ASSCOS SC 54911 #056-05-1987 L1988 **U** *020 †95

VOGEL, Lee Marie. 229 S MORRISON ST 54911 #026-04-1983 L1990 **FM IMG** *020 †18

VOGT, Philip Anthony. 1818 N MEADE ST, FOX VALLEY SURGICAL 54911 #019-02-1979 L1985 **GS VS** *020 †85

VOSKUIL, Chad Eric. 229 S MORRISON ST 54911 #056-06-2004 L2005 **FM** *020 †18

VRABEC, Michael Paul. 21 PARK PL, VALLEY EYE ASSOC 54914 #056-05-1983 L1984 **OPH** *020 †35 ‡

WAEDEKIN, Barbara Jean. 477 S NICOLET RD, APPLETON PSYCHIATRIC & COU 54914 #649-14-1981 L1995 **P** *020

WAGENER, Christopher W. 1531 S MADISON ST 54915 #056-06-1995 L1996 **OBG** *020 †30

WAGNER, Christopher T. 1501 S MADISON ST 54915 #056-06-1995 L2000 **GS** *020 †85

WALDROP, Sheila Leigh. 181 N MEADE ST 54911 #001-02-1997 L2002 **IM** *020 †20

WALSH, Cyril. 1818 N MEADE ST 54911 #063-01-1980 L1995 *020

WARRICK, Paul David. 1501 S MADISON ST 54915 #065-10-1999 L2004 **OTO** *020 †45

WEBSTER, Hilary J. 2701 E ENTERPRISE AVE 54913 #056-06-1991 L1992 **PD** *020 †55

WEED, Brent Robert. 2700 E ENTERPRISE AVE, DERMATOLOGY ASSOCIATES OF 54913 #031-01-2003 L2008 **DMP** *012 †15

WEINLANDER, Chris Martin. 2105 E ENTERPRISE AVE, ORTHOPEDIC & SPORTS SURGER 54913 #025-01-1980 L1986 **AN PMM** *020 †05 ‡

WEISBROD, Louis W. 301 E FLORIDA AVE # 228 54911 #056-05-1953 L1954 **FM GS** *071

WENDELBORN, Daniel Frank. 436 E LONGVIEW DR STE B, APPLETON ALLERGISTS LTD 54911 #056-05-1980 L1987 **AI IG** *020 †20,03

WILLIAMS, Lloyd Parrish. 401 N ONEIDA ST 54911 #056-05-1944 L1945 **PD** *071 †55

WILSON, Robert Leeson. 1818 N MEADE ST, APPLETON CARDIOLOGY 54911 #018-03-1978 L1985 **CD** *020 †20

WINEK, Thomas Greg. 1818 N MEADE ST, FOX VALLEY SURGICAL 54911 #056-05-1981 L1982 **GS VS** *020 †85

WOODBRIDGE, Brian Scott. 1506 S ONEIDA ST 54915 #056-05-2000 L2003 **IM** *020 †20

WRIGHT, Frank, Jr. 54915 #016-11-1950 L1952 **GP** *071

WYCOFF, Timothy Dean. 2809 N PARK DRIVE LN 54911 #030-05-1987 L1988 **FM** *020 †18

XIONG, Xa Xavier. 229 S MORRISON ST 54911 #306-01-2000 **FP** *012

YACOUB, Hayan. 1501 S MADISON ST 54915 #875-01-1996 L2001 **IM** *020 †20

YANG, Kuang Min. 315 W WISCONSIN AVE 54911 #244-04-1970 L1976 **AN** *020

YEATMAN, Douglas Scott. 842 N WESTHILL BLVD, AASCEND PAIN INSTITUTE SC 54914 #422-01-1999 L2004 **APM** *020

YUN, Byung Sun Bobby. 1506 S ONEIDA ST 54915 #056-05-1998 L2004 **FM EM** *020 †18

ZELLER, Corey Jay. 229 S MORRISON ST 54911 #056-05-2003 L2004 **FM** *020 †18

ZHOU, Li. 1818 N MEADE ST, APPLETON CARDIOLOGY 54911 #243-78-1986 L2006 **CD** *020 †20

ARCADIA — TREMPEALEAU

ALEXANDER, Janice. 464 S SAINT JOSEPH AVE, FRANCISCAN SKEMP HEALTHCAR 54612 #025-07-1979 L1989 **OBG FM** *020 †18,30 ‡

BURGGRAF, Jodi Rae. 464 S SAINT JOSEPH AVE 54612 #056-05-1998 L2001 **FM** *020 †18

HAM, Clayton Lore. 464 S SAINT JOSEPH AVE 54612 #068-01-1970 L1994 *100

HODOUS, Bert Stephen. 464 S SAINT JOSEPH AVE 54612 #016-01-1987 L2003 **FM** *020 †18

ROBERTS, William Virgil. 464 S SAINT JOSEPH AVE 54612 #028-02-1972 L1984 **P GPM** *020 †75 ‡

SCHULTZ, Matthew Donald. 464 S SAINT JOSEPH AVE 54612 #026-04-2002 L2005 **FM** *020 †18 ‡

ARGYLE — LAFAYETTE

GARRETT, Norma Patricia. ■ 53504 #004-01-1988 L1990 **P** *020

ROBIOLIO, Michael Edward. 311 MILL ST 53504 #010-01-1992 L1994 **FM** *020 †18

SOLVERSON, Matthew W. 311 MILL ST 53504 #056-05-2003 L2005 **FM** *020 †18

ASHLAND — ASHLAND

ANDERSON, Mary Ann. 206 6TH AVE W, RM 101 54806 #056-05-1984 L1987 **FM** *071 †18

ANDRZEJEWSKI, Jerzy J. 1625 MAPLE LN, DULUTH CLINIC-ASHLAND 54806 #759-06-1980 L2003 **IMG** *020 †20

ARESON, Peter Dewitt. 1625 MAPLE LN, ASHLAND CLINIC 54806 #024-07-1982 L2003 **GS GE** *020 ‡

ASBELL, Michael Dean. 1625 MAPLE LN 54806 #026-04-1985 L1995 **EM** *020

ASPLUND, Terrence Paul. 1615 MAPLE LN, MEMORIAL MED CTR-EMER DEPT 54806 #025-01-1986 L1987 **FM** *020 †18

BENNINGTON, Judith Zwemer. 2111 BEASER AVE, NORTHERN WATERS OPHTH 54806 #025-01-1967 L1977 **OPH** *020 †35

BETZOLD, Nancy Lee. 1625 MAPLE LN 54806 #056-06-1985 L1986 **FM** *020 †18

BURROWS, Stephanie Lynne. 1635 MAPLE LN 54806 #056-06-1999 L2003 **P** *020

CAPPS, Brian Andrew. 415 ELLIS AVE, CHEQUAMEGON CLINIC 54806 #016-43-2000 L2003 **FM** *020 †18

CHAMBERS, James Dale. 2101 BEASER AVE STE 6 54806 #030-06-1964 L1971 **ORS** *020 †40

CUNNINGHAM, Thomas Charle. 415 ELLIS AVE 54806 #030-06-1979 L1980 **FM** *020 †18

DOTY, John Wm. 1615 MAPLE LN 54806 #056-06-1985 L1966 **OPH** *071 †35

DRYER, Deborah Anne. 1001 MAIN ST W 54806 #056-05-2000 L2003 **FM** *020 †18

ESPE, Marty J. 1419 BEASER AVE, SURGEONS, P.A. 54806 #026-08-1996 L1998 *020

EVANSON, Jeffrey Allyn. 415 ELLIS AVE 54806 #026-04-1994 L1998 **D DS** *020 †15

FALL, George Anthony. 216 3RD ST W STE 201 54806 #026-04-1988 L1993 **GS** *020 †85

FLORINE, Craig Wally. 2111 BEASER AVE, NORTHERN WATERS OPHTHALOMO 54806 #026-04-1988 L1993 **OPH** *020 †35

FREDERICKSON, Margie A. 1615 MAPLE LN 54806 #026-04-1983 L2000 **FM EM** *020 †18

GANG, Kathleen Marie. 1001 MAIN ST W, MAIN STREET CLINIC INC 54806 #016-11-1992 L1997 **FM** *020 †18

GOESE, Richard E. 1625 MAPLE LN, DULUTH CLINIC-ASHLAND 54806 #026-04-1969 L1985 **CD IM** *020 †20

GROTH, Boyd Joman. 221 PRENTICE HEIGHTS RD 54806 #016-06-1971 L1976 **FM** *020 †18

GUFFY, Thomas Andrew. 2101 BEASER AVE, STE 6 54806 #016-01-1988 L1993 **OPH** *020 †35

HAMMOND, Sharon Marie. 415 ELLIS AVE 54806 #056-06-1998 L2001 **FM** *020 †18 ‡

HAMP, James Arthur. 1625 MAPLE LN 54806 #025-01-1974 L1979 **OTO A** *020 †45 ‡

HARRISON, Matthew Scott. 415 ELLIS AVE 54806 #026-04-1990 L1994 **PM** *020 †60

HART, Cynthia Marie. 415 ELLIS AVE 54806 #038-45-1991 L2001 **FM OBS** *020 †18

HAWKINS, Furman E, Jr. 415 ELLIS AVE 54806 #045-01-1981 L2004 **GS** *020 †85

HEITSCH, Grace Margaret. 1625 MAPLE LN 54806 #026-04-1987 L1989 **PD** *020 †55

HENRY, Keith Allen. 1615 MAPLE LN 54806 #056-05-1986 L1989 **PTH** *020 †50

HUSSA, John Florian. 1615 MAPLE LN 54806 #056-05-1969 L1970 **GP ADM** *062

JAUQUET, Joseph Martin. 1615 MAPLE LN 54806 #056-06-1943 L1943 **GP** *071 †18

KANAKIRIYA, Sharan K R. 1625 MAPLE LN, ASHLAND CLINIC 54806 #495-95-1986 L2002 **NEP** *020 †20

KLEE, David Karl. 1001 MAIN ST W, MAIN STREET CLINIC INC 54806 #026-04-1997 L2000 **FM** *020 †18

KOELLER, Arlyn Arnold. 415 ELLIS AVE 54806 #056-05-1961 L1962 **FM** *020 †18

KONASIEWICZ, Stefan J. 415 ELLIS AVE 54806 #065-05-1989 L1997 **NS** *020 †25

KOZIEL-ANDRZEJEWSKA, A. 1625 MAPLE LN, DULUTH CLINIC-ASHLAND 54806 #759-06-1980 L2003 **N** *020 †20

KRUTSCH, Kenneth Norman. 2101 BEASER AVE 54806 #056-05-1973 L1974 **U** *020 †95

LEAN, James Eldon. 1615 MAPLE LN 54806 #030-06-1990 L1994 **P** *020 †75

LEWIS, Jeffrey David. 1615 MAPLE LN 54806 #041-12-1982 L1995 **FM OBS** *020 †18

LIND, Robert Gordon. 1625 MAPLE LN 54806 #026-04-1971 L1977 **DR** *020 †80

MATHEUS, Andrew Troy. 1001 MAIN ST W, MAINSTREET CLINIC 54806 #056-05-1989 L1992 **FM** *020 †18

MC CLELLAND, Kevin Jos. 2101 BEASER AVE STE 5 54806 #038-06-1987 L1992 **GE** *020

MC CUE, John Patrick. 415 ELLIS AVE 54806 #007-02-1977 L1978 **FM** *020 †18

MESCHIEVITZ, Carlton Koon. 1224 MACARTHUR AVE 54806 #056-05-1973 L1974 **PHP ID** *050

MITCHELL, Sheila Annette. ■ 54806 #539-06-1984 L1988 **EM** *020

MOEN, Clinton Tetrick. 1615 MAPLE LN 54806 #026-04-1973 L1983 **ORS FM** *020 †18,40

MORUD, Clair Marcus. 1625 MAPLE LN 54806 #028-34-1985 L1988 **IM** *020 †20

NIBLER, James Glenn. 415 ELLIS AVE 54806 #056-05-1966 L1967 **GS** *020

NIEDRINGHAUS, Robert Dale. 1625 MAPLE LN, DULUTH CLINIC- ASHLAND 54806 #026-04-1968 L1985 **OS HEM** *020 †20

OLSEN, Clark Orville. 2101 BEASER AVE, ORTHO RECNSTRCTV SURG LTD 54806 #056-05-1962 L1963 **ORS** *071 †40

OUJIRI, John Chas. 1625 MAPLE LN 54806 #018-03-1975 L1978 **FM** *020 †18

PARKER, Eugenia Horne. MEMORIAL MED CTR 54806 #038-06-1962 L1975 **PTH** *020 †50

PATTON, Donald Gene. 1615 MAPLE LN 54806 #654-01-1989 L1991 **FM** *020 †18

RAINA, Dheeraj Kanhayalal. 1625 MAPLE LN, DULUTH CLINIC-ASHLAND 54806 #495-83-1994 L2000 **P** *020 †75

RALLES, Lizabeth Jane. 415 ELLIS AVE 54806 #003-01-1988 L1989 **GP** *020

RICH, Michael Ray. 1625 MAPLE LN, ASHLAND CLINIC 54806 #016-43-1989 L2002 **CD** *020 †20

SAARINEN, David Michael. 1625 MAPLE LN 54806 #025-01-1975 L1978 **FM** *020 †18

SANDIN, Howard Nils. 1625 MAPLE LN 54806 #056-05-1973 L1977 **OBG** *020 †30

SAUER, John Andrew. 2101 BEASER AVE, STE 1 54806 #038-06-1988 L1993 **ORS** *020 †40

SJOBERG, Robert John. 415 ELLIS AVE 54806 #048-14-1979 L1999 **END DIA** *020 †20

SPEARS, Nyasha L. 415 ELLIS AVE 54806 #026-04-2001 L2004 **FM** *020 †18

STANLEY, Robert Afton. 1625 MAPLE LN 54806 #016-11-1955 L1958 **EM** *071 †18

STONE, Barbara Ann. ■ 54806 #038-41-1979 **CHP** *075

TEOH, Ivan. 2101 BEASER AVE STE 5 54806 #209-01-1968 L1976 **GS VS** *020

TROMBINO, Laura Jean. 1625 MAPLE LN, DULUTH CLINIC - ASHLAND 54806 #016-06-1984 L1997 **ORS** *020 †18

VAN PERNIS, Paul. 1625 MAPLE LN 54806 #016-01-1975 L1978 **FM** *020 †18

VERNIER, Edward Marcel. ■ 54806 #028-34-1970 L1977 **OBG** *071 †30

VORDERBRUG, Candy Lynn. 1615 MAPLE LN 54806 #012-22-1997 L2000 **FM** *020 †18

YUNUS, Uzma. 1625 MAPLE LN, DULUTH CLINIC - ASHLAND 54806 #704-25-1995 L2001 **P** *020 †75

ZAHM, Dennis Lee. 1625 MAPLE LN 54806 #025-12-1985 L1988 **IM** *020 †20

ZIMMERMAN, Paul Edward. 1625 MAPLE LN, DULUTH CLINIC-ASHLAND 54806 #019-02-1986 L2003 **PUD** *020 †20

ATHENS — MARATHON

CAMERON, Vinoo. 702 PINE ST, HOPE CLINIC 54411 #495-08-1971 L1979 **FM** *020

SULLIVAN, Melissa Peeples. 625 W LIMIT RD 54411 #024-07-2004 L2006 **AN** *012

AUBURNDALE — WOOD

SAUL, Jennifer Susan. 5580 YELLOWSTONE DR 54412 #025-12-1997 L2003 **CHP** *020 †75

AUGUSTA — EAU CLAIRE

CAYLEY, William Edward, Jr. 207 W LINCOLN ST, STE 1 54722 #056-06-1996 L1997 **FM** *020 †18

LEASUM, Robert Nels, Jr. 131 CROCKER ST 54722 #041-02-1954 L1958 **GE IMG** *071 †18

ROESKE, Jad Colby. 207 W LINCOLN ST, AUGUSTA FMLY MED CLINIC 54722 #056-05-1990 L1992 **FM** *020 †18

AVOCA — IOWA

DOWNS, David Ross. ■ 53506 #056-05-1957 L1959 **GP** *071

JONES, George Wm. 53506 #026-04-1946 L1948 **IM** *071 †20

BAILEYS HARBOR – DOOR

BARTA, Rudolph A, Jr. ■ 54202 #038-06-1960 L1961 **NPM OS** *071 †55

PERLOFF, William Harry. ■ 54202 #038-06-1977 L1982 **PD OS** *071 †55

RUSY, Ben Franklin. ■ 54202 #056-05-1956 L1957 **AN OS** *071 †65

SAPERSTEIN, Henry Ira. 8430 W BUES POINT RD 54202 #056-06-1972 L1973 **EM IM** *020 †20,16

BALDWIN – SAINT CROIX

KLINGLER, Marvin Daryl. 730 10TH AVE, BOX 300 54002 #068-01-1984 L1994 **FM** *020 †18 ‡
ROLOFF, Nicole Marie. ■ 54002 #056-06-2006 **FM** *100
STOECKELER, Joel Stoick. 750 11TH AVE W 54002 #026-04-1985 L1990 **N** *062 †18
SULEMANKHIL, Shaima Kakar. 730 10TH AVE 54002 #496-07-1987 L2006 **FM** *020 †18

BALSAM LAKE – POLK

ARMSTRONG, Michele E. 1482 190TH AVE 54810 #048-12-1994 L1997 **FM** *020 †18
BEYER, William David. 1482 190TH AVE 54810 #026-04-1983 L1984 **FM** *020 †18
BOYKEN, Mark Edward. 1482 190TH AVE 54810 #018-03-1971 L1974 **FM** *020 †18
HALL, Jeffrey Mark. 1482 190TH AVE, UNITY CLINIC 54810 #030-05-1998 L2001 **FM** *020 †18
KLEIN, Kevin Gerard. 1482 190TH AVE 54810 #026-04-1995 L1996 **FM** *020 †18

BARABOO – SAUK

AILSWORTH, Karen Sue. 1700 TUTTLE ST 53913 #034-01-1990 L1994 **PD** *020 †55
BEAVER, Daniel James. 707 14TH ST 53913 #054-04-1986 L1999 **FM** *020 †18
BUENO, Edward. 707 14TH ST 53913 #056-05-1985 L1986 **FM** *020 †18
CARLSON, Ethan Wendell. 1700 TUTTLE ST 53913 #018-03-1993 L1996 **FM** *020 †18
CLEVELAND, Peter Grant. 53913 #016-01-1974 L1976 **GP** *020
DALE, Christopher Peter. 1700 TUTTLE ST 53913 #056-05-1999 L2005 **ORS** *020
DAMOS, James Robt. 1700 TUTTLE ST 53913 #028-34-1974 L1977 **FM** *040 †18
DEERING, Timothy A Mical. 1700 TUTTLE ST 53913 #047-05-1998 L1999 **FM** *020 †18
DE LONG, Amy Jo. S2845 WHITE EAGLE RD, HO-CHUNK HOUSE OF WELLNESS 53913 #026-04-1998 L2002 **FM** *020 †18
DIRAIMONDO, Linda Anne. 1002 LINCOLN AVE 53913 #056-05-1999 L2000 **P** *020 †75
DUBRAY, Kansas Lee. S2845 WHITE EAGLE RD 53913 #026-04-1998 L2000 **MPD** *020 †20
FLYGT, Thomas Rex. 637 15TH ST 53913 #023-07-1977 L1982 **IM IMG** *020 †20
GEHIN, Cheryl Louise. 1700 TUTTLE ST 53913 #056-05-1999 L2000 **FM** *020 †18
GERL, Sarah Kathleen. 219 10TH ST 53913 #056-05-2006 L2007 **FP** *012
GOECKERMANN, Cheryl Renee. 1700 TUTTLE ST, MEDICAL ASSOCIATES 53913 #056-06-1995 L1996 **FM** *020 †18
HAMBURG, Eric Daryl. 1700 TUTTLE ST 53913 #028-34-1977 L1978 **IM CCM** *020 †20
HAMMER, Edwin Jon. 1700 TUTTLE ST 53913 #025-01-1964 L1972 **GS** *020
HOLMEN, Gerald James. 1700 TUTTLE ST 53913 #056-05-1961 L1962 **OM** *020 †18
JOSHI, Divya-Devi. 707 14TH ST 53913 #154-07-1994 L2003 **PHO** *055
KEELING, Gregory Scott. 707 14TH ST 53913 #018-03-1983 L1990 **EM** *020
KING, Teresa Ann. 637 15TH ST, STE 300 53913 #056-06-1996 L2000 **IM** *020 †20
KRSZJZANIEK, Randy James. 1700 TUTTLE ST, MEDICAL ASSOC 53913 #056-05-1989 L1991 **FM** *020 †18
MATHERS, James Donald. 1700 TUTTLE ST, MEDICAL ASSOC 53913 #056-05-1981 L1984 **FM** *040 †18
MAY, Tim Clyde. ■ 53913 #035-06-1984 L1995 **EM GP** *020 †16
MC CAFFERTY, Patricia F. 703 14TH ST, ST. CLARE HOSPITAL 53913 #026-04-1992 L2001 **CHP P** *020 †75
MENDOZA, Manuel A, III. 707 14TH ST, ST CLARE HOSP 53913 #018-03-1994 L1996 **FM** *020 †18 ‡
MENDOZA, Teresa M Maveus. 1700 TUTTLE ST 53913 #056-05-1992 L1996 **PD** *020 †55
MUNNEKE, Sharilyn B. 1700 TUTTLE ST, MEDICAL ASSOCIATES OF BARA 53913 #026-08-1992 L1993 **FM** *020 †18
MURPHY, James Thos, Jr. 703 14TH ST, ST CLARE HOSP-EMERG DEPT 53913 #056-05-1989 L1990 **EM PEM** *020 †55
MYERS, Theodore Arthur. 707 14TH ST, ST. CLARE HOSPITAL 53913 #056-06-1984 L1985 **PM** *020 †60
PLOOSTER, Michael Dwain. 635 15TH ST 53913 #030-05-1976 L1981 **ORS** *020 †40
SCHNEE, Bradley Kent. 707 14TH ST 53913 #026-04-1993 L1996 **FM** *020 †18
SESSLER, Danny Ray. 637 15TH ST 53913 #056-06-1979 L1984 **IM ADM** *020 †20
SIVESIND, Rienera. 1700 TUTTLE ST 53913 #067-01-2007 **FP** *012
TROTTER, Daniel Dwight. 1700 TUTTLE ST, MEDICAL ASSOCIATES OF BARA 53913 #056-05-1990 L1991 **FM** *020 †18
VALENZUELA, Mario R. 1002 LINCOLN AVE 53913 #012-05-1995 L1999 **P** *020 †75
WEBER, Kevin Jay. 635 15TH ST, STE 200 53913 #056-05-1985 L1987 **ORS** *020 †40
WELLS, Kristen Marie. 1700 TUTTLE ST 53913 #016-01-1997 L2002 **GS** *020 †85

BARNEVELD – IOWA

MULLIN, Peter George. 103 QUAIL RIDGE DR, FAMILY PRACTICE ASSOCIATES 53507 #019-02-2004 L2005 **FM** *020 †18
PETERSON, Jodi Lynn. 103 QUAIL RIDGE DR 53507 #056-05-1996 L1997 **FM** *020 †18
WOLKOMIR, Michael S. 8139 LEE DR 53507 #065-10-1974 L1977 **OBS FM** *040 †18

BARRON – BARRON

BRICKNER, Gregory Charles. 1220 E WOODLAND AVE 54812 #030-06-1995 L2000 **DR** *020 †80
BURNS, Dan Phillip. 1220 E WOODLAND AVE 54812 #026-04-1988 L1991 **ON IM** *020 †20
DAMROTH, Michael Stanley. 1220 E WOODLAND AVE, BARRON MEDICAL CLINIC 54812 #016-06-1970 L1973 **FM** *020 †18
FOLZ, Steve Jos. 1220 E WOODLAND AVE 54812 #025-01-1992 L1996 **DR** *020 †80
GOODWIN, Jeffrey Thos. 1220 E WOODLAND AVE 54812 #038-06-1986 L1991 **R N** *020 †80
KYSER, Perry Leroy. 1220 E WOODLAND AVE 54812 #038-40-1977 L1992 **DR** *020 †80
MAIERHOFER, William James. 1220 E WOODLAND AVE 54812 #016-11-1975 L1977 **IM NEP** *020 †20
MARKET, Jewel Marie. 1220 E WOODLAND AVE 54812 #056-05-1994 L1995 **FM** *020 †18
MINIER, Veronica. 1220 E WOODLAND AVE 54812 #005-12-1998 L2003 **FM** *020 †18
MYERS, David Lynn. 1220 E WOODLAND AVE 54812 #018-03-1986 L1987 **FM** *020 †18
NAMBUDIRI, Gopakumar S. 1220 E WOODLAND AVE 54812 #690-02-1989 L2000 **HO IM** *020 †20
NIJHAWAN, Vinay Kumar. 1220 E WOODLAND AVE 54812 #030-06-1993 L2001 **DR** *020 †80

NORDSTROM, Charles R. 1220 E WOODLAND AVE 54812 #028-34-1972 L1978 **IM GE** *020 †20
NYE, David Andrew. 1220 E WOODLAND AVE 54812 #050-02-1978 L1982 **N** *020 †75
PETERSON, Robert Paul. 1220 E WOODLAND AVE 54812 #056-05-1994 L1995 **FM** *020 †18
RHODES, Barry Jos. 1220 E WOODLAND AVE 54812 #007-02-1975 L1986 **AI IM** *020 †20,03
RIPECKYJ, Geo Theodosius. 1220 E WOODLAND AVE 54812 #016-45-1985 L1990 **DR RNR** *020 †80
SAMPSON, Richard Raymond. 1222 E WOODLAND AVE, LUTHER MIDELFORT NORTHLAND 54812 #026-04-1990 L1993 **FM** *020 †18
THALACKER, Howard Albert. 1220 E WOODLAND AVE 54812 #056-05-1972 L1973 **FM** *020 †18
WHALEY, Ralph Clarence. 1220 E WOODLAND AVE 54812 #056-05-1955 L1958 **GP** *075

BAY CITY – PIERCE

LEAF, Donn Stanton. W7052 250TH AVE 54723 #026-04-1962 L1971 **PTH CLP** *071 †50

BAY VIEW – MILWAUKEE

CLOTHIER, W J Kilburn, Jr. 316 E GAUER CIR 53207 #010-01-1963 L1965 **FM P** *020 †18
HAFRAN, Michael John. 3056 S KINNICKINNIC AVE 53207 #056-05-1999 L2006 **FM** *020 †18
SKIER, Mark Danl. 3119 S CLEMENT AVE 53207 #035-46-1991 L1993 **IM** *020 †20

BAYFIELD – BAYFIELD

PIERPONT, David Burton. ■ 54814 #056-05-1964 L1968 **FM** *020 †18
PURCELL, Thomas W. ■ 54814 #018-03-1968 L1969 **OPH** *071 †35
ROBNIK, Spencer Louis. ■ 54814 #026-04-1963 L1987 **R NM** *071 †80,28
ROEMHILD, Franklin N. ■ 54814 #016-11-1949 L1959 **GP** *071
TELFORD, John Garvin. ■ 54814 #016-06-1959 L1961 **EM GP** *071

BAYSIDE – MILWAUKEE

ARYA, Sunita. 9081 N REXLEIGH DR 53217 #495-05-1964 L1977 **PTH** *074 †50
BERCOVICI, Edwin Bryl. ■ 53217 #030-05-1963 L1972 **OPH PS** *071 †35
CHHABRIA, Prakash B. 500 W BROWN DEER RD, STE 202 53217 #495-17-1972 L1979 **DR** *020 †80
FIELD, Laura Renee. 500 W BROWN DEER RD 53217 #016-11-1991 L2005 **DR** *020 †80
GREAVES, William Walter. 8851 N BAYSIDE DR 53217 #016-11-1975 L1982 **PHP OM** *030 †18,70
HART, Jonathan David. ■ 53217 #030-05-2004 L2006 **DR** *012
KIM, Mitchel. 500 W BROWN DEER RD, STE 202 53217 #016-11-1991 L1997 **DR NM** *020 †80
ORIGENES, Frederick F. 500 W BROWN DEER RD, STE 202 53217 #056-06-1998 L2004 **DR** *020 †80
PRATT, Charles David. ■ 53217 #017-20-1993 L1994 **GS** *020
REGNER, Dawn M. 500 W BROWN DEER RD # 202, WRS 53217 #056-06-2001 L2007 **DR** *100 †80
TOMASHEK, John Paul. 500 W BROWN DEER RD, STE 202 53217 #056-05-1996 L2001 **VIR DR** *020 †80
WAGNER, David Keith. ■ 53217 #016-11-1979 L1982 **ID** *050 †20
WESSELS, Charles Robt. 9495 N FAIRWAY CIR 53217 #025-01-1973 L1985 **IM** *020 †20,16

BEAVER DAM – DODGE

AAMODT, David Sherman. 705 S UNIVERSITY AVE, STE 510 53916 #035-09-2001 L2004 **FM** *020 †18
ALI, Asra Ahmed. ■ 53916 #056-05-2005 L2005 **AN** *012
ALI, Laeekha Ahmed. 130 WARREN ST 53916 #495-21-1978 L1987 **PTH** *020 †50
ALI, M Ahmed. 130 WARREN ST STE 102 53916 #495-65-1967 L1976 **GS VS** *020 †85
ALLEN, Bradley Andrew. 130 WARREN ST STE 122 53916 #003-01-1991 L1994 **FM** *020 †18
ARMATO, Douglas Paul. 116 MONROE ST 53916 #019-02-1986 L1987 **DR** *020 †80
AUGUSTSON, Michael Keith. 705 S UNIVERSITY AVE, STE 510 53916 #025-12-1980 L1986 **FM** *020 †18
BACHHUBER, Brian Gerard. 130 WARREN ST, STE 122 53916 #056-05-1988 L1996 **CD IM** *020 †20
BARTHOLMAI, Jack Robt. 116 MONROE ST, RADY ASSOCS BVR DAM COLUM 53916 #056-06-1968 L1969 **R DR** *071 †20
BEATTY, Peter Ayer. 130 WARREN ST, STE 122 53916 #016-11-1977 L1984 **HO** *020 †20
BERGEN, Paul Marie. ■ 53916 #056-06-1945 L1946 **GP** *071
BONEBRAKE, Frank Clinton. 130 WARREN ST, STE 122 53916 #016-01-1985 L1986 **PUD CCM** *020 †20
BRICKER, Douglas Earl. 116 MONROE ST 53916 #005-12-1976 L1981 **DR** *020 †80
CACERES, Victor. 919 S UNIVERSITY AVE 53916 #847-03-1971 L1976 **FM PTH** *020 †50
CODY, Edward Frank. 705 S UNIVERSITY AVE, STE 510 53916 #056-05-1975 L1976 **FM** *020 †18
COE, Robert Allen. 118 W MAPLE AVE, FAMILY & SPORTS ORTHOPAEDI 53916 #041-09-1986 L1995 **ORS OSM** *020 †40
CUPERY, Stanley Gene. 130 WARREN ST 53916 #056-05-1967 L1970 **FM** *020 †18
DAVIS, George Eugene. ■ 53916 #056-05-1977 L1978 **OPH** *020 †35
DE VRIES, Jamie Sue. 705 S UNIVERSITY AVE, 4TH & 5TH FLOOR 53916 #056-05-1998 L1999 **FM** *020 †18
DIANCIN, Renato Clar. 707 S UNIVERSITY AVE 53916 #748-08-1962 L1972 **OBG** *020
DOMINSKI, Mary Kathleen. 130 WARREN ST, STE 122 53916 #056-05-1978 L1984 **N CHN** *020 †55,75
EHRHARDT, Alan August. ■ 53916 #056-05-1959 L1960 **OPH** *071 †35
ENGLAND, Rebecca Lynn. 705 S UNIVERSITY AVE, STE 300 53916 #025-01-1997 L2003 **OBG** *020 †30
FRINAK, Charles Wray. 130 WARREN ST, STE 122 53916 #056-05-1977 L1981 **FM** *020 †18
FUNCKE, William Edward. 707 S UNIVERSITY AVE 53916 #016-11-1951 L1956 **AS GS** *071
GONZALEZ-RODRIGUEZ, Erick. 130 WARREN ST, STE 118 53916 #308-12-1985 L1992 **PTH** *020 †50
GRAUPNER, Kenneth Carl. 707 S UNIVERSITY AVE 53916 #056-05-1968 L1970 **P** *020 †75

GREMMINGER, Roger Anthony. 707 S UNIVERSITY AVE 53916 #056-06-1976 L1978 EM PHP *071 †16

HAASE, Sharon Louise. 801 S UNIVERSITY AVE 53916 #056-05-1985 L1986 IM *020 †20

HAHNFELD, Lynn Ellen. 130 WARREN ST, STE 122 53916 #016-01-1994 L1995 U *020 †95

JASKUNAS, Jeremy William. 801 S UNIVERSITY AVE 53916 #017-20-2001 L2002 IM *020

JENNINGS, Richard Paul. 109 WARREN ST 53916 #016-76-1982, ▲ L1988 OTO A *020 †45

JOHNSON, Devin Brooke. 130 WARREN ST, STE 122 53916 #028-02-1997 L1998 U *020 †95

JONES, David Brynley. 707 S UNIVERSITY AVE 53916 #451-01-1985 L1999 FM *020 †18

JUNG, Frank. 130 WARREN ST, STE 122 53916 #409-05-1990 L2003 GP *020

KESSLER, Andrew Jay. 108 N LINCOLN AVE 53916 #305-01-1984 L1985 CHP P *020 †75

KHAN, Waqar Arshad. 205 S UNIVERSITY AVE 53916 #704-01-1977 L1981 FM IMG *020 †18

KOOISTRA, Jon Brent. 130 WARREN ST, STE 122 53916 #025-12-1972 L1973 PDA *020 †55,03

KUEHNL, Kenneth Leo. 705 S UNIVERSITY AVE, STE 200 53916 #056-05-1977 L1981 IM *020 †20

KURTZ, Roberta Gail. 130 WARREN ST, STE 122 53916 #038-43-1975 L2002 CD *020 †20

LANDDECK, Daniel Scott. 705 S UNIVERSITY AVE, STE 200 53916 #056-05-1992 L1993 FM *020 †18

LEMKE, Deborah Lynn. 707 S UNIVERSITY AVE 53916 #011-02-1995 L1998 IM *020 †20

LOVELL, Jeffrey Howard. 707 S UNIVERSITY AVE, BEAVER DAM EMERGENCY PHYS 53916 #016-11-1980 L1991 EM OM *020 †18

LUSKIN, Allan T. 130 WARREN ST, STE 122 53916 #016-11-1968 L1993 AI IM *020 †20,03

LUY TAN, Wilson Haw. 705 S UNIVERSITY AVE, STE 380 53916 #748-02-1979 L1987 N *020 †75

MALONEY, James Driscoll. 705 S UNIVERSITY AVE, STE 200 53916 #038-06-1995 L1996 TS *020 †85,90

MEYER, Dianne Kay. 707 S UNIVERSITY AVE, BEAVER DAM COMMUNITY HOSPI 53916 #056-05-1978 L1980 GP *020

MILITELLO, Joseph Michael. 705 S UNIVERSITY AVE, STE 350 53916 #028-34-1969 L1970 GS *020 †85

MILLER, Eric Davis. 130 WARREN ST, UNIV COM CLINICS WARREN 53916 #056-05-1993 L1994 FM *020 †18

MUCHOW, Amy Jileen. 705 S UNIVERSITY AVE, STE 200 53916 #056-05-2002 L2006 IM *100 †20

OSTERMANN, Kenneth V. 705 S UNIVERSITY AVE, STE 300 53916 #041-09-1987 L1995 OBG OS *020 †30 ‡

OSTERMANN, Mary Frances. 705 S UNIVERSITY AVE, STE 300 53916 #030-05-1988 L1995 OBG *020 †30

PALMER, Paul Anthony. 705 S UNIVERSITY AVE, STE 350 53916 #056-05-1997 L2002 GS *020 †80

PALS, Steven Dewane. 705 S UNIVERSITY AVE STE 1, BEAVER DAM ORTHOPAEDIC 53916 #024-07-1985 L1994 ORS *020 †40

PASSOW, Tara L. 700 HILLCREST CT 53916 #056-05-1981 L1982 D *020 †15

PETERSON, Elizabeth M. 109 WARREN ST, STE 4 53916 #028-02-2002 L2004 PD *020 †55

RAMAN, Bharat. 130 WARREN ST, STE 122 53916 #495-04-1987 L2001 END IM *020 †20

RAWLINS, Steven Joe. 116 MONROE ST 53916 #016-06-1968 L1978 DR GP *072 †80

REICH, Scott Bradley. 707 S UNIVERSITY AVE 53916 #056-05-1985 L1986 PTH *020 †50

RENTMEESTER, Timothy J. 705 S UNIVERSITY AVE, STE 510 53916 #056-05-1983 L1984 FM *020 †18

RICHARDS, William G. ■ 53916 #056-05-1952 L1953 PTH NM *071 †50

ROWAN, Theodore. 707 S UNIVERSITY AVE 53916 #352-07-1955 L1960 PTH NM *071 †50

SAMADANI, Ayaz Mahmud. 148 WARREN ST, STE A 53916 #704-08-1964 L1976 FM PD *020 ‡

SCHULZ, Norman H. 130 WARREN ST 53916 #056-05-1963 L1954 GP OS *071

SNOOK, William Henry. ■ 53916 #010-01-1960 L1962 FM *020

TANCREDI, Robert Gustin. 130 WARREN ST, STE 122 53916 #041-01-1962 L2005 CD IM *020 †20

WALTON, Alan James. 116 MONROE ST 53916 #056-05-1985 L1986 DR *020 †80

WEGNER, Mark Vincent. ■ 53916 #056-05-1999 L2000 *020 †70

WESSON, Penny Ann. 216 STARKWEATHER DR, PENNY A WESSON MD LLC 53916 #016-11-1991 L2004 AN *020 †05

WHANG, Ki Jun. 130 WARREN ST 53916 #583-04-1963 L1972 U *020 †95

WIEBENGA, Jeanne E. 707 S UNIVERSITY AVE 53916 #660-03-1973 L2002 OBG *020 †30

WILKINS, Jay Murray. 707 S UNIVERSITY AVE 53916 #056-06-2000 L2004 OPH *020 †35

WILSON, John David. 130 WARREN ST, STE 122 53916 #056-05-1988 L1994 PUD CCM *020 †20

WITKE, Christopher Jacob. 705 S UNIVERSITY AVE, STE 510 53916 #056-05-2000 L2003 FM *020 †18 ‡

YEE, Mon Lun. 130 WARREN ST, STE 235 53916 #016-11-1994 L1995 FM *020 †18

YOSELOFF, Marlin David. 116 MONROE ST 53916 #039-01-1969 L1991 DR *020 †80

ZHANG, Xiaogang. 705 S UNIVERSITY AVE, VITA PARK 4TH FL 53916 #243-43-1984 L1998 IM *020 †20

BELGIUM – OZAUKEE

GAUTHIER, Lorraine Marie. 309 LAKEVIEW DR, STE A 53004 #056-06-1992 L1993 FM *020 †18

BELLEVILLE – DANE

BURROW, Kara Lee. 21 S VINE ST, STE D 53508 #056-05-2005 L2006 FP *012

DURST, Sarah Catherine. 21 S VINE ST, STE D 53508 #056-05-2005 L2006 FP *012

GEURKINK, Terry Frederick. 1675 BARTLETT CT, 1675 BARTLETT CT 53508 #056-05-1978 L1980 EM ESM *020 †16

GOETZ, Sarah Noren. ■ 53508 #056-05-2008 *012

SMITH, Paul Douglas. 21 S VINE ST 53508 #038-45-1982 L1995 FM *020 †18

STILES, Melissa Marie. 21 S VINE ST, STE D 53508 #018-03-1988 L1989 FM *020 †18

BELOIT – ROCK

ABERNETHY, Michael Kurt. 1969 W HART RD 53511 #038-41-1988 L1992 EM *020 †16

AKBAR, Muhammad Javaid. 1905 E HUEBBE PKWY 53511 #704-21-1991 L2000 IM *020 †20

ANTLE, Shawn Douglas. 1905 HUEBBE PKWY, BELOIT CLINIC, S.C. 53511 #016-11-1990 L2004 IM IMG *020 †20

BARNEY, Richard Nolan. 1969 W HART RD 53511 #016-01-1986 L1989 EM *020 †16

BEHRENS, Susan Florence. 1905 HUEBBE PKWY 53511 #056-05-1975 L1976 CRS GS *071 †10,85

BELTRAN, Juan Cruz. 1905 HUEBBE PKWY 53511 #847-06-1951 L1959 U *020 †95

BENEDICT, Charles Palmer. ■ 53511 #008-02-1980 L1985 N *071 †75

BENNETT, Paul, II. 1905 HUEBBE PKWY 53511 #016-06-1960 L1968 OBG *071 †30

BHASKAR, David Ravi. 1905 HUEBBE PKWY 53511 #016-43-1988 L1994 OBG *020 †30

BLAKESLEE, Beth Ann. 822 BROAD ST 53511 #056-05-1995 L1996 P *020 †75

BLUMOFE, Karin Annika. 1905 E HUEBBE PKWY 53511 #005-06-1994 L2001 GS *020 †85

BOARDMAN, Charles Ruggles. 1905 HUEBBE PKWY 53511 #016-02-1955 L1962 D *020 †15

BOUC, Geoffrey Thomas. 3005 RIVERSIDE DR STE 101 53511 #056-06-1994 L1995 FM *020 †18

BRACO, Robert J. 1905 E HUEBBE PKWY 53511 #035-06-1980 L1991 OM PRS *020 †45,70

BURANDT, Donald Chas. 1905 HUEBBE PKWY 53511 #056-05-1959 L1960 PD *071 †55

CHARLES, Pierre Sourial. 1905 HUEBBE PKWY 53511 #021-05-1986 L1996 GS *020 †85

CHERIAN, George. 1969 W HART RD 53511 #495-27-1985 L1998 DR *020 †80

CHOUNG, Steven S. 1969 W HART RD 53511 #583-10-1970 L1979 AN *020 †05

CRESSMAN, Nancy Jane. 2228 PARKMEADOW DR, JANESVILLE COUNSELING CENT 53511 #025-12-1989 L1996 P PYG *020

CRISWELL, David Kerns. 1905 E HUEBBE PKWY 53511 #016-11-1983 L1996 OBG *020 †30

DIEBOLD, Steven Eric. 1969 W HART RD 53511 #016-02-1990 L1992 EM *020 †16

DRUCKREY, Gerald Richard. 1905 HUEBBE PKWY, BELOIT CLINIC SC 53511 #016-11-1957 L1959 OPH *071 †35

DURKEE, Paul F. ■ 53512 #056-06-1950 L1980 ADM *071

EGBUJIOBI, Leo Chuks. 1905 E HUEBBE PKWY 53511 #654-01-1987 L1989 CD IM *020 †20

FANOPOULOS, Dimitrios. 1905 E HUEBBE PKWY 53511 #418-02-1986 L1994 IMG *020 †20

FASS, Steven Joshua. 1905 E HUEBBE PKWY 53511 #035-01-1971 L1977 GE IM *020 †20

FITZGERALD, Wm Matthew. 1905 E HUEBBE PKWY 53511 #016-06-1980 L1983 IM *020 †20

FLANAGAN, Patrick Michael. 2825 PRAIRIE AVE 53511 #021-01-1962 L1962 GYN *071 †30

FROM, Leland Jerrald. 1905 E HUEBBE PKWY 53511 #016-42-1978 L1981 IM *020 †20

FUDALA, Stanley John. 2250 TALLGRASS CT UNIT 4 53511 #759-06-1990 L1999 CHP *020 †75

GHADIALI, Nafisa Yunus. 1969 W HART RD, BELOIT MEMORIAL HOSPITAL 53511 #495-28-1976 L2002 P *020 †75

GOETZEN, Krzysztof. 1905 E HUEBBE PKWY 53511 #759-09-1982 L1999 N *020 †75

GOLD, Kenneth Ira. 1905 E HUEBBE PKWY 53511 #035-08-1961 L1968 IM *020

GONZALES, Eugene Adrian. 1735 MADISON RD, WESTSIDE MEDICAL CENTER 53511 #007-02-1981 L1995 FM *020 †18 ‡

HERNANDEZ DURAN, Juan Car. 2825 PRAIRIE AVE 53511 #264-14-1993 L2006 FM *020

HO, Emmy. 1905 E HUEBBE PKWY 53511 #010-02-1991 L2004 ORS *020 †40

HUIZENGA, Roger Edward. 1905 E HUEBBE PKWY 53511 #016-05-1974 L1975 ORS *020 †40

IQBAL, Atiya. 1735 MADISON RD 53511 #704-02-1990 L1999 FM *020 †18 ‡

JIMENEZ, Miguel A. 1969 W HART RD 53511 #847-04-1968 L1985 DR *020 †80

JOHANSON, John Frederick. 1905 HUEBBE PKWY 53511 #016-11-1985 L1986 GE EP *020 †20

JONES, George Thos. 1905 E HUEBBE PKWY 53511 #024-01-1971 L1977 IM *020 †20

JUAN, Henry S. 2825 PRAIRIE AVE 53511 #748-16-1986 L1996 IM *020 †20

JUNCK, Marlen Frederick. 1969 W HART RD 53511 #056-05-1969 L1972 DR NM *020 †80,28

KLEIN, Kenneth Lawrence. 1969 W HART RD, BELOIT MEMORIAL HOSPITAL 53511 #016-42-1989 L1993 PM *020 †60

KLESPIS-WICK, Kathleen Ma. 1904 E HUEBBE PKWY 53511 #056-05-1984 L1987 OBG *020 †18

KODRAS, Ronald Lee. 1905 E HUEBBE PKWY 53511 #019-02-1982 L1983 IMG *020 †20

LANG, Thomas Jos. 1905 HUEBBE PKWY 53511 #028-34-1954 L1960 IM *071

LAUTH, Sheree. 1905 E HUEBBE PKWY 53511 #422-01-1988 L1989 IM *020 †20

LEE, Jong Man. 1905 E HUEBBE PKWY 53511 #583-04-1963 L1981 OTO GS *020

LEE, Peter Uy. 1905 HUEBBE PKWY 53511 #748-01-1963 L1976 OTO PUD *071

LIM, Nancy Benemerito. ■ 53511 #748-01-1963 IM *074

LIM, Roger Go. 1905 E HUEBBE PKWY 53511 #748-01-1963 L1972 CD IM *020 †20

LIND, George Herbert, III. 1905 HUEBBE PKWY 53511 #056-05-1978 L1979 P *012 †20

LISK, Thomas Jos. 1969 W HART RD 53511 #016-11-1979 L1989 R *020 †80

LOFTUS, Kerilynn. 1905 E HUEBBE PKWY 53511 #056-06-1991 L1992 OBG *020 †30

MAHER, John J. 1969 W HART RD 53511 #051-07-1982 L1985 EM *020 †16

MANNING, Timothy Arthur. 1904 HUEBBE PKWY 53511 #016-11-1953 L1969 GP *020

MARTONFFY, Andrea Ildiko. 74 BELOIT MALL, BELOIT AREA COMM. HEALTH C 53511 #016-11-2002 L2003 FM *020 †18

MATLOOB, Ajmal A. 1905 E HUEBBE PKWY 53511 #528-01-1973 L1989 ORS *020

MATTHEWS, Jessica Tabor. 1969 W HART RD 53511 #016-43-2000 L2003 EM *020 †16

MAUERMANN, William J. ■ 53511 #056-06-1939 L1939 GP *071

MENSAH, Victor Olawale. 74 ECLIPSE CTR, PROVIDENT HOSP OF COOK COU 53511 #690-02-1992 L2007 FM *100 †18

MERINO, Rodrigo R. 1905 E HUEBBE PKWY 53511 #016-06-1974 L1990 N *020 †75

MILLER, Cheryl Marie. 1905 E HUEBBE PKWY 53511 #018-03-1996 L1999 IM *020 †20

MILLER, James Raymond. 1905 E HUEBBE PKWY 53511 #056-05-1971 L1972 IM *020 †20

MOHIUDDIN, Mohammed J. 1969 W HART RD 53511 #495-21-1992 L2001 AN *020

MYERS, Cris P. 1969 W HART RD, HART ROAD PATHOLOGY S.C. 53511 #023-12-1983 L2004 PTH DMP *020 †50

OJEDA, Larry Michael. 1905 E HUEBBE PKWY 53511 #016-11-1977 L1987 U *050 †95

OKOCHA, Chukwunonye. 2825 PRAIRIE AVE 53511 #026-04-2002 L2006 OBG *020

OLSZEWSKI, Pawel. 1905 E HUEBBE PKWY 53511 #759-01-1989 L1997 IM *020 †20

OUGH, Yon Doo. 1969 W HART RD 53511 #583-10-1969 L1983 AN *020 †50,05

PATEL, Sushrut R. 1905 E HUEBBE PKWY 53511 #495-23-1984 L1989 PUD CCM *020 †20

PEREZ, Enrique Francisco. 74 ECLIPSE CTR 53511 #056-06-2002 L2003 FM *020 †18

PETERSON, Cheryl Scott. 2958 PRAIRIE AVE, STE A 53511 #016-45-1987 L1990 FM *020 †18

POPLAWSKA-GOETZEN, Maria. 1904 HUEBBE PKWY, FAMILY HEALTH ASSOCIATES 53511 #759-09-1982 L2005 FM *020

PRUETT, William Alfred. ■ 53511 #048-04-1958 L1960 FM OBG *071 †18

RIEKER, Willis J, Jr. 1969 W HART RD 53511 #016-43-1984 L1994 PCP CLP *020 †50

ROJAS, Amelia Rybinski. 1905 E HUEBBE PKWY 53511 #016-43-1986 L1991 AI PD *020 †55,03

ROJAS, Mario. 1905 E HUEBBE PKWY 53511 #016-11-1986 L1991 OPH *020 †35

RUDISILL, Stephen Randall. 1904 E HUEBBE PKWY 53511 #016-11-1985 L1988 FM *020 †20

RYAN, Diane Alice. ■ 53511 #649-14-1978 FM *100

SALVADOR, Fernando E. 2031 RIVERSIDE DR 53511 #748-01-1958 L1968 GP AS *071

SAUER, Paul Albert. 1905 E HUEBBE PKWY 53511 #016-01-1989 L1995 ORS *020 †40

SCHOLTEN, Walter A, Jr. 1905 HUEBBE PKWY 53511 #016-06-1954 L1959 OBG *071 †30

SDANO, Matthew Thaddeus. 1905 E HUEBBE PKWY 53511 #056-05-2001 L2006 OTO *020 †45

SEGAL, Paul Miles. 1905 E HUEBBE PKWY 53511 #028-02-1982 L1983 D *020 †15

SIDDIQI, Nadeem Ahson. 74 BELOIT MALL, BELOIT AREA COMMUNITY 53511 #704-01-1984 L1997 IMG IM *020 †20

STROUD, Christopher Byron. ■ 53511 #011-03-1991 L1995 OBG *020 †30

TAN, Glenn Anthony A. 1905 HUEBBE PKWY, BELOIT CLINIC, S.C. 53511 #748-01-1988 L2007 OBG *020 †30 ‡

TAVERAS, Maria Emperatriz. 1905 E HUEBBE PKWY 53511 #005-02-1978 L1992 **CD IM** *020 †20
TOWNSHEND, Alice M. 1905 E HUEBBE PKWY 53511 #025-07-1990 L1995 **OPH** *020 †35 ‡
TRIPP, Warren Earl. 1969 W HART RD 53511 #017-20-1986 L1991 **EM** *020 †16
TSE, Jimson Chiuhung. 1969 W HART RD 53511 #056-05-1990 L1995 **AN PME** *020 †05
TUFTEE, Allen O. ■ 53511 #016-11-1951 L1958 **ORS** *071 †40
VISWANATHAN, Kanchana. 1905 E HUEBBE PKWY 53511 #495-16-1983 L1993 **END IM** *020 †20
VOGEL, Walter Clifford. 1905 E HUEBBE PKWY 53511 #016-42-1980 L1987 **ON HEM** *020 †20
WAGNER, Alan Scott. 1969 W HART RD, BELOIT MEMORIAL HOSPITAL 53511 #056-05-1993 L2007 **DR** *020 †80
WANG, Jackky. 1904 HUEBBE PKWY, BELOIT CLINIC 53511 #305-01-1999 L2007 **FM** *020 †18
WANG, Tsu-Hon. 1905 HUEBBE PKWY 53511 #305-01-1997 L2004 **GE** *020 †20
WERNER, Stephen Cole. 2825 PRAIRIE AVE 53511 #056-06-1972 L1973 **PD** *020 †55
WILSON, Shawn Paul. 1969 W HART RD 53511 #018-03-1987 L1990 **EM** *020 †16
WOODINGTON, George Fraser. ■ 53511 #056-05-1953 L1960 **GS TS** *071 †85
YOUNT, Beth Judy. 1904 HUEBBE PKWY 53511 #056-06-1993 L1994 **FM** *020 †18

BERLIN – GREEN LAKE

ATASSI, Omar. 225 MEMORIAL DR 54923 #016-43-1990 L1996 **U** *020 †95
BATLEY, Craig M. W832 STATE ROAD 91 54923 #018-75-2000, ▲ L2003 **FM** *020 †18
BENTSON, Jeffrey George. 225 MEMORIAL DR, STE 2020 54923 #025-07-1997 L2002 **ORS** *020 †40
BRADSHAW, Todd Michael. 225 MEMORIAL DR, STE 1200 54923 #056-06-1992 L1995 **FM** *020 †18
BRUCE, Mary Jean. 225 MEMORIAL DR STE 12 54923 #056-05-1986 L1987 **FM** *030 †18
BRUNO, Patrick Lewis. 225 MEMORIAL DR STE 2030 54923 #028-03-1989 L2002 **OBG** *020 †30
CARROLL, Jeffrey J. 225 MEMORIAL DR # 1100 54923 #056-06-1978 L1979 **IM** *020 †20
CAVES, Chandler Donald. 225 MEMORIAL DR 54923 #056-05-1997 L1998 **EM** *020 †18
COLEMAN, David Eugene. 225 MEMORIAL DR 54923 #030-06-1982 L1983 **EM FM** *020 †18
EASTMAN, Robert Royal. 225 MEMORIAL DR 54923 #030-06-1995 L1998 **FM** *020 †18
EBERTS, Eric G. 225 MEMORIAL DR, AT BERLIN MEMORIAL 54923 #048-12-1993 L1999 **OBG** *020 †30
EKSTROM, Shawn Christine. 225 MEMORIAL DR, STE 1200 54923 #054-04-1994 L1995 **FM** *020 †18
FLICKINGER, Frederick Wm. 225 MEMORIAL DR, CHN RADIOLOGY SERVICES 54923 #016-06-1965 L1991 **DR** *020 †80,28
GIMENEZ, Alonzo Rudolfo. 144 N PEARL ST 54923 #028-34-1954 L1955 **GS** *071
GROSSKLAUS, Mark Dennis. 225 MEMORIAL DR, STE 1200 54923 #056-05-1994 L1995 **FM** *072 †18
HIGGINS, Daniel James. 225 MEMORIAL DR 54923 #056-06-1999 L2001 **U** *020 †95
JEROME, Peter Steven. 225 MEMORIAL DR, COMMUNITY HEALTH NETWORK 54923 #018-03-1980 L1981 **PUD CCM** *020 †20
JONES, David Rees. 191 MEMORIAL DR 54923 #035-20-1975 L1979 **ORS** *020 †40
KURTZ, David Wm. 225 MEMORIAL DR, BERLIN MEMORIAL HOSP 54923 #024-01-1975 L1994 **R** *020 †80
LEIKNESS, Mary Hallman. 225 MEMORIAL DR 54923 #056-05-1976 L1977 **U** *020 †95
LO, Horace Pei. 225 MEMORIAL DR, STE 2000 54923 #056-05-1996 L1997 **GS** *020 †85
MOORE, Freeman Mark. 225 MEMORIAL DR, BERLIN MEM HOSP ED 54923 #038-41-1968 L1973 **EM** *020
MURPHY, Renee Anne. 225 MEMORIAL DR 54923 #056-06-1990 L1991 **FM** *020 †18
NELSEN, Paul Douglas. 225 MEMORIAL DR 54923 #030-05-1975 L1976 **FM** *020 †18
NELSON, Darren Glenn. 225 MEMORIAL DR, STE 2000 54923 #016-43-1992 L1997 **GS** *020 †85
RACKI, Anthony John. 225 MEMORIAL DR 54923 #016-11-1974 L1994 **IM** *020 †20
RESEN, David Edwin. 225 MEMORIAL DR 54923 #046-01-1986 L1992 **PTH IM** *020 †50
RESOP, Daniel Jos. 225 MEMORIAL DR, ANESTHESIA DEPARTMENT-CHN 54923 #056-05-1989 L1993 **AN** *020 †05
ROGERS, Barry Leonard. 225 MEMORIAL DR STE 2000 54923 #012-05-1976 L1981 **GS** *020 †85
ROSELAAR, Simon Edwin. 225 MEMORIAL DR, APPLETON CARDIOLOGY 54923 #917-19-1986 L1999 **CD** *020 †20
SEITZINGER, Michael Roy. 225 MEMORIAL DR STE 1400 54923 #021-01-1975 L1995 **OBG** *020 †30
SULLIVAN, Kenneth Todd. 225 MEMORIAL DR 54923 #026-04-1995 L1998 **FM** *020 †18
WILLIAMS, James Matthews. 225 MEMORIAL DR 54923 #051-07-1979 L2002 **FM EM** *020 †18

BIG BEND – WAUKESHA

DROESE, Karl. ■ 53103 #056-05-2004 L2006 **FM** *100

BIRCHWOOD – WASHBURN

BURGFECHTEL, Robt Francis. ■ 54817 #018-03-1967 L1970 **EM FM** *020 †18
FREITAG, Rick Danl. W2876 COUNTY ROAD A 54817 #056-05-1972 L1977 **DR** *071 †80
GREEN, Joseph Edgar, III. ■ 54817 #041-13-1960 L1961 **IM** *071 †20
GUNDERSON, Finn Olaf. ■ 54817 #056-05-1959 L1960 **ORS** *071 †40

BLACK CREEK – OUTAGAMIE

FAUDREE, Michael Stephen. 400 S MAPLE ST 54106 #054-04-1974 L1975 **FM** *020 †18
RAWLING, Jon Daniel. W4794 DEER RUN DR 54106 #056-05-1995 L2002 **EM** *020 †16

BLACK EARTH – DANE

HUPP, Janelle Kay. 1529 STATE ST, STE A 53515 #016-11-1995 L2004 **FM** *020 †18
MC DERMOTT, Michael F. ■ 53515 #056-06-1970 L1997 **IM** *020 †16

BLACK RIVER FALLS – JACKSON

ANDERSON, Kevin Mark. 610 W ADAMS ST 54615 #028-34-1998 L2005 **FM** *020 †18

ANTONELLI, Darrin. 711 W ADAMS ST 54615 #422-01-1995 L2000 **GS** *020 †85
BOARDMAN, Benjamin J. W9855 AIRPORT RD 54615 #056-47-1992 L1997 **FM** *020 †18
CAMERON, Etson, Jr. 711 W ADAMS ST 54615 #010-03-1995 L2001 **FM** *020 †18
DICKMAN, James Joseph, III. 711 W ADAMS ST 54615 #056-06-1970 L1972 **FM** *020 †18
GUESS, Lea Donelle. 610 W ADAMS ST 54615 #048-02-2003 L2006 **FM** *020 †18
GUVENLI, Gokhan. 711 W ADAMS ST 54615 #902-04-1986 L2002 **FM** *020 †18
HICKS, Edgar Obadiah. 711 W ADAMS ST 54615 #018-03-1973 L1978 **ORS** *020 †40
JACOBSON, Lang O. ■ 54615 #056-06-2007 L2007 *012
KELLEN, David Bryan. 711 W ADAMS ST 54615 #056-05-1987 L1990 **FM** *062 †18
KESLER, James Miguel. 711 W ADAMS ST 54615 #034-01-2000 L2003 **FM** *020 †18
KITOWSKI, Jerome Carl. 711 W ADAMS ST 54615 #056-06-1982 L1983 **FM** *020 †18
KROHN, Eugene. 421 HARRISON ST 54615 #056-05-1959 L1962 **FM** *071 †20
LANE, Kirk Edward. 711 W ADAMS ST 54615 #048-12-1998 L2001 **FM** *020 †18
LAVOIE, Daniel Louis. 711 W ADAMS ST 54615 #016-11-1988 L1993 **FM** *020 †18
MAHAN, Michael Allan. 711 W ADAMS ST 54615 #017-20-1987 L1988 **FM** *020 †18
MARTIN, Carol Ann. 610 W ADAMS ST 54615 #018-03-1993 L1994 **FM** *020 †18
MERRITT, David Barry. 610 W ADAMS ST, KROHN CLINIC LTD 54615 #665-01-2000 L2003 **FM** *020 †18
NOBLE, John Henry. ■ 54615 #016-11-1947 L1950 **FM** *071 †18
PETERSEN, Gary Kent. 711 W ADAMS ST 54615 #028-03-1971 L1974 **FM** *020 †18
POLZIN, Jeffrey Kenneth. 711 W ADAMS ST 54615 #026-08-1978 L1981 **FM FSM** *020 †18
ROGERS, Delbert Wade. 711 W ADAMS ST 54615 #016-01-1998 L2001 **FM** *020 †18
ROGGE, Richard Wayne. 711 W ADAMS ST 54615 #018-03-1996 L1997 **FM** *020 †18
SPEGMAN, Howard Francis. 711 W ADAMS ST 54615 #054-04-1986 L1995 **FM** *020 †18
SPRINGS, Fern. ■ 54615 #026-08-1991 L1992 **IM** *020
WHITEHOUSE, Catherine A. 711 W ADAMS ST 54615 #056-05-1990 L1994 **P** *020 †75
WOOLSEY, Guy Hamilton. 610 W ADAMS ST, KROHN CLINIC 54615 #060-01-1991 *100

BLAIR – TREMPEALEAU

GILBERT, Kenyon Roger. ■ 54616 #016-11-1964 L1967 **FM** *071

BLANCHARDVILLE – LAFAYETTE

HUNTER, Richard E. 309 N MAIN ST 53516 #056-05-1953 L1954 **GP OS** *072

BLOOMER – CHIPPEWA

BEUNING, Alex John. 1501 THOMPSON ST 54724 #026-04-1998 L2001 **FM** *020 †18
BLAIR, David Russell. 1501 THOMPSON ST 54724 #036-07-1994 L2005 **FM** *020 †18
BRUXVOORT, Kristen R. 1501 THOMPSON ST 54724 #056-05-1988 L1991 **FM** *020 †18
FLOREN, Lydia F Lowe. 1501 THOMPSON ST 54724 #012-01-1983 L2003 **FM** *074 †18
LARSON, John Leonard. 1501 THOMPSON ST 54724 #056-05-1976 L1982 **FM EM** *020 †18
LEAVITT, James Robt. 1503 THOMPSON ST, LUTHER MIDELFORT 54724 #028-34-1972 L1977 **ORS** *020 †40
ROSENBROOK, Gordon H. 1501 THOMPSON ST, MIDELFORT CLINIC BLOOMER 54724 #056-05-1971 L1973 **FM GS** *020 †18
SILL, Allan John. 1501 THOMPSON ST 54724 #018-03-1972 L1973 **END** *020 †20
VOSS, Martin Jos. 1501 THOMPSON ST 54724 #056-05-1977 L1980 **AI PD** *020 †55,03
WANKEL, Albert J. 1501 THOMPSON ST 54724 #016-11-1980 L1981 **GS TS** *020 †85

BLUE MOUNDS – DANE

KELLEY, Christopher John. ■ 53517 #056-06-1984 L1989 **DR** *062 †80

BLUE RIVER – RICHLAND

HEERSMA, James R. ■ 53518 #016-06-1949 L1953 **PD PDA** *071 †55

BOSCOBEL – GRANT

CHIRIAC, Irinel Ruxandra. 205 PARKER ST, BOSCOBEL AREA HEALTH CARE 53805 #781-01-1994 L2004 **P** *020 †75 ‡
FAST, William Paul. 208 PARKER ST 53805 #026-04-1975 L1978 **FM** *020 †18
MUELLER, Carol E. ■ 53805 #056-05-1952 L1954 **FM** *071 †18
PALMER, Douglas Ronald. 205 PARKER ST 53805 #056-06-1981 L1986 **ORS** *020 †40
WILHELM, Kurt, II. 208 PARKER ST 53805 #016-45-1988 L1989 **FM** *020 †18

BOWLER – SHAWANO

DALVE, Richard Dean. W12802 COUNTY ROAD A 54416 #026-04-1981 L1983 **FM** *020 †18

BOYCEVILLE – DUNN

BAUDER, Martha Wynne. ■ 54725 #056-06-1991 L1994 **EM** *020 †16

BRILLION – CALUMET

LEE, John J.. 708 W RYAN ST 54110 #661-02-2002 L2004 **FSM** *020 †18
SIPPLE, Christopher John. 964 WEST RYAN ST, STE B 54110 #056-06-1998 L1999 **FM** *020 †18

BRODHEAD – GREEN

BLUEMEL, Kevin Michael. 2310 1ST CENTER AVE, MERCY BRODHEAD MED CTR 53520 #017-20-1994 L1995 **FM** *020 †18

CATES, Robert Chas. 1904 1ST CENTER AVE, BRODHEAD 53520 #056-05-1987 L1989 FM FSM *020 †18

OLSON, Stuart Kenneth. 2310 1ST CENTER AVE 53520 #016-06-1954 L1990 IM OS *071 †20

BROOKFIELD – WAUKESHA

ABOUDOLA, Samer. ■ 53005 #875-01-1995 L2006 HMP *020

ADAMS, Mark Douglas. 225 S EXECUTIVE DR 53005 #056-06-1987 L1988 AN *020 †05

AKBAR, A Nisar. 225 S EXECUTIVE DR 53005 #704-01-1987 L1992 AN *020 †05

ALEXIS, Athlene Agnes. 1125 ASHBOURNE CT 53045 #056-06-1991 L1993 AN *020

ANDREJAT, Georgiann. 19650 WHITEHALL DR 53045 #056-05-1979 L1981 PTH *020 †50

ANNESLEY, Wm Henry, Jr. 17000 W NORTH AVE, STE 108 53005 #056-06-1977 L1978 U *020 †95

ANSARI, Shamim Ahmad. ■ 53005 #704-02-1974 L1978 AN *020 †05

APPLE, Bryan Stanley. 225 S EXECUTIVE DR 53005 #028-02-1981 L1996 AN *020 †05

ARMAGAN, Senekerim. 13595 W JAMES ST 53005 #902-01-1958 L1967 OTO HNS *020 †45

ARNOLD, Sara. 19333 W NORTH AVE 53045 #016-11-1983 L1984 R *020 †80

ARYA, Basant. ■ 53005 #495-04-1996 L2005 CD *012 †20

AUGER, Jon Joseph. 17000 W NORTH AVE, STE 108 53005 #056-06-1996 L1997 U *020 †95

BACCUS, Donald Jos. 17280 W NORTH AVE, STE 200 53045 #025-01-1976 L1977 GYN *020 †30

BANASIAK, Michael Francis. 17000 W NORTH AVE 53005 #056-06-1969 L1972 IM END *020 †20

BARWIG, Patricia A. 19475 W NORTH AVE, STE 400 53045 #056-06-1981 L1982 OBG *020 †30

BATAYIAS, George Edward. 2455 N 124TH ST 53005 #012-01-1960 L1967 OM PTH *020 †50,70

BAUTISTA, Soliven Cruz. 19333 W NORTH AVE 53005 #748-10-1989 L2002 PM *020 †60

BEHNKE, Paula Jean. ■ 53005 #056-06-2005 L2007 PD *012

BERNSTEIN, Joseph Sidney. 225 S EXECUTIVE DR 53005 #056-06-1980 L1981 AN PME *020 †05

BHARGAVA, Rajesh. 1150 WINSTON PARK CT, ST JOES REGIONAL MEDICAL C 53045 #495-73-1979 L1994 MPD HOS *020 †55,20

BHATTI, Azam M. 3260N PILGRIM RD 53005 #704-21-1982 L2001 GPM *020

BHATTI, Zagum Abid. ■ 53045 #056-06-2008 *012

BIAGTAN, Juan Tanopo. 19475 W NORTH AVE STE 308 53045 #748-01-1971 L1981 PD *020

BIELKE, Stephen Roy. 17000 W NORTH AVE 53045 #026-04-1979 L1980 IM *020 †20

BIRGE, Edward Asahel. 3140 LILLY RD, RM 195 53005 #023-07-1936 L1940 PTH CLP *071 †50

BLACKWOOD, John Stoddart. 17050 W NORTH AVE, STE 107 53005 #056-06-1964 L1967 GS VS *020 †85

BLANKENBURG, Russell Neil. 17000 W NORTH AVE 53005 #056-05-1993 L1994 IM *020 †20

BLASCHKE, Ulrik Thos. 225 S EXECUTIVE DR 53005 #056-06-1987 L1991 AN *020 †05

BOEDECKER, Robert Allan. ■ 53005 #056-06-1972 L1973 DR NR *071 †80

BOSCHEK, Michael Steven. 13950 W CAPITOL DR, HARWOOD CLINIC CAPITOL 53005 #030-06-1995 L1996 IM *020 †20

BOSNJAK, Lisa Marie. ■ 53005 #056-06-2008 *012

BRAHMBHATT, Tejas N. ■ 53005 #495-76-1993 L1998 CD *012 †20

BRAKER, J Christopher. 17100 W NORTH AVE, STE 200 53005 #025-01-1984 L1988 D *020 †15

BRODZINSKI, George T, Jr. 225 S EXECUTIVE DR 53005 #024-16-1984 L2000 AN *030 †05

BUECHLER, Anthony Alan. 225 S EXECUTIVE DR 53005 #018-03-1977 L1978 AN *020 †05

BUGGY, William J. ■ 53005 #026-04-1948 L1951 OBG *071 †30

BULLOCK, Richard Wayne. 20070 FREEDOM CT 53045 #065-10-1984 L1996 EM *020

BURHOP, James Wm. 17050 W NORTH AVE, STE 108 53005 #056-06-1986 L1987 GS *020 †85

BURKE, Donna Bienlein. 12690 W NORTH AVE, ELMBROOK FAMILY COUNSELING 53005 #056-06-1968 L1975 P CHP *020

BURKE, Eugene Paul. 2085 N CALHOUN RD 53005 #016-11-1966 L1975 IM *020

BURKERT, Lawrence Blythe. 17000 W NORTH AVE 53005 #038-06-1965 L1966 HO IM *020 †20

BUTLER, Brian Patrick. 17000 W NORTH AVE, STE 108 53005 #025-01-1990 L1995 U *020 †95

CALIMIN, Elnora Mendoza. ■ 53045 #748-08-1971 L1991 R *020

CALKINS, Barbara B. ■ 53045 #056-06-1996 L2005 PD *020 †55

CANITZ, Christopher John. 19333 W NORTH AVE 53045 #056-06-1992 L1994 DR *020 †80

CANTIERI, John Stephen. 17100 W NORTH AVE 53005 #028-02-1976 L1993 D IM *020 †15

CAPELLI-SCHELLPFEFFER, M. 20070 FREEDOM CT 53045 #011-03-1982 L1985 OM GPM *040 †70

CARPENTER, Matthew. ■ 53045 #037-01-2007 ORS *012

CERLETTY, James Mathias. 1355 HELENE DR 53045 #056-06-1958 L1961 END IM *040 †20

CHANG, James Owen. ■ 53005 #056-06-2007 TY *012

CHERWENKA, Richard Wayne. ■ 53045 #056-06-1971 L1972 AN *071 †05

CHIANG, Manfred Chiming. 17000 W NORTH AVE, STE 107 53005 #056-06-1987 L1988 GS VS *020 †85

CHOI, Hongyung. 19762 BRAMPTON CT 53045 #583-04-1959 L1973 PTH *020 †50

CHRISTIANSON, Eric Ellis. 19333 W NORTH AVE, UNITED HEALTHCARE OF WIS 53045 #056-06-1983 L1984 FM MDM *030 †18

CHRZAN, Donald Gerard. 225 S EXECUTIVE DR 53005 #056-06-1983 L1984 AN *020 †05

CLARK, Douglas Owen. ■ 53045 #038-40-1961 L1968 GYN *071 †30

CLAVERIA, Joanne Kristine. ■ 53045 #016-06-2007 PD *012

COFFEY, John Michael. 18940 WILDERNESS CT UNIT D 53045 #056-06-1957 L1959 ADM OBG *020 †30

CORISH, Robert Anthony. 225 S EXECUTIVE DR 53005 #011-02-1991 L1993 AN *020 †05

CUETO, Janelorelie P. ■ 53045 #056-05-2001 L2001 AN *100

DAHLGREN, Karie Naomi. ■ 53005 #056-05-2006 PM *012

DAS GUPTA, Krishna. 12690 W NORTH AVE 53005 #056-05-1982 L1987 P *020 †75

DAVIES, William Alexander. 2085 N CALHOUN RD 53005 #056-06-1993 L1998 OSM *020 †40

DEGUEME, Amy Marie. ■ 53045 #056-06-2008 *012

DEVINE, Irisa Melitapaka. ■ 53045 #056-06-2008 *012

DHEIN, Robert Mark. 19333 W NORTH AVE 53045 #056-06-1987 L1988 AN *020 †05

DINU, Eliza Cristina. ■ 53045 #781-01-1999 L2007 N *012

DJOKOVIC, Jovan Ljubomir. 1265 VALLEY RIDGE DR 53005 #957-02-1963 L1981 AN *071 †05

DONOFRIO, Joseph John. 19333 W NORTH AVE 53045 #016-01-1978 L1992 EM *020 †20,16

DORMAN, David Kent. 19475 W NORTH AVE, STE 302 53045 #056-06-1968 L1969 PS HS *020 †65

DOROW, Mark Allen. 2085 N CALHOUN RD 53005 #056-06-1980 L1981 FM *020 †18

DOUCETTE, Benjamin David. 250 N SUNNY SLOPE RD, STE 250 53045 #024-07-2005 *100

DRINKA, Joseph Mark. 345 N ELM GROVE RD, UNIT D 53045 #056-05-1979 L1980 CHP P *075

DRISCOLL, Collin Dean. ■ 53045 #025-01-2003 L2004 RO *012

DRISCOLL, Susanna Mg. ■ 53045 #025-01-2003 L2005 IM *100

DUA, Harminder Singh. ■ 53045 #495-83-1975 L1993 *020

DU CANTO, James Charner. 225 S EXECUTIVE DR 53005 #016-01-1992 L1997 AN *020 †05

DUFFRIN, Henry Jos. 17000 W NORTH AVE, STE 200E 53005 #056-05-1984 L1988 DR *020 †80

DZUBINSKI, David Lee. ■ 53045 #025-12-1982 L1989 P CHP *020 †75

EGGERT, Wendy Watson. ■ 53045 #017-20-1981 L1988 AN *020 †05

ELCONIN, Howard Victor. 225 S EXECUTIVE DR, PHYSICIANS ACCOUNTING 53005 #056-06-1981 L1993 AN PME *020 †05

ELSON, Matthew W. ■ 53005 #038-40-1949 L1961 R NM *071 †80,28

ENGLE, David Edward. 2085 N CALHOUN RD STE 203 53005 #026-04-1977 L1978 CD IM *020 †20

ENGSTRAND, David J. 17000 W NORTH AVE STE 107W 53005 #056-06-1981 L1982 GS OS *020 †85

FAERSTAIN, Steven Arthur. ■ 53045 #056-06-2008 *012

FARLEY, Thomas Michael. 225 S EXECUTIVE DR 53005 #056-06-1985 L1990 EM *020 †05

FELTON, David Alan. 225 S EXECUTIVE DR 53005 #023-01-1986 L2000 AN GS *020 †05

FELTON, Thomas Owen. 225 S EXECUTIVE DR 53005 #056-05-1989 L1990 AN *020 †05

FERIA, Paul V. ■ 53005 #056-06-1995 *100

FINGARD, David Hollet. 225 S EXECUTIVE DR 53005 #064-01-1971 L1983 AN *020 †05

FLATLEY, Michael Edward. 19333 W NORTH AVE 53045 #056-06-1990 L1991 PCC *020 †20

FORWARD, Daniel Jos. 19475 W NORTH AVE, STE 305 53045 #028-34-1969 L1973 IM CD *020 †20

FOSTER, Lawrence Lee. 13255 W BLUEMOUND RD 53005 #056-06-1963 L1964 ORS HS *020 †20

FOX, Amy Marie. 19475 W NORTH AVE, STE 400 53045 #056-05-1991 L1995 OBG *020 †30

FOX, Paul Stephen. 19333 W NORTH AVE 53045 #056-06-1968 L1969 GS *020 †85

FRANK, Richard Alan. 3305 N 124TH ST 53005 #008-01-1976 L1992 P CHP *020 †75

FUIKS, Kimball Sands. 12780 W NORTH AVE, # 204 53005 #008-02-1978 L1991 NS N *020 †75,25

GALDIERI, Ralph James, Jr. 2085 N CALHOUN RD, STE 203 53005 #561-17-1978 L2003 TS *020 †85,90

GANDHAVADI, Ranjini B. 19250 HAYDEN CT 53045 #495-33-1972 L1980 RO *020 †80

GAWRISCH, Ellen Lou. 19333 W NORTH AVE 53045 #056-06-1986 L1987 AN *020 †05

GERBER, Daniel Thos. 19333 W NORTH AVE 53045 #056-06-1981 L1982 AN IM *020 †20,05

GERSTNER, Gary Lee. 19333 W NORTH AVE 53045 #056-05-1976 L1981 GE IM *020 †20

GOELL, William Stuart. ■ 53045 #056-05-1984 L1985 R *071 †80

GOLOPOL, Lawrence Allen. 13850 W CAPITOL DR, ADVANCED HEALTHCARE 53005 #056-06-1983 L1984 IM *020 †20

GONZAGA, Jason Elias. ■ 53045 #016-41-2006 IM *012

GONZAGA, Katherine Ann. ■ 53045 #016-43-2006 PD *012

GOVIN, Gerald Gerard. 16535 W BLUEMOUND RD, STE 222 53005 #056-06-1973 L1978 PS GS *020 †85,65

GRIEVE, Bonnie-Jo Mc Lean. 18910 HIVIEW DR, HARBECKE MEDICAL 53045 #049-01-1973 L1974 MG PD *020 †55,19

GRODEN, David Lee. 2085 N CALHOUN RD, STE 203 53005 #038-40-1984 L1990 CD IM *020 †20

GRUM, Clement Martin. 225 S EXECUTIVE DR 53005 #056-06-1981 L1982 AN *020 †05

GUENTHER, Neil Roman. 225 S EXECUTIVE DR 53005 #056-06-1983 L1984 AN IM *020 †20,05

HAMBROOK, Megan E. 1305 N BARKER RD, STE 1 53045 #056-06-2001 L2003 PD *020 †55

HAMDA, Hossam Khamis. ■ 53045 #915-03-1994 L2004 R RNR *020

HANSEN, Peter Thorwald. 19333 W NORTH AVE 53045 #056-06-1967 L1968 AN *020 †05

HANSON, Rita Marie. 13950 W CAPITOL DR 53005 #016-43-1976 L1977 IM IMG *020 †20

HASELOW, Kent David. 4735 HASTINGS DR, STE 105 53045 #056-05-1992 L1999 AN *020 †05

HASSAN, Mushir Bin. 17000 W NORTH AVE 53005 #016-06-1995 L1999 IM ISM *020 †20

HAWKINS, Marjorie Curcio. 3305 N 124TH ST 53005 #924-01-1981 L1994 P *020 †75

HAWORTH, Nancy Robinson. 17000 W NORTH AVE, STE 110 53005 #056-06-1980 L1981 PD *020 †55

HAYSSEN, Theresa Karich. 17000 W NORTH AVE 53005 #016-45-1992 L1998 CRS *020 †10,85

HEANEY, Stephen John. 225 S EXECUTIVE DR 53005 #018-03-1986 L1991 AN *020 †05

HEIGHWAY, John Stephen. 19333 W NORTH AVE 53045 #056-06-1985 L1986 DR *020 †80

HEIN, Joel Evan. ■ 53045 #056-06-2008 *012

HEMPEL, Douglas John. 601 N BARKER RD 53045 #056-06-1998 L2000 RHU *020 †20

HEPPERLA, Roger Lawrence. 225 S EXECUTIVE DR 53005 #056-06-1957 L1959 AN GP *020 †05

HERNANDEZ, Juan Miguel. ■ 53045 #847-03-1979 L2004 P *020 †75

HERTLER, Melissa Ann. ■ 53045 #056-05-2001 L2003 OTO *100 †45

HESS, Timothy Richard. 2085 N CALHOUN RD STE 203, WISC HEART GRP SC 53005 #056-06-1975 L1977 CD IM *020 †20

HEYDARPOUR, Mehran. 125 N EXECUTIVE DR 53005 #018-03-1988 L1989 PME AN *020 †05

HILL, Joanne Lynn. 1350 S SUNNY SLOPE RD 53005 #056-06-1995 L1996 FM *020 †18

HIRUDAYARAJ, Purnima. ■ 53045 #495-42-1995 IM *012

HO, Sun-O Gregory. ■ 53045 #143-02-1969 L1975 AN *071 †05

HOLMBERG, James Richard. 19333 W NORTH AVE 53045 #308-11-1986 L1987 EM *020 †16

HOLZHAUER, Peter John. 19333 W NORTH AVE 53045 #056-06-1972 L1973 EM *020 †16

HORKHEIMER, Ronald Wm. ■ 53045 #056-06-1967 L1970 EM FM *074 †16

HOUGHTON, Mary Alice B. 3305 N 124TH ST 53005 #008-01-1966 L1971 P *020 †75

HOUGHTON, Wm John, Jr. 3305 N 124TH ST 53005 #008-01-1964 L1970 P N *020 †75

HUGHES, Chas Vincent, Jr. 17425 W RIVER BIRCH DR 53045 #055-01-1963 L1966 IM CD *071 †20

HUGHES, Jack Lindley. 19333 W NORTH AVE 53045 #007-02-1968 L1974 OPH *020 †35 ‡

HUR, John K. 19333 W NORTH AVE 53045 #016-11-1988 L1994 AN *020 †05

IGNACIO, Alfredo Garcia. ■ 53005 #748-01-1956 L1969 DR *071 †80

IRELAND, Ivan Andrew. 18110 W BLUEMOUND RD, STOP 8 53045 #056-05-1993 L2000 OPH *020 †35

IRLAND, Jacqueline Marie. 19475 W NORTH AVE, STE 400 53045 #025-12-1986 L1990 OBG *020 †30

JACKSON, David Bradley. 225 S EXECUTIVE DR 53005 #036-05-1992 L2000 AN *020 †05

JAFFURS, Daniel C. ■ 53005 #041-12-2000 L2001 CFS *012 †85

JEST, Timothy Marvin. 19475 W NORTH AVE, STE 305 53045 #056-06-1982 L1983 IM *020 †20

JOHNSON, Frank Kenneth. ■ 53005 #016-11-1942 L1948 CHP PD *071 †55

JOHNSON, Joel Mark. 225 S EXECUTIVE DR 53005 #016-11-1980 L1981 AN *020 †05

JOHNSON, Thomas Andrew. 17000 W NORTH AVE 53005 #016-11-1984 L1985 IM *020 †20

JOHNSON, Wenner Dudley. 350 BISHOPS WAY STE 202 53005 #016-11-1955 L1959 TS CD *071 †85,90

KAMARAJU, Yeseswini. ■ 53045 #495-50-1995 L1998 **P** *020

KARIER, Monica Jeanne. ■ 53045 #056-06-1979 L1997 **PTH** *074 †50

KAYATA, Sahar. 3215 HOLSEN CT 53005 #396-32-1981 L1985 **NPM PD** *020 †55

KELLEY, Scott William. 12805 W BURLEIGH RD 53005 #056-06-1994 L1995 **DMP** *020 †50

KLEINER, Jeff Alan. 19333 W NORTH AVE 53045 #056-05-2001 L2005 **PM PME** *020 †60

KLEVEN, Kristina Ann. 13800 W NORTH AVE, STE 100 53005 #056-06-2001 L2002 **D** *020 †15

KNAUTZ, Michael Harry. 2085 N CALHOUN RD 53005 #056-06-1980 L1981 **FM** *020 †18

KOMAR, Robert Raymond. ■ 53005 #056-06-1955 L1956 **GP OS** *071

KOMATINENI, Aparna. ■ 53045 #495-70-2003 **N** *012

KONDURI, Kameswari Surya. 12605 W NORTH AVE 53005 #004-01-1988 L2000 **AI** *020 †03,55

KOVACEVIC, Vladimir. 225 S EXECUTIVE DR 53005 #957-01-1970 L1974 **AN** *020 †05

KRAEGEL, John Hilder. 13950 W CAPITOL DR, WESTBROOK PEDIATRICS 53005 #010-02-1982 L1983 **PD** *020 †55

KRAFT, John Marshall. ■ 53005 #056-06-1971 L1972 **P** *020

KROPP, Marina Leonidovna. 3305 N 124TH ST, REHABILITATION 53005 #913-99-1982 L2000 **PM** *020 †60

KRUG, Scott James. 225 S EXECUTIVE DR 53005 #056-06-1996 L1997 **AN** *020 †05 ‡

KUKREJA, Promil. ■ 53045 #495-30-1995 L2006 **AN** *012

KULA, Ayse Oge. ■ 53045 #902-04-1994 L2006 **AN** *012

KULKARNI, Vivekanand P. ■ 53045 #495-17-1968 L1973 **HEM** *020

LAMMERS, John Philip. 19333 W NORTH AVE 53045 #018-03-1969 L1971 **DR NM** *020 †80,28

LAWRENCE, Lee James. ■ 53005 #056-06-1985 L1988 **EM** *020 †16

LEH, Steven Lim. ■ 53045 #056-05-2000 L2006 **PCC** *100 †20

LEHRMANN, Mary C. 13950 W CAPITOL DR 53005 #056-06-1990 L1991 **PD** *020 †55

LITZOW, J Kim. 19355 TANALA DR 53045 #056-06-1986 L1987 **CHP P** *020

LIU, Henry. ■ 53045 #016-42-1997 L2001 **AN** *020 †05

LLOYD, James Robert. 13105 W BLUEMOUND RD, STE 150 53005 #016-11-1979 L1980 **NS** *020 †25

LOEWENSTEIN, Paul Willon. 13800 W NORTH AVE, STE 110 53005 #017-20-1976 L1982 **PS** *020 †85,65

LOGAN, Michael Jeffrey. 16535 W BLUEMOUND RD, STE 200 53005 #056-06-1964 L1968 **P OS** *020 †75

LUEDKE, Donald Max. 17050 W NORTH AVE 53005 #056-05-1962 L1963 **IM** *071

MADDEN, Peter Neville. 19333 W NORTH AVE 53045 #026-04-1962 L1972 **DR** *071 †80

MADDIKUNTA, Rajesh Venkat. ■ 53045 #495-65-1997 L2001 **CD** *012 †20

MAIER, Joseph Thomas. 17000 W NORTH AVE, STE 200E 53005 #056-06-1968 L1969 **EM GP** *020

MAKHIJA, Veronica. ■ 53045 #056-05-2008 *012

MANION, Lorelle M. 1305 N BARKER RD, STE 1 53045 #056-06-1993 L1994 **PD** *020 †55

MANN, Dale Henry. ■ 53045 #056-05-1956 L1957 **PD** *071

MARESCA, Anthony P. ■ 53045 #308-03-1982 L1985 **AN** *020 †05

MARKELOVA, Natalia V. ■ 53045 #913-01-1987 L2005 **ATP PCP** *100 †10

MARTENS, William Earl. 19475 W NORTH AVE, STE 400 53045 #056-05-1962 L1963 **GYN** *020 †30

MAS, Maria Isabel. 3305 N 124TH ST 53005 #308-03-1984 L1988 **P** *020 †75 ‡

MASKOUN, Waddah. ■ 53045 #875-02-2000 L2007 **IM** *100 †20

MATSIS, John Peter. 4560 COMPTON CT, ELMBROOK HOSPITAL 53045 #017-20-1962 L1967 **DR NM** *020 †80,28

MC CANN, Steven Bruce. 19475 W NORTH AVE, STE 400 53045 #035-08-1993 L1997 **OBG** *020 †30

MC KESSON, Catherine C. ■ 53005 #051-04-1992 L1997 **FTH** *020 †18 ‡

MCNEELY, Parren Scott. ■ 53005 #016-11-2005 L2008 **NM** *012

MELIN, Thomas John. 19333 W NORTH AVE 53045 #056-06-1986 L1987 **AN** *020 †05

MELZER, Daryl John. 13950 W CAPITOL DR, WESTWOOD MEDICAL GROUP 53005 #056-06-1977 L1978 **IM IMG** *020 †20

METOFF, Joanne E. 17280 W NORTH AVE, STE 200 53045 #056-06-1977 L1979 **OBG** *020

MEVES, Theodore Frederick. ■ 53005 #017-20-1948 L1950 **AN** *071 †05

MEYERS, Richard Winston. ■ 53045 #016-06-1968 L1977 **GP** *020

MILBRATH, Mary Maud. 19475 W NORTH AVE, STE 301 53045 #056-05-1987 L1988 **OTO** *020 †45

MILLER, Safiyun Sugra. 19333 W NORTH AVE 53045 #056-05-1994 L1995 **DR** *020 †80,28

MINGO, Catherine Cay. 14135 GOLF PKWY, 14135 GOLF PARKWAY 53005 #056-06-1993 L1994 **AN** *020 †05

MINIKEL, Susan Carol. 15905 HEATHER HILL DR, P O BOX 387 53005 #056-06-1982 L1983 **DR** *020 †80

MITRA, Samir Kumar. ■ 53005 #495-15-1957 L1976 **AN** *072

MODRZYNSKI, John Paul. 2085 N CALHOUN RD, 2085 N CALHOUN ROAD 53005 #056-06-1979 L1980 **FM** *020 †18

MORRIS, Janie Powell. 225 S EXECUTIVE DR 53005 #056-06-1999 L2002 **AN** *020 †05 ‡

MUNOZ, Andrea Lynn. 13850 W CAPITOL DR, BROOKFIELD CLINIC 53005 #056-05-1992 L1993 **PD** *020 †55

MUSZYNSKI, Cheryl Ann. ■ 53005 #028-02-1988 L2000 **NS NSP** *071 †25 ‡

NAKATA, Steven Keiji. 19333 W NORTH AVE 53045 #056-06-1988 L1989 **AN** *020 †05

NANGIA, Samir. ■ 53005 #422-01-2006 L2008 **IM** *012

NEMCEK, Albert Andrew. ■ 53045 #056-06-1956 L1958 **R** *071 †80

NEWHALL, Melissa. 13850 W CAPITOL DR, AURORA ADVANCED HEALTHCARE 53005 #020-12-1989 L1996 **FM** *020 †18 ‡

NORMAN, Sharniecia L. 1350 S SUNNY SLOPE RD 53005 #056-06-2002 L2004 **FM** *020 †18

NULAND, Stanley John. ■ 53045 #056-05-1955 L1958 **OM OS** *071 †85

OLANDER, Tina Mina. 19475 W NORTH AVE STE 30 53005 #038-41-1996 L1999 **IM** *020 †20

OLINGER, Gordon Nodell. 19635 PUTNEYS CT 53045 #035-45-1968 L1976 **TS** *020 †85,90

OLSON, David Carl. 2085 N CALHOUN RD 53005 #056-06-1986 L1987 **FM FPG** *020 †18 ‡

OPATKEN, Clifford John. 225 S EXECUTIVE DR, PHYSICIAN'S ACCOUNTING 53005 #020-12-1982 L1985 **AN** *020 †05

OSTERGAARD, John Michael. 2085 N CALHOUN RD, PROHEALTH CARE MEDICAL CEN 53005 #056-06-1986 L1987 **FM** *020 †18

PAGEL, Julie Margaret. 2650 GLENMAURA PL 53005 #056-06-1983 L1990 **PM** *020 †60

PAPIN, Michael Manion. 3305 N 124TH ST 53005 #056-06-2000 L2001 **P** *020 †75

PARIKH, Rajulkumar Rashmi. ■ 53045 #495-22-2003 L2007 **N** *012 †20

PARK, Tracy Alan. 19333 W NORTH AVE 53045 #056-06-1987 L1989 **PM** *020 †60

PATEL, Atulkumar Natu. 19333 W NORTH AVE 53045 #056-06-1987 L1989 **AN** *020 †05

PATTERSON, Maria Portello. 12690 W NORTH AVE 53045 #041-01-1992 L2000 **PO** *020 †35

PAULSEN, Richard Alan. 225 S EXECUTIVE DR 53005 #056-06-1998 L1999 **AN** *020 †05

PAVLIC, Robert Stephen. 19333 W NORTH AVE 53045 #056-06-1954 L1955 **OBG** *071 †30

PEARCE, Jan Dalrymple. 17000 W NORTH AVE, STE 200E 53005 #020-02-1970 L1971 **DR** *020 †80

PEARSON, Larry Chas. 601 N BARKER RD, STE 110 53045 #056-06-1975 L1978 **RHU** *020 †20

PEARSON, Mark Edward. 601 N BARKER RD, STE 110 53045 #056-06-1982 L1987 **RHU IM** *020 †20

PELLEGRINI, Jorge Gaston. 3275 MONTILLA CT 53005 #429-01-1964 L1975 **ATP FOP** *020 †50

PELUSO, Carl Joseph. 17000 W NORTH AVE 11 53005 #056-06-2000 L2002 **PD** *020 †55 ‡

PERKINS, Cathy Ann. 3305 N 124TH ST 53005 #035-06-1988 L1996 **P** *020 †75

PERRAULT, Daniel Joseph. 19035 W CAPITOL DR STE 101 53045 #056-06-1996 L1997 **EM** *020 †18

PHILLIPS, John Richard. 13255 W BLUEMOUND RD 53005 #056-05-1970 L1971 **ORS** *020 †40

PINTAR, Karl. ■ 53045 #154-07-1954 L1967 **PTH** *030 †50

POSTLES, Jeffery Scott. 13950 W CAPITOL DR 53005 #056-06-1989 L1990 **IM** *020 †20

PURTOCK, Robert V. 225 S EXECUTIVE DR 53005 #056-06-1980 L1981 **AN** *020 †05

RAKOVSHIK, Anna Golod. 18725 BROOKFIELD LAKE DR 53045 #016-06-2003 L2005 **PD** *100 †55

RAMAN, Lakshmi. ■ 53045 #496-59-2003 L2006 **IM** *100

RANDHAWA, Jasleen Kaur. ■ 53045 #495-43-2005 *100

RAO, Rajesh Chalamalase. ■ 53005 #008-01-2007 L2008 **TY** *012

REIK, Robert P. 19475 W NORTH AVE, STE 400 53045 #056-06-1951 L1952 **GYN** *072 †30

REYNALDO, Primitivo I. ■ 53045 #748-01-1961 L1976 **AN** *071 †05

RHOMBERG, Bernard B. 225 S EXECUTIVE DR 53005 #016-02-1965 L1966 **AN** *020 †05

RICHTER, Theresa Mary. 20775 BARTLETT DR, ANES SOLUTIONS OF MILWAUKE 53045 #056-06-1982 L1983 **AN** *020 †05

ROACH, Donald Glenn. 19475 W NORTH AVE, STE 305 53045 #026-04-1979 L1980 **IM** *020 †20

ROTHWELL, David James. ■ 53005 #025-07-1961 L1970 **PTH** *071 †50

ROUMAN, William C. 225 S EXECUTIVE DR 53005 #056-05-1956 L1957 **AN** *020 †05

RUEHL, Roger Le Roy. ■ 53005 #056-06-1954 L1955 **IM** *071

RUGGERI, Sunyoung. 13800 W NORTH AVE, STE 100 53005 #048-04-2003 L2004 **D** *020 †15

RUSCH, Richard Lee. 225 S EXECUTIVE DR 53005 #056-06-1983 L1984 **AN** *020 †05

RUSSELL, James Patrick. 13800 W NORTH AVE, STE 100 53005 #056-06-2001 L2005 **D** *020 †15

RUSSELL, Thomas Joseph. 13800 W NORTH AVE, STE 100 53005 #056-06-1962 L1964 **D** *020 †15

RUVALCABA, Randal Karl. 19333 W NORTH AVE, EMERGENCY DEPT. 53045 #056-06-1992 L1993 **EM** *020 †16

RYPEL, Gregory Donald. 19333 W NORTH AVE, ELMBROOK MEMORIAL HOSPITAL 53045 #056-06-1986 L1990 **AN** *020 †05

SALGUERO, Hugo Stanley. ■ 53005 #005-18-2005 L2007 **AN** *012

SAN AGUSTIN, Eleazar S. 4390 DRUID CT 53005 #748-08-1972 L1978 **P** *020

SANTAMARIA-RUBIO, Julio J. ■ 53005 #715-01-1981 L1987 **HEM IM** *020 †20

SARRACINO, Susan Margaret. 225 S EXECUTIVE DR 53005 #018-03-1985 L1989 **AN** *020 †05

SCHAEFER, Richard Matthew. 225 S EXECUTIVE DR 53005 #056-06-1983 L1984 **AN NUP** *020

SCHAPER, Aysha L. 1350 S SUNNY SLOPE RD, 390927165 53005 #056-06-1993 L1998 **IM** *020 †05

SCHMIDT, Kathleen Ann. 225 S EXECUTIVE DR 53005 #056-06-1985 L1986 **AN OS** *020 †05

SCHNEIDER, George Robt. 1350 S SUNNY SLOPE RD 53005 #056-06-1970 L1973 **IM** *020 †20

SCHNEIDER, Mary Lynn. 225 S EXECUTIVE DR 53005 #056-06-2003 L2004 **AN** *020

SCHNEIDER, Michael Daniel. 17000 W NORTH AVE 53005 #056-06-1995 L1998 **IM** *020 †20

SCHWIETERING, Eric B. 16535 W BLUEMOUND RD, STE 200 53005 #038-40-1993 L1994 **CHP** *020 †75

SEKHAR, Kiran Polisetty. ■ 53045 #056-06-2008 *012

SETTIMI, Albino L. ■ 53005 #026-04-1948 L1950 **IM** *071 †20

SEWELL, Robert Harold. 17000 W NORTH AVE, STE 107W 53005 #016-11-1959 L1962 **GS** *071 †85

SHANKAR, Hariharan. ■ 53045 #495-16-1983 L2002 **APM** *100 †05

SIDDIQUI, Nighat D. 3270 FORDHAM CT, 1121 E NORTH AVE. 53005 #704-06-1986 L2006 **FM** *100 †18

SIDHU, Jasdeep Singh. ■ 53045 #056-06-2007 L2007 **IM** *012

SILIUNAS, Mindas. 17280 W NORTH AVE STE 203 53045 #016-01-1981 L1983 **P GPM** *020 †75

SIMHAN, Shwetha. ■ 53005 #496-34-2004 **AN** *012

SMOLIK, John Aloyauie, Jr. 2085 N CALHOUN RD, PROHEALTH CARE MEDICAL CEN 53005 #056-05-1981 L1982 **FM** *020 †18

SOBCZAK, Dennis Anthony. 19475 W NORTH AVE, STE 400 53045 #056-06-1986 L1987 **OBG** *020 †30

SONDAG, Glenn Eugene. 13800 W NORTH AVE, STE 100 53005 #016-06-1969 L1978 **D** *020 †20,15

SONDERMAN, Philip Lee. 13800 W NORTH AVE, STE 110 53005 #056-05-1985 L1986 **PS HS** *020 †85,65

SOUTHERN, James Fount. ■ 53045 #039-01-1979 L1996 **PP** *020 †50

SPIELBAUER, Gregory Paul. 17000 W NORTH AVE, STE 200E 53005 #018-03-1995 L2000 **IM** *020 †20

STADLER, Eric Robert. ■ 53005 #056-06-2000 L2008 **IM** *020 †20

STASZKIEWICZ, Mark Robert. 17000 W NORTH AVE STE 1, STE 110E 53005 #056-05-1995 L1996 **PD** *020 †55

STEIN, Ronald Wayne. 225 S EXECUTIVE DR 53005 #056-05-1964 L1966 **AN** *020 †05

STEINHOFF, Jennifer Erin. ■ 53005 #056-06-2008 *012

STEPHENSON, Jack Baker. ■ 53045 #048-04-2007 **PS** *012

STEWART, Edward T. 2470 ANITA DR 53045 #028-02-1962 L1971 **R** *071 †80

STOECKL, Joseph. 19333 W NORTH AVE 53045 #056-05-1988 L1989 **AN** *020 †05

STOKES, Kathleen Sarah. 13800 W NORTH AVE, STE 100 53005 #056-06-1987 L1988 **D** *020 †15 ‡

STOLARSKI, Amy Joann. 13950 W CAPITOL DR, WESTBROOK PEDIATRICS 53005 #056-06-1992 L1993 **PD** *020 †55

STRAKA, Bradley. 13800 W NORTH AVE, STE 100 53005 #016-11-1998 L2002 **D** *020 †15

STROTHER, Stephen Vance. 13950 W CAPITOL DR 53005 #056-05-1977 L1985 **IM** *020 †20
SWART, Gary Lee. 19333 W NORTH AVE 53045 #056-06-1989 L1992 **EM** *020 †16
SWEIDAN, Raed. ■ 53045 #875-01-1981 L1994 **CD** *020 †20
SYTSMA, Mark Jonathan. ■ 53005 #056-06-2004 L2005 **ORS** *012
TANTY, Daniel Chas. 13850 W CAPITOL DR, BROOKFIELD CLINIC 53005 #056-06-1973 L1975 **IM** *020 †20
TAWADROUS, Zakaria Solima. ■ 53045 #915-02-1999 **IM** *012
TELEGA, Dorota Halina. 13950 W CAPITOL DR STE 200, WESTBROOK PEDS 53005 #759-01-1989 L2000 **CHN** *012 †55
TENGE, Jackie Ralph. 19333 W NORTH AVE 53045 #056-05-1973 L1975 **PTH** *072 †50
THOMAS, Jaren G. ■ 53005 #056-06-2007 **IM** *012
THOMAS, John Everett. 1350 S SUNNY SLOPE RD 53005 #056-06-2002 L2003 **FM** *020 †18
THOMAS, Manuel De Jesus. ■ 53005 #308-04-1995 L2004 **PD** *020 †55
THOMAS, Sayana Rachel. ■ 53045 #056-05-2007 **IM** *012
THOMSON, Jeffrey Robt. 225 S EXECUTIVE DR 53005 #056-06-1984 L1985 **AN** *020 †05
TORRES, Katherine M. ■ 53005 #003-75-2006, ▲ L2007 **IM** *012
TRAMPE, Erin Joelle. 2085 N CALHOUN RD 53005 #028-34-2002 L2005 **FM** *020 †18
TREVINO, Melanie Kay. 12805 W BURLEIGH RD 53005 #003-01-1993 L1999 **DMP D** *062 †15
TREVINO, Richard C, II. 19475 W NORTH AVE, STE 201 53045 #048-15-1994 L1998 **HS** *020 †40
TRINKL, Denise Marie. 225 S EXECUTIVE DR 53005 #056-06-1991 L1992 **AN** *020 †05
TROY, James Lawrence. 13800 W NORTH AVE, STE 100 53005 #024-01-1975 L1981 **DMP D** *020 †20,15
TURCO, Glenn Raymond. 2240 VINCENT DR, GLENN TURCO 53045 #028-79-1989, ▲ L1993 **AN PAN** *05
TURCO, Kathy Lynn. ■ 53005 #056-05-1987 L1993 **P** *074 †75
URBAN, Frank Henry. ■ 53005 #056-05-1954 L1955 **D OS** *071 †15
URLAKIS, Kenneth James. 17280 W NORTH AVE STE 200, LIFETIME OB/GYN 53045 #056-06-1958 L1959 **OBG** *071 †30
VAN GILDER, Jane Mary. ■ 53005 #056-06-1987 *100
VARGHESE, Abraham. 13950 W CAPITOL DR 53005 #016-11-1991 L1992 **IM** *020 †20
VARGHESE, Thomas. 19475 W NORTH AVE STE 306, ELMBROOK NEUROLOGY 53045 #496-30-1994 L2005 **CN** *075
VASQUEZ, Eufrocina Cruz. ■ 53045 #748-02-1955 L1977 **AN** *071
VELIVELA, Sarat Kumar. 19333 W NORTH AVE, ELMBROOK MEMORIAL HOSPITAL 53045 #496-34-2003 L2007 **IM** *020 †20
VIERNES, Patricio F. 13845 W CAPITOL DR 53005 #748-02-1964 L1976 **IM PUD** *020
VINCENT, Suzanne Leigh. 13950 W CAPITOL DR, WESTBROOK PEDIATRICS 53005 #654-01-1983 L1985 **PD OPH** *020 †55
VONDRAK, Ben Frank. ■ 53005 #016-11-1961 L1962 **OBG OS** *071 †30
VONDRELL, John Jos. 19333 W NORTH AVE, ELMBROOK MEMORIAL HOSP 53045 #056-06-1963 L1969 **AN OS** *071 †05
VOSTERS, Randal Leonard. 13950 W CAPITOL DR 53005 #056-06-1987 L1991 **FM FSM** *020 †18
WALTON, Timothy Michael. 225 S EXECUTIVE DR 53005 #056-06-1984 L1987 **AN** *020 †05
WARSH, James Richard. 225 S EXECUTIVE DR 53005 #056-06-1971 L1976 **AN PME** *020 †05
WHITE, James Everelt. 12720 W NORTH AVE 53005 #025-01-1973 L1977 **PS HS** *020 †85,65
WILSON, James Michael. 225 S EXECUTIVE DR 53005 #021-01-1983 L2002 **AN** *020 †05
WOMACK, Greg Neil. 17000 W NORTH AVE, STE 108 53005 #019-02-1996 L2002 **U** *020 †95
WU, Bobby. 17000 W NORTH AVE, BROOKFIELD SURGICAL ASSOCI 53005 #056-06-2000 L2002 **GS** *020 †85 ‡
WYNSEN, John Chas. 2085 N CALHOUN RD, STE 203 53005 #038-41-1982 L1985 **IM CD** *020 †20
YAHNKE, David Paul. ■ 53045 #056-06-1974 L1975 **EM** *050
YAN, Yuhui. ■ 53045 #243-16-1999 **PS** *012
YARD, Albert Chas. ■ 53005 #056-06-1961 L1962 **DR** *071 †80
YUG, Anthony Geo. ■ 53008 #056-06-1989 L1990 **D** *020 †15
YUG, David. ■ 53005 #056-06-1994 L2001 **DR** *020 †80
ZAMAN, Abunasar F. ■ 53045 #704-03-1955 L1974 **PTH** *030 †50
ZEBALLOS CHAVEZ, Juan Car. ■ 53005 #737-11-1999 L2006 **PCC** *012
ZHU, Hongsheng. 2085 N CALHOUN RD 53005 #056-06-1995 L1996 **ORS OFA** *020 †40

BROOKLYN – GREEN

BEASLEY, Penelope E N. ■ 53521 #026-04-1969 L1973 **GP** *074
BURANT, Dolores. W702 HORAN RD 53521 #056-05-1970 L1991 **FM ADM** *020 †18

BROWN DEER – MILWAUKEE

ERWIN, Charles R. ■ 53209 #016-06-1945 L1956 **PHP D** *071
FRIEDRICHS, Edward Slade. ■ 53223 #016-06-1958 L1962 **IM ADM** *040
GRADE, Charles Michael. 4555 W SCHROEDER DR 53223 #056-05-1989 L1991 **P** *020 †75
JOHNSTONE, Michael F. 9233 N GREEN BAY RD 53209 #056-06-1982 L1983 **FM** *020 †18
KLEIN, Thomas Gerard. ■ 53223 #018-75-2004, ▲ L2004 **IM** *012
MEDINA, Jeanne Marie. 9233 N GREEN BAY RD 53209 #056-05-1979 L1980 **FM** *020 †18
PLOTKIN, Michael David. 9233 N GREEN BAY RD 53209 #011-02-1972 L1973 **OPH** *071 †35
ROWE, Bruce Evan. 9233 N GREEN BAY RD 53209 #018-03-1994 L1995 **FM OBS** *020 †18
SIMONS, John P. ■ 53223 #048-78-2002, ▲ L2006 **AN** *012
ZIMMERMAN, Richard Carl. 4600 W SCHROEDER DR 53223 #056-06-1966 L1967 **CHP P** *072 †75

BROWNSVILLE – DODGE

FRIEDRICH, Leland Edward. 501 HIGHLAND AVE 53006 #056-05-1941 L1942 **GP** *071

BRUCE – RUSK

BARKER, Edward Theodore. ■ 54819 #028-02-1957 L1957 **PD** *071 †55
CHATTERTON, Howard Treat. ■ 54819 #036-07-1976 L1979 **FM** *071 †18

BURLINGTON – RACINE

BANDEALY, Malik Tajuddin. 252 MCHENRY ST 53105 #704-02-1988 L1997 **HO** *020 †20
BATSLEER, Robert Louis. 141 S PINE ST 53105 #165-02-1959 L1966 **GP PDS** *071 †18
BAUR, Martin Cesar. 248 MCHENRY ST, AURORA BURLINGTON CLINIC 53105 #056-06-2003 L2007 **FM** *020 †18
BERNSTEIN, Steven Alan. 248 MCHENRY ST 53105 #035-08-1982 L1988 **U** *020 †95
BILLINGSLEY, Sandra Lynn. 248 MCHENRY ST, AURORA MEDICAL GROUP INC. 53105 #056-06-1989 L1990 **FM** *020 †20
BOTKA-WUNDER, Gabriella M. ■ 53105 #473-01-1951 L1965 **IM P** *071
DRESDEN, Scott Mcneill. 248 MCHENRY ST, AURORA OCCUPATIONAL HLTH S 53105 #056-05-1994 L1995 **FM** *020 †18
ELLINGSTAD, Richard Allen. 248 MCHENRY ST 53105 #056-05-1968 L1969 **FM** *020 †18
ERICKSON, Lief, Sr. 248 MCHENRY ST 53105 #026-04-1950 L1950 **FM PLM** *020
ERICKSON, Lief W, Jr. 248 MCHENRY ST 53105 #056-06-1974 L1975 **GS** *020 †85
FIETE, Randall Lee. 137 E CHESTNUT ST 53105 #028-34-1986 L1987 **PD** *020
GEIMER, Nicholas F. 252 MCHENRY ST 53105 #056-05-1963 L1965 **ON IM** *075 †20
HAIDER, Syed N. 252 MCHENRY ST 53105 #704-21-1990 L1995 **HO** *020
JINDAL, Vishnu. 252 MCHENRY ST, MEMORIAL HOSPITAL OF BURLI 53105 #038-43-1999 L2006 **IM** *020 †20
JOSHI, Shailesh G. 252 MCHENRY ST 53105 #495-22-1976 L1978 **AN** *020 †05 ‡
KRISMER, George John. 248 MCHENRY ST 53105 #030-06-1956 L1957 **GP** *020
LARMORE, Gerry Kent. 248 MCHENRY ST, BURLINGTON CLINIC S.C. 53105 #056-05-1975 L1976 **FM** *020 †18
LEE, Linda. 248 MCHENRY ST, AURORA MEDICAL GROUP 53105 #011-02-1995 L1997 **FM** *020 †18
MAJEWSKI, Michael Jos. 248 MCHENRY ST 53105 #032-01-1978 L1979 **OBG** *020 †30
MAKER, George Edward. 248 MCHENRY ST 53105 #050-02-1976 L1977 **OBG** *020 †30
MOLOT, Mark David. ■ 53105 #065-09-1962 L1964 **PTH OS** *020 †50
MURRAY, Barbara Joan. 190 GARDNER AVE, STE 3 53105 #010-02-1980 L1986 **P PYG** *020 †75 ‡
NGO-GRACIOSA, Elena Y. 248 MCHENRY ST 53105 #748-11-1972 L1982 **OBG GYN** *020 †30
NGUYEN, Tri Van. 248 MCHENRY ST 53105 #016-06-1989 L1994 **D OS** *020 †15
PRCHAL, Carol Louise. 252 MCHENRY ST 53105 #016-11-1983 L1988 **ORS** *071 †40
REIN, Arthur Kevin. 248 MCHENRY ST 53105 #056-06-1981 L1982 **IM** *020 †20
SCHIEFFER, James Paul. 248 MCHENRY ST, AURORA HEALTH CTR 53105 #056-06-1970 L1974 **FM** *071 †18
SCHMIDT, Randall Wm. 248 MC HENRY ST 53105 #422-01-1982 L1983 **IM OS** *020 †20
SMITH, Sharon Anne. 425 MILWAUKEE AVE STE 1 53105 #035-46-1977 L1979 **FM** *020
STEFFANIDES, Gilbert D. 231 MILLGATE DR, PROHEALTH CARE MEDICAL CEN 53105 #056-05-1990 L1992 **FM** *020 †18
STONE, Addison Thomas. ■ 53105 #056-05-2004 L2004 **ORS** *012
STONE, William Henry. 248 MCHENRY ST, BURLINGTON CLINIC 53105 #016-11-1967 L1977 **OS HEM** *071 †20
SVASTA, Paula Cristiana. 252 MCHENRY ST, BURLINGTON MEMORIAL HOSPIT 53105 #781-01-1993 L2002 **IM** *020 †20
TAYLOR, David Lawrence. 248 MCHENRY ST 53105 #023-01-1982 L1989 **FM** *020 †18
THACHENKARY, Ted George. 252 MCHENRY ST, AURORA MEMORIAL HOSPITAL O 53105 #305-01-2002 L2008 **IM** *020 †20
TWARDY, Jolanata Martyna. 248 MCHENRY ST 53105 #759-03-1991 L2002 **IMG** *020 †20
WAGNER, Paul Francis. 308 MCHENRY ST 53105 #056-05-1968 L1969 **OPH** *020 †35
WAGNER, Richard F. 252 MCHENRY ST 53105 #056-05-1975 L1978 **EM IM** *020 †20,16
WAGNER, Stephen Paul. 308 MC HENRY ST 53105 #056-05-1998 L1999 **OPH** *020 †35
WEBBER, Paul Robt. 248 MCHENRY ST 53105 #016-06-1973 L1974 **FM** *020 †18
WHEATON, Robert Carroll. ■ 53105 #056-05-1955 L1956 **GP** *071
WHITE, Samuel Crawford. 248 MCHENRY ST, AURORA BURLINGTON CLINIC 53105 #045-01-2003 L2007 **FM** *020 †18
ZAREMBA, Katarzyna Iwona. 248 MCHENRY ST 53105 #759-03-1991 L1998 **IM** *020 †20

BUTTE DES MORTS – WINNEBAGO

KELLEY, Thomas Jos, Jr. 5139 WASHINGTON ST 54927 #041-02-1952 L1965 **P** *071 †75

BUTTERNUT – ASHLAND

SHAFFER, Martin Chas. 6642 W FLAMBEAU DAM RD 54514 #016-11-1969 L1970 **GS** *020 †85

CABLE – BAYFIELD

LINDBERG, Evan Florian. ■ 54821 #023-07-1956 L1961 **TS GS** *071 †85,90
TULLY, Timothy Eugene. ■ 54821 #016-06-1969 L1972 **DR NM** *020 †80,28

CADOTT – CHIPPEWA

BOWE, Clifford Thos. 322 N MAIN ST, CADOTT MEDICAL CENTER 54727 #056-06-1958 L1959 **FM AM** *020 †18
JOSEPH, Amrish Roshan. 305 STATE HWY 27, MARSHFIELD CLN-CADOTT CTR 54727 #495-52-2003 L2007 **FM** *020
OBCENA, Ricardo Sanchez. 305 S HIGHWAY 27 54727 #748-01-1964 L1976 **GP IM** *020
SANCHEZ, Romulo Manalo. 305 S HIGHWAY 27, MARSHFIELD CLINIC-CADITT C 54727 #748-07-1964 L1976 **FM IM** *020 †18

CALEDONIA – RACINE

BOTE, Rommel Ortiz. 6900 NICHOLSON RD, VILLAGE OF CALEDONIA FIRE 53108 #016-43-1995 L1999 **EM** *020 †16
HERNANDEZ, Antoinette. ■ 53108 #016-01-2003 L2004 **PD** *100 †55
SILKEY, John Willard. ■ 53108 #308-11-1988 L1989 **FM EM** *020 †18

■ = Address Information Privacy Protected

CAMBRIDGE – DANE

DANGLE, Harland C. ■ 53523 #056-06-1944 L1945 **PTH** *071 †50
GAY, George Lewis, Jr. 704 KATIE CT 53523 #056-05-1972 L1973 **FM FPG** *020 †18
LINS, Robert Jos. ■ 53523 #056-05-1969 L1971 **IM** *074 †20
NOTTESTAD, Stephanie Lee. 704 KATIE CT 53523 #056-05-2002 L2003 **FM** *020 †18
WENDLAND, Diane Lynn. 704 KATIE CT, FORT HEALTH CARE 53523 #056-05-1986 L1987
    FM *020 †18

CAMERON – BARRON

BARTYNSKI, Jeffrey M. 2049 15TH AVE 54822 #041-07-1985 L1990 **OTO FPS** *020 †45
BENNETT, Craig Scott. 2049 15TH AVE 54822 #026-04-1999 L2000 **FM** *020 †18
SKAAR, Phillip James. 2049 15TH AVE 54822 #046-01-2003 L2004 **FM** *020 †18
ZUROB, Adel S. 1001 W MAIN ST 54822 #539-06-1989 L2004 **PCC IM** *020 †20

CAMP DOUGLAS – JUNEAU

SALVO, Emile Wm. III. 16288 HUCKLEBERRY RD 54618 #056-05-1985 L1988 **EM** *020

CASCO – KEWAUNEE

RIES, Peter Marshall. N6364 TOWNLINE RD 54205 #056-05-1978 L1979 **IM** *020 †20

CASHTON – MONROE

ERICKSON, Joel David. 238 FRONT ST, CASHTON SCENIC BLUFFS 54619 #026-04-1999 L2000
    FM *020 †18

CEDAR GROVE – SHEBOYGAN

DEMASTER, Brian Jon. 313 S MAIN ST 53013 #056-06-1992 L1993 **FM** *020 †18
NETZOW, Earl John. 6958 SAUK TRAIL RD 53013 #035-20-1943 L1944 **FM** *071
NOCK, Gilbert John, Jr. ■ 53013 #056-06-1963 L1965 **P OS** *071
PFEFFER, Robert Aloysius. N263 CLAERVUE SHRS 53013 #056-06-1970 L1975 **FM** *020 †18

CEDARBURG – OZAUKEE

BLASKOWSKI, Paul Leo. 7861 STATE HWY 60, AURORA HEALTH CARE 53012
    #056-06-1997 L1999 **FM** *020 †18
BUDNY, Christopher. N143W6515 PIONEER RD 53012 #056-06-1988 L1990 **IM** *020 †20
CHEMOTTI, M Thomas. N54W6135 MILL ST, PO BOX 503 53012 #056-06-1974 L1978
    OPH *020 †35
CHICKS, Julie Ann. 4922 COLUMBIA RD, STE 200 53012 #056-05-1995 L1998 **IM** *020 †20
DEL ROSARIO, Salvador V. N54W6135 MILL ST 53012 #748-08-1968 L1976 **IM FM** *020
DONEGAN, Judith F Higgins. ■ 53012 #028-02-1964 L1974 **AN** *071 †05
ESTILL, Carol Jean. N143W6515 PIONEER RD, CEDAR MILLS MEDICAL GROUP 53012
    #056-06-1996 L1997 **PD** *020 †55
GARCIA, Arthur F. ■ 53012 #016-11-1966 L1967 **OPH** *071 †35
GEIGER, Jason Eric. ■ 53012 #056-06-2003 L2006 **FM** *020
GEIGER, Tracy Merle. ■ 53012 #056-06-2007 **FP** *012
GONIU, Kevin John. N143W6515 PIONEER RD 53012 #056-06-1980 L1981 **IM** *020 †20
HAGEN, Elizabeth Rose. N143W6515 PIONEER RD 53012 #056-06-1993 L1994 **PD** *020 †55
HAGERMAN, Daniel Alan. N143W6515 PIONEER RD 53012 #056-05-1989 L1990 **PD** *020 †55
HEISE, James Freeman. N143W6515 PIONEER RD, CEDAR MILLS MEDICAL GROUP 53012
    #056-06-2002 L2004 **IM** *020 †20
HRON, John Raymond. ■ 53012 #056-06-1974 L1975 **FM** *020
HUCKABY, Audrey L Straka. ■ 53012 #056-05-1951 L1952 **DR NR** *071 †80
JABLONSKI, Daniel F. N143W6515 PIONEER RD 53012 #056-05-1984 L1988 **IM** *020 †20
JOHNSTON, Jane Kelly. N143W6515 PIONEER RD 53012 #056-06-1999 L2000 **PD** *020 †55
KRAUSE, Bobbi Lynn. 1700 PIONEER RD 53012 #305-01-2004 L2006 **PM** *012
LOHAUS, Gary H. ■ 53012 #017-20-1975 L1976 **PUD IM** *020 †20
MAMMEN, Indira. 4922 COLUMBIA RD 53012 #495-31-1971 L1978 **OBG** *020 †30
MEULER, David Gregory. N143W6515 PIONEER RD 53012 #056-05-2002 L2004 **PD** *020 †55
MOLONEY, Kathleen Rose. W62N179 WASHINGTON AVE, STE 1 53012 #654-01-2003 L2005
    FM *020 †18
MONDLOCH, Victoria Jeanne. W62N225 WASHINGTON AVE, WOMEN'S HEALTH
    CENTER 53012 #056-06-1983 L1984 **OBG** *020 †30
MONTGOMERY, Edwin Geo, Jr. N143W6515 PIONEER RD 53012 #056-06-1961 L1962
    PD ADL *071 †55
NITSCHKE, Leann F. W67N710 FRANKLIN AVE 53012 #056-06-1988 L1989 **GS** *030 †85
ROGERS, Jeffrey Phillip. ■ 53012 #016-11-1969 L1980 **CD IM** *071 †20
SHEWCZYK, Thomas John. 4922 COLUMBIA RD 53012 #056-05-1974 L1975 **FM** *020 †18
STEPHANY, Jeffrey John. N54W6135 MILL ST, STE 200 53012 #056-06-1995 L1997
    ORS *020 †40
STREMSKI, Ernest Stan. ■ 53012 #056-06-1986 L1987 **EM** *020 †55
TILLER, Mary Rose. ■ 53012 #305-01-1987 L1993 **APM** *020 †05
ZAJACKOWSKI, Mark Eugene. ■ 53012 #056-06-1974 L1975 **FM** *020

CHETEK – BARRON

ESSWEIN, James Lee. 220 DOUGLAS ST, MIDELFORT CLC CHETEK 54728 #056-05-1965 L1968
    FM *020 †18
KRISTENSEN, Lowell Andrew. 528 PLEASURE ST 54728 #008-01-1954 L1955 **FM** *071 †18
MARQUARDT, Jeffrey M. 806 2ND ST 54728 #056-05-1989 L1994 **FM** *020 †18
REISNER, Peter D. 220 DOUGLAS ST, MIDELFORT CLINIC - CHETEK 54728 #048-02-2001 L2002
    FM *020
TURNER, Benjamin Forbes. ■ 54728 #026-04-2008 *012

CHILTON – CALUMET

ACKELL, Peter Hummel. 614 MEMORIAL DR, APPLETON CARDIO ASSC 53014
    #051-01-1981 L1988 **CD IC** *020 †20
ANSARI, Bakhtiar B. 618 MEMORIAL DR 53014 #704-02-1984 L1997 **N** *020
BOCKHORN, Christine. 618 MEMORIAL DR 53014 #025-07-1986 L1992 **FM** *020 †18
CAMPBELL, John Thos. 618 MEMORIAL DR 53014 #038-06-1964 L1972 **U** *020 †95
CHAKRAVARTI, Neetu. 618 MEMORIAL DR 53014 #654-01-2003 L2006 **FM** *020 †18
DREMEL, Catherine Marie. 614 MEMORIAL DR 53014 #056-06-1988 L1993
    PM CHP *020 †60,55
GINDER, Michael Gayle. 614 MEMORIAL DR 53014 #026-04-1985 L1988 **EM** *020 †18
HOLDER, Michele A. 614 MEMORIAL DR 53014 #018-03-1991 L1994 **D** *020 †15
KNAUF, James Wm. 451 E BROOKLYN ST 53014 #056-06-1946 L1947 **GP GS** *071
LESCHKE, John Michael. 614 MEMORIAL DR 53014 #056-06-1984 L1985 **AN** *020 †05
MEYER, Kathryn Marie. 614 MEMORIAL DR 53014 #056-05-1999 L2000 **OBG** *020 †30
THEILER, Alvin Carl. 614 MEMORIAL DR 53014 #056-06-1945 L1948 **GP** *072
THEILER, Randy Thos. 451 E BROOKLYN ST 53014 #056-05-1977 L1978 **FM** *020 †18
TIPLER, Gene Arthur. 618 MEMORIAL DR 53014 #056-05-1980 L1981 **FM** *020 †18

CHIPPEWA FALLS – CHIPPEWA

AYER, Patrick Craig. 2661 COUNTY HIGHWAY I 54729 #028-02-1973 L1977 **EM** *020
BABARIA, Dharmesh. 2655 COUNTY HIGHWAY I 54729 #495-14-1996 L2004 **IM** *020
BARKLEY, Sharon Marie. 2655 COUNTY HIGHWAY I 54729 #038-41-1986 L1993 **PD** *020 †55
BARKLEY, William Jos. 2655 COUNTY HIGHWAY I 54729 #038-41-1986 L1993 **PD** *020 †55
BIEGING, Deborah Tierney. 2655 COUNTY HIGHWAY I 54729 #026-04-1979 L1985 **PD** *020 †55
BROWN, Jeffrey Frederic. 2525 COUNTY HIGHWAY I 54729 #056-05-1981 L1985 **OPH** *020 †35
BYRD, Jane Dinnies. 611 1ST AVE 54729 #056-05-1984 L1995 **PD** *020 †55
CABREROS, Helen R. THE DEV DISABLED, NORTHERN WISCONSIN CTR FOR 54729
    #748-11-1967 L1975 **PD** *071 †55
CARLSON, Stephen Frank. 2655 COUNTY HIGHWAY I 54729 #056-06-1997 L1999 **FM** *020 †18
COCHRANE, Peter Jos. 2655 COUNTY HIGHWAY I, MARSHFIELD CLINIC - CHIPPE 54729
    #041-13-1985 L2002 **GS VS** *020 †85
COCHRANE, Sara Lynne Orr. 2655 COUNTY HIGHWAY I 54729 #041-13-1983 L2003
    OBG *020 †30
COOK, Frederick Donald. ■ 54729 #056-05-1947 L1948 **AN** *071 †05
CROWSER, Aaron Jay. 611 1ST AVE, LUTHER MIDELFORT CHIPPEWA 54729
    #026-04-2004 L2005 **FM** *020 †18
DEISZ, Megan Stumm. ■ 54729 #056-05-2005 L2007 **PD** *012
DRAWBERT, John Paul. 2501 COUNTY HIGHWAY I 54729 #056-05-1980 L1986 **ORS** *020 †40
EBERT, Edward Louis. 2655 COUNTY HIGHWAY I, MARSHFIELD CLINIC 54729 #018-75-1975,
    ▲ L2006 **PUD IM** *020 †20
ETMUND, Kari Leah. ■ 54729 #025-07-2007 L2007 **AN** *012
EZENAGU, Leonard Chike. 611 1ST AVE 54729 #038-45-1992 L1999 **OBG** *020 †30
FLEMING, George Edward. ■ 54729 #016-11-1969 L1976 **ORS** *071 †40
FORSTER, Jeremy Scott. 2655 COUNTY HIGHWAY I 54729 #056-05-2001 L2004 **PD** *020 †55
FROHLING, Sandra Jean. 2655 COUNTY HIGHWAY I 54729 #054-04-1996 L1999 **IM** *020 †20
GAERLAN, Evangelina A. PO BOX 340 54729 #748-01-1953 L1978 **OS IM** *071
GEHL, Gerald Andrew. 7635 161ST ST 54729 #056-05-1964 L1965 **P CHP** *071
GERING, Kristie Lynn. 2449 COUNTY HIGHWAY I 54729 #046-01-1996 L1997 **FM** *020 †18
HANSEN, Steven Fredrick. 2661 COUNTY HIGHWAY I, ST. JOSEPH HOSPITAL 54729
    #026-04-1988 L1989 **FM** *020
HARRISON, Les Paul. 2655 COUNTY HIGHWAY I 54729 #037-01-1977 L1980 **IM** *020 †20
HERZOG, Bernard Frederick. 8397 163RD ST 54729 #056-05-1966 L1985 **GS** *020 †85
HOLM, Peter Wm. 2525 COUNTY HIGHWAY I 54729 #016-06-1977 L1978 **OPH** *020 †35
IPPEL, Paul Martin. 2449 COUNTY HIGHWAY I 54729 #056-05-1978 L1979 **FM** *020 †18 ‡
JULIAN, Scott Earl. 2655 COUNTY HIGHWAY I 54729 #026-04-1989 L1992 **OBG** *020 †30
KEMPER, Charles Alexander. 2661 COUNTY TRUNK I 54729 #023-01-1943 L1948 **GP CD** *071
KREITLOW, Sharlene P. 2655 COUNTY HIGHWAY I 54729 #056-06-1991 L1995 **OBG** *020 †30
KUEHL, Mary J. 611 1ST AVE 54729 #056-06-1990 L1991 **FM** *020 †18
LANDWEHR, Mary Lisa. 2449 COUNTY HIGHWAY I 54729 #409-38-1999 L2003 **FM** *020 †18
LEA, Robert S. 2449 COUNTY HIGHWAY I 54729 #016-06-1980 L1982 **FM** *020 †18
LENHART, Jill Gunlikson. 611 1ST AVE 54729 #037-01-1993 L1994 **FM** *020 †18
LINDSTROM, John Russel. 2655 COUNTY HIGHWAY I, MARSHFIELD CLNC 54729
    #016-06-1972 L1979 **ORS** *020 †40
MANIQUIZ, Reynaldo C. 2655 COUNTY HIGHWAY I 54729 #748-08-1965 L1976 **FM IM** *020 †18
MC CANNA, Terrence Danl. 2525 COUNTY HIGHWAY I, CHIPPEWA VALLEY EYE CLINIC 54729
    #056-05-1991 L1995 **OPH** *020 †35
MILLER, Vincent Thos. 2655 COUNTY HIGHWAY I, MARSHFIELD CLINIC 54729
    #016-11-1976 L1991 **N** *020 †75
MITCHELL, Kenneth Richard. 611 1ST AVE 54729 #026-04-1989 L1990 **FM** *020 †18
MOMI, Rajinder Singh. 2029 COUNTY HIGHWAY I, MARSHFIELD CLINIC-CHIPPEWA 54729
    #495-03-1992 L2005 **P** *020 †75
ONUIGBO, Macaulay Amechi. 611 1ST AVE 54729 #690-04-1981 L2002 **NEP IM** *020 †20 ‡
O'SHIELDS, Wm Richard. ■ 54729 #026-04-1978 L1983 **GP EM** *071
OTTOMAN, Nizar. 2655 COUNTY HIGHWAY I, MARSHFIELD CLINIC-CHIPPEWA 54729
    #875-03-1996 L2004 **IM** *020
PETER, Laura Elizabeth. 2655 COUNTY HIGHWAY I, MARSHFIELD CLN-CHIPPEWA 54729
    #030-05-1993 L2007 **ORS** *100
REGEHR, Edward Henry. ■ 54729 #062-01-1962 L1964 **GP** *071
RHOADES, Bruce Cecil. 2655 COUNTY HIGHWAY I 54729 #030-05-1964 L1972 **P** *020 †75
ROGERS, Carla C. 611 1ST AVE 54729 #030-06-1986 L1989 **OBG** *020 †30
ROGERS, Stephen Michael. 611 1ST AVE 54729 #030-06-1986 L1987 **IM** *020 †20
SAMUELSON, Clarence. 694 DUTCHMAN DR 54729 #056-06-1946 L1948 **FM GP** *071
SAZAMA, John James. 2661 COUNTY TRUNK I 54729 #056-05-1937 L1938 **EM U** *071
SCHAUS, Kathryn Klimovitz. 2655 COUNTY HIGHWAY I, MARSHFIELD CLINIC-CHIPPEWA 54729
    #056-05-1989 L1993 **PD** *020 †55
SCHROEDER, Jeanne M. 611 1ST AVE 54729 #056-05-1978 L1979 **GYN** *020 †30
SINTSOV, Dmitriy R. 2655 COUNTY HIGHWAY I, MARSHFIELD CLN-CHIPPEWA 54729
    #913-29-1990 L2007 **AN CCA** *020
STEWART, Nathaniel James. 2501 COUNTY HIGHWAY I 54729 #026-04-1992 L1997
    ORS *020 †40
TAMAN, Mahmoud Shawky. 2655 COUNTY HIGHWAY I 54729 #915-03-1957 L1973 **P** *020 ‡

TOPLIFF, Aaron Jerome. 2655 COUNTY HIGHWAY I, MARSHFIELD CLINIC-CHIPPEWA 54729 #040-02-1998 L2005 **AN** *020
VANYO, Maureen Gloria. 611 1ST AVE 54729 #026-04-1996 L1997 **FM** *020 †18
WALTON, Michael Harold. 2661 COUNTY HIGHWAY I, ST JOSEPH'S HOSPITAL 54729 #026-04-1973 L1976 **FM** *020 †18
WEINDORFER, Jason John. 611 1ST AVE 54729 #056-06-2004 L2005 **FM** *020 †18
WHITLEY, Rhonda Rae. 2655 COUNTY HIGHWAY I, MARSHFIELD CLINIC-CHIPPEWA 54729 #045-04-1987 L1993 **OTO GS** *020 †45
WIGHTON, Harold Bruce. 610 DUTCHMAN DR, APT 2 54729 #041-02-1974 L2005 **FM** *020 †16,18
WILDES, Thomas Oliver. 2655 COUNTY HIGHWAY I, CHIPPEWA CENTER 54729 #021-01-1971 L1984 **OTO FPS** *020 †45
WIRT, Marcia Louise. 2655 COUNTY HIGHWAY I 54729 #016-01-1978 L1993 **PD RHU** *020 †55
WOLDUM, Lane Andrew. 611 1ST AVE 54729 #026-04-1989 L1995 **FM** *020 †18
WOLTER, Timothy John. 716 W COLUMBIA ST 54729 #026-04-1982 L1985 **FM** *020 †18
ZANDER, Margaret B. 2655 COUNTY HIGHWAY I 54729 #026-04-1990 L1993 **PD** *020 †55

CLEVELAND – MANITOWOC

BHATIA, Gurmeet Singh. 1205 NORTH AVE, CLEVELAND VA OUTPATIENT CL 53015 #495-05-1993 L1998 **IM** *020 †20
BIRKHOLZ, Steven Wm. ■ 53015 #056-06-1974 L1975 **ORS** *020 †40
REISKYTL, John Richard. 1205 NORTH AVE, CLEVELAND VA CLINIC 53015 #056-06-1988 L1990 **FM** *020 †18

CLINTON – ROCK

ADAMSKI, Gary Bernard. 307 OGDEN AVE 53525 #056-05-1976 L1979 **PD** *020 †55
JOHNSEN, Shelly Lea. 307 OGDEN AVE 53525 #056-05-2000 L2003 **FM** *020 †18
MURTHY, Sanjay. 601 JOHNSON AVE, UNIT 15B 53525 #495-37-1997 L2007 **FM GPM** *020
PATEL, Tejesh N. 307 OGDEN AVE 53525 #496-21-1996 L2001 **FM** *020 †18

CLINTONVILLE – WAUPACA

BEIMBORN, Karen Alyce. W8386 RUSTIC DR 54929 #056-06-1987 L1988 **FM** *020 †18
CASKEY, Harry Saml. 61 ANNE ST 54929 #056-06-1948 L1949 **GP** *071
EGAN, Cynthia. 370 S MAIN ST 54929 #056-05-1979 L1980 **FM** *020 †18
FANG, Yuchin. 370 S MAIN ST 54929 #056-05-1998 L1999 **FM** *020 †18
GOEDDERZ, Steven Anthony. 370 S MAIN ST 54929 #308-11-1984 L1996 **FM** *020 †18
GRAY, Leslie Howard. 370 S MAIN ST 54929 #056-05-1979 L1980 **FM** *020 †18
KANDARAJ, Jeyakumar. 61 ANNE ST 54929 #495-04-1987 L1999 **IM** *020 †20
KOLBECK, Scott Charles. 370 S MAIN ST 54929 #056-05-1987 L1993 **U** *020 †95

COLBY – CLARK

ADOLPHSON, John David. 111 DEHNE DR, MARSHFIELD CLINIC-COLBY/AB 54421 #026-04-1974 L1988 **FM** *020 †18
GILBERT, Janet Carol Aud. 111 DEHNE DR, MARSHFIELD CLINIC-COLBY CE 54421 #004-01-1985 L1992 **FM** *020 †18
HOERNEMAN, Tanya Kausch. 111 DEHNE DR 54421 #056-05-2000 L2004 **FM** *020 †18 ‡
KRENZKE, Karen Beaudet. 111 DEHNE DR 54421 #056-06-1988 L1989 **FM EM** *020 †18
WRITZ, Paul Lawrence. 111 DEHNE DR, COLBY/ABBOTSFORD CENTER 54421 #056-06-1983 L1986 **FM** *020 †18

COLFAX – DUNN

EARNHART, H Harlan. 809 HIGH ST 54730 #038-41-1958 L1961 **EM GP** *071
GLADITSCH, Richard Ernest. 1010 HIGH ST 54730 #056-05-1977 L1980 **FM** *020 †18

COLGATE – WASHINGTON

BAYLISS, Margaret Mary. 4800 MONCHES RD 53017 #056-06-1983 *100
CLARKE, William Robt. 6102 HIGHWAY Q 53017 #036-07-1979 L2004 **PD AN** *020 †55,05
HELD, Michael Barton. ■ 53017 #056-05-1991 L1992 **P** *020

COLUMBUS – COLUMBIA

BYRD, Janis Ellen. 1513 PARK AVE, COLUMBUS CLINIC 53925 #056-05-1976 L1977 **FM** *020 †18
GALVIN, Gary James. 1513 PARK AVE 53925 #018-03-1986 L2003 **GS** *020 †85
GULL, Nazi. 1511 PARK AVE 53925 #704-02-1987 L1990 **PUD** *020 †20
HADJIEV, Christo A. 1513 PARK AVE 53925 #198-01-1985 L2001 **FM** *020 †18
HANSELL, Charles Earl. 1513 PARK AVE 53925 #017-20-1973 L1976 **FM** *020 †18
KRAUS, Bruce Allan. 1515 PARK AVE 53925 #056-05-1974 L1978 **IM** *020 †20 ‡
KUGLITSCH, Michael Ervin. 53925 #056-43-1980 L1981 **U** *020 †95
MITCHELL, Thomas. 1511 PARK AVE, UW MEDICAL FOUNDATION 53925 #965-01-1986 L1995 **FM IM** *020 †18,20 ‡
POSER, Rolf F. 635 PARK AVE 53925 #056-06-1978 L1983 **IM CD** *020 †20
POSER, Samuel Groom. PO BOX 229, 625 PARK AVE 53925 #056-05-1982 L1985 **IM** *020 †20
WALZ, John Edward. 1511 PARK AVE 53925 #056-06-1977 L1978 **GS** *020
YOUNG, Paul Brooke. 1513 PARK AVE, COLUMBUS CLINIC 53925 #049-01-1985 L1986 **PD** *020 †55

COMBINED LOCKS – OUTAGAMIE

CLAYPOOL, Blaine W, Jr. ■ 54113 #016-06-1951 L1954 **IM** *072 †20

COMSTOCK – BARRON

MEARS, Thomas Val. 203 220TH AVE 54826 #026-04-1965 L1966 **OM IM** *071 †20

COON VALLEY – VERNON

SCHALDACH, Fred August. RR 1 54623 #056-05-1961 L1964 **GS** *071 †85

CORNELL – CHIPPEWA

DICKSON, Erik J. 600 WOODSIDE DR 54732 #037-01-1997 L1998 **FM** *020 †18

COTTAGE GROVE – DANE

CAMBRAY, Robert William. 535 SOUTHING GRANGE 53527 #025-12-2000 L2001 **FM** *020 †18
CLEVIDENCE, Derek Edward. 500 WESTLAWN DR, UW HEALTH COTTAGE GROVE 53527 #016-11-1997 L2000 **FM** *020 †18
FLANNERY, Ellen Anne. 535 SOUTHING GRANGE 53527 #041-07-1977 L1978 **FM** *020 †18
GIORGI, Gaspar Gary. 535 SOUTHING GRANGE 53527 #010-02-1980 L1987 **FM** *020 †18
LENTFER, Karen Rose. 535 SOUTHING GRANGE 53527 #040-02-1992 L1996 **FM** *020 †18
POGUE, Frances Lema. ■ 53527 #001-02-1995 L1997 **IM** *020 †20
SIEWERT, Lynda Ann. 535 SOUTHING GRANGE, WILDWOOD FAMILY CLINIC SC 53527 #056-05-1994 L1995 **FM** *020 †18
SIEWERT, Steven Peter. 535 SOUTHING GRANGE 53527 #056-05-1996 L1997 **FM** *020 †18
SPITZER-RESNICK, Sheryl. 535 SOUTHING GRANGE 53527 #024-01-1985 L1986 **FM OBS** *020 †18
WERTSCH, Paul Anthony. 535 SOUTHING GRANGE 53527 #056-05-1970 L1971 **FM** *020 †18
WINKLER, Andrew Alexander. ■ 53527 #056-05-2002 L2007 **OTO** *100

CRANDON – FOREST

ABRAMS, Bruce Rankin. 209 E ELM ST 54520 #056-05-1984 L1988 **OBG** *020 †30
BENTLEY, Jodelle Lea. 209 E ELM ST 54520 #011-03-1979 L1985 **OBG** *020 †30
BRANDNER, Richard Arthur. 209 E ELM ST 54520 #056-06-1975 L1976 **FM** *020 †18
FROST, John Fairfax. 209 E ELM ST 54520 #056-05-1971 L1972 **IM** *020 †20
KANSARIWALA, Indravadan. 209 E ELM ST 54520 #495-89-1982 L1993 **IM RHU** *020 †20
PERRY, Rebecca Dawn. 209 E ELM ST, MINISTRY MEDICAL GRP-CRAND 54520 #056-05-1978 L1979 **IM** *020 †20
TAN, Hongjiu. 209 E ELM ST 54520 #243-69-1982 L2000 **PM** *020 †60
WALDO, Chris Todd. 4959 LAKE LUCERNE DR 54520 #017-20-1990 L1994 **PTH** *020 †50

CRIVITZ – MARINETTE

CURIO, Peter Robert. 218 S HWY 141 54114 #016-11-1994 L1996 **FM** *020 †18

CROSS PLAINS – DANE

BLISS, Lauren Beth. ■ 53528 #036-05-1999 *100
GRELLE, Amy Rongstad. 2418 BREWERY RD 53528 #056-05-1996 L1998 **FM** *020 †18
JARZEMSKY, Daniel Richard. 2418 BREWERY RD 53528 #016-01-1981 L1982 **FM** *020 †18
KNOX, Barbara Lou. ■ 53528 #056-05-2002 L2005 **PD** *020
LONG, Sara Jane Clope. ■ 53528 #041-07-1990 L1991 **P** *020
OLSON, Pamela Ann. 2418 BREWERY RD 53528 #056-05-1987 L1994 **FM** *020 †18
WILKIE, James M. RR 2 53528 #056-05-1940 L1941 **OM PUD** *071 †20

CUBA CITY – GRANT

CAYLOR, Duane Kent. 117 S MADISON ST 53807 #018-03-1983 L1990 **FM** *020 †18
KANTAMNENI, Maruthi P M. 117 S MADISON ST 53807 #495-50-1960 L1978 **IM CD** *020 †20
RUOHONIEMI, Lisa Anne. ■ 53807 #016-11-1994 L1997 **PD** *020 †55

CUDAHY – MILWAUKEE

ABDALLAH, Wadie A. 3533 E RAMSEY AVE 53110 #330-02-1948 L1976 **IM CD** *071
ALLEN, Timothy William. 5900 S LAKE DR 53110 #056-06-2001 L2003 **FM** *020 †18
ANDERSON, Margaret M. 5900 S LAKE DR, PATHOLOGY DEPARTMENT 53110 #025-01-1987 L1999 **PTH HMP** *020 †55,50
BAHAL, Rajinder Kumar. 3533 E RAMSEY AVE, FINE-LANDO CLINIC 53110 #495-29-1967 L1977 **OBG** *071 †30
BROIHIER, Thomas Jos. 5900 S LAKE DR 53110 #056-06-1989 L1990 **CD** *020 †20
BURGOS, Rodolfo G. 3533 E RAMSEY AVE 53110 #748-01-1965 L1976 **DR** *020 †80
CORNELL, John Wm. 3533 E RAMSEY AVE 53110 #056-06-1963 L1966 **GP** *020
DAVITO, Richard Glenn. 3533 E RAMSEY AVE 53110 #016-11-1975 L1976 **ORS** *020 †40
DE QUINA, Magtangol R. 5900 S LAKE DR 53110 #748-08-1966 L1976 **FM** *075
FREDERICK, John J. 5900 S LAKE DR 53110 #056-06-1951 L1952 **GS** *072 †85
GABRIEL, Reynaldo Perez. 4819 S PACKARD AVE 53110 #748-01-1954 L1966 **OM GP** *071
GARCHITORENA, Noel Kare. 5900 S LAKE DR, STE 100 53110 #748-09-1981 L1996 **P** *020
GARG, Nirmal Anil Kumar. 5900 S LAKE DR, PHTYSCL MED & REHAB 53110 #495-29-1959 L1978 **PM** *020 †60
GUPTA, Kul Bhushan. 5900 S LAKE DR 53110 #495-08-1988 L2001 **FM** *020 †20
HAIDER-SHAH, Hammad Raza. 3533 E RAMSEY AVE, COVENANT MEDICAL GROUP 53110 #422-01-1999 L2002 **IM** *020
KIPNIS, Gerald. 5900 S LAKE DR 53110 #422-01-1984 L2004 **P** *020
LAMBERTON, Stephen C. 5900 S LAKE DR, STE 100 53110 #056-06-1993 L1995 **FM** *020 †18
MALIK, Mohammad I. 5900 S LAKE DR, PATHOLOGY DEPARTMENT 53110 #704-01-1961 L1970 **PTH HEM** *071 †50
MATHAI, Mathew George. 5900 S LAKE DR 53110 #654-01-1996 L2003 **PCC SME** *020 †20

■ = Address Information Privacy Protected

MISRA, Virendra K. 3533 E RAMSEY AVE 53110 #495-41-1982 L1997 **N** *020 †75
MODY, Manoj V. 5900 S LAKE DR, STE 100 53110 #495-22-1982 L1992 **IM** *020 †20
NUNAG, Armando Narciso. 3533 E RAMSEY AVE 53110 #748-01-1964 L1976 **IM CD** *020
#056-06-1966 L1967 **FM FSM** *020 †18
O'CONNOR, Thomas Anthony. 4775 S PACKARD AVE, CUDAHY MED ASSOC 53110
#056-06-1966 L1967 **FM FSM** *020 †18
OZMAN, Bridget. ■ 53110 #704-20-1996 L2001 **FM** *020 †18
RAMIREZ, Sacha Melissa. 5900 S LAKE DR, STE 100 53110 #056-05-2000 L2002 **FM** *020 †18
REBANCOS, Dexter Relucio. 5900 S LAKE DR, STE 100 53110 #748-08-1986 L1992
FM *020 †18
ROBERTS, Jeffrey Aldon. 5900 S LAKE DR, PATHOLOGY DEPARTMENT 53110
#005-02-1995 L1999 **PTH** *020 †50
ROSNER, Gregory Mason. 5900 S LAKE DR, STE 100 53110 #035-09-1984 L1991 **GS** *020 †85
SHAH, Ami Pragnesh. 5900 S LAKE DR 53110 #496-44-1999 L2004 **FM** *100 †18
SHAH, Meenaxi D. 3533 E RAMSEY AVE 53110 #495-18-1983 L1992 **IM** *020 †20
SHUKLA, Sanjeev Nalin. 3533 E RAMSEY AVE, FINE LANDO CLINIC 53110 #495-76-1982 L1991
PD *020 †55
SILABAN, Danette Marie. ■ 53110 #056-06-2007 **FP** *012
SUP, Stephen James. 5900 S LAKE DR, PATHOLOGY DEPARTMENT 53110 #041-01-1999 L2003
PTH *020
TABET, Robert Chas. 5900 S LAKE DR 53110 #330-04-1955 L1961 **CD IM** *071
TAVAF MOTAMEN, Ali. FINE-LANDO CLINIC 53110 #517-01-1964 L1978 **GS** *020 †85
TERTADIAN, Jack Avak. 3533 E RAMSEY AVE 53110 #056-06-1990 L1993 **IM** *020 †20
THEISEN, Charles Edward. 5900 S LAKE DR 53110 #056-06-1954 L1955 **FM** *071 †18
TIEU, Thu Minh. ■ 53110 #941-01-1966 L1979 **PTH PCP** *071 †50
VITULLI, Vito Nick. 5900 S LAKE DR 53110 #056-06-1957 L1958 **OBG** *071 †30
WASIULLAH, Masood. 5900 S LAKE DR 53110 #308-07-1983 L1984 **FM** *020 †18
WEISENTHAL, Chas Leonard. 5656 S PACKARD AVE, UROLOGY CONSULTANTS SC 53110
#016-42-1955 L1956 **U** *072 †95
WILLIAMS, James Edward. 5900 S LAKE DR, PATHOLOGY DEPARTMENT 53110
#016-06-1969 L1981 **PTH** *020 †50

CUMBERLAND – BARRON

ANKARLO, Barbara Ann. 1110 7TH AVE 54829 #026-04-1997 L2000 **FM** *020 †18
BIROS, Dennis Gerald. 1150 7TH AVE, CUMBERLAND MEMORIAL HOSPIT 54829
#026-04-1964 L1971 **P** *020
CARLSON, Alan Ross. 1110 7TH AVE 54829 #026-04-1984 L1987 **FM** *020 †18 ‡
GARRISON, Kenneth Joe. 1475 WEBB ST 54829 #011-02-1973 L2003 **GS** *020 †85
HEANEY, Joseph Aloysius. ■ 54829 #041-02-1955 L1989 **P CHP** *071
LINGEN, Thomas Alan. 1475 WEBB ST, CUMBERLAND CLINIC 54829 #056-05-1976 L1977
FM *020 †18
MAHLER, John Herbert. PO BOX 1255 54829 #026-04-1963 L1971 **U** *071 †95
MAYO, Charles Wm, II. 1140 6TH AVE, CUMBERLAND MEM HOSP 54829 #026-04-1988 L1996
CHP P *020 †75
UPRETY, Madan Kumar. 1110 7TH AVE 54829 #672-01-1998 L2005 **P** *020
YOUNGREN, Thomas Russell. 1110 7TH AVE 54829 #026-04-1974 L1977 **FM** *020 †18

CURTISS – CLARK

SCHAFER, Kelly M. ■ 54422 #012-01-2002 L2004 **GP** *062

DANBURY – BURNETT

LESLIE, William Robt. 31009 S WEBB LAKE DR 54830 #007-02-1956 L1993 **ORS** *071 †40
STELLMACHER, Virginia Mae. ■ 54830 #041-07-1972 L1973 **P** *071

DARIEN – WALWORTH

PULERA, M L L. ■ 53114 #056-05-1973 L1976 **GPM PHP** *062

DARLINGTON – LAFAYETTE

BERNARDONI, Robert James. 731 CLAY ST, MEDICAL ASSOCIATES 53530 #016-01-1978 L1979
FM *020 †18
GRAF, Richard Andrew. 800 CLAY ST 53530 #056-05-1956 L1957 **U** *020 †95
LUCAS, Ann Marie. 731 CLAY ST 53530 #019-02-1992 L1994 **FM** *020 †18
NAJAT, Hushang. 800 CLAY ST 53530 #056-03-1957 L1967 **ORS** *020 †40
NEUMANN, Lori Lynn. 731 CLAY ST, C/O MEDICAL ASSOCIATES 53530 #056-05-1980 L1981
FM *020 †18
RUF, David Frederick. ■ 53530 #056-05-1959 L1960 **FM** *071 †18

DE FOREST – DANE

DEMING, Dustin Alan. ■ 53532 #056-05-2007 **IM** *012
GAGE, Robert Bruce. 100 E NORTH ST 53532 #056-05-1978 L1979 **FM** *020 †18 ‡
MILLER, Scott Bolles. 815 S MAIN ST 53532 #038-43-1979 L1993 **FM** *020 †18 ‡
PICKHARDT, Peter Alex. 100 E NORTH ST 53532 #056-05-1999 L2002 **FM** *020 †18
RINGDAHL, David John. 100 E NORTH ST 53532 #018-03-1985 L1988 **FM** *020 †18
SCHMIDT, Erich Martin. ■ 53532 #407-01-1942 L1961 **GP OS** *075
TITEL, Robyn Leigh. 100 E NORTH ST 53532 #056-06-2003 L2004 **FM** *020 †18

DE PERE – BROWN

ANDHOLE, Indira P. 1881 CHICAGO ST 54115 #495-21-1994 L1998 **PD** *020 †55
ANDRES-PALINES, Jesusa S. 1881 CHICAGO ST 54115 #748-01-1989 L2001 **IM** *020 †20
ASMA, Stephen Matthew. 3860 MONROE RD 54115 #056-06-1984 L1985 **FM** *020 †18
BACHHUBER, Raymond Geo. 1881 CHICAGO ST, AURORA HEALTH CENTER 54115
#056-05-1978 L1982 **IM** *020 †20
BAUMANN, Danielle Ann. 1972 DICKINSON RD 54115 #056-05-2005 L2005 **PD** *012

BIERNAT, Bozena Jadwiga. 555 REDBIRD CIR 54115 #759-03-1986 L2003 **IM** *020 †20
BOCCHECIAMP, Harold W. 555 REDBIRD CIR, STE 300 54115 #030-06-1998 L2001
FM *020 †18 ‡
BURNEY, Paul Charles. ■ 54115 #023-12-1995 L2005 **P** *020 †75
CAMILLI, Karen M De Groot. 555 REDBIRD CIR 54115 #056-05-1972 L1973 **PD** *020 †55
CHERKASKY, Alan Hugh. 1881 CHICAGO ST 54115 #016-42-1977 L1979 **FM OBS** *020 †18
CIPRES-JAUCIAN, Rose Mila. ■ 54115 #748-02-1970 L1980 **NPM** *020 †55
COLASSACCO, Lawrence Earl. 1881 CHICAGO ST 54115 #056-05-2001 L2003 **FM** *020 †18
DZWONKOWSKI, Malena. 3860 MONROE RD 54115 #759-04-1980 L2000 **IM** *020 †20
FULLAN, Neil Patrick. 1325 ANGELS PATH, STE 110 54115 #016-01-1982 L1987 **CHP P** *020
GALLAGHER, Tracy Lynn. 3860 MONROE RD 54115 #056-05-1994 L1995 **FM** *020 †18
GAPINSKI, James Peter. 1881 CHICAGO ST 54115 #056-05-1988 L1991 **IM** *020 †20
GRACE, Joseph B. ■ 54115 #016-06-1950 L1956 **IM CD** *071 †20
GRAY, John David. 1881 CHICAGO ST 54115 #026-04-1980 L1986 **FM** *020 †18
GRIEBEN, Leo. 1881 CHICAGO ST, AURORA HEALTH CENTER 54115 #132-01-1957 L1966
P *020
HAFNER, Rance J. 2366 OAK RIDGE CIR 54115 #037-01-1992 L1996 **FM PLM** *020 †18
HANDELAND, Joan Zinkgraf. 3860 MONROE RD 54115 #056-05-1984 L1985 **PD** *020 †55
HARDER, Tim Gilbert. 3860 MONROE RD 54115 #056-05-1984 L1987 **PD** *020 †55
HOYER, Jennifer Lynn. 1881 CHICAGO ST, AURORA HEALTH CARE 54115 #056-06-1996 L2001
PD *020 †55
INYART, Jack Russell. 1881 CHICAGO ST 54115 #017-20-1960 L1964 **EM GP** *071 †16
JACQUEZ-DEAN, Susan M. 1881 CHICAGO ST, AURORA BEHAVIORAL HEALTH 54115
#016-01-2002 L2003 **CHP P** *020 †75 ‡
JAMES, Alan Wayne. 555 REDBIRD CIR, STE 100 54115 #055-01-1994 L2004 **AI IM** *020 †20,03
KAFTAN, George Robt. 1316 FOX RIVER DR 54115 #056-05-1959 L1960 **PD** *030 †55
KELLNER, W Joseph. 555 REDBIRD CIR 54115 #056-05-1979 L1980 **PD** *020 †55
LARSON, Chris Norman. 1325 ANGELS PATH 54115 #018-03-1978 L1991 **CHP P** *020 †75
LASECKI, Cynthia Berner. 1800 LAWRENCE DR 54115 #056-05-1993 L1996 **FM** *020 †18 ‡
LEONG, Gary. 1800 LAWRENCE DR 54115 #060-02-1981 L1995 **FM** *020 †18
LINDGREN, Kristen Ann. 3860 MONROE RD 54115 #056-05-2002 L2003 **FM** *020 †18
LUTHAR, Anshu. 555 REDBIRD CIR, BELLIN HEALTH CLINIC 54115 #495-45-1988 L1999
FM *020 †18
MAC CARTHY, John Phillip. 1016 N BROADWAY, ST NORBERT ABBEY 54115
#016-43-1977 L1980 **IM OBS** *020 †20
MC KENNA, David Hurley. ■ 54115 #028-34-1959 L1963 **IM CD** *071
METZLER, Erich Gilbert. 3860 MONROE RD 54115 #041-02-1988 L2003 **OBG** *020 †30
MEYER, Michael James. 1800 LAWRENCE DR 54115 #056-05-1984 L1985 **FM** *020 †18
MICKLE, Kenneth Cochran. ■ 54115 #056-05-1947 L1948 **PD** *071 †55
MIHAILESCU, Gabriel. 1881 CHICAGO ST 54115 #781-01-1996 L1999 **IM** *020 †20
MOHAMMAD-ZADEH, Ali A. ■ 54115 #517-01-1961 L1975 **NM** *071 †28
O'NEILL, Michael John. 1511 W MAIN AVE, # 100 54115 #016-02-1969 L1972 **P** *020 †75 ‡
ORMAN, Edward Sidney. 1348 N SUMMER RANGE RD 54115 #056-05-1957 L1958
CHP P *020 †75
PALINES, Reynaldo V. 1881 CHICAGO ST, AURORA HEALTH CENTER 54115
#748-01-1987 L2001 **RHU IM** *020 †20
PATEL, Anoo Prabhudas. 4351 CREAMERY RD 54115 #495-17-1956 L1969 **ORS HS** *062 †40
PETERS, Earl E. ■ 54115 #005-12-1953 L1954 **EM** *071
PLANK, Thomas John. 1881 CHICAGO ST 54115 #056-05-1984 L1987 **EM** *020 †16
REYNOLDS, Todd Parker. 1686 EISENHOWER RD, PREVEA HEALTH LAWRENCE SI 54115
#056-05-1986 L1996 **FM** *020 †18
RICHARDS, David Gearhart. 3860 MONROE RD 54115 #056-06-1997 L1998 **IM** *020 †20
ROSIC, Aleksandar V. 1881 CHICAGO ST 54115 #957-07-1990 L2001 **IM** *020 †20
ROSTEING, Kevin Peter. 3860 MONROE RD 54115 #035-06-1984 L1988 **IM** *020
ROTH, Karla Jean. 3860 MONROE RD 54115 #056-05-1992 L1996 **FM** *020 †18
ROUP, Ronald Eugene. 1881 CHICAGO ST 54115 #056-05-1979 L1982 **PD** *020 †55
RUSTAD, Dale Robt. 3860 MONROE RD 54115 #056-05-1991 L1994 **PD** *020 †55
SCHUMACHER, John Peter. ■ 54115 #056-06-1956 L1957 **AN** *071
SEKHON, Satpreet Singh. 1881 CHICAGO ST 54115 #495-08-1997 L2001 **NEP** *012 †20
SIPES, Don Ralph. 1881 CHICAGO ST 54115 #028-03-1960 L1966 **OBG** *071 †30
SMYTH, Riley Alexander. ■ 54115 #012-05-2008 *012
SOETER, John Randolph. ■ 54115 #035-03-1962 L1975 **TS** *071 †85,90
SPIKA, David Thomas. 1686 EISENHOWER RD 54115 #056-05-1995 L1996 **FM** *020 †18
SPIKA, Karla Jean. 1686 EISENHOWER RD 54115 #056-05-1995 L1996 **FM** *020 †18
STAMM, John Robt. 1325 ANGELS PATH, STE 110 54115 #056-06-1971 L1989 **P** *020 †75
STEFFEL, Rhonda Sue. 3860 MONROE RD 54115 #056-05-1997 L2000 **FM** *020 †18
STEVENS, Robert James. 1881 CHICAGO ST 54115 #056-06-1984 L1985 **FM** *020 †18
TORREANO, Lori Ann. ■ 54115 #025-12-1989 L1993 **FM** *071 †18
VAISHNAV, Abhilash R. 1881 CHICAGO ST, AURORA HEALTH CTR 54115 #023-07-2000 L2005
AI IM *020 †20,03
VANDE LOO, Francis B. ■ 54115 #056-06-1940 L1940 **EM** *071
WAMPLER, Robert Elwood, Jr. 3860 MONROE RD 54115 #018-03-1969 L1977 **IM** *020 †20
WARGIN, Roger Chas. 1881 CHICAGO ST 54115 #056-06-1968 L1969 **DR NM** *020 †80
WARREN, John Tracy. 1686 EISENHOWER RD 54115 #056-05-1986 L1988 **FM** *020 †18
WATTS, Edwin Scully. 5760 LEDGE CREST RD 54115 #016-43-1962 L1969 **P** *020

DEERBROOK – LANGLADE

LEEK, James Arthur. W9876 FORMAN RD 54424 #035-09-1992 L1996 **AN PMM** *020

DEERFIELD – DANE

KEIL, Jeffrey Mark. 103 LAKE ST 53531 #056-05-1994 L1995 **FM** *020 †18
OLSON, Irene Renuka. ■ 53531 #495-19-1967 L1977 **AN** *020
PEPPER, Kyla Nicole. ■ 53531 #550-04-2007 **FP** *012
ZALAPA, Leah Christine. ■ 53531 #056-05-2000 L2003 **IM** *020 †20

DELAFIELD – WAUKESHA

BERGOM, Carmen Renee. ■ 53018 #056-06-2008 *012
GREENUP, Rachel Adams. ■ 53018 #056-06-2004 L2006 **GS** *012
HATFIELD, Hayes H. ■ 53018 #017-20-1969 L1970 **IM END** *071 †20

JAHNKE, Jeffrey Compton. ■ 53018 #056-06-1990 **OPH** *100
KALT, Melissa Anne. 2750 GOLF RD, PROHEALTH CARE MEDICAL CEN 53018 #056-06-1997 L2001 **MPD** *020 †20,55
KAMSLER, Mark. 2574 SUN VALLEY DR, DELEAFIELD PED SC STE 201 53018 #025-01-1992 L1995 **PD** *020 †55
LO, Romeo Ciriaco. 634 MILWAUKEE ST 53018 #748-01-1963 L1976 **IM** *020
MILBRATH, John Richard. 2574 SUN VALLEY DR, STE 100 53018 #056-05-1965 L1972 **DR OS** *020 †80
OLSON, Debra Jane. 2750 GOLF RD, PROHEALTH CARE MEDICAL CEN 53018 #026-04-1990 L1991 **OBG** *020 †30
OSTROMECKI, Christopher J. 385 WILLIAMSTOWNE, STE 101 53018 #759-03-1982 L1993 **CD EM** *020 †20
OSTROMECKI, Elzbieta E K. 385 WILLIAMSTOWNE, 385 WILLIAMSTOWNE SUITE 1 53018 #759-03-1982 L1993 **IM** *020 †20
PTACIN, Michael John. 708 SAINT JOHNS DR 53018 #016-43-1974 L1976 **IM CD** *040 †20
SCHOPER, Glenn Whitman. ■ 53018 #054-04-1959 L1960 **GP** *071 †18
SZERENYI, Jennifer Amend. ■ 53018 #056-06-1993 L1995 **IM** *020
THOMPSON, Melanie Marie. 2750 GOLF RD, PROHEALTH CARE MEDICAL CEN 53018 #056-06-1995 L1996 **FM** *020 †18
TOTH, Glenn Albert. 2725 HILLSIDE DR 53018 #056-06-1991 L1992 **FM AI** *020 †18
UEBELACKER, Carol J. 700 MILWAUKEE ST 53018 #056-06-1989 L1989 **FM EM** *020 †18
URBAN, Michelle Elizabeth. TIMBERLINE CICLE, SIIW 32975 53018 #056-06-1987 L1988 **PM** *020 †55,60
WALDREN, Henry Mowat, Jr. 824 BACK BAY 53018 #056-06-1957 L1958 **OBG** *071
WATSON, Roger Dale. 3832 HILLSIDE DR 53018 #038-06-1999 L2001 **MPD** *020 †55,20

DELAVAN – WALWORTH

BRUECKERT, Kurt Erik. 1550 HOBBS DR 53115 #016-11-1998 L2000 **FM** *020 †18
BURNELL, Ernest Lenon. ■ 53115 #004-01-1957 L1962 **R IM** *071 †80
CANDA, Alex Canlas. 1550 HOBBS DR 53115 #748-01-1987 L1993 **IM** *020 †20
FEHLING, Michael Jos. 1550 HOBBS DR 53115 #056-06-1985 L1986 **FM** *020 †18
GILMAN, Christopher John. 540 BOWERS BLVD 53115 #016-11-1975 L1999 **RO FPG** *020 †80,18
GOETTSCH, Brett Dee. 540 BOWERS BLVD 53115 #018-03-1993 L1994 **FM** *020 †18
GRACIOSA, Joseph Dominise. 1550 HOBBS DR 53115 #748-11-1972 L1994 **PD** *020 †55
HICKS, John Howell, III. 5411 HIGHWAY 50 53115 #020-02-1981 L2002 **PD** *020 †55
MAHON, David Kenneth. 1550 HOBBS DR, AURORA HEALTH CENTER-DELAV 53115 #016-11-1989 L1990 **FM** *020 †18 ‡
POPLAR, Clifford Robt. 915 E GENEVA ST 53115 #649-33-1983 L1987 **IM** *020
SMILEY, Glenn A. ■ 53115 #056-06-1951 L1952 **GP** *071
SQUIRE, George Varnum. ■ 53115 #026-04-1952 L1952 **GPM A** *072
TYDRICH, James Joseph. 540 BOWERS BLVD, DEAN DELAVAN CLINIC 53115 #056-05-1962 L1963 **FM** *071 †18
VIVERO, Manuel. 1550 HOBBS DR 53115 #748-10-1972 L1993 **PD NPM** *020 †55 ‡

DODGEVILLE – IOWA

ALMASY, David Scott. 833 S IOWA ST 53533 #016-45-2003 L2008 **OBG** *100
ARBAJE, Yamil Miguel. 800 COMPASSION WAY, STE 136 53533 #308-05-1985 L1990 **IM** *020 †20
BISHOP, Mark Paul. 1204 JOSEPH ST 53533 #056-05-1973 L1974 **FM** *020 †18
BREIER, Harald Peter L. 800 COMPASSION WAY 53533 #660-01-1953 L1958 **GP** *071
CRUMMY, Timothy Andrew. 868 COMPASSION WAY 53533 #056-06-1997 L2004 **VIR** *020 †80
DALSING, Kathryn Olson. 833 S IOWA ST, STE 102 53533 #056-05-1990 L1991 **FM** *020 †18
DESOUKY, Samy Shehata M. 800 COMPASSION WAY 53533 #915-04-1978 L1991 **PTH** *020 †50
ELIASSON, Sven Gustav. ■ 53533 #858-01-1956 L1957 **N** *071 †75
GRUNOW, Gary Joseph. 1204 JOSEPH ST 53533 #056-05-1993 L1994 **FM** *020 †18 ‡
KAISER, Cathryn Isabel. 833 S IOWA ST 53533 #010-01-1975 L1976 **FM** *020 †18
KIM, Young II. 833 S IOWA ST, STE 106 53533 #583-09-1965 L1973 **GS GP** *020
LEHMAN, John Mark. 800 COMPASSION WAY 53533 #016-76-1977, ▲ L1978 **GP FPG** *020
LINDSEY, Everett Raymond. 800 COMPASSION WAY 53533 #038-40-1973 L1974 **OBG IM** *020 †20,30
SHANNAHAN, Sean Kevin. 868 COMPASSION WAY 53533 #016-42-1997 L2002 **DR** *020 †80
SHLIMOVITZ, Cary Lyle. 868 COMPASSION WAY 53533 #056-06-1998 L1999 **RNR** *020 †80
ZIRNESKIE, Joseph David. 800 COMPASSION WAY 53533 #056-05-1985 L1986 **EM GP** *020

DOUSMAN – WAUKESHA

CHECK, Nancy Dwyer. W345S3702 MORAINE HLS DR D 53118 #056-05-1995 L1996 **P** *020 †18
CLAUDE, John Laurence. 410 N MAIN ST, # 5B 53118 #056-06-1953 L1954 **OBG** *071 †30
DORFF, Gerald Jos. ■ 53118 #056-06-1964 L1967 **ID IM** *071 †20
GAVER, Jeffrey Wm. 370 VENTURE DR 53118 #056-05-1987 L1988 **IM EM** *020 †16,20
JAKUBAITIS, Terry Carl. W331S3342 HAWTHORNE HOLW 53118 #016-01-1989 L1990 **FM EM** *020 †18
KLAAS, Mark Alan. S35W35601 HIGHWAY D 53118 #030-06-1985 L1990 **IM PUD** *020 †20
KROENING, Paul Merritt. 535 W33275 HONEYSUCKLE CT 53118 #056-05-1957 L1958 **RO R** *071 †80
LAWNICZAK, Rebecca Ann. ■ 53118 #047-05-2008 *012
MATTHEWS, Robert Danl. ■ 53118 #056-05-1992 L1996 **AN PME** *020 †05
OSTROWSKI, Charles A. ■ 53118 #016-76-1962, ▲ L1965 **AN** *071

DURAND – PEPIN

BANDY, Michelle Lynnette. ■ 54736 #016-42-2003 L2007 **FM** *020 †18
DOHLMAN, Robert Lanier. 905 7TH AVE W 54736 #005-12-1973 L1981 **GP** *020
MYERS, Maurice Eugene. 204 W MAIN ST 54736 #056-06-1963 L1964 **OTR** *020
RUCKER, Kenneth Marcel. 1250 3RD AVE W 54736 #025-12-1982 L1988 **N** *020 †20
SANDIN, Robyn. 1220 3RD AVE W 54736 #005-12-2000 L2001 **FM** *020 †18

EAGLE – WAUKESHA

MC ADOO, Marcy Lynn. W355S9085 GODFREY LN 53119 #021-05-1985 L1988 **IM** *020 †20
SMYERS, David D. S92W35340 BARBARY CT 53119 #048-16-1982 L1987 **EM** *020 †16

EAGLE RIVER – VILAS

BARTOS, Robert Edwin. ■ 54521 #056-06-1957 L1958 **GS** *071 †85
BRODHEAD, Roderick Scott. 201 HOSPITAL RD 54521 #056-05-1982 L1985 **EM** *020 †16
BYRNE, Michael Paul. 930 E WALL ST 54521 #305-01-1990 L1992 **FM** *020 †18
FLETCHER, Fred Wm. ■ 54521 #018-03-1956 L1963 **CD IM** *020 ‡
GONZALEZ-CERRA, Maria C. 930 E WALL ST, MINISTRY MED GROUP-EAGLE R 54521 #011-02-1995 L2000 **PD** *020 †55
HOLAN, Cali Alexandra. 201 HOSPITAL RD 54521 #038-06-1996 L2002 **EM** *020 †16
JACKSON, James, Jr. 930 E WALL ST, MINISTRY MEDICAL GROUP 54521 #025-76-1985, ▲ L2007 **FM** *020 †18
JACOBSON, Lewis Leo. 920 E WALL ST 54521 #016-42-1954 L1955 **FM** *071 †18
LEACH, Jennie A Miller. 1741 LIGHTHOUSE LODGE RD 54521 #050-02-1996 L1999 **FM** *020 †18
MOE, Terrance David. ■ 54521 #026-04-1975 L1989 **FM EM** *020 †18
MRAZ, Frank Anthony. 930 E WALL ST, MINISTRY MEDICAL GROUP 54521 #016-11-1999 L2002 **FM** *020 †18
PUSATERI, Gary Michael. 859 HIGHWAY 17 S 54521 #016-42-1987 L1988 **EM** *020
RICHARDS, James Mark. 201 HOSPITAL RD 54521 #064-01-1996 L1998 **FM** *020 †18
SCHUMAKER, James Dale. 500 COMMERCE DR, EAGLE RIVER CENTER 54521 #056-05-1978 L1982 **FM** *020 †18
SOOKOCHOFF, Robt Michael. 930 E WALL ST 54521 #061-01-1980 L1993 **FM** *020 †18
STEFFENSON, John Le Roy. ■ 54521 #056-06-1957 L1958 **AN** *020 †05
WOOD, Donald Lintz. ■ 54521 #056-05-1954 L1955 **FM** *071 †18
WRIGHT, William Eugene. 930 E WALL ST, MINISTRY MEDICAL GROUP - E 54521 #028-78-2001, ▲ L2002 **FM** *020

EAST TROY – WALWORTH

BEATSE, Scott Neal. 2483 CORPORATE CIR 53120 #021-01-1989 L1996 **OBG** *020 †30
BONNEAU, Laura Ann. ■ 53120 #056-05-2008 *012
FRODERMAN, Timothy Carl. 2483 CORPORATE CIR 53120 #305-01-2002 L2006 **FM** *020 †18
JAYNE, Dorothy Jaeger. 2483 CORPORATE CIR 53120 #056-05-1977 L1978 **FM** *020 †18
KESSEL, Kenneth Frank. ■ 53120 #016-11-1958 L1959 **FM FPG** *071 †18
KNIGHT, Margaret Mary. 2483 CORPORATE CIR 53120 #056-05-1980 L1983 **FM** *020 †18
SELDERA, Juanilito N. 2483 CORPORATE CIR 53120 #748-10-1972 L1981 **GS GP** *020 †85
SHEPHERDSON, Gary Lee. PO BOX 294, 3108 MAIN ST 53120 #847-12-1975 L1977 **FM EM** *020 †18
THOMPSON, Stephen Robt. ■ 53120 #056-06-1981 L1984 **AN** *020 †05
ZWICK, Christopher Allan. 2483 CORPORATE CIR 53120 #056-05-1984 L1985 **PTH** *020 †20,50

EAU CLAIRE – EAU CLAIRE

ABIODUN, Olufemi Joseph. 2116 CRAIG RD 54701 #690-02-1996 L2004 **IM GE** *020 †20
ADEL, Gina Lynn. 1400 BELLINGER ST, STE 2 54703 #056-05-1984 L1990 **IM RHU** *020 †20
ADKINS, Aron Shawn. 2116 CRAIG RD, MARSHFIELD CLINIC 54701 #038-43-1996 L2002 **END** *020 †20
ADLER, Kenneth Paul. 1000 STARR AVE, MARSHFIELD CLINIC-RIVERCLI 54703 #056-05-1987 L1989 **FM** *020 †18
AHLUWALIA, Arundhathi S. 2116 CRAIG RD, EAU CLAIRE CENTER 54701 #495-37-1987 L2002 **AN** *020
AHLUWALIA, Sharat. 2116 CRAIG RD, MARSHFIELD CLINIC 54701 #495-53-1988 L2002 **N** *020 †75
AHMAD, Afroze A. 1400 BELLINGER ST 54703 #704-02-1983 L2003 **CD** *020 †20
AHMED, Mahmoud Mostafa. 2116 CRAIG RD, MARSHFIELD CLINIC-EAU CLAI 54701 #915-02-1979 L1987 **P ADP** *020 †75
AKFALY, Abdulla. 733 W CLAIREMONT AVE 54701 #875-02-1991 L2000 **IM** *020 †20
AL-ABBAS, Amel. PO BOX 1510, 1400 BELLINGER ST 54702 #759-03-1995 L2000 **IM** *020 †20
ALFUTH, Richard Peter. 733 W CLAIREMONT AVE 54701 #028-34-1980 L1981 **FM** *020 †18
ALSOUS, Fadi. 703 W HAMILTON AVE, EAU CLAIRE MEDICAL CLINIC, 54701 #875-01-1993 L2004 **CD** *020 †20
ANDERSON, Jean Marie. 1400 BELLINGER ST, SYSTEM 54703 #026-04-1988 L1996 **IM** *020 †20
ANGELL, David Clark. 900 W CLAIREMONT AVE 54701 #067-01-1955 L1964 **PTH** *071 †50
ANWAR, Shamim. 1400 BELLINGER ST, MAYO HEALTH SYSTEM 54703 #704-16-1984 L2007 **P** *020
ARNHOLT, Jeffrey Craig. 2116 CRAIG RD, MARSHFIELD CLINIC-EAU CLAI 54701 #026-08-1998 L2004 **DR** *020 †80
ARZOUMAN, David Allen. 2116 CRAIG RD, EAU CLAIRE CENTER 54701 #016-06-1986 L2007 **TS** *020 †85,90
ATTERMEIER, Mark Henry. 733 W CLAIREMONT AVE 54701 #056-05-1975 L1976 **FM** *020 †18
AUGUSTYN, Mark Alan. 2715 FRANK ST 54703 #025-12-1996 L2002 **DR** *020 †80
BADDIGAM, Krishnamohan Re. 1221 WHIPPLE ST, PAIN CLNC OF NW WIS 54703 #496-01-2000 L2006 **AN** *100
BALDING, Carmen. 2116 CRAIG RD, MARSHFIELD CLINIC 54701 #737-06-1990 L2004 **D** *020 †15
BANICH, James Christopher. ■ 54701 #016-43-1999 L2006 **PS** *020 †45
BARTHOLOW, John Alpheus. 733 W CLAIREMONT AVE 54701 #026-04-1988 L1990 **P** *020 †75
BASSETT, Jenifer Ivy. 714 W HAMILTON AVE 54701 #056-05-1999 L2003 **MPD** *020 †20,55
BATAMBUZE, Ephraim W. 2116 CRAIG RD 54701 #905-01-1974 L2006 **CD IM** *020
BATES, Patrick James. ■ 54703 #056-05-1947 L1949 **OS** *072
BAYLEY, Bruce Covell. 733 W CLAIREMONT AVE 54701 #026-04-1962 L1969 **U** *071 †95
BEAUDRIE, Michael Lee. 3802 OAKWOOD MALL DR 54701 #018-75-1997, ▲ L2001 **AN** *020 †05
BELMONT, Richard Edgar. 3802 OAKWOOD MALL DR 54701 #018-75-1996, ▲ L2000 **AN** *020 †20
BERG, Troy Lyman. 4212 SOUTHTOWN DR 54701 #026-04-1993 L1998 **ORS** *020 †40

■ = Address Information Privacy Protected

BERLIE, Cecil Loe. 733 W CLAIREMONT AVE 54701 #030-06-1998 L2004 **OPH** *020 †35

BILDSOE, Mark Christian. 1400 BELLINGER ST, LUTHER MIDELFORT 54703 #026-04-1988 L1994 **DR** *020 †80

BINGHAM, Charles Thos. 1400 BELLINGER ST, STE 2 54703 #023-07-1987 L2003 **END IM** *020 †20

BISCHOF, Timothy Scott. 2116 CRAIG RD, MARSHFIELD CLINIC 54701 #028-34-2001 L2002 **ID** *020 ‡

BLINK, Donald Vernon. 733 W CLAIREMONT AVE 54701 #056-05-1960 L1962 **FM GS** *020 †18

BODEAU, Donald Thos. 733 W CLAIREMONT AVE, MIDELFORT CLINIC 54701 #026-08-1982 L1991 **OM OS** *020 †70

BOLLINGER, John Thos. 733 W CLAIREMONT AVE 54701 #056-05-1970 L1971 **FM** *020 †18

BORMAN, Terrance Randell. 1400 BELLINGER ST 54703 #026-04-1973 L1976 **IM** *030 †20

BOUNDS, James Vincent, Jr. 1400 BELLINGER ST, LUTHER MIDELFORT 54703 #003-01-1972 L1976 **N** *020 †75

BOWMAN, Daniel John. 3802 OAKWOOD MALL DR 54701 #056-05-1981 L1983 **AN** *020 †05

BREEN, Dennis Patrick. 617 W CLAIREMONT AVE 54701 #026-04-1978 L2000 **FM** *040 †18

BRUCKER, Wallace B, Jr. 2116 CRAIG RD, MARSHFIELD CLINIC-EAU CLAI 54701 #048-02-1990 L2005 **ORS** *020 †40

BUENGER, Lisa Constance. 1110 OAK RIDGE DR, OAKLEAF PEDIATRICS 54701 #026-08-1999 L2003 **PD** *020 †55

BURGESS, Sarah Kay. 1400 BELLINGER ST, LUTHER MIDELFORT 54703 #017-20-1982 L1983 **OBG** *020 †30

BURNETT, Greg Allen. 2116 CRAIG RD DEPT OB, MARSHFIELD CLC EAU CLAIRE 54701 #056-06-1986 L1987 **OBG** *030 †30

CAMERON, Scott Edward. 2116 CRAIG RD, AMBULATORY SURGERY CENTER 54701 #056-06-1985 L1993 **ORS GS** *020 †40

CASPER, Randall Jay. 1400 BELLINGER ST, STE 2 54703 #026-04-1981 L1985 **IM** *020 †20

CAVANAUGH, Daniel Geo. 2116 CRAIG RD, EAU CLAINE CENTER 54701 #019-02-1969 L1986 **TS GS** *020 †85,90 ‡

CHADA, Satish. 1400 BELLINGER ST, LUTHER MIDELFORT 54703 #495-57-1994 L2006 **CCM** *020 †20

CHRISTIANSON, Lon Douglas. 733 W CLAIREMONT AVE, MIDELFORT CLC 54701 #026-04-1977 L1978 **D DS** *020 †15

CHUKWUDELUNZU, Felix E. 1400 BELLINGER ST, STE 2 54703 #025-07-1994 L1999 **N** *020 †75

CIRESI, David Lee. 1400 BELLINGER ST, STE 2 54703 #026-08-1992 L1998 **GS CCS** *020 †85

CLARK, Daniel Monroe, III. 1400 BELLINGER ST, LUTHER MIDELFORT 54703 #016-11-1969 L1973 **GYN** *020 †30

CLARK, Eleanor Suzanne. ■ 54701 #024-05-1979 L1985 **PTH** *020 †50

CLARKE, Janice. 1600 BELLINGER ST, CARDIOLOGY DIVISION 54703 #038-06-1972 L1982 **CD IM** *020 †20

COCHRANE, Richard Narland. 3802 OAKWOOD MALL DR 54701 #056-06-1981 L1984 **AN** *020 †05

COLE, Scott Jeffrey. 1400 BELLINGER ST, LUTHER MIDELFORT HOSP 54703 #026-04-1999 L2004 **DR** *020 †80

COLLIER, Jay Hugh. ■ 54701 #038-41-1990 L2004 **P** *020 †75

COOK, David Frederick. 2116 CRAIG RD, CENTER 54701 #056-05-1981 L1982 **FM** *020 †18

COOK, Steven Dean. 703 W HAMILTON AVE 54701 #016-06-1976 L1978 **EM** *020 †16

CRANE, Richard Turner. 2119 HEIGHTS DR 54701 #017-20-1978 L1985 **OTO A** *020 †45

CROWTHER BESSET, Valerie. ■ 54703 #396-27-1991 L2006 **FM** *100

CULLINAN, Susan Marie. 1400 BELLINGER ST, LUTHER MIDELFORT 54703 #037-01-1998 L2000 **EM** *020 †16

DAHL, Kirk Victor. 900 W CLAIREMONT AVE 54701 #026-04-1980 L1981 **EM PHM** *020 †16

DANIELS, Richard James. 719 W HAMILTON AVE, STE C 54701 #030-06-1991 L1996 **GS** *020 †85

DANYLKOVA, Nataliya. 617 W CLAIREMONT AVE, EAU CLAIRE FAMILY MED CLIN 54701 #913-57-1996 **FP** *012

DAVIS, Claude Dewey. 836 RICHARD DR 54701 #056-05-1967 L1975 **ORS** *020 †40

DE CESARE, Wm Francis. 431 E CLAIREMONT AVE, DECESARE ORTHOPEDIC CLINIC 54701 #024-01-1972 L1977 **ORS** *020 †40

DECKER, Catharine C. 733 W CLAIREMONT AVE, MAYS HEALTH SYSTEM 54701 #056-05-1995 L1996 **FM** *020 †18

DELMASTRO, Dean Allen. 900 W CLAIREMONT AVE, SACRED HEART REGIONAL CANC 54701 #016-01-1988 L1995 **HO IM** *020 †20

DERFUS, Gregory Alan. 1221 WHIPPLE ST, LUTHER HOSPITAL 54703 #056-06-1984 L1987 **GE IM** *020 †20

DETTBARN, Kyle James. 703 W HAMILTON AVE, STE 4 54701 #018-03-1997 L2003 **PCC** *020 †20

DEXTER, Donn David, Jr. 1221 WHIPPLE ST, DEPT NEURO SCIENCES 54703 #026-08-1986 L1993 **N SME** *020 †75

DIBBLE, James B. RR 4 BOX 222 54701 #016-11-1949 L1957 **GS OS** *071 †85

DIESTELMEIER, Michael R. 733 W CLAIREMONT AVE, MIDELFORT CLINIC LTD 54701 #018-03-1978 L1985 **D** *020 †15

DOLAN, Joseph Wm. 733 W CLAIREMONT AVE 54701 #026-08-1992 L1999 **OPH** *020 †35

DOVRE, Erik John. 1400 BELLINGER ST, STE 2 54703 #026-04-1989 L1992 **OBG** *020 †30

DOW, Coad Thomas. 2715 DAMON ST 54701 #056-05-1974 L1975 **OPH** *020 †35

DOYLE, Thomas James. ■ 54701 #056-06-1967 L1970 **U** *071 †95

DRECHSEL, Kevin M. 1400 BELLINGER ST, STE 2 54703 #014-01-1995 L2001 **EM** *020 †16

EBEL, Daniel Chas. 900 W CLAIREMONT AVE 54701 #018-03-1991 L1994 **EM FM** *040 †18,16

EDDY, Jennifer Jeanne. 617 W CLAIREMONT AVE 54701 #024-16-1995 L2002 **FM** *020 †18

EDSTROM, Mark Edwin. 1400 BELLINGER ST, LUTHER MIDELFORT 54703 #026-04-1980 L1983 **IM** *020 †20

EDWARDS, Merle Thomas, Jr. 2715 FRANK ST 54703 #018-03-1977 L1980 **DR PD** *020 †55,80

EKREM, Frederic Paul. 900 W CLAIREMONT AVE, SACRED HEART HOSPITAL 54701 #026-04-1972 L1987 **PM FM** *020 †60

EL KHATIB, Abd El Ghany. 659 W HAMILTON AVE 54701 #875-02-1974 L1983 **CD IM** *020 †20

ELVIG, David Peter. 800 WISCONSIN ST 54703 #026-04-1983 L1986 **FM** *030 †18

EMMERICH, Melissa L. 2116 CRAIG RD, EAU CLAIRE CENTER 54701 #056-06-1993 L2001 **OBG** *020 †30

ENDERS, Gene Geo. 733 W CLAIREMONT AVE, LUTHER MIDELFORD CLINIC 54701 #056-05-1970 L1972 **FM** *020 †18

ENDRES, Stephen Mathias. 1221 WHIPPLE ST, PAIN CLNC OF NW MI 54703 #026-04-1982 L1985 **AN PME** *020 †05

ERICKSON, Michael David. 1400 BELLINGER ST, STE 2 54701 #056-06-1989 L1990 **GS** *020 †85

ETZEL, Eric D. 3802 OAKWOOD MALL DR 54701 #018-75-1997, ▲ L2002 **AN** *020 †05

EVANS, John Martin. 3802 OAKWOOD MALL DR 54701 #018-03-1973 L1976 **AN** *020 †05

FABINY, Robert John. 1400 BELLINGER ST, STE 2 54703 #038-06-1965 L1966 **OBG** *071 †30

FAVRET, Gerald Wm. 3501 GOLF RD 54701 #038-43-1981 L1985 **FM** *020 †18

FELDMEIER, John Elery. 2715 FRANK ST 54703 #056-05-1984 L1985 **DR** *020 †80

FENNO, James Andrew. 900 W CLAIREMONT AVE, SACRED HEART HOSPITAL 54701 #056-06-1997 L2000 **EM** *020 †16

FERNANDES, Regis I. 1400 BELLINGER ST, LUTHER MIDELFORT 54703 #187-73-1989 L2002 **CD IM** *020 †20

FINK, Robert Joel. 900 W CLAIREMONT AVE 54701 #016-43-1947 L1956 **PTH** *071 †50

FITZ, Ralph Woelfel. 2116 CRAIG RD 54701 #021-01-1979 L2006 **CD IM** *020 †20

FLOREN, Andrew Eugene. 733 W CLAIREMONT AVE, LUTHER MIDELFONT 54701 #048-02-1985 L2003 **OM FM** *020 †70,18

GARDNER, Brett Louis. 3802 OAKWOOD MALL DR 54701 #056-06-1977 L1978 **AN** *020 †05

GASSER, Gary Lynn. 2116 CRAIG RD, EAU CLAIRE CENTER 54701 #056-06-1988 L1999 **NS** *020 †25

GERACI, Rose Marie. ■ 54701 #056-05-1999 L2000 **GE** *100

GERAGHTY, James Joseph. 2715 FRANK ST 54703 #018-03-1987 L1991 **DR** *020 †80

GERLINGER, Bruce Allen. 733 W CLAIREMONT AVE, MIDELFORT CLINIC LTD 54701 #038-06-1986 L1989 **FM** *020 †18

GERRY, Timothy Robert. 3802 OAKWOOD MALL DR 54701 #056-05-1992 L1994 **AN** *020 †05

GIANLUPI, Adriane. 2116 CRAIG RD, MARSHFIELD CLINIC-EAU CLAI 54701 #187-02-1990 L1993 **CCM** *020 †20

GIDEONSEN, Mark David. 617 W CLAIREMONT AVE, EAU CLAIRE FAMILY MEDICINE 54701 #016-01-1994 L2002 **FM** *020 †18

GILBERSTADT, Philip M. 3802 OAKWOOD MALL DR 54701 #026-04-1989 L1993 **AN** *020 †05

GILLETTE, Lisa Braner. 733 W CLAIREMONT AVE 54701 #016-45-1990 L1991 **FM** *020 †18

GILMARTIN, Kevin Michael. 733 W CLAIREMONT AVE 54701 #005-02-1996 L1997 **PD** *020 †55

GLEESON, Joseph Thomas. 617 W CLAIREMONT AVE 54701 #654-01-1996 L2001 **FM** *020

GOGIA, Sudhanshu. ■ 54703 #495-36-2000 L2004 **IM** *020 †20

GONZAGA, Caesar R. 2116 CRAIG RD, MARSHFIELD CLINIC-EAU CLAI 54701 #748-01-1962 L1976 **GS** *020

GONZAGA, Michael. 2116 CRAIG RD, MARSHFIELD CLNC 54701 #748-11-1968 L1975 **IM NEP** *020 †20

GRAY, Pamela Jean. ■ 54703 #056-05-1987 L1998 **FM** *020 †18

GRAY, Roger Sloan. ■ 54701 #056-06-1947 L1948 **FM** *071 †18

GREEN, Paul Wm. 733 W CLAIREMONT AVE, MIDELFORT CLINIC LTD 54701 #030-05-1983 L1984 **FM** *020 †18

GREWE, Bradley Kent. 1400 BELLINGER ST, STE 2 54703 #056-05-1982 L1987 **GS VS** *020 †85

GRIFFITH, Donald R. 1356 PRIORY RD 54701 #025-01-1951 L1957 **IM** *071 †20

HADLEY, Thomas Wright. 900 W CLAIREMONT AVE 54701 #026-04-1970 L1977 **PTH** *020 †50

HAIGH, James Danl. 733 W CLAIREMONT AVE, MIDELFORT CLINIIC LTD 54701 #037-01-1977 L1978 **PD** *020 †55

HALGRIMSON, Kenneth Wayne. ■ 54701 #023-01-1954 L1955 **P N** *071

HALLIN, Roger P. ■ 54701 #026-04-1943 **PM** *071

HAMBLIN, Joan Elizabeth. 617 W CLAIREMONT AVE 54701 #016-06-1980 L1997 **FM FPG** *020 †18

HANNA, Richard Douglas. 1400 BELLINGER ST, LUTHER-MIDELFORT 54703 #056-06-1989 L1990 **CD IM** *020 †20

HANSEN, Jahn Sigmund. 2125 HEIGHTS DR STE 3E, SUITE 3E 54701 #054-04-1991 L1996 **GE** *020 †20

HANSON, Peter Sven. 2715 FRANK ST 54703 #018-03-1995 L2001 **DR VIR** *020 †80

HANSON, Rae Richard. 1400 BELLINGER ST, STE 2 54703 #003-01-1976 L1996 **CHN PD** *020 †55,75

HANSON, William R. 2741 N CLAIREMONT AVE, PINE GROVE FAMILY 54703 #018-75-1981, ▲ L1983 **FM** *020 †18

HAPPE, Philip John. ■ 54701 #030-06-1964 L1970 **IM** *071 †20

HARMER, Amy Louise. 2116 CRAIG RD, DEPT OF OB/GYN 54701 #037-01-1998 L2002 **OBG** *020 †30

HARTMAN, Michael Aaron. ■ 54701 #056-06-1998 L1999 **EM** *020 †16

HAWN, William Francis. 2715 DAMON ST 54701 #030-05-1977 L1981 **OPH** *020 †35

HAYES, Edward Patrick. 2116 CRAIG RD 54701 #041-01-1994 L1995 **ORS** *020 †40

HEBL, Joseph Terry. 1400 BELLINGER ST, LUTHER MIDELFORT 54703 #038-41-1985 L1991 **FM** *020 †18

HEILER, Greg Crane. 900 W CLAIREMONT AVE 54701 #026-04-1987 L1992 **PTH** *040 †50

HELLAND, David Jay. 2116 CRAIG RD, EAU CLAIRE CENTER 54701 #026-04-1998 L1999 **FM** *020 †18

HENLY, David Reeves. 1400 BELLINGER ST, MAYO HEALTH SYSTEM , 54703 #026-08-1988 L1996 **U** *020 †95

HERR, Molly Mayo-Hilgenbe. ■ 54701 #056-05-1999 L2005 **AN** *020 †05

HETH, William Leon. 1400 BELLINGER ST, STE 2 54703 #056-05-1984 L1989 **U** *020 †95

HICKS, Patrice M L. 1400 BELLINGER ST, LUTHER MIDELFORT 54703 #026-04-1988 L1994 **D** *020 †15

HIDALGO, Jose Alfredo. ■ 54703 #737-01-1989 **ID** *100 †20

HIDALGO, Martha Alcira. 2116 CRAIG RD, MARSHFIELD CLINIC 54701 #737-01-1990 L2002 **IM** *020 †20

HILLERUD, Andrea Chung. ■ 54701 #060-01-1995 L1998 **FM OBG** *020 †18

HIRSH, Michael Schoen. 3203 STEIN BLVD, WESTERN WISCONSIN UROLOGY 54701 #021-01-1993 L1998 **U** *020 †95

HOFER, Lee Allan. 2715 DAMON ST 54701 #026-04-1983 L1988 **OPH** *020 †35

HOFER, Mark Wayne. 900 W CLAIREMONT AVE 54701 #026-04-1985 L1986 **PTH** *020 †50

HOFF, Donald E. 1221 WHIPPLE ST 54703 #019-02-1946 L1949 **GP IM** *071 †20

HOGUE, David Kenneth. 733 W CLAIREMONT AVE 54701 #038-41-1971 L1972 **OPH** *071 †35

HOWER, Chris Donnell. 1400 BELLINGER ST, STE 2 54703 #026-04-1995 L1996 **GS** *020 †85

HOWER, Deborah Joan. 1221 WHIPPLE ST 54703 #056-06-1996 L1998 **IM** *020 †20

HUDSON, Ann Netalia. ■ 54703 #130-01-2002 L2007 **IMG** *020 †20

HUDSON, Ralph F. 3834 CLAYMORE LN 54701 #016-11-1949 L1957 **GS** *071 †85

HUMPHREYS, Chris Ewing. 3802 OAKWOOD MALL DR 54701 #018-03-1982 L1983 **AN** *020 †05

HUNT, Thomas K. 2116 CRAIG RD, URGENT CARE DEPT 54701 #037-01-1997 L1999 **FM** *020 †18

HUSAIN, Naghma. 2116 CRAIG RD 54701 #690-02-1986 L2000 **PD** *020 †55

IHLE, Charles Vaudreuil. 1400 BELLINGER ST, MIDELFORT CLN 54703 #056-05-1965 L1966 **ORS** *020 †40

IMMERMAN, Steven Curt. 719 W HAMILTON AVE 54701 #016-06-1976 L1981 **GS TS** *020 †85

ISRAEL, T Andrew. 1400 BELLINGER ST, LUTHER MILFORT 54703 #056-05-1993 L1999 **ORS** *020 †40

IWAKIRI, James Seitaro. 3203 STEIN BLVD, WESTERN WISCONSIN UROLOGY 54701 #016-06-1988 L1994 **U** *020 †95

JACOBY, Philip Emery. 3501 GOLF RD 54701 #056-05-1984 L1985 **FM** *020 †18

JALIL, S Nathaniel. 2116 CRAIG RD, EAU CLAIRE CENTER 54701 #160-05-1982 L1993 **NEP** *020 †20

JARECKI, Heidi Leanne. 2715 DAMON ST 54701 #056-05-2001 L2003 **OPH** *020 †35

JAVAHERIAN, Abolghasem D. 3587 GATEWAY DR 54701 #517-08-1979 L1993 **IM** *020 †20

JOHNSON, Daniel Fremont. 3652 TAMARACK LN 54701 #028-02-1961 L1964 **OBG** *071 †30

JOHNSON, Deborah L. 3802 OAKWOOD MALL DR 54701 #422-01-1989 L2003 **AN** *020 †05

JOHNSON, Robert John. 3587 GATEWAY DR, STE 110 54701 #422-01-1990 L2003 **FM** *020 †18

JOHNSON, Steven Danl. 1400 BELLINGER ST, MIDELFORT CLINIC LTD 54703 #056-05-1986 L1991 **GS VS** *020 †85

JOLES, Thomas Ivan. 617 W CLAIREMONT AVE, UW - HEALTH 54701 #056-06-2006 **FP** *012

JONES, Daniel Lewis. ■ 54701 #038-40-1968 L1974 **D** *020 †15

KAMRANI, Farzad T. ■ 54701 #517-01-1972 L1978 **IM** *020 †20

KAPLA, Steven M. 3802 OAKWOOD MALL DR 54701 #026-04-1989 L1993 **AN** *020 †05

KATZ, David Jeffrey. 3203 STEIN BLVD, WESTERN WISCONSIN UROLOGY 54701 #041-02-1969 L1970 **U** *020 †95

KEBEDE, Asegid Hassen. 1400 BELLINGER ST, LUTHER MIDELFORT 54703 #366-03-1992 L2008 **PCC** *020 †20

KEEBAUGH, Kathy Klein. 733 W CLAIREMONT AVE, LUTHER MIDELFORT 54701 #012-22-1997 L2007 **FM** *020 †18

KELLEY, Walter M. ■ 54701 #056-05-1950 L1951 **AN** *071 †05

KHAN, Ayesha. 2116 CRAIG RD, EAU CLAIRE CENTER 54701 #704-02-1972 L1995 **PD** *020

KHAN, Humayun A. 2116 CRAIG RD, EAU CLAIRE CENTER 54701 #308-11-1986 L1993 **NEP** *020 †20

KHATTAB, Mahmoud. 2116 CRAIG RD, MARSHFIELD CLINIC-EAU CLAI 54701 #875-01-1993 L2007 **IM** *100 †20

KIDESS, Anton Issa. 703 W HAMILTON AVE, STE 4 54701 #575-01-1987 L1990 **PCC IM** *020 †20

KINCAID, Daniel Thos. 1400 BELLINGER ST, STE 2 54703 #023-07-1966 L1972 **CD IM** *020 †20

KING, Brian John. 2102 CRAIG RD 54701 #352-03-1958 L1968 **GS** *020 †85

KISHABA, Richard Gregg. 733 W CLAIREMONT AVE, LUTHER/MIDELFORT CLAIRMNT 54701 #056-06-1984 L1985 **PD** *020 †55

KLESSIG, Heidi Telfer. 1221 WHIPPLE ST, PAIN CLNC OF NW WI 54703 #056-05-1988 L1989 **AN PME** *071 †05

KOKAN, Farhat Nasreen. 2116 CRAIG RD, EAU CLAIRE CENTER 54701 #690-03-1983 L1996 **AI PD** *020 †03,55

KOKEMOOR, Richard Herbert. S5456 STATE ROAD 37 54701 #048-13-1979 L1985 **NS LM** *062

KOLLROSS, Linda K. 2116 CRAIG RD, EAU CLAIRE CENTER 54701 #056-05-1990 L1998 **P** *020 †75

KONZEN, Jon P. 719 W HAMILTON AVE, STE A 54701 #016-76-1988, ▲ L1995 **N** *020 †75

KRESS, Patricia Lou. 2741 N CLAIREMONT AVE, PINE GROVE FAMILY 54703 #026-04-1986 L1987 **FM** *020 †18

KYLE, Julia Irene. 2116 CRAIG RD, MARSHFIELD CLINIC-EAU CLAI 54701 #056-05-1995 L1999 **MPD PD** *020 †20,55

LAMOUREUX, John T L. 900 W CLAIREMONT AVE 54701 #025-07-1978 L1981 **PM** *020 †60

LANGE, Ronald Herbert. 2715 DAMON ST, CHIPPEWA VALLEY EYE CLINIC 54701 #056-06-1980 L1981 **OPH OS** *020 †35

LAYDE, John Patrick. 733 W CLAIREMONT AVE 54701 #016-06-1965 L1969 **PD** *071 †55

LIEGEL, Steven Sylvester. ■ 54701 #056-05-1977 L1978 **DR** *020 †80

LINDEN, Michael Andrew. ■ 54701 #026-04-2006 L2006 **PTH** *012

LINDEN, Richard Phelps. 1400 BELLINGER ST, STE 2 54703 #026-04-1966 L1972 **PTH** *020 †50

LINDSAY, Christopher W. ■ 54701 #026-04-1999 L1999 **RNR** *020 †80

LINDSAY, Mark Edward. 1400 BELLINGER ST, STE 2 54703 #005-06-1981 L1997 **IM** *020 †20

LINTON, Randall Lynn. 733 W CLAIREMONT AVE 54701 #030-05-1978 L1981 **PD** *020 †55

LIU, Lily Har. 1000 STARR AVE 54703 #654-01-1984 L1986 **FM FPG** *020 †18

LODAHL, James. ■ 54701 #056-05-2003 L2004 **AN** *020

LOFTSGAARDEN, Jay Davis. 1400 BELLINGER ST, LUTHER MIDELFORT CLINIC 54703 #056-06-1991 L1995 **PM** *020 †60

LOKKESMOE, Darren Kyle. 733 W CLAIREMONT AVE 54701 #026-04-1991 L1998 **IM** *020 †20

LONGBELLA, Chris Richard. 2116 CRAIG RD, EAU CLAIRE CENTER 54701 #026-04-1989 L1992 **OBG** *020 †30

LOOMIS, Paul Danl. 733 W CLAIREMONT AVE, MIDELFORT CLINIC FAMILY ME 54701 #056-05-1988 L1990 **EM FM** *020 †20

LORUSSO, Frank Paul. 2116 CRAIG RD 54701 #017-20-2002 L2006 **OBG** *020

LOTZ, Robert Major. 1400 BELLINGER ST 54703 #056-05-1943 L1944 **GS GP** *071

LUTHER, Dennis Michael. 2116 CRAIG RD, MARSHFIELD CLINIC-EAU CLAI 54701 #041-12-1984 L1991 **IM** *020

LYNCH, Michael James. ■ 54701 #016-11-1980 L1981 **IM IMG** *030 †20

MACKEN, Patrick D. 1400 BELLINGER ST, LUTHER MIDELFORT 54703 #539-04-1969 L1976 **NEP** *020 †20

MANZ, Carl Walton. 1400 BELLINGER ST, STE 2 54703 #056-05-1963 L1964 **GS** *020 †85

MANZ, James Walton. 1400 BELLINGER ST, LUTHER MIDELFORT 54703 #056-06-1985 1986 **OSS ORS** *020 †40

MANZ, Sharon Harris. 3802 OAKWOOD MALL DR 54701 #038-45-1983 L1984 **AN** *020 †05

MARTIN, Keith Edward. 1400 BELLINGER ST, MIDELFORT CLINIC LTD 54703 #016-02-1976 L1981 **GS** *020 †85

MARTIN, Scott A. 1221 WHIPPLE ST, DEPT OF PATH LUTHER HOSP 54703 #037-01-1998 L2002 **PTH** *020

MASTERS, Lynnette A. 617 W CLAIREMONT AVE, EAU CLAIRE FAMILY MEDICINE 54701 #048-02-2006 **FP** *012

MAUTZ, William Thos. 204 SKYLINE DR 54703 #056-05-1940 L1941 **GP** *071

MAYER, Leland Robt. 1400 BELLINGER ST, LUTHER/MIDELFORT 54703 #056-06-1981 L1982 **ORS** *020 †40

MC CLAFLIN, Richard Ray. 617 W CLAIREMONT AVE, UW HEALTH 54701 #030-05-1977 L1998 **FM** *040 †18

MC DOUGALL, Wm Alexander. 900 W CLAIREMONT AVE 54701 #919-05-1976 L2004 **GS AM** *020 †85

MC ELROY, Neil Daniel. 2818 URANUS AVE 54703 #056-06-1993 L1994 **AN** *020

MC ENANY, Michael Terry. 1400 BELLINGER ST, MIDELFORT CLNC DEPT CARD D 54703 #023-07-1964 L1993 **TS** *075 †85,90

MC LEOD, David James. ■ 54703 #056-05-1956 **OS** *075

MC QUILLAN, Kathryn Irene. 2116 CRAIG RD, MARSHFIELD CLINIC- EAU CLA 54701 #056-06-2003 L2007 **PD** *020 †55

MC QUILLAN, Lance. ■ 54701 #056-06-2003 L2007 **FM** *100 †18

MELLEMA, Joanne Ruth. 619 RIPLEY AVE, CREST WELLNESS CENTER 54701 #026-04-1984 L1985 **FM** *020 †18

MERRICK, John Clinton. 3221 STEIN BLVD 54701 #028-02-1998 L2005 **HS** *020 †65

MERRITT, James Woodward. ■ 54701 #018-03-1952 L1953 **GS TS** *020 †85,90

MICHALK, Kathleen R. 900 W CLAIREMONT AVE 54701 #016-76-1997, ▲ L2005 **OBG** *020 †30

MIETTUNEN, James Brian. 733 W CLAIREMONT AVE, MIDELFORT CLINIC LTD 54701 #026-04-1982 L1987 **OTO** *020 †45

MILZ, Michael Quentin. 3802 OAKWOOD MALL DR 54701 #056-05-1990 L1991 **AN** *020 †05

MOBERG, Thomas David. 723 RORK AVE 54703 #026-04-1948 L1957 **R** *071 †80

MOLLDREM, Nathan David. 4315 MEADOW LN 54701 #016-06-1969 L1976 **PD** *071

MORE, Rolando Ramon. 2116 CRAIG RD 54701 #056-06-1991 L1998 **N CN** *020 †75

MORGAN, Odette Angela. 2116 CRAIG RD 54701 #566-01-1991 L2003 **IM END** *020 †20

MORIN, William David. 1400 BELLINGER ST, STE 2 54703 #026-04-1982 L1994 **ORS AM** *020 †40

MOURAD, Wael Sayed. 617 W CLAIREMONT AVE, UW HEALTH FAMILY MED CLIN 54701 #654-01-2004 L2005 **FM** *100 †18

MUELLER, John Michael. 733 W CLAIREMONT AVE 54701 #056-05-1975 L1976 **FM** *020 †18

MURPHY, Christine M. 2116 CRAIG RD, MARSHFIELD CLINIC-EAU CLAI 54701 #048-02-1992 L1999 **D** *020 †20

MURPHY, Michael Martin. 900 W CLAIREMONT AVE, 6TH FL 54701 #016-45-1978 L1993 **N IM** *020 †20,75

MURRAY, Michael John. 826 S HASTINGS WAY 54701 #056-06-1982 L1985 **P** *020 †75

MUSLIM, Muhammad. 900 W CLAIREMONT AVE, MARSHFIELD CLINIC-REGIONAL 54701 #704-01-1988 L2002 **HO** *020 †20 ‡

MYHRE, Karen Lynne. 733 W CLAIREMONT AVE, LUTHER MIDELFORT 54701 #016-06-1998 L1999 **PD** *020 †55

NAQVI, Syed Muhammed B. 900 W CLAIREMONT AVE, MARSHFIELD CLINIC-REGIONAL 54701 #704-01-1995 L2002 **HO IM** *020 †20

NAVARRO, Marlon Joseph. 2116 CRAIG RD, MARSHFIELD CLINIC-EAU CLAI 54701 #021-05-1996 L2001 **RHU** *020 †20

NIXON, Nadine Elizabeth. 617 W CLAIREMONT AVE, EAU CLAIRE FAMILY MED PGM 54701 #056-05-2007 **FP** *012

NOLTNER, Stephen William. 3802 OAKWOOD MALL DR 54701 #056-06-1985 L1992 **AN** *020 †05

NORDSTROM, Charles W. ■ 54701 #056-06-2001 L2004 **IM** *020

NORMAN, Stanley Gerald. 2116 CRAIG RD 54701 #026-04-1965 L1973 **OTO** *020 †45

NOYCE, Robert Dearborn. 1400 BELLINGER ST, STE 2 54703 #005-02-1979 L1990 **ID IM** *020 †20

OBAID, Saleh. 703 W HAMILTON AVE, STE 4 54701 #875-01-1969 L1976 **IM PUD** *020 †20

O'CARROLL, Donnan I. 900 W CLAIREMONT AVE 54701 #539-04-1969 L1976 **PTH** *020 †50

O'COCHLAIN, Brendan J. ■ 54701 #539-05-1990 L1995 **ICE** *020 †20

O'CONNOR, James J. 1400 BELLINGER ST, MIDELFORT CLINIC 54703 #010-02-1975 L1980 **ORS** *020 †40

OGUNLESI, Christianah Y O. 2116 CRAIG RD, MARSHFIELD CLNC EYE CLAIRE 54701 #690-02-1995 L2006 **CHP P** *020 †75

O'HALLORAN, Michael James. 1312 CUMMINGS AVE 54701 #030-06-1967 L1972 **PD** *071 †55

OLSON, David Warren. 2116 CRAIG RD 54701 #038-40-1974 L2000 **VS GS** *020 †85

OLSON, Roy Arnold. 2715 DAMON ST 54701 #056-05-1969 L1970 **OPH** *020 †35

ORTIZ, Jose Antonio, Jr. 1400 BELLINGER ST, LUTHER MIDELFORT 54703 #035-46-1992 L2000 **ORS HS** *020 †40

OTTEVAERE, James Alphonse. 3802 OAKWOOD MALL DR 54701 #025-01-1993 L1997 **AN** *020 †05

OWEN, George Edward. 3421 MCELROY CT 54701 #035-20-1956 L1962 **IM CD** *020 †20

PADILLA, Jose Abran. 4212 SOUTHTOWN DR 54701 #005-11-1992 L2005 **ORS** *020 †40

PAKPREO, Somrat. 2116 CRAIG RD, MARSHFIELD CLINIC-EAU CLAI 54701 #891-02-1968 L1974 **OBG** *020 †30

PARKHURST, Brandon Lynn. 1000 STARR AVE 54703 #028-03-1997 L1998 **FM** *020 †18

PAST, Larry Robt. 1221 WHIPPLE ST 54703 #026-04-1981 L2004 **RO** *020 †80

PASTERNACK, Morris, Jr. 1400 BELLINGER ST, STE 2 54703 #024-05-1984 L1995 **PUD CCM** *050 †20

PAYNE, Nicole Marie. 617 W CLAIREMONT AVE 54701 #665-02-2008 *100

PECK, Robert Curtiss, Jr. 1221 WHIPPLE ST BOX 4105, MIDELFORT CLNC 54703 #041-09-1987 L1993 **P ADP** *020 †75

PEIKERT, Johann Markus. 733 W CLAIREMONT AVE 54701 #026-04-1990 L1994 **D** *020 †15

PELLER, Thomas Patrick. 714 W HAMILTON AVE 54701 #026-04-1985 L1993 **GE IM** *020 †20

PELTIER, Suzette Kay. 1400 BELLINGER ST, STE 2 54703 #037-01-1985 L1987 **OBG** *020 †30

PEPPERL, James Eric. 2116 CRAIG RD, MARSHFIELD CLINIC-EAU CLAI 54701 #035-09-1988 L1999 **OPH** *020 †35

PEREZ, Eduardo J. 1221 WHIPPLE ST, STAFF NEUROSURGEON 54703 #035-15-1998 L2007 **NS** *020 †25

PETERSON, Christian F. 1400 BELLINGER ST, STE 2 54703 #056-05-1980 L1981 **EM FM** *020 †18,16

PETERSON, Laurie L. 2116 CRAIG RD, EAU CLAIRE CENTER 54701 #048-04-1986 L1989 **PD** *020 †55

PETERSON, Thomas Louis. 900 W CLAIREMONT AVE, CHIPPEWA VALLEY EMERGENCY 54701 #016-11-1982 L1985 **EM** *030 †16

PITCHFORD, Timothy James. ■ 54701 #037-01-1995 L2000 **GS** *020 †85

PLEWA, John Joseph. 733 W CLAIREMONT AVE, CLAIREMONT CAMPUS 54701 #028-34-1997 L2013 **PD** *020 †55

POESCHEL, Bernard Bruce. 1400 BELLINGER ST, STE 2 54703 #036-07-1974 L1976 **PTH** *020 †50

POLUS, Jacqueline. 2741 N CLAIREMONT AVE, PINE GROVE FAMILY 54703 #056-05-1986 L1987 **FM** *020 †18

PORTER, Phillip James. 900 W CLAIREMONT AVE, SACRED HEART HOSPITAL 54701 #065-01-1991 L2002 **NS** *020

PROETT, Alois Frederick. 4212 SOUTHTOWN DR 54701 #030-05-1973 L1979 **ORS** *071 †40

RAHMAN, Seema. 2116 CRAIG RD, MARSHFIELD CLINIC-EAU CLAI 54701 #704-02-1989 L2002 **IM** *020 †20

RAIKAR, Vasant Amrut. ■ 54701 #496-38-1954 L1988 **FM EM** *071

RAMAGE, Jack Ira, Jr. 1221 WHIPPLE ST, LUTHER MIDELFORT-MAYO HLTH 54703 #012-01-1997 L2013 **GE** *020 †20

RANKIN, Thomas Vincent. 900 W CLAIREMONT AVE, SACRED HEART HOSP 54701 #023-01-1968 L1993 **NS** *075 †25

RANTALA, Amy Lynn. PO BOX 1510, 1400 BELLINGER ST 54702 #026-04-1999 L2000 **FM** *020 †18

READ, William Tolbert. 733 W CLAIREMONT AVE, BOX 1510 54701 #019-02-1974 L1976 **PD** *020 †55

REDDY, Kurapati Bhaskar. 900 W CLAIREMONT AVE 54701 #495-50-1973 L1983 **P PYG** *020 †75

■ = Address Information Privacy Protected

REDMANN, James Oliver. 733 W CLAIREMONT AVE 54701 #056-06-1981 L1982 **OPH** *020 †35

REID, Dale Lee. 733 W CLAIREMONT AVE 54701 #056-05-1976 L1977 **FM** *020 †18

RENTZEPIS, Michael John. 1400 BELLINGER ST, LUTHER MIDELFORT CLINIC 54703 #035-01-1990 L1998 **U** *020 †95

RESAR, Roger Kieth. 1221 WHIPPLE ST 54703 #056-05-1972 L1975 **PUD CCM** *020 †20

RIDENOUR, Robt Vincent, Jr. 900 W CLAIREMONT AVE 54701 #016-43-1975 L1986 **PTH** *020 †50

RILEY, Mari. 2116 CRAIG RD, EAU CLAIRE CENTER 54701 #007-02-2002 L2004 **FM** *020 †18

RITSCH, Jodi Hansen. 1400 BELLINGER ST, STE 2 54703 #056-06-1994 L1996 **FM** *020 †20

RIVERO SANCHEZ-COVISA, Mar. 617 W CLAIREMONT AVE, EAU CLAIRE FAMILY MED PGM 54701 #847-13-1986 **FP** *012

ROBERTS, Christopher T. 1400 BELLINGER ST, STE 2 54703 #056-05-1995 L1998 **IM** *020 †20

ROBERTS, James Allan. 733 W CLAIREMONT AVE, LUTHER-MIDELFORT 54701 #026-04-1984 L1985 **IM** *020 †20

ROBERTSON, Timothy John. 1400 BELLINGER ST, LUTHER-MIDELFORT 54701 #056-06-1980 L1981 **CHP P** *020 †75

ROSADO, Angel Luis. ■ 54703 #042-03-2003 L2007 **IM** *020 †20

ROWE, Susan Kathryn. 733 W CLAIREMONT AVE 54701 #056-06-1980 L1981 **FM** *020 †18

ROZICH, John Dale. 1400 BELLINGER ST, STE 2 54703 #016-06-1980 L2000 **CD IM** *020 †20

RUCKER, Joseph W, Jr. 900 W CLAIREMONT AVE 54701 #025-12-1978 L1984 **PS** *020 †65

RUCKER-KEEGAN, Rebecca. 733 W CLAIREMONT AVE 54701 #025-07-1982 L1988 **IM** *020 †20

RUSKIN, James Alan. 1400 BELLINGER ST, LUTHER - MIDLFORT 54703 #035-08-1982 L1983 **NM** *020 †20

RYAN, Anne Margarethe. 5940 WILD ROSE LN 54701 #025-12-1996 L2002 **ORS** *020

SABBAGH, Fadi. 703 W HAMILTON AVE, STE 4 54701 #875-02-1993 L2006 **CCM PUD** *020 †20

SAHAKIAN, Nancy Margaret. ■ 54701 #056-06-1985 L1992 **FM** *020 †70,18

SANDAGER, Thomas Dean. 1000 STARR AVE 54703 #026-04-1980 L1983 **FM** *020 †18

SANTOLIN, Craig J. 2116 CRAIG RD 54701 #654-01-1982 L1989 **CD IM** *020 †20

SARFRAZ, Asif. 1000 STARR AVE, MARSHFIELD CLINIC-RIVERVIE 54703 #704-01-2000 L2007 **FM** *020 †18

SARUMI, Oludayo Olubukola. 2116 CRAIG RD, EAU CLAIRE CENTER 54701 #010-01-2003 L2007 **PD** *020

SATTEM, David Norman. 1104 CUMMINGS AVE 54701 #016-11-1964 L1973 **R NM** *020 †28,80

SAVITT, Susan Momont. 900 W CLAIREMONT AVE 54701 #056-05-1990 L1991 **OBG** *020 †30

SAZAMA, Richard Cline. 2116 CRAIG RD 54701 #056-05-1975 L1981 **U** *020 †95

SCHAUS, Paul Walter. 2116 CRAIG RD, MARSHFIELD CLINIC-EAU CLAI 54701 #056-05-1989 L1993 **AN** *020 †05

SCHERRER, Lawrence Clark. 2116 CRAIG RD, EAU CLAIRE CENTER 54701 #026-04-1994 L1998 **D** *020 †15

SCHIFELING, David John. 900 W CLAIREMONT AVE, MARSHFIELD CLINIC-REGIONAL 54701 #016-02-1980 L1983 **IM PLM** *020 †20

SCHLICHT, Anneke. 807 S FARWELL ST 54701 #056-05-2003 L2005 **FM** *020 †18

SCHLIMGEN, Karla Stelling. 1110 OAK RIDGE DR, OAK LEAF PEDIATRICS 54701 #030-05-1992 L1999 **PD** *020 †55

SCHLOSSER, Paul Mitchell. 200 MAIN ST, TWO RIVERS CLINIC, SC 54701 #035-20-1981 L1991 **OBG** *020 †30

SCHMIDT-KRINGS, Diane Ros. 2116 CRAIG RD, MARSHFIELD CLINIC-EAU CLAI 54701 #026-04-1995 L2005 **PS** *020 †85,65

SCHOENFELDER, Donna Lynn. 1110 OAK RIDGE DR 54701 #046-01-1987 L1992 **OBG** *020 †30

SCHREITER, Steven Walter. 1400 BELLINGER ST, STE 2 54703 #016-43-1988 L2000 **CD IM** *020 †20

SCHULZ, Caryn Irene. 4638 GOLF RD 54701 #056-05-1976 L1978 **D** *020 †15

SCHULZ, Emil. ■ 54701 #026-04-1956 L1961 **DR RO** *071 †80

SCHYNOLL, Wolfram Guido. 900 W CLAIREMONT AVE 54701 #026-04-1987 L1990 **EM** *020 †16

SENINGEN, Ronald Perry. ■ 54701 #036-07-1968 L1991 **DR** *020 †80

SETLA, Joanna. 1400 BELLINGER ST, STE 2 54703 #759-03-1992 L1997 **IM** *020 †20

SHARMA, Vinay. 3349 S ROBIN MEADOWS LN 54701 #661-03-2007 *100

SHELLEY, Timothy Mark. 733 W CLAIREMONT AVE, MIDELFORT CLINIC 54701 #030-05-1994 L1982 **RHU IM** *020 †20

SHEPICH, Jeffrey Ryan. 2116 CRAIG RD 54701 #025-01-1996 L1997 **FM** *020 †18

SHINNERS, Patrick Anthony. 733 W CLAIREMONT AVE, LUTHER MIDELFORT 54701 #056-05-1995 L2000 **OTO** *020 †45

SIMON, Rita Rae. 2440 RIDGE RD, COMM HLTH PARTNERSHIO 54701 #026-04-1985 L1988 **FM** *030 †18

SINGH, Gurpreet Kaur. 2116 CRAIG RD, MARSHFIELD CLINIC-EAU CLAI 54701 #654-01-2000 L2005 **FM** *100 †18

SINGH, Paramvir. 2005 RICE CT 54701 #495-36-1994 L2004 **IM GE** *100 †20

SLINKARD, Tamara Jean. 900 W CLAIREMONT AVE 54701 #026-04-1997 L1998 **FM** *020 †18

SMITH, Margaret Ann. ■ 54703 #056-05-1994 L1996 *020

SMITH, Michael J. 714 W HAMILTON AVE 54701 #030-06-1988 L1992 **IM PD** *020 †20,55 ‡

SMITHBERG, Nathan Edward. 1400 BELLINGER ST, STE 2 54703 #026-04-1986 L1988 **IM** *020 †20

SNYDER, John Roger, Jr. 733 W CLAIREMONT AVE, LUTHER MIDELFORT 54701 #026-04-1989 L1992 **FM** *020 †18

SONTAG, Mark Timothy. 3802 OAKWOOD MALL DR 54701 #026-04-1983 L1988 **AN** *020 †05

SOOMAR, Nasima R. 3501 GOLF RD, MARSHFIELD CLINIC-OAKWOOD 54701 #704-16-1987 L1997 **IM** *020 †20

SOUTHARD, Mark Robert. ■ 54703 #056-06-2001 L2002 **DR** *020 †80

SPAK, Michael John. 2715 FRANK ST 54703 #016-43-1972 L1976 **DR N** *020 †80

SPERLINGAS, Stacey Jo. 617 W CLAIREMONT AVE 54701 #056-05-2005 L2006 **FP** *012

SPERRY, Verne Allen. 240 SKYLINE DR 54703 #016-43-1957 L1963 **AN** *071 †05

SPITZ, Leslie Mike. 1400 BELLINGER ST, STE 2 54703 #024-01-1969 L1975 **IM GP** *020 †20

SPRECHER, Lawrence Jay. 733 W CLAIREMONT AVE, INTERNAL MED DPT 54701 #017-20-1986 L2005 **IM** *020 †20

STAKE, Sharon Lynn. 733 W CLAIREMONT AVE, LUTHER MIDELFORT 54701 #056-05-1990 L1991 **FM** *020 †18

STARK, Jane Marie. 2116 CRAIG RD, MARSHFIELD CLINIC-EAU CLAI 54701 #056-06-1988 L1989 **OM GPM** *020 †70

STEINMETZ, Mark Chas. 900 W CLAIREMONT AVE 54701 #056-05-1986 L1987 **RO** *020 †80

STEINMETZ, Steven Wallace. 617 W CLAIREMONT AVE 54701 #056-05-2005 L2006 **FP** *012

STENZEL, Steven Darrell. 1030 OAK RIDGE DR 54701 #018-03-1974 L1978 **GYN** *030 †30

STERNER, Carleen A M. 1400 BELLINGER ST, LUTHER MIDELFORT 54703 #060-02-1988 L1997 **FM** *020 †18

STEVENSON, Teri Glee. 1400 BELLINGER ST, LUTHER MIDELFORT 54703 #018-03-1995 L1998 **PD** *020 †55

STIEN, John Craig. 2715 W FRANK ST 54703 #056-06-1993 L1994 **DR** *020 †80

STIEN, Karl Edwin. 2715 FRANK ST 54703 #025-01-1999 L2004 **DR** *020 †80

STIEN, Kim Patrick. 1212 CUMMINGS AVE, SACRED HEART HOSPITAL 54701 #056-05-1966 L1967 **R** *020 †80

STRINGER, Elena Aleksandr. 617 W CLAIREMONT AVE 54701 #913-55-1999 **FP** *012

STRYCZEK, Andrzej Piotr. 2116 CRAIG RD, MARSHFIELD CLINIC-EAU CLAI 54701 #759-17-1993 L2002 **IM** *020 †20

STUDT, Larry Charles, Jr. 900 W CLAIREMONT AVE 54701 #018-03-1994 L1995 **PMM** *020 †18

SUBRAMANIAN, Anand. ■ 54703 #495-16-1998 L2007 **IM** *100

SUELDO, Efrain. 2116 CRAIG RD, MARSHFIELD CLINIC 54701 #737-06-1987 L1996 **IM** *020 †20

SULTAN, Michel. ■ 54701 #605-02-1964 L1977 **GE** *071

SWANSON, Steven Elliott. PO BOX 1510, 1400 BELLINGER ST 54702 #026-08-1979 L2004 **NS** *020 †25

SWENSON, Richard Alan. 1221 WHIPPLE ST 54703 #016-11-1974 L1976 **FM** *040 †18

SWORSKI, Stephanie A. 1400 BELLINGER ST, LUTHER-MIDELFORT 54703 #026-04-1994 L1995 **FM** *020 †18

TANAWATTANACHAROEN, P. 2116 CRAIG RD 54701 #891-02-1987 L2000 **HEM ON** *020 †20

TASCH, Gail Ann. S5456 STATE ROAD 37 54701 #016-43-1981 L1985 **P** *020 †75

THAPAR, Kamal. 900 W CLAIREMONT AVE, SACRED HEART HOSP-NEUROSUR 54701 #060-02-1985 L2001 **NS OS** *020

THIMKE, Harry E. 3746 PATTON ST 54701 #056-05-1951 L1952 **AN** *071 †05

THISTLE, Johnson Logan. 1400 BELLINGER ST, MIDEFORT CLINIC-LUTHER CAM 54703 #041-13-1964 L1999 **GE** *100 †20

THOMAS, Sunil. 3213 STEIN BLVD, EAU CLAIRE SPINE & ORTHOPE 54701 #035-03-1990 L1996 **OSS GS** *020 †40

THORPE-SWENSON, Amy Jo. 733 W CLAIREMONT AVE 54701 #003-01-1987 L1988 **IM** *020 †20

TOBIN, Joseph Malcolm. 800 WISCONSIN ST 54703 #024-05-1946 L1963 **P OS** *071 †75

TOMASI, Mark Richard. 1400 BELLINGER ST, STE 2 54703 #039-01-1983 L1986 **EM FM** *020 †18

TORNEHL, Christopher Karl. 3203 STEIN BLVD 54701 #056-05-2002 L2007 **U** *020

TORNEHL, Mary Catherine. 2116 CRAIG RD, EAU CLAIRE CENTER 54701 #056-05-2002 L2007 **PD** *020 †15

TRIVEDI, Vipul Alkesh. 1221 WHIPPLE ST, LUTHER HOSP DEPT PATH 54703 #016-45-1994 L1995 **PTH** *020 †50

ULLRICH, Peter Helmuth. 1400 BELLINGER ST 54703 #026-04-1962 L1970 **R** *071 †80

USHER, David John. 733 W CLAIREMONT AVE 54701 #018-03-1993 L1998 **FM** *020 †18

VAN DE LOO, David A. 733 W CLAIREMONT AVE, LUTHER MIDELFORT 54701 #056-05-1988 L1994 **PD PSM** *020 †55

VAN DER HEIDE, Chas Joep. 321 SUMMIT AVE, EAU CLAIRE CENTER 54701 #056-05-1961 L1992 **CHP P** *020 †20

VAN WYHE, Jodie Kay. 4255 ELK CREEK RD 54703 #030-05-1997 L2002 **DR** *020 †80

VELKOVA, Diana Staykova. 2214 PETERS DR APT 219 54703 #198-05-1988 *100

VERMA, Rajnish. 1400 BELLINGER ST, LUTHER MIDELFORT 54703 #495-30-2001 L2006 **IM** *012

VIDIC, Nino Anton. 4907 KEYSTONE XING, LIFE SKILLS SUPPORT CTR 54701 #654-01-1996 L2007 **CHP P** *020

VIRATA, Andrew Roehr. 1221 WHIPPLE ST, DEPARTMENT OF PATHOLOGY 54703 #047-07-2002 L2005 **PTH** *100 †50

VOLMAR, Fritz Henry. 2116 CRAIG RD 54701 #016-06-1999 L2005 **GE** *020 †20

WAGNER, Peter Jon. 1400 BELLINGER ST, MIDELFORT CLINIC 54703 #026-08-1983 L1994 **IM** *020 †20

WAITS, Ronald Keith, Jr. 2116 CRAIG RD, MARSHFIELD CLINIC-EAU CLAI 54701 #018-03-1987 L1992 **GS** *020 †85

WALKER, Joy Penelope. 733 W CLAIREMONT AVE 54701 #026-04-1994 L1995 **D** *020 †15

WALTER, William Henry. ■ 54701 #028-34-1955 L1959 **GS** *071

WARFFUEL, Morgan Ernest. 3501 GOLF RD 54701 #654-01-1983 L1986 **FM** *020 †18 ‡

WATSON, Robert Forrest. 733 W CLAIREMONT AVE 54701 #016-11-1982 L1984 **FM EM** *020 †18

WEBER, Donald Frank. 1400 BELLINGER ST, BOX 1510 54701 #037-01-1982 L1983 **OBG** *020 †18

WEGGEL, William James. 1221 WHIPPLE ST 54703 #056-05-1981 L1985 **P** *020 †75

WEIMER, Kenneth Charles. 1000 STARR AVE 54703 #026-04-2000 L2001 **PD** *020 †55 ‡

WEISS, Steven David. 1400 BELLINGER ST, STE 2 54703 #056-05-1985 L1988 **IM** *020 †20

WHITEHOUSE, Donna Pauline. 900 W CLAIREMONT AVE, CITY OF EAU CLAIRE FIRE DE 54701 #056-06-1998 L1999 **EM** *020 †16

WHITIS, Benjamin Michael. 2715 FRANK ST 54703 #018-03-1991 L2001 **DR** *020 †80

WHITIS, Lori Jo Jessen. ■ 54701 #018-03-1989 L2001 **FM** *020 †18

WIECHMANN, Robert Jerome. 1400 BELLINGER ST, LUTHER MIDELFORT 54703 #026-04-1986 L1999 **TS** *020 †85,90

WIEDBUSCH, Robert Bruce. 3501 GOLF RD 54701 #025-07-1979 L2000 **PD** *020 †55

WILLIAMS, Mark Wesley. ■ 54701 #056-05-1983 L1986 **FM** *020 †18

WILSON, Louis James. 807 S FARWELL ST BOX 1 54701 #026-04-1952 L1980 **FM P** *040 †18

WINANDY, Marlys Regina. 617 W CLAIREMONT AVE 54701 #026-04-1996 L1997 **FM** *020 †18

WINTER, David Bruce. 733 W CLAIREMONT AVE, LUTHER MIDELFORTT 54701 #026-04-1989 L1990 **DR** *020 †80

WOGAHN, Brent Matthew. 719 W HAMILTON AVE STE C 54701 #018-03-1990 L1995 **GS VS** *020 †85

WOGAHN, Kristin Huebner. 703 W HAMILTON AVE, STE 4 54701 #018-03-1990 L1995 **FM** *020 †18

WOOD, William Jonathan. 2107 HEIGHTS DR, EAU CLAIRE ANESTHESIOLOGIS 54701 #041-02-2003 L2004 **AN** *100

WOODHOUSE, Charles L, Jr. 1400 BELLINGER ST 54703 #019-02-1974 L1978 **ON IM** *071 †20

WOODS, Roderick Dale. 2116 CRAIG RD 54701 #023-07-1979 L2003 **IM** *020 †20

WRIGHT, Todd Walker. 1400 BELLINGER ST, LUTHER MIDELFORT 54703 #005-14-1989 L1991 **ORS** *020 †40

WYNKOOP, Robert David. ■ 54701 #040-02-1997 L2004 **EM** *020 †16

YOUNG, George. 2116 CRAIG RD 54701 #010-01-1975 L1988 **DR PDR** *020 †80

YOUNG, Timothy John. 1400 BELLINGER ST, ST JOHNS CLINIC 54703 #026-04-2001 L2008 **N** *020 †75

ZHEREBITSKIY, Viktor. 617 W CLAIREMONT AVE 54701 #913-07-1989 **FM** *100

ZIGHELBOIM, Jaime. 1400 BELLINGER ST, MIDELFORT CLINIC 54703 #935-01-1987 L1998 **GE IM** *020 †20

EDGAR – MARATHON

STOFFEL, Thomas G. 103 S 3RD AVE 54426 #030-05-1987 L1988 **FM** *020 †18

■ = Address Information Privacy Protected

EDGERTON – ROCK

BETTS, Kenneth Roger. 528 STOUGHTON RD 53534 #068-01-1982 L1998 **GP** *020
DHILLON, Sartaj K. 1011 N MAIN ST 53534 #495-29-1986 L1993 **IM** *040 †20
GATTUSO, David Brian. 92 E STATE ROAD 59 53534 #306-01-1983 L1986 **IM CD** *020
HOBSON, Douglas Jay. 217 N MAIN ST 53534 #018-03-2000 L2003 **FM** *100 †18
KNISELY, Barbara Lynn. 313 STOUGHTON RD 53534 #041-14-1990 L1994 **DR** *020 †80
KRONQUIST, Gordon Eric. 1011 N MAIN ST 53534 #056-05-1959 L1960 **PD** *071 †55
LARSON, James Herbert. 313 STOUGHTON RD, EDGERTON HOSP & HLTH SYS 53534 #026-04-1972 L1991 **ATP CLP** *020 †50
MC GOREY, Thomas Michael. 313 STOUGHTON RD, MEMORIAL COMMUNITY HOSPITA 53534 #016-43-1995 L1996 **FM** *020 †18
MOSES, John. 313 STOUGHTON RD 53534 #056-05-1991 L1992 **CD** *020 †20
NORDLAND, Thomas James. 528 STOUGHTON RD 53534 #016-06-1980 L1984 **ORS** *020 †40
PARTELLO, Vernon S, III. 217 N MAIN ST 53534 #305-01-1997 L1998 **FM** *020 †18
ROBINSON, Harrison Lewis. 1011 N MAIN ST 53534 #018-03-1991 L1991 **IM** *020 †20
ROWE, David Shaw. 528 STOUGHTON RD 53534 #041-13-1969 L1977 **OTO** *020 †45
ROWELL, Katja Joanne. 1011 N MAIN ST 53534 #025-01-1998 L2001 **FM** *020 †18
SCHMIDT, Christopher Step. ■ 53534 #056-05-2007 **AN** *012
SHEARER, Thomas M. 1011 N MAIN ST 53534 #016-06-1951 L1952 **GS GP** *072 †85
STEWART, Bonne Lee. ■ 53534 #422-01-2000 L2001 **FM** *020

EGG HARBOR – DOOR

FELTON, Owen Lester. ■ 54209 #056-05-1960 L1961 **ATP CLP** *071 †50
KIRKHAM, Bruce Curtis. ■ 54209 #056-05-1966 L1967 **R** *071 †80
WILL, Frederic B. PO BOX 410 54209 #041-09-1979 L1983 **P** *020 †75

ELCHO – LANGLADE

DEEP, Lakshmi. W10618 CLINIC ST 54428 #495-21-1995 L2001 **IM** *020 †20

ELEVA – EAU CLAIRE

NELSON, Sandra Kay. ■ 54738 #054-04-1992 L2007 **CHP** *020 †75
SHUJA, Suhail Bin. ■ 54738 #704-01-1984 L2006 **NEP IM** *020 †20

ELKHART LAKE – SHEBOYGAN

JAEKELS, Michael Thos. ■ 53020 #056-06-1955 L1956 **GYN IMG** *071 †30
KARRAS, Thomas James. PO BOX 333 53020 #056-05-1969 L1973 **CD** *020 †20

ELKHORN – WALWORTH

ANGERMEIER, Paul Alan. W3985 COUNTY ROAD NN, PATHOLOGY DEPARTEMENT 53121 #017-20-1982 L1993 **PTH OS** *020 †50
BATESKY, Douglas Edward. W3985 COUNTY ROAD NN, LAKELAND MEDICAL CENTER 53121 #016-11-1991 L2003 **EM** *020 †16
BELLINO, Michael Peter. W3985 COUNTY ROAD NN, AURORA LAKELAND MED CTR 53121 #016-11-1988 L2002 **EM** *020 †16
BERKOWITZ, Cary Edward. W3985 COUNTY ROAD NN, LAKELAND MEDICAL CENTER 53121 #016-42-1972 L2004 **CD IM** *020 †20 ‡
BORTIN, Kenneth Baurse. W3985 COUNTY ROAD NN 53121 #041-09-1979 L1984 **CD IM** *020 †20
CABABA, Ernesto C. W3985 COUNTY ROAD NN, ANESTHESIOLOGY AT 53121 #748-01-1967 L1978 **AN** *020
CONRARDY, Anthony Gregory. W3985 COUNTY ROAD NN, ANESTHESIOLOGY AT 53121 #654-01-1996 L2001 **AN** *020 ‡
CONRARDY, Philip Gerard. W3985 COUNTY ROAD NN, ANESTHESIOLOGY AT 53121 #654-01-1987 L1989 **AN** *020 †05
DALTON, David Earl. W3985 COUNTY ROAD NN, LAKELAND MEDICAL CENTER 53121 #016-42-1999 L2004 **EM** *020 †16
FOLLANSBEE, Jeffrey Thos. W3985 COUNTY ROAD NN, ANESTHESIOLOGY AT 53121 #654-01-1988 L1991 **AN PME** *020
FREMGEN, Patrick M. 1311 S LINCOLN ST, EYE PHYSICIANS & SURGEONS 53121 #016-11-1992 L1996 **OPH** *020 †35
GOLDMANN, Robert Warren. W3648 SCOTCH BUSH RD 53121 #035-08-1978 L1979 **CCM UM** *020 †18
GROUT, David Clark. 20 N CHURCH ST 53121 #038-40-1965 L1970 **U** *071 †95
HANSEN, Daniel Roth. HWY N N 53121 #016-43-1958 L1960 **FM IM** *071
HOBBS, Michael Samuel. 205 COMMERCE CT 53121 #056-06-1997 L1998 **FM** *020 †18
JACOBS, Stephen C, Jr. W3985 COUNTY ROAD NN, ANESTHESIOLOGY AT 53121 #023-01-2000 L2003 **AN** *020 ‡
JOHNSON, Craig Joel. W3985 COUNTY ROAD NN 53121 #016-42-1984 L1988 **N** *020
KOCHAR, Arvind. HIGHWAY NN 53121 #495-20-1969 L1976 **DR NR** *071 †80
KORT, Chad Alden. 20 N CHURCH ST, AURORA HEALTH CARE 53121 #016-11-1989 L1994 **GS** *020 †85
LANZAROTTI, Charles J. 100 S WASHINGTON ST 53121 #016-43-1990 L1997 **CD** *020 †20
MADAMBA, Rossana M. W3985 COUNTY ROAD NN 53121 #748-01-1988 L1995 **ON** *020
MC HUGH, Ruth. HWY N N 53121 #056-05-1984 L1988 **OBG** *020 †30
MOL, Henry Roger. RR 4 BOX 469B 53121 #018-03-1954 L1955 **FM** *071 †18
MUZAFFAR, Kamal Syed. 100 S WASHINGTON ST 53121 #704-16-1990 L2001 **FM** *020 †18
NIAZI, Imran Ali Khan. 100 S WASHINGTON ST 53121 #704-01-1977 L1985 **ICE CD** *020 †20
OHAIR, Daniel Patrick. W3985 COUNTY ROAD NN 53121 #056-06-1988 L1989 **TS** *020 †90,85
ONG, Robert O. W3985 COUNTY ROAD NN, ANESTHESIOLOGY AT 53121 #748-10-1984 L1998 **AN PME** *020 †05
PHAN, Nguyen Hong. 100 S WASHINGTON ST 53121 #016-43-1996 L2003 **CD** *020 †20
PRASAD, Ashwini. W3985 COUNTY ROAD NN, MEDICAL COLLEGE OF WISCONS 53121 #495-57-1992 L2004 **AN** *020 ‡
QURESHI, Mehboob M. HWY N N 53121 #539-04-1963 L1969 **IMG PUD** *071

RAO, Kusuma C. W3985 COUNTY ROAD NN 53121 #495-50-1976 L1989 **PM** *050 †60
ROGERS, Richard Jos. ■ 53121 #056-06-1954 L1955 **GP** *071
ROSSING, Mark Harold. 1 1/2 W GENEVA ST 53121 #056-06-1991 L1992 **P** *020
SEEGERS, James Victor. 20 N CHURCH ST 53121 #028-02-1973 L1978 **GS GE** *020 †85
TAVERA, Menandro V, Jr. W3930 HWY NN, LAKELAND HEALTH CARE CENTE 53121 #748-02-1961 L1968 **AN IMG** *020
THIES, David Claude. 205 COMMERCE CT 53121 #018-03-1980 L1983 **FM** *020 †18
WOLTER, Robert Kurt. 20 N CHURCH ST 53121 #016-11-1979 L1980 **OTO** *020 †45

ELLISON BAY – DOOR

FIEDLER, Geo Adolph, Jr. ■ 54210 #004-01-1968 L1968 **U GP** *020 †95
HANSOTIA, Phiroze L. PO BOX 168 54210 #495-19-1962 L1970 **N CN** *020 †75
RADEMACHER, Lon Dietrig. PO BOX 138, 1276 GARRET BAY RD 54210 #016-11-1964 L1965 **DR** *071 †80

ELLSWORTH – PIERCE

JONAS, Eugene R. RR 1 BOX 13 54011 #026-04-1960 L1961 **GP** *072 †18
MC CANN, George Lester. ■ 54011 #026-04-1976 L1977 **FM** *075 †18
SHERRY, Daniel Richard. 530 W CAIRNS ST 54011 #026-04-1973 L1983 **FM OM** *020 †18
TASHJIAN, Christopher H. 144 S PLUM ST 54011 #026-04-1985 L1992 **FM** *020 †18
WILSON, Kerith Elise. 144 S PLUM ST 54011 #055-02-2000 L2003 **FM** *020 †18

ELM GROVE – WAUKESHA

AKHTAR, Khurshid Masood. ■ 53122 #704-01-1968 L1982 **NM PD** *020 †28
AMLIE-LEFOND, Catherine M. ■ 53122 #005-14-1989 L2004 **PD N** *020 †55,75
ANDRADE, Michele A. 15285 WATERTOWN PLANK RD 53122 #056-05-1997 L1999 **P** *020
ANDRLE, Terese Eileen. ■ 53122 #016-06-1985 L1989 **P** *020 †75
BRESNAHAN, Boyd Keith. ■ 53122 #060-01-1956 L1992 **P** *020 †75
CONMY, Michael Francis. 12500 W BLUEMOUND RD 53122 #056-06-1958 L1959 **DR OS** *020
CORDES, John Edwin. 13050 W BLUEMOUND RD 53122 #056-06-1954 L1955 **IM** *020
CURTIS, William C. ■ 53122 #056-06-1947 L1948 **OM** *071
DAVIS, Denise Elizabeth. 15285 WATERTOWN PLANK RD 53122 #056-06-1994 L1995 **P** *020 †75
FILLMORE, Capri Mara. 1220 WOODSIDE LN 53122 #047-05-1989 L2001 **GPM FM** *050 †70,18
GARBER, Susan Elisabeth. ■ 53122 #060-02-1987 *020
GARDNER, Weston Deuain. ■ 53122 #041-12-1942 L1948 **OS** *071
GOBLIRSCH, Thomas James. ■ 53122 #016-43-1985 L1991 **AN AM** *071 †05 ‡
GOLDBERG, Henry M. ■ 53122 #056-06-1962 L1964 **OM FM** *071 †18
GUTGUTIA, Kanan. 14840 JUNEAU BLVD, ST JOES REGIONAL MEDICAL C 53122 #495-29-1994 L1999 **IM** *020 †20
HANSON, Emmet Robt. ■ 53122 #056-06-1942 L1942 **U** *071
HART, Terrence Nicholas. ■ 53122 #038-40-1962 L1963 **IM** *071
HAUGHEY, Stephen A. 1050 LEGION DR 53122 #165-06-1981 L1982 **FM** *020 †18
HOANG, Anthony. 890 ELM GROVE RD STE 211 53122 #038-44-1992 L1996 **OBG** *020 †30
HOGAN, M Rosalie Henneke. ■ 53122 #056-06-1959 L1960 **IM AI** *071
HOTANALLI, Vaishali Rajen. ■ 53122 #305-01-2005 L2008 **IM** *012
KASPER, John David. ■ 53122 #026-04-1976 L1977 **R** *020 †80
KASTELIC, Robert. ■ 53122 #056-06-1961 L1962 **OPH** *071 †35
KAUNAS, Roman. ■ 53122 #056-06-1970 L1973 **PYG P** *020 †75
KAWECKI, Andrzej M. 12425 KNOLL RD, HLTH PROMOTION & REHAB CLI 53122 #759-12-1984 L1997 **GPM** *020
KLINGBEIL, Gerda Galambos. ■ 53122 #016-11-1957 L1958 **PM** *071 †60
KLINGBEIL, Robert Edward. ■ 53122 #016-11-1957 L1958 **AN** *071 †05
KOEPKE, Donald E. ■ 53122 #056-05-1953 L1954 **TS** *071 †85,90
KOHANYI, Mioara Argentina. PO BOX 406 53122 #308-01-1984 L1990 **P** *020
LEONHARDT, Kathryn Kraft. 12500 W BLUEMOUND RD # 301 53122 #025-01-1987 L1994 **PHP** *030 †70
LOFFREDO, Michael Anthony. ■ 53122 #033-06-2004 L2005 **PS** *012
MALLILLIN, Adoracion. 12500 W BLUEMOUND RD 53122 #748-07-1963 L1978 **GP** *020 †50
MATEICKA, William E. ■ 53122 #056-06-1953 L1954 **AN** *071 †05
MUELLER, Karl Heinz. ■ 53122 #407-32-1952 L1965 **ORS** *071 †40
O'CONNOR, Thomas Michael. ■ 53122 #056-06-1955 L1956 **TS** *071 †90,85
REIFENRATH, Wm Edward. ■ 53122 #056-06-1956 L1957 **GS** *071 †85
RHEE, Yong Hee. 13820 FAIRFIELD CT 53122 #583-03-1962 L1975 **OBG** *071 †30
RICHARDS, Marcia J S. ■ 53122 #056-05-1970 L1971 **RO** *071 †80
ROBINSON, Jonathan. 13600 JUNEAU BLVD, VILLAGE OF ELM GROVE 53122 #016-42-1980 L1983 **EM** *030 †10
RUTTUM, David Mark. ■ 53122 #056-05-2005 L2006 **AN** *012
STERGIADES, Frank Geo. 1690 BERKSHIRE DR, VA MEDICAL CENTER 53122 #056-06-1956 L1957 **IM IMG** *071
STOBBE, Knud Christian. 1435 VICTORIA CIR N 53122 #020-02-1959 L1962 **GS** *020 †85
UNGER, George Francis. ■ 53122 #041-02-1957 L1962 **R** *030 †80
VAN GILDER, John Henry. ■ 53122 #056-06-1955 L1956 **AN** *071 †05
VAN GILDER, Thomas Jos. 13005 WRAYBURN RD 53122 #048-12-1989 L2005 **GPM IM** *020 †70,20
VAN RUISWYK, Jerome Vern. 1040 WOODLAND AVE 53122 #056-05-1985 L1986 **IM** *020 †20
VINCENT, William Joseph. ■ 53122 #654-01-1983 L1987 **OPH PTH** *071
WALKER, John Anthony. ■ 53122 #056-06-1956 L1957 **CD** *071 †20
WIEGMANN, Otto A. ■ 53122 #057-05-1952 L1966 **OPH** *071 †35
WILLIAMS, Delore. 15190 MARILYN DR 53122 #026-06-1948 L1949 **IM CD** *071 †20
ZELLMER, Richard E. ■ 53122 #026-04-1953 L1959 **R** *071 †80

ELMWOOD – PIERCE

FLORY, Sonja Knebel Myhre. ■ 54740 #026-04-1959 L1996 **GP** *071
FLORY, William Danl. W1467 530TH AVE 54740 #026-04-1959 L1995 **IM** *071 †20
SPRINGER, Frank Albert. 236 SPRINGER AVE 54740 #056-05-1946 L1947 **FM** *020 †18

■ = Address Information Privacy Protected

ELROY – JUNEAU

AHLSTROM, Howard Byron. ■ 53929 #005-15-1962 L1975 **OBG GP** *071
BRIESKE, Timothy Andrew. 1705 OMAHA ST 53929 #056-05-1994 L2001 **FM** *020 †18
COOKE, William Thos. 1705 OMAHA ST 53929 #016-02-1979 L1980 **FM** *020 †18
LUDWIKOWSKI, Amy Michelle. 1705 OMAHA ST 53929 #016-11-1999 L2000 **FM** *020 †18

EPHRAIM – DOOR

STOEHR, Bruce Jos. ■ 54211 #056-05-1957 L1960 **GS VS** *071 †85

EVANSVILLE – ROCK

DEEGAN, Janet Ruth. 10 N WATER ST 53536 #056-05-1988 L1992 **FM** *020 †18
HARKIN, Christopher P. 300 UNION ST 53536 #056-05-1989 L1993 **FM** *020 †05
KRUSER, Timothy J. ■ 53536 #056-05-2006 *012
LEJA, Catherine Michelle. ■ 53536 #056-05-2004 L2006 **GE** *012 †20

FENNIMORE – GRANT

AGUILAR, Eulogio G. 220 LINCOLN AVE 53809 #748-11-1967 L1985 **GP EM** *020
BLAIR, David Murray. ■ 53809 #064-01-1979 L1984 **GP** *020
HAHN KEENEY, Christina M. ■ 53809 #056-05-1998 **FM** *100
SLANE, Eric George. 1255 11TH ST 53809 #039-01-2000 L2002 **FM** *020 †18 ‡
STADER, Eric Edwin. 1255 11TH ST 53809 #039-01-2000 L2001 **FM** *020 †18 ‡
STUPEK, Warren S. ■ 53809 #539-02-1962 L1968 **DR IM** *071 †80
WALKER, Scott Abbott. 220 LINCOLN AVE, FENNIMORE FAMILY MEDICINE 53809
#038-06-2003 L2004 **FM** *020 †18

FERRYVILLE – CRAWFORD

DUNN, Paul J. ■ 54628 #016-43-1951 L1980 **GPM OS** *071 †55
HEALY, Alfred. ■ 54628 #018-03-1963 L1964 **PD** *071 †55
SAMPSON, Alan B. ■ 54628 #016-05-1950 L1975 **OBG** *071 †30

FISH CREEK – DOOR

ARNOLD, Phillip Bonner. 3711 STATE HIGHWAY 42, NORTH SHORE MEDICAL CLINIC 54212
#018-75-2001, ▲ L2002 **FM** *020
GRUESEN, Robert Arthur. PO BOX 225, 9162 COTTAGE ROW 54212 #056-06-1957 L1958
NS *071
REBHAN, Joseph Joshua. 3711 STATE HIGHWAY 42 54212 #035-06-1998 L1999 **FM** *020 †18
TRUPIN, Lewis. ■ 54212 #035-09-1955 L1956 **OBG** *071 †30

FITCHBURG – DANE

ABLOVE, Tova Stram. 5543 E CHERYL PKWY 53711 #035-06-1996 L2003 **OBG** *020 †30
AGNEBERG, Bruce Edward. 5395 E CHERYL PKWY, VISITING NURSE ASSOCIATION 53711
#028-34-1974 L2007 **PLM FM** *030 †18
AGUILAR-SINCABAN, V. M. ■ 53575 #748-02-1957 L1967 **P** *020
ALFONSO-JAUME, Maria A. 3034 FISH HATCHERY RD, STE B 53713 #132-01-1984 L2004
IM *020 †20
AMBAY, Raj. ■ 53711 #041-15-2002 L2005 **PS** *012
BARIGALA, Ravikiran Abrah. ■ 53719 #495-21-2001 L2007 **ID** *012 †20
BAUMAN, Edward Eugene. ■ 53711 #038-06-1943 L1943 **GS** *071 †40
BECKER, Bryan Neil. 3034 FISH HATCHERY RD, UW NEPHROLOGY, SUITE B 53713
#019-02-1988 L1997 **NEP** *020 †20
BERGERON, Kimberly Green. 2955 TRIVERTON PIKE DR 53711 #030-06-2000 L2004 **OBG** *020
BERNHARDT, Louis Chas. ■ 53711 #056-05-1963 L1964 **TS GS** *071 †85,90
BOELKE, Kristi Lynn. ■ 53719 #030-06-2006 **PD** *012
BOGNER, Mark Paul. 5415 KING JAMES WAY, FITCH-RONA EMS DISTRICT 53719
#056-05-1993 L1994 **EM** *020 †16
BRIDGWATER, Gary Robt. 5209 NANNYBERRY DR 53711 #016-11-1975 L1976 **IM** *020 †20
CALLEAR, Robert Thos. ■ 53711 #035-03-1981 L1982 **IM** *020 †20
CARDWELL, Michael Carey. 2955 TRIVERTON PIKE DR 53711 #016-01-1992 L1993
OBG *020 †30
CHAN, Micah. 3034 FISH HATCHERY RD, DIVISION OF NEPHROLOGY 53713
#422-01-2002 L2003 **NEP** *012 †20
CHAN, Pik Sha Ting. ■ 53575 #748-01-1990 L2000 **OPH** *100
CHANDRUPATLA, Chethana Ve. ■ 53711 #016-11-2005 L2006 **D** *012
DASGUPTA, Vijaya. ■ 53711 #495-02-1963 L1978 **AN** *020
DJAMALI, Arjang. 3034 FISH HATCHERY RD, STE B 53713 #396-04-1998 L2001 **NEP** *020 †20
DODWAD, Mohammed-Iqbal M. ■ 53711 #495-35-1978 L1995 **EM** *020
DONOVAN, Timothy Jay. ■ 53711 #056-05-1964 L1965 **OTO** *071 †45
DONOVAN, Wm Nelson, Jr. 2844 INDEX RD 53713 #056-05-1972 L1981 **IM** *020 †20
DOXTATER, Lana Ann. ■ 53719 #056-05-2001 L2007 **FM** *020 †18
DUTRA, Katherine Elizabet. ■ 53711 #030-06-2007 **P** *012
EGGERT, Christopher H. 2840 INDEX RD, MADISON AREA RENAL SPECIAL 53713
#016-43-2000 L2007 **NEP** *020 †20
ELLIS, Richard Lyall. 5543 E CHERYL PKWY 53711 #016-01-1977 L1980 **PD CHP** *020 †55
ENGLE, David Bryan. ■ 53711 #004-01-2002 L2006 **OBG** *020 †30
EVERTS, Shawn Stacy. 5713 MARGATE ST 53711 #018-03-1994 L2004 **FM** *020 †18
FARRO, Kouros. 72 S GARDENS WAY 53711 #409-04-1998 L2005 **FM** *020 †18 ‡
FRANCOIS, Sarah Margaret. 5550 CADDIS BND, UNIV OF WI DEPT OF FAMILY 53711
#056-06-2006 L2007 **FP** *012
FRANDY, Jennifer Ann. ■ 53719 #056-05-2001 *100
FREITAG, Mary Jo. ■ 53711 #056-05-1970 L1972 **PD HEM** *050 †55
GLOWACKI, Christopher Mic. ■ 53711 #030-06-2007 **OBG** *012
GOLDEN, Robert Andrew. 5543 E CHERYL PKWY 53711 #056-05-1998 L2001 **FM** *020 †18

GOUELI, Hisam Said. ■ 53711 #056-05-2004 L2004 **FPP** *012
GREEN, Aileen Louise. ■ 53711 #005-11-2006 **FP** *012
GREEN, Dena Ann. 5395 E CHERYL PKWY, HOSPICE CARE, INC. 53711 #056-06-1995 L1998
HO PLM *020 †20
GURKOW, Helen Jean. ■ 53711 #056-06-1962 L1963 **GP AM** *072
HARTWELL, Jennifer Renee. ■ 53711 #017-20-2008 *012
HASLER, Galen Rolf. 5395 E CHERYL PKWY 53711 #056-05-1972 L2007 **PLM ON** *020
HAYES, Matthew John. ■ 53711 #407-05-1964 L1966 **GP EM** *020 †16
HOFMANN, Ronald Michael. 3034 FISH HATCHERY RD, DEPT. OF MEDICINE/NEPHROLO 53713
#018-03-1992 L1998 **NEP CCM** *020 †20
HUDDLESTON, Jennifer Rena. ■ 53711 #007-02-2006 L2007 **DR** *012
HUTH, Mark Preston. 3051 CAHILL MAIN, GROUP HEALTH COOPERATIVE 53711
#040-02-2003 L2004 **FM** *100 †18
IYER, Lalitha Venkateshwa. 5543 E CHERYL PKWY 53711 #495-96-1995 L2003 **PD** *020 †55
JAFFERY, Jonathan Bret. 3034 FISH HATCHERY RD 53713 #038-40-1997 L2002 **NEP** *020 †20
JOHNSON, Curtis Michael. ■ 53719 #056-05-2008 *012
KELLERMAN, Paul Stephen. 3034 FISH HATCHERY RD 53713 #005-06-1982 L2002
NEP IM *020 †20
KHAN, Farhat Abbas. 6200 NESBITT RD, MADISON URGENT CARE SC 53719
#704-20-1988 L1999 **IM EM** *020 †20
LAKE, Wendell Bradley. ■ 53711 #020-12-2007 **GS** *012
LENTZ, Elizabeth Watson. ■ 53711 #020-12-2007 **N** *012
LEVERENTZ, Erin Gayle. ■ 53711 #026-04-2002 L2006 **OPH** *100
LO, Stephen Shihchung. 3051 CAHILL MAIN 53711 #056-05-1994 L1995 **PD** *020 †55
LUND, Gregory Scott. ■ 53711 #056-06-2006 L2008 **IM** *012
MANDARINO, Debra Ann. ■ 53711 #016-01-1992 L2006 **FM** *020 †18
MAYO, Steven David. 5500 E CHERYL PKWY, STE 108 53711 #056-05-1988 L1992 **AN** *020 †05
MELIUS, Frederic Arnold. 2955 TRIVERTON PIKE DR 53711 #030-06-1987 L1988 **OBG** *020 †30
MIDDLETON, Kathryn L. 2844 INDEX RD 53713 #025-01-1983 L1994 **IM PUD** *020 †20
MIROCHA, Sarah Jon. ■ 53711 #056-05-2002 L2006 **END** *012
MOORTHY, Aroor Vishnu. 3034 FISH HATCHERY RD 53713 #495-16-1968 L1975
NEP IM *020 †20
NAVARRO, Bernardita Cruz. ■ 53575 #748-01-1983 **OPH** *100
NELSON, Jacalyn Ann. 2844 INDEX RD 53713 #056-05-1990 L2006 **N** *020 †75
OLAJOS, Arpad S. 6200 NESBITT RD, AURORA BAYCARE MEDICAL CTR 53719
#473-04-1992 L2001 **IM** *020 †20
OLINGER, Mark Byron. 3051 CAHILL MAIN 53711 #056-05-1976 L1983 **FM** *020 †18
PETERS, Mary Ellen. ■ 53711 #056-05-1967 L1969 **R** *071 †80
POLAND, Alan Paul. ■ 53713 #035-45-1966 L1977 **IM** *050
PUCHNER, Thomas Carlyle. 5763 N HILL CT 53711 #056-06-1946 L1948 **CD** *020
PUENT, Jodie Janine. ■ 53711 #056-05-2004 L2006 **PD** *020
RAJAGOPALAN, Lavanya N. 3051 CAHILL MAIN, GROUP HEALTH COOPERATIVE 53711
#017-20-1995 L2003 **FM** *020 †18
RASMUSSEN, Jessica Sue. ■ 53711 #046-01-2007 **OBG** *012
REARDON, Claudia Louise. ■ 53713 #056-05-2006 L2007 **P** *012
REPPLINGER, Michael Dean. ■ 53711 #056-05-2007 **EM** *012
ROCK, William P. 5395 E CHERYL PKWY 53711 #016-43-1953 L1957 **PLM IMG** *071 †20
SABO, Laura Anne. 5543 E CHERYL PKWY 53711 #020-02-2000 L2001 **OBG** *020
SAMANIEGO-PICOTA, M. 3034 FISH HATCHERY RD 53713 #715-01-1984 L2004 **NEP** *020 †20
SANDMIRE, David Alan. 2454 HIGH RIDGE TRL, APT 20 53713 #056-05-1989 L1989 **IM** *075
SCHMEHIL, Amanda Lynn. ■ 53711 #056-05-2007 **OBG** *012
SCHURR, Julie Alexander. 2955 TRIVERTON PIKE DR 53711 #038-41-1989 L1990
OBG *020 †30
SHARKUS, Kristi Ann. ■ 53711 #056-05-1993 L1996 **PD** *020
SHENASSA, Mohammad Mehdi. ■ 53711 #517-01-1961 L1980 **PD** *100
SHENOI, Debra A. 3051 CAHILL MAIN 53711 #026-08-1994 L1997 **FM** *020 †18
SINGER, Steven. 5944 SEMINOLE CENTRE CT, STE B 53711 #016-01-1992 L2001 **P** *020 †75
STANGER, Ann E. 2940 CHAPEL VALLEY RD 53711 #017-20-1989 L1990 **GP OBG** *020
STEWART, Jimmie, III. ■ 53711 #004-01-1992 L2004 **PTH** *020 †50
TROSTEL, Kendrick Ann. 2840 INDEX RD 53713 #023-07-1996 L1997 **NEP** *020 †20
VOLZ, Lana Marie. ■ 53711 #056-05-2008 *012
WAIT, Erik Jon. 5543 E CHERYL PKWY 53711 #046-01-1991 L2000 **OBG** *020 †20
WEN, Sung-Feng. 3034 FISH HATCHERY RD, STE B 53713 #385-02-1958 L1975 **NEP IM** *020
WICHMAN, Bryan Stuart. ■ 53711 #056-05-2002 L2005 **AN** *100 †05
WILKE, Catherine Bedford. 3051 CAHILL MAIN 53711 #056-05-2001 L2005 **FM** *020 †18
WILSON, William Michael. 5543 E CHERYL PKWY, UNIVERSITY MADISON DEPT OF 53711
#143-02-1976 L1993 **FM OBS** *020 †18
YEVZLIN, Alexander Sasha. 3034 FISH HATCHERY RD 53713 #038-40-1998 L2004
NEP *020 †20
ZIMMERMAN, Stephen Wm. 2840 INDEX RD 53713 #056-05-1966 L1967 **NEP** *071 †20
ZOLOT, Marvin Mitchell. ■ 53711 #016-11-1956 L1960 **IM** *071 †20

FLORENCE – FLORENCE

BACKUS, Ronald Arthur. ■ 54121 #067-01-1964 L1968 **IM** *071
CARLSON, Ralph Everett. ■ 54121 #016-11-1946 L1952 **GS** *071 †85

FOND DU LAC – FOND DU LAC

ABLER, Sandra L. ■ 54937 #056-06-1989 L1990 **PTH** *020
ADAR, Eric. 430 E DIVISION ST 54935 #035-08-2000 L2006 **EM** *020 †16
AI, Quan Chen. 145 N MAIN ST 54935 #243-16-1998 L2003 **IM** *020 †20
AI, Zhaowei. 420 E DIVISION ST 54935 #243-16-1985 L2003 **CD IC** *020 †20
ANTLFINGER, Thomas John. ■ 54935 #056-06-1967 L1980 **DR** *020 †80
AVERY, James Alan. 210 WISCONSIN AMERICAN DR 54935 #016-06-1977 L1982 **GS** *075 †85
AYALA, Elpidio Tomas. 92 E DIVISION ST 54935 #056-05-1975 L1978 **IM** *071 †20
BACHHUBER, Michael Wm. 420 E DIVISION ST 54935 #056-06-1963 L1964 **GP PD** *071
BENNETT, Charles. ■ 54935 #056-05-1998 L2006 **AN** *020 †05
BENSEN, Elizabeth S. 420 E DIVISION ST 54935 #056-05-1992 L1996 **PM PME** *020 †60
BILLINSKY, John Milton. 430 E DIVISION ST 54935 #024-05-1978 L1992 **P OS** *020 †75 ‡
BOWMAN, David Ray. 420 E DIVISION ST, FOND DU LAC REGIONAL CLINI 54935
#017-20-1977 L1978 **CD IM** *020 †20
BRADLEY, Richard Dale. 430 E DIVISION ST 54935 #016-11-1971 L1996 **ATP CLP** *071 †50

BRILLA, Roland H C. 210 WISCONSIN AMERICAN DR 54935 #409-23-1996 L2003 **N** *020 †75
BRIMHALL, Conrad Lance. 145 N MAIN ST 54935 #028-34-1986 L1987 **D** *020 †15
BRUSKY, William John. 420 DIVISION 54935 #056-06-1974 L1975 **EM** *020 †16
CAHEE, Steven Michael. 420 E DIVISION ST, FOND DU LAC REGIONAL CLINI 54935 #017-20-1995 L1996 **GS** *020 †85
CARLSON, Thomas Jos. 145 N MAIN ST 54935 #056-05-1965 L1966 **GS** *020 †85
CEPOI, Sanda. 420 E DIVISION ST, FOND DU LAC REGIONAL CLINI 54935 #781-01-1987 L2003 **IM** *020 †20
CHAMBERS, Paul Richard. 420 E DIVISION ST 54935 #056-06-1977 L1980 **FM** *020 †18
CHAMSEDDIN, Ayham. ■ 54935 #875-01-1996 L2006 **IM** *020 †20
CHARLES, John E. ■ 54935 #016-02-1949 L1957 **R** *071 †80
CHOI, John Kwokkuen. 421 CAMELOT DR 54935 #056-06-1984 L1988 **AN** *020 †05
CHRISTENSON, Brian Curtis. 430 E DIVISION ST 54935 #018-03-1975 L1979 **P** *020 †75
CLEMENTS, Oliver Adsit. 420 E DIVISION ST 54935 #016-11-1982 L1991 **IM** *020 †20
COLMENARES, Derek Ismar. 420 E DIVISION ST 54935 #017-20-1998 L2001 **FM** *020 †18
CULLEN, Robert E. ■ 54935 #056-05-1952 L1953 **IM A** *071 †20
CUMMINS, Mary Swieskowski. N5840 HICKORY RD, MERCURY MARINE FAMILY MEDI 54935 #018-03-1982 L1985 **FM** *020 †18
DAR, Zahid Nadeem. 210 WISCONSIN AMERICAN DR 54935 #704-01-1988 L2003 **HO** *020 †20
DENNIS, Sara Jo. 420 E DIVISION ST 54935 #056-05-2001 L2005 **OBG** *020 †30
DHONAU, Howard Lloyd. 420 E DIVISION ST 54935 #016-11-1987 L1998 **PD** *020 †55
DIAZ, Juan Francisco. 420 E DIVISION ST, FOND DU LAC REGIONAL CLINI 54935 #016-11-1982 L1999 **CD IM** *020 †20
DI GIOSIA, Juliana Lynne. 210 WISCONSIN AMERICAN DR 54935 #026-04-1992 L1994 **OBG** *020 †30
DOROIN-HORN, Elsa B. 430 E DIVISION ST 54935 #748-01-1965 L1975 **IM GE** *020 †20
EMMER-SHELDON, Amy Sue. 210 WISCONSIN AMERICAN DR 54935 #056-06-2000 L2002 **PD** *020 †55
EVANS, Jerry Christopher. 420 E DIVISION ST 54935 #030-05-1990 L1994 **GE** *020 †20
EVERSON, Gina M. 420 E DIVISION ST 54935 #056-06-2001 L2004 **FM** *020 †18
FISCHER, Louis Calvin. 481 E DIVISION ST 54935 #056-05-1965 L1966 **DR NM** *020 †80
FITZPATRICK, Dennis. 430 E DIVISION ST 54935 #016-11-1993 L2003 **AN CCA** *020 †05
FLURRY, Steven D. ■ 54935 #056-06-2002 L2006 **AN** *020 †05
FOWNES, Douglas Robt. 420 E DIVISION ST 54935 #062-01-1971 L1978 **FM FSM** *020 †18
FREDERICK, Thomas Bayard. ■ 54935 #056-05-1977 L1978 **IM IMG** *075 †20
FREUND, Marian E. 210 WISCONSIN AMERICAN DR 54935 #016-43-1992 L1993 **PD** *020 †55
GAUTHIER, Richard John. 420 E DIVISION ST, SILVER CREEK MED ASSOC LTD 54935 #056-06-1984 L1985 **FM** *020 †18
GRAF, James Chas. 430 E DIVISION ST, ANESTHESIOLOGY 54935 #026-04-1986 L1990 **AN** *020 †05
GRASS, Brenda Jo. 420 E DIVISION ST 54935 #056-06-1997 L2001 **MPD** *020 †55,20
GRASS, Robert James. 420 E DIVISION ST, FOND DU LAC REGIONAL CLINI 54935 #056-06-1997 L2001 **MPD** *020 †55,20
GU, Xian Feng. 210 WISCONSIN AMERICAN DR 54935 #243-44-1982 L1995 **N** *020 †75
GYOROG, Scott Michael. ■ 54935 #056-05-2006 L2006 **MPD** *012
HABIB, Isam Hasan. PO BOX 385, 430 E DIVISION ST 54936 #575-01-1986 L1992 **IM** *020 †20
HAGEL, Hans. 92 E DIVISION ST 54935 #660-01-1953 L1959 **OBG** *071
HARIRI, Suhail Mahmood. 420 E DIVISION ST 54935 #010-01-1993 L2000 **OTO** *020 †45
HATAHET, Yasir. 430 E DIVISION ST 54935 #875-01-1979 L2003 **PUD CCM** *020 †20
HAY, Darrell E M. 420 E DIVISION ST 54935 #065-01-1976 L1980 **GP** *020
HELLER, Larry Leslie. 430 E DIVISION ST, ST AGNES HOSPITAL 54935 #038-40-1965 L1972 **ADM IM** *020
HITSELBERGER, James F. 310 E DIVISION ST 54935 #023-07-1956 L1961 **D** *020 †15
HORD, Eugenia-Daniela. 430 E DIVISION ST, MGH PAIN CENTER 54935 #781-01-1987 L2005 **N** *020 †75
HUIBREGTSE, Chas Albert. 210 WISCONSIN AMERICAN DR, AURORA HEALTH CENTER 54935 #649-33-1983 L1999 **FM** *020 †18
IGNACIO, Maria Revina O. 420 E DIVISION ST, FOND DU LAC REGIONAL CLINI 54935 #748-01-1990 L1994 **IM** *020 †20
ILEA, Dana Georgeta. 420 E DIVISION ST 54935 #781-01-1987 L1995 **IM** *020 †20
ISAACS, Juanita Joyce. 430 E DIVISION ST, P O BOX 385 54935 #021-01-1972 L1997 **P** *020 †75
JANSSEN, John Theodore. 430 E DIVISION ST 54935 #056-06-1967 L1969 **ORS HS** *020 †40
JESSEN, Kevin Andrew. N5840 HICKORY RD, MERCURY MARINE FAMILY MED 54935 #026-04-1978 L1982 **FM** *020 †18
JONES, Michael Wayne. 420 E DIVISION ST 54935 #030-05-1994 L1995 **IM** *020 †20
JUNIG, Jeffrey T. 1020 S MAIN ST, FOND DU LAC PSYCHIATRY, LL 54935 #035-45-1988 L1991 **P** *100 †05
KAILAS, Sujatha. 420 E DIVISION ST 54935 #495-11-1981 L1989 **GE** *020 †20
KANCA, Milan. 80 SHEBOYGAN ST 54935 #286-02-1960 L1976 **PD** *071 †55
KAPALA, Gregory B. 125 AURORA LN, RADIOLOGY - FOND DU LAC 54935 #056-06-1978 L1979 **DR** *020 †80
KARRY MOHANRAO, Shailender. ■ 54935 #495-65-2000 L2006 **IM** *020 †20
KASPER, Lynda Jeanne. 420 E DIVISION ST 54935 #056-05-1988 L1989 **FM** *020 †18
KELLER, Philip Edward. 420 E DIVISION ST 54935 #035-15-1980 L1981 **FM** *020 †18
KEMP, Glen Jos, Jr. 210 WISCONSIN AMERICAN DR, STE 235 54935 #056-05-1987 L1992 **ORS OSM** *020 †40
KETCHUM, Kevin Lee. 481 E DIVISION ST, RADIOLOGY FOND DU LAC 54935 #056-05-1987 L1996 **DR** *020 †80
KEYES, Michael Jos. 430 E DIVISION ST 54935 #021-01-1970 L1997 **P OS** *020 †75
KIRKWOOD, Mary Veronica. 430 E DIVISION ST, BEHAVIORAL HEALTH SERVICES 54935 #056-06-1998 L1999 **P** *020 †75
KONZ, Fredric Stephen. 403 PLEASANT ST 54935 #056-05-1966 L1967 **PD** *020 †55
KWON, Tai Ho. 430 DIVISION, ST AGNES HOSPITAL 54935 #583-03-1966 L1981 **AN** *020
LAMBERT, Eugene Kent. 430 DIVISION 54935 #016-11-1970 L1986 **ON HEM** *020 †20
LARSEN, Nathan Michael. 420 E DIVISION ST 54935 #056-06-2004 L2005 **EM** *020
LAWRENCE, David Lee. 420 E DIVISION ST 54935 #056-05-1956 L1957 **PD** *020 †55
LEIBEL, Mark Alan. 420 E DIVISION ST 54935 #025-12-1996 L2002 **FM** *020 †18
LENT, John Emery. 210 WISCONSIN AMERICAN DR, AURORA HLTH CTR 54935 #010-02-1966 L1967 **CD IM** *071 †20
LIM, Douglas. ■ 54935 #016-76-1999, ▲ L2007 **AN** *100
LINGAM, Suchit Kumar. ■ 54935 #495-36-2001 L2006 **IM** *020 †20
LITMAN, Gabriel. 210 WISCONSIN AMERICAN DR, AURORA HEALTH 54935 #030-06-1989 L1992 **IM** *020 †20
LLOREN, Jose Tavora, Jr. ■ 54935 #748-08-1964 L1975 **FM PD** *071
LUNDBERG, Joel Hjalmar. 480 E DIVISION ST 54935 #056-06-1981 L1988 **ON HEM** *020 †20
MAGOLINE, Steven Alfred. 421 CAMELOT DR 54935 #038-06-1992 L2001 **ORS** *020 †40
MALLATT, Wm Frederick. ■ 54935 #017-20-1968 L1974 **OPH** *071 †35
MANNEBACH, Michael Drew. 421 CAMELOT DR 54935 #056-06-1988 L1993 **ORS** *020 †40
MARIK, Joseph Phillip. 420 E DIVISION ST 54935 #016-11-1983 L1992 **IM** *020 †20
MARUSKA, David Vincent. 420 E DIVISION ST 54935 #056-05-1986 L1987 **FM** *020 †18
MASSICK, Stephen Aloysius. 420 E DIVISION ST 54935 #018-03-1967 L1970 **OBG** *020 †30
MATTHEWS, David Patrick. 430 E DIVISION ST, ST. AGNES HOSPITAL 54935 #056-05-1993 L1995 **IM** *020
MC BRIDE, Frank Fuller. ■ 54935 #056-06-1961 L1962 **GYN** *071 †30
MC CULLOUGH, Jack C. 430 E DIVISION ST 54935 #056-05-1945 L1946 **GP GS** *071
MC CULLOUGH, John Patrick. 420 E DIVISION ST 54935 #056-05-1976 L1981 **EM FM** *020 †18
MERESS, Steven Gregory. 180 KNIGHTS WAY, FOX VALLEY WELLNESS CTR 54935 #422-01-1986 L1987 **IM OS** *020 †20
MEYER, Karen Leslie. 420 E DIVISION ST, FOND DU LAC REGIONAL CLI 54935 #422-01-2000 L2001 **OBG** *020
MIKKELSEN, Robert Harold. 420 E DIVISION ST 54935 #016-06-1971 L1976 **GS VS** *020 †85
MILLER, Theodore Donald. 420 E DIVISION ST 54935 #030-05-1985 L1989 **OBG** *020 †30 ‡
MIROT, Max Steven. 430 DIVISION 54935 #016-43-1988 L2005 **PTH NM** *020 †50
MOEN, Jon Thos. 420 E DIVISION ST 54935 #056-05-1984 L1985 **GS** *020 †85
MOORE, C E Mc Daniel. ■ 54935 #018-03-1964 L1968 **P** *071 †75
MUELLER, Joan Louise. 430 E DIVISION ST 54935 #056-05-1980 L1981 **PTH** *020 †50
MUSUNURU, Jagadeeswara. 459 E 1ST ST 54935 #495-58-1971 L1980 **P** *020 †75
NELEZEN, Gerald P. 420 E DIVISION ST 54935 #016-76-1976, ▲ L1977 **GP EM** *020
NIXON, Karen Lynn. 420 E DIVISION ST 54935 #038-06-1994 L2006 **OPH** *020 †35
OBMA, Robert Tjeerdt. 420 E DIVISION ST, FOND DU LAC REGIONAL CLINI 54935 #056-05-1965 L1969 **CD IM** *020 †20
OSTMAN, Lars Gosta Pontus. 421 CAMELOT DR, AGNESIAN HEALTHCARE CTR FO 54935 #374-01-1981 L1993 **PMM AN** *020 †05
OTT, Christopher Eugene. 420 E DIVISION ST, FOND DU LAC REGIONAL CLINI 54935 #056-06-2000 L2004 **OBG** *020 †30
OWENS, Jeanna L. 430 E DIVISION ST 54935 #012-01-1981 L1984 **RHU IM** *020 †20
PANDYA, Hitesh N. 430 E DIVISION ST 54935 #495-48-1991 L2002 **P** *020 †75
PAREEK, Yogesh. ■ 54935 #495-74-1989 L1995 **P** *020
PEARSON, Heather R. ■ 54935 #016-76-2002, ▲ L2005 **FM** *020 †18
PECH, Michael Louis. 210 WISCONSIN AMERICAN DR 54935 #056-06-1986 L1989 **OBG** *020 †30
PENDERGAST, Robert L, Jr. 430 E DIVISION ST 54935 #056-06-1970 L1971 **U** *071 †95
PENNAU, Karl Ludwig, Jr. 421 CAMELOT DR 54935 #016-43-1973 L1981 **ORS** *020 †40
PENTON, Lutti. 430 E DIVISION ST 54935 #891-01-1961 L1976 **PS** *071 †65
PESCHONG, Barbara Ann. 420 E DIVISION ST 54935 #056-05-1988 L1992 **OBG** *020 †30 ‡
PHILLIPS, Elliott Richard. 430 E DIVISION ST, ST. AGNES HOSPITAL 54935 #016-11-1975 L2002 **P SME** *020 †75
POST, Warren Michael. 420 DIVISION 54935 #016-02-1978 L1982 **PD** *020 †55
PRUSKI, Judith Diane. 420 E DIVISION ST 54935 #056-05-1978 L1985 **PD** *020 †55
QUEJADA, Ma Estelita F G. 210 WISCONSIN AMERICAN DR, HWY. 23 EAST 54935 #748-02-1991 L1994 **PD** *020 †55
REVELIS, John. 210 WISCONSIN AMERICAN DR 54935 #039-01-1996 L2001 **OTO** *020 †45
ROETKER, Alan Walter. 210 WISCONSIN AMERICAN DR, STE 235 54935 #018-03-1983 L1984 **ORS** *020 †40
ROSCULET, John Peter. 420 E DIVISION ST 54935 #025-01-1988 L1993 **OPH** *020 †35
RUPPLE, James Hugh. 420 E DIVISION ST, FOND DULAC REG CLINIC 54935 #025-07-1957 L1961 **OPH** *071 †35
SACKSTEDER, Wm Anthony. 210 WISCONSIN AMERICAN DR 54935 #020-02-1976 L2004 **PD GS** *020 †85,90
SAGGIO, Carl John. 420 E DIVISION ST 54935 #056-06-1968 L1969 **FM** *071 †18
SAKER, Denise Marie. 420 E DIVISION ST 54935 #038-41-1989 L2003 **PDC** *020 †55
SALEH, Haydar Khaled. 210 WISCONSIN AMERICAN DR, AURORA HEALTH CENTER 54935 #875-01-1990 L1999 **IM** *020 †20
SANTA-CRUZ, Richard A. 420 E DIVISION ST 54935 #011-02-1999 L2006 **IC** *020 †20
SANTA ROSARIO, Daisy Ines. 420 E DIVISION ST 54935 #042-01-1989 L1993 **PD** *020 †55
SCHAEFER, Richard Barrett. 420 E DIVISION ST 54935 #016-01-1999 L2001 **PS** *020 †65
SCHATEN, Mark Allan. 210 WISCONSIN AMERICAN DR 54935 #056-06-1988 L2001 **IM** *020 †20
SCHLECHT, Lorne Porter. 210 WISCONSIN AMERICAN DR 54935 #026-08-1987 L1991 **OPH PS** *020 †35
SCHOFF, Erik Obin. 420 E DIVISION ST 54935 #056-05-1993 L1999 **OPH OS** *020 †35
SCHULTZ, Mary M. 92 E DIVISION ST 54935 #056-05-1996 L2000 **OBG** *020 †30
SCHUSTER, James Edward. 145 N MAIN ST 54935 #056-05-1967 L1969 **D** *020 †15
SCHUSTER, Robert Jos, Jr. 420 E DIVISION ST 54935 #016-11-1969 L1973 **OBG** *020 †30
SEARLE, Clark P, III. 420 E DIVISION ST 54935 #038-06-1993 L2006 **ORS** *020 †40
SERGI, Michael. 210 WISCONSIN AMERICAN DR 54935 #561-26-1981 L1986 **IM** *020 †20
SHARPE, Harvey Roy, Jr. 92 E DIVISION ST 54935 #016-06-1943 L1943 **GS** *071 †85
SHELDON, Amy Marie. 430 E DIVISION ST 54935 #056-05-1987 L1988 **PTH PCP** *062 †50
SIERRA, Lewis Albert. 145 N MAIN ST 54935 #056-05-1978 L1985 **EM IM** *020 †20,16
STALLER, Bernard Jay. 210 WISCONSIN AMERICAN DR 54935 #041-09-1966 L1973 **CD** *020 †20
STANLEY, Toni Lee. 420 E DIVISION ST 54935 #056-06-1993 L2004 **GS** *020 †85
STEELE, Gary Francis. 420 E DIVISION ST 54935 #055-01-1974 L1985 **FM** *020 †18
STEINER, John David. 210 WISCONSIN AMERICAN DR, AURORA HEALTH CENTER 54935 #056-06-1991 L1992 **IM** *020 †20
STELLMACHER, Scott John. 210 WISCONSIN AMERICAN DR 54935 #056-06-1987 L1988 **FM** *020 †18
STEWARD, Donald Chas. 206 WISCONSIN AMERICAN DR 54935 #056-05-1982 L1985 **PD** *020 †55
STORMO, K Alan. ■ 54935 #030-05-1963 L1971 **FOP** *071 †50
STRIGENZ, Anthony Kurt. 430 E DIVISION ST, ST AGNES HOSP 54935 #056-06-1989 L1990 **AN** *020 †05
STRIGENZ, Michael Anthony. 421 CAMELOT DR 54935 #056-06-1983 L1984 **OTO** *020 †45
STRONG, Jeffrey Alan. 420 E DIVISION ST 54935 #056-05-1981 L1982 **FM FPG** *020 †18
SWEET, David Fraley. 420 E DIVISION ST 54935 #026-04-1966 L1969 **OPH** *071 †35
SYBESMA, William Gene. 421 CAMELOT DR 54935 #018-03-1972 L1978 **OTO** *020 †45
TAIVALMAA, Kristine Sue. 420 E DIVISION ST 54935 #056-06-1997 L2000 **PD** *020 †55
TAPP, Cheryl R. 430 E DIVISION ST, P O BOX 385 54935 #048-13-1997 L2002 **PYG P** *020 †75
TAYLOR, Peter Brien. ■ 54935 #011-02-1981 L1982 **OPH** *020 †35
TREFFERT, Darold Allen. 430 E DIVISION ST 54935 #056-05-1958 L1959 **P** *071 †75

■ = Address Information Privacy Protected

TREPANIER, Gay David. ■ 54935 #056-06-1968 L1969 **FM FPG** *071 †18
TSAI, Shogi Ten. 430 E DIVISION ST, ST AGNES HOSPITAL 54935 #244-04-1969 L1975
  AN *020 †05
TUVESON, Christopher C. 420 DIVISION 54935 #016-11-1992 L1998 **U** *072 †95
UDLIS, Seth David. 912 S HICKORY ST 54935 #065-06-1990 L1995 **FM MDM** *020 †18
VAN BEEK, Donald Floyd. 210 WISCONSIN AMERICAN DR, FOUNTAIN CITY SURG
  ASSOCS 54935 #037-01-1980 L1981 **GS VS** *020 †85
VANDER KOOY, Michael J. 480 E DIVISION ST 54935 #056-05-1993 L1996 **RO** *020 †80
VEIT, Henry. ■ 54935 #056-06-1943 L1943 **P** *071
VEIT, Kirk Andre. 420 E DIVISION ST 54935 #056-05-1970 L1973 **PD MDM** *020 †55
VENUTI, Susan Elizabeth. ■ 54935 #019-02-1993 L1997 **ATP FOP** *020 †50
VRTILEK, Mojmir Rudolf. 430 E DIVISION ST 54935 #869-07-1953 L1955 **IM** *071
WALBY, Linda Lee. 420 E DIVISION ST 54935 #056-05-1984 L1987 **PM** *020 †60
WANG, Hong Chu. 480 E DIVISION ST 54935 #244-04-1970 L1980 **RO** *020 †80
WEBER, David R. ■ 54935 #017-20-1962 L1963 **IM** *071 †20
WELLS, Timothy Gerard. 210 WISCONSIN AMERICAN DR, STE 235 54935 #056-06-1987 L1988
  ORS OSM *020 †40
WELSCH, John Aloysius. ■ 54935 #056-06-1965 L1972 **ORS** *071 †40
WERMELING, Amy Knipschild. 420 DIVISION, DEPT OF PEDS 54935 #056-05-1996 L1997
  PD *020 †55
WHEELER, Joanell Kathryn. 481 E DIVISION ST 54935 #030-05-1989 L1990 **NR DR** *020 †80,28
WHELAN, John Danl. 459 E 1ST ST, DIV OF COMMUNITY PROGRAMS 54935
  #306-01-1987 L1994 **P** *020
WHITMORE, Mark Allan. 420 E DIVISION ST 54935 #016-11-1981 L1993 **IM** *020 †20
WIGG, Dwight Anthony. 420 E DIVISION ST 54935 #030-05-1989 L1990 **FM** *020 †18
WINDSOR, Richard B, Jr. 210 WISCONSIN AMERICAN DR 54935 #056-05-1985 L1986
  U *020 †95
WONDER, Douglas C. 420 E DIVISION ST, FOND DU LAC REGIONAL CLINI 54935 #016-76-1986,
  ▲ L1987 **FM** *020 †18
WOODHALL, Dennis Dale. 420 E DIVISION ST 54935 #016-45-1978 L1987 **TS** *020 †85,90
WRENN, Robert Mc Donald. 430 E DIVISION ST, AGNESIAN HEALTHCARE 54935
  #056-05-2003 L2004 **AN** *020
WRIGHT, James Arthur. 420 E DIVISION ST 54935 #056-06-1986 L1987 **U** *020 †95
YUAN, David Dong. 420 E DIVISION ST, FOND DU LAC REGIONAL CLINI 54935
  #243-47-1990 L2004 **NEP IM** *020 †20
ZINK, Barbara Ann Dewitz. 420 E DIVISION ST 54935 #040-02-1985 L1986 **PD** *020 †55

FOOTVILLE – ROCK

SCHWAEGLER, Robert Roy. 144 DEPOT 53537 #018-03-1961 L1965 **FM** *071

FORT ATKINSON – JEFFERSON

ANDERSON, Michael Roger. 426 MCMILLEN ST 53538 #056-05-1998 L2003 **OTO** *020 †45
ANSCHUETZ, Harold Fredric. 740 REENA AVE 53538 #056-06-1977 L1978 **FM** *020 †18
AUFDERHAAR, Henry Wm. 740 REENA AVE 53538 #056-05-1957 L1958 **GP** *020
BAIRD, Drew Craig. ■ 53538 #021-01-2006 L2008 **FP** *012
BATES, Donald E. 500 EDWARD ST 53538 #020-02-1964 L1965 **FM** *020 †18
BERAN, Frank V. 211 MEMORIAL DR 53538 #018-03-1960 L1963 **FM GS** *071
BRADT, Jack Oldham. 611 SHERMAN AVE E 53538 #041-09-1955 L1987 **P CHP** *020 †75
CALHOUN, Barbara Louise. 509 MCMILLEN ST 53538 #056-05-1981 L1982 **P** *020 †75
CAREY, Mark Richard. 512 WILCOX ST 53538 #025-12-2001 L2005 **NEP** *020 †20
CASH, Barry Phillip. 740 REENA AVE 53538 #016-11-1988 L1989 **FM** *020 †18
CHUPPA, Christine Ann. 650 MCMILLEN ST, CENTER FOR WOMENS HLTH 53538
  #056-05-1998 L2002 **OBG** *020 †30
CONLEY, C Sue. 426 MCMILLEN ST 53538 #030-05-1989 L1992 **D** *020 †15
DAVIS, Dawn Belt. ■ 53538 #016-02-2003 L2005 **END** *012 †20
DHILLON, Satwant Singh. 650 MCMILLEN ST 53538 #025-07-1987 L1988 **OBG** *020 †30
ELANGOVAN, Loganathan. 512 WILCOX ST 53538 #495-61-1988 L1999 **IM NEP** *020 †20
ENGELER, James Edward, Jr. 525 HANDEYSIDE LN, STE 2 53538 #017-20-1966 L1969
  ON HEM *071 †20
ERICKSON, Marc Helge. 426 MCMILLEN ST 53538 #056-06-1989 L1994 **GS** *020 †85
GEHRED, Gregory Andrew. 601 HANDEYSIDE LN 53538 #038-06-1967 L1994 **FM** *020 †18
GLINERT, Robert John. 611 SHERMAN AVE E 3RD FL, FORT HEALTCARE 53538
  #016-01-1980 L1990 **D AI** *020 †20,03,15
GRAZIANO, Anthony Francis. 611 SHERMAN AVE E 53538 #056-05-1982 L1992 **EM** *020 †16
GROSSMAN, Timothy Bruce. 520 HANDEYSIDE LN 53538 #030-05-1995 L1996 **U** *020 †95
GUCFA, Cornelius Jason. 509 MCMILLEN ST, BEHAVIORAL HEALTH 53538 #654-01-1999 L2002
  P *100
HARRIS, Nancy Louise. 520 HANDEYSIDE LN, STE 2 53538 #048-12-1991 L1998 **FM** *020 †18
HELLMAN, Charles Kenneth. 601 HANDEYSIDE LN 53538 #056-05-1971 L1972 **CD** *020
JIONGCO, Edgardo Cruz. 611 SHERMAN AVE E, FORT ATKINSON MEMORIAL HOS 53538
  #748-08-1966 L1976 **R** *020 †80
KAPUSTKA, Edward Stanley. 426 MCMILLEN ST 53538 #016-06-1966 L1973 **U** *071 †95
KENG, George. 611 SHERMAN AVE E 53538 #028-34-1998 L2001 **EM** *020 †16
KONTNY, Billie Gerard. 426 MCMILLEN ST 53538 #056-06-1988 L1993 **GS** *020 †85
KRUK, Kathleen A. 211 MEMORIAL DR 53538 #056-05-1984 L1990 **FM** *020 †18
KRUK, Michael Lawrence. 740 REENA AVE 53538 #056-05-1984 L1990 **FM OBG** *020 †18
MC GUIRE, Jeffrey Patrick. 601 HANDEYSIDE LN 53538 #056-05-1985 L1986 **FM FPG** *020 †18
MC LAUGHLIN, Jonathan G. 426 MCMILLEN ST 53538 #026-04-1988 L1997 **GS VS** *020 †85
MEYER, Ronald Kevin. 611 SHERMAN AVE E 53538 #056-06-1996 L1997 **EM** *020 †16
MEYER, Shauna Jolynn. 601 HANDEYSIDE LN 53538 #046-01-1999 L2001 **FM** *020 †18
MODE, Georgia Knox. ■ 53538 #056-05-1982 L1983 **FM** *071 †18
MOMIN, Jahangir. 512 WILCOX ST 53538 #660-02-1993 L2004 **NEP IM** *020
MORITZ, Walter Danl. ■ 53538 #016-06-1964 L1966 **ORS** *071 †40
NEUFELD, Mark Victor. 611 SHERMAN AVE E, SPETRUM EYE CENTER 53538
  #062-01-1993 L1999 **OPH** *020 †35
RIGGS, Stephen Carl. 740 REENA AVE, FORT ATKINSON MEDICAL CENT 53538
  #035-15-1993 L1996 **FM** *020 †18
SCHLAISHUNT, Scott T. 611 SHERMAN AVE E 53538 #038-41-1994 L1995 **EM** *072 †16
SHEA, Joseph Wm. 650 MCMILLEN ST 53538 #056-06-1988 L1991 **OBG** *020 †30
WILLIAMS, Donald Lee. 500 MCMILLEN ST, INT MEDICINE & PEDS 53538 #016-11-1976 L1980
  IM PD *020 †20,55

WOELFLE, Wade William. 611 SHERMAN AVE E 53538 #056-05-1995 L1998 **EM OS** *020 †16
YAO, Filemon C. 611 SHERMAN AVE E 53538 #748-01-1958 L1967 **GS GP** *071

FOX POINT – MILWAUKEE

GEORGE, Ben. ■ 53217 #495-31-1999 L2007 **HO** *012 †20
KAPLAN, Michael Miller. ■ 53217 #035-46-1982 L1993 **CHP** *012 †75
KHAN, Ahmed Jalaluddin. ■ 53217 #160-01-1993 L2005 **PCC** *100 †20
ROE, Patrick Aloysius. ■ 53217 #056-06-1964 L1967 **IM** *071 †20
SCHWARTZ, Norman Wolfe. 7950 N PORT WASHINGTON RD, STE 100 53217
  #041-09-1975 L1977 **GP** *020
SOROKA, Lidia. ■ 53217 #913-01-1998 **FM** *100
WALBERGH, Eric James. 8100 N LAKE DR 53217 #005-18-1981 L1986 **PAN CCP** *020 †05
WEISS, Bruce Alan. ■ 53217 #016-42-1982 L2006 **IM GPM** *030 †20
WU, Hui Tien. ■ 53217 #572-08-1970 L1978 **OBG** *071

FRANKLIN – MILWAUKEE

ADAMCZYK, Michal. ■ 53132 #759-01-1977 L1981 **GS** *071 †85
AHUJA, Mandeep Singh. ■ 53132 #016-42-1994 L1999 **DR** *020 †80
ALBRECHT, Donald J. ■ 53132 #056-06-1949 L1950 **OBG** *071 †30
AMOLI, Sean Reza. 3111 W RAWSON AVE, STE 105 53132 #039-01-1993 L1998
  DR RNR *020 †20
ANDERSON, Norwood Ralph. 7400 W RAWSON AVE, STE 240 53132 #016-11-1971 L2003
  ON IM *020 †20
BARR, Carmela Ann. 7400 W RAWSON AVE, STE 120 53132 #016-11-1979 L1980 **OBG** *020 †30
BASHAM, Mark Cash. 3111 W RAWSON AVE, STE 105 53132 #051-04-1986 L1998
  RNR R *020 †20,80
BERES, Robert Allen. 3111 W RAWSON AVE, STE 105 53132 #056-05-1987 L1988
  VIR DR *020 †80
BESSETTE, Peter Richard. 3111 W RAWSON AVE, STE 105 53132 #056-06-1987 L1988
  DR *020 †80
BLOOMGARDEN, Daniel Caleb. 3111 W RAWSON AVE, STE 105 53132 #041-01-1996 L2002
  VIR DR *020 †80
BREGER, Robert Karl. 3111 W RAWSON AVE, STE 105 53132 #056-06-1984 L1985 **R** *020 †80
BRENNER, Tracy Michelle. ■ 53132 #035-08-2004 L2007 **IM** *012
BROWN, Gregory Laurence. 9612 S FRANKLIN DR, ARCH MEDICAL SERVICES LLC 53132
  #030-05-1984 L1985 **IM** *020 †20
BUCZYNA, John. 3111 W RAWSON AVE, STE 105 53132 #759-01-2000 L2001 **RNR** *020 †80
CARPITA, Rosanna A. 9200 W LOOMIS RD 53132 #016-42-1997 L2002 **PD** *020
CERVENANSKY, James M. 8530 W HAWTHORNE LN 53132 #056-06-1971 L1972 **EM GP** *020
CHELIUS, Carl-Juergen W H. ■ 53132 #407-12-1954 L1958 **CD IM** *020
CIANCIOLO, Michael S. 9200 W LOOMIS RD 53132 #056-06-1987 L1988 **PD** *020 †55
COHEN, Ronald Ian. 7400 W RAWSON AVE, STE 143 53132 #305-01-2001 L2004 **IM** *020
COOLEY, Peter Alexander. 3111 W RAWSON AVE, STE 105 53132 #056-05-1978 L1979
  DR *020 †80
CRONSELL, Christopher All. ■ 53132 #016-43-2007 *012
DERUS, Jeffrey Arnold. 3111 W RAWSON AVE, STE 235 53132 #056-06-1985 L1986 **U** *020 †95
DESAI, Paresh B. 3111 W RAWSON AVE, STE 105 53132 #495-01-1982 L1991
  DR NM *020 †80,28
DICUS, William Tegtmeier. 7400 W RAWSON AVE, STE 210 53132 #016-06-1963 L1964
  ORS *020 †40
DOMKE, Lewis Richard, Jr. 7400 W RAWSON AVE, STE 240 53132 #561-17-1976 L2004
  HO IMG *020 †20
DOZER, David Wesley. 7400 W RAWSON AVE, STE 241 53132 #056-05-1987 L1992
  GE IM *020 †20
FERBER, Marie Grace. 9200 W LOOMIS RD 53132 #056-05-1993 L1994 **P** *020 †75
FON-SING, Max Kenny K. 9200 W LOOMIS RD 53132 #917-29-1989 L1998 **IM** *020 †20
FOOTE, Peter Stedman. 9200 W LOOMIS RD, STE 204 53132 #056-05-1979 L1980
  OPH *020 †35
GAL, Aviva. 9200 W LOOMIS RD, STE 204 53132 #550-03-1977 L1987 **OPH** *020
GILLES, Carol Eleanor. 10101 S 27TH ST 53132 #038-43-1990 L2004 **OBG** *020 †30
GLUNZ, Paul Richard. ■ 53132 #056-06-1957 L1959 **PTH** *071 †50
GRAFF, Kimberly Anne. ■ 53132 #016-43-2007 **PD** *012
GRAY, Dana Ann. 3111 W RAWSON AVE, STE 105 53132 #056-06-2000 L2006 **DR** *020 †80
GREBNER, Michael Crispin. 8885 S 68TH ST, MILWAUKEE CO HOUSE OF CORR 53132
  #025-12-1976 L1992 **FM** *030 †20
GREENLEE, James Edward. 9200 W LOOMIS RD, STE 204 53132 #016-06-1970 L1976
  OPH *020 †35
GUDA, Nalini Mohan. 3111 W RAWSON AVE, STE 240 53132 #495-62-1994 L1998
  GE IM *020 †20
GUEHLSTORF, Daniel Wayne. 3111 W RAWSON AVE STE 200 53132 #056-06-1993 L1994
  ORS *020 †40
HANDRICH, Stephen James. 3111 W RAWSON AVE, STE 105 53132 #056-06-1998 L2004
  NM *020 †80,28
HANSON, Jerome Thos. 7400 W RAWSON AVE, STE 241 53132 #056-05-1974 L1975
  GE IM *020 †20
HARDIE, Robert Chas. 3111 W RAWSON AVE, STE 105 53132 #056-05-1987 L1988
  PDR *020 †20
HARRINGTON, Alexandra Mar. ■ 53132 #056-06-2004 L2005 **PTH** *012
HARRINGTON, Daniel George. 3111 W RAWSON AVE, STE 105 53132 #056-06-1993 L1994
  R *020 †80
HATFIELD, Malcolm Keith. 3111 W RAWSON AVE, STE 105 53132 #025-07-1983 L1988
  DR *020 †80
HEITMAN, Timothy David. 9200 W LOOMIS RD 53132 #016-42-1982 L1988 **OBG** *020 †30
HILL, Susan J. 7400 W RAWSON AVE, STE G30 53132 #056-06-1989 L1990 **FM** *020 †18
HURST, Emil Douglas. 3111 W RAWSON AVE, STE 105 53132 #025-01-1992 L1995
  DR *020 †16,80
IDARRAGA, George A. 9200 W LOOMIS RD, STE 116 53132 #056-06-1995 L1998 **PD** *020 †55
IRELAND, Kimberly Claire. 9200 W LOOMIS RD, STE 204 53132 #035-03-1996 L2000
  OPH *020 †35
JAIN, Arun Kumar. 9200 W LOOMIS RD 53132 #495-29-1995 L2003 **IM** *020 †20
JAIN, Parag Nandlal. ■ 53132 #495-28-2005 **PD** *012

JAWORSKI, Janelle Alane. ■ 53132 #017-20-1988 L1994 **FOP PTH** *030

JENOURI, Gilbert Anthony. 7245 S 76TH ST, APT 311 53132 #308-12-1991 **PCC** *100

JOSHI, Jaideep S. 3111 W RAWSON AVE, STE 105 53132 #056-06-1998 L1999 **DR** *020 †80

KAMER, Gary Louis. 9200 W LOOMIS RD 53132 #020-12-1982 L1983 **FM** *020 †18

KEHOE, Michael Ernest. 3111 W RAWSON AVE, STE 105 53132 #056-05-1974 L1975 **DR VIR** *020 †20,80

KHAN, Abdul. 3203 W LINKS DR 53132 #495-21-1985 L1993 **AN** *020

KIM, Steve J. 7380 S CAMBRIDGE DR 53132 #016-01-1995 L1998 **IM PLM** *020 †20

KNECHTGES, Thomas Edmund. 3111 W RAWSON AVE, STE 105 53132 #056-05-1970 L1971 **R OS** *020 †80

KODURI, Sudha. ■ 53132 #496-01-1986 L1988 **P GP** *020

KUGLITSCH, Ervin F. 10835 W RAWSON AVE 53132 #056-06-1952 L1953 **AN FM** *020

KUMAR, Parmod. 9200 W LOOMIS RD STE 106 53132 #495-29-1974 L1978 **GS** *020 †85

LAHIRI AHUJA, Namrata A. 7400 W RAWSON AVE, STE 241 53132 #056-06-1988 L1991 **IM** *071 †20

LAUS, Colleen Margaret. 9200 W LOOMIS RD, STE 116 53132 #056-06-2001 L2004 **PD** *020 †55

LERNER, Jerome Alan. 7400 W RAWSON AVE, STE 130 53132 #056-06-1983 L1984 **PM PMM** *020 †60

LEVIN, Jonathan Michael. 3111 W RAWSON AVE, STE 105 53132 #016-43-1997 L2004 **DR** *020 †80

LOO, Franklin David. 7400 W RAWSON AVE, STE 241 53132 #056-06-1975 L1977 **IM GE** *020 †20

LUTZ, Michelle Marie. ■ 53132 #056-06-2008 *012

MALLOY, Thomas G, Jr. 7400 W RAWSON AVE, STE 241 53132 #056-06-1984 L1990 **GE** *020 †20

MANAGO, Joseph Andrew. ■ 53132 #016-43-1953 L1954 **DR** *071 †85,80

MASTEY, Lynn Allison. 3111 W RAWSON AVE, STE 105 53132 #056-06-1991 L1992 **DR** *020 †80

MC BRIDE, Michael Fuller. 9200 W LOOMIS RD 53132 #056-06-1992 L1993 **CHP** *020 †75

MEDVED, Peter Michael. 9200 W LOOMIS RD, STE 221 53132 #056-05-1981 L1982 **OTO** *020 †45

MEINERS, Ryan Jacob. 3111 W RAWSON AVE, STE 105 53132 #016-06-2001 L2002 **DR** *020 †80

MINOR, Paul Loren. 3111 W RAWSON AVE, STE 105 53132 #056-06-1986 L1987 **DR** *020 †80

MINTER, Michael Geo. 9200 W LOOMIS RD 53132 #017-20-1969 L1973 **PD** *020 †55

MONTGOMERY, Robert Gowen. 8885 S 68TH ST 53132 #054-04-1978 L1980 **FM** *020 †05

MOORE, Lauren Joan. 7400 W RAWSON AVE 53132 #030-06-2003 L2007 **OBG** *020

MORTENSEN, Gordon Lee, Jr. 3111 W RAWSON AVE STE 210 53132 #025-07-1981 L1984 **AN** *020 †18,05

MURPHY, Ryan Mcniven. ■ 53132 #056-06-2003 L2004 **AN** *020

NORDYKE, Gary Duane. 10500 W LOOMIS RD, STE 100 53132 #018-03-1986 L1989 **PD** *020 †55

OLSON, David Lewis. 3111 W RAWSON AVE, STE 105 53132 #028-02-1980 L1981 **DR** *020 †80

ORIGENES, Edna F. 7407 W PINEBERRY RDG 53132 #748-08-1968 L1976 **P** *020 †75

PARKER, Edward Clayton. ■ 53132 #056-06-1964 L1966 **OBG** *071 †30

PARMAR, Harpreet Singh. ■ 53132 #030-05-2007 **IM** *012

PETERSEN-FISHER, Anne L. 3111 W RAWSON AVE, STE 105 53132 #056-05-1991 L2001 **DR** *020 †80

PRIEHS, Timothy Wm. 3111 W RAWSON AVE STE 210, INNOVATIVE PAIN CARE LLC 53132 #654-01-1989 L1990 **PMM AN** *020 †05

PRIETO, Noemi A. 9200 W LOOMIS RD 53132 #308-07-1981 L1984 **PD** *020 †55

QUMSEYA, Bashar Jeryes. ■ 53132 #422-01-2007 **IM** *012

RAFFERTY, Hugh Peter. ■ 53132 #056-06-1954 L1955 **OBG** *071 †30

RUIZ, Juan Pablo. ■ 53132 #264-18-1993 L2004 **PDP** *012 †18

SALEH, Mohammad A. ■ 53132 #016-11-2004 L2006 **MPD** *012

SANE, Shekhar Shashikant. 3111 W RAWSON AVE, STE 105 53132 #026-04-1993 L2000 **VIR DR** *020 †80

SCALZITTI, Sandra Lynn. 7400 W RAWSON AVE STE G30 53132 #016-11-1992 L1996 **MPD PD** *020 †55,20

SCHAPER, Dale Steven. 7400 W RAWSON AVE, STE 143 53132 #018-03-1995 L1998 **IM** *020 †20

SCHUSTER, Thomas Alan. 3111 W RAWSON AVE, STE 105 53132 #056-06-1982 L1983 **DR** *020 †80

SHAH, Indu Mugatlal. ■ 53132 #496-38-1961 L1976 **PTH** *071 †50

SHARMA, Vipul. ■ 53132 #056-06-2004 L2005 **DR** *012

SIRUS, Steven Richard. 9200 W LOOMIS RD 53132 #422-01-1982 L1983 **FM** *020 †18

SKOWLUND, Christopher Jon. 3111 W RAWSON AVE, STE 105 53132 #056-06-1998 L1999 **DR** *020 †80

SMITH, Jacqueline. 3396 W SYCAMORE ST 53132 #051-04-1996 L1998 **DR** *020 †80

SMITH, William Bert. 7400 W RAWSON AVE, STE 210 53132 #016-06-1970 L1971 **ORS** *020 †40

SNELL, Mary Beth. 7400 W RAWSON AVE, STE 143 53132 #056-06-1981 L1986 **IM** *020 †20

SPIERING, Patrick Ryan. 7400 W RAWSON AVE, STE G30 53132 #016-11-1992 L1998 **FM** *020 †18

SPLITTGERBER, Gerald Fred. 3111 W RAWSON AVE, STE 105 53132 #056-05-1971 L1985 **DR IM** *020 †20,80

STAUFF, Abigail Katherine. ■ 53132 #056-06-2007 **IM** *012

STEIN, Paul Gregory. ■ 53132 #028-34-1955 L1963 **P OS** *071 †75

STINEMAN, William F. 9200 W LOOMIS RD 53132 #654-01-1981 L1983 **FM** *020 †18

SURIYANARAYANAN, Uma. 3111 W RAWSON AVE, STE 105 53132 #496-07-1991 L1995 **DR NM** *020 †80,28

SZYMSKI, George Xavier. 3111 W RAWSON AVE, STE 105 53132 #016-02-1989 L1998 **DR** *020 †80

TCHEKANOV, Guennady V.. ■ 53132 #305-01-2002 L2005 **PM** *100

TIBBETTS, Palmer Geo. ■ 53132 #056-05-1964 L1965 **D DMP** *071 †15

TREICHEL, William Allan. 7400 W RAWSON AVE, STE G30 53132 #056-05-1971 L1972 **FM** *020 †18

TRIVEDI, Madhuri. 7400 W RAWSON AVE, STE 241 53132 #495-01-1986 L2004 **GE** *020 †20

WALKER, James Michael. 3111 W RAWSON AVE, STE 105 53132 #025-01-1999 L2005 **VIR** *020 †80

WEBER, Jeffrey Mark. 7400 W RAWSON AVE, STE 241 53132 #056-05-1974 L1977 **GE IM** *020 †20

WEINBERG, Jennifer Ann. ■ 53132 #016-43-2004 L2006 **PD** *100

WENZEL, Mark Steven. 3111 W RAWSON AVE, STE 105 53132 #056-06-1984 L1985 **DR** *020 †80

WILSON, Robin Sue. 9200 W LOOMIS RD, STE 204 53132 #056-05-1983 L1984 **OPH** *020 †35

WOZNIEWICZ, Dorota B. 9200 W LOOMIS RD 53132 #759-03-1987 L2002 **IM** *020 †20

YUILLE, David Lawrence. 3111 W RAWSON AVE, STE 105 53132 #025-01-1969 L1978 **NM R** *020 †80,28

ZIEGLER, Dean Wayne. 7400 W RAWSON AVE, STE 210 53132 #056-05-1989 L1995 **ORS** *020 †40

ZUEGE, Robert Calvin. 7400 W RAWSON AVE, STE 210 53132 #056-06-1955 L1956 **ORS** *071 †40

FRANKSVILLE – RACINE

GASS, Howard Irving. ■ 53126 #056-05-1954 L1955 **GYN OS** *072 †30

GEROL, A Yale. 2985 FORESTVIEW CIR 53126 #016-02-1952 L1957 **N** *071 †25

HARRIS, William C. 17527 TWO MILE RD 53126 #041-13-1950 L1951 **GS TS** *071 †85

KESSLER, Richard Arthur. ■ 53126 #056-06-1963 L1964 **R** *071 †80

LEITSCHUH, Thomas Henry. ■ 53126 #026-04-1943 L1952 **P IM** *071 †75

MAC VICAR, Ernest L, Jr. ■ 53126 #056-05-1943 L1947 **OPH** *071 †35

FREDERIC – POLK

AMMEND, David Allan. 203 UNITED WAY, N.W. PEDIATRIC SPECIALTIE, 54837 #026-04-1989 L1992 **PD** *020 †55

JOHNSON, Bradley Dean. 204 UNITED WAY 54837 #026-04-1963 L1997 **FM** *071 †18

MAYO, Andrew Graham. 107 OAK ST E 54837 #026-04-1994 L1997 **FM** *020 †18

MC CORMACK, Greg William. ■ 54837 #060-01-1973 L2004 **ON IM** *020 †20

FREDONIA – OZAUKEE

HINZ, William Max. ■ 53021 #010-01-1964 L1970 **PD AM** *071 †55

FREMONT – WAUPACA

HANKEY, Terry Lee. N430 WOOD DUCK DR 54940 #036-07-1972 L1973 **FM** *020 †18 ‡

FRIENDSHIP – ADAMS

ESMAILI, Jaleh Hamidieh. ■ 53934 #517-03-1969 L1979 **PTH** *020 †50

ESMAILI, Muhammad. 302 W LAKE ST 53934 #517-03-1969 L1978 **FM GS** *020 †85

JANSSEN, Martin Lowell. 302 W LAKE ST 53934 #056-05-1959 L1960 **FM** *020 †18

MIRZA, Muzaffar Baig. 206 W LAKE ST, MUZAFFAR B MIRZA MD SC 53934 #704-02-1967 L1975 **GS VS** *071 †85

REED, James W, Jr. 402 W LAKE ST 53934 #024-07-1984 L1987 **AN EM** *020

SANKARAN, Ramakrishan. 302 W LAKE ST 53934 #495-16-1972 L1977 **PD** *020 †55

SHAPIRO, Michael Barry. 402 W LAKE ST 53934 #028-02-1980 L1981 **OPH** *050 †35

SIMANI, Rahmatullah. 302 W LAKE ST 53934 #517-01-1958 L1972 **FM GS** *071

STODOLA, Carol Diane. 402 W LAKE ST 53934 #056-05-1980 L1981 **FM** *020 †18

GALESVILLE – TREMPEALEAU

EKERN, Samuel Jay. 16734 S 12TH ST 54630 #056-05-1985 L1987 **P IM** *020

KLOSTER, Geoffrey Chas. ■ 54630 #028-34-1971 L1976 **FM** *020 †18

ROHDE, Elmer Patzer. ■ 54630 #056-05-1942 L1943 **GP** *071

GAYS MILLS – CRAWFORD

SCHUCH, Rick J. ■ 54631 #056-05-1973 L1975 **FM** *050 †18

GERMANTOWN – WASHINGTON

ABRAHAM, Maritoni Molina. W176N9830 RIVERCREST DR, STE 104 53022 #748-21-1986 L1997 **CHP** *020 †75

ASIJA, Priya. N112W17975 MEQUON RD, ADVANCED HEALTHCARE, S.C. 53022 #495-74-1993 L2006 **FM** *020

BERTRAM, Karl John. W168N11237 WESTERN AVE 53022 #038-41-1994 L1999 **GS** *020 †85

BOYD, Bruce Huntington. N112W17975 MEQUON RD 53022 #040-02-1975 L1985 **FM** *020 †18

CHAN, Cesar A, Jr. N112W17975 MEQUON RD 53022 #748-19-1989 L2000 **GE** *020 †20

DAHLMAN, Kevin James. ■ 53022 #056-05-2005 L2006 **PD** *012

DIESTELHORST, Amy Lea. W168N11237 WESTERN AVE 53022 #028-34-1999 L2003 **OBG** *020 †20

FECHNER, Darcy Lynne. N112W15415 MEQUON RD 53022 #056-06-2000 L2002 **PD** *020 †55

GOLLUP, Howard Jeffrey. N112W17975 MEQUON RD 53022 #056-05-1978 L1981 **PD** *020 †55

HEYRMAN, Julie A. N112W17975 MEQUON RD 53022 #422-01-1998 L1999 **FM** *020 †18

HIATT, William R. ■ 53022 #017-20-1950 L1953 **GP** *071

HUIZENGA, Thomas Benjamin. N112W15415 MEQUON RD 53022 #056-06-2001 L2006 **ORS** *020 †20

IMSE, David Philip. W168N11237 WESTERN AVE, MED ASSOCS HLTH CTR 53022 #020-12-1973 L1974 **FM** *020 †18

JARZEMBOWSKI, Jason A. ■ 53022 #056-06-2002 L2007 **PTH** *100 †50

KAMINSKI, Henry Michael. N112W17975 MEQUON RD 53022 #016-11-1983 L1984 **OBG** *020 †30

KAMINSKI, John Henry. ■ 53022 #056-05-2008 *012

KNOERNSCHILD, Andrew M. W168N11237 WESTERN AVE 53022 #018-03-1997 L1998 **FM** *020 †18

KONKEL, Kurt Frederick. N112W17975 MEQUON RD 53022 #056-05-1970 L1971 **ORS** *020 †40

KONKEL, Philip David. N112W17975 MEQUON RD 53022 #056-06-1982 L1983 **HS ORS** *020 †40

MAYS, Bradley Wolfe. N112W15415 MEQUON RD 53022 #020-02-1991 L1993 **VS** *020 †85

MILLER, Amy Lynn. W168N11237 WESTERN AVE, MEDICAL ASSOCIATES 53022 #056-06-2001 L2003 **FM** *020 †18

MILLER, Paul Richard. N112W17975 MEQUON RD 53022 #016-02-1986 L1995
ORS OSM *020 †40
MONROE, Eugene Warren. W180N11070 RIVER LN, AURORA ADVANCED HEALTHCARE 53022
#025-01-1972 L1976 D *020 †15
NAUM, Efstathios Steve. N112W17975 MEQUON RD 53022 #016-43-1997 L2003 CD *020 †20
PLAMBECK, Christopher J. ■ 53022 #056-06-2000 L2003 AN *020 †05
SINGHAL, Peeush. N112W17975 MEQUON RD 53022 #025-07-1998 L1999 ORS *020 †40
STANLEY, Jerrel Lee. N112W17975 MEQUON RD 53022 #035-15-1978 L1979 FM EM *020 †18
STEINERT, Dirk Henry. N112W15415 MEQUON RD, GERMANTOWN CLNC CSM 53022
#016-11-1994 L2004 MPD *020 †20,55
SZWALEK, Kathleen E. N112W17975 MEQUON RD 53022 #038-06-2000 L2001 OBG *020 †30
TIMM, Mark Allan. W168N11237 WESTERN AVE 53022 #037-01-1987 L1988 GS VS *020 †85
VAN FOSSEN, Katharine S. W168N11237 WESTERN AVE 53022 #056-05-1996 L2000
OBG *020 †30
WEBER, Thomas Stephen. N112W17975 MEQUON RD 53022 #056-06-1998 L2002
FSM *020 †18
WHITE, Michael Gerard. N112 W16760 MEQUON RD 53022 #016-43-1984 L1988 FM *020 †18
WOOD, Carol Anne. N112W15415 MEQUON RD 53022 #016-01-2003 L2005 IM *020

GILLETT — OCONTO

BALMADRID, Luz L. 340 N GREEN BAY AVE 54124 #748-01-1972 L1992 FM *020 †18
MALTINSKI, Genadi. 340 N GREEN BAY AVE, CMH PRIMARY CARE CLINIC 54124
#561-06-1988 L1997 FM *020 †18

GLENDALE — MILWAUKEE

ARASSI, Siamak Baghai. 309 W SILVER SPRING DR, MED ALLIANCE 53217 #305-01-1997 L1999
FM GP *020 †18
BERGQUIST, Steven Robt. 7080 N PORT WASHINGTON RD, RHEUMATIC DISEASE CTR 53217
#056-06-1987 L1993 RHU IM *020 †20
BOUSOUNIS, Dimitrios P. 200 W SILVER SPRING DR, STE 255 53217 #418-01-1975 L1985
CHN CN *020 †55,75
BROWN, Steven Mark. 4655 N PORT WASHINGTON RD, STE 325 53212 #008-01-1981 L1988
PUD CCM *020 †20
CAIN, James E, Jr. 575 W RIVER WODS PKWY #100, ORTHOPAEDIC HOSP OF WISC 53212
#010-02-1982 L1992 OSS *020 †40
CARDAMONE, Stephen M. 400 W RIVER WOODS PKWY 53212 #018-75-1985, ▲ 2007
FM *030 †18
DZAKPASU, Promise. 5650 N GREEN BAY AVE, STE 210 53209 #408-30-1984 L1995
PD PG *020 †55
ELEJALDE, Benigno Rafael. 2311 W GOOD HOPE RD 53209 #264-03-1967 L1978
CG CCG *020 †19
FAISON, Barbara Ann. 309 W SILVER SPRING DR, MED ALLIANCE PAIN CARE 53217
#047-07-1979 L1982 FM *020
FISHER, Robert Henri. 350 W GREEN TREE RD, ALLERGY RESEARCH & CARE 53217
#035-45-1981 L1993 AI IM *020 †20,03
GILMAN, Michael H. 4655 N PORT WASHINGTON RD, STE 100 53212 #018-75-1979, ▲ L1980
OBG *020 †30
GIMBEL, Barry Kent. 5205 N IRONWOOD RD, STE 104 53217 #056-06-1977 L1982 CD IM *020
GRUENWALD, Lee Michael. 6791 N GREEN BAY AVE 53209 #056-06-2000 L2002 CHP *020 †75
HANNA, Miriam Naoum. 7080 N PORT WASHINGTON RD, RHEUMATIC DISEASE CENTER 53217
#025-07-1980 L1985 RHU IM *020 †20
HELLMAN, Daniel Roy. 2135 W EDWARD LN 53209 #056-05-1978 L1979 AN *020 †05
HOWELL, Jacqueline Coates. 2500 W SILVER SPRING DR, STE C 53209 #010-03-1954 L1960
PD *020 †55
KANIN, Harry Jerome. 2501 W SILVER SPRING DR, MEDPOINT FAMILY CARE CTR 53209
#056-06-1947 L1948 IM GE *020 †20
LENETT, Harold Glenn. ■ 53209 #038-40-1995 L2006 NEP *020
MASCI, Vance Andrew. 377 W RIVER WOODS PKWY, STE 111 53212 #034-01-1981 L1995
OM *020 †70,18
MELBYE, David Enos. 6373 N JEAN NICOLET RD, BAYSHORE PEDS STE 110 53217
#056-06-2002 L2003 PD *020 †55
NAZAREY, Pradeep P. ■ 53217 #024-05-2000 L2000 PDS *020
NIEDFELDT, Jennifer W. 575 W RIVER WOODS PKWY, ORTHOPAEDIC HOSP OF WI 53212
#056-06-1993 L1994 AN *020 †05
NORTON, Paul E. 6791 N GREEN BAY AVE 53209 #056-06-1978 L1979 PD *020 †55
OELKE, Kurt Robert. 7080 N PORT WASHINGTON RD 53217 #056-05-1997 L2003
RHU IG *020 †20
POWELL, Guy Robert. 5650 N GREEN BAY AVE, STE 200 53209 #306-01-2000 L2002
FM *100 †18
POWONDRA, Philip Frank. 575 W RIVER WOODS PKWY, WISCONSIN 53212
#056-05-1965 L1966 AN *071 †05
SADIQ, Raja Adnan. ■ 53217 #704-26-2004 FP *012
SEMON, Bruce A. 5555 N PT WASHNGTN RD #200 53218 #056-05-1984 L1985
CHP NTR *020 †75
SHIMSHAK, Karen S. 377 W RIVER WOODS PKWY, STE 115 53212 #056-06-1985 L1986
OPH PO *020 †35
SIMANONOK, Kirsten J. 575 W RIVER WOODS PKWY 53212 #409-36-1991 L2002 AN *020 †05
SO, Conchita Gue. ■ 53209 #748-01-1960 L1969 IM EM *071
STETZER, Joan Lee. 7007 N RANGE LINE RD 53209 #056-06-1992 L1993 AN *020 †05
STRAUB, Robert Harold. 200 W SILVER SPRING DR, STE 300 53217 #056-05-1983 L1984
FM *020 †18
SWEENEY, Brian Terence. ■ 53209 #539-04-1992 L2003 *020
TAMAYO, Primo R. 2501 W SILVER SPRING DR 53209 #748-08-1965 L1971 IM OS *020
TSENG, Justina Jennan. 377 W RIVER WOODS PKWY, STE 113 53212 #024-05-1998 L2006
RHU *020 †20
WAELTZ, John Lee. 4655 N PORT WASHINGTON RD, STE 100 53212 #017-20-1980 L1984
OBG *020 †30
WILSON, Jeffrey Whitside. 5225 N IRONWOOD RD, STE 102 53217 #056-05-1965 L1966
P *020 †18
WRIGHT, Rory Ray. 545 W RIVER WOODS PKWY, STE 100 53212 #056-06-1988 L1989
ORS *020 †40
YOUNG, Carol Edith. 200 W SILVER SPRING DR 53217 #056-05-1960 L1961 PD *071

GLENWOOD CITY – SAINT CROIX

SORENSON, Eric Wayne. 219 E OAK ST 54013 #026-04-1997 L1999 FM *020 †18

GRAFTON – OZAUKEE

BONILLA, Melinda C. 215 WASHINGTON ST, STE 60 53024 #748-01-1990 L1994 IM *020 †20
BUNTING, Richard Wm. 215 WASHINGTON ST, STE 60 53024 #026-04-1977 L1978 IM *020 †20
CHAROUS, B Lauren. 215 WASHINGTON ST, CREEK CLINIC 53024 #016-11-1978 L1984
AI RHU *020 †20,03
CHATTON, Thomas Barbour. 215 WASHINGTON ST, STE 60 53024 #056-06-1972 L1973
PD *020 †55
CORNELL, Ann Elizabeth. 215 WASHINGTON ST, STE 60 53024 #018-03-1986 L1991
OBG *020 †30
EBINGER, William Allen. 215 WASHINGTON ST, STE 60 53024 #016-02-1980 L1983 IM *020 †20
GRABOYES, Joseph Hillel. 215 WASHINGTON ST, STE 60 53024 #028-02-1980 L1985
OTO *020 †45
HONG, Domingo T. 1990 WISCONSIN AVE 53024 #748-03-1966 L1973 IM PUD *020
HOOLBOOM, Beatrice Lucie. 215 WASHINGTON ST, STE 60 53024 #056-05-1986 L1987
EM IM *020 †20
HUNG, Winny W. ■ 53024 #036-01-1999 L2005 EM *020 †16
KAPUR, Sunil. 215 WASHINGTON ST, STE 60 53024 #035-09-1996 L2002 GE *020 †20
LUY, Jerome John, Jr. 1220 LAKE SHORE RD 53024 #056-06-1964 L1968 PS HS *062
MOTARJEME, Steven Cyrus. 2109 CHEROKEE ST 53024 #016-43-1992 L1998
EM PD *020 †20,16
PAVLOVITZ, Gwenn Karen. 215 WASHINGTON ST, STE 60 53024 #028-02-1980 L1985
GS *020 †85
PHILLIPS, Darcy Ann. ■ 53024 #054-04-1994 L1995 FM *020
PHILLIPS, Kenneth Jay, Jr. 215 WASHINGTON ST, STE 60 53024 #056-06-1986 L1998
CD *020 †20
SHEWCZYK, Mark Dennis. 1990 WISCONSIN AVE 53024 #005-15-1983 L1986 FM *020 †18
YADGIR, John D, Jr. 215 WASHINGTON ST, AURORA ADVANCED HEALTHCARE 53024
#016-11-1983 L1990 D IM *020 †15

GRANTSBURG – BURNETT

BROTHERS, Alexander Bain. 513 PARKVIEW DR, GRANTSBURG CLINIC 54840
#060-02-1994 L1996 *020
HARTZELL, Richard Layton. PO BOX 169 54840 #038-06-1948 L1949 GS GP *071 †18
HUSET, Richard Alfred. 513 PARKVIEW DR 54840 #005-11-1973 L1991 FM OM *020
KAMMAN, Lee Michael. 257 W SAINT GEORGE AVE, BURNETT MEDICAL CENTER 54840
#026-04-1977 L1983 PUD IM *020 †20
KUMAR, Anil. 257 W SAINT GEORGE AVE 54840 #495-37-1999 L2003 FM *020 †18
NOVICK, Timothy George. 513 PARKVIEW DR 54840 #026-04-1983 L1999 FM *020 †18
SCHISSEL, Gregory A. 513 PARKVIEW DR 54840 #030-06-1951 L1991 FM *071 †18
VITALE, Blaise Paul. 513 PARKVIEW DR 54840 #035-48-1988 L1991 FM FSM *020 †18 ‡

GREEN BAY – BROWN

ABDEL-HALIM, Olan Mohamed. 1821 S WEBSTER AVE 54301 #575-01-1996 L2006 IM *020
ABUJAMRA, Fawzi Nicola. 704 S WEBSTER AVE 54301 #605-01-1958 L1977 PS *075 †85,65
AHMAD, Sahar. ■ 54313 #704-02-1994 L2004 CCM *062 †20
AHMED, Ashraf Nabil. 301 E SAINT JOSEPH ST 54301 #915-04-1990 L2004 PYG *020 †75
AHN, Joyce Sunghee. 2253 W MASON ST, STE 200 54303 #050-02-1998 L2001 IM *020 †20
AL-KHALISY, Mazen. 725 S WEBSTER AVE 54301 #305-01-1998 L2002 *020 †20
AL-SHAHROURI, Manar K. 1821 S WEBSTER AVE 54301 #473-02-1994 L2006 PCC *020 †20 ‡
AMARNANI, Narayan H. 725 S WEBSTER AVE 54301 #495-22-1971 L1976 GE IM *020 †20
AMENT, Alan Simon. PO BOX 22425 54305 #016-02-1992 L1999 CD *020 †20
AMENT, Joel Steven. 835 S VAN BUREN ST 54301 #005-19-1987 L1999 CCP *020 †55
ANDERSON, Marc Hanson. 1630 COMMANCHE AVE, ORTHOPAEDIC ASSOCIATES OF 54313
#017-20-1980 L1981 ORS *020 †40
ANDREWS, John Frederick. 720 S VAN BUREN ST, P O BOX 19070 54301 #026-04-1979 L1985
PUD AI *020
ANGUS, Darel C. 1381 W MASON ST 54303 #056-05-1949 L1950 GS *020 †85
ANTHONY, Lewis Geo. 704 S WEBSTER AVE 54301 #041-02-1961 L1973 CD IM *071 †20
APATA, Olusegun O. 744 S WEBSTER AVE, 7TH FL 54301 #690-05-1986 L2004
PUD CCM *020 †20
ARAUJO, Marco. 1928 RIVERSIDE DR 54301 #187-03-1994 L2007 AN PME *020 †05
ARORA, Kanwar. 725 S WEBSTER AVE # 303 54301 #495-29-1990 L2002 GE *020 †20
ASSEF, Saied. 744 S WEBSTER AVE 54301 #005-11-1986 L1987 AN *020 †05
AUCHTER, Richard Martin. 835 S VAN BUREN ST, RADIATION ONCOLOGY 54301
#056-05-1989 L1992 RO *020 †20,80
BAETEN, Pamela Cuene. 704 S WEBSTER AVE STE 500 54301 #054-04-1992 L1997 END *020
BANNASCH, Gerald John. 1821 S WEBSTER AVE, PREVEA CLINIC 54301 #038-43-1976 L2001
CN *020 †75
BANTAMOI, Edward John. 760 PILGRIM WAY 54304 #561-13-1996 L2005 FM *020 †18
BARKOW, Kathleen Marie M. 1821 S WEBSTER AVE 54301 #056-05-1975 L1978 PD *020 †55
BARTEL, Mary Lynn. 835 S VAN BUREN ST 54301 #056-06-1996 L1997 PD *020 †55
BARYLAK, Edward John. 2845 GREENBRIER RD 54311 #041-02-1970 L1971 HO *020 †20
BASTIN, Kenneth Tyrone. 2845 GREENBRIER RD 54311 #047-05-1988 L1989 RO GP *020 †80
BAYER, Gerald Kurt. 835 S VAN BUREN ST 54301 #056-05-1974 L1979 ON HEM *020 †20
BEACHLEY, Brenda Ruth. ■ 54301 #056-05-1986 L1988 PD *062 †55
BEDI, Sabeeha Shefali. 725 S WEBSTER AVE 54301 #495-90-1991 L1998 FM *020 †18 ‡
BENO, Donald James. 2845 GREENBRIER RD, STE 440 54311 #056-06-2001 L2003
PD *020 †55
BENO, Thomas John. 835 S VAN BUREN ST 54301 #056-05-1946 L1947 GS TS *071 †85
BERKO, Yaw Dankyi. 1715 DOUSMAN ST 54303 #412-01-2001 L2006 IM *020 †20
BERTAGNOLI, Mark Wm. 835 S VAN BUREN ST, ST VINCENT HOSP NJCU 54301
#026-04-1989 L1999 NPM *020 †55
BETKA, Thomas Charles. ■ 54311 #056-05-1998 L1999 FM *020 †18
BIENVENU, Louis Maurice. 835 S VAN BUREN ST 54301 #021-05-1987 L2002 EM *020 †16
BISHOP, John Champion. 1203 S MILITARY AVE 54304 #056-06-1967 L1968 GS GP *020

BITTORF, Steven Victor. 1821 S WEBSTER AVE, PREVEA CLC ALLOUEZ SITE 54301 #056-05-1994 L2003 **PCC** *020 †20
BJORAKER, Robt Wayne, Jr. 164 N BROADWAY, BAYCARE 54303 #023-12-1990 L2001 **AN** *020 †05
BLACK, Julie Anne. ■ 54311 #056-05-1984 L1987 **PD** *071 †55
BLAHNIK, Clarence Louis. 1515 N BAY HIGHLANDS DR 54311 #056-06-1954 L1956 **OPH** *071 †35
BLANK, Jules Harris. 835 S VAN BUREN ST 54301 #016-43-1978 L1985 **ON HEM** *020 †20
BLINK, Jeffrey Alan. 2845 GREENBRIER RD, STE 230 54311 #056-05-1984 L1989 **GS VS** *020 †85
BLOCK, Jeffrey A. 2845 GREENBRIER RD, STE 220 54311 #037-01-1991 L1997 **OTO** *020 †45
BOEHM-MATTIA, Shelley K. 300 CROOKS ST 54301 #056-05-1988 L1998 **P** *020 †75
BOLICH, Paul Randolph. 2941 S RIDGE RD 54304 #025-01-1970 L1971 **DR** *071 †80
BOLLOM, Steven James. 2793 LINEVILLE RD 54313 #056-06-1989 L1990 **IM** *020 †20
BOMMAKANTI, Chandralekha. 2900 SAINT ANTHONY DR, MENTAL HEALTH CENTER 54311 #495-50-1971 L1990 **P** *020 †75 ‡
BORDEWICK, Dianna Lee. 2140 VELP AVE 54303 #018-03-1994 L1999 **OPH** *020 †35
BOTTEI, Gregory Matthew. 835 S VAN BUREN ST 54301 #016-02-1988 L1999 **PUD CCM** *072 †20
BOYD, Thomas Clyde. 725 S WEBSTER AVE, STE 215 54301 #016-11-1983 L1986 **FM** *020 †18
BRACHMANN, Denise Ann. ■ 54301 #030-06-1986 L1991 **CHP** *020 †75
BRADA, Stephen Andrew. 2253 W MASON ST, STE 200 54303 #032-01-1994 L1998 **AN** *020 †05
BRANDT, Jon Marc. 835 S VAN BUREN ST 54301 #047-05-1991 L1999 **PHO** *020 †55
BRAULT, Robert Granger. 704 S WEBSTER AVE 54301 #056-06-1957 L1960 **GS TS** *071 †85,90
BREBURDA, Christian. 2845 GREENBRIER RD STE 31, BAYCARE CLINIC 54311 #409-06-1988 L2000 **CD** *020 †20
BRESSLER, Bruce Clarke. 3117 BAY VIEW DR 54311 #030-05-1967 L1971 **NS** *020 †25
BROCKMAN, Michael John. 2845 GREENBRIER RD, STE 420 54311 #030-06-1984 L1988 **OBG** *020 †30
BROWN-SULLIVAN, Cynthia J. 2845 GREENBRIER RD, STE 480 54311 #024-05-1996 L2000 **OBG** *020 †30
BRUSKY, Eugene S. 1726 SHAWANO AVE 54303 #056-06-1945 L1946 **GP OS** *062
BRUSKY, John Dean. 835 S VAN BUREN ST 54301 #056-06-1963 L1966 **IM FM** *071 †20
BUDDI, Rajeev. 1821 S WEBSTER AVE 54301 #495-28-1986 L2000 **OPH** *020 †35
BUDZAK, Lynn Marie. 141 SIEGLER ST, DEPT OF VET AFFAIRS 54303 #056-05-1990 L1991 **FM** *020 †18
BUIKUS, William R. 2640 W POINT RD 54304 #028-78-1983, ▲ L1984 **P ADP** *020 †75
BURNS, Jennifer Ann. 1821 S WEBSTER AVE 54301 #018-03-1996 L2005 **U** *020 †95
CAIN, Thomas Leo. 720 S VAN BUREN ST, STE 303 54301 #026-04-1977 L1984 **TS** *020 †85,90
CARELS, Gail Schwartz. 760 PILGRIM WAY 54304 #056-05-1993 L1994 **FM** *020 †18
CARRIGAN, Patrick Mel. 1241 LOMBARDI ACCESS RD 54304 #026-04-1976 L1977 **DR** *020 †80
CASE, C E. 720 S VAN BUREN ST STE 201, NEURLGY CONSLTS NE WISC 54301 #034-01-1991 L1993 **N** *020
CASEY, Paul David. ■ 54301 #010-01-1986 L2004 **EM** *020 †16
CASIS, Ferdinand C. 2845 GREENBRIER RD, STE 430 54311 #748-01-1991 L2005 **END** *020 †20
CASPER, James Theodore. 835 S VAN BUREN ST 54301 #056-06-1970 L1971 **ON PD** *050 †55
CASTILLO, Carlos S. 301 E SAINT JOSEPH ST, BELLIN BEHAVIORAL HEALTH C 54301 #649-33-1983 L2006 **CHP P** *020
CAVALLIN, Geffrey Edward. 835 S VAN BUREN ST 54301 #018-03-1992 L2000 **IM** *020 †20
CAVANAUGH, Robert Alan. 124 SIEGLER ST 54303 #016-45-1979 L1983 **OBG** *020 †30
CHAMBERLAIN, Timothy Lee. 2845 GREENBRIER RD, PATHOLOGY DEPARTMENT 54311 #017-20-1991 L1996 **PTH** *020 †50
CHARLES, John Christopher. 301 E SAINT JOSEPH ST 54301 #056-05-1994 L2000 **P** *020 †75
CHRISTEL, Diane Kathryn. 141 SIEGLER ST 54303 #056-05-1981 L1982 **IM** *020 †20
CHRISTIAN, Roland B. 1715 DOUSMAN ST 54303 #018-03-1985 L1986 **GE** *020 †20
CHUN, Yoon Wook. 704 S WEBSTER AVE, STOP 100 54301 #025-07-1995 L2001 **OBG** *020 †30
CHUNG, Kum Young. 1726 SHAWANO AVE 54303 #583-01-1959 L1976 **GP PME** *071 †50
CLEMENS, James Richard. 1821 S WEBSTER AVE 54301 #038-41-1990 L1997 **OTO** *020 †45
COALMON, Perry Gene. ■ 54305 #056-06-1984 L1989 **IM** *075
COHEN, Staci Michele. 124 SIEGLER ST 54303 #016-42-1996 L1999 **PD** *020 †55
COHEN, Toby Linda. 2845 GREENBRIER RD, 4TH FL 54311 #021-01-1994 L2003 **NPM** *020 †55
COLEMAN, Edward J. 835 S VAN BUREN ST 54301 #035-06-1983 L1990 **TS** *020 †90,85 ‡
CONNELLY, Mary Alice. 2020 S WEBSTER AVE 54301 #045-01-1988 L1992 **FM** *020 †18
COOLEY, Gregory Mark. 835 S VAN BUREN ST, ST VINCENT HOSP 54301 #056-06-1987 L1988 **RO** *020 †80
COOLEY, Richard Lawrence. 1726 SHAWANO AVE 54303 #035-03-1966 L1972 **AI PD** *020 †55
COOPER, Timothy Russell. 2845 GREENBRIER RD, STE 340 54311 #056-05-1990 L1992 **APM** *020 †05 ‡
COUSINEAU, Anthony James. 1821 S WEBSTER AVE 54301 #025-12-1987 L1993 **PDC** *020 †55
COYLE, Douglas. 1241 LOMBARDI ACCESS RD 54304 #056-06-1999 L2000 **DR** *020 †80
CRAWFORD, Chester W. 744 S WEBSTER AVE 54301 #005-12-1953 L1953 **GPM GP** *072 †18
CROSS, William Michael. 835 S VAN BUREN ST, HOSPITALIST OFFICE 54301 #028-34-1963 L1969 **IM** *071 †20
CRUZ, Lorenzo Reyes. ■ 54301 #748-07-1963 L1976 **RO** *071
CRUZ, Norma Picio. 744 S WEBSTER AVE 54301 #748-01-1964 L1977 **P** *020
CULLEN, Joseph Patrick. 1715 DOUSMAN ST, PREVEA HEALTH 54303 #036-07-1988 L1994 **ORS** *020 †40
CUTLAN, Robert Thomas. 1715 DOUSMAN ST 54303 #056-06-1996 L2002 **PTH** *020 †50
CVITKOVICH, Donald Gerard. 704 S WEBSTER AVE, STOP 102 54301 #016-06-1974 L2008 **PUD IM** *020 †20
DAIS, Charles F, II. 835 S VAN BUREN ST 54301 #056-05-1995 L1996 **PTH** *020
DAIS, Charles Franklin. 835 S VAN BUREN ST 54301 #047-06-1968 L1972 **CLP PTH** *062 †50
DALE, Daniel Lawrence. 1525 PARK PL 54304 #047-05-1981 L1989 **OPH AM** *020 †35
DANNER, John H, III. 744 S WEBSTER AVE 54301 #056-05-1991 L1995 **AN** *020 †05
DANOWIT, Herbert Danl. 744 S WEBSTER AVE 54301 #026-04-1986 L1999 **IM** *020 †20
DANOWIT, Jane Hansen. 124 SIEGLER ST 54303 #026-04-1985 L1999 **PD** *020 †55
DARNELL, Michael Paul. 704 S WEBSTER AVE 54301 #019-02-1985 L1992 **GS IM** *020 †85
DAVIS, Howard Wells. 301 E SAINT JOSEPH ST 54301 #017-20-1971 L1982 **CHP** *020 †75
DAVIS, Mark Embrey. 720 S VAN BUREN ST, STE 101 54301 #018-75-1988, ▲ L1993 **RHU** *020 †20
DAVIS, Peter Wm. 670 CORMIER RD 54304 #048-04-1987 L1998 **GS** *020 †85
DAVIS, Ronald Dale. 704 S WEBSTER AVE STOP 102 54301 #018-03-1976 L1989 **PUD ID** *020 †20
DAVISON, Robert Francis. 835 S VAN BUREN ST, ST VINCENT HOSP 54301 #654-01-2000 L2003 **NM** *100 †28
DE ARTEAGA, Julio C. 1595 ALLOUEZ AVE 54311 #847-10-1957 L1965 **FM** *020 †18
DEGROOT, Daniel Lawrence. 1821 S WEBSTER AVE 54301 #056-06-1989 L1990 **U** *020 †95
DE MOTT, Robert Knox. 704 S WEBSTER AVE, STOP 100 54301 #056-05-1981 L1985 **OBG** *020 †30
DETTMANN, John Ernst. ■ 54301 #020-02-1946 L1947 **FM P** *071
DIERBERG, William Jeffrey. 704 S WEBSTER AVE, STE 401 54301 #028-03-1984 L1990 **PS HS** *020 †85,65
DIERSCHKE, Brenda Jeanne. 704 S WEBSTER AVE 54301 #056-05-1985 L1991 **PM** *020 †60
DITCHEN, Izabela Joanna. 2714 RIVERVIEW DR, BELLIN FAMILY MEDICAL CENT 54313 #759-12-1996 L2002 **FM OBS** *020 †18
DOBBINS, Brian Dale. 1715 DOUSMAN ST 54303 #030-06-1994 L1998 **OBG** *020 †30
DONARSKI, David Paul. ■ 54301 #056-06-1960 L1962 **P** *071 †75
DOUGHERTY, Donn Michael. 760 PILGRIM WAY 54304 #308-11-1984 L1987 **FM** *020 †18
DOVIN, Nancy Lynn. 835 S VAN BUREN ST 54301 #056-06-1991 L1994 **GS** *020
DRAHEIM, John H. 1726 SHAWANO AVE 54303 #026-04-1949 L1953 **PTH** *071 †50
DUFFY, Mark Thos. 2253 W MASON ST 54303 #016-11-1992 L2004 **OPH** *020 †35
DZWONKOWSKI, Peter. 1715 DOUSMAN ST 54303 #759-04-1980 L2000 **IM GE** *020 †20
EBBEN, James Robt. 1630 COMMANCHE AVE 54313 #056-05-1987 L1988 **FM OS** *020 †18
ECLAVEA, Anthony. PO BOX 13508, 835 S VAN BUREN ST 54307 #019-02-1994 L2007 **VIR** *020 †80
EDGAR, Terence Shaun. 1821 S WEBSTER AVE 54301 #836-03-1984 L1993 **CHN PD** *020 †55,75
EL-EKIABY, Amr Saad. 835 S VAN BUREN ST, PREVEA CLINIC 54301 #915-02-1990 L2003 **PCC** *020 †20
ERDMAN, Richard Louis. 835 S VAN BUREN ST 54301 #056-06-1981 L1982 **EM IM** *020 †20,16
ERICKSON, Milo Rodney. 1726 SHAWANO AVE 54303 #056-05-1954 L1955 **GP** *071
ERRICO, Charles Anthony. 2253 W MASON ST, STE 100 54303 #056-06-1971 L1972 **OPH** *020 †35
FAGRE, Tim Alan. 1565 ALLOUEZ AVE, AMG-THE WILLOWS 54311 #018-03-1995 L1998 **FM** *020 †18
FALK, Manuel James. 670 CORMIER RD 54304 #056-05-1961 L1962 **GP** *071
FALK, Peter Michael. 670 CORMIER RD 54304 #039-05-1986 L1993 **CRS GS** *020 †10,85
FALLER, William. 1726 SHAWANO AVE 54303 #016-06-1965 L1966 **ATP CLP** *071 †50
FANGMAN, Edmund Stephen. 835 S VAN BUREN ST, DEPARTMENT OF ANESTHESIOLO 54301 #030-06-2000 L2003 **AN** *020 †05
FENSTER, Bruce Paul. 1726 SHAWANO AVE 54303 #016-02-1978 L1981 **IM** *020 †20
FENSTER, Diane Lind. 1715 DOUSMAN ST, PREVEA CLINIC 54303 #016-02-1978 L1981 **PD** *020 †55
FINESILVER, Alan Geo. 2253 W MASON ST, 2ND FL 54303 #008-01-1968 L1982 **RHU IM** *020 †20
FISCHER, Deborah Sue. 1715 DOUSMAN ST 54303 #025-12-1987 L1988 **OBG** *020 †30
FISCHER, Peter Morris. 2845 GREENBRIER RD 54311 #056-06-1991 L1996 **P** *020 †75
FISHER, David Jude. 2941 S RIDGE RD, GREEN BAY RADIOLOGY 54304 #018-03-1994 L2007 **DR NRN** *020 †80
FLORACK, Thomas Michael. 1821 S WEBSTER AVE 54301 #035-45-1985 L2003 **ORS** *020 †40
FOSTER, Stephen Michael. 725 S WEBSTER AVE, STE 303 54301 #028-02-1991 L1995 **AN** *020 †05
FREDEEN, Thomas Scott. ■ 54301 #049-01-1987 L1989 **PTH** *020 †50
FREEMAN, Timothy John. 744 S WEBSTER AVE 54301 #056-05-1979 L1980 **CD NM** *020 †20
FUGLESTAD, Loren C. 2714 RIVERVIEW DR 54313 #056-05-1993 L1994 **FM** *020 †18
GADSBY, Alessandra Mae. 760 PILGRIM WAY 54304 #010-03-1993 L1994 **FM** *020 †18 ‡
GALLAGHER, John C. 2845 GREENBRIER RD, STE 420 54311 #016-43-1976 L1980 **OBG** *020 †30
GALLAGHER, Michael L. 141 SIEGLER ST 54303 #016-43-1979 L1980 **IM** *020 †20
GALLAGHER, Thomas James. 2845 GREENBRIER RD, STE 420 54311 #056-06-1986 L1989 **OBG** *020 †30
GALLION, Todd Patrick. 835 S VAN BUREN ST, P O BOX 19070 54301 #016-45-1992 L1995 **IM** *020 †20
GAPINSKI, Peter Vincent. 2845 GREENBRIER RD 54311 #056-06-1976 L1977 **GS PDS** *020 †85
GASSNER, John Richard. 1241 LOMBARDI ACCESS RD 54304 #056-06-1986 L1987 **DR** *020 †80
GAST, James William. 1630 COMMANCHE AVE 54313 #056-06-1996 L1999 **FM** *020 †18
GEMER, Linda Susan. 835 S VAN BUREN ST, DEPT OF RADIATION ONCOLOGY 54301 #056-06-1982 L1983 **RO** *020 †80
GEOCARIS, Cynthia Louise. 720 S VAN BUREN ST, STE 202 54301 #016-43-1995 L1996 **GS VS** *020 †85
GEOCARIS, Thomas Victor. 720 S VAN BUREN ST STE 202 54301 #016-43-1968 L1976 **GS VS** *020 †85
GERNDT, Steven James. 720 S VAN BUREN ST, STE 303 54301 #056-05-1989 L1997 **TS** *020 †85,90
GIBSON, James Joseph. 2845 GREENBRIER RD, STE 420 54311 #016-11-1994 L1995 **OBG** *020 †30
GIFFORD, Stewart W. 704 S WEBSTER AVE 54301 #016-11-1977 L1984 **GS VS** *020 †85
GOELZ, John Robt. 519 S MONROE AVE 54301 #056-06-1940 L1940 **GP GS** *071
GOOLSBY, Philip Lane. 1565 ALLOUEZ AVE, AMG - THE WILLOWS 54311 #045-01-1982 L2000 **FM** *020 †18
GRACE, James Norton. 720 S VAN BUREN ST STE 101 54301 #028-34-1984 L1989 **ORS** *020 †40
GRAZZIOTIN, Marcello U. 720 S VAN BUREN ST, STE 202 54301 #187-80-1992 L2003 **GS** *020 †85
GREEN, Jeremy Raleigh. 1821 S WEBSTER AVE 54301 #836-01-1954 L1964 **IM** *020
GREENE, Richard Carl. 2495 EDGEWOOD CT, AURORA BAY CLINIC 54302 #016-43-1972 L1975 **IM** *020
GREER, Kevin Allen. 720 S VAN BUREN ST, STE 303 54301 #016-06-1992 L2001 **GS** *020 †85,90
GREWE, Gregory Mark. 744 S WEBSTER AVE 54301 #016-11-1984 L1989 **DR** *020 †80
GRIESSER, Robert Conrad. 2253 W MASON ST, STE 200 54303 #056-06-1982 L1985 **AN CCM** *020 †05
GRIGGS, Stewart Latham. 1821 S WEBSTER AVE 54301 #035-06-1943 L1947 **PDA PD** *020 †55,03
GROSSMAN, Daniel Robt. 1630 COMMANCHE AVE 54313 #007-02-1980 L1999 **FM** *020 †18
GROTELUSCHEN, David Louis. 835 S VAN BUREN ST, GREEN BAY ONCOLOGY 54301 #018-03-2001 L2002 **ON** *020
GUO, Danqing. 3021 VOYAGER DR 54311 #243-47-1988 L2006 **FM** *020 †18

■ = Address Information Privacy Protected

GUO, Ziwen. 744 S WEBSTER AVE, DEPT OF PATH 54301 #243-45-1984 L1999 **PCP** *062 †50
GUY, Fraser. 2640 WEST POINT RD, ONEIDA BEHAVIORAL HEALTH 54304 #051-01-1966 L1986 **P OPH** *071 †75
HALE, John Michael. 2845 GREENBRIER RD, STE 420 54311 #010-02-1986 L1993 **OBG FM** *020 †18,30
HALLOIN, Thomas Jos. 2845 GREENBRIER RD, STE 420 54311 #056-06-1980 L1984 **OBG** *020 †30
HALSEY, Steven Alan. 725 S WEBSTER AVE 54301 #026-08-1982 L1983 **FM** *020 †18
HART, Loren E, Jr. ■ 54301 #016-06-1950 L1958 **R** *071 †80
HARTIG, Donald Edward, Jr. 2714 RIVERVIEW DR 54313 #019-02-1992 L1993 **IM** *020 †20
HARTMAN, John William. 425 PACKERLAND DR, STE F 54303 #025-01-1995 L2000 **NEP** *020 †20
HATHWAY, Stephen Dallas. ■ 54305 #017-20-1968 L1974 **PTH** *071 †50
HECKERT, Richard Raymond. 2253 W MASON ST, STE 100 54303 #041-02-1981 L1991 **OPH PO** *020 †35
HEJNY, Charles. 2835 OGDAN WOODS DR 54313 #056-06-1997 L2002 **OPH** *020
HERING, George Vosburgh. 744 S WEBSTER AVE 54301 #026-04-1945 L1946 **OS GP** *071
HERMITANIO, Marlon Lim. 1714 E SONATA DR 54311 #748-01-1986 L1995 **RHU** *020 †20
HERON, Charles Richard. 1726 SHAWANO AVE 54303 #025-12-1990 L1992 **AN** *020 †05
HILL, John Robert. 835 S VAN BUREN ST 54301 #054-04-1994 L1994 **PHO** *020 †55
HINCKLEY, James Arthur. 760 PILGRIM WAY, PREVEA CLINIC 54304 #016-11-1971 L1978 **ORS** *020 †40
HINGTGEN, William Laverne. 1241 LOMBARDI ACCESS RD 54304 #018-03-1981 L1986 **DR** *020 †80
HOBSON, Paula Mae. 1537 PARK PL STE 200, WOMEN'S HEALTH CARE OB-GYN 54304 #016-01-2003 L2007 **OBG** *020
HODGDON, Scott Michael. 2253 W MASON ST, STE 200 54303 #056-06-1982 L1985 **AN** *020 †05
HODGES, Paul Chesley, Jr. ■ 54301 #023-07-1955 L1962 **EM** *020 †80
HOEGEMEIER, Harry W. ■ 54301 #017-20-1950 L1961 **IM** *071 †20
HOLZMAN, Paul Russell. 1715 DOUSMAN ST 54303 #056-05-1983 L1984 **PTH** *020 †50
HOLZWARTH, Peter David. 1715 DOUSMAN ST 54303 #046-01-1991 L1994 **PD** *020 †55
HOOPS, Harold John, Jr. 835 S VAN BUREN ST 54301 #035-01-1954 L1961 **PS HS** *071
HOPPE, Jason William. 1821 S WEBSTER AVE 54301 #056-05-1995 L1997 **IM** *020 †20
HORAK, Richard David. 720 S VAN BUREN ST, STE 101 54301 #056-05-1970 L1971 **ORS FM** *020 †40
HOUN, Kristina Ann. 3021 VOYAGER DR 54311 #037-01-2000 L2003 **PD** *020 †55
HOYER, David James. 744 S WEBSTER AVE, BELLIN MEMORIAL HOSPITAL 54301 #056-05-1999 L2001 **EM** *020 †16
HUDSON, Dennis Michael. 1715 DOUSMAN ST 54303 #034-01-1991 L1993 **PM** *020 †60
HUFFER, Thomas Carl. 1715 DOUSMAN ST 54303 #056-05-1989 L1991 **PD** *030 †55
HUJET, Kenneth John. 1726 SHAWANO AVE 54303 #056-06-1980 L1983 **IM** *020 †20
HUNT, Scott Matthew. 1821 S WEBSTER AVE 54301 #017-20-1994 L1999 **OTO** *020 †45
HUTTO, John David. 1821 S WEBSTER AVE 54301 #056-05-2000 L2000 **GS** *100 †85
IGLER, Franz Otto. 744 S WEBSTER AVE BOX 23, BELLIN HOSP., DEPT. OF ANE 54301 #056-06-1980 L1981 **AN PME** *020 †05
JACKSON, Suzanne Victoria. 1715 DOUSMAN ST 54303 #016-11-1999 L2002 **IM** *020 †20
JACQUES, Thomas John. ■ 54311 #056-05-2006 **AN** *012
JAGETIA, Rakesh. 2845 GREENBRIER RD 54311 #038-06-1993 L1997 **RO** *020 †80
JAHN, Timothy Wm. 835 S VAN BUREN ST 54301 #056-05-1989 L1998 **EM** *020 †16
JAMES, Amy A. 744 S WEBSTER AVE 54301 #056-06-1996 L2004 **IM** *020
JANCZAKOWSKI, John M. 2793 LINEVILLE RD, PREVEA CLINIC 54313 #054-04-1992 L1995 **PD** *020 †55
JANITCH, Michael Allen. 1715 DOUSMAN ST 54303 #028-46-1993 L2000 **PS** *020 †85,65
JANQUART, Stephen Jos. 2253 W MASON ST, STE 200 54303 #056-06-1990 L1991 **AN** *020 †05
JASLOWSKI, Anthony John. 1726 SHAWANO AVE, GREEN BAY ONCOLOGY 54303 #016-43-1987 L1988 **ON HEM** *020 †20
JAZAYERI, Allahyar. 2641 DEVELOPMENT DR, NEW MOMS OF GREEN BAY, SC 54311 #048-02-1992 L2002 **OBG** *020 †30
JAZAYERI, Mohammed-Reza. 744 S WEBSTER AVE, 744 S WESTER AVENUE 54301 #517-01-1977 L1985 **ICE CD** *020 †20
JENSON, Mark Krueger. 1747 SHAWANO AVE 54303 #748-10-1986 L1988 **FM EM** *020 †18
JERZAK, James Thos. 1630 COMMANCHE AVE, BELLIN HEALTH ASHWAUBENON 54313 #056-05-1983 L1984 **FM** *050 †18
JOHNSON, Edward Jos. 1922 UNIVERSITY AVE 54302 #056-06-1971 L1972 **P ADP** *020 †75
JOHNSON, Janet Marie. 1715 DOUSMAN ST, PREVEA CLINIC 54303 #056-05-1993 L1996 **IM** *020 †20
JOHNSON, Kenneth Michael. 835 S VAN BUREN ST 54301 #021-05-1987 L1994 **EM** *020 †16
JOHNSON, Matthew John. 1715 DOUSMAN ST 54303 #056-06-1990 L1991 **GS** *020 †85
JONES, William David. 704 S WEBSTER AVE 54301 #056-06-1965 L1966 **ORS** *071 †40
JOYCE, Daniel Mark. 835 S VAN BUREN ST 54301 #024-07-1983 L1999 **EM GS** *020 †16
JULIEN, Reginald. 835 S VAN BUREN ST 54301 #035-08-2001 L2006 **AN** *020 †05
KADILE, Eleazar Mira. 1538 BELLEVUE ST 54311 #748-11-1965 L1976 **AI P** *020 ‡
KASDORF, Gayle Marie. 704 S WEBSTER AVE STE 500 54301 #056-06-1981 L1982 **END** *020 †20
KATHURIA, Sabeena. 835 S VAN BUREN ST 54301 #965-01-1991 L1998 **PD** *020 †55
KATMEH, Ghazwan. 1727 SHAWANO AVE 54303 #528-01-1980 L1988 **CD** *020 †20
KEIM, David Ralph. 3021 VOYAGER DR 54311 #007-02-1982 L1992 **PD PPR** *020 †55
KEISER, Orris S. 835 S VAN BUREN ST 54301 #005-12-1953 L1954 **FM** *020
KELLER, Jeffery Wm. 2253 W MASON ST, STE 200 54303 #056-05-1990 L1996 **VS** *020 †85
KEMMERLING, James M. 670 CORMIER RD, NEW SURGICAL ASSOCIATES 54304 #056-06-1986 L1994 **GS** *020 †85
KEMPKEN, Thomas Geo. 3208 SAINT ANDREWS CT, GREEN BAY 54301 #056-06-1965 L1966 **ORS** *071 †40
KENNY, John Andrew. 1176 E WALNUT ST 54301 #056-06-1960 L1963 **D** *071
KHAN, Naser Mohammed. 1715 DOUSMAN ST 54303 #496-27-2003 L2007 **IM** *020 †20
KIEFER, Patrick James. 835 S VAN BUREN ST, PREVEA CLINIC 54301 #030-06-1981 L1986 **GS** *020 †85
KINCHELOE, Michael J. 2845 GREENBRIER RD, STE 420 54311 #037-01-1984 L1988 **OBG** *020 †30
KISER, John Patrick. 2253 W MASON ST STE 2 54303 #056-06-1979 L1980 **GP OM** *020
KITCHER, Paulina Dameki. 301 E SAINT JOSEPH ST 54301 #913-48-1990 L2003 **CHP** *020
KLEIN, Jason P. 720 S VAN BUREN ST, STE 101 54301 #048-04-1995 L2005 **OSM** *020 †40
KLEMENS, Lee James. 744 S WEBSTER AVE, BELLIN HEALTH 54301 #041-12-1981 L1997 **IM PM** *020 †20
KNUTSON, Thomas James. 1727 SHAWANO AVE, STE 201 54303 #056-05-1980 L1983 **FM EM** *020 †18
KOCH, John Michael. PO BOX 19070, PREVEA CLINIC 54307 #056-05-1995 L2004 **PM PMM** *020 †60
KOCH, Paul David. 835 S VAN BUREN ST, ST VINCENT HOSPITAL 54301 #017-20-1968 L1976 **ON** *020 †20
KOEHLER, Thomas Paul. PO BOX 8960, 3189 VOYAGER DR 54308 #038-43-1979 L1982 **IM MDM** *020 †20
KOHL, Robert. 2845 GREENBRIER RD 54311 #018-75-2001, ▲ L2006 **RO** *020 †80
KOKOSZKA, Melissa Jo. ■ 54304 #422-01-2003 L2007 **AN** *100
KONDAVEETI, Ravi. 2845 GREENBRIER RD 54311 #422-01-1997 L2003 **GE** *020 †20
KOSTER, Daniel Garrison. 744 S WEBSTER AVE 54301 #025-01-1987 L1988 **FM** *020 †18
KOUZOV, Eugeni Todorov. 835 S VAN BUREN ST, PATH DEPT 54301 #198-01-1988 L2004 **PTH** *020 †50
KUBSCH, Kenneth R. 1715 DOUSMAN ST 54303 #056-06-1968 L1976 **IM** *071 †20
KULKOSKI, Bernard. 744 S WEBSTER AVE 54301 #056-06-1950 L1951 **FM** *071
KURITZ, Jay Jacob. ■ 54302 #056-05-1973 L1974 **AN** *071 †05
LANDA, Martin Jeffrey. 835 S VAN BUREN ST 54301 #049-01-1990 L1999 **EM** *020 †16
LAUKKA, Mark Alan. 1715 DOUSMAN ST 54303 #025-01-1988 L1994 **GE IM** *020 †20
LAWTON, John Michael. 2020 RIVERSIDE DR, STE 200 54301 #026-04-1978 L1984 **NEP CCM** *020 †20
LEAHY, Jesse Isobel. 3021 VOYAGER DR, PREVEA CLINIC FAMILY PRACT 54311 #062-01-1994 L2004 **FM** *020 †18
LEE, Alice Myungjae. 835 S VAN BUREN ST 54301 #583-08-1953 L1970 **GP PD** *071
LEE, James. 704 S WEBSTER AVE STE 401, GREEN BAY PLASTIC SURGICAL 54301 #041-13-1994 L2006 **PS** *020 †65
LEH, Patrick Siu Shing. 1745 DOUSMAN ST, STE 101 54303 #748-01-1960 L1970 **FM GS** *071 †18
LEMKUIL, Daniel Carl. 1630 COMMANCHE AVE 54313 #056-05-1995 L1996 **FM** *020 †18
LEONARD, Thomas Jos. 2763 MANITOWOC RD, BELLEVUE TOTAL HEALTH 54311 #026-04-1982 L1984 **IM** *020 †20
LEVY, Charles Lewis. 835 S VAN BUREN ST, SAINT VINCENT HOSPITAL/PRE 54301 #041-09-1998 L2005 **NS** *020 †25
LEWIS, Ernest Christopher. 835 S VAN BUREN ST 54301 #019-02-1994 L2003 **ON HEM** *020 †20 ‡
LINEHAN, Daniel John. 1630 COMMANCHE AVE, STE 101 54313 #056-06-1989 L1990 **ORS** *020 †40
LISOWSKI, James Benedict. 124 SIEGLER ST 54303 #051-04-1994 L2002 **IM** *020 †20
LULLOFF, Rolf Smart. 835 S VAN BUREN ST 54301 #056-05-1967 L1968 **ORS** *020 †40
LULLOFF, Sarah Jane. 1821 S WEBSTER AVE 54301 #056-06-1997 L1999 **ID** *020 †20
LUX, Beth Anne. 744 S WEBSTER AVE, BELLIN HEALTH CARE 54301 #056-06-1982 L1983 **EM FM** *020 †18,16
LYLES, William B. 840 WILLARD DR STE 201 54304 #011-04-1985 L1998 **CHP P** *020 †75
LYNCH, Jennifer Barry. 923 ELIZA ST 54301 #056-06-1996 L1998 **OTO** *020 †45
MAC DONALD, John Douglas. 744 S WEBSTER AVE, BELLIN HOSPITAL 54301 #056-06-1984 L1985 **IM EM** *020 †20
MACKEY, James Patrick. ■ 54311 #028-34-1958 L1959 **AN** *071
MAGNIN, Julie Ann. 1747 SHAWANO AVE 54303 #056-05-1987 L1988 **FM** *020 †18
MAHONEY, Thomas Lee. 744 S WEBSTER AVE 54301 #046-01-1985 L1986 **OBG** *020 †30
MALLOY, Kelly Kathleen. ■ 54313 #030-06-2007 **OBG** *012
MAMONOV, Alexander Boriso. 2845 GREENBRIER RD, STE 420 54311 #913-97-1989 L2003 **OBG** *020
MANKE, David Alvin. 1715 DOUSMAN ST, PREVEA CLINIC 54303 #038-41-1972 L1981 **GS VS** *020 †85
MANNEM, Koti R. 130 E WALNUT ST, STE 706 54301 #495-50-1975 L1981 **P** *020
MANNING, Ronald George. 1821 S WEBSTER AVE 54301 #007-02-1995 L1996 **PM** *020 †60
MANTHEY, Mitchell W. 1821 S WEBSTER AVE 54301 #056-05-1989 L1992 **GE** *020 †20
MARADA, Ramana Rao N. PO BOX 8900, 2845 GREENBRIER RD STE 320 54308 #495-11-1982 L2005 **CCM** *020 †20
MARCHLEWSKI, Anthony J. 301 E SAINT JOSEPH ST 54301 #016-06-1986 L1996 **P CHP** *020 †75
MARIFKE, Jerald Peter. 704 S WEBSTER AVE 54301 #056-06-1994 L1995 **END IM** *020 †20
MARSHALL, Thomas Gregory. 744 S WEBSTER AVE 54301 #056-05-1987 L1992 **AN PD** *020 †55,05
MATHIAS, David Wm. 2845 GREENBRIER RD 54311 #016-43-1982 L1983 **CD IM** *020 †20
MATTIA, Frank Raymond. 2845 GREENBRIER RD, 4TH FL 54311 #056-05-1988 L1991 **NPM** *020 †55
MATTSON, James Richard. 141 SIEGLER ST 54303 #016-06-1966 L1974 **A IM** *071 †20,03
MAYLAND, Diane Marie. 2845 GREENBRIER RD, STE 220 54311 #056-05-1986 L1987 **OTO HNS** *020 †45
MC GOVERN, James D. 835 S VAN BUREN ST 54301 #028-34-1975 L1982 **ON** *071 †20
MC HENRY, Michael Gerald. 725 S WEBSTER AVE 54301 #056-05-1979 L1980 **FM** *020 †18
MC KENZIE, Patrick James. 1630 COMMANCHE AVE, ORTHOPAEDIC ASSOCIATES OF 54313 #056-06-1983 L1984 **ORS** *020 †40
MC NUTT, Richard Kevin. 720 S VAN BUREN ST, STE 303 54301 #056-06-1985 L1986 **AS VS** *020 †85
MEAD, Robert Chas. 1630 COMMANCHE AVE 54313 #056-05-1984 L1985 **FM** *020 †18
MENDOZA, Raul. 2845 GREENBRIER RD, STE 320 54311 #649-01-1983 L1987 **CD IM** *020 †20
MEREDITH, Robert Loren. 2595 DEVELOPMENT DR, STE 120 54311 #017-20-1992 L1993 **NM** *020 †28
MEVES, Roderick Lynn. 2845 GREENBRIER RD 54311 #021-01-1981 L1982 **IM** *020 †20
MEYER, Larry Alan. 2253 W MASON ST, STE 100 54303 #056-06-1984 L1985 **OPH** *020 †35
MIAN, Hamayun Saeed. 720 S VAN BUREN ST, STE 301 54301 #041-09-1992 L2004 **U** *020 †95
MIHAILESCU, Violeta. 2253 W MASON ST, STE 200 54303 #781-01-1996 L1999 **IMG** *020 †20
MILLER, Gary Stuart. 720 S VAN BUREN ST, STE 201 54301 #056-06-2002 L2007 **CN** *020
MILLER, Gary Thos. ■ 54313 #016-11-1976 L1977 **OTO** *071 †45
MILLER, Thomas Paul. 1747 SHAWANO AVE, 1745 DOUSMAN 54303 #017-20-1977 L2001 **FM** *020 †18
MILLS, John Manierre. 923 ELIZA ST 54301 #016-11-1959 L1967 **OTO** *071 †45
MILSON, Bertram Irving. 1747 SHAWANO AVE 54303 #056-06-1956 L1957 **EM GP** *020 †85
MISSBACH, Timm Scott. 3021 VOYAGER DR 54311 #056-05-1993 L1996 **PD** *020 †55
MOHR, Wayne Steven. 720 S VAN BUREN ST STE 101 54301 #026-04-1975 L1981 **ORS** *020 †40
MONETTE, Robert John. 1241 LOMBARDI ACCESS RD 54304 #056-05-1988 L1989 **DR** *020 †80
MOORE, Terry Jay. 1087 W MASON ST 54303 #048-04-1992 L1999 **OPH** *020 †35

■ = Address Information Privacy Protected

MOORMAN, Matthew Lee. 2845 GREENBRIER RD, STE 230 54311 #038-40-2001 L2006 **GS** *020
MORRISSEY, William Gerard. 2845 GREENBRIER RD, STE 420 54311 #016-01-1997 L2001 **OBG** *020 †30
MOYER, Robert Donald, Jr. 1715 DOUSMAN ST, PREVEA CLINIC 54303 #041-12-1992 L2002 **OBG** *020 †30
MULLER, Joseph Christian. 670 CORMIER RD, NEW SURGICAL ASSOCIATES 54304 #045-04-1998 L2007 **CRS** *020 †85
MUNOZ-ROCHE, Wanda Y. ■ 54313 #042-02-1996 **FM** *020
MURPHY, Robert Joseph. 1726 SHAWANO AVE 54303 #056-06-1994 L1995 **PTH** *020 †50
MURTHY, Geetha. 1726 SHAWANO AVE, ST MARYS HOSPITAL 54303 #496-01-1974 L1983 **AN** *020 †05
MURTHY, Gowdar Sadashiv. 2253 W MASON ST, STE 200 54303 #495-09-1964 L1977 **IM** *020 †20
MYERS, Richard L. ■ 54301 #028-34-1951 L1957 **PD PDA** *071 †55
NASSIFF, Marie Diane. 2253 W MASON ST # 100 54303 #021-01-1984 L1992 **OPH OS** *062 †35 ‡
NEU, Steven Edwin. 2020 RIVERSIDE DR, STE 200 54301 #030-06-1979 L1988 **NEP IM** *020 †20
NEUHAUS, Ellen Mary. 2793 LINEVILLE RD 54313 #056-05-1992 L1993 **CCP** *020 †55
NICHOLAS, Shaytone. 744 S WEBSTER AVE 54301 #008-02-2000 L2004 **EM** *100 †16
NITKE, Jason M. 3276 SITKA ST 54311 #018-75-2001, ▲ L2004 **IM** *020
NITKE, Leah A. 2845 GREENBRIER RD 54311 #018-75-2001, ▲ L2004 **IM** *020
NORDELL, Charles. 2845 GREENBRIER RD, AURORA MEDICAL GROUP POB 8 54311 #024-05-1968 L1979 **IM GE** *020 †20
NWAEZE, Ijeoma. 760 PILGRIM WAY 54304 #305-01-2000 L2004 **FSM** *020 †18
ONUAGULUCHI, Maureen O. 1630 COMMANCHE AVE, BELLIN HEALTH, FMC-ASHWAUB 54313 #690-04-1981 **P** *100
O'REILLY, Michael Dennis. 1715 DOUSMAN ST 54303 #016-06-1975 L1980 **ORS** *020 †40
ORTWEIN, Robert Keith. 1634 MAIN ST 54302 #030-06-1961 L1969 **PD** *071 †55
OSWALD, Terri Ann. 3021 VOYAGER DR 54311 #056-06-1989 L1993 **PM IM** *020 †60
PALUBIAK, David Joseph. 2020 RIVERSIDE DR, STE 200 54301 #016-11-1999 L2003 **NEP** *020 †20
PANNKE, Thomas Scott. 835 S VAN BUREN ST 54301 #016-43-1989 L1999 **EM** *020 †16
PARDINI, Pamela Jean. 2253 W MASON ST, AURORA BAYCARE CLC 54303 #025-12-1999 L2003 **OBG** *020 †30
PATEL, Dhimant R. 2845 GREENBRIER RD, LOMBARDI CANCER CTR-PO BOX 54311 #495-23-1980 L1987 **ON IM** *020 †20
PATIL, Veeranagouda A. 2900 SAINT ANTHONY DR 54311 #495-35-1978 L1989 **P** *020 †75
PATRICK, Robert Kenneth. ■ 54305 #143-03-1968 L1993 **OPH** *020
PAVEK, Timothy Steven. 835 S VAN BUREN ST 54301 #037-01-1986 L1987 **EM ESM** *020 †16
PEARSON, Paul Jos. 1821 S WEBSTER AVE 54301 #026-08-1991 L1999 **TS** *020 †85,90
PEARSON, Sayuri Virginia. 835 S VAN BUREN ST 54301 #054-04-1987 L1992 **APM AN** *020 †05
PECHMAN, Kenneth Jos. 1525 PARK PL, STE 300 54304 #016-11-1977 L1981 **D** *020 †15
PEREIRA, Bryan M. ■ 54311 #495-52-1978 L1998 **NS** *020
PERKOVICH, Brian Thos. 2253 W MASON ST, STE 100 54303 #056-06-1985 L1990 **OPH** *020 †35
PETERS, Eric John. 164 N BROADWAY 54303 #056-05-2000 L2001 **AN** *020 †05 ‡
PETERS, Kelly Lynn. ■ 54313 #056-05-2006 L2006 **OBG** *012
PETERS, Michelle C. 164 N BROADWAY, BAYCARE 54303 #041-15-2001 L2004 **EM** *020 †16
PETERSEN, Steven John. 2253 W MASON ST, STE 200 54303 #047-06-1999 L2003 **AN** *020 †05 ‡
PHILLIPS, Maureen. 1630 COMMANCHE AVE 54313 #056-06-1997 L1998 **FM** *020 †18
PHILLIPS, Michael Earl. 164 N BROADWAY 54303 #017-20-1972 L1982 **EM** *020 †16
PIECHOWSKI, Susan Marie. 835 S VAN BUREN ST 54301 #056-05-1977 L1985 **IM** *020 †20
PINN, Christopher Chas. ■ 54301 #016-11-1967 L1968 **IM** *020 †20
PLEMENTOSH, Nicky. 1537 PARK PL, STE 200 54304 #001-02-1993 L2002 **OBG** *020 †30
PLOUFF, Louis Thos. ■ 54301 #056-06-1955 L1957 **R** *071 †80
POLEY, Carl Robt. 1726 SHAWANO AVE 54303 #056-06-1971 L1972 **OBG** *071 †30
POREMBSKI, Michael Victor. 1821 S WEBSTER AVE 54301 #016-02-1971 L1978 **PD NPM** *020 †55
POTTS, Richard G. 1821 S WEBSTER AVE 54301 #025-76-1987, ▲ L1991 **PUD PCC** *020 †20
PRICE, Michael Alan. 2941 S RIDGE RD 54304 #008-01-1989 L2007 **DR** *020 †80
PRITCHARD, Michelle Lynn. ■ 54302 #056-06-1997 *100
PRITCHARD, Paul M. 3021 VOYAGER DR 54311 #056-06-1996 L1997 **IM** *020 †20
PUKEL, Clifford Stuart. 2845 GREENBRIER RD 54311 #011-02-1991 L2000 **HO IM** *020 †20
RAHR, Henry Carl. ■ 54302 #056-05-1958 L1959 **FM GP** *071
RAI, Ashok Nand. 2710 EXECUTIVE DR 54304 #056-06-1997 L2001 **MPD** *020 †20,55
RAJALA, Mary Margaret. 1726 SHAWANO AVE 54303 #026-08-1988 L1994 **AN PME** *020 †05
RANDALL, John Hammond. 211 N BROADWAY 54303 #018-03-1959 L1960 **IM HEM** *071
RANK, John Jos. 1715 DOUSMAN ST 54303 #056-05-1971 L1972 **IM RHU** *020 †20
RATSCHAN, Walter John. 744 S WEBSTER AVE 54301 #056-06-1992 L1996 **AN** *020 †05
RECKARD, Paul Eugene. 1821 S WEBSTER AVE 54301 #026-04-1984 L1992 **GS FM** *020 †85
REINKE, Mark Kevin. 923 ELIZA ST 54301 #016-01-1992 L1997 **OTO** *020 †45
RENTMEESTER, David W. 835 S VAN BUREN ST 54301 #056-05-1991 L1993 **IM** *020 †20
REYES, Metodio Mercado. 744 S WEBSTER AVE 54301 #748-01-1956 L1967 **GP FM** *071
REYNDERS, William Michael. 1630 COMMANCHE AVE 54313 #056-06-1980 L1986 **FM** *020 †18
RICHARDSON, B Lee. ■ 54301 #038-40-1960 L1963 **END IM** *071 †20
RIDER, James Elliot. 704 S WEBSTER AVE 54301 #036-01-2000 L2007 **CD** *020 †20
RIPP, Daniel Jos. 835 S VAN BUREN ST 54301 #056-05-1985 L1988 **IM** *020 †20
RIQUELME, Jean Marie. 725 S WEBSTER AVE, STE 100 54301 #056-06-1993 L1994 **FM** *020 †18
ROBINSON, Brock Lyndsey. 3021 VOYAGER DR 54311 #026-04-1981 L1985 **PM PMM** *020 †60
ROBINSON, James Ernest. ■ 54311 #019-02-1971 L1975 **DR** *071 †80
RODRIGUEZ-POJAS, Josefina. 2900 SAINT ANTHONY DR 54311 #748-07-1976 L1997 **P** *020
ROH, Steven Sukwoo. 1821 S WEBSTER AVE 54301 #017-20-1993 L2003 **IC** *020 †20
ROHDE, David Carl. 2845 GREENBRIER RD 54311 #056-05-1987 L1988 **RO** *020 †80
ROITSTEIN, Alexander. 2845 GREENBRIER RD, STE 310 54311 #035-45-1990 L2001 **TS** *020 †90,85
ROLSTON, Richard David. 2793 LINEVILLE RD 54313 #034-01-1987 L2005 **PD** *020 †55
ROSS, Michael Anthony. 1241 LOMBARDI ACCESS RD 54304 #056-06-1981 L1991 **DR FM** *020 †18,80
RUGGLES, Scott Lewis. 670 CORMIER RD, NEW SURGICAL ASSOCIATES 54304 #010-02-1996 L2002 **CRS GS** *020 †85,10
RUSSELL, Elizabeth Joyce. 1630 COMMANCHE AVE, BELLIN MED GRP 54313 #060-02-1990 L1995 **EM** *020 †18
SALETTA, Charles Walter. 1821 S WEBSTER AVE 54301 #016-42-1973 L2001 **GS VS** *020 †85
SALMI, Allen Wayne. 835 S VAN BUREN ST 54301 #025-12-1996 L1999 **EM** *020 †16
SALM-SCHMID, Colette Ann. 2845 GREENBRIER RD 54311 #016-06-1996 L1998 **GS** *020 †85
SANDMIRE, Herbert F. 704 S WEBSTER AVE, STOP 100 54301 #056-05-1953 L1956 **OBG** *020 †30
SANDMIRE, Kevin Wayne. 1715 DOUSMAN ST 54303 #056-05-1983 L1986 **IM** *020 †20
SAPHNER, Thomas James. 1726 SHAWANO AVE, GREEN BAY ONCOLOGY 54303 #056-05-1985 L1987 **ON IM** *020 †20
SAROS, Peter Gabor. 835 S VAN BUREN ST 54301 #473-01-1996 L2006 **IM** *020 †05
SATHOFF, Rodney Harold. 1726 SHAWANO AVE, ST MARY'S HOSPITAL 54303 #016-11-1982 L1986 **AN** *020 †05
SAUVEY, Mary Alice. 1595 ALLOUEZ AVE, MERCY FAMILY PRACTICE 54311 #030-06-1983 L1996 **FM** *020
SCATTERGOOD, Kirk David. 2253 W MASON ST, STE 100 54303 #023-07-1983 L1994 **OPH** *020 †35
SCHIBLY, William Jos. 424 S MONROE AVE STE 106, EAST WALNUT FAM PRAC 54301 #030-05-1958 L1959 **GP** *020
SCHICK, Mark Robt. 1821 S WEBSTER AVE 54301 #016-43-1988 L1997 **ORS** *020 †40
SCHICK, Patricia Anne. 1715 DOUSMAN ST 54303 #038-41-1988 L1997 **OP** *020 †40
SCHIEBLER, John Chas. 2021 S WEBSTER AVE, UROLOGICAL SURGEONS LTD 54301 #035-20-1961 L1970 **U** *071 †95
SCHLUETER, Thomas Robt. 900 S WEBSTER AVE 54301 #056-06-1992 L1993 **U** *020 †95
SCHMIDT, Frederic Wm. 923 ELIZA ST 54301 #056-06-1983 L1984 **OTO HNS** *020 †45
SCHMIDT, Robert Thos, Jr. 720 S VAN BUREN ST, STE 201 54301 #056-06-1970 L1975 **N** *020 †75
SCHMITT, Eugene Henry, III. 704 S WEBSTER AVE, STE 401 54301 #016-11-1977 L1985 **PS HS** *020 †85,65
SCHMITZ, Paul Jerome. 3021 VOYAGER DR 54311 #056-05-1986 L1990 **IM** *020 †20
SCHNEIDER, Rayfel. 2140 S RIDGE RD, ECHO RIDGE DENTAL CLINIC 54304 #836-01-1980 **PD** *100 †55
SCHNEIDER, William F. 704 S WEBSTER AVE 54301 #056-06-1960 L1961 **ORS** *071 †40
SCHROEDER, Jeffrey David. 2845 GREENBRIER RD 54311 #028-78-2004, ▲ L2005 **PCC** *012
SCHUCHARD, Gregory Harold. 1821 S WEBSTER AVE 54301 #026-04-1979 L1982 **CD IM** *020 †20
SCHUECKLER, Amy Katherine. ■ 54311 #035-06-1984 L1988 **OBG** *071 †30
SCHWIESOW, Kurt August. 1087 W MASON ST, TOWER CLOCK EYE CENTER 54303 #056-05-2000 L2004 **OPH** *020 †35
SCHWIESOW, Tyson Karl. 1087 W MASON ST, STE 1 54303 #056-06-1997 L1999 **OPH** *020 †35
SECCOMBE, John Forrest. 1821 S WEBSTER AVE 54301 #026-08-1990 L1999 **TS GS** *020 †85,90 ‡
SEHRING, Stephen F. 2845 GREENBRIER RD, STE 420 54311 #056-06-1985 L1988 **OBG** *020 †30
SHAH, Fauzia Rafat. 1715 DOUSMAN ST 54303 #495-77-1998 L2004 **IM** *020
SHEA, Daniel W. 835 S VAN BUREN ST 54301 #028-34-1951 L1957 **PD** *071 †55
SHERWOOD, Donald Leroy. 1551 DOUSMAN ST BOX 19070 54303 #056-05-1958 L1959 **FM** *071
SHRAKE, John Fredrick. 1821 S WEBSTER AVE 54301 #056-05-1974 L1977 **IM** *020 †20
SIAS, Patricia Elizabeth. 3461 BAYWATCH DR 54311 #025-07-1993 L1997 **IM** *020 †20
SINCLAIR, Tangee Noel. 1715 DOUSMAN ST, PREVEA CLINIC 54303 #056-05-1995 L1998 **IM** *020 †20
SIPES, Donald Ralph, Jr. 2845 GREENBRIER RD, 4TH FL 54311 #056-05-1989 L1993 **OBG** *020 †30
SIPES, Susan Louise. ■ 54304 #016-06-1985 L1997 **MFM MG** *020 †19,30
SKALETSKI, Brian Bernard. 835 S VAN BUREN ST 54301 #056-06-1993 L1994 **AN** *020 †05
SKUMATZ, Primus John, Jr. ■ 54307 #026-04-1970 L1971 **FM** *020 †18
SLIWINSKI, Jane Kilsdonk. 3021 VOYAGER DR 54311 #056-06-1982 L1983 **OM PHP** *020 †70
SMITH, Charles Copland. ■ 54301 #016-06-1954 L1956 **U** *071 †95
SMITH, Seth Edgar. 1715 DOUSMAN ST 54303 #030-05-1994 L1999 **GS** *020 †85
SMITH, Thomas Jos. 2020 RIVERSIDE DR, STE 200 54301 #056-05-1986 L1992 **NEP IM** *020 †20
SMULLEN, Michael James. 1239 W MASON ST 54303 #056-05-1968 L1969 **D DMP** *020 †15
SMYTH, Ronan Hugh. 2941 S RIDGE RD 54304 #056-05-1992 L1993 **DR** *020 †80
SOMERVILLE, Stephen V. 1241 LOMBARDI ACCESS RD 54304 #056-05-1971 L1975 **N RNR** *020 †75
SONG, Hwe-Jae. 835 S VAN BUREN ST, ST VINCENT HOSP 54301 #583-04-1962 L1975 **AN** *071 †05
SOROKOUMOV, Oleg. 835 S VAN BUREN ST, ST. VINCENT'S HOSPITAL 54301 #913-99-1997 L2005 **CCM** *020 †20
SORRELLS, Christopher C. 164 N BROADWAY, BAYCARE CLINIC LLP 54303 #017-20-1988 L1991 **EM** *020 †16
SOUTHWICK, Robert David. 1715 DOUSMAN ST 54303 #028-02-1994 L1995 **OBG** *020 †30
SPEARS, James Raymond. 1630 COMMANCHE AVE, ORTHOPAEDIC ASSOCIATES OF 54313 #011-03-1983 L1997 **ORS** *020 †40
STAMPFL, David Anton. 725 S WEBSTER AVE STE 303, GASTROENTEROLOGY ASSOCS 54301 #024-05-1984 L1985 **GE IM** *020 †20
STANKEVYCH, Anatol John. 923 ELIZA ST 54301 #016-11-1976 L1980 **OPH** *020 †35
STANKO, Heather Alissa. 720 S VAN BUREN ST, STE 201 54301 #056-06-1998 L1999 **N** *020 †75
STANKO, Peter Michael. 900 S WEBSTER AVE 54301 #056-06-1998 L1999 **GE** *020 †20
STANLAW, Karen Ann. 835 S VAN BUREN ST 54301 #016-11-1987 L1990 **EM** *020 †16
STEELE, C Danae. 704 S WEBSTER AVE, STOP 100 54301 #040-02-1990 L2006 **OBG MFM** *020 †30
STEVENS, Clark W, Jr. 704 S WEBSTER AVE, OB-GYN ASSOCIATES 54301 #051-01-1984 L1998 **OBG** *020 †30
STEVENSON, John Eric. 2845 GREENBRIER RD 54311 #024-01-1966 L1977 **IM PUD** *020 †20
STORCH, Shimon. 1910 RIVERSIDE DR, ROYCE CLINDIALYSIS CTR 54301 #550-03-1982 L1990 **NEP** *020
STOVER, Paul Michael. 1525 PARK PL, STE 300 54304 #018-03-1985 L1997 **D** *020 †15
STRANCKE, Charles Richard. 164 N BROADWAY, BAYCARE CLINIC LLP 54303 #056-05-1988 L1995 **EM** *020 †16
STROMAN, Steven Jon. 164 N BROADWAY, BAYCARE CLINIC LLP 54303 #017-20-1988 L1991 **EM** *020 †16
STRUNGS, Gunars R. 1726 SHAWANO AVE 54303 #056-06-1983 L1985 **IM** *020 †20
SULLIVAN, Thomas Andrew. 835 S VAN BUREN ST 54301 #030-05-1997 L2002 **ORS** *020 †40
SWELSTAD, Jack Alan. 2845 GREENBRIER RD, STE 230 54311 #016-06-1971 L1978 **GS VS** *020 †85

SZE, David Bartholomew. 1715 DOUSMAN ST 54303 #056-05-1995 L1997 **IM** *020 †20

TAMMELA, Jonathan Edward. 835 S VAN BUREN ST, ST. VINCENT HOSPITAL 54301 #017-20-1998 L2005 **OBG** *020 †30

TAMMELA, Karen Demers. 835 S VAN BUREN ST 54301 #047-05-1997 L2005 **OBG** *020 †30

TANKE, Timothy Edward. 1821 S WEBSTER AVE, P O BOX 19070 54301 #056-05-1993 L1994 **CD** *020 †20

TAYLOR, James Hamilton. 2845 GREENBRIER RD 54311 #051-01-1981 L1990 **RO** *020 †80

TEETZEN, Merle Lee. 2845 GREENBRIER RD, STE 140 54311 #056-06-1976 L1978 **N SCI** *020 †75

THOMAS, Jonathan Wesley. 1543 PARK PL, STE 800 54304 #001-02-1988 L1992 **P** *020 †75

THOMS, Carrie Ann. 1821 S WEBSTER AVE 54301 #007-02-1983 L2005 **GS** *020 †85

TIBBETTS, Jay Jeremy. 1551 DOUSMAN ST 54303 #056-05-1966 L1967 **FM** *020

TIMMONS, Richard J, Jr. 744 S WEBSTER AVE, CARDIOLOGY ASSOCIATES 54301 #038-41-1984 L1993 **CD IC** *020 †20

TONELLI, Danielle Gloria. 120 W BRIAR LN 54301 #016-76-2005, ▲ L2006 **FP** *012

TRESSLER, Hubert Allen. 720 S VAN BUREN ST STE 101 54301 #016-01-1968 L1975 **ORS** *071 †40

TRESSLER, Michael Allen. 720 S VAN BUREN ST, STE 101 54301 #010-02-1995 L1999 **ORS** *071 †40

TROUP, Richard H. 2021 S WEBSTER AVE 54301 #016-06-1950 L1952 **U** *071 †95

TSCHOEKE, Richard Walter. 744 S WEBSTER AVE 54301 #056-05-1987 L1992 **AN** *020 †05

TUNIO, Javed H. 2845 GREENBRIER RD 54311 #704-16-1989 L2006 **CD** *020 †20

TURBA, Rose Marie. 1715 DOUSMAN ST 54303 #056-05-1989 L1993 **PM** *020 †60

ULIBARRI, James Allan. 1715 DOUSMAN ST 54303 #056-05-2000 L2001 **ORS** *020

UTRIE, John Wendel. 160 DETRIE DR 54301 #056-06-1959 L1962 **GYN** *071 †30

VALLEY, Joseph Edward. 2253 W MASON ST, STE 200 54303 #025-01-1985 L2002 **AN** *020 †05,18

VANDEN HEUVEL, Chad G. 835 S VAN BUREN ST 54301 #056-06-1996 L1998 **AN** *020 †05

VANDERWALL, Pamela Jean. 835 S VAN BUREN ST 54301 #056-06-1986 L1988 **RO** *020 †80

VANDER WOUDE, Sherwood Wm. 2845 GREENBRIER RD, STE 220 54311 #025-01-1966 L1974 **OTO** *020 †45

VAN DORP, William Leonard. 1715 DOUSMAN ST 54303 #016-42-1998 L2001 **PM** *020 †60

VANSADERS, Christopher J. 1715 DOUSMAN ST 54303 #016-06-1988 L1994 **OSS** *020 †40

VARDIS, Ralph Jos. 835 S VAN BUREN ST 54301 #035-48-1992 L1999 **CCP** *020 †55

VERMA, Anupama. 2020 RIVERSIDE DR, STE 204 54301 #690-04-1992 L2002 **IM** *020 †20

VIEBAHN, Martin. 1087 W MASON ST 54303 #409-16-1986 L1995 **OPH** *020 †35

VILLWOCK, Mark Kurt. 3021 VOYAGER DR 54311 #056-06-1982 L1983 **FM** *020 †18

VOGEL, Edward Corradin. 2845 GREENBRIER RD 54311 #016-43-1997 L2001 **EM** *020 †16

VOGEL-SCHWARTZ, Laura L. 164 N BROADWAY 54303 #056-05-1991 L1992 **EM** *020

VOLK, Michael Josef. 835 S VAN BUREN ST 54301 #409-10-1985 L1988 **ON HEM** *020 †20

WACKWITZ, Donald Leo. 760 PILGRIM WAY 54304 #056-05-1979 L1980 **ORS EM** *020 †40

WAHL, Leonard John. 725 S WEBSTER AVE, STE 303 54301 #005-15-1971 L1979 **GE IM** *071 †20

WALBRUN, Fred H. 1715 DOUSMAN ST, PREVEA CLINIC 4TH FLOOR 54303 #010-02-1976 L1979 **IMG IM** *020 †20

WALDKIRCH, Bernard P. 835 S VAN BUREN ST 54301 #056-06-1943 L1943 **FM** *071 †18

WALKER, Thomas F. ■ 54302 #056-05-1963 L1964 **AN** *020

WANAMAKER, William Meade. 1901 S WEBSTER AVE, GREEN BAY NEUROLOGY LTD 54301 #030-06-1964 L1965 **N** *071 †75

WANG, Wei-Chuan. 2253 W MASON ST STE 100 54303 #051-01-2002 L2007 **OPH** *012

WARACZYNSKI, Susan Ellen. 744 S WEBSTER AVE 54301 #056-06-1979 L1981 **AN** *020 †05

WARD, Kay Lynn. 835 S VAN BUREN ST 54301 #018-03-2000 L2006 **NPM** *020 †55 ‡

WARGOWSKI, David Stephan. 835 S VAN BUREN ST 54301 #056-05-1985 L1990 **PD** *020 †19,55

WARPINSKI, James Robt. 519 S MONROE AVE 54301 #056-05-1977 L1984 **AI** *020 †55,03

WARPINSKI, Luke Thos. 2100 RIVERSIDE DR 54301 #056-06-1985 L1986 **FM** *020 †18 ‡

WATSON, Christopher. 725 S WEBSTER AVE STE 215 54301 #056-05-1980 L1981 **FM MDM** *020 †18

WATSON, Jo Ann. ■ 54301 #056-05-1980 L1981 **FM** *062 †18

WEINHOLD, Frank Meredith. 425 ARROWHEAD DR 54301 #056-05-1966 L1968 **R** *020 †80

WELLS, Susan Jane. 2793 LINEVILLE RD 54313 #056-05-1991 L1995 **PD** *020 †55

WENCK, Mark Eric. 835 S VAN BUREN ST, ST. VINCENT HOSPITAL 54301 #025-07-1981 L1983 **AN** *020 †05

WENTWORTH, Alan F. ■ 54301 #018-03-1956 L1970 **NS AM** *071 †25

WERNER, Linda. 835 S VAN BUREN ST 54301 #019-02-1987 L1988 **IM** *020 †20

WESTENBERG, Scott Curtis. 164 N BROADWAY 54303 #056-05-1988 L1991 **EM** *020 †16

WIACEK, Marzena. 54311 #305-01-2001 L2007 **PCP** *100

WIEST, Mark Eugene. 2710 EXECUTIVE DR, P O BOX 19070 54304 #037-01-1977 L2004 **FM IMG** *030 †18

WILKINS, Thomas James. 2845 GREENBRIER RD 54311 #056-05-2000 L2001 **PM** *020 †60

WILSON, Kafi. 835 S VAN BUREN ST 54301 #001-02-2001 L2006 **IM** *020 †20

WILSON, Roderick Bernius. 1931 W TELEMARK CIR 54313 #026-04-1984 L1985 **AN PME** *020 †05

WINBURN, Kimberly Ann. 2845 GREENBRIER RD, STE 420 54311 #056-05-1996 L2000 **OBG** *020 †30

WINSTON, James Frederick. ■ 54313 #028-03-1979 L1983 **PD** *020 †55

WITMAN, Jane Kay. 164 N BROADWAY 54303 #056-06-1991 L1996 **EM** *020 †16

WOKHLU, Nina. 744 S WEBSTER AVE, 2ND FL 54301 #033-05-1998 L2005 **CD** *020 †20

WOLBERG, Faith Lena. 54304 #018-03-1978 L1982 **N** *074

WOLFRAM, Christopher M. 704 S WEBSTER AVE 54301 #056-06-2000 L2007 **IC** *020 †20

WURTH, Jason Theodore. 1630 COMMANCHE AVE 54313 #046-01-1995 L2002 **FM** *020 †18

YAP, Wen Tjoen. 720 S VAN BUREN ST STE 301 54301 #056-14-1975 L2004 **U EM** *020 †95

ZAHN, Scott Gerald. 2253 W MASON ST, AURORA BAYCARE HEALTH CENT 54303 #026-04-1991 L1992 **PD** *020 †55

ZANKOUL, Fuad E. 1726 SHAWANO AVE 54303 #605-01-1992 L2002 **TS** *020 †85,90 ‡

ZENT, Steve A. 2253 W MASON ST, STE 200 54303 #020-12-1997 L1999 **OS** *020

ZIMMERMAN, Donald Alfred. 2845 GREENBRIER RD 54311 #056-05-1979 L1982 **PD** *020 †55

ZIMMERMAN, Robert Chas. 164 N BROADWAY 54303 #056-05-1977 L1981 **EM** *020 †20

ZIMMERMANN, Kolleen L. 715 SUPERIOR RD, STE 120 54311 #056-06-1995 L1996 **D** *020 †15

ZONDLO, Joseph Geo. 2333 RIVERSIDE DR 54301 #056-05-1966 L1967 **A PDA** *020 †55 ‡

GREEN LAKE – GREEN LAKE

BARBOUR, James Humphrey. ■ 54941 #056-05-1946 L1947 **AN** *071 †05

CHIER, Dean Richard. ■ 54941 #056-06-1989 L1990 **FM** *020 †18

MUELLER, Gustave Chas E. ■ 54941 #024-01-1957 L1965 **TS TRS** *071 †85,90

ROGERS, William Kirke. ■ 54941 #056-05-2008 *012

GREENDALE – MILWAUKEE

ANDERSON, Robert Francis. 4745 STRATFORD DR 53129 #665-01-2002 L2003 **AN** *020

GROGAN, Michael John. ■ 53129 #056-06-2006 **DR** *012

HERT, Robert C. ■ 53129 #056-05-1975 L1976 **AN** *075

KRAUTKRAMER, Ronald R. ■ 53129 #038-41-1965 L1966 **GP** *071 †50

LAMEKA, Peter, Jr. 7930 W EDGERTON AVE 53129 #056-06-1960 L1961 **AN** *071 †05

LUBING, John Flint. 6601 NORTHWAY # D 53129 #396-04-1980 L1981 **IM** *020 †20

MATHEWSON, Randy Chris. 6601 NORTHWAY # D 53129 #056-06-1979 L1980 **IM** *020 †20

RODRIGUEZ, Humberto A. ■ 53129 #056-05-1982 L1983 **IM** *020 †20

SHAKIR, Mohammed Ebrahim. ■ 53129 #030-06-2005 L2007 **PD** *012

STONELY, Troy Brent. ■ 53129 #028-34-2004 L2005 **DR** *012

TAN, Leonilo Damian. ■ 53129 #748-02-1976 **IM** *100

WALSH-KELLY, Christine M. 6329 PARKVIEW RD 53129 #016-43-1977 L1979 **PEM** *020 †55

ZAMORA, Alfredo P, Jr. ■ 53129 #748-01-1955 L1972 **GP** *071

GREENFIELD – MILWAUKEE

AGUILAR, Francisco J. 5381 S 48TH ST, GREENFIELD WI 53220 53220 #429-01-1944 **EM ID** *020

ALICDAN, Christina Rivera. ■ 53220 #030-06-2004 **OBG** *012

BARTON, James Robt. 4600 W LOOMIS RD 53220 #055-01-1971 L1976 **OTO** *020 †45

BRUEGGEMAN, Robert Edward. 4848 S 76TH ST STE 210 53220 #056-06-1996 L2001 **MPD** *020 †20,55

BRUMWELL, Melanie Marie. ■ 53221 #056-06-2008 *012

CEESAY, Fatoumata. ■ 53221 #016-42-2004 L2006 **PD** *020

CHANG, Denise Marie. 4131 W LOOMIS RD, STE 300 53221 #035-09-2002 L2003 **PM** *020

COOPER-YOUNG, Helen M. ■ 53228 #024-07-1949 L1958 **FOP PTH** *020

DOMINSKI, Cheryl J. 4848 S 76TH ST STE 210 53220 #016-01-1997 L2001 **PD IM** *020 †20,55

DRESCHER, Peter. 4448 W LOOMIS RD, STE 100 53220 #409-37-1988 L1994 **VIR** *020 †80

ERDELT, Kurt Allan. ■ 53220 #056-06-2007 *012

FAGAN, Ann M. 5332 S 46TH ST, ANESTHESIOLOGY ASSOC. OF W 53220 #002-01-1969 L1973 **AN** *020 †05

FRENN, Recia Louise. ■ 53228 #056-06-2007 L2007 **OBG** *012

KEANE, Sean Declan. ■ 53228 #539-02-2000 L2006 **GS** *100

KOMOZEC, Pero Gojko. 2745 W LAYTON AVE, STE 206 53221 #957-07-1979 L1992 **FM** *020 †18

LAHIRI, Prasanta K. 4448 W LOOMIS RD 53220 #495-38-1962 L1976 **IM PA** *020 †20

LIU, Cheng-Chi. 4666 S 35TH ST 53221 #056-06-1962 L1965 **PD** *071

MACAK, James Richard. 6901 W EDGERTON AVE 53220 #056-06-1980 L1981 **OBG** *020

MACCOUX, Darin Allen. 4448 W LOOMIS RD, STE 100 53220 #056-05-1993 L1994 **FM** *020 †18

MANDICH, Milka. 4448 W LOOMIS RD, STE 102 53220 #056-05-1991 L1992 **FM** *020 †18

MAYR, James Francis. 4715 S 39TH ST 53221 #056-06-1971 L1972 **OM UM** *020 †70

MENDOZA-LEMES, Maria N. 4448 W LOOMIS RD STE 100, LAKESHORE MEDICAL CLINIC, 53220 #014-01-2000 L2002 **FM** *020 †18

MOHIUDDIN, Maaz Syed. ■ 53220 #056-06-2008 *012

NEFF, Donald Alan. ■ 53220 #056-06-2008 *012

ORAVETZ, Thomas Gerard. 4432 S 113TH ST 53228 #056-06-1983 L1984 **NS** *020

PAREKH, Ajitkumar M. 4448 W LOOMIS RD, STE 100 53220 #496-38-1971 L1998 **PUD** *020 †20

POLACHECK, Elizabeth Anne. 8575 W FOREST HOME AVE, STE 50 53228 #056-06-1990 L1994 **PM** *020 †60

PRINTZ, Magnolia Cagang. ■ 53228 #056-05-2008 *012

SALUJA, Rajit. 4448 W LOOMIS RD STE 202 53220 #056-05-1988 L1997 **ORS** *020 †40

SHAH, Hemant Bharat. ■ 53220 #016-11-2004 L2005 **DR** *012

SHIN, Kwan Je. ■ 53228 #583-04-1956 L1978 **P** *071

STEVEN, Gary C. 8585 W FOREST HOME AVE, ALLERGY, ASTHMA & SINUS CE 53228 #056-06-1991 L1992 **AI** *020 †20,03

TAN, Aileen Serrano. 4448 W LOOMIS RD, STE 204 53220 #748-08-1987 L1998 **IM** *020 †20

TOMBULOGLU, Bedriye. 4325 S 60TH ST 53220 #902-03-1968 L1978 **CLP GP** *020 †50

TOVAR, Mauricio. 4931 S 27TH ST STE 100 53221 #264-04-1984 L1990 **OBG** *020 †30

YOUNG, Kathryn Adele. ■ 53221 #034-01-2002 L2005 **CCP** *012 †55

GREENLEAF – BROWN

KAGEN, Marvin Stanley. ■ 54126 #016-11-1941 L1948 **D** *071

GREENVILLE – OUTAGAMIE

ALEXANDER, Darya Ann. W6981 PARKVIEW DR 54942 #019-02-1999 L2004 **FM** *020 †18

KAPRELIAN, Vallie Michael. W6981 PARKVIEW DR, AFFINITY MEDICAL GROUP 54942 #056-05-1996 L1999 **FM** *020 †18

LATHROP CAPAUL, Kari L. W6981 PARKVIEW DR 54942 #056-05-1998 L1999 **FM** *020 †18

PRICE, David Leland. W6941 ROCKDALE LN 54942 #056-05-1969 L1972 **FM** *020 †18

PRICE, Robin Terese. W6981 PARKVIEW DR, AFFINITY MEDICAL GROUP 54942 #030-06-1982 L1985 **FM** *020 †18

GREENWOOD – CLARK

DEAN, Russell Allyn. ■ 54437 #026-04-1970 L1983 **FM** *020 †18

GROSSMAN, Stuart Alan. ■ 54437 #035-45-1973 L1976 **ON IM** *020 †20

JANSSEN, Gary James. 102 CANNERY ST 54437 #056-05-1972 L1979 **FM** *020 †18

HAGER CITY – PIERCE

WEILAND, Louis H. ■ 54014 #056-06-1964 L1966 **PTH** *071 †50

■ = Address Information Privacy Protected

HALES CORNERS – MILWAUKEE

BAUER, Mark Ahrens. 11035 W FOREST HOME AVE 53130 #056-06-1973 L1974 **ORS** *020 †40

BERG, Jennifer Kaye. ■ 53130 #056-06-2008 *012

CLEMENCE, James Allen. 6080 S 108TH ST 53130 #056-06-1960 L1962 **GP** *020

CLEMENCE, Mark Alan. 6080 S 108TH ST 53130 #422-01-1986 L1993 **IM PD** *020 †20

CZAJKA, John Jos. 11035 W FOREST HOME AVE, FOREST VIEW PEDIATRICS SC 53130 #056-06-1956 L1959 **PD** *071

DORRINGTON, Arthur Jordan. 11035 W FOREST HOME AVE, STE 105 53130 #056-06-1972 L1973 **PD** †55

DORRINGTON, Daniel Jordan. 11035 W FOREST HOME AVE 53130 #056-06-2001 L2003 **PD** *020 †55

GENTILE, Jeffrey David. 6080 S 108TH ST 53130 #056-06-2004 L2005 **FM** *020 †18

GIANNINI, Mary Therese. 11035 W FOREST HOME AVE, FOREST VIEW PEDIATRICS 53130 #017-20-1999 L2003 **PD** *020 †55

GRUNSKE, Laurie Ann. 11035 W FOREST HOME AVE, STE 105 53130 #056-06-1989 L1990 **PD** *020 †55

HARTMANN, Robert Gerard. 11035 W FOREST HOME AVE 53130 #056-06-1985 L1986 **PD** *020 †55

HARVEY, Steven Andrew. 11035 W FOREST HOME AVE 53130 #030-06-1985 L1986 **OTO** *020 †45

KUWAYAMA, S Paul. 11035 W FOREST HOME AVE 53130 #572-29-1959 L1968 **AI PDA** *020 †55,03

LAUTZ, David Alan. 11035 W FOREST HOME AVE, STE 105 53130 #017-20-1981 L1982 **PD** *020 †55

LEONHARDT, Margaret M. 5757 S 108TH ST 53130 #056-06-1983 L1984 **FM** *020 †18

MARTIN, Eric Fleming. ■ 53130 #422-01-2007 **IM** *012

MILLEN, Steven Jon. 11035 W FOREST HOME AVE 53130 #056-06-1973 L1974 **OTO NO** *020 †45

MILLER, Robert John. 11035 W FOREST HOME AVE 53130 #056-05-1976 L1977 **PD** *020 †55

MOHIUDDIN, Syed Gouse. 11800 W WOODLAND CIR 53130 #496-24-1995 L1999 **IM** *020 †20

MOLONEY, Michael Eugene. ■ 53130 #539-03-1975 L1977 **GPM FM** *020 †70 ‡

PETERSON, Vanessa Lynn. ■ 53130 #305-01-2007 **IM** *012

RANTA, Marylyn Sutton. 11035 W FOREST HOME AVE, STE 105 53130 #017-20-1982 L1985 **PD** *020 †55

SMUCKLER, Mark Burton. 12065 W JANESVILLE RD 53130 #056-05-1966 L1967 **CHP P** *020 †75

ZUKOWSKI, Chris Michael. 11035 W FOREST HOME AVE, STE 105 53130 #056-06-1991 L1993 **PD** *020 †55

HANCOCK – WAUSHARA

PEARSALL, Margaret Mary. ■ 54943 #056-06-1994 L1995 **FM EM** *020 †18

HARTFORD – WASHINGTON

ABU-SALIH, Majdi M. 1640 E SUMNER ST 53027 #575-02-1991 L1996 **PD** *020 †55

ALLEN, Jeffrey Steven. 1640 E SUMNER ST 53027 #030-05-1982 L1983 **FM** *020 †18

AL-WATHIQUI, Mahmood H. 110 LONE OAK LN 53027 #020-02-1981 L1986 **CD IM** *020 †20

BRODISH, Robert John. 110 LONE OAK LN 53027 #016-43-1988 L1995 **GS VS** *020 †85

BUBOLTZ, Jerome Benedict. 1032 E SUMNER ST 53027 #025-12-1992 L1993 **IM** *020 †20

BULLIS, Paul Vander. 1640 E SUMNER ST 53027 #056-05-1996 L1999 **FM** *020 †18 ‡

BUTLER, Jeffrey J. 1004 E SUMNER ST 53027 #020-12-1981 L1982 **ORS** *020 †40

CHEN, David. 1640 E SUMNER ST, AURORA MEDICAL GROUP 53027 #038-40-1985 L1992 **IM GE** *020 †20

DUNICAN, Annmarie Lucy. 1640 E SUMNER ST 53027 #033-05-1996 L2004 **GS** *020 †85

EIS, Michael Johannes. 110 LONE OAK LN 53027 #038-41-1997 L2001 **P** *020 †75 ‡

FABICH, Douglas Ryan. 1032 E SUMNER ST 53027 #056-06-1975 L1975 **PTH NM** *071 †50,28

FLORESCU, Luiza-Irina Nic. 1640 E SUMNER ST, AURORA HEALTH CENTER 53027 #781-01-1995 L2003 **IM** *020 †20

GEIGER, Chas Stephen, Jr. 1032 E SUMNER ST 53027 #016-43-1963 L1966 **IM** *071 †20

GORELIK, Maxim. 1032 E SUMNER ST 53027 #016-01-2001 L2006 **N** *020

GRITT, Ronald Geo. 1640 E SUMNER ST 53027 #056-05-1973 L1974 **PD** *020 †55

GUPTE, Uday Vasant. 1004 E SUMNER ST 53027 #495-17-1965 L1979 **GE IM** *020 †20

HAAS, Deborah Suzanne. 402 W SUMNER ST, SYNERGY HEALTH HARTFORD 53027 #056-06-2001 L2004 **FM** *020 †18

HAGLER, Nathaniel Geo. 1004 E SUMNER ST 53027 #023-01-1977 L1997 **DR** *020 †80

HEINZEN, James Scott. 1032 E SUMNER ST, HARTFORD EMERGENCY PHYSICA 53027 #056-05-1996 L1997 **FM EM** *020 †18 ‡

HERRELL, Daniel Wayne. 110 LONE OAK LN 53027 #056-05-1975 L1980 **PUD IM** *020 †20

HICKMAN, Bruce Edward. 1004 E SUMNER ST 53027 #056-06-1996 L1998 **FM** *020 †18

HILDEBRANDT, Amber E. 110 LONE OAK LN 53027 #056-06-2001 L2003 **FM** *020 †18

KASHYAP, Kiran. 110 LONE OAK LN 53027 #495-36-1993 L1997 **CD** *020 †20

LEWIS, Richard Allen. 110 LONE OAK LN 53027 #016-11-1994 L1995 **FM** *020 †18

LIEDTKE, Robert Russell. 110 LONE OAK LN 53027 #016-11-1995 L1996 **FM** *020 †18

LIETHEN, Patricia Jean. 1640 E SUMNER ST 53027 #056-06-1987 L1988 **FM** *020 †18

MALLY, Michael Joseph. 1004 E SUMNER ST 53027 #056-06-1962 L1964 **IM** *071

MANSHEIM, Bernard Jos. 1032 E SUMNER ST 53027 #018-03-1943 L1947 **OPH** *071 †35

MAUTZ, Alan Paul. ■ 53027 #016-11-2004 L2005 **DR** *012

MC CROSSIN, James Murray. 1004 E SUMNER ST, HARTFORD PARKVIEW CLINIC 53027 #064-01-1990 L1995 *100

MEHDI, Syed H. 110 LONE OAK LN 53027 #704-02-1985 L1997 **GE** *020 †20

MORETTI, Scott Thos. 1640 E SUMNER ST 53027 #016-43-1990 L1994 **OPH** *020 †35

NAJEEB, Waleed S. 1640 E SUMNER ST 53027 #875-01-1983 L1991 **PUD IM** *020 †20

NICKELS, Robert John. ■ 53027 #017-20-1955 L1956 **GS** *071 †85

NIENHUIS, David Mark. 110 LONE OAK LN 53027 #056-05-1987 L1992 **OTO** *020 †45

PAYKEL, Jacquelyn Marie. 110 LONE OAK LN 53027 #056-05-1997 L1999 **OBG** *020 †30

PFOTENHAUER, Joseph R. 1640 E SUMNER ST 53027 #056-06-1983 L1984 **IM** *020 †20

PIRVANESCU, Radu Eugen. 1640 E SUMNER ST 53027 #781-01-1993 L2003 **IM** *020 †20

RIVERA, Manuel A. 1032 E SUMNER ST 53027 #048-12-1983 L1985 **EM** *020

SELTHAFNER, John V. 1032 E SUMNER ST 53027 #056-05-1988 L1990 **AN** *012

SMITH, David Seibert, III. 402 W SUMNER ST, SYNERGY HEALTH HARTFORD 53027 #008-02-1980 L1981 **FM EM** *020 †18

SNYDER, Matthew Lane. 1640 E SUMNER ST 53027 #019-02-1998 L2004 **PTH** *020

STICKNEY, Peggy Ann. 110 LONE OAK LN 53027 #056-06-2002 L2003 **FM** *020 †18

TKACHUK, Megan Ann. 1640 E SUMNER ST 53027 #056-06-2003 L2004 **FM** *020 †18

TYE, Michael Kenneth. 1640 E SUMNER ST 53027 #056-06-1996 L1997 **FM** *020 †18

WEBER, Eric Frank. 1640 E SUMNER ST 53027 #056-06-1975 L1978 **IM** *020 †20

WILLIAMSON, Terry Sewell. 1640 E SUMNER ST 53027 #060-02-1986 L1996 **FM** *020 †18

HARTLAND – WAUKESHA

ADAMSON, Andrew James. ■ 53029 #056-06-1998 L1999 **DR** *020 †80

ATLEE, John Light. ■ 53029 #041-13-1967 L1973 **AN** *071 †05

BERK, Richard Alan. ■ 53029 #056-06-1956 L1957 **PD** *020 †55

BONG, Matthew Robert. 1500 WALNUT RIDGE DR 53029 #056-06-1999 L2006 **OTR** *100

BRUNO, James Vincent. 600 WALNUT RIDGE DR 53029 #056-05-1985 L1990 **ORS** *020 †40

BUDARAPU, Suseela. 700 N PONDEROSA DR, 700 N PONDEROSA DRIVE 53029 #495-50-1964 L1982 **OBG GYN** *020 †30

COPE, Miriam Pya. 1500 WALNUT RIDGE DR, PROHEALTH CARE MEDICAL CEN 53029 #016-01-1991 L1992 **FM** *020 †18

FICKEL, Ronald Dean. 1500 WALNUT RIDGE DR 53029 #018-03-1998 L1999 **FM** *020 †18

GERALTS, Mary Lou. 600 WALNUT RIDGE DR 53029 #056-06-1986 L1993 **IM** *020 †20

HANNULA, Todd Taylor. 600 WALNUT RIDGE DR 53029 #056-05-1989 L1998 **ORS** *020 †40

JANOWAK, Michael Chas. 1500 WALNUT RIDGE DR 53029 #016-43-1972 L1973 **OTO A** *020 †45 ‡

KAMARAJU, Sailaja C. 600 WALNUT RIDGE DR 53029 #495-50-1993 L2002 **HO** *020 †20

KHAN, Fawad Karim. 600 WALNUT RIDGE DR 53029 #704-09-1986 L1997 **IM** *020 †20

KUGLITSCH, John Francis. ■ 53029 #056-06-1969 L1973 **IM** *071 †20

KULTGEN, Karin I. 1500 WALNUT RIDGE DR 53029 #056-06-1985 L1986 **FM** *020 †18

KWONG, Helen Dasal. 600 WALNUT RIDGE DR, WILKINSON MEDICAL CLINIC 53029 #016-11-1995 L1997 **IM** *020 †20

LEE, Kimberly Jane. ■ 53029 #025-07-1998 L2001 **CCP** *020 †55

LINDSTROM, Dean Richard. 1500 WALNUT RIDGE DR 53029 #016-01-1999 L2001 **OTO** *020 †45

MARTINELLI, Dean Louis. 1500 WALNUT RIDGE DR 53029 #016-43-1971 L1972 **OTO A** *020 †45

MERKOW, Steven Jon. 1500 WALNUT RIDGE DR 53029 #056-05-1980 L1985 **ORS OSM** *020 †40

NOVACEK, Paul James. W329N8390 WEST SHORE DR 53029 #056-06-1964 L1965 **AN** *071 †05

PAMULAPATI, Srinivasa Rao. 1604 E JUNIPER WAY, ST JOES REGIONAL MEDICAL C 53029 #496-24-1990 L2000 **IM** *020 †20

PANCHAL, Arti. ■ 53029 #056-06-1990 L1991 **AN** *020 †05

PHELAN, Kathleen Marie. 1500 WALNUT RIDGE DR 53029 #018-03-1994 L1995 **FM** *020 †18

POPPENS, Arthur D. ■ 53029 #016-21-1952 L1953 **EM TRS** *071 †85

RIDLEY, John F. 105 NORTH AVE 53029 #056-06-1950 L1951 **GP** *072

SERB, Cheryl Christine. 1500 WALNUT RIDGE DR 53029 #037-01-2000 L2001 **FM** *020 †18

SHANDER, James Edward. 600 WALNUT RIDGE DR 53029 #016-02-1982 L1986 **PD ADL** *020 †55

SMITH, Franklin L, Jr. 600 WALNUT RIDGE DR 53029 #016-06-1982 L1987 **U** *020 †95

STENGER, George Scott. ■ 53029 #016-76-1970, ▲ L1971 **FM** *071 †18

SWANSON, Karen Ann. 600 WALNUT RIDGE DR 53029 #056-05-1994 L1996 **PD** *020 †55

UY, Michael Mario. 1500 WALNUT RIDGE DR 53029 #056-05-1991 L1992 **FM** *020 †18 ‡

WARTH, Robert Lee. ■ 53029 #056-06-1968 L1969 **GYN** *071 †30

WAY, Catherine Elizabeth. 1500 WALNUT RIDGE DR, PROHEALTH CARE MED-HARTLND 53029 #056-06-1996 L1997 **FM** *020 †18

YACOBOZZI, Margaret Anton. ■ 53029 #056-06-2008 *012

ZOREK, Karen Lynn. 600 WALNUT RIDGE DR 53029 #016-01-1993 L1994 **PD** *020 †55

HAYWARD – SAWYER

ANDREI, Vicentiu. 11134 N STATE ROAD 77, HAYWARD CLINIC 54843 #781-01-1979 L1995 **FM GS** *020 †18

BAERTSCH, Lloyd Marvin. 11134 N STATE ROAD 77 54843 #056-05-1956 L1957 **GP** *071

BERLAGE, Ann Renee. 11113 N FULLINGTON RD 54843 #056-06-1982 L1983 **FM** *020 †18

BLEIDORN, David Francis. 11134 N STATE ROAD 77, HAYWARD CLINIC 54843 #056-05-2000 L2003 **IM** *020 †20

CERMAN, Jennifer Elizabet. ■ 54843 #016-01-2005 **PD** *012

DECKER, John Paul. 11128 N STATE ROAD 77, FAMILY CARE CLINIC 54843 #026-04-1976 L2007 **FM** *020 †18

DUNLAP, Sabrina Ann. 11128 N STATE ROAD 77 54843 #056-05-1994 L1997 **FM** *020 †18

EDER, Richard Lee. 221 KANSAS AV 54843 #019-02-1965 L1969 **LM IMG** *072

FERRER, Modesto Marcial. 16184 W WOODLAND HILLS DR 54843 #748-07-1959 L1972 **GP GS** *020

FOGARTY, James Patrick. 11128 N STATE ROAD 77, DBA: FOGARTY SURGICAL SERV 54843 #056-05-1972 L1974 **GS** *020 †85

GILBERG, Nina June. 11128 N STATE ROAD 77 54843 #026-04-1984 L1985 **FM** *020 †18

GOTTSCHALK, Paul G, Jr. ■ 54843 #016-11-1960 L1968 **N** *071 †75

HALLQUIST, Roberta Ruth. 11134 N STATE ROAD 77, DULUTH CLINIC-HAYWARD 54843 #026-04-1980 L1988 **N** *020 †75

HARMSEN, Jody Marie. 11128 N STATE ROAD 77 54843 #016-02-2002 L2005 **FM** *020 †18

HENGEL, James Alvin, Jr. 9925 N RICHARDSON BAY RD 54843 #026-04-1967 L1990 **AN** *071 †05

HOFFMAN, Douglas F. 11134 N STATE ROAD 77, DULUTH CLINIC - HAYWARD 54843 #050-02-1988 L1991 **FSM FM** *020 †18

KINTZINGER, Thomas Lee. 12550 W MORELAND RD, P O BOX 67 54843 #018-03-1979 L1983 **DR** *020

LEFF, Robert Dana. 11134 N STATE ROAD 77, HAYWARD CLINIC 54843 #017-20-1977 L1985 **IM RHU** *020 †20

LUEDKE, Matthew James. 11134 N STATE ROAD 77, HAYWARD CLINIC 54843 #030-05-1993 L1996 **FM** *020 †18

MALCOLM, Dayle Quigley. 15910 W COMPANY LAKE RD 54843 #041-13-1988 L1996 **FM** *020 †18

MALCOLM, Harry Douglas. 11134 N STATE ROAD 77 54843 #041-13-1988 L1996 **FM** *020 †18

MOHAMED, Imtiaz. 11040 N STATE ROAD 77, HAYWARD AREA MEMORIAL HOSP 54843 #495-45-1991 L1999 *020 †20

NOVAK, Dorothy Agnes. 11040 N STATE ROAD 77 54843 #056-05-1977 L1978 **EM FM** *020 †18,16

RADUEGE, Elizabeth Marie. 11134 N STATE ROAD 77, DULUTH CLINIC - HAYWARD 54843 #056-06-1993 L1996 **FM** *020 †18

RUGOWSKI, James Anthony. 7804 N COUNTY ROAD K 54843 #056-05-1971 L1972 **P** *020 †75

RYAN, John Francis. 11040 N STATE ROAD 77 54843 #016-43-1959 L2000 **GS** *071 †85 ‡

STRAPON, Paul, III. 13380 W TREPANIA RD 54843 #017-20-1969 L1970 **FM** *020

SWENSON, Robert R. 11040 N STATE ROAD 77 54843 #026-04-1979 L1982 **EM** *020 †18

VESELY, Ronald. 11128 N STATE ROAD 77 54843 #016-11-1983 L1987 **EM** *020 †20

WARREN, Scott Harold. 11134 N STATE ROAD 77, SOUTH SHORE ORTHOPEDICS 54843 #056-06-1982 L1988 **ORS** *020 †40

HERBSTER — BAYFIELD

BUCY, James G. ■ 54844 #016-06-1962 L1963 **U** *071 †95

HERTEL — BURNETT

DEVLIN, Larry Patrick. ST CROIX CENTER 54845 #026-04-1989 L1995 **FM** *071 †18

HIGH BRIDGE — ASHLAND

CAMPION, Tee Selmon. PO BOX 5, RR 1 54846 #048-13-1974 L1990 **ORS** *020 †40

HIGHLAND — IOWA

SONG, Gloria Unyoung. 600 S HIGHLAND, DEPT OF INTERNAL MEDICINE 53543 #041-02-1998 L2004 **NEP** *012 †20

STODDARD, Steven Carlton. ■ 53543 #056-05-1970 L1978 **ORS** *020 †40

HILLSBORO — VERNON

PATEL, Sheila Ambalal. 400 WATER AVE 54634 #056-05-1994 L2001 **FM** *020 †18

RESAN, Thomas Kristz. 300 WATER AVE, P O BOX 546 54634 #056-05-1970 L1971 **GP EM** *020 †18

SANCHEZ, Lawrence David. S1901 COUNTY HIGHWAY F 54634 #018-03-1998 L1999 **FM** *020 †18

SHAH, Sandhya. 300 WATER AVE, HILLSBORO CLINIC 54634 #654-01-1986 L1989 **IM** *020 †20

TAYLOR, Stewart Ferguson, Jr. 400 WATER AVE 54634 #016-02-1974 L1980 **ORS** *020 †40

WILLIAMS, Warren Lee. ■ 54634 #007-02-1962 L1999 **GP** *071 †18

HOBART — BROWN

BERTLER, David Eugene. 1400 SCHEURING RD, DERMATOLOGY ASSOCIATES OF 54115 #023-12-1985 L1988 **D** *020 †15

BINARD, Joseph Elise Chas. 525 AIRPORT DR, ONEIDA COMMUNITY HEALTH CE 54155 #165-04-1958 L1966 **U** *030 ‡

CANNELLA, N Kendall. ■ 54155 #004-01-1980 L1984 **GP** *020

DIAZ, Yoloxochitl. ■ 54155 #649-13-1994 L2001 **PD** *020 †55

FULLER, Richard Eugene. 525 AIRPORT DR, HEALTH CENTER 54155 #051-04-1988 L1992 **PD** *020 †18,55

HAASE, Michael Anthony. 525 AIRPORT DR, ONEIDA COMM HLTH CLNC 54155 #016-43-1980 L1983 **IM** *020 †20

LACEY, James Vincent. 525 AIRPORT DR, POB 365 54155 #025-01-1970 L1977 **IM HEM** *020 †20

MC GUAN, Austin Regan. ■ 54313 #016-06-1972 L1973 **AN** *071 †05

MC INTYRE, James Angus. ■ 54155 #056-05-1958 L1960 **PTH** *071 †50

SEHRING, Frederick G. ■ 54155 #056-06-1956 L1957 **GYN GO** *071 †30

SHAH, Syed Jirgis. ■ 54155 #495-51-1995 L2007 **PCC** *020 †20

VIR, Ravinder. 525 AIRPORT DR, ONEIDA COMMUNITY HEALTH CE 54155 #495-45-1989 L1995 **IM** *020 †20

HOLCOMBE — CHIPPEWA

KOCH, James W. 29074 263RD ST 54745 #056-05-1950 L1951 **GP** *071

HOLMEN — LA CROSSE

BINN, Martha Christine. 520 AMY DR 54636 #056-06-2001 L2002 **FM MDM** *020 †18

HANSON, Pamela Ann. 520 AMY DR 54636 #026-04-1984 L1995 **PD** *020 †55

OHLROGGE, Dennis Donn. 520 AMY DR 54636 #026-04-1979 L1980 **FM** *020 †18

WITCIK, Michael Adam. ■ 54636 #056-05-2007 **IM** *012

HORICON — DODGE

LEE, Joann Kathy. 610 WASHINGTON ST, UNIV OF WI MADISON 53032 #038-44-2001 L2004 **FM** *020 †18

PAJARILLO, Ramon Sumagit. 610 WASHINGTON ST 53032 #748-13-1985 L1994 **FM** *020 †18

HORTONVILLE — OUTAGAMIE

KHANNA, Ann. ■ 54944 #422-01-1986 L1988 **PD** *075

HOULTON — SAINT CROIX

SYDLEWSKI, Wendy Lee. ■ 54082 #026-04-2004 L2004 **OTO** *100

HOWARDS GROVE — SHEBOYGAN

REMINGTON, Robert Joseph. 620 S WISCONSIN DR, HOWARDS GROVE CENTER 53083 #025-12-1997 L1998 **FM** *020 †18

HUBERTUS — WASHINGTON

BALLIET, Kelly Andrew. 4360 HIGHWAY 167, EMERGENCY ROOM SPECIALISTS 53033 #056-05-1988 L1989 **ID IM** *020 †20

CIURLIK, Elizabeth Wilson. 3055 HUBERTUS RD, HUBERTUS CLINIC 53033 #056-05-1989 L1993 **MPD** *020 †20,55

FANCHER, Jennifer Marie. ■ 53033 #056-06-2008 *012

JOHNSON, Gwen A. 3055 HUBERTUS RD, AURORA ADVANCED HEALTHCARE 53033 #016-42-1988 L1989 **FM** *020 †18

KELLEY, Philip Douglas. ■ 53033 #016-45-1992 L1998 **FOP** *062 †50

MILLER, Michael Robert. 3055 HUBERTUS RD, HUBERTUS CLINIC 53033 #056-06-1989 L1991 **FM** *020 †18

HUDSON — SAINT CROIX

ADORN, Steven Frank. 403 STAGELINE RD 54016 #026-04-1989 L1992 **FM** *020 †18

ANDERSON, Myron Geo. 400 WISCONSIN ST 54016 #026-04-1947 L1950 **IM GP** *071

ANKEL, Felix Karlgeorge. 400 WISCONSIN ST, HUDSON MERICK CENTER 54016 #056-05-1989 L1991 **EM** *020 †16

BIROS, Teresa Lee. 403 STAGELINE RD, STE 1 54016 #048-14-1987 L2001 **FM** *020 †18

CAMPBELL, Kari Mc Intire. 403 STAGELINE RD, STE 1 54016 #026-08-1990 L1993 **PD** *020 †55

CARR, Mary. 405 STAGELINE RD, HUDSON HOSPITAL 54016 #025-01-1980 L1984 **EM IM** *020 †16

COMFORT, Thomas Krebs. 405 STAGELINE RD 54016 #026-04-1990 L2007 **ORS** *020 †40

COOK, Jeremy William. ■ 54016 #026-04-2008 *012

DAHL, Dana Marie. 403 STAGELINE RD 54016 #026-04-2000 L2003 **FM** *020 †18

DIEFENBACH, Jeanne E Dahl. ■ 54016 #026-04-1949 L1996 **IMG** *071

DRUFFNER, Mark Richard. 403 STAGELINE RD 54016 #041-02-1991 L1997 **GS** *020 †18

ENGELS, Donald Henry. ■ 54016 #056-06-1946 L1963 **P** *071

FERMIN, Ruben Espinas. 593 GILBERT RD 54016 #748-10-1965 L1975 **GS** *071

GORDON, Bradley Dean. 405 STAGELINE RD, HUDSON HOSPITAL EMERGENCY 54016 #030-06-1999 L2002 **EM** *020 †16

HALLER, Paul Richard. 405 STAGELINE RD, HUDSON MEDICAL CENTER 54016 #026-04-1984 L1998 **IM** *020 †20

HARTUNG, Dennis Ray. 403 STAGELINE RD, STE 1 54016 #023-12-1990 L2005 **OBG** *020 †30

HASS, Wayne Frederick. 405 STAGELINE RD 54016 #026-04-1971 L1999 **EM IM** *030 †20,16

HELMEN, Kevin Duane. 403 STAGELINE RD, HUDSON PHYSICIANS 54016 #039-05-1984 L1987 **FM EM** *020 †18

HERNANDEZ, Bradley Scott. 405 STAGE LINE, HUDSON MEDICAL CENTER 54016 #018-03-1998 L2001 **EM** *020 †16

HIPPCHEN, Ray C. ■ 54016 #035-06-1961 L1968 **PD FM** *020 †55

HOLLENDER, Heather Lynne. 405 STAGELINE RD, DEPARTMENT OF SURGERY 54016 #026-04-1992 L1998 **HS PS** *020 †65

HUNT, Vincent Robt. ■ 54016 #026-04-1960 L1986 **FM** *071 †18

JACOBSON, Kirk. 403 STAGELINE RD, HUDSON PHYSICIANS 54016 #056-05-1985 L1990 **GS** *020 †85

KAYE, Koren Linda. 400 WISCONSIN ST, HUDSON MEDICAL CENTER 54016 #046-01-1986 L1995 **EM** *020 †16

KRETZ, Michael Jacob. ■ 54016 #056-05-1974 L1975 **FM OBG** *071

LAMON, Richard Paul. 405 STAGELINE RD, HUDSON MEMORIAL HOSPITAL, 54016 #005-12-1972 L1998 **EM FM** *020 †18,16 ‡

LEFEVERE, Robert C. 405 STAGELINE RD, HUDSON HOSPITAL EMERGENCY 54016 #030-06-2001 L2004 **EM** *020 †16

LE TOURNEAU, Barbara C. 400 WISCONSIN ST 54016 #026-04-1975 L2004 **MDM EM** *020 †16

LEYDA, George Wm, Jr. 403 STAGELINE RD, STE 1 54016 #026-04-1992 L1994 **FM** *020 †18

MADIGAN, Joseph Callaghan. ■ 54016 #026-04-2004 L2004 **EM** *100

MATEVA, Vesselina S. 405 STAGELINE RD, HUDSON HOSPITAL 54016 #198-02-1984 L2003 **N** *020 †75

MAYER, Vicki Lynn. 403 STAGELINE RD 54016 #026-04-1974 L1978 **FM FPG** *020 †18 ‡

MC CANN, Patrick John. 403 STAGELINE RD, STE 1 54016 #026-04-1983 L1987 **FM** *020 †18

MC GINNIS, Paul Wm. 403 STAGELINE RD, HUDSON PHYSICIANS 54016 #030-06-1984 L1987 **FM** *020 †18

MC NALLAN, Annette Mary. 403 STAGELINE RD, STE 1 54016 #026-04-1996 L1999 **FM** *020 †18

MOETTUS, Alda Ligita. 405 STAGELINE RD, HUDSON HOSPITAL 54016 #026-04-1994 L2003 **EM** *020 †16

MUSACK, Randy. ■ 54016 #018-75-2002, ▲ L2004 **DR** *100 †80

NAHUM, Avi. 405 STAGELINE RD, HUDSON HOSPITAL 54016 #016-02-1985 L1986 **PUD** *020 †20

NELSON, Scott Gerald. 268 SAINT ANNES PKWY 54016 #026-04-1993 L1994 **AN** *020 †05

NOVAK, Anthony Frank. 2215 VINE ST STE C, EYE SURGERY & LASER CENTER 54016 #026-04-1985 L1989 **OPH GP** *020 †35

PITTMAN, Donna M. ■ 54016 #056-05-1985 L1990 **FM** *074 †18

PLOTNIK, Tammi Sue. 1610 MAXWELL DR, STE 245 54016 #026-04-1998 L2007 **PD** *020 †55

REARDON, Eileen Margaret. 1610 MAXWELL DR, STE 200 54016 #007-02-1992 L1997 **OBG** *020 †30

SCHERTZ, Elizabeth M. 403 STAGELINE RD, HUDSON PHYSICIANS 54016 #026-04-1989 L1994 **PD** *020 †55 ‡

SCHMITZ, Stephen Richard. 403 STAGELINE RD, HUDSON PHYSICIANS 54016 #017-20-1978 L1979 **FM** *020 †18 ‡

SIEGEL, Steven Wm. 401 STAGELINE RD, STE 5 54016 #025-01-1981 L1997 **U** *020 †95

SPAULDING, John Scott. ■ 54016 #016-02-1959 L1982 **PD END** *071 †55

STANNARD, Mark Donald. 403 STAGELINE RD 54016 #026-04-1995 L1998 **FM** *020 †18

STOY, Robert Jos. 403 STAGELINE RD, HUDSON PHYSICIANS 54016 #016-43-1976 L1979 **FM** *020 †18

YOUNG, Gregory Louis. 403 STAGELINE RD, HUDSON PHYSICIANS 54016 #056-06-1998 L1999 **FM** *020 †18

YOUNG, John Burton. 418 N GLOVER RD 54016 #016-02-1966 L1973 **OTO** *071 †45

HURLEY – IRON

BALAS, Mark Stephen. 502 COPPER ST, STE 5 54534 #056-06-1991 L1996 **ORS** *020 †40
HORSWILL, Robert N. 502 COPPER ST 54534 #056-05-1968 L1975 **ORS** *020 †40
MARREN, Thomas Fitzgerald. 501 GRANITE ST 54534 #016-43-2000 L2003 **FM** *020 †18 ‡
SCHROETER, Lea Ann. 501 GRANITE ST, GRAND VIEW CLC-HURLEY 54534
 #056-06-1983 L1984 **PD** *020 †55

IOLA – WAUPACA

HOLLERO, Numeriano, Jr. ■ 54945 #748-01-1960 L1966 **GP** *071

IRON RIVER – BAYFIELD

OGLE, Kim Marie. ■ 54847 #026-04-2006 L2006 **IM** *012

JACKSON – WASHINGTON

BYERLY, Sandra Kay. N168W20060 MAIN ST 53037 #040-02-1978 L1979 **FM** *071 †18
CAMERON, Carey Meyer. W225N16711 CEDAR PARK CT, SYNERGY HEALTH JACKSON 53037
 #056-06-1998 L1999 **FM** *020 †18
CORNELIUS, Peter Lee. W225N16711 CEDAR PARK CT, SYNERGY HEALTH JACKSON 53037
 #056-06-1982 L1983 **FM** *020 †18
RUSSO, Joycelyn Gael. N168W20060 MAIN ST 53037 #056-06-1998 L1999 **FM** *020 †18
SCHACHTER, Alvin J. ■ 53037 #035-06-1966 L1975 **PUD** *020 †20

JANESVILLE – ROCK

ADIET, John A. 849 KELLOGG AVE 53546 #305-01-2004 L2006 **FP** *012
ALKHAN, Muhammad B. 2844 N WRIGHT RD 53546 #875-01-1988 L2001 **CCM** *020 †20
ALMEKY, Essam M. 849 KELLOGG AVE 53546 #915-03-1999 L2007 **FP** *012
ALTBUCH, Arthur Mark. 849 KELLOGG AVE, MERY CLINIC SOUTH 53546 #035-03-1976 L2000
 FPG FSM *030 †18
ANDELIN, Samuel Forsyth. 849 KELLOGG AVE 53546 #305-01-2007 **FP** *012
ANDERSON, Anthony Judd. 1000 MINERAL POINT AVE 53548 #305-01-2007 **FP** *012
ANDERSON, Derek Nathan. 1000 MINERAL POINT AVE 53548 #018-03-2004 L2005 **FM** *020
ANDERSON, Jane Elizabeth. 1010 N WASHINGTON ST 53548 #056-05-2000 L2002 **FM** *020
ANDREAKOS, Thanh Tran. 1000 MINERAL POINT AVE 53548 #048-14-1994 L1998 **EM** *020 †16
ANGEVINE, Mark Patrick. 3524 E MILWAUKEE ST 53546 #038-43-1973 L1974 **FM** *020 †20
ARTER, Deborah Lynn. 35 S MAIN ST, ROCK COUNTY HUMAN SERVICES 53545
 #056-05-1992 L1994 **P PYG** *020 †75
BABUWE-NGOBI, Joy G. 1000 MINERAL POINT AVE 53548 #905-01-1992 L2003 **AN** *020 †05
BAKER, Charles Sydney. 580 N WASHINGTON ST 53548 #016-11-1959 L1963 **IM** *020
BARSNESS, Brigg William. 849 KELLOGG AVE 53546 #034-01-2006 L2008 **FP** *012
BARTZ, Steven David. 849 KELLOGG AVE 53546 #038-41-1995 L2005 **FM FPG** *040 †18
BAUTISTA, Ryndon Negrillo. 3524 E MILWAUKEE ST 53546 #748-02-2001 L2006 **IM** *020 †20
BEACH, Rebecca Ann. 849 KELLOGG AVE 53546 #016-02-1990 L1992 **FM** *040 †18
BEDROSSIAN, Philip Saml. 3430 PALMER DR, 2770 53546 #038-43-1979 L2001 **EM** *020 †16
BERENTSEN, Thomas Richard. 580 N WASHINGTON ST, RIVERVIEW CLINIC 53546
 #056-05-1977 L1981 **N** *020 †75
BEST, Aaron Patrick. 580 N WASHINGTON ST, STE 551 53548 #422-01-2001 L2004 **EM** *020
BETLACH, Dorothy Wittmann. ■ 53548 #056-05-1946 L1949 **AN** *071 †05
BINGOL, Hilary Danielle. 580 N WASHINGTON ST 53548 #422-01-2000 L2004 **IM** *020
BLAGOGEE, Benjamin Omamog. 849 KELLOGG AVE 53546 #690-02-1990 **FP** *012
BOETTCHER, Mark Chas. 580 N WASHINGTON ST, STE 551 53548 #037-01-1991 L1992
 PD *020 †55
BOSTIAN, Karl Eugene. ■ 53548 #036-01-1962 L1963 **PD** *071 †55
BOSWELL, Harold Craig. 1000 MINERAL POINT AVE 53548 #018-03-1973 L1985 **AN** *020 †20
BOWERS, Ronald Kent. 1000 MINERAL POINT AVE 53548 #038-40-1975 L1984 **FM** *020 †18
BRANDT, William Norman. 580 N WASHINGTON ST, STE 551 53548 #017-20-1968 L1973
 GE IM *020 †20
BRICKMAN, David Michael. 1000 MINERAL POINT AVE 53548 #001-02-1970 L1996
 EM FM *020 †18,16
BRODKEY, Frank Donald. 1000 MINERAL POINT AVE, MERCY CLINIC WEST 53548
 #030-06-1979 L1980 **IM CCM** *020 †20
BROOKS, Gregory Daniel. 2540 E US HIGHWAY 14 53545 #030-05-1996 L1998 **AI** *020 †20,03
BRUNS, Cristin Marie. 2540 E US HIGHWAY 14 53545 #028-34-1998 L1999 **END** *020 †20
BUSSA, John Jos. 1000 MINERAL POINT AVE 53548 #048-13-1978 L1988 **OPH** *020 †35
CALLISON, Sue Ann. 113 S FRANKLIN ST 53548 #003-01-1983 L1997 **P CHP** *020 †75
CARIMI, Sanford Allen. 1000 MINERAL POINT AVE 53548 #011-02-1984 L1985 **IM** *020 †20
CARLSON, Edward Ewald. 1000 MINERAL POINT AVE, MERCY HEALTH SYSTEM 53548
 #016-11-1973 L1974 **FM** *020 †18
CASTILLO, Rodrigo A. 3524 E MILWAUKEE ST, MERCY CLINIC EAST 53546 #264-04-1989 L2001
 GE *020 †20
CERVANTES, Christopher W. 580 N WASHINGTON ST, STE 551 53548 #038-40-1987 L1993
 CCM *020 †20
CHARNECKI, George. 1000 MINERAL POINT AVE 53548 #016-11-1964 L1971 **OPH** *020
CHICKS, Calvin Orvis. 37 S MAIN ST, POST OFFICE 8190 53545 #056-05-1956 L1957 **P** *020
CLANFIELD, William Kent. 580 N WASHINGTON ST, STE 551 53548 #016-11-1987 L1990
 IM *020 †20
CODY, Graham Allen. 1 S MAIN ST 53545 #019-02-1986 L1987 **CHP** *020 †75
COOGAN, Michael Vincent. 1000 MINERAL POINT AVE 53548 #016-43-1992 L1995 **EM** *020 †16
CROSIER, Jonathan Pry. 849 KELLOGG AVE 53546 #661-02-2002 L2005 **FM** *020 †18
DE JONGH, Leon Francis. 1000 MINERAL POINT AVE 53548 #056-05-1978 L1979
 DR NM *020 †80
DEMING, Nancy Lynne. 849 KELLOGG AVE 53546 #026-04-1994 L1995 **FM** *100 †18
DENISON, Gregory Lewis. 1000 MINERAL POINT AVE, RADIOLOGY DEPARTMENT 53548
 #038-40-1991 L2004 **DR** *020 †80
DILLON, Christopher Colin. ■ 53548 #056-05-2005 L2006 **EM** *012
DOWNING, John J. 580 N WASHINGTON ST, STE 551 53548 #024-16-1978 L1982 **OPH** *020
DURKES, Shane Michael. 849 KELLOGG AVE 53546 #305-01-2005 L2006 **FP** *012

EDELMAN, Harlan David. 557 N WASHINGTON ST 53548 #016-11-1983 L2000 **ORS** *020 †40
EJERCITO, Michael Pecson. 1446 N RANDALL AVE 53545 #056-05-2001 L2005 **EM** *020 †16 ‡
ELKINS, Keith Warren. 849 KELLOGG AVE 53546 #305-01-2004 L2005 **FP** *012
ELLISON, Warren Ross. 580 N WASHINGTON ST, RIVERVIEW CLINIC 53548 #018-03-1979 L1984
 OTO *020 †45
ELTARAWY, Islam Ghoneim. 849 KELLOGG AVE 53546 #915-03-2000 **FP** *012
ENRIQUEZ, Gilberto D. 3202 SPRUCE CT 53546 #748-21-1983 L2002 **AN PME** *020 †05
FALK, Steven Louis. 510 N TERRACE ST 53548 #056-06-1976 L1977 **GS** *020 †85
FAST, Spencer William. 849 KELLOGG AVE 53546 #056-06-2005 L2006 **FP** *012
FERNANDO, Manellema N. 15 W MILWAUKEE ST, STE 206 53548 #220-01-1965 L1994 **FM** *020
FRECHETTE, Paul Francis. 301 E MILWAUKEE ST 53545 #056-05-1962 L1964 **P** *020
FREY, James Kenneth. 1446 N RANDALL AVE 53545 #038-45-1984 L1987 **FM** *020 †16
GARCIA, Michael Jerome. 1000 MINERAL POINT AVE, MERCY HEALTH SYSTEM 53548
 #016-43-1972 L2001 **DR** *020 †80
GARCIA, Ronald Allan M. 1000 MINERAL POINT AVE 53548 #748-10-1992 L2001
 PM SCI *020 †60
GARNER, Patricia Diane. 510 N TERRACE ST 53548 #004-01-1993 L2004 **GS** *020 †85
GASAL SPILDE, Jeannette M. 580 N WASHINGTON ST, DEAN RIVERVIEW CLINIC 53548
 #048-13-1995 L1996 **DR** *020 †80
GERZENSHTEIN, Jacob. 1000 MINERAL POINT AVE, MERCY HOSPITAL 53548
 #016-43-1997 L2005 **PS GS** *020 †85,65
GILESTRA, Rosa A. 580 N WASHINGTON ST, STE 551 53548 #042-01-1992 L1993 **FM** *020 †18
GODAR, Jeanne Marie. 3524 E MILWAUKEE ST, MERCY CLINIC EAST 53546
 #036-05-1985 L1992 **D DMP** *020 †20
GOELZER, Kristen Marna. 3524 E MILWAUKEE ST 53546 #056-06-1999 L2000
 MPD *020 †20,55
GOELZER, Mark Lee. 1000 MINERAL POINT AVE 53548 #056-05-1973 L1978 **PD** *020 †55
GOLDSTEIN, A Sandor. 1000 MINERAL POINT AVE 53548 #067-01-1975 L1989 **TS** *020 †85,90
GORDON, Christal Ann. 1000 MINERAL POINT AVE 53548 #030-06-1978 L1981 **PD** *020 †55
GORDON, Sharon Anne. 1000 MINERAL POINT AVE 53548 #056-05-1991 L1992 **AN** *020 †05
GREDLER, Gerald P. 580 N WASHINGTON ST, DEAN MEDICAL CTR 53548 #056-05-1951 L1952
 ORS OS *071 †40
GRITT, Lisa Renee. 849 KELLOGG AVE, MERCY CLINIC SOUTH 53546 #305-01-2006 **FP** *012
GRUHN, Stanley Wm. 580 N WASHINGTON ST, STE 551 53548 #018-03-1972 L1975
 IM *020 †20
GUTMANN, George E. 580 N WASHINGTON ST 53548 #020-02-1943 L1947 **IM** *071 †20
HAHN, Michael Frederick. 1000 MINERAL POINT AVE 53548 #056-05-1963 L1964 **PTH** *071 †50
HAHN-SCHUMACHER, Leanne K. 1000 MINERAL POINT AVE 53548 #056-06-1996 L1997
 FM *020 †18
HANGAN, Daniela Nicoleta. 849 KELLOGG AVE 53546 #781-03-1997 L2006 **FP** *012
HANN, Marek. 17 S RIVER ST, STE 254 53548 #759-03-1963 L1970 **P CHP** *020 †75
HANSEN, Thomas Royal. 1000 E MEMORIAL DR, MERCY HOSP OF JANESVILLE 53545
 #016-11-1954 L1961 **DR NM** *071 †20
HAROON, Ayaz Mahmood. 849 KELLOGG AVE, MERCY HEALTH SYSTEM 53546
 #704-05-1992 L2007 **IM** *020 †18
HATCH, James Louis. 707 THORNECREST CT, JAMES L HATCH, M.D. 53546
 #030-05-1974 L1979 **DR** *020 †80
HAZRA, David. 1000 GENERAL MOTORS DR 53546 #422-01-1998 L2004 **GPM** *020 †70
HENIGES, Matthew Wiley. 1000 MINERAL POINT AVE 53548 #016-42-1988 L1989 **AN** *020 †05
HENRICKSON, Kerry H. 1000 MINERAL POINT AVE 53548 #043-01-1982 L1983
 CCM IM *020 †20
HONARKHAH, Nader. 1000 MINERAL POINT AVE 53548 #038-43-1997 L2000 **IM** *020 †20
HORTON, James Glenn. 849 KELLOGG AVE 53546 #048-14-1985 L1986 **FM** *040 †18
HUIBREGTSE, David Mark. 580 N WASHINGTON ST, STE 551 53548 #056-05-1981 L1986
 ORS OSM *020 †40
HUSSLI, Jennifer Anne. 849 KELLOGG AVE, CLINIC SOUTH 53546 #665-02-2004 L2006
 FM *020 †18
JACKSON, Amanda Tucker. 1000 MINERAL POINT AVE, MERCY HEALTH SYSTEM 53548
 #056-05-2004 L2007 **EM** *020
JAFARY, Fahim Haider. 1000 MINERAL POINT AVE, MERCY HEART AND VASCULAR C 53548
 #704-25-1990 L1995 **CD** *020 †20
JAIKUMAR, S. 1000 MINERAL POINT AVE 53548 #048-13-1996 L2001 **NS** *020 †25
JASEK, Andrzej Michal. 1000 MINERAL POINT AVE 53548 #759-03-1985 L2000 **RHU** *020 †20
KALEMBER, Robert Leroy. 17 S RIVER ST, STE 254 53548 #025-01-1963 L1969 **P** *020
KARZEL, Ronald Paul. 580 N WASHINGTON ST 53548 #016-06-1956 L1959 **GS** *071 †85
KAVEGGIA, Francis F. 1000 MINERAL POINT AVE 53548 #056-05-1985 L1986 **U GS** *020 †95
KELLER, Francis Leo. 3524 E MILWAUKEE ST 53546 #869-01-1969 L1971 **IM GE** *020 †20
KELLY, David Jon. 849 KELLOGG AVE 53546 #305-01-2003 L2004 **FM** *020 †18
KHABBAZ, Sany T. 1000 MINERAL POINT AVE, MERCY HEALTH SYSTEM 53548
 #605-01-1997 L2001 **N OS** *020 †75
KHAN, Kauseruzzaman A K M. 3524 E MILWAUKEE ST 53546 #160-02-1992 L2003 **IM** *020 †20
KHAN, Lubna. 849 KELLOGG AVE 53546 #308-03-2001 L2006 **FP** *012
KHOURY, Ramez Mounir. 1000 MINERAL POINT AVE, MERCY HEALTH SYSTEM 53548
 #875-01-1989 L2002 **GE** *020 †20
KING, Noreen Renee. 580 N WASHINGTON ST, STE 551 53548 #025-12-1993 L1997
 OBG *020 †30
KIRSCHBAUM, James Gerard. 1000 MINERAL POINT AVE 53548 #056-05-1989 L1994
 DR *020 †80
KNEPEL, Donald. 580 N WASHINGTON ST 53548 #005-12-1962 L1963 **EM** *071
KNUIJT, Kristi Emilie. 580 N WASHINGTON ST, STE 551 53548 #056-05-1982 L1984 **D** *020
 FM *020 †18
KOLSTE, Rex J. 849 KELLOGG AVE, 849 KELLOGG AVE 53546 #030-05-1979 L1994
 FM *020 †18
KONKOL, Keith Allan. 1000 MINERAL POINT AVE 53548 #056-05-1984 L1996 **IM** *020 †20
KOPNICK, Mitchell Alan. 580 N WASHINGTON ST, STE 551 53548 #025-01-1987 L1998
 U *020 †95
KOSNAR, Tina Lynn. 1000 MINERAL POINT AVE 53548 #030-06-1989 L1995 **CHP P** *020 †75
KREILKAMP, Tawnya Jean. 1159 PRAIRIE AVE 53545 #654-01-2005 L2007 **FP** *012
KULAS, Daniel John. 1000 MINERAL POINT AVE 53548 #056-06-2004 L2005 **FM** *020
LA BRECHE, Michael Jos. NORTH PARKER DRIVE 53547 #056-06-1965 L1966 **IMG** *071
LIEBMAN, Lori Kay. 710 PRINCETON CT 53546 #056-06-1985 L1986 **IM** *020 †20
LILLEY, Kathryn Ann. 2540 E US HIGHWAY 14 53545 #056-06-1994 L2000 **IM** *020 †20
LINDAHL, Stephen Arthur. 1010 N WASHINGTON ST 53548 #026-04-1970 L1972
 IM OS *020 †18,70
LITSHEIM, Dennis Edward. 580 N WASHINGTON ST, STE 551 53548 #056-05-1982 L1983
 DR NS *020 †80
LOVE, Greg Allen. 1000 MINERAL POINT AVE 53548 #028-03-1980 L1987 **AN** *020 †05

LUNAAS, Kimberly M. 1000 MINERAL POINT AVE 53548 #056-05-1992 L1996 **AN** *020 †05
LUPTON, Mark Danl. ■ 53548 #016-11-1972 L1992 **N** *020 †75
LYON, Steven Lambert. 580 N WASHINGTON ST, DEAN RIVERVIEW CLINIC 53548 #016-01-1991 L2004 **OTO** *020 †45 ‡
MACIOLEK, Steven Paul. 580 N WASHINGTON ST, STE 551 53548 #056-05-1972 L1980 **RHU** *020 †20
MALDONADO, Dennys Eduardo. 849 KELLOGG AVE 53546 #305-01-2007 L2008 **FP** *012
MANNINO, Paul Edward. 3524 E MILWAUKEE ST 53546 #056-05-1993 L1994 **FM** *020 †18
MARTIN, William James, III. 1163 EDGEVIEW DR 53549 #305-01-2006 L2008 **FP** *012
MARUTHOOR, Jim Kuruvilla. 1000 MINERAL POINT AVE, MERCY HOSPITAL 53548 #495-63-2002 L2007 **IM** *020 †20
MARZEC, Andrzej Jacek. ■ 53545 #759-10-1993 L2005 **GE** *020 †20
MC DADE, Mark Edward. 580 N WASHINGTON ST, STE 551 53548 #035-03-1989 L1995 **GS** *020 †85
MC GROGAN, James Carl. 1446 N RANDALL AVE, SWEA 53545 #017-20-2003 L2006 **EM** *020 †16
MC SWEENY, Austin J. 415 DODGE ST BOX 897 53548 #016-43-1949 L1957 **GE IM** *020 †20
MEMON, Mohammed I. 1000 MINERAL POINT AVE 53548 #704-16-1988 L2005 **HO** *020 †20
MENDOZA, Alfredo F. 580 N WASHINGTON ST, STE 551 53548 #748-10-1985 L1990 **PD** *020 †55
MEYER, Patrick David. 580 N WASHINGTON ST, STE 551 53548 #038-40-1974 L1986 **PD** *020 †20
MICHALSKI, Matthew Mark. 1000 MINERAL POINT AVE 53548 #056-05-1993 L1997 **EM** *020 †16
MILLER, Dale Eugene. 580 N WASHINGTON ST, STE 551 53548 #056-05-1980 L1983 **IM** *020 †20
MILLER, Edward Chas. 1000 MINERAL POINT AVE 53548 #018-03-1974 L1978 **OBG** *020 †30
MILLER, Scott Edward. 580 N WASHINGTON ST, DEAN RIVERVIEW CLINIC 53548 #056-05-1990 L1991 **AN** *020 †05
MONTGOMERY, Susan E. 580 N WASHINGTON ST 53548 #056-05-1993 L1994 **FM** *020 †20
MOORE, Jeffrey Norman. 557 N WASHINGTON ST, MERCY SPORTS MED & REHAB 53548 #047-06-1997 L1999 **PM** *020 †60
MUNNS, Meridyth Katherine. 1000 MINERAL POINT AVE, P O BOX 5003 53548 #016-42-1988 L1989 **OBG** *020 †30
MURAKI, Alan Shigemi. 1000 MINERAL POINT AVE 53548 #049-01-1978 L1997 **NRN** *040 †20,80
MYKLEBUST, Anna Maria. 580 N WASHINGTON ST, STE 551 53548 #026-04-1985 L1993 **DR** *020 †80
NADEEM, Amin-Ur-Rehman. 1000 MINERAL POINT AVE, CRITICAL CARE CLINIC 53548 #704-02-1992 L2004 **CCM** *020 †20
NAGLE, Bruce Kenton. 1814 PINE RIDGE DR 53545 #008-01-1969 L1974 **PD** *020 †55
NAHN, Patricia A K. 1000 MINERAL POINT AVE, MERCY WEST 53548 #056-05-1988 L1995 **OBG** *020 †30 ‡
NARYSHKIN, Sonya. 1000 MINERAL POINT AVE, MERCY HOSPITAL LABORATORY 53548 #020-02-1981 L1991 **PTH PCP** *020 †50 ‡
NEENO, Katsumi. 580 N WASHINGTON ST 53548 #041-09-1954 L1957 **PD** *020 †55
NEUMAN, Carol J. 1000 MINERAL POINT AVE 53548 #012-05-1984 L1993 **OBG** *020 †30
NEWCOMB, N Robert. 580 N WASHINGTON ST, STE 551 53548 #005-14-1978 L1992 **PUD IM** *020 †20
NEWMARK, Dorothy. 1000 MINERAL POINT AVE, MERCY CLINIC WEST 53548 #035-15-1997 L1999 **OBG** *020 †30
NICKELS, Arnold Carl. ■ 53545 #016-11-1922 L1922 **OS** *020
NIENHUIS, Herman Dale. ■ 53546 #025-01-1958 L1964 **OBG** *071
NOWAK, Blaine B. 1000 MINERAL POINT AVE 53548 #056-06-1978 L1979 **PD** *020 †55
O'BRIEN, Ellen Marie. 5026 N NORTHWOOD TRCE 53545 #038-43-1989 L1990 **ORS** *020 †40
O'BRIEN, James Neal. 580 N WASHINGTON ST, DEAN MEDICAL CTR 53548 #056-06-1958 L1959 **OBG** *030 †30
O'DONNELL, Craig D. 1000 GENERAL MOTORS DR 53546 #023-01-1972 L2004 **IM GP** *020
ODUWOLE, Adedapo M A. 1000 MINERAL POINT AVE, 1000 MINERAL POINT ROAD 53548 #690-08-1988 L2001 **ADP** *020 †20,75
OHARA, Narumi. PO BOX 505 53547 #016-02-1981 L1993 **GE IM** *020 †20
OLSON, Laird E. 1000 MINERAL POINT AVE, MERCY REGIONAL CANCER CENT 53548 #016-11-1978 L1980 **RO** *020 †80
OLSON, Susan Jayne. 1000 MINERAL POINT AVE 53548 #056-05-1983 L1984 **P** *020 †75
OMARI, Bashar A. 510 N TERRACE ST 53548 #575-02-1991 L1994 **NEP** *020 †20
ORGAN, Mirian Boyd. 580 N WASHINGTON ST, RIVERVIEW CLINIC 53548 #025-07-1989 L2006 **OBG** *020 †30
O'ROURKE, Colleen Joyce. 1000 MINERAL POINT AVE 53548 #056-05-1982 L1985 **P CHP** *020 †75
OVERTON, Richard S. 1000 MINERAL POINT AVE 53548 #056-05-1952 L1953 **FM** *071
PALMER, Julie. 1 S MAIN ST 53545 #035-06-1970 L1971 **P** *020 †75,18
PANG, Willett Wakin. 580 N WASHINGTON ST, STE 551 53548 #021-01-1986 L1991 **RNR DR** *020 †80
PATERSON, John James. 3634 SHEFFIELD DR 53546 #028-34-1972 L1995 **OBG** *020 †30 ‡
PEARSON, Bruce Reuel. 2801 CAMBRIDGE CT 53548 #030-05-1968 L1975 **D** *071 †15
PEMBER, John Frank. 580 N WASHINGTON ST, DEAN MEDICAL CTR 53548 #016-06-1947 L1948 **OPH** *071 †35
PEPLINSKI, Gary Ronald. 510 N TERRACE ST 53548 #016-06-1991 L2003 **GS SO** *020 †85
PETERSON, Daniel Thorsten. 580 N WASHINGTON ST, RIVERVIEW CLINIC 53548 #005-11-1973 L1977 **IM** *020 †20
PITTENGER, David Edward. 557 N WASHINGTON ST, MEDICINE CENTER 53548 #056-06-1985 L1991 **ORS** *020 †40
POPESCU, Marcela Ionela. ■ 53545 #781-05-1992 L2007 **PHO** *100 †55
POSADA, Ruben Dario. PO BOX 5003 53547 #264-13-1992 **FM** *100
POSNER, Christian John. 1000 MINERAL POINT AVE 53548 #005-05-1967 L1993 **CD IC** *020 †20
POZO, Milton Leonardo. 1000 MINERAL POINT AVE 53548 #847-23-1973 L1992 **EM IM** *020 †20,16
PRATT, Marshall Curtis. 849 KELLOGG AVE, FAMILY PRA 53546 #016-76-2007, ▲ **FP** *012
PURDY, Marshall Frank. 3530 N US HIGHWAY 51 53545 #025-07-1943 L1947 **IM** *072
RADAK, Richard Edward. 1000 MINERAL POINT AVE 53548 #016-01-1991 L1995 **EM** *020 †16
RAGOTZY, Ronald Lee. 3524 E MILWAUKEE ST, MERCY CLINIC EAST 53546 #025-07-1983 L1987 **A PD** *020 †55,03
RAINIERO, Michael. 580 N WASHINGTON ST, STE 551 53548 #016-01-1986 L1987 **GS** *020 †85
RAINIERO, Nancy C. 580 N WASHINGTON ST, STE 551 53548 #017-20-1987 L1988 **IM** *020 †20
RAMSEY, Harry Richard. 580 N WASHINGTON ST, STE 551 53548 #026-04-1984 L1985 **IM** *020 †20

RAO, Ramachandra. 1305 WOODMAN RD, JANESVILLE DIALYSIS CENTER 53545 #495-09-1964 L1974 **IM NEP** *020 †20
REID, Timothy Shawn. 1010 N WASHINGTON ST, MERCY REGIONAL DIABETES CE 53545 #038-43-1989 L1999 **FM DIA** *020 †18
RIGGS, Landon Cornell. 3524 E MILWAUKEE ST, MERCY CLINIC EAST 53546 #016-43-1994 L1999 **OTO** *020 †45
ROBERTS, John Austin. 17 S RIVER ST STE 254, CROSSROADS COUNSELING CTR 53548 #056-05-1982 L1983 **P** *020 †75
ROBINSON, Emily G. 1000 MINERAL POINT AVE, MERCY CLINIC WEST 53548 #056-05-1991 L1996 **HO** *020 †20
ROE, Jonathan David. 1000 MINERAL POINT AVE 53548 #056-06-1991 L1994 **PD** *020 †55
ROZEBOOM, Dale Evan. 580 N WASHINGTON ST, STE 551 53548 #018-03-1984 L1988 **OBG** *020 †30
RUSSO, Francis Robt. ■ 53548 #035-01-1947 L1951 **GS TS** *071 †85
RUTHERFORD, Darin Scott. 557 N WASHINGTON ST, MERCY SPORTS MEDICINE CENT 53548 #038-03-1995 L1996 **FSM** *020 †18
SACHS, Marc A. 3524 E MILWAUKEE ST, MERCY EAST 53546 #024-05-1980 L1990 **OTO** *020 †45
SALISBURY, Steven Matthew. 1000 MINERAL POINT AVE 53548 #056-05-1992 L1993 **ATP NM** *020 †50,28 ‡
SCHMIDT, Bart John. 1000 MINERAL POINT AVE 53548 #056-06-1991 L1992 **DR AR** *020 †80
SCHULMAN, Sidney. 580 N WASHINGTON ST 53548 #065-01-1977 L1997 **ORS** *020 †40
SELLMAN, Daniel Clay. 557 N WASHINGTON ST 53548 #038-06-1989 L2000 **ORS** *020 †40
SELLMAN, Susan P B. ■ 53545 #056-06-1987 L2001 **PD** *020 †55
SHAMSEE, Saleem Iqbal A. 580 N WASHINGTON ST, RIVERVIEW CLINIC 53548 #704-02-1993 L2007 **FM** *020 †18
SHARMA, Divya. 580 N WASHINGTON ST, STE 551 53548 #495-55-1983 L1989 **FM** *020 †18
SHEA, Lawrence Michael. 3524 E MILWAUKEE ST, JANESVILLE MED CTR 53546 #011-04-1981 L1993 **FM** *020 †18
SIMON, Laura Joan. 3524 E MILWAUKEE ST 53546 #016-11-1971 L1992 **IM END** *020 †20
SINGH, Nidhi. 580 N WASHINGTON ST, RIVERVIEW CLINIC 53548 #495-45-2000 L2007 **IM** *020 †20
SITORIUS, Patrick Lynn. 1000 MINERAL POINT AVE 53548 #030-05-1978 L1988 **FM** *020 †18
SKINNER, Julie Claire. 1 PARKER PL STE 150 53545 #056-05-1988 L1990 **PD** *020
SMITH, David A. ■ 53545 #056-05-1952 L1953 **IM** *072 †20
SNODGRASS, Herbert M. ■ 53546 #020-02-1940 L1945 **IM** *071 †20
SPONSELLER, Brian Randall. 4118 DEER CROSSING DR 53546 #305-01-2006 L2007 **FP** *012
SPYROPOULOS, Basil. 113 S FRANKLIN ST 53546 #016-45-1992 L2004 **P** *020 †75
SQUIRES, William H. 580 N WASHINGTON ST, STE 551 53548 #056-06-1975 L1976 **GS** *020 †85
STADDLER, Daniel James. 580 N WASHINGTON ST, STE 551 53548 #056-05-1991 L1999 **FM** *020 †18
STRASSMAN, Michael John. 1000 MINERAL POINT AVE 53548 #056-05-1986 L1987 **PTH** *020 †50
STRUCK, Michael Cary. 3524 E MILWAUKEE ST 53546 #056-05-1991 L1992 **OPH PO** *020 †35
STURM, Christopher D. 1000 MINERAL POINT AVE 53548 #028-34-1992 L2001 **NS** *020 †25
SZEKELY, Gabriel Andrew. 3524 E MILWAUKEE ST 53546 #056-06-1979 L1987 **FM** *020 †18
TARJAN, Andrea Veronika. 3524 E MILWAUKEE ST 53546 #473-01-1978 L1992 **IM** *020 †20
TARRAR, Wais. 849 KELLOGG AVE 53546 #305-01-2005 **FP** *012
THOMAS, Jeffrey Chapman. 23 W MILWAUKEE ST 53548 #056-05-1966 L1969 **ORS** *020 †40
THOMAS, Nadine Verona. 580 N WASHINGTON ST, STE 551 53548 #010-03-1990 L2006 **CD** *020 †20
THOMASSEN, Thom Scott. 3524 E MILWAUKEE ST 53546 #036-07-1977 L1993 **OPH** *020 †35
TOMLINSON, Carol. ■ 53548 #056-05-1942 L1943 **DR** *071 †80
TREGONING, Paul Conrad. ■ 53545 #041-13-1960 L1964 **GP** *071
VOGEL, James Geo. 580 N WASHINGTON ST, STE 551 53548 #018-03-1972 L1978 **OBG** *071 †30
VRAA, Eric Patrick. 1446 N RANDALL AVE, FAIRVIEW - UNIVERSITY MED 53545 #026-04-1992 L1993 **EM** *020 †16
WANG, Hailong. 3928 PARK VIEW DR 53546 #243-36-1984 L2002 **AN** *020 †05
WARAKSA, Julie Ann. 2540 E US HIGHWAY 14 53545 #056-06-1998 L2001 **PD** *020 †55
WASILJEW, Bohdan K. 1000 MINERAL POINT AVE 53548 #016-06-1976 L1993 **GS SO** *020 †85 ‡
WINKLER, William. 849 KELLOGG AVE, MERCY CLINIC SOUTH 53546 #028-34-1976 L2000 **FM** *040 †18
WISEMAN, Terrance Lee. 580 N WASHINGTON ST, DEAN MEDICAL CTR 53548 #016-11-1970 L1975 **A IM** *020
WOOD, William Allen. 557 N WASHINGTON ST 53548 #056-05-1981 L1982 **PS GS** *020 †85,65
YAP, Bobby Lee. 3524 E MILWAUKEE ST, MERCY CLINIC EAST 53546 #748-17-1986 L1996 **FM UCM** *020 †18
ZAJAC, Dorothy Jean. ■ 53547 #030-06-1976 L1980 **IM EM** *020 †20 ‡
ZIEGLER, John Marshall. 580 N WASHINGTON ST, STE 551 53548 #017-20-1982 L1989 **PD ID** *020 †55
ZIEGLER, Judy Price. 1000 MINERAL POINT AVE 53548 #018-03-1980 L1989 **PD** *074 †55
ZIKEL, Ofer Michael. 1000 MINERAL POINT AVE, MERCY REG NEURO SURGERY CT 53548 #016-06-1994 L2003 **NS** *020 †25

JEFFERSON – JEFFERSON

HAGGART, Melvin Anderson. N3995 ANNEX RD 53549 #048-02-1972 L1978 **CHP GP** *020 †75
MEYERS, F Bradford. 152 W GARLAND ST 53549 #047-05-1981 L1987 **FM OS** *020 †18
QUANDT, Raymond W. ■ 53549 #056-05-1942 L1943 **GP** *071
RUTLEDGE, David A. 840 W RACINE ST 53549 #016-06-1979 L1982 **FM** *020 †18

JOHNSON CREEK – JEFFERSON

ARMATYS-GRIFFEL, Sandra. 400 DOCTORS CT 53038 #016-06-2000 L2006 **U** *020
BASARICH, John Robert. 540 VILLAGE WALK LN 53038 #056-06-2001 L2004 **FM** *020
CHITNIS, Amit Satish. ■ 53038 #005-18-2006 L2008 **IM** *012
DAJANI, Hatem Marwan. ■ 53038 #040-02-2005 L2006 **IM** *012
HOWARD, Steven Paul. 250 DOCTORS CT 53038 #056-06-1990 L1998 **RO** *020 †80
MILFORD, James Alexander. 540 VILLAGE WALK LN 53038 #016-43-1990 L1991 **FM** *020 †18

JUNEAU - DODGE

EENIGENBURG, Royle Glen. 199 HOME RD, DODGE COUNTY HUMAN SERVICE 53039 #016-01-1992 L1993 **P** *020 †75
FULLERTON, Nathaniel J. 153 E OAK ST 53039 #056-05-1995 L1997 **IM** *020 †20
MANNIS, Kent S. 199 HOME RD 53039 #056-05-1960 L1961 **P** *020 †75
MILLER, Rhonda Susan. 153 E OAK ST 53039 #025-12-1985 L1998 **OBG** *020 †30

KANSASVILLE - RACINE

LAVIN, Maureen Patrice. 23615 GOLF RD, FORENSIC PATHOLOGY CONSULT 53139 #056-05-1987 L1988 **OM FOP** *020

KAUKAUNA - OUTAGAMIE

CULLIGAN, Timothy Patrick. 305 E 12TH ST 54130 #016-43-1999 L2000 **FM** *020 †18
DANZ, Bruce Robert. 305 E 12TH ST 54130 #016-45-1980 L1981 **FM** *020 †18
EWERT, Brian Howard. 2259 PROGRESS WAY, FMCNA KAUKAUNA 54130 #016-06-1985 L1992 **NEP IM** *020 †20
FRIEDRICH, Michal Ford. 2601 FIELDCREST DR 54130 #016-43-2000 L2001 **FM** *020 †18
GRAUNKE, Joseph Corbin. 305 E 12TH ST 54130 #025-07-1992 L1995 **FM** *020 †18
GUSTAFSON, William Gustv. 305 E 12TH ST 54130 #026-04-1989 L1990 **EM FM** *020 †18
JEFFREY, James Stanley. 305 E 12TH ST 54130 #030-05-1954 L1955 **FM** *020
JOHNSON, Gregory Alan. 305 E 12TH ST 54130 #026-04-1986 L1987 **FM ESM** *020 †18
REISNER, Terry Ray. ■ 54130 #018-03-1985 L2001 **FM** *020 †18
RUSSO, John Gregory. ■ 54130 #016-43-1938 L1941 **IM PUD** *071
RUSSO, Paul Henry. 305 E 12TH ST 54130 #016-45-1987 L1988 **FM** *020 †18
SCHIMKE, Andrea Carol. 2700 CROOKS AVE 54130 #037-01-1998 L2001 **FM** *020 †18
SCHOENING, Jennifer Lynn. 305 E 12TH ST 54130 #056-05-1997 L1998 **FM** *020 †18
WERNER, Michael Thomas. 305 E 12TH ST 54130 #056-06-2003 L2004 **FM** *020 †18
WOLFMEYER, Waldemar W. 305 E 12TH ST, KAUKAUNA CLINIC SC 54130 #056-05-1962 L1963 **FM** *071

KENNAN - PRICE

REDFALL, Margaret Ellen. N3470 RILEY RD 54537 #026-04-2001 L2002 **FM** *020 †18

KENOSHA - KENOSHA

ABBO, Katherine Marie. 6308 8TH AVE, STE 3060 53143 #030-05-1987 L1995 **CD IM** *020 †20
ABRAHAM, Sheryn. 6308 8TH AVE, CHILDRENS HOSPITAL OF 53143 #016-06-1996 L1997 **PD** *020 †55
ACHARYA, Arvind N. 6308 8TH AVE 53143 #495-48-1970 L1977 **GS** *071
AGAIBY, John Mounir. 10400 75TH ST, STE 201 53142 #056-06-1996 L1999 **FM** *020 †18
AHMAD, Amtul R. 3601 30TH AVE STE 101 53144 #704-06-1982 L1998 **PD GP** *020 †55 ‡
ALI, M Yusuf. 10400 75TH ST, STE 305 53142 #704-02-1960 L1976 **IM GP** *020
AL-SINAWI, Lubna A. 4536 22ND AVE, KENOSHA COMM HEALTH CNTR, 53140 #528-01-1979 L1997 **FM GS** *020 †18
AMBRO, Thomas Michael. 6308 8TH AVE 53143 #056-06-1990 L1991 **OBG** *020 †30
ANSARI, Aftab Ahmed. 3535 30TH AVE, STE 101 53144 #704-08-1971 L1978 **ORS HS** *020 †40
ANTOO, Elizabeth. 10400 75TH ST, WALK IN CLINIC 53142 #495-37-1998 L2006 **FM** *020 †18
ARANA, Maria Chela Cruz. 4536 22ND AVE 53140 #748-02-2000 L2004 **FM** *020 †18
ARIF, Abdul Q. 10400 75TH ST 53142 #495-57-1981 L1994 **IM** *020
ASCHENBRENER, Scott John. 6308 8TH AVE, DEPT ANESTHESIA 53143 #056-05-1987 L1992 **AN** *020 †05
ATCHA, Shahid Ali. 6308 8TH AVE, # 2000 53143 #422-01-1997 L2004 **OBG** *020 †30
AZUMA, Steven Akira. 6215 10TH AVE 53143 #016-06-1970 L1972 **OBG** *071 †30
BABUSUKUMAR, Pushparanee. 3535 30TH AVE, STE 201 53144 #220-01-1976 L1992 **P** *020
BALIGA, Narayan. 6308 8TH AVE, KENOSHA HOSPITAL 53143 #495-52-1983 L1995 **AN** *020 †05
BANDEALY, Geetha. 10400 75TH ST 53142 #495-04-1988 L1997 **IM** *020 †20
BARR, Mary Beth. 6530 SHERIDAN RD 53143 #056-05-1987 L1992 **DR** *020 †80
BILAK, Roman. 3556 7TH AVE 53140 #165-04-1953 L1956 **GP GS** *071
BIRNDORF, Michael S. 6308 8TH AVE 53143 #016-01-1987 L1992 **HS** *020 †65
BJORK, Harold Albert. ■ 53143 #016-01-1941 L1952 **R** *071 †80
BJORK, Robert D. 6308 8TH AVE 53143 #056-06-1983 L1984 **PTH FOP** *020 †50
BLACK, Robert Leo, Jr. 10400 75TH ST, MIDWEST EMERGENCY ASSOCIAT 53142 #016-11-1989 L1993 **EM** *020 †16
BLOOM, Joshua Alexander. 6308 8TH AVE # 108 53143 #016-11-1982 L1988 **PUD CCM** *020 †20
BONELL, Blair Thos. ■ 53144 #056-06-1945 L1947 **GS** *071
BORMAN, Richard Joseph. 3601 30TH AVE, STE 205 53144 #056-06-1979 L1986 **FM** *020 †18
BUENCAMINO, Ernesto E. 3734 7TH AVE STE 11 53140 #748-01-1965 L1976 **IM CD** *020
BURANOSKY, Julie. 6308 8TH AVE, KENOSHA MEMORIAL 53143 #016-11-1991 L1995 **EM** *020 †16
BURHANI, A Walid. ■ 53144 #704-01-1955 L1961 **GS** *071 †85
CABALLERO, Antonio C. 10400 75TH ST 53142 #748-01-1985 L1997 **AN** *020 †05 ‡
CALDERWOOD, David Alexis. 1020 35TH ST, GENESIS MEDICAL CENTER 53140 #049-01-1999 L2000 **FM** *020 †18
CAPELLI, Alfred John. 7540 22ND AVE 53143 #056-06-1978 L1979 **IM GP** *020 †20
CAPELLI, Paul Alfred. 3601 30TH AVE, STE 204 53144 #056-06-1956 L1958 **OBG** *071 †30
CAPELLI, Paul Vincent. 10400 75TH ST, STE 201 53142 #422-01-1989 L1991 **FM** *020 †18
CAPELLI-SCHEIDT, Regina A. 3601 30TH AVE, STE 204 53144 #056-06-1989 L1990 **AN** *020 †05
CASACLANG, Sergio Cruz. 10400 75TH ST, AURORA HEALTH CENTER 53142 #308-11-1985 L1995 **FM** *020 †18
CASTRO, Magdalena. 5525 GREEN BAY RD, WAYNE PERKINS 53144 #264-04-1969 L1974 **AN** *020
CETTA, Nicholas Mark. ■ 53144 #561-01-1971 L1979 **PD** *071
CHANG, Vanessa Quyen. 12225 71ST ST, AURORA MEDICAL CENTER 53142 #038-44-2001 L2005 **P** *020 †75
CHANTELOIS, Judith Lynn. 6308 8TH AVE, STE 2000 53143 #056-06-1981 L2001 **OBG PHP** *020 †70,30
CHAUHAN, Suneet Bhushan. 10400 75TH ST 53142 #041-02-1983 L2005 **OBG** *020 †30
CLUBB, Meredith Carter. 6308 8TH AVE # 503 53143 #016-06-1972 L1978 **U** *020 †95
CONZELMAN, Dorothy R. 10400 75TH ST 53142 #041-07-1956 L1960 **PD** *071
COOK, Robert Geo. 6308 8TH AVE # 301 53143 #016-43-1973 L1979 **GS OS** *020 †85
CRAIN, Martin Richard. 10400 75TH ST, STE 201 53142 #018-03-1986 L1992 **VIR R** *020 †80
CULLINANE, Natalie Dolore. ■ 53144 #016-11-2005 L2007 **AN** *012
DANKLE, Jon Anthony. 10400 75TH ST 53142 #018-03-1990 L1995 **OTO** *020 †45
DAVID, Diana. 10400 75TH ST 53142 #528-02-1989 L2001 **IM** *020 †20
DAVIS, David Winningham. 6213 10TH AVE 53143 #030-05-1953 L1956 **PD** *071 †55
DE GROAT, Jesse Varney, Jr. ■ 53140 #056-05-2000 L2002 **FM** *040 †18 ‡
DE LA CRUZ, Rolando Yu. 10400 75TH ST 53142 #748-11-1974 L1994 **PD AI** *020 †55,03
DHALIWAL, Amrit Kaur. 4906 39TH AVE 53144 #495-29-1965 L1976 **AI** *020
DHALIWAL, Kulwant Singh. 4906 39TH AVE 53144 #495-29-1959 L1971 **AI PUD** *020 †03
DUNCAN, James T, Jr. ■ 53143 #028-02-1949 L1953 **IM** *071
DURRANI, Abdul G. 3601 30TH AVE, STE 102 53144 #308-11-1986 L1993 **FM** *020 †18
ELDRIDGE, Eugene John. 1400 75TH ST 53143 #016-06-1983 L1984 **OPH** *020 †35
ELDRIDGE, Mary Patricia. ■ 53144 #056-06-2008 *012
EYZAGUIRRE, Arturo E. 10400 75TH ST 53142 #737-06-1997 L2005 **PCC** *020 †20
FAGAN, Leonard Simon. 7201 GREEN BAY RD, STE C 53142 #016-01-1984 L2003 **OBG** *020 †30
FAI, Leslie. ■ 53143 #473-01-1952 L1960 **P** *071
FARKAS, David Eric. 10400 75TH ST, AURORA MEDICAL CENTER 53142 #016-11-1990 L1991 **EM** *020 †16
FERWERDA, James Russell. 8020 SHERIDAN RD, VICTOR S SLANA MD 53143 #056-05-1957 L1958 **OPH** *072 †35
FETTER, Marvin Ray. 10400 75TH ST, ATTN: MEDICAL STAFF OFFIC 53142 #012-05-1970 L1997 **ORS** *020 †40
FEUERBACH, Stephen P. 3556 7TH AVE 53140 #305-01-1987 L1989 **FPG** *020 †18
FIELDS, Robert Lewis. 6308 8TH AVE, KENOSHA MEMORIAL HOSPITAL 53143 #016-11-1973 L1985 **EM FM** *020 †16,18
FIFIELD, Elizabeth Anne. 7201 GREEN BAY RD, STE C 53142 #016-11-1979 L2003 **OBG** *020 †30
FOSTER, James Campbell. 9916 75TH ST 53142 #016-11-1977 L1984 **OM PD** *020 †55,70
FRIEDL, Wendel Mathew, Jr. 6308 8TH AVE 53143 #038-40-1976 L1981 **IM** *020 †20
FRIEDLANDER, Jason Robert. 6308 8TH AVE, CHILDRENS HOSPITAL OF 53143 #016-06-1997 L1998 **PD** *020 †55
FULLIN, Kevin Jos. 6308 8TH AVE STE 306 53143 #038-40-1980 L1986 **CD IM** *030 †20
GARRETTO, Mario. 6308 8TH AVE, STE 202 53143 #016-01-1978 L1983 **GE IM** *020 †20
GEOTSALITIS, Geo Nicholas. 10400 75TH ST, AURORA HLTH CTR 53142 #305-01-1987 L1992 **FM** *020
GOLDBERG, Richard Jay. 6308 8TH AVE 53143 #016-06-1985 L1997 **EM OM** *020 †16
GRINIS, Gedas Marius. 10400 75TH ST, AURORA MED CTR 53142 #028-34-1983 L1998 **U** *020 †95 ‡
GUZMAN, Mariano Flores De. 3734 7TH AVE 53140 #748-01-1965 L1973 **PD** *020 †55
HABEL, Alfred Martin. 6308 8TH AVE 53143 #056-06-1990 L1997 **PCC** *020 †20
HAHN, Sigrid Gabriele. 6308 8TH AVE, FLATTENDING LNGE 1 53143 #025-12-1998 L2002 **EM** *020 †16
HAIDER, Syed Naqi. ■ 53142 #704-02-1990 L2004 **IM** *020 †20
HAUSCHILD, Werner Albert. ■ 53143 #407-30-1948 L1960 **GS** *075
HEDLUND, Kelly Anne. 6308 8TH AVE, UNITED HOSP SYSTEMS 53143 #016-01-2003 L2006 **EM** *020 †16
HOLLANT, Gladys E. 800 55TH ST 53140 #016-42-1990 L1999 **IM** *020 †20
HOLT, Stephen H. 6308 8TH AVE 53143 #020-02-1950 L1957 **PTH** *020 †50
HORSLEY, D Boyd. 6308 8TH AVE 53143 #051-01-1951 L1957 **IM** *072
HULL, Annette Rae. 6308 8TH AVE 53143 #056-05-1993 L1996 **IM** *020 †20
HUTSON, Rick John. ■ 53143 #056-06-1994 L1995 **AN** *020 †05
ILAO, Maria Concepcion M. 10400 75TH ST 53142 #748-10-1982 *100
INVEISS, Anita Ilze. 3535 30TH AVE, STE 101 53144 #056-06-1983 L1984 **FM** *020 †18
IYER, Jaya Venkateshwaran. 6125 GREEN BAY RD, KENOSHA PEDIATRICS 53142 #495-99-1994 L2001 **PD** *020 †55
JANDALI, Majed. 6308 8TH AVE, STE 3050 53143 #875-01-1980 L1993 **GS** *020 †85
JERANEK, William J. 3556 7TH AVE 53140 #056-05-1976 L1977 **FM** *020 †18
JOHNSON, Howard Herbert. 10400 75TH ST 53142 #056-05-1967 L1969 **DR** *020 †80
JOLLY, Christine Marie. 6308 8TH AVE, CHILDRENS HOSPITAL OF 53143 #019-02-1992 L1999 **PD** *020 †55
JONES, Robert W, Jr. 6308 8TH AVE # 303, KENOSHA HOSP & MED CTR 53143 #038-41-1984 L1987 **CN N** *020 †75
KABINS, Laurie A. 6308 8TH AVE, KENOSHA HOSPITAL & MEDICAL 53143 #016-11-1990 L1996 **APM AN** *020 †05
KACHAPPILLY, Alby Antoo. 10400 75TH ST STE 210 53142 #495-37-1998 L2005 **FM** *100 †18
KAMBOL, James J. 6308 8TH AVE, KENOSHA HOSP & MEDICAL CEN 53143 #017-20-1989 L1992 **EM** *020 †16
KAYEUM, Nina. 10400 75TH ST, STE 201 53142 #422-01-1990 L1991 **IM** *020 †20
KELLER, Theodore Adam. 6530 SHERIDAN RD 53143 #056-06-1961 L1963 **R NM** *071 †80
KHAN, Abdul Hamid. 10400 75TH ST, STE 201 53142 #495-20-1964 L1976 **ORS** *020 †40
KHAN, Mehjabein Yacoob. ■ 53142 #704-02-1989 L2004 **RHU** *020 †20
KHAN, Muhammad S. 10400 75TH ST, STE 201 53142 #308-11-1986 L1991 **FM** *020 †18
KHAN, Seema. 6308 8TH AVE, UNITED HOSPITAL SYSTEM 53143 #495-74-1992 L2007 **IM** *020 †20
KLEIN, Kenneth Allan. 10400 75TH ST 53142 #035-19-1969 L1972 **RO** *020 †80
KNIGHT, Melinda K. 6308 8TH AVE, STE 3040 53143 #023-07-1994 L2001 **U** *020 †95
KNIGHT, Raymond Wm. 6308 8TH AVE, STE 2000 53143 #038-40-1970 L1974 **ON HEM** *020
KREAGER, Michael Curtis. 6308 8TH AVE 53143 #308-11-1987 L1994 **CD** *020 †20
KUMPATI, Ganesh Sundar. 6308 8TH AVE, STE 300 53143 #038-40-1998 L2006 **TS** *020 †85,90
KUZYCZ, Markian Jurij. 10400 75TH ST, DEPT. OF SURGERY 53142 #016-11-1997 L2003 **GS** *020 †85
LABRADOR, Andrew G. 10400 75TH ST STE 30, INNOVATIVE EMERGENCY PHYSI 53142 #748-01-1967 L1999 **EM** *020 †16
LAUFENBURG, Herbert F. ■ 53142 #056-05-1953 L1954 **FM** *071 †18
LAYDE, Michael Jos. 6308 8TH AVE 53143 #056-05-1972 L1973 **EM** *020 †18
LESLIE, Andrew Campbell. 6308 8TH AVE, CHILDRENS HOSPITAL OF 53143 #038-40-1988 L1991 **PD** *020 †55
LEWIS, Trevor Justin. 10400 75TH ST, STE 201 53142 #016-42-1992 L2004 **EM** *020 †16
LIEBERMAN, David Eli. 6308 8TH AVE, OF EM 53143 #016-43-2002 L2006 **EM** *020 †16
MAIN, Jonathan Danl. 6308 8TH AVE STE 505 53143 #016-06-1987 L1997 **OSM** *040 †40

■ = Address Information Privacy Protected

MAINLAND, Mary Kathryn. 3508 WASHINGTON RD, KENOSHA COUNTY MEDICAL EXA 53144 #056-06-1995 L1996 **FOP PTH** *020 †50

MANDA, Ramanuja Rao. 6308 8TH AVE, STE 3060 53143 #495-65-1975 L1986 **CD IM** *020 †20

MANSKE, Michael Gerard. 625 52ND ST, CITY OF KENOSHA FIRE DEPT 53140 #056-05-1985 L1989 **EM** *020 †16

MARIANI, Peter. 6308 8TH AVE STE 108 53143 #561-01-1975 L1981 **PCC IM** *020 †20

MARTIN, Carroll M, Jr. 6308 8TH AVE, STE 3060 53143 #005-02-1966 L1976 **CD** *020 †20 ‡

MATA, Rodrigo Ayento. 6123 GREEN BAY RD, STE 120 53142 #748-01-1960 L1980 **GP** *020

MATA, Rodrigo B, III. 6123 GREEN BAY RD, STE 120 53142 #748-10-1986 L1992 **IM** *020 †20

MATSON, Jonathan Edward. 10400 75TH ST, MIDWEST EMERGENCY ASSOCIAT 53142 #016-42-1990 L2002 **EM** *020 †16

MATTEUCCI, David Jos. 5004 22ND AVE 53140 #030-06-1974 L1982 **CRS GS** *020 †10,85

MATTEUCCI, John Chas. 6127 GREEN BAY RD, STE 600 53142 #016-42-1990 L1997 **U** *020 †95

MATTOX, Suzanne P. 6308 8TH AVE, STE 401 53143 #016-43-1988 L1991 **IM** *020 †20

MAUDUDI, Shagufta. ■ 53144 #704-16-2000 L2006 **FM** *100

MENDEZ, Jose Cuitlahuac. 10400 75TH ST 53142 #649-14-1980 L2004 **CD CCM** *020 †20

MILNER, Thomas Gordon. 1246 40TH AVE 53144 #409-05-1988 L1997 **PTH** *020 †50

MILOSAVLJEVIC, Douglas. 10400 75TH ST, PAIN MGMT CTR 53142 #654-01-1987 L1991 **AN** *020

MIRZA, Shazia. 1020 35TH ST 53140 #704-02-1997 L2006 **IM** *020 †20

MYHRE, Adam Paul. 10400 75TH ST 53142 #047-05-2000 L2006 **DR** *020 †80

NAIK, Suresh Ramchandra. 3535 30TH AVE STE 207 53144 #495-01-1962 L1976 **IM RHU** *020

NANUL, Dragos Gabriel. 6308 8TH AVE 53143 #781-01-1986 L1999 **FM** *020 †18

NAYAR, Rajeev. 10400 75TH ST, STE 201 53142 #495-45-1984 L1998 **GE IM** *020 †20

NEEDLE, David Michael. 7540 22ND AVE 53143 #012-05-1989 L2005 **GS** *020 †85

NELSON, Kirk. ■ 53144 #016-11-1996 L2000 **IMG** *020 †20

NELSON, Shellyl Brodjeski. 3122 13TH ST 53144 #056-06-1989 L1990 **FPG** *020 †18

NERVI, Christopher August. 6308 8TH AVE, STE 3050 53143 #033-05-1999 L2004 **GS** *020 †85

NEWMAN, Julian Jos. 1605 BIRCH RD 53140 #056-05-1956 L1979 **P CHP** *071 †75

NEWTON, Carolyn Genevieve. 8600 75TH ST, STE 103 53142 #047-20-1982 L1986 **FM** *020 †18

NICCOLAI, Thomas Albert. 10400 75TH ST 53142 #056-06-1980 L1989 **ORS GP** *020 †40

NIEZGODA, Jeffrey Alan. 10400 75TH ST 53142 #023-12-1985 L1998 **EM** *020 †16

NIMMER, Wilbur A. 914 GREEN BAY RD 53144 #005-17-1962 L1972 **PM** *071 †60

NOVSAM, Ned Richard. 6308 8TH AVE, STE 503 53143 #024-05-1979 L1989 **U** *020 †95 ‡

O NEILL, Gregory Scott. 10400 75TH ST, AURORA MEDICAL CENTER 53142 #018-03-1987 L2005 **FM** *020 †18

ORTIZ, Simeon B. 3556 7TH AVE 53140 #748-10-1962 L1976 **IM** *020

PACANOWSKI, Roger Thos. 6308 8TH AVE, STE 302 53143 #018-03-1966 L1967 **GS** *020 †85

PAKKALA, Divakar Mombrana. 3535 30TH AVE, STE 207 53144 #495-04-1964 L1982 **NEP IM** *071 †20

PATEL, Dilip P. 10400 75TH ST, STE 201 53142 #495-22-1970 L1981 **EM** *020 †16

PATEL, Priti Dilip. 6308 8TH AVE, STE 302 53143 #495-22-1972 L1982 **IM IMG** *020 †20 ‡

PATEL, Priti Jashubhai. 10400 75TH ST, AURORA MEDICAL CENTER 53142 #305-01-2001 L2005 **FM** *020 †18

PAUKNER, Joseph Leopold. 7540 22ND AVE 53143 #016-43-1986 L1987 **FM** *020 †18

PECHOUS, Chas Edward, Jr. 3556 7TH AVE 53140 #016-43-1956 L1957 **GS** *071 †85

PEDDICORD, Clifford R. 7305 98TH AVE, UNIT C 53142 #016-11-1962 L2001 **DR** *020

PETERSON, Clifton Edward. 6308 8TH AVE, CLIFTON E PETERSON DR SC 53143 #035-45-1954 L1961 **ORS IM** *071 †40

PINKUS, Walter Howard. 5525 GREEN BAY RD 53144 #016-11-1947 L1955 **GS** *071 †85

PULIDO, Adalene Flora. ■ 53140 #748-08-1986 **FM** *100

PULLA, Bharathi. 6125 GREEN BAY RD, STE 100 53142 #496-22-1988 L1999 **IMG** *020 †18 ‡

PULLA, Ganesh N. 6125 GREEN BAY RD, STE 100 53142 #495-65-1982 L1999 **NEP IM** *020 †20

QUDDUS, Jawaid. 4536 22ND AVE, KENOSHA COMMUNITY HEALTH C 53140 #654-01-1996 L2003 **FM** *020 †18

RASHID, Ikram Ur. 10400 75TH ST, STE 201 53142 #704-02-1982 L1992 **IM** *020 †20

RASKIN, Kenneth Scott. 7540 22ND AVE 53143 #056-06-1994 L2002 **OBG** *020 †30 ‡

RAZZAK, Maysoon Abdul. 10400 75TH ST, PATHOLOGY DEPARTMENT 53142 #528-01-1976 L1992 **PCP ATP** *020 †50

RICKER, Justin Lynn. ■ 53144 #019-02-2002 *100

RIZZO, Michael James. 10400 75TH ST, STE 201 53142 #056-05-1978 L1979 **FM** *020 †18 ‡

RIZZO, Vincent Michael. 10400 75TH ST, STE 201 53142 #056-06-1997 L1998 **FM** *020 †18

ROBINSON, Barbara S. 7201 GREEN BAY RD, STE C 53142 #016-11-1983 L2003 **OBG OS** *020 †30

ROBINSON, Kelly Anthony. 10400 75TH ST, MIDWEST EMERGENCY ASSOCIAT 53142 #035-08-1986 L1997 **EM IM** *020 †20,16

ROCCO, Gregory Neal. 10400 75TH ST 53142 #016-42-1998 L2002 **FSM** *020 †18

ROCCO, Sheri Silva. 10400 75TH ST, AURORA MEDICAL CTR 53142 #016-42-1996 L1999 **PD** *020 †55

ROEHRICH, Herbert Geo. 12225 71ST ST 53142 #056-05-1980 L1988 **P OS** *020 †75

ROSEN, Stanley Russell. 7807 15TH AVE, C/O DR. J. VAN 53143 #869-07-1965 L1972 **IM HEM** *074

RUBIN, Ronald Glen. 3618 8TH AVE, STE 2 53140 #016-42-1981 L1995 **P GP** *020 †75

RUSTIA, Ricardo Merced. 6308 8TH AVE 53143 #748-01-1957 L1967 **FM** *071

SALAHUDDIN, Farah. 3535 30TH AVE, STE 101B 53144 #704-01-1988 L2003 **IM END** *020 †20

SANCHEZ-GIMENO, Francisco. ■ 53142 #847-08-1946 L1964 **AN** *071

SANSON, John Gustilo. ■ 53142 #748-01-1958 L1968 **PTH FOP** *071 †50

SANTARELLI, James Michael. 2707 15TH PL, AURORA HEALTH CENTER 53140 #056-06-1993 L1996 **FM** *020 †18

SAVAGLIO, Vincent Paul. 3535 30TH AVE 53144 #056-06-1967 L1968 **OPH** *071 †35

SCALZO, David Anthony. 10400 75TH ST 53142 #041-07-1992 L1998 **PTH** *020 †50

SCHEIDT, Karl Burton. 3601 30TH AVE STE 204 53144 #016-02-1987 L1988 **ORS** *020 †40

SCHELLPFEFFER, Michael A. 1400 8TH ST 53143 #056-06-1980 L1983 **OBG** *020 †30

SCHLENKER, Thomas Lee. 6308 8TH AVE, CHILDREN'S HOSPITAL KENOSH 53143 #016-06-1978 L1979 **PD** *030 †55

SCHROEDER-CAPELLI, Mary. 10400 75TH ST 53142 #056-06-1990 L1991 **OPH** *020 †35

SEIPEL, Robert Clement. 6308 8TH AVE 53143 #056-06-1994 L1995 **ORS** *020 †40

SETHI, Ashwani Kumar. 6308 8TH AVE, STE 202 53143 #495-74-1982 L1987 **GE IM** *020 †20

SHAH, Ashok Kantilal. 3734 7TH AVE, STE 24 53140 #495-23-1982 L1992 **P ADP** *020 †75

SHAPIRO, James Adam. 6308 8TH AVE, STE 505 53143 #016-01-1984 L1989 **ORS** *020 †40 ‡

SHARMA, Venkatakrishna. 3535 30TH AVE, STE 201 53144 #495-33-1970 L1978 **P PYG** *020 †75

SHENFELD, Ronald Marc. 10400 75TH ST, STE 201 53142 #016-45-1991 L2000 **EM** *020 †16

SIMANONOK, John Paul. 10400 75TH ST 53142 #005-06-1987 L2002 **GP UM** *020 †70

SIMMONS, Scott Clay. 10400 75TH ST 53142 #030-06-1990 L2002 **ORS** *020 †40

SINGH, Satnam Kaur. 9916 75TH ST, STE 102 53142 #496-07-1966 L1971 **IM GP** *020

SLANA, Victor Stephen. 6125 GREEN BAY RD, STE 800 53142 #016-43-1988 L1992 **OPH** *020 †35

SMITH, Ralph Amon, Jr. ■ 53142 #007-02-1946 L1946 **GP OM** *071

SOBIN, W Harley. 6308 8TH AVE, RM 202 53143 #035-19-1977 L1993 **GE** *020 †20

SPOTTSWOOD, Paul Gregory. 6308 8TH AVE, DEPARTMENT OF ANESTHESIA 53143 #023-01-1975 L1985 **AN PMM** *020 †10

STAACKE, Timothy Scott. 10400 75TH ST 53142 #056-05-1993 L1997 **AN PME** *020 †05

STA INES, Mark Carlos. ■ 53142 #665-02-2003 L2005 **FM** *020

STA ROMANA, Leilane U. 3734 7TH AVE, STE 15 53140 #056-06-1990 L1991 **IM** *020 †20

STONE, Christopher Durant. 6308 8TH AVE 53143 #039-01-1984 L1997 **TS GS** *020 †85,90

ST VILLE, Edward Wm. 10400 75TH ST, STE 201 53142 #048-14-1985 L1995 **DR** *020 †80

SUNDARESON, Annmarie M. 6125 GREEN BAY RD, KENOSHA PEDIATRICS 53142 #025-07-1999 L2003 **PD** *020 †55

SUNN, Laura Ann. 3618 8TH AVE, STE 2 53140 #028-03-1981 L1984 **CHP P** *020 †75

SWEE, Robert Jeffry. 6308 8TH AVE, KENOSHA HOSP EMERG HOSP 53143 #016-06-1980 L1989 **EM** *020 †16

SWERDLIN, Hilel. 3535 30TH AVE STE 204 53144 #067-01-1992 L1997 **OTO** *020 †45

TARABICHI, Muaaz. 3535 30TH AVE STE 204 53144 #654-01-1983 L1988 **OS** *040 †45

TERRELL, John Archer. 10400 75TH ST, STE 201 53142 #041-14-1991 L1992 **DR** *020 †80

THACHENKARY, Leelamma C. ■ 53142 #495-44-1967 L1982 **PTH CLP** *020 †50

THOMPSON, Junith. 6530 SHERIDAN RD 53143 #056-06-1984 L1989 **OBG** *020 †30

TOLENTINO, Phillip Robert. 10400 75TH ST 53142 #016-42-1995 L2003 **GP EM** *020

TONIOLO, James Anthony. 10400 75TH ST 53142 #016-42-1988 L1991 **DR** *020 †80

TRAN, Thao Nguyen. 6125 GREEN BAY RD STE 800 53142 #048-04-1994 L2002 **OPH** *020 †35 ‡

TRIMARK, Jeffrey Reid. 6308 8TH AVE # 2000, KENOSHA MED CTR CLN 53143 #016-02-1992 L1993 **IM** *020 †20

TSUCHIYA, Goro. 3535 30TH AVE, STE 205 53144 #572-20-1953 L1968 **N NS** *020 †25

TURNER, Lewis, III. 6308 8TH AVE 53143 #041-12-1953 L1968 **GP OS** *020

VANDERVORT, Glenn Eugene. ■ 53143 #056-05-1960 L1961 **P** *071

VASHI, Hardik A. 3556 7TH AVE 53140 #028-78-1997, ▲ L2003 **PM** *020 †60

VEDDER, Jeanne Sue. 1400 75TH ST, STE 4 53143 #056-06-1990 L2002 **OTO HNS** *020 †45

VLAHOS, Patricia S. 6213 10TH AVE 53143 #016-11-1994 L1999 **PD** *100 †55

VYTLACIL, Mark Robt. 6308 8TH AVE, DEPT OF PATHOLOGY 53143 #056-06-1982 L2003 **PTH** *020 †50

WALROD, Leiah Terese. 2800 80TH ST 53143 #038-43-2001 L2007 **FM** *020

WERBIE, Thomas Stanley. 6308 8TH AVE 53143 #056-06-1977 L1978 **ORS** *020 †40

WHETSTONE, Oliver Harvey. 6308 8TH AVE 53143 #016-43-1954 L1956 **OM GS** *072

WITECK, Mark Jos. 3556 7TH AVE 53140 #308-07-1982 L1986 **FOP ATP** *020

WOOD, Fredrick, Jr. 604 74TH ST 53143 #016-06-1951 L1956 **IM** *071

YOUNG, Gregory Walter. 6125 GREEN BAY RD, KENOSHA PEDIATRICS 53142 #056-06-1975 L1976 **PD** *020 †55

ZEIHEN, Michael. 6308 8TH AVE, RM 401 53143 #056-06-1974 L1975 **IM** *020 †20

ZELL, Antoinette Marie. 10400 75TH ST 53142 #056-06-1980 L1981 **EM GS** *020

ZIARKO, Mitchell Jacob, Jr. 6308 8TH AVE 53143 #016-11-1975 L1978 **IM** *020 †20

ZIMMERMAN, Mark Cleary. 5525 GREEN BAY RD 53144 #016-11-1986 L1987 **AN** *020 †05

KESHENA – MENOMINEE

CULHANE, John Kevin. PO BOX 970 54135 #040-02-1984 L1990 **FM** *020 †18

GUENTHER, Joseph E. PO BOX 970, W3275 WOLF RIVER RD 54135 #056-05-1998 L1999 **FM** *020 †18

ZINCK, Rebecca Watt. PO BOX 970 54135 #028-03-1992 L1993 **FM** *020 †18

KEWASKUM – WASHINGTON

CASTRO, Florizel F. 1701 FOND DU LAC AVE 53040 #748-08-1963 L1976 **GP** *020

GUMINSKI, Andrew Michael. 1701 FOND DU LAC AVE, KEWASKUM CLINIC 53040 #422-01-1998 L2002 **MPD** *020 †20,55

REED, Alan Eliot, Jr. 1421 FOND DU LAC AVE 53040 #056-06-1968 L1969 **P** *075

SISON, Aurora Alonzo. ■ 53040 #748-08-1964 L1977 **AN** *020

SISON, Cesar V. 1701 FOND DU LAC AVE 53040 #748-08-1964 L1977 **GS GP** *071

KEWAUNEE – KEWAUNEE

MASTER, Suketu. 1304 1ST ST, KEWAUNEE MEDICAL CENTER 54216 #064-01-1990 **FM** *020

MC CLELLAN, Stephen Lee. ■ 54216 #056-05-1978 L1979 **PTH FOP** *071 †50

NESEMANN, Reynold M. 575 4TH ST, BELLINHLTH FAMILY MEDICAL 54216 #056-05-1942 L1943 **GP** *071

POWELL, Kristen Aline. E5593 3RD RD 54216 #036-05-1997 L1998 **FM** *020 †18

REINARDY, Arthur L. ■ 54216 #056-05-1937 L1938 **GP** *071

ZENNER, Thomas Michael. 1ST & LINCOLN 54216 #056-06-1980 L1981 **FM** *020 †18

KIEL – MANITOWOC

DEUBLER, David John. 1001 SERVICE RD, AURORA SHEBOYGAN CLINIC 53042 #056-05-1983 L1984 **FM** *020 †18

TWOHIG, George Jos. ■ 53042 #056-06-1941 L1941 **FM** *071

KIMBERLY – OUTAGAMIE

BAUER, Joyce Miller. 520 W 3RD ST 54136 #056-05-1984 L1985 **FM** *020 †18

BLANC, Carolyn Monique. 520 W 3RD ST 54136 #005-18-1997 L1998 **FM OS** *020 †18

ELMER, Montgomery John. 520 W 3RD ST 54136 #018-03-1986 L1987 **FM** *020 †18

GAGE, Ralph Sylvester. ■ 54136 #056-06-1947 L1948 **GP** *071

MOARD, Douglas Paul. 520 W 3RD ST, THEDACARE PHYSICIANS-KIMBE 54136 #018-03-1984 L1985 **FM** *020 †18

VAN GOMPEL, Jamie Joseph. ■ 54136 #056-05-2005 L2005 **NS** *012

VEUM, James S. ■ 54136 #056-05-1950 L1951 **PD** *071 †55

■ = Address Information Privacy Protected

KING – WAUPACA

DRINKA, Paul Jos. N2665 COUNTY ROAD QQ 54946 #056-05-1972 L1974 **IMG IM** *020 †20
HOLMES, Chester L. 800 MITCHELL AVE 54946 #047-06-1942 L1951 **GS PUD** *071 †85,90

KOHLER – SHEBOYGAN

BICK, Ilsa J. 1099 HIGHLAND DR, KOHLER 53044 #010-01-1982 L2001 **CHP P** *020 †75
PRATT, Dean Byron. ■ 53044 #026-04-1963 L1972 **GS** *071 †85

LA CROSSE – LA CROSSE

ABBOTT, Mark Fredric. ■ 54601 #018-03-2007 **TY** *012
ABELLERA, R Mario. 1900 SOUTH AVE 54601 #748-01-1955 L1976 **ATP** *020 †50
ABERGER, Frank J. 1836 SOUTH AVE, GUNDERSEN CLINIC LTD 54601 #017-20-1977 L1984 **GE IM** *020 †20
ADAMS, Annell Elisabeth. ■ 54601 #016-43-2000 L2002 **P** *020 †75 ‡
AGGER, William Allan. 1900 SOUTH AVE 54601 #016-11-1972 L1974 **IM ID** *020 †20
AILIANI, Renuka Raju. 1836 SOUTH AVE, GUNDERSEN LUTHERAN CLINIC 54601 #496-38-1993 L2003 **IM** *020 †20
ALLEN, Laura Marie. ■ 54601 #016-42-2007 **TY** *012
ALVARADO, Mary Seigman. 1900 SOUTH AVE, MAIL STOP HO3-007 54601 #048-14-1996 L2004 **OBG** *020 †30
ANDERSEN, Ivy Marie. 1836 SOUTH AVE, GUNDERSEN LUTHERAN 54601 #018-03-2002 L2007 **N** *100
ANDERSEN, Jeremiah John. ■ 54601 #018-03-2002 L2007 **PTH** *100 †50
ANDERSON, Ben Hilton. ■ 54601 #005-11-1960 L1961 **GP** *072
ANDERSON, Hans Pierce. 1836 SOUTH AVE, GUNDERSEN CLINIC, LTD 54601 #026-04-1963 L1972 **P** *071 †75
ANDRESEN, Kristen Marie. 1836 SOUTH AVE 54601 #035-06-1998 L2006 **CD** *020 †20
ANIL, Gokhan. ■ 54601 #902-03-1999 L2007 **OBG** *020
ANNIS, Byron Lester. 1836 SOUTH AVE 54601 #017-20-1963 L1964 **NS** *071
ARIDA, Muammar. ■ 54601 #875-01-1996 L2006 **DMP** *020 †50
ASLAM, Rakshanda. 1900 SOUTH AVE, GUNDERSEN LUTHERAN MEDICAL 54601 #496-17-2002 **IM** *012
ASP, Arnold Allan. 1900 SOUTH AVE 54601 #023-12-1982 L1986 **END IM** *020 †20
BAKER, Matthew Todd. 1900 SOUTH AVE 54601 #010-01-1993 L2004 **GS** *020 †85
BAKER, William Vance. 603 KING ST 54601 #020-02-1947 L1952 **IM** *071 †20
BANDHAKAVI, Vijay Madhav. 1900 SOUTH AVE, DEPT OF INTERNAL MED 54601 #495-45-1999 **IM** *012
BANDYOPADHYAY, Sankar. 800 WEST AVE S 54601 #495-39-1988 L1998 **N** *020 †75
BANK, Paula Ann. 1707 MAIN ST, FAMILY & CHILDRENS CTR 54601 #025-12-1997 L2002 **CHP P** *020 †75
BAORTO, Marisa Anne. 700 WEST AVE S 54601 #024-05-1990 L2005 **IM** *020 †05
BARBIER, Arthur Gottfried. ■ 54601 #030-06-1962 L1971 **IM RHU** *071
BARTHEL, Mary Frances. 1900 SOUTH AVE, GUNDERSEN LUTHERAN 54601 #056-05-1999 L2000 **IM HOS** *020 †20
BARTOS, Craig Lee. 815 10TH ST S 54601 #016-01-1981 L1992 **FM** *040 †18
BEAHM, Mark Richard. ■ 54601 #056-06-2008 *012
BECKENBAUGH, Jeffrey P. 1900 SOUTH AVE 54601 #018-75-1997, ▲ L2005 **OAR** *020 †40
BEIER-HANRATTY, Sue Ann. 1900 SOUTH AVE 54601 #056-06-1980 L1981 **R IM** *020 †20,80
BENACCI, Joseph Carl. 1900 SOUTH AVE 54601 #041-01-1988 L2000 **PS** *020 †85,65
BENDEN, Dana Marie. 1900 SOUTH AVE 54601 #056-05-1997 L2000 **OBG** *020 †30
BERG, Laurence Clifford. 1900 SOUTH AVE, DEPT OF PATHOLOGY 54601 #026-04-1985 L1989 **ATP** *020 †50
BERKSETH, Timothy John. ■ 54601 #056-06-2008 *012
BILBISI, Montaser A. ■ 54601 #575-01-1991 L1994 **ID** *020 †20
BINEGAR, Joseph Brent. 1836 SOUTH AVE, GUNDERSEN LUTHERAN 54601 #037-01-1997 L2001 **PM** *020 †60
BIRD, Julio Javier. ■ 54601 #028-34-2005 L2008 **GS** *012
BIRKHOLZ, Emily Susan. ■ 54601 #026-04-2007 L2008 **TY** *012
BLANK, William Alden. W5843 VISTA DR 54601 #038-06-1968 L1973 **OPH** *020 †35
BLICHFELDT, Tracy Carol. ■ 54601 #056-05-2007 **IM** *012
BORGE, Karl Olaf. 1836 SOUTH AVE, URGENT CARE - C01-003 54601 #037-01-2000 L2001 **FM** *020 †18
BOTTCHER, Michael Louis. 1900 SOUTH AVE, GUNDERSEN CLINIC LTD 54601 #056-06-1986 L1987 **AN** *020 †05
BOTTNER, Wayne Arthur. 1900 SOUTH AVE, GUNDERSEN CLINIC LTD 54601 #035-20-1977 L1988 **HEM ON** *020 †20
BOURI, Manjeet Kaur. 1836 SOUTH AVE 54601 #495-08-1970 L1980 **P** *020
BOYD, William Chas. 1836 SOUTH AVE 54601 #018-03-1966 L1976 **GS** *020 †85
BRANDES, Angela Christine. 815 10TH ST S 54601 #026-04-2006 L2007 **FP** *012
BRASIC, Gerlyn Mae. 1900 SOUTH AVE 54601 #056-05-2000 L2000 **IM** *020 †20
BRAUNSCHWEIG, Jennifer Ly. 1900 SOUTH AVE 54601 #056-06-2000 L2001 **AN** *020 †05
BREKKE, Eric Fred. 1900 SOUTH AVE 54601 #056-05-1987 L1988 **GS** *020 †85
BROWN, Neil Eric. 800 WEST AVE S, FRANCISCAN SKEMP HEALTHCAR 54601 #036-05-1998 L2004 **OTO** *020 †45
BROWN, Ward Martin. 1836 SOUTH AVE, GUNDERSON CLINIC LTD 54601 #654-01-1981 L1982 **CD ICE** *020 †20
BRUMM, Jennifer L. 800 WEST AVE S 54601 #056-05-1993 L1996 **PD** *020 †55
BRUMM, Mark Roger. 800 WEST AVE S 54601 #056-05-1993 L1995 **FM** *020 †18
BRUNK, Scott Derauf. 1900 SOUTH AVE 54601 #018-03-1985 L1986 **EM FM** *020 †18
BURELBACH, John Charles. 1836 SOUTH AVE, GUNDERSEN LUTHERAN 54601 #016-11-1997 L2001 **AN** *020 †05
BUTLER, Aaron Mk. 800 WEST AVE S, FSH DEPT OF ORTHO 54601 #056-05-1997 L2002 **ORS** *020 †40
CAMPBELL, Lori Ann. 700 WEST AVE S 54601 #056-05-1984 L1985 **D** *020 †15
CAPLAN, Robert Henry. 1900 SOUTH AVE, GUNDERSEN CLINIC LTD 54601 #016-02-1961 L1969 **END IM** *020 †20
CARLISLE, Eugene James. 800 WEST AVE S 54601 #016-43-1967 L1974 **ORS** *020 †40
CARLISLE, Stephen Eugene. 1900 SOUTH AVE 54601 #026-08-1992 L1993 **AN** *020 †05
CARLSON, Bruce Allen. 700 WEST AVE S 54601 #056-05-1976 L1977 **FM** *020 †18
CARRASCO, Antonio Jose. 815 10TH ST S, MED PGM 54601 #026-08-2006 **FP** *012

CARROLL, Stephanie Lyn. 1900 SOUTH AVE 54601 #056-06-2001 L2004 **IM** *100 †20
CEJPEK, Karel Oto. 700 WEST AVE S 54601 #869-07-1954 L1957 **A PD** *071 †55,03
CHANEY, Ronald Geo. 1836 SOUTH AVE, GUNDERSEN CLINIC LTD 54601 #007-02-1982 L1983 **IM** *020 †20
CHAPMAN, Jennifer Rachel. 800 WEST AVE S 54601 #035-45-1997 L2004 **CRS** *020 †85,10
CHAPMAN, Scott C. 800 WEST AVE S 54601 #016-43-1998 L2003 **GS** *020 †85
CHESTNUT, David Hill. 1900 SOUTH AVE, GUNDERSEN LUTHERAN 54601 #001-02-1978 L2005 **AN OBG** *020 †30,05
CHIAL, Heather Joy. 1900 SOUTH AVE, GASTROENTEROLOGY C04-001 54601 #026-04-1997 L2003 **GE** *020 †20
CHIPLUNKER, Susmita. 700 WEST AVE S, FSH HEALTHCARE MAYO HEALTH 54601 #495-28-1973 L1983 **AN** *020 †20
CHRISTENSEN, Heather. 800 WEST AVE S 54601 #046-01-1992 L1993 **FM** *020 †18
CHRISTIAN, Mary Kathleen. 800 WEST AVE S 54601 #019-02-1991 L1996 **GS** *020 †85
CLEMONS, John Edward. 1836 SOUTH AVE 54601 #056-05-1962 L1963 **OTO HNS** *071 †45
CLOUSE, Kelly Thomas. 1900 SOUTH AVE 54601 #018-03-2000 L2004 **P** *020 †20
COGBILL, Thomas Hull. 1900 SOUTH AVE, GUNDERSEN CLINIC 54601 #007-02-1977 L1982 **VS GS** *020 †85
COLE, Craig Emmitt. 1900 SOUTH AVE 54601 #038-40-1995 L2003 **HO IM** *020
CONDIT, Randall Scott. ■ 54601 #056-05-1980 L1981 **OPH** *071 †35
CONNELLY, Mark Vincent. 1900 SOUTH AVE, GUNDERSEN CLINIC LTD 54601 #018-03-1969 L1971 **FPS OTO** *020 †45
CONNOLLY, James. ■ 54601 #539-06-1950 L1964 *020
CONWAY, Patrick Donald. 1836 SOUTH AVE, GUNDERSEN CLINIC LTD. 54601 #056-06-1988 L1989 **RO** *020 †80
CONZEMIUS, John Joseph. 1900 SOUTH AVE MS CO2-007, GUNDERSEN LUTHERAN 54601 #026-04-2000 L2001 **IM** *020 †20 ‡
COPPS, Stephen Clinton, Jr. 1900 SOUTH AVE, EMERGENCY SERVICES 54601 #026-04-2001 L2002 **EM** *020 †16
CORSER, David Hewson. 621 9TH ST S, APT 309 54601 #028-02-1954 L1959 **PD** *071 †55
COSTAKOS, Dennis Theodore. 700 WEST AVE S, FSH-MAYO HLTH SYSTEM 54601 #032-01-1984 L1989 **NPM PD** *020 †55 ‡
COWAN, Karen Korb. 815 10TH ST S, FRANCISCAN SKEMP-MAYO HLTH 54601 #056-05-1981 L1982 **FM** *040 †18
COX, Fred Ward. 1836 SOUTH AVE, GUNDERSEN LUTHERAN 54601 #041-13-1977 L2001 **IM OM** *020
COX, Timothy Raymond. 700 WEST AVE S, C/O URGENT CARE DEPT 54601 #019-02-2000 L2003 **FM** *020 †18 ‡
CRAMER, Gregory Lee. 800 WEST AVE S 54601 #016-11-1980 L1989 **GE IM** *020 †20
CULP, Kimberley Erbes. 1900 SOUTH AVE 54601 #035-03-1998 L2004 **AN CCA** *020 †05
DA COSTA, Wanir Correa. 700 WEST AVE S 54601 #187-13-1955 L1963 **OBG** *071 †30
DAILY, Wayne Wm. 1836 SOUTH AVE, GUNDERSEN CLINIC LTD 54601 #028-03-1972 L1982 **OTO** *020 †45
DALTON, Kathryn Elizabeth. ■ 54601 #038-40-2007 **FP** *012
DALTON, Ruth Margaret. N1946 FOREST RIDGE DR 54601 #016-11-1953 L1955 **PTH CLP** *071 †50
DAUN, Shannon Bobbie. 815 10TH ST S 54601 #056-06-2003 L2004 **FM** *020 †18
DAVIS, Clark Allan. 1836 SOUTH AVE, SURGERY - C05-001 54601 #054-04-1994 L1995 **VS** *020 †85
DAVIS, Jerry Arthur, II. 1900 SOUTH AVE, MS EB3-004 GUNDERSEN CLINI 54601 #001-02-1992 L1998 **NS** *020 †25
DEETZ, Daniel Craig. 800 WEST AVE S 54601 #026-04-1988 L1993 **PCC** *020 †20
DEGENHARDT, Jeffry Allan. 800 WEST AVE S 54601 #056-05-1992 L1997 **PTH** *020 †50
DERRIG, Pearse. 1900 SOUTH AVE 54601 #005-06-1979 L2003 **DR AM** *020 †80
DEVINE, Lori Anne. 800 WEST AVE S 54601 #026-04-1991 L1992 **FM** *020 †18
DEVINE, Stephen Michael. 1900 SOUTH AVE, GUNDERSEN LUTHERAN 54601 #028-34-1974 L1975 **IM** *020 †20
DHANAK, Kalpana Bankim. 1900 SOUTH AVE, GUNDERSEN CLINIC LTD 54601 #495-22-1977 L1984 **AN** *020 †05
DI BELLA, Michael David. 700 WEST AVE S 54601 #305-01-1988 L2001 **IM** *020 †20 ‡
DIETRICH, Leah Lizbeth. 1900 SOUTH AVE 54601 #026-04-1995 L1996 **ON** *020 †20
DIVI, Rama. 1836 SOUTH AVE 54601 #495-70-2002 **IM** *012
DOESCHER, Philip Orville. 1836 SOUTH AVE, GUNDERSEN LUTHERAN 54601 #026-04-1976 L1980 **RO** *020 †80
DOLAN, Michael James. 1836 SOUTH AVE 54601 #056-05-1987 L1988 **IM EM** *020 †20
DOMROESE, Mark Eric. 1836 SOUTH AVE 54601 #056-05-2001 L2003 **PM** *020 †60
DORIA, Maria Renee. 1836 SOUTH AVE, GUNDERSEN LUTHERAN HOSP 54601 #023-12-1995 L2007 **FM OM** *020 †18
DOUGLAS, Aaron Scott. 815 10TH ST S 54601 #026-04-2005 L2006 **FP** *012
DURST, Joseph B. 700 WEST AVE S 54601 #056-06-1951 L1952 **OBG** *071 †30
DYWAN-CORDER, Jolanta. 1900 SOUTH AVE 54601 #759-09-1987 **IM** *100
EARLE, Guy Harmon. 700 WEST AVE S 54601 #025-12-1976 L2005 **FM EM** *020 †18
EBERLEIN, Chris Matthew. 1900 SOUTH AVE 54601 #056-05-2001 L2002 **EM** *020 †16
EBERSOLD, Michael John. 800 WEST AVE S, FRANCISCAN SKEMP HEALTHCAR 54601 #056-05-1970 L1971 **NS** *020 †25
ECKLUND, Daniel John. 1900 SOUTH AVE 54601 #026-04-1995 L1996 **IM** *020 †20
EDLAND, Robert Wm. ■ 54601 #056-05-1956 L1957 **RO** *071 †80
EHLE, Joseph James. 1836 SOUTH AVE 54601 #026-04-2003 L2007 **AM** *020 *020
EILERS, Gayleen Marie. 1300 BADGER ST, UWL STUDENT HEALTH CENTER 54601 #030-05-1982 L1989 **FM** *020 †18
ELLENZ, George B. 805 CLIFFWOOD LN 54601 #016-43-1951 L1952 **R** *071 †80
ELLIS, Richard Leroy. 1900 SOUTH AVE 54601 #016-45-1991 L1992 **DR** *020 †80
ELLWEIN, Robert Wm. 700 WEST AVE S, FRANCISCAN SKEMP HLTHCARE 54601 #026-04-1975 L1976 **IM EM** *020 †20
ELSTON, Asaph Clayton, III. 2005 CASS ST 54601 #056-05-1964 L1965 **PDC PD** *020 †55
EMME, Matthew Albert. ■ 54601 #026-04-1997 L2003 **U** *020 †95
ENDRIZZI, Joseph Michael. 1900 SOUTH AVE, GUNDERSEN LUTHERAN 54601 #048-13-1991 L1993 **U** *020 †95
ENGEL, Charles Henry. 700 WEST AVE S 54601 #056-05-1964 L1965 **FM** *030
ENGELLAND, Emily Lynn. ■ 54601 #028-02-2001 L2005 **OM** *020 †70
ENGLISH, John T, Jr. 700 WEST AVE S 54601 #035-20-1964 L1987 **DR NM** *020 †80
ETTINGER, Robert S. 1900 SOUTH AVE 54601 #023-01-1976 L1997 **PHO PD** *020 †55
FAILLACE, Walter Joseph. 1900 SOUTH AVE, NEUROSCIENCE CENTER EB3-00 54601 #561-17-1980 L2002 **NS NSP** *020 †25
FALLER, Annette. 1900 SOUTH AVE 54601 #056-05-1994 L1995 **IM** *020 †20
FANTZ, Jon Scott. 700 WEST AVE S, FRANCISCAN SKEMP HEALTHCAR 54601 #016-06-1967 L2004 **IM GE** *020 †20

FARNEN, John Patrick. 1836 SOUTH AVE, GUNDERSEN LUTHERAN EB1-001 54601 #030-06-1982 L1991 **HEM ON** *020 †20

FEIGHNER, Brett Alan. 630 10TH ST S 54601 #025-01-1975 L1985 **FM** *040 †18

FELION, Paul Leegard. 1117 CLIFFWOOD LN 54601 #026-04-1958 L1966 **GYN** *071 †30

FERNANDES, Felix J. 1900 SOUTH AVE 54601 #917-02-1975 L1985 **AN PMM** *020 †05

FIELDS, Mary Christine. 1900 SOUTH AVE #048-02-1997 L2004 **P** *020 †75

FILLA, Joan Ellen. 1900 SOUTH AVE, GUNDERSEN-LUTHERAN 54601 #056-05-1996 L1997 **IM** *020 †20

FINK, Richard Alan. 1836 SOUTH AVE #021-01-1968 L1973 **HS OTR** *071 †40

FIRARY, Sylvie A. 1900 SOUTH AVE 54601 #016-43-1990 L1991 **ID IM** *020 †20

FISCHER, Gregory Glen. 1900 SOUTH AVE, GUNDERSEN CLINIC LTD 54601 #026-04-1979 L1983 **N** *020

FISHER, Caroline F. 800 WEST AVE S, FRANCISCAN SKEMP HEALTHCAR 54601 #056-05-1993 L1994 **IM** *020 †20

FLEISCHMANN, James Alan. 700 WEST AVE S 54601 #539-02-1975 L1990 *020

FOURNIER, Neesha Elizabet. ■ 54601 #025-12-2007 **IM** *012

FOWLER, Amy Marie. ■ 54601 #056-05-2007 L2008 **TY** *012

FRANTA, Peter John. 700 WEST AVE S, FRANCISCAN SKEMP MEDICAL C 54601 #026-04-1989 L1990 **FM** *020 †18

FREEDLAND, Robert Jos. 800 WEST AVE S 54601 #005-19-1980 L1986 **OPH** *020 †35

FRERKS, Tara Lee. ■ 54601 #026-04-2007 **FP** *012

FRIESEMA, Jill Suzanne. ■ 54601 #056-06-2008 *012

FRISBY, Thomas G. 1900 SOUTH AVE 54601 #026-08-1976 L1977 **FM** *020 †18

FROEMMING, Adam Timothy. 815 10TH ST S, MED PGM 54601 #028-02-2006 L2007 **DR** *012

FROHNAUER, Mary Kathleen. 1836 SOUTH AVE, GUNDERSEN LUTHERAN 54601 #017-20-1994 L1999 **END** *020 †20

FROMAN, Joshua Paul. ■ 54601 #026-04-2007 **GS** *012

FUNDELL, Larry James. 1836 SOUTH AVE, MAIL STOP C02-002 54601 #016-06-1972 L1997 **R** *020 †80

FURLONG, Lawrence D, Jr. 700 WEST AVE S, FRANCISCAN SKEMP HEALTHCAR 54601 #004-01-1971 L1974 **DR** *020 †80 ‡

GALL, Randall Jay. 1836 SOUTH AVE, GUNDERSEN-LUTHERAN 54601 #056-05-1968 L1971 **ORS OFA** *020 †40

GARZA, Ann Budzak. 1900 SOUTH AVE 54601 #056-05-1986 L1987 **PD** *020 †55

GEHAN, Beth Ann. 1910 SOUTH AVE, GUNDERSEN LUTHERAN MEDICAL 54601 #041-01-1999 L2003 **AN** *020 †05

GERHARD, David Gary. 1900 SOUTH AVE, GUNDERSEN LUTHERAN HOSP 54601 #056-05-2003 L2004 **PD** *100 †55

GHANDOUR, Fadi Z. 1836 SOUTH AVE 54601 #605-01-1988 L1999 **NEP** *020 †20

GILL, Paula. 700 WEST AVE S, FRANCISCAN SKEMP 54601 #038-06-1998 L2005 **HO** *020 †20

GILLEN, Benjamin Clark. ■ 54601 #035-06-2007 L2008 **TY** *012

GLASSER, James Edward. 1910 SOUTH AVE 54601 #023-07-1964 L1970 **IM ID** *020 †20

GLENNA REIN, Michelle Lee. 800 WEST AVE S 54601 #026-04-2001 L2002 **FM** *020 †18

GLOMSET, Daniel Anders. 2575 7TH ST S 54601 #016-21-1938 L1940 **IM GE** *071 †20

GO, Ronald S. 1900 SOUTH AVE 54601 #748-01-1991 L2000 **HO IM** *020 †20

GOODNOUGH, David Edwin. 1910 SOUTH AVE 54601 #056-05-1959 L1960 **AN CCM** *071 †05

GOODSETT, Mary Louise. 1900 SOUTH AVE EB3-002, GUNDERSEN LUTHERAN 54601 #056-05-1985 L1999 **N** *020 †75

GRAU, Harold John. ■ 54601 #018-03-1947 L1948 **GP OS** *071

GRAU, Thomas John. 815 10TH ST S 54601 #046-01-1977 L1988 **FM** *040 †18

GREENBERG, Todd David. ■ 54601 #038-06-1997 L2003 **DR R** *062 †80

GRENIER, Yannick. 1900 SOUTH AVE 54601 #016-02-1993 L2006 **NS** *020 †25

GRENISEN, Margaret Mary. 800 WEST AVE S, FRANCISCAN SKEMP HEALTHCAR 54601 #056-06-1984 L1992 **FM** *020 †18 ‡

GRILL, Karl Peter. 401 26TH PL N 54601 #056-05-1964 L1965 **OPH** *071 †35

GROON, Linda Christine. 1900 SOUTH AVE, H03-017 54601 #046-01-1996 L1997 **IM** *020 †20

GROOTWASSINK, Lois Wilma. 1900 SOUTH AVE, H02-002 54601 #026-04-1976 L1979 **AN** *020 †05

GROSHEK, Robert Ralph. 1900 SOUTH AVE 54601 #056-05-1991 L1995 **AN** *020 †05

GROSKREUTZ, James Lee. 1900 SOUTH AVE, GUNDERSEN LUTHERAN MEDICAL 54601 #026-04-1984 L1999 **GE IM** *020 †20

GUNDERSEN, A Erik. 1900 SOUTH AVE 54601 #024-01-1955 L1964 **CD TS** *071 †85,90

GUNDERSEN, Cameron B. ■ 54601 #024-05-1956 L1961 **PD** *071 †55

GUNDERSEN, Gunnar Adolf. 1836 SOUTH AVE 54601 #024-01-1948 L1950 **R NM** *071 †80,28

GUNDERSEN, Jerome Head. 1836 SOUTH AVE 54601 #056-05-1962 L1966 **OBG GP** *071 †30

GUNDERSEN, Lincoln Hugh. 1836 SOUTH AVE, GUNDERSEN CLINIC LTD 54601 #010-01-1984 L1987 **DR** *020 †80

GUNDERSEN, Sigurd B, Jr. 1836 SOUTH AVE 54601 #024-01-1948 L1952 **GS** *071 †85

GUNDERSEN, Sigurd B, III. 1836 SOUTH AVE 54601 #016-06-1983 L1984 **GS OS** *020 †85

HABEL, Theodor. 615 10TH ST S 54601 #056-05-1966 L1967 **OS FM** *020

HAGAN, Brian Michael. 1900 SOUTH AVE, GUNDERSEN LUTHERAN 54601 #030-06-1986 L1992 **PUD PCC** *020 †20

HAHN, Myung Ho. 700 WEST AVE S, FRANCICAN-SKEM HEALTHCARE 54601 #583-01-1967 L2000 **PCC IM** *020 †20

HALBERT, Helen E. RR 2 54601 #041-07-1953 L1970 **P** *071 †75

HALLER, Karen Elizabeth. 20 COPELAND AVE 54603 #056-05-1988 L1989 **OBG** *020 †30

HAND, Andy Allan. 1900 SOUTH AVE, MAIL STOP C05-001 54601 #045-04-2004 L2006 **GS** *012

HANMER, Clark Beryl. N1961 HICKORY LN 54601 #025-07-1977 L1996 **FM** *020 †18

HANNA, James D, Jr. 1836 SOUTH AVE, GUNDERSEN LUTHERAN 54601 #056-06-1983 L1984 **PD** *020 †20

HARBIN, Adie Danl, III. 1900 SOUTH AVE, GUNDERSEN LUTHERAN 54601 #038-41-1978 L1984 **CD** *020 †20

HARBST, Timothy Alexander. 1836 SOUTH AVE, GUNDERSEN CLINIC LTD 54601 #020-02-1984 L1985 **PM PMM** *020 †60

HARELSON, Jennifer Jo. 700 WEST AVE S, FRANCISCAN-SKEMP 54601 #056-05-2002 L2003 **FM** *020 †18

HARPENAU, Judith S. 800 WEST AVE S, FRANCISCAN SKEMP HEALTHCARE 54601 #018-03-1992 L1995 **FM** *020 †18

HARTIGAN, J Michael. 125 16TH ST S 54601 #035-15-1963 L1970 **PD NPM** *020 †55

HAUS, Lindsay Mae. ■ 54601 #056-06-2008 *012

HAWKER, Rachel M. 1836 SOUTH AVE, MB C01-005 54601 #037-01-2002 L2004 **IM HOS** *020 †20

HAYDEN, Charles Hamilton. 1900 SOUTH AVE 54601 #016-06-1981 L1984 **ORS HS** *020 †40

HAYDEN, John Wood. W5831 COULEE SPRINGS LN 54601 #035-15-1947 L1958 **ORS** *071 †40

HELLIESEN, Per Jakob. GUNDERSON CLINIC 54601 #869-07-1951 L1958 **PD** *020 †55

HENDRICKSON, David John. 800 WEST AVE S 54601 #056-05-1974 L1975 **EM** *020 †16

HENRY, Michael John. 1900 SOUTH AVE MS H05-007, GUNDERSON CLINIC LTD 54601 #005-06-1985 L1990 **DIA IM** *020 †20

HER, Cheng. 1900 SOUTH AVE 54601 #026-04-1996 L1997 **FM** *020 †18

HER, Stacy Ann. 1900 SOUTH AVE 54601 #026-04-1996 L1997 **PM** *020 †60,55

HILL, Marie Eleanore. 700 WEST AVE S 54601 #026-04-2004 L2005 **FM** *020 †18

HILLESLAND, Jeffery D. 1836 SOUTH AVE 54601 #037-01-1985 L1988 **EM** *020 †16

HLAING, Win Cho. 700 WEST AVE S, FRANCISCAN SKEMP 54601 #209-01-1990 L2006 **IM** *020 †20

HOEFERT, James Ralph. 1900 SOUTH AVE, GUNDERSEN LUTHERAN FAMILY 54601 #056-05-1974 L1975 **FM** *020 †18

HOEG, Rasmus Tetens. 1900 SOUTH AVE 54601 #297-01-2005 L2007 **IM** *012

HOLROYD, Michelle Marie. 815 10TH ST S, MED PGM 54601 #056-06-2005 L2006 **FP** *012

HOOYMAN, Joseph Robt. 700 WEST AVE S, FRANCISCAN SKEMP HEALTHCAR 54601 #026-08-1983 L2005 **DR** *020 †80

HORTH, Kenneth Sherman. 1910 SOUTH AVE, GASTROENTEROLOGY C04-001 54601 #038-06-1979 L1998 **IM GE** *020 †20

HOUSKAMP, John Rhine. 1836 SOUTH AVE, GUNDERSEN LUTHERAN 54601 #025-01-1992 L2007 **IM** *020 †20

HOWARD, Richard Staunton. 1836 SOUTH AVE, GUNDERSEN CLINIC 54601 #041-01-1957 L1966 **U** *020 †95

HOWELLS, Kathryn Sally. 800 WEST AVE S, FRANCISCAN SKEMP HEALTH CA 54601 #010-02-1987 L1996 **FM** *020 †18

HRUSKA, Kerry Lee. 815 10TH ST S 54601 #026-04-1975 L1980 **N** *020

HUIRAS, Christopher M. 800 WEST AVE S 54601 #056-05-1983 L1984 **GS VS** *020 †85

HUTTER, Richard Donald. 1900 SOUTH AVE, GUNDERSEN LUTHERAN 54601 #026-04-1976 L1981 **N** *020 †75

IHLE, Peter Mandelert. 1836 SOUTH AVE 54601 #056-05-1967 L1968 **ORS** *071 †40

INFANTE, Mauricio. 700 WEST AVE S, FRANCISCAN SKEMP-MAYO HEAL 54601 #264-05-1995 L2004 **P** *020 †75

IYER, Varsha V. 1900 SOUTH AVE 54601 #035-03-1999 L2000 **NR** *020 †80

IYER, Venkateshwaran. 800 WEST AVE S, FRANCISCAN SKEMP HEALTHCAR 54601 #495-17-1989 L1999 **NEP** *020 †20

JACKSON, Pauline M. 1836 SOUTH AVE 54601 #005-11-1961 L1972 **P** *071 †75

JAEGER, John Gustave. 800 WEST AVE S 54601 #056-05-1967 L1968 **AN** *020 †05

JAHANGIR, Mory. 700 WEST AVE S, SKEMP HEALTHCARE 54601 #016-06-1974 L2001 **DR PD** *020 †80

JANIS, John Francis. 2769 HAGEN RD 54601 #056-06-1959 L1968 **PTH DMP** *020 †50

JARMAN, Benjamin Thomas. ■ 54601 #017-20-1999 L2004 **GS** *020

JARRETT, Anthony M. 700 WEST AVE S 54601 #016-06-1983 L1990 **OPH** *020 †35

JEDELE, Kerry Baldwin. 1900 SOUTH AVE 54601 #056-05-1985 L2005 **PD** *020 †19,55

JENSEN, Arno Lee. 700 WEST AVE S, FRANCISCAN SKEMP MEDICAL 54601 #018-03-1956 L2003 **R GPM** *020 †80

JOHNSON, Benjamin Henry. 1900 SOUTH AVE 54601 #026-04-1988 L1989 **EM** *020 †18

JOHNSON, Gordon Le Roy. 1836 SOUTH AVE 54601 #018-03-1968 L1971 **CD IM** *020 †20

JOHNSON, Jeanne Marie. 1900 SOUTH AVE, GUNDERSEN CLINIC 54601 #026-04-1994 L1995 **GS SO** *020 †85

JOHNSON, Lee Ann. 800 WEST AVE S 54601 #018-03-1991 L2000 **PD** *020 †55

JURIA, Ruth P. 1836 SOUTH AVE, GUNDERSEN FNDN/LA CROS LUT 54601 #748-07-1981 **IM** *100

JUVVIGUNTA, Vasthala. 1900 SOUTH AVE, DEPT OF INTERNAL MED 54601 #495-11-2002 **IM** *012

KADER, Nabil Mohamed. 700 WEST AVE S 54601 #330-04-1956 L1971 **U** *071 †95

KAMPSHOFF, Jesse Leigh. 1900 SOUTH AVE 54601 #046-01-2004 L2006 **GS** *012

KANAGALA, Anita. 800 WEST AVE S 54601 #919-02-1994 L2004 **FM** *020 †18

KANG, Seuk Bong. 1910 SOUTH AVE 54601 #583-04-1965 L1971 **AN** *020 †05

KAUPHUSMAN, James Richard. 1836 SOUTH AVE, GUNDERSEN CLINIC LTD 54601 #037-01-1976 L1980 **IM NTR** *020 †20

KAZAKS, Klavs. 1836 SOUTH AVE, GUNDERSEN CLINIC LTD 54601 #065-05-1973 L1978 **DR** *062 †80

KEON, Joy Elizabeth. N1979 JOY LN 54601 #065-09-1986 L2000 **FM** *020

KISKEN, William Albert. 1910 SOUTH AVE 54601 #016-02-1958 L1961 **GS END** *071 †85

KITOWSKI, Nicholas Jerome. 1900 SOUTH AVE, GUNDERSEN LUTHERAN HOSPITA 54601 #056-06-2006 L2007 **GS** *012

KLEMOND, Thomas James, Jr. 1900 SOUTH AVE 54601 #026-04-1999 L2000 **IM** *020 †20

KLEVEN, James Gross. 1900 SOUTH AVE 54601 #056-06-1999 L2003 **AN** *020 †05

KLINE, Kelly Hodgson. 1836 SOUTH AVE, GUNDERSEN LUTHERAN 54601 #056-05-1997 L2000 **PD** *020 †55

KNORR, Gregory Mark. 1836 SOUTH AVE, GUNDERSEN LUTHERAN 54601 #056-06-2000 L2001 **IM** *020 †20

KNUFFMAN, Jason Edward. 1836 SOUTH AVE, GUNDERSEN LUTHER 54601 #028-34-2001 L2002 **AI** *020 †20,03

KONERU, Praveen. 800 WEST AVE S, FRANCISCAN SKEMP HEALTHCAR 54601 #495-50-1997 L2007 **IM** *020 †20

KORDUCKI, Jane Marie. 700 WEST AVE S 54601 #056-06-1985 L1987 **END IM** *020 †20

KOSIAK, Brian J. 700 WEST AVE S 54601 #025-12-1984 L2004 **IM GP** *020 †20

KOSTAMO, Katherine Louise. 800 WEST AVE S 54601 #026-04-1986 L1995 **NM** *020 †20,28

KOTHARI, Shanu Nikhil. 1836 SOUTH AVE, GUNDERSEN LUTHERAN 54601 #016-11-1995 L1996 **GS** *020 †85

KRAUSE, Forrest Jon. 1836 SOUTH AVE, GUNDERSEN LUTHERAN 54601 #056-05-1987 L2002 **AN** *020 †05

KRISTER, Laura Elizabeth. 1900 SOUTH AVE, GUNDERSON CLINIC LTD 54601 #038-43-1982 L1983 **FM** *020 †20

KROKER, George Frederick. 700 WEST AVE S 54601 #034-01-1975 L1981 **A IM** *020 †20

KRUECKEBERG, Steven Thos. 1910 SOUTH AVE 54601 #017-20-1980 L1988 **DR** *020 †80

KRUMHOLZ, Alan Jay. 800 WEST AVE S 54601 #035-08-1976 L2001 **PD ADL** *030 †55

KUFFEL, Mary Elizabeth. 1900 SOUTH AVE 54601 #018-03-1993 L1997 **OBG** *020 †30

KULKARNI, Amit Prakash. 1900 SOUTH AVE 54601 #056-06-2004 L2005 **IM** *020 †20

KWONG, Roger Waynsan. 1836 SOUTH AVE, GUNDERSEN CLINIC LTD 54601 #026-04-1972 L1977 **ON IM** *020 †20

LA BREC, Henry Clayton. ■ 54601 #056-05-1956 L1957 **D** *071 †15

LABUZZETTA, James Wm. 700 WEST AVE S, FRANCISCAN SKEMP HEALTH CA 54601 #035-06-1990 L1999 **IM** *020 †20

LAHMANN, Jennifer Sue. 1836 SOUTH AVE, GUNDERSEN LUTHERAN 54601 #026-04-1996 L2004 **CHP** *020 †75

LANDERCASPER, Jeffrey. 1900 SOUTH AVE 54601 #007-02-1980 L1982 **GS** *020 †85

LANGE, Danny Burton. 1900 SOUTH AVE, GUNDERSEN CLINIC LTD 54601 #026-04-1982 L1987 OPH *020 †35

LANKIREDDY, Srilakshmi. 1900 SOUTH AVE, DEPT OF INTERNAL MED 54601 #495-50-2003 IM *012

LANSING, Kimberly Miller. 1900 SOUTH AVE, DEPT OF FAMILY MED 54601 #014-01-1995 L1997 FM *020 †18

LARSEN, Brian Keith. 700 WEST AVE S, FRANCISCAN SKEMP HEALTHCARE 54601 #056-05-1998 L2002 AN *020

LARSON, Shawn Gene. 212 11TH ST S 54601 #056-05-1997 L1998 P *020

LATHROP, Thomas Paul. 1900 SOUTH AVE 54601 #056-05-1969 L1970 IM *020 †20

LAUGHLIN, Michael John, Jr. 800 WEST AVE S 54601 #016-11-2000 L2003 EM *020 †16

LAUTZ, David Wm. 1900 SOUTH AVE 54601 #056-05-1981 L1986 DR RNR *020

LEACH, Christopher Lane. 1836 SOUTH AVE, GUNDERSEN LUTHERAN 54601 #041-02-1973 L1989 TS *020 †85,90

LEBEAU, Michael E. 1900 SOUTH AVE 54601 #037-01-2002 L2003 NEP *012 †20

LEDBETTER, Emma Katherine. 1836 SOUTH AVE 54601 #048-15-1974 L1975 EM *020 †16

LEE, Jeffrey Allan. 1836 SOUTH AVE, GUNDERSEN LUTHERAN 54601 #023-12-1994 L1996 GPM *020

LEE, Kyla Renee. 1900 SOUTH AVE 54601 #056-05-1998 L2000 IM *020 †20

LEE, Tracy Jaewon. 1900 SOUTH AVE 54601 #035-08-1999 L2003 DR *020 †80

LEE, Young Kyoon. 1900 SOUTH AVE, GUNDESEN LUTHERAN 54601 #583-02-1967 L1976 AN *020 †05

LEEHEY, Paul Jos. 1900 SOUTH AVE 54601 #018-03-1982 L1990 R *020 †80

LENSELINK, Daniel R. 700 WEST AVE S, FRANCISCAN SKEMP HEALTHCAR 54601 #056-06-1995 L1996 FM *020 †20

LERBERG, Kristen Marjorie. 800 WEST AVE S, FRANCISCAN SKEMP HLTHCARE 54601 #056-05-2004 L2005 FM *020 †18

LINDESMITH, Larry Alan. W4965 WOODHAVEN DR 54601 #036-05-1963 L1969 OM PUD *071 †20

LINEBARGER, Jared Harris. 1836 SOUTH AVE 54601 #017-20-2006 L2008 GS *012

LINK, Charles Elmer. 1900 SOUTH AVE, GUNDERSEN LUTHERAN 54601 #056-06-1962 L1965 OS *030 †20

LOEPFE, Thomas Roy. 700 WEST AVE S, FRANCISCAN SKEMP 54601 #026-08-1992 L1996 IMG PLM *012

LONDERGAN, Thomas Andrew. 1900 SOUTH AVE 54601 #041-02-1988 L1994 U UP *020 †95

MACCHARLES, Daniel C. 1900 SOUTH AVE 54601 #041-09-1996 L1999 FM *020 †18

MACLELLAN TOBERT, Susan G. 1910 SOUTH AVE, GUNDERSEN LUTHERAN MEDICAL 54601 #060-01-1989 L1995 PDC PD *020 †55

MAHAIRAS, Gregory Harry. 1836 SOUTH AVE 54601 #035-05-1959 L1966 OBG *071 †30

MAIN, Laura. 1836 SOUTH AVE, GUNDERSEN LUTHERAN HOSP 54601 #028-79-2007, ▲ IM *012

MANNION, James Patrick. 700 WEST AVE S 54601 #028-03-1987 L1990 FM *020 †18

MANSKE, Brian Richard. 1836 SOUTH AVE, GUNDERSEN CLINIC LTD 54601 #056-05-1978 L1982 DR *020 †80

MANSON, Steven Robt. 1900 SOUTH AVE, GUNDERSON CLINIC LTD 54601 #016-45-1981 L1982 PD ADL *020 †55

MARCHIANDO, Richard Jos. 1836 SOUTH AVE 54601 #056-05-1969 L1972 ORS *020 †40

MARSHALL, Angus. 800 WEST AVE S 54601 #048-13-1992 L1997 DR *020 †80

MARTIN, Lynn Thos. 1836 SOUTH AVE, GUNDERSEN CLINIC LTD 54601 #056-05-1977 L1982 PS OTO *020 †45,65

MATEY, Joan Patricia. 1900 SOUTH AVE, GUNDERSEN LUTHERAN 54601 #025-07-1981 L1985 IM IMG *020 †20

MATTINGLEY, Jennifer Susa. 1836 SOUTH AVE, GUNDERSEN LUTHERAN 54601 #037-01-2005 L2006 IM *012

MAVES, Stephanie Novak. 815 10TH ST S 54601 #056-06-2005 L2006 FP *012

MC CARTHY, David Danl. 1836 SOUTH AVE, GUNDERSEN CLINIC, LTD 54601 #056-05-1985 L1999 N DR *020 †75

MC DONNELL, Dennis Edward. 1900 SOUTH AVE 54601 #030-06-1962 L2000 NS *020 †25

MC MILLEN, Milton Remes. 700 WEST AVE S 54601 #056-05-1974 L1975 EM *020 †16 ‡

MEADE, Andrew Allen. 1836 SOUTH AVE, 1836 SOUTH AVE 54601 #025-01-1974 L1993 R *020 †80

MELNYK, George John. 700 WEST AVE S, FRANCISCAN SKEMP HRALTHCAR 54601 #748-18-1983 L1986 P ADM *020 †75 ‡

MENAGH, Clayton John. 700 WEST AVE S 54601 #030-05-1980 L1983 PD NPM *020 †18,55

MENKE, Tyler Craig. ■ 54601 #018-03-2007 FP *012

MERFELD, John Michael. 815 10TH ST S 54601 #056-06-1995 L1996 FM *020 †18

MERKITCH, Kenneth Wm. 1900 SOUTH AVE, MAIL STOP C03-002 54601 #016-06-1984 L1988 OBG *020 †30

METZLER, David Walter. 1836 SOUTH AVE, GUNDERSEN LUTHERAN 54601 #056-06-1988 L1991 P *020 †75

MEYERS, Michael Stephen. 700 WEST AVE S, FRANCISCAN SKEMP HEALTHCAR 54601 #005-06-1984 L1986 AN *030 †05

MEYERS, Mike Scott. 800 WEST AVE S 54601 #056-06-1991 L1996 CD *020 †20

MIDTHUN, Mark Alan. 1836 SOUTH AVE, NORFOLK REGIONAL CENTER 54601 #018-03-1989 L2007 P *020 †75 ‡

MILLER, Charles H, III. 3305 GREENSPIRE LN 54601 #056-05-1962 L1963 GS *071 †85

MILLER, Christine Diane. 1836 SOUTH AVE 54601 #026-04-1987 L1988 IM ADM *020 †20

MILLER, Christine Maria. 1900 SOUTH AVE 54601 #056-05-1996 L1997 DR *020 †80

MILLER, Jerry James, II. 1900 SOUTH AVE, GUNDERSEN CLINIC LTD 54601 #056-05-1988 L1989 D *020 †15

MINER, Edward Budd. 1836 SOUTH AVE 54601 #056-05-1957 L1964 IM *071 †20

MOMONT, David Alex. 1900 SOUTH AVE, GUNDERSEN LUTHERAN 54601 #026-04-1985 L1986 IM EM *020 †20

MOMONT, Sheila L. 1910 SOUTH AVE 54601 #018-03-1985 L1986 IM IMG *020 †20

MONAGHAN, Kathleen Lynn. 1836 SOUTH AVE 54601 #054-04-1996 L1997 GS *020 †85

MORGAN, William Alfred. 1836 SOUTH AVE 54601 #035-20-1956 L1964 IM ID *071 †20

MORRELL, David Scott. 1900 SOUTH AVE, MAIL CODE C02-002 54601 #056-05-1998 L2006 DR *020 †80

MORRIS, David Leslie. 615 10TH ST S 54601 #056-05-1954 L1956 A *020 †18,03

MORRIS, Mary Sacia. 615 10TH ST S 54601 #056-05-1983 L1984 IM A *020 †20

MORRISON, David John. 1900 SOUTH AVE 54601 #030-06-1982 L1987 AN CCM *020 †05

MORRISSEY, John Edward. 700 WEST AVE S 54601 #016-06-1981 L1989 ORS *020 †40

MOST, Robert Elmer. 513 MAIN ST STE C 54601 #036-01-1989 L1994 P *020

MOUSER, Matthew James. 1836 SOUTH AVE 54601 #026-04-2004 L2005 IM *100 †20

MUELLER, Kurt Karl. 1900 SOUTH AVE, DEPT OF DERMATOLOGY 54601 #030-05-1990 L1998 D *020 †15

MULRENNAN, Brian Malcolm. 1900 SOUTH AVE 54601 #026-04-1984 L1985 IM IMG *020 †20

MUMME, Daniel Elroy. 1900 SOUTH AVE 54601 #026-04-2005 L2006 GS *012

NAIK, Vinay Shamkant. ■ 54601 #495-01-1993 L2006 HMP *100 †50

NARAYANA RAO GARI, Swapna. 1900 SOUTH AVE, DEPT OF INTERNAL MED 54601 #495-21-2003 IM *012

NAYAK, Tanaya. 1900 SOUTH AVE 54601 #495-79-1997 L2005 IM *020 †20

NELSON, David Lee. 800 WEST AVE S 54601 #056-06-1973 L1976 PD *020 †20

NELSON, Douglas Raymond. 700 WEST AVE S 54601 #026-04-1984 L1989 AI PD *020 †03,55

NELSON, Evan Robert. 800 WEST AVE S, FRANCISCAN SKEMP HEALTHCAR 54601 #016-11-1993 L1997 PM *020 †60

NELSON, Martin John. 700 WEST AVE S, FRANCISCAN SKEMP HEALTH CA 54601 #023-07-1983 L1994 DR *020 †80

NELSON, Mary N. 1900 SOUTH AVE 54601 #056-06-1978 L1979 DR *020 †80

NELSON, Peter J. 2605 BAUMGARTNER DR, MEMORIAL HOSPITAL 54603 #056-06-1978 L1979 AN *020 †05

NEWCOMER, Kermit Lee. ■ 54601 #038-06-1959 L1967 NEP IM *071 †20

NIGOGOSYAN, Mark Aram. 1836 SOUTH AVE, GUNDERSEN CLINIC LTD 54601 #035-06-1984 L1989 DR *020 †80

NOACK, Nelleen Grace. 1900 SOUTH AVE 54601 #056-05-1977 L1993 PD *020 †55

NORENBERG, David Del. 1900 SOUTH AVE, GUNDERSEN LUTHERAN 54601 #056-05-1970 L1971 IM *020 †20

NYGREN, Eric. 700 WEST AVE S, FRANCISCAN SKEMP 54601 #026-08-2001 L2006 AN *020 †05

O'BRIEN, Michael John. 700 WEST AVE S 54601 #056-06-1984 L1988 IM *020 †20

O'BRIEN, Sylvia V. 1300 BADGER ST, STUDENT HEALTH CENTER 54601 #056-06-1984 L1988 FM *020 †18

O'LEARY, William Jos, Jr. W5437 HORSESHOE PL 54601 #056-06-1962 L1963 OBG *071 †30

OLIVEIRA, Alice Santoro. 700 WEST AVE S, DEPT FM 54601 #047-07-2007 FP *012

OLSEN, Thomas Gary. ■ 54603 #056-05-1956 L1957 R *071 †80

OLSON, Cheri Lynn. 815 10TH ST S 54601 #026-04-1984 L1989 FM FPG *040 †18

OLSON, Gregory Dean. 1836 SOUTH AVE 54601 #016-11-1988 L1994 FM *020 †18

OLSON, Richard Alan. 1836 SOUTH AVE, GUNDERSEN CLINIC LTD 54601 #026-04-1975 L1985 AN FM *020 †05

OMANS, Judson Frank. 1900 SOUTH AVE 54601 #026-04-1981 L1984 EM *020 †16

O'MEARA, Mark Thos. 2536 MADISON PL 54601 #056-06-1942 L1943 GS OM *071 †85

OSWALD, Sarah Lynn. 1900 SOUTH AVE 54601 #056-06-2003 L2005 AN *012

OTTO, William Carl. ■ 54601 #045-04-2000 L2002 GPM *020 †70

OVERHOLT, Edwin Lowell. N1965 HICKORY LN 54601 #018-03-1948 L1958 IM *071 †20

OVERHOLT, Steven Lowell. 1836 SOUTH AVE, GUNDERSEN CLINIC LTD 54601 #016-02-1972 L1980 OTO *020 †45

PANGILINAN, Willie M. 800 WEST AVE S 54601 #748-01-1987 L1994 IM *020 †20

PARAMESH, Venki. 1900 SOUTH AVE 54601 #019-02-1989 L2001 TS *020 †85,90

PATEL, Divya Umang. 1900 SOUTH AVE, GUNDERSEN LUTHERAN 54601 #495-23-1999 L2005 IM *020

PATEL, Nirav Yashwantrai. 1900 SOUTH AVE 54601 #056-05-1992 L1993 CCS *020 †85

PAVELA, Stephen Lawrence. 700 WEST AVE S 54601 #026-04-1975 L1979 IM *020 †20

PEARSON, Steven Bradley. 1836 SOUTH AVE, GUNDERSEN LUTHERAN 54601 #056-06-1983 L1984 IM *020 †20

PECK, Theodore Morton. 1836 SOUTH AVE, GUNDERSEN CLINIC LTD 54601 #007-02-1972 L1979 OBG *020 †30

PEDERSON, John Francis. W5237 BOMA RD 54601 #056-05-1972 L1973 PTH *071 †50

PERPICH, Mark Stephen. 800 WEST AVE S 54601 #056-05-1977 L1978 ORS *020 †40

PERSHING, John Joseph. 1836 SOUTH AVE, GUNDERSEN LUTHERAN 54601 #056-05-1984 L1985 EM IM *020 †20,16

PETERS, Antoinette Marie. 1900 SOUTH AVE, EB2-002 54601 #056-05-2000 L2006 PHO *100 †55

PETERSON, Kristen. 1900 SOUTH AVE 54601 #026-04-1996 L1996 PD *020 †55

PHILLIPS, Todd Christian. 1900 SOUTH AVE 54601 #056-05-1996 L2000 EM *020 †16

PICK, Peter Wm. 700 WEST AVE S, NEUROLOGY SERVICE-FRANCISC 54601 #016-06-1975 L1998 N NP *020 †50,75

PIDADY, Vrushali Vinayak. ■ 54601 #496-30-1993 L1996 IMG *020 †18 ‡

PILLAI, Ajit Kesara. 1836 SOUTH AVE 54601 #495-73-1974 L1979 P *020 †75

PINGALI, Sai Ravi Kiran. 1836 SOUTH AVE 54601 #495-21-2003 IM *012

PLAGMAN, Ewa. 1836 SOUTH AVE, GUNDERSEN LUTHERAN 54601 #759-09-1986 L2004 DR *020 †80

PORTER, Michael Brent. 800 WEST AVE S 54601 #024-07-1984 L1993 PTH *020 †50

PRACHTHAUSER, Tracy Beth. ■ 54601 #056-06-2006 L2007 TY *012

PRATT, Alan Duane. 1900 SOUTH AVE, GUNDERSON LUTHERON 54601 #056-05-1980 L1996 PUD *020 †20

PRICE, Michael John. 800 WEST AVE S 54601 #040-02-1975 L1995 U *020 †95

PROCTOR, Brian Dale. 212 11TH ST S, FRANCISCAN SKEMP HEALTHACR 54601 #018-03-1983 L1998 P *020 †75

PROPER, Jacqueline Ann. 1900 SOUTH AVE 54601 #026-08-1995 L2004 AN PME *020 †05

PUCHAKAYALA, Bharat Kumar. 1836 SOUTH AVE 54601 #495-73-2004 IM *012

QUETSCH, Joseph Leonard. ■ 54601 #018-03-1979 L1980 GP EM *020

RABINDRANAUTH, Prem. 1900 SOUTH AVE 54601 #041-02-1993 L2002 TS *020 †85,90

RADEMACHER, Dana Ellis. 800 WEST AVE S 54601 #067-02-1992 L1998 U *020 †95

RAGHAVENDRA, Meghana. 1900 SOUTH AVE 54601 #496-31-2003 L2006 IM *012

RAJASEKARAN, Smita Yvonne. 1836 SOUTH AVE, GUNDERSEN LUTHERAN 54601 #690-02-1992 L2007 IM *100 †20

RAMLOW, Robert W. 1910 SOUTH AVE 54601 #056-05-1943 L1946 IM *071

RASOOL, Haleem Jawed. 700 WEST AVE S, FRANCISCAN SKEMP HEALTHCARE 54601 #704-02-1987 L2003 HO *020 †20

RATHGABER, Mary Dively. ■ 54601 #017-20-1988 L1989 N *020 †75

RATHGABER, Scott Wm. 1900 SOUTH AVE 54601 #017-20-1988 L1997 GE *020 †20

REIMANN, Leah. 1836 SOUTH AVE, GUNDERSON CLINIC LTD 54601 #056-05-1974 L1975 PD *020 †55

RENNEBOHM, John A. 1910 SOUTH AVE, GUNDERSEN LUTHERAN 54601 #056-05-1952 L1955 P *071 †75

RENWICK, Richard Francis. 1900 SOUTH AVE 54601 #056-05-1976 L1992 OBG *020 †30

REYNERTSON, Richard H. 1900 SOUTH AVE 54601 #016-11-1965 L1986 END IM *020 †20

RHO, David Seungwoo. 800 WEST AVE S 54601 #583-06-1962 L1975 AN *071 †05

RICHARDSON, James Dale. 700 WEST AVE S 54601 #056-05-1977 L1978 FM *020 †18

RIEGERT-JOHNSON, Vanessa. 1836 SOUTH AVE C01-005, MEDICAL FOU 54601 #026-08-2003 L2005 IM *020 †18

RIGDEN, Jonathan Robt. 800 WEST AVE S, SKEMP CLINIC LTD 54601 #028-03-1984 L1991 FM *020 †18

ROBERTS, Cameron Frank. 1900 SOUTH AVE 54601 #056-05-1971 L1972 **DR** *020 †80

RODMAN, Charles A, II. ■ 54601 #035-20-1961 L1970 **NS** *071 †25

ROLTGEN, Carmen Marie. 815 10TH ST S 54601 #056-06-2003 L2004 **FM** *100 †18

ROSKOS, Michael C. 700 WEST AVE S 54601 #056-05-1994 L1999 **GS** *020 †85

RUMBALL, Kevin M. 1836 SOUTH AVE 54601 #065-05-1987 L1997 **ORS** *020 †40

RUSHLOW, David Robt. 815 10TH ST S 54601 #056-06-1990 L1991 **FM** *020 †18

RYAN, Catherine Rose. 1836 SOUTH AVE, GUNDERSEN CLINIC, LTD. 54601
#026-04-1990 L1993 **OBG REN** *020 †30

RYAN, Dennis Kohlmann. 1836 SOUTH AVE, GUNDERSEN CLINIC LTD 54601
#024-04-1966 L1974 **OPH PO** *071 †35

SABNIS, Vijay Keshav. 615 10TH ST S, ALLERGY ASSC. OF LACROSSE 54601
#496-38-1966 L1982 **AI PD** *071 †25

SALEH, Ezzeldin Abdulgadi. 800 WEST AVE S 54601 #848-01-1995 L2007 **PD** *020 †55

SALLAWAY, Rhonda. 1900 SOUTH AVE, GUNDERSON LUTHERAL 54601 #056-05-1996 L1997
IM *020 †20

SARTIN, Jeffrey Scott. 1836 SOUTH AVE, GUNDERSON CLINIC 54601 #012-05-1986 L2000
IM ID *020 †20

SATERBAK, Andrew Todd. 1836 SOUTH AVE, DEPT OF ORTHOPAEDIC SURGER 54601
#056-06-1988 L1993 **ORS** *020 †40

SCHAER, Rachel Anne. 1900 SOUTH AVE 54601 #016-43-1995 L1996 **FM** *020 †18

SCHAMS, Peter John. 700 WEST AVE S 54601 #056-06-2001 L2005 **AN** *020 †05

SCHAUBERGER, Charles Wm. 1900 SOUTH AVE, GUNDERSON CLINIC 54601
#018-03-1978 L1982 **OBG REN** *020 †30

SCHAWE, Allen Frederick. 800 WEST AVE S, FRANCISCAN SKEMP HEALTHCAR 54601
#035-15-1989 L1990 **FM** *020 †18

SCHLACK, Steven Craig. 1900 SOUTH AVE, MS H05-007 54601 #056-05-1991 L1992
GE *020 †20

SCHMIDT, Carl Frederick. 1908 29TH ST S 54601 #056-05-1956 L1957 **OPH** *071 †35

SCHMIDT, Gregory Linn. 2316 ADAMS ST 54601 #041-01-1977 L1978 **P** *020 †75

SCHMITZ, John Joseph. ■ 54601 #030-06-2007 L2008 **TY** *012

SCHOENFELD, Paul Michael. 1836 SOUTH AVE, GUNDERESEN LUTHERAN 54601
#016-01-1974 L1975 **CD IM** *020 †18,20

SCHRAITH, Daniel Frank. 1900 SOUTH AVE 54601 #056-05-1999 L2003 **PTH** *020 †50

SCHULDT, Dennis Rene. 1900 SOUTH AVE 54601 #018-03-1969 L1988 **DR** *020 †80

SCHWARTZ, Barrett F. 615 10TH ST S 54601 #030-06-1975 L1999 **D PA** *020

SCHWARZ, Dayna Patricia. 800 WEST AVE S, FRANCISCAN SKEMP HEALTHCAR 54601
#021-06-1991 L2007 **OBG** *020 †30

SCOTT, Patrick John. 3454 LOSEY BLVD S 54601 #056-05-1987 L1988 **GP EM** *020

SEERING, Melinda Svoboda. 700 WEST AVE S 54601 #018-03-2002 L2006 **AN** *020 †05

SETTY, Sampoornima. 1900 SOUTH AVE 54601 #495-42-2000 L2008 **CD** *012

SEVEREID, Larry Robt. 2524 ZEPHYR CIR 54601 #018-03-1963 L1971 **OTO PS** *071 †45

SHAFFER, Robert Denton. 800 WEST AVE S 54601 #016-11-1964 L1967 **GE** *071 †20

SHAHIDI, Nasrollah T. 1836 SOUTH AVE 54601 #396-06-1954 L1968 **ORS** *050 †55

SHARP, Mickel Blake. ■ 54601 #056-06-2007 **TY** *012

SHORT, Daniel Kaufman. 1900 SOUTH AVE, ENDOCRINOLOGY 54601 #018-03-1999 L2004
END *100 †20

SHORTER, Ann Marie. 800 WEST AVE S 54601 #065-10-1984 L2003 *020

SHULTZ, Paul Stephen. 700 WEST AVE S 54601 #016-11-1973 L1976 **PD OS** *030 †55

SHURTLEFF, Robert Glenn. 1836 SOUTH AVE 54601 #016-11-1976 L1980 **AN** *020 †20

SIECK, Sandra Onder. W5447 PINE BLUFF RD 54601 #028-46-1989 L1989 **IM** *020 †20

SIERRA, Jesus M. ■ 54601 #649-14-1960 L1976 **ORS** *071

SILVA, Diane Elisabeth. 1836 SOUTH AVE, GUNDERSEN CLNC LTD 54601 #005-19-1981 L1988
END *050

SIMMONS, Lonnie Dean. 1836 SOUTH AVE, MS C02-002 54601 #056-05-1993 L1999
DR *020 †80

SINGH, Mandeep. 800 WEST AVE S 54601 #495-77-1985 L2002 **IC** *020

SKAUDIS, Darin Joseph. ■ 54601 #026-04-2007 **IM** *012

SKEMP, Frederick C, Jr. 2210 PARK DR 54601 #847-11-1970 L1972 **FM** *071

SKEMP, Joseph Patrick. 800 WEST AVE S, DEPT OF SURG 54601 #026-04-1984 L1989
GS *020 †85

SKEMP, Samuel Jos. W4075 COUNTY ROAD YY 54601 #056-06-1955 L1956 **OPH** *071 †35

SKIBO, Scott Douglas. 1836 SOUTH AVE, MEMORIAL HOSPITAL OF R.I. 54601
#056-05-1998 L2006 **PCC** *020 †20

SKOBIC, Mario. 800 WEST AVE S, FRANCISCAN SKEMP/MAYO HLTH 54601
#957-08-1985 L2000 **IM PLM** *020 †20 ‡

SLUNGAARD, Rolv Kjelberg. 1836 SOUTH AVE 54601 #693-01-1950 L1956 **PD HEM** *071 †55

SMALLEY, John James, Jr. 3121 LAUDERDALE CT 54603 #016-11-1964 L1970 **GP GS** *071 †85

SMITH, Martin Jay. ■ 54601 #035-01-1959 L1966 **CLP HEM** *071 †50,20

SMITH, Travis Jon. ■ 54601 #026-08-2007 **GS** *012

SONGSIRIDEJ, Vanee. 1836 SOUTH AVE 54601 #891-02-1974 L1980 **AI IM** *020 †20,03

SPRINGER, David D. ■ 54601 #056-05-1987 L1989 **PTH** *020 †50

SRINIVASAN, Balaji. 1900 SOUTH AVE 54601 #495-53-1992 L2001 **NEP** *020 †20

STANCIC, Zoran. 1836 SOUTH AVE, GUNDERSEN CLINIC, LTD. 54601 #957-01-1986 L1999
AN *020 †05

STEBBINS, Jill Marie. 1900 SOUTH AVE, FAMILY MEDICINE 54601 #026-04-1983 L1985
FM *020 †18 ‡

STEINGRAEBER, Paul Henry. 800 WEST AVE S 54601 #056-06-1973 L1974 **OBG** *020 †30

STEVENS, Mark Kenneth. 800 WEST AVE S 54601 #035-45-1980 L1994 **NS OSS** *075 †25

STIERS, Gary Ripley. 1836 SOUTH AVE, GUNDERSEN CLINIC LTD 54601 #016-11-1970 L1974
PD ADL *020 †55

STOA, Thomas Arnold. 700 WEST AVE S, FRANCISCAN SKEMP HEALTHCAR 54601
#048-04-1985 L1996 **EM** *020 †16

STOLL, Sharon Ann. ■ 54601 #025-12-2006 **FP** *012

STRAUSS, Richard Henry. 1900 SOUTH AVE, GUNDERSEN CLINIC LTD 54601
#035-19-1980 L1986 **PD CCM** *020 †55

STREBE, Kenneth Lee. 1836 SOUTH AVE 54601 #056-06-1962 L1963 **FM** *071

STROSAHL, Amanda Lou. 1836 SOUTH AVE, GUNDERSEN CLINIC 54601 #056-05-1986 L1987
IM *020 †20

SULLIVAN, Humbert Giroude. 1836 SOUTH AVE, NEUROSUR GUNDERSEN CLINIC 54601
#038-40-1970 L1987 **NS** *020 †25

SUSAG, Gary Ardean. 1900 SOUTH AVE, GUNDERSEN LUTHERAN 54601 #037-01-1983 L1984
IM *020 †20

SWANSON, Kristin Elna. 1300 BADGER ST, UW-LA CROSSE STUDENT HEALT 54601
#018-03-1984 L1985 **FM** *020 †18

TANDON, Abhishek. 1836 SOUTH AVE, GUNDERSEN LUTHERAN HOSPITA 54601
#495-37-2002 L2006 **IM** *012

TATA, Sujatha. 1836 SOUTH AVE 54601 #495-65-2003 **IM** *012

TAYLOR, Neal. 1836 SOUTH AVE 54601 #054-04-1962 L1973 **PM PMM** *071 †60

TEMPLE, John-Peter. 1900 SOUTH AVE 54601 #016-01-1985 L1991 **CHN PD** *020 †55,75

TERHORST, Thomas Ralph. 1900 SOUTH AVE 54601 #026-04-1970 L1976 **DR** *020 †80

TERMAN, James Wm. 1900 SOUTH AVE, GUNDERSEN LUTHERAN 54601 #017-20-1965 L1971
IM *020 †20

TESKE, John Michael, Jr. 800 WEST AVE S, SKEMP HEALTHCARE 54601 #056-05-1992 L1993
IM *020 †20 ‡

THATCHER, Lionel Gilbert. 1836 S AVE GUNDERSEN CLIN 54601 #056-05-1955 L1957
PHO PD *071 †55

THIEL, James Richard. 615 10TH ST S 54601 #056-05-1975 L1981 **P** *075

THOMPSON, James Cameron. 615 10TH ST S 54601 #048-13-1997 L1998 **PD PDE** *020 †55

THOMPSON, Jeffrey Evan. 1836 SOUTH AVE, GUNDERSEN CLINIC LTD 54601
#056-05-1978 L1984 **NPM CCM** *020 †55

THOMPSON, Teddy Leonard. 1836 SOUTH AVE, 1900 SOUTH AVE 54601 #028-34-1973 L1976
FM *020 †18

TOBERT, Daren Gerald. 1900 SOUTH AVE 54601 #060-01-1989 L2002 **PCC IM** *020 †20

TOCE, Suzanne Shanley. 1836 SOUTH AVE, PEDIATRIC DEPARTMENT 54601
#056-05-1976 L1978 **PD NPM** *020 †55

TOMPKINS, Douglas G. 122 16TH ST N 54601 #035-01-1950 L1958 **ORS** *071 †40

TRAVELLI, Renato. 1836 SOUTH AVE, GUNDERSEN LUTHERAN 54601 #561-17-1956 L1975
DR *020 †80

TROK, Benjamin Michael. ■ 54603 #026-04-2005 L2006 **IM** *012

TROTT, Kathleen Anne. 1900 SOUTH AVE, BEHAVIORAL HEALTH HO4-004 54601
#007-02-1999 L2003 **P** *020 †75

TRUMBULL, Kathy Ann. 1900 SOUTH AVE, FERTILITY CENTER, C03-002 54601
#028-34-1987 L2007 **REN GYN** *020 †30

UDELL, John Lawrence. 1900 SOUTH AVE 54601 #056-05-1987 L1988 **IM** *020 †20

UJDA, John Riordan. ■ 54603 #056-06-1969 L1973 **IM PUD** *020 †20

UNDELAND, Duane Kyle. 1836 SOUTH AVE C01-005, MEDICAL FOU 54601 #026-04-2007
IM *012

USHA, Kumari. 1836 SOUTH AVE 54601 #495-47-1983 L1999 **NEP IM** *020 †20

UY, Jonathan Jos. 800 WEST AVE S 54601 #041-13-1991 L1996 **VIR** *071

VANDENBERG, Jos Patrick. 1836 SOUTH AVE, GUNDERSEN CLINIC LTD 54601
#056-05-1979 L1981 **ORS** *020 †40

VAN GELDER, Timothy Dean. ■ 54601 #018-03-2007 **FP** *012

VAN NORSTRAND, Michael D. 700 WEST AVE S, FRANCISCAN SKEMP 54601
#026-08-1986 L1998 **GE IM** *020 †20

VILLARREAL, Armando A. 1900 SOUTH AVE, GUNDERSON LUTHERAN MED CTR 54601
#715-01-1990 L2004 **APM AN** *020 †05 ‡

VIRATA, Rodelino Legaspi. 1836 SOUTH AVE, GUNDERSEN CLINIC LTD 54601
#748-08-1964 L1975 **PTH** *062 †50

VOTER, Eric Wilsey. 221 BUCHNER PL, TRI-STATE AMBULANCE 54603 #056-06-1990 L1993
EM *020 †16

WADE, Alexander Donald. 1900 SOUTH AVE 54601 #034-01-2003 L2006 **GS** *012

WAGNER, Danyon James. 1836 SOUTH AVE, GUNDERSEN LUTHERAN 54601
#056-05-2003 L2007 **IM** *100 †20

WANIGER, Ricky Jos. 1836 SOUTH AVE, FOUNDERS BLDG FAM PRAC 54601
#056-05-1987 L1988 **FM** *020 †18

WEBER, Lori Sue. 1900 SOUTH AVE 54601 #056-05-1998 L1999 **PD** *020 †55

WEBSTER, Margaret E. 1836 SOUTH AVE, GUNDERSEN CLINIC LTD 54601 #016-06-1989 L1992
IM *020 †20

WEDRO, Benjamin C. 1900 SOUTH AVE 54601 #060-01-1979 L1982 **EM** *020 †16 ‡

WEETH, John B. 1616 KING ST 54601 #035-08-1952 L1965 **IM ON** *071 †20

WERGELAND, Kevin James. 1900 SOUTH AVE 54601 #026-04-2005 L2006 **IM** *012

WHELAN, John Charles. ■ 54601 #018-03-2002 L2004 **FM** *071

WHITE, Kerry Thos. 1836 SOUTH AVE, GUNDERSEN CLINIC 54601 #035-09-1977 L2003
NS *012

WHITE, Michael J. 700 WEST AVE S, FRANCISCAN SKEMPDERMATOLOG 54601
#025-07-1977 L2005 **D** *020 †15

WHITEWAY, Dean Everson. 2600 STATE RD, VA RIVER VALLEY CLINIC 54601
#056-05-1977 L1979 **IM** *020 †20

WHITEWAY, Robert E. ■ 54601 #016-06-1946 L1961 **GP AM** *072

WIEMAN, Stephanie Marie. 1900 SOUTH AVE 54601 #046-01-2005 L2006 **AN** *012

WILLIAMSON, Gehrig Robert. 815 10TH ST S 54601 #056-06-2005 L2006 **FP** *012

WINGA, Edward Rees. 1900 SOUTH AVE 54601 #018-03-1962 L1969 **PUD IM** *020 †20

WINTER, Gilda Belinda. 212 11TH ST S, FRANCISCAN SKEMP 54601 #038-06-1996 L2003
P *020

WITTCHOW, Richard James. 1900 SOUTH AVE 54601 #056-05-1985 L1986 **PTH IM** *020 †20,50

WITTE, Robert S. 1900 SOUTH AVE, GUNDERSEN LUTHERAN MED. CE 54601
#035-45-1974 L1980 **ON PLM** *020 †20

WOOD, Cindy Lou. 1900 SOUTH AVE, GUNDERSON CLINIC 54601 #056-05-1980 L1981
P GS *020 †70,75

YOON, Joon. 1836 SOUTH AVE, GUNDERSON CLINIC LTD 54601 #583-02-1967 L1980
AN *020 †05

YOUNG, Margaret Susan. 800 WEST AVE S, FRANCISCAN SKEMP HEALTH CA 54601
#038-40-1987 L1992 **OBG** *020 †30

YUTUC, Wilfrido R. 1836 SOUTH AVE, GUNDERSEN CLINICLTD 54601 #748-02-1957 L1962
NEP IM *020

YUVIENCO, Jose M. 700 WEST AVE S 54601 #748-19-1989 L2004 **NPM** *020 †55

ZAKY, Mary Amina. 1900 SOUTH AVE 54601 #041-02-1995 L2002 **IM** *020 †20

ZENG, Gordon Guangyuan. 1900 SOUTH AVE 54601 #243-76-1986 L2005 **PTH** *100 †50

ZERNIA, John Allen. 1900 SOUTH AVE, GUNDERSEN CLINIC LTD 54601 #056-06-1985 L1986
EM IM *020 †20

ZIEGELBEIN, Kurt James. 1836 SOUTH AVE, GUNDERSEN CLINIC 54601 #018-03-1994 L1999
DR *020 †80

ZINK, Julie Stiles. 1900 SOUTH AVE 54601 #026-04-1991 L1996 **EM** *020 †16

ZINK, Robert Russell. 1836 SOUTH AVE, GUNDERSEN CLINIC LTD 54601 #026-04-1991 L1996
EM *020 †16

ZLABEK, Jonathan Alan. 1900 SOUTH AVE 54601 #056-05-1997 L1998 **IM VM** *020 †20

LA FARGE – VERNON

SEDGWICK, Shawn Thomas. 111 W SNOW ST, LAFARGE MEDICAL CLINIC - V 54639
#056-05-1994 L1997 **FM** *020 †18 ‡

LA VALLE – SAUK

WATERS, Robert Scott. S3163 LARUE RD 53941 #016-11-1976 L1986 **GP** *020

LAC DU FLAMBEAU – VILAS

CARY, Brenda Lee. 450 OLD ABE RD, PETER CHRISTENSEN HEALTH C 54538 #026-04-2003 L2006 **FM** *020 †18

CORON, Alfred Jos. 2115 COUNTY ROAD D 54538 #056-05-1965 L1966 **FM** *020

KOTHANUR MARAPPA, Chandras. PO BOX 9, 2932 HIGHWAY 47 N 54538 #495-99-1984 L2004 **DIA** *100

LAVERDURE, Adrienne D. 450 OLD ABE RD 54538 #037-01-1994 L1998 **FM** *020 †18

POINTER, Robert Wayne. ■ 54538 #056-05-1957 L1958 **OPH** *071 †35

SPELLMEYER, John Clair. ■ 54538 #016-11-1955 L1994 **R NM** *071 †80

WITTCHOW, Allen W. ■ 54538 #056-05-1950 L1957 **OPH FM** *071 †35

LADYSMITH – RUSK

AHN, Helen Haeng Kang. 900 COLLEGE AVE W 54848 #583-08-1966 L1978 **GP NM** *020

ALLEN, Rebecca Joann. 906 COLLEGE AVE W 54848 #026-04-1984 L1985 **PD** *020 †55

AVECILLA, Constante S. 906 COLLEGE AVE W, MARSHFIELD CLINIC-LADYSMIT 54848 #748-10-1962 L1976 **CRS GS** *020 †10,85

BACHIR, Joseph Simon. 906 COLLEGE AVE W, LADYSMITH CENTER 54848 #913-15-1968 L1981 **GS** *020

BENNETT, Ralph P. ■ 54848 #056-05-1951 L1952 **FM** *071 †18

BIEGING, James Kenneth. 906 COLLEGE AVE W 54848 #026-04-1978 L1985 **IM** *020 †20

CHARIPAR, Ron M. 906 COLLEGE AVE W, LADYSMITH CENTER 54848 #016-43-1980 L1981 **IM IMG** *020 †20 ‡

COTTON, Paul Edward. 900 COLLEGE AVE W 54848 #041-02-1969 L1970 **EM GS** *020 †85,16

HAWN, Vicki Lynn. 906 COLLEGE AVE W 54848 #030-05-1976 L1981 **DR** *075 †80

HOLT, Joseph Paynter, III. 906 COLLEGE AVE W, CENTER 54848 #020-02-1995 L1999 **IM** *020 †20

KLIESE, Kenneth Alan. 311 MINER AVE E, STE L361 54848 #056-05-1969 L1970 **P** *071

MASLONKOWSKI, Robert Roy. 900 COLLEGE AVE W 54848 #026-04-1989 L1993 **OBG** *020 †30

NOGLER, Robert Allen. 906 COLLEGE AVE W, MARSHFIELD CLINIC-LADYSMIT 54848 #005-12-1978 L1983 **FM** *020 †18

PAULSEN, Thomas Peter. 906 COLLEGE AVE W, MARSHFIELD CLINIC 54848 #056-05-1978 L1986 **FM** *020 †18

ROBERTS, Mark R. 906 COLLEGE AVE W, MARSHFIELD CLINIC-LADYSMIT 54848 #018-75-1998, ▲ L2001 **IM** *020 †20

ROMEIS, Richard James. ■ 54848 #056-05-1975 L1976 **IM GP** *020 †20

SALACH, Thomas Jos. 906 COLLEGE AVE W, LADYSMITH CENTER 54848 #847-12-1978 L1980 **GP** *020

SCHEIN, Moshe. 906 COLLEGE AVE W, MARSHFIELD CLINIC 54848 #550-01-1980 L1994 **GS** *020

ZIEMER, John Leonard. 906 COLLEGE AVE W 54848 #056-05-1978 L1981 **FM** *020 †18

LAKE DELTON – SAUK

EWING, John Read. 530 WISCONSIN DELLS PKWY S 53940 #034-01-1995 L2005 **FM** *020 †18

LAKE GENEVA – WALWORTH

ALABARCA, Nestor Catigbe. 146 E GENEVA SQ 53147 #748-10-1969 L1977 **IM PUD** *020 †20

ALWA, Rathna V K. 717 GENEVA ST, SAI HOLISTIC HEALTH CENTER 53147 #495-16-1945 L1976 **FM NTR** *071

BACCHUS, Austin Frank. 146 E GENEVA SQ 53147 #005-12-2004 L2007 **FM** *020 †18

BHUSHAN, Shashi. 146 E GENEVA SQ 53147 #665-01-2003 L2006 *020 †20

BLUE, Debra L. 146 E GENEVA SQ 53147 #016-01-1990 L1991 **FM** *020 †18

COMPTON, Marguerite R. N2950 STATE ROAD 67 53147 #056-06-1992 L1993 **D** *020 †15

DE BIASE, Norbert George. 350 PELLER RD 53147 #132-01-1996 L2007 **FM** *020 †18

DUFFY, Thomas Edward. N2950 STATE ROAD 67, MERCY WALWORTH MED CTR 53147 #016-01-1973 L1987 **EM GP** *020 †16

DUSSAULT, Michael C. 146 E GENEVA SQ 53147 #056-06-1974 L1978 **ORS** *020 †40

FASANO, Robert Andrew. N2950 STATE ROAD 67, MERCY WALWORTH MED CTR 53147 #016-43-1994 L1997 **IM** *020 †20

FIDELER, Bradley Michael. N2950 STATE ROAD 67, MERCY WALWORTH MED CTR 53147 #018-03-1989 L1994 **OSM** *020 †40

FOX, Barry Michael. N2950 STATE ROAD 67, HWY 50 & 67 53147 #005-14-1977 L2003 **OBG EM** *020 †30

FRANDOLIG, John Earnest. ■ 53147 #048-02-1970 L1970 **OM PD** *071 †55

FUEREDI, George A. 400 S EDWARDS BLVD # 247 53147 #654-01-1985 L1986 **VIR** *020 †80

GALVANI, Theodore John. 146 E GENEVA SQ 53147 #016-11-1982 L1983 **IM** *020 †16

GERBER, Greg James. 146 E GENEVA SQ 53147 #056-05-1979 L1980 **FM OBS** *020 †18

GIBSON, Mark Stephen. N2950 STATE ROAD 67, MERCY WALWORTH MED CTR 53147 #016-11-1972 L1978 **EM OM** *020 †16

GIBSON, Mark Thomas. N2950 STATE ROAD 67 53147 #016-01-1994 L1994 **EM** *020 †16

GOOD, Nancy Ellen. N2950 STATE ROAD 67, MERCY WALWORTH MEDICAL CEN 53147 #008-01-1978 L1992 **IM OS** *020 †20

HADLEY, June L. ■ 53147 #047-05-1957 L1979 **P CHP** *071 †75

HAGNELL, Susan Marie. N2950 STATE ROAD 67, MERCY WALWORTH MEDICAL CEN 53147 #016-11-1991 L2003 **OBG** *020 †30

HAHN, Roberta R. N2950 STATE ROAD 67, MERCY WALWORTH MED CTR 53147 #038-41-1998 L2001 **PD** *020 †55

HANLEY, James Chas. 725 CENTER ST 53147 #016-11-1965 L1968 **LM OBG** *075

HINDALL, Boyd Crawford. ■ 53147 #028-02-1948 L1952 **GP AM** *074

KLENSKE, Jennifer. N2950 STATE ROAD 67, MERCY WALWORTH MEDICAL CEN 53147 #016-11-2002 L1996 **IM** *020 †20

KNAVEL, James Lee. 352 PELLER RD 53147 #018-03-1969 L1974 **ORS** *020 †40

KOLAR, Britton Ward. 146 E GENEVA SQ 53147 #016-06-1976 L1978 **FPG** *030 †18

LIEBMAN, Monte Harris. ■ 53147 #056-05-1957 L1958 **P** *071

MC NEILL, Thomas William. ■ 53147 #016-11-1962 L1963 **ORS OSS** *020 †40

MCNERNEY, Megan Elizabeth. ■ 53147 #016-02-2008 *012

MEADOR, Linda Kathleen. 146 E GENEVA SQ, AURORA HEALTH CENTER 53147 #056-06-1996 L2003 **OBG** *020 †30

MYRON, Gary. 350 PELLER RD 53147 #305-01-2004 L2007 **FM** *020 †18

NARUT, Noel Francis. ■ 53147 #016-43-1973 L1976 **CHP** *020

NEMEROVSKI, Randall Scott. N2950 STATE ROAD 67 53147 #016-11-1980 L2000 **AN PME** *025

OSTROW, David Gene. 700 GENEVA PKWY N, STE B 53147 #016-02-1975 L1994 **P PA** *071 †75

PARK, John Raymond. 146 E GENEVA SQ 53147 #010-01-1968 L1981 **OTO PS** *071 †45

QUEZADA, Jaime. 350 PELLER RD, MERCY LAKE GENEVA MED CTR 53147 #016-11-2000 L2004 **FM** *020 †18

ROSOL, Laura Marie. 146 E GENEVA SQ 53147 #016-01-1995 L1998 **FM** *020 †18

SCHNEIDER, Garth Robt. 146 E GENEVA SQ 53147 #016-06-1978 L1979 **FM IM** *020 †20,18

SELDERA, Joy Z. 146 E GENEVA SQ 53147 #748-10-1972 L1981 **OBG** *020

SWANSON, Erika Lee. ■ 53147 #056-06-2006 **RO** *012

VACARELLA, Jake Saml. N2950 STATE ROAD 67, MERCY WALWORTH MEDICAL CTR 53147 #001-06-1979 L1995 **PD** *020 †55

VEITH, Nicholas Wm. 7363 STATE ROAD 50 53147 #030-06-1969 L1973 **OPH** *020 †35

VUPER, Kathryn Ann. 144 E GENEVA SQ 53147 #030-05-1995 L2002 **P** *020 †75

YAO, George Lim. 146 E GENEVA SQ 53147 #748-01-1963 L1983 **OBG** *071 †30

LAKE MILLS – JEFFERSON

AAFREEN, Tahmina. 1025 MULBERRY ST 53551 #016-06-1996 L2002 **OBG** *020 †30

BRODIE, Jonathan J. 200 E TYRANENA PARK RD, URGENT CARE LAKE MILLS 53551 #008-02-1988 L1989 **D EM** *020 †18 ‡

EFFENHAUSER, Manfred. 200 E TYRANENA PARK RD 53551 #407-05-1958 L1962 **FM** *071 †18

FISCHER, Edwin Dyreby. 200 E TYRANENA PARK RD 53551 #056-05-1978 L1979 **FM EM** *020 †18

KAZI, Wahab A. 200 E TYRANENA PARK RD 53551 #915-04-1981 L1991 **FM** *020 †18

LIEBENOW, Roland Rudolph. ■ 53551 #056-05-1948 L1949 **NM** *071

MC GUINNESS, John Jos. 1025 MULBERRY ST 53551 #016-43-1991 L1999 **OBG** *020 †30

MILLER, Mary Elaine. 200 E TYRANENA PARK RD 53551 #025-12-1997 L2007 **FM** *020 †18

QUACKENBUSH, James Earl. 200 E TYRANENA PARK RD, FORT MEDICAL GROUP 53551 #046-01-1996 L1998 **FM** *020 †18

REED, William Homer. ■ 53551 #016-06-1954 L1961 **FM EM** *072 †85

WISHAU, James Patrick. 200 E TYRANENA PARK RD 53551 #056-05-1978 L1981 **IM GE** *020 †20

LAKE TOMAHAWK – ONEIDA

COOPER, Ronald Jeffrey. ■ 54539 #056-06-1982 L1983 **FM** *020 †18

VERANTH, Jerome Jos. ■ 54539 #056-06-1961 L1962 **OTO A** *071 †45

LAKEWOOD – OCONTO

PALOP, Rey Rayco. ■ 54138 #003-01-1999 L2002 **FM** *020

LANCASTER – GRANT

AHMED, Muhammad Khwaja Ma. 500 S MADISON ST 53813 #704-25-1995 L2003 **IMG** *020 †20 ‡

CULLEN, Randall Keith. 200 W ALONA LN 53813 #008-01-1976 L1977 **P FM** *020 †18,75

GROTZ, Gregory Richard. 507 S MONROE ST 53813 #005-12-1992 L1998 **DR** *020 †80

HUEBSCHMAN, Erin Leigh. 500 S MADISON ST 53813 #030-05-1998 L2003 **FM** *020 †18

MARISKANISH, Paul C. 9177 OLD POTOSI RD, LANCASTER FAMILY MEDICAL C 53813 #041-13-1992 L1999 **FM** *020 †18

OYEN, Mary Jo. 500 N MADISON ST, STE 2 53813 #056-05-1993 L1994 **OPH** *072 †24

PECHOUS, Bryan Paul. 507 S MONROE ST, GRANT REGIONAL HEALTH CENT 53813 #016-01-1983 L1988 **OPH** *020 †35 ‡

SCHMIDT, Clemens Sichling. 200 W ALONA LN 53813 #056-05-1958 L1959 **P** *020

SMITH, Robert James. 500 S MADISON ST 53813 #060-01-1980 L1991 **FM** *020

SORIANO, Romeo C. 500 S MADISON ST 53813 #748-08-1967 L1984 **GS** *071

STADER, Robert Edwin. 507 S MONROE ST 53813 #056-05-1975 L1978 **FM** *020 †18

VERGER, Lynn Rosel. 200 W ALONA LN, UNIFIED COMMUNITY SERVICES 53813 #056-05-1987 L1989 **P PYG** *020 †75

YURCEK, James Joseph. 500 S MADISON ST 53813 #026-04-1997 L2006 **GS** *020 †85

LANNON – WAUKESHA

WHITT, Stephanie Lynn. ■ 53046 #056-05-2003 L2005 **PD** *020 †55

LARSEN – WINNEBAGO

HULL, Stephen Bruhn. ■ 54947 #056-05-1963 L1964 **P GP** *020

LEOPOLIS – SHAWANO

HALLE, Judy Lynn. ■ 54948 #018-03-1982 L1983 **GS** *071

LITTLE CHUTE – OUTAGAMIE

BEUTLER, Karen Weyenberg. 117 E NORTH AVE 54140 #016-43-1999 L2000 **FM** *020 †18

MEYER, Jack Robinson. 117 E NORTH AVE 54140 #019-02-1976 L1985 **FM** *020 †18

SCOTT, Brian Keith. 200 PATRIOT DR 54140 #018-03-1993 L1995 **FM** *020 †18

SHOENBILL, Kimberly Ann. 200 PATRIOT DR 54140 #056-05-1997 L1998 **FM** *020 †18

VIR, Meena Pradhan. 200 PATRIOT DR 54140 #495-12-1994 L2003 **FM** *020 †18

LIVINGSTON – GRANT

MC NEEL, Laird. ■ 53554 #056-05-1943 L1947 **GS GP** *071

LODI – COLUMBIA

CHAO, Andrea M. 601 CLARK ST 53555 #056-06-1995 L2000 **PD** *020 †55
FANNEY, Dale Phillips. 601 CLARK ST 53555 #038-06-1976 L1980 **FM** *020
HALANSKI, Amy Denise. 601 CLARK ST 53555 #025-07-2000 L2003 **PD** *020 †55
KEENER, John Robt. 601 CLARK ST 53555 #056-05-1982 L1983 **FM** *020
OLSON, Janet Elaine. 601 CLARK ST 53555 #035-45-1974 L1975 **FM** *020 †18
SODERQUIST, Catherine C. 601 CLARK ST 53555 #026-04-1977 L1985 **FM** *020 †18
SULLIVAN, Thomas Patrick. 601 CLARK ST 53555 #016-06-1975 L1976 **FM** *020 †18

LOMIRA – DODGE

ARNDT, Mary. N11896 HWY 175, QUAD MED CLINIC 53048 #048-12-1988 L2001 **PD** *020 †55
MALEKI, Massoud. 375 EAST AVE 53048 #517-01-1965 L1968 **CD IM** *020 †20

LONE ROCK – RICHLAND

PETERSEN, Kim Paul. S10448 STRANG HOLLOW RD, S10448 STRANGE HOLLOW ROAD 53556 #018-03-1972 L1987 **FM IMG** *040 †18

LOYAL – CLARK

ZDOR-NORTH, Deborah Ann. 141 N MAIN ST 54446 #056-05-1989 L1998 **FM** *020 †18

LUCK – POLK

BJORNSON, Bjorn Rolf. 137 E 1ST AVE 54853 #026-04-1985 L1986 **FM** *020 †18

LUXEMBURG – KEWAUNEE

KROLL, Mark Robt. 101 SCHOOL RD, CREEK TRAIL P O BOX 99 54217 #018-75-1988, ▲ L1989 **FM** *020 †18
QUIDZINSKI, Erich J. 101 SCHOOL CREEK TRL 54217 #016-76-1993, ▲ L1996 **FM** *020 †18

LYNDON STATION – JUNEAU

REYNOLDS, Bret Aaron. ■ 53944 #056-05-1995 L1996 **PFP** *020

MADISON – DANE

ABAD, Cybele Lara Rivera. 600 HIGHLAND AVE, AVE H4/831-8320 53792 #748-02-2002 L2006 **ID** *012 †20
ABDELRAHMAN, Sahar Mustaf. ■ 53705 #056-05-2007 *012
ABERNETHY, Heather Ann. 202 S PARK ST 4, MERITER HOSP 53715 #056-05-2000 L2001 **AN** *012
ABLOVE, Robert Harold. 600 HIGHLAND AVE, K4/7 CLINICAL SCIENCE CENT 53792 #035-15-1989 L2003 **HS** *020 †40
ABRONS, Ron Owen. 600 HIGHLAND AVE, H4/831-8320 53792 #018-03-2004 L2006 **AN** *012
ACEVEDO ESPINOZA, Sonia M. 701 DANE ST 53713 #682-01-2003 L2006 **FP** *012
ACHER, Charles Wm. 600 HIGHLAND AVE, RM G5/322 53792 #017-20-1973 L1975 **VS GS** *020 †85
ADAMICK, Richard David. 1313 FISH HATCHERY RD, DEAN MEDICAL CENTER 53715 #016-11-1980 L1990 **CD** *020 †20
ADAMS, Alexandra King. 701 DANE ST 53713 #016-11-1994 L1995 **FM** *020 †18
ADAMS, Wendy Lee. 1313 FISH HATCHERY RD, DEAN CLINICS 53715 #041-07-1982 L1985 **IM IMG** *020 †20
ADDINGTON-WHITE, Joan F. 2880 UNIVERSITY AVE, INTERNAL MEDICINE 53705 #016-02-1990 L1996 **IM** *020 †20
ADEYEMI, Oluyemisi Adedoy. ■ 53705 #056-05-2008 *012
ADEYEMO, Bamidele Oyebami. ■ 53705 #056-05-2008 *012
ADIB, Khosro. 202 S PARK ST, MERITER HEART CENTER 53715 #517-01-1971 L1978 **TS** *020 †85,90
ADKINS, William Norman, Jr. 317 KNUTSON DR 53704 #038-40-1970 L1977 **PD CG** *020 †55
ADKISON, Jarrod Bartlett. 600 HIGHLAND AVE H4/831, UW HOSPITAL AND CLINICS 53792 #001-06-2005 L2007 **RO** *012
AGARWAL, Robert Ravi. 600 HIGHLAND AVE 53792 #539-03-2004 L2007 **IM** *012
AGARWAL, Swati. 2880 UNIVERSITY AVE, BLDG 9030 53705 #495-30-1994 L2007 **OPH** *100
AGNI, Rashmi Mahajan. UNIV WI HOSP & CLI, DEPT PATH 53792 #495-45-1985 L1997 **PTH** *020 †50
AGRAWAL, Basheal Mohan. ■ 53705 #056-05-2006 L2008 **NS** *012
AGRIANTONIS, Demetrios Jo. ■ 53719 #033-05-2004 L2007 **NM** *012
AGUIRRE, Nancy Lynn. 600 HIGHLAND AVE, AVE H4/831-8320 53792 #056-05-2004 L2006 **OBG** *012
AHEARN, Eileen Patricia. 2500 OVERLOOK TER, VETERAN'S ADMINISTRATION H 53705 #036-07-1990 L2002 **P** *020 †18
AHMED, Azam Syed. 600 HIGHLAND AVE H4/831, UW HOSPITAL AND CLINICS 53792 #016-43-2003 L2007 **NS** *012
AHMED, Vaqar. ■ 53717 #704-28-2001 L2007 **IM** *020 †20
AHRENS, Edward Robt. 707 S MILLS ST, ST MARYS HOSPOL HOSPITAL 53715 #025-07-1983 L1986 **NEP IM** *020 †20

AKINYEDE, Olufemi Olumuyi. 600 HIGHLAND AVE 53792 #690-02-1994 L2006 **FM** *020 †18
ALBERT, Clark Jae. 1313 FISH HATCHERY RD, DEAN MEDICAL CENTER 53715 #028-02-1984 L1985 **AN** *020 †05
ALBERT, Daniel Myron. 2880 UNIVERSITY AVE 53705 #041-01-1962 L1992 **OPH PTH** *020 †35
ALBERTE-LISTA, Cesar. 600 HIGHLAND AVE, UNIVERSITY OF WISCONSIN 53792 #847-05-1994 L2003 **CD** *020 †20
ALBERTINI, Mark Richard. 600 HIGHLAND AVE, K4/414 CSC UNIT OF WISC 53792 #050-02-1984 L1985 **ON IM** *050 †20
ALBRIGHT, A Leland. 600 HIGHLAND AVE K4/836, UNIVERSITY OF WISCONSIN 53792 #021-05-1969 L2006 **NSP** *020 †25
ALBRIGHT, John Garth. 1821 S STOUGHTON RD 53716 #026-04-1960 L1966 **FM** *071
ALBRIGHT, Lisa Marie. ■ 53726 #056-05-2008 *012
ALEXANDER, Suzanne M. 20 S PARK ST 53715 #056-05-1989 L1990 **IM** *020 †20
ALGAN, Ahmet Mitat. ■ 53711 #902-01-1954 L1970 **IM FM** *020
ALGIER, Leah Nicole. 3209 DRYDEN DR 53704 #041-12-2004 L2005 **FM** *020 †18
AL HASHIMI, Omar Basil. ■ 53705 #056-05-2008 *012
ALLAN, Melissa Y. 752 N HIGH POINT RD 53717 #056-05-1997 L2003 **IM** *020 †20
ALLAN, Michael Leslie. 1821 S STOUGHTON RD 53716 #056-05-1997 L2003 **GE** *020 †20
ALLEN, Gail Susan. 7102 MINERAL POINT RD 53717 #056-05-1991 L1994 **PD** *020 †55
ALLEN, James Colton. 600 HIGHLAND AVE, #F4/336, MAIL 3220 53792 #056-06-1959 L1960 **OPH** *071 †35
ALLICK, Albert P. 210 GLEN HOLLOW RD 53705 #026-04-2000 L2004 **P** *020
AL-NIAIMI, Ahmed Numan. 700 REGENT ST, STE 301 53715 #528-07-1995 L2005 **OBG** *012
ALSALEEM, Ahmad Samer. 600 HIGHLAND AVE 53792 #875-01-1994 L2007 **PCC** *012 †20
ALSUM, Pamela Beth. 20 S PARK ST 53715 #056-05-1993 L1994 **IM** *020 †20
ALT, Jennifer Marie. 6001 RESEARCH PARK BLVD, INST & 53719 #056-05-2006 **P** *012
ALT, Robert Leo. 1821 S STOUGHTON RD, EAST CLINIC 53716 #016-43-1982 L1988 **IM** *020 †20
AL TAMIMI, Mazin. 600 HIGHLAND AVE 53792 #528-03-1984 L2004 **APM** *020 †20
ALTAWEEL, Mike Mostafa. 2870 UNIVERSITY AVE, STE 206 53705 #064-01-1990 L1998 **OPH** *020 †35
ALTER, Albert J, Jr. 6701 SEYBOLD RD STE 204 53719 #038-06-1969 L1976 **R RP** *020 †80
ALWABEL, Abdulhamid A. ■ 53705 #797-01-1980 L1985 **IM** *020 †20
AMADOR, Araceli. 1300 UNIVERSITY AVE 53706 #649-03-1999 **FP** *012
AMBAY, Aparna. 1 S PARK ST 53715 #041-15-2002 L2004 **D** *020 †15
ANACLETO, Eduardo F. 330 E LAKESIDE ST 53715 #748-01-1958 L1969 **GP** *071
ANDERS, Jeffrey Lawrence. 115 N ORCHARD ST 53715 #050-02-1990 L1991 **P** *020 †75
ANDERSEN, Aaron D. ■ 53711 #056-05-2008 *012
ANDERSEN, James Richard. 1313 FISH HATCHERY RD 53715 #056-05-1988 L1994 **DR NM** *020 †80
ANDERSON, Aaron David. ■ 53704 #056-05-2006 L2008 **AN** *012
ANDERSON, Alexandra Louis. ■ 53705 #056-05-2005 L2007 **AN** *012
ANDERSON, Alton Duane. ■ 53705 #056-05-1943 L1948 **GS** *071 †85
ANDERSON, Ashley Gould, Jr. 1 S PARK ST, FL 7 53715 #056-05-1977 L1978 **HNS FPS** *020 †45
ANDERSON, Bethany Marie. 600 HIGHLAND AVE, UNIVERSITY OF WI HOSPITAL 53792 #056-05-2005 L2006 **RO** *012
ANDERSON, Charles Jos. 1200 JOHN Q HAMMONS DR 53717 #056-05-1973 L1974 **OPH OS** *020 †35
ANDERSON, Clifford Jon. 752 N HIGH POINT RD, DEAN MEDICAL CENTER 53717 #026-04-1988 L1989 **IM** *020 †20
ANDERSON, Cynthie Kay. 600 HIGHLAND AVE, BOX 6188 53792 #023-07-2002 L2004 **OBG** *100
ANDERSON, Gary David. 202 S PARK ST 53715 #056-05-1978 L1979 **EM IM** *020 †20,16
ANDERSON, Henry Adolph. 1 W WILSON ST RM 150, DIV OF PUBLIC HLTH 53702 #056-05-1972 L1973 **PHP EP** *062 †70
ANDERSON, James Allen. 1200 JOHN Q HAMMONS DR, STE 400 53717 #056-05-1965 L1971 **DR** *020 †80
ANDERSON, Odette Adean. ■ 53705 #056-05-2008 *012
ANDERSON, Paul Alan. 600 HIGHLAND AVE RM K4, ORTHOPEDICS REHA 53792 #025-07-1979 L2002 **OSS** *020 †40
ANDERSON, Richard Boethin. 330 E LAKESIDE ST 53715 #056-05-1947 L1948 **P** *071 †55
ANDERSON, Scott Allen. 600 HIGHLAND AVE, RM H4/831 53792 #056-05-2005 L2006 **ORS** *012
ANDES, David Robt. 600 HIGHLAND AVE, AVE. RM.J5/230 53792 #028-03-1992 L1993 **ID** *020 †20
ANDREWS, Douglas Raymond. 1313 FISH HATCHERY RD 53715 #016-11-1981 L1983 **DR** *020 †80
ANDRINGA, Conrad Lloyd. 752 N HIGH POINT RD, DEPT OF PEDIATRICS 53717 #056-05-1963 L1965 **PD** *020 †55
ANDRUS, Candye R. 5249 E TERRACE DR 53718 #048-16-1987 L1988 **PD** *020 †55
ANGELINI, Giuditta. 600 HIGHLAND AVE, B6 319 CLINICAL SCIENCE CT 53792 #056-05-1995 L1996 **CCA** *020 †20,05
ANGEVINE, James Murray. 600 HIGHLAND AVE 53792 #056-05-1959 L1968 **PTH** *071 †50
ANGLIN, Melissa. 202 S PARK ST 53715 #056-05-1994 L2000 **AN** *020 †05
ANIAKUDO, Maureen O. ■ 53719 #056-05-2007 **FP** *012
ANSFIELD, Thomas Jos. 4410 REGENT ST 53705 #056-05-1966 L1967 **CD IM** *020
ANSUSINHA, Chirawan K. 1552 UNIVERSITY AVE 53705 #891-01-1958 L1968 **IM CD** *020
ANSUSINHA, Tamnit. 6601 GRAND TETON PLZ, MADISON RADIOLOGISTS, S.C. 53719 #891-02-1957 L1963 **R NM** *071 †80,28
APPEN, Richard Everett. 6118 N HIGHLANDS AVE 53705 #036-07-1966 L1969 **OPH** *071 †35
ARMSTRONG, Charles Benjam. 600 HIGHLAND AVE, RM H4/831 53792 #038-06-2004 L2005 **OTO** *012
ARMSTRONG, Richard Glenn. 350 S HAMILTON ST 53703 #016-06-1968 L1974 **IM** *020 †20
ARNDT, Daniel Henry. 202 S PARK ST, BLDG 3 53715 #056-05-1973 L1974 **DR** *020 †80
ARNDT, George Arthur. 600 HIGHLAND AVE, B6 319 CLINICAL SCIENCE CT 53792 #056-05-1984 L1989 **AN** *020 †05
ARNDT, Kimberly Kegel. 600 HIGHLAND AVE, AVE H4/831-8320 53792 #056-05-2005 L2006 **PM** *012
ARNOLD, Douglas Randolph. ■ 53717 #011-03-2007 **ORS** *012
ARYA, Bhaskar S. 330 E LAKESIDE ST 53715 #495-33-1988 L1994 **PYG** *020
ASAKEVICH, Scott Alan. 600 HIGHLAND AVE, BOX 2454 53792 #025-12-2005 L2006 **IM** *012
ASCHBACHER, Ann Christine. 301 TROY DR, MMHI GTU 53704 #018-03-1989 L1990 **P PYG** *075
ASCHENBRENNER, Jacquelyn. 600 HIGHLAND AVE, UNIV OF WISCONSIN HOSPITAL 53792 #007-02-1997 L1999 **GS** *020

ASGHAR, Hannah Sughra. 600 HIGHLAND AVE H4/831, UW HOSPITAL AND CLINICS 53792 #704-25-2003 L2008 **IM** *012

ASHMAN, Hubert C. ■ 53711 #021-05-1943 L1948 **IM** *071 †20

ASIRVATHAM, Michael J. ■ 53705 #495-04-1952 L1977 **FM EM** *071

ASTHANA, Sanjay. 2870 UNIVERSITY AVE, STE 106 53705 #496-09-1980 L2001 **IMG** *020 †20

ASTON, Paula Amy. 600 HIGHLAND AVE, BOX 5132 53792 #039-01-2005 L2006 M *012

ATHAS, David Paul. 202 S PARK ST 53715 #056-05-1980 L1986 **IM** *020 †20,16

ATKINSON, Benjamin Walter. 5249 E TERRACE DR, EAST CLINIC 53718 #026-04-1975 L1978 **FM** *071 †18

ATKINSON, M E. 600 HIGHLAND AVE, UNIV OF WISCONSIN HOSP & C 53792 #037-01-1986 L1987 **HEM BBK** *020 †20

ATWELL, David Truman. 1313 FISH HATCHERY RD 53715 #021-01-1968 L1969 **R** *020 †80

AUGHENBAUGH, William D. 451 JUNCTION RD, STE 9903 53717 #056-05-1997 L1998 **D** *020 †15

AUSTIN, Stephen Mark. 3402 KINSMAN BLVD, CONVANCE CLOCL RES UNIT 53704 #035-08-1967 L1992 **CD IM** *050 †20

AVEY, Gregory David. 600 HIGHLAND AVE BOX 3252, UNIVERSITY HOSP 53792 #054-04-2005 L2006 **DR** *012

AVGERIS, Aristides Charle. 777 S MILLS ST 53715 #422-01-2006 L2008 **FP** *012

AYETEY, William E. 301 TROY DR, MENDOTA MENTAL HEALTH INST 53704 #026-04-1991 L1992 **P** *020 †75

AZEN, Edwin Allan. 600 HIGHLAND AVE 53792 #041-12-1955 L1960 **HEM** *050 †20

BABAIAN, Kara Noelle. 600 HIGHLAND AVE RM G5/333, UW HOSP & CLINICS 53792 #048-14-2006 L2008 **U** *012

BACHHUBER, Tracy Lynn. 600 HIGHLAND AVE, UNIV OF WISCONSIN 53792 #051-01-1991 L1996 **IM** *020 †20

BACKONJA, Miroslav. 5249 E TERRACE DR 53718 #957-01-1980 L1985 **N PMM** *050 †75

BADGER, Amy Noelle. ■ 53704 #016-06-2006 L2008 **OPH** *012

BADYLAK, John Stephen. SCIENCE CTR, K4/755 CLINICAL 53792 #017-20-2006 **ORS** *012

BAE, Jean Sook. 700 RAY O VAC DR STE 220, FAMILY THERAPY CTR OF MADI 53711 #035-06-1997 L1998 **P** *012

BAER, Geoffrey Scott. OF SPOR, DEPT OF ORTHOPAEDIC SURGER 53792 #047-05-2000 L2007 **ORS** *100

BAGUL, Nitin Dharma. 6001 RESEARCH PARK BLVD, DEPT OF PSYCHIATRY 53719 #495-28-2000 **P** *012

BAIN, Philip Arthur. 1821 S STOUGHTON RD 53716 #056-05-1985 L1986 **IM OS** *020 †20

BAKER, Catherine Ann. ■ 53705 #056-05-1986 *074

BAKER, Richard Joint, Jr. 1221 JOHN Q HAMMONS DR, MADISON RADIOLOGISTS 53717 #032-01-1989 L1997 **DR** *020 †80

BAKER, Robert Morris. 20 S PARK ST STE 307 53715 #026-04-1962 L1965 **OBG** *071 †30

BALASUBRAMANIAN, Prakash. 600 HIGHLAND AVE, UW HOSPITAL AND CLINICS 53792 #495-27-1998 L2008 **IM** *012

BALES, Alicia Lishan. ■ 53705 #056-05-2008 *012

BALKIN, Daniel Michael. ■ 53705 #008-01-2008 *012

BALLANTYNE, Ford, III. 600 HIGHLAND AVE, UNIVERSITY OF WISCONSIN 53792 #035-20-1969 L1970 **CD IM** *020 †20

BALLIAN, Nikiforos. ■ 53703 #917-31-1999 L2008 **GS** *020

BALOUGH, Kathryn Mclain. 1 S PARK ST 53715 #016-11-1984 L1993 **A PDA** *075 †55

BAMBER, Amy. ■ 53705 #056-05-2008 *012

BANDOW, Paul Wm. ■ 53713 #012-01-1974 L1976 **P** *020

BANE, Regina Ann. 600 HIGHLAND AVE, RM H4 831 UNIV HOSP 53792 #016-45-2003 L2005 **PCP** *012 †50

BARANCIN, Courtney Ellen. H6/5 CSC, 600 HIGHLAND AVE 53792 #017-20-2000 L2001 **GE** *012 †20

BARANOWSKI, Walter. 1821 S STOUGHTON RD 53716 #065-06-1962 L1978 **ORS** *071 †40

BARANSKI, Bruce Gordon. 2500 OVERLOOK TER, MIDDLETON VA HOSPITAL 53705 #038-41-1983 L1988 **IM HEM** *020 †20

BARASH, Harvey Louis. 1 S PARK ST, FL 7 53715 #035-46-1965 L1971 **ORS** *020 †40

BARBOUCHE, Ellen Mattes. 451 JUNCTION RD, GEN INTERNAL MED 53717 #039-01-1996 L1997 **IM** *020 †20

BARCZI, Steven Robt. 2500 OVERLOOK TER, VA GRECC MADISON 53705 #016-11-1989 L1994 **IMG SME** *020 †20

BARKER, Carrie Katherine. 600 HIGHLAND AVE, BOX 4108 53792 #018-03-2005 L2007 **PD** *012

BARKLAGE, Nancy Elizabeth. 6001 RESEARCH PARK BLVD 53719 #028-03-1979 L1980 **P** *020 †75

BARLOW, Jonathan David. ■ 53715 #056-05-2008 *012

BARNEY, Neal Paul. 2880 UNIVERSITY AVE 53705 #038-45-1983 L1992 **OPH** *020 †35

BARRERAS, Robert Francis. 600 HIGHLAND AVE, CLINICAL SCIENCE CTR 53792 #035-20-1957 L1962 **GE** *071 †20

BARRETT, Bruce Patrick. 777 S MILLS ST, DEPARTMENT OF FAMILY MEDIC 53715 #056-05-1992 L1995 **FM** *020 †18

BARRETT, Kay Miller. 1821 S STOUGHTON RD 53716 #025-01-1972 L1977 **CD IM** *020 †20

BARRY, Daniel Jos, III. 777 S MILLS ST DEPT FP 53715 #005-02-1973 L1974 **FM** *075 †18

BARRY, George Richard. ■ 53705 #016-02-1942 L1948 **IM CD** *071 †20

BARTELL, Jessica M. 1265 JOHN Q HAMMONS DR, GROUP HEALTH COOPERATIVE 53717 #056-05-1999 L2000 **FM** *020

BARTELL, Thomas Hunter. 6418 NORMANDY LN STE 210 53719 #056-05-1983 L1990 **PS** *020 †65

BARTELS, Christie Michels. J5/230 CSC-2454, 600 HIGHLAND AVE 53792 #030-06-2001 L2002 **RHU** *100

BARTHOLOMEW, Michael Lee. 600 HIGHLAND AVE, AVE H4/831-8320 53792 #032-01-2003 L2006 **PD** *020 †55

BARTLETT, David Heiner. 340 S WHITNEY WAY 53705 #056-05-1973 L1978 **ORS** *020 †40 ‡

BARTLETT, William H. 1313 FISH HATCHERY RD 53715 #025-01-1953 L1957 **PD PSM** *071 †55

BARTOSH, Sharon M. 600 HIGHLAND AVE 53792 #041-13-1983 L1998 **NP PD** *020 †55

BASKAYA, Mustafa Kemal. 600 HIGHLAND AVE, DEPT OF NEUROSURGERY, K4/8 53792 #902-03-1987 L2005 **NS** *100

BATHKE, Kristine Ann. 752 N HIGH POINT RD 53717 #056-05-1997 L1998 **OBG** *020 †30

BATSON, John Frederick. 2 W GORHAM ST 53703 #048-04-1957 L1959 **GS TS** *071 †85,90

BATTAGLIA, John. 600 WILLIAMSON ST, STE A 53703 #038-40-1984 L2000 **P** *020 †75

BAUER, Andrew Michael. ■ 53719 #028-03-2006 L2008 **NS** *012

BAUMAN, Billy J. ■ 53717 #017-20-1953 L1962 **PTH FOP** *062 †50

BAUMANN-BLACKMORE, Nicole. 600 HIGHLAND AVE, BOX 4108 53792 #056-05-2005 L2006 **PD** *012

BAUMBLATT, Michael Jon. 722 WILLIAMSON ST 53703 #056-05-1959 L1960 **OBG** *020

BAUMGARTNER, John Thos. 1310 MENDOTA ST STE 107 53714 #056-06-1972 **R** *075

BAUS, Kathleen Marie. 202 S PARK ST, BLDG 3 53715 #056-05-1986 L1987 **DR** *020 †80

BAWA, Nimrat. ■ 53719 #495-36-1989 L1995 **PTH** *100 †50

BAYER, Edward Dennis. 1313 FISH HATCHERY RD 53715 #056-05-1994 L1997 **PD** *020 †55

BAYLY, Erica Elliott. 600 HIGHLAND AVE, AVE H4/831-8320 53792 #021-01-2004 L2006 **ORS** *012

BEAMSLEY, Mark Bergen. 5618 ODANA RD 53719 #016-43-1999 L2000 **FM** *020 †18

BEAN, Darren Bruce. 707 S MILLS ST, DEPT OF EMERGENCY MEDICINE 53715 #050-02-1999 L2002 **EM** *020 †16

BEAN, Stacey T. 700 S PARK ST 53715 #050-02-1999 L2002 **EM** *020 †16

BEARDEN, Allison Lynn. ■ 53703 #021-01-2004 L2006 **MPD** *012

BEASLEY, John Wagner. 777 S MILLS ST 53715 #026-04-1969 L1973 **FM** *020 †18

BEAVER, Janet Rae. 752 N HIGH POINT RD, DEAN MEDICAL CENTER 53717 #056-05-1984 L1985 **IM** *020 †20

BECK, James Paul. 1821 S STOUGHTON RD 53716 #056-05-1963 L1964 **OBG** *020 †30

BECKER, Beth Christine. ■ 53719 #056-05-2007 **PD** *012

BECKER, Gary Alan. 600 HIGHLAND AVE 53792 #056-06-1960 L1961 **BBK** *030 †20

BECKER, Michael Edward. 1 S PARK ST, FL 7 53715 #038-41-1978 L1979 **OTO FPS** *020 †45

BECKER, Yolanda Tai. 600 HIGHLAND AVE, H4/754 CSC TRANSPLANT 53792 #023-07-1990 L1997 **GS TTS** *020 †85 ‡

BEDI, Surmeet. ■ 53705 #496-43-1997 L2007 **NEP** *012 †20

BEEN, Mark Joseph. ■ 53705 #056-05-2008 *012

BEHLING, Ronald Edwin. 1313 FISH HATCHERY RD, DEAN MEDICAL CENTER 53715 #056-05-1977 L1978 **AN** *020 †05

BEHRMANN, Ann Thompson. 8202 EXCELSIOR DR, SAUK TRAILS CLINIC 53717 #038-41-1978 L1979 **PD NEP** *020 †55

BEHRS, Theresa Lynn. 1821 S STOUGHTON RD 53716 #056-05-1993 L1994 **D** *020 †15

BEILMAN, Robert Lewis. 53711 #035-01-1953 L1957 **IM** *071

BEIRNE, Gregory James. 2500 OVERLOOK TER 53705 #016-43-1958 L1961 **NEP IM** *071 †20

BEKX, Mary Terese. 451 JUNCTION RD, STE 9903 53717 #056-06-1997 L2000 **PDE** *020 †55

BELL, Carolyn Lee. 451 JUNCTION RD, STE 9903 53717 #016-11-1971 L1979 **RHU IM** *020 †20

BELLAK, Jason Michael. 600 HIGHLAND AVE 53792 #031-01-2000 L2005 **AI** *100 †20

BELLAZZINI, Marc Anthony. F2/208 CSC, 600 HIGHLAND AVE 53792 #016-43-1996 L1997 **EM** *020 †20,16

BELLINGHAM, Janet Marie. ■ 53705 #026-04-2001 L2007 **CCS** *100

BELLISSIMO, Joseph A. 202 S PARK ST 53715 #056-05-1989 L1990 **CD** *020 †20

BELLISSIMO, Patricia L. 1821 S STOUGHTON RD 53716 #056-05-1989 L1990 **PD** *020 †55

BELSKY, Lorna Evleen. 451 JUNCTION RD, STE 9903 53717 #025-01-1992 L1993 **IM** *020 †20

BENARDETTE, Arnold. 675 W WASHINGTON AVE 53703 #035-48-1976 L1981 **PD FM** *020 †20

BENCA, Joan Francis. 600 HIGHLAND AVE B6/319, UNIVERSITY OF WISCONSIN MA 53792 #016-11-1980 L2001 **AN PD** *020 †05

BENCA, Ruth Myra. 600 HIGHLAND AVE DEPT P, B6 210 CLNC SCI CTR 53792 #016-02-1981 L1993 **P SME** *020 †75

BENDER, Cynthia Marie. 1821 S STOUGHTON RD 53716 #017-20-1985 L1991 **PM** *020 †60

BENNETT, Eleanor Maxine. ■ 53719 #030-05-1942 L1943 **OTO** *071 †45

BENNETT, Eliza Apple. 600 HIGHLAND AVE, UNIV OF WI HOSP & CLINIC 53792 #019-02-2006 L2008 **OBG** *012

BENNETT, Harold F. 1313 FISH HATCHERY RD 53715 #016-11-1988 L1999 **DR** *020 †80

BENNETT, Lindsey Knowles. 600 HIGHLAND AVE, UNIVERSITY OF WI HOSPITAL 53792 #056-05-2003 L2004 **IMD** *012

BENSON, Holly Andrea. 5249 E TERRACE DR 53718 #035-09-1999 L2006 **IM** *020 †20

BENTON, George David. 752 N HIGH POINT RD, DEAN MEDICAL CENTER 53717 #016-01-1975 L1976 **FM** *020 †18

BENTZ, Michael Lloyd. 451 JUNCTION RD, STE 9903 53717 #041-13-1984 L1999 **PS HS** *020 †65,85

BENWAY, Brian Michael. 600 HIGHLAND AVE, AVE H4/831-8320 53792 #017-20-2003 L2006 **U** *012

BERENDES, Brian Kenneth. 6001 RESEARCH PARK BLVD, INST & 53719 #046-01-2006 L2008 **P** *012

BERESKY, Donald E. 1821 S STOUGHTON RD 53716 #010-02-1981 L1988 **OPH** *020 †35

BERG, Mary C. ■ 53711 #056-05-1950 L1951 **P** *071 †75

BERGER, Karen Berger. 675 W WASHINGTON AVE, GROUP HEALTH COOPERATIVE 53703 #056-05-1989 L1990 **FM** *020 †18

BERGER, Kirk David. 1821 S STOUGHTON RD 53716 #041-14-1974 L1975 **FM** *020 †18

BERGER-DURNBAUGH, Bonnie. ■ 53711 #016-11-1991 L1992 **FM** *040 †18

BERGHAHN, Laura. 4122 E TOWNE BLVD 53704 #056-05-1998 L1999 **OBG** *020 †30

BERGIN, Jennifer Thiel. 600 HIGHLAND AVE, AVE H4/831-8320 53792 #056-05-2003 L2004 **DR** *012 †20

BERMANT, Christopher Sean. ■ 53715 #056-05-2008 *012

BERN, Lauren. 53703 #005-02-1977 L1979 **PYG** *020 †20,75

BERNHARDT, David Ted. 2870 UNIVERSITY AVE # 200, DEPARTMENT OF PEDIATRICS 53705 #056-05-1989 L1990 **PD** *020 †18

BERNHARDT, Norval Eldred. ■ 53719 #056-05-1967 L1971 **OTO** *071 †45

BERNSTEIN, Leslie Ellen. 1821 S STOUGHTON RD 53716 #035-03-1986 L1996 **FM** *020 †18

BERTRAM, John Robt. 1821 S STOUGHTON RD 53716 #056-05-1970 L1971 **D** *020 †15

BERTRAND, Robert Leo. 202 S PARK ST, MERITER HOSPITAL, INC. 53715 #067-01-1975 L1993 **EM OM** *020 †70,16

BEST, Sara Lynn. 600 HIGHLAND AVE, AVE H4/831-8320 53792 #056-05-2003 L2006 **U** *012

BEVACQUA, Brian Kriss. 2500 OVERLOOK TER 112A, MADISON VAMC 53705 #016-02-1980 L1981 **AN IM** *020 †20,05

BHAMB, Bhushan Lal. 777 S MILLS ST 53715 #495-29-1971 L2006 *100

BHATNAGAR, Ritu Smita. ■ 53719 #018-03-2006 L2008 **P** *012

BHATT, Amit Kirit. 1300 UNIVERSITY AVE, RM. # 2765 MSC 53706 #016-01-2006 L2007 **RO** *012

BHATT, Archana Prabhakar. 202 S PARK ST 53715 #016-11-2003 L2007 **PM** *020

BHATTI, Sabha. 600 HIGHLAND AVE, BOX 2454 53792 #704-25-2003 L2008 **IM** *012

BIAGTAN, Mark John. ■ 53705 #056-05-2008 *012

BIANCO, Jesus. 600 HIGHLAND AVE, UW HOSPITAL & CLINICS 53792 #935-01-1963 L1987 **NM CD** *050 †20,28

BIEDERMANN, Christine H. 202 S PARK ST 53715 #018-03-1989 L1993 **AN** *020 †05

BILHORN, Anna Kathleen. 707 S MILLS ST, ST. MARY'S HOSPITAL 53715 #056-05-2002 L2004 **IM** *020 †20

BILLS, Gregory Dean. 451 JUNCTION RD, STE 9903 53717 #056-05-1991 L1992 **OBG** *020 †30

BINKLEY, Neil Chas. 451 JUNCTION RD, STE 9903 53717 #056-05-1979 L1980 **IMG** *020 †20

BIRNBAUM, Marvin Lyle. 600 HIGHLAND AVE 53792 #056-05-1960 L1962 **OS PUD** *062

BISHOP, Erin Anderson. ■ 53711 #056-05-2006 L2008 *012

BITTAR, Evelyn Edward. UNIV WIS SCH MED, DEPT PHYS 53706 #008-01-1955 L1961 **OS** *050

BITTAR, Neville. 600 HIGHLAND AVE 53792 #067-01-1961 L1967 **CD IM** *050 †20
BIXLER, Heather Anne. ■ 53704 #034-01-2006 **PTH** *012
BJOERNSEN, Lars Petter Ba. 600 HIGHLAND AVE 53792 #693-01-2006 **EM** *012
BJORNSDOTTIR, Unnur S. ■ 53705 #484-01-1984 **AI** *020 †20,03
BLACK, Sara. 600 HIGHLAND AVE 53792 #858-01-2001 **P** *100
BLAKE, Jocelyn Marie. ■ 53719 #056-05-2006 L2008 **AN** *012
BLANCHARD, John Evan. 7102 MINERAL POINT RD 53717 #030-05-1983 L1984 **IM IMG** *020 †20
BLANCKE, Frederick Wm. ■ 53704 #660-01-1950 L1959 **IMG IM** *020
BLANK, Robert Danl. 451 JUNCTION RD, STE 9903 53717 #035-19-1988 L1995 **END IM** *050 †20
BLANKENBAKER, Donna G. 600 HIGHLAND AVE, STE E-3/366 53792 #030-05-1996 L1997 **DR** *020 †80
BLECHA, Matthew John. ■ 53703 #041-02-2001 L2001 **VS** *100 †85
BLEIER, Ruth H. ■ 53705 #041-07-1949 L1974 **OS** *050
BLISS, Matthew Scott. 5 MADELINE IS 53719 #034-01-1997 L2003 **HS** *020 †40
BLOCK, Jeffrey Bertram. 1313 FISH HATCHERY RD 53715 #035-46-1982 L1983 **DR** *020 †80
BLOCK, Robert Theodore. ■ 53711 #056-05-1961 L1962 **IM CD** *071
BLODI, Barbara Ann. 2880 UNIVERSITY AVE, 2ND FL 53705 #018-03-1987 L1997 **OPH** *020 †35
BLOMBERG, Joshua Robert. ■ 53705 #026-04-2001 **ORS** *012
BLOODWORTH, J M B, Jr. 2500 OVERLOOK TER 53705 #012-05-1948 L1962 **PTH END** *071 †50
BLUME, David Evelyn. 301 TROY DR, STOVALL HALL MMHI 53704 #028-34-1988 L1989 **IM** *020 †20
BOBADILLA, Joseph Louis. 600 HIGHLAND AVE, AVE H4/831-8320 53792 #056-05-2003 L2005 **GS** *012
BODEMER, Apple. 1 S PARK ST, DEPARTMENT OF DERMATOLOGY 53715 #056-05-2001 L2002 **D** *020 †15
BOGDANOWICZ, Marta Maria. 1313 FISH HATCHERY RD 53715 #056-05-1995 L1999 **DR** *020 †80
BOGDANOWICZ, Wojciech M. 1313 FISH HATCHERY RD, DEAN CLINIC 53715 #759-01-1960 L1972 **NS** *020 †25
BOGOST, Gregg Alan. 1313 FISH HATCHERY RD 53715 #056-05-1988 L1997 **DR** *020 †80
BOHLMAN, Diane Christine. 2500 OVERLOOK TER 53705 #056-05-1956 L1958 **AN** *040 †05
BOHLMANN, Brian Jeffrey. 1313 FISH HATCHERY RD 53715 #056-05-1987 L1988 **IM OM** *020 †20
BOHN, John Matthew. 600 HIGHLAND AVE 53792 #056-05-1984 L1985 **PD** *020 †55
BOHON, Scott Alan. 1821 S STOUGHTON RD, EAST CLINIC 53716 #016-02-1984 L1990 **P** *020 †75
BOLEK, Jilaine Mary. 600 HIGHLAND AVE, BOX 2454 53792 #016-11-2004 L2005 **IM** *100 †20
BOLLES, John Craig. 36 S BROOKS ST 53715 #041-01-1972 L1976 **PTH** *020 †50
BOLTE, Stefanie Lynn. 600 HIGHLAND AVE, AVE H4/831-8320 53792 #016-43-2001 L2002 **U** *020 †95
BONCYK, John Clement. 600 HIGHLAND AVE, B6/319 CLINICAL SCIENCE CE 53792 #056-05-1979 L1980 **AN** *020 †05
BONEBRAKE, Robert Alan. 600 HIGHLAND AVE 53792 #016-06-1963 L1970 **RHU IM** *020 †20
BONJOUR, Karen Margaret. 451 JUNCTION RD, STE 9903 53717 #056-05-1989 L1990 **IM** *020 †20
BOORSTEIN, Stephen M. 752 N HIGH POINT RD 53717 #025-01-1992 L1998 **OPH** *020 †35
BORA, Suhani Sudhir. ■ 53703 #025-01-2007 **FP** *012
BORMAN, Edward James. ■ 53717 #056-06-2001 L2005 **DR** *020 †80
BOTHAM, Richard J. 1313 FISH HATCHERY RD 53715 #056-05-1952 L1957 **GS TS** *071 †85
BOTTOMS, Holly I. J5/230 CSC-2454, 600 HIGHLAND AVE 53792 #017-20-2000 L2001 **IM** *020 †20
BOURNE, Amy Evelyn. 5534 MEDICAL CIR 53719 #056-05-1995 L1997 **P** *020
BOUSHEA, Deborah Knutson. 20 S PARK ST, STE 207 53715 #056-05-1984 L1985 **GP RHU** *020 †20
BOWMAN, H Michael. 600 HIGHLAND AVE, MED FLIGHT PROGRAM 53792 #025-12-1974 L1983 **EM** *020,16
BOYCE, Cody James. ■ 53711 #056-05-2004 L2008 **DR** *012
BOYER, Stanley Wade. 1313 FISH HATCHERY RD, DEAN CLINIC NEUROLOGY DEPT 53715 #017-20-1962 L1970 **N** *020 †75
BOYLE, Robert William. 1821 S STOUGHTON RD 53716 #026-04-2001 L2004 **IM** *020
BRAATEN, Randy A. 600 HIGHLAND AVE, AVE H4/831-8320 53792 #026-04-2004 L2006 **AN** *012
BRADFIELD, Yasmin. 2870 UNIVERSITY AVE, STE 206 53705 #016-06-1998 L2003 **OPH** *020 †35
BRADFORD, Leslie Siriya. ■ 53703 #050-02-2006 L2007 **OBG** *012
BRADLEY, David Paul. ■ 53711 #025-07-2005 **IM** *012
BRADLEY, Elisa Ann. J5/230 CSC-2454, 600 HIGHLAND AVENUE 53792 #016-11-2007 **IM** *012
BRADLEY, Kristin Ann. 600 HIGHLAND AVE, K4/B100 53792 #056-05-1999 L2000 **RO** *020 †80
BRANCH, Paul Kenneth. 2122 LUANN LN STE 102 53713 #030-05-1996 L1999 **FM** *020 †18
BRAND, Stacey Lynn. UNIV OF WISCONSIN HOSP, F2/214 CLINICAL SCIENCES C 53792 #035-75-2006, ▲ **EM** *012
BRANDABUR, John Jos, Jr. 4410 REGENT ST 53705 #028-34-1958 L1960 **IM IMG** *020 †20
BRANDENBURG, James Harold. 600 HIGHLAND AVE, CLINICAL SCIENCE CENTER 53792 #056-05-1956 L1958 **OTO AM** *071 †45
BRANDON, Jodee Rae. 20 S PARK ST, STE 207 53715 #033-01-1996 L2000 **OBG** *020 †30
BRAUER, William Richard. 600 HIGHLAND AVE E3/311, RADIOLOGY DEPT UNIV WISCON 53792 #056-05-1971 L1973 **R** *020 †80
BRAUS, Anthony James. 2500 OVERLOOK TER 53705 #025-12-1979 L1984 **P** *020 †75
BRAZELTON, Thomas Berry. 600 HIGHLAND AVE H4/466, DEPT OF PEDIATRICS 53792 #024-07-1994 L2000 **CCP** *020 †55
BRAZY, Jane E. 202 S PARK ST 53715 #022-07-1972 L1988 **NPM PD** *040 †55
BRAZY, Peter Coffin. 2500 OVERLOOK TER, B-3059 53792 #028-02-1972 L1988 **NEP IM** *050 †20
BRECKBILL, Don Eric. 1821 S STOUGHTON RD 53716 #051-01-1993 L1994 **FM** *020 †18
BREED, Alan Lewis. 600 HIGHLAND AVE, DEPT ORTHOPEDICS 53792 #035-15-1965 L1974 **ORS** *020
BREGMAN, Howard Steven. ■ 53719 #041-01-1990 L1993 **PD** *020 †55
BRENNAN, Meghan Beth. J5/230 CSC-2454, 600 HIGHLAND AVENUE 53792 #050-02-2006 **IM** *012
BRESLIN, Tara Margaret. 600 HIGHLAND AVE, H4/744/CSC 53792 #048-04-1992 L2000 **SO** *020 †85
BRETT, Maria Kristina. ■ 53718 #056-06-2007 **PD** *012
BREUNIG, Adam Charles. ■ 53705 #056-05-2008 *012

BRIDGES, Alan Jay. 600 HIGHLAND AVE, H6/363 CLINICAL SCI CTR 53792 #016-11-1983 L1984 **RHU** *020 †20
BRIDGES, Allison Duke. 600 HIGHLAND AVE, UNIVERSITY OF WI HOSPITAL 53792 #001-06-2002 L2004 **GE** *012 †20
BRIDSON, William Ernest. 600 HIGHLAND AVE, J5 219 CLINICAL SCIENCE CE 53792 #028-02-1965 L1972 **END IM** *050
BRILL, James Jos. 202 S PARK ST, DR JAMES B TORHORST 53715 #056-06-1968 L1969 **AN** *071 †05
BRODERICK, Lynn Swab. 600 HIGHLAND AVE 311, OF RADIOLOGY 53792 #038-41-1987 L1998 **DR** *020 †80
BRODERICK, Thomas P. 1 S PARK ST, FL 7 53715 #016-01-1990 L1998 **AN** *020 †05
BRODSKY, Jon Frederick. ■ 53726 #016-11-1989 L1990 **CCM** *020 †20
BROGUNIER, Michele E. 675 W WASHINGTON AVE 53703 #050-02-1996 L1997 **FM** *020 †18
BROOKS, Benjamin Rix. 600 HIGHLAND AVE, UNIV OF WI HOSP & CLINICS 53792 #024-01-1970 L1982 **N IM** *020 †20,75 ‡
BROOKS, Laurel May. ■ 53711 #016-45-1980 L1981 **GP IM** *071
BROOKS, Margaret Alison. 2870 UNIVERSITY AVE, STE 200 53705 #047-06-2000 L2006 **PSM** *100 †55
BROOKS, Nathaniel P. 600 HIGHLAND AVE, UNIVERSITY OF WI HOSPITAL 53792 #056-06-2002 L2004 **NS** *012
BROWN, Arnold L. 1300 UNIVERSITY AVE 53706 #051-04-1949 L1980 **PTH** *071 †50
BROWN, Julianne Joy. 1313 FISH HATCHERY RD 53715 #056-05-1999 L2002 **CHP** *020 †75
BROWN, Laura Jane. ■ 53711 #028-02-1981 L1982 **OS** *050
BROWN, Randall Todd. ■ 53704 #054-04-1996 L2001 **FM** *020 †18
BROWN, Richard L. 777 S MILLS ST, DEPT OF FAM MED & PRAC 53715 #043-01-1981 L1990 **FM** *050 †18
BROWNING, Thomas Hughes. 20 S PARK ST STE 355 53715 #049-01-1960 L1961 **GE IM** *020 †20
BRUCE, Calvin Sumner. 707 S MILLS ST 53715 #024-01-1975 L1976 **FM FPG** *020 †18
BRUCE, Richard J. 600 HIGHLAND AVE H4/831, UW HOSPITAL AND CLINICS 53792 #048-12-2003 L2007 **DR** *012
BRUNGARD, Karen Ruth. 4122 E TOWNE BLVD 53704 #041-01-1977 L1980 **IM** *020 †20
BRUSKEWITZ, Reginald Chas. 451 JUNCTION RD, STE 9903 53717 #056-05-1973 L1974 **U** *020 †95
BRYAN, George Terrell. 600 HIGHLAND AVE, UW MEDICAL ONCOLOGY CLINIC 53792 #056-05-1957 L1959 **ON PA** *071
BRYANT, Tyson. 707 S MILLS ST, ST MARY'S HOSPITAL 53715 #016-11-2003 L2006 **EM** *016
BUCHANAN, Joel R. 600 HIGHLAND AVE H4/847, UNIV OF WI HOSP & CLINICS 53792 #047-05-1981 L1982 **EM IM** *020 †20,16
BUCHHOLZ, Andrew Paul. 600 HIGHLAND AVE RM B6-319, HOSPITAL AND 53792 #007-02-2006 L2008 **AN** *012
BUCHLER, Dolores Ann. ■ 53704 #041-07-1961 L1969 **OBG RO** *071 †30,80
BUCKMAN, Sara Anne. ■ 53726 #056-05-2008 *012
BUDZAK, Kathryn Sue. 1313 FISH HATCHERY RD 53715 #056-05-1969 L1970 **OS FM** *071
BUEHRING, Bjoern. 600 HIGHLAND AVE 53792 #409-46-2005 **IM** *012
BUENCAMINO, Amy C Pivovar. 4410 REGENT ST, ASSOCIATED PHYSICIANS 53705 #056-05-1999 L2004 **PD** *020 †55 ‡
BUENCAMINO, Cenon Michael. 1313 FISH HATCHERY RD 53715 #056-06-1997 L1998 **DR** *020 †20,80 ‡
BUKSTEIN, Don Abram. 1313 FISH HATCHERY RD, DEAN CLINIC 53715 #028-03-1977 L1982 **A PUD** *020 †55,03
BULL, Rebecca. 675 W WASHINGTON AVE, CAPITOL HLTH CTR 53703 #038-41-1986 L1987 **FM** *020 †18
BURG, Kenneth Richard. 600 HIGHLAND AVE, AVE H4/831-8320 53792 #056-05-2001 L2005 **P** *020
BURGER, Amberly Lyn. J5/230 CSC-2454, 600 HIGHLAND AVENUE 53792 #038-40-2006 **IM** *012
BURK, Renee Elizabeth. 5249 E TERRACE DR 53718 #056-05-1996 L1997 **PD** *020 †55
BURKAT, Cathy K Nguyen. 2880 UNIVERSITY AVE 53705 #035-45-1999 L2002 **OPH** *020 †35 ‡
BURKE, Mary Quinn. 2500 OVERLOOK TER 53705 #045-04-1981 L1987 **IM** *020 †20
BURNER, Richard William. 1 S PARK ST, MADISON SURGERY CENTER, IN 53715 #016-11-1968 L1973 **AN** *072 †05
BURNS, Charlotte Ann. ■ 53726 #056-05-1962 L1963 **OPH** *071 †35
BURNS, Deirdre Ann. 4122 E TOWNE BLVD 53704 #036-01-1989 L1990 **PD** *020 †55
BURNS, Robert O. 4410 REGENT ST 53705 #051-04-1952 L1958 **IM NEP** *020 †20
BURNSIDE, Elizabeth S. 600 HIGHLAND AVE E3/311 53792 #024-07-1993 L2001 **DR** *020 †80
BUSAROW, Sara Beth. ■ 53703 #016-06-2006 *012
BUSH, Arianna Kay. 1300 UNIVERSITY AVE, UNIV OF WI MED SCH 53706 #056-05-1998 **FM** *100
BUSH, Curtis Wells. 20 S PARK ST, UW MEDICAL FOUNDATION SUIT 53715 #017-20-1969 L1972 **FM** *020 †18
BUSH, George Lynn. 600 HIGHLAND AVE, DEPT ANES 53792 #038-41-1968 L1974 **AN** *071 †05
BUSH, Robert Kyle. 2500 OVERLOOK TER, WM S MIDDLETON MEM VA HOSP 53705 #055-01-1970 L1973 **AI IM** *050 †20,03
BUSHMAN, Wade Alan. 600 HIGHLAND AVE 53792 #016-02-1986 L2002 **U** *020 †95
BUSSAN, Kenneth Luverne. ■ 53705 #056-05-1975 L1976 **IM** *020 †20
BUSSE, William Walter. 600 HIGHLAND AVE 53792 #056-05-1966 L1967 **A IM** *050 †20,03
BUSSEY, Mary Emily. 707 S MILLS ST 53715 #016-06-1977 L1992 **NPM PD** *020 †55
BUTLER, John Bernard. 777 S MILLS ST, ST MARYS HOSPITAL 53715 #056-05-1980 L1992 **IM** *020 †20
BUTLER, Samuel L. 5301 TOKAY BLVD 53711 #011-04-1982 L2003 **PUD IM** *030 †20
BUTTAR, Amna B. 600 HIGHLAND AVE, DEPT. OF MEDICINE 53792 #704-06-1987 L1993 **IM** *020 †20
BUYAN-DENT, Laura J. 600 HIGHLAND AVE H6/574, DEPT. OF NEUROLOGY 53792 #056-05-1998 L1999 **N** *020 †75
BUZOGANY, William Michael. ■ 53705 #035-45-1958 L1960 **P** *020 †75
BYCE, Kenneth Robert. 202 S PARK ST 53715 #026-04-1962 L1964 **OBG** *071 †30
BYERLY, Dianne Marie. 1 S PARK ST 53715 #005-02-1987 L1994 **AN** *040 †05
BYERS, Rebecca Lucich. 2202 S PARK ST 53713 #056-05-1986 L1987 **FM** *020 †18
BYRNE, Frank Dewey. 700 S PARK ST 53715 #035-08-1977 L1978 **PUD CCM** *030 †20 ‡
BYRNE, Siobhan Mairead. 600 HIGHLAND AVE H4/831, UW HOSPITAL AND CLINICS 53792 #054-04-2005 L2007 **IM** *012
CABAY, Marcus Esker. 600 HIGHLAND AVE, AVE H4/831-8320 53792 #016-11-2003 L2006 **DR** *012
CAHILL, Kathryn Horras. 600 HIGHLAND AVE, BOX 4108 53792 #056-05-2005 L2007 **PD** *012
CAISSIE, Amanda Jo. ■ 53705 #056-05-2008 *012

CALDER, Robert A. ■ 53703 #056-06-1982 L1983 **PHP** *030 †70
CALLANDER, Natalie Scott. 600 HIGHLAND AVE, HEM/ONC SECTION MAIL CODE 53792 #024-07-1985 L2004 **HEM ON** *020 †20
CALLCUT, Rachael Anne. 600 HIGHLAND AVE H4/831, UW HOSPITAL & CLINICS 53792 #038-41-2001 L2002 **GS** *012
CALLISTER, Todd Richard. 313 GLENWAY ST 53705 #056-06-1996 L2001 **P** *020
CALLISTO, Anthony Jay. 707 S MILLS ST, ST. MARY'S HOSPITAL 53715 #028-02-2004 L2007 **EM** *100
CAMBRAY, Adam Joseph. 600 HIGHLAND AVE, UNIVERSITY OF WI HOSPITAL 53792 #056-05-2003 L2004 **AN** *012
CAMPANILE, Maria Kay. 1552 UNIVERSITY AVE, UNIVERSITY HEALTH SERVICES 53726 #038-40-2000 L2001 **IM** *020 †20 ‡
CAMPBELL, Toby C. 600 HIGHLAND AVE, HEMATOLOGY/ONCOLOGY K6/5 53792 #051-01-2001 L2003 **HO** *100
CANNON, George Mackey. 600 HIGHLAND AVE K4/B100, HOSPITAL AND 53792 #049-01-2002 L2006 **RO** *012
CAPONI, Bartho, III. 600 HIGHLAND AVE, BOX 2454 53792 #016-11-2005 L2006 **IM** *020
CARD, William Hays. 707 S MILLS ST 53715 #056-05-1954 L1955 **PTH CLP** *071 †50
CARDWELL, Jill Marie. 202 S PARK ST 53715 #056-05-1992 L1993 **AN** *020 †05
CARLSON, Philip Randall. 202 S PARK ST, BLDG 3 53715 #026-08-1979 L1984 **DR NM** *020 †20,80
CARLSON, Sheila Kay. 9 WHITE OAKS LN, C/O DAVIS DUEHR DEAN SURGE 53711 #056-05-1977 L1978 **AN** *020 †05
CARLSSON, Cynthia M. 2500 OVERLOOK TER, VA GRECC (11G) 53705 #025-01-1995 L1996 **IM** *020 †20
CARMICHAEL, Bradley John. 600 HIGHLAND AVE, AVE H4/831-8320 53792 #030-05-2001 L2005 **PCP** *100 †50
CARNES, Mary Lindsey. 600 HIGHLAND AVE, DEPT OF MEDICINE J5/220 53792 #035-06-1978 L1979 **IMG** *050 †20
CAROPRESO, David Keir. 1821 S STOUGHTON RD 53716 #018-03-1998 L1999 **U** *020 †95
CARR, Kathleen Elizabeth. 1552 UNIVERSITY AVE 53726 #056-05-1997 L2000 **FM FSM** *020 †18
CARR, Richard M. 1 W WILSON ST RM 272 53703 #005-11-1965 L1970 **IM ON** *030 †20
CARR, Sandra Colleen. 202 S PARK ST 53715 #028-34-1989 L1997 **PHL** *020 †85
CARREL, Aaron Lawrence. 600 HIGHLAND AVE, H4/455 CSC PEDIATRICS 53792 #035-06-1992 L1996 **PDE** *020 †55
CARRIGAN, Kevin James. ■ 53705 #025-12-1994 L1996 **P** *020
CARTER, Richard Leland. 1200 JOHN Q HAMMONS DR, STE 400 53717 #025-01-1984 L2003 **NS** *020 †25
CARTER, Thomas Lynn. 202 S PARK ST, MERITER HOSPITAL 53715 #038-06-1963 L1968 **R** *020 †80
CASANOVA, James Edward. 707 S MILLS ST 53715 #056-05-1974 L1975 **IM MDM** *030 †20
CASEY, Marie Ann. 600 HIGHLAND AVE H4/831 53792 #026-04-1995 L2007 **P** *012
CASIMIR, Kenneth Charles. 301 TROY DR, MENDOTA MENTAL HEALTH INST 53704 #048-15-1989 L2001 **CHP** *020 †75
CASPER, N Thomas. 20 S PARK ST, ST-INTERNAL MEDICINE 53715 #056-05-1991 L1992 **IM** *020 †20
CASSADAY, Ryan Daniel. J5/230 CSC-2454, 600 HIGHLAND AVENUE 53792 #056-05-2007 **IM** *012
CASTILLO, Marcelo E, Jr. 301 TROY DR, MENDOTA MENTAL HEALTH INST 53704 #748-10-1983 L1986 **P** *020
CASTRO, Michael Jerome. ■ 53705 #012-01-2004 L2008 **PTH** *012
CATLETT-SIRCHIO, Ann. 202 S PARK ST 53715 #056-05-2000 L2003 **IM** *020
CATTAPAN, Steven Eugene. 202 S PARK ST 53715 #016-43-1996 L2002 **PCC** *020 †20
CENTER, Barbara H. 2727 MARSHALL CT 53705 #056-05-1988 L1989 **CHP** *020 †75
CERTAIN, Heather E. 2500 OVERLOOK TER, TERRACE D4208 53705 #056-05-2003 L2006 **IM** *100 †20
CHAIET, Scott Randolph. ■ 53703 #048-04-2007 **OTO** *012
CHAIREZ, Ariel. ■ 53705 #056-05-2008 *012
CHALMERS, Aaron. ■ 53703 #037-01-2007 **GS** *012
CHAN, Pennapa Sujatanond. 1313 FISH HATCHERY RD 53715 #016-45-1998 L1999 **END** *020
CHANBUSARAKUM, Krisada. 20 S PARK ST, STE 207 53715 #891-04-1971 L1977 **NS** *020 †25
CHANBUSARAKUM, Puangpetch. 202 S PARK ST 53715 #891-04-1971 L1977 **GP ID** *062 †20
CHANDRA, Suresh R. 2828 MARSHALL CT, STE 106 53705 #495-05-1961 L1974 **OPH GS** *020 †35
CHANG, Chen-Kang. 707 S MILLS ST 53715 #244-02-1971 L1976 **ATP PTH** *020 †50
CHANG, Faye L. UNIV HOSP AND CLINICS, B4/243-2472 CSC 53792 #038-03-2007 **PTH** *012
CHANG, Julie Elizabeth. 600 HIGHLAND AVE, CSC H4/534 53792 #017-20-2000 L2001 **HEM** *100 †20
CHANG, Tony S. 20 S PARK ST, STE 207 53715 #056-05-1995 L2000 **IM** *020 †20
CHAPMAN, Carrie Beth. 600 HIGHLAND AVE, BOX 2454 53792 #056-05-2004 L2005 **CD** *012 †20
CHARBONEAU, Susan. 752 N HIGH POINT RD 53717 #016-43-1996 L2001 **GS** *020 †85
CHARLES, Rebecca Lea. 752 N HIGH POINT RD, WEST CLINIC 53717 #056-06-1999 L2000 **PD** *020 †55
CHARLES, Samuel Stephen. 600 HIGHLAND AVE, AVE H4/831-8320 53792 #056-06-2001 L2002 **DR** *020 †80
CHARLIER, Nancy L. 301 TROY DR, MENDOTA MENTAL HLTHINSTITU 53704 #055-01-1991 L1992 **P** *020
CHASE, Peter Joseph. 202 S PARK ST, BLDG 3 53715 #028-34-2001 L2002 **DR** *020 †80
CHEEMA, Yusra Rifaquat. ■ 53711 #056-05-2008 *012
CHEN, Herbert. 600 HIGHLAND AVE, H4/750 CSC 53792 #036-07-1992 L2000 **GS SO** *020 †85
CHEN, Ping-Sun K. 600 HIGHLAND AVE, DEPT OF RADIOLOGY, NEURORA 53792 #048-02-2002 L2007 **RNR** *012 †80
CHEN, Xueyan. 6000 HIGHLANDS AVE 53792 #243-47-1995 **PTH** *020
CHENE, Robin Louise. 6001 RESEARCH PARK BLVD, DEPT PSYCHIATRY 53719 #025-01-1984 L1985 **P PA** *050
CHEUNG, Victoria Manching. ■ 53717 #016-11-2006 L2008 **IM** *012
CHHEDA, Shobhina Girish. 451 JUNCTION RD, STE 9903 53717 #035-06-1990 L2002 **IM PD** *020 †55,20
CHI, Kwan-Hwa. ■ 53705 #244-08-1982 **ON** *020
CHINNAIYAN, Prakash. 600 HIGHLAND AVE, K4 342 53792 #025-07-2000 L2004 **RO** *020 †80
CHO, Clifford Suhyun. 600 HIGHLAND AVE, H4/724 CLINICAL SCIENCE CE 53792 #047-05-1997 L1999 **GS** *020 †85
CHOHANEY, Marilyn Jean. 5618 ODANA RD 53719 #038-41-1979 L1984 **FM** *020 †18

CHOI, Brian Seungwook. 600 HIGHLAND AVE, UNIVERSITY OF WI HOSPITAL 53792 #016-06-2003 L2004 **ON** *012 †20
CHOI, James Jeong. 621 SCIENCE DR 53711 #018-03-1995 L2000 **DR** *020 †80
CHOI, Jinhee. 600 HIGHLAND AVE, BOX 7375 53792 #056-05-2005 L2006 **GS** *012
CHOLES, Diana Psihos. 707 S MILLS ST 53715 #026-04-1993 L1995 **HOS IM** *020 †20
CHONG, Laura Kimberley. 600 HIGHLAND AVE, AVE H4/831-8320 53792 #016-11-2004 L2006 **IM** *100 †20
CHOPRA, Paramjeet S. 600 HIGHLAND AVE 53792 #495-32-1962 L1971 **TS** *040 †85,90
CHOSY, Julius John. ■ 53711 #038-40-1955 L1960 **IM P** *071
CHOSY, Louis Wm. 600 HIGHLAND AVE 53792 #038-40-1959 L1961 **PUD IM** *040
CHOU, Maggie Yachyn. 600 HIGHLAND AVE H4/831, UW HOSPITAL AND CLINICS 53792 #054-04-2005 L2007 **PD** *012
CHOW, Clement Chikai. ■ 53719 #056-05-2007 **TY** *012
CHRISTENSEN, Michael Evan. ■ 53719 #056-05-2008 *012
CHRISTIAN, Matthew Winter. 600 HIGHLAND AVE, BOX 3236 53792 #024-07-2005 L2006 **GS** *020
CHRISTIAN, Nicole S. 707 S MILLS ST, ST. MARY'S HOSPITAL 53715 #026-04-2003 L2004 **IM** *100 †20
CHRISTIANSEN, Abigail M. 752 N HIGH POINT RD 53717 #030-05-1985 L1988 **GE IM** *020 †20
CHRISTIE, Nathan. ■ 53717 #056-06-2003 L2006 **AN** *012
CHUN, Memee King. ■ 53717 #035-01-1955 L1963 **PD** *071 †55
CHUN, Raymond Wai Mun. 600 HIGHLAND AVE 53792 #010-02-1955 L1961 **CHN** *071 †55
CHUNDURI, Srinivas. 1300 UNIVERSITY AVE 53706 #496-24-2002 **FM** *100
CHYBOWSKI, Timothy John. 20 S PARK ST, STE 207 53715 #056-05-1980 L1981 **PD** *020 †55
CISKE, David J. 20 S PARK ST, STE 207 53715 #056-05-2002 L2004 **IM** *020 †20
CLEARY, James Francis. 600 HIGHLAND AVE 53792 #143-01-1984 L2000 †120
CLINE, Joseph Robt. 600 HIGHLAND AVE 53792 #016-01-1979 L1986 **EM IM** *020 †20,16
CLUTSON, Richard Anthony. 202 S PARK ST, BLDG 3 53715 #026-04-1987 L1993 **DR** *040 †80
CODNER, Panna Ashok. ■ 53711 #056-05-1999 L2000 **CCS** *020 †85
COHEN, Candace Agress. 301 TROY DR, MENDOTA MENTAL HLTH INST 53704 #020-12-1990 L1992 **P** *020 †75
COHEN, Marcus. 600 HIGHLAND AVE, DEPARTMENT OF PEDIATRICS 53792 #056-05-1962 L1963 **PDA PD** *020 †55,03
COHEN, Philip Tepper. 2828 MARSHALL CT STE 100, DEPT OF INTERNAL MEDICINE 53705 #005-02-1975 L2005 **IM** *020 †20
COLAS, Antonio E. 600 HIGHLAND AVE 53792 #847-04-1953 *071
COLBURN, Ralph Marshall. 1313 FISH HATCHERY RD 53715 #016-06-1966 L1974 **DR** *020 †80
COLE, Jean Louise. 600 HIGHLAND AVE, UNIV OF WI HOSP 53792 #028-03-2006 L2006 **PM** *012
COLE, Robert Lockey. 5618 ODANA RD 53719 #028-34-1973 L1976 **FM** *020 †18
COLEMAN, Frederick Wm. 625 W WASHINGTON AVE, MENTAL HLTH CTR DANE CO 53703 #041-01-1974 L1976 **P CHP** *020
COLEMAN, Wendy L Sterne. 7102 MINERAL POINT RD 53717 #041-07-1971 L1975 **PD CHP** *020 †55
COLLINS, Jannette. 600 HIGHLAND AVE, DEPT OF RADIOLOGY 53792 #038-43-1989 L1990 **DR** *020 †20
COLLINS, Margaret Alice. ■ 53711 #056-06-2004 L2008 **D** *012
COLLINS, Michael Mcgowin. 600 HIGHLAND AVE, BOX 4108 53792 #030-06-2004 L2006 **AN** *012 †55
COLMENARES, John Phillip. 1821 S STOUGHTON RD, EAST CLINIC 53716 #041-13-1992 L2004 **EM** *020 †16
CONLEY, Dierdre Antoinett. ■ 53704 #056-05-2007 **AN** *012
CONLEY, James Patrick. 600 HIGHLAND AVE H4/831, UW HOSPITAL AND CLINICS 53792 #030-06-2005 L2007 **IM** *012
CONNELL, Amy Marie. 1821 S STOUGHTON RD, DEAN EAST CLINIC 53716 #018-03-2000 L2001 **P** *020 †75
CONNER, Joseph Patrick. 600 HIGHLAND AVE, UNIV OF WISC RM H4/636 CSC 53792 #038-41-1987 L2001 **GO** *020 †30
CONNER, Neil Patrick. 707 S MILLS ST, DEPT OF PEDS-ST MARYS HOSP 53715 #021-06-1991 L1994 **CCP PD** *020 †55
CONNORS, Charlotte V B. ■ 53726 #051-04-1954 L1956 **P** *071
CONNORS, Dean M. 707 S MILLS ST 53715 #056-05-1952 L1955 **PTH OS** *030 †50
CONRAD, David Norbert. ■ 53719 #056-05-2007 **ORS** *012
CONTRERAS, Carlo Mario. 600 HIGHLAND AVE, UNIVERSITY OF WI HOSPITAL 53792 #016-06-2003 L2004 **GS** *012
CONWAY, James Hyde. ■ 53711 #035-20-1990 L2005 **PD PDI** *020 †55
COOK, Jeffrey Randolph. 600 HIGHLAND AVE, BOX 2454 53792 #016-11-2005 L2007 **IM** *012
COOK, Shelly Marie. ■ 53715 #016-11-2001 L2001 **PTH** *012
COOKSON, David Upjohn. ■ 53705 #024-01-1956 L1957 **IM A** *071 †20
COOLEY, Mary Huber. 600 HIGHLAND AVE, BOX 9601 53792 #036-07-2004 L2005 **PD** *100 †55
COOPER, David Michael. 1200 JOHN Q HAMMONS DR, STE 400 53717 #016-06-1997 L2001 **IM** *020 †20
COOPER, Karen Ann. 1 S PARK ST, FL 7 53715 #047-05-1997 L1999 **OTO** *020
COPELAND, Travis Burton. 752 N HIGH POINT RD 53717 #016-11-1997 L1998 **CHP** *020 †75
CORDEN, Sarah Swanson. 451 JUNCTION RD, STE 9903 53717 #016-06-1985 L1988 **PD ADL** *020 †55
CORDES, Blueleaf Ann. ■ 53704 #056-05-2006 **IM** *012
CORDES, Timothy John. ■ 53704 #056-05-2004 **P** *012
CORLISS, Robert Frederick. 600 HIGHLAND AVE H4/823 53792 #056-05-2000 L2003 **FOP** *100 †50 ‡
CORLISS, Robert James. 800 S BROOKS ST, SURGERY & CARE 53715 #041-02-1959 L1961 **PDC IM** *020.20,55
CORNETT, Chris Alan. 600 HIGHLAND AVE, RM H4/831 53792 #030-05-2005 L2006 **ORS** *012
CORNETT, Daniel Duane. 600 HIGHLAND AVE, AVE H4/831-8320 53792 #020-12-2003 L2005 **IM** *100 †20
CORNWELL, Richard Dean. 600 HIGHLAND AVE, PULMONARY SECTION 53792 #035-15-1984 L1985 **PUD IM** *020 †55
CORRELL, Timothy A. 950 W SHORE DR 53715 #001-02-1972 L1973 **IM** *020
CORYELL, John L. ■ 53713 #056-05-1953 L1954 **IM** *071
COSTANZO, Christine Marie. 16 N CARROLL ST STE 710, OF WISCONSIN 53703 #038-40-1993 L1994 **P** *020 †75
COTTER, Tracy Patrick. 1313 FISH HATCHERY RD, DEAN MEDICAL CTR 53715 #025-12-1987 L1988 **AN IM** *020 †05
COUNTS, Helen Elizabeth. 202 S PARK ST 53715 #051-01-1998 L1999 **FM** *040 †18
COURSIN, Douglas Baird. 506 BLUE RIDGE PKWY 53705 #035-03-1976 L1978 **AN IM** *020 †20,05

■ = Address Information Privacy Protected

COUSER, James Isaac. 1200 JOHN Q HAMMONS DR, STE 400 53717 #050-02-1982 L1994 **IM PUD** *020 †20

COUTO, Francesca. J5/230 CSC-2454, 600 HIGHLAND AVE 53792 #042-03-2001 L2002 **END** *100

COWGILL, Lale Douglas. 1313 FISH HATCHERY RD, DEAN CLINIC 53715 #005-06-1973 L1985 **TS GS** *020 †85,90

COX, Elizabeth D. 600 HIGHLAND AVE, 44/455 CSC PEDIATRICS] 53792 #055-01-1991 L1992 **PD** *020 †55

COYLE, Michelle Leticia. ■ 53705 #056-05-1998 *100

CRABTREE, Sandra Ann. 3602 ATWOOD AVE 53714 #056-05-1989 L1990 **FM** *020

CRAIG, Alison. 675 W WASHINGTON AVE 53703 #056-05-1998 L1999 **PD** *020 †55

CRAIG, Rebecca Anne. J5/230 CSC-2454, 600 HIGHLAND AVENUE 53792 #018-03-2006 L2008 **IM** *012

CRAIG, William Alexander. 2500 OVERLOOK TER 53705 #024-07-1965 L1966 **ID IM** *050 †20

CRAWFORD, David Gerald. 6515 WATTS RD, STE 206 53719 #039-01-1976 L1977 **P** *020 †75

CRESWELL, Caleb Howe. ■ 53705 #056-05-2007 **TY** *012

CRIPPS, Derek James. 1 S PARK ST, DEPT OF DERMATOLOGY 53715 #352-07-1953 L1965 **D** *020 †15

CRNICH, Christopher John. 600 HIGHLAND AVE, UWSMPH - DEPARTMENT OF MED 53792 #016-01-1997 L1998 **ID** *100 †20

CROASDALE, Christopher R. 707 S MILLS ST 53715 #025-01-1990 L1992 **OPH** *020 †35

CROCKER, Laurence Gordon. 451 JUNCTION RD # 9902 53717 #028-02-1955 L1958 **IM** *071 †20

CROFT, Donita Ruth. 600 HIGHLAND AVE 53792 #056-05-1992 L2002 **PCC** *020 †20

CROUSE, Byron James. 777 S MILLS ST, UW OF MADISON DEPT OF FAMI 53715 #026-08-1977 L1980 **FM** *040 †18

CROWE, Matthew Eric. 600 HIGHLAND AVE, BOX 2454 53792 #038-45-2001 L2003 **RHU** *100 †10

CRUMMY, Andrew Bernard. 600 HIGHLAND AVE, D4-354 53792 #024-05-1955 L1958 **R VIR** *071 †80

CRYLEN, Curtis Edward. 600 HIGHLAND AVE, AVE H4/831-8320 53792 #016-06-2003 L2005 **U** *012

CUBIN, Frederick Wm. ■ 53719 #016-11-1964 L2006 **IM** *020

CULBERTSON, Eric John. ■ 53715 #056-05-2006 L2007 **GS** *012

CULLENWARD, Michael J. 1313 FISH HATCHERY RD 53715 #056-05-1983 L1984 **DR** *020 †80

CUNNINGHAM, Milfred Allen. ■ 53718 #056-05-1961 L1962 **ORS** *071

CURTIN, Michael Jos. 1313 FISH HATCHERY RD, DEAN CLINIC 53715 #023-07-1967 L1975 **DR PDR** *071 †80

CURTIS, Erin Melissa. ■ 53703 #041-12-2003 L2007 **P** *012

CURTIS, Vanessa Ann. 600 HIGHLAND AVE, AVE H4/831-8320 53792 #056-05-2004 L2005 **PD** *012

CZERWONKA, Lukasz. ■ 53703 #056-05-2008 *012

DAHLBERG, Paul Eric. 600 HIGHLAND AVE, AVE H4/831-8320 53792 #023-07-2004 L2005 **AI** *012 †20

DAILEY, Seth H. 600 HIGHLAND AVE, K4/719 CSC 53792 #035-19-1996 L2004 **OTO** *020 †45

D'ALESSANDRO, Anthony, Jr. 600 HIGHLAND AVE 53792 #041-09-1981 L1982 **GS** *020 †85

D'ALESSIO, Donn Jos. 610 WALNUT ST 53726 #035-20-1960 L1967 **ID IM** *071

DALEY, Amy Lynn. 1200 JOHN Q HAMMONS DR, STE 400 53717 #030-05-1995 L1996 **IM** *020 †20

DALEY, Timothy John. ■ 53705 #056-05-2007 **IM** *012

DALLY, Alfred David. ■ 53705 #056-06-1960 L1961 **IM** *071 †20

DALTON, Debra Ann. 600 HIGHLAND AVE, BOX 4108 53792 #025-12-2005 L2007 **PD** *012

DAMM, Michael Geo. 202 S PARK ST, MERITER HOSPITAL 53715 #016-43-1965 L1970 **DR** *020 †80

DANAHY, Daniel Thos. 1313 FISH HATCHERY RD, DEAN MEDICAL CENTER 53715 #035-45-1968 L1978 **CD** *020 †20

DANIOLOS, Athena. 1552 UNIVERSITY AVE, UNIVERSITY STUDENT HEALTH 53726 #048-12-1986 L1991 **D** *020 †15

DANIS, Ronald P, Jr. 2880 UNIVERSITY AVE 53705 #016-06-1983 L1984 **OPH** *020 †35

DANKO, Istvan. 600 HIGHLAND AVE, CSC H4/432 UW HOSPITAL 53792 #473-03-1978 L1998 **PG** *020 †55

DANOV, Zoran Risto. 600 HIGHLAND AVE, AVE H4/831-8320 53792 #957-04-1982 L2005 **PDP** *012 †55

DAR, Wasim Akram. 600 HIGHLAND AVE H4/823, PO BOX 7375 53792 #038-06-2000 L2001 **GS** *012

DARCY, Teresa A. 600 HIGHLAND AVE 53792 #018-03-1982 L2001 **PTH MDM** *030 †50

DAS, Maya. 325 S YELLOWSTONE DR # 3 53705 #056-05-2005 L2006 *020

DASHER, Kevin John. 600 HIGHLAND AVE 53792 #048-14-2003 L2005 **GE** *012 †20

DAUGHERTY, Donald Albert. 1200 JOHN Q HAMMONS DR, STE 400 53717 #056-06-1958 L1965 **IM END** *020 †20

DAVENPORT, Gordon, Jr. ■ 53711 #035-45-1948 L1956 **PS** *071 †65

DAVID-LANTZ, Krista J. 600 HIGHLAND AVE 53792 #046-01-2000 L2001 **P** *020 †75

DAVIDSON, Paul Lane. ■ 53718 #035-01-1954 L1961 **OS IM** *071 †20

DAVIDSON, Susan Rubin. 707 S MILLS ST 53715 #035-46-1982 L1986 **MFM OBG** *020 †30

DAVIS, Ashley Jean. ■ 53717 #056-06-2008 *012

DAVIS, Frederick J. ■ 53704 #056-05-1946 L1947 **OPH** *071 †35

DAVIS, James Earl. 675 W WASHINGTON AVE 53703 #010-01-1975 L1976 **FM** *040 †18

DAVIS, James Mcdowell, Jr. 1802 MONROE ST, UNIT 412 53711 #016-45-1997 L2004 **IM** *020 †20

DAVIS, Jeffrey Dinsdale. 752 N HIGH POINT RD 53717 #056-05-1974 L1980 **GE IM** *020 †20

DAVIS, Jeffrey Paul. 8007 EXCELSIOR DR 53717 #016-02-1971 L1979 **PHP ID** *050 †55

DAVIS, Jeffrey Paul. ■ 53705 #035-01-1977 L1978 **IM** *035 †20

DAVIS, Kirkland Westbury. 600 HIGHLAND AVE, STE E-3/366 53792 #045-01-1994 L2000 **DR** *020 †80

DAVIS, Mark Foster. 20 S PARK ST 53715 #003-01-1986 L1988 **IM EM** *020 †20

DAVIS, Matthew D. 600 HIGHLAND AVE, DEPT OF OPHTH & VISUAL SVC 53792 #041-01-1950 L1951 **OPH** *071 †35

DAVIS, William Thomas. 7102 MINERAL POINT RD 53717 #056-05-1983 L1987 **IM** *030 †20

DAWSON, Shirley Joy. 301 TROY DR 53704 #026-04-1990 L1991 **PYG** *020 †75

DAY, Richard Perrin. 20 S PARK ST, STE 207 53715 #005-11-1978 L1985 **IM PA** *050 †20

DEAL, Eric Michael. ■ 53719 #037-01-2007 **ORS** *012

DEAN, Shannon Leah. 600 HIGHLAND AVE, UNIV OF WI HOSPITAL & CLIN 53792 #056-05-2002 L2003 **PHO** *012 †55

DE ANGELES, David Alan. 1313 FISH HATCHERY RD 53715 #016-45-1991 L1992 **GS** *020 †85

DEATON, Nancy Kathleen. 5249 E TERRACE DR 53718 #016-01-1986 L1991 **FM** *020 †18

DE COCK, David Gibson. 707 S MILLS ST 53715 #056-06-1971 L1972 **GS TS** *020 †90,85

DEFFNER-VALLEY, Patricia. 4122 E TOWNE BLVD, UW HEALTH 53704 #056-05-1995 L1998 **PD** *020 †55

DE GROOT, Beverly Jeanne. 317 KNUTSON DR, CENTRAL WISCONSIN CENTER 53704 #056-05-1992 L1994 **PM** *020

DELGADILLO, Cristina M. 600 HIGHLAND AVE H4/447 53792 #056-05-2007 **PD** *012

DELGADO, David Carl. 600 HIGHLAND AVE, AVE H4/831-8320 53792 #016-11-2002 L2005 **PHO** *012 †55

DELONG, Bridget Stephanie. ■ 53726 #056-05-2008 *012

DELVENTHAL, Jennifer Kay. ■ 53726 #056-05-1980 *075

DEMOPOULOS, Jean. 1821 S STOUGHTON RD 53716 #056-05-1980 L1981 **OBG** *020 †30

DEMORE, Jennifer Preston. 600 HIGHLAND AVE, AVE H4/831-8320 53792 #025-01-2002 L2006 **AI** *012 †20

DEMPSEY, Robert John. 600 HIGHLAND AVE 53792 #016-02-1977 L1995 **NS** *020 †25 ‡

DE MURI, Gregory Paul. 2202 S PARK ST 53713 #025-01-1989 L1990 **PD** *020 †55

DENHOLM, Todd Andrew. 1313 FISH HATCHERY RD 53715 #028-02-1981 L1990 **DR** *020 †80

DENLINGER, Loren Clark. 600 HIGHLAND AVE, J5/230 CSC-2454 53792 #056-05-1998 L1999 **PCC** *100 †20

DENNIE, Trevor Wayne. 600 HIGHLAND AVE RM K4/546, AND CLI 53792 #054-04-2003 L2007 **ON** *012 †20

DE OLIVEIRA, Nilto. 555 ZOR SHRINE PL, NNE KELLEY UWMF-HR 53719 #187-08-1990 L2004 **TS** *100 †85,90

DESAI, Atit Rajendra. 600 HIGHLAND AVE, BOX 9601 53792 #016-11-2004 L2006 **CHP** *012

DE SANTES, Kathleen A. 4122 E TOWNE BLVD 53704 #005-18-1985 L1998 **PD** *020 †55

DESANTES, Kenneth B. 600 HIGHLAND AVE, 44/4 CSC PEDIATRICS 53792 #035-09-1984 L1998 **PHO PD** *020 †55

DESHMUKH, Praveen. 5249 E TERRACE DR 53718 #001-06-1995 L2001 **NS** *020

DE SMET, Arthur August. 600 HIGHLAND AVE, RADIOLOGY E3/311 53792 #025-01-1972 L1985 **R DR** *020 †80 ‡

DE VENECIA, Guillermo B. 600 HIGHLAND AVE, UNIVERSITY OF WISCONSIN MD 53792 #748-01-1954 L1967 **OPH PTH** *020 †35

DE VRIES, Keith Lorne. 202 S PARK ST, WISCONSIN HEART 53715 #062-01-1981 L1987 **CD** *050

DEWEY, Julia Ruthashton. ■ 53711 #041-14-2007 **PD** *012

DE WITT, Richard Thos. 4122 E TOWNE BLVD 53704 #021-01-1968 L1976 **IM ON** *020 †20

DEYO, Christopher Neal. 600 HIGHLAND AVE RM B6-319, HOSPITAL AND 53792 #056-06-2006 **AN** *012

DEYOUNG, Peter Menser. 202 S PARK ST 53715 #025-07-2001 L2004 **NPM** *020 †55

DHOLAKIA, Chirag Ashok. ■ 53705 #016-11-2004 L2008 **GS** *012

DIAMOND, Ronald J. 625 W WASHINGTON AVE 53703 #041-01-1973 L1977 **P** *020 †75

DIAZ, Zobeida Margarita. ■ 53705 #056-05-2008 *012

DIAZ-COTRINA, Victor Adol. 600 HIGHLAND AVE, AVE H4/831-8320 53792 #737-03-1997 L2005 **N** *020

DIBBELL, David Gilmore. 600 HIGHLAND AVE 53792 #041-01-1959 L1975 **PS GS** *040 †85,65

DIBBLE, Phillip Allyn. ■ 53717 #056-05-1955 L1964 **OTO** *071 †45

DICKMEYER, Karla Jean. 4410 REGENT ST 53705 #056-05-1994 L1998 **OBG** *020 †30

DIEDRICH, Dana Renee. 301 TROY DR, MENDOTA MENTAL HLTH INST 53704 #056-06-1995 L1996 **PFP** *020 †75

DIEM, Klaus Dieter. 20 S PARK ST, STE 207 53715 #048-04-1974 L1975 **OBG** *020 †30

DIGGS, Charles Hallam. 1200 JOHN Q HAMMONS DR, STE 400 53717 #023-07-1972 L1979 **ON HEM** *020 †20

DI MAGGIO, Marjorie A. 1821 S STOUGHTON RD 53716 #035-06-1991 L1992 **IM** *020 †20

DIMOND, Alan Randall. ■ 53711 #056-05-2008 *012

DIXON, Russell Mills. 451 JUNCTION RD, STE 9903 53717 #038-41-1976 L1978 **IM END** *020

DOCTER, Timothy J. 1313 FISH HATCHERY RD, DEAN MEDICAL CENTER 53715 #016-11-1982 L1985 **ORS HS** *020 †40

DODSON, Vernon N. ■ 53711 #056-06-1951 L1971 **IM OM** *071 †70

DOELER, Terrence Eugene. 707 S MILLS ST, ST. MARY'S HOSPITAL 53715 #017-20-1976 L1979 **AN** *105

DOMBOURIAN, Melkon Garabe. ■ 53711 #056-05-2008 *012

DONART, Teresa Marie. 600 HIGHLAND AVE, UNIVERSITY OF WI HOSPITAL 53792 #056-05-2003 L2004 **AN** *100

DONG, Sheng-Jing. 1313 FISH HATCHERY RD 53715 #243-44-1982 L2004 **CD** *020 †20

DONOVAN, Stanley Thos. 1313 FISH HATCHERY RD 53715 #056-06-1969 L1972 **OTO** *020 †45

DOOMS, Kevin Todd. 600 HIGHLAND AVE, AVE H4/831-8320 53792 #054-04-2004 L2006 **AI** *012 †55

DOPF, Craig Anthony. 1 S PARK ST, FL 7 53715 #007-02-1987 L1993 **ORS OSS** *072 †40

DO PICO, Guillermo Adolfo. 600 HIGHLAND AVE 53792 #132-01-1961 L1968 **PUD IM** *020

DORESWAMY, Meghana. 600 HIGHLAND AVE, UNIV OF WI HOSP & CLI 53792 #496-39-2002 L2005 **N** *012

DORESWAMY, Vinod. 7453 W VALLEY RIDGE DR, MEDICAL COLLEGE OF WISCONS 53719 #495-09-1994 L2004 **PD** *020 †55

DORMAN, Stephen Michael. 4230 E TOWNE BLVD STE 288 53704 #036-01-1974 L1976 **AN** *020

DORTZBACH, Richard Karl. 600 HIGHLAND AVE, CSC F4-370 53792 #041-01-1963 L1964 **FPS PS** *071 †35

DOUCET, Herman Lee. J5/230 CSC-2454, 600 HIGHLAND AVENUE 53792 #024-01-2006 **IM** *012

DOVAT, Sinisa. ■ 53792 #957-07-1988 L2004 **PHO** *020 †55

DOVER, Crystal Michelle. ■ 53719 #051-01-2007 **GS** *012

DOWELL, David S. 752 N HIGH POINT RD, DEAN WEST CLINIC 53717 #048-12-1986 L1991 **P** *020 †75

DOWLING, Patrick Allen. 202 S PARK ST 53715 #056-06-1991 L1992 **PCC** *020 †20

DREHER, Daniel Jefferson. 600 HIGHLAND AVE, BOX 3272 53792 #016-11-2003 L2004 **AN** *020

DREIZIN, Ivy. 600 HIGHLAND AVE 53792 #041-07-1974 L1980 **N OS** *020 †75

DRESANG, Lee Timberlake. 777 S MILLS ST, UNIV OF WI-MADISON DEPT OF 53715 #017-20-1994 L1998 **FM** *020 †18

DREYFUS, Deborah Elizabet. 777 S MILLS ST, FAMILY MEDICINE DEPT 53715 #033-06-2006 L2007 **FP** *012

DREZNER, Marc Kenneth. 451 JUNCTION RD, STE 9903 53717 #041-12-1970 L2000 **END IM** *020 †20

DROESSLER, Janet Ann. 1821 S STOUGHTON RD 53716 #056-06-1998 L1999 **FM** *020 †18

DROSTE, Sabine. 202 S PARK ST 53715 #046-01-1984 L1985 **MFM OBG** *020 †30

DRUMMOND, Bruce Charles. 1821 S STOUGHTON RD 53716 #056-05-1993 L1997 **OBG** *020 †30

DRYE, Thomas Arthur. 600 HIGHLAND AVE, AVE H4/831-8320 53792 #026-08-2004 L2006 **AN** *012

DRYER, Bryan Christopher. 600 HIGHLAND AVE, BOX 4108 53792 #025-07-2005 L2006 **PD** *012

DUCK, Holly Jean. 340 S WHITNEY WAY 53705 #035-45-1985 L1990 **ORS OSM** *020 †40

DUFF, Thomas Alexander. 600 HIGHLAND H4/336 AVE 53792 #038-06-1969 L1975 **NS** *020 †25

DUFFY, Briar Leigh. ■ 53703 #056-06-2006 L2008 **IM** *012

DULLI, Douglas Anthony. 600 HIGHLAND AVE 53792 #050-02-1984 L1985 **N** *020 †75

DUMERMUTH, Brent David. 600 HIGHLAND AVE, BOX 6188 53792 #056-06-2005 L2007 **OBG** *012

DUNBAR, William Henry. 600 HIGHLAND AVE, AVE H4/831-8320 53792 #422-01-2003 L2005 **ORS** *012

DU PREEZ, Amanda E. 600 HIGHLAND AVE BOX 2454, UNIVERSITY HOSP 53792 #037-01-2003 L2006 **IM PLM** *100 †20

DUREJA, Parul. 600 HIGHLAND AVE, BOX 2454 53792 #539-03-2004 L2006 **GE** *012 †20

DURKIN, Emily Tompkins. 600 HIGHLAND AVE, AVE H4/831-8320 53792 #025-12-2004 L2005 **GS** *012

DURNIN, Robert Eugene. 6601 GRAND TETON PLZ, MADISON RADIOLOGISTS SC 53719 #018-03-1959 L1974 **DR PDC** *071 †55,80

DURST, Janelle Marie. ■ 53726 #056-05-2008 *012

DUTTON, Caryn Ruth. 5249 E TERRACE DR, STE 9952 53718 #008-02-1996 L2002 **OBG** *020 †30

DVORAK, David Paul. 1300 UNIVERSITY AVE, UNIV OF WI MED SCH 53706 #056-05-1996 L2006 *100

DVORAK, Paul Franklin. 1200 JOHN Q HAMMONS DR, STE 400 53717 #016-11-1966 L1972 **PD PHO** *020 †55

EBENHOE, Emily Louise. J5/230 CSC-2454, 600 HIGHLAND AVENUE 53792 #030-06-2004 **NEP** *012 †20

ECKERLE, David E. 675 W WASHINGTON AVE 53703 #056-05-1991 L1992 **IM** *020 †20

ECKHARDT, L Lee Lochbaum. 600 HIGHLAND AVE, AVE H4/831-8320 53792 #010-02-1999 L2003 **ICE ICE** *012 †20

ECKLUND, L A. ■ 53705 #016-06-1956 L1962 **P** *071 †75

EDELMAN, Frederick S. 20 S PARK ST, CENTER S 53715 #041-01-1974 L1980 **N CHN** *020 †55,75

EDMONSON, M Bruce. 2880 UNIVERSITY AVE, AND CLINICS 53705 #054-04-1975 L1976 **PD** *020 †55

EDWARDS, Jennifer Tyson. 5618 ODANA RD 53719 #056-05-2001 L2002 **FM** *020 †18

EDWARDS, John Sanford. 202 S PARK ST, BLDG 3 53715 #025-01-1965 L1971 **R** *020 †80,28

EDWARDS, Niloo Mario. 600 HIGHLAND AVE, BLDG H4-358 CLNCL SCI CTR 53792 #035-01-1986 L2003 **TS** *020 †85,90

EGGLESTON, Kevin Lee. J5/230 CSC-2454, 600 HIGHLAND AVENUE 53792 #056-06-2006 L2008 **IM** *012

EHRHARDT, William Milton. 1313 FISH HATCHERY RD, DEAN CLINIC 53715 #056-05-1999 L2000 **GE** *020 †20

EHRLICH, Edward Norman. 600 HIGHLAND AVE 53792 #025-01-1952 L1974 **END IM** *050 †20

EHRLICH, Frances Elliott. 409 E WASHINGTON AVE 53703 #035-03-1949 L1956 **P** *071

EHRLICH, Susan Dale. 20 S PARK ST, STE 207 53715 #005-02-1982 L1993 **PD** *020 †55

EICHELMAN, Burr S, Jr. 600 HIGHLAND AVE, B6/585 CLINICAL SCI CTR 53792 #016-02-1968 L1976 **P** *020 †75

EICHHORN, Kevin Jon. 707 S MILLS ST 53715 #017-20-2000 L2004 **MPD** *020 †20,55

EICHMAN, Peter L. 600 HIGHLAND AVE 53792 #041-02-1949 L1955 **N IM** *071 †20,75

EILER, Donald Martin. 202 S PARK ST, MADISON ANESTHESIOLOGY CON 53715 #028-02-1964 L1970 **AN** *020 †05

EIMERSON, Daniel Allen. 2727 MARSHALL CT 53705 #056-06-1978 L1979 **P** *020 †75

EIMERMANN, Heidi Marie. 1821 S STOUGHTON RD 53716 #056-06-1993 L1996 **FM** *020 †18

EINARSSON, Siguraur. 451 JUNCTION RD, STE 9903 53717 #484-01-1994 L1999 **GE** *020 †20

ELDRIDGE, Marlowe Wayne. 600 HIGHLAND AVE, H4/422 CSC 53792 #034-01-1986 L1999 **CCP** *020

ELFMAN, Lawrence Alan. 752 N HIGH POINT RD 53717 #041-01-1985 L1988 **PD** *020 †55

ELSON, Diane Frances. 451 JUNCTION RD, STE 9903 53717 #016-11-1985 L1989 **END** *020

EMSPAK, Dolores Merrick. 451 JUNCTION RD, STE 9903 53717 #024-07-1979 L1999 **OBG** *020 †30

ENDE, David Jay. 202 S PARK ST, WISCONSIN HEART 53715 #016-43-1980 L1981 **CD IM** *020 †20

ENDO, Justin Osamu. 600 HIGHLAND AVE BOX 2454, UNIV HOSP 53792 #030-05-2005 L2006 **IM** *012

ENGBER, William Dean. 600 HIGHLAND AVE 53792 #019-02-1969 L1970 **ORS** *020 †40 ‡

ENRIGHT, Timothy Richard. 600 HIGHLAND AVE, AVE H4/831-8320 53792 #056-05-2005 L2006 **DR** *012

ENRIGHT, William Joseph. 600 HIGHLAND AVE, AVE H4/831-8320 53792 #056-05-2004 L2005 **ORS** *012

ENZ, Sarah Jane. 1313 FISH HATCHERY RD 53715 #056-05-1997 L1998 **D** *020 †15

ERICKSON, Chris. 600 HIGHLAND AVE # K4447 53792 #028-34-1976 L1982 **IG PD** *020 †55

ERICKSON, Matthew George. 600 HIGHLAND AVE H4/821, HOUSTE STAFF/ MED STAFF OF 53792 #012-01-1996 L1998 **ID** *020 †20

ERSKINE, Charles Peter. ■ 53711 #023-01-1973 L1975 **EM PD** *071 †55,16

ERTL, Melissa Joanne. ■ 53703 #056-05-2008 *012

ESPINOZA, Kristina Elizab. 777 S MILLS ST, UNIV OF WI-MADISON DEPT OF 53715 #056-05-2005 L2007 **FP** *012

ESPINOZA, Sonia Maria. ■ 53719 #682-01-1982 L2007 **FM** *100

ETHRIDGE, Clarisse Patric. 1200 JOHN Q HAMMONS DR, STE 400 53717 #056-05-1994 L1995 **END** *020 †20

EVANS, Alida Marie. 5618 ODANA RD 53719 #056-05-1995 L1996 **FM** *020 †18

EVANS, Anthony C, Jr. 600 HIGHLAND AVE, H4/636 HSC 53792 #012-01-1990 L1998 **GO GYN** *020 †30

EVANS, William Stroter. 202 S PARK ST, WISCONSIN HEART, MERITER H 53715 #019-02-1985 L1986 **VS** *020 †85

EWALT, John Edward. 202 S PARK ST 53715 #017-20-1979 L1982 **IM** *020 †20

FACTOR, Robert M. 625 W WASHINGTON AVE 53703 #041-01-1979 L1980 **P** *020 †75

FAGAN, Julie Ruth. 451 JUNCTION RD, STE 9903 53717 #024-07-1981 L1982 **IM** *020 †20

FAGERHOLM, Margaret I. 202 S PARK ST, BLDG 3 53715 #026-08-1981 L1984 **R** *040 †80

FAHIEN, Leonard August. ■ 53705 #028-02-1960 L1972 **OS PA** *071

FALK, David Keer. 1821 S STOUGHTON RD 53716 #016-01-1980 L1984 **D** *020 †15

FARNHAM, Dennis John. 202 S PARK ST, WISCONSIN HEART, S.C. 53715 #035-03-1967 L1975 **CD** *020 †20

FARRELL, Carolyn Jane. 600 HIGHLAND AVE BOX 3272, UNIV OF WISCONSIN SCHOOL M 53792 #056-05-1983 L1984 **AN** *020 †05

FARRELL, Philip Marshall. 750 HIGHLAND AVE 53705 #028-34-1970 L1977 **PD** *020 †55

FARRELL, Thomas Adam. 600 HIGHLAND AVE, DEPT OF OPHTH & VISUAL SVC 53792 #067-01-1961 L1993 **OPH** *071 †35

FASSBINDER, Katie Renee. 600 HIGHLAND AVE, AVE H4/831-8320 53792 #018-03-2004 L2006 **P** *012

FAUCHER, Lee David. H4/732 CSC, 600 HIGHLAND AVENUE 53792 #056-05-1996 L2004 **TRS OS** *020 †85

FAULKNER, Gordon T. 2202 S PARK ST 53713 #056-06-1978 L1979 **PD** *074 †55

FAULKNER, Nathan David. ■ 53719 #049-01-2008 *012

FEBBO, Mary Ann. 1821 S STOUGHTON RD 53716 #041-13-1984 L1985 **UCM IM** *020 †20

FEDERMAN, Christopher A. 752 N HIGH POINT RD 53717 #011-02-1987 L1988 **OBG** *020 †30

FEHR, Kevin Eilert. 3434 E WASHINGTON AVE, ACCESS COMMUNITY HEALTH CE 53704 #018-03-1997 L1998 **FM** *020 †18

FEHRENBACHER, Kelly. 600 HIGHLAND AVE, AVE H4/831-8320 53792 #016-43-2004 L2005 **IMG** *012 †20

FEIERABEND, Theodore C. ■ 53714 #028-02-1951 L1964 **PS** *071

FEIFAREK, Michael John. 2880 UNIVERSITY AVE 53705 #056-05-1982 L1983 **OPH** *020 †35

FEINSILBER, Doron. & C, UNIV of WISCONSIN HOSPITAL 53792 #305-01-2006 L2006 **NM** *020 †20

FEIX, James Alexander. ■ 53726 #056-05-2008 *012

FELDSTEIN, David Alan. 600 HIGHLAND AVE, DEPT OF MEDICINE, J5/220 C 53792 #035-48-1996 L2000 **IM** *020 †20

FELGUS, Matthew Abby. 660 W WASHINGTON AVE, STE 307 53703 #041-09-1991 L1997 *020 †75

FENNEMA, Karen Elizabeth. 7102 MINERAL POINT RD 53717 #056-05-1983 L1984 **FM** *020 †18

FERGUSON, Edwin Earle, Jr. 451 JUNCTION RD, STE 9903 53717 #010-01-1974 L1975 **IM** *020 †20

FERNANDEZ, Luis Alberto. H4/782 CSC, 600 HIGHLAND AVE 53792 #935-01-1988 L2000 **GS** *020 †85

FERRELLA, Thomas James. 202 S PARK ST 53715 #038-43-1982 L1983 **EM** *020 †16

FETT, Nicole Marie. 1 S PARK ST, 7TH FL 53715 #056-05-2004 L2005 **IMD** *012

FEX, Anders Claesgoran. 1313 FISH HATCHERY RD, DEAN MEDICAL CENTER 53715 #017-20-1981 L1984 **AN** *020 †05

FIELD, Aaron Scott. 600 HIGHLAND AVE E3-311, DEPT OF RADIOLOGY 53792 #016-11-1993 L2001 **RNR DR** *020 †80

FIELDS, Marshall. 1821 S STOUGHTON RD 53716 #056-06-1972 L1973 **FM** *020 †18

FINCH, William Wesley. 1 S PARK ST, FL 7 53715 #056-05-1973 L1974 **OTO** *020 †45

FIORE, Michael C. 2880 UNIVERSITY AVE 53705 #016-06-1981 L1986 **IMG PHP** *030 †20

FISCHER, Nicole Marie. ■ 53719 #056-05-2008 *012

FISHER-BECKFIELD, Paul W. 1821 S STOUGHTON RD 53716 #018-03-1977 L1978 **IM EM** *020 †20,16

FITZGERALD, Judith Elise. 1025 REGENT ST, DAVIS DUEHR 53715 #016-06-1982 L1990 **OPH** *020 †35

FITZPATRICK, James Henry. AND CL, UNIVERSITY OF WISCONSIN HO 53792 #056-05-1977 L1978 **AN** *020 †05

FLADER, William Albert. ■ 53704 #056-05-1964 L1965 **GP** *071

FLANUM, Mark Evans. 600 HIGHLAND AVE 53792 #056-05-2002 L2004 **ORS** *100

FLEMING, John Oleson. 600 HIGHLAND AVE 53792 #035-08-1971 L1989 **N IM** *050 †20,75

FLEMING, Lawrence Albert. 451 JUNCTION RD, STE 9903 53717 #023-01-1971 L1979 **IM** *040 †20

FLEMING, Michael Francis. 777 S MILLS ST, DEPT FAMILY MEDICINE 53715 #025-07-1974 L1975 **FM** *040 †20

FLETCHER, Christopher Dav. J5/230 CSC-2454, 600 HIGHLAND AVENUE 53792 #016-43-2007 **IM** *012

FLICKINGER, John A. 707 S MILLS ST 53715 #017-20-1984 L1993 **PTH** *020 †50

FLIEGEL, Martin B. ■ 53719 #056-05-1950 L1951 **CHP** *071 †75

FLIMAN, Paola Joanna. 707 S MILLS ST 53715 #038-40-1999 L2005 **NPM** *020 †55

FLOOD, Grace Ellen. 610 WALNUT ST RM 656, DEPT POPULATION HLTH SCI 53726 #025-01-1992 L2000 **GPM** *020 †70,18

FLOWERS, Flora Patricia. 600 HIGHLAND AVE 53792 #451-01-1986 **CCP** *100

FOK, Joseph Shiu-Fai. 1313 FISH HATCHERY RD, DEAN MEDICAL CENTER 53715 #056-05-1978 L1979 **OBG** *020 †30

FOLEY, Eugene F, III. H4/738 CSC, 600 HIGHLAND AVE, 53792 #024-01-1985 L1988 **CRS** *020 †85,10

FOLEY, Michael James. 700 S PARK ST 53715 #056-05-1996 L1999 **EM** *020 †16

FORD, Charles N. 600 HIGHLAND AVE, ENT CLINIC F4 270 53792 #020-02-1965 L1973 **OTO** *020 †45

FORD, Edward John. 1619 N STOUGHTON RD, CONCENTRA HEALTH CENTER 53704 #018-03-1986 L1987 **RHU FM** *020 †20

FORD, Michael Patrick. 600 HIGHLAND AVE, 86/319 CLINICAL SCIENCE CE 53792 #056-06-1982 L1999 **AN** *020 †05

FOSS, John Thos. 1821 S STOUGHTON RD 53716 #018-03-1977 L1987 **GE IM** *020 †20

FOST, Norman Chas. 600 HIGHLAND AVE, DEPT PEDIATRICS 53792 #008-01-1964 L1974 **PD OS** *050 †55

FOWLER, William Edward. 202 S PARK ST 53715 #037-01-1988 L1992 **PM** *020 †60

FOX, Barry Chas. 20 S PARK ST, STE 207 53715 #047-05-1982 L1983 **IB IM** *020 †20

FOX, Bradley Marion. 7102 MINERAL POINT RD, UW HEALTH WEST TOWNE 53717 #018-03-1995 L2001 **FM** *020 †18

FOX, Sarah Elizabeth. 701 DANE ST 53713 #056-05-2005 L2006 **FP** *012

FRANCE, Thomas Douglas. 2870 UNIVERSITY AVE, DEPT OPHTH & VIS SCI 53705 #016-06-1962 L1970 **OPH PO** *020 †35

FRANCOIS, Christopher J. 600 HIGHLAND AVE 53792 #016-06-2000 L2007 **DR** *020 †80

FRANK, Daniel Jacob. 600 HIGHLAND AVE 53792 #016-06-2006 L2007 **IM** *012

FRANK, Terrence Wayne. 242 JUNCTION RD 53717 #056-05-1977 L1978 **OTO HNS** *071 †45

FRANZ, Carolyn Therese. ■ 53705 #056-05-2007 **PD** *012

FREDERICKS, Nancy Carol. 1 S PARK ST, MADISON SURGERY CTR 53715 #056-05-1979 L1980 **AN** *020 †05

FREY, John Joseph. 777 S MILLS ST, UNIV OF WI DEPT OF FAMILY 53715 #016-06-1970 L1993 **FM** *020 †18

FRICK, Terrence John. 451 JUNCTION RD, STE 9903 53717 #016-11-1987 L1988 **GE** *020 †20

FRIDAY, Richard Oliver. 600 HIGHLAND AVE E3/311 53792 #041-12-1968 L1969 **DR** *020 †80

FRIEDBERG, Jennifer Ann. 6001 RESEARCH PARK BLVD 53719 #012-01-2002 L2003 **CHP** *100 †75

FRIEDL, Andreas. 600 HIGHLAND AVE, DEPT PATH K4/850 CSC 53792 #409-04-1985 L1990 **PTH** *050 †50

FRITSCH, Michael Kevin. 600 HIGHLAND AVE 53792 #056-05-1985 L1986 **PP PTH** *020 †50

FROELICH, Ralph Donald. 675 W WASHINGTON AVE 53703 #056-05-1963 L1964 **P** *020 †75

FROHNA, John Gerard. 600 HIGHLAND AVE, H4/455 CSC 53792 #056-05-1990 L2007 **MPD** *020 †55,20

FRONTIERA, Michael S. 1200 JOHN Q HAMMONS DR, STE 400 53717 #019-02-1980 L1986 **ON HEM** *020 †20

FROST, Natasha Lanaeh. 1313 FISH HATCHERY RD, DEAN CLINIC 53715 #056-06-2001 L2001 N *020 †75

FRUCHT, Michael Martin. 1200 JOHN Q HAMMONS DR, STE 400 53717 #036-07-1995 L2001 CN N *020 †75

FUAD, Nazia. 600 HIGHLAND AVE 53792 #704-06-1996 PTH *100

FUH, Annie. 600 HIGHLAND AVE, AVE HA/831-8320 53792 #038-40-2002 L2004 CD *012 †20

FULLER, Nancy Sue. 451 JUNCTION RD, STE 9903 53717 #025-07-1982 L1985 IM *020 †20

FULLERTON, Donald T. 600 HIGHLAND AVE 53792 #016-11-1957 L1965 P *072 †75

FUNG, Kam-Pui. 600 HIGHLAND AVE 53792 #462-01-1975 L1987 *020

FUNTE, Lisa Renee. UNIV HOSPITAL AND CLINICS, B4/243 CSC 53792 #018-03-2001 L2006 FOP *020 †50

FUTTERER, Rise Ann. 2500 OVERLOOK TER, WM MIDDLETON VA HOSPITAL 53705 #056-05-1992 L1993 P PHM *050 †75

GABRIEL, Geoffrey Matthew. 1313 FISH HATCHERY RD 53715 #010-02-1996 L2005 P PYG *020 †75

GADBAW, Brian Christopher. 600 HIGHLAND AVE, AVE H4/831-8320 53792 #025-12-2004 L2005 PHO *012

GAGLIANELLO, Nunzio Anton. J5/230 CSC-2454, 600 HIGHLAND AVENUE 53792 #056-06-2006 L2008 IM *012

GALLAGHER, Catherine Lee. 600 HIGHLAND AVE 53792 #007-02-1993 L1994 N *020 †75

GALVEZ, Timoteo L. 202 S PARK ST 53715 #748-10-1960 L1976 AN *071 †05

GAMM, David Matthew. 2880 UNIVERSITY AVE 53705 #025-01-1997 L1999 OPH *050 †35

GANGIREDDY, Sreedevi. 600 HIGHLAND AVE, AVE H4/831-8320 53792 #495-21-1999 L2006 PCC *012 †20

GANNAGE, Melissa Anne. ■ 53705 #056-05-2007 PTH *012

GAO, Jianjun. ■ 53711 #019-02-2006 IM *012

GARCIA, Erica Maria. ■ 53717 #056-05-2008 *012

GARDNER, Eric James. ■ 53718 #016-11-2006 L2007 ORS *012

GARG, Sandhya. 451 JUNCTION RD STE 9902, UNIV OF WISCONSIN HOSP & C 53717 #016-11-1991 L2005 IM *020 †20

GARITI, James Charles. 358 JUNCTION RD 53717 #016-11-1997 L2004 FM *020 †18

GARNETT, Gordon M. ■ 53711 #056-05-1946 L1947 AN *071 †05

GARNETT, James Gordon. 202 S PARK ST 53715 #056-05-1976 L1978 AN *020 †05

GARRELS, Kathryn Lee. 600 HIGHLAND AVE, BOX 7375 53792 #018-03-2005 L2006 ORS *012

GARREN, Michael Jos. 1 S PARK ST, FL 7 53715 #056-05-1989 L1990 GS *020 †85

GARRETT, Andrea. ■ 53705 #028-03-2003 L2006 D *020 †15

GARRETT, Robert Walker. 600 HIGHLAND AVE, AVE H4/831-8320 53792 #028-03-2003 L2006 DR *012

GARRISON, Dana Sue. 7102 MINERAL POINT RD 53717 #056-05-1988 L1989 FM *020 †18

GARVIE, Maryanne Ballard. 600 HIGHLAND AVE, BOX 6188 53792 #539-04-2004 L2005 OBG *012

GASSNER, Kyle Richard. ■ 53705 #056-05-2008 *012

GAUMNITZ, Eric Alan. 451 JUNCTION RD, STE 9903 53717 #019-02-1989 L1992 GE *020 †20

GAUTHIER, Gregory Mark. 600 HIGHLAND AVE, J5/230 CSC-2454 53792 #038-40-1999 L2000 ID *100 †20

GEANON, John Demetrios. 1821 S STOUGHTON RD 53716 #016-02-1989 L1993 OPH *020 †35

GEE, Jason Robert. 600 HIGHLAND AVE 53792 #024-01-1994 L2003 U *020 †95

GEISSLER, Felix E. 600 HIGHLAND AVE, H4-780 53792 #409-40-1992 GS TTS *020

GELENBERG, Alan J. 7617 MINERAL POINT RD, STE 300 53717 #041-01-1969 L2008 P PA *050 †75

GENCHEFF, Christopher A. 2830 DRYDEN DR 53704 #018-75-1980, ▲ L1981 OS GP *020 ‡

GENSLER, Arminda Lee. ■ 53715 #036-05-2007 FP *012

GENTRY, Lindell Ray. 600 HIGHLAND AVE, STE E-3/366 53792 #020-12-1978 L1981 R RNR *075 †80

GEORGE, Elizabeth. 20 S PARK ST, STE 207 53715 #495-37-1995 L2000 IM *020 †20

GEPPERT, Thomas Vincent. ■ 53715 #028-02-1943 L1948 PD OS *071 †55

GERDES, Dale Allen. 600 HIGHLAND AVE, EMERG DEPT 53792 #030-05-1980 L1983 EM *020 †16

GERLACH, Sara Rae. 700 S PARK ST 53715 #056-06-2001 L2003 EM *020 †16

GERN, James Elliot. 600 HIGHLAND AVE, DEPT PED 53792 #011-04-1981 L1992 AI PD *050 †55,03

GERVAIS, Claire M. 5618 ODANA RD 53719 #037-01-1990 L1991 FM *020 †18

GETTO, Carl Jos. 6001 RESEARCH PARK BLVD 53719 #016-43-1972 L1979 P *030 †75

GHABSHA, Ahmad. 600 HIGHLAND AVE H4/831, UW HOSPITAL AND CLINICS 53792 #875-01-2000 L2006 PCC *012 †20

GHERLAN, Claudiu Gabriel. 8202 EXCELSIOR DR, SUAK TRAILS CLNC 53717 #781-05-1994 L2003 IM IMG *020 †20

GHIA, Amol Jitendra. 600 HIGHLAND AVE, RM H4/831 53702 #007-02-2004 L2006 NS *100

GHOUSE, Mohammed. 2929 CURRY PKWY 53713 #495-65-1980 L1996 N *020

GIBSON, Jeffrey Scott. 4726 E TOWNE BLVD STE 120 53704 #041-12-1989 L2000 PHL *020 †16

GIBSON, Scott Wayne. 1821 S STOUGHTON RD 53716 #025-07-1994 L2004 GS *020 †85

GIESEN, James Moreau. 4122 E TOWNE BLVD 53704 #056-05-1979 L1980 IM *020 †20

GILBERT, James Bryson. ■ 53704 #024-02-1946 L1955 OS *050

GILBERT, Robert Dudley. 1802 W BELTLINE HWY 53713 #008-01-1970 L1976 IM IMG *020 †20

GILCHRIST, Kennedy Wenger. 600 HIGHLAND AVE 53792 #041-01-1964 L1969 ATP *071 †50

GILCHRIST, Valerie Jean. 777 S MILLS ST 53715 #065-01-1977 L2008 FM *030 †18

GILLMAN, Brad Michael. ■ 53705 #056-05-2008 *012

GIMELLI, Giorgio. 600 HIGHLAND AVE, CARDIOVASCULAR SETION HC/3 53792 #561-07-1990 L2001 CD *020 †20

GLAD, Richard Wayne. 800 S BROOKS ST, SURGERY AND CARE CENTER 53715 #056-05-1983 L1984 ORS *020 †40

GLICK, Norris Randle. 317 KNUTSON DR, CENTRAL CENTER STATE 53704 #016-11-1971 L1987 PD OS *020 †55

GLINBERG, Simone L. 600 HIGHLAND AVE, UNIVERSITY OF WI HOSPITAL 53792 #016-01-2003 L2004 END *012 †20

GO, Leonard Lim. 1313 FISH HATCHERY RD, DEAN CLINIC 53715 #016-06-1990 L1991 PDS *020 †20

GOCEY, Julie Ann. 7102 MINERAL POINT RD 53717 #016-45-1997 L1998 PD *020 †55

GODISH, Mark Thad. J5/230 CSC-2454, 600 HIGHLAND AVENUE 53792 #017-20-2004 IM *100 †20

GOEL, Manju. ■ 53717 #056-06-1994 L1996 PHL *020 †18

GOELZER, Susan Lorry. 600 HIGHLAND AVE, DEPT OF ANESTHESIOLOGY 53792 #056-05-1981 L1982 AN CCA *030 †05

GOETZ, Elizabeth Matthew. 600 HIGHLAND AVE, RM 4/831 53792 #026-04-2002 L2005 PD *100 †55

GOGINENI, Jyothi. ■ 53717 #495-37-2001 L2007 END *012 †20

GOLD, Jay Alexander. 2909 LANDMARK PL, METASTAR 53713 #048-16-1986 L1987 PHP LM *040 †70

GOLDBERG, Burton D. 470 N CHARTER ST 53706 #016-06-1950 L1986 PTH *050 †50

GOLDEN, Robert Neal. 750 HIGHLAND AVE 53705 #024-05-1979 L2006 P PA *020 †75

GOLDFARB, Stanley. 1300 UNIV AVE 53706 #035-06-1955 L1972 GP PTH *020 †50

GOLDROSEN, Michael Isaac. 707 S MILLS ST 53715 #016-43-1996 L1997 IM *020 †20

GOLESTANIAN, Ellie. 600 HIGHLAND AVE, K4/926 CSC-UWHC 53792 #917-26-1989 L2001 PCC *050 †20

GOMEZ, Robert Cesar. ■ 53704 #056-06-1969 L1970 TS GS *071 †85,90

GOODFRIEND, Theodore L. 2500 OVERLOOK TER 53705 #041-01-1957 L1965 IM OS *030

GOODMAN, David Alan. 9 CHEROKEE CIR, UNIT 203 53704 #036-05-1977 L1979 OM *020 †70

GOODMAN, Jeremy. ■ 53703 #005-06-1999 L2006 GS *100 †85

GOODSETT, James Robert. 1821 S STOUGHTON RD 53716 #056-06-1994 L1995 IM *020 †20

GOPAL, Deepak Venu. 451 JUNCTION RD, STE 9903 53717 #063-01-1993 L2002 GE *020 †20

GORGES, Melissa Linnae. ■ 53703 #016-42-2006 L2006 OTO *012

GOTTLIEB, Justin Louis. 2880 UNIVERSITY AVE 53705 #036-07-1990 L1997 OPH *020 †35

GOTTLIEB, Lawrence Irwin. 330 E LAKESIDE ST 53715 #016-02-1956 L1960 PTH *020 †50

GOULD, Jon Charles. 600 HIGHLAND AVE, ROON H4-726 53792 #056-05-1996 L1997 GS *020 †85

GRACE, Colleen Conway. 2870 UNIVERSITY AVE, STE 206 53705 #025-01-2003 L2007 OPH *020

GRAETTINGER, Kristine Ren. 600 HIGHLAND AVE, BOX 6188 53792 #001-02-2005 L2006 OBG *012

GRAF, Andrew Kingston. 1 S PARK ST, FL 7 53715 #048-13-1987 L1992 U *020 †95

GRAF, Ben Kim. 600 HIGHLAND AVE K4-735, DEPT. OF ORTHOPEDICS & REH 53792 #056-05-1979 L1980 ORS *020 †40

GRAHAM, Timothy Patrick. ■ 53726 #056-05-2008 *012

GRAYEV, Allison Michele. 600 HIGHLAND AVE, UNIV HOSPTIAL & CLINICS 53792 #041-14-2001 L2005 RNR *100 †10

GREBLO, Zorislav. ■ 53717 #957-01-1953 L1966 P *071 †75

GREEN, Christopher G. 600 HIGHLAND AVE, H4/450 CLINICAL SCIENCES C 53792 #035-45-1977 L1978 PDP *020 †55

GREEN, Joseph M. ■ 53792 #016-06-1952 L1959 CHP P *071 †75

GREEN, Judith Nancy. 1 S PARK ST, FL 7 53715 #008-01-1978 L1983 OTO *020 †45

GREENBERG, Alvin J. ■ 53719 #035-19-1951 L1971 RO *071

GREENBERG, Earl Barry. 707 S MILLS ST 53715 #011-02-1963 L1972 U *071 †95

GREENBLATT, David Yu. ■ 53705 #035-01-2005 GS *012

GREENE, Lauren Ann. 1423 S PARK ST, MENTAL HEALTH CTR OF DANE 53715 #056-05-1988 L1989 P *020 †75

GREENLAW, Paul Norman. 600 HIGHLAND AVE 53792 #759-01-2003 L2006 FM *020 †18

GREENSPAN, Leslie. 707 S MILLS ST, ST MARYS HOSP 53715 #017-20-1990 L1991 P *020 †75

GREER, Frank Roland. 202 S PARK ST 53715 #041-01-1972 L1980 NPM PD *050 †55

GREIST, John Huth. 7617 MINERAL POINT RD 53717 #017-20-1965 L1966 P IM *020 †75

GREKIN, David Allen. 1 S PARK ST 7TH FL, DEPARTMENT OF DERMATOLOGY 53715 #025-01-1971 L1997 D *040 †15 ‡

GRIFFITH, Jeanne A. ■ 53705 #056-05-1950 L1951 PD PHP *071 †55

GRIMES, Ian Christopher. ■ 53719 #016-45-2007 IM *012

GRIST, Thomas Martin. 600 HIGHLAND AVE, E3/366 CSC 53792 #056-06-1985 L1987 R *020 †80

GROESSL, Sarah Anne. 1821 S STOUGHTON RD 53716 #056-06-1992 L1993 OPH *020 †35

GROGAN, Earl Wayne, Jr. 202 S PARK ST 53715 #023-01-1976 L1985 CD IM *020 †20

GRONSKI, David James. 1313 FISH HATCHERY RD, DEAN MEDICAL CTR 53715 #025-01-1991 L1992 FM FSM *020 †18

GROSS, Ann Victoria. 5618 ODANA RD 53719 #041-02-1992 L1993 FM *020 †18

GROSSBERG, Paul Mitchell. 1552 UNIVERSITY AVE 53726 #035-15-1975 L1976 PD *020 †55

GROSSMAN, Jeffrey Eliot. 600 HIGHLAND AVE, H4/863 CSC MC 8310 53792 #035-15-1975 L1976 PUD CCM *030 †20

GROSSMAN, Jeffrey Wayne. ■ 53719 #048-02-2002 L2007 DR *100 †80

GROSSMAN, Jennifer Lyn. ■ 53703 #035-01-2007 *012

GUDMUNDSSON, Adalsteinn. 2870 UNIVERSITY AVE, STE 106 53705 #484-01-1986 L1992 IMG IM *020 †20

GUEND, Hamza. ■ 53705 #056-05-2008 *012

GUHA, Rahul. J5/230 CSC-2454, 600 HIGHLAND AVENUE 53792 #025-12-2007 IM *012

GUIAO, Ronald Peter. 1 S PARK ST, FL 7 53715 #038-06-1995 L2002 ORS *020 †40

GUILBERT, Theresa Wendy. 600 HIGHLAND AVE K4/944, PEDIATRIC PULMONARY DIVISI 53792 #026-04-1992 L2006 PDP *020 †55

GUITE, Christopher Alan. 600 HIGHLAND AVE RM B6-319, AND CLI 53792 #056-05-2007 AN *012

GULLIVER, Gene Allen, Jr. 600 HIGHLAND AVE, AVE H4/831-8320 53792 #056-06-2001 L2002 IC *012

GUNDERSON, Alan Eric. ■ 53705 #035-09-2007 IM *012

GUNKEL, Juliet Lynn. 451 JUNCTION RD, STE 9903 53717 #056-05-2000 L2001 D *020 †15

GUNNARSSON, Bjorn. 600 HIGHLAND AVE, UNIV WI HOSP & CLI 53792 #484-01-1990 NPM *100 †55

GUNTHER, Jonathan Blaine. 2870 UNIVERSITY AVE, STE 206 53705 #035-01-2004 L2008 OPH *012

GUPTA, Pankaj. 1313 FISH HATCHERY RD, DEAN CLINIC 53715 #016-06-1992 L1999 OTO *020 †45

GUSTAFSON, Brooke Megan. ■ 53703 #007-02-2007 N *012

GUSTAFSON, James Paul. 6001 RESEARCH PARK BLVD, U OF WISCONSIN MEDICAL SCH 53719 #024-01-1967 L1973 P OS *020 †75

GUTOWSKI, Karol Artur. 600 HIGHLAND AVE, G5/360 53792 #025-12-1992 L2000 PS HS *020 †65

HAAG, Mary Kathleen. 752 N HIGH POINT RD, DEAN WEST CLINIC 53717 #016-01-1984 L2004 OBG *020 †30

HAAS, Randall Scott. 752 N HIGH POINT RD 53717 #056-05-1987 L1988 IM *020 †20

HABEEB, Katherine Sophia. 202 S PARK ST, MERITER ATRIUM 53715 #001-06-1994 L2006 PCC *020 †20

HABIB, Taimur Hassan. 600 HIGHLAND AVE MC2454, HOSPITALS AND CLINICS 53792 #704-02-1995 L2007 IM IMG *020 †20

HACKFORTH-JONES, Jenny T. 4410 REGENT ST 53705 #025-01-1982 L1983 OBG *020 †30

HACKMAN, Sarah Abigail. 1821 S STOUGHTON RD 53716 #016-11-2004 L2006 FM *020 †18

HAEMEL, Anna Kaye. 1 S PARK ST, 7TH FL 53715 #043-01-2006 L2008 IMD *012

HAERR, Carolyn Anna. 600 HIGHLAND AVE, E3/311 53792 #030-05-1983 L2001 DR PD *020 †55,80

HAFEZ, Gholam Reza. 600 HIGHLAND AVE 53792 #517-04-1970 L1977 PTH DMP *020 †50

HAGEN, Scott Allen. 600 HIGHLAND AVE, H4/ 464 CSC 53792 #056-05-1987 L1990 CCP *020 †55

HAGLUND, Theodore Eric. 675 W WASHINGTON AVE 53703 #026-04-1977 L1987 GP *020

HAHN, David Louis. 1821 S STOUGHTON RD 53716 #005-11-1973 L1974 FM *020 †18

HAIN, Kendra Sue. ■ 53705 #056-05-2006 L2007 DR *012

HAKEEM, Abdul. 600 HIGHLAND AVE BOX 2454 53792 #704-25-2003 L2007 IM *012

HALKOVA, Tatsiana. 1300 UNIVERSITY AVE 53706 #913-43-1996 FP *012

HALL, Aric Cameron. ■ 53705 #056-05-2008 *012

HALLS, Juanita Jax. 2828 MARSHALL CT, STE 100 53705 #056-05-1981 L1982 IM *020 †20

HALVERSON, Jerry Lee, II. 6001 RESEARCH PARK BLVD 53719 #056-05-1999 L2001 P PYM *020 †75

HAMACHER, John Eugene. 20 S PARK ST, STE 360 53715 #056-05-1964 L1965 PS *020 †65

HAMEDANI, Azita Gnrad. F2/211 CLINICAL SCIENCE CE, 600 HIGHLAND AVE 53792 #008-01-2000 L2006 EM *020 †16

HAMMELMAN, Benjamin David. ■ 53703 #038-41-2007 IM *012

HAMMES, Kathryn Anne. 3009 UNIVERSITY AVE, APT 401 53705 #056-05-2008 *012

HANCOCK, Shawn Michael. 600 HIGHLAND AVE, UW HOSPITAL AND CLINICS 53792 #016-76-2005, ▲ IM *012

HANDA, Yoshio. ■ 53705 #030-06-1951 L1952 AN *071 †05

HANNAMAN, Michael J. 600 HIGHLAND AVE, BOX 3272 53792 #048-13-2005 L2006 AN *012

HANSEN, John Peter. 1265 JOHN Q HAMMONS DR 53717 #056-05-1969 L1970 FM *040 †18

HANSEN, Karen Elizabeth. 451 JUNCTION RD, STE 9903 53717 #056-05-1993 L1994 RHU *020 †20

HANSEN, Kurt Wm. 2870 UNIVERSITY AVE, STE 106 53705 #056-05-1992 L1993 IMG *020 †20

HANSEN, Mark A. 1821 S STOUGHTON RD 53716 #056-06-1979 L1981 FM *020 †18

HANSEN, Sherri M. 440 SCIENCE DR STE 200, CAPITOL ASSOC LLC 53711 #025-01-1991 L1996 P *020 †75

HANSON, Adam Charles. 202 S PARK ST, EMERGENCY DEPT. 53715 #003-01-1998 L2004 EM *020 †16

HANSON, Carleen Lynn. 5249 E TERRACE DR, STE 9962 53792 #056-05-2003 L2004 PD *020 †55

HANSON, James Adam. ■ 53711 #007-02-2007 DR *012

HANSON, Jeffrey Wm. 600 HIGHLAND AVE RM B6-319, HOSPITAL AND 53792 #046-01-1981 L1983 AN *020 †20

HANSON, Peter G. 600 HIGHLAND AVE, CARDIOVASCULAR MED #3248 53792 #034-01-1971 L1974 CD *071

HANSON, Stephanie Marie. 600 HIGHLAND AVE, BOX 4108 53792 #030-06-2005 L2007 PD *012

HANSON, Summer Elizabeth. ■ 53705 #056-05-2005 L2007 PS *012

HAQ, Cynthia Lawrence. 750 HIGHLAND AVE, 4235 HLTH SCI LEARNING CTR 53705 #017-20-1983 L1984 FM *020 †18

HARALDSSON, Haraldur M. 600 HIGHLAND AVE H4/821, HOUSE STAFF/MED STAFF OFFI 53792 #484-01-1994 L1999 P *020

HARARI, Paul Maurice. 600 HIGHLAND AVE, CLINICAL SCIENCE CTR 53792 #051-01-1984 L1990 RO *020 †80

HARDEN, Oliver Pierre. 330 E LAKESIDE ST 53715 #047-07-1994 L1995 IM *020 †20

HARDY, Paul Andrew John. 600 HIGHLAND AVE, B6/319 CLIN SCI CTR 53792 #917-08-1979 *100

HARKNESS, Donald Richard. 600 HIGHLAND AVE # IM 53792 #028-02-1958 L1980 IM HEM *030

HARKNESS, Mary Nishi. ■ 53705 #028-02-1958 L1980 PD A *071 †55

HARMS, Bruce Alan. 451 JUNCTION RD, STE 9903 53717 #030-05-1977 L1978 GS CRS *020 †85

HARNED, Lewis B. ■ 53704 #041-09-1951 L1984 ORS *071 †40

HARNISH, Peter Randolf. 1821 S STOUGHTON RD 53716 #041-13-1998 L1999 FM *020 †18

HARRINGTON, John T, Jr. 600 HIGHLAND AVE, DEPT OF MEDICINE J5/219 53792 #056-05-1965 L1966 RHU *020 †20

HARRIS, Justin Daniel. 600 HIGHLAND AVE, HOUSE STAFF AFFAIRS H4/831 53792 #030-05-2002 L2007 OSM *012

HARRISON, Michael Roger. 600 HIGHLAND AVE H4/831, UW HOSPITAL AND CLINICS 53792 #021-01-2004 L2007 ON *012 †20

HART, Michael Noel. 2500 OVERLOOK TER 53705 #056-06-1965 L1995 NP PTH *050 †50

HARTENBACH, Ellen Marie. 600 HIGHLAND AVE, H4 636 CLINICAL SCIENCE CT 53792 #028-03-1988 L1995 OBG GO *020 †30

HARTER, Josephine Miriam. 600 HIGHLAND AVE C7/350, UNIV OF WISC HOSP CLINICS 53792 #025-01-1994 L2001 PTH PCP *020 †50

HARTIG, Gregory Karl. 600 HIGHLAND AVE 53792 #025-01-1988 L1994 OTO HNS *020 †45

HARTJES, Thomas L. 8202 EXCELSIOR DR 53717 #056-06-1980 L1984 FM *020 †18

HARTMAN, Michael James. 2500 OVERLOOK TER, DEPT. OF RADIOLOGY 53705 #056-06-1997 L1998 RNR *020 †80

HARTMANN, Henrik A L. 10 S KENOSHA DR 53705 #693-01-1949 L1951 NP PTH *050 †50

HARTRIDGE, Theodore L. ■ 53705 #041-01-1934 L1936 A OTO *071 †45

HAUBENSCHILD, Michael Tho. ■ 53705 #056-05-2007 IM *012

HAUGAN, Gordon Dale. 707 S MILLS ST 53715 #026-04-1977 L1980 PD *020 †55

HAUGHTON, Victor Mellet. 600 HIGHLAND AVE E3/311, DEPT OF RADIOLOGY 53792 #008-01-1967 L1974 DR RNR *020 †20

HAUGHWOUT, Jean Campbell. 777 S MILLS ST 53715 #035-45-1994 L1995 FM *020 †18

HAUSTEIN, Silke Verena. 600 HIGHLAND AVE, UNIVERSITY OF WI HOSPITAL 53792 #001-02-2003 L2004 GS *012

HAYES, John P. 1104 JOHN NOLEN DR 53713 #055-01-1987 L2004 RO *020 †80

HAYMART, Megan Renae. ■ 53719 #023-07-2002 L2007 END *100 †20

HE, Rong. 600 HIGHLAND AVE H4/831, UW HOSPITAL AND CLINICS 53792 #243-76-1994 L2008 PTH *012

HEACOX, Robert Bruce. ■ 53704 #025-01-1973 L1974 EM FM *020 †18,16

HEAD, Diane Elizabeth. 600 HIGHLAND AVE, DEPT OF ANETHESIOLOGY 53792 #019-02-1993 L1999 CCA AN *020 †05

HEALY, Christopher Thomas. 20 S PARK ST, STE 460 53715 #030-06-1998 L1999 PDA *020 †55,03

HEASLETT, Ann Marie. 301 TROY DR, MENDOTA MENTAL HEALTH INST 53704 #056-05-1991 L1995 CHP P *020 †75

HEATLEY, Diane Gallo. 600 HIGHLAND AVE K4-765, UNIVERSITY OF WISCONSIN HO 53792 #056-05-1987 L1988 PDO OTO *020 †45

HEATLEY, Gregg Alan. 2870 UNIVERSITY AVE, STE 206 53705 #056-05-1987 L1988 OPH *020 †35

HECHT, Rudolph Caro. ■ 53703 #649-01-1954 L1973 FM *071 †18

HECKMAN, William Wesley. ■ 53711 #020-02-2007 OTO *012

HEDICAN, Sean Patrick. 451 JUNCTION RD, STE 9903 53717 #018-03-1991 L2001 U *020 †95

HEGEMAN, Kari Ann. 752 N HIGH POINT RD, DEAN WEST CLINIC 53717 #056-06-1996 L2006 PD *020 †55

HEGEMAN, Robert Blake. 1 S PARK ST 53715 #019-02-1994 L1996 ON *020 †20

HEGGESTAD, Kay A. 110 BELMONT RD, BELMONT NURSING & REHAB 53714 #056-05-1970 L1971 FM PLM *062 †18

HEI, David Larry. 1 S PARK ST, FL 7 53715 #056-05-1993 L2001 HO *020 †20

HEIDEL, Randy Scott. 707 S MILLS ST 53715 #041-01-1992 L1995 IM *020 †20

HEIDEN, Jack Dick. 1 S PARK ST, FL 7 53715 #056-05-1958 L1959 ORS *020 †40

HEIKS, Samuel James. ■ 53715 #056-05-2008 *012

HEILIGENSTEIN, Eric Lee. 115 N ORCHARD ST 53715 #016-45-1980 L1989 CHP *020 †55,75

HEILMAN, Pamela Jean. 202 S PARK ST 53715 #056-05-1990 L1991 FM *020 †18

HEINEN, Robert Delano. 4100 MONONA DR 53716 #056-05-1964 L1965 FM A *071 †18

HEINER, John Pershing, III. 600 HIGHLAND AVE, G5-360 CSC 53792 #016-06-1979 L1987 ORS *020 †40

HEINZEN, Benjamin Joseph. ■ 53704 #056-05-2008 *012

HEISE, Charles Paul, Jr. 451 JUNCTION RD, STE 9903 53717 #026-04-1994 L1995 CRS *020 †85,10

HELFFRICH, Richard S. PO BOX 6493 53716 #041-13-1968 L2001 FM GP *020

HELLING, Kevin Donald. ■ 53719 #054-04-2007 OBG *012

HEMATTI, Peiman. 600 HIGHLAND AVE, HEMATOLOGY OFFICE H4/534 C 53792 #517-01-1990 L2004 HEM *020 †20,55

HENDERSON, Perry Anderson. 202 S PARK ST 53715 #038-06-1958 L1976 MFM OBG *071 †30

HENDRICKS, Richard Jos. ■ 53711 #016-43-1960 L1966 IM *071

HENKE, Timothy Kerr. 722 WILLIAMSON ST, DISABILITY DETERMINATION B 53703 #056-05-1963 L1965 N *062 †75

HENRY, Joel Bradley. 451 JUNCTION RD, STE 9903 53717 #056-05-1990 L1991 OBG *020 †30

HERALD, Matthew Robert. ■ 53705 #048-13-2007 P *012 #016-06-1997 L2008 END IM *050 †20

HERAS-HERZIG, Ailleen. 451 JUNCTION RD, UW HEALTH WEST MC 3284 53717 #016-06-1997 L2008 END IM *050 †20

HERLACHE, April Leah. ■ 53705 #056-05-2006 L2008 AN *012

HERM, John Whitton. 202 S PARK ST 53715 #056-05-1975 L1976 EM *020 †16

HERMSEN, Joshua Leon. 600 HIGHLAND AVE, BOX 7375 53792 #045-01-2004 L2007 GS *012

HERMUNDSTAD, Orin Allen. 1025 REGENT ST 53715 #048-04-1954 L1957 OPH *071 †35

HERMUS, Russell James. 1313 FISH HATCHERY RD, DEAN MEDICAL CENTER 53715 #056-05-1989 L1990 FM *020 †18

HERNANDEZ, Santiago. 707 S MILLS ST 53715 #005-14-1998 L2001 IM *020 †20

HEROLD, Kelly Ag. ■ 53717 #056-05-2007 IM *012

HERRMANN, Kenneth James. 625 W WASHINGTON AVE 53703 #016-42-1988 L1993 CHP *020 †20

HERRON, Julie Louise. ■ 53711 #031-01-2004 L2004 FM *020 †18

HESS, Christopher Joel. ■ 53726 #056-05-2008 *012

HESS, Russell O, III. 675 W WASHINGTON AVE 53703 #041-13-1971 L1972 PD *020 †55

HETLAND, Andrew Ryan. 600 HIGHLAND AVE, AVE H4/831-8320 53792 #037-01-2004 L2007 GS *012

HETSKO, Cyril Michael. 309 W WASHINGTON AVE 53703 #035-45-1968 L1969 IM ID *030 †20

HEUN, James Michael. 600 HIGHLAND AVE, BOX 2454 53792 #018-03-2005 L2006 IM *012

HEVESI, Zoltan G. 600 HIGHLAND AVE, B6 319 CLINICAL SCIENCE CT 53792 #473-01-1990 L2003 AN PME *020 †05

HIBBARD, A J. 600 HIGHLAND AVE, CLINICAL SCIENCE CTR 53792 #016-11-1976 L1980 BBK *030 †50

HIGUERA, Emiliano Sol. ■ 53705 #056-05-2008 *012

HIGUERA, Griselda. ■ 53705 #056-05-2008 *012

HILDEBRAND, Christoper J. 2500 OVERLOOK TER 53705 #018-03-1992 L1995 IM *020 †20

HILDEBRAND, Julie Patrice. 4410 REGENT ST, ASSOC PHYS LLP 53705 #048-13-1998 L1999 RHU IM *020 †20

HILLERY, Karen Marie. 451 JUNCTION RD, STE 9903 53717 #036-01-1995 L1996 PD *020 †55

HILQUIST, Eric William. 752 N HIGH POINT RD 53717 #016-06-1999 L2003 FSM *020 †18

HINKE, Marvin Lee. ■ 53705 #056-05-1955 L1956 DR *071 †80

HINSHAW, James Louis. 600 HIGHLAND AVE, UNIVERSITY OF WISCONSIN SC 53792 #056-05-2000 L2001 DR *020 †80

HINSHAW, Molly Ann. 1 S PARK ST 7TH FL, DEPT OF DERMATOLOGY 53715 #056-05-2000 L2001 D *020 †15

HINSLEY, Matthew Lee. 1313 FISH HATCHERY RD, DEAN CLINIC 53715 #030-05-2002 L2004 OTO *012

HIPPS, John Bates. ■ 53703 #036-01-2003 PHO *012 †55

HIREKATUR, Ravishankar V. 7102 MINERAL POINT RD 53717 #019-02-2000 L2003 FM *020 †18

HIRSCH, Thomas Jos. 1313 FISH HATCHERY RD 53715 #023-07-1974 L1980 RHU *020 †20

HIRSCHLER, Charles Wm. ■ 53704 #018-03-1960 L1968 AN *071 †05

HISGEN, William Jerrold. 202 S PARK ST, MERITER HOSPITAL 53715 #056-05-1967 L1968 IM *030 †20

HLA, Khin Mae. 2880 UNIVERSITY AVE 53705 #209-01-1971 L1990 IM *020 †20

HO, Libin. 752 N HIGH POINT RD, WEST CLINIC 53717 #038-40-2000 L2007 MPD *020 †20,55

HOANG, Tien. 600 HIGHLAND AVE, K6/566 53792 #942-01-1987 L2001 HO *020 †20

HOBBINS, William Bell. 5510 MEDICAL CIR 53719 #016-06-1947 L1948 SO GS *050 †85

HOCH, John R, II. 451 JUNCTION RD, STE 9903 53717 #041-02-1983 L1991 VS *020 †85

HODGE, Charles Wesley. ■ 53711 #011-03-2004 L2007 RO *012

HODULIK, Charles James. 2727 MARSHALL CT 53705 #056-05-1976 L1979 P *020 †75

HOEFER, Daniel Joseph. 1313 FISH HATCHERY RD 53715 #018-03-1996 L2000 VIR *020 †80

HOEL, Mark Jos. 1313 FISH HATCHERY RD, DEAN MEDICAL CENTER 53715 #056-05-1984 L1985 AN *020 †05

HOENECKE, Mark Alan. 707 S MILLS ST 53715 #056-05-1986 L1987 AN *020 †05

HOERL, Howard Daniel. 707 S MILLS ST 53715 #056-05-1994 L1998 PCP *020 †50

HOFF, Allan Dale. ■ 53705 #056-05-1945 L1946 AN *071 †05

HOFFMAN, Philip Anthony. ■ 53713 #056-05-1957 L1958 AN *071 †05

HOFFMAN, Robert Jeremy. ■ 53703 #056-05-2001 L2005 IM *020

HOFFMAN, William Kenneth. 330 E LAKESIDE ST 53715 #056-06-1947 L1948 OBG *071 †30

HOGAN, Kirk Jeffrey. 600 HIGHLAND AVE, UNIV OF WISCONSIN HOSPITAL 53792 #056-05-1976 L1977 AN *071 †05

HOGDEN, Laurie. 707 S MILLS ST, NEONATAL RESOURCES OF WISC 53715 #056-05-1998 L2004 NPM *020 †55

HOGENDORN, Courtney Todd. 202 S PARK ST, MERITER HOSPITAL 53715 #056-05-1995 L1999 PM *020 †60

HOGG, William Edward, Jr. ■ 53719 #048-12-1979 L1993 IM FM *020 †20

HOHLER, Eugene Jos. 330 E LAKESIDE ST 53715 #056-06-1946 L1948 GP *071

HOKANSON, John Michael. 202 S PARK ST 53715 #056-05-1990 L1993 **PDC** *020 †55
HOKIN, Lowell Edward. 1300 UNIVERSITY AVE 53706 #020-02-1948 L1974 **OS** *071
HOLEN, Kyle Douglas. 600 HIGHLAND AVE, CLINICAL SCIENCE CENTER 53792 #035-01-1996 L2002 **HO** *020 †20
HOLLAND, Robert Bruce. ■ 53703 #041-14-2002 L2005 **PCC** *100 †20
HOLLATZ, Andrew Allan. ■ 53719 #026-04-2007 **AN** *012
HOLLATZ, Trina. ■ 53719 #026-04-2006 L2006 **IM** *012
HOLLISTER, Mary. 2500 OVERLOOK TER, WM S MIDDLETON VAH 53705 #056-05-1988 L1995 **DR** *020 †80
HOLLMAN, Greg Allen. 600 HIGHLAND AVE, DEPT OF PEDIATRICS 53792 #056-06-1984 L1985 **PD CCM** *020 †55
HOLT, Michael Craigie. 700 S PARK ST 53715 #024-01-1980 L1981 **FM EM** *020 †18,16
HONG, Andrew Suk. ■ 53726 #056-05-2008 L2008 *012
HOOK, Jaime Lynn. ■ 53711 #056-05-2008 *012
HOPE, Anne Elizabeth. 7102 MINERAL POINT RD 53717 #005-14-1994 L1999 **FM** *020 †18
HOPKINS, Keith Alfred. ■ 53719 #016-11-1998 **NEP** *012
HORBUL, Julie Elizabeth. ■ 53719 #026-04-2008 *012
HORSTMEYER, Carl Geo. ■ 53704 #056-06-1991 *100
HOSTETLER, Barbara Ruth. 20 S PARK ST, STE 207 53715 #038-41-1988 L1998 **OBG** *020 †30
HOUSER, Laura Marie. 600 HIGHLAND AVE H4/447 53792 #028-02-2007 **PD** *012
HOWARD, Janet. 600 HIGHLAND AVE H41823, UINIVERSITY HOSPITAL & CLI 53792 #049-01-1999 L2000 **OPH** *071
HOWARD, Jeanne Marie. ■ 53711 #056-06-1994 L2003 **IMG** *020 †20
HOWELL, Timothy. 2500 OVERLOOK TER 53705 #005-11-1978 L1979 **PYG P** *040 †75
HSU, Benson Shihhan. 600 HIGHLAND AVE, BOX 4108 53792 #028-03-2005 L2007 **PD** *012
HSU, David Ambrose. 600 HIGHLAND AVE 53792 #041-12-1997 L2003 **CHN** *020 †55,75
HSU, Jennifer Lynn. 600 HIGHLAND AVE, BOX 2454 53792 #028-03-2005 L2007 **IM** *012
HSU, Phillip T. 1 S PARK ST, 7TH FL 53715 #005-11-2005 L2007 **IMD** *012
HU, Johnny Liao. ■ 53726 #056-06-2004 L2007 **PTH** *012
HUANG, Wei. 600 HIGHLAND AVE, UW HOSP & CLINICS, PATHOLO 53792 #243-94-1986 L2005 **PTH** *020 †50
HUBBARD, Derek Ralph. 5618 ODANA RD 53719 #056-05-1997 L1999 **FM** *020 †18
HUBER, Robert Gordon. 707 S MILLS ST, ST MARYS HOSP LAB 53715 #038-40-1976 L1991 **PTH** *071 †50,18
HUEBSCHMANN, Joan Norma. ■ 53705 #017-20-1969 L1976 **PTH** *075
HUEPENBECKER, Paul Elwood. 752 N HIGH POINT RD 53717 #026-04-1981 L1982 **GS AS** *020 †85
HUFFER, James Morse. ■ 53717 #016-02-1958 L1965 **ORS** *071 †40
HUGHES, Patrick Jos. 600 HIGHLAND AVE, U OF WI, SCHOOL OF MEDICIN 53792 #016-43-1980 L1981 **CD IM** *020 †20
HUIE, Michael Scott. 1 S PARK ST, FL 7 53715 #056-05-2000 L2003 **ON** *020 †20
HULS, Christopher Kevin. 202 S PARK ST 53715 #018-03-2001 L2005 **OBG MFM** *020
HUNSAKER, R Dale. 3 QUAIL RIDGE DR 53717 #040-02-1950 L1971 **PHP OBG** *030
HUNTER, Lisa Marlene. 675 W WASHINGTON AVE 53703 #035-06-1992 L1993 **P** *020 †75
HUNTINGTON, Robert W, III. 2074 ABINGTON RD, DEPT PATH 53706 #035-45-1964 L1971 **PTH** *062 †50
HUPPLER, Anna Ruth. ■ 53713 #032-01-2006 L2008 **PD** *012
HURLEY, James Woodson. 917 HARBOR HOUSE DR, UNIT 3 53719 #021-01-1969 L1973 **FM** *020 †18
HURST, Dorsey Wm. 1 S PARK ST 53715 #028-02-1956 L1957 **IM PUD** *071 †20
HUTSON, Clare Frederick. 2880 UNIVERSITY AVE 53705 #056-05-1956 L1957 **OPH** *071 †35
HUTTENLOCHER, Anna. 451 JUNCTION RD, PEDIATRIC RHEUMATOLOGY 53717 #024-01-1988 L1999 **PD** *020 †55
HWANG, Joanna. 600 HIGHLAND AVE, AVE H4/831-8320 53792 #047-05-2003 L2005 **OTO** *012
HYZER, Thomas Scott. 4410 REGENT ST 53705 #018-03-1975 L1979 **IM** *020 †20
IBELE-RISLEY, Anna Rose. 600 HIGHLAND AVE H4/831, UW HOSPITAL AND CLINICS 53792 #036-05-2003 L2007 **GS** *012
IDSVOOG, Peter Bruce. 7102 MINERAL POINT RD, U.W. HEALTH HOSPTIAL AND C 53717 #056-05-1982 L1983 **IM** *020 †20
IGIC, Petar Gordan. 202 S PARK ST 53715 #016-02-1999 L2006 **ICE** *020 †20
IKEGWUONU, Fidelis Ifeany. ■ 53719 #104-01-2003 **GP** *020
ILBAWI, Nadim Michel. ■ 53703 #016-06-2007 **FP** *012
ILLGEN, Richard L, II. K4/739 CSC, 600 HIGHLAND AVENUE 53792 #016-02-1993 L2000 **ORS** *020 †40
ILLICHMANN, Mitchell Loui. ■ 53719 #056-05-2006 L2007 **P** *012
INGRISANO, Nicole Marie. ■ 53715 #056-05-2006 **OBG** *012
INHORN, Stanley L. 8007 EXCELSIOR DR 53717 #035-01-1953 L1956 **PCP CCG** *071 †50
IP, Michael Shunnun. 2880 UNIVERSITY AVE 53705 #035-19-1993 L1999 **OPH** *020 †35
IRURETAGOYENA FERNANDEZ, J. ■ 53703 #935-07-2002 L2007 **OBG** *100
ISENBERG, Jason Steven. 600 HIGHLAND AVE, UW HOSPITAL AND CLINICS 53792 #017-20-2003 L2004 **OTO** *012
ISENSEE, Susan Nordstrom. 752 N HIGH POINT RD 53717 #056-05-1983 L1984 **FM** *020 †18
ISHII, Mutsumi Michael. 1821 S STOUGHTON RD 53716 #056-06-1991 L1995 **P** *020 †75
ISHIKAWA, Shizen. ■ 53715 #572-26-1971 *100
ISRAELSTAM, David Michael. 330 S WHITNEY WAY STE 104 53705 #038-06-1963 L1971 **CHP P** *020 †75
ITANI, Muhammad M. 700 S PARK ST, ATTN: ANESTHESIOLOGY 53715 #605-01-1993 L2003 **AN CCA** *020 †05 ‡
ITO, Fumito. ■ 53705 #572-67-1995 L2007 **GS** *012
IVSIN, Olga. 33 UNIVERSITY SQ STE 195 53715 #286-02-1953 L1974 **P** *075
IYAMA, Christina M. 1500 HIGHLAND AVE 53705 #025-01-1976 L1979 **PD** *020 †55
JACKSON, Daniel James. 600 HIGHLAND AVE K4/91, CSC 9988 53792 #056-05-2003 L2007 **AI** *012 †55
JACOBSEN, Paul Mill. 1313 FISH HATCHERY RD, DEAN MEDICAL CENTER 53715 #056-05-1968 L1969 **AN GP** *071 †05
JACOBSON, Kurt Martin. 600 HIGHLAND AVE, CLINICAL SCIENCE CENTER H6 53792 #019-02-2004 L2007 **CD** *012 †20
JACOBSON, Steven Marvin. 700 S PARK ST 53715 #001-02-1976 L1979 **EM** *020 †16
JAIN, Neal. 1821 S STOUGHTON RD 53716 #056-06-1999 L2004 **AI PD** *020 †55,03
JAJOUR, Nizar Najib. 600 HIGHLAND AVE 53792 #875-01-1980 L1986 **PUD CCM** *050 †20
JAKEL, Rebekah J. ■ 53714 #056-05-2008 *012
JAMES, Catherine Thompson. 5618 ODANA RD 53719 #054-04-1988 L1989 **FM** *020 †18
JAMZADEH, Gohar. ■ 53726 #517-08-1977 *100
JANICEK, Don R. 3434 E WASHINGTON AVE 53704 #056-05-1951 L1955 **FM** *071 †18
JANIS, Angela Christine. ■ 53718 #016-11-2007 **P** *012
JANUARY, Craig Taylor. 600 HIGHLAND AVE, UNIV OF WI HOSP 53792 #018-03-1976 L1994 **CD IM** *040 †20
JARRARD, David Frazier. 600 HIGHLAND AVE 53792 #051-01-1989 L1996 **U** *020 †95
JAUME, Juan C. 451 JUNCTION RD, STE 9903 53717 #132-01-1985 L2004 **IM END** *020 †20
JAVID, Manucher. 600 HIGHLAND AVE, CLINICAL SCIENCE CTR 53792 #016-11-1946 L1954 **NS** *071 †25
JEAN-LOUIS, Garry. 1313 FISH HATCHERY RD 53715 #440-01-1991 L2003 **ID IM** *020 †20
JEFFERSON, James Walter. 7617 MINERAL POINT RD, HEALTHCARE TECHNOLOGY SYST 53717 #056-05-1964 L1965 **P IM** *040 †20,75 ‡
JEFFRIES, Mark Wm. 752 N HIGH POINT RD 53717 #007-02-1973 L1982 **FM OS** *071 †18,16
JENKIN, Brenda Kim. 4122 E TOWNE BLVD 53704 #041-07-1987 L1993 **OBG** *020 †30
JENS, Patricia J. ■ 53705 #055-01-1985 L1986 **P** *020 †75
JENSEN, Hans Christopher. 600 HIGHLAND AVE, BOX 9601 53792 #056-05-2005 L2007 **P** *012
JENSEN, Norman Maynard. 2828 MARSHALL CT 53705 #056-05-1965 L1967 **IM** *040 †20
JEPPSEN, Paul Scott. 2870 UNIVERSITY AVE, STE 206 53705 #056-06-2004 L2005 **OPH** *012
JEPSEN, Jan Viberg. 600 HIGHLAND AVE 53792 #297-02-1995 L2003 **U** *020
JERISHA, John Anthony. 202 S PARK ST, BLDG 3 53715 #016-06-1976 L1977 **DR NM** *020 †80
JOHN, Vineeth Philip. 6001 RESEARCH PARK BLVD, & CLINICS ; C/O M. BANOVET 53719 #495-27-1991 L2006 **PYG** *020 †75
JOHNSON, Aaron Richard. 600 HIGHLAND AVE, AVE H4/831-8320 53792 #056-05-2000 L2005 **U** *020
JOHNSON, Clarence Edward. 707 S MILLS ST 53715 #056-05-1981 L1984 **AN** *030 †05
JOHNSON, Dana Marie. ■ 53719 #018-03-2006 L2008 **PD** *012
JOHNSON, David Leonard. ■ 53704 #045-04-2002 L2006 **OPH** *100
JOHNSON, Donald A. ■ 53718 #010-01-1945 L1949 **NS N** *020 †25,75
JOHNSON, Erik Edward. 600 HIGHLAND AVE, AVE H4/831-8320 53792 #056-06-2003 L2005 **GS** *012
JOHNSON, Gary Lee. 5133 CRESCENT OAKS DR, GARY L. JOHNSON MD 53704 #025-12-1978 L1984 **FM OBG** *020 †18
JOHNSON, Lindsey Nicol. 600 HIGHLAND AVE, AVE H4/831-8320 53792 #054-04-2004 L2006 **PDE** *012 †55
JOHNSON, Maryl Rae. 600 HIGHLAND AVE, E5/582 CSC 5710 53792 #018-03-1977 L2002 **CD IM** *020 †20
JOHNSON, Milton Henry, Jr. 1821 S STOUGHTON RD 53716 #056-05-1990 L1991 **FM** *020 †18
JOHNSON, Tasha Renee. 1360 REGENT ST, # 314 53715 #018-03-2004 L2006 **OBG** *012
JOHNSTON, Hugh F. 600 HIGHLAND AVE 53792 #056-05-1982 L1983 **CHP AM** *040 †75
JONES, Jeffrey Malden. 2500 OVERLOOK TER 53705 #016-11-1972 L1975 **ID IM** *030 †20
JONES, John Chas. 600 HIGHLAND AVE, H6/574 UWHC/CSC 53792 #041-14-1982 L1983 **N IM** *020 †20
JONES, Thomas Moss. SCIENCE CTR, K4/755 CLINICAL 53792 #012-01-2005 L2007 **ORS** *012
JONES, Todd Dwyer. ■ 53714 #041-02-2007 **OTO** *012
JONKER, Mark Andrew. ■ 53711 #056-06-2006 L2008 **GS** *012
JONUZI, Zinije. 701 DANE ST 53713 #056-05-2003 L2005 **FM** *020
JOO, Patricia Ann. ■ 53703 #056-05-1961 L1963 **PD ON** *071 †55
JOSVAI, Samuel Paxton. 600 HIGHLAND AVE 53792 #056-05-1998 L2001 **EM** *020 †16
JOU, Janice Hsiao-Lun. 600 HIGHLAND AVE, AVE H4/831-8320 53792 #016-06-2003 L2005 **GE** *012 †20
JU, Andrew Wenhua. ■ 53726 #056-05-2008 *012
JUCKETT, Mark Brumleve. 600 HIGHLAND AVE 53792 #020-02-1987 L1994 **IM HEM** *020 †20
JUDD, Robert Henley. CSC H4 428-600 HIGHLAND AV, UNIV OF WIS HOSP 53792 #017-20-1971 L1988 **PG PD** *020 †55
JUERGENS, Timothy Michael. 600 HIGHLAND AVE H4/823, UNIVERSITY HOSPITAL & CLIN 53792 #028-03-1999 L2000 **PYG** *020 †75
JUHL, John Harold. ■ 53705 #025-01-1940 L1941 **DR** *072 †80
JULIAN, Thomas Michael. 600 HIGHLAND AVE, RM H4-649 53792 #026-04-1978 L1988 **GYN** *020 †30 ‡
JUOZEVICIUS, John Linas. 1 S PARK ST, UW MEDICAL FOUNDATION 53715 #016-11-1981 L2000 **RHU IM** *020 †20
JUSTL, Robert Norman. 1821 S STOUGHTON RD 53716 #056-05-1972 L1973 **EM FM** *020 †18
KABBANI, Loay S.. 302 N SEGOE RD 53705 #875-01-1997 L2004 **VS** *012 †85
KADELL, Jerome Gilbert. 752 N HIGH POINT RD 53717 #056-05-1966 L1969 **OPH** *020 †35
KAFKA, Adam Timothy. 600 HIGHLAND AVE, AVE H4/831-8320 53792 #030-05-2005 L2006 **PM** *012
KAHL, Brad Steven. 600 HIGHLAND AVE 53792 #024-07-1994 L1995 **HEM** *020 †20
KAHLE, William Keith. 752 N HIGH POINT RD 53717 #051-01-1975 L1988 **OP** *020 †40
KAJI, Eugene Hideo. 5249 E TERRACE DR 53718 #024-01-1994 L2001 **CD** *020 †20
KAKUMANU, Sujani Sarada I. ■ 53703 #041-14-2002 L2002 **AI** *012 †20,03
KALAYOGLU, Munci. 600 HIGHLAND AVE, DEPT SURG H4/780 53792 #902-03-1963 L1983 **OS PDS** *040
KALIN, Ned Henry. 600 HIGHLAND AVE 53792 #041-02-1976 L1977 **P** *020 †75
KALLAS, Kevin Patrick. 3099 E WASHINGTON AVE, WISCONSIN DEPT OF CORRECTI 53704 #056-06-1988 L1998 **PFP P** *020 †75
KAMENSHIKOV, Dimitri Alek. 600 HIGHLAND AVE, UNIVERSITY OF WI HOSPITAL 53792 #056-05-2004 L2006 **OBG** *012
KAMMERZELT, Todd Jason. ■ 53705 #056-05-2008 *012
KAMP, Timothy Jos. 600 HIGHLAND AVE 53792 #016-02-1989 L1996 **CD** *050 †20
KANE, Mollie Lauren. 119 ASH ST 53726 #024-07-1996 L2003 **FM** *020 †18
KANG, Matthew Minwoo. 330 E LAKESIDE ST 53715 #056-06-2002 L2006 **NS** *012
KANNER, Albert Victor. 1025 REGENT ST 53715 #023-01-1956 L1957 **OPH** *071 †35
KANTAMNENI, Vijay Kumer. 1313 FISH HATCHERY RD, C/O SURGERY DEPT 53715 #056-05-1985 L1986 **TS GS** *020 †85,90
KANTOR, Kim Murphy. 7102 MINERAL POINT RD 53717 #050-02-1989 L1991 **PD** *020 †55
KAO, Walter G. 600 HIGHLAND AVE J5/210, MC 2454 53792 #035-20-1984 L2005 **CD** *020 †20
KAPELL, Murray Lee. 5534 MEDICAL CIR 53719 #056-05-2000 L2001 **CHP P** *020 †75 ‡
KAPLAN, Lee David. 621 SCIENCE DR 53711 #010-01-1995 L2002 **OSM** *020 †40
KAPPES, Ashley Lynn. ■ 53726 #056-05-2008 *012
KARK, Richard Allen. 1552 UNIVERSITY AVE, UW - MADISON 53726 #056-06-1975 L1976 **FM** *071 †18
KARMALI, Kunal Narendra. J5/230 CSC-2454, 600 HIGHLAND AVENUE 53792 #016-06-2007 **IM** *012
KARWOWSKI, Mateusz Piotr. ■ 53705 #040-02-2006 L2008 **PD** *012
KASKE, Earl Thos. 5249 E TERRACE DR 53718 #056-05-1959 L1960 **GP** *020
KASTMAN, Christian Clay. 777 S MILLS ST, UNIV WI DEPT OF FAMILY MED 53715 #056-05-2006 L2007 **FP** *012
KASUBOSKI, David Allen. 780 REGENT ST, STE 300 53715 #056-05-1969 L1970 **P** *020 †75

■ = Address Information Privacy Protected

KATCHER, Murray L. 600 HIGHLAND AVE H6/4, UNIV OF WISCONSIN 53792 #056-05-1975 L1976 **PD ADL** *020 †55

KATWALA, Kashyap N. 20 S PARK ST, STE 207 53715 #035-48-1998 L2004 **GE** *020 †20

KAUFMAN, Mark Alan. 1277 DEMING WAY, DEAN HEALTH PLAN 53717 #041-01-1977 L1978 **IM** *020 †20

KAUFMAN, Paul Leon. 2880 UNIVERSITY AVE 53705 #035-19-1967 L1975 **OPH** *050 †35

KAVEGGIA, Erzsebet Gathy. 1512 WHEELER RD 53704 #473-01-1950 L1960 **PD** *071

KAZI, Waseemuddin. 1821 S STOUGHTON RD 53716 #704-20-1984 L1998 **ICE CD** *020 †20

KAZKAZ, Bassel. 1200 JOHN Q HAMMONS DR, STE 400 53717 #875-02-1992 L1996 **CN** *100 †75

KEELING, Richard Powell. 1552 UNIVERSITY AVE, UNIVERSITY HEATH SERVICES 53726 #024-07-1913 L1993 **ADL HEM** *030 †20

KEENE, James Stephen. 621 SCIENCE DR 53711 #056-05-1970 L1971 **OSM** *020 †40

KEEVIL, Hannah Matilda. ■ 53719 #035-15-1990 L1992 **FM** *020 †18

KEEVIL, Jonathan Gregory. 600 HIGHLAND AVE H6/349, CV MEDICINE # 3248 53792 #035-45-1994 L1995 **CD** *020 †20

KEHOE, Meghan Colleen. ■ 53726 #056-05-2005 **AN** *012

KEHOE, Ryan James. 600 HIGHLAND AVE, AVE H4/831-8320 53792 #056-05-2001 L2002 **OSM** *100

KELCZ, Frederick. 600 HIGHLAND AVE, E3/366-3252 C5C 53792 #011-02-1982 L1985 **DR** *020 †80

KELLER, Dean Richard. 451 JUNCTION RD, STE 9903 53717 #056-06-1985 L1986 **IM** *020 †20

KELLEY, Catherine. 600 HIGHLAND AVE, UNIVERSITY OF WI HOSPITAL 53792 #056-05-1986 L1987 **PD** *040 †20

KELLOGG, Lloyd Stephen. 1313 FISH HATCHERY RD 53715 #016-11-1948 L1949 **GP** *071

KELLY, John Terence. 600 HIGHLAND AVE, UNIVERSITY OF WI HOSPITAL 53792 #056-05-2003 L2004 **AI** *012 †20

KEMP, Allen David. 1808 W BELTLINE HWY, DEAN BUSINES OFFICE 53713 #056-05-1976 L1977 **AN** *020 †05

KEMP, Thomas S. ■ 53703 #026-04-1948 L1954 **D** *071 †15

KENDZIORSKI, Alexander. 707 S MILLS ST, ST MARYS HOSP 53715 #056-05-2001 L2004 **IM** *020 †20

KENNEDY, Gregory Dean. 600 HIGHLAND AVE, CSC H4/761 53792 #054-04-1996 L1997 **CRS** *100 †85

KENNEY, Shannon Celeste. 1400 UNIVERSITY AVE, UNIVERSITY OF WISCONSIN 53706 #008-01-1979 L2006 **ID PD** *020 †20,55

KENNY, John Dillard. ■ 53711 #010-01-1968 L1985 **NPM** *071 †55

KEPECS, Joseph G. 600 HIGHLAND AVE 53792 #016-01-1937 L1965 **PYA P** *020 †75

KERKUTA, Ryan Charles. 600 HIGHLAND AVE, DEPT OF OB/GYN 53792 #018-03-2006 **OBG** *012

KERWIN, Robert Earl, Jr. 1552 UNIVERSITY AVE 53726 #056-05-1991 L1992 **FM** *020 †18

KESSEL, Julie Marie. 202 S PARK ST, MERITER HOSPITAL 53715 #005-02-1991 L1998 **NPM** *020 †55

KETHIREDDY, Shravan Kumar. 600 HIGHLAND AVE 53792 #496-23-2003 L2007 **ID** *012

KETZLER, Jonathan Taylor. 600 HIGHLAND AVE 53792 #030-05-1992 L1993 **CCA** *020 †05

KHAN, Mohammad S A. 440 SCIENCE DR STE 200 53711 #704-19-1980 L2002 **CHP** *020

KHAN, Sahahida R. 752 N HIGH POINT RD 53717 #704-09-1972 L1982 **PD** *020

KHATIB, Irfane M. 600 HIGHLAND AVE 53792 #875-01-1967 L1976 **OBG** *020 †30

KHUNTIA, Deepak. 600 HIGHLAND AVE, RADIATION ONCOLOGY DEPT 53792 #016-11-1999 L2004 **RO** *020 †80

KHUU, Linh My. 1200 JOHN Q HAMMONS DR, STE 400 53717 #001-06-1992 L2007 **HO** *020 †20

KIEKHAEFER, Carol Marie. K6/435 CLINICAL SCIENCE CE, 600 HIGHLAND AVEUNE 53792 #016-06-1978 L1987 **PCC EM** *020 †20

KIENITZ, Beverly Aagaard. 600 HIGHLAND AVE, CSC E3/311 53792 #005-19-1988 L2000 **RNR** *020 †80

KIESER, Randall John. 2909 LANDMARK PL, METASTAR INC 53713 #056-05-1984 L1985 **ADM** *030 †18

KILPATRICK, Frank W. 20 S PARK ST, ST-INTERNAL MEDICINE 53715 #050-02-1970 L1981 **RHU IM** *050 †20

KIM, David H. 600 HIGHLAND AVE, E3/311 53792 #025-01-1993 L2005 **DR** *020 †80

KIM, Nancy. ■ 53703 #025-01-2003 L2003 **OPH** *100

KIM, Newrhee. 202 S PARK ST, BLDG 3 53715 #035-15-2000 L2005 **RNR** *100 †80

KIM, Robert Dong. 600 HIGHLAND AVE 53792 #056-05-2002 L2005 **PCC** *012 †20

KIM, Roy Hyuk. 1200 JOHN Q HAMMONS DR, 4TH FL 53717 #041-01-1994 L2001 **HO IM** *020 †20

KIMMEL, Glenn. 600 HIGHLAND AVE, CLINICAL SCIENCE CTR 53792 #016-42-1980 L1981 **FM** *020 †18

KIMURA, Ibuki Anne. 707 S MILLS ST 53715 #016-02-1996 L1997 **IM** *020 †20

KIMURA, Ray. 202 S PARK ST 53715 #067-01-1997 L1998 **IM** *071 †20

KIND, Amy Jo. 2500 OVERLOOK TER, WILLIAM S MIDDLETON VA HOS 53705 #056-05-2001 L2004 **IMG** *050 †20

KINDA, Hajnal Klara. 7102 MINERAL POINT RD, UW HEALTH WEST TOWNE CLINI 53717 #781-05-1997 L2007 *100

KINDIG, David Anthony. 610 WALNUT ST STE 760 53726 #016-02-1968 L1981 **PHP PD** *030

KINDSCHI, Kari Ellen. 777 S MILLS ST 53715 #056-05-2006 L2008 **FP** *012

KING, Andre Christian. ■ 53719 #010-01-2007 **GS** *012

KING, Clifford. 752 N HIGH POINT RD, WEST CLINIC 53717 #010-02-1998 L1997 **HS GS** *020 †65

KING, Jonathan Douglass. ■ 53717 #056-06-2008 *012

KINGREE, William Blaine. ■ 53705 #051-01-1959 L1959 **FM** *071

KIPP, Ryan Timothy. ■ 53719 #056-05-2007 **IM** *012

KIRCHER, Kip Alan. 600 HIGHLAND AVE 53792 #030-05-1991 L1994 **EM** *020 †16

KISSEL, Gregg Edward. 7102 MINERAL POINT RD 53717 #035-06-1997 L1998 **FM** *020 †18

KISSING, Dominik. 600 HIGHLAND AVE, UNIV OF WI HOSP & CLI 53792 #409-22-2001 L2005 **OBG** *012

KLATT, Kenneth Munson. 1 S PARK ST 53715 #023-01-1956 L1957 **GS CD** *020 †85,90

KLEIN, Barbara E Kobrin. 610 WALNUT ST, 409 WARF OFFICE BUILDING 53726 #035-19-1969 L1976 **OPH GPM** *050 †70,35

KLEIN, Bruce Steven. 600 HIGHLAND AVE, WISCONSIN HOSPIT 53792 #024-05-1978 L1983 **IM PD** *020 †55

KLEIN, Matthew David. 707 S MILLS ST, ST. MARY'S HOSPITAL 53715 #026-08-1993 L1999 **IM** *020 †20

KLEIN, Ronald. 610 WALNUT ST RM 450, DEPT OF OPHTHALMOLOGY 53726 #035-19-1969 L1976 **OPH PHP** *050 †35

KLEINFELDT, Katherine Ann. 600 HIGHLAND AVE, AVE H4/831-8320 53792 #056-05-2005 L2007 **PD** *012

KLEIST, Troy James. 600 HIGHLAND AVE, UNIVERSITY OF WI HOSPITAL 53792 #056-05-2001 L2005 **PD** *100 †55

KLEMIN, Jill Maire. ■ 53719 #037-01-2007 *012

KLEMIN, Peter Lawrence. ■ 53719 #037-01-2007 **OBG** *012

KLEVENE, Bary Michael. ■ 53715 #056-05-2008 *012

KLIEWER, Mark Alan. 600 HIGHLAND AVE, STE E-3/366 53792 #036-07-1985 L2001 **DR** *020 †80

KLING, Pamela Jean. 202 S PARK ST 53715 #018-03-1985 L1986 **NPM** *050 †55

KLINK, Mary Elizabeth. 6001 RESEARCH PARK BLVD 53719 #056-06-1979 L1981 **PUD IM** *020 †20

KLOMBERG, Gerald Herman. 1313 FISH HATCHERY RD 53715 #056-06-1960 L1961 **IM IMG** *071

KLOOSTERBOER, Thomas B. 600 HIGHLAND AVE, B6/319 CLINICAL SCI CTR 53792 #056-05-1982 L1983 **AN** *020 †05

KNECHTLE, Stuart Johnston. 600 HIGHLAND AVE, UNIV OF WISCONSIN HOSPITAL 53792 #035-20-1982 L1989 **GS** *020 †85

KNEZEVIC, Ivan D. ■ 53719 #957-02-1958 L1963 **DR NM** *071 †80,28

KNIAZ, Harry. ■ 53719 #056-05-1966 L1967 **CHP PYG** *072 †75

KNIOLA, Renee Hess. 600 HIGHLAND AVE RM B6-319, UNIV OF WISCONSIN 53792 #661-02-2006 L2007 **AN** *012

KNOCH, Daniel William. 600 HIGHLAND AVE, AVE H4/831-8320 53792 #056-05-2003 L2004 **OPH** *100

KNOEDLER, William Henry. 108 S WEBSTER ST 53703 #056-05-1971 L1972 **P** *020 †75

KNOEDLER, William Henry. 600 WILLIAMSON ST, STE A 53703 #056-06-1943 L1944 **GP** *071

KNOEPKE, Kristen Lynn. 675 W WASHINGTON AVE, GROUP HEALTH COOPERTIVE 53703 #056-05-1994 L1995 **FM** *020 †18

KNOESTER, Peter Anthony. 600 HIGHLAND AVE, HOSPITAL AND 53792 #025-01-2006 L2008 *012

KNOTTS, Mary Helen. 1821 S STOUGHTON RD 53716 #017-20-1977 L2000 **IM** *020 †20

KNUDSON, Erik David. 301 TROY DR, MENDOTA MENTAL HEALTH INST 53704 #056-06-1998 L1999 **PFP** *012

KNUPPEL, Jeffrey William. 317 KNUTSON DR, CENTRAL WI CTR 53704 #016-01-1994 L1995 **P PYG** *020 †75

KNUTZEN, David Bruce. 301 TROY DR, MENDOTA MENTAL HEALTH INST 53704 #056-05-1966 L1968 **CHP P** *071

KOBER, Philip Mason. ■ 53704 #016-01-1994 **IM** *100

KOBITARY, Majd. 600 HIGHLAND AVE, UNIVERSITY OF WIS. HOSPITA 53792 #875-01-1996 L2001 **PCC** *012 †20

KOENIG, Erwin Fred. ■ 53704 #056-06-1960 L1964 **GP** *071

KOKOTAILO, Patricia K. 2880 UNIVERSITY AVE 53705 #056-06-1982 L1989 **PD ADL** *020 †55

KOLEHMAINEN, Christine Ja. ■ 53717 #025-12-2008 *012

KOLIMAS, Christopher J. 1821 S STOUGHTON RD 53716 #016-11-1979 L2001 **EM FM** *020 †16,70,18

KOLLER, William Seigfried. 752 N HIGH POINT RD 53717 #038-40-1973 L1975 **OBG** *020 †30

KOLPA, Emily Margaret. ■ 53713 #050-02-2008 *012

KOLPIN, Sarah Elizabeth. ■ 53726 #056-05-2008 *012

KOOPMANN, Matthew Charles. 600 HIGHLAND AVE, AVE H4/831-8320 53792 #038-40-2005 L2007 **GS** *012

KOPLIN, Stephanie. 402 N EAU CLAIRE AVE 53705 #056-05-2004 L2007 **GS** *012

KOPP, Douglas Earl. 600 HIGHLAND AVE, CSC G7/347-MC3248 53792 #056-05-1986 L2001 **ICE CD** *020 †20

KORDLAR, Bahram Ataei. 600 HIGHLAND AVE, AVE H4/831-8320 53792 #517-01-2000 L2005 **CN** *012

KOSLOV, Steven Saul. 7102 MINERAL POINT RD 53717 #028-03-1977 L1978 **PD** *020 †55

KOSOLCHAROEN, Peter. 2500 OVERLOOK TER, DEPT CARD 53705 #016-06-1974 L1975 **CD IM** *020 †20

KOSSEFF, Andrew L. 707 S MILLS ST 53715 #056-05-1974 L1977 **IM** *020 †20

KOSTELYNA, Orest Ilko. 1200 JOHN Q HAMMONS DR, STE 400 53717 #016-43-1986 L1990 **IM** *020 †20

KOVAZ, Joseph Michael. 451 JUNCTION RD 53717 #012-05-1974 L1994 **IM** *020 †20 ‡

KOZAREK, John Andrew. 1313 FISH HATCHERY RD 53715 #056-05-1975 L1976 **R DR** *020 †80

KRAEMER, Patricia Sue. 345 W WASHINGTON AVE 53703 #056-05-1985 L1986 **IM ADM** *072 †20

KRAEMER, Paul Edward. 600 HIGHLAND AVE K4/739, WISCONSIN HOSPIT 53792 #018-03-2002 L2004 **ORS** *020

KRAFT, Sally Ann. 202 S PARK ST, ST-MERITER ATRIUM 53715 #025-01-1983 L1993 **IM** *020 †20

KRAHN, Dean Dennis. 2500 OVERLOOK TER 53705 #056-05-1980 L1992 **P ADP** *020 †75

KRAJEWSKI, Kenneth Anthon. 53705 #020-02-2008 *012

KRAMER, Douglas Alan. 780 REGENT ST 53715 #056-05-1971 L1974 **CHP P** *020 †75

KRANNER, Paul William. 600 HIGHLAND AVE, B6 319 CLINICAL SCIENCE CT 53792 #056-05-1988 L1989 **AN** *020 †05

KRECKMAN, Sara E. H4/4 CSC, 600 HIGHLAND AVENUE 53792 #025-12-2000 L2001 **PD** *020 †55

KREUL, John Frederick. 600 HIGHLAND AVE 53792 #016-43-1972 L1975 **AN** *071 †05

KRIEGE, Joanne Marie. 1200 JOHN Q HAMMONS DR, STE 400 53717 #056-05-1988 L1989 **RHU** *020 †20

KRISS, Fred Chas. 20 S PARK ST STE 205 53715 #024-01-1961 L1968 **NS** *020 †25

KROHN, Amy Cortright. 2500 OVERLOOK TER, VA HOSPITAL 53705 #056-05-1992 L1994 **P** *020 †75

KRONCKE, George Michael. 6006 GALLEY CT 53705 #056-05-1954 L1955 **TS** *071 †85,90

KRUCK, Mark Edward. 707 S MILLS ST, DEPT OF ANESTHESIOLOGY 53715 #056-06-1998 L2002 **AN** *020 †05

KRUEGER, Kelly Therese. ■ 53715 #056-05-2008 *012

KRUEGER, Timothy James. 600 HIGHLAND AVE H4/831, UW HOSPITAL AND CLINICS 53792 #017-20-2005 **AN** *012

KRUPP, Jennifer Lynn. 600 HIGHLAND AVE, AVE H4/831-8320 53792 #056-05-2005 L2007 **OBG** *012

KUDSK, Kenneth Allan. 600 HIGHLAND AVE, H4/736 CSC 53792 #016-11-1975 L2001 **GS TRS** *020 †85

KUESTER, Jessica Lynn. ■ 53705 #056-05-2008 *012

KUHLMAN, Janet Elaine. 600 HIGHLAND AVE, STE E-3/366 53792 #024-01-1981 L1994 **DR IM** *020 †20,80

KULIE, Teresa Irene. 3209 DRYDEN DR, NORTHEAST CLINIC 53704 #023-01-2001 L2002 **FM** *020 †18

KUMAR, Girish Chander. 202 S PARK ST 53715 #495-45-1980 L1999 **CCA** *020 †05

KUNIN, Kalman Clarence. ■ 53705 #067-01-1943 L1988 **OBG** *071 †30

KUNSTMAN, David Thomas. 5618 ODANA RD 53719 #056-05-1995 L1996 **FM** *020 †18

KUNTZ, Kevin Douglas. 780 REGENT ST 53715 #018-03-1990 L1994 **P** *020 †75

KUNZ, Jeffrey R M. PO BOX 6157 53716 #056-05-1977 **IMG PM** *030

KUO, John Shushin. K3/803 CSC 8660, 600 HIGHLAND AVE 53792 #024-01-1998 L2005 **NS** *100

KUPHAL, Greta Jane. 777 S MILLS ST, UNIVERSITY OF WISCONSIN, M 53715 #056-05-2006 L2008 **FP** *012

KURITZ, Robert Ronald. 5714 ODANA RD, ODANA MEDICAL CENTER 53719 #056-06-1975 L1976 **FM** *071 †18

KURLE, Philip. 20 S PARK ST, STE 207 53715 #016-11-1998 L1999 **N** *020 †75

KURTYCZ, Daniel Frank. 465 HENRY MALL, MED CIR WISC STATE LAB HYG 53706 #025-01-1976 L1979 **PTH PCP** *020 †50

KURTZ, Kevin Andrew. 707 S MILLS ST 53715 #056-05-2000 L2004 **PTH** *100 †50

KUSHNER, Burton Jay. 2880 UNIVERSITY AVE 53705 #016-06-1969 L1970 **OPH PO** *020 †35 ‡

KUSHNER, David Marc. 600 HIGHLAND AVE H4-636, DEPT OF OB / GYN 53792 #025-07-1994 L2001 **GO GYN** *020 †30

KUSHNER, Jeffrey Alan. 1200 JOHN Q HAMMONS DR, STE 400 53717 #025-01-1982 L1989 **ICE CD** *020 †20

KUTER, David Paul. 1102 JOHN NOLEN DR 53713 #016-11-1968 L1971 **FM** *020 †18

KUTZ, Douglas Chas. 20 S PARK ST, STE 207 53715 #056-05-1992 L1993 **IM** *020 †20

KWON, Tea Gil. 301 TROY DR 53704 #583-03-1968 L1979 **CHP P** *020 †75

LACHARITE, Desiree D. 600 HIGHLAND AVE, F2/209 CLINICAL SCIENCE CE 53792 #020-12-1998 L2001 **EM** *020 †16

LADD, Charlotte Allison. 6001 RESEARCH PARK BLVD, INST & 53719 #012-05-2003 L2005 **P** *100

LAGMAN, Steven Randall. 202 S PARK ST 53715 #056-05-1987 L1988 **AN** *020 †05

LAIRD, Anna Kane. ■ 53705 #041-01-1946 L1947 **P** *071

LALICH, Mihailo. 600 HIGHLAND AVE H4/823, UW HOSPITAL & CLINICS 53792 #056-05-2001 L2003 **ON** *020

LAMAN, Brian David. 600 HIGHLAND AVE, AVE H4/831-8320 53792 #048-04-2004 L2005 **ORS** *012

LAMBOURNE, Kathryn Paulin. ■ 53704 #056-06-2007 **AN** *012

LA MONICA, Carolyn Ann. 502 W SHORE DR, H4/572 53715 #030-05-1993 L2004 **ID** *020 †20 ‡

LANDRY, Gregory Lance. 2880 UNIVERSITY AVE 53705 #017-20-1980 L1981 **PD PSM** *020 †55

LANDRY, Mary Sue Schlack. 1552 UNIVERSITY AVE 53726 #056-05-1992 L1994 **OBG** *020 †30

LANE, Linda Diane. ■ 53705 #016-43-1974 L1975 **P OS** *020

LANG, Gerald Jos. 600 HIGHLAND AVE, K4/744 53792 #056-05-1988 L1994 **OTR** *020 †40

LANG, Joshua Michael. ■ 53717 #016-11-2006 L2007 **IM** *012

LANGE, Richard H. 600 HIGHLAND AVE 53792 #056-06-1978 L1979 **ORS** *020 †40

LANGE, Rollo Du Bois. 202 S PARK ST 53705 #028-34-1945 L1956 **OTO** *071 †45

LANGER, Leonard O, Jr. ■ 53713 #026-04-1953 L1960 **PDR DR** *050 †80

LANGHEIM, Frederick J. ■ 53705 #026-04-2007 **P** *012

LARAVUSO, Raymond Bruce. 600 HIGHLAND AVE 53792 #035-46-1969 L1980 **AN** *071 †05

LARDY, Diana Elizabeth. 3706 ORIN RD 53704 #056-05-1977 L1978 **FM** *020 †18

LARKIN, Charles B. ■ 53711 #056-05-1949 L1950 **P N** *071 †75

LARSON, Frank Clark. 600 HIGHLAND AVE # B4251 53792 #030-05-1944 L1948 **END CLP** *030 †20

LARSON, Jeffrey David. ■ 53719 #056-06-2006 **PS** *012

LARUE, Shane Joseph. 600 HIGHLAND AVE, AVE H4/831-8320 53792 #056-06-2005 L2007 **IM** *012

LATHROP, Deborah. 4122 E TOWNE BLVD, EAST TOWNE IMMEDIATE CARE 53704 #036-01-1998 L2003 **FM** *020 †18

LATTERELL, Louise Frances. 1552 UNIVERSITY AVE, UNIVERSITY HEALTH SERVICES 53726 #026-04-1997 L2001 **FM** *020 †18

LAUBE, Douglas Wm. 1 S PARK ST STE 555, DEPARTMENT OF OBGYN 53715 #018-03-1970 L1993 **OBG** *030 †30 ‡

LAVELL, Beatriz Isabel. 1821 S STOUGHTON RD 53716 #715-01-1990 L2001 **FM** *020 †18

LAWRENCE, Susan Judith. 600 HIGHLAND AVE H6/363 53792 #056-06-1999 L2000 **RHU** *012

LAXOVA, Renata. 1500 HIGHLAND AVE 53705 #286-04-1956 L1980 **PD IMG** *071 †19

LEAL, Miguel Angelo Gomes. 600 HIGHLAND AVE, HOUSE STAFF AFFAIRS H4/831 53792 #187-10-2001 L2007 **CD** *012 †20

LEAL, Ticiana A B. 600 HIGHLAND AVE, HOUSE STAFF AFFAIRS H4/831 53792 #187-10-2001 L2007 **ON** *012 †20

LEAVITT, Lewis A. 600 HIGHLAND AVE, H414 CSC-PEDIATRICS 53792 #016-02-1965 L1970 **PD NPM** *050 †55

LEBLANC, Vanessa Monique. ■ 53703 #056-05-2008 *012

LECHMAIER, Timothy Edward. 752 N HIGH POINT RD 53717 #056-06-1977 L1980 **IM** *020 †20

LEE, Andrew Dehan. 600 HIGHLAND AVE, AVE H4/831-8320 53792 #026-04-2002 L2006 **DR** *020 †80

LEE, Fred Tonghoi, Jr. 600 HIGHLAND AVE, E3 311 HEALTH SCIENCES CEN 53792 #024-05-1986 L1991 **DR** *020 †80

LEE, Jonas Jooyoung. 600 HIGHLAND AVE FAM PR 53792 #019-02-1996 L1997 **FM** *020 †18

LEE, Peter Ju-Heung. 1313 FISH HATCHERY RD, DEAN CLINIC 53715 #025-01-1995 L2006 **CD IM** *020 †20

LEE, Suzanne Bosen. ■ 53703 #025-07-1986 L1986 **CHP** *020

LEE, Tracy. ■ 53705 #035-15-1999 L2005 **PD** *020 †55

LEHMAN, James Gregory. ■ 53705 #056-05-2008 *012

LEIKENSOHN, Adam Robert. ■ 53703 #011-02-2004 L2007 **IM** *100 †20

LEIN, Arild. 1300 UNIVERSITY AVE 53706 #665-02-2006 **FP** *012

LEITH, Catherine P. 600 HIGHLAND AVE 53792 #917-19-1983 L2000 **PTH** *020 †50

LEITNER, Thomas Laurence. ■ 53705 #016-02-1994 L2007 **IM** *012

LEMANSKE, Robert F, Jr. 600 HIGHLAND AVE, H6-367 53792 #056-05-1975 L1976 **PD PDA** *020 †55,03

LEMBERGER, Terrence Lee. 752 N HIGH POINT RD 53717 #016-11-1979 L2000 **EM** *020 †16

LEMKE, Bradley Nathanael. 1200 JOHN Q HAMMONS DR #10 53717 #038-06-1975 L1976 **OPH FPS** *020 †35

LEMKUIL, Amy Elizabeth. ■ 53711 #056-05-2001 *100

LEMON, Richard Aubrey. 1 S PARK ST, FL 7 53715 #025-01-1980 L1981 **ORS AM** *020 †40

LEONOVICZ, Peter F, Jr. 707 S MILLS ST, ST. MARY'S HOSPITAL 53715 #030-05-1979 L1980 **AN** *020 †05

LEPAK, Alexander John. 600 HIGHLAND AVE, BOX 2454 53792 #056-05-2005 L2007 **IM** *012

LEPEAK, Lisa Marie. J5/230 CSC-2454, 600 HIGHLAND AVENUE 53792 #025-07-2006 L2006 **IM** *012

LEPINSKI-MURRELL, Susan M. 20 S PARK ST, STE 207 53715 #056-05-1984 L1985 **GE IM** *020 †20

LEUNG, Winifred K. 600 HIGHLAND AVE, AVE H4/831-8320 53792 #041-15-2004 L2006 **DR** *012

LEVENICK, Kathleen S. 700 RAY O VAC DR STE 220, FAM THERAPY CTR OF MADISON 53711 #030-05-1982 L1984 **P** *020

LEVIN, Allan Bertram. 600 HIGHLAND AVE 53792 #016-42-1965 L1969 **NS** *062 †25

LEVIN, James Michael. 1313 FISH HATCHERY RD 53715 #056-06-1988 L1992 **ID** *020 †20

LEVIN, Kenneth Ellis. 1313 FISH HATCHERY RD, DEAN MEDICAL CTR 53715 #056-05-1982 L1990 **FP** *085,10

LEVIN, Leonard Abraham. 600 HIGHLAND AVE, K6/456 53792 #024-01-1988 L1993 **OPH OS** *050 †35

LEVINE, Ross Lewis. 600 HIGHLAND AVE 53792 #056-05-1978 L1979 **N** *050 †75

LEVY, Andrea Hillary. 115 N ORCHARD ST, COUNSELING & CONSULTATION 53715 #012-01-1991 L1996 **P** *020 †75

LEVY, Jay Milford. 600 HIGHLAND AVE 53792 #023-07-1955 L1966 **PDC PD** *020

LEVY, Robert Barnett. ■ 53705 #035-48-2006 **AN** *012

LEWIS, David Henry. 309 W WASHINGTON AVE 53703 #056-05-1995 L2002 **CD IC** *020 †20

LEWIS, Emily H. 202 S PARK ST, BLDG 3 53715 #025-07-1989 L2004 **DR** *020 †80

LEWIS, Mitchell Laine. ■ 53717 #030-05-1994 L2007 **EM** *020 †16

LIAO, Jenny Peichin. 600 HIGHLAND AVE H6/5, DEPARTMENT OF NEUROLOGY 53792 #041-02-1998 L1999 **N** *020 †75

LICKLIDER, Gary Melvin. 1313 FISH HATCHERY RD 53715 #056-05-1971 L1972 **U** *071 †95

LIEBL, Edmund R. ■ 53705 #056-05-1952 L1953 **GP** *071

LIEDTKE, Arthur James. 600 HIGHLAND AVE, UW HOSPITAL - CSC 53792 #016-12-1964 L1971 **CD** *030 †20

LIEGEL, Jessica Jayne. ■ 53703 #056-05-2008 *012

LIEW, Elaine Chiew Lin. ■ 53705 #143-04-1992 L2007 **CCA** *012

LILLEAS, Finn Erik Green. U W I HLTH SCI CTR, DEPT RAD 53706 #693-01-1971 L1979 **R** *020

LINDBLADE, James Alfred. 1552 UNIVERSITY AVE 53726 #016-02-1962 L1969 **GYN** *071 †30

LINDGREN, Jan Urban. 8007 EXCELSIOR DR 53717 #858-04-1970 L1984 **ORS** *020 †40

LINDGREN, Richard Dan. 600 HIGHLAND AVE 53792 #018-03-1956 L1962 **R NM** *072 †80,28

LINDSAY, Malcolm Bruce. 600 HIGHLAND AVE, E5768 53792 #016-42-1992 L1996 **EM** *020 †16

LINHART, Heinz Gerta. UNIV WI HOSP AND CLI, DEPT MED 53792 #409-07-1994 **IM** *100

LINK, Rudolf Walter. ■ 53705 #030-05-1959 L1960 **P OS** *071 †75

LINZER, Mark. 600 HIGHLAND AVE, UNIV WISCONSIN 53792 #023-07-1977 L1993 **GPM IM** *020 †20

LITTLE, Margaret. 309 W WASHINGTON AVE 53703 #005-11-1978 L1979 **CHP P** *020 †75

LIU, Glenn. 600 HIGHLAND AVE DEPT MED 53792 #041-02-1997 L1998 **ON** *020 †20

LIU, Rosemarie H. 1 S PARK ST 7TH FL, UNI OF WI, DEPT OF DERM 53715 #051-07-2005 L2008 **D** *012

LLOYD, Rita. 1 S PARK ST, 7TH FL 53715 #005-15-1984 L1999 **D** *020 †15

LOCONTE, Matthew Daniel. 2500 OVERLOOK TER, MIDDLETON MEM VA HOSP 53705 #016-11-2000 L2004 **IMG PLM** *012

LOEFFLER, Christopher J. ■ 53705 #040-02-1984 L1985 **AN IM** *071 †20,05

LOEVINGER, Barbara Lee. 2500 OVERLOOK TER, GRECC WM S MIDDLETON VA HO 53705 #023-01-1979 L1980 **P OS** *100 †75

LOMAS, Philip Neil. 301 TROY DR, MENDOTA MENTAL HEALTH INST 53704 #005-02-1987 L1991 **P** *020 †75

LONG, James P. 675 W WASHINGTON AVE 53703 #649-14-1977 L1981 **FM** *020 †18

LONG, Webb Ellis. ■ 53703 #050-02-2006 L2007 **PD** *012

LONGLEY, B Jack, Jr. 451 JUNCTION RD, STE 9903 53717 #056-05-1979 L1980 **DMP** *050 †50

LONGLEY, Bruce Jack. ■ 53726 #056-05-1942 L1943 **CD GS** *071 †85,90

LONGO, Jude Michael. 600 HIGHLAND AVE, DEPT RAD E3-311 53792 #018-03-1996 L2001 **DR** *020 †80

LONSDORF, David Belew. 7102 MINERAL POINT RD 53717 #038-41-1979 L1984 **FM** *020 †18

LOPUKHIN, Olga Valeri. 600 HIGHLAND AVE, B5/319 53792 #913-15-1992 L2002 **AN** *020 †05

LOPUKHIN, Sergeui Yuri. 600 HIGHLAND AVE, CSC, B6/319 53792 #913-15-1978 L1998 **AN** *020

LOTZ, Barend Petrus. 600 HIGHLAND AVE, UNIVERSITY HOSPITAL &CLINI 53792 #836-03-1976 L1991 **N** *020

LOVE, Robert B. 600 HIGHLAND AVE H4/344, DEPT OF SURGERY 53792 #016-01-1982 L1983 **TS GS** *020 †90,85

LOVING, Kenneth Raymond. 2202 S PARK ST 53713 #016-11-1993 L1996 **FM** *020 †18

LOWERY, Sarah Elisabeth. 707 S MILLS ST 53715 #056-05-2003 L2004 **FM** *020 †18

LOWREY, Jonathan Stanley. 202 S PARK ST, MERITER HOSPITAL 53715 #038-41-1984 L1985 **AN** *020 †05

LOZEAU, Annemarie. 3209 DRYDEN DR, UW FAMILY MED CLINIC 53704 #032-01-1998 L1999 **FM** *020 †18

LOZIER, Alan Paul. 1200 JOHN Q HAMMONS DR, STE 400 53717 #005-14-1998 L2004 **NS** *020

LOZONSCHI, Lucian. ■ 53717 #781-02-1995 L2006 **GS** *020 †85,90

LU, Katherine Susan. 1200 JOHN Q HAMMONS DR, STE 400 53717 #025-01-1999 L2000 **IM** *020 †20

LU, Zhen. 1552 UNIVERSITY AVE 53726 #243-47-1991 L2001 **IM** *020 †20

LUCARELLI, Mark Jos. 600 HIGHLAND AVE, DEPT OF OPHTH F4/348 53792 #028-02-1991 L1996 **OPH** *020 †35

LUCCHESE, Neil James. 1025 REGENT ST, DAVIS DUEHR DEAN 53715 #016-06-1978 L1981 **OPH PO** *020 †35

LUCEY, Michael R. 451 JUNCTION RD, STE 9903 53717 #539-03-1976 L2001 **GE** *020 †20

LUDWIG, Brian Joseph. 600 HIGHLAND AVE, AVE H4/831-8320 53792 #018-03-2004 L2005 **ORS** *012

LUETKE, William Vernon. ■ 53715 #056-05-1942 L1947 **GYN** *071 †30

LUM, Darren Pakying. 600 HIGHLAND AVE E3/311, UNIV OF WI HOSPITAL AND CL 53792 #014-01-2002 L2004 **DR** *100 †80

LUNT, William Webb. 600 HIGHLAND AVE 53792 #030-06-1992 L1993 **GE** *020 †20

LUX, Marcia Louise. 202 S PARK ST 53715 #024-01-2001 L2006 **IM** *020

LUYET, Francois Maurice. 2202 S PARK ST 53713 #869-04-1970 L1978 **PD** *020 †55

LUZZIO, Christopher C. 600 HIGHLAND AVE 53792 #020-02-1993 L1994 **N** *020 †75

LYONS, Melissa Elaine. ■ 53703 #028-03-2006 L2008 **D** *012

LYSLOFF, George Odet. 17204 MAPLEWOOD LN 53704 #165-04-1951 L1965 **P** *020 †75

MAASSEN, Nicholas Henry. ■ 53705 #056-05-2008 *012

MACDONALD, Kevin Michael. 600 HIGHLAND AVE, AVE H4/831-8320 53792 #056-05-2004 L2005 **ORS** *012

MAC DONALD, Michael John. 1300 UNIVERSITY AVE, UNIV HOSPITAL 53706 #028-02-1970 L1974 **DIA END** *020 †55

MACK, Eberhard Alfred. 600 HIGHLAND AVE, DEPT OF SURGERY H4/744 53792 #407-19-1964 L1976 **GS** *020 †85

MACKEY, K Christopher. 451 JUNCTION RD, STE 9903 53717 #035-46-1995 L2001 **OBG** *020 †30

■ = Address Information Privacy Protected

MACKIN, Kelly Marie. ■ 53705 #056-05-2008 *012
MAC KINNEY, Archie Allen. 330 E LAKESIDE ST 53715 #035-45-1955 L1957 **HEM IM** *071 †20
MADSEN, Paul Ove. 2500 OVERLOOK TER, DEPT UROL 53705 #297-01-1952 L1962 **U** *071 †95
MADSEN, Renate Elisabeth. 600 HIGHLAND AVENUE, DEPT OF ANESTHESIOLOGY 53706 #407-10-1955 L1962 **AN** *071 †05
MAGENHEIM, Bryan L. 20 S PARK ST, STE 207 53715 #654-01-1989 L1991 **GE** *020 †20
MAGINOT, Kathleen Rose. 600 HIGHLAND AVE, H4/412 CSC 53792 #056-05-1989 L2003 **PDC PD** *020 †55
MAHAFFEY, Megan Elizabeth. 752 N HIGH POINT RD 53717 #056-05-1999 L2004 **PD** *020 †55
MAHAJAN, Ashish Yogindera. 600 HIGHLAND AVE RM G5-361, AND CLI 53792 #041-12-2005 L2006 **PS** *012
MAHONEY, Jane Ellen. 600 HIGHLAND AVE J5/220, DEPT. OF MEDICINE 53792 #005-02-1986 L1987 **IMG IM** *050 †20
MAHVI, David Mehdi. 600 HIGHLAND AVE 53792 #045-01-1981 L1989 **GS** *020 †85
MAIER, Gary Jos. 301 TROY DR, MENDOTA MENTAL HEALTH INST 53704 #065-06-1968 L1979 **P PFP** *020 †75
MAIXNER, Andrew Holden. 600 HIGHLAND AVE RM B6-319, HOSPITAL AND 53792 #054-04-2005 L2008 **AN** *012
MAKI, Dennis Geo. 600 HIGHLAND AVE, INFECTIOUS DISEASE 53792 #056-05-1967 L1974 **ID CCM** *040 †20
MAKIELSKI, Jonathan C. 600 HIGHLAND AVE, H6/300 CLNC SCIENCE CTR 53792 #016-02-1979 L1995 **IM CD** *050 †20
MALEK, Gohlam-Hossein. 1 S PARK ST 53715 #517-03-1962 L1976 **U GS** *020 †95
MALIK, Farhat Bashir. 7102 MINERAL POINT RD 53717 #704-06-1984 L2000 **FM** *020 †18
MALIK, Jeffrey Tariq. 600 HIGHLAND AVE H4/831, UW HOSPITAL AND CLINICS 53792 #422-01-2005 L2008 **PTH** *012
MALIK, Mahr Afroz. 2500 OVERLOOK TER, DEPT RADIOLOGY 53705 #704-21-1995 L1998 **DR** *020 †80
MALLOF, Mary Clare. J5/230 CSC-2454, 600 HIGHLAND AVENUE 53792 #056-06-2005 L2006 **IM** *012
MALLORY, Dorothy Jill. 701 DANE ST 53713 #012-01-2005 L2006 **FP** *012
MALONE, Daniel Gary. 451 JUNCTION RD, STE 9903 53717 #016-11-1976 L1987 **RHU IM** *050 †20
MALTER, James Saml. 1500 HIGHLAND AVE, 509 WAISMAN CTR U WISCONSI 53705 #028-02-1983 L1991 **PTH** *050 †50
MAMEROW, Brian Robert. 707 S MILLS ST, ST. MARY'S HOSPITAL/MEP 53715 #056-05-2003 L2006 **EM** *020 †16
MANAKAS, Christopher Mich. 600 HIGHLAND AVE, BOX 3236 53792 #017-20-2005 L2006 **GS** *020
MANALO, Felipe. 675 W WASHINGTON AVE 53703 #748-01-1962 L1976 **IM ON** *020 †20
MANDEL, Benjamin Alden. 600 HIGHLAND AVE H4/831, UW HOSPITAL AND CLINICS 53792 #023-07-2004 L2007 **GS** *012
MANDEL, Christopher Barcl. ■ 53719 #056-06-2005 L2007 **AN** *012
MANGOLD, Michael Norbert. 600 HIGHLAND AVE 53792 #016-42-1990 L1991 **GP** *020
MANN, David Chas. 621 SCIENCE DR 53711 #016-42-1978 L1988 **OP ORS** *020 †40
MANNING, Bradley L, Jr. 600 HIGHLAND AVE, AVE H4/831-8320 53792 #016-11-1974 L1975 **PS GS** *020 †85,65
MANOUSAKIS, Georgios. ■ 53726 #418-01-2003 **IM** *100
MARCHAND, Lucille Rachel. 777 S MILLS ST, UNIV WI DPT FAM MED 53715 #005-02-1987 L1991 **FM** *020 †18
MARCU, David Mihai. ■ 53705 #016-06-2006 L2007 **ORS** *012
MARCUS, Jeffrey Allen. 13717 KNUTSON DR 53704 #056-05-1992 L1994 **P** *020 †75
MARK, Laurel Blima. 1 S PARK ST 53715 #035-20-1979 L1982 **IM NEP** *020 †20
MARKS, Stanton A. 330 E LAKESIDE ST 53715 #056-06-1952 L1953 **RO** *071 †80
MARLOW, Gordon V. ■ 53705 #056-05-1949 L1953 **CRS** *071
MARSH, Anne Michele. 600 HIGHLAND AVE H4/447 53792 #056-05-2007 **PD** *012
MARSHALL, John Richard. 6001 RESEARCH PARK BLVD, DEPT PSYCHIATRY 53719 #056-05-1964 L1966 **P** *071 †75
MARTIN, Chester Barton. 600 HIGHLAND AVE, CLINICAL SCIENCE CTR 53792 #041-01-1958 L1985 **OBG MFM** *071 †30
MARTIN, James Paul. 621 SCIENCE DR 53711 #056-06-1986 L1996 **OM IM** *020 †20,70
MARTIN, Kyle Rainey. 700 S PARK ST 53715 #026-08-2002 L2005 **EM** *020 †16
MARTINEZ, Wanda Melanie. 600 HIGHLAND AVE, BOX 9090 53792 #056-05-2004 L2005 **OPH** *012
MARZANO, Joseph Sweeny. ■ 53705 #025-07-2004 L2007 **P** *012
MASCIOPINTO, Jeffery E. 1200 JOHN Q HAMMONS DR, STE 400 53717 #016-06-1990 L1992 **NS** *020 †25
MASKEL, Jennifer Lynn. 1313 FISH HATCHERY RD 53715 #056-05-2000 L2003 **U** *020 †95
MASKEL, Lynn Ann. 2701 UNIVERSITY AVE, SUITE B 1. #305 53705 #056-05-1976 L1977 **P CHP** *020 †75
MASLIAH, Daniel Solomon. 202 S PARK ST, MADISON ANESTHESIOLOGY CON 53715 #016-43-1986 L2004 **AN** *020 †05
MASON, Peter James. 202 S PARK ST 53715 #024-16-1997 L2006 **CD** *020 †20
MATHUR, Madhulika. 8202 EXCELSIOR DR 53717 #035-06-1995 L2003 **PD** *020 †55
MATHUR, Sameer Kumar. 5249 E TERRACE DR 53718 #016-06-2000 L2005 **AI** *050 †20,03
MATIOC, Adrian A. 2500 OVERLOOK TER, DEPT OF ANESTHESIOLOGY 53705 #781-04-1980 L1993 **AN** *020 †05
MATTHEW, Robert Guy. 675 W WASHINGTON AVE 53703 #016-01-1999 L2000 **FM** *020 †18
MATTHEWS, Camilla Kay. 5249 E TERRACE DR 53718 #018-03-1999 L2003 **PD** *020 †55
MATTHEWS, Heather Maria. 600 HIGHLAND AVE, AVE H4/831-8320 53792 #056-05-2002 L2004 **CD** *012 †20
MATZKE, Gregory Michael. 1821 S STOUGHTON RD 53716 #056-05-2000 L2004 **GS AS** *020 †85
MAZEPA, Marshall Andrew. 1300 UNIVERSITY AVE, UNIV OF WI MED SCH 53706 #056-05-2006 L2008 **IM** *012
MCALLISTER, Kevin Sean. 202 S PARK ST 53715 #016-01-1990 L1996 **PUD** *020 †20
MC BRIDE, Ann Marie. 2880 UNIVERSITY AVE MC9020 53792 #019-02-1976 L1991 **IM** *040 †20
MC BRIDE, Patrick E. 600 HIGHLAND AVE, H6/360 CSC 53792 #056-05-1980 L1984 **CD FM** *020 †18
MCCAFFREY, Diane Marie. 600 HIGHLAND AVE, AVE H4/831-8320 53792 #056-05-2005 L2006 **AN** *012
MC CANNA, Peter Jos. 1011 OAK WAY 53705 #056-05-1978 L1979 **OPH** *020 †35
MC CARTHY, James Jos. 600 HIGHLAND AVE, RM K4/735 53792 #036-01-1991 L2007 **ORS** *020 †40
MC CARTHY, Thomas Michael. 2880 UNIVERSITY AVE 53705 #056-06-1959 L1960 **IM PUD** *020 †20

MC CARTNEY, John George. 600 HIGHLAND AVE H4/831, UNIVERSITY OF WISCONSIN HO 53792 #056-05-1997 L1998 **PCC** *012 †20
MC CLAIN, Gregory Dewayne. ■ 53714 #007-02-2003 L2007 **GS** *012
MC CLUNG, John L. 202 S PARK ST 53715 #025-01-1945 L1953 **AN ILI** *072 †05
MCCORD, Jaime Heather. ■ 53711 #041-13-2005 **GS** *012
MC CUE, Jeremy Boone. 600 HIGHLAND AVE H4/823, UNIVERSITY HOSPITALS & CLI 53792 #003-01-1999 L2000 **RNR** *020 †80
MC CULLOCH, Timothy M. UNIVERSITY OF WISCONSIN, HOSPITAL AND CLIN 53792 #030-05-1985 L2007 **OTO** *020 †45
MC DERMOTT, John Craig. 600 HIGHLAND AVE RM E3/311, UNIV OF WIS HOSP AND CLINI 53792 #056-05-1979 L1980 **DR R** *020 †80
MC DERMOTT, John Peter. 4522 HAMMERSLEY RD 53711 #016-06-1945 L1945 **GS** *071 †85
MC DONALD, Michael Healy. 600 HIGHLAND AVE 53792 #016-11-1974 L1976 **OTO FPS** *020 †45
MC DONALD, Robert Alan. 752 N HIGH POINT RD 53717 #018-03-1973 L1975 **D** *020 †15
MC DOWELL, Kimberly Ann. ■ 53711 #051-01-1993 **PD** *100
MC DOWELL, Thomas Stephen. 600 HIGHLAND AVE, B6/319 CSC 53792 #018-03-1991 L1996 **AN** *020 †05
MC ELDOWNEY, Steven J. 600 HIGHLAND AVE 53792 #016-11-2002 L2007 **AI** *012 †20,03
MC FARLAND, Thomas Allen. 1 S PARK ST, FL 7 53715 #016-11-1987 L1994 **ON** *020 †20
MC GRATH, Joan Marie. 1025 REGENT ST, DAVIS DUEHR DAY SURGERY 53715 #056-05-1987 L1996 **AN** *020 †05
MCHAFFIE, Derek Ryan. ■ 53711 #047-20-2006 L2008 **RO** *012
MC HUGH, Timothy Richard. 1821 S STOUGHTON RD 53716 #030-06-1990 L1996 **IM RHU** *020 †20
MC ILLECE, Patricia E. ■ 53703 #030-05-1947 L1950 **CHP P** *072 †55,75
MC INTOSH, Gwenevere C. 5249 E TERRACE DR 53718 #056-05-1996 L2000 **PD** *020 †55
MC INTOSH, James Frederic. 1 S PARK ST 53715 #056-05-1947 L1948 **U** *071 †95
MC KENNA, Daniel Timothy. 600 HIGHLAND AVE, AVE H4/831-8320 53792 #030-06-2003 L2005 **GS** *012
MCKENNA, Patrick Aloysiou. ■ 53713 #056-05-2008 *012 ‡
MCKENNA, Virginia Clara. 1821 S STOUGHTON RD 53716 #056-06-2004 L2005 **FM** *020 †18
MC KINNON, Sally Teresa. 1313 FISH HATCHERY RD 53715 #026-04-1991 L1992 **RNR R** *020 †80
MC KOWN, Kevin Mark. 600 HIGHLAND AVE, H6/ 363 53792 #025-07-1983 L2000 **RHU** *040 †20
MC LEOD, Paul Arthur. 1 S PARK ST, STE 555 53715 #056-05-1960 L1961 **GYN** *020 †30
MC MAHON, Joseph Peter. 202 S PARK ST, PULMONARY MEDICINE 53715 #056-06-1987 L2001 **IM CCM** *020 †20
MC MAHON, Susan Renee. 600 HIGHLAND AVE, B6 319 CLINICAL SCIENCE CT 53792 #056-06-1987 L2001 **AN** *020 †05,55
MC MILLAN, Willis G. 1 S PARK ST 6TH FL 53715 #062-01-1962 L1967 **OTO** *071 †45
MC MURRAY, Alexandria. 2727 MARSHALL CT 53705 #016-11-1992 L1997 **P** *020 †75
MCMURRAY, J Scott. 451 JUNCTION RD, STE 9903 53717 #054-04-1990 L1998 **PDO OTO** *020 †45
MC MURRAY, Julia E. 2880 UNIVERSITY AVE 53705 #036-01-1979 L1993 **IM** *020 †20
MC NAMAR, Justin Patrick. 600 HIGHLAND AVE, AVE H4/831-832 53792 #056-06-2002 L2003 **OTO** *020
MC NEEL, Douglas Gordon. 600 HIGHLAND AVE, K4/518 CLINICAL SCIENCE CE 53792 #016-02-1994 L2001 **ON** *020 †20
MC SWEENEY, Mary Eb. 600 HIGHLAND AVE, B6/319 CLINICAL SCIENCE CE 53792 #056-05-1991 L1993 **AN** *020 †05
MC VEAN, Randall Wayne. 202 S PARK ST, MERITER HOSPITAL 53715 #026-04-1999 L2000 **IM** *020 †20
MC VEY, John Edward. 202 S PARK ST 53715 #038-06-1987 L1988 **TS** *020 †85,90
MEAD, Scott Michael. 600 HIGHLAND AVE, DEPT OF MED RES OFF 53792 #056-05-2002 L2004 **IM** *020 †20
MEANY, Thomas B. 600 HIGHLAND AVE # 6315, UW HOSP-CARDIOLOGY 53792 #539-02-1981 L1991 **CD** *020
MEDOW, Joshua Eric. UNIV OF WISCONSIN, CLINICAL SCIENCE CTR K4/82 53792 #016-11-1999 L2000 **NS** *020 ‡
MEEHAN, Kathryn Ann. J5/230 CSC-2454, 600 HIGHLAND AVENUE 53792 #016-01-2005 **IM** *012
MEHTA, Minesh P. 600 HIGHLAND AVE, # K4-312 53792 #965-01-1981 L1987 **RO** *020 †80
MEIER, Thomas David. 20 S PARK ST, STE 207 53715 #056-05-1979 L1980 **PD** *020 †55
MEJIA, Gualberto Bisquera. 1 S PARK ST 53715 #017-01-1956 L1996 **IM PUD** *071
MEJICANO, George Chas. 750 HIGHLAND AVE, 4263 HEALTH SCIENCES LRNG 53705 #016-11-1990 L1991 **ID IM** *040 †20
MELL, Matthew Wm. 451 JUNCTION RD, STE 9903 53717 #024-01-1987 L2006 **VS** *020 †85
MELLINGER, Jessica Leigh. ■ 53705 #016-06-2007 **IM** *012
MELNICK, David Marc. 1 S PARK ST, FL 7 53715 #024-07-1996 L2002 **GS** *020 †85
MENDELIN, Joel Edward. 707 S MILLS ST 53715 #016-07-1999 L2007 **PTH** *020 †50
MENDYK, Laura Lubawy. ■ 53704 #016-45-2007 **FP** *012
MENET, Mark Wesley. J5/230 CSC-2454, 600 HIGHLAND AVENUE 53792 #016-11-2007 **IM** *012
MEREDITH, Kenneth Lee, Jr. 600 HIGHLAND AVE, H4/823 53792 #020-02-2000 L2002 **GS** *100 †85
MEREDITH, Melissa. 451 JUNCTION RD, STE 9903 53717 #016-11-1988 L1989 **END** *020 †20
MESCHER, Thomas John. 1025 REGENT ST 53715 #056-05-1958 L1959 **AN** *020 †05
MESKIN, Scott Alan. 202 S PARK ST 53715 #012-05-1990 L2002 **EM** *020 †16
MET, Jay Alan. 1200 JOHN Q HAMMONS DR 53717 #035-46-1984 L1997 **OPH** *020 †35
METCALF, Robert Alan. 600 HIGHLAND AVE 53792 #016-11-1985 **ATP OS** *100
MEYER, Andrew Richard. ■ 53717 #056-05-2008 *012
MEYER, Cari Lynn. 600 HIGHLAND AVE B6/319, U OF WASHINGTON HOSP CSC 53792 #056-05-2000 L2001 **PAN AN** *020 †20
MEYER, Charles Ted. 20 S PARK ST STE 403 53715 #041-09-1971 L1972 **P** *020 †75
MEYER, Irene Mary Ibler. 147 WAISMAN CTR 53706 #836-01-1952 L1962 **PD OS** *020
MEYER, Keith Carl. 600 HIGHLAND AVE RM K4/930 53792 #056-05-1981 L1982 **PUD CCM** *050 †20
MEYER, Matthew Elliot. 780 REGENT ST 53715 #028-34-1998 L1999 **P** *020
MEYER, Nicholas Albert. 600 HIGHLAND AVE 53792 #056-05-1990 L1991 **GS** *020 †85
MEYER, Thomas Carl. 2715 MARSHALL CT, ADMIN OFFICE 53705 #836-01-1950 L1961 **CD** *071 †55
MEYER, Thomas Donald. 600 HIGHLAND AVE 53792 #056-05-1973 L1976 **FM** *020 †18,16
MEYERS, David Michael. 2500 OVERLOOK TER, WILLIAM S MIDDLETON MEM 53705 #048-02-2002 L2003 **IM** *020 †20
MEYERS, Sonia Kiran. 600 HIGHLAND AVE H4/831, UW HOSPITAL AND CLINICS 53792 #056-05-2004 L2007 **OBG** *012

■ = Address Information Privacy Protected

MEZRICH, Joshua David. ■ 53717 #035-20-1997 L2005 **TTS** *100 †85

MICKE, Bernard Francis. 5618 ODANA RD 53719 #056-06-1974 L1978 **FM** *020 †18

MIDELFORT, Leila Rebecca. 701 DANE ST 53713 #056-05-2006 L2007 **FP** *012

MIDTHUN, Thomas Tenney. 1200 JOHN Q HAMMONS DR, STE 400 53717 #056-05-1975 L1978 **OM** *020 †70,18

MILEY, Charles Edward, III. 1313 FISH HATCHERY RD, DEAN CLINIC S.C 53715 #051-01-1971 L1976 **N** *020 †75

MILEY, Katherine Finch. 1313 FISH HATCHERY RD, DEAN MEDICAL CENTER 53715 #051-04-1997 L2001 **PD** *020 †55

MILLER, Eugene Chas. 4 W TOWNE MALL, 202 S PARK STREET 53719 #032-01-1984 L1986 **AN** *020 †05

MILLER, Jeanette D. 5702 RAYMOND RD 53711 #056-06-1994 L1995 **FM** *020 †18

MILLER, Kim Joanne. 7102 MINERAL POINT RD 53717 #056-05-1983 L1987 **OBG** *020 †30

MILLER, Michael Michel. 1015 GAMMON LN, MERITER NEW START 53719 #021-01-1979 L1980 **ADM P** *020 †75

MILLER, William Chas. 4410 REGENT ST, ASSOCIATED PHYSICIANS 53705 #056-06-1943 L1945 **D A** *071 †15

MILLIN, Kristin Marie. 451 JUNCTION RD, STE 9903 53717 #016-11-1997 L1998 **PD** *020 †55

MINOR, Kyle Daniel. ■ 53717 #016-11-2008 *012

MIRANPURI, Amrendra Singh. 600 HIGHLAND AVE, RM H4/831 53792 #056-05-2005 L2005 **NS** *012

MITBY, Julie Kampen. 1313 FISH HATCHERY RD 53715 #056-05-1985 L1986 **DR** *020 †80

MOFFET, Hugh Lamson. 330 E LAKESIDE ST 53715 #008-01-1957 L1971 **PD** *071 †55

MOFFET, Mark Alan. 780 REGENT ST STE 300, PHYSICIANS PLUS MED GRP 53715 #025-12-1989 L1990 **CHP** *020 †75

MOFTAKHAR, Roham. ■ 53719 #010-01-2001 L2004 **NS** *012

MOHAGHEGH, Arefeh. ■ 53719 #517-11-2000 *100

MOLANDER, Rachel Celene. 600 HIGHLAND AVE, AVE H4/831-8320 53792 #005-11-2004 L2005 **P** *012

MOLOT, Ross Jonathan. 707 S MILLS ST 53715 #056-06-1988 L1993 **PTH** *020 †50

MONAT, Eric Joseph. 1221 JOHN Q HAMMONS DR, P O BOX 44428 53717 #035-08-1996 L1997 **VIR** *020 †80

MONCHER, Karen Lou. 451 JUNCTION RD, STE 9903 53717 #056-05-1998 L1999 **CD** *020 †20

MONTGOMERY, Erwin B, Jr. 600 HIGHLAND AVE 53792 #035-06-1976 L2003 **N** *050 †75

MOON, Timothy David. 600 HIGHLAND AVE, CLINIC SCI CTR G5/341 53792 #919-03-1972 L1990 **U** *020 †95

MOORE, Andrew D. 440 SCIENCE DR, STE 200 53711 #043-01-1988 L1989 **P** *020 †18,75

MOORE, Mark Clifford. 1313 FISH HATCHERY RD, DEAN MEDICAL CENTER 53715 #007-02-1973 L1992 **OM IM** *020 †20,70

MOORE, Nathan Wesley. ■ 53719 #056-05-2006 L2008 **GS** *012

MOORE, Richard Roth, Jr. 600 HIGHLAND AVE 53792 #035-01-1990 L1996 **NEP IM** *020 †20

MOORE, Sarah Catherine. 600 HIGHLAND AVE, UNIVERSITY OF WI HOSPITAL 53792 #056-05-2002 L2003 **P** *100

MORLEDGE, John Howard. 202 S PARK ST 53715 #038-06-1952 L1959 **CD IM** *020 †20

MOSHER, Dean Fremont, Jr. 1300 UNIVERSITY AVE 53706 #024-01-1968 L1977 **HEM GP** *050 †20

MOSKOVLJEVIC, Predrag M. ■ 53718 #957-02-1985 L1994 **IM** *020 †20

MOSS, Hart Beaman. ■ 53705 #056-05-2008 *012

MOSS, Hubert Vencill, Jr. ■ 53717 #051-04-1962 L1968 **D** *020 †15

MOSS, Mark Hubert. 600 HIGHLAND AVE, ROOM K4/934 CSC #9988 53792 #056-05-1994 L1999 **AI** *020 †55,03

MOSTAGHIMI-TEHRANI, Ladan. 451 JUNCTION RD, STE 9903 53717 #517-01-1985 L1999 **P** *020 †75

MOTT, William James. 1 S PARK ST, UNIVERSITY OF WISCONSIN ME 53715 #056-05-1988 L1989 **ORS** *020 †40

MOUA, Teng. 600 HIGHLAND AVE, BOX 2454 53792 #026-04-2005 L2007 **IM** *012

MOUNT, Delora Louise. UNIVERSITY WISCONSIN HOSPI, 600 ISLAND AVE G5/360 53792 #016-11-1992 L2001 **PS** *020 †85,65

MOVAGHAR, Mansoor. 1025 REGENT ST 53715 #033-06-1995 L1999 **OPH PO** *020 †35

MUEGGENBERG, Jim Joseph. 600 HIGHLAND AVE, AVE H4/831-8320 53792 #030-06-2002 L2005 **PD** *100 †55

MUELLER, Gerald C. 1300 UNIVERSITY AVE 53706 #056-05-1946 L1947 **OS** *071

MULDOWNEY, Bridget Lynn. ■ 53726 #056-06-2004 **AN** *012

MULHERIN, Brian Patrick. ■ 53719 #016-43-2006 L2008 **IM** *012

MULKERIN, Daniel L. 600 HIGHLAND AVE, DEPARTMENT OF MEDICINE 53792 #041-02-1992 L1993 **OM** *020 †20

MULLINS, Maureen Ann. 4122 E TOWNE BLVD 53704 #056-05-1979 L1980 **OBG** *020 †30

MUMM, Gregory E. 600 HIGHLAND AVE, AVE H4/831-8320 53792 #037-01-2004 L2005 **RHU** *012 †20

MURDY, David Chas. 1821 S STOUGHTON RD 53716 #043-01-1984 L1987 **IM IMG** *020 †20

MURPHY, Jennifer Ann. 600 HIGHLAND AVE, AVE H4/831-8320 53792 #048-02-2002 L2003 **PS** *012

MURPHY, M John. ■ 53717 #030-06-1967 L1969 **N** *071 †75

MURPHY, Marion Estabrooks. ■ 53705 #056-05-1946 L1951 **A IM** *071 †20,03

MURRAY, David Robt. 2500 OVERLOOK TER, WILLIAM MIDDLETON MEM VA 53705 #016-11-1986 L2004 **CD IM** *040 †20

MUSA, Albert John. 1821 S STOUGHTON RD 53716 #016-01-1983 L1984 **IM FM** *020 †20,18

MUSAT, Alexander. 451 JUNCTION RD, STE 9903 53717 #858-02-1985 L1988 **GE** *020 †20

MUSSER, Wayne Eugene. 202 S PARK ST, MED SCHOOL 53715 #028-02-1972 L1979 **CD** *020 †20

MUSSEY, William Clive. 1313 FISH HATCHERY RD 53715 #026-04-1946 L1955 **GYN** *071 †30

MUSUNURU, Sandeepa. 600 HIGHLAND AVE, BOX 3236 53792 #056-05-2005 L2006 **GS** *012

MYERS, Franklin Lewis. 600 HIGHLAND AVE, DEPT OF OPHTH & VISUAL SVC 53792 #018-03-1957 L1964 **OPH** *071 †35

MYUNG, Karen Sookyung. 600 HIGHLAND AVE, UW HOSPITAL AND CLINICS 53792 #018-03-2002 L2004 **ORS** *012

NAKADA, Stephen Yuzo. 600 HIGHLAND AVE, G5/339 CLINICAL SCIENCE CE 53792 #035-45-1988 L1995 **U** *020 †95

NAKAMURA, Teruya. 600 HIGHLAND AVE, H4/360 CSC CARDIO SURGERY 53792 #572-85-1992 L2006 **GS** *100

NALWA, Sarvi. 1313 FISH HATCHERY RD, DEAN CLINIC 53715 #016-11-1996 L1997 **OTO HNS** *020 †45

NAMASIVAYAM, Dhanalakshmi. 202 S PARK ST, MERITER HOSPITAL 53715 #495-04-1993 L2005 **IM** *020 †20

NARANG, Ritu. 600 HIGHLAND AVE 53792 #016-06-2007 **P** *012

NASH, Lawrence Thomas. 700 RAY O VAC DR 53711 #005-11-1996 L2002 **CHP P** *020 †75

NASON, Katie Sue. 600 HIGHLAND AVE - H4/366 53792 #040-02-1997 L2007 **TS** *100 †85

NAVEED, Mohammad. 600 HIGHLAND AVE, STE 52793-3252 53792 #704-09-1992 L2000 **DR** *020

NAVSARIA, Dipesh. ■ 53705 #016-11-2006 L2008 **PD** *012

NAWALANY, Michal. ■ 53719 #759-01-2001 L2008 **VS** *012 †85

NAYLOR, Michelle Christin. ■ 53703 #026-04-2007 **OTO** *012

NEARY, Elizabeth J. 600 HIGHLAND AVE 53792 #056-05-1991 L1994 **PD** *020 †55

NEEKHRA, Aneesh. 600 HIGHLAND AVE, F4/336 53792 #495-34-2000 *100

NEHLS, Sarah Marie. 2870 UNIVERSITY AVE, STE 206 53705 #056-05-1999 L2005 **OPH** *100 †35

NEIDHART, Linda Renee. 1200 JOHN Q HAMMONS DR, STE 400 53717 #028-02-1996 L1997 **OBG** *020 †30

NEIDLINGER, Nikole A. H4/780 CSC, 600 HIGHLAND AVE, 53792 #021-01-2000 L2007 **GS** *020

NELSON, Josiah Daniel. 600 HIGHLAND AVE, AVE H4/831-8320 53792 #018-03-2004 L2005 **U** *012

NELSON, Margaret Viola. 600 HIGHLAND AVE 53792 #026-04-1966 L1968 **IM** *020 †20

NEMETH, Blaise Alexander. 2870 UNIVERSITY AVE, F4/336 53792 #056-05-1999 L2005 #028-02-1997 L1998 **PD OP** *020 †55

NESTLER, Kimberly Sharp. 124 W MIFFLIN ST 53703 #016-11-1985 L1988 **P** *020 †75

NETT, Jeniel Emily. 600 HIGHLAND AVE, UNIVERSITY OF WI HOSPITAL 53792 #056-05-2003 L2004 **IM** *012 †20

NETTUM, James Carl. 1313 FISH HATCHERY RD, DEAN CLINIC 53715 #056-05-1987 L1988 **FM** *020 †18

NEUHAUSER, Charles Allen. 1313 FISH HATCHERY RD 53715 #056-05-1961 L1962 **FM** *071

NEUMANN, Mark Allen. 600 HIGHLAND AVE, HOUSE STAFF AFFAIRS H4/831 53792 #028-34-1982 L2000 **CCP** *012 †55

NEWCOMER, Peter Daniel. 451 JUNCTION RD, STE 9903 53717 #056-05-1995 L2000 **IM** *020 †20

NEWMAN, Geri Sue. 46 OAK CREEK TRL 53717 #026-04-1996 L1997 **PD** *020 †55

NEWTON, Douglas Andrew. 600 HIGHLAND AVE, HOUSE STAFF AFFAIRS H4/831 53792 #056-05-2004 L2007 **CHP** *012

NG, Benton Yee. 600 HIGHLAND AVE H4/447 53792 #048-12-2006 L2008 **PD** *012

NGUYEN, Steve Minhthanh. ■ 53705 #056-05-2008 *012

NI, Oliver Kangwei. 1313 FISH HATCHERY RD, WUSM DEPT OF NEUROLOGY 53715 #011-03-2000 L2001 **N** *100 †75

NIELSEN, Christopher M. 202 S PARK ST, MERITER HOSPITAL 53715 #037-01-1999 L2002 **EM** *020 †16

NIELSEN, Christopher S. 600 HIGHLAND AVE 53792 #018-03-1992 L1997 **GS** *020 †85

NIELSEN, Julie Kay. ■ 53715 #056-05-1990 L1991 **CHP P** *020 †75

NIEMANN, David Bartlett. 600 HIGHLAND AVE 53792 #056-06-1993 L1995 **NS** *020

NIETO, Juan Carlos. ■ 53717 #035-01-2006 L2007 **OPH** *012

NIJHAWAN, Niraj. ■ 53726 #056-05-1992 L1994 **AN** *020 †05

NILLES, Eric James. ■ 53703 #056-05-2000 L2004 **EM** *020 †16

NILSSON, Torgny. UNIV HOSP DEPT UROL 53706 #858-01-1964 L1974 *020

NINAN, Jacob Anil. J5/230 CSC-2454, 600 HIGHLAND AVE 53792 #025-01-2002 L2004 **HEM** *012 †20

NIXDORF, Kathryn Elise. ■ 53704 #056-05-2006 L2008 **N** *012

NODINE, Robert Carlton. ■ 53705 #008-01-1955 L1957 **P** *071 †75

NOLTEN, Wolfram Eduard. 451 JUNCTION RD, STE 9903 53717 #407-16-1961 L1974 **END IM** *030 †20

NONDAHL, Susan R. 4410 REGENT ST 53705 #056-05-1981 L1982 **PD** *020 †55

NOON, John Francis. 752 N HIGH POINT RD 53717 #056-05-1979 L1980 **PS** *020 †85,65

NORBACK, Diane Hageman. 600 HIGHLAND AVE, B4/259 53792 #056-05-1974 L1975 **HMP PTH** *040 †50

NORD, Jo Ellen. ■ 53715 #040-02-2007 **FP** *012

NORDBY, Eugene Jorgen. ■ 53719 #056-05-1943 L1943 **ORS** *071 †40 ‡

NORK, Thomas Michael. 600 HIGHLAND AVE F4/3, UNIV WISCONSIN DEPT OF OPH 53792 #048-13-1980 L1985 **OPH** *062 †35

NORTHROP, Gretajo. 402 VIRGINIA TER 53726 #056-05-1965 L2002 **FM** *071

NOUR, Seema Elkhider. 600 HIGHLAND AVE #539-06-2003 L2007 **CD** *012 †20

NUENNINGHOFF, Dirk Markus. 1313 FISH HATCHERY RD 53715 #409-36-1997 L2003 **RHU** *020 †20

NYENHUIS, Sharmilee Maria. ■ 53719 #016-11-2003 L2006 **AI** *012 †20

OBASI, Chinyere Ngozi. 600 HIGHLAND AVE 53782 #690-01-1985 L1999 **NS** *020

OBERLEY, Terry De Wayne. 2500 OVERLOOK TER, RM A-24 53705 #016-06-1974 L1975 **PTH** *020 †50

O'BRIEN, Elizabeth Eilene. 4410 REGENT ST 53705 #016-45-1998 L1999 **IM** *020 †20

O'BRIEN, Michael Patrick. 600 HIGHLAND AVE, AVE H4/831-8320 53792 #018-03-2004 L2005 **DR** *012

O'BRIEN, Shawn D. 700 S PARK ST 53715 #056-06-1995 L1996 **EM** *020 †16

O'CONNELL, Barbara Jean. 20 S PARK ST, STE 450 53715 #056-05-1985 L1986 **OBG OS** *020 †30

O'CONNOR, Daniel Thomas. ■ 53703 #016-42-2005 L2007 **FM** *100

O'CONNOR, Erin Stephanie. ■ 53704 #054-04-2006 L2008 **GS** *012

O'CONNOR, Sheilah Marie. ■ 53705 #016-11-1967 L1999 **DR** *071 †80

O'CONNOR, Stacy Dorothy. UNIV HOSP AND CLINICS, E3-311 CLIN SCI CTR 53792 #035-47-2006 L2008 **DR** *012

ODEH, Yousef Mustafa. 600 HIGHLAND AVE, RM H4/366 53792 #654-01-2001 L2006 **TS** *012

O'DONNELL, Ann Marie. 600 HIGHLAND AVE H4/831, UW HOSPITAL AND CLINICS 53792 #026-04-2005 L2007 **OBG** *012

ODORICO, Jon Scott. 600 HIGHLAND AVE, CLINICAL SCIENCE CTR 53792 #035-19-1987 L1994 **GS** *020 †85

OGDEN, Meghan E. 451 JUNCTION RD, STE 9903 53717 #035-15-2001 L2005 **OBG** *020

OH, Simon Chin. 600 HIGHLAND AVE, BOX 5132 53792 #023-01-2004 L2006 **N** *012

OLESZKOWICZ, Andrew Mark. 701 DANE ST 53713 #025-07-2006 L2007 **FP** *012

OLIN, Justine Claire. ■ 53719 #023-07-2007 **PD** *012

OLSEN, Ward Alan. 600 HIGHLAND AVE, H6 /516 CLINICAL SCI CTR 53792 #056-05-1959 L1964 **GE IM** *071

OLSON, Daniel. 600 HIGHLAND AVE H4/447 53792 #025-12-2007 **PD** *012

OLSON, Elizabeth Christin. ■ 53705 #056-05-2008 *012

OLSON, Erik William. 600 HIGHLAND AVE, AVE H4/831-8320 53792 #056-06-2005 L2006 **DR** *012

OLSON, James Goodell. 1313 FISH HATCHERY RD 53715 #018-03-1979 L1983 **DR** *020 †80

OLSON, John Jerome. 202 S PARK ST - 4T, MADISON ANESTHESIOLOGY CON 53715 #056-05-1999 L2000 **AN** *020 †05

OLSON, Jordan Erik. ■ 53705 #056-05-2008 *012

OLSON, Reid Martin. 752 N HIGH POINT RD 53717 #040-02-1983 L1989 **AI IM** *020 †20,03
OLSON, Robert W. 4410 REGENT ST 53705 #037-01-1986 L1987 **IM** *020 †20
OLSON, Ronald Wayne. ■ 53705 #056-05-1957 L1958 **OBG MFM** *071 †30
OLSON, Terrah Jean. ■ 53718 #056-05-2008 *012
OMBRELLO, Christopher Ter. 600 HIGHLAND AVE, RM H4/831 53792 #025-07-2004 L2007 **IM** *100 †20
OMOHUNDRO, James Edward. 3434 E WASHINGTON AVE 53704 #018-03-1989 L1990 **PD** *020 †55
O'NEIL, Timothy John. 1821 S STOUGHTON RD 53716 #056-05-1983 L1985 **FM** *020 †18
OOSTERHOUS, George Edward. 6175 MINERAL POINT RD, # 302 53705 #056-05-1938 L1939 **OPH** *071 †55,35
ORECK, Steven Lewis. 1 S PARK ST, FL 7 53715 #021-05-1979 L1992 **HS ORS** *020 †40
ORIEL, Kathleen Anne. 3209 DRYDEN DR, NORTHEAST FAM MED CTR 53704 #028-03-1992 L1995 **FM** *040 †18
OROURKE, Ann Puryear. 600 HIGHLAND AVE H4/831, UNIVERSITY OF WI HOSPITAL 53792 #056-05-2002 L2004 **GS** *012
ORR, James Alexanderwa. ■ 53705 #026-04-2001 L2007 **CCS** *020
ORWIN, John Frederick. 600 HIGHLAND AVE, K4/7 CLINICAL SCIENCES CEN 53792 #025-01-1984 L1990 **ORS OSM** *020 †40
OSBORN, Sandra Ladehoff. 750 HIGHLAND AVE, UNIV. OF WIS. MED. SCHOOL 53705 #056-05-1970 L1973 **PD** *062 †55
OSTROV, Michael. 1265 JOHN Q HAMMONS DR, GROUP HEALTH COOPERATIVE 53717 #028-34-1978 L1979 **FM** *030 †18
OTITOJU, Foluke Abiodun. 202 S PARK ST 53715 #690-01-1991 L2005 **DR** *020 †80
OUELLETTE, John J. 20 S PARK ST 53715 #050-02-1960 L1962 **A IM** *071 †20,03
OUJIRI, James Aaron. 600 HIGHLAND AVE, BOX 2454 53792 #024-05-2005 L2007 **IM** *012
OWENS, Richard Lee. 1920 MONROE ST 53711 #017-20-1974 L1994 **GP OS** *020 †16
OZEL, Bora. 600 HIGHLAND AVE, AVE H4/831-8320 53792 #056-06-2002 L2005 **DR** *100 †80
OZERS, Lawrence James. 1313 FISH HATCHERY RD, DEAN MEDICAL CENTER 53715 #016-02-1993 L1994 **IM** *020 †20
PACK, Quinn Russell. ■ 53711 #025-01-2005 **IM** *012
PADBERG, Susan Elizabeth. 3800 REGENT ST, STE 1B 53705 #016-45-1984 L1988 **FM** *020 †18
PADDOCK, Elizabeth Denise. ■ 53715 #035-03-2008 *012
PAGEL, Christine Diamond. 600 HIGHLAND AVE, BOX 4108 53792 #056-05-2005 L2007 **PD** *012
PAK, Mary Huiok. 600 HIGHLAND AVE 53792 #041-09-1993 L2000 **IM** *030 †20
PAMMI, Bhawani Achyutalak. 6001 RESEARCH PARK BLVD 53719 #913-07-1995 **CHP** *020
PANBEHI, Bahman. ■ 53705 #056-05-2008 *012
PANDHI, Nancy Ananda. 777 S MILLS ST, UNIV OF WISC DEPT FAM MED 53715 #051-04-2001 L2004 **FM** *050 †18
PANKRATZ, Gerald Todd. J5/230 CSC-2454, 600 HIGHLAND AVENUE 53792 #038-40-2007 **IM** *012
PANSEGRAU, Kim John. 45 JUNCTION CT 53717 #021-06-1998 L1999 **GS** *020
PAOLONE, David Ralph. 1 S PARK ST, FL 7 53715 #016-02-1995 L2001 **U** *020 †95
PARDON, Edward John. 1 S PINCKNEY ST, BOX 1806 53703 #056-05-1988 L1989 **GP P** *062
PARK, John Kiewyone. 202 S PARK ST, BLDG 3 53715 #017-20-1998 L2004 **RNR** *020 †80
PARKS, H K. 3410 SUNSET DR 53705 #056-05-1944 L1945 **IM OS** *020
PARKS, Samuel David. 600 HIGHLAND AVE H4/831, UNIV OF WI HOSPITAL AND CL 53792 #056-06-2002 L2004 **AN** *020 †05
PARQUETTE, Brian Thos. 600 HIGHLAND AVE 53792 #038-40-1985 L1988 **EM IM** *020 †20
PARTON, Ronald Allen. 22 E MIFFLIN ST, STE 200 53703 #018-03-1983 L2001 **FM PHP** *062 †18
PASIC, Thomas Randall. 451 JUNCTION RD, STE 9903 53717 #030-06-1984 L1991 **OTO HNS** *020 †45
PASSINI, Jennifer Cleair. J5/230 CSC-2454, 600 HIGHLAND AVENUE 53792 #016-01-2006 L2008 **IM** *012
PATEL, Ashvinkumar I. 2500 OVERLOOK TER 53705 #905-01-1966 L1976 **CD IM** *020 †20
PATEL, Nirav Jay. ■ 53703 #010-02-2004 L2008 **NS** *012
PATEL, Rakesh R. 600 HIGHLAND AVE, K4/B100 53792 #017-20-1999 L2003 **RO** *020 †80
PATEL, Vivek Ravindra. 2870 UNIVERSITY AVE STE 10 53705 #068-01-2001 L2006 **OPH N** *020
PATRO, Pragyan. 1200 JOHN Q HAMMONS DR, STE 400 53717 #495-13-1992 L2001 **IM** *020 †20
PATZ, Jonathan Alan. ■ 53726 #038-06-1987 L1989 **OM FM** *020 †18,70
PATZNER, Jill Marie. 600 HIGHLAND AVE, AVE H4/831-8320 53792 #056-05-2005 L2006 **AN** *012
PAUL, Caroline Rose. 600 HIGHLAND AVE, H4/454CLINICAL SCIENCE CEN 53792 #016-43-1994 L2003 **PD** *020 †55
PAUL, Russell Kelly. 600 HIGHLAND AVE 53792 #010-03-1992 L2004 **VIR** *020 †80
PAULI, Richard Martin. 1500 HIGHLAND AVE 53705 #016-02-1975 L1980 **CG PD** *020 †19
PEACOCK, Jeremy Lee. 600 HIGHLAND AVE, UW HOSPITAL AND CLINICS 53792 #028-34-2003 L2004 **PYG** *012
PEARCE, Robert Allen. B6/340 600 HIGHLAND AVE BO, DEPT OF ANESTHESIOLOGY 53792 #051-01-1986 L1989 **AN** *050 †05
PEARLMAN, Mary. 236 LAKEWOOD BLVD 53704 #025-07-1971 L1973 **CHP P** *020 †75
PEARLMAN, Melvyn Alan. 202 S PARK ST 53715 #020-02-1970 L1973 **EM** *020 †16
PEARSON, Jane King. 1821 S STOUGHTON RD 53716 #056-06-1989 L1990 **IM** *020 †20
PEASLEE, Douglas Fox. ■ 53711 #056-05-1987 L1988 **IM** *020 †20
PELLEGRINO, Ernest A, Jr. 1313 FISH HATCHERY RD 53715 #056-05-1964 L1966 **ORS** *020 †40
PELLETT, John Roger. 600 HIGHLAND AVE, CLINICAL SCIENCE CENTER 53792 #041-01-1954 L1956 **TS PDS** *020 †85,90
PELLEY, Elaine Michelle. 451 JUNCTION RD, STE 9903 53717 #005-12-2001 L2006 **END IM** *100 †20
PELLINO, Thomas Michael. 202 S PARK ST 53715 #016-01-1982 L1986 **AN** *020 †05
PENDLEY, Sarah Ruth. 600 HIGHLAND AVE, HOUSE STAFF AFFAIRS 53792 #039-01-2004 L2007 **PTH** *012
PENLY, Don H. ■ 53719 #018-03-1941 L1946 **GP** *071
PENZOTTI, Jennifer Louise. 2500 OVERLOOK TER, DEPARTMENT OF CARDIOLOGY, 53705 #016-02-1999 L2006 **CD** *020 †20
PEREZ, Efrain. 1313 FISH HATCHERY RD 53715 #042-01-1986 L2003 **N** *020 †75
PERLMAN, Scott Bradley. 600 HIGHLAND AVE, STE E-3/366 53792 #016-42-1980 L1981 **NM OM** *020 †28
PERNA, Giuseppe. 330 E LAKESIDE ST 53715 #561-19-1958 L1965 **GE IM** *020
PEROUANSKY, Michael. 600 HIGHLAND AVE, RM B6319 53792 #409-40-1986 L2002 *020
PESKO, Meghan Catherine. ■ 53704 #056-05-2008 *012
PETERS, David Kellogg. 36 S BROOKS ST 53715 #056-05-1995 L1997 **HMP ATP** *020 †50
PETERS, Henry Augustus. ■ 53711 #056-05-1945 L1946 **N P** *071 †75
PETERSON, Andrew Robert. 600 HIGHLAND AVE, AVE H4/831-8320 53792 #056-05-2004 L2006 **PD** *020 †55
PETERSON, Laura Alice. ■ 53719 #056-05-2008 *012
PETERSON, Michael John. 6001 RESEARCH PARK BLVD, 6001 RESEARCH PARK BLVD 53719 #056-06-2001 L2002 **P** *100 †75
PETRICH, Adam Matthew. 600 HIGHLAND AVE, AVE H4/831-8320 53792 #016-11-2005 L2006 **IM** *012
PETROVIC-DOVAT, Lidija. 1313 FISH HATCHERY RD 53715 #957-07-1992 L2005 **CHP** *020 †75
PFAEHLER, Gothardt Thos. 780 REGENT ST, STE 300 53715 #056-05-1966 L1967 **P FM** *020 †75
PFAU, Patrick Raymond. 451 JUNCTION RD, STE 9903 53717 #016-06-1994 L2001 **GE** *020 †20
PFEFFERKORN, Branden Jame. ■ 53726 #056-05-2008 *012
PHELAN, John Michael. 1821 S STOUGHTON RD 53716 #035-45-1984 L1996 **CD IM** *020 †20
PHELPS, Lynn A. ■ 53703 #025-01-1953 L1973 **FM** *072 †18
PHILLIPS, Jeffrey Michael. ■ 53703 #056-05-2008 *012
PHROMRATANAPONGSE, P. UNIV WISCONSIN HOSP 53792 #891-04-1979 L1985 **DR** *100
PIASECKI, Justin Howard. 600 HIGHLAND AVE RM G5-361, HOSPITAL AND 53792 #047-05-2002 L2003 **PS** *100
PICKHARDT, Perry Joseph. 202 S PARK ST 53715 #025-01-1995 L2003 **DR** *020 †80
PIERCE, Surya John. ■ 53715 #056-05-2007 **FP** *012
PIERNER, Tammy Ann. 301 TROY DR, HLTH INST 53704 #056-05-1998 L1999 **P** *020
PILLAI, Krishna Ragnar. 202 S PARK ST, BLDG 3 53715 #016-01-1996 L2001 **DR** *020 †80
PINCHOT, Scott Nathan. 600 HIGHLAND AVE, BOX 3236 53792 #056-06-2005 **GS** *012
PINNEY, Tanner Austin. ■ 53719 #056-05-2006 L2008 **AN** *012
PIRSCH, John David. 600 HIGHLAND AVE 53792 #026-04-1980 L1981 **IM** *020 †20
PITHAN, Mark Allen. 600 HIGHLAND AVE, UNIVERSITY OF HOSPITAL & C 53792 #016-45-2002 L2003 **SME** *012 †75
PITOT, Henry Clement. 1400 UNIVERSITY AVE 53706 #021-01-1955 L1961 **OS PTH** *071 †50
PITT, Susan Clare. ■ 53704 #056-06-2005 **GS** *012
PITTS, Frederick Robt. ■ 53715 #035-45-1954 L1958 **NS** *071 †25
PIZER, Evan Frederick. 2870 UNIVERSITY AVE, DOCTOR'S OFFICE 53705 #056-05-1959 L1960 **CHP P** *071 †75
PLETTA, Karen Harris. 600 HIGHLAND AVE 53792 #056-05-1990 L1996 **PD** *020 †55 ‡
PLUMB, Amy Joanne Nelson. 5249 E TERRACE DR, STE 9952 53718 #026-08-1988 L1989 **PD** *020 †55
PLZAK, George John. 1313 FISH HATCHERY RD 53715 #016-02-1964 L1968 **ORS** *020 †40
PODEIN, Rian John. 621 SCIENCE DR 53711 #041-13-2002 L2003 **FM** *020 †18
POE, Susan Lorick. 451 JUNCTION RD, UW HEALTH WEST CLINIC: WOM 53717 #045-01-1984 L1991 **IM** *020 †20
POI, Elizabeth Ann. 2202 S PARK ST 53713 #056-05-1997 L2006 **FM** *020 †18
POLYAK, Frank Paul. 202 S PARK ST 53715 #056-05-1975 L1977 **IM ID** *020 †20
POONAWALLA, Tasneem Aziz. 1 S PARK ST, 7TH FL 53715 #048-02-2005 L2007 **D** *012
POORE, Samuel Oliver. 600 HIGHLAND AVE, AVE H4/831-8320 53792 #043-01-2004 L2006 **PS** *012
POPIC, Peter Mario. 600 HIGHLAND AVE, OFC F8/347 53792 #056-05-1982 L1984 **AN** *020 †05
PORTER, Emily Bernice. 777 S MILLS ST, WISCONSIN 53715 #056-06-2006 L2008 **FP** *012
PORTER, James Frederick. 1200 JOHN Q HAMMONS DR, STE 400 53717 #056-06-1980 L1985 **RHU IM** *020 †20
POTTER, Beth Ellen. 701 DANE ST, WINGRA CLINIC 53713 #016-01-1996 L1997 **FM** *020 †18
POTTER, Heather A D. 451 JUNCTION RD, STE 9903 53717 #018-03-2001 L2003 **OPH** *020 †35
POWELL, Mario Ralph. 3814 DOLPHIN DR 53719 #016-11-2001 L2004 **NPM** *020 †55
POWELL, Robert Ian. 7102 MINERAL POINT RD 53717 #038-43-1996 L1997 **IM** *020 †20
PRENDERGAST, Edward. 1200 JOHN Q HAMMONS DR, STE 400 53717 #016-02-1973 L1974 **ON HEM** *020 †20
PRIBBENOW, Bridget Anne. 1821 S STOUGHTON RD 53716 #056-05-2003 L2005 **FM** *020 †18
PRICE, Patrick. PO BOX 8667 53708 #003-01-1983 L1985 **PD** *030 †55
PRIEST, Geoffrey Rush. 202 S PARK ST 53715 #016-06-1974 L1980 **PUD CCM** *030 †20
PROCTOR, Lester Talley. 600 HIGHLAND AVE, B6 319 CLINICAL SCIENCE CT 53792 #056-06-1982 L1987 **AN** *020 †05
PROCTOR, Richard Allan. 600 HIGHLAND AVE, DEPT OF MEDICINE; DEPT OF 53792 #025-01-1970 L1976 **ID IM** *050 †20
PROKUSKI, Laura Jean. 600 HIGHLAND AVE 53792 #018-03-1992 L1998 **ORS** *020 †40
PROPECK, Pamela Ann. 202 S PARK ST, BLDG 3 53715 #024-05-1986 L1987 **DR** *020 †80
PROUT, Tyler Marshall. 600 HIGHLAND AVE, AVE H4/831-8320 53792 #018-03-1997 L2005 **DR** *020 †80
PRUNUSKE, Jacob Paul. 1552 UNIVERSITY AVE, RM 201D 53726 #056-05-2000 L2006 **FM** *020 †18 ‡
PRYDE, Peter Girard. 202 S PARK ST, MADISON ANESTHESIA CONSULT 53715 #025-07-1985 L1998 **AN** *020 †30,19,05
PRZYBELSKI, Robert John. 1133 RISSER RD . 53792 #056-05-1979 L1991 **FM** *050 †18
PUCCETTI, Diane Marie. 600 HIGHLAND AVE RM K4426, U WI CHILDRENS HOSP PEDS 53792 #038-43-1985 L1991 **PHO PD** *020 †55
PUCHALSKY, David Ralph. 1 S PARK ST 7TH FL, UW HEALTH 53715 #028-02-1983 L1989 **D IM** *020 †20,15
PYLE, Garrold M, II. K4718 600 HIGHLAND AVENUE 53792 #056-05-1984 L1985 **NO HNS** *020 †45
QUALEY, Peter Eric. 202 S PARK ST 53715 #056-05-1991 L1995 **AN** *020 †05
QUANDT, Courtney E. 1 S PARK ST 53715 #056-06-1952 L1953 **GP** *020
QUANN, Philip John. 600 HIGHLAND AVE, RM H4/831-UNIV HOSP 53792 #036-01-2004 L2007 **PTH** *012
QUI, Catherine O. ■ 53705 #748-01-1988 **OPH** *100
QUIAMBAO, Leonila Songco. ■ 53704 #748-02-2002 L2004 **IM** *020 †20
QUIGLEY, Patricia Daniell. ■ 53705 #024-07-2006 L2007 **PD** *012
RABAGO, David Patrick. 3209 DRYDEN DR 53704 #056-05-1997 L1999 **FM** *020 †18
RABSON, Laurel Dale. 1200 JOHN Q HAMMONS DR, STE 400 53717 #035-48-1992 L1993 **IM** *020 †20
RACA, Gordana. 465 HENRY MALL, UW CYTOGENETICS SERVICE 53706 #957-07-1992 *100 †19
RACHU, Gregory. ■ 53705 #056-05-2008 *012
RAETZ, Christian R H. 420 HENRY MALL 53706 #024-01-1973 L1978 **IM** *100
RAHKO, Peter Saml. 600 HIGHLAND AVE, CARDIO MED G7-343 CSC 53792 #026-04-1979 L1985 **CD IM** *020 †20
RAJPAL, Sharad. 600 HIGHLAND AVE, UWI HOSPITAL & CLINIC 53792 #056-05-2002 L2003 **NS** *012
RAMAIYA, Dharmindra. 1821 S STOUGHTON RD 53716 #037-01-1997 L1999 **PYG** *020 †75
RAMAMURTHY, Rekha. 600 HIGHLAND AVE, H4/568 CSC(5148) 53792 #016-02-2000 L2006 **END** *020 †20

■ = Address Information Privacy Protected

RAMAN, Prasanna. 7102 MINERAL POINT RD 53717 #496-38-1983 L2001 **NPM** *020 †55

RAMIREZ, Guillermo. 600 HIGHLAND AVE 53792 #264-01-1958 L1968 **ON PO** *071

RAMIREZ, Lincoln Franklin. 600 HIGHLAND AVE, UWHC DEPT NEUROSURGERY 53792 #016-11-1971 L1979 **OS HNS** *040 †25

RANHEIM, Erik Arthur. 600 HIGHLAND AVE 53792 #026-04-1996 L2003 **PTH** *020 †50

RAO, Anupama Kumar. 600 HIGHLAND AVE, AVE H4/831-8320 53792 #038-06-2004 L2006 **IM** *020 †20

RAPKIN, Mitchell Arthur. 4 W TOWNE MALL, 202 S PARK STREET 53719 #056-05-1960 L1961 **AN** *020

RAVAL, Amish Naresh. 451 JUNCTION RD, STE 9903 53717 #065-06-1996 L2005 **CD** *020 †20

RAVAL, Nilam Amin. 752 N HIGH POINT RD 53717 #654-01-1999 L2005 **FM** *020 †18

RAY, Soma. ■ 53719 #056-05-2008 L2007 *012

RAZA, Syed Abbas. 600 HIGHLAND AVE 53792 #704-21-1996 L2002 **END** *100 †20

REBSAMEN, Susan Lynne. 600 HIGHLAND AVE E1/334, RADIOLOGY DEPT. 53792 #004-01-1987 L2007 **RNR** *020 †80

REDDIG, Robert Thomas. 53704 #019-02-2006 L2007 **N** *012

REDFORD, Peter Alan. 202 S PARK ST 53715 #019-02-1993 L1994 **ID** *020 †20

REDMER, Jacqueline Sue. ■ 53715 #056-05-2007 *012

REED, Ann Sheehy. H6/169 CSC MC2454, 600 HIGHLAND AVE 53792 #026-08-2000 L2005 **IM** *100 †20

REED, Karen Alice. 3209 DRYDEN DR 53704 #025-12-2005 L2006 **FP** *012

REED, Steven Wayne. 1821 S STOUGHTON RD 53716 #026-04-1991 L1996 **FM** *020 †18

REEDER, Brian Michael. 1821 S STOUGHTON RD 53716 #056-05-1999 L2003 **PD PSM** *020 †55

REEDER, Scott Brian. 1 S PARK ST, FL 7 53715 #023-07-1999 L2005 **DR** *020 †80

REGAN, Margo Hoover. 600 HIGHLAND AVE, DEPARTMENT OF PEDIATRICS 53792 #016-11-1990 L2002 **PHO PD** *020 †55

REGNE-KARLSSON, Maud H. ■ 53711 #858-02-1967 L1991 **PD GPM** *020 †55,70

REHM, Jennifer Leigh. ■ 53704 #011-03-2006 L2008 **PD** *012

REICH, Richard Merrit. 600 HIGHLAND AVE, DEPT OF MEDICINE 53792 #035-20-1975 L1976 **IMG ID** *020 †20

REICHELDERFER, Mark. 4410 REGENT ST 53705 #035-01-1974 L1977 **GE IM** *020 †20

REICHMUTH, Tracy Suzanne. 7102 MINERAL POINT RD 53717 #030-05-1999 L2000 **FM** *020 †18

REIKERSDORFER, Christian. 707 S MILLS ST, ST. MARY'S HOSPITAL 53715 #051-01-1991 L2004 **AN** *020 †05

REINKE, Lisa Louise. 202 S PARK ST 53715 #056-05-1998 L1999 **AN** *020

REIS, Jacqueline J Rebbe. ■ 53704 #030-06-1950 L1957 **OS** *075

REIZNER, George Terry. 1 S PARK ST, 7TH FL 53715 #010-01-1980 L1981 **D** *020 †15

REMINGTON, Patrick L. 610 WALNUT ST RM 760, UNIV OF WISC MADISON 53726 #056-05-1981 L1988 **PHP GPM** *040 †70

RENIER, Marsha. 2500 OVERLOOK TER 53705 #046-01-1985 L1986 **IM** *020 †20

RESCHKE, Julia Kruger. ■ 53705 #051-01-1984 L1987 **P** *020 †75

RESNICK, Daniel Karel. 621 SCIENCE DR 53711 #041-01-1991 L1998 **NS** *020 †20

REYNOLDS, Ernest W, Jr. ■ 53717 #039-01-1946 L1972 **CD IM** *020 †20

RICE, Gregory Maurice. 600 HIGHLAND AVE, AVE H4/831-8320 53792 #056-05-2000 L2002 **MG** *100 †55,19

RICE, Justin Chad. J5/230 CSC-2454, 600 HIGHLAND AVE 53792 #030-05-2001 L2004 **GE** *100

RICE, Laurel Wysong. 1 S PARK ST STE 555 53715 #007-02-1983 L2007 **GO** *020 †30

RICE, Richard Lee. 309 W WASHINGTON AVE 53703 #018-03-1968 L1973 **PD** *020 †55

RICH, Mark Frederick. 1313 FISH HATCHERY RD 53715 #047-05-1988 L1989 **DR** *020 †80

RICHARDS, Gregory Michael. 600 HIGHLAND AVE, UW - RAD/ONCO CLNC 53792 #033-05-2001 L2007 **RO** *012

RICHARDS, Norman Roland. 1821 S STOUGHTON RD, EAST CLINIC 53716 #047-05-1985 L1986 **U** *020 †95

RICHMOND, Burke Samuel. 600 HIGHLAND AVE, K4768 CLINICAL SCIENCE CEN 53792 #050-02-1996 L1997 **FM** *020 †18

RICKETTS, Karene Joanna. 600 HIGHLAND AVE, AVE H4/831-8320 53792 #056-05-2004 L2005 **AN** *012

RICKMAN, Christian Jacob. 707 S MILLS ST 53715 #056-06-2004 L2007 **EM** *100

RIEDESEL, Erica Lynn. ■ 53703 #018-03-2006 **PD** *012

RIESELBACH, Richard Edgar. 750 HIGHLAND AVE, RM 2126 53705 #024-01-1958 L1960 **NEP IM** *071 †20

RIFKIN, Allan Ross. 1552 UNIVERSITY AVE 53726 #020-12-1979 L1980 **FM N** *020 †18

RIHERD, Jody Michelle. 600 HIGHLAND AVE, AVE H4/831-8320 53792 #046-01-2003 L2006 **DR** *012

RIKKERS, Layton Frederick. 600 HIGHLAND AVE - H4/710, DEPARTMENT OF SURGERY 53792 #005-11-1970 L1996 **GS** *020 †85

RINDFLEISCH, James Adams, Jr. 621 SCIENCE DR 53711 #023-07-2000 L2001 **FM** *020 †18

RINDFLEISCH, Kirsten S. 701 DANE ST 53713 #023-07-2000 L2001 **FM** *020 †18

RINGWALA, Sukit Mayur. ■ 53705 #056-05-2008 *012

RIS, Hania W. 600 HIGHLAND AVE 53792 #869-07-1937 L1951 **ID PD** *062 †55

RISSE, Guenter Bernhard. ■ 53711 #132-01-1958 L1972 **OS** *071

RITTER, Dorothy Ann. 707 S MILLS ST, ST MARY'S HOSPITAL MEDICAL 53715 #026-04-1973 L1985 **NPM** *020 †55

RITTER, Mark Alfred. 600 HIGHLAND AVE 53792 #011-02-1984 L1988 **RO** *020 †80

RITTER, Michael Wm. 20 S PARK ST, STE 460 53715 #056-05-1986 L1987 **PDA PD** *020 †55,03

RIZK, Mary Nabil N. ■ 53715 #915-02-1992 L1999 **END** *020

ROBERSON, Erica Nadine. ■ 53713 #018-03-2005 L2007 **IM** *012

ROBERTS, Leigh Milton. 8007 EXCELSIOR DR 53717 #016-11-1947 L1954 **P** *040 †75

ROBERTS, Richard Guy. 777 S MILLS ST, DEPT FAM MED 53715 #010-01-1980 L1983 **FM** *020 †18 ‡

ROBINS, H Ian. 600 HIGHLAND AVE, DEPT ONCOLOGY 53792 #024-05-1976 L1977 **ON IM** *050 †20

ROCK, Michael Jos. 600 HIGHLAND AVE K4/946, UNIV OF WI OSP & CLINICS 53792 #039-01-1983 L1986 **PDP** *020 †55

ROCQUE, Brandon George. 600 HIGHLAND AVE, BOX 8660 53792 #028-02-2005 L2006 **NS** *012

RODRIGUEZ, Justo. ■ 53705 #847-04-1957 L1968 **R RO** *071

ROETHLISBERGER, Marie L. 5618 ODANA RD 53719 #026-04-1996 L1997 **FM** *020 †18

ROGALL, Benjamin. 2500 OVERLOOK TER, DEPT. OF RADIOLOGY 53705 #008-01-1990 L1991 **DR** *020 †80

ROGERS, Carolyn Ruth. ■ 53717 #041-12-2007 **PS** *012

ROGERS, Roby L. 600 HIGHLAND AVE 53792 #007-02-1987 L1999 **BBK** *020 †50

ROGERSON, John Sargent. 2 SCIENCE CT, UNIV RESEARCH PARK 53711 #018-03-1975 L1976 **ORS** *020 †40

ROGGE, Paula Ann. ■ 53713 #016-11-1980 L2006 **EM FM** *020 †18

ROGGENSACK, Geo Frederic. 6601 GRAND TETON PLZ, MADISON RADIOLOGISTS SC 53719 #018-03-1962 L1970 **R NM** *071 †80,28

ROHAN, James S. 625 W WASHINGTON AVE 53703 #016-45-1978 L1979 **P** *020 †75

ROLLE, Timothy Jon. ■ 53705 #056-05-2008 *012

ROLLI, Martha Leigh. 600 HIGHLAND AVE 53792 #026-08-1992 L1993 **P** *020 †75

ROLNICK, David Jay. 1 S PARK ST, FL 7 53715 #035-15-1968 L1973 **ORS OSM** *020 †40

ROMAN, Katharine Mae. ■ 53705 #056-05-2007 *012

ROMER, Laurel Lynne. 451 JUNCTION RD, STE 9903 53717 #023-01-1997 L2002 **IM** *020 †20

RONEY, Ellen Elizabeth. 5249 E TERRACE DR, GHC CLINIC 53718 #016-11-1977 L2006 **IM** *020 †20

RONGSTAD, Kurt Marshall. 1 S PARK ST 53715 #056-05-1990 L1995 **ORS** *020 †40

RONGSTAD, Meriel Susan. 20 S PARK ST 53715 #056-05-1990 L1996 **PD** *020 †55

ROSE, James Wm, Jr. 1313 FISH HATCHERY RD 53715 #036-01-1964 L1970 **IM PUD** *071

ROSE, Jerzy E. 1300 UNIVERSITY AVE 53706 #759-01-1931 L1941 **N** *075

ROSE, John Gerard, Jr. 1025 REGENT ST, DEAN HEALTH SYSTEMS 53715 #036-07-1997 L2001 **OPH** *020 †35

ROSIN, Anne Ellen. 2880 UNIVERSITY AVE, 1 SOUTH PARK ST 7TH FLOOR 53705 #056-05-1993 L1995 **D** *020 †15

ROSIN, Louis R. 330 E LAKESIDE ST 53715 #056-06-1952 L1953 **FM** *030 †18

ROSS, Jeffrey. ■ 53705 #028-02-1969 **ON** *040

ROSSI, Alessandro Ranieri. 1313 FISH HATCHERY RD 53715 #297-01-1988 L1990 **DR** *020 †80

ROSSI, Solveig Otzen. 707 S MILLS ST 53715 #297-01-1988 L1991 **PTH** *062 †50

ROTH, Harry. 1025 REGENT ST, DAVIS DUEHR DEAN 53715 #038-06-1962 L1966 **OPH** *020 †35

ROTHBERGER, Edward H. 600 HIGHLAND AVE, UNIVERSITY OF WI HOSPITAL 53792 #036-05-2002 L2004 **IM** *020 †20

ROTH-CLINE, Michelle Deni. ■ 53705 #056-05-2008 *012

ROTHSTEIN, Laurence Ross. 202 S PARK ST - 4 53715 #056-05-1984 L1985 **AN IM** *020,05

ROTTER, Royal. ■ 53711 #056-05-1947 L1948 **IM** *071 †20

ROWE, George Giles. 330 E LAKESIDE ST 53715 #056-05-1945 L1946 **CD IM** *071 †20

ROWE, Mary Goehle. 20 S PARK ST, STE 405 53715 #056-05-1985 L1986 **FM** *020 †18

ROWLEY, Howard Andrew. 6002 S HIGHLANDS AVE 53705 #028-02-1985 L1999 **DR N** *020 †75,80

RUCHALA, Joanna Blythe. 20 S PARK ST, STE 207 53715 #056-05-2003 L2004 **IM** *020 †20

RUDAT, Karl August. 1200 JOHN Q HAMMONS DR, STE 400 53717 #056-05-1973 L1977 **OBG** *020 †30

RUDIN, Nathan J. 5249 E TERRACE DR 53718 #023-07-1991 L2000 **PM PME** *020 †60

RUDMAN, Sherwin Michael. 7102 MINERAL POINT RD 53717 #016-11-1974 L1977 **OBG** *020 †30

RUEFENACHT, Daniel A. 600 HIGHLAND AVE 53792 #869-02-1981 *100

RUNCHEY, Michelle Marie. 600 HIGHLAND AVE, RM H4 831 UNIV OF WISC 53792 #019-02-2003 L2004 **HO** *012 †20

RUNO, James Russell. 600 HIGHLAND AVE, DEPARTMENT OF MEDICINE 53792 #017-20-1997 L2004 **PCC** *020 †20

RUSCH, Brett Daniel. 600 HIGHLAND AVE, BOX 9601 53792 #056-05-2005 L2007 **P** *012

RUSCHER, Ann Elizabeth. 600 HIGHLAND AVE, B6 319 CLINICAL SCIENCE CT 53792 #056-05-1991 L1993 **AN** *020 †05

RUSS, Andrew Joseph. 600 HIGHLAND AVE, HOSPITAL AND 53792 #038-45-2006 **GS** *012

RUSSELL, Douglas Campbell. 2500 OVERLOOK TER, CARDIOLOGY SECTION 53705 #917-03-1969 L1997 **CD** *020 †20

RUSSELL, Paul Lewis. ■ 53711 #067-01-1960 L1991 **IM** *071

RUSY, Deborah Ann. 600 HIGHLAND AVE, B6 319 CLINICAL SCIENCE CE 53792 #056-05-1992 L1994 **AN** *020 †05

RUTECKI, Paul Anthony. 600 HIGHLAND AVE 53792 #035-06-1978 L1992 **N CN** *050 †75

RUTKOWSKI, Anthony John. 600 HIGHLAND AVE, AVE H4/831-8320 53792 #056-05-2004 L2005 **DR** *012

RYAN, Gerald Gene. 1552 UNIVERSITY AVE 53726 #038-43-1978 L1991 **FM** *040 †18

RYAN, Pamela Marie. 451 JUNCTION RD, UW HEALTH WEST CLINIC 53717 #018-03-1997 L1998 **IM** *020 †20

SABB, Patricia Camille. 780 REGENT ST, # 306 53715 #025-01-1993 L1997 **OPH** *020 †35

SADOWSKI, Elizabeth. 600 HIGHLAND AVE, E3/311 CLINICAL SCIENCE CT 53792 #016-43-1996 L2001 **DR** *020 †80

SAFDAR, Nasia. 2501 WHITLOCK ST 53719 #704-25-1995 L1999 **IM** *100 †20

SAGER, Julie Anne. ■ 53726 #671-02-1998 L2007 **FM** *100 †18

SAGER, Matthew Steven. 707 S MILLS ST, ST MARYS HOSP 53715 #056-05-2001 L2006 **P** *020 †75

SAID, Adnan. 451 JUNCTION RD, STE 9903 53717 #704-25-1995 L1999 **GE HEP** *050 †20

SAINI, Narinder Kumar. 301 TROY DR 53704 #495-69-1971 L1981 **P** *020

SALAMAT, Shahriar M. 600 HIGHLAND AVE, U.W. CLINICAL SCIENCE CENT 53792 #422-01-1985 L1994 **ATP NP** *020 †50

SALIH, Sana Mohamed. 600 HIGHLAND AVE, H4/628 53792 #848-01-1985 L2007 **OBG** *100 †20,30

SALINAS, Pedro Daniel. 600 HIGHLAND AVE, H6/169 CSC 53792 #649-30-2002 L2007 **IM** *100 †20

SALINGER, Robert Jules. 780 REGENT ST 53715 #025-01-1971 L1973 **P** *020 †75

SALKOWSKI, Lonie Rose. 1 S PARK ST, FL 7 53715 #056-06-1991 L1992 **DR** *020 †80,28

SALTER, Benjamin Scott. 701 DANE ST 53713 #021-01-2005 L2006 **FP** *012

SALYAPONGSE, Amorn Neil. 1 S PARK ST, FL 7 53715 #016-06-1995 L2006 **PS** *020 †65

SAMANIEGO, Edgar Andres. 600 HIGHLAND AVE, AVE H4/831-8320 53792 #319-01-2000 L2006 **N** *012

SAMPLE, Katherine Scanlon. 600 HIGHLAND AVE, UNIVERSITY OF WI HOSPITAL 53792 #054-04-2001 L2004 **OBG** *020

SANCHEZ, Cheryl P. 600 HIGHLAND AVE, DEPT OF PEDIATRICS,H41444 53792 #748-02-1986 L1998 **PN PD** *050 †55

SANCHEZ, Richard. 600 HIGHLAND AVE H4/823, UNIVERSITY HOSPITAL & CLIN 53792 #017-20-1998 L1999 **RNR** *100 †80

SANDGREN BIRKELO, Maria E. 451 JUNCTION RD, STE 9903 53717 #858-02-1985 L1995 **OBG** *020 †30

SANDHU, Neil. ■ 53705 #056-05-2008 *012

SANDIN, John Allen, III. 20 S PARK ST, STE 207 53715 #025-01-1993 L1994 **NS** *020

SANGHVI, Shalin Rajendra. J5/230 CSC-2454, 600 HIGHLAND AVE 53792 #025-12-2002 L2004 **NEP** *020 †20

SANNER, Louis Anthony. 777 S MILLS ST, FAM MED & PRAC 53715 #005-11-1983 L1988 **FM EM** *040 †18

SANTANA, Marcus Guena. 1313 FISH HATCHERY RD 53715 #187-01-1995 L2000 **PCC** *020 †20

SANYAL, Amit. 1200 JOHN Q HAMMONS DR, SAUK TRAILS PLZ STE 400 53717 #495-53-1988 L1995 **ON** *020 †20

SARAKBI, Housam Aldeen. 600 HIGHLAND AVE, H61363 RHEUMATOLOGY 53792 #875-01-1990 L1998 **RHU** *020 †20

SARDA, Rakesh. 36 S BROOKS ST 53715 #495-53-1991 L1997 **PTH** *100 †50

SARTO, Gloria Elizabeth. 202 S PARK ST, MERITER HOSP 6 WEST 53715 #056-05-1958 L1960 **OBG OS** *071 †30

SASSE, Frank Jos. 600 HIGHLAND AVE, ANESTHLGY DEPT B6/319 CSC 53792 #020-12-1975 L1976 **AN** *040 †05

SASSE, Mark Frederic. 451 JUNCTION RD, STE 9903 53717 #035-45-1994 L2005 **IC** *020 †20

SASSE, Sara. ■ 53719 #016-11-2001 **PD** *100

SATTIN, Justin Alan. 600 HIGHLAND AVE, BOX 5132 53792 #041-02-2000 L2006 **N OS** *020 †75

SAUER, Stephen Kostur. 2828 MARSHALL CT, STE 106 53705 #038-06-1997 L2001 **OPH** *020 †35

SAUERHAMMER, Tina Marie. 600 HIGHLAND AVE, BOX 3236 53792 #056-05-2003 L2006 **GS** *012

SAVIELLO, George M. 600 HIGHLAND AVE B6/319, OF WISC HOSPITAL AND CLINI 53792 #016-06-1967 L1969 **AN** *020 †05

SAWETAWAN, Chiravudh. 226 CORPORATE DR, REPRODUCTIVE HEALTH AND 53714 #016-01-1988 L2002 **OBG REN** *020 †30

SAWMA, Vincent Anthony, Jr. J5/230 CSC-2454, 600 HIGHLAND AVENUE 53792 #038-41-2007 **IM** *012

SCALLON, Peggy Sue. 6001 RESEARCH PARK BLVD 53719 #056-05-1992 L1995 **CHP** *020 †75

SCHAEFER, Daniel William. ■ 53704 #056-05-2000 L2006 **FM** *020 †18

SCHAEFER, Holly Elizabeth. 6001 RESEARCH PARK BLVD 53719 #024-07-2000 L2005 **P** *020 †75

SCHAETTLE, Sarah C. 6001 RESEARCH PARK BLVD 53719 #056-05-2002 L2004 **CHP** *020 †75

SCHALCH, Don Sylvester. 451 JUNCTION RD, STE 9903 53717 #038-41-1960 L1982 **IM PD** *020 †20

SCHALICK, Walton Orvyl. ■ 53711 #023-07-1995 L2000 **PM PD** *020

SCHECKLER, William Edward. 777 S MILLS ST 53715 #041-01-1964 L1965 **IM ID** *050 †20

SCHEID, Terrance Michael. ■ 53717 #056-05-1975 L1992 **OBG OS** *020 †30

SCHELMAN, William Russell. 600 HIGHLAND AVE, BOX 5669 53792 #016-11-2000 L2001 **ON** *100 †20

SCHEMMEL, James C. 1821 S STOUGHTON RD 53716 #056-06-1986 L1987 **OTO** *020 †45

SCHIEBLER, Mark Lincourt. 601 HIGHLAND AVE, E3/378 CLINCAL SCIENCE CEN 53792 #011-03-1982 L1983 **DR** *020

SCHIFFMAN, Jeffrey Howard. 5534 MEDICAL CIR 53719 #011-02-1982 L1986 **P** *020 †75

SCHILLER, Joan Hoff. 600 HIGHLAND AVE, K4/548 53792 #016-11-1980 L1983 **ON** *020 †20

SCHILLING, Robert F. 1300 UNIVERSITY AVE, MED HEMATOLOGY UNIV WI 53706 #056-05-1943 L1943 **HEM IM** *071 †20

SCHINITSKY, Michael Robt. ■ 53705 #047-07-1968 L1970 **PTH** *100

SCHMALTZ, Lisa Marie. 202 S PARK ST, BLDG 3 53715 #028-46-1991 L1992 **DR** *020 †80

SCHMELZER, Richard Gerald. 5618 ODANA RD, ODANA ATRIUM CLINIC 53719 #026-04-1975 L1978 **FM** *020 †18

SCHMIDT, Ann Marie. 7102 MINERAL POINT RD 53717 #056-05-1987 L1988 **IM RHU** *020 †20

SCHMIDT, Bradley Jennings. 707 S MILLS ST, ST. MARYS HOSPITAL 53715 #056-06-1998 L2002 **IM** *020 †20

SCHMIDT, Noelle Kirsten. 600 HIGHLAND AVE, K4/548 CSC 53792 #016-11-2000 L2003 **ON** *020 †20

SCHMITT, Katherine Anne. 600 HIGHLAND AVE, BOX 9601 53792 #056-06-2005 L2006 **P** *012

SCHMITT, William Robert. ■ 53711 #056-05-2008 L2008 *012

SCHMITZ, Peter Walter. ■ 53715 #056-05-1971 L1972 **ORS** *071 †40

SCHNEIDER, James Edward. 2500 OVERLOOK TER, WM S MIDDLETON VA MED CTR 53705 #056-06-1982 L1986 **IM** *020 †20

SCHNEIDER, John. 600 HIGHLAND AVE, BOX 5132 53792 #030-05-2005 L2007 **N** *012

SCHOEN, Justin Wade. 600 HIGHLAND AVE, BOX 9601 53792 #025-12-2004 L2006 **P** *012

SCHOENWETTER, Charles D. 600 HIGHLAND AVE 53792 #056-05-1957 L1958 **PD** *040 †55

SCHRAGER, Sarina Beth. 3209 DRYDEN DR 53704 #016-11-1992 L1996 **FM** *020 †18

SCHRAMM, Richard Carl. 752 N HIGH POINT RD, DEAN MED CTR 53717 #056-06-1986 L1990 **P** *020 †75

SCHREIBMAN, Ken. 621 SCIENCE DR 53711 #038-06-1991 L1999 **DR OS** *020 †80

SCHROEDER, Kristopher M. 600 HIGHLAND AVE, AVE H4/831-8320 53792 #056-05-2003 L2005 **AN** *100

SCHROEDER, Mark Edwin. 600 HIGHLAND AVE RM6-305, UNIVERSITY OF WISCONSIN HO 53792 #056-05-1979 L1980 **AN PME** *020 †05

SCHROTH, Mary Kay. 600 HIGHLAND AVE K4938C, UW CHILDREN'S HOSPITAL 53792 #056-05-1986 L1993 **PDP PD** *040 †55

SCHUELLER, Kathryn Elizab. 3209 DRYDEN DR 53704 #056-06-2006 L2008 **FP** *012

SCHUETZ, John Gustave. 1200 JOHN Q HAMMONS DR, STE 400 53717 #016-11-1984 L1988 **IM** *020 †20

SCHUH, James Jerard. 202 S PARK ST, MERITER HOSPITAL 53715 #030-06-1987 L1995 **AN EM** *020 †05

SCHULTZ, Robert John. 707 S MILLS ST 53715 #056-05-1989 L1996 **AN** *020 †05

SCHULZ, James Trotter. 1821 S STOUGHTON RD 53716 #056-06-1956 L1957 **GS** *020

SCHUMACHER, Clark. 600 HIGHLAND AVE, UNIVERSITY OF WI HOSPITAL 53792 #026-04-2002 L2006 **VIR** *012 †80

SCHUMACHER, Daniel John. 700 HIGHLAND AVE 53792 #056-05-2005 L2007 **PD** *012

SCHUMACHER, Jayna Blythe. ■ 53703 #056-05-2008 *012

SCHUMACHER, Rosemarie L. 675 W WASHINGTON AVE 53703 #016-06-1991 L1992 **FM** *020 †18

SCHURR, Michael John. 600 HIGHLAND AVE 53792 #038-41-1988 L1989 **CCS TRS** *020 †85

SCHUSSLERFIORENZ, Chris M. 610 WALNUT ST, 640 WARF BLDG 53726 #041-01-2001 L2002 **GS** *100

SCHUSTER, Donald S. 4414 REGENT ST 53705 #056-05-1951 L1953 **D** *020 †15 ‡

SCHWAB, William Eric. 3209 DRYDEN DR 53704 #038-06-1980 L1985 **FM** *020 †18

SCHWARTZ, Howard Stuart. ■ 53703 #035-19-1966 L1994 **EM OS** *030 †20,16

SCHWARZE, Margaret Lee. 451 JUNCTION RD, STE 9903 53717 #024-01-1995 L2005 **VS** *020 †85

SCOTT, Jessica Alysia. 600 HIGHLAND AVE, BOX 4108 53792 #056-05-2005 L2007 **PD** *012

SCRIMGER, Rufus A. ■ 53711 #060-01-1994 L2000 *020

SEABORG, Kristin Ann. 5249 E TERRACE DR, GROUP HEALTH COOPERATIVE 53718 #056-05-2001 L2002 **PD** *020 †55

SEAMON, Meredith Leigh. ■ 53717 #030-06-2006 L2008 **PD** *012

SEBRANEK, Joshua James. 600 HIGHLAND AVE, AVE H4/831-8320 53792 #056-05-2002 L2005 **AN** *100

SEEGER, Susanne Katharina. 600 HIGHLAND AVE, UW HOSPITAL AND CLINICS 53792 #409-23-1983 L2001 **N CN** *020 †75

SEGAR, William Elias. UNIV WIS MED SCH, DEPT PED 53706 #017-20-1947 L1971 **PD** *071 †55

SEHLOFF, James W. 1821 S STOUGHTON RD 53716 #056-05-1981 L1982 **PUD CCM** *030 †20

SEIBERT, Christine S. 5249 E TERRACE DR 53718 #016-06-1992 L1995 **IM** *020 †20

SELF, James E. 340 S WHITNEY WAY, BONE AND JOINT SURGERY ASS 53705 #048-02-1986 L1993 **ORS OAR** *020 †40

SELTZ, Jeffrey Neale. 317 KNUTSON DR, CENTRAL WI CENTER 53704 #055-01-1969 L1986 **PD** *020 †55

SELVAGGI, Suzanne M. 451 JUNCTION RD 53717 #035-46-1978 L2001 **ATP** *020 †50

SELZER, Peter Michael. 600 HIGHLAND AVE, E3/311 53792 #011-02-1981 L1986 **DR** *020 †80

SEROOGY, Christine Marie. 451 JUNCTION RD, STE 9903 53717 #026-04-1993 L2003 **AI PD** *020 †03,55

SERRANO, Karen Denise. 600 HIGHLAND AVE, BOX 2454 53792 #016-02-2005 L2007 **IM** *100

SHAABAN, Aimen Farouk. 600 HIGHLAND AVE, H4/785 CLINICAL SCIENCE CE 53792 #016-11-1991 L2002 **PDS** *020 †85

SHADDIX WHITE, Jeremy R. ■ 53711 #039-01-2003 L2005 **ORS** *012

SHAFIEI, Majid. ■ 53726 #055-01-2006 **OTO** *012

SHAH, Dinesh Manilal. 202 S PARK ST 53715 #495-17-1973 L2004 **MFM OBS** *020 †30

SHAH, Neena. 202 S PARK ST, 6-CENTER 53715 #495-17-1977 L2004 **PD NPM** *020 †55

SHAH, Neha Nitin. 2870 UNIVERSITY AVE, STE 206 53705 #005-18-2006 L2008 **OPH** *012

SHAH, Roopa K. 752 N HIGH POINT RD 53717 #025-12-1999 L2000 **FM** *020 †18

SHAKHNOVICH, Valentina. ■ 53705 #056-05-2008 *012

SHALEV, Anath. 451 JUNCTION RD, STE 9903 53717 #869-01-1993 L2002 **END** *020

SHAMA, Liat N. 600 HIGHLAND AVE, BOX 7375 53792 #034-01-2005 **GS** *012

SHAMES, Brian Douglas. UNIV OF WI HOSP & CLNC, DEPT SURGERY 53792 #008-02-1994 L2001 **GS** *020 †85

SHANNAHAN, John Michael. 1313 FISH HATCHERY RD 53715 #028-03-1969 L1970 **TS GS** *071 †85,90

SHANNAHAN, Meghan E W. 600 HIGHLAND AVE, B6/319 CSC 53792 #028-79-1998, ▲ L1999 **AN** *020 †05

SHANNON, Brian Daniel. 600 HIGHLAND AVE, UW HOSPITAL AND CLINICS 53792 #047-05-2003 L2004 **ORS** *012 ‡

SHANNON, William Patrick. 202 S PARK ST 53715 #003-01-1984 L1985 **PM** *020 †60

SHAO, Haipeng. 600 HIGHLAND AVE 53792 #243-70-1993 L2006 **PTH** *012

SHAPIRO, Robert Barnet. 675 W WASHINGTON AVE 53703 #035-08-1961 L1969 **CHP P** *020 †75

SHAPIRO, Sander Sheaman. 600 HIGHLAND AVE, UNIVERSITY HOSPITAL 53792 #025-01-1963 L1974 **REN** *071 †30

SHARATA, Harry H. 6510 GRAND TETON PLZ, STE 302 53719 #056-05-1990 L1994 **D** *020 †15

SHAW, Laura Kristine. 2545 UNIVERSITY AVE 53705 #056-05-2003 L2004 **FM** *100

SHAW, Ronald Parry. 317 KNUTSON DR, CENTRAL COLONY 53704 #056-05-1970 L1971 **N** *020 †75

SHAW, Timothy John. 752 N HIGH POINT RD 53717 #056-05-1976 L1980 **OTO AM** *020 †45

SHAY, Gerald Walter. 1821 S STOUGHTON RD 53716 #016-11-1968 L1969 **OBG** *020 †30

SHEARER, David Robert. 1821 S STOUGHTON RD 53716 #018-03-2001 L2004 **FM** *020

SHEARER, Robert Dale. ■ 53705 #007-02-1967 L1993 **CHP P** *071 †75

SHEEHAN, John P, Jr. 1300 UNIVERSITY AVE, MED SCI CTR UNIV OF WISCON 53706 #028-03-1985 L2001 **ON HEM** *050 †20

SHEEHY, Gregory Leonard. 451 JUNCTION RD, UW HEALTH WEST CLINIC 53717 #056-05-1973 L1974 **IM** *020 †20

SHELDON, Edwin Oliver. 675 W WASHINGTON AVE 53703 #025-01-1957 L1958 **P** *020

SHELDON, Ruth E Torrant. 2727 MARSHALL CT 53705 #025-01-1957 L1958 **P** *020 †75

SHELEF, Miriam Anne. J5/230 CSC-2454, 600 HIGHLAND AVENUE 53792 #035-01-2006 L2008 *012

SHELP, Weldon Donald. 707 S MILLS ST 53715 #056-05-1961 L1962 **NEP IM** *020 †20

SHENKER, Yoram. 600 HIGHLAND AVE 53792 #550-01-1978 L1986 **END IM** *020 †20

SHEPARD, Peter Michael. 600 HIGHLAND AVE, AVE H4/831-8320 53792 #038-06-2004 L2005 **OTO** *012

SHETH, Raj Dilip. 600 HIGHLAND AVE 53792 #627-01-1982 L1997 **N PD** *020 †75,55

SHRAGO, Earl. 600 HIGHLAND AVE, CLINICAL SCIENCE CTR 53792 #030-05-1952 L1960 **IM NTR** *075 †20

SHRIVIDYA, Sethuratnam. ■ 53717 #495-17-1992 L2001 **PTH** *100 †50

SHULTZ, Philip Michael. 700 S PARK ST 53715 #017-20-1972 L1975 **EM FM** *020 †16,18

SIA, Elma Ong. 4410 REGENT ST 53705 #748-10-1981 L1988 **PD ID** *020 †55

SIDHU, Pamil. 1300 UNIVERSITY AVE 53706 #665-02-2006 **FP** *012

SIEBERS, Michael James. 5249 E TERRACE DR 53718 #056-05-1980 L1981 **IMG IM** *050 †20

SIEBERS, Nicholas Mark. 5249 E TERRACE DR 53718 #056-05-2000 L2002 **IM** *020 †20 ‡

SILLAY, Karl Arthur. 600 HIGHLAND AVE, UWHC K4/842 53792 #012-01-1999 L2007 **NS** *020

SILVERMAN, Carl Geo. 2202 S PARK ST 53713 #024-01-1960 L1967 **IM** *071 †20

SILVERMAN, Elizabeth B. 2500 OVERLOOK TER 53705 #024-01-1962 L1967 **IM HEM** *040 †20

SIMENSTAD, Paul Otis. 1313 FISH HATCHERY RD 53715 #035-45-1954 L1956 **IM PUD** *071 †20

SIMON, Deborah Ann. 600 HIGHLAND AVE H4/831, PO BOX 6188 53792 #046-01-2003 L2004 **OBG** *020

SINGER, Alan Howard. 1313 FISH HATCHERY RD, DEAN CLINIC 53715 #016-02-1985 L2004 **CD IM** *020 †20

SINGH, Anne Marie. ■ 53718 #035-46-2002 L2005 **AI** *012 †55,03

SINGH, Neeraj. 600 HIGHLAND AVE, DEPARTMENT OF SURGERY, H4/ 53792 #495-36-1999 L2007 **NEP** *020

SINGH, Steven Thein. ■ 53726 #056-05-2008 *012

SINGLEY, Cynthia Marie. 202 S PARK ST, 1EAST PSYCHIATRY 53715 #056-05-2003 L2004 **P** *020

SIOMOS, Effie Evangelia. ■ 53713 #056-05-2006 L2008 **OBG** *012

SIPPEL, Rebecca Sue. 600 HIGHLAND AVE 53792 #028-02-1999 L2000 **GS** *100 †85

SISK, Elizabeth A. 451 JUNCTION RD, STE 9903 53717 #056-05-1997 L2004 **OTO** *020 †45

SISNEY, Gale Anne. 600 HIGHLAND AVE, UNIV OF WISC HOSPITAL AND 53792 #016-11-1988 L2004 **DR** *020 †80

SIVERHUS, W James. 1313 FISH HATCHERY RD 53715 #026-04-1961 L1962 **OBG** *071 †30

SIZER, Teresa Ann. 8202 EXCELSIOR DR 53717 #018-03-1979 L1982 **FM** *020 †18

SKARPHEDINSDOTTIR, Sigurbj. 600 HIGHLAND AVE, UNIV HOSP 53792 #484-01-2000 **AN** *012

SKLADZIEN, Stephanie Ann. 777 S MILLS ST, UW DEPT OF FAMILY MEDICIN 53715 #016-42-2006 L2007 **FP** *012

SKRIPKA, David Victor. 600 HIGHLAND AVE 53792 #026-04-1997 L1999 **CHP** *020 †75

SKROCH, Eugene E. ■ 53719 #056-05-1943 L1944 **GS VS** *071 †85

SLATER, Bruce. 600 HIGHLAND AVE, BOX 2454 53792 #011-03-1977 L2003 **IM GP** *020 †20 ‡

SLATTERY, Marcia Jean. 6001 RESEARCH PARK BLVD 53719 #056-05-1988 L1992 **P CHP** *020 †75

SLEETH, Jeffrey Scott. 20 S PARK ST, STE 207 53715 #003-01-1989 L1990 **PD** *020 †55
SLOAN, Michael Patrick. 1 S PARK ST, FL 7 53715 #056-05-2001 L2002 **GS** *020
SLUKVIN, Igor Ivanovich. 2500 OVERLOOK TER, 1220 CAPITOL COURT 53792 #913-05-1984 L2001 **ATP SP** *050 †50
SMALLEY, Rebecca Marie. 600 HIGHLAND AVE, BOX 2454 53792 #019-02-2005 L2006 **IM** *012
SMITH, Aubrey Merrijane. 600 HIGHLAND AVE, UNIVERSITY OF WI HOSPITAL 53792 #041-13-2004 L2006 **OBG** *012
SMITH, Brad Edward Reed. 301 TROY DR 53704 #056-05-1996 L1997 **PFP P** *020 †75
SMITH, Carter T. ■ 53705 #048-14-2007 **GS** *012
SMITH, Clayton Allen. 600 HIGHLAND AVE, AVE H4/831-8320 53792 #025-01-2005 L2006 **AN** *012
SMITH, Daniel Jos. 600 HIGHLAND AVE, DEPARTMENT OF MEDICINE 53792 #056-05-1978 L1979 **GE HEP** *020 †20
SMITH, Dean Barton. ■ 53705 #016-06-1952 L1955 **GS GP** *071 †85
SMITH, Elisabeth Esther. ■ 53706 #056-05-2008 *012
SMITH, Gregory Gene. 1821 S STOUGHTON RD 53716 #056-05-1973 L1977 **PD** *020 †55
SMITH, Judian Harris. 625 W WASHINGTON AVE 53703 #056-05-1982 L1983 **P** *020 †75
SMITH, Judith Anne. 451 JUNCTION RD, STE 9903 53717 #016-02-1999 L2006 **PPR** *020 †55
SMITH, Maureen Annette. 360 W WASHINGTON AVE 53703 #008-01-1992 **PHP** *100
SMITH, Robert Geo. 309 W WASHINGTON AVE 53703 #056-06-1978 L1991 **OPH GP** *020 †35
SNIDER, Andrew David. ■ 53713 #056-05-2008 *012
SNIDER, John Matthew. 1200 JOHN Q HAMMONS DR, STE 400 53717 #019-02-1989 L1999 **TS** *020 †85,90
SNOW, Stephen Ningta. 451 JUNCTION RD, UNIVERSITY OF WISCONSIN DE 53717 #035-08-1975 L1981 **D PD** *020 †55,15
SOBKOWICZ, Hanna Maria. 1300 UNIVERSITY AVE 53706 #759-03-1954 **N** *050
SOLFELT, David Allan. 202 S PARK ST 53715 #026-04-1979 L1984 **ORS** *020 †40
SOLLINGER, Hans Werner. 600 HIGHLAND AVE 53792 #409-16-1974 L1980 **OS GS** *030 †85
SOMOZA-BLANCO, Beatriz. 7102 MINERAL POINT RD 53717 #308-07-1982 L1991 **FM OBG** *020 †18
SONDEL, Paul Mark. UNV WI H4 442 CLNC SCI CTR 53792 #024-01-1977 L1978 **PD HEM** *050 †55
SONI, Anurag. 600 HIGHLAND AVE H6/516 53792 #496-09-1994 L2007 **GE** *020 †20
SONNTAG, Paul David. J5/230 CSC-2454, 600 HIGHLAND AVENUE 53792 #049-01-2007 **DR** *012
SOPER, Thomas Edward. 1300 UNIVERSITY AVE 53706 #654-01-2006 **FP** *012
SORBER, David A. 752 N HIGH POINT RD 53717 #041-09-1979 L1980 **IM IMG** *020 †20
SORIANO, Benjamin Joseph. ■ 53705 #056-05-2008 *012
SOSMAN, James Michael. 2828 MARSHALL CT STE 100 53705 #016-02-1985 L1994 **IM ID** *020 †20
SPEAS, Laura Lynn. ■ 53726 #056-06-1997 *100
SPERLING, Keith Burr. 1414 MACARTHUR RD 53714 #056-05-1966 L1971 **PM GP** *030 †60
SPIEGELMAN, Karuna Purnim. 202 S PARK ST 53715 #913-15-1993 L2005 **IM** *020
SPIELDOCH, Rachel Louise. ■ 53792 #028-03-2002 L2004 **OBG** *020
SPIER, Bret Jason. 600 HIGHLAND AVE H4/831, UNIV OF WI HOSPITAL AND CL 53792 #038-41-2003 L2004 **GE** *012 †20
SPRINGMAN, Scott Richard. 600 HIGHLAND AVE, F8/345 CSC 53792 #056-05-1978 L1979 **AN** *020 †05
SRAMEK, Stephen J. 1025 REGENT ST, DAVIS DUEHR DEAN 53715 #048-13-1982 L1983 **OPH** *020 †35
SRINIVASAN, Shardha. 202 S PARK ST 53715 #495-20-1987 L2000 **PDC PD** *020 †55
STAATS, Patricia Vrabec. 7102 MINERAL POINT RD 53717 #056-06-1977 L1978 **PD** *030 †55
STABLER, Stacy Marie. 600 HIGHLAND AVE, UNIV OF WISCONSIN HOSPITAL 53792 #023-01-2003 L2005 **HO** *012 †20
STACEY, Adriana Unger. 600 HIGHLAND AVE, AVE H4/831-8320 53792 #004-01-2004 L2005 **P** *012
STACEY, David Heath. 600 HIGHLAND AVE RM H4/831, UNIVERSITY HOSP 53792 #004-01-2004 L2005 **PS** *012
STAFSTROM, Carl. 600 HIGHLAND AVE 53792 #054-04-1985 L1999 **CHN PD** *050 †75
STAII, Anca. ■ 53705 #781-04-1999 L2008 **END** *012 †20
STALEY, Richard Lee. ■ 53705 #050-02-1977 L1978 **EM** *071 †16
STANEK, Nicholas Wm. 600 HIGHLAND AVE, DEPT. OF NEUROLOGY 53792 #056-05-1988 L1991 **N** *020 †75
STANLEY, Edwin Cruz. ■ 53711 #495-04-2005 L2006 **GS** *012
STANLEY, Robert John. 1821 S STOUGHTON RD 53716 #056-05-1977 L1988 **OTO ATP** *020 †50,45 ‡
STANTON, Paul Thomas. 600 HIGHLAND AVE, AVE H4/831-8320 53792 #056-05-2005 L2006 **DR** *012
STARLING, James Ralph. 2500 OVERLOOK TER, HOSPITAL ROOM 7052 53705 #035-45-1969 L1977 **GS** *020 †85 ‡
STASKOWSKI, Paul Andrew. 451 JUNCTION RD, STE 9903 53717 #026-08-1992 L1993 **OTO** *020 †45
STEADY, Henry Maduka. 36 S BROOKS ST 53715 #917-09-1972 L1982 **PTH** *020 †50
STEELE, Robert Stuart. 1821 S STOUGHTON RD 53716 #025-12-1992 L1995 **FM** *020 †18
STEELE, Thomas Hartman. 600 HIGHLAND AVE, OF MEDICINE 53792 #035-01-1962 L1963 **NEP IM** *040 †20
STEEVES, Richard A. 600 HIGHLAND AVE 53792 #065-06-1961 L1980 **RO** *020 †80
STEFFEN, Dennis Henry. 309 W WASHINGTON AVE 53703 #018-03-1964 L1965 **R** *071 †80
STEFFEN, Kristin Anne. 451 JUNCTION RD, STE 9903 53717 #056-05-1996 L1997 **IM** *020 †20
STEIN, Ann P. 8202 EXCELSIOR DR 53717 #028-03-1981 L1998 **FM** *074 †18
STEIN, James Howard. 600 HIGHLAND AVE, ROOM G7/341-3248 53792 #008-01-1990 L1996 **CD** *020 †20
STEIN, Leonard Irving. ■ 53705 #056-05-1960 L1962 **P** *071 †75
STEINMETZ, George Philip. ■ 53705 #056-05-1956 L1958 **GS TS** *071 †85,90
STELZER, Marie Kathryne. 600 HIGHLAND AVE H4/831, UW HOSPITAL AND CLINICS 53792 #030-05-2006 L2007 **GS** *012
STEPHANI, Nicholas G. 1 S PARK ST, FL 7 53715 #056-06-1999 L2004 **DR** *020 †80
STEPHENSON, John Nieman. 600 HIGHLAND AVE, UNIVERSITY OF WI HOSPITAL 53792 #024-05-1963 L1972 **ADL PD** *040 †55
STEVENS, Christian D. 600 HIGHLAND AVE RM B6-319, HOSPITAL AND 53792 #046-01-2004 L2005 **AN** *012
STEWARD, Tyler Harvey. 600 HIGHLAND AVE H4/831, UW HOSPITAL AND CLINICS 53792 #018-03-2004 L2008 **IM** *012
STEWART, Barbara Ann. 202 S PARK ST 53715 #018-03-1997 L2002 **AN** *020
STEWART, James Alexander. 600 HIGHLAND AVE RM K6548 53792 #016-02-1975 L1991 **ON IM** *020 †20
STEWART, Katharina T. 202 S PARK ST 53715 #038-40-1992 L1998 **OBG** *020 †30
STIEGHORST, Michael F. 1313 FISH HATCHERY RD 53715 #056-05-1976 L1977 **DR** *020 †80
STIEGLER, Paul Martin. 700 S PARK ST 53715 #026-04-1977 L1981 **GP EM** *020 †18,16
STIER, Michael Anthony. 600 HIGHLAND AVE, CLINICAL SCIENCE CTR 53792 #056-05-1994 L1998 **FOP** *020 †50
STIER, Peter Andrew. 707 S MILLS ST, ST. MARY'S HOSPITAL EMERGE 53715 #016-01-1998 L2001 **EM** *020 †16
STITGEN, Jeffrey Robt. 1821 S STOUGHTON RD 53716 #056-05-1980 L1985 **ORS** *020 †40
STITGEN, Stuart Harold. 1821 S STOUGHTON RD 53716 #056-05-1986 L1990 **ORS** *020 †40
STOFFEL, Mary Lynn. 4410 REGENT ST 53705 #016-45-1986 L1990 **OBG** *020 †30
STOIBER, Thomas Ray. 202 S PARK ST 53715 #056-05-1988 L1989 **CD IM** *020 †20
STONE, Charles Kingsbury. 600 HIGHLAND AVE, H6/317, UNIV OF WISCONSIN 53792 #035-20-1981 L1988 **CD NR** *020 †20
STONE, Dennis Wayne. 36 S BROOKS ST 53715 #026-04-1973 L1978 **PTH** *020 †50
STORM, Frederick K, III. 600 HIGHLAND AVE 53792 #005-14-1970 L1987 **OS GS** *020 †85
STOWE-CARPENTER, Barbara. 451 JUNCTION RD, STE 9903 53717 #056-05-1982 L1983 **IM** *020 †20
STREICHER, Eric Michael. 1313 FISH HATCHERY RD 53715 #035-01-1977 L1978 **IM** *020 †20
STRIKER, Robert Todd. 600 HIGHLAND AVE 53792 #028-02-1995 L2001 **ID** *020 †20
STROHM, John Michael. 202 S PARK ST 53715 #056-05-1979 L1980 **AN** *020 †05
STROTHER, Charles Milton. 5008 RISSER RD 53705 #048-02-1967 L1976 **R N** *020 †80
STRUPP, Kim Mary. ■ 53726 #056-05-2008 *012
STUESSER, Glen J. 1 S PARK ST 53715 #056-05-1953 L1954 **GS** *020 †85
STURM, Rodney James. 752 N HIGH POINT RD 53717 #056-05-1956 L1957 **OPH** *071 †35
SULMAN, David. 1552 UNIVERSITY AVE 53726 #035-08-1959 L1966 **GE IM** *071 †20
SUMKIN, Joan Toby. 2500 OVERLOOK TER, WM. S. MIDDLETON MEM VET. 53705 #038-40-1982 L1992 **IM** *020 †20
SUNBY, Carl Richard. 1821 S STOUGHTON RD 53716 #056-05-1982 L1992 **GS** *020 †85
SUNDSTROM, Walter Roach. 2880 UNIVERSITY AVE 53705 #016-43-1957 L1964 **RHU IM** *071 †20
SUNKARA, Srinivasu. ■ 53726 #056-05-2008 *012
SUTTON, Daniel M, Jr. ■ 53705 #056-05-2008 *012
SUTULA, Thomas Peter. 600 HIGHLAND AVE 53792 #041-01-1975 L1984 **N** *050 †20,75
SVENSON, James Ernest. 600 HIGHLAND AVE 53792 #016-02-1980 L1985 **PD** *020 †55,16
SWANSON, Kyle Ian. ■ 53705 #056-05-2008 *012
SWEITZER, Nancy K. 600 HIGHLAND AVE, CARDIO SECT H6/3 CSC 53792 #056-05-1993 L2002 **CD** *050 †20
SWENSON, Amanda Kate. 777 S MILLS ST, UW SMPH DEPT OF FAMILY MED 53715 #028-03-2006 L2007 **FP** *012
SWENSON, Erik Dean. 600 HIGHLAND AVE, UNIVERSITY OF WI HOSPITAL 53792 #018-03-2003 L2004 **RHU** *012 †20
SWIZE, Lisa Rebecca. ■ 53717 #007-02-2004 L2007 **GE** *012 †20
SY, Mary Lynn. 600 HIGHLAND AVE, UNIVERSITY OF WI HOSPITAL 53792 #056-05-2002 L2004 **PD** *100
SYDNOR, Ryan Henry. ■ 53705 #056-05-2008 *012
SYKES, William Stuart. 600 HIGHLAND AVE 53792 #352-09-1955 L1967 **AN OS** *071
SYTH, Cara Nicole. 600 HIGHLAND AVE, BOX 6188 53792 #056-05-2005 L2006 **OBG** *012
SYVERUD, Thomas Andrew. ■ 53705 #056-05-2004 **AN** *012
SZACHNOWSKA, Barbara M. 600 HIGHLAND AVE 53792 #759-03-1984 L1992 **N** *071 †75
SZEWCZYK, Karl Fredric. 707 S MILLS ST 53715 #028-34-1978 L1987 **NPM** *020 †55
SZWEDA, John Alexander. 1605 S GOLF GLN UNIT H, JOHN A SZWEDA MD 53704 #016-43-1952 L1953 **IM CD** *072 †20
TAKAHASHI, Hitoshi. 1300 UNIVERSITY AVE 53706 #572-07-1948 **GS OS** *040
TAMPA, Linda C. 5249 E TERRACE DR 53718 #016-42-1999 L2002 **FM** *020 †18
TAN, Chee-Hian. ■ 53705 #143-03-1994 L2008 **OPH** *012
TANNER, William A. 330 E LAKESIDE ST 53715 #019-02-1944 L1948 **PD PTH** *071 †55
TAYLOR, Andrew John. 600 HIGHLAND AVE, CLINICAL SCIENCE CENTER 53792 #016-06-1977 L1978 **DR** *020 †80
TAYLOR, Benton C. 2500 OVERLOOK TER 53705 #048-04-1950 L1952 **IM PUD** *071 †20
TAYLOR, Claude Adams. 600 HIGHLAND AVE 53792 #038-41-1956 L1957 **AN** *071 †05
TEELIN, Thomas Corcoran. H6/349 CSC 3248, 600 HIGHLAND AVE 53792 #056-06-2003 L2004 **CD** *012 †20
TEFERA, Girma. 451 JUNCTION RD, STE 9903 53717 #561-16-1982 L2000 **GS** *020 †85
TEGTMEYER, Gamber F, Jr. 1 S PARK ST 53715 #035-01-1959 L1960 **N** *071 †75
TEIGEN, Elizabeth Louise. 202 S PARK ST, BLDG 3 53715 #056-05-1993 L1997 **DR** *020 †80
TELLEZ-GIRON, Patricia A. 701 DANE ST 53713 #649-01-1993 L1998 **FM** *020 †18
TEMPLETON, Katherine M. 707 S MILLS ST 53715 #056-05-1983 L1984 **IM** *020
TEMPRANO, John Edward. 1 S PARK ST, FL 7 53715 #056-05-1993 L1997 **OPH** *020 †35
TEMTE, Jonathan Lane. 701 DANE ST 53713 #056-05-1987 L1991 **FM** *040 †18
TENG, Joyce Mingcao. 1 S PARK ST, FL 7 53715 #047-05-2001 L2006 **D** *020 †15
TENG, Ming. 1104 JOHN NOLEN DR, RADIATION ONCOLOGY 53713 #243-16-1987 L2005 **RO** *020 †80
TENNEY, Horace Kent, III. PO BOX 7841 53707 #016-06-1946 L1950 **PD** *072 †55
TEODORESCU, Mihaela. 600 HIGHLAND AVE, UNIV OF WI, MEDICINE AND P 53792 #781-01-1992 L2006 **PCC** *020 †20
TEODORESCU, Mihai C. 2500 OVERLOOK TER, B5056 53705 #781-01-1992 L2006 **IMG** *020 †20
TEVAARWERK, Amye Juliet. K6/516 CSC, 600 HIGHLAND AVENUE 53792 #028-02-2002 L2006 **ON** *012 †20
THAKOR, Sheila K. 625 W WASHINGTON AVE 53703 #037-01-1989 L1990 **P N** *020 †75
THET, Lyn Aung. 600 HIGHLAND AVE, CSC K4910 53792 #209-01-1971 L1990 **IM** *050 †20
THILEN, Stephan R. 805 HIDDEN CAVE RD 53717 #858-02-1980 L2002 **CCA** *020 †05
THLIVERIS, Andrew Tom. 2500 OVERLOOK TER 53705 #049-01-1994 L1998 **OPH** *020 †35
THOM, Michael Lyle. 451 JUNCTION RD # 9902 53717 #056-05-1976 L1977 **IM** *020 †20
THOMAS, Alex. 600 HIGHLAND AVE H4/447 53792 #016-01-2007 **PD** *012
THOMPSON, Mary Greene. 5618 ODANA RD 53719 #035-45-1987 L1988 **FM** *020 †18
THOMSEN, James Harry. 8007 EXCELSIOR DR 53717 #056-05-1962 L1963 **CD IM** *020 †20
THORNBERY, James Meredith. 36 S BROOKS ST 53715 #056-06-1977 L1982 **PTH CLP** *062 †50
THORNTON, Francis Joseph. 202 S PARK ST, BLDG 3 53715 #539-02-1991 L2002 **DR** *020 †80
THOUSAND, Rebecca Ann. 1821 S STOUGHTON RD, DEAN HEALTH SYSTEM 53716 #056-06-2001 L2002 **OBG** *020 †30
THURLOW, Peter Munroe. 4410 REGENT ST 53705 #024-01-1977 L1985 **GS VS** *020 †85
THURRELL, Richard J. ■ 53705 #056-05-1954 L1958 **P** *071 †75
TIBBETTS, James C. 20 S PARK ST STE 202 53715 #035-06-1964 L1967 **NS** *020 †25
TIERNEY, Adam Charles. 1200 JOHN Q HAMMONS DR, STE 400 53717 #056-05-1998 L1999 **U** *020 †95

■ = Address Information Privacy Protected

TIPNIS, Parag A. 2500 OVERLOOK TER, CARDIOLOGY DEPT 53705 #056-05-1999 L2006 **CD** *020 †20

TOMASSON, Gunnar. 600 HIGHLAND AVE, UNIVERSITY OF WI HOSPITAL 53792 #484-01-2000 L2004 **RHU** *012 †20

TOMCZAK, Mark Lewis. 707 S MILLS ST 53715 #056-05-1976 L1979 **AN IM** *020 †20,05

TOMPKINS, Bonnie M. 600 HIGHLAND AVE 53792 #041-07-1972 L1974 **AN** *071 †05

TOMPKINS, Wm Alexander. ■ 53717 #016-11-1947 L1949 **GS OS** *071 †85

TONG, Carl Weichan. ■ 53711 #048-16-2002 L2008 **CD** *012 †20

TORHORST, Susan Marie. 7102 MINERAL POINT RD 53717 #056-06-1985 L1987 **FM OBG** *020 †18

TORREALBA, Jose Ramon. 600 HIGHLAND AVE, UNIV OF WISC HOSP CLCS 53792 #935-01-1994 L2002 **PTH** *020

TORSTENSON, Ordean Lloyd. 707 S MILLS ST 53715 #026-04-1967 L1971 **PD** *020 †55

TOTH, Susan Irene. 1 S PARK ST, FL 4 53715 #011-02-1989 L1990 **GS** *020 †85

TOUSSAINT, John B. 53703 #056-05-1951 L1952 **N** *071

TOUSSAINT, Norbert F. 7102 MINERAL POINT RD 53717 #028-34-1975 L1980 **OPH** *020 †35

TRAVER, Myrna. 8007 EXCELSIOR DR 53717 #056-05-1962 L1964 **CLP** *030

TREWARTHA, Mark. 313 PRICE PL STE 109 53705 #056-05-1964 L1966 **PYA P** *020 †75

TRIAS, Michael James. 1821 S STOUGHTON RD 53716 #016-11-1999 L2000 **PD** *020 †55

TRIBUS, Clifford Boehe. 621 SCIENCE DR 53711 #023-07-1987 L1993 **OSS ORS** *020 †40

TRIER, Todd Timothy. 1200 JOHN Q HAMMONS DR, STE 400 53717 #003-01-1993 L2000 **NS** *020 †25

TROST, Gregory Raymond. 600 HIGHLAND AVE K3/805, UNIV OF WI HOSP & CLINICS 53792 #056-05-1988 L1989 **NS** *020 †25

TROWBRIDGE, Elizabeth R. 20 S PARK ST, STE 207 53715 #056-05-1991 L1993 **IM** *020 †20

TUETING, Jonathan Leif. 53705 #016-02-2001 L2003 **HS** *020

TUFFAHA, Amjad S. 600 HIGHLAND AVE, UNIVERSITY HOSPITAL & CLIN 53792 #575-01-1988 L2000 **AI** *020 †55,03

TUFFLI, Gordon Andrew. 20 S PARK ST 53715 #056-05-1964 L1966 **PD END** *071 †55

TUITE, Michael John. 621 SCIENCE DR 53711 #024-01-1987 L1992 **DR** *020 †80

TURNER, Stuart Paul. 1821 S STOUGHTON RD 53716 #025-01-1980 L1981 **FM** *020 †18

TURNEY, Susan Kaye. 330 E LAKESIDE ST 53715 #056-05-1979 L1980 **IM** *030 †20

TURNIPSEED, Wm Derrick. 600 HIGHLAND AVE, H4-730 53792 #012-05-1969 L1976 **GS CD** *020 †20

TURSKI, Deborah Louise. 707 S MILLS ST 53715 #016-01-1975 L1976 **PTH** *020 †50

TURSKI, Patrick Alan. 600 HIGHLAND AVE, PROFESSOR OF RADIOLOGY 53792 #016-01-1975 L1976 **DR** *020 †80

TUSA, Reka. 3209 DRYDEN DR 53704 #016-01-2003 **FM** *100

TWEETEN, J Kent. 1 S PARK ST 53715 #056-05-1942 L1943 **FM** *071

TWOHIG, Matthew Hamilton. 600 HIGHLAND AVE, AVE H4/831-8320 53792 #056-05-2003 L2005 **HMP** *012 †50

TYLER, Chanel Torian. 202 S PARK ST, MERITER HOSPITAL DEPT. OB& 53715 #041-15-2002 L2006 **OBG** *100

TYLER, Robert J. 707 S MILLS ST 53715 #056-05-1977 L1990 **DMP** *020 †50

TYSKA, Steven Blaise. 4122 E TOWNE BLVD 53704 #016-11-1993 L1999 **FM** *020 †18

UEHLING, David Theodore. 600 HIGHLAND AVE 53792 #016-06-1959 L1965 **U** *071 †95

ULLAND, Erik Johnston. ■ 53705 #005-12-2003 L2007 **CHP** *012

ULLRICK, Steven Ray. 600 HIGHLAND AVE, AVE H4/831-8320 53792 #016-11-2003 L2006 **DR** *012

UMPHREY, Lisa Ann-Marie. ■ 53711 #007-02-2007 **PD** *012

UMSTEAD, Deborah Mae. 625 W WASHINGTON AVE 53703 #034-01-1984 L1985 **CHP P** *020 †75

UPDIKE, Stuart James. 2880 UNIVERSITY AVE 53705 #035-45-1962 L1963 **NEP** *020

UPTON, David Christopher. ■ 53719 #056-05-2006 L2007 **OTO** *012

URBAN, Andrew Wm. 600 HIGHLAND AVE # H4570, UNIV WI HOSP 53792 #016-11-1991 L1993 **ID** *020 †20

URBELYTE, Asta. 202 S PARK ST 53715 #913-49-1994 L1998 **AN** *020 †05

URTES, Mary-Anne. 8202 EXCELSIOR DR 53717 #035-41-1982 L1983 **FM** *020 †18

UTRIE, Gina Andrea. 1821 S STOUGHTON RD, EAST CLINIC 53716 #056-05-2000 L2001 **IM** *020

VAIDYANATHAN, Gayatri. 6001 RESEARCH PARK BLVD, INST & 53719 #056-06-2006 **P** *012

VALDER, Ann M. 600 HIGHLAND AVE, RM H4/831 53792 #037-01-2005 **PTH** *012

VALLEJO, David, Jr. ■ 53705 #056-05-2008 *012

VALMADRID, Cassandra Joy. 451 JUNCTION RD, STE 9903 53717 #748-02-1989 L1996

VAN BUER, Michael Gerard. 600 HIGHLAND AVE, HOSPITAL AND 53792 #016-11-2006 **GS** *100

VAN BUREN, Jeremy James. 600 HIGHLAND AVE, AVE H4/831-8320 53792 #056-05-2005 L2006 **OPH** *012

VANDER ARK, Condon Ray. 600 HIGHLAND AVE # H6-338 53792 #025-01-1961 L1972 **CD IM** *020 †20

VANDER MEER, James Edward. 1200 JOHN Q HAMMONS DR, STE 400 53717 #025-01-1969 L1970 **GE IM** *020 †20

VANDERSLUIS, Stephen H. 700 S PARK ST, ST. MARY'S HOSPITAL 53715 #012-05-1989 L2003 **AN** *020 †05

VAN DYKE, Kenneth John, Jr. 600 HIGHLAND AVE, UNIVERSITY OF WI HOSPITAL 53792 #056-05-2002 L2004 **AN** *100 †05

VAN GEMERT, John G. ■ 53705 #002-01-1941 L1942 **EM** *020

VANGOR, Donald William. 1604 S GOLF GLN, UNIT D 53704 #016-11-1962 L1966 **FM** *071 †18

VANNESS, Erin Ruth. 555 ZOR SHRINE PL 53719 #056-05-1999 L2003 **D** *020 †15

VAN SUSTEREN, John A. 1 W WILSON ST 53702 #056-06-1946 L1947 **PM** *020 †70

VARMA, Adarsh Kumar. J5/230 CSC-2454, 600 HIGHLAND AVENUE 53792 #016-11-2007 **IM** *012

VARNESS, Todd Steven. 600 HIGHLAND AVE, UNIVERSITY OF WI HOSPITAL 53792 #023-07-2002 L2004 **PDE** *012 †55

VASEY, Brian Alexander. 780 REGENT ST STE 300 53715 #035-15-1995 L1996 **CHP** *020

VASTOLA, Anthony P, Jr. 53711 #024-05-1953 L1959 **IM RHU** *071

VEDDER, Kathryn N. 125 N HAMILTON ST, UNIT 601 53703 #016-06-1968 L2002 **PD** *030 †55

VEGA, Roland James. 1 S PARK ST, FL 7 53715 #033-05-1979 L1980 **GS** *020 †85

VEIT, Brian Thomas. 202 S PARK ST 53715 #056-06-2001 L2004 **EM** *020 †16

VELEZ, Mauricio. ■ 53703 #264-12-1999 L2006 **IM** *100 †20

VERGERONT, James Michael. 1 W WILSON ST, RM 318 53702 #056-05-1978 L1979 **ID PHP** *030

VESELY, James John. 2500 OVERLOOK TER, RADIOLOGY SERV/114 DG226 53705 #016-43-1981 L2001 **DR NM** *020 †80

VICKERY, Jennifer Janelle. 600 HIGHLAND AVE, UNIVERSITY OF WI HOSPITAL 53792 #056-05-2003 L2006 **AN** *020

VICKREY, Robert James. 301 TROY DR, GOODLAND HALL 53704 #016-11-2002 L2004 **PFP** *012

VIDARSSON, Brynjar. 600 HIGHLAND AVE H4/821, HOUSE STAFF/MED STAFF OFC 53792 #484-01-1990 L1996 **HEM** *020 †20

VINCENT, Robert Allen. 600 HIGHLAND AVE, STE E-3/366 53792 #056-05-1970 L1971 **DR NM** *020 †80 ‡

VIRNIG, Christine Marie. 600 HIGHLAND AVE, UNIVERSITY OF WI HOSPITAL 53792 #056-05-2002 L2006 **AI** *012

VISWANATHAN, Ravi K. J5/230 CSC-2454, 600 HIGHLAND AVENUE 53792 #016-01-2006 **IM** *012

VOGEL, Heinz Gerhard. ■ 53717 #407-23-1955 L1961 **P** *020 †75

VOGT, Kevin Michael. 752 N HIGH POINT RD 53717 #056-05-2003 L2004 **FM** *020 †18

VOHMANN, Monica. 675 W WASHINGTON AVE, CAPITOL CLINIC GH C 53703 #056-05-1997 L1999 **FM** *020 †18

VOLLRATH, Victoria Ann. 5702 RAYMOND RD 53711 #056-06-1977 L1978 **FM OS** *020 †18

VOLSKY, Nadezhda Ivanouna. 777 S MILLS ST, UNIV OF WI-MADISON DEPT OF 53715 #913-36-2000 L2006 **FP** *012

VONK, Jantina Rose. 1050 REGENT ST, STE 201 53715 #025-12-1992 L1993 **P** *020 †75

VOSS, Ching Ye. 600 UNIVERSITY AVE H4/823, UNIVERSITY HOSPITAL & CLIN 53792 #243-33-1983 L2004 **BBK** *020 †50

VOYTOVICH, Marta C. 2500 OVERLOOK TER, MIDDLETON VA HOSP-PATH 53705 #016-11-1983 L1986 **PTH** *020 †50

VUKICH, Carolyn Ogland. 752 N HIGH POINT RD, WEST CLINIC 53717 #056-06-1986 L1989 **PD** *020 †55

VUKICH, John Allan. 1025 REGENT ST, DAVIS DUEHR DEAN 53715 #012-05-1985 L1989 **OPH** *020 †35

WACKER, Joel Douglas. 700 S PARK ST 53715 #030-05-1979 L1981 **EM** *020 †20,16

WACLAWIK, Andrew John. 600 HIGHLAND AVE 53792 #759-03-1982 L1988 **N** *020 †75

WAECHTER, Anastasia Chris. 2500 OVERLOOK TER, WILLIAMS MIDDLETON VA MEDI 53705 #025-01-2001 L2002 **GE** *012

WAGGONER, Jesse J. ■ 53713 #036-07-2006 **IM** *012

WALASZEK, Arthur C. 6001 RESEARCH PARK BLVD, UNIVERSITY OF WISCONSIN 53719 #016-06-1997 L2002 **P PYG** *040 †75

WALD, Arnold. H6 / 516, 600 HIGHLAND AVENUE 53792 #035-08-1968 L2006 **GE IM** *040 †20

WALD, Ellen F Rashkow. 2880 UNIVERSITY AVE 53705 #035-08-1968 L2006 **PD PDI** *030 †55

WALKER, Andrew Joseph. ■ 53705 #028-34-2007 **IM** *012

WALKER, Duard Lee. 1300 UNIVERSITY AVE 53706 #005-02-1945 L1953 **ID OS** *071

WALKER, Kae Isabel. 8007 EXCELSIOR DR 53717 #056-05-1968 L1969 **IM ON** *020 †20

WALLHAUS, Thomas Robt. 202 S PARK ST, WISCONSIN HEART 53715 #016-45-1990 L1991 **CD** *020 †20

WALLOW, Ingolf Horst L. 600 HIGHLAND AVE, DEPT OF OPHTH & VISUAL SVC 53792 #409-12-1964 L1976 **OPH** *071 †35

WALSH, Brian Patrick. 20 S PARK ST, STE 205 53715 #056-06-1996 L1997 **NS** *020

WALSH, Le Roy Geo. 707 S MILLS ST 53715 #056-05-1958 L1959 **FM** *072

WALTERS, Beth. 4510 REGENT ST, STE 2A 53705 #025-12-1978 L1984 **P CHP** *020 †75

WALTERS, Michael C. 600 HIGHLAND AVE 53792 #056-06-2001 L2004 **IM** *020 †16

WANG, Jining I. 1821 S STOUGHTON RD 53716 #028-46-1994 L2001 **D** *020 †15

WARD, James Edward, III. ■ 53703 #016-43-2006 L2008 **IM** *012

WARD, Joshua James. 600 HIGHLAND AVE, UNIVERSITY OF WI HOSPITAL 53792 #056-05-2002 L2003 **PM** *020 †60

WARNER, Jeremy Patrick. 600 HIGHLAND AVE, AVE H4/831-8320 53792 #010-01-2003 L2005 **PS** *012

WARNER, Thomas Frederick. 600 HIGHLAND AVE RM E51317 53792 #539-05-1965 L1979 **PTH IM** *020 †50

WARWICK, Scott Wm. 330 E LAKESIDE ST 53715 #056-06-1991 L1995 **AN** *020

WASHBURN, Walter L. ■ 53705 #056-05-1949 L1956 **FM** *071 †18

WASSENAAR, Timothy Robert. J5/230 CSC-2454, 600 HIGHLAND AVE 53792 #016-42-2002 L2003 **HEM** *012 †20

WATERMAN, Robert Wm. 625 W WASHINGTON AVE 53703 #056-05-1986 L1988 **P** *020 †75

WATERS, Gary Edward. 1313 FISH HATCHERY RD 53715 #016-01-1987 L2002 **OBG** *020 †30

WATERS, Raul Fernando. 1313 FISH HATCHERY RD, DEAN CLINIC 53715 #025-07-1961 L1963 **U** *020 †95

WATHNE, Natascha. ■ 53703 #056-05-2007 *012

WATKINS, Josh Andrew. 600 HIGHLAND AVE RM B6-319, HOSPITAL AND 53792 #017-20-2004 L2006 **AN** *012

WATSON, Maren Lee. ■ 53711 #026-04-1992 L1996 **FM** *020 †18

WATTS, David Thos. 2880 UNIVERSITY AVE 53705 #054-04-1979 L1981 **IMG IM** *020 †20

WEATHERHOGG, Curtis Ramon. 20 S PARK ST STE 303 53715 #030-05-1955 L1958 **PD** *071 †55

WEBB, Heather. UNIV HOSP AND CLINICS, E3-311 CLIN SCI CTR 53792 #028-02-2006 L2008 **DR** *012

WEBB, Richard Marshall. 25 KESSEL CT, STE 200 53711 #016-11-1983 L1984 **P ADP** *020 †75

WEBER, Charles Alfred. 600 HIGHLAND AVE, 202 S PARK DEPT OF MEDICIN 53792 #016-43-1982 L1990 **PUD CCM** *020 †20

WEBER, Sharon Marie. 600 HIGHLAND AVE, H4/752CSC 53792 #056-05-1993 L1994 **GS** *020 †85

WEBSTER, Benjamin Harris. 600 HIGHLAND AVE, BOX 3272 53792 #054-04-2005 L2006 **AN** *012

WEDDLE, Melissa Carol. 2880 UNIVERSITY AVE 53705 #051-01-1985 L1997 **PD** *020 †55

WEGENKE, John Duane. 1 S PARK ST, FL 7 53715 #056-05-1971 L1972 **U** *020 †95

WEIDEN, Evan Todd. 1200 JOHN Q HAMMONS DR, STE 400 53717 #038-43-1999 L2000 **P** *020 †75

WEIGEL, Tracey Lee. 600 HIGHLAND AVE, H4/316 53792 #035-45-1986 L1995 **TS SO** *020 †85,90

WEIGERT, Bonnie J. 621 SCIENCE DR 53711 #038-41-1993 L1994 **PM** *020 †60

WEILER, Stephen James. 6001 RESEARCH PARK BLVD 53719 #038-40-1973 L1981 **P SME** *040 †75

WEIN, Francine Bryna. 600 HIGHLAND AVE, DEPARTMENT OF OPHTHALMOLOG 53792 #067-01-1993 L2002 **OPH** *020 †35

WEINER, Michael Amram. 6418 NORMANDY LN, STE 210 53719 #056-05-1974 L1975 **PS** *020

WEINHAUS, Larry Howard. 1313 FISH HATCHERY RD, DEAN MEDICAL CENTER 53715 #028-03-1982 L1989 **PDC PD** *020 †20

WEINMAN, Mary Sue. ■ 53705 #056-05-1967 L1968 **AN** *020 †05

WEINSTEIN, Marie E R. 707 S MILLS ST 53715 #028-03-1974 L1987 **NPM PD** *020 †55

WEINTRAUB, Breton M. 2500 OVERLOOK TER, WM E. MIDDLETON MVH 53705 #038-41-1991 L2002 **IM** *020 †20

WEINTRAUB, Frances Herman. 4122 E TOWNE BLVD 53704 #016-45-1991 L2002 **PD** *020 †55

WEIR, Robert Michael. 707 S MILLS ST 53715 #016-06-1969 L2004 **OPH FM** *071 †35

WEISBLUM, Bernard. UNIV-WI MED SCH PHARMA 53706 #035-08-1961 **OS** *050

WEISS, Jennifer Michelle. J5/230 CSC-2454, 600 HIGHLAND AVE 53792 #035-45-2002 L2004 **GE** *012 †20

WEISS, John Wm. 2500 OVERLOOK TER 53705 #056-05-1971 L1972 **PTH** *020 †50

WEISSE, Mark Otto. 115 W DOTY ST, PHS C/O DANE COUNTY JAIL 53703 #056-05-1976 L1977 **FM** *020 †18

WEITZEL, Aimee Marie. 600 HIGHLAND AVE H4/832, UW HOSPITAL & CLINICS 53792 #056-05-2001 L2004 **AN** *020 †05

WELCH, Jeffrey John. 1821 S STOUGHTON RD 53716 #016-02-1982 L1987 **ORS** *020 †40

WELLING, Catherine C. 1 S PARK ST, FL 7 53715 #056-05-1981 L1991 **GS** *072 †85

WELLS, Jason Charles. ■ 53704 #035-20-2006 L2008 **IM** *012

WELLS, Jeffrey Allen. 600 HIGHLAND AVE K4/930, UNIV. OF WISCONSIN HOSPITA 53792 #028-03-1987 L1988 **CCM IM** *020 †20

WELLS, Jennifer T. 600 HIGHLAND AVE, UNIVERSITY OF WI HOSPITAL 53792 #048-15-2002 L2004 **GE** *012 †20

WELNICK, Richard Otto. 20 S PARK ST STE 355 53715 #056-05-1973 L1974 **IM** *030 †20

WELSCH, Suzanne Marie. 451 JUNCTION RD, UW W CLINIC 53717 #056-06-1994 L1998 **OBG** *020 †30

WENDLAND, Claire Leone. ■ 53711 #025-12-1990 L1990 **OBG** *020 †30

WENDRICKS, Lori Marie. 1821 S STOUGHTON RD 53716 #056-05-1996 L2000 **OBG** *020 †30

WENDT, Gary John. 600 HIGHLAND AVE, STE E-3/366 53792 #056-05-1991 L1992 **DR** *020 †80

WENGER, Ronald David. 1821 S STOUGHTON RD 53716 #038-06-1970 L1977 **GS SO** *020

WEST, Jesse Lyle, IV. 600 HIGHLAND AVE H4/831, UNIV OF WI HOSPITAL AND CL 53792 #036-07-2002 L2004 **ORS** *012

WESTCOTT, Thomas S. 330 E LAKESIDE ST 53715 #019-02-1953 L1954 **GP FM** *071 †18

WESTER, Susan Muriel. ■ 53703 #056-05-1977 L1978 **PTH** *020 †50

WESTMAN, Jack C. 600 HIGHLAND AVE, CLINICAL SCIENCE CTR 53792 #025-01-1952 L1965 **CHP P** *071 †75

WESTON, Carl Burton. 166 LAKEWOOD BLVD 53704 #041-01-1960 L1962 **IM** *040 †20

WESTRING, David Williams. 53703 #056-05-1958 L1960 **IM HEM** *074

WETTERNECK, Tosha Beth. 600 HIGHLAND AVE, J5/222 CSC MC 2454 UW HOSP 53792 #056-06-1995 L1996 **IM** *050 †20

WHALEN, Bonny Lyn. 5249 E TERRACE DR 53718 #050-02-1996 L1999 **PD** *020 †55

WHIFFEN, James Douglass. 600 HIGHLAND AVE 53792 #056-05-1955 L1956 **GS** *030 †85

WHITE, John David. ■ 53708 #018-03-1973 L1992 **EM** *020

WHITE, Katherine Margaret. ■ 53719 #017-20-2006 L2008 **IM** *012

WHITE, Matthew Joseph. ■ 53719 #017-20-2006 L2008 **ORS** *012

WIEDEL, Beth Ann. 600 HIGHLAND AVE, UNIVERSITY OF WI HOSPITAL 53792 #056-05-2002 L2004 **OBG** *020

WIGFIELD, Christopher. 600 HIGHLAND AVE 53792 #409-33-1993 *100

WIGGINS, Lora Lee. 2802 INTERNATIONAL LN, CARE WISCONSIN 53704 #035-08-1987 L1990 **IMG** *020 †20

WILCOTS, Margaret C. 4410 REGENT ST, ASSOCIATED PHYS LLP 53705 #005-02-1991 L1995 **PD** *020 †55

WILHITE, Beth Louise. ■ 53704 #038-41-1989 L1990 **IM** *020

WILK, Alev Inez. H6/169 CSC, 600 HIGHLAND AVE 53792 #005-19-1989 L1992 **IM** *020 †20

WILLIAMS, Daniel Harrison. 1 S PARK ST, FL 7 53715 #035-01-1999 L2006 **U** *020 †95

WILLIAMS, Deborah Claire. 675 W WASHINGTON AVE 53703 #056-05-2001 L2004 **IM** *020

WILLIAMS, Eliot C, III. UNIVERSITY HOSPITAL 53792 #017-20-1976 L1977 **HEM IM** *074

WILLIAMS, Eric Mccammon. 600 HIGHLAND AVE, AVE H4/831-8320 53792 #016-45-2004 L2006 **CD** *012 †20

WILLIAMS, Gary Philip. 2880 UNIVERSITY AVE 53792 #041-01-1974 L1985 **PD IM** *040 †55

WILLIAMS, John Byron. 20 S PARK ST, STE 207 53715 #028-34-2000 L2001 **GE** *100 †20

WILLIAMS, Laurence Lyman. 20 S PARK ST STE 504, UW HEALTH INTERNAL MEDICIN 53715 #035-08-2000 L2002 **IM** *020 †20

WILLIAMSON, Shawn Sebasti. ■ 53718 #056-05-2008 *012

WILLMANN, Karl. 600 HIGHLAND AVE, B6 319 CLINICAL SCIENCE CT 53792 #056-05-1997 L1998 **AN** *020 †20

WILLS, Brian Philipdonal. 600 HIGHLAND AVE, BOX 7375 53792 #041-01-2005 L2006 **ORS** *012

WILLS, John Orrin Basil. 4230 E TOWNE BLVD, # 286 53704 #566-01-1981 L1985 **EM** *020 †18

WILMETH, Alison Smith. 1313 FISH HATCHERY RD, OCCUP MED DEPT 53715 #056-05-1978 L1980 **OM** *020 †70

WILSON, Allen David. 600 HIGHLAND AVE, DEPT PEDIATRICS CSC 53792 #016-11-1974 L1979 **PD PDC** *020 †55 ‡

WILSON, Charis. 3434 E WASHINGTON AVE, DEAN URGENT CARE CTR 53704 #024-07-1981 L1986 **IM** *020 †20

WILSON, Michael Andrew. 600 HIGHLAND AVE, HOSPITAL 53792 #671-01-1968 L1979 **NM IM** *020 †28

WILSON, Pamela Aird. 600 HIGHLAND AVE 53792 #023-01-1976 L1979 **PUD** *020 †20

WILSON, Siobhan Deire. 53705 #056-05-2008 *012

WINKEL, Elaine Marie. 600 HIGHLAND AVE, E5/582B, CSC/CARD. MED SEC 53792 #016-43-1987 L2005 **CD** *020 †20

WINSTON, Margaret C. ■ 53703 #016-06-1952 L1954 **DR** *071 †80

WINTER, Thomas Chas. 600 HIGHLAND AVE, STE E-3/366 53792 #036-07-1986 L1999 **DR** *020 †80

WIRINGA, Karen S. 707 S MILLS ST, ST MARY'S HOSPITAL MED CEN 53715 #016-06-1974 L1987 **NPM** *020 †55

WISE, James Parry. 1821 S STOUGHTON RD 53716 #025-01-1969 L1980 **OPH** *020 †35

WISE, Steven M. ■ 53704 #056-05-2006 L2008 **DR** *012

WITKOVSKY, Michael Thos. 600 HIGHLAND AVE 53792 #016-11-1989 L1991 **CHP** *020 †75

WITTE, Karin Elisabeth. ■ 53703 #056-05-2006 **DR** *012

WOJDYLA, Piotr Jozef. 600 HIGHLAND AVE, AND CLI 53792 #759-06-1996 L2006 **PCC** *012 †20

WOJTOWYCZ, Myron M. 600 HIGHLAND AVE, UNIV WI CSC DEPT RADLGY 53792 #016-01-1978 L1979 **DR VIR** *020 †80

WOLBERG, William Harvey. 600 HIGHLAND AVE 53792 #056-05-1956 L1957 **GS CRS** *040 †85

WOLF, Mitchell Dennis. 707 S MILLS ST 53715 #025-01-1986 L1991 **OPH** *020 †35

WOLFE, Adam. ■ 53719 #016-11-2008 *012

WOLFF, David Alfred. 1313 FISH HATCHERY RD 53715 #016-06-1988 L1995 **OAR ORS** *020 †40

WOLFF, Jan. 1500 HIGHLAND AVE, UW BIOCHEM GENETICS LAB 53705 #024-01-1953 L2009 **OS** *100

WOLFF, Jon Asher. 1500 HIGHLAND AVE 53705 #023-07-1980 L1988 **PD MG** *050 †55,19

WOLFF, Matthew R. 451 JUNCTION RD, STE 9903 53717 #023-07-1986 L1992 **CD IM** *020 †20

WOLLAEGER, John Kingsbury. 1 S PARK ST, FL 7 53715 #005-14-1995 L1996 **ORS** *020 †40

WOLMAN, Richard Lee. 600 HIGHLAND AVE, B6 319 CLINICAL SCIENCE CT 53792 #035-47-1979 L1999 **AN OS** *020 †05 ‡

WONG, Gordon Wayne. 600 HIGHLAND AVE BOX 3684 53792 #017-20-2003 L2005 **RO** *012

WONG, William Ka-Lox. 1300 UNIVERSITY AVE, UNIV OF WI MED SCH 53706 #056-05-2004 L2004 **DR** *012

WOOD, Gary Stewart. 451 JUNCTION RD, STE 9903 53717 #016-11-1979 L2001 **D DMP** *020 †50,15

WOOD, Jeffrey Marion. 752 N HIGH POINT RD 53717 #056-05-1995 L1996 **IM** *020 †20

WOODFORD, John Elmer. 1808 W BELTLINE HWY 53713 #056-05-1969 L1970 **NS** *030 †25

WOODS, Jon Pointon. ■ 53705 #036-01-1989 **IM** *100

WOODS, Monty. 8322 INVERNESS DR 53717 #036-05-1970 L1993 **GS** *020

WOODS, Ryan William. ■ 53703 #056-05-2008 *012

WOODSON, Robert David. 600 HIGHLAND AVE, DEPT OF MEDICINE H4 540 CS 53792 #016-02-1963 L1974 **HEM IM** *050 †20

WOODWARD, Thomas Woodrow. 1821 S STOUGHTON RD 53716 #018-03-1996 L1997 **FM** *020 †18

WORKNEH, Fikre. UNIV HOSPS, DEPT PSYCH 53706 #605-01-1962 **P** *100

WORLEDGE, James Nicholas. 707 S MILLS ST, ST MARYS HOSPITAL 53715 #051-01-1997 L1998 **P** *020 †75

WOROCH, Gary Ward. 2500 OVERLOOK TER 53705 #056-05-1974 L1975 **IM** *020 †20

WOZNIAK, Marye Elizabeth. J5/230 CSC-2454, 600 HIGHLAND AVENUE 53792 #040-02-2006 L2008 **IM** *012

WRIGHT, Clyde Jason. 600 HIGHLAND AVE H4/823, UW HOSPITAL AND CLINICS 53792 #023-07-2001 L2003 **NPM** *012 †55

WRIGHT, Julia Walden. 600 HIGHLAND AVE 53792 #025-01-1993 L1994 **IM** *030 †20

WRIGHT, Robin Mc Ginn. 7102 MINERAL POINT RD, U W HEALTH 53717 #040-02-1993 L1996 **PD** *020 †55

WU, Nancy Nan-Hwa. ■ 53711 #242-17-1945 L1964 **AN** *071 †05

WUBBEN, Deborah Patrick. H4/568 CSC, 600 HIGHLAND AVE 53792 #056-05-1998 L2003 **END** *100 †20,70

WYMAN, John Bryant. 451 JUNCTION RD, STE 9903 53717 #056-05-1958 L1959 **IM GE** *072 †20

WYNN, Martha Marie. DEPT ANES B6/319 CSC, 600 HIGHLAND AVE. 53792 #056-05-1977 L1978 **AN** *040 †05

WYNN, Shawn Warren. 600 HIGHLAND AVE K4/7, UNIVERSITY OF WISCONSIN 53792 #016-01-2001 L2006 **OSM** *020

YAFFE, Michael Reed. 1200 JOHN Q HAMMONS DR, STE 400 53717 #016-01-1979 L1984 **PG PD** *020 †55

YANDOW, Donald Robt, II. 600 HIGHLAND AVE, UNIV OF WISCONSIN HOSP 53792 #050-02-1977 L1978 **DR** *020 †80

YANG, David Tsunchi. ■ 53726 #005-12-1994 L1997 **HMP** *100 †20,50

YAO-LONG, Michelle S. ■ 53792 #025-01-1993 L1994 **RO** *020 †80

YEAZEL, Roy Vernon. 6425 ODANA RD 53719 #056-06-1961 L1962 **AM GP** *020

YOST, John Chas. 437 VIRGINIA TER 53726 #056-05-1979 L1980 **FM** *020 †16,18

YOUNG, Abigail M. 700 RAY O VAC DR, STE 220 53711 #035-45-1988 L1989 **P** *020

YOUNG, Alexander Jon. 777 S MILLS ST, UW - MADISON DEPT OF FAMIL 53715 #051-04-2004 L2006 **FP** *012

YOUNG, Ken He. 600 HIGHLAND AVE, B4-263 UWHC 53792 #243-43-1984 L2005 **PTH HMP** *100

YOUNG, William Paul. 600 HIGHLAND AVE, RM HR348 53792 #056-05-1941 L1942 **TS** *071 †85,90

YU, Kok Peng. 4122 E TOWNE BLVD 53704 #035-15-1977 L1978 **PD** *020 †55

YUCUS, Chad Joseph. 1313 FISH HATCHERY RD 53715 #016-11-2002 L2007 **N** *100 †75

YUEN, Lawrence M. 600 HIGHLAND AVE, BOX 2454 53792 #016-11-2005 **IM** *012

YUN, Elizabeth Sohee. 600 HIGHLAND AVE, DEPARTMENT OF ANESTHESIOLO 53792 #041-09-1993 L1998 **AN PAN** *020 †05

YUSKA, Kenneth H. 4726 E TOWNE BLVD, STE 110 53704 #035-09-1971 L1978 **ORS OSS** *020 †40

YUSUF-SAFAVI, Yasmin N. 210 MARTN LTHR KNG JR BLVD, KING BLVD. 53703 #690-03-1978 L2001 **FM** *020 †18

ZACHMAN, Richard Dean. 202 S PARK ST, MADISON GENERAL HOSPITAL 53715 #011-03-1966 L1968 **NPM OS** *071

ZAHED, Cameron. J5/230 CSC-2454, 600 HIGHLAND AVE 53792 #016-42-2002 L2004 **AN** *012 †20

ZAKOWSKI, Laura Jean. 750 HIGHLAND AVE, 1190 HLTH SCI LEARNING CTR 53705 #056-05-1990 L1995 **IM** *020 †20

ZASADIL, Mary Lee. 600 HIGHLAND AVE MC3248, UNIV OF WI HOSPITAL AND CL 53792 #422-01-1998 L2003 **CD** *020 †20

ZDEBLICK, Thomas Arthur. 621 SCIENCE DR 53711 #024-07-1982 L1989 **ORS** *020 †40

ZEHEL, Guadalupe Negron. 4122 E TOWNE BLVD 53704 #056-05-1986 L1988 **IM** *020

ZEINEMANN, John Ernst. 202 S PARK ST 53715 #056-06-1983 L1993 **EM** *020 †16

ZELENSKI, Steven G. 317 KNUTSON DR, CENTRAL WISCONSIN CENTER 53704 #018-75-1984, ▲ L1992 **P PPN** *020 †75

ZELINSKI, Nathan Mark. 600 HIGHLAND AVE, AVE H4/831-8320 53792 #056-06-2005 L2006 **DR** *012

ZELLER, Frank Henry. 36 S BROOKS ST 53715 #056-05-1979 L1980 **PTH** *030 †50

ZEMAN, David Rudy. 1821 S STOUGHTON RD 53716 #016-06-1976 L1982 **ORS** *062 †40

ZEROFSKY, Ronald Aaron. 600 HIGHLAND AVE 53792 #041-13-1973 L1978 **N IM** *020 †20,75

ZGIERSKA, Aleksandra Ewa. 777 S MILLS ST, DEPT FAM MED 53715 #759-03-1995 L2003 **FM** *050 †18

ZHAO, Song Qing. 707 S MILLS ST 53715 #243-31-1984 L2003 **PTH** *020 †50

ZHARIKOVA, Darya Georgiev. 600 HIGHLAND AVE 53792 #913-64-2001 **PTH** *012

ZHONG, Weixiong. 2500 OVERLOOK TER 53705 #243-21-1982 L1998 **ATP** *020 †50

ZHUANG, Lei. 330 E LAKESIDE ST 53715 #056-06-2002 L2004 **OTO** *012

ZIEBARTH, Angela Jo. ■ 53718 #046-01-2006 **OBG** *012

ZIEGERT, Andrew Jonathan. 600 HIGHLAND AVE, UNIVRESITY OF WI HOSPITAL 53792 #056-05-2002 L2004 **DR** *100 †80

ZINDA, Michael Wm. 1104 JOHN NOLEN DR, ONCOLOGY CENTER 53713 #056-06-1979 L2001 **RO** *020 †80

ZMOLIK, Jessica Marie. ■ 53717 #048-12-2007 **IMD** *012

ZOLINSKI, Michael David. 4 W TOWNE MALL, 202 SOUTH PARK STREET 53719 #056-05-2000 L2001 **AN** *020 †05

ZU RHEIN, Gabriele Marie. 470 N CHARTER ST 53706 #407-16-1953 **PTH** *040

MANITOWISH WATERS – VILAS

BECKLUND, Roger W. ■ 54545 #016-02-1961 L1965 **GS** *071 †85

COMBS, James Arnold. ■ 54545 #056-05-1962 L1963 **R NM** *071 †80

MANITOWOC – MANITOWOC

ALVAREZ, William. 1900 WOODLAND DR 54220 #132-02-1984 L2003 **GE HEP** *020 †20
ANDRUS, David Earl. 1650 S 41ST ST 54220 #056-06-1998 L2000 **FM** *020 †18
ASCHE, Dale Edwin. 601 REED AVE 54220 #038-43-1980 L1999 **IM** *020
AUGUSTINE, David Earl. 1650 S 41ST ST 54220 #018-03-1989 L1992 **FM** *020 †18
BAATZ, Lynn Marie. 2300 WESTERN AVE 54220 #038-40-1986 L1999 **ON HEM** *020 †20
BAST, Barry Vincent. 1650 S 41ST ST 54220 #056-05-1967 L1969 **ORS** *020 †40
BAUMGARDT, M Anne. 4150 DEWEY ST 54220 #028-34-1983 L1984 **PD** *020 †55
BELL, Roger A. 4303 MICHIGAN AVE 54220 #054-04-1966 L1977 **OTO GP** *071 †45
BENHAM, Sean T. 2300 WESTERN AVE 54220 #422-01-1985 L1992 **GS** *020 †85
BENZMILLER, James Albert. 1515 RANDOLPH CT, DERMATOLOGY ASSOCIATES 54220 #030-06-1994 L2005 **D** *020 †15
BEST, John Donald. 601 REED AVE 54220 #016-11-1959 L1967 **IM** *071 †20
BHATT, Krishna. 339 REED AVE 54220 #495-98-1974 L1982 **N P** *020
BUSH, Robert Duane. PO BOX 1270 54221 #026-04-1956 L1959 **PD** *071 †55
BUSHLAND, Anne Elizabeth. 4303 MICHIGAN AVE 54220 #056-05-1998 L2006 **PD** *020 †55
BUTLER, Nancy Nguyen. 300 E REED AVE 54220 #021-01-2002 L2002 **OTO** *020
CAHILL, Charles Adams. 926 S 8TH ST, SERVICES DEPT. 54220 #024-01-1955 L1961 **P PFP** *020 †75
CANTAGALLO, Patricia Jean. 601 REED AVE, AURORA MANITOWOC CLINIC 54220 #016-11-1983 L1999 **OM** *020 †20,70
CHILINSKI, Steven Gerard. 2300 WESTERN AVE, HOLY FAMILY MEMORIAL MED C 54220 #056-05-1986 L1990 **EM** *020 †16
CHIU, Michal. 601 REED AVE 54220 #759-09-1985 L1996 **PD** *020 †55
CUTLAN, Jonathan Eugene. ■ 54220 #056-06-2005 L2005 **PTH** *012
CZERWONKA, Grazyna. 2300 WESTERN AVE 54220 #759-06-1981 L1998 **AN** *020 †05
DAHLKE, Francis Gene. ■ 54220 #010-01-1961 L1969 **GS** *071
DANBY, David Michael. 1650 S 41ST ST 54220 #056-06-1986 L1988 **FM** *020 †18
DE BRUYN, Donald J. 601 REED AVE 54220 #025-01-1977 L1980 **IM** *020 †20
DERNLAN, Robert Lewis. ■ 54220 #038-41-1956 L1967 **GS** *071 †85
DI RAIMONDO, Carl Alan. 501 N 10TH ST 54220 #056-06-1995 L2001 **OSM** *020 †40
DI RAIMONDO, Joseph Charl. 501 N 10TH ST 54220 #028-02-1965 L1966 **ORS** *071 †40
DOPIRAK, Ryan Michael. 1650 S 41ST ST, LAKESHORE ORTHO 54220 #038-40-2000 L2006 **ORS OSM** *020
DRIGGERS, Steven Durand. 2300 WESTERN AVE 54220 #016-11-1975 L1978 **EM FM** *030 †16,18
DUDEK, Stephen Lawrence. 4303 MICHIGAN AVE 54220 #056-06-1981 L1982 **DR** *020 †80
FINNEGAN, Thomas Lyman. 1650 S 41ST ST 54220 #016-11-1970 L1977 **ORS GP** *020 †40
GARVIN-CRESS, Jennifer A. 600 YORK ST, LAKESHORE WOMENS HEALTH 54220 #056-05-1985 L1993 **OBG** *020 †30
GENTILE, Matthew Kent. 2300 WESTERN AVE, HOLY FAMILY MEMORIAL HLTHC 54220 #305-01-1987 L2003 **CD** *020 †20
GIRIYAPPA, Pradeep. 1900 WOODLAND DR 54220 #495-33-1987 L1991 **CCM** *020 †20
GONZALEZ, Maryann. 1650 S 41ST ST 54220 #038-43-1993 L2002 **FM** *020 †18
GOVIER, Mary Atherton. 1900 WOODLAND DR 54220 #028-03-1977 L1980 **IM** *020 †20
GRABOWSKI, Adam S. 2417 DEWEY ST UNIT 19 54220 #759-03-1976 L1985 **P** *020
GREENE, Robert Henry. 4303 MICHIGAN AVE 54220 #016-11-1995 L1999 **PD** *020 †55
GUELDNER, Terry Louis. 940 MARITIME DR STE 4 54220 #056-06-1970 L1975 **GS TS** *020 †85
HALVORSEN, Rodney Jos. 1900 WOODLAND DR 54220 #056-06-1989 L1990 **OBG** *020 †30
HARMAN, Jill Pamela. 2300 WESTERN AVE 54220 #056-05-1979 L1980 **FM** *020 †16,18
HAYFORD, Kara Elizabeth. 339 REED AVE, TAMARACK BEHVRL HLTH CTR 54220 #056-05-1993 L2002 **PYG** *020 †75
HAYWARD, David R. 1900 WOODLAND DR 54220 #048-15-1999 L2002 **IM** *020 †20
HENDRICKS, Mark Ralph. 4100 DEWEY ST 54220 #026-04-1981 L1982 **EM** *020 †20
HERRING, Mark Leonard. 1355 JOHNSTON DR 54220 #018-03-1981 L1982 **IM** *020 †20
HOFFMAN, Michael Herbert. 1900 WOODLAND DR 54220 #056-05-1993 L1996 **FM** *020 †18 ‡
HOFFMAN, Tracy Lee. 2021 S ALVERNO RD 54220 #056-05-1993 L1996 **FPG** *020 †18 ‡
HOFTIEZER, James Wallace. 1900 WOODLAND DR, WOODLAND CLC 54220 #016-11-1975 L1980 **GE IM** *020 †20
HUDZINSKI, Janeen May. 1650 S 41ST ST 54220 #056-06-2002 L2005 **FM** *020 †18
JACOBY, Jeffrey Allen. 1650 S 41ST ST 54220 #016-43-1995 L1996 **OSS ORS** *020
JACQUES, Dana R. 600 YORK ST 54220 #041-01-1993 L2000 **OBG** *020 †30
KANER, Seymour Lawrence. 601 REED AVE, MANITOWOC CLINIC 54220 #056-05-1956 L1957 **FM** *071 †18
KANGAYAPPAN, Sivakami. 1220 FLEETWOOD DR 54220 #495-04-1965 L1976 **OBG** *071 †30 ‡
KATZ, Giora. 1818 MEMORIAL DR 54220 #550-01-1978 L2000 **U** *020
KATZ, Henry Jos. ■ 54220 #056-06-1943 L1944 **GP** *071
KATZ, Henry Michael. 801 YORK ST 54220 #056-06-1971 L1972 **D** *020 †15
KATZ, Kenneth Henry. 801 YORK ST 54220 #056-05-1996 L1997 **D DS** *020 †15
KIYAK, James Jos. 2300 WESTERN AVE 54220 #561-20-1982 L2002 **OBS GYN** *020 †30
KLASSEN, Richard Lee. 1650 S 41ST ST 54220 #019-02-1978 L1987 **FM** *020 †70,18
KLATT, Jonathan Lee. 2300 WESTERN AVE 54220 #056-06-1993 L1998 **AN** *020 †05
KLATT, Margaret Lucille. 2300 WESTERN AVE 54220 #056-06-1994 L1998 **APM AN** *020 †05
KOBELT, Carl Conrad. 601 REED AVE 54220 #016-11-1954 L1960 **CD IM** *071 †20 ‡
KORDIYAK, Christopher. 601 N 8TH ST 54220 #422-01-1987 L1989 **FM** *020 †18
KOWALEWSKA-CHIU, Joanna. 601 REED AVE 54220 #759-09-1988 L1998 **IM** *020 †20
LAMPSA, Diana Jean. 1425 MEMORIAL DR, G LAKES PSYCH CTR POB 400 54220 #056-05-1985 L1987 **P** *020 †75
LARSEN, John Revedahl. 4303 MICHIGAN AVE 54220 #056-05-1959 L1960 **OTO** *071 †45
LEWELLEN, Donald R, Jr. 4801 EXPO DR, P O BOX 1900 54220 #038-06-1981 L1985 **OPH** *020 †35
LIMONI, Patrick Francis. 1130 WESTWOOD LN 54220 #056-06-1963 L1964 **U** *020 †95
LOIS, Dean Mark. 2300 WESTERN AVE, HFMMC 54220 #056-06-1985 L1987 **EM OM** *020
LOPEZ, Nicole D. 1650 S 41ST ST, LAKESHORE FAMILY MEDICINE 54220 #048-15-1999 L2008 **FM** *040 †18
LYNCH, John D. 601 REED AVE BOX 1270 54220 #016-11-1942 L1943 **IM GE** *071
MAJOR, Judith Arnold. 1425 MEMORIAL DR 54220 #056-06-1988 L1989 **CHP** *020 †75
MARTIN, Julie Helen. 1900 WOODLAND DR 54220 #056-05-2001 L2005 **OBG** *020 †30
MC CORMICK, Michael B. 2300 WESTERN AVE 54220 #039-01-1977 L1996 **PTH FM** *020 †50,18
MENDOZA, Cecilio Tomas. ■ 54220 #748-02-1954 L1973 **GP GS** *071
MIRZA, Mansoor H.. 1900 WOODLAND DR 54220 #306-01-1997 L2005 **IM** *020 †20
MOHR, Mark David. 601 REED AVE 54220 #048-02-1986 L1987 **IM** *020 †20
MOLTENI, Kevin Henry. 4303 MICHIGAN AVE, LAKESHORE PEDIATRICS 54220 #033-05-1985 L1986 **PD NEP** *020 †55
MOORE, Julia F Tybor. ■ 54220 #056-06-1969 L1970 **CHP P** *020 †75
NAPIER, James L. 601 REED AVE 54220 #016-11-1978 L2002 **N** *020 †20,75
NELSON, Todd A. 2300 WESTERN AVE 54220 #016-11-1999 L2002 **EM** *020 †16
NUSSBAUM, Kim Cassandra. 1515 RANDOLPH CT, DERMATOLOGY ASSOC. OF WISC 54220 #016-02-2001 L2007 **D** *100 †15
O'CONNOR, Guy Alfred. 2300 WESTERN AVE 54220 #018-03-1981 L1984 **EM** *020 †16
OLSON, Craig Ladd. 501 N 10TH ST 54220 #016-01-1988 L2005 **ORS OSM** *020 †40
OOSTING, Ganna Vladimirov. 1900 WOODLAND DR 54220 #913-10-1990 L2002 **IM** *020 †20
OYEDIJO, Dotun Isaac. 2300 WESTERN AVE 54220 #025-01-1995 L2002 **RO** *020
PALAY, Howard Jerome. 601 REED AVE 54220 #056-06-1965 L1967 **CD IM** *071 †20
PATTEE, Sean Forrest. 1515 RANDOLPH CT, DERMATOLOGY ASSOC. OF WISC 54220 #003-01-2001 L2006 **D** *020 †15
PIASECKI, Shelley Diane. 339 REED AVE 54220 #056-06-2000 L2001 **P** *020 †75
QAZI, Qamaruddin. 601 REED AVE 54220 #704-16-1985 L1997 **IM** *020 †20
RAJPAL, Surinder Kumar. 601 REED AVE 54220 #905-01-1965 L1978 **PD** *020 †55
RANDOLPH, Robert Carlton. ■ 54220 #056-05-1941 L1942 **OPH** *071 †35
RAUSCHENBERGER, Thomas R. 1650 S 41ST ST 54220 #016-11-1976 L1979 **FM** *020 †18
REIMER, Darla Joy. 1650 S 41ST ST 54220 #019-02-1977 L1987 **FM** *075 †18
RILEY, Suzanne Maureen. 2300 WESTERN AVE 54220 #026-04-1985 L1992 **PTH** *020 †50
RISH, Ronald Lee, Jr. 300 E REED AVE 54220 #011-03-1970 L2000 **OTO A** *020 †45
SARGEANT, Charles D. 1825 NEW YORK AVE 54220 #016-06-1955 L1956 **GP OS** *072
SATCHELL, David Allan. 600 YORK ST 54220 #025-07-1971 L1976 **GS GP** *020 †85
SATYANATH, Siram. 601 REED AVE 54220 #495-62-1972 L2002 **DR** *020 †80
SBAR, Alan D. 2300 WESTERN AVE BOX 1450, HFM - DEPT OF SURGERY 54220 #010-01-1996 L2005 **GS** *020 †85
SCHLERNITZAUER, Donald A. 4801 EXPO DR, EYE CLINIC OF MANITOWOC SC 54220 #035-20-1967 L1978 **OPH** *071 †35
SCHMIDT, Gary Allan. 1650 S 41ST ST 54220 #056-05-1975 L1978 **FM** *020 †18
SCHROEDER, Norman Carl. 2300 WESTERN AVE 54220 #056-05-1962 L1963 **FM GP** *020 †18
SCHROEDER, Todd James. 2300 WESTERN AVE 54220 #056-05-1989 L1990 **R** *020 †80
SCHROEDER, Todd Wilson. ■ 54220 #016-02-1991 *100
SCHUETTE, Anne Hammond. 601 REED AVE 54220 #056-05-1987 L1988 **PD** *020 †55
SHAH, Dinesh Chandra P. 2300 WESTERN AVE 54220 #495-22-1961 L1976 **AN OS** *071
SHARIFF, Mansoor. 1900 WOODLAND DR 54220 #056-05-1987 L1992 **GE IM** *020 †20
SHARMA, Rajesh. 601 REED AVE, AURORA MANITOWOC CLC 54220 #495-03-1986 L2001 **GE IM** *020 †20
STANLEY, Evelyn D. 600 YORK ST 54220 #048-15-1999 L2005 **FM** *020 †18
STERN, John Michael. 1818 MEMORIAL DR 54220 #056-06-1975 L1980 **U** *020 †95
STOCKHAUSEN, Amy Lynn. 2316 HUNTERS RIDGE CT, LAKESHORE PEDIATRICS 54220 #056-05-1999 L2000 **PD** *020 †55
STUNTZ, Edgar Cheadle. ■ 54220 #016-06-1954 L1982 **P** *071
SWERCHOWSKY, Vladimir N. 2300 WESTERN AVE, BOX 487 54220 #038-06-1970 L2004 **CD IM** *020 †20
TAUSCHECK, Aloys L, Jr. 1900 WOODLAND DR 54220 #056-05-1980 L1981 **D EM** *020 †15
TEEHAN, Tresa Ann. 601 REED AVE 54220 #305-01-1996 L1997 **IM** *020 †20
THEOBALD, Richard Walrath. 601 REED AVE 54220 #018-03-1982 L1983 **IM** *020 †20
TRADER, Joseph Edgar. 501 N 10TH ST 54220 #056-06-1971 L1972 **ORS EM** *020 †40 ‡
TROCHLELL, Andrew Edward. 2300 WESTERN AVE 54220 #056-06-2003 L2004 **AN** *100
UMHOEFER, Steven Gregory. 2300 WESTERN AVE 54220 #056-05-1983 L1984 **EM** *020 †18
VAN DREEL, Richard Alan. 601 REED AVE 54220 #056-05-1962 L1963 **PD** *020 †55
VERLINDEN, Laurence J. 1650 S 41ST ST 54220 #056-06-1983 L1984 **FM** *020 †18
VOLKERT, Michael Jos. 601 REED AVE 54220 #056-05-1976 L1982 **GS VS** *020 †85
WHITE, Wayne Franklin. 2300 WESTERN AVE 54220 #039-01-1957 L1960 **AN** *071
YOUSSEF, Mary George H. ■ 54220 #915-03-1991 L2008 **CD IM** *020 †20
ZAGRODNIK, Dennis F, II. 940 MARITIME DR, STE 4 54220 #056-06-1997 L2006 **GS TS** *020 †85

MARATHON – MARATHON

SCHOOLER, Sheldon Arthur. 798 SPRING RD 54448 #018-03-1972 L1973 **FM PD** *071 †55
WARE, Robert Jerome. PO BOX 178 54448 #056-05-1964 L1966 **GP** *020

MARINETTE – MARINETTE

ARNOLD, James Michael. 3130 SHORE DR, STE 106 54143 #016-43-1984 L1988 **OBG** *020 †30
ARNOLD, James Schoonover. 2311 RIVERSIDE AVE 54143 #036-07-1948 L1990 **PTH GO** *020 †50,28
BAEK, Paul Nam-Shin. 4061 OLD PESHTIGO RD 54143 #056-06-1988 L1989 **NS** *020 †25
BALISON, David Jeffrey. 3100 SHORE DR 54143 #049-01-1992 L1993 **DR** *020 †80
BALLARD, Elisabeth Vogel. 3100 SHORE DR 54143 #030-06-1992 L1999 **RNR** *020 †80
BAROUD, Khalil S. 1106 UNIVERSITY DR 54143 #915-02-1980 L2001 **IM** *020
BARRETTE, Antoine. ■ 54143 #056-06-1953 L1954 **GP** *071
BIELKE, Dennis James. 3100 SHORE DR 54143 #056-06-1982 L1991 **DR VIR** *020 †80
BOREN, Clark Henry. 3100 SHORE DR 54143 #056-06-1946 L1947 **GP** *071
BOREN, James A. ■ 54143 #016-06-1948 L1948 **GP GS** *071 †85
BOZELKA, Brian Edward. 1400 UNIVERSITY DR 54143 #021-05-1990 L1994 **OPH IM** *020 †35
BOZOVICH, Pablo Gabriel. 3130 SHORE DR 54143 #132-02-1999 L2003 **IM** *020 †20
BRADY, John Gilchrist. 3100 SHORE DR 54143 #034-01-1992 L1997 **PCP** *020 †50
BRIODY, John Patrick. 3123 SHORE DR, STE 201 54143 #025-07-1978 L1982 **OBG** *020 †30
CAI, Jiaxin. 3100 SHORE DR 54143 #243-52-1984 L2004 **PTH** *020 †50
CARLSON, Vernette Marie. 3100 SHORE DR 54143 #056-06-1984 L1985 **FM** *020 ‡
CASELTON, Stephen Chas. 1510 UNIVERSITY DR 54143 #038-43-1973 L1977 **PD EM** *020 †55
CHAKRABARTI, Sakti. 3100 SHORE DR 54143 #495-02-1992 L2004 **IM HO** *020 †20
CRISSINGER, Harold Paul. 3100 SHORE DR 54143 #041-02-1972 L1975 **FM A** *020 †18
DAHIR, George Alex. ■ 54143 #056-05-1978 **LM** *050
DAROACH, Gian C. 3130 SHORE DR, POB XO 54143 #495-03-1983 L1993 **IM** *020 †20
DIZOR, Robert Patrick. 4061 OLD PESHTIGO RD 54143 #011-04-1997 L2004 **DR** *020
DOSHI, Mehul Mahendra. 3100 SHORE DR 54143 #056-05-2001 L2006 **DR** *100 †80
EL JACK, Mohamed Sid Ahme. 3100 SHORE DR 54143 #848-01-1991 L2002 *020
ESCOBAR, Miguel R. 3100 SHORE DR 54143 #065-01-1999 L2004 **NEP** *020 †20

■ = Address Information Privacy Protected

FALK, Barbara Ann. 3100 SHORE DR 54143 #025-07-1975 L2001 **PD** *020 †55
FEIDER, Henry Kenneth. 3100 SHORE DR 54143 #056-06-1986 L1987 **DR** *020 †80
FEJER, Szabolcs I. 1510 UNIVERSITY DR 54143 #473-04-1965 L1992 **PD EM** *071 †55 ‡
FERGUS, Peter Andrew. 1106 UNIVERSITY DR, PREVEA GREEN BAY HEARTCARE 54143
 #035-45-1970 L1975 **CD** *020 †20
FISHER, David Ross. 3100 SHORE DR 54143 #019-02-1979 L1983 **DR OS** *020 †80
FLYNN, James Bryan. 3130 SHORE DR 54143 #035-08-1976 L1982 **VS** *020 †85
GAMEZ, Francisco Jose. 3100 SHORE DR 54143 #308-02-1994 L2004 **CD** *020 †20
GARDON, Mark Anthony. 4061 OLD PESHTIGO RD 54143 #056-06-1990 L1991 **NS** *020 †25
GATES, Thomas Mooney. 3100 SHORE DR, BAY AREA MEDICAL CENTER 54143
 #030-06-1982 L1988 **DR** *020 †80
GAYLORD, Gregg Michael. 3100 SHORE DR 54143 #038-41-1981 L1996 **DR VIR** *020 †80
GOSSMAN, David Garrett. 3200 SHORE DR, PO BOX 437 54143 #020-12-2002 L2007 **OTO** *020
HALAWEH, Osama Mahmoud. 4061 OLD PESHTIGO RD, AURORA MED GRP 54143
 #575-01-1996 L2006 **HO** *020 †20
HALLFRISCH, John Thos. 1915 HALL AVE 54143 #025-01-1984 L1986 **FM OM** *020 †18
HARRINGTON, Virginia V. 3100 SHORE DR 54143 #748-10-1982 L1994 **NEP PTH** *020 †20
HEVERLY, David N. 3100 SHORE DR 54143 #047-06-1996 L2000 N *020 †75
HIMMEL, Karen Baranski. 3130 SHORE DR, STE 104 54143 #025-07-1988 L1993
 IM GYN *020 †20
HOYME, Steven Howard. 1939 HALL AVE 54143 #056-05-1971 L1972 **OPH GP** *071 †35
KAUFMAN, David Karl. 3100 SHORE DR 54143 #026-04-1989 L1993 **N** *020 †75
KENNEDY, Denise Abbott. 3100 SHORE DR 54143 #007-02-1990 L1995 **PTH** *020 †50
KENNEDY, Timothy J. 3100 SHORE DR 54143 #018-03-1983 L1989 **U UP** *020 †95
KHAYAT, Ahmad. 3130 SHORE DR 54143 #875-02-1992 L2000 **IM PCC** *020 †20
KIELER, Nathanial Ivan. 3100 SHORE DR 54143 #056-05-2002 L2006 **PTH** *020 †50
KLOUB, Mamoun Ahmad. 3130 SHORE DR STE 111, BAY AREA MEDICAL CENTER 54143
 #913-13-1986 L2007 **CN** *100 †75
KOHLHASE, Randall K H. 3100 SHORE DR 54143 #016-11-1983 L1988 **DR** *020 †80
KURAN, Lionel Vincent. 3900 HALL AVE, BOX 797 54143 #025-01-1956 L1984
 OTO HNS *020 †45
LEOW, Nicole Ann. 3123 SHORE DR STE 102 54143 #025-12-1995 L1998 **IM** *020 †20
LEOW, Thomas Edward, Jr. 3117 SHORE DR 54143 #056-05-1993 L1998 **ORS** *020
LOOMANS, Henry John. 4061 OLD PESHTIGO RD 54143 #056-06-1992 L1994 **ID IM** *020
MAC ARTHUR, Sandra B. 1106 UNIVERSITY DR, NORTHREACH PEDIATRICS 54143
 #051-04-2000 L2003 **PD** *020 †55
MACK, Thomas V. 3100 SHORE DR, BAMC 54143 #056-06-1976 L1977 **EM GP** *020
MAGNIN, Dean Alexander. N3027 SHORE DR 54143 #056-05-1961 L1963 **GS** *071
MALLORY, William James. 3100 SHORE DR 54143 #056-05-1978 L1979 **DR** *020 †80
MANTEI, Elwyn Curtis. 3100 SHORE DR 54143 #056-05-1978 L1979 **IM IMG** *020 †20
MARS, Anthony R. ■ 54143 #305-01-1981 L1986 **AN IM** *071 †05
MASSEE, Michael Gustav. 3123 SHORE DR, STE 201 54143 #021-01-1995 L1999 **OBG** *020 †30
MC CARTHY, Gerald James. 3100 SHORE DR, BAY AREA MEDICAL CENTER 54143
 #016-06-1975 L1979 **IM** *030 †20
MC GUIRE, John Kellogg. 3100 SHORE DR 54143 #030-06-1983 L1984 **IM** *020 †20
MC QUEENEY, Robert T. 1602 MAIN ST 54143 #305-01-1984 L1992 **P** *020
MERTENS, David Raymond. 3100 SHORE DR 54143 #056-05-1976 L1977 **ON IM** *020 †20
MOEDE, Allan Jos. 4061 OLD PESHTIGO RD 54143 #056-05-1985 L2003 **ORS** *020 †40
NEAL, Bruce Michael. 3130 SHORE DR STE 109 54143 #056-05-1986 L1987 **U** *020 †95
NEZIRI, Qefli. 3100 SHORE DR 54143 #056-05-1997 L2000 **IM** *020
OPOIEN, James Wayne. 3123 SHORE DR, NORTHREACH HEALTHCARE 54143
 #011-02-1980 L1995 **FM** *020 †18
PANJA, Srinivas Rao. 3130 SHORE DR 54143 #495-62-1993 L2002 **IM** *020 †20
PETERLIN, Melinda Hough. 3100 SHORE DR 54143 #016-06-1998 L2002 **PD** *020 †55
POST, Michael James. 4061 OLD PESHTIGO RD 54143 #025-07-1980 L2000 **IM** *020 †20
POWERS, Guy. N2734 STANLEY LN 54143 #016-11-1997 L2001 **P** *020
POWERS, Lara Marie. 3100 SHORE DR STE 202 54143 #016-11-1996 L2003 **FM** *020 †18
RAMLI, Nor Hasiah. 1510 UNIVERSITY DR 54143 #624-01-1995 L2006 **PD** *020 †55
REIM, Rebecca Marie. ■ 54143 #056-06-2002 L2003 **FM** *020 †18
REITER, Brian Z. 3100 SHORE DR, DEPT. OF PHYSICIAN SERVICE 54143 #048-02-1994 L2004
 AN *020 †05
RIEBE, Joshua David. 3100 SHORE DR 54143 #056-05-1999 L2000 **DR** *020 †80
ROARTY, Timothy P. 3123 SHORE DR 54143 #056-06-1989 L1995 **GE IM** *020 †20
SALEM, Yasser Salah M. 4061 OLD PESHTIGO RD 54143 #915-03-1994 L2005 **CD** *020 †20
SANTILLAN, Concepcion E. 3100 SHORE DR 54143 #748-10-1985 L2005 **N** *020 †75
SCHMIDT, Steven Clifford. 4061 OLD PESHTIGO RD 54143 #028-02-1989 L2003 **GS** *020 †65
SEEGER, Richard Walter. 2003 MARINETTE, # 240 54143 #056-05-1980 L2007
 GS VS *020 †85
SIMMONS, Jon Lee. 3123 SHORE DR, NORTHREACH HEALTHCARE 54143 #056-05-1994 L1995
 FM *020 †18
SLADKY, James Ignatius. 3100 SHORE DR 54143 #028-34-1993 L2003 **DR** *020 †80
SPROAT, Ian Alan. 3100 SHORE DR 54143 #065-06-1985 L1991 **DR VIR** *020 †80
STIENNON, Michael John. 4061 OLD PESHTIGO RD 54143 #056-05-1976 L1977 **DR** *020 †80
STIENNON, O Arthur. 4061 OLD PESHTIGO RD 54143 #056-06-1973 L1979 **R** *020 †80
STRIPLING, Burnell Donald. 3130 SHORE DR 54143 #035-09-1960 L1968 **IM PD** *071 †20
SUN, Yeping. 3100 SHORE DR 54143 #243-46-1985 L2002 **PTH** *020
TAMBEAUX, Robert Hale. 3100 SHORE DR 54143 #005-19-1990 L1991 **DR** *020 †80
THILL, James Elton. 2720 CAHILL RD, NORTHREACH HEALTHCARE LLC 54143
 #039-05-1985 L1988 **FM** *020 †18
THYES, Rick G. 3130 SHORE DR 54143 #056-05-1996 L2001 **DR** *020 †80
TICK, David Bruce. 1106 UNIVERSITY DR 54143 #016-01-1983 L1993 **IM PD** *020 †19,55
TILLSON, Martha Ann. 3100 SHORE DR 54143 #007-02-1962 L1972 **F 7H** *020 †30
TSAI, Jung Nan. 1510 UNIVERSITY DR 54143 #385-02-1967 L1976 **PD GP** *020 †55
URBAN, Jeffrey Robt. 1106 UNIVERSITY DR 54143 #026-04-1991 L2006 **PD** *020 †55
VICUNA-RIOS, Juan Manuel. ■ 54143 #737-01-1973 L1976 **EM GS** *075 †16
WINECK, Edward Marcus. 3100 SHORE DR 54143 #003-01-1989 L1998 **DR** *020 †80
ZARVAN, Nami Patrick. 3100 SHORE DR 54143 #056-05-1991 L1992 **DR VIR** *020 †80

MARION – WAUPACA

MC INNIS, Michael J. PO BOX 266 54950 #056-06-1976 L1977 **FM EM** *075 †18

MARKESAN – GREEN LAKE

FENSKE, Jill Noelle. ■ 53946 #056-05-2003 L2006 **FM** *100 †18

KREUTER, George Carlton. RR 1 BOX 109 53946 #056-06-1943 L1947 **AN** *071 †05
PLUEDDEMAN, Paul Martin. ■ 53946 #016-11-1957 L1960 **EM FM** *071 †18,16
WATERHOUSE, Blake Elwin. ■ 53946 #017-20-1961 L1965 **OS** *071 †20

MARSHALL – DANE

SCHMIDT, Mary E Helmer. 617 ROSEWOOD AVE, BOX 428 53559 #056-05-1962 L1971 **GP** *071

MARSHFIELD – WOOD

ABDALRAHMAN, Ihab Babiker. 1000 N OAK AVE 54449 #848-01-1994 L2003 **IM** *020 †20 ‡
ABLETT, Charles Timothy. 1000 N OAK AVE 54449 #024-01-1971 L1991 **IM** *020 †20
ABO-KAMIL, Raid. 1000 N OAK AVE, MARSHFIELD CLINIC 54449 #154-01-1997 L2006 **PD** *012
ALI, Pamela S. ■ 54449 #035-46-1998 L2000 **IM** *075 †20
AL KASSAR, Ghiath. 1000 N OAK AVE 54449 #875-01-2004 **PD** *012
AL-SHARIF, Bashar Labib. 1000 N OAK AVE 54449 #575-02-2003 L2008 **PD** *012
ANDERSEN, Niels Christian. 1000 N OAK AVE, MARSHFIELD CLINIC 54449 #154-02-1981 L1988
 FM *020 †18
ANDERSEN, Victoria E. 1000 N OAK AVE, MARSHFIELD CLINIC 54449 #154-02-1981 L1997
 FM *020 †18
ANDERSON, Dennis Richard. 1000 N OAK AVE 54449 #018-03-1983 L1991 **OPH** *020 †35
ANDERSON, Gregory Allen. 1000 N OAK AVE, MARSHFIELD CLINIC 54449 #056-05-1988 L1989
 U *020 †95
ANDERSON, Kelley Pierce. 1000 N OAK AVE, MARSHFIELD CLINIC - HEARTC 54449
 #035-45-1977 L2000 **CD** *020 †20
ASWANI, Vijay Hotchand. 1000 N OAK AVE, MAIL ROUTE 1B3 54449 #661-02-2005 L2006
 MPD *012
AUGHENBAUGH, David Kim. 611 SAINT JOSEPH AVE 54449 #025-01-1965 L1970
 IM PUD *020 †20
BABCOCK, Gregory Allen. 1000 N OAK AVE, MARSHFIELD CLINIC 54449 #016-45-2000 L2005
 DR *020 †80 ‡
BACHHUBER, Michele Bauer. 1000 N OAK AVE 54449 #056-05-1991 L1992 **IM** *020 †20
BAJWA, Raza Ullah. 1000 N OAK AVE 54449 #704-01-2005 *100
BALDAUF, Mary C C. 1000 N OAK AVE 54449 #017-20-1974 L1977 **BBK CLP** *020 †50
BALINGHASAY, Celestino P. 1000 N OAK AVE 54449 #748-10-1988 L2005 **ADP** *020 †75
BANERJEE, Tarit Kumar. 1000 N OAK AVE, STE 3A1 54449 #495-39-1962 L1972 **ON** *020 †20
BARTOW, Rebecca Margaret. 1000 N OAK AVE 54449 #036-07-1980 L1987 **OPH** *020 †35
BARTOW, Thomas Jos. 1000 N OAK AVE 54449 #035-48-1980 L1990 **RHU IM** *020 †20
BASSI, Deepa. 1000 N OAK AVE 54449 #495-37-1993 L2004 **PTH** *020
BASSI, Tarun. 1000 N OAK AVE 54449 #495-37-1993 L2004 **IM** *020
BELL, Wendell Dean. 1000 N OAK AVE 54449 #056-06-1988 L1992 **P** *020
BELONGIA, Edward. 1000 N OAK AVE, MARSHFIELD MED RES FOUND 54449
 #025-12-1982 L1983 **EM IM** *050 †20
BELTAOS, Efstathios. 1000 N OAK AVE 54449 #418-01-1960 L1965 **ATP** *020 †50 ‡
BENSON, Lisa Suzanne Poss. 1000 N OAK AVE, MARSHFIELD CLINIC 54449
 #026-04-1992 L1995 **IM** *020 †20 ‡
BERSALONA, Fernando B. 1000 N OAK AVE, MARSHFIELD CLINIC 54449 #748-02-1961 L1969
 OTO *071 †45
BHATTACHARJEE, Nandita R. 1000 N OAK AVE, MARSHFIELD CLINIC 54449
 #038-40-1991 L1997 **DR** *020 †80
BHUPATHI, Satya Sai Venka. 1000 N OAK AVE, MARSHFIELD CLINIC 54449 #495-11-2001 L2005
 IM *020
BILLINGS, Kenneth Jos. 1000 N OAK AVE, MARSHFIELD CLINIC 54449 #024-07-1965 L1979
 DR *071 †80
BJARNASON, David F. 1000 N OAK AVE, MARSHFIELD CLINIC 54449 #061-01-1966 L1973
 RHU IM *020 †20
BLAU, Edward Bernard. 1000 N OAK AVE 54449 #028-34-1964 L1977 **NEP PD** *071 †55
BOERO, Jaime Alberto. 1000 N OAK AVE, MARSHFIELD CLINIC 54449 #737-06-1992 L2007
 N *100 †75
BOHON, Charles Randall. 1000 N OAK AVE 54449 #039-05-1988 L1989 **AN** *020 †05
BOL-DE GREVE, B Danielle. 1000 N OAK AVE, MARSHFIELD CLINIC 54449 #917-08-1976 L1993
 ON *020 †20
BOLLOW, Frederic Wm. 1000 N OAK AVE 54449 #056-06-1981 L1984 **AN** *020 †05
BOULET, Wilbur Jos. ■ 54449 #056-06-1954 L1956 **FM EM** *071
BOVET, Philip Michael. 1000 N OAK AVE, MARSHFIELD CLINIC 54449 #018-75-2006, ▲ L2007
 GS *012
BOYLE, Timothy Richard. 1000 N OAK AVE, MARSHFIELD CLINIC 54449 #018-03-1989 L1994
 OTO *020 †45
BRINK, Bruce Edward. 1000 N OAK AVE, MARSHFIELD CLINIC 54449 #025-01-1966 L1985
 GS *071 †85
BROWELL, John Nelson. ■ 54449 #023-01-1961 L1967 **CD IM** *071
BSEISO, Ali Walid Saleh. 1000 N OAK AVE # 3A2 54449 #575-01-1988 L2000 **IM HO** *020 †20
BUCHOLTZ, Gerald Arthur. 1000 N OAK AVE, MARSHFIELD CLINIC 54449 #056-05-1973 L1979
 AI IM *020 †20,03
BUDDEMEIER, Kamilla J. 1000 N OAK AVE 54449 #017-20-1987 L1988 **CD IC** *020 †20
BUFFORD, Jeremy Daniel. ■ 54449 #004-01-2001 L2007 **AI** *020 †55,03
BURNS, John Leo, Jr. ■ 54449 #056-06-1942 L1947 **AN OS** *071
BURRILL, Raymond Eugene. 611 SAINT JOSEPH AVE 54449 #016-43-1961 L1967
 OBG *071 †30
CALDWELL, Michael De Foix. 1000 N OAK AVE, EDUCATION FDN. 54449 #045-01-1968 L2000
 VS GS *030 †85
CALLAGHAN, Eric Brian. 1000 N OAK AVE, DEPT. OF RADIOLOGY 54449 #025-01-2000 L2006
 DR *100 †80
CAMPBELL, Harold Thomas. 1000 N OAK AVE 54449 #021-01-1977 L1990 **NEP IM** *020 †20
CAMPBELL, John Alexander. 1000 N OAK AVE 54449 #016-01-1974 L1979 **PUD IM** *071 †20
CAMPBELL, Lois Rebecca. 1000 N OAK AVE 54449 #021-01-1977 L1990 **CHN** *020 †55,75
CANCEL, Efrain M. 1000 N OAK AVE 54449 #042-01-1985 L1991 **OPH OS** *020 †35
CANGELOSI, Christopher J. 1000 N OAK AVE 54449 #021-05-1997 L2003 **MSR** *020 †80
CARLSON, Robert Allen. 1000 N OAK AVE, MARSHFIELD CLINIC 54449 #056-05-1983 L1984
 PTH *020 †50
CARLSON, Robert David. ■ 54449 #041-13-1962 L1968 **R** *071 †80
CASHIN, Sean Michel. 1000 N OAK AVE, MARSHFIELD CLINIC 54449 #056-05-2003 L2006
 GS *012

CHALASANI, Sreelatha. 1000 N OAK AVE, MARSHFIELD CLINIC 54449 #495-11-2001 L2005 IM *020

CHANG, Sheng-Hsiung. 1000 N OAK AVE, MARSHFIELD CLINIC 54449 #385-01-1965 L1975 CLP HMP *020 †50

CHEN, Jane Ellen. 611 SAINT JOSEPH AVE 54449 #056-05-1984 L1987 AN *020 †05

CHERIAN, Veneetha. 1000 N OAK AVE 54449 #495-31-1989 IM *100

CHIKKALA, Jane S. 1222 E 18TH ST 54449 #495-27-1990 L2004 PD *020

CHU, Dominic Shiu Kei. 1000 N OAK AVE 54449 #462-01-1975 L1983 PM *020 †60

CLAESSENS, Michael Thos. 1000 N OAK AVE, MARSHFIELD CLINIC 54449 #026-04-1992 L1999 IM PLM *050 †20

CLEVELAND, David Alan. 1000 N OAK AVE, MARSHFIELD CLINIC 54449 #056-06-1986 L1987 EM IM *020 †20,16

CLOUSE, Lawrence Henry. 1000 N OAK AVE, MARSHFIELD CLINIC 54449 #005-18-1976 L1989 HEM ON *020 †20

CODY, Lee Bailey. 1000 N OAK AVE, MARSHFIELD CLINIC 54449 #028-34-1997 L2001 MPD *020 †55,20

COHEN, Kenneth Benj. 1000 N OAK AVE 54449 #056-06-1987 L1990 IM *020 †20

COLD, Christopher James. 1000 N OAK AVE, MARSHFIELD CLINIC 54449 #056-05-1984 L1993 PTH *030 †50

CONDE, Autumn D. 1000 N OAK AVE, DEPT OF GENERAL SURGERY 54449 #038-75-2007, ▲ L2008 GS *012

CONTERATO, James P. ■ 54449 #016-01-1979 L1980 AN CCM *020 †20,05

COPPENS, Alon. 1000 N OAK AVE, MARSHFIELD CLINIC 54449 #035-06-1986 L1992 DR *020 †80

CORTEEN, Darren Patric. 1000 N OAK AVE, MARSHFIELD CLINIC 54449 #056-05-1996 L1997 OSM *020 †40

COUSINS, Margo B. 1000 N OAK AVE 54449 #007-02-1988 L1994 DR *020 †80

CRUMP, John Wm. 1000 N OAK AVE, MARSHFIELD CLINIC 54449 #026-04-1983 L1998 PUD IM *020 †20

CRUZ, Adrienne Margaret. 1000 N OAK AVE, MARSHFIELD CLINIC 54449 #056-05-2000 L2001 PD *020 †55

CURTISS, Healther Marie. ■ 54449 #056-05-2007 *012

CUSIC, Marshall E, Jr. 1000 N OAK AVE 54449 #056-06-1969 L1976 AI PD *020 †55,03

DALUM, Peter Jos. 1000 N OAK AVE, MARSHFIELD CLINIC 54449 #028-03-1976 L1992 FM *020 †18

DALY-O'NEILL, Linda. 1000 N OAK AVE, MARSHFIELD CLINIC 54449 #539-06-1991 L1997 IM *020 †20

DART, Richard Allen. 1000 N OAK AVE 54449 #016-11-1965 L1973 NEP IM *020 †20

DEETS, Cheryl C. 1000 N OAK AVE, MARSHFIELD CLINIC 54449 #026-04-1993 L1997 OBG *020 †30

DEHNER, Michael Andrew. 1000 N OAK AVE 54449 #018-03-1977 L1999 FM *020

DENNY, Edward Chas. 1000 N OAK AVE, MARSHFIELD CLINIC 54449 #041-02-1976 L1992 NPM PD *020 †55

DEVADAS, Grace C. 1000 N OAK AVE, MARSHFIELD CLINIC 54449 #495-94-1991 L1997 IM *020 †20

DEVRIES, Edna Ohalloran. 1000 N OAK AVE, ADM 1K4 54449 #016-11-1989 L1990 PD *030 †55

DHARMASHANKAR, Kodlipet C. 1000 N OAK AVE 54449 #495-09-1998 L2003 IM *020 †20

DIETZ, Julie Carol. 1000 N OAK AVE, MARSHFIELD CLINIC 54449 #026-04-1987 L1994 PDC *020 †55

DILLON, Ade Robt. 1000 N OAK AVE 54449 #055-01-1978 L1979 PM *020 †60

DISSANAYAKE, Ruwan Rasika. 1000 N OAK AVE, MARSHFIELD CLINIC 54449 #913-01-1999 L2007 IM *020 †20

DOUGLAS-JONES, John W. 1000 N OAK AVE 54449 #030-05-1975 L1983 GS *020 †85,90

DUFFY, Douglas Paul. 1000 N OAK AVE, MARSHFIELD CLNC 54449 #025-12-1973 L1983 NEP IM *020 †20

DUNLAP, Wade Wilcock. 1000 N OAK AVE, MARSHFIELD CLNC 54449 #048-16-2006 L2007 GS *012

DUPERRET, Donald Lucien. 1000 N OAK AVE 54449 #035-20-1957 L1988 R *020 †80

DYKE, Peter Cummins, II. 1000 N OAK AVE, MARSHFIELD CLINIC 54449 #051-04-2000 L2007 PDC *100 †55

EARNHART, Todd Douglas. 1000 N OAK AVE 54449 #026-04-1985 L1988 IM *020 †20

EDELSTEIN, Barry Bernard. 1000 N OAK AVE 54449 #035-08-1963 L1985 DR NM *020 †80,28

EJERCITO, Victor Santos. 1000 N OAK AVE 54449 #748-02-1972 L1979 OTO *020 †45

ELHENDY, Abdou Abdelhamid. 1000 N OAK AVE 54449 #915-02-1985 L2005 IM *020 †20

ELLIAS, Yakub Abdulmasih. 1000 N OAK AVE, THE MARSHFIELD CLINIC 54449 #528-03-1977 L2007 EM *020 †18

EMANUEL, Dean Albert. 611 SAINT JOSEPH AVE 54449 #056-05-1947 CD PUD *071 †20

ERICKSON, Scott Stephen. 1000 N OAK AVE 54449 #016-11-1975 L1978 IM IMG *020 †20

ESPADA, Ramon A. 1000 N OAK AVE 54449 #042-01-1987 L1996 FM *020 †18

FACISZEWSKI, Tom. 1000 N OAK AVE 54449 #007-02-1987 L1993 ORS GS *020 †40

FAGBEMI, Seth O. 1000 N OAK AVE 54449 #690-01-1982 L1993 HO *020 †20

FAROOQUE, Mustafa. 1000 N OAK AVE, MARSHFIELD CLINIC 54449 #160-02-1983 L2002 PM PRS *020 †60

FERNANDEZ, Edward Gerard. 1000 N OAK AVE, MARSHFIELD CLINIC 54449 #495-83-1984 L1995 CCP PD *020 †55

FINTA, Kathleen Marie. 1000 N OAK AVE 54449 #023-07-1986 L1992 PDC *020 †55

FISCHER, Herbert K J. 54449 #407-19-1951 L1965 PM *071 †60

FISH, Daryl L. 1000 N OAK AVE, MARSHFIELD CLINIC 54449 #028-79-1998, ▲ L2000 PG *020 †55

FORNCROOK, Jonathan A. 1000 N OAK AVE, MARSHFIELD CLINIC 54449 #005-76-1996, ▲ L1997 MPD *040 †20,55

FRENS, David Bruce. MARSHFIELD CLINIC NEUR 54449 #025-01-1970 L1979 CHN N *071 †55,75

FU, Qingquan. 1000 N OAK AVE 54449 #243-47-1990 L2001 IM *020 †20

GALLANT, Thomas Emanuel. 1000 N OAK AVE 54449 #048-04-1974 L1986 VIR R *020 †80

GANGINENI, Srinivas Kalya. 1000 N OAK AVE, DEPT OF INTERNAL MED 54449 #913-48-1999 L2007 IM *012

GANGLOFF, Michael Anthony. 611 SAINT JOSEPH AVE 54449 #041-02-1967 L1993 DR VIR *020 †80

GANITSKY, Alberto. MARSHFIELD CLINIC, DEPT MED 54449 #264-04-1978 IM *100

GAULKE, Mark Ernest. 1000 N OAK AVE 54449 #056-06-2006 L2007 MPD *012

GBADEBO, Olufuowobi Sunday. 1000 N OAK AVE, MARSHFIELD CLINIC 54449 #690-01-1991 L1998 CHP P *020 †75

GERNDT, Harold Leroy. ■ 54449 #018-03-1958 L1963 GS *071 †85

GERNDT, Kristin Marie. 1000 N OAK AVE 54449 #056-05-1992 L1998 VIR *020 †80

GHBEIS, Muhammad Bakr. 1000 N OAK AVE 54449 #875-01-2003 L2005 MPD *012

GHELLER-RIGONI, Anita. 1000 N OAK AVE, MARSHFIELD CLINIC 54449 #018-75-2003, ▲ L2004 AI *012 †20

GHERA, Princy. 1000 N OAK AVE 54449 #495-29-2005 *100

GIAMPIETRO, Philip F. 1000 N OAK AVE, MARSHFIELD CLINIC 54449 #035-48-1986 L2001 PD *020 †55,19

GILBERT, Steven Ronald. 1000 N OAK AVE 54449 #035-45-1984 L1992 PUD IM *020 †20

GONUGUNTLA, Veena Vandana. 1000 N OAK AVE, MARSHFIELD CLINIC 54449 #495-99-2000 PD *012

GORDON, Ellen Marie. 1000 N OAK AVE, MARSHFIELD CLINIC 54449 #011-03-1998 L2000 D *020 †15

GOTTLIEB, Viktor. 1000 N OAK AVE 54449 #016-11-1972 L1985 PS GS *020 †85,65 ‡

GRANDHE, Naga Prasad. 1000 N OAK AVE 54449 #495-62-1998 L2007 IM *012

GRANT, Henry Irvin, III. 1000 N OAK AVE 54449 #001-02-1979 L1991 GS CCS *020 †85

GREENBURG, Marian Lee. 1000 N OAK AVE 54449 #008-01-1987 L2004 IM *020 †20

GREENLAW, Robert H. M622 BIRCH ST 54449 #035-45-1952 L1970 RO *071 †80

GRIBBLE, Robert Kelly. 1000 N OAK AVE 54449 #056-05-1981 L1982 OBG *030 †30

GRIERSON, David Scott. 1000 N OAK AVE 54449 #038-40-1978 L1985 CD *020 †20

GROSS, Jody Roselyn. 1000 N OAK AVE 54449 #005-15-1978 L1984 NPM PD *020 †55

GUI, Gaojun. 1000 N OAK AVE 54449 #243-62-1982 L2001 IM *020 †20

GUNGOR, Bahri O. ■ 54449 #902-01-1954 L1962 FM *071 †20

GUZOWSKI, Frank Steven. 1000 N OAK AVE, MARSHFIELD CLINIC 54449 #025-12-1978 L1981 IM *020 †20

HABASH, Dana Esam. 1000 N OAK AVE 54449 #575-01-1998 L2003 IM *020 †20

HALDES, Tula. 1000 N OAK AVE 54449 #016-42-1979 L1990 IMG IM *020 †20

HALL, Matthew Charles. 1000 N OAK AVE 54449 #003-01-1997 L1998 ID *020 †55,20

HAMILTON, Gurdon Hubbard. 1000 N OAK AVE 54449 #016-02-1968 L1976 IMG PHP *020 †20

HAMMEKE, Michael Dennis. 1000 N OAK AVE 4A1 54449 #030-06-1972 L2002 NEP *020 †20

HAMPTON, Tracy Ann. 1000 N OAK AVE 54449 #056-05-1985 L1990 AN *020 †05

HANSEN, Raymond L. 1801 WOODSVIEW DR 54449 #056-05-1952 L1953 PDA *071 †55,03

HARDACRE, Jerry Medaris. 512 QUENTIN AVE 54449 #038-40-1959 L1966 GS *071 †85

HAWS, Robert M. 1000 N OAK AVE 54449 #049-01-1986 L2003 PN PD *020 †55

HAYES, John Jos. 1000 N OAK AVE 54449 #016-01-1985 L1991 ICE CD *020 †20

HEATH, Larry Kent. 1000 N OAK AVE 54449 #005-02-1972 L1991 IM ID *020 †20

HEBERT, Lisa Ann. 1000 N OAK AVE 54449 #056-06-1988 L1989 FM *020 †18

HEEGEMAN, David James. 1000 N OAK AVE, MARSHFIELD CLINIC 54449 #056-06-1991 L1992 IM *020 †20

HEFFERNON, Jeffrey J. 1000 N OAK AVE, DEPT OF RADIOLOGY 2B 54449 #005-15-1976 L1994 DR *020 †80

HEIKENEN, Janice B. 1000 N OAK AVE, MARSHFIELD CLINIC 54449 #056-05-1990 L1991 PG *020 †55

HENNICK, Mark Roy. 1000 N OAK AVE 54449 #056-06-1986 L1987 IM *040 †20

HERBST, Amy Louise. 310 MARYKNOLL AVE 54449 #056-05-1997 L1998 PD *020 †55

HEYWOOD, Robert Monroe. 1204 W 5TH ST 54449 #010-01-1954 L1960 AI IM *071 †20

HEYWOOD, William Harvey. 611 SAINT JOSEPH AVE 54449 #040-02-1947 L1949 P *071 †75

HILBELINK, Elizabeth V. 1000 N OAK AVE 54449 #056-05-1994 L1995 PD *020 †55

HILLE, Rachel Carol. 1000 N OAK AVE, MARSHFIELD CLINIC 54449 #037-01-2003 L2005 D *012

HILLMAN, Michael Alan. 1000 N OAK AVE, MARSHFIELD CLINIC 4F 54449 #041-07-1979 L1988 N MDM *030 †75

HINKE, Thomas Dayton. 1000 N OAK AVE 54449 #056-05-1968 L1969 AR R *020 †80

HINSON, Mark Matthew. 1000 N OAK AVE 54449 #018-03-1997 L2003 DR *020 †80

HITCHCOCK, Thomas Floyd. 1000 N OAK AVE 54449 #028-02-1982 L1991 HS *050 †40

HOCKING, William Gray. 1000 N OAK AVE 54449 #021-01-1973 L1983 HO IM *020 †20

HOEHN, George Jacob. 1000 N OAK AVE 54449 #016-11-1967 L1969 NPM *020 †55

HOEHN, James Lloyd. 1000 N OAK AVE 54449 #016-11-1966 L1974 GS SO *071 †85

HOERNEMAN, Brian David. 1000 N OAK AVE 54449 #056-05-2000 L2004 EM *020

HOLT, James Jos. 1000 N OAK AVE 54449 #030-06-1975 L1984 OTO NO *020 †45

HOLZBERGER, James August. 1000 N OAK AVE 54449 #056-05-1984 L1988 OPH *020 †35

HORTON, Peter Danl. 1000 N OAK AVE 54449 #035-45-1976 L1982 CD IM *020 †20,28

HOYNACKE, Renee Ann. 1000 N OAK AVE 54449 #025-01-2000 L2001 IM *020 †20

HUTCHINS, Lawrence Guy. 1000 N OAK AVE 54449 #056-05-1983 L1989 DR *020 †80

IDARRAGA, Samuel. 1003 W BLODGETT ST 54449 #264-06-1963 L1976 PM *071 †60

INAGANTI, Anupama. 1000 N OAK AVE, MARSHFIELD CLINIC 54449 #496-52-2002 L2006 IM *012

INDEN, Ronald Thos. 1000 N OAK AVE 54449 #056-06-1971 L1972 FM OM *020 †85

ISKANDER, Gaby Philippe. 1000 N OAK AVE, MARSHFIELD CLINIC 54449 #915-04-1988 L1998 GS TRS *020 †85

IZUORA, Kenneth Ejikeme. 1000 N OAK AVE, MARSHFIELD CLINIC 54449 #690-04-2003 L2007 IM *020 †20

JACOBSEN, F Stig. 1000 N OAK AVE 54449 #297-01-1968 L1986 OP *020 †40

JAKOPIN, Paul Bryan. 1000 N OAK AVE 54449 #017-20-1993 L1997 EM *020 †16

JANSEN, Matthew John. 1000 N OAK AVE 54449 #056-05-1994 L1995 IM *020 †20

JOHNSON, Sidney Edward. 1000 N OAK AVE 54449 #056-05-1961 L1966 OS IM *071 †20

JOSE, Deepa. 1000 N OAK AVE, DEPT OF INTERNAL MED 54449 #495-63-1998 L2007 IM *012

JOSEPH, Pradeep. 1000 N OAK AVE, MARSHFIELD CLINIC 54449 #495-63-1998 L2004 IM *020

KADAM, Brijesh Hanumant. 1000 N OAK AVE, MARSHFIELD CLINIC 54449 #495-28-2000 PD *012

KAHLE, Donald Lee. 1000 N OAK AVE 54449 #018-03-1965 L1971 DR *071 †80

KAILA, Rahul. 1000 N OAK AVE, MFLD PEDIATRIC RES PRGM 54449 #496-59-2002 L2006 PD *012

KAPLAN, Katherine M. 1000 N OAK AVE, OBSTETRICS DEPARTMENT 54449 #056-05-1985 L1986 OBG *020 †30

KAR, Papia. 1000 N OAK AVE 54449 #495-32-2002 *100

KARANJIA, Percy Naval. 1000 N OAK AVE 54449 #495-01-1970 L1984 N EM *020 †75

KASIRYE, Yusuf. 1000 N OAK AVE 54449 #905-01-2003 *100

KEENAN, Owen Bernard. 1000 N OAK AVE 54449 #011-04-1979 L1988 ORS OSM *020 †40

KELMAN, Donald Brian. ■ 54449 #068-01-1968 L1979 NS *071 †25

KENNEDY, Jane E. 1000 N OAK AVE 54449 #026-08-1977 L1989 GE *020 †20

KENNEY, Charles Victor. 1000 N OAK AVE, MARSHFIELD CLINIC 54449 #016-45-2000 L2006 DR *100 †80

KENNEY, Heidi Katherine. 1000 N OAK AVE, MARSHFIELD CLINIC 54449 #016-45-2000 L2006 DR *100 †80

KERR, Sarah Christine. 1000 N OAK AVE, MARSHFIELD CLINIC 54449 #046-01-2006 L2007 D *012

KETHIREDDY, Rajesh Babu. 1000 N OAK AVE 54449 #495-14-2002 *100

KHAMO-SOSKOS, Jian. 1000 N OAK AVE, MARSHFIELD CLINIC 54449 #528-04-1994 MPD *012

KHAN, Amir Afsar. 1000 N OAK AVE 54449 #704-21-2000 L2007 IM *100

■ = Address Information Privacy Protected

KHAN, Mohammad Qaseem. 1000 N OAK AVE 54449 #704-16-1986 L2001 **ON IM** *020 †20

KINKELLA, Albert M. 1609 SAWYER DR 54449 #025-01-1951 L1957 **OTO** *071 †45

KIRCHNER, John Patrick. 1000 N OAK AVE 54449 #016-43-1967 L1977 **HEP GE** *020 †20

KIRKHORN, Steven Reid. 1000 N OAK AVE 54449 #026-04-1977 L1987 **OM FM** *050 †70,18

KNUTH, Ronald Chas. 1000 N OAK AVE 54449 #056-05-1982 L1985 **AN** *020 †05

KOCH, Edgar Le Roy. ■ 54449 #056-05-1964 L1972 **DR** *020 †80

KOEHLER, Roderick Douglas. 1000 N OAK AVE 54449 #016-43-1986 L1987 **IM** *020 †20

KOEHN, Monica Anne. 1000 N OAK AVE, MARSHFIELD CLNC DEPT NEURO 54449 #037-01-1994 L1999 **PD** *020 †75

KOH, Yea Suk. 1000 N OAK AVE 54449 #231-03-1996 L2004 **IM** *020 †20

KOLQUIST, Kathryn Ann. 1000 N OAK AVE 54449 #020-12-1992 L1998 **SP** *020 †50

KOLTS, Robert Lee. 1000 N OAK AVE, MARSHFIELD CLINIC 54449 #049-01-1980 L1981 **GS VS** *020

KRALL, Edward Jos. 1000 N OAK AVE, DEPT OF PSYCHIATRY 54449 #056-06-1977 L1986 **P** *075

KRAWISZ, Bruce Raymond. 1000 N OAK AVE 54449 #026-08-1978 L1989 **ATP MGP** *071 †50

KRONZER, William Wagner. 1000 N OAK AVE 54449 #056-05-1968 L1969 **DR NM** *020 †80

KUBICA, Ewa. 1010 N WALNUT 54449 #759-12-1987 L1995 **IM** *020 †20

KUEHNER, Marvin Ernest. 1000 N OAK AVE 54449 #028-02-1961 L1974 **VS GS** *020 †85

KUHN, John M Ryan. 611 SAINT JOSEPH AVE 54449 #056-06-1964 L1968 **IM** *020 †20

KULSTAD, Roger Martin. 1000 N OAK AVE 54449 #308-05-1999 L2003 **END** *012 †20,55

KUMARAPERU, Indrani L. 1000 N OAK AVE 54449 #220-01-1969 L1984 **P CHP** *020 †75

KUZEL, Russel John. 1000 N OAK AVE, MARSHFIELD CLINIC 54449 #037-01-1979 L2003 **FM OS** *030 †18

LAMBERSON, Steven Alan. 1000 N OAK AVE 54449 #040-02-1983 L1984 **PM** *020 †60

LANG, Kevin A. 1000 N OAK AVE, MARSHFIELD CLINIC 54449 #056-05-1988 L1991 **GE** *020 †20

LARSON, Carol Ann. 1000 N OAK AVE 54449 #026-04-1965 L1969 **P** *071

LARSON, Dale Mark. 1000 N OAK AVE, MARSHFIELD CLINIC 54449 #025-01-1980 L1987 **GO GYN** *020 †30

LAWLER, Benjamin. 1000 N OAK AVE, MARSHFIELD CLINIC 54449 #016-11-1996 L2002 **N HO** *020 †75

LEDFORD, Jamie Randall. 1000 N OAK AVE 54449 #305-01-2008 *100

LEE, John Douglas. 1000 N OAK AVE 54449 #056-05-1970 L1976 **IM ID** *030 †20

LEE, Martha Louise K. 1101 W 5TH ST 54449 #023-07-1971 L1976 **RHU IM** *071 †20

LEER, Richard Arnold. 1000 N OAK AVE 54449 #048-12-1971 L1977 **FM EM** *020 †18

LEGGON, Robert. 1000 N OAK AVE, MARSHFIELD CLINIC 54449 #008-01-1987 L2002 **OTR** *020 †40

LEIFHEIT, Thomas Lee. 1000 N OAK AVE 54449 #016-43-1986 L1989 **AN** *020 †05

LENARTOVA, Martina. 1000 N OAK AVE, MARSHFIELD CLINIC 54449 #286-06-2000 L2002 **RHU** *100

LE PAGE, Mark Anthony. 1000 N OAK AVE 54449 #025-01-1995 L2003 **DR** *020 †80

LEWIS, Russell F. ■ 54449 #056-05-1941 L1946 **OBG** *071 †20

LIAN, Fangru. 1000 N OAK AVE 54449 #243-16-1991 L2006 **DMP** *100 †50

LIEBERMAN, Kristin Anne. 1000 N OAK AVE, MARSHFIELD CLINIC 54449 #056-05-1995 L2003 **RNR** *020 †80

LIN, Yeenan G. 1000 N OAK AVE 54449 #385-04-1966 L1981 **ON HEM** *020

LINGAIAH, Sheela Rama. 1000 N OAK AVE, MARSHFIELD CLINIC 54449 #496-39-2000 L2004 **PD** *100 †55

LISS, Paul Lloyd. 1000 N OAK AVE 54449 #056-06-1976 L1979 **IM** *030 †20

LIZAKOWSKI, Laura A. 1000 N OAK AVE, MARSHFIELD CLINIC 54449 #037-01-2005 L2006 **IM** *012

LONSDALE, Jacob William. ■ 54449 #049-01-2007 **PD** *012

LUND, Jared Jacob. 1000 N OAK AVE, MARSHFIELD CLINIC 54449 #048-16-2005 L2006 **D** *012

LUO, Jiangming. 1000 N OAK AVE 54449 #243-33-1982 L1999 **IM** *020 †20

MAC DONALD, Sanford Dale. 1000 N OAK AVE, MARSHFIELD CLINIC 54449 #026-04-1971 L1975 **IM** *071 †20

MACK, Jonathan Eberhard. 1000 N OAK AVE, MARSHFIELD CLINIC 54449 #035-46-1999 L2007 **OSM** *020 †40

MACKAY, Christopher Ian. 1000 N OAK AVE, MARSHFIELD CLINIC 54449 #065-09-1994 L2002 **NS** *020 †20

MADDEN, Kenneth Patrick. 1000 N OAK AVE 54449 #048-13-1985 L1990 **N OS** *020 †75

MAGID, Gail Avrum. 1000 N OAK AVE, DEPT. OF NEUROSURGERY 4K3 54449 #016-42-1958 L2002 **NS** *020 †25 ‡

MAGNIN, George Ernest. ■ 54449 #056-05-1946 L1947 **IM** *071 †20

MAHONEY, Kevin Richard. 1000 N OAK AVE, MARSHFIELD CENTER 54449 #026-04-1988 L2001 **CCS GS** *020 †85

MAKI, Hope Stephanie. 1000 N OAK AVE 54449 #026-04-1983 L1984 **TS** *020 †85,90

MAMCARZ, Ewelina Kinga. 1000 N OAK AVE, MARSHFIEL CLINIC 54449 #759-12-2003 **PD** *012

MAMILLAPALLI, Chaitanya K. 1000 N OAK AVE, MARSHFIELD CLINIC 54449 #495-50-2001 **IM** *012

MANANDHAR, Pradita. 1000 N OAK AVE, MARSHFILED CLINIC 54449 #672-03-2003 **IM** *012

MANICKAM, Panneer Selvan. 1000 N OAK AVE, MARSHFIELD CLINIC 54449 #495-66-1986 L2001 **IM** *020 †20

MANNE, Janaki Rami Reddy. 1000 N OAK AVE 54449 #495-62-2003 *100

MANOR, William F. 1000 N OAK AVE 54449 #018-75-1972, ▲ L1974 **EM IM** *020 †20,80

MAREEDU, Ravi Kiran. 1000 N OAK AVE, MARSHFIELD CLINIC 54449 #495-65-2003 L2006 **IM** *012

MARION, Michael Dean. 1000 N OAK AVE 54449 #422-01-2005 L2007 **GS** *012

MARTIN, Ronald Frederick. 1000 N OAK AVE, MARSHFIELD CLINIC 54449 #024-16-1988 L2004 **GS** *020 †85

MASCOLA, Maria Anne. 1000 N OAK AVE 54449 #024-07-1989 L2000 **OBG MFM** *030 †20

MAURER, William James. 1000 N OAK AVE, MARSHFIELD CLINIC 54449 #056-06-1961 L1962 **IM** *030 †20

MAYEUX, Allyson B. M645 BIRCH ST 54449 #021-05-1986 L1990 **IM** *020 †20

MAYEUX, Gary Paul. 1000 N OAK AVE, MARSHFIELD CLINIC 54449 #021-05-1984 L1990 **GE** *020 †20

MAZZA, Joseph John. 1000 N OAK AVE 54449 #016-43-1962 L1969 **HEM IM** *030 †20

MBAKWE, Ogechi Helen C.. 1000 N OAK AVE 54449 #690-07-1998 L2007 **IM** *100

MC CAULEY, Charles S. 1000 N OAK AVE 54449 #016-11-1976 L1980 **CD** *020 †20

MC FARLANE, Lawrence Geo. 1000 N OAK AVE, MARSHFIELD CLINIC 54449 #056-05-1978 L1979 **PD ADM** *020 †55

MC GILL, Charles Wilkie. 1000 N OAK AVE, MARSHFIELD CLINIC 54449 #048-04-1972 L1998 **PDS** *020 †85

MC KENZIE, Alan Kenneth. 1000 N OAK AVE, MARSHFIELD CLINIC 54449 #025-01-1969 L1977 **END IM** *020 †20

MC KIERNAN, Fergus Eoin. 1000 N OAK AVE, MARSHFIELD CLINIC 54449 #026-04-1980 L1987 **RHU IM** *020 †20

MC MANUS, Michael John. 1000 N OAK AVE, MARSHFIELD CLINIC 54449 #010-02-1983 L2002 **PHO** *020 †55

MEIER, Paul Richard. 1000 N OAK AVE 54449 #005-12-1973 L1985 **OBG MFM** *020 †30

MEILAHN, Jill Rae. 1000 N OAK AVE, DEPT OF PHYS MED & REHABIL 54449 #018-75-1988, ▲ L2006 **PM OSM** *020 †60

MELSKI, John Wm. 1000 N OAK AVE 54449 #023-07-1972 L1983 **D** *020 †20,15

MENNEN, Joseph. 1000 N OAK AVE, MARSHFIELD CLINIC 54449 #021-01-1983 L2003 **U GS** *020 †95

MERCIER, Richard J. 1000 N OAK AVE 54449 #024-16-1979 L1989 **ON HEM** *030 †20

MESA, Juan E. 1000 N OAK AVE, DEPARTMENT OF CARDIOLOGY 2 54449 #264-13-1982 L2000 **CD** *020 †20

MEYER, James Alan. 1000 N OAK AVE, DEPT OF PEDIATRICS 54449 #056-06-1982 L1983 **ADL** *020 †55

MEYER, Kathleen Marie. 1000 N OAK AVE 54449 #025-01-1984 L1991 **PS HS** *020 †85,65

MEYER, Peter Camillus. 1000 N OAK AVE, MARSHFIELD CLINIC 54449 #056-05-1983 L1987 **IM UCM** *020 †20

MICKEL, Steven Hayford. 1000 N OAK AVE 54449 #012-05-1982 L1987 **IM** *020 †20,16

MICKEL, Susan Funkhouser. 1000 N OAK AVE 54449 #012-05-1979 L1987 **N OS** *020 †75

MIECH, Donald Jos. 1000 N OAK AVE, MARSHFIELD CLINIC 54449 #007-02-1969 L1975 **D DMP** *020 †15

MILBAUER, John Patrick. 1000 N OAK AVE, MARSHFIELD CLINIC 54449 #033-05-1961 L1975 **ORS** *020 †40

MILLER, Richard Wilbur. 611 SAINT JOSEPH AVE 54449 #041-01-1961 L1970 **NM END** *020 †28,20

MIRANDA, Warren L. 1000 N OAK AVE, MARSHFIELD CLINIC 54449 #748-01-1965 L1976 **AN OS** *020

MITRA, Subhashis. 1000 N OAK AVE 54449 #495-02-1997 **IM** *012

MODHIA, Falgun Mahendraku. 1000 N OAK AVE, MARSHFIELD CLINIC 54449 #495-89-1999 L2006 **IM** *012

MOFFAT, Nelson Aird. 611 SAINT JOSEPH AVE 54449 #016-02-1955 L1962 **U** *072 †95

MOIZUDDIN, Mohammed. 1000 N OAK AVE, HOSP OFFICE 3J3 54449 #496-27-1995 L2005 **IM** *020 †20

MOLDYSZ, Urszula Jozefa. 1000 N OAK AVE 54449 #759-12-1985 L2001 **IM** *020 †20

MOREHOUSE, Dan Lee. 1000 N OAK AVE, MARSHFIELD CLINIC 54449 #018-03-1990 L2001 **VS** *020 †85

MORGAN, William Robert. 1000 N OAK AVE, MARSHFIELD CLINIC 54449 #665-01-2002 L2005 **GS** *012

MUKHERJEE, Rama Prosad. 1000 N OAK AVE, MARSHFIELD CLINIC 54449 #495-02-1958 L1981 **PS HS** *020 †65 ‡

MULLIGAN, Gerald Michael. 1000 N OAK AVE, MARSHFIELD CLINIC 54449 #026-04-1977 L1983 **R** *020 †80

MURALI, Hema Raghuram. 1000 N OAK AVE, MARSHFIELD CLINIC 54449 #495-09-1995 L2006 **CHN** *020 †55,75

MURALI, Narayana Shankar. 1000 N OAK AVE, MARSHFIELD CLINIC 54449 #495-59-1991 L2006 **NEP** *020

MUSANA, Kenneth Apollo. 1000 N OAK AVE, MARSHFIELD CLINIC 54449 #905-01-1995 L2002 **IM** *020 †20

MYERS, Lee Alan. ■ 54449 #016-42-2007 **TY** *012

MYERS, William Osgood. 1000 N OAK AVE 54449 #016-06-1955 L1968 **TS** *071 †85,90

MYKLEJORD, Duane Jaden. 1000 N OAK AVE 54449 #319-01-1995 L2001 **AN** *020 †05

NAIK, Yashoda G. 1000 N OAK AVE 54449 #496-15-1992 L2004 **PD** *100 †55

NANRA, Jasjyot Kaur. 1000 N OAK AVE, MARSHFIELD CLINIC 54449 #495-89-2001 L2005 **IM** *020 †20

NAQVI, S Hasan. 1000 N OAK AVE, MARSHFIELD CLINIC 54449 #704-01-1978 L1994 **CD** *020 †20

NAQVI, Syed Hasan Raza. ■ 54449 #704-21-2000 L2007 **IM** *100

NASH, Carolyn Rae. 1000 N OAK AVE, MARSHFIELD CLINIC 54449 #056-05-1993 L2000 **PD** *020 †55

NASSER, Rana M. 1000 N OAK AVE, MARSHFIELD CLINIC 54449 #605-01-1991 L1996 **ID** *020 †20

NEAL, John Heermann. 1000 N OAK AVE, MARSHFIELD CLINIC 54449 #008-01-1983 L1994 **NS** *020 †25

NEKKANTI, Swapna. 1000 N OAK AVE, MARSHFIELD CLINIC 54449 #496-66-2004 **IM** *012

NELSON, Lawrence Eric. 1000 N OAK AVE, MARSHFIELD CLINIC 54449 #005-02-1964 L1965 **PTH** *030 †50

NEMEC, George. 901 N COLUMBUS AVE 54449 #016-11-1954 L1957 **FM** *071 †35

NGUYEN, Thanhcuong T. 1000 N OAK AVE, MARSHFIELD CLINIC 54449 #010-01-1982 L1994 **PTH PCP** *020 †50

NICKERSON, Harlan James. 1000 N OAK AVE 54449 #018-03-1963 L1970 **PD PHO** *071 †55

NIKOLAI, Thomas F. ■ 54449 #056-16-1956 L1957 **END IM** *071 †20

NIRUJOGI, Vijaya Lakshmi. 1000 N OAK AVE, MARSHFIELD CLINIC 54449 #495-21-1994 L2007 **GS** *020

NORDIN, Ned Glen. 1000 N OAK AVE, MARSHFIELD CLINIC 54449 #056-05-1988 L1991 **AN** *020 †05

NORTH, Frank Peter. 1000 N OAK AVE, MARSHFIELD CLINIC 54449 #056-05-1989 L1998 **AN** *020 †05

OBERG, Michael Stephen. 1000 N OAK AVE, MARSHFIELD CLINIC 54449 #026-04-1979 L1998 **P** *020

OGUNMODEDE, Folashade Abi. 1000 N OAK AVE 54449 #690-01-1995 L2005 **IM** *020 †20

OKON, Tomasz Robert. 1000 N OAK AVE, MARSHFIELD CLINIC 54449 #038-43-1997 L2002 **IM PLM** *020 †20

OLDS, Warren Woodson. 1000 N OAK AVE 54449 #051-01-1978 L1993 **R** *020 †80

OMOBA, Emmanuel Aderemi. 1000 N OAK AVE, MARSHFIELD CLINIC 54449 #690-01-1984 L1992 **DR R** *020 †20,80

O'NEILL, Dermot Alphonsus. 1000 N OAK AVE 54449 #539-06-1960 L1970 **OBG U** *020 †30

O'NEILL, Diarmuid Anthony. 1000 N OAK AVE 54449 #539-06-1987 L1997 **OS** *020 †05

ONITILO, Adedayo Ayodeji. 1000 N OAK AVE 54449 #690-05-1995 L2003 **HO** *020 †20

OPITZ, James C. 1000 N OAK AVE, MARSHFIELD CLINIC 54449 #030-05-1962 L1969 **PD OS** *020 †55

OUSLEY, Joseph L. ■ 54449 #016-02-1951 L1953 **IM ON** *071 †20

OWENS, Kevin Scott. ■ 54449 #305-01-2004 L2005 **IM** *020

PAGE, Robert Wm. ■ 54449 #041-13-1972 L1977 **N** *020 †75

PARIMANATH, Sherine Jos. 1000 N OAK AVE 54449 #495-44-1990 L1997 **IM** *020 †20

PARK, Myung Ha. 1000 N OAK AVE 54449 #583-10-2007 *100

PARK, Roger Walter. 1000 N OAK AVE 54449 #019-02-1969 L1988 **GE PD** *020 †55

PARKER, John Philip. 1000 N OAK AVE 54449 #017-20-1965 L1968 **NEP IM** *020 †20

PATCHETT, Richard Bryant. 1000 N OAK AVE 54449 #005-12-1983 L1990 **OPH** *020 †35

PATHAK, Ram Dinkar. 1000 N OAK AVE 54449 #495-19-1987 L2006 **END** *020 †20

PATHAK, Sumedha Ram. 1000 N OAK AVE 54449 #495-83-1989 **IM** *012

PATTEN, Stella Frunza. 1000 N OAK AVE, MARSHFIELD CLINIC 54449 #056-05-1984 L1988 **D** *020 †15

PAULMAN, Scott Jeffrey. 1000 N OAK AVE, MARSHFIELD CLINIC 54449 #056-05-1992 L1998 **OPH** *020 †35

PAULSON, Steven Q. 1000 N OAK AVE 54449 #037-01-1977 L1980 **IM** *020 †20

PERCELL, Denis E. 1000 N OAK AVE, MARSHFIELD CLINIC 54449 #018-75-1984, ▲ L2007 **OBG** *020 †30

PERVEZ, Adnan. 1000 N OAK AVE, MARSHFIELD CLINIC 54449 #704-20-2000 L2005 **IM** *020

PESICKA, Gary Allen. 1000 N OAK AVE 54449 #028-02-1981 L1987 **OPH** *020 †35

PETERSON, Douglas Bergen. 1000 N OAK AVE 54449 #024-01-1969 L1977 **IM** *020 †20

PETERSON, Douglas Wayne. 1000 N OAK AVE, MARSHFIELD CLINIC 54449 #030-05-1965 L1991 **OTO** *020 †45

PHILLIPS, Robert Edwin. 1000 N OAK AVE, MARSHFIELD CLINIC 54449 #016-06-1975 L1979 **IM IMG** *020 †20

POONURU, Sujani. 1000 N OAK AVE, MARSHFIELD CLINIC 54449 #495-65-2004 **IM** *012

POTLURI, Satish. 1000 N OAK AVE, MARSHFIELD CLINIC 54449 #495-99-2000 L2007 **IM** *020 †20

POTT, Markus Philipp. 1000 N OAK AVE 54449 #409-25-2001 **IM** *100

PRAXEL, Theodore Allen. 1000 N OAK AVE 54449 #056-06-1982 L1983 **IM** *020 †20 ‡

PREBBLE, Thomas Burton. 1000 N OAK AVE 54449 #036-01-1979 L1983 **IM** *020 †20

PRZYBYLINSKI, John Paul. 1000 N OAK AVE 54449 #056-05-1981 L1982 **IM** *020 †20

PTACEK, Louis J. 720 SYCAMORE AVE 54449 #056-06-1952 L1953 **CHN** *071 †55

PULVERMACHER, Keith Willi. 1000 N OAK AVE, MARSHFIELD CLINIC 54449 #056-06-2005 L2006 **PD** *012

QUINN, Daniel Lester. 1000 N OAK AVE 54449 #001-02-1976 L1984 **PCC IM** *020 †20

RAHIM, Eram. 1000 N OAK AVE, DEPT OF GEN INT MED 54449 #704-02-1995 L2001 **IM** *020 †20

RAHMAN, Nataliya. 1000 N OAK AVE, MARSHFIELD CLINIC 54449 #913-01-1994 L2006 **IM** *020 †20

RALL, Christopher J. 1000 N OAK AVE, MARSHFIELD CLINIC 54449 #051-04-1988 L1995 **IM GE** *020 †20

RANGU, Venu Mohan. 1000 N OAK AVE 54449 #495-21-2002 *100

RAO, Sanjay C. 1000 N OAK AVE, MARSHFIELD CLINIC 54449 #035-47-1991 L1998 **NS** *020 †25

RASHID, Zahir Alislam. 611 SAINT JOSEPH AVE 54449 #495-38-1986 L1999 **TS** *020 †85,90

RASHID, Zarzina. ■ 54449 #160-06-1988 L2004 **AN** *020

RAZA, Qasim. 1000 N OAK AVE 54449 #704-02-1988 L2000 **IM** *020 †20

REDING, Douglas James. 1000 N OAK AVE 54449 #018-03-1980 L1986 **ON HEM** *020 †20

REED, Kurt Danl. 1000 N OAK AVE, MARSHFIELD CLINIC 54449 #056-05-1980 L1982 **MM PTH** *020 †50

REED, Suanne Michelle. 1000 N OAK AVE 54449 #048-13-1986 L1987 **P PYG** *020 †75

REESER, Jonathan Charles. 1000 N OAK AVE, MARSHFIELD CLINIC 54449 #038-40-1993 L1997 **PM** *020 †60

REHMAN, Ateeq Ur. 1000 N OAK AVE, BAKA HEIDA PHYS. RECRUITME 54449 #704-21-2000 L2007 **IM** *020 †20

REMEIKA, Lori Jean. 1000 N OAK AVE, MARSHFIELD CLINIC 54449 #038-45-1982 L1989 **IM** *020 †20

RESNICK, Jeffrey M. 1000 N OAK AVE 54449 #035-03-1989 L1998 **PTH** *020 †50

REZKALLA, Shereif Hallim. 1000 N OAK AVE 54449 #915-05-1974 L1989 **CD IM** *020 †20

RICE, Thomas John. 1408 W 8TH ST 54449 #056-05-1945 L1949 **OBG** *071 †30

RICHARDSON, Gaines Edward. 1000 N OAK AVE, MARSHFIELD CLINIC 54449 #021-05-1994 L1997 **FM** *020 †18

RIEPE, Roger Eugene. 1000 N OAK AVE 54449 #018-03-1974 L1987 **PTH** *020 †50

ROKEY, Roxann. 1000 N OAK AVE 54449 #003-01-1978 L1994 **CD IM** *020 †20

ROLAK, Loren Andrew. 1000 N OAK AVE, MARSHFIELD CLINIC 54449 #003-01-1978 L1994 **N** *020 †75

ROTHFUSZ, Ronald Ray. 1000 N OAK AVE 54449 #056-05-1985 L1986 **IM** *020 †20

RUDOLPH, Laurel Ann. 1000 N OAK AVE 54449 #056-06-1988 L1989 **FM FSM** *020 †18

RUPP, George Mac Donald. 1000 N OAK AVE, MARSHFIELD CLINIC 54449 #038-45-1984 L1991 **PTH PCP** *020 †50

RUSS, Homer Hugh. 1000 N OAK AVE 54449 #026-04-1959 L1974 **RO** *071 †80

RYAN, Michael Edward. 1000 N OAK AVE, 1001 N OAK ST 54449 #026-04-1977 L1980 **GE IM** *020 †20

SA, Daniel Simoes De. 1000 N OAK AVE, NEUROLOGY - 4F5 54449 #187-17-1997 L2006 **N** *100 †75

SAHA, Sanjoy. 1000 N OAK AVE, MARSHFIELD CLINIC 54449 #495-67-1976 L2007 **SO GS** *020 †85

SAJJAD, Syed Mir. 611 SAINT JOSEPH AVE 54449 #495-51-1972 L1983 **PTH** *020 †50

SALIBI, Bahij S. ■ 54449 #024-01-1950 L1958 **NS** *071 †25

SAMSON, Julie Anne. 1000 N OAK AVE, MARSHFIELD CLINIC 54449 #026-04-1989 L2006 **ORS** *020 †40

SANCHEZ, Claire Emeline. 1000 N OAK AVE 54449 #028-34-1997 L2003 **FM** *020 †18

SANDOK, Evan Kendall. 1000 N OAK AVE, MARSHFIELD CLINIC 54449 #026-08-1993 L1998 **N** *020 †75

SARINO, Epafrodito Cruz. ■ 54449 #748-01-1938 L1968 **GP** *071

SCHAEFER, Wendelin W. 1000 N OAK AVE 54449 #056-06-1964 L1974 **ORS HS** *020 †40

SCHALLER, John W. 221 S SCHMIDT AVE 54449 #016-11-1951 L1952 **FM** *071 †18

SCHORR, William F. 1105 WEISTER CT 54449 #056-06-1957 L1963 **D** *071 †15

SCHREIBER, Donald John. 1000 N OAK AVE 54449 #018-03-1973 L1978 **ATP** *020 †50

SCHWARTZ, Mark Joseph. 1000 N OAK AVE, MARSHFIELD CLINIC 54449 #025-07-1996 L1997 **IM** *020 †20

SCRIVEN, Kimberly Anne. ■ 54449 #038-06-1995 L2005 **GS** *020 †85

SEELEN, Michael C. 1000 N OAK AVE 54449 #010-02-1970 L1978 **U** *020 †95

SELL, Patricia Ann Kuzma. 1000 N OAK AVE 54449 #025-07-1977 L1986 **GE IM** *020 †20

SELL, Thomas Lee. 1000 N OAK AVE 54449 #025-07-1977 L1986 **ID IM** *020 †20

SHAH, Alpa Chandrakant. 1000 N OAK AVE, STE RL1 54449 #495-22-1990 L2000 **P** *020 †75

SHAH, Milind S. 1000 N OAK AVE, DEPT OF CARDIOLOGY 54449 #495-76-1984 L2000 **IC CD** *020 †20

SHARMA, Param P. 1000 N OAK AVE 54449 #495-10-1984 L1998 **CD** *020 †20

SHAW, Gene Ronald. 611 SAINT JOSEPH AVE 54449 #026-04-1987 L1993 **PTH IM** *020 †50

SHEFLIN, John Richard. 1000 N OAK AVE 54449 #007-02-1970 L1978 **R** *020 †80

SHOLL, John Sargent. 1000 N OAK AVE 54449 #016-02-1975 L2008 **MFM OBG** *020 †30

SHULMAN, Garry Brent. 1000 N OAK AVE, MARSHFIELD CLINIC 54449 #065-06-1993 L1998 **AN** *020 †05

SIASOCO, Senen Villanueva. 1000 N OAK AVE 54449 #748-10-1975 L1983 **AN** *020

SILBERMAN, Teresa. 1000 N OAK AVE, MARSHFIELD CLINIC 54449 #132-01-1962 L1974 **PHO PD** *020 †55

SILFA MAZARA, Francheyska. 1000 N OAK AVE, MARSHFIELD CL/ST JOSEPH HP 54449 #308-05-1999 L2005 **NPM** *012

SIMENSTAD, David John. 1000 N OAK AVE, MARSHFIELD CLINIC 54449 #056-05-1986 L1994 **ORS GS** *020 †40

SINGH, Raj Vir. 1000 N OAK AVE 54449 #495-77-1973 L1995 **IM** *020 †20

SINGH, Rama. 1000 N OAK AVE, MARSHFIELD CLINIC 54449 #495-30-1979 L1996 **IM** *020 †20

SLOMINSKI, Corey Lee. 1000 N OAK AVE 54449 #056-06-2005 L2006 **GS** *012

SMITH, Ann Coleman. 1000 N OAK AVE 54449 #007-02-1988 L1994 **D** *020 †15

SMITH, Peter N. 1000 N OAK AVE 54449 #016-42-1983 L1989 **CD ICE** *020 †20

SMITH, Reginald A. ■ 54449 #060-01-1942 L1949 **GYN** *071 †30

SPARKS, George Mann. 611 SAINT JOSEPH AVE 54449 #016-11-1962 L1966 **OPH** *071 †35

SPELLMAN, Jeanne Marie R. 1000 N OAK AVE 54449 #023-07-1980 L1994 **ID IM** *020 †20

SPIETH, Michael Ernest. 1000 N OAK AVE, MARSHFIELD CLINIC NUC MED 54449 #005-12-1982 L1999 **NM DR** *020 †28,80

SPIREK, Gerald Henry. 1000 N OAK AVE 54449 #016-43-1962 L1997 **PTH** *020 †50

STAMAS, Peter, Jr. 1000 N OAK AVE 54449 #056-05-1983 L1986 **EM IM** *020 †20,16

STARREN, Justin Bruce. ■ 54449 #028-02-1987 L1989 **OS** *050

STEPIEN, Kathy Ann. ■ 54449 #054-04-2007 **PD** *012

STEVENS, Michael Lawrence. 1000 N OAK AVE 54449 #016-43-1965 L1966 **OBG** *071 †30

STEWART, C Todd. 1000 N OAK AVE, DEPT PEDS 1A4 54449 #016-01-1996 L2003 **CCP** *020 †55 ‡

STOJIC, Andrey Sasha. 1000 N OAK AVE, MARSHFIELD CLINIC 54449 #038-43-2002 L2007 **CN** *100

STONE, Gwen Elizabeth. 1000 N OAK AVE, MARSHFIELD CLINIC 54449 #056-05-1984 L1993 **OTO EM** *020 †45

STONE, Kenneth Dale. 1000 N OAK AVE 54449 #048-04-1990 L1998 **ORS** *020 †40

STRACHAN, Charles Patrick. 1000 N OAK AVE, DEPT OF ANES 54449 #056-05-1984 L1988 **AN** *020 †05

STRAM, Thomas Wm. 1000 N OAK AVE, MARSHFIELD CLINIC 54449 #056-05-1964 L1967 **OPH** *071 †35

STRATMAN, Erik Joseph. 1000 N OAK AVE, MARSHFIELD CLINIC 54449 #028-03-1998 L1999 **D** *020 †15

STRICKER, Jaye Jacquelyn. 1000 N OAK AVE 54449 #016-42-1988 L1994 **AN PME** *020 †05

SULLIVAN, Bradley John. 1000 N OAK AVE 54449 #024-07-1975 L1979 **PD ID** *020 †55

SULLIVAN, Michael Patrick. 1000 N OAK AVE, MARSHFIELD CLINIC 54449 #056-05-2001 L2005 **PD** *020 †55

SULLIVAN, Patrick Jos. 1000 N OAK AVE 54449 #039-05-1987 L1991 **AN** *020 †05

SUTTER, Brian Wilhelm. 1000 N OAK AVE, MARSHFIELD CLNC 54449 #026-04-2004 L2006 **PD** *012

SWAMY, Pandy G. 1133 RIDGE RD 54449 #495-09-1960 L1968 **AN PUD** *020

SWAN, Timothy Lee. 611 SAINT JOSEPH AVE, ST. JOSEPH'S HOSPITAL 54449 #026-04-1989 L1994 **VIR DR** *020 †80

SWANSON, Mark Kenneth. 1000 N OAK AVE, MARSHFIELD CLINIC 54449 #019-02-1969 L1971 **VS GS** *020 †85

SWANSON, Philip Arthur. 1000 N OAK AVE 54449 #016-11-1963 L1970 **AN** *071 †05

SWINK, Traci Diane. 1000 N OAK AVE 54449 #028-34-1991 L2001 **CHN** *020 †55,75

SZLABICK, Randolph E. 1000 N OAK AVE 54449 #025-07-1977 L1999 **GS CCS** *040 †85

TAM, Clarence Geetow. 1000 N OAK AVE 54449 #048-04-1995 L1999 **OPH** *020 †35

TANAWATTANACHAROEN, S. 1000 N OAK AVE 54449 #891-02-1987 L2000 **NEP** *020 †20

TAYLOR, Steven Douglas. 1000 N OAK AVE, MARSHFIELD CLINIC 54449 #305-01-1999 L2006 **GS** *020

THAPPETA, Sushma. 1000 N OAK AVE, MARSHFIELD CLINIC 54449 #495-21-2003 L2007 **PD** *012

THEISS, Thomas Edward. 1000 N OAK AVE 54449 #028-03-1999 L2003 **PTH** *020

THEODOROPOULOS, Demetrios. ■ 54449 #418-04-1987 L2001 **ALI** *020 †03,55,19

THEODOSIOU, Elena Nikou. 1000 N OAK AVE 54449 #418-01-1996 L2007 **HO IM** *020 †20

THOMALLA, James Vincent. 1000 N OAK AVE 54449 #016-45-1979 L1989 **U UP** *020 †95

THOMASGARD, Michael C. 1000 N OAK AVE, MARSHFIELD CLINIC 54449 #056-05-1986 L2007 **PD** *020 †55

THOMPSON, Alice Dale. 1000 N OAK AVE 54449 #048-13-1997 L1998 **PD** *020 †55

THORNE, Wayne Edward. 1000 N OAK AVE, MARSHFIELD CLINIC 54449 #056-06-1982 L1989 **IM** *020 †20

TIERNEY, Richard Price. 1000 N OAK AVE 54449 #008-01-1987 L2004 **AN GS** *020 †05

TIPPING, James Stanton. ■ 54449 #041-12-1941 L1942 **IM IMG** *071 †20

TIPPING, Stuart James. 1000 N OAK AVE, MARSHFIELD CLINIC 54449 #041-12-1977 L1983 **ON IM** *020 †20

TORBEY, Camille F. 1000 N OAK AVE 54449 #605-01-1991 L1993 **GE IM** *020 †20

TORKELSON, Erik Ole. ■ 54449 #056-05-1978 L1984 **HS ORS** *020 †40

TOYAMA, William M. 1810 WOODSVIEW DR 54449 #025-01-1957 L1967 **PDS GS** *071 †85

TRINH, Thuthao Thi. 1000 N OAK AVE, MARSHFIELD CLINIC 54449 #010-02-1990 L1998 **PD** *020 †55

TUTTLE, Thomas Floyd. 611 SAINT JOSEPH AVE 54449 #025-07-1980 L1986 **IM** *020 †20

TWIGGS, John Thos. 1000 N OAK AVE 54449 #026-04-1973 L1982 **PDA A** *020 †55,03

TYLER, Gregory Chase. 1000 N OAK AVE, MARSHFIELD CLINIC 54449 #010-02-1990 L1998 **OBG** *020 †30

ULMER, Richard Henry. 1320 N SHAWANO DR 54449 #016-43-1961 L1969 **CD IM** *071 †20 ‡

ULRICH, Karl James. 1000 N OAK AVE 54449 #034-01-1980 L1995 **MDM ADP** *030

UNOKANJO, Isioma Awele. 1000 N OAK AVE, MARSHFIELD CLINIC 54449 #690-02-2003 **MPD** *012

URQUHART, Andrew C. 1000 N OAK AVE 54449 #836-04-1983 L1992 **OTO HNS** *020

VAISMAN, Uri. 1000 N OAK AVE 54449 #035-08-1974 L1978 **DR VIR** *020 †80

VANDERSPEK, Hans Gerard. M134 RUBY LN 54449 #660-06-1960 L1979 **NS** *071 †25

VANDE ZANDE, Victoria L. 1000 N OAK AVE 54449 #056-06-2000 L2001 **IM** *020 †20

VAN EREM, Alayne Julie. 1000 N OAK AVE 54449 #037-01-1977 L1985 **PD** *020 †55

VANOUDENHOVEN, Gary Paul. 1000 N OAK AVE 54449 #056-06-1987 L1991 **IM** *020 †20

VARESKO, Rudolph W. 1000 N OAK AVE, RONC-H1N 54449 #005-12-1978 L2001 **RO** *020 †80

VARIA, Panna Virendra. 1000 N OAK AVE 54449 #495-48-1972 L1981 **PM** *020 †60

VARIA, Virendra Jechand. 1000 N OAK AVE 54449 #495-48-1972 L1981 **P** *020

VATS, Hemender Singh. 1000 N OAK AVE 54449 #496-43-1997 L2004 **IM** *020 †20

VEDRE, Jayanthgopalreddy. 1000 N OAK AVE, MARSHFIELD CLINIC 54449 #496-59-2003 L2007 **IM** *012

VELASCO, Alfonso Luis. 1000 N OAK AVE, GENERAL SURGERY 54449 #649-13-1981 L2001 **CRS GS** *020 †85,10

VELUVOLU, Purushotham. 1000 N OAK AVE 54449 #495-50-1974 L1984 **NM R** *020
VIDAILLET, Humberto J, Jr. 1000 N OAK AVE 54449 #039-01-1981 L1987 **CD OS** *020 †20
VIEGUT, Victoria Lynn. 1000 N OAK AVE, PEDIATRICS 54449 #056-05-1991 L1992 **PD** *020 †55
VINODU, Vinaya Susan. 1000 N OAK AVE, MARSHFIELD CLINIC 54449 #495-63-2000 L2007 **IM** *012
VISEKRUNA, Maja. 1000 N OAK AVE, MARSHFIELD CLINIC 54449 #957-02-1994 L2007 **MPD** *012
VO, Andrew Nguyen. 1000 N OAK AVE 54449 #005-19-1997 L2001 **PM** *020 †60
VOMOCIL, Boyd Earl. 1000 N OAK AVE, MARSHFIELD CLINIC 54449 #041-09-1990 L2006 **NM R** *020 †28
VOSS, Dieter Martin. ■ 54449 #407-05-1958 L1966 **CD IM** *072
VUDDAGIRI, Satyananda Kum. 1000 N OAK AVE, MFLD PEDIATRIC RES PRGM 54449 #495-11-1992 **PD** *100
WAGNER, Diana. 611 SAINT JOSEPH AVE 54449 #781-01-1997 L2004 **IM** *020 †20
WAGNER, Stephen Faust. MARSHFIELD CLINIC 54449 #056-05-1965 L1966 **PD CG** *071 †55,19
WARNER, John James. 1000 N OAK AVE, MARSHFIELD CLINIC 54449 #056-05-1983 L1987 **RNR DR** *020 †80
WASHINGTON, William Lee. 1000 N OAK AVE, MARSHFIELD CLINIC 54449 #028-03-1973 L1980 **RHU IM** *020 †20
WATERS, John Ingersol. 1000 N OAK AVE, MARSHFIELD CLINIC 54449 #016-11-1983 L1998 **P** *020 †75
WATKINS, Bruce James. 1000 N OAK AVE, MARSHFIELD CLINIC 54449 #654-01-2002 L2005 **GS** *012
WEBER, Andrew Robert. 1000 N OAK AVE 54449 #422-01-2002 L2004 **IM** *100
WEESNER, Kenneth Martin. ■ 54449 #003-01-1977 L1994 **PDC PA** *075 †55
WEISSMAN, Mark Neil. 1000 N OAK AVE, MARSHFIELD CLINIC 54449 #165-03-1978 L1994 **NS** *025
WELTER, Joseph Donald. 1000 N OAK AVE, MARSHFIELD CLINIC 54449 #056-06-1982 L1983 **OBG** *020 †30
WENGERT, Timothy Jos. 1000 N OAK AVE 54449 #018-03-1985 L1986 **CRS GS** *020 †85,10
WERNBERG, Jessica A. 1000 N OAK AVE, MARSHFIELD CLINIC 54449 #056-06-2000 L2001 **GS** *100 †85
WESBROOK, Frederic Paul. 1000 N OAK AVE 54449 #017-20-1970 L1976 **OS IM** *030 †20
WHITENACK, Donald Clark. 1000 N OAK AVE 54449 #054-04-1958 L1975 **FM PM** *020 †18
WILLIAMS, K J. 1000 N OAK AVE 54449 #056-05-2000 L2002 **FM** *020
WILSON, Deborah Anna. 1000 N OAK AVE, MARSHFIELD CLINIC 54449 #017-20-1974 L1986 **IM RHU** *020 †20
WINDER, Audra Ann. 1000 N OAK AVE, DEPT. OF PEDIATRICS 54449 #049-01-1998 L2007 **NPM** *020 †55
WISNEFSKE, Mark Dennis. 1000 N OAK AVE 54449 #056-06-1977 L1982 **ORS** *020 †40
WITKOWSKY, Roman Bohdan. 1000 N OAK AVE 54449 #016-43-1971 L1975 **AN EM** *020 †05
WITTMANN, Dietmar H. 1000 N OAK AVE, MARSHFIELD CLINIC 54449 #407-21-1969 L1989 **GS AS** *071
WOLFE, Craig Arthur. 1000 N OAK AVE 54449 #038-45-1983 L1989 **IM PUD** *020 †20
WONG, Shannon Lindsay. 1000 N OAK AVE 54449 #422-01-2007 *012
WOOD, Michael Thos. 1000 N OAK AVE 54449 #016-06-1969 L1973 **P MDM** *030 †75
WORD, Ronnie. ■ 54449 #935-01-1991 L2000 **GS** *020 †85
WRIGHT, Suzanne. 1000 N OAK AVE, MARSHFIELD CLINIC 54449 #048-04-1992 L1998 **PD** *020 †55
XIA, Ling. 1000 N OAK AVE 54449 #243-16-1984 L2004 **PTH D** *020
YAKOVLEV, Alexander E. 1000 N OAK AVE 54449 #913-06-1983 L1994 **APM** *020 †05
YALE, Eileen Scott. 1000 N OAK AVE, MARSHFIELD CLINIC 54449 #035-03-1991 L1999 **IM** *020 †20
YALE, Steven H. 1000 N OAK AVE, MARSHFIELD CLINIC 54449 #035-03-1991 L1999 **IM** *020 †20
YANKE, William Ervin. 1000 N OAK AVE, MARSHFIELD CLINIC 54449 #056-06-1981 L1983 **IMG IM** *030 †20 ‡
YAO, Lei. 1000 N OAK AVE, MARSHFIELD CLINIC 54449 #243-32-1983 L2000 **AN** *020 †05
YAZIGI, Natalia. 1000 N OAK AVE 54449 #913-01-2000 *100
ZADOR, Ivan. 1000 N OAK AVE 54449 #286-13-1981 L1999 **PDE** *020 †55
ZEKARIAS, Kidmealem Lulse. 1000 N OAK AVE 54449 #366-03-1994 **IM** *012

MAUSTON – JUNEAU

BUSS, Robert Christopher. 1040 DIVISION ST, MILE BLUFF CLINIC 53948 #056-05-1996 L1997 **FM** *020 †18
FARNE, Rey Fortaleza. 121 MONROE ST 53948 #748-01-1962 L1977 **FM UCM** *020
GILLIAM, Haywood Stirling. 1050 DIVISION ST 53948 #030-06-1977 L1989 **TS GS** *020 †85,90
HAACK, Susan M. 1040 DIVISION ST 53948 #048-02-1982 L1987 **OBG** *020 †30
HEANEY, Eric Sproat. 1040 DIVISION ST 53948 #056-05-1974 L1977 **FM IM** *020 †20,18
HOFFMANN, Ann H. 1040 DIVISION ST 53948 #010-02-1983 L1990 **FM FPG** *020 †18
HOFFMANN, David Martin. 1040 DIVISION ST 53948 #010-02-1983 L1990 **FM FPG** *020 †18 ‡
KATTENBRAKER, Daniel Wade. 1040 DIVISION ST 53948 #016-11-1999 L2000 **FM** *020 †18
LARSON, Charles Edward. 1040 DIVISION ST 53948 #026-04-1984 L1985 **FM** *020 †18
LEWANDOSKI, June R. 1040 DIVISION ST, MILE BLUFF CLINIC 53948 #056-05-1999 L2000 **FM** *020 †18
LOGAN, James Jos. 1040 DIVISION ST 53948 #048-12-1978 L1981 **FM PD** *020 †18
MALINOWSKI, Rodney Wayne. 1040 DIVISION ST, MILE BLUFF CLNC LLP 53948 #056-06-1975 L1980 **GS HS** *020 †85 ‡
MARCULIS, William. 1040 DIVISION ST 53948 #028-79-1987, ▲ L1996 **GS** *020
NAPIER, Timothy Erin. 1040 DIVISION ST 53948 #016-01-1987 L1988 **GS VS** *020 †85
NESS, Dennis Keith. 1040 DIVISION ST 53948 #056-05-1975 L1976 **FM** *020 †18
NESS, Nancy E B. 1040 DIVISION ST 53948 #056-05-1975 L1976 **FM** *074 †18
PETERSON-KATTENBRAKER, J. 1040 DIVISION ST 53948 #016-11-1999 L2000 **FM** *020 †18
RADANT, Leon Jerome. 1040 DIVISION ST, MILE BLUFF CLINIC 53948 #056-05-1977 L1978 **FM** *020 †18
RIEDLE, Robert R. 1040 DIVISION ST, MILE BLUFF CLINIC LLP 53948 #016-01-1984 L1991 **ORS** *020 †40
ROLEY, Everett Lee. 1040 DIVISION ST 53948 #030-06-1956 L1959 **GYN** *020 †30
SPEICHINGER, James Peter. 1040 DIVISION ST 53948 #030-05-1970 L1976 **GYN FM** *020 †30
STRONG, Jack. 1040 DIVISION ST 53948 #016-11-1953 L1958 **GP** *020 †18

MAYVILLE – DODGE

COLLISTER, Beth. 316 S MOUNTIN DR 53050 #025-07-1985 L1992 **FM** *020 †18

KETTERER, Alisha Lori. ■ 53050 #056-05-2006 L2007 **FP** *012

MAZOMANIE – DANE

MOREY, Jonathan Blake. ■ 53560 #010-02-1979 L1980 **FM** *020 †18

MC FARLAND – DANE

JACOB, Aaron Lee. 3323 COUNTY ROAD MN 53558 #026-04-1996 L1999 **GPM** *012
KRAMPER, Edward Jos. 5020 FARWELL ST 53558 #028-03-1976 L1979 **FM** *020 †18
KURTZ, R Compton, II. 5020 FARWELL ST 53558 #654-01-2000 L2001 **FM** *020 †18 ‡
LIVINGSTON, Stanley, III. 5020 FARWELL ST 53558 #043-01-1981 L1982 **FM** *020 †18
PARKER, Megeen. 5020 FARWELL ST 53558 #012-05-1986 L1994 **FM** *040 †18
RICH, Frederick M, Jr. ■ 53558 #018-03-1950 L1964 **R RO** *071 †80

MEDFORD – TAYLOR

CAROTHERS, Kelly Ann. 135 S GIBSON ST, EMERGENCY DEPARTMENT 54451 #056-05-1997 L1998 **FM** *020 †18
EKWUEME, Ngozi J. 143 S GIBSON ST, MEMORIAL HEALTH CENTER CLI 54451 #690-07-1990 L1997 **FM** *020 †18 ‡
FALKENBERG, Amy Arlene. 143 S GIBSON ST, MEMORIAL HEALTH CENTER 54451 #056-05-1995 L1996 **FM** *020 †18
FOLTZ, Richard Newton. 724 S 8TH ST 54451 #056-05-1975 L1976 **ORS** *020 †40
GAUTAM, Hind Mirza. 724 S 8TH ST 54451 #495-17-1997 L2006 **AN PME** *020 †05
HACKETT, Benjamin James. 724 S 8TH ST 54451 #056-06-2001 L2006 **ORS OSS** *020
HALEEM, Shahid. 143 S GIBSON ST, MEMORIAL HEALTH CENTER CLI 54451 #704-02-1995 L2002 **IM** *020
KOWLE, Ronald Lee. 143 S GIBSON ST, MEMORIAL HEALTH CENTER CLI 54451 #056-05-1976 L1979 **GS** *020
MC HUGH, Frank Jos. 143 S GIBSON ST, MEMORIAL HEALTH CENTER 54451 #031-01-1980 L2006 **EM** *020 †16
MC NABB, Daniel Mark. 135 S GIBSON ST, MEMORIAL CARE HLTH CARE CT 54451 #847-02-1979 L2004 **EM FPG** *020 †16,18
MEYER, Walther Wm. ■ 54451 #016-02-1947 L1948 **GP** *071
MOSCOSO, Romulo Pobre. 101 S GIBSON ST 54451 #748-08-1962 L1976 **GS GP** *071
REUTER, Catherine Fahien. 143 S GIBSON ST 54451 #056-06-1992 L1993 **PD** *020 †55
REUTER, Mark Geoffrey. 143 S GIBSON ST 54451 #056-06-1992 L1993 **FM** *020 †18
RITTER, Carol Ann. 135 S GIBSON ST 54451 #025-07-1975 L1979 **PTH** *020 †50
ROBINSON, James K. W5238 JOLLY AVE 54451 #028-79-1965, ▲ L1967 **FM** *071
SEABUL, Ricky Lee. 143 S GIBSON ST, MEMORIAL HEALTH CENTER 54451 #056-06-1997 L1998 **FM** *020 †18
UHRI, Vladimir. 107 S GIBSON ST 54451 #286-04-1960 L1973 **GE IM** *020
WAGONER, Amy Lynne. 143 S GIBSON ST, MEMORIAL HEALTH CENTER CLI 54451 #046-01-1997 L1998 **FM** *020 †18
WESSELS, William Reese. 724 S 8TH ST 54451 #018-03-1954 L1955 **AN** *071 †05
WRAGE, Darla. 143 S GIBSON ST, MEMORIAL HEALTH CENTER CLI 54451 #046-01-1994 L2002 **PD** *020 †55

MELLEN – ASHLAND

SCHLOESSER, Lee Lyon. PO BOX 517, 75767 TOWN ROAD 37 54546 #019-02-1951 L1952 **HEM IM** *020 †20

MENASHA – WINNEBAGO

ALAM, Khalid. 1550 MIDWAY PL, OUTPATIENT SURGERY CTR 54952 #704-19-1983 L1993 **GE** *020 †20
ALT, Stephen Kay. 1186 APPLETON RD 54952 #056-05-1970 L1973 **OM IM** *071 †20
BACHMAN, Joseph Frederick. 1550 MIDWAY PL 54952 #025-01-1959 L1973 **IM GE** *020 †20
BARKMEIER, John Ray. 2005 MIDWAY RD 54952 #018-03-1975 L1978 **FM FPG** *030 †18
BELD, John Thomas. 1095 MIDWAY RD 54952 #020-02-1994 L2002 **P** *020 †75
BLOOMHUFF, Suzanne. 2005 MIDWAY RD 54952 #025-07-1998 L2001 **FM** *020 †18
BUFFO, Janine Marie. 2005 MIDWAY RD 54952 #018-03-1984 L1985 **FM** *020 †18
CROWE, John Michael. ■ 54952 #056-05-1968 L1972 **GS** *020
DONATELLE, Lawrence R. 878 W AIRPORT RD 54952 #037-01-1982 L1983 **FM** *020 †18
ERICKSON, Gregg Richard. 878 W AIRPORT RD 54952 #056-06-1980 L1982 **N PD** *020
GEHRINGER, Natalie Ann. 878 W AIRPORT RD 54952 #030-05-1975 L1981 **PD** *020 †55
GEHRINGER, Robt Edward, Jr. 1071 BRIGHTON DR 54952 #030-05-1975 L1981 **PD** *020 †55
GOWDA, Shubha Aladahalli. ■ 54952 #496-22-1989 L1998 **IM** *020 †20
GROENEWOLD, Sandra K. 2005 MIDWAY RD 54952 #056-06-1994 L1995 **FM** *020 †18
GRUNWALD, Nathan C. 2005 MIDWAY RD 54952 #056-06-2003 L2004 **FM** *020 †18
GUSTAFSON, Glenn E, Jr. 222 WASHINGTON ST 54952 #016-11-1961 L1962 **GP** *072
HALL, Ada Mc Intire. 1550 MIDWAY PL 54952 #038-43-1980 L1986 **OPH** *075 †35
HANSEN, Kenneth Duane. 1134 MORGAN TAYLOR CT, KENNETH D. HANSEN, MD 54952 #056-06-2000 L2005 *020 †05
HEIFNER, Gary Mark. 878 W AIRPORT RD 54952 #018-03-1979 L1980 **FM** *020 †18
HENRY, Charles Stephen. 325 LAKE RD 54952 #025-07-1997 L2003 **DR** *020 †80
HUSS, Barbara Amelida. 1800 APPLETON RD, FOX CITIES COMMUNITY HEALT 54952 #056-06-1979 L2006 **PD** *071 †55
KENNEDY, Ralph O. ■ 54952 #056-05-1950 L1955 **R** *071 †80
KHALAF, Tagreed Mansour. 1550 MIDWAY PL 54952 #056-05-2001 L2005 **PM** *020 †60
MADDEN, Michael Allan. 1814 APPLETON RD 54952 #047-05-1976 L1979 **IM NEP** *020 †20
MITCHELL, Elizabeth M. ■ 54952 #056-05-1987 L1992 **FM** *020 †18
NYGAARD, Scott David. 1570 MIDWAY PL, AFFINITY HEALTH SYSTEM 54952 #026-04-1987 L1993 **PUD CCM** *030 †20
PARK, Tai Jin. ■ 54952 #583-02-1962 L1978 **PMM PM** *020 †60
PITRE, Cheryl-Lynn Marie. 878 W AIRPORT RD, AFFINITY MEDICAL GROUP 54952 #065-01-1986 L1999 **FM** *020 †18
RATHERT, Roger Arthur. 878 W AIRPORT RD 54952 #056-05-1966 L1968 **PD** *071 †55

SCANLAN, Edward Scott. 1570 MIDWAY PL 54952 #016-11-1966 L1973 **CD IM** *020 †20
SODHI, Sudeep Singh. 1550 MIDWAY PL 54952 #495-90-1990 L2000 **GE** *020 †20
SOUSEK, Reid Alexander. 878 W AIRPORT RD 54952 #016-43-2004 L2005 **FM** *020 †18
SPENCER, John Robert. 2005 MIDWAY RD 54952 #065-05-1990 L1994 **FM** *020
THOMSEN, Kristen Lee. 2005 MIDWAY RD 54952 #016-43-1994 L1997 **FM** *020 †18
VOGEL, Kathy Ann. 1550 MIDWAY PL 54952 #056-05-1984 L1985 **OPH OS** *020 †35
WAGE, Michael Lee. 1550 MIDWAY PL, OUTPATIENT SURGERY CTR 54952 #024-01-1982 L1983 **OPH** *020 †35

MENOMONEE FALLS – WAUKESHA

AGGARWAL, Anil. W180N8085 TOWN HALL RD 53051 #495-29-1979 L1987 **AN** *040 †05
ANDREW, Michelle Rae. W180N8085 TOWN HALL RD 53051 #030-05-1994 L1995 **U** *020 †95
ANDRYK, Jolene E. N84W16889 MENOMONEE AVE, MENOMONEE FALLS CLINIC 53051 #056-05-1996 L1996 **OTO** *020 †45
ATALLAH, Ehab Latif. ■ 53051 #915-02-1994 L2007 **ON** *020 †20
BARTL, George Richard. W180N8085 TOWN HALL RD, COMMUNITY MEMORIAL HOSP 53051 #025-07-1964 L1971 **NS** *020 †25
BARTL, Lynn Margaret. W180N8085 TOWN HALL RD, NEUROLOGIC ASSOCIATES OF 53051 #056-06-1993 L1999 **NS** *020 †25
BECKER, David Leonard. W180N7950 TOWN HALL RD 53051 #016-11-1969 L1970 **ORS** *020 †40
BECKER, Robert John. W172N8478 SHADY LN 53051 #056-06-1980 L1982 **P** *020 †75
BELANI, Mahesh G. W180N8085 TOWN HALL RD 53051 #495-52-1982 L1987 **AN PME** *020 †05
BHOSEKAR, Chitra Sadasiwa. W129 N7055 NORTHFIELD DR, NORTH HILLS PRIMARY CARE 53051 #495-01-1999 L2007 **IM** *020
BIBLER, Richard Henry. W180N7950 TOWN HALL RD 53051 #017-20-1957 L1960 **PD** *071 †55
BLATNIK, Steven. W180N7950 TOWN HALL RD 53051 #056-05-1971 L1977 **ORS** *020 †40
BOFFELI, Todd Jos. N91W17271 APPLETON AVE 53051 #018-03-1988 L1992 **P** *020 †75
BOTTICELLI, James Thos. N84W16889 MENOMONEE AVE 53051 #016-43-1955 L1959 **CD IM** *071 †20
BRANNEN, Chas Howard, Jr. W180N7950 TOWN HALL RD 53051 #030-06-1968 L1973 **PD** *071 †55
BRENNAN, William Michael. W180N8085 TOWN HALL RD 53051 #056-06-1959 L1961 **IM PUD** *020
BRODY, Patrick J. N84W16889 MENOMONEE AVE, MENOMONEE FALLS CLINIC 53051 #056-06-1978 L1979 **IM** *020 †20
BROOKS, Joanne Renelle. W180N7950 TOWN HALL RD, MEDICAL ASSOC HLTH 53051 #056-05-1997 L1998 **FM** *020 †18
BROWNING, Meghen Brooke. ■ 53051 #028-03-1995 L1996 **PHO** *020 †55
BUCK, James Darrell. W180N7950 TOWN HALL RD 53051 #056-06-1982 L1985 **IM** *020 †20
BUTLER, Pamela Jean. N84W16889 MENOMONEE AVE, MENOMONEE FALLS CLINIC 53051 #048-02-1990 L1991 **D** *072 †15
CHARLTON, Nicola Marie. N84W16889 MENOMONEE AVE, MENOMONEE FALLS CLINIC 53051 #016-42-1989 L1994 **FM PD** *020 †18
CHATTOPADHYAY, Kumkum. N84W16889 MENOMONEE AVE, MENOMONEE FALLS CLINIC 53051 #024-05-1991 L2001 **IM** *020 †20
CHEN, Yaoju. ■ 53051 #243-46-1983 **IM** *100
CHERMAK, James Arthur. N84W16889 MENOMONEE AVE 53051 #056-06-1973 L1976 **OTO** *020 †45
CHIANG, Melissa Phyllis. N84W16889 MENOMONEE AVE 53051 #008-01-2003 L2004 **D** *020 †15
CHOITHANI, Ashok C. W180N8085 TOWN HALL RD 53051 #305-01-1986 L1989 **IM** *020 †20
CHUMBLEY, Clyde Marion, II. W180N7950 TOWN HALL RD, MEDICAL ASSOCIATES 53051 #028-03-1975 L1976 **GYN** *030 †30
CUEVAS, Francis Joseph Sy. ■ 53051 #748-10-1992 L2007 **HO IM** *020 †20
DE ANGELIS, Alan A. N84W16889 MENOMONEE AVE, MENOMONEE FALLS CLINIC 53051 #016-11-1980 L1981 **PD** *020 †55
DEUSTER, Jeanmarie P. W180N7950 TOWN HALL RD 53051 #056-06-1986 L1987 **FM** *020 †18
DE WERTH, John Homer. ■ 53051 #056-06-1937 L1937 **P GP** *075
DOUGHERTY, Philip James. W180N7950 TOWN HALL RD 53051 #016-11-1956 L1959 **IM** *071 †20
DRAYER, Henry Danl. W180N7950 TOWN HALL RD 53051 #016-11-1963 L1964 **PD** *071
DYKSTRA, Mark Jerome. N84W16889 MENOMONEE AVE, MENOMONEE FALLS CLINIC 53051 #056-06-1982 L2001 **U** *020 †95
FEILBACH, John Allen. N84W16889 MENOMONEE AVE 53051 #056-05-1991 L1992 **IM** *020 †20
FERNANDEZ, Mary Catherine. W180N8085 TOWN HALL RD, COMMUNITY MEMORIAL HOSP 53051 #056-06-1970 L1973 **PTH** *020 †20
FLANARY, Casey James. W180N7950 TOWN HALL RD 53051 #056-05-1987 L1988 **OTO** *020 †45
FLINK, Paul Fredrick. W180N7950 TOWN HALL RD 53051 #055-01-1981 L1989 **IM** *020 †20
FRANCK, Laura Louise. W180N7950 TOWN HALL RD, MED ASSOC PEDIATRICS 53051 #018-03-2003 L2005 **PD** *020 †55
FRONDA, Gerardo Polanco. W180N8085 TOWN HALL RD, COMMUNITY MEM HOSP 53051 #748-01-1980 L2005 **ATP PCP** *020 †50
GANDHAVADI, Balaraju. W180N8085 TOWN HALL RD 53051 #495-70-1971 L1978 **PM** *020 †60
GEANON, George Demetrios. N84W16889 MENOMONEE AVE, MENOMONEE FALLS CLINIC 53051 #016-43-1986 L1987 **OBG** *030 †30
GERSHAN, Robert Nathan. W180N7950 TOWN HALL RD 53051 #056-05-1976 L1980 **IM** *020 †20
GILBERTSON, Kenneth Gerar. ■ 53051 #056-06-2006 L2008 **TY** *012
GILL, Sonia Boparai. ■ 53051 #496-07-1993 L2005 **RNR** *100
GOY, Peter Wm. N84W16889 MENOMONEE AVE, MENOMONEE FALLS CLINIC 53051 #056-06-1986 L1987 **IM** *075 †20
GRANT-ACQUAH, Nana K. W180N8085 TOWN HALL RD, COMMUNITY MEMORIAL HOSP 53051 #056-05-1979 L1986 **AN** *020 †05
GRAYSON, Mitchell Harry. ■ 53051 #016-02-1993 L1996 **AI IM** *050 †20,03
GRONOWSKI, Jill Marie. N84W16889 MENOMONEE AVE, MENOMONEE FALLS CLINIC 53051 #056-06-1999 L2002 **PD** *020
GRUBOR, Milosh. W180N8085 TOWN HALL RD 53051 #056-06-1990 L1991 **AN** *020 †05
GRUNKE, Richard John. N84W16889 MENOMONEE AVE, MENOMONEE FALLS CLINIC 53051 #056-06-1977 L1978 **OTO A** *020 †45
GUNDAMRAJ, Yoganand. N84W16889 MENOMONEE AVE 53051 #306-01-1997 L2001 **IM** *020 †20

GUPTA, Nilesh Indra M. N84W16889 MENOMONEE AVE 53051 #495-01-1995 L2001 **PCC** *020 †20
GUTTERSEN, Rita V. W180N8085 TOWN HALL RD, FALLS ANESTHESIA ASSOC, SC 53051 #748-16-1989 L1997 **AN** *020 †05
GVORA, Thomas Jos. W180N7950 TOWN HALL RD 53051 #056-05-1986 L1991 **IM** *020 †20
HALLERMAN, Elizabeth Anne. W180N7950 TOWN HALL RD 53051 #016-06-1989 L1990 **IM** *020 †20
HALLORAN, Daniel Richard. N84W16889 MENOMONEE AVE, MENOMONEE FALLS CLINIC 53051 #035-15-1978 L1986 **IM CCM** *020 †20
HALSTROM, Paul Frank. N84W16889 MENOMONEE AVE, MENOMONEE FALLS CLINIC 53051 #056-06-1987 L1988 **IM** *020 †20
HARRINGTON, Kenneth John. N84W16889 MENOMONEE AVE 53051 #056-06-1956 L1957 **FM** *071 †18
HEGMANN, Karen Marie. N84W16889 MENOMONEE AVE, MENOMONEE FALLS CLINIC 53051 #056-06-1990 L1991 **IM** *020 †18
HENNESSY, Donald Jos, Jr. W180N7950 TOWN HALL RD 53051 #016-43-1980 L1981 **IM** *020 †20
HEYRMAN, Daniel Jos. N84W16889 MENOMONEE AVE, MENOMONEE FALLS CLINIC 53051 #422-01-1986 L1988 **FM** *020 †18
HEYRMAN, Donald Jos. N84W16889 MENOMONEE AVE, MENOMONEE FALLS CLINIC 53051 #056-06-1956 L1957 **FM** *020 †18
HEYRMAN, Thomas Peter. N84W16889 MENOMONEE AVE, MENOMONEE FALLS CLINIC 53051 #056-06-1988 L1992 **OPH** *020 †35
HOLMBURG, Charles Estes. W180N7950 TOWN HALL RD 53051 #056-05-1966 L1969 **IM** *020 †20
HRYCIUK, Jeanne Ellen. W180N8085 TOWN HALL RD, COMM MEMORIAL HOSP 53051 #056-06-1992 L1993 **PTH** *020 †20
HUGHES, Stephen Douglas. W180N8085 TOWN HALL RD 53051 #039-01-1995 L1996 **FM** *020 †18
JACKSON, Edgar Basil. W142N7867 THORNDELL DR 53051 #539-01-1957 L1961 **P CHP** *020 †75
JACOBSON, Karen M. N84W16889 MENOMONEE AVE, MENOMONEE FALLS CLINIC 53051 #040-02-1985 L1986 **PD** *020 †55
JAIN, Rajeev Kumar. N84W16889 MENOMONEE AVE, MENOMONEE FALLS CLINIC 53051 #495-36-1980 L1989 **END** *020 †20
JENSEN, Thomas Robt. N84W16889 MENOMONEE AVE 53051 #056-05-1980 L1983 **FM OS** *020 †18
JOANNIDES, Tina Margaret. N84W16889 MENOMONEE AVE, MENOMONEE FALLS CLINIC 53051 #016-11-1985 L1986 **PD** *020 †55
JOOSSE, Peter Clifford. W180N7950 TOWN HALL RD 53051 #056-05-1973 L1974 **P** *020 †75
JUBECK, Brian Thomas. ■ 53051 #056-06-2007 **IM** *012
KANITZ, Dan David. W180N7950 TOWN HALL RD 53051 #056-06-1986 L1987 **AN** *020 †05
KANITZ, Kristi. W180N8085 TOWN HALL RD 53051 #056-06-1988 L1990 **AN** *020 †05
KELLER, Daniel Arthur. N84W16889 MENOMONEE AVE 53051 #056-05-1983 L1985 **IM** *020 †20
KELLY, John Jos. N87W16462 JACOBSON DR 53051 #056-06-1967 L1976 **OTO HNS** *020 †45
KHAMBATTA, Sunita Sarosh. W180N7950 TOWN HALL RD 53051 #016-11-1995 L1996 **PD** *020 †55
KIS, Anne Marie. W180N8085 TOWN HALL RD, COMMUNITY MEMORIAL HOSP 53051 #056-05-1992 L1995 **IM** *020 †20
KOTHUR, Hanumantha R. N84W16889 MENOMONEE AVE 53051 #495-21-1977 L1992 **FM** *020 †18
KOVNAR, Edward Harry. N84W16889 MENOMONEE AVE 53051 #028-02-1977 L1982 **CHN** *020 †55,75
LASTRILLA, Rudolfo Sabili. W180N8085 TOWN HALL RD 53051 #748-01-1958 L1963 **AN** *020 †05
LINTON, Scott. W180N8085 TOWN HALL RD 53051 #016-06-1986 L1994 **AN** *020 †05 ‡
LISTER, Matthew Thomas. N84W16889 MENOMONEE AVE 53051 #056-05-2002 L2007 **OTO** *020
LUDEMAN, Lucas Brian. ■ 53051 #056-06-2006 L2008 **DR** *012
MALONE, Trudy J. N84W16889 MENOMONEE AVE, FALLS MEDICAL GROUP S C 53051 #056-05-1993 L1997 **OBG** *020 †30
MAROWSKI, Christopher M. N84W16889 MENOMONEE AVE, MENOMONEE FALLS CLINIC 53051 #759-09-1987 L1999 **CD** *020 †20
MAST, Alan Edward. ■ 53051 #036-07-1991 L2003 **PTH** *020 †50
MAZUMDAR, Shaibal. N84W16889 MENOMONEE AVE, MENOMONEE FALLS CLINIC 53051 #495-02-1987 L2000 **IM** *020 †20
MC CANN, Francis X. N84W16889 MENOMONEE AVE, MENOMONEE FALLS CLINIC 53051 #422-01-1986 L1987 **IM** *020 †20
MEI, David Anthony. W180N8085 TOWN HALL RD 53051 #056-06-1998 L1999 **AN** *020 †05 ‡
MENEZES, Margaret Lynn. W180N8085 TOWN HALL RD, DEPT OF PATHOLOGY-CMH 53051 #026-04-1996 L2004 **ATP CLP** *062 †50
MERRY, Steven Leigh. N84W16889 MENOMONEE AVE, MENOMONEE FALLS CLINIC 53051 #018-03-1975 L1979 **IM CD** *020 †20
MILLER, Natalya Shannon. ■ 53051 #030-05-2005 L2007 **PD** *012
MONTES, Artemio M. W180N8085 TOWN HALL RD 53051 #748-08-1968 L1973 **AN** *020
MORTON, Timothy Jos. W180N8085 TOWN HALL RD, FORWARD ORTHOPEDICS, S.C. 53051 #016-01-1986 L1992 **ORS** *020 †40
MUGGLER, Debra Ann. W180N7950 TOWN HALL RD 53051 #016-43-1995 L1999 **IM** *020 †20.
ONESON, Susan Richards. N84W16889 MENOMONEE AVE 53051 #056-05-1988 L1993 **DR** *020 †80
PAHUJA, Reshma. ■ 53051 #495-37-1998 L2007 **IM** *012
PELISKA, Jean Marie. N84W16889 MENOMONEE AVE, MENOMONEE FALLS CLINIC 53051 #056-06-1987 L1993 **ON** *020 †20
PETERS, Kenneth Ronald. W180N7950 TOWN HALL RD 53051 #056-06-1961 L1962 **OTO** *071 †45
PIER, William Jos, Jr. ■ 53051 #056-06-1961 L1965 **PTH NM** *071 †50,28
POPE, Jennifer Marie. ■ 53051 #016-45-2005 L2007 **PD** *012
PREWITT, Zane Patrick. N84W16889 MENOMONEE AVE, MENOMONEE FALLS CLINIC 53051 #016-42-1989 L1994 **GS** *020 †85
QUERIMIT, Alberto S. N84W16889 MENOMONEE AVE, MENOMONEE FALLS CLINIC 53051 #748-10-1962 L1975 **CD IM** *020 †20
QUINN, Curtis Campbell. W180N8085 TOWN HALL RD, 3 SW STE 4 53051 #024-07-1987 L1995 **TS GS** *020 †85,90
RAMAN, Anuradha. W180N7950 TOWN HALL RD 53051 #495-65-1985 L1998 **OBG** *020 †30
RENCH-REBELLA, Tiffany. N84W16889 MENOMONEE AVE, MENOMONEE FALLS CLINIC 53051 #056-05-2000 L2004 **D** *020 †15 ‡

■ = Address Information Privacy Protected

RIEDER, Anthony Allan. ■ 53051 #056-06-2000 L2001 **OTO** *020 †45

RIESCH, John D. W180N8085 TOWN HALL RD 53051 #056-05-1958 L1959 **GS** *020 †85

ROBERTS, Thomas Henry. ■ 53051 #056-06-1964 L1965 **GS** *071 †85

ROMANO, Joseph Mario. N84W16889 MENOMONEE AVE 53051 #035-08-1981 L1992 **EM** *020 †20,16

SABNIS, Samir Suman. W180N7950 TOWN HALL RD 53051 #495-37-1990 L1991 **PD** *020 †55

SANTIAGO, L Mina. W180N8085 TOWN HALL RD 53051 #748-01-1978 L1988 **PD** *020 †85

SCHAEFER, Kent Carlton. W180N8085 TOWN HALL RD 53051 #056-06-1964 L1968 **AN** *071

SCHATZMAN, Michael John. W129 N7055 NORTHFIELD DR, BLDG A 53051 #056-06-1997 L2000 *020 †20

SCHENCK, Beth Amsterdam. N79W14756 APPLETON AVE, # 200 53051 #017-20-1980 L1981 **D** *020 †15

SCHLIDT, Scott Alan. W180N7950 TOWN HALL RD 53051 #016-02-1994 L2004 **TS** *020 †85

SCHNEIDER, Joseph P. N84W16889 MENOMONEE AVE, MENOMONEE FALLS CLINIC 53051 #056-06-1990 L1991 **FM** *020 †18

SCHREIBER, Jennifer Cunni. ■ 53051 #056-06-2005 L2007 **PD** *012

SCHWARZ, Robert Lewis. ■ 53051 #018-03-1971 L1972 **FM** *071 †18

SETHI, Amanpreet Kaur. ■ 53051 #016-45-2002 L2008 **FM** *020 †18

SHAHZAD, Abdul R. N88W17015 MAIN ST, EMERGENCY RESOURCES GROUP 53051 #308-11-1983 L1998 **GS** *020 †85

SHAPSON, Mark Stuart. N84W16889 MENOMONEE AVE, MENOMONEE FALLS CLINIC 53051 #056-05-1987 L1988 **IM** *020

SHARMA, Sameer Kumar. N84W16889 MENOMONEE AVE 53051 #051-01-1997 L2007 **U** *020 †95

SIMS, Malini. W180N7950 TOWN HALL RD 53051 #495-99-1988 L1991 **IM** *020 †20

SKRUPKY, Ryan Anthony. W180N8085 TOWN HALL RD, COMMUNITY MEMORIAL EMERGEN 53051 #056-05-2000 L2003 **EM** *020 †16

SMITH, Douglas Sanford. N84W16889 MENOMONEE AVE, MENOMONEE FALLS CLINIC 53051 #038-40-1981 L1986 **EM** *020 †55

SMITH, Edward Beck. N84W16889 MENOMONEE AVE, MENOMONEE FALLS CLINIC 53051 #017-20-1981 L1983 **GS** *020 †85

SODHI, Manila. W165N5595 CREEKWOOD XING 53051 #495-29-1994 L1998 **IM** *020 †20

STARSHAK, Robert Jos. N84W16889 MENOMONEE AVE, MENOMONEE FALLS CLINIC 53051 #056-06-1968 L1969 **PDR DR** *020 †80

STEINMETZ, Thomas E. W180N7950 TOWN HALL RD 53051 #056-05-1972 L1973 **FM** *020 †18

STEPHENS, Tori Lynn. N84W16889 MENOMONEE AVE, MENOMONEE FALLS CLINIC 53051 #056-06-1991 L1992 **OBG** *020 †30

STEWART, Gary Wilkinson. N84W16889 MENOMONEE AVE 53051 #048-14-1979 L1981 **GS VS** *075 †85

SWENSON, Todd Michael. W180N7950 TOWN HALL RD 53051 #056-05-1989 L1995 **ORS OSM** *020 †40

SWIDERSKI, Mary Katherine. N84W16889 MENOMONEE AVE, MENOMONEE FALLS CLINIC 53051 #056-06-1993 L1997 **OBG** *020 †30

TESCH, Bonnie Jean. N84W16889 MENOMONEE AVE, MENOMONEE FALLS CLINIC 53051 #038-41-1978 L1981 **IM** *075 †20

TIPTON, Sarah Elizabeth. N84W16889 MENOMONEE AVE, MENOMONEE FALLS CLINIC 53051 #028-03-1994 L1999 **NM** *071 †80,28

TODD, Paul Clark. N91W17271 APPLETON AVE 53051 #025-01-1971 L1980 **P** *020 †75 ‡

TOPP, Jeremy D. N84W16889 MENOMONEE AVE 53051 #018-75-2003, ▲ L2005 **FM** *020 †18

TOTH, David William. N84W16889 MENOMONEE AVE, MENOMONEE FALLS CLINIC 53051 #035-45-1996 L2002 **END** *020 †20

TOTZKE-VAN VOORHIS, Lara. W180N7950 TOWN HALL RD 53051 #056-06-2001 L2003 **PD** *020

UNGER, Michael John. W180N8085 TOWN HALL RD, COMMUNITY MEMORIAL HOSP 53051 #056-06-1981 L1982 **IM** *020

VALESTIN, Gary Robt. W180N7950 TOWN HALL RD 53051 #041-09-1977 L1978 **GYN** *020 †30

VAN BOMMEL, Jesse Jacob. N51W16911 OLD HICKORY RD, DEPT OF ANESTHESIOLOGY 53051 #056-06-1998 L1999 **AN** *020 †05

VAN STEEN, Scott Drew. N84W16889 MENOMONEE AVE, MENOMONEE FALLS CLINIC 53051 #056-05-1978 L1982 **N** *020 †75

VAN WHY, Laura Imig. N84W16889 MENOMONEE AVE 53051 #056-05-1989 L2001 **D IM** *020 †20,15

VAN WINKLE, Gregory Nolan. W180N8085 TOWN HALL RD, FORWARD ORTHOPEDICS S.C. 53051 #016-45-1979 L1985 **ORS** *020 †40

VARONA, Guillermo D, Jr. N88W16624 APPLETON AVE 53051 #748-08-1959 L1977 **FM** *020 †18

VASUDEV, Brahm Sarup. ■ 53051 #495-73-1996 L2002 **NEP** *020 †20

VERRE, William Paul. N89W16785 APPLETON AVE 53051 #016-01-1981 L1982 **OPH** *020 †35

WACKER, William David. W180N7950 TOWN HALL RD, MEDICAL ASSOCIATES 53051 #021-05-1985 L1986 **D IM** *020 †20,15

WAKEFIELD, Richard James. N84W16889 MENOMONEE AVE, MENOMONEE FALLS CLINIC 53051 #056-06-1977 L1978 **CD IM** *020

WARRIER, Anil. N84W16889 MENOMONEE AVE 53051 #496-09-1996 L2005 **RHU** *020 †20

WOLFF, Yolanda Stephenson. ■ 53051 #056-06-2004 L2006 **PD** *020 †55

YOUNG, Jeffrey Stephen. N89W16785 APPLETON AVE, VERRE YOUNG EYE CLINIC, S. 53051 #016-43-1988 L1989 **OPH** *020 †35

MENOMONIE – DUNN

BENOIST, Louis Armand, III. 700 WOLSKE BAY RD, STE 225 54751 #027-01-1970 L1995 **HS** *020 †40

BROWN, Steven Geo. 2211 STOUT RD 54751 #016-42-1972 L1975 **IM** *020 †20

CUPERY, James Howard. 2321 STOUT RD, MYRTLE WERTH HOSPITAL 54751 #041-01-1966 L1973 **R** *020 †20

DEYO-SVENDSEN, Mark Emory. 2211 STOUT RD 54751 #026-04-1983 L1986 **FM** *020 †18

DSOUZA, Jacqueline Simone. 2321 STOUT RD 54751 #046-01-1999 L2002 **IM** *020 †20

EITRHEIM, David Craig. 2321 STOUT RD 54751 #026-04-1983 L1986 **FM FPG** *020 †18

FEIGAL, Michael Dean. 2211 STOUT RD 54751 #026-04-1975 L1978 **FM** *020 †18

FENNELL, Elton Garret. 2321 STOUT RD, RED CEDAR CLINIC 54751 #654-01-1982 L2002 **OBG** *020 †30,18

FICKE, Albert John. N6622 530TH ST 54751 #026-04-1965 L1970 **ORS OS** *030 †40

FOLKESTAD, Charles Le Roy. 2211 STOUT RD 54751 #026-04-1974 L1978 **FM** *020 †18

FOSTER, Allen Curtis. 2321 STOUT RD, RED CEDAR CLINIC 54751 #016-11-1993 L1996 **IM** *020 †20

HAEMMERLE, James Henry. 2211 STOUT RD 54751 #026-04-1973 L1978 **ORS** *071 †40

HARVEY, Thomas Michael. 710 WOLSKE BAY RD 54751 #056-06-2000 L2005 **OPH** *020 †35

HAVLOVIC, Julia. ■ 54751 #056-05-2008 *012

HEIMLER, Joseph William. 2211 STOUT RD 54751 #026-04-1983 L1987 **FM** *020 †18

HERRMANN, Sarajean Marie. 2321 STOUT RD 54751 #026-04-1990 L2000 **PD** *020 †55

HERRMANN, Thomas Michael. 2321 STOUT RD, RED CEDAR MEDICAL CTR 54751 #035-19-1991 L2000 **GS** *020 †85

HESSLER, Ronald Jason. 2409 STOUT RD, MIDELFORT CLINIC - MENOMON 54751 #025-01-2001 L2005 **OPH** *020

HOLLINS-JACKSON, Viola R. 2321 STOUT RD, RED CEDAR MEDICAL CENTER 54751 #019-02-1993 L2006 **OBG** *020 †30

HSIAO, Albert Kechung. 2321 STOUT RD 54751 #026-04-1988 L2002 **EM** *020 †55

KAMINSKI, Marek. 2321 STOUT RD 54751 #759-11-1974 L1988 **EM IM** *020 †20

LEE, Sherman R. 934 TAINTER ST D 54751 #056-05-1949 L1950 **FM** *071

LIMBERG, Allen Wm. 2321 STOUT RD 54751 #056-05-1946 L1947 **CD** *071

MOHROR, Jason Allan. 3603 SCHNEIDER AVE SE 54751 #046-01-1999 L2002 **MPD** *020 †20,55

MUREL, Lynn Mary. 103 1ST AVE W, UW STOUT STUDENT HEALTH 54751 #026-04-1991 L1993 **FM** *020 †18

MURTY, Annavarapu Gale. 2211 STOUT RD 54751 #026-04-1983 L1986 **FM FPG** *074 †18

NADEN, David Clifford. 2211 STOUT RD 54751 #016-11-1958 L1968 **ORS** *071 †40

NATWICK, Roger Dennis. 609 FAGSTAD ST 54751 #024-07-1958 L1964 **GS** *075

NELSON, Carrie Jo. 2321 STOUT RD 54751 #026-04-1976 L1981 **IM IMG** *020 †20

PEDERSON, Thomas E, Jr. 710 WOLSKE BAY RD 54751 #018-03-1969 L1978 **OPH** *020 †35

PERSING, James Scott. 2211 STOUT RD 54751 #046-01-1994 L1999 **OS P** *020 †20,75

PHILLIPS, Michael Robert. 2321 STOUT RD, RED CEDAR MEDICAL CENTER 54751 #056-06-2001 L2002 **FM** *020 †18

RICH, Nathan Lyle. 2321 STOUT RD 54751 #026-04-1983 L1986 **FM** *020 †18

ROSAS, Steven Louis. 2321 STOUT RD 54751 #026-04-1983 L1984 **FM** *020 †18

RUND, Carroll Duane. 2409 STOUT RD 54751 #026-04-1967 L1973 **OPH** *071 †35

RUTH, Donald Henry, II. 3603 SCHNEIDER AVE SE, MENOMONIE CENTER 54751 #041-02-1995 L1996 **FM** *100 †18 ‡

RUTH, Gregory Douglas. 2211 STOUT RD 54751 #026-04-1999 L2004 **GS** *020 †85

SCAMMELL, Derek Arthur. 2321 STOUT RD 54751 #056-05-1987 L1992 **GS** *020 †85

SCHLEIFER, Philip John. 817 BROADWAY ST S, UW-STOUT 54751 #056-06-1967 L1968 **FM EM** *020 †18

SIMPSON, Henry Joseph. 2321 STOUT RD 54751 #056-05-1987 L1988 **FM MDM** *020 †18

STYGAR, Kyja Karolina. 2321 STOUT RD, RED CEDARMEDICAL CENTER 54751 #056-06-1997 L1998 **FM** *020 †20

SWAENEPOEL, Shawn. 2321 STOUT RD 54751 #018-75-2002, ▲ L2003 **FM** *020 †18

VEDDER, Lorene Lillian. 2321 STOUT RD 54751 #056-05-1973 L1974 **IM** *020 †20

WAHLGREN, Van Eugene. 2321 STOUT RD 54751 #030-05-1979 L2005 **ORS** *020 †40

WALKER, James Allen. 2321 STOUT RD 54751 #026-04-1973 L1976 **FM** *020 †18

WESTPHAL, Nola Ruth. N2598 730TH ST, WESTPHAL HOME 54751 #026-04-1994 L1995 **FM** *071 †18

WILLARD, James Eldene. ■ 54751 #028-03-1965 L1971 **GP** *020

WITGERT, Johann Christoph. 2321 STOUT RD, RED CEDAR MEDICAL CENTER 54751 #409-06-1972 L1984 **OBG** *020 †30

MEQUON – OZAUKEE

ABRAMSON, Beth E. 1240 W RANCHITO LN 53092 #056-05-1985 L1990 **P PYG** *020 †75

ADEDOKUN, Olanrewaju Oluw. ■ 53092 #016-11-2008 *012

ADL, Dima. 13111 N PORT WASHINGTON RD 53097 #875-02-1997 L2007 **PCC** *020 †20

AKBAR, Muhammad Tariq. ■ 53092 #704-25-1998 L2005 **IM** *020 †20

AKBAR, Saima T. ■ 53092 #704-01-1997 L2003 **IM** *020

AL-SAGHIR, Rula. 12203 CORPORATE PKWY, MEQUON CLINIC 53092 #875-02-1986 L1998 **PCC** *020 †20

AMEEN, Nadia A. ■ 53092 #566-01-1985 L1988 **PD** *020 †55

AMMON, Sandra F. ■ 53092 #041-01-1974 L1974 **IM** *020

ANDERSON, Michael John. 12203 CORPORATE PKWY, AURORA ADVANCED HEALTHCARE 53092 #056-06-1988 L1994 **ORS** *020 †40

ANSFIELD, James Jos. 10033 N PORT WASHINGTON RD, STE 125 53092 #056-06-1968 L1969 **GE IM** *020 †20

APPLEGATE, Glenn Leslie. 13111 N PORT WASHINGTON RD 53097 #016-06-1993 L1998 **RO** *020 †80

ASGHAR, Huma Ali. 7030 TAMARACK CT 53092 #704-06-1990 L2004 **IM** *020 †20

AZIMI-ZAVAREI, Minoudokht. ■ 53092 #517-11-1994 L2001 **IMG** *020 †20

BARRON, Margaret Mary. 1035 W GLEN OAKS LN, STE 101 53092 #016-02-1978 L2003 **EM IM** *030 †20,55,16

BARTHELL, Edward Nickol. 1035 W GLEN OAKS LN STE 10, INFINITY HEALTHCARE 53092 #056-05-1983 L1984 **EM** *030 †16

BENDER, Ray S, Jr. 1017 W GLEN OAKS LN STE 20 53092 #056-06-1992 L1993 **P** *020 †75 ‡

BEREJAN, Boris. 1251 W GLEN OAKS LN, INFINITY HEALTHCARE 53092 #016-06-1982 L1997 **EM** *020 †16

BOCK, Harvey Michael. 13133 N PORT WASHINGTON RD, STE 208 53097 #056-05-1971 L1972 **PS GS** *020 †85,65

BODNAR, Adriana Stach. ■ 53092 #917-06-1988 L1997 **PTH** *020 †50

BONFIGLIO, Anthony. 10303 N PORT WASHINGTON RD, STE 101 53092 #056-06-1981 L1983 **D** *020 †15

BORCA, Heidi Ann. 13133 N PORT WASHINGTON RD, STE 116 53097 #056-06-1993 L1994 **PM** *020 †60

BRACKETT, Nathaniel S. 1035 W GLEN OAKS LN, STE 101 53092 #025-01-2001 L2004 **EM** *020 †16

BRODERICK, John Scott. 13133 N PT WASHINGTON RD, STE 110 53097 #056-06-2002 L2004 **CN** *075

BROOKS, Andrew James. 12203 CORPORATE PKWY, MEQUON CLINIC 53092 #056-05-1994 L2000 **GS** *020 †85

BYRNE, Richard Row. ■ 53092 #025-01-1955 L1960 **R RO** *071 †80

CABATINGAN, Jaime D. 13111 N PORT WASHINGTON RD 53097 #748-01-1970 L1975 **FM** *020 †18

CALLAHAN, Peggy Ann. 12800 N PORT WASHINGTON RD 53097 #016-11-1988 L1996 **FM** *020 †18

CALVERT, Andrew Wayne. ■ 53092 #016-01-2002 L2005 **EM** *020 †16

CHAPMAN, Elizabeth Nicole. ■ 53092 #056-05-2008 *012

CHAYER, Robert Paul. 10303 N PORT WASHINGTON RD, STE 203 53092 #016-01-1987 L1989 CHP P *020 †75

CHEEMA, Mohammed Aslam. ■ 53092 #704-01-1951 L1974 CD TS *071 †85,90

CHEN, Xiao-Lan. ■ 53097 #243-48-1988 L2002 PTH *020 †50

CHURCHILL, Robert Sean. 12203 CORPORATE PKWY, MEQUON 53092 #025-01-1995 L2001 ORS *020 †40

COSTAKOS, Deborah Mehl. 11307 N PORT WASHINGTON RD 53092 #056-06-1998 L1999 PO OPH *035

COULTER, Renee Rae. 12203 CORPORATE PKWY, MEQUON CLINIC 53092 #056-05-1979 L1980 OBG OS *020 †30

DAVIES, Joseph Francis. 13133 N PORT WASHINGTON RD, STE 104 53092 #056-06-1982 L1988 ORS *020 †40

DAVIS, Marsha Fleming. 1220 W RANCHITO LN 53092 #056-06-1993 L1994 IM PD *020 †20,55

DAVISON, Walter Todd. 11501 N PT WASHINGTON RD, # 630 53092 #045-01-1966 L1985 PYA P *020 †75

DECKER, Michael C. 1251 W GLEN OAKS LN, INFINITY HEALTHCARE 53092 #025-12-1991 L1992 EM *020 †16

DINAPOLI, Kevin John. 13133 N PORT WASHINGTON RD, STE G16 53097 #038-40-1985 L1988 IM *020 †20

DJELMAMI-HANI, Mohamed. 10123 N FOXKIRK CIR 53097 #125-01-1996 L2001 CD *012 †20

DOERS, Thomas Michael. 12203 CORPORATE PKWY 53092 #056-05-1991 L1999 OSS *020 †40

DOLHUN, Patricia Jean. 13133 N PORT WASHINGTON RD, STE G16 53097 #056-05-1981 L1993 OBG *020 †30

DOTSON, Rose Marie. 11016 N WYNGATE TRCE 53092 #056-05-1980 L1981 N *020 †75

DRAKE, Neil L. 9311 W CONCORD DR 53097 #030-05-1976 L1994 PTH *020 †50

DRAYNA, Christopher John. 13133 N PORT WASHINGTON RD, STE G16 53097 #056-06-1976 L1977 IM *020 †20

DUNN, Bruce Edward. ■ 53092 #045-01-1981 L1991 CLP *050 †50

EATON, Thomas L. 11725 N PT WASHINGTON RD, STE 250 53092 #016-01-1982 L1998 PHL VM *020

EISEMAN, Marc Steven. 1220 W RANCHITO LN, ADVANCED CARE WELLNESS CTR 53092 #016-06-1995 L1999 FM OS *020 †18

ELGIN, Drew Michael. 13133 N PORT WASHINGTON RD, STE G16 53097 #018-03-1980 L1985 GE IM *020 †20

ELIAS, Sharon Louise. 10945 N PT WASHINGTON RD, STE 100 53092 #005-11-1967 L1972 PS *020 †65

ENGLEBERT, Christina V. 10046 N PORT WASHINGTON RD, NORTH SHORE PEDIATRICS 53092 #056-06-1998 L1999 PD *020 †55

ERICKSON, James David. 1251 W GLEN OAKS LN, INFINITY HEALTHCARE 53092 #056-06-2002 L2006 EM *020 †16

FABER, Julie Eileen. 11348 N LAGUNA DR 53092 #016-43-2001 L2004 EM *020 †16

FAURE, Bruce Terrence. 12203 CORPORATE PKWY, MEQUON CLINIC 53092 #056-05-1985 L1991 ORS *020 †40

FELTON, Christopher W. 1035 W GLEN OAKS LN, INFINITY HEALTHCARE 53092 #028-34-1986 L1988 EM *020 †16

FLESCH, James Richard. 13133 N PORT WASHINGTON RD, STE 116 53097 #056-05-1972 L1977 ORS *020 †20

FLYNN, George Francis. ■ 53092 #056-06-1956 L1957 GS *071 †85

FORMAN, Sheldon Ray. 2625 W LAKE ISLE DR 53092 #056-06-1969 L1970 A *020 †20,03

FROMMELL, George Thos. 12203 CORPORATE PKWY, MEQUON CLINIC 53092 #056-06-1970 L1971 PD *020 †55

GAENSLEN, Eric Steven. 12203 CORPORATE PKWY, MEQUON CLINIC 53092 #056-05-1989 L1995 ORS HS *020 †20

GANJI, Masoud. ■ 53092 #517-01-1997 L2004 PTH *020

GARDEZI, Maryam. 6807 MENDOTA CT 53092 #704-21-1991 L2004 CD *012

GERSHAN, Lynn A. 10046 N PORT WASHINGTON RD, NORTH SHORE PEDIATRICS 53092 #067-01-1984 L1990 NPM PD *020 †55 ‡

GERTEL, Theodore Hilliard. 13133 N PORT WASHINGTON RD, STE 104 53097 #035-19-1983 L1989 ORS GS *020 †40

GITTER, Joyce Brandl. ■ 53097 #056-05-1985 L1992 PD *020 †55

GLINSKI, Jeffrey John. 1035 W GLEN OAKS LN, STE 101 53092 #056-05-2002 L2005 EM *020 †16

GOLDMAN, Janet Beth. 13133 N PT WASHINGTON RD, STE 204 53097 #005-02-1993 L1994 OBG *020 †30

GREEN, William Harry. 1220 W RANCHITO LN, ADVANCED CARE CLINIC 53092 #024-07-1975 L1985 IM *062 †20

GROSSMAN, Ronald Earl. ■ 53092 #056-06-1961 L1962 R *020 †80

GUMMIN, David Dana. 1251 W GLEN OAKS LN, INFINITY HEALTH CARE 53092 #056-05-1990 L2000 EM ETX *020 †16

HANDRICH, Thomas Alfred. ■ 53092 #056-05-1964 L1965 OBG *071 †30

HANNAH, Stuart Garth. 10526 N PORT WASHINGTON RD, WFMG - MEQUON 53092 #047-05-2000 L2001 FM *020 †18 ‡

HASELOW, William Carl. 1035 W GLEN OAKS LN, ADMINISTRATION SUITE 101 53092 #025-07-1984 L1989 EM AM *020 †16

HEINRICH, John Thomas. 13133 N PORT WASHINGTON RD, STE 104 53097 #056-05-1988 L1989 ORS OSM *020 †40

HEINRICH, Lori Nelson. 10303 N PORT WASHINGTON RD, STE 101 53092 #056-05-1987 L1988 D *020 †15

HEISDORF, John Gerard. 13110 N PORT WASHINGTON RD, CSM OZAUKEE-ANES DEPT 53097 #056-05-1992 L1993 AN *020 †05

HERSHEY, Jonathan Marc. 11307 N PORT WASHINGTON RD 53092 #028-02-1985 L1992 OPH *020 †35

HILANDER, Swen James. 1035 W GLEN OAKS LN, STE 101 53092 #056-06-1995 L1996 EM *020 †16

HIRSCH, Erwin Oskar. ■ 53092 #024-01-1946 L1970 IM *071 †20

HONG, Bruce Sidney. ■ 53092 #014-01-1979 L1984 RHU IM *020 †20

HONIGBERG, Robert M. ■ 53092 #016-06-1986 L1988 PHM GS *050

HORWITZ, S Fredric. 13622 N LAKEWOOD DR 53097 #016-42-1962 L1963 OTO *071 †45

HUETTL, Brian Michael. 13111 N PORT WASHINGTON RD 53097 #056-06-1992 L2002 EM *020 †16

HUNT, Sally Gluek. 10046 N PORT WASHINGTON RD, NORTH SHORE PEDIATRICS 53092 #165-01-1979 L1990 PD *020 †55

JACOBS, Paul Alan. 13133 N PORT WASHINGTON RD, STE 104 53097 #035-08-1954 L1961 ORS *071 †40

JACOBSON, Mitchell Mayer. 13133 N PORT WASHINGTON RD, STE G16 53097 #016-06-1964 L1965 IM END *020 †20

JAY, Martha F. 11307 N PORT WASHINGTON RD 53092 #045-04-1988 L1992 OPH *020 †35

JORDAN, Jeffrey Paul. ■ 53092 #654-01-1987 L1993 IM *020

JORGENSEN, Scott Alan. 13111 N PORT WASHINGTON RD 53097 #056-06-1986 L1990 IM *020 †20

KAREWICZ, Adam Piotr. 12203 CORPORATE PKWY 53092 #759-03-1994 L2000 IM *020 †20

KARR, Richard Karpowitz. 13133 N PORT WASHINGTON RD 53097 #056-06-1977 L1978 OSS ORS *020 †40

KAUFMAN, Kiesl Karl. ■ 53092 #056-06-1946 L1947 PUD *071 †20

KEPPEL, Christina C. 1017 W GLEN OAKS LN STE 20 53092 #016-43-1977 L1981 P *020 †75

KERR, Harry Davidson. 1035 W GLEN OAKS LN # 101, INFINITY HEALTHCARE 53092 #035-09-1975 L1983 IM EM *020 †20,16

KINSFOGEL, Edward Robt. 13116 N FOX HOLLOW RD 53097 #056-05-1967 L1970 DR *071 †80

KLEIN, Mitchell Alan. 10936 N PORT WASHINGTON RD, # 208 53092 #028-02-1985 L1990 DR *020 †80

KLUIBER, Rudolph Mark. 12203 CORPORATE PKWY, MEQUON CLINIC 53092 #016-06-1986 L1987 GS *020 †85,10

KOENIG, Robert R. ■ 53092 #056-05-1952 L1953 PTH *071 †50

KONON, Irina. ■ 53092 #056-06-2002 L2004 RHU *100 †20

KRETCHMAR, Joseph S. ■ 53092 #056-06-1949 L1950 PS *020 †65

KUMAR, Radhika Lingam. ■ 53092 #038-06-2005 L2007 OPH *012

LE FEBER, William Polk. 12203 CORPORATE PKWY 53092 #032-01-1979 L1980 D *020 †15

LEVIN, Michael Isaac. 12203 CORPORATE PKWY, AURORA ADVANCED HEALTHCARE 53092 #028-02-1993 L2006 N *020 †20

LEVY, Michael B. 10520 N PORT WASHINGTON RD 53092 #056-05-1981 L1982 AI IM *020 †20,03

LEVY, Stuart A. 1516 W MEQUON RD 53092 #035-46-1965 L1971 PUD IM *062 †20

LEWIS, Kimberley Dawn. 1035 W GLEN OAKS LN, STE 101 53092 #028-03-1995 L2006 EM *020 †16

LIPINSKI, Anne Mary. 13133 N PORT WASHINGTON RD, STE 204 53097 #025-12-1988 L1989 OBG *020 †30

LOIBEN, Robert Louis. 1240 W RANCHITO LN 53092 #016-42-1987 L1989 P *020 †75

LUCKE, David Patrick. 13133 N PORT WASHINGTON RD, STE G16 53097 #056-05-1993 L1994 IM *020 †20

MAGALSKI, Anthony Edward. 1035 W GLEN OAKS LN, STE 101 53092 #038-43-1995 L2006 IM *020 †16

MAI, David William. 12203 CORPORATE PKWY, ADVANCED HEALTHCARE, S.C. 53092 #016-11-1997 L1999 D *020 †15

MALICKY, Eric Scott. 12203 CORPORATE PKWY, MEQUON CLINIC 53092 #038-06-1992 L1998 ORS *020 †40

MALONEY, Jack Edward. 13133 N PORT WASHINGTON RD, STE G6 53097 #026-04-1995 L2002 D *020 †15

MATTSON, Anne Lee. 6425 W MEQUON RD, MEQUON CLINIC 53092 #025-12-1990 L1991 FM *020 †18

MC DONAGH, Andrew Michael. 4403 N MADERO DR, ST JOES REGIONAL MEDICAL C 53092 #017-20-1987 L1995 IM *020 †20

MC FARLAND, Janice Gail. 13030 BIRCH CREEK RD 53097 #040-02-1977 L1984 HEM OS *020 †20

MELTZER, Sylvia Mae. 6425 W MEQUON RD, MEQUON CLINIC 53092 #016-11-1987 L1988 FM *020 †18

MENKVELD, Sharon R. ■ 53092 #025-12-1975 L1986 ORS *071 †40

METSKAS, Nanette Mary. 10936 N PORT WASHINGTON RD, STE 104 53092 #016-06-1976 L1979 P *074

MEYERS, Sidney Stanley. ■ 53092 #016-11-1943 L1948 OBG *071 †30

MICKE, Jennifer Rose. 6425 W MEQUON RD, MEQUON CLINIC 53092 #026-04-1986 L1987 FM *020 †18

MILLER, Edward Carl W. 3926 W LE MONT BLVD 53092 #016-11-1977 L1985 EM FM *020 †18,16

MOUSSAVI, Nadia. 10532 N PORT WASHINGTON RD 53092 #056-06-1991 L1993 CD *020 †20

MUNKWITZ, Geo Albert, Jr. ■ 53097 #056-06-1974 L1977 IM *020 †20

MUNRO, Ian James. 1035 W GLEN OAKS LN, INFINITY HEALTHCARE 53092 #047-07-1994 L1999 EM *020 †16

NAZARETH, Norine. 12203 CORPORATE PKWY, MEQUON CLINIC 53092 #495-52-1992 L1998 IM *020 †20

NOONAN, Patrick Jos. 10520 N PORT WASHINGTON RD 53092 #056-06-1957 L1958 OTO *071 †45

O'MALLEY, Richard Jos. ■ 53097 #016-06-1948 L1948 GP PHP *071

OSTROVSKY, Benjamin. 1035 W GLEN OAKS LN, STE 101 53092 #016-01-2003 L2007 EM *020

PANAGOS, Alexander C. 1035 W GLEN OAKS LN, STE 101 53092 #781-01-1987 L1993 IM *020 †20

PANDEY, Krishna Pratap. 7123 W LANTERN LN, ST JOES REGIONAL MEDICAL C 53092 #495-41-1995 L2003 IM *020 †20

PENN, Julia Hinkle. 11501 N PT WASHINGTON RD, STE 202 53092 #028-03-1978 L1981 P GP *020 †75

PESEK-MC COY, Michelle C. 1251 W GLEN OAKS LN 53092 #056-06-2002 L2005 EM *020 †16

PIRYANI, Chandur. 10945 N PORT WASHINGTON RD, PAIN DIAGNOSTIC 53092 #704-16-1990 L1999 APM AN *020 †05

PLICHTA, Stephen Delore. 1035 W GLEN OAKS LN, STE 101 53092 #016-11-1986 L2007 DR *020 †80

PUCCINELLI, Joseph M. 13133 N PORT WASHINGTON RD, STE 116 53097 #028-34-1986 L1992 ORS *020 †20

PUERNER, James Allen. 13111 N PORT WASHINGTON RD, COLUMBIA-ST.MARY'S OZAUKEE 53097 #016-42-1992 L1997 PTH *020 †50

PULITO, Domenic Jos. 13133 N PORT WASHINGTON RD, STE 116 53097 #056-06-1976 L1980 ORS *020

RAIN, Barbara Ann. 6425 W MEQUON RD, MEQUON CLINIC 53092 #018-03-1994 L1999 OBG *020 †30

RAISINGHANI, Mohini K. ■ 53092 #495-17-1960 L1977 AN *071 †05

RAJA, Sharath Chandra. 11307 N PORT WASHINGTON RD 53092 #016-02-1992 L2001 OPH *020 †35

RAJKUMAR, Srutha P. 1240 W RANCHITO LN 53092 #495-21-1987 L1992 CHP *020 †75

RAMANUJAM, Srihari R. 13133 N PORT WASHINGTON RD, STE G16 53097 #056-06-2001 L2004 GE *020

RASANSKY, Marc. 13133 N PORT WASHINGTON RD, STE 206 53097 #056-05-1975 L1980 PUD CCM *020 †20

REESER, Frederick H, Jr. 11307 N PORT WASHINGTON RD 53092 #041-01-1965 L1973 OPH *020 †35

REHRAUER, Luke Francis. 12203 CORPORATE PKWY, MEQUON CLINIC 53092 #056-06-1982 L1983 **IM** *020 †20

REMINGA, Thomas Alan. 1035 W GLEN OAKS LN, STE 101 53092 #025-01-1973 L1976 **EM** *030 †16

RIEGG, Susan Joan. 13111 N PORT WASHINGTON RD 53097 #056-06-1990 L1992 **PTH** *020 †50

RILLING, Robert John. 1340 W TOWNE SQUARE RD 53092 #056-05-1995 L1996 **DR** *020 †80

RUGGERO, Robert Santo. 12203 CORPORATE PKWY 53092 #016-06-1978 L1983 **DR OS** *020 †80

RUSSO, John Louis. 1035 W GLEN OAKS LN, INFINITY HEALTHCARE, SUITE 53092 #056-05-2001 L2005 **EM** *020 †16

SABNIS, Sushil Suman. 12203 CORPORATE PKWY, MEQUON CLINIC 53092 #016-06-1991 L2004 **DR** *020 †80

SALAYMEH, Basil Muhammad. 6425 W MEQUON RD, MEQUON CLINIC 53092 #016-11-1986 L1987 **GS** *020 †85

SALUD, Antonio De Villa, II. 13111 N PORT WASHINGTON RD 53097 #056-06-1999 L2007 **PCC** *020 †20

SCHENCK, Jeffrey Wayne. 13133 N PT WASHINGTON RD, STE G16 53097 #017-20-1980 L1981 **GE IM** *020 †20

SCHMIDT, Mary Susan. 12203 CORPORATE PKWY 53092 #056-06-1994 L1995 **DR** *020 †80

SCHNITZLER, Henry Jos. 12800 N PORT WASHINGTON RD, HIGHLAND FAM. HLTH CTR 53097 #056-06-1990 L1991 **FM** *020 †18

SCHUCK, John Ellsworth. 12203 CORPORATE PKWY 53092 #037-01-1986 L1987 **DR** *020 †80

SCHULTZ, Rosemary Theresa. 12203 CORPORATE PKWY, MEQUON CLINIC 53092 #056-05-1985 L1992 **ORS** *020 †40

SCHWARTZ, Ann E. ■ 53092 #016-06-1984 L1989 **OPH OS** *071 †35

SCRIMENTI, Rudolph Jos. ■ 53092 #056-06-1958 L1959 **D** *071 †15

SENNETT, Jordan Avery. 12203 CORPORATE PKWY 53092 #024-01-1977 L1977 **END IM** *020 †20

SENNETT, Louis W. 10046 N PT WASHNGTN RD 13W 53092 #056-05-1943 L1944 **IM CD** *072 †20

SHAMAH, Corey Justin. 12203 CORPORATE PKWY 53092 #056-06-2001 L2003 **HO** *020 †20

SHAW, Donald Kevin. 1045 W GLEN OAKS LN, STE 3 53092 #056-06-1965 L1966 **R** *071 †80

SHIMP, Richard John. 1251 W GLEN OAKS LN, INFINITY HEALTHCARE 53092 #016-06-1994 L1998 **EM** *020 †16

SHOHAM, Charles. 11701 N EUGENE AVE 53092 #024-05-1976 L1993 **PM** *020 †60

SIEGERT, John Jos. 12300 N PORT WASHINGTON RD 53092 #056-06-1983 L1987 **HS ORS** *020 †40

SIEGERT, Theresa Ann. 12300 N PT WASHINGTON RD 53092 #056-06-1982 L1983 **HS GS** *020 †85

SILBERMAN, Adam F. ■ 53092 #056-05-2007 **P** *012

SIMON, Bozena. 11203 N BUNTROCK AVE, STE 204 53092 #759-08-1989 L1995 **IM** *020 †20

SLOCUM, Peter Albert. 13133 N PORT WASHINGTON RD, STE G16 53097 #056-05-1983 L1988 **U** *020 †16

SOVELL, Paul Jos. 1035 W GLEN OAKS LN, STE 101 53092 #026-04-1989 L1991 **EM** *020 †16

SPOERL, Margaret Mary. 12203 CORPORATE PKWY, MEQUON CLINIC 53092 #056-06-1988 L1992 **IM** *020 †20

SPRUNG, Larry Ross. 1240 W RANCHITO LN 53092 #016-11-1986 L1987 **P** *020 †75

STANLEY, Mark Danton. 1017 W GLEN OAKS LN, STE 109 53092 #018-03-1980 L2000 **DR** *020 †80

STEIGER, Fredric Adams. 13111 N PORT WASHINGTON RD 53092 #016-06-1971 L1975 **CHP P** *020 †75

STEVENS, Bruce Robt. 13111 N PORT WASHINGTON RD 53097 #056-06-1992 L1993 **P** *020 †75

STROTTMANN, James Michael. 1340 W TOWNE SQUARE RD 53092 #018-03-1987 L2000 **RNR** *020 †80

STUMPF, Robert Rudolf. 13133 N PORT WASHINGTON RD, STE 204 53097 #056-06-1988 L1989 **OBG** *020 †30

SUNDARAM, Mecheri M. 1045 W GLEN OAKS LN, STE 2 53092 #495-16-1973 L1993 **N CN** *020

TAXMAN, Jeffrey Earle. 11501 N PORT WASHINGTON RD 53092 #056-05-1982 L1984 **P** *020 †75

TEPLIN, Ervin. 10995 N MARKET ST, RM 205 53092 #056-05-1946 L1947 **P** *071 †75

TEPLIN, Robert Wayne. ■ 53092 #056-05-1970 L1971 **OTO GP** *020 †45

THAKUR, Anita. ■ 53097 #495-08-1977 L2001 **PCP** *020 †50

THOMPSON, Wm Clyne, III. 10234 N TRILLIUM RD 53092 #025-07-1967 L1999 **DR NM** *071 †80,28 ‡

TOCCO, Christopher John. 1251 W GLEN OAKS LN, INFINITY HEALTHCARE INC 53092 #028-03-1994 L1998 **EM** *020 †16

TODD, Stephanie Jeanne. ■ 53097 #056-05-2002 L2004 **PEM** *100 †55

TONG, Peggy. 12203 CORPORATE PKWY 53092 #016-02-1992 L1997 **D** *020 †15

TOVAR, Richard Toby. 1035 W GLEN OAKS LN, STE 101 53092 #048-02-1984 L1985 **EM** *020 †16

TUCKER, William Thos, Jr. 1251 W GLEN OAKS LN 53092 #016-01-1992 L2000 **EM** *020 †16

VASUDHAR, Sridhar V. 3705 W MARSEILLES DR 53092 #495-56-1971 L1976 **PM PMM** *020 †60

VILLANUEVA, Ethel Ruiz. 12203 CORPORATE PKWY, MEQUON CLINIC 53092 #016-01-1994 L2004 **R** *020 †80

VITAMVAS, Gerald L. 12203 CORPORATE PKWY, MEQUON CLINIC 53092 #030-05-1975 L1979 **OBG** *020 †30

WAGNER, Richard Otto. 1045 W GLEN OAKS LN, STE 3 53092 #056-06-1974 L1975 **DR** *020 †80

WALKER, Gene Edward, Jr. ■ 53092 #048-14-1979 L2002 **FM EM** *020 †16

WARTINBEE, Daniel Robert. 13133 N PORT WASHINGTON RD, STE 104 53097 #056-06-1977 L1978 **ORS** *020 †40

WATCHMAKER, Greg Peter. 1535 W MARKET ST 53092 #028-02-1989 L1996 **HS** *020 †65

WEFFENSTETTE, Bruce E. 13111 N PORT WASHINGTON RD 53097 #017-20-1977 L1978 **P ADP** *020 †75

WEISSLER, Joseph Bernard. ■ 53092 #028-34-1948 L1954 **P** *071 †75

WESTREICH, Frederick G. 13133 N PORT WASHINGTON RD, STE 204 53097 #056-06-1995 L1997 **OBG** *020 †30

WHITE, Steffen Peter. 7448 W RIDGEVIEW CT 53092 #056-06-1990 L1991 **AN** *020 †05

WHITFIELD, Robert M. 12203 CORPORATE PKWY 53092 #031-01-1996 L2005 **PS** *100 †85,65

WILKERSON, Suzanne M. 13111 N PORT WASHINGTON RD 53097 #016-11-1995 L1996 **FM** *020 †18

WILSON, Bruce Campbell. 1330 W TOWNE SQUARE RD 53092 #056-05-1980 L1991 **CD IM** *020 †20

WILSON, Cory Allan. 3411 W RIVER DR 53097 #016-43-1989 L1993 **EM** *020 †16

WILSON, Susan J. ■ 53097 #016-43-1989 L1990 **EM** *020 †16

YALE, Russell Steven. 10520 N PORT WASHINGTON RD 53092 #016-42-1973 L1979 **OTO PS** *020 †45

YANG, John Joonhwan. 6425 W MEQUON RD, MEQUON CLINIC 53092 #054-04-1994 L1995 **FM** *020 †18

YORKE, Victoria Lynn. 10526 N PORT WASHINGTON RD 53092 #010-01-1986 L1994 **FM** *020 †18

YOUNG, Laurens Dolan. 11514 N PORT WASHINGTON RD, STE 4 53092 #016-02-1969 L1972 **P PFP** *020 †75

ZACHARIAS, Alex. 12203 CORPORATE PKWY, MEQUON CLINIC 53092 #016-11-1992 L1994 **U** *020 †95

ZASTROW, Raymond Jude. 13111 N PORT WASHINGTON RD 53097 #056-06-1983 L1986 **FM** *030 †18

ZELLMER, Christopher J. 12203 CORPORATE PKWY 53092 #056-06-1990 L1991 **DR** *020 †80

ZIMMERS, Herbert John. 12203 CORPORATE PKWY 53092 #056-06-1970 L1973 **DR** *020 †80

MERCER – IRON

DOUD, J Richard. PO BOX 649 54547 #035-45-1958 L1985 **GS** *071 †85

PIERPONT, John M. ■ 54547 #025-01-1938 L1939 **GP OM** *075

MERRILL – LINCOLN

ADAMS-STICH, James Nathan. 1205 O DAY ST 54452 #026-08-1997 L2001 **FM** *020 †18

ALDRICH, Michael G. 601 S CENTER AVE, GOOD SAM HLTH CTR ER 54452 #056-06-1983 L1984 **EM IM** *020 †20

ASINAS, Ildefonso L. ■ 54452 #748-01-1955 L1961 **FM OBG** *071

CRAPSTER-PREGONT, Barbara. 1205 O DAY ST, MARSHFIELD CLINIC MERRILL 54452 #008-02-1982 L1983 **FM** *020 †18

CRAPSTER-PREGONT, Mark G. 1205 O DAY ST 54452 #008-02-1982 L1983 **FM** *020 †18

DAHM, Steven David. 1205 O DAY ST, MARSHFIELD CLINIC-MERRILL 54452 #056-06-1983 L1989 **GS** *020 †85

DODGE, Gregory Glenn. 1205 O DAY ST, FAMILY MEDICAL CLINIC S.C. 54452 #046-01-1990 L1992 **GS** *020 †85

EVANS, Donald L. 1205 O DAY ST 54452 #025-12-1977 L1980 **FM** *020 †18

FISHMAN, Robert Alan. ■ 54452 #649-03-2002 L2005 **FP** *012

GILL, Gregory Lee. 1205 O DAY ST 54452 #056-05-1982 L1983 **FM OBG** *020 †18

HEESE, Jason P. 601 S CENTER AVE 54452 #037-01-1995 L2000 **PTH** *020 †20

HEITZ, Joseph Alan. 600 S CENTER AVE, RADIOLOGY MERRILL 54452 #038-41-1983 L1984 **DR** *020 †80

HENRY, Catherine Gail. 3333 E MAIN ST, ASPIRUS MERRILL CLINIC 54452 #028-02-1976 L1984 **FM PD** *020 †55,18

JANOWIAK, James Stanley. 2404 COTTER CT 54452 #056-06-1961 L1965 **FM** *071 †18

KRAJNIK, Ronald John. 1205 O DAY ST, MARSHFIELD CLINIC MERRILL 54452 #056-06-1993 L1994 **FM** *020 †18

KROHN-GILL, Kathryn Ann. 1205 O DAY ST 54452 #056-05-1983 L1984 **FM** *020 †18 ‡

KRUEGER, Le Roy August. 601 S CENTER AVE 54452 #056-05-1964 L1969 **PTH** *020 †50

LEE, Christian Erwin. 3333 E MAIN ST, ASPIRUS MERRILL CLINIC 54452 #748-10-1986 L1996 **IM** *020 †20

MARQUIS, Arthur Sylvester. 1205 O DAY ST, MARSHFIELD CLINIC-MERRILL 54452 #056-06-1971 L1972 **FM EM** *020 †18

MOORE, Jeffrey Lewis. 1205 O DAY ST 54452 #056-05-1980 L1981 **FM** *020 †18

ODEA, Christine Joy. 1205 O DAY ST, MARSHFIELD CLINIC 54452 #026-08-1997 L2001 **FM** *020 †18 ‡

OLLROGGE, Jane. 1205 O DAY ST, MARSHFIELD CLINIC-MERRILL 54452 #056-06-1988 L1989 **FM** *020 †20

SWEET, Amy Ann. ■ 54452 #056-06-2003 L2004 **MPD** *020 †20,55

SWEET, Gary Theodore, Jr. ■ 54452 #056-06-2003 L2004 **GS** *012

THOMPSON, Paul Alan. 1205 O DAY ST 54452 #028-02-1987 L1988 **FM** *020 †18

WASKIN, Randolph Benj. ■ 54452 #048-04-1984 L1992 **EM FM** *020 †18

MERRIMAC – SAUK

COHEN, Martin Robt. E13365 SUE KAY DR 53561 #051-04-1971 L1994 **P** *050 †75

YARD, Raymond R R, Jr. W11758 THRESHER RD 53561 #030-06-1978 L1991 **PUD IM** *050 †20

MIDDLETON – DANE

ADAMS, Erik Stuart. 2521 ALLEN BLVD, MIDWEST INST SPORTS MED 53562 #016-11-1994 L1995 **FSM** *020 †55

ADULLA, Madhurima Reddy. ■ 53562 #495-57-1997 L2003 **IM** *020 †20

ARBUCKLE, Jacquelynn Dawn. 2349 DEMING WAY 53562 #056-05-1995 L2000 **GS** *020 †85

AVERY, Pamela Gayle. 2349 DEMING WAY 53562 #039-01-1977 L1978 **AN PMM** *020 †05

BACH-Y-RITA, Paul. 6630 UNIVERSITY AVE 53562 #649-01-1959 L1983 **PM** *030 †60

BELT, William Alvin, III. ■ 53562 #038-41-1970 L1972 **AN** *071 †05

BERG, Eric Roy. 2349 DEMING WAY 53562 #056-05-1983 L1988 **D DS** *020 †15

BIEK, Richard Wm. 8501 OLD SAUK RD, APT 131 53562 #016-11-1957 L1969 **PHP** *071 †70

CAMBRAY, Rachel Lamb. ■ 53562 #056-05-2004 L2006 **AN** *012

CHRISTENSEN, Sara Ann. 6630 UNIVERSITY AVE 53562 #056-05-2002 L2006 **PM** *020 †60

COOKE, Robert Edmund. ■ 53562 #056-01-1944 L1974 **PD P** *071

COOMBS, Guerdon Jos. ■ 53562 #035-45-1958 L1963 **END** *071 †54

CROW, Austin Jay. ■ 53562 #028-34-2008 *012

CURRIE, Jonathan William. ■ 53562 #016-06-2006 L2007 **DR** *012

DAS, Ram. ■ 53562 #495-44-1965 L1978 **OM PS** *071

DAVID, John Edward. ■ 53562 #056-05-2001 L2002 **IM** *020 ‡

DAVIS, John Borton. ■ 53562 #056-05-1954 L1955 **R** *071 †80

DEUTSCH, Stephan Martin. 6630 UNIVERSITY AVE 53562 #056-05-1997 L1998 **PM** *020 †60

DOLIN, Ronald Jay. ■ 53562 #016-11-2001 L2007 **DR** *020 †80

DORSEY, Sarah Suzanne. ■ 53562 #038-06-2001 L2004 **IM** *020

EBERT, Jerome Charles. 6630 UNIVERSITY AVE 53562 #056-05-1995 L1996 **PM** *020 †60

EL EZABY, Mai Amin Mahmou. ■ 53562 #915-02-1997 L2006 *100

ERDMAN, Boyd Eric. 2275 DEMING WAY, STE 280 53562 #056-05-1996 L1999 **PHL IM** *020 †20

FATTOUH, Maher Wahed. 3230 DEMING WAY, STE 100 53562 #875-02-1991 L2002 **APM** *020 †05 ‡

FELZ, Kenneth. 7780 ELMWOOD AVE, MERITER MED CLINIC 53562 #038-40-1985 L1988 **IM** *020 †20

FOSDAL, Frederick Allen. 6647 COLUMBUS DR, FORNSIC PSYCH 53562 #056-05-1964 L1965 **LM P** *020 †75

FRIEDMAN, Lisa C. 1420 WILLOW TRL, DEAN CLINIC 53562 #028-03-1979 L1980 **IM** *020 †20

GILSON, Robert Ellsworth. 3000 W BELTLINE HWY 53562 #056-05-1973 **D** *075

HATCHELL, Ryan Neil. ■ 53562 #056-05-2008 *012

HEALY, John R. ■ 53562 #041-02-1949 L1955 **OBG** *071 †30

HECKER, Travis Michael. ■ 53562 #036-08-2007 **AN** *012

HINDERAKER, Paul Hugh. 8383 GREENWAY BLVD STE 1 53562 #056-05-1975 L1980 **CD IM** *020 †20

HOGAN, Larry Howlett. ■ 53562 #056-05-1944 L1946 **AN** *072 †05

IRWIN, Matthew John. ■ 53562 #056-05-2006 L2008 **AN** *012

JAYALAKSHMI, B. 8383 GREENWAY BLVD, STE 100 53562 #495-04-1990 L2004 **CD** *020 †20

JENSEN, Brent William. ■ 53562 #056-05-2006 L2008 **PD** *012

JOHNSON, Eric Averill. ■ 53562 #056-06-2006 L2008 **IM** *012

JOVANOVIC, Dusan. ■ 53562 #957-02-1952 L1971 **GYN** *071 †30

KAROFSKY, Peter Stuart. 1406 SHADY OAK CIR 53562 #024-07-1966 L1967 **PD GP** *071 †55

KATZELNICK, David Joel. 2711 ALLEN BLVD 53562 #007-02-1986 L1990 **P** *050 †75

KRISHNAMACHARY, Mohan Kas. ■ 53562 #495-57-1997 L2004 **HEM** *012 †20

LANGHEIM, Werner. 4505 FOX BLUFF LN, NEUROLOGICAL SURGEON 53562 #407-21-1954 L1964 **NS** *020 †25

LEE, Kenneth Seunghoon. ■ 53562 #024-07-2002 L2007 **DR** *100 †80

LEVY, Carol Spiegel. 3111 PHEASANT BRANCH RD, APT 103 53562 #056-05-1961 L1962 **PYA CHP** *020

LOGAN, Donald Chas. 2515 MIDDLETON BEACH RD 53562 #025-01-1968 L1975 **IM CD** *071 †20

MARCUS, Benjamin Carl. 2349 DEMING WAY 53562 #016-02-1999 L2005 **OTO** *020 †45

MARKS, Erich Nicholas. ■ 53562 #020-02-2007 **AN** *012

MC GUIRE, Shawn Michael. ■ 53562 #023-07-2001 L2007 **DR** *020 †80

MC LEISH, Deborah Lynn. 6630 UNIVERSITY AVE, U.W. HOSPITAL AND CLINICS 53562 #056-05-1986 L1987 **PM PD** *020 †60,55

MC VEAN, Jennifer J. ■ 53562 #026-04-2002 L2005 **PDE** *012 †55

MENDENHALL, Sally Cornell. 4617 FOX BLUFF LN 53562 #023-07-1943 L1951 **GP PD** *071

MIRKIN, Irene Renee. 7780 ELMWOOD AVE, STE 201 53562 #038-40-1984 L1988 **IM** *020 †20

MOON, Richard Lee. ■ 53562 #056-05-1960 L1961 **CHP P** *020 †75

MORGAN, Adam Steven. ■ 53562 #017-20-2008 *012

MULLANEY, Paul B. 1230 SWEENEY DR 53562 #539-06-1982 **OPH** *020

NAHN, Charles Edward. ■ 53562 #056-06-1959 L1969 **OPH** *071 †35

NARAYAN, Shoba Bangalore. ■ 53562 #496-39-2000 L2007 **IM** *100

NARRA, Hemalatha. ■ 53562 #495-50-2001 L2004 **N** *012

NEMOVITZ, Paul Michael. 7780 ELMWOOD AVE, STE 201 53562 #056-05-1973 L1975 **IM** *020 †20

NESTLEROAD, Christopher A. 7780 ELMWOOD AVE, STE 201 53562 #028-03-2001 L2003 **IM** *020

OLIVE, David Leon. 3146 DEMING WAY 53562 #048-04-1979 L2002 **OBG REN** *040 †30

PAGE, Nathan. 1639 POND VIEW CT 53562 #056-06-1976 L1977 **MDM PHP** *030

PARFITT, Richard C, II. 2261 DEMING WAY 53562 #056-05-1982 L1996 **FPS OTO** *020 †45

PEDERSON, Donald P. ■ 53562 #035-45-1951 L1959 **AN** *071 †05

PRITTS, Elizabeth Anna. 9526 BLUE HERON DR 53562 #041-02-1994 L2002 **OBG** *020 †30

RAO, Venkat Konangi. 2349 DEMING WAY 53562 #495-04-1970 L1982 **PS HS** *020 †85,65

ROBERTSON, Kevin Mccrae. 3205 GLACIER RIDGE RD 53562 #056-05-1990 L1996 **FPS** *020 †45

RODRIGUEZ, Nestor Salvado. ■ 53562 #056-05-2007 **EM** *012

RUDY, Ronald Chas. ■ 53562 #056-06-1959 L1960 **ORS** *020 †40

SAMP, Robert J. ■ 53562 #056-05-1951 L1952 **GS** *071

SARGEANT, Thomas Sherman. ■ 53562 #056-06-1954 L1955 **IM** *071

SCHMID, Daniel Benjamin. ■ 53562 #016-06-2007 **PS** *012

SCHNEIDER, Chad Edward. ■ 53562 #422-01-2002 L2004 **IM** *020 †20

SCHNEIDER-BRAUS, Kathleen. ■ 53562 #025-12-1979 L1984 **P** *020 †75

SCRUGGS, Jesse Earl. ■ 53562 #047-20-2003 L2005 **AN** *012 †20

SEHGAL, Nalini. 6630 UNIVERSITY AVE, DEPT OF REHAB MED 53562 #496-02-1975 L1996 **PM** *020 †60

SIEBERT, John Weston. 2349 DEMING WAY 53562 #056-05-1981 L2006 **GS** *020 †85,65

SIELAFF, Gerald Waldemar. ■ 53562 #056-05-1980 L1986 **EM** *012 †16

SMALL-BEMENT, Shiloh Nico. ■ 53562 #046-01-2008 *012

STAUSS, Thomas Gerard. 3230 DEMING WAY, STE 100 53562 #056-05-1985 L1986 **AN PME** *020 †05

STERKEN, Gary Wayne. 2349 DEMING WAY 53562 #056-05-1985 L1986 **OPH** *020 †35

TAYLOR, Leslie Vanhouten. 2711 ALLEN BLVD, RESEARCH AND EDUCATION 53562 #025-12-1988 L1989 **P** *050 †75

THOEN, Larynda Denine. ■ 53562 #016-06-1995 L1997 **OBG** *020 †30

THOMAS, Jojy George. 6630 UNIVERSITY AVE 53562 #495-31-1990 L2004 **SCI** *020

THOMPSON, Debra Marie. ■ 53562 #056-05-2004 L2005 **ID** *012 †20

TRINKL, Jeffrey Gene. ■ 53562 #056-05-1992 L1994 **DR** *020

TURLEY, David Paul. ■ 53562 #055-02-2007 **EM** *012

WADE, Lauren Rae. ■ 53562 #017-20-2008 *012

WARD, Michael John. 6630 UNIVERSITY AVE, UNIVERSITY OF WI S., MADI 53562 #025-01-1986 L1996 **PM** *020 †60

WARRICK, Louis Frederick. 8301 OLD SAUK RD 53562 #010-01-1957 L1963 **IM** *030

WATSON, Margaret L. 6630 UNIVERSITY AVE 53562 #037-01-2003 L2007 **PM** *100

WONG, Long. ■ 53562 #243-92-1990 L2005 **FP** *012

XU, Yaohui. ■ 53562 #243-21-1995 L2007 **D** *100 †15

YAEGER, Jeffrey Paul. ■ 53562 #035-06-2007 **PD** *012

YAMANE, Brett Haru. ■ 53562 #014-01-2005 L2007 **GS** *012

MILLADORE — WOOD

KANE, Norman M. ■ 54454 #016-11-1980 L1982 **FM** *062

MILTON — ROCK

DORR, James Arnold. ■ 53563 #056-05-1961 L1962 **FM EM** *030 †18

HOLMES, John Francis. ■ 53563 #005-12-1938 L1946 **GP** *071

KRAMER, Tamara Axelsen. ■ 53563 #056-05-2007 **FP** *012

LYERLA, Eric Ray. 710 S JANESVILLE ST 53563 #016-01-1981 L1984 **FM** *020 †18

MADURA, Angela S. 725 S JANESVILLE ST 53563 #016-01-1994 L2002 **FM** *020 †18

MC NICHOLS, Edwin Francis. ■ 53563 #016-43-1952 L1953 **IM GP** *071 †20

SHACKELFORD, Gary Dean. ■ 53563 #028-02-1968 L1970 **PDR** *071 †80

VANBEEK, Rodney Joel. 725 S JANESVILLE ST 53563 #039-01-1996 L1997 **FM** *020 †18

WEST, William Peter. 831 ARTHUR DR 53563 #026-04-1971 L1980 **FM FPG** *030 †18

MILWAUKEE — MILWAUKEE

AASBO, Johan D. 9200 W WISCONSIN AVE, MEDICINE CENTER 53226 #016-76-2002, ▲ L2005 **CD** *012 †20

AASEN, Mark Kevin. 4570 S 27TH ST 53221 #056-05-1987 L1996 **AN PME** *020 †05

ABAD, Lilia Sales. 5000 W NATIONAL AVE 53295 #748-07-1962 L1980 **P** *040

ABBURI, Madhava S. 1971 W CAPITOL DR 53206 #496-09-1995 L2001 **IM** *020 †20

ABDELGADIR TAHA, Mohamed. 3000 W MONTANA ST 53215 #848-01-1995 L2007 **IM** *012

ABDUL HUSSAIN, Maysa Hamz. 3000 W MONTANA ST, DEPT OF INT MED 53215 #528-01-2003 L2008 **IM** *012

ABELSON, David S. 1834 W WISCONSIN AVE, STE 100 53233 #306-01-1985 L1991 **FM** *020 †18

ABRAM, Stephen Edward. 9200 W WISCONSIN AVE, DEPT ANESTHESIOLOGY MED CO 53226 #041-02-1970 L1975 **AN PMM** *020 †05

ABU ERREISH, Muna Asmahan. 9200 W WISCONSIN AVE, STE 5100 53226 #575-01-2000 L2006 **ID** *012 †20

ACETO, James Christopher. 2025 E NEWPORT AVE, WISCONSIN RADIOLOGY 53211 #056-06-1988 L1993 **DR** *020 †80

ADAMIAK, Tonya Renee. 8701 W WATERTOWN PLANK RD, PEDIATRIC GI AND NUTRITION 53226 #026-04-2003 L2006 **PG** *012 †55

ADAMKIEWICZ, Joseph J, Jr. 2900 W OKLAHOMA AVE 53215 #056-06-1957 L1961 **DR NS** *020 †25,80

ADAMS, Albert Henry. ■ 53213 #016-43-1967 L1970 **IM** *071

ADAMS, Alex Arnold. 9200 W WISCONSIN AVE 53226 #913-45-1995 L2006 **AN** *012

ADAVADKAR, Pranshu Anant. 626 E KILBOURN AVE 53202 #496-38-1999 L2006 **PD** *020 †55

ADLAM, Robert Thos. 3071 N 51ST ST, STE P404 53210 #056-06-1958 L1959 **PUD IM** *072

ADLER, Jeffrey Michael. 2900 W OKLAHOMA AVE, ERMED, S.C. 53215 #016-42-1996 L2000 **EM** *020 †16

AGARWAL, Avadh Behari. 4267 W FOND DU LAC AVE 53216 #495-05-1954 L1967 **PD** *030

AGOR, Ramon Agcaoili. 1834 W WISCONSIN AVE, 2ND FL 53233 #748-02-1970 L1985 **FM** *020 †18

AGUILAR-TORRES, Francisco. 3237 S 16TH ST 53215 #649-04-1969 L1974 **ID EM** *020 †20,16

AHMAD, Maqsood. 5434 W CAPITOL DR, STE 1 53216 #704-21-1982 L1992 **CD** *020 †20

AHMAD, Semina. ■ 53202 #665-02-2006 **FP** *012

AHMED, Arshad. 2801 W KK RIVER PKWY # 630 53215 #495-59-1993 L2003 **N** *020 †75

AHMED, Atif Umair. ■ 53208 #056-06-2008 *012

AHMED, Mohamed S. 9200 W WISCONSIN AVE, NEOPLASTIC DISEASE 53226 #422-01-2002 L2005 **HO** *012 †20

AHMED, Syed Mansoor. 8701 W WATERTOWN PLANK RD, MEDICAL COLLEGE OF WISCONS 53226 #160-03-1979 L2001 **FM PHP** *030 †18

AHMED, Urooj. 2801 W KK PKWY, STE 1030 53215 #704-02-1990 L2004 **GE** *100 †20

AHUJA, Arvind. 2901 W KINNICKINC RVR PKWY 53215 #938-49-1987 L1991 **NS** *020 †25

AHUJA, Manohar. 5650 N GREEN BAY AVE, STE 100 53209 #495-74-1980 L1998 **NEP** *020 †20

AHUJA, Om Prakash. 9200 W WISCONSIN AVE, FROEDTERT HOSPITAL DEPT-ME 53226 #495-74-1998 L2004 **PCC** *012 †20

AIKEN, John J, Jr. 999 N 92ND ST 53226 #038-41-1984 L1993 **PDS** *020 †85

AIMAN, Edward James. 8701 W WATERTOWN PLANK RD, DEPT OBG 53226 #056-06-1969 L1970 **OBG END** *020 †30

AINA, Oluyemi Adetokunbo. 9200 W WISCONSIN AVE, FROEDTERT HOSPITAL 53226 #690-14-1994 L2006 **FM SME** *020 †18,75

AKANSEL, Gur. 2115 N 67TH ST 53213 #902-05-1986 L1993 **NM** *020 †28

AKANSEL, Sertac. ■ 53213 #902-05-1984 **NM** *100

AKERS, Brian Paul. ■ 53211 #024-07-1975 L1978 **IM** *020 †20

AKHTAR, Shamsuddin. 8701 W WATERTOWN PLANK RD, OF WIS AFFILIATED HOS, BX2 53226 #704-25-1989 L1995 **AN** *020 †16

AKHTER, Sabreen. 9000 W WISCONSIN AVE, DEPT OF 53226 #016-76-2003, ▲ L2006 **PEM** *012 †55

AKIYA, Yoshiaki. ■ 53222 #665-01-2006 L2008 **FP** *012

AKTAY, Atiye Nur. 2801 W KINNICKINC RVR PKWY, STE 1030 53215 #902-10-1991 L1997 **PG** *020 †55

AKTAY, Recayi. 5000 W NATIONAL AVE 53295 #902-07-1989 L1998 **DR NM** *020 †80,28

AL-AKASHEH, Marwan Salti. 9200 W WISCONSIN AVE, MEDICAL COLLEGE OF WISCONS 53226 #575-01-1982 L1999 **HO** *020

ALBA, Henry Marion. 4710 W LOOMIS RD, PAIN MGMT CTR OF WISCONSIN 53220 #561-01-1978 L1982 **PM OS** *020 †60

AL-BASSAM, Omar A. Aziz E. ■ 53220 #797-03-1982 *100

ALBERS, Bradley Mark. ■ 53211 #056-06-2007 **TY** *012

ALBERT, John Auxilium. 2500 W LAYTON AVE, STE 280 53221 #495-16-1991 L1998 **RHU** *020 †20

ALBERTI, John B. 4141 W BRADLEY RD 53209 #056-06-1959 L1961 **DR OS** *071 †80

ALBERTS, Jay Laurence. 8701 W WATERTOWN PLANK RD, DEPT OBG 53226 #396-06-1977 **OBG** *100

ALBRIGHT, Emily Laraine. 4130 N 104TH ST UNIT F 53222 #028-34-2005 L2007 **GS** *012

ALCERA-POE, Remedios. 2727 W CLEVELAND AVE, STE 2000 53215 #748-08-1977 L1998 **PD** *020 †55

ALDRED, Jeffrey Allen. 2500 W LAYTON AVE, STE 10 53221 #016-11-1990 L1993 **IM** *020 †20

ALEMAN, Alvaro. 3527 W NATIONAL AVE, HISPANIC MEDICAL CENTER 53215 #682-01-1974 L1986 **GP EM** *020

ALEMAN, Catherine Vollmer. 2311 N PROSPECT AVE, STE 401 53211 #016-43-1997 L2000 **IM** *020 †20

ALEMZADEH, Ramin. 8701 W WATERTOWN PLANK RD, MED CLG OF WI 53226 #422-01-1982 L1991 **PDE PD** *020 †55

ALEXANDER, Andrew Kyle. ■ 53222 #056-06-2005 L2007 **PD** *012

■ = Address Information Privacy Protected

ALEXANDER, Russell Tod. 933 W HIGHLAND AVE, MILW CNTY MED EXMNRS OFF 53233 #035-46-1999 L2005 **FOP** *020 †50

ALEXANIAN, David Manuel. 5000 W NATIONAL AVE, ZOLLULUI VAMC 53295 #056-05-1986 L1987 **IM** *020 †20

ALGIERS, James Leonard. 9200 W WISCONSIN AVE, MED COLLEGE OF WIS 53226 #056-06-1953 L1954 **IM** *071 †20

ALI, Adnan Wajid. 5000 W CHAMBERS ST, DEPT RAD 53210 #016-43-2006 L2006 **DR** *012

ALI, Hussain. 945 N 12TH ST, AURORA OB/GYN RESIDENCY 53233 #704-20-1999 L2007 **OBG** *012

ALI, Omar. 9000 W WISCONSIN AVE, MS C520 53226 #704-01-1986 L2005 **PDE** *100 †55

ALI, Zulfiqar. 8701 W WATERTOWN PLANK RD, MED COLL WI AFFIL HOSPS 53226 #704-22-1992 L2004 **IM** *020

ALLAQABAND, Suhail Qadir. 2801 W KK RIVER PKWY # 777 53215 #495-51-1995 L1997 **IC CD** *020 †20

ALMAGRO, Urias Alcantara. 3237 S 16TH ST 53215 #748-09-1968 L1989 **PTH** *020 †50

ALMASSI, Gholam Hossein. 9200 W WISCONSIN AVE 53226 #517-05-1976 L1984 **TS** *020 †85,90

ALMOUJAHED, Mohammad O. 8701 W WATERTOWN PLANK RD 53226 #875-02-1994 L2001 **ID** *020 †20

ALSAYEGH, Laith Ghazi. 2801 W KINNICKINC RVR PKWY 53215 #038-40-2002 L2006 **IM** *020 †20

ALSHEIK, Nila H. 9200 W WISCONSN AVE #FROED, DEPARTMENT OF ORTHOPAEDICS 53226 #043-01-2003 L2004 **DR** *012

ALTAF, Muhammad Adnan. 8701 W WATERTOWN PLANK RD, OF WISCONSIN 53226 #704-01-2000 L2004 **PG** *012 †55

ALTMAN, S David Paul. 1218 W KILBOURN AVE, STE 101 53233 #056-05-1961 L1962 **GS** *071 †85

ALTMANN, Claudia Lia. 2025 E NEWPORT AVE 53211 #056-06-1984 L1985 **ID IM** *020 †20

ALTSTADT, John Francis. 9000 W WISCONSIN AVE 53226 #056-06-1959 L1960 **PD** *071 †55

ALVARAN, Jerico Isiderio. ■ 53227 #748-02-2002 L2007 **PD** *020 †55

ALVAREZ, Orlando Ernesto. 5000 W CHAMBERS ST, EMERGENCY DEPT 53210 #056-06-1992 L1994 **IM** *020 †20

ALVERNO, Luca Alessandro. 9455 W WATERTOWN PLANK RD 53226 #561-07-1953 L1963 **P** *020 †75

AMBARDEKAR, Amar. ■ 53226 #028-79-2007, ▲ **IM** *012

AMIN, Kamal. 2901 W KINNICKINC RVR PKWY, STE 405 53215 #704-01-1994 L2001 **NEP** *020 †20

AMMON, Helmut Volker C H. 788 N JEFFERSON ST STE 300 53202 #407-16-1962 L1973 **GE IM** *020 †20

AMOS, David E. 5800 W BURLEIGH ST 53210 #748-08-1970 L1976 **FM EM** *020 †18

AMOS, Louella Beltran. 3001 S 56TH ST 53219 #056-05-2003 L2004 **PDP** *012 †55

AMUZU, Betty Jean. 945 N 12TH ST, FL 1 53233 #056-05-1988 L1990 **OBG** *020 †30

AMUZU, John Kanyi. 5000 W CHAMBERS ST 53210 #056-05-1988 L1991 **AN** *020 †20

ANANTHAKRISHNAN, Ashwin N. 9200 W WISCONSIN AVE 53226 #495-53-2003 L2005 **GE** *012 †20

ANBALAGAN, Uma. 10400 W NORTH AVE, STE 300 53226 #495-59-1982 L1987 **IM** *020 †05

ANDERSON, Danielle Louise. 8701 W WATERTOWN PLANK RD, MEDICAL COLLEGE OF WISCONS 53226 #016-02-2002 L2002 **P** *100

ANDERSON, Dustin Cade. 8701 W WATERTOWN PLANK RD, MED COLL OF WI 53226 #049-01-2007 **PD** *012

ANDERSON, Matthew Wilson. ■ 53211 #056-06-2006 L2007 **PTH** *012

ANDERSON, Vicki Leatrice. ■ 53226 #016-02-2002 L2006 **SCI** *012

ANDERSON, William Gray. 5000 W NATIONAL AVE, WOOD VA HOSP 53295 #056-06-1982 L1983 **P GP** *020

ANDREEV, Mihail Andreev. 3000 W MONTANA ST 53215 #198-01-1997 **IM** *012

ANDREWS, Steven Scott. 9200 W WISCONSIN AVE, DEPARTMENT OF EMERGENCY ME 53226 #026-04-1995 L1998 **EM PE** *020 †16

ANNE, Venkata Vijay Kumar. 3267 S 16TH ST, STE 103 53215 #495-21-1995 L2003 **CCM IM** *020 †20

ANSARI, Shan Nur. 8701 W WATERTOWN PLANK RD, MED COL OF WI 53226 #905-02-2004 L2004 **PCC** *012

ANTAPLI, Mursel Mehmet. 9200 W WISCONSIN AVE, MEDICAL COLLEGE OF WI ANES 53226 #902-01-1985 L2001 **AN** *020

ANTONESCU-TURCU, Andreea. 5000 W NATIONAL AVE 53295 #781-01-1997 L2005 **PCC IM** *020

ANTONIK, Melissa Johnson. 9200 W WISCONSIN AVE, DEPT OF ENDOCRINOLOGY 53226 #016-43-2002 L2006 **END** *100 †55

ANTONIK, Stephen John. 9200 W WISCONSIN AVE, DEPT OF GASTROENTEROLOGY 53226 #016-43-2002 L2006 **GE** *012 †20

ANTONY DOSS, Sharon. 8430 W CAPITOL DR 53222 #495-52-1996 L1999 **IM** *020

ANTUONO, Piero. 9200 W WATERTOWN PLANK RD 53226 #561-06-1975 L1981 **N** *050 †75

ANUPAM, Anupam. 180 W GRANGE AVE, AURORA ELCU CARE CENTER 53207 #495-54-1993 L2006 **CCM** *020 †20

ANWAR, Mohammad. ■ 53213 #704-15-1987 **PS** *100

APONTE, Leonardo. 1238 S 16TH ST 53204 #409-05-1962 L1974 **NM GP** *020 †28

APRAHAMIAN, Charles. 8700 W WISCONSIN AVE 53226 #056-06-1962 L1963 **GS TRS** *040 †85

AQUINO, Manuel Mendoza. 8923 W BROWN DEER RD 53224 #748-01-1952 L1960 **GP EM** *071

ARAIN, Rizwanullah. 6026 W LISBON AVE 53210 #422-01-1985 L1989 **N** *020

ARAIN, Shahbaz Rasool. 5000 W NATIONAL AVE # 112A, DEPT OF ANESTH VA MED CTR 53295 #704-15-1984 **AN** *050

ARALASMAK, Ayse. 8701 W WATERTOWN PLANK RD 53226 #902-05-1995 **RNR** *100

ARANA, Emilia Isabel. 1032 S CESAR E CHAVEZ DR, 16TH STREET COMMUNITY HEAL 53204 #737-06-1996 L2001 **PD** *020 †55

ARAUJO, Jose Gonzalo. 10425 W NORTH AVE, STE 215 53226 #187-23-1977 L1987 **PTH BBK** *020

ARCA, Marjorie Judith. 999 N 92ND ST 53226 #005-14-1990 L2003 **PDS** *020 †85

ARCE BETANCOURT, Sandra M. 2906 S 20TH ST 53215 #264-04-1996 L2004 **PD** *020

ARFMAN, Robert Christian. 10000 W BLUEMOUND RD 53226 #056-06-1977 L1978 **AN** *020 †05

ARIAS, Joseph Jeremy. 2400 VILLARD AVE 53209 #748-01-1996 L2004 **FM** *020 †18

ARIF, Murtaza. 8701 W WATERTOWN PLANK RD 53226 #704-02-2000 L2006 **IM** *012

ARMAGANIJAN, Lisa L. 2801 W KINNICKINC RVR PKWY, STE 425 53215 #056-06-1990 L1991 **CD** *020 †20

ARMSTRONG, Nicholas N. 2801 W KINNICKINC RVR PKWY, STE 330 53215 #056-05-1993 L1994 **GS** *020 †85

ARMSTRONG, Stacey Alece. ■ 53216 #056-06-2008 *012

ARNDT, Angela Margaret. 10000 W BLUEMOUND RD 53226 #056-05-2002 L2006 **AN** *020 †05

ARNOLD, Brent Wayne. 3070 N 51ST ST 53210 #048-02-1984 L1989 **NPM PD** *020 †55

AROLE, Adebola Oyedele. 8901 W LINCOLN AVE, CONSULTANTS AT WEST ALLIS 53227 #690-02-1986 L2006 **AN** *020 †05

ARONOW, Cedor B, II. 9000 W WISCONSIN AVE 53226 #028-34-1962 L1963 **PD** *071 †55

ARORA, Hena Subash. ■ 53226 #016-01-2007 **PD** *012

ARORA, Jaspal Singh. 2906 S 20TH ST, AURORA HEALTH CENTER 53215 #495-55-1992 L2005 **FM** *100 †18,70 ‡

ARSHAD, Ijaz Ibrahim. 3201 S 16TH ST, STE 2020 53215 #704-21-1995 L2004 **IM** *020 †20

ARSHAD, Maqbool. 3201 S 16TH ST STE 2020 53215 #704-01-1980 L1985 **PUD IM** *020 †20

ARTANG, Ramin. 9200 W WISCONSIN AVE, MEDICAL COLLEGE OF WISCONS 53226 #297-01-1994 L2007 **CD** *100

ARTLEY, Devin Teilhard. 8901 W LINCOLN AVE, CONSULTANTS AT WEST ALLIS 53227 #016-42-2000 L2003 **AN** *020 †05

ARUL, Nandini. 8701 W WATERTOWN PLANK RD, MEDICAL COLLEGE OF WISCONS 53226 #495-04-1999 L2004 **NPM** *100 †55

ASAKURA, Hiroyuki. 2000 W KILBOURN AVE 53233 #572-01-1986 L1996 **OBG** *020 †30

ASCHLIMAN, Mark Randall. 3970 N OAKLAND AVE, STE 300 53211 #016-02-1980 L1986 **ORS OSM** *020 †40

ASHPOLE, David Kenneth. 2801 W KINNICKINC RVR PKWY, STE 425 53215 #026-04-1982 L1987 **CD** *020 †20 ‡

ASHWATHNARAYAN, Ramesh. 2025 E NEWPORT AVE, STE 217 53211 #495-33-1992 L2003 **GE** *012 †20

ASIDDAO, Caridad Bobon. 8700 W WISCONSIN AVE 53226 #748-01-1956 L1975 **AN** *020 †05

ASKOT, Melvin Morris. 2400 W VILLARD AVE 53209 #056-06-1953 L1954 **PD** *071 †55

ASLESON, John Christopher. ■ 53222 #026-04-2004 L2007 **DR** *012

ASMA, Richard Matthew. 2400 W VILLARD AVE 53209 #056-06-1959 L1960 **GP** *071

ASSEL, Barbara Gail. 8905 W LINCOLN AVE, MATERNAL FETAL MEDICINE , 53227 #030-05-1979 L2007 **MFM OBG** *020 †30

ASTER, Richard Herbert. 638 N 18TH ST, THE BLOOD CENTER OF SOUTHE 53233 #025-01-1957 L1970 **HEM IM** *071 †20

AUER, James Edward. 2900 W OKLAHOMA AVE 53215 #018-03-1963 L1970 **TS GS** *071 †85,90

AUFDERHEIDE, Tom Paul. 9200 W WISCONSIN AVE, FROEDTERT EAST 53226 #026-04-1979 L1984 **EM IM** *020 †20,16

AUGER, Gerald Elmer. 2801 W KINNICKINC RVR PKWY, STE 135 53215 #056-06-1970 L1973 **IM EM** *020

AUSMAN, Robert King. 9200 W WISCONSIN AVE, DEPT OF SURGERY 53226 #056-06-1957 L1959 **SO PA** *050

AUSSEM, John Wm. 2400 W VILLARD AVE 53209 #056-06-1966 L1974 **PTH** *020 †50

AVERILL, Kevin Jay. 2900 W OKLAHOMA AVE, ERMED, SC 53215 #036-05-1996 L1999 **EM** *020 †16

AVILES, Alberto Julian. 8700 W WATERTOWN PLANK RD, DEPARTMENT OF PLASTIC SURG 53226 #016-11-1999 L2006 **PS** *012 †85

AVNER, Ellis David. 9000 W WISCONSIN AVE, CHILDREN'S HOSPITAL OF WIS 53226 #041-01-1975 L2004 **PN PD** *030 †55

AWAN, Saleem Ashraf. 4570 S 27TH ST, ADVANCED PAIN MANAGEMENT 53221 #704-09-1989 L2001 **AN PME** *020 †05

AXELROD, Bruce Henry. 5150 N PORT WASHINGTON RD, STE 200 53217 #035-45-1967 L1977 **P CHP** *020 †55,75

AXTELL, Roger Forsyth. 945 N 12TH ST 53233 #048-15-1995 L1996 **DR** *020 †80

AZCUETA, Cesar Segui. 2311 N PROSPECT AVE, STE 5B 53211 #748-01-1955 L1975 **FM EM** *020 †18

AZCUETA, Czarina O. 2311 N PROSPECT AVE, STE 401 53211 #016-06-1994 L1998 **OBG** *020 †30

AZCUETA, Ester Segui. 9235 N THRUSH LN 53217 #748-01-1952 L1964 **GYN** *071

AZCUETA, Renato Serrano. 7220 W NATIONAL AVE 53214 #748-10-1976 L1984 **FM** *020 †18

BABAR, Ghufran Saeed. 8701 W WATERTOWN PLANK RD, OF WISCONSIN 53226 #704-24-1991 L2005 **PDE** *012

BABBITT, Jill Ann. 2025 W OKLAHOMA AVE, STE 114 53215 #422-01-1988 L1989 **ID** *020 †20

BABBITZ, Allen Henry. 2350 N LAKE DR, STE 201 53211 #056-05-1968 L1969 **OBG** *020 †30

BACHHUBER, Thomas Michael. 1032 S 16TH ST, 16TH ST COMMUNITY HLTH CTR 53204 #056-06-1987 L1988 **FM** *020 †18

BACKUS, Michelle Anne. 3070 N 51ST ST, STE 305 53210 #025-12-2000 L2004 **OBG** *020

BADE, Elizabeth Ruth. 1020 N 12TH ST STE 202, FAMILY CARE CTR 53233 #056-05-2003 L2004 **FM** *020 †18

BADER, Jill Marie. ■ 53202 #056-06-2004 L2006 **OBG** *012

BADI, Arunkumar Narayansa. 9200 W WISCONSIN AVE, OTOLARYNGOLOGY, MCW 53226 #495-73-1996 L2005 **OTO** *012

BAGHERLI, Sabiheh. 245 N 110TH ST 53226 #517-01-1966 L1976 **PD** *020 †55

BAHAL, Santosh Kumari. 2025 W OKLAHOMA AVE, STE 108 53215 #495-29-1967 L1977 **PM** *020 †60

BAHR, Jeffrey Kevin. 3003 W GOOD HOPE RD, HOPE ROAD CLINIC 53209 #056-06-1998 L1999 **IM** *020 †20

BAILET, Jeffrey Wayne. 3000 W MONTANA ST, AURORA MEDICAL GROUP 53215 #054-04-1987 L2004 **HNS** *030 †45

BAILEY, Laurie Ann. 2801 W KINNICKINC RVR PKWY, STE 250 53215 #056-06-2003 L2004 **FM** *020 †18

BAILEY, Smita Sane. 8522 W CAPITOL DR, PEDIATRIC DIAGNOSTIC 53222 #026-04-1991 L1998 **PDR** *020

BAILEY, Timmothy Don. ■ 53211 #305-01-2006 L2008 *012

BAIN, Carole Page. 1000 N 92ND ST 53226 #056-05-1986 L1987 **GPM PD** *020 †70

BAINBRIDGE, Phillip E, Jr. 3237 S 16TH ST, RADIOLOGY DEPARTMENT 53215 #017-20-1993 L1998 **DR** *020 †80

BAISDEN, Jamie Lynn. 9200 W WISCONSIN AVE 53226 #055-01-1987 L1994 **NS** *020 †25

BAJAJ, Jasmohan Singh. 9200 W WISCONSIN AVE, FROEDTERT HOSP DIV OF GI 53226 #495-45-1998 L2003 **GE** *100 †20

BAJGROWICZ, Alexander Seb. 2900 W OKLAHOMA AVE, DEPARTMENT OF RADIOLOGY 53215 #016-01-2006 L2007 **DR** *012

BAJWA, Tanvir Khalid. 960 N 12TH ST # 400, MILWAUKEE HEART INSTITUTE 53233 #704-17-1985 L1991 **CD IM** *020 †20

BAKER, Stephen Trent. 10950 W CAPITOL DR 53222 #056-06-1984 L1985 **IM** *020

BAKER, William Vance. 9200 W WISCONSIN AVE 53226 #056-05-1980 L1981 **P** *020 †75

BAKER-FRANCKOWIAK, A L. 8701 W WATERTOWN PLANK RD, PLANK ROAD 53226 #056-06-2001 L2003 **PD** *020 †55

BAKHTIAR, Karim. 945 N 12TH ST 53233 #704-02-1984 L1988 **IM PLM** *020 †50,20

BAKHTIAR, Saleem. 1218 W KILBOURN AVE, SURGICAL GRP., SUITE 101 53233 #704-02-1975 L1981 **GS AN** *020 †85

BALAKRISHNAN, Vetrivel R. 8901 W LINCOLN AVE, CONSULTANTS AT WEST ALLIS 53227 #495-66-1984 L1997 **AN** *020 †05

BALASUBRAMANIAN, Vijay Pu. 9200 W WISCONSIN AVE, MEDICAL COLLEGE OF WISCONS 53226 #495-16-1993 L2002 **PCC** *100

BALCOM, Anthony H. 9000 W WISCONSIN AVE, CHLDRNS HOSP OFFICE BLDG 53226 #056-06-1984 L1985 **UP U** *020 †95

BALIJA, Ramadevi. 8200 N SILVER SPRING DR, HEALTH CENTER 53218 #495-62-1979 L1999 **PD** *020 †55

BALKHY, Husam H. 3070 N 51ST ST, CARDIO THORACIC SURGERY 53210 #797-02-1986 L1997 **TS CD** *020 †85,90

BALLA, Andre Kajdacsy. 9200 W WISCONSIN AVE, MDCL CLLGE CLNCS AT FRDTRT 53226 #187-08-1972 L1994 **PTH** *020 †50

BALLECER, Raymond Roy. 10400 W NORTH AVE, STE 200 53226 #748-02-1979 L1990 **IM** *020 †20

BALZER, Rudolph. ■ 53208 #957-01-1937 L1958 **GP IM** *020

BAMRAH, Bindu Singh. 2801 W KINNICKINC RVR PKWY, STE 575 53215 #056-06-1996 L1997 **OSM** *020 †40

BAMRAH, Virinderjit Singh. 2801 W KINNICKINC RVR PKWY, STE 840 53215 #495-03-1964 L1972 **CD IM** *020 †20

BANDA, Pedro Miguel. 2311 N PROSPECT AVE 53211 #056-05-1993 L2003 **U** *020 †95

BANDA, Pedro Nel. 6030 W CAPITOL DR 53216 #264-02-1960 L1967 **PD A** *071

BANDARI, Armin Jay. 945 N 12TH ST 53233 #016-01-2002 L2005 **CD** *012 †20

BANE, Gina Carol. ■ 53213 #025-01-2007 **PD** *012

BANGASH, Andleeb Salma. 740 W WISCONSIN AVE # 52 53233 #704-09-1999 L2003 **CD** *012 †20

BANGASH, Muhammad-Fuad. 2501 W SILVER SPRING DR 53209 #704-09-1995 L1997 **IM PCC** *020 †20

BANIUKIEWICZ, Andrew Paul. 3237 S 16TH ST 53215 #056-06-1998 L2001 **EM** *020 †16

BARATTA, Lisa Ann. 2801 W KINNICKINC RVR PKWY, STE 840 53215 #016-06-1988 L1989 **CD** *020 †20

BARBOI, Alexandru Cezar. 9200 W WISCONSIN AVE, MEDICAL COLLEGE OF WISCONS 53226 #781-01-1990 L2001 **N** *020 †75,20

BARBOI, Cristina. 8901 W LINCOLN AVE, CONSULTANTS AT WEST ALLIS 53227 #781-01-1990 L2001 **CCA** *020 †05

BARGOUT, Raed. 2500 W LAYTON AVE, STE 200 53221 #875-02-1995 L2003 **CD** *020 †20

BARKHAUS, Paul Edward. 9200 W WISCONSIN AVE, DEPT OF NEURLGY 53226 #025-07-1975 L1993 **N CN** *020 †75

BARKIMER, Brett A. 9200 W WISCONSIN AVE, PRIMARY CARE INITIATIVE 53226 #017-20-2004 L2007 **MPD** *012

BARNABEI, Vanessa Marie. 9200 W WISCONSIN AVE 53226 #051-01-1985 L1998 **OBG CCG** *020 †19,30

BARNAS, Gary Paul. 5000 W NATIONAL AVE, VA MEDICAL CENTER (PC-00) 53295 #016-06-1980 L1981 **IM** *020 †20

BARNETT, James H. 2600 N MAYFAIR RD STE 810 53226 #056-06-1979 L1980 **D DMP** *020 †15

BARNETT, Vernie Theodore. 9200 W WISCONSIN AVE #5200, PULMONARY & CRIT CARE 53226 #016-11-1985 L2004 **CCM PUD** *012

BARNOSKY, Adrienne. ■ 53208 #028-79-2007, ▲ **IM** *012

BARON-KUHN, Elizabeth. W129 N7055 NORTHFIELD DR, BLDG A STE 100 53227 #056-06-1982 L2004 **OBG GYN** *012

BAROUMAND SHAMSALDINI, Far. 9200 W WISCONSIN AVE, MCW PHYSICAL MEDICINE & RE 53226 #517-26-1997 L2006 **PM** *012

BARRAGRY, Thomas Peter. 2901 W KINNICKINC RVR PKWY, STE 310 53215 #056-05-1981 L1991 **TS** *020 †85,90

BARRETTO, Karen Tengco. 2906 S 20TH ST 53215 #748-27-1996 L2005 **PD** *020 †55

BARRON, Matthew James. ■ 53222 #056-06-2006 L2008 **IM** *012

BAR-SELA, Shlomo. ■ 53217 #550-01-1976 L1983 **AI IM** *050 †20,03

BARTEL, Anne Elizabeth. 2025 E NEWPORT AVE, WISCONSIN RADIOLOGY 53211 #047-05-1989 L1996 **DR VIR** *020 †80

BARTEL, Shawn David. 9000 W WISCONSIN AVE, C/O MEDICAL EDUCATION 53226 #046-01-2002 L2004 **MPD** *020 †20,55

BARTH, Christopher David. ■ 53213 #016-01-2000 L2003 **CCA** *100 †05

BARTHEL, Richard Paul. 9000 W WISCONSIN AVE 53226 #056-06-1970 L1972 **CHP PD** *020 †55,75

BARTON, James Clyde, Jr. 3033 S 27TH ST STE 302 53215 #041-12-1970 L1977 **N** *020 †75

BARTYZAL, Donna Mae. ■ 53222 #056-06-2008 *012

BARTZ, Peter Jeffrey. 9000 W WISCONSIN AVE, CHILDREN'S HOSPITAL OF WIS 53226 #026-04-1999 L2006 **PDC** *100 †20,55

BARUAH, Jitendra Kumar. 3201 S 16TH ST, STE 200 EUCLID BLD 53215 #495-78-1969 L1979 **N PMM** *020 †75

BARUDIN, Seth Mathew. 2320 N LAKE DR 53211 #018-03-2001 L2002 **FM** *020 †18

BASHIR, Hiba. ■ 53203 #056-06-2007 **MPD** *012

BASIR, Mir A. 8701 W WATERTOWN PLANK RD, MS213A 53226 #704-04-1982 L1998 **NPM** *020 †55

BASIR, Zainab. 9200 W WISCONSIN AVE, DEPT OF PATH MED CLGE WI 53226 #704-02-1983 L1998 **CLP PCP** *020 †50

BATES, Barbara Ayers. 5408 W BURLEIGH ST 53210 #050-02-1993 L1995 **FM** *020 †18

BATTIOLA, Richard John. 2801 W KINNICKINC RVR PKWY, STE 730 53215 #056-06-1983 L1984 **IM** *020 †20

BATTISTA, Joseph C. 6200 W BLUEMOUND RD 53213 #016-06-1983 L1984 **GS VS** *020 †85

BATTISTINI, Humberto. 9200 W WISCONSIN AVE, DEPT OF NEUROLOGY 53226 #042-01-1990 L1991 **N** *020 †75

BATWARA, Ruchika. 9200 W WISCONSIN AVE 53226 #495-36-2003 L2005 **IM** *100 †20

BAUER, Anderson Ahrens. ■ 53213 #056-06-2007 **IM** *012

BAUER, Cynthia A W. 2900 W OKLAHOMA AVE 53215 #056-06-1974 L1975 **EM** *075 †16

BAUER, Paul Nicolas. ■ 53210 #056-06-2004 L2005 **CCP** *012 †55

BAUER, Terese Ann. 2801 W KINNICKINC RVR PKWY, STE 175 53215 #056-06-2003 L2005 **FM** *100 †18

BAUER, William. 330 E KILBOURN AVE, STE 1170 53202 #051-04-1956 L1979 **P OS** *071

BAUGRUD, Kathleen Ann. 788 N JEFFERSON ST, STE 300 53202 #056-06-1985 L1986 **IM** *020 †20

BAUMGARDNER, Dennis Jay. 2801 W KINNICKINC RVR PKWY, STE 250 53215 #016-11-1983 L1986 **FM** *040 †18

BAYE, Peter Jos. 3237 S 16TH ST 53215 #056-06-1991 L1994 **EM** *020 †16

BAYLON, Joselito A. 756 N 35TH ST, STE 101 53208 #748-10-1988 L1994 **FM** *020 †18

BEAR, Brian Jeffrey. 3289 N MAYFAIR RD, ADVANCED HEALTHCARE, S.C. 53222 #056-06-1984 L1985 **OBG** *020 †30

BEAR, Laurel M. 9000 W WISCONSIN AVE 53226 #056-06-1984 L1985 **PD** *020 †55

BEAULIEU, Phillip Leslie. 9200 W WISCONSIN AVE, MCW DEPT. OF ANESTHESIOLOG 53226 #047-06-2003 L2005 **AN** *020

BEAUMONT, Andrew. 9200 W WISCONSIN AVE, DEPARTMENT OF NEUROSURGERY 53226 #919-03-1998 L2002 **NS** *012

BECKER, Carl Geo. 8701 W WATERTOWN PLANK RD, MEDICAL CLG OF WI PATH DEP 53226 #035-20-1961 L1990 **PTH CLP** *030 †50

BECKER, Irvin Marvin. 945 N 12TH ST 53233 #056-05-1947 L1948 **GE IM** *071 †20

BECKER, John F. 25 E NEWPORT AVE 53211 #056-06-1951 L1952 **IM** *071 †20

BECKER, Michael D. 2801 W KINNICKINC RVR PKWY, STE 840 53215 #056-06-1979 L1981 **CD IM** *020 †20 ‡

BECKER, Michael Lorenz. 2900 W OKLAHOMA AVE, ERMED ST LUKE'S HOSPITAL 53215 #016-43-2002 L2005 **EM** *020 †16

BECKER, Stephen Chas. 2025 E NEWPORT AVE 53211 #056-06-1982 L1983 **AN CCM** *020 †05

BECKMAN, Marshall Allen. 8701 W WATERTOWN PLANK RD, MEDICAL COLLEGE AFFIL HOSP 53226 #056-06-1999 L2002 **GS** *020 ‡

BECTOR, Sumit. 3000 W MONTANA ST, AURORA HLTH CARE 53215 #495-43-2001 L2006 **IM** *012

BEDI, Ashok Ramprakash. 1220 DEWEY AVE 53213 #495-22-1971 L1977 **P PYA** *020 †75

BEDINGHAUS, Joan Marie. 9000 W WISCONSIN AVE 53226 #024-01-1982 L1996 **FM** *020 †18

BEG, Maria. 3000 W MONTANA 53215 #704-02-2002 **IM** *012

BEGAZ, Tomer Jacob. 9200 W WISCONSIN AVE, FROEDTERT EMERGENCY MEDICI 53226 #035-47-2002 L2006 **EM** *020 †16

BEGUN, Frank Philip. 9200 W WISCONSIN AVE, MEDICAL COLLEGE OF 53226 #025-01-1979 L1984 **U** *020 †95

BEHFAR-RAD, Mahmoud. 5000 W NATIONAL AVE, VA MEDICAL CENTER 53295 #517-01-1956 L1994 **P** *020

BEHMARAN, Behanz. 9200 W WISCONSIN AVE, MCW DEPT OF PATHOLOGY 53226 #517-01-1974 L2004 **PTH** *020 †50

BEHRENS, Timothy Wayne. ■ 53208 #016-45-1982 L1983 **RHU IM** *020 †20

BELETE, Michael Eyasu. 5818 W CAPITOL DR 53216 #056-05-1995 L1998 **IM** *020 †20

BELITS, Rachel. 4555 W SCHROEDER DR, STE 170 53223 #913-49-1981 L1995 **AN** *020 †05

BELL, Douglas James. 8901 W LINCOLN AVE, CONSULTANTS AT WEST ALLIS 53227 #056-06-2000 L2001 **AN** *020 †05 ‡

BELL, Michael Anthony. 8200 W SILVER SPRING DR, HEALTH CENTER 53218 #047-07-2000 L2004 **P** *020 †75 ‡

BELLIS, David Norman. 7635 W OKLAHOMA AVE 53219 #056-06-1971 L1972 **OBG** *020

BELLIZZI, John A, Jr. 8701 W WATERTOWN PLANK RD, DIV. OF INFECTIOUS DISEASE 53226 #051-01-1971 L2004 **ID** *020 †20

BENAE, Jeanlouis. 9200 W WISCONSIN AVE, MCW FROEDTERT HOSP NEURSUR 53226 #005-14-2002 L2005 **NS** *012

BENES, Paula Sue. 5000 W NATIONAL AVE, SCI-128 53295 #056-06-1996 L1998 **SCI PM** *100 †60

BENGANA, Chafik. ■ 53217 #125-04-1988 L2005 **SP** *100 †50

BENIWAL, Kaushalya. 2500 W LAYTON AVE, STE 230 53221 #495-55-1974 L1983 **GP** *020 ‡

BENJAMIN, Heather Louise. 9200 W WISCONSIN AVE, 4TH FL 53226 #305-01-2005 L2006 **IM** *012

BENNER, Marshall Hershel. 9000 W WISCONSIN AVE 53226 #056-05-1961 L1962 **A IM** *020 †20,03

BENNETT, Andrew Stephen. ■ 53217 #035-01-1997 L2006 **ADP** *100 †75

BENSON, Jeffrey Charles. 9000 W WISCONSIN AVE, MS 681 CRITICAL CARE 53226 #016-45-1996 L2000 **PDP** *020 †55

BENSON, Laurie Lynn. 2900 W OKLAHOMA AVE, ST LUKES MEDICAL CTR 53215 #056-06-1995 L1996 **EM** *020 †16

BENSON, Mark M. 2323 N MAYFAIR RD, MARK M BENSON MD SC 53226 #056-06-1978 L1979 **ORS** *075 †40

BENTLE, Michelle Kathleen. ■ 53228 #038-43-2007 **P** *012

BENZ, Lisa Marie. ■ 53210 #056-06-2008 *012

BERCEANU, Luciana C. 201 N MAYFAIR RD 53226 #781-01-1991 L2000 **APM AN** *020

BERDAN, Elizabeth Ann. 53212 #056-06-2007 L2007 **GS** *012

BERENS, Richard Jos. 9000 W WISCONSIN AVE, DEPT OF ANESTHESIOLOGY 53226 #056-06-1984 L1985 **AN CCM** *020 †05,55

BERES, James Jos. 2025 E NEWPORT AVE, WISCONSIN RADIOLOGY 53211 #056-05-1980 L1981 **DR** *020 †80

BEREZOVSKIY, Roman G. 9120 W CAPITOL DR 53222 #913-37-1995 L2005 **APM** *100 †60

BERG, Christine Mary. 7878 N 76TH ST, NORTHWEST CLINIC 53223 #056-06-1994 L1995 **OBG** *020 †30

BERG, Randall Neal. ■ 53210 #056-06-1987 L1988 **AN** *075 †05

BERGER, Marcie Gail. 2015 E NEWPORT AVE, STE 703 53211 #056-05-1992 L1993 **ICE CD** *020 †20

BERGER, Michael John. 9200 W WISCONSIN AVE 53226 #056-06-2004 L2005 **EM** *020

BERGER, Stuart. 9000 W WISCONSIN AVE 53226 #056-05-1979 L1990 **PDC PD** *020 †55

BERGER, William Langston. 9000 W WISCONSIN AVE 53226 #019-02-1980 L1991 **GE IM** *020 †20

BERKOFF, Jonathan Hale. 2350 N LAKE DR, STE 500 53211 #056-05-1991 L1996 **OBG** *020 †30

BERLIN, Jon Scott. 9455 W WATERTOWN PLANK RD, MILWUAKEE CNTY MENTAL HLTH 53226 #016-43-1979 L1997 **P** *020 †75

BERMAN, James Edward. 7400 W BROWN DEER RD 53223 #056-05-1984 L1986 **D** *020 †15

BERNARD, Keith Gerard. 945 N 12TH ST 53233 #021-05-1976 L1986 **DR** *020 †80

BERNS, Thomas Francis. 2025 E NEWPORT AVE, WISCONSIN RADIOLOGY 53211 #056-06-1975 L1976 **DR** *020 †80

BERNSTEIN, Barry Michael. 8700 W WISCONSIN AVE # 117 53226 #036-07-1977 L1982 **ID OS** *020 †20

BERNSTEIN, Deborah Weigle. 201 N MAYFAIR RD, MEDICAL EYE ASSOCIATES SC 53226 #056-06-1999 L2003 **OPH** *020 †35

BERNSTEIN, Harvey Hiller. 6400 W CAPITOL DR 53216 #056-06-1956 L1957 **GP** *020 ‡

BERNSTEIN, Karen Sue. 9000 W WISCONSIN AVE, CHILDRENS HOSPITAL OF WISC 53226 #016-01-2001 L2003 **ADL** *100 †55

BERNSTEIN, Paul Steven. 2801 W KINNICKINC RVR PKWY, STE 840 53215 #016-02-1976 L1981 **CD** *020 †20

BERNSTEIN, Susan Reah. 2311 N PROSPECT AVE, STE 401 53211 #016-06-1978 L1981 **PD NPM** *020 †55

BERRIDGE, Debra Lee. 500 W BROWN DEER RD, WISCONSIN RADIOLOGY 53217 #019-02-1988 L1989 **DR** *020 †80

BERRIDGE, Frank E, Jr. 5000 W NATIONAL AVE 53295 #024-05-1952 L1960 **GS** *071 †85

BERRY, Bruce Bart. 2801 W KINNICKINC RVR PKWY, STE 135 53215 #056-06-1983 L1984 **IM OM** *020 †20

BERRYHILL, Kenyita Tamara. 8200 W SILVER SPRING DR 53218 #056-05-2003 L2005 PD *020 †55

BERRY-HOOKS, Maisha K. 1121 E NORTH AVE 53212 #056-05-2006 L2008 FP *012

BESTE, David John. 9000 W WISCONSIN AVE, STE 208 53226 #056-06-1979 L1980 OTO PDO *020 †45

BETZ, John Richard. 788 N JEFFERSON ST, STE 300 53202 #056-06-2000 L2003 IM *020 †20

BETZOLD, Rose Amy. 788 N JEFFERSON ST, STE 300 53202 #056-06-1991 L1992 PUD *020 †20

BEUTLER, Selena Rae. 9200 W WISCONSIN AVE, RM 1870 53226 #056-05-2003 L2004 EM *020 †16

BHALA, Ram Parvesh. 2900 W OKLAHOMA AVE 53215 #495-29-1959 L1978 PM OS *020 †60

BHARATKUMAR, Agrahara G. 2925 W OKLAHOMA AVE 53215 #495-09-1981 L1995 DR *020 †20

BHATIA, Neal Dayal. 400 N BROADWAY, UNIT 801 53202 #056-05-1993 L1994 D *020 †15

BHATIA, Rambha. 2801 W KINNICKINC RVR PKWY, STE 250 53215 #495-05-1971 L1991 FM *020 †18

BHATIA, Sandeep K. ■ 53202 #016-02-2006 L2006 OPH *012

BHATTI, Allah Wadhayo. 614 W BROWN DEER RD, STE 221 53217 #704-08-1962 L1974 ORS EM *071 †40

BIANK, Vincent Franco. 9000 W WISCONSIN AVE, CHILDREN'S HOSPITAL OF WIS 53226 #016-11-2001 L2002 PG *100 †55

BIBLO, Lee Arnold. 9200 W WISCONSIN AVE, MEDICINE SUITE 4100 53226 #038-06-1981 L2002 CD *020 †20

BICK, David Paul. 8701 W WATERTOWN PLANK RD, MED CLGE OF WISC 53226 #010-01-1981 L2001 CG PD *020 †55,19

BIDWELL, Jacob Lee. 2801 W KINNICKINC RVR PKWY, STE 250 53215 #056-05-1999 L2000 FM *020 †18

BIGGERSTAFF, Matthew Clar. 9200 W WISCONSIN AVE 53226 #018-75-2004, ▲ L2006 AN *012

BILAL, Chihab Eddin. 6901 W EDGERTON AVE 53220 #875-01-1983 L1992 FM *020 †18

BILLER, Harold Bruce. ■ 53217 #056-06-1959 L1960 PTH *062 †50

BILLER, Julie Ann. 9200 W WISCONSIN AVE, MDCL CLLGE CLNCS AT FRDTRT 53226 #016-02-1983 L1991 PUD AN *020 †20

BINDER, Jeffrey Robt. 9200 W WISCONSIN AVE, DEPT OF NEUROLOGY 53226 #030-05-1986 L1992 N IM *020 †75

BINET, Scott Francis. ■ 53207 #004-01-1990 L1996 FM *020 †18

BINION, David Geo. 9200 W WISCONSIN AVE, DIV GASTRO 53226 #035-06-1988 L1997 GE *020 †20

BIRCHALL, Dennis Carl. 8901 W LINCOLN AVE 53227 #038-43-1983 L1984 EM *020 †16

BIRD, Thomas Ferguson. 320 E BUFFALO ST 53202 #025-01-1983 L1984 AN *020 †05

BIRKU, Yoseph Abaseran. 9200 W WISCONSIN AVE 53226 #366-02-1990 L2007 IM *012

BIVINS, John David, II. 2323 S 102ND ST, WEST ALLIS MEDICAL CLINIC 53227 #032-01-1999 L2003 FM *020 †18

BIXLER, Robin. 8701 W WATERTOWN PLANK RD 53226 #018-75-2004, ▲ L2005 FPP *012

BJERK, Sonja Maurie. 8701 W WATERTOWN PLANK RD, MED COLL WI AFFIL HOSPS 53226 #654-01-2005 L2007 IM *012 †20

BJORK, John Theodore. 2901 W KINNICKINC RVR PKWY, STE 414 53215 #056-06-1971 L1974 GE IM *020 †20

BLACHER, Stuart Evan. 5000 W CHAMBERS ST 53210 #056-05-1981 L1982 R RO *020 †80

BLACK, Brian Edward. 2424 S 90TH ST, STE 418 53227 #016-11-1984 L1990 ORS *020 †40

BLACKWELL, Barry. 2000 W KILBOURN AVE 53233 #352-03-1966 L1981 P PA *062

BLAIVAS, Michael. 9200 W WISCONSIN AVE, EMERGENCY MED/FROEDTERT HO 53226 #025-01-1995 L1999 EM *020 †16

BLAKE, Kyle Matthew. ■ 53213 #056-06-2008 *012

BLANCAS, Shirley. 1238 S CESAR E CHAVEZ DR 53204 #056-06-1999 L2003 FP *012

BLANCK, Zalmen. 2801 W KK RIVER PKWY, STE 777 53215 #649-01-1984 L1986 CD *020 †20

BLANK, Ellen Louise. 8701 W WATERTOWN PLANK RD, DEPT OF PEDS 53226 #019-02-1978 L1979 PG PD *020 †55

BLANKENSHIP, Nancy Jean. 8901 W LINCOLN AVE 53227 #056-06-1985 L1986 DR *020 †80

BLASCHKE, U Michael. 7080 N PORT WASHINGTON RD 53217 #056-06-1981 L1982 IM *020 †20

BLENKER, Ryan Daniel. 9200 W WISCONSIN AVE, FROEDTERT EAST CLINIC 53226 #056-06-2004 L2006 IM *012 †20

BLETZINGER, Deborah Sue. 1575 N RIVERCENTER DR 53212 #056-05-1999 L2001 FM *020 †18

BLICK, Michael John. 2025 E NEWPORT AVE, STE 208 53211 #016-43-1970 L1975 IM *020 †20

BLINDAUER, Karen Ann. 9200 W WISCONSIN AVE, DEPT. OF NEUROLOGY 53226 #056-06-1993 L1994 N *020 †75

BLOCK, Joseph Robert. ■ 53202 #035-09-2006 PD *012

BLOCK, Margo L. 9200 W WISCONSIN AVE, NEUROLOGY DEPT. 53226 #016-76-2003, ▲ L2005 CN *012

BLOCK, Spencer Jonathan. 960 N 12TH ST, STE 1800 53233 #016-06-1987 L1993 NS GS *020 †25

BLOM, Dennis. 9200 W WISCONSIN AVE, DEPT. SURGERY 53226 #035-03-1992 L2001 GS *020 †85

BLOOM, Thomas David. 5150 N PORT WASHINGTON RD, NO 251 53217 #016-11-1983 L1987 OPH *020 †35

BLOOMSTEIN, Jerry M. 1220 DEWEY AVE, BLDG 2 53213 #024-05-1986 L1987 CHP P *020 †75

BLOOMSTEIN, Joanne R. 9455 W WATERTOWN PLANK RD, MILWAUKEE CTY MENTAL HLTH 53226 #016-11-1990 L1994 P *020 †75

BLUMENTHAL, Samuel S. 9200 W WISCONSIN AVE, FRUEDTERT HOSPITAL-NEPHROL 53226 #035-19-1977 L1978 OS IM *050 †20

BLUMIN, Joel Howard. 9200 W WISCONSIN AVE, MEDICAL COLLEGE OF WISCONS 53226 #018-03-1993 L2005 OTO *020 †45 ‡

BLUST, Linda Sue. 9200 W WISCONSIN AVE, MEDICAL COLLEGE OF WISCONS 53226 #056-06-1998 L1999 IM *020 †20

BLUSTEIN, Joseph Nathan. 1032 S CESAR E CHAVEZ DR 53204 #016-11-1984 L1988 OPH PHP *062 †35

BOBLIN, James D. 3201 S 16TH ST, STE 1005 53215 #056-05-1984 L1985 N *020

BODNAR, Myron Oleh. 3003 W GOOD HOPE RD 53209 #016-42-1987 L1988 IM *020 †20

BODNER, Aaron Chaim. 1218 W KILBOURN AVE, STE 511 53233 #056-05-1966 L1967 OBG *071 †30

BOGOST, Keith Evan. ■ 53211 #056-05-1959 L1960 P *071

BOGUNOVIC, Dragan. 5663 S 27TH ST 53221 #957-02-1958 L1976 EM FM *071

BOHN, Michael James. 1220 DEWEY AVE 53213 #056-05-1985 L1987 ADP P *020 †75

BOKERMAN, David Matthew. 2900 W OKLAHOMA AVE, ERMED ST LUKES MEDICAL CEN 53215 #025-07-1997 L2003 EM *020 †16

BOKU, Abinet Mulat. 3000 W MONTANA ST 53215 #366-02-1993 L2007 IM *012

BOLDT, Rhonda Rae. 2524 E WEBSTER PL, STE 301 53211 #016-45-1987 L1988 PD *020 †55

BOMMAKANTI, Satya Venkata. ■ 53202 #021-01-2005 IM *012

BOMZER, Charles Alan. 2025 E NEWPORT AVE, STE 1000 53211 #016-06-1978 L1986 HO HEM *020 †20 ‡

BONAVIA, John Peter. 210 W CAPITOL DR, RIVER GLEN MED CLNC 53212 #016-06-1980 L1981 FM *020 †18

BONDOW, Steven Edward. 1155 N MAYFAIR RD 53226 #026-04-1980 L1981 FM *020 †18

BONKOWSKI, Colleen Marie. 3237 S 16TH ST, ST. FRANCIS HOSPITAL 53215 #016-01-1995 L2002 DR *020 †80

BONNE, Valerie Jean. 9200 W WISCONSIN AVE, STE 4100 53226 #016-43-2000 L2002 PCC *100 †20

BONNER, Theodore Robt. 4111 W MITCHELL ST, AURORA HEALTH CARE 53215 #021-01-1977 L1988 OM *020 †20,18,70

BOOK, Diane Sonia. 9200 W WATERTOWN PLANK RD 53226 #056-06-1991 L1992 N *020 †75

BORKOVEC, John Clarence. 6200 W BLUEMOUND RD 53213 #056-06-1987 L1988 FM *020 †18

BORKOVEC, Terre Marie. 2350 N LAKE DR STE 500, BORKOWF & BORKOVEC MD SC 53211 #056-06-1984 L1985 OBG *020 †30

BORMAN, Jesse Jon. 10400 W NORTH AVE, RADIOLOGY ASSOCIATES OF MI 53226 #056-06-1999 L2000 MSR *100 †20

BORNS, Laurie Lee. ■ 53213 #056-06-1993 FM *100

BOROWSKI, Bret John. 8901 W LINCOLN AVE, CONSULTANTS AT WEST ALLIS 53227 #056-06-1989 L1991 AN *020 †05

BORUTA, David Michael, II. 9200 W WISCONSIN AVE, DEPT OBG 53226 #025-01-1996 L2003 GO *020 †30

BOSBOUS, Mark Walter. 8700 W WATERTOWN PLANK RD, MCW DEPT. OF PLASTIC SURGE 53226 #056-06-2005 L2006 PS *012

BOSE, Diwata Hope Abeleda. 3000 W MONTANA ST, DEPT OBG 53215 #748-02-1998 L2007 OBG *012

BOTROS, Emad S. 1218 W KILBOURN AVE, SETHI MEDICAL SERVICES 53233 #915-03-1985 L2000 PUD *020 †20

BOTROS, Nazih Youssef. 6901 W EDGERTON AVE 53220 #915-04-1982 L2004 FM *020 †18

BOTTUM, Michael Wm. 2901 W KINNICKINC RVR PKWY, STE LL8 53215 #056-06-1959 L1961 IM CCM *020 †20

BOUHABIB, Rania. 2315 N LAKE DR, STE 501 53211 #067-06-1997 L2002 *100

BOULANGER, Gregory John. 12129 W FEERICK ST 53222 #056-06-1981 L1982 AN *020 †05

BOULANGER, Wayne J. 2025 E NEWPORT AVE 53211 #056-06-1952 L1953 GS *030 †85

BOURNE, Charles Warren. 3003 W GOOD HOPE RD 53209 #025-01-1959 L1967 U *071 †95

BOVI, Joseph Anthony. 8701 W WATERTOWN PLANK RD, MEDICAL COLLEGE OF WISCONS 53226 #016-43-2002 L2003 RO *100

BOWER, Douglas John. 9200 W WISCONSIN AVE, MEDICINE 53226 #056-05-1979 L1982 FM *020 †18

BOWMAN, John Wilson. 2424 S 90TH ST 53227 #038-41-1966 L1967 GS OS *020 †85

BOYD, Andrew. ■ 53211 #041-01-1954 L1955 GYN *071 †30

BOYLES, Margie Elaine. ■ 53211 #012-01-1973 L1978 PD *071 †55

BOZORGI, Kenny. 9200 W WISCONSIN AVE, DEPT OBGYN 53226 #016-06-1992 L1999 GO *020 †30

BRAAK, Beverly L. 2311 N PROSPECT AVE, CSMCP PROSPECT MED COMMONS 53211 #048-13-1988 L1992 OBG *020 †30

BRADLEY, Ciaran Thomas. 8701 W WATERTOWN PLANK RD, MCWAH- GENERAL SURGERY PRO 53226 #539-04-2004 L2006 GS *012

BRADLEY, Henry Jos. 2025 E NEWPORT AVE, WISCONSIN RADIOLOGY 53211 #539-04-1970 L1976 R *020 †80

BRADSHAW, Michael Blair. ■ 53226 #056-06-2008 *012

BRAHMACHARI, Chandra Shek. ■ 53227 #496-34-1998 N *012

BRAKER, Arlene Magon. 5000 W CHAMBERS ST 53210 #025-01-1984 L1988 PM *020 †60

BRAMHADEVI, Srinivas Rao. 3505 W WISCONSIN AVE 53208 #495-21-1994 L2002 FM *020 †18

BRAMMER, Harry Murray. 7878 N 76TH ST, NORTHWEST CLINIC 53223 #056-06-1979 L1995 DR PDR *020 †80

BRANCHFORD, Brian Re. ■ 53202 #056-05-2005 L2006 PD *012

BRAND, Thomas R. 2500 W LAYTON AVE STE 10 53221 #016-43-1993 L1994 IM *020 †20

BRANDOW, Amanda M. 1020 N 12TH ST 53233 #016-76-2001, ▲ L2003 PHO *012 †55

BRANNEN, John Herbert. 3000 W MONTANA ST 53215 #056-06-2003 L2008 DR *012 †20

BRASEL, Karen Jean. 9200 W WISCONSIN AVE, MED COL OF WI DEPT SURG 53226 #018-03-1991 L1999 CCS *020 †85

BRATANOW, Nancy Constance. 2500 N MAYFAIR RD, STE 300 53226 #056-05-1980 L1982 PMM AN *020 †05,20

BRAUN, Andrew James. 9200 W WISCONSIN AVE, DEPT. OF ANESTHESIOLOGY (E 53226 #056-05-2004 L2006 AN *012

BRAUN, Michael Andrew. 500 W BROWN DEER RD 53217 #056-05-1986 L1992 DR VIR *020 †80

BRAUN, Theresa Marie. ■ 53217 #035-03-1987 L1993 N *020 †75

BRAVO-FERNANDEZ, Caridad. 9200 W WISCONSIN AVE, ANESTHESIOLOGY/FROEDTERT E 53224 #026-04-1983 L2003 AN PME *040 †05

BRAZA, Diane Wolf. 1155 N MAYFAIR RD STE B 53226 #056-06-1987 L1988 PM IM *020 †20,60

BREDESON, Christopher N. 9200 W WISCONSIN AVE, MEDICAL COLLEGE OF WISCONS 53226 #065-09-1987 L2000 HEM *020

BREGER, Mary Therese. 7007 N RANGE LINE RD, NORTH SHORE SURG CTR 53209 #056-06-1984 L1985 AN *071 †05

BRENNAN, John Jos. 2051 W WISCONSIN AVE 53233 #056-06-1946 L1947 OBG *020 †30

BRENOWITZ, Jerold Barry. 2315 N LAKE DR STE 605 53211 #035-19-1971 L1980 TS *071 †85,90

BRESNAHAN, Barbara Ann. 9200 W WISCONSIN AVE 53226 #028-34-1981 L1982 NEP IM *020 †20

BRESNAHAN, David Boyd. 8700 W WISCONSIN AVE 53226 #028-34-1981 L1982 P *020 †75

BRESNAHAN, Jill Marie. 2524 E WEBSTER PL, # 301 53211 #056-06-1994 L1997 PD *020 †55

BRETHAUER, Jon. 8701 W WATERTOWN PLANK RD, MCW DEPARTMENT OF ANESTHES 53226 #018-75-2004, ▲ L2005 AN *012

BRETZA, Joseph Anthony. 3003 W GOOD HOPE RD, HOPE ROAD CLINIC 53209 #056-06-1972 L1980 RHU IM *020 †20,03

BREWER, Matthew Robert. 945 N 12TH ST 53233 #056-06-1999 L2005 RNR *020 †80

BRICKNER, Robert Chas. 2801 W KINNICKINNIC PKWY, STE 245 53215 #056-06-1986 L1987 END *020 †20

BRILL, John Roger. 2801 W KINNICKINC RVR PKWY, STE 250 53215 #056-06-1991 L1992 FM *020 †18

BRIONES, Carmen Cabailo. 8701 W WATERTOWN PLANK RD 53226 #748-02-1997 L2007 N *012

BRIXEY, Suzanne Nicole. 1020 N 12TH ST 53233 #051-01-1998 L1999 **PD** *020 †55

BROEKHUIZEN, Fredrik F. 9200 W WISCONSIN AVE 53226 #660-04-1970 L1978 **OBG MFM** *020 †30

BROEREN, Alicia Marie. 1032 S 16TH ST, HEALTH CENTER 53204 #056-06-1993 L1994 **FM** *020 †18

BROGHAMMER, Benjamin G. 2025 E NEWPORT AVE, WISCONSIN RADIOLOGY 53211 #018-03-1988 L1989 **DR** *020 †80

BROOR, Shobha. 8701 W WATERTOWN PLANK RD 53226 #495-03-1969 **PTH** *100

BROTZMAN, Gregory Lyle. 1121 E NORTH AVE 53212 #016-45-1984 L1988 **FM** *040 †18

BROUSSEAU, David Carl. 999 N 92ND ST STE CCC550 53226 #051-01-1993 L1996 **PE PEM** *050 †55

BROUWER, Nathan Aaron. ■ 53210 #056-06-2008 *012

BROWN, Dennis Gregory. 2901 W KINNICKNC PKWY #317 53215 #056-06-1979 L1980 **PM** *020 †60

BROWN, Dwight Herman. 2315 N LAKE DR 53211 #056-06-1963 L1964 **OPH** *020 †35

BROWN, John Robt. 2901 W KINNICKINC RVR PKWY, STE 317 53215 #056-06-1968 L1969 **GS** *020 †20

BROWN, Kellie Rene. 8700 W WISCONSIN AVE, COMPREHENSIVE VEIN CLINIC 53226 #056-06-1993 L1998 **VS** *020 †85

BROWN, Matthew Douglass. 9000 W WISCONSIN AVE, MS713 53226 #049-01-2001 L2004 **PDC** *012 †55

BROWN, Richard Everett. 2901 W KINNICKINC RVR PKWY, AUITE 317 53215 #056-06-1973 L1974 **TS** *020 †85

BROWN, Robin Skaufle. 545 N 15TH ST 53233 #030-05-1984 L1985 **IM FM** *020 †20

BROWN, Sarah Prentis. 9000 W WISCONSIN AVE 350, CHILDRENS CORP CENTER 53226 #018-03-2003 L2004 **PD** *020 †55

BROWN, Stacy Jean. 5000 W CHAMBERS ST, ST. JOSEP 53210 #047-06-2007 **TY** *012

BROWN, W Douglas. 9200 W WISCONSIN AVE, RADIOLOGY, FEC/FROEDTERT H 53226 #048-12-1984 L1986 **RNR NM** *020 †28,80

BROWNING, Carol Anne. ■ 53217 #056-05-1962 L1970 **NPM** *071 †55

BRUCKER, Thomas Danl. 2900 W OKLAHOMA AVE, DEPT OF PATHOLOGY 53215 #056-05-1989 L1994 **PTH** *020 †50

BRUCKMAN, James Eugene. 3237 S 16TH ST 53215 #056-05-1970 L1971 **RO** *020 †80

BRUMBLAY, Raymond Scott. 501 W MICHIGAN ST, ASSURANT HLTH 53203 #056-05-1972 L1973 **IM** *030 †20 ‡

BRUMMITT, Charles Francis. 1032 S CESAR E CHAVEZ DR 53204 #056-05-1982 L1986 **ID IM** *020 †20

BRUNO, Domenick Stephen. ■ 53217 #056-06-1956 L1957 **ORS** *071 †40

BRUNO, Kristine Dawn. 3003 W GOOD HOPE RD, HOPE ROAD CLINIC 53209 #016-06-1996 L1999 **IM** *020 †20

BRUSKY, John Edward. 2801 W KK RIVER PKWY # 453, ANESTHESIOLOGY ASSOC OF WI 53215 #056-05-1984 L1985 **AN OS** *020 †05

BRUSKY, Laura Torrico. ■ 53213 #561-17-1995 **FP** *012

BRYANT, John Michael. 3003 W GOOD HOPE RD, HOPE ROAD CLINIC 53209 #056-06-1976 L1979 **IM** *020 †20

BRYKE, Christine Roberts. 3720 N 124TH ST, STE I 53222 #016-11-1982 L1992 **MG PD** *020 †55,19

BRYKE, Edward A. 2300 N LAKE DR, ST MARY'S HOSPITAL 53211 #016-11-1982 L1992 **AN** *020 †05

BUBOLZ, Laura Marie. 2323 N LAKE DR, ST. MARY'S ANESTHESIA ASSO 53211 #056-06-1998 L1999 **AN** *020

BUCK, Gregory Bruce. 3289 N MAYFAIR RD, AURORA ADVANCED HEALTHCARE 53222 #016-01-1982 L1983 **IM** *020 †20

BUDDE, Morgan. ■ 53212 #654-01-2005 L2007 **PM** *012

BUDITHI, Rachel. 9200 W WISCONSIN AVE, DEPARMENT OF ANESTHESIOLOG 53226 #495-16-1995 L2003 **AN** *020 †05

BUDOVEC, Joseph John. 9200 W WISCONSIN AVE 53226 #016-43-1999 L2003 **DR** *100 †80

BUEBENDORF, Norman Donald. 575 W RIVER WOODS PKWY, STE 202 53212 #028-03-1983 L1988 **HS PS** *020 †20

BUEGEL, Dale Mark. 6980 N PORT WASHINGTON RD, STE 202 53217 #026-04-1976 L1978 **GP P** *075 †75

BUGGY, Brian Patrick. 2801 W KINNICKINC RVR PKWY, STE 475 53215 #056-06-1977 L1983 **ID IM** *020 †20

BULACAN, Frederick Keith. 2500 W LAYTON AVE STE 10 53221 #056-06-1993 L1994 **IM** *020 †20

BURCHBY, Kathleen Kay. 3003 W GOOD HOPE RD, GGOD HOPE CLINIC 53209 #016-45-1979 L1982 **PD** *020 †20

BURCHMAN, Sheldon L. ■ 53217 #056-06-1955 L1956 **PME** *071

BURDICK, Evelyn Eileen. 1901 E CAPITOL DR, SHOREWOOD FAMILY 53211 #056-06-1984 L1985 **FM** *020 †18

BURFEIND, John David. 2311 N PROSPECT AVE, CSMCP PROSPECT MEDICAL COM 53211 #056-05-1993 L1995 **ON** *020 †20

BURG, Edward Arthur, Jr. 2025 E NEWPORT AVE 53211 #041-13-1960 L1964 **PTH** *071 †50

BURGARINO, Joseph Jude. 1220 DEWEY AVE 53213 #056-06-1979 L1980 **P N** *020 †75

BURGOS, Loures Galay. VET ADMIN HOSP, DEPT AN 53295 #748-01-1964 L1976 **AN IM** *020 †05

BURKO, Henry. ■ 53211 #025-07-1953 L1976 **R** *071 †80

BURNS, Edith Ann. 5000 W NATIONAL AVE, SECTION OF GERIATRICS, PC- 53295 #056-05-1981 L1982 **IM IMG** *050 †20

BURNS, William. 3237 S 16TH ST 53215 #016-06-1978 L1981 **IM** *020 †20

BURSTEIN, Paul David. 2350 N LAKE DR, STE 201 53211 #025-01-1972 L1973 **OBG** *020 †30

BUSEY, Sharon Linda. 1020 N 12TH ST, DOWNTOWN HEALTH CENTER 53233 #038-40-1989 L1995 **PD** *020 †55

BUSTOS, Teresita T. 4555 W SCHROEDER DR, STE 170 53223 #748-10-1969 L1979 **AN** *020

BUTALA, Nitin Santosh. 9200 W WISCONSIN AVE, LUTHERAN HO 53226 #495-01-2003 **N** *012

BUTCHART, Andrew M. 8701 W WATERTOWN PLANK RD 53226 #016-76-2000, ▲ L2007 **P** *012

BUTLER, Carolyn Peterson. 201 N MAYFAIR RD, MEDICAL EYE ASSOCIATES SC 53226 #056-05-1990 L1995 **OPH** *020 †35 ‡

BUTLER, Elizabeth G. 9200 W WISCONSIN AVE, CARDIOTHORACIC SURGERY 53226 #048-13-2000 L2006 **TS** *012

BUTTERFIELD, Gail E. 5000 W CHAMBERS ST, DEPT OF ANESTHESIOLOGY 53210 #056-06-1986 L1990 **AN** *020 †05

BUTZ, Steven Frederick. 3223 S 103RD ST 53227 #016-06-1993 L1998 **AN** *020 †05

BYHARDT, Roger Warren. 8700 W WISCONSIN AVE 53226 #056-06-1968 L1973 **RO** *020 †80

CABALLERO, Gerardo Adan. 2801 W KINNICKINC RVR PKWY, STE 330 53215 #649-19-1983 L1984 **GS** *020 †85

CABRAL, Patricia. 1032 S CESAR E CHAVEZ DR 53204 #016-11-2000 L2001 **FM** *020 †18

CACERES, Anthony Eusebio. 1020 N 12TH ST, FL 2 53233 #024-01-1981 L1984 **IM** *020 †20

CADY, Charles Edward, Jr. 9200 W WISCONSIN AVE, FROEDTERT HOSP EAST 53226 #056-06-1997 L2000 **EM** *020 †16

CAFARO, Anthony Francis. 5000 W CHAMBERS ST, ST. JOSEPHS 53210 #056-06-1956 L1958 **PTH** *071 †50

CAFARO, Anthony Francis. ■ 53202 #030-06-1984 L1988 **PCP** *020 †50

CAFARO, John Anthony. 2311 N PROSPECT AVE, STE 401 53211 #030-06-1997 L1999 **FM** *020 †18

CAFARO, John Richard. 5000 W CHAMBERS ST 53210 #030-06-1959 L1966 **PTH** *020 †50

CAFARO, Theresa Stolz. 2311 N PROSPECT AVE, STE 401 53211 #030-06-1997 L1999 **PD** *020 †55

CAIMACAN, Dumitru Timotei. 5000 W CHAMBERS ST 53210 #781-01-1950 L1979 **GP** *071

CAINE, Donald. ■ 53217 #041-13-1949 L1950 **IM** *071

CAINE, Marc Randall. 2801 W KINNICKINC RVR PKWY, STE 135 53215 #016-06-1974 L1977 **IM** *020 †20

CALDWELL, Scott David. 8905 W LINCOLN AVE, STE 411 53227 #056-05-1993 L1998 **OBG** *020 †30

CALKINS, Casey Matthew. 999 N 92ND ST 53226 #056-06-1996 L2005 **PDS** *020 †85

CALL, Jason Andrew. ■ 53210 #056-06-2007 L2008 **TY** *012

CALLAHAN, Edward Paul. 9200 W WISCONSIN AVE, DEPT OF EMERGENCY MEDICINE 53226 #016-11-1988 L1995 **EM** *020 †16

CALVY, Thomas Matthew. 945 N 12TH ST 53233 #056-05-1979 L1985 **RNR DR** *020 †80

CAMERON, Cheryl Marie. 9000 W WISCONSIN AVE 53226 #056-06-2003 L2004 **PHO** *012 †55

CAMERON, Jeffrey Scott. 2025 E NEWPORT AVE 53211 #016-06-1979 L1993 **PM** *020 †16

CAMILLERI, Bruce Hinman. 3003 W GOOD HOPE RD, HOPE ROAD CLINIC 53209 #165-04-1986 L1991 **IM** *020 †20

CAMITTA, Bruce Matthew. 8701 W WATERTOWN PLANK RD, MEDICAL COLLEGE OF WISCONS 53226 #023-07-1966 L1976 **PHO PD** *020 †55

CAMPBELL, Bruce Hegstad. 9200 W WISCONSIN AVE, MCW OTOLARYNGOLOGY 53226 #016-01-1980 L1981 **OTO HNS** *020 †45

CAMPBELL, William Henry. 8901 W LINCOLN AVE, CONSULTANTS AT WEST ALLIS 53227 #056-05-1990 L1991 **AN** *020 †05

CANGA, Cristino Caayao. 2801 W KINNICKINC RVR PKWY, STE 1030 53215 #748-19-1993 L1999 **GE** *020 †20

CANNON, Shanklin B. 720 E WISCONSIN AVE 53202 #016-06-1973 L1980 **OS ON** *030 †20

CAPELLI, Gregory Joseph. 2323 N LAKE DR, ST MARYS HOSPITAL 53211 #422-01-1989 L1992 **AN** *020 †05

CARBALLO, Richard Ernest. 2801 W KINNICKINC RVR PKWY 53215 #016-11-1988 L1993 **VS GS** *020 †85

CARDINAL, Sean Patrick. 1121 E NORTH AVE, COLUMBIA-ST MARY'S HOSP 53212 #056-05-2006 L2007 **FP** *012

CARDONA, Marylynn. ■ 53212 #031-01-2006 **OBG** *012

CARDONE, Bruce Wm. 4601 N OAKLAND AVE 53211 #561-20-1984 L1990 **DR** *020 †80

CARDONI, Andrew Lee. 9200 W WISCONSIN AVE, MCW DEPT OF EMERGENCY MEDI 53226 #056-05-2004 L2005 **EM** *100

CARLSON, Alisa Anne. ■ 53222 #056-06-2006 L2008 **PD** *012

CARLSON, Douglas Lee. 2457 N MAYFAIR RD, MILWAUKEE OB GYN SC 53226 #056-05-1985 L1988 **OBG** *020 †30

CARLSON, Judith Ann. 5000 W CHAMBERS ST 53210 #056-05-1982 L1983 **N** *020 †75

CARNEOL, Mitchell Grant. 2311 N PROSPECT AVE, STE 401 53211 #056-05-1985 L1997 **IM** *020 †20

CARPENTER, Diane Ellen. 53223 #056-05-1984 L1987 **PD** *020 †55

CARPENTER, John Wm. 5555 N PORT WASHINGTON RD, STE 200 53217 #056-06-1980 L1981 **P** *020 †75

CARPENTER, Suresh M. ■ 53233 #495-33-1966 **FM** *100

CARPENTER-EDMOND, Regenia. 5000 W CHAMBERS ST, DEPT OF EMERGENCY MEDICINE 53210 #024-01-1988 L1999 **EM** *020 †20,16

CARR, Donald Jos. 10950 W CAPITOL DR 53222 #056-06-1985 L1986 **IM** *020 †20

CARR, Jane Anne. 2900 W OKLAHOMA AVE, ST. LUKE'S MEDICAL CENTER 53215 #030-06-2007 **TY** *012

CARR, Margaret Herzog. 201 N MAYFAIR RD, FL 3 53226 #056-05-1989 L1990 **OBG MFM** *020 †30

CARRERA, Guillermo F. 9200 W WISCONSIN AVE, FROEDTERT MEM'RL LUTHERAN 53226 #024-01-1972 L1977 **R** *020 †80

CARROLL, Benjamin Joseph. 8701 W WATERTOWN PLANK RD 53226 #018-75-2005, ▲ L2007 **AN** *012

CARROLL, Ty Brian. 9200 W WISCONSIN AVE 53226 #056-06-2002 L2004 **END** *012 †20

CARRON, Angela Colarelli. 1020 N 12TH ST, FL 5 53233 #028-34-1986 L1987 **PD** *020 †55

CARRON, David Anthony. 2801 W KINNICKINC RVR PKWY, STE 1030 53215 #028-34-1986 L1987 **GE IM** *020 †20

CARTER, Jacqueline. 2311 N PROSPECT AVE, CSMCP PROSPECT MEDICAL COM 53211 #016-06-1978 L2006 **N P** *020 †75

CARTER, Katrina M.. ■ 53217 #056-06-2008 *012

CARTES, Alfredo. 155 E SILVER SPRNG DR #206 53217 #726-01-1954 L1963 **IM** *071

CASE, Graham. 2900 W OKLAHOMA AVE, ST LUKE'S MED CTR 53215 #041-15-2004 **DR** *012

CASE, Mark Patrick. 2300 N LAKE DR 53211 #056-05-1998 L1999 **AN** *020 †05

CASPARY-SULLIVAN, E A. 1220 DEWEY AVE 53213 #056-06-1975 L1977 **P** *020 †75

CASPER, Ryan Matthew. 9000 W WISCONSIN AVE, ASTHMA AND ALLERGY CTR STE 53226 #056-06-2001 L2004 **AI** *100 †55,03

CASSIDY, Erin Kathleen. ■ 53217 #016-42-1996 L2000 **GPM** *100

CASTERLINE, Vernon Dale. 2424 S 90TH ST, STE 206 53227 #040-02-1980 L1983 **D EM** *020 †15

CASTILLO, Marcelo Gaite. 9720 W BLUEMOUND RD 53226 #748-02-1952 L1970 **OBG** *071 †30

CASTILLO, Wilfrido E. 10000 W BLUEMOUND RD 53226 #056-05-1982 L2001 **AN** *020 †05

CASTRO, Mary Ames. 9200 W WISCONSIN AVE, DEPT OF OBGYN 53226 #038-41-1989 L1999 **OBG** *020 †30

CATALANO, Marc Fabian. 2801 W KINNICKINC RVR PKWY, STE 1030 53215 #048-14-1986 L1993 **IM GE** *020 †20

CATTEY, Richard Paul. 2015 E NEWPORT AVE STE 305 53211 #056-06-1984 L1985 **GS VS** *020 †85

CEDERBERG, Christopher Al. 9200 W WISCONSIN AVE 53226 #030-05-2004 L2005 **OTO** *012

CENTENA, Edmundo Franco. 1220 DEWEY AVE, BLDG 2 53213 #748-01-1971 L1978 **P** *020

CERNIGLIA, Ross Michael. ■ 53226 #056-06-2005 L2006 **DR** *012

CESAR, Louis-Marcel A. 3237 S 16TH ST, EMERGENCY MEDICINE SPECIAL 53215 #041-07-1986 L1992 **EM CCM** *020 †16

CESARZ, Thomas John. 2300 N MAYFAIR RD STE 1155 53226 #056-06-1966 L1967 **OPH OTO** *020 †35 ‡

CHADDA, Nader Hussain. ■ 53202 #035-08-2002 L2006 **CD** *012 †20

CHAI, Krisna Potewiratan. 9200 W WISCONSIN AVE, DIVISION OF GI/HEPATOLOGY 53226 #048-04-2002 L2005 **GE** *012 †20

CHAMBERLAIN, John O. 324 E WISC AVE 53202 #056-06-1952 L1953 **IM** *071 †20

CHAMBERS, Charles Hoy. 2308 W WISCONSIN AVE, # 306 53233 #036-05-1970 L1973 **FOP** *020 †50

CHAMBERS, La Royce F. 945 N 12TH ST, FL 1 53233 #025-01-1970 L1976 **OBG** *020 †30

CHAMOY, Lewis. 575 W RIVER WOODS PKWY, STE 202 53212 #035-08-1968 L1969 **HS GS** *020 †85

CHAN, Carlyle Hung-Lun. 2025 E NEWPORT AVE # 4FLR 53211 #056-06-1975 L1980 **P** *040 †75

CHAN, Wong I-Ling. ■ 53217 #243-03-1958 L1975 **FM** *071 †55

CHANDRASEKHARAN, Raja G. ■ 53216 #495-16-1953 L1969 **IM CD** *072

CHANDY, George K. 2040 W WISCONSIN AVE, APT 466 53233 #495-27-1978 L1987 *020

CHANG, Edward Chip. 3201 S 16TH ST, SOUTH CENTER MEDICAL 53215 #243-32-1982 L1997 **IM** *020 †20

CHANG, Helen. ■ 53214 #056-06-2008 *012

CHANG, Steve Iksoo. 5757 W OKLAHOMA AVE, STE 201 53219 #035-48-1994 L1997 **IM** *020 †20

CHANG, Titus Chenglee. 9000 W WISCONSIN AVE, ASTHMA AND ALLERGY CTR STE 53226 #016-11-2000 L2006 **AI** *012 †55

CHAPA, Ajay Rama. 5000 W CHAMBERS ST, DEPT RAD 53210 #016-11-2006 L2006 **DR** *012

CHAPLIN, Robert Newton. 9000 W WISCONSIN AVE, MS 681 PO 1997 53226 #019-02-2002 L2005 **CCP** *012 †55

CHARLSON, John Alan. 9200 W WISCONSIN AVE, MEDICINE FEC E 4200 53226 #018-03-1999 L2001 **HO** *100 †20

CHARME, Larry Sanford. ■ 53216 #038-40-1963 L2005 **OBG** *071 †30

CHAROUS, Matthew Todd. ■ 53217 #025-01-2005 L2005 **AN** *012

CHAUSOW, Douglas D. 2900 W OKLAHOMA AVE 53215 #016-11-1990 L1991 **PTH** *020 †50

CHAWLA, S Paramjith S. 5000 W CHAMBERS ST 53210 #495-57-1992 L2002 **IM** *020 †20

CHELMOWSKI, Mark Kenneth. 3003 W GOOD HOPE RD, HOPE ROAD CLINIC 53209 #016-11-1985 L1986 **IM** *020 †20

CHEN, Hong. 9200 W WISCONSIN AVE, DEPT OF RAD/NM 53226 #243-72-1983 L2002 **GS** *020 †28

CHEN, Hong Mo. 9200 W WISCONSIN AVE, FROEDTERT HOSPITAL 53226 #385-02-1958 L1976 **ORS HS** *020

CHEN, Jenny. 1121 E NORTH AVE 53212 #016-11-2005 **FP** *012

CHEN, Jenny Yichen. 1121 E NORTH AVE 53212 #056-06-2005 L2006 **FP** *012

CHEN, Poly. 9200 W WISCONSIN AVE, MEDICAL COLLEGE OF WISCONS 53226 #056-05-2004 L2005 **AN** *012

CHEN, Qian. 2801 W KK RVR PKWY 53215 #243-43-1986 L2000 **AN** *020 †05

CHENG, Chihlynn. 9200 W WISCONSIN AVE, DEPT OF DERMATOLOGY 53226 #036-07-2005 L2006 **D** *012

CHENG, Dong-Yuan. ■ 53213 #243-16-1991 L2000 **AN** *020 †05

CHENG, Yee Chung Chua. 9200 W WISCONSIN AVE, MED CLG OF WISC 53226 #748-01-1992 L2003 **ON HEM** *020 †20

CHEPLIN, Muriel June. ■ 53217 #035-15-1947 L1950 **IM** *071

CHESSHIRE, Susan Hindman. 1684 N PROSPECT AVE, MILWAUKEE EYE CARE ASSOCIA 53202 #018-03-1985 L1986 **OPH** *020 †35

CHEVAKO, Jane Ann. 9000 W WISCONSIN AVE 53226 #056-06-1984 L1985 **PD** *020 †55

CHEVALIER, Jennifer Marie. 9000 W WISCONSIN AVE, MS 677 53226 #056-06-1999 L2000 **PD** *020 †55

CHILDREY, Valerie Alexis. 750 W VIRGINIA ST 53204 #016-11-1985 L1985 **FM** *020 †18

CHINTAMANENI, Jagan Mohan. 2311 N PROSPECT AVE, STE 401 53211 #495-58-1969 L1977 **IM** *020 †20

CHINTAMANENI, Krishna Sri. 3267 S 16TH ST, STE 103 53215 #495-58-1977 L1987 **CCM IM** *020

CHINTAMANENI, Kumari S. 3267 S 16TH ST, STE 103 53215 #495-58-1978 L1987 **IM PTH** *020 †50,20

CHISHOLM, Donald Edward. 10425 W NORTH AVE STE 2, 46 53226 #056-06-1956 L1957 **OPH** *071 †35

CHITAMBAR, Christopher R. 9200 W WISCONSIN AVE, DIV NEOPLASTIC DISEASES 53226 #495-08-1976 L1984 **HO IM** *020 †20

CHITCHYAN, Ara. ■ 53213 #913-38-1999 L2006 **PM** *012

CHIU, Asriani Marisa. 9000 W WISCONSIN AVE # 411 53226 #056-06-1992 L1993 **AI IM** *020 †03,20

CHIU, Yvonne Efen. 9200 W WISCONSIN AVE, DEPARTMENT OF DERMATOLOGY 53226 #005-06-2006 L2007 **D** *012

CHO, Jung K. 5000 W NATIONAL AVE, VA HOSPITAL DEPT OF PSYCH 53295 #583-08-1966 L1976 **ADM P** *020 †55

CHO, Younghoon Ronald. 8700 W WATERTOWN PLANK RD, PLASTIC SURGERY DEPT 53226 #008-01-2003 L2004 **PS** *012

CHOI, Byung-Il. 9200 W WISCONSIN AVE, FROEDTERT HOSPITAL AND MCW 53226 #583-02-1965 L2004 **IM CD** *040 †20

CHOITHANI, Chanderbhan M. 9200 W WISCONSIN AVE, MEDICAL COLLEGE OF 53226 #495-17-1955 L1979 **U** *020 †95

CHOITHANI, Hansa G. 4359 S HOWELL AVE 53207 #496-38-1956 L1979 **OBG** *071 †30

CHOU, Clarence Paul. 9000 W WISCONSIN AVE 53226 #056-06-1977 L1978 **CHP P** *020 †75

CHOUDHURI, Indrajit. 3163A S 29TH ST 53215 #654-01-1999 L2008 **ICE** *012 †20

CHRISTENSEN, Richard H. 1515 N RIVERCENTER DR, PREFERRED PROVIDER OPTION 53212 #056-05-1969 L1976 **DR OS** *030 †80

CHRISTIANS, Kathleen Kay. 9200 W WISCONSIN AVE 53226 #018-03-1993 L1994 **GS CCS** *020 †85

CHRISTIANSON, John C. 2025 W OKLAHOMA AVE, STE 114 53215 #056-06-1983 L1986 **ID IM** *020 †20

CHRZAN, Donald John. 2900 W OKLAHOMA AVE 53215 #056-06-1957 L1965 **OTO PS** *071 †45

CHUA, Thomas Yu. 945 N 12TH ST, STE 1042 53233 #748-08-1970 L1977 **VS GS** *020 †85

CHUNG, Maurice W. 801 S 70TH ST 53214 #056-06-1984 L1985 **GE IM** *020 †20

CHUNG, Ui-Il. 4555 W SCHROEDER DR, STE 170 53223 #583-04-1967 L1975 **AN** *020 †05

CHUNG, William. 3201 S 16TH ST, SOUTH CENTER MEDICAL 53215 #005-14-1971 L1972 **IM** *020 †20

CHUNG, William W. 3201 S 16TH ST, SOUTH CENTER MEDICAL 53215 #583-04-1963 L1974 **IM** *020 †20

CHUSID, Michael Jos. 8701 W WATERTOWN PLANK RD, MACC FUND RESEARCH BLDG 53226 #008-01-1970 L1976 **ID PD** *030 †55,03

CIHLAR, Krista Louise. ■ 53213 #056-06-2004 L2005 **PTH** *012

CINQUEGRANI, Michael P. 9200 W WISCONSIN AVE, MED COLL OF WI 53226 #016-43-1978 L1985 **CD IC** *020 †20

CIRALSKY, Robert H. 3289 N MAYFAIR RD, MAYFAIR ROAD CLINIC 53222 #038-40-1969 L1978 **OTO** *020 †45

CLARK, Kenneth Edward. 2025 E NEWPORT AVE, WISCONSIN RADIOLOGY 53211 #056-05-1974 L1979 **DR** *020 †80

CLARKE, Shanelle Alicia. 9000 W WISCONSIN AVE, MS 681 53226 #056-05-2004 L2007 **CCP** *012 †55

CLAY, Leonard Kenneth. 9200 W WISCONSIN AVE, HOSP-GENERAL SURGERY 53226 #016-11-1994 L1996 **GS** *100

CLAY, Ross Lyman. 9200 W WISCONSIN AVE 53226 #026-04-1983 L1989 **OM** *020 †70

CLIFFORD, Richard M. 2400 S 90TH ST, RICHARD M CLIFFORD MD SC 53227 #056-06-1962 L1963 **OBG OS** *071 †30

CLINE, John Chas. 945 N 12TH ST, SINAI SAMARITAN MEDICAL CE 53233 #025-01-1989 L1996 **DR** *020 †80

CLINTON, Gerald La Verne. 2770 N 5TH ST, MILWAUKEE HEALTH SERVICE, 53212 #056-05-1957 L1958 **P** *071

CLOUD, Patrick Michael. 4555 W SCHROEDER DR, C/O KAY HANRAHAN 53223 #017-20-1999 L2003 **AN** *020 †05

CO, Dominic Oliverso. ■ 53226 #016-06-2006 L2008 **PD** *012

CO, Eddy Dronila. 3267 S 16TH ST STE 105 53215 #748-08-1966 L1976 **CD IM** *020 †20

CO, Jennifer Go. 9000 W WISCONSIN AVE MS 7 53226 #748-02-2001 L2003 **PDC** *012 †55

COBBS, Sarah B Williams. 2555 N DR MRTN LTHR KNG DR, CENTER 53212 #016-11-1973 L1998 **PD** *020 †55

CODY, Paula Jo. ■ 53226 #056-06-2007 **PD** *012

COE, Anthony. 756 N 35TH ST STE 202 53208 #748-01-1956 L1967 **PD** *071

COE, Maria Rita Yao. 756 N 35TH ST 53208 #748-01-1961 L1976 **FM** *071 †80

COHAN, Mary Elizabeth. 9200 W WISCONSIN AVE, FROEDTERT MEM LUTHRAN HOSPI 53226 #028-34-1984 L1985 **IMG IM** *020 †20

COHEN, Donald Jason. 6200 W BLUEMOUND RD 53233 #056-05-1956 L1957 **PD** *071 †55

COHEN, Eric Phin. 9200 W WISCONSIN AVE, HOSP 53226 #165-03-1980 L1987 **NEP IM** *020 †20

COHEN, Gary Allen. 8701 W WATERTOWN PLANK RD 53226 #056-06-1980 L1981 **PD** *020 †55

COHEN, Miriam Richter. 7080 N PT WASHINGTON RD, RHEUMATIC DISEASE CTR 53217 #021-01-1980 L1987 **RHU IM** *020 †20

COHEN, Norman Ervin. 735 W WISCONSIN AVE, EYE CARE SPECIALISTS SC 53233 #056-05-1969 L1970 **OPH** *020 †35

COHEN, Roger David. ■ 53202 #035-01-1963 L1971 **PDS TS** *071 †85,90

COHN, Jerry S. ■ 53211 #056-05-1976 L1990 **P** *020 †75

COKE, Helena Mary. 2555 N MARTIN LUTHR KNG DR, MILWAUKEE HEALTH SERVICES, 53212 #056-06-1991 L1996 **OBG** *020

COLEMAN, William A. ■ 53208 #409-21-1966 **PM** *020

COLES, Elliot L. 1218 W KILBOURN AVE, ELLIOT L COLES MD SC 53233 #023-07-1949 L1952 **ORS** *071 †40

COLINCO, Maelynn Dawn. 4555 W SCHROEDER DR, STE 170 53223 #056-06-1992 L1993 **AN** *020 †05

COLLIER, Bert David, Jr. 945 N 12TH ST 53233 #008-01-1974 L1980 **NM R** *062 †80,28

COLLIER, Shawna Renee. 8701 W WATERTOWN PLANK RD 53226 #018-03-2003 L2004 **OPH** *020

COLLINS, Ligeia Jamillah[1]. ■ 53206 #305-01-2006 **FP** *012

COLLINS, Michael Paul. 9200 W WISCONSIN AVE, NEUROLOGY DEPARTMENT 53226 #046-01-1986 L2002 **N** *020 †75

COLLIS-GEERS, Jane Marie. 10855 W PARK PL 53224 #056-06-1975 L1976 **OPH** *020 †35

COLLOPY, Michael Charles. 2801 W KINNICKINC RVR PKWY, STE 575 53215 #056-06-1963 L1966 **ORS** *071 †40

COMPTON, Ralph Theodore. 201 N MAYFAIR RD, MEDICAL EYE ASSOCIATES SC 53226 #038-40-1985 L1998 **OPH** *020 †35

CONLEY, Stephen Francis. 9200 W WISCONSIN AVE 53226 #048-04-1978 L1989 **OTO PD** *040 †55,45

CONNELLY, Jennifer Marie. 9200 W WISCONSIN AVE, FMLH - DEPT. OF NEUROLOGY 53226 #056-06-2003 L2004 **MN** *012

CONNOLLY, Lois Ann. 9200 W WISCONSIN AVE, DEPT OF ANESTHESIOLOGY 53226 #056-06-1984 L1985 **AN** *020 †05

CONNOR, Douglas James. ■ 53215 #056-06-2007 **MPD** *012

CONNOR, Thomas Byrne, Jr. 925 N 87TH ST 53226 #023-07-1988 L1994 **OPH** *020 †35

CONRAD, Edward Patrick. ■ 53202 #038-06-2006 L2006 **D** *012

CONRADSON, Eric Paul. 201 N MAYFAIR RD 53226 #016-06-1974 L1977 **IM** *020 †20

CONTI, Carolina Gueco. 2040 W WISCONSIN AVE # 50, CAROLINA G. CONTI, M.D., S 53233 #748-10-1993 L1999 **IM** *020 †20

COOGAN, Paul Jordan. 2400 W VILLARD AVE 53209 #016-42-1990 L1991 **EM** *020 †16

COOK, Craig Ralph. ■ 53242 #056-06-2008 *012

COOLEY, Ryan Lindsay. 2801 W KINNICKINC RVR PKWY, STE 777 53215 #056-05-1992 L1998 **ICE CD** *020 †20

COONEY, Edward. 11414 W PARK PL, SENSIA HEALTHCARE 53224 #016-11-1987 L1991 **IM** *020 †20

COOPER, Carroll Donell. 9200 W WISCONSIN AVE 53226 #001-02-2004 L2006 **PM** *012

COOPER, Philippe J. 10000 W BLUEMOUND RD 53226 #067-01-1986 L2001 **AN PMM** *020 †05 ‡

COOPER, Robert David. 7635 W OKLAHOMA AVE, STE 202 53219 #038-40-1984 L1989 **IM** *020 †20

COPE, James Wilburn, Jr. 8901 W LINCOLN AVE 53227 #023-01-1981 L1982 **FM** *020 †18,16

CORAN, David Lawrence. 2424 S 90TH ST, STE 418 53227 #025-01-1989 L1997 **OSS OP** *020 †40

CORAN, Judith Becker. 2424 S 90TH ST, RICHARD DAVENPORT MD & 53227 #056-05-1989 L1997 **OPH** *020 †35

CORBETT, Shaun Carsten. ■ 53202 #056-06-2008 *012

CORDEN, Timothy Evans. 9200 W WISCONSIN AVE, CHILDRENS HOSP OF WISC 53226 #025-07-1986 L1999 **CCP PD** *020 †55

CORNELL, Robert Franklin. ■ 53226 #016-06-2008 *012

CORNFIELD, Jerome R. 53209 #056-05-1951 L1952 **GP OS** *071

CORTES, Wilberto Gil. 4225 W HIGHLAND BLVD 53208 #042-02-2001 L2003 **PS** *100

CORTEZ, Edmundo Padilla. 9000 W WISCONSIN AVE, MS 681 53226 #016-43-1994 L1998 **CCP** *020 †55

CORY, David Wm. ■ 53211 #056-05-1991 L1992 **P** *020 †75

COSTA, Dennis James. 9200 W WISCONSIN AVE, IOWA METHODIST MEDICAL CEN 53226 #056-06-2001 L2006 **VS** *012

COSTELLO, Jill Catherine. 9200 W WISCONSIN AVE, DIVISION OF RHEUMATOLOGY-F 53226 #018-03-1999 L2000 **RHU** *020 †20

COTTRELL, Joseph James. 5000 W NATIONAL AVE, VA MED CTR 53295 #016-43-1975 L1976 **IM PUD** *071 †20

COUGHLAN, Michael Gerard. ■ 53213 #539-05-1982 L1992 **AN** *020 †05

COVERT, Douglas John. 925 N 87TH ST 53226 #036-01-2004 L2005 **OPH** *012

COX, Bart Leroy. 4448 W LOOMIS RD, STE 201 53220 #017-20-1986 L1987 **CD** *020 †20

COX, Matthew David. ■ 53202 #016-11-2006 **GS** *012

COX, Thomas John. 9233 N GREEN BAY RD 53209 #056-06-1954 L1955 **FM** *071 †18

CRAVEN, Ian Andrew. ■ 53222 #056-06-2008 *012

CREPEAU, Alexandra Susan. 3000 W MONTANA ST 53215 #305-01-2004 L2006 **OBG** *012

CRIMMINS, Curtis Allen. 575 W RIVER WOODS PKWY, STE 202 53212 #025-07-1988 L1994 **HS** *020 †65

CROMWELL, Charles Leon. 2311 N PROSPECT AVE, CSMCP PROSPECT MEDICAL COM 53211 #051-04-1969 L1976 **IM** *071

CRONIN, Mary E. 9200 W WISCONSIN AVE, RHEUMATOLOGY 53226 #016-43-1979 L1980 **RHU IM** *020 †20

CRONIN, Robert Patrick. 11716 W GREENFIELD AVE 53214 #033-05-1969 L1978 **R** *020 †80

CROUCH, John David. 2901 W KINNICKINC RVR PKWY, STE 310 53215 #016-45-1980 L1988 **TS TTS** *020 †85,90

CROWLEY, William J. 1428 N FARWELL AVE STE 210 53202 #056-06-1953 L1954 **P** *020

CRUIKSHANK, Dwight P, IV. 9200 W WISCONSIN AVE, FROEDTERT MEM LUTH OB-GYN 53226 #036-07-1969 L1991 **MFM OBG** *040 †30

CRUZ, Elizabeth Marie. 9200 W WISCONSIN AVE, DEPARTMENT OF MEDICINE 53226 #056-06-2005 L2006 **IM** *012

CRUZ, Samuel J. 5000 W NATIONAL AVE 53295 #275-01-1945 L1969 **GP** *100

CSUKA, M E. 9200 W WISCONSIN AVE, FMLH-EAST 53226 #035-09-1977 L1980 **RHU IMG** *020 †20

CUETO, Maximo L, Jr. 2745 W LAYTON AVE 53221 #748-08-1971 L1976 **P CHP** *020 †75

CUMMINGS, Patrick W, Jr. 7220 W NATIONAL AVE 53214 #020-02-1970 L1973 **ORS** *020 †40

CUMMINS, Frank E. 601 N 99TH ST, STE 304 53226 #017-20-1969 L1970 **CD IM** *020 †20

CUNNINGHAM, James Alan. 2801 W KINNICKINC RVR PKWY, STE 1030 53215 #056-06-1979 L1980 **GE IM** *020 †20

CUNNINGHAM, Lew S. MARQUETTE U SCH OF MED 53233 #040-02-1949 **OS** *040

CURLEY, Michael Edward. ■ 53213 #056-05-2007 **IM** *012

CURREY, Adam Douglas. 8701 W WATERTOWN PLANK RD, RADIATION ONCOLOGY DEPT. 53226 #056-06-2005 L2006 **RO** *012

CURTIN, John Joseph. ■ 53202 #539-02-1985 **R** *100

CUSICK, Joseph Francis. 9200 W WISCONSIN AVE 53226 #010-02-1965 L1974 **NS PMM** *020 †25

CUTTING, Harry Martin. ■ 53228 #056-06-1953 L1954 **GP** *071

DABBAGH-REHMERT, Nadira. ■ 53226 #409-37-1990 **AN** *100

DABROWSKI, Russell C. 1140 E BYWATER LN 53217 #024-05-1976 L1977 **CD IM** *020 †20

DAEMMRICH, Debra Marie. ■ 53219 #056-05-2008 *012

DAGAM, Shekhar Acharya. 2801 W KINNICKINC RVR PKWY, STE 570 53215 #010-01-1994 L2001 **NS** *020

DAGHER, Nabil. 1111 N ASTOR ST 53202 #056-06-2003 L2008 **GS** *012

DAHLGREN, Matthew Alan. 1684 N PROSPECT AVE, MILWAUKEE EYE CARE ASSOCIA 53202 #056-06-2001 L2006 **OPH** *020 †35

DALE, Kyle Laird. 2900 W OKLAHOMA AVE 53215 #024-34-2003 L2004 **DR** *012

DALEY, Roger Alan. 9200 W WISCONSIN AVE, MCM CLINICS FROEDTERT EA 53226 #035-06-1985 L1992 **ORS** *020 †40

DALL, Aaron Thomas. 9200 W WISCONSIN AVE, MEDICAL COLLEGE OF WISCONS 53226 #056-06-2002 L2004 **NEP** *012 †20

DALY, Mackenzie Duncan. 8701 W WATERTOWN PLANK RD, DEPT. OF RADIATION ONCOLOG 53226 #028-46-2005 L2006 **RO** *012

DAMITZ, Beth Anne. 2400 W VILLARD AVE, GLENDALE FCC 53209 #056-06-1996 L1998 **FM** *020 †18

D'ANDREA, Lynn Ann. 9000 W WISCONSIN AVE #777A, CHILDRENS HOSP OF WISC 53226 #056-06-1987 L1988 **PD PDP** *020 †55

DANGVU, Huong Van. 3003 W GOOD HOPE RD 53209 #025-07-1993 L1996 **IM** *020 †20

DANIEL, Alan. 2025 E NEWPORT AVE 53211 #024-01-1967 L1977 **IM CD** *071 †20

DANIELS, David Lee. 9200 W WISCONSIN AVE, FROEDTERT MEMORIAL LUTHHOS 53226 #016-11-1975 L1976 **DR** *020 †80

DANKLE, Steven Kie. 7220 W NATIONAL AVE 53214 #018-03-1982 L1987 **OTO HNS** *020 †45

DANNINGER, Carol Joyce D. 5000 W NATIONAL AVE, ZABLOCKI VA HOSPITAL 53295 #056-05-1972 L1973 **IM** *020 †20

DANTO-NOCTON, Ellen S. 9255 N 76TH ST 53223 #035-47-1987 L1994 **IMG IM** *020 †20

DAO, Marc Khacvinh. 2025 E NEWPORT AVE, RM 217 53211 #056-06-2002 L2005 **IM** *020 †20

DARAM, Sumanth Reddy. 5000 W CHAMBERS ST 53210 #495-21-1998 L2003 **IM** *020 †20

DARAMOLA, Opeyemi. ■ 53224 #026-04-2008 *012

DARIEN, Gholi Ghashghai. 788 N JEFFERSON ST, STE 300 53202 #056-06-1962 L1963 **IM OS** *020 †20

DARNELL, Kathryn Ann. MED COLL OF WISCONSIN 53233 #056-06-1979 *100

DARNIEDER, Michael Victor. 8535 W CAPITOL DR 53222 #056-06-1981 L1985 **OPH** *020 †35

DARR, Omar Jesse. 2025 E NEWPORT AVE 53211 #038-06-1997 L2003 **OSM** *020 †40

DAS, Dipan. 9200 W WISCONSIN AVE, MEDICAL COLLEGE OF WISCONS 53226 #495-37-2001 L2004 **GS** *012

DASKAL, Anatoliy. 4555 W SCHROEDER DR, STE 170 53223 #913-05-1977 L1998 **AN** *020 †05

DATKA, Gordon Leo. 5757 W OKLAHOMA AVE, STE 105 53219 #056-06-1963 L1964 **PD** *071 †55

DAVE, Heman Kirit. ■ 53221 #056-06-2007 **TY** *012

DAVENPORT, Richard Drake. 2424 S 90TH ST, RICHARD DAVENPORT MD & 53227 #041-02-1970 L1976 **OPH** *020 †20

DAVID, Alan Kent. 1155 N MAYFAIR RD 53226 #028-03-1971 L1998 **FM** *030 †18

DAVIDOFF, Donna Dee. 2323 N LAKE DR 53211 #056-06-1978 L1979 **PM OS** *020 †60 ‡

DAVIDS, Susan Lynn. 9200 W WISCONSIN AVE 53226 #056-05-1995 L1997 **IM** *020 †20

DAVIDSON, Arthur Jerome. 10000 W BLUEMOUND RD 53226 #016-11-1978 L1979 **AN** *020 †05

DAVIES, Glena O. 3289 N MAYFAIR RD, MAYFAIR ROAD CLINIC 53222 #610-01-1983 L1991 **PD** *020 †55

DAVIS, Elizabeth Ann. 2025 E NEWPORT AVE 53211 #020-02-1982 L1995 **PM** *020 †60

DAVIS, Hugh Lloyd. 9200 W WISCONSIN AVE, FMLH EAST 53226 #016-02-1954 L1967 **ON IM** *040 †20

DAVIS, Nancy Barrett. 9200 W WISCONSIN AVE FEC39 53226 #048-14-1997 L2003 **HO** *020 †20

DAVIS, Starkey Dee. 8701 W WATERTOWN PLANK RD, MED COL OF WISC/DEPT OF PE 53226 #048-04-1957 L1975 **ID PD** *030 †55

DAWSON, Michael John. 2424 S 90TH ST, STE 206 53227 #056-05-1984 L1985 **IM** *020 †20 ‡

DAYER, Anne M I. 10425 W NORTH AVE, STE 215 53226 #869-04-1977 L1989 **PTH PCP** *020 †50

DEAN, Alice Rogers. ■ 53233 #038-06-1962 L1966 **CHP** *071

DEAN, Larry Bryce. 3003 W GOOD HOPE RD, HOPE ROAD CLINIC 53209 #024-07-1974 L1975 **IM IMG** *020 †20

DEBBINK, Nancy L. 161 W WISCONSIN AVE, STE 5180 53203 #056-05-1993 L1994 **CHP** *020 †75

DEBEHNKE, Daniel James. 9200 W WISCONSIN AVE, FROEDTERT HOSPITAL EAST 53226 #056-05-1988 L1991 **EM** *020 †20

DE BOE, Frederick M, Jr. 1575 N RIVERCENTER DR, STE 112 53212 #016-06-1979 L1980 **FM** *020 †18 ‡

DE CARLO, John Dominic. 2500 N MAYFAIR RD 53226 #016-43-1974 L1978 **OPH** *020 †35

DECKARD, Jack H. 2025 E NEWPORT AVE # 140 53211 #017-20-1976 L1982 **NS** *020 †25

DECKER, Mark Henry. 1218 W KILBOURN AVE, STE 101 53233 #037-01-1984 L1985 **OBG** *020 †30

DEE, Thomas Herbert. 3237 S 16TH ST 53215 #030-06-1967 L1972 **IM OS** *040 †20

DEEKEN, Michael G. 1220 DEWEY AVE 53213 #056-06-1977 L1986 **P** *020 †75

DE FRANCO, Anthony Carl. 2801 W KK RIVER PKWY, STE 840 53215 #024-07-1985 L2008 **CD IM** *020 †20

DE FRANK, Michael Robert. 111 E WISCONSIN AVE, STE 2100 53202 #056-06-1996 L1999 **EM** *020 †16

DE GRANDVILLE, Konrad Wal. 3000 W MONTANA ST 53215 #759-06-2005 **FP** *012

DEIPARINE, Alfonso B, Jr. 945 N 12TH ST 53233 #748-01-1957 L1965 **PTH** *071 †50

DEISZ, Robert Jason. 9200 W WISCONSIN AVE, DEPARTMENT OF EMERGENCY ME 53226 #056-05-2005 L2007 **EM** *012

DE LA CRUZ, Marcos Martin. 2906 S 20TH ST 53215 #025-01-2004 L2006 **PD** *020 †55

DELAHUNT, Stephen Patrick. 2801 W KK RIVER PKWY, STE 355 53215 #056-06-1972 L1974 **OSS** *020 †18,40

DE LEO, Nicholas C. 5404 N LOVERS LANE RD 53225 #056-06-1952 L1954 **FM EM** *072 †18

DE LIA, Julian Emilio. 5000 W CHAMBERS ST 53210 #033-05-1972 L1991 **OBG** *020 †30

DEL TORO, David Ruben. 9200 W WISCONSIN AVE 53226 #017-20-1988 L1989 **PM** *020 †60

DEMARCO, Rebecca Ann. 1121 E NORTH AVE 53212 #056-06-2005 L2007 **FP** *012

DEMIDOVICH, Yulia M. 9000 W WISCONSIN AVE, MS 735 53226 #030-05-2000 L2004 **PAN** *040 †05

DEMIRCIOGLU, Ahmet Umit. 12232 W FLORIST AVE 53225 #902-05-1989 L2003 **IM** *020 †20

DEMIRCIOGLU, Reyhan. 1020 N 12TH ST, FL 2 53233 #902-18-1992 L2002 **IMG** *020 †20 ‡

DEMPSEY, Rania Louise. 1000 N 92ND ST 53226 #016-02-1996 L1999 **FSM** *020 †20

DENNIS, Niloufer Siddiqui. 945 N 12TH ST, AURORA SINAI MEDICAL CENTE 53233 #305-01-2002 L2007 **OBG** *100

DENNY, Arlen Dwight. 9200 W WISCONSIN AVE 53226 #026-04-1976 L1986 **PS GS** *020 †65

DENSMORE, Emily Myrick. 999 N 92ND ST 53226 #016-11-2000 L2002 **PD** *020 †55 ‡

DENSMORE, John C. 9000 W WISCONSIN AVE 53226 #016-11-2000 L2002 **PDS** *012 †85 ‡

DENSON, Steven. 9200 W WISCONSIN AVE, GENERAL INTERNAL MEDICINE 53226 #016-11-1997 L1998 **IMG** *100 †20

DENT, Chloe Melissa. 9200 W WISCONSIN AVE 53226 #038-06-2004 L2008 **AN** *012

DEOL, Mandeep Kaur. 3000 W MONTANA ST 53215 #305-01-2006 **FP** *012

DERENNE, Jennifer Lynn. ■ 53202 #056-05-2001 L2001 **CHP** *100

DERFUS, Beth Ann. 9200 W WISCONSIN AVE, MEDICAL COLL WI DIV RHEUM 53226 #023-07-1986 L1991 **RHU** *050 †20

DERUS, Kevin Gerald. 945 N 12TH ST, AURORA SINAI MED CTR 53233 #056-06-1982 L1985 **EM** *020 †16

DESAI, Heena Yogendra. PO BOX 1997, DEPT OF PHYSCHIATRY 53201 #016-11-2003 L2008 **P** *012

DESAI, Shobha Paresh. 2025 E NEWPORT AVE, WISCONSIN RADIOLOGY 53211 #495-01-1983 L1991 **DR** *020 †20

DESHMUKH, Abhishek Jay. ■ 53226 #496-49-2004 *100

DESHPANDE, Sanjay S. 2015 E NEWPORT AVE, STE 703 53211 #496-38-1982 L1990 **CD IM** *020 †20

DESHUR, William Ralph. 2801 W KINNICKINC RVR PKWY, STE 330 53215 #056-05-1975 L1980 **GS VS** *020 †85

DESTINO, Lauren Ann. 1812 E LAFAYETTE PL # 303 53202 #016-06-2004 L2005 **PD** *100 †55

DEVCIC, Ante. 8901 W LINCOLN AVE, CONSULTANTS AT WEST ALLIS 53227 #957-01-1982 L1989 **IM** *020 †05

DEVERA HERNANDEZ, Lyndon. 2801 W KINNICKINC RVR PKWY, STE 1030 53215 #748-01-1990 L1993 **GE** *020 †20

DEWALL, Jeremy Scott. ■ 53214 #056-06-2007 **EM** *012

DEWIRE, Douglas Michael. 2015 E NEWPORT AVE, STE 707 53211 #017-20-1987 L1988 **U** *020 †95

DHALA, Anwer Ali. 2801 W KINNICKINC RVR PKWY, STE 777 53215 #495-04-1979 L1990 **CD IM** *020 †20

DHAMEE, Mohammed Saeed. 9200 W WISCONSIN AVE, DEPT ANESTH E FRMH 53226 #704-02-1960 L1976 **AN** *020 †05

DHESI, Satvinder Singh. 4131 W LOOMIS RD, STE 300 53221 #016-11-1994 L2007 **APM** *020 †05

DHIR, Sumer Kumar. 2801 W KINNICKINC RVR PKWY, PARKWAY SUITE 777 53215 #495-45-1994 L2006 **ICE** *100 †20 ‡

DIAMOND, Leon. ■ 53202 #020-02-1946 L1947 **P** *030 †75

DIAZ, Christina Doris. 9200 W WISCONSIN AVE, DEPT OF ANESTHESIOLOGY 53226 #048-04-2003 L2004 **AN** *020

DIAZ, Santo De Jesus. 2900 W OKLAHOMA AVE 53215 #018-03-1980 L1985 **IM CCM** *020 †20

DICK, Carol Ann W. 5423 W HEMLOCK RD 53223 #056-06-1960 L1961 **PHP GP** *020

DIEHR, Sabina. 8701 W WATERTOWN PLANK RD, MED. COLLEGE OF WISCONSIN 53226 #041-13-1988 L1991 **FM** *020 †18

DIETERLE, Carl Herbert. 7205 N BARNETT LN 53217 #035-20-1963 L1969 **ORS OS** *071 †40

DIGILIO, William Francis. 9233 N GREEN BAY RD 53209 #016-01-1986 L1987 **GS** *020 †85

DIKSHIT, Kalpana. 8430 W CAPITOL DR 53222 #496-07-1990 L1996 **IM** *020 †20

DILLIG, Katherine Mary. ■ 53211 #056-06-1984 L1985 **EM** *020 †20

DILLON, David Andrew. ■ 53211 #056-06-1973 L1974 **N** *020

DIMITROV, Rosen Kirilov. 9200 W WISCONSIN AVE 53226 #198-01-1990 L2003 **PCP** *100 †50

DINCER, Huseyin Erhan. 9200 W WISCONSIN AVE, MEDICAL COLLEGE OF WISCONS 53226 #902-07-1992 L2001 **PCC** *100 †20

DINDZANS, Linda J Coffman. 8532 W CAPITOL DR 53222 #067-01-1980 L1990 **OTO PDO** *020 †45

DINDZANS, Vincents James. 2350 N LAKE DR, STE 303 53211 #067-01-1980 L1990 **GE** *020 †20

DINH, Nguyet-Nga Thi. 8701 W WATERTOWN PLANK RD, MED COLL OF WI 53226 #030-05-2007 **PD** *012

DI ULIO, Robert Anthony. 2801 W KINNICKINC RVR PKWY, STE 575 53215 #056-06-1972 L1973 **ORS** *020 †40

DIVGI, Ajit B. 2900 W OKLAHOMA AVE 53215 #495-17-1969 L1978 **ON HEM** *020 †20

DOBBS, June Milne. ■ 53211 #803-01-1951 L1965 **PD** *071 †55

DOBBS, Karen Elizabeth. 8905 W LINCOLN AVE, STE 501 53227 #056-06-1988 L1989 **OBG** *020 †30

DOBMEYER, Kathryn Marie. 9200 W WISCONSIN AVE, ASST PROF OF MED/GERIATRIC 53226 #028-34-1996 L1997 **IMG** *040 †20

DOERMANN, Andreas. 2015 E NEWPORT AVE 53211 #056-05-1981 L1988 **PS** *020 †85,65

DOGRA, Anil. 2323 N LAKE DR, ST MARY'S HOSPITAL 53211 #496-09-1981 L1997 **AN PME** *020 †05

DOLAN, James Dominick. 8905 W LINCOLN AVE, STE 515 53227 #539-05-1973 L1976 **OBG** *020 †20

DOLAN, Stephen. 9200 W WISCONSIN AVE, MDCL CLLGE CLNCS AT FRDTRT 53226 #010-01-1988 L1998 **CCM** *020 †20

D'OLHABERRIAGUE, Luis. 730 N PLANKINTON AVE 53203 #847-04-1983 **CN** *020

DOLINSKI, Sylvia Yvonne. 9200 W WISCONSIN AVE, DEPT OF ANESTHESIOLGY 53226 #056-05-1988 L1990 **AN CCA** *020 †05,20

DOMINGO, Angela Fagela. 9200 W WISCONSIN AVE, DEPT OF INTERNAL MEDICINE 53226 #748-02-2001 L2004 **IM** *100 †20

DONATELLO, Steven James. 2323 N LAKE DR, ST MARYS HOSPITAL-MILW 53211 #056-05-1991 L1996 **PME AN** *020 †05

DONNELL, Robert Francis. 9200 W WISCONSIN AVE, MEDICAL COLLEGE OF 53226 #056-05-1987 L1988 **U** *020 †95

DONOHOE, Christopher. 3522 W LISBON AVE, LISBON AVENUE HEALTH CENTE 53208 #016-06-2001 L2004 **PD** *020 †55

DONOVAN, Murray Sean. 2025 E NEWPORT AVE, WISCONSIN RADIOLOGY 53211 #023-12-1989 L1990 **DR** *020 †20

DOOLEY, John Edward. 10400 W NORTH AVE, SUUITE 445 53226 #056-06-1954 L1962 **GE IM** *071 †20

DOOS, Wilhelm Gustav. 2900 W OKLAHOMA AVE, DEPT LABORATORY MEDICINE 53215 #056-05-1970 L1989 **PTH OS** *020 †50

DOPPALAPUDI, Anil Vamsi. ■ 53226 #495-73-2003 L2005 **IM** *100 †20

DORN, Eric Menzner. 2025 E NEWPORT AVE, WISCONSIN RADIOLOGY 53211 #056-06-1996 L2000 **DR** *020 †80

DOUROS, Demetrios J. 9200 W WISCONSIN AVE, MED COLL OF WISCONSIN 53226 #016-11-2007 **ORS** *012

DOWNEY, Francis Xavier. 2015 E NEWPORT AVE, STE 208 53211 #038-43-1986 L1993 **TS TTS** *020 †85,90

DOYLE, Maryam M. 7007 N RANGE LINE RD, NORTH SHORE SURGI CENTER 53209 #056-06-1987 L1989 **AN** *020 †05

DRAKE, Linda Florine. 1555 S LAYTON BLVD 53215 #056-05-1982 L1987 **IM** *020 †20

DRALLE, William G. 4448 W LOOMIS RD STE 100 53220 #308-11-1985 L1986 **FM FPG** *020 †18 ‡

DRAYNA, Patrick Christoph. ■ 53208 #056-05-2006 L2008 **PD** *012

DREHOBL, Kristina Ann. 555 W LAYTON AVE, STE 390 53207 #038-41-1993 L1994 **FM** *020 †18

DRESSLER, Joachim A W. ■ 53217 #407-32-1947 L1970 **PTH CLP** *071 †50

DREXLER, Catherine M. 2323 N LAKE DR, ST MARYS HOSPITAL 53211 #056-06-1995 L1996 **AN** *020 †05

DRISCOLL, Thomas Paul. 5000 W CHAMBERS ST 53210 #056-06-1969 L1973 **IM END** *030 †20

DROBNY, Elaine Claire. 788 N JEFFERSON ST, STE 300 53202 #003-01-1977 L1983 **END IM** *020 †20

DROBYSKI, William Raymond. 9200 W WISCONSIN AVE, MDCL CLLGE CLNCS AT FRDTRT 53226 #035-45-1983 L1988 **HEM IM** *020 †20

DROLET, Beth Ann. 9200 W WISCONSIN AVE 53226 #016-43-1991 L1994 **D** *020 †15

DRUKER, Robert Henry. 2577 N DOWNER AVE, STE 215 53211 #016-11-1985 L1986 **P** *020 †75

DRURY, David Lee. 215 N 35TH ST, CONCENTRA MED CTRS 53208 #056-06-1985 L1992 **OM** *020 †70

DRVARIC, Emil Jos. ■ 53215 #024-01-1953 L1958 **OBG** *071 †30

DUA, Kulwinder Singh. 9200 W WISCONSIN AVE, FROEDTERT MEM LUTH HOSP 53226 #495-19-1978 L1992 *020 †20

DUBIN, Lawrence Mark. 10919 W BLUEMOUND RD 53226 #056-06-1982 L1987 **DR RNR** *020 †80

DUBNER, Howard Niles. 2025 E NEWPORT AVE, STE 1000 53211 #016-11-1969 L1972 **ON HO** *020 †20

DUBOIS, Melissa Sue Hoffm. ■ 53210 #016-11-2004 L2005 **DR** *012

DUBRY, Seth Marion. 2801 W KINNICKINC RVR PKWY, STE 250 53215 #003-01-1993 L2000 **FM** *020 †18

DUCHOWSKA, Helena Liliana. 9000 W WISCONSIN AVE 53226 #759-03-1957 L1992 **FM GP** *020

DU CLOUX, Harold P, Jr. 945 N 12TH ST, EMPEC 53233 #001-06-1978 L2008 **FM** *040 †18 ‡

DUCREST, Antoinette Marie. 9455 W WATERTOWN PLANK RD, MILWAUKEE COUNTY MENTAL HE 53226 #043-01-1988 L2003 **P** *020 †75

DUEKER, David Kenneth. 925 N 87TH ST 53226 #008-01-1970 L2006 **OPH** *020 †35

DUFFIE, Meghan Russell. ■ 53202 #010-01-2007 **FP** *012

DUFFY, Daniel Patrick. 2400 W VILLARD AVE 53209 #030-06-1987 L1988 **FM** *020 †18

DUKE, Rebecca Lynn. 9200 W WISCONSIN AVE, DEPT. OF OTOLARYNGOLOGY 53226 #016-43-2001 L2003 **OTO** *100 †45

DUNCAN-WIEBE, Greta Lynn. 9200 W WISCONSIN AVE, DEPT. OF ANESTHESIOLOGY 53226 #030-05-2002 L2004 **PAN** *100 †05

DUNEK, Tracie M. 2801 W KK RIVER PKWY 53215 #016-76-2005, ▲ L2006 **FP** *012

DUNIGAN, Thomas H. 9000 W WISCONSIN AVE 53226 #056-06-1978 L1979 **PD** *030 †55

DUNN, David Kircher. 324 E WISCONSIN AVE 53202 #056-05-1961 L1963 **NS PD** *020 †25

DUNN, James Charles. 9200 W WISCONSIN AVE, WISC-FROEDTERT HOS 53226 #038-41-2001 L2003 **DR** *100 †20

DUNN, John Matthew. 1032 S 16TH ST, SIXTEENTH STREET COMM HLTH 53204 #056-06-1990 L1994 **PD** *020 †20

DUNN, Margaret M. 1032 S CESAR E CHAVEZ DR, SIXTEENTH COMMUNITY 53204 #056-05-1994 L1995 **FM** *020 †18

DUNN, Michael John. 8701 W WATERTOWN PLANK RD, OFFICE OF THE DEAN 53226 #056-06-1962 L1995 **IM NEP** *020 †20

DUNN, Noelle Christine. 555 W LAYTON AVE, STE 390 53207 #056-06-1995 L1996 **FM** *020 †18

DUQUESNOY, Rudolf. 9233 N GREEN BAY RD, GLENDALE CLINIC 53209 #660-06-1973 L1976 **PD** *020 †55

DURGA, Anita. ■ 53202 #018-75-2002, ▲ L2006 **PM** *012 †20

DURKEE, Charles Thos. 9200 WISCONSIN AVE, MEDICAL COLLEGE OF 53226 #017-20-1975 L1977 **U UP** *020 †95

DURKIN, Eugene C. ■ 53202 #035-03-1978 L1981 **AN** *020 †05

DURKIN, Gretchen. 2315 N LAKE DR, STE 1005 53211 #017-20-1981 L1982 **OTO** *020 †45

DURRANT, Julia Christine. 9200 W WISCONSIN AVE, DEPARTMENT OF NEUROLOGY 53226 #049-01-2006 L2008 **MN** *012

DURST, Milo Gerald. 2600 N MAYFAIR RD, STE 650 53226 #026-04-1976 L1977 **P** *030 †75

DUTHIE, Edmund H, Jr. VAMC MILWAUKEE 53295 #010-02-1976 L1977 **IMG IM** *020 †20

DU VALL, Dorothy Valaire. ■ 53214 #041-07-1945 1972 **P** *071

DVORACEK, Francine L. 2323 N LAKE DR 53211 #056-06-1980 L1981 **OBG** *020 †30

DWARAKANATH, Kishan. ■ 53220 #422-01-2006 **AN** *012

DYSART, Amy Rodriguez. 2457 N MAYFAIR RD, MILWAUKEE OB GYN SC 53226 #016-43-2000 L2001 **OBG** *020

DZELZKALNS, Ray Robt. 2025 E NEWPORT AVE 53211 #056-06-1981 L1985 **AN PTH** *030 †05

DZWIERZYNSKI, William W. 8700 W WATERTOWN PLANK RD, DEPT OF PLASTIC SURG 53226 #016-42-1984 L1991 **PS HS** *020 †85,65

EAPEN, Mary. 8701 W WATERTOWN PLANK RD 53226 #690-03-1986 L2000 **PHO** *020 †55

EARING, Michael Gaylord. 9200 W WISCONSIN AVE, CHILDREN'S HOSPITAL OF WIS 53226 #016-01-1997 L2003 **PDC CD** *040 †20,55

EARLE, Sandra Hurlbut. 2350 N LAKE DR, STE 500 53211 #016-01-1983 L1987 **OBG** *020 †30

EASOM, Harry August. 377 W RIVER WOODS PKWY, STE 100 53212 #025-01-1958 L1962 **OPH** *020 †35

EBEL, Rachel Heather. ■ 53212 #305-01-2006 L2008 **GS** *012

EBERT, Thomas Jay. ■ 53217 #056-06-1983 L1984 **AN** *020 †05

EDALATPOUR, Mehran. 2025 E NEWPORT AVE, COLUMBIA HOSPITAL 53211 #305-01-1989 L1992 **IM** *020 †20

EDDU, Ganiu Abimbola. ■ 53218 #016-11-2005 L2007 **AN** *012

EDLEBECK, Anna Borisovna. 3000 W MONTANA ST 53215 #913-39-1995 L2006 **IM** *012

EDMONDS, Jason Nathaniel. ■ 53202 #028-03-2008 *012

EDWARDS, Kevin Brian. 500 N 19TH ST, SAMI 53233 #018-03-1990 L1991 **PTH OS** *062 †50

EDWARDS, Margaret Dulles. ■ 53233 #025-07-1977 L1978 **PD** *074 †55

EDWARDS, Robb Alan. ■ 53222 #056-06-2006 **GS** *012

EFEMINI, Ese Paul. 9200 W WISCONSIN AVE 53226 #016-11-2006 L2008 **OBG** *012

EGAN, John Craig. 999 N 92ND ST, STE C320 53226 #016-43-1995 L2006 **PDS** *012 †85

EGGE, Beret Ann. ■ 53222 #056-06-2008 *012

EHLERT, Carey Ann. 8701 W WATERTOWN PLANK RD, ED COLL OF WI 53226 #030-05-1997 L2000 **NPM** *020 †55

EHRHARDT, Matthew James. ■ 53222 #016-11-2007 **MPD** *012

EHRMAN, Wendi Gay. 1020 N 12TH ST, HEALTH CE 53233 #056-06-1988 L1993 **ADL PD** *040 †55

EISENBERG, Carl Spencer. 2025 E NEWPORT AVE 53211 #036-07-1968 L1972 **PD PN** *020 †55

EISENSTEIN, Reuben. 945 N 12TH ST 53233 #021-05-1953 L1980 **PTH** *030 †50

EKBOM, Gregory Alan. 10400 W NORTH AVE, STE 480 53226 #026-04-1975 L1976 **GS** *020 †85

EL AMM, Christian Albert. 9000 W WISCONSIN AVE, CRANIFOFACIAL OFFICES 53226 #605-02-1995 L2003 **GS** *012

ELANGOVAN, Rakki Goundan. ■ 53217 #495-04-1969 L1976 **AN** *020 †05

ELBICH, Jeffrey David. ■ 53222 #016-42-2007 **IM** *012

EL-GHARBAWY, Areeg H. 8701 W WATERTOWN PLANK RD, MEDICAL COLLEGE OF WISCONS 53226 #915-02-1989 L1999 **MG** *100 †20,19 ‡

ELLINAS, Elizabeth H. 5000 W CHAMBERS ST, DEPT OF OB ANESTHESIA 53210 #016-02-1992 L1999 **AN** *020 †05

ELLINAS, Herodotos. 9200 W WISCONSIN AVE 53226 #016-02-1992 L1999 **AN** *012 †55,20

ELLIOTT, William C, Jr. 2901 W KINNICKINC RVR PKWY, STE 405 53215 #017-20-1984 L1985 **NEP** *020 †20

ELLIS, Mary Kathryn. 2900 W OKLAHOMA AVE, FL 1 53215 #056-06-1995 L1998 **PCC EP** *020 †20

ELNAGAR, Elwaleed. ■ 53215 #848-01-1998 **IM** *012

EL RAMAH, Mohsen Mahmoud. 3000 W MONTANA ST 53215 #915-02-2001 **IM** *012

ELSON, Mark A. 945 N 12TH ST 53233 #024-05-1980 L1984 **DR** *020 †80

EMMERICH, Kate Marie. ■ 53228 #016-45-2007 **FP** *012

EMRAN, Muhammad. 2801 W KK RIVER PKWY # 175, ST LUKES MEDICAL CENTER 53215 #665-01-2005 L2006 **FP** *012

ENGBRING, Norman H. ■ 53213 #056-06-1951 L1952 **END IM** *071 †20

ENGLISH, Rachel Allen. 3237 S 16TH ST 53215 #056-06-1990 L1991 **EM FM** *020 †18

ENRIQUEZ, Francisco J. 1032 S CESAR E CHAVEZ DR 53204 #429-01-1993 L1998 **PD** *020 †55 ‡

ENTRESS, Jeffrey Jay. 8700 W WISCONSN AVE #ANEST 53226 #056-06-1982 L1983 **AN** *020 †05

EPPERSON, Keith Dallas. 2323 N LAKE DR, ST MARYS HOSPITAL 53211 #016-06-1947 L1950 **DR RO** *020

ERDMANN, Kenneth J. 1220 DEWEY AVE 53213 #308-07-1982 L1984 **P GP** *020 †75

ERDMANN, Michael David. VA MED CTR 5000 W NAT'L 53295 #056-05-1983 L1984 **IM ID** *030 †20

ERICKSON, Beth Ann. 8700 W WISCONSIN AVE 53226 #056-06-1984 L1985 **RO** *020 †80

ERICKSON, Eric Matthew. 9200 W WISCONSIN AVE, DEPT RADIOLOGY 53226 #016-42-2003 L2005 **DR** *012

ERICKSON, Marc Thos. ■ 53209 #054-04-1966 L1968 **EM** *072

ERLINDER, Kevin Douglas. 8901 W LINCOLN AVE, CONSULTANTS AT WEST ALLIS 53227 #056-06-2000 L2001 **AN** *020 †05 ‡

ESHOA, Camellia. 2025 E NEWPORT AVE, COLUMBIA HOSP-PATH DEPT 53211 #875-02-1989 L1995 **PTH HMP** *020 †50

ESKINDER, Hanna. 945 N 12TH ST 53233 #056-06-1995 L1996 **PM** *020 †60

ESPEJO, Evalynne J. 3237 S 16TH ST, ST FRANCIS HOSPITAL 53215 #748-01-1985 L2000 **HMP** *020 †50

ESSER, Jerome Anthony. 3040 N 117TH ST, STE 100 53222 #056-06-1995 L1996 **PD** *020 †55

ESSER, John H. ■ 53217 #016-06-1951 L1951 **IM** *071

ESTERLY, Nancy Burton. 9200 W WISCONSIN AVE 53226 #023-07-1960 L1987 **D PD** *071 †55,15

ETHINGTON, James Edward. 2424 S 90TH ST, STE 206 53227 #016-43-1974 L1979 **DS D** *020 †15

ETIM, Ann Ekaetepat. ■ 53209 #056-06-2008 *012

ETINGEN, Margarita Lazare. 3000 W MONTANA ST 53215 #913-99-1992 L2006 **IM** *012

EVANICH, Christopher J. 2801 W KINNICKINC RVR PKWY, STE 575 53215 #056-06-1990 L1991 **OAR** *020 †40

EVANS, Richard Neal. 2266 N PROSPECT AVE, STE 518 53202 #047-07-1976 L1984 **GS VS** *020 †85

EVANS, Wayne. 950 N 12TH ST, CENTER OB 53233 #038-43-1981 L1985 **OBG** *020 †30

EVERSMAN, John Jos. 8701 W WATERTOWN PLANK RD, MED COLLEGE OF WISCONSON 53226 #018-03-1960 L1993 **IM END** *072 ‡20

EVERTON, Jennifer Lee. 8701 W WATERTOWN PLANK RD, MED COLL OF WI AFFIL HOSP 53226 #018-75-2006, ▲ L2008 **IM** *012

EWING, Mike James. 2266 N PROSPECT AVE, STE 608 53202 #035-45-1985 L1986 **P** *020 †75

EXTEN, Emily Louise. ■ 53222 #038-45-2007 **ORS** *012

FABRIC, Kenneth Stuart. 5150 N PORT WASHINGTON RD, STE 251 53217 #056-06-1967 L1968 **OPH** *020 †35

FABRIZIO, Matthew Joseph. ■ 53202 #016-11-2007 **TY** *012

FAHEY, John Jos. 201 N MAYFAIR RD 53226 #056-06-1981 L1982 **RHU IM** *020 †20

FAIRCHILD, Ralph B, III. 2900 W OKLAHOMA AVE, FL 5 53215 #048-14-1981 L2000 **GS CCS** *020 †85

FAIT, Gary Paul. 6200 W BLUEMOUND RD 53213 #056-06-1984 L1988 **OBG** *020 †30

FAIT, Jeffrey Scott. 8701 W WATERTOWN PLANK RD, DEPARTMENT OF PSYCHIATRY 53226 #056-06-2001 L2003 **PFP** *020

FALCI, Lori Ann. 6200 W BLUEMOUND RD 53213 #026-04-1999 L2000 **PD** *020 †55

FALENDER, Michael Jay. 8901 W LINCOLN AVE, CONSULTANTS AT WEST ALLIS 53227 #017-20-1996 L2001 **AN** *010 †05

FANGMAN, John Josephwill. 9200 W WISCONSIN AVE, STE 5500 53226 #026-04-1994 L2005 **ID PD** *020 †20,55

FANNING, Jeffrey John. 9000 W WISCONSIN AVE, CRITICAL CARE OFFICE 53226 #039-01-2003 L2005 **CCP** *012

FARBER, Neil Elliott. 9000 W WISCONSIN AVE, CHILDREN'S HOSPITAL OF WI 53226 #056-06-1990 L1991 **AN** *020 †05

FAREED, Mohammad N. 8430 W CAPITOL DR 53222 #704-09-1980 L1996 **IM** *020 †20

FARRELL, Michael Henry. 1155 N MAYFAIR RD 53226 #028-34-1993 L2004 **MPD OS** *050 †20,55

FATHKE, Carrie. 8701 W WATERTOWN PLANK RD, MED COLL OF WI 53226 #054-04-2007 **PD** *012

FAUST, Deidre Leigh. 1155 N MAYFAIR RD 53226 #056-06-2001 L2002 **IM** *020

FEDDERLY, Raymond Todd. 9000 W WISCONSIN AVE # 713, CHILDRENS HOSP WI HRT CTR 53226 #056-05-1988 L1991 **PDC** *020 †55

FEENEY, James Michael. 9200 W WISCONSIN AVE, & CRITICAL CARE 53226 #032-01-2000 L2006 **CCS** *020 †85

FEIGES, Lewis Michael. 2900 W OKLAHOMA AVE 53215 #056-05-1961 L1962 **IM** *020

FEIRING, Andrew Jonathan. 2015 E NEWPORT AVE, STE 600 53211 #035-47-1978 L1979 **CD IM** *020 †20

FELIZMENA, Renato C. 3237 S 16TH ST, ST FRANCIS HOSPITAL 53215 #748-01-1954 L1969 **AN** *071

FELSENTHAL, Susan. 544 E OGDEN AVE, STE 700 53202 #016-42-1977 L2004 **IM** *020 †20

FELSHEIM, Gregory Alan. 10000 W BLUEMOUND RD 53226 #056-05-1982 L1986 **AN** *020 †05

FENSKE, Lucinda Kaye. 2350 N LAKE DR, STE 502 53211 #017-20-1984 L1986 **OBG** *020 †30

FENSKE, Thomas Gerald. 2801 W KINNICKINC RVR PKWY, STE 925 53215 #056-06-1990 L1991 **CD** *020 †20

FENSKE, Timothy Sean. 9200 W WISCONSIN AVE, NEOPLASTIC DISEASES 53226 #056-05-1999 L2000 **HO** *100 †20

FERBER, David Andrew. 10425 W NORTH AVE, STE 215 53226 #056-05-1992 L1993 **PTH** *020 †50

FERGUSON, Anthony Arlo. 3970 N OAKLAND AVE, STE 300 53211 #024-07-1994 L1995 **ORS** *020 †40

FERGUSON, Daniel Kenneth. 735 W WISCONSIN AVE, EYE CARE SPECIALISTS SC 53233 #056-05-2001 L2005 **OPH** *020 †35

FERNANDES, Vanessa Caesar. 3070 N 51ST ST, STE 510 53210 #495-17-1993 L2005 **FM** *100

FERREIRA, Joao Paulo Albu. 8701 W WATERTOWN PLANK RD 53226 #187-01-2003 L2007 **IM** *012

FERRER, Modesonsamu Banez. ■ 53202 #056-06-2004 L2006 **PTH** *012

FERRON, Robin R. 5301 W CAPITOL DR, MILWAUKEE COMMUNITY MED. C 53216 #056-06-1983 L1984 **AN** *020

FETHERSTON, Michael P. 9233 N GREEN BAY RD 53209 #056-06-1977 L1978 **FM** *020 †18

FETTER, Victoria Lewin. 2040 W WISCONSIN AVE # 515 53233 #165-01-1966 L1968 **P PM** *020

FEUERSTEIN, Carol Ann. 7878 N 76TH ST, NORTHWEST CLINIC 53223 #025-12-1988 L1989 **FM** *020 †18

FICKEL, Holly Anne. ■ 53226 #030-06-1995 **PTH** *100

FICKEL, Karen Louise. 840 N 87TH ST 53226 #018-03-1998 L1999 **IM** *020 †20

FIELD, Brenton H, Jr. 3003 W GOOD HOPE RD 53209 #016-06-1965 L1972 **IM OS** *020 †20

FILMANOWICZ, Edward V, Jr. 10400 W NORTH AVE, STE 440 53226 #016-02-1961 L1964 **ON HEM** *071 †20

FINDLAY, William Adolphus. 11101 W LINCOLN AVE, ROGERS HOSPITAL 53227 #016-11-1997 L1999 **CHP** *100 †75

FINDLING, James Wayne, Jr. 2801 W KINNICKINC RVR PKWY 53215 #016-06-1975 L1976 **END DIA** *020 †20

FINE, Stuart Wolfe. 2801 W KINNICKINNIC PKWY, STE 370 53215 #020-02-1963 L1964 **U** *020 †95

FINGER, William A. 9200 W WISCONSIN AVE, FROEDTERT HOSP RAD DEPT 53226 #056-06-1956 L1957 **DR** *020 †80

FINK, Jordan Norman. 9000 W WISCONSIN AVE, STE 411 53226 #056-05-1959 L1960 **AI IM** *020 †20,03

FINKLE, David Meyer. ■ 53202 #016-06-2007 **EM** *012

FINLAYSON, William E. 945 N 12TH ST 53233 #047-07-1953 L1958 **OBG** *020 †30

FINNEY, Roger. 5000 W CHAMBERS ST, DEPT OF RAD THERPY 53210 #917-23-1944 L1977 **RO** *020

FIRCHAU, Dennis John. ■ 53202 #025-07-2004 L2005 **PTH** *012

FISCHER, Brian Anthony. 8701 W WATERTOWN PLANK RD, DEPT OF NEUROSURGERY 53226 #016-01-2003 L2004 **AN** *012

FISCHER, Donald Chas. 1522 N PROSPECT AVE, UNIT 1403 53202 #056-05-1977 L1979 **P** *020

FISCHER-WILLIAMS, M. ■ 53211 #803-09-1947 L1968 **OS N** *072

FISH, Robert Isaac. ■ 53204 #017-20-2005 L2006 **OPH** *012

FISHER, Richard Michael. 3238 S 16TH ST 53215 #056-05-1985 L1986 **FM** *020 †18

FISHER, Travis Jeron. 8701 W WATERTOWN PLANK RD 53226 #056-06-2006 L2008 **P** *012

FISHMAN, Paul Alan. 2025 E NEWPORT AVE, WISCONSIN RADIOLOGY 53211 #018-03-1974 L1978 **R DR** *062 †80

FITZSIMMONS, Brian-Fred M. 9200 W WISCONSIN AVE, FROEDTERT MEMORIAL LUTHERA 53226 #011-03-1996 L1998 **N** *020 †75

FIXMER, Jared Michael. ■ 53226 #056-06-2008 *012

FLANARY, Lawrence Michael. 10425 W NORTH AVE, LAWRENCE M FLANARY MD SC 53233 #056-06-1956 L1961 **OTO** *020 †45

FLATLEY, Thomas Jos. 9200 W WISCONSIN AVE, DEPT OF ORTHO 53226 #056-06-1959 L1960 **ORS** *020 †40

FLEJSIEROWICZ, Magdalena. 2901 W KINNICKINC RVR PKWY 53215 #759-04-1992 L1997 **HO** *020 †20

FLEMING, Catherine Anne. ■ 53211 #539-04-1990 L1993 **IM** *020 †20

FLEMING, Matthew Gray. 9200 W WISCONSIN AVE 53226 #035-08-1982 L1994 **D DMP** *020 †15

FLETCHER, Kathlyn Emma. 9200 W WISCONSIN AVE 53226 #016-02-1996 L2003 **IM** *020 †20

FLEWELLING, Daniel Thacke. ■ 53202 #025-01-2007 **U** *012

FLICKINGER, Roger R, Jr. 201 N MAYFAIR RD, MEDICAL EYE ASSOCIATES SC 53226 #018-03-1964 L1971 **OPH** *030 †35 ‡

FLOOD, Robert Emmet. 9233 N GREEN BAY RD 53209 #056-06-1946 L1947 **GP** *020

FLOOD, Veronica Heather. 8701 W WATERTOWN PLANK RD, SECTION OF HEMATOLOGY/ONCO 53226 #024-07-1999 L2006 **PHO** *100 †55

FLORCZAK, Jonathan W. 9200 W WISCONSIN AVE, DEPARTMENT OF 53226 #017-20-2001 L2006 **N** *100 †75

FLUGSTAD, Nicholas Adam. ■ 53222 #056-06-2008 *012

FOERSTER, Harry Robt, Jr. ■ 53217 #056-06-1948 L1951 **D** *071 †15

FOIL, Jason Eugene. ■ 53222 #028-03-2008 *012

FOLEY, David V. 5000 W CHAMBERS ST 53210 #056-06-1952 L1953 **ON OBG** *071 †30

FOLEY, James Alexander. 9200 W WISCONSIN AVE, DEPT OF ORTHOPAEDIC SURGE 53226 #056-06-2003 L2004 **ORS** *012

FOLEY, Sharon Ann. ■ 53211 #030-05-1986 L1996 **D** *020 †20,15

FOLEY, William Dennis. 9200 W WISCONSIN AVE, FROEDTERT HOSPITAL 53226 #143-03-1967 L1977 **R DR** *020 †80

FOLEY, William Jude. ■ 53213 #056-06-1955 L1956 **OS** *071 †85,90

FONG, Christine Marie. 3070 N 51ST ST, STE 309 53210 #018-03-1993 L1997 **NPM** *020 †55

FONK, James Richard. 2315 N LAKE DR 53211 #056-06-1969 L1970 **IM** *020 †20

FONS, Mark Edward. 8701 W WATERTOWN PLANK RD, MED CO WI AFFIL HOSPS 53226 #018-75-2006, ▲ L2007 **PTH** *012

FONS, Roger Allan. 7620 W BURLEIGH ST, INNOVATIVE HEALTH CARE 53222 #056-05-1994 L1995 **FM** *020 †18

FORD, Dennis Dale. 8701 W WATERTOWN PLANK RD, MEDICAL COLLEGE OF WISCONS 53226 #054-04-2004 L2006 **EM** *020

FOREGGER, Richard. 6708 W APPLETON AVE 53216 #056-06-1938 L1946 **AN** *072 †05

FOUTZ, Renee Annette. 2900 W OKLAHOMA AVE, ERMED 53215 #038-41-2000 L2001 **EM** *020 †16

FOWLER, Curtis Wilhite. 6200 W BLUEMOUND RD 53213 #019-02-1962 L1968 **IM PUD** *020 †20

FRANCE, Nancy Knutsen. 9200 W WISCONSIN AVE, MDCL CLLGE CLNCS AT FRDTRT 53226 #016-06-1963 L1970 **AN** *071 †05

FRANCIOSI, Ralph Anthony. PO BOX 1997 53201 #033-05-1962 L1988 **PTH PD** *062 †50

FRANCO, Jose. 9200 W WISCONSIN AVE 53226 #056-06-1990 L1991 **GE** *020 †20

FRANCOLLA, Karen Ann. 8701 W WATERTOWN PLANK RD, RD #26509 53226 #035-15-2002 L2005 **PG** *012 †55

FRANCZAK, Malgorzata B. 9200 W WISCONSIN AVE 53226 #759-01-1988 L1996 **N** *020 †75

FRANGER, Alfred Lanier. 2222 N MAYFAIR RD STE 101, OB-GYN ASSOCIATES, SC 53226 #048-02-1958 L1979 **OBG P** *040 †30

FRANK, Kimberly Hammes. 6980 N PORT WASHINGTON RD, STE 202 53217 #056-06-1990 L1992 **CHP** *020 †75

FRANK, Michael Orville. 8701 W WATERTOWN PLANK RD, IFECTIOUS DISEASE DIVISION 53226 #056-05-1988 L1999 **IM** *020 †20

FRANK, Robert Matthew. 7878 N 76TH ST, NORTHWEST CLINIC 53223 #038-40-1988 L1989 **FM** *020 †18

FRANKOWSKI, Wieslaw. 3201 S 16TH ST, STE 1010 53215 #759-03-1968 L1988 **FM** *020 †18

FRASER, Colin D. ■ 53215 #919-02-1990 L1994 **IMG** *020 †18

FRASER, Lori Lavon. ■ 53212 #025-12-2000 L2007 **GS** *100 †85

FRAZIN, Lawrence Jeffery. 3201 S 15TH ST, # 2200 53215 #056-05-1972 L1973 **NS** *020 †25

FREEDMAN, Mark Ian. 735 W WISCONSIN AVE, EYE CARE SPECIALISTS SC 53233 #056-06-1983 L1987 **OPH** *020 †35

FREEDMAN, Milton Saml. 1218 W KILBOURN AVE, MILTON S FREEDMAN MD SC 53233 #065-01-1941 L1943 **GP** *071

FREEMAN, Jonathan Andrew. ■ 53222 #019-02-2002 L2006 **CD** *012 †20

FREETO, Brian David. 9200 W WISCONSIN AVE, DEPARTMENT ORTHOPAEDIC SUR 53226 #025-07-2003 L2004 **ORS** *012

FREGIEN, Sue M. 2901 W KINNICKINNIC PKWY, RIVER PKWY STE 311 53215 #056-05-1986 L1987 **EM IM** *020 †20

FRICANO, Salvatore. 2900 W OKLAHOMA AVE 53215 #056-06-1954 L1955 **IM** *071 †20

FRIDRIKSSON, Theodor. 9000 W WISCONSIN AVE # 67 53226 #484-01-1987 L1996 **PD PE** *020 †55

FRIEDBERG, David Zachary. 9000 W WISCONSIN AVE, STE 401 CHILD HLTH SYS BLD 53226 #024-01-1962 L1970 **PDC PD** *020 †55

FRIEDLAND, David Richard. 9200 W WISCONSIN AVE 53226 #035-47-1995 L2002 **OTO** *050 †45

FRIEDMAN, Burton Jerry. 2600 N MAYFAIR RD, STE 880 53226 #056-05-1959 L1960 **CD IM** *020 †20

FRIEDMAN, Kenneth Dale. 638 N 18TH ST, BLOOD CENTER SE WISCONSIN 53233 #035-15-1980 L1986 **HEM BBK** *030 †20

FRITZ, Richard David. 788 N JEFFERSON ST STE 300 53202 #056-05-1954 L1958 **IM ON** *071 †20

FRITZ, Robert James. 3535 W OKLAHOMA AVE 53215 #056-06-1957 L1958 **OBG** *020 †30

FROMMELT, Michele A. 9000 W WISCONSIN AVE, CHILDREN'S HOPSITAL OF WIS 53226 #035-08-1984 L1991 **PDC PD** *020 †55

FROMMELT, Peter Cyril. 9000 W WISCONSIN AVE, DEPT OF PEDIATRIC CARDIOLO 53226 #018-03-1985 L1991 **PDC PD** *020 †55

FULLER, Christopher K. 9200 W WISCONSIN AVE, DEPT OF DERMATOLOGY 53226 #039-01-2002 L2007 **D** *012

FULLER, Julie Ann. 2524 E WEBSTER PL, STE 301 53211 #056-06-1992 L1995 **PD** *020 †55

FULLER, Patrick John. 2524 E WEBSTER PL, # 301 53211 #056-06-1992 L1995 **PD** *020 †55

FULMER, Susan Laurel. ■ 53213 #035-15-2007 **OTO** *012

GABBY, Samuel Lee, Jr. ■ 53226 #020-02-1947 L1973 **OM AM** *071

GABELA, Johanna Gabriela. ■ 53202 #016-06-2007 **OBG** *012

GABLER, Nathan Paul. 8901 W LINCOLN AVE, CONSULTANTS AT WEST ALLIS 53227 #056-06-2003 L2004 **AN** *020

GADDI, Marie Anne. ■ 53217 #748-10-1977 *100

GAEBLER-UHING, Charlene. 1020 N 12TH ST, DOWNTOWN HEALTH CENTER 53233 #016-11-1987 L2002 **PD** *040 †55

GAGE, Sandra Mc Clelland. 8701 W WATERTOWN PLANK RD, DEPT OF PEDIATRICS REHAB. 53226 #017-20-1991 L1995 **PD** *020 †55

GAGRAT, Dinshah Dhun. 600 E MASON ST STE 401 53202 #496-38-1970 L1977 **P** *020 †75

GAILANS, Ivars Janis. 215 N 35TH ST 53208 #056-05-1969 L1970 **EM** *020 †16

GAINES, Carol M. 1324 W SHERIDAN CT 53209 #056-06-1982 L1983 **GPM** *020

GAL, Rami A. 960 N 12TH ST 53233 #550-03-1976 L1986 **IM CD** *020 †20

GALANG, Luis L. 2350 W VILLARD AVE, STE 311 53209 #748-01-1954 L1965 **GP GS** *075

GALANG, Miguel T, Jr. 9008 W BURLEIGH ST 53222 #748-01-1955 L1968 **IM** *071

GALANG, Redentor Lapuz. 3267 S 16TH ST, STE 209 53215 #748-07-1981 L2005 **P** *020

GALBRAITH, Sheila Sue. 9200 W WISCONSIN AVE, DEPT OF DERMATOLOGY 53226 #018-03-1999 L2003 **D** *020 †15

GALDABINI, James Jos. 5410 N MOHAWK AVE 53217 #024-01-1964 L1983 **FM P** *020 †50

GALEZOWSKA, Joanna E. 2015 E NEWPORT AVE, STE 308 53211 #759-09-1983 L1990 **N SME** *020 †75

GALVAN, Kristofer I. ■ 53202 #048-04-2005 L2007 **IM** *012

GANAPES, Constance Mary. 2500 W LAYTON AVE, STE 250 53221 #026-04-1977 L1980 **IM** *020

GANDHI, Bhavesh. 2400 W VILLARD AVE 53209 #305-01-2004 L2006 **IMG** *012

GANDHI, Devang Vadilal. 6030 W CAPITOL DR 53216 #495-76-1989 L1995 **PD** *020 †55

GANDHI, Shantilal K. 9200 W WISCONSIN AVE 53226 #495-17-1963 L1969 **AN** *020 †05

GANDHI, Sweeta Devang. 8701 W WATERTOWN PLANK RD, DEPARTMENT OF ANESTHESIOLO 53226 #495-76-1989 L1999 **AN** *020 †05

GANESAN, Geetha. 8200 W SILVER SPRING DR, HEALTH CENTER 53218 #496-39-1994 L2001 **IM** *071 †20

GANSKI, Amber Lynn. 9200 W WISCONSIN AVE, DEPT OF OB/GYN 53226 #056-06-2005 **OBG** *012

GARAY, Fema So. 3003 W GOOD HOPE RD 53209 #748-01-1961 L1977 **OBG** *071

GARCIA BONILLA, Moises An. 1032 S CESAR E CHAVEZ DR 53204 #682-03-1996 L2002 **IM** *020

GARDEZI, Syed Ali Afzal. 2501 W SILVER SPRING DR 53209 #704-20-1987 L2004 **END** *020 †20

GARDNER, Tae Joseph. 53213 #056-06-2008 *012

GARG, Anil Kumar. 3305 S 20TH ST, STE 100 53215 #495-29-1959 L1977 **IM IMG** *020 †20

GARG, Tullika. 9200 W WISCONSIN AVE 53226 #048-04-2005 L2006 **U** *012

GARITI, Dominique Leeann. 8905 W LINCOLN AVE, STE 401 53227 #016-01-2000 L2004 **OBG** *020

GARLAND, Jeffery Scott. 3070 N 51ST ST, STE P309 53210 #056-06-1981 L1982 **NPM PD** *020 †55

GARRISON, Camille Brianne. ■ 53205 #056-06-2006 L2008 **FP** *012

GARTLAND, Patrick Thomas. 1505 W KILBOURN AVE 53233 #056-06-2006 L2007 **DR** *012

GARVEY, Benjamin Lange. 2353 N 57TH ST 53210 #056-06-2008 *012

GASPARRI, Mario Giacomo. 9200 W WISCONSIN AVE, MEDICAL COLLEGE OF WISCONS 53226 #056-06-1993 L1999 **GS** *020 †85,90

GASTON, Luther Lamar. 945 N 12TH ST 1K 53233 #016-01-1991 L2006 **OBG** *020 †30

GAVINSKI, Mary Parish. 1555 S LAYTON BLVD, COMM CARE FOR THE ELDERLY 53215 #056-06-1983 L1984 **IMG** *020

GAWRIEH, Samer. 9200 W WISCONSIN AVE, GI DIV, EAST CLINIC 4TH FL 53226 #875-02-1996 L2001 **GE** *020 †20

GEBREYESUS, Esayas Tekleh. 945 N 12TH ST 53233 #366-03-2000 L2007 **IM** *012

GECHT, Eli Alexander. ■ 53217 #056-06-1943 L1945 **PD** *071

GEDANKE, Susan Dale. 2400 W VILLARD AVE 53209 #056-06-1992 L1993 **EM** *020 †16

GEDDAM, Mamatha. 8701 W WATERTOWN PLANK RD 53226 #305-01-2004 **FP** *012

GEDEIT, Rainer Gerhart. 9000 W WISCONSIN AVE, CHILDREN'S HOSPITAL OF WIS 53226 #016-43-1987 L1990 **CCP PD** *020 †55

GEDRAITTIS, Jessica Ann. 9200 W WISCONSIN AVE, DEPT EMGY MED 53226 #016-11-2006 **EM** *012

GEE, Kevin Ross. 2015 E NEWPORT AVE STE 500 53211 #018-03-1994 L1999 **U** *020 †95

GEENEN, Daniel Jude. 2801 W KINNICKINC RVR PKWY, STE 1030 53215 #056-06-1989 L1990 **GE** *020 †20

GEENEN, Joseph Edward. 2424 S 90TH ST, STE 508 53227 #056-06-1960 L1961 **GE IM** *020 †20

GEFFROS, Lisa Michelle. 9200 W WISCONSIN AVE, MDCL CLLGE CLNCS AT FRDTRT 53226 #028-03-1993 L1994 **PTH** *020 †50

GEHL, Suzanne Van Brunt. 1121 E NORTH AVE 53212 #056-05-1986 L1987 **FM** *020 †18

GEIGER, Jason. ■ 53202 #010-01-1945 L1946 **PUD IM** *075

GEIGER, William Jos. 1121 E NORTH AVE 53212 #028-40-1972 L2000 **FM** *040 †18

GEIST, Jack Emil. ■ 53217 #026-04-1948 L1956 **CHP PFP** *071 †75

GENNARELLI, Thomas Anton. 9200 W WISCONSIN AVE 53226 #016-43-1968 L1999 **NS N** *020 †25

GENNIS, Mark Alan. 1020 N 12TH ST, FL 2 53233 #041-01-1975 L1985 **IM ON** *040 †20

GENNIS, Virginia Myers. 9200 W WISCONSIN AVE 53226 #041-02-1976 L1985 **IM** *040 †20

GENNRICH, Joan Marie. 8024 N 76TH ST 53223 #407-10-1969 L1976 **FM EM** *020

GEORGAKOPOULOS, Nikolaos. 1029 N JACKSON ST, APT 706A 53202 #418-01-1989 L1997 **CD** *020 †20

GEORGE, Chandy V. 9000 W WISCONSIN AVE 53226 #495-31-1971 L1976 **PD** *020 †55

GEORGE, Reena Annie. 9000 W WISCONSIN AVE, ASTHMA & ALLERGY CTR 53226 #495-31-1994 L1998 **AI** *020 †55,03

GERLACH, John Paul. 2311 N PROSPECT AVE, STE 401 53211 #056-05-1977 L1982 **IM** *020 †20

GERLEMAN, Mary Catherine. 2015 E NEWPORT AVE 53211 #056-06-1985 L1986 **GE IM** *020 †20

GEROULIS, Sophos. 9200 W WISCONSIN AVE, MCW CLINIC AT FROEDTERT 53226 #665-01-2003 L2006 **N** *012

GERSHAN, William Mark. 9000 W WISCONSIN AVE 53226 #056-06-1983 L1990 **PDP** *020 †55

GESSERT, Glenn Edmund. 8901 W LINCOLN AVE 53227 #056-06-1983 L1984 **EM IM** *020 †20,16

GHANAYEM, Nancy Suhare. 9200 W WISCONSIN AVE, MDCL CLLGE CLNCS AT FRDTRT 53226 #016-01-1993 L1994 **CCP PD** *020 †55

GHARIA, Manish Jash. 788 N JEFFERSON ST, STE 300 53202 #056-06-1996 L1998 **D** *020 †15

GHEITH, Ayman Ahmad. ■ 53226 #305-01-2005 **N** *012

GIANNATTASIO, Vincent A. 161 W WISCONSIN AVE 53203 #030-06-1958 L1964 **P** *075 †75

GIBBONS, David John. 9200 W WISCONSIN AVE, MCWAH DEPT OF ORTHOPAEDIC 53226 #032-01-2003 L2004 **ORS** *012

GIBSON, Richard Henry. 5000 W NATIONAL AVE, VA MEDICAL CENTER 53295 #056-06-1980 L1990 **P** *030 †75

GILANI, Syed Abbas Raza. 9200 W WISCONSIN AVE, STE 5100 53226 #704-21-1996 L2005 **CD** *012 †20

GILBERT, Ileen Adrianne. 9200 W WISCONSIN AVE, MEDICAL COLLEGE OF WISCONS 53226 #038-06-1981 L2003 **IM** *020 †20

GILGENBACH, Jayme Susan. ■ 53204 #056-06-2008 *012

GILL, Amandeep Singh. 8701 W WATERTOWN PLANK RD, DEPT OF INT MEDICINE, MCW 53226 #495-29-1992 L2003 **PCC** *020 †20

GILL, Joan Cox. 8739 W WATERTOWN PLANK RD, CCBD, BLOODCENTER OF WI 53226 #056-06-1976 L1977 **PHO HEM** *020 †55

GILLER, Herbert. 1575 N RIVERCENTER DR, EYE PHYSICIANS ASSOCS 53212 #056-05-1947 L1948 **OPH** *071 †35

GILLIGAN, Maryann C. 9200 W WISCONSIN AVE 53226 #017-20-1987 L1988 **IM** *050 †20

GILLIS, Rick David. 840 N 87TH ST 53226 #056-06-1988 L1989 **IM** *020 †20

GILLMORE, John Michael. 5000 W NATIONAL AVE, ZABLOCKI VETERANS HOSPITAL 53295 #028-34-2000 L2003 **P** *020 †75

GILSON, Ian Herman. 1575 N RIVERCENTER DR 53212 #016-11-1974 L1977 **IM** *020 †20

GIMENEZ, Alfredo C. 7635 W OKLAHOMA AVE 53219 #748-08-1965 L1976 **GP** *020

GIMENEZ, Leslie May. 9000 W WISCONSIN AVE, P O BOX 1997 53226 #056-06-1996 L1997 **AI** *020 †20,03

GINGRASS, Ruedi Peter. 9800 W BLUEMOUND RD 53226 #025-01-1958 L1960 **PS** *071 †85,65

GINKEL, Paul Donald. 8905 W LINCOLN AVE, GYNECOLOGY LTD 53227 #051-04-1992 L2003 **OBG** *020 †30

GIRGIS, Medhat Abdelmalak. 8701 W WATERTOWN PLANK RD 53226 #915-03-1981 L2005 **AN** *012

GIROTRA, Saket. 8701 W WATERTOWN PLANK RD, MED COLL WI AFFIL HOSPS 53226 #495-36-2003 L2006 **IM** *012

GITTER, Daniel Geo. 3003 W GOOD HOPE RD, HOPE ROAD CLINIC 53209 #056-05-1985 L1991 **D** *020 †20,15

GLADYSZ, Margaret. 8701 W WATERTOWN PLANK RD 53226 #305-01-2006 L2008 **IM** *012

GLASPEY, John Calvin. 3070 N 51ST ST 53210 #056-06-1972 L1977 **NPM PD** *020 †55

GLASPY, Jeffrey Norman. 2900 W OKLAHOMA AVE, ERMED SC 53215 #056-06-1998 L1999 **EM** *020 †16

GLASSNER, David M. 2025 E NEWPORT AVE 53211 #056-05-1953 L1954 **A** *071 †03

GLAZER, Mark Steven. 10919 W BLUEMOUND RD 53226 #550-02-1988 L1996 **R** *020 †80

GLEASON, Sheena Marie. 9200 W WISCONSIN AVE 53226 #028-34-2005 L2007 **MPD** *012

GLEESON, Robert Klinger. 720 E WISCONSIN AVE 53202 #016-01-1975 L1982 **IM OS** *030 †20

GLICKLICH, Marvin. 9000 W WISCONSIN AVE 53226 #056-05-1950 L1951 **PDS TS** *071 †85,90

GLICKLICH-ROSENBERG, L. ■ 53211 #056-05-1950 L1951 **CHP PD** *071 †55,75

GNADT, Gregory James. 2015 E NEWPORT AVE STE 607 53211 #056-06-1974 L1975 **ORS** *020 †40

GNADT, Joan Therese. 2315 N LAKE DR, STE 901 53211 #056-06-1976 L1987 **CD IMG** *020 †20

GO, Simplicio. 1218 W KILBOURN AVE, STE 403 53233 #748-08-1964 L1976 **IM** *020

GOBIS, John Edward. 10000 W BLUEMOUND RD 53226 #056-05-1984 L1987 **AN** *020 †05 ‡

GODAY, Praveen S. 8701 W WATERTOWN PLANK RD, PEDIATRIC GASTRO., MED.COL 53226 #495-04-1991 L2004 **PG** *020 †55

GODBERT, Sarah Lyne. ■ 53222 #056-06-2005 **PD** *012

GODDARD, Adam. 925 N 87TH ST, EYE INSTIT 53217 #018-75-2006, ▲ L2006 **OPH** *012

GOETZ, Gregory Glenn. 9431 W BELOIT RD, STE 119 53227 #048-12-1979 L1980 **FM** *020 †18

GOFRON, Antoni Jan. 788 N JEFFERSON ST, STE 300 53202 #759-01-1991 L2006 **END** *020

GOGAN, Robert Jos. 2727 W CLEVELAND AVE 53215 #028-02-1975 L1979 **OTO** *020 †45

GOGINENI, Sireesha. 9200 W WISCONSIN AVE 53226 #495-58-1999 L2003 **PCC** *012 †20

GOITIA, Hugo Fernando. 637 W MITCHELL ST 53204 #132-01-1975 L1985 **FM** *020

GOLCHINI, Ramin Jeffery. 2025 E NEWPORT AVE, WISCONSIN RADIOLOGY 53211 #016-43-1996 L1998 **RNR** *020 †80

GOLDBERG, Aaron Israel. 2900 W OKLAHOMA AVE, ERMED, SC 53215 #016-43-1997 L2000 **EM** *020 †16

GOLDBERG, Alan Herbert. 8700 W WISCONSIN AVE #ANES 53226 #024-05-1957 L1981 **AN** *071 †05

GOLDBERG, Jerry W. 11925 W LAKE PARK DR, STE 100 53224 #005-15-1978 L1984 **RHU IM** *020 †20

GOLDBERG, Steven Harold. 2500 N MAYFAIR RD, STE 570 53226 #041-01-2000 L2006 **HS** *020

GOLDING, Jacob Lessner. ■ 53212 #004-01-1961 L1968 **GS** *071

GOLDMAN, Allan Louis. 2901 W KINNICKINC RVR PKWY, STE 301 53215 #041-09-1966 L1972 **RHU** *071 †20

GOLDMAN, Margaret Taxen. 7101 N GREEN BAY AVE 53209 #056-05-1950 L1954 **P OS** *020

GOLDMAN, Robert Semerik. 2801 W KINNICKINC RVR PKWY, STE 135 53215 #008-01-1981 L1990 **N** *020 †75

GOLDSTEIN, David Jonathan. 1121 E NORTH AVE 53212 #033-06-2001 L2007 **AM** *020

GOLGERT, William Alan. 9200 W WISCONSIN AVE, MEDICAL COLLEGE OF WISCONS 53226 #056-06-2003 L2004 **NEP** *012 †20

GOLLAPUDY, Suneeta. 9200 W WISCONSIN AVE, FROEDTERT MEM LUTH HOSP 53226 #495-49-1990 L2001 **AN** *020 †05

GOMBUS, Leslie Howard. 9201 W WATERTOWN PLANK RD 53226 #017-20-1972 L1973 **P CHP** *020

GOMILLA, Severino G. ■ 53211 #748-01-1956 L1967 **AN** *075

GONNERING, Russell S. 2900 W OKLAHOMA AVE, ST LUKE'S MED CTR 53215 #056-05-1976 L1976 **OPH** *020 †35

GONYO, James Edward. 9200 W WISCONSIN AVE 53226 #056-06-1956 L1957 **DR GP** *020 †80

GONYO, Mary Beth. 9200 W WISCONSIN AVE, DEPT OF RADIOLOGY 53226 #056-06-1993 L1994 **DR** *020 †80

GONZALEZ, Ramon Angelico. 1308 S 16TH ST 53204 #308-01-1951 L1968 **GP DR** *071

GOODMAN, Joseph Jay. 5150 N PORT WASHINGTON RD, STE 151 53217 #056-06-1971 L1972 **GS** *020 †85

GOODMAN, Lawrence R. 8700 W WISCONSIN AVE 53226 #035-08-1968 L1983 **DR** *020 †80

GOODMAN, William Martin. 4655 N PORT WASHINGTON RD, STE 100 53212 #056-05-1972 L1973 **OBG** *020 †20

GOPAL, Kandavar Muniyappa. 5000 W CHAMBERS ST 53210 #495-33-1970 L1977 **PM** *020 †60

GORDON, John Bernard. 9200 W WISCONSIN AVE, MDCL CLLGE CLNCS AT FRDTRT 53226 #067-01-1977 L1996 **AN PD** *020 †55

GORDON, Michael David. 1218 W KILBOURN AVE # 301, STE 301 53233 #024-01-1997 L2003 **ORS OSM** *020

GORDON, Norvan F. ■ 53217 #056-05-1943 L1946 **IM** *071 †20

GORE, Elizabeth Marie. 9200 W WISCONSIN AVE, FROEDTERT HOSPITAL 53226 #056-06-1990 L1991 **RO** *020 †80

GORELICK, Marc Harris. 9000 W WISCONSIN AVE MS 6, EMERGENCY MEDICINE SECTION 53226 #036-07-1987 L2000 **PD PEM** *020 †55

GORENSTEIN, Leonard. 1218 W KILBOURN AVE 53233 *056-06-1942 L1943 **PD** *072 †55

GOSAIN, Arun Kumar. 9200 W WISCONSIN AVE, MED COLLEGE OF WISCONSIN 53226 #005-14-1981 L1988 **HS PS** *020 †85,65

GOSHTASBI, Mana. 3000 W MONTANA ST 53215 #517-12-2004 L2008 **IM** *012

GOSHTASBI, Saeid. 3000 W MONTANA ST, AURORA HLTH CARE 53215 #517-11-1994 L2003 **GE** *012 †20

GOSS, Michael Patrick. 6900 N PORT WASHINGTON RD 53217 #056-06-1983 L1984 **FM** *020 †18

GOSSET, James Baudouin. 9200 W WISCONSIN AVE 53226 #056-05-1990 L1991 **VM** *020 †20

GOSWAMI, Monica. 8701 W WATERTOWN PLANK RD, MED COLL WI 53226 #495-78-1996 L2002 **PCP** *012

GOTTSCHALL, Jerome Louis. 638 N 18TH ST, BLOODCENTER OF WISCONSIN 53233 #038-40-1974 L1979 **BBK CLP** *030 †50

GOTTWALD, Sandra Danielle. 3003 W GOOD HOPE RD 53209 #025-01-1986 L1990 **OBG** *020 †30

GOTWALT, Karen Theresa. 201 N MAYFAIR RD 53226 #056-06-1986 L1987 **OBG** *020 †30

GOULD, Robert John. 3237 S 16TH ST, RADIOLOGY DEPARTMENT 53215 #016-11-1981 L2000 **R** *020 †80

GOURLAY, David Michael. 999 N 92ND ST 53226 #056-06-1997 L2004 **PDS** *100 †85

GOVANDE, Vinayak Prabhaka. 999 N 92ND ST, CHILDREN'S CORPORATE CENTE 53226 #496-38-1995 L2005 **NPM** *012 †55

GOVEAS, Joseph Santam. 8701 W WATERTOWN PLANK RD, DEPT OF PYCH & BEHAV 53226 #495-37-1996 L2002 **PYG** *100 †75 ‡

GOYAL, Abhijeet. 9200 W WISCONSIN AVE, MCW-DEPT OF MEDICINE,FEC E 53226 #495-37-2000 L2005 **IM** *020 †20

GOYAL, Alok. 5000 W CHAMBERS ST 53210 #913-12-1991 L2003 **IM** *020 †20

GOYAL, Amit. ■ 53202 #016-01-2006 L2007 **IM** *012

GOZON, Benjamin S, III. 7220 W CAPITOL DR 53216 #748-02-1992 L2001 **PM** *020 †60

GRACA, Simone Simas. 3000 W MONTANA ST 53215 #187-46-1999 **OBG** *012

GRAEWIN, Shannon Jean. 9200 W WISCONSIN AVE # O 53226 #056-06-2000 L2003 **GS** *100 †85

GRAHAM, Gerard William. 2323 N LAKE DR, ANESTHESIOLOGY DEPT 53211 #007-02-1998 L1999 **AN** *020 †05

GRAHAM, Mary Beth. 8701 W WATERTOWN PLANK RD, INFECTIOUS DISEASE DIVISIO 53226 #016-06-1984 L2001 **ID IM** *040 †20

GRALL, Kristi Joy. 9200 W WISCONSIN AVE, DEPT.OF EMERGENCY MEDICINE 53226 #056-06-2001 L2004 **EM** *020 †16

GRAMBOW, David William. 2350 N LAKE DR, STE 400 53211 #047-05-1986 L1987 **CD IM** *020 †20

GRANT, Jonathan Reagan. 8701 W WATERTOWN PLANK RD, MEDICAL COLLEGE OF WISCONS 53226 #048-04-2003 L2005 **OTO** *012

GRAUPE, Menachem Henny. 201 N MAYFAIR RD, FL 3 53226 #035-46-1996 L2003 **OBG MFM** *020 †30

GRAVES, Terry Spencer. 2500 N MAYFAIR RD, STE 220 53226 #056-06-1973 L1977 **AI IM** *020 †20,03

GRAY, Matthew Philip. ■ 53211 #056-06-2007 **PD** *012

GRAY, Todd William. 8701 W WATERTOWN PLANK RD, MEDICAL COLLEGE OF WISCONS 53226 #305-01-2005 L2007 **IM** *012

GRAYBURN, Ryan. ■ 53226 #016-76-2007, ▲ **IM** *012

GRAZIANO, Samuel Anthony. 5000 W CHAMBERS ST 53210 #056-06-1954 L1955 **GP OM** *020

GREEN, Erin Mae. ■ 53222 #056-06-2006 L2008 **EM** *012

GREEN, Jeffrey Alan. ■ 53209 #035-06-1988 L1989 **FM** *020 †18

GREEN, Sandra Sue. 840 N 87TH ST 53226 #017-20-1980 L1987 **IM** *020 †20

GREENMAN, Steven Barry. 3900 W BROWN DEER RD 53209 #016-11-1973 L1974 **IM** *075 †20

GREGG, David Christopher. 4890 N LAKE DR, CHILDREN'S HOSP OF WISCONS 53217 #056-06-1982 L1983 **DR** *020 †80

GREGORIO, Fernando Q. 2315 N LAKE DR 53211 #748-01-1958 L1969 **FM** *020

GREGORIO, Maria Asuncion. 4448 W LOOMIS RD 53220 #748-01-1961 L1975 **GP** *020

GREGORY, Darin Ray. 9200 W WISCONSIN AVE 53226 #028-34-2004 L2006 **OBG** *012

GREWAL, Alma. ■ 53214 #056-06-2007 **P** *012

GRIBOVSKAJA, Irena. ■ 53213 #056-06-2007 **GS** *012

GRIEM, Melvin L. 8701 W WATERTOWN PLANK RD 53226 #056-05-1953 L1955 **RO** *071 †80

GRIESHOP, Richard Jos. 2424 S 90TH ST 53227 #056-05-1987 L1992 **GS VS** *020 †85

GRIFFITHS, Jennifer Beth. 1121 E NORTH AVE, MEDICAL COLLEGE OF WISCONS 53212 #008-01-2000 L2001 **FM** *020 †18

GRILL, Jennifer Carol. ■ 53219 #016-42-2006 **GS** *012

GRIM, Clarence Ezra. 2821 N 4TH ST, STE 410 53212 #028-03-1964 L1995 **END IM** *050 †20

GRINDEL, Steven Ira. 9200 W WISCONSIN AVE, ORTHOPAEDIC SURGERY 53226 #016-11-1990 L1996 **ORS** *020 †40

GRODA-LEWIS, Mary Louise. 1121 E NORTH AVE 53212 #035-03-1984 L2002 **FM OBS** *040 †18

GRONAU, Rachel Tarajoy. ■ 53221 #056-06-2005 L2007 **FP** *012

GRONSKI, Theodore Joseph. 2900 W OKLAHOMA AVE, FL 1 53215 #056-06-1985 L1998 **PCC IM** *020 †20

GROSENICK, Deborah Jane. 3351 N DOWNER AVE, NORRIS HEALTH CENTER,UWM 53211 #056-05-1978 L1980 **IM** *020 †20

GROSS, Eric Richard. ■ 53211 #056-06-2007 **TY** *012

GROSSBERG, Josette B. 924 E JUNEAU AVE UNIT 823 53202 #396-06-1954 L1969 **AN** *071 †05

GROSSBERG, Sidney Edward. 8701 W WATERTOWN PLANK RD, MEDICAL COLLEGE OF WISCONS 53226 #012-05-1954 L1996 **MM IG** *050

GROSSMAN, Thomas Whitney. ■ 53223 #056-06-1958 L1959 **OTO** *071 †45

GROSSMAN, William Jon. 8701 W WATERTOWN PLANK RD, MEDICAL COLLEGE OF WISCONS 53226 #028-02-1999 L2004 **PHO IG** *050 †55

GROTH, Travis William. 8701 W WATERTOWN PLANK RD, MEDICAL COLLEGE OF WISCONS 53226 #026-04-2003 L2005 **U** *012

GROVE, Andrew Jonathon. 545 N 15TH ST 53233 #028-03-1998 L2006 **PD PSM** *020 †55

GRUM, John Thos. 5000 W CHAMBERS ST 53210 #056-05-1977 L1978 **DR** *020 †80

GRUM, Katherine Ann. ■ 53202 #056-05-2005 L2006 **DR** *012

GRYNIEWICZ, Steven M. 5000 W CHAMBERS ST, DEPT RAD D 53210 #056-06-1988 L1989 **DR** *020 †80

GRZABA-GRACZ, Barbara. 2801 W KINNICKINC RVR PKWY, STE 135 53215 #759-01-1987 L1998 **IM** *020 †20

GUADALUPE, Keyla. 180 N MILWAUKEE ST, LAKESHORE MEDICAL CLINIC 53202 #056-05-2002 L2003 **FM** *020 †18

GUDEMAN, Jon Edward. 2025 E NEWPORT AVE, COLUMBIA HOSP PSYCH CTR 53211 #024-01-1963 L1987 **P PYA** *020 †75

GUEDET, Patty Jane. 5000 W NATIONAL AVE, VA MEDICAL CTR 53295 #018-03-1985 L1991 **P** *020 †75

GUHL, James Frederick. 3237 S 16TH ST 53215 #056-06-1954 L1955 **ORS OS** *071 †40

GUHL, Thomas James. 8901 W LINCOLN AVE, CONSULTANTS AT WEST ALLIS 53227 #056-06-1990 L1991 **AN** *020 †05

GUINN, Judy Helen. 9000 W WISCONSIN AVE 53226 #016-45-1982 L1983 **PD** *020 †55

GUISE, Amy Irene. 9200 W WISCONSIN AVE, STE 5700 53226 #017-20-2005 **U** *012

GUMINA, Roseann. 3070 N 51ST ST, STE 305 53210 #056-06-1989 L1999 **OBG** *020 †18,30

GUNDAMRAJ, Sunitha. 3289 N MAYFAIR RD, MAYFAIR ROAD CLINIC 53222 #495-21-1994 L1999 **IM** *020 †20

GUPTA, Anjan. 2801 W KINNICKINC RVR PKWY, STE 777 53215 #495-44-1991 L1996 **CD IC** *020 †20

GUPTA, Champalal. 5300 W VILLARD AVE 53218 #495-30-1967 L1981 **IM FM** *020 †20

GUPTA, Dipti. 2900 W OKLAHOMA AVE 53215 #016-11-2006 L2008 **DR** *012

GUPTA, Lata M.. 945 N 12TH ST 53233 #665-02-2003 L2006 **OBG** *020

GUPTA, Madhu Nilesh. 2801 W KINNICKINC RVR PKWY, STE 135 53215 #496-44-1998 L2003 **IM** *020

GUPTA, Neeraj. ■ 53214 #495-36-1999 L2003 **PCC** *100 †20

GUPTA, Nidhi. ■ 53202 #010-01-2006 L2008 **OTO** *012

GUPTA, Ruby. 8701 W WATERTOWN PLANK RD 53226 #496-04-1998 L2007 **NPM** *012 †20

GUPTA, Sonika. 8701 W WATERTOWN PLANK RD, MEDICAL COLLEGE OF WISCONS 53226 #495-90-2001 L2005 **IM** *100 †20

GURALNICK, Michael L. 9200 W WISCONSIN AVE, MEDICAL COLLEGE OF 53226 #067-01-1994 L2000 **U** *020 †95

GUTE, Daniel Browne. ■ 53217 #016-06-1956 L1957 **U** *071 †95

GUTEN, Gary Neal. 2424 S 90TH ST, STE 418 53227 #056-05-1964 L1965 **ORS OSM** *020 †40

GUTENBERGER, Daniel James. 750 W VIRGINIA ST 53204 #056-05-1989 L1992 **IM** *062 †20

GUTGLASS, Milton F. ■ 53217 #056-06-1950 L1951 **GYN OBG** *071 †30

GUTGUTIA, Nikhil. 3237 S 16TH ST 53215 #495-36-1993 L1998 **IMG** *020 †20

GUTIERREZ, Norma Bautista. 9455 W WATERTOWN PLANK RD 53226 #016-43-1962 L1981 **CHP** *071 †75

GUTIERREZ, Sherrill Denee. ■ 53222 #056-06-2008 *012

GUTTERMAN, David Drew. 8701 W WATERTOWN PLANK RD, CVRC MED COLL WISCONSIN 53226 #056-06-1974 L1980 L1998 **TS IM** *040 †20

GUYON, Andrea Helenenoell. ■ 53222 #016-45-2003 L2004 **AN** *020

GUZZETTA, Paul Michael. 2300 N MAYFAIR RD STE 960 53226 #056-06-1977 L1982 **PUD CCM** *020 †20

HAAKE, Rachel Marie. 9200 W WISCONSIN AVE, FROEDTERT EAST CLNC 53226 #056-06-2006 **AN** *012

HAAS, Richard Andrew. 4570 S 27TH ST 53221 #065-05-1977 L1978 **AN** *020 †05

HAASLER, George Bruce. 9200 W WISCONSIN AVE 53226 #035-01-1977 L1985 **TS CD** *020 †85,90

HABECK, Donna Jean. 945 N 12TH ST 53233 #056-05-2003 L2004 **IM** *100 †20

HABIBI, Saeed. 2323 N LAKE DR, ST MARYS HOSPITAL 53211 #517-01-1981 L1992 **CCA** *020 †05,20

HACKBARTH, Donald A. 9200 W WISCONSIN AVE, ORTHOPAEDIC SURGERY CLINIC 53226 #056-06-1977 L1978 **ORS OMO** *020 †40

HACKETT, James Glenn. 7878 N 76TH ST, NORTHWEST CLINIC 53223 #018-03-1973 L1980 **ORS OSS** *020 †40

HADCOCK, David Andrew. 9233 N GREEN BAY RD, CSMCP GLENDALE CLINIC 53209 #056-05-1995 L1998 **FM** *020 †18

HADDADIAN, Babak. 3000 W MONTANA ST, AURORA HLTH CARE 53215 #517-21-1997 L2006 **IM** *100

HAEFNER, Rebecca Ann. 10000 W BLUEMOUND RD 53226 #028-03-1988 L1989 **AN** *020 †05

HAFEEZ, Abdul. 8430 W CAPITOL DR, PR OFFICE 53222 #704-02-1990 L1999 **IM RHU** *020 †20

HAFEEZ, Samina. 4555 W SCHROEDER DR, STE 170 53223 #704-02-1990 L2002 **AN** *020

HAGEN, Thad Chilson. 9200 W WISCONSIN AVE 53226 #056-05-1965 L1966 **END IM** *020

HAGO, Patricia Ivonne. 1032 S CESAR E CHAVEZ DR, 16TH STREET COMMUNITY HEAL 53204 #319-03-1988 L1999 **FM** *020 †18

HAIDER, Nadia. ■ 53202 #056-06-2004 L2006 **AN** *012

HAKE, Christopher Ronald. 9200 W WISCONSIN AVE, DEPT OF MEDICINE SUITE 410 53226 #056-06-2002 L2004 **HO** *012 †20

HALBERT, Kevin Eugene. 3070 N 51ST ST STE P309 53210 #019-02-1981 L1996 **NPM** *020 †55

HALE-RICHLEN, Barbara L. 8701 W WATERTOWN PLANK RD, MCW DEPARTMENT OF PSYCHIAT 53226 #056-06-2003 L2004 **CHP** *012

HALL, John Michael. 8901 W LINCOLN AVE, CONSULTANTS AT WEST ALLIS 53227 #016-45-1995 L1998 **AN** *020 †05

HALL, Judith Katherine. 611 W NATIONAL AVE, WALKER'S POINT COMM CLINIC 53204 #056-06-1980 L1981 **P** *071 †75,18

HALL, Michele Marie. 2323 S 102ND ST 53227 #018-03-1993 L1994 **FM** *020 †18

HALL, William Lamb, Jr. 1901 E CAPITOL DR, SHOREWOOD FAMILY 53211 #056-06-1994 L1995 **FM** *020 †18

HALLER, Lisa U. 2901 W KINNICKINNIC PKWY, STE 405 53215 #016-11-1995 L2001 **NEP** *020 †20

HALM, Josiah Kwesi. 945 N 12TH ST, STE 3506 53233 #412-01-1996 L2001 **IM** *020 †20

HALSTROM, Melody Ann. ■ 53217 #056-06-1991 **IM** *100

HALVERSON, Gloria M. 9200 W WISCONSIN AVE 53226 #056-06-1973 L1974 **OBG REN** *040 †30

HALVERSON, Paul Brekke. 9200 W WISCONSIN AVE 53226 #056-06-1973 L1974 **RHU IM** *020 †20

HALVERSON, Philip Clair. ■ 53211 #026-04-1979 L1980 **A** *020 †20,03

HAMBROOK, George Willard. 945 N 12TH ST 53233 #028-34-1969 L1985 **N** *020 †55

HAMBROOK, M Sarah. 2524 E WEBSTER PL, STE 301 53211 #056-06-1997 L1998 **PD** *020 †55

HAMED, Raed Ahmad. 960 N 12TH ST, FIRST FLOOR CONSULT SUITE 53233 #575-01-1995 L2003 **PCC** *020 †20

HAMER, John Forrest. 3237 S 16TH ST, DEPT. OF RADIOLOGY 53215 #056-06-1999 L2000 **RNR** *020 †80

HAMIZADEH, Leyla Maria. ■ 53217 #056-05-2007 **PD** *012

HAN, Dennis Peter. 925 N 87TH ST 53226 #025-01-1981 L1986 **OPH** *020 †35

HANKO-SPACEK, Eva. 9200 W WISCONSIN AVE, MCWAH-DEPT OF ANESTHESIOL0 53226 #286-13-1983 L2001 **AN** *020 †5

HANKWITZ, Paul Edward. 8520 W OKLAHOMA AVE, OLSEN MEDICAL CLINIC 53227 #056-06-1974 L1975 **IM IMG** *020 †20 ‡

HANNA, Matthew Harvey. 3003 W GOOD HOPE RD 53209 #016-45-1979 L1984 **NEP IM** *020 †20

HANNA, Nickolas Fred. 2400 W VILLARD AVE 53209 #654-01-2005 **FP** *012

HANSEN, Kim Allen. 2901 W KK RIVER PKWY, STE 106 53215 #056-06-1986 L1993 **PM IM** *020 †60

HANSEN, Kirk Alan. 8901 W LINCOLN AVE, CONSULTANTS AT WEST ALLIS 53227 #056-05-1990 L1991 **AN** *05

HANSEN, Kyle Jory. 9200 W WISCONSIN AVE, FROEDTERT EAST HOSPITAL 53226 #016-42-2000 L2001 **EM** *020

HANSEN, Thomas Nicholas. 9000 W WISCONSIN AVE, DEPARTMENT OF ANESTHESIOLO 53226 #056-06-2004 L2006 **AN** *012

HANSON, John Pierrus. 2901 W KINNICKINC RVR PKWY 53215 #056-06-1964 L1971 **ON HO** *020

HANSON, Sheila. 9000 W WISCONSIN AVE 53226 #056-06-1999 L2000 **CCP** *020 †55

HAQ, Zahida P. 9000 W WISCONSIN AVE, CHILDRENS HOSP OF WI 53226 #704-05-1986 L1992 **PD** *020 †55

HAQUE, Ammar Ansarul. ■ 53213 #665-02-2007 **IM** *012

HARACZ, Johnny Lee. MED COLL OF WISCONSIN 53233 #056-06-1980 *100

HARBECKE, Richard Geo. 3003 W GOOD HOPE RD, ADVANCED HEALTHCARE 53209 #056-06-1972 L1973 **PUD IM** *012

HARDIN, Scott Thomas. 2901 W KINNICKINC RVR PKWY, STE 106 53215 #056-06-1993 L1994 **PM** *020 †60 ‡

HARDING, Thomas Robt. 9455 W WATERTOWN PLANK RD 53226 #025-07-1983 L1984 **P** *020 †75

HARE, James Willis. 10701 W RESEARCH DR 53226 #035-20-1976 L1977 **FM** *030 †18

HARGARTEN, Stephen Wm. 9200 W WISCONSIN AVE, RM 1870 53226 #056-06-1975 L1976 **EM** *016

HARI, Parameswaran Nair. 9200 W WISCONSIN AVE 53226 #495-31-1992 L2002 **HO** *020 †20

HARIHARAN, Jaishree. 9200 W WISCONSIN AVE, MILWAUKEE 53226 #495-96-1980 L1995 **IM** *020 †20

HARIHARAN, Sundaram. 9200 W WISCONSIN AVE, FROEDTERT MEMORIAL LUTHERA 53226 #495-96-1977 L1995 **NEP IM** *020 †20

HARKAVY, Raymond. 2315 N LAKE DR 53211 #056-05-1953 L1954 **U** *020 †95

HARKINS, Charles John. 9200 W WISCONSIN AVE, DEPT OF OTOLARYNGOLOGY 53226 #056-05-1983 L1984 **OTO FPS** *020 †45

HARKINS, Heidi Jane. 2900 W OKLAHOMA AVE 53215 #056-06-1980 L1981 **EM** *020 †20,16

HARMELINK, Neal Arthur. 2400 W VILLARD AVE 53209 #056-06-2000 L2003 **EM** *020 †16

HARPER, Deann Leah. 9200 W WISCONSIN AVE, OB/GYN DEPARTMENT 53226 #028-78-2005, ▲ L2007 **OBG** *012

HARRINGTON, Gregory J. 9200 W WISCONSIN AVE, FROEDTERT HOSP NEUROLOGY 53226 #056-06-1967 L1968 **N P** *020 †75

HARRIS, Gerald Jay. 925 N 87TH ST 53226 #016-06-1970 L1977 **OPH** *020 †35

HARRIS, Paul Wayne. 3237 S 16TH ST, ST. FRANCIS HOSPITAL 53215 #065-10-1979 L2003 **ADP** *020 †05,75

HARRIS, Stephanie E. 9200 W WISCONSIN AVE, MCW DEPT. OF UROLOGY 53226 #047-05-2003 L2005 **U** *012

HARRIS, Theodore Alfred. ■ 53217 #062-01-1952 L1965 **P** *072

HARRISON, Rebecca Ann. 8701 W WATERTOWN PLANK RD 53226 #056-06-2006 L2007 **P** *012

HARSCH, Harold Harvey. 8701 W WATERTOWN PLANK RD, TOSA CTR 53226 #056-06-1976 L1982 **P PYG** *020 †75

HARSHBARGER, William T. 8901 W LINCOLN AVE, WEST ALLIS MEMORIAL HOSPIT 53227 #017-20-1998 L2002 **EM** *020 †16

HART, Ronald Dixon. 2900 W OKLAHOMA AVE 53215 #067-01-1975 L1980 **ON** *020 †20

HARTGRAVES, Hallie. 3288 N LAKE DR, ST MARYS CONVENT 53211 #048-02-1926 L1972 **OS** *071 †35

HARTLAUB, Paul Philip. 7950 N PORT WASHINGTON RD 53217 #056-05-1987 L1988 **FM PHP** *040 †70,18

HARTMANN, Bradley John. ■ 53226 #056-06-2006 L2008 **DR** *012

HARTMANN, Kathryn Ann. ■ 53226 #056-06-2006 L2007 **IM** *012

HASAN, Nosheen. 2400 W VILLARD AVE 53209 #704-02-1995 L2002 **AN** *100 †05

HASANADKA, Ravishankar. 9200 W WISCONSIN AVE, DEPARTMENT OF SURGERY 53226 #017-20-2002 L2004 **GS** *012

HASENYAGER, Carol A. 9200 W WISCONSIN AVE, MEDICAL COLLEGE OF WISCONS 53226 #016-11-1980 L1986 **OBG** *020 †30

HASHIKAWA, Andrew Nobuhid. 999 N 92ND ST C550, CHILDREN'S CORPORATE CENTE 53226 #026-08-2004 L2007 **PEM** *012 †55

HASHIM, Abdelazim Osman. 2224 W WISCONSIN AVE # 208 53233 #848-01-1995 L2005 **CD** *012 †20

HASHIM, Zulfiqar Ali. 2900 W OKLAHOMA AVE 53215 #704-02-2003 **FP** *012

HASLER, David J. 4555 W SCHROEDER DR, STE 170 53223 #305-01-1992 L1994 **AN** *020 †05

HATFIELD, Lynn Ann. ■ 53215 #056-06-1990 L1991 **PD** *020 †55

HAUGSTAD, Bradley Neil. 12129 W FEERICK ST 53222 #018-03-1990 L1994 **AN** *020 †05

HAUKE, Gary Steven. 2901 W KINNICKINC RVR PKWY, STE 417 53215 #056-06-1979 L1980 **OBG** *020 †30 ‡

HAVAS, Nancy E. 8701 W WATERTOWN PLANK RD, MCW DEPT OF FAM & COMM MED 53226 #056-06-1999 L2000 **FM PLM** *040 †18

HAVENS, Peter Lucas. 8701 W WATERTOWN PLANK RD, MED OF COLLEGE OF WISCONSI 53226 #028-46-1980 L1987 **PDI CCP** *020 †55

HAVEY, Elizabeth Ann. 9200 W WISCONSIN AVE, DEPT OF DERMATOLOGY 53226 #028-03-2006 L2008 **D** *012

HAVLIK, Heather Schlesner. 8700 W WATERTOWN PLANK RD 53226 #056-06-2003 L2007 **PM** *020

HAW, Jeehea Sonya. ■ 53226 #056-06-2008 *012

HAWES, Jane Alice. 2015 E NEWPORT AVE, MEDICAL CLINIC 53211 #056-06-1977 L1978 **IM** *020 †20

HAWKINS, Alexander Todd. 2901 W KINNICKINC RVR PKWY, STE 300 53215 #016-11-1997 L2003 **NS** *020

HAWPETOS, Kate A. ■ 53222 #037-01-1997 L1998 **P** *020

HAYES, Avery Marquis. 9200 W WISCONSIN AVE 53226 #056-06-1998 L1999 **IM** *020 †20

HAYES, Ellen Carol. ■ 53211 #016-43-1997 L1998 **OBG** *020 †30

HAYES, John Menke. 5000 W NATIONAL AVE, MILWAUKEE VA MEDICAL CENTE 53295 #016-43-1997 L1998 **IM** *020 †20

HAYES, Valerie Annette. 9000 W WISCONSN AVE MS782A 53226 #016-11-1989 L1990 **OTO PD** *020 †45

HAZELBERG, Michael David. 8701 W WATERTOWN PLANK RD 53226 #018-75-2005, ▲ L2007 **FP** *012

HEAL, Gregory Thos. 555 S 108TH ST 53214 #056-06-1989 L1990 **OBG** *020 †30

HEARN, Richard Forrest. 2315 N LAKE DR 53211 #056-06-1962 L1963 **EM** *020 †85

HEATH, Mary Delphine. ■ 53222 #550-04-2006 L2008 **PD** *012

HEFFEZ, Dan Salomon. 960 N 12TH ST, STE 1800 53233 #067-01-1979 L2004 **NS** *020 †25

HEFFNER, Viday Audra. ■ 53214 #056-06-2002 L2005 **PEM** *012 †55

HEIDEMAN, Gregory M. 5000 W CHAMBERS ST 53210 #056-05-2005 L2006 **DR** *012

HEIDENREICH, Charlotte A. 501 W MICHIGAN ST, BOX 3050 53203 #041-07-1982 L1989 **IM** *030 †20

HEIDENREICH, Wayne F. 720 E WISCONSIN AVE, NORTHWESTERN MUTUAL 53202 #056-05-1982 L1988 **IM** *030 †20

HEIMLER, Ruth. 8700 W WISCONSIN AVE, MEDICAL CLINICS AT FRDTRT 53226 #550-01-1960 L1976 **PD** *071 †55

HEINRICH, Tanya Karina. 9455 W WATERTOWN PLANK RD 53226 #016-45-1997 L1998 **P** *020 †75

HEINRICH, Thomas William. 8701 W WATERTOWN PLANK RD, DEPT. OF PSYCHIATRY 53226 #056-06-1996 L1997 **FM P** *020 †18,75

HELLMAN, Elissa Rose. ■ 53209 #035-19-2006 L2007 **OBG** *012

HELLMAN, Robert Steven. 9200 W WISCONSIN AVE, NUCLEAR MEDICINE 53226 #056-05-1977 L1980 **NM** *020 †20,28

HELM, Robin Lyn. 2400 W VILLARD AVE, FAMILY CARE CENTER 53209 #056-06-1994 L1995 **FM** *020 †20

HELMS, Ann Katherine. 9200 W WISCONSIN AVE, DEPARTMENT OF NEUROLOGY 53226 #016-43-1999 L2003 **N** *100 †75

HEMMY, David Christian. 9000 W WISCONSIN AVE 53226 #041-09-1967 L1968 **NS NSP** *072 †25

HEMSWORTH, Daniel Edward. ■ 53222 #056-05-2002 L2005 **CD** *012 †20

HENEGHAN, Marykathleen A. 9000 W WISCONSIN AVE, MS C 53226 #016-43-2004 L2007 **PDE** *012 †55

HENNES, Halim Mahfouz A. 9000 W WISCONSIN AVE 53226 #915-04-1973 L1994 **PEM PD** *020 †55

HENRICKSON, Kelly John. 999 N 92ND ST, CHILDREN'S HOSPITAL OF WIS 53226 #054-04-1984 L1990 **ID PD** *020 †55

HENRIKSEN, Lisa Marie. 1121 E NORTH AVE, COLUMBIA-ST MARYS, FPC 53212 #056-06-2001 L2003 **P** *100 †18

HENRY, David Allan. 3237 S 16TH ST, ST FRANCIS HOSP 53215 #030-06-1986 L2000 **R VIR** *020 †80

HENRY, Lyle Gene. 2015 E NEWPORT AVE 53211 #017-20-1970 L1973 **GS VS** *020 †85

HENSIEN, Michael Andrew. 10000 W BLUEMOUND RD 53226 #056-06-1993 L2002 **AN** *020 †05

HERATH, Nihal Koralalage. 2801 W KINNICKINC RVR PKWY, STE 135 53215 #220-01-1982 L1999 **N** *020 †75

HERGAN, David Jeremy. 9200 W WISCONSIN AVE, ORTHO. DEPT. P.O. BOX 2609 53226 #016-42-2003 L2004 **ORS** *012

HERINGTON, Aaron Christop. ■ 53226 #056-06-2008 *012

HERNANDEZ, Kathy Susan. 1032 S CESAR E CHAVEZ DR 53204 #005-18-1988 L1991 **FM** *020 †18

HERNANDEZ-ENGSTRAND, G. 2015 E NEWPORT AVE 53211 #056-06-1981 L1983 **AN** *020 †20

HERRELL, Nancy C Cross. 3070 N 51ST ST STE 309, NEWBORN CARE PHYSICIANS 53210 #056-05-1975 L1980 **NPM PD** *020 †55

HERRMANN, Ronald Anthony. 9455 W WATERTOWN PLANK RD, MILWAUKEE COUNTY BEHAVIORA 53226 #016-11-1993 L1994 **P** *020 †75

HERSCHER, Anne Marie. 2400 W VILLARD AVE 53209 #016-76-2005, ▲ **FP** *012

HERSZENSON, Sidney. 3077 N MAYFAIR RD, STE 305 53222 #056-05-1972 L1973 **D** *020 †15

HERZOG, Joseph Paul. 3070 N 51ST ST, STE 305 53210 #056-05-1990 L1991 **OBG** *020 †30

HETTINGER, Patrick Christ. ■ 53227 #056-06-2006 L2008 **PS** *012

HEUER, Dale Kennedy. 925 N 87TH ST 53226 #016-06-1978 L1979 **OPH** *020 †35

HEWES, Harvey Ferris. 2424 S 90TH ST, STE 206 53227 #041-12-1964 L1972 **IM CD** *020 †20

HEYDEN, Steven James. 7878 N 76TH ST, NORTHWEST CLINIC 53223 #016-11-1990 L1991 **FM** *020 †18

HEYWOOD, Patricia A. 945 N 12TH ST 53233 #016-43-1994 L1996 **OBG** *020 †30

HICKMAN, Jennifer Ann. ■ 53226 #056-06-2004 L2006 **AN** *012

HIEB, Robert Alexander. 9200 W WISCONSIN AVE 53226 #037-01-1992 L1997 **VIR** *020 †80

HIEBERT, Michelle Denise. 2900 W OKLAHOMA AVE 53215 #047-05-1995 L1999 **EM** *020 †16

HIJJAWI, John B. 8700 W WATERTOWN PLANK RD, MED CLG OF WI DEPT PLAS SR 53226 #016-02-1997 L2005 **PS** *020 †65

HILL, Janice Marie. 2400 W VILLARD AVE 53209 #038-45-1993 L1999 **FM** *020 †18

HILL, Tristram Christophe. 6901 W EDGERTON AVE 53220 #422-01-2002 L2004 **FM** *020 †18

HILLERY, Cheryl Ann. 8701 W WATERTOWN PLANK RD, MEDICAL COLLEGE OF WISCONS 53226 #036-07-1984 L1991 **PHO IM** *050 †20,55

HILLMANN, Sylvia Martina. 1020 N 12TH ST 53233 #030-06-1987 L1988 **PD** *040 †55

HILRICH, Nathan M. ■ 53211 #056-05-1951 L1952 **OBG** *071 †30

HIMELSTEIN, Bruce Philip. 7950 N PORT WASHINGTON RD 53217 #035-19-1987 L2001 **PHO** *050 †55

HIMES, Joseph. ■ 53217 #016-42-1946 L1952 **AN** *071 †05

HINDE, Brian Charles. 1733 N CAMBRIDGE AVE 53202 #056-06-2003 L2007 **AN** *012

HINDLE, David Christopher. 9200 W WISCONSIN AVE, DEPT OF EMERGENCY MEDICINE 53226 #917-33-1999 L2001 **EM** *020 †16

HINE, Joseph James. 9200 W WISCONSIN AVE, STE 5200 53226 #011-02-1999 L2001 **PCC** *020 †80

HINER, Bradley Collins. 9200 W WISCONSIN AVE, MED COLLEGE OF WI 53226 #038-40-1982 L1987 **N** *020 †75

HING, Ellen. 9000 W WISCONSIN AVE 53226 #025-07-1982 L1983 **PD** *020 †55

HINKE, David Henry. 2925 W OKLAHOMA AVE 53215 #056-05-1987 L1988 **DR** *020 †80

HINKLE, Stephen Currier. 2500 W LAYTON AVE, STE 280 53221 #032-01-1973 L1978 **RHU IM** *020 †20

HINSON, Robert Eugene. 6530 N PINE SHORE DR 53209 #018-03-1960 L1966 **DR** *020 †80 ‡

HIRANO, Brian Satoru. 2025 E NEWPORT AVE, COLUMBIA ST. MARY'S HOSPIT 53211 #026-04-1995 L1997 **IM** *020 †20

HIRT, Amy Joy. ■ 53226 #056-06-2007 **IM** *012

HLAVA, Mark Andrew. 2900 W OKLAHOMA AVE 53215 #056-06-1991 L1992 **EM** *020 †16

HLAVAC, Robert Jos. 3338 S WHITNALL AVE 53207 #056-05-1960 L1963 **AN** *020 †05

HLODNICKI, Bruce John. 3237 S 16TH ST 53215 #017-20-1982 L1998 **EM** *020 †16

HO, Khang-Cheng. 9200 W WISCONSIN AVE 53226 #385-01-1965 L1975 **NP ATP** *020 †50,75

HODGES, Kelly Rae. ■ 53213 #016-11-2007 **OBG** *012

HODGSON, Mark Emory. 9200 W WISCONSIN AVE, BOX 26099 53226 #025-01-1999 L2005 **HS** *100 †40

HODGSON, Norman B. 2600 N MAYFAIR RD STE 545 53226 #020-01-1951 L1958 **U** *071 †95

HOEFFLEUR, Norman A. 11803 W NORTH AVE 53226 #016-76-1964, ▲ L1965 **GP** *020

HOFFMAN, Burton Paul. ■ 53202 #035-19-1943 L1944 **ORS** *071 †40

HOFFMAN, George Milliard. 9000 W WISCONSIN AVE, CHILDRENS HOSPITAL 53226 #041-01-1980 L1987 **PAN CCP** *020 †55,05

HOGAN, Christine Marie. ■ 53211 #005-02-1995 L2008 ID *020 †20
HOGAN, Quinn Howlett. 9200 W WISCONSIN AVE, DEPT OF ANESTHESIOLOGY 53226 #024-01-1978 L1989 AN OTO *020 †05
HOGAN, Walter Jos. 9200 W WISCONSIN AVE 53226 #056-06-1958 L1959 GE IM *020 †20
HOHENWALTER, Eric J. 9200 W WISCONSIN AVE, FROEDTERT MEMORIAL LUTHERA 53226 #056-06-1998 L1999 VIR *020 †80
HOHENWALTER, Mark David. 9200 W WISCONSIN AVE, DEPT RAD MED COLL OF WISC 53226 #056-05-1993 L1994 DR *020 †80
HOKE, Samuel Edwin. 201 N MAYFAIR RD 53226 #038-41-1966 L1968 GE IM *020 †20
HOLAK, Elena J. 9200 W WISCONSIN AVE 53226 #047-06-1989 L1992 AN *040 †05
HOLBROOK, Meredith Ann. ■ 53222 #056-06-2006 L2008 P *012
HOLLAND, Kristen E. 9200 W WISCONSIN AVE, DERMATOLOGY DEPT 53226 #038-43-2000 L2003 D *020 †15
HOLLENBAUGH, Raina Leanne. 3223 S 103RD ST 53227 #054-04-1988 L1989 AN *020 †05
HOLLINGSWORTH, Margarita. 9200 W WISCONSIN AVE, MEDICAL COLLEGE OF 53226 #016-42-2000 L2002 U *100 ‡
HOLLISTER, Winston Ned. 10425 W NORTH AVE, STE 215 53226 #056-06-1971 L1973 PTH IM *020 †20,50
HOLTH, Michael David. ■ 53224 #056-06-2008 *012
HONG, Sang Hun. 925 N 87TH ST, THE EYE INSTITUTE 53226 #016-06-1993 L2003 OPH *020
HONG, Stephen Victor. 53210 #016-11-2005 PD *100
HOOGERLAND, David Lee. 2323 N LAKE DR 53211 #025-01-1970 L1971 GO OBG *020 †30
HOOP, Jinger Gail. 8701 W WATERTOWN PLANK RD, DEPT OF PSYCH MCW 53226 #016-02-2000 L2006 P *020 †75
HOOPFER, Jean Ann. 3365 S 103RD ST 53227 #056-06-1998 L1999 PD *020 †55
HOPE, William Gerard. 9200 W WISCONSIN AVE, FMLH-EAST 53226 #048-02-1991 L1993 AN *020 †05
HORNEFFER, Elizabeth Ann. 9000 W WISCONSIN AVE 53226 #025-01-1990 L1993 PD *071 †55
HORNER-IBLER, Barbara A. 8320 W BLUEMOUND RD, STE 125 53213 #056-05-1998 L2000 IM *020 †20
HOROWITZ, Mary Frances. 8701 W WATERTOWN PLANK RD, STE H2500 53226 #056-06-1980 L1981 ON *050 †20
HOROWITZ, Noah. 735 N WATER ST STE 911 53202 #065-06-1999 L2000 P *020 †75
HOWARDS, Lawrence Allen. ■ 53209 #056-05-1958 L1959 AN PME *071 †05
HOYT, Alastair. ■ 53213 #030-05-2005 NS *012
HUANG, Allen Tzu-Chuan. 4421 N 73RD ST 53218 #242-03-1943 L1959 PD *071 †55
HUANG, Chuong Chun. 9200 W WISCONSIN AVE 53226 #385-02-1962 L1977 P *020 ‡
HUANG, Kou Chou. ■ 53208 #020-02-1975 L1976 AN *020
HUANG, Nancy Yee. ■ 53208 #016-01-2007 IM *012
HUBER, Anne Louise. ■ 53211 #056-06-2007 *012
HUBER, Brad Settle. 9200 W WISCONSIN AVE, OF DERMATOLOGY 53226 #001-02-2005 L2006 D *012
HUBLEY, Theodore James. 2900 W OKLAHOMA AVE, FL 1 53215 #056-06-1990 L1991 PCC SME *020 †20
HUMPHREY, John Atwell. 9000 W WISCONSIN AVE, PALLIATIVE CARE DEPT. MAIL 53226 #045-01-1978 L1979 PD *020
HUMPHREY, Stephen Michael. 3237 S 16TH ST 53215 #048-14-1996 L2002 VIR *020 †80
HUNG, Serena Wansi. 9200 W WISCONSIN AVE 53226 #036-05-1998 L2005 N *020 †75
HUNTER, Paul Henry. 1825 N PROSPECT AVE 53202 #056-05-1989 L1990 FM *020 †18
HUR, Su-Ryong. 8700 W WISCONSIN AVE, DEPT ANESTH 53226 #583-02-1966 L1976 AN *020 †05
HURLEY, Patrick Thomas. ■ 53202 #055-01-2002 L2004 DR *100 †80
HURST, Denise Lynn. 2801 W KINNICKINC RVR PKWY, STE 777 53215 #021-01-1991 L1991 ICE *100 †20
HURWITZ, Lawrence Sheldon. 2266 N PROSPECT AVE, STE 503 53202 #005-11-1968 L1973 ON HEM *020
HUSKE, Alisen Brie. ■ 53222 #028-02-2005 L2007 PD *012
HUSNAIN, Fouad Jamal-Ul. 8701 W WATERTOWN PLANK RD 53226 #704-25-2000 L2006 PCC *012 †20
HUSSAIN, Syed Ather. 9200 W WISCONSIN AVE, MED COLL OF WISCONSIN 53226 #704-02-1994 L2000 NEP OS *020 †20
HUSSAINI, Syed N. 4555 W SCHROEDER DR, STE 170 53223 #495-21-1985 L1995 APM *020 †05
HUSSUSSIAN, Jacques. 2323 N LAKE DR 53211 #330-03-1955 L1966 ORS *071 †40
HUSTON, Erwin S. ■ 53217 #056-05-1950 L1951 OM IM *071 †20
HUXLEY, Eliot Jeral. 3000 W MONTANA AVE 53215 #056-05-1972 L1973 PUD IM *030 †20
HUXLEY, Robert Leslie. 3056 S KINNICKINNIC AVE, # 300 53207 #056-05-1977 L1978 CD *020
HYNDIUK, Robert Anthony. 925 N 87TH ST 53226 #016-43-1962 L1971 OPH *071 †35
IBSA, Fisseha Tadesse. 5818 W CAPITOL DR 53216 #366-01-1994 L2004 IM *040 †20
IDRESS, Rozina Sohail. 2555 N DR MRTN LTHR KNG DR, CENTER 53212 #704-02-1995 L2001 IM *020 †20
IFARINDE, Joan O. 555 S 108TH ST 53214 #690-08-1990 L1994 PD *020 †55
ILCHENKO, Boris G. 2801 W KK RIVER PKWY, STE 453 53215 #913-63-1991 L2004 AN *020 †05 ‡
INGLESE, Christopher M. 2801 W KINNICKINC RVR PKWY, STE 570 53215 #561-01-1982 L1992 NSP N *020 †75
IQBAL, Asma. 8200 W SILVER SPRING DR, ISAAC COGGS HERITAGE HEALT 53218 #704-25-2000 L2006 P *100
IQBAL, Muhammad Asif. 9200 W WISCONSIN AVE, INTERAL MEDICINE 53226 #704-01-1997 L2004 ID *012
IQBAL, Zafar. 5000 W NATIONAL AVE 112A, VAMC ANESTHESIOLOGY 53295 #704-01-1987 L2001 AN CCA *012
IRION, Richard Nelson. ■ 53216 #056-06-2008 *012
ISITMAN, Ali T. 8700 W WISCONSIN AVE 53226 #902-03-1952 L1981 NM IM *040 †28
ISOM, Ryan Franklin. ■ 53215 #035-09-2007 TY *012
ISSA, Mazen. 9200 W WISCONSIN AVE, DEPT OF MEDICINE 53226 #875-02-1996 L2005 IM *020 †20
ITABLE, Fernando Tan. 2745 W LAYTON AVE, STE 201 53221 #028-34-1993 L1994 IM *020 †20
ITABLE, Rodrigo R. 2315 N LAKE DR 53211 #748-01-1967 L1976 GP IM *020
IVSIN, Rostislav. 5300 W VILLARD AVE 53218 #286-02-1957 L1975 GP *020
IZARD, Kevin Dwayne. 1452 N 7TH ST 53205 #056-06-1995 L1997 FM *020 †18
IZARD, Tito Lamont. 2555 N DR MRTN LTHR KNG DR, CENTER 53212 #056-05-1996 L1998 FM *020 †18
JABLONSKI, Chester Wm. 2323 N LAKE DR BOX 503 53211 #017-20-1976 L1980 PTH *020 †50
JACKSON, Leon Jos. 3237 S 16TH ST 53215 #056-06-1971 L1972 ID *020 †16
JACKSON, Thomas Carleton. 1020 N 12TH ST 53233 #056-05-1967 L1970 IM *071 †20

JACOB, Shibin Thomas. 945 N 12TH ST, DEPT OF INTERNAL MEDICINE 53233 #495-44-1996 L2000 PCC *012 †20
JACOBS, Elizabeth H. 8701 W WATERTOWN PLANK RD, MEDICAL COLLEGE WISCONSIN 53226 #019-02-1977 L1989 PUD IM *050 †20
JACOBSOHN, Harold Alfred. 2900 W OKLAHOMA AVE 53215 #056-06-1967 L1968 U *020 †95
JACOBSON, Foster Jos. 7020 N PORT WASHINGTON RD 53217 #056-06-1945 L1946 GYN *071 †30
JACOBSON, Richard David. 9000 W WISCONSIN AVE, BOX 1997 53226 #016-02-1982 L1990 CHN CN *020 †75,55
JAIN, Asha. 8675 N PORT WASHINGTON RD, STE 120 53217 #495-08-1974 L1978 PD *020
JAIN, Dharam Pal. 2311 N PROSPECT AVE, CSMCP PROSPECT MEDICAL COM 53211 #495-08-1973 L1978 CD IM *020 †20
JAIN, Nitin. 8701 W WATERTOWN PLANK RD, DEPARTMENT OF MEDICINE, MC 53226 #495-36-2003 L2005 IM *100 †20
JAMES, Janine A. 4038 N 39TH ST, THE PERINATAL CTR OF WISC 53216 #016-11-1979 L1985 MFM OBG *040 †30
JAMMULA, Praveen. 960 N 12TH ST 4TH FL, AURORA SINAI MEDICAL CENT 53233 #495-65-1997 L2006 ICE *020 †20
JANIK, Grace Marie. 2015 E NEWPORT AVE, STE 707 53211 #056-06-1984 L1986 REN *020 †30
JANKINS, Daniel Bryan. 10950 W CAPITOL DR, COLUMBIA WESTMEDICAL CLINI 53222 #056-06-1985 L1993 IM *020 †20
JAQUISS, Robert Douglas. 9000 W WISCONSIN AVE, MCOW/CHOW/FMLH 53226 #047-05-1986 L2000 TS GS *020 †85,90
JARADEH, Safwan Salim. 9200 W WISCONSIN AVE, FROEDTERT MEMORIAL HOSPITA 53226 #875-01-1979 L1989 N CHN *020 †75
JARAMILLO, Luis Alejandro. 8700 W WATERTOWN PLANK RD, DEPARTMENT OF PLASTIC SURG 53226 #264-03-1996 L2006 PS *012 †85
JARENWATTANANON, Apichai. 2025 E NEWPORT AVE, WISCONSIN RADIOLOGY 53211 #891-01-1974 L1986 DR RNR *020 †80
JAVADI, Pardis. ■ 53221 #056-06-2008 *012
JAY, Allison Meredith. 8701 W WATERTOWN PLANK RD, MED COLL WI 53226 #016-02-2007 PD *012
JAY, Mary Susan. 8701 W WATERTOWN PLANK RD, DEPT. OF PED 53226 #016-11-1976 L2004 PD ADL *020 †55
JAY, Rodney Gillman, Jr. ■ 53216 #056-06-2008 *012
JAYARAMAN, Vijay. 9200 W WISCONSIN AVE, ROOM 295, DYNACARE LAB 53226 #016-06-2004 L2006 GS *012
JAZAYERI, Pooya John. ■ 53208 #056-06-2004 AN *012
JEDNACAK, Marijan. 10000 W BLUEMOUND RD 53226 #957-01-1993 L2002 AN *020
JELENCHICK, Erwin John. ■ 53226 #056-06-1941 L1941 GP *071
JELLA, Abhay K. 2901 W KINNICKINC RVR PKWY 53215 #495-21-1990 L2005 IM *020 †20
JENK, Lloyd Francis. 2400 W VILLARD AVE 53209 #018-03-1943 L1948 P N *071 †75
JENKINS, Paul Geo. 1575 N RIVERCENTER DR, DRIVE #104 53212 #056-05-1969 L1971 NEP IM *020 †20
JENKS, David Mark. 3003 W GOOD HOPE RD, HOPE ROAD CLINIC 53209 #016-43-1996 L1999 IM *020 †20
JENSEN, John Newcomb. ■ 53202 #028-02-1994 L2003 PS *020 †65
JENSEN, Michael Kyle. 9000 W WISCONSIN AVE, PEDIATRIC GASTROENTEROLOGY 53226 #049-01-2004 L2007 PG *012
JENSON, James Jos. 8701 W WATERTOWN PLANK RD, TOSA CENTER 3RD FLOOR 53226 #041-02-1987 L2002 CHP P *040 †75 ‡
JENTZEN, Jeffrey Mitchell. 933 W HIGHLAND AVE 53233 #025-07-1980 L1987 FOP PTH *020 †50
JEVTIC, Jasna. 9200 W WISCONSIN AVE 53226 #056-06-1991 L2001 IM *020 †20
JEYARAJ, Hamilton. 2801 W KK RIVER PKWY, STE 175 53215 #495-37-2003 L2006 FM *100
JHANSALE, Sheila. 10950 W CAPITOL DR 53222 #056-06-1995 L2002 IM *020 †20
JOCHEM, Richard Jefferey. 8901 W LINCOLN AVE, MEMORIAL HOSPITAL 53227 #038-41-1985 L1990 DR *020 †80
JOCHEN, Albert Lawrence. 9200 W WISCONSIN AVE, DIV OF ENDOC & METABOLISM 53226 #023-01-1979 L1987 END IM *020 †20
JOGAL, Sachin Sharad. 8701 W WATERTOWN PLANK RD, HEMATOLOGY/ONCOLOGY STE 3 53226 #033-06-1992 L2001 PHO *020 †55
JOHN, Abie Jacob. 8701 W WATERTOWN PLANK RD, ANESTHESIOLOGY EAST OFFICE 53226 #495-37-2002 L2006 AN *012
JOHNSON, Anne Marie. 9200 W WISCONSIN AVE, DEPT OF EMERGENCY MEDICINE 53226 #016-43-2003 L2004 EM *020 †16
JOHNSON, Beth Ann. 9000 W WISCONSIN AVE, HERMA HEART CENTER MS713 53226 #016-11-1997 L2002 CCP *012 †15
JOHNSON, Brian Chas. 12129 W FEERICK ST 53222 #056-05-1985 L1986 AN *020 †20
JOHNSON, Christopher P. 9200 W WISCONSIN AVE 53226 #056-05-1979 L1986 GS VS *020 †85
JOHNSON, David Paul. 1121 E NORTH AVE 53212 #056-06-1996 L1997 FM *020 †18
JOHNSON, George Kenneth. 9200 W WISCONSIN AVE, GI-HEPATOLOGY 53226 #049-01-1965 L1967 GE IM *020 †20
JOHNSON, Jennifer Holaday. 3003 W GOOD HOPE RD, HOPE ROAD CLINIC 53209 #056-06-1986 L1991 IM *020 †20
JOHNSON, Kenneth Edward. 2015 E NEWPORT AVE STE 409 53211 #016-11-1985 L1986 P *020 †75
JOHNSON, Matthew Wayne. 2801 W KINNICKINC RVR PKWY, STE 370 53215 #016-01-1996 L1997 U SO *020 †95
JOHNSON, Michael Albert. 801 S 70TH ST 53214 #016-43-1995 L1996 PD *020 †55
JOHNSON, Roger Paul. 5233 W MORGAN AVE 53220 #056-06-1967 L1968 ORS *071 †40
JOHNSON, Shalini. 925 N 87TH ST, EYE INSTIT 53226 #016-11-2004 L2005 OPH *012
JOHNSON, Shannon Marie. ■ 53202 #028-34-2005 L2007 MPD *012
JOHNSON, Sydney J. ■ 53211 #016-76-1956, ▲ L1957 AN *071
JOHNSON, Tad Mark. 400 W RIVER WOODS PKWY 53212 #026-08-1982 L1983 PD AI *020 †55,03 ‡
JOHNSTON, Steve Russell. 2320 N LAKE DR 53211 #056-05-1994 L2002 FM *020 ‡
JONES, Melissa Chanel. ■ 53212 #056-06-2008 *012
JONES, Paula Geo. 1020 N 12TH ST 53233 #056-05-1977 L1985 ID *020 †20
JONES, Robert Mc Laren. 8701 W WATERTOWN PLANK RD 53226 #671-01-1974 L1987 GS *100
JONES, Seth Reuben. 9200 W WISCONSIN AVE, DEPT OF PLASTIC SURGERY 53226 #031-01-2004 L2005 PS *012
JONES, Thomas Robert. ■ 53214 #012-05-2005 L2006 ORS *012
JONES-NOSACEK, Cynthia. 2311 N PROSPECT AVE, STE 401 53211 #016-43-1980 L1983 FM OBS *020 †18

JORDAHL, Clarence Wm. ■ 53211 #035-03-1954 L1963 **IM PUD** *071 †20

JORDAN, Ruth Ann. ■ 53211 #035-01-1957 L1959 **IM OM** *071

JOSEPH, Manuel. 180 W GRANGE AVE, FAMILY HEALTH PLAN 53207 #495-52-1979 L1992 **IM** *020 †20

JOSEPH, Reshmi. 5000 W CHAMBERS ST 53210 #495-63-2000 L2007 **IM** *020 †20

JOSEPHSON, Morton. ■ 53210 #016-42-1950 L1959 **P** *071 †75

JOY, Brian Francis. ■ 53217 #026-04-2004 L2005 **CCP** *012 †55

JUGOVAC, Izabela. ■ 53226 #957-05-2001 **GS** *012

JULY, Laura Violet. 945 N 12TH ST, STE 1042 53233 #068-01-1995 L2006 **GS** *020

JUNKERMAN, Charles Lee. 9200 W WISCONSIN AVE 53226 #056-06-1947 L1948 **IM** *071 †20

JURISIC, Anthony. 9455 W WATERTOWN PLANK RD 53226 #957-01-1950 L1963 **P** *020

JURISIC, Maja Antonia. 8923 W BROWN DEER RD 53224 #056-05-1980 L1981 **OM** *020 †16,70

JURVA, Jason Weldon. 9200 W WISCONSIN AVE, MEDICAL COLLEGE OF WISCONS 53226 #025-01-1997 L1999 **CD** *100 †20

JUST, John Francis. 3333 N MAYFAIR RD, STE 209 53222 #016-11-1961 L1962 **TS** *020 †85,90

KACKA, Michael J. 8701 W WATERTOWN PLANK RD 53226 #048-12-2006 **PD** *012

KACZMAROWSKI, Amy Lynn. ■ 53226 #056-06-2008 *012

KADEMIAN, Michael Thos. ■ 53217 #005-02-1972 L1973 **RO** *020 †80

KAEHLER, Susan Lee. 2015 E NEWPORT AVE, STE 409 53211 #396-18-1980 L1985 **P** *020 †75

KAFTAN, Gregory Robt. ■ 53211 #030-06-1991 L1993 **OM** *020 †70

KAHLON, Pundeep Kaur. ■ 53223 #661-03-2007 *100

KAHN, Charles Edward, Jr. 9200 W WISCONSIN AVE 53226 #016-11-1985 L1991 **DR** *020 †80

KAIKOBAD, Mahazarin Rumi. 9200 W WISCONSIN AVE, FROEDTERT AND MEDICAL COLL 53226 #495-96-2002 L2006 **IM** *012

KALENAK, Jeffrey Ward. 2600 N MAYFAIR RD STE 600 53226 #025-01-1983 L1985 **OPH** *020 †35

KALLAS, Gerald J. 2315 N LAKE DR 53211 #056-06-1962 L1963 **ON HEM** *071 †20

KALOGJERA, Ikar Jaksa. 1220 DEWEY AVE 53213 #957-01-1970 L1973 **P CHP** *020 †75

KAMATH, M Laxman. 3900 W BROWN DEER RD, STE A308 53209 #495-37-1966 L1977 **TS** *020 †85,90

KAMELLE, Scott Ahmed. 2801 W KINNICKINC RVR PKWY, STE 525 53215 #024-05-1995 L2007 **OBG** *020 †30

KAMPALATH, Balagopalan. 9200 W WISCONSIN AVE, MDCL CLLGE CLNCS AT FRDTRT 53226 #495-44-1979 L1998 **SP** *020 †50

KAMPALATH, Latha N. 9000 W WISCONSIN AVE, CHILDREN'S HOSPITAL/WISCON 53226 #495-39-1978 L1998 **AN** *020 †05,55

KAMPINE, John Paul. 8700 W WISCONSIN AVE, DEPT OF ANES BOX 150 53226 #056-06-1961 L1962 **AN OS** *050 †05

KAMPSCHROER, Bernard Hugh. 5000 W CHAMBERS ST, ST JOSEPHS HOSPITAL 53210 #056-05-1967 L1968 **R** *072 †80

KANAGALA, Rajesh. 9200 W WISCONSIN AVE 53226 #495-21-1999 L2005 **IM** *020 †20

KANDEEPAN, Jeyachelvi. 3000 W MONTANA ST 53215 #665-01-2005 **FM** *100

KANDIAH, Prem Anand. 1920 N FARWELL AVE UNIT 4 53202 #894-01-2000 L2005 **MN** *012

KANDULA, Madan Narayana. 555 S 108TH ST 53214 #041-09-1998 L2002 **OTO** *020 †45

KANE, Derek Douglas. 9200 W WISCONSIN AVE, STE 3510 53226 #016-01-2004 L2005 **GS** *012

KANE, Jason Marc. 9000 W WISCONSIN AVE MS 6, PEDIATRIC CRITICAL CARE ME 53226 #016-01-1999 L2003 **CCP** *020 †20

KANE, Richard Scott. 1020 N 12TH ST, FL 3 53233 #056-05-1973 L1974 **IM IMG** *020

KANSRA, Alvina R. 8701 W WATERTOWN PLANK RD 53226 #496-26-1995 L2007 **PDE** *100 †20,55

KANTER, Eric Stuart. ■ 53202 #056-06-2000 L2002 **CHP** *020

KAO, Dennis Shun Jen. 8700 W WATERTOWN PLANK RD, DEPARTMENT OF PLASTIC SURG 53226 #048-02-2003 L2005 **PS** *012

KAPETSONIS, Mario. 734 N JACKSON ST 53202 #306-01-1998 L2001 **FM** *020 †18

KAPLAN, Eric W. 2025 E NEWPORT AVE RM 110, COLUMBIA HOSPITAL 53211 #016-01-1983 L1993 **PYG P** *020 †75

KAPLUNSKY, Polina. 5000 W NATIONAL AVE, ZABLOCKI VA MEDICAL CENTER 53295 #913-19-1987 L1998 **P** *020

KAPPES, Steven Kenneth. 3003 W GOOD HOPE RD, HOPE ROAD CLINIC 53209 #017-20-1977 L1978 **GS CD** *020 †85

KARICH LAUER, Kathryn Ann. 9200 W WISCONSIN AVE 53226 #056-06-1984 L1986 **AN** *020 †05

KARIM, Minhaz. 1218 W KILBOURN AVE # 124, PROCARE MED CLNC 53233 #160-02-1994 L2004 **IM** *020

KARKOS, Jerie Beth. 9000 W WISCONSIN AVE, CHILDREN'S CORPORATE CENTE 53226 #016-11-1979 L2007 **PD** *020 †55

KARMAKAR, Phullara. 2025 E NEWPORT AVE, CAMPUS OF COLUMBIA ST MARY 53211 #495-02-1995 L2004 **IM** *020

KARMARKAR, Ravindra S. 3070 N 51ST ST, # 540 53210 #495-28-1990 L2000 **ID** *020 †20

KARNES, Mack Alan. 945 N 12TH ST 53233 #016-11-1971 L1978 **R** *020 †80

KARRICK, Andrea Michelle. ■ 53208 #028-34-2007 **EM** *012

KASARABADA, Aditya. 8701 W WATERTOWN PLANK RD, MED COLL WI AFFIL HOSPS 53226 #495-73-2002 L2007 **IM** *012

KASLOW, Olga Yuryevna. 9200 W WISCONSIN AVE, DEPT ANESTHESIOLOGY-FMLH 53226 #913-15-1984 L2002 **AN** *020 †05

KASNER, Jay R. 2315 N LAKE DR 53211 #056-05-1974 L1975 **NM** *020 †28

KATAYAMA, K Paul. 2801 W KINNICKINC RVR PKWY, STE 535 53215 #572-03-1962 L1975 **OBG REN** *020 †30

KATT, Jeffrey Alan. 3003 W GOOD HOPE RD, AURORA ADVANCED HEALTHCARE 53209 #025-01-1988 L1989 **IM** *020 †20

KATZ, Peter John. ■ 53226 #056-06-2007 **TY** *012

KATZOFF, Michael Noah. 2801 W KINNICKINC RVR PKWY, STE 445 53215 #035-09-1976 L1979 **PUD SME** *020 †20

KAUFMAN, Bruce Allen. 9200 W WISCONSIN AVE, CHILDRENS HOSP 53226 #038-06-1982 L2000 **NS NSP** *020 †25

KAUFMAN, Jack. 9200 W WISCONSIN AVE 53226 #038-40-1960 L1971 **IM PUD** *020 †20

KAUR, Kawaljeet. 8701 W WATERTOWN PLANK RD, MED COLL WI AFFIL HOSPS 53226 #495-41-1998 L2006 **END** *012 †20

KAUTH, Laurence Chas. 1220 DEWEY AVE 53213 #056-06-1968 L1969 **P** *020

KAY, Jonathan. 2801 W KK RIVER PKWY, STE 453 53215 #041-02-1975 L1976 **AN IM** *020 †20,05

KAY, Marilyn Joan C. 2801 W KINNICKINC RVR PKWY, STE 170 53215 #041-02-1975 L1976 **OPH N** *020 †35

KAYE, Robin Diane. 8522 W CAPITOL DR, PEDIATRIC DIAGNOSTIC 53222 #007-02-1986 L2006 **R PDR** *020 †80

KAZI, Fahim Ud Din. 9000 W WISCONSIN AVE 53226 #704-25-1993 L2001 **AN** *020 †05

KEANE, Sean Patrick. 2315 N LAKE DR STE 1007 53211 #539-02-1961 L1970 **ORS TRS** *020

KEARNS, Christopher M. 2015 E NEWPORT AVE, MILW UROLOGICAL S.C. 53211 #056-06-1989 L1990 **U** *020 †95

KEARNS, John Westhofen. 2015 E NEWPORT AVE STE 20 53211 #023-07-1947 L1955 **U** *071 †95

KEBBEKUS, Robert A. 5000 W CHAMBERS ST 53210 #056-05-1952 L1953 **OM** *072

KEENAN, Andrew George. ■ 53213 #056-06-2008 *012

KEIM, Rebecca Lynn. 2801 W KINNICKINC RVR PKWY, STE 330 53215 #056-06-2003 L2005 **GS** *012

KEISERMAN, Wayne Mark. 10701 W RESEARCH DR, UNITED HLTH CARE OF WI 53226 #041-02-1970 L1998 **FM U** *100 †18

KEITH, Philip Adamson. 9200 W WISCONSIN AVE, DEPT DIAG RAD 53226 #038-41-2003 L2005 **DR** *012

KELLEY, William Bernard. 2675 N MAYFAIR RD, STE 110 53226 #028-34-1967 L1969 **GS** *020 †85 ‡

KELLY, Michael Edward. 8701 W WATERTOWN PLANK RD, CHILDREN'S HOSPITAL OF WIS 53226 #038-41-1993 L2005 **PHO** *055

KELLY, Thomas M. 201 N MAYFAIR RD, 2ND FL 53226 #035-20-1975 L1990 **END IM** *020 †20

KELLY, Tracy Rebecca. 8701 W WATERTOWN PLANK RD, DEPT OF RADIATION ONCOLOGY 53226 #056-06-2003 L2004 **RO** *012

KENNEDY, Jennifer Alphons. 2025 E NEWPORT AVE 53211 #495-04-1988 L2007 **PM** *020 †60

KENNY, Dermot Jos. 9200 W WISCONSIN AVE, CARDIOVASCULAR MEDICINE 53226 #539-06-1982 L1990 **CD** *020 †20

KENNY, Eugene Charles, IV. 1730 N FRANKLIN PL # 2R 53202 #056-05-2002 L2003 **EM** *020 †16

KENWOOD, Stanley Norbert. ■ 53223 #056-06-1956 L1957 **PD** *071 †55

KEPPELER, Paula Elizabeth. 3003 W GOOD HOPE RD 53209 #056-05-2003 L2005 **PD** *020 †55

KERMGARD, Mark Stephen. 5000 W CHAMBERS ST 53210 #016-06-1985 L1993 **EM** *020 †16

KERRIGAN, Gerald Austin. 8701 W WATERTOWN PLANK RD 53226 #024-01-1946 L1956 **PD END** *072 †55

KERSCHNER, Joseph Edward. 9000 W WISCONSIN AVE, MAIL STATION 782A 53226 #056-06-1990 L1996 **PDO OTO** *020 †45

KERSTEN, Judy Rae. 8701 W WATERTOWN PLANK RD, MED COLLEGE OF WISCONSIN 53226 #056-05-1988 L1992 **AN** *050 †05

KERWIN, Diana Rose. 9200 W WISCONSIN AVE, FROEDERT-EAST CLINIC BUILD 53226 #056-06-1996 L2002 **IM** *020 †20

KESKEY, Charles Wm. 2315 N LAKE DR 53211 #025-01-1954 L1958 **OPH** *020 †35

KESSLER, Elizabeth Anne. ■ 53202 #016-43-2007 **PD** *012

KETCHUM, Nicholas Clare. ■ 53202 #056-05-2006 **PM** *012

KETTERHAGEN, James P. 2025 E NEWPORT AVE 53211 #056-06-1978 L1979 **MDM VS** *020 †80

KETTLER, Robert Earl. 8700 W WISCONSIN AVE, MILWAUKEE COUNTY MED CMPLX 53226 #056-06-1979 L1982 **AN PME** *020 †05

KHAIR, Gamil Zaki. 9000 W NATIONAL AVE 53295 #330-02-1958 L1973 **CD IM** *071 †20

KHALIL, Johnmichael Nessi. ■ 53227 #056-05-2004 L2005 **DR** *012

KHAN, Ariba. 1020 N 12TH ST, FL 2 53233 #704-21-1997 L2001 **IMG** *020 †20

KHAN, Gouhar Yusuof. 3070 N 51ST ST, STE 408 53210 #665-01-2002 L2006 **OBG** *020

KHAN, Ijaz Mohammad. 3237 S 16TH ST 53215 #704-09-1982 L1993 **GE** *020 †20

KHAN, Jawad Hasan. 3201 S 16TH ST, STE 2006 53215 #704-21-1991 L2000 **PCC** *020 †20

KHAN, Mir. 6901 W EDGERTON AVE, AURORA EDGERTON CLINIC 53220 #495-21-1983 L1992 **FM** *020 †18

KHAN, Mohammad Q. 2727 W CLEVELAND AVE 53215 #704-19-1980 L1994 **IM** *020 †20

KHAN, Muhammad Yusuof. 1218 W KILBOURN AVE # 101 53233 #704-02-1968 L1976 **GS GP** *020 †85

KHAN, Saira Mahnoor Aslam. ■ 53214 #704-01-2004 **FP** *012

KHAN, Saniya. 8701 W WATERTOWN PLANK RD, MED COLL OF WI 53226 #704-25-2002 L2004 **PCC** *012 †20

KHANNA, Raman. 7878 N 76TH ST, NORTHWEST CLINIC 53223 #495-45-1980 L2003 **GE** *020 †20

KHATRI, Bhupendra Odhavji. 2801 W KINNICKINC RVR PKWY, STE 135 53215 #495-01-1974 L1981 **N** *020 †75

KHATRI, Vikram. ■ 53226 #496-59-2001 L2008 *100

KHATTAB, Razan. 945 N 12TH ST 53233 #875-01-2000 L2006 **IM** *012

KHAWARI, Maryam. 9200 W WISCONSIN AVE, MCW DEPARTMENT OF MEDICINE 53226 #704-02-1999 L2004 **RHU** *012 †20

KHITHA, Jayant. 2801 W KK RIVER PKWY, STE 840 53215 #913-99-1997 L2006 **IC** *020 †20

KHOGALI, Aymen Mohammed. 2224 W WISCONSIN AVE # 2 53233 #848-01-2000 L2008 **IM** *012

KIDAMBI, Srividya. 9200 W WISCONSIN AVE, FROEDTERT EAST 53226 #495-65-1996 L2001 **END** *100 †20

KIDDER, Thomas Michael. 9200 W WISCONSIN AVE 53226 #056-06-1968 L1969 **OTO** *020 †45

KIELY, James Mark. 9200 W WISCONSIN AVE 53226 #539-03-1999 **GS** *012

KIM, Hak-Joong. 5757 W OKLAHOMA AVE # 101, END/INTERNAL MED 53219 #583-02-1963 L1977 **END IM** *020 †20

KIM, Joseph Myoungsik. 900 W BLUEMOUND RD 53226 #583-10-1970 L1979 **AN** *020 †05

KIM, Judy E. 925 N 87TH ST, THE EYE INST 53226 #023-07-1990 L1994 **OPH** *020 †35

KIM, Michael Kwang. 999 N 92ND ST C550, CHILDREN'S CORPORATE CENTE 53226 #016-42-1988 L1994 **PEM** *020 †55

KIM, S John. 2900 W OKLAHOMA AVE 53215 #583-10-1974 L1982 **P** *020

KIM, Sungwon. ■ 53202 #010-01-2007 **OTO** *012

KIM, Una Olivia. 8701 W WATERTOWN PLANK RD 53226 #017-20-1998 L2004 **PD** *020 †55

KIM, Yong Woo. 2323 N LAKE DR 53211 #583-04-1952 L1970 **DR** *071 †80

KING, Adam Gideon. ■ 53217 #056-06-2006 L2008 **MPD** *012

KING, Arthur Roy. 2414 N FARWELL AVE 53211 #056-05-1982 L1983 **FM** *020 †18

KING, David Matthew. 9200 W WISCONSIN AVE, MED CLG OF WISC ORTHO SURG 53226 #018-03-1996 L2002 **ORS SO** *020 †40

KING, Douglas. 5000 W CHAMBERS ST 53210 #539-03-1954 L1969 **RO** *071 †80

KING, Ericka Francine. 9200 W WISCONSIN AVE 53226 #054-04-2005 L2006 **OTO** *012

KING, Kathy Ann. 9200 W WISCONSIN AVE, DEPT OF OB/GYN 53226 #056-05-1997 L1998 **OBG** *020 †30

KING, Stacey Lynn. ■ 53202 #056-06-2007 **FP** *012

KINGCAID, Evette Claretta. 5818 W CAPITOL DR 53216 #056-05-1998 L2000 **FM** *020 †18

KINGHORN, Katherine Ann. 9200 W WISCONSIN AVE, ANESTHESIA 53226 #056-06-2000 L2001 **AN** *020 †05

KIRVAITIS, Romas Jos. 960 N 12TH ST, 4TH FL 53233 #056-05-1992 L2006 **CD** *012 †20

KISPERT, John Fay. 2424 S 90TH ST 53227 #025-07-1984 L1985 **GS VS** *020 †85

KISSEBAH, Ahmed Hamed. 9200 W WISCONSIN AVE, FROEDTERT MEMORIAL LUTHERN 53226 #915-02-1961 L1979 **IM END** *020

KISTLER, Lane Andrew. 2901 W KINNICKINNIC PKWY, STE 414 53215 #035-19-1972 L1973 **GE IM** *020 †20

KIVLIN, Jane Douglas. 925 N 87TH ST 53226 #023-07-1975 L1990 **PO** *020 †35

KIYONO, Kathryn Margit. 4448 W LOOMIS RD 53220 #056-06-1992 L1993 **FM** *020 †18

KLAMECKI, Bernard Jos. 3237 S 16TH ST 53215 #056-06-1957 L1958 **CRS** *071

KLAMIK, James G. 2025 E NEWPORT AVE, COLUMBIA HOSP DEPT ANESTH 53211 #056-05-1979 L1982 **AN** *020 †05

KLAS, James Victor. 2801 W KINNICKINC RVR PKWY, STE 330 53215 #056-05-1990 L1991 **CRS** *020 †85,10

KLATT, Timothy Egon. 9200 W WISCONSIN AVE, DEPT OBGYN 53226 #041-12-1992 L2004 **OBG** *020 †30

KLECZKA, James Fredrick. 9200 W WISCONSIN AVE, STE 5100 53226 #056-06-1996 L1997 **CD** *020 †20

KLECZKA, Laura Marie. 840 N 87TH ST 53226 #056-06-1992 L1993 **IM** *020 †20

KLEHM, David Harry. 6901 W EDGERTON AVE 53220 #056-05-1975 L1976 **FM** *020 †18

KLEIMAN, Molly May. 9000 W WISCONSIN AVE, CGO MEDICAL EDUCATION 53226 #056-06-2006 L2008 **MPD** *012

KLEIN, Andrew Paul. 2900 W OKLAHOMA AVE, ST LUKES MEDICAL CENTER 53215 #030-06-2003 L2004 **DR** *012

KLEIN, Jared Leb. 311 E ERIE ST, UNIT 205 53202 #038-06-1978 L2006 **HEM PD** *050 †55

KLEIN, Jeffrey Allen. ■ 53203 #016-45-2007 **TY** *012

KLEIN, Morris. ■ 53217 #026-04-1948 L1949 **IM** *071 †20

KLEINER, Harvey. 9200 W WISCONSIN AVE 53226 #056-06-1972 L1973 **OTO** *020 †45

KLEINMAN, Jack G. VA MED CTR RENAL 111K 53295 #035-19-1968 L1975 **NEP IM** *050 †20

KLEINMAN, Leonard H. 2901 W KINNICKINC RVR PKWY, STE 310 53215 #035-19-1970 L1978 **TS** *020 †85,90

KLEINMAN, Mark Ellsworth. ■ 53217 #035-19-2005 **GS** *100

KLIEGMAN, Robert Mark. 999 N 92ND ST, CHILDREN'S CORPORATE CENTE 53226 #035-08-1974 L1993 **PD** *050 †55

KLIMOPOULOS, Serafim N. ■ 53220 #418-01-1974 *100

KLINGBEIL, Frederick T. 9000 W WISCONSIN AVE, CHILDREN'S HOSPITAL OF WIS 53226 #025-07-1990 L2002 **OS PM** *020 †60

KLINGBEIL, Mark Allen. 999 N 92ND ST, STE 350 53226 #056-06-1985 L1986 **PM PD** *020 †55,60

KLINGER, Dean Edward. 2801 W KK RIVER PKWY 53215 #056-06-1980 L1981 **GS** *020 †85

KLINK, Douglas Dean. 1121 E NORTH AVE 53212 #018-03-1956 L1964 **END IM** *071 †20

KLINKNER, Denise Barbara. 9200 W WISCONSIN AVE 53226 #026-04-2001 L2003 **GS** *012

KLOEHN, Roger Walter. ■ 53217 #056-06-1961 L1963 **IM CD** *020

KLUESSENDORF, Kari Ann. 5000 W CHAMBERS ST, ST JOSEPH'S HOSPITAL 53210 #056-06-1995 L1996 **DR** *020 †80,28

KNABEL, Mark Raymond. 2801 W KINNICKINC RVR PKWY, STE 250 53215 #018-03-1979 L1982 **D** *020 †15

KNAPP, Brian Allan. 9200 W WISCONSIN AVE, DEPARTMENT OF PHYSICAL MED 53226 #017-20-2006 L2007 **PM** *012

KNEPSHIELD, Robert Shane. ■ 53214 #056-06-2008 *012

KNIPPEL, Martin Wm. 2025 W OKLAHOMA AVE 53215 #028-34-1984 L1985 **PD** *020 †55

KNOEDLER, Darly M. ■ 53222 #056-06-2003 L2004 **PTH** *100 †50

KNUDSON, Paul Edward. 9200 W WISCONSIN AVE, DIV OF ENDOCRINOLOGY/FEC/4 53226 #056-06-1988 L1989 **END** *020 †20

KNUTSON, Sara Marie. 9200 W WISCONSIN AVE, MEDICAL COLLEGE OF WISCONS 53226 #037-01-2003 L2005 **AN** *020

KO, Unchu. 788 N JEFFERSON ST, MADISON MEDICAL AFFILIATES 53202 #051-01-1997 L2000 **IM** *020 †20

KOCAK, Mehmet. 5000 W NATIONAL AVE, DEPT OF RAD VA MED CTR 53295 #902-10-1991 L1999 **RNR NM** *020 †28,80

KOCH, Claudia A. 2025 E NEWPORT AVE 53211 #409-36-1999 L2001 **FM** *020 †18

KOCH, Paul Eric. 1121 E NORTH AVE, STE 175 53212 #056-05-1994 L2000 **FM** *020 †18

KOCHAR, Jinesh. ■ 53214 #495-55-2002 **IM** *012

KOCHAR, Mahendr Singh. 8701 W WATERTOWN PLANK RD 53226 #495-36-1965 L1972 **IM NEP** *030 †18,20

KODALI, Satish. 7220 W NATIONAL AVE 53214 #056-06-1993 L1994 **OTO** *020 †45

KODURI, Sumana. 9200 W WISCONSIN AVE 53226 #016-06-1994 L1995 **OBG** *020 †30

KOEBERT, Robert Frank. 5000 W CHAMBERS ST, WHEATON FRANCISCAN HEALTHC 53210 #056-06-1983 L1984 **AN** *040 †05

KOENIG, Steven Brand. 925 N 87TH ST 53226 #035-20-1977 L1983 **OPH** *020 †35

KOEPPLER, Raven Ann. 9200 W WISCONSIN AVE, OB/GYN DEPT 53226 #056-06-2006 L2008 **OBG** *012

KOGAN, Dmitriy. ■ 53227 #016-01-2007 **IM** *012

KOH, Charles H. 2015 E NEWPORT AVE, STE 707 53211 #825-01-1967 L1978 **GYN OS** *020 †30

KOH, Tong Chui. 2801 W KINNICKINC RVR PKWY, STE 453 53215 #624-01-1970 L1977 **AN** *020 †05

KOHLER, Sidney Herman. ■ 53217 #056-06-1945 L1948 **GP** *071

KOHLER-NEUWIRTH, Stephanie. 8701 W WATERTOWN PLANK RD, WISCONSIN HOSPS 53226 #016-42-2006 **P** *012

KOHLMEIER, Lynn Beth. 10909 W BLUEMOUND RD, WISCONSIN 53226 #056-06-1989 L1990 **PD** *020 †55

KOHN, Harvey S. 2424 S 90TH ST, STE 418 53227 #035-46-1970 L1979 **ORS** *020 †40

KOKANOVIC, Simonida. ■ 53225 #957-02-1995 L2007 **FM** *020

KOLANOWSKI, Piotr J. 3316 W WISCONSIN AVE, FAMILY MEDICAL CLINIC, 53208 #759-04-1990 L1994 **FM** *020 †18

KOLESARI, Gary Lee. 1155 N MAYFAIR RD 53226 #056-06-1977 L1978 **OS FM** *040 ‡

KOLP, Barbara Lynn. 3003 W GOOD HOPE RD, ADVANCED HEALTH CARE 53209 #012-22-1995 L1997 **PD** *020 †55

KOMISAR, Jeffrey Malcolm. 3237 S 16TH ST 53215 #056-06-1976 L1987 **PTH** *071 †50

KOMMER, Curtis Geo. 734 N JACKSON ST, CATHEDRAL SQ U C CTR 53202 #005-19-1985 L1986 **FM** *020 †18

KOMOROWSKI, Richard A. 9200 W WISCONSIN AVE, DEPT PTH 53226 #056-06-1967 L1968 **PTH** *050 †50

KONDURI, Girija Ganesh. 8701 W WATERTOWN PLANK RD, MEDICAL COLLEGE OF WI MS21 53226 #495-11-1981 L2000 **NPM PD** *050 †55

KONIDALA, Srilakshmi. 9121 W DIXON ST, APT 8 53214 #495-70-2000 L2005 **IM** *020 †20

KONKEL, John Karl. 7878 N 76TH ST, NORTHWEST CLINIC 53223 #056-06-1977 L1978 **ORS** *020 †40

KOO, Min Kook. 8701 W WATERTOWN PLANK RD, MED COLL OF WI 53226 #048-12-2006 L2007 **AN** *012

KOPELL, Brian Harris. 9200 W WISCONSIN AVE, MEDICAL COLLEGE OF WI-NEUR 53226 #035-19-1996 L2004 **NS** *020

KOPLIN, Anne I. ■ 53209 #550-02-1988 L1990 **P** *020 †75

KORDAS, Werner. 945 N 12TH ST 53233 #016-11-1978 L1979 **DR** *020 †80

KORENIC, John Chas. 5000 W CHAMBERS ST 53210 #056-06-1971 L1978 **RO** *020 †80

KORI, Adriana A. 9200 W WISCONSIN AVE 53226 #132-01-1985 L2003 **N** *020 †75

KORNAK, Jodi Marie. 8532 W CAPITOL DR 53222 #056-06-1995 L2001 **OTO** *020 †45

KORNREICH, David B. 6200 W BLUEMOUND RD 53213 #016-76-1995, ▲ L2000 **ORS** *020

KOSASIH, Judith Budiono. 5000 W NATIONAL AVE 53295 #056-06-1988 L1989 **PM** *020 †60

KOSHY, Daniel P. 10000 W BLUEMOUND RD 53226 #495-37-1997 L2003 **AN** *020 †05 ‡

KOSTIC, Mark. ■ 53211 #041-02-1994 L1995 **EM** *020 †16

KOSTOPOULOS, Louie Nickol. 2025 E NEWPORT AVE, COLUMBIA HOSPITAL 53211 #665-01-2001 L2003 **CD** *012 †20

KOTCHEN, Jane E Morley. 8701 W WATERTOWN PLANK RD 53226 #038-06-1964 L1992 **EP** *050 †70

KOTCHEN, Theodore Allan. 9200 W WISCONSIN AVE, MDCL CLLGE CLNCS AT FRDTRT 53226 #038-06-1964 L1992 **END IM** *071 †20

KOTHARI, Samip Dhiren. ■ 53202 #056-05-2005 L2008 **PD** *012

KOTRLY, Karel J. VET ADMIN CENTER, DEPT ANES 53295 #286-02-1965 L1976 **AN** *020 †05

KOUNEV, Venelin Jekov. 9200 W WISCONSIN AVE, FMLH, DEPARTMENT OF MEDICI 53226 #198-01-1996 L2003 **GE** *100

KOWALKE, Kathy Joy. 8701 W WATERTOWN PLANK RD, CAMPUS CLINIC PSYCHIATRY 53226 #016-45-1987 L1991 **P** *020 †75

KOWALSKI, Jacek Marian. 3237 S 16TH ST 53215 #056-06-1984 L1985 **OBG** *020 †30

KOWOL, Mary-Anne Ottilie. 8701 W WATERTOWN PLANK RD, DEPARTMENT OF PSYCHIATRY 53226 #409-20-2000 L2007 **P** *012

KOZEL, Dennis Dean. 6980 N PORT WASHINGTON RD, STE 202 53217 #030-06-1982 L1983 **CHP IM** *020 †75

KRAMER, Sophie Marianne. 10950 W CAPITOL DR 53222 #012-05-1986 L1989 **IM** *020 †20

KRANZ, James Chas. 9000 W WISCONSIN AVE 53226 #056-06-1988 L1989 **PTH** *020 †50

KRASNOW, Arthur Z. 9200 W WISCONSIN AVE 53226 #016-11-1980 L1981 **NM IM** *020 †20,28

KRAUS, Jonathan Charles. ■ 53213 #028-34-2007 **ORS** *012

KRAUSE, Peter Alan. ■ 53211 #056-06-1996 L1999 **FM** *020 †18

KRAUSEN, Anthony Sharnik. ■ 53217 #025-01-1969 L1976 **OTO** *020 †45

KRAWCZYK, Konrad Walter. 3738 S 60TH ST, STE 101 53220 #016-42-1981 L1982 **FM** *020 †18

KREMBS, Francis Gregory. ■ 53202 #056-05-1969 L1970 **P N** *075

KRESS, David Charles. 2901 W KINNICKINC RVR PKWY 53215 #056-05-1983 L1984 **TS TTS** *020 †85,90

KRESS, Julianna Marie. 3237 S 16TH ST, ST FRANCIS HOSPITAL ED 53215 #038-43-1993 L1996 **EM** *020 †16

KREUZPAINTER, Manfred M. 10000 W BLUEMOUND RD 53226 #308-11-1986 L1990 **AN** *020

KRIEG, Kathryn Carol. 1155 N MAYFAIR RD 53226 #056-05-1981 L1982 **P IM** *020 †20,75

KRIPPENDORF, Robert L. 9200 W WISCONSIN AVE 53226 #056-06-1990 L1991 **IM** *020 †20

KRISHNAN, Santosh N. 2801 W KINNICKINC RVR PKWY 53215 #008-01-1997 L2004 **TS** *020 †85,90

KRISHNANEY, Ashok Kumar R. 4555 W SCHROEDER DR, STE 170 53223 #495-01-1964 L1975 **AN** *020 †05

KRON, Michael Andrew. 8701 W WATERTOWN PLANK RD, MEDICAL COLLEGE OF WISCONS 53226 #016-06-1980 L2006 **ID GPM** *050 †20

KRONER, Eric Lee. ■ 53222 #056-05-2003 L2004 **PEM** *012 †55

KRONER, John Thos. 2350 N LAKE DR, GROUND FLOOR 53211 #056-06-1982 L1983 **ORS** *020 †40

KRONER, Joseph M. ■ 53213 #056-06-2007 **ORS** *012

KROUWER, Hendrikus G J. 9200 W WISCONSIN AVE, MEDICAL COLLEGE OF WISCONS 53226 #660-03-1978 L1995 **N** *020

KRUEGER, John Ralph. 8200 W SILVER SPRING DR, HEALTH CENTER 53218 #056-05-1979 L1980 **FM** *020 †18

KRYDA, Michael James. ■ 53224 #016-11-1972 L1977 **PUD CCM** *030 †20

KRYNICKI, Michal. 2025 E NEWPORT AVE, COLUMBIA ST. MARY'S HOSPIT 53211 #759-11-1991 L2005 **IM** *020 †20

KUBLY, Michael Chas. ■ 53233 #056-06-1963 L1965 **ORS** *020 †40

KUBRICAN, Tomas. ■ 53222 #286-12-1999 **FP** *012

KUCHLING, Sonja Nicole. ■ 53214 #056-06-2008 *012

KUEHN, Donald Norman, Jr. 2350 N LAKE DR, STE 350 53211 #056-06-1980 L1987 **ORS** *075 †40

KUGATHASAN, Subramaniam. 9000 W WISCONSIN AVE, CHILDREN HOSP OF WISCONSIN 53226 #220-01-1985 L1998 **PD PG** *050 †55

KUHLMANN, Randall Scott. 8700 W WISCONSIN AVE 53226 #056-06-1984 L1990 **MFM OBG** *020 †30

KUHN, Michael John, III. 8901 W LINCOLN AVE, CONSULTANTS AT WEST ALLIS 53227 #056-06-1987 L1991 **AN** *020 †05

KULINSKI, Jacquelyn Patri. ■ 53226 #056-06-2008 *012

KULKARNI, Vijay Vitthal. 2315 N LAKE DR STE 71 53211 #495-19-1955 L1975 **ORS** *071 †40

KULKARNI, Vineet P. 11101 W LINCOLN AVE 53227 #495-17-1973 L1980 **P CHP** *020 †75

KUMAR, Gagan. 9200 W WISCONSIN AVE, FROEDTERT EAST CLINICS 53226 #495-36-1998 L2006 **IM** *012

KUMAR, K V Ashok. 3033 S 27TH ST STE 200 53215 #495-09-1971 L1974 **TS GS** *020 †85

KUMAR, Krishna. 2801 W KINNICKINC RVR PKWY, STE 425 53215 #495-61-1982 L1992 **IC CD** *020 †20

KUMAR, Nidhi. 9200 W WISCONSIN AVE, DEPT PATHOLOGY 53226 #495-77-1998 L2004 **PCP** *020

KUMAR, Nilay. 8701 W WATERTOWN PLANK RD, MED COLL WI AFFIL HOSPS 53226 #496-38-2004 L2006 **IM** *012

KUMAR, Pradeep Gopi. 1711 S 11TH ST, GERALD L IGNACE INDIAN HEA 53204 #495-99-1994 L2000 **PD** *020 †55

KUMAR, Punit. 9200 W WISCONSIN AVE, STE 4200FEC 53226 #496-09-1995 L2000 **IM** *020 †20

KUMAR, Renuka Lingam. 3267 S 16TH ST, STE 104 53215 #495-21-1975 L1980 **PM** *020

KUMAR, Swati. ■ 53202 #495-14-1998 L2007 **PDI** *100 †55

KUMAR, Vikas. ■ 53215 #496-39-1999 *100

KUPRIYENKO, Lidiya. 3000 W MONTANA ST 53215 #913-42-1984 L2006 **IM** *012

KURAKULA, Preethi Carolin. 3000 W MONTANA ST 53215 #495-50-2000 L2006 **IM** *100 †20

KURANZ, Sarah Brodrick. 8905 W LINCOLN AVE, STE 401 53227 #056-06-1995 L1999 **OBG** *020 †30

KURRE, Kamlesh Reddy. 9200 W WISCONSIN AVE, GEN INTERNAL MEDICINE CLIN 53226 #495-21-1997 L2005 **IM** *100 †20

KURRE, Lakshmi Hima Bindu. ■ 53226 #496-34-1999 **FP** *012

KURTER, Selahattin S. 803 W OKLAHOMA AVE 53215 #056-05-2002 L2005 **P** *020

KURUDIYARA, Preetha Yasmi. 8532 W CAPITOL DR 53222 #422-01-2002 L2006 **PD** *020

KUSHI, Jonathan Kiichiro. ■ 53202 #005-06-2006 **IM** *012

KUSHNARYOV, Michael. ■ 53208 #056-06-1982 L1983 **IM OS** *075

KUSTERMANN, Stuart Dean. 1904 E BELLEVIEW PL 53211 #026-04-1948 L1968
CLP FOP *071 †50

KUTEYI, Olugbenga Bantale. ■ 53214 #690-02-1983 **CHP** *012

KUTLUAY, Ekrem. 9200 W WISCONSIN AVE, DEPARATMENT OF NEUROLOGY, 53226
#902-20-1992 L2004 **CN** *020

KUTTY, Kesavan. 5000 W CHAMBERS ST 53210 #495-73-1972 L1977 **PCC SME** *040 †20

KWASNY, Gregory Paul. 2300 N MAYFAIR RD STE 1030 53226 #017-20-1970 L1971
OPH *020 †35 ‡

KWIATT, James Thomas. ■ 53213 #016-43-2004 L2005 **IM** *100 †20

KWOCK, Lindon Theodore. 3237 S 16TH ST, ST. FRANCIS HOSPITAL 53215
#021-01-1992 L2000 **DR** *020 †80

KWON, Elena Namkoong. ■ 53202 #654-01-2004 L2007 **PDC** *012 †55

KWON, Ohhoon. 5000 W CHAMBERS ST 53210 #016-11-1999 L2004 **RO** *100 †80

LAABS, Sarah Maria. ■ 53233 #016-06-2007 **PM** *012

LA CROSSE, Larry Edward. 5000 W CHAMBERS ST, ST JOSEPH REG MED CTR 53210
#056-06-1988 L1989 **EM IM** *040

LACUNA, Eduardo Malvin Bu, Jr. 3000 W MONTANA 53215 #748-02-1997 **OBG** *012

LADWIG, Daniel August. 2801 W KINNICKINC RVR PKWY, STE 575 53215 #056-06-1985 L1986
ORS *020 †40

LAFFERTY, Wesley Voris. 2025 E NEWPORT AVE, STE 217 53211 #654-01-1999 L2002
FM *100 †18 ‡

LAGUNA, Mario Alberto. 9200 W WISCONSIN AVE, DEPT OF RADIO 53226 #649-31-1991 L2002
DR *020 †80

LAGUNA, Maritza. 2906 S 20TH ST 53215 #649-03-1993 L2004 **IM** *020 †20

LAHM, Michael Christopher. ■ 53217 #038-43-2004 L2008 **DR** *012

LAL, Alysandra. ■ 53213 #054-04-2002 L2005 **GS** *100 †85

LAL, Dave Raj. 999 N 92ND ST 53226 #030-06-1998 L1999 **PDS** *100 †85

LAL, Neena. 8701 W WATERTOWN PLANK RD, MED COLL WI AFFIL HOSPS 53226 #495-36-2003
IM *100

LAMB, Geoffrey Campbell. 9200 W WISCONSIN AVE, C/O FMLH EAST 53226
#032-01-1979 L1987 **IM** *040 †20

LAMBERT, Steven Bruce. 2900 W OKLAHOMA AVE 53215 #025-01-1987 L1988
PUD CCM *020 †20

LAMBERTON, John C. 1231 W MITCHELL ST 53204 #056-06-1997 L1998 **P** *020 †75

LAMERS, Luke Joseph. 9000 W WISCONSIN AVE, MEDICAL COLLEGE OF WISCONS 53226
#056-06-1998 L2005 **PDC** *020 †55

LAMNARI, Anna Magdalena. 9255 N 76TH ST 53223 #759-11-1991 L2000 **IMG IM** *020 †20

LAMPING, Barbara Jean. 8905 W LINCOLN AVE, GYNECOLOGY LTD 53227 #016-11-1985 L1986
OBG *020 †30

LANCASTER, Shanyn Colleen. 1121 E NORTH AVE 53212 #025-07-2005 L2006 **FP** *012

LANDIS, Francis Bertold. ■ 53227 #056-06-1941 L1941 **IM PUD** *071 †20

LANDISCH, James H. 3289 N MAYFAIR RD, MAYFAIR ROAD CLINIC 53222 #056-06-1978 L1979
IM *020 †20

LANE, John David. 2025 E NEWPORT AVE, WISCONSIN RADIOLOGY 53211 #016-43-1991 L1996
DR VIR *020 †80

LANG, Gordon Edward. 2323 N LAKE DR # 503, ST MARYS HOSP 53211 #056-05-1959 L1960
PTH BBK *071 †50 ‡

LANG, Jean P Le Febvre. ■ 53217 #056-05-1959 L1960 **PTH** *071 †50

LANG, Tanner Fred. ■ 53217 #056-06-1946 L1948 **AN** *012

LANGE, George Melvin. 8430 W CAPITOL DR 53222 #056-06-1975 L1976 **IM IMG** *020 †20

LANGE, Marlene Melzer. 9000 W WISCONSIN AVE, CCC 550 53226 #056-06-1975 L1976
PEM PD *030 †55

LANGENKAMP, James Halberg. 6200 W BLUEMOUND RD 53213 #056-05-1973 L1980
ORS *020 †40

LANGENSTROER, Peter. 9200 W WISCONSIN AVE, MEDICAL COLLEGE OF 53226
#056-06-1992 L1993 **U** *020 †95

LANKIEWICZ, Michael W. PO BOX 2178, 638 N 18TH ST 53201 #024-16-1987 L2003
BBK IM *020 †20

LANTZ, Helen. 2801 W KINNICKINC RVR PKWY, STE 1030 53215 #001-02-1998 L2002
GE *020

LANZAROTTI, Stephen. 9200 W WISCONSIN AVE, CRITICAL CARE 53226 #048-13-2000 L2006
CCS *100 †85

LARKEY, Deborah Mickel. 2311 N PROSPECT AVE, CSMCP PROSPECT MEDICAL COM 53211
#056-06-1988 L1990 **OBG** *020 †30

LARKEY, Jay Allen. ■ 53217 #056-06-1946 L1948 **OBG** *071 †30

LAROSE, Rosario Bernard. 555 S 108TH ST 53214 #654-01-1986 L1992 **IM DIA** *020 †20

LARSON, Craig. 2100 N MAYFAIR RD, STE 105 53226 #056-06-1956 L1957 **P** *020

LARSON, David Lee. 8700 W WATERTOWN PLANK RD 53226 #021-05-1969 L1986
PS OTO *020 †45,65

LARSON, Gunnar Lawrence. 5000 W NATIONAL AVE # 116A, MILWAUKEE VAMC DEPT
PSYC 53295 #016-42-1984 L1988 **P PYG** *020 †75

LARSON, Jeffrey Edward. 2424 S 90TH ST, STE 206 53227 #056-06-1984 L1990 **ORS** *020 †40

LARSON, Lawrence Stanley. 2025 E NEWPORT AVE 53211 #056-06-1963 L1964
IM NEP *071 †20

LARSON, Sanford John. 9200 W WISCONSIN AVE, MDCL CLLGE CLNCS AT FRDTRT 53226
#016-06-1954 L1963 **NS** *071 †25

LARSON, Susan Manz. 7220 W NATIONAL AVE 53214 #056-06-1984 L1990 **PM** *020 †60

LASS, Thomas Erwin. 8901 W LINCOLN AVE 53227 #056-06-1967 L1968 **AN** *071 †05

LATORRACA, Carol White. 5000 W CHAMBERS ST 53210 #024-07-1949 L1958 **AN** *071

LAUBENHEIMER, Roger E. 324 E WISCONSIN AVE # 925 53202 #056-05-1950 L1951
D *071 †15

LAUNDRIE, Dennis Jay. 2423 W LISBON AVE, CURTIS AMBULANCE SERVICE 53205
#056-06-1996 L1997 **EM** *16

LAURENCIN, Denis Louis. 5818 W CAPITOL DR 53216 #056-05-1979 L1988 **IM** *020

LAUTZ, Amy Michelle. 919 N GLENVIEW AVE 53213 #056-06-2003 L2005 **PD** *020 †55

LAUWASSER, Marvin Edward. 3070 N 51ST ST, STE 402 53210 #056-06-1972 L1973
ID IM *020 †20

LAVEN, Brett Anthony. 2801 W KINNICKINC RVR PKWY, STE 370 53215 #012-05-1999 L2006
U *020 †95

LAW, Brian Chunwah. ■ 53208 #056-06-2005 L2006 **ORS** *012

LAWAL, Adegboyega Hakeem. 8901 W LINCOLN AVE, CONSULTANTS AT WEST ALLIS 53227
#690-01-1987 L2001 **AN PME** *020 †05 ‡

LAWAL, Adeyemi Adekunle. 9200 W WISCONSIN AVE, MEDICAL COLLEGE OF WISCONS 53226
#690-02-1992 L2003 **GE** *100 †20

LAWAL, Moshood Adebayo. ■ 53217 #690-01-1999 L2007 **IM** *020 †20

LAWNICKI, Lyle Casey. 3237 S 16TH ST 53215 #056-06-1995 L2002 **HMP** *020 †50

LAWRENCE, Lakesha Yolanda. 2555 N DR MRTN LTHR KNG DR, CENTER 53212
#012-21-2001 L2005 **OBG** *020

LAWRENCE, Rebecca A. 3040 N 117TH ST 53222 #056-06-1983 L1984 **OBG** *020 †30

LAWRENCE, Steven Lee. 8701 W WATERTOWN PLANK RD, MEDICAL COLLEGE OF
WISCONS 53226 #056-05-1970 L1971 **FM** *020 †18

LAWSON, Thomas Longley. 945 N 12TH ST 53233 #025-01-1965 L1978 **DR** *020 †80

LAWTON, Colleen Anne. 9200 W WISCONSIN AVE 53226 #056-06-1983 L1984 **RO** *020 †80

LAYDE, Joseph Bernard. 9455 W WATERTOWN PLANK RD 53226 #056-05-1979 L1980
P LM *030 †75

LAYDE, Margaret Mary. 1020 N 12TH ST, DOWNTOWN HEALTH CTR 53233 #038-40-1974 L1977
PD *040 †55

LAYDE, Peter Mark. 8701 W WATERTOWN PLANK RD, DEPT POPULATION HEALTH 53226
#056-05-1976 L1988 **GPM EP** *050 †70

LAYMAN, Ralph Eugene. 9200 W WISCONSIN AVE, DEPARTMENT OF SURGERY 53226
#016-02-2001 L2003 **GS** *020

LAZARIDES, Toula. 950 N 12TH ST 53233 #056-06-1985 L1986 **EM IM** *020 †20

LAZORITZ, Stephen. 1020 N 12TH ST 53233 #035-06-1976 L1987 **PD** *020 †55

LEAVITT, Mitchell Hugh. 2900 W OKLAHOMA AVE, ST LUKES MEDICAL CENTER EM 53215
#025-01-1979 L1983 **EM** *020 †14

LEDESMA, Wendy Marie. ■ 53215 #016-45-2006 L2008 **IM** *012

LEE, Cha. 6810 W CAPITOL DR, STE 217 53216 #422-01-1999 L2000 **FM** *020 †18

LEE, David S. 7220 W NATIONAL AVE 53214 #025-01-1992 L2000 **OTO** *020 †45

LEE, Don Suk. 2025 E NEWPORT AVE, COLUMBIA HOSPITAL 53211 #056-05-2002 L2003
IM *020 †20

LEE, Glenda Marie. 8905 W LINCOLN AVE, GYNECOLOGY LTD 53227 #037-01-1984 L1985
OBG *020 †30

LEE, Henry Kai. 5015 W BURLEIGH ST 53210 #025-07-1985 L2001 **RO DR** *020 †80

LEE, Karen Morales. 8701 W WATERTOWN PLANK RD 53226 #305-01-2006 **IM** *012

LEE, Kenneth Kyungkeun. 5000 W NATIONAL AVE, ZABLOCK VAMC SCI-128 53295
#056-06-1993 L1996 **PM SCI** *020 †60

LEE, Matthew Bishop. 3040 N 117TH ST 53222 #056-06-1012-01-1995 L1996 **OBG** *020 †30

LEE, Max. 960 N 12TH ST, STE 1800 53233 #016-11-1998 L2005 **NS** *020

LEE, Saeyeal Kevin. 9200 W WISCONSIN AVE, OBGYN 53226 #056-06-2005 L2006 **OBG** *012

LEE, Sarha. 945 N 12TH ST 53233 #016-01-1996 L2005 **DR** *020 †20

LEENEY, Ellen Margaret. 7878 N 76TH ST, NORTHWEST CLINIC 53223 #018-03-1992 L1993
FM *020 †18

LEEPER, Heather Elisabeth. ■ 53211 #016-42-2008 *012

LEHMAN, Elmer G. 4655 N PORT WASHINGTON RD, STE 100 53212 #056-06-1983 L1984
GO GYN *020 †30

LEIB, Ari David. 8701 W WATERTOWN PLANK RD 53226 #016-45-2004 L2006 **EM** *100

LEIB, Melissa Louise. 9200 W WISCONSIN AVE, MEDICAL COLLEGE OF WISCONS 53226
#056-05-2006 L2008 **EM** *012

LEICHTER, Heinz Erich. ■ 53211 #409-21-1978 L1985 **PN PD** *020 †55

LEIDER, Holly Anne. 3003 W GOOD HOPE RD, HOPE ROAD CLINIC 53209 #056-06-1997 L1998
IM *020 †20

LEININGER, Jean Anne. 4555 W SCHROEDER DR, STE 170 53223 #056-06-1993 L1994
AN *020 †05

LEITSCHUH, Mark Linus. 2025 E NEWPORT AVE 53211 #040-02-1982 L1990 **CD IM** *020 †20

LEMONT, Laura Elizabeth. ■ 53202 #056-06-2007 **FP** *012

LENNERTZ, Richard C, Jr. 8901 W LINCOLN AVE, CONSULTANTS AT WEST ALLIS 53227
#056-06-1983 L1984 **AN GP** *020 †05

LEO, Gary Jos. 945 N 12TH ST # 4602 53233 #018-75-1979, ▲ L1981 **N SME** *020 †75

LEONARD, Sharleen Martha. 901 E HAMPTON RD 53217 #018-03-1977 L1978 **FM** *020 †18

LEONOVICZ, Peter Francis. 2801 W KINNICKINC RVR PKWY, STE 370 53215
#030-06-1996 L1997 **U** *020 †95

LERNER, Benjamin Michael. 413 N 2ND ST, UNIT 280 53203 #056-05-2002 L2004 **GS** *012

LESCHKE, Robert R. 9200 W WISCONSIN AVE, FROEDERDT HOSPITAL EMERGEN 53226
#056-06-1995 L1996 **EM** *016

LESKO, Gary Nicholas. 7878 N 76TH ST, NORTHWEST CLINIC 53223 #038-40-1976 L1977
FM *020 †18

LESKO, John Francis. 1242 N 13TH ST, RIVERSIDE ORTHOPEDIC CONSU 53205
#016-43-1980 L1985 **ORS** *020 †40

LESSARD, Lauren Catherine. ■ 53213 #056-06-2008 *012

LETZER, David M. 601 N 99TH ST, STE 103 53226 #025-76-1985, ▲ L1989 **ID** *020

LEUNG, Belinda Vaifan. 8905 W LINCOLN AVE, STE 401 53227 #005-06-1993 L1997
OBG *020 †30

LEUTHNER, Steven Raymond. 8701 W WATERTOWN PLANK RD, DEPT PEDS 53226
#016-02-1989 L1995 **NPM PD** *020 †20

LEVINE, Michael Ira. 2901 W KINNICKINC RVR PKWY, STE 405 53215 #035-47-1982 L1996
NEP *020 †20

LEW, Sean Morten. 999 N 92ND ST STE 310 53226 #040-02-1995 L2004 **NS** *020 †25

LEWIN, Ruben Fernando. 2025 W OKLAHOMA AVE, STE 114 53215 #132-01-1974 L1987
CD *020

LEWIS, Brian David. 9200 W WISCONSIN AVE, DEPT OF SURGERY 53226 #016-45-1997 L1998
VS *020 †85

LEWIS, Rozmond Johnson. 2906 S 20TH ST 53215 #047-20-2004 L2007 **FM** *020 †18

LEYBISHKIS, Biana. 1020 N 12TH ST, FL 2 53233 #913-21-1992 L2003 **IM** *020 †20

LI, B Uk. 8701 W WATERTOWN PLANK RD, DIV OF PEDIATRIC GI 53226 #019-02-1974 L1977
GE NTR *020 †55

LI, Ricardo Augusto. 2801 W KINNICKINC RVR PKWY, STE 1030 53226 #016-06-1992 L1998
GE *020 †20

LIBNOCH, Joseph Anthony. VET ADMIN MED CTR 53295 #016-11-1958 L1968
HEM ON *020

LICHTY, James Edward. 2025 E NEWPORT AVE 53211 #018-03-1962 L1967 **DR** *071 †80

LIDAR-DERGICZ, Zvi Michae. 9200 W WISCONSIN AVE 53226 #550-02-1996 L2003 *020

LIEBERMAN, Leonard. ■ 53226 #056-06-1944 L1945 **P IM** *030

LIEBERTHAL, Alan S. 1218 W KILBOURN AVE 53233 #056-05-1949 L1951 **END NM** *020 †28

LIEBMAN, Albert. 2315 N LAKE DR 53211 #056-05-1946 L1947 **P IM** *020 †20

LIGLER, Lindsay Marie. 9000 W WISCONSIN AVE P, CGO MEDICAL EDUCATION 53226
#017-20-2006 L2008 **PD** *012

LIKNESS, Lincoln Paul. 2801 W KINNICKINC RVR PKWY, STE 250 53215 #028-78-2005, ▲ L2006
FP *012

LILLICH, David Wm. 1155 N MAYFAIR RD 53226 #016-11-1974 L1979 **FM FPG** *020 †18

LILLIE, Douglas Wm. 2424 S 90TH ST, STE 206 53227 #016-11-1985 L1989 **IM** *020 †20

LILLY, Ronald Eric. 9200 W WISCONSIN AVE, STE E5700 53226 #036-07-1992 L2006 **TS** *020 †85,90

LIM, Robert Ang. 3237 S 16TH ST, ST FRANCIS HOSPITAL 53215 #748-01-1955 L1967 **GP** *020

LIN, Helen Curie. 8701 W WATERTOWN PLANK RD, DEPT. OF NEUROLOGY 53226 #035-09-2001 L2007 **N** *020 †75

LIN, Jessica Shuwen. 9200 W WISCONSIN AVE, DEPARTMENT OF NEUROSURGERY 53226 #041-12-2004 L2007 **NS** *012

LIN, Joyce Ying. ■ 53213 #056-06-2008 *012

LINABURY, Virginia Mae. 250 W COVENTRY CT STE 209 53217 #016-01-1983 L1988 **P PYA** *020 †75

LINDBERG, James Benjamin. 773 N WATER ST, UNIT 35 53202 #056-06-1997 L2000 **EM** *020 †16

LINDENBAUM, Larry. 9200 W WISCONSIN AVE 53226 #016-11-1993 L1994 **AN** *012

LINN, Anthony James. 2311 N PROSPECT AVE, CSMCP PROSPECT MEDICAL COM 53211 #056-06-1975 L1980 **GS** *020 †85

LINN, James Gerard. 1032 S CESAR E CHAVEZ DR 53204 #056-06-1980 L1984 **OBS** *020 †30

LINSMEIER, Michelle Marie. 6373 N JEAN NICOLET RD 53217 #056-06-2000 L2002 **PD** *020 †55

LIPCHIK, Elliot O. ■ 53211 #869-01-1958 L1976 **CD DR** *020 †80

LIPCHIK, Randolph J. 9200 W WISCONSIN AVE, PULMONARY & CRITICAL CARE 53226 #067-01-1984 L1990 **PUD CCM** *040 †20

LIPKOWITZ, Allan. 10919 W BLUEMOUND RD 53226 #062-01-1980 L1997 **R VIR** *020 †80

LIPUSCH, Claudia E. 930 E KNAPP ST 53202 #016-45-1981 L1986 **P** *020 †75

LISI, Paul. ■ 53213 #018-75-2007, ▲ *100

LISTWAN, William Jos. 840 N 87TH ST 53226 #056-06-1968 L1969 **IM OM** *020 †20

LIU, Jason Marc. 9200 W WISCONSIN AVE, DEPT. OF EMERGENCY MEDICIN 53226 #016-06-2001 L2003 **EM** *020 †16

LIU, Suyan. 9200 W WISCONSIN AVE, DPT ANESTH 53226 #243-70-1982 L2003 **AN** *020 †05

LLOYD, Lisa Beth. 8905 W LINCOLN AVE, STE 501 53227 #654-01-1984 L1986 **OBG** *020 †30

LOBECK, Lorri Jo. 3003 W GOOD HOPE RD, HOPE ROAD CLINIC 53209 #027-01-1987 L1988 *020 †75

LOBEL, Martin Lewis. 324 E WISCONSIN AVE STE 9 53202 #016-42-1968 L1975 **AI PDA** *020 †55,03

LOCHEN, Gregory Robt. 201 N MAYFAIR RD, MEDICAL EYE ASSOCIATES SC 53226 #056-05-1972 L1973 **OPH** *020 †35

LOCHER, Charles J. 53211 #056-06-1962 L1963 **R** *020 †80

LOCHOWITZ, Norbert J. 6200 W BLUEMOUND RD 53213 #056-06-1952 L1953 **GP** *020

LOCURTO, Anthony Geo. 2801 W KINNICKINC RVR PKWY, STE 840 53215 #056-06-1990 L1991 **CD** *020 †20

LODES, Mark William. 1155 N MAYFAIR RD 53226 #056-06-1997 L1998 **MPD** *020 †55,20

LOEHRL, Todd Alfred. 9200 W WISCONSIN AVE 53226 #056-06-1991 L1993 **OTO** *020 †45

LOGIUDICE, John Anthony. 9200 W WISCONSIN AVE, DEPT OF PLASTIC SURGERY 53226 #016-43-2000 L2003 **HS** *020

LONDON, Richard Laurence. 9255 N 76TH ST, WHEATON FRANCISCAN GER MED 53223 #025-01-1973 L1984 **FM FPG** *020 †18

LONG, Catherine Anne. ■ 53202 #016-11-2008 *012

LONG, Christopher Michael. 7220 W NATIONAL AVE 53214 #056-06-1996 L1997 **OTO** *020 †45

LONG, Douglas Mathew. 3003 W GOOD HOPE RD, HOPE ROAD CLINIC 53209 #016-45-1993 L1998 **OPH** *020 †35

LONGEWAY, Maureen Poag. ■ 53202 #056-06-2008 *012

LONGNECKER, Marshall A. 12129 W FEERICK ST, ATTN: MIKE LATTOS 53222 #016-02-1987 L1992 **AN** *020 †05

LONGO, Lance Peter. 1020 N 12TH ST, FL 4 53233 #056-06-1990 L1996 **P ADP** *020 †75

LONTOK, Emilio. 2040 W WISCONSIN AVE, APT 667 53233 #748-08-1957 L1970 **OBG** *071

LOO, Jon Warren. ■ 53213 #056-06-2008 L2008 *012

LOOK, Stacey Marie. ■ 53210 #056-06-2001 L2003 **CD** *012

LOPEZ, Hector. 4931 S 27TH ST, STE 200 53221 #042-01-1990 L1992 **FM** *020 †18

LOPEZ VICENTE, Marta. 8701 W WATERTOWN PLANK RD 53226 #847-07-2002 L2007 **FP** *012

LOREK, Jennifer D. 9200 W WISCONSIN AVE, PATH DEPT 53226 #048-12-2000 L2002 **PTH** *100 †50

LOVE, Cynthia Sawyer. 8701 W WATERTOWN PLANK RD, DEPARTMENT OF PSYCHIATRY M 53226 #028-03-1978 L2002 **CHP** *100

LOVELL, Candice Dion. 9200 W WISCONSIN AVE, DEPT OF OB/ GYN 53226 #056-06-2004 L2006 **OBG** *012

LOYA, Rizwan. 2900 W OKLAHOMA AVE, ERMED SC 53215 #016-42-1998 L2004 **EM** *020 †16

LU, Feng. 8701 W WATERTOWN PLANK RD, DEPARTMENT OF PMR MEDICAL 53226 #243-46-1985 L2003 **APM** *100 †60

LUBAR, Sidney. ■ 53209 #056-06-1952 L1953 **IM** *071

LUBINSKY, Mark Stephen. 8701 W WATERTOWN PLANK RD, DEPT PED 53226 #035-08-1974 L1975 **OS PD** *071 †55,19

LUBSEY, Vincent Geo. 5300 W VILLARD AVE 53218 #010-03-1975 L1978 **FM** *020 †18

LUCCA, Paul Alan. 3003 W GOOD HOPE RD 53209 #056-06-1969 L1972 **OBG** *020 †30

LUCK, Allan. 3267 S 16TH ST STE 209 53215 #056-05-1963 L1964 **P** *020

LUDWIG, Kirk Allen. 9200 W WISCONSIN AVE, THE MEDICAL COLLEGE OF WI 53226 #038-41-1988 L1989 **CRS GS** *020 †85,10

LUDWIG, Maida Ann. 8700 W WATERTOWN PLANK RD 53226 #016-11-2005 L2006 **PS** *012

LUN, Agnes Minne. 2015 E NEWPORT AVE, MEDICAL CLINIC 53211 #026-04-1992 L1995 **IM** *020 †20

LUND, Michael Robert. 9200 W WISCONSIN AVE, DEPT OF OB-GYN 53226 #018-03-1996 L1997 **OBG** *020 †30

LUNDEEN, Brian Edward. 8522 W CAPITOL DR, PEDIATRIC DIAGNOSTIC 53222 #016-42-1988 L1989 **PDR RNR** *020 †20

LUNDH, Christopher Jeffre. ■ 53210 #056-06-2007 **EM** *012

LUPO, Elisabetta. ■ 53210 #869-07-1992 *100

LUPU, Veronica Daniela. 8701 W WATERTOWN PLANK RD 53226 #654-01-2004 L2008 **FP** *012

LUSIS, Richard John. 2015 E NEWPORT AVE, STE 208 53211 #056-06-1999 L2000 **IM** *020 †20

LUSSIER, Louis. 9455 W WATERTOWN PLANK RD 53226 #067-02-1969 L1983 **PM** *020 †60

LUSTIG, James Vincent. 9000 W WISCONSIN AVE, DIVISION OF ALLERGY 53226 #016-02-1972 L2004 **A IG** *020 †55,03

LUTTER, Stephanie Ann. 9000 W WISCONSIN AVE, CHILDRENS HOSPITAL OF WI 53226 #056-06-2001 L2003 **PDI** *020 †55

LUX, Alison Eileen. 2555 N DR MRTN LTHR KNG DR, CENTER 53212 #024-01-1997 L1998 **FM** *020 †18

LUY, Eric Ungos. 11211 W LINCOLN AVE 53227 #056-06-1992 L1995 **IM** *020 †20

LUY, Neil Kevin. 840 N 87TH ST 53226 #056-06-2000 L2002 **IM** *040 †20

LYE, Patricia Ann. 8701 W WATERTOWN PLANK RD, DEPT OF PEDIATRICS 53226 #049-01-1984 L1985 **PD** *020 †55

LYNCH, John Roborg. ■ 53226 #036-07-1994 L2006 **OS N** *020 †20,75

LYND, Francesca Marie. 3003 W GOOD HOPE RD, HOPE ROAD CLINIC 53209 #020-12-1996 L2000 **OBG** *020 †30

LYON, Robert Douglas. 2025 E NEWPORT AVE, WISCONSIN RADIOLOGY 53211 #010-01-1989 L2000 **VIR** *020 †80

LYON, Robert K. 1121 E NORTH AVE 53212 #036-07-1986 L1998 **FM** *020 †18

LYON, Roger Morton. 9000 W WISCONSIN AVE, PEDIATRIC ORTHOPAEDICS 53226 #016-02-1985 L1993 **OP** *020 †40

MAAS, Eric Francis. 3003 W GOOD HOPE RD, HOPE ROAD CLINIC 53209 #056-06-1985 L1990 **N** *020 †75

MABINI, Evelina L Mendoza. 3510 W BURNHAM ST 53215 #748-01-1968 L1977 **PD PP** *020

MAC GAFFEY, Jennifer E. 3289 N MAYFAIR RD, MAYFAIR ROAD CLINIC 53222 #035-45-1992 L1994 **IM** *020 †20

MACGAFFEY, Keith. 3305 W FOREST HOME AVE 53215 #035-45-1959 L1997 **IM** *071 †20

MAC GILLIS, Alexander Jos. 9200 W WISCONSIN AVE, DEPT OF UROLOGY 53226 #056-06-1956 L1957 **U** *071 †95

MACHHI, Jinobya K. 9200 W WISCONSIN AVE, DEPT. OF PATHOLOGY 53226 #495-01-1991 L1997 **PTH** *020 †50

MACHI, Jane Marie. 999 N 92ND ST, STE C550 53226 #056-06-1988 L1989 **PD PEM** *020 †55

MACIAS, Melissa Yvonne. 9200 W WISCONSIN AVE, DEPT OF NEUROSURGERY 53226 #056-06-2002 L2003 **NS** *012

MACIOLEK, Lawrence John. 575 W RIVER WOODS PKWY, STE 100 53212 #056-05-2001 L2003 **ORS** *012

MAC KINNEY, Theodore G. 9200 W WISCONSIN AVE, FROEDTERT HOSPITAL 53226 #056-06-1985 L1991 **IM PHP** *020 †20

MADIEDO, Gonzalo. 8700 W WISCONSIN AVE 53226 #264-03-1973 L1976 **PTH** *020 †50

MADSEN, Paul Byram. 10919 W BLUEMOUND RD 53226 #037-01-1982 L1984 **DR** *020 †80

MAEHL, Jeffrey Richard. 4301 W BROWN DEER RD 53223 #422-01-1997 L1998 **FM** *020 †18

MAGILL, Steven B. 2801 W KINNICKINC RVR PKWY 53215 #037-01-1990 L1991 **END IM** *020 †20

MAGLIO, Robert Carl. 5000 W NATIONAL AVE, CLEMENT J ZABLOCKI MEDICAL 53295 #056-06-1975 L1976 **IM PUD** *020 †20,16

MAGSI, Homa. 9255 N 76TH ST 53223 #308-13-1998 L2004 **IMG** *100 †18

MAGUIRE, Ann Margaret. 9200 W WISCONSIN AVE 53226 #041-01-1990 L1998 **IM** *020 †20

MAHAJAN, Namit. ■ 53213 #028-34-2007 **TY** *012

MAHESHWARI, Mohit. ■ 53214 #495-01-2000 L2008 **RNR** *100

MAHKORN, Sandra Kathleen. ■ 53207 #056-05-1981 L1992 **FM** *030 †18

MAHN, Thomas Henning. 3070 N 51ST ST, STE 106 53210 #056-05-1980 L1985 **CD IM** *020 †20

MAHONEY, James Leo. 2801 W KINNICKINC RVR PKWY, STE 330 53215 #021-06-1983 L1984 **GS** *020 †85

MAIERHOFER, Verona. ■ 53223 #104-01-2004 L2007 **FP** *012

MAIMAN, Dennis Jay. 9200 W WISCONSIN AVE 53226 #056-06-1977 L1978 **NS** *020 †25 ‡

MAJOR, Michael Robt. 2350 N LAKE DR, GROUND FLOOR 53211 #030-06-1975 L1976 **ORS OS** *020 †40

MAKOWSKI, Andrew Louis. 9200 W WISCONSIN AVE, DEPT. OF EMERGENCY MEDICIN 53226 #016-43-2003 L2005 **EM** *020 †16

MALAMIS, Angelo Peter. 9200 W WISCONSIN AVE, RM 2803 53226 #016-01-2002 L2007 **VIR** *012 †80

MALAN, Michael Joshua. ■ 53202 #049-01-2004 L2007 **AN** *012

MALAPIRA, Antonio Abella. 756 N 35TH ST 53208 #748-07-1959 L1974 **GP FM** *071

MALECKI, Elise. ■ 53203 #023-01-2006 L2008 **GS** *012

MALHOTRA, Abha. 9200 W WISCONSIN AVE, STE 5100 53226 #056-05-1995 L1996 **CD** *020 †20

MALHOTRA, Sameer. 8701 W WATERTOWN PLANK RD, MED COLL WI AFFIL HOSPS 53226 #495-36-2003 L2007 **IM** *012

MALIK, Ahmed Mehdi. 2901 W KINNICKINC RVR PKWY, STE 405 53215 #704-01-1985 L2001 **NEP** *020 †20

MALIK, Ijaz Ali. 2801 W KINNICKINC RVR PKWY, STE 777 53215 #704-01-1985 L1991 **CD** *020 †20

MALINENI, Krishna C. 960 N 12TH ST, MILWAUKEE HEART INSTITUTE 53233 #025-07-1997 L2005 **ICE** *020 †20

MALINIS, Lamberto Yabut, Jr. 2801 W KINNICKINC RVR PKWY 53215 #748-07-2003 L2008 **FP** *012

MALKIN, Mark Gordon. 9200 W WISCONSIN AVE, RM 2546 53226 #065-01-1979 L2004 **N OS** *020

MALLICK, Mohammad S A. 9455 W WATERTOWN PLANK RD, MILWAU CO MNTL HLTH COMPLX 53226 #654-01-1982 L1986 **P PYG** *020

MALLIN, Sanford Richard. 788 N JEFFERSON ST, STE 201 53202 #056-05-1957 L1958 **END IM** *020 †20

MALONE, Daniel Patrick. 10919 W BLUEMOUND RD 53226 #026-04-1990 L1997 **DR** *020 †80

MALONE, John A. 3305 S 20TH ST, STE 100 53215 #056-06-1952 L1953 **FM** *020

MALONE, Michael Lawrence. 1020 N 12TH ST, STE 301 53233 #048-15-1983 L1985 **IM** *020 †20

MAMMEN, Aykarethu O. 3070 N 51ST ST STE 604 53210 #495-31-1964 L1976 **GS** *020 †85

MANDEL, Jordan David. 2040 W WISCONSIN AVE, APT 650 53233 #017-20-1987 L1991 **PM** *020 †60

MANDEL, Paul David. 5150 N PORT WASHINGTON RD, UNIT167 53217 #016-11-1980 L1981 **OPH** *020 †35

MANDELIN, Brenda Marie. 9000 W WISCONSIN AVE, MEDICAL EDUCATION, PO BOX 53226 #016-42-2004 L2006 **CCP** *012 †55

MANEY, James P, Jr. 10000 W BLUEMOUND RD 53226 #056-06-1982 L1983 **AN** *020 †05

MANKUS, Paul J. 3056 S KINNICKINNIC AVE 53207 #030-06-1982 L1983 **FM** *020 †18 ‡

MANN, Sarah Lynn. ■ 53211 #305-01-2006 **IM** *012

MANNING, Tyshunda L. 9200 W WISCONSIN AVE, DEPT. OF OBSTETRICS/GYNECO 53226 #011-04-2001 L2003 **OBG** *020 †30

MANOLI, Rajashri S. 5000 W CHAMBERS ST 53210 #495-33-1966 L1976 **NM GP** *020 †28

MANOR, Betsy Lynne. 1121 E NORTH AVE 53212 #056-06-2005 L2006 **FP** *012

MANUEL, Emmanuel S. 3201 S 16TH ST, SOUTH CENTER MEDICAL 53215 #748-01-1971 L1980 **U** *020 †95

MARAMATTOM, Leena Varkey. 8701 W WATERTOWN PLANK RD, MEDICAL COLLEGE OF WISCONS 53226 #495-37-1999 L2006 **IM** *020

MARANAN, Isidro L. 2400 W VILLARD AVE 53209 #748-01-1956 L1962 **AN** *071 †05

MARCANGELO, Michael James. 8701 W WATERTOWN PLANK RD 53226 #016-11-2002 L2007 **PYM** *100 †75

MARCDANTE, Karen Jean. 9000 W WISCONSIN AVE, MS681 53226 #056-06-1980 L1981 PD CCP *020 †55

MARGOLIS, David Arthur. 8701 W WATERTOWN PLANK RD, DEPT PHO 53226 #056-05-1989 L1990 PHO *020 †55

MARGOLIS, Irwin. 2900 W OKLAHOMA AVE 53215 #035-19-1963 L1971 PUD IM *071 †20

MARINO, Rita Mary. 161 W WISCONSIN AVE, RITA M MARINO MD SC 53203 #056-06-1958 L1959 GYN *071 †30

MARK, Leighton P. 9200 W WISCONSIN AVE, DEPT DIAGN.RAD.FROEDTERT H 53226 #035-19-1978 L1983 DR *020 †80

MARKS, David Scott. 9200 W WISCONSIN AVE, MED COL WI DEPT CD # E5100 53226 #005-02-1989 L2000 CD IM *020 †20

MARKS, Richard M. 9200 W WISCONSIN AVE 53226 #041-02-1988 L1998 ORS *020 †40

MARKS, Sean Michael. 9200 W WISCONSIN AVE, FREODTERT HOSPITAL 53226 #056-06-2004 L2007 IM *100 †55

MARLA, Rammohan. 9200 W WISCONSIN AVE #5700, CT SURGERY,FROEDTERT EAST 53226 #495-58-1988 L2004 TS *012 †85

MARLOWE, Taylor E. 9000 W WISCONSIN AVE 53226 #016-43-1991 L1994 PD *020 †55

MARN, Charles Stephen. 9200 W WISCONSIN AVE, DEPT OF RADIOLOGY, RM 2840 53226 #028-02-1982 L2006 DR *020 †80

MARONN, Mandi Lynne. 8701 W WATERTOWN PLANK RD, MEDICAL COLLEGE OF WISCONS 53226 #056-06-2004 L2005 D *012

MARQUEZ, Gilbert. 2801 W KINNICKINC RVR PKWY, STE 135 53215 #016-11-2003 L2004 IM *020

MARQUEZ, Jonathan Pangili. 1218 W KILBOURN AVE, STE 124 53233 #748-02-2002 L2006 IM *020 †18

MARR, Lisa Anne. 9200 W WISCONSIN AVE, PALLIATIVE CARE CTR 9200 W 53226 #023-01-1990 L2003 IM *020 †20

MARRA, Thomas Russell. 1575 N RIVERCENTER DR 53212 #056-05-1974 L1975 N *020 †75

MARTIN, Cheryl Renee. 544 E OGDEN AVE, # 700-343 53202 #005-06-1978 L1993 CD *020 †20

MARTIN, John Thos. 2315 N LAKE DR 53211 #030-06-1974 L1975 PD *020 †55

MARTIN, Timothy John. 9200 W WISCONSIN AVE, DEPT OF OTOLARYNGOLOGY MC 53226 #056-06-2002 L2003 OTO *020

MARTINEZ, Alfonso M. 8701 W WATERTOWN PLANK RD 53226 #649-14-1979 L1996 PG PD *020 †55

MARTINEZ, Francisco Jose. 3033 S 27TH ST STE 200 53215 #649-01-1972 L1977 GS CD *020 †85

MARTINEZ-TORRES, G. 2025 E NEWPORT AVE 53211 #016-11-1988 L2001 PTH FOP *020 †50

MARUTA, Ikuko Ui. ■ 53217 #572-18-1985 L1994 P *020

MARWAHA, Amitoj Singh. ■ 53202 #056-06-2004 L2007 CD *012 †20

MARWAHA, Anjali. ■ 53202 #028-34-2007 *012

MASON, Tina Clair. 945 N 12TH ST, FL 1 53233 #018-03-1984 L2006 OBG *040 †30

MASSARO, Bruce Michael. 2600 N MAYFAIR RD, STE 600 53226 #016-06-1981 L1982 OPH PS *020 †35

MASSEY, Becky Lynn. 9200 W WISCONSIN AVE, DEPT OTO 53226 #056-06-2000 L2006 OTO *100 †45

MASSEY, Benson Talmage. 9200 W WISCONSIN AVE, GI DIVISION/FROEDTERT HOSP 53226 #023-07-1983 L1987 GE IM *020 †20

MASUNUNGURE, Ratidzai. 8532 W CAPITOL DR 53222 #775-01-1989 L1999 PD *020 †55

MATESKON, Charles Andrew. 2025 E NEWPORT AVE, STE 1000 53211 #028-34-1982 L1983 RO *020 †80

MATHEW, James. 2350 N LAKE DR, STE 400 53211 #495-31-1981 L2003 CD *020 †20

MATHEW, Jinu Jacob. 1121 E NORTH AVE 53212 #495-37-2002 L2006 FM *020 †18

MATHEWS, Richard Joseph. 2388 N LAKE DR, NORTH POINT MEDICAL GRP LT 53211 #056-06-1962 L1963 OBG *071 †30

MATLOUB, Hani Selman. 8700 W WATERTOWN PLANK RD 53226 #528-01-1970 L1978 PS HS *020 †85,65

MATTERN, Quentin James. 2025 E NEWPORT AVE, STE 217 53211 #016-01-2000 L2002 FM *020 †18

MATTEUCCI, Michael Joseph. 9200 W WISCONSIN AVE, DEPT OF UROLOGY 53226 #056-06-2004 L2006 U *012

MATTHAEUS, William Gerard. 2025 E NEWPORT AVE, STE 1000 53211 #056-06-1983 L1984 HEM IM *020 †20

MATTHEWS, Brian Paul. 2478 N 66TH ST 53213 #056-06-2006 L2007 AN *012

MATTHEWS, Gregory Jos. 9233 N GREEN BAY RD 53209 #056-06-1990 L1991 FM *020 †18

MATZ, Cory James. 2801 W KK RIVER PKWY, STE 453 53215 #056-06-2001 L2002 AN *020 †05

MAUL, John Scott. 2025 E NEWPORT AVE, STE 1000 53211 #056-06-1999 L2005 HO *020 †20

MAURER, Adrienne Michelle. 801 S 70TH ST 53214 #056-06-2003 L2005 FM *020 †18

MAVIGLIA, Marcello Argeo. 1231 W MITCHELL ST 53204 #561-17-1980 L2004 P *020 †75

MAXEY, Christine Ann. 9200 W WISCONSIN AVE 53226 #056-05-1988 L1989 PM *020

MAXFIELD, Bradley Andrew. 8522 W CAPITOL DR, PEDIATRIC DIAGNOSTIC 53222 #056-06-1994 L1995 PDR *020 †80

MAY, Judith Ann. 9200 W WISCONSIN AVE, MDCL CLLGE CLNCS AT FRDTRT 53226 #056-06-1985 L1986 AN *020 †05

MAYA, Alberto Adrian. 3223 S 103RD ST, SURGICENTER OF GREATER MIL 53227 #649-19-1987 L1998 AN *020 †05

MAYER, Alan Neil. 8701 W WATERTOWN PLANK RD, IATRIC GASTROENTERLOGY & N 53226 #035-20-1995 L2003 PD *020 †55

MAYHORN, Rodney Richard. 9000 W WISCONSIN AVE, CHILDREN'S HOSPITAL OF WIS 53226 #028-34-2002 L2004 MPD *100 †20,55

MAZUMDAR, Debesh Chandra. 1575 N RIVERCENTER DR 53212 #495-36-1964 L1979 IM NEP *020 †20

MAZURCZAK, Christina Mari. ■ 53203 #056-05-2007 FP *012

MAZZEO, Anthony Jos. 10000 W BLUEMOUND RD 53226 #056-06-1987 L1988 AN CCM *020 †05

MAZZULLA, James Patrick. 2500 W LAYTON AVE, STE 250 53221 #016-06-1975 L1977 IM EM *020 †20

MC AULIFFE, Janet M. 2727 W CLEVELAND AVE 53215 #050-02-1987 L1991 PD *020 †55

MC CABE, Robert Wm. 2323 N MAYFAIR RD STE 310 53226 #056-06-1957 L1958 ORS *020 †40

MC CARTHY, Geraldine M. 9200 W WISCONSIN AVE, STE 650 53226 #539-04-1981 L1988 RHU *050 †20

MC CARTY, Brian Albert. 2801 W KINNICKINC RVR PKWY, STE 575 53226 #056-06-1995 L2000 ORS *020 †40

MC CARTY, Daniel John. 8701 W WATERTOWN PLANK RD, DEPT MED 53226 #041-01-1954 L1974 RHU IM *050 †20

MC CARVER, Deborah Gail. 8701 W WATERTOWN PLANK RD, DEPT OF PEDIATRICS 53226 #047-06-1978 L1999 PA PD *050 †55

MC CLYMONDS, Megan Elise. 9455 W WATERTOWN PLANK RD, HEALTH - CAIS/53B 53226 #056-05-2000 L2002 CHP *100 †75

MCCORMICK, Joseph Charles. 9200 W WISCONSIN AVE, DEPT. OF ORTHOPAEDIC SURGE 53226 #056-06-2005 L2006 ORS *012

MC CORMICK, Thomas F. ■ 53217 #056-06-1952 L1953 AN *071 †05

MC COY, Audrey Kay. 8901 W LINCOLN AVE, CONSULTANTS AT WEST ALLIS 53227 #056-05-1995 L1999 AN *020 †05

MC COY, Mary Giambrone. 6901 W EDGERTON AVE, AURORA HEALTH CENTER EDGER 53220 #016-06-1987 L1993 FM *020 †18

MC CULLOUGH, William T. 2901 W KINNICKINC RVR PKWY 53215 #028-34-1997 L2006 NS *020

MC DEVITT, Wm Patrick. 2323 N MAYFAIR RD 53226 #018-03-1958 L1961 ORS *071 †40

MC DONALD, Monica Lee. 2015 E NEWPORT AVE, COLUMBIA CARDIAC CLINIC 53211 #008-01-1991 L1999 TS *020 †90,85

MCEVOY, Taryn Marie. ■ 53213 #056-06-2005 L2007 OBG *012

MC FADDEN, Edith Anne. 3201 S 16TH ST STE 400 53215 #041-01-1979 L1988 OTO A *020 †15

MCGARGILL, Shawn Michael. ■ 53218 #056-06-2008 *012

MCGARTLAND, Laura Pfouts. 2025 E NEWPORT AVE, STE 1000 53211 #539-06-2000 L2006 HO *100 †20

MCGOWAN, Jacqueline Renee. ■ 53213 #056-06-2008 *012

MC GOWN, Andrew John. 2015 E NEWPORT AVE, MEDICAL CLINIC 53211 #025-07-2001 L2002 IM *020 †20

MC GUIRE, John Rhode. 9200 W WISCONSIN AVE, DEPT OF PM & R 53226 #026-04-1987 L1997 PM CN *020 †60

MC LAUGHLIN, Brian Chas. ■ 53223 #028-34-1945 L1946 OPH *071 †35

MC LEAN, Zarah Gean. 4016C W GOOD HOPE RD, # C 53209 #010-03-1968 L1969 PD *020 †55

MCMAHON, Chadd James. ■ 53202 #030-05-2006 L2008 DR *012

MCMILLAN, Terry Lee. ■ 53222 #054-04-2007 AN *012

MC MULLIN, Brian T. ■ 53222 #048-13-2005 L2006 OTO *012

MC NAMARA, Peter J. 3003 W GOOD HOPE RD, MILWAUKEE MEDICAL CLINIC 53209 #035-09-1953 L1958 GE IM *071 †20

MC NEAR, Deborah Jean. 2716 E NEWBERRY BLVD 2308 53211 #016-06-1982 L1988 PUD IM *020 †20

MC NEELY, James Kenneth. 575 W RIVER WOODS PKWY 53212 #056-06-1984 L1988 AN PAN *020 †05

MC QUEEN, Amanda Marie. 9200 W WISCONSIN AVE 53226 #030-06-2003 L2004 AN *020

MC SORLEY, Brian Patrick. 3615 W OKLAHOMA AVE 53215 #056-06-1983 L1984 FM *020 †18

MC WEY, Patrick J. 2025 E NEWPORT AVE, WISCONSIN RADIOLOGY 53211 #056-06-1978 L1979 DR *020 †80

MEANS, James Andrew, III. ■ 53223 #056-06-1947 L1948 IM NEP *071

MEDIPALLI, Radhika. 9200 W WISCONSIN AVE 53226 #496-01-2000 L2003 NEP *012 †20

MEGAN, Nancy L. 2025 E NEWPORT AVE 53211 #056-06-1988 L1989 AN *020 †05

MEHRABY, Katayoun. 5000 W NATIONAL AVE, RM 5136 53295 #517-26-1997 L2006 IMG *100 †20

MEHROTRA, Asheesh. 635 N 35TH ST 53208 #495-05-2000 L2004 PD *020 †55

MEIDL, John Joseph. 2801 W KINNICKINC RVR PKWY, STE 475 53215 #051-04-1990 L2000 ID *020 †20

MEIER, Julie Davis. 925 N 87TH ST 53226 #038-40-2002 L2004 OPH *012

MEISTER, Andrew N. 9200 W WISCONSIN AVE, DEPARTMENT OF EMERGENCY ME 53226 #056-05-2006 L2008 EM *012

MEISTER, Morris Milton. ■ 53217 #056-05-1948 L1951 D *071 †15

MELKONIAN, Abdallah Geo. 9233 N GREEN BAY RD 53209 #330-04-1955 L1964 GS *071 †85

MELLENCAMP, David Dixon. 3970 N OAKLAND AVE STE 501 53211 #056-05-1966 L1968 ORS FM *020 †40

MELNYCZENKO, Walter Ihor. 2727 W CLEVELAND AVE, STE 2000 53215 #649-33-1979 L1987 OBG IM *020

MELZER, Anne Catherine. ■ 53208 #056-06-2008 *012

MENDELL, Jeffery Paul. 2900 W OKLAHOMA AVE 53215 #016-45-2002 L2004 DR *020 †80

MENDELOFF, Gale Lee. 2025 E NEWPORT AVE 53211 #056-06-1958 L1959 GS VS *071 †85

MENDIOLA, Rolando M. 2745 W LAYTON AVE, STE 202 53221 #748-01-1971 L1979 VS *020

MENDIS, Nimali D. 2901 W KINNICKINC RVR PKWY, STE 301 53215 #422-01-1993 L2004 IM *020 †20

MENETREY, Jammie. ■ 53212 #028-78-2007, ▲ IM *012

MEPANI, Jay Bhupen. 8701 W WATERTOWN PLANK RD, MED OF WI 53226 #035-06-2002 L2006 END *012 †20

MEPANI, Rachel. 9200 W WISCONSIN AVE, FMLH, DIV OF GI & HEPATOLO 53226 #035-06-2002 L2006 GE *012 †20

MERRIMAN, Kim Alan. 1901 E CAPITOL DR, SHOREWOOD FAMILY 53211 #056-05-1981 L1982 FM FPG *020 †18

MESKIN, Joshua Albert. 9200 W WISCONSIN AVE, STE 51 53226 #016-43-2003 L2006 CD *012 †20

MESROBIAN, Hrair-George J. 999 N 92ND ST # 330, CHILDREN'S CORPORATE CENTE 53226 #605-01-1978 L1995 OS U *020 †95

MESROBIAN, James Randall. 10000 W BLUEMOUND RD 53226 #016-06-1989 L2003 AN *020 †05

MESSER, Peter W. 2801 W KINNICKINC RVR PKWY, STE 250 53215 #056-05-1973 L1978 D *020 †15

METZLER, John Paul. 1000 N 92ND ST, DEPT PM & R 53226 #048-02-1995 L1997 PM *020 †60

MEURER, John Richard. 1020 N 12TH ST, MEDICAL COLLEGE OF WISCONS 53233 #056-05-1986 L1994 PD *050 †55

MEURER, Linda Nicholson. 1000 N 92ND ST 53226 #025-07-1989 L1994 FM *040 †18 ‡

MEWISSEN, Mark W. 2801 W KINNICKINC RVR PKWY 53215 #016-02-1983 L1987 VIR R *020 †80

MEYER, Christina Tate. 1121 E NORTH AVE 53212 #016-43-2003 L2004 FM *020 †18

MEYERS, Alfred. ■ 53217 #056-06-1957 L1958 CLP PTH *071 †50

MICHEL, Michelle Anne. 9200 W WISCONSIN AVE, DEPT OF RADIOLOGY 53226 #038-41-1991 L1999 RNR *020 †80

MICKELSON, Julie Anne. 1032 S CESAR E CHAVEZ DR 53204 #026-04-1992 L1996 OBG *020 †30

MIDDLETON, Donald Kevin. 3970 N OAKLAND AVE, STE 300 53211 #016-06-1988 L1989 ORS OSM *020 †40

MIGRINO, Raymond Q. 9200 W WISCONSIN AVE, MED COLLEGE OF WISCONSIN 53226 #748-02-1990 L2004 CD IM *020 †20

MIJAL, Sara Ann. ■ 53208 #056-06-2007 GS *012

MIKHAEEL, Hany Gaber. 6901 W EDGERTON AVE, AURORA HEALTH CENTER - EDG 53220 #915-02-1990 L2000 FM *020 †18

MIKHAILOV, Konstantin Y. 575 W RIVER WOODS PKWY 53212 #913-69-1984 L2000 AN *020 †05

MIKHAILOV, Theresa A. 9000 W WISCONSIN AVE, CHILDRENS HOSP WI/MS 681 53226 #016-06-1986 L1999 CCP *020 †55

MIKKELSON, Wendy Marie. 2801 W KINNICKINC RVR PKWY, STE 160 53215 #056-06-1980 L1983 GS *020 †85

MIKOLAJCZAK, Norbert A. ■ 53222 #056-06-1945 L1948 GS *071

MIKUS, Mary Ann. 9455 W WATERTOWN PLANK RD 53226 #018-75-1990, ▲ L1991 P FM *020 †75

MILBURN, Mason Wayne. 9200 W WISCONSIN AVE, ORTHOPAEDIC DEPT. 53226 #047-06-2004 L2005 ORS *012

MILDENBERG, Christopher F. 1020 N 12TH ST, FL 2 53233 #056-06-2001 L2006 IM *020 †20

MILLAN, Alfredo C. 1834 W WISCONSIN AVE, 2ND FL 53233 #748-08-1961 L1976 OBG *020

MILLAR, Iluminado Meera. 7220 W NATIONAL AVE, HERRINGTON CLINIC 53214 #748-01-1964 L1976 FM *020 †18

MILLARD, Jennifer Louise. 843 N 13TH ST 53233 #047-06-1985 L1987 P IM *020

MILLEN, Francis Jos. ■ 53217 #056-06-1942 L1943 N P *071 †75

MILLER, Boyd Donald. 2311 N PROSPECT AVE, STE 401 53211 #028-02-1988 L1990 PD *020 †55

MILLER, Dennis Paul. 7878 N 76TH ST, NORTHWEST CLINIC 53223 #056-06-1984 L1985 OBG *020 †30

MILLER, John Jos. 1901 E CAPITOL DR, SHOREWOOD FAMILY 53211 #056-06-1979 L1980 FM FPG *020 †18

MILLER, Jordan Jay. 9200 W WISCONSIN AVE 53226 #056-06-2005 L2006 D *012

MILLER, Matthew Louis. 9200 W WISCONSIN AVE, DEPARTMENT OF NEUROSURGERY 53226 #030-05-2004 L2005 NS *012

MILLER, Shenell Yvette. 7878 N 76TH ST, NORTHWEST CLINIC 53223 #056-06-2002 L2004 PD *020 †55

MILLEVILLE, Gregory Scott. 3070 N 51ST ST STE 309 53210 #018-03-1979 L1984 NPM PD *020 †55

MILOSAVLJEVIC, Staci Lynn. 9200 W WISCONSIN AVE, FROEDTERT HOSPITAL DEPT ME 53226 #056-06-2003 L2004 CD *012

MILSHTEYN, Mark. 8901 W LINCOLN AVE, CONSULTANTS AT WEST ALLIS 53227 #913-16-1993 L2001 AN *020 †05

MINAR, Phillip Paul. 8701 W WATERTOWN PLANK RD, MED COLL OF WI 53226 #056-06-2007 PD *012

MINES, Arthur. 8200 W SILVER SPRING DR, HEALTH CENTER 53218 #016-11-1978 L1979 FM *020 †18

MINHAS, Sheeba. 2323 S 102ND ST 53227 #306-01-1999 L2005 FM *020 †18

MINIKEL, James Eric. 5233 W MORGAN AVE 53220 #020-02-1970 L1973 ORS *071 †40

MINIKEL, Jeffrey Lee. 5233 W MORGAN AVE, MILWAUKEE CLINIC OF 53220 #020-02-1977 L1978 ORS *020 †40

MINIOR, Thomas Matthew. 2770 N 5TH ST, MILWAUKEE HEALTH SERVICES 53212 #024-07-2000 L2003 IM *020 †20

MINKEL, Daniel Thomas. 2801 W KINNICKINNIC PKWY 53215 #649-33-1981 L1982 AN *020 †05

MINKLEY, Richard Eric. 2801 W KINNICKINC RVR PKWY, STE 1030 53215 #056-05-1982 L1987 GE IM *020 †20

MINKO, Myron Boris. 2511 E BELLEVIEW PL 53211 #056-06-1976 L1977 P *020 †75

MIRANDA, Adrian. 8701 W WATERTOWN PLANK RD, MEDICAL COLLEGE OF WISCONS 53226 #056-06-1998 L1999 PG *020 †55

MIRHOSEINI, Mahmood. 1400 W OKLAHOMA AVE 53215 #517-01-1955 L1962 CD TS *071 †85,90

MIRVISS, Marshall Jay. 2500 W LAYTON AVE, STE 10 53221 #056-06-1975 L1976 IM *020

MISHEFSKE, Mary Jean. 3070 N 51ST ST 53210 #056-05-1985 L1986 NPM PD *020 †55

MISHLOVE, Linda Rebekah. ■ 53217 #056-05-1977 L1995 FM *020 †18

MISRA, Suresh Kumar. 3267 S 16TH ST STE 208 53215 #495-29-1972 L1978 FM *020 †18

MISSETT, Andrew Mark. ■ 53211 #008-02-1978 L1983 EM PD *040 †55

MISTRY, Rakesh Dilip. 9000 W WISCONSIN AVE, MS-677 53226 #033-06-1998 L2002 PEM PD *020 †55

MITCHANIS, Mary Ellen. 3003 W GOOD HOPE RD, HOPE ROAD CLINIC 53209 #016-01-1988 L1991 IM *020 †20

MITCHELL, Julie Lyn. 9200 W WISCONSIN AVE 53226 #056-05-1995 L1999 IM OS *020 †20

MITCHELL, Mark J. 3003 W GOOD HOPE RD 53209 #030-06-1976 L1977 PD *020 †55

MITCHELL, Michael Edward. 9000 W WISCONSIN AVE, CHILDREN HOSPITAL WI 53226 #024-01-1995 L2006 TS PDS *020 †85,90

MITCHELL, Michael Ernst. 999 N 92ND ST, CHILDRENS CORP CTR STE 330 53226 #024-01-1969 L2006 UP U *020 †95

MITCHELL, Michael James. 801 S 70TH ST 53214 #056-06-1997 L1998 N *020 †75

MITTAL, Prabhas. 2901 W KINNICKINC RVR PKWY, STE 516 53215 #495-36-1993 L2007 HEM *020 †20

MIXTER, Roger Conant. 5201 N PORT WASHINGTON RD 53217 #035-01-1976 L1984 PS *020 †85,65

M.K., Mallikarjunappa. 8701 W WATERTOWN PLANK RD 53226 #495-09-2000 RNR *012

MOBERG-WOLFF, Elizabeth. 999 N 92ND ST, PM&R 53226 #056-05-1990 L1991 PM *020 †60

MODY, Rita. 3305 S 20TH ST 53215 #308-32-1970 L1978 FM *020 †18

MOE, Craig Edward. 5233 W MORGAN AVE, MILWAUKEE CLINIC OF 53220 #016-11-1999 L2004 ORS *020

MOECKER, Neil Arthur. 3738 S 60TH ST, STE 101 53220 #056-06-1975 L1976 FM *020 †18

MOFFIC, H Steven. 8701 W WATERTOWN PLANK RD 53226 #008-01-1971 L1989 P GP *020

MOHANRAM, Arvind. ■ 53202 #305-01-2003 L2006 AN *012

MOHIUDDIN, Jaweed Mohamme. 4555 W SCHROEDER DR, STE 170 53223 #495-99-1988 L2001 AN *020 †05

MOISIO, Shane Victor. 9000 W WISCONSIN AVE 53226 #038-41-2001 L2002 P CHP *020 †75

MOLLOY, Robert Michael. 2801 W KINNICKINC RVR PKWY, STE 1030 53215 #025-07-2000 L2000 ORS *100

MOLYAKO, Tatiana Borisovn. 3000 W MONTANA ST 53215 #913-08-1995 L2008 IM *012

MOMI, Jaspreet Kaur. ■ 53215 #305-01-2001 OBG *020

MONESE, George Molemo. 9455 W WATERTOWN PLANK RD, DENCY EDUCATION 53226 #913-97-1989 L1997 CHP *100 †75

MONTANO, Sandra T. 535 N 27TH ST 53208 #748-14-1986 L1990 PD *020 †55

MONTENEGRO, Jose Vita, III. 10400 W NORTH AVE 53226 #748-08-1958 L1966 OM GS *071

MONTGOMERY, Robert R, Jr. 1000 N 92ND ST 53226 #041-12-1969 L1980 PHO HEM *050 †55

MOORE, Nicholas J. 8901 W LINCOLN AVE 53227 #001-02-2000 L2006 DR *020 †80

MORAL, Gregg Emil. 2323 N LAKE DR, WISCONSIN RADIOLOGY 53211 #035-03-1986 L1987 DR IM *020 †20,80

MORAN, Jill Kathleen. 9200 W WISCONSIN AVE, DEPT OBGYN FMLH/E 53226 #016-43-1999 L2000 OBG *020 †30

MORAN, Rebecca Howard. 8701 W WATERTOWN PLANK RD, DIVISION OF NEONATOLOGY 53226 #020-02-1998 L2004 NPM *020 †55

MORENO, Jose Miguel. 637 W MITCHELL ST 53204 #264-01-1967 L1982 TS *020

MORENO, Luz Stella. 637 W MITCHELL ST 53204 #264-01-1968 L1986 GP *020

MORKER, Ketan N. ■ 53225 #305-01-2005 FP *012

MORRIS, George L, III. 2801 W KINNICKINNIC PKWY 53215 #030-05-1984 L1985 N *050 †75

MORRIS, Robert Du Bois. 136 HARRISON AVE, TUFT UNIV DEPT MED 53207 #056-06-1991 OS *040

MORRISON, Joshua Lewis. 9200 W WISCONSIN AVE, NEUROLOGY DEPARTMENT 53226 #056-06-2005 L2006 N *012

MORTADA, Mohammad Eyman. 945 N 12TH ST 53233 #875-01-1996 L2001 CD ICE *020 †20

MOSCHELL, Amy Marie. 2424 S 90TH ST, STE 204 53227 #056-05-1998 L2002 OPH *020 †35

MOSER, Barbara Elizabeth. 3351 N DOWNER AVE, UW-MILWAUKEE 53211 #016-06-1984 L1993 FM *020 †18

MOSER, Michael John. 3000 W MONTANA ST 53215 #143-11-2006 TY *012

MOSESSON, Michael Wm. 945 N 12TH ST 53233 #035-08-1959 L1981 IM HEM *050

MOSLETH, Michael Bertrum. 3003 W GOOD HOPE RD, HOPE ROAD CLINIC 53209 #026-08-1977 L1980 PCC IM *020 †20

MOSS, David Howard. 5000 W CHAMBERS ST 53210 #056-05-1978 L1979 EM *071 †16

MOSSEY, Richard Orville. ■ 53226 #016-06-1948 L1949 GS *071

MOUNTS, Kyle Owen. 3070 N 51ST ST # P309 53210 #035-06-1987 L1994 NPM *020 †55

MOY, Raymond W. 6917 W OKLAHOMA AVE 53219 #035-08-1976 L1977 P *020 †75,18

MOYER, Carl Frederic. 201 N MAYFAIR RD 53226 #056-06-1966 L1972 ORS OS *020 †40

MUDERLAK, Shannon Sarah. 1720 W FLORIST AVE 53209 #056-06-1999 L2004 FM *020

MUELLER, Wade Martin. 9200 W WISCONSIN AVE 53226 #056-05-1983 L1984 NS *020 †25

MUELLERLEILE, Edward J. 2025 W OKLAHOMA AVE, SUITE 105 53215 #026-04-1992 L1995 PD *020 †55

MULLANE, Michael P. 2025 E NEWPORT AVE, STE 1000 53211 #023-07-1985 L1995 ON IM *020 †20

MULLICK, Samir. 4267 W FOND DU LAC AVE 53216 #495-36-1989 L1996 PD *020 †55

MULLIN, Timothy Ian. 9200 W WISCONSIN AVE, DEPT OF ORTHO SURG 53226 #056-06-2004 L2005 ORS *012

MULLOOLY, John Peter. 5000 W CHAMBERS ST 53210 #056-06-1960 L1961 IM *071

MULLOOLY, John Peter, II. 1220 DEWEY AVE 53213 #056-06-1993 L1994 P N *020 †75

MULROONEY, Neil Patrick. 8701 W WATERTOWN PLANK RD, DIVISION OF NEONATOLOGY 53226 #026-04-1998 L2004 NPM *020 †55

MUNAGIAN, Michael William. ■ 53202 #056-06-2003 L2005 DR *012

MUNDEY, Kavita. 8701 W WATERTOWN PLANK RD, MCWAH 53226 #495-36-1995 L2000 IM *020 †20

MUNSHI, Charul Ambrish. 9200 W WISCONSIN AVE, DEPT ANES 53226 #495-17-1969 L1974 AN *020 †05

MUNTZ, Carla Jean. ■ 53222 #016-45-2005 L2007 DR *012

MUNTZ, Martin Daniel. 9200 W WISCONSIN AVE, GENERAL INTER'L MEDICINE E 53226 #016-45-2001 L2003 IM *020

MUQEET, Khazi Abdul. 8701 W WATERTOWN PLANK RD 53226 #495-72-2001 L2006 P *012

MURPHY, Heather C. 9000 W WISCONSIN AVE 53226 #018-03-1996 L1997 OTO *020 †45

MURPHY, Michael Lloyd. 201 N MAYFAIR RD, MEDICAL EYE ASSOCIATES SC 53226 #056-06-1990 L1992 OPH *020 †35 ‡

MURTHY, Vishnubhakta S. 2801 W KINNICKINC RVR PKWY, STE 135 53215 #495-20-1965 L1980 PA IM *050

MUSA, Ndidiamaka L. 9000 W WISCONSIN AVE, CRITICAL CARE OFFICE-MS 68 53226 #610-01-1987 L2002 CCP PD *012

MUSEITIF, Raaid I. ■ 53202 #056-05-2001 L2003 CD *012

MUSHTAQ, Romila. 9200 W WISCONSIN AVE, DEPARTMENT OF NEUROLOGY 53226 #704-06-1998 L2005 CN *100

MUZI, Michael. 10000 W BLUEMOUND RD 53226 #056-05-1987 L1988 AN *020 †05

NADAR, Donald Jos. 2900 W OKLAHOMA AVE 53215 #016-11-1983 L1995 FM *020 †18

NADEEM, Iram. 9200 W WISCONSIN AVE, OF IN 53226 #704-02-1987 L1996 IM ID *020 †20

NADEEM, Muhammad. 3201 S 16TH ST STE 2006 53215 #704-02-1987 L1996 PUD *020 †20

NAGARJUN RAO, Rayasam K S. 9200 W WISCONSIN AVE 53226 #496-18-1985 L2000 PTH *020 †50

NAHRA, Kareem Rizkallah. ■ 53204 #016-11-2006 N *012

NAIDA, John David. 1020 N 12TH ST 53233 #025-01-1992 L1997 RO *020 †80

NAIK, Amar Satish. ■ 53233 #016-11-2005 IM *012

NAIK, Kavita V. ■ 53212 #056-06-2007 IM *012

NAIK, Niravkumar Ashokkum. 8701 W WATERTOWN PLANK RD 53226 #422-01-2005 IM *012

NAIR, B Ramachandran. 3975 N 68TH ST, CAPITOL DRIVE PEDIATRICS 53216 #495-31-1965 L1973 PD PTH *020 †55

NAIR, Suresh Ramachandran. 8701 W WATERTOWN PLANK RD, MED COLL WI AFFIL HOSPS 53226 #495-31-1988 *100

NAJAM, Nadeem Waheed. 3201 S 16TH ST, STE 2006 53215 #704-01-1997 L2004 IM *020

NAMDARI, Bahram. 6000 S 27TH ST 53221 #517-01-1966 L1976 GS VS *071 †85

NAND, Ranveer Kumar. 8701 W WATERTOWN PLANK RD, MCWAH 53226 #016-01-2003 L2005 HO *012

NANDA, Thim P. 11716 W GREENFIELD AVE 53214 #495-09-1964 L1978 PM ORS *071 †60

NANDA, Usha. 3056 S KINNICKINNIC AVE 53207 #495-09-1964 L1980 PM *020 †60

NANDALUR, Karunakar Reddi. ■ 53215 #056-06-1996 L1997 IM *020 †20

NANGIA, Vikram. 2801 W KINNICKINC RVR PKWY, STE 777 53215 #495-36-1994 L1995 ICE *020 †20

NARAYAN, Raj. 9200 W WISCONSIN AVE, DEPT OBG 53226 #495-53-1982 L2000 OBG *020 †30,18

NASH, David Steven. 2350 N LAKE DR, STE 201 53211 #056-05-1975 L1976 OBG *020 †30

NASH, John Joseph. ■ 53202 #056-06-2006 L2007 OTO *012

NASH, Tammon Antoinette. ■ 53213 #025-07-2002 L2005 BBK *100 †50

NASSARALLA, Claudia Lage. 2906 S 20TH ST 53215 #025-12-2004 L2007 IM *020 †20

NASSIF, Kamal Fuad. 2300 N MAYFAIR RD STE 1155 53226 #605-01-1976 L1980 OPH OS *020 †35

NATTINGER, Ann Butler. 9200 W WISCONSIN AVE, FEC DIV OF GIM STE 4200 53226 #016-11-1983 L1988 IM *050 †20

NAUGHTON, Thomas Michael. 5000 W NATIONAL AVE 53295 #056-06-1984 L1992 IMG FM *020 †18

NAUSIEDA, Paul Anthony. 945 N 12TH ST # 4602 53233 #016-02-1972 L1982 N PA *020 †75

NAVARRA, Miguel. PO BOX 340051 53234 #264-04-1963 L1975 EM FM *071

NAZIR, Adnan. 5300 W VILLARD AVE 53218 #704-22-1999 L2004 IM *020 †20

NEAVES, Noe, Jr. 1032 S 16TH ST 53204 #056-05-1991 L1993 **PD** *020

NEGRETTE, Gina G. ■ 53219 #056-06-2007 **P** *012

NEGRON, Jose Manuel. 1032 S CESAR E CHAVEZ DR 53204 #035-45-2003 L2006 **FM** *020 †18

NEIDEEN, Todd Andrew. 9200 W WISCONSIN AVE, DEPARTMENT OF SURGERY 53226 #016-11-2002 L2004 **GS** *100

NEILSON, John Curtis. 9200 W WISCONSIN AVE, WISCONSIN O 53226 #046-01-2004 L2005 **ORS** *012

NEIMON, Robert Emmett. 5000 W CHAMBERS ST, DEPT RAD D 53210 #056-06-1989 L1990 **RNR** *020 †80

NEITZEL, Gary Frank. 2900 W OKLAHOMA AVE, LABORATORY-ST. LUKE'S MED 53215 #056-06-1982 L1983 **PTH** *020 †50

NELLEN, James Raymond. 2900 W OKLAHOMA AVE 53215 #056-06-1955 L1956 **R** *071 †80

NELSON, Anthony Carl. ■ 53210 #056-06-2007 **GS** *012

NELSON, Eric Allen. 8901 W LINCOLN AVE, CONSULTANTS AT WEST ALLIS 53227 #025-07-1991 L1998 **AN** *020 †05

NELSON, Mark Alan. 8901 W LINCOLN AVE, CONSULTANTS AT WEST ALLIS 53227 #056-06-1981 L1982 **AN** *020 †05

NELSON, Michael Lee. 7878 N 76TH ST, NORTHWEST CLINIC 53223 #028-34-1980 L1981 **FM** *020 †18

NELSON, Reed Young. 8701 W WATERTOWN PLANK RD 53226 #010-01-2004 L2005 **AN** *012

NELSON, Rory Michael. 2900 W OKLAHOMA AVE, ST. LUKES MEDICAL CENTER 53215 #056-06-2003 L2004 **DR** *012

NESIAMA, Jo-Ann Oyaide. 1060 N 115TH ST 53226 #690-06-1990 L2005 **PEM** *012 †55

NESS, Mary Ellen. 2901 W KINNICKINNIC PKWY, STE 106 53215 #056-06-1983 L1984 **P** *020 †60

NESS-WENUM, Sherry Lynn. 2025 E NEWPORT AVE, WISCONSIN RADIOLOGY 53211 #056-06-1977 L1978 **DR** *020 †80

NESTA, Jeffrey Scott. ■ 53202 #056-05-1991 L1992 **FM** *020 †18

NEUBURG, Marcelle. 9200 W WISCONSIN AVE 53226 #040-02-1982 L1990 **D GS** *020 †20,15

NEUNER, Joan Marie. 9200 W WISCONSIN AVE 4TH, FROEDTERT EAST OFFICE BLDG 53226 #056-05-1994 L2000 **IM** *050 †20

NEVIN, David Narcy. 6200 W BLUEMOUND RD 53213 #056-05-1982 L1983 **END IM** *020 †20

NEWBY, Diana Lynn. 8701 W WATERTOWN PLANK RD 53226 #056-06-2004 L2005 **AN** *012

NEWCOMER, Julianne Ruth. 9200 W WISCONSIN AVE 53226 #056-06-1987 L1988 **OBG** *020 †30

NFOR, Tonga Karngong. 3000 W MONTANA ST 53215 #217-01-2003 **IM** *012

NGO, Tuyen Pham. ■ 53214 #056-05-2006 L2006 **PM** *012

NGUYEN, Canh Minh. ■ 53211 #941-01-1959 *074

NGUYEN, Hang Thi-Thuy. ■ 53227 #056-06-2008 *012

NGUYEN, Hanh Huu. 9200 W WISCONSIN AVE, DEPT OF PLASTIC SURG 53226 #143-06-1990 L2002 **HS** *020

NGUYEN, Lan Thi. ■ 53202 #026-04-2000 L2008 **VS** *012

NGUYEN, Nancy Thi. ■ 53219 #056-05-2008 *012

NGUYEN, Steven T.. ■ 53219 #665-02-2004 **FM** *100

NGUYEN, Vinh Trong. ■ 53202 #018-03-2005 L2007 **DR** *012

NICHOL, Kathryn E Piziali. 2323 N LAKE DR 53211 #056-05-1962 L1963 **PD** *030 †55

NICHOLAS, Joseph Andrew. 4448 W LOOMIS RD, STE 100 53220 #018-03-2003 L2006 **FM** *020 †18

NICHOLAS, Paul Elliott. 4800 S 10TH ST UNIT 1, MILWAUKEE HEALTH SERVICE S 53221 #025-01-2000 L2004 **P** *100

NICHOLS, Colleen Mary. 2801 W KINNICKINC RVR PKWY, STE 730 53215 #056-06-1992 L1993 **IM** *040 †20

NICOLOSI, Alfred Carl. 9200 W WISCONSIN AVE, MEDICAL COLLEGE OF WISCONS 53226 #033-06-1984 L1985 **TS** *020 †85,90

NIEBLER, Robert Aaron. 9000 W WISCONSIN AVE, CRITICAL CARE DIVISION, MS 53226 #056-06-2001 L2005 **CCP** *012 †55

NIELSEN, Micah Kirk. ■ 53222 #056-06-2008 *012

NIEVERA, Conrad Cruz, Jr. 9200 W WISCONSIN AVE, DEPT OF NEUROLOGY 53226 #748-02-1991 L1994 **N CN** *020 †75

NILSSON, Elizabeth Dianne. 9455 W WATERTOWN PLANK RD, MILWAUKEE COUNTY BEHAVIORA 53226 #056-06-2002 L2003 **P** *100

NIMMER, Donald David. 6200 W BLUEMOUND RD 53213 #056-06-1987 L1988 **FM** *020 †18

NINNEMAN, Robert Walter. 2801 W KK RIVER PKWY, STE 840 53215 #056-06-1976 L1979 **CD IM** *020 †20

NINOMIYA, James Toshio. 8701 W WATERTOWN PLANK RD 53226 #050-02-1985 L1993 **ORS** *020 †40

NKWAZI, Geoffrey C K. 6001 W CENTER ST, STE 104 53210 #917-23-1971 L1994 **IM D** *020 †20

NOCTON, James John, Jr. 9000 W WISCONSIN AVE, STE C465 53226 #023-07-1987 L1994 **PPR** *020 †55

NOEL, Richard Joseph. 8701 W WATERTOWN PLANK RD, NUTRITION 53226 #048-12-1998 L2004 **PG** *012

NOHL, Jacquelyn Christine. 8701 W WATERTOWN PLANK RD, CHILDRENS HOSP WISC 53226 #056-05-2005 L2007 **PD** *012

NOLAN, Sean Michael. 8701 W WATERTOWN PLANK RD, MED COLL WI HOSPS 53226 #016-76-2006, ▲ L2008 **EM** *012

NOLASCO, Thomas C, Jr. 10425 W NORTH AVE, STE 215 53226 #748-01-1963 L1971 **PTH** *020 †50

NOOR, Aijaz Ahmed. 2801 W KINNICKINC RVR PKWY, STE 135 53215 #495-21-1989 L1999 **IM** *040 †20

NORDIN, Daniel Jon. 2801 W KINNICKINC RVR PKWY, STE 135 53215 #056-05-1990 L1991 **IM** *020 †20

NORDNESS, Mark Edward. 9000 W WISCONSIN AVE, P O BOX 1997 53226 #056-06-1998 L1999 **AI** *020 †55,03

NORDSTROM, Michael R. 7220 W NATIONAL AVE 53214 #016-11-1987 L1992 **OTO** *020 †45

NORTH, Paula Elizabeth. ■ 53226 #004-01-1992 L2005 **PTH** *020 †50

NORTHWAY, Sara Elizabeth. ■ 53228 #056-05-2007 **EM** *012

NORTON, Andrew John. 840 N 87TH ST 53226 #041-02-1982 L1983 **IM** *020 †20

NOSEIR, Randa Kamel. 10000 W BLUEMOUND RD 53226 #915-04-1988 L2000 **AN** *020 †05 ‡

NOSIR, Hany Radwan. 7007 N RANGE LINE RD 53209 #915-07-1985 L2004 **APM** *020 †60

NOVAK, Joseph Anthony. 2025 E NEWPORT AVE, DEPT MED COL HOSP 53211 #957-03-1990 L1997 **PTH** *020 †50

NOVALIJA, Jutta. 5000 W NATIONAL AVE 53295 #409-36-1998 L2005 **AN** *020 †05

NOVOA-TAKARA, Kendall L. 840 N 87TH ST 53226 #028-34-1995 L2002 **IM** *020 †20

NOVOA-TAKARA, Louis J. 9200 W WISCONSIN AVE, DEPT OF PATH MED CLG OF WI 53226 #028-02-1992 L2001 **HMP PTH** *020 †50

NOVOM, Marc Jeffrey. 8989 N PORT WA RD 122 53217 #056-06-1972 L1977 **N IM** *020 †20,75

NUMAAN, Ahmed. 9455 W WATERTOWN PLANK RD, BEHAVIORAL HEALTH DIVISION 53226 #704-21-1989 L2004 **P** *020 ‡

NUNYAKPE, Abalo K Eli. 7810 W GOOD HOPE RD, OMNI FAMILY MEDICAL CLINIC 53223 #243-03-1987 L1994 **FM** *020 †18

NUTTLEMAN, Peter Roy. 9200 W WISCONSIN AVE, DIVISION OF GENERAL SURGER 53226 #056-06-1997 L1999 **GS** *040 †85

NWILATI, Mhd Ziad. 1218 W KILBOURN AVE, STE 124 53233 #875-01-1991 L1994 **IM** *020 †20

NYGARD, Neal Richard. 9200 W WISCONSIN AVE, MDCL CLLGE CLNCS AT FRDTRT 53226 #016-43-1981 L2001 **RHU IM** *050 †20

OAKLEY, Carlene Marie. 8701 W WATERTOWN PLANK RD 53226 #056-05-2002 L2003 **CHP** *020

OCAMPO, Thadfranci Layson. ■ 53233 #056-06-2007 **PD** *012

OCASIO, Maria Aurelia. 9200 W WISCONSIN AVE, OF WISCONSIN 53226 #042-01-2002 L2006 **PM** *012 †60

OCHALEK, Daniel Jerome. 9233 N GREEN BAY RD 53209 #056-06-1993 L1999 **GS** *020 †85

OCHOA, Cesar Omar. ■ 53202 #056-05-2007 **TY** *012

OCKERT, Doris Bertha M. 5000 W NATIONAL AVE 53295 #836-03-1981 L1992 **AN** *020 †05

O'CONNOR, Elizabeth Amy. 8701 W WATERTOWN PLANK RD, MED COLL OF WI 53226 #025-07-2007 **PS** *012

O'CONNOR, Robert Corey. 9200 W WISCONSIN AVE, MEDICAL COLLEGE OF 53226 #025-07-1998 L2005 **U** *100 †95

O'CONNOR, Theresa C. ■ 53202 #539-05-1985 L1994 **APM AN** *020

O'DELL, Kristin Renee. ■ 53210 #056-06-2008 *012

OECHLER, Herbert Wright. 9000 W WISCONSIN AVE 53226 #056-05-1960 L1961 **PTH** *020 †50

OESTERLING, Kurt F. 2025 E NEWPORT AVE, STE 1000 53211 #035-20-1977 L1978 **ON HEM** *020 †20

O'GRADY, Joseph P, Jr. 1744 N FARWELL AVE, PHOENIX CARE SYSTEMS 53202 #026-04-1979 L1980 **CHP PD** *020 †55

O'KEEFE, Gwendolyn Becker. 9200 W WISCONSIN AVE 53226 #035-08-1995 L2004 **IM** *020 †20

OKIA, Zelda Ikulumet. 2025 E NEWPORT AVE 53211 #056-05-1995 L2000 **PTH** *020 †50

OKOKON, Enid Akaninyene. 5650 N GREEN BAY AVE 53209 #056-05-1981 L1986 **PD** *020 †55

OKUSANYA, Adedapo Fisayo. 7810 W GOOD HOPE RD 53223 #690-02-1999 L2005 **FM** *020 †18

OLACIREGUI, Michael Glenn. 573 W LINCOLN AVE, LINCOLN HEALTH CENTER 53207 #264-12-1984 L2000 **IM** *020

OLASZ, Edit Barbara. 9200 W WISCONSIN AVE 53226 #473-02-1995 L2005 **D** *012

OLDHAM, Keith Thos. 999 N 92ND ST 53226 #051-04-1976 L1998 **PDS CCS** *020 †85

OLDS, Glenn Richard. 9200 W WISCONSIN AVE, # 4100 53226 #038-06-1976 L2000 **ID IM** *030 †20

OLEN, Douglas Walter. 10400 W NORTH AVE, STE 300 53226 #056-06-1967 L1968 **R** *071 †80

OLMEDO-ESTRADA, Francisca. 5408 W BURLEIGH ST, WHEATON FRANCISCAN MEDICAL 53210 #016-11-1997 L1998 **FM** *020 †18

O'LOUGHLIN, Colm Joseph. 9200 W WISCONSIN AVE, FREODTERT HOSPITAL 53226 #539-02-1991 L2003 **GE** *020 †20

OLSEN, Marc A. 7878 N 76TH ST, NORTHWEST CLINIC 53223 #056-06-1977 L1978 **FM** *040 †18

OLSEN, Whitney William. ■ 53226 #056-06-2000 *100

OLSON, Carl Erling. 2025 E NEWPORT AVE 53211 #056-05-1969 L1970 **RO ON** *020 †80 ‡

OLSON, David Walter. 575 W RIVER WOODS PKWY, STE 202 53212 #038-40-1973 L1975 **ORS** *020 †40

OLSON, David Wm. ■ 53226 #030-05-1978 L1981 **FM OS** *020 †16

OLSON, Judyann C. 8701 W WATERTOWN PLANK RD 53226 #016-43-1979 L1980 **PPR RHU** *020 †55

OLTEANU, Horatiu. 8701 W WATERTOWN PLANK RD, MED COLLEGE OF WI 53226 #781-03-1996 L2007 **HMP** *012 †50

OLUND, Timothy John. 8700 W WISCONSIN AVE # AN 53226 #025-01-1982 L1985 **AN IM** *020 †05

OMARI, Saadoun Issam. 10909 W BLUEMOUND RD, WISCONSIN 53226 #528-01-1982 L1993 **PD** *020 †55

OMER, Diab Sidahmed. 3000 W MONTANA ST 53215 #848-01-1998 L2007 **IM** *012

O'NEIL, Peter Joseph. ■ 53222 #017-20-2004 L2006 **AN** *012

O'NEILL, William Wade. 5000 W NATIONAL AVE, ZAGLOCKI VA HOSP 53295 #039-01-1969 L1986 **PUD SME** *040 †20

ONG, Seng Hoo. 8522 W CAPITOL DR, PEDIATRIC DIAGNOSTIC 53222 #143-11-1995 L2001 **PDR** *020 †80

ONGWIJITWAT, Sakkapol. ■ 53233 #056-06-2007 **ORS** *012

ONYEMA, Judepatricks Mmae. ■ 53223 #056-06-2008 *012

OPPENHEIMER, John Paul. 2323 N LAKE DR 53211 #056-06-1987 L1988 **AN** *020 †05

O'QUINN, Kirsten Lynn. 6900 N PORT WASHINGTON RD 53217 #056-06-2002 L2003 **FM** *020 †18

O'QUINN, Robert John. 8901 W LINCOLN AVE, CONSULTANTS AT WEST ALLIS 53227 #056-06-2002 L2004 **AN** *020 †05

O'REILLY, Julie Comerford. 2457 N MAYFAIR RD, MILWAUKEE OB GYN SC 53226 #056-06-1983 L1984 **OBG** *020 †30

ORR, Merle. ■ 53210 #056-05-2000 L2005 **SCI** *100 †60 ‡

ORTEGA GUTIERREZ, Santiago. 9200 W WISCONSIN AVE 53226 #847-07-2003 L2006 **MN** *012

ORTELL, Steven Wm. 711 W CAPITOL DR, HLTHCARE FOR THE HOMELESS 53206 #056-06-1987 L1989 **P** *020 †75

ORTH, Karl Gary. 9200 W WISCONSIN AVE, MEDICAL COLLEGE OF WISCONS 53226 #056-06-1999 L2000 **AN** *020 †05

ORTON, Derek James. 2424 S 90TH ST, STE 418 53227 #056-06-2000 L2006 **ORS** *020 ‡

OSBORNE, Janet Lynn. 9200 W WISCONSIN AVE, DEPT. OF OB/GYN FMLH 53226 #056-06-1991 L2000 **GO GYN** *020 †30

O'SHAUGHNESSY, Irene. 9200 W WISCONSIN AVE, ENDOCRINE-METABOLICSERVICE 53226 #016-11-1983 L1984 **END DIA** *020 †20

OSIPOV, Vladimir O. 9200 W WISCONSIN AVE, DEPT OF PATHOLOGY 53226 #913-01-1992 L2001 **PTH** *020 †50

OSMAN, Dafaallah Hassabel. 3000 W MONTANA ST 53215 #848-01-2000 L2007 **IM** *012

OSPINA, Maria Cristina. 945 N 12TH ST STE 4602 53233 #422-01-1998 L2006 **N** *020 ‡

OTA, David Masao. ■ 53226 #016-02-1973 L2001 **GS NTR** *020 †85

OTTENSTEIN, Harold H. 9418 N GREEN BAY RD 53209 #056-06-1940 L1940 **GP** *071

OTTERSON, Mary Francis. 9200 W WISCONSIN AVE, SURGERY 53226 #056-06-1984 L1985 **GS** *050 †85

OTTO, Marjorie C. 4555 W SCHROEDER DR STE 1, LAKEFRONT BILLING SERV INC 53223 #012-05-1992 L1996 **AN** *020 †05

OTTO, Samuel James. 2801 W KINNICKINNIC PKWY, STE 370 53215 #056-05-1971 L1975 **U** *020 †95

OWEN, Haley Lyn. 8701 W WATERTOWN PLANK RD, OF ANESTHESIOLOGY 53226
#018-03-2005 L2006 **AN** *012

OWEN, Nicholas Loyd. 2015 E NEWPORT AVE, MILWAUKEE MEDICAL CLINIC 53211
#028-02-1959 L1964 **IMG IM** *071 †20

OXMAN, Herbert Arthur. 2350 N LAKE DR 53211 #056-05-1966 L1967 **CD IM** *020 †20

OYESANYA, Olusoji O. 6001 W CENTER ST STE 102, ALPHA MEDICAL CLINIC S.C. 53210
#690-01-1979 L1989 **FM GP** *020

OZCAN, Cevher. 9200 W WISCONSIN AVE, MCW DEPARTMENT OF MEDICINE 53226
#902-09-1991 L2005 **CD** *012 †20

PACHNER, Robert William. 946 N VAN BUREN ST, AURORA SINAI DOWNTOWN 53202
#056-06-1994 L1995 **FM** *020 †18

PACKMAN, Kevin Scott. 5150 N PORT WASHINGTON RD, STE 151 53217 #025-07-1991 L1992
GS VS *020 †85

PADALA, Kiran Kumar. 2025 E NEWPORT AVE, COLUMBIA HOSPITAL 53211
#495-50-1999 L2005 **IM** *100 †20

PADUREAN, Adrian Mircea. 10425 W NORTH AVE, STE 215 53226 #781-04-1986 L2004
PTH HMP *020 †50

PAGEL, Paul Stanley. 9200 W WISCONSIN AVE 53226 #056-06-1986 L1987 **AN** *050 †05

PAIS, Priya Josephine. 9000 W WISCONSIN AVE, CHILDRENS HOSPITAL OF WISC 53226
#495-52-2001 L2004 **PN** *012 †55

PAK, Chol Y. 8701 W WATERTOWN PLANK RD, MED COLL OF WI 53226 #047-06-2006 L2008
AN *012

PALABRICA, Cynthia Louise. 6200 W BLUEMOUND RD 53213 #030-06-1988 L1992
OBG *020 †30

PALENCIA, Mauricio E. 1818 W NATIONAL AVE 53204 #451-01-1989 L2001 **FM** *040 †18

PALEY, Sharyl G. 6373 N JEAN NICOLET RD 53217 #056-05-1993 L1994 **PD** *020 †55

PALIN, William Drew. 312 E WISCONSIN AVE 53202 #026-08-1981 L1982 **FM** *030 †18

PALISCH, Andrew Ryan. ■ 53202 #056-06-2007 **TY** *012

PALMER, Caroline Nicole. 8701 W WATERTOWN PLANK RD, DEPT OF PSYCHIATRY 53226
#056-06-2006 **P** *012

PALMISANO, Barbara W. 8701 W WATERTOWN PLANK RD 53226 #021-01-1977 L1985
AN PD *020 †55,05

PAMIDI, Srinivas Reddy. 2801 W KINNICKINC RVR PKWY, STE 425 53215 #495-58-1990 L1997
CD *020 †20

PAN, Cynthia Gail. 8701 W WATERTOWN PLANK RD 53226 #056-06-1983 L1989
PN PD *020 †55

PANAGIS, Constantine. 2266 N PROSPECT AVE, STE 312 53202 #056-06-1946 L1948
PHP GPM *062 †20

PANCHAL, Parag Ramanlal. 10000 W BLUEMOUND RD 53226 #495-76-1988 L1991
AN *020 †05

PANDYA, Dhruvil J. 8701 W WATERTOWN PLANK RD 53226 #305-01-2005 L2006 **MN** *012

PANEPINTO, Julie Ann. 9200 W WISCONSIN AVE 53226 #016-45-1991 L1992 **PHO** *020 †55

PANISH, Richard Michael. 945 N 12TH ST 53233 #016-11-1966 L1969 **DR NM** *071 †80,28

PANKIEWICZ, John. 544 E OGDEN AVE STE 700, PMB 223 53202 #016-11-1985 L1988
P *020 †75

PANNU, Yashdip Singh. 2901 W KINNICKINC RVR PKWY 53215 #023-01-1994 L2003 **NS** *020

PANSZI, Shannon Hope. ■ 53217 #025-01-2000 L2000 **OBG** *100 †30

PANTHER, Robert Leonard. 2801 W KINNICKINC RVR PKWY, STE 840 53215
#016-43-1990 L1991 **CD NC** *020 †20

PAO, William Jos. 2900 W OKLAHOMA AVE, RADIATION ONCOLOGY 53215 #056-06-1983 L1989
RO *020 †80

PAPIN, Kayleen Paige. 1155 N MAYFAIR RD 53226 #056-06-2001 L2003 **FM** *020 †18

PAPP, Michael Louis. 8701 W WATERTOWN PLANK RD 53226 #016-76-2005, ▲ L2007 **IM** *012

PAPPAS, Sam George. 9200 W WISCONSIN AVE 53226 #016-01-1998 L2007 **GS** *100 †85

PAPPENHEIM, John Eugene. 9455 W WATERTOWN PLANK RD 53226 #056-06-1985 L1986
P *020 †75

PARAKININKAS, Daiva Elena. 9000 W WISCONSIN AVE, MS 681 53226 #016-11-1995 L1996
PDP *020 †55

PARASU, Narayana Rao. 2901 W KK RIVER PKWY # 106, PHYSICAL MEDICINE & REHAB 53215
#495-70-1981 L2006 **PM** *020 †60

PARCON, Jazmin D. 2315 N LAKE DR STE 717 53211 #748-01-1965 L1976 **OBG** *020 †30

PARENT, Gerard Thos. 2901 W KINNICKINC RVR PKWY 53215 #023-07-1971 L1977
IM CD *020 †20

PARIKH, Keyur Hareshbhai. 8701 W WATERTOWN PLANK RD 53226 #495-76-2001 L2007
P *012

PARISI, Jonathan Antanino. 9200 W WISCONSIN AVE, MEDICAL COLLEGE OF WISCONS 53226
#056-06-2005 L2007 **GS** *012

PARK, Matthew Vaughn. 9000 W WISCONSIN AVE, CHW MS 713 53226 #056-06-2002 L2005
PDC *012

PARKER, Martha Simon. ■ 53211 #016-11-1935 L1935 **PD** *071

PARKER, Wayman Louis. ■ 53209 #025-12-1974 L1978 **OBG** *020

PARRINO, Peter G, Jr. 1522 N PROSPECT AVE, UNIT 603 53202 #021-06-1994 L1995
EM *020 †16

PARVIN, Aliyar A. ■ 53202 #056-06-2006 **FP** *012

PASCH, Allan Richard. 5150 N PORT WASHINGTON RD, STE 151 53217 #056-05-1979 L1986
VS GS *020 †85

PASQUINI, Marcelo Camargo. 5000 W NATIONAL AVE, STE 4300 53295 #187-57-1997 L2004
HO *100 †20

PATEL, Ankur N. 10400 W NORTH AVE, STE 200 53226 #496-16-1990 L1995 **IM** *020 †20

PATEL, Jiten Jayantilal. ■ 53202 #016-11-2005 L2006 **AN** *012

PATEL, Malti Mahendra. 10625 W NORTH AVE STE 208 53226 #495-17-1971 L1976 **P** *020 †75

PATEL, Muni H. 2600 N MAYFAIR RD, STE 850 53226 #495-23-1971 L1979 **CHP P** *020 †75

PATEL, Nikhil Hasmukh. 8701 W WATERTOWN PLANK RD 53226 #305-01-2006 **PM** *012

PATEL, Rupesh Parag. ■ 53202 #016-11-2004 L2006 **DR** *012

PATEL, Shailendra B. 9200 W WISCONSIN AVE, FEC 4TH. FLOOR E4950 53226
#917-09-1985 L2005 **END** *050 †20

PATEL, Shirish Popatlal. 2901 W KINNICKINC RVR PKWY 53215 #025-01-1996 L2002
DR *020 †80

PATEL, Sima Indubhai. 9200 W WISCONSIN AVE, LUTHERAN HO 53226 #016-01-2006 **N** *012

PATEL, Smita N. 8700 W WISCONSIN AVE, DEPT OF ANESTH-MED CLGE WI 53226
#495-96-1974 L1982 **AN** *040 †05

PATTERSON, Barbara Joann. 945 N 12TH ST STE 3506 53233 #056-06-2001 L2003 **MPD** *020

PATTIS, Susan Elaine. 6040 W LISBON AVE STE 200 53210 #038-06-1994 L1995 **IM** *020

PAUL, Jasmeet Singh. 9200 W WISCONSIN AVE, STE 3510 53226 #056-06-2004 L2006 **GS** *012

PAULEY, Brian Nicholas. 111 E WISCONSIN AVE, STE 2100 53202 #026-04-1993 L1996
EM *020 †16

PAYDAK, Hakan. 9200 W WISCONSIN AVE, EAST BLDG. 5TH FLOOR 53226 #902-05-1988 L2002
CD *020 †20

PAYNE, Ryan Adam. 9200 W WISCONSIN AVE, DEPARTMENT OF UROLOGY 53226
#019-02-2004 L2006 **U** *012

PAZ, Eduardo. 2025 W OKLAHOMA AVE 53215 #847-12-1975 L1979 **IM** *020

PEARLSTEIN, Daryl Phillip. 3333 N MAYFAIR RD, STE 209 53222 #047-05-1996 L2006
TS *020 †85,90

PELECH, Andrew Nicholas. 9000 W WISCONSIN AVE, CHILDRENS HOSP OF WI 53226
#060-01-1977 L1993 **PD PDC** *020 †55

PELES, Shachar. ■ 53214 #056-06-2008 *012

PELTIER, Wendy L. 9200 W WISCONSIN AVE, MEMORIAL LUTHERAN HOSPITAL 53226
#016-01-1991 L1996 **N** *020 †75

PENNINGTON, William T. 2901 W KINNICKINC RVR PKWY, STE 102 53215 #056-06-1994 L1996
ORS *020 †20

PENTALA, Jolanta. 2424 S 90TH ST, STE 310 53227 #759-09-1997 L2006 **IM** *020 †20

PERCHIK, Robert. ■ 53211 #064-01-1980 L1981 **EM GP** *020 †16

PERELMAN, Ana. 1155 N MAYFAIR RD 53226 #550-03-2001 L2005 **IM** *020 †20

PERERA, Lilani Priyadarsh. 9200 W WISCONSIN AVE, FROEDTERT MEMORIAL LUTHERA 53226
#220-01-1998 L2005 **GE** *012

PERFETTO PILA, Patricia. 945 N 12TH ST 53233 #935-01-1994 **OBG** *012

PERIQUET, Maria I. 9200 W WISCONSIN AVE, DEPT OF NEUROLOGY 53226
#748-02-1991 L1994 **N** *020 †75

PERLEWITZ, Thomas John. 2801 W KINNICKINC RVR PKWY, STE 730 53215
#056-06-1998 L1999 **ORS** *020 †40

PERLSON, Samuel G. ■ 53209 #056-05-1951 L1952 **OBG** *040 †30

PERME, Aaron Michael. 53224 #654-01-2002 L2004 **GS** *012

PERRY, Elzbieta. 3000 W MONTANA ST 53215 #759-03-1997 L2008 **IM** *012

PERRY, Marcus Todd. 2311 N PROSPECT AVE, STE 401 53211 #056-05-1996 L2004
IM *020 †20

PERSHMAN, Yuliy Mukh. 5000 W CHAMBERS ST, MEDICAL REHABVLTN ASSOC 53210
#913-21-1979 L2001 **PM** *020 †60

PERSON, Amy Darhui. 1020 N 12TH ST, CLINIC 53233 #016-11-1989 L1990 **PD** *020 †55

PETERSON, Danielle Bezill. 999 N 92ND ST, STE 320 53226 #038-41-2004 L2006 **GS** *012

PETERSON, Karina Marie. 6900 W NORTH AVE, WASHINGTON ROAD 53213
#056-06-1998 L1999 **FM** *020 †18

PETKOVA, Jenny Harizanova. 9200 W WISCONSIN AVE, DEPT OF MEDICINE 53226
#198-01-1993 L2005 **IM** *020 †20

PETRO, Nancy Christine. 4111 W MITCHELL ST, STE 300 53215 #025-01-1978 L1979
GS OM *020

PETROLL, Andrew Elias. 9200 W WISCONSIN AVE, FEC, STE 5700 53226 #056-05-2001 L2003
ID IM *020

PETRUZELLA, Frank David. 9000 W WISCONSIN AVE, CHILDREN'S HOSPITAL OF WIS 53226
#051-01-2003 L2007 **PEM** *012 †55

PETTY, Mc Kinley. 2555 N DR MRTN LTHR KNG DR, CENTER 53212 #056-05-1976 L1978
FM *020

PFEIFER, Kurt James. 9200 W WISCONSIN AVE 53226 #056-06-1999 L2000 **IM** *020 †20

PFLEGER, Susan Lynn. 8675 N PORT WASHINGTON RD, STE 120 53217 #047-05-1981 L1989
OBG GS *020 †30

PHAM, Khanh Ngoc. ■ 53213 #056-06-2008 *012

PHANSALKAR, Arvind G. 2400 W VILLARD AVE 53209 #495-28-1968 L1977 **P IM** *020 †75

PHELAN, Marybeth. 9200 W WISCONSIN AVE, FM/PAVILION BLDG 1P 53226
#056-06-1988 L1992 **EM** *020 †16

PHILLIPS, Morton F. 5916 N GREEN BAY AVE 53209 #056-06-1953 L1954 **AN** *071 †05

PICK, James Wm. ■ 53202 #016-06-1941 L1946 **U ADM** *071

PIDIKITI, Sudha. 9200 W WISCONSIN AVE 53226 #496-24-2000 L2006 **NEP** *012 †20

PIENKOS, Paul Stephen. 945 N 12TH ST, AURORA SINAI MEDICAL CENTE 53233
#056-05-2001 L2003 **CD** *012

PIERCE, Brenda Marie. 2900 W OKLAHOMA AVE 53215 #016-43-1992 L1998 **HO IM** *020 †20

PIERCE, Sarah Elizabeth. ■ 53215 #056-05-2007 **FP** *012

PIERING, Walter Frederick. 9200 W WISCONSIN AVE 53226 #056-05-1962 L1963
NEP IM *040 †20

PIERRE, Isaac Douglas. 1121 E NORTH AVE 53212 #056-06-1998 L1999 **FM** *020 †18

PIERSTORFF, Craig Alan. 8700 W WATERTOWN PLANK RD, DEPT. OF ANESTHESIOLOGY 53226
#056-05-2004 L2006 **AN** *012

PIFEL, Tiffany Laura. 2801 W KINNICKINC RVR PKWY, STE 245 53215 #056-06-1999 L2001
END *020 †20

PILLA, Prashanti. 3000 W MONTANA ST 53215 #496-24-2000 L2006 **OBG** *012

PINCUS, Mitchell Hal. 1020 N 12TH ST 53233 #011-04-1981 L1988 **RO OM** *020 †80

PINKERTON, Carolyn. ■ 53202 #028-34-2008 *012

PINZON, Adrian Lee. 8701 W WATERTOWN PLANK RD 53226 #820-02-2003 **FP** *012

PIRCON, Richard Adam. 2323 N LAKE DR, ASSESSMENT CENTER 53211 #016-01-1983 L1989
OBG MFM *020 †30

PIRALLO, Ronald Gerard. 9200 W WISCONSIN AVE, EMERGENCY MEDICINE 53226
#025-07-1987 L1992 **EM** *020 †16

PITTELKOW, Robert B. 2600 N 32ND ST 53210 #056-06-1952 L1955 **D OM** *071 †15

PITTER, Donna Elaine. 6001 W CENTER ST STE 200 53210 #025-07-1981 L1984 **PD** *020

PITTS, Nathan Arnold. ■ 53217 #030-05-2005 L2006 **AN** *012

PLANTES, Peter James. 9200 W WISCONSIN AVE, CEO-MEDICAL COLLEGE PHYSIC 53226
#041-01-1982 L2007 **MDM IM** *030 †20

PLATZKER, Daniel. ■ 53202 #056-06-2005 *100

PLUMB, Mark David. 2424 S 90TH ST, STE 206 53227 #028-02-1988 L1990 **PUD** *020 †20

PLZAK, Christina Maria. 8901 W LINCOLN AVE 53227 #016-42-1993 L1996 **EM** *020 †16

POETKER, David Morton. 9200 W WISCONSIN AVE, DEPT OF OTOLARYNGOLOGY 53226
#018-03-2001 L2002 **OTO** *020 †45

POGGENBURG, Colleen M. 9200 W WISCONSIN AVE, DEPT OF GENERAL SURGERY 53226
#056-06-1998 L1999 **FM** *100 †18

POHL, Alan L. 2350 W VILLARD AVE, STE 302 53209 #035-06-1962 L1973 **PS HS** *020 †85,65

POHL, Carol Ann Castleman. 3003 W GOOD HOPE RD 53209 #024-05-1967 L1973 **DR** *020 †80

POHLE, Edward Louis. 3970 N OAKLAND AVE, STE 603 53211 #056-05-1963 L1965
D DMP *015

POHLMANN, Guenther Peter. 2025 E NEWPORT AVE 53211 #056-06-1961 L1962
IM PUD *040 †28,20

POLACHECK, Larry Jean. 5900 N PORT WASHINGTON RD, BAYSHORE PEDIATRICS 53217
#056-05-1959 L1963 **PD** *020 †55

POLIANSKA, Marina I. 8901 W LINCOLN AVE, CONSULTANTS AT WEST ALLIS 53227
#913-70-1985 L1998 **AN** *020 †05

POLK, Janice Renee. 7961 N 76TH ST 53223 #056-06-2002 L2004 **FM** *020 ‡
POLL, Marvin. 2906 S 20TH ST 53215 #056-05-1954 L1955 **GS OM** *071
POLLARD, Randle E. 2040 W WISCONSIN AVE, DR RANDLE POLLARD 53233 #047-07-1951 L1956 **U IMG** *071 †95
POLLEMA, Matthew Gerald. ■ 53226 #026-04-2003 L2005 **DR** *012
POMERANZ, Albert Jos. 1020 N 12TH ST 53233 #030-06-1977 L1989 **PD** *020 †55
PONTUS, Stephen Peter, Jr. 3223 S 103RD ST 53227 #030-06-1975 L1976 **PD AN** *020 †55,05
POPE, John F. 2424 S 90TH ST, SU 304 53227 #422-01-1981 L1982 **U** *020 †95
POPOVICH, Miodrag M. 4601 N OAKLAND AVE 53211 #957-02-1974 L1977 **R NM** *020 †80
POPP, Deidre Meredith. 3000 W MONTANA ST 53215 #305-01-2006 L2007 **DR** *012
POREMSKI, Tod Jos. 3040 N 117TH ST 53222 #016-43-1975 L1977 **OBG** *020 †30
PORT, Steven C. 2901 W KINNICKINC RVR PKWY, PKWY 53215 #035-47-1972 L1982 **IM CD** *020 †20
POTEET-SCHWARTZ, Kim L. ■ 53226 #050-02-1998 L2008 **IM** *020
POTOS, William Basil. 2500 W LAYTON AVE, STE 290 53221 #056-06-1960 L1961 **FM OM** *020 †18
POTTER, Charles Francis. 3070 N 51ST ST ♯ P309 53210 #056-06-1991 L1999 **NPM** *020 †55
POWELL, Kathleen Mary. ■ 53219 #056-05-2004 L2006 **OBG** *012
POWELL, Richard Randolph. 720 E WISCONSIN AVE 53202 #036-01-1971 L1986 **IM OS** *020
PRASAD, Jaya C. 2323 N LAKE DR 53211 #495-50-1969 L1974 **IM RHU** *020 †20
PRATT, Sarah J. 9000 W WISCONSIN AVE, CHILDRENS HOSP OF WISC 53226 #056-06-1978 L1979 **PD** *071 †55
PRESBERG, Kenneth Wm. 9200 W WISCONSIN AVE, & CRIT CARE 53226 #016-11-1984 L1990 **PUD CCM** *020 †20
PRETELL, Judith Olive. 8701 W WATERTOWN PLANK RD, MED COLLEGE OF WISC PATH 53226 #041-02-1989 L1995 **HMP PTH** *020 †50
PRIBEK, Robert Andrew. ■ 53217 #056-06-1953 L1954 **IM OS** *072 †20
PROSEN, Harry. 8701 W WATERTOWN PLANK RD 53226 #062-01-1955 L1987 **P** *071 †75
PROSEN, Leandrea Sue. 1231 W MITCHELL ST, MEDICAL COLLEGE OF WISCONS 53204 #023-01-1997 L1998 **FM** *020 †18,75
PRUDLOW, William Frank. 9200 W WISCONSIN AVE 53226 #056-06-1970 L1971 **OTO** *020 †45
PRUITT, Marion Eugene. 9200 W WISCONSIN AVE, FEC 4TH FL 53226 #010-03-1977 L1980 **IM** *020 †20
PRYBA, David Eugene. 1155 N MAYFAIR RD 53226 #056-06-1993 L1994 **IM** *020 †20
PUBBI, Dinesh. 960 N 12TH ST ♯ 400 53233 #495-03-1991 L1994 **ICE** *012 †20
PUCA, K E. 2900 W OKLAHOMA AVE 53215 #016-45-1996 L2002 **PTH** *020 †50
PUDUR, Archana. 2400 W VILLARD AVE, ST MICHAEL HOSPITAL 53209 #496-35-2001 L2006 **FP** *012
PUGELY, James Michael. 2311 N PROSPECT AVE, CSMCP PROSPECT MEDICAL COM 53211 #056-06-1973 L1974 **AI PD** *020 †55,03
PULS, Dawn Jennine. 9455 W WATERTOWN PLANK RD 53226 #056-06-1998 L1999 **FM** *020
PULS, Thomas Brian. 3267 S 16TH ST 53215 #056-06-1953 L1954 **P** *071
PUNZALAN, Rowena C C. 638 N 18TH ST, BLOOD CENTER OF WISCONSIN 53233 #748-02-1991 L1994 **PHO** *020 †55
PUREWAL, Navtej. 9120 W CAPITOL DR 53222 #495-08-1983 L1993 **APM** *020 †05
PUTERBAUGH, Kim Marie. 945 N 12TH ST, FL 1 53233 #023-07-1994 L2006 **OBG** *020 †30
PUTERBAUGH, Rex Marcum. ■ 53226 #056-06-2008 *012
PYASTA, Roman T. 9200 W WISCONSIN AVE, DEPARTMENT OF MEDICINE 53226 #913-42-1994 L2000 **IM** *020 †20
QAMAR, Rubina. 2025 E NEWPORT AVE, STE 1000 53211 #704-02-1989 L2001 **IM** *020 †20
QAMAR, Shahid. 945 N 12TH ST, RESIDENT PROGRAM 53233 #704-02-2001 L2007 **IM** *012
QHAVI, Ajaz M. 3305 S 20TH ST, STE 100 53215 #495-21-1996 L2004 **N CN** *020 †75
QIAN, Liqing. 9200 W WISCONSIN AVE, DEPT. OF ANESTHESIOLOGY 53226 #243-45-1993 L2002 **AN** *020 †05
QUANDT, Peter Jude. 2025 E NEWPORT AVE, CAMPUS OF COLUMBIA ST MARY 53211 #023-07-1985 L1999 **IM** *020 †20
QUEJADA, Ma Remedios B. 2040 W WISCONSIN AVE, APT 466 53233 #748-10-1988 L1992 **PD** *020 †55
QUINN, Theresa Marie. 9200 W WISCONSIN AVE 53226 #024-01-1992 L2002 **GS** *020 †85
QUINONES, Eduardo. 5000 W CHAMBERS ST, ST JOSEP 53210 #056-06-2005 L2006 **DR** *012
QUINTERO, Diana Rebeca. 9000 W WISCONSIN AVE, M/C 777A 53226 #264-05-1993 L2002 **PDP** *020 †55
QUITZON, Andres Fernando. 2400 W VILLARD AVE, ST. MICHAEL FAMILY CARE CT 53209 #748-01-1955 L1966 **AN** *071
QURASHI, Mir Ismail. 377 W RIVER WOODS PKWY, STE 100 53212 #495-35-1994 L1999 **IM** *020 †20
QURESHI, Jamal Ahmad. 3000 W MONTANA ST, AURORA HLTH CARE 53215 #665-01-2002 L2003 **IM** *100 †20
RAAB, Karlo. 3070 N 51ST ST STE 309 53210 #957-01-1959 L1970 **NPM PD** *030 †55
RAASCH, William Glenn. 9200 W WISCONSIN AVE 53226 #016-02-1986 L1992 **OSM ORS** *020 †40
RABENN, William Bernard. ■ 53217 #056-05-1954 L1958 **AN** *071 †05
RABINOWITZ, Linda Gail. 9000 W WISCONSIN AVE ♯ 411 53226 #035-06-1982 L1991 **D PD** *020 †55,15
RACU, Camellia. 9200 W WISCONSIN AVE, DEPARTMENT OF SURGERY 53226 #056-06-2004 L2005 **GS** *012
RADAFSHAR, Mohamad Reza. 2801 W KINNICKINC RVR PKWY, STE 453 53215 #517-08-1981 L1997 **PMM** *020 †05
RADEMACHER, Ruth Marie. 999 N 92ND ST, PEDS NEONATOLOGY CCC-C410 53226 #016-42-1980 L1981 **PD** *020
RADER, Keith Alvin. 2900 W OKLAHOMA AVE, ERMED 53215 #025-01-1997 L2000 **EM** *020 †16
RADIUS, Ronald Lee. 8700 W WISCONSIN AVE 53226 #023-07-1973 L1979 **OPH** *020 †35
RADKE, Marcia Ann. 2311 N PROSPECT AVE 53211 #026-04-2004 L2007 **IM** *020
RAGATZ, Stephen Chas. 3070 N 51ST ST STE 309 53210 #056-06-1977 L1978 **NPM PD** *020 †55
RAGHAVAN, Manoj. 9200 W WISCONSIN AVE, FROEDTERT WEST CLINICS 53226 #495-53-1987 L2003 **CN** *020 †75
RAHIM, Syed Abdur. ■ 53221 #496-27-1992 L2005 **CHP** *012
RAHMAN, Mohamed Shakeelur. 960 N 12TH ST, 4TH FL 53233 #495-33-1994 L2007 **CD** *012 †20
RAINEY, Charles James. 1155 N MAYFAIR RD, MCW TOSA CENTER 3RD FLOOR 53226 #016-43-1994 L1995 **PFP P** *020
RAJAGOPAL, Manuraj. 2801 W KINNICKINC RVR PKWY, STE 730 53215 #496-22-1999 L2006 **IM** *020
RAJA SHANKAR, Latha. 734 N JACKSON ST, CATHEDRAL SQ URGENT CARE 53202 #495-04-1998 L2001 **FM** *020 †18 ‡

RAKOWSKI, Tara Antoinette. 2311 N PROSPECT AVE, STE 401 53211 #056-05-1989 L1992 **FM OBG** *020 †18
RAMAIAH, Shobha. 3000 W MONTANA ST, AURORA HLTH CARE 53215 #496-22-2001 L2006 **IM** *012
RAMAMURTHY, Suresh. 8701 W WATERTOWN PLANK RD, MEDICAL COLLEGE OF WISCONS 53226 #495-66-1999 L2003 **CD** *012 †20
RAMASAMY, Dhanasekaran. 2801 W KINNICKINC RVR PKWY, STE 1030 53215 #495-04-1997 L2007 **GE** *020 †20
RAND, Harold. ■ 53233 #035-19-1938 L1944 **IM** *071
RANDLE, Delicia Lynn. ■ 53223 #056-06-1995 L1997 **FM** *100
RANOLA, Pedro O. 1218 W KILBOURN AVE, STE 200 53233 #748-01-1967 L1978 **FM** *020 †18
RAO, Aparna Rohit. 9000 W WISCONSIN AVE, CRITCAL CARE PULMONARY/MC 53226 #495-01-1990 L2002 **PDP** *100 †55
RAO, Raj D. 9200 W WISCONSIN AVE, PB 26099 DEPT OSS 53226 #496-38-1984 L1999 **ORS OSS** *020 †40
RAO, Rohit Prabhakara. 9000 W WISCONSIN AVE ♯ 681, CHILDREN'S HOSPITAL WISCON 53226 #495-01-1990 L1999 **PDC** *012 †55
RAO, V Kutumba. 3201 S 16TH ST, SOUTH CENTER MEDICAL 53215 #495-50-1971 L1976 **IM** *020 †20
RAPP, Daniel Thos. 945 N 12TH ST 53233 #016-01-1989 L1994 **DR** *020 †80
RASMUSSEN, Nathan Trudeau. ■ 53210 #056-05-2006 **U** *012
RASSOULI, Mohammad E. 3201 S 16TH ST, STE 1019 53215 #517-08-1974 L1990 **N CHN** *020
RATER, Cornelius James. 5818 N SHORE DR, 5818 N. SHORE DR 53217 #018-03-1961 L1970 **DR** *020 †80
RATHOUR, Rajendra Singh. 3201 S 16TH ST STE 1000, SOUTH CENTER MEDICAL 53215 #496-04-1978 L1992 **IM END** *020 †20
RATKALKAR, Vishal Narendr. 5000 W CHAMBERS ST 53210 #495-73-1998 L2004 **IM** *020
RATKE, Donald. 3970 N OAKLAND AVE 53211 #056-06-1947 L1948 **P** *020
RAUEN, Leonard Carl. 3003 W GOOD HOPE RD 53209 #056-06-1968 L1969 **IM** *020
RAVELO, Henry V. 950 N 12TH ST, PATHOLOGY 53233 #748-08-1965 L1971 **PTH CLP** *071 †50
RAVICHANDRAN, T. 2025 W OKLAHOMA AVE, STE 122 53215 #495-66-1978 L1997 **N** *020 †75
RAWSKI, Robert John. 544 E OGDEN AVE, STE 700-223 53202 #056-06-1992 L1993 **P** *020 †75
RAY, Vani. 1020 N 12TH ST, FL 4 53233 #495-70-1981 L1994 **P** *020 †75
RAYAN, Lalitha C. 1218 W KILBOURN AVE, STE 124 53233 #495-62-1972 L1977 **PD** *020 †55
RAYAN, Sonya Chalasani. 1218 W KILBOURN AVE 53233 #905-02-2003 L2007 **IM** *100 †20
RAYMAN, Lea Harding. 9200 W WISCONSIN AVE, FROEDTERT MEMORIAL LUTHERA 53226 #036-05-1986 L1995 **N** *020 †75
RAZA, Tasleem. 5000 W NATIONAL AVE 53295 #704-02-1985 L1995 **PCC SME** *020 †20
RAZZAQ, Mohammad A. 1218 W KILBOURN AVE, STE 124 53233 #704-02-1989 L1993 **N IM** *020 †75
RAZZAQ, Mohammad S. 1218 W KILBOURN AVE, STE 124 53233 #704-02-1988 L1994 **N GP** *020 †75
REASA, Douglas Alan. 2400 W VILLARD AVE, ST MICHAEL HOSP 53209 #056-05-1965 L1966 **R NR** *020 †80
REBELLA, Gregory Scott. 999 N 92ND ST STE C550, CHILDRENS CORPORATE CENTER 53226 #056-05-2000 L2004 **PEM** *012
RECKA, Katherine Ann. ■ 53202 #056-06-2006 **MPD** *012
REDDY, Linga Vinay. 9200 W WISCONSIN AVE 53226 #495-36-1998 L2006 **N** *012
REDDY, Moitreyee Bandyopa. 8701 W WATERTOWN PLANK RD, DIVISION OF CHILD PSYCHIAT 53226 #495-36-2001 L2006 **CHP** *012
REDDY, Nanjappareddy Muni. 1000 N 92ND ST 53226 #495-33-1971 L1978 **PM** *020 †60
REDDY, Naveen Gunda. 8701 W WATERTOWN PLANK RD 53226 #025-07-2006 L2008 **IM** *012
REDLICH, Philip Norman. 9200 W WISCONSIN AVE, DEPT GENERAL SURGERY 53226 #017-20-1979 L1984 **GS** *020 †85
REDLIN, Kenneth Chas. 2025 W OKLAHOMA AVE, STE 121 53215 #654-01-1983 L1984 **FM** *020 †18
REEDER, Nancy Suzanne. 2015 E NEWPORT AVE, MEDICAL CLINIC 53211 #016-11-1989 L1991 **IM** *020 †20
REESE, Yolanda. 3975 N 68TH ST, CAPITOL DRIVE PEDIATRICS 53216 #016-11-1996 L1998 **PD** *020 †55
REGAN, Joseph Patrick. 2015 E NEWPORT AVE, STE 305 53211 #016-06-1996 L2003 **GS** *020 †20
REGAN, Patrick Thos. 2350 N LAKE DR, STE 303 53211 #016-06-1972 L1976 **GE IM** *020 †20
REGNER, Kevin Richard. 8701 W WATERTOWN PLANK RD, MEDICAL COLLEGE OF WISCONS 53226 #056-06-2001 L2007 **NEP** *100
REHS, Mary Theresa. 9200 W WISCONSIN AVE 53226 #056-06-1993 L1994 **IM** *020 †20
REICH, Craig Alan. 1845 N FARWELL AVE STE 207 53202 #836-02-1988 L1995 **FM** *020 †18
REID, Kern Aundre. 1020 N 12TH ST, FL 2 53233 #056-06-1987 L1989 **IM** *020 †20
REID, Michael Stuart. 201 N MAYFAIR RD 53226 #056-06-1967 L1969 **CD IM** *071 †20
REIDY, Christopher Michae. ■ 53222 #056-05-2006 L2006 **AN** *012
REIN, David Arnold. 2900 W OKLAHOMA AVE, FL 1 53215 #056-05-1986 L1989 **PUD CCM** *020 †20
REINARD, Kevin Arash. ■ 53227 #056-06-2008 *012
REIS, Werner Adam. ■ 53211 #056-06-1973 L1975 **PTH** *075 †50
RELACION, Jose R. ■ 53213 #748-01-1957 L1965 **AN** *075
REMLER, Bernd F. 9200 W WISCONSIN AVE, MCW CLINIC AT FROEDTERT 53226 #409-06-1978 L1997 **N OS** *020 †75
REMSBERG, Elizabeth Anne. ■ 53211 #056-06-2008 *012
REMSHAK, Mark S. 3657 S 92ND ST 53228 #957-03-1987 L1998 **AN** *020
REMUS-GARCIA, Cesar Jose. VET ADMIN HOSP 53295 #042-01-1956 L1963 **AN** *071 †05
RENCH, Adam James. 8701 W WATERTOWN PLANK RD, MED COLL WI AFFIL HOSPS 53226 #305-01-2005 L2007 **IM** *012
RENCH, Jennifer Ann. 1121 E NORTH AVE 53212 #305-01-2005 **FP** *012
RESK, David Michael. 3237 S 16TH ST 53215 #016-11-1965 L1972 **PTH** *071 †50
RETZACK, Susan Margaret. PO BOX 1991, 9000 W WISCONSIN AVE 53201 #056-06-1986 L1987 **PD** *020 †05,55
REUBEN, Charles Frederic. 3070 N 51ST ST, STE 411 53210 #056-06-1972 L1973 **TS** *020 †85,90
REVOLINSKI, Jason Paul. 9200 W WISCONSIN AVE 53226 #056-06-2005 L2007 **IM** *012
REYNOLDS, Kristen H. 8320 W BLUEMOUND RD, STE 125 53213 #056-05-1999 L2000 **FM** *020 †18
REYNOLDS, Norman Clark. 9200 W WATERTOWN PLANK RD 53226 #026-04-1972 L1976 **N** *050 †75
RHEAD, William James. 9000 W WISCONSIN AVE, CHW GENETICS CTR ♯716 53226 #005-18-1974 L2000 **CG PD** *050 †55,19
RHEE, John Sungjung. 9200 W WISCONSIN AVE, DEPT OF OTOLARNGOLOGY 53226 #035-48-1993 L1999 **OTO** *020 †45

■ = Address Information Privacy Protected

RHODE, Brett W. 945 N 12TH ST 53233 #056-05-1991 L1992 **OPH** *020 †35

RHYNER, Mark David. 555 W LAYTON AVE, AIRPORT MEDICAL CLINIC 53207 #056-06-1995 L1996 **FM** *020 †18

RICE, Cynthia Ann. 2025 E NEWPORT AVE, WISCONSIN RADIOLOGY 53211 #056-06-1982 L1986 **DR** *020 †80

RICE, Thomas Bernard. 9000 W WISCONSIN AVE 53226 #030-06-1975 L1976 **PD CCM** *020 †55

RICH, Lisa Matuszewski. 2901 W KK RIVER PKWY, STE 405 53215 #056-06-1988 L1989 **NEP** *020 †20

RICHARD, Jeanette. 9000 W WISCONSIN AVE 53226 #056-06-1983 L1984 **PD** *071 †55

RICHBURG, Gregory Thomas. 3201 S 16TH ST, EUCLID OFFICE BUILDING S 53215 #056-06-2000 L2003 **EM** *020

RICHER, Thomas Jos. 7900 W BURLEIGH ST 53222 #056-06-1971 L1972 **PD** *020 †55

RICHLEN, Matthew Michael. 7961 N 76TH ST 53223 #056-06-2003 L2004 **FM** *020 †18

RICHTER, Michael Alphonse. 3305 S 20TH ST, STE 100 53215 #056-05-1979 L1982 **OBG** *020 †30

RICHTER, Michael Joe. 1575 N RIVERCENTER DR 53212 #056-06-1991 L1993 **FM** *020 †18

RICKERT, Kim L. 9200 W WISCONSIN AVE, FROEDTERT HOSPITAL 53226 #035-15-2000 L2001 **NS** *100

RIDDLE, Kristina Jean. 8701 W WATERTOWN PLANK RD, DEPT OF ANESTHESIOLOGY 53226 #028-79-2005, ▲ L2005 **AN** *012

RIDL, Kimberly Ann. 5000 W NATIONAL AVE, VETERANS ADMINISTRATION ME 53295 #056-05-1993 L1995 **GS** *020

RIDLEY, John Ewing, III. 2315 N LAKE DR STE 1001 53211 #017-20-1960 L1963 **OPH** *071 †35

RIECAN, Jan. 2500 N MAYFAIR RD STE 410 53226 #286-03-1966 L1976 **GS** *020 †85

RIEDL, Cornelia Monika. 2323 N LAKE DR, COLUMBIA ST MARYS MILW 53211 #056-05-1993 L1994 **AN** *020 †05

RIEGELMAN, John H R. ■ 53210 #056-06-1941 L1941 **GP GS** *071

RIESS, Matthias Ludwig. 8701 W WATERTOWN PLANK RD, MEDICAL COLLEGE OF WISCONS 53226 #409-05-1997 L2005 **AN** *012

RIHAWI, Mouhammed. 2801 W KINNICKINC RVR PKWY, STE 445 53215 #875-01-1993 L1998 **PUD** *020 †20

RILEY, Aaron Vincent. ■ 53212 #056-06-2007 **P** *012

RILLING, William Scott. 9200 W WISCONSIN AVE 53226 #056-05-1990 L1991 **VIR DR** *020 †80

RINCON, Mariana. 1032 S CESAR E CHAVEZ DR 53204 #035-48-1987 L1992 **IM PD** *020 †55,20

RINDER, Ruth Schnapper. ■ 53211 #056-06-1959 L1960 **P LM** *072

RING, Allison Marie. 2311 N PROSPECT AVE, CSMCP PROSPECT MEDICAL COM 53211 #016-43-2002 L2004 **OBG** *020

RINGGER, Benjamin Carl. ■ 53223 #056-06-2008 *012

RINIKER, Robert Paul. 9200 W WISCONSIN AVE 53226 #026-04-1982 L1996 **IM** *020 †20

RIORDAN, Margaret Alice. ■ 53217 #018-03-2008 *012

RIPPLE, Timothy Patrick. 9200 W WISCONSIN AVE, FROEDTERT HOSPITAL RADIOLO 53226 #056-06-2000 L2002 **RNR** *100 †80

RISINGER, Robert Clair. 1155 N MAYFAIR RD, HLTH CTR/TOSA CENTER RM 33 53226 #041-12-1988 L1997 **P** *020

RISSELL, Michael Tod. 2801 W KK RIVER PKWY # 170, EYE PHYSICIAN ASSOC S C 53215 #016-01-1988 L1993 **OPH** *020 †35

RITCH, Paul Steven. 8701 W WATERTOWN PLANK RD, HEMATOLOGY/ONCOLOGY 53226 #024-07-1973 L1980 **ON IM** *062 †20

RIVERA, Mariateresita D. 2801 W KINNICKINC RVR PKWY, STE 1030 53215 #748-01-1990 L1995 **PG** *020 †55

RIZZO, James Douglas. 8701 W WATERTOWN PLANK RD, P O BOX 26509 53226 #023-07-1990 L1998 **ON** *020 †20

ROBB, Paul Anderson. 9200 W WISCONSIN AVE, DEPARTMENT OF OB/GYN 53226 #065-01-1996 L2004 **OBG** *020

ROBBINS, Amber Christine. 9200 W WISCONSIN AVE, MEDICAL COLLEGE OF WISCONS 53226 #054-04-2004 L2005 **D** *012

ROBBINS, Regina Frances. 2555 N DR MRTN LTHR KNG DR, CENTER 53212 #056-06-2003 L2006 **PD** *020

ROBBINS, Stephen Eric. 2015 E NEWPORT AVE, MILWAUKEE SPINAL SPECIALIS 53211 #016-11-1982 L1983 **ORS** *020 †40

ROBERTS, Laura W. 8701 W WATERTOWN PLANK RD, DEPT OF PSYCHIATRY 53226 #016-02-1998 L2003 **P** *030 †75

ROBERTS, Niles Milton. ■ 53211 #026-04-2002 L2006 **PM** *100

ROBERTSON, Frederick A. 3223 S 103RD ST 53227 #056-05-1980 L1981 **AN** *020 †05

ROBEY, Thomas Charles. 9000 W WISCONSIN AVE, STE 208 53226 #028-02-1995 L2001 **OTO PDO** *020 †45

ROBINSON, Davida A. ■ 53213 #016-11-1999 L2000 **TS** *012

ROBINSON, James Colin. 925 N 87TH ST 53226 #056-05-1985 L1986 **OPH GS** *020

ROBINSON, Tanya Joy. 1121 E NORTH AVE 53212 #038-40-1996 L1997 **FM** *020 †18

ROCK, Andrea Jean. ■ 53211 #056-06-2008 *012

RODRIGUES, Gilberto De A. 2025 E NEWPORT AVE, STE 1000 53211 #187-30-1984 L2000 **HO** *020 †20

RODRIGUEZ, Carlos Javier. 2311 N PROSPECT AVE, CSMCP PROSPECT MEDICAL COM 53211 #056-06-2000 L2001 **OBG** *020

RODRIGUEZ-CANSECO, Rica B. 2900 W OKLAHOMA AVE 53215 #748-02-1997 L2007 **FP** *012

ROESSLER, Ronald David. 2900 W OKLAHOMA AVE, ERMED, SC 53215 #016-06-2000 L2001 **EM** *020 †16

ROFFERS, John Anthony. 2025 E NEWPORT AVE 53211 #056-06-1985 L1989 **PM** *030 †60

ROGACZEWSKI, Aaron Lee. 2109 N 60TH ST 53208 #011-04-2002 L2004 **GS** *100

ROGERS, John Chas. 3738 S 60TH ST 53220 #030-05-1975 L1976 **OBG** *020

ROGINSKY, Alexandra B. 9200 W WISCONSIN AVE, FROEDTERT HOSPITAL/MCW 53226 #016-06-2001 L2002 **GS** *012

ROH, Byung Lim. 5000 W NATIONAL AVE 53295 #583-02-1947 L1975 **GP PA** *071

ROHR, John Mc Lean, Jr. 9401 W BELOIT RD, STE 315 53227 #056-05-1972 L1973 **P ADM** *020 †75

ROKOPETZ, Sonia Ann. ■ 53233 #056-06-1985 **OS** *020 †20

ROLOFF, Russell Ryan. 1121 E NORTH AVE 53212 #056-06-2004 L2006 **FM** *020 †18

ROMAN-MARCIAL, Lucia C. 413 N 2ND ST UNIT 330 53203 #042-03-1995 L1999 **PD** *020 †55

ROMASHKO, Amy R. 9000 W WISCONSIN AVE 53226 #056-05-2000 L2005 **PD** *020 †55

ROMERO, Ruben P. 7220 W NATIONAL AVE 53214 #748-01-1968 L1977 **OTO** *020 †45

ROMMELFANGER, Stephen G. 2801 W KK RIVER PKWY, STE 175 53215 #056-05-2003 L2005 **FM** *100 †18

RONAYNE, Sean Patrick. 4301 W BROWN DEER RD 53223 #039-01-1999 L2000 **FM** *020 †18

ROSE, Brian Gerard. 2801 W KINNICKINC RVR PKWY, STE 245 53215 #016-11-1995 L1996 **END** *020 †20

ROSEN, Leon Besthoff. 2801 W KINNICKINC RVR PKWY, STE 460 53215 #649-01-1983 L1984 **CD IM** *020 †20

ROSENBERG, Jason Gregory. 788 N JEFFERSON ST, STE 300 53202 #019-02-1999 L2002 **D** *020 †15

ROSENTHAL, Ann Kathryn. 9200 W WISCONSIN AVE, DEPT OF RHEUMATOLOGY 53226 #023-07-1983 L1987 **RHU IM** *020 †20

ROSENTHAL, Edward Jay. 2350 W VILLARD AVE STE 205 53209 #028-03-1988 L1989 **U** *020 †95

ROSENZWEIG, David Yates. 8700 W WISCONSIN AVE 53226 #025-07-1957 L1962 **PUD IM** *040 †20

ROSIELLE, Drew Arnold. 9200 W WISCONSIN AVE, MEDICAL COLLEGE OF WISCONS 53226 #026-04-2002 L2005 **IM** *100 †20

ROSKOS, Thomas. 5310 W CAPITOL DR 53216 #005-15-1962 L1975 **DR NM** *020

ROSLER, Daniel H. 2901 W KK RIVER PKWY # 30 53215 #649-14-1985 L1994 **RHU IM** *020 †20

ROSLER, Henry N. 4710 W LOOMIS RD 53220 #737-06-1983 L1989 **PM** *020 †60

ROSNER, Diane Ruth. 9200 W WISCONSIN AVE, MDCL CLLGE CLNCS AT FRDTRT 53226 #036-05-1982 L1986 **AN** *020 †20

ROSSITER, James Lawrence. 2350 N LAKE DR, STE 406 53211 #017-20-1987 L1999 **OTO FPS** *020 †45

ROTH, James Adam. 9200 W WISCONSIN AVE, MEDICAL COLLEGE OF WISCONS 53226 #041-01-1982 L1994 **ICE CD** *020 †20

ROTH, Robert Barry. 2350 N LAKE DR, STE 400 53211 #021-01-1982 L1988 **CD IM** *020 †20

ROTH, Terence Vincent. 2900 W OKLAHOMA AVE 53215 #056-06-1968 L1973 **GS SO** *071 †85

ROTTER, Francis Jos. 7545 W NORTH AVE, WASHINGTON ROAD 53213 #007-02-1967 L1974 **ORS** *020 †40

ROUKHADZE, Elena. ■ 53211 #913-15-1981 L2007 **SP** *020 †50

ROUMANI, Sami Ali. 3046 S 13TH ST 53215 #875-01-1978 L1993 **FM** *020 †18

ROUTES, John Michael. 9000 W WISCONSIN AVE, MEDICAL COLLEGE OF WISCONS 53226 #017-20-1981 L2006 **IG IM** *050 †20,03

ROWLETT, Randall R. 8989 N PT WASHINGTON RD, STE 220 53217 #016-02-1980 L1990 **CHP P** *020 †75

ROWLEY, Michael William. ■ 53202 #305-01-2007 **IM** *012

ROY, Paige Calhoun. 9200 W WISCONSIN AVE, MCW, DEPT. PM&R, C/O K. HA 53226 #051-07-2002 L2006 **PM** *100 †60

ROYCE, Owen, Jr. 2025 E NEWPORT AVE 53211 #021-01-1935 L1946 **IM** *071 †20

ROZA, Allan Michael. 9200 W WISCONSIN AVE 53226 #065-01-1977 L1988 **TTS** *020 †85

ROZRAN, Richard Stephen. 2025 E NEWPORT AVE, WISCONSIN RADIOLOGY 53211 #056-05-1981 L1985 **DR** *020 †80

RUBIN, Jonathan Michael. 9200 W WISCONSIN AVE, FMLH EAST 53226 #032-01-1989 L1992 **EM** *020 †16

RUDIC, Goran Todor. 5663 S 27TH ST 53221 #957-02-1991 L1999 **IM** *020 †20

RUDOLPH, Colin D. 8701 W WATERTOWN PLANK RD, PEDIATRICS/GASTROENTEROLOG 53226 #038-06-1982 L2000 **PD GE** *020 †55

RUFER, Lawrence. 945 N 12TH ST 53233 #016-11-1989 L1999 **VIR** *020 †60

RUFER, Linda Jones. 8701 W WATERTOWN PLANK RD, DEPARTMENT OF PEDIATRICS 53226 #016-01-1988 L2000 **PD** *020 †55

RUFF, Louis L. ■ 53229 #016-42-1949 L1957 **A IM** *020 †03

RUIZ, Franklin Jesus. 3223 S 103RD ST 53227 #319-03-1987 L1996 **PAN AN** *040 †05

RUSCH, James Robt. 8901 W LINCOLN AVE, CONSULTANTS AT WEST ALLIS 53227 #056-06-1979 L1980 **GS** *020 †20

RUSCH, Susan Witt. 10425 W NORTH AVE, STE 215 53226 #056-06-1983 L1984 **PTH** *020 †50

RUSKIEWICZ, Robert Jerome. 9201 W WATERTOWN PLANK RD, P O BOX 341663 53226 #056-06-1985 L1986 **P** *020 †75

RUSSELL, Elizabeth B. 9200 W WISCONSIN AVE, DIV RHEUM MED CLGE WISC 53226 #033-06-1977 L1985 **RHU IM** *020 †20

RUSSELL, Rebecca Ann. 9000 W WISCONSIN AVE, PEDIATRIC CRITICAL CARE MS 53226 #056-05-2003 L2006 **CCP** *012 †55

RUSSETH, Kathy Jean. 1155 N MAYFAIR RD, MCW DEPARTMENT OF PSYCHIAT 53226 #056-06-2005 L2006 **P** *012

RUSSLER, Susan Kathleen. 2900 W OKLAHOMA AVE 53215 #030-05-1985 L1986 **ID IM** *071 †20

RUSTERHOLZ, Kristin Ruth. 5000 W CHAMBERS ST, ST JOSEPH REG MED CTR 53210 #056-05-2003 L2005 **DR** *020

RUSY, Lynn Marie. 9000 W WISCONSIN AVE 53226 #056-05-1987 L1989 **AN** *020 †05

RUTLEN, David Lee. 9200 W WISCONSIN AVE 53226 #024-01-1973 L2000 **CD IM** *050 †20

RUTTUM, Mark Stuart. 925 N 87TH ST 53226 #024-01-1976 L1978 **OPH PO** *020 †35

RUVALCABA, Jaime G. 1032 S CESAR E CHAVEZ DR 53204 #649-01-1981 L1993 **CHP** *020

RYAN, Lawrence Matthew. 8700 W WISCONSIN AVE, DEPT MED 53226 #016-43-1971 L1972 **RHU IM** *050 †20

RYAN, Thomas John. 10000 W BLUEMOUND RD 53226 #056-06-1980 L1993 **AN** *020 †55,05

RYDLEWICZ, James Allen. 5233 W MORGAN AVE, MILWAUKEE CLINIC OF 53220 #056-06-1967 L1970 **ORS** *020 †40

RYDLEWICZ, James Andrew. ■ 53202 #056-06-2006 **GS** *012

RYDLEWICZ, Mark James. 8701 W WATERTOWN PLANK RD, MEDICAL COLLEGE OF WISCONS 53226 #056-05-2000 L2002 **IM** *020 †20

RYKWALDER, Paul Jos. 2900 W OKLAHOMA AVE, DEPT OF PATHOLOGY 53215 #025-01-1975 L1981 **PTH** *020 †50

RYMUT, August Frank, Jr. ■ 53202 #028-34-1962 L1970 **DR** *071 †80

RYTEL, Krystyna D. 1220 DEWEY AVE 53213 #759-03-1958 L1976 **P** *071

SAAD, Ehab Ramses. 9200 W WISCONSIN AVE, MEDICAP COLLEGE OF WISCONS 53226 #915-02-1987 L2005 **IM NEP** *100 †20

SABHARWAL, Shakti S. 4402 S 68TH ST STE 102, KENITZER INVESTMENT GROUP 53220 #422-01-1992 L1995 **IM** *020 †20

SABLJAK, Edward J. 5535 W ANDOVER RD 53219 #056-06-1952 L1953 **D GP** *020 †70,18

SABNIS, Svapna Samir. 1020 N 12TH ST, DOWNTOWN HEALTH CENTER 53233 #495-37-1990 L1991 **PD** *020 †55

SACHDEVA, Ashutosh. 2501 W SILVER SPRING DR 53209 #495-45-1997 L2003 **PCC** *012 †20

SACHDEVA, Ramesh C. 9000 W WISCONSIN AVE, CHILDREN'S HOSP OF WI MS- 53226 #495-73-1985 L1990 **CCP** *040 †55

SADAGOPAN, Madhu Shyam. 8901 W LINCOLN AVE 53227 #016-11-2000 L2001 **RNR** *020 †20

SADHU, Srikanth. 9200 W WISCONSIN AVE 53226 #495-11-1997 L2003 **IC** *012

SAEED, Athar Muhammad. 2120 W LAYTON AVE, APT 214 53221 #704-22-2005 **IM** *012

SAEIAN, Kia. 9200 W WISCONSIN AVE, HEPATOLOGY - MED COLLEG OF 53226 #005-18-1992 L1993 **GE** *020 †20

SAFAVI, Kayvon Taher. 2801 W KINNICKINC RVR PKWY, STE 700 53215 #016-06-1985 L1992 **IM PD** *071 †20,55

SAFAVI, Patricia Holzemer. 2545 N 29TH ST 53210 #046-01-1985 L1992 **PD** *020 †55

SAGAR, Kiran Bala. 2801 W KINNICKINC RVR PKWY, STE 777 53215 #495-03-1966 L1985 **CD IM** *020 †20

SAICHEK, Robert Parker. 1218 W KILBOURN AVE, ROBERT P SAICHEK MD SC 53233 #056-06-1946 L1948 **CD IM** *071

SAINT LOUIS, Leigh. ■ 53212 #016-11-2006 L2008 **FP** *012

SAJJAD, Rehan. 8701 W WATERTOWN PLANK RD, DEPT. OF NEUROLOGY 53226 #704-04-1990 L1996 **N** *012 †20

SAJJAD, Shabbar. 3000 W MONTANA ST, DEPT OF INTERNAL MEDICINE 53215 #704-21-1991 **IM** *012

SALA, Guglielmo C. 2311 N PROSPECT AVE, STE 401 53211 #056-06-1994 L1997 **IM** *020 †20

SALIH, Samia Sied Ahmed. 3000 W MONTANA ST, DEPT OF INTERNAL MEDICINE 53215 #848-01-1989 **IM** *012

SALKINI, Anas. 9000 W WISCONSIN AVE, HERMA HEART CENTER- MAIL S 53226 #875-02-2001 L2005 **PDC** *012 †55

SALM, Cindy Margaret. ■ 53208 #056-06-2007 **TY** *012

SALVANA, Edsel Maurice T. 9200 W WISCONSIN AVE, MEDICAL COLLEGE OF WISCONS 53226 #748-02-2001 L2004 **ID** *100 †20

SALVI, Frank Jos, Jr. 5000 W CHAMBERS ST 53210 #016-11-1992 L1993 **PM PME** *020 †60

SALZMAN, Nita Helene. 8701 W WATERTOWN PLANK RD, DEPT OF PEDIATRICS/GI 53226 #035-19-1990 L2006 **ATP** *050 †50

SAMARA, Mohammad. 5300 W VILLARD AVE 53218 #561-03-1979 L1995 **GP IMG** *020

SAMAVEDY, Nalini. 3131 S 29TH ST 53215 #495-27-1994 L2006 **P** *100

SAMAVEDY, Ramanujan. 2801 W KINNICKINC RVR PKWY, STE 1030 53215 #495-53-1993 L2006 **GE** *100 †20

SAMIEE, Omied. ■ 53211 #056-06-2008 **IM** *012

SAMUEL, Martin Everett. 2741 W LAYTON AVE STE 206 53221 #056-06-1975 L1976 **OTO HNS** *020 †45

SAMUELS, Elaine Anne. 821 W STATE MED EXAM OFF 53233 #869-05-1970 L1976 **FOP PTH** *020

SAMYN, Margaret Mary. 9000 W WISCONSIN AVE, MS 713 53226 #025-07-1989 L2006 **PDC PD** *020 †55

SANABRIA, Carlos R. 2900 W OKLAHOMA AVE, ST. LUKES HOSPITAL 53215 #056-06-1984 L1987 **EM IM** *020 †20

SANCHEZ, Cecilia R. 925 N 87TH ST, EYE INSTITUTE 53226 #048-03-2005 L2007 **OPH** *012

SANCHEZ, Federico Augusto. 2025 E NEWPORT AVE, STE 1000 53211 #429-02-1985 L1990 **ON HEM** *020 †20

SANDERS, James David. 1121 E NORTH AVE 53212 #016-01-1990 L2002 **FM** *020 †18

SANDERS, Thomas Briggs. 2900 W OKLAHOMA AVE 53215 #056-06-2003 L2004 **DR** *012

SANDFORD, Paul Richard. 5000 W NATIONAL AVE, VA MEDICAL CENTER SCI 128 53295 #056-06-1984 L1987 **PM SCI** *060

SANDHU, Manmeet Kaur. 3000 W MONTANA ST 53215 #496-59-2002 **OBG** *012

SANDHU, Sarbjeet Singh. 8018 W CAPITOL DR 53222 #495-43-1976 L1995 **PD** *020

SANDLER, Mitchell Steven. ■ 53209 #041-09-1978 L1985 **DR** *020 †80,28

SANDLOW, Jay. 9200 W WISCONSIN AVE, MEDICAL COLLEGE OF 53226 #016-01-1987 L2003 **U** *020 †95

SANDOCK, David Scott. 2311 N PROSPECT AVE, CSMCP PROSPECT MEDICAL COM 53211 #003-01-1990 L1996 **U** *020 †95

SANDOVAL, Evelyn Abrogar. ■ 53217 #748-08-1960 L1976 **PTH** *074

SANFT, Tara Beth. 8701 W WATERTOWN PLANK RD 53226 #056-06-2004 L2004 **HO** *012 †20

SANGER, James Robt. 8700 W WATERTOWN PLANK RD, DEPT OF PLASTIC SURG 53226 #056-05-1974 L1979 **HS PS** *020 †65,85

SANIDAS, John George. 788 N JEFFERSON ST, SUIET 300 53202 #056-06-1995 L1996 **IM** *020 †20

SANKARAIAH, Budarapu. 945 N 12TH ST 53233 #495-50-1963 L1979 **AN** *020

SANTELLE, Susan Laura. 945 N 12TH ST 53233 #056-06-1980 L1981 **AN** *020

SANTHARAM, Rajesh. 2801 W KINNICKINC RVR PKWY, STE 1030 53215 #056-06-1999 L2000 **GE** *020 †20

SANTILLI, Robert James. ■ 53217 #056-05-1966 L1967 **IM NEP** *071

SANTOS, Amadeu Federico. 8701 W WATERTOWN PLANK RD, STE 604 53226 #054-04-2000 L2002 **DR** *012 †28

SANTO TOMAS, Linus John H. 9200 W WISCONSIN AVE, PULM CRITICAL CARE 53226 #748-02-1991 L1996 **PCC IM** *030 †20

SARANTOPOULOS, C. 8701 W WATERTOWN PLANK RD, MEDICAL COLLEGE OF WISCONS 53226 #418-01-1985 L1998 **APM** *100 †05

SARASOMBATH, Pichaya Ann. 9200 W WISCONSIN AVE, DEPT OF DERMATOLOGY 53226 #891-04-1999 L2005 **D** *012 †20 ‡

SASI, Akhila Lalita. ■ 53217 #422-01-2007 **IM** *012

SASIDHARAN, Maya. 9000 W WISCONSIN AVE 53226 #495-33-1971 L1990 **PTH** *020 †50 ‡

SASIDHARAN, P. 999 N 92ND ST 53226 #495-44-1969 L1987 **NPM PD** *020 †55

SATCHIE, Brenda N. 2801 W KINNICKINNIC PKWY, STE 330 53215 #056-05-2000 L2002 **GS** *020 †85

SATO, Thomas Tad. 999 N 92ND ST 53226 #005-06-1988 L1997 **PDS** *020 †85

SATTLER, Marvin Edward. 1218 W KILBOURN AVE # 401 53233 #056-06-1946 L1948 **GP** *020 †85

SAUCIER, William Jos, Jr. 2900 W OKLAHOMA AVE 53215 #056-05-1980 L1981 **AN PAN** *020 †05

SAUDEK, David Eliot. 9000 W WISCONSIN AVE, CHILDREN'S HOSPITAL OF WIS 53226 #012-01-2001 L2007 **PDC** *100 †55

SAUNDERS, Evan Keith. 2901 W KINNICKINC RVR PKWY, STE 417 53215 #028-02-1990 L1994 **OBG** *020 †30

SAUTER, Carley Nicole. ■ 53211 #056-06-2007 **TY** *012

SAUTER, Douglas Cameron. 3305 S 20TH ST, STE 130 53215 #016-11-1992 L1999 **GS VS** *020 †85 ‡

SAVIN, Virginia E Jenkins. 9200 W WISCONSIN AVE 53226 #041-12-1970 L1994 **NEP** *050 †20

SAVING, Allegra Malin. ■ 53202 #025-07-2007 **GS** *012

SAVITT, Michael Andrew. 2901 W KINNICKINC RVR PKWY 53215 #036-07-1989 L2005 **TS** *020 †85,90

SAWASKY, Kathleen M. 8700 W WISCONSIN AVE, HOSPITALS 53226 #056-06-1993 L1994 **IM** *020 †20

SAWHNEY, Niraj. 2025 W OKLAHOMA AVE, STE 114 53215 #495-67-1979 L1995 **ID IM** *020 †20

SAXENA, Varun Kumar. 2801 W KINNICKINC RVR PKWY, STE 135 53215 #495-45-1968 L1977 **N** *020 †75

SAYEED, Shaik O. 5818 W CAPITOL DR 53216 #495-21-1996 L2004 **CN** *020

SAYKO, Oksana Y. 9200 W WISCONSIN AVE, FROEDTERT MEMORIAL HOSP. W 53226 #913-89-1988 L2004 **PM** *020 †20,60

SCAFFIDI, Linda E. 9200 W WISCONSIN AVE, MEDICAL COLLEGE OF WISCONS 53226 #038-41-1980 L2006 **CD** *050 †20

SCANLON, Matthew Chas. 9000 W WISCONSIN AVE 53226 #016-43-1992 L1996 **CCP** *020 †55

SCHAEFER, Mark Jos. 8901 W LINCOLN AVE, CONSULTANTS AT WEST ALLIS 53227 #056-06-1989 L1991 **AN** *020 †05

SCHAPIRA, Marilyn May. 5000 W NATIONAL AVE 53295 #025-01-1986 L1990 **IM GP** *040 †20

SCHAPIRA, Ralph Mark. 5000 W NATIONAL AVE, VA MEDICAL CTR RM 111E 53295 #048-12-1984 L1990 **PUD CCM** *050 †20

SCHARKO, Alexander M. 6800 N 76TH ST, STE 200 53223 #056-05-1993 L1996 **CHP P** *020 †75

SCHAUFELBERGER, Kenneth L. 2801 W KINNICKINC RVR PKWY, STE 575 53215 #056-05-1997 L1998 **ORS** *020

SCHECTMAN, Gordon. 5000 W NATIONAL AVE, PC- 00 VA MEDICAL CENTER 53295 #056-06-1978 L1984 **IM ON** *020 †20

SCHEDEWIE, Heinrich K. ■ 53228 #409-21-1965 L1988 **AN PD** *071 †55,05

SCHELL, Debra Lu. 2801 W KINNICKINNIC PKWY, STE 535 53215 #005-12-1985 L1997 **OBG** *020 †30

SCHELLHASE, Kenneth G. 8701 W WATERTOWN PLANK RD, DEPT OF FAM & COMM MED 53226 #041-01-1994 L2001 **FM** *020 †18

SCHER, Kenneth S. 3267 S 16TH ST, OHIO BUILDING SUITE 200 53215 #041-01-1971 L1990 **GS VS** *020 †85

SCHERER, Jeffery Grant. 8901 W LINCOLN AVE 53227 #056-05-1979 L1982 **DR** *020 †80

SCHERMAN, Francis Geo. 2388 N LAKE DR 53211 #056-06-1955 L1960 **IM** *071 †20

SCHEU, Kevin Leslie. 2025 E NEWPORT AVE, DEPT OF ANESTHESIOLOGY 53211 #056-06-1993 L1995 **AN** *020 †20

SCHILLER, Edward D. ■ 53207 #048-12-2006 L2008 **AN** *012

SCHILLING, John Patrick. 8701 W WATERTOWN PLANK RD, MED COLL OF WI 53226 #010-02-2001 L2007 **HSO** *012

SCHILLING, John Philip. 9200 W WISCONSIN AVE, MEDICAL COLLEGE OF WISCONS 53226 #028-02-1976 L1981 **CCM PUD** *020 †20

SCHLOSSER, Robert J. 9200 W WISCONSIN AVE, DEPT. OF ANESTHESIOLOGY 53226 #056-06-2000 L2001 **AN** *020 †05

SCHLUETER, Donald Paul. 9200 W WISCONSIN AVE, MDCL CLLGE CLNCS AT FRDTRT 53226 #056-06-1959 L1960 **PUD IM** *071 †20

SCHMAHL, Karen D Stevens. 3237 S 16TH ST 53215 #056-06-1972 L1973 **AN** *020 †05

SCHMAHL, Terence Malcolm. 2901 W KINNICKINC RVR PKWY, STE 511 53215 #038-40-1967 L1968 **TS** *071 †85,90

SCHMALZ, Michael Johannes. 2424 S 90TH ST, STE 508 53227 #056-06-1983 L1984 **GE IM** *020 †20

SCHMELING, Gregory Jack. 9200 W WISCONSIN AVE, MCW CLINICS AT FMLH EAST 53226 #056-05-1984 L1985 **ORS** *040 †40

SCHMELING, William Thos. 5000 W NATIONAL AVE, ZABLOCKI VA MED CTR ANES 53295 #056-06-1981 L1983 **AN PA** *050 †05

SCHMIDT, Donald Henry. 2500 W LAYTON AVE STE 220 53221 #056-05-1960 L1964 **CD IM** *020

SCHMIDT, John Phillip. 9200 W WISCONSIN AVE, MEDICAL COLLEGE OF 53226 #016-06-1968 L1969 **U** *020 †95

SCHMIDT, Katherine Jean. 8701 W WATERTOWN PLANK RD 53226 #038-45-2003 L2005 **P** *012

SCHMIDT, Matthew Aaron. ■ 53222 #056-06-2006 **IM** *012

SCHMIDT, Richard Nikolaus. 2350 N LAKE DR, STE 406 53211 #025-01-1987 L1993 **OTO** *020 †45

SCHMIDT, Robert Miles. 2025 E NEWPORT AVE 53211 #035-20-1964 L1972 **GS** *071 †85

SCHMITZ, Donna L. 2311 N PROSPECT AVE, STE 401 53211 #056-05-1973 L1976 **PD** *020 †55

SCHMITZ, Gerard Paul. 7878 N 76TH ST, NORTHWEST CLINIC 53223 #056-06-1983 L1987 **OPH** *020 †35

SCHMITZ, Lisa Marie. 3000 W MONTANA ST, AURORA HLTH CARE 53215 #018-75-2006, ▲ L2008 **IM** *012

SCHNAPP, Peter. 8923 W BROWN DEER RD 53224 #286-02-1967 L1990 **FM** *020

SCHNEEBERGER, Benjamin Mi. 9200 W WISCONSIN AVE 53226 #056-06-2005 L2007 **IM** *012

SCHNEIDER, Derek Thomas. 2900 W OKLAHOMA AVE, ERMED, SC 53215 #056-05-2002 L2005 **EM** *020 †16

SCHNEIDER, John Arthur. 2424 S 90TH ST, STE 418 53227 #056-06-1995 L2001 **ORS HS** *020 †40

SCHNEIDER, John Henry. 9455 W WATERTOWN PLANK RD, MCBHD 53226 #056-06-1999 L2000 **P** *100 †79

SCHNEIDER, Thomas Carl. 2311 N PROSPECT AVE, STE 401 53211 #056-06-1974 L1975 **GS TRS** *020 †85

SCHNEIDER-DE CORTEZ, Amy. ■ 53225 #056-06-2008 *012

SCHNELL, Gary Keith. 1220 DEWEY AVE 53213 #056-06-1983 L1984 **CHP P** *020 †75

SCHOFIELD, Sara Jane. 10400 W NORTH AVE 53226 #056-06-1998 L1999 **FM** *020 †18

SCHRAGER, Mark A. 7080 N PORT WASHINGTON RD 53217 #010-02-1970 L1971 **RHU IM** *020 †20

SCHREIBER, Brian T. 10000 W BLUEMOUND RD 53226 #056-05-2001 L2002 **AN** *020 †05

SCHROEDER, John M. ■ 53211 #056-05-1951 L1953 **ON** *071

SCHUBERT, Matthew James. ■ 53208 #056-06-2007 **FP** *012

SCHUETZ, Michael Wm. 3003 W GOOD HOPE RD 53209 #016-43-1970 L1978 **ON IM** *020 †20

SCHULGIT, James Lawrence. 2901 W KINNICKINC RVR PKWY, STE 105 53215 #056-06-1981 L1982 **CD** *020 †20

SCHULLER, Julie Beyer. 1032 S CESAR E CHAVEZ DR 53204 #016-06-1992 L1993 **IM** *020 †20

SCHULTE, Michael Anthony. 3237 S 16TH ST, ST. FRANCIS HOSPITAL 53215 #056-06-1984 L1989 **PTH PCP** *020 †50

SCHULTE, William John. 9200 W WISCONSIN AVE, RM 145 53226 #038-40-1956 L1959 **GS** *030 †85

SCHULTZ, Christopher John. 8700 W WISCONSIN AVE 53226 #056-06-1985 L1989 **RO** *020 †80

SCHULTZ, Dennis E, Jr. 555 S 108TH ST 53214 #056-05-1980 L1987 **OM FM** *020 †18,70

SCHULTZ, Melanie Kay. 2457 N MAYFAIR RD, MILWAUKEE OB GYN SC 53226 #056-06-1984 L1985 **OBG** *020 †18,30

SCHULTZ, Richard Otto. 925 N 87TH ST, MCW EYE INST 53226 #035-03-1956 L1961 **OPH** *071 †35

SCHULZ, David Wm. 2400 W VILLARD AVE 53209 #056-06-1992 L1993 **P** *020

SCHULZ, Rita E. 4448 W LOOMIS RD 53220 #056-06-1991 L1992 **FM** *020 †18

SCHUM, Timothy Russell. 1020 N 12TH ST, DOWNTOWN HEALTH CENTER 53233 #056-06-1977 L1978 **PD** *040 †55

SCHWAB, Joseph Michael. 9200 W WISCONSIN AVE, DEPARTMENT OF ORTHOPAEDIC 53226 #056-06-2006 **ORS** *012

SCHWABE, Michael James. 9000 W WISCONSIN AVE, MOB STE 205 DIV.PEDS NERO 53226 #056-06-1991 L1998 **CHN** *020 †75

SCHWABE, Stefan Klaus F. 5000 W NATIONAL AVE 53295 #409-16-1982 L1985 **N** *100

SCHWARTZ, Marlene. 1220 DEWEY AVE 53213 #035-08-1988 L1989 **IM PUD** *020 †20

SCHWARTZ, Robert Lawrence. 3003 W GOOD HOPE RD, HOPE ROAD CLINIC 53209 #056-05-1986 L1990 **IM** *020 †20

SCHWARZ, Stephanie Elizab. ■ 53202 #005-76-2004, ▲ L2006 **IM** *020 †20

SCHWEINSBERG, Bjorn Steph. 9200 W WISCONSIN AVE 53226 #038-43-2005 L2006 **EM** *012

SCHWIND, Joseph Peter. 9233 N GREEN BAY RD 53209 #056-06-1986 L1987 **FM** *020 †18

SCOTT, Andrew Henry Chas. 9200 W WISCONSIN AVE 53226 #917-19-1973 L1982 **AN** *020 †05

SCOTT, Geoffrey Alan. 210 W CAPITOL DR 53212 #056-05-1990 L1991 **FM** *020 †18

SCOTT, John Paul. ■ 53213 #056-05-2000 L2002 **PAN** *100 †55,05

SEABROOK, Gary Robt. 9200 W WISCONSIN AVE, DEPT VASCULAR SURG 53226 #025-07-1982 L1983 **VS** *020 †85

SEBASTIAN, James Leo. 9200 W WISCONSIN AVE, FMLH-E CLINIC BLDG #4100 53226 #017-20-1979 L1980 **IM** *020 †70

SEE, William Adelbert. 9200 W WISCONSIN AVE, DEPARTMENT OF UROLOGY 53226 #016-02-1982 L1999 **U** *020 †95

SEGURA, Annette Diane. 9000 W WISCONSIN AVE # 701, DEPARTMENT OF PATHOLOGY 53226 #016-11-1980 L1981 **PP** *020 †50

SEIDL, John Jos. 1121 E NORTH AVE 53212 #056-06-1982 L1983 **FM** *020 †18

SEIDMANN, Tamara. ■ 53226 #286-03-1979 L1991 **AN** *020 †05

SEIFERT, Scott Alan. 2900 W OKLAHOMA AVE 53215 #017-20-1996 L1999 **EM** *020 †16

SEKARAN, Palaniandy. 2801 W KINNICKINNIC PKWY, PKWY #453 53215 #495-66-1987 L2001 **AN** *020 †05

SEKHAR, Polisetty. 9000 W WISCONSIN AVE 53226 #495-58-1972 L1980 **AN** *020

SELL, Linda Lou. 9000 W WISCONSIN AVE 53226 #056-06-1980 L1981 **PDS** *071 †85

SELZER, Ann Rae Brauer. 3003 W GOOD HOPE RD, HOPE ROAD CLINIC 53209 #056-05-1970 L1971 **IM** *020 †20

SEMLER, William L. 2350 W VILLARD AVE STE 106 53209 #056-05-1949 L1952 **GYN** *071

SENANAYAKE, Shamila Chatu. 8701 W WATERTOWN PLANK RD, MEDICAL COLLEGE OF WISCONS 53226 #220-01-2000 L2005 **IM** *020 †20

SENDER, Neville. 2400 W VILLARD AVE 53209 #352-10-1955 L1961 **OBG** *020 †30

SENDOW, Randy Ferdinand. ■ 53225 #661-02-2005 **FP** *012

SENO, Louis Steven. 8675 N PORT WASHINGTON RD, STE 120 53217 #016-42-1975 L1976 **FM PM** *020 †18

SEPAHPANAH, Farhad. 5000 W NATIONAL AVE, SCI UNIT VA MEDICAL CTR 53295 #517-01-1990 L2004 **PM SCI** *020 †60

SEPP, Ingeborg Elizabeth. 1545 S LAYTON BLVD, INGEBORG SEPP MD 53215 #407-10-1960 L1966 **IM RHU** *071

SETER, Andrew John. 875 W LAYTON AVE, SENSIA HEALTHCARE, INC. 53221 #016-11-1984 L1991 **OM IM** *020 †20,70

SETHI, Mohammed Rafiq. 6815 W CAPITOL DR, STE 313 53216 #704-08-1968 L1975 **IM END** *020

SETLOCK, Mary A. 9000 W WISCONSIN AVE 53226 #016-43-1979 L1985 **AN EM** *020 †16,05

SEVERANCE, David Allan. 4400 W STATE ST, BLDG 54 53208 #056-06-1990 L1995 **FM** *020 †18

SHAD, Umar. 2900 W OKLAHOMA AVE 53215 #308-11-1997 **FP** *012

SHAFFER, Katherine A H. 9200 W WISCONSIN AVE, FROEDTERT HOSPITAL 53226 #025-01-1968 L1974 **DR** *020 †80 ‡

SHAFFER, William Rankin. 10400 W NORTH AVE, STE 200 53226 #056-06-1979 L1980 **FM** *020 †18

SHAFI, Mohammad. 1218 W KILBOURN AVE, STE 200 53233 #704-04-1965 L1976 **OBG** *020 †30

SHAFRIN, Fred Max. 5150 N PT WASH RD STE 25 53217 #056-05-1978 L1982 **OPH** *020 †35

SHAH, Bimal Dinesh. ■ 53202 #016-11-2004 L2006 **AN** *012

SHAH, Dharmen Subodhchand. 3175 S 28TH ST 53215 #495-22-1998 L2003 **SME** *012 †75

SHAH, Janaki. ■ 53202 #033-75-2007, ▲ **IM** *012

SHAH, Kanak Kishore. 3003 W GOOD HOPE RD, HOPE ROAD CLINIC 53209 #917-23-1963 L1976 **IM PUD** *020 †20

SHAH, Prakash Dhirajlal. 2801 W KINNICKINC RVR PKWY, STE 840 53215 #056-06-1990 L1991 **CD** *020 †20

SHAH, Samir Prashant. ■ 53222 #016-45-2007 **IM** *012

SHAH, Sandeep Niranjan. 925 N 87TH ST, ATTN: DIANE LOPEZ 53226 #039-01-2002 L2006 **OPH** *100

SHAHIR, Kaushik Shankar. ■ 53214 #496-38-1999 *100

SHAIK, Shabeena. 945 N 12TH ST 53233 #496-22-2001 **IM** *012

SHAIKH, Nosheen Naz. 9000 W WISCONSIN AVE, C/O MEDICAL EDUCATION 53226 #028-34-2002 L2004 **PD** *100

SHAKER, Reza. 9200 W WISCONSIN AVE, MDCL CLLGE CLNCS AT FRDTRT 53226 #517-01-1975 L1985 **GE** *075

SHALEV, Yoseph. 2801 W KINNICKINC RVR PKWY, STE 777 53215 #550-01-1974 L1988 **CD** *020 †20

SHALLOW, Kathleen Ann. 9575 N REGENT RD 53217 #056-06-1993 L1994 **EM** *020 †16

SHAMMO, Salim Mikhail. 2500 W LAYTON AVE, STE 200 53221 #875-02-1982 L1994 **CD** *020 †20

SHAPIRO, David Herman. 10950 W CAPITOL DR 53222 #056-06-1977 L1978 **IM** *020 †20

SHAPIRO, Walter D. 8520 W OKLAHOMA AVE, OLSEN MEDICAL CLC 53227 #056-05-1951 L1952 **IM** *020 †20

SHAPIRO-BARR, Tania Ann. ■ 53217 #056-05-2005 *100

SHAPSON, Milton. 700 N WATER ST, # 1227 53202 #056-05-1955 L1957 **P** *071

SHARIF, Mohammad Hasanat. ■ 53202 #704-02-1984 L1996 **CD** *100

SHARMA, Anjali Jain. 9000 W WISCONSIN AVE, P O BOX 1997 53226 #056-06-2005 L2006 **PD** *012

SHARMA, Rakesh Bhikanlal. 8701 W WATERTOWN PLANK RD, MILWAUKEEE 53226 #495-96-1998 L2008 **NPM** *012

SHARMA, Sanjay Kumar. 9200 W WISCONSIN AVE, DEPT OF PHYS MED & REHAB 53226 #496-09-1993 L2001 **IM** *020 †20,60

SHARMA, Shalini Ashokkuma. ■ 53214 #496-46-2000 **AN** *012

SHARPLESS, Philip B. 9200 W WISCONSIN AVE 53226 #056-05-1987 L1992 **EM** *020 †20,16

SHASTRI, Nikhil J.. 8701 W WATERTOWN PLANK RD 53226 #305-01-2005 L2007 **IM** *012

SHEIKH, Asad. 9200 W WISCONSIN AVE, DEPARTMENT OF MEDICINE 53226 #422-01-2006 L2008 **IM** *012

SHEIKH, Imran Rashid. 836 N 12TH ST STE 426 53233 #305-01-2000 L2003 **CD** *012 †20

SHELDON, Dana Joy. 8701 W WATERTOWN PLANK RD 53226 #665-01-2005 L2006 **OBG** *012

SHELGIKAR, Suhas K. 3267 S 16TH ST, STE 207 53215 #495-56-1966 L1976 **CD IM** *020 †20

SHEMIRANI, Nima L. 9200 W WISCONSIN AVE 53226 #056-06-2004 L2005 **OTO** *012

SHERMAN, Brock Van Every. 3003 W GOOD HOPE RD, AURORA ADVANCED HEALTHCARE 53209 #024-07-1970 L1978 **AI PD** *020 †55,03

SHETH, Bhavna Pravin. 925 N 87TH ST 53226 #056-01-1992 L1993 **OPH** *020 †35

SHETH, Kumudchandra. 9000 W WISCONSIN AVE 53226 #495-01-1961 L1976 **NEP PD** *071 †55

SHETH, Mehul K. 8701 W WATERTOWN PLANK RD, MEDICAL COLLEGE OF WISCONS 53226 #016-76-2003, ▲ L2007 **PG** *012

SHETH, Neela K. VET ADMIN HOSP 53295 #495-01-1961 L1976 **CLP MM** *020 †50

SHETH, Pravin Champaklal. 945 N 12TH ST 53233 #495-01-1961 L1980 **AN** *075

SHETTY, Kaup R. VA CENTER 53295 #495-09-1965 L1976 **IM END** *020 †20

SHIDHAM, Vinod Baburao. 9200 W WISCONSIN AVE, FROEDTERT EAST HOSP 53226 #495-83-1977 L1998 **PTH PCP** *020 †50

SHILYANSKY, Joel. 9000 W WISCONSIN AVE, STE 403 53226 #005-14-1988 L2000 **GS** *020 †85

SHIMSHAK, Thomas Michael. 6200 W BLUEMOUND RD 53213 #056-06-1980 L1981 **CD IM** *020 †20

SHINDELL, Sidney. 1011 N MAYFAIR RD 53226 #035-08-1946 L1966 **GPM OM** *071 †70

SHIRES, Adam Lee. 8701 W WATERTOWN PLANK RD 53226 #018-75-2005, ▲ L2006 **AN** *012

SHIVARAM, M S. 4111 W MITCHELL ST 53215 #495-09-1973 L1979 **ORS PTH** *020 †40

SHIVPURI, Chandra Rekha. 3070 N 51ST ST # P309 53210 #495-77-1972 L1983 **NPM** *020 †55

SHOVERS, Jeffrey Benj. 4111 W MITCHELL ST 53215 #056-05-1984 L1989 **ORS OSM** *020

SHOVERS, Philip. 9400 W LINCOLN AVE 53227 #056-05-1958 L1959 **ORS** *071 †40

SHRIDHARANI, Anand. ■ 53202 #024-16-2006 **U** *012

SIDDALINGAIAH, Vasanth K. 3003 W GOOD HOPE RD 53209 #495-33-1988 L2003 **GE** *020 †20

SIDDIQI, Aamir. 1020 N 12TH ST, FL 2 53233 #704-25-1989 L1993 **FM** *020 †18

SIDDIQI, Nauman A. 9200 W WISCONSIN AVE, DEPARTEMNT OF NEPHROLOGY 53226 #704-25-1991 L1999 **NEP** *020 †20

SIDDIQUE, Ishrat. 8701 W WATERTOWN PLANK RD, PLANK RD 53226 #704-02-1989 L2006 **PD** *040 †55

SIDDIQUI, Danish Shariat. 945 N 12TH ST, FL 1 53233 #704-25-1989 L2003 **OBG** *020 †30

SIDDIQUI, Khadija. ■ 53213 #048-78-2007, ▲ *012

SIDHU, Dilraj Singh. 2025 E NEWPORT AVE, COLUMBIA HOSPITAL 53211 #016-11-1992 L2000 **IM PA** *020 †20

SIEGAL, Eric Matthew. 2900 W OKLAHOMA AVE, COGENT HLTHCARE OF WISCONS 53215 #056-06-1994 L2003 **IM** *020 †20

SIEGEL, Ronald. 8700 W WISCONSIN AVE, DEPARTMENT OF CARDIOLOGY 53226 #016-43-1971 L1973 **IM** *020

SIEHR, Stephanie Leigh. ■ 53202 #056-06-2008 *012

SIELAFF, Heather Leigh. ■ 53202 #056-06-2008 *012

SIEVERS, Mary Elizabeth. 9200 W WISCONSIN AVE, AND GYNECOLOGY 53226 #018-03-2006 L2008 **OBG** *012

SIEVERS, Stephen Glenn. 2901 W KINNICKINC RVR PKWY, STE 405 53215 #056-06-1984 L1985 **IM** *020 †20

SIGMANN, Peter. 10000 W INNOVATION DR 53226 #407-05-1963 L1980 **IM IMG** *071 †18,20

SIKER, Daniel. 9000 W WISCONSIN AVE 53226 #005-02-1979 L1985 **AN CCM** *020 †05,55

SIKER, Malika Lisa. ■ 53226 #056-05-2006 L2007 **RO** *012

SILBAR, Elliott Cheplin. 2801 W KINNICKINC RVR PKWY, STE 370 53215 #038-41-1981 L1986 **U** *020 †95

SILCOX, Wendy Lynn. 2900 W OKLAHOMA AVE 53215 #016-11-2004 L2005 **DR** *012

SILVER, Ted Steven. 2350 N LAKE DR, STE 400 53211 #011-02-1975 L1979 **TS** *020 †20

SILVEY KALLAS, Gail Jean. 9200 W WISCONSIN AVE 53226 #056-06-1998 L1998 **IM** *020 †20

SIMMONS, John David. 8901 W LINCOLN AVE, CONSULTANTS AT WEST ALLIS 53227 #056-06-1991 L1992 **AN** *020 †05

SIMMS, Mark Douglas. 9000 W WISCONSIN AVE, CHILDREN'S HOSPITAL OF WIS 53226 #035-15-1974 L1994 **PD OS** *020 †55

SIMON, Jeffrey Scott. 9275 N 49TH ST, STE 200 53223 #056-06-1981 L1985 **P** *020 †75

SIMONS, George W, III. 8701 W WATERTOWN PLANK RD, STE 3018 53226 #010-01-1960 L1978 **ORS** *071 †40

SIMONS, Kenneth Bernard. 8701 W WATERTOWN PLANK RD 53226 #024-05-1980 L1989 **OPH PTH** *040 †15

SIMS, Farrol Hyman. 1020 N 12TH ST, FL 3 53233 #836-01-1960 L1980 **FM** *040

SINCABAN, Marilyn Jane. 5228 W FOND DU LAC AVE 53216 #748-08-1992 L1995 **IMG PLM** *020 †20

SINCLAIR, Eugene Perle. 4555 W SCHROEDER DR, STE 170 53223 #056-06-1961 L1964 **AN** *020 †05

SINENSE, Ricardo Rabang. 2501 W SILVER SPRING DR 53209 #748-08-1964 L1977 **U OS** *020

SINGH, Aman. 2801 W KINNICKINC RVR PKWY, STE 1030 53215 #028-46-1998 L2005 **GE** *020 †20

SINGH, Anilkumar M. 2745 W LAYTON AVE 53221 #539-06-1972 L1977 **GS** *020 †85

SINGH, S Dalip. 5000 W NATIONAL AVE #111-C, CLEMENT J ZABLOCKI VA MED 53295 #495-73-1993 L2002 **ICE CD** *020 †20

SINGSON, Juanito Parel. 3237 S 16TH ST 53215 #748-02-1967 L1976 **ON HEM** *020

SINGSON, Violeta A. 535 N 27TH ST 53208 #748-02-1967 L1976 **PD** *020

SINHA, Sumit. ■ 53220 #894-01-2002 **FM** *100

SINOPOLI, Renee. 2311 N PROSPECT AVE, STE 403 53211 #016-43-1994 L1995 **FM** *020 †18

SINSKY, John Edward. 5000 W CHAMBERS ST 53210 #056-06-1946 L1947 **OBG** *071 †30

SINSON, Grant Paul. 9200 W WISCONSIN AVE, DEPT NEURO SURGERY 53226 #016-06-1989 L2002 **NS** *020 †25

SISTO, Paola A Palma. 8701 W WATERTOWN PLANK RD, MEDICAL COLLEGE OF WISCONS 53226 #035-46-1994 L2000 **PDE** *020 †55

SIVERHUS, Craig Alan. 2015 E NEWPORT AVE, STE 305 53211 #056-06-1988 L1989 **VS GS** *020 †85

SIVERHUS, David James. 575 W RIVER WOODS PKWY, STE 202 53212 #056-06-1991 L1997 **ORS** *020 †40

SIY, Lucio Co. 2350 W VILLARD AVE STE 108 53209 #748-01-1960 L1968 **IM** *071 †20

SIZENSKY, Joseph Albert. 9200 W WISCONSIN AVE, PO BOX 26099 53226 #017-20-1995 L2002 **ORS OFA** *020 †40

SJULSON, Neil Bryan. 10000 W BLUEMOUND RD 53226 #026-04-1987 L1990 **AN** *020 †05

SLAMER, James R. ■ 53209 #056-06-1950 L1952 **GP** *020

SLAVIC-SVIRCEV, Vera. 8901 W LINCOLN AVE, CONSULTANTS AT WEST ALLIS 53227 #957-07-1969 L1977 **AN** *071 †05

SLAWSKI, Barbara Ann. 9200 W WISCONSIN AVE, GENERAL INTERNAL MEDICINE 53226 #056-06-1997 L1998 **IM** *020 †20

SLAWSON, James Gray. 2400 W VILLARD AVE, WHEATON FRANCISCAN FAM CTR 53209 #025-07-1988 L1989 **FM** *020 †18

SLAWTER, Amy Elizabeth. 9200 W WISCONSIN AVE, MEDICAL COLLEGE OF WI DEPT 53226 #056-05-2005 L2006 **EM** *012

SLOMOWITZ, Jonathan. ■ 53216 #056-06-1944 L1945 **IM** *071

SLOTA, Thomas. 2350 W VILLARD AVE 53209 #016-43-1975 L1978 **GE IM** *071 †20

SMADI, Tarif. 9200 W WISCONSIN AVE, FROEDTERT HOSPITAL 53226 #875-01-1997 L2003 PCC *100 †20

SMEDBERG, Thomas Carl. 8701 W WATERTOWN PLANK RD, MEDICAL COLLEGE OF WISCONS 53226 #056-06-2006 L2007 ORS *012

SMILTNEEK, Eric August. 1121 E NORTH AVE 53212 #056-05-2006 L2007 FP *012

SMITH, Bernard. 1428 N FARWELL AVE, AFFILIATED MED SVCS 53202 #016-06-1975 L1988 EM *020

SMITH, Carolyn Shannon. 545 N 15TH ST, MARQUETTE UNIVERSITY 53233 #016-11-1995 L1996 FM FSM *020 †18

SMITH, Emily Elizabeth. 8701 W WATERTOWN PLANK RD 53226 #016-01-2003 L2004 AN *012

SMITH, Gerald Patrick. 945 N 12TH ST, DEPT OF PATHLGY 53233 #016-45-1993 L2000 PTH *020 †50

SMITH, Jeffrey A. 1020 N 12TH ST, STE 5120 53233 #011-02-1994 L1999 IM *020 †20

SMITH, Jeremiah John. ■ 53211 #539-02-1985 AN *100

SMITH, Joshua David. 5000 W CHAMBERS ST 53210 #056-05-2001 L2004 RNR *100 †80

SMITH, Richard Allen. 8901 W LINCOLN AVE, CONSULTANTS AT WEST ALLIS 53227 #056-06-1977 L1978 AN *020 †20

SMUKOWSKI, Joel D. 3237 S 16TH ST 53215 #056-05-1994 L1998 EM *020 †16

SMULLEN, Daniel Michael. 8901 W LINCOLN AVE, CONSULTANTS AT WEST ALLIS 53227 #056-05-2002 L2004 AN *020

SMULLEN, William Alfred. 10400 W NORTH AVE, STE 300 53226 #056-06-1964 L1970 DR *071 †20

SOERGEL, Konrad Hermann. 9200 W WISCONSIN AVE, DIV OF GI/HEPATOLOGY 53226 #407-04-1957 L1961 GE IM *071 †20

SOHNLE, Peter Geo. VET ADMIN HOSP 53295 #035-20-1971 L1976 ID AI *050 †20

SOIFER, Morton Marshall. 8675 N PORT WASHINGTON RD, ALLERGY ASSOCIATES 53217 #024-07-1961 L1970 AI PD *071 †55,03

SOLBERG, Matthew Alan. 3289 N MAYFAIR RD, MAYFAIR ROAD CLINIC 53222 #056-05-1987 L1990 PD *020 †55

SOLIS, Joaquin. 2801 W KINNICKINC RVR PKWY, STE 777 53215 #682-03-1996 L1999 IC *020 †20

SOMBERG, Lewis Brian. 9200 W WISCONSIN AVE 53226 #012-05-1987 L1997 CCS *020 †85

SONNENBERG, Gabriele E. 9200 W WISCONSIN AVE, MED COLLEGE OF WISCONSIN 53226 #409-25-1974 L1989 *020

SOO, Kam Kwang. 2015 E NEWPORT AVE, STE 307 53211 #825-01-1969 L1975 P *020 †75

SOOD, Manu Raj. 9000 W WISCONSIN AVE 53226 #495-90-1986 L2004 *020

SOOD, Puneet. 8701 W WATERTOWN PLANK RD, MED COLL WI AFFIL HOSPS 53226 #495-36-2002 L2005 IM *100

SOO HOO, Melvin Jay. 1220 DEWEY AVE, WAUWATOSA 53213 #025-07-1982 L1983 P *020 †75

SORIN, Luda Mila. ■ 53217 #016-42-2008 *012

SORYAL, Soryal Ayoub. 1020 N 12TH ST 53233 #915-03-1996 L2006 IMG *020 †20

SOSA, Veronica. 2801 W KINNICKINNIC PKWY, STE 570 53215 #008-02-1992 L2005 N SME *020 †75

SOSTAK, James Patrick. 9200 W WISCONSIN AVE, MCW DEPT OF ORTHOPAEDICS 53226 #016-43-2005 L2006 ORS *012

SOTO, Francisco Javier. 9200 W WISCONSIN AVE, STE 5200 53226 #264-05-1992 L2002 PCC *020

SPEARS, Terry Lynn. 2801 W KINNICKINC RVR PKWY, STE 135 53215 #056-05-1987 L1988 IM *020 †20

SPENCER, Warren Scott. ■ 53210 #056-06-2007 L2008 TY *012

SPICUZZA, Salvatore A. 2400 W VILLARD AVE, ST. MICHAEL FAMILY CARE CT 53209 #056-06-1962 L1963 PM *071 †60

SPIEGELHOFF, Don Ray. 2900 W OKLAHOMA AVE 53215 #056-06-1966 L1967 NM DR *020 †80,28

SPIEKERMAN, Jill Marie. 4301 W BROWN DEER RD 53223 #056-06-1997 L1998 FM *020 †18

SPINELLI, Kristine Shackl. 7878 N 76TH ST, NORTHWEST CLINIC 53223 #016-06-1994 L1995 DR *020 †80

SPIRO, Herzl Robt. 777 N PROSPECT AVE, UNIT 303 53202 #050-02-1960 L1975 P PHP *040 †75 ‡

SPITZ, Milton Baron. 1218 W KILBOURN AVE STOP 1 53233 #056-05-1954 L1955 IM PUD *071

SPIVACK, Jonathan Wood. 3003 W GOOD HOPE RD, HOPE ROAD CLINIC 53209 #041-09-1997 L1997 N OS *020 †75

SPODEN, Darrin John. ■ 53222 #016-76-2007, ▲ TY *012

SPONAGLE, Stephen Kenneth. 740 W WISCONSIN AVE # 301 53233 #011-04-1999 L2004 P *100 †75

SPORTIELLO, Debora Jean. 2457 N MAYFAIR RD, MILWAUKEE OB GYN SC 53226 #056-06-1987 L1988 OBG REN *020 †30

SPRADLEY, Wayne Bernard. 6901 W EDGERTON AVE 53220 #056-06-1985 L1986 IM *020 †20

SPREITZER, Alberta Marie. 9200 W WISCONSIN AVE, MDCL CLLGE CLNCS AT FRDTRT 53226 #025-07-1988 L1991 PM *020 †60

SRA, Jasbir S. 2801 W KINNICKINC RVR PKWY, STE 777 53215 #495-75-1979 L1987 CD *020 †20

SRINIVASAN, Srividya. 8701 W WATERTOWN PLANK RD, MEDICAL COLLEGE OF WISCONS 53226 #495-04-1997 L2002 ID *020 †20

SRIVATSAL, Sindhu Rajalak. ■ 53226 #496-39-2003 N *012

STABELFELDT, Ellen Ann. 9000 W WISCONSIN AVE, CHILDRENS HOSP OF WIL CGO 53226 #056-06-2006 L2008 PD *012

STADLER, Francis Jos. ■ 53207 #056-06-1957 L1958 PHP *071

STADLER, James A, II. 555 S 108TH ST 53214 #056-06-1973 L1974 OBG *020 †30

STAFL, Adolf. 2801 W KINNICKINC RVR PKWY, STE 535 53215 #286-02-1957 L1970 OBG *020 †30

STANCO, Lynn Marie. 2323 S 102ND ST 53227 #056-06-1992 L1993 FM *020 †18

STANCZ, Henrietta. 9200 W WISCONSIN AVE, DEPT OF OB-GYN FMLH 53226 #286-13-1998 OBG *100

STAVES, Nicholas Peter. 3238 S 16TH ST 53215 #418-01-1949 L1962 GS *071

STAVRAKOS, John Evans. 9200 W WISCONSIN AVE, DEPARTMENT OF ORTHOPAEDICS 53226 #016-42-2001 L2005 PM *100 †60

ST CLAIR, Nicole Erin. ■ 53211 #056-05-2003 L2007 PD *100 †55

STEARNS, Jeffrey Alan. 1020 N 12TH ST RM 5120, AURORA SINAI MED CTR OHC 53233 #025-01-1974 L2000 FM *040 †18

STEIN, David Irving. 5400 N 118TH CT, SERVICES 53225 #056-05-1987 L1991 AN PMM *020 †05

STEIN, Phillip Lawrence. 1020 N 12TH ST, FL 4 53233 #056-05-1958 L1959 P *020 †75

STEINER, Robert Edward. ■ 53211 #056-06-1955 L1958 NS *071

STEKIEL, Thomas Anthony. 8701 W WATERTOWN PLANK RD, DEPT OF ANESTHESIOLOGY 53226 #056-06-1985 L1986 AN *020 †05

STELIGA, Richard Allen. 3070 N 51ST ST STE 405 53210 #056-05-1972 L1973 GS OS *020 †85

STEPEK, Magdalena. 2801 W KK RIVER PKWY # 250, AURORA ST LUKE'S MEDICAL C 53215 #018-75-2005, ▲ L2007 FP *012

STEPHENS, Jill. 945 N 12TH ST 53233 #017-20-1989 L1993 DR *020 †80

STEPIEN, Kimberly Ellen. 925 N 87TH ST, EYE INSTITUTE 53226 #056-05-2002 L2007 OPH OS *020 †35

STEPKE, Chad Joseph. 2350 N LAKE DR, STE 303 53211 #056-06-1998 L2001 GE IM *020 †20

STERN, Karice. 8701 W WATERTOWN PLANK RD, MEDICAL COLLEGE OF WISCONS 53226 #016-43-2002 L2003 EM *020 †16

STERN, Robert Marc. 3237 S 16TH ST 53215 #649-33-1981 L1987 PM EM *020 †60

STERNLIEB, Richard Owen. 2323 N LAKE DR 53211 #056-05-1953 L1954 RHU IM *071 †20

STEVANOVIC, Nebojsa. 5020 W OKLAHOMA AVE 53219 #957-02-1980 L1997 FM *020 †18

STEVENS, Martha Wood. 999 N 92ND ST C550, CHILDRENS HOSPITAL WISCONS 53226 #036-01-1989 L2002 PD *020 †55

STICKELS, Susan Fredi. 6901 W EDGERTON AVE, AURORA MEDICAL GROUP 53220 #056-05-1977 L1978 FM *020 †20

STIEHL, James Bowen. 575 W RIVER WOODS PKWY 53212 #016-11-1975 L1987 ORS *020 †40

STILES, Adam Christopher. 9200 W WISCONSIN AVE, MCW DEPT OF EMERGENCY MEDI 53226 #049-01-2004 L2006 EM *100

STOCK, E Lee. 925 N 87TH ST, THE EYE INSTITUTE 53226 #025-01-1968 L1999 OPH *035

STOCKHAUSEN, Rebecca Chri. ■ 53210 #056-06-2007 FP *012

STOESZ, Michael James. ■ 53213 #056-06-2008 *012

STOKES, Annette S. 7620 W BURLEIGH ST 53222 #030-06-1994 L1995 FM *020 †18

STOLL, James Edwin, Jr. 2015 E NEWPORT AVE STE 605 53211 #016-06-1978 L1984 OSS *020 †20

STOLLENWERK, Kenneth J. 3237 S 16TH ST 53215 #056-06-1947 L1948 GP EM *071

STONE, John Edward. 2801 W KINNICKINC RVR PKWY, STE 1030 53215 #038-06-1980 L1981 GE *020 †20

STONE, Lucy. 2311 N PROSPECT AVE, STE 401 53211 #244-04-1986 L1993 IM *020 †20

STONE, Richard. 2801 W KK RIVER PKWY, STE 170 53215 #056-05-1969 L1975 OPH *071 †35

STONER, Kimberly Michele. 9200 W WISCONSIN AVE, FEC STE 4200 53226 #016-43-2000 L2004 IMG PYM *020 †20,75

STOWE, David F. VA MEDICAL CTR RES SER 151 53295 #056-06-1983 L1985 AN *020

STRACK, Margery Ann. 1020 N 12TH ST 53233 #748-02-1980 L1993 HO *020 †20

STRANDE, Jennifer Lynn. 9200 W WISCONSIN AVE, FROEDTERT MEMORIAL LUTHERA 53226 #016-43-2002 L2004 CD *012 †20

STRASSBURGER, Richard H. 3033 S 27TH ST STE 201 53215 #028-34-1953 L1954 NS *071 †25

STRAUS, Todd Douglas. ■ 53225 #056-06-2005 L2006 PTH *012

STRAWN, Estil Young. 2388 N LAKE DR 53211 #047-07-1952 L1958 OBG *071 †30

STRAWN, Estil Young, Jr. 9200 W WISCONSIN AVE, DEPARTMENT OF OB/GYN 53226 #056-05-1980 L1981 OBG *020 †30

STRECKERT, Matthew Daniel. 9200 W WISCONSIN AVE, DEPT. OF EMERGENCY MEDICIN 53226 #008-01-2005 L2006 EM *012

STRELNICK, Karl Ira. 9455 W WATERTOWN PLANK RD, MCBHD 53226 #056-05-1975 L1976 P *020

STRITTMATER, Jamey Jill. 9200 W WISCONSIN AVE, DEPT OF MEDICINE 53226 #056-06-2005 L2006 IM *012

STRNAD, Renee Rachelle. 1660 N PROSPECT AVE 53202 #017-20-2003 L2004 AN *020

STROHM, Cindy Ann. 5000 W CHAMBERS ST 53210 #016-45-1990 L1984 RO *074 †80

STRONG, Tatyana. 8701 W WATERTOWN PLANK RD 53226 #056-06-1997 L1999 *020 †05

STRUNIN, Leo. 5000 W NATL AVE, MEDICAL COLLEGE WIS 53226 #917-04-1960 L1977 *020

STUCKE GENANNT MEINERT, As. 8701 W WATERTOWN PLANK RD 53226 #409-10-1995 L2004 PD *020

STUHLER, John Dunham. ■ 53226 #018-03-1948 L1950 ADM *030 †55

STUKENBERG, Lisa Marie. 555 S 108TH ST 53214 #016-45-1990 L1991 PD *020 †55

STULA, Gojko D. 3238 S 16TH ST 53215 #957-02-1958 L1962 GP *020

STURZU, Mirela O. 6901 W EDGERTON AVE 53220 #781-02-1992 L2006 IM *020 †20

STUTH, Eckehard E A. 9000 W WISCONSIN AVE, DIV OF ANESTH CLHDN HOSP 53226 #409-10-1983 L1987 AN *020 †05

SUAVERDEZ, Rodolfo P. 7220 W NATIONAL AVE 53214 #748-08-1965 L1978 GP *020

SUCHER, Robert Alan. 9200 W WISCONSIN AVE, EYE CARE SPECIALISTS SC 53233 #056-06-1972 L1973 OPH *020 †35

SUCHI, Mariko. 9000 W WISCONSIN AVE 53226 #572-47-1983 L2005 PTH *020 †50

SUDAKOFF, Gary Steven. 9200 W WISCONSIN AVE, DEPT OF RADIOLOGY/ROOM 288 53226 #016-01-1983 L1990 DR *020 †80

SULAIMAN, Olawale Adeniyi. 9200 W WISCONSIN AVE 53226 #198-03-1997 L2006 *100

SULLIVAN, Dennis Michael. 1218 W KILBOURN AVE, MILWAUKEE ORTHOPEDIC GROUP 53233 #056-06-1974 L1975 ORS *020 †40

SULLIVAN, Gerald Edward. 6040 W LISBON AVE, STE 200 53210 #056-06-1994 L1995 IM ADM *020

SULMAN, Aaron. 9200 W WISCONSIN AVE, MEDICAL COLLEGE OF 53226 #056-06-1996 L2006 U *020 †95

SULMAN, Cecille Gail. 9000 W WISCONSIN AVE 53226 #038-06-1999 L2006 OTO *100 †45

SUMMERILL, Shaun Stephen. ■ 53226 #056-06-2004 L2006 PD *100

SUN, Kai. ■ 53202 #243-72-1999 *100

SUN, Rosalio C. 3237 S 16TH ST 53215 #748-01-1961 GS *062

SUNDARAM, Candadai M. 1218 W KILBOURN AVE, STE 124 53233 #495-16-1968 L1978 GE *020 †20

SUNDER, Nithya. 9000 W WISCONSIN AVE, C/O MEDICAL EDUCATION 53226 #016-11-2003 L2005 PD *020 †55

SUNDLASS, Jaswinderjit S. ■ 53215 #495-20-1977 L1984 IM EM *020 †20

SURAPANENI, Sri Naveen. 9200 W WISCONSIN AVE #495-73-2003 L2005 GE *012 †20

SUSINI, Vincenzo Rocco. 8701 W WATERTOWN PLANK RD 53226 #665-01-2007 FP *012

SUSON, Elieser Basiga. 2300 N MAYFAIR RD 53226 #748-02-1955 L1968 OPH *020 †35

SUSON, John David. 2300 N MAYFAIR RD 53226 #056-06-1992 L1993 OPH *020 †35

SUSTER, Saul Marcos. 9200 W WISCONSIN AVE, DEPT OF PTH-MCW 53226 #319-04-1976 L1987 PTH *020 †50

SWADER, Gloria. 2311 N PROSPECT AVE, STE 401 53211 #056-06-2003 L2005 IM *020 †20

SWAIN, Geoffrey Robt. 841 N BROADWAY RM 315, CITY OF MILWAUKEE HLTH DEP 53202 #056-06-1985 L1986 FM PHP *030 †18

SWANK, Michael. 2315 N LAKE DR, STE 703 53211 #041-09-1970 L1975 TS *020 †85,90

SWANSON, Howard James. 11925 W LAKE PARK DR, STE 100 53224 #019-02-1973 L1990 RHU IM *020 †20

SWEENEY, Anthony Jos. 2400 W VILLARD AVE 53209 #016-11-1973 L1986 FM NTR *020 †18

SWEET, Margaret E. 3070 N 51ST ST, STE 507 53210 #065-10-1986 L2006 N *020 †75

SWENSON, Eldon Jon. 8901 W LINCOLN AVE, CONSULTANTS AT WEST ALLIS 53227 #018-03-1967 L1976 **AN** *020 †05

SWENSON, Jeanine Marie. 3003 W GOOD HOPE RD, P O BOX 090996 53209 #056-05-1989 L1995 **PDC PD** *020 †55

SWIETLIK, Andrew Philip. 2323 S 102ND ST 53227 #056-05-1995 L1997 **PD** *020 †55

SWINARSKA, Monika Agata. 9200 W WISCONSIN AVE 53226 #759-07-1992 L2001 **PM PME** *020 †60

SY, Santiago. 4666 S 35TH ST 53221 #748-08-1965 L1975 **PD** *020

SYED, Amina Yasmeen. 2900 W OKLAHOMA AVE 53215 #496-27-2004 **FP** *012

SYED, Faiz Imad. ■ 53220 #056-05-2008 *012

SYED, Vaqaruddin Mansoor. 9200 W WISCONSIN AVE, MDCL CLLGE CLNCS AT FRDTRT 53226 #704-02-1980 L1999 **AN** *020 †05

SYVERSON, Grant Douglas. 9000 W WISCONSIN AVE, CO MED ED 53226 #037-01-2005 L2006 **PD** *012

SZABO, Sara. 9000 W WISCONSIN AVE, CHILD HOSP OF WI DEPT PATH 53226 #473-03-1989 L2006 **PTH PP** *020 †50

SZEDER PHD, Viktor. 9200 W WISCONSIN AVE, DEPT NEURLGY MED CLGE-WI 53226 #286-13-1998 L2006 **N** *012

SZOKE, Ervin. 788 N JEFFERSON ST, STE 201 53202 #473-03-1991 L2007 **IM** *020

SZYMANSKI, Czeslaw. 2323 N LAKE DR 53211 #759-09-1975 L1990 **AN** *020 †05

TADDEI, Kimberlee Jo. ■ 53207 #056-06-1992 L1998 **AN** *020

TADIMETI, Himabindu. 9200 W WISCONSIN AVE, MED COLL OF WI-FROEDTERT M 53226 #496-41-1998 L2007 **RNR** *100

TAINTOR, Adam Read. ■ 53222 #049-01-2007 *012

TAKAHASHI, Dai. 6100 W STATE ST # 72, RESERVE AT WAUWATOSA VILLA 53213 #011-75-2003, ▲ L2004 **IM** *100 †20

TALANO, Juliean Marie. 8701 W WATERTOWN PLANK RD, MACC FUND RESEARCH CENTER 53226 #016-06-1995 L1999 **PHO** *020 †55

TALISMAN, Ran. ■ 53216 #550-02-1991 L1996 **PS** *020

TAN, Carlos Castillo. 4600 W LOOMIS RD, STE 201 53220 #748-08-1977 L2004 **GS VS** *020 †85

TAN, Djerrick Cu. 500 W BROWN DEER RD, WISCONSIN RADIOLOGY 53217 #017-20-1999 L2005 **DR** *020 †80 ‡

TAN, Khai Ling. 9200 W WISCONSIN AVE, ATTN: KHAI LING TAN MD 53226 #060-02-2003 L2005 **OBG** *012

TAN, Khai-Tong. ■ 53202 #825-01-1982 *100

TAN, Simon T. 1218 W KILBOURN AVE, STE 200 53233 #748-01-1960 L1976 **PD** *020 †55

TANG, Thomas T. 9000 W WISCONSIN AVE 53226 #010-01-1958 L1964 **PTH NM** *071 †50,28

TANNEHILL, Scott Patrick. 2025 E NEWPORT AVE, RADIOTHERAPY 53211 #056-05-1993 L1994 **RO** *040 †80 ‡

TARAWNEH, Husam Saleh. 1020 N 12TH ST 53233 #913-04-1981 L1990 **HO** *020 †20

TASSONE, J Channing. 8701 W WATERTOWN PLANK RD, ORTHOPEDICS, SUITE 3018 53226 #054-04-1996 L1997 **OP** *020 †40

TAYLOR, Jessica Catherine. 8701 W WATERTOWN PLANK RD, DEPARTMENT OF PSYCHIATRY A 53226 #035-15-2006 L2008 **P** *012

TAYLOR, Robert Fredrick. 2900 W OKLAHOMA AVE 53215 #008-01-1976 L1984 **HEM** *020 †20

TAYLOR, Susan P. 9000 W WISCONSIN AVE 53226 #051-07-1979 L1990 **GS** *020 †05

TECTOR, Alfred Jos, Jr. 2901 W KINNICKINC RVR PKWY 53215 #028-34-1963 L1970 **TS TTS** *020 †85,90

TEEHAN, Robert Glenn. 2025 E NEWPORT AVE, COLUMBIA HOSPITAL 53211 #305-01-1996 L1997 **IM** *020 †20

TEITELBAUM, Benjamin Joel. 7220 W NATIONAL AVE 53214 #016-11-1989 L1994 **OTO HNS** *020 †45

TEITGEN, Ralph E. 1684 N PROSPECT AVE 53202 #041-01-1944 L1945 **OPH OS** *071 †35

TELEGA, Grzegorz Wojciech. 9000 W WATERTOWN PLANK RD, DEPT PED GI & NUTRITION 53226 #759-01-1989 L2000 **PG OS** *020 †55

TELFORD, Gordon Laing. 9200 W WISCONSIN AVE 53226 #016-02-1971 L1982 **GS CRS** *030 †85

TELFORD, Lynn Sarah. 10400 W NORTH AVE, STE 200 53226 #056-06-1996 L1997 **FM** *020 †18

TERLIZZI, Carmen L, III. 3040 N 117TH ST 53222 #038-45-1989 L1990 **OBG** *020 †30

TERRY, Leon Cass. 4677 N WILSHIRE RD, STE 200 53211 #056-06-1969 L1989 **N OS** *020 †75

TEVES, Denise Angelica. 9200 W WISCONSIN AVE, ENDOCRINE FEC 4TH FLOOR 53226 #737-01-1997 L2004 **END** *020 †20

THENAPPAN, Mala. 3070 N 51ST ST, STE 100 53210 #056-06-1993 L1995 **GS** *020 †85

THERIOT, Kenneth Robert. ■ 53216 #056-06-2007 **TY** *012

THIEL, Brad John. 8701 W WATERTOWN PLANK RD 53226 #056-06-2004 L2005 **P** *012

THIEL, Elizabeth L. 8701 W WATERTOWN PLANK RD 53226 #056-06-2004 L2006 **PHO** *012

THOMAS, John Patrick, Jr. 10625 N NORTH AVE, WIS PED CARDIOLOGY ASSOCSC 53226 #056-06-1968 L1975 **PDC PD** *020 †55

THOMAS, Leno Mammen. 8701 W WATERTOWN PLANK RD, MED COLL WI 53226 #905-02-2003 L2007 **PDP** *012

THOMAS, Upton Haskin, III. 7330 W LAYTON AVE 53220 #056-06-2000 L2003 **P** *020

THOMAS-KING, Pamela Y. 8901 N 76TH ST 53223 #056-05-1989 L1995 **APM** *020 †05

THOMASON, Jessica L. 2015 E NEWPORT AVE, STE 803 53211 #036-01-1974 L1984 **GYN ID** *071 †30

THOMETZ, John Gerard. 9000 W WISCONSIN AVE, CHILDRENS HOSPITAL OF WI. 53226 #016-06-1978 L1985 **ORS** *020 †85

THOMPSON, Ashley Allen. 8701 W WATERTOWN PLANK RD, MCWAH 53226 #046-01-2003 L2004 **PFP** *012

THOMPSON, Daniel Jos. 3289 N MAYFAIR RD, MAYFAIR ROAD CLINIC 53222 #016-11-1985 L1986 **IM** *020 †20

THOMPSON, Melish A. 2015 E NEWPORT AVE # M114 53211 #005-18-1972 L1977 **CD** *020 †20

THOMPSON, Nathan Eric. 53210 #017-20-2008 *012

THOMPSON, Rachel Therese. ■ 53226 #056-06-2008 *012

THOMPSON, Sarah Louise. ■ 53207 #026-04-2002 L2002 **PD** *100

THOPPIL, Ephrem. 2900 W OKLAHOMA AVE 53215 #495-52-1971 L1977 **P PM** *020 †60

THORNQUIST, Peter William. 3003 W GOOD HOPE RD, ADVANCED HEALTHCARE 53209 #056-06-1994 L1995 **GPM** *020 †20

THORSTEINSSON, Vigfus O. 8700 WEST WISC AVE, DPT PATH 53226 #484-01-1970 **PTH** *100

THOTA, Venkata Krishna. 4448 W LOOMIS RD 53220 #308-11-1985 L1987 **FM EM** *020 †18

TIBBS, Christen Augustus. 53213 #056-06-2008 *012

TIBER, Charles H I. 2025 E NEWPORT AVE 53211 #038-40-1975 L1980 **IM ON** *020 †20

TIETZ, Katie Marie. 9200 W WISCONSIN AVE, FROEDTORT HOSP 53226 #056-06-2005 L2006 **N** *012

TIGER, Paul. 8701 W WATERTOWN PLANK RD 53226 #056-06-2002 L2004 **P** *100 †75

TILLEMANS, Kim Marie. ■ 53204 #018-75-2004, ▲ L2007 **OBG** *012

TIMINS, Michael Elliot. 9200 W WISCONSIN AVE, DEPARTMENT OF RADIOLOGY 53226 #016-11-1986 L1991 **DR** *020 †80

TIMM, William Donald. 601 N 99TH ST, STE 103 53226 #056-06-1991 L1992 **ID** *020 †20

TINGUELY, Matthew Joseph. 9200 W WISCONSIN AVE, DEPARTMENT OF MEDICINE 53226 #030-06-2004 L2006 **HO** *012 †20

TIPNIS, Neelesh Ajit. ■ 53226 #056-06-1997 L2004 **PG** *020 †55

TIPNIS, Sajani Matai. 8701 W WATERTOWN PLANK RD, MCW DIVISION OF NEONATOLOG 53226 #056-06-1997 L2004 **NPM** *020 †55

TISOL, William Blair. 9200 W WISCONSIN AVE, DIV OF CARDIOTHORACIC SURG 53226 #025-12-1997 L2002 **TS** *100 †85,90

TISONE, James Jacob. ■ 53222 #056-06-1957 L1958 **AN** *071

TITLER, Sarah Sue. ■ 53202 #018-03-2004 L2008 **AN** *012

TIU, Alfonso L. 2424 S 90TH ST, STE 418 53227 #748-11-1965 L1976 **CD IM** *071 †20 ‡

TJOE, Judy Angela. 2801 W KINNICKINC RVR PKWY, STE 160 53215 #005-02-1995 L1996 **SO** *020 †85

TLOMAK, Wieslawa. 933 W HIGHLAND AVE, MILWAUKEE COUNTY MED EXAM 53233 #759-10-1989 L2006 **FOP** *020 †50

TOBIN, Benjamin, Jr. 9200 W WISCONSIN AVE, MEDICAL COLLEGE OF WISCONS 53226 #056-06-1996 L1997 **IM** *020 †20

TOLAT, Parag Pradip. ■ 53213 #030-06-2004 L2005 **DR** *012

TOLEDO, Jose O. 8430 W CAPITOL DR STE 2 53222 #748-08-1985 L1994 **IM** *020 †20

TOMASIAN, Ardases. 8701 W WATERTOWN PLANK RD, MEDICAL COLLEGE OF WISCONS 53226 #781-01-1993 L2001 **PFP** *075

TOMBAK, Henrietta Natalia. ■ 53221 #913-03-1959 L1991 **P** *071

TOMBULOGLU, Lutfi. 1425 S 60TH ST 53214 #902-10-1957 L1970 **EM PD** *020

TOMES, Lana Lisa. 8701 W WATERTOWN PLANK RD 53226 #056-06-2001 L2003 **EM** *020

TOMIC, Rade. ■ 53202 #957-01-1989 L2004 **PCC** *020 †20

TOMPA, David. 133 N JACKSON ST, APT 432 53202 #028-79-2006, ▲ **AN** *012

TONKOVIC-CAPIN, Mislav. 10000 W BLUEMOUND RD 53226 #957-01-1987 L1993 **AN CCM** *020 †05

TOOHILL, Robert James. 9200 W WISCONSIN AVE 53226 #056-06-1960 L1967 **OTO** *072 †45

TOPETZES, Gregory John. 6200 W BLUEMOUND RD 53213 #056-06-1961 L1965 **IM OS** *071

TORANIA, Salim A. 945 N 12TH ST 53233 #704-02-1988 L1998 **ID IM** *020 †20

TORBEY, Michel Toni. 9200 W WISCONSIN AVE, MEDICAL CLGE OF WISC 53226 #605-01-1993 L2003 **N** *020 †75

TORRE, Dario. 9200 W WISCONSIN AVE 53226 #561-17-1990 L2002 **IM** *020 †20

TOTEMCHOKCHYAKARN, Piya. ■ 53220 #891-02-1986 *100

TOTH, Heather Louise. 9000 W WISCONSIN AVE, AVE MS214A 53226 #056-05-2001 L2002 **MPD** *020 †20,55

TOTODOVA, Zinoviya. 3970 N OAKLAND AVE, FL 2 53211 #913-08-1972 L2003 **IM** *020 †20 ‡

TOUZIOS, John George. 9200 W WISCONSIN AVE 53226 #016-06-2001 L2003 **GS** *012

TOWER, Kara. 8701 W WATERTOWN PLANK RD, MED COLL OF WI HOSP 53226 #005-76-2006, ▲ **N** *012

TOWER, Richard Lynn, II. 8701 W WATERTOWN PLANK RD 53226 #056-05-2001 L2007 **PHO** *100 †55

TOWNE, Jonathon Baker. 9200 W WISCONSIN AVE 53226 #035-45-1967 L1975 **VS** *020 †85

TOWNSEND, Wm Frederick. ZABLOCKI VA MED CTR 53295 #005-11-1972 L1973 **IM GE** *020 †20

TRAEGER, Kelly Ann. ■ 53202 #056-05-2007 **PD** *012

TRAN, Khoi Quang. 9200 W WISCONSIN AVE, DEPARTMENT OF SURGERY 53226 #005-19-1999 L2003 **GS** *012

TRAN, Sonya Myhien. 9200 W WISCONSIN AVE, DEPARTMENT OF OBSTETRICS A 53226 #030-06-2005 L2007 **OBG** *012

TRAN, Tony Khanh. ■ 53211 #016-42-2006 L2008 **IM** *012

TRAPANE, Pamela L Smith. 9000 W WISCONSIN AVE, MS 716 53226 #048-13-1996 L2005 **MG PD** *020 †19,55

TRAVIS, Natasha Annora. 840 N 87TH ST 53226 #016-01-2002 L2003 **IM** *020 †20

TRAXLER, John Saml. ■ 53211 #056-06-1989 L1991 **NM** *020 †28

TREBIAN, Kathleen. 2524 E WEBSTER PL, # 303 53211 #056-06-1990 L1992 **OBG** *020 †30 ‡

TRIBBLE, Jennifer Ellen. 4601 N OAKLAND AVE 53211 #026-04-1992 L1996 **RNR** *020 †80

TRINKL, Steven Robt. 2901 W KINNICKINC RVR PKWY, STE 102 53215 #056-06-1989 L1990 **ORS** *020 †40

TRIPP, Patrick M. 5000 W NATIONAL AVE, DEPT OF RAD ONCOLOGY 53295 #048-14-2000 L2005 **RO** *100 †80

TRIVEDI, Chinmaya Bharat. 2025 E NEWPORT AVE, COLUMBIA ST. MARY'S HOSP M 53211 #056-06-1998 L2004 **IM** *020 †20

TRIVEDI, Hariprasad S. 2901 W KK RIVER PKWY, STE 414 53215 #495-01-1984 L2004 **IM NEP** *020 †20

TRIYAMBAKA RAJ, C. 2311 N PROSPECT AVE, STE 401 53211 #495-33-1969 L1975 **IM** *020 †20

TROIANO, Philip F, III. 945 N 12TH ST, MEDICAL CENTER 53233 #056-05-1980 L1981 **EM** *020 †16

TROJAN, Joseph Gerard. 2500 W LAYTON AVE, STE 10 53221 #056-05-1983 L1984 **IM** *020 †20

TROSHYNSKI, Todd Jos. 9000 W WISCONSIN AVE, CHILDREN'S HOSPITAL OF WIS 53226 #030-05-1986 L1987 **AN** *020 †05,55

TROST, Beth Ann. 9200 W WISCONSIN AVE, MDCL CLLGE CLNCS AT FRDTRT 53226 #056-05-1990 L1995 **PTH** *020 †50

TROTMAN, Enid Althea. 2311 N PROSPECT AVE, STE 401 53211 #056-06-1985 L1988 **IM** *020

TROUTMAN, Roy M. 9455 W WATERTOWN PLANK RD, MILWAUKEE COUNTY MENTAL HE 53226 #056-06-1979 L1983 **P** *020

TROY, Benjamin Louis. 8701 W WATERTOWN PLANK RD, DEPARTMENT OF PSYCHIATRY 53226 #025-01-2002 L2004 **CHP** *012

TRUONG, Trinh Gia. 2015 E NEWPORT AVE, STE 302 53211 #005-19-1991 L1995 **PM** *020 †60

TRUPPE, Robert E, II. 945 N 12TH ST 53233 #056-06-1988 L1989 **EM** *020 †18

TRZPUC, Trent Damian. 9200 W WISCONSIN AVE, DEPT OF PATHOLOGY 53226 #037-01-2000 L2002 **PTH** *020 †50

TSAO, Carol Iping. 5000 W NATIONAL AVE, ZABLOCKI VA MEDICA CTR 53295 #016-11-1989 L1990 **P** *020 †75

TSAO, Elaine Ya-Wei. ■ 53213 #056-06-2008 *012

TSCHOPP, Michele Renee. 3289 N MAYFAIR RD, MAYFAIR ROAD CLINIC 53222 #056-05-1991 L1993 **IM** *020 †20

TSENG, Jeffrey. ■ 53204 #056-06-2003 L2004 **OTO** *012

TSOULFAS, Kostandinos C. ■ 53221 #063-01-2002 L2006 **FM** *100

TSUJI, Miles Kei. 3070 N 51ST ST # P309 53210 #005-02-1986 L1995 **NPM PD** *020 †55

TUCHMAN, Herman. 5150 N PORT WASHINGTON RD 53217 #056-05-1951 L1952 **CD IM** *071 †20

TUCKER, Alex Surba. 210 W CAPITOL DR 53212 #056-05-1975 L1977 **FM EM** *020 †18

TUCKER, Erskine Ramsey. 3237 S 16TH ST 53215 #047-07-1963 L1964 **PTH** *071 †50

■ = Address Information Privacy Protected

TUCKER, John Frederick. 2900 W OKLAHOMA AVE, ST.LUKES HOSPITAL 53215 #016-01-1979 L1980 **EM ETX** *020 †16

TUCKER, Kevin Peyton. ■ 53213 #056-06-2006 L2008 **IM** *012

TULLY, Madelaine Therese. 5818 W CAPITOL DR, MIDTOWN HEALTH CENTER 53216 #056-05-2000 L2001 **FM** *020 †18

TUMMALA, Aruna Kumari. 1155 N MAYFAIR RD, DEPARTMENT OF PSYCHIATRY 53226 #495-72-2001 L2005 **P** *012

TUMPACH, Elizabeth Anne. 9000 W WISCONSIN AVE, EMERGENCY DEPARTMENT 53226 #056-06-2005 L2006 **EM** *012

TUMULURI, Ramagopal J. 2801 W KK RIVER PKWY # 777 53215 #495-22-1989 L1997 **CD** *020 †20

TURA, Ismael Haji. 3000 W MONTANA ST 53215 #366-02-1996 **IM** *012

TURECKI, Marcin B. 2900 W OKLAHOMA AVE, DEPT OF RADIOLOGY 53215 #759-11-1995 L2003 **DR** *012

TURKAL, Nick W. 3000 W MONTANA ST, AURORA HEALTH CARE 53215 #030-06-1982 L1983 **FM** *030 †18

TURNER, Arthur James. 2801 W KINNICKINIC RVR PKWY, STE 135 53215 #035-19-1961 L1968 **N** *020 †75

TURNER, Diana Lynn. 945 N 12TH ST 53233 #056-06-2002 L2005 **IM** *020

TURNER, Lawrence Alan. 9200 W WISCONSIN AVE, FROEDTERT MEMORIAL LUTH HO 53226 #016-42-1971 L1974 **AN** *020 †05

TURNER, Todd Delance. ■ 53216 #056-06-2008 *012

TUTTON, Sean Merrill. 9200 W WISCONSIN AVE, MEDICAL COLLEGE OF WISCONS 53226 #033-05-1991 L2005 **VIR** *020 †80

TWEDDELL, James Scott. 9000 W WISCONSIN AVE, MS715 53226 #038-41-1985 L1993 **TS** *020 †85,90

TWENTE, Brett Elliot. 2015 E NEWPORT AVE, MEDICAL CLINIC 53211 #056-05-2002 L2007 **IM** *020 †20

TWENTE, Jennifer Lee. 2524 E WEBSTER PL, STE 301 53211 #056-05-2001 L2007 **PD** *020 †55

TYNE, Lee Martin. 7220 W NATIONAL AVE 53214 #056-05-1967 L1971 **ORS HS** *020 †40

UBELL, Matthew Lee. 9200 W WISCONSIN AVE, DEPARTMENT OF OTOLARYNGOLO 53226 #025-01-2001 L2004 **OTO** *020

UBEROI-NANGIA, Rupika. 8675 N PORT WASHINGTON RD, STE 120 53217 #495-20-1993 L1996 **IM** *020 †20

UGOLINI, Corrado. 3237 S 16TH ST, WHEATON FRANCISCAN MEDICAL 53215 #016-11-1986 L2007 **IM OM** *020 †20

UHERICK, Lisa Ann. 9000 W WISCONSIN AVE, CHILDRENS HOSPITAL OF WI 53226 #056-06-2001 L2004 **PEM** *100 †55

UHING, Michael Roman. 8701 W WATERTOWN PLANK RD, MEDICAL COLLEGE OF WISCONS 53226 #018-03-1986 L2002 **NPM** *020 †55

UIHLEIN, Michael Joseph. 2900 W OKLAHOMA AVE, ERMED 53215 #056-06-2000 L2002 **EM** *020 †16

ULITSKY, Alex. ■ 53226 #016-11-2003 L2007 **GE** *012 †20

ULMER, John Lipscomb. 9200 W WISCONSIN AVE, FROEDTERT HOSPITAL 53226 #020-12-1988 L1995 **DR** *020 †80

ULRICH, Steven Slack. ■ 53217 #056-06-1977 L1979 **P N** *020

UMEONYIDO, Chigolum Chidi. ■ 53226 #690-04-2000 **N** *012

UNNI, Chandra Sheila. ■ 53202 #495-36-1964 L1983 **P CHP** *020 †75

URBAN, John Thomas. 10000 W BLUEMOUND RD 53226 #056-06-1994 L1995 **AN** *020 †05

URBAN, Michael Joseph. 2900 W OKLAHOMA AVE, ERMED, SC - ST LUKES MED C 53215 #016-43-1995 L1997 **EM** *020 †16

URUETA MAZZILLI, Hedy. ■ 53221 #264-04-1999 L2006 **FM** *020

USATINSKY, Julia Michelle. 3000 W MONTANA ST, AURORA HLTH CARE 53215 #913-36-1997 L2003 **IM** *020 †20

USOW, Barry Howard. 2801 W KINNICKINNIC PKWY, STE 370 53215 #056-05-1969 L1970 **U** *020 †95

UY, Mario Lim. ■ 53209 #748-01-1956 L1968 **OBG** *071

UY, Teresa Marie. ■ 53208 #056-05-2002 L2004 **PHO** *012

UYAR, Denise Sevim. 9200 W WISCONSIN AVE 53226 #050-02-1997 L2004 **OBG** *020

UZQUIANO, Jorge. 3201 S 16TH ST, SOUTH CENTER MEDICAL 53215 #176-01-1965 L1975 **IM** *020 †20

VAISHNAVI, Kuruvalli. 9200 W WISCONSIN AVE 53226 #495-72-2001 L2005 **SCI** *012

VALENCIA VELEZ, Maria Del. ■ 53214 #264-16-2000 **RNR** *012

VALERI, Andrea Diane. 8701 W WATERTOWN PLANK RD, MCW DEPT OF OB/GYN 53226 #030-06-2004 L2006 **OBG** *012

VANBLARCOM, Stephen T. 201 N MAYFAIR RD 53226 #056-05-1986 L1987 **DR** *020 †80

VANDENBERGH, Teresa Ellen. ■ 53210 #025-07-2007 **PD** *012

VANDROVEC, Chad Matthew. 8701 W WATERTOWN PLANK RD, MEDICAL COLLEGE OF WISCONS 53226 #037-01-2002 L2003 **PAN** *100

VAN HEEST, James Allen. 6200 W BLUEMOUND RD 53213 #016-42-1973 L1974 **GS VS** *020 †85

VAN HEUKELOM, Jon Norman. 9200 W WISCONSIN AVE 53226 #018-03-2006 L2008 **EM** *012

VANHOOF, Jody Alice. ■ 53202 #056-06-2008 *012

VAN LIERE, Timothy John. 5007 S HOWELL AVE 53207 #056-06-1979 L1980 **FM EM** *020 †18

VAN NOSTRAND, Allan F. 945 N 12TH ST 53233 #020-12-1978 L1982 **DR** *020 †80

VAN ROO, Jane E. ■ 53213 #056-06-1994 L1995 **EM** *020 †16

VAN SANTEN, Lenore. 2801 W KINNICKINC RVR PKWY, STE 135 53215 #026-04-1973 L1975 **IM** *020 †20

VAN VALIN, Scott Erwin. 2424 S 90TH ST, STE 418 53227 #056-06-1993 L1995 **ORS** *020 †40

VAN VALKENBURGH, Ilva. 8200 W SILVER SPRING DR, MILWAUKEE HEALTH SERVICES, 53218 #913-16-1992 L1996 **P** *020 †75

VAN WHY, Scott Keith. 8701 W WATERTOWN PLANK RD, MEDICAL COLLEGE OF WISCONS 53226 #018-03-1986 L1987 **PN** *020 †20

VARADARAJAN, Jaya L. 8701 W WATERTOWN PLANK RD, ANESTHESIOLOGY 53226 #496-39-1988 L2001 **PAN** *100 †05

VARADARAJAN, Srinivasan. 8701 W WATERTOWN PLANK RD, MEB 4280 ANES 53226 #495-16-1979 L1984 **AN** *020 †05

VARANASI, Jyothi Priya. ■ 53214 #016-45-2007 **IM** *012

VARGHESE, Reny. 9255 N 76TH ST 53223 #495-99-1998 L2005 **IMG** *020

VARKEY, Basil. 9200 W WISCONSIN AVE, PULM & CRIT DIV STE E5200 53226 #495-31-1964 L1976 **PUD CCM** *020 †20

VARMA, Rajiv Ranjan. 9200 W WISCONSIN AVE 53226 #495-36-1963 L1976 **GE IM** *020

VARSEGI, George Michael. 8701 W WATERTOWN PLANK RD 53226 #665-02-2004 L2005 **PTH** *012

VASUDEV, Monica. 9200 W WISCONSIN AVE, DIV OF ALLE & IMM STE 411 53226 #496-21-2002 L2005 **AI** *012 †20

VATANDOUST, Gita. 5000 W CHAMBERS ST 53210 #517-01-1997 L2004 **IM** *020 †20

VATTAKATTCHERRY, Omana G. 2040 W WISCONSIN AVE, APT 466 53233 #495-80-1971 L1976 **PM** *020 †60

VAUGHN, Ericka Carter. 5408 W BURLEIGH ST 53210 #056-06-1999 L2001 **OBG** *020 †30

VAZQUEZ, Luis. 8200 W SILVER SPRING DR, HEALTH CENTER 53218 #042-01-1999 L2003 **P** *020 †75

VAZQUEZ, Victor M. 1032 S 16TH ST STE 2 53204 #042-01-1998 L2004 **CHP P** *020

VEDDER, Lisa Sullivan. 1020 N 12TH ST, FL 2 53233 #028-46-2000 L2002 **FM** *020 †18

VEERAMACHANENI, Jyothi. 2400 W VILLARD AVE 53209 #495-99-2002 L2007 **FP** *012

VELAGAPUDI, Satish. 3000 W MONTANA ST 53215 #495-21-2002 **IM** *012

VELLINGA, Timothy. 2801 W KINNICKINC RVR PKWY, STE 425 53215 #018-03-1982 L1983 **CD IM** *020 †20

VENKATAPURAM, Suneetha. 9200 W WISCONSIN AVE, STE 51 53226 #495-70-1998 L2006 **CD** *012 †20

VENKATASUBRAMANI, Narayana. 8701 W WATERTOWN PLANK RD, MAIL STOP 756 53226 #495-04-1995 L2005 **PG** *012

VENKATESAN, Thangam. 8701 W WATERTOWN PLANK RD, MEDICAL COLLEGE OF WISCONS 53226 #495-59-1992 L2004 **GE** *012

VENTRAPRAGADA, Sailaja Ve. 945 N 12TH ST 53233 #495-50-2000 L2007 **IM** *012

VENU, Mukund. ■ 53202 #028-34-2007 **IM** *012

VERBSKY, James. 8701 W WATERTOWN PLANK RD, OF WISCONSIN 53226 #028-02-2000 L2005 **PPR** *100 †55

VERNON, Matthew Raymond. ■ 53213 #056-06-2008 *012

VETTER, Carole S. 9200 W WISCONSIN AVE 53226 #056-06-1993 L1994 **OSM** *020 †40

VEYTSMAN, Anna-Maria. 9200 W WISCONSIN AVE, MDCL CLLGE CLNCS AT FRDTRT 53226 #056-06-1985 L1986 **AN** *020 †05

VICE, Jessica Lynn. ■ 53222 #056-05-2007 **PD** *012

VIDYARANYA, Ajjampur R. 2901 W KINNICKINC RVR PKWY, STE 405 53215 #495-33-1983 L1995 **IM** *020 †20

VIEL, Robert Sprague. 5000 W CHAMBERS ST 53210 #056-06-1964 L1965 **FM FPG** *020

VIJAYABHANU, Kalluru. 5228 W FOND DU LAC AVE 53216 #495-70-1989 L1995 **IM** *020 †20

VIJAYAKUMAR, Anita. 1155 N MAYFAIR RD, TOSA CENTER, 3RD FLOOR 53226 #026-11-2004 L2007 **P** *012

VIJAYAPAL, Aravind S. 9200 W WISCONSIN AVE 53226 #056-06-2001 L2003 **GE** *012

VILLADONIGA, Graciela B. 1032 S 16TH ST, 16TH STREET COMMUNITY HEAL 53204 #924-01-1994 L2001 **PD** *020 †20

VILLANUEVA, Alvin Puno. 2025 W OKLAHOMA AVE, STE 122 53215 #748-02-1995 L2001 **IMG** *020 †20

VILLWOCK, Jeffrey Scott. 950 N 12TH ST 53233 #035-09-1992 L1994 **EM IM** *020 †20

VINLUAN, Alejandro M. 756 N 35TH ST STE 201 53208 #748-01-1955 L1962 **GS FM** *020

VINLUAN, Jeremias B, Jr. 756 N 35TH ST, STE 204 53208 #748-01-1969 L1975 **GP GS** *020

VIPOND, Jennifer Hoppe. 9000 W WISCONSIN AVE 53226 #056-05-1988 L1991 **PD** *020 †55

VIRDI, Amarjit Singh. 8701 W WATERTOWN PLANK RD 53226 #495-79-2000 L2006 **AN** *012

VISAMA, Maria Fe Q. 1218 W KILBOURN AVE, SETHI MEDICAL SERVICES 53233 #748-02-1993 L2000 **PD** *020 †55

VISAYA, Marciano Cadiz. 2025 W OKLAHOMA AVE, STE 126 53215 #748-01-1959 L1969 **GP** *071

VOLBERDING, James Paul. 788 N JEFFERSON ST STE 30 53202 #016-45-1982 L1983 **IM** *020 †20

VOLOSHIN, Emma. 2350 W VILLARD AVE, STE 210 53209 #913-21-1975 L1983 **FM** *020 †18

VOONG, David. ■ 53214 #056-06-2008 *012

VORA, Sheetal Suresh. 9000 W WISCONSIN AVE, RHEUMATOLOGY, C465 53226 #005-14-1998 L2005 **PPR** *012 †55

VOSS, Erika Marie. 8700 W WISCONSIN AVE, MEDICAL CLINICS AT FRDTRT 53226 #010-02-1956 L1976 **IM GP** *071

VUCINS, Eduards Janis. 8901 W LINCOLN AVE, CONSULTANTS AT WEST ALLIS 53227 #056-06-1979 L1980 **AN** *040 †05

WACKYM, Phillip Ashley. 9200 W WISCONSIN AVE, DEPT OTOLARYNGOLOGY 53226 #047-05-1985 L1998 **NO OTO** *020 †45

WADE, James Clive. 9200 W WISCONSIN AVE, # 63A 53226 #049-01-1974 L2002 **IM ID** *020 †20

WAGHRAY, Rakesh. 3267 S 16TH ST, STE 103 53215 #495-50-1987 L1998 **CCM** *020 †20

WAGNER, Marvin. 5150 N PORT WASHINGTON RD, STE 151 53217 #056-06-1944 L1945 **GS VS** *020 †85 ‡

WAHEED, Rubina. 2400 W VILLARD AVE 53209 #704-02-1991 L1999 **P** *020 †75

WAHLBERG, Neil Evan. 2015 E NEWPORT AVE # M118 53211 #035-03-1977 L1980 **IM** *020 †20

WAISBREN, Burton Armin. 3077 N MAYFAIR RD, STE 100 53222 #056-05-1946 L1951 **IM IG** *020 †20

WAISBREN, Charles Jay. 3077 N MAYFAIR RD 53222 #035-20-1980 L1983 **IM** *020 †20

WAKE, Linda. 8701 W WATERTOWN PLANK RD, DEPARTMENT OF PSYCHIATRY 53226 #041-09-1988 L2004 **GP BBK** *020

WALBRANDT, Melissa Ann. 4301 W BROWN DEER RD 53223 #056-06-1997 L1998 **FM** *020 †18

WALCOTT, George. 2015 E NEWPORT AVE, STE 208 53211 #024-05-1962 L1968 **IM CD** *020 †20

WALDECK, Edward Wm. 2900 W OKLAHOMA AVE 53215 #056-06-1965 L1969 **OPH** *030 †35

WALIUDDIN, Syed. ■ 53221 #495-65-1996 L2007 **CHP** *100

WALKER, Alonzo Patrick. 9200 W WISCONSIN AVE 53226 #011-03-1976 L1983 **GS SO** *020 †85

WALKER, Tarik Dobbs. ■ 53226 #023-07-1999 **PD IM** *100

WALKIEWICZ, Dorota. 8701 W WATERTOWN PLANK RD 53226 #759-03-1989 **PG** *100

WALKIEWICZ-JEDRZEJCZAK, D. 8701 W WATERTOWN PLANK RD 53226 #759-03-1989 L1999 **PD** *012

WALLACE, Brian Ken. 2801 W KINNICKINC RVR PKWY, STE 250 53215 #056-05-1984 L1985 **FM** *020 †18

WALLACE, James Robt. 9200 W WISCONSIN AVE 53226 #025-07-1980 L1992 **GS** *020 †85

WALLACE, Timothy Michael. 2900 W OKLAHOMA AVE 53215 #012-01-1993 L1999 **PTH** *020 †50

WALLACH, Jeffrey Donn. 2901 W KINNICKINC RVR PKWY, STE 405 53215 #041-01-1975 L1980 **NEP IM** *020 †20

WALLSKOG, Joel Anthony. 2901 W KINNICKINC RVR PKWY, STE 102 53215 #056-05-1996 L1997 **ORS** *020

WALSH, Christopher John. 2600 N MAYFAIR RD 53226 #010-02-1994 L2000 **U** *020 †95

WALSH, John Patrick. 2600 N MAYFAIR RD STE 545 53226 #056-06-1967 L1972 **U** *020 †95

WALSH, Patrick Robt. 9200 W WISCONSIN AVE, DEPT NEUROSURGERY 53226 #056-06-1973 L1974 **NS** *020 †25

WALTER, Frank Lynn. 9200 W WISCONSIN AVE 53226 #056-06-2001 L2005 **HS** *020

WALTER, Kevin. 9000 W WISCONSIN AVE, PEDS ORTH STE C360 53226 #016-11-1998 L1999 **PD PSM** *020 †55

WALTERS, Michael Shane. ■ 53223 #039-01-2003 L2006 **DR** *012
WANG, Dian. 8701 W WATERTOWN PLANK RD, MEDICAL COLLEGE OF WISCONS 53226 #243-52-1984 L2002 **RO** *020 †80
WANG, Marjorie Carol. 9200 W WISCONSIN AVE, DEPT. OF NEUROSURGERY 53226 #016-43-1996 L2005 **NS** *020 †25
WANG, Richard I-Hsiang. 4608 W BURLEIGH ST 53210 #016-06-1955 L1964 **PA ADM** *071
WANG, Ronggang. 10000 W BLUEMOUND RD 53226 #243-67-1985 L2000 **AN** *020 †05 ‡
WANG, Shihtien. 8701 W WATERTOWN PLANK RD, MED COLL OF WI 53226 #016-06-2007 **PD** *012
WANG, Tracy Szemay. ■ 53202 #035-46-2000 L2001 **GS** *100 †85
WANN, Lee Saml. 9200 W WISCONSIN AVE, CARDIOVASCULAR MEDICINE CL 53226 #017-20-1971 L1979 **CD IM** *020 †20
WAPLES, Mark James. 2801 W KK RIVER PKWY STE 3, CLINIC OF UROLOGY SC 53215 #038-06-1989 L1990 **U** *020 †95
WARD, Kimberlie Ann. 2500 W SILVER SPRING DR, GLENDALE PEDIATRICS 53209 #056-06-1996 L1999 **PD** *020 †55
WARD, Linda Margaret. 3056 S KINNICKINNIC AVE 53207 #056-06-1995 L1996 **FM** *020 †18
WARING, William Patrick. 9200 W WISCONSIN AVE, FROEDTERT HOSPITAL 53226 #026-04-1978 L1998 **PM** *050 †60
WARLTIER, David C. 9200 W WISCONSIN AVE, FROEDTERT HOSPITAL 53226 #056-06-1982 L1986 **AN CD** *030 †05
WARNER, Jeffrey Louis. 1126 S 70TH ST, STE S306 53214 #056-05-1983 L1984 **IM** *020 †20
WARWICK, Anne Benedicta. 8701 W WATERTOWN PLANK RD, DEPT OF PED-MED COL OF WI 53226 #026-04-1985 L1996 **PHO OBG** *020 †55 ‡
WASHINGTON, Janie Marie. 1575 N RIVERCENTER DR 53212 #056-05-1983 L1984 **OBG** *020 †30
WASHINGTON, Lacey. 9200 W WISCONSIN AVE 53226 #041-01-1993 L2000 **DR** *020 †80
WASILOWSKI, Kristen Miche. 8701 W WATERTOWN PLANK RD, MED COLL OF WI 53226 #030-06-2007 **PD** *012
WASSERMAN, Sheldon Allan. 10950 W CAPITOL DR 53222 #056-06-1987 L1988 **OBG** *020 †30
WATERS, David Allen. 1032 S CESAR E CHAVEZ DR 53204 #056-06-1983 L1987 **PD** *020 †55
WATERS, Richard Daniel. 5000 W CHAMBERS ST 53210 #016-42-2003 L2006 **DR** *012
WATSON, John Davis. 950 N 12TH ST 53233 #026-04-1963 L1966 **OBG** *071 †30
WATSON, Karen Sue. 1620 E CAPITOL DR, P O BOX 11565 53211 #056-05-1991 L1994 **OBG** *020 †30
WATT, John E. 2311 N PROSPECT AVE, CSMCP PROSPECT MEDICAL COM 53211 #019-02-1962 L1992 **END IM** *020
WATTERS, Shelley Kaye. 10400 W NORTH AVE 2ND FL, ALLERGY ASSOCIATES 53226 #056-06-1990 L1991 **AI IM** *020 †20 ‡
WATTS, Christopher Jamarl. 104 E MASON ST, UNIT 606 53202 #045-01-2003 L2006 **ID** *012 †20
WEAN, John David. 1220 DEWEY AVE 53218 #056-05-1983 L1984 **P** *020 †75
WEBB, Cristal Chanel. ■ 53227 #056-06-2008 *012
WEBB, Julie Ann. 2311 N PROSPECT AVE, CSMCP PROSPECT MEDICAL COM 53211 #056-06-1992 L1993 **OBG** *020 †30
WEBB, Travis Paul. 9200 W WISCONSIN AVE, MEDICAL COLLEGE OF WISCONS 53226 #016-45-1999 L2000 **GS** *100 †85
WEBER, Craig Allan. ■ 53202 #056-06-2006 **AN** *012
WECSLER, Petre Iosif. 7019 N BARNETT LN, SEMIRETIRED,DOING TEMPORAR 53217 #781-01-1961 L1987 **DR NM** *020 †80
WEEKES, Richard Gene. 945 N 12TH ST 53233 #056-06-1982 L1988 **DR** *020 †80
WEGNER, Karen Marie. 2500 N MAYFAIR RD 53226 #056-06-1994 L1995 **PD** *020 †55
WEIDMAN, Kevin Addington. 625 E SAINT PAUL AVE 53202 #026-08-1979 L1994 **HS ORS** *020 †40
WEIGELT, John August. 9200 W WISCONSIN AVE, DEPT OF SURGERY 53226 #056-06-1974 L1992 **GS CCS** *040 †85
WEIGLE, Carl George M. 9000 W WISCONSIN AVE 53226 #035-03-1976 L1990 **CCP PD** *020 †55
WEILER, Michael Benjamin. 2900 W OKLAHOMA AVE, STE G8370 53215 #056-06-1994 L1995 **IM** *020 †20
WEINBERG, David Val. 925 N 87TH ST 53226 #016-11-1985 L2005 **OPH** *020 †35
WEINBERG, Matthew Nathan. 8701 W WATERTOWN PLANK RD, MED COLL OF WI 53226 #016-01-2004 L2007 **CD** *012 †20
WEINDLING, Howard Keith. 3237 S 16TH ST 53215 #025-01-1966 L1974 **PTH** *020 †50
WEINER, H Richard. ■ 53202 #048-02-1986 L1988 **IM EM** *020 †20
WEINER, Joel Scott. 720 E WISCONSIN AVE –E14B 53202 #016-01-1993 L1999 **IM** *030 †20
WEINGARTEN, Maxwell H S. 3237 S 16TH ST 53215 #065-01-1945 L1958 **AN PHP** *071 †05
WEIRICH, Richard Thos. 3305 S 20TH ST, LAKESHORE MEDICAL CLINIC 53215 #026-04-1990 L1998 **END IM** *020 †20
WEIS, Sarah Anne. 8701 W WATERTOWN PLANK RD, DEPT OBG 53226 #056-06-2007 **OBG** *012
WEISGERBER, Michael Carl. 8701 W WATERTOWN PLANK RD, MACC FUND RESEARCH BUILDIN 53226 #056-06-1999 L2002 **PD** *020 †55
WEISMAN, Paul Stuart. 3003 W GOOD HOPE RD, AURORA ADVANCED HEALTHCARE 53209 #028-02-1986 L1992 **CD** *020 †20
WEISMAN, Steven J. 9000 W WISCONSIN AVE, MS 792 53226 #035-46-1978 L1998 **AN PD** *020 †55,05
WEISS, Aaron Myer. ■ 53208 #049-01-2004 L2008 **PD** *012
WEISS, Ann Marie. ■ 53208 #049-01-2006 L2008 **EM** *012
WEISS, Jonathan Wade. 9200 W WISCONSIN AVE, WISC-FROEDTERT HOS 53226 #017-20-2003 L2004 **DR** *020
WEISSMAN, David Edward. 9200 W WISCONSIN AVE, FROEDTERT HOSP 53226 #005-18-1980 L1986 **PLM** *020 †20
WEISTROP, Leonard. 3003 W GOOD HOPE RD, HOPE ROAD CLINIC 53209 #055-01-1969 L1971 **IM** *020 †20
WELLS, Robert George. 8522 W CAPITOL DR, PEDIATRIC DIAGNOSTIC 53222 #056-06-1980 L1981 **DR** *020 †80
WELLS, Ronald Kenneth. 9000 W WISCONSIN AVE 53226 #016-06-1956 L1957 **PD** *071 †55
WELLS, Timothy Scott. 925 N 87TH ST 53226 #017-20-1999 L2003 **OPH** *100 †35
WELLS-HOLTEY, Heather M. 788 N JEFFERSON ST STE 300, MADISON MEDICDAL AFFILIATE 53202 #056-05-1998 L1999 **D** *020 †15
WELSCHER, Kathleen Ellen. ■ 53214 #056-06-2008 *012
WENDERS, James Anthony. 6200 W BLUEMOUND RD 53213 #056-06-1959 L1960 **PD** *020 †55
WENGELEWSKI, Henry Bruno. 5757 W OKLAHOMA AVE, HENRY B WENGELEWSKI MD SC 53219 #016-43-1954 L1957 **GS** *071 †85
WENZEL, Michael Peter. 500 W BROWN DEER RD SU, WISCONSIN RADIOLOGY SPECIA 53217 #056-06-1998 L1999 **DR** *020 †80

WERMUTH, Douglas John. 8430 W CAPITOL DR 53222 #056-06-1984 L1989 **OTO HNS** *020 †45
WERNER, Paul Herbert. 2901 W KINNICKINC RVR PKWY, STE 310 53215 #016-01-1975 L1976 **TS** *020 †85,90
WERTSCH, Jacqueline J. 5000 W NATIONAL AVE # 117D, ZABLOCKI VA MED CTR 53295 #041-07-1974 L1980 **PM N** *020 †60
WESKE, Paul Robert. 2323 N LAKE DR, METROPOLITAN ANESTHESIOLOG 53211 #056-05-2001 L2002 **AN** *020 †05
WESSON, Jeffrey Alan. 9200 W WISCONSIN AVE, DEPT OF MEDICINE/NEPHROLOG 53226 #056-06-1994 L1995 **NEP IM** *020 †20
WEST, Matthew Paul. ■ 53210 #030-06-2005 L2006 **PM** *012
WEST, Pamela Hesse. 2500 N MAYFAIR RD 53226 #030-05-1999 L2000 **PD** *020 †55
WESTLEY, William, Jr. 2727 W CLEVELAND AVE 53215 #056-05-1960 L1961 **PD** *020 †55
WETHERBEE, Jule Elizabeth. 2025 W OKLAHOMA AVE, STE 102 53215 #028-34-1980 L1981 **CD IM** *020 †20
WETZLER, Robert Jos. 208A E CAPITOL DR, RIVERWEST CLINIC 53212 #056-06-1968 L1969 **OBG** *020
WHALEN, John Patrick. 2025 E NEWPORT AVE, WISCONSIN RADIOLOGY 53211 #016-11-1976 L1977 **NM** *020 †20
WHEELER, Amanda Leigh. ■ 53204 #016-45-2007 **GS** *012
WHELAN, Harry Thos. 9000 W WISCONSIN AVE 53226 #056-05-1979 L1987 **CHN** *020 †75
WHITCOMB, John Elmer. 2900 W OKLAHOMA AVE 53215 #008-01-1977 L1983 **EM** *030 †20,16
WHITE, Gilbert Case, II. PO BOX 2178, 8727 WATERTOWN PLANK RD 53201 #036-01-1971 L2005 **HEM IM** *050 †20
WHITE, Julia Rose. 9200 W WISCONSIN AVE 53226 #025-12-1988 L1993 **U** *020 †80
WHITEHEAD, John Joseph. 925 N 87TH ST, THE EYE INSTITUTE 53226 #003-01-2004 L2006 **OPH** *012
WHITEHOUSE, Jill Suzanne. 9200 W WISCONSIN AVE, DEPT OF SURGERY 53226 #025-07-2005 L2007 **GS** *012
WHITEHURST, James Howell. 5015 W BURLEIGH ST, WHEATON FRANCISCAN 53210 #035-01-1984 L2007 **RO** *020,80
WHITNEY, Robert Theodore. 8901 W LINCOLN AVE, CONSULTANTS AT WEST ALLIS 53227 #056-05-1988 L1989 **AN** *020 †05
WHITTIER, Stephen Allen. ■ 53227 #036-08-1994 L1997 **IM** *075
WHITTLE, Donna Iles. 2801 W KINNICKINC RVR PKWY, STE 475 53215 #036-05-1986 L2005 **ID IM** *020 †20
WHITTLE, Jeffrey Clement. 5000 W NATIONAL AVE, MAIL STOP 00/PC 53295 #056-06-1984 L2005 **IM** *050 †20
WIDELL, Jeffrey L. 2900 W OKLAHOMA AVE, FL 1 53215 #048-12-1985 L1991 **CCM IM** *020 †20
WIDLANSKY, Michael Eric. 9200 W WISCONSIN AVE, FEC SUITE E5100 53226 #025-01-1999 L2001 **CD** *100 †20
WIEDMEYER, Debra Ann. 3237 S 16TH ST 53215 #056-06-1985 L1986 **R IM** *020 †80
WIGER, Krista Michelle. 1155 N MAYFAIR RD, STE A 53226 #026-04-2000 L2002 **MPD** *020
WIGTON, Thomas Richard. 9200 W WISCONSIN AVE, DEPT OBG 53226 #038-43-1987 L1993 **MFM OBG** *020 †30
WILCOX, Mark Daniel. 8901 W LINCOLN AVE, CONSULTANTS AT WEST ALLIS 53227 #056-06-1989 L1992 **AN** *020 †05
WILKE, Russell Alan. 9200 W WISCONSIN AVE, DEPT OF MEDICINE FEC E4194 53226 #056-06-1995 L1996 **IM** *020 †20
WILKINS, Terrence James. 2015 E NEWPORT AVE, SIUTE 401 53211 #056-06-1972 L1973 **PS** *020 †85,65
WILLEMS, William Jos. ■ 53214 #056-06-1970 L1971 **N CD** *075 †75
WILLEY, Sean T. 9200 W WISCONSIN AVE, MCW-PHYSICAL MED & REHAB 53226 #028-79-2004, ▲ L2006 **PM** *012
WILLIAMS, Aronica Vonice. 1121 E NORTH AVE 53212 #016-11-2005 L2007 **FP** *012
WILLIAMS, Linnea M. 300 W MONTANA ST 53215 #028-78-2005, ▲ L2006 **FP** *012
WILLIAMS, O'Rell Ronald. 7810 W GOOD HOPE RD, MINISTRY MEDICAL GROUP 53223 #056-05-2001 L2003 **IM** *020
WILLIS, Ernestine. 1020 N 12TH ST 53233 #024-01-1977 L1994 **PD PHP** *040
WILLOUGHBY, John Austin. 12313 W OKLAHOMA AVE # 34, 8701 WATERTOWN PLANK ROAD 53227 #018-03-1981 L2006 **P** *012 †18
WILLOUGHBY, Rodney E, Jr. 999 N 92ND ST, STE C450 53226 #023-07-1982 L2003 **PD** *050 †55
WILSON, Barbara Dahl. 9200 W WISCONSIN AVE 53226 #026-04-1981 L1992 **D** *020 †15
WILSON, Christopher S. 10400 W NORTH AVE STE 480 53226 #056-06-1992 L1998 **GS** *020 †85
WILSON, Donald James. ■ 53217 #056-06-1987 L1988 **AN** *020 †05
WILSON, J Frank. 8701 W WATERTOWN PLANK RD, DEPT OF RADATION ONCOLOGY 53226 #028-03-1965 L1974 **RO** *030 †80 ‡
WILSON, Jessica Ann. ■ 53223 #016-42-2006 **MPD** *012
WILSON, Pamela Denise. 2906 S 20TH ST 53215 #056-06-1999 L2000 **FM** *020 †18
WILSON, Stuart Dickinson. 9200 W WISCONSIN AVE, MEDICAL COLLEGE OF WISCONS 53226 #016-11-1960 L1961 **GS OS** *020 †85
WINCE, Tiffany Janelle. ■ 53202 #017-20-2005 L2007 **EM** *012
WINDSOR, Annamarie B. 3003 W GOOD HOPE RD, HOPE ROAD CLINIC 53209 #056-05-1990 L1991 **OBG** *020 †30
WINSTON, Evonne Marie. 2350 N LAKE DR, STE 301 53211 #016-01-1975 L1982 **D** *020 †20,15
WINSTON, James Barry. 9720 W BLUEMOUND RD 53226 #056-05-1981 L1984 **P** *020 †75
WINTHROP, Andrea L. 999 N 92ND ST C320, CHILDRENS HOSP OF WSICONSI 53226 #065-05-1981 L1997 **PDS** *020
WIROSTKO, William Joseph. 925 N 87TH ST, MEDICAL COLLEGE OF WISCONS 53226 #051-01-1994 L1996 **OPH** *020 †35
WITT, Anna Marie. 1121 E NORTH AVE 53212 #028-03-2006 L2008 **FP** *012
WITTE, Gerhard L. ■ 53211 #041-13-1964 L1975 **IM ID** *071 †20
WITTMAACK, Frank M. 8901 W LINCOLN AVE, WEST ALLIS MEMORIAL HOSPIT 53227 #409-21-1983 L1989 **OBG REN** *020 †30
WLODARSKI, John Charles. 8901 W LINCOLN AVE, CONSULTANTS AT WEST ALLIS 53227 #016-01-1991 L1995 **AN** *020 †05
WOEHLCK, Harvey Jay. 9200 W WISCONSIN AVE, DEPT OF ANESTHESIOLOGY 53226 #032-01-1985 L1986 **AN** *020 †05
WOHLFEIL, Eric Robt. 8701 W WATERTOWN PLANK RD 53226 #025-07-1989 L1993 **AN** *020 †05
WOLF, Catherine Elizabeth. 3070 N 51ST ST, STE 510 53210 #016-06-1978 L1979 **EM IM** *020 †20
WOLF, John Wm. 3070 N 51ST ST STE 309 53210 #056-06-1981 L1986 **NPM PD** *020 †55
WOLF, Lawrence Philip. ■ 53217 #056-06-1946 L1948 **CD OS** *071

WOLFE, Pamela Bliss. 9200 W WISCONSIN AVE, MDCL CLLGE CLNCS AT FRDTRT 53226 #056-05-1978 L1979 **P IM** *040 †20,75

WOLFE, Thomas Andrew. 8923 W BROWN DEER RD 53224 #017-20-1984 L1988 **FM OBS** *020 †18

WOLFE, Thomas James. 9200 W WISCONSIN AVE 53226 #056-06-2003 L2005 **N** *100

WOLFLA, Christopher E. 9200 W WISCONSIN AVE, DEPT. OF NEUROSURGERY 53226 #017-20-1991 L1996 **NS** *020 †25

WOLSKI, Le Roy Richard. ■ 53210 #056-06-1953 L1959 **OS** *075

WOLTER, Brian Roland. 400 W RIVER WOODS PKWY 53212 #056-06-2002 L2003 **FM** *020 †18

WOMACK, Seth Patrick. 9200 W WISCONSIN AVE, MCW EMERGENCY DEPARTMENT 53226 #021-06-2005 L2007 **EM** *012

WONG, Denise Linda. ■ 53226 #056-06-1993 *100

WONG, Eric Che. ■ 53226 #056-06-1994 *100

WONG, Kimberley Laura. ■ 53217 #056-06-2007 **IM** *012

WONG, Stuart John. 9200 W WISCONSIN AVE, NEO PLASTIC DISEASES RELAT 53226 #056-06-1990 L1992 **ON** *020 †20

WONG, Walter Khe Tian. 2424 S 90TH ST STE 202 53227 #748-02-1976 L1981 **N** *020 †75

WONPAT, Elizabeth Corrine. 2801 W KINNICKINC RVR PKWY, STE 175 53215 #104-01-2005 L2007 **FP** *012

WOO, Douglas Anthony. 9200 W WISCONSIN AVE, NEUROLOGY DEPARTMENT 53226 #056-06-2001 L2003 **N** *100 †75

WOO, Sung Kyun. 12129 W FEERICK ST 53222 #583-10-1967 L1975 **AN** *071 †05

WOOD, Earl Clinton. ■ 53226 #020-12-2006 L2007 **RO** *012

WOOD, James Platt. 7220 W NATIONAL AVE 53214 #025-01-1976 L1981 **ORS** *020 †40

WOODS, James Harley. 10400 W NORTH AVE STE 480 53226 #017-20-1968 L1969 **GS SO** *071 †85

WOODS, Timothy Danl. 9200 W WISCONSIN AVE 53226 #038-44-1992 L1995 **CD** *020 †20

WOODSON, B Tucker. 9200 W WISCONSIN AVE 53226 #028-03-1983 L1988 **OTO SME** *020 †45

WOOLF, Cameron J.. ■ 53222 #056-06-2008 *012

WOOSENCRAFT, David Michae. 9200 W WISCONSIN AVE, FROEDTERT EAST CLINICS 53226 #056-05-2005 L2007 **AN** *012

WOOTEN, Marvin Ray. 3003 W GOOD HOPE RD 53209 #017-20-1979 L1983 **N OS** *075

WORKMAN, Timothy L. 2025 E NEWPORT AVE, WISCONSIN RADIOLOGY 53211 #023-12-1987 L1999 **DR** *020 †80

WORM, George John. ■ 53226 #056-06-1940 L1940 **GP** *071

WORMAN, Daniel Jos. 9200 W WISCONSIN AVE, DEPT EM 53226 #056-06-1992 L1996 **EM** *020 †16

WORSENCROFT, Helen May. ■ 53217 #056-05-1956 L1958 **GYN OBG** *071 †30

WORTHINGTON, Dennis. 201 N MAYFAIR RD, FL 3 53226 #803-03-1966 L1980 **OBS** *020 †30

WREN, Julia Margaret. 9000 W WISCONSIN AVE, MEDICAL EDUCATION, POB 199 53226 #056-06-2004 L2005 **MPD** *012

WRIGHT, Carla Louise. 2555 N DR MRTN LTHR KNG DR, CENTER 53212 #025-01-1982 L1987 **PM** *020 †60

WRIGHT, Mark Thos. 8701 W WATERTOWN PLANK RD, MEDICAL COLLEGE OF WISCONS 53226 #001-02-1989 L2004 **P** *020 †75

WROBLEWSKI, Ronald John. 7635 W OKLAHOMA AVE, STE 109 53219 #041-09-1963 L1966 **GP** *075

WU, Hong. 9200 W WISCONSIN AVE, DEPT P M & R 53226 #243-52-1988 L2002 **PM** *100 †60

WU, Po-Hui Michael. ■ 53227 #056-06-2008 *012

WURSTER, Beverly J. 53211 #026-04-1956 L1957 **PHP PD** *071

WURSTER, Wallace Harvey. ■ 53211 #056-06-1956 L1957 **GP PD** *020

WYATT, David Thurman. 9000 W WISCONSIN AVE, CCC C520 53226 #048-12-1977 L1984 **END PD** *020 †55

WYLLIE, Tanritai. ■ 53213 #056-05-2008 *012

WYNN, Hillary D. 3200 W HIGHLAND BLVD 53208 #041-09-1994 L2004 **CHP** *020 †75

XIA, Chunzhi. 3000 W MONTANA ST 53215 #242-72-1992 **IM** *012

XIE, Liping. 3000 W MONTANA ST 53215 #243-43-1997 **IM** *012

YAHIAOUI, Hassiba. 2025 E NEWPORT AVE, COLUMBIA ST. MARY'S HOSPIT 53211 #125-01-1989 L2003 **FM** *020 †18

YAMAT, Jaime Bonifacio. 3305 S 20TH ST, STE 150 53215 #748-07-1964 L1975 **AN EM** *020

YAN, Lester. 6901 W EDGERTON AVE 53220 #030-06-1989 L1992 **FM** *020 †18

YANG, Pafoua Julliette. 535 N 27TH ST, NOUKEY CLINIC SC 53208 #056-05-1995 L1997 **OBG** *020 †18

YAO, Xin. 8701 W WATERTOWN PLANK RD, MED COL OF WI 53226 #243-36-1993 **HO** *012 †20

YARBOROUGH, Garland W. 3077 N MAYFAIR RD STE 100 53222 #036-05-1975 L1980 **GE IM** *020 †20

YATSO, Michael Gary. ■ 53213 #056-06-1953 L1954 **FM OBG** *071

YEE, Albert Shelman. 3237 S 16TH ST, ST FRANCES HOSP. 53215 #025-01-1976 L1982 **EM** *020 †16

YEE, Consuelo Aprecio. 4666 S 35TH ST 53221 #748-01-1964 L1978 **PD** *020 †55

YEH, Jeffrey. 8701 W WATERTOWN PLANK RD, MED COLL OF WI 53226 #016-11-2006 L2008 **AN** *012

YELLICK, Clyde Wm. 2388 N LAKE DR 53211 #056-06-1956 L1957 **OBG** *071 †30

YEN, Kenneth. 9000 W WISCONSIN AVE # 677 53226 #016-11-1996 L1999 **PEM** *020 †55

YEN, Tina Weifang. 9200 W WISCONSIN AVE, DEPARTMENT OF SURGERY 53226 #024-01-1995 L2008 **SO GS** *020 †85

YOON, Hie Jin. 1155 N MAYFAIR RD 3RD FL, DEPT OF PSYCHIATRY 53226 #583-08-1992 L2006 **P** *012

YOON, Michele Yuna. 1522 N PROSPECT AVE, UNIT 604 53202 #035-19-2006 L2008 **ORS** *012

YOOSEFIAN, Farideh. 1230 W GRANT ST 53215 #517-05-1985 L1995 **AN** *020 †20

YOSELEVITZ, Moises. 8901 W LINCOLN AVE 53227 #649-31-1979 L2005 **DR CD** *020 †80

YOSHIDA, Michael K. 9200 W WISCONSIN AVE, MDCL CLLGE CLNCS AT FRDTRT 53226 #572-34-1972 L1997 **PM** *020 †60

YOUKER, James Edward. 9200 W WISCONSIN AVE, DEPT RADIOLOGY 53226 #035-06-1954 L1968 **DR** *040 †80

YOUNG, Craig Chun. 8700 W WATERTOWN PLANK RD 53226 #005-18-1988 L1992 **FM FSM** *020 †18

YOUSEF AGHA, Jawad. 2555 N KING DR, MILWAUKEE HEALTH SERVICES, 53212 #875-01-1998 L2003 **IM** *100 †20

YU, George Chengchi. 8901 W LINCOLN AVE, WEST ALLIS MEMORIAL HOSP 53227 #020-12-1989 L1996 **PTH** *020 †50

YUE, Jin. 8701 W WATERTOWN PLANK RD, MEDICAL COLLEGE OF WISCONS 53226 #243-92-1983 **PM** *100

YUNUS, Hafiz Mohammad. 2315 N LAKE DR 53211 #704-01-1963 L1976 **GS EM** *020 †85,16

ZABORS, Thomas Edward. ■ 53211 #056-06-1958 L1959 **P** *071

ZACHARISEN, Michael C. 9000 W WISCONSIN AVE, STE 411 53226 #056-06-1988 L1989 **AI PD** *020 †03,55 ‡

ZAFRA, Heidi Teresa V. 9000 W WISCONSIN AVE, ALLERGY DEPT-STE 411 53226 #748-10-1990 L2001 **PD AI** *020 †03,55

ZAGORAC, Drazen. 8701 W WATERTOWN PLANK RD, MED COLL WI AFFIL HOSPS 53226 #957-01-1995 **AN** *012

ZAIDI, Adnan Ali. 9200 W WISCONSIN AVE, DEPT OF HEMATOLOGY ONCOLOG 53226 #704-25-1994 L2000 **HO** *020

ZAINER, Christine Mary. 8701 W WATERTOWN PLANK RD, DEPT ANEST 53226 #056-06-1982 L1983 **AN** *040 †05

ZAKI, Maggie Kamal. 6901 W EDGERTON AVE 53220 #915-02-1990 L2001 **FM** *020 †18

ZALUT, Todd Eric. 5000 W CHAMBERS ST, EMERGENCY DEPT. 53210 #003-01-1985 L2001 **EM** *016

ZANGWILL, Steven David. 9000 W WISCONSIN AVE, DIV OF PEDIATRIC CARDIOLOG 53226 #035-46-1989 L2002 **PDC** *020 †55

ZAREM, Norton Lewis. ■ 53217 #056-05-1961 L1962 **P** *020

ZEBROSKI, Jeremy Paul. 8701 W WATERTOWN PLANK RD 53226 #030-06-2004 L2005 **ORS** *012

ZEC, Slobodan. 1714 S 52ND ST 53214 #957-02-1978 L2004 **AN** *020

ZEFT, Howard Joel. 2901 W KINNICKINC RVR PKWY 53215 #035-01-1962 L1970 **CD IM** *020 †20

ZELLMER, James Herbert. 5000 W CHAMBERS ST 53210 #056-06-1964 L1967 **FM** *071 †18

ZENZ, Carl Nicholas. ■ 53227 #041-02-1978 L1980 **OM PTX** *030

ZEPS, Aivars Andrejs. 759 N MILWAUKEE ST 53202 #056-06-1956 L1957 **CHP P** *071

ZETLEY, Linda Rae. 8989 N PORT WASHINGTON RD, STE 220 53217 #056-05-1980 L1990 **CHP P** *020 †75

ZETLEY, Lisa W. 1020 N 12TH ST, DOWNTOWN HEALTH CENTER 53233 #056-06-1991 L1992 **PD** *020 †55

ZHANG, Chenyang. 9200 W WISCONSIN AVE, MILWAUKEE, WI 53226 53226 #243-47-1991 L2004 **AN** *020 †05

ZHANG, Guojun. 8701 W WATERTOWN PLANK RD, MED COLL OF WI 53226 #243-72-1986 **PD** *012

ZHANG, John J. 2801 W KINNICKINC RVR PKWY, STE 535 53215 #243-43-1984 L2000 **OBG** *020

ZHU, Jessica Y. 9000 W WISCONSIN AVE 53226 #056-06-1992 L1994 **PD** *020 †55

ZIA, Turgut Zafar. 2025 W OKLAHOMA AVE, STE 122 53215 #704-20-2000 L2004 **IM** *100

ZIAJA, Ellen L. 2900 W OKLAHOMA AVE, RADIATION ONCOLOGY 53215 #025-07-1993 L1998 **RO** *020 †80

ZIDAN, Hanaa Jamal Alhaj. 8701 W WATERTOWN PLANK RD, MEDICAL COLLEGE OF WISCONS 53226 #575-01-1998 L2006 **PDE** *012

ZIEBERT, Monica Mary. 9200 W WISCONSIN AVE 53226 #056-06-1999 L2002 **IM** *020 †20

ZIEHL, Frank Lawrence. ■ 53226 #056-06-1946 L1950 **PTH GP** *071

ZIGUN, Jeffrey Robt. 5325 W BURLEIGH ST STE 200, COMPREHENSIVE NEURO SVC 53210 #008-02-1985 L1993 **P PFP** *020 †75

ZIKOS, Aggeliki. ■ 53202 #016-42-2006 L2008 **IM** *012

ZILS, Steven William. 9200 W WISCONSIN AVE, DEPARTMENT OF EMERGENCY ME 53226 #016-43-2006 L2008 **EM** *012

ZIMMER, Mary Jo. 3003 W GOOD HOPE RD, HOPE ROAD CLINIC 53209 #056-05-1981 L1984 **PD** *020 †55

ZIMMER, Michelle G. 3003 W GOOD HOPE RD 53209 #056-05-1976 L1977 **IM** *020 †20

ZIMMERMAN, Daniel Dwight. 720 E WISCONSIN AVE 53202 #056-05-1990 L2006 **IM PD** *020 †55,20

ZIMMERMAN, Jessica Lynn. 1032 S CESAR E CHAVEZ DR 53204 #008-02-2003 L2007 **PD** *020 †55

ZIMMERMANN, Burton M. 1020 N 12TH ST 53233 #056-05-1943 L1943 **FM** *072

ZIRBEL, Gretchen Mary. 2300 N MAYFAIR RD STE 855 53226 #012-05-1990 L1991 **D** *020 †15

ZOLTAN, Donald James. 2424 S 90TH ST, STE 418 53227 #016-11-1981 L1982 **ORS OSM** *020 †40

ZOMPA, Joseph Michael. 8200 W TOWER AVE, GEMS-IT CLINIC MC: 240 53223 #024-07-1980 L1998 **OM** *020 †70

ZORN, Adam Peter. 3000 W MONTANA ST 53215 #422-01-2007 **TY** *012

ZOURAS, Wendy Kay. 9200 W WISCONSIN AVE 53226 #016-01-2000 L2003 **PCC** *100 †20

ZUKOWSKI, Thomas Harry. 2025 E NEWPORT AVE, STE 1000 53211 #016-11-1994 L2000 **ON** *020 †20

ZUPANC, Mary Lynn. 8701 W WATERTOWN PLANK RD, MACC FUND RESEARCH BLDG. 3 53226 #005-14-1979 L1982 **CHN PD** *020 †55,75

ZUPNIK, Gerald R. 2675 N MAYFAIR RD 53226 #056-06-1951 L1952 **GS ORS** *062 †85

ZURKINA, Svetlana. 3000 W MONTANA ST 53215 #913-16-1993 **IM** *012

ZVULUNOV, Alexander. ■ 53220 #550-02-1987 *100

ZWICKE, Dianne Lynn. 2801 W KK RIVER PKWY, STE 777 53215 #036-01-1982 L1984 **CD IM** *020 †20

ZWIENENBERG, Marike. 999 N 92ND ST, STE 310 53226 #660-07-1997 L2007 **NS** *100

MINERAL POINT – IOWA

BIERE, Paul Fredric. 227 COMMERCE ST 53565 #018-03-1977 L1982 **FM** *020 †18

DUNN, Aaron Augustine. 227 COMMERCE ST 53565 #019-02-2002 L2003 **FM** *020 †18

GRIESHABER, Gordon James. 104 HIGH ST, MINERAL POINT MED CTR 53565 #019-02-1986 L1993 **FM** *020 †18

KRAMER, Kent Steven. 104 HIGH ST 53565 #056-05-1999 L2000 **FM** *020 †18

ROELLI, Michele Ann. 104 HIGH ST, MINERAL POINT MEDICAL CTR 53565 #056-06-2001 L2002 **FM** *020 †18

MINOCQUA – ONEIDA

AHMANN, David Lawrence. 12970 BLACKBERRY LN 54548 #056-06-1958 L1963 **ON** *071 †20

ANICH, Stephen Edward. 9601 TOWNLINE RD, LAKELAND CTR., P.O. BX 139 54548 #056-05-1979 L1980 **EM** *020 †18,16

BAILEY, Gary Alan. 9601 TOWNLINE RD 54548 #055-01-1974 L1990 **U** *020 †95

BAKKEN, Lloyd A. 9601 TOWNLINE RD, MARSHFIELD CLINIC-LAKELAND 54548 #037-01-1986 L2003 **OBG** *020 †30 ‡

BENSEN, Michelle Anne. 9601 TOWNLINE RD 54548 #056-06-1995 L1996 **IM** *020 †20

BOGUMILL, Hugh Pierce. 9601 TOWNLINE RD 54548 #010-02-1982 L1987 **ORS** *020 †40

BOURKLAND, Bradley Alan. 9601 TOWNLINE RD, LAKELAND CENTER 54548 #056-05-1992 L1993 **EM** *020 †16

■ = Address Information Privacy Protected

BOWERS, Victor M, Jr. ■ 54548 #016-06-1948 L1988 **OBG** *071 †30
BOYER, Barbara J. 9601 TOWNLINE RD 54548 #056-06-1992 L1999 **GS** *020 †85
BROZ, Raymond Wm. ■ 54548 #016-43-1943 L1982 **GP** *072
CHEN, Lin. 9601 TOWNLINE RD, LAKELAND CENTER 54548 #243-16-1986 L2003 **OPH** *020
DE GROOT, Michael Arthur. 9601 TOWNLINE RD, MARSHFIELD CLINIC MINOCQUA 54548
  #016-42-1987 L1998 **OBG** *020 †30
DREWRY, Anne Judith. 9601 TOWNLINE RD 54548 #056-05-1991 L1994 **FM** *020 †18
DREWRY, Matthew Michael. 9601 TOWNLINE RD, MARSHFIELD CLINIC-LAKELAND 54548
  #056-05-1990 L1994 **IM** *020 †20
FLANIGAN, Michael John. 9601 TOWNLINE RD, MARSHFIELD CLINIC - LAKELA 54548
  #056-05-1975 L1976 **NEP IM** *020 †20
FOSSEN, Richard Fredrick. 9601 TOWNLINE RD, LAKELAND CENTER 54548
  #056-06-1984 L1985 **IM CD** *020 †20 ‡
FRANKS, Michael F. 9601 TOWNLINE RD, MINOCQUA CENTER 54548 #649-33-1985 L2002
  GE *020 †20
GABERT, Thomas Carmody. 9601 TOWNLINE RD 54548 #056-05-1985 L1986 **IM IMG** *020 †20
GORAL, Joanna Krystyna. 9601 TOWNLINE RD, MARSHFIELD CLINIC-LAKELAND 54548
  #759-03-1981 L1989 **PD** *020 †55
GORAL, Tomasz. 9601 TOWNLINE RD 54548 #759-03-1980 L1989 **IM** *020 †20
HAMMEL, Laura Lane. 9601 TOWNLINE RD, MARSHFIELD CLNC BOX 1390 54548
  #017-20-1989 L1992 **AN** *012 †20
HARKINS, Paul Gregory. 9601 TOWNLINE RD 54548 #056-05-1975 L1976 **OBG** *020 †30
HAUG, Gary Alan. 9637 MANITOU PARK DR 54548 #056-05-1971 L1972 **OPH EM** *071
HOLSINGER, Jill Rene. 9601 TOWNLINE RD, MARSHFIELD CLINIC-MINOCQUA 54548
  #016-01-1997 L1998 **DR** *020 †80
HOULIHAN, James Thos. 8263 US HIGHWAY 51 S 54548 #016-43-1944 L1970 **OS** *100
JAIN, Sanjeev Ramswaroop. 9601 TOWNLINE RD 54548 #495-17-1994 L2002 **PD** *020 †55
JANAK, Steve Wm. 9601 TOWNLINE RD, MARSHFIELD CLINIC-MINOCQUA 54548
  #056-06-1975 L1978 **FM** *020 †18
KAHANA, Baruch Ephraim. 9601 TOWNLINE RD, LAKELAND CENTER 54548
  #028-02-1974 L1999 **RO GP** *020 †80
KEUER, James Robt. 9601 TOWNLINE RD 54548 #016-42-1954 L1955 **GS** *072 †85
KOZISEK, John A. 9601 TOWNLINE RD 54548 #028-34-1976 L1981 **ORS** *020 †40
KREUTZER, D Louise. 9601 TOWNLINE RD 54548 #005-12-1967 L1994 **R NM** *071 †80
KROCK, Felix Anthony. ■ 54548 #016-43-1919 L1960 **IM** *071 †20
LANDAUER, Kurt. 9601 TOWNLINE RD, MARSHFIELD CLINIC-MINOCQUA 54548
  #056-05-1988 L1992 **FM** *020 †18
LAURENCE, Kevin Jos. 9601 TOWNLINE RD, MARSHFIELD CLINIC - LAKELA 54548
  #016-11-1990 L1994 **IM** *020 †20
LI, Paul Kin Wah. 9601 TOWNLINE RD, P O BOX 1390 54548 #048-16-1991 L1996
  PS *020 †85,65
LONSDORF, Charles Andrew. 9601 TOWNLINE RD, MARSHFIELD CLINIC 54548
  #056-06-1977 L1979 **FM EM** *020 †18
MELMS, Frederick Alfred. ■ 54548 #056-05-1959 L1960 **FM** *071 †18
MIN, Young Bok. 9601 TOWNLINE RD 54548 #005-11-1992 L2001 **OTO** *020 †45
MONSON, Michael Jon. 9601 TOWNLINE RD, MARSHFIELD CLINIC-MINOCQUA 54548
  #056-06-1981 L1997 **GS VS** *020 †20
MROZ, Jolanta. 9601 TOWNLINE RD, MARSHFIELD CLINIC-MINOCQUA 54548
  #759-01-1985 L1997 **IM** *020 †20
NELAPOLU, Durga Prasad S.. 9601 TOWNLINE RD, MARSHFEILD CLINIC/LAKELAND 54548
  #496-34-1993 L2004 **IM** *020
NELSON, Laura Malinda. 9601 TOWNLINE RD, MARSHFIELD CLINIC-MINOCQUA 54548
  #056-05-1991 L1992 **IM MDM** *030 †20
NEMCEK, John Gregory. 9601 TOWNLINE RD, MARSHFIELD CLINIC-LAKELAND 54548
  #056-05-1988 L1991 **IM** *020 †20
OFFORD, James Patrick. 9601 TOWNLINE RD 54548 #056-05-1988 L1993 **GS VS** *020 †85
PETER, Elvis. 9601 TOWNLINE RD, MARSHFIELD CLINIC-MINOCQUA 54548 #495-73-1998 L2002
  IM *020 †20
PHILLIPS, Timothy Scott. 9601 TOWNLINE RD, MARSHFIELD CLINIC-MINOCQUA 54548
  #041-09-1991 L2005 **GS** *020 †85
POGODZINSKI, Anthony E. 9601 TOWNLINE RD, MARSHFIELD CLINIC 54548
  #056-06-1968 L1969 **GS** *020 †85
RASSIER, Mark Edward. 9601 TOWNLINE RD, MARSHFIELD CLINIC-MINOCQUA 54548
  #026-04-1986 L1994 **NEP IM** *020 †20
ROACH, Richard Michael. 9601 TOWNLINE RD, MARSHFIELD CLINIC-MINOCQUA 54548
  #056-05-1982 L1983 **U** *020 †95
ROMANENKO, Maria Orysia. 9601 TOWNLINE RD, LAKELAND CENTER 54548
  #056-05-1994 L1995 **EM** *020 †16
ROY, Thomas Michael. 9601 TOWNLINE RD, MARSHFIELD CLINIC-LAKELAND 54548
  #025-07-1989 L1995 **CD** *020 †20
SAUER, James Richard. ■ 54548 #038-06-1963 L1998 **IM** *071
SCHAARS, Michael John. 9601 TOWNLINE RD, MARSHFIELD CLINIC-MINOCQUA 54548
  #056-06-1994 L1998 **EM** *020 †16
SCHELL, Charles A. 7814 HACKER DR 54548 #016-11-1952 L1977 **GP** *071
SCHOENEMAN, Robert H. 12440 WARPATH LN 54548 #056-06-1950 L1951 **AN** *071 †05
SEALE, Linda Ruth. 9601 TOWNLINE RD 54548 #021-01-1980 L1997 **ID IM** *020 †20
SEIDEL, Barry John. 9601 TOWNLINE RD 54548 #056-06-1967 L1968 **GS VS** *020 †85
SHANKS, Michael John. 9601 TOWNLINE RD, MINOCQUA CENTER 54548 #025-01-1983 L2001
  DR *020 †80 ‡
SHANNON, Richard C. 8453 PINK DRIVE 54548 #056-05-1941 L1942 **EM GS** *071
SHARMA, Umesh Moolchand. 9601 TOWNLINE RD 54548 #495-28-1999 L2006 **IM** *020 †20
SIMIC, William James, Jr. 9601 TOWNLINE RD, MARSHFIELD CLINIC-LAKELAND 54548
  #030-05-1964 L1990 **OTO** *020 †45
SIMPSON, Thomas Harry. 9601 TOWNLINE RD 54548 #064-01-1978 L1999 **AN** *020 †05
SMITH, Robert L. ■ 54548 #056-06-1951 L1952 **R** *071 †80
SULE, Oghomwen Kizito. 9601 TOWNLINE RD 54548 #690-06-1995 L2006 **IM** *020 †20
TADYCH, Kevin Lee. 7520 US HIGHWAY 51 S 54548 #056-06-1982 L1988 **ORS** *020 †40
THOMAS, Matthew Allen. 9601 TOWNLINE RD, DEPT. OF UROLOGY 54548 #032-01-1999 L2005
  U *020 †95
TWELMEYER, John Morgan. 9601 TOWNLINE RD, MARSHFIELD CLC LAKELND CTR 54548
  #056-06-1989 L1993 **OBG** *020 †30
VASSALLO, Charles J. 9601 TOWNLINE RD, MINOCQUA CENTER 54548 #010-02-1976 L1994
  DR OS *040 †80
VAUGHN, Cary Dean. 9601 TOWNLINE RD, MARSHFIELD CLINIC-LAKELAND 54548
  #034-01-1983 L1994 **P** *020 †75
WEISS, Matthias. 9601 TOWNLINE RD 54548 #409-10-1986 L1989 **HO IM** *020 †20

WENMAN, Michael Scott. 9601 TOWNLINE RD, MARSHFIELD CLINIC-MINOCQUA 54548
  #056-06-1983 L1988 **EM** *020 †16
WIESNER, James Kenneth. 9601 TOWNLINE RD, MINOCQUA CENTER 54548
  #056-06-1974 L1975 **IM** *020 †20
YEUNG, Joseph Ching-Hoi. 9601 TOWNLINE RD 54548 #056-06-1983 L1984 **OPH** *020 †35
YI, Xiang-Yan. 9601 TOWNLINE RD 54548 #243-47-1987 L2003 **N** *020 †75
YOUNG, James Jos. 9601 TOWNLINE RD 54548 #026-04-1978 L1985 **FM** *020 †18
ZHANG, Dai-Wei. 9601 TOWNLINE RD, MINOCQUA CENTER BOX 1390 54548
  #243-47-1988 L2000 **DR** *020 †80
ZHAO, Qi. ■ 54548 #243-47-1982 L1996 **AN** *020

MINONG – WASHBURN

FULLER, Lauren Ingrid. 600 W SHELL CREEK RD, NORTHWOODS COMMUNITY HEALT 54859
  #056-06-1981 L1982 **FM** *020 †18

MONDOVI – BUFFALO

DUNCANSON, Emma Lee. ■ 54755 #056-05-2008 *012
KURAPATI, Rani S. 700 BUFFALO ST 54755 #495-50-1976 L1983 **FM** *020 †18
STASKO, John C. ■ 54755 #025-07-2007 **FP** *012
STOUGHTON, Rick Wm. 700 BUFFALO ST 54755 #056-05-1991 L1992 **FM** *020 †18
WALTER, Karl E. S11675 S HEMLOCK RD 54755 #028-34-1949 L1950 **GP GS** *071

MONONA – DANE

BINCER, Wanda Lawendel. ■ 53716 #539-04-1956 L1973 **P** *071
CLARK, Michael Robert. 5900 MONONA DR, STE 301 53716 #056-06-2006 L2007 **EM** *012
GIGOT, Michelle Lynn. 5001 MONONA DR 53716 #056-05-1995 L1998 **FM** *020 †18
GROGAN, Brian Foley. ■ 53716 #056-05-2008 *012
HENNEN, Richard John. ■ 53716 #056-05-1943 L1946 **GP** *071
JOHNSON, Anne Volk. 5001 MONONA DR 53716 #016-45-2002 L2003 **FM** *020 †18
JOHNSON, Noel Mc Kinley. ■ 53714 #028-02-1963 L1963 **P** *071 †75
KAMNETZ, Sandra Ann. 5001 MONONA DR 53716 #056-05-1981 L1982 **FM** *020 †18
KRALL, Lindsay. ■ 53716 #021-01-2006 L2007 **EM** *012
LOCHEN, Brian Earl. 300 FEMRITE DR, TELLURIAN 53716 #056-05-1978 L1979
  ADM EM *020 †18
LUCE, David Barclay. 1717 W BROADWAY, P O BOX 8190 53713 #005-14-1970 L1999
  FM *030 †18 ‡
MANNING, Bradley Laine. ■ 53716 #056-05-2004 L2005 **IM** *100 †20
PLAUTZ, Arthur Carl. 6516 MONONA DR 53716 #056-06-1958 L1959 **U** *071 †95
RAUCH, Sarah Elizabeth. ■ 53716 #016-11-2003 L2006 **EM** *020 †16
SHROPSHIRE, James Harry. 5001 MONONA DR, UW HEALTH MONONA 53716
  #056-05-1989 L1992 **FM** *020 †18
SHROPSHIRE, Richard Wayne. ■ 53716 #018-03-1953 L1957 **FM** *071 †18
TIERNEY, Jon Paul. ■ 53716 #056-05-1962 L1970 **OPH OS** *020 †35
VRABEC, Joshua Peter. ■ 53716 #056-05-2005 L2008 **OPH** *012
WALSH, Eugene John. ■ 53716 #056-06-1959 L1960 **GP OBG** *072
WANG, Jie. 5001 MONONA DR 53716 #243-97-1991 L2004 **FM** *020 †18
WEGNER, Gene Paul. ■ 53716 #056-05-1963 L1965 **R NM** *020 †80

MONROE – GREEN

AHMAD, Arif. 515 22ND AVE, MONROE CLINIC 53566 #704-21-1987 L1996 **CD** *020 †20
ALEXANDER, John. 515 22ND AVE, MONROE CLINIC 53566 #495-80-1997 L2006 **IM** *020
ANDERSON, Eric Kenneth. 515 22ND AVE 53566 #016-11-1981 L1982 **FM** *020 †18
ANDRASKI, Dorota. 515 22ND AVE 53566 #759-01-1986 L1993 **IM** *020 †20
AQUINO, Edmundo C. 515 22ND ST, MONROE 53566 #748-01-1959 L1967 **GP AS** *071
ARNOLD, Martin Long. 515 22ND AVE, THE MONROE CLINIC 53566 #030-05-1988 L1992
  AN *020 †05
BAKER, William Leslie. 2009 5TH ST 53566 #048-04-1961 L1969 **OPH** *071 †35
BAUMANN, Robert Reed. 721 30TH AVE 53566 #023-07-1954 L1961 **D** *071 †15
BAZLEY, John Alvin. 515 22ND AVE 53566 #056-06-1993 L2001 **OBG** *020 †30
BHASKAR, Karen Elaine. 515 22ND AVE, MONROE CLINIC 53566 #016-43-1990 L1994
  OPH *020 †35 ‡
BOYER, Richard Peter. 515 22ND AVE 53566 #024-07-1968 L1976 **GS VS** *072 †85
BREADON, George Edward. 201 11TH ST 53566 #539-04-1968 L1977 **OTO FPS** *071 †45
BRINK, Kristin Erin. 515 22ND AVE, MONROE CLINIC 53566 #056-05-1998 L2002 **P** *020 †75
DAVIDSON, James Russell. 515 22ND AVE 53566 #056-05-1982 L1983 **RHU IM** *020 †20
DAVIS, Carleton B, Jr. 515 22ND AVE, MONROE CLINIC HOSP 53566 #051-01-1970 L1977
  GE IM *020 †20
DIMALALUAN, Ana Cecilia G. 515 22ND AVE 53566 #748-08-1990 L2001 **IM** *020 †20
ERLANDSON, Jan Eberly. 515 22ND AVE, MONROE CLNC 53566 #056-05-1968 L1973
  IM *071 †20
FRANTZ, John A. 515 22ND AVE 53566 #035-45-1946 L1955 **IM** *071 †20
FRANTZ, Mary W Hodge. 515 22ND AVE 53566 #007-02-1951 L1956 **IM** *020 †20
FREY, William Burton. 2009 5TH ST 53566 #026-04-1943 L1946 **PD** *071 †55
FULLER, John Riess. 515 22ND AVE 53566 #050-02-1946 L1963 **OTO** *071
GOGIN, Marie. 515 22ND AVE, THE MONROE CLINIC 53566 #056-06-1989 L1994 **AN** *020 †05
GOSSET, Franz. 515 22ND AVE 53566 #165-04-1960 L1969 **PTH FOP** *020 †50
GUDJONSSON, Thorbjorn. 515 22ND ST, THE MONROE CLINIC 53566 #484-01-1993 L1996
  IC *020 †20
GUL, Ambreen. 515 22ND AVE, THE MONROE CLINIC 53566 #704-25-1998 L2006 **NEP** *020 ‡
HAMEL, Timothy James. 515 22ND AVE, THE MONROE CLINIC 53566 #056-05-1980 L1983
  FM *020 †18
HULS, Valerie. 515 22ND AVE 53566 #028-78-2001, ▲ L2006 **D** *100
INMAN, John Emerson. ■ 53566 #056-06-1970 L1974 **OBG** *071 †30
IRVIN, John Martin. 515 22ND AVE 53566 #056-05-1945 L1946 **IM** *071 †20
JARAMILLO, Carlos A. ■ 53566 #737-01-1950 L1967 **PTH** *071 †50
KAZA, Harsha. 515 22ND AVE 53566 #495-21-1997 L2003 **IM** *020 †20
KEILHAUER, Franz Anton. ■ 53566 #056-06-1991 L1995 **EM** *020 †16

■ = Address Information Privacy Protected

KELLY, James E. 515 22ND AVE 53566 #028-34-1951 L1993 **IM** *071 †20

KILLE, Tony Lee. 515 22ND AVE, OTOLARYNGOLOGY DEPT. 53566 #056-05-2001 L2002 **OTO** *020 †45

KINAST-PORTER, Susan. 515 22ND AVE 53566 #016-11-1979 L1980 **FM OBG** *020 †18

KINDSCHI, George Wm. ■ 53566 #056-05-1968 L1972 **PTH DMP** *071 †50

KNEUBUHLER, Hans Arnold. ■ 53566 #056-05-1958 L1959 **IM OS** *071

KNUTESON, Edward Lee Roy. 515 22ND AVE 53566 #028-02-1969 L1973 **D** *071 †15

KOPPIKAR, Vinaya Shyam. 515 22ND AVE, MONROE CLINIC 53566 #495-35-1970 L1996 **P** *020 †75

LANGEMO, Christine Ellen. 515 22ND AVE 53566 #026-04-1987 L1992 **EM** *020 †18

LONG, Rachel Ann. 515 22ND AVE 53566 #030-05-1987 L1992 **P** *020 †75

MANOHARAN, Umavathy. 515 22ND AVE 53566 #220-04-1998 L2005 **IM** *020 †20

MAXWELL, Nicholas Peter T. 515 22ND AVE 53566 #067-01-1984 L1989 **GS** *020 †85

MILLER, Angela Liszek. 515 22ND AVE 53566 #016-43-1988 L1991 **PD** *020 †55

MILLS, William R. 515 22ND AVE, MONROE CLNC 53566 #056-06-1959 L1960 **GP GS** *071 †18

MIRZA, Rubina Asif. 515 22ND AVE 53566 #704-26-1995 L2004 **CD** *020 †20 ‡

NETZEL, Michael Anthony. 515 22ND AVE, MONROE CLINIC 53566 #030-06-1987 L1995 **PUD AI** *020 †20,03

NIDER, Lester L. 515 22ND AVE 53566 #016-11-1982 L1994 **IM** *020 †20

OLSKY, Mark. 515 22ND AVE 53566 #016-06-1969 L1981 **EM IM** *030 †20,16

OLSON, Merlin Johnson. 515 22ND AVE 53566 #056-05-1947 L1953 **OBG** *071

PARISEAU, Brett James. 515 22ND AVE, MONROE CLINIC 53566 #005-11-2003 L2005 **OPH** *020 †20

PATEL, Vasudev Manibhai. 515 22ND AVE, THE MONROE CLINIC 53566 #495-23-1974 L1984 **AN** *020 ‡

PERRY, Thomas Russell. 1905 5TH ST 53566 #056-05-1978 L1979 **N SME** *020 †75

PIPP, Darren John. 515 22ND AVE 53566 #025-07-1996 L1999 **FM** *020 †18

PIPP, Michele Leeann. 515 22ND AVE, MONROE HOSPITALS AND CLINI 53566 #025-07-1996 L1999 **ON** *020 †20

POLLOCK, James Currier. 515 22ND AVE 53566 #016-11-1975 L1980 **GE IM** *020 †20

RANA, Kishor Gulabbhai. 515 22ND AVE, DEPT OF ANESTHESIA 53566 #495-48-1978 L1988 **AN** *020

RIESE, David Chas. ■ 53566 #056-05-1968 L1969 **AN** *071 †05

ROGERSON, Tony Richard. 515 22ND AVE 53566 #018-03-1989 L1994 **OTO** *040 †45

SANTIAGO, Fernando Saenz. 515 22ND AVE 53566 #748-01-1956 L1966 **OBG FM** *020

SATHOFF, Lance Edward. 515 22ND AVE 53566 #056-06-1993 L1994 **ORS** *020 †40

SMITH, Christopher James. ■ 53566 #028-79-2000, ▲ L2007 **FM** *020

SMITH, Jane Costello. 515 22ND AVE 53566 #048-04-1973 L1978 **P CHP** *020 †75

SPARR, Kenneth Edward. 515 22ND AVE, DEPT UROLOGY MONROE CLINIC 53566 #056-06-1993 L1994 **U** *020 †95

STORMONT, Annette Zeeb. 515 22ND AVE, MONROE CLINIC 53566 #056-06-1980 L1985 **OPH** *020 †35

STORMONT, Daniel Mac Leod. 1905 5TH ST 53566 #056-06-1980 L1985 **ORS** *020 †40

STORMONT, James Russell. 515 22ND AVE, MONROE CLINIC 53566 #010-01-1954 L1959 **IM** *020 †20

SZACHNOWSKI, Peter Paul. 515 22ND ST, THE MONROE CLINIC 53566 #759-03-1984 L1992 **RHU PMM** *020 †20

THOMPSON, Mark James. 515 22ND AVE, FOX VALLEY REGIONAL CAMPUS 53566 #025-12-1995 L2002 **FM** *020 †18

TULLETT, Geoffrey L. W5824 OLD ARGYLE RD 53566 #917-30-1958 L1969 **IM CD** *071 †20

VICKERMAN, Robert Lynn. 2106 19TH AVE 53566 #018-03-1967 L1979 **OBG** *020 †30

VILLACREZ, Jose A. ■ 53566 #737-01-1958 L1964 **AN** *071

WISNEFSKE, David Douglas. ■ 53566 #056-06-1975 L1976 **R NM** *071 †80

YIN, Jane Jianfang. 515 22ND AVE, MONROE CLINIC 53566 #243-16-1984 L2003 **PTH PCP** *020 †50

MONTELLO — MARQUETTE

FRANKS, William Thos. 215 CHURCH ST, MONTELLO FAM MED PRAC 53949 #017-20-1977 L1994 **FM** *020 †18

GARITI, James Thos. 480 UNDERWOOD AVE, MARQUETTE COUNTY EMS 53949 #016-11-1976 L1980 **EM** *020 †18,16

MONTICELLO — GREEN

BLUM, Fred G, Jr. W6303 HEFTY RD 53570 #010-01-1954 L1956 **OPH** *071 †35

INGALLS, Jerry Milton. ■ 53570 #036-07-1958 L1988 **OS GS** *071

MOSINEE — MARATHON

ANDRES, Jerome Carl. 390 ORBITING DR 54455 #056-05-1984 L1985 **FM CCM** *020 †18

BACHHUBER, Gregory Jos. ■ 54455 #056-05-1940 L1941 **EM FM** *071

BARR, Elizabeth Gleason. 1881 COUNTY ROAD XX, ASPIRUS KRONENWETTER 54455 #016-11-1982 L1983 **FM** *020 †18

BEIER, James John. 2191 RIVER FOREST LN, UNION STATION 54455 #016-11-1970 L1979 **FM** *020 †18

DILLON, David Patrick. 390 ORBITING DR, MARSHFIELD CLINIC-MOSINEE 54455 #026-04-1991 L2000 **FM** *020 †18

FULLINGTON, Ann Louise. 1881 COUNTY ROAD XX, ASPIRUS KRONENWETTER 54455 #016-42-1997 L1998 **FM** *020 †18

GRIM, Gerald Wm. 390 ORBITING DR, MARSHFIELD CLNC-MOSINEE 54455 #026-04-1976 L1977 **FM** *020 †18

JOHNSTON, William Henry. 1881 COUNTY ROAD XX, ASPIRUS KRONENWETTER 54455 #005-19-2003 L2005 **FM** *020

MONTGOMERY, Jean Chas. 1881 COUNTY ROAD XX, ASPIRUS KRONENWETTER 54455 #023-12-1983 L1999 **IM** *020 †20

NASH, Richard Gene. 390 ORBITING DR, MARSHFIELD CLINIC-MOSINEE 54455 #026-04-1976 L1977 **FM** *020 †18

NIETERT, William C. 1881 COUNTY ROAD XX, ASPIRUS KRONENWETTER 54455 #056-05-1978 L1979 **FM FPG** *020 †18

SCHNEIDER, Susie Marie. 1881 COUNTY ROAD XX, ASPIRUS KRONENWETTER 54455 #056-06-1993 L1994 **FM** *020 †18

TANGE, David Bruce. 1881 COUNTY ROAD XX, ASPIRUS KRONENWETTER CLINI 54455 #035-46-1975 L1977 **IM IMG** *020 †20

WESTERN, Dennis Wayne. 774 BLACK CREEK DR 54455 #056-05-1968 L1969 **FM OS** *020 †18

WILLIAMS, Amy Jo. ■ 54455 #028-34-2006 L2006 **PD** *012

WITT, Darrell Lee. ■ 54455 #018-03-1966 L1967 **FM** *071 †18

ZIMBRIC, Susan Elaine. 1881 COUNTY ROAD XX, ASPIRUS KRONENWETTER 54455 #056-05-1978 L1979 **GP** *075

MOUNT HOREB — DANE

EGLASH, Anne Rochelle. 600 N 8TH ST 53572 #056-05-1986 L1994 **FM** *020 †18

GARDNER, Russell, Jr. 202 E LINCOLN ST, STE E 53572 #016-02-1962 L1998 **P** *020 †75

IRWIN, Heather Lynn. 600 N 8TH ST 53572 #056-05-2002 L2003 **FM** *020 †18

ISRAEL, Kenneth. 600 N 8TH ST 53572 #051-04-1975 L1980 **IM** *020 †20

IVEY, E Rackley. 1406 BUSINESS 18 AND 151 E, STE 106 53572 #012-22-1993 L2002 **PFP LM** *020

KNOWLTON, Joshua Quincy. ■ 53572 #049-01-2004 L2007 **DR** *012

MAYS, David Vernon. 473 STATE ROAD 78 53572 #017-20-1983 L1984 **P PFP** *071 †75

MUKWONAGO — WAUKESHA

ALLEN-GRYZWA, Shannon P. 240 MAPLE AVE 53149 #056-06-1997 L1998 **FM** *020 †18

AMADON, Sandra Gwen. 240 MAPLE AVE 53149 #056-06-1993 L1994 **FM** *020 †18

BELSON, Thomas Patrick. 240 MAPLE AVE, MORELAND EAR NOSE & 53149 #056-06-1963 L1966 **OTO** *020 †45

CUMMENS, Michael Loyal. 400 BAY VIEW RD 53149 #056-05-1978 L1982 **FM ADM** *020 †18

ELLENBOLT, Darren Richard. 240 MAPLE AVE, PROHEALTH CARE MEDICAL CEN 53149 #056-05-2003 L2005 **FM** *100 †18

FARIS, Sean Michael. 240 MAPLE AVE, MUKWONAGO 53149 #048-04-1996 L2001 **PD** *020 †55

FEHR, Steven Charles. 240 MAPLE AVE, MUKWONAGO 53149 #018-03-1993 L1994 **FM** *020 †18

GATTER, Maripat Loftus. 225 EAGLE LAKE AVE 53149 #010-02-1989 L1993 **EM** *012 †18

HAMMER, Steven Garey. 240 MAPLE AVE, PRO HEALTH CARE MED CTR 53149 #056-05-1983 L1984 **FM** *020 †18

JOCHIMS, Sean Anthony. 240 MAPLE AVE, NEUROLOGIC ASSOCIATES OF 53149 #056-06-1996 L1998 **GP CN** *020 †75

JOHNSON, Daniel Edward. 240 MAPLE AVE, PRO HEALTH CARE MED CTR 53149 #018-03-1995 L1996 **FM** *020 †18

MARTIN, Scott Alan. 240 MAPLE AVE, PROHEALTH CARE MEDICAL CEN 53149 #056-05-2001 L2002 **PD** *020 †55

MEISNER, Steven Carl. 240 MAPLE AVE, MUKWONAGO 53149 #056-06-1998 L1999 **FM** *020 †18

MULLER, Karen Alfreda. ■ 53149 #035-03-1980 L1982 **OBG** *020

MULROONEY, Karin L. 240 MAPLE AVE, MUKWONAGO 53149 #026-04-1996 L1997 **PD** *020 †55

NORELLI, Anthony. 240 MAPLE AVE, MUKWONAGO 53149 #056-06-1992 L1994 **FM** *020 †18

PETERSON, Wayne Walter. 240 MAPLE AVE, PROHEALTH CARE MEDICAL CEN 53149 #056-11-1982 L1985 **FM ID** *020 †18

REINERS, Thomas Kurt. 225 EAGLE LAKE AVE 53149 #035-03-1985 L1991 **FM GP** *020 †18

STEELE, Frederick Jos. 225 EAGLE LAKE AVE 53149 #038-41-1982 L1991 **GS GP** *020 †85

STREHLOW, Scott Raymond. 240 MAPLE AVE 53149 #056-05-1979 L1980 **FM** *020 †18

VAKIL, Nimish Bhupendra. 225 EAGLE LAKE AVE 53149 #496-38-1980 L1993 **GE IM** *020 †20

WALLOCH, Jane Louise. 240 MAPLE AVE, PROHEALTH CARE MED CTRS 53149 #056-06-2002 L2002 **FM** *100 †18

WOOLEVER, Jon L. 240 MAPLE AVE, MUKWONAGO 53149 #016-11-2000 L2001 **FM** *020 †18

MUSCODA — GRANT

HASSELHOF, Gert Herman R. 525 N WISCONSIN AVE 53573 #409-12-1988 L1993 **FM EM** *020

MUSKEGO — WAUKESHA

CHAPMAN, James Michael. S69W15636 JANESVILLE RD, WMC MUSKEGO 53150 #056-05-1994 L1997 **IM** *020 †20

CHENG, Daniel. S69W15636 JANESVILLE RD, PROHEALTH CARE MEDICAL CEN 53150 #016-11-1989 L1992 **IM** *020 †20

DEKKER, Cornelis. S77W12929 MCSHANE DR 53150 #660-01-1953 L1957 **FM** *071

DUDOR, Brian Joseph. S74W16775 JANESVILLE RD, LAKESHORE MEDICAL CLINIC 53150 #056-06-1996 L1997 **FM** *020 †18

EGHBALI, Hassan. S66W13597 SAROYAN RD 53150 #517-01-1960 L1974 **TS** *020

FOWLER, Timothy Patrick. S69W15636 JANESVILLE RD 53150 #016-02-2000 L2006 **ORS HS** *020

HASTINGS, Thomas Edward. W195S7750 ANCIENT OAKS DR 53150 #028-78-1976, ▲ L1983 **CD IM** *020 †20

KOCOUREK, Genevie Loree. ■ 53150 #056-05-2008 *012

MAMEROW, Steven James. S69W15636 JANESVILLE RD 53150 #056-05-1978 L1979 **IM** *020 †20

PATTERSON, Richard Henry. ■ 53150 #056-06-1956 L1957 **P** *071 †75

QUINTANA, Jeffrey Scott. ■ 53150 #056-06-2006 **AN** *012

SCHULTZ, Timothy Karl. S69W15636 JANESVILLE RD 53150 #056-05-1985 L1986 **ORS** *020 †40

SONSALLA, Mary Ann. S69W15636 JANESVILLE RD, WAUKESHA HEALTH CARE 53150 #056-05-1994 L1999 **IM** *020 †20

VEGEAIS, Donna Sue. S69W15636 JANESVILLE RD, PROHEALTH CARE MEDICAL CEN 53150 #016-02-1985 L2005 **MPD PD** *020 †20,55

NASHOTAH — WAUKESHA

BROWN, Douglas Lloyd. ■ 53058 #056-06-2003 L2005 **IM** *020

GAYNOR, Victoria Olson. 5430 N. PAULINE(S WOOD DR 53058 #056-05-1984 L1985 **IM** *075

OTTERS, Anthony Alan. N54W33820 ROAD N 53058 #056-05-1989 L1991 **IM** *020 †20

■ = Address Information Privacy Protected

PUCHNER, John David. ■ 53058 #056-06-1989 L1990 **CD** *100 †20

NECEDAH – JUNEAU

O'LOUGHLIN, Peter Danl. N10461 QUEENS WAY 54646 #056-06-1955 L1957 **P PM** *020 †60

NEENAH – WINNEBAGO

ACHANTI, Satish Kumar. 130 2ND ST 54956 #495-11-2000 L2006 **IM** *100 †20

AHMAD, Osaid Khalid. 200 THEDA CLARK MEDICL PLZ, STE 250 54956 #704-02-1995 L2000 **NEP** *020 †20

ALBA, Jose J. 307 S COMMERCIAL ST, STE 103 54956 #056-06-1982 L1986 **P** *020

ANDREWS, Laura Allison. 411 LINCOLN ST 54956 #056-06-1999 L2004 **END** *020 †20

ARISTIGUETA-MERKHOFER, M. 130 2ND ST 54956 #011-03-1982 L1987 **IM PCC** *020 †20

ASBURY, Corbin C. 333 N COMMERCIAL ST 54956 #025-01-1993 L2003 **DR** *020 †80

ATASSI, Safouh Adel. 200 THEDA CLARK MEDICL PLZ 54956 #875-01-1955 L1967 **U** *071 †95

AUFDERHEIDE, John F. 333 N COMMERCIAL ST, VALLEY, S.C. 54956 #028-02-1976 L1983 **NRN RNR** *020 †80 ‡

BALTZ, Curtis Coulter. 200 THEDA CLARK MEDICL PLZ, STE 390 54956 #016-11-1973 L1976 **IM** *020 †20

BARBER, Frank Ernest. 333 N COMMERCIAL ST 54956 #028-02-1979 L1989 **DR EM** *020 †80,16

BARTIZAL, Frederick J, Jr. ■ 54956 #016-42-1971 L1975 **OBG** *071 †30

BATES, Forrest Thos. 333 N COMMERCIAL ST 54956 #056-06-1982 L1983 **DR IM** *020 †20,80

BAUER, Deedric W. PO BOX 408 54957 #056-06-1962 L1964 **AN OS** *071 †05

BAUER, Lawrence Lee. 333 N COMMERCIAL ST, STE 100 54956 #056-06-1979 L1983 **DR NM** *020 †20

BEHRENS, Scott Arthur. 1029 ROCK LEDGE LN 54956 #056-05-1978 L1979 **AN** *020

BELLG, Laurin A. 130 2ND ST 54956 #047-06-1996 L1998 **IM CCM** *020 †20

BELTZ, David Eugene. 1504 S COMMERCIAL ST 54956 #056-05-1976 L1977 **FM** *020 †18

BERG, Kimberly Ann. 1380 TULLAR RD 54956 #026-04-1996 L1997 **FM** *020 †18

BHATTACHARJEE, Sumon. 1305 W AMERICAN DR, NEUROSCIENCE GROUP OF NE W 54956 #047-07-1997 L2003 **NS** *020

BLOOMHUFF, Kurt Michael. 1504 S COMMERCIAL ST 54956 #025-07-1998 L2001 **FM** *020 †18

BOGNER, Dallas Melvin. 1380 TULLAR RD 54956 #018-03-1994 L1993 **FM** *020 †18

BORMES, Jerome Edward. 130 2ND ST, DEPT OF ANESTHESILOGY 54956 #046-01-1989 L1993 **AN** *020 †05

BRENNAN, Patrick James. 100 THEDA CLARK MEDICL PLZ, STE 400 54956 #056-05-1997 L2002 **GS** *020 †85

BULLARD, Stephen Mark. 1540 LYON DR 54956 #048-15-1991 L1997 **IM** *020 †20

BURKETT, Jeffrey Scott. 200 THEDA CLARK MEDICL PLZ, STE 410 54956 #016-11-1989 L1994 **GS** *020 †85

BURNS, James Robt. 411 LINCOLN ST 54956 #028-03-1974 L1977 **IM** *020 †20

CAMACHO, Daniel Luis. 333 N COMMERCIAL ST 54956 #036-07-1998 L2005 **RNR** *020 †80

CHANG, Young. ■ 54956 #038-43-2001 L2007 **VIR** *020 †80

CHANTELOIS, Allen Edward. 333 N COMMERCIAL ST 54956 #056-06-1984 L1994 **DR** *040 †80

CHARAVEJASARN, Vipaton. ■ 54956 #891-02-1966 L1974 **GP PTH** *020 †50

CHAUDHARI, Swati. 130 2ND ST, N 157 54956 #033-05-1998 L2005 **GE** *020 †20

CHOI, Man Young. 130 2ND ST 54956 #583-01-1971 L1981 **AN** *020 †05

CLARK, Kristin Lyn. 200 THEDA CLARK MEDICL PLZ, STE 130 54956 #056-05-2000 L2004 **OBG** *020

COENEN, Steven R. ■ 54956 #306-01-1985 L1989 **FM** *020 †18

COLE, Brian. 333 N COMMERCIAL ST 54956 #016-11-1998 L2001 **DR** *020 †80

COLGAN, Harry Jos. ■ 54956 #041-12-1944 L1951 **P** *071 †75

COLLINS, Marley Leona. 200 THEDA CLARK MEDICL PLZ 54956 #016-01-1993 L2000 **OBG** *020 †30

CORRIGAN, Tiffany E. 130 2ND ST, THEDA CLARK MED CTR -LAB 54956 #056-05-1987 L1988 **PTH** *020 †50

DALY, Patrick Edward. 1136 WESTOWNE DR 54956 #038-41-1986 L2004 **GS VS** *030 †85 ‡

DAVIS, Scott Edward. 1380 TULLAR RD 54956 #005-14-1985 L1993 **FM** *020 †18

DEDMON, Robert Ernest. ■ 54956 #017-20-1956 L1963 **IM OM** *071 †20,70 ‡

DE WITT, Liza Concetta. 640 DEERWOOD AVE 54956 #016-43-2000 L2001 **PD** *020 †55

DOSS, Jerry Coleman. 325 N COMMERCIAL ST 54956 #038-40-1966 L1969 **DR NR** *020 †80

DOUGLAS, Bruce Robert. 333 N COMMERCIAL ST, STE 100 54956 #056-05-1993 L2003 **DR** *020 †80

DOUGLAS, Robert Frederick. 325 N COMMERCIAL ST, VALLEY, S.C. 54956 #056-05-1955 L1956 **R NR** *071 †80

DUNCAN, Thomas Keith. 200 THEDA CLARK MEDICL PLZ, STE 240 54956 #016-06-1975 L1979 **IM** *020 †20

ELISBERG, John Morton. 200 THEDA CLARK MEDICL PLZ, STE 240 54956 #016-06-1974 L1976 **IM** *020 †20

FEHRER, Michael Raymond. 200 THEDA CLARK MEDICL PLZ, STE 240 54956 #056-06-1976 L1977 **IM** *020 †20

FITZSIMMONS, Dennis M. 130 2ND ST 54956 #847-06-1996 L2001 **P** *020

FLAHERTY, Timothy Thos. 325 N COMMERCIAL ST 54956 #056-06-1959 L1961 **R** *020 †80

GAROFALO, Robert Silvano. 333 N COMMERCIAL ST 54956 #056-05-1992 L1995 **VIR** *020 †80

GELASHVILI, Mariam. 130 2ND ST, THEDACARE 54956 #912-02-2002 L2006 **IM** *020 †20

GENTILE, Kevin Edward. 740 DEERWOOD AVE, AFFINITY MEDICAL GROUP 54956 #056-05-2004 L2005 **PD** *020 †55

GEORGEN, Raymond Frank. 200 THEDA CLARK MEDICL PLZ, STE 410 54956 #016-43-1985 L1990 **GS VS** *020 †85

GRANDONE, John Thos. 200 THEDA CLARK MEDICL PLZ, STE 350 54956 #028-34-1973 L1978 **RHU IM** *020 †20

GURSOY, Erdal Yasar. ■ 54956 #902-03-1956 L1962 **IM** *071

HANSCH, Ernst Christian. 333 N COMMERCIAL ST 54956 #008-01-1994 L2003 **VIR** *020 †80

HARDING, Harold Walter. ■ 54956 #016-11-1964 L1966 **TS VS** *071

HASELOW, John Richard. 307 S COMMERCIAL ST 54956 #056-06-1958 L1959 **GP FSM** *071

HEITZLER, Arthur Phillip. ■ 54956 #016-42-1985 L1986 **AN** *020 †05

HENDRIX, Lloyd E. 333 N COMMERCIAL ST 54956 #019-02-1979 L1986 **DR** *020 †80

HERMANS, Mark Gerard. 200 THEDA CLARK MEDICL PLZ, STE 240 54956 #056-06-1984 L1985 **IM** *020 †20

HIBBS, Susan G. 1305 W AMERICAN DR, THE NEUROSCIENCE GROUP 54956 #020-02-2000 L2004 **N** *020 †75

HILDEBRAND, Fredric L, Sr. ■ 54956 #041-01-1960 L1964 **PUD IM** *071 †20

HILL, Wendy Carroll. 130 2ND ST, WEST PAVILION 54956 #056-05-1994 L1995 **PD** *020 †55

HOLLY, Robert Jos. 1136 WESTOWNE DR 54956 #056-06-1976 L1977 **OBG** *020 †30

HONG, Sung-Nok. ■ 54956 #583-01-1951 **GS OS** *020

HONKAMP, Jill Theresa. 200 THEDA CLARK MEDICL PLZ, STE 270 54956 #018-03-1991 L2004 **OBG** *020 †30

HORAK, David Michael. 333 N COMMERCIAL ST 54956 #056-06-1998 L1999 **DR** *020 †80

HUGO, Christopher Patrick. 124 ASHBROOKE PL 54956 #056-05-1995 L1998 **EM** *020 †16

JADIN-CARDELLI, Roxanne L. 1136 WESTOWNE DR, AURORA MEDICAL GROUP 54956 #056-05-1994 L2006 **IM** *020 †20

JANKUS, Ward Raymond. ■ 54956 #026-04-1989 L1994 **PM PMM** *020 †60

JEKOT, Eileen Clare. 640 DEERWOOD AVE 54956 #048-12-1993 L1996 **PD** *020 †55

JOHNSON, Randall Roy. FL 2 54956 #028-02-1997 L2004 **NS** *020

JOLLY, Eugene Richard. KIMBERLY-CLARK CORP 54956 #025-01-1957 **OS PA** *062

KALDAS, Rami Samir. 200 THEDA CLARK MEDICL PLZ, STE 130 54956 #036-01-1992 L1996 **OBG** *020 †30

KASPER, Patricia Howe. 740 DEERWOOD AVE 54956 #048-14-1984 L1992 **PD** *020 †55

KASPER, William Jos. 740 DEERWOOD AVE, AFFINITY MEDICAL GROUP 54956 #016-06-1982 L1992 **PD** *020 †55

KERINS, Emily Diana. ■ 54956 #056-05-2008 *012

KHAN, Farah Deeba. 411 LINCOLN ST, AFFINITY MEDICAL GROUP 54956 #160-02-1987 L2007 **FM** *020 †18

KIDD, Howard Lee. 517 MAPLE LN, FOX VALLEY NEONATOLOGY 54956 #016-06-1964 L1969 **NPM PD** *020 †55

KIDD, John Aaron. 130 2ND ST 54956 #056-05-1992 L1998 **AN** *020 †05

KING-KUBIAK, Mary Kath. 2100 WINCHESTER RD 54956 #056-05-1954 L1955 **OM** *020 †70

KLAMM, Richard Dale. 1504 S COMMERCIAL ST 54956 #016-43-1975 L1981 **FM** *020 †18

KLEIN, Fred Emil. 333 N COMMERCIAL ST 54956 #026-04-1975 L1982 **DR RNR** *020 †80

KNAUS, Steven Eric. 200 THEDA CLARK, MEDICAL PLAZA STE 380 54956 #056-06-1990 L1991 **IM** *020 †05

KOKONTIS, Lisa Mary. 1305 W AMERICAN DR, WEST PAVILION 54956 #018-03-1992 L1998 **N OS** *020 †75

KONSEK, John P. 411 LINCOLN ST, LASALLE CLINIC 54956 #035-06-1964 L1970 **ON HEM** *071 †20

KRETCHMAR, Kent Allen. 1136 WESTOWNE DR 54956 #021-01-1970 L1980 **R DR** *020 †80

KRUEGER, David Aaron. 130 2ND ST, FOX VALLEY EMERGENCY MEDIC 54956 #016-02-1997 L2003 **EM** *020 †16

LAABS, John Edward. 2100 WINCHESTER RD, KIMBERLY-CLARK CORPORATION 54956 #056-05-1975 L1976 **FM OM** *050 †70,18

LAMPS, Gary Martin. 315 1ST ST 54956 #028-34-1976 L1981 **D IM** *071 †20,15

LARMON, J Elaine. ■ 54956 #012-01-1991 L2007 **OBG** *020 †30

LARSEN, Kristin Marie. 130 2ND ST, CHILDREN'S HOSPITAL FOX VA 54956 #056-05-1999 L2002 **PD** *100 †55

LARSON, Gizell Rossetti. 1305 W AMERICAN DR, NEUROSCIENCE GROUP OF NE W 54956 #041-07-1978 L1985 **N** *020 †75

LARSON, Paul Albert. 333 N COMMERCIAL ST 54956 #008-02-1982 L1986 **R VIR** *020 †80 ‡

LAUDERDALE, Barbara Lewis. 411 LINCOLN ST 54956 #035-01-1980 L1986 **ID IM** *020 †20

LAWATSCH, Eric Jon. 200 THEDA CLARK MEDICL PLZ, STE 310 54956 #026-04-2002 L2003 **U** *020

LEIGH, Cynthia Campbell. 411 LINCOLN ST 54956 #030-05-1980 L1987 **END** *020 †20

LEWANDOWSKI, Nancy J. ■ 54956 #035-45-1992 L2002 **IM** *020 †20

LIN, Rudolph Yi-Min. 333 N COMMERCIAL ST, STE 100 54956 #056-05-1996 L2001 **DR** *020 †80

LITTMAN, Noam Tzvi. 333 N COMMERCIAL ST 54956 #033-06-1997 L2003 **R VIR** *020 †80

LOPEZ, Michelle Alise. 1504 S COMMERCIAL ST 54956 #056-05-1976 L2001 **FM** *020 †18

LULLOFF, Kim Harold. R130 2ND ST 54956 #056-06-1960 L1963 **ORS** *071 †40

LYONS, Thomas Alston. 1305 W AMERICAN DR, NEUROSCIENCE GROUP OF NE W 54956 #056-06-1967 L1991 **NS** *020 †25

MACKSOOD, Daniel Joseph. 333 N COMMERCIAL ST 54956 #025-01-1995 L2006 **DR** *020 †80

MADHUSUDHAN, Ramegowda V. 333 N COMMERCIAL ST 54956 #495-33-1986 L2004 **DR** *020 †80

MAGUIRE, Michael Francis. 130 2ND ST 54956 #016-43-1989 L1995 **PUD CCM** *020 †20

MALTRY, David Emile. 7765 JOSEPH PETERS DR 54956 #030-05-1979 L1986 **AN** *040 †05

MALUEG, Thomas John. ■ 54956 #056-05-1961 L1962 **P** *030 †75

MATTIO, Thomas Gerard. 1305 W AMERICAN DR, NEUROSCIENCE GROUP OF NE W 54956 #016-45-1988 L1993 **N** *020 †75

MC AVOY, Paul Brian. 411 LINCOLN ST, AFFINITY MEDICAL GROUP 54956 #016-43-1969 L1975 **IMG** *020 †20

MC GLOIN, Mary T Stanczak. 924 OAK ST 54956 #016-43-1957 L1967 **AN** *071 †05

MC KENZIE, Paul Todd. 640 DEERWOOD AVE 54956 #054-04-2000 L2001 **PD** *020

MILLER, Marc Jason. 333 N COMMERCIAL ST 54956 #056-06-1995 L1996 **DR** *020 †80

MJAANES, Christopher M. 220 BOSWORTH LN 54956 #056-05-2000 L2001 **AI** *020 †55,03

MOORE, Brian Paul. 111 E NORTH WATER ST 54956 #056-05-1968 L1976 **PTH** *020 †50

MORTARA, Kevin Lee. 200 THEDA CLARK MEDICL PLZ, STE 430 54956 #003-01-1996 L2006 **HO** *020 †20

MURPHY, Thomas F. 333 N COMMERCIAL ST 54956 #025-01-1984 L2001 **DR** *020 †80

MYERS, Paul Robt. 130 2ND ST, CHW-FOX VALLEY 54956 #026-04-1979 L1989 **NPM PD** *020 †55

NELSON, Jeri Anne Leekley. ■ 54956 #038-41-1972 L1977 **PD** *020

NELSON, William Lawrence. 411 LINCOLN ST 54956 #038-41-1972 L1977 **IM FM** *020 †20

NEWBY, Kenneth Geo. ■ 54956 #016-11-1957 L1964 **OPH** *071 †35

NICHOLS, Thomas Harley. 130 2ND ST, CHW-FOX VALLEY 54956 #016-01-2002 L2004 **PD** *020 †55

NOLTEN, Audrey Elisabeth. 333 N COMMERCIAL ST, STE 100 54956 #056-05-1993 L2003 **DR** *020 †80

NONN, Robert Allen. 130 2ND ST 54956 #016-43-1992 L1998 **PCC** *020 †20

NOVAK, Russell Arthur. 130 2ND ST 54956 #030-05-1973 L2006 **CCM IM** *020 †20

OKUNDAYE, Ifueko B. 1540 LYON DR 54956 #690-06-1987 L1996 **IM NEP** *020 †20

O LEARY, James Vincent. 200 THEDA CLARK MEDICL PLZ, STE 270 54956 #016-43-1985 L1995 **OBG** *020 †30

PANTE, Rogelio Ortega. 130 2ND ST 54956 #748-01-1996 L2006 **IM** *020 †20

PEEBLES, Todd Robert. 333 N COMMERCIAL ST 54956 #035-15-1994 L1999 **RNR** *020 †80

PELLEGRINI, James Alfred. ■ 54956 #016-02-2001 L2006 **DR** *100 †80

PFAFFENBACH, Elina Xanos. 200 THEDA CLARK MEDICL PLZ, STE 270 54956 #016-06-1994 L1995 **OBG** *020 †30

PHILLIPS, Anthony Wayne. 200 THEDA CLARK MEDICL PLZ, STE 430 54956 #056-05-1986 L1987 **HO** *020 †20

PIERSON, Michael Ray. 130 2ND ST, THEDA CLARK HOSPITAL 54956 #056-05-1992 L1993 **AN** *020 †05

POWLEY, Scott Gerald. 130 2ND ST 54956 #038-41-1987 L1991 **PM** *020 †60

PRICE, Kathleen R. 130 2ND ST, THEDA CLARK MEDICAL CTR 54956 #016-06-1986 L1992 **EM** *020 †16

PRICE, Steven James. 130 2ND ST, 2ND FLOOR 54956 #016-06-1986 L1992 **N** *020 †75

PUJALS, John S. 315 1ST ST 54956 #035-03-1992 L2000 **DMP** *020 †15

QUINN, Kevin Francis. 111 E NORTH WATER ST 54956 #056-06-1977 L1978 **GS** *020 †85

QUINONES-TALEON, Andrea C. 130 2ND ST 54956 #748-10-1993 L2001 **PD** *020 †55

RADTKE, Brian Earl. 130 2ND ST, EMERGENCY DEPARTMENT 54956 #041-02-1998 L2002 **EM** *020 †16

RAJ, Radhika Palani. 411 LINCOLN ST 54956 #495-94-1989 L1998 **IM** *020 †20

RAMSEY, Tina Suzanne. 200 THEDA CLARK MEDICL PLZ, STE 270 54956 #016-11-1996 L2000 **OBG** *020 †30

RAO, Sandeep Katikineni. 333 N COMMERCIAL ST, STE 100 54956 #025-01-1994 L2002 **DR** *020 †30

REILLY, Steven Douglas. 130 2ND ST 54956 #056-06-1994 L1995 **AN** *020 †05

REINARDY, Thomas Edward. 740 DEERWOOD AVE 54956 #056-05-1993 L1994 **OBG** *020 †30

RENFREW, Donald Lee. 333 N COMMERCIAL ST, RADIOLOGY ASSOC. OF THE FO 54956 #018-03-1982 L1993 **DR** *020 †80 ‡

RICCITELLI, Guy. 517 E FOREST AVE 54956 #016-11-1991 L1993 **OBG** *020

RIDLEHOOVER, Annika K. 640 DEERWOOD AVE 54956 #056-05-1999 L2000 **PD** *020 †55

RIEDER, Michael Jos. 421 KITTIVER CT 54956 #056-05-1968 L1969 **N PM** *071 †75 ‡

RIESS-SAGERS, Kim Renee. 200 THEDA CLARK MEDICL PLZ, STE 250 54956 #056-05-1990 L1991 **NEP** *020 †20

ROGERS, Leslie Dawn. 130 2ND ST, 3RD FL 54956 #048-14-1994 L2000 **FM** *020 †18

ROLOFF, Peter Arnold. 740 DEERWOOD AVE 54956 #056-05-1997 L2000 **PD** *020 †55

ROSCULET, Katrina A. 333 N COMMERCIAL ST 54956 #025-01-1987 L1993 **DR** *020 †80

RUBNER, Pamela Maria. 740 DEERWOOD AVE 54956 #056-06-2000 L2002 **PD** *020 †55

RYLAK, David Albert. 130 2ND ST, THEADA CLARK EMERGENCY DEP 54956 #035-20-2000 L2001 **EM** *020 †20,16

SALO, Bruce Carlton. 333 N COMMERCIAL ST 54956 #016-43-1976 L1983 **DR NR** *020 †80

SAN DRETTO, Michael A. 333 N COMMERCIAL ST, STE 100 54956 #056-06-1976 L1977 **DR** *020 †80

SARNECKI, Jan Chas. ■ 54956 #026-04-1966 L1975 **ORS** *020 †40

SCHRANG, Eugene Arnold. 414 E WISCONSIN AVE, 414 E. WISCONSIN AVE 54956 #016-43-1957 L1959 **PS GS** *071 †65

SCHULTZ, David John. 100 THEDA CLARK MEDICL PLZ, STE 400 54956 #016-01-1998 L1999 **GS** *020 †85

SEKHAR, Nikhilesh Royapet. 100 THEDA CLARK MEDICL PLZ, STE 400 54956 #033-05-1999 L2006 **GS** *020 †85

SELINE, Timothy Herbert. 333 N COMMERCIAL ST 54956 #026-04-1986 L1994 **R** *020 †80

SHAHBANDAR, Hassan. 200 THEDA CLARK MEDICL PLZ, STE 270 54956 #875-01-1970 L1974 **GYN** *020 †30

SHAPIRO, Ilan Isaac. 1136 WESTOWNE DR 54956 #056-05-1981 L1987 **ORS OSM** *020 †40

SHOBERG, Teresa Lea. 1504 S COMMERCIAL ST, 1504 S COMMERCIAL ST 54956 #056-06-1989 L1990 **FM** *020 †18

SICKELS, David Lawrence. ■ 54956 #056-05-1993 L1996 **EM** *020 †16

SICKELS, Wm Frederick. 411 LINCOLN ST 54956 #016-06-1961 L1965 **IM** *020 †20

SOLIS-ROHR, Veronica. 1380 TULLAR RD 54956 #231-03-1984 L1991 **FM** *020 †18

STACHOWICZ, Pawel Piotr. 425 S COMMERCIAL ST 54956 #026-04-1993 L2008 **PS** *020 †65

STRASBURGER, Janette Fae. 130 2ND ST, # 2FL 54956 #030-05-1980 L2001 **PDC PD** *020 †55

STREBEL, Ronald Lee. 1136 WESTOWNE DR 54956 #056-05-1963 L1964 **OBG** *020 †30

SUNG, Susan. ■ 54956 #016-02-2002 L2007 **DR** *100 †80

SWANSON, Gregory John. 411 LINCOLN ST 54956 #016-01-1996 L2002 **OTO** *020 †45

SWANSON, Suzanne Chaffee. 640 DEERWOOD AVE 54956 #018-03-1983 L1992 **OBG** *075 †30

SWARTWOUT, Paul Richard. ■ 54956 #056-06-1971 L1973 **P** *074

SWEET, Philip Albert. ■ 54956 #016-45-1986 L1987 **DR** *020 †75

SZABO, Edward Jos. 411 LINCOLN ST, LA SALLE CLINICSYSTEM 54956 #056-06-1991 L1993 **FM** *020 †18

SZANISZLO, Katalin. 120 2ND ST, NEONATAL ICU 54956 #473-02-1976 L2001 **NPM** *020 †55

THALACKER, Craig Steven. ■ 54956 #007-02-2001 L2005 **EM** *020 †16

THEARLE, Daniel Stephen. 200 THEDA CLARK MEDICL PLZ, STE 410 54956 #056-06-1961 L1971 **TS** *071 †90,85

THEYERL, Kay Ellen. 200 THEDA CLARK MEDICL PLZ, STE 240 54956 #056-06-2001 L2003 **IM** *020

TOLLY, Thomas Lee. 333 N COMMERCIAL ST 54956 #025-07-1984 L1985 **DR** *020 †80

TSISKARISHVILI, Vasil. 130 2ND ST, THEDACARE 54956 #912-02-2002 L2006 **IM** *020 †20

TURNER, Donald Craig. 325 N COMMERCIAL ST, VALLEY, S.C. 54956 #056-06-1967 L1977 **R** *020 †80

ULLRICH, Cari Hamilton. 640 DEERWOOD AVE 54956 #056-05-1990 L1995 **PD** *074 †55

VAN SISTINE, Thomas Kevin. 130 2ND ST, CENTER FOR REHABILITATION 54956 #056-06-1988 L1995 **PM** *020 †60

VAN YE, Todd Michael. 425 S COMMERCIAL ST 54956 #048-12-1989 L1990 **PS GS** *020 †85,65

VARBERG, Waldo Raymond. ■ 54956 #040-02-1957 L1961 **ORS** *071 †40

VONGSA, Sourasack. 1136 WESTOWNE DR 54956 #104-01-2003 L2004 **FM** *020 †18

WASCO, Kevin Edward. 100 THEDA CLARK MEDICL PLZ, STE 400 54956 #056-05-1994 L1995 **GS** *020 †85

WEST, Michael E. 200 THEDA CLARK MEDICL PLZ 54956 #056-06-1979 L1980 **OBG** *020 †30

WESTRA, Christopher Shawn. 2100 WINCHESTER RD, KIMBERLY CLARK CORP 54956 #018-03-1992 L1998 **IM OM** *020 †70,20

WHITESIDE, Jeffrey Robt. 130 2ND ST 54956 #018-03-1977 L1982 **PUD CCM** *020 †20

WILKE, Andrew Mark. 7350 MURRAY RD 54956 #056-05-1997 L2006 **EM FM** *020 †18

WILSON, Edwin Earl. 411 LINCOLN ST 54956 #026-04-1974 L1977 **IM** *020 †20

XIE, Hong. 333 N COMMERCIAL ST, STE 100 54956 #243-47-1989 L2004 **DR** *020 †80

YAZBAK, Philip Andrew. 1305 W AMERICAN DR, NEUROSCIENCE GROUP OF NE W 54956 #032-01-1989 L1995 **NS** *020 †25

ZANTOW, Ryan Thomas. 130 2ND ST 54956 #056-05-2001 L2002 **PM** *020 †60

ZAPOLSKY, Jeffrey Howard. 333 N COMMERCIAL ST, STE 100 54956 #035-45-1982 L2001 **DR** *020 †80 ‡

ZERRIEN, David Wm. 211 N COMMERCIAL ST, DEPT OF HUMAN SVCS 54956 #056-06-1986 L1987 **P** *020 †75

ZIMMERMAN, Delano Elmer. ■ 54956 #056-05-1965 L1966 **EM OS** *071

ZOCH, Thomas Wm. 200 THEDA CLARK MEDICL PLZ, STE 240 54956 #056-06-1983 L1984 **EM IM** *020 †20,16

NEILLSVILLE – CLARK

ASINAS, Teodorico Y. ■ 54456 #748-08-1962 L1989 **GP IM** *071 †18

CAPATI, Ana Camaya. ■ 54456 #748-01-1959 L1968 **GP IMG** *071

CAPATI, Nazario Reyes. NEILLSVILLE CLINIC 54456 #748-07-1959 L1967 **GS GP** *075

CRUZ, Maria Graziella A. 216 SUNSET PL, MEMORIAL MEDICAL CENTER 54456 #748-01-1959 L1968 **GP IMG** *071

FUNK, Dean W. 216 SUNSET PL, MEMORIAL MEDICAL CENTER 54456 #308-03-1984 L1996 **FM EM** *020 †18

HALAC, Mehmet Emin. ■ 54456 #902-03-1959 L1973 **IM GP** *020

JOVELLANA, Apolinar E. 216 SUNSET PL 54456 #748-10-1975 L1983 **GP** *020

KWIECINSKI, Brooke Renee. ■ 54456 #056-05-2008 *012

LLEVA, Florentino E. 216 SUNSET PL 54456 #748-07-1956 L1970 **FM GS** *071

LUCINA, Pedro A. 216 SUNSET PL 54456 #748-01-1957 L1991 **GS** *020

MAGUIGAD, Demetrio C. 216 SUNSET PL, MEMORIAL MEDICAL CTR 54456 #748-01-1965 L1990 **DR CLP** *075

MARTIN, Steven Carl. 216 SUNSET PL, MEMORIAL MEDICAL CENTER 54456 #011-04-1998 L2005 **FM** *020 †18

OZTURK, Cahit H. 510 W 5TH ST 54456 #902-10-1943 L1967 **GS ORS** *071

PACIS, Armando A. 216 SUNSET PL 54456 #748-08-1968 L2003 **GS** *020

PACIS, Wilhelmina V. 216 SUNSET PL 54456 #748-08-1968 L2004 **GP** *020

STANGA, Christina Yvonne. ■ 54456 #019-02-1991 L2001 **P** *020 †75

STANGA, James Andrew. 216 SUNSET PL, MEMORIAL MEDICAL CTR 54456 #019-02-1991 L1999 **FM** *020 †18 ‡

TAGUBA, Leslie C R. 216 SUNSET PL 54456 #748-02-1995 L2001 **END** *020 †20

NEKOOSA – WOOD

ALLEN, William. 1128 W QUEENS WAY 54457 #038-40-1957 L1964 **IM** *071

ALMONTE, Ricardo A. 315 1ST ST, RIVERWOOD CLINIC SC 54457 #748-10-1964 L1975 **IM** *071

CABALTICA, Josefino B. 1015 ANGELUS DR 54457 #748-01-1966 L1976 **GP EM** *020

CLASEN, Richard Walter. 1015 ANGELUS DR 54457 #056-05-1976 L1980 **IM IMG** *020 †20

PFEIFFER, Louis R. 515 PROSPECT AVE 54457 #056-05-1951 L1952 **GP** *071

PRICE, Cheston E. 1160 ROME CENTER DR 54457 #025-12-1996 L1999 **FM** *020 †18

RODRIGUEZ, Richie-Ann G. ■ 54457 #748-10-2000 L2007 **FM** *020 †18

NESHKORO – MARQUETTE

WAGNER, William Arthur. ■ 54960 #056-05-1948 L1949 **CD GP** *071

NEW AUBURN – CHIPPEWA

FRASE, Louis Harvey. ■ 54757 #016-11-1964 L1971 **IMG IM** *071 †20

NEW BERLIN – WAUKESHA

ABDULAL, Ghudran Adel. 2801 S MOORLAND RD, AURORA HEALTH CARE 53151 #875-01-1990 L2003 **FM** *020 †18

AHAMMEDKUTTY, Shelby. ■ 53151 #495-44-1995 L2003 **PDC** *012 †55

ALPREN, Thomas Victor P. 14555 W NATIONAL AVE 53151 #024-07-1971 L1974 **OPH OS** *020 †35

ALQUINTO, Aileen R. 12555 W NATIONAL AVE, STE 201 53151 #748-01-1990 L1994 **IM** *020 †20

ANDERSON, Steven Paul. 14555 W NATIONAL AVE 53151 #056-05-1985 L1990 **ORS** *020 †40

ANGOVE, Arthur E. ■ 53146 #018-75-1962, ▲ L1966 **GS UCM** *071

BAILEY, Shannon Lee. 2801 S MOORLAND RD 53151 #019-02-1991 L2007 **OBG** *020 †30

BASILE, Richard D, Jr. 14555 W NATIONAL AVE # 170 53151 #016-11-1992 L1995 **IM** *020 †20

BELL, Matthew Lee. 14075 LENOX DR 53151 #056-06-2001 L2002 **DR** *100 †80

BLAKE, David Gary. 14555 W NATIONAL AVE, STE 165 53151 #056-06-1974 L1975 **HEM ON** *020 †20

BLOCHER, Kathleen Sue. 14999 W BELOIT RD, STE C 53151 #030-05-1986 L1989 **IM** *020 †20

BUCHANAN, Timothy Geo. 14555 W NATIONAL AVE, STE 165 53151 #308-07-1982 L1983 **FM PTH** *020 †18

BUNGE, William Rodolfo. ■ 53151 #132-01-1942 L1950 **GP** *071 †55

BURROWS, Katherine N. ■ 53151 #018-75-2007, ▲ **MPD** *012

CASTELAR-TORRES, Sandra C. 12555 W NATIONAL AVE, STE 201 53151 #748-01-1985 L1994 **PD** *020 †55

CATANZARO, Andrew Jos. 12901 W NATIONAL AVE, POINTE CENTER 53151 #038-40-1973 L1974 **IM** *020 †20

CENSKY, James Anthony. 3610 MICHELLE WTMR MMRL DR 53151 #056-06-1994 L1995 **FM** *020 †18

CESAREC, Robert G. 3610 MICHELLE WTMR MMRL DR 53151 #056-06-1978 L1979 **FM** *020 †18

CHUNG, Eunjin. ■ 53151 #056-06-2008 *012

CONNERS, Douglas Robert. ■ 53151 #056-05-2006 **DR** *012

CURRAN, Margaret Mary. 14555 W NATIONAL AVE # 160 53151 #005-19-1984 L1991 **EM** *020 †16

DANFORTH, R Clarke. 14555 W NATIONAL AVE, NEUROLOGY ASSOCIATES SC 53151 #056-05-1958 L1960 **N** *071 †75

DARLING, Ronald John. 13900 W NATIONAL AVE, MORELAND EAR NOSE & 53151 #056-06-1962 L1963 **OTO** *020 †45

DARLING, William Anthony. 13900 W NATIONAL AVE, MORELAND EAR NOSE & 53151 #056-06-1969 L1970 **OTO HNS** *020 †45

DELP, Arlen R. 14555 W NATIONAL AVE, STE 165 53151 #041-77-1967, ▲ L1968 **FM** *071 †18

DESIDERO, Stephen Joseph. 14555 W NATIONAL AVE, STE 170 53151 #016-11-1992 L1995 **IM** *020 †20

DUNBAR, Amy Therese. ■ 53151 #028-34-2006 L2008 **OBG** *012

DUNCAN, Laura S. 12901 W NATIONAL AVE, POINTE CENTER 53151 #056-06-1993 L1994 **MPD** *020 †55,20

DUNCAN, Neville Winston. 15417 W NATIONAL AVE # 217 53151 #035-46-1973 L1996 **OBG** *075

ENG, Tin Yam. 14555 W NATIONAL AVE 53151 #017-20-1971 L1976 **D** *020 †15

FENSKE, Scott Darrell. 14555 W NATIONAL AVE 53151 #017-20-1984 L1985 **IM** *020 †20 ‡

FISHBURN, Charles Wylie. ■ 53151 #007-02-1963 L1966 **OM** *020 †70

FOX, Mary Celine. 13900 W NATIONAL AVE, MORELAND EAR NOSE & 53151
#056-06-1995 L1996 **OTO** *020 †45
GOBLIRSCH, Dean E. ■ 53151 #028-79-1959, ▲ L1973 **OTO AI** *071
GOUTHRO, Robert Vincent, Jr. ■ 53151 #056-06-2007 **P** *012
GRAVES, Glenn Edward. 14555 W NATIONAL AVE 53151 #035-48-1985 L1986 **OPH** *020 †35
GRIEBEN, Cristina Andrea. ■ 53151 #056-06-1984 L1987 **FM** *020 †18
GUTZEIT, Michael Francis. 3610 MICHELLE WTMR MMRL DR 53151 #016-43-1985 L1986
PD *020 †55
HARDEMAN, Jamie Lee. ■ 53151 #056-06-2007 **TY** *012
HEIDLBERG, Jeannette Anne. ■ 53151 #056-06-2008 *012
HEINTZ, Norman V. 16310 W COACHLIGHT DR 53151 #016-11-1964 L1978 **P CHP** *020
HENDLEY, Gail Edmee. ■ 53151 #051-01-1979 L1980 **EM IM** *020 †20,16
HIDA, Catherine Ann. ■ 53151 #041-07-1992 L1999 **PCP PTH** *020 †50
HOYER, Katherine Marie. 14555 W NATIONAL AVE 53151 #056-06-1989 L1990 **FM** *020 †18
ISAACS, David Lawrence. 2875 S 171ST ST, GREAT LAKES RADIOLOGISTS, 53151
#036-01-2000 L2005 **DR** *100 †80
ISAACSON, Stuart. 15465 W HOWARD AVE 53151 #018-75-1983, ▲ L2003 **FM OM** *020
JERUC, William Donald. 3610 MICHELLE WTMR MMRL DR 53151 #056-06-1990 L1991
PD *020 †55
JONES, Michael. ■ 53151 #028-78-2006, ▲ **FP** *012
JORDAN, Mark Vernon. 12801 W WYNDRIDGE CT # 2 53151 #836-03-1998 L2005 **IM** *020 †20
KANTOLA, Scott James. ■ 53151 #056-06-2008 *012
KASS, Edward Gerard. 13900 W NATIONAL AVE, MORELAND EAR NOSE & 53151
#056-06-1987 L1988 **OTO** *020 †45
KESSEN, Marci Denee. 13900 W NATIONAL AVE, PROHEALTH CARE MEDICAL CEN 53151
#018-03-1996 L1997 **FM** *020 †18
KHAZI, Abdul Mateen. ■ 53151 #495-72-2001 **P** *012
KHEMKA, Sanjay Vishwanath. 2801 S MOORLAND RD 53151 #496-46-1998 L2005 **IM** *020 †20
KHMOUR, Ayman Yousef. 12540 DUNCAN LN 53151 #575-02-2000 L2006 **NPM** *012 †55
KOLB, Marvin Otto. ■ 53151 #030-06-1965 L1995 **PD** *030 †55
KORDUCKI, Stanley A. ■ 53151 #056-06-1949 L1950 **OBG** *071 †30
KOTSONIS, Steven M.. ■ 53151 #056-06-2008 *012
KUHR, Gregory Jerome. 14555 W NATIONAL AVE 53151 #056-06-1975 L1976 **FM FPG** *020 †18
LAMBERT, Jessica Layne. ■ 53151 #056-06-2008 *012
LIEB, Roger Leroy. ■ 53151 #018-03-1985 L1986 **DR** *020
LOE, Meridith Ann. 2801 S MOORLAND RD 53151 #037-01-2002 L2004 **OBG** *100
LOHR, Nicole Lynn. ■ 53151 #056-06-2006 L2008 **IM** *012
LUM, Hillary Eileen. ■ 53151 #056-06-2008 *012
MA, Lin. 2801 S MOORLAND RD 53151 #243-47-1987 L1999 **IM** *020 †75
MANKIEWICZ, Thomas J. 3610 MICHELLE WTMR MMRL DR 53151 #056-06-1978 L1979
FM EM *020 †18
MANNINO, Dennis Patrick. 14555 W NATIONAL AVE 53151 #035-08-1982 L1983 **IM** *020 †20
MAREK, Cynthia Jean. ■ 53151 #056-06-1988 *075
MATHAI, Malaika Mary. 14555 W NATIONAL AVE 53151 #056-06-1993 L1994 **IM** *020 †20
MEIER, Mark A. 14555 W NATIONAL AVE, STE 160 53151 #037-01-1988 L1994 **GS** *020 †85
MEIER, Mark Alan. 14555 W NATIONAL AVE 53151 #016-02-1984 L1985 **FM** *020 †18
MOLDVAN, June C. 3610 MICHELLE WTMR MMRL DR 53151 #781-01-1982 L1992
FM *020 †18 ‡
MULLER, Janissa Kaye. ■ 53151 #030-06-2008 *012
MUSHTAQ, Adnan. ■ 53151 #704-01-1999 L2001 **ID** *020
NAGPAL, Pooja. ■ 53151 #016-11-2005 L2007 **IM** *012
NESS, Beverly Ruth. 12901 W NATIONAL AVE, POINTE CENTER 53151 #056-05-1998 L1999
IM *020 †20
OLSON, Carroll Robt. 2665 S MOORLAND RD 53151 #056-06-1943 L1944 **IM** *071
OWSIAK, Andrew Mark. ■ 53151 #016-43-1978 L1980 **GS** *020 †16
PALESE, John Anthony. 2801 S MOORLAND RD 53151 #056-05-1948 L1952
GPM FM *030 †70,18
PAPANDREA, Rick Frank. 13900 W NATIONAL AVE, STE 100 53151 #056-05-1992 L1998
OAR HS *020 †40
PARSA, Abbas. 12901 W NATIONAL AVE 53151 #517-01-1963 L1975 **IM** *071 †20
POLK, Joyce Elaine. ■ 53151 #056-05-1977 L1978 **IM** *100 †20
PORTER, Ryan Frederick. ■ 53151 #056-06-2008 *012
RAJURKAR, Piyush Kamlakar. 14555 W NATIONAL AVE 53151 #030-05-1998 L2002
OPH *020 †35
REMENIUK, Eudokia. ■ 53151 #407-02-1953 L1965 **PTH OS** *071
RICHTER, Connie Lorraine. 3610 MICHELLE WTMR MMRL DR 53151 #056-06-1991 L1992
PD *020 †55
RITTER, Jodi L. 2801 S MOORLAND RD 53151 #016-76-1994, ▲ L1995 **FM** *020 †18
ROHLOFF, Robert Thos. 3610 MICHELLE WTMR MMRL DR 53151 #056-06-1981 L1982
PD *020 †55
SAMEH, Maysa Lynn. 14555 W NATIONAL AVE # 165 53151 #056-06-1999 L2002 **FM** *020 †18
SAMI, Zeba. 14555 W NATIONAL AVE 53151 #704-02-1983 L1994 **P** *020
SCHWAKE, Christopher J. 3610 MICHELLE WTMR MMRL DR 53151 #016-11-2002 L2004
PD *020 †55
SIEBRING, Barton Gearhard. 14555 W NATIONAL AVE 53151 #039-05-1987 L1991 **FM** *020 †18
SIEGEL, Mark. 14555 W NATIONAL AVE 53151 #056-06-1978 L1980 **CHP P** *020 †75
SLINDE, Nathan Eric. 14060 SOLITAIRE CT 53151 #056-06-1999 L2000 **GE** *020 †20
SMELTZ, Angela Rose. ■ 53146 #056-06-2008 **EM** *012
SPELLMAN, Robert John. ■ 53151 #023-07-1973 L1976 **IM** *071 †20
STOLZMANN, Amy Nicole. ■ 53151 #028-79-2005, ▲ L2005 **PD** *012
STUART, Robert Williston. 14555 W NATIONAL AVE, ST. LUKE'S NEW BERLIN URGE 53151
#025-12-1982 L1983 **EM** *020 †16
SWOBODA, Robert Jos. 2875 S 171ST ST 53151 #056-06-1980 L1984 **R** *020 †80
TAN, Corazon Cabrera. 2801 S MOORLAND RD 53151 #748-08-1977 L2005 **FM** *020 †18 ‡
TORRES, Roger Ven Soriano. 12555 W NATIONAL AVE, STE 201 53151 #748-01-1985 L1994
IMG IM *020 †20
TURCIOS, Rosa Elizabeth. ■ 53151 #451-01-1993 L2002 **CCS** *100
VINCENT, Dennis Galen. 14555 W NATIONAL AVE, STE 175 53151 #056-06-1982 L1988
GS VS *020 †85
WHEATLEY, Philip Owen. 2801 S MOORLAND RD 53151 #016-02-1982 L1984 **IM** *020 †20
WHITE, Tara Megan. ■ 53151 #056-05-2005 L2007 **PD** *012
WILLIAMS, Robert Edward. 12901 W NATIONAL AVE, POINTE CENTER 53151
#038-45-1997 L2001 **MPD** *020 †20,55
WINKOSKI, Jeffrey Duane. 13900 W NATIONAL AVE 53151 #048-02-1991 L1994 **FM** *020 †18
WUI, Marilou Arrozal. 12555 W NATIONAL AVE, STE 201 53151 #748-02-1996 L2003
IM IMG *020 †20

YOUNG, Patti Marie. 3610 MICHELLE WTMR MMRL DR 53151 #016-43-1993 L1996 **PD** *020 †55

NEW GLARUS — GREEN

JOSEPH, Anly. 1800 2ND ST, MONROE CLINIC 53574 #495-37-1996 L2004 **FM** *020 †18
SMITHERMAN, Marvin Lee. ■ 53574 #026-04-1973 L1974 **GS** *050 †85

NEW LISBON — JUNEAU

HINTON, Timothy Raymond. 901 W BRIDGE ST 53950 #026-04-1978 L1981 **FM** *020 †18

NEW LONDON — WAUPACA

ANDERSON, Robert Cleland. 1405 MILL ST, NEW LONDON FAMILY MEDICAL 54961
#038-44-1998 L2006 **FM** *020 †18
AVERY, Bryan Allen. 1420 ALGOMA ST 54961 #056-06-1985 L1986 **PUD IM** *020 †20
BELDEN, Allan D. ■ 54961 #026-04-1961 L1967 **P OS** *075 †75
CHYBOWSKI, Frank Matthew. 1420 ALGOMA ST 54961 #056-05-1987 L1993 **U** *020 †95
FISHER, Dirk Thos. 1420 ALGOMA ST 54961 #056-05-1979 L1980 **U** *020 †95
FLETCHER, William Ogden. 1405 MILL ST, APPLETON CARDIO ASSC 54961
#024-01-1985 L1990 **CD IM** *020 †20
FUHRMANN, Donn Darrel. 1405 MILL ST 54961 #056-05-1976 L1978 **FM** *020 †18
GARVIDA, Cesar Acoba. 1405 MILL ST 54961 #748-10-1963 L1969 **FM** *071 †18
HAMMES, David Arthur. 1405 MILL ST 54961 #056-05-1954 L1955 **R NM** *072
HILDEBRAND, Fredric L, Jr. 1420 ALGOMA ST 54961 #056-05-1986 L1993 **CD IM** *020 †18
HOULIHAN, Timothy John. 1405 MILL ST 54961 #056-06-1988 L1989 **FM** *020 †18
LAMB, Joseph Raymond. 1620 N SHAWANO ST 54961 #056-06-1987 L1988 **FM** *020 †18
LEIVA, Jose Miguel. 1420 ALGOMA ST, NEW LONDON CLINIC 54961 #451-01-1993 L2002
FM *020 †18
METZ, Daniel Peter. 1420 ALGOMA ST 54961 #056-06-1997 L2002 **ORS** *020 †40
PAJEK, Emil M. 1401 MILL ST, NEW LONDON FAMILY MED CTR 54961 #759-07-1988 L1995
IM *020 †20
PARTAIN, Kent L. 1420 ALGOMA ST 54961 #056-05-1981 L1986 **RHU IM** *020 †20
PINIACH, Donald Matthew. 1405 MILL ST, NEW LONDON FAMILY MEDICAL 54961
#068-01-1988 L1996 *020
RASOR, Timothy Brian. 1370 N SHAWANO ST 54961 #038-40-1985 L1986 **DMP EM** *020 †18
SCHILKE, Sarah Marie. 1405 MILL ST 54961 #056-06-2002 L2006 **FM** *100 †18
SCHLAIS, Dale Lawrence. 1420 ALGOMA ST, NEW LONDON CLINIC 54961 #056-06-1980 L1981
FM FPG *020 †18
SCHULER, Renae Sue. 1405 MILL ST 54961 #016-43-1994 L1997 **FM** *020 †18
TAAKE, Elmer Robert. 1420 ALGOMA ST, NEW LONDON CLINIC 54961 #056-05-1957 L1958
FM EM *071
WEBER, Joseph Westmore. 1420 ALGOMA ST 54961 #030-05-1956 L1959 **GP** *071 †18
WEBER, Marie T. 1420 ALGOMA ST, NEW LONDON CLINIC 54961 #016-06-1985 L1986
IM *020 †20
YOUNG, Brett Douglass. 1420 ALGOMA ST 54961 #056-06-1997 L2002 **ORS** *020 †40
YU, Carlos C. 1405 MILL ST 54961 #748-08-1966 L1973 **GS FM** *020 †85

NEW RICHMOND — SAINT CROIX

BECKEN, Eric Thomas. 551 HOSPITAL RD, MIDWEST ENT SPECIALISTS 54017
#026-04-2000 L2005 **OTO** *020 †45
CRAIG, James Langemo. 535 HOSPITAL RD 54017 #056-05-1952 L1956 **FM** *071 †18
DIETZLER, Joseph Aaron. 551 HOSPITAL RD, NEW RICHMOND CLINIC 54017
#056-05-2004 L2005 **FM** *100 †18
DRURY, Colin Jordan. 246 TIERNEY DR 54017 #056-05-1970 L1971 **GS FM** *020 †18 ‡
NEFF, Taylor Eugene. 246 TIERNEY DR, FAMILY MED CTR 54017 #035-01-1988 L1992 **EM** *020
OKNER, Thomas Luke. 551 HOSPITAL RD 54017 #035-09-1975 L1985 **OTO A** *020 †45 ‡
ORSELLO, Christopher A. ■ 54017 #026-04-1998 L2000 **FM** *020 †18
POWELL, Joseph Edward. 551 HOSPITAL RD 54017 #017-20-1960 L1961 **FM FPG** *071 †18
ROACH, Charles Albert. 821 W 8TH ST 54017 #026-04-1957 L1957 **OPH** *071 †35
WEISS, Nicholas Gregory. 535 HOSPITAL RD 54017 #056-06-1997 L2002 **OSM** *020 †40

NIAGARA — MARINETTE

BASU, Sandeep Kumar. 1601 ROOSEVELT RD, PAIN DIAGNOSTIC ASSOCIATES 54151
#496-09-1987 L2001 **HO ON** *020
HNATUK, Lorrence A. 500 ROOSEVELT RD 54151 #068-01-1988 L1999 **OTO** *020 †45
JAKEL, Victoria Ann. 1601 ROOSEVELT RD, PAIN DIAGNOSTIC 54151 #025-07-1990 L1991
FM *020 †18
LIAO, Katherine Go. 1601 ROOSEVELT RD, PAIN DIAGNOSTICS ASSOC 54151
#748-08-1991 L2000 **AN PME** *020
LOEWEN, John Lloyd. 615 WASHINGTON AVE 54151 #062-01-1975 L1977 **FM** *020
MAGINN, Richard Jos. ■ 54151 #016-01-1942 L1946 **OS GP** *071
SINGH, Francoise. PO BOX 6 54151 #396-32-1979 L1982 **NPM PD** *020 †55
SINGH, Vijay. 1601 ROOSEVELT RD, PAIN DIAGNOSTICS ASSOCS 54151 #495-67-1976 L1993
AN PME *020 †05
SONNENBURG, Robert Elmer, Jr. 500 ROOSEVELT RD 54151 #056-06-2000 L2005
OTO *020 †45

NORTH FOND DU LAC — FOND DU LAC

CLARK, Dwayne Charles. 723 PARK RIDGE LN, NORTH FOND DU LAC CLNC 54937
#036-07-1994 L2005 **FM** *020 †18
FRANCK, Barbara Helen. 723 PARK RIDGE LN, AGNESIAN HEALTH CARE 54937
#018-03-1997 L1998 **FM** *020 †18
FREDRICKSON, Russell John. 723 PARK RIDGE LN 54937 #056-05-2001 L2002 **FM** *020 †18
KHANPARA, Vipul Dharamshi. ■ 54937 #025-07-2004 L2007 **EM** *100

■ = Address Information Privacy Protected

NORTH FREEDOM – SAUK

KINDSCHI, Donald Rex. RR 1 BOX 673 53951 #041-01-1941 L1942 **AN** *020 †05

NORTH PRAIRIE – WAUKESHA

PLUDEMAN, Jay Bernard. ■ 53153 #056-06-2007 **FP** *012

OAK CREEK – MILWAUKEE

ABROL, Rahul Dev. ■ 53154 #305-01-2002 L2003 **SCI** *100

AGRAWAL, Ruchir. 2603 W RAWSON AVE STE 137 53154 #495-73-1994 L2001 **PD AI** *020 †03,55

ALI, Malik Sajid. 2603 W RAWSON AVE, SERVICES 53154 #704-25-1995 L1999 **IM** *020 †20

ALMAS, Rakhshinda. 2603 W RAWSON AVE, SERVICES 53154 #704-06-1983 L1995 **IM GP** *020 †20

BOGLE, Warren Cyrus. ■ 53154 #018-03-1944 L1956 **AN** *071 †05

BOLEK, George. 2603 W RAWSON AVE 53154 #759-01-1971 L1986 **FM** *020

CALDWELL-CHOR, Kelly Ann. 331 E PUETZ RD, STE 104 53154 #016-45-2000 L2002 **FM** *020 †18 ‡

COLAN, Richard Vincent. 8825 S HOWELL AVE, STE 101 53154 #041-14-1974 L1987 **CHN** *020 †55,75

DAHAM, Bassam. ■ 53154 #875-02-1994 L2006 **IM** *100

D'AMICO, Michael Dennis. 331 E PUETZ RD STE 104, LAKESHORE MED CLINIC 53154 #056-06-1994 L1995 **FM** *020 †18

DELGADO, Maria Anna. ■ 53154 #056-06-2008 *012

FAROOKI, Moeed. 10140 S WINDSOR DR 53154 #495-21-1961 L1977 **IM** *020 †20

FIKREE, Moin. 2603 W RAWSON AVE, MIDWEST URGENT MEDICAL SER 53154 #704-16-1985 L1990 **IM EM** *020 †20

FLORES, Suzanne Rodriguez. ■ 53154 #748-10-2006 *100

FREA, Anne Marie. ■ 53154 #056-06-2007 **PD** *012

HARRIS, Julia Grace. ■ 53154 #056-06-2008 *012

HUSSAIN, Fahmina Yasmeen. 200 E RYAN RD 53154 #016-45-1998 L2002 **MPD** *020 †20,55

JAKA, Arif G. 2603 W RAWSON AVE, SERVICES 53154 #704-16-1985 L1994 **FM** *020 †18

JEREB, Steven James. 8375 S HOWELL AVE 53154 #016-11-2000 L2001 **PD** *020 †55

KASTNER, Kimberly Joy. 8661 S HOWELL AVE 53154 #056-06-2001 L2003 **PD** *020 †55

KHARE, Smriti S. 8661 S HOWELL AVE, OAK CREEK PEDIATRICS 53154 #495-19-1985 L1993 **PD** *020 †55

KIM, Zaezeung. ■ 53154 #583-02-1960 L1976 **AI** *071 †03

LIPO, Robert Frank. 140 E RYAN RD 53154 #056-06-1958 L1960 **PTH** *071 †50

LUETZOW-FRANSON, Deborah. 2413 W RAWSON AVE 53154 #056-06-1987 L1988 **FM** *020 †18

MACDOUGALL, Ryan Scott. ■ 53154 #056-06-2006 L2008 **IM** *012

MARVIN, Joy Dawn. 331 E PUETZ RD, STE 104 53154 #016-42-1989 L2004 **GS** *020 †85

MEINERZ, Andrea Lee. ■ 53154 #056-06-2006 **N** *012

MOHIS, Shereen. 331 E PUETZ RD, STE 104 53154 #495-31-1998 L2003 **FM** *020 †18

NAIR, Ajit Velayudhan. ■ 53154 #016-42-2003 L2004 **DR** *012

PAGEDAS, Tony Gus. 2603 W RAWSON AVE, STE 105 53154 #017-20-1963 L1970 **OBG** *020 †30

PAREKH, Madhavi. 2603 W RAWSON AVE, STE 108 53154 #495-01-1971 L1998 **GP** *020 †50

PATEL, Rajesh Ashok. ■ 53154 #056-06-2008 *012

ROMINE, Kathryn Lynn. ■ 53154 #654-01-1989 L1991 **CHP** *020 †75

SAEDI, Saed F. 2603 W RAWSON AVE, STE 135 53154 #517-01-1966 L1975 **TS** *020 †85,90

SALAM, Yasser. ■ 53154 #875-01-1988 L2001 **N IM** *020 †75,20

SHAH, Vinodkumar S. 147 W RYAN RD 53154 #495-48-1975 L1985 **IM** *020

SKOLD, Craig Lindsey. 8201 S HOWELL AVE STE 400 53154 #025-07-1978 L1986 **EM** *020 †20,55,16

SONI, Nalin S. 147 W RYAN RD 53154 #495-23-1970 L1976 **IM ON** *020 †20

STAR-ADAMCZYK, Ursula H. 331 E PUETZ RD, STE 104 53154 #759-01-1978 L2004 **OBG** *020 †30

STEWART, Paul Gerard. ■ 53154 #056-06-1997 *100

SUKUMARAN, Sunitha. ■ 53154 #495-80-1998 L2006 **IM** *100 †20

TETTING, Gregg Edward. 331 E PUETZ RD, 331 E PUETZ RD 53154 #056-06-1993 L1996 **PD ADL** *020 †55

WELLS, Alvin Francis. 200 E RYAN RD, STE 101 53154 #011-04-1996 L2003 **RHU IM** *020 †20

OCONOMOWOC – WAUKESHA

ADLER, Gerard Geo. 915 SUMMIT AVE, AURORA WILKINSON MEDICAL C 53066 #056-05-1989 L1994 **ORS OSM** *020 †40

BAJIC, Jurica. ■ 53066 #957-01-1985 L1996 **AN** *020

BAKER, Barbara Alison. 791 SUMMIT AVE, AT OCONOMOWOC MEMORIAL 53066 #038-06-1993 L1999 **PCP** *020 †50

BALTZ, Aaron Coulter. 791 SUMMIT AVE 53066 #056-06-2000 L2006 **GE** *020 †20

BAMRAH, Paramjit Kaur. 915 SUMMIT AVE 53066 #495-29-1968 L1976 **FM PTH** *020 †50,18

BARDEEN-HENSCHEL, Ann. ■ 53066 #056-05-1945 L1946 **AN** *071 †05

BAYLISS, Katherine Marie. 791 SUMMIT AVE, AT OCONOMOWOC MEMORIAL 53066 #056-06-1986 L1987 **PTH** *020 †50

BERGOM, Michael Allen. 915 SUMMIT AVE 53066 #037-01-2001 L2003 **GS** *020

BHATIA, Atul. 915 SUMMIT AVE 53066 #495-29-1988 L1995 **ICE CD** *020 †20

BOSCHEK, Brenda Lynn. 1185 CORPORATE CENTER DR 53066 #030-06-1998 L1999 **MPD** *020 †20,55

BOSSHARD, Lisa Sue. 915 SUMMIT AVE 53066 #056-06-1998 L1999 **PD** *020 †55

BREYER, Julius Thos. ■ 53066 #056-06-1967 L1969 **IM OS** *071

CESCHI, Jeffrey. 791 SUMMIT AVE, OCONOMOWOC MEMORIAL HOSPIT 53066 #056-06-1985 L1986 **AN** *020 †05

CHAMBERS, Richard K. ■ 53066 #056-06-1946 L1948 **FPG AS** *071 †18

CLEARY, Dan Thos. 1229 ROBRUCK DR 53066 #056-05-1971 L1977 **IM** *020 †20

COLVIN, Jill Hatfield. 915 SUMMIT AVE 53066 #056-05-1996 L1999 **D** *020 †15

COOPER, William Rollin. 1185 CORPORATE CENTER DR 53066 #056-05-1993 L2006 **IM** *020 †20

CORNELLA-CARLSON, Tracey. 34700 VALLEY RD 53066 #016-42-1992 L2005 **CHP** *020 †75

CULLINANE, David Wm. ■ 53066 #056-05-1991 L2007 **CD** *020 †20

DALL, Tara Lynn. 1185 CORPORATE CENTER DR, CHOLESTEROL & LIFESTYLE CT 53066 #056-05-1998 L1999 **OS FM** *020 †18

DAUFENBACH, Donna Ruth. 915 SUMMIT AVE 53066 #056-06-1991 L1992 **OPH** *020 †35

DE JONG, Julie Marie. 1284 SUMMIT AVE 53066 #056-05-1991 L1995 **OBG** *020 †30

DERRIG, Thomas M. 915 SUMMIT AVE 53066 #037-01-1996 L2001 **GS** *020 †85

D'OLEIRE, Floriane Romy. ■ 53066 #409-19-1988 L1995 **CHP** *020 †75

DUFFY, Deirdre Ann. ■ 53066 #035-47-1992 L2005 **OBG** *020 †30

DUMA, Matthew Albert. 970 S SILVER LAKE ST # 102 53066 #016-11-1986 L1987 **PD** *020 †55

DVORAK, Eric Maitland. ■ 53066 #056-05-2005 L2006 **PM** *012

ELLIS, Mary K. 915 SUMMIT AVE, WILKINSON MEDICAL CLINICS 53066 #056-05-1987 L1988 **OPH** *020 †35

FERGUSON, David James. 791 SUMMIT AVE, AT OCONOMOWOC MEMORIAL 53066 #048-13-1988 L1994 **PCP** *020 †50

FEULNER, Robert Chas. ■ 53066 #035-19-1953 L1955 **DR NM** *071 †80,28

GATTO, James Joseph. 915 SUMMIT AVE 53066 #016-06-1995 L1998 **FM** *020 †18

GAYNOR, Terrence John. 791 SUMMIT AVE # ANES 53066 #056-05-1984 L1985 **AN** *020 †05

GILL, Kara G. ■ 53066 #056-06-2005 L2006 **DR** *012

GILMORE, George Edgar, IV. 791 SUMMIT AVE, OCONOMOWOC MEMORIAL HOSPIT 53066 #056-06-1998 L1999 **EM** *020 †16

GOEL, Poonam. 970 S SILVER LAKE ST # 102 53066 #495-29-1992 L2000 **PD** *020 †55

GUCCIARDI, John W, Jr. 1185 CORPORATE CENTER DR, STE 175 53066 #654-01-1986 L1987 **FM** *020 †18

GUSTIN, Alan Ellsworth. 1284 SUMMIT AVE 53066 #018-03-1974 L1975 **OBG** *020 †30

HAGUE, Karin. 791 SUMMIT AVE, AT OCONOMOWOC MEMORIAL 53066 #035-47-1991 L2002 **NP** *020 †50

HAIGHT, Richard Orlo. ■ 53066 #018-03-1974 L1977 **FM** *071 †18

HANSEN, Richard Morris. 791 SUMMIT AVE 53066 #017-20-1973 L1974 **ON HEM** *020 †20

HARSHBARGER, Lisa Louise. 1284 SUMMIT AVE 53066 #056-06-1998 L2000 **OBG** *020 †30

HERMANOFF, Mark Heinrick. 915 SUMMIT AVE 53066 #016-06-1991 L1999 **AI** *020 †20,03

HILL, Timothy John. 791 SUMMIT AVE 53066 #016-11-1982 L1985 **EM** *020 †16

HOLBROOK, Thomas Lincoln. 34700 VALLEY RD 53066 #048-04-1970 L1971 **P** *075 †75

HUNTER, Steven Jay. 915 SUMMIT AVE 53066 #056-05-1989 L1990 **D** *020 †20,15

HUTJENS, Kirk Jos. 915 SUMMIT AVE, MEDICINE DIV 53066 #056-05-1991 L1995 **IM** *020 †20

IBRIC, Jean Anne. 34784 SCHIMMEL RD 53066 #403-01-1990 L1990 **FM** *020 †18

IRFAN, Tariq Bin. 915 SUMMIT AVE 53066 #704-02-1992 L2002 **N CN** *020 †18

JANUSONIS, Palmira A. 791 SUMMIT AVE, OCONOMOWOC MEMORIAL HOSPIT 53066 #016-11-1966 L1967 **AN** *020 †05

JOHNSON, Collin Bruce. 791 SUMMIT AVE, AT OCONOMOWOC MEMORIAL 53066 #056-05-1973 L1974 **PTH BBK** *020 †50

JOHNSON, Dale Alan. 820 SUMMIT AVE 53066 #016-11-1978 L1979 **FM** *020 †18

JOHNSON, Kenneth Oscar. 5722 N MARY LN 53066 #016-06-1958 L1961 **PD OS** *030 †55

KASS, Kevin Jay. 915 SUMMIT AVE 53066 #056-06-1985 L1989 **DR** *020 †80

KEFER, Michael P. 791 SUMMIT AVE, LAKE COUNTRY EMERGENCY PHY 53066 #016-01-1986 L1987 **EM** *020 †20,16

KELLY, John Edward. 820 SUMMIT AVE 53066 #748-01-1979 L1982 **FM EM** *020 †18

KIDD, Charles Frederick. 1185 CORPORATE CENTER DR 53066 #056-05-1996 L2004 **U** *020 †95

KRIEGER, Robert Wm. 915 SUMMIT AVE 53066 #056-05-1975 L1976 **PD** *020 †55

KUECK, Brian Dale. 791 SUMMIT AVE, AT OCONOMOWOC MEMORIAL 53066 #056-06-1981 L1982 **PTH HMP** *020 †50

LAKE, Peter Matthew. 34700 VALLEY RD, ROGERS MEMORIAL HOSPITAL. 53066 #018-03-1986 L1991 **CHP P** *020 †75

LEAHY, Erin Jeanette. ■ 53066 #056-06-2007 **IM** *012

LEAHY, John M, III. 915 SUMMIT AVE 53066 #038-41-1992 L2000 **DR** *020 †80

LENZ, Michael Allen. 1260B BROWN ST, PROHEALTH CARE MEDICAL CEN 53066 #056-06-1996 L2000 **MPD** *020 †20

LEVENHAGEN, Tim C. 34700 VALLEY RD 53066 #056-05-1991 L1992 **P** *020 †75

LIPSCOMB, Steven John. 791 SUMMIT AVE 53066 #056-05-1989 L2001 **GE IM** *020 †20

LUHN, Roger Duane. 34700 VALLEY RD, ROGERS MEMORIAL HOSP 53066 #005-18-1986 L1996 **P** *020 †75

LUNDGREN, Ralph Joseph. 38075 MAINLAND DR 53066 #038-41-1962 L1966 **PD** *071 †55

MANN, Sherri Jo. 791 SUMMIT AVE, AT OCONOMOWOC MEMORIAL 53066 #021-01-1996 L2002 **PTH** *020 †50

MARDEN, Philip Manuel. 340 SUMMIT AVE 53066 #056-05-1962 L1963 **PD OS** *020 †55

MARIANO, Elpidio Abanilla. 34700 VALLEY RD 53066 #018-03-2002 L2006 **P** *020

MARKUS, Stan Lawrence. 1185 CORPORATE CENTER DR, # 200 53066 #038-45-1982 L1987 **GS** *020 †85

MARSHALL, Michael Bruce. 1079 SUMMIT AVE, AURORA MEDICAL GROUP 53066 #836-01-1988 L2007 **FM** *020 †18

MARSZALEK, Renee Beth. 915 SUMMIT AVE, AURORA WILKINSON MEDICAL C 53066 #422-01-2001 L2004 **IM** *020

MIDTLING, John Edward, III. PO BOX 388 53066 #026-04-1976 L1989 **FM** *030 †18

MIELKE, Michelle Marie. 915 SUMMIT AVE, WILKINSON MEDICAL CLINIC 53066 #056-05-1996 L2001 **PD** *020 †55

MILLER, G Danl. ■ 53066 #056-06-1954 L1956 **AN EM** *071 †05

MILLER, Maren Elizabeth. ■ 53066 #056-06-2007 **PD** *012

MOLLOY, Robert Michael, Jr. 791 SUMMIT AVE 53066 #017-20-1990 L1991 **GE IM** *020 †20

MOTZEL, Albert J, Jr. 915 SUMMIT AVE 53066 #028-34-1953 L1954 **OS GS** *071 †85

MOYER, Gregory Michael. 970 S SILVER LAKE ST, STE 102 53066 #056-06-1993 L1994 **PD** *020 †55

MULLER, Marta Cristina. ■ 53066 #056-06-1967 L1968 **P CHP** *020

MURPHY, John W. 915 SUMMIT AVE 53066 #020-02-1967 L1968 **GS** *020 †85

MURPHY, John Wm. 915 SUMMIT AVE, WILKINSON MED CLINICS S.C. 53066 #056-05-1985 L1989 **FM** *020 †18

MURRAY, Timothy J.. ■ 53066 #305-01-2003 L2004 **AN** *012

NARKIS, Carrie Anne. 915 SUMMIT AVE 53066 #056-05-2002 L2005 **IM** *020 †20

NEILS, Richard Ervin. 888 THACKERAY TRL 53066 #026-04-1974 L1976 **D IM** *020 †20,15

O'MARA, Michael Guy. 888 THACKERAY TRL, STE 201 53066 #040-02-1966 L1967 **IM** *020 †20

PANGALLO, Cynthia Ann. 1185 CORPORATE CENTER DR, STE 200 53066 #056-05-1986 L1991 **GS** *020 †85

PENG, Ruth Yuanmei. 791 SUMMIT AVE, AT OCONOMOWOC MEMORIAL 53066 #035-46-1999 L2005 **PTH** *020 †50

PETERSON, Freddie N. 6151 SAND BEACH RD 53066 #016-06-1940 L1958 **PD PDS** *071 †65

PHILLIPS, Michael J. 791 SUMMIT AVE 53066 #056-06-1976 L1977 **PTH** *020 †50

■ = Address Information Privacy Protected

PHILLIPS, Michael Jay. 1185 CORPORATE CENTER DR 53066 #030-05-1986 L1994
GS VS *020 †85

PRASAD, Krishna. 791 SUMMIT AVE 53066 #495-31-1979 L1988 EM IM *020 †16

RASMUSSEN, Karen Kusba. 915 SUMMIT AVE, WILKINSON CLINIC 53066 #056-05-1980 L1981
DR *075 †80

RASMUSSEN, Paul David. 915 SUMMIT AVE, WILKINSON CLINIC 53066 #056-05-1980 L1981
ORS *020 †40

RIETBROCK, Michael John. 915 SUMMIT AVE 53066 #026-04-1968 L1972 IM CD *020 †20 ‡

ROGAHN, Denise Carol. ■ 53066 #056-06-1996 L1997 FM *020 †18

SCHLOMER, David Duane. 1185 CORPORATE CENTER DR 53066 #056-06-1996 L2000
MPD *020 †20,55

SCHMIDT, Suzanne Hoch. W205 ALLEN RD, RENEU WOMEN'S HEALTH & MED 53066
#056-06-1987 L1988 OBG *020 †30

SCHMIDT OLIVER, Kari Ann. 785 SUMMIT AVE STE 203, PROHEALTH CARE MEDICAL
CEN #028-02-1995 L1999 OBG *020 †30

SCHNEIDER, Scott Bennett. 1205 CORPORATE CENTER DR 53066 #056-06-1999 L2006
ORS *020

SCHROEDER, Thomas Andrew. 915 SUMMIT AVE 53066 #018-03-1959 L1963 OBG *071 †30

SCHROETTNER, Andrew John. 888 THACKERAY TRL STE 211 53066 #056-06-1992 L1993
P *020 †30

SCHUMACHER, Bernhard John. 791 SUMMIT AVE 53066 #056-06-1954 L1955 IM *071 †20

SCHWAB, John Damian. 791 SUMMIT AVE 53066 #056-06-1994 L1995 IM *020 †20

SIMONS, Kristin Jean. ■ 53066 #056-06-1995 L1997 FM *071 †18

SIMS, Patrick Jos. 1284 SUMMIT AVE 53066 #016-43-1992 L1996 OBG *020 †30

SMARRELLA, Jeffrey Justin. 34700 VALLEY RD, ROGERS MEMORIAL HOSPITAL 53066
#038-40-2002 L2005 CHP *100 †75

SMITH, Jeffrey Adam. ■ 53066 #038-43-1998 L2001 EM *020 †16

STANWYCK, T Scott. 1205 CORPORATE CENTER DR 53066 #050-02-1984 L1993
ORS GS *020 †40

STODDARD, Emily Elizabeth. 1185 CORPORATE CENTER DR, STE 200 53066
#056-05-1996 L1997 GS *020 †85

TAYLOR, Thomas Fleming. 888 THACKERAY TRL, WHITMAN PK PROF BLDG 53066
#056-05-1967 L1968 OPH *020 †35

TJARKSEN, Michael Eugene. 1205 CORPORATE CENTER DR 53066 #025-01-1991 L1998
ORS *020 †40

TYLICKI, David George. 915 SUMMIT AVE 53066 #056-05-2000 L2002 APM *020 †60

ULERY, David Orville. 915 SUMMIT AVE 53066 #038-40-1973 L1974 PD PSM *020 †55

VARMA, Deep Kumar. 34700 VALLEY RD 53066 #041-12-1998 L2003 P *020

VIEL, Robert Sprague, Jr. ■ 53066 #056-06-1981 L1985 P *020 †18

WEISENSEL, Nicolette Ella. 34700 VALLEY RD, ROGERS MEMORIAL HOSP 53066
#056-05-2000 L2001 P OS *020 †75

WELTZIN, Theodore Eldon. 34700 VALLEY RD 53066 #026-04-1984 L1994 P *020 †75

WESSLING, Mark Raymond. 915 SUMMIT AVE, WILKINSON CLINIC SC 53066
#018-03-1979 L1980 PD *020 †55

WESTLAKE, Timothy W. 791 SUMMIT AVE, LAKE COUNTRY EMERGENCY PHY 53066
#056-06-1995 L1999 EM *020 †16

WHITTAKER, Michael Henry. 791 SUMMIT AVE, AT OCONOMOWOC MEMORIAL 53066
#017-20-1983 L1992 PTH HEM *020 †50

WOHLFEIL, Jill Parker. 785 SUMMIT AVE # 203 53066 #025-07-1988 L1993 OBG *020 †30

ZOELLER, Robert Lawrence. 791 SUMMIT AVE 53066 #056-05-1989 L1990 PM PMM *020 †60

ZUZICK, Paul H. 915 SUMMIT AVE, WILKINSIN MEDICAL CLINIC 53066 #056-05-1999 L2000
FM *020 †18

OCONTO – OCONTO

AWEN, Charles F. 230 WASHBURN AVE 54153 #583-02-1957 L1976 PTH GP *020 †50

BIVINS, Robert Anthony. 820 ARBUTUS AVE 54153 #025-07-2000 L2003 FM *020 †18

CONANT, Scott Henry. 103 1ST ST, OCONTO MEDICAL CENTER 54153 #039-05-1984 L1985
GP IM *020

HONISH, John Sylvester. 620 SMITH AVE 54153 #056-05-1964 L1965 GP *020

KUMAR, Sarvadaman J. 620 SMITH AVE 54153 #495-43-1978 L1998 IM *020 †20

PHILBIN, Jennifer Michele. 620 SMITH AVE 54153 #016-11-1998 L2002 FM *020 †18

PINKERTON, John Douglas. 405 1ST ST 54153 #010-01-1960 L1967 GS *071 †85

RALLS, Frank Mike. 103 1ST ST 54153 #056-05-1994 L1995 IMG *012 †18

OCONTO FALLS – OCONTO

BOWERS, Judith E. 835 S MAIN ST, STE 2 54154 #025-76-1992, ▲ L2006 OBG *020 †30

COATES, John Thos. 855 S MAIN ST, COMMUNITY MEMORIAL HOSPITA 54154
#038-43-1982 L1983 EM *020 †18,16

COUSSONS, Herbert Stanley. 833 S MAIN ST 54154 #021-06-1992 L2001 OBG *020 †30

CUPINO, Isaias R, Jr. 855 S MAIN ST 54154 #748-10-1984 L1995 FM *020 †18

DOLIBOIS, John Michael. 835 S MAIN ST 54154 #038-41-1970 L2001 ORS *020 †40

GARNER, Harold Benj. 815 S MAIN ST, 315 S MAIN ST 54154 #020-12-1985 L1986 IM *020 †20

GREMBAN, Douglas Carl. 815 S MAIN ST 54154 #026-04-1978 L1981 FM *020 †18

HEYKA, Charles John. 833 S MAIN ST 54154 #025-07-1985 L2006 FM FPG *020 †18

LIEBL, R Scott. 835 S MAIN ST 54154 #056-06-1973 L1978 GS *020 †85

MARLETT, Myron Max. 835 S MAIN ST 54154 #016-11-1971 L1978 U EM *020 †95

O'TOOLE, Michael C. 833 S MAIN ST 54154 #001-06-1998 L2002 OBG *020

PEREZ, Iris Theodora C. 855 S MAIN ST, COMMUNITY MEM HOSP 54154 #748-02-1986 L1996
FM *020 †18

SIEFERT, Clyde E. 833 S MAIN ST 54154 #038-41-1952 L1953 GP *071

TALENS, Antonio Calica. ■ 54154 #748-01-1962 L1969 AN *071

TANDIAS, James. 855 S MAIN ST 54154 #026-04-1972 L1981 ORS *020 †40

TEMP, Megan Elise. 833 S MAIN ST 54154 #038-34-1994 L2002 OBG *020 †30

VOGEL, Edward Geo. 833 S MAIN ST 54154 #016-43-1965 L1972 OBG *020 †30

WITTMAN, William James. 833 S MAIN ST 54154 #026-04-1980 L1981 IM *020 †20

WONG, James R P. 855 S MAIN ST 54154 #016-43-1951 L1958 EM GP *071

ODANAH – ASHLAND

MATING, Narwhals. PO BOX 250, 72718 MAPLE ST 54861 #026-04-2000 L2001 FM *020 †18

OMRO – WINNEBAGO

BAKER, Peter Nicholas. ■ 54963 #016-11-1960 L1961 PD *071 †55

ONALASKA – LA CROSSE

BAHR, Kelley Ann. 3111 GUNDERSEN DR, ONALASKA CLINIC 54650 #056-05-1997 L2000
FM *020 †18

BOOMER, Robert B. N5141 GREEN COULEE RD 54650 #024-01-1951 L1970 OPH *071 †35

BORGE, Robyn Brady. 3111 GUNDERSEN DR 54650 #037-01-2000 L2001 FM *020

BRUBAKER, Stephen James. 3111 GUNDERSEN DR, CLINIC ONALASKA 54650
#016-11-1970 L1977 OPH *020 †35

CAPELLI, David Paul. 191 THEATRE RD 54650 #016-42-1996 L2002 PD *020 †55

CARR, Craig Cordelle. 3111 GUNDERSEN DR, ONALASKA CLINIC 54650 #026-04-1976 L1977
FM *020 †18

CARSKADON, William Edward. ■ 54650 #016-11-1970 L1972 EM OM *020

CHAIKIN, Gary Dean. 704 SAND LAKE RD 54650 #012-05-1982 L1998 P *020 †75

CUNDIFF, Jerald E, Jr. 1107 PINE ST 54650 #016-43-1993 L1997 OPH *020 †35

DANNING, Carol Lynn. 3111 GUNDERSEN DR, GUNDERSEN CLNC 54650 #056-06-1990 L1993
RHU *020 †20

DAVIDSON, Jill. 3111 GUNDERSEN DR, ONALASKA CLINIC 54650 #018-03-1988 L1992
OBG *020 †30

DONOHUE, Micca Kathleen. 3111 GUNDERSEN DR, GUNDERSEN LUTHERAN 54650
#018-03-2003 L2007 OBG *020

DU CHARME, Wanda Marie. 3111 GUNDERSEN DR, ONALASKA CLINIC 54650
#056-06-1981 L1982 FM *020 †18

ERICKSON, Nancy Lynn. 191 THEATRE RD, ONALASKA CLINIC 54650 #056-05-1999 L2000
FM *020 †18

ESCHER, Scott Arthur. 3111 GUNDERSEN DR, ONALASKA CLINIC 54650 #056-05-1987 L1989
FM FSM *020 †18

FITZGERALD, Kevin Michael. 191 THEATRE RD, ONALASKA CLINIC 54650 #030-06-1995 L1996
FM *020 †18

FOWLER, Bradley Lawrence. 3111 GUNDERSEN DR 54650 #025-01-1987 L2001
ORS OSM *020 †40

GERIG, Julie Rebecca. 3111 GUNDERSEN DR 54650 #056-05-2004 L2004 FM *020 †18

GUNDERSEN, Erik Adolf. 3111 GUNDERSEN DR, ONALASKA CLINIC 54650
#056-05-1994 L1995 FM *020 †18

HAIK, Nedira E. 191 THEATRE RD, FRANCISCAN SKEMP - ONALASK 54650 #048-13-1993 L2006
FM *020 †18

HALVERSON, Peter Anthony. ■ 54650 #056-05-2006 IM *012

HANSON, Timothy Scott. 191 THEATRE RD, ONALASKA CLINIC 54650 #026-04-1985 L1995
FM *020 †18

HERATH, John Frederick. 3111 GUNDERSEN DR 54650 #026-04-1999 L2000 IM *020 †20

HOFFMAN, Donna Lynn. 3111 GUNDERSEN DR, ONALASKA CLINIC 54650 #056-05-1995 L1999
FM *020 †18

HOULIHAN, David John. 509 GREEN COULEE RD 54650 #018-03-1990 L1994 P *020 †75

INMAN, Catherine Jane. 3111 GUNDERSEN DR 54650 #038-06-1991 L1992 OM *020 †70

IVERSON, Gary O'Neil. 3111 GUNDERSEN DR, ONALASKA CLINIC 54650 #056-05-1974 L1975
IM *020 †20

JAEGER, Kevin Matthew. 3111 GUNDERSEN DR, ONALASKA CLINIC 54650
#056-06-1983 L1986 CD IM *020 †20

JOHNSON, Steven J. 3111 GUNDERSEN DR, ONALASKA CLINIC 54650 #018-75-1986, ▲ L1994
PD *020 †55

JUNGCK, Mark Cameron. 191 THEATRE RD, ONALASKA CLINIC 54650 #025-07-1981 L1984
FM *020 †18

KERR, Bruce Jay Arthur. 3111 GUNDERSEN DR, ONALASKA CLINIC 54650 #026-04-1979 L1996
EM IM *020 †20

KLAS, Paul Thomas. 3111 GUNDERSEN DR 54650 #056-05-1983 L2006 FM *020 †18

KLEVAN, Judy Lynn. 3111 GUNDERSEN DR, ONALASKA CLINIC 54650 #035-06-1984 L1989
PD *020 †55

KLEVEN, Jennifer E. 3111 GUNDERSEN DR 54650 #056-06-1998 L2003 PD *020 †55

KRIEN, Joseph Scott. 191 THEATRE RD, ONALASKA CLINIC 54650 #056-05-1993 L1994
FM *020 †18

LAWNICKI, Clyde Casimir. 2902 HEATHER CT 54650 #056-06-1968 L1969 U UP *071 †95

LOCKETZ, Alan Michael. ■ 54650 #016-42-1966 L1967 OPH OS *050 †35

LOCKHART, Jack Mc Kamey. 3111 GUNDERSEN DR, GUNDERSEN-LUTHERAN
ONALASK 54650 #024-01-1977 L1977 RHU IM *020 †20

MAC EWEN, Almon R. 5884 COUNTY OS 54650 #064-01-1950 L1954 U *071 †95

MAHR, Todd Alan. 3111 GUNDERSEN DR, ONALASKA CLINIC 54650 #056-05-1984 L1985
AI PDA *020 †03,55

MARCHIANDO, Laura K. 3111 GUNDERSEN DR, ONALASKA CLINIC 54650 #018-03-2000 L2005
FM *020 †18 ‡

MERCHLEWITZ, John Frank. 3111 GUNDERSEN DR, GUNDERSEN CLINIC 54650
#026-04-1992 L1993 FM *020 †18

MUNN, James Hugh. 3111 GUNDERSEN DR, ONALASKA CLINIC 54650 #056-05-1970 L1973
IM GP *020 †20

MURPHY, John Michael. 3111 GUNDERSEN DR, ONALASKA CLINIC 54650 #056-06-1994 L1995
FM *020 †18

NAIK, Rajiv Michael. 3111 GUNDERSEN DR, ONALASKA CLINIC 54650 #056-05-1995 L1999
PD *020 †55

NAIK, Sarah S. 3111 GUNDERSEN DR, ONALASKA CLINIC 54650 #056-05-1995 L1999
IM *072 †20

NOLL, Karl Ray. 3111 GUNDERSEN DR, ONALASKA CLINIC 54650 #056-05-1984 L1988
D *020 †15

PECK, Christopher Previn. 3111 GUNDERSEN DR, ONALASKA CLINIC 54650
#056-05-2002 L2005 *020 †18

PEHLING, Gregory Burton. 3111 GUNDERSEN DR, GUNDERSEN CLNC-ONALASKA 54650
#026-04-1977 L1983 END IM *020 †20

RILEY, Edward H, II. 3111 GUNDERSEN DR, ONALASKA CLINIC 54650 #026-08-1987 L1997
ORS EM *020 †40

ROBERTS, Thomas Newman. 3111 GUNDERSEN DR, ONALASKA CLINIC 54650
#056-05-1968 L1969 PD DIA *020 †55

RODZAK, Jeffrey E. 3111 GUNDERSEN DR, ONALASKA CLINIC 54650 #016-42-1988 L2001
OBG *020 †30

SAXTON, Mark Lewis. 3111 GUNDERSEN DR, ONALASKA CLINIC 54650 #026-04-1988 L2004 **PDS GS** *020 †85
SHAPIRO, Stephen Barnet. 3111 GUNDERSEN DR, ONALASKA CLINIC 54650 #056-05-1994 L2002 **GS** *020 †85
SHERMAN, Roger. ■ 54650 #038-44-1998 L2007 **OBG** *020 †30
SILVA, Paul Douglas. 191 THEATRE RD, FRANCISCAN SKEMP HEALTHCAR 54650 #005-19-1981 L1987 **REN OBG** *020 †30
STEPHENS, Shannan K. 3111 GUNDERSEN DR 54650 #056-05-1999 L2003 **OBG** *020 †30
TANNER, Suzanne Marie. 3111 GUNDERSEN DR, ONALASKA CLINIC 54650 #007-02-1984 L2002 **ORS PD** *020 †55,40
TAUKE, Ralph Edward. 3111 GUNDERSEN DR, ONALASKA CLINIC 54650 #018-03-1976 L1979 **FM** *020 †18
THURMAN, Chad Michael. 3111 GUNDERSEN DR, ONALASKA CLINIC 54650 #046-01-2000 L2001 **FM** *020 †18
TRANNEL, Thomas J. ■ 54650 #016-11-1991 L1996 **CHP P** *020 †75
URUSOPONE, Pakorn. ■ 54650 #891-01-1992 L1999 **AN** *020 †05
VALEN, Peter Arndt. 3111 GUNDERSEN DR, ONALASKA CLINIC 54650 #026-04-1978 L1983 **RHU** *020 †20 ‡
VISHWANAT, Balaji. ■ 54650 #495-37-1966 L1975 **N** *071 †75
WASHA, Darryl Milo. W7371 COUNTY ROAD Z 54650 #026-04-1963 L1970 **DR NM** *020 †80,28
WEBSTER, Stephen Burtis. 3111 GUNDERSEN DR, MAIL STOP NC3-006 54650 #016-06-1960 L1971 **D** *020 †15 ‡
WHYTE, Brett Steven. 3111 GUNDERSEN DR 54650 #056-05-1994 L1995 **EM** *020 †18
WINTERSTEEN, Virginia G. 3111 GUNDERSEN DR, ONALASKA CLINIC 54650 #056-05-1982 L1988 **ORS P** *020 †40
WISSINK, Stephen Craig. 3111 GUNDERSEN DR, ONALASKA CLINIC 54650 #028-02-1994 L1996 **IM** *020 †20
ZIMMERMAN, Lisa Marie L. ■ 54650 #056-05-1978 L1987 **GPM AM** *020
ZURBRIGGEN, Thomas Lee. 3111 GUNDERSEN DR, ONALASKA CLINIC 54650 #018-03-1978 L1979 **IM** *020 †20

ONEIDA – BROWN

JOHNSON, Brian Lee. 4611 HILLCREST DR 54155 #047-06-1998 L2001 **IM** *020 †20

OOSTBURG – SHEBOYGAN

HEFFELFINGER-JUTTNER, M J. ■ 53070 #018-03-1967 L1968 **PTH** *071 †50
JUTTNER, Hans-Udo. ■ 53070 #407-12-1961 L2003 **R** *071 †80
PAWLAK, James Ronald. 927 CENTER AVE 53070 #649-14-1975 L1977 **FM EM** *020 †18 ‡

OREGON – DANE

BALIN, Adam Hunter. 753 N MAIN ST 53575 #028-03-1986 L1989 **FM** *020 †18
BISGROVE, Joanna Turner. 753 N MAIN ST, OREGON CLINIC 53575 #016-01-2003 L2007 **FM** *100 †18
BONNELL, Sanee Marie. 137 S MAIN ST 53575 #056-05-1984 L1987 **FM** *020 †18
CRENNELL, Ean Henry. 1457 STORYTOWN RD 53575 #539-03-1955 L1961 **EM** *071
DREWS, Timothy Donald. 137 S MAIN ST 53575 #056-05-2003 L2004 **FM** *020 †18
DUKERSCHEIN, Franklin N. 753 N MAIN ST, OREGON CLINIC 53575 #056-05-1949 L1950 **FM** *071
GRAZIANO, Franklin M. 853 TIPPERARY RD 53575 #051-01-1973 L1974 **RHU AI** *050 †20,03
HEIFNER, William Ray. 137 S MAIN ST 53575 #028-03-1985 L1986 **FM** *020 †18
KULLERSTRAND, Donald S. ■ 53575 #016-11-1961 L1965 **OBG GP** *071
LA MANNA, Lorraine Jean. ■ 53575 #034-01-1990 L2007 **GS** *020
MARSH, Ryan Scott. ■ 53575 #007-02-1998 L2002 **IM** *020 †20
OKADA, David Jos. 753 N MAIN ST 53575 #056-05-1983 L1986 **FM** *020 †18
PASTER, Robert Merrill. 753 N MAIN ST 53575 #016-11-1974 L1976 **FM EM** *020 †18
SCHROEDER, R Walter. ■ 53575 #056-05-1953 L1966 **PD FM** *071 †55
SCHWARTZSTEIN, Alan I. 753 N MAIN ST, OREGON CLINIC 53575 #033-06-1978 L1987 **FM UCM** *020 †18
SHILLINGSTAD, Robert Bret. ■ 53575 #034-01-1990 L1991 **GS CCS** *020 †85
SOMMERS, Martha Anne. ■ 53575 #056-05-1990 L1994 **FM** *020 †18
WARBASSE, Eric Andrew. 137 S MAIN ST 53575 #025-07-2001 L2002 **FM** *020

OSCEOLA – POLK

BARTLESON, Jerry Russell. 301 RIVER ST 54020 #035-15-1983 L1987 **GP** *020
BRUNCLIK, Jeanine Leann. ■ 54020 #026-04-2003 L2006 **FM** *020 †18
CIEGLER, Glenn Warren. 301 RIVER ST 54020 #016-11-1989 L1994 **ORS** *020 †40
COX, Victor Stuart, III. 301 RIVER ST 54020 #026-04-1994 L2001 **OTO** *020 †45
DEZIEL, Dennis Patrick. 301 RIVER ST, OSCEOLA MEDICAL CENTER 54020 #026-04-1985 L1989 **FM** *020
DUBOIS, Christian Michael. 301 RIVER ST 54020 #016-02-1998 L2004 **ORS OSS** *020 †40
DYBVIG, Robert Holms. 301 RIVER ST 54020 #026-04-1987 L1999 **FM** *030 †18
JOHNSON, Thomas Jos. 2252 60TH AVE, 2252 60TH AVE. 54020 #030-05-1987 L1996 **CCS** *020 †85
MATTSON, Greg Dale. 301 RIVER ST 54020 #016-11-1987 L1993 **FM** *062 †18
ROHR, Bonnie Jean. 301 RIVER ST 54020 #026-04-1988 L1999 **FM** *020 †18
SALAZAR-TIER, Maryruth G. 301 RIVER ST 54020 #007-02-1984 L2000 **FM OBG** *020 †18 ‡
SEVERSON, Erik Arlen. 301 RIVER ST, P O BOX 218 54020 #026-08-2002 L2005 **FM** *020 †18
SLETTEN, Paul William. 301 RIVER ST 54020 #028-03-1982 L1988 **FM** *020 †18
SMITH, Kari Jean. 301 RIVER ST 54020 #026-04-1999 L2002 **FM** *020 †18
STRATE, Richard Gordon. 301 RIVER ST, RAMSEY CLINIC-OSCEOLA 54020 #026-04-1964 L1978 **GS TS** *071 †85

OSHKOSH – WINNEBAGO

ABOUZELAM, Zenoun Omar. 2700 W 9TH AVE 54904 #915-04-1978 L1987 **TS CD** *020 †85,90
AL-NOURI, Mamoun Bashir. 2700 W 9TH AVE 54904 #875-01-1971 L1978 **CD** *020 †20
ALZOUBI, Ammar. 855 N WESTHAVEN DR 54904 #875-01-1990 L1999 **IM** *020 †20
AMBAS, Felipe Patino. 303 PEARL AVE, MENTAL HEALTH CONSULTANTS 54901 #748-08-1973 L1991 **P** *020
ANDERSON, Matthew S. 600 N WESTHAVEN DR 54904 #007-02-1995 L2001 **U** *020 †95
ANDERSON, Sheila Marbeth. 414 DOCTORS CT, AURORA MEDICAL GROUP OSHKO 54901 #036-01-1985 L1989 **OBG** *020 †30
ANDRASKO, Kevin Paul. 1128 E PARKWAY AVE 54901 #056-06-1978 L1979 **IM EM** *020 †20
ANDREINI, Jeffrey Paul. 2700 W 9TH AVE STE 315A 54904 #025-01-1986 L1993 **GE IM** *020 †20
APELL, Melvin Geo. ■ 54901 #056-05-1946 L1947 **AI PDA** *071 †55,03
BAKER, Ralph Kendrick. 303 PEARL AVE, STE C 54901 #056-05-1962 L1963 **P PFP** *020 †75
BARRETT, Morgan. 2700 W 9TH AVE, STE 11 54904 #012-01-1985 L2002 **RO** *020
BAYER, Matthew Arthur. 600 N WESTHAVEN DR 54904 #056-06-2001 L2002 **P** *020 †75
BEARDWOOD, Gordon Alan. 500 S OAKWOOD RD 54904 #005-12-1992 L2006 **AN** *020 †05
BECKETT, Michael Charles. 500 S OAKWOOD RD 54904 #018-03-2002 L2004 **IM** *020 †20
BEGLEY, Benjamin Wm. 2130 W 9TH AVE 54904 #017-20-1987 L1988 **ORS** *020 †40
BERNSTEIN, Robert Louis. 855 N WESTHAVEN DR, AURORA MEDICAL CTR 54904 #016-11-1975 L1984 **PTH** *020 †50
BLAHA, Steven Chas. 855 N WESTHAVEN DR 54904 #056-05-1985 L1986 **IM** *020 †20
BOEDER, Paul Allan. 2700 W 9TH AVE STE 230 54904 #056-06-1989 L1990 **OBG** *020 †30
BOMMAKANTI, Swami Saran. ■ 54901 #495-50-1966 L1984 **OPH** *020 †35 ‡
BOYLE, John Scott. 414 DOCTORS CT 54901 #016-43-1970 L1974 **ORS** *020 †40
BRESCIA, Donald Jos. 2700 W 9TH AVE # 106 54904 #016-43-1976 L1982 **CD IM** *020 †20
BUCK, Roy Eugene. 2700 W 9TH AVE 54904 #025-01-1964 L1971 **ORS** *020 †40
BULLARD, Karen M. 2700 W 9TH AVE, STE 11 54904 #048-15-1991 L1997 **HO** *020 †20
CAPASSO, Charles Anthony. 2700 W 9TH AVE 54904 #041-09-1979 L1980 **OM** *020 †70
CARDELLI, Dominic T. 2953 RYF RD 54904 #026-04-1991 L1992 **N** *020 †75
CARLSON, Jon Kenneth. 855 N WESTHAVEN DR 54904 #056-06-1997 L1998 **FM** *020 †18
CAULEY, James Edward. 2700 W 9TH AVE STE 305 54904 #017-20-1981 L1982 **U** *020 †95
CHARAVEJASARN, Chiaw C. 500 S OAKWOOD RD 54904 #891-02-1964 L1973 **AI** *071 †55,03
CHULSKI, Thomas Geo. 1855 S KOELLER ST 54902 #056-06-1980 L2000 **FM AM** *030 †18
CLARK, David Dick. 2700 W 9TH AVE, STE 310 54904 #056-06-1966 L1974 **GS** *020 †85
CLARKE, Gerald Paul. 509 S WASHBURN ST 54904 #016-43-1976 L1978 **OPH EM** *020 †35
CLER, Joel Warren. 855 N WESTHAVEN DR, AURORA MEDICAL GROUP 54904 #016-11-1985 L1989 **ORS** *020 †40
COLLAR, Mark W. 855 N WESTHAVEN DR 54904 #028-34-1994 L1997 **AN** *020 †05
COLLINS, Andrew Jordan. 600 N WESTHAVEN DR 54904 #056-05-1992 L2003 **PD** *020 †55
COOPER, Janelle Lunette. 2700 W 9TH AVE STE 104, MERCY MED CTR OAKWOOD 54904 #047-05-1986 L1998 **N PYG** *020 †75
CRAWFORD, William Albert. 2700 W 9TH AVE STE 210 54904 #018-03-1959 L1967 **OTO EM** *071 †45
CUARESMA, Milagros R. ■ 54902 #748-08-1973 L1991 **P** *020
CUNNINGHAM, Thomas E. ■ 54901 #016-43-1953 L1968 **GP** *071
DANFORTH, Harold J. ■ 54904 #056-06-1944 L1945 **EM** *071
DAVE, Indu Jaodish. ■ 54904 #495-48-1966 L1992 **P** *020 †75
DEDRICK, David John. 500 S OAKWOOD RD 54904 #056-05-1994 L1997 **PTH** *020 †50
DERVISH, Ahmet. 500 S OAKWOOD RD 54904 #902-01-1986 L1992 **AN PME** *020 †05
DEVERMANN, Robert Bruce. 500 S OAKWOOD RD 54904 #018-03-1979 L1994 **FM** *030 †18
DIAS, Jose Carlos B. 500 S OAKWOOD RD 54904 #062-01-1994 L1997 *020
DOUBEK, William G. 2700 W 9TH AVE, STE 205 54904 #028-34-1953 L1953 **PS GS** *071
DOUBEK, William Geo. 2400 WITZEL AVE 54904 #028-34-1991 L1998 **PS HS** *020 †85,65
DUDLEY, Stephen Sherman. 503 DOCTORS CT 54901 #056-05-1970 L1973 **OPH** *020 †35
DUFFY, Michael Alan. 855 N WESTHAVEN DR, MERCY OAKWOOD 54904 #025-01-1978 L1982 **IM** *020 †20
DUWELL, Eric Chas. 855 N WESTHAVEN DR 54904 #056-06-1989 L1990 **FM** *020 †18
EISMA, Alejandro A. 500 S OAKWOOD RD 54904 #748-01-1968 L2001 **IM** *020 †20,18
ELLIOTT, John Thos, Jr. ■ 54904 #017-20-1965 L1973 **U AM** *071 †95
ELLIS ZAPOLSKY, Valerie A. ■ 54902 #035-45-1983 L2001 **PD** *020 †55
ESPIRITU, Rolando Lauro G. 1855 S KOELLER ST 54902 #748-10-1977 L2000 **IM** *020 †20
FINGER, Michael Carl. 500 S OAKWOOD RD 54904 #056-05-1978 L1981 **EM** *020 †18
FISCHER, Matthew Peter. 855 N WESTHAVEN DR 54904 #018-03-1983 L1986 **FM** *020 †18
FISHER, Albert Lee. 400 CEAPE AVE STE 14 54901 #056-06-1980 L1982 **FM EM** *020 †18
FOLEY, Michael James. 2700 W 9TH AVE 54904 #018-03-1996 L2001 **GS** *020 †85
GALAZKA, Pawel. 500 S OAKWOOD RD, MERCY MEDICAL CENTER 54904 #759-03-1989 L1996 **AN** *020 †05
GARCIA, Raul R. 500 S OAKWOOD RD, UW HEALTH MERCY MEDICAL 54904 #748-02-1989 L1994 **IM** *020 †20
GARDNER, Jeremy Garret. 343 SUNNYBROOK DR 54904 #056-06-2000 L2001 **PD** *020 †55
GOLDSHLACK, Brian L. 855 N WESTHAVEN DR 54904 #305-01-1986 L1990 **FM** *020 †18
GOWING, Eric Charles. 1855 S KOELLER ST 54902 #025-07-1997 L1998 **RHU** *020 †20
GREEN, Kevin Robt. 631 HAZEL ST 54901 #018-03-1990 L1993 **FM AM** *020 †18
GREENE, Karl Anthony. 700 N WESTHAVEN DR, FL 2 54904 #005-11-1989 L2001 **NS** *020 †25
GREENWOOD, Benjamin Saml. ■ 54902 #028-02-1943 L1947 **IM OM** *071
GREGOR, Bozidar. ■ 54901 #957-01-1953 L1961 **P OS** *071 †75
HAFFAR, Ahmad Yahya. 555 S WASHBURN ST, VALLEY NEUROLOGY CLINIC S. 54904 #875-01-1972 L1980 **N** *020 †75
HARRISON, Brian D. 2700 W 9TH AVE 54904 #026-08-1982 L1983 **OM EM** *020 †18,70
HARTZ, Jay M. 1866 SCARLET OAK TRL 54904 #654-01-1987 L1990 **P** *020 †75
HATTON, Mark Edward. 500 S OAKWOOD RD 54904 #016-43-1981 L1994 **FM** *020 †18
HAYNES, James Manley. PO BOX 3370, MERCY MEDICAL CENTER 54903 #054-04-1961 L1994 **N** *071 †75
HENDRICKS, Douglas Jon. 700 N WESTHAVEN DR, FL 2 54904 #056-05-1994 L1995 **PM** *020 †60
HIEBERT, Michael Eugene. 500 S OAKWOOD RD 54904 #056-06-1994 L1997 **IM** *020 †20
HOLZ, David Anthony. 1855 S KOELLER ST 54902 #056-06-1999 L2000 **FM** *020 †18
HORAN, Douglas B. 1855 S KOELLER ST 54902 #048-04-1979 L1987 **D DS** *020 †15
HORAN, John Wm Patrick. 2700 W 9TH AVE, STE 220 54904 #056-06-1990 L2007 **ORS** *020 †40
HOUSE, Pamela T. 855 N WESTHAVEN DR 54904 #319-01-1991 L1996 **FM** *020 †18
HOWARD, Walter Tasker. 1855 S KOELLER ST, LASALLE CLINIC PEDIATRICS 54902 #056-05-1994 L1997 **PD** *020 †55
HUGHES, John Byron. 2700 W 9TH AVE, MERCY OAKWOOD 54904 #056-05-1955 L1956 **PD** *071 †55
HUGHES, Richard C. 855 N WESTHAVEN DR 54904 #056-05-1960 L1961 **IM** *071 †20
JACOBS, Lois J. 1510 ARBORETUM DR 54901 #056-05-1987 L1989 **IM A** *020
JACOBSON, Joel Curtis. ■ 54904 #056-06-1987 L1988 **AN PME** *020 †05
JANSSEN, David Alan. 2400 WITZEL AVE 54904 #056-05-1986 L1993 **PS HS** *020 †85,65

■ = Address Information Privacy Protected

JANUSONIS, Rimas Viktoras. 600 N WESTHAVEN DR 54904 #016-01-1996 L2003 **FM** *020 †18
JOHNSON, Scott Bradley. 500 S OAKWOOD RD 54904 #056-05-1997 L1998 **PD** *020 †55
JORDAN, Milan. 500 S OAKWOOD RD, UW HEALTH MERCY MEDICAL 54904 #016-42-1990 L1991 **GS** *020 †85
JOSEPH, John. 555 S WASHBURN ST 54904 #495-52-1992 L1998 **APM AN** *020 †05
KAMMHOLZ, Larry Palmer. ■ 54901 #056-06-1964 L1965 **PD** *071 †55
KAPLAN, Roman. 1730 W SNELL RD, OSHKOSH CORRECTIONAL INST. 54901 #913-05-1973 L1994 **FM** *020
KEHRBERG, Mark Wayne. 500 S OAKWOOD RD, ADMINSTRATION 54904 #056-05-1976 L1993 **PD** *030 †55
KERSWILL, Randy Michael. 600 S MAIN ST, WESTSHORE PSYCHC ASSOCS SC 54902 #056-06-1980 L1982 **P** *020 †75
KHATIB, Mohamad Y. 2700 W 9TH AVE, STE 106 54904 #875-01-1995 L2007 **PUD** *020 †20
KIM, Eun Young. 296 OHIO ST, OSHKOSH ALLERGY CTR 54902 #583-08-1979 L1990 **AI PD** *020 †03,55
KIMBROUGH, Elizabeth L. 1855 S KOELLER ST 54902 #048-13-1992 L2000 **IM** *020 †20
KNIER, Michael Steven. 855 N WESTHAVEN DR 54904 #056-05-1978 L1981 **FM** *020 †18
LAIBLY, Shawn Walter. 855 N WESTHAVEN DR 54904 #026-04-1997 L2001 **OBG** *020 †30
LANDAUER, Megan. 855 N WESTHAVEN DR 54904 #056-05-1978 L1982 **OBG** *050 †30
LARSON, Alyson Paige. ■ 54904 #016-06-1996 L2003 **FM** *020 †18
LARSON, Eric Matthew. 1885 W POINTE DR 54902 #026-04-1998 L2003 **OPH** *020 †35
LASERNA, Amelia De Leon. ■ 54904 #748-01-1971 L1983 **P** *020 †75
LASERNA, Ramon V. ■ 54904 #748-01-1971 L1979 **FM GP** *020
LAUFER, Christopher James. 500 S OAKWOOD RD 54904 #056-05-1994 L1999 **PD** *020 †55
LESCHKE, John Anthony. ■ 54901 #056-06-1957 L1958 **AN** *071 †05
LEWANDOWSKI, Thomas J. 600 N WESTHAVEN DR, APPLETON CARDIO ASSC 54904 #035-45-1992 L1999 **IM** *020 †20
LONG, Gregory Lee. 600 N WESTHAVEN DR 54904 #016-45-1990 L1993 **FM** *020 †18
LY, Vee Tom. 855 N WESTHAVEN DR 54904 #056-06-2001 L2003 **PD** *020 †55
MAASSEN, Stephen James. 855 N WESTHAVEN DR 54904 #025-01-1983 L1984 **FM** *020 †18
MACACHOR, Jesus D. ■ 54902 #748-11-1964 L1976 **EM GS** *071
MALIK, Iftikhar Ahmed. 600 N WESTHAVEN DR 54904 #704-05-1991 L2005 **IM** *020
MANN, Robert Fredrick. 815 W 20TH AVE 54902 #025-01-1982 L1989 **PD** *020 †25
MATHISON, Johan Alfred. 712 DOCTORS CT 54901 #056-05-1961 L1962 **GS** *071 †85
MC ANDREW, John Burton. ■ 54901 #030-05-1959 L1963 **P** *071 †75
MC DONALD, Caroline C. 500 S OAKWOOD RD 54904 #048-04-1989 L1991 **AN** *020 †05
MC DONALD, Donald James. 500 S OAKWOOD RD 54904 #056-06-1983 L1984 **AN PME** *020 †05
MC DONALD, Mary Frances. 2700 W 9TH AVE, STE 300 54904 #056-06-1985 L1986 **GE HEP** *020 †20
MC DONALD, Robert Scott. 2700 W 9TH AVE, STE 310 54904 #056-06-1984 L1987 **GS TS** *030 †85,90
MC DONALD, Shaun P. 515 S WASHBURN ST, STE 204 54904 #048-13-1992 L2000 **D** *020 †20,15
MC KENZIE, John Redmond. ■ 54902 #056-06-1955 L1956 **R GP** *071 †80
MC LAUGHLIN, Jeffrey R. 2700 W 9TH AVE STE 125, MERCY MED CTR 54904 #023-01-1986 L1992 **ORS OAR** *020 †40
MENET, Richard Alan. 2700 W 9TH AVE 54904 #016-01-1977 L1981 **OM IM** *020 †20,70
MERFELD, Stephen John. 1885 W POINTE DR 54902 #018-03-1986 L1993 **OPH** *020 †35
MONDRY, Martin Gary. 3763 CANDLISH HARBOR LN 54902 #748-18-1987 L1992 **AN** *020 †05
MORGAN, Charles Dignam. 2700 W 9TH AVE, STE 320 54904 #024-07-1973 L1999 **P** *020 †75
MULLER, Jay Ronald. 500 S OAKWOOD RD, UW HEALTH MERCY MEDICAL 54904 #028-34-1998 L2002 **IM** *020 †20
MULLER, Laurie Lynn. 500 S OAKWOOD RD 54904 #028-34-1999 L2002 **PD** *020 †55
NEUBECKER, Mary Smith. ■ 54901 #048-02-1947 L1967 **GPM OM** *071
NEUBECKER, Robert D. ■ 54901 #035-45-1949 L1961 **PTH** *071 †50
NORDEN, Jennifer Anne. 500 S OAKWOOD RD 54904 #056-05-1994 L1999 **IM** *020 †20
O'CONNOR, Paul C. 2700 W 9TH AVE STE 220 54904 #016-43-1963 L1971 **ORS HS** *071 †40
OELSCHLAGER, Jean Kay. 855 N WESTHAVEN DR, AURORA HEALTH CENTER 54904 #017-20-1984 L1990 **P** *020 †75
ORTA-ROSARIO, Porfirio. ■ 54904 #042-01-1985 L2001 **FM** *020
PATEL, Rina Akxay. ■ 54904 #496-30-1995 L2007 **FM** *020 †18
PATEL, Sangita A. 1945 HICKORY LN 54901 #495-65-1981 L1988 **PYG** *050 †75
PAUL, Kamaljit Singh. 2700 W 9TH AVE, STE 120 54904 #495-05-1968 L1986 **NS** *020
PAYNE, James Chas. ■ 54901 #056-05-1957 L1958 **P** *020
PING, Er Chang, Jr. ■ 54902 #018-03-1963 L1969 **P** *020 †75
PREHN, Denise Miller. 855 N WESTHAVEN DR, AUROA MEDICAL GRP 54904 #056-05-1991 L1993 **IM** *030 †20
PULAKANDUM, Indira. ■ 54904 #495-70-1990 L2004 **IMG** *100 †20
PUNG, Brian Jos. 500 S OAKWOOD RD 54904 #056-05-1988 L1992 **AN** *020 †05
QURESHI, Ghayyur Abbas. 2700 W 9TH AVE, STE 106 54904 #041-07-1995 L2006 **PCC** *020 †20 ‡
RADFORD, Curtis Duff. 500 S OAKWOOD RD 54904 #056-05-1981 L1984 **IM VIR** *020 †20
RAYMOND, James Robt. 515 DOCTORS CT 54901 #038-40-1959 L1964 **OTO** *071 †45
REVORD, John Patrick. 700 N WESTHAVEN DR, FL 2 54904 #016-11-1988 L1992 **PM PMM** *020 †60
RINGWALA, Kirtida N. 10 E IRVING AVE # A 54901 #495-76-1976 L1982 **IM PD** *020 †20
ROMOND, David Hunter. 2700 W 9TH AVE STE 220 54904 #008-01-1972 L1979 **ORS HS** *020 †40
ROZUM, L Thos. ■ 54902 #056-06-1967 L1968 **D** *020 †15
SABIH, Asma. 855 N WESTHAVEN DR 54904 #704-02-1992 L2004 **IM** *020
SCHEUERMANN, Nyal Morgan. ■ 54901 #056-06-1954 L1955 **GP AM** *071
SCHULTZ, Margaret Ann. 855 N WESTHAVEN DR, AURORA HLTH CTR 54904 #056-05-2001 L2005 **AN** *020 †05
SCHULTZ, Randall James. 700 N WESTHAVEN DR, FL 2 54904 #016-43-1988 L1992 **PM** *020 †60
SHARMA, Sandeep. ■ 54904 #495-29-1992 L2000 **AN** *020 †05
SHOPBELL, Stephen Louis. 2700 W 9TH AVE 54904 #024-16-1996 L2002 **P FM** *020 †18,75
SHROEDER, Rebekah R. 855 N WESTHAVEN DR 54904 #056-05-1995 L1997 **IM** *020 †20
SIDDIQUI, Ather Saeed A. ■ 54901 #704-02-1993 L1997 **P PFP** *020 †75
SIEPMANN, James Patrick. ■ 54904 #026-08-1986 L1989 **FM FSM** *071 †18
SIMONSON, M James. ■ 54901 #016-06-1960 L1968 **U** *071 †95
SMITH, Erica Lynn. 600 N WESTHAVEN DR 54904 #056-06-2002 L2003 **FSM** *020
SMRECEK, James Wm. 1855 S KOELLER ST 54902 #056-05-1981 L1982 **FM** *020 †18
STAEHLER, Richard Allen. 700 N WESTHAVEN DR, FL 2 54904 #056-05-1994 L1995 **PM** *020 †60

STILP, Lyall Carlton, II. ■ 54903 #008-01-1964 L1969 **ORS OSM** *071 †40
STRAM, Mark Lawrence. 500 S OAKWOOD RD, UW HEALTH MERCY MEDICAL 54904 #038-45-1997 L2000 **AN** *012 †20
STRAND, Barbara Joan. 500 S OAKWOOD RD 54904 #016-01-1985 L1992 **PD** *020 †55
STURM, Richard Edward. 855 N WESTHAVEN DR, AURORA MEDICAL GROUP 54904 #025-12-1978 L1998 **OM IM** *020 †20,70
SUBRAMANI, Govindaraju. 480 N KOELLER ST 54902 #495-09-1973 L1986 **CD IM** *020 †20
SUZUKI, Joshua. 2700 W 9TH AVE STE 2 54904 #572-10-1968 L1999 **OBG** *020 †30
SWANSON, John David. 777 ALGOMA BLVD 54901 #030-05-1973 L1978 **PD** *020 †55
SWANSON, Lars Victor. 500 S OAKWOOD RD 54904 #016-11-1999 L2002 **IM** *020 †20
SZABO, Susan M. 1855 S KOELLER ST, AFFINITY MEDICAL GROUP 54902 #010-01-1985 L1986 **PD** *020 †55 ‡
TANNAN, Dilip Kumar. 555 S WASHBURN ST, STE C2 54904 #495-19-1979 L1984 **GP** *020
TEVIOTDALE, Brian M. 855 N WESTHAVEN DR 54904 #671-01-1967 L1976 **AN** *020
THOMAE, Daniel Herbert. 855 N WESTHAVEN DR 54904 #056-05-1984 L1992 **GS** *020
TOMPKINS, Daren M. 500 S OAKWOOD RD, MERCY MED CTR 54904 #037-01-1991 L1996 **PTH** *020 †50
TRESP, Michael Gerard. 855 N WESTHAVEN DR 54904 #056-06-1983 L1984 **PTH** *020 †50
TSAI, David Chang-Chur. 3475 OMRO RD STE 400 54904 #244-04-1970 L1976 **OBG GS** *075 †30
TSAI, Davis Chengyu. 2700 W 9TH AVE, STE 125 54904 #016-06-1994 L1999 **ORS** *020 †40
TURCHAN, Steven James. 2370 STATE ROAD 44, STE D 54904 #035-48-1988 L1995 **P** *020 †75
ULLRICH, Peter F, Jr. 700 N WESTHAVEN DR, FL 2 54904 #056-05-1989 L1995 **ORS** *020 †40
VICENTE, Michael R. ■ 54904 #056-06-1995 L1999 **P** *020 †75
VOLKERT, Paul Donald. 2700 W 9TH AVE, STE 106 54904 #056-06-1987 L1988 **CD** *020 †20
WASCHER, Thomas Michael. 700 N WESTHAVEN DR, FL 2 54904 #016-43-1985 L1992 **NS** *020 †25
WEBB, Rebecca L. 855 N WESTHAVEN DR 54904 #016-01-1989 L1996 **PD** *020 †55
WEBER, John Richard S. 414 DOCTORS CT 54901 #056-05-1997 L1998 **FM** *020 †18
WEBER, Robert Raymond. 2700 W 9TH AVE 54904 #056-06-1984 L1989 **GS VS** *020 †85
WEBER, William Geo. 500 S OAKWOOD RD 54904 #056-06-1960 L1961 **IM IMG** *071 †20
WERNBERG, Charles Edward. 1855 S KOELLER ST 54902 #056-05-1967 L1972 **GP PD** *020 †55
WESTON, Clayton L. ■ 54904 #056-05-1951 L1952 **FM GP** *071
WESTON, Robert Lee. 631 HAZEL ST 54901 #056-05-1978 L1979 **IM** *075 †20
WEX, Thomas Edward. 500 S OAKWOOD RD 54904 #047-05-1973 L1974 **FM** *020 †18
WILSON, Eric Birger. ■ 54904 #016-11-1963 L1964 **OBG NM** *071 †80
WILSON, Stephen Boyd. 855 N WESTHAVEN DR STE 2, AURORA MEDICAL GROUP 54904 #056-06-1984 L1985 **PUD SME** *020 †20
WOLFGRAM, Richard Chas. ■ 54904 #056-05-1955 L1956 **GYN** *071 †30
WOODRUFF, Roland Neal. 500 S OAKWOOD RD 54904 #030-06-1970 L1975 **IM GE** *020 †20
ZERNZACK, Lance Edward. 500 S OAKWOOD RD 54904 #056-05-1975 L1976 **FM** *020 †18
ZMOLEK, Ernest Jos. ■ 54901 #018-03-1948 L1950 **GS** *071 †85
ZORNOSA, Francisco J. 2700 W 9TH AVE, STE 101 54904 #264-05-1990 L2000 **NEP** *020 †20

OSSEO — TREMPEALEAU

DOWNEY, Walter Gerald. 13025 8TH ST, OSSEO MEDICAL CENTER 54758 #056-06-1995 L2006 **FM** *020 †18
FITZGERALD, Michael John. 13031 8TH ST, MIDELFORT CLINIC - OSSEO 54758 #016-45-1990 L1991 **FM** *020 †18
GARBER, Bradley Gilbert. 13031 8TH ST 54758 #038-40-1960 L1961 **EM GS** *020 †18
GARBER, Richard Dean. 13029 9TH ST BOX 370 54758 #038-40-1964 L1965 **GP** *071 †18
SCRENOCK, Thomas. 12830 COX LN 54758 #056-05-1969 L1970 **GP FPG** *020 ‡
WEINMEISTER, Donald Duane. 13029 9TH ST, OSSEO MEDICAL CLINIC 54758 #019-02-1986 L1987 **FM FSM** *020 †18

OWEN — CLARK

WIRTZ, Charles Earl. 6 JOHNSON ST 54460 #018-03-1984 L1985 **IM** *020 †20

OXFORD — MARQUETTE

QUALY, Richard James. N4390 CROSSROAD CLINIC RD, UNIV. OF WOSCONSIN 53952 #056-05-1986 L1987 **FM** *020 †18

PARDEEVILLE — COLUMBIA

GLOWACKI, Gayl Marcia. 102 GILLETTE ST, PARDEEVILLE CLINIC 53954 #001-02-1994 L1996 **FM** *020 †18 ‡

PARK FALLS — PRICE

AHMAD, Syed Mashud. ■ 54552 #704-15-1991 L2006 **IMG** *020 †20
ARGUELLO ARGUELLO, Adriana. ■ 54552 #264-18-1989 L2007 **IM** *100
BROWN, Kurt A. 50 SHERRY AVE 54552 #035-03-1989 L1991 **PG** *020 †55
CARPENTER, William Scott. 50 SHERRY AVE, MARSHFIELD CLINIC 54552 #030-05-1979 L1991 **EM IM** *020 †20
GAYLE, Arlene A. 98 SHERRY AVE 54552 #566-01-1993 L2001 **IMG** *020 †20
HARRISON, Geoffrey S. 222 LAWRENCE AVE 54552 #026-04-1988 L1997 **FM** *020 †18
HOUKOM, Everin Claire. 50 SHERRY AVE, MARSHFIELD CLINIC PARK FAL 54552 #056-06-1986 L1987 **FM** *020 †18
LINDGREN, Timothy James. 50 SHERRY AVE, PF CENTER 54552 #056-05-1977 L1978 **FM PLM** *020 †18
MILLER, Kenneth Andrew. 50 SHERRY AVE 54552 #056-05-1987 L1988 **IM** *020 †20
MURPHY, Maurice O. 50 SHERRY AVE, PARK FALLS CENTER 54552 #051-07-1981 L2005 **EM** *020 †16
PUTLUR, Pradeep. 50 SHERRY AVE 54552 #495-65-2002 L2007 **IM** *100 †20
THORNGATE, Stephen. ■ 54552 #038-06-1952 L1984 **GS DR** *071 †85

PEMBINE – MARINETTE

THIEL, Glenn Alan. ■ 54156 #056-06-1982 L1983 EM *020

PEPIN – PEPIN

HOVDE, De Larry Ruel. 410 LAKE ST 54759 #026-04-1956 L1958 GP *071

PESHTIGO – MARINETTE

ADORJAN, Mark Gyorgy. 441 FRENCH ST 54157 #473-04-1997 L2002 FM *020 †18
PUPPALA, Venkata Krishna. ■ 54157 #495-50-2001 L2005 IM *100 †20
STORY, Rodney Richard. 441 FRENCH ST 54157 #054-04-2002 L2003 FM *020 †18

PEWAUKEE – WAUKESHA

CHHOKAR, Vikramjit Singh. ■ 53072 #308-13-1999 L2000 IC *012 †20 ‡
CONRAD, Arthur Baier. ■ 53072 #056-06-1958 L1959 PTH *020 †50
DE GUZMAN, Eleuterio A. ■ 53072 #748-01-1957 L1963 AN *020
DONIPARTHI, Anilkumar. 1155 QUAIL CT 53072 #495-11-1989 L1996 IM *020 †20
GOWDA, Santosh. N34W23344 HUNTERS CT # 303 53072 #496-39-1998 L2006 HO *012
GREEN, Lauri Theresa. 1177 QUAIL CT STE 101 53072 #056-06-1995 L1996 CHP P *020 †75
GUPTA, Sweta Lalitmohan. ■ 53072 #495-23-1999 L2005 PHO *012 †55
HOFBAUER, Thomas Anton. ■ 53072 #056-06-1956 L1957 OBG *071 †30
HOGAN, John Patrick. 1104 RIVERWAY CT 53072 #016-06-1962 L1963 PS GS *071 †85,65
KELM, Michael Andrew. ■ 53072 #056-06-2008 *012
KIM, Jin. 1292 W CAPITOL DR 53072 #056-06-1996 L2000 FM *020 †18
KLOEHN, Ralph Anthony. 161 W WISCONSIN AVE, STE 1G 53072 #056-06-1958 L1963 PS HS *020 †65
KUKREJA, Sandeep Surendra. ■ 53072 #495-23-1999 L2005 PCC *012 †20
KUMAR, Amit. ■ 53072 #035-15-2004 L2007 AI *012 †20
KUMAR, Kalpana M. 1166 QUAIL CT STE 21 53072 #035-46-1986 L1992 IM *020 †20
LARSEN, Julie Ann. 2900 GOLF RD 53072 #016-45-1984 L1985 FM FSM *020 †18
LOPEZ-TAN, Daniel W. 1155 QUAIL CT 53072 #748-01-1990 L1994 IM *020 †20
MANJONEY, Deborah Lynn. 1231 GEORGE TOWNE DR, STE G 53072 #050-02-1978 L1992 TS PHL *020 †85,90
MERKOW, William. W224N3322 DUPLAINVILLE RD 53072 #056-05-1943 L1944 OM *072 †85
MEYER, Anthony David. N35W28146 TAYLORS WOODS RD 53072 #056-06-1963 L1964 CHP P *020 †75
MUCENO, Dar. ■ 53072 #748-01-1961 L1999 IM GE *062 †20
POWERS, Susan Jane. ■ 53072 #020-12-1983 L1997 P *020 †75
QUINONES, Eric Mauricio. ■ 53072 #308-03-1983 L1991 GP *020
STRONG, Donald Hiroshi. ■ 53072 #056-06-1996 L1998 IM *020 †20
TORPHY, Daniel Englund. ■ 53072 #056-05-1962 L1963 PD GP *040 †55
WISNEFSKI, Lori Lynn. 1292 CAPITOL DR, WHEATON FRANCISCAN MED GRO 53072 #056-06-1994 L1997 FM *020 †18

PHELPS – VILAS

ZELINSKI, James Wm. 2383 HIGHWAY 17, FAMILY HEALTH CENTER 54554 #025-01-1974 L1979 GP GS *020 †85

PHILLIPS – PRICE

ANDERSON, Lee Angelique. 104 TRINITY DR, MARSHFIELD CLINIC-PHILLIPS 54555 #056-06-1996 L1997 FM *020 †18
DAHLIE, Peter Norman. 104 TRINITY DR 54555 #056-05-1978 L1981 FM *020 †18
DEVANEY, Elizabeth J. 104 TRINITY DR 54555 #016-11-1990 L1991 FM *020 †18
KOZAK, Deborah Anne. 104 TRINITY DR, MARSHFIELD CLINIC-PHILLIPS 54555 #056-06-1996 L1997 FM *020 †18
NIEBAUER, Walter Edward. ■ 54555 #056-05-1943 L1946 GP *071

PIGEON FALLS – TREMPEALEAU

ENGLAND, Douglas Marlo. PO BOX 340 54760 #016-42-1973 L1983 PTH *020 †50

PLAIN – SAUK

COLLINS, Jeffrey Michael. 825 MAIN ST 53577 #056-05-1997 L1998 FM *020 †18 ‡
GALARNYK, Ihor Anton. 825 MAIN ST, MEDICAL BLDG 53577 #062-01-1955 L1956 FM *071 †18

PLATTEVILLE – GRANT

BOSWORTH, Hobart Hunt. 1450 EASTSIDE RD 53818 #005-18-1978 L1997 OTO *062 †45
CARR, Kevin George. 1450 EASTSIDE RD 53818 #056-06-1986 L1987 FM *020 †18
CASTANEDA, Edwin T. 1240 BIG JACK RD, MEDICAL ASSOCIATES CLINIC 53818 #019-02-1979 L1995 ORS HS *020 †40
DURANCEAU, Christine M. 1400 EASTSIDE RD 53818 #008-01-1981 L2000 EM *020 †16
GRIFFIN, Vernon Mathew. ■ 53818 #040-02-1938 L1946 GP GS *071
HAUPT, Alice Susan. 1450 EASTSIDE RD 53818 #038-40-1992 L2005 OBG *020 †30
HUEBNER, Jerome Allen. 1450 EASTSIDE RD 53818 #056-05-1976 L1977 FM *020 †18
MASKI, Meenakshi Ravikant. 1250 E BUSINESS HIGHWAY 151, STE A 53818 #495-65-1969 L1980 PD FM *020 †55
MASKI, Ravikant. 1250 E BUSINS HGHWY 151 #A 53818 #495-21-1965 L1980 GS FM *020 †85
PARIKH, Divya Narendra. ■ 53818 #495-65-1978 *100
PETERSON, Jennifer Sue. 1450 EASTSIDE RD 53818 #056-06-1998 L1999 D *020 †15
REBCHOOK, Allen Gregory. 1450 EASTSIDE RD 53818 #016-06-1980 L1999 GS HS *020 †85

RILEY, Todd Roger. 1 UNIVERSITY PLZ, STUDENT HEALTH SVCS 53818 #056-06-1988 L1989 PTH *020 †50
SCOTT, Edward Homer. 1240 BIG JACK RD, ATTN: SUSAN HERMSEN 53818 #018-03-1967 L1982 OPH *020 †35
SLOAN, Raymond Joseph. 1450 EASTSIDE RD 53818 #056-06-1974 L1975 FM OBS *020 †18
STABENOW, David Lee. 1240 BIG JACK RD 53818 #028-02-1968 L1981 D DMP *020 †15
SUKHWAL, Aditya. 1450 EASTSIDE RD 53818 #654-01-1995 L1998 FM OBS *020 †18 ‡
VARELDZIS, Basil P. 1 UNIVERSITY PLZ, STUDENT HEALTH SERVICES 53818 #017-20-1986 L1999 GPM FM *020
WILSON, Virginia K. 1450 EASTSIDE RD 53818 #041-12-1988 L1994 RHU *020 †20

PLEASANT PRAIRIE – KENOSHA

ACHARYA, Manish. 8044 88TH AVE 53158 #016-11-1996 L1999 EM *030 †16
AFFINITO, John Henry. 9555 76TH ST 53158 #016-06-1994 L2008 FM *020 †18
ARMUS, Steven Louis. 9555 76TH ST, STE 2600 53158 #056-05-1988 L1993 D *020 †15
ARROYO, Martha Patricia. 9555 76TH ST, STE 2600 53158 #005-11-1999 L2005 D *020 †15 ‡
CHUA, Janet Tan. 53158 #748-01-1988 L1995 FM *020 †18
FERNANDO, Aimee Claire. 9555 76TH ST, SCMC FAMILY PRACTICE 53158 #028-34-2002 L2005 FM *020 †18
GOJRATY, Sattar Mehdie. 53158 #041-01-2008 *012
HAWKINS, Richard Alfred. 9555 76TH ST 53158 #016-42-2000 L2004 AN *020
JANKOVIC, Goran. ■ 53158 #018-75-2004, ▲ L2006 FM *020 †18
LYNOTT, James Vincent. 9555 76TH ST 53158 #016-11-1999 L2004 D *020 †15
MILOSEVIC, Rade. 9555 76TH ST 53158 #654-01-1984 L1987 NEP IM *020
MONTEMURRO, Angelina M. 9555 76TH ST 53158 #056-06-1985 L1986 FM *020 †18
MONTEMURRO, Leonardo D. 9555 76TH ST 53158 #056-06-1997 L1998 FM *020 †18
PAGE, John Geo. 53158 #067-01-1956 L1991 PD *071 †55
QUETS, Jerome Philippe. 9555 76TH ST, RADIOLOGY DEPT 53158 #017-20-1989 L2000 RNR R *020 †18
RANIERI, Rosanna Maria. 9555 76TH ST 53158 #561-01-1971 L1978 IM NEP *020
REIF, Lawrence James. 9555 76TH ST, RADIOLOGY DEPT 53158 #056-06-1980 L1981 DR AR *020 †80 ‡
SHAH, Nandini Ashokkumar. 9555 76TH ST 53158 #495-23-1989 L1994 FM *020 †18
SHAPIRO, Julie Michelle. 9555 76TH ST 53158 #016-42-1997 L2006 FM *020 †18
SHEPLER, Neil A. 9555 76TH ST, RADIOLOGY DEPT 53158 #037-01-1983 L1984 FM *020 †18
TOMIC, James Edward. 9555 76TH ST, RADIOLOGY DEPT 53158 #056-05-1983 L2000 DR OS *020 †80
WALROD, Bryant James. 9555 76TH ST 53158 #038-43-2000 L2003 FSM *012 †18
WILBUR, Michael James. 9555 76TH ST, RADIOLOGY DEPT 53158 #005-12-1992 L2004 DR *020 †80

PLOVER – PORTAGE

ARNOLD, Lloyd Herbert. 54467 #056-06-1984 L1985 PTH *062 †50
BAHRKE, Steven John. 2401 PLOVER RD 54467 #056-05-1979 L1981 FM *020 †18
BRIGDEN, Malcolm L. ■ 54467 #067-01-1971 L2001 PTH *020 †20
FATCHIKOV, Tzvetan Todoro. ■ 54467 #198-01-1989 L2007 OBG *100
FENLON, Mark Leslie. 2401 PLOVER RD 54467 #056-05-1984 L1985 FM *020 †18
JONES, Jeffrey Jon. 2401 PLOVER RD 54467 #056-05-1995 L1996 IM *020 †20
LOTEYRO, Corazon Bigata. 2401 PLOVER RD 54467 #748-10-1976 L1985 FM *020 †18 ‡
SANDERSON, Peter Ashley. 2401 PLOVER RD 54467 #012-01-1980 L1981 FM *030 †18
WHITMAN, John Chas. ■ 54467 #056-05-1971 L1972 EM AM *020 †16
WIERSEMA, Channing C. 2401 PLOVER RD 54467 #056-06-1994 L1997 FM *020 †18
WIRTZ, Tim J. 2401 PLOVER RD 54467 #028-79-1989, ▲ L1990 FM *020 †18

PLYMOUTH – SHEBOYGAN

ALVAREZ, Ricardo Jose. RR 3 53073 #056-06-1957 L1961 EM GP *071
ARENBERG, Mary E. 1000 EASTERN AVE 53073 #016-11-1980 L1981 FM *020 †18
BOSTWICK, Allon Howard. 2600 KILEY WAY 53073 #056-05-1978 L1979 FM EM *020 †18
MURTHY, Dharmesh. 2636 EASTERN AVE 53073 #305-01-1998 L2001 FM *020 †18
OLSON, Dean Matthew. 2600 KILEY WAY 53073 #056-06-2000 L2003 FM *020 †18
PESCHKE, Scott Robt. 2600 KILEY WAY 53073 #056-05-1981 L1983 FM *020 †18
SCHROEDER, George Spencer. 1000 EASTERN AVE 53073 #056-05-1979 L1980 FM *020 †18
SCOTT, Robert Jos. W7177 COUNTY ROAD Z, RSCS LTD 53073 #056-06-1970 L1974 DR *020 †80
SHARON, Mark Wm. 2600 KILEY WAY 53073 #056-06-1979 L1982 FM *020 †18
STAEHLING, Renee Ann. 515 E MILL ST, 515 E MILL ST 53073 #056-05-1992 L1993 FM *020 †18
STAEHLING, Steven John. 515 E MILL ST, 515 E MILL ST 53073 #056-05-1992 L1993 FM *020 †18 ‡
SZYMANSKI, Walter Gerard. PO BOX 31 53073 #056-06-1980 L1981 ESM GP *075
WEBB, William Christopher. ■ 53073 #056-06-1948 L1949 IM *072 †20

POPLAR – DOUGLAS

LUNDBERG, William Irvin. ■ 54864 #056-05-1966 L1967 OBG *030 †30

PORT EDWARDS – WOOD

JOHNSON, Robert Lee. ■ 54469 #016-06-1956 L1958 FM *071 †18

PORT WASHINGTON – OZAUKEE

BOSTWICK, Mark Steven. 1777 W GRAND AVE, STE 33 53074 #056-06-1978 L1979 IM *020 †20
BRAZA, Edward Anthony. 1777 W GRAND AVE, STE 33 53074 #056-06-1986 L1987 OPH *020 †35
COSNER, Francine Laura. 1777 W GRAND AVE, STE 33 53074 #038-41-1992 L2005 OBG *020 †30

FITZSIMMONS, Mark Robt. 1475 W GRAND AVE 53074 #056-06-1991 L1992 **FM OBG** *020 †18
GERHARDSTEIN, Richard P. 1317 W GRAND AVE, COMPREHENSIVE COUNSELING 53074 #028-34-1962 L1968 **P ADM** *071
GOETZ, John Norbert. 1777 W GRAND AVE, AURORA ADVANCED HEALTHCARE 53074 #056-06-1979 L1982 **PD** *020 †55
GUNDELLY, Ashwini. 1777 W GRAND AVE, STE 33 53074 #495-57-1998 L2002 **IM** *020 †20
HENKLE, Robert Fenton. ■ 53074 #018-03-1953 L1956 **GP** *071
HURTH, James Philip. 121 W MAIN ST 53074 #056-06-1981 L1985 **P** *071 †75
JENSEN, Kenneth F, Jr. 1777 W GRAND AVE, STE 33 53074 #056-05-1977 L1978 **IM** *075 †20
KARRI, Roopa. 1777 W GRAND AVE, STE 33 53074 #495-65-1991 L1998 **PDE** *020 †55
KOSTIC, Kathryn Jeanette. 1777 W GRAND AVE, STE 33 53074 #038-06-1993 L1998 **OBG** *020 †30
KRCO, Michael Joseph. 1777 W GRAND AVE, STE 33 53074 #016-11-1978 L1980 **U** *020 †95
KROL, Pamela. ■ 53074 #016-01-2002 L2002 **EM** *020 †16
MAITRA, Anita Marisa. ■ 53074 #495-17-1973 L1977 **AN** *020 †05
MARUSINEC, Laura Ellen. 1777 W GRAND AVE 53074 #056-06-1995 L1996 **PD** *020 †55
MC MANUS, Douglas Brian. 1777 W GRAND AVE, STE 33 53074 #046-01-1977 L1978 **IM EM** *020 †20
MOCARSKI, Jill Frances. 1777 W GRAND AVE, MILWAUKEE MEDICAL CLINIC 53074 #056-05-1986 L1990 **IM** *020 †20
O'REILLY, Tedmond Robt. 1475 W GRAND AVE 53074 #028-34-1988 L1989 **FM** *020 †18
PEREZ, Celestino M. 126 E PIER ST 53074 #748-07-1963 L1976 **IM IMG** *020
PUETZ, Thomas Robt. 1777 W GRAND AVE, STE 33 53074 #056-05-1990 L1991 **GE** *020 †20
SCAMMELL, Kevin Bruce. 1777 W GRAND AVE, STE 33 53074 #056-05-1988 L1991 **PD** *020 †55
WALL, Thomas. 1317 W GRAND AVE 53074 #038-06-1952 L1958 **GS** *071 †85

PORTAGE – COLUMBIA

ANDREW, Reed Chadwick. 1011 W PLEASANT ST 53901 #025-01-1958 L1966 **OPH** *071 †35
ARNASON, Jon A. 1116 PROSPECT AVE, PORTAGE FAMILY CARE CENTER 53901 #484-01-1987 L1992 **RHU IM** *020 †20
BEINLICH, Brad Robt. 2817 NEW PINERY RD 53901 #025-12-1983 L1985 **N** *040 †75
BLOHM, Brenda Ann. PO BOX 387, 2817 NEW PINERY RD 53901 #016-06-1994 L1997 **FM** *020 †18
BOURSIER, Charles Lemont. 2817 NEW PINERY RD, DIVINE SAVIOR HEALTHCARE I 53901 #026-04-1984 L2001 **EM** *020
CALLAHAN, Bert Clark. 2817 NEW PINERY RD, BEAVER DAM ORTHOPAEDIC 53901 #028-34-1987 L1988 **ORS OSM** *020 †40
CASTROVINCI, Robt Vincent. 2851 NEW PINERY RD 53901 #028-34-1973 L1974 **OPH** *020 †35
CLEVELAND, Langston B. 1115 W PLEASANT ST 53901 #016-11-1992 L1996 **PM** *020 †60
COONEY, Robert Thos. 2825 HUNTERS TRL 53901 #024-05-1948 L1950 **GP** *071
DOYLE, Kathleen. 2825 HUNTERS TRL 53901 #028-34-1974 L1976 **PD OS** *020
ESCOBEDO, Antonio. 2825 HUNTERS TRL 53901 #007-02-1998 L2001 **FM** *020 †18
GREGORY, David Dixson. 2825 HUNTERS TRL, PORTAGE CLINIC LTD 53901 #018-03-1977 L1980 **FM** *020 †18
GUZMAN, Victor C, Jr. ■ 53901 #748-07-1956 L1977 **GP** *071
JACKSON, Thomas Victor. 2817 NEW PINERY RD 53901 #056-06-1976 L1977 **EM FM** *020
KRECKMAN, Susan Halasz. 2817 NEW PINERY RD, DEVINE SAVIOR HC STE 107 53901 #025-07-1994 L1997 **FM** *020 †18
KRUMPOS, Gerald Lawrence. 2825 HUNTERS TRL 53901 #056-05-1991 L1994 **FM** *020 †18
LOCAS-FRENCH, Nadine M. 1116 PROSPECT AVE, UNIV COMMUNITY CLINICS-POR 53901 #063-01-1994 L1997 **FM** *020 †18
LONGO, Walter Leo. 2817 NEW PINERY RD 53901 #030-05-1977 L1982 **ON HEM** *020 †20
LYNCH, Matthew Lawrence. 2817 NEW PINERY RD, DIVINE SAVIOR HEALTHCARE 53901 #056-05-2002 L2002 **GS** *020
MAENNER, Gerald Francis. 2817 NEW PINERY RD 53901 #041-02-1992 L2004 **OBG** *020 †30
MAGAR, Namrata Arun. 2977 COUNTY ROAD CX 53901 #495-96-1993 L2006 **FM** *020 †18
MAGNES, Craig Neil. 2817 NEW PINERY RD, RADIOLOGY DEPARTMENT 53901 #016-42-1989 L1999 **NR** *020 †80
NOVACHECK, Steven James. 2817 NEW PINERY RD 53901 #056-05-1977 L1978 **EM FM** *020 †18
OH, Kenneth Kim. PO BOX 387, 128 EASTRIDGE DR 53901 #035-19-1993 L1999 **GPM OS** *020 †60,70
PAULK, Stephen Chas. 1115 W PLEASANT ST, STE 200 53901 #018-03-1973 L1995 **GS** *020 †85
PAVELSEK, Joseph Wm. ■ 53901 #056-05-1945 L1948 **IM GP** *072
PINEDA, Susan E. 2977 COUNTY ROAD CX 53901 #748-01-1975 L1994 **FM** *020 †18
PUCHNER, Thomas C, Jr. 2977 COUNTY ROAD CX 53901 #056-06-1984 L1985 **AI** *020 †20,03
RAK, Kevin Martin. 2817 NEW PINERY RD P, DIVINE SAVIOR HLTH DEPOT R 53901 #056-06-1984 L1994 **DR** *020 †80
SAGER, Mark Alan. 1011 W PLEASANT ST 53901 #025-01-1972 L1975 **IMG IM** *030 †20
SAJJAD, Imran. 2825 HUNTERS TRL 53901 #704-20-2002 L2006 **IM** *020 †20
SCHMUS, Robert. 2817 NEW PINERY RD 53901 #056-06-1977 L1978 **GS VS** *020 †85
SHULER, Paul Fredric. 2817 NEW PINERY RD, BEAVER DAM ORTHOPAEDIC 53901 #025-12-1996 L2001 **ORS** *020 †40
SIMON, Patrick Michael. 2817 NEW PINERY RD, BEAVER DAM ORTHOPAEDIC 53901 #056-06-1999 L2004 **ORS** *020 †40
SLAVIK, Paul Jos. 2825 HUNTERS TRL 53901 #028-34-1974 L1976 **IM** *020 †20
SONDERSON, Jeon M. ■ 53901 #056-05-1949 L1950 **OS** *075
STEIDINGER, Charles L. ■ 53901 #016-11-1953 L1956 **FM** *071 †18
STRABEL, Elizabeth Ruth. 2825 HUNTERS TRL 53901 #021-06-1991 L1998 **FM** *020 †18
STRAIN, Amy Lynn. 2825 HUNTERS TRL 53901 #018-03-1995 L2002 **FM** *020 †18
STUBITSCH, Brian Thomas. 2817 NEW PINERY RD, DIVINE SAVIOR HEALTH CARE 53901 #422-01-1997 L2001 **EM** *020 †16
SULAS, Leonas Pranas. 2825 HUNTERS TRL 53901 #154-07-1974 L1985 **U OS** *020
SULIENE, Dalia. ■ 53901 #913-96-1975 L1986 **IM** *020
TAYLOR, Stewart F. 108 E COOK ST, STEWART F TAYLOR JR MD 53901 #016-02-1945 L1948 **GP** *071
VERZOSA, Raymundo Munoz. 2315 HAMILTON ST 53901 #748-09-1972 L1983 **DR** *020

PORTERFIELD – MARINETTE

OSTROWSKI, David Michael. ■ 54159 #056-06-1974 L1979 **OTO** *071 †45

POUND – MARINETTE

NOGLER, Calvin Dean. 2026 COUNTY ROAD Q 54161 #005-12-1982 L1985 **FM** *020 †18

POYNETTE – COLUMBIA

KASTENBERG, Ira Seth. 237 W SEWARD ST, STE 97 53955 #035-15-1975 L1976 **FM** *020 †18

PRAIRIE DU CHIEN – CRAWFORD

BINTZ, Marilu. 610 E TAYLOR ST, PRAIRIE DU CHIEN CLINIC 53821 #017-20-1983 L1984 **GS** *020 †85
BIRD, Julio Jose. 610 E TAYLOR ST 53821 #042-01-1976 L1986 **CD IM** *020 †20
BOISVERT, Walter Ray. 610 E TAYLOR ST, PRAIRIE DU CHIEN CLINIC 53821 #056-05-1985 L1986 **FM FPG** *020 †18
BORN, Christopher Paul. 213 W BLACKHAWK AVE, CLINIC PRAIRIE DU CHIEN 53821 #028-02-1977 L1982 **OPH** *020 †35
BURROWS, Christopher R. 705 E TAYLOR ST, PRAIRIE DER CHIEN MEMOR HO 53821 #061-01-1992 L1996 **FM** *020
CASE, Michael Keith. 610 E TAYLOR ST, PRAIRIE DU CHIEN CLINIC 53821 #056-05-1988 L1993 **OTO GS** *020 †45
DEHART, David Bradford. 800 E BLACKHAWK AVE 53821 #016-43-1998 L1999 **FM** *020 †18
EPLEY, Verne Carbauh. 610 E TAYLOR ST 53821 #039-01-1942 L1946 **GP GS** *075
FITZNER, Ronald Timothy. 705 E TAYLOR ST 53821 #060-01-1987 L1996 **EM** *020
GARRITY, Michael Stephen. ■ 53821 #056-06-1959 L1960 **FM FPG** *071 †18
GOODLUND, Larry Shenehon. 610 E TAYLOR ST, BEHAVIORAL HEALTH PRAIRIE 53821 #026-04-1972 L1978 **CHP P** *020 †75
GRIMM, Gayette Fauniece. 610 E TAYLOR ST, PRAIRIE DU CHIEN CLINIC 53821 #018-03-1999 L2004 **GS** *020 †85
GRUNWALD, Ann L. 610 E TAYLOR ST 53821 #056-05-1979 L1980 **FM** *020 †18
GRUNWALD, Mark Andrew. 610 E TAYLOR ST, PRAIRIE DU CHIEN CLINIC 53821 #005-11-1979 L1980 **FM FPG** *020 †18
JOHNSON, William Lee. ■ 53821 #024-06-1948 L1950 **OS** *075
JORGENSEN, Kurt James. 610 E TAYLOR ST, GUNDERSEN CLINIC-PRAIRIE D 53821 #018-03-1977 L1980 **FM** *020 †18
KEY, Robert Terry, Jr. 800 E BLACKHAWK AVE 53821 #026-04-1996 L1997 **FM** *020 †18
KVIDERA, Amy Allisan. 61750 PARK VIEW LN, PRAIRIE DU CHIEN 53821 #018-03-1996 L2003 **FM** *020 †18
MEESTER, Gerald Le Roy. 705 E TAYLOR ST, SURGEONS PC AT PDC 53821 #018-03-1970 L1971 **ORS HS** *020 †40
PEARSON, James August. 705 E TAYLOR ST, SURGEONS PC AT PDC 53821 #018-03-1959 L1995 **ORS** *071 †40
PFEIFFER, Donald Wayne. 705 E TAYLOR ST 53821 #018-03-1947 L1966 **GP** *071
PIEROTTI, Stephen Eugene. 705 E TAYLOR ST, SURGEONS PC AT PDC 53821 #018-03-1989 L1995 **ORS** *020 †40
ROGGE, Michael John. 800 E BLACKHAWK AVE, PRAIRIE DU CHIEN CLINIC 53821 #018-03-1996 L1997 **FM** *020 †18
ROLLIE, Thomas Richard. 610 E TAYLOR ST, PRAIRIE DU CHIEN 53821 #026-04-1978 L2007 **FM** *020 †18
RYBARCZYK, Sara Jane. 610 E TAYLOR ST, PRAIRIE DU CHIEN CLINIC 53821 #056-05-1993 L1994 **IM** *020 †20
VOSIKA, Mariana K. 610 E TAYLOR ST, BEHAVIORAL HEALTH PRAIRIE 53821 #957-01-1980 L2001 **P** *020 †75
WHITAKER, Ren Romaine. 610 E TAYLOR ST, GUNDERSON-PRAIRIE CLINIC 53821 #054-04-1966 L1988 **FM CD** *071 †18

PRAIRIE DU SAC – SAUK

BEKX, Paul Andrew. 35 PRAIRIE AVE, STE 325 53578 #056-06-1995 L1996 **END** *020 †20
BERTRAM, Dale Thos. 80 1ST ST, SAUK PRAIRIE MEMORIAL HOSP 53578 #056-05-1982 L1983 **EM** *020 †16
BISHOP, Paul R. 80 1ST ST 53578 #056-05-1949 L1950 **GP FM** *071
CARLSON, Haakon Paralie. ■ 53578 #056-05-1964 L1966 **FM** *071 †18
COX, Carol Christine. 35 PRAIRIE AVE, STE 325 53578 #036-01-1980 L1989 **RHU IM** *020 †20
DE GIOVANNI, John Anthony. 35 PRAIRIE AVE, STE 315 53578 #016-11-1972 L1973 **GS GYN** *020 †85
HAUBENSCHILD, David Thoma. ■ 53578 #056-05-2008 *012
HEBERT, Matthew Meade. 35 PRAIRIE AVE, ORTHOPEDIC ASSOCIATES OF 53578 #056-05-1999 L2000 **ORS** *020 †40
KRIZ, Robert John. 80 1ST ST 53578 #035-19-1969 L1974 **A IM** *020 †20,03
LAMSON, Michael Davidc. 35 PRAIRIE AVE, ORTHOPEDIC ASSOCIATES OF 53578 #056-05-1997 L1998 **ORS** *020 †40
NIEDERMEIER, William Robt. 35 PRAIRIE AVE, ORTHOPEDIC ASSOCIATES OF 53578 #056-05-1973 L1976 **ORS** *020 †40
PARINS, Theodore Sheldon. 35 PRAIRIE AVE, STE 315 53578 #056-05-1993 L1994 **GS** *020 †85 ‡
PUCILLO, Kelly Nelson. 818 E WOODLAND TRL, MEDICINE 53578 #056-06-2005 L2006 **FP** *012
ROSENTHAL, Arnold Neil. 35 PRAIRIE AVE STE 200, ORTHOPEDIC ASSOCIATES OF 53578 #032-01-1977 L1979 **ORS** *020 †40
SLATTERY, James Stephen. 80 1ST ST 53578 #018-03-1976 L1978 **ORS** *071 †40
STRAUB, Norbert Ralph. 80 1ST ST, SAUK PTSITIR HOSPITAL 53578 #056-05-1996 L1997 **FM** *020 †18
STRICKLER, John Chas. 80 1ST ST, SAUK PRAIRIE MEMORIAL HOSP 53578 #026-04-1980 L1983 **EM FM** *020 †18

PRAIRIE FARM – BARRON

NAGLER, Richard Dell. 224 RIVER AVE S 54762 #025-01-1985 L1996 **IM** *020 †20

PRENTICE – PRICE

LOFLAND, Leo James. 1511 RAILROAD AVE, MEMORIAL HEALTH CENTER CLI 54556 #056-05-1977 L1978 **FM** *020 †18

PRESCOTT – PIERCE

FUCHS, Kurt Richard. 1400 N ACRES RD, STE 30 54021 #026-04-1990 L1995 FM *020 †18
KUSSKE, Bradley Walter. ■ 54021 #026-04-1945 OTO *071 †45
LANEY, Howard John. 604 ORANGE ST 54021 #056-05-1935 L1937 GP P *072

PRESQUE ISLE – VILAS

CASEY, Peter Nicholas. ■ 54557 #056-06-1961 L1962 PTH *071 †50
ZEISS, John Chetwick. ■ 54557 #016-06-1960 L1961 OPH *071 †35

PRINCETON – GREEN LAKE

LEE, Phyllis Eileen. 502 W WATER ST, PRINCETON FAM MC 54968 #005-02-1986 L1998 FM *020 †18

PULASKI – SHAWANO

ALDRICH, Peri Johnson. 331 W GREEN BAY ST 54162 #043-01-1977 L1978 FM *020 †18
FERGUS, Christina Loumari. 940 S SAINT AUGUSTINE ST 54162 #025-01-2001 L2006 FP *012
RICHTER, James Allen. ■ 54162 #046-01-1988 L1989 P *020 †75
VERSTOPPEN, Gerald R. 940 S SAINT AUGUSTINE ST 54162 #165-04-1981 L1983 FM *020 †18

RACINE – RACINE

AFIFI, Najwa Khalil. 5142 CITATION DR 53402 #575-01-1989 L1998 NPM *020 †55
AKGULIAN, Nicholas Arthur. ■ 53402 #056-05-1990 L1995 FM *020 †18
ALEXANDER, A Chas. 1320 WISCONSIN AVE 53403 #016-06-1951 L1960 OBG *020 †30 ‡
ALEXANDER, Andrew Charles. 3801 SPRING ST, ALL SAINTS MEDICAL GROUP 53405 #016-06-1996 L2000 OBG *020 †30
ALLEN, Lori Joyce Rens. 1007 ROBIN LN 53402 #056-05-1985 L1987 PTH *020 †50
ALLISON, Curt Alan. 3811 SPRING ST 53405 #056-06-1989 L1990 OTO *020 †45
ALTENBERG, Barry Mathew. 5802 WASHINGTON AVE # 201 53406 #561-01-1963 L1966 P *020
AMAN, Saleem. 1320 WISCONSIN AVE 53403 #704-02-1990 L1993 IM *020 †20
AMES, Brian Michael. ■ 53403 #016-42-2008 *012
ANDERSEN, Dennis James. 3811 SPRING ST, STE 102 53405 #016-02-1989 L1995 HS *020 †40
ARMAGAN, Osep Ezagel. 3811 SPRING ST, # 102 53405 #056-06-1991 L1996 ORS OSM *020 †40
ASSAAD, Haney Nabil. 6232 BANKERS RD 53403 #016-11-1996 L1999 IM *020 †20
AYRES, Loren Ray. ■ 53406 #005-02-1969 L1970 PTH *020 †50
BADER, Iftekhar Hussain. 3807 SPRING ST 53405 #495-65-1984 L1991 PUD IM *020 †20 ‡
BAHADUR, Shivendra. 1320 WISCONSIN AVE 53403 #305-01-2003 L2007 FP *012
BAHZAD, Christobel Grant. 3807 SPRING ST 53405 #919-01-1971 L1976 OBG *020
BARNHARDT, Todd Thos. 3811 SPRING ST # 102, WHEATON FRANCISCAN MEDICAL 53405 #056-06-1990 L1991 ORS *020 †40
BARTLETT, James Clifford. 3805 SPRING ST, STE 310 53405 #018-75-1984, ▲ L1987 CD IM *020 †20
BARTZEN, Peter James, Jr. 8348 WASHINGTON AVE 53406 #026-04-1979 L1980 GS *020 †85
BAUMBLATT, Don Phillip. 1244 WISCONSIN AVE, STE 206 53403 #056-05-1958 L1960 IM *071
BECK, David. ■ 53402 #016-42-2007 FP *012
BEGGS, Bradley Kluth. 3801 SPRING ST, LABORATORY 53405 #017-20-1984 L1985 PTH *020 †50
BERCE, Paul Joseph. 3807 SPRING ST, ALL SAINTS HEALTHCARE 53405 #056-06-2003 L2005 IM *020 †20
BERGS, Joseph Theodore. 3805B SPRING ST STE 240, WHEATON HEALTHCARE 53405 #056-06-1984 L1989 P *020 †75
BHARAT, Yogendra. 3801 SPRING ST 53405 #495-69-1978 L1986 AN *020 †05
BIBOSO, Romeo Blam. 5401 DOUGLAS AVE 53402 #748-01-1959 L1970 GP *020
BJERREGAARD, Wm James. 1244 WISCONSIN AVE STE 303 53403 #056-05-1981 L1986 P *020 †75
BORDAK, Glen Alan. 1007 ROBIN LN 53402 #056-06-1985 L1986 PTH *020 †50
BOYCE, Lorenzo C. 2405 NORTHWESTERN AVE, KURTEN MEDICAL GROUP 53404 #016-11-1985 L1989 OBG IM *020 †30
BOYE, Roger. 3801 SPRING ST 53405 #412-02-1987 L2007 CCM *020 †20
BRENNAN, John F, III. 3807 SPRING ST 53405 #016-42-1991 L1990 NEP *020 †20
BRIGGS, Joy D. 3807 SPRING ST, ALL SAINTS HEALTHCARE 53405 #025-12-1996 L1999 PD *020 †55
BRITTIG, Jennifer Joline. 2408 FOUR MILE RD, ALL SAINTS HEALTHCARE SYST 53402 #016-42-1991 L1996 FM *020 †18
BROCKMAN, Lenora Marie. 3821 SPRING ST, ALL SAINTS MED GROUP 53405 #068-01-1980 L1985 OBG *020 †30
BROOKS, Jerome Clifford. ■ 53406 #056-06-1961 L1964 IM NEP *071 †20
BROWN, Robert Wm. 8348 WASHINGTON AVE, BLDG E 53406 #048-04-1982 L1991 FM *020 †18
BURKE, Donald Richard. 3801 SPRING ST 53405 #016-43-1954 L1957 GS *071 †85
BYRNE, John James. 3807 SPRING ST, WHEATON FRANCISCAN MEDICAL 53405 #056-06-1979 L1988 IM *020 †20
BYRON, Rudy Vallee, Jr. 3807 SPRING ST 53405 #016-06-1997 L2000 FM *020 †18
CAIN, Tedd Peter. 3805 SPRING ST, STE 212 53406 #056-06-1986 L1988 GE *020 †20
CALLAGHAN, Robert S. 1244 WISCONSIN AVE, PSYCHIATRIC SERVICES 53403 #016-06-1990 L1994 CHP *020 †75
CARVER, Veronica Giple. 3821 SPRING ST, STE 200 53405 #056-06-1988 L1991 OBG *020 †30
CATHERALL, Mark Thomas. 3801 SPRING ST, ALL SAINTS MEDICAL GROUP 53405 #016-43-1998 L2005 IM *020 †20
CHEN, Emmie Andrea. 3801 SPRING ST, ALL SAINTS HEALTHCARE 53405 #016-42-2001 L2005 EM *020 †16
CHRISTENSON, James B. 1320 WISCONSIN AVE 53403 #026-04-2002 L2006 P *020 †75
CIOS, Adam T. 3801 SPRING ST 53405 #759-01-1983 L1994 EM GP *020 †16
CLARK, David John. ■ 53402 #016-01-2001 L2007 ORS *100
CLARK, Richard Irving. 1320 WISCONSIN AVE 53403 #056-05-12-1956 L1957 GPM *020
CLARK, Richard Rangecroft. 2408 FOUR MILE RD, WHEATON FRANCISCAN MED GRP 53402 #041-02-1988 L1997 FM *020 †18

COHILL, Donald F. 3811 SPRING ST 201, WHEATON FRANCISCAN MEDICAL 53405 #041-01-1960 L1964 GS OS *020 †85
CONNOLLY, Matthew F. 5354 HUNT CLUB RD 53402 #056-05-1995 L1999 IM *020 †20
COTY, Paulette Yvonne. 3807 SPRING ST, ALL SAINTS MEDICAL GROUP 53405 #017-20-1980 L1991 PD *020 †55
CREVIER, Carlynn Hill. 6232 BANKERS RD, WHEATON FRANCISCAN MEDICAL 53403 #056-06-2003 L2007 IM *020 †20
CULEN, Gregory Martin. 3807 SPRING ST 53405 #016-01-1997 L2000 IM *020 †20
CUNNINGHAM, Ruthann Marie. 3803 SPRING ST, STE LL1 53405 #025-07-1993 L2000 EM *020 †16
CURRIE, Robert E. ■ 53402 #007-02-1952 L1955 AN *020 †05
CUSHMAN, Stephen Marshall. 3805B SPRING ST STE 320 53405 #056-06-1956 L1961 NS *020 †85,25
DASOVIC, William Joseph. 3801 SPRING ST 53405 #030-05-1996 L1999 IM *020 †20
DAVIS, Glenn Stuart. 3801 SPRING ST 53405 #016-45-1980 L1986 AN *020 †20,05
DE CHECK, Mark Edward. 3805B SPRING ST, STE 250 53405 #056-05-1983 L1986 FM *020 †18
DE GRANDVILLE, Catherine. ■ 53406 #759-01-2004 FP *012
DE KRAAY, Warren Henry. 3803 SPRING ST, STE 206 53405 #018-03-1955 L1981 TS VS *020 †85,90
DEUSTER, Anthony Wm. 3801 SPRING ST, SAINT MARY'S MEDICAL CENTE 53405 #056-06-1991 L1997 EM *020 †16
DHINGRA, Pankaj Kumar. 3807 SPRING ST 53405 #038-44-2002 L2002 NEP *020 †20
DI ZADJI, Desiree Madelyn. 3803 SPRING ST 53406 #016-06-1995 L2004 CD *020 †20
DIZADJI, Hadi. 3805A SPRING ST, STE 310 53405 #517-01-1953 L1963 CD *071 †20
DOUGLAS, Eustace Fitz O. ■ 53402 #061-01-1962 L1976 N *071
DRAKE, David J. 5333 DOUGLAS AVE 53402 #056-06-1996 L1998 FM *020 †18
DRAYTON, Kimberley Anasta. ■ 53406 #305-01-2006 FP *012
DRIZIN, Mikhail. 2405 NORTHWESTERN AVE 53404 #913-16-1968 L1993 PM *020
DUDLEY, Suzana Ivanov. 2408 4 MILE RD 53402 #056-05-1992 L1993 FM *020 †18
DURBIN, Paul Christian. 3807 SPRING ST, WHEATON FRANCISCAN MEDICAL 53405 #016-11-1995 L1998 IM *020 †20
EARNEST, Barbara L. 3801 SPRING ST 53405 #047-05-1982 L1995 PTH *020 †20
ELFERING, Sandra Lee. 3821 SPRING ST, ST LUKES HEALTH PAVILLION 53405 #016-06-1996 L2005 OBG *020 †30
ENGLANDER, Stanley Mark. 2405 NORTHWESTERN AVE 53404 #016-06-1959 L1964 PD *071 †55
ERICSON, H Leslie. 3811 SPRING ST, STE 102 53405 #016-06-1965 L1972 ORS *020 †40
FASSEAS, Panayotis. 3805A SPRING ST, WFH-ALL SAINTS WEST PROFES 53405 #561-20-1991 L2002 CD *020 †20
FEIDER, Dennis E. 3811 SPRING ST, STE 303 53405 #056-06-1978 L1979 OTO *020 †45
FLEMING, Maureen Therese. 1320 WISCONSIN AVE 53403 #007-02-1994 L1998 OBG *020 †30
FLOCH, Louis John. 3807 SPRING ST, RACINE MED CLNC 53405 #062-01-1956 L1965 GYN *071 †30
FLOX, Stephen Thos. 3807 SPRING ST 53405 #016-42-1980 L1981 PD *020 †55
FODOR, Adriana Corina. 3801 SPRING ST, WHEATON FRANCISCAN MEDICAL 53405 #781-05-1997 L2008 IM *020 †20
FOLEY, Thomas Frank. 1 MAIN ST 53403 #011-02-1967 L1973 IM PUD *020 †20
FOREMAN, John Woods. 3807 SPRING ST 53405 #008-01-1962 L1967 PD *071 †55
FOX, Leslie Maria. 3807 SPRING ST, WHEATON FRANCISCAN MEDICAL 53405 #016-43-1988 L1996 PD *020 †55
FOX, Stuart Aaron. 3821 SPRING ST 53405 #016-43-1988 L1995 OBG AM *020 †30
GALBIS-REIG, David. 3801 SPRING ST 53405 #051-04-1999 L2002 IM *020
GANANSKY, Rhonda S. 3801 SPRING ST 53405 #016-42-1989 L1990 D *071 †15
GANDER, E Paul. 904 STATE ST 53404 #056-06-1957 L1958 GP *071
GANDHI, Liza Bhupendra. 1320 WISCONSIN AVE 53403 #305-01-2001 L2004 FM *020 †18
GANZ, Michael Aaron. 1515 S GREENBAY RD 53406 #016-42-1985 L1991 AI IM *020 †20,03
GARDETTO, Peter August. 1320 WISCONSIN AVE 53403 #056-06-1954 L1957 PD *071 †55
GAUSCHE, Eric David. ■ 53406 #056-05-2005 L2005 P *012
GIERAHN, James Paul. 1 MAIN ST 53403 #056-05-1975 L1978 IM *020 †20
GIST, Darnella D. 6232 BANKERS RD LL, ALL SAINTS HEALTHCARE-PK S 53403 #016-42-1998 L2001 FM *020 †18
GOODRICH, Thomas Edward. 1244 WISCONSIN AVE STE 105 53403 #016-11-1986 L1987 FM *020 †18
GOSWAMI, Rupashi. ■ 53406 #305-01-2006 FP *012
GRAF, Alfred Edmond. 3807 SPRING ST, RACINE MEDICAL CLNC 53405 #024-07-1947 L1950 PD *071
GRUETER, Jean Ann. 3801 SPRING ST 53405 #056-06-1980 L1989 AN *020 †05
GULLBERG, Robert Martin. 3807 SPRING ST 53405 #016-11-1981 L1986 ID IM *020 †20
HALLMON, William Nicholas. 3811 SPRING ST STE 202, ALL SAINTS MEDICAL GROUP 53405 #041-12-1985 L1990 GE IM *020 †20
HAMMES, James Roger. ■ 53402 #056-06-1955 L1956 ORS *071 †40
HAN, Peter Duhee. 3811 SPRING ST, STE 201 53405 #041-01-1998 L2004 GE *020 †20
HARDACRE, Jerry M, II. 3811 SPRING ST STE 201 53405 #056-05-1985 L1989 GS *020 †85 ‡
HEMPHILL, Donna Jeanette. 8400 WASHINGTON AVE 53406 #016-11-1995 L1997 OBG *020 †30
HENNESSY, Margaret Mary. 3807 SPRING ST 53405 #056-06-1996 L1998 PD *020 †55 ‡
HERNANDEZ, Diego Alberto. 3811 SPRING ST, ALL SAINTS ST MARYS MED CT 53405 #017-20-1994 L2000 GS VS *020
HERRMANN, Anthony Albert. ■ 53402 #056-06-1960 L1961 OM GPM *071 †70
HOLTEBECK, Aaron Charles. 3805B SPRING ST, STE 140 53405 #056-06-2002 L2006 OPH *020
HSU, Chung-Yen Philip. 1320 WISCONSIN AVE 53403 #654-01-2000 L2005 FM *100 †18
HULBERT, Karen Ann. 1320 WISCONSIN AVE 53403 #016-42-1994 L2003 FM *020 †18
ILADA, Patricio Luis B. 5439 DURAND AVE, STE 202 53406 #748-08-1983 L1994 FM *020 †18
INFUSINO, Giovanni Annunz. ■ 53404 #016-42-2007 IM *012
INPANBUTR-MARTINKUS, Melis. ■ 53405 #016-11-2006 L2008 FP *012
JACKSON, Gregory Bernard. 1147 WARWICK WAY, CONCENTRA MEDICAL CENTERS 53406 #056-06-1980 L1985 AN *012
JACOBSON, Donald Melvin. 3701 DURAND AVE STE 325 53405 #047-05-1981 L1992 P *020 †75
JACOBSON, Michael P. 3807 SPRING ST, ST. MARY'S MEDICAL GROUP 53405 #017-20-1974 L1989 IM NEP *020 †20
JAMES, Jehana Asaidra. ■ 53402 #033-06-2004 L2007 IM *020 †20
JAYAPRAKASH, Subbanna. 6015 DURAND AVE STE 500 53406 #495-33-1978 L1986 PM PMM *020 †60
JOHNSON, P Spencer. TWO ELEVEN NINTH ST 53403 #539-06-1968 OS *030

■ = Address Information Privacy Protected

JOHNSON, Steven Ronald. 3807 SPRING ST 53405 #016-11-1982 L1985 **PUD IM** *020 †20 ‡
JONES, Michael Peter. 3801 SPRING ST, EMERGENCY DEPARTMENT 53405 #016-06-1999 L2003 **EM** *020 †16
JOSEPH, Elizabeth T. 3807 SPRING ST, ALL SAINTS MEDICAL GROUP 53405 #016-11-1992 L2001 **IM** *020 †20
KAARAKKA, Olli F. ■ 53405 #374-01-1951 L1959 **AN** *071
KALEKA, Aaronjit Singh. 1320 WISCONSIN AVE 53403 #305-01-2003 L2008 **FP** *012
KANTER, Alan Marc. 2405 NORTHWESTERN AVE, STE 141 53404 #016-06-1991 L2008 **FM** *020 †18 ‡
KAZ, Ari Jacob. 3811 SPRING ST, ATRIUM ORTHOPEDICS 53405 #016-42-2001 L2007 **ORS OFA** *020
KENNEDY, Marc Vinson. 3811 SPRING ST STE 202 53405 #016-11-1994 L2000 **GE** *020 †20
KHAN, Ahmad Z. 1244 WISCONSIN AVE, PSYCHIATRIC SERVICES 53403 #308-10-1987 L1999 **CHP** *020 †75
KIM, David Young. 1244 WISCONSIN AVE STE 303 53403 #583-03-1971 L1977 **P** *075 †75
KIM, Robert Byung Hoon. 1055 PRAIRIE DR, RK LTD 53406 #583-01-1965 L1969 **R** *020 †80,28
KIM, Soo Yun. ■ 53402 #583-10-1965 L1976 **PTH** *075
KIRAGES, Thomas John. 3801 SPRING ST, ST MARYS MEDICAL CTR 53405 #016-42-1998 L2003 **EM** *020 †16
KOENIGSKNECHT, Steven Jos. 3805B SPRING ST, STE 230 53405 #025-01-1977 L1982 **EM** *071 †16
KONTRA, Dennis James. 5802 WASHINGTON AVE 53406 #016-06-1965 L1966 **OPH** *020 †35
LAING, Robert E. 3811 SPRING ST STE 102, GROUP 53405 #016-43-1979 L1985 **ORS OS** *020 †40 ‡
LAST, Allen R. 1320 WISCONSIN AVE 53403 #056-05-2000 L2005 **FM** *020 †18
LEADHOLM, Charles Richard. 3801 SPRING ST 53405 #056-05-1975 L1976 **IM** *020 †20,16
LEHNER, Robert H, Jr. 3805A SPRING ST, EYE CLINIC OF RACINE LTD 53405 #056-06-1978 L1982 **OPH** *020 †35
LEHNER, Robert Harold, Sr. 3805 SPRING ST, EYE CLINIC OF RACINE LTD 53405 #016-01-1941 L1943 **OPH OS** *071 †35
LEIBER, Michael Thomas. ■ 53402 #056-06-2007 **IM** *012
LE SAGE, Timothy B. 3811 SPRING ST, STE 201 53405 #056-05-1995 L2000 **GS VS** *020 †85
LINSTROTH, John Wm. 1320 WISCONSIN AVE 53403 #056-05-1975 L1976 **IM** *020 †16
LIPPMAN, Harry Herman. 3805B SPRING ST, STE 220 53405 #016-42-1967 L1976 **NS** *020 †25
LITTLE, William James, Jr. 904 STATE ST, HEALTH CARE NETWORK INC 53404 #056-05-1944 L1945 **IM PUD** *071 †20
LIU, Terry Chong Yo. 3811 SPRING ST STE 303, ALL SAINTS MEDICAL GROUP 53405 #065-01-1991 L1999 **OTO** *020 †45
LO CURTO, John Jos, Jr. 8400 WASHINGTON AVE, TRAUMA/SURGICAL CRITICAL C 53406 #561-01-1977 L1979 **GS** *020 †85
LOPEZ, John Michael. 3807 SPRING ST, ST MARY'S MEDICAL CENTER 53405 #016-43-1995 L1998 **IM** *020 †20
LUCCAS, Bruce Alan. 3805 SPRING ST, STE 130B 53405 #056-06-1987 L1988 **FM** *020 †18
MADDEN, William James. 47 STEEPLECHASE DR 53402 #056-06-1946 L1947 **GYN** *071 †30
MANLOVE, Jeffrey Carl. 3807 SPRING ST 53405 #056-05-1985 L1986 **EM** *020 †18
MANNE, Sridevi. 8348 WASHINGTON AVE, BLDG E 53406 #495-11-1995 L1997 **FM** *020 †18
MARRIOTT, Elizabeth Ann. 3805B SPRING ST, STE 320 53405 #016-43-2003 L2003 **N** *020
MARTINEZ, Mike. 3801 SPRING ST, ALL SAINTS - ST MARY'S MED 53405 #028-02-1981 L1982 **AN IM** *020 †20,05
MARTINI, John Anthony. 3805B SPRING ST STE 250 53405 #056-06-1983 L1984 **FM P** *020 †18
MATACZYNSKI, James Dean. 829 S GREENBAY RD, STE 102 53406 #030-06-1986 L1990 **FM** *020 †18
MATHEW, Joseph Paul. 2408 FOUR MILE RD, ALL SAINTS MEDICAL GROUP 53402 #016-45-1994 L1999 **IM** *020 †20
MATKOV, Thomas George. 3811 SPRING ST STE 302, WHEATON FRANCISCAN MEDICAL 53405 #016-01-1995 L2001 **U** *020 †95
MAWN, Karen E. 3807 SPRING ST 53405 #008-02-1980 L2001 **CHN N** *020 †55
MAWN, Stephen Vincent. 3805B SPRING ST STE 260, ALL SAINTS MED GRP OCCUP M 53405 #010-02-1981 L2001 **GPM** *020 †70
MCCABE, Jennifer Ann. ■ 53402 #028-34-2005 L2005 **OBG** *012
MC CABE, Kevin Wayne. 1525 HOWE ST, SC JOHNSON 53403 #028-34-1977 L1982 **IM OM** *020 †20
MC CORD, Melinda Louise. 3811 SPRING ST, STE 301 53405 #036-01-1987 L1993 **D IM** *020 †15
MEILS, Carol Margaret. 3805A SPRING ST, STE 310 53405 #056-06-1983 L1991 **CD IM** *020 †20
MEJALLI, Nedal. 8348 WASHINGTON AVE 53406 #308-03-1984 L1994 **FM** *020 †18
MEYER, Loren Marc. 3807 SPRING ST, WHEATON FRANCISCAN MED GRP 53405 #055-01-1983 L1986 **PD DIA** *030 †55
MEYER, Scott Walter. 3807 SPRING ST, BOX 085001 53405 #018-03-1984 L1985 **PD** *020 †55
MIKAELIAN, Myron David. 3811 SPRING ST, STE 102 53405 #056-06-1983 L1984 **ORS** *020 †40
MILLER, Michelle Marie. 3821 SPRING ST, WOMEN'S HEALTH PAVILION 53405 #016-01-1995 L2001 **OBG** *020 †30
MILONAS, George. 3807 SPRING ST 53405 #016-01-1995 L1999 **PD** *020 †55
MINTON, Richard. ■ 53402 #056-06-1946 L1947 **IM** *071 †20
MONT-LOUIS, Emelide. ■ 53402 #306-01-2003 L2007 **FP** *012
MOORE, Kelan A. 3801 SPRING ST, ALL SAINTS HEALTHCARE SYST 53405 #025-12-1991 L2000 **AN** *020 †05
MOSES, Lynda Phillips. 3807 SPRING ST 53405 #048-02-1996 L1999 **IM** *020 †20
MURPHY, Thomas Michael. ■ 53406 #016-06-2000 L2007 **RHU** *020 †20
MUSSON, Jeffrey Linn. 3821 SPRING ST 53405 #025-12-1977 L1989 **GYN OBG** *020 †30
NAHIN, David Ralph. 1320 WISCONSIN AVE 53403 #056-06-1976 L1977 **EM** *020 †16
NAUS, Jeffrey Paul. 3807 SPRING ST 53405 #056-06-1986 L1987 **PD** *020 †55
NEAU, Yvonne Sophie. 1320 WISCONSIN AVE 53403 #016-42-2005 L2007 **FM** *100
NELSON, Daniel Leroy. ■ 53403 #018-03-1992 L1995 **IM** *020 †20
NELSON, Marvin Wilfred. ■ 53402 #056-05-1948 L1949 **ORS** *071 †40
NETTLES, Willard H. 3807 SPRING ST 53405 #045-01-1970 L1982 **PD** *020 †55
NICHOLSON, William F. 3807 SPRING ST 53405 #010-01-1991 L1996 **FM** *020 †18
NICOARA-KASTI, Giana L. 3807 SPRING ST, ALL SAINTS MEDICAL GROUP 53405 #038-43-1993 L1999 **ALI** *020
ODDERS, Richard N. 3809 SPRING ST 53405 #056-05-1973 L1978 **ON HO** *072
OHRINGER, Jack David. 3811 SPRING ST STE 202, ALL SAINTS MEDICAL GROUP 53405 #016-02-1982 L2004 **GE IM** *020 †20
OMDAHL, Nicholas Saml. 3807 SPRING ST 53405 #056-05-1974 L1977 **PUD IM** *020 †20
PAE, Gregory Heichang. 3821 SPRING ST, ALL SAINTS HEALTHCARE 53405 #016-01-1988 L1994 **OBG** *020 †30
PAGANO, Mary. 5333 DOUGLAS AVE 53402 #038-40-1982 L1989 **IM** *020 †20
PAGANO, Stephen J. 3807 SPRING ST, ALL SAINTS HEALTH CARE INC 53405 #016-43-1979 L1988 **N RHU** *020 †20
PAHM, Maria Gina Ilao. 8348 WASHINGTON AVE 53406 #748-02-1986 L1993 **FM** *020 †18
PAIDISETTY, Nagendram. 3821 SPRING ST, WOMENS & INFANTS PAVILLION 53405 #495-11-1972 L1992 **NPM PD** *020 †55
PALM, Robert Allen. 3811 SPRING ST, # 302 53405 #056-05-1969 L1971 **U EM** *020 †95
PAQUETTE-SCHULGIT, C. 3807 SPRING ST 53405 #016-43-1979 L1980 **FM FSM** *020 †18
PARIKH, Arun Vasudev. 840 LAKE AVE, STE 101 53403 #495-73-1973 L1980 **P ADP** *020 †75
PARK, Anthony Joon Y. 8400 WASHINGTON AVE 53406 #016-11-1992 L1996 **OBG** *020 †30
PARK, Byung Hai. 3805B SPRING ST, STE 320 53405 #583-06-1971 L1981 **N** *020 †75
PARK, Woosuk. 3811 SPRING ST, STE 202 53405 #016-11-2000 L2006 **GE** *020 †20 ‡
PATTERSON, John Andrew. 3821 SPRING ST 53405 #016-02-1989 L1995 **OBG** *020 †30
PATTON, Charles Hatch. ■ 53402 #016-11-1959 L1967 **D** *071 †15
PEGIS, Bernard Thomas. 3805B SPRING ST, STE 130 53405 #028-34-2002 L2005 **FM** *020 †18
PETERS, David Sidney. 1147 WARWICK WAY 53406 #017-20-1980 L2007 **FM** *020 †18
PETERSEN, James John Geo. 1320 WISCONSIN AVE 53403 #024-07-1948 L1953 **GP** *071
PETTINGER, John David. 3801 SPRING ST 53405 #016-43-1996 L1999 **EM** *020 †16
PIERCE-RUHLAND, Richard A. 3807 SPRING ST 53405 #048-13-1985 L1988 **IM** *020 †20 ‡
PLATT, Lawrence William. 3805A SPRING ST, EYE CLINIC OF RACINE LTD 53405 #016-11-1986 L1987 **OPH** *020 †35
POTTS, Carol Ann. 1500 DE KOVEN AVE 53403 #030-05-1984 L1987 **IM OM** *020
PRPA, Branko. 3811 SPRING ST STE 102, ST. MARY'S MEDICAL GROUP 53405 #026-08-1995 L2002 **ORS** *020 ‡
PUDZISZ, Bogdan. 3807 SPRING ST, WHEATON FRANCISCAN MEDICAL 53405 #016-06-1995 L1999 **IM** *020 †20
PUFFER, Douglas Edward. 3809 SPRING ST, ALL SAINTS CANCER CENTER 53405 #038-40-1997 L1998 **HO** *020 †20
PURATH, Traci Ann. 3805 SPRING ST 53405 #539-05-1995 L1998 **OS N** *020
RAFIULLAH, Mohammed. 3001 MICHIGAN BLVD, NEUROLOGICAL CLINIC, SC 53402 #704-08-1956 L1967 **NS** *020 †25
RINGWALT, Eric Chas. 3801 SPRING ST 53405 #047-05-1991 L2001 **AN** *020 †05 ‡
ROSS, Daniel Brian. 1 MAIN ST 53403 #016-11-1984 L1987 **IM** *020 †20
ROSS, David Lee, Jr. 3807 SPRING ST, WHEATON FRANCISCAN MEDICAL 53405 #038-45-1998 L2006 **FM** *020 †18
RUSTIA, Fernando Francia. 8348 WASHINGTON AVE, BLDG E 53406 #056-06-1992 L1996 **PD** *020
RYBICKI, Raymond Jos. 3805B SPRING ST, STE 120 53405 #016-43-1981 L1986 **N EM** *020
RYDER, Steven John. 3811 SPRING ST, STE 201 53405 #056-06-1991 L1996 **GS VS** *020 †85
SALTI, Nader Isa. 8400 WASHINGTON AVE, WISCONSIN SURGICAL ASSOCIA 53406 #016-02-1993 L1999 **CRS** *020 †85
SAMUEL, James. ■ 53406 #104-01-2004 **FP** *012
SANGHVI, Reema. 3801 SPRING ST, ST. MARY'S MEDICAL CENTER 53405 #016-06-1986 L2001 **AN** *020 †05
SCHIMMING, Michael B. 6232 BANKERS RD, WHEATON FRANCISCAN HEALTHC 53403 #056-06-1998 L2000 **PD** *020 †55
SCHLEPER, Albin John. 5625 WASHINGTON AVE 53406 #056-06-1945 L1949 **GP OS** *071 †18
SCHNEIDER, Janel Sue. 3807 SPRING ST 53405 #028-46-1999 L2005 **CN** *020 †75
SCHULGIT, Ronald E. 3807 SPRING ST, WHEATON FRANCISCAN MED GRO 53405 #056-06-1978 L1979 **FM IM** *020 †18
SCHULLER, Gert Jorg. 5515 W BRANCH TRL 53402 #407-12-1963 L1973 **CD IM** *071
SCHUSTER, Myron. ■ 53406 #056-06-1941 L1941 **ATP CLP** *071 †50
SCUMACI, Michael Jos. 3801 SPRING ST 53405 #016-42-1991 L1997 **AN** *020 †05
SHACK, James Bruce. 4700 21ST ST, EMERSON ELECTRIC MED DEPT 53406 #016-43-1956 L1959 **FM P** *020
SHAMSUDDIN, Laeeq Syed. 3801 SPRING ST, ALL SAINTS HEALTHCARE 53405 #665-01-2001 L2007 **PCC** *020 †20
SHANKAR, Vijayashree. 3807 SPRING ST 53405 #495-04-1990 L1998 **AN** *100 †20
SHARMA, Sonia. 3807 SPRING ST 3, INFECTOUS DISEASES 53405 #665-01-2002 L2004 **ID** *020 †20
SHORT, Howard Wendell. 3803 SPRING ST, STE 410 53405 #038-41-1961 L1964 **CD IM** *020 †20
SHOVE, Gregory Alan. 3807 SPRING ST, ALL SAINTS HEALTHCARE 53405 #016-11-1979 L1984 **RHU IM** *020 †20
SIDHU, Devinder Kaur. 3801 SPRING ST, ST MARY'S MEDICAL CENTER 53405 #495-29-1974 L1999 **AN** *020 †05
SIEGERT, Robert Frederick. 1525 HOWE ST, SC JOHNSON 53403 #016-11-1963 L1964 **GS OM** *071 †85
SIGARI, Farhad. 8348 WASHINGTON AVE, BLDG E 53406 #016-42-2001 L2006 **OTO** *020
SILVER, Sarah Simcha. 3801 SPRING ST 53405 #035-09-1997 L2000 **EM** *020 †16
SINGH, Inder Paul. 3805 SPRING ST STE 140, & KENOSHA 53405 #016-42-1999 L2004 **OPH** *020 †35
SINGH, Kanwar Amarjit. 3805B SPRING ST STE 140 53405 #495-45-1966 L1971 **OPH** *020 †35
SINGH, Satnam A. 3803 SPRING ST 53405 #495-45-1966 L1970 **NM PTH** *020 †50
SINHA, Shashank Shekhar. 5910 WYNBROOK CT 53406 #016-02-2008 *012
SKANTZ, John M. 105 HOLIDAY DR, MEDICAL COLLEGE OF WISCONS 53402 #056-06-1990 L1991 **N** *020 †75
SMITS, Ronald La Vern. 3811 SPRING ST, STE 301 53405 #056-05-1964 L1971 **D** *020 †15
SMUDDE, Stephanie Jayne. ■ 53406 #056-05-2008 *012
SNYDERMAN, Michelle. 3807 SPRING ST 53405 #016-11-1986 L1987 **PD DBP** *020 †55
SOYKA, James Michael. 3801 SPRING ST, RACINE EMER PHYS SC 53405 #016-42-1985 L1992 **EM** *020 †16
SPIERING, Ellen Cecilia. 6232 BANKERS RD 53403 #016-06-1996 L2001 **FM** *020 †18
SRIRAM, Ranganatha Rao. 1 MAIN ST 53403 #495-99-1977 L1991 **CD** *020 †20
STALIVONENKO, Dmitriy. 3801 SPRING ST, ST MARY'S HOSPITAL 53405 #913-32-1986 L1999 **AN** *020 †05
STA ROMANA, Ismael R. ■ 53403 #748-10-1973 L1982 **AN** *020 †05
STEWART, Richard Donald. ■ 53402 #025-01-1955 L1967 **IM ETX** *071 †20 ‡
STIKA, Edward Andrew. ■ 53402 #016-11-1947 L1957 **U** *071 †95
STOLTENBERG, Richard L. 3811 SPRING ST, ATRIUM OFFICES 53405 #016-11-1990 L1991 **GS VS** *020 †85
SWEARINGEN, Sujan Michael. ■ 53406 #104-01-2007 *100
SWEET, Michael Ervin. 3811 SPRING ST, STE 203 53405 #056-05-1988 L1989 **PS** *020 †85,65
TAGALAKIS, Harry Anthony. 3801 SPRING ST 53405 #011-03-1999 L2005 **APM** *020 †05 ‡
THOMAS, Jennifer Rucka. 3807 SPRING ST 53405 #056-06-1993 L1994 **PD IM** *020 †55
THORWEST, Anke. ■ 53406 #409-20-1999 L2002 **FM** *020

9486

■ = Address Information Privacy Protected

TIERNEY, James Franklin. 3805A SPRING ST, STE 310 53405 #026-04-1975 L1980 **CD IM** *020 †20

TOLSON, Lawrence S. 3805B SPRING ST, STE 260 53405 #056-05-1977 L1978 **OM IM** *020 †20,70

TOMKIEWICZ, Ralph Eugene. 5802 WASHINGTON AVE 53406 #056-06-1959 L1960 **P** *071

TROTTER, Dana R. 5439 DURAND AVE, STE 103 53406 #016-11-1983 L1988 **RHU** *020 †20

TROTTER, Johnny Louis. 8400 WASHINGTON AVE 53406 #016-11-1983 L1988 **ORS** *020 †40

TURNER, Derek Sorton. 3807 SPRING ST, WHEATON FRANCISCAN MEDICAL 53405 #016-43-1997 L2000 **IM** *020 †20

ULMER, Laura Black. 1320 WISCONSIN AVE, RADIATION ONCOLOGY 53403 #055-01-1989 L1995 **RO** *020 †20

VAGHASIYA, Alpa D. 3801 SPRING ST 53405 #003-75-2002, ▲ L2008 **IM** *100 †20

VAHIDY, Ali Ahmed. 1320 WISCONSIN AVE, RACINE FAMILY PRACTICE PRO 53403 #654-01-2001 **FM** *100

VANBENDEGOM, Jeffrey M. 3801 SPRING ST 53405 #056-06-1997 L2001 **EM** *020 †16

VANSLOUN, Joan Ann. 8400 WASHINGTON AVE 53406 #056-06-1989 L1993 **AN** *020 †05

VEMAREDDY, Sarada. 5333 DOUGLAS AVE 53402 #495-65-2001 L2007 **FM** *020 †18

VOLKMAN, Kristen Koto. 3807 SPRING ST, WHEATON FRANCISCAN MED GRP 53405 #056-06-2001 L2003 **AI** *055,03

VRAVICK, Thomas Edward. 3807 SPRING ST, ALL SAINTS MEDICAL GROUP 53405 #016-11-1984 L1987 **IM** *020 †20

WADHWANI, Indur Bhojraj. 3811 SPRING ST 53405 #495-17-1954 L1973 **U** *020 †95

WALRATH, Daniel Laurens. 1320 WISCONSIN AVE 53403 #030-05-1978 L1979 **EM FM** *020 †16,18

WALTENBERGER, James M. 3811 SPRING ST, 2ND FLOOR ATRIUM BUILDING 53405 #056-06-1998 L2003 **GS** *020 †85

WELCH, Jonathan Robert. ■ 53402 #024-01-2007 L2007 **EM** *012

WELSH, Brady Thos. 8348 WASHINGTON AVE, BLDG E 53406 #016-06-1982 L1991 **FM** *020 †18

WIDEBURG, Charles Allen. 3801 SPRING ST 53405 #016-11-1978 L1982 **AN IM** *020 †20,05

WILCZYNSKI, Joseph Robt. 3821 SPRING ST 53405 #017-20-1966 L1969 **OBG** *020

WILLARD, Kaye-Eileen. 2408 FOUR MILE RD, MEDICAL NORTHSIDE 53402 #054-04-1979 L1999 **IM** *020 †20

WILLIAMSON, Warren H. ■ 53402 #016-06-1948 L1949 **GP** *072 †18

WIRFS, Bonnie Lee. 2000 DOMANIK DR 53404 #016-45-1983 L1986 **IMG OS** *020 †20

WISNIEWSKI, Gerald Roman. 2405 NORTHWESTERN AVE, ALL SAINTS KURTEN MEDICAL 53404 #056-06-1973 L1974 **IM** *020 †20

WOLF, Lisa Ann. 2408 4 MILE RD 53402 #056-06-1994 L1995 **FM** *020 †18

WONG, Walter. 1320 WISCONSIN AVE, RADIATION ONCOLOGY 53403 #025-07-1983 L1987 **RO** *020 †80 ‡

WOOD, Thomas Wm. 3811 SPRING ST # 302 53405 #056-05-1982 L1987 **U** *020 †95

WOODS, Justin James. ■ 53406 #305-01-2006 L2008 **FP** *012

YUN, Elizabeth Kyongyil. 3807 SPRING ST, ALL SAINTS MEDICAL GROUP 53405 #016-11-2001 L2003 **IM** *020

ZABLOTNEY, David Chas. 5333 DOUGLAS AVE 53402 #038-41-1981 L1989 **FM** *020 †18

RANDOLPH – DODGE

LUCARELLI, Melissa E. 504 S HIGH ST 53956 #016-11-1994 L1995 **FM** *020 †18

RANDOM LAKE – SHEBOYGAN

WEBER, Barbara Alice. N639 SILVER CREEK CASCD RD 53075 #026-04-1991 L1998 **FM** *020 †18

WITT, Raymond Wm. ■ 53075 #016-11-1966 L1967 **OBG** *071 †30

REDGRANITE – WAUSHARA

GELDNER, Barbara. N2909 COUNTY RD E 54970 #759-03-1951 L1965 **OPH** *071

GRAY, David Andrew. 402 PRESTON LN 54970 #026-04-1997 L1998 **FM** *020 †18

REEDSBURG – SAUK

BENISH, Deanna Dawn. 1900 N DEWEY AVE, REEDSBURG PHYSICIANS GROUP 53959 #056-06-1998 L1999 **FM** *020 †18

CHRABASZCZ, Gerry Jos. 2000 N DEWEY AVE 53959 #016-11-1982 L1987 **ORS HS** *020 †40

CLAY, James Wm. 1104 21ST ST, STE B 53959 #025-07-1974 L1983 **GS** *020 †85

CLEARY, John Patrick. ■ 53959 #056-05-1959 L1969 **OS** *075

HOFFMANN, Karl Mathias. 1900 N DEWEY AVE, STE A 53959 #056-05-1981 L1982 **FM** *020 †18

KINCAID, Steven William. 1900 N DEWEY AVE, STE A 53959 #056-05-1994 L1995 **PD** *020 †55

KLINGBEIL, Eric William. 1104 21ST ST, STE B 53959 #056-05-1996 L1997 **GS** *020 †85

KNIGHT, Robert Geo. 1900 N DEWEY AVE 53959 #038-06-1948 L1950 **GP** *071

KOONTZ, Anne Elizabeth. ■ 53959 #056-06-2007 **FP** *020

KOONTZ, Robert James. 1900 N DEWEY AVE STE A, REEDSBURG PHYSICIANS GROU, 53959 #025-07-1977 L1980 **FM** *020 †18

LAUKANT, Joanna Lara. 1900 N DEWEY AVE STE A, REEDSBURG PHSYCIANS GROUP, 53959 #056-06-1995 L1996 **FM** *020 †18

MORTIMORE, Robert Harry. 1900 N DEWEY AVE, STE A 53959 #016-06-1974 L1977 **FM** *020 †18

PERKINS, Todd Wendell. 251 2ND ST 53959 #005-14-1981 L1989 **OPH** *040 †35

RAMSEY, Alan Huguenin. 2000 N DEWEY AVE, RAMC 53959 #021-01-1997 L1998 **FM** *020 †18

SCHONFELD, Michael Roy. 1900 N DEWEY AVE STE A, REEDSBURG PHY GROUP, S.C. 53959 #025-07-1974 L1977 **FM** *020 †18

SHEAR, Mary Beth. 1900 N DEWEY AVE, STE A 53959 #016-11-1982 L2007 **FM** *020 †18

STOCK, Jonathan Grover. 211 2ND ST 53959 #056-06-1982 L1984 **OPH FM** *020 †18,35 ‡

TURNER, Robert Craig. 1900 N DEWEY AVE, REEDSBURG PHYSICIANS GROUP 53959 #056-05-1984 L1991 **CD** *020 †20

WENNINGER, Christopher J. 1900 N DEWEY AVE, REEDSBURG PHYSICIAN GROUP 53959 #056-06-2001 L2002 **FM** *020

REEDSVILLE – MANITOWOC

IMP, Janet Jenkin. 106 MILL ST 54230 #036-07-2000 L2005 **PD** *020 †55

STEVENS, Jennifer Feinste. 106 MILL ST 54230 #016-02-1996 L1997 **FM** *020 †18

RHINELANDER – ONEIDA

ABEL, Margaret. 2251 N SHORE DR STE 200 54501 #048-02-1990 L1994 **IM** *020

AGRE, James Courtland. 2251 N SHORE DR 54501 #026-04-1976 L1984 **PM** *020 †60

AYLESWORTH, Robt John, Jr. 550 E TIMBER DR 54501 #056-05-1978 L1982 **D** *020 †15

BAKER, Dawn Elisabeth. 2251 N SHORE DR, STE 100 54501 #035-47-1993 L1999 **VIR IM** *020 †80

BARBER, Carol Dianne. 2251 N SHORE DR, STE 100 54501 #026-04-1990 L1991 **P** *020 †75

BARUDIN, Barry Seth. 70 N STEVENS ST 54501 #016-42-1972 L1995 **PD** *020 †55

BELLVILLE, John Kyper. 1044 KABEL AVE, SAINT MARY'S HOSPITAL 54501 #026-04-1982 L2006 **P** *020

BODENSTEINER, Jos Adams. 2251 N SHORE DR 54501 #018-03-1967 L1974 **GS VS** *020 †85

BOISMENUE, Stuart N. 138 S STEVENS ST, CHILD HEALTH CARE CTR 54501 #056-05-1977 L1980 **PD** *020

BROOKS, Steven Raymond. 2251 N SHORE DR 54501 #056-05-1996 L1997 **IM** *020 †20

BROWN, Steven Robt. 2251 N SHORE DR 54501 #026-04-1987 L1999 **DR FM** *020 †18,80

BURTON, Charlene Geniece. 1020 KABEL AVE 54501 #020-02-1977 L1986 **P** *020

CATTAU, David Paul. 2251 N SHORE DR 54501 #056-06-1980 L1986 **RO** *020 †80

DEAN, Joseph Oliver, Jr. ■ 54501 #023-01-1957 L1964 **PTH** *071 †50

DURETTE, Marc Roland. 586 SHEPARD ST 54501 #028-34-1986 L1987 **PM** *020 †60

DYREBY, James Richard, Jr. 444 E TIMBER DR, NORTHLAND ORTHOPEDIC ASSOC 54501 #056-05-1978 L1979 **ORS** *020 †40

ERDMANN, Brian Jon. 2251 N SHORE DR, STE 200 54501 #056-06-1996 L1997 **IM** *020 †20

ERDMANN, Kim Marie. 140 S BROWN ST 54501 #056-06-1997 L1998 **IM** *020 †20

FERNANDES, Harry. 2251 N SHORE DR 54501 #495-09-1992 L1999 **IM** *020 †20

GRAHAM, Peter Edgar. 2251 N SHORE DR, STE 200 54501 #035-08-1973 L2006 **ON IM** *020 †20

GREBNER, James Vincent. 2251 N SHORE DR 54501 #041-14-1981 L1982 **FM EM** *020 †18

GROTENHUIS, Paul Willard. 4085 N BAY RD 54501 #056-05-1966 L1969 **R** *071 †80

HAUSSERMAN, Sue A Hall. 2251 N SHORE DR 54501 #030-05-1971 L1975 **R** *071 †80

HENRY, Michael James. 2251 N SHORE DR, STE 200 54501 #026-04-1978 L1982 **IM** *020 †20

HERTEL, Bruce Frederick. 1044 KABEL AVE 54501 #028-02-1972 L1977 **ATP** *020 †50

HOOPER, Larry Albert. 2251 N SHORE DR 54501 #025-07-1986 L1992 **FM** *020 †18

IMMLER, Richard Edward. 1020 KABEL AVE, P O BOX 1390 54501 #056-05-1978 L1998 **P CHP** *020 †75

INCHA, Eunice Corujo. 2251 N SHORE DR 54501 #042-01-1986 L1994 **PD** *020

JACOBSON, Bruce K. 2251 N SHORE DR 54501 #008-01-1986 L1988 **GS** *020 †85

JAIN, Raj Kumar. 1020 KABEL AVE, ST MARYS HOSP RIVERSDE CLC 54501 #495-29-1977 L1985 **OM PTH** *020 †50,70

KESSINGER, Rovena Louise. 1044 KABEL AVE 54501 #028-03-1998 L2003 **PTH** *020

KIEF, John Jos. 2930 CRESTWOOD DR 54501 #056-06-1965 L1967 **IM GE** *020 †20

KIM, Joseph Peter. 2251 N SHORE DR 54501 #056-06-1995 L1996 **GE** *020 †20

KITZMAN, Robert Harvey. 431 SPRING LAKE RD 54501 #056-06-1965 L1966 **ORS** *020 †40

KOEPPL, Christopher Geo. 2251 N SHORE DR 54501 #036-01-1983 L1986 **IM** *020 †20

KOTILA, Bruce Andrew. 2251 N SHORE DR 54501 #016-06-1974 L1975 **IM** *020 †20

KRUPKA, Lisa Marie. ■ 54501 #016-42-2002 L2008 **GS** *012 †85

LOWRY, Kent Jason. 444 E TIMBER DR 54501 #028-03-1996 L2001 **ORS** *020 †40

LOWRY, Laura Beth. 2251 N SHORE DR, STE 100 54501 #028-03-1994 L2004 **PD** *020 †55

LUNDBERG, Danny Alan. 2251 N SHORE DR 54501 #056-06-1988 L1989 **IM** *020 †20

MARSAN, Scott Lee. 2251 N SHORE DR 54501 #056-06-1993 L1994 **EM** *020 †16

MAYRER, Richard Jos. 2251 N SHORE DR 54501 #038-44-1991 L1992 **FM** *020 †18

MICKEVICIUS, Richard F. 2251 N SHORE DR 54501 #028-02-1995 L1998 **EM** *020 †16

MOORE, Vincent Jos, Jr. 2251 N SHORE DR, MINISTRY MEDICAL GROUP 54501 #048-13-1976 L1977 **OBG** *020 †30

MULLEN, James Evans. 902 BOYCE DR, WELLNESS CLINIC 54501 #056-05-1988 L1992 **PM** *020 †60

NEVIN, Ismail Nik. 1044 KABEL AVE 54501 #008-01-1951 L1958 **R NM** *020 †80

NILES, Sarah Ellen. ■ 54501 #048-14-2004 L2005 **GS** *100 †70

NORDEN, Leo Geo. 2251 N SHORE DR, MINISTRY MEDICAL GROUP 54501 #018-03-1967 L1973 **IM** *020 †20

O'HANLON, Miles Edward. 1020 KABEL AVE, TAMARACK BEHAVIORAL HLTH C 54501 #422-01-1989 L2004 **P** *020 †75

PADGETT, William Robert. 1044 KABEL AVE 54501 #038-40-1996 L1997 **ORS** *020 †40

PAGANO, Judith Stephanie. 2251 N SHORE DR, STE 200 54501 #025-01-1970 L1978 **OBG GYN** *020 †30

PANTALONE, Richard Albert. 2251 N SHORE DR, STE 200 54501 #041-12-1979 L2003 **GS VS** *020 †85

PARMAR, Mona. 2251 N SHORE DR 54501 #495-03-1995 L2003 **FM** *020 †18

PARRIS, Ellen Lee. 3716 COUNTRY DR, STE 6 54501 #011-02-1976 L1983 **N** *020 †75

POTTER, Lee H. 3716 COUNTRY DR STE 6, VA-CBOC 54501 #056-06-1972 L1986 **FM** *020 †18

PRATT, George Francis. ■ 54501 #024-01-1948 L1957 **GS** *071 †85

SCHIEK, Irving Edward, III. 5380 LAKE VIEW LN 54501 #056-06-1967 L1969 **GS GP** *071 †85

SCHIPITSCH, Douglas A. 1044 KABEL AVE 54501 #016-43-1975 L1981 **GS GP** *020 †85

SHANMUGHAM, Vadivelu. 1044 KABEL AVE 54501 #495-04-1976 L1978 **AN** *020 †05

SHETH, Shishir N. 2251 N SHORE DR 54501 #011-02-1993 L2000 **OTO** *020 †45

SHINNERS, Theodore John. 2251 N SHORE DR 54501 #056-05-1999 L2000 **DR** *020 †80

SIKKA, Gurkirpal Singh. 1044 KABEL AVE 54501 #495-29-1977 L1985 **AN** *075 †05

SKYE, Dorothy Virginia. 1020 KABEL AVE 54501 #034-01-1978 L1984 **OBG** *020 †30

SKYE, Harry Wm. 2251 N SHORE DR 54501 #041-13-1974 L1985 **DR EM** *020 †80

SLETTE, Amy Michelle. 2251 N SHORE DR 54501 #017-20-1999 L2002 **PD** *020 †55

STOCKWELL, Debra Ann. 2251 N SHORE DR, STE 200 54501 #025-07-1991 L1998 **OBG** *020 †30

STONEFELD, Donald Frank. ■ 54501 #010-01-1965 L1994 **P N** *020

SWANK, Adam Charles. ■ 54501 #056-06-2003 L2003 **FM** *100 †18

SWANK, Lee Allen. 2251 N SHORE DR, STE 200 54501 #016-11-1972 L1975 **IM EM** *020 †20

TVEDTEN, Daniel Ernest. 444 E TIMBER DR, NORTHLAND ORTHOPEDICS 54501 #026-04-1989 L1997 **ORS** *020 †40

WATSON, Raymond Roger. 7501 CLEAR LAKE RD 54501 #056-05-1948 L1949 **TS GS** *071 †85,90

WEGEHAUPT, Paul Karl. 2251 N SHORE DR, MINISTRY MEDICAL GROUP 54501 #016-11-1970 L1989 **PD** *020 †55

WHITE, Herbert C. 1020 KABEL AVE 54501 #016-76-1964, ▲ L1965 **P ADP** *020 †75

■ = Address Information Privacy Protected

WILSON, Nancy J. 2251 N SHORE DR 54501 #654-01-1987 L1989 **P** *020 †75

ZENTI, Peter Jos. 2251 N SHORE DR 54501 #025-01-1973 L1989 **FM EM** *020 †16,18

RICE LAKE – BARRON

ALAOUA, Mohammad D. 1020 LAKESHORE DR, INDIANHEAD CENTER 54868 #875-01-1993 L2004 **CD IM** *020

ANDEREGG, Jeffrey James. 1020 LAKESHORE DR, INDIANHEAD CENTER 54868 #018-03-2000 L2003 **AN** *020 †05 ‡

BEKKUM, Bradley Peter. 1215 W KNAPP ST 54868 #056-05-1996 L1999 **IM PLM** *030 †20

BENDER, William Logan. 1100 N MAIN ST, LAKE MEDICAL CENTER 54868 #056-05-1969 L1970 **EM FM** *020

BIHRLE, David Michael. 1700 W STOUT ST, RICE LAKE CENTER 54868 #026-04-1987 L1996 **OBG** *020 †30

BRANHAM, Roger Vawter. 1035 N MAIN ST 54868 #038-06-1973 L1974 **ORS** *020

BRENDEL, John Keith, Jr. 2021 CENEX DR, UNIT J 54868 #056-05-1989 L1993 **PMM** *020 †05

BYRON, Michele Christine. 1700 W STOUT ST, RICE LAKE CENTER 54868 #048-04-1992 L1996 **OBG** *020 †30

CARLSEN, Eric Nystuen. 1700 W STOUT ST 54868 #026-04-1990 L1991 **PM** *020 †60

CARLSON, Lawrence Dean. 1020 LAKESHORE DR 54868 #026-04-1975 L1981 **FM** *020 †18

CESNIK, John Anthony, II. 331 S MAIN ST STE H, RICE LAKE OFFICE 54868 #026-04-1974 L2000 **FM** *020 †18 ‡

CHETTY, Srinivas. 1020 LAKESHORE DR, INDIANHEAD CENTER 54868 #496-15-1993 L2001 **IM** *020 †20

COTTS, Lloyd Ralph. ■ 54868 #056-05-1954 L1957 **FM GP** *071 †18

CRAGG, John Arthur. 1700 W STOUT ST, RICE LAKE CENTER 54868 #026-04-1978 L1989 **ORS** *020 †40

CRAGG, Michael Macoubrey. 1020 LAKESHORE DR 54868 #026-04-1975 L1978 **FM** *020 †18

CRANDALL, Leland Douglas. 1020 LAKESHORE DR 54868 #005-14-1968 L1975 **IM ON** *020 †20

DEGERMAN, Gary Randal. 1700 W STOUT ST, RICE LAKE CENTER 54868 #026-04-1988 L1993 **OBG** *020 †30

EASTWOLD, Conrad Engwold. 1020 LAKESHORE DR 54868 #026-04-1974 L1978 **IM** *020 †20

ERICKSON, Daniel Roy. 1215 W KNAPP ST, MARSHFIELD CLINIC-LAKEWOOD 54868 #056-05-1980 L1982 **FM** *020 †18

ESCHENBAUM, Edward G, Jr. 1020 LAKESHORE DR 54868 #016-11-1965 L1968 **U** *020 †95

ESTER, John Bolinger. 1700 W STOUT ST, RICE LAKE CENTER 54868 #026-04-1997 L2004 **OBG** *020 †30

FEINSTEIN-HUSAK, Michael. 1700 W STOUT ST, RICE LAKE CENTER 54868 #041-07-1982 L2006 **EM** *020 †20

FLORENCE, David Wood. 1020 LAKESHORE DR 54868 #016-43-1955 L1964 **OS ORS** *071 †40

GERBER, Thomas Gerald, Jr. 1700 W STOUT ST, RICE LAKE CENTER 54868 #056-06-1975 L1976 **OTO** *020 †45

GILBERT, Rachel Marie. 1700 W STOUT ST, RICE LAKE CENTER 54868 #056-06-2002 L2007 **OBG** *100

GOZA, George Merlin. ■ 54868 #012-05-1954 L1970 **IM CD** *071

GRAY, Lori Ann Click. 1100 N MAIN ST 54868 #056-06-1986 L1990 **PD** *020 †55

GRAY, Roger Sloan, Jr. 2820 S WISCONSIN AVE 54868 #056-06-1986 L1990 **OPH** *020 †35

HEALY, Patrick Michael. 1035 N MAIN ST 54868 #056-05-1972 L1974 **ORS** *020 †40

HENKEL, Philip Stephen. 1020 LAKESHORE DR, INDIANHEAD CENTER 54868 #056-05-1982 L1984 **AN** *020 †05

HENNINGSEN, David John. 1700 W STOUT ST, RICE LAKE CENTER 54868 #056-05-1991 L1992 **FM** *020 †18

HENNINGSEN, John Thorvald. ■ 54868 #030-05-1962 L1965 **FM** *071 †18

HOLTHAUS, Stephen Thomas. 1700 W STOUT ST 54868 #016-06-1995 L1998 **FM** *020 †18

HOYER, Jean Elise. 331 S MAIN ST, STE E304 54868 #056-05-1990 L1993 **FM** *020 †18

JOHNSTON, Paul David. 1020 LAKESHORE DR 54868 #056-06-1985 L1990 **FM** *020 †18

KOOB, Lynn David. 1020 LAKESHORE DR 54868 #018-03-1973 L1976 **GS** *020 †85

LANGRECK, Laura Ann. 1700 W STOUT ST 54868 #028-78-2004, ▲ L2007 **PD** *020 †55

LARSON, Bryan Hammond. 1700 W STOUT ST, RICE LAKE CENTER 54868 #046-01-1994 L2000 **OAR** *020 †40 ‡

LOCHMANN, Daniel Paul. 1020 LAKESHORE DR 54868 #056-06-1986 L1987 **ORS** *020 †40

LUNDQUIST, Thomas Warren. 1020 LAKESHORE DR 54868 #026-04-1983 L1986 **FM** *020 †18

MARTIN, Gwen D. 1020 LAKESHORE DR 54868 #037-01-1986 L1987 **GS** *020 †85

MC CLELLAND, Janice Marie. 1700 W STOUT ST 54868 #056-05-1989 L1995 **FM** *020 †18

MEYER, Diane Joy. 1020 LAKESHORE DR 54868 #048-13-1991 L1995 **D** *020 †15

MINK, Lisa Ann. 1700 W STOUT ST, RICE LAKE CENTER 54868 #028-02-1982 L1983 **FM** *020 †18

MOFLE, Philip Jeffrey. 1700 W STOUT ST, RICE LAKE CENTER 54868 #056-06-2002 L2003 **GS** *020 †85

NAMBOODIRI, Neelakantan. 1700 W STOUT ST, RICE LAKE CENTER 54868 #495-63-1985 L1998 **NEP** *020 †20

NARINS, Voldemars. 1020 LAKESHORE DR, MARSHFIELD CLC INDHD CTR 54868 #018-03-1972 L1975 **FM** *020 †18

NIAZI, Shehzad Khan. 1020 LAKESHORE DR 54868 #704-01-1997 L2005 **P** *020 †75

NYMO, Mark Thomas. 1700 W STOUT ST 54868 #026-04-1975 L1978 **FM** *020 †18

OCWIEJA, Mary Ann. 1020 LAKESHORE DR 54868 #016-01-1983 L1986 **FM PHP** *075 †18

OLSON, John L. 1700 W STOUT ST, INDIANHEAD CENTER 54868 #056-05-1982 L1988 **IM** *020 †20

OLSON, Rodney Geo. 1020 LAKESHORE DR 54868 #026-04-1976 L1978 **FM** *020 †18

OSTERBAUER, Joseph Jay. 1700 W STOUT ST, RICE LAKE CENTER 54868 #056-05-1981 L1982 **IM** *020 †20

PEBLER, Richard Frank. 1700 W STOUT ST, RICE LAKE CENTER 54868 #024-16-1984 L1992 **FM** *020 †18

PETERS, James M. 1020 LAKESHORE DR 54868 #016-76-1998, ▲ L1999 **FM** *020 †18

RAETHER, Douglas John. 1700 W STOUT ST 54868 #056-06-1979 L1980 **AN** *020 †05

ROBERTSON, Andrew Lind. 1700 W STOUT ST 54868 #025-12-1997 L2000 **PD** *020 †55

SELEZNEVA, Irina. 1020 LAKESHORE DR, MARSHFIELD CLINIC-INDIANHE 54868 #913-15-1986 L2004 **PD** *020 ‡

SITENGA, Neil Harry, Jr. ■ 54868 #056-05-1991 L1993 **DR AM** *020 †80

SMITH, William Alexander. 1020 LAKESHORE DR 54868 #056-05-1983 L1986 **FM EM** *020 †18

STELZER, Gary Urban. 1215 W KNAPP ST, LAKEWOODS FAMILY CENTER 54868 #026-04-1976 L1978 **FM** *020 †18

VALENZUELA, Fabio E. 1700 W STOUT ST, RICE LAKE CENTER 54868 #308-05-1994 L2007 **RO** *020 †80

VERVILLE, Kristin E. 1020 LAKESHORE DR, INDIANHEAD CENTER 54868 #026-04-2000 L2001 **FM** *020 †18

WALDRON, John Becker. 1020 LAKESHORE DR, INDIANHEAD CENTER 54868 #026-04-1982 L1983 **FM EM** *020 †18

WEBER, Mark Allen. 1020 LAKESHORE DR, MARSHFIELD CLINIC-INDIANHE 54868 #018-03-1994 L2000 **AN** *020 †20

WOLNER, Daniel Michael. 1700 W STOUT ST, RICE LAKE CENTER 54868 #026-04-1988 L1992 **OPH** *020 †35

RICHFIELD – WASHINGTON

MOMPER, Stephanie Proko. ■ 53076 #056-06-2005 L2007 **MPD** *012

RICHLAND CENTER – RICHLAND

BALINK, Kay Margaret M. 301 E 2ND ST 53581 #422-01-1986 L1987 **FM** *020 †18

BARD, Neil Nathan. 301 E 2ND ST 53581 #010-02-1977 L1978 **FM** *020 †18

BECK, Thomas S. 301 E 2ND ST, RICHLAND MEDICAL CENTER 53581 #048-04-1993 L2001 **ORS** *020 †40

BERMUDEZ, Eduardo Renan. ■ 53581 #649-06-1957 L1983 **EM P** *071 †18,16

BERRES, Jerel Thos. RR 5 BOX 570A 53581 #056-05-1977 L1994 **EM** *020 †16

BRYCE, David Anthony. 333 E 2ND ST 53581 #028-34-1977 L1989 **AN IM** *020 †20,05

BUTRICK, Robin Marie. 301 E 2ND ST 53581 #056-05-1998 L1999 **FM** *020 †18

CORNELIUS, Cristine Lynn. 301 E 2ND ST 53581 #016-45-1996 L1997 **FM** *020 †18

DELVENTHAL, Stephen John. 301 E 2ND ST 53581 #033-05-1974 L1975 **GS** *020 †85

DICKMAN, James Joseph. 301 E 2ND ST 53581 #305-01-1999 L2000 **FM** *020 †18

EDWARDS, Richard Wilmer. ■ 53581 #056-05-1960 L1961 **FM** *071 †18

GLISE, Roy C. 301 E 2ND ST 53581 #018-03-1949 L1950 **GP PHP** *100

HAGEN, Tamara Sue. 301 E 2ND ST 53581 #056-06-1981 L1984 **CD** *020 †20

KELERTAS, Julius Herbert. ■ 53581 #407-20-1951 L1961 **GS GP** *071

KLOESS, Michael Gerard. 301 E 2ND ST 53581 #016-45-2000 L2003 **FM** *020 †18

KOENECKE, Fred H, Jr. ■ 53581 #026-04-1949 L1960 **P** *071 †75

MOTHS, Bruce Frederic. 333 E 2ND ST, THE RICHLAND HOSP 53581 #056-05-1986 L1987 **IM** *020 †20

MYERS, Bryan Lee. 301 E 2ND ST 53581 #056-06-2003 L2004 **FM** *020 †18

MYSZKOWSKI, Jennifer Mary. 301 E 2ND ST 53581 #056-06-1996 L1997 **FM** *020 †18

PIPPIN, Maramon L. PO BOX 649 53581 #020-02-1943 L1943 **GP** *071

RICH, Barry Howard. 301 E 2ND ST 53581 #016-02-1974 L1988 **PD PDE** *020 †55

RICH, Nancy Ellen. 301 E 2ND ST 53581 #016-02-1971 L1988 **OBG** *020 †30

SINNETT, Dale Frederick. 301 E 2ND ST 53581 #005-12-1975 L1979 **IM** *020

SMITH, Robert Patrick. 1313 W SEMINARY ST, RICHLAND MEDICAL CENTER 53581 #016-06-1976 L1980 **FM FPG** *020 †18

WENTZ, John Munro. ■ 53581 #020-12-1970 L1985 **DR** *020 †80

WHITNEY, Kevin Richard. 301 E 2ND ST 53581 #016-42-1996 L1998 **FM** *020 †18

WRIGHT, Andrew J. ■ 53581 #048-04-2003 L2005 **M** *100 †18

WRIGHT, Andrew Stone. 301 E 2ND ST 53581 #020-02-1998 L1999 **GS** *020 †85

RINGLE – MARATHON

JENKINS, David Douglas. 6605 PENINSULA LN 54471 #020-02-1973 L1974 **ON HEM** *071 †20

RIO – COLUMBIA

SCHULTZ, Allison Ann. N3102 BERKVAM RD, SAFE AND SOUND ANESTHESIA 53960 #037-01-1984 L2004 **AN** *020 †05

RIPON – FOND DU LAC

AL-BITAR, Issam. 933 NEWBURY ST 54971 #875-01-1979 L1984 **CD IM** *020 †20

BECHARD, Robert John. 635 W OSHKOSH ST 54971 #056-05-1989 L1990 **OTO HNS** *020 †45

BROWN, David Franklin. 933 NEWBURY ST 54971 #056-06-1993 L1996 **FM** *020 †18

BURTON, Larry Kenneth, Jr. 635 W OSHKOSH ST 54971 #028-03-1998 L2003 **OTO** *020 †45

CHOLEWA, Ryszard. 635 W OSHKOSH ST 54971 #759-04-1997 L2003 **FM** *020 †18 ‡

COMBS, Michael John. ■ 54971 #056-05-1988 L1989 **EM OM** *020

GELLER, Kenneth Alan. 933 NEWBURY ST 54971 #038-41-1971 L1976 **CD IM** *020 †20

GREGORY, Patrick Brennan. 933 NEWBURY ST 54971 #035-15-1991 L2003 **CD** *020 †20

HOUSE, Robert Herbert. 635 W OSHKOSH ST 54971 #056-05-1968 L1970 **FM HS** *071 †18

JOHNSON, Jean E. 635 W OSHKOSH ST 54971 #056-05-1968 L1970 **FM** *020 †18

KELLER, Christopher John. 635 W OSHKOSH ST 54971 #056-05-1989 L1995 **OTO** *020 †45

LAKHDHIR, Amin Abdul Ali. ■ 54971 #704-16-1990 L2002 **IM** *020 †20 ‡

LYKE, Jeanne M. 635 W OSHKOSH ST 54971 #038-41-1990 L1993 **PD** *020 †55

MIELKE, Douglas Wm. 1080 W FOND DU LAC ST, APPLETON CARDIO ASSC 54971 #056-05-1987 L1994 **CD** *020 †20

MURPHY, Michael James. 635 W OSHKOSH ST 54971 #025-12-2001 L2002 **U** *020 †95

PELTON, Russell S. ■ 54971 #020-02-1942 L1946 **GP** *071

PREHN, Robert Booth. 635 W OSHKOSH ST 54971 #056-05-1991 L1992 **OTO** *020 †45

SAKRISON, Christal Rahjes. 635 W OSHKOSH ST 54971 #056-05-1978 L1982 **FM** *020 †18

SWANSON, Catherine D. 550 RUSSELL DR 54971 #018-03-1991 L1995 **FM** *020 †18

TUMAS, Vydunas Geo. 933 NEWBURY ST, BADGER EMERGENCY PHYSICIAN 54971 #005-06-1986 L1996 **FM** *020 †18

VERDE, Diana L. 649 W OSHKOSH ST 54971 #748-08-1985 L1993 **P** *020

RIVER FALLS – PIERCE

ANDERSON, Kelle. 1687 E DIVISION ST, RIVER FALLS MEDICAL CLINIC 54022 #030-06-2001 L2002 **FM** *020 †18

AVESTRUZ, Alex P. 670 WASHINGTON ST 54022 #748-01-1955 L1968 **OS GS** *020

AVESTRUZ, Nerissa L. 670 WASHINGTON ST 54022 #748-01-1955 L1968 **OS GP** *020

BEIX, James Robt. 1629 E DIVISION ST 54022 #056-06-1967 L1970 **FM** *020 †18

CICERO, James Jos. ■ 54022 #016-06-1963 L1967 **EM FM** *071 †18,16

CLAYTON, Matthew Chas. 1687 E DIVISION ST, RIVER FALLS MEDICAL CLINIC 54022 #026-04-1989 L1998 **GS** *020 †85

DAHLBERG, Peter Scott. 1687 E DIVISION ST, UNIV. OF MINNESOTA 54022 #026-04-1990 L2007 **TS** *020 †85,90

DE GEAR, David Orion. 1687 E DIVISION ST, WESTERN WISCONSIN MEDICAL 54022 #026-04-1983 L1986 **FM** *040 †18

ESTLUND, Gregory John. ■ 54022 #048-04-1975 L1987 **FM** *020 †18

FRAZIER, Susan Jean. 1687 E DIVISION ST, WESTERN WISCONSIN MEDICAL 54022 #026-04-1991 L1993 **FM** *020 †18

GOBLIRSCH, Gregory T. 1687 E DIVISION ST 54022 #026-04-1990 L1993 **FM** *020 †18

GOLDIN, Phyllis R. ■ 54022 #062-01-1966 L1968 **P** *020

HANSON, Bruce Geo. 1687 E DIVISION ST, WESTERN WISCONSIN MEDICAL 54022 #056-05-1975 L1976 **FM** *020 †18

HANSON, Daniel Wells. 1629 E DIVISION ST 54022 #026-04-1998 L2005 **ORS** *020 †40

HARROLD, Stephen Joseph. 1687 E DIVISION ST, WESTERN WISCONSIN MEDICAL 54022 #017-20-2002 L2005 **FM** *020 †18

HECHT, Anthony Curtis. 1687 E DIVISION ST, WESTERN WISCONSIN MEDICAL 54022 #056-05-1991 L1994 **GE** *020 †18

HOBERG, Glenn. 504 S MAIN ST 54022 #028-79-1958, ▲ L1959 **GP** *071

JOHNSON, Robert Bennett. 1687 E DIVISION ST 54022 #026-04-1975 L1978 **FM** *020 †18

KARLSTAD, Ryan Richard. 1629 E DIVISION ST 54022 #023-07-1997 L2003 **ORS** *020 †40

KOVAR, Joseph L. 1629 E DIVISION ST 54022 #030-06-1979 L1983 **DR** *020 †80

LARSEN, Jeffrey David. 1687 E DIVISION ST 54022 #026-04-1988 L1996 **IM** *020 †20

MANTEUFEL, Viola Maria. ■ 54022 #024-07-2008 *012

MC MILLAN, Paul Ramon. 1687 E DIVISION ST 54022 #025-12-1989 L1992 **FM** *020 †18

MEDINI, Allen Michael. 1687 E DIVISION ST, WESTERN WISCONSIN MEDICAL 54022 #026-04-2000 L2001 **FM** *020 †18

MELBY, Michael Judd. 1687 E DIVISION ST, WESTERN WISCONSIN MEDICAL 54022 #026-04-1996 L2001 **GS** *020 †85

MELBY, Neal Arthur. 1687 E DIVISION ST, WESTERN WISCONSIN MEDICAL 54022 #056-05-1965 L1968 **GS GP** *020 †85

MILLER, Greg John. 1687 E DIVISION ST 54022 #056-06-1996 L2000 **FM** *020 †18

NYGREN, Linda Jean. 1687 E DIVISION ST, WESTERN WISCONSIN MEDICAL 54022 #025-01-1981 L2001 **PD** *020 †55

OLSON, David Laverne. 1687 E DIVISION ST, WESTERN WISCONSIN MEDICAL 54022 #056-05-1977 L1978 **FM** *020 †18

ONGSTAD, Curtis Dean. 1687 E DIVISION ST, WESTERN WISCONSIN MEDICAL 54022 #037-01-1982 L2004 **FM AI** *020 †18

RAVERTY, Rita Marie. 1687 E DIVISION ST 54022 #026-04-1998 L2001 **FM** *020 †18

REICHERT, Robin M. 1687 E DIVISION ST, WESTERN WISCONSIN MEDICAL 54022 #056-06-1995 L1996 **FM** *020 †18

SATERBAK, Andrea Marie. 1629 E DIVISION ST 54022 #030-04-1992 L1998 **OSM** *072 †40

STEINMETZ, Timothy F. 1687 E DIVISION ST 54022 #056-05-1983 L1984 **FM** *020 †18

SURA, Patrick Dennis. 1687 E DIVISION ST 54022 #056-05-1985 L1986 **FM** *020 †18

TENNER, Clifford C. 1687 E DIVISION ST, WESTERN WISCONSIN MEDICAL 54022 #048-13-1989 L1992 **FM** *020 †18

TVEDT, Heather Jean. 1687 E DIVISION ST 54022 #037-01-2000 L2006 **PD** *020 †55

WILHELM, David Mark. 1687 E DIVISION ST 54022 #026-04-1984 L1987 **FM** *020 †18

WOESTE, David M. 1687 E DIVISION ST 54022 #026-04-1972 L1975 **FM** *071 †18 ‡

ZIMMERMAN, Daniel Wm. 1687 E DIVISION ST 54022 #026-08-1989 L1996 **FM** *020 †18

RIVER HILLS — MILWAUKEE

BAE, Ik Hak. ■ 53217 #583-04-1963 L1971 **OBG** *072 †30

BERRY, Jonathan Ronald. 2485 W FAIRY CHASM RD 53217 #026-04-1984 L1989 **ORS** *020 †40

CHANG, Sekon. ■ 53217 #583-02-1963 L1972 **GE IM** *071 †20

DACKO, Lenia Maryann. ■ 53217 #008-02-1974 L1975 **AN OBG** *071 †05

ELANGOVAN, Ganesh Kumar. ■ 53217 #036-07-2006 **GS** *012

LEVIN, Jonathan Jay. ■ 53217 #056-06-2007 L2008 **TY** *012

MUSSAK, Erich Nicholai. ■ 53217 #035-20-2007 *012

PECINA, Ivo. ■ 53217 #957-01-1954 L1970 **AN OTO** *071 †05

PINEDA, Claudia Alejandra. 718 W GREEN TREE RD 53217 #264-11-1994 L2003 **IM** *020 †20

ROTHSCHILD — MARATHON

KANEMOTO, Henry Hideki. 8005 SOUTHRIDGE DR 54474 #005-11-1971 L1976 **DR NM** *020 †80

RUDOLPH — WOOD

SHUFFSTALL, Richard M. ■ 54475 #041-09-1948 L1974 **PTH** *071 †50

SAINT CROIX FALLS — POLK

BEYER, Marsha Jean. 204 S ADAMS ST 54024 #026-04-1979 L1981 **FM** *074 †18

CATLIN, Mark Grady. 204 S ADAMS ST, THREE RIVERS PATHOLOGY 54024 #026-04-1980 L1985 **PTH** *020 †50

CEAGLSKE, Randall Norman. 204 S ADAMS ST 54024 #046-01-1994 L1995 **DR** *020 †80

CONWAY, Lars T. 204 S ADAMS ST, THREE RIVERS PATHOLOGY 54024 #047-06-1977 L2007 **PTH PCP** *062 †50

GAERTNER, Robert Adams. 204 S ADAMS ST, METROPOLITAN UROLOGY 54024 #010-02-1988 L1996 **U GS** *020 †95

HALL, Melissa Steiner. 208 S ADAMS ST 54024 #030-05-1998 L2001 **FM** *020 †18

HANSEN, Carl Wm. 208 S ADAMS ST, RIVER VALLEY MED CTR S.C. 54024 #026-04-1970 L1971 **IM FM** *020 †20

HANSON, Gail Jeanine. 208 S ADAMS ST, RIVER VALLEY MEDICAL CENTE 54024 #018-03-1980 L1984 **FM** *020 †18

HEDLUND, Patrick Carl. 204 S ADAMS ST 54024 #056-05-1984 L1985 **FM** *020 †18

HINCK, Thomas Eugene. 208 S ADAMS ST, RIVER VALLEY MEDICAL CENTE 54024 #026-04-1983 L1986 **FM** *020 †18

HOLMGREN, Jeffrey Paul. 809 US HIGHWAY 8 54024 #026-04-1984 L1987 **P ADP** *020 †75 ‡

HONKE-KARUN, Allison A. 208 S ADAMS ST 54024 #046-01-2000 L2002 **OBG** *020 †30 ‡

HUBER, Robert W. ■ 54024 #026-04-1946 L1956 **DR** *071

JOHNSON, Gary Alan. 204 S ADAMS ST 54024 #016-11-1978 L1979 **DR IM** *020 †20,80

JOHNSON, Thomas Hagge. 208 S ADAMS ST 54024 #026-04-1984 L1992 **IM** *020 †20

KRAH, Steven Frank. 204 S ADAMS ST 54024 #056-06-1994 L1995 **RNR** *020 †80

KRAVIG, James Robt. 204 S ADAMS ST 54024 #026-04-1979 L1985 **IM** *020 †20

LAGUS, Arne T. 204 S ADAMS ST 54024 #026-04-1965 L1967 **FM FPG** *020 †18

LO, Muaj Christian. ■ 54024 #026-04-2003 L2004 **FM** *020 †18

LYMAN, Rebecca Ray. 204 S ADAMS ST 54024 #056-06-1993 L1996 **FM** *020 †18

MAHONEY, Brian Daniel. 208 S ADAMS ST 54024 #035-45-1997 L1998 **CD** *020 †20

MARSH, Donald Gene. 204 S ADAMS ST 54024 #018-03-1962 L1968 **DR NR** *020 †80

MILNER, Rene Brian. 205 S ADAMS ST, MILNER FAMILY MEDICAL CENT 54024 #062-01-1988 L1996 **FM** *020 †18

MUELLER, Donald R. ■ 54024 #026-04-1953 L1964 **R** *071 †80

NICKELE, Glenn Albert. 204 S ADAMS ST 54024 #025-01-1993 L1991 **CD** *020 †20

NUNES, Wendy Ann. 208 S ADAMS ST 54024 #028-03-2001 L2007 **GS** *020

NUNES FILHO, Claudio Fern. ■ 54024 #187-03-1999 L2007 **CCS** *020

OLSON, Lloyd Laures. 219 N DAY RD 54024 #054-04-1954 L1959 **GS** *020 †85

PATEL, Sunil Natvarlal. 204 S ADAMS ST, THREE RIVERS PATHOLOGY 54024 #495-23-1981 L1990 **PTH BBK** *062 †50

PELANT, Thomas Michael. 204 S ADAMS ST 54024 #056-06-1970 L1971 **DR** *020 †80

PFALTZGRAFF, Geo Hackman. 411 SIMONSON RD 54024 #041-13-1971 L1991 **GS** *020 †85 ‡

RATLIFF, Norman Burbridge. 204 S ADAMS ST 54024 #056-04-1995 L2004 **CD** *020 †20

RIENDL, Stephen Chas. 204 S ADAMS ST 54024 #023-07-1978 L2003 **CD IM** *020 †20

STEVENS, David Clarke. 208 S ADAMS ST, RIVER VALLEY MEDICAL CENTE 54024 #026-04-1999 L2002 **IM** *020 †20

STEVENS, Kristen Lee. 204 S ADAMS ST 54024 #026-04-1999 L2002 **IM** *020 †20

ULLAND, Anders Eugene. 204 S ADAMS ST 54024 #026-04-1989 L2003 **GS** *020 †85

VANDERLIJN, Pieter J. 204 S ADAMS ST 54024 #048-04-1997 L2002 **DR** *020

WALLACE, Jim Mahlon. 208 S ADAMS ST, RIVER VALLEY MED CENTER SC 54024 #026-04-1994 L1995 **IM PD** *020 †20,55

WEGNER, Marwood E. 208 S ADAMS ST 54024 #026-04-1953 L1955 **FM** *072 †18

WIKENHEISER, Mark Anthony. 204 S ADAMS ST 54024 #037-01-1987 L1998 **ORS** *020 †40

SAINT FRANCIS — MILWAUKEE

AKHTAR, Masood. 2000 E LAYTON AVE, STE 100 53235 #704-01-1966 L1977 **IM** *020 †20

ALLEN, Nikki Jo. 2000 E LAYTON AVE 53235 #056-06-2000 L2001 **FM** *020 †18

BAMAN, Sarang Bhasker. 2000 E LAYTON AVE, STE 100 53235 #016-01-1998 L1999 **FM OS** *020 †18

BRUEGGEMAN, Rosemarie E. 2000 E LAYTON AVE, STE 110 53235 #016-11-1998 L2002 **OPH** *020 †35

CRAFT, Samuel Colvin. 2000 E LAYTON AVE, STE 100 53235 #056-06-1976 L1977 **OBG** *020 †18,30

CRAWFORD, Jessica Anne. ■ 53235 #025-12-2007 **OBG** *012

CRUZ, Meredith Ordonez. ■ 53235 #056-05-2005 L2006 **OBG** *012

FUHR, Walter Alexander. 2000 E LAYTON AVE, LAKESHORE MEDICAL CLINIC, 53235 #033-05-1993 L1996 **FM** *020 †18

GOLDSTEIN, Paul Henry. 2000 E LAYTON AVE, STE 110 53235 #016-11-1960 L1964 **OPH** *020 †35

HAYES, Richard Michael. 2000 E LAYTON AVE, STE 100 53235 #305-01-1996 L1997 **IM** *020 †20

HIRSCH, Marc Daniel. 2000 E LAYTON AVE, STE 110 53235 #016-42-1998 L2005 **OPH** *020 †35

KORITALA, Sridevi. 2000 E LAYTON AVE, STE 100 53235 #496-24-1991 L1997 **FM** *020 †18

KOWALSKI, Thomas Henry. 3872 S LAKE DR, UNIT 404 53235 #056-06-1963 L1964 **PD NPM** *071 †55

KUMAR, Ullattil Nanda. 2000 E LAYTON AVE, STE 100 53235 #495-31-1970 L1975 **PUD IM** *020 †20

LERNOR, Richard Elliot. 2000 E LAYTON AVE, STE 110 53235 #028-02-1964 L1970 **OPH** *020 †35

LINSCOTT, John R, Jr. 2000 E LAYTON AVE, STE 100 53235 #422-01-1987 L1988 **FM** *020

LUBENS, Jonathan Martin. 2000 E LAYTON AVE, STE 100 53235 #025-01-1980 L1982 **END IM** *020 †20

MYLAVARAPU, Srikrishna. 2000 E LAYTON AVE, STE 250 53235 #495-50-1992 L2002 **P** *020 †75

NATHAN, Denis Chas B. 2000 E LAYTON AVE, STE 100 53235 #836-02-1964 L1978 **N** *020 †75

NORD, Stephen Lynn. 2000 E LAYTON AVE, STE 100 53235 #056-06-1978 L1983 **ORS OSS** *020 †40

ROBERTS, Erin Marie. 2000 E LAYTON AVE, STE 100 53235 #041-12-1999 L2001 **FM** *020 †18

SARAN, Praveen. ■ 53235 #495-73-1987 L1996 **IM** *020 †20

SHERMAN, David M. 2000 E LAYTON AVE, STE 100 53235 #035-03-1985 L1998 **PD AM** *020 †55

SIDHU, Navneet. ■ 53235 #305-01-2005 L2007 **IM** *012

SOLIS, Leyla Maria. 2000 E LAYTON AVE, STE 100 53235 #682-03-1992 L1997 **IMG** *020 †18

WEBER, Marshall L. 2000 E LAYTON AVE 53235 #056-05-1944 L1945 **GP** *071

YANG, Charles Borchau. 2000 E LAYTON AVE, STE 110 53235 #016-02-1992 L1997 **OPH** *020 †35

SAINT GERMAIN — VILAS

LAUDER, Tamara Gerlach. 7556 HIGHWAY J 54558 #046-01-1990 L1991 **PM** *020 †60

MUSGJERD, David Gene. ■ 54558 #023-01-1962 L1970 **R NM** *071 †80,28

SALEM — KENOSHA

BURY, James Michael. 7137 236TH AVE, STE 103 53168 #016-11-1995 L2000 **FM EM** *020 †18

CARROLL, Joel P. 25320 75TH ST, # 102 53168 #056-06-1978 L1982 **FM** *020 †18

DIDINSKY, Michael. 25100 75TH ST 53168 #016-76-1999, ▲ L2005 **OSS ORS** *020

GERSHTENSON, Joshua Mark. 25100 75TH ST 53168 #010-02-1999 L2005 **HS** *020

HETTRICK, Brian John. 7137 236TH AVE, STE 103 53168 #004-01-1995 L1999 **FM** *020 †18

HUSSAIN, Rubina S. 25320 75TH ST STE 102 53168 #704-08-1983 L2007 **FM** *020 †18

MAYER, Steve Lloyd. ■ 53168 #056-05-1987 **OS** *050
WILSON, Robert Emett. 24906 75TH ST 53168 #038-40-1960 L1965 **PD** *020

SARONA – WASHBURN

SWANSON, Richard Walter. W3948 CHURCH RD 54870 #016-11-1979 L1980 **DR NM** *020 †80

SAUK CITY – SAUK

BAKER, Maribeth. 112 HELEN ST 53583 #056-05-1992 L1993 **FM** *020 †18
BARTHOLOW, Timothy Lisle. 112 HELEN ST 53583 #028-02-1989 L1992 **FM** *020 †18
BREUNIG, Scott Robert. 112 HELEN ST, PRAIRIE CLINIC, SC 53583 #056-05-1997 L2000 **IM** *020 †20
BRINN, Lisa Michele. 112 HELEN ST 53583 #025-12-1998 L1999 **FM** *020 †18
BUSS, Trevver Chandler. 112 HELEN ST 53583 #056-05-1997 L2000 **FM** *020 †18 ‡
GRADE, Matthew Paul. 112 HELEN ST 53583 #016-06-1977 L1978 **FM** *020 †18
GUDLAUGSSON, Olafur. PO BOX 490, 880 INDEPENDENCE LN 53583 #484-01-1992 L1997 **ID** *020 †20
HANSEN, Marc Frederick. 840 CAROLINA ST, U-CARE HMO INC 53583 #024-01-1956 L1957 **PD** *030 †55
JOHNSON, Steven James. 112 HELEN ST 53583 #056-06-1981 L1982 **FM** *020 †18 ‡
KOCH, John James. 112 HELEN ST 53583 #028-34-1974 L1975 **FM** *020
KRUSE, Diana Lynn. 208 PHILLIPS BLVD 53583 #056-05-1977 L1978 **ORS** *020 †40
MC AULIFFE, John Austin. 112 HELEN ST 53583 #056-05-1973 L1978 **FM** *020 †18
SCHAD, Todd Alan. 112 HELEN ST 53583 #026-04-1998 L2001 **OBG** *020 †30
SHULTZ, Edwin Barclay. 112 HELEN ST 53583 #025-01-1982 L1986 **FM** *020 †18
SMITH, Linnea Jean. 112 HELEN ST 53583 #056-05-1984 L1985 **FM** *020 †20
SPURGEON, Joseph Paul. 112 HELEN ST 53583 #018-03-1988 L1991 **FM** *020 †18
VARLEY, Thomas James. 112 HELEN ST 53583 #018-03-1990 L1994 **FM** *020 †18

SAUKVILLE – OZAUKEE

GERARD, Michael James. 830 E GREEN BAY AVE, STE 100 53080 #016-42-1996 L2005 **FM** *020 †18
SMITH, Deeann Marie. 830 E GREEN BAY AVE, STE S100 53080 #030-06-1998 L2000 **FM** *020 †18
ZUCCARO, Cheryl Rae. 830 E GREEN BAY AVE # 100, PRACTICE CLIN 53080 #056-05-1990 L1991 **FM** *020 †18

SCHOFIELD – MARATHON

ABREGO, Pablo Hernandez. 3501 CRANBERRY BLVD 54476 #649-01-1989 L1999 **NEP IM** *020 †20
ANDERSON, Dale Burr. 3501 CRANBERRY BLVD 54476 #030-05-1970 L1971 **IM** *020
ARENSON, Naomi Elizabeth. 3501 CRANBERRY BLVD, MARSHFIELD CLINIC-WESTON C 54476 #016-01-2000 L2008 **N** *020 †75
BANGI, Edwin Tolete. 3301 CRANBERRY BLVD 54476 #748-10-1994 L2004 **FM** *020 †20
COLE, Harry Clifford, III. 3501 CRANBERRY BLVD, WESTON CENTER 54476 #051-01-1987 L1993 **ORS** *020 †40
CRAY, William Keith, Jr. 3501 CRANBERRY BLVD, WESTON CENTER 54476 #409-24-1983 L2008 **GS** *020 †85
CZYZEWSKI, E Ann. 3401 CRANBERRY BLVD, WESTON CENTER 54476 #016-01-1994 L1996 **RO** *020 †40
DE KONING, Joel Richard. 3501 CRANBERRY BLVD, MARSHFIELD CLINIC-WESTON C 54476 #025-01-1971 L1975 **OBG** *020 †30
DERNBACH, William Kiefer. 3501 CRANBERRY BLVD 54476 #056-05-1971 L1972 **GE IM** *020
DOERING, Matthew Paul. 3501 CRANBERRY BLVD, WESTON CENTER 54476 #056-05-1984 L1989 **GS** *020 †85
EARLL, Mark David. 3501 CRANBERRY BLVD 54476 #056-05-1993 L2000 **ORS** *020 †40
GO, Rosita Sio. 3501 CRANBERRY BLVD 54476 #748-10-1972 L1982 **DR** *020 †80
HEGLAND, Larry Thos. 3400 MINISTRY PKWY 54476 #026-04-1990 L2006 **AN CCA** *030 †05
HESSEL, Melissa Lynne. 3501 CRANBERRY BLVD 54476 #056-06-1998 L2001 **PD** *020 †55
HONG, Im Sun. 3501 CRANBERRY BLVD, WESTON CENTER 54476 #187-12-1977 L1990 **PM PMM** *020 †60
HUPY, Thomas Craig. 3501 CRANBERRY BLVD 54476 #025-01-1982 L1985 **FM** *020 †18
ISAACSON, Bart Jon. 3501 CRANBERRY BLVD, WESTON CENTER 54476 #056-06-1995 L1998 **IM** *020 †18
ISLAM, Rezwan. 3501 CRANBERRY BLVD 54476 #160-02-1987 L1999 **HO** *020 †20
KABIR-ISLAM, Lopa S. 3501 CRANBERRY BLVD, WESTON CENTER 54476 #160-02-1993 L2001 **IM** *020
KLIMANT, Eiko. 3501 CRANBERRY BLVD, WESTON CENTER 54476 #409-25-1995 L2002 **IM ON** *020 †20
LAMONT, Jeffrey Harwood. 3501 CRANBERRY BLVD, WESTON CENTER 54476 #016-11-1979 L1985 **PD** *020 †18
LEE, Chong Chin. 3501 CRANBERRY BLVD 54476 #051-04-1987 L2001 **TS** *020 †85,90
LENOIR, Jeanette Marie. 3501 CRANBERRY BLVD 54476 #005-15-1992 L2000 **FM** *020 †18
LEON, Frank, Jr. 3501 CRANBERRY BLVD 54476 #028-78-1997, ▲ L2004 **GE** *020 †20
LUCE, Joshua L. 3501 CRANBERRY BLVD, MARSHFIELD CLINIC-WESTON C 54476 #035-09-1987 L2007 **CD** *020 †20
MACALALAD, J F Herbert R. 3501 CRANBERRY BLVD 54476 #748-07-1983 L2000 **IM** *020 †20
MAC DONALD, Joseph Gerard. 3501 CRANBERRY BLVD 54476 #064-01-1979 L2001 **OTO** *020 †45
MC COOL, Thomas John. 3501 CRANBERRY BLVD 54476 #018-03-1977 L1981 **FM** *020 †18
MEYER, David. 3501 CRANBERRY BLVD, MARSHFIELD CLNC 54476 #001-02-1983 L2007 **OBG** *020 †30
MOE, Ronelle Marie. 3301 CRANBERRY BLVD 54476 #056-05-1992 L1995 **IM** *020 †20
MONACO, Joseph Michael. 3501 CRANBERRY BLVD, MARSHFIELD CLINIC-WESTON C 54476 #050-02-1974 L1977 **PD** *020 †55
MORAN, William J. 3501 CRANBERRY BLVD 54476 #054-04-1978 L2006 **HNS OTO** *020 †45
NAIK, Guruprasad Datta. 3501 CRANBERRY BLVD 54476 #496-15-1992 L2003 **IC CD** *020 †20
NESKOVIC, Verica. 3501 CRANBERRY BLVD 54476 #957-02-1986 L2003 **N** *020 †75
OLMANSON, Douglas Vern. 3501 CRANBERRY BLVD 54476 #026-04-1982 L1989 **FM** *020 †18

PACHECO, Juan Manuel. 3501 CRANBERRY BLVD 54476 #264-18-1993 L1996 **CCM** *020 †20
PINKE, Lori Ann. 3501 CRANBERRY BLVD, MARSHFIELD CLINIC-WESTON C 54476 #026-04-1997 L2007 **U** *020 †95
RATANAWONG, Chirasakdi. 3501 CRANBERRY BLVD, MARSHFIELD CLINIC-WESTON C 54476 #016-11-1993 L1999 **U** *020 †95
SCHUMANN, Ellen Maria. 3501 CRANBERRY BLVD, WESTON CENTER 54476 #056-05-1981 L1984 **PD** *030 †55
SHAW, William Frederick. 3501 CRANBERRY BLVD, WESTON CENTER 54476 #025-01-1986 L2000 **CD** *020 †20
SHEEHAN, Michael Todd. 3501 CRANBERRY BLVD 54476 #026-08-1994 L1995 **END** *020 †20
TAUCHMAN, Cary Geo. 3501 CRANBERRY BLVD, MARSHFIELD CLINIC 54476 #016-45-1981 L1985 **EM** *020 †55
TAYLOR, Gregg W. 3501 CRANBERRY BLVD 54476 #030-06-1979 L2003 **ORS** *020 †40
THAYAPARAN, Thevalojini. ■ 54476 #220-04-1998 L2006 **IM** *020 †20
THOGARUCHEETI, Anil Babu. 3400 MINISTRY PKWY 54476 #495-62-2000 L2003 **IM** *020 †20
TROBEC, Michael J. 3501 CRANBERRY BLVD 54476 #022-75-1994, ▲ L2006 **FM** *020 †18
VARMA, Anshu. 3501 CRANBERRY BLVD, WESTON CENTER 54476 #495-45-1989 L1998 **IM** *020 †20
WEBB, John Francis. 3501 CRANBERRY BLVD 54476 #016-11-1978 L1979 **FM UCM** *020 †18
WESTDORP, Ellen Jean. 3400 MINISTRY PKWY, EMERGENCY DEPT. 54476 #056-06-1987 L2005 **EM** *020 †16
WILLIAMS, Alan Curtis. 3501 CRANBERRY BLVD, WESTON CENTER 54476 #016-43-1975 L1988 **R** *020
WILSON, Jason Allen. 3501 CRANBERRY BLVD 54476 #038-40-1998 L1999 **U** *020 †95
WYSKOARKO, Nicholas Peter. 3501 CRANBERRY BLVD, MARSHFIELD CLINIC-WESTON C 54476 #035-08-1973 L1996 **CD IC** *020 †20

SEYMOUR – OUTAGAMIE

LAMONT, Frederick Jos. 1100 ORCHARD DR 54165 #056-05-1967 L1968 **IM** *020 †20
MIASKOWSKI, Tomasz Konrad. 405 COMMERCIAL ST 54165 #759-07-1987 L1992 **FM** *020 †18
TURZINSKI, Steven David. 958 FOOTE ST 54165 #028-34-1994 L1997 **FM** *020 †18

SHARON – WALWORTH

HITT, Rockton Wm. 118 PLAIN ST 53585 #016-01-1984 L2000 **FM** *020 †18

SHAWANO – SHAWANO

ALBRIGHT, John Jos. 1555 N BRODER RD 54166 #056-05-1959 L1960 **GP** *071
ANDREWS-FIKE, Christa M. 100 COUNTY ROAD B, THEDACARE SHAWANO 54166 #037-01-1996 L2006 **FM** *020 †18
ARVOLD, David Schewe. ■ 54166 #056-05-1946 L1947 **GP OBG** *071
BERGMANN, Franklyn Thos. 117 E GREEN BAY ST 54166 #056-05-1960 L1964 **GP** *071
BETANCOURT, Edgar. 309 N BARTLETT ST 54166 #042-01-1996 L2001 **PTH** *020
BONNIN, Julie Joy. 100 COUNTY ROAD B 54166 #056-06-1982 L1983 **FM** *020 †18
DAUPHINEE, Patricia K. 118 E DIVISION ST 54166 #064-01-1982 L1993 **GP OBG** *020
GILLIS, Beth L. 100 COUNTY ROAD B 54166 #056-06-1982 L1983 **FM** *020 †18
HART, John David. 100 COUNTY ROAD B 54166 #018-03-1966 L1969 **FM** *071 †18
HENKE, Frederick Wm. ■ 54166 #056-05-1945 L1946 **R NM** *071 †80,28
HILTGEN, Gregrey G. 503 S MAIN ST, AURORA MED GRP 54166 #056-06-1994 L1996 **FM** *020 †18
JEFFRIES, Donald Allan. ■ 54166 #056-05-1947 L1948 **GS GP** *071
KEENAN, Peter C. 309 N BARTLETT ST 54166 #028-34-1994 L1997 **FM** *020 †18
KENNARD, Jay Kelly. 309 N BARTLETT ST 54166 #038-41-1996 L2006 **FM** *020 †18
LANGLEY, John Richard. 100 COUNTY ROAD B, GREATER ATLANTA VEIN CLINI 54166 #045-01-1968 L2001 **GS** *020 †85
LEWIS, Tod Clifford. 100 COUNTY B 54166 #026-04-1990 L1991 **FM** *020 †18
MALFESE, David C. 100 COUNTY 54166 #016-45-1998 L1999 **FM** *020 †18
PETERS, Randall B. 100 COUNTY ROAD B 54166 #048-14-1983 L2004 **GS** *020
QUALHEIM, Kathleen. 100 COUNTY B 54166 #649-30-1986 L1991 **FM** *020 †18
SCHWIESOW, Karl Lee. 309 N BARTLETT ST 54166 #016-11-1968 L1980 **OPH** *020 †35
SHALINI, Kshamata. 116 N MAIN ST 54166 #495-15-1990 L1999 **IM** *020 †20
SLAGLE, Amy Jo. ■ 54166 #028-03-1991 L1992 **FM** *020 †18
STOUGHTON, Richard R. 100 COUNTY ROAD B 54166 #056-00-1962 L1976 **FM** *020 †18
THATCHER, Gregory Bruce. 100 COUNTY ROAD B 54166 #019-02-1976 L1979 **FM** *020 †18
THOMAS, Thomas J. 100 COUNTY B 54166 #056-05-1974 L1977 **FM** *020 †18
VIDALAKIS, Geo Emmanuel. 309 N BARTLETT ST, SHAWANO CTY HOSP EMERGENCY 54166 #016-45-1979 L1982 **EM FM** *020 †16,18
WILLIAMS, Michael Duane. 100 COUNTY ROAD B 54166 #007-02-2003 L2006 **FM** *020 †18

SHEBOYGAN – SHEBOYGAN

ABITZ, Leslie Cheryl. 2414 KOHLER MEMORIAL DR 53081 #025-12-1985 L1989 **OBG** *020 †30
AMBELANG, Charles Arthur. ■ 53081 #056-05-2008 *012
AMBELANG, Jessica Menn. 318 SAINT CLAIR AVE 53081 #056-05-1976 L1982 **OBG** *020 †30
AMBELANG, Thomas Matthew. 2414 KOHLER MEMORIAL DR 53081 #056-05-1976 L1982 **FM OM** *020 †18
AYMOND, David King. 1414 N TAYLOR DR, STE 105 53081 #048-14-1978 L1981 **OPH** *020 †35
BASSEWITZ, Paul Peter. ■ 53081 #056-05-1941 L1942 **GP** *071
BATZNER, David John. 1601 N TAYLOR DR 53081 #056-06-1956 L1957 **OBG** *020 †30
BAUER, Paul Manfred. 1223 N 23RD ST 53081 #409-19-1996 L1999 **PD** *020 †55
BEIERSDORF, Rieck Wilfred. 1223 N 23RD ST 53081 #056-05-1978 L1979 **FM** *020 †18
BEMIS, Heidi A. 2629 N 7TH ST 53083 #056-05-2000 L2005 **IM** *100 †20
BERI, Vijay Kumar. 2414 KOHLER MEMORIAL DR 53081 #495-69-1974 L1981 **AI IM** *020 †20,03
BEST, Catherine Marie. 620 S WISCONSIN ST 53081 #056-05-1988 L1992 **FM** *020 †18
BETTAG, Steven Mark. 1621 N TAYLOR DR, STE 100 53081 #016-01-1989 L1995 **ON HEM** *020 †20
BLACK, Charles Byron. 2414 KOHLER MEMORIAL DR 53081 #018-03-1995 L2000 **GS** *020 †85
BOARDMAN, John Robt. 2629 N 7TH ST 53083 #056-05-1974 L1986 **EM PD** *020 †55,16
BRAUER, Warren Allen. 1703 N TAYLOR DR 53081 #028-03-1975 L1978 **FM** *020 †18 ‡

■ = Address Information Privacy Protected

BRAULT, Jenny. 2920 SUPERIOR AVE, SHEBOYGAN PEDIATRIC ASSOIC 53081 #056-05-2003 L2006 **PD** *020 †55
BRENNAN, John T, Jr. ■ 53083 #024-01-1950 L1957 **GS TRS** *071 †85
BRENTON, Jennifer Lynn. 1621 N TAYLOR DR, STE 300 53081 #025-01-1997 L2004 **OBG** *020 †30
BRIMHALL, Kathryn W. 2203 S MEMORIAL PL 53081 #028-34-1987 L1988 **P OBG** *020
BRITTON, Jeffrey Wells. 2414 KOHLER MEMORIAL DR, AURORA SHEBOYGAN CLINIC 53081 #056-05-1987 L1989 **PD** *020 †55
BROOKS, Lori. 2629 N 7TH ST 53083 #056-06-1990 L1991 **PM** *020 †60
BROOKS, Michael Robt. 2414 KOHLER MEMORIAL DR, THE SHEBOYGAN CLINIC 53081 #056-06-1989 L1990 **NEP IM** *020 †20
BRUEGL, Amanda Sue. ■ 53081 #054-04-2007 **OBG** *012
CAMPBELL, Andrew Carl. 1411 N TAYLOR DR, SHEBOYGAN EAR NOSE THROAT 53081 #017-20-1993 L1998 **OTO FPS** *020 †45
CAMPBELL, Richard L. 2414 KOHLER MEMORIAL DR 53081 #056-05-1976 L1980 **DR NM** *020 †80
CHESNA, Edward J. 2414 KOHLER MEMORIAL DR, AURORA SHEBOYGAN CLINIC 53081 #016-43-1979 L1988 **DR NM** *020 †80
CHLEBORAD, William Paul. 2414 KOHLER MEMORIAL DR 53081 #030-05-1983 L1990 **GS VS** *020 †85
CLEVELAND, Katherine C. 2414 KOHLER MEMORIAL DR 53081 #016-43-1998 L1999 **OBG** *020 †30
CORRIGAN, Jeffrey Kent. 1813 ASHLAND AVE 53081 #038-43-1996 L1999 **FM** *020 †18
COULIS, Louie. 1414 N TAYLOR DR 53081 #017-20-1986 L1993 **CD** *020 †20
CRAWFORD, Wm Carl, III. 2414 KOHLER MEMORIAL DR 53081 #023-01-1974 L1977 **GP** *020
DE LEON, Manuel Cruz, III. ■ 53081 #748-01-1971 L1977 **IM** *020
DEMERY, Patricia Maureen. 2629 N 7TH ST 53083 #025-07-1983 L1991 **EM** *020 †16
DENKER, Stephen Ty. 2414 KOHLER MEMORIAL DR 53081 #025-01-1975 L1978 **CD ICE** *020 †20
DE ROOS, Jan Pierre. 2414 KOHLER MEMORIAL DR 53081 #016-02-1973 L1977 **ORS** *020 †40
DERSE, Theodore Scott. 1813 ASHLAND AVE 53081 #023-12-1992 L1993 **FM** *020 †18
DETRANA, Philip M. 2920 SUPERIOR AVE 53081 #016-11-1986 L1995 **PCC SME** *020 †20
DIELENTHEIS, David Peter. 2414 KOHLER MEMORIAL DR 53081 #026-04-1984 L1985 **OBG** *020 †30
DUENK, Larry L. 1703 N TAYLOR DR 53081 #056-06-1989 L1990 **FM EM** *020 †18 ‡
DY, Edmund Cheng. 2414 KOHLER MEMORIAL DR 53081 #016-45-1993 L1997 **P** *020 †75
DYKSTERHOUSE, Dwight L. 2414 KOHLER MEMORIAL DR 53081 #025-01-1988 L1997 **OBG** *020 †30
EDDLEMAN, Frank Clinton, Jr. 2414 KOHLER MEMORIAL DR, AURORA SHEBOYGAN CLINIC 53081 #028-03-1998 L2007 **IM** *020 †20
EHRHART, Robert Henry. 2414 KOHLER MEMORIAL DR, THE SHEBOYGAN CLINIC 53081 #041-12-1974 L1985 **RHU IM** *020 †20
FALCONER, Steven Hogan. 2414 KOHLER MEMORIAL DR, THE SHEBOYGAN CLINIC-RADIO 53081 #026-04-1993 L1997 **DR** *020 †80
FARRELL, John C, Jr. 2414 KOHLER MEMORIAL DR 53081 #010-01-1944 L1945 **D OS** *071 †15
FEHRMAN, Douglas Armin. 2414 KOHLER MEMORIAL DR, AURORA SHEBOYGAN CLINIC 53081 #056-05-1991 L1992 **ORS** *020 †40
FERNANDEZ, Pedro B. 2414 KOHLER MEMORIAL DR 53081 #748-08-1963 L1975 **OBG** *071 †30
FLEMING, Paul Michael. 2629 N 7TH ST 53083 #056-06-1966 L1975 **OTO** *020 †45
FULTZ, George S. ■ 53081 #038-43-1980 L1984 **DR** *020 †80
GALE, Henry Hamon. 2414 KOHLER MEMORIAL DR, THE SHEBOYGAN CLINIC 53081 #061-01-1954 L1966 **CD** *020
GANJU, Badri Nath. 2414 KOHLER MEMORIAL DR 53081 #495-19-1970 L1977 **GS VS** *020 †85
GASSNER, Kevin James. 2920 SUPERIOR AVE 53081 #056-05-1980 L1986 **ORS** *020 †40
GAVIN, Andrea Maria. 2414 KOHLER MEMORIAL DR, AURORA SHEBOYGAN CLINIC 53081 #016-45-1988 L1989 **FM** *020 †18
GEHRING, Charles John, Jr. 2414 KOHLER MEMORIAL DR 53081 #056-05-1982 L1983 **AN PME** *020 †05
GENTINE, Mary Josephine. 1703 N TAYLOR DR 53081 #033-05-1997 L1998 **FM** *020 †18
GEREND, Jacob Michael. 2414 KOHLER MEMORIAL DR 53081 #030-06-1967 L1970 **DR** *071 †80
GLAESER, Scott Thos. 1601 N TAYLOR DR 53081 #016-06-1986 L1987 **ORS** *020 †40 ‡
GOLUBSKI, Joseph Frank. 2629 N 7TH ST, SHEBOYGAN MEMORIAL HOSP 53083 #028-78-1980, ▲ L1988 **PTH DMP** *020 †50 ‡
GORE, Donald Ray. 2920 SUPERIOR AVE 53081 #016-11-1960 L1961 **ORS** *020 †40
GRAF, Christopher A. 1720 N 8TH ST 53081 #056-05-1954 L1957 **U** *071 †95
GREEN, Kathryn Ann. 1442 N 31ST ST 53081 #017-20-1980 L1981 **OPH** *020 †35
GREEN, Thomas John. ■ 53083 #016-42-2006 L2008 **AN** *012
GROSE, Gregory Stephen. 1414 N TAYLOR DR, STE 210 53081 #054-04-1990 L1991 **U** *020 †95
GUEVARA, Esteban. ■ 53081 #649-01-1965 L1982 **ON HEM** *071
GUZZO, Matthew Hart. 2920 SUPERIOR AVE 53081 #018-03-1998 L1999 **GS** *020 †85
HAID, Max. 1223 N 23RD ST 53081 #016-11-1971 L2002 **ON HEM** *020 †20
HALLER, David Lee. 3100 SUPERIOR AVE, THIRD FLOOR 53081 #016-11-1995 L2001 **GE** *020 †20
HANCOCK, Curtis Wayne. 2414 KOHLER MEMORIAL DR 53081 #056-05-1976 L1979 **IM IMG** *020 †20
HANSMANN, Jeffrey Thos. 1601 N TAYLOR DR 53081 #056-05-1992 L1996 **AN** *020 †05
HARMS, Jay Scot. 2414 KOHLER MEMORIAL DR, AURORA SHEBOYGAN CLINIC 53081 #047-05-1997 L2004 **FM** *020 †18
HARVEY, Donald James. 2124 KOHLER MEMORIAL DR 53081 #056-06-1976 L1977 **AN** *075 †05
HEESACKER, Darren Michael. 2629 N 7TH ST 53083 #056-06-1992 L1995 **EM** *020 †16
HEILI, Michael John. 2920 SUPERIOR AVE, SHEBOYGAN MEDICAL ASSOC 53081 #056-05-1987 L1990 **GS** *020 †85 ‡
HEINS, Craig Lee. 1621 N TAYLOR DR 53081 #030-06-1996 L2004 **OBG** *020 †30
HELMINIAK, Robert Anthony. 2414 KOHLER MEMORIAL DR 53081 #056-05-1974 L1975 **IM** *020 †20
HERMANN, John Peter. 2414 KOHLER MEMORIAL DR 53081 #056-05-1974 L1975 **U** *020 †95
HERNANDEZ, Manuel. 2629 N 7TH ST 53083 #056-06-2002 L2005 **EM** *020 †16
HEROLD, Jeffrey Anthony. 1526 N TAYLOR DR 53081 #051-01-1990 L1998 **PS** *020 †85,65
HEROLD, Suzanne S. 2920 SUPERIOR AVE 53081 #051-01-1993 L1999 **IM** *071 †20
HESS, George Leonard, Jr. 1601 N TAYLOR DR 53081 #056-06-1976 L1977 **AN** *020 †05
HILDEBRAND, James F. ■ 53081 #056-05-1943 L1945 **D A** *071 †20,15
HODGSON, Joseph L. 2629 N 7TH ST 53083 #016-43-1982 L1987 **EM** *020 †16
HOELL, James Steven. 2629 N 7TH ST, SHEBOYGAN MEMORIAL CEDICAL 53083 #056-06-1996 L1997 **AN** *020 †05
JOERRES, Sarah Geenen. 2629 N 7TH ST, REHAB SPEC SHEBOYGAN MEML 53083 #056-06-1987 L1988 **PM** *020 †60
JOHNSON, Kevin M. 2414 KOHLER MEMORIAL DR 53081 #048-12-1985 L1986 **REN GYN** *020 †30
JOHNSON, Kevin Marke. 2414 KOHLER MEMORIAL DR 53081 #025-12-1986 L1989 **IM** *020 †20
JOHNSON, Michael David. 2629 N 7TH ST 53083 #038-40-1997 L2000 **IM** *020 †20
JOHNSON, Rodney Chas. 1306 N 3RD ST 53081 #026-04-1961 L1965 **P OM** *071 †75
JONES, Jerry, III. 2629 N 7TH ST 53083 #038-40-1984 L1989 **EM IM** *020 †20 ‡
JUMES, Marvin Geo. 1202 N 31ST ST 53081 #056-05-1958 L1959 **AN** *072
KANTER, Steven Kenneth. ■ 53081 #056-05-1980 L1991 **DR** *020 †80
KAPUR, Chanda. 2414 KOHLER MEMORIAL DR, AURORA SHEBOYGAN CLINIC 53081 #495-51-1971 L1976 **IM FM** *020
KELLER, Robert Arthur. ■ 53083 #056-05-1958 L1959 **FM** *071 †18
KERPE, Vytas Kazimieras. 2920 SUPERIOR AVE 53081 #016-43-1975 L1979 **IM** *020 †20
KIM, Steven Cheulwoo. 2414 KOHLER MEMORIAL DR 53081 #016-11-1994 L2000 **U** *020 †95
KLETTKE, Roger Gordon. 1601 N TAYLOR DR 53081 #025-01-1972 L1981 **PTH** *020 †50
KNOEDLER, Daniel Wm. 1807 RIDGE RD 53083 #026-04-1985 L1992 **P** *020 †75
KOTIHAL, Ramesh Murugappa. 2414 KOHLER MEMORIAL DR, NEPHROLOGY CLINICS 53081 #496-42-2001 L2008 **NEP** *012 †20
KROPP, August Donald. ■ 53081 #056-06-1964 L1968 **P** *071
KRUMMEL, Stephen John. 2414 KOHLER MEMORIAL DR, THE SHEBOYGAN CLINIC 53081 #056-06-1983 L1987 **P** *020 †75
KUNKEL, Stephen P. 2414 KOHLER MEMORIAL DR 53081 #048-13-1985 L1989 **N** *020 †75
KUPLIC, James Bradley. 2920 SUPERIOR AVE 53081 #056-05-1967 L1971 **IM OM** *020
KUTTICKAT, George. 2414 KOHLER MEMORIAL DR, AURORA SHEBOYGAN CLINIC 53081 #495-52-1986 L1997 **CD** *020 †20
LANG, Mark Stephen. 2414 KOHLER MEMORIAL DR, THE SHEBOYGAN CLINIC 53081 #056-05-1996 L1997 **ORS** *020 †40
LARSON, Christopher L. 1442 N 31ST ST 53081 #056-05-1975 L1976 **OPH** *020 †35
LISBERG, Kenneth Jay. 2920 SUPERIOR AVE 53081 #028-02-1972 L1973 **GS VS** *020 †85
LIVERMORE, John Tillotson. 2414 KOHLER MEMORIAL DR 53081 #056-05-1982 L1988 **ORS** *020 †40
LOGAN, Alexandra. 2629 N 7TH ST, AURORA SHEBOYGAN MEMORIAL 53083 #422-01-1987 L1990 **IM** *020 †20
LUEDTKE, Jeremy Ray. ■ 53083 #056-06-2005 L2006 **GS** *012
LULLOFF, Lynn Kathryn. 2629 N 7TH ST 53083 #056-06-2003 L2006 **EM** *020 †16
LYNDS, Jeffrey Clark. 1813 ASHLAND AVE 53081 #016-45-1988 L1989 **FM** *020 †18
MALEWISKI, Larry J. 1930 N 8TH ST 53081 #056-05-1965 L1966 **GP** *020
MAMALAKIS, John Markos. 1601 N TAYLOR DR 53081 #056-05-1999 L2003 **AN** *020 †05
MANCHESKI, Dean Anthony. 1703 N TAYLOR DR 53081 #056-05-1979 L1980 **FM** *020 †18
MARSHO, Bernard S. 1703 N TAYLOR DR 53081 #056-06-1943 L1944 **GP OBG** *072
MARSHO, Patrick Robt. 1703 N TAYLOR DR 53081 #056-06-1975 L1978 **FM FPG** *020 †18
MARTENS, Suzanne Jean. 3100 SUPERIOR AVE, EMERGENCY DEPT 53081 #056-06-1995 L1996 **EM** *020 †16
MARTIN, Clifford Glenn. 1621 N TAYLOR DR 53081 #021-01-1982 L1990 **GYN** *020 †30
MATTHEWS, H Marshall. 1621 N TAYLOR DR 53081 #007-02-1985 L1986 **HO PLM** *020 †20
MEDICH, Michael George. 2629 N 7TH ST 53083 #026-04-1985 L1989 **EM** *020 †16 ‡
MICHAEL, James D. ■ 53081 #028-02-1953 L1960 **IM** *071 †20
MILLER, Brian David. 2629 N 7TH ST 53083 #056-05-1999 L2002 **EM** *020 †16
MOCKERT, Thomas, Jr. ■ 53083 #056-05-1964 L1965 **IM** *071
MOHAMMAD, Ghulam. 2414 KOHLER MEMORIAL DR 53081 #704-02-1962 L1976 **PD PHO** *071 †55
MORENO, Roland Pascasio. 2414 KOHLER MEMORIAL DR, THE SHEBOYGAN CLINIC 53081 #748-10-1992 L1999 **PM** *020 †60
MORE O'FERRALL, Dermot J. 2124 KOHLER MEMORIAL DR 53081 #539-06-1990 L2001 **PM** *020 †60
MORGENWECK, Cynthiane J. 1601 N TAYLOR DR 53081 #056-06-1977 L1978 **AN** *071 †05
MOULTON, Jonathan Vail. 2414 KOHLER MEMORIAL DR 53081 #038-40-1971 L1976 **GE IM** *020 †20
MURPHY, Patrick James. 2414 KOHLER MEMORIAL DR, THE SHEBOYGAN CLINIC 53081 #056-06-1986 L1987 **FM** *020 †18
MYERS, Kevin Scott. 1440 N 25TH ST 53081 #039-01-1978 L1982 **D DS** *020 †15
NICHOLSON, James J. 2414 KOHLER MEMORIAL DR, THE SHEBOYGAN CLINIC 53081 #056-05-1985 L1993 **AN PMM** *020 †85,05
NIXON-MONROE, Rachel L. 2414 KOHLER MEMORIAL DR, AURORA SHEBOYGAN CLINIC 53081 #025-76-1999, ▲ L2002 **FM** *020
NORA, Elizabeth Hart. 2414 KOHLER MEMORIAL DR 53081 #056-06-2000 L2004 **END** *020 †20
NORRIS, Clint A. 2414 KOHLER MEMORIAL DR 53081 #308-11-1984 L1988 **CHP P** *020 †75
NORTHUP, Cole Stanley. 2414 KOHLER MEMORIAL DR 53081 #016-06-1974 L1979 **ORS** *071 †40
NORTHUP, Cynthia V Peska. 1223 N 23RD ST 53081 #016-06-1974 L1979 **FM** *020 †18
O'NEILL, Thaddeus Patrick. 2414 KOHLER MEMORIAL DR 53081 #016-01-1999 L2006 **PS** *020 †85
OPEL, Elise Haru. 2414 KOHLER MEMORIAL DR, AURORA SHEBOYGAN CLC 53081 #016-06-1999 L2002 **PD** *020 †55
PETERSON, Daniel A. 2414 KOHLER MEMORIAL DR, THE SHEBOYGAN CLINIC 53081 #016-01-1994 L1998 **DR** *020 †80
PHELAN, David Michael. 2414 KOHLER MEMORIAL DR 53081 #056-06-1995 L2002 **ID IM** *020 †20
PHILLIPS, Philip Perry. 2414 KOHLER MEM DR, SHEBOYGAN CLINIC 53081 #039-01-1985 L1991 **OTO** *020 †45
PIZER, Steven Jos. 2414 KOHLER MEMORIAL DR 53081 #056-05-1985 L1988 **PD** *020 †55
PLEVIAK, Denis James. 2629 N 7TH ST 53083 #016-11-1977 L1980 **FM** *020 †18
POND, Jonathan Daines. 2414 KOHLER MEMORIAL DR 53081 #054-04-1999 L2000 **ORS** *020
POULLETTE, George Thos. 2414 KOHLER MEMORIAL DR, AURORA SHEBOYGAN CLINIC 53081 #056-05-1988 L1989 **FM** *020 †18
QUINN, Garry Arthur. 2414 KOHLER MEMORIAL DR 53081 #056-06-1957 L1958 **GYN** *020 †30
QUINONES, Nikolo Calabio. 2414 KOHLER MEMORIAL DR 53081 #748-10-1993 L1998 **IM** *020 †20
RAMMER, Martin Astor. ■ 53083 #056-05-1959 L1961 **FM GS** *071 †18
REEDYK, Leonard. 2414 KOHLER MEMORIAL DR, 2414 KOHLER MEMORIAL DRIVE 53081 #060-01-1976 L1986 **GP** *020
REINEMANN, John Michael. ■ 53081 #056-05-1956 L1957 **PD** *071
REISER, Gregory. 2414 KOHLER MEMORIAL DR 53081 #308-11-1984 L1985 **CD IM** *020 †20 ‡
RIES, Thomas. 2414 KOHLER MEMORIAL DR 53081 #056-05-1978 L1979 **OBG** *020 †30
ROEHRBORN, Julie Ann. 2920 SUPERIOR AVE 53081 #030-05-1995 L1998 **PD** *020 †55

■ = Address Information Privacy Protected

ROIGER, Michelle M. 1601 N TAYLOR DR 53081 #025-12-1996 L1999 **EM** *020 †16
ROSEBUSH, John Mcnaughton. 2629 N 7TH ST 53083 #056-05-1984 L1987 **EM** *020 †16
SANFELIPPO, Elizabeth T. 1703 N TAYLOR DR 53081 #056-06-1971 L1972 **AI IM** *020 †20
SANTHOSH-KUMAR, C. 1222 N 23RD ST 53081 #495-31-1975 L2002 **HO IM** *020 †20
SANTINO, Steven George. 2414 KOHLER MEMORIAL DR 53081 #028-03-1998 L2002 **PM** *020 †60
SCHERR, Gary Ross. ■ 53081 #048-13-1989 L2004 **PTH BBK** *020 †50
SCHLEEVOGT, Charlie Fred. 2920 SUPERIOR AVE 53081 #016-11-1989 L1993 **IM** *020 †20
SCHMITT, Bryan Thos. 2414 KOHLER MEMORIAL DR 53081 #056-05-1990 L1991 **IM** *020 †20
SCHMITT, Charles A. 1202 N 31ST ST 53081 #056-05-1979 L1982 **AN** *020 †05
SCHMITT, Jill I. 2414 KOHLER MEMORIAL DR 53081 #056-05-1990 L1991 **IM** *020 †20
SCHOTT, Jean Harriet. 2209 S MEMORIAL PL 53081 #016-06-1975 L1981 **PO OPH** *020 †35
SCHULTZ, Wade Thomas. 1407 N 8TH ST 53081 #026-08-2002 L2004 **OMF** *020
SCHULZ, Craig Allan. 1222 N 23RD ST 53081 #056-05-1995 L1996 **RO** *020 †80
SCHWALBACH, John Francis. 2414 KOHLER MEMORIAL DR 53081 #026-04-1968 L1976 **CD IM** *071 †20
SCIARRA, Paschal A. ■ 53081 #038-41-1951 L1958 **OTO** *071 †45
SELLINGER, David Scott. 2920 SUPERIOR AVE 53081 #056-05-1973 L1974 **ORS** *020 †40
SHAH, Asghar Ali. 2414 KOHLER MEMORIAL DR 53081 #704-01-1964 L1973 **P** *020 †75
SIDDIQUE, Awais. 2414 KOHLER MEMORIAL DR 53081 #025-07-1997 L2003 **VIR DR** *020 †80
SIMONSON, Rolf Lee. 2414 KOHLER MEMORIAL DR 53081 #056-05-1968 L1974 **PD OS** *020 †55
SMITH, David Ross. 2414 KOHLER MEMORIAL DR 53081 #016-45-1979 L1990 **FM EM** *020 †70,18
SOKHI, Rana Paramvir. 2414 KOHLER MEMORIAL DR 53081 #495-12-1994 L2003 **GE IM** *020 †20
STASTNY, William Jos. 1223 N 23RD ST 53081 #056-06-1980 L1981 **FM** *020 †18
STERNER, David James. 2629 N 7TH ST 53083 #001-02-1993 L1999 **PTH** *072 †50
STEWART, Otto K, Jr. ■ 53083 #010-02-1952 L1961 **ORS HS** *071 †40
STILLWELL, Scott Michael. 1703 N TAYLOR DR 53081 #056-06-1985 L1986 **FM** *020 †18 ‡
SUMMERSIDE, Paul Robt. 2629 N 7TH ST 53083 #018-03-1985 L1988 **EM** *030 †16
SUTHAR, Sanjay Bhikhalal. 2414 KOHLER MEMORIAL DR, SHEBOYGAN CLINIC 53081 #305-01-1991 L1994 **FM** *020 †18
TARAN, Martha. 2414 KOHLER MEMORIAL DR, SHEBOYGAN CLINIC WALK IN C 53081 #016-11-1987 L1998 **FM** *020 †18
TOLENTINO, Jose Quimzon. 1601 N TAYLOR DR 53081 #748-08-1962 L1969 **AS GP** *020
TRAGER, William L. 2920 SUPERIOR AVE 53081 #016-11-1983 L1986 **PD** *020 †55
TUTTLE, Paul Vernon, III. 2414 KOHLER MEMORIAL DR 53081 #036-01-1980 L1994 **N** *020 †75
VALICENTI, Jeanne Marie. 2414 KOHLER MEMORIAL DR, AURORA SHEBOYGAN CLINIC 53081 #035-48-1988 L1992 **D** *020 †15
VAN DOMMELEN, Bruce Alan. 2920 SUPERIOR AVE 53081 #025-07-1981 L1986 **ORS OSM** *020 †40
VRZAL, Kari Marie Stauffe. ■ 53081 #056-06-2004 L2004 **FM** *020 †18
WAGNER, William Geo. ■ 53081 #056-06-1967 L1970 **GS CD** *020 †85
WAKE, Brian Douglas. 2414 KOHLER MEMORIAL DR 53081 #025-01-1969 L1980 **DR** *071 †80
WAKE, Kristine Marie. 2414 KOHLER MEMORIAL DR 53081 #056-05-1997 L2000 **PD** *020 †55
WALKER, Philip Howard. 2920 SUPERIOR AVE 53081 #016-11-1974 L1977 **IM** *020 †20
WELSCH, Jeffrey Michael. 1414 N TAYLOR DR, SHEBOYGEN UROLOGY SPEC 53081 #056-06-1996 L2002 **U** *020 †95
WERNER, David A. ■ 53083 #056-05-1953 L1955 **OS GP** *071
WERNER, Stephen John. 2920 SUPERIOR AVE 53081 #028-34-1980 L1986 **GS VS** *020 †85
WESTCOTT, Stephen C. 2414 KOHLER MEMORIAL DR 53081 #056-05-1974 L1977 **IM** *020 †20
WILLIS, Robert Thos. 2414 KOHLER MEMORIAL DR 53081 #048-04-1964 L1972 **PUD IM** *020 †20
WORTHINGTON, Ross Alan. 2629 N 7TH ST 53083 #016-01-1998 L2003 **PTH** *020
ZABROWSKI, Randal James. 2414 KOHLER MEMORIAL DR 53081 #056-05-1982 L1987 **DR** *020 †80
ZANDT-STASTNY, Debra Ann. 2414 KOHLER MEMORIAL DR, THE SHEBOYGAN CLINIC 53081 #056-06-1982 L1983 **DR GP** *071 †80
ZWEBEN, Larry Michael. 2414 KOHLER MEMORIAL DR 53081 #005-18-1978 L1999 **OPH** *020 †35

SHEBOYGAN FALLS — SHEBOYGAN

REJMAN, Michelle L. 1146 PLANKVIEW GREEN BLVD 53085 #016-01-1993 L1998 **FM** *020 †18
WEYGANDT, James L. ■ 53085 #038-06-1952 L1954 **OM** *071

SHELL LAKE — WASHBURN

DUNHAM, Jeffrey Allen. PO BOX 336, 105 4TH AVE 54871 #026-04-1987 L1989 **FM** *020 †18

SHERWOOD — CALUMET

PILON, Joseph Edward. ■ 54169 #056-06-1965 L1968 **ORS** *071 †40

SHOREWOOD — MILWAUKEE

BALKER, Shemsu Detamo. 4424 N WILSON DR 53211 #366-03-1991 L2004 **IM** *020 †20
DAHL, David Selmer. ■ 53211 #018-03-1963 L1968 **N** *020 †75
DERSE, Arthur Ralph. ■ 53211 #056-05-1980 L1981 **EM** *020 †16
DIETZ, Nicholas Edward. ■ 53211 #030-05-2006 L2008 **PTH** *012
DONGAS, Barbara S. ■ 53211 #038-06-1981 L1982 **IM** *071 †20
HANLEY, Kathryn Sullivan. 4410 N FREDERICK AVE, FROEDTERT HOSPITAL 53211 #016-02-1998 L2004 **IM** *020 †20
JARENWATTANANON, Marisa Y. ■ 53211 #891-03-1975 L1986 **NPM PD** *020 †55
KOEWLER, Thomas Jos. ■ 53211 #017-20-1981 L1982 **FM** *020 †18
LINN, John C. ■ 53211 #056-06-1951 L1952 **GYN OS** *071 †30
PHELPS, Mark Christian. ■ 53211 #035-15-2007 **P** *012
RICKLES, Aaron Saul. ■ 53211 #056-06-2008 *012
TYLER, Israel Lloyd. ■ 53211 #011-02-1980 L1996 **AN** *020 †05
WEIDA, Billy Joe. ■ 53211 #017-20-1971 L1982 **OS FM** *030 †18

WESTON, Matthew Morris. ■ 53211 #056-06-2007 **AN** *012

SHULLSBURG — LAFAYETTE

DGANI, Ram. 29 EDGEHILL RD 53586 #550-01-1969 L1976 **OBG** *100

SISTER BAY — DOOR

CHOPYAK, John Alan. 330 MEADOW LN 54234 #056-06-1959 L1960 **GS OS** *071
KRUMENACHER, Frederick P. ■ 54234 #056-05-1949 L1950 **IM** *071 †20
LARSON, Owen E. ■ 54234 #056-06-1950 L1951 **AN** *071
POLAND, Maynard Dillon. ■ 54234 #056-06-1961 L1968 **IM DIA** *071 †20
QURESHI, Ijaz Nasim. PO BOX 736, 9501 MARSHALL'S PT – BAY 54234 #704-01-1962 L1970 **PTH** *020 †50
STANNARD, Gilbert H, Jr. ■ 54234 #056-05-1946 L1949 **R** *072 †80
TRAVER, Joan Amalia. 275 SMITH DR 54234 #041-07-1975 L1978 **IM EM** *020 †20
WIXSON, Richard Cotts. ■ 54234 #025-01-1942 L1951 **ORS** *071 †40
ZEMEL, Harry Jos. PO BOX 560 54234 #028-03-1968 L1974 **PTH** *020 †50

SLINGER — WASHINGTON

BULLIS, Therese Jean. 4656 LAKEVIEW CIR 53086 #056-05-1996 L1999 **EM** *020 †16
FERNANDEZ, Edmund Juco. 1061 E COMMERCE BLVD, AURORA HEALTH CENTER 53086 #305-01-1998 L2000 **FM** *020 †18
ISAACSON, Harold Edmund. ■ 53086 #025-07-1946 L1991 **IM** *071
LINDSEY, Stephen Moore. 1061 HIGHWAY 60 E 53086 #038-40-1973 L1974 **DR** *020 †80
PATEL, Rina Ankur. 1061 E COMMERCE BLVD 53086 #496-21-1989 L1992 **PYG** *020 †75
TORKELSON, Allan Wm. 1061 E COMMERCE BLVD 53086 #056-05-1976 L1977 **ON HEM** *020 †20
TREISMAN, Jonathan Scott. 1061 E COMMERCE BLVD 53086 #025-07-1984 L1995 **HO IM** *020 †20
VUKELICH, Marjorie Ann. 1061 E COMMERCE BLVD H, AURORA HEALTH CTR 53086 #026-04-1981 L1985 **ON HEM** *020 †20

SOLDIERS GROVE — CRAWFORD

DEVITT, Timothy James. 102 SUNSET AVE 54655 #056-06-1971 L1977 **FM** *020 †18

SOMERSET — SAINT CROIX

ADAMS, Beth Allison. 700 RIVARD ST, STILLWATER MED GROUP PA 54025 #026-04-1996 L2003 **FM** *020 †18
DEVAN, Douglas Gregory. ■ 54025 #056-05-1974 L1975 **GS TRS** *071 †85
SIKKINK, Jeffrey Lloyd. 700 RIVARD ST, STILLWATER MED GROUP PA 54025 #026-04-1981 L1988 **FM** *020 †18
ULLAND, Rolf Peter. 700 RIVARD ST, SOMERSET CLINIC 54025 #026-04-1975 L1981 **OBG** *020 †30

SOUTH MILWAUKEE — MILWAUKEE

BRUTVAN, Ferdinand M, II. 827 MICHIGAN AVE 53172 #056-05-1979 L1980 **DR** *020 †80
CHERAYIL, George D, Jr. 902 MILWAUKEE AVE 53172 #056-06-1994 L1995 **FM** *020 †18
FEDDERLY, Bradley Jay. 902 MILWAUKEE AVE, COVENANT MEDICAL GROUP 53172 #056-05-1985 L1989 **FM FPG** *020 †18
ISMAILI, Agron S.. 3611 S CHICAGO AVE 53172 #957-08-1991 L2006 **IM** *020 †20
MC FADDEN, Wayne Leland. ■ 53172 #038-40-1954 L1962 **FM PHP** *072
MITTAL, Ram Kishan. 902 MILWAUKEE AVE 53172 #495-03-1969 L1971 **GS VS** *020 †85
MUNOZ, David. 3611 S CHICAGO AVE, LAKESHORE MEDICAL CLINIC 53172 #042-03-1991 L1993 **FM** *020 †18
MURRAY, Jack Francis. 301 BROOKDALE DR 53172 #051-01-1948 L1950 **GS OS** *071
PATEL, Dixie Mafat. 3611 S CHICAGO AVE 53172 #056-06-2001 L2003 **FM** *020 †18
SCERPELLA, James John. 114 LAKE DR 53172 #308-11-1986 L1997 **FM** *020 †18
SCERPELLA, Rebecca L. 3611 S CHICAGO AVE 53172 #030-05-1996 L1998 **FM** *020 †18
SHET KANEKAR, Sangam Guru. ■ 53172 #496-15-1988 L2004 *100
SUREDDI, Sandhya. 902 MILWAUKEE AVE 53172 #495-99-1992 L1997 **IM** *020 †20

SPARTA — MONROE

ALBRECHT, Paul Gerhardt. 1522 S HIGHLAND DR 54656 #026-04-1960 L1961 **FM** *020 †18
ATKINS, Douglas Marshal. 310 W MAIN ST 54656 #056-05-1984 L1987 **FM** *020 †18
BRENNAN, John Thaddeus. 310 W MAIN ST, FAMILY PRACTICE CLINIC 54656 #056-05-1967 L1968 **IM FM** *020 †20
CHAMBERS, Peter R. 310 W MAIN ST, FRANCISCAN SKEMP HEALTHCAR 54656 #022-75-1999, ▲ L2000 **FM** *020 †18
DEGEN, Shane Jeffry. 315 W OAK ST, CLINIC 54656 #026-04-2004 L2007 **FM** *020 †18
JAIARJ, Parnjai. 218 W MAIN ST, BEHAVIORAL HEALTH SPARTA 54656 #891-02-1992 L1999 **CHP P** *020 †75
KRONER, Thomas Chas. ■ 54656 #028-34-1965 L1966 **P** *075
LOGAN, Laurie Ann. 310 W MAIN ST 54656 #016-11-1990 L1993 **FM** *020 †18
PACE, Michael Thos. 315 W OAK ST, CLINIC 54656 #018-03-1980 L1983 **FM** *020 †18
PATTERSON, Mark John. 315 W OAK ST, CLINIC 54656 #056-05-1990 L1991 **IM** *020 †20
SCHUMAKER, Howard Dale. 618 STELTING ST, SPARTA AREA AMBULANCE SERV 54656 #056-05-1991 L1992 **EM FM** *020 †18
THOMPSON, Gregory Paul. 315 W OAK ST, CLINIC 54656 #007-02-1987 L1988 **PUD CCM** *020 †20
TUMERMAN, Marc David. 310 W MAIN ST, FRANCISCAN SKEMP HEALTHCAR 54656 #016-45-1979 L1982 **FM** *020 †18
WARSING, Tracy Ann. 310 W MAIN ST, FRANCISCAN SKEMP HEALTHCAR 54656 #056-06-1999 L2000 **FM** *020 †18

WHITFORD, Steven William. 400 JEFFERSON AVE, CLINIC SPARTA 54656 #056-05-2000 L2004 OPH *020 †35

SPOONER – WASHBURN

BOHAC, Beverly Jean. 707 ASH ST 54801 #030-05-1980 L1983 FM *020 †18
BRAY, Bruce Edward. 707 ASH ST 54801 #018-03-1985 L1994 FM *020 †18
BRAY, Laura Boehlke. 707 ASH ST, DULUTH CLINIC - SPOONER 54801 #047-05-1985 L1995 FM *020 †18
CARLSON, Stephen John. 819 ASH ST, SPOONER HEALTH SYSTEM 54801 #016-06-1971 L1976 FM *020 †18
DANNER, Leah Anne. W7164 GREEN VALLEY RD, NORTHERN WATERS 54801 #056-05-1994 L1998 OPH *072
GOELLNER, Paul Godwin. 707 ASH ST 54801 #018-03-1972 L1974 FM *020 †18
HARPER, David Geo. W7164 GREEN VALLEY RD, NORTHERN WATERS 54801 #056-05-1963 L1965 OPH *020 †35
LA ROQUE, Chas Augustus. 1217 MICHIGAN ST 54801 #056-06-1981 L1982 FM *020
MATZKE, Rudolf Wm. 707 ASH ST 54801 #056-05-1954 L1955 FM *071 †18
PARKINSON, Katherine E. 114 TIMBERLANE RD, PARKINSON DERMATOLOGY 54801 #028-03-1989 L1995 D *020 †15
RECHSTEINER, Hans. N6142 LITTLE VALLEY RD 54801 #026-04-1977 L1978 GS *020 †85
SEEBER, Lisa Ann. 707 ASH ST, SPOONER CLINIC 54801 #054-04-1995 L2004 FM *020 †18
SNEED, Mark Wm. W7164 GREEN VALLEY RD, NORTHERN WATERS 54801 #026-04-1986 L1987 OPH *035
VAN ETTEN, Mark Aeppli. 707 ASH ST 54801 #018-03-1980 L1983 FM FPG *020 †18

SPRING GREEN – SAUK

GRAVES, Richard Harwood. E7859 MILL RD 53588 #017-20-1958 L1959 BBK GP *071
OSMAN, Hisham A. 156 W JEFFERSON ST, P O BOX 250 53588 #915-04-1988 L1996 FM *020 †18 ‡
RICHARDS, Christine Shaw. 150 E JEFFERSON ST 53588 #016-11-1997 L2000 FM *020 †18 ‡
RICHARDSON, Thomas Lee. 150 E JEFFERSON ST 53588 #056-05-1979 L1980 FM *020 †18
TIMMERMAN, Mark Gesner. 436 SUNRISE DR 53588 #026-08-1989 L1990 FM SME *020 †18
WERMUTH, Ellen Louise. 436 SUNRISE DR, RIVER VALLEY MEDICAL CLINI 53588 #016-11-1995 L1996 FM *020 †18
WOLPERT, Edward A. ■ 53588 #016-02-1960 L1973 P PYA *020 †75 ‡

SPRING VALLEY – PIERCE

SOLBERG, Norman Sigurd. ■ 54767 #026-04-1966 L1967 OBG *020 †30

STANLEY – CHIPPEWA

CASING, Myrna A. ■ 54768 #748-08-1968 L1975 FM *020
CASING, Roberto L. ■ 54768 #748-08-1968 L1975 GS *071
HAYWARD, Sharon Rose. 1120 PINE ST 54768 #025-07-1985 L1998 GS *020 †85
HEIDORN, Richard Gordon. 100 CORRECTIONS DR, STANLEY CORRECTIONAL INSTI 54768 #007-02-1964 L1978 GP *020 †18
LUXFORD, Betsy Ann. 100 CORRECTIONS DR, STANLEY CORRECTIONAL INSTI 54768 #051-01-1985 L1993 P *020 †75

STEVENS POINT – PORTAGE

AHMED, Mubashir. 824 ILLINOIS AVE, RICE MEDICAL CENTER 54481 #496-27-1996 L2002 HOS IM *020 †20
ALDINGER, Karl Dean. 824 ILLINOIS AVE 54481 #018-03-1966 L1972 OPH *071 †35
ALINEA, Augusto M. 500 VINCENT ST, STEVENS POINT 54481 #305-01-1986 L1991 AN *020 †05
ALMQUIST, John E. 824 ILLINOIS AVE, MINISTRY MEDICAL GROUP 54481 #056-06-1979 L1982 IM PUD *020 †20
ANDREWS, Ryan Michael. 824 ILLINOIS AVE 54481 #025-07-1997 L1998 FM *020 †18
ATKINSON, Paul Brian. ■ 54481 #056-05-2003 L2008 N *100
BANOVETZ, James M, Jr. 824 ILLINOIS AVE 54481 #016-06-1990 L1996 OSM ORS *020 †40
BARAKEH, Romeo Michel. 824 ILLINOIS AVE 54481 #605-03-2001 L2006 IM *071 †20
BEDELEY, Emmanuel Narh. 824 ILLINOIS AVE, MINISTRY MEDICAL GROUP 54481 #412-01-2002 L2006 IM *100 †20
BENN, William Herbert. 5409 VERN HOLMES DR 54481 #056-05-1984 L1985 FM *020 †18
BOEHM, Frederick Jos. 900 ILLINOIS AVE 54481 #016-45-1976 L1980 OBG *020 †30
BOERO, Joseph Francis. 824 ILLINOIS AVE, RICE MEDICAL CENTER 54481 #016-11-1983 L1992 IM *020 †20
BRAUN, Andrew Jos. 824 ILLINOIS AVE 54481 #056-05-1983 L1990 IM *020 †20
BRICK, Daniel Lee. 824 ILLINOIS AVE 54481 #056-05-1969 L1970 GP *020
BUCHL, Andrew Charles. 5409 VERN HOLMES DR, ASPIRUS STEVENS POINT CLIN 54481 #025-07-1998 L1999 FM *020 †18
BUTLER, James David. 900 ILLINOIS AVE 54481 #005-06-1973 L1979 EM *020 †18,16
CHANG, Fong-Chung. 900 ILLINOIS AVE 54481 #244-05-1968 L1983 AN *071
COTHRON, Anna Wilson. 520 VINCENT ST, ASPIRUS PSYCHIATRY 54481 #048-02-1991 L1996 P *020 †75
COTTER, Jonathan Joseph. 824 ILLINOIS AVE, RICE MEDICAL CENTER 54481 #654-21-2001 L2004 FM *020 †18
CURTIS, Michael Dougherty. 1701 FRANKLIN ST, STEVENS POINT FIRE DEPARTM 54481 #056-06-1989 L1992 EM *020 †16
DE WEERD, James Henry, Jr. ■ 54481 #036-05-1972 L1978 ORS *071 †40
DOTTI, Marco Claudio. 824 ILLINOIS AVE 54481 #561-03-1987 L2002 N SME *020 †75
DUNLAP, Roy John, II. 824 ILLINOIS AVE 54481 #026-04-1971 L1978 OTO *020 †45
ENERSON, David Earl. 900 ILLINOIS AVE 54481 #056-05-1968 L1971 DR *071 †80
ESKRITT, Nyles Richard. 3508 E MARIA DR 54481 #056-05-1966 L1969 D *020
FIAKPORNOO, Sylvanus Kwam. 900 ILLINOIS AVE, MINISTRY MEDICAL GROUP/ ST 54481 #412-01-2001 L2007 IM *020 †20
FOLDY, Seth Leonard. 900 ILLINOIS AVE 54481 #038-06-1982 L1996 FM *030 †18,70

FRIEDRICH, Robert Carl. ■ 54481 #056-06-1977 L1982 DR GP *020 †80
FULLER, John Robt. 500 VINCENT ST, STE D 54481 #018-03-1989 L1995 U *020 †95
GAUDER, John Paul. 824 ILLINOIS AVE 54481 #017-20-1973 L1974 IM IMG *020 †20
GIROD, Susan Jane. 3398 E MARIA DR, MINISTRY MEDICAL GROUP - P 54481 #017-20-1988 L2002 P PYG *020 †75
GRISWOLD, Stephen L. 900 ILLINOIS AVE 54481 #019-02-1976 L1980 IM *020 †20
GROOS, Jeanne Taccolini. 824 ILLINOIS AVE 54481 #025-07-1984 L1987 PD *020 †55
GUSE, Thomas Randall. 500 VINCENT ST 54481 #056-05-1988 L1995 ORS OSM *020 †40
HACKER, Philip Kearny. 1786 CLARICES CIR 54481 #021-01-1961 L1964 U *071 †95
HAGNESS, Dean Robt. 3301 STANLEY ST 54481 #056-06-1980 L1981 FM *020 †18
HAHN, Katharina Leonore. 824 ILLINOIS AVE 54481 #409-15-1992 L2001 FM *020 †18
HAHN, Terri A. 824 ILLINOIS AVE, RICE MEDICAL CENTER 54481 #056-06-1996 L1999 IM *020 †20
HARTER, Jerold Jamison. 3398 E MARIA DR 54481 #017-20-1988 L2002 P *020 †55
HARTKE, Raymond Louis. 5409 VERN HOLMES DR 54481 #038-40-1990 L1995 GE IM *020 †20
HEINS, Joanne Lynn. 1100 CENTERPOINT DR # 303, STEVENS POINT ANESTHE ASSO 54481 #665-01-2001 L2003 AN *020 †05
HETTLER, Gerhard Wm, III. 910 FREMONT ST 54481 #038-41-1969 L1972 GP *020
HOUTING, Thomas Vernon. 316 VINCENT ST 54481 #016-06-1988 L1989 OS *020
JACKSON, Lorraine H M. 3340 WHITING AVE, UNIT N 54481 #308-11-1987 L1992 ID *020 †20
JAEGER, Robert John. 824 ILLINOIS AVE, RICE MEDICAL CENTER 54481 #056-05-1971 L1972 OBG *020 †30 ‡
JAMISON, Lisa Marie. 824 ILLINOIS AVE 54481 #033-05-1986 L2001 OBG *020 †30
JARABEK, Joseph Frank. 824 ILLINOIS AVE 54481 #016-43-1971 L1976 IM IMG *020 †20
JEAN, Robert James. 824 ILLINOIS AVE 54481 #025-12-1975 L1983 GE IM *020 †20
JEWELL, Kay E. 23 PARK RIDGE DR 54481 #056-05-1979 L1980 IM IMG *030 †20
JOHNSON, Bradley Fred. 824 ILLINOIS AVE 54481 #056-05-1980 L1981 IM EM *020 †20,16
JOHNSON, Donald David. 2878 MAPLE RIDGE RD 54481 #048-04-1958 L1969 FM *071 †20
KASUKONIS, James Allan. 824 ILLINOIS AVE, RICE CLINIC 54481 #048-78-1986, ▲ L1990 PD *020 †55
KINSMAN, David Ignatius. 900 ILLINOIS AVE, ST. MICHAEL'S HOSPITAL 54481 #056-06-2001 L2003 AN *020 †05
KLASINSKI, Clarence A. 217 PRENTICE ST 54481 #016-43-1960 L1961 HS ORS *071 †40
KLASINSKI, Michele Mary. 500 VINCENT ST 54481 #056-06-1984 L1985 N *020 †75
KOCHIU, Naim Veliko. 900 ILLINOIS AVE 54481 #056-06-1997 L2001 IM *020 †05
KRAEGER, Daniel R. 824 ILLINOIS AVE 54481 #018-75-1987, ▲ L1992 FSM FM *020 †18
LEAHY, Maureen Anne. 817 WHITING AVE 54481 #056-06-1991 L1992 P *020 †75
LOCASCIO, Ronald Thos. 824 ILLINOIS AVE, MINISTRY MED GRP 54481 #308-03-1979 L1982 PD *020
LOCHER, Ralph Martin. 824 ILLINOIS AVE 54481 #306-01-1988 L1991 PD *020 †55
LOPEZ RUIZ, Juan B. 106 MCDILL AVE, MCDILL PROF BLDG 54481 #649-14-1971 L1980 PD *020 †55
MAGEE, Harry Jos. 3398 E MARIA DR, RICE MEDICAL CENTER 54481 #055-02-1983 L1999 CHP P *020 †75
MASON, Bruce Douglas. 900 ILLINOIS AVE 54481 #047-06-1965 L1986 PTH *071 †50
MAY, E Geo. 5466 HIGHLAND AVE 54481 #016-43-1963 L1970 OBG *020 †30
MC GINNIS, Kathleen Jean. 910 FREMONT ST, UNIV OF WISC STEVENS POINT 54481 #016-43-1975 L1976 FM GP *020 ‡
MC INTEE, Thomas Jos. 824 ILLINOIS AVE 54481 #024-01-1991 L1996 PD *020 †55
MILANO, Angelo. 3925 JORDAN LN 54481 #028-34-1955 L1963 PTH CLP *071 †50
MILLER, Herbert Payne, Jr. 900 ILLINOIS AVE 54481 #018-03-1954 L1966 PTH *071 †50
MILLER, James David. 900 ILLINOIS AVE 54481 #056-06-1965 L1966 GP *020
MUNCK, Paul Elroy. 824 ILLINOIS AVE 54481 #018-03-1983 L1989 IM *020 †20
NEUHOFF, Alfred Louis, Jr. 3301 STANLEY ST 54481 #018-03-1988 L1989 FM *020 †18
NOVINSKA, Brian David. 1100 CENTERPOINT DR # 303 54481 #035-45-1997 L2001 AN *020 †05
NUMSEN, Gene Harlan. 120 WILSHIRE BLVD N 54481 #016-06-1964 L1971 PD *071 †55
O'MALLEY, Thomas Patrick. 824 ILLINOIS AVE 54481 #033-06-1988 L1992 OPH *020 †35
ONGNA, Daniel Lawrence. 3140 STANLEY ST 54481 #056-05-1987 L1992 DR *020 †80
OO, Tin Nwe. 824 ILLINOIS AVE 54481 #209-01-2001 L2007 IM *020 †20
OO, Yin Htwe. 824 ILLINOIS AVE 54481 #209-01-2002 L2007 IM *020 †20
PERRY, David Alan. 900 ILLINOIS AVE, ST. MICHAELS HOSPITAL 54481 #026-04-1978 L1981 FM *020 †18
PICCONATTO, John Arthur. 5534 WOODLAND ST 54481 #056-06-1969 L1970 OBG *071 †30
POLOMIS, David Alan. 824 ILLINOIS AVE, MINISTRY MEDICAL GROUP 54481 #025-01-1989 L1992 PCC *012 †20
PRINGLE, David L. ■ 54481 #017-20-1963 L1969 NEP IM *071 †20
RAMESH, Chembu Vidyasagar. 824 ILLINOIS AVE 54481 #495-42-1988 L2004 IM *020
RAVE, Carol Sieck. 824 ILLINOIS AVE, RICE MEDICAL CENTER 54481 #048-04-1990 L1996 FM *020 †18
RAVE, Todd Alan. 824 ILLINOIS AVE 54481 #030-05-1991 L1996 N *020 †75
REED, Anne Marie. 824 ILLINOIS AVE, RICE MEDICAL CTR 54481 #046-01-1995 L1996 PD *020 †55 ‡
REZAZADEH, Hamied Reza. 900 ILLINOIS AVE 54481 #422-01-1987 L1990 ON HEM *020 †20
RIFLEMAN, Robert H. ■ 54481 #056-06-1952 L1954 EM *071
RIORDAN, Matthew Thos. 500 VINCENT ST 54481 #056-06-1987 L1991 ORS *020 †40
RUSEK, Jay John. 824 ILLINOIS AVE 54481 #056-06-1986 L1992 GS *020 †85
SANDER, Robert Wm. 824 ILLINOIS AVE, MINISTRY MEDICAL GROUP 54481 #017-20-1978 L1992 FM *040 †18
SCHIERL, Anne M Gilfry. 733 RIDGE RD 54481 #056-05-1957 L1958 AN GP *071
SCHLAIS, James Ray. 5409 VERN HOLMES DR 54481 #056-05-1983 L1988 GE IM *020 †20
SCHNEEBERGER, E Michael. 824 ILLINOIS AVE 54481 #056-05-1974 L1977 IM *020 †20
SCIARRONE, Francesco. 2517 PRAIS ST 54481 #028-34-1956 L1963 PTH *071 †50
SELWYN, Calvin A, Jr. 824 ILLINOIS AVE, DEPT OF SURGERY 54481 #026-04-1997 L1998 GS *020 †85
SEVENICH, James Robt. 1324 4TH AVE 54481 #056-06-1955 L1956 GP OBG *071
SHAW, Henry Hastings. 824 ILLINOIS AVE 54481 #649-14-1969 L1974 FM *020 †18
SHEWMAKE, Karl Eric. 824 ILLINOIS AVE 54481 #056-05-1976 L1979 N NP *020 †75
SIMONS, Shiloh A. 824 ILLINOIS AVE, MINISTRY MEDICAL GROUP 54481 #005-76-1999, ▲ L2004 OPH *020
SIMPSON, Richard Emery. 3410 STANLEY ST, RADIOLOGY FOND DU LAC LTD 54481 #025-07-1995 L2000 DR *020 †80
SLEZAK, Steven Jay. 824 ILLINOIS AVE 54481 #016-01-1997 L2001 OPH *020 †35
SMYTH, Rose Louise. 900 ILLINOIS AVE, SAINT MICHAEL'S HOSPITAL 54481 #060-02-1987 L1995 FM EM *020 †18

SOROKA, Paul Z. ■ 54481 #056-06-1977 L1985 **FM OBG** *020 †18
SOWKA, Albin Jos. 900 ILLINOIS AVE 54481 #016-43-1947 L1954 **GS GP** *071 †85
SULLIVAN, William John. 824 ILLINOIS AVE 54481 #056-06-1974 L1988 **P GP** *020 †75
SWISHER, Nancy K. 824 ILLINOIS AVE, MINISTRY MEDICAL CENTER 54481 #048-02-1998 L2001 **FM** *020 †18
THIELMAN, Michael James. 824 ILLINOIS AVE 54481 #030-06-1995 L1996 **OTO** *020 †45
TIESZEN, Myles Eldon. 824 ILLINOIS AVE 54481 #046-01-1989 L2006 **GS** *020 †85
TREMBLE, Luke Jonathon. 824 ILLINOIS AVE, RICE MEDICAL CENTER 54481 #056-06-1999 L2000 **PD** *020 †55
VO-HILL, Hien T. 824 ILLINOIS AVE, RICE MEDICAL CENTER 54481 #056-05-1998 L1999 **OBG** *020 †30
WADINA, Mark Stephen. 3410 STANLEY ST, ST MICHAELS HOSPITAL 54481 #056-06-1990 L1991 **DR RNR** *020 †80
WANG, Kei-Chia. 900 ILLINOIS AVE 54481 #244-05-1969 L1986 **AN GS** *100
WEISER, Jennifer Isabel. 824 ILLINOIS AVE 54481 #056-05-2002 L2006 **PD** *020 †55
WILLIAMS, Todd Martin. 824 ILLINOIS AVE, RICE MEDICAL CENTER 54481 #056-05-1993 L1998 **ORS** *020 †40
YOUNG, Christopher Arthur. 5409 VERN HOLMES DR 54481 #038-45-1983 L1984 **GE IM** *020 †20
YOUNG, Jessica Katherine. 824 ILLINOIS AVE 54481 #056-05-1997 L2002 **IM** *020 †20
YOUNG, Marc Andrew. 824 ILLINOIS AVE, DEPT OF SURG 54481 #056-05-1997 L2002 **GS** *020 †85
ZACH, James Robt. 900 ILLINOIS AVE 54481 #056-05-1976 L1977 **FM D** *020 †18 ‡

STODDARD — VERNON

SEAGER, Glenn Marvin. ■ 54658 #050-02-1959 L1969 **OTO** *071 †45

STONE LAKE — SAWYER

EASTWOOD, Elton Bayard. ■ 54876 #056-05-1954 L1992 **IM** *071
HAESEMEYER, Allan Jay. 16887 2ND ST S 54876 #019-02-1978 L1981 **FM** *020 †18
MC KICHAN, John Malcolm. 16719 SISSABAGAMA RD 54876 #056-05-1969 L1971 **FM** *020 †18
RIEMER, Donald Eugene. 16887 2ND ST S, STONE LAKE MEDICAL CLINIC 54876 #056-05-1966 L1967 **FM** *020 †18
SODETZ, Richard Alan. ■ 54876 #016-11-1969 L1970 **ORS** *071 †40

STOUGHTON — DANE

AGNI, Guirish. 225 CHURCH ST 53589 #495-45-1983 L1995 **IM** *020 †20
BERESKY, Ronald E. 225 CHURCH ST, STOUGHTON CLINIC 53589 #010-02-1981 L1989 **GS** *020 †85
BREHM, Joyce Marie. 225 CHURCH ST 53589 #056-05-1981 L1984 **IM** *020 †20
ECCLES, Deanne Kay. 225 CHURCH ST 53589 #056-05-1994 L1998 **FM** *020 †20
GRAEBNER, Robert Wm. 900 RIDGE ST 53589 #056-05-1968 L1969 **N CN** *071 †75 ‡
HANSON, Meghan Elizabeth. ■ 53589 #056-05-2006 L2008 **DR** *012
HILL, Richard Wayne. 225 CHURCH ST 53589 #056-05-1973 L1975 **FM** *020 †18
KHALID, Ahsan. 100 SILVERADO DR, STOUGHTON CLINIC 53589 #704-21-1992 L2005 **IM** *020 †20
KOKX, Bryan Dayfield. 1115 VIRGIN LAKE DR 53589 #047-05-1997 L2003 **IM** *020 †20
KRESGE, Dean Grant. 225 CHURCH ST, DEAN CLINIC 53589 #056-05-1983 L1984 **FM** *020 †18 ‡
LANSER, Mark Edward. 225 CHURCH ST 53589 #056-05-1986 L1990 **N** *020 †75
LUY, Enrique W. 900 RIDGE ST 53589 #748-10-1965 L1976 **GP UCM** *071
MC MULLIN, Bradford W. ■ 53589 #067-01-1972 L1979 **FM PD** *020
MEANS, Anne Catherine. 100 SILVERADO DR 53589 #018-03-1988 L1989 **PD** *020 †55
MURWIN, Thomas James. 225 CHURCH ST 53589 #056-05-1991 L1992 **PD** *020 †55
NELSON, David Leroy. 225 CHURCH ST 53589 #026-04-1963 L1966 **FM** *020
PAIK, Woo Chun Whang. ■ 53589 #583-03-1956 L1978 **PD** *071 †55
PETERSON, Rodney K. ■ 53589 #056-05-1940 L1941 **FM AM** *020
RHOADES, Erin Megann. 611 S ACADEMY ST 53589 #050-02-1996 L2001 **FM** *020 †18
RILLING, Richard G. 225 CHURCH ST 53589 #056-05-1992 L1993 **ORS** *020 †40
ROBBINS, Kenneth Ian. 900 RIDGE ST 53589 #025-01-1977 L1982 **P IM** *020 †20,75
SCHAMMEL, Francis Michael. 225 CHURCH ST, DEAN MEDICAL CENTER 53589 #016-11-1954 L1957 **FM** *071 †18
SHAH, Meetul. 225 CHURCH ST 53589 #016-11-1998 L2005 **FM** *020 †18
WELCH, Stanley Weldon. 900 RIDGE ST, STOUGHTON HOSPITAL 53589 #016-42-1990 L1998 **EM** *020 †16

STRATFORD — MARATHON

KRUEGER, Kori Kal. 101 S WISCONSIN AVE, STRATFORD CENTER 54484 #056-05-1999 L2000 **MPD** *020 †20,55
SHULMAN, Karen Ann. 101 S WISCONSIN AVE, STRATFORD CENTER 54484 #065-06-1993 L1998 **FM** *020 †18

STRUM — TREMPEALEAU

EDSON, Jack Dee. RR 1 BOX 200 54770 #056-05-1957 L1958 **P** *071
VOSMEK, Josef Fredrick. 106 5TH AVE N 54770 #056-05-1964 L1969 **FM** *020 †18

STURGEON BAY — DOOR

ALZUHN-HANSEN, Leslie Kay. 323 S 18TH AVE 54235 #056-06-1998 L2002 **OBG** *020 †30
ANTONIO, Maria Chona Segi. 323 S 18TH AVE 54235 #748-08-1988 L2005 **FM** *020 †18
BECK, John Jay. 323 S 18TH AVE 54235 #016-06-1965 L1966 **FM** *020 †18
BOARD, Paul Steven. 323 S 18TH AVE 54235 #016-11-1982 L2008 **ADM** *020 †18
BORGNES, Erik Mathew. 228 S 18TH AVE, ADVANCED IMAGING 54235 #025-07-1992 L1993 **DR** *020 †80

BOYD, Joseph David. 421 NEBRASKA ST, DOOR CNTY DEPT COMM PROGRM 54235 #016-11-1963 L2002 **P** *030 †75
BROOK, Jeffrey J, Jr. 323 S 18TH AVE 54235 #016-06-1951 L1951 **FM FPG** *072 †18
BRUNO, Michael Stephen. 323 S 18TH AVE 54235 #056-05-1990 L1994 **AN** *020 †05
BRYANT, Frederick Wm. ■ 54235 #025-01-1948 L1949 **OPH** *071 †35
BUTLER, Karen Lind. 1009 EGG HARBOR RD STE 113 54235 #305-01-2000 L2001 **FM OM** *020 ‡
CONGER, David Glenn. 1910 ALABAMA ST 54235 #017-20-1970 L1974 **IM** *020 †20
DAVIS, Steven Scott. 323 S 18TH AVE, NORTH SHORE MEDICAL CLINIC 54235 #021-06-1987 L2003 **ORS** *020 †40
DEMPSTER, Dorene E. 323 S 18TH AVE 54235 #025-12-1990 L1994 **OBG** *020 †30
DOWNING, Edwin Lee. PO BOX 806 54235 #041-02-1964 L1977 **OPH** *071 †35
ECKSTROM, Philip Truman. ■ 54235 #025-01-1965 L1968 **OS EM** *071
FENTON, Sarah Hack. 323 S 18TH AVE 54235 #025-07-1988 L1998 **CD** *020 †20
FINCK, Martin. 323 S 18TH AVE 54235 #396-08-1988 L1994 **AN** *020 †05
FOSTER, William James. 30 N 18TH AVE, STE 7 54235 #025-01-1969 L1977 **OPH** *020 †35
FUCHS, Matthias Arthur. 323 S 18TH AVE 54235 #056-05-1974 L1976 **CD IM** *020 †20
GLOSS, Frank Edward. 133 S 16TH PL 54235 #056-05-1976 L1980 **ORS** *020 †40
GREAVES, Alison J Ash. ■ 54235 #016-11-1962 L1979 **OM PD** *071 †55
HAMMOND, Susan Elisabeth. 1910 ALABAMA ST, AURORA HEALTHCARE 54235 #056-06-1998 L2003 **FM** *020 †18
HARRIS, Kurt Gene. 228 S 18TH AVE 54235 #018-03-1987 L1997 **DR** *020 †80
HERLACHE, John Lawrence. 5258 BUFFALO RIDGE TRL 54235 #056-05-1968 L1969 **GS** *071 †85
HICKEY, C Hugh. 345 S 18TH AVE, FRANK E GLOSS MD 54235 #056-05-1948 L1954 **OFA** *072 †40
HOGAN, Richard Anthony. 323 S 18TH AVE 54235 #016-01-1978 L1993 **IM PUD** *020 †20
JENNY, Donald Benj. 323 S 18TH AVE 54235 #028-34-1976 L1979 **CD IM** *020 †20
JOHNSON, Rory Michael. 323 S 18TH AVE 54235 #037-01-1998 L1999 **FM** *020 †18 ‡
KELLER, Sarah June. 323 S 18TH AVE, DOOR COUNTY MEMORIAL HOSPI 54235 #023-01-2002 L2002 **IM** *020 †20
KIM, David Dououk. 30 N 18TH AVE, STE 7 54235 #016-43-1990 L1991 **OPH** *020 †35
KRUEGER, Roderick Waldo. ■ 54235 #056-05-1972 L1980 **NPM** *020 †55
LEWIS, James Michael. 323 S 18TH AVE 54235 #056-06-1966 L1967 **FM** *071 †18 ‡
MARTENS, Sandra Isabel. 323 S 18TH AVE, NORTH SHORE MEDICAL CLINIC 54235 #409-16-1993 L1998 **FM** *020 †18
MC CORMACK, Francis X. 323 S 18TH AVE, EMERGENCY DEPARTMENT 54235 #016-11-1987 L2004 **FM** *020 †18
MELARVIE, Shaun J. 1843 MICHIGAN ST 54235 #037-01-1989 L1994 **GS GE** *020 †85
MERKIN, Donald H. ■ 54235 #649-33-1978 L1988 **IM** *020
MILLER, Anne. 421 NEBRASKA ST 54235 #038-44-1990 L2005 **P PYG** *020 †75
MURRAY, Richard Cleary. ■ 54235 #056-06-1957 L1958 **OBG** *071 †30
NELL, Patricia Ann. ■ 54235 #018-03-1960 L1969 **AI PD** *062 †55,03
NELSON, Charles Eugene. 1910 ALABAMA ST 54235 #016-01-1995 L1996 **FM OBS** *020 †18
NELSON, Ralph B. 323 S 18TH AVE 54235 #016-76-2001, ▲ L2002 **IM** *020
NUTT, Richard Leverne. 323 S 18TH AVE 54235 #045-01-1972 L2001 **ORS** *020 †40
PAT, Ileana Margareta. 323 S 18TH AVE, NORTH SHORE MEDICAL CLINIC 54235 #781-01-1983 L2001 **IM END** *020 †20
PATHAKJEE, Bharat Y. 323 S 18TH AVE 54235 #495-23-1971 L1979 **CD** *020 †20
REITZ, Kelton J. 323 S 18TH AVE 54235 #025-76-1992, ▲ L2005 **IM** *020 †20
ROENNING, George Harlan. 323 S 18TH AVE 54235 #033-06-1976 L1977 **FM** *020 †18
ROWE, Donald M. ■ 54235 #056-06-1951 L1952 **OM** *071
ROWE, Thomas Michael. 323 S 18TH AVE 54235 #056-06-1983 L1984 **OBG** *075
SAYEGH, Kamil Nadim. 323 S 18TH AVE, DOOR COUNTY MEMORIAL HOSPI 54235 #605-01-1995 L2005 **PDC** *020 †55
SCHEER, Kurtis D. 1843 MICHIGAN ST 54235 #037-01-1992 L1993 **GS** *072 †85
SCHLISE, Sally Marion. 323 S 18TH AVE, DOOR COUNTY CANCER CTR 54235 #056-05-1976 L1978 **RO** *020
SCHUEPPERT, Thomas Wm. ■ 54235 #056-06-1971 L1973 **ORS** *071 †40
SHUTT, Charles Brian. 323 S 18TH AVE, 188 LILIA PL 54235 #019-02-1982 L1990 **OBG** *020 †30
STAMPFL, Connie Lynette. 323 S 18TH AVE 54235 #056-05-1987 L1990 **EM** *020 †16
THALER, Diane. 33 GREEN BAY RD 54235 #056-05-1979 L1980 **D** *020 †15
THEADO, Matthew R. 323 S 18TH AVE 54235 #056-06-1995 L1998 **PD** *020 †55
VERMA, Rahul. 323 S 18TH AVE 54235 #495-90-1988 L2002 **CD** *020 †20
WAGENER, Nicholas Roger. 323 S 18TH AVE 54235 #056-05-1957 L1962 **GP** *072
WAKE, Joan Peddie. 1910 ALABAMA ST 54235 #025-01-1969 L1980 **FM ADL** *071
WEINSHEL, Steven Saml. 323 S 18TH AVE 54235 #056-06-1983 L1984 **NS** *020 †25
WIENKERS, Kevin Paul. 30 N 18TH AVE, 7 BUILDING 54235 #056-05-1981 L1984 **OPH** *020 †35
WITMER, William Timothy. 1910 ALABAMA ST 54235 #047-05-1988 L1989 **CD** *020 †20

STURTEVANT — RACINE

CATALDI, Christopher Vinc. ■ 53177 #665-01-2003 L2007 **FM** *020
KEEGAN, John A. 1837 COUNTY ROAD V 53177 #018-75-1995, ▲ L1999 **OBG** *020
SKUPNIEWICZ, Raymond E. 8311 16TH ST, SC JOHNSON WAX 53177 #056-05-1955 L1956 **OM** *071 †18

SUAMICO — BROWN

WINICK, Jeffrey P. 3058 HARBOR WINDS DR 54173 #035-20-1979 L2007 **OPH** *020 †35 ‡

SUN PRAIRIE — DANE

AUGHEY, Michael John. 10 TOWER DR 53590 #056-05-1993 L1996 **FM** *020 †18
COERT, Lesley Anne. 1270 W MAIN ST 53590 #056-06-2000 L2005 **FM** *020 †18
DELANY, Christina Marie. 10 TOWER DR 53590 #016-42-2001 L2005 **OPH** *020 †35
EDWARDS, Robert Zachary. 1270 W MAIN ST 53590 #018-03-2000 L2002 **FM** *020 †18
GINDLESBERGER, Danielle R. 10 TOWER DR 53590 #025-12-2004 L2005 **FM** *020 †18
GREEN, Ray Edward. ■ 53590 #056-05-1945 L1946 **OS AN** *071 †05
HALE, Christine L. 855 DUNCANNON WAY 53590 #016-01-1993 L2003 **FM** *020 †18
HARTUNG, Kent Burdair. 1270 W MAIN ST 53590 #018-03-1982 L1992 **FM** *020 †18
HAWKINS, John Gary. 1270 W MAIN ST 53590 #056-05-2002 L2005 **FM** *020 †18

KINNUNEN, Nina Marieanne. 10 TOWER DR, DEAN CLINIC 53590 #056-05-1999 L2000 **FM** *020 †18 ‡

KORNAUS, Paul Alvin. 10 TOWER DR, SUN PRARIE CLINIC 53590 #056-05-1979 L1981 **FM PRS** *020 †18

KRUBSACK, Arnold Jos. ■ 53590 #056-05-1981 L1982 **NM FM** *071 †28

LANE, Nicholas Charles. 10 TOWER DR 53590 #007-02-1999 L2000 **CHP** *020 †75

MEHTA, Cynthia Lee. 3527 SWANSEE RDG, 3527 SWANSEE RIDGE 53590 #046-01-1993 L1994 **D** *020 †15

MICHELS, Eileen Carol. 10 TOWER DR 53590 #056-05-1993 L1994 **FM** *020 †18

MOTL, Gregory H. 10 TOWER DR 53590 #016-45-1980 L1981 **IM IMG** *020 †20

NEWQUIST, Michele Lynn. 10 TOWER DR 53590 #016-11-2000 L2004 **IM** *020 †20

NOSAL, James Martin. 10 TOWER DR 53590 #016-01-1984 L1987 **FM** *020 †18

OWEN, Natalie Ann. 10 TOWER DR 53590 #065-10-1978 L1983 **FM** *020 †18

QUEOFF, David Wm. 1270 W MAIN ST, UNIVERSITY OF WI MADISON D 53590 #056-05-1991 L1992 **FM** *020 †18

RAM, Sumita. 10 TOWER DR, SUN PRAIRIE CLINIC 53590 #038-40-1990 L2006 **PD** *020 †55

RUSSELL, William Timothy. ■ 53590 #056-05-1946 L1947 *071

SCHMIDT, Paul Luther. 10 TOWER DR 53590 #028-03-1974 L1975 **FM** *020 †18

SCHUG, Leo A. 10 TOWER DR 53590 #056-05-1992 L1996 **IM** *020 †20

SELFRIDGE, Nancy Jane. 1270 W MAIN 53590 #016-45-1979 L1982 **FM** *075

SYTY, Joseph. ■ 53590 #056-05-1959 L1960 **FM GP** *071

TAYLOR, Joanne Jensen. 10 TOWER DR 53590 #056-05-1985 L1986 **PD** *020 †55

THOMAS, Stephen Chas. 10 TOWER DR 53590 #035-08-1975 L1978 **FM** *020 †18

WEBER, David Lee. 10 TOWER DR 53590 #038-41-1974 L1975 **FM** *071 †18

WILLIAMS, Lisa Ann. ■ 53590 #056-05-2008 *012

ZENNER, Tyler Dean. 10 TOWER DR 53590 #026-04-1998 L2001 **FM** *020 †18

SUPERIOR – DOUGLAS

ALBIN, Glenn. 3500 TOWER AVE, SMHS DULUTH CLINIC-SUPERIO 54880 #048-04-1983 L1986 **CD IM** *020 †20

ANDERSEN, Steven Lynn. 3500 TOWER AVE, ST. MARY'S HOSPITAL OF SUP 54880 #026-04-1982 L2001 **FM** *020 †18

AVELLO, Waldo L. 109 N 28TH ST E, MARINER MEDICAL CLINIC 54880 #033-06-1978 L2002 **GE IM** *020 †20

BAMBENEK, Gregory Peter. 39 N 25TH ST E 54880 #026-04-1974 L1980 **P** *020 †75

BAUER, Steven James. 39 N 25TH ST E 54880 #026-04-1990 L1991 **CHP** *020 †75

BERNADINO, Kirk Patrick. 3500 TOWER AVE, SUPERIOR CLINIC 54880 #050-02-1998 L2005 **GE** *100 †20

BONNER, Wendell Rhett. 3500 TOWER AVE, ST MARY'S HOSPITAL OF SUPE 54880 #026-04-1995 L1997 **FM** *020 †18

CABOT, Daniel T. 3500 TOWER AVE, SMHS DULUTH CLINIC SUPERIO 54880 #028-79-1999, ▲ L2007 **FM** *020 †18

DEUTSCH, John Christopher. 3500 TOWER AVE, DULUTH CLINIC SUPERIOR 54880 #056-05-1980 L2000 **GE HO** *020 †20

DOBIS, James Henry. 3520 TOWER AVE 54880 #026-04-1974 L1975 **FM** *020 †18

EDGERTON, Bradley Craig. 3500 TOWER AVE, ST. MARY'S HOSPITAL SUPER 54880 #007-02-1983 L1994 **ORS** *020 †40

ERICKSON, Robert Victor. 3500 TOWER AVE, SMHS DULUTH CLINIC - SUPER 54880 #026-04-1984 L1993 **GE IM** *020 †20

EYER, Steven Duane. 3500 TOWER AVE, DULUTH CLINIC-SUPERIOR 54880 #016-42-1977 L1985 **OS GS** *050 †85

FROEHLING, Rodney Chas. 3500 TOWER AVE 54880 #030-05-1971 L1980 **PTH** *071 †50

GALLITO, Amida Tirol. 3520 TOWER AVE, TWIN PORTS VA CLNC 54880 #748-11-1991 L1999 **FM** *020 †18 ‡

GILDERSLEEVE, John Wm. 3500 TOWER AVE 54880 #056-05-1967 L1968 **AN** *020 †05

GINETE, Wilson. 3500 TOWER AVE, SUPERIOR CLINIC 54880 #748-11-1991 L2005 **IC** *020 †20

GLICK, John Wm. 39 N 25TH ST E 54880 #026-04-1987 L1988 **P** *020 †75

GREGORY, James Paul. 3500 TOWER AVE, SUPERIOR CLINIC 54880 #030-05-1985 L2007 **AN** *020 †05

HANSON, Allen Stuart. 3500 TOWER AVE, ST MARY'S HOSPITAL OF SUPE 54880 #056-05-1976 L1979 **FM** *020 †18

HANSON, David J. 3500 TOWER AVE, ST. MARY'S HOSP. OF SUPERI 54880 #037-01-1998 L2004 **AN** *020 †05

HANSTEIN, Conrad Georg. 3500 TOWER AVE 54880 #654-01-1998 L1999 **EM FM** *020 †18

HOLLIDAY, George Francis. 3500 TOWER AVE, SMHS DULUTH CLINIC - SUPER 54880 #026-04-1994 L1996 **MPD** *020 †20,55

HUSSEIN, Ahmad D. ■ 54880 #575-01-1982 L1994 **GS** *020

JAMES, Claudia Ann. 2501 N 22ND ST 54880 #025-07-1978 L1981 **FM PTH** *020 †50,18

JOHNSON, Randall L. 820 N 22ND ST 54880 #026-04-1964 L1984 **IM** *020 †20

KIRBY, David J. 109 N 28TH ST E 54880 #063-01-1978 L1988 **FM OBG** *020 †18

KONOWALCHUK, Brian Keith. 3500 TOWER AVE, SMHS DULUTH CLINIC SUPERIO 54880 #026-04-2000 L2006 **GPM** *020 †70

KULKARNI, Suresh. 3500 TOWER AVE 54880 #495-21-1985 L2002 **IM** *020 †20

LAO, Antonio Lim. 3500 TOWER AVE 54880 #748-10-1970 L1975 **IM** *020

MATACZYNSKI, Robt Raymond. 3500 TOWER AVE 54880 #056-05-1955 L1956 **FM** *072 †18

MC LEAN, Joseph Allen. 109 N 28TH ST E 54880 #005-12-1982 L1989 **FM** *020 †18

MITTELSTADT, Paul Everett. 3500 TOWER AVE, ST MARY'S HOSPITAL OF SUPE 54880 #026-04-1979 L1984 **EM FM** *020 †18,16

MONGE, James Jos. 3500 TOWER AVE 54880 #016-06-1955 L1999 **GS VS** *071 †85

MOREHOUSE, Joseph Davis. 3500 TOWER AVE, SMDC SUPERIOR 54880 #010-02-1990 L1999 **OPH AM** *020 †35

MULLINS, Daniel John. 3500 TOWER AVE, DULUTH CLINIC-SUPERIOR 54880 #041-13-1991 L2003 **DR** *020 †80

MUNDHENKE, Jeffrey Alan. 3500 TOWER AVE, ST. MARY'S HOSPITAL - SUPE 54880 #046-01-1984 L2003 **AN** *020 †05

NEWMAN, Douglas James. 3500 TOWER AVE 54880 #025-07-1982 L1990 **FM** *020 †18

OKORO, Robert Ugwu. 3500 TOWER AVE, ST MARY'S HOSPITAL OF SUPE 54880 #690-04-1994 L2004 **FM** *020

PETERSON, Craig Norman. 3500 TOWER AVE, ST. MARY'S HOSP. OF SUPERI 54880 #026-04-1998 L2003 **AN** *020 †05

PETERSON, Steven Frank. 3500 TOWER AVE 54880 #026-04-1985 L1990 **FM** *020 †18 ‡

PIERPONT, Robert Bruce. 3500 TOWER AVE, SUPERIOR CLINIC 54880 #026-04-1989 L1990 **FM** *020 †18

RAVN, Erling Oscar, Jr. 50 BILLINGS DR 54880 #056-06-1954 L1955 **GS GP** *071

RICHARDS, Joseph Van. 3500 TOWER AVE, SUPERIOR CLINIC 54880 #056-05-1988 L1989 **FM FSM** *020 †18

ROVA, Nancy Louise. 3500 TOWER AVE, SMHS DULUTH CLINIC SUPERIO 54880 #026-04-1991 L2007 **FM** *020 †20

RUBIN, Timothy Alan. 3500 TOWER AVE, SMHS DULUTH CLINIC -SUPERI 54880 #026-04-1993 L2002 **GE** *020 †20

RYAN, Edward Anthony. 1419 HILL AVE, HEALTH CARE CENTER 54880 #056-06-1957 L1958 **CD IM** *071 †20

SARACINO, Margaret Mary. 39 N 25TH ST E 54880 #026-04-1990 L1999 **CHP P** *020 †75

SCOTT, C Malcolm. 3500 TOWER AVE 54880 #056-05-1962 L1963 **FM** *071 †18

SHARMA, Sarojini. 3500 TOWER AVE, STE 1 54880 #495-08-1990 L1994 **IM FM** *020 †20

STEPHENSON, Jon Chas. 109 N 28TH ST E 54880 #026-04-1976 L1977 **FM** *020 †18

SUDOH, Ann Caroline. 3500 TOWER AVE, DULUTH CLINIC-SUPERIOR 54880 #026-04-1997 L2001 **FM** *020 †18

SUTHERLAND, Steven John. 39 N 25TH ST E 54880 #026-08-1991 L1992 **CHP P** *020 †75

SWENSON, Sonja Ursula. 109 N 28TH ST E, MARINER CLINIC 54880 #026-04-1999 L2001 **FM** *020 †18

VUJKOVIC, Sinisa. 3500 TOWER AVE, SUPERIOR CLINIC 54880 #957-01-1997 L2003 **IM** *020 †20

YOON, John Sukhoon. 109 N 28TH ST E, C/O MARINER MED CLINIC 54880 #025-01-1987 L1994 **OPH** *020 †35

SUSSEX – WAUKESHA

ABAD-SANTOS, Jose Singson. W227N6103 SUSSEX RD 53089 #748-02-1991 L1993 **PD** *020 †55

AUNE, Carter Allen. N64W24086 MAIN ST 53089 #056-06-2000 L2002 **FM** *020 †18

BUONO, Gina Marie. N57W24950 N CORPORATE CIR 53089 #035-03-1985 L1998 **OM IM** *020

FRISVOLD, James M. W227N6103 SUSSEX RD 53089 #016-76-1979, ▲ L1980 **GP** *020

JOHNSON, Julie. N57W24950 N CORPORATE CIR 53089 #056-05-1983 L1984 **DR** *020 †80

LENTZNER, Alan Neil. N57W24950 N CORPORATE CIR 53089 #051-07-1993 L2002 **PTH HMP** *020

LUCKEY, William Thos. N57W24950 N CORPORATE CIR 53089 #017-20-1957 L1958 **P DR** *071 †75,80 ‡

MC ELROY, Kimberly Lynne. W227N6103 SUSSEX RD 53089 #056-06-1990 L1991 **PD** *020 †55

RAND, Scott Douglas. N57W24950 N CORPORATE CIR 53089 #005-11-1988 L1995 **RNR** *020 †80

RYPKEMA, David John. ■ 53089 #016-43-1991 L1992 **AN** *020 †05

SHEETS, Lynn Kathleen. ■ 53089 #019-02-1983 L2005 **PD** *020 †55 ‡

SMITH, Cathy Cleone. W227N6103 SUSSEX RD 53089 #038-40-1975 L1994 **IM** *020 †20

STRICKROOT, Rick Lawton. N 57 W 24950 N CORPOR CIRL 53089 #028-34-1996 L2000 **FM** *020 †18

URLAKIS, Kenneth J, Jr. N57W24950 N CORPORATE CIR 53089 #056-06-1994 L1995 **FM** *020 †18

WEISGERBER, Jennifer M. N57W24950 N CORPORATE CIR 53089 #056-06-1999 L2002 **FM** *020 †18

THIENSVILLE – OZAUKEE

BREHM, Donna Jo. 216 GREEN BAY RD, STE 201 53092 #056-05-1985 L1990 **P CHP** *020 †75

DIETRICH, Thomas Jeffrey. 250 ELM ST, THIENSVILE FIRE DEPT 53092 #041-14-1996 L2002 **EM** *020 †16

HERMAN, Bruce Chas. 407 N MAIN ST 53092 #056-06-1977 L1978 **IM IMG** *020 †20 ‡

KARLIN, Henry Robert. PO BOX 637 53092 #056-06-1958 L1959 **AI** *020 †03

KEVICH, Nevenka T. ■ 53092 #957-02-1961 L1974 **AN** *071

LEWIS, Gary Stephen. 140 S MAIN ST, THIENSVILLE FAMILY HEALTH 53092 #836-01-1982 L1992 **FM** *020 †18

LORD, Guy Russell. 216 GREEN BAY RD 201 53092 #036-07-1970 L1977 **CHP P** *020 †75

STEINHAUS, Brian Thos. 216 GREEN BAY RD, STE 201 53092 #056-06-1966 L1967 **P OS** *020

STEINHAUS, Lyndon K. PO BOX 127, 216 N GREEN BAY RD # 201 53092 #422-01-1988 L1990 **P CHP** *020

VOGT, Wess Richard. 216 GREEN BAY RD, STE 201 53092 #056-06-1965 L1966 **P** *020 †75

ZAIDI, Syed Tahawar A. 108 W IRONWOOD LN 53092 #704-25-1995 L1998 **CD** *020 †20

THORP – CLARK

ALISKY, Joseph Martin. 704 S CLARK ST, MARSHFIELD CLINIC-THORP CE 54771 #028-34-1996 L2002 **FPG** *020 †20

CHERTKOVA, Elena Lvovna. 704 S CLARK ST 54771 #913-01-1994 L2001 **FM** *020 †18

LOOZE, Thomas Edward. 704 S CLARK ST 54771 #056-05-1983 L1984 **IM** *020 †20

THREE LAKES – ONEIDA

PFEFFERKORN, Ethan Dolf. ■ 54562 #056-05-1957 L1958 **GP** *071

TIGERTON – SHAWANO

WEISFLOCK, Cynthia Jean. 110 SPAULDING ST 54486 #056-05-1981 L1982 **FM** *020 †18

TOMAH – MONROE

AHN, Richard. 500 E VETERANS ST 54660 #583-01-1965 L1977 **ADL PTH** *020

AKHTAR, Naheed. 500 E VETERANS ST BLDG 408, TOMAH VA HOSPITAL 54660 #704-06-1988 L2000 **P** *020 †75

BABCOCK, Steven Wm. 1330 N SUPERIOR AVE 54660 #041-01-1959 L1963 **IM IMG** *020

BATEMAN, William Dudley. 500 E VETERANS ST 54660 #017-20-1975 L1979 **FM GP** *020

BERRY, John Frederick. 500 E VETERANS ST, VAMC-TOMAH 54660 #016-11-1982 L1994 **PM** *020 †60

■ = Address Information Privacy Protected

BUAN, Rolando Ramos. 1330 N SUPERIOR AVE, GUNDERSEN LUTHERAN-TOMAH C 54660 #748-08-1965 L1975 **GS** *020

CAVANESS, Jeffrey Scott. 325 BUTTS AVE 54660 #026-08-1996 L1999 **FM** *020 †18 ‡

CHU, Ming. 500 E VETERANS ST 54660 #638-01-1945 L1970 **IM** *020

COFFEY, John. 500 E VETERANS ST, VA MEDICAL CENTER 54660 #016-11-1998 L2001 **FM** *020 †18

CONWAY, Alan David. 1330 N SUPERIOR AVE, CLINIC 54660 #016-11-1997 L2006 **FM** *020 †18

DEMING, James Roy. 325 BUTTS AVE 54660 #056-05-1982 L1985 **FM** *020 †18

ERDMAN, Rick Alan. 1330 N SUPERIOR AVE, CLINIC 54660 #654-01-1993 L1995 **IM** *020 †20

ERICKSON, Rodney Alan. 325 BUTTS AVE 54660 #056-06-1981 L1991 **FM FPG** *020 †18

HENDRICKSON, Jill Elizabe. 325 BUTTS AVE 54660 #030-05-2004 L2006 **FM** *100 †18

HOGAN, James Danl. 1330 N SUPERIOR AVE, CLINIC 54660 #056-06-1977 L1978 **D PD** *020 †15

HOGANSON, Donald E. ■ 54660 #026-04-1945 L1945 **GP** *071

KANSAL, Tapeesh. 500 E VETERANS ST 54660 #495-05-1993 L2000 **P** *020 †75

KLINE, Robb Evan. 1330 N SUPERIOR AVE, CLINIC 54660 #056-05-1997 L2000 **FM** *020 †18

KNUDSON, Ralph Heerens. 1330 N SUPERIOR AVE, CLINIC 54660 #018-03-1972 L2003 **FM** *020 †18

KOZAREK, Clarence E. ■ 54660 #026-04-1945 L1947 **GP** *071

LANDMANN, Gustave A, Jr. 7015 COUNTY HIGHWAY M 54660 #056-06-1951 L1952 **GP** *071 †18

LANSKA, Douglas John. 500 E VETERANS ST 54660 #056-06-1984 L1998 **N** *050 †75 ‡

LANSKA, Mary Jo. 1330 N SUPERIOR AVE, CLINIC 54660 #056-06-1984 L1998 **PD N** *074 †75,55 ‡

LIEBERT, Paul Lawrence. 321 BUTTS AVE 54660 #041-07-1980 L2005 **ORS** *020 †40

LLOYD, Baldwin E. 18845 STATE HIGHWAY 21 54660 #056-05-1952 L1955 **FM** *071 †18

LOTTMANN, J. 1330 N SUPERIOR AVE, CLINIC 54660 #016-01-1976 L1983 **GS** *020 †85

LU, Carol Youkai. 500 E VETERANS ST 54660 #243-45-1990 L2003 **IM** *020 †20

LUCEK, Donald Walter. 325 BUTTS AVE, LAKE TOMAH CLINIC 54660 #016-11-1974 L2008 **GS** *020 †85

MADER, Michael Henry. 1330 N SUPERIOR AVE, CLINIC 54660 #056-05-1974 L1975 **OBG** *020 †30

MARTIN, Sharel Ann. 325 BUTTS AVE 54660 #056-05-1993 L1995 **FM** *020 †18

MAZUR, Larisa Ivanovna. ■ 54660 #913-32-1973 L2007 **FM** *020 †18

MC CLELLAN, Eugene Karl. VET ADMIN MED CTR PATH 54660 #005-16-1962 L1975 **PTH FOP** *050 †50

MC CONNELL, Mark Everett. 500 E VETERANS ST, TOMAH VA MEDICAL CENTER 54660 #020-12-1985 L1988 **IM** *020 †20

MC MULLEN, Jill Patricia. 1330 N SUPERIOR AVE, CLINIC 54660 #005-11-1998 L2005 **FM** *020 †18

MOEDE, James Gordon. 321 BUTTS AVE 54660 #056-05-1973 L1974 **EM FM** *020 †18

PEITZMEIER, Gary Allen. 325 BUTTS AVE 54660 #030-06-1984 L1989 **GS GYN** *020 †85

POLENDER, Bruce Albert. 1330 N SUPERIOR AVE, CLINIC 54660 #016-06-1963 L1972 **IM IMG** *020 †20,03

PURDY, Raymond Howard. 321 BUTTS AVE 54660 #047-05-1981 L1982 **GP** *020 †20

RIOS, Bruno. ■ 54660 #308-01-1980 L1996 **IM** *020

ROBERTS, Cathryn Irene. 500 E VETERANS ST 54660 #025-12-1990 L1993 **FM OS** *020 †18

RUNDE, Matthew Robert. 1330 N SUPERIOR AVE, CLINIC TOMAH 54660 #056-05-1993 L2000 **OPH** *020 †35

SALTZGIVER, Craig Norris. 25044 FOLEY AVE 54660 #046-01-1993 L1995 **IM** *020

SAMMOUR, Mohammed Ali. 1330 N SUPERIOR AVE 54660 #561-14-1978 L1988 **FM** *020 †18

SAUNDERS, Michael Jos. 325 BUTTS AVE 54660 #026-04-1981 L1984 **FM** *020 †18

SCHANHOFER, Willard K, Jr. 325 BUTTS AVE 54660 #056-05-2000 L2001 **FM** *020 †18

SHEIKH, Zaheeruddin. 500 E VETERANS ST, VA HOSPITAL 54660 #704-08-1989 L2002 **IMG RHU** *020

SINGH, Jyotila. 500 E VETERANS ST, # 6 54660 #495-05-1996 L2003 **P** *020

SLATER, Edward John. 15188 HENNEPIN RD 54660 #025-07-1965 L1966 **IM** *020 †20

SZCZERBANIUK, George B. 500 E VETERANS ST 54660 #016-11-1978 L1982 **DR GP** *020

TRAN, Tuyen Thanh. 206 N LAWRENCE AVE 54660 #028-46-1992 L1993 **IM** *012

TRAYNOR, Eugene James. VA MEDICAL CENTER 54660 #056-06-1956 L1957 **P** *071

URBATSCH, Susan Elizabeth. 500 E VETERANS ST, TOMAH V.A. 54660 #016-06-1974 L1975 **FM FPG** *040 †18

WICKLUND, Dale G. 500 E VETERANS ST, VETERANS AFFAIRS MEDICAL C 54660 #014-01-1976 L1983 **FM EM** *020 †18

WIERSMA, Rustan John. 321 BUTTS AVE 54660 #016-43-1975 L1980 **OTO** *020 †45

TOMAHAWK – LINCOLN

AMUNDSON, Gail Marie. ■ 54487 #056-05-1980 L1983 **IM IMG** *030 †20

CARROLL, James Lynn. 221 E WASHINGTON AVE, BOX 305 54487 #025-01-1977 L1980 **FM** *075 †18

CHEEMA, Puneet Singh. 401 W MOHAWK DR STE 200, MINISTRY MED GROUP-TOMAHAW 54487 #495-03-1995 L2003 **HO** *020 †20

CORTTE, Ronald Geo. 401 W MOHAWK DR 54487 #054-04-1992 L1993 **FM** *020 †18

CRAIG, Jeffrey Charles. 401 W MOHAWK DR STE 200 54487 #056-05-1996 L1998 **FM** *020 †18

DICHSEN, Eric Donald. 401 W MOHAWK DR 54487 #016-45-1993 L2000 **FM** *020 †18

JONES, William Wayne. ■ 54487 #018-03-1963 L1972 **GS** *071 †85

PALLAGI, Jeanne Eskau. 401 W MOHAWK DR 54487 #056-06-1991 L1992 **N** *020 †75

SUDBURY, Russell Scott. 401 W MOHAWK DR 54487 #016-11-1987 L1988 **FM** *020 †18

THEILER, George J. N 11445 BUS HWY 51A 54487 #056-05-1953 L1954 **OBG** *071 †30

TREMPEALEAU – TREMPEALEAU

SKEMP, Joseph Jerome. ■ 54661 #056-06-1953 L1954 **IM** *071 †20

TURTLE LAKE – BARRON

HALBERG, Avery Carl. ■ 54889 #056-05-1945 L1946 **GP** *071

LEITHEISER, Gregory J. 550 MARTIN AVE W 54889 #056-06-1982 L1988 **FM** *020 †18

TWIN LAKES – KENOSHA

CASSIDY, Kristin K. 700 N LAKE AVE, # 102 53181 #056-05-1997 L1998 **IM** *020 †20

JOOSS, Robert Louis. ■ 53181 #056-05-1967 L1985 **AN** *071 †05

MEHDI, Ali A. 118 S LAKE AVE, TWIN LAKES CLINIC 53181 #704-16-1985 L1993 **IM** *020

SCHULMAN, Jerome L. 37200 128TH ST 53181 #035-01-1949 L1989 **CHP PD** *030 †55,75

TWO RIVERS – MANITOWOC

ANDERAS, Per Roland. 5300 MEMORIAL DR, STE 105 54241 #016-06-1981 L1982 **GS VS** *020 †85

BENTLEY, Laura Christine. 2219 GARFIELD ST, AURORA TWO RIVERS CLINIC 54241 #018-03-2004 L2007 **FM** *020

CARROLL, Andrea Joyce. 2219 GARFIELD ST, AURORA CLINIC 54241 #018-03-1990 L1992 **IM** *020

CHRISTIANSON, Ronald F. 5000 MEMORIAL DR 54241 #023-01-1982 L2003 **DR EM** *020 †80

DAHNERT, Wolfgang F. 5000 MEMORIAL DR 54241 #409-32-1976 L2004 **R OS** *020 †80

DEMPSEY, James E. 5000 MEMORIAL DR 54241 #539-01-1978 L2004 **DR** *020 †80

DIAZ, Alfredo. 2219 GARFIELD ST, TWO RIVERS CLINIC AMG INC 54241 #030-05-1995 L1998 **IM** *020 †20

DICKENS, Robert Allen. 2500 GARFIELD ST 54241 #024-07-1967 L1989 **P** *020 †75

DOUGHERTY, William Scott. 5300 MEMORIAL DR, STE 105 54241 #019-02-1989 L1995 **U** *020 †95

FEDER, Joseph Mark. 5300 MEMORIAL DR, AURORA VISION CENTER 54241 #025-01-1983 L1988 **OPH** *020 †35

FOSTER, Kenneth James. 5300 MEMORIAL DR, STE 105 54241 #016-01-1990 L1999 **GS** *020 †85

GAGE, Scott William. 5000 MEMORIAL DR 54241 #017-20-1988 L1992 **DR** *020 †80

GAHL, Robert A. 1516 WASHINGTON ST 54241 #056-05-1993 L1994 **FM** *020 †18

GAINEY, Steven Paul. 1603 WASHINGTON ST, EYE CLINIC OF MANITOWOC 54241 #030-06-1984 L1989 **OPH** *020 †35

GLENN, Bradley Jerome. 5000 MEMORIAL DR 54241 #005-06-1987 L2004 **R RNR** *020 †80

GOSWITZ, John Thos. 5000 MEMORIAL DR 54241 #056-06-1958 L1960 **GS** *071 †85

GUO, Danzhu. 5000 MEMORIAL DR 54241 #243-95-1984 L2001 **PM** *020 †60

HALLER, Robert Wayne. 5000 MEMORIAL DR 54241 #056-05-1993 L2002 **DR** *020 †80

HENNIGAN, Shawn Patrick. 5300 MEMORIAL DR, STE 105 54241 #041-13-1994 L2003 **ORS** *020 †40

HENRY, Jonathon Charles. 5300 MEMORIAL DR, STE 105 54241 #056-05-1995 L2001 **ORS** *020 †40

HESTER-DIAZ, Julia D. 2219 GARFIELD ST, 2219 GARFIELD ST 54241 #030-05-1995 L1998 **FM** *020 †18

HOFTIEZER, Michael Don. ■ 54241 #016-11-1980 L1987 **IM EM** *020 †20

HOLDER, Lynn Wayman. 2219 GARFIELD ST 54241 #016-11-1961 L1968 **IM** *020

KUESTER, David James. 5000 MEMORIAL DR 54241 #035-01-1986 L1991 **ORS OSM** *020 †40

LALIBERTE, Brian Patrick. 2219 GARFIELD ST, TWO RIVERS CLINIC 54241 #056-06-1993 L1997 **MPD** *020 †20,55

LAMBERT, Hye Chong Lois. 5300 MEMORIAL DR, STE 105 54241 #056-06-1993 L1997 **OBG** *020 †30

LARSON, Karl Christian. 3310 45TH ST 54241 #056-06-1981 L1987 **FM OBS** *020 †18

LEE, John Kent. 5000 MEMORIAL DR 54241 #062-01-1991 L1994 **DR** *020 †28,80

LIMONI, Robert Patrick. 5300 MEMORIAL DR, STE 105 54241 #056-06-1996 L2001 **ORS** *020 †40

MAATMAN, Timothy James. 5000 MEMORIAL DR 54241 #025-01-1978 L1982 **IM** *020 †20

MARTIN-FOSTER, Cheryl A. 2219 GARFIELD ST 54241 #016-42-1990 L1999 **FM** *020 †18

MENDOZA-AYALA, Raul M. 5300 MEMORIAL DR, STE 105 54241 #649-13-1991 L2000 **PCC** *020 †20

MIHALAKAKOS, Paul. 5300 MEMORIAL DR 54241 #030-06-1992 L2001 **AN** *020 †05

MIR, Ali Akbar. 2219 GARFIELD ST, TWO RIVERS CLINIC-AMG, INC 54241 #517-05-1959 L1966 **PD** *071

MYERS, Robert Earl. 2219 GARFIELD ST 54241 #056-06-1961 L1962 **OBG** *071

NILLES, John E. ■ 54241 #056-06-1951 L1952 **GP IMG** *072

PFAFFENBACH, David Dean. 1603 WASHINGTON ST 54241 #056-05-1967 L1972 **OPH** *071 †35

PHILLIPS, Benjamin Edward. 1603 WASHINGTON ST, EYE CLINIC OF MANITOWOC 54241 #026-08-1998 L2002 **OPH** *020

RAPISARDA, Douglas Edward. 5300 MEMORIAL DR, STE 105 54241 #024-07-1986 L1994 **OTO HNS** *020

ROMAN, Ekaterina. 2219 GARFIELD ST 54241 #913-81-1995 L2003 **FM** *020 †18

RUH, Paul James. 2219 GARFIELD ST 54241 #056-05-1991 L1996 **GE** *020 †20

SCHNAUBELT, Michael A. 5000 MEMORIAL DR 54241 #056-05-1997 L2004 **ORS** *020 †40

SHARMA, Supriya. 5000 MEMORIAL DR 54241 #496-07-1987 L2001 **DR** *020 †80

SMITH, Glenn Arthur. 2219 GARFIELD ST 54241 #056-05-1989 L1990 **FM FSM** *020 †18

SONNELAND, Arthur M, III. 5300 MEMORIAL DR, STE 105 54241 #056-05-1978 L1979 **U** *095

STAUDINGER, Diane L. 2219 GARFIELD ST, AURORA HEALTH CARE 54241 #056-05-1991 L1992 **FM** *020 †18

THAYER, Cedric Verl. 2219 GARFIELD ST 54241 #056-05-1979 L1982 **IM** *020

TRAGER, Marc Harris. 5000 MEMORIAL DR 54241 #024-07-1971 L1999 **DR NM** *071 †80 ‡

VOSKUIL, Scott William. 5300 MEMORIAL DR, STE 105 54241 #056-06-1997 L2002 **OBG** *020 †30

WINGA, Betsy Michele. 5300 MEMORIAL DR, STE 105 54241 #018-03-2001 L2005 **OBG** *020 †30

WOLF, Francis Gilbert. 5300 MEMORIAL DR, STE 105 54241 #056-05-1973 L1974 **CD IM** *020 †20

YETTER, Andrew Walter. 5000 MEMORIAL DR 54241 #016-11-1990 L1996 **ON HO** *020 †20

ZAMBRANO, Isidoro V. 5300 MEMORIAL DR, STE 203 54241 #056-06-2000 L2005 **ORS** *020

ZASULY, James M. 5300 MEMORIAL DR, STE 105 54241 #048-16-1993 L2001 **PS** *020 †65

ZELDENRUST, John Chas. 5300 MEMORIAL DR, STE 105 54241 #025-01-1970 L1981 **GS** *020 †85

ZUEHL, Richard Wm. 5000 MEMORIAL DR 54241 #056-05-1979 L1982 **PTH** *020 †50

UNION GROVE – RACINE

BIENEMANN, Mary Elizabeth. 1120 MAIN ST 53182 #056-06-2000 L2002 **FM** *020 †18

DEMERS, Gerald Allen. 4320 67TH DR 53182 #016-11-1983 L1986 **FM** *020 †18

FIVEYSKY, Vladimir D. 21425 SPRING ST, SOUTHERN WISCONSIN 53182 #913-15-1960 L1984 **GP** *020

HALLER, Daniel Joseph. 4320 67TH DR, AURORA HEALTH CENTER 53182 #016-11-1979 L2006 FM *020 †18

LIKHTEREV, Alla Yuryevna. 21425 SPRING ST, MENTAL HEALTH CLINIC 53182 #913-69-1972 L1995 P *020

SCHLIMGEN, Anne Marie. 21425 SPRING ST, VA MEDICAL UNION GROVE CBO 53182 #056-05-1993 L1993 IM *020 †20

SIMONDS, James David. 1120 MAIN ST 53182 #056-05-1985 L1988 FM *020 †18

SIMONDS, Lisa Maria. 1120 MAIN ST 53182 #056-05-1985 L1988 FM *020 †18

STEFANOWICZ, Albert. 1114 15TH AVE 53182 #759-08-1953 L1972 GP R *020

VALDERS — MANITOWOC

SAMUNDSEN, Paul Carl. 721 S CALUMET ST, AURORA HEALTH CENTER 54245 #016-06-1996 L2003 FM *020 †18 ‡

VERONA — DANE

ALBAN, Christopher John. 1979 MILKY WAY 53593 #041-07-1991 L1994 EM *062 †16

ARNDT, Brian Gerald. 100 N NINE MOUND RD 53593 #056-05-2005 L2006 FP *012

BASKE, R F. ■ 53593 #025-01-1966 L1969 OPH *071 †35

BRONSON, Fredrick Howard. 46 HAWKS LANDING CIR 53593 #056-05-1963 L1964 GP GS *071

CAPE, Robert Edwards. 100 N NINE MOUND RD 53593 #016-42-1980 L1983 FM *020 †18

CARSON, Susan Jeannette. 100 N NINE MOUND RD, VERONA CLINIC 53593 #056-05-1986 L1987 FM *071 †18

CARUFEL-WERT, Donald Alan. 100 N NINE MOUND RD 53593 #017-20-1992 L1993 FM *020 †18

CHANDLER, John Wm, Jr. ■ 53593 #056-05-1965 L1967 OPH *071 †35

CULP, John Andrew. 100 N NINE MOUND RD 53593 #017-20-2004 L2006 FP *012

CUTA, Lindsay Marie. ■ 53593 #056-05-2007 PD *012

DUFFEK, Cory Christophe. ■ 53593 #016-11-2004 L2007 DR *012

EGGERT, Cari Anne. ■ 53593 #016-43-2000 L2004 PM *020 †60

EHRHARDT, Jonathan Peter. ■ 53593 #016-02-2002 L2006 DR *020 †80

EICHHORST, Bradley Craig. 1979 MILKY WAY, EPIC SYS CORP 53593 #026-08-1980 L1981 FM OS *062 †18

EVENSEN, Ann Elizabeth. 100 N NINE MOUND RD 53593 #056-05-1995 L1999 FM *020 †18

FARLEY, Eugene Shedden. ■ 53593 #035-45-1954 L1982 FM GPM *071 †18

FARLEY, Linda Fabry. ■ 53593 #035-45-1955 L1982 FM FPG *071

FORTNEY, Luke William. 100 N NINE MOUND RD 53593 #056-05-2003 L2004 FM *020 †18

FRAZER, Samuel Leo. 9110 EAGLEWOOD DR 53593 #056-05-1972 L1975 IM *071 †20

HAMILTON, John William. 7748 ALMOR DR 53593 #016-11-1978 L1981 IM GE *020 †20

JOSEPH, Craig Maurice. 1979 MILKY WAY, EPIC SYSTEMS CORP 53593 #025-07-1994 L1996 PD *062 †55

KOBBERVIG, Catherine E. 3900 MERIDIAN CIR 53593 #056-05-1999 L2000 HEM *020 †20

LARSON, Paul Orwin. ■ 53593 #056-05-1972 L1973 D DS *071 †18,15

LI, Yu. ■ 53593 #243-72-1985 L2004 PTH *100 †50

MC AWEENEY, William Jos. ■ 53593 #010-01-1959 L1963 IM *020 †20

MORGAN, Miles Thomas. 100 N NINE MOUND RD, VERONA FAMILY MEDICAL CLIN 53593 #056-05-1999 L2000 FM *020 †18

MUCHOW, Ryan David. ■ 53593 #056-05-2006 L2007 ORS *012

MULLER, Daniel. 3539 SABAKA TRL 53593 #035-48-1985 L1991 RHU IM *050 †20

NEIDHART, David James. ■ 53593 #028-02-1996 *100

PREIMESBERGER, Amanda Ray. 100 N NINE MOUND RD 53593 #056-05-2005 L2006 FP *012

QUINN, Rachel Ann. 100 N NINE MOUND RD 53593 #056-05-2004 L2005 FM *020 †18

RAKEL, David Paul. 100 N NINE MOUND RD 53593 #048-04-1991 L2001 FM *020 †18

ROTERT, Eric M. 100 N NINE MOUND RD, VERONA FAM MED CLINIC 53593 #036-05-2000 L2001 FM *020 †18

SANSONE, Jason Matthew. ■ 53593 #056-05-2007 ORS *012

SCHEIBEL, William Roy. 100 N NINE MOUND RD 53593 #056-05-1974 L1975 FM *020 †18

SELZER, Jadwiga. ■ 53593 #759-02-1936 L1939 PHP *071

SKOCHELAK, Susan Eva. 100 N NINE MOUND RD 53593 #025-01-1981 L1986 FM GPM *030 †18

SMITH, Douglas Leroy. 100 N NINE MOUND RD 53593 #016-11-1979 L1980 FM FPG *020 †18

SOOD, Vidushi. ■ 53593 #496-09-1994 L1998 END *020 †20

WEBER, Maria Therese. ■ 53593 #056-05-1988 L1989 IM *020 †20

WEBER, Michael Joseph. 100 N NINE MOUND RD 53593 #051-01-2006 L2008 FP *012

WILSON, John James. 100 N NINE MOUND RD 53593 #056-05-2003 L2004 PSM *012 †18

VIOLA — VERNON

DINGES, Carol Margaret. 338 N COMMERCIAL ST 54664 #056-05-1980 L1982 IM *020

VIROQUA — VERNON

ANDREW, Mark Henry. 407 S MAIN ST, STE 400 54665 #056-05-1980 L1985 GS *020 †85

BERGQUIST, Paul Edward. 507 S MAIN ST 54665 #026-04-1986 L1989 FM *020

BRAULT, Yvonne Marie. E8569 COUNTY ROAD Y 54665 #056-05-1990 L1992 GS *020

CADWELL, Frank James. 407 S MAIN ST, VIROQUA CLINIC 54665 #026-04-1977 L1980 ON IM *020 †20

CALKINS, William Norman. 507 S MAIN ST 54665 #056-05-1977 L1978 FM *020

CHAKOIAN, David Edward. 497 S MAIN ST 54665 #026-08-1986 L1989 FM *020 †18

DAHL, Kristina Anne. ■ 54665 #016-01-1983 L1988 N *075

DE LINE, James Michael. 507 S MAIN ST 54665 #016-11-1980 L1981 FM FPG *020 †18

ECKLUND, Dan Leonard. ■ 54665 #056-05-1987 L1990 FM *020 †18

FELTES, James Robt. 407 S MAIN ST, VIROQUA CLINIC 54665 #056-05-1987 L1988 FM *020 †18

FIORUCCI, Michael Raymond. 407 S MAIN ST, VIROQUA CLINIC 54665 #016-11-1995 L2004 GS *020 †18

ICENOGLE, Daniel Lee. 507 S MAIN ST 54665 #016-43-1981 L1987 FM *020 †18

KOONS, Duane Melvin. 497 S MAIN ST, STE 400 54665 #025-07-1985 L1989 FM *020 †18

KUCK, Paul Arthur. 407 S MAIN ST, CLINIC VIROQUA 54665 #038-40-1974 L1995 OPH OS *071 †35

LAWRENCE, Jeffrey Michael. 507 S MAIN ST 54665 #016-06-1987 L1997 ORS OAR *020 †40

LONG, Richard Ernest. 407 S MAIN ST, VIROQUA CLINIC 54665 #016-43-1984 L1987 FM OS *020 †18

MACASAET, Anthony Lloyd. 507 S MAIN ST, VERNON MEMORIAL HEALTHCARE 54665 #056-05-1995 L1997 EM *020 †16

MACASAET, Rolando A. 318 W DECKER ST, HIRSCH CLINIC 54665 #748-08-1964 L1973 AS GP *020 ‡

MENN, Jeffrey Fletcher. 497 S MAIN ST, STE 400 54665 #056-05-1974 L1976 PD *020 †55

OPPERT, Harold Erwin. 15 WASHINGTON HTS 54665 #056-05-1946 L1948 GP *071

OVERHOLT, Edwin Morgan. 407 S MAIN ST, VIROQUA CLINIC 54665 #056-05-1986 L1992 OTO HNS *020 †45

PRIOR, Deborah Lynn. 407 S MAIN ST STE 400 54665 #061-01-1985 L1995 FM *020

STARR, Robert A. 1003 JOHNSON ST 54665 #056-05-1950 L1951 FM GP *071 †18

SUNDARAM, Rajah Sridhar. 407 S MAIN ST, VIROQUA CLINIC 54665 #065-09-1978 L1992 CD *020 †20

VALENTINI, Eugene John. 507 S MAIN ST 54665 #028-02-1963 L1971 R NM *020 †80,28

VAN DYKE, David Allyn. 122 W SOUTH ST 54665 #025-12-1974 L1975 P *020 †75

VIG, David E. 407 S MAIN ST, STE 200 54665 #056-05-1951 L1952 GP *020

VIG, De Verne W. 18 WASHINGTON HTS 54665 #056-05-1951 L1952 GP *071

WOODY, Brian Rodgers. 407 S MAIN ST STE 400, HIRSCH CLINIC 54665 #016-11-1991 L1994 FM *020 †18

WALES — WAUKESHA

BALDWIN, Lynn L. 300B E SUMMIT AVE 53183 #056-06-1989 L1990 FM *020 †18

BURNETT, David Eugene. 115 N ELIAS ST 53183 #056-05-1983 L1997 FM *020 †18

DAUENHAUER, Marie Alana. 144 E SUMMIT AVE, STE 100 53183 #056-06-2001 L2002 D *020 †15

FITZPATRICK, Paul Jerome. ■ 53183 #056-06-1961 L1962 AN *020 †05

MILLER, Todd Anthony. 144 E SUMMIT AVE, STE 100 53183 #018-03-1990 L2005 FM *020 †18

WALWORTH — WALWORTH

COURIER, Deana Leeon. 525 KENOSHA ST, STE A 53184 #016-45-1996 L1997 FM *020 †18

HOPE, A. ■ 53184 #056-05-2002 RO *100

JACOBSON, Dale Gary. 525 KENOSHA ST, STE A 53184 #056-05-1978 L1981 FM *020 †18

KOLNIK, Sarah Elizabeth. ■ 53184 #056-05-2007 PD *012

LOWELL, Janis Anne. 525 KENOSHA ST, STE A 53184 #056-06-1985 L1986 FM *020 †18

PASIKHOV, Dmitry. 525 KENOSHA ST, STE A 53184 #016-42-1997 L2002 GS *020 †85

WASHBURN — BAYFIELD

CHRISTENSEN, Donnan L. ■ 54891 #026-04-1972 L1980 FM GP *020 †18

KREUSER, Stephen Robt. 320 SUPERIOR AVE 54891 #038-41-1983 L1985 GP *020

MERCER, Wayne Clay. ■ 54891 #018-03-1952 L1966 P *071 †75

SNEED, Sara Knapp. ■ 54891 #026-04-1989 L1997 EM *020

WASHINGTON ISLAND — DOOR

BASS, Marjorie Darrow. ■ 54246 #056-05-1981 L1983 FM *071 †18

WATERFORD — RACINE

BAUER, Aaron Jurgens. 818 FORREST DR 53185 #056-06-2002 L2005 PD *020 †55

COHN, James Howard. 1701 SHARP RD 53185 #056-05-1983 L1997 PM *020 †60

DECKER, Jennifer Jayne. 818 FORREST DR 53185 #016-43-1995 L1996 FM *020 †18

DIGNAN, Christine Marie. 818 FORREST DR 53185 #056-06-1997 L1998 PD *020 †55

KMECAK, Stephen Clay. 818 FORREST DR 53185 #020-02-1991 L1993 GS *020 †85

LAHIRI, Satish. 818 FORREST DR, PHEUMATOLOGY 53185 #496-07-1961 L1977 RHU IM *020 †20

LIVERMAN, Elaine Maria. 818 FORREST DR 53185 #056-06-1996 L1997 OBG *020 †30

LORENZO, Jose Paulo P. ■ 53185 #748-02-1989 L1995 RHU *100

MAJEED, Mustansir. 1701 SHARP RD, LAKEVIEW SPEC HOSP & REHAB 53185 #704-20-1988 L1998 FM EM *020 †18 ‡

MAJEWSKI, Joseph Thos. 818 FORREST DR 53185 #056-06-1976 L1977 GS *020 †85

MORAN, James Thos. 818 FORREST DR 53185 #054-04-1986 L1992 IM *020 †20

RAMIREZ-SALDANA, Iliana. ■ 53185 #042-01-2005 L2008 GP *100

SLADKY, James Aloysius. ■ 53185 #056-06-1962 L1963 PM *030 †60

SRIVASTAVA, Alok Kumar. 818 FORREST DR 53185 #038-41-1995 L1996 IM *020 †20

WATERLOO — JEFFERSON

FLOOD, James C. 105 HIGHLAND TER 53594 #025-01-1992 L2000 FM *020 †18

LUNDE, Britt Marie. ■ 53594 #056-05-2006 L2008 OBG *012

SCHMIDT, Benjamin T, Jr. 111 ANNA ST 53594 #056-06-1988 L1989 FM *020 †18 ‡

WATERTOWN — DODGE

CHIN, Moe Louie. 123 HOSPITAL DR, STE 2004 53098 #054-04-1977 L1978 FM FPG *020 †18

CLAR, Alberto Calingasan. 125 HOSPITAL DR 53098 #748-08-1969 L1977 AN *020

COCHRANE, Bruce John. 127 HOSPITAL DR 53098 #016-42-1976 L1978 FM *020 †18

DOUGLAS, Linda Olson. 134 HOSPITAL DR, FAMILY PRACTICE CENTER 53098 #028-02-1982 L1997 FM ADL *020 †18

ESTRELLA, Aurora A. 123 HOSPITAL DR STE 104 53098 #748-08-1967 L1978 FM *071 †18

ESTRELLA, Renato Soriano. 128 HOSPITAL DR, CTR FOR WOMENS HLTH 53098 #748-08-1968 L1975 OBG *071 †30

FOSTER, Edward Jos. 125 HOSPITAL DR 53098 #016-01-1989 L1990 EM *020

GEORGE, Christopher R. 125 HOSPITAL DR, EMERGENCY DEPARTMENT 53098 #016-43-1999 L2000 EM *020 †16

GROSSMAN, Thomas W, Jr. 123 HOSPITAL DR, STE 1008 53098 #023-12-1986 L1995 ORS OSM *020 †40

HARGARTEN, Kathleen. 125 HOSPITAL DR 53098 #056-06-1982 L1983 EM *020 †16

HAUSER, Gary Curtis. 129 HOSPITAL DR 53098 #035-06-1962 L1963 P ADM *020 †75

HOLDEN, Richard C. 127 HOSPITAL DR 53098 #028-03-1976 L1977 FM *020 †18

HOY, Edward John. 123 HOSPITAL DR, STE 1002 53098 #028-34-1977 L1981 OPH *020 †35

LEE, Jason Huongtzern. 125 HOSPITAL DR 53098 #056-05-1995 L2001 EM *020 †16

MANTEY, Karie Anne. 134 HOSPITAL DR, MEADE MEDICAL CLC 53098 #056-06-1998 L2003 PD *020 †55

MEADE, James Edward. 134 HOSPITAL DR, MEADE MEDICAL CLINIC 53098 #056-05-1988 L1998 FSM FM *020 †18

MEADE, Jeffrey Alan. 134 HOSPITAL DR 53098 #056-05-1995 L1998 PD *020 †55

MEIER, Pierce James. 123 HOSPITAL DR, STE 100 53098 #056-05-1967 L1968 R *020 †80

MULTHAUF, Cecilia Marie. 125 HOSPITAL DR 53098 #056-06-1987 L1988 OPH IM *020

OHALLORAN, Kevin Louis. 123 HOSPITAL DR STE 2000 53098 #016-11-1987 L1993 ORS *020 †40

RHODES, Steven Paul. 123 HOSPITAL DR, STE 1008 53098 #016-43-1986 L1987 ORS *020 †40

SAMDANI, Moazam Jah. 123 HOSPITAL DR STE 214 53098 #704-08-1968 L1975 IM HEM *020 †20

SANDSTROM, Todd Alan. 123 HOSPITAL DR, STE 2006 53098 #056-05-1991 L1996 GS *020 †85

SCHOENECKER, Craig Jerome. 129 HOSPITAL DR 53098 #056-05-2001 L2005 PFP *020 †75

SCHOENECKER, Erin Michele. 128 HOSPITAL DR 53098 #056-05-2001 L2005 OBG *020 †30

SOKOVICH, Ronald Scott. 123 HOSPITAL DR, STE 2002 53098 #016-45-1988 L1992 U *020 †95

SOLIS, Kenneth Martin. 125 HOSPITAL DR 53098 #056-05-1985 L1986 EM *020

SULLIVAN, Michael Edward. 125 HOSPITAL DR 53098 #016-11-2001 L2004 FM *020

THORSTENSON, Michael E. 125 HOSPITAL DR 53098 #056-05-1978 L1984 GS VS *020 †85

TURKE, Terry Lester. 132 HOSPITAL DR 53098 #056-05-1973 L1974 FM *020 †18

VAN HECKE, Holly C. 123 HOSPITAL DR, STE 1002 53098 #016-11-1990 L1994 OPH *020 †35

YAFAI, Mohamed H. 123 HOSPITAL DR, STE 2001 53098 #305-01-1987 L1991 IM *020 †20

WATERTOWN – JEFFERSON

CALADO, Brigido Caasi. 1532 UTAH ST 53094 #748-02-1968 L1976 PD *020

GRAJEWSKI, Michael Andrew. 1507 DOCTORS CT 53094 #056-05-1982 L1985 FM *020 †18

JOHNSON, Thomas Duane. 53094 #036-08-1990 L1992 FM *020

KEEFE, Beth Greenhalgh. 109 AIR PARK DR 53094 #026-04-1998 L2002 MPD *020 †20,55

LEE, Ok Soon. 700 HOFFMANN DR 53094 #583-03-1952 L1965 PHP PD *062

LINZER, Brett Adam. 109 AIR PARK DR 53094 #016-43-1996 L2000 MPD OS *020 †20,55

LUETZOW, Thomas John. N7406 CT E 53094 #056-05-1976 L1978 FM EM *020 †16,18

QUANBECK, David Thomas. ■ 53094 #016-02-1962 L1965 U *071 †95

SCHLOEMER, Nathan John. ■ 53094 #056-05-2008 *012

WOLLHEIM, Donald Alan. N8748 HUSTISFORD RD, IMPLEXUS WOUND CARE SERVIC 53094 #056-06-1976 L1977 GS *020 †85

WAUKESHA – WAUKESHA

ABUHAJIR, Majed. N14W23900 STONE RIDGE DR 53188 #575-01-1984 L1992 HO *020 †20

AFFI, Aboud. W231N1440 CORPORATE CT, CT #307 53186 #875-02-1989 L1994 GE *020 †20

AFZAL, Omer. 721 AMERICAN AVE, STE 511 53188 #704-21-1996 L2002 NEP *020 †20

AGNEW, Michelle Marie. 2130 BIG BEND RD, PRO HEALTH CARE MED CTR 53189 #056-06-1992 L1995 IM *020 †20

AGPOON, Jose S. 1859 E MORELAND BLVD 53186 #748-08-1967 L1974 IM *020

AGPOON, Perla Panahon. 1859 E MORELAND BLVD 53186 #748-08-1967 L1974 PD *020

AMORDE, Robert William. ■ 53188 #016-43-2007 *012

ANDERSON, Robert G. 222 PARK PL, # 270 53186 #016-06-1952 L1975 OPH *071 †35

ATTWELL, Amy Jean. 1111 DELAFIELD ST, STE 115 53188 #038-41-1994 L1995 PD *020 †55

AUSHWITZ, Margaret Louise. ■ 53188 #016-06-2005 PD *012

BAJAJ, Shailesh. 410 KOSSOW RD 53186 #495-12-1995 L2000 GE *100 †20

BAKALARS, Mark Glen. 725 AMERICAN AVE, WAUKESHA MEMORIAL HOSPITAL 53188 #056-06-1997 L1998 VIR *020 †80

BANKER, Vincent Phillips. 1111 DELAFIELD ST, STE 301 53188 #056-06-1964 L1970 DR NM *071 †80,28

BARBER, Jergen Leroy. ■ 53186 #030-05-1959 L1962 AN EM *071 †05

BARTOS, Stephen Robt. 1111 DELAFIELD ST STE 209 53188 #056-05-1987 L1996 VS GS *020 †85

BASELGA, Eulalia. ■ 53186 #847-12-1989 D *100

BASICH, John Ewald. 1111 DELAFIELD ST, STE 213 53188 #016-43-1974 L1978 AI IM *020 †20,03

BEECH, Melinda Veronyca. ■ 53186 #056-06-2007 OTO *012

BEHNKE, Stephanie Jean. ■ 53186 #056-06-2006 L2008 PD *012

BERMAN, Gerald Neil. 1111 DELAFIELD ST 53188 #016-43-1971 L1975 IM *020 †20

BEYER, Gary Anthony. 725 AMERICAN AVE, DEPT OF RADIOLOGY 53188 #056-06-1986 L1987 DR *020 †80

BEYKOVSKY, Andrew Victor. 1111 DELAFIELD ST, NEUROLOGIC ASSOCIATES OF 53188 #429-02-1993 L1995 NS *020

BHATHENA, Dhun Noshir. 1111 DELAFIELD ST, STE 311 53188 #495-97-1977 L1979 OBG *020 †30

BIEBEL, Matthew Robert. 1111 DELAFIELD ST, STE 115 53188 #056-06-1994 L1995 PD *020 †55

BIEDRZYCKI, Lynda Marie. 515 W MORELAND BLVD 53188 #056-06-1980 L1981 PTH FOP *062 †50

BIEHL, Mark David. 500 RIVERVIEW AVE 53188 #056-05-1962 L1963 P *020 †75

BINDRA, Rajvinder Singh. 1111 DELAFIELD ST, STE 205 53188 #495-03-1986 L1998 IM *020 †20

BISCHEL, Jerome Raymond. 222 PARK PL, # 341 53186 #056-06-1954 L1955 PD *071

BLACKSTONE, Carolyn Sue. N14W23900 STONE RIDGE DR 53188 #056-06-1985 L1986 IM *071 †20

BLAVAT, Renee Marie. 210 NW BARSTOW STE 201 53188 #056-06-2003 L2004 FM *020 †18

BLEIL, David C. ■ 53188 #056-06-1951 L1953 D OS *071

BOEHM, William James. N14W23900 STONE RIDGE DR 53188 #056-06-1991 L1992

BOEX, Robert Murray. 725 AMERICAN AVE 53188 #056-05-1974 L1975 DR *020 †80

BOLGER, John Thos. 1111 DELAFIELD ST STE 120, ORTH ASSOCIATES OF WI 53188 #016-06-1975 L1980 HS ORS *020 †40 ‡

BONNESS, Michelle Rae. 20611 WATERTOWN RD, SEEGER MED BLDG STE D 53186 #056-05-1989 L1997 PS *020 †85,65

BORKOWSKI, Michael A. N14W23900 STONE RIDGE DR 53188 #056-06-1990 L1992 OM *020 †70

BOYLE, Austin J, III. W231N1440 CORPORATE CT, STE 200 53186 #016-11-1979 L1985 ORS *020 †40

BRANDES, James Carmen. 721 AMERICAN AVE, STE 511 53188 #056-06-1985 L1986 NEP IM *020 †20

BRASS, Kathleen Amanda. ■ 53188 #016-01-2007 FP *012

BREMER, Sharon Anne. 721 AMERICAN AVE STE 203 53188 #056-06-1989 L1990 N *020 †75

BROWN, Bruce Alan. 1111 DELAFIELD ST, STE 10 53188 #056-06-1981 L1982 OPH *020 †35

BROWNELL, Caryn Ernster. 2130 BIG BEND RD, WMC-SOUTH 53189 #056-06-1990 L1991 FM *020 †18

BROWNELL, Elizabeth Ellen. N17W24100 RIVERWOOD DR, STE 150 53188 #422-01-1988 L1989 FM *020 †18

BRUMMUND, Walter, Jr. 1111 DELAFIELD ST, STE 213 53188 #041-01-1980 L1983 A PDA *020 †20,03

BUERGER, Edward J. 1111 DELAFIELD ST 53188 #056-06-1963 L1964 OBG *071 †30

BUFFINGTON, Nathaniel Jam. 210 NW BARSTOW ST STE 201 53188 #056-06-2004 L2005 FM *020 †18

BUHL, John L. 725 AMERICAN AVE 53188 #056-06-1950 L1951 GP GS *020

BURNS, William Brian. 721 AMERICAN AVE STE 403 53188 #056-06-1989 L1995 CD *020 †20

BURTON, Thomas C. ■ 53186 #016-06-1964 L1984 OPH *071 †35

CADBURY, Jane Balderston. W288S5023 ROCKWOOD TRL 53189 #008-01-1943 L1974 OS *071

CANTIERI, Thomas Patrick. 2130 BIG BEND RD, SOUTH 53189 #023-07-1977 L1990 IM *020 †20

CASE, Kerry Ann. 210 NW BARSTOW ST, STE 201 53188 #016-42-2005 L2008 FP *012

CATRINE, Kristina Eir. ■ 53188 #026-04-2004 PD *012

CHAPMAN, Brian Alan. 1111 DELAFIELD ST, NEUROLOGIC ASSOCIATES OF 53188 #056-06-1979 L1983 N *020 †75

CHAPMAN, Peter David. N14W23900 STONE RIDGE DR 53188 #035-15-1979 L1980 ICE CD *020 †20

CHUDNOW-YOPPS, Melissa. N14W23900 STONE RIDGE DR 53188 #056-06-1999 L2000 AI *020 †55,03

CLAPPER, Wingate Foster. 725 AMERICAN AVE 53188 #038-44-1985 L1989 RO *020 †80

COMISKEY, Ellen B. 1111 DELAFIELD ST, STE 311 53188 #056-05-1989 L1996 OBG *020 †30

CONDON, Kenneth Gerard. N4W22370 BLUEMOUND RD, STE 202 53186 #056-06-1980 L1981 OTO HNS *020 †45

CONNELLY, James Friedrich. 725 AMERICAN AVE, WAUKESHA MEMORIAL HOSPITAL 53188 #056-06-2002 L2004 AN *020 †05

CONNOR, Michael Scott. 1111 DELAFIELD ST, STE 222 53188 #021-06-2003 L2005 GS *100

COOPER, Wendy Pamela. N14W23900 STONE RIDGE DR 53188 #025-01-1982 L1987 IM PD *020 †20,55

CRANBERG, James Allan. 1111 DELAFIELD ST, STE 213 53188 #018-03-1984 L1989 AI IM *020 †20,03

CRELIN, William Chas. 721 AMERICAN AVE STE 509 53188 #056-06-1983 L1989 IM END *020 †20

CRISOSTOMO, J Arthur C. N14W23900 STONE RIDGE DR 53188 #748-08-1979 L1987 PCC SME *020

CROSBY, David Lloyd. W231N1440 CORPORATE CT 53186 #004-01-1986 L1990 D *020 †15

CZARNECKI, David Jos. 725 AMERICAN AVE 53188 #056-06-1983 L1984 DR *020 †80

DALEIDEN, James Patrick. 1111 DELAFIELD ST STE 311 53188 #026-04-1969 L1970 OBG *071 †30

DALL, James Edward. 210 NW BARSTOW ST, STE 201 53188 #056-06-1974 L1977 FM *020 †18

DANIEL, Amir. 721 AMERICAN AVE, STE 511 53188 #517-01-1980 L1991 NEP *020 †20

DAVIES, Christopher Bowen. 1111 DELAFIELD ST STE 209, WAUKESHA GEN & VASCULAR SU 53188 #056-05-1988 L1996 GS VS *020 †85

DAVIES, Elizabeth M. 717 W MORELAND BLVD 53188 #056-06-1995 L1996 FM *020 †18 ‡

DAVIES, William Bowen. 1111 DELAFIELD ST, STE 209 53188 #056-05-1965 L1966 GS VS *020 †85

DELISLE, Dorothy Mary. N14W23900 STONE RIDGE DR 53188 #056-05-1992 L1996 PD *020 †55

DEUTSCH, Jerrold Marshall. 1111 DELAFIELD ST, STE 115 53188 #056-06-1982 L1983 PD GP *020 †55

DHAMEE, Margaret Angela. ■ 53188 #919-03-1963 L1974 PD *071 †55

DI ULIO, Lynn Knitter. 20611 WATERTOWN RD 53186 #056-06-1974 L1975 OBG *020 †30

DIVJAK, Angela Dawn. ■ 53186 #056-05-2008 *012

DOENIER, Jan Alexis. 1111 DELAFIELD ST, STE 321 53188 #056-06-1991 L1993 FM *020 †18

DOENIER, Paul Brian. 1111 DELAFIELD ST, STE 321 53188 #056-06-2003 L2006 FM *020 †18

DOENIER, Todd Michael. 1111 DELAFIELD ST STE 321, DOENIER FAMILY MED 53188 #056-06-1991 L1992 FM *020 †18

DONIPARTHI, Padmaja. 725 AMERICAN AVE 53188 #056-06-1992 L1995 AN *020 †05

DONOVAN, Mary Wisniewski. 20611 WATERTOWN RD, PEDIATRIC HEALTHCARE S.C. 53186 #056-06-1985 L1986 PD *020 †55

DOUGHERTY, Thomas Jos. 1111 DELAFIELD ST, STE 203 53188 #018-03-1968 L1974 IM *020 †20

DREYER, Mark Walter. 1111 DELAFIELD ST, STE 216 53188 #056-05-1976 L1981 GE *020 †20

DUA, Arnavaz. 1111 DELAFIELD ST, STE 203 53188 #495-19-1978 L1994 IM *020 †20

DUFRESNE, Stephen John. N17W24100 RIVERWOOD DR, STE 250 53188 #056-05-1982 L1986 IM *020 †20

DYOCO, Lorree Lynn. 1111 DELAFIELD ST, STE 311 53188 #030-06-1997 L1998 OBG *020 †30

EAPEN, Sunu Sara. ■ 53188 #056-05-2003 L2004 IM *100 †20

ENGEL, Charles John. 2422 N GRANDVIEW BLVD 53188 #025-01-1972 L1982 ADM D *020 †15

ENGLUND, Stanley Allan. 725 AMERICAN AVE 53188 #016-02-1964 L1971 AN *020 †05

EPPERSON, Laura Ellen. 721 AMERICAN AVE, STE 304 53188 #051-01-1993 L1997 OBG *020 †30

ESBENSEN, Leif Erik. 717 W MORELAND BLVD 53188 #056-05-1990 L1991 FM *020 †18

EVANGELISTA, Teofilo. ■ 53188 #748-01-1952 L1965 GP *071

FAHEY, Norbert James, Jr. ■ 53186 #056-06-1985 L1986 IM *075 †20

FAY, David Lawrence. 210 NW BARSTOW ST STE 20, WAUKESHA FAMILY PRACTICE C 53188 #051-07-1987 L2000 FM *020 †18

FERSTENFELD, Julian Erwin. 210 NW BARSTOW ST, STE 201 53188 #018-03-1966 L1969 ID IM *020 †20

FETE, Jeffrey Michael. 725 AMERICAN AVE 53188 #016-06-1984 L1988 **R** *020 †80
FISH, John Titus. 1111 DELAFIELD ST, STE 300 53188 #056-06-1978 L1979 **IM** *020
FISHER, Eric Robt. 725 AMERICAN AVE 53188 #024-07-1989 L2001 **R** *020 †80
FLANAGAN, Wm Patrick, Jr. 1111 DELAFIELD ST, STE 12 53188 #021-05-1980 L1988
  U *020 †95
FOLEY, John Jos. N14W23900 STONE RIDGE DR 53188 #016-43-1956 L1959 **OM GP** *071 †85
FOX, Christopher John. 1111 DELAFIELD ST STE 209, SURGERY, S.C. 53188
  #056-06-1998 L1999 **GS** *020 †85
FOX, Paul Fabian, II. 725 AMERICAN AVE, WAUKESHA MEMORIAL HOSPITAL 53188
  #056-06-1994 L1995 **VIR R** *020 †80
FRANCIS, Robert James. 721 AMERICAN AVE 53188 #056-06-1960 L1962 **P** *071
FRANCKEN, Gregory Allen. 725 AMERICAN AVE 53188 #056-05-1990 L1991 **NM R** *020 †80,28
FRANTA, Amy Katherine. 721 AMERICAN AVE, STE 205 53188 #056-05-1999 L2000
  ORS *020 †40
FRANTZ, Richard Geo. ■ 53186 #056-05-1954 L1955 **GS** *071 †85
FRITSCHE, Claire. 721 AMERICAN AVE, STE 511 53188 #056-06-1978 L1979 **IM NEP** *020
GAGER, Walter Edward. 725 AMERICAN AVE 53188 #056-06-1963 L1965 **OPH** *071 †35
GALLAGHER, Thomas J. N14W23900 STONE RIDGE DR 53188 #056-06-1978 L1979
  IM *020 †20
GANNE, Vasundhara. 721 AMERICAN AVE, STE 511 53188 #495-62-1996 L2001 **NEP** *020 †20
GARD, Anne Lajean. ■ 53186 #056-06-2007 **FP** *012
GARDNER, James David. 725 AMERICAN AVE, MEDICAL STAFF OFFICE 53188
  #056-06-1975 L1976 **FM** *030 †18
GEISS, Peter Thos. N17W24100 RIVERWOOD DR, STE 130 53188 #028-34-1978 L1982
  IM IMG *020 †20
GILES, Steven Alan. 717 W MORELAND BLVD 53188 #016-01-1979 L1980 **FM FSM** *020
GILL, Harinder Singh. 1111 DELAFIELD ST, STE 215 53188 #917-12-1982 L1990 **CD** *020 †20
GINN, Patrick Hing, Jr. 210 NW BARSTOW ST STE 201, RESIDENCY PROGRAM 53188
  #032-01-1993 L1994 **FM** *020 †18
GOLDSTONE, Michael Saul. 2422 N GRANDVIEW BLVD 53188 #028-34-1986 L1987
  ADM IM *020 †20
GOTH, Eric Joseph. ■ 53189 #056-06-2006 L2008 **DR** *012
GRIFFAY, Anthony Mack. 725 AMERICAN AVE 53188 #005-06-1988 L1992 **EM** *020 †16
GROGAN, John Robert. 725 AMERICAN AVE 53188 #056-06-1996 L1997 **RNR** *020 †80
HAHN, Lisa Marie. ■ 53186 #056-06-2008 *012
HAINZLSPERGER, Kory Richa. ■ 53186 #056-06-2007 **IM** *012
HANSON, James Coe. 1111 DELAFIELD ST, STE 105 53188 #056-05-1965 L1966 **N** *071 †75
HARDY, Kimberly Jean. N17W24100 RIVERWOOD DR, STE 150 53188 #018-03-1997 L1998
  FM *020 †18
HARLAND, Russell William. N14W23900 STONE RIDGE DR 53188 #056-06-1987 L1988
  PCC *020 †20
HARRIS, John A. 1111 DELAFIELD ST 53188 #056-06-1960 L1961 **GE IM** *071 †20
HART, Kevin Scott. 1111 DELAFIELD ST STE 209, WAUKESHA SURGICAL SPECIALI 53188
  #056-05-1987 L1988 **GS VS** *020 †85
HARTKE, Kathy D. 20611 WATERTOWN RD 53186 #056-06-1983 L1984 **OBG** *020 †30
HAUPERT, A Peter. ■ 53186 #041-01-1963 L1965 **GP GS** *071 †85,16
HEIN, Richard Curtis. 1111 DELAFIELD ST, WAUKESHA UROLOGY SC 53188
  #016-06-1966 L1975 **U** *020 †95
HELLING, Robert David. 725 AMERICAN AVE 53188 #056-06-1962 L1964 **R GP** *020 †80
HELZ, Timothy James. 725 AMERICAN AVE, ER DEPT 53188 #056-06-1973 L1974 **EM** *020 †16
HERMAN, Lavern Harry. 725 AMERICAN AVE 53188 #056-05-1956 L1968 **NS** *071
HIGGINS-LARKEY, Susan M. 1111 DELAFIELD ST, STE 213 53188 #056-06-1991 L1992
  AI *020 †20,03
HILGEMAN, Alan Carl. N14W23900 STONE RIDGE DR 53188 #017-20-1975 L1976
  RHU *020 †20
HILLAN, Donald D. 725 AMERICAN AVE 53188 #041-13-1949 L1954 **PD** *020
HOLLISTER, Mark Clifford. 725 AMERICAN AVE 53188 #056-05-1987 L1995 **DR** *020 †80
HOLLOWAY, David Edwin. 2717 N GRANDVIEW BLVD, STE 303 53188 #011-02-1985 L1986
  P N *020 †75
HOLUB, Daniel Patrick. 1111 DELAFIELD ST, STE 120 53188 #056-06-1992 L1993 **ORS** *020 †40
HOLZMACHER, Ryan Daniel. 1111 DELAFIELD ST STE 212, NEPHROLOGY ASSOCIATES 53188
  #016-45-1999 L2000 **NEP** *020 †20
HOSTETLER, Harry Benton. N17W24100 RIVERWOOD DR, STE 250 53188 #016-01-2002 L2005
  IM *020 †20
HUBER, Karri A. ■ 53188 #028-78-2006, ▲ L2008 **IM** *012
HUCKSTORF, Brian Leslie. 725 AMERICAN AVE, EMERGENCY MEDICAL ASSOCIAT 53188
  #056-06-1999 L2002 **EM** *020 †16
HUEBLER, Stephen Mitchell. 725 AMERICAN AVE 53188 #056-06-1989 L1992 **AN** *020 †05
HUGHET, Keith R. 21300 JILL CT 53186 #018-03-1951 L1970 **P** *020
HUNTER, Susan Kay. 1111 DELAFIELD ST, STE 311 53188 #056-05-1982 L1987 **GYN** *020 †30
HUSSUSSIAN, Christopher J. N4W22370 BLUEMOUND RD, ASSOCIATES 53186
  #008-01-1990 L2004 **PS GS** *020 †85,65
IORIO, Kathryn Dykstra. 1111 DELAFIELD ST, STE 115, WAUKESHA PEDIATRIC ASSOCIA 53188
  #035-15-1968 L1974 **PD** *020 †55
JAEGER, John Michael Jos. N17W24100 RIVERWOOD DR 53188 #056-05-1978 L1981 **FM** *030 †18
JAHNKE, Jacqueline P. 725 AMERICAN AVE 53188 #056-06-1990 L1991 **VIR R** *020 †80
JOHNSON, Stephanie Lee. ■ 53189 #056-06-2007 **FP** *012
JOLIN, James Louis. 707 W MORELAND BLVD STE 6 53188 #056-05-1966 L1967
  GS VS *071 †85
JONES, Genevieve Marie. N14W23900 STONE RIDGE DR 53188 #056-06-1998 L2002 **N** *020
JONES, James Curtis. 725 AMERICAN AVE, DEPT RAD ONCOLOGY 53188 #017-20-1989 L1993
  RO *020 †80
JOSEPH, Meena M. N14W23900 STONE RIDGE DR 53188 #495-63-1978 L1992
  IM IMG *020 †20
KAJUCH, Anna Lucia. 20700 WATERTOWN RD 53186 #286-06-1964 L1999 **P** *020
KANE, Kevin John. 725 AMERICAN AVE, WAUKESHA MEMORIAL HOSPITAL 53188
  #056-06-1993 L1994 **AN** *020 †05
KAPLAN, Steven Jay. W231N1440 CORPORATE CT, STE 200 53186 #035-06-1978 L1983
  ORS OSM *020 †40
KASCHT, Robert Lawrence. ■ 53186 #016-06-1948 L1948 **PTH** *071 †50
KASS, Gregory Allen. 725 AMERICAN AVE 53188 #056-06-1985 L1988 **DR NR** *020 †80
KATIB, Imad. 721 AMERICAN AVE STE 410 53188 #915-04-1977 L1987 **IM CD** *020 †20
KENGIS, Janis John. 1111 DELAFIELD ST, STE 216 53188 #025-07-1966 L1969 **GE IM** *020 †20
KERN, Martin Wm. 1111 DELAFIELD ST STE 203 53188 #056-06-1969 L1970 **IM** *020 †20
KESHAVA BHAT, Kshama. ■ 53188 #496-33-2003 *100
KHALIL, Moeen. 2130 BIG BEND RD, SOUTH 53189 #016-11-2000 L2002 **IM** *020 †20

KIM, Moon Ja. W231N1440 CORPORATE CT, STE 310 53186 #187-76-1984 L1994 **P** *020 †75
KING, Christopher. 725 AMERICAN AVE 53188 #028-79-1985, ▲ L1992 **NS** *020
KISICKI, Judith Marie. 725 AMERICAN AVE, CTR OF BEHAVIORAL HLTH 53188
  #030-05-1993 L1994 **P** *020 †75
KLAAS, Kathleen Kay. 725 AMERICAN AVE 53188 #030-06-1990 L1991 **DR** *020 †80
KLEMISH, Steven Wesley. 2130 BIG BEND RD, WAUKESHA MED CTR SOUTH 53189
  #018-03-1995 L1996 **FM** *020 †18
KLEWIN, Kristine Marie. W238N1610 BUSSE RD, STE 100 53188 #056-05-1978 L1979
  OPH *020 †35
KLOS, Stephen Scott. 210 NW BARSTOW ST STE 201, PRACTICE PRGM 53188
  #056-05-2004 L2007 **FP** *012
KLOSS, Raymond John. 725 AMERICAN AVE # 501 53188 #038-41-1987 L1992 **P** *020 †75
KNAPP, Meghan Therese. 1111 DELAFIELD ST, STE 115 53188 #010-02-2003 L2007
  PD *020 †55
KOENIG, Patrick Neal. W238N1610 BUSSE RD, THE ORTHOPAEDIC SURGERY CE 53188
  #038-45-1994 L1996 **AN** *020 †05
KOHLENBERG, Cary Jay. 2717 GRANDVIEW BLVD, STE 202 53188 #056-05-1989 L1990
  P *020 †75
KOHLI, Alka. 725 AMERICAN AVE 53188 #495-41-1972 L1981 **PM** *020 †60
KONETZKI, Wayne Harry. 403 N GRAND AVE 53186 #016-11-1961 L1962 **A IM** *020
KORKOR, Adel. 1111 DELAFIELD ST STE 327 53188 #875-01-1974 L1981 **NEP IM** *020 †20
KORKOS, George James. N4W22370 BLUEMOUND RD, ASSOCIATES 53186
  #056-06-1959 L1960 **PS HS** *020 †65
KORKOS, Thomas Geo. N4W22370 BLUEMOUND RD, ASSOCIATES 53186 #056-06-1990 L1993
  PS *020 †65
KOSS, Scott Allen. 725 AMERICAN AVE 53188 #056-06-1998 L1999 **DR** *020 †80
KOUZOVA, Margarita K. 20611 WATERTOWN RD, STE J 53186 #198-01-1988 L2002 **PTH** *020
KRAKLOW, William M. 721 AMERICAN AVE, STE 511 53188 #056-06-1992 L1993 **NEP** *020 †20
KRASOVICH, Susanne Marie. 210 NW BARSTOW ST, STE 201 53188 #032-01-1993 L2004
  FM *020 †18
KRETZSCHMAR, Susan D. 725 AMERICAN AVE, WMH LABATORY 53188 #018-03-1984 L1986
  PTH PCP *020 †50
KRISMER, Patrick Geo. W231N1440 CORPORATE CT, AURORA HEALTH CENTER 53186
  #056-05-1992 L1993 **FM** *020 †18
KULICK, Steven Kenneth. 725 AMERICAN AVE, ER DEPT 53188 #056-06-1988 L1992
  EM *020 †16
KUMAR, Rajesh. 500 RIVERVIEW AVE 53188 #495-21-1985 L1990 **P** *020 †75
KURIAN, Seira. 2600 FOX HILL DR 53189 #422-01-1998 L2004 **GPM** *020 †70
LA JOIE, William J. ■ 53189 #010-02-1946 L1976 **PM** *071 †60
LALICH, Roger A. 721 AMERICAN AVE, STE 304 53188 #039-79-1977, ▲ L1978
  OBG REN *030
LANE, Jack Tuttle. ■ 53186 #018-03-1966 L1969 **MDM** *071 †20
LANS, Joel Isidore. 1111 DELAFIELD ST, STE 216 53188 #056-06-1985 L1990 **GE IM** *020 †20
LARSON, Jill C. 210 NW BARSTOW ST, STE 201 53188 #025-76-2005, ▲ L2006 **FP** *012
LARSON, Paul Richard. 721 AMERICAN AVE, STE 501 53188 #046-01-1996 L1997
  CHP *020 †75
LAWSON, Russell Kenneth. 721 AMERICAN AVE, STE 402 53188 #040-02-1963 L1976
  U OS *040 †95
LEECH, Richard Butler. 721 AMERICAN AVE, WAUKESHA 53188 #016-11-1983 L1986
  CD IM *020 †20
LEMARBRE, Gabrielle Betty. ■ 53186 #056-05-2007 **IM** *012
LE MARBRE, Paul Jos. 725 AMERICAN AVE 53188 #026-04-1974 L1991 **ON HEM** *020 †20
LEONHARDT, James Gates. 1111 DELAFIELD ST, STE 311 53188 #025-01-1987 L1994
  OBG *020 †30
LESNIAK, John Charles. N4W22370 BLUEMOUND RD, STE 200 53186 #056-06-1997 L1998
  FM *020 †18
LESNIAK, Robert Joseph. 725 AMERICAN AVE 53188 #056-06-1997 L1998 **VIR R** *020 †80
LEWAN, Richard B, Jr. N17W24100 RIVERWOOD DR, STE 250 53188 #016-02-1979 L1982
  FM *040 †20
LEWIS, Tracy Marie. 2130 BIG BEND RD, MEDICAL CENTERS-SOUTH 53189
  #016-45-1997 L1998 **FM** *020 †18
LINDBERG, Ruth F. 210 NW BARSTOW ST STE 201, WAUKESHA FAMILY PRACTICE 53188
  #016-43-2003 L2004 **FM** *020 †18
LINDORFER, Donald B J. ■ 53186 #056-06-1956 L1957 **FM EM** *071 †18
LIPMAN, Brian Thos. 725 AMERICAN AVE, DEPARTMENT RADIOLOGY 53188
  #056-06-1987 L1988 **PDR** *020 †80,28
LLOYD, Brian Emory. 1501 AIRPORT RD, CENTER 53188 #016-11-1967 L1979 **P N** *071 †75
LONG, Michael Jos. N4W22370 BLUEMOUND RD 53186 #056-06-1990 L1991 **FM** *020 †18
LOPEZ, Gertrudez. ■ 53186 #018-03-1981 L1986 **IM** *074
LO PRESTI, Leigh Stewart. 210 NW BARSTOW ST, STE 201 53188 #050-02-1983 L2004
  FM *020 †18
LORENZEN, Kraig Elmer. 122 DOUGLAS AVE 53186 #016-42-1979 L1980 **CD IC** *020
LUNDE, Michael Roy. 1111 DELAFIELD ST, STE 218 53188 #023-01-1980 L1981 **FM** *020 †18
LUTZ, William Frederick. 1111 DELAFIELD ST, STE 203 53188 #056-06-1986 L1987 **IM** *020 †20
MACKIEL, Punnoose. ■ 53188 #495-98-1970 L1986 **GP** *072
MAJEED, Lubna. 721 AMERICAN AVE, STE 511 53188 #704-25-1990 L1999 **CCM** *020 †20
MAKHIJA, Sarita. N14W23900 STONE RIDGE DR 53188 #495-67-1978 L1985 **IM** *020 †20
MALINOVIC, Rada. 1501 AIRPORT RD, WAUKESHA COUNTY MENTAL HEA 53188
  #056-05-1993 L1994 **P** *020
MANSOUR-SHAMMO, Faye E. 20611 WATERTOWN RD 53186 #875-02-1987 L1994
  PD *020 †55
MARTIN, Matthew Steven. ■ 53186 #056-05-2007 *012
MARTIN, Tracy. 725 AMERICAN AVE 53188 #056-06-1998 L1999 **DR** *020 †80
MARTINELLI, Anne T. N14W23900 STONE RIDGE DR 53188 #056-06-2001 L2005 **OBG** *020
MATEER, James Robt. 725 AMERICAN AVE, ER DEPT 53188 #016-45-1980 L1981 **EM** *020 †16
MATHER, Michael Cory. W231N1440 CORPORATE CT, AURORA HLTH CTR 53186
  #056-06-1984 L1985 **FM** *020 †18
MATHEWS, Edwin L, Jr. 725 AMERICAN AVE, WAUKESHA MEMORIAL HOSPITAL 53188
  #056-05-1982 L1983 **GS AN** *020 †05
MAUSNER, Keith Lincoln. 725 AMERICAN AVE, EMERG DEPT 53188 #007-02-1986 L1992
  EM *020 †16
MAZZONE, Michael Francis. 210 NW BARSTOW ST, STE 201 53188 #041-02-1992 L1999
  FM *020 †18
MC AVOY, Timothy Gerard. 1751 E MAIN ST 53188 #035-09-1973 L1979 **IM** *020 †20
MC CALL, Tracy Evelyn. N4W22370 BLUEMOUND RD 53186 #038-45-1993 L2001
  PS GS *020 †65

MC COMIS, Mary Louise. N14W23900 STONE RIDGE DR, MEDICAL ASSOCIATES 53188 #016-01-1989 L1993 **OBG** *020 †30

MEIER, Ann. 725 AMERICAN AVE 53188 #056-06-1993 L1995 **DR** *020 †80

MEYER, Glenn Arthur. 1111 DELAFIELD ST, NEUROLOGIC ASSOCIATES OF 53188 #056-05-1960 L1961 **NS** *020 †25

MEYER, Matthew A. 721 AMERICAN AVE, STE 304 53188 #010-02-1971 L1975 **OBG** *020 †30

MISORSKI, David Andrew. W231N1440 CORPORATE CT 53186 #056-06-1991 L1992 **FM** *020 †18

MOEHRING, Grant William. 725 AMERICAN AVE, ER DEPT 53188 #016-43-1999 L2000 **EM** *020 †16

MOONEY, John P. W231N1440 CORPORATE CT 53186 #056-06-1996 L1997 **FM** *020 †18

MORGAN, Stephen Edward. N17W24100 RIVERWOOD DR, STE 150 53188 #040-02-1999 L2000 **FM** *020 †18

MOSS, Kevin Vincent. N14W23900 STONE RIDGE DR 53188 #016-01-1986 L1991 **GS** *020 †85

MOTHS, Robert Wayne. 725 AMERICAN AVE 53188 #056-05-1974 L1975 **DR** *020 †80

MUCHE, Todd James. 721 AMERICAN AVE, STE 511 53188 #025-07-1990 L1991 **IM NEP** *020 †20

NAGEL, James Henry. 1111 DELAFIELD ST, STE 314 53188 #028-34-1973 L1974 **OPH** *020

NAKATA, Marie Louise. 2717 N GRANDVIEW BLVD, STE 101 53188 #056-06-1989 L1991 **D** *020 †15

NANCHAL, Rahul Sudhir. ■ 53188 #495-45-1999 L2005 **CCM** *020

NELSON, Brian Donald. 1111 DELAFIELD ST, STE 215 53188 #056-05-1991 L1997 **IC** *020 †20

NEUMANN, Jane L Schneider. 725 AMERICAN AVE 53188 #056-06-1970 L1971 **PUD IM** *020

NIEDFELDT, Mark Wm. 210 NW BARSTOW ST, STE 201 53188 #056-06-1992 L1994 **FSM** *020 †18

NORTON, Laura Elaine. ■ 53186 #026-04-2007 **PD** *012

O'NEILL, Paul Jos. N14W23900 STONE RIDGE DR 53188 #025-07-1988 L1992 **IM PD** *020 †20,55

OSTENDORF, Julia. 1111 DELAFIELD ST STE 115, WAUKESHA PEDIATRIC ASSOC L 53188 #033-06-1988 L1989 **PD** *020 †55

OVERLIN, Amy Jo Fink. 210 NW BARSTOW ST 53188 #017-20-2002 L2003 **FM** *100 †18

OWENS, Dawn Patrice. 210 NW BARSTOW ST, STE 201 53188 #038-75-2005, ▲ L2006 **FP** *012

PALLIN, J Cary. 725 AMERICAN AVE 53188 #004-01-1983 L1988 **DR** *020 †80

PALLIN, John Steven. 725 AMERICAN AVE 53188 #056-06-1980 L1988 **DR** *020 †80

PALMER, Thomas Edward. 721 AMERICAN AVE, WAUKESHA 53188 #056-06-1971 L1974 **CD** *020 †20

PARTHUM, Peter John. 725 AMERICAN AVE 53188 #056-06-1976 L1977 **FM GPM** *020 †70

PATEL, Asmita Ramji. ■ 53189 #905-02-2002 L2003 **RHU** *012 †20

PATEL, Dhaval Bhupendrabh. ■ 53186 #495-89-2001 L2004 **IM** *012 †20

PEQUET, Archebald J. 1111 DELAFIELD ST STE 209 53188 #025-01-1981 L1982 **GS VS** *020 †85

PEREZ, Francisco. 725 AMERICAN AVE, WAUKESHA MEMORIAL HOSPITAL 53188 #056-06-1991 L1992 **AN** *020 †05

PETERSEN, Deborah Jean. 1111 DELAFIELD ST STE 115, WAUKESHA PEDIATRIC ASSOCIA 53188 #030-05-1982 L1990 **PD PDE** *020 †55

PETERSON, Brian Lee. 515 W MORELAND BLVD 53188 #056-06-1980 L2006 **FOP PTH** *062 †50

PIERNOT, Ellen Elizabeth. ■ 53188 #056-06-2004 L2005 **FM** *020 †18

PIKNA, David John. 20611 WATERTOWN RD, STE C 53186 #056-06-1982 L1983 **PD** *020 †55

PLETZKE, Frank Ted. 500 RIVERVIEW AVE, WAUKESHA COUNTY HHS 53188 #056-05-1973 L1983 **P** *020 †75

POLLEMA, Andrea M. N17W24100 RIVERWOOD DR, STE 250 53188 #026-04-2002 L2005 **IM** *100 †20

PRINCE, Darryl Marc. 1111 DELAFIELD ST, NEUROLOGIC ASSOCIATES OF 53188 #030-06-1992 L1996 **N** *020 †75

PROWATZKE, Sherry L. 20611 WATERTOWN RD 53186 #056-06-1986 L1990 **OBG** *020 †30

PYNE, Lynn Shallberg. N14W23900 STONE RIDGE DR 53188 #047-05-1981 L1987 **PD** *020 †55

QUASNEY, Michael William. ■ 53189 #016-11-1988 L2006 **PD CCP** *020 †55

QURAISHI, Kamran Raza. 725 AMERICAN AVE 53188 #665-01-2004 L2007 **IM** *020

RADUEGE, John William. 2130 BIG BEND RD, WAUKESHA MED CTR S 53189 #056-05-1995 L1998 **FM** *020 †18

RAMOS, Manuel Posadas. 1501 AIRPORT RD 53188 #748-01-1971 L1980 **P** *020

RASLAU, Flavius Daniel. ■ 53188 #016-42-2005 L2006 **DR** *012

RASMUSSEN, Robert James. N14W23900 STONE RIDGE DR 53188 #056-05-1957 L1958 **U** *071 †95

RASTER, Michael Joseph. 721 AMERICAN AVE, STE 501 53188 #025-07-1993 L1998 **P** *020 †75

REED, Jennifer Lynn. 2130 BIG BEND RD, % PROHEALTH CARE MEDICAL C 53189 #056-06-2004 L2006 **FM** *020 †18

REICHERT, Kenneth Wm. 1111 DELAFIELD ST, NEUROLOGIC ASSOCIATES OF 53188 #056-06-1986 L1987 **NS** *020 †20

REIS, Bridget Kathleen. 210 NW BARSTOW ST 53188 #056-06-2005 L2006 **FP** *012

RESHEL, Edward Gerald. N14W23900 STONE RIDGE DR 53188 #030-06-1986 L1987 **N** *020 †75

RIENDL, Anne Marie. 721 AMERICAN AVE STE 310 53188 #056-06-1977 L1978 **OBG** *020 †30

ROGERS, David Wesley. 1111 DELAFIELD ST STE 216 53188 #017-20-1986 L1992 **GE IM** *020 †20

ROLFES-LO, Maryjo Rose. 2130 BIG BEND RD 53189 #026-04-1990 L1997 **AI IM** *020 †20,03

ROMASHKO, Alexander A. 721 AMERICAN AVE STE 510 53188 #056-05-2000 L2004 **OTO** *020 †45

ROZNIK, Mark Thos. N14W23900 STONE RIDGE DR 53188 #056-06-1985 L1988 **IM** *020 †20

RUGGERI, Antony. N14W23833 STONE RIDGE DR, STE 200 53188 #048-04-1998 L2004 **ON** *020 †20

RUTHERFORD, James Lee. 1501 AIRPORT RD, WAUKESHA COUNTY MNTL HLTH 53188 #018-03-1980 L2004 **P PYG** *020 †75

RYNDA, Joy Ann. W231N1440 CORPORATE CT 53186 #056-06-1985 L1986 **PD** *020 †55

SAEIAN, Kooroush. 721 AMERICAN AVE, WAUKESHA 53188 #056-06-1985 L1988 **CD IM** *020

SARAN, Dennis James. 20611 WATERTOWN RD 53186 #016-43-1980 L1981 **PD** *020 †55

SAWALL, Gerhard Frank. N14W23900 STONE RIDGE DR 53188 #056-06-1988 L1991 **PD** *020 †55

SCANDURA-ENGDAHL, M. 721 AMERICAN AVE STE 309 53188 #041-07-1994 L1996 **PD** *020 †55

SCHELLINGER, Robert E. 717 W MORELAND BLVD 53188 #056-06-1995 L1996 **FM** *020 †18

SCHIEDERMAYER, David L. 725 AMERICAN AVE, WAUKESHA MEMORIAL HOSPITAL 53188 #056-06-1982 L1982 **IM** *020 †20

SCHMITT, David Dale. 1111 DELAFIELD ST STE 209 53188 #056-06-1982 L1983 **VS** *020 †85

SCOTT, Robert Douglas. 210 NW BARSTOW ST STE 201, PRACTICE PRGM 53188 #056-06-2006 **FM** *100

SEIFERT, Paul Edward. 725 AMERICAN AVE 53188 #011-03-1979 L1986 **TS GS** *020 †85,90

SEMMLER, Steven Duane. ■ 53189 #028-34-2005 L2005 **FP** *012

SHEEDY, Thomas Jude. 721 AMERICAN AVE, STE 309 53188 #056-06-1989 L1996 **PD** *020 †55

SIDHU, Sarfraz Singh. 725 AMERICAN AVE, RM 2036 53188 #305-01-2003 L2006 **IM** *020

SIERASKI, Madelyn Carol. 2130 BIG BEND RD, PROHEALTH CARE MEDICAL CEN 53189 #016-01-1990 L1991 **FM** *020 †18

SINGH, Sanjay. 1111 DELAFIELD ST STE 215, WAUKESHA HEART INSTITUTE 53188 #495-41-1977 L1981 **CD IM** *020 †20

SINGH, Shaila. 1111 DELAFIELD ST STE 218 53188 #495-74-1981 L1985 **FM** *020 †18

SKULASON, Thorsteinn. N17W24100 RIVERWOOD DR, WAUKESHA HEALTH CARE 53188 #484-01-1988 L2004 **D** *020 †20,15

SMITH, Stanya. 1111 DELAFIELD ST STE 105, NEUROLOGIC ASSOCIATES OF 53188 #759-11-1977 L2004 **N CN** *020 †75

SMITH, William Dean. 725 AMERICAN AVE 53188 #038-41-1959 L1960 **D** *071 †15

SORE, Michael. 725 AMERICAN AVE, ER DEPT 53188 #011-04-1998 L2002 **EM** *020 †16

SPONAGLE, Christine Ann. 1111 DELAFIELD ST, STE 311 53188 #056-05-2000 L2001 **OBG** *020

STAFF, David Mitchell. N14W23900 STONE RIDGE DR 53188 #056-06-1991 L1992 **GE** *020 †20

STAUDACHER, Richard A. 721 AMERICAN AVE STE 3, CARDIOLOGY ASSOCIATES OF 53188 #056-06-1983 L1990 **CD IM** *020 †20

STAUDT, Susan Revers. ■ 53188 #041-01-1988 L2001 **CCA** *020 †05,55

STEINBAUER, Marian C. ■ 53188 #025-01-1963 L1964 **OS** *074

STERNITZKY, Nicole Lynn. 20611 WATERTOWN RD 53186 #056-06-1997 L2006 **OBG** *020 †30

STEVENSON, Katherine R. 725 AMERICAN AVE 53188 #016-06-1989 L1996 **OBG** *020 †30

STUEVEN, Harlan Alvin. 725 AMERICAN AVE, ER DEPT 53188 #026-04-1977 L1981 **EM AM** *020 †16

SUKOWATY, Laura Catherine. 725 AMERICAN AVE 53188 #056-06-1993 L1995 **FM** *020 †18

SUWANABOL, Pasithorn Amy. ■ 53186 #056-05-2007 **GS** *012

SWIONTONIOWSKI, Mary C. 725 AMERICAN AVE 53188 #047-05-1981 L2004 **IM IMG** *020 †20

SZATKOWSKI, Frank Scott. 725 AMERICAN AVE 53188 #016-43-1999 L2004 **EM** *020 †16

TANEL, Gwendolyn Ann. 717 W MORELAND BLVD 53188 #056-06-1984 L1985 **FM** *020 †18

TAYLOR, Matthew William. 1111 DELAFIELD ST, STE 311 53188 #056-06-1999 L2001 **OBG** *020 †30

THILL, Andrew Robert. ■ 53186 #056-06-2008 *012

THIRUMAKIZHMARAN, Uma. N14W23900 STONE RIDGE DR 53188 #495-66-1992 L1997 **IM** *020 †20

THOMPSON, Michael Alan. 725 AMERICAN AVE STE 108, WAUKESHA MEMORIAL HOSPITAL 53188 #026-08-2001 L2007 **HO** *020 †20

THORGERSEN, Thor Magnus. 725 AMERICAN AVE 53188 #056-06-1953 L1958 **PTH** *071 †50

THORSEN, Marie Kristin. 725 AMERICAN AVE, WAUKESHA MEM HOSP RAD DEPT 53188 #035-01-1977 L1981 **DR** *020 †80

TOMASELLO, Dean Michael. W296N535 BLODWEN DR 53188 #056-06-1993 L1996 **FM** *020 †18 ‡

TONSFELDT, Denis John. 725 AMERICAN AVE, ER DEPT 53188 #018-03-1975 L1982 **EM** *020 †16

TOUSIGNANT, Ann Marie. 721 AMERICAN AVE, STE 304 53188 #056-06-1980 L1981 **OBG** *020 †30

TROTIER, Anna Han. 20611 WATERTOWN RD, STE E 53186 #056-06-1995 L1996 **OBG** *020 †30

TROTIER, Timothy S. 725 AMERICAN AVE 53188 #056-06-1995 L1996 **AN** *020 †05

TRUEMAN, Laurence Wm. 1501 AIRPORT RD, CENTER 53188 #025-07-1992 L1993 **P** *020 †75

TZEEL, Eyal Albert. N19W24133 RIVERWOOD DR, STE 300 53188 #025-01-1986 L1999 **PD MDM** *030 †55

TZOUGROS, Joseph Nicholas. N14W23900 STONE RIDGE DR 53188 #056-06-1989 L1990 **PD** *020 †55

ULATOWSKI, Tami L. W231N1440 CORPORATE CT 53186 #056-06-1985 L1986 **AN IM** *020 †20,05

USOLTSEV, Nikolay. ■ 53186 #913-08-2005 **AN** *012

UY, Kathleen Wan. 721 AMERICAN AVE, STE 511 53188 #748-10-1993 L1999 **NEP** *020 †20

VACEK, Steven James. 210 NW BARSTOW ST, STE 201 53188 #056-06-1992 L1993 **FM** *020 †18

VAN BEEK, Jeffrey Thomas. 725 AMERICAN AVE 53188 #056-06-1996 L2000 **DR** *020 †80

VARMA, Som Datta. 725 AMERICAN AVE 53188 #495-21-1955 L1966 **PTH** *071 †50

VERMA, Ashish. 721 AMERICAN AVE, STE 409 53188 #038-41-1996 L1997 **IM** *020 †20

VORPERIAN, Vicken Roupen. 721 AMERICAN AVE, STE 410 53188 #605-01-1985 L1993 **ICE CD** *020 †20

WAHMHOFF, Christine Ann. N14W23900 STONE RIDGE DR 53188 #018-03-1991 L1994 **IM** *030 †20

WAKEFIELD, David Walter. 725 AMERICAN AVE 53188 #056-06-1982 L1983 **AN** *020 †05

WARREN, Gregory V. 721 AMERICAN AVE, STE 511 53188 #495-09-1977 L1984 **NEP IM** *020 †20

WARREN, Paul James. 721 AMERICAN AVE, STE 511 53188 #422-01-1987 L1989 **NEP IM** *020 †20

WELNIAK, Linda Marie. W231N1440 CORPORATE CT 53186 #056-06-1992 L1993 **FM** *020 †18

WICHMAN, Harvey Mitchell. W231N1440 CORPORATE CT, STE 200 53186 #056-05-1965 L1966 **ORS** *020 †40

WICHMAN, Mark Todd. W231N1440 CORPORATE CT, STE 200 53186 #056-05-1990 L1996 **OSM** *020 †40

WILKES, Geoffrey Owen. ■ 53189 #025-01-2008 *012

WILLIAMS-ANGSTEN, Beth M. 725 AMERICAN AVE 53188 #016-01-1982 L1986 **OBG** *020 †30

WILSON, Janell Renee. 210 NW BARSTOW ST, STE 201 53188 #056-05-2005 L2006 **FP** *012

WILSON, Thomas Jerome. 500 RIVERVIEW AVE 53188 #056-06-1971 L1977 **P** *020 †75

WITEK, Diane Marie. ■ 53188 #056-05-2007 **FP** *012

WITTMANN, Thomas Glen. 717 W MORELAND BLVD 53188 #056-06-1984 L1985 **FM** *020 †18

WOODS, Michael P. 725 AMERICAN AVE, WAUKECHA MEM HOSP INC 53188 #056-06-1979 L1981 **AN** *020 †05

YAGODA, Brian Mitchell. N17W24100 RIVERWOOD DR, STE 250 53188 #016-11-1986 L1994 **PD** *020 †55

YENERICH, David Orlin. 725 AMERICAN AVE 53188 #056-05-1986 L1987 **DR N** *020 †80

YIANNIAS, Chris A. N14W23900 STONE RIDGE DR, MEDICAL ASSOC 53188 #028-78-1997, ▲ L1999 **IM** *020 †20

YOUSIF, N John. W231N1440 CORPORATE CT, # 201 53186 #165-01-1979 L1982 **PS** *020 †65

ZANDT, John Robt. 725 AMERICAN AVE, RM 2036 53188 #056-05-1988 L1991 **IM** *020 †20

ZARLING, Terry Allen. 721 AMERICAN AVE, WAUKESHA 53188 #056-05-1986 L1987 **CD IM** *040 †20

ZARWELL, David Harvey. 741 N GRAND AVE STE 302, CORNERSTONE COUNSELING SVC 53186 #056-05-1965 L1968 **CHP P** *071

ZBLEWSKI, Randall Joseph. W231N1440 CORPORATE CT, STE 310 53186 #056-06-1981 L1982 P *020 †75

WAUNAKEE – DANE

BARTLETT, Cheryl Anne. ■ 53597 #056-05-1973 L1978 PD *074 †55
CRUZ, Nazario Ramirez. ■ 53597 #748-01-1955 L1966 FM *020
DAVENPORT, Douglas James. ■ 53597 #056-06-2007 IM *012
FLYNN, Mary Catherine. 208 S CENTURY AVE 53597 #040-02-1984 L1994 IM *020 †20
HOUNSHELL, Jennie Burr. 208 S CENTURY AVE, UW HEALH-WAUNAKEE 53597 #041-12-2004 L2005 FM *020 †18
MISCHLER, Nicholas Emory. PO BOX 7 53597 #041-01-1970 L1977 MDM IM *071 †20
O'CONNOR, Angela M. ■ 53597 #026-04-1993 L2002 PD *020 †55
RANUM, William Howard, Jr. 202 S CENTURY AVE 53597 #056-05-1987 L1988 FM OBG *020 †18
ROSEN, Melvin Harris. 202 S CENTURY AVE 53597 #011-02-1977 L1978 FM *020 †18
ROWE, John Wm. ■ 53597 #056-05-1977 L1978 EM *020 †16
THOMPSON, Trent Daniel. 202 S CENTURY AVE, DEAN CLINIC WAUANAKEE 53597 #056-05-1994 L2000 FM *020 †18 ‡

WAUPACA – WAUPACA

ANDERSON, Earl Lamar. 710 RIVERSIDE DR 54981 #026-04-1984 L1985 FM *020 †18
ARBOLEDA, Reginaldo V. ■ 54981 #748-29-1988 L1998 FM *020 †18
BAUER, Michael Henry. 710 RIVERSIDE DR 54981 #026-04-1984 L1986 FM *020 †18
BLUM, Barton Jerome. 710 RIVERSIDE DR 54981 #016-43-1969 L1977 GS *071 †85
BROWN, John Francis. ■ 54981 #056-06-1960 L1961 IM *071
BURGSTEDE, Gilbert C. 800 RIVERSIDE DR 54981 #056-06-1976 L1979 EM *020 †18
BUTKIEWICZ, Russell Felix. 710 RIVERSIDE DR 54981 #056-05-1987 L1988 FM *020 †18
CARLOVSKY, Robert Eugene. ■ 54981 #056-05-1958 L1959 PTH *071 †50
COMEAU, Dorothy Ellen. 800 RIVERSIDE DR 54981 #035-01-1991 L1998 EM GP *020
DENT, Robert Arlie. 710 RIVERSIDE DR 54981 #056-05-1973 L1974 FM *020 †18
DOWLING, Noelle Kristine. 710 RIVERSIDE DR 54981 #056-05-1997 L2004 FM *020 †18
EDELMAN, Gary Chas. 902 RIVERSIDE DR, STE 201 54981 #032-01-1988 L1989 GS *020 †85
GEORGE, Anthony Dean. 800 RIVERSIDE DR, RIVERSIDE MEDICAL CENTER E 54981 #004-01-1981 L1998 EM IM *020 †20
HALE, Sabine Jutta. 800 RIVERSIDE DR 54981 #408-09-1978 L1997 PTH *020
HATHAWAY, David Saml. ■ 54981 #048-04-1963 L1969 NEP IM *071 †20
HILL, Karen Ruth. 1439 CHURCHILL ST STE 202, WAUPACA INT MED 54981 #048-15-1986 L2000 IM GYN *020 †20
HOELL, Paul Thomas. 800 RIVERSIDE DR 54981 #056-06-1994 L1995 AN *020 †05
HUBBARD, Stephen. 800 RIVERSIDE DR 54981 #016-11-1996 L1998 EM *020
HURST, Kenneth Arnold. W5589 N PINE LAKE RD 54981 #056-05-1956 L1957 R NM *071 †80
KENNEDY, Wm Frederick. ■ 54981 #056-06-1956 L1957 ORS *071 †40
KILE, Patti Ann. 710 RIVERSIDE DR 54981 #026-04-1980 L1994 FM *020 †18
LEWIS, Russell, Jr. 190 GRAND SEASONS DR 54981 #010-03-2002 L2006 FM *020 †18
LOCHNER, Donald Mark. 710 RIVERSIDE DR 54981 #056-05-1972 L1973 FM FPG *020 †18
MARTIN, Catherine C. 710 RIVERSIDE DR 54981 #021-01-1994 L1997 FM *020 †18
MCCAUSLAND, Joseph Daniel. 190 GRAND SEASONS DR 54981 #028-79-1999, ▲ L2002 IM *020
MC CRORY, Thomas Edwin. 710 RIVERSIDE DR 54981 #023-12-1993 L2005 GS *020 †85
MITCHELL, James Robert. 902 RIVERSIDE DR, STE 203 54981 #056-05-1987 L1992 ORS OFA *020 †40 ‡
OETKEN, Matthew S. 710 RIVERSIDE DR 54981 #018-75-1999, ▲ L2000 FM *020 †18
PETERSON, Robert Lester. 900 RIVERSIDE DR STE III 54981 #016-06-1972 L1975 FM EM *020 †18
PRECIADO RIESTRA, Juan Se. ■ 54981 #649-03-1999 L2004 FM *020 †18
RALSTON, Jeffrey Lee. 902 RIVERSIDE DR, STE 203 54981 #018-03-1993 L2000 ORS *020 †40
RATHJEN, Charles James. 710 RIVERSIDE DR 54981 #030-05-1985 L1986 FM *020 †18
SALAN, Jerry Richard. 710 RIVERSIDE DR 54981 #016-06-1960 L1961 FM *020 †18
SANO, Keith Kenji. 800 RIVERSIDE DR 54981 #014-01-1983 L1997 EM *020 †16
SEARS, Brian Richard. 902 RIVERSIDE DR, STE 203 54981 #038-40-1994 L1999 ORS OTR *020 †40
STEINER, John Herbert. 800 RIVERSIDE DR 54981 #056-06-1945 L1946 FM *071
STROBUSCH, Alan Dean. 710 RIVERSIDE DR 54981 #056-05-1980 L1981 FM *020 †18
STUBLER, Kathryn Marie. ■ 54981 #056-05-2008 *012
VEIGA, Richard Secundino. 800 RIVERSIDE DR 54981 #308-07-1983 L1987 PTH FOP *020 †50
WENBERG, Ellen Turner. 710 RIVERSIDE DR 54981 #056-06-2003 L2003 IMG *020 †18
WILLIAMS, James Stuart. 800 RIVERSIDE DR, RIVERSIDE MEDICAL CENTER 54981 #060-02-1991 L1997 FM *020 †18
WINCH, Thomas Riggs. ■ 54981 #056-05-1967 L1971 DR *071 †80
WUBBEN, Robert C. 902 RIVERSIDE DR, STE 203 54981 #056-06-1980 L1981 ORS *020 †40

WAUPUN – DODGE

ARELLANO, Corazon P. 612 W BROWN ST 53963 #748-01-1963 L1974 PD GP *020 †55
ARELLANO, Eduardo G. 608 W BROWN ST, WAUPUN MEMORIAL HOSPITAL 53963 #748-01-1963 L1976 OBG *020 †30
CHANG, Henry Ta-Shen. 620 W BROWN ST 53963 #244-04-1971 L1977 AN *020 †05
GEDYE, Jonathan. 620 W BROWN ST 53963 #016-02-1985 L1991 PTH *020 †50
HANSFIELD, Scott Merrill. 14 BEAVER DAM ST 53963 #016-06-1981 L2003 OBG *020 †30
HOFTIEZER, Scott Allen. 1 W LINCOLN ST BOX 661, DCI 53963 #023-07-1983 L1985 FM *020 †18
KIRSCH, John Michael. 620 W BROWN ST 53963 #028-11-1964 L1967 ORS *020 †40
NEWTON, Robert D. 14 BEAVER DAM ST 53963 #028-79-1995, ▲ L1998 FM OBS *020 †18
PAUSMA, Andrea Jenae. ■ 53963 #056-05-2007 *012
ROSALES, Mariano L, Jr. 600 FERN ST 53963 #748-11-1970 L1978 IM *020
SCHULZ, Gregory Leonard. 620 W BROWN ST, EMERGENCY DEPARTMENT 53963 #056-06-1984 L1987 IM *020 †18
SIRIN, Kerim Fikret. 1 W LINCOLN ST, DODGE CORRECT INSTIT HLT 53963 #902-03-1949 L1969 OBG *020 †30
TIMMERMANS, Peter Wm. 14 BEAVER DAM ST 53963 #065-06-1979 L1980 FM *020

TU, Her-Lang. 14 BEAVER DAM ST 53963 #244-01-1966 L1976 IM NEP *020 †20
VASQUEZ, Juan Angel. 14 BEAVER DAM ST, WAUPUN AREA CLINIC 53963 #025-01-1990 L2005 IM *020
WILLIAMS, Thomas Hugh. 1 W LINCOLN ST, DEPARTMENT OF CORRECTIONS 53963 #056-05-1975 L1976 FM *020 †18

WAUSAU – MARATHON

ABADEER, Samir Labib. 333 PINE RIDGE BLVD 54401 #330-03-1964 L1972 OBG *071 †30 ‡
ABRAHAM, Jeanette Marie. 2108 MEADOWBROOK WAY 54403 #041-07-1987 L1992 FM *020
ABUZZAHAB, Faruk Said, Jr. 3200 WESTHILL DR, STE 201 54401 #026-04-1999 L2005 ORS *020 †40
AFRIDI, Sayed Belal. 425 WIND RIDGE DR 54401 #118-01-1992 L2004 FM *020 †18
ALBERT, Philip Richard. 4149 BOULDER RDG, DEPARTMENT OF RADIOLOGY 54401 #056-05-1970 L1971 DR *020 †80
ALDEN, Charles Renwick. 425 PINE RIDGE BLVD, STE 200 54401 #026-04-1979 L1984 GS *020 †85
AL-HAMDAN, Farouq Amer. 425 PINE RIDGE BLVD, BONE AND JOINT CLINIC 54401 #528-04-1983 L1999 OSS *020
ALVAREZ-JACINTO, Orestes. 2720 PLAZA DR, ASPIRUS OB GYN ASSOCIATES 54401 #275-01-1951 L1972 OBG GP *071 †30
ALVAREZ-JACINTO, Orestes. 2720 PLAZA DR, STE 2100 54401 #308-03-1982 L1997 GYN *071 †30
ANDERSON, Erik Paul. 2720 PLAZA DR STE 1400, ASPIRIUS WESTHILL MEDICAL 54401 #026-08-1991 L1995 IM *020 †20
ANDERSON, Margaret D. 3200 WESTHILL DR STE 102, ASPIRUS SPINE & NEUROSCIEN 54401 #026-08-1991 L1995 PM *020 †60
ASPLUND, Mark Wm. 2400 PINE RIDGE BLVD 54401 #056-05-1982 L1983 GS VS *020 †85
BABIARZ, Joseph Wm. 2800 WESTHILL DR, STE 200 54401 #025-01-1987 L1993 U OS *020 †95
BACKER, Gordon Lewis. 614 N 1ST AVE, EYE CLINIC OF WISCONSIN SC 54401 #026-04-1955 L1963 OPH *071 †35
BACKER, William Duane. ■ 54403 #026-04-1958 L1965 OPH *071 †35
BAKER, Vicky Ann. 3605 STEWART AVE, STE 200 54401 #056-05-1993 L1994 FM *020 †18
BANASZYNSKI, Brenda Jean. 1810 2ND ST 54403 #056-05-2003 L2006 FM *020 †18
BARANI, Riccardo. 2720 PLAZA DR, ASPIRIUS WESTHILL MEDICAL 54401 #561-09-1987 L2001 IM *020 †20
BARTON, Darryl Roderick. 215 N 28TH AVE 54401 #045-04-1986 L1991 RO *020 †80
BASU, Sailendra Nath. 1100 LAKE VIEW DR 54403 #495-38-1943 L1976 IM FM *071
BATTINO, Benjamin Sadik. 2800 WESTHILL DR STE 200, UROLOGY SPECIALISTS OF WI 54401 #038-40-1996 L2005 U *020 †95
BATTINO, Gillian M. 3200 WESTHILL DR, STE 210 54401 #038-40-1996 L2005 DR *020 †80
BAYBA, Jonathan Leslie. 333 PINE RIDGE BLVD 54401 #003-01-1985 L1986 AN PME *020 †05
BEAUCHENE, Robert N. 800 1ST ST 54401 #065-06-1982 L2002 OPH *020 †35
BELGEA, Kathy Pauline. 404 S 3RD AVE 54401 #026-04-1965 L1967 PTH OS *071 †50
BELTON, Austin Lawrence. 3200 WESTHILL DR, STE 210 54401 #016-11-1995 L2001 DR *020 †80
BIELEFELD, David Robert. 995 W CAMPUS DR, WAUSAW FAM PRAC CTR 54401 #665-01-1998 FM *100
BINDER, James Patrick. 425 PINE RIDGE BLVD STE 20 54401 #056-05-1978 L1979 GS VS *020 †85
BISWAS, Amit. 2727 PLAZA DR, WAUSAU MEDICAL CENTER 54401 #495-45-1986 L1999 N SME *020 †75
BISWAS, Swati Sisodia. 3605 STEWART AVE, MARSHFIELD CLINIC-STETTIN 54401 #496-07-1992 L1999 PM *020 †60
BLONSKY, Stephen Lawrence. 2727 PLAZA DR 54401 #748-10-1981 L1986 NEP IM *020 †20 ‡
BLUESTEIN, David L. 2800 WESTHILL DR, STE 200 54401 #005-14-1990 L1995 U *020 †95
BLUESTEIN, Linda S. 333 PINE RIDGE BLVD 54401 #005-14-1990 L1995 AN PME *020 †05
BOBINSKI, John Edward. 333 PINE RIDGE BLVD 54401 #028-34-1967 L1972 PD *071
BOCOUN, Vera. 2727 PLAZA DR 54401 #286-02-1994 L2004 RHU *020 †20
BODEMER, Steven Edwin. 2800 WESTHILL DR, STE 208 54401 #056-05-1972 L1973 PTH *071 †50
BOORNAZIAN, Zaven Charles. 333 PINE RIDGE BLVD 54401 #024-07-1982 L1988 AN *020 †05
BOURQUE, Adrian Richard. 1817 N 10TH ST 54403 #030-06-1967 L1976 RO *071 †80
BOUSH, George Andrew. 800 1ST ST 54401 #056-05-1989 L1990 OPH *020 †35
BOWLER, William Arthur. 2727 PLAZA DR 54401 #036-05-1981 L1988 ID IM *020 †20
BREARLEY, Wayne Alan. 3200 WESTHILL DR, STE 201 54401 #023-12-1988 L2002 HS *020 †40
BREBRICK, Robert Thos. 425 PINE RIDGE BLVD 54401 #056-06-1996 L1997 GS *020 †20,85
BRISTER, G H. 2211 RIDGE VIEW DR 54401 #048-02-1956 L1960 R *071 †80
BROOKER, Robert Fredrick. ■ 54403 #016-02-1988 L2003 AN *020 †05
BROTZ, Brian Michael. 333 PINE RIDGE BLVD 54401 #056-05-1985 L1993 AN PME *020 †05
BROWN, Christopher Wm. 425 PINE RIDGE BLVD # 317 54401 #067-01-1982 L1990 PG PD *020 †55
BROWNE, Sally A. 425 PINE RIDGE BLVD, STE 317 54401 #056-06-1984 L1985 GE IM *071 †20
BUNCH, Brian Edward. 3200 WESTHILL DR 54401 #056-06-1996 L1999 NS *020
BURR, Thurl C, Jr. 325 STURGEON EDDY RD 54403 #017-20-1950 L1952 GP *071
BURT, Glenn Brigham, III. 1500 MERRILL AVE 54401 #048-13-1985 L1986 GP EM *020 †18
BUSHMAN-SIMPSON, Nicole. ■ 54401 #038-45-2001 L2005 AN *100 †05
BUTLER, John Andrew. 425 PINE RIDGE BLVD, STE 205 54401 #056-05-1980 L1981 PS *020 †85,65
CADWELL, Robert Edward. 995 W CAMPUS DR 54401 #018-03-1966 L1967 FM *071 †18
CAMPUS, Hieu Trong. 425 WIND RIDGE DR 54401 #054-04-2006 FP *012
CARROLL, John Edmund, Jr. 2720 PLAZA DR, ASPIRIUS WESTHILL MEDICAL 54401 #056-05-1974 L1975 END IM *020 †20
CLANCY, Matthew Thos. 8001 WOODBINE LN 54401 #016-02-1988 L2000 AN *020 †05
CLARK, Matthew Lynn. 2720 PLAZA DR, ASPIRIUS WESTHILL MEDICAL 54401 #018-03-1988 L1989 IM *020 †20
COLE, Catherine Gilchrist. ■ 54403 #051-04-1987 FM *020
COLLISON, James Steele. 3200 WESTHILL DR, STE 210 54401 #018-03-1987 L1993 DR *020 †80
COUSINS, Tracy Lynn. 2800 WESTHILL DR, STE 208 54401 #051-04-1989 L1994 PTH PCP *062 †50
CRISPELL, Jeffrey Hall. 333 PINE RIDGE BLVD 54401 #056-05-1985 L1986 AN *020 †05
CYGAN, James Michael. 425 PINE RIDGE BLVD, STE 220A 54401 #016-06-1996 L2003 PCC *020 †20

DAHLIN, John Eric. ■ 54403 #305-01-2000 L2002 **NM** *100 †28
DAY, Kenneth L. 2727 PLAZA DR 54401 #018-03-1960 L1961 **U** *071 †95
DE CLUTE, Mark Warren. 2727 PLAZA DR, MARSHFIELD CLINIC-WAUSAU C 54401 #056-05-1983 L1995 **DR** *062 †80
DEFFNER, Norman Fred. ■ 54401 #056-05-1968 L1969 **D A** *071 †15
DEGREGORIO, Christian. 520 N 28TH AVE, BEHAVIORAL HEALTH 54401 #023-12-1993 L2005 **P** *020 †75
DENNETT, Mike Allen. 425 PINE RIDGE BLVD, STE 200 54401 #019-02-1995 L2007 **GS** *020 †85
DEVANI, Sindhu Maganlal. 2720 PLAZA DR, ASPIRUS WESTHILL MEDICAL 54401 #495-01-1984 L2004 **END** *020 †20
DEVECCHI, Fausto Giacomo. ■ 54401 #561-20-1996 L2007 **ICE CD** *020 †20
DINGER, Craig Phillip. 212 STURGEON EDDY RD 54403 #016-43-1975 L1999 **FM EM** *071 †18
DO, Jean-Anthony Phuong. 425 WIND RIDGE DR 54401 #051-04-2006 L2007 **OBG** *012
DOAN, Nam Dinh. 333 PINE RIDGE BLVD 54401 #941-01-1968 L1980 **AN** *020 †05
DOVENBARGER, Wm Vance. ■ 54403 #038-41-1955 L1961 **PUD IM** *071 †20
DRAKE, Ellet Haller. 2100 STEWART AVE STE 240 54401 #030-05-1939 L1976 **CD** *071 †20
DREWRY, Andrew Geo. 425 PINE RIDGE BLVD, STE 211 54401 #056-05-1984 L1985 **AN PD** *020 †55,05
DZIADZIO, Laura Lynn. 2727 PLAZA DR, MARSHFIELD CLINIC-WAUSAU C 54401 #025-01-1997 L1999 **AI** *020 †03,55
EDMONDSON, David Allen. 2801 WESTHILL DR 54401 #005-76-2001, ▲ L2002 **AI** *020 †20,03
EDWARDS, Douglas Troy. 800 1ST ST 54403 #018-03-1999 L2003 **OPH** *020 †35
EGGENER, Brian Jos. 1100 LAKE VIEW DR 54403 #056-05-1985 L1986 **P** *020 †75
FERNANDEZ, Juan, III. 2600 STEWART AVE STE 270 54401 #308-07-1982 L1989 **P CHP** *020 †75
FISHER, Darrell Ervin. 2727 PLAZA DR 54401 #018-03-1961 L2000 **ORS** *071 †40
FLAHERTY, Kevin Thos. 800 1ST ST 54403 #016-43-1984 L1989 **OPH** *020 †35
FLANNERY, John V, III. 20 N HILL RD 54403 #056-06-1960 L1962 **OTO** *071 †45
FOLTZ, Alexander Stewart. 425 PINE RIDGE BLVD # 300 54401 #056-05-1969 L1970 **ORS GS** *071 †40
FOX, Stephen Patrick. 425 PINE RIDGE BLVD, STE 205 54401 #056-05-1986 L1995 **PS** *020 †65
FRANKSON, Jane L. 2727 PLAZA DR, MARSHFIELD CLINIC-WAUSAU C 54401 #056-06-1986 L1987 **PD** *020 †55
FREEMAN, David J. ■ 54403 #056-05-1952 L1953 **CD IM** *071 †20
FREEMAN, Mary Jo. 2720 PLAZA DR, ASPIRUS FREEMAN ADULT 54401 #056-05-1976 L1977 **IM** *020 †20
GABRIEL, Youssef Habib. 2727 PLAZA DR 54401 #330-03-1964 L1979 **NS** *020
GALANG, L Ferdinand N. 800 1ST ST 54403 #018-75-2000, ▲ L2004 **OPH** *020
GALANG, Luis Christopher. 800 1ST ST 54403 #018-75-1996, ▲ L2002 **PO OPH** *020
GALLOWAY, Pamela Gail. 413 N 17TH AVE, STE 120 54401 #051-04-1980 L2002 **GS PTH** *020 †50,85
GARVEY, Chas Albert, III. 520 N 28TH AVE STE 200 54401 #056-05-1972 L1973 **P** *020 †75
GAUTAM, Umang. 215 N 28TH AVE 54401 #496-04-1995 L2002 **HO** *020 †20
GAVIN, Eileen S. 2720 PLAZA DR, ASPIRUS FAMILY WALK IN 54401 #016-01-1994 L1995 **FM** *020 †18
GILLES, Gregory Thomas. 1131 EASTHILL PL 54403 #654-01-2001 L2004 **AN** *020 †05
GLENNON, Pamela Ellen. 333 PINE RIDGE BLVD 54401 #041-09-1998 L2004 **ORS** *020 †40
GOSSETT, Ryan Allison. 995 W CAMPUS DR, UNIV OF WISCONSIN 54401 #056-06-2002 L2007 **FP** *012
GRAUER, Curt G. 302 S 9TH AVE 54401 #016-06-1950 L1953 **FPG** *071 †18
GREEN, Leonard Judson. ■ 54401 #017-20-1976 L1976 **FP** *012 †30
GROSHAN, Edward Harrison. 2727 PLAZA DR 54401 #056-06-1983 L1984 **PD** *020 †55
GRULING, Kay Ann. 2727 PLAZA DR, MARSHFIELD CLINIC-WAUSAU C 54401 #056-05-1988 L1989 **FM** *020 †18 ‡
HACKWORTH, Craig Allen. 3200 WESTHILL DR STE 210, RADIOLOGY ASSOCIATES OF WA 54401 #038-40-1988 L1997 **DR** *020 †80
HACKWORTH, Sarah G. 2720 PLAZA DR, ASPIRUS PEDIATRIC CLINIC 54401 #016-11-1988 L1997 **PD** *020 †55
HANGIANDREOU, Gabriella A. 1100 LAKE VIEW DR, NORTH CENTRAL HEALTH CARE 54403 #056-05-1993 L1994 **CHP P** *020 †75
HANNEMAN, Wendy Lou. 2720 PLAZA DR, STE 1300 54401 #056-05-1984 L1985 **FM** *020 †18
HATTENHAUER, John Milo. ■ 54403 #016-11-1964 L1969 **OPH** *071 †35
HATTENHAUER, Matthew G. 800 1ST ST 54403 #056-05-1992 L1999 **OPH** *020 †35
HEALY, Shelbe Kuzminsky. 2720 PLAZA DR, ASPIRUS PEDIATRIC CLINIC 54401 #056-06-1996 L1999 **PD** *020 †55
HEINZL, Glen J. 333 PINE RIDGE BLVD 54401 #056-06-1977 L1980 **FM FPG** *040 †18
HERMAN, Stephen Jos. 614 1ST ST 54403 #016-11-1965 L1972 **OPH** *071 †35
HILLIKER, Kim M. ■ 54401 #056-05-1979 L1980 **DR** *020 †80
HOBSON, Bartholomew D. 2727 PLAZA DR, MARSHFIELD CLINIC-WAUSAU C 54401 #035-45-1975 L1982 **FM** *020 †18
HOLM, William. 333 PINE RIDGE BLVD 54401 #037-01-2000 L2004 **AN** *020 †05
HOWELLS, Scott David. 333 PINE RIDGE BLVD 54401 #056-06-1985 L1994 **EM** *020 †16
HOYUM, Allen Sander. ■ 54401 #028-79-1943, ▲ L1950 **GP** *071
HSU, Jonathan Chong. ■ 54401 #016-06-2005 L2005 **IM** *012
HUFTEL, Mark Alexander. 2727 PLAZA DR 54401 #056-05-1986 L1987 **AI IM** *020 †20,03
HUGUS, John Jay. 3200 WESTHILL DR, STE 101 54401 #036-01-1982 L1988 **OSS** *020 †40
JABBOUR, Samer. 500 WIND RIDGE DR, CARDIOVASCULAR ASSOCIATES 54401 #875-02-1989 L2007 **CD** *020 †20
JAFAR, Tazeen Hasan. 333 PINE RIDGE BLVD 54401 #704-25-1990 L1995 **NEP PD** *020 †55,20
JARVIS, William John, II. 425 PINE RIDGE BLVD 54401 #016-01-1992 L1998 **OSM** *020 †40
JAYASINGHA, Eromi S. 1100 LAKE VIEW DR, NORTH CENTRAL HLTH CARE FA 54403 #422-01-1993 L1998 **IM** *020 †20
JENSEN, Robert Arthur. 212 STURGEON EDDY RD 54403 #027-01-1966 L1998 **PD** *071 †55
JOHNKOSKI, John Anthony. 425 PINE RIDGE BLVD, STE 209 54401 #025-01-1988 L1997 **TS VS** *020 †85,90
JOLIN, David Wayne. 2727 PLAZA DR, WAUSAU CENTER 54401 #056-05-1985 L1986 **NEP IM** *020 †20
KAUPIE, Robert Charles. 212 STURGEON EDDY RD 54403 #056-05-1969 L1971 **FM** *020 †18 ‡
KESSEL, Jeffrey Francis. 2727 PLAZA DR, WAUSAU MEDICAL CENTER S.C. 54401 #026-04-1979 L1986 **OM FM** *020 †18,70
KIM, Sungha Paul. 2727 PLAZA DR 54401 #026-04-1981 L1986 **AN** *020
KLEMM, Frederick Arnold. 333 PINE RIDGE BLVD, WAUSAU HOSPITALS 54401 #016-11-1971 L1977 **EM FM** *071 †16,18
KLINE, Patrick C. 2600 STEWART AVE STE 226, WAUSAU ORAL & MAXILLOFACIA 54401 #024-01-1993 L2005 **OS** *020
KOEPKE, Thomas Allan. 333 PINE RIDGE BLVD 54401 #016-45-1989 L1990 **EM** *020 †16
KOH, Peter Tong Bak. 333 PINE RIDGE BLVD 54401 #825-01-1968 L1976 **AN** *071 †05
KORDIYAK, George. 333 PINE RIDGE BLVD 54401 #016-43-1943 L1950 **GP** *075
KOSLOFF, Alex Harvey. 2727 PLAZA DR 54401 #028-34-1980 L2007 **IM DIA** *020 †20
KROLICKI, Thaddeus James. 800 1ST ST 54403 #028-03-1986 L1999 **OPH OS** *020 †35
KUMM, Randal Chas. 510 N 17TH AVE, STE B 54401 #056-05-1986 L1987 **D** *020 †15
KURTH, Ian Edward. 3200 WESTHILL DR, STE 210 54401 #025-12-2001 L2007 **RNR** *020 †80
KURTZ, Jeffrey Alan. 425 PINE RIDGE BLVD STE 20, WAUSAU HOSPITAL CENTER 54401 #030-06-1973 L1974 **PS HS** *020 †85,65
LAHREN, Kris Michael. 425 PINE RIDGE BLVD, SULTANTS 54401 #028-34-1988 L1998 **PUD CCM** *020 †20
LANGE, Ross Alan. 2720 PLAZA DR, STE 1300 54401 #056-05-1989 L1990 **FM** *020 †18
LARSON, David Lynn. 333 PINE RIDGE BLVD 54401 #035-06-1967 L1980 **P** *020 †75
LAYNES, Grace V. 2727 PLAZA DR, MARSHFIELD CLINIC - WAUSAU 54401 #748-01-1981 L2000 **IM** *020 †20
LIPSMAN, Rocky Alan. 2801 WESTHILL DR 54401 #030-05-1981 L1991 **OTO** *020 †45
LOCHER, Wolfram Geo. ■ 54403 #035-15-1947 L1950 **AN** *071 †05
LOW, Suzanne G. 333 PINE RIDGE BLVD 54401 #825-01-1970 L1976 **AN** *071 †05
LUKS, Julie Hope. 333 PINE RIDGE BLVD 54401 #067-01-1983 L1988 **OBG** *020 †30
LUTHRA, Madhu Vinay. 2727 PLAZA DR 54401 #495-96-1973 L1981 **PD** *020 †55
LUTHRA, Vinay Desraj. 2800 WESTHILL DR, STE 106 54401 #495-96-1973 L1980 **DR** *020 †80
MAC CARTHY, Chas Francis. 1226 HIGHLAND CT 54403 #016-43-1963 L1970 **OPH** *071 †35
MADAGAME, Elisabeth T. 2720 PLAZA DR, ASPIRUS PEDIATRIC CLINIC 54401 #056-06-1988 L1989 **PD** *020 †55
MADAGAME, Jimmy Bruce. 2720 PLAZA DR, STE 1400 54401 #025-07-1987 L1990 **END IM** *020
MAGIERA, Christopher J. 413 N 17TH AVE, STE 120 54401 #038-06-1982 L2002 **GE IM** *020 †20
MAHONY, William Minch. ■ 54403 #056-06-1971 L1972 **DR** *071 †80
MANAHAN, Luisa S. 3302 TERRACE CT 54401 #748-10-1973 **FM** *100
MARKEY, Edmund Lawrence. 425 PINE RIDGE BLVD, STE 300 54401 #025-07-1969 L1970 **ORS** *020 †40
MARKWARDT, Debra K. 333 PINE RIDGE BLVD 54401 #056-05-1985 L1987 **AN** *020 †05
MARS, Christa Johnson. 2727 PLAZA DR, MARSHFIELD CLINIC 54401 #048-13-1976 L2000 **GS** *020 †85
MARTENS, Jacob H. 414 KENT ST 54403 #035-08-1960 L1961 **DR RO** *071 †80
MASON, Albert. 2800 WESTHILL DR, STE 208 54401 #016-42-1974 L1998 **PTH PD** *062 †55,50
MATTINGLY, Sally S. 333 PINE RIDGE BLVD 54401 #047-05-1972 L1987 **GS VS** *020 †85
MATTINGLY, William Taylor. ■ 54403 #047-05-1973 L1987 **TS** *071 †85,90
MAXFIELD, Barry Alan. 333 PINE RIDGE BLVD 54401 #056-06-1971 L1976 **AN** *071
MC GUCKEN, Robert Michael. 333 PINE RIDGE BLVD 54401 #056-05-1991 L1992 **AN** *020 †05
MELMS, William Frederick. 3605 STEWART AVE, MARSHFIELD CLINIC-STETTIN 54401 #056-05-1986 L1987 **FM** *020 †18
MICHELENA, Ana Maria. ■ 54403 #935-07-1994 L2007 **AN** *020 †05
MILES, Ronald Howard. 425 PINE RIDGE BLVD 54401 #007-02-1988 L2001 **TS VS** *020 †85,90
MILLICAN, Robert Jos. 2600 STEWART AVE, STE 144 54401 #030-06-1984 L1987 **NEP IM** *020 †20
MINNIHAN, Richard Louis. 520 N 28TH AVE, STE 200 54401 #018-03-1965 L1969 **P** *020 †75
MIRICK, Mark J. 333 PINE RIDGE BLVD 54401 #018-03-1978 L1982 **EM** *020 †16
MISCHLER, Elaine N Hall. 1800 WESTWOOD CENTER BLVD, WAUSAU BENEFITS, INC. 54401 #041-01-1970 L1977 **PDP PD** *030 †55
MODI, Haresh Bansilal. 1201 W WAUSAU AVE 54401 #495-76-1980 L2005 **NPM PD** *020 †55
MOLINARO, Albert J. 333 PINE RIDGE BLVD 54401 #056-05-1950 L1957 **GS CD** *062 †85
MONTGOMERY, Michele H. 2720 PLAZA DR, STE 1300 54401 #065-10-1989 L1991 **FM** *020 †18
MOREHEAD, Richard Thos. 211 FOREST ST 54403 #018-03-1968 L1975 **PTH** *071 †50
MUEHLENBECK, Erich C. 500 W CAMPUS DR 54401 #407-23-1959 L1966 **GS ORS** *071
NICHOLS, Steven Dale. 212 STURGEON EDDY RD 54403 #016-45-1987 L1988 **FM** *020 †18 ‡
NIELSEN, Thomas Luke. 333 PINE RIDGE BLVD 54401 #018-03-1997 L1999 **EM** *020 †16
NORTH, David Perl. 995 W CAMPUS DR, PRACTICE RESIDENCY 54401 #038-40-1968 L1973 **FM PLM** *071 †18
NOWINSKI, Donald M, Jr. 3200 WESTHILL DR, STE 210 54401 #056-05-1983 L1988 **DR** *020 †80
NOWINSKI, Donald Michael. 3200 WESTHILL DR, STE 210 54401 #056-05-1961 L1962 **R** *071 †80
NUNEZ, Anselmo Alcides. 2600 STEWART AVE, STE 148 54401 #011-02-1978 L1997 **MDM VS** *030 †85
OBST, Gregory. 333 PINE RIDGE BLVD 54401 #067-01-1992 L1994 **EM** *020 †16
O'CONNELL, Kevin John. 425 WIND RIDGE DR, UW HEALTH WAUSAU FAMILY ME 54401 #056-05-1979 L1980 **FM** *030 †18
ODULIO, Teofilo O. 3310 CHRISTIAN AVE 54401 #748-02-1964 L1977 **NS N** *071 †25
OMOLAYO, Olumuyiwa Oluwat. ■ 54401 #690-01-2002 L2007 **IM** *020 †20
OSWALD, Jeffrey Sylvan. 3605 STEWART AVE, MARSHFIELD CLINIC-SETTIN C 54401 #056-05-1983 L1995 **FM** *020 †18
OWEN, William Roy. 2727 PLAZA DR 54401 #018-03-1972 L1980 **D** *020 †15
PALARSKI, Jeffrey David. 333 PINE RIDGE BLVD 54401 #056-05-1988 L1995 **AN** *020 †05,20
PARMLEY, Vernon Clay. 800 1ST ST 54403 #023-12-1982 L2003 **OPH** *020 †35
PASSINI, Barry Thos. 3200 WESTHILL DR, STE 101 54401 #016-11-1985 L1999 **N** *020 †75
PATTERSON, Katherine P. 2727 PLAZA DR 54401 #056-05-1981 L1989 **FM FPG** *020 †18
PEREZ, Oscar. 425 WIND RIDGE DR 54401 #048-13-2002 L2005 **FM** *020
PETERSON, Christopher G. 215 N 28TH AVE, UW CANCER CENTER ASPIRUS 54401 #056-06-1998 L1999 **HEM** *020 †20
PETERSON, Thomas Hull. 995 W CAMPUS DR 54401 #056-05-1958 L1959 **FM GP** *071 †18
PICONE, Saml Bartholomew. 425 PINE RIDGE BLVD, STE 200 54401 #016-42-1977 L1992 **GS CRS** *020 †85 ‡
PIERRE, Edeck Saintilien. 333 PINE RIDGE BLVD 54401 #306-01-2003 L2007 **IM** *020 †20
POOLE, Robert Rollin. 2727 PLAZA DR 54401 #056-05-1971 L1972 **PD** *020
PRASAD, Rupesh. 2727 PLAZA DR, MARSHFIELD CLINIC-WAUSAU C 54401 #496-01-2001 L2005 **IM** *020 †20 ‡
PRZLOMSKI, Andrew Thos. 2720 PLAZA DR, STE 1100 54401 #056-06-1969 L1971 **UCM FM** *020 ‡
PUNKE, Jodi A B. 2727 PLAZA DR, MARSHFIELD CLINIC-WAUSAU 54401 #016-76-1994, ▲ L2001 **FM** *020 †18
QUINN, Margo Jean. 4149 BOULDER RDG, UNIVERSITY OF WISCONSIN 54401 #654-01-1986 L1987 **NM** *020 †18
RABKINA, Diana. 2720 PLAZA DR, ASPIRUS PEDIATRIC CLINIC 54401 #913-06-1984 L2004 **PD** *020 †55

9502

■ = Address Information Privacy Protected

REDING, Rick Raphael. 2720 PLAZA DR, ASPIRIUS WESTHILL MEDICAL 54401 #056-06-1977 L1978 **IM** *020 †20

REED, Claire H. 2720 PLAZA DR, ASPIRUS FAMILY WALK IN 54401 #048-16-1993 L2002 **FM** *020 †18

REINEKE, Lisa A. 2720 PLAZA DR, ASPIRUS FAMILY WALK IN 54401 #018-75-1992, ▲ L1993 **FM** *020

REINHART, Richard Alan. 2727 PLAZA DR, MARSHFIELD CLINIC WAUSAU C 54401 #038-40-1971 L1980 **CD IM** *040 †20

REISING, Christopher A. 2400 PINE RIDGE BLVD, SURGICAL ASSOCIATES, S.C. 54401 #017-20-1996 L2002 **GS** *020 †85

RENGEL, Thomas Neil. 425 PINE RIDGE BLVD # 220 54401 #028-34-1971 L1978 **IM CCM** *020 †20

REYES, Edgardo Apostol. ■ 54401 #748-01-1991 L2002 **IMG** *020 †18

REYNOLDS, Alan Chas. 333 PINE RIDGE BLVD 54401 #056-06-1976 L1977 **AN** *020 †05

RHEE, Peter. 2727 PLAZA DR, MARSHFIELD CLINIC-WAUSAU C 54401 #023-07-1995 L1996 **OPH** *020 †35

RICHETTO, Mark Arthur. 2727 PLAZA DR, MARSHFIELD CLINIC-WAUSAU C 54401 #056-05-1986 L1987 **IM** *020 †20

RIECK, Paul Edwin. 3200 WESTHILL DR, STE 210 54401 #046-01-1994 L2002 **DR R** *020 †80

RISHI, Daljeet. 2727 PLAZA DR, MARSHFIELD CLNC-WAUSAU C 54401 #495-29-1986 L2004 **IM** *020

RIVERON, Fernando. 425 PINE RIDGE BLVD, STE 209 54401 #016-42-1983 L1996 **TS GS** *020 †85,90

RIZVI, Shambeel Hussain. 2720 PLAZA DR, ASPIRUS RHEUMATOLOGY 54401 #704-02-1990 L2006 **RHU** *020 †20

ROMANG, Timothy Chas. 3200 WESTHILL DR, STE 101 54401 #056-05-1990 L1994 **PM** *020 †60

ROUSH, Stephen Craig. 2727 PLAZA DR, MARSHFIELD CLINIC-WAUSAU 54401 #056-05-1979 L1982 **FM** *020 †18

RUBINO, Frank Joseph. 2720 PLAZA DR STE 1300 54401 #016-43-1975 L1978 **FM OBG** *020 †18

RUTHBERG, Andrew D. 2727 PLAZA DR, MARSHFIELD CLINIC - WAUSAU 54401 #043-01-1977 L2006 **RHU** *020 †20

RYAN, Winston Daniel. 333 PINE RIDGE BLVD, WISCONSIN EMERGENCY MEDICA 54401 #030-06-1993 L1994 **EM** *020 †16

SACK, Joseph Garry. 2801 WESTHILL DR 54401 #028-03-1972 L1973 **OTO** *020 †45

SAEGER, Stephen Lyle. 2720 PLAZA DR, STE 1300 54401 #017-20-1978 L1979 **FM** *020 †18

SAMUELSON, Bonnie M. 2720 PLAZA DR, STE 1100 54401 #056-05-1994 L2001 **EM** *020 †16

SCHALLER, Ivan Bruce. 2727 PLAZA DR 54401 #056-05-1980 L1986 **IM** *020 †20

SCHNEIDER, Thomas G. 3000 WESTHILL DR STE 108 54401 #016-11-1990 L1991 **NEP IM** *020 †20

SCHUCHART, Kristin Jo. 3605 STEWART AVE 54401 #018-03-1995 L1996 **FM** *074 †18

SCHULER, Mark John. 3605 STEWART AVE, MARSHFIELD CLINIC-STETTIN 54401 #056-06-1996 L1999 **FM** *020 †60

SCULLY, Hilary Palm. 2720 PLAZA DR, STE 1300 54401 #005-14-1990 L1991 **FM** *020 †18

SEWALL, Gregory Knowlton. 2801 WESTHILL DR, ENT ASSOCIATES 54401 #056-06-1999 L2000 **OTO** *020 †45

SEWALL, Sarah Ann. 2800 WESTHILL DR, STE 208 54401 #056-06-2002 L2005 **PTH** *100 †50

SEYBOLD, Daniel M. 3200 WESTHILL DR STE 20 54401 #056-05-1980 L1981 **ORS OSM** *020 †40

SHABINO, Charles Lynn. 333 PINE RIDGE BLVD 54401 #016-06-1970 L1993 **PD CCM** *030 †55

SHAH, Gaurav Rohitkumar. 2727 PLAZA DR, WAUSAU CENTER 54401 #495-48-2001 L2005 **IM HOS** *020 †20

SHEFF, Jerome R. 2727 PLAZA DR, MARSHFIELD CLINIC-WAUSAU C 54401 #056-05-1981 L1982 **FM** *020 †18

SHEKAR, Chandra Kurudi. 1100 LAKE VIEW DR, NORTH CENTRAL HLTH CARE FA 54403 #495-57-1979 L1993 **P** *020 †75

SHEPHERD, Lori Lynn. 2727 PLAZA DR, WAUSAU MEDICAL CENTER 54401 #056-06-1985 L1994 **PD** *020 †55

SHERRILL, Laura Elizabeth. 3300 WESTHILL DR 54401 #035-03-1997 L2004 **U** *100 †95

SIEBERT, Derrick Robson. ■ 54402 #056-06-2008 L2008 †12

SMITH, Brian David. 212 STURGEON EDDY RD 54403 #056-05-1983 L1984 **FM** *020 †18

SMITH, Burton K. 212 STURGEON EDDY RD 54403 #056-05-1951 L1952 **FM GP** *071 †18

SMITH, Katrina Ann. 333 PINE RIDGE BLVD 54401 #018-03-2000 L2004 **D** *020 †15

SOBHANI-MAHDABI, Aref. 333 PINE RIDGE BLVD, ASPIRUS WAUSAU HOSPITAL 54401 #517-01-1996 L2007 **IM** *020 †20

SOMMERS, Alexander Louis. 333 PINE RIDGE BLVD 54401 #056-06-1999 L2000 **EM** *020 †16

SONNEK, Noel K. 212 STURGEON EDDY RD 54403 #030-06-2001 L2002 **FM** *020 †18

SORENSON, John Robt. 2800 WESTHILL DR, STE 106 54401 #056-05-1983 L1988 **DR** *020 †80

SORENSON, Kay Beth. 1810 2ND ST 54403 #056-05-1983 L1988 **PD** *030 †55

SPELTZ, Stephen Michael. ■ 54403 #026-04-1977 L1978 **EM** *020 †16

SPRIK, Calvin Dale. 800 1ST ST 54403 #046-01-1984 L1997 **OPH** *020 †35 ‡

SPURGEON, Gizelle Ann. 2727 PLAZA DR, MARSHFIELD CLINIC-WAUSAU C 54401 #018-03-1978 L1982 **N** *020 †75

STAHMER, Karl Henry. ■ 54403 #056-05-1939 L1940 **GS** *071 †85

STANKO, Ivan. 2727 PLAZA DR 54401 #286-03-1962 L1973 **N** *071 †75

STARKEY, Thomas Austin. 333 PINE RIDGE BLVD 54401 #016-06-1964 L1969 **OBG** *071 †30

STINE, Stephen Bradley. 3200 WESTHILL DR, STE 210 54401 #056-06-1993 L1999 **VIR** *020 †80

STRICK, Thomas Jos. 995 W CAMPUS DR, WAUSAU FAMILY PRACTICE CTR 54401 #056-06-1985 L1986 **FM** *020 †18

SUTHERLAND, James P, Jr. 3200 WESTHILL DR STE 20 54401 #020-02-1989 L1998 **ORS** *020 †40

SUTHERLAND, Kay Lockwood. 2720 PLAZA DR, ASPIRUS FAMILY WALK IN 54401 #020-02-1989 L2001 **GP** *020

SUTO, Bonnie Lyn. 995 W CAMPUS DR 54401 #056-06-2004 L2006 **FM** *100

SWIFT, Ian Richard. 2801 WESTHILL DR 54401 #041-14-1994 L1995 **OTO** *020 †45

TABAO, Nunila Grace C. 2727 PLAZA DR, MARSHFIELD CLINIC - WAUSAU 54401 #748-10-1998 L2002 **IM** *020

TANNER, George Reid. 3200 WESTHILL DR STE 201 54401 #028-34-1971 L1980 **ORS GS** *020 †40

TERRY, Wanda K. 333 PINE RIDGE BLVD, ASPIRUS WAUSAU HOSP 54401 #048-04-1988 L2006 **P CHP** *020 †75

TICHO, Gabriel Chaim. 1100 LAKE VIEW DR 54403 #041-07-1987 L1991 **P** *020 †75

TOMASI, Marie Ann. 2727 PLAZA DR, WAUSAU CENTER 54401 #056-06-1997 L2002 **N CN** *020 †75

TON, Kiet Anh That. 995 W CAMPUS DR, UNIV WIS FAMILY MEDICINE 54401 #665-01-2003 L2007 **FP** *012

TUMAN, David Christopher. 800 1ST ST 54403 #016-11-1991 L2000 **OPH** *020 †35

UMLAND, Michael Allen. 995 W CAMPUS DR 54401 #305-01-2005 **FP** *012

VELDHUIZEN, Leon Paul. 3605 STEWART AVE, MARSHFIELD CLINIC-SETTIN C 54401 #018-03-1998 L1999 **FM** *020 †18

VIVIANO, Carl Jos. 333 PINE RIDGE BLVD 54401 #016-42-1985 L1991 **U** *020 †95

VOSS, Mark Andrew. 2801 WESTHILL DR 54401 #007-02-1991 L2001 **OTO** *020 †45

WADE, Judith Elaine. 333 PINE RIDGE BLVD 54401 #048-12-1977 L1986 **AN** *071 †05

WALD, Thomas Christopher. 425 PINE RIDGE BLVD, STE 220 54401 #026-04-1989 L1995 **PUD CCM** *020 †20

WALDMAN, Arthur Myron. 2727 PLAZA DR 54401 #025-01-1974 L1977 **FM** *020 †18

WCISEL, Gregory James. 425 PINE RIDGE BLVD, STE 220A 54401 #016-43-1994 L2002 **PCC** *020 †20

WEBB, Roxana O. 209 W WASHINGTON ST 54403 #017-20-1978 L1980 **FM** *020 †18

WEILAND, Steven Thomas. 2400 PINE RIDGE BLVD 54401 #056-06-1997 L1998 **GS VS** *020 †85

WENDLING, Mary Jo. 2720 PLAZA DR, ASPIRUS PEDIATRIC CLINIC 54401 #056-06-1998 L2002 **PD** *020 †55

WESSELS, Wm Edward, Jr. 425 PINE RIDGE BLVD # 300 54401 #018-03-1985 L1990 **OSM ORS** *020 †40

WHITEHEAD, Allan Jeffrey. 800 1ST ST 54403 #056-05-2000 L2004 **OPH** *020 †35

WILLIAMS, John Michael. 3000 WESTHILL DR, STE 100 54401 #048-12-1982 L1991 **OM OPH** *020 †35,70

WILSON-WARD, Elizabeth J. 333 PINE RIDGE BLVD 54401 #026-04-1986 L1989 **EM** *020 †16

WITTEMAN, George John. 2103 RIDGE VIEW DR 54401 #016-11-1971 L1977 **OPH** *020 †35

WOHLRABE, Heidi H. ■ 54403 #016-42-1983 L1997 **P** *020 †75

WOLF, Laurie Lee. 3200 WESTHILL DR, STE 101 54401 #016-11-1985 L1989 **PM** *020 †60

WURMAN, Leonard Howard. T5942 N TROY ST 54403 #024-07-1967 L1975 **OTO GP** *071 †45

XU, Fushen. 2800 WESTHILL DR, ASSOC IN PATHOLOGY 54401 #243-69-1985 L2002 **PTH** *020 †50

YAKUB ELLIAS, Mazin A. 333 PINE RIDGE BLVD 54401 #528-03-1979 L1998 **PME** *020 †05

YANG, Kou Kevin. 2727 PLAZA DR, MARSHFIELD CLINIC-WAUSAU C 54401 #305-01-1996 L2001 **FM** *020 †18

YI, Xing. ■ 54401 #243-52-1986 L2008 **FP** *012

ZABEL, Earl Wayne. 2727 PLAZA DR 54401 #056-05-1971 L1977 **OBG** *020 †30

ZICKERMAN, Philip Martin. 2727 PLAZA DR, MARSHFIELD CLINIC-WAUSAU C 54401 #035-08-1969 L1977 **U** *020 †95

ZIMBRIC, Gabrielle Amelia. ■ 54401 #056-05-2008 *012

ZIMBRIC, Gary Alan. 2727 PLAZA DR, MARSHFIELD CLINIC-WAUSAU C 54401 #056-05-1978 L1979 **EM** *020 †16

WAUTOMA – WAUSHARA

ALVI, Fozia Sarwar. 900 E DIVISION ST 54982 #704-01-1997 L2004 **FM** *020 †18

GOMMERMANN, John Alois. ■ 54982 #056-05-1978 L1979 **DR** *020 †80

GROOS, Fred Litchfield. 400 S TOWNLINE RD, DENTAL CENTER - P.O. BOX 1 54982 #025-07-1984 L1987 **FM** *020 †18

HOLLING, Heide Lore. N3421 BLACKHAWK RD 54982 #407-24-1967 L1981 **R** *020 †80

KIEFER, Richard Louis. 900 E DIVISION ST 54982 #028-34-1987 L2000 **GS** *020 †85

LAKE, Edward Wm. 900 E DIVISION ST 54982 #016-11-1987 L1988 **IM NEP** *020 †20

RYAN, Thomas Anthony. 900 E DIVISION ST 54982 #018-03-1961 L1962 **IM GP** *020 †20 ‡

SHATTUCK, Paul Michael. N2934 STATE ROAD 22 54982 #017-20-1982 L1983 **FM** *020 †18

WAUWATOSA – MILWAUKEE

ABDEL-MAGUID, Amani. 2500 N MAYFAIR RD STE 440 53226 #915-02-1969 L1988 **D IM** *020

AKATA, Deniz. ■ 53226 #902-07-1989 *100

ALLEN, Brian James. ■ 53226 #026-04-2002 L2006 **APM** *020

ALLEN, Ronald Lee. 2300 N MAYFAIR RD, STE 460 53226 #056-05-1984 L1985 **OPH** *020 †35

ANDRES, Francis I. 2500 N MAYFAIR RD 53226 #056-06-1958 L1959 **U** *071 †95

ANTULA-JOVANOVIC, Ljubica. 1248 N 68TH ST 53213 #957-02-1955 L1972 **PM** *074

ARCILLA, Senen S. 10900 W POTTER RD, LIMITED PARTNERSHIP 53226 #748-08-1965 L1976 **AN** *020

ARGANBRIGHT, Jill Marie. ■ 53226 #056-06-2008 *012

ARPILLEDA, Joyce C. ■ 53213 #039-01-1995 L1998 **PEM** *020 †55

ASHRAF, Hebatollah Said. 949 GLENVIEW AVE 53213 #517-01-1958 L1968 **PD** *020

AYENGAR, Shanta. 949 GLENVIEW AVE 53213 #496-07-1956 L1976 **PD** *020 †55

BATORY, Mark Andrew. 53213 #016-11-2003 L2007 **CHP** *012

BAUER, Matthew. ■ 53226 #016-76-2007, ▲ *012

BAUGHN, Julie Marie. ■ 53226 #056-05-2004 L2006 **PD** *100 †55

BAUWENS, Dale Edward. 2500 N MAYFAIR RD, STE 500 53226 #016-11-1979 L1980 **ORS EM** *020 †40

BAYNES, Keith Edward. 2445 N MAYFAIR RD, STE 100 53226 #030-05-2002 L2003 **DR** *100 †80

BEASLEY, Charles A G. ■ 53226 #671-02-1978 *100

BECHERER, Elizabeth Ann. ■ 53226 #056-06-2007 **PTH** *012

BEECHER, Ann Cecile. 3300 N 124TH ST, DOOR W-14 53222 #016-06-1975 L1976 **FM** *040 †18

BERES, Joseph Anthony. 9200 W WISCONSIN AVE, FROEDTERT MEM LUTH HOSP 53226 #016-43-1952 L1957 **NEP IM** *020 †20

BERMUDEZ, Christopher Jos. ■ 53226 #056-06-2008 *012

BERNSTEIN, Avi Nathan. ■ 53213 #056-06-2006 IM *012

BERROYA, Maye Rayos. 601 N 99TH ST, STE 103 53226 #748-10-1992 L2007 **IM ID** *020 †20

BHARUCHA, Sanaya Darayus. ■ 53226 #026-04-2006 L2008 **PD** *012

BORDINI, Brett John. ■ 53213 #056-05-2006 L2008 **PD** *012

BORROMEO, Dawn Marie. ■ 53213 #047-06-2003 L2005 **GE** *012

BREEDLOVE, Huston Harold. 1155 N MAYFAIR RD 3RD FL, MED CLG OF WI DEPT OF PSYC 53226 #847-19-1994 **P** *100

BRUCKNER, Julia Anne. 3289 N MAYFAIR RD 53222 #016-06-1995 L2005 **DR** *020 †80

BURTON, Jared Blaine. ■ 53213 #056-06-2008 *012

BYRD, Gregory Floyd. 8134 GRIDLEY AVE 53213 #054-04-2002 L2004 **U** *020

CARDINA, Adam Michael. ■ 53213 #035-15-2007 **EM** *012

CARTER, Benjamin Gill. 9200 W WISCONSIN AVE, DEPARTMENT OF DERMATOLOGY 53226 #056-06-2006 L2008 **D** *012

CARTER, Kenny Bertlyn, Jr. 9200 W WISCONSIN AVE, DEPARTMENT OF OTOLARYNGOLO 53226 #048-04-2006 L2007 **OTO** *012

CHAHAL, Diljon Singh. ■ 53226 #056-06-2008 *012

CHAPERON, Amy Dianne. ■ 53213 #025-07-2006 **IM** *012
CHOWDHARY, Yashwant Mohan. 11809 W DIANE DR 53213 #495-73-1982 L2001 **IM** *100 †20
CHUNG, David Youngcho. 1155 N MAYFAIR RD, TOSA CENTER 53226 #010-03-2004 L2006 **P** *012
CICCANTELLI, Mark Jos. 6745 W WELLS ST 53213 #041-01-1945 L1948 **IM RHU** *071 †20
CLOWRY, Lawrence John. 7504 MAPLE TER 53213 #023-07-1959 L1967 **PTH DMP** *020 †20
COTTON, Lavaughn. ■ 53226 #056-05-2006 **PD** *012
CRENNAN, Joan Marie. ■ 53226 #035-08-1980 L1997 **IM ID** *071 †20 ‡
CRIOLLO, Roman Ulises. ■ 53213 #016-11-2005 L2007 **PD** *012
CROMWELL, Lewis Ronald. 9455 W WATERTOWN PLANK RD 53226 #056-06-1973 L1975 **P** *071
CROTTY, Paul. ■ 53213 #539-05-1987 L1989 **PTH** *100 †50
CRUZ, Robert Cojuangco. ■ 53226 #056-06-2005 L2006 **OBG** *012
CULLEN, Gerald Michael. 10400 W NORTH AVE, STE 300 53226 #056-05-1971 L1976 **DR** *020 †80
CURRIER, George Edmund. ■ 53226 #024-07-1936 L1960 **P** *071 †75
DARMSTADTER, Susan Lee. 2300 N MAYFAIR RD, STE 960 53226 #038-40-1989 L1990 **CCM** *020 †20
DAS, Utpala Gopal. 999 N 92ND ST, STE 410 53226 #017-20-1991 L1999 **NPM PD** *020 †55
DASSLER, Amy Catherine. ■ 53222 #056-06-2005 **PD** *012
DAVIS, William Raymond. 2600 N MAYFAIR RD, STE 950 53226 #028-34-1985 L1994 **CD IM** *020 †20
DEAN, Marissa Lynne. ■ 53213 #056-06-2007 **TY** *012
DECKERS, Elizabeth Ann. 10400 W NORTH AVE, AURORA HEALTH CENTER MAYFA 53226 #008-02-1995 L2001 **OBG** *020 †30
DEDIANOUS, David Keith. 1155 N MAYFAIR RD, STE B 53226 #028-34-1992 L1993 **PM** *020 †60
DELINE, Christopher James. 9200 W WISCONSIN AVE, MEDICAL COLLEGE OF WISCONS 53226 #305-01-2005 L2007 **NS** *012
DEMBNY, Kenneth D, II. 201 N MAYFAIR RD, STE 530 53226 #056-05-1992 L1994 **PS GS** *020 †65
DE MURI, Bernadette. 2600 N MAYFAIR RD, STE 305 53226 #056-06-1983 L1984 **P N** *020 †75
DHALIWAL, Sharon Kaur. ■ 53226 #016-06-2006 L2008 **PD** *012
DINUSSON, Jacquelyn Faye. 1155 N MAYFAIR RD STE A 53226 #026-04-2000 L2001 **FM** *020 †18 ‡
DRINKA, Eva Katherine. ■ 53213 #056-06-2008 *012
DUCHELLE, Richard Allen. ■ 53226 #010-02-1959 L1968 **CD** *071
EICHE, Jocelyn K. 3040 N 117TH ST, STE 200 53222 #056-06-1982 L1983 **OBG** *020 †30
ELIASON, Benjamin Ray. ■ 53213 #056-06-2005 L2007 **P** *012
ENGLAND, Mark Joseph. ■ 53226 #056-06-2008 *012
ENGLUND, Jon Michael. 8320 W BLUEMOUND RD, STE 125 53213 #056-05-2002 L2004 **FSM** *020 †18
ERICKSON, Scott John. 2445 N MAYFAIR RD, CENTER FOR DIAONOSTIC IMAG 53226 #056-06-1983 L1987 **DR** *020 †80
FARWELL, Kathryn Rae. ■ 53226 #056-05-2006 **PD** *012
FAUGHT, Samuel Ryan. 9200 W WISCONSIN AVE, MEDICAL COLLEGE WISCONSIN 53226 #020-02-2004 L2005 **RO** *012
FEE, Kathrynn Anne. ■ 53226 #016-06-2008 *012
FERGUSON, George Jos. 1220 DEWEY AVE 53213 #056-06-1967 L1969 **CHP P** *020 †75
FIRAT, Selim Yusuf. 9200 W WISCONSIN AVE, MEDICAL COLLEGE OF WISCONS 53226 #902-05-1994 L1998 **RO** *020 †80
FLEISCHFRESSER, Sharon A. ■ 53213 #048-04-1983 L1984 **PD PHP** *020 †55
FORT, Jamie Lee. ■ 53225 #026-04-2006 **DR** *012
FREUND, Edward M Nelsen. 9200 W WISCONSIN AVE 53226 #056-05-1993 L2000 **ORS** *020 †40
FRIEDMAN, Jerry Eli. ■ 53226 #016-11-1961 L1968 **OTO** *071 †45
GAGRAT, Shobha Simon. 1220 DEWEY AVE 53213 #496-38-1970 L1977 **P** *020 †75
GALLIMORE, Harriet L S. ■ 53213 #030-06-1943 L1955 **PHP PM** *071
GAUS, David Paul. ■ 53226 #021-01-1992 L1993 **FM** *020 †18
GEORGE, Mathews Lal. ■ 53225 #495-37-1991 **IM** *012
GODIWALLA, Shirley Yezdi. 10625 W NORTH AVE STE 201 53226 #495-17-1975 L1985 **U UP** *020
GOERS, Trudie Anne. 2566 N 64TH ST 53213 #056-06-2002 L2004 **GS** *012
GORELICK, Jeffrey Bruce. 2626 N 76TH ST, STE 105 53213 #056-06-1981 L1982 **PM** *020 †60
GOULD, Lindsay Marie. ■ 53213 #056-06-2007 L2008 **PD** *012
GRANTACQUAH, Kweku Willia. ■ 53222 #016-02-2008 *012
GREIDANUS, Heather Susan. ■ 53226 #056-06-2008 *012
GUPTA, Ravi. 10625 W NORTH AVE, STE 230 53226 #495-05-1970 L1977 **GP IM** *020
HANSON, Gerald Arthur. 11020 W PLANK CT STE 100 53226 #056-06-1971 L1972 **HMP PTH** *071 †50
HARDEL, Michael David. ■ 53213 #056-06-2006 L2008 **AN** *012
HARRIS, Michael Stephan. ■ 53226 #056-06-2008 *012
HARTEMINK, David Arent. 9200 W WISCONSIN AVE 53226 #056-06-2005 L2007 **OTO** *012
HASKELL, David Stilwell. 2323 N MAYFAIR RD, STE 310 53226 #056-06-1967 L1968 **ORS** *020 †40
HAUSHALTER, Robert Allen. 2500 N MAYFAIR RD STE 400 53226 #056-06-1967 L1968 **GS VS** *020 †85
HENNES, Magda Maher. 201 N MAYFAIR RD, WHEATON FRANCISCAN MEDICAL 53226 #915-02-1981 L1999 **IM** *020 †20
HERRMANN, Jurgen Peter R. 2323 N MAYFAIR RD, STE 410 53226 #407-21-1967 L1973 **PD MG** *020 †55,19
HILBELINK, Ryan Thomas. 10400 W NORTH AVE, MAYFAIR RADIOLOGY 53226 #056-06-1999 L2000 **DR** *020 †20
HOEPPNER, Edith M. ■ 53226 #056-06-1949 **PTH** *075
HOGGATT, Judy Paz. 2300 N MAYFAIR RD, STE 1101 53226 #056-05-1990 L1992 **OPH** *020 †35 ‡
HORNEFFER, Mark Douglas. 10950 W CAPITOL DR, COLUMBIA WEST 53222 #025-01-1990 L1993 **IM** *020 †20
HOTTER, John Thos. 2500 N MAYFAIR RD 53226 #056-06-1946 L1948 **U** *071 †95
HUANG, Jonathan Chii-En. ■ 53226 #016-76-2004, ▲ L2007 **GE** *012 †20
HUSSAIN, Syed Mansoor. ■ 53213 #704-02-1977 **PM** *020 †60
IDARRAGA, Samuel Hernan. 2645 N MAYFAIR RD, STE 200 53226 #056-06-1989 L1992 **IM** *020 †20
IGNACE, Gerald Lewis. 201 N MAYFAIR RD, WHEATON FRANCISCAN MEDICAL 53226 #056-06-1965 L1969 **IM** *020 †20
JACKSON, Gloria Machel. 6230 W NORTH AVE 53213 #038-41-1978 **P** *030
JAIN, Shaili. ■ 53213 #917-06-1998 L2003 **P** *020

JAQUES, Kimberly Dawn. ■ 53226 #056-06-2005 **IM** *012
JENNINGS, Jonathan Elliot. 10400 W NORTH AVE, RADIOLOGY ASSOC. OF MILWAU 53226 #056-06-1999 L2004 **RNR** *020 †80
JOHNSON, Bridget Eileen. ■ 53226 #016-42-2006 L2006 **AN** *012
JONES, Sumi Denniston. 1155 N MAYFAIR RD, STE B 53226 #056-06-2001 L2004 **IM** *100
JUREK, Sara Kristin. ■ 53213 #039-01-2006 L2008 **ORS** *012
KAMPER, David Gary. 10425 W NORTH AVE STE 216 53226 #024-01-1960 L1967 **CD IM** *020
KANE, Roxanne Jennifer. 3040 N 117TH ST, STE 100 53222 #056-05-1993 L1994 **PD** *020 †55
KEELAN, Michael H, Jr. 9200 W WISCONSIN AVE 53226 #056-06-1960 L1961 **CD IM** *040 †20
KEGEL, Thomas Andrew. ■ 53213 #056-06-1960 L1961 **AN** *020
KENNEDY, Brian Wm. 3289 N MAYFAIR RD, MEDICAL CLINIC 53222 #018-03-1965 L1968 **IM** *020 †20
KESSARIS, Christos. 12226 W BLUEMOUND RD 53226 #418-01-1995 L2003 **AN** *100
KETTERHAGEN, Donald Wm. ■ 53213 #056-06-1974 L1975 **OBG** *020 †30
KEYES, Jill Carpenter. ■ 53213 #028-34-2006 L2008 **PD** *012
KIM, Andrew Chinhoe. 2645 N MAYFAIR RD, STE 200 53226 #056-06-1989 L1990 **IM** *020 †20
KIM, Eunice. ■ 53213 #056-06-2008 *012
KING, James Frederick. 601 N 99TH ST, STE 201 53226 #019-02-1966 L1973 **CD** *020
KLEIN, Charles Anthony. 2500 N MAYFAIR RD STE 500 53226 #056-06-1981 L1982 **ORS** *020 †40
KLOPFSTEIN, Jennifer Nell. 201 N MAYFAIR RD 53226 #038-45-1986 L1990 **PM** *020 †60
KOOZEKANANI, Dara David. ■ 53226 #038-40-2003 L2007 **OPH** *020
KRAMER, Lorelle Lynn. 620 N MAYFAIR RD 53226 #056-06-1990 L1995 **PS** *020
KREEGER, Anne Marie. ■ 53226 #018-03-2007 **OBG** *012
KREITZER, Frank Victor. ■ 53226 #056-06-1962 L1964 **R** *071 †80
KROLL, Alexandra Pauline. ■ 53226 #056-06-2008 *012
KRYNIAK, Minerva Pacana. ■ 53213 #748-09-1978 L1984 **PTH** *020 †50
KUHN, Michael John, Jr. 2500 N MAYFAIR RD STE 330 53226 #056-06-1958 L1959 **OBG** *071 †30
KUMPREY, William Todd. 10000 W BLUEMOUND RD, ATTN: EMERGENCY DEPARTMENT 53226 #056-06-1998 L2001 **EM** *020 †16
LA BISSONIERE, Paul Geo. ■ 53213 #056-06-1943 L1943 **IM CD** *071 †20
LEE, Victor Chiavee. ■ 53213 #055-01-1982 L1986 **AN** *020 †05
LEIBSOHN, James Alan. 1233 N MAYFAIR RD, STE 201 53226 #056-06-1975 L1975 **CD IM** *020 †20
LEISHMAN-BARB, Andrea M. ■ 53213 #028-78-2006, ▲ **OBG** *012
LERAND, Sarah Jennifer. ■ 53226 #028-03-1998 L2006 **ADL** *100 †55
LEVIN, Igor. 201 N MAYFAIR RD 53226 #913-37-1980 L1995 **APM** *020 †05
LEWIS, Samantha Claire. ■ 53213 #056-06-2008 *012
LIANG, Mei-Ying. 6523 W CLARKE ST 53213 #243-16-1991 L2003 **APM** *100
LIM, Swee Yang. ■ 53226 #056-06-2008 *012
LIN, Catherine Pei-Wun. ■ 53213 #056-06-2008 *012
LINCER, James David. 2525 N MAYFAIR RD, STE 200 53226 #016-11-1986 L1987 **PM PMM** *020 †60
LINDERT, Merlyn C F. 10400 W NORTH AVE, AURORA HEALTH CTR-MAYFAIR 53226 #026-04-1939 L1940 **GE IM** *071 †20
LIPSCOMB, Thomas Chas. 6745 W WELLS ST 53213 #056-06-1946 L1948 **R PDR** *072 †80
LIU, Chris Yuan Kang. ■ 53213 #056-06-2008 *012
LUTES, Michael Steven. 9200 W WISCONSIN AVE, DEPT OF EMGY MED 53226 #016-43-2000 L2004 **EM** *020 †16
MADDEN, James Anthony. ■ 53226 #056-06-1966 L1967 **P** *012
MADDEN, Robert Francis. 6200 W BLUEMOUND RD 53213 #056-06-1953 L1954 **IM PUD** *071 †20
MADSEN, Karin Editha. 9200 W WISCONSIN AVE, FMLJ, ANESTHSIOLOGY DEPT 53226 #056-05-1984 L1985 **AN** *020 †05
MALCOM, Stephen Christoph. ■ 53213 #016-11-2007 **MPD** *012
MALIK, Steven William. ■ 53213 #011-02-2003 L2006 **ORS** *012
MALMSTEN, Catharine D. ■ 53226 #005-02-2003 L2008 **CD** *012 †20
MANLEY, Ann-Marie. ■ 53226 #056-06-2006 L2007 **IM** *012
MANLEY, John Chas. 601 N 99TH ST STE 201, WI HEART & VASCULAR CLINIC 53226 #028-34-1959 L1961 **CD IM** *020 †20
MANNING, Erika Lyn. ■ 53213 #045-01-2006 **NS** *012
MARQUART, Michael James. 10400 W NORTH AVE STE 300, RADIOLOGY ASSOCIATES OF MI 53226 #056-06-1999 L2000 **VIR** *020 †80
MARTIN, Leslie Frederick. 6814 W WELLS ST, MARTIN OCCUPATIONAL MEDICI 53213 #396-02-1985 L1992 **OM GPM** *040 †70
MASSART, Peter Allan. ■ 53222 #028-78-2004, ▲ L2006 **IM** *012
MC CORMICK, Michael Robt. 201 N MAYFAIR RD, STE 525 53226 #016-06-1961 L1965 **OPH** *020 †35
MCNALLY, Madeline Anne. ■ 53213 #056-06-2008 *012
MCQUILLAN, Brea Lynn. 9200 W WISCONSIN AVE, OBGYN DEPARTMENT 53226 #030-06-2005 L2007 **OBG** *012
MEADE, Robert C. 2620 NORMANDY CT 53226 #026-04-1951 L1953 **NM IM** *071 †20,28
MEYER, Nicholas Carl. ■ 53213 #056-06-2008 *012
MILLER, Nathaniel Edmond. ■ 53213 #056-06-2008 *012
MLSNA, Jacqueline Sue. 2500 N MAYFAIR RD STE 500, BAUWENS & KLEIN MD SC 53226 #016-11-1987 L1988 **ORS** *020 †40
MODRIC-JEDNACAK, Ksenija. ■ 53226 #957-01-1992 L2005 **AN** *100
MONTALBO, Marionito N. 1155 N MAYFAIR RD, STE B 53226 #041-12-1991 L2003 **IM** *020 †20
MORRISON, Paul E.. ■ 53226 #056-06-2008 *012
MORTIMORE, Wendy Rae. 1155 N MAYFAIR RD, MEDICAL COLLEGE OF WISCONS 53226 #056-06-2000 L2005 **MPD** *100 †55,20
MOSS, Sheryl Lynn. 10625 W NORTH AVE STE 222 53226 #056-06-1980 L1981 **PD** *020 †55
MUELLER, Paul Lawrence. 949 GLENVIEW AVE, PEDIATRIC ENDOCRINOLOGY 53213 #038-40-1969 L1995 **PD** *020 †55
MUI, Daniel. 10950 W CAPITOL DR 53222 #056-06-1991 L1992 **IM** *020 †20
MULLIN, Jamie Hensen. ■ 53213 #056-06-2005 L2006 **EM** *012
MUTHUSAMY, Anbu Durai. 999 N 92ND ST, CHILDREN'S CORPORATE CTR,N 53226 #495-59-1998 L2007 **NPM** *012 †55
MYRE, Brian Christopher. ■ 53226 #056-06-2008 *012
NASSIF, Ninette A. 2300 N MAYFAIR RD STE 755 53226 #056-06-1987 L1988 **IM** *020 †20
NAVRATIL, Marcie A. ■ 53226 #056-05-2008 *012
NELSON, Eileen Josephine. ■ 53213 #056-06-2008 *012
NELSON, Philip Andrew. 1155 N MAYFAIR RD, SPINE CARE 53226 #017-20-1999 L2003 **PM** *020 †60

NICKOLOFF, Sarah Jane. ■ 53226 #056-06-2008 *012
NOTO, Louis Fred. 9200 W WISCONSIN AVE, DEPARTMENT OF ANESTHESIA 53226 #056-06-2005 L2007 AN *012
NUSBAUM, Anna Marie. ■ 53226 #038-43-2005 L2007 P *012
O'MEALLY, William C. 6617 W WELLS ST 53213 #023-01-1996 L1998 FM *020 †18
ONUORA, Tochukwu Obinna. ■ 53226 #028-02-2006 AN *012
ORAKA, Chinwe Nneka. ■ 53226 #016-11-2005 MPD *012
PALMER, Christine Mary. ■ 53213 #056-06-2008 *012
PALOUCEK, James Truman. 11020 W PLANK CT 53226 #016-43-1963 L1973 PTH PCP *071 †50
PANIAN, Gwen Marie. ■ 53213 #056-06-2008 *012
PARK, Sun Ok. 12000 W BLUEMOUND RD 53226 #583-13-2001 L2007 ID *012 †20
PARKER, Harrison Worley. 1033 N MAYFAIR RD, STE 101 53226 #017-20-1969 L1972 GE IM *072 †20
PARKINS, David Graham. ■ 53226 #016-11-2005 L2007 AN *012
PATEL, Sima Balubhai. ■ 53226 #011-04-2005 L2007 PD *012
PAULSON, Elizabeth Ann. ■ 53226 #056-06-2006 L2008 PD *012
PAWAR, Sachin S. ■ 53213 #056-06-2007 OTO *012
PEAK, Daniel Thos. ■ 53213 #056-05-1959 L1975 P *071 †75
PEQUET, Archebald Russell. 10425 W NORTH AVE 53226 #025-01-1956 L1961 PD *020 †55
PERRY, Jennifer Lynn. ■ 53226 #025-07-2001 L2004 PD *020 †55
PETERSEN, John Robt. ■ 53226 #056-05-1954 L1955 IM END *071 †20
PETTIT, Kelli Ann. 8701 W WATERTOWN PLANK RD 53226 #028-02-2003 L2005 GS *012
PHILLIPS, Brandon Nickola. ■ 53213 #056-06-2008 *012
PLETCHER, Pamela Marie. 7439 HARWOOD AVE, STE 303 53213 #026-04-1992 L1996 P *020 †75
POLACEK, Michael A. ■ 53213 #016-06-1957 L1960 GS GE *071 †85
POLENTINI, Mark Scott. 2336 N 81ST ST 53213 #056-06-2001 L2003 EM *020 †16
PORTER, Craig Chas. 999 N 92ND ST, STE 510 53226 #038-40-1980 L2008 PN *020 †55
POULOS, Christopher Kreag. ■ 53213 #017-20-2001 L2005 FOP *100 †50
PUGH, David Byron. ■ 53213 #056-06-2007 TY *012
QUEBBEMAN, Edward John. 8700 W WISCONSIN AVE 53226 #016-11-1972 L1973 GS *050 †85
RAGALIE, Glenn Francis. 1155 N HONEY CREEK PKWY, AURORA VNA ZILBERT FAM HSP 53213 #016-11-1977 L1978 PLM IM *020 †20
RAMOS, Leigh Maria K. 9200 W WISCONSIN AVE, MED COLLEGE OF WI AFFILIAT 53226 #014-01-2001 L2005 CN *012 †55
RANA, Vipulkumar Bhupen. 8701 W WATERTOWN PLANK RD, MEDICAL COLLEGE OF WISCONS 53226 #028-34-2004 L2007 IM *020 †20
RAO, Venkatarama. 10400 W NORTH AVE, AURORA MEDICAL GROUP 53226 #495-33-1976 L1992 IM *020 †20
REBHOLZ, Brandon John. ■ 53213 #056-06-2006 L2007 ORS *012
REHMAN, Naima Obaidur. ■ 53226 #025-01-2007 MPD *012
REISWIG, Amanda Courtney. ■ 53213 #056-06-2007 TY *012
RICHER, Timothy Matthew. 8651 W NORTH AVE 53226 #056-05-1998 L2002 PD *020 †55
RICHTER, Alphonse Michael. 725 AMERICAN AVE 53213 #056-06-1955 L1956 DR *071 †80
RIDOLFI, Timothy Joseph. ■ 53226 #056-06-2005 L2008 GS *012
RIORDAN, Katherine Collee. ■ 53226 #056-06-2008 *012
ROBERTSON, Felicia Denise. 10400 W NORTH AVE, AURORA HEALTH CTR - MAYFAI 53226 #038-45-1996 L1998 FM *020 †18
ROBERTSON, John Allan. 1011 N MAYFAIR RD, STE 301 53226 #024-15-1938 PM *071
RUSSO, Carla Rae. ■ 53213 #056-06-2006 L2008 OBG *012
RYBICKI, Katherine Nicole. ■ 53213 #056-06-2008 *012
SAGERT, Larry Paul. ■ 53226 #056-05-1987 *100
SAMPATH, Venkatesh. 999 N 92ND ST, STE C410 53226 #495-59-1995 L2006 NPM *100 †55
SANDLER, Alberto. ■ 53213 #132-01-1959 L1986 IM CD *071
SANVANSON, Patrick Paul. ■ 53213 #056-06-2008 *012
SAUDEK, Kristine Ann. ■ 53213 #012-01-2001 L2007 PD *020 †55
SAULSBERRY, Alexandria De. ■ 53226 #056-06-2005 L2008 PD *012
SCHECHTER, Miriam. 2600 N MAYFAIR RD, STE 305 53226 #028-03-1977 L1986 P *020 †75
SCHNEIDER, Kathleen Mary. 2675 N MAYFAIR RD, STE 500 53226 #056-06-1984 L1985 EM IM *020 †20,16
SCHROEDERUS, Jennifer L. 2600 N MAYFAIR RD, STE 785 53226 #056-06-2000 L2002 P PYG *020 †75 ‡
SCHULTZ, Marvin Allen. 3330 N 107TH ST 53222 #056-05-1956 L1957 CHP P *071 †55,75
SCHWAB, Jeffrey Philip. 9200 W WISCONSIN AVE, DEPT ORTHOPEDIC SURG 53226 #026-04-1971 L1972 ORS *020 †40
SCHWARTZ, Walter Richard. 2949 N MAYFAIR RD STE 309 53222 #056-05-1955 L1956 GYN *071 †30
SCOTT, John Paul. 2350 N 71ST ST 53213 #016-43-1974 L1987 PHO OS *050 †55
SHARIF, Uzma M. 9000 W WISCONSIN AVE, CHILDREN'S HOSPITAL OF WIS 53226 #704-02-1990 L2007 CHN *020
SIDHU, Jaswinder Kaur. 201 N MAYFAIR RD, WHEATON FRANCISCAN MEDICAL 53226 #495-29-1980 L1999 IM *020 †20
SILBERMAN, Richard Eugene. 1233 N MAYFAIR RD, STE 201 53226 #056-05-1966 L1967 CD *020
SILVER, Elizabeth Anne. 999 N 92ND ST, STE C550 53226 #005-14-1987 L2005 PD *020 †55
SIMON, Andrew David. 10400 W NORTH AVE 53226 #056-06-1999 L2000 DR *020 †80
SIMONSEN, Hubert Willard. ■ 53213 #056-05-1957 L1958 IM *071
SLOAN, Kirstin Barrow. 1284 N 63RD CT, PREVEA CLINIC 53213 #016-01-1997 L1998 PD *020 †55
SMITH, Christopher Todd. 2500 N MAYFAIR RD, STE 400 53226 #056-05-1994 L2003 CRS *020 †85,10
SOBCZAK, Christopher Paul. 1155 N MAYFAIR RD, STE A 53226 #056-06-1997 L1998 MPD *020 †20,55
SOREM, Elaine M. 1220 DEWEY AVE 53213 #016-42-1987 L1988 P *020 †75
SORKIN, Sheila W. 11430 W BLUEMOUND RD, STE 109 53226 #016-06-1969 L1980 ADM *020
SREEDHARAN, Rajasree. 999 N 92ND ST, CHILDREN'S CORPORATE CENTE 53226 #495-44-1993 L2006 PN *100 †55
STARK, Ron H. 3077 N MAYFAIR RD STE 306 53222 #056-06-1978 L1979 HS GS *020 †85 ‡
STAUNTON, Marie Jeanne. ■ 53226 #539-05-1989 PTH *100
STEIN, Daniel John. 820 N 117TH ST 53226 #030-06-2003 L2007 GE *012 †20
STERKIN, Lawrence Alan. 201 N MAYFAIR RD, STE 530 53226 #005-06-1984 L1989 PS GS *020 †85,65
STEWART, William Arnold. 2525 N MAYFAIR RD, STE 200 53226 #017-20-1980 L1985 PM N *020 †75,60

STOLP, Sherwood Bernard. ■ 53213 #056-06-1954 L1955 IM OS *071
STUEVE, Michele Heidi. ■ 53213 #056-05-2003 L2007 PM *020
SUBRAMANIAN, Sharath Sesh. ■ 53213 #496-23-2001 IM *012
SUNDLASS, Karanjot Singh. ■ 53213 #056-06-2008 *012
SWITALA, Jean M. 10400 W NORTH AVE, AURORA HEALTH CTR-MAYFAIR 53226 #056-06-1976 L1977 IM *020 †20
SZABO, Elod Zala. 1125 N GLENVIEW AVE 53213 #473-02-1995 L2005 AN *100 †05
TAFT, Thomas Allan. 601 N 99TH ST STE 103 53226 #056-06-1981 L1982 ID IM *020 †20
TAKAHASHI, Takashi. ■ 53222 #056-06-2008 L2008 *012
TAMBURRINO, Amy Michelle. 3040 N 117TH ST 53222 #056-06-2003 L2005 OBG *020
TAYLOR, An'Drea Danielle. ■ 53213 #056-06-2008 *012
TEH, Hui-Pin. ■ 53226 #539-06-1964 L1969 AN *020 †05
TEJADA, Generose Villanue. 999 N 92ND ST, STE C410 53226 #748-01-1993 L2006 NPM *100
TEMME, Russell Gregory. 1220 DEWEY AVE 53213 #056-05-1995 L1996 P *020 †75
TENG, Ru-Jeng. 999 N 92ND ST, SUITE C410, CHILDREN'S COR 53226 #244-02-1985 L2006 PD NPM *020 †55
TESCHAN, Rudolf R. 4025 N 92ND ST, AURORA HEALTH CARE 53222 #056-06-1985 L1986 FM *020 †18
TIEU, Cuong Chi. ■ 53213 #056-06-2004 L2005 CHP *012
TIMM, Fred John. 8651 W NORTH AVE 53226 #056-06-1980 L1981 PD *020 †55
TONKIN, Paul Robert. ■ 53222 #026-04-2006 *100
TURCOTT, Carolyn Joyce. 2600 N MAYFAIR RD STE 785, TURCOTT MED & PSY ASSOC 53226 #056-06-2000 L2002 CHP P *020
TURCOTT, Richard Dennis. 2600 N MAYFAIR RD, STE 785 53226 #056-05-1972 L1974 P GP *020
TYSON, Jared John. ■ 53213 #056-06-2008 *012
UBELL, Katrina Rieflin. 8651 W NORTH AVE, TOSA PEDIATRICS 53226 #025-01-2002 L2004 PD *020 †55
UGUREL, Mehmet Sahin. ■ 53213 #902-05-1990 L2003 RNR *100
VANDER LUGT, Mark Thomas. ■ 53213 #056-06-2006 PD *012
VANREGENMORTER, Adam Alan. ■ 53213 #025-12-2007 PTH *012
VASSEL, Jennifer King. 933 N MAYFAIR RD STE 308 53226 #056-06-1994 L1995 CHP *020 †75
VAUGHAN, Christopher Jame. ■ 53226 #056-06-2008 *012
WALTERS, Matthew Patrick. ■ 53213 #056-06-2006 L2008 PTH *012
WANAT, Karolyn Ann. ■ 53213 #022-02-2008 *012
WEBER, Christopher Edward. ■ 53226 #056-06-2008 *012
WEIN, Melissa Marie. 9200 W WISCONSIN AVE 53226 #017-20-1999 L2003 DR *100 †80
WEINSTEIN, Michael B. 2500 N MAYFAIR RD, STE C410 53226 #056-06-1970 L1972 IM *020
WEISS, Clarissa Justine. ■ 53226 #016-43-2007 OBG *012
WEPFER, Joseph F. ■ 53226 #056-05-1945 L1949 R *071 †80
WIENER, Marvin. 10701 W RESEARCH DR 53226 #056-06-1974 L1975 FM *030 †18
WIENER, Sarah Jeane. ■ 53213 #056-06-2008 *012
WINTERS, Thomas Francis. 10400 W NORTH AVE, AURORA HEALTH CTR - MAYFAI 53226 #056-05-1978 L1982 FM *020 †18
WU, Tzong-Jin. 999 N 92ND ST, DEPT. OF PEDIATRICS 53226 #244-02-1989 L2006 PD NPM *020 †55
WYER, Laura E. 201 N MAYFAIR RD, # 2FL 53226 #056-05-1982 L1983 IM *020 †20
YOUNG, Mandick. ■ 53213 #016-06-2005 L2007 GS *100
ZELLER, James Richard. 9200 W WISCONSIN AVE, FMLH-EAST 53226 #056-06-1959 L1960 IM *040 †20
ZIOLKOWSKI, James Stanley. 7400 HARWOOD AVE, HARWOOD MEDICAL ASSOCIATES 53213 #056-06-1958 L1959 IM IMG *072 †20

WEBSTER – BURNETT

INGALLS, John Wm. 7456 MAIN ST W 54893 #056-05-1989 L1990 FM *020 †18

WEST ALLIS – MILWAUKEE

AHLGRIM, Gwenda Jeanne. 8901 W LINCOLN AVE 53227 #047-05-1989 L2002 PTH *020 †50
AMBROSE, Rustin Eugene. ■ 53227 #056-06-1982 L1983 IM *062
ATNAFU, Belay Woldegiorgi. 2014 S 102ND ST 53227 #366-01-1996 L2007 IM *012
BACHHUBER, Patricia Ann. 8901 W LINCOLN AVE, PATHOLOGY DEPARTMENT 53227 #018-03-1985 L1986 PTH *020 †50
BARROWS, Linda Jean. 8901 W LINCOLN AVE, OUT-PATIENT DEPARTMENT 53227 #056-06-1989 L1990 PM *062 †60
BARTOS, Christine E P. 2424 S 90TH ST STE 2 53227 #041-02-1987 L1996 OPH *071 †20,35
BEROUKHIM, Feridoun. 2424 S 90TH ST, STE 504 53227 #517-01-1965 L1973 N *020 †55
BLATNIK, Donald Steven. 2424 S 90TH ST STE 404 53227 #056-06-1961 L1962 OTO *020 †45
BLIWAS, Crain Henry. 11101 W LINCOLN AVE 53227 #056-06-1975 L1976 P *020 †75
BONELLI, Landy E. 8901 W LINCOLN AVE, WEST ALLIS MEMORIAL HOSPIT 53227 #056-06-1974 L1975 EM *020 †16
BRAYER, Andrew Paul. 10243 W NATIONAL AVE, ST. MARY'S MEDICAL CLINIC 53227 #056-06-1996 L1997 FM *020 †18
BRISELLI, Michael Fels. 8901 W LINCOLN AVE, PATHOLOGY DEPARTMENT 53227 #041-14-1974 L1980 OS PCP *020 †50
BUSS, Robert Orville. 8901 W LINCOLN AVE 53227 #056-06-1966 L1967 ORS *071 †40
BUSTOS, Alice C. 7220 W NATIONAL AVE 53214 #748-12-1986 L1993 FM *020 †18
CASTRO, Eduardo Enrique. 8901 W LINCOLN AVE 53227 #005-14-1991 L1999 EM *020 †16
CHATTERJEE, Asok Kumar. ■ 53227 #495-02-1962 L1972 END OBG *071 †30
CLARK, Jimmy Ray. 8901 W LINCOLN AVE, GREAT LAKES PATHOLOGISTS 53227 #047-06-1984 L1988 PTH *020 †50
COHEN, Steven Howard. 11121 W OKLAHOMA AVE 53227 #038-40-1972 L1973 AI IM *020 †20,03 ‡
COUCH, James Russell. ■ 53219 #056-06-1947 L1948 GP OS *071
DANIELS, John Elliott. 2400 S 90TH ST, STE 106 53227 #056-05-1996 L2000 IM *020 †20
DURHAM, Janet Richards. 8901 W LINCOLN AVE, PATHOLOGY DEPARTMENT 53227 #025-07-1991 L1996 PTH *020 †50
ERDOGAN, Barbaros Levent. ■ 53227 #902-10-1991 NM *100
ESKAROUS, Nady Ibrahim. 8901 W LINCOLN AVE 53213 #915-05-1973 L1992 FM *020 †18
GAERTNER, William J. 8901 W LINCOLN AVE 53227 #016-11-1979 L1980 FM *020 †18
GRESSEAU, Shirley. 555 S 108TH ST 53214 #035-09-1992 L1996 OBG *020 †30
HALL, Robert Brooks. 8901 W LINCOLN AVE, WEST ALLIS MEMORIAL HOSPIT 53227 #056-06-1987 L1996 PTH *020 †50

HARDEN, Don Albert. 2356 S 102ND ST, SLEEP WELLNESS INSTITUTE 53227 #016-11-1983 L2005 **PDP PD** *020 †55

HAVENS, Kathryn Klein. 8901 W LINCOLN AVE, ST LUKES FAMILY PRACTICE 53227 #028-46-1982 L1987 **IM** *020 †20

HAYES, James Roger. 10150 W NATIONAL AVE, STE 100 53227 #016-11-1985 L1986 **OBG** *020 †30

HEBER, David Leon. 2424 S 90TH ST, STE 212 53227 #056-05-1972 L1978 **GS** *020 †85

HEINTZ, Patrick Walter. 8901 W LINCOLN AVE, PATHOLOGY DEPARTMENT 53227 #056-06-1993 L2001 **DMP** *020 †50

HESSERT, Mary Josephine. ■ 53227 #022-75-2005, ▲ L2006 *020

HICKS, Scott Christopher. ■ 53227 #056-06-2005 L2006 **ORS** *012

HUBBARD, Tiffany Anne. 11211 W LINCOLN AVE, LINCOLN AVENUE CLINIC 53227 #056-06-1993 L1999 **IM** *020 †20

HUMMEL, Barbara Ann. 2424 S 90TH ST, STE 302 53227 #056-06-1988 L1989 **FM** *020 †18

JAGLAN, Amarjit Singh. 8905 W LINCOLN AVE STE 501 53227 #654-01-1986 L1987 **OBG FM** *020 †18,30

JENNISON, Marshall Reed. 8901 W LINCOLN AVE 53227 #038-40-1961 L1962 **AN** *071 †05

JOHNSON, Peter Robert. 8901 W LINCOLN AVE, 1ST FL 53227 #056-05-1987 L1996 **OBG GO** *020 †30

JONES, Rushton Michael. ■ 53219 #056-06-2008 *012

KLECZEWSKI, Heather Ann. ■ 53219 #056-06-2007 **PD** *012

KONG, Nam Sik. ■ 53214 #056-06-2008 *012

KRUG, Alvin Karl. 9400 W LINCOLN AVE 53227 #056-06-1973 L1977 **ORS** *020 †40

KUENSTNER, John Todd. 8901 W LINCOLN AVE, PATHOLOGY DEPARTMENT 53227 #035-03-1981 L2002 **PTH** *020 †50

KUNTZ, Rebecca Lynn. ■ 53214 #005-12-2007 **TY** *012

LASSER, Michael John. 11211 W LINCOLN AVE, LINCOLN AVE CLINIC 53227 #046-01-1993 L1994 **OBG** *020 †30

LATHERS, Eugene Gerald. 8800 W LINCOLN AVE 53227 #056-06-1958 L1959 **OBG** *071 †30

LESHAN, Loren Andrea. 2424 S 90TH ST, STE 310 53227 #024-07-1980 L1983 **FM** *020 †18

LEVIN, Randall Myles. 8901 W LINCOLN AVE 53227 #056-06-1976 L1977 **EM** *071 †16

LISCHAK, Michael William. 801 S 70TH ST, GATEWAY CLINIC 53214 #023-12-1981 L2004 **OM AM** *020 †70

LOPEZ, Lauren S. 10201 W LINCOLN AVE # 100 53227 #056-05-1983 L1987 **PUD PCC** *020 †20

MAGANN, Everett Francisco. 8901 W LINCOLN AVE, STE 505 53227 #051-04-1975 L2006 **MFM OBG** *020 †30

MAN, Leslie Ann. 8905 W LINCOLN AVE, STE 515 53227 #005-06-1990 L1995 **OBG** *020 †30

MARGOLIS, Michael Thos. 8905 W LINCOLN AVE, CENTER FOR PELVIC SURGERY 53227 #019-02-1987 L1991 **OBG IM** *020 †30

MASON, Cynthia Lynn. 555 S 108TH ST, QUAD MED-WEST ALLIS 53214 #056-06-1987 L1988 **FM** *020 †18 ‡

MC AVOY, Stephen Patrick. 8905 W LINCOLN AVE, STE 515 53227 #030-06-2002 L2004 **OBG** *020 †30

MC MANUS, Robert Patrick. 10150 W NATIONAL AVE, STE 190 53227 #024-05-1979 L1987 **TS** *020 †85,90

MEHTA, Malini Atul. 2424 S 90TH ST, STE 214 53227 #495-59-1989 L1996 **IM** *020 †20

MEIER, Tim Michael. ■ 53227 #038-41-2002 L2003 **RNR** *012 †80

MERKOW, Ann Bartos. 555 S 108TH ST 53214 #056-05-1979 L1985 **IM** *020 †20

MILLER-MC CARTHEY, Amy Jo. 8905 W LINCOLN AVE, STE 501 53227 #056-05-1992 L1993 **OBG** *020 †30

MILOTT, Joan Laurie. 11211 W LINCOLN AVE 53227 #016-43-1981 L1987 **IM** *020 †20

MOKROHISKY, Rebecca Ann. 8905 W LINCOLN AVE, STE 515 53227 #030-06-1996 L2001 **OBG** *020 †30

MUNIM, Masroor. 7200 W GREENFIELD AVE 53214 #704-16-1984 L1996 **IM** *020 †20

MUNIM, Shahida. 7200 W GREENFIELD AVE 53214 #704-18-1988 L1997 **IM** *020 †20

MUSNI, Roberto B. 7220 W NATIONAL AVE, AURORA HEALTH CENTER 53214 #748-10-1980 L1986 **FM** *020 †18

NASS, Lisa Beth. 8901 W LINCOLN AVE, GLPISC 53227 #016-11-1991 L1996 **PTH PCP** *020 †50

NELSON, Lillian Sonja. ■ 53227 #041-07-1948 L1950 **GP OM** *071

NESEMANN, Sam Perry. 9400 W LINCOLN AVE 53227 #056-06-1964 L1967 **ORS** *071 †40

OLSON, Susan Carroll. ■ 53227 #056-06-1996 *100

PAGEDAS, Thos Constantine. 9400 W LINCOLN AVE 53227 #017-20-1958 L1964 **ORS** *071 †40

PAHLAVAN, Kambiz. 11101 W LINCOLN AVE 53227 #517-08-1970 L1992 **CHP P** *020 †75

PICKERAL, John J, III. 8901 W LINCOLN AVE, PATHOLOGY DEPARTMENT 53227 #051-01-1993 L1999 **PCP** *020 †50

POTNIS, Payal Saiprasad. ■ 53227 #056-06-2008 *012

PRIETO, Argelia. ■ 53219 #275-01-1954 L1997 **P** *071

QUADRACCI, Leonard Jon. 555 S 108TH ST 53214 #056-06-1965 L1995 **IM NEP** *071 †20

RAO, L Mohan. 10243 W NATIONAL AVE 53227 #495-04-1956 L1973 **PD HEM** *020 †55

REZNICEK, Mary Karen. 8901 W LINCOLN AVE, PATHOLOGY DEPARTMENT 53227 #048-13-1985 L1991 **PTH PCP** *020 †50

RINCON, Javier A. 801 S 70TH ST, ST.MARY'S MEDICAL CLINIC 53214 #649-19-1986 L1988 **FM EM** *020 †18

RUMHOFF, Gordon. 8901 W LINCOLN AVE 53227 #056-06-1956 L1957 **GP** *071

RUZICKA, Francis Xavier. 801 S 70TH ST, ST MARY'S MEDICAL CLINIC 53214 #056-06-1991 L1992 **FM** *020 †18

SADOWSKI-JOHNSON, M. 2323 W 102ND ST 53227 #056-06-1996 L1997 **FM** *020 †18

SAMUEL, Erica Ann. ■ 53227 #056-06-2007 **IM** *012

SANCHEZ, Armando. 801 S 70TH ST, GATEWAY HEALTH CENTER 53214 #056-06-1990 L1991 **FM** *020 †18

SCHAMBERG, Jay F. 8901 W LINCOLN AVE, DPT PATH 53227 #041-09-1972 L1978 **PTH PHP** *030 †50

SCHAUFELBERGER, Adriana J. 8905 W LINCOLN AVE STE 515 53227 #056-05-1997 L2000 **OBG** *020 †30

SCHMITT, Karl Wm. 8901 W LINCOLN AVE, GMP WAMH 53227 #041-12-1967 L1976 **PTH OS** *062 †50

SELLERS, Erika Susan. 8905 W LINCOLN AVE, STE 409 53227 #056-05-2001 L2002 **FM** *020 †18 ‡

SHU, Tiffany Hsinling. ■ 53227 #016-11-2008 *012

SIDHU, Mahtab Kaur. 1361 S 109TH ST, ST JOES REGIONAL MEDICAL C 53214 #305-01-1993 L2003 **IM** *020 †20

SIENKIEWICZ, Paul John. 9400 W LINCOLN AVE 53227 #056-05-1979 L1980 **ORS** *020 †40

SIRISANTHANA, Thira. ■ 53227 #891-04-1973 L1978 **ID IM** *020 †20

SOLOCHEK, Sheldon Morris. 8901 W LINCOLN AVE 53227 #056-05-1967 L1969 **GS CRS** *020 †85

SOSENKO, Alexandra. 5631 W LINCOLN AVE 53219 #056-06-1978 L1979 **FM** *020 †18

STOLP, David Scott. 2424 S 90TH ST, STE 214 53227 #056-05-1999 L2002 **FM** *020 †18

STRIET, Becky Marie. 2424 S 90TH ST, STE 310 53227 #038-45-1997 L2002 **PCC** *020 †20

SUBERVIOLA, Pedro Danl. 8901 W LINCOLN AVE 53227 #132-03-1969 L1980 **NS** *020 †25

TANDINGAN, Patrick Galvan. ■ 53214 #056-06-2004 L2006 **MPD** *012

TAUGHER, Philip James. 8901 W LINCOLN AVE 53227 #056-06-1964 L1965 **OPH** *071 †35

TIUSECO, Domingo Robles. ■ 53214 #748-02-1953 L1983 **GP** *020

TOLENTINO, Mario Granatin. 8901 W LINCOLN AVE 53227 #748-07-1956 L1963 **CRS IM** *020

UNDERHILL, Shelly Briggs. 8901 W LINCOLN AVE, PATHOLOGY DEPARTMENT 53227 #016-02-1985 L1990 **PTH PCP** *020 †50

VAIDYANATHAN, Rama Sundar. 2448 S 102ND ST, STE 270 53227 #495-59-1993 L2004 **IM** *020 †20

VANDERKOOY, Kris Rudy. ■ 53219 #056-06-2008 *012

VON ROENN, W Gregory. 11101 W LINCOLN AVE, ROGERS MEMORIAL HOSPITAL 53227 #020-12-1973 L1974 **IM** *020 †20

VONRUEDEN, Michael Thos. 2323 S 102ND ST, COLUMBIA ST MARYS CLINIC 53227 #056-06-1992 L1994 **FM** *020 †18

WADDADAR, Jay. 2448 S 102ND ST 53227 #495-73-1986 L2007 **IMG** *020 †20

WAGNER, Patrick Nathan. ■ 53227 #056-06-2008 *012

WALLACE, Virginia C. 8901 W LINCOLN AVE, PATHOLOGY DEPARTMENT 53227 #012-01-1993 L1999 **PCP PTH** *020 †50

WASHBURNE, Mary D. 801 S 70TH ST, ST MARY'S MEDICAL CLINIC 53214 #041-13-1991 L1993 **FM** *020 †18

WEIDIG, David John. 8901 W LINCOLN AVE, RM 295 53227 #016-06-1991 L2007 **IM** *020 †20

ZAWORSKI, Bernard Edward. 2448 S 102ND ST STE 2 53227 #759-01-1988 L1997 **FM** *020 †20

ZENZ, Carl. ■ 53227 #041-02-1949 L1951 **OM** *071 †70

ZIEBERT, Anthony Paul. 2400 S 90TH ST, STE 206 53227 #056-06-1960 L1961 **IM HEM** *071 †20

WEST BEND – WASHINGTON

ALI, Abbas. 205 VALLEY AVE 53095 #704-02-1990 L2000 **PCC** *020 †20

AMUNDSEN, Laurie Beth. 1010 E WASHINGTON ST 53095 #056-05-1987 L1998 **AN** *020 †05

ANDERSON, Mary Beth E. 205 VALLEY AVE 53095 #056-06-1999 L2003 **OBG** *020 †30

BARUAH, Gita R. 205 VALLEY AVE 53095 #495-78-1973 L1981 **PM PMM** *020 †60

BEERENDS, Jerold John. 205 VALLEY AVE 53095 #018-03-1974 L1977 **PD** *020 †55

BLOMMEL, Gregory Geo. 1700 W PARADISE DR, WEST BEND CLINIC INC 53095 #056-06-1985 L1986 **IM EM** *020 †20

BODENSTEINER, Robert T. 1700 W PARADISE DR, WEST BEND CLINIC INC 53095 #018-03-1974 L1975 **FM** *020 †18

BURT, Michael Allen. ■ 53095 #056-06-2002 L2008 **AN** *020

BUTTERFIELD, Lisa Kay. 205 VALLEY AVE 53095 #056-06-1997 L1998 **PD** *020

CHIKKALA, Deepak N R. 205 VALLEY AVE 53095 #306-01-1998 L2001 **IM** *020 †20

CLAYBAUGH, William Morris. 1700 W PARADISE DR, WEST BEND CLINIC INC 53095 #056-06-1965 L1969 **R** *020 †80

DONOVAN, Scott Wm. 3200 PLEASANT VALLEY RD, BEND CLINIC 53095 #010-01-1980 L1982 **OBG** *020 †30

DRIESSEL, Richard Henry. ■ 53095 #056-06-1941 L1941 **GP AM** *071

EARNEST, Melissa Lee. 1700 W PARADISE DR 53095 #056-06-1988 L1989 **GE** *020 †20

EDWARDS, Jamie Obrian. 205 VALLEY AVE 53095 #056-05-1998 L1999 **FSM** *020 †18

FINK, John Gilmore. 551 S SILVERBROOK DR 53095 #056-06-1989 L1990 **PTH** *020 †50

FLEISCHMANN, Michelle D. 3200 PLEASANT VALLEY RD, ST JOSEPH COMM HOSP 53095 #056-06-1997 L1998 **AN** *020 †05

FRANK, Clay Jamison. 1700 W PARADISE DR, WEST BEND CLINIC INC 53095 #056-06-1990 L1996 **ORS** *020 †40

FROEHLICH, James Dennis. 1700 W PARADISE DR, WEST BEND CLINIC INC 53095 #056-05-1973 L1976 **FM** *020 †18

GAJIC, Zoran Dragutin. 1700 W PARADISE DR, WEST BEND CLINIC INC 53095 #957-02-1995 L2005 **IM** *020 †20

GARDNER, Patrick Michael. 3200 PLEASANT VALLEY RD 53095 #056-06-1993 L1994 **CLP** *020

GARDNER, Robert J. PO BOX 1980 53095 #016-06-1951 L1952 **GS TS** *071 †85,90

GIBSON, Richard D. 1700 W PARADISE DR 53095 #016-06-1951 L1954 **GP GS** *071

GIBSON, Robert Davis. 1700 W PARADISE DR, WEST BEND CLINIC INC 53095 #056-05-1986 L1987 **IM** *020 †20

GILL, Lawrence Albert. 1700 W PARADISE DR, WEST BEND CLINIC INC 53095 #040-02-1976 L1977 **FM** *020 †18

GILLES, Lynn Marie. 1700 W PARADISE DR, WEST BEND CLINIC INC 53095 #056-06-1989 L1990 **R NM** *020 †80,28

GOULD, Perry Matthew. 1110 OAK ST, STE 1300 53095 #056-05-1994 L1998 **RO** *020 †80

GREBE, Paul John. 1700 W PARADISE DR, WEST BEND CLINIC INC 53095 #056-06-1989 L1990 **DR VIR** *020 †80

GRISWOLD, Bruce Guy. 1700 W PARADISE DR, WEST BEND CLINIC INC 53095 #056-06-1976 L1977 **FM** *020 †18

GROGAN, John Paul. 1700 W PARADISE DR, WEST BEND CLINIC INC 53095 #056-06-1966 L1967 **R N** *020 †80

GRUNDAHL, Alvin Theodore. 551 S SILVERBROOK DR 53095 #018-03-1943 L1946 **FM** *071

HACK, Howard Mark. 1700 W PARADISE DR, WEST BEND CLINIC INC 53095 #028-02-1988 L1990 **GE IM** *020 †20

HAMBROOK, Daniel Wright. 1700 W PARADISE DR, WEST BEND CLINIC 53095 #056-06-2000 L2002 **AI** *020 †55,03

HAMMER, Todd Jerome. 1700 W PARADISE DR, WEST BEND CLINIC INC 53095 #056-05-1974 L1977 **FM** *020 †18

HARTWICK, Jeffrey Michael. 1700 W PARADISE DR, WEST BEND CLINIC INC 53095 #056-06-1983 L1988 **DR** *020 †80

HARVEY, Julie Elizabeth. 3200 PLEASANT VALLEY RD, SYNERGY HEALTH WEST BEND 53095 #038-43-1999 L2000 **PD** *020 †55

HELLMAN, Barry David. 205 VALLEY AVE, AURORA HLTH CARE CTR 53095 #056-05-1970 L1971 **D** *020 †15

HERDRICH, Gary Micheal. 1700 W PARADISE DR, WEST BEND CLINIC INC 53095 #056-05-1978 L1979 **FM** *020 †18

HILTY, Louise Clara. ■ 53095 #056-06-1960 L1961 **P** *071 †75

HOITINK, Chad Everett. 1700 W PARADISE DR, WEST BEND CLINIC INC 53095 #056-05-2000 L2001 **OPH** *020 †35

HOLCOMB, Steven Wm. 5595 COUNTY ROAD Z 53095 #018-03-1989 L1992 **FM** *020 †18

HOLLOWELL, James Parker. 1700 W PARADISE DR, WEST BEND CLINIC INC 53095 #005-14-1984 L1991 **NS** *020 †25

JEWETT, Bryan Edward. 205 VALLEY AVE 53095 #010-02-1983 L2006 **GS AS** *020 †85

KAROS, Michael Gust. 1710 VOGT DR, WEST BEND SURG CTR 53095 #056-06-1962 L1966 **AN** *020

KELLER, Patrick Ray. 1700 W PARADISE DR, WEST BEND CLINIC INC 53095 #056-05-1998 L1999 **DR** *020 †80

KLAUSMEIER, Nicole Lynn. 1700 W PARADISE DR, WEST BEND CLINIC INC 53095 #056-06-1998 L1999 **IM** *020 †20

LACEY, John Patrick, Jr. 1700 W PARADISE DR, WEST BEND CLINIC INC 53095 #056-06-1989 L1990 **U** *020 †95

LAU, Lee Ann Rae. 205 VALLEY AVE 53095 #056-06-2002 **GS** *020 †85

LAWTON, Mark Thos. 1700 W PARADISE DR, WEST BEND CLINIC INC 53095 #056-06-1987 L1988 **DR ORS** *020 †80

LEICHLITER, Christopher J. 1700 W PARADISE DR 53095 #056-06-2002 L2006 **AN** *020 †05

LEIKNES, Renee Rose. 205 VALLEY AVE, GENERAL CLINIC OF WEST BEN 53095 #056-05-1994 L1996 **IM** *020 †20

LITZAU, David William. 1700 W PARADISE DR, WEST BEND CLINIC INC 53095 #056-06-1998 L1999 **RNR** *020 †80

LYE, Dale James. 1700 W PARADISE DR, WEST BEND CLINIC INC 53095 #049-01-1984 L1985 **DR** *020 †80

MAAS, Diana Lee. 1700 W PARADISE DR 53095 #056-06-1985 L1986 **END IM** *020 †20

MAC DONALD, William B. 1700 W PARADISE DR, WEST BEND CLINIC INC 53095 #025-07-1989 L1996 **DR** *020 †80

MACHHI, Kaizad P. 3200 PLEASANT VALLEY RD, SYNERGY HEALTH WEST BEND 53095 #690-02-1985 L1996 **VS GS** *020 †85

MAKSTENIEKS, Gatis. 205 VALLEY AVE 53095 #913-94-1981 L2002 **PM** *020 †60

MANZ, Robert Carl. 1700 W PARADISE DR, WEST BEND CLINIC INC 53095 #056-06-1997 L1998 **ORS** *020 †40

MASKALA, Kristen Lucy. 1700 W PARADISE DR, WEST BEND CLINIC INC 53095 #016-01-1998 L1999 **ORS** *020 †40

MIAN, Muhammad Z. 5595 COUNTY ROAD Z 53095 #308-11-1986 L1993 **IM** *040 †20

MIRANDA, Rory F. 1700 W PARADISE DR, WEST BEND CLINIC 53095 #016-11-1995 L2003 **OBG** *020 †30

MOSLEY, George Michael. 1700 W PARADISE DR 53095 #030-06-1986 L1987 **IM** *020 †20

MUELLER, Gilbert F, Jr. ■ 53095 #025-01-1954 L1960 **GS** *071 †85

MUTH, Donald Marshall. 551 S SILVERBROOK DR 53095 #056-05-1965 L1966 **IM** *071 †20

MYLOTT, Brandt Michael. 1700 W PARADISE DR, WEST BEND CLINIC INC 53095 #016-01-1999 L2000 **PD** *020 †55

NEPPLE, Earl Wm. 1201 OAK ST 53095 #056-05-1974 L1976 **OPH** *020 †35 ‡

NIELSEN, William Arthur. ■ 53095 #056-05-1945 L1946 **FM** *071

OLAFSSON, Eric Jon. 3202 PLEASANT VALLEY RD 53095 #056-05-1999 L2000 **PCC SME** *020 †20

OLSEN, Ralph Norman. 205 VALLEY AVE 53095 #056-05-1954 L1955 **PD** *071 †55

O'MEARA, Mark Thos. 1700 W PARADISE DR, WEST BEND CLINIC INC 53095 #056-06-1977 L1978 **ORS** *020 †40

OSBORN, Heather Ihrke. 3200 PLEASANT VALLEY RD, SYNERGY HEALTH WEST BEND 53095 #056-06-2000 L2001 **PD** *020 †55

OWENS, William Lewis, Jr. 3200 PLEASANT VALLEY RD, SYNERGY HEALTH WEST BEND 53095 #056-05-1985 L1991 **OS** *020 †85

PAHL, Andrew Charles. 1700 W PARADISE DR, WEST BEND CLINIC INC 53095 #056-05-1995 L1996 **IM** *020

PELLMANN, Roger Allen. 1700 W PARADISE DR, WEST BEND CLINIC INC 53095 #422-01-1981 L1982 **DR** *020 †80

PIFEL, Eric Bruce. 205 VALLEY AVE 53095 #038-43-1999 L2000 **OSM** *020 †40

POLLNOW, Dean Michael. 205 VALLEY AVE, GENERAL CLINIC OF WEST AVE 53095 #056-06-1990 L1991 **OBG** *020 †30

RADKE, Laura Lee. 1700 W PARADISE DR 53095 #056-06-1989 L1990 **IM ID** *030 †20

REICHEL, Colleen Jean. 205 VALLEY AVE 53095 #016-01-1992 L1994 **PD** *020 †55

REINEKE, Michael Chas. 1201 OAK ST, OAKBROOK MEDICAL COMPLEX 53095 #056-05-1970 L1971 **ORS** *020 †40

ROSENMEIER, Gary John. 1190 E PARADISE DR, WEST BEND CLINIC EAST 53095 #016-11-1984 L1996 **D** *020 †15 ‡

RYZKA, Rafal Jerzy. 1700 W PARADISE DR 53095 #759-01-1999 L2007 **RHU** *020 †20

SAINI, Bhupinder Singh. 1700 W PARADISE DR, WEST BEND CLINIC INC 53095 #495-29-1979 L2004 **AN** *020 †05

SCHNEIDER, Paul Richard. 1201 OAK ST 53095 #056-06-1970 L1974 **ORS EM** *020 †40

SHERKOW, Larry Hersh. 1700 W PARADISE DR, WEST BEND CLINIC INC 53095 #035-09-1975 L1976 **DR NM** *071 †80 ‡

SHIM, Jae Yong. 551 S SILVERBROOK DR 53095 #583-04-1964 L1993 **P N** *020

SMALE, Jeffery Roy. 3200 PLEASANT VALLEY RD, SYNERGY HEALTH WEST BEND 53095 #056-06-1989 L1990 **PUD CCM** *020 †20

SMITH, Hugh Saml. 333 E WASHINGTON ST, STE 2000 53095 #038-40-1969 L1998 **P** *071 †75

SODERLING, Michael James. 1041 TIMBERLINE DR 53095 #056-06-1987 L1991 **OBG** *071 †30

SONESON, Eric Andrew. 3200 PLEASANT VALLEY RD, SYNERGY HEALTH WEST BEND 53095 #056-06-1996 L1997 **GS** *020 †85

STEINHAUS, Randall Brian. 400 W RIVER DR, AFFILIATED CLINICAL 53090 #056-06-1985 L1990 **P CHP** *020 †75

STONE, James Wilkins. 205 VALLEY AVE 53095 #024-01-1982 L1989 **ORS** *020 †40

SULLIVAN, Lawrence P. 1700 W PARADISE DR, WEST BEND CLINIC INC 53095 #056-06-1984 L1988 **N** *020 †75

TAMEZ, Chad Fredrick. 1700 W PARADISE DR 53095 #056-06-2002 L2003 **FM** *020 †18

TRIVEDI, Rajesh Mukundray. 205 VALLEY AVE, AURORA HEALTH CENTER-WEST 53095 #495-76-1991 L1998 **IM** *020 †20 ‡

VANDER ZANDEN, Matthew Th. ■ 53095 #056-05-2008 *012

VEGAFRIA, Jesse Occena. 422 MEADOWBROOK DR 53090 #748-07-1962 L1970 **AN GP** *071

WEST MILWAUKEE – MILWAUKEE

AFRASIABI, Cyrus. ■ 53214 #517-01-1963 L1971 **IM** *071 †20

FRICK, Jacob Chas. 2801 W KK RIVER PKWY, STE 930 53215 #056-06-1979 L1980 **ON IM** *020 †20

LIEBER, William David. 2900 W OKLAHOMA AVE, ERMED SC 53215 #056-05-2000 L2001 **EM** *020 †16

WEST SALEM – LA CROSSE

GERSCH, George Peter. N5021 OAKVIEW DR 54669 #056-06-1961 L1963 **FM** *072 †18

WESTBY – VERNON

BLAND, Phillips Thos. 100 MELBY ST 54667 #056-05-1947 L1948 **GP** *071

DITTER, Ronda. ■ 54667 #305-01-1999 L2004 **FM** *020 †18

SCRENOCK, Jonathan David. 100 MELBY ST 54667 #056-05-1997 L1998 **FM** *020 †18

WESTFIELD – MARQUETTE

SHALASH, Shahada G. PO BOX 245, 104 E 2ND ST 53964 #875-01-1981 L1992 **N** *020

WESTON – MARATHON

ARAYA, Alberto Hernan. 4005 COMMUNITY CENTER DR, ASPIRUS WESTON WALK-IN CLI 54476 #005-18-1994 L2004 **FM** *020 †18

BAILEY, Richard Hall. 3400 MINISTRY PKWY 54476 #028-03-1993 L2004 **IM** *030 †20

BERGIN, Steve Chas. 4005 COMMUNITY CENTER DR, ASPIRUS WESTON CLINIC 54476 #056-06-1974 L1975 **OBG** *020 †30

BURRER-SCHUSTER, Debra. 3301 CRANBERRY BLVD, MINISTRY MEDICAL GROUP 54476 #028-02-1984 L1985 **AN** *020 †05 ‡

CAPRIOLO, Mark Jos. 3301 CRANBERRY BLVD 54476 #056-05-1992 L1999 **IM** *020 †20

EGE, Hilmi. 3501 CRANBERRY BLVD, CLINIC WESTON CTR 54476 #902-04-1991 L2002 **BBK** *100 †20

GARVER, Thomas Hunter. 3501 CRANBERRY BLVD, MARSHFIELD CLINIC ORTHOPED 54476 #023-12-1988 L2002 **ORS GP** *020 †40

HANSON, Jason Lee. 3400 MINISTRY PKWY, SAINT CLARE'S HOSPITAL 54476 #056-06-2001 L2005 **IM** *020 †05

HANUMAIAH, Ravindra. 3400 MINISTRY PKWY 54476 #495-35-1986 L2005 **IM** *020 †20

HAO, Lei. 3401 CRANBERRY BLVD 54476 #243-95-1980 L2003 **PTH** *020 †50

HENNEGHAN, David Michael. 4005 COMMUNITY CENTER DR, STE 203 54476 #025-12-1984 L1990 **OS** *020 †40

HOMA, Bruce Allan. 3301 CRANBERRY BLVD 54476 #026-04-1980 L1983 **FM** *020 †18

JOSEPH, Mary Loods Regini. 3400 MINISTRY PKWY 54476 #220-04-1998 L2005 **IM** *020 †20

LANGE, David Eugene. 3501 CRANBERRY BLVD, MARSHFIELD CLINIC-WESTON C 54476 #026-04-1992 L1993 **FM** *020 †18

MATHIAS, David Lee. 3501 CRANBERRY BLVD, DEPARTMENT OF PEDIATRICS 54476 #025-01-1999 L2005 **PD** *020 †55

MUHLE, Steven Anthony. 3400 MINISTRY PKWY, ST. CLARES HOSPITAL 54476 #047-05-2002 L2005 **EM** *020 †16

ONUNKWO, Chiedu Charles. 3400 MINISTRY PKWY, SAINT CLARE'S HOSPITAL 54476 #690-04-1998 L2005 **ID** *012 †20

PAULSON, John Keith. 4005 COMMUNITY CENTER DR 54476 #026-04-1980 L1981 **IM IMG** *020 †20

PFAENDTNER, Christopher R. 3400 MINISTRY PKWY, SAINT CLARES HOSPITAL 54476 #056-06-1988 L1991 **EM** *020 †16

P'NG, Choon Heong. 3400 MINISTRY PKWY, ED ST CLARES HOSP 54476 #060-01-1985 L2004 **FM EM** *020 †18

RAHN, Kristen Rae. 4005 COMMUNITY CENTER DR 54476 #056-05-1998 L1999 **FM** *020 †18

SIKORA, Jerzy Boleslaw. 3400 MINISTRY PKWY 54476 #759-12-1996 L2005 **HOS** *020 †20

SRIVASTAVA, Rohit. 3501 CRANBERRY BLVD, WESTON REG MED CTR 54476 #495-45-1989 L1996 **CD** *020 †20

THOMPSON, John Michael. 3400 MINISTRY PKWY 54476 #056-05-1975 L1991 **EM FM** *020 †18,16

TURBETT, Timothy James. 4005 COMMUNITY CENTER DR 54476 #018-03-1997 L1998 **FM** *020 †18

WATSON, James Stewart. 3400 MINISTRY PKWY 54476 #038-41-1980 L2004 **EM** *030 †16

WEYAUWEGA – WAUPACA

BUCHHOLZ, Roy Russell. 206 S MILL ST 54983 #056-05-1978 L1980 **FM** *020 †18

MAASCH, Lloyd Palmer. ■ 54983 #056-06-1953 L1954 **FM** *071 †18

WHITEFISH BAY – MILWAUKEE

BAYNTON, Charles Graham. ■ 53211 #007-02-1979 L1981 **IM** *020 †20

BONNER, Michael Harvey. 702 E BEAUMONT AVE 53217 #047-05-1994 L2006 **IM** *020 †20

CORNELL, Jean Marie. 53217 #021-05-1997 L2007 **PD** *020 †55

HELMCHEN, Donna Jane. 4764 N NEWHALL ST 53211 #016-43-1991 L1993 **EM** *020 †16

HERNANDEZ, Natasha Marie. ■ 53217 #056-06-2003 L2007 **OBG** *100

HUGHES, George Raymond. ■ 53217 #035-09-1963 L1966 **IM CD** *071 †20

IVES, Donald G. 409 E SILVER SPRING DR 53217 #056-06-1951 L1952 **P N** *071

JOSEPH, Susan Elizabeth. 633 E HENRY CLAY ST 53217 #021-05-1989 L1990 **FM PLM** *020 †18

KANNEGANTI, Prameela Rani. ■ 53217 #495-21-1997 L2002 **IM** *100 †20

KLEMER, David Patrick. ■ 53217 #035-01-1999 L2004 **IM** *020 ‡

KOZIOL, Raymond Stanley. ■ 53217 #016-43-1965 L1969 **P GP** *075

LEHRMANN, Jon Arthur. ■ 53217 #056-06-1990 L1991 **P** *040 †75

MOORE, Jordan Alan. 121 E SILVER SPRING DR 53217 #038-41-1979 L1985 **D FM** *020 †18,15

PANDAZI, Andrew A. ■ 53211 #056-06-1963 L1964 **FM IM** *071 †95

REABE, Scott Matthew. ■ 53217 #056-06-2001 L2006 **RNR** *100 †80

TAYLOR, Jessica Ann. ■ 53217 #016-06-2001 L2002 **FP** *012

VAN SCHAIK, Jan Cornelius. 4530 N OAKLAND AVE 53211 #005-14-1979 L1980 **P PYA** *020 †75

ZEHMS, Chad Thomas. ■ 53217 #056-06-2001 L2001 **OSM** *012

WHITEHALL – TREMPEALEAU

ADAMS, Reuben James. 18606 ERVIN ST, WHITEHALL CLINIC 54773 #056-05-1975 L1976 **IM IMG** *020 †20

AULTBRINKER, Elizabeth A. 18606 ERVIN ST, CLINIC WHITEHALL 54773 #038-06-1985 L1991 OPH IM *020 †35

BELL, Barbara Jo. 18606 ERVIN ST, CLINIC 54773 #028-79-1983, ▲ L2001 FM *020

MARTIN, Wayne Bradford. 18606 ERVIN ST, WHITEHALL CLINIC 54773 #056-05-1969 L1972 GS *020 †85

OETTEL, Kurt Robert. 18606 ERVIN ST, WHITEHALL CLINIC 54773 #056-05-1995 L1998 ON IM *020 †20

SELKURT, Joanne Amanda. 18606 ERVIN ST, WHITEHALL CLINIC 54773 #056-05-1968 L1969 PD *020 †55

VAN EVERY, Marvin John. 18606 ERVIN ST, WHITEHALL CLINIC 54773 #005-06-1980 L1988 U *020 †95

WHITELAW — MANITOWOC

DOWNS, Dennis Ray. ■ 54247 #305-01-1980 L1981 FM EM *020

WHITEWATER — WALWORTH

ALWIN, Sean Padraic. 1305 W MAIN ST 53190 #056-05-1983 L1984 FM *020 †18

ANDERSEN, Eric Alan. 1461 W MAIN ST, STE A 53190 #025-01-1994 L1997 PD *020 †55

ANDERSON, Anna Lisa. 396 PANTHER CT 53190 #056-05-2007 OBG *012

CIASTO, Judith Anne. 710 W STARIN RD 53190 #016-11-1978 L1987 FM OS *020 †18

DELO, Marjorie Jean. 507 W MAIN ST 53190 #035-19-2000 L2004 FSM *020 †18 ‡

DETWILER, Alan Lee. 1461 W MAIN ST, STE A 53190 #016-11-1976 L1977 IM *020 †20

FARY, Daniel R B. 1461 W MAIN ST 53190 #017-20-1974 L1979 OPH *020 †35

FECHTER, Janet Marie. 507 W MAIN ST, MERCY WHITEWATER MEDICAL C 53190 #422-01-2000 L2001 FM *020 †18

GEORGE, Steven Chas. 1461 W MAIN ST, STE A 53190 #016-11-1982 L1985 IM *020 †20

GRIFFITHS, Anne Elizabeth. 1305 W MAIN ST 53190 #025-01-1976 L1977 FM *020 †18

HOLLAND, Robert A. ■ 53190 #028-02-1953 L1957 GYN OBG *072 †30

JENNINGS, Randall Wayne. 1461 W MAIN ST 53190 #012-05-1991 L2001 OSM *020 †40

KELLUM, Rebecca Irja. 1461 W MAIN ST, STE A 53190 #016-01-2003 L2006 IM *020 †20

KIDD, Kenneth Robert. 1305 W MAIN ST 53190 #016-01-1978 L1981 FM *020 †18

KOENIG, Laura Marie. 1461 W MAIN ST, STE A 53190 #056-05-1995 L1996 IM *020 †20

KOZLER, Craig Joseph. 1461 W MAIN ST 53190 #025-12-1998 L2004 U *020 †95

LEE, Catherine Haesook. 1461 W MAIN ST 53190 #041-01-1990 L1995 OPH *020 †35

MOKHTAR, Julie M. 1461 W MAIN ST 53190 #018-75-1990, ▲ L1995 OBG *020 †30

MULRY, James Thos. 507 W MAIN ST, MED CENTER 53190 #018-03-1973 L1988 FM OS *020 †18

NEARY, Paul James. 1461 W MAIN ST, STE A 53190 #010-02-1984 L1985 PD *020 †55

NELSON, Lawrence Frank. ■ 53190 #016-11-1947 L1950 GP *071

PETERSON, Stanley Eugene. 1461 W MAIN ST 53190 #018-03-1974 L1980 ORS HS *020 †40 ‡

ROWE, Donene Adele. 710 W STARIN RD 53190 #056-05-1989 L1990 FM *020 †18

SACHS, Nancy. ■ 53190 #016-11-1974 L2000 EM PD *020 †55,16

SALOV, Leslie Howard. ■ 53190 #869-02-1958 L1970 OPH FM *072

TACKMAN, Thomas John. 1461 W MAIN ST 53190 #056-06-1988 L1989 IM *030 †20

WEDL, Roberta Jo. 1305 W MAIN ST 53190 #056-05-1995 L1996 FM *020 †18

WINTER, Julia Robin. 1461 W MAIN ST, STE A 53190 #016-11-1994 L2001 PD *020 †55

WILD ROSE — WAUSHARA

ROMANA, Teodoro P, Jr. ■ 54984 #748-08-1962 L1982 UCM IM *020

ROMANA, Teresita Ungos. 701 GROVE AVE, P O BOX 314 54984 #748-10-1963 L1983 IM FM *071

STAUDINGER, Michael R. 701 GROVE AVE, WAUSHARA FAMILY PHYSICIANS 54984 #056-05-2003 L2004 FM *020 †18

WICHMANN, Rodney D. 601 GROVE AVE 54984 #056-05-1952 L1953 GP *071

WILLIAMS BAY — WALWORTH

GONCHAROVA, Irina. ■ 53191 #016-02-1999 L2006 VS *020 †85

MC CARTHY, Rebecca Jean. ■ 53191 #016-11-1979 *074

STUTZMAN, E Delroy, Jr. ■ 53191 #041-12-1961 L1962 ADM IM *071 †20

WINDSOR — DANE

TRAUTMAN, Christine Marie. ■ 53598 #056-05-2008 *012

WINNEBAGO — WINNEBAGO

ARONG, Chona Tesaluna. ■ 54985 #748-11-1991 L1999 P *020 †75

BALDOMERO, Maria Luisa B. PO BOX 9, WINNEBAGO MENTAL HEALTH IN 54985 #748-08-1990 L2001 CHP *020 †75

DE JESUS, Raul M. PO BOX 9 54985 #748-10-1965 L1994 P *020

GAANAN, Carlo Gallo. ■ 54985 #748-11-1991 L2002 FM *020 †18

LEE, Connie Mae Corlett. BUTLER AVE 54985 #056-05-1961 L1962 P *020

MICHLOWSKI, Thomas John. ■ 54985 #748-11-1976 L1979 P N *020 †75

SARINO, Wilbur Amoranto. PO BOX 9, 1300 SOUTH DR 54985 #748-10-1988 L1999 P *020 †75

WINNECONNE — WINNEBAGO

ANDERSON, Gay Raymond. ■ 54986 #016-06-1964 L1967 ORS OM *071 †40,75

FAUST, Marvin Clyde. ■ 54986 #517-05-1968 L1971 FM OM *020

LORIA, Loyda Ong. 916 E MAIN ST, WINNECOME CLINIC . 54986 #748-08-1980 L1989 IM *020 †20

MALLILIN, Carolyn T. 916 E MAIN ST, # D204 54986 #748-01-1994 L2002 GS FM *020 †18

MC DONALD, Donald H. 19 S 3RD ST, D H MC DONALD CLINIC SC 54986 #056-06-1951 L1952 FM FM *071

MORK, Harold Craig. 5184 SOUTHWIND DR 54986 #028-34-1976 L1981 IM IMG *020 †20

REINARDY, Michael Jos. 916 E MAIN ST, WINNECONNE CLINIC 54986 #056-06-1966 L1967 FM GP *071 †18

WINTER — SAWYER

SORENSEN, Charles Cordell. ■ 54896 #049-01-1968 L1969 U *071 †95

WISCONSIN DELLS — COLUMBIA

FAYLONA, Renato Tanzuaco. 1310 BROADWAY, STE 325 53965 #748-01-1961 L1972 GS *020 †85

HOOK, Christina Dianne. 1310 BROADWAY 53965 #056-05-2004 L2005 FM *020 †18

HOWARD, Stephen Donald. ■ 53965 #024-01-1963 L1992 P CHP *071 †75

JARVIS, David L. 1310 BROADWAY, DELLS CLINIC 53965 #054-04-1998 L1999 FM *020 †18

MILLER, Gerald Jos. ■ 53965 #056-06-1965 L1968 R NR *071 †80,28 ‡

MURPHY, Maureen. 1310 BROADWAY, STE 325 53965 #028-34-1981 L1984 FM *020 †18

SABOURIN, Mary Ellen. 530 WISCONSIN DELLS PKWY S 53965 #038-40-1990 L1991 FM *020 †18

WESTPHAL, Richard Kurt. 1310 BROADWAY, STE 325 53965 #056-06-1980 L1981 FM *020 †18

WISCONSIN RAPIDS — WOOD

AHMAD, Khadijah Binte S. 220 24TH ST S, MARSHFIELD CLNC 54494 #422-01-1997 L2001 FM *020 †18

AHUJA, Harish Gangaram. 410 DEWEY ST, FL 1 54494 #495-01-1978 L2000 ON *050 †20

ANDREWS, Steven Craig. 2611 12TH ST S 54494 #030-05-1974 L1978 P *020 †75

BOETTCHER, Bradley Scott. 420 DEWEY ST 54494 #028-34-1989 L1990 FM *020 †18

BRANDELL, Roy Alex. 400 DEWEY ST, UROLOGY SPEC OF WI 54494 #016-06-1989 L1995 U *020 †95

CARLSON, Joel Martin. 410 DEWEY ST, CARLSON GI CLINIC 54494 #026-04-1986 L1992 GE *020 †20

CHAMBERLIN, Regis Richard. 400 DEWEY ST 54494 #017-20-1982 L1985 PD *020 †55

CHRISTIE, Wayne Roger. 410 DEWEY ST 54494 #035-03-1977 L1995 OSM *020 †18

CHUNG, Dong Joon. 420 DEWEY ST, ASPIRUS DOCTORS CLINIC 54494 #583-03-1994 L2007 FM *020 †18

CONGER, Charles. PO BOX 8080 54495 #016-06-1973 L1974 EM FM *020 †18

CROWTHER, David Noel. 420 DEWEY ST 54494 #065-09-1982 L1995 FM *020 †18

DAUENHAUER, Floyd L, Jr. 420 DEWEY ST, DOCTORS CLINIC 54494 #048-02-1978 L1982 OBG *020 †18

DE LAS ALAS, Mercedes T. PO BOX 8080, 410 DEWEY ST 54495 #748-01-1989 L1998 IM *020 †20

DICKMAN, Scott Eugene. 420 DEWEY ST, DOCTOR'S CLINIC 54494 #056-06-2002 L2003 FM *020 †18

DRAKE, Thomas R. 420 DEWEY ST 54494 #048-13-1996 L2000 DR *020 †80

DUELLMAN, Todd Joseph. PO BOX 8005 54495 #056-06-2001 L2006 ORS *020

EGGE, Paul Richard. 420 DEWEY ST 54494 #046-01-1980 L1981 IM *020 †20

ESSER, Michael James. 420 DEWEY ST 54494 #056-06-1983 L1984 GS CCS *020 †85

ESTRADA, Deogracias R. 420 DEWEY ST 54494 #748-01-1980 L2000 IM *020 †20

FERREIRA, Kevin Juan. ■ 54494 #305-01-2002 L2006 IM *100 †20

FLETCHER, Brent Paul. PO BOX 8040, 420 DEWEY ST 54495 #024-16-1979 L1999 OBG *020 †30

GALUK, Douglas Peter. 140 24TH ST S 54494 #026-04-1990 L1995 ORS *020 †40 ‡

GARDE, Joseph Richard. 410 DEWEY ST 54494 #056-05-1987 L1989 GS *020 †85

GHINAZZI, Scott Ronald. 420 DEWEY ST 54494 #016-01-1981 L1982 FM *020 †18

GORDON, Bruce David. 410 DEWEY ST, RIVERVIEW HOSP EMERG DEPT 54494 #038-06-1974 L1976 EM OS *020

HO, Thomas Alton. 420 DEWEY ST 54494 #026-04-1984 L1985 IM *020 †20

HONG, Hi Young. 410 DEWEY ST, RIVERVIEW HOSPITAL 54494 #583-10-1982 L1990 PTH PCP *020 †50

HUEBNER, Timothy Keith. 420 DEWEY ST 54494 #056-05-1974 L1977 FM *020 †18

JOHNSON, James Alan. 140 24TH ST S 54494 #018-03-1977 L1978 ORS *020 †40 ‡

KIRSCHLING, Ronnie James. 410 DEWEY ST, RIVERVIEW UW CANCER CTR 54494 #056-06-1979 L1997 HO PLM *020 †20

KOTHARI, Nileshkumar K. 710 E GRAND AVE, CR ASSOCIATES 54494 #495-22-1985 L1994 EM FM *020

LEIBERT, Lawrence Glenn. 420 DEWEY ST 54494 #062-01-1985 L1996 PD *020 †55

LOVITT, Etta. ■ 54495 #012-05-1982 L2005 EM *020

LUCAS, Andrew Mc Keon. ■ 54494 #056-06-1958 L1959 DR *071 †80

LUCAS, Daniel Mckeon. ■ 54494 #056-06-1989 L1994 DR *020 †80

MATANGUIHAN, Eva Tiquis. 420 DEWEY ST 54494 #748-10-1983 L1995 PD *020 †55

MC DONOUGH, John Wm. 400 DEWEY ST 54494 #018-75-1968, ▲ L1975 ORS OSM *020 †40 ‡

MEHR, Michael Patrick. 420 DEWEY ST, RIVERWOOD CLINIC SC 54494 #010-02-1959 L1963 IM *071 †20

MILLER, Kevin B. PO BOX 309 54495 #056-06-1980 L1984 OPH *020 †35 ‡

MILLER, Marjorie S. 410 DEWEY ST, 3RD FL 54494 #035-47-1997 L2002 GS *020 †85

NAM, Moon-Woo. ■ 54494 #583-03-1998 L2006 PCP *020 †50

NAZE, Gregory Scott. 410 DEWEY ST 54494 #056-06-1981 L1982 AN *020

OLSON, Lisa Lyn. 420 DEWEY ST 54494 #018-03-1995 L1999 FM *020 †18

PAKALNS, Ruta Melita. ■ 54494 #056-06-1979 L1980 FM *020 †18

PATTERSON, James A, Jr. 410 DEWEY ST, EMERGENCY DEPT 54494 #025-07-1979 L1994 FM EM *020 †18,16

PERRYMAN, Fred Arthur. 420 DEWEY ST 54494 #016-45-1978 L1981 FM *020 †18

PONCE, Mario V. 520 BRUCE LN 54494 #748-07-1965 L1976 GS GP *071 †85

PONCE, Minerva Nicolas. 520 BRUCE LN 54494 #748-01-1965 L1976 IM *020 †20

RIMPILA, Charles Robt. 4421 EASTWOOD DR, P O BOX 182 54494 #016-42-1972 L1987 OM EM *071 †16

ROENIUS, Robert James. 1041 HILL ST, DOCTORS CLINIC SC 54494 #056-06-1987 L1988 FM *020 †18

SCHERWINSKI, David Louis. 410 DEWEY ST 54494 #056-05-1984 L1987 AN PMM *020 †05

SEIFERT, Matthew Roman. 410 DEWEY ST 54494 #030-06-1981 L1984 AN *020

SNOW, Steven Paul. 420 DEWEY ST 54494 #025-07-1989 L2006 IM *020 †20

STARR, Clifford Harold. 231 1ST AVE N 54495 #056-06-1956 L1957 OM GS *071 †85

STORCH, Todd Dennis. 410 DEWEY ST 54494 #056-05-1990 L1992 **AN** *020 †05

TANG, Shee-Chang. ■ 54494 #065-01-1989 L1999 **FM** *020 †18

TETER, Allen Lavern. 410 DEWEY ST 54494 #056-05-1981 L1995 **EM GS** *020 †85

UBER, Christine Louise. 420 DEWEY ST 54494 #056-05-1979 L1982 **IM** *072 †20

VAN DER VEEN, Rhonda L. 410 DEWEY ST, RIVERVIEW HOSPITAL ASSOCIA 54494 #016-76-1996, ▲ L2004 **DR** *020 †80

VAN DYKEN, Robt La Verne. 420 DEWEY ST 54494 #048-02-1973 L1977 **OBG** *020

VOELKER, Thomas Anthony. 420 DEWEY ST, ASPIRUS DOCTORS CLINIC, IN 54494 #026-04-1984 L1987 **FM** *020 †18

VOS, Marvin Arnold. 3220 15TH ST S 54494 #018-03-1969 L1972 **FM OS** *071 †18

WEILAND, Jennifer Ann. ■ 54494 #056-06-2001 L2002 **FM** *020 †18

WELSH, James. 410 DEWEY ST, FL 1 54494 #035-48-1994 L2002 **RO** *020 †80

WESSLING, Richard Stephen. 420 DEWEY ST 54494 #036-05-1995 L1998 **IM** *020 †20

WILKES, James Alhen. 140 24TH ST S 54494 #056-06-1982 L1987 **ORS** *020 †40 ‡

WILSON, Janet Adele. 541 GARFIELD ST 54494 #038-06-1969 L1970 **IM** *071 †20

WOGAHN, Timothy Paul. 420 DEWEY ST, P O BOX 8040 54494 #018-03-1995 L1998 **FM** *020 †18

WITTENBERG — SHAWANO

ALMAZAR, Deogracias C, Jr. 600 S WEBB ST 54499 #748-08-1965 L1976 **FM** *020 †18

HANSON, Susan Elizabeth. ■ 54499 #016-02-1963 L1992 **P** *075

WONEWOC — JUNEAU

CORNELL, Lea. 505 CENTER ST 53968 #056-05-1975 L1978 **EM** *020 †18

WOODRUFF — VILAS

ANSELMO, Paul Jay. 311 ELM ST 54568 #056-06-1970 L1971 **CD IM** *020 †20

BECHTEL, Richard C, Jr. ■ 54568 #036-07-1966 L1974 **OBG** *071 †30

ENGELMEIER, Richard S. 311 ELM ST 54568 #056-05-1978 L1986 **CD** *020 †20

FURDA, Joel Lee. 311 ELM ST 54568 #018-03-1974 L1978 **IM** *020 †20

GELINAS, Michel Pierre. 1020 3RD AVE, EYECARE ASSOC 54568 #007-02-1988 L1998 **OPH** *020 †35

GUIGAOURI, Pavel. 311 ELM ST 54568 #913-06-1984 L2004 **IM** *020 †20

HOFFMANN, Mark T. 311 ELM ST 54568 #056-05-1987 L1994 **CD IC** *020 †20

KOSKI, David Walter. 240 MAPLE ST 54568 #025-01-1974 L1982 **AN** *020 †05

LARRAIN, German. 311 ELM ST 54568 #231-01-1985 L2000 **CD IC** *020 †20

LOGEMANN, Timothy Neal. 311 ELM ST 54568 #056-05-1986 L1989 **CD IM** *020 †20

LUETMER, Paul A. 311 ELM ST 54568 #026-04-1984 L1997 **IM** *020 †20

MURDOCK, David Kent. 311 ELM ST 54568 #016-43-1977 L1987 **CD** *020 †20

RAETTIG, James Arthur. ■ 54568 #016-43-1967 L1973 **PD** *040 †55

SCHLOTTERBECK, Phyllis C. ■ 54568 #016-06-1950 L1950 **IMG** *071

WRIGHTSTOWN — BROWN

SLIGHTAM, Pierre Eduard. 229 MAIN ST 54180 #056-05-1958 L1959 **GP** *075

STANELLE, Eric Jon. ■ 54180 #056-05-2008 *012

WOZNEY, Bradley Bernard. 555 QUALITY CT 54180 #056-05-1995 L1996 **FM** *020 †18

AFTON – LINCOLN

BENDER, David Scott. PO BOX 1695, 110 HOSPITAL LN 83110 #035-08-1988 L2001 **GS VS** *020 †85

CARTER, Allen D. 120 HOSPITAL LN 83110 #054-04-1983 L1986 **FM EM** *020 †18

HEAD, Kitchener Paul. PO BOX 280 83110 #308-11-1985 L1989 **FM** *020 †18

PERKES, Orson Dee. 110 HOSPITAL LN 83110 #049-01-1955 L1956 **GP** *020

STIBOR, Noel Bruce. PO BOX 280 83110 #028-34-1986 L1987 **FM** *020 †18

ALBIN – LARAMIE

SCHMIDT, Elizabeth Anne. PO BOX 217, 404 WOLCOTT 82050 #030-06-1983 L1984 *074

ALPINE – LINCOLN

GORMAN, George Newell. ■ 83128 #048-04-1957 L1957 **OTO AM** *071

ALTA – TETON

THOMAS, Scott David. 155 YELLOW ROSE DR, . 83414 #026-04-1982 L1983 **EM** *020 †16

ARAPAHOE – FREMONT

GILROY, Tabitha Marie. 14 GREAT PLAINS RD, INDIAN HEALTH MEDICAL CENT 82510 #017-20-1999 L2000 **FM** *020 †18

BANNER – SHERIDAN

MUNDY, Gary Duane. 1087 HIGHWAY 14 82832 #040-02-1977 L1993 **EM** *020 †16

BASIN – BIG HORN

DURNEY, Sarah E. ■ 82410 #054-04-2008 *012

FITZSIMMONS, Brendan Hugh. 388 HIGHWAY 20 S 82410 #030-06-1995 L1998 **FM** *020 †18

HILL, Demar David. 388 US HIGHWAY 20 S, MIDWAY CLINIC 82410 #305-01-1995 L1996 **FM** *020 †18

BIG HORN – SHERIDAN

ALZHEIMER, Daniel Robt. PO BOX 708 82833 #054-04-1984 L1993 **DR NRN** *020 †80

BIG PINEY – SUBLETTE

BURNETT, William David. PO BOX 130 83113 #027-01-1982 L1987 **FM** *020

CLOSE, William T. ■ 83113 #035-01-1951 L1976 **FM** *062

BONDURANT – SUBLETTE

CRENSHAW, John L, Jr. PO BOX 959 82922 #016-06-1945 L1964 **OBG** *075 †30

ELLWOOD, Paul M, Jr. ■ 82922 #005-11-1953 L1953 **PM N** *062 †60

BUFFALO – JOHNSON

BLACK, Norman R. ■ 82834 #021-01-1944 L1951 **U** *071 †95

DARNELL, Brian M. 497 W LOTT ST 82834 #048-78-2001, ▲ L2002 **FM** *020 †18

FEHIR, Kim Michele. 497 W LOTT ST 82834 #016-01-1978 L1998 **IM ON** *020 †20

GARDNER, Ronald Shearer. ■ 82834 #017-20-1966 L1992 **GS** *020 †85

GONZALEZ, Hermilo, Jr. 497 W LOTT ST 82834 #003-01-1989 L1990 **FM** *020 †18

GOSAR, Grace Marie. 497 W LOTT ST 82834 #049-01-1990 L1993 **FM** *020 †18

HOWELL, Marsha T. PO BOX 66, 1 DEER HVN 82834 #004-01-1974 L1974 **GYN** *020 †30

KIRVEN, Lawrence Edward. 497 W LOTT ST, FAMILY MEDICAL CENTER 82834 #030-06-1982 L1985 **FM** *020 †18

KNIERIM, Gabriele Susanne. 497 W LOTT ST 82834 #030-06-1995 L2004 **FM** *020 †18

MATTHEWS, Frederick A. 497 W LOTT ST 82834 #041-01-1965 L1971 **R** *020 †80

NOLAN, Patrick David. 497 W LOTT ST 82834 #049-01-1963 L1966 **GP** *071

RUBY, Blaine J. 497 W LOTT ST 82834 #054-04-2002 L2004 **GS** *020 †85

SCHUELER, Mark Steven. 497 W LOTT ST 82834 #049-01-1986 L1990 **FM** *020 †18

TABB, Aubrey Dozier. 497 W LOTT ST, OF JOHNSON COUNTY 82834 #012-22-1991 L1992 **FM FSM** *020 †18

WAGNER, Robert Morris. ■ 82834 #035-20-1952 L1957 **OBG** *071 †30

CASPER – NATRONA

ALLERHEILIGEN, David A. ■ 82604 #030-05-1975 L1992 **FM** *020 †70,18

ANDERSON, James Allen. 410 S WASHINGTON ST, STE 102 82601 #007-02-1976 L1980 **GS VS** *020 †85

ARNDT, William F, Jr. 262 S WASHINGTON ST 82601 #010-02-1963 L1968 **PA AM** *071

ASHBAUGH, R Dale. ■ 82601 #007-02-1941 L1946 **GP** *071

BAILEY, John Dyches. 4140 CENTENNIAL HILLS BLVD, STE A 82609 #048-02-1970 L1978 **ORS** *020 †40

BAILEY, Tarver Bryant. 1416 E A ST, STE 101 82601 #048-02-1969 L1978 **U** *071 †95

BARAHAL, David. 301 THELMA DR, # 172 82609 #025-07-1991 L2000 **AN** *020 †05

BARRASSO, John A. 4140 CENTENNIAL HILLS BLVD, STE A 82609 #010-02-1978 L1983 **ORS** *020 †40

BATTY, Trent Walter. 1522 E A ST 82601 #003-01-2006 L2007 **FP** *012

BAUM, Jamie Leona. 1522 E A ST, COMMUNITY HEALTH CENTER 82601 #016-45-2003 L2004 **FM** *100 †18

BAXTER, David Albert, IV. ■ 82609 #030-05-1997 L2006 **AN** *020 †05

BECKSTEAD, Todd Harrison. 419 S WASHINGTON ST, STE 102 82601 #049-01-1994 L1999 **GS** *020 †85

BEHRENS, Jerome Allen. 4140 CENTENNIAL HILLS BLVD, STE A 82609 #056-05-1966 L1973 **ORS** *020 †40

BENNETT, Bruce Cyrus. 2521 E 15TH ST, WYOMING BEHAVIORAL INSTITU 82609 #041-02-1997 L2008 **P** *020

BETTINGER, Paul Thos. 419 S WASHINGTON ST, STE 200 82601 #024-05-1990 L2000 **IM** *020 †20

BICEK, Joseph Geo. ■ 82604 #016-42-1965 L1973 **R** *071 †80

BILLINGS, John Alan. 1233 E 2ND ST 82601 #026-04-1979 L1992 **AN** *020 †05

BINDER, Jonathan Paul. 1233 E 2ND ST 82601 #030-05-1984 L1987 **EM FM** *020 †18

BOWDEN, Robert Horton. ■ 82601 #056-06-1946 L1948 **OBG** *071

BRONDOS, Gregory Alan. 1233 E 2ND ST 82601 #036-05-1964 L1970 **PTH** *071 †50

BROWN, Robert Oakley. 1233 E 2ND ST 82601 #056-05-1955 L1960 **GP ADM** *020

BROWN, Stephen Loyd. 2417 E 15TH ST 82609 #005-06-1985 L1990 **CHP P** *020 †75

BRUBAKER, Elbridge Lee. 1311 E 3RD ST 82601 #047-06-1965 L1968 **FM OBG** *020 †18

BRUCKER, Anne Wolff. 1233 E 2ND ST, WYOMING MEDICAL CENTER 82601 #306-01-1995 L2006 **IM** *020 †20

BRUNO, Michael Rudolph. 1233 E 2ND ST, EMERGENCY ROOM 82601 #049-01-1987 L1988 **FM** *020 †18

BURGFECHTEL, John Stephen. 4140 S POPLAR ST 82601 #018-03-1977 L1977 **FM** *020 †18

BURKE, Mary F Russ. 940 E 3RD ST 82601 #028-46-1979 L1982 **FM** *074 †18

BURKE, Thomas Malachy. 940F E 3RD ST, STE 202 82601 #028-46-1978 L1982 **IM** *020 †20

BURSTEN, Marian Stager. 419 S WASHINGTON ST, STE 200 82601 #038-40-1993 L2007 **FM** *020 †20

BUSSO, Oscar Mendez. 1233 E 2ND ST, WYOMING MEDICAL CENTER 82601 #737-01-1988 L2006 **IM** *020 †20

CARNAHAN, Robert Curtis. ■ 82609 #030-05-1955 L1956 **ORS** *071 †40

CHEN, Han Kuang. 1233 E 2ND ST, UNIV OF WYOMING 82601 #759-04-2001 L2008 **FP** *012

CLIFFORD, Ryan T. 1233 E 2ND ST, STE 600 82609 #037-01-1999 L2000 **FM** *020 †18

COLE, Malvin. 246 S WASHINGTON ST 82601 #010-02-1957 L1972 **N** *071 †75

COLYAR, Willis Oren. 2350 GARDEN CREEK HTS 82601 #004-01-1958 L1989 **AN** *071 †05

CORBETT, John Jensen. 280 W COLLINS DR, STE 2 82601 #007-02-1954 L1959 **GS FM** *071 †85

CORSON, Rishona Y.. 1522 E A ST, COMMUNITY HEALTH CENTER OF 82601 #820-02-2005 L2007 **FP** *012

CUBIN, Frederick William. ■ 82604 #054-04-2005 **DR** *012

CUMMINGS, Daniel Clyde. 940 E 3RD ST STE 209, CASPER CLINIC 82601 #049-01-1975 L2005 **FM** *020 †18

CUNNINGHAM, Thomas M, III. 419 S WASHINGTON ST, STE 101 82601 #047-06-1994 L2000 **VIR** *020 †80

DEAKINS, Jacob Charles. 1522 E A ST 82601 #820-02-2006 **FP** *012

DEISS, Frederick. 1450 E A ST 82601 #005-12-1957 L1959 **GP OS** *071

DE PAOLO, Hugh Danl. 1450 E A ST, STE 1 82601 #001-02-1978 L1979 **OBG** *020

DODDS, Matthew Taylor. 1421 WILKINS CIR 82601 #054-04-1981 L1990 **OPH AM** *020 †35

DOWELL, Mark Edward. 5810 E 2ND ST STE 100, ROCKY MTN. INFECTIOUS DISE 82609 #024-16-1985 L1993 **ID IM** *020 †20

DOWNEY-MC MILLIN, Kelly L. ■ 82601 #007-02-2007 **FP** *012

DUDO, James Edward. 1522 E A ST, COMMUNITY HEALTH CLINIC 82601 #665-01-2000 L2007 **FM** *100

DURHAM, Harry Blaine, Jr. ■ 82609 #016-06-1945 L1952 **GS** *071 †85

EDWARDS, Diane J Rose. 915 S DAVID ST 82601 #036-07-1969 L1993 **PD** *050 †55

ELLBOGEN, David Arnold. 1720 S POPLAR ST STE 1 82601 #030-06-1989 L1992 **PD** *020 †55

ELLBOGEN, Martin Healey. 1233 E 2ND ST, HOSPITALIST SERVICES OF WY 82601 #030-06-1956 L1959 **FM** *020 †18

ELLBOGEN, Martin Healey. ■ 82609 #030-06-1994 L2000 **ID IM** *020 †20

EMCH, Rita Marie. 940 E 3RD ST, STE 210 82601 #023-07-1976 L1979 **IM** *020 †20

ENGELKING, Kerry Glenn. 1233 E 2ND ST 82601 #030-06-1981 L1984 **AN** *020 †05

ERK, David John. 419 S WASHINGTON ST, STE 200 82601 #046-01-1979 L1994 **IM** *020 †20

FERGUSON, Donald Ewing. 3800 S COFFMAN AVE 82604 #054-04-1960 L1968 **U** *071 †95

FOLEY, Matthew Vaughn. ■ 82609 #016-06-1996 L2006 **AN** *020

FOX, Sherrill Anne. 6500 E 2ND ST STE 200 82609 #036-08-1996 L2006 **FM** *020 †18

GHANEM, Ghazi Antoun. 5810 E 2ND ST STE 100, ROCKY MTN INFECTIOUS DISEA 82609 #605-02-1999 L2006 **ID** *100

GIBSON, Ronald Eugene. 1705 E 12TH ST 82601 #007-02-1978 L1983 **OPH** *020 †35

GODDIK, Steen. 2521 E 15TH ST, WYOMING BEHAVIORAL INSTITU 82609 #046-01-2001 L2007 **CHP** *020

GOODER, Ronald Lee. ■ 82604 #005-02-1978 L1981 **FM** *020 †18

GORDY, Philip D. ■ 82604 #025-01-1943 L1973 **NS** *071 †25

GORMAN, Matthew Thomas. 4140 CENTENNIAL HILLS BLVD, STE A 82609 #016-43-2001 L2007 **ORS** *020

GRANUM, Michael James. 940 E 3RD ST, STE 205 82601 #037-01-1977 L1980 **PD** *020 †55

GREEN, Richard Dewar. 940 E 3RD ST STE 102 82601 #039-01-1969 L1974 **PD** *020 †55 ‡

GREER, Donald Merrill, Jr. 1300 E A ST STE 207 82601 #038-41-1962 L1987 **PS** *071 †65

HAMMOND, Todd Alan. 1026 E 2ND ST 82601 #030-06-2000 L2004 **AN** *020 †05

HAYNES, Coleen Marie. 1522 E A ST, UNIV WY FAMILY RESIDENCY 82601 #305-01-2004 L2007 **FP** *012

HISER, Wesley Wayne. 1230 E 1ST ST 82601 #038-40-1966 L1976 **CD PUD** *020 †20

HOBART, Edward Danl, Jr. ■ 82601 #016-43-1966 L1993 **CLP ATP** *071 †50

HOLMES, Roy Willis. ■ 82604 #048-02-1946 L1956 **NM** *071 †20

HORN, Steven Ray. 419 S WASHINGTON ST 82601 #021-01-1978 L1987 **DR AM** *020 †80

HRNICEK, Gary Englebert. 1020 S CONWELL ST 82601 #030-05-1973 L1992 **IM** *020 †20

HUDSON, Timothy Bartlett. 2417 E 15TH ST 82609 #017-20-1980 L2004 **P** *020 †75

HYNDMAN, Marlene C. 3830 E 20TH ST 82609 #422-01-1995 L2001 **EM** *020

IDEEN, Dana Ray. 1315 E A ST, FAMILY CLNC 82601 #030-06-1984 L1985 **FM** *020 †18

IVERSON, Ronald Dean. 1233 E 2ND ST, WYOMING MEDICAL CENTER 82601 #007-02-1979 L1983 **EM FM** *020 †18,16

JOHNSON, Paul Kyrean. 1233 E 2ND ST 82601 #005-11-1962 L1975 **IM HEM** *020

JOHNSON, Ted Dean. 1300 E A ST STE 206 82601 #054-04-1957 L1987 **NS** *071 †25

JONES, J Paul, III. 1416 E A ST 82601 #048-02-1987 L1990 **U** *020 †95

JOUBRAN, Raoul Boulos. 1201 E 3RD ST 82601 #038-45-1994 L2001 **GE** *020 †20

KAIGH, Jodi. 1204 E 2ND ST 82601 #019-02-1988 L1997 **OBG** *020 †30

KARAMAN, Boris Alexander. 419 S WASHINGTON ST 82601 #041-02-1983 L2003 DR IM *020 †20,80

KARNES, Sharon Ruth. 1522 E A ST 82601 #054-04-2001 L2004 FM *020 †18

KATZ, Kent Douglas. 1201 E 3RD ST 82601 #054-04-1981 L2000 GE IM *020

KLINKER, Timothy Grant. 351 N LENNOX ST 82601 #049-01-2001 L2003 FM *020

KNOTT, James Arden. 4619 SMOKE RISE RD 82604 #040-02-1997 L2001 AN *020 †05

KOPITNIK, Thomas Anthony. 1026 E 2ND ST, CENTRAL WYOMING NEUROSURGE 82601 #055-01-1984 L2004 NS OS *020 †25

KRMPOTICH, Phillip Thos. 1201 E 3RD ST 82601 #030-06-1991 L1996 GE *020 †20

LANDON, Tom Wedgeworth. 4140 CENTENNIAL HILLS BLVD, STE A 82609 #021-05-1971 L1979 ORS *020 †40

LARCOM, Gordon Danforth. ■ 82601 #024-07-1958 L1967 AN *071 †05

LEGAN, Eugenia. PO BOX 2356 82602 #030-06-1977 L1977 IM CCM *020 †20

LI, Curtis Kimky. 1300 E A ST, STE 209 82601 #005-06-1977 L1995 CD ICE *020 †20

LLOYD, Jason Wayne. 419 S WASHINGTON ST, STE 200 82601 #018-03-1999 L2002 FM *020 †18

LYNCH, Kathy Sue. ■ 82601 #016-45-2007 FP *012

MAC GUIRE, Anne Marie. 940 E 3RD ST 82601 #030-06-1980 L1980 RHU *020 †18

MAC GUIRE, Mary Elizabeth. 1450 E A ST, STE 3 82601 #007-02-1979 L1991 GS GE *020 †85

MACKENZIE, Janet S. 1450 E A ST, STE 2 82601 #041-01-1992 L2000 GS *020 †65

MADDY, James Allen. 940 E 3RD ST, CASPER CLINIC 82601 #047-05-1963 L1971 IM END *071 †20

MAHNKE, Donald Fred. ■ 82601 #035-20-1956 L1961 GS *071 †85

MATTERN, Allan Lee. 1230 E 1ST ST, SERVICES P.C. 82601 #008-01-1962 L1980 CD IM *071 †20

MCGINLEY, Mark J. 1300 E A ST, STE 206 82601 #836-02-1990 L2003 PUD CCM *020 †20

MCLANAHAN, Andrew Gregg, Jr. ■ 82609 #054-04-2007 MPD *012

METZ, Albert Victor, Jr. 1233 E 2ND ST 82601 #041-02-1969 L1976 NS *020

MICKELSON, Joseph E, IV. 6500 E 2ND ST STE 200 82609 #030-06-1994 L1995 FM *020 †18

MILLER, Meredith Hodes. 1026 E 2ND ST 82601 #010-01-1963 L1991 NS N *020 †25

MILLS, Keith R. 6501 E 2ND ST 82609 #041-13-1973 L2001 ON IM *020 †20

MITCHELL, Kirk Ernest. 1522 E A ST 82601 #820-02-2006 FP *012

MITCHELL, Matthew Eugene. 4140 CENTENNIAL HILLS BLVD, STE A 82609 #024-01-1991 L2007 ORS *020 †40

MOHR, Michele Rene. 1233 E 2ND ST 82601 #007-02-2001 L2002 FM *020 †18

MORRISON, Kerry Dean. 111 W 2ND ST, STE 415 82601 #030-06-1980 L1984 AN *020 †05

MORSE, Jeremy Charles. ■ 82604 #422-01-2003 L2005 FM *020 †18

MOSHER, Jennifer Christen. ■ 82601 #054-04-2008 *012

MUEHL, Karen Louise. 1522 E A ST, WYOMING FAMILY MEDICINE RE 82601 #005-06-1985 L1992 FM *040 †18

MUNDAY, George David. 1416 E A ST, STE 101 82601 #038-41-1986 L2003 U *020 †95

MUNOZ, Eric. 805 E 2ND ST, WYOMING CARDIAC SURGERY 82601 #005-11-1988 L1999 TS *020 †85,90

MYERS, Harlen Dale. 940 E 3RD ST 82601 #005-15-1965 L1971 PD PHO *020 †55

MYERS, Rachel Nicole. ■ 82601 #016-45-2007 FP *012

NAROTZKY, Robert Allan. 1026 E 2ND ST 82601 #016-06-1974 L1999 NS GS *020 †25

NELSON, Vera. 419 S WASHINGTON ST, STE 200 82601 #017-20-1996 L2001 NEP *020 †20

NICHOLS, Carrie Jean. 1522 E A ST 82601 #037-01-2000 L2001 FM *100 †18

NORCROSS, David Copeland. 6500 E 2ND ST, STE 101 82609 #048-12-2001 L2006 OTO *020 †45

NOVICK, Robert Allen. 1230 E 1ST ST 82601 #016-11-1984 L1992 CD IM *020 †20

ORCUTT, Steven Allyn. 4140 CENTENNIAL HILLS BLVD, STE A 82609 #005-18-1985 L2003 ORS HS *020 †40

ORFORD, James Langley. 1230 E 1ST ST 82601 #836-02-1993 L2004 CD *020 †20

PAZOOKI, Babak. 419 S WASHINGTON ST, STE 200 82601 #517-11-1994 L2006 END *020

PETERS, Paul Leon. 419 S WASHINGTON ST 82601 #030-05-1980 L1987 DR *020 †80

PICKRELL, John William. 1233 E 2ND ST 82601 #049-01-1996 L2003 CD *020 †20

PODRAZIK, Eugene Peter. 6500 E 2ND ST 82609 #016-01-1984 L2000 OTO *020 †45

POPE, Karla Rae. 1522 E A ST 82601 #104-01-2006 FP *012

PRYPCHAN, Lida Daria. 2521 E 15TH ST, WYOMING BEHAVIORAL INSTITU 82609 #935-04-1986 L2007 CHP *020

PURVIANCE, John David. 6501 E 2ND ST, ROCKY MOUNTAIN ONCOLOGY 82609 #024-07-2002 L2007 RO *100

QUINN, Michael Jos. 940 E 3RD ST, STE 208 82601 #050-02-1975 L1980 PD *020 †55

RADOSEVICH, Thomas Edward. 1522 E A ST 82601 #030-06-1999 L2000 FM *020 †18

RAO, Peddada Ramachandra. 307 S JACKSON ST 82601 #023-01-1999 L2005 OPH *020 †35 ‡

RATCLIFF, Robert Craig. 419 S WASHINGTON ST, STE 102 82601 #049-01-1983 L1988 GS *020 †85,10

REALING, Jr. ■ 82601 #049-01-2003 L2007 EM *020

REASONER, Edward Earl. 940 E 3RD ST, STE 203 82601 #007-02-1959 L1963 IM *071

RICHARD, Jack Vernon. 167 S CONWELL ST STE 5, CASPER OBSTETRICAL & GYN A 82601 #030-05-1967 L1973 OBG *071 †30

ROBERTS, Andrew L. 5110 S OAK ST 82601 #048-78-2002, ▲ L2006 FM *100

ROBITAILLE, Beth E. 1522 E A ST, COMMUNITY HEALTH CENTER OF 82601 #030-06-1995 L1999 FM *020 †18

ROUSSALIS, John Louis. 1129 E 2ND ST 82601 #030-06-2000 L2007 PS *020 †85

ROUSSALIS, Louis John. 1129 E 2ND ST 82601 #021-01-1961 L1962 FM GS *071 †18

RUBEN, Stuart Jay. 1300 E A ST STE 101 82601 #038-40-1971 L1996 IM *020 †20

RUPP, James Clarke. 1141 WILKINS CIR 82601 #019-02-1989 L1995 NEP IM *020 †20

RYAN, Keith Aaron. 2501 E 15TH ST, STE 2 82609 #056-06-2001 L2005 AN *020 †05

SANTIAGO, Angelo Mario M. 1026 E 2ND ST 82601 #748-16-1987 L1993 N *020 †75

SCALING, Sam Tilden. 1125 E 2ND ST 82601 #047-06-1971 L1978 OBG *020 †20

SCHLIDT, Robert Anthony. 1441 WILKINS CIR 82601 #056-06-1989 L1994 GE IM *020 †20

SCHOEBER, Joe K. 6500 E 2ND ST STE 20 82609 #030-06-1985 L1986 FM *030 †18

SHAH, Kamlesh. 2222 E 2ND ST 82609 #495-22-1980 L1996 AI *020 †20,03

SHARFAEI, Soraya. 1233 E 2ND ST, WYOMING MEDICAL CENTER 82601 #517-11-1996 L2006 IM *020 †20

SHEIKH, Shoaib. 1522 E A ST 82601 #665-01-2003 L2006 FM *100 †18

SHEPPARD, Benjamin Wilbur. 167 S CONWELL ST, STE 5 82601 #037-01-1976 L1980 OBG *020 †30

SHERIDAN, Susan Marie. ■ 82601 #054-04-2003 L2007 OBG *020

SKAF, Michel Wadih. 1230 E 1ST ST 82601 #605-01-1996 L2005 CD *020 †20

SMITH, Craig Patrick. 4140 CENTENNIAL HILLS BLVD, STE A 82609 #007-02-1988 L1994 ORS OTR *020 †40

SMITH, Donald Dee. 940 E 3RD ST STE 207 82601 #025-01-1970 L1979 PCC FM *020 †20

SMITH, Geoffrey Giles. 419 S WASHINGTON ST 82601 #048-04-1986 L1991 DR *020 †80

SMOTHERS, Lane L. 419 S WASHINGTON ST, STE 102 82601 #048-12-1996 L2001 GS *020 †85

SMOTHERS, Laura Ann. 1125 E 2ND ST 82601 #048-12-1993 L2001 OBG *020 †30

SNYDER, Christopher M. 1522 E A ST 82601 #041-77-1977, ▲ L2006 IM *030

SRAMEK, Joseph Gerald. 419 S WASHINGTON ST, STE 202 82601 #016-01-1994 L2000 GS NS *020 †25

STANSILL, Jason Tyler. 1522 E A ST 82601 #054-04-2001 L2004 IM *020

STEELE, Debra Lynn. 1026 E 2ND ST, NEUROSCIENCE CENTER OF WYO 82601 #030-05-1998 L2005 NS *020

STEPLOCK, Albert Louis, Jr. 805 E 2ND ST, STE 2 82601 #021-01-1976 L1985 TS GS *020 †85,90

STINSON, Anita Jean. 1233 E 2ND ST 82601 #030-06-1989 L1993 PTH *020 †50

STINSON, Ronald Grover. 1233 E 2ND ST 82601 #030-06-1987 L1991 PTH *020 †50

STIRLING, Cory James. 1300 E A ST STE 104 82601 #019-02-1995 L1999 IM *020 †20

STIRLING, Renee Dawn. 1300 E A ST, STE 104 82601 #038-06-1995 L1999 AN *020

STUDER, Werner Alvin. 6500 E 2ND ST STE 200 82609 #030-06-1987 L1988 FM *020 †18

SULLIVAN, Daniel Jos. 1233 E 2ND ST 82601 #005-15-1969 L1977 PTH *030 †50

SULLIVAN, Patrick Garner. 4010 S POPLAR ST A, PMB 176 82601 #056-06-1968 L1977 DR *020 †80

SULSER, Daniel Fridolin. 419 S WASHINGTON ST 82601 #047-05-1990 L2001 DR *020 †80,28

SWAN, Ryan Thomas. 1233 E 2ND ST, WYOMING MEDICAL CENTER 82601 #048-13-1996 L2003 PM *020 †60

SWEDBERG, Jay Andrew. 6500 E 2ND ST STE 200 82609 #007-02-1974 L1982 FM FPG *020 †18

TEAGUE, Lonnie Arthur. ■ 82604 #661-02-2005 L2008 FP *012

TELCK, Lynnette Claire. 1522 E A ST 82601 #007-02-2002 L2003 FM *020 †18

THORPEN, James Werts. 200 N CENTER ST # 10, NATRONA CO CORONER 82601 #023-07-1954 L1960 ATP FOP *062 †50

TICHENOR, Rowan Edwin. 1119 E 3RD ST 82601 #019-02-1971 L1977 D DMP *020 †15

TOBIN, Robert Lawrence. 6501 E 2ND ST 82609 #030-06-1986 L1990 RO *020 †80

TOEWS, Berton James. 231 S WILSON ST 82601 #038-41-1976 L1977 ADM FM *020 †18 ‡

TOOKE, Johnny Mack. 2241 FARNUM ST STE 105 82609 #021-05-1974 L1976 FM *020 †18

TURNER, Clayton Earl. 4140 CENTENNIAL HILLS BLVD, STE A 82609 #048-04-1988 L1998 OSS *072 †40

TURNER, Diane Clay. 6501 E 2ND ST 82609 #048-04-1988 L1998 IM HEM *075 †20

VEAUTHIER, Brian Michael. 1522 E A ST, UW FP RESIDENCY 82601 #010-02-2001 L2002 FM *020 †18

VIGNERI, Joseph Michael. 6500 E 2ND ST 82609 #026-04-1967 L1974 OTO *020 †45

VIGNERI, Robert Anthony. 940 E 3RD ST, STE 203 82601 #030-06-1996 L1999 PD *020 †55

VIGNERI, Samuel Joseph. 1125 E 2ND ST 82601 #030-06-1998 L2002 OBG *020 †30

VIRAY, Arlene P. 111 W 2ND ST, STE 305 82601 #748-01-1988 L1995 P *020

VUOLO, Mark D. 300 S WOLCOTT ST, STE 330 82601 #016-11-1981 L1993 P *020 †75

WEBB, Sherilyn Mc Dade. 1233 E 2ND ST, EMERGENCY DEPARTMENT 82601 #004-01-1991 L1992 FM OBS *020 †18 ‡

WEBER, Mary B. ■ 82605 #026-08-1987 L1999 AN *020 †05

WELLS, Marjorie Lynn. 1315 E A ST 82601 #035-48-1995 L1996 FM *020 †18

WELO, Bob Leonard. ■ 82604 #067-01-1955 L1962 OPH *071 †35

WHALEN, Richard Michael. ■ 82604 #010-01-1970 L1977 GS GP *020 †85

WHEELER, David Brockman. 419 S WASHINGTON ST, STE 201 82601 #005-11-2000 L2004 N CN *020 †75

WICKS, Allan Benj. 1230 E 1ST ST 82601 #041-13-1992 L1998 CD *020 †20

WIEDER, Brian Howard. 419 S WASHINGTON ST, STE 202 82601 #005-06-1991 L2006 NS GS *020 †20

WITZELING, Todd Michael. 1044 S WOLCOTT ST 82601 #030-06-1984 L1990 AN *020 †05

WOODWARD, Ralph Andrew. 304 S PARK ST 82601 #034-01-1993 L1994 FM *020 †20

WORKS, Cynthia Ann. 1522 E A ST 82601 #003-01-1985 L1991 FM *071 †18 ‡

WRIGHT, Aaron Davidlee. 419 S WASHINGTON ST, STE 101 82601 #019-02-2001 L2006 DR *020 †80

YOST, Linda Ann. 1233 E 2ND ST 82601 #019-02-1979 L1983 PTH *020 †50

YOUMANS, Jerry Lee. 230 S WASHINGTON ST 82601 #016-06-1965 L1969 IM *071

YOUNG, Clarke Murray. 940 E 3RD ST STE 207 82601 #016-01-1942 L1951 OBG *071

ZONDAG, Tuenis Dowe. 1026 E 2ND ST, CENTRAL WYOMING NEUROSURGE 82601 #056-05-1970 L2002 OM FM *020 †18,70

CHEYENNE – LARAMIE

ALDRICH, Alvin S. ■ 82009 #024-01-1946 L1958 GS *071 †85

ANDERSON, Rodney Arthur. ■ 82009 #018-03-1962 L1970 OPH *071 †35

ANDERSON-RAY, Janet L. 800 E 20TH ST, STE 350 82001 #005-12-2003 L2007 OBG *020

ANSARI, Saqib Shawn. ■ 82001 #305-01-2002 L2004 FM *100

AREFIE, Afsaneh. 821 E 18TH ST, UNIV WYO FAMILY MED RESIDE 82001 #517-01-1991 FP *012

ARMSTRONG, Bruce W. 2360 E PERSHING BLVD 82001 #028-02-1944 L1944 IM OS *030

ARNOLD, Janet S. ■ 82001 #025-07-1984 L1985 FM *020 †18

ASHLEY, John Daniels. ■ 82009 #030-05-1963 L1963 OPH *071 †35

BABSON, John Hurst. 1331 PRAIRIE AVE, STE 1 82009 #065-09-1978 L1980 GP AM *020

BASTA, Jean Denise. 2301 HOUSE AVE, STE 505 82001 #054-04-1999 L2003 ORS *020 †40

BATEZINI, Maristela. 214 E 23RD ST, UNITED MEDICAL CENTER 82001 #187-02-1997 L2006 IM *100

BECKMAN, John Waldo. 2301 HOUSE AVE, STE 300 82001 #039-01-1981 L1986 GE IM *071 †20

BEER, Steven Jos. 1950 BLUEGRASS CIR STE 170, WYOMING SPINE-NEURO ASSOC 82009 #018-03-1992 L2001 NS OSS *020 †25

BELL, Valerie Jean. 2301 HOUSE AVE, STE 405 82001 #038-41-1983 L1988 PD *020 †55

BINDSCHADLER, Darryl D. ■ 82001 #035-45-1963 L1969 PUD IM *071 †20

BLOOMBERG, Jason Michael. 3100 HENDERSON DR, MOUNT VIEW PK MED CTR 82001 #046-01-2001 L2002 FM *020 †18

BOLOURIAN, Houman. 821 E 18TH ST 82001 #517-31-2001 L2007 FP *012

BRACKETT, Deborah Susan. 821 E 18TH ST, UM FAMILY PRACTICE 82001 #130-01-2004 L2007 FP *012

BRANDES, Lisa Kae. 821 E 18TH ST, UNIVERSITY OF WYOMING FAMI 82001 #019-02-1993 L2006 FM *020 †18

BRAUSCH, Laura M. 5050 POWDERHOUSE RD, CHEYENNE MEDICAL SPECIALIS 82009 #021-01-1987 L1992 PUD *020 †20

BRAVO, Lazaro Oscar, Jr. ■ 82009 #308-03-1983 L2008 IM *020 †20

BRENTLINGER, Dale Clyde. ■ 82009 #041-02-1963 L1980 **IM** *071 †20
BROOMFIELD, James Floid. 820 E 17TH ST 82001 #004-01-1990 L1999 **FM** *020 †18
BROOMFIELD, Kim R. 9525 BUCK BRUSH RD 82009 #007-02-1992 L1999 **FM** *020 †18
BROWN, Craig Stephon. 1723 LOGAN AVE 82001 #033-05-1970 L1993 **EM TS** *020
BROWNING, James W. 2360 E PERSHING BLVD 82001 #039-01-1969 L1976 **P CHP** *020
BRYANT, John Frank. 2301 HOUSE AVE, STE 502 82001 #047-06-1978 L2002 **U** *020 †95
BULLARD, Kathryn Kimberly. 2301 HOUSE AVE, STE 400 82001 #034-01-2002 L2006 **OBG** *020
CALKINS, Jerry Milan. ■ 82009 #003-01-1976 L1998 **AN** *071 †05
CARLTON, Jeffrey Chas. 300 E 23RD ST, UNITED MED CTR DEPT RO 82001 #047-05-1985 L1994 **RO** *020 †80
CARMEN, George Wm. 1950 BLUEGRASS CIR, C/O EMERGENCY MEDICAL 82009 #049-01-1988 L1993 **IM EM** *020 †20
CASSIDY, Thomas Geo. 2360 E PERSHING BLVD 82001 #016-43-1974 L1992 **IM IMG** *020 †20
CHOY, Cynthia Noriko. 800 E 20TH ST, STE 350 82001 #037-01-1999 L2000 **FM** *020 †18
CLARKE, Jason Halsey. 5201 YELLOWSTONE RD 82009 #007-02-1999 L2006 **GS** *020
COESTER, Hans Carl. 800 E 20TH ST, STE 200 82001 #018-03-1986 L1994 **NS** *020 †25
COLE, Mary Eileen. 123 WESTERN HILLS BLVD 82009 #016-06-1997 L1999 **IM** *020
COOK, Judson Howard. 1950 BLUEGRASS CIR STE 170 82009 #021-01-1996 L2004 **NS** *020 †25
COTTAM, Tamara Odegard. 840 GOLDEN HILL ST 82009 #030-06-1994 L1995 **FM** *020 †18
CRAWFORD, Harry Cooper. ■ 82001 #021-01-1958 L1964 **OBG** *071 †30
DANCZIK, Irena. ■ 82009 #286-13-1992 L2006 **P** *100 †75
DANCZIK, Jiri John. 2600 E 18TH ST 82001 #286-13-1991 L2006 *020 †75
DANIEL, Robert Edwin. 919 RIDGELAND ST 82009 #021-01-1969 L1990 **AN EM** *071 †16,05
DAVIS, Harmon Howard, II. 2301 HOUSE AVE, STE 300 82001 #049-01-1972 L1979 **PUD IM** *020 †20
DAVIS, Joan E. 821 E 18TH ST 82001 #820-02-2006 **FP** *012
DAVIS, Meade, III. 433 E 19TH ST, DAVIS ORTHOPEDIC CLINIC 82001 #016-06-1969 L1975 **ORS** *020 †40
DAVIS, Robert James, II. 2301 HOUSE AVE, STE 300 82001 #038-41-1965 L1973 **CD** *071 †20
DEBROS, James Anthony. ■ 82001 #016-43-1968 L1969 **FM GP** *071 †18
DICKERSON, Don Ricardo. 214 E 23RD ST, CHEYENNE REGIONAL MED CTR 82001 #011-03-1970 L2003 **RO** *020 †80
DIJKSTAL, Dirk. 1300 E 20TH ST 82001 #660-01-1974 L1984 **OPH GP** *020 †35
DILMAGHANIAN, Omid Gillan. 821 E 18TH ST, UM FAMILY PRACTICE 82001 #104-01-2003 L2008 **FP** *012
DOBSON, Joseph. 300 E 23RD ST 82001 #051-07-1993 L1994 **FM** *020 †18
DRAMKO, Joseph George, Jr. 2301 HOUSE AVE, STE 405 82001 #035-08-1991 L2006 **PD** *020 †55
EDMONDS, Hope Johanna. 2030 BLUEGRASS CIR 82009 #019-02-1999 L2002 **FM EM** *020 †18
EICHBAUM, Edgar Gad. 2360 E PERSHING BLVD 82001 #550-01-1958 L1983 **GS GP** *020 †85
EL-TARABILY, Mohamed E. 2301 HOUSE AVE, STE 201 82001 #915-04-1980 L2008 **HO IM** *020 †20
EMAMI, Sarvin. 5050 POWDERHOUSE RD, SPECIALISTS PC 82009 #409-22-1993 L2000 **IM** *020 †20
ESKAM, Sharon Kay. 2301 HOUSE AVE, STE 400 82001 #030-05-1982 L1988 **OBG** *020 †30
EVANS, Kayleen A. 2360 E PERSHING BLVD, VA MEDICAL CENTER 82001 #308-03-1987 L1989 **ID** *020 †20
FERMELIA, Richard A. 5201 YELLOWSTONE RD 82009 #049-01-1989 L1994 **GS VS** *020 †85 ‡
FEUER, David Scott. ■ 82001 #035-08-1992 L1994 **VS** *020 †85
FILBY, Paul Alexander. 214 E 23RD ST 82001 #007-02-1985 L1998 **AN** *020 †05
FISCHER, Carol Anne. 1331 PRAIRIE AVE, STE 2 82009 #030-06-1982 L1983 **FM** *020 †18
FLICK, William Fredrick. ■ 82009 #010-02-1966 L1973 **OS** *030 †85
FOLEY, Mary Ellen. 2301 HOUSE AVE, STE 400 82001 #011-04-1987 L1997 **OBG** *020 †30
GAJDA, David J. 6228 YELLOWSTONE RD 82009 #065-05-1988 L1994 **OPH** *020 †35
GARDNER, Harold Hepworth. ■ 82009 #035-45-1965 L1967 **IM GE** *030
GARDNER, Timothy Mabry. 2301 HOUSE AVE, STE 300 82001 #048-04-1989 L1996 **CD** *020 †20
GASSER, Thomas John. 300 E 23RD ST 82001 #056-05-1969 L1974 **ORS GP** *020 †40
GIBBENS, William Paxton. 5320 EDUCATION DR 82009 #039-01-1968 L1976 **OTO** *020 †45
GILTNER, Lloyd A. 2030 BLUEGRASS CIR 82009 #016-06-1953 L1991 **EM FM** *071 †18
GLODE, John Edward. 2301 HOUSE AVE, STE 300 82001 #030-06-1971 L1990 **CD IM** *020 †20
GONDALIA, Lakhman L. 6252 YELLOWSTONE RD, STE 1300 82009 #495-22-1978 L1988 **AI PD** *020 †55,03
GRAVATT, Rayna Elizabeth. 2301 HOUSE AVE, STE 405 82001 #305-01-2003 L2007 **PD** *020 †55
GREEN, Elizabeth Anne. ■ 82009 #050-02-2006 **FP** *012
GREEN, Ronald Stephen. ■ 82009 #016-43-1962 L1968 **AM GPM** *071 †70
GREER, Dan B. 2600 E 18TH ST 82001 #047-06-1943 L1952 **GS** *071 †85
GRIZZLE, Claude Oliver. ■ 82001 #005-11-1954 L1958 **NS OS** *071 †25
GRUBER, Amy Lynn. 5416 EDUCATION DR 82009 #017-20-1979 L1980 **FM** *020 †18
GUIDRY, George Jos, III. 1950 BLUEGRASS CIR, STE 170 82009 #021-05-1970 L1994 **NS** *071 †25
GUIDRY, Sandra Abreu. 5050 POWDERHOUSE RD 82009 #021-06-1993 L1998 **IM** *020 †20
HABERMAN, Phillip John. 2301 HOUSE AVE, STE 108 82001 #030-05-1988 L2000 **PTH PCP** *020 †50
HALES, Joseph Sloan. 1920 EVANS AVE 82001 #038-41-1966 L1975 **AN GS** *020 ‡
HALLER, James Geo. 123 COLE SHOPPING CTR 82001 #030-06-1963 L1964 **CD ADM** *020
HALPERN, Jean Alvin. 1111 LOGAN AVE, FRESENIUS MEDICAL CARE 82001 #041-02-1977 L1982 **NEP IM** *020 †20
HANNA, Peter. 821 E 18TH ST 82001 #166-02-2002 **FP** *012
HARNISH, Amy Jo. 1950 BLUEGRASS CIR, STE 200 82009 #049-01-1993 L1996 **FM** *020 †18
HARPER, James Augustus. ■ 82003 #048-04-1963 L1997 **TS** *071 †85,90
HARRIS, Bill Douglas. 2301 HOUSE AVE STE 502 82001 #028-79-1978, ▲ L2004 **GP** *020
HARTMAN, Stanley Edward. 214 E 23RD ST, STE 4111 82001 #038-41-1982 L1986 **EM IM** *020 †20
HATTEL, Larry James. 2301 HOUSE AVE, STE 300 82001 #020-02-1983 L1991 **CD IM** *020 †20
HAYDEN, Scott Allen. 800 E 20TH ST, STE 110 82001 #049-01-1984 L1988 **DR** *020 †80
HAYNES, Taylor Henry. 300 E 23RD ST 82001 #049-01-1975 L1984 **U** *020 †95
HEALEY, John Patrick. 2003 BLUEGRASS CIR 82009 #030-06-1991 L1992 **FM EM** *020 †18
HECKER, James A. 2301 HOUSE AVE, STE 405 82001 #019-02-1963 L1971 **PD** *072 †55
HERBER, Michael C. 1950 BLUEGRASS CIR, STE 200 82009 #030-06-1979 L1980 **FM** *020 †18
HETTINGER, Thomas Edward. 10804 PORTUGEE PHILLIPS RD 82009 #016-06-1964 L1970 **R** *071 †80
HIGGINBOTHAM, Michael B. 2301 HOUSE AVE, STE 300 82001 #143-02-1973 L2004 **CD** *050
HILLMAN, J Richard. 300 E 23RD ST 82001 #048-15-1976 L1979 **EM PD** *020 †55
HINKLE, Dan Cheatham. ■ 82009 #021-01-1966 L1972 **GYN** *071 †30
HINKLE, Rene Margot. 800 E 20TH ST STE 350, CHEYENNE WOMEN'S CLINIC 82001 #011-02-1991 L1999 **OBG** *020 †30
HOPFENSPERGER, Kathryn A. 2526 SEYMOUR AVE, PEAK WELLNESS CENTER 82001 #016-11-1988 L2001 **P** *020 †75
HOPFENSPERGER, Kurt James. 2301 HOUSE AVE STE 203, WYOMING NEUROLOGY, PC 82001 #016-11-1988 L2000 **N** *020 †75
HORAM, William Jos. 2301 HOUSE AVE, STE 405 82001 #007-02-1987 L1993 **PD** *020 †55
HOYER, Eric Richard. 800 E 20TH ST, STE 110 82001 #007-02-1991 L2007 **DR** *020 †80
HUMMEL, Jonathan Acton. 2360 E PERSHING BLVD 82001 #035-19-1958 L1999 **GS** *020 †85
HUNTON, Donald Bothen. 1200 E 20TH ST 82001 #035-45-1954 L1956 **IM GE** *071 †20
IAMS, Helen Drake. 820 E 17TH ST 82001 #016-43-2000 L2004 **FSM** *020 †18
IVERSON, Donald Gordon. 2600 E 18TH ST 82001 #007-02-1958 L1966 **OPH** *071 †35
IZADARA, Alireza. ■ 82001 #517-01-1968 L1977 **IM** *071 †20
JOHNSON, Alan Boyd. 821 E 18TH ST 82001 #166-02-2002 L2005 **FM** *100
JOHNSON, James Vernon. 2600 E 18TH ST 82001 #037-01-1980 L1981 **EM FM** *020 †16,18
JOHNSON, Regina. 214 E 23RD ST, CHEYENNE REG MED CTR 82001 #010-02-1980 L2007 **P** *020 †75
JOHNSON, Roger Milborn. 2360 E PERSHING BLVD, VA MED CTR 82001 #030-05-1968 L1968 **P GP** *030 †75
JOHNSTON, Randolph Leigh. 1300 E 20TH ST 82001 #049-01-1979 L1982 **OPH** *020 †35
JOHNSTON, Theodore L. PO BOX 407 82003 #016-02-1950 L1955 **OPH** *071 †35
JOY, Michael Fieldings. 520 E 18TH ST 82001 #007-02-1968 L1995 **P PYA** *020 †75
KAHN, Robert Jakob. 800 E 20TH ST, STE 10 82001 #049-01-1957 L1999 **R** *072 †80
KAHRE, James Wm. 214 E 23RD ST 82001 #030-05-1977 L1980 **AN** *020 †05
KANARD, Robert Roessler. ■ 82009 #028-34-1963 L1970 **IM RHU** *020 †20
KANDALA, Ranganath. ■ 82009 #496-01-2001 L2007 **IMG** *100 †20
KERBER, Mary L. 5050 POWDERHOUSE RD, SPECIALISTS PC 82009 #048-13-1995 L2004 **N** *020 †75
KILPATRICK, David M. 2360 E PERSHING BLVD 82001 #030-05-1979 L1994 **IM IMG** *030 †20
KINCAID, Terese Marie. 820 E 17TH ST 82001 #054-04-2001 L2006 **FP** *012
KLINE, Duane M, Jr. ■ 82001 #019-02-1946 L1953 **ORS** *071 †40
KNAPPENBERGER, Joshua A. 2301 HOUSE AVE, STE 203 82001 #049-01-2000 L2006 **CN** *020 †75
KOUGL, Donald Alfred. 1950 BLUEGRASS CIR, BOX 805 82009 #051-04-1968 L1975 **EM IM** *030 †20,16
KRAEFT, Stine Kathrein. ■ 82009 #408-17-1987 L2007 **PCP** *020 †50
KRANER, Thomas Orval. ■ 82009 #049-01-1989 L1995 **CCS** *020 †85
KRANZ, Kenneth Ray. 2301 HOUSE AVE, STE 300 82001 #035-09-1980 L1991 **GE IM** *020 †20
KUCKEL, Charles Lee. 2301 HOUSE AVE, STE 300 82001 #033-05-1992 L2002 **GE** *020 †20
KUHN, Michael Peter. 5307 YELLOWSTONE RD 82009 #030-06-1985 L1994 **ORS** *020 †40
LANIER, Robert Lewis. 421 E 17TH ST, CHEYENNE HEM/ONC SVCS 82001 #007-02-1970 L1977 **HO ON** *020 †20 ‡
LAPKIN, Leonard. 2301 HOUSE AVE, STE 207 82001 #016-11-1985 L2003 **TS CCS** *020 †85,90
LAPKIN, Patricia G. ■ 82009 #016-11-1987 L2003 **P PYG** *020 †75
LARSEN, Nicholas James. ■ 82009 #028-79-2003, ▲ L2007 **AN** *020
LARSON, Trenette Ann. 1202 CLEVELAND AVE 82001 #030-06-1981 L1984 **IM** *020 †20
LAWLER, Donald Jerome. 1300 E 20TH ST 82001 #026-04-1958 L1970 **OPH** *071 †35
LE BEAUMONT, Ronald W. 214 E 23RD ST 82001 #035-45-1987 L1991 **AN** *020 †05
LELAND, Robert Wallace. 2301 HOUSE AVE, STE 405 82001 #026-04-1971 L1976 **PD** *020 †55
LEUNG, Karen W.. 821 E 18TH ST, FAMILY MED RESIDENCY PROG 82001 #305-01-2004 **FP** *012
LIND, David Mark. 2301 HOUSE AVE STE 400 82001 #030-06-1982 L1983 **OBG FM** *020 †30
LOWER, Dennis La Moine. 2360 E PERSHING BLVD 82001 #030-05-1965 L1991 **IM** *020
LUCAS, John Louis. ■ 82009 #060-01-1970 L1975 **FM GPM** *071 †70,18
LUGG, James Arthur, Jr. 2301 HOUSE AVE STE 502 82001 #016-06-1990 L2000 **U UP** *020 †95
MACKEY, Chas Edward, III. 5050 POWDERHOUSE RD, SPECIALISTS PC 82009 #045-01-1967 L1991 **IM PUD** *020 †20
MANCIET, Lorraine Hanna. 821 E 18TH ST 82001 #166-01-2007 **FP** *012
MARTIN, Michael Paul. 126 QUINCY RD, EAR NOSE & THROAT CLINIC 82009 #010-02-1983 L1992 **OTO GS** *020 †45
MAZHAR-UDDIN, Mohammed. 6143 SHAUN AVE 82009 #495-21-1962 L1972 **IM HO** *020 †20
MC CLEERY, Richard Grimes. ■ 82001 #018-03-1954 L1960 **CLP PTH** *071 †50
MC CORMICK, Harry M. ■ 82001 #025-01-1946 L1974 **ADM PTH** *071 †50
MC COY, Theodore Neal. ■ 82001 #019-02-1960 L1968 **U** *020
MC GUIRE, Robert Lee. 2301 HOUSE AVE, STE 400 82001 #041-13-1971 L1975 **GYN** *020 †30
MC KUSKER, Shauna Kay. 1300 E 20TH ST 82001 #018-03-1981 L1987 **OPH PO** *020 †35
MC MULLEN, Douglas Bruce. ■ 82009 #010-01-1966 L1972 **AN** *020
MC NAUL, David Wayne. 800 E 20TH ST, STE 110 82001 #005-15-1991 L2005 **DR** *020 †80
MEANS, Michael James. 616 CROOK AVE, AMERICAN MEDICAL RESPONSE 82001 #036-08-1999 L2005 **EM** *020
MEARES, Ageselaos John. 2301 HOUSE AVE, STE 201 82001 #030-06-1993 L2004 **NEP** *020 †20
MELINKOVICH, Gary. 418 HATHAWAY BLDG 82002 #030-06-1980 L1983 **PD** *020 †55
MERRELL, Arthur Nelson. 2526 SEYMOUR AVE 82001 #007-02-1967 L1974 **P** *020 †75
MEULI, R Larry. 100 CENTRAL AVE 82007 #019-02-1962 L1980 **PHP PD** *071 †55
MILLER, Anne Elizabeth. 1300 E 20TH ST 82001 #007-02-1996 L2001 **OPH** *020 †35
MILLER, Michael Edward. 2301 HOUSE AVE, STE 300 82001 #036-01-1976 L2001 **IM** *020 †20
MILLIN, John Andrew. 1300 E 20TH ST 82001 #024-05-1988 L1993 **OPH** *020 †35
MILMONT, Bruce Mark. 214 E 23RD ST 82001 #030-06-1987 L1991 **AN** *020 †05
MONGER, Robert Matthew. 5050 POWDERHOUSE RD, SPECIALISTS PC 82009 #049-01-1992 L1997 **RHU** *020 †20 ‡
MONIE, Paul Eric. 821 E 18TH ST 82001 #422-01-2006 **FP** *012
MOTL, John Michael. 2360 E PERSHING BLVD, CHEYENNE VA MEDICAL CENTER 82001 #030-06-1973 L1979 **P N** *020 †75
MUBARAK, Mona Asaad. ■ 82009 #007-02-1990 L1991 **FM** *020 †18
MURPHY, Tracy Douglas. HATHAWAY BLDG, 4TH FLOOR, 2300 CAPITOL AVE 82002 #019-02-1993 L2004 **PTH** *020 †50
NELSON, Robert Allen. ■ 82009 #016-11-1952 L1954 **NM IM** *071
NEVILLE, Julie Anne. ■ 82001 #030-05-2002 L2007 **D DS** *071 †15
O'HOLLERAN, Lawrence Wm. 1616 E 19TH ST, STE 8 82001 #030-05-1979 L2000 **GS** *020 †85
ORAHOVATS, Dimitar A. 5050 POWDERHOUSE RD, SPECIALISTS PC 82009 #198-01-1992 L2003 **IM** *020 †20
ORCUTT, Terri Ann. 2360 E PERSHING BLVD, CHEYENNE VA MED CTR 82001 #048-16-1990 L2004 **P** *020

■ = Address Information Privacy Protected

OZBAY, Behice. 821 E 18TH ST 82001 #902-05-1981 **FP** *012

PARKS, Douglas Stephen. 821 E 18TH ST, FAMILY PRACTICE RESIDENCY 82001 #019-02-1984 L1993 **FM** *040 †18

PARNELL, M Whitney. 5201 YELLOWSTONE RD 82009 #030-06-1995 L2000 **GS** *020 †85

PATEL, Mihir V. 5416 EDUCATION DR 82009 #550-03-2003 L2006 **FM** *020 †18

PECKHAM, Robyn Harold. ■ 82009 #005-12-1989 L1990 **ORS** *020 †40

PERAKOS, Peter Geo. 5050 POWDERHOUSE RD, SPECIALISTS PC 82009 #010-02-1977 L1983 **GE IM** *020

PIECZALSKA, Marta Agniesz. 2600 E 18TH ST, CHEYENNE REGIONAL MEDICAL 82001 #759-01-1993 L2005 **CHP** *020 †75

POPOVA-ORAHOVATZ, Guergana. 5050 POWDERHOUSE RD, SPECIALISTS PC 82009 #198-01-1992 L2003 **FM** *020 †18 ‡

PRENTICE, Robert Reid. 2301 HOUSE AVE, STE 405 82001 #026-04-1967 L1973 **PD** *030 †55

PULLOS, Take G. 2301 HOUSE AVE, STE 200 82001 #034-01-1977 L1983 **GS** *020 †85

RANGITSCH, Mark Richard. 2301 HOUSE AVE, STE 505 82001 #030-06-1989 L1994 **ORS** *020 †40

RASHKOW, Andrew Mark. ■ 82009 #154-01-1978 L2008 **CD IC** *020 †20

RECKLING, W Carlton. 800 E 20TH ST STE 300, RMOS 82001 #030-06-1989 L1996 **OSS ORS** *020 †40

REEB, Steven Douglas. 2301 HOUSE AVE, STE 300 82001 #030-06-1989 L1994 **PUD IM** *020 †20

RIBNIK, Harlan Robt. 903 S GREELEY HWY STE A, THE ROCKIES 82007 #007-02-1985 L1989 **PME AN** *020 †05

RIDEOUT, Elmer Wm, Jr. 2360 E PERSHING BLVD 82001 #035-06-1945 L1946 **IM** *071

ROBISON, Earl Willoughby. 5050 POWDERHOUSE RD 82009 #041-02-1969 L1976 **IM ON** *020 †20

RODEBAUGH, Maria R. 2301 HOUSE AVE, STE 300 82001 #748-02-1989 L2002 **END IM** *020 †20

RODRIGUEZ-MORVELI, Dante. 214 E 23RD ST 82001 #451-01-1992 L2003 **AN** *020 †05

ROMANO, John Edward. 5320 EDUCATION DR 82009 #003-01-1984 L2002 **OTO** *020 †45

ROMANOW, John Harris. 5320 EDUCATION DR, OTOLARYNGOLOGY SERVICE 82009 #024-07-1988 L2006 **OTO** *020 †45

ROSS, Vincent John. 5307 YELLOWSTONE RD 82009 #030-06-1985 L1986 **FM FSM** *020 †18

SANDICK, Stanley Martin. 214 E 23RD ST 82001 #041-01-1976 L1983 **AN PME** *020 †05

SCHIEL, Carol Ann. 2301 HOUSE AVE, STE 405 82001 #030-06-1981 L1988 **PD ADL** *020 †55

SCHIEL, Philip James. 5416 EDUCATION DR 82009 #030-06-1981 L1988 **FM** *020 †18

SCHLEYER, Otis. 1723 LOGAN AVE 82001 #048-12-1950 L1951 **GP** *071

SCHMID, Walter Carl. ■ 82001 #019-02-1960 L1968 **GE IM** *071 †20

SEGAL, Radu Adrian. ■ 82009 #422-01-2004 L2006 **FM** *020 †18 ‡

SEITZ, Larry Eugene. 2112 SEYMOUR AVE 82001 #007-02-1973 L1977 **D PTH** *020 †15

SHAFER, Reed Clifton. 5050 POWDERHOUSE RD, SPECIALISTS PC 82009 #025-01-1974 L1979 **N** *020 †75

SHAMLEY, Kirk Thos. 1616 E 19TH ST, STE 1 82001 #030-06-1988 L1994 **GYN** *020 †30

SHANNON, Michael James. 2301 HOUSE AVE, STE 505 82001 #030-06-2000 L2007 **ORS** *020

SHARP, Philip Marion. 214 E 23RD ST, WOUND CLINIC 82001 #048-02-1967 L1974 **ID** *020 †20

SHERARD, Brent Donald. 401 HATHAWAY BLDG 82002 #030-06-1979 L1981 **IM** *030 †20

SILVER, David Gary. ■ 82001 #025-07-1976 L1988 **TS** *020 †85,90

SILVER, Martha H. 5320 EDUCATION DR 82009 #001-02-1980 L1988 **OTO** *020 †45

SINGER, Jonathan Wm. 1401 AIRPORT PKWY, STE 150 82001 #018-75-1983, ▲ L1985 **FM PM** *020

SLATER, Paul Vernon. 2232 DEL RANGE BLVD 82001 #023-01-1956 L1967 **PS** *071 †85,65

SLOAN, Michael Linwood. 214 E 23RD ST 82001 #047-06-1986 L1992 **VIR R** *020 †80

SMITH, Gerald L. 5320 EDUCATION DR 82009 #028-02-1951 L1956 **OTO A** *020 †45

SPAULDING, Michael Robert. 2301 HOUSE AVE STE 300, INTERNAL MEDICINE GROUP 82001 #035-09-1991 L1999 **CD** *020 †20

SPEER, Christopher Robert. 2030 BLUEGRASS CIR 82009 #049-01-1993 L2000 **FM** *020 †18

STAMPFLI, Danae. 2301 HOUSE AVE, STE 405 82001 #030-06-1996 L1999 **PD** *020

STAMPFLI, Greg Howard. 5416 EDUCATION DR 82009 #030-06-1996 L1999 **FM** *020 †18

STEFKA, Jakub. ■ 82001 #286-05-1995 L2006 **HMP** *020 †50

STEFKA, Kristina Louise. 1688 MORNINGSTAR RD 82009 #025-01-1997 L2006 **IMG** *020 †20

STEVENS, Ronald E. 214 E 23RD ST 82001 #005-12-1980 L1991 **AN** *020 †05

STOREY, Jeffrey Dean. 800 E 20TH ST 82001 #032-01-1993 L1999 **OBG** *020 †30 ‡

STOUT, Rex Allen. ■ 82009 #011-02-1965 L1973 **AN** *071 †05

STUART, Robert Jos, Jr. ■ 82001 #040-02-1970 L2000 **CD IM** *072 †20

SUNDARALINGAM, Dhakshayani. 214 E 23RD ST, CHEYENNE REGIONAL MEDICAL 82001 #422-01-2000 L2008 **IM** *020

SURBRUGG, Sandra Kathleen. 123 WESTERN HILLS BLVD 82009 #007-02-1981 L1983 **D** *020 †15

SURDAM, Daniel Edward. 214 E 18TH ST, CHEYENNE REGIONAL MEDICAL 82001 #030-06-2002 L2005 **EM** *100 †16

TANNER, Mindy D. ■ 82009 #020-02-1993 L1994 **D** *020

THOMAS, Kathleen Ann. 123 WESTERN HILLS BLVD, CHEYENNE SKIN CLINIC 82009 #030-06-1994 L1997 **PD** *020 †20

THORNTON, Andrea Sue. 3235 SPARKS RD STE 200 82001 #007-02-1993 L1999 **PCC** *020 †20

TIETJEN, Charisse S. 401 STETSON DR 82009 #028-46-1990 L1994 **AN** *020 †05

TOFT, Thomas Victor. ■ 82009 #030-05-1962 L1969 **PTH** *071 †50

TORKELSON, Richard Eugene. 2301 HOUSE AVE, STE 505 82001 #007-02-1971 L1977 **ORS** *020 †40

TRAVERS, Daniel James. 2360 E PERSHING BLVD, CHEYENNE VA MEDICAL CENTER 82001 #038-44-1983 L1984 **GS** *020 †85

TRAVIS, Bane Thurlow. ■ 82003 #016-11-1945 L1951 **OBG** *071 †30

TRELEASE-BELL, Amy L. 820 E 17TH ST 82001 #030-06-1996 L2001 **FM** *020 †18

TURNER, Donn Martin. 800 E 20TH ST, STE 200 82001 #028-02-1978 L1994 **NS** *020 †25

VESSEY, Jill Wisely. 214 E 23RD ST, ATTN: EMERGENCY DEPARTMENT 82001 #005-18-2002 L2006 **EM** *100 †16

VIOLA, John Jos, Jr. 800 E 20TH ST, STE 200 82001 #041-02-1989 L1996 **NS** *020 †25

WAECKERLIN, Ronald Wayne. 2301 HOUSE AVE, STE 108 82001 #049-01-1977 L1981 **PTH** *020 †50

WAGNER, Philip L. 2301 HOUSE AVE, STE 400 82001 #030-06-1988 L1992 **OBG** *020 †30

WAHL, William Ray. ■ 82009 #007-02-1960 L1961 **FM** *071

WALLACE, Andrew Applequis. ■ 82001 #270-02-2000 L2001 *020

WARSON, James Stickney. 800 E 20TH ST, STE 200 82001 #047-05-1966 L1994 **NS** *071 †25

WEDELL, Eric James. 2301 HOUSE AVE STE 300 82001 #056-05-1967 L1974 **END IM** *071 †20

WILKINS, Anna Roth. 821 E 18TH ST 82001 #654-01-2007 **FP** *012

WILLIAMS, Russell I. ■ 82009 #030-05-1936 L1942 **A OTO** *071 †45

WILLIAMS, Russell I, Jr. 2301 HOUSE AVE, STE 405 82001 #035-45-1966 L1971 **PD OS** *020 †55,03

WILSON, Edith D. 433 E 19TH ST 82001 #060-01-1985 L1994 **U UP** *020 †95

WINTER, John Eric, II. ■ 82009 #019-02-1972 L1976 **ORS** *071 †40

WIRT, Timothy Craig. 800 E 20TH ST, STE 200 82001 #025-01-1974 L1993 **NS GS** *020 †25

WISE, Cleothus Rogers. 6812 PASADENA DR 82009 #869-05-1960 L1964 **AN OS** *071

WRIGHT, John W. 800 E 20TH ST, STE 110 82001 #048-04-1984 L1990 **DR** *020 †80

YOST, Patrick Allan. 1950 BLUEGRASS CIR, STE 200 82009 #030-06-1999 L2000 **FM** *020 †18

ZAVERI, Lopa Bakul. 5050 POWDERHOUSE RD, CHEYENNE MEDICAL SPECIALIS 82009 #654-01-1998 L2005 **FM** *020

CODY – PARK

AJAX, Theodore John. 732 LINDSAY LN, NORTHERN WYOMING SURGICAL 82414 #049-01-1986 L2001 **AN** *020 †05

ANDERSON, Tom. 1025 9TH ST UNIT B 82414 #005-11-1969 L2001 **ON HEM** *020 †20

BEASLEY, Benjamin Edward. 532 E CIRCLE DR 82414 #055-01-2003 L2007 **EM** *020

BIRCH, Warren Adair. 726 ALLEN AVE, P O BOX 774 82414 #049-01-1987 L1991 **AN** *020 †05

BOLLINGER, Kirk Alan. 707 SHERIDAN AVE, WEST PARK HOSPITAL 82414 #049-01-1995 L1996 **EM FM** *020 †18

BOWLBY, Adair Marie. 201 YELLOWSTONE AVE, BILLINGS CODY CLINIC 82414 #050-02-1994 L2004 **FM** *020 †18

BROADBENT, Robert V. ■ 82414 #005-06-1950 L1985 **DR** *071 †80

CODIGA, Michael Alan. 720 LINDSAY LN, STE A 82414 #422-01-1997 L2005 **IM** *020 †20

COHEN, Harry Bernard. 50 PARTRIDGE LN 82414 #030-06-1974 L2002 **AN** *020 ‡

COLLIE, Ross James. 12 ROCKY MOUNTAIN DR, LOCUM TENEN RADIOLOGY 82414 #065-04-1961 L1969 **DR NM** *020 †80,28

CROSS, Gregory Hachikian. 707 SHERIDAN AVE 82414 #023-12-1987 L1999 **DR** *020 †80

CRUZ, Rodni Noelle. 721 SHERIDAN AVE, STE 260 82414 #011-03-2001 L2007 **OBG** *020

DEBENHAM, Kyle Windsor. 707 SHERIDAN AVE, WEST PARK HOSPITAL 82414 #035-09-1991 L1995 **EM** *020 †16

EMERY, Stephen Foster. 720 LINDSAY LN STE C 82414 #048-02-1980 L1990 **ORS OSS** *020 †40

FLORY, Rand E. 721 SHERIDAN AVE, STE 100 82414 #028-34-1977 L1982 **OBG** *071

GAUTSCH, Joseph Arthur. 1207 MONUMENT ST 82414 #056-06-1939 L1948 **GP** *071

GEE, Allen Lyle. 720 LINDSAY LN 82414 #030-05-1996 L2000 **N** *020 †75

GRAHAM, Travis Scott. ■ 82414 #030-06-2000 L2006 **DR** *100 †80

HAKE, Lawrence Willis. ■ 82414 #030-05-1973 L2004 **U** *071 †95

HERMANN, Lee Kennan. 707 SHERIDAN AVE 82414 #030-05-1961 L1972 **PTH** *020 †50

HINES, Jonie M. 707 SHERIDAN AVE 82414 #018-03-1999 L2006 **FM** *020 †18

HOPKINS, Matthew Vernon. 721 SHERIDAN AVE STE 230 82414 #048-16-1999 L2006 **ADP** *020

JAMIESON, Charles Edward. 721 SHERIDAN AVE STE 270 82414 #049-01-1984 L1987 **PD** *020 †55

JOHNSON, James Lewis. ■ 82414 #039-01-1966 L1966 **U GP** *071

JOHNSON, James Lewis, II. 1021 9TH ST 82414 #030-06-1992 L1998 **GS VS** *020 †85

KOEHLER, Donald Robt. 707 SHERIDAN AVE 82414 #041-12-1955 L1961 **GP** *071

LOWTHER, Christopher M. 802 GERRANS AVE 82414 #033-05-1976 L1993 **D ID** *020 †20

MAININI, Stephen Eugene. 201 YELLOWSTONE AVE, BILLINGS CODY CLINIC 82414 #308-11-1983 L1993 **IM PUD** *020 †20

MARCHELLO, Benjamin Thos. 1025 9TH ST UNIT B, OF THE NORTHERN ROCKIES 82414 #049-01-1973 L1993 **ON IM** *020 †20

MCCUE, Gregory Patrick. 201 YELLOWSTONE AVE, BILLINGS CODY CLINIC 82414 #030-06-1979 L1982 **FM** *020 †18 ‡

MC FARLAND, Ian Wm Albert. 201 YELLOWSTONE AVE 82414 #919-02-1951 L1972 **EM GS** *020

MORTON, Douglas Earl. 201 YELLOWSTONE AVE, BILLINGS CODY CLINIC 82414 #030-06-1984 L1988 **FM PLM** *020 †20

MYERS, Dale Ray. 721 SHERIDAN AVE STE 220 82414 #025-07-1988 L2004 **OBG** *020 †30

NUTT, Benjamin Worth. ■ 82414 #027-01-1968 L1968 **N IMG** *020

OBERNUEFEMANN, Timothy. 707 SHERIDAN AVE 82414 #027-01-1980 L1980 **EM FM** *020 †18,16

ONDERS, Robert Paul. 707 SHERIDAN AVE 82414 #038-44-1997 L1998 **FM** *020 †18 ‡

PETERS, Stanley Wm. 707 SHERIDAN AVE, WEST PARK HOSPITAL 82414 #041-02-1978 L1981 **FM EM** *020

POLLEY, Charles S. 707 SHERIDAN AVE, WEST PARK HOSPITAL E.R. 82414 #048-16-1993 L1994 **FM** *020 †18

SCHMIDT, Catherine Carter. 720 LINDSAY LN 82414 #048-04-1983 L1988 **AN** *020 †05

SCHMIDT, Frank Hall. 720 LINDSAY LN STE C 82414 #048-04-1983 L1988 **ORS** *020 †40

SLIGHT, Kim Lewis. 720 LINDSAY LN, STE A 82414 #005-06-1986 L1991 **IM** *020 †20

STANLEY, Leland Eugene. 1220 SUNSHINE AVE 82414 #019-02-1960 L1964 **FM** *071 †18

STEWART, Gregory Stuart. 721 SHERIDAN AVE, STE 160 82414 #005-19-1996 L2005 **U** *020 †95

STROUBE, John A. ■ 82414 #017-20-1952 L1952 **GP GS** *020

TARR, John Relton. 4861 POWELL HWY 82414 #041-12-1954 L1975 **EM FM** *020

TROTTER, John Carroll. 201 YELLOWSTONE AVE, BILLINGS CODY CLINIC 82414 #036-01-1978 L2003 **FM** *020 †18

VAN NEWKIRK, Mylan Roscoe. ■ 82414 #030-05-1968 L1986 **OPH** *040 †35

WALTER, Mark Wayne. 721 SHERIDAN AVE, STE 230 82414 #036-05-2002 L2006 **P** *020

WELCH, Barry Peterson. 721 SHERIDAN AVE STE 280 82414 #030-06-1991 L1995 **OPH** *020 †35

WELCH, Charles Gilbert. 1021 9TH ST 82414 #030-06-1991 L2001 **GS** *020 †85

WHEELER, Joe Sidney. ■ 82414 #021-01-1957 L1975 **OBG** *071

WILLIAMS, Lisa Berryman. 721 SHERIDAN AVE STE 100 82414 #048-15-1987 L2002 **OBG** *020 †30

WINZENRIED, Jay Albert. 721 SHERIDAN AVE STE 130 82414 #048-13-1985 L2000 **ORS GS** *020 †40

DANIEL – SUBLETTE

BOYLE, Judith Marie. PO BOX 228, 12882 US HWY 189 83115 #003-01-1990 L1996 **IM PD** *020 †55,20

DEVILS TOWER – CROOK

STY, John Robert. ■ 82714 #028-34-1970 L2004 **PDR DR** *071 †80

■ = Address Information Privacy Protected

DOUGLAS – CONVERSE

BLANCHARD, Sherri. 111 S 5TH ST 82633 #048-16-1998 L2004 **FM** *020 †18

ENGLE, Deeanne Johnson. 111 S 5TH ST 82633 #054-04-2004 L2007 **FM** *020

HEYER, Deborah Susan. ■ 82633 #021-05-1978 L2003 **UCM OS** *020

HOSKINS, Thomas Henry. 111 S 5TH ST, CONVERSE COUNTY HOSPITAL 82633 #016-11-1974 L2004 **FM** *020 †18

KINBROOK, Michelle. 111 S 5TH ST, STE 6 82633 #020-12-2001 L2005 **MPD** *020 †20

KIRKLAND, Kirby Calvin. 111 S 5TH ST APT 1 82633 #024-07-1958 L1981 **GS** *071 †85

MORGAN, James Forrest. 111 S 5TH ST 82633 #024-05-1980 L1980 **FM PME** *020 †18

PEASLEY, Steven Pierce. 222 S 5TH ST 82633 #010-02-1993 L1995 **FM** *020 †18

ROBERTSON, Patrick Aaron. 111 S 5TH ST, THUNDERBASIN ORTHO 82633 #024-07-1988 L2004 **ORS** *020 †40

SCHMUNK, Robert Frank. ■ 82633 #025-01-1955 L1975 **GP** *075

SMITH, H Thomas. 111 S 5TH ST # 5 82633 #011-02-1978 L1995 **OBG EM** *020 †30

THALKEN, John Phillip. 111 S 5TH ST, STE 7 82633 #034-01-1981 L1984 **IM** *020 †20

TOBLER, Lori Pamela. ■ 82633 #033-06-1981 L2005 **IM** *020 †20

UNDERWOOD, Kara Lee. 111 S 5TH ST 82633 #018-03-1999 L2005 **FM** *020 †18

WHITE, Kraig Arthur. 111 S 5TH ST, PORTER FAMILY MEDICINE CLI 82633 #054-04-2004 L2007 **FM** *020 †18

WHITE, William Leslie. 111 S 5TH ST, STE 8 82633 #040-02-1984 L2005 **GS** *020 †85

WOODS, Willard Morton. 222 S 5TH ST 82633 #039-01-1972 L1978 **OBG GP** *020 †30

WORTHAM, Rex Emerson. 111 S 5TH ST STE 2 82633 #030-06-1986 L2006 **FM** *020 †18

YUTANI, Dennis Shigeo. 111 S 5TH ST 82633 #038-41-1971 L2000 **DR RNR** *020 †80

DUBOIS – FREMONT

BALCER, Charlotte Marie. ■ 82513 #028-46-1985 L2007 **P** *075

CAVANAH, Harold Stewart. ■ 82513 #020-02-1963 L1967 **AN** *075 †05

HOLMES, Keith Marshall. ■ 82513 #021-01-1961 L1974 **OTO** *071 †45

MORGAN, Vaughn Michael. 5647 US HIGHWAY 26 WAY 82513 #050-02-1979 L1982 **EM FM** *020 †18

EVANSTON – UINTA

ADAMS, David Frederick. 170 ARROWHEAD DR, STE 2 82930 #030-06-1998 L2001 **CCP** *012 †55

ADAMS, Michael Dean. 75 YELLOW CREEK RD STE 102 82930 #049-01-1986 L1989 **FM** *020 †18

ARCHER, Frank Jay. 196 ARROWHEAD DR STE 1, UINTA FAMILY PRACT 82930 #023-12-1987 L1989 **FM** *020 †18

BENNETT, Jack B. ■ 82931 #016-02-1947 L1950 **GS** *071

BENNETT, John Romney. 196 ARROWHEAD DR, STE 5 82930 #034-01-1991 L2004 **FPS OTO** *020 †45

BISHOP, Marion Cathryn. 190 ARROWHEAD DR, EMERGENCY DEPARTMENT 82930 #049-01-2004 L2007 **EM** *020

CHING, Rebecca Sy. 170 ARROWHEAD DR, STE 2 82930 #748-08-1991 L1998 **PD** *020 †55 ‡

CROWE, David B. 831 HIGHWAY 150 S, WYOMING STATE HOSPITAL 82930 #010-02-1985 L1993 **P** *020 †75

EVERETT, James C, Jr. PO BOX 1569 82931 #048-02-1969 L1969 **U** *071 †95

FRIEDENBERG, Marvin J. ■ 82931 #024-07-1955 L1992 **R NR** *020 †80,28

GEORGE, Catherine Marie. ■ 82930 #048-12-1982 L2005 **PD** *020 †55

HANSEN, Eric Christopher. 150 ARROWHEAD DR, STE 2 82930 #030-06-1996 L2000 **OBG** *020 †30

KAUNITZ, Victor H. ■ 82930 #035-19-1943 L1976 **TS** *071 †85,90

KEMMLER, Ardella Mary. 150 ARROWHEAD DR 82930 #041-13-1978 L1988 **RHU IM** *020 †20,70 ‡

LAUCOMER, Thomas Charles. 190 ARROWHEAD DR, EVANSTON REGIONAL HOSPITAL 82930 #007-02-1996 L1998 **FM EM** *020 †18

MAGGIOLO, Julie B. PO BOX 177 82931 #012-22-1997 L2006 **P** *020 †75

MILLER, Thomas E. ■ 82930 #047-06-1959 L1994 **P N** *071

NASH, Robert Alan. 831 HIGHWAY 150 S 82930 #019-02-1955 L1992 **P** *030 ‡

NOE, Gary Randal. 190 ARROWHEAD DR 82930 #040-02-1984 L1987 **FM** *020 †18

NOWICKI, Edmund John. 196 ARROWHEAD DR, STE 1 82930 #049-01-1995 L1999 **FM** *020 †18

O CONNOR, Michael John. 196 ARROWHEAD DR, STE 8 82930 #030-06-1987 L1992 **GS** *020

OLSON, John Chas. 190 ARROWHEAD DR, RADIOLOGY 82930 #020-02-1977 L1998 **DR** *020 †80

O'MEARA, Kevin Francis. 190 ARROWHEAD DR 82930 #030-05-1985 L1989 **EM FM** *020 †18

POWEL, Tanya Karen. 830 HIGHWAY 150 S, WYOMING STATE HOSPITAL 82930 #043-01-1981 L2003 **IM** *020

RAMAN, Anasuya Ambur. 831 HIGHWAY 150 S, WYOMING STATE HOSPITAL 82930 #495-50-1962 L1990 **P** *020

RODEFFER-EVANS, Karen M. 150 ARROWHEAD DR, STE 2 82930 #047-20-1992 L2007 **OBG** *020 †30

RONIGER, Joseph John. 831 HIGHWAY 150 S 82930 #021-01-1971 L2005 **P** *020 †75

SCHAFER, Nathan C. ■ 82930 #038-06-1979 L1997 **EM** *030 †16

SEGARRA, David Peter. 196 ARROWHEAD DR, STE 2 82930 #033-05-1985 L2001 **IM** *020 †20

SIMON, Thomas James. 150 ARROWHEAD DR STE 1 82930 #004-01-1982 L1985 **IM** *020 †20

SULLIVAN, Philip. PO BOX 177 82931 #021-01-1966 L1992 **P** *020 †75

YASUDA, Gregory Mark. 75 YELLOW CREEK RD, STE 101 82930 #034-01-1986 L1994 **GS** *020 †85

EVANSVILLE – NATRONA

ROSS, Dale Jay. ■ 82636 #032-01-2005 L2006 **FP** *012

FORT WASHAKIE – FREMONT

CALDER, William Alexander. PO BOX 128 82514 #003-01-1983 L1987 **FM** *020 †18

FRANCIS E WARREN AIR FORCE BASE – LARAMIE

BARTHOLOMEW, Dean W. 6900 ALDEN DR, MEDICAL CLINIC 82005 #030-06-2001 L2004 **FM** *020 †18

CRONIN, Peter Joshua. 6900 ALDEN DR, ATTN: CREDENTIAL OFFICE 82005 #056-06-2002 L2002 **FM** *020 †18

HAYES, Brian Patrick. 6900 ALDEN DR, 90 MDG 82005 #011-02-1990 L1992 **AM** *020 †70

KIEL, Mary Anne. 6900 ALDEN DR, ATTN: CREDENTIAL OFFICE 82005 #048-13-2003 L2005 **PD** *020 †55

PFLANZ, Steven Edward. 6900 ALDEN DR, 90TH MEDICAL GROUP/SGHQ 82005 #035-45-1994 L1996 **P** *020 †75

REED, Heather Ruth. 6900 ALDEN DR 82005 #003-01-1999 L2002 **AI** *012 †55

STETSON, John Batterson, V. 6900 ALDEN DR, 90 MDG/SGHQ 82005 #023-12-2000 L2002 *020 ‡

SWANSON, Leigh Alexandra. 6900 ALDEN DR, 90TH MEDICAL GROUP 82005 #056-06-1997 L1999 **GPM** *020 †18,70

TINGEY, Justin J. 6900 ALDEN DR, 90 MDG/SGHQ 82005 #023-12-2002 L2003 *020

GILLETTE – CAMPBELL

ABUJABER-AMMARI, Linda. 1300 W 4TH ST 82716 #575-01-1985 L1997 **PD PDI** *020 †55

ALLEGRETTO, Joseph F. 109 W LAKEWAY RD, STE A 82718 #038-44-1987 L1993 **ORS OS** *074 †40

ALMOHAMMED, Salah Naser. 1300 W 4TH ST, ABC PEDIATRICS 82716 #575-02-1999 L2005 **PD** *020 †55 ‡

AMMARI, Ramzi T. 430 S MEDICAL ARTS CT 82716 #575-01-1981 L1997 **IM PCC** *020 †20

ANDERS, Laura Ann. 709 W 8TH ST STE 4 82716 #030-06-1991 L1994 **FM** *020 †18

ANDREW, Thomas Todd. 201 W LAKEWAY RD, STE 300 82718 #049-01-1994 L1995 **FM** *020 †18

BAGNARELLO, Adolfo G. 302 S DOUGLAS HWY 82716 #270-01-1968 L1979 **IM ID** *020 †20

BAKER, Gerald Lee. 508 STOCKTRAIL AVE, STE A 82716 #030-05-1974 L1980 **ORS** *020 †40

BARRIOS, Jose. 501 S BURMA AVE 82716 #029-02-1988 L1995 **PG PD** *020 †55

BECK, David Alan. 1402 W 4TH ST 82716 #016-01-1989 L1994 **OBG** *020 †30

BECKER, Garry Gordon. 709 W 8TH ST STE 4 82716 #048-13-1970 L1974 **FM** *020 †18

BIGGS, Angela L. 1414 W 4TH ST, OBGYN SPECIALISTS 82716 #030-06-2000 L2005 **OBG** *020

BIGGS, Rodney Cooper. 1206 W 4TH ST STE 2 82716 #030-06-2000 L2005 **GS** *020 †85

DEARING, Paul David. 501 S BURMA AVE, 501 S. BURMA 82716 #048-13-1985 L2004 **GS** *020 †85

DE BOER, Laurence Wm Vail. ■ 82716 #048-04-1973 L1996 **CD IM** *020 †20

DUCK, Sigsbee Walter. 1405 W 4TH ST 82716 #036-08-1981 L1995 **OTO** *020 †45

DUNN, John Patrick. 508 STOCKTRAIL AVE, STE A 82716 #025-12-1995 L2000 **ORS** *020 †40

DUTTER, Tamara Lynn. 2001 W LAKEWAY RD, NORTHERN PLAINS ANESTHESIA 82718 #026-04-2000 L2004 **AN** *020 †05 ‡

FALL, David Robt. 1308 W 4TH ST 82716 #030-06-1981 L1985 **PD** *020 †55

FALL, Julie Shibata. 1308 W 4TH ST 82716 #030-06-1981 L1985 **PD** *020 †55

FAREED, Sameera. 407 S MEDICAL ARTS CT, STE F 82716 #704-25-1990 L2007 **IM** *020 †20

FORMAN, William James. CAMPBELL CO MEM HOSP, DEPT OF ANESTHESIOLOGY 82716 #031-01-1980 L1986 **AN** *020 †05

FRANDRUP, Christopher J. 501 S BURMA AVE 82716 #026-04-2000 L2007 **AN APM** *020 †05

GERARD, Daniela Simona. 5601 STONE GATE AVE, UNITED MEDICAL CENTER 82718 #035-48-1998 L2005 **FM** *020 †18

HALLINAN, Timothy Patrick. 709 W 8TH ST STE 4 82716 #049-01-1975 L1982 **FM** *020 †18

HARTSAW, Sara Louise. 310 W LAKEWAY RD, STE 1 82718 #030-06-1985 L1990 **GS** *020 †85

HWANG, Sandy T. 501 S BURMA AVE 82716 #011-02-1991 L1993 **PG** *020 †55

JAVAID, Farrukh. 407 S MEDICAL ARTS CT, STE F 82716 #704-02-1990 L2007 **IM** *020 †20

JOHNSRUD, Erik Peter. 906 W 6TH ST, STE C 82716 #056-05-1982 L1986 **AN** *020 †05

KALKE, Hein Hartmut. ■ 82718 #143-02-1965 L1977 **GYN** *071 †30

KIOSCHOS, Hans C. 508 STOCKTRAIL AVE, STE A 82716 #030-06-1992 L1997 **ORS** *020 †40

LA MANNA, James Raymond. 501 S DOUGLAS HWY, STE A-220 82716 #020-02-1977 L1981 **DR** *020 †80

LAWSON, Stanley Lee. 501 S BURMA AVE, CAMPBELL COUNTY MEM HOSP 82716 #028-34-1992 L1995 **EM** *020 †16

LAWSON, Theodore Geo. ■ 82716 #028-34-1990 L1997 **EM** *020 †16

LONG, Lawrence Erie. 407 S MEDICAL ARTS CT, STE D 82716 #030-06-1985 L1988 **IM** *020 †20

MARSHALL, Toby Reid. 1414 W 4TH ST, OBSTETRICS & GYNECOLOGY 82716 #030-06-1999 L2003 **OBG** *020 †30

MC CREERY, Margaret Sarah. 1701 PHILLIPS CIR UNIT A 82718 #034-01-1974 L2004 **FM** *020 †18

MC MAHILL, Philip Conrad. 501 S BURMA AVE 82716 #011-03-1980 L1999 **ON HEM** *020 †20

MC MURTREY, George Boone. 416 W JUNIPER LN 82718 #030-05-1944 L1962 **GS TRS** *072 †85

MITCHELL, Alan Lynn. ■ 82716 #021-06-1990 L1999 **NR** *020 †80

MORMAN, Monica Leigh. 508 STOCKTRAIL AVE, STE A 82716 #001-02-1997 L2003 **ORS** *020 †40

NARAMORE, James Jos. 407 S MEDICAL ARTS CT, STE D 82716 #049-01-1977 L1978 **FM** *020 †18

NEUWIRTH, Robert. 407 S MEDICAL ARTS CT, STE F 82716 #308-03-1981 L2006 **IM NEP** *020 †20 ‡

PAINTER, Rebecca Ann. 201 W LAKEWAY RD, STE 300 82718 #030-06-1983 L1987 **IM** *020 †20

PARKER, Donald W. 1307 W 3RD ST STE A 82716 #025-07-1980 L1984 **OBG** *020 †30

PATEL, Kirtikumar L. 407 S MEDICAL ARTS CT # D 82716 #495-23-1982 L1991 **IM** *020 †20

PESHEK, Brian Alexander. ■ 82718 #025-07-2002 L2007 **OTO** *020

PETERSON, Jennifer Michel. 1308 W 4TH ST 82716 #037-01-1997 L2001 **PD** *020 †55

RUSSELL, Laine Chantel. PO BOX 3011, 501 S BURMA AVE 82717 #018-75-1998, ▲ L2001 **FM** *100 †18

SHEPARD, Shelley Marie. 1206 W 4TH ST STE 1 82716 #019-02-1989 L1999 **OBG** *020 †30

SIMPSON, Nathan S. 508 STOCKTRAIL AVE, STE A 82716 #048-13-1992 L2000 **ORS** *020 †40

STATHOS, Theodore Harry. 501 S BURMA AVE 82716 #030-05-1988 L1991 **PG** *020

TAYLOR, Jack Eugene. PO BOX 2645 82717 #019-02-1957 L1970 **GP** *020 †18

THOMAS, Jennifer J. 709 W 8TH ST, STE 4 82716 #030-05-1993 L1994 **FM OBG** *020 †18

TOBI, Patricia Kuncheff. 1710 W US HIGHWAY 14-16 82716 #049-01-1990 L1993 **AN** *020 †05

WASSER, Michael. 4 J CT, STE A 82716 #033-05-1981 L1987 **ORS OSM** *020 †40

WILKERSON, Billie Jo. 407 S MEDICAL ARTS CT, STE D 82716 #030-06-1999 L2002 **FM** *020 †18

WOODWARD, William B, Jr. 501 S BURMA AVE 82716 #031-01-1984 L1994 **PTH** *020 †50
ZOLCIK, Wojciech. 5600 CENTENNIAL DR 82716 #286-11-1992 L1999 **P** *020

GLENROCK – CONVERSE

LYFORD, Charles Le Roy. ■ 82637 #018-03-1967 L1975 **GE IM** *071 †20

GREEN RIVER – SWEETWATER

BALKA, Gordon Lee. 1400 UINTA DR BOX 219 82935 #049-01-1972 L1981 **OM FM** *020
HATCH, Francis Jos. ■ 82935 #038-06-1954 L1979 **PTH FOP** *072 †50
HOLLAND, Michael Stephen. 82935 #048-02-1991 L2007 **PTH** *020 †50
LONG, Marilyn Ann. ■ 82935 #030-06-1981 L1984 **FM OBG** *020
SLOAN, John Stephen. 1400 UINTA DR, CASTLE ROCK MEDICAL CENTER 82935 #049-01-1983 L1986 **FM OM** *020 †18
SMITH, Dean A. 1400 UINTA DR 82935 #048-13-1986 L2003 **PD** *020 †55

GREYBULL – BIG HORN

PULL, Joel Michael. 444 GREYBULL AVE 82426 #037-01-1993 L1996 **FM** *020 †18
ROGERS, Anthony S. 425 W 5TH STREET 82426 #007-02-1939 L1946 **GP** *072

JACKSON HOLE – TETON

ANTHONY, Giovannina Maria. ■ 83001 #005-06-1992 L2005 **OBG** *020 †30
BALLIRO, James M. PO BOX 12976 83002 #024-16-1978 L2004 **VS** *020 †85
BEGELMAN, Kenneth Marc. PO BOX 764 83001 #016-02-1971 L1972 **TS** *072 †85,90
BERG, Robert Noble. 625 E BROADWAY 83001 #028-03-1966 L1997 **IM PUD** *020 †20
BERLIN, Robert Carl. PO BOX 428, ST JOHNS HOSPITAL 83001 #035-15-1985 L1990 **DR NM** *020 †80
BLUM, Philip Clarke. PO BOX 12530, 150 BUFFALO WAY 83002 #030-05-1974 L1997 **AN** *020 †05
BUTCHER, Dennis Lynn. 555 E BROADWAY STE 220, TETON INTERNAL MEDICINE 83001 #038-06-1977 L1979 **IM** *020 †20
CAVALIERE, Guy Samuel. 970 W BROADWAY, STE 472 83001 #038-45-1992 L2004 **AN** *020 †05
CLAYTON, L Whitney. ■ 83001 #049-01-1947 L1986 **GYN** *071 †30
FLECK, Roland. PO BOX 1766 83001 #154-02-1957 L1978 **GS U** *071 †18
FOGARTY, William Anthony. ■ 83001 #016-02-1961 L1973 **PTH GP** *071 †50
FOUNTAIN, James Alan. ■ 83001 #025-01-1972 L1974 **OPH** *071 †35
FREDSTROM, O'Ann Karin. 625 E BROADWAY 83001 #056-05-1988 L1992 **P** *020
FRENCH, Steven P. ■ 83002 #048-14-1976 L1980 **GS** *020
GREENBAUM, Jeffrey David. 625 E BROADWAY 83001 #005-14-1997 L2000 **EM** *020 †16
HALING, Christopher Sean. ■ 83002 #054-04-1995 L2000 **DR** *020 †80
HAYSE, Bruce Mc Lain. PO BOX 1884 83001 #040-02-1980 L1983 **FM** *020
HIRSCHFELD, Arthur James. PO BOX 13005, 800 N BARY RD 83002 #016-02-1964 L2000 **PD** *071 †55
HOCHHEISER, Louis I. ■ 83001 #033-05-1962 L1969 **FM PD** *030 †55,18
HUFF, Charles W. PO BOX 1394 83001 #041-02-1949 L1976 **FM CD** *040 †18
KING, Martin Francis. ■ 83001 #035-45-1965 L1972 **PTH** *071 †50
KNOBLOCH, Emily Jean. 625 E BROADWAY 83001 #026-04-1999 L2002 **IM** *020 †20
LANGER, Robert Dale. ■ 83001 #016-11-1978 L2004 **GPM FM** *050 †70
LINDENFELD, Etta Ann. PO BOX 1868, JACKSON HOLE COMM CTR 83001 #016-11-1978 L2007 **P** *040 †75
LITTLE, James Russell. 557 E BROADWAY, JACKSON PEDIATRICS PC 83001 #007-12-1969 L1972 **PD** *020 †55
LOFARO, Maura Jean. ■ 83001 #007-02-1993 L1997 **OBG** *020 †30
LOWE, Phillip. 555 E BROADWAY 83001 #030-05-12-1973 L1999 **U OS** *020 †95
LUEBBERS, James Arnold. ■ 83001 #023-07-1971 L2000 **OPH** *071 †35
MAHONY, Cheryl. 625 E BROADWAY 83001 #036-07-1976 L1996 **CD IM** *075 †20
MC KAY, Richard A, Jr. 890 CACHE CREEK DR 83001 #016-43-1983 L1989 **EM GS** *020 †16
MENOLASCINO, Mark P. PO BOX 4816, 555 E BROADWAY 83001 #030-05-2000 L2003 **IM** *020 †20
MENOLASCINO, Michael J. PO BOX 358, 555 E BROADWAY 83001 #030-05-1986 L1990 **IM** *020 †20
MEYERS, Ellen. ■ 83002 #035-47-1987 L1996 **IM** *020 †20
NEAL, William Caldwell. PO BOX 7434, 555 E BROADWAY 83002 #005-11-1979 L1998 **ORS** *020 †40
PAYNE, Charles L, Jr. 970 W BROADWAY # 378 83001 #001-02-1982 L1999 **AN** *020 †05
PAYNE, Holly Gail. ■ 83002 #041-77-1983, ▲ L2003 **NPM PD** *071
PAYNE, John C. 555 E BROADWAY, STE 211 83001 #041-77-1987, ▲ L2002 **PS** *020
POCKAT, Thomas Joseph. PO BOX 4182, 555 E BROADWAY 83001 #056-05-1979 L1981 **PD** *020 †55
POORE, Philip Geo. ■ 83001 #054-04-1978 L1996 **GS VS** *020 †85
RAMSAY, William John. 555 E BROADWAY 83001 #062-01-1973 L1981 **OPH** *020 †35 ‡
RIDGWAY, Elizabeth W. PO BOX 1029, 557 E BROADWAY 83001 #007-02-1969 L1972 **PD ADL** *020
RIESER, Aloys Martin, Jr. ■ 83002 #028-34-1962 L1962 **CLP PTH** *071 †50
RIVERS, Franklin M, Jr. 988 S US HIGHWAY 89 83001 #048-02-1972 L1995 **IM FM** *020 †16
ROBERTS, Shannon Christin. PO BOX 15570, 555 E BROADWAY 83002 #665-01-1998 L2002 **OBG** *020 †30
ROLAND, Norman Barry. PO BOX 412 83001 #023-01-1963 L1982 **GS VS** *072 †85
RORK, Peter Ernest. PO BOX 7434, 555 E BROADWAY 83002 #023-01-1979 L1990 **OSM HS** *020 †40
RUTTLE, Paul Edward. MOOSE WILSON RD, THE ASPENS 83001 #047-05-1977 L1983 **ORS** *020
RYEL, James W. ■ 83001 #005-06-1950 L1973 **R** *071 †80
SHLIM, David R. 557 E BROADWAY 83001 #016-01-1976 L1998 **GP** *062
SMITH, William Robert. ■ 83001 #054-04-2001 L2004 **EM** *020 †16
SOBIESKI, Kathryn Ann. PO BOX 4057, 269 W BROADWAY 83001 #005-14-1974 L1997 **IM** *020 †20
STEARN, Martha Gene. 625 E BROADWAY 83001 #035-45-1976 L1980 **IM** *020 †20

SUGARMAN, Stuart Ronald. PO BOX 15540 83002 #041-01-1973 L1996 **P** *020 †75
SUGDEN, Richard Greer. PO BOX 2468, 557 E BROADWAY 83001 #048-04-1969 L1974 **FM AM** *020 †16,18 ‡
TOMLINSON, David Jason. ■ 83001 #012-01-1999 L2006 **AN** *020 †05
TOMLINSON, Ruth Anne. PO BOX 1029, 557 E BROADWAY 83001 #012-01-1999 L2007 **PD** *020 †55
TRYKA, Anna Francine. PO BOX 3789 83001 #014-01-1976 L2000 **ATP PP** *050 †50
VAN GENDEREN, Larry. ■ 83001 #016-06-1962 L1973 **ORS HS** *071 †40 ‡
VIGNAROLI, Laura Marie. PO BOX 14230, 62 REDMOND ST 83002 #030-06-2000 L2004 **FM** *020 †18
WATERHOUSE, George. PO BOX 4197, 557 E BROADWAY 83001 #036-01-1975 L1992 **GS VS** *072 †85
WEBB, Kipp Bradley. PO BOX 603, MONTANA HEART INSTITUTE 83001 #030-05-1976 L1981 **CD IM** *071 †18
WEGNER, Kenneth James. 557 E BROADWAY 83001 #025-01-1963 L1991 **D** *020 †15
WHEELER, Albert Richard. ■ 83002 #038-40-2002 L2005 **EM** *020 †16
WHEELER, Keri Ann. PO BOX 7890 83002 #038-40-2002 L2005 **PD** *100
WOODFIN, Blane Anthony. 555 E BROADWAY 83001 #021-01-1982 L2002 **ORS** *020 †40

KAYCEE – JOHNSON

RENKERT, Elizabeth Emeny. ■ 82639 #041-07-1981 L1997 **FM** *020 †18

KEMMERER – LINCOLN

KRELL, George Christopher. MOOSE & ONUX STS, S LINCOLN MED CTR 83101 #049-01-1994 L1995 **FM** *020 †18

LAGRANGE – GOSHEN

NASHELSKY, Gunter Martin. ■ 82221 #007-02-1953 L1954 **RHU IM** *072

LANDER – FREMONT

ALLEN, Charles Ross. 815 E MAIN ST 82520 #020-12-1967 L1974 **ORS** *071 †40
BARNES, Richard Eugene. 115 WYOMING ST 82520 #019-02-1984 L1996 **PD** *020 †55
BEVERIDGE, Jacques David. 1460 MAIN ST, STE B 82520 #030-06-1995 L1999 **OBG** *020 †30
BLAIR, A James. ■ 82520 #035-20-1951 L1960 **IM END** *020
BLAKEMORE, Tonya Renee. 115 WYOMING ST 82520 #054-04-2002 L2005 **PD** *020 †55
BRITT, Cornelius Le Roy. 815 E MAIN ST 82520 #028-03-1978 L2003 **ORS** *020 †40
BRUBAKER, James C. 745 BUENA VISTA DR, LANDER MEDICAL CLNC 82520 #016-42-1988 L1998 **OBG** *020
CLIFFORD, Gregory Paul. 1320 BISHOP RANDALL DR 82520 #037-01-1996 L1997 **FM** *020 †18
COOK, Perry Fletcher. 1320 BISHOP RANDALL DR, LANDER VALLEY MEDICAL CTR 82520 #036-07-1988 L1992 **R** *020 †80
CRANE, Peter Oliver. 295 GARFIELD ST 82520 #054-04-1972 L1974 **N** *020
DEL REAL, Frank, III. ■ 82520 #005-18-1983 L2005 **P** *020
DOLL, David Andrew. ■ 82520 #019-02-1972 L1975 **AN** *071 †05
EBBERT, Paul James. ■ 82520 #049-01-1980 L2008 **FM** *020 †18
ERICKSON, William Gardner. 745 BUENA VISTA DR 82520 #030-02-1943 L1960 **GP** *071 †85
FALLIN, Cheryl P. 115 WYOMING ST 82520 #048-02-1994 L2003 **PD** *020 †55
FISCHER, Robert Louis. 8185 HIGHWAY 789 82520 #056-06-1985 L2003 **OTO** *020 †45
FONTAINE, James Heryford. 191 WYOMING ST 82520 #040-02-1966 L1968 **OPH** *071 †35
FOWLER, Jeffrey Ben. 2986 SINKS CANYON RD 82520 #049-01-1991 L1998 **AN** *020 †05
GEE, Brian Dale. ■ 82520 #016-06-1994 L1995 **FM** *020 †18
GILBERTSON, Phillip Roy. 707 BELLVUE ST 82520 #040-02-1973 L1975 **FM** *020
GULLICKSON, Donald Albert. 745 BUENA VISTA DR 82520 #016-06-1966 L1968 **IM CD** *020 †20
HARRIS, John David. 78 SNYDER RD 82520 #041-12-1966 L1973 **PTH** *020 †50
HASAN, Sanjida. 8204 STATE HIGHWAY 789 82520 #495-65-1966 L1995 **GP** *020
HEDIGER, Roy Gary. 295 GARFIELD ST, WIND RIVER RADIOLOGY 82520 #010-02-1982 L1996 **DR** *020 †80
HILLMER, Norman Roland. L V R M C 82520 #019-02-1956 L1975 **AN** *071 †05
JACOBSEN, Hart. ■ 82520 #016-11-1969 L1977 **OTO** *071 †45
JARRARD, Jerry Stephen. 1320 BISHOP RANDALL DR 82520 #014-01-1978 L1988 **FM** *100 †16
JEREB, John August. ■ 82520 #010-02-1963 L1964 **PTH OS** *020 †50
JONES, Troy R. 125 WYOMING ST 82520 #016-42-1982 L2006 **FM** *020 †18
KLINKENBORG, John Curtis. 1320 BISHOP RANDALL DR, LANDER VALLEY MEDICAL CENT 82520 #005-19-1985 L1993 **FM** *020 †18
LEWIS, Ray Blaine. ■ 82520 #016-06-1943 L1949 **PD** *071 †55
LOWHAM, Anthony Steve. 195 CAPITOL ST, LOWHAM SURGERY AND ENDOSC 82520 #030-06-1993 L1999 **GS** *020 †85
MARLER, Mary Elizabeth. ■ 82520 #016-43-1970 L1981 **EM** *075
MC MAHON, Charles. 195 CAPITOL AVE 82520 #040-02-1963 L1966 **N** *071 †75
MICHELSEN-JOST, Heidi E. 1320 BISHOP RANDALL DR 82520 #035-01-1994 L2001 **HS OFA** *020 †40
MILLER, Malachi. 745 BUENA VISTA DR 82520 #030-06-1999 L2002 **FM** *020 †18
MONDORF, Pamela Eva. ■ 82520 #021-05-1995 L2004 **AN** *020 †05
MOSEMANN, Mark Jonathan. 1322 BISHOP RANDALL DR 82520 #017-20-1999 L2000 **FM** *020 †18
NAGY, Robert Eugene. ■ 82520 #038-40-1968 L1976 **OTO** *071 †45
PEARSON, Susan Marshall. 8185 HIGHWAY 789 82520 #047-06-1988 L1991 **FM** *020 †18
PHIPPS, Charles Rex. ■ 82520 #019-02-1957 L1968 **GP** *071
PHIPPS, Douglas Rex. 745 BUENA VISTA DR 82520 #030-06-1980 L1983 **FM** *020 †18
PRASKA, Sheryl Jean. ■ 82520 #030-06-1983 L1992 **FM** *020 †18
PRUETT, Thomas Carl. ■ 82520 #007-02-1978 L1979 **EM GP** *020 †16
PRYOR, Wilbur Michael. 815 E MAIN ST 82520 #041-02-1971 L1978 **ORS** *020 †40
RATIGAN, Daniel. 1320 BISHOP RANDALL DR 82520 #007-02-1978 L1982 **EM** *020
SCHEER, Gentian Ann. 745 BUENA VISTA DR 82520 #054-04-2001 L2004 **IM** *020
SHIPLEY, William T. ■ 82520 #028-46-1978 L1982 **AN** *020 †05
STEVENS, Cynthia Brown. 172 ROSEWOOD AVE 82520 #010-02-1985 L2006 **P PYA** *020 †75 ‡

■ = Address Information Privacy Protected

THOMAS, Daniel Dale. 745 BUENA VISTA DR 82520 #007-02-1990 L1995 **GS** *020 †85
WAGNER, Karla Lee. 745 BUENA VISTA DR, LANDER MEDICAL CLINIC 82520 #038-43-1989 L1994 **OBG** *020 †30
WHEELER, Frank R. 1320 BISHOP RANDALL DR, LANDER VALLEY MEDICAL CENT 82520 #422-01-1982 L2003 **P** *020 †75
WHIPP, John Ashley. 815 E MAIN ST 82520 #020-12-1968 L1975 **ORS** *020 †40
WISE, Christopher Scott. 1320 BISHOP RANDALL DR, LANDER REGIONAL HOSPITAL 82520 #305-01-2002 L2007 **AN** *100
WOODARD, Mark Downing. ■ 82520 #007-02-1982 L1995 **PTH** *020 †50

LARAMIE — ALBANY

ALLAIS, Jean M. 1000 E UNIVERSITY AVE, DEPT 3068 82071 #030-06-1983 L1992 **IM ID** *020 †20
ANDERSON, David M, Jr. 204 MCCOLLUM ST 82070 #036-01-1954 L1954 **OBG** *071 †30
ANDERSON, Debra Lund. 2710 HARNEY ST, STE 100 82070 #049-01-1991 L1994 **PD** *020 †55
AUKERMAN, Ryan Anthony. 1909 VISTA DR 82070 #007-02-2000 L2006 **OSM** *020
BALLARD, Charles Donald. 255 N 30TH ST 82072 #048-15-1981 L2005 **EM** *020
BATTERSHELL, Ty Lee. 3908 E GRAND AVE, INTRAWEST MEDICAL SERVICE, 82070 #049-01-1992 L1995 **EM** *020 †16
BRAGG, John David. 2710 HARNEY ST, STE 100 82072 #030-06-1997 L2001 **OBG** *020 †30
CANTWAY, Donald Lee. 255 N 30TH ST 82072 #016-02-1967 L1976 **EM GP** *020 †16
CARLSON, Julie A. 1000 E UNIVERSITY AVE 82071 #030-06-1989 L1994 **IM** *020 †20
CARLSON, Marten Alvin. 3116 WILLETT DR, DEPT OF INTERNAL MEDICINE 82072 #030-06-1991 L1994 **IM** *020 †20
COATES, Winifred Jean. 1303 E GRAND AVE 82070 #352-02-1953 L1969 **FM OBS** *071 †18
COFFEY, Charles Roy. 204 MCCOLLUM ST, STE 101 82070 #019-02-1982 L2000 **AN** *020 †05
COMLY, William Michael. 3116 WILLETT DR 82072 #030-06-1980 L1983 **IM** *020 †20
COUSINS, Jody Ann. ■ 82070 #054-04-2006 L2006 **FP** *012
CRECCA, John David. ■ 82072 #038-40-1987 L1995 **AN PME** *020 †20,05
DEHART, Kathryn A. 2710 HARNEY ST STE 100, THE CHILDRENS CLINIC 82072 #054-04-2001 L2006 **PD** *020 †55
ELIASON, Nathan Bert. ■ 82072 #041-13-1995 L2004 **PTH** *020 †18,50
FERTIG, Henry H, Jr. ■ 82072 #041-01-1943 L1972 **IM CD** *071 †20
FLOCK, William Dean. 2606 E GRAND AVE 82070 #030-05-1970 L1975 **U** *020 †95
FULLER, Samuel Edward. 255 N 30TH ST, RADIOLOGY - IMH 82072 #028-34-1999 L2005 **DR** *100 †80
GREEN, Charles Patrick. 3116 WILLETT DR 82072 #019-02-1993 L1999 **CD** *020 †20
GREENE, Laurence W, Jr. ■ 82072 #007-02-1947 L1958 **GS TS** *071 †85
HAIGHT, Geo Steiner, III. 204 MCCOLLUM ST, STE 101 82070 #041-13-1970 L1977 **GS** *020 †85
HALL, Alan Herman. ■ 82072 #017-20-1977 L1977 **ETX EM** *062 †16
HANDRICH, Eldon Michael. 4363 WELSH LN 82070 #007-02-1981 L1984 **FM EM** *020 †18,16
HAROKOPIS, Michael Steven. 255 N 30TH ST 82072 #028-34-1978 L1983 **DR NR** *020 †80
HORST, Brian Paul. 2710 HARNEY ST STE 1, LARAMIE PHYSICIANS FOR WOM 82072 #030-06-1997 L2000 **PD** *020 †55
HOWDESHELL, Angela E I. 3625 E GRAND AVE 82070 #748-01-1962 L1969 **P ADP** *020 †75
JOHNSON, Kurt Samuel. 2020 E GRAND AVE, STE 410 82070 #005-14-1998 L2003 **FM** *020 †18
JONES, Harry Alex. 204 MCCOLLUM ST, STE 101 82070 #047-06-1975 L1978 **AN PD** *020 †55,05
KAPLAN, Michael Chas. 1909 VISTA DR 82070 #024-07-1992 L1998 **PM** *020 †60
KEELER, Timothy David. 2710 HARNEY ST STE 100 82072 #021-06-1998 L2004 **OBG** *020 †30
KLELE, Michael A. PO BOX 3434 82071 #820-02-2005 **FP** *012
KLEPPINGER, Kent Myron. 1252 N 22ND ST, UNIT B 82072 #030-06-1981 L1985 **PD** *020 †55
KLINGLER, Travis Don. 2710 HARNEY ST, LARAMIE PHYS FOR WOMENS 82072 #030-06-1998 L2002 **OBG** *020 †30
KOPLYAY, Peter D. 255 N 30TH ST, IMH - RADIOLOGY 82072 #048-13-1992 L2005 **DR** *020 †80
KURY, Wendell Michael. ■ 82070 #041-01-1966 L1989 **P** *020 †75
MAINS, Thane Michael. ■ 82070 #049-01-1981 L1986 **EM** *020 †16
MARTINCHICK, James F. 255 N 30TH ST, IVINSON MEM HOSP 82072 #049-01-1994 L1998 **PTH** *020 †50
MERRILL, Clinton F, Jr. 255 N 30TH ST 82072 #030-06-1979 L1982 **ON HEM** *020 †20
MEYER, Michael Peter. 1000 E UNIVERSITY AVE # 3, CHEYENNE HEALTH AND WELLNE 82071 #056-05-1990 L2005 **FM** *020 †18
MOORE, Charles Herbert. ■ 82072 #056-06-1948 L1954 **AN** *071 †05
NACHTIGAL, Tom Allen. 3125 E GRAND AVE UNIT B 82070 #046-01-1985 L1990 **GS** *020 †85
PAGE, James Brent. ■ 82072 #007-02-1997 L1999 **P** *020 †75
PEARSON, Gary Scott. 255 N 30TH ST 82072 #038-40-1990 L2007 **FM** *020 †18
PETERSON, Lars Erik. 3116 WILLETT DR 82072 #030-06-2000 L2004 **IM** *020 †20
PHENEGER, Paul Wm, Jr. 204 MCCOLLUM ST, STE 201 82070 #011-02-1977 L1981 **OPH** *020 †35
PIERCE, Harold Lyle. 2710 HARNEY ST, STE 200 82072 #048-12-1991 L1997 **U** *020 †95
PROCTOR, Lance A. 204 MCCOLLUM ST STE 101 82070 #048-14-1989 L2001 **AN** *020 †05
RADOSEVICH, Daniel Geo. 1022 E SHERIDAN ST 82070 #007-02-1991 L1993 **FM** *020 †18
RAGLAND, Forrest Scott. 204 MCCOLLUM ST, STE 101 82070 #056-05-1998 L2003 **AN** *020 †05
RANGITSCH, Thomas Raymond. 3908 E GRAND AVE, STE 201 82070 #030-06-2000 L2003 **EM** *020 †16
RAY, Esten W. ■ 82070 #005-02-1953 L1961 **PD** *071 †55
RINGDAHL, Irving Clayton. 255 N 30TH ST, BEHAVIORAL HEALTH UNIT 82072 #019-02-1957 L1989 **CHP FM** *071 †75
ROBERTSON, Kenneth Lee. 3116 WILLETT DR 82072 #023-01-1972 L1977 **IM** *020 †20
ROTH, Albert Harold. STUDENT HEALTH SERVICE 82071 #026-04-1962 L1983 **FM** *071 †18
SALVINO, Cora Frances. ■ 82072 #016-42-1978 L2006 **OBG** *020 †30
SAUNDERS, Walter Gerald. 2612 LODGEPOLE LN, UNIT 705 82072 #007-02-1966 L1972 **OBG** *071 †30
SHAFER, Shaun Stewart. 204 MCCOLLUM ST, CENTER STE 201 82070 #038-41-1991 L1997 **OPH** *020
SHINE, Robert Michael. ■ 82070 #017-20-1968 L1975 **OBG** *020 †30
STAHL, Galyn Millage. 255 N 30TH ST 82072 #007-02-1967 L1972 **PTH FOP** *020 †50
STEANE, Joanne Elizabeth. 1000 E UNIVERSITY AVE, DEPT 3068 82071 #051-01-1982 L1994 **GP ADL** *020 †55
STRAND, Jason Trevor. PO BOX 3432 82071 #021-01-2006 L2008 **FP** *012
SWIATEK, Donald Stanley. 255 N 30TH ST 82072 #028-34-1970 L1978 **GP** *020 †16
THEDIECK, Ann Holzgrefe. 3810 E GRAND AVE, ANN H. THEDIECK 82070 #007-02-2001 L2002 **FM** *020 †18

VAN BAALEN, Annette. 807 S 3RD ST 82070 #007-02-1999 L2002 **FM** *020 †18
WEINSTEIN, Stanley W. 255 N 30TH ST, RADIOLOGY - IMH 82072 #056-06-1995 L2005 **DR** *020 †80

LOVELL — BIG HORN

BAUMSTARCK, Joseph, Jr. 342 E MAIN ST, STRONG TREE CLINIC 82431 #037-01-1990 L1994 **GP UCM** *020
CALDWELL, Troy J. 1115 LANE 12, NBHH 82431 #028-34-1996 L1997 **FM** *020 †18
GILBERT, Derek Harvey. 1115 LANE 12, NORTH BIG HORN HOSPITAL CL 82431 #046-01-2002 L2005 **FM** *020 †18
HOFFMAN, David Evans. 1115 LANE 12, NORTH BIG HORN HOSPITAL 82431 #030-06-1984 L1989 **GS** *075
STORY, John Huntington. 1115 LANE 12 82431 #030-05-1955 L1958 **GP GS** *075

LUSK — NIOBRARA

HUITT, Carlton Duane. PO BOX 360, 225 S MAIN 82225 #004-01-1958 L1976 **GP AM** *020

MARBLETON — SUBLETTE

CZARNIK, Tamarack Robt. PO BOX 787, 17 W 3RD ST 83113 #038-40-1992 L1993 **GPM** *020 †18

MOORCROFT — CROOK

CASEY, Cynthia M. PO BOX 187, 101 W CROOK 82721 #030-06-1995 L1996 **FM** *020 †18
MONTGOMERY, Guy Edwin. ■ 82721 #018-03-1965 L1979 **EM** *020
STITELER, Ellin Mary. 101 W. CROOK, ELLIN STITELER 82721 #030-06-1980 L1981 **FM** *020 †18

MORAN — TETON

LA VALLEE, Dale Arthur. PO BOX 380, 27610 N WHETSTONE RD 83013 #016-06-1965 L1971 **AN** *071 †05
MC FARLAND, John Zehner. ■ 83013 #021-05-1966 L1990 **R** *020 †80

NEWCASTLE — WESTON

ECKRICH, Stephen G. 1124 WASHINGTON BLVD 82701 #048-04-1986 L1999 **ORS** *020 †40
FRANKLIN, Duane Charles. 1121 WASHINGTON BLVD 82701 #005-12-1979 L1983 **FM** *020 †18
FRANZ, Willis Martin. 1124 WASHINGTON BLVD 82701 #026-04-1946 L1950 **GP** *071
JORDING, Michael Allen. 1121 WASHINGTON BLVD 82701 #030-06-1980 L1983 **FM** *020 †18
REIMER, Lanny Bruce. 1121 WASHINGTON BLVD 82701 #007-02-1976 L1979 **FM** *020 †18
STEPHENSON, Henry N, Jr. ■ 82701 #056-05-1950 L1954 **GP** *071
STERCHI, John Michael. 1124 WASHINGTON BLVD 82701 #038-41-1966 L2003 **GS GE** *020 †85

PINEDALE — SUBLETTE

JOHNSTON, J Thos. PO BOX 1877 82941 #041-09-1957 L1958 **GP** *020 †18
KAPPENMAN, David Patrick. ■ 82941 #046-01-2002 L2006 **FM** *020 †18
QUIRK, James Hanlon, Jr. PO BOX 627, 619 E HENNICK 82941 #007-02-1999 L2006 **FM** *020 †18 ‡
STOFER, Barbara. ■ 82941 #005-11-1950 L1950 **A GP** *071

POWELL — PARK

BILES, Jimmie Gene. 639 W COULTER AVE 82435 #048-14-1981 L1986 **ORS** *020 †40
BOHLMAN, Michael Keith. 450 MOUNTAIN VIEW ST, CENTER 82435 #039-01-1991 L1994 **FM** *020 †18
BRYAN, Roy Glynn, Jr. ■ 82435 #030-06-1993 L1994 **FM** *020 †18
CHANDLER, Robert Lyle. 450 MOUNTAIN VIEW ST, CENTER 82435 #030-06-1997 L2000 **FM** *020 †18
CHRISTENSEN, Kelly Eugene. 450 MOUNTAIN VIEW ST, CENTER 82435 #049-01-1992 L1995 **FM** *020 †18
DICKERSON, Robert Milam. 450 MOUNTAIN VIEW ST, CENTER 82435 #019-02-1964 L1990 **IM** *020
DIRKSEN, Lawrence John. ■ 82435 #005-11-1968 L1994 **DR** *020 †80
ELLIS, Robert F. 450 MOUNTAIN VIEW ST, CENTER 82435 #649-14-1980 L1988 **OBG** *020
HABERLAND, Lyle F. 808 E 5TH ST 82435 #026-04-1953 L1959 **GP** *071
HANSEN, Jeffrey Norman. 450 MOUNTAIN VIEW ST, CENTER 82435 #054-04-1980 L2005 **HS ORS** *020 †40
HORTON, Lynn Stewart. 450 MOUNTAIN VIEW ST, UNIT A 82435 #041-07-1983 L1998 **FM** *020 †18
MILLER, Joseph Allan. 777 AVENUE H 82435 #038-06-1957 L1957 **PTH NM** *071 †50,28
MORRIS, Nicholas Waln. 450 MOUNTAIN VIEW ST, CENTER 82435 #041-13-1969 L1991 **GS** *020 †85
PRESTON, Clinton Earl. 777 AVENUE H 82435 #049-01-1997 L1999 **FM EM** *020 †18
SPOMER, Elizabeth Laura. 450 MOUNTAIN VIEW ST, CENTER 82435 #030-06-1998 L2001 **FM** *020 †18
TRACY, Michael Duane. 450 MOUNTAIN VIEW ST, CENTER 82435 #007-02-1994 L2002 **MPD** *020 †20,05
WURZEL, John F. 450 MOUNTAIN VIEW ST, UNIT A2 82435 #028-34-1953 L1984 **GYN** *071 †30
WURZEL, Mark Steven. 450 MOUNTAIN VIEW ST, CENTER 82435 #003-01-1982 L1985 **FM** *020 †18

RANCHESTER — SHERIDAN

KREMER, Jerome Lawrence. PO BOX 547 82839 #056-06-1963 L1964 **OS GP** *071

RAWLINS – CARBON

CESKO, David Ray. ■ 82301 #030-06-1994 L1997 **FM** *020 †18
CHANDRA, Raja V. 519 8TH ST BOX 1768 82301 #495-66-1971 L1978 **GP** *020
COUCH, M Wayne, II. 606 23RD ST 82301 #048-14-1994 L1995 **FM OBS** *020 †18
FLINNER, Mark Andrew. 2012 ELM ST 82301 #049-01-1990 L1991 **FM** *020 †18
JOHNSON, Gregory James. 2221 ELM ST, CARBON COUNTY 82301 #026-04-1982 L1985 **EM FM** *020 †18
KIRSCH, Archie Patrick. ■ 82301 #028-34-1966 L1969 **FM** *020 †18
LARSEN, James C, II. 408 DALEY ST 82301 #030-06-1983 L1990 **P IM** *020
POWELL, Jack Payne, Jr. 507 9TH ST 82301 #020-12-1969 L1974 **EM** *020 †16
REYBURN, Christopher B. 721 W MAPLE ST 82301 #030-06-1993 L1997 **P** *020 †75
SCHULZE, Kenneth Wm, Jr. 2012 ELM ST 82301 #025-01-1964 L1992 **ORS** *020
SRIDHARAN, Palur. 2221 ELM ST 82301 #495-04-1972 L1979 **GS VS** *020 †85
STEELE, Phillip Martin. 606 23RD ST 82301 #049-01-1996 L2000 **FSM FM** *020 †18
YOUNG, Charles Chester. 2213 E CEDAR ST 82301 #308-03-1980 L1993 **GP GS** *020

RIVERTON – FREMONT

ALLISON, Archie Brooks. 2100 W SUNSET DR, RIVERTON MEMORIAL HOSPITAL 82501 #047-06-1967 L1990 **PTH** *020
AVILES, Ricardo Alfonso. 1005 COLLEGE VIEW DR 82501 #032-01-2000 L2007 **OPH** *020 †35
BILLIN, Aaron Robert. 2100 W SUNSET DR 82501 #028-34-1995 L2007 **FM** *020 †18
BROHM, William Bates. 2100 W SUNSET DR 82501 #041-13-1965 L1973 **GS** *071
CAPRICCHIONE, Angelo M. 511 N 12TH ST E 82501 #305-01-1997 L2003 **END** *020 †20
CARRICABURU, Pierre A. 2300 ROSE LN, VA RIVERTON CLINIC 82501 #049-01-1977 L1979 **FM** *020 †18
COLLINS, Kathryn Ann. 2100 W SUNSET DR 82501 #005-11-1977 L1979 **EM** *020 †16
CROSBY, William Michael. ■ 82501 #017-20-1976 L1988 **AN** *020
FERRIS, John Delos. 300 N BROADWAY AVE 82501 #049-01-1969 L1970 **EM** *020
FISHER, Michael R. 1005 COLLEGE VIEW DR 82501 #048-15-2002 L2005 **PD** *020 †55
GOSE, Roger Lamar. 1005 COLLEGE VIEW DR, WIND RIVER INTERNAL MEDICI 82501 #048-02-1966 L1978 **IM CD** *020 †20
HANNANEY, Maryanne. 1005 COLLEGE VIEW DR 82501 #528-01-1975 L2003 **OBG** *020 †30
HEDGECOCK, Linda Joanne. 1025 COLLEGE VIEW DR 82501 #030-05-1982 L1983 **FM** *020 †18
HOPKINS, Ralph Edward. 705 E WASHINGTON AVE 82501 #020-12-1967 L1974 **U GS** *020 †95
JENKINS, Lawrence Alan. 1025 COLLEGE VIEW DR 82501 #005-06-1983 L1994 **ORS OSS** *020 †40
JODER, Donald Kenneth. ■ 82501 #007-02-1958 L1959 **AM GP** *020
JONES, Richard Lawrence. 1005 COLLEGE VIEW DR 82501 #030-06-1996 L1998 **IM** *020 †20
KADRI, Sheikh Mohammed Z. 2002 W SUNSET DR, STE 2 82501 #495-42-1967 L2006 **OTO FPS** *020 †45
KUCERA, Wallace K. ■ 82501 #030-06-1953 L1964 **FM** *071 †18
LEE, Michael John. 2300 ROSE LN, RIVERTON VA CLINIC 82501 #007-02-1974 L1998 **FM** *020 †18
LEVENE, Daniel Ellis. 1025 COLLEGE VIEW DR 82501 #007-02-1993 L2002 **ORS** *020 †40
LEWIS, Dennis Michael. 1005 COLLEGE VIEW DR 82501 #011-03-1983 L1995 **GS** *020 †85
MAGRUDER, Joy Lynn. 1620 RIVERVIEW RD, WESTERN FAMILY CARE 82501 #041-02-1997 L2005 **FM** *020 †18
MC CALLUM, Thomas Lee. 1001 W MAIN ST 82501 #038-06-1966 L1977 **DR** *020 †80
MILLER, Michael William. 1620 RIVERVIEW RD, WESTERN FAMILY CARE 82501 #056-06-1985 L1986 **FM** *020 †18
MILSTEIN, Stephen Howard. 716 COLLEGE VIEW DR STE A 82501 #034-01-1973 L1998 **VS GS** *020 †85
MOSSBROOK, Sandra Slade. 4251 VALLEY GREEN CIR 82501 #041-02-1972 L1982 **FM PG** *020 †55
MUZAFFAR, Sana Taj. ■ 82501 #054-04-2006 L2007 **IM** *012
PORTWOOD, Cheryl Collins. 1110 MAJOR AVE 82501 #037-01-1995 L2001 **CHP P** *020
RECKLING, John Frederick. 1005 COLLEGE VIEW DR 82501 #049-01-1990 L1993 **IM** *020 †20
RIDGWAY, Eric M. 1620 RIVERVIEW RD 82501 #007-02-1983 L1984 **FM** *020 †18
RIVERA HURTADO, Aida Del. 716 COLLEGE VIEW DR, RIVERTON MEMORIAL HOSPITAL 82501 #264-10-1989 L2007 **IM IMG** *071
ROTHOLZ, Stephen Saml. 1005 COLLEGE VIEW DR 82501 #003-01-1989 L2003 **OBG** *020 †30
SJOSTROM, Rebecca Ashley. ■ 82501 #021-01-2008 L2008 *012
SORENSON, Richard Russell. 1005 COLLEGE VIEW DR, WINDRIVER CLINIC 82501 #039-01-1975 L1980 **IM HEM** *020 †20
STEGER, David Jos. 1130 MAJOR AVE 82501 #028-34-1976 L1981 **FM EM** *020 †18
STENFORS-DACRE, Celia C. 904 W SUNSET DR, CANYON ORTHOPAEDICS & REHA 82501 #005-12-1994 L1997 **PM** *020
STOCKTON, Kent De Lano. 1620 RIVERVIEW RD 82501 #019-02-1969 L1973 **FM EM** *020 †18
TAYLOR, James Robt. 1001 W MAIN ST 82501 #030-06-1991 L1995 **DR** *020 †80
WECKER, Richard Carl. 711 E MAIN ST, # 241 82501 #030-05-1971 L1975 **ORS CLP** *020 †40

ROCK SPRINGS – SWEETWATER

AIELLO, James John. 1200 COLLEGE DR 82901 #016-01-1995 L2007 **EM** *020 †16
ALLYN, Peter Geo. 1204 HILLTOP DR STE 111 82901 #016-06-1981 L1985 **OBG** *020 †30
BECK, Joshua David. 2761 COMMERCIAL WAY 82901 #033-05-2000 L2006 **ORS** *020 ‡
BEIA, Todd. 1200 COLLEGE DR 82901 #016-76-1997, ▲ 2001 **EM** *020 †16
BENDER, Sean Patrick. 1200 COLLEGE DR 82901 #025-07-2002 L2006 **EM** *020 †16
BIENZ, Thomas Alexander. 2950 COLLEGE DR 82901 #024-07-1993 L1999 **HS** *020 †40
BOESE, Edmund Cone. ■ 82901 #041-14-1974 L1992 **AN** *020 †05
CARSON, Jay G. 2950 COLLEGE DR 82901 #048-02-1995 L2000 **ORS** *020 †40
CIANFLONE, Alexander G. 1200 COLLEGE DR 82901 #007-02-1978 L1995 **FM EM** *020 †16,18
CLIMACO, Jesus Lledo. T1200 COLLEGE DR 82901 #748-01-1961 L1972 **PD** *075
COURNOYER, Gerard P. 1208 HILLTOP DR, STE 102 82901 #067-02-1978 L1994 **GP** *020
CYGAN, Ronald Walter. 2515 FOOTHILL BLVD, STE 202 82901 #021-01-1972 L2000 **PD** *020 †55
D'AMORE, Daniel Thomas. 1200 COLLEGE DR 82901 #011-02-2002 L2008 **EM** *012 †20
DILLARD, Faith Anne. 1200 COLLEGE DR 82901 #654-01-1999 L2007 **EM** *020 †16
DONALDSON, Terry Robt. 1204 HILLTOP DR, STE 108 82901 #030-06-1992 L1995 **IM** *020 †20
ELIOPOULOS, Vassily T. 1200 COLLEGE DR 82901 #035-20-2003 L2007 **EM** *100

FRANKS, Chad Keith. 1204 HILLTOP DR, STE 108 82901 #305-01-2001 L2007 **GS** *020
GARCIA-PRIETO, Carlos E. 1124 COLLEGE DR, SOUTHWEST COUNSELING SERVI 82901 #341-03-1993 L2004 **P** *020
GOLDBERG, Lauren Sue. 1200 COLLEGE DR 82901 #035-47-1990 L1993 **EM** *020 †16
GRANT, Michael. 2908 FOOTHILL BLVD STE B 82901 #495-67-1989 L2002 **IM** *020 †20
HOLTAN, Brian Alan. 1993 DEWAR DR, UNIT1 82901 #054-04-1982 L1986 **DR** *020 †80
HUNTER, Kurt Leroy. 2751 COMMERCIAL WAY 82901 #030-06-1997 L1998 **FM** *020 †18
ILIYA, John Andrew. 1208 HILLTOP DR STE 105 82901 #048-12-1981 L1986 **GS** *020 †85 ‡
JENSEN, Peter M. 1208 HILLTOP DR STE 200 82901 #039-79-1991, ▲ L1995 **OPH** *020
JOHNSON, Frederick. 1200 COLLEGE DR 82901 #016-06-1977 L2006 **EM PD** *020 †55,16
KAAN, Daryl James. 3000 COLLEGE DR 82901 #030-06-1989 L1992 **OBG** *020 †30
KATTAN, Samer Emile. 3000 COLLEGE DR, COLLEGE HILL WOMEN'S HEALT 82901 #605-03-2001 L2007 **OBG** *020
KRAMER, Michael John. 1200 COLLEGE DR 82901 #016-11-1974 L1975 **GP EM** *020 †16
KRONER, Ludwig F, III. 1204 HILLTOP DR, STE 102 82901 #056-05-1974 L1981 **ORS HS** *062 †40
LANSANG, Rodolfo R. ■ 82901 #748-01-1955 L1964 **R** *071
LEA, Mark Stratton. 1204 HILLTOP DR, STE 109 82901 #030-06-1985 L2000 **GS VS** *020 †85
LEMON, Charles Herbert. 1200 COLLEGE DR 82901 #030-06-1989 L2006 **EM** *020 †16
MADSEN, Kenneth Robert. 1208 HILLTOP DR STE 205 82901 #010-01-1993 L2004 **VS** *020 †85
MAJEED, Mohammed. 1200 COLLEGE DR, SWEETWATER COUNTY 82901 #528-01-1990 L2004 **IM** *020 †20
MARTIN, James Douglas. 1200 COLLEGE DR 82901 #041-02-1995 L2005 **EM** *020 †16
MATTI, Frederick Leo. 1200 COLLEGE DR, MEDICAL IMAGING DEPARTMENT 82901 #011-04-1999 L2005 **DR** *020 †80
MC KEE, Ronald James. 1200 COLLEGE DR 82901 #056-05-1980 L1981 **EM FM** *020 †18,16 ‡
MEYER, Mel Rea. 1200 COLLEGE DR 82901 #049-01-1993 L1994 **FM** *020 †18
MOSER, Chris S. 3000 COLLEGE DR STE C 82901 #049-01-1989 L1990 **FM** *020 †18
OANA, Iulia. 1200 COLLEGE DR, SWEETWATER MEMORIAL HOSPIT 82901 #781-01-1997 L2003 **IM** *020 †20
OLIVER, Joseph John. 1204 HILLTOP DR 82901 #035-06-1972 L1977 **ORS** *020 †40
PRYICH, William Vladimir. ■ 82901 #030-06-1956 L1957 **GP OS** *071
RAINEY, Debra Kaycole. ■ 82902 #030-06-1986 L1990 **P** *020
RAJU-SWAMI, Rathna. 1200 COLLEGE DR 82901 #024-05-1998 L2003 **EM** *020 †16
RICE, Matthew Morrow. 1200 COLLEGE DR 82901 #041-14-1977 L2003 **EM LM** *020 †16
RICHARDSON, Alan. 1204 HILLTOP DR, STE 107 82901 #030-06-1985 L1987 **FM** *020 †18
ROBERTS, Margaret Louise. 3000 COLLEGE DR, STE C 82901 #049-01-1999 L2002 **FM** *020 †18 ‡
RODDY, Jonathan Richard. 1200 COLLEGE DR 82901 #024-05-1998 L2002 **EM** *020 †16
ROGERS, Douglas Melvin. ■ 82902 #004-01-1976 L1992 **AN PME** *020
SHERMAN, John A. 1200 COLLEGE DR 82901 #043-01-1990 L1994 **EM** *020 †16
SOWADA, David Felix. 1200 COLLEGE DR, C/O MEMORIAL HOSPITAL 82901 #049-01-1971 L1976 **PTH** *020 †50
SPICER, Thomas Eldon. 1208 HILLTOP DR, STE 103 82901 #054-04-1973 L1976 **PS** *020 †85,65
STACHON, Jean A. 1208 HILLTOP DR STE 105 82901 #049-01-1983 L1986 **FM** *020 †18
STIEGLITZ, Jeffrey Brian. 1200 COLLEGE DR 82901 #005-19-1982 L1984 **EM GP** *020 †16
SUTPHIN, Michael David. 1208 HILLTOP DR STE 204 82901 #049-01-1979 L1984 **U** *020 †95
WALLACE, Stephen Wright. 1200 COLLEGE DR 82901 #005-11-1988 L2004 **EM** *020 †16
WHITLING, David Michael. 1200 COLLEGE DR 82901 #035-47-2004 L2004 **EM** *012
YESHLUR, Chandrashekar P. 1204 HILLTOP DR, STE 106 82901 #495-09-1991 L2003 **PD** *020 †55

SARATOGA – CARBON

LUNT, John. ■ 82331 #035-01-1954 L1977 **FM EM** *071 †85
NOTON, Diane Lesley. 1208 S RIVER ST 82331 #030-06-1995 L1996 **FM** *020 †18
WARD, William Todd. 1 BOOZER CREEK RD 82331 #023-01-1958 L1962 **R** *071 †80

SHAWNEE – CONVERSE

HORNER, George M. ■ 82229 #030-05-1946 L1985 **GYN** *071 †30

SHERIDAN – SHERIDAN

ADAMS, Herbert V. ■ 82801 #056-06-1943 L1947 **GP D** *071
ADLER, Jacqueline. PO BOX 6046 82801 #048-02-1992 L2004 **ID** *020
ARAAS, Frederick J. PO BOX 643 82801 #030-06-1951 L1952 **FM** *071 †18
BATEMAN, Scott Neldon. 330 W DOW ST 82801 #048-13-1990 L1995 **OTO** *020 †45
BATTY, Hugh Kenworthy. 1262 W 5TH ST 82801 #649-33-1977 L1979 **IM** *020
BENEPE, James Lorimer, Jr. ■ 82801 #028-02-1954 L1969 **P PM** *071
BENNETT, Michele Lynn. 248 W WORKS ST 82801 #049-01-1995 L1998 **FM** *020 †18
BOWERS, Mary Imogen. 1701 W 5TH ST STE A, GOOSE CREEK PEDS 82801 #054-04-1982 L1993 **PD ADL** *020 †55
CARMEN, John C. 1898 FORT RD, APT 16-A 82801 #010-01-1975 L1980 **FM** *020 †18
CHERNI-SMITH, Rita. 1898 FORT RD 111 82801 #048-14-1983 L1996 **IM** *020 †20
COE, Tracy Lynn. 1585 W 5TH ST, WELCH CANCER 82801 #048-13-1989 L2008 **HO** *020 †20
CURNOW, Robert John. 1458 W 5TH ST 82801 #028-03-1971 L1975 **ORS** *020 †40
DOUGHTY, William Edward. 1401 W 5TH ST 82801 #034-01-1969 L1976 **PTH** *020 †50
EDWARDS, John Zener. 1458 W 5TH ST 82801 #041-12-1999 L2004 **ORS** *020 †40
FARS, Roberto. ■ 82801 #561-01-1995 L2002 **IM** *020 †20
FERRIES, James Scott. 1050 MYDLAND RD 82801 #034-01-1990 L1995 **ORS** *020 †40
FERRIES, Laura M. 1401 W 5TH ST 82801 #034-01-1990 L1995 **IM** *020 †20
FINLEY, John W. 1949 SUGARLAND DR, STE 192 82801 #048-13-1984 L1995 **FM** *020 †18
FRISBIE, Dennis Clinton. ■ 82801 #026-04-1963 L1973 **CHP** *071
GILL, Lawrence G, III. 1333 W 5TH ST, STE 203 82801 #035-19-1977 L1984 **OBG REN** *020 †30
GOULD, Walter Harry. 340 W DOW ST 82801 #040-02-1968 L1976 **GS** *020 †85
GRAVES, Charles Bruce. 1898 FORT RD 82801 #028-02-1988 L1991 **IM** *020 †20
HALL, Andrew Foster. 350 S BROOKS ST 82801 #036-01-1993 L1997 **OPH** *020
HANEBRINK, Bradley G. 1401 W 5TH ST 82801 #028-79-1986, ▲ L1992 **AN IM** *020 †05
HANNA, Robert Saml. 340 W DOW ST 82801 #030-05-1975 L2006 **OPH** *020
HERSCHLER, Jonathan. 350 S BROOKS ST 82801 #007-02-1969 L1988 **OPH** *071 †35
HILLER, Michael Wilson. VET ADM FORT MAC KENZIE 82801 #038-06-1973 L1977 **IM GE** *020 †20

■ = Address Information Privacy Protected

HUNT, Karl Raymond. 110 S GOULD ST 82801 #017-20-1962 L1965 **AN** *071

HUNTER, Ian James. 1333 W 5TH ST, STE 103 82801 #054-04-2003 L2007 **IM** *100 †20

JOST, Corey James. 1333 W 5TH ST 82801 #019-02-1994 L2005 **VS GS** *020 †85

JUNG, Roger Wm. 1842 SUGARLAND DR STE 108, PMB 178 82801 #026-04-1976 L1977 **P** *020

LINDEMANN, Fred Carl. 1401 W 5TH ST 82801 #056-06-1964 L1970 **RO R** *020 †80

LUDWIG, Ryan Richard. ■ 82801 #025-12-2008 L2008 *012

MAERTENS, Steven R. 1401 W 5TH ST, MEMORIAL HOSP/SHERIDAN CTY 82801 #049-01-1987 L1988 **EM GP** *020 †16 ‡

MANGUS, Barry Eugene. ■ 82801 #049-01-2002 L2007 **GS** *020 †85

MAYER, Thomas Otto. 1050 MYDLAND RD 82801 #017-20-1998 L2003 **N** *020 †75

MC KIE, Robert Allan. 1898 FORT RD, QUARTERS 10 82801 #054-04-2000 L2001 **IM** *100

MILNER, Brenton Faulkner. 1050 MYDLAND RD 82801 #051-01-1998 L2003 **ORS** *020 †40

MURPHY, Robert C. ■ 82801 #035-20-1942 L1978 **P** *071 †75

MUSSELL, Howard L. 1926 W 5TH ST 82801 #028-03-1967 L1977 **GS** *071 †85

NICKERSON, David Scott. 340 W DOW ST 82801 #023-07-1971 L1977 **ORS** *071 †40

NIETHAMMER, Thomas Herman. 1333 W 5TH ST 82801 #049-01-1980 L1983 **IM** *020 †20

OLSON, David Mark. 1898 FORT RD, # 8 82801 #049-14-1988 L1990 **P PFP** *020

OSS, Suzanne Eva. 916 JACKSON AVE, NORTHEAST WYOMING PEDIATRI 82801 #047-06-2002 L2006 **PD** *100

PRADHAN, Neelima. 1898 FORT RD, SHERIDAN VAMC 82801 #495-92-1981 L1994 **P** *020

QUINN, Anthony Bernard. 1050 MYDLAND RD 82801 #023-01-1994 L1999 **ORS** *020 †40

REED, Margaret A. ■ 82801 #030-06-1951 L1963 **IMG** *071 †18

RICHARDS, Tom Jason. 1401 W 5TH ST, MEMORIAL HOSP OF SHERIDAN 82801 #049-01-1991 L1996 **FM** *020 †18

RITTERBUSCH, John Fred. 1050 MYDLAND RD 82801 #023-07-1980 L1997 **ORS OP** *020 †40

ROBINSON, Irving E. 1401 W 5TH ST 82801 #049-01-1991 L1994 **FM** *020 †18

ROBISON, Wendell Jesse. VET ADMIN HOSP 82801 #049-01-1978 L1985 **IM IMG** *020

ROGERS, Stanley James. VET ADMIN HOSP, DEPT PSYCH 82801 #352-06-1951 L1956 **P** *030 †75

ROJO, Oscar Jimenez. ■ 82801 #275-01-1944 L1949 **OBG AS** *071 †30

SCHREFFLER, Dennis Dale. 1401 W 5TH ST, MEMORIAL HOSPITAL 82801 #004-01-1973 L1990 **PTH** *020 †50

SCHULTZ, David Michael. 1401 W 5TH ST 82801 #030-06-1980 L1983 **AN** *020 †05

SCOTT, Timothy James. 212 W BURKITT ST 82801 #038-41-1974 L1978 **OBG** *020 †30 ‡

SIDHU, Anup Singh. 1456 W 5TH ST, THE WILLIAMS CLINIC 82801 #495-29-1980 L1989 **P** *020 †75

SMITH, Alan Edward, Jr. 1401 W 5TH ST 82801 #019-02-1997 L2004 **AN** *020 †05

SMITH, Christopher T. 1050 MYDLAND RD 82801 #020-02-1969 L1974 **ORS** *020 †40

SOTO RIVAS, Ismael Hiram. PO BOX 6758 82801 #649-14-1997 L1999 **FM** *020 †18 ‡

SPRINGER, Roy Abbott. 1842 SUGARLAND DR STE 108 82801 #035-15-1954 L1997 **R** *020 †80

STAMATO, John Patrick. 1585 W 5TH ST, CANCER CTR OF NORTHERN WY 82801 #017-20-1992 L1996 **RO** *020

STEARS, Robert L Grant. 1458 W 5TH ST 82801 #007-02-1990 L1995 **R** *020 †80

STRAHAN, Michael James. 1401 W 5TH ST 82801 #049-01-1980 L1983 **GP** *020 ‡

SWAN, Davis Mc Kean. 1524 W 5TH ST, SHERIDAN SURGICAL CENTER 82801 #028-02-1969 L1981 **AN OS** *071 †55,05

TENNEY, Stephen Scott. 1898 FORT RD 82801 #003-01-1978 L1981 **IM** *020 †20

THICKMAN, Seymour. 1754 BIG HORN AVE, 1401 WEST FIFTH STREET 82801 #035-03-1947 L1954 **IM** *020 †20

TREHAN, Rajeev Ratan. 1898 FORT RD, # 15 82801 #495-36-1978 L1982 **P N** *030 †75

WALSH, Thomas Lee. 1401 W 5TH ST 82801 #030-06-1997 L1998 **EM** *020 †18

WALTER, Charles Frederick. MEM HSP SHERIDAN DEP PTH 82801 #041-01-1964 L1971 **PTH** *020 †50

WATSON, George Nolin. 1898 FORT RD 82801 #020-02-1943 L1944 **P** *071

WHITE, Jason Matthew. 1401 W 5TH ST, RADIOLOGY 82801 #038-40-1998 L2005 **RNR** *020 †80

WILLIAMS, William Morgan. 1456 W 5TH ST 82801 #023-01-1968 L1974 **IM CD** *020 †20

WILSON, Michal Richard. 1848 FORT RD, STE 17A 82801 #054-04-1994 L1996 **P** *020

WILSON, Robert W. ■ 82801 #007-02-1951 L1980 **OBG** *040 †30

WOHL, Barry Michael. 916 JACKSON AVE 82801 #041-01-1975 L1978 **PD** *020 †55

STORY — SHERIDAN

RAINS, Garry Ewell. PO BOX 99, 18 TRAPPER RD 82842 #038-40-1977 L1994 **AN** *020 †05 ‡

SUNDANCE — CROOK

ROGERS-NOBACK, Erin L. ■ 82729 #016-01-1997 L2000 **FM** *020 †18

VILLANO, Jeremi. 713 OAK ST 82729 #035-08-1972 L1976 **FM** *020 †18

TETON VILLAGE — TETON

ANKENBRANDT, Ivan S. ■ 83025 #016-11-1954 L1982 **GP** *071

BROUS, Julie Anne. ■ 83025 #007-02-1965 L1967 **OS D** *071 †15

LARIMER, Jack Austin. 3630 CURTISS DR 83025 #038-06-1967 L1973 **R OTO** *071 †80

MELLION, Morris Bernard. ■ 83025 #008-01-1970 L1971 **MDM FSM** *071 †18 ‡

THAYNE — LINCOLN

HAGEMAN, Martha Susan. 122 PETERSEN PKWY, STE 4 83127 #038-41-1992 L1995 **FM** *020 †18 ‡

KIRK, Donald J. 122 PETERSEN PKWY STE 4 83127 #038-41-1992 L1995 **FM** *020 †18

THERMOPOLIS — HOT SPRINGS

BOMENGEN, Wade Travis. ■ 82443 #048-04-1996 L1997 **FM** *020 †18 ‡

COOK, David Arthur. 150 E ARAPAHOE ST 82443 #005-15-1964 L2001 **ORS** *020 †40

MAHONEY, Kevin Robert. 120 N C AVE, RED ROCK FAMILY PRACTICE 82443 #056-06-1994 L1995 **FM** *020 †18

MILLER, Vernon Walter. 112 E ARAPAHOE ST 82443 #030-05-1973 L1979 **GS** *020 †85

PETTIPIECE, Kurt R. 110 E ARAPAHOE ST 82443 #030-05-1984 L1985 **FM** *020 †18

WEYER, Jason Christopher. 120 N C AVE 82443 #018-75-2003, ▲ L2006 **FM** *020 †18

WILLSON, Howard Todd. 703 US HIGHWAY 20 N 82443 #011-03-1965 L1975 **FM** *020 †18

TORRINGTON — GOSHEN

BERRY, Millard Todd. 625 ALBANY AVE, BHS PHYSICIAN SERVICES 82240 #007-02-1999 L2000 **FM** *020 †18

COLIP, Michael Floyd. 2000 CAMPBELL DR, COMMUNITY HOSPITAL 82240 #019-02-1995 L2005 **FM** *020 †18

EVANS, Breck Irene. 625 ALBANY AVE 82240 #054-04-2004 L2007 **FM** *020 †18

FLUCKIGER, Ezdan A. 625 ALBANY AVE 82240 #049-01-1995 L1998 **FM** *020 †18 ‡

KNITTEL, Peggy. ■ 82240 #030-05-1981 L1994 **GP PTH** *020

LEHMITZ, Paul Glen. 625 ALBANY AVE 82240 #049-01-1987 L2003 **IM IMG** *020 †20

MCCARTY, Craig Willard. 625 ALBANY AVE 82240 #422-01-2004 L2007 **FM** *020 †18

MORGAN, Loran B. ■ 82240 #026-04-1943 L1946 **OPH FM** *071 †35,18

OAKLEY, Richard Stuart. 665 ALBANY AVE 82240 #051-04-1966 L2005 **GS** *020 †85

RANDOLPH, Bonnie L. 2000 CAMPBELL DR 82240 #049-01-1993 L1994 **FM** *020 †18

RUTT, Rodney Ray. 625 ALBANY AVE 82240 #030-05-1960 L1967 **GP** *071

SCHMITZ, Gary Douglas. 665 ALBANY AVE 82240 #030-05-1979 L1984 **GS** *020 †85

SMITH, Kayo. 625 ALBANY AVE 82240 #030-05-1954 L1957 **GP** *020

SMITH, Marion Nolan. 625 ALBANY AVE, BHS PHYSICIAN SERVICES 82240 #030-06-1982 L1985 **FM** *020 †18

SOUTHWELL, Richard Bull. 2000 CAMPBELL DR 82240 #035-15-1975 L1980 **ORS** *020 †40

WAKAMATSU, Jon Paul. 625 ALBANY AVE, BHS PHYSICIAN SERVICES 82240 #040-02-1989 L1994 **FM** *020 †18

WARREN, Garth Dylan. PO BOX 897 82240 #007-02-2007 L2007 **PTH** *012

WAPITI — PARK

ROBINSON, Michael Luther. ■ 82450 #021-06-1977 L1979 **DR** *071 †80

WHEATLAND — PLATTE

CECIL, Jeffrey A. 1551 BRICE ST 82201 #030-06-2001 L2004 **FM** *020

HAWLEY, James Wesley, Jr. 201 14TH ST 82201 #004-01-1988 L1994 **EM GP** *020

MURPHY, Mark Gregory. 201 14TH ST 82201 #043-01-1987 L1997 **ORS AM** *020 †40

PALMER, Lauri Ann. 1551 BRICE ST 82201 #049-01-1991 L1995 **FM** *020 †18

SCHULTZ, Pennie Lyn. 1551 BRICE ST, CHEYENNE CHILDREN'S CLINIC 82201 #030-06-1992 L1998 **PD** *020 †55

WILSON, William D. 1356 SHIEK ST 82201 #010-01-1951 L1952 **GP** *071

WILSON — TETON

BRECHEEN, Roger Malcolm. PO BOX 243, WILSON GYNECOLOGY 83014 #005-11-1987 L1993 **OBG** *020 †30

CASPERSON, Paul Conrad. ■ 83014 #026-04-1967 L1995 **ORS OSM** *071 †40

CHIDSEY, Charles Augustus. PO BOX 711, 5025 W RAINBOW TROUT LN 83014 #035-01-1954 L1976 **FM CD** *072 †20

GOODER, Ronald Brent. PO BOX 669, 2311 YARROW THE ASPENS 83014 #007-02-1956 L1957 **FM** *071 †18

HANKS, Jonathan Paul. PO BOX 247, 982 W BROADWAY 83014 #003-01-1988 L2003 **EM** *020

ODELL, William Douglas. ■ 83014 #016-02-1956 L1997 **IM END** *071 †20

OWENS, Hugh Simon, Jr. PO BOX 309, 3450 ASTER LN 83014 #036-01-1971 L1975 **AN** *020

ROUX, Jacques F. 3625 LAKE CREEK DR N 83014 #869-04-1955 L1980 **OBS OS** *071 †30

WILSON, Maria Ester. PO BOX 1986 83014 #035-15-1998 L2006 **IM** *020 †20

WORLAND — WASHAKIE

BARKHAUSEN, Regina. 400 S 15TH ST 82401 #409-20-1993 L2003 **IM** *020 †20

BENSON, Kjell Andrew. 400 S 15TH ST, WMC CLINIC 82401 #018-03-2002 L2005 **FM** *020 †18

BOLTON, William Edward. 400 S 15TH ST 82401 #016-11-1966 L1974 **GS GP** *071 †85

DEISS, Zachory Fred. 400 S 15TH ST 82401 #030-06-1987 L1988 **FM** *020 †18

HORSLEY, Edward Croft. 400 S 15TH ST 82401 #007-02-1959 L1961 **FM GS** *071

RANDOLPH, James Guerry. 151 S 6TH ST 82401 #048-14-1981 L1993 **ORS** *020

RICHARDSON, George G, Jr. 500 S 15TH ST, WASHAKIE MEDICAL CENTER 82401 #040-02-1970 L2005 **ORS** *020 †40

THURSTON, John Edward. 401 S 15TH ST, FAMILY PRACTICE & OBSTETRI 82401 #019-02-1993 L1994 **FM** *020 †18

WEAVER, Gerald Edward. 1511 CHARLES AVE 82401 #005-12-1990 L1995 **GS** *020

ZIMMERMAN, Edward Doyle. 400 S 15TH ST, WASHAKIE MED CLINIC 82401 #019-02-1998 L1998 **FM OBS** *020 †18 ‡

WRIGHT — CAMPBELL

JOHNSTON, Scott L. 500 LATIGO DRIVE, CCMH-WRIGHT CLINIC 82732 #023-12-1987 L1998 **FM** *020

YODER — GOSHEN

IRONS, Annabel Miller. ■ 82244 #035-06-1946 L1986 **IM PUD** *071 †20

■ = Address Information Privacy Protected

AGANA – GUAM

ATENDIDO, Winifredo Asis. GUAM MEM HOSP 96910 #748-08-1960 L1968 **IM OS** *020
BASILIO, Lourdes Cruz. ■ 96921 #748-01-1961 L1974 **AN** *020
ESPALDON, Leticia Virata. ■ 96910 #748-01-1954 L1967 **AN GP** *030
KIM, Young Whan. ■ 96910 #583-10-1964 L1977 **OBG** *020
MARTINEZ, Juanita Arce. FHP CMC BOX 6690 C 96910 #748-01-1954 L1960 **GP PD** *020
SABLAN, Ralph Guerrero. TOTO CANADA ROAD, TOTO DERMATOLOGY CLINIC 96910
  #039-01-1959 L1966 **D** *020 †15 ‡

AGANA HEIGHTS – GUAM

CHISHOLM, Christopher B. PO BOX 197829 96919 #028-34-1997 L1999 **EM** *020 †16
CORWIN, Christian Hobart. ■ 96919 #008-02-2001 L2002 **GS** *020 †85
PARAMAGURU, Rudradevi. 313 FARENHOLT RD, DEPT OF VET AFFAIRS US NAV. 96910
  #220-02-1967 L1972 **IM** *020
RAHN, Andrea Teresa. ■ 96919 #037-01-1998 L1999 **PD** *100 †55
WEIS, Daniel Richard. PO BOX 197834 96919 #038-43-2002 L2003 *020 †75

BARRIGADA – GUAM

CASTRO, Troadio B. ■ 96921 #748-02-1964 L1991 **R** *071
CORTEZ, Felipe R. ■ 96913 #748-01-1962 L1970 **AN GP** *020
KALLINGAL, Matilda Joseph. 101 PEDRO AGUON ST, LOWER BARRIGADA HEIGHTS 96913
  #495-63-1969 L1978 **IM** *020
KALLINGAL, Sebastian K. ■ 96913 #495-44-1968 L1977 **IM** *020
MARFORI, Goldelina L. ■ 96921 #748-11-1968 L1993 **AN** *020
PARENT, Charles H. PO BOX 24209, DEPT OF PUB HLTH & SOCIAL 96921 #067-03-1946 L1976
  PHP *071 †85

DEDEDO – GUAM

CHEN, Wen Yen. 330 W MARINE DR, CENTRAL MEDICAL CLINIC 96929 #385-04-1966 L1974
  PD GP *020 ‡
CHENET, Alix L. 612 W MARINE DR, GUAM ADULT PEDIATRIC CLINI 96929 #010-03-1980 L1991
  IM *020 †20
DAUTERMAN, Philip A. 674 HARMON LOOP RD, STE 111 96929 #305-01-1991 L1996
  PTH *020 †50
ESPERANZA, Rodolfo O. 172 E BUENA VISTA AVE, DEDEDO POLYMEDIC CLINIC 96929
  #748-02-1965 L1992 **IM** *020 †20
HAHN, Byung Du. 330 W MARINE DR STE 2, CENTRAL MEDICAL CLINIC 96929
  #583-01-1947 L1995 **OBG** *020 †30
OCAMPO, Teresito P. ■ 96912 #748-02-1967 L1975 **P** *020 †75
PANGILINAN, Ronald Felipe. ■ 96929 #014-01-2006 L2006 **IM** *012
RAMASAMY, Rengaraju. 520 W SANTA MONICA AVE, COMMUNITY HEALTH CENTER 96929
  #495-66-1982 L2002 **IM** *020 †20
WERTHMANN, Florian John. ■ 96912 #054-04-1962 L1983 **GP GS** *020 †85

HAGATNA – GUAM

CRUZ, Michael Warren. ■ 96932 #005-12-1984 L1992 **GS** *020 †85
CRUZ, Olivia L. T. 277 W CH SANTO PAPA 96910 #041-07-1962 L1967 **EM IM** *020
FLORES, Francisco Claudio. PO BOX AX 96932 #748-08-1957 L1976 **GS** *020
PEREZ, Victor Martin. 238 ARCHBISHOP FLORES ST, STE 403C 96910 #008-01-1983 L1987
  P *020
SALTZGABER, Lee Gerald. PO BOX 1732 96932 #023-12-1992 L1994 **AM FM** *030 †18,70
SISON, Benjamin Sitier. ■ 96932 #748-02-1957 L1967 **IM PHP** *071 †20
TOLENTINO, Sinforoso C. ■ 96910 #748-02-1943 L1961 **ORS GS** *020

INARAJAN – GUAM

ONG, Percival M. 162 ABMAN DR, SOUTHERN REG COMM HLTH CTR 96917
  #748-01-1955 L1967 **ID EM** *020

MAJURO – MARSHALL ISLANDS

RIKLON, Sheldon. ■ 96960 #014-01-1998 L1998 **FM** *020 †18

MANGILAO – GUAM

AHN, Ik Jo. ■ 96913 #010-01-1999 L2000 *020 †05
BAASEN, Chad Michael. ■ 96913 #023-12-1995 L1997 **EM** *020
PITTNER, Douglas Edward. ■ 96913 #038-06-2002 L2002 **ORS** *020
SZYFRES, Luis. ■ 96913 #132-01-1977 **P PHP** *030

PAGO PAGO – AMERICAN SAMOA

BEALES, Peter Frederick. LBJ TROPICAL MED CENTER 96799 #352-06-1968 **PHP OS** *030
DOSS, John W. LBJ HOSP 96799 #023-07-1952 L1952 **PHP FM** *030
DRAPER, Fred Haven. LBJ TROPICAL MED CTR 96799 #005-11-1945 L1945 **PTH** *071 †50
FLICK, John Jervis. C/O LBJ TROPICAL MED CTR 96799 #017-20-1940 **OPH** *071 †35
GRACH, Julia Lagarejos. LBJ TROPICAL MED CTR 96799 #748-01-1955 **PUD PD** *100
LEE, Jong Wook. LBJ TROPICAL MED CTR 96799 #583-02-1976 L1980 **GPM** *100
LYONS, Thomas Jos, Jr. ■ 96799 #041-13-1945 L1975 **OBG OS** *071 †30
MAGINN, R Reilly. ■ 96799 #028-34-1960 L1960 **GS TS** *071 †85
MARRONE, James Richard. PO BOX LBJ 96799 #021-01-1997 L1998 **PD** *020 †55
PERRY, Wm Darrell, Jr. ■ 96799 #407-10-1964 L1966 **FM P** *020

SALEAPAGA, Iotamo Tilofa. ■ 96799 #014-01-1979 L1985 **IM** *020
WILES, Stacey Diane. ■ 96799 #025-12-2004 L2005 **PD** *020
WILLIAMS, Victor Terenuku. PO BOX 997343 96799 #024-05-1966 L1967 **OBG** *020 †85

PALAU – PALAU

KUARTEI, Stevenson Jakey. ■ 96940 #014-01-1987 L1988 **FM** *020 †18
ROBERTS, Emais. ■ 96940 #014-01-1991 L1991 **GS** *020 †85
YALAP, Francisca. ■ 96940 #014-01-1977 **GS** *100
YANO, Victor. PO BOX 822 96940 #014-01-1978 L1979 **IM GP** *020

PITI – GUAM

SULLIVAN, Michael Stanley. ■ 96915 #023-12-1996 L1998 **PD** *100 †55

POHNPEI – FEDERATED STATES OF MICRO

ISAAC, Bryan Alik. PO BOX 1841 96941 #014-01-1986 L1986 **IM** *020
O'LEARY, Michael John. ■ 96941 #026-04-1977 **PHP IM** *062 †20
PAVLIN, Boris Igor. ■ 96941 #047-05-2003 L2005 **GPM** *012
SOUTHERLAND, John Gavin. PONAPE HOSP-CAROLINE ISLS 96941 #067-01-1958
  ORS GS *020 †40

SAIPAN – NORTHERN MARIANA ISLANDS

ADA, Norma Seman. ■ 96950 #021-01-1993 L1995 **MPD PD** *020 †55,20
ALDAN, Vicente Sablan. CHALAN KIYA, SAIPAN HEALTH CLINIC 96950 #014-01-1990 L1991
  FM *020 †18
ALOU, Ahmad Al. PO BOX 501908, PACIFIC MED CTR BLDG 96950 #308-11-1985 L1991
  IM GYN *020 †20
ARCILLA, Leopoldo C, Jr. ■ 96950 #748-01-1991 L1997 **IM** *020 †20 ‡
AUSTIN, Thomas M. PO BOX 10000, PMB 362 96950 #060-02-1986 *100
BORJA, Leticia Pangelinan. ■ 96950 #010-02-2000 L2000 **PD** *020 †55 ‡
BRAIG, Florian Gustav A. ■ 96950 #409-16-1976 **OTO** *020 †45
DE CHABRIS, Lionel Rush M. AAA 3669 BOX 10 001 96950 #067-01-1988 L1999 **EM** *020
DE GUZMAN, Gabriel Banu. PO BOX 501908, PMC BLDG, MIDDLE RD 96950
  #748-10-1990 L1996 **ID** *020 †20
FAUSTINO, Alfonso. PO BOX 409, CK 96950 #054-04-1971 L1973 **IM GP** *071
HART, Michael. ■ 96950 #847-10-1997 L2004 **AN** *020
HERNANDEZ, Mary Elizabeth. COMMONWEALTH HEALTH CTR, MIDDLE ROAD 96950
  #748-02-1993 L1998 **PDP PD** *020 †55
HOCOG, Loreto Borja. CHALAN KIYA, SAIPAN HEALTH CLINIC 96950 #014-01-1984 L1985
  FM *020 †18
HOFSCHNEIDER, James U. ■ 96950 #014-01-1983 L1985 **IM EM** *020 †20
JOHNSON, Mark Brian. 409 CK MIDDLE ROAD, COMMONWEALTH HEALTH CENTER 96950
  #030-05-1979 L1982 **FM** *020 †18
KHORRAM, K David. PO BOX 503900 96950 #020-12-1988 L1988 **OPH** *020 †35
LAMAR, Daniel Caine. ■ 96950 #040-02-1990 L1991 **FM** *020 †18
LAMKIN, Celia B. ■ 96950 #748-20-1984 *071
POST, Laura L. PO BOX 7920, SAN VICENTE RURAL BRANCH 96950 #035-06-1987 L1988
  P ADM *020 †75
RAMSEY, Gary Griffin. ■ 96950 #005-14-1990 L1991 **OBG** *020 †30
SECKLER, Michael David. ■ 96950 #023-01-2003 L2006 **PD** *100
SHEVY, Laura Elyse. ■ 96950 #035-48-2004 L2004 **IM** *020 †20
STEARNS, Anthony Richard. PO BOX 218 96950 #005-06-1981 L1982 **EM FM** *020 †18
VAN EFFEN, Kathleen Mary. ■ 96950 #056-05-1981 L1984 **FM** *020
WEINSTEIN, Stephen R. PO BOX CK 96950 #297-01-1978 L1984 **PTH** *020 †50

SANTA RITA – GUAM

MOORE, Kevin Dale. ■ 96915 #020-12-1987 L1991 **P PFP** *062 †75
RICEHOUSE, Karen Jean. PO BOX 153174 96915 #028-46-1998 L1998 **FM** *020 †18

TAMUNING – GUAM

ACOSTA, Eleuterio C. ■ 96931 #748-01-1957 L1972 **GP FM** *020
ADOLPHSON, Arania O. 177 CHALAN PASAHERU STE C, PMC ISLA HEALTH SYSTEM 96913
  #043-01-2003 L2003 **FM** *100 †18
AIREL, Peter Stephen. ■ 96913 #041-14-2000 L2002 **IM** *012
AKIMOTO, Vincent Taijeron. 1244 N MARINE CORPS DR, AMERICAN MEDICAL CENTER 96913
  #025-12-1994 L1994 **FM** *020 †18
ALANO, Maria Andrea R. 548 S MARINE CORPS DR, TAKE CARE INSURANCE CLINIC 96913
  #748-02-1986 **PD NPM** *020 †55
AQUINO, Ernesto P. 231 GUERRERO DR, PACIFICARE ASIA PACIFIC 96913 #748-01-1957 L1967
  U *020 †95
ARAFILES, Ruben Pasion. PO BOX 9220, GUAM MEDICAL PLAZA #212 96931
  #748-02-1971 L1978 **ORS EM** *074
ARGUELLES, Luis Golez. 590 S MARINE DR, SUITE 126 GITC BLDG 96913 #748-01-1957 L1966
  GP *020
AUSTIN, Taylor Gentry. ■ 96913 #036-05-2004 L2005 *020
BATES, Brian Elbert. 388 YPAO RD 96913 #005-12-1986 L1997 **GS** *020 †85
BERG, Nathaniel Benj. 633 GOV CARLOS G CAMACH RD, STE 210 96913 #024-07-1990 L1995
  DR *020 †80
BEZ, Ellen. 472 CHALAN SAN ANTONIO, MARIANAS PHYSICIANS GROUP 96913
  #010-03-1990 L1993 **IM** *020 †20
BIELING, Friedrich C. ■ 96931 #409-21-1971 L1975 **OBG** *020 †30
BLANCAFLOR, Maria. 396 CHALAN SAN ANTONIO, BRI BUILDING STE 103 96913
  #748-01-1990 L1993 **PD D** *020 †55 ‡
BOLLINGER, Jan Anders. 850 GOV CARLOS G CAMACH RD, GUAM MED PLZ STE 212 96913
  #035-45-1970 L1978 **ORS** *020 †40

BOONPRAKONG, Putchara. ■ 96931 #891-02-1970 L1974 **GP** *020

BOONPRAKONG, Vallop. 850 GOV CARLOS G CAMACH RD 96913 #891-02-1967 L1974 **GYN GP** *020 †30

BORDALLO, Annie Underwood. 472 CHALAN SAN ANTONIO 96913 #010-03-1989 L1993 **OBG** *020 †30

BORROMEO, Jose Roberto M. ■ 96913 #748-02-1993 L1999 **VS** *100 †85 ‡

BROOKS, Peter Andrew. 415 CHALAN SAN ANTONIO, HEALTH SERVICES OF THE PAC 96913 #041-02-1993 L1995 **IMG** *020 †20

CARIAGA, Jose Capistrano. PO BOX 6578, FHP GUAM MED CTR 96931 #748-01-1952 L1965 **IM** *020

CARLOS, Ramel Asuncion. 472 CHALAN SAN ANTONIO, STE 101 96913 #748-08-1992 L2000 **CN** *020 †55,75 ‡

CARR, Elizabeth M. 280 PALE SAN VITORES RD, SUNFLOWER VILLA 96913 #035-09-1998 L2000 **PCC** *020 †20

CARRERA, Yolanda M. 1757 ARMY DR, STE 109 96913 #748-01-1977 L1983 **PD** *020 †55

CHANG, Young Kyo. 416 CHALAN SAN ANTONIO, GOOD SAMARITAN CLINIC 96913 #583-01-1988 L1995 **IM** *020

CHEN, Jiun Nan. 241 FARENHOLT AVE, STE 202 96913 #244-01-1968 L1974 **GS** *020

CHEN, Kwang Ming. ■ 96931 #385-02-1957 L1965 **N** *071

CHIU, John Jeng Jyi. 138 YPAO RD, GUAM POLYCLINIC 96913 #385-05-1968 L1973 **GP** *020

CHOI, Chang Sig. ■ 96931 #583-02-1960 L1977 **GS** *020

COLE, Farrell Anthony. 548 S MARINE CORPS DR 96913 #038-41-1973 L1994 **OBG U** *020 †30

COVILL, Raymond Wade. PO BOX 6578 96931 #050-02-1961 L1985 **OS FM** *030 †18

CRUZ, Edwardo Justo. PO BOX 9160 96931 #014-01-1979 L1984 **GS** *020

CUNNINGHAM, Glenn D, Jr. ■ 96913 #018-03-1976 L1978 **ORS HS** *020 †40

DAVID, Annette Mascunana. 590 S MARINE CORPS DR #226, HEALTH PARTNERS LLC 96913 #748-02-1986 L2005 **PHP IM** *062 †20,70 ‡

DE GUZMAN, Fernan F. 850 GOV CARLOS G CAMACH RD, GUAM MEMORIAL HOSPITAL 96913 #748-21-1990 L1994 **APM** *100

DOMALANTA, Dina D. 428 CHALAN SAN ANTONIO, # 101 96913 #748-13-1989 L1998 **PD ADL** *020 †55 ‡

ESPINOLA, Aurelio A. 325 DUENAS DR, OFF OF THE CHIEF MEDICAL E 96913 #748-07-1963 L1993 **PTH FOP** *062 †20

EUSEBIO, Ricardo Brownlee. 633 GOV CARLOS G CAMACH RD 96913 #010-01-1981 L1992 **GS VS** *020 †85

FEGURGUR, John Arrco. 280 PALE SAN VITORES RD, SUNFLOWER VILLA 96913 #035-09-1992 L1992 **PS** *020 †85

FELL, William Russell. 633 CAROLS CAMACHO RD G, 203 GUAM MEDICAL PLAZA 96913 #040-02-1991 L1994 **OTO** *020 †45

FLEMING, James Gregory. 231 GUERRERO DR 96913 #056-06-1966 L1967 **OBG** *020 †30

FLORES, Lisa Denise. 388 YPAO RD 96913 #005-12-1999 L2000 **FM** *020 †18

FREEMAN, William Shourds. 541 S MARINE DR, STE 211 SECOND FL 96913 #005-15-1970 L1991 **OBG** *072 †30 ‡

FRICKEL, Wendy Douglas. PO BOX 6578 96931 #010-02-1984 L1985 **FM** *020 †18

GALGO, Geoffrey Perpetua. 744 N MARINE DR, STE 105 96913 #748-16-1991 L1996 **FM** *100 †18

GARRIDO, John Marco. 241 FARENHOLT AVE STE 106 96913 #014-01-1985 L1992 **PD** *020

GESLANI, Bevan Ali Same. 388 YPAO RD 96913 #748-08-1981 L1992 **IM** *020 †20

GILL, Joan Huennekens. ■ 96931 #056-06-1988 L1993 **P** *020 †75

GRILEY, Edmund A. 138 YPAO RD 96913 #847-01-1974 L1981 **OBG** *020

GUZMAN, Pablo S. 543 CHALAN GUMA YUOS ST 96913 #748-02-1961 L1977 **IM ON** *020 †20

HAWKINS, Elizabeth Beverl. 177 CHALAN PASAHERU STE C, PMC ISLA HEALTH SYSTEMS 96913 #012-01-1975 L1991 **OBG** *020 †30

HEBERLE, Marjorie Fricke. 415 CHALAN SAN ANTONIO, STE 214 96913 #005-06-1992 L1993 **OPH** *020 †35

HIDALGO, Edgardo C. 428 CHALAN SAN ANTONIO, # 101 96913 #748-01-1981 L1997 **PD** *020 †55

HONG, Rai Bok. 850 GOV CARLOS G CAMACH RD 96913 #583-04-1965 L1976 **OTO PS** *020 †45

HOOKS, Wm Kendall, Jr. ■ 96931 #016-11-1953 L1990 **DR OS** *020 †80

INNIS-SHELTON, Racquel D. 548 S MARINE DR, PACIFICARE ASIA PACIFIC 96913 #012-01-1998 L2001 **HO** *012 †20

ISMAEL, Ariel Arceo. 199 CHALAN SAN ANTONIO, MARIANAS CLINIC 96913 #748-10-1992 L1999 **P** *020 †75

JACK, Robert Stephen. 415 SAN ANTONIO RD, STE 214 96913 #035-20-1995 L1997 **OPH** *030

JACKSON, Minal Damani. ■ 96913 #023-12-1999 L2000 **D** *020 †15

JONES, Lindsay E. ■ 96913 #025-01-2003 L2003 *100 †20

KIM, Chong Suhl. ■ 96931 #583-02-1947 L1976 **GP IM** *020

LANDSTROM, Jerone T. 633 GOV CARLOS G CAMACH RD, STE 212 96913 #025-07-1981 L1990 **HS GS** *020 †85

LAST, James Peter. 850 GOV CARLOS G CAMACH RD, GUAM MEMORIAL HOSPITAL 96913 #005-06-1972 L1996 **EM IM** *020 †20,16

LEON GUERRERO, Robert Jos. 548 S MARINE CORPS DR, FHP HEALTH CENTER 96913 #014-01-1981 L1982 **PD** *020 †55

LIM, Doris Po. 590 S MARINE DR, ITC BLDG. STE 126 96913 #748-11-1989 L2001 **IM** *020 †20

LIM, Johnny Cua, Jr. 177 CHALAN PASAHERU 96913 #748-10-1993 L1997 **IMG** *020 †20

LIM, Reynald Te. 850 GOV CARLOS G CAMACH RD, GUAM MEMORIAL HOSPITAL 96913 #748-11-1991 L1996 **AN** *020 †05

LINSANGAN, Maria Gladys M. 816 N MARINE DR, STE 108 96913 #748-01-1989 L1995 **PD** *020 †55

LIZAMA, Florencio Tudela. 177 CHALAN PASAHERU STE C, PMC ISLA HEALTH CLINIC SYS 96913 #054-04-1986 L1989 **IM** *020 †20

LIZAMA, Vincent Victor. ■ 96931 #014-01-1982 L1986 **DR** *020

LOERZEL, Arthur Jos. 850 GOV CARLOS G CAMACH RD 96913 #026-04-1961 L1969 **PTH GP** *030 †50

LOM, Jitka. 280 PALE SAN VITORES RD, SUNFLOWER VILLA 96913 #065-01-1992 L1997 **AN** *020 †18

LOMBARD, Gabriel Peter N. 851 GOV CARLOS G CAMACH RD, THE DOCTORS CLINIC 96913 #005-15-1967 L1974 **GP EM** *020

LUJAN, Davina Marie. 177A CHALAN PASAHERU, PMC ISLA HEALTH SYS 96913 #005-14-1990 L1994 **FM** *020 †18

MACARAEG, Godofredo Gomez. PO BOX 6067 96931 #748-01-1945 L1970 **GS OBG** *071 †85

MAGCALAS, Edgar M. 548 S MARINE DR 96913 #748-08-1991 L1998 **ID** *020 †20 ‡

MANALOTO, Ma Cristina Q. 1244 N MARINE CORPS DR 96913 #748-01-1992 L1997 **PD** *020 †55

MATHEW, Annakutty. 850 GOV CARLOS G CAMACH RD 96913 #495-63-1978 L1989 **IM ID** *020 †20

MC DARBY, James Vincent. 415 CHALAN SAN ANTONIO, STE 214 96913 #539-05-1973 L1994 **OPH** *020 †35

MEADOWS, Lee H. 388 YPAO RD 96913 #005-12-1982 L1992 **FM** *020 †18

MONSOD, Teresa Patricia C. 280 PALE SAN VITORES RD #2 96913 #748-02-1993 L1998 **PDE** *020 †55 ‡

MUDD, David Michael. 388 YPAO RD, SEVENTH DAY ADVENTIST CLIN 96913 #020-02-1976 L1985 **DR** *020 †80

MURPHY, James Warren. 850 GOV CARLOS G CAMACH RD, GUAM MEMORIAL HOSPITAL- ER 96913 #011-02-1971 L1976 **EM FM** *020 †20,16,18

NGUYEN, Hoa Van. 1244 N MARINE CORPS DR, AMERICAN MED CTR 96913 #001-06-1992 L1996 **FM** *020 †18

NOZAKI, James Kenji. 388 YPAO RD 96913 #005-12-1995 L2006 **FM** *100 †18

OCONER, Thaddeo C. 633 GOV CARLOS G CAMACH RD, STE 205 96913 #748-24-1988 L1997 **NEP** *100 †20

OUHADI, Faraz. 633 GOV CARLOS G CAMACH RD, STE 205 96913 #154-07-1996 L2000 **IM** *071 †20

PARK, Hee-Yong. PO BOX 7147 96931 #583-01-1948 L1972 **FOP PTH** *071 †50

PARK, Soong Kook. ■ 96931 #583-04-1963 L1977 **IM GE** *020

PEREZ, Walter Chris. 851 GOV CARLOS G CAMACH RD 96913 #005-02-1978 L1981 **FM** *020 †18

PHILIPS, Sherif Antoun. 1406 N MARINE CORPS DR 96913 #915-04-1981 L1993 **NEP** *020 †20

PITMAN, Shannon Lawrance. 388 YPAO RD 96913 #005-12-1998 L1999 **FM** *020 †18 ‡

PLATT, Rory P. PO BOX 6155 96931 #748-01-1957 L1972 **AS TRS** *071

PRESTON, Donald Curry. 612 N MARINE DR, STE 8 96913 #040-02-1982 L1988 **IM** *020 †20

RAHMANI, Kia M. 280 PALE SAN VITORES RD 96913 #065-05-1991 L1997 **GS** *072 †85 ‡

REDDING, Estelita. 790 GOV CARLOS G CAMACH RD, DEPT OF MENTAL HEALTH AND 96913 #748-08-1966 L1989 **P** *020

RICHARD, Elisabeth G. 280 PALE SAN VITORES RD, HAFA ADAI SPECIALIST GRP 96913 #024-16-2001 L2001 **D** *020 †15

RICHARDSON, Darius A. 318 DUENAS DR 96913 #048-13-1996 L1997 **GS** *100

RICHTER, Jaroslav Kenneth. 241 FARENHOLT AVE, OKA BLDG 202 96913 #016-43-1963 L1991 **U AM** *020 †95

ROBINSON, Michael Jon. 388 YPAO RD 96913 #005-12-1995 L1996 **FM** *020 †18

ROZYCKI, Thomas Jos. 548 S MARINE CORPS DR, FHP HEALTH CENTER 96913 #026-04-1970 L1979 **FM** *020 †18

RUBIO, Joel. PO BOX 6578, 231 GUERRERO DR 96931 #748-10-1985 L1991 **END IM** *020 †20

RYAN, Robert Patton. 850 GOV CARLOS G CAMACH RD 96913 #019-02-1974 L1975 **EM AM** *020 †70,16

SAFABAKHSH, Saied. 633 GOV CARLOS G CAMACH RD, STE 205 96913 #654-01-1988 L1994 **NEP IM** *020 †20

SAGISI, Glocrito Guerrero. PO BOX 6276, HOSPITAL ROAD TAMUNING GU 96931 #748-02-1964 L1970 **OBG** *020

SAGISI, Vivien R Betoyon. 416 CHALAN SAN ANTONIO, POB 6276 96913 #748-02-1965 L1970 **OBG** *020

SAMONTE, Romeo M. 1757 ROUTE 16, GUAM BUSINESS CENTER, STE 96913 #748-01-1967 L1995 **IM** *020 †20

SANTOS, Edna V. 125 CARLOS LN, CARLOS HEIGHTS 96913 #748-01-1988 L1997 **PD** *020 †55 ‡

SANTOS, Marciano Santos. ■ 96931 #748-01-1958 L1966 **PD GP** *071 †55

SANTOS, Patrick Charles. 125 CARLOS LN, TUMON MEDICAL OFFICE 96913 #748-01-1989 L1996 **FM** *020 †80

SANTOS, Raymund Castro. 850 GOV CARLOS G CAMACH RD, MEDICAL STAFF OFFICE GUAM 96913 #748-10-1994 **AN** *100

SARMIENTO, Dennis Antonio. 548 S MARINE CORPS DR, TAKECARE INSURANCE COMPANY 96913 #748-08-1991 L2001 **PD** *020 †55 ‡

SCHROEDER, Edmund F, Jr. 633 GOV CARLOS G CAMACH RD, STE 2 96913 #038-06-1973 L1984 **FM IMG** *020 †18

SCHUSTER, Grae Lee. 633 GOV CARLOS G CAMACH RD, CANCER CENTER OF GUAM 96913 #032-01-1986 L1987 **RO** *020 †80

SHIEH, Thomas. 643 CHALAN SAN ANTONIO, STE 108 96913 #056-06-1992 L1996 **OBG** *020 †30

SILAN, Rodolfo Dacasin. ■ 96931 #748-01-1959 L1968 **GP** *020

SILK, Robert. ■ 96913 #023-12-2000 L2001 **DR** *100 †80

SIMEON, Arnette Galimba. 850 GOV CARLOS G CAMACH RD, GUAM MEMORIAL HOSPITAL AUT 96913 #748-10-1994 **AN** *100 †05

SLOOP, Christine Huse. 388 YPAO RD, GUAM SDA CLINIC 96913 #005-12-1987 L1988 **OBG** *020 †30

SLOOP, Jay Randal. 388 YPAO RD 96913 #005-12-1986 L1987 **OBG** *020 †30

SPAK, Eric Wm. 633 GOV CARLOS G CAMACH RD, GUAM RADIOLOGY CONSULTANTS 96913 #010-02-1984 L1987 **DR VIR** *020 †80

SRIKUREJA, Wichit. 388 YPAO RD 96913 #005-12-1997 L1997 **GE** *020 †20

STADLER, James Jos. 548 S MARINE CORPS DR, FHP HEALTH CENTER 96913 #025-01-1974 L1977 **PD** *020 †55

SUGUITAN, Demetrio B, Jr. ■ 96913 #748-10-1992 L1996 **FM** *020 †18

SUPIT, Edwin Jess. 388 YPAO RD 96913 #005-12-1996 L2000 **IM** *020

TINSAY, Ramon Arevalo. 205 VIVIAN WAY 96913 #748-01-1954 L1966 **GS GP** *020

TOBIAS, Maria Melissa S. 744 N MARINE DR, STE 105 96913 #748-01-1995 L2002 **FM** *020 †18

YAMASHITA, Hideyuki. 388 YPAO RD 96913 #005-12-1987 L1991 **PD** *020 †55

ZVONIK, Kaaren Ann. 472 CHALAN SAN ANTONIO, MARIANAS PHYSICIANS GROUP 96913 #035-08-1972 L1993 **OBG** *020

YIGO – GUAM

CAYCE, Walter Robertson. ■ 96929 #038-43-1981 L1982 **AM FM** *020 †70,18

VOLQUARTSEN, Dale A. ■ 96929 #023-12-1992 L1995 **PD** *020 †55

■ = Address Information Privacy Protected

APO – AA

BAUDER, Mary E Schorpp. AMER EMBASSY BX ECO BECKER 34002 #041-07-1931 L1932 **P** *071
BOWEN, Ronaldo Enrique. GORGAS ARMY HOSP 34004 #649-14-1974 L1981 **OBG** *020
CATTAN, Jaime. USA MEDD PANAMA GORGA HOSP 34004 #715-01-1972 **IM** *020
CHIARI CENTELLA, Juan J. GORGAS ARMY COMM HOSP 34008 #715-01-1957 **RHU IM** *020
CONRAD, Larry Lee. ■ 34002 #017-20-1964 L1964 **EM** *020
DIEZ, Felipe. ■ 34002 #016-02-1977 L1986 **D** *071 †15
GONZALEZ, Hipolito Rene. GORGAS ARMY COMM HOSP DERM 34004 #847-08-1963 **D** *020
HENRY, Ismay Estriana. PSC 2 BOX 1451 34002 #005-12-1958 L1962 **P N** *020
KOURANY, Gabriel. GORGAS ARMY HSP USA MEDDAC 34004 #017-20-1953 L1953 **IM HEM** *020
LENNAN, Hedley Clarence. MADD PANAMA GORGA ARM HSP 34004 #715-01-1953 **IM IMG** *020
LOKEE, Alexis Manuel. HSXU PC ER UNIT 7139, USA MEDDAC PANAMA GACH 34004 #715-01-1966 L1991 **OS** *075
MANS AGUIRRE, Ricardo. GORGAS ARMY HOSP PATH 34004 #264-05-1964 **PTH** *020 †50
MAVES, Ryan Cory. UNIT 3800, NAVAL MEDICAL RESEARCH 34031 #054-04-1999 L2001 **ID IM** *020 †20
MAZZI, Eduardo. US EMBASSY LA PAZ POST MED 34032 #176-01-1969 L1974 **PD NPM** *020 †55
MC CORMICK, Georges F. UNIT 3120, US EMBASSY SAN SALVADOR 34023 #005-02-1976 L1977 **IM N** *020 †20,75
PINZON, Maximino Adolfo. USA MEDDAC PANAMA OBGYN 34004 #649-14-1970 L1981 **OBG** *020
ROBLES, Wanda Ivelisse. ■ 34004 #042-01-1981 *020
ROGNONI, Paulina Amelia. GORGAS ARMY HSP PANAMA 34004 #021-01-1973 L1976 **CD IM** *020
STANDAERT, Richard Ernest. ■ 34001 #023-12-1992 L1996 **GS** *020 †85
VEGA-RICH, Mario Gilberto. PSC BOX 2292 34002 #715-01-1978 **OBG** *020

APO – AE

ADAMS, Jaye Elaine. ■ 09464 #024-07-1996 L1999 **OBG** *020 †30
ALARCON, Alfonso Santos. ■ 09112 #023-12-1990 L1992 **ORS** *020 †40
ALBRIGHT, George Havard. CMR 402 BOX 477 09180 #021-05-1968 L1968 **D** *020 †15
ALCAZAR, Esteban A. USAF HOSP INCIRLIK ABS 09824 #847-04-1954 **PTH** *100
ALICEA, Edgardo. ■ 09139 #042-01-2002 L2004 **FM** *020 †18
ALLGOOD, Norma Lynne. ■ 09180 #045-04-1987 L1990 **PDC** *020 †55
AMJADI, Darius Kave'H, II. ■ 09042 #036-01-1996 L1998 **NP** *020 †50
ANDERSON, Carl Andre. 196 TU HOSPITAL 09705 #035-09-1959 L1964 **OBG** *020 †30
ANDERSON, Joseph Benson. ■ 09464 #023-12-1990 L1992 **FM** *020 †70,18
ANGLADE, Andres. UNIT 25717 BOX 44 09242 #042-01-1971 L1973 **DR PD** *020 †80
AQUILINA, Joseph Charles. ■ 09421 #016-43-1993 L1994 **FM** *020 †18
ARBITER, David. BOX R 09102 #869-05-1955 **ID PTH** *030 †50
ARGYLE, Joseph Craig. ■ 09464 #049-01-1980 L1981 **PTH** *030 †50
ASEMOTA, Edwin Scott. CMR 431 BOX 2289 09175 #690-01-1980 **IM** *062
AUNGST, Matthew James. ■ 09464 #041-15-2000 L2001 *020 †30
AYALA, Carlos. ■ 09180 #005-14-1999 L2001 **OTO FPS** *020 †45
BACMEISTER, Erwin. UNIT 26610, 67 CSH 09244 #407-10-1960 L1969 **P** *020
BAIK, Kris Kongsun. ■ 09464 #040-02-2000 L2001 **PD** *020 †55
BAKER, Brian Leslie. CMR 402 BOX 1992, L R M C 09180 #917-29-1969 L1971 **FM** *020 †18
BAKER, Richard D, III. ■ 09824 #050-02-1992 L1993 **GPM** *020 †18,70
BANKS, Jeffrey Allan. ■ 09630 #023-12-2000 L2002 **PD** *020 †55
BARBER, David Houghton. CMR 402 BOX 381, 2ND GENERAL HOSPITAL 09180 #016-02-1961 L1965 **CHN PD** *020 †55
BARTELL, Silas A. 34TH GEN HOSP DEPT ANES 09178 #649-14-1974 **AN** *020
BAUGHMAN, Steven Matthew. ■ 09464 #028-03-1998 **U** *020 †95
BEECH, Douglas Bruce. UNIT 31403, BOX 13 09630 #026-04-1993 L1996 **FM** *020 †18
BEHLEN, Shelly Frances. PSC 41, BOX 4042 09464 #048-14-2003 L2005 **EM** *020
BEIGHLEY, Paul S. UNIT 64900, BOX 19 09839 #048-13-1987 L1991 **P** *062 †75
BELLAFIORE, Vincent A. PO BOX 2, UNIT NR 20916 09169 #407-05-1966 L1971 **ORS PS** *020
BENENSON, Michael Wm. UNIT 29223 09102 #023-01-1968 L1972 **GPM ID** *030 †70
BENTLEY, Vincent Carl. ■ 09714 #012-01-1983 L1984 **FM** *030 †18
BERGMANN, Elizabeth E. ■ 09494 #051-01-1994 L1996 **FM** *020
BERGMANN, Michele. CMR 442 BOX 786 09042 #007-02-1994 L1996 **OBG** *020 †30
BHAVSAR, Amit Kiritkumar. ■ 09128 #023-12-2000 L2002 **FM** *020 †18
BLACK, Alexander Brooks. ■ 09464 #056-06-1996 L1998 **PD** *020 †55
BLOHM, Raymond Wm, Jr. HQ USA MED COMM MED CONSUL 09014 #035-06-1947 **IM** *030 †20
BODEN, Stephen Richard. ■ 09137 #030-06-1997 L1999 **PD** *020 †55
BOREMAN, Craig Dean. ■ 09464 #038-41-1998 L1999 **PD** *020 †55
BOSTROM, Paul Fredrick. ■ 09180 #041-01-1992 L1994 **D** *020 †15 ‡
BOUCHER, Rebecca Ann. ■ 09042 #023-12-2002 L2004 **P** *020 †75
BRADLEY, Kent Loring. ■ 09180 #023-12-1988 L1990 **PHP** *062 †70
BRASLOW, Kenneth Joshua. ■ 09123 #005-06-2001 L2003 **CHP** *020 †75
BRASWELL, William Norman. CMR 402 BOX 2095 09180 #422-01-1995 L1998 **FM** *020 †18
BRAUNLICH, Earl Fritz. ■ 09180 #055-02-1994 L1996 **ORS** *100 †40
BRENNEN, David M. ■ 09180 #035-06-2002 L2004 **PD** *020
BRICKER, Dean A. ■ 09180 #041-14-1987 L1989 **IM** *040 †20
BROPHY, Gwendolyn Marie. ■ 09180 #041-12-2001 L2002 **N** *020 †75
BROWN, Brandon Dalton. ■ 09042 #023-12-2002 L2004 **GS** *020 †85
BROWN, Darin Shayne. UNIT 3215, 435 MDG/SGOPF 09094 #001-06-1998 L1999 **FM** *020 †18
BROWN, Markham Jay. ■ 09123 #021-01-1991 L1992 **FM** *020 †18
BRUNI, Christine Yvonne. ■ 09042 #051-04-1988 L1989 **GP** *020
BRUZZINI, Daniel Blaise. ■ 09180 #023-12-1994 L1995 **PD** *020 †55
BUCK, Alfred A. USAID OFFICE OF HEALTH 09839 #407-21-1945 **PHP ID** *040
BUCK, Donald Edward. CMR 442 BOX 558, HMEDDAC 09042 #308-12-1986 L1991 **EM IM** *020 †20
BUDIK, Edith M. ■ 09139 #035-15-1974 L1976 **PDR** *100 †55,80
BUI, Jeffrey Silvio. ■ 09603 #023-12-1999 L2000 **ORS** *020 †40
CAFFREY, Timothy Joseph. ■ 09630 #032-01-1995 L1997 **FM** *020 †18
CAIN, Albert Delane. CMR 430 BOX 994 09096 #036-01-1978 L1989 **PD** *020
CALHOUN, Aris Jeannette. CMR 459 BOX 01706, UNIT USAHC 09139 #004-01-1996 L1997 **FM** *020 †18
CAMPBELL, Rebecca C. ■ 09601 #007-02-1991 **PD** *100
CAMPBELL, Ronald. CMR 402 BOX 608, LRMC 09180 #048-13-1980 L1981 **P** *020 †75
CANTILINA, Thomas James. ■ 09824 #023-12-1997 L1999 **FM** *020 †18
CARANDANG, Francisray R. PSC 2 BOX 9573 09012 #023-12-1999 L2000 **PD** *020 †55
CARBOGNIN, Susan Jennifer. ■ 09012 #023-12-2005 L2006 **IM** *100
CARPENTER, A Noelle. ■ 09137 #038-40-2001 L2003 **PD** *020 †55 ‡
CASHMAN, Thos Michael, Jr. 10TH MED LAB 09180 #033-05-1962 L1967 **OS PA** *020 †55,70
CASSIMATIS, Dimitri C. ■ 09180 #024-01-1999 L2001 **CD** *020 †20
CHAPA, Artemio Cerda. ■ 09009 #005-19-1995 L1998 **FM** *020 †18
CHIOU, Shing Kwei. ■ 09617 #035-09-1995 L1996 **IM** *020 †20
CHOI, Mary Joungwom. ■ 09180 #010-01-1999 L1999 **EM** *100
CHOW, Jennifer C. PSC 2 BOX 9686 09012 #051-04-2000 L2002 **CHP** *020 †75
CHRISTIAN, Dixon Lorenzo. UNIT 5210 BOX 230, 48 AMDS/SGPF-1 09464 #010-03-1995 L1998 **FM AM** *020 †18
CHUA, George So Vin Hu. OPC/ER 34TH GEN HOSP 09178 #748-10-1974 *020
CLEVELAND, Chris Lee. ■ 09603 #037-01-2000 L2001 **PD** *020 †55 ‡
CLINT, Brandon. ■ 09459 #048-12-1989 L1992 **IM** *020 †20
COLEMAN, Amy Elizabeth. ■ 09012 #036-08-2002 L2003 **FM** *100
COLEMAN, Jason Channing. ■ 09182 #001-02-2002 L2004 **PD** *100 †55
COLGAN, Martha Ellen. ■ 09180 #010-02-1996 L1997 **PD** *020 †55
COLLINS, John William. ■ 09244 #025-12-1997 L1999 **P** *020
COMBS, John Joseph. ■ 09042 #023-12-1998 L1999 **DR** *020 †80
CONGDON, David Raymond. PSC 827 BOX 1000 09617 #023-12-1998 L2000 **FM** *020 †18
CORNFELD, Robert James. ■ 09042 #023-12-2004 L2006 **PD** *020 †55
CORR, William Philip, III. ■ 09180 #023-12-1991 L1992 **GPM** *030 †70
COVINGTON, Mark Owen. ■ 09180 #049-01-1995 L1996 **OTO** *020 †45
CRANNEY, Dean Ross. ■ 09824 #305-01-2001 L2002 **FM** *020 †18
CRAWLEY, Geoffrey Wallace. ■ 09601 #020-02-1989 L1990 **R** *020 †80
CRITTENDON, William Floyd. CMR 402 BOX 222, 2ND GENERAL HOSPITAL 09180 #039-01-1954 L1954 **GYN** *071 †30
CROSLAND, Telita. ■ 09114 #023-12-1993 L1994 **FM** *020 †18
CROWE, John Martin, Jr. ■ 09142 #016-43-2001 L2001 **FM** *020 †18
CUENCA, Phillip Benjamin. ■ 09042 #023-12-2001 L2002 *020 †05
CUMMINGS, Justin Lee. ■ 09180 #021-01-2002 L2004 **IM** *020 †20 ‡
CUMMISS, Scott Michael. ■ 09459 #023-12-1998 L2000 **GPM** *012 †70
CUNNINGHAM, Geo Robinson. ■ 09045 #027-01-1978 L1980 **FM** *020 †18
CUNNINGHAM, Paul James. ■ 09180 #010-02-1997 L1998 **DR** *020 †80
CZECH, Jeanine Marie. ■ 09824 #026-08-1982 L1984 **OM** *020 †18,70
DARKEN, Jill Elizabeth. ■ 09817 #016-11-1990 L1992 **FM** *020 †18
DAUBY, Pierrealai Lucien. ■ 09464 #023-12-1996 L1998 **IM** *020 †20,03
DAVIS, Cornelia Estelle. ■ 09831 #005-02-1972 L1973 **PHP PD** *030
DAVIS, Edwin Patton, Jr. ■ 09464 #045-04-2000 L2002 **FM** *020 †18
DAVIS, Karla Lowe. ■ 09180 #051-07-2001 L2002 **AI** *020 †55,03
DAVISON, Jonathan Merlin. ■ 09180 #035-20-2000 L2002 **NM** *100 †20,28
DEGOES, J Jeffrey. PSC 103 BOX 4262 09603 #023-12-1989 L1992 **IM** *020 †20
DELO, Robert I. ■ 09601 #048-13-1999 **GS FPS** *020
DENNISON, David Houston. ■ 09180 #023-12-2000 L2001 **CHN** *100 †75
DENNISON, Sheri Katrina. ■ 09180 #023-12-2000 L2001 **HO** *020
DICKIE, Mark H. ■ 09137 #048-16-1996 L1998 **FM** *020 †18
DIRNBERGER, Daniel Robert. CMR 402 BOX 526, LRMC/NICU 09180 #023-12-1994 L1997 **NPM** *020 †55
DOAN, Paul Son-Anh. ■ 09012 #023-12-1989 L1991 **GPM** *020 †18,70
DOMENICHINI, Aldo John. ■ 09180 #023-12-1989 L1993 **FM OBS** *020 †18
DOYNE, Holly Linn. UNIT 29223 BOX 552, 95TH C S H 09102 #026-04-1975 L1976 **OM FM** *030 †70,18
DRAKE, David Fulster. CMR 415 BOX 4532 09114 #031-01-1997 L1997 **PM PRS** *020 †60
DREW, Christopher David. ■ 09012 #024-01-2000 L2001 *020
DRIFMEYER, Erin Beth. ■ 09334 #051-01-2004 L2005 **FM** *020 †18
DUCHARME, Sarah Elizabeth. ■ 09464 #025-07-1997 L2000 **GS** *020 †85
DUFF, Arthur Denning. ■ 09630 #049-01-1971 L1980 **PD** *020
DUQUE, Elizabeth Hill. ■ 09173 #023-12-2003 L2005 **FM** *100 †18
EDIGER, Mark Alan. UNIT 3050 BOX 130 09094 #028-46-1978 L1979 **FM AM** *020 †70,18
EGAN, Thomas Joseph. BOX 25 UNIT 25717, 97TH GENERAL HOSP 09242 #539-02-1961 L1990 *020
ELLIS, Bradley Charles. ■ 09824 #030-05-2004 L2005 **FM** *100
ELROD, Darryl Glen, Jr. ■ 09464 #017-20-1997 L1998 **OBG** *020 †30
ENSLEY, Robert John. ■ 09042 #047-06-1994 L1996 **CHP** *020 †75
ERICKSON, Elizabeth Ann. ■ 09824 #026-04-2003 L2004 **FM** *020 †18
ESHBACH, Richard Earl. ■ 09841 #041-02-1958 L1962 **ADM** *071
ESQUILIN, Migdia Yolanda. CMR 430 BOX 262, HHS 1ST MI BN 09096 #308-03-1984 L1987 **GP** *075
ESSEN, Theresa M. CMR 467 BOX 1493 09096 #033-75-1994, ▲ L1997 **IM AM** *020
EVANS, Karen Christine. ■ 96205 #023-12-1995 L1996 **U** *020 †95
FANG, Raymond. CMR 402 BOX 506 09180 #028-34-1995 L1997 **CCS GS** *020 †85
FARKAS, Ladislaus. LANDSTUHL M C 2ND GEN HOSP 09180 #473-01-1976 L1983 **EM** *020 †18
FELDE, Anne. ■ 09112 #035-01-1993 L1996 **P PYM** *020 †75
FENNELL, John. ■ 09086 #539-06-1969 L1977 **IM P** *020 †55
FERNALD, John Patrick. ■ 09180 #036-08-2001 L2003 **PD** *020 †55
FERNANDEZ, Margaret Mc Gi. ■ 09642 #035-03-2001 L2003 **PD** *020 †55
FICHTNER, John Zbigniew. UNIT 9234, 196TH STATION HOSP 09102 #407-10-1951 L1957 **GS OBG** *020 †85
FINNILA, Teresa Lee. ■ 09464 #056-06-2003 L2005 **N** *020
FISCHER, Collin Jon. ■ 09630 #005-12-2003 L2005 **IM** *020 †20
FLAHERTY, Stephen Francis. ■ 09180 #024-07-1988 L1990 **CCS** *020 †85
FLOOD, Daniel Kevin. ■ 09464 #040-02-1991 L1993 **IM** *020 †20
FLYNN, Christopher F. UNIT 2020 BOX 10 09817 #012-01-1985 L1987 **P AM** *020 †75
FOGARTY, Brian Thomas. ■ 09096 #010-02-1999 L2001 **DR** *012
FOGLIA, Lisa Marie. CMR 402 BOX 2076, REGIONAL MEDICAL CENTER 09180 #008-02-1998 L2000 **OBG** *020 †30
FOLARIN, Victor Abayomi. CMR 480 BOX 494 09128 #047-06-1985 L1987 **GPM** *030 †18,70
FOX, Charles Wm, Jr. CMR 442 BOX 746 09042 #023-12-1981 L1986 **U GS** *020 †95
FRATTAROLI, Nicholas F. USA MADDAD SHAPE 09705 #561-01-1965 L1967 **OBG GP** *020 †30
FREILINO, Julie Alexandra. ■ 09464 #041-02-2002 L2004 **FM** *100 †18

■ = Address Information Privacy Protected

FUGITT, Jonathan Brett. ■ 09617 #041-02-1998 L2004 **DR** *100 †80
GALGON, Richard Edward. ■ 09045 #035-03-2003 L2004 **GP** *100
GALINDO, Roger Martinez. ■ 09617 #048-14-1999 L2001 **GS** *020
GAMMILL, Amy Elizabeth. ■ 09464 #023-12-2003 L2005 **IM** *100 †20
GANCARCZYK, Kevin Joseph. ■ 09180 #004-01-1995 L1997 **U** *020 †95
GARCIA, Eulogio Fernandez. BOX 3984 09641 #847-09-1971 L1977 **PDC** *020 †55
GARDINER, Bradley Clark. ■ 09140 #023-12-2001 L2003 **GPM** *012
GARR, John Harold. ■ 09042 #048-13-1998 L1999 **EM** *020 †16
GASPER, Kirk Peter. ■ 09617 #028-02-1993 L1994 **FM** *020 †18
GASPER, Michele Lynn. PSC 827 BOX 1000, US NAVAL HOPS 09617 #028-02-1993 L1994 **PD** *020 †55
GEBHART, Harold Eugene. UNIT 29223 BOX #, 130TH STATION HOSP 09102 #001-02-1968 L1969 **EM GP** *020
GEITNER, Erika Katherine. ■ 09012 #041-12-1998 L1998 **FM** *020 †18
GELBER, George Leopold. PO BOX 236 09154 #759-02-1937 L1970 **PD** *071
GEORGE, Dale Wayne. ■ 09180 #023-12-2001 L2002 *020
GHIM, Anthony Tongwon. ■ 09012 #010-02-1985 L1986 **FM** *020 †18
GIEM, James Lawrence. ■ 09603 #005-12-1982 L1983 **OBG GP** *020 †30
GIESE, Elizabeth Ann. ■ 09076 #005-12-2002 L2002 **FM** *020 †18
GIESE, Russell James, Jr. ■ 09076 #005-12-2002 L2002 **FM** *020 †18
GIL, Francisco Miguel. UNIT 27401 09105 #847-03-1974 **U** *020
GLEASON, Bruce Alan. ■ 09264 #019-02-1999 L2000 **EM** *012
GLOVER, Jamie. UNIT 5210 BOX 230, 48TH MDOS/SGOPF 09464 #023-12-1999 L2001 **FM** *020 †18
GOINGS, Kathleen Marie. ■ 09042 #016-01-2001 L2003 **GS** *020 †85
GOLLE, Rogelio F. PSC 50 BOX 447 09494 #748-09-1964 L1975 **R** *020
GONZALEZ, Felipe De Jesus. ■ 09107 #005-14-1978 L1979 **GS** *020
GONZALEZ, Veronica Mayela. ■ 09601 #048-02-1999 L2000 **OBG** *020 †30
GOODMAN, Brian Travis. ■ 09464 #004-01-2003 L2005 **AN** *020
GORDON, David Kent, II. ■ 09824 #023-12-2003 L2004 **FM** *100 †18
GORSKE, Julie Ann. ■ 09180 #036-07-1996 L1998 **PTH** *020
GRAHAM, Erinne Ayanna. ■ 09617 #011-04-2000 L2002 **OBG** *100
GRAHAM, James Wagter. ■ 09180 #023-12-2000 L2007 **DR** *020 †80
GRAL, Thomas. 24TH MED DETACHMENT 09033 #286-03-1951 L1969 **IM NEP** *020
GRIFFITH, James Carter. ■ 09244 #041-13-1976 L1988 **DR** *020
GUHLKE, Alan Douglas. CMR 402 BOX 1092, LRMC 09180 #023-12-2002 L2003 **AN** *020 †05
HALLGREN, John David. ■ 09468 #023-12-1995 L1998 **FM** *020 †18
HANS, Alexandra Gudrun. ■ 09112 #028-03-2000 **FM** *020 †18
HANSEN, Dan Roland. ■ 09012 #040-02-1984 L1985 **IM** *020 †20
HARDER-SIM, Thelma. 97TH GEN HOSP BOX 22 09242 #748-08-1963 L1978 **PTH** *020
HARPER, Bradley Neal. ■ 09630 #023-12-1983 L1985 **PTH IM** *030 †50
HARRELL, Thomas Wesley. ■ 09012 #011-04-1992 L1997 **CD** *020 †20
HARRISON, Cary Elizabeth. ■ 09617 #036-07-1994 L1995 **OPH** *020 †35
HARVEY, Robert Clinton. ■ 09180 #036-07-1975 L1976 **IM IMG** *020 †20
HATCH, Douglas Lloyd. UNIT 64902, HRDC/H USAID-CAIRO 09839 #035-03-1977 L1981 **EP ID** *050 †55
HAYES, Christopher George. ■ 09824 #038-40-1999 L2001 **FM** *020 †18
HAYES, Jason Thorin. ■ 09012 #054-04-1997 L1998 **FM** *020 †18
HEGSTROM, George Robt, Jr. ■ 09803 #040-02-1963 L1990 **OS EM** *020
HEINRICHS, Christopher N. PSC 1 BOX 1981 09009 #048-15-1979 L1979 **AM GP** *071 †70
HENNION, Duane Richard. ■ 09244 #023-12-1998 L2007 **FM** *020 †18
HEPBURN, Matthew Jerrad. PSC 821 BOX 84 09421 #036-07-1996 L1997 **ID** *020 †20
HESS, Todd David. ■ 09180 #056-06-1985 L1986 **OPH** *020 †35
HESTER, Marc Anthony. ■ 09012 #023-12-1992 L1994 **OBG** *020 †30
HICKS, Robert Scott. ■ 09042 #011-02-2002 L2005 **DR** *020 †80
HILDEBRAND, Jessica Dawn. ■ 09464 #039-01-2004 L2006 **EM** *020
HILL, Jeffrey Von. CMR 402 BOX 1356 09180 #023-12-1997 L1998 **CHP** *020 †75
HILL, Patrick Edwin. ■ 09180 #011-04-1996 L1998 **DR** *020 †80
HING, Matthew Stanton. ■ 09630 #023-12-2001 L2002 **GP** *020
HIPP, Sean Joseph. ■ 09042 #041-13-2002 L2004 **PD** *020 †55
HODGES, Michael Glenn. ■ 09012 #036-08-1999 L2001 **FM** *020 †18
HOGGAN, Mark Edward. ■ 09468 #054-04-1997 L1997 **FM** *020 †18
HOLLAND, Robert H. ■ 09244 #023-12-1997 L1999 **OBG** *020
HOLLISTER, Paul. USAF HOSP UPPER HEYFRD RAF 09466 #035-45-1968 L1971 **HEM IM** *020 †20
HORVATH, Brian Chas. ■ 09180 #035-46-1985 L1987 **CD IM** *020 †20
HUGHES, Kathryn Ann. ■ 09470 #030-05-1999 L1999 **AM** *062
HUITINK, Jonathan Scott. ■ 09042 #004-01-2001 L2003 **PD** *020 †55
HUMBERD, Christina M. ■ 09012 #028-03-2000 L2003 **ID** *100 †20
HUNT, Harold Eugene, II. ■ 09244 #048-14-1996 L1998 **ORS** *020 †40
HYDE, George Terrence. 33RD FIELD HOSP MARYBURG 09244 #407-10-1962 L1968 **IM OS** *020
HYLAND, Stephen Paul. CMR 454 BOX 1535 09250 #005-12-1999 L2001 **FM** *020 †18
INGWERSEN, Kathleen Mason. ■ 09180 #041-07-1986 L1989 **FOP** *020 †50
IOSIF, Stefania G. 2ND GEN HOSP BOX 10 09180 #781-01-1954 **PTH** *020
JACKSON, Richard B. PO BOX 28, FRANKFURT MEDDAC 25717 09242 #010-01-1989 **OBG** *020 †30
JACOBSON, Eric John. ■ 09250 #051-07-2005 L2007 **IM** *020
JACOBY, Elinor Elisabeth. BOX 2378 09009 #869-07-1964 **GP** *020
JARRETT, Miriam E. USAF HOSP BOX 2591 09464 #847-01-1967 L1973 **GP** *020
JENNINGS, Barbara Louise. ■ 09244 #045-04-1988 L1990 **OBG** *020 †30
JOHANSEN, Karen Perusse. ■ 09180 #023-12-1988 L1991 **CHP** *020 †75
JONES, Delbert Emmanuel. ■ 09042 #026-04-1977 L1979 **HS ORS** *020 †40
JONES, Michael Duncan. ■ 09182 #035-46-2000 L2002 **EM** *020
JOSLOW, Barbara. 2ND GENERAL HOSP 1598 09180 #023-12-1987 L1989 **N** *020 †75
JULIAN, Wayne Edmond. PSC 77, MEDICAL UNIT 09721 #021-01-1977 L1979 **P** *020 †75
KANE, Edward Jos, Jr. ■ 09617 #023-12-1985 L1987 **PTH** *020 †50
KELSICK, Cavelle Maria. W2HX, JFC HQ W2XH13 09620 #024-01-1981 L1981 **IM** *020 †20
KENNEDY, Olga Vladimirovn. ■ 09063 #913-01-1992 L2005 **IM** *020 †20
KESSLER, Karl Martin. ■ 09112 #008-02-1987 L1989 **P** *020 †75
KILLIAN, Peter James. ■ 09617 #023-12-1998 L1999 **OTO** *100 †45
KIM, Daniel Eijune. ■ 09180 #023-12-2001 L2002 **GS** *020
KING, Ronald Peter. PSC 821 BOX 84 09421 #023-12-1990 L1992 **AM** *050 †18
KIRK, Genoveva Du-Uy. PSC 1203 BOX 1221 09803 #748-01-1966 **AN** *020
KNETSCHE, Robert Paul. CMR 402 BOX 652, LANDSTUHL REGIONAL MEDICAL 09180 #045-01-1994 L1995 **ORS** *020 †40
KOBES, Peter Jeffery. ■ 09180 #047-06-1996 L1997 **GE** *020 †20
KOKKONEN, Jana Suzanne. ■ 09180 #010-02-1999 L2001 **EM** *020 †16
KOWDLEY, Gopal Chandru. UNIT 26610, USAMEDDAC 09244 #051-01-1996 L1996 **GS** *020 †85
KRATT, Logan Frederick. ■ 09096 #028-03-2003 L2005 **FM** *020 †18
KRAUTHEIM, Mark M. ■ 09123 #010-02-1981 L1983 **GPM** *020 †25,70
KUTZ, David Leonard. ■ 09464 #023-12-1991 L1994 **CHP** *020 †75
KYLE, George Mc Clelland. ■ 09112 #038-45-1998 L2000 **FM** *020 †18
LABOVICH, Marc Hartmut. ■ 09180 #023-12-1993 L1995 **PTH** *020 †50
LAGUNA-RAMOS, Javier E. ■ 09045 #042-01-1995 L1997 **FM** *020 †18
LALENA, Christine Erdie. ■ 09180 #021-06-1995 L1996 **PD** *020 †55
LAM, David Martin. PSC 79 BOX 145 09714 #026-04-1972 L1978 **AM** *030 †70
LANDEW, Melvin. ■ 09012 #035-19-1957 L1960 **GS** *020 †85
LAVOPA, Louis Vincent. ■ 09617 #050-02-1991 L1993 **GP EM** *020 †16
LAWSON, Patrick Louis. ■ 09617 #025-07-1990 L1996 **PTH** *020 †50
LE, Hamilton S. ■ 09237 #048-14-2001 L2002 **GS** *020 †85
LEAPLEY, Megan Adele. PSC 827 BOX 4697, USNH NAPLES ITALY 09617 #028-46-1997 L1998 **EM** *020 †16
LEBEDOVYCH, Victor Bohdon. CMR 402 BOX 753, LANDSTUHL REG MED CTR 09180 #025-01-1968 L1969 **GS VS** *020 †85
LECLAIRE, Edgar Louis. PSC 41 BOX 592 09464 #039-01-2003 L2004 **OBG** *020
LEE, Chang Ho. PSC BOX 398 09109 #040-02-1957 **GS** *020
LEIBRECHT, Murl Edwin. CMR 402 BOX 1147, LRMC 09180 #049-01-1971 L1976 **AM OM** *020 †70
LEITNAKER, Frank C. CMR 403 BOX 5169, MIESAU ARMY DEPOT 09059 #019-02-1952 L1952 **GP GPM** *071 †70
LEJA, Ivars. CMR 402 BOX 1742 09180 #035-09-1961 L1979 **PTH CLP** *020 †50
LEONG, Jonathan Gilbert. ■ 09630 #030-06-1992 L1993 **ORS** *020
LILLIE, Michele Cathy Ann. ■ 09464 #018-03-1981 L1988 **PD** *075 †55
LIM, Romeo Ng. ■ 09267 #748-07-1985 L1997 **FM** *020 †18
LISHKA, Catherine Brenier. OPC/ER 34TH GEN HOSP 09178 #396-18-1982 *020
LLANSO, Theodore Towles. ■ 09042 #048-02-2000 L2001 **DR** *100
LODICO, Peter Jacob. ■ 09603 #025-07-1998 L2000 **FM** *020 †18
LOWELL, George Henry. USDAO EMBASY OF US 09830 #035-46-1971 L1973 **PD** *100
LOWRY, Mark A. ■ 09721 #023-12-1987 L1989 **PTH FOP** *020 †50
LUCAS, William Matthew. ■ 09617 #016-43-2002 L2004 **FM** *020 †18
LUNDQUIST, Erik Jon. PSC 827 BOX 15 09617 #028-34-2000 **FM** *020 †18
LUTHER, David James. PSC 37 BOX 8 09459 #056-06-1985 L1986 **FM** *020 †18
LUU, Huy Quoc. ■ 09267 #023-12-1999 L2001 **FM** *020 †18
MA, Kai-Wood. ■ 09720 #244-02-1989 L1994 **FM** *020 †18
MAC DONALD, Bruce S. USA HSP STA 500 KREUCH GER 09252 #035-45-1966 **IM OS** *020
MAHER, Cornelius Creedon. ■ 09042 #028-34-1986 L1988 **N AM** *030 †75
MARCHESSAULT, Jeffrey A. ■ 09464 #023-12-1991 L1993 **ORS** *020 †40
MARCO, Peter Anthony. ■ 09180 #028-34-1989 L1991 **PCC** *020 †20
MARINO, Paul F. ■ 09630 #561-01-1973 L1977 **PD OS** *020 †55
MARIUS, Kjersti Ann. PSC 47, RAF UPWOOD CLINIC 09470 #023-12-1999 L2001 **FM** *020 †18
MARPLE, Richard L. CMR 480 BOX 1432 09128 #023-12-1982 L1986 **IM** *030 †20
MARSHALL, Robert C. CMR 402, BOX 1473 09180 #005-06-1988 L1989 **IM** *020 †20
MARTIN, Barry Don. CMR 402 BOX 630, LRMC DEPT OF PLASTIC SURG 09180 #004-01-1992 L1994 **PS GS** *020 †85,65
MARTINEZ, Louis Marty. ■ 09464 #045-01-1996 L1996 **OPH** *020 †35
MASON, Carl Jeffries. UNIT 64109, USA MRU K 09831 #041-13-1984 L1987 **PHP IM** *050 †20,70
MAYBEE, Gabrielle. ■ 09042 #041-13-2002 L2004 **OBG** *020 †30
MC BETH, Michael John. ■ 09459 #023-12-2000 L2004 **FM AM** *020 †18
MC COY, Kelly Lynn. PSC 827 BOX 94 09617 #041-09-1998 L1999 **GS** *020 †85
MC DERMOTT, Joseph Edward. CMR 402 BOX 318, LANDSTUHL REG MED CENTER 09180 #055-01-1978 L1980 **N** *020 †75
MCDERMOTT, Joseph Harris. ■ 09464 #023-12-2002 L2002 **PTH** *020 †50
MC DONALD, Tonya Patrice. ■ 09244 #024-01-1998 L2001 **ADL** *020 †55
MC DONNELL, Elizabeth L. ■ 09464 #023-12-1990 L1994 **OBG** *020 †30
MC GRATH, John Michael. ■ 09096 #023-12-1990 L1992 **EM** *020 †16
MC KENNA, John Paul, Jr. CMR 402 BOX 563 09180 #048-02-1992 L1993 **END IM** *020 †20
MCKINNEY, Krystie Kay. ■ 09630 #025-07-2002 L2003 **PD** *020
MEADE, Kenneth Wayne. CMR 402 BOX 684 09180 #005-14-1972 L1977 **OBG** *020 †30
MEADOWS, Sean Michael. ■ 09180 #039-01-2003 L2005 **EM** *020 †16
MEDINA, Anibal. ■ 09180 #451-01-1962 L1969 **U** *071 †95
MEGHOO, Colin A. ■ 09244 #035-19-1998 L1999 **GS** *020 †85
MENDENHALL, Marshall C. ■ 09705 #023-12-1998 L1999 **FM** *020 †18
MENDOZA, Edward. USAF HSP TORREJON BX 4653 09641 #264-01-1963 **GP AM** *020
MERCER, Jett J. ■ 09464 #048-13-2000 L2002 **AN** *100 †05
MICHAUD, Vincent Joel. ■ 09012 #048-12-1988 L1989 **AM OM** *030 †70
MILLER, Carolyn Yvette. ■ 09042 #048-13-1994 L1996 **AN** *020 †05
MILLER, Lee Hart. 196TH STATION HOSP 09705 #165-01-1960 **OTO GP** *020 †45
MIRON, Edward Joseph. UNIT 61307, AMEMBASSY 09803 #012-01-1980 L1981 **FM** *020 †18
MIRZA, Inam Ul-Haque. 34TH GEN HOSP 09178 #704-01-1961 *020
MODLIN, Randolph Eugene. CMR 402 BOX 1560, LANDSTUHL REG MED CTR 09180 #023-12-1985 L1988 **CD IM** *020 †20
MOFFITT, Mitchell Jackson. ■ 09244 #010-01-2000 L2002 **PD** *020 †55 ‡
MOLLOY, Jeffrey William. ■ 09464 #023-12-2001 L2003 **IM** *020
MONTALVO RODRIGUEZ, Roque. US AIR FORCE HOSP PED 09824 #847-04-1958 L1960 **PD OS** *020
MORGAN, Jeffrey Scott. UNIT 26610 BOX 516, 67TH FST CMR 446 09244 #047-20-1998 L1999 **ORS** *020 ‡
MORRISON, Pamela Louise. ■ 09421 #041-02-1997 L1999 **FM** *020 †18
MORTLAND, Angela Joy. PSC 2 BOX 15451 09012 #018-03-1998 L1999 **OPH** *020
MOUNTS, Anthony Wayne. ■ 09812 #020-02-1983 L1987 **IM PD** *020 †20,55
MULVANEY, Sean William. ■ 09046 #023-12-2000 L2001 **FM** *020 †18
MUNDO-GUZMAN, Josefa M. CMR 470 BOX 4842, USAHC 09165 #264-05-1975 L1980 **PD OS** *020
MYRTUE, Andrew Jason. ■ 09137 #023-12-1997 L1998 **ORS** *020 †40
NALESNIK, Jeffrey George. ■ 09180 #023-12-1996 L1997 **U** *020 †95
NALESNIK, Sally Wonderly. ■ 09180 #023-12-1996 L1997 **OBG** *020 †30
NASR, Hafez Ali. PSC 94 BOX 252 09824 #305-01-1998 L1998 **FM** *020 †18
NASSIF, Walid Michel. ■ 09180 #605-02-1984 L1988 **PYG** *020 †75
NASSIRKHANI, Shahin. CMR 454 BOX 1725, USA HEALTH CLINIC KATTERBA 09250 #023-12-2003 L2004 **AM FM** *020

9524

■ = Address Information Privacy Protected

NAYLOR, Jacqueline Nadine. ■ 09630 #011-03-2001 L2001 FM *100
NEGIN, Nathan Samuel. ■ 09042 #033-06-2000 L2002 IM *020 †20
NEWMAN, Michaeltodd. ■ 09617 #020-12-1998 L2000 GP *020
NGUYEN, Cuong Dinh. ■ 09180 #024-07-2000 L2000 PM *020 †60
NIEVES, Wilfredo Javier. ■ 09459 #042-02-1993 L1995 IM *020
NORTH-WILHELM, Kathleen. UNIT 26610 BOX 212, USAMEDDAC WUERZBURG 09244 #005-14-1981 L1982 FM *030 †18
NYSTUEN, Christopher M. ■ 09114 #025-01-2001 L2002 ORS *100
OCHOA-FLORES, Michelle S. ■ 09042 #048-04-1997 PD *020 †55
ODUWA, Felix Osabohien. ■ 09112 #024-05-1996 L1999 FM *020
OLDHAM, Marriner Verlin. ■ 09720 #049-01-1993 L1996 FM *020 †18
OLSEN, James Michael. ■ 09042 #023-12-1985 L1987 OPH GP *020 †35
OVERFIELD, A Scott. ■ 09464 #019-02-1984 L1984 N *020 †75
PAGAN, Rafael Angel. ■ 09464 #042-01-1988 L1990 DR *020 †80
PARIS, Robert Mc Clary. USAMC AFRIMS 96546 #016-43-1994 L1996 IM EP *050 †70,20
PARSONS, Rosangela. UNIT 31401 BOX 85 09630 #187-55-1978 L1992 P *020 †75
PATRIN, George David. CMR 402 BOX 1946, 2ND GENERAL HOSPITAL 09180 #026-04-1988 L1990 PD *020 †55
PENDERGRASS, Timothy Lee. ■ 09137 #023-12-1987 L1989 DR AM *030 †80
PETERS, Gordon Chas. ■ 09603 #023-12-1989 L1990 GPM *020 †70
PETERSON, William Dwight. ■ 09165 #067-01-1981 L1981 P CHP *020 †75
PETROFSKY, Yolanta V. ■ 09123 #016-43-2000 L2001 IM *020
PHILLIPS, Dan Emory. ■ 09603 #012-05-1994 L1995 P *020
PHILLIPS, James Daniel. ■ 09175 #021-01-2003 L2003 FM *020 †18
PIETSZAK, Kimberly Diane. ■ 09601 #023-12-1996 L1999 IM *020 †20
PINZON, Renato De-Peralta. ■ 09244 #748-02-1973 L1977 FM PTH *020 †18
PLACE, Ronald Jos. CMR 402, BOX 1756 09180 #030-06-1990 L1993 CRS *020 †10,85
PLOTKIN, Fredric Robt. ■ 09180 #047-05-1989 L1989 EM *020 †70,16
POLHEMUS, Mark Edward. ■ 09831 #043-01-1995 L1997 ID *020 †20
POPEY, Tracy Croll. ■ 09180 #041-07-1992 L1993 ORS *020 †40
PRAGER, Harris Robert. PSC 2 BOX 5333 09012 #016-42-1994 L1994 OBG *020 †30
PRUITT, Valerie Marie. ■ 09180 #020-02-1997 L1998 CCS *020 †85
PUCHTA, Pawel. ■ 09012 #759-03-1986 L2005 *100
PULIDO-BOTTGE, Leticia. 34TH GENERAL HOSPITAL 09178 #748-10-1973 *020
QUEZADA, Carlos E. ■ 09617 #048-13-1999 L2003 OBG *020 †30
QUINONES-ACOSTA, F. USA MED AC VICENZA ITA 09630 #231-01-1953 L1955 IM *020
RACZNIAK PHD, Gregory Aar. UNIT 2020 BOX 69 09817 #051-07-2004 L2005 OBG *020
RAEZ, Abigail Carmen. ■ 09264 #001-06-2003 L2005 EM *020 †16
REINDEL, Rebecca. ■ 09459 #016-02-2002 L2002 PD *100 †55
RICHARDS, Joseph Ronald. PSC 2 BOX 7063 09012 #023-12-1998 L2000 P *100 †75
RIEKER, Mark Garrett. ■ 09012 #023-07-1999 L2001 PD *020 †55
RILEY, Lyrad Kelly. PSC 37 BOX 3028 09459 #028-34-1997 L1998 FM *020 †18
ROBERTSON, Brian David. ■ 09250 #023-12-1999 L2001 PD *020 †55
ROELLIG, Martha Susan. SINA HOSPITAL, 86TH CSH TF BAGHDAD 09348 #028-34-2001 L2001 EM *020 †16
ROGERS, David Michael. ■ 09459 #023-12-1996 L1999 FM *020 †18
ROHATGI, Anand Kumar. ■ 09244 #036-07-2002 L2002 CD *012 †20
ROLLI, Michael Laurence. ■ 09705 #035-19-1999 L2003 NS *020
ROSSMAN, Michael Glenn. CMR 442 BOX 53 09042 #048-16-1994 L1996 IM AM *020 †20
RUARK, Sylvan Ross. ■ 09102 #054-04-1964 L1966 PHP OM *030 †20
RUCINSKI, Robert James. CMR 442 BOX 703 09042 #056-05-1995 L1995 CHP *020 †75
RUCK, Richard Charles, II. ■ 09180 #016-06-1995 L1997 PD UM *020 †55
RUMBAUGH, John George. ■ 09705 #041-02-2000 L2002 FM *020 †18
RUZE, Patricia. UNIT 64107 09831 #032-01-1990 L1990 IM *020 †20 ‡
RYAN, Paul Mccafferty. ■ 09042 #021-01-1999 L2001 ORS *020
SAGUIL, Aaron Albert. ■ 09114 #011-03-1999 L2001 FM *100 †18
SALOUM, David Elias. ■ 09180 #041-15-2001 L2004 EM *020 †16
SALZMAN, Keith Lawrence. ■ 09042 #026-08-1989 L1991 FM *030 †18
SANDBERG, Douglas Herbert. ■ 09244 #036-05-1955 L1960 PD PG *020 †55
SANTANA, Jorge A. USAF HOSP BOX 74 09220 #042-01-1968 L1973 PD GP *020 †55
SAUNDERS, Charles L, Jr. USAE-JUSMA C C 09841 #048-02-1951 L1951 GPM *020
SAYLES, Timothy Everett. ■ 09617 #051-04-1997 L1998 OBG *020 †30
SCHALL, David Gordon. ■ 09128 #028-46-1977 L1978 NO AM *020 †70,45
SCHEIRMAN, Katherine E. ■ 09012 #039-01-1976 L1977 IM *020 †20
SCHERLE, Gregory Allen. CMR 467 BOX 1096 09096 #016-43-1998 L1998 FM *020 †18
SCHICK, John David. CMR 402 BOX 1335, C/O LRMC 09180 #004-01-1989 L1989 N *020
SCHISSEL, Daniel John. CMR 442 BOX 688 09042 #023-12-1993 L1995 D UM *020 †15
SCHMUKER, Gerald Nicholas. ■ 09617 #025-07-2000 L2002 P *020 †75
SCHROEDER, Peter. HQS 5TH GENERAL HOSP 09154 #407-12-1948 L1956 OS *030 †85
SCOTT, John Switzer. ■ 09180 #023-12-1990 L1992 PDC *020 †55
SCULLY, Shawna E. ■ 09180 #005-76-1999, ▲ L2001 N *020 †75
SEIGERMAN, Jedd A. ■ 09464 #041-13-2003 L2005 IM *020 †20
SELTZER, Joel. UNIT 6010 BOX 142 09825 #306-01-1986 L1991 P PFP *020 †75 ‡
SEM, Shobha. ■ 09839 #495-12-1969 L1980 FM *020 †18
SEPDHAM, Dan. ■ 09464 #051-04-1997 L1999 FM *020 †18
SERWACKI, Michael James. ■ 09180 #054-04-1991 L1993 PDC *100 †55
SESSIONS, Cecili K. ■ 09824 #005-06-2000 L2000 PD *020 †55
SEYFERTH, Jacqueline R. 34TH GEN HOSP 09178 #917-30-1963 *020
SHAFFER, Douglas Neale. ■ 09831 #055-01-1993 L1994 IM *100 †20
SHIRLEY, Darren Layne. ■ 09137 #020-12-2000 L2002 DR *100 †80
SIGMOND, Benjamin Ronald. ■ 09180 #024-05-2002 L2002 GS *020
SILVEY, Stephen Van. ■ 09180 #048-12-1990 L1993 IM *020 †20
SIM, Roselynn Wee. ■ 09042 #023-12-2002 PD *020
SIMONET, Luke Benjamin. ■ 09123 #023-12-2000 L2001 IM *020
SIMPSON, Carole Ann. CMR 437 BOX 1220 09267 #038-06-1982 L1984 PD PM *020 †60,55
SLOCUM, Kathleen Anne. PSC 827 BOX 4602 09617 #035-15-1978 L1988 DR *020 †80
SMITH, Bryan Lee. ■ 09832 #023-12-1992 L1994 FM *020 †18
SMITH, Daniel Thomas. ■ 09180 #023-12-1995 L1997 EM *020 †16
SMITH, Larry Oliver. ■ 09464 #017-20-1997 L1999 EM *020 †16
SMULLEN, Brian Dennis. PSC 821 BOX 22 09421 #033-06-1988 L1991 P *020 †75
SOHA, Albert John. USAHN MEDDAC UROL SER 09222 #035-06-1961 U *020
SOLTIS, Christopher Brian. ■ 09165 #023-12-1999 L1999 PD *020 †55,03
SPRENGER, Paul H. UNIT 61305 09803 #869-02-1976 L1981 FM *020 †18
SPRING, Henry, Jr. ■ 09036 #024-05-1981 L1984 OBG LM *020 †30
SPRINGER, Matthew William. ■ 09096 #051-07-2004 L2004 PD *100
SRIDHAR, Anjali Natasha. ■ 09180 #023-12-2002 L2004 PD *020
STAATS, Julie Stark. ■ 09705 #028-78-1995, ▲ L1997 FM EM *030 †18 ‡
STACEY, Michael William. ■ 09464 #041-13-2001 L2003 FM *100 †18
STACKLE, Mark Edward. ■ 09089 #010-02-2001 L2002 FM *020
STANDAERT, Brynne B. ■ 09012 #023-12-1992 L1993 PD *020 †55
STANEK, Lidia. ■ 09705 #759-01-1980 L1995 FM *020 †18
STARK, Craig Garrett. UNIT 21414 BOX 148, SHAPE HEALTHCARE FACILITY 09705 #024-07-1998 L1999 IM AM *020 †20
STECHER, William Alfred. CMR 402 BOX 1881 09180 #041-02-1958 L1971 DR *071 †80
STEFKO, John Gerald. UNIT 29223 09102 #038-40-1968 L1968 CHP P *020 †75
STEIL, Evan Neil. CMR 429, BOX 536 09054 #041-12-1993 L1995 FM OM *020 †18 ‡
STEIN, James John. ■ 09244 #037-01-1995 L1996 GPM *020 †70,55
STEVENS, Michael David. ■ 09603 #023-12-1995 L1998 PD *020 †55
STEVENSON, Harriet Hogue. ■ 09180 #048-02-1990 L1991 FM *020
STOCKMASTER, Neil Richard. CMR 402 BOX 656 09180 #023-12-2000 L2002 GS VS *020 †85
STORMS, Patrick R. ■ 09464 #048-04-1981 L1981 GPM *020 †20,70
STOUTE, Jose Antonio. ■ 09831 #011-02-1985 L1987 ID *020 †20
STRALEY, Daryn Richard. PSC 9 BOX 3844 09123 #028-78-2000, ▲ L2000 FM EM *020 †18 ‡
STROBEL, David Lane. ■ 09464 #038-41-1991 L1993 PTH *072 †50
STUPARICH, Michael A. ■ 09180 #021-01-2002 L2004 IM *020 †20 ‡
SUBRAMANIAN, Sreekumar. ■ 09137 #035-03-1996 L1998 TS *012 †85
SWANTON, Edward Joseph. ■ 09180 #023-12-1996 L1997 OS *020 †20,75
SWITAJ, Timothy Lawrence. ■ 09046 #023-12-2002 L2003 FM *020 †18
TEBROCK, Christopher Eric. ■ 09180 #023-12-1998 L2000 GS *020 †05
TEBROCK, Melissa Jane. ■ 09180 #023-12-1998 L2000 FM *020 †18
TELIAN, Simon Hovannes. ■ 09036 #024-05-1998 L2000 GS *020 †85
THEURER, Wesley M. ■ 09096 #048-78-2002, ▲ L2004 FM *020 †18
THOMPSON, Heather M. ■ 09042 #047-06-1994 L1995 P *020 †75
TIBBETTS, Grant Parker. ■ 09464 #023-12-1993 L1998 DR *020 †80
TIFFANY, Carolyn Lane. ■ 09042 #025-12-1991 L1993 EM *020 †16
TINDALL, John Philip. ■ 09464 #036-07-1959 L1959 D AM *071 †15,70
TIROL, Tristan Gella. 97 MEDDAC UNIT 25717 BX 50 09242 #748-10-1973 GP *020
TOKOLA, Nancy Smith. PSC 71 BOX 9, AMERICAN EMBASSY 09715 #038-06-1989 PTH *020
TOMSYCK, Rebecca R. CMR 442 BOX 645 09042 #036-05-1978 L1981 P PD *020 †55,75
TOUFEXIS, Christina E. CMR 467 BOX 4686, WIESBADEN HEALTH CLINIC 09096 #422-01-1997 L2000 PD *020 †55
TSAI, Jenny. UNIT 25560, CASUAL MAIL DIRECTORY 09237 #025-01-1998 L2001 FM *020 †18 ‡
TUJO, Charles Albert. ■ 09180 #023-12-1995 L1996 DR *020 †80
UENG, Timothy. ■ 09086 #005-12-1998 L1999 AN *100 †18
UZOGARA, Ngozi Eugenia. ■ 09464 #010-01-2001 L2004 OBG *020
VAN HORNE, Anne Katherine. ■ 09464 #035-09-2003 L2005 OBG *020
VAUGHAN, Eric Weston. ■ 09180 #019-02-2003 L2003 EM *020 †16
VEDDER, Timothy George. UNIT 21414 BOX 188 09705 #026-04-2001 L2002 PD AM *020 †55
VEGA-MORALES, Marisol. ■ 09180 #042-02-1995 L1997 PD *020 †55
VINING, Neil Carroll. ■ 09180 #036-01-2000 L2002 ORS *020 †40
VO, Dai Tran. ■ 09112 #942-01-1995 L2004 IM *020 †20
VON SCHLIPPE, Katherine E. 34TH GEN HOSP PED 09178 #409-16-1982 L1988 PD *020 †55
VYVERBERG, Bryan Michael. PSC 41 09464 #025-07-1993 L1996 CHP *020 †75
WAGERS, Steven A, Jr. ■ 09042 #051-04-1994 L1996 DR *020 †80
WAKEFIELD, Chas Theodore. ■ 09009 #016-11-1955 L1960 GP *020
WALKER, Robert Bell. CMR 442 BOX 492 09042 #041-02-1985 L1986 FM EM *020 †18
WALKER, Stacy S. ■ 09464 #021-01-1993 L1994 GS *020 †85
WALLACE, Graham Wilson. ■ 09603 #019-02-1998 L1999 FM *020 †18
WALSH, Douglas Shawn. UNIT 64109, USAMRU-K 09831 #010-01-1989 L1991 D *020 †15
WANEK, Sandra Michelle. ■ 09180 #025-07-1997 L2000 GS *020 †85
WARD, Alison M. ■ 09244 #043-01-1993 L1995 CHP *020 †75
WATTERS, Raymond Wendell. PSC 36 BOX 524 09456 #847-14-1981 L1983 FM AM *020 †18
WHITE, Douglas Wesley. ■ 09464 #023-12-2001 L2002 DR *100 †80
WHITE, Ronald Lemond. ■ 09180 #023-12-2000 L2002 AN *020 †05
WICHMAN, Todd Anthony. ■ 09180 #023-12-2004 L2006 PM *012
WICKLUND, Matthew Paul. ■ 09464 #007-02-1987 L1989 N *020 †75
WIGLE, Richard L. UNIT 26610, BOX 5062 09244 #035-06-1973 L1974 TRS GS *020 †16,85 ‡
WILKS, Gerald Lee. ■ 09042 #030-05-1968 L1968 ORS *020
WILLIAMS, Charles Dale. ■ 09012 #005-06-1980 L1981 ORS *020 †40
WINKLER, Warren Harry. AMCONGEN 09827 #025-01-1955 L1956 FM GPM *020
WITHERS, Mark Robt. ■ 09831 #055-01-1986 L1987 AM *020 †20,70
WOOD, Joann Louise. ■ 09822 #039-05-1989 L1991 FM *020 †18
WOOD-MORRIS, Robert N. ■ 09034 #048-13-1998 L2000 ID *012 †20
WOODS, Timothy David. ■ 09180 #030-06-1997 L1999 GS *020 †85
WOODSON, Jennifer Lee. PSC 827 BOX 72, US NAVAL HOSP 09617 #050-02-1992 L1993 FM *020 †18
WOS, Aldona. ■ 09723 #759-03-1980 L1984 IM PUD *020 †20
WOYDICK, Daniel Paul. ■ 09114 #056-06-2003 L2006 FM *020 †18
YORK, Brian Melvin. ■ 09464 #027-01-1997 L1997 OBG *020 †30
YOUNG, Jeremie Joseph. ■ 09012 #055-02-1999 L2003 OBG *020
YOUNG, Paul Albert. PSC 2 BOX 10533 09012 #036-01-1987 L1989 AM OM *020 †70
ZARUTSKIE, Susan Engel. CMR 410 BOX 139 09096 #036-07-1972 L1973 PD *020 †55 ‡
ZOOK, Jason David. ■ 09617 #036-05-2002 L2002 ORS *100

APO – AP

ABRAMES, Erik Lee. ■ 96319 #023-12-2005 L2006 GS *100
AGEE, Brian Floyd. ■ 96319 #051-07-1993 L1995 FM *020 †18
AHMED, Syed Imraan. ■ 96205 #035-19-2002 L2004 ORS *020
ALVARADO, Amarillys. PSC 80 BOX 15493 96367 #042-01-1990 L1992 *020
ANGELES, Abdiel Mateo. PO BOX 716 96206 #748-02-1960 L1971 IM GP *020
AOKI, Armando. PSC 77 BOX 4713 96325 #132-02-1968 L1976 PTH *020
AYER, David Thomas. ■ 96218 #016-01-2004 L2006 PD *020 †55
BAILEY, Keisha Yema. ■ 96319 #305-01-2002 L2006 OBG *020
BALINTONA, Joanne M. ■ 96326 #023-12-2003 L2004 *020
BARD, Catherine E. ■ 96326 #048-13-1991 L1992 FM *020 †18
BARNETT, Andrew Russell. ■ 96266 #005-12-2006 L2006 *100
BAUMGARTNER, Brian James. ■ 96205 #016-42-1999 L2001 OTO *020 †45
BELENKIY, Slava M. ■ 96266 #023-12-2003 L2004 GS *020

BERMUDEZ, James Eric. PSC 80 BOX 14477 96367 #023-12-1998 L1999 **FM** *020

BRIZZELL, Rebecca E. ■ 96266 #035-03-2003 L2005 **FM** *020 †18

BROWN, Tyson Craig. ■ 96326 #023-12-2004 L2005 **PD** *100 †55

BUCKNAM, Barbara R. PSC 3 BOX 11 96266 #051-07-1987 L1989 **AM** *020

BUTLER, William Patrick. ■ 96367 #051-01-1979 L1980 **AM GS** *020 †70,85

CASTILLO, Craig Yuichi. PSC BOX 1345 96262 #010-01-1989 L1990 **GPM** *020 †70

CHA, Yong Kwon. ■ 96206 #012-01-1995 L1996 **FM** *020

CHAMBERS, Elise Marie. ■ 96319 #034-01-2005 L2006 **FM** *020

CHAMPOUX, Edward. ■ 96326 #035-03-2002 L2004 **PD** *020 †55

CHIN, David Lee. ■ 96319 #048-02-1989 L1992 **PHP OS** *020 †70

CHOI, Bong Joon. PSC 450 BOX 743 96206 #583-04-1969 L1975 **GE IM** *020 †20

CHOI, Wan Hee. ■ 96205 #583-02-1982 L1991 **IM** *020 †20

CHUNG, Kyung Park. 121ST GENERAL HOSPITAL 96205 #030-05-1985 L1986 **IM** *020 †20

CLARK, Justin Stiles. ■ 96384 #048-13-2006 L2007 **FM** *020

COAKWELL, Mark Richard. UNIT 5024, 35 AMDS/SGP 96319 #038-43-1992 L1994 **AM OM** *020 †70

COLE, Daniel Edward. ■ 96367 #056-05-1999 L2001 **IM** *020 †20

CONNOLLY, Eve Alison. ■ 96319 #051-04-1996 L1998 **FM** *020 †18

CONNOLLY, Kevin Patrick. ■ 96319 #051-04-1995 L1998 **GPM** *020 †70,18

CUNNINGHAM, David Lane. PSC 80 BOX 14172 96367 #025-12-1992 L1994 **GPM** *020 †18

DAVEY, Kathleen Mara. ■ 96326 #051-04-2003 L2003 **IM** *020 †20

DELOS SANTOS, Alan John S. PSC 80 BOX 21326 96367 #748-22-1986 L2000 **IM** *020 †20

DINTAMAN, Jay Michael. ■ 96202 #023-12-2003 L2005 **PD** *100 †55

DOMBROWSKI, James Albert. ■ 96319 #023-01-1996 L1997 **ORS** *020

ELNICKY, Carol Jean. PSC 78 BOX 3695 96326 #036-05-1997 L1999 **PD** *020

FARRISH, Susan Catherine. PSC 78 BOX 7463 96326 #023-12-1998 L1999 **FM** *020 †18

FAY, Charles P. ■ 96367 #048-02-1997 L1998 **AM** *020

FERNANDES, Jacqueline S. ■ 96326 #010-03-2002 L2002 **OBG** *020 †30

GAYDOS, Steven John. UNIT 45011, USA MEDDAC JAPAN 96338 #010-02-2002 L2003 **EM AM** *020 †16

GERSTENBERGER, Duane F. HHC 2ND INF DIV 96224 #054-04-1964 **PHP** *062

GRIFFIN, Erica Joan. UNIT 5269, KADENA FAMILY PRACTICE 96368 #025-12-2000 L2001 **FM** *020 †18

GRINAGE, Brad David. ■ 96319 #019-02-1990 L1993 **P PFP** *040 †75

HAGBERG, Stephen Mark. ■ 96319 #041-13-2003 L2004 **FM** *020 †18

HAMPTON, David Akinyele. ■ 96384 #028-02-2004 L2005 **GP** *020

HANLEY, Lenonie Melisia. PSC 78 BOX 2908 96326 #012-21-2001 L2001 **FM** *020

HARDER, Evelyn Mae. ■ 96266 #023-12-2001 L2002 **AM** *020

HARDY, John Henry, Jr. PSC 78 BOX 3046 96326 #040-02-1992 L1994 **FM** *020 †18

HARTWICH, Scott Alan. ■ 96367 #023-12-1995 L1996 **GP AM** *020 †70

HENDRICKS, Susan Lesher. UNIT 15244 BOX 3, 121 GENERAL HOSP 96205 #039-05-1985 L1986 **CHP P** *020 †75 ‡

HERSACK, Richard Allan. PSC 3 BOX 7738 96266 #028-34-1983 L1985 **AN AM** *020 †05

HEUMAN, Michael David. UNIT 15244 BOX 369, HHC 121 GEN HOSP 96205 #025-07-2000 L2002 **GS** *020 †85 ‡

HIGHT, Rachel Ann. PSC 76 BOX 8384 96319 #023-12-1998 L2000 **GS** *020 †85

HILL, Kenisha Renee. ■ 96264 #023-12-2003 L2005 *100 †18

HILTON, Alden Douglas. ■ 96266 #048-02-1994 L1995 **GPM** *020 †70

HOCHHEIMER, Sven Markus. ■ 96266 #023-12-2005 L2006 **GS** *100

HOFFMANN, Thomas Nathan. ■ 96376 #023-12-2004 L2004 **IM** *020 †20

HOLLANDER, Matthew Colby. ■ 96319 #024-07-2004 L2006 *100 †55

HORNER, Jillian Elizabeth. PO BOX 1702 96555 #019-02-1989 L1990 **FM** *020 †18

HUBNER, Mark Edward. ■ 96367 #041-09-1990 L1992 **P** *020 †18

HUIET, James Frederick. PSC 80 BOX 11765 96367 #045-04-1998 L1999 **IM** *020 †20

HUR, Gham. UNIT 15550, AMERICAN EMBASSY 96205 #583-03-1972 **DR** *020 †80

IRELAN, Wendy Ann. ■ 96326 #047-20-2003 L2003 **OBG** *020

JAMES, Randolph Lee. PSC 76 BOX 7694 96319 #019-02-1998 L1999 **FM** *020 †18

JANSON, Lee William. ■ 96264 #048-12-2000 L2002 **FM AM** *020 †18

JENSEN, Scott Todd. ■ 96326 #049-01-2003 L2005 **AN** *020

JEPSEN, Kerry. PSC 3 BOX 6126 96266 #023-12-1993 L1995 **ORS** *020 †40

JOERS, Kathy Joan. PSC 80 BOX 16892 96367 #023-12-1998 **FM** *020 †18

JOHNSON, Jerodene P. ■ 96260 #047-07-1978 **GP GPM** *062

JOHNSON-WALL, Helen N. PSC 76 BOX 8462 96319 #023-12-1998 L2000 **IM** *020 †20

JOHNSON-WALL, Joseph C. PSC 76 BOX 8462 96319 #023-12-1997 L1998 **PD** *020

KANG, Daniel Won. ■ 96205 #035-09-2002 L2002 **IM** *020 †20

KANG, Helen. ■ 96205 #025-01-2001 L2002 **IM** *020 †20

KARWACKI, Jerome J, Jr. ■ 96546 #023-01-1980 L1982 **GPM OM** *030 †70

KENT, Robert S. PSC 80 BOX 14818 96367 #048-02-1995 L1997 **FM AM** *020 †18

KIM, Beum Saeng. ■ 96205 #583-10-1972 L1976 **N P** *020 †75

KIM, Gary S. ■ 96367 #023-12-2002 L2002 **IM** *020 †20

KIM, Hyung Ki. 121ST GENERAL HOSP, BOX 565 96205 #583-10-1971 L1979 **OBG** *020

KIM, Kyoung-Hi Park. UNIT 15244 BOX 568, 121ST EVACUATION HOSP 96205 #583-03-1954 L1972 **PD** *020 †55

KIM, Seung Il. 121 GENERAL HOSP BOX 282 96205 #583-02-1968 L1975 **OBG** *030 †30

KIM, Sok Min. HHC 121ST GENERAL HOSP, BOX 24 96205 #583-12-1975 L1986 **PM** *020 †60

KNIGHT, Leslie Ann. ■ 96326 #023-12-1994 L1997 **FM** *020 †18

KOO, Cha Oeok. 121 EVAC HOSP BX 68 U15244 96205 #583-03-1965 L1974 **P FM** *030

KURITSKY, Joel Norman. ■ 96206 #035-46-1975 L1977 **IM FM** *020 †20

KWON, Herbert Peter. ■ 96338 #023-12-2001 L2003 **IM** *020 †20

LARSON, Kerry Kevin. ■ 96367 #005-12-1986 L1987 **IM** *020 †20

LEARY, Rose M. PSC 3 BOX 3772 96266 #048-13-2000 *100

LEDERER, Benjamin David. ■ 96266 #041-01-2002 L2004 **P** *020

LEE, Hee-Choon S. ■ 96205 #023-12-1987 L1989 **FM** *020 †18,70

LEE, Sook L. HHC 18TH MEDCOM, BOX 318 96205 #041-02-1996 L1997 **FM** *020 †18

LEWIS, Jeffrey Daniel. PSC 3 BOX 1938, OSAN AFB KOREA 96266 #039-01-1998 L2001 **GS** *020 †85

LINDBORG, C Eric. PO BOX 1448 96555 #017-20-1975 L1975 **FM EM** *020 †16

LYONS, Terence J. UNIT 45002 BOX 316 96337 #008-02-1973 L1979 **AM FM** *020 †70,18

MAC ALPINE, Daniel Mark. ■ 96326 #018-03-1995 L1995 **D** *020 †18,15

MALABANAN, Elena Joya. USAF RMC CLARK PSC, BX 15639 96432 #748-01-1961 **AN** *020

MALABANAN, Francisco L. PSC 3 BOX 15639 96266 #748-07-1965 L1973 **U GS** *020 †95

MALAN, Matthew Micah. ■ 96367 #040-02-2002 L2003 *020

MARAT, Olga. ■ 96319 #024-16-2004 L2005 **FM** *020

MARCHANT, Bryant Gene. ■ 96205 #023-12-1998 L2000 **ORS** *020 †40

MAYERS, Richard J. ■ 96319 #016-06-1993 L1998 **GS** *020 †85

MCDONALD, Lucas Stevenson. ■ 96386 #021-01-2005 L2006 **GS** *020

MEZA-VALENCIA, Beatriz E. P.O. BOX 712, 121 COMBAT SUP HOSP 96205 #023-12-2000 L2000 **PD** *020 †55

MILLER, Todd Alan. ■ 96224 #010-02-1994 **U** *020 †95

MINIHANE, Keith Peter. UNIT 15244, BOX 23 96205 #016-01-2000 L2001 **ORS** *020

MITCHELL, Stephen Wilfred. ■ 96367 #012-21-1993 L1995 **FM** *020 †18

MOBLEY, Sarita Darlene. PSC 303 BOX 31 96204 #012-21-1997 L1999 **FM** *020 †18

MOON, Garth Geung I. PSC 3, BOX 3716 96266 #010-02-1994 L1996 **GS** *020

MOON, Jae Ho. 121 US ARMY HOSP 96205 #583-01-1970 L1975 **PM GP** *020 †60

MORGAN, Eric David. ■ 96338 #005-12-1991 L1993 **FM** *020 †18

MORGANSTEIN, Joshua Chaim. ■ 96319 #023-12-2001 L2003 **P** *100 †18,75 ‡

MORITA, Keith Hideo. PSC 80 BOX 12341 96367 #005-12-1992 L1995 **FM** *020 †18

MOSES, Kennett Jesse. ■ 96386 #049-01-1998 L2007 **ORS** *012

MURRAY, Dan Hugh. ■ 96367 #048-16-1999 L2001 **FM** *020 †18

NEFCY, Christine Ann. ■ 96326 #023-12-1997 L1998 **PD** *020 †55

NELSON, Eric Andrew. ■ 96326 #025-12-1991 L1994 **GPM** *020 †18,70

NEWMAN, John W. PO BOX 1731 96555 #065-01-1944 L1946 **FM** *020 †18

NGUYEN, Richard Hung. PSC 78 BOX 2166 96326 #942-01-1978 L1987 **DR** *020

NICHOLS, Shawnn Derrek. ■ 96266 #048-02-2002 L2002 **GS** *020 †85

OH, John Yoonsik. PSC 76 BOX 5487 96319 #041-14-1992 L1995 **GPM** *020 †70,20

O'ROURKE, Thomas Francis. NAMRU 2 DPT TROPICAL MED 96440 #014-01-1979 L1980 **ID PHP** *050

OSBORN, Patrick Marshall. PSC 3, BOX 1942 96266 #048-14-2002 L2002 **ORS** *020

OTERO, Luis Benito, Jr. ■ 96326 #011-02-2001 L2001 **FM** *020 †18

PARK, Joseph Rae. ■ 96224 #016-45-2003 L2005 **GS** *100

PARK, Pyong Seok. 131 GENERAL HOSPITAL ORTHO 96205 #583-04-1963 L1972 **HS ORS** *020 †40

PERCY, Jacqueline Jane. PSC 3 BOX 4298 96266 #056-06-2001 L2003 **FM** *100 †18

PIERCE, Brian Richard. ■ 96319 #032-01-1995 L1998 **FM** *020 †18

PIKE, Andrew Nathan. ■ 96326 #010-02-2002 L2002 **ORS** *100

PINKSTON, Brian Sean. ■ 96319 #023-12-1994 L1996 **AM** *020 †18,70

PIOVESAN, Nathan Edward. ■ 96326 #038-45-2000 L2000 **GS** *020 †85

PORCHIA, Robert R. ■ 96319 #654-01-1998 L2001 **FM** *020 †18

PRICE, Kelly Ann. ■ 96319 #028-34-2004 L2004 **PD** *020 †55

PRUSS, Jeanne Elizabeth. UNIT 5071 BOX 4408, 374 MEDICAL GROUP 96328 #010-02-1996 L1997 **D** *020 †15

QUIGLESS, Milton D, Jr. ■ 96326 #047-07-1971 L1972 **GS** *030 †85

REED, Zarifah Hussain. UNIT 8129 96520 #624-01-1991 L1998 **GPM** *100 †55

RICHARDSON, Joann Yuki. PSC 3, BOX 7731 96266 #036-08-1993 L1996 **PD** *020 †55

RIEDESEL, Matthew Kent. ■ 96326 #035-15-1997 L1999 **ORS** *020

ROBERTS, Kismet T. PSC 80 BOX 21494 96367 #007-02-1998 L1999 **FM** *020 †18

ROBERTS, Owen William. ■ 96326 #023-12-2003 L2005 **IM** *020 †20

ROHAL, Patrick Michael. PSC 3 BOX 4433 96266 #023-01-2004 L2006 **FM** *100 †18

ROUSE, Christopher Allen. ■ 96266 #016-43-2003 L2005 **PD** *100 †55

RUSSELL, Timothy Paul. UNIT 45011, USA MEDDAC JAPAN 96338 #056-05-1977 L1978 **FM EM** *020 †18

SAMPSON, James Buchanan. ■ 96266 #011-04-1998 L2002 **GS** *020 †85

SAMUELS, Christopher P. ■ 96367 #030-05-1999 L2000 **FM** *020 †18

SANIDAD, Leonard G. PSC NO 3 BOX 15712 96262 #748-07-1961 L1974 **GS GP** *020

SARNOW, David Alan. PSC 80 BOX 15149 96367 #011-04-1994 L1997 **GPM** *020 †18,70

SASTRI, Siri. ■ 96319 #048-04-2000 L2001 **GS** *020

SESSIONS, Raymond Renard. ■ 96326 #011-03-1998 L1999 **AN** *020 †05

SHEFFIELD, Ryan Christoph. ■ 96367 #001-06-2004 L2005 **FM** *020 †18

SIU, K Kenneth. PSC 77 BOX 4709 96325 #014-01-1976 L1979 **PD ADL** *020

SMETANA, Christine Anne. ■ 96266 #041-14-2004 L2005 **FM** *100 †18

SOMSEL, Elizabeth Lee. ■ 96326 #028-02-2003 L2006 **PD** *020 †55

SONG, Soon Hi Tak. 121ST EVACUATION HOSP 96205 #583-03-1962 L1974 **GP PD** *020

STEINKRAUS, Lawrence, Jr. ■ 96367 #051-04-1982 L1982 **FM** *030 †18,70

STOKES, Shayne C. ■ 96319 #023-12-2001 L2003 **PD** *020 †55

SUCHOSKI, John Peter. PSC NO 3 BOX 16312 96262 #056-06-1967 L1970 **D** *020 †15

TELLEZ, Guillermo Jose. ■ 96319 #048-15-1985 L1986 **OTO HNS** *020 †45

THILL, Bridget Anne. PSC 78 BOX 2924 96326 #031-01-1999 L2000 **IM** *020

THOLEN, Christine Elaine. ■ 96319 #023-12-2000 L2001 **FM AM** *020 †18 ‡

THOMASMA, Christa Mae. ■ 96319 #025-07-2005 L2006 **FM** *020

THOMSON, Sara B. ■ 96205 #023-12-2002 L2004 **OBG** *020 †30

TILLMAN, Monica Jean. ■ 96319 #023-12-2002 L2003 **GS** *020

TREADGOLD, Jeffrey Mark. PSC BOX 3872 96262 #012-05-1979 **AM** *020

TULIS, Matthew Robert. ■ 96386 #010-02-2001 L2003 *020

VALENCERINA, Rodolfo R. PSC NO 3 BOX 15889 96262 #748-08-1963 L1973 **PTH** *020 †50

WALKER, Shaka Malik. ■ 96326 #010-02-2000 L2002 **ORS** *100 †40

WANKER, Charles Joseph. ■ 96319 #055-01-2001 L2001 **FM** *020

WARDEN, Graham Ingersoll. ■ 96326 #005-14-2002 L2004 **DR** *020 †80

WOLIN, Ely Allen. ■ 96326 #023-12-2003 L2004 **GS** *020

WOLKEN, David William. ■ 96271 #030-05-1996 L1997 **FM** *020 †18

WOODS, Claire K. PSC 76 BOX 8484 96319 #030-05-1985 L1987 **P** *020

WORTHING, Robert Michaelc. ■ 96386 #036-05-2005 L2006 **FM** *020

WREDE, Valerie G. ■ 96319 #048-12-2002 L2002 **FM** *020 †18

YAN, Lun Sheung. PSC 78 BOX 7275 96326 #396-31-1987 L1989 **FM** *020 †18

YIP, Sandy K. ■ 96367 #024-07-2004 L2005 **PD** *100 †55

YOON, Kun Chul. 121 EVAC HOSP BOX 135 96205 #583-09-1966 L1975 **PD** *020 †55

ZALESKI, Scott D. ■ 96266 #048-14-1986 L1987 **FM** *020 †18

ZIMMERER, Gabriel. ■ 96326 #005-18-1997 L1998 **FM** *020 †18

ZOLLINGER, David Jesse. ■ 96266 #023-12-1999 **FM** *020 †18

FPO – AA

JULIA-RODRIQUEZ, Luis M. US NAVAL HOSP BOX 3007 34051 #847-04-1961 L1964 **OBG** *020

PRINCE, Andrea Marie. ■ 34099 #027-01-1994 L1996 **FM** *020 †18

SMITH, Robert Wayne. US NAV HOSP BOX 3007 RAD 34051 #048-12-1963 **R** *020

FPO – AE

ALSINA, Manuel Fernando. ■ 09622 #048-04-1999 L2001 **FM** *020 †18

■ = Address Information Privacy Protected

AUSTIN, David Allen. ■ 09636 #010-02-1999 L2001 **PD** *020 †55
AUSTIN, Katherine C. PSC 836 BOX 156 09636 #023-12-2000 L2002 **OBG** *020
BAHADOSINGH-TIEN, Suzanne. ■ 09636 #025-01-1991 L1994 **PD** *020 †55
BENDER, Malinda Joan. ■ 09622 #030-05-2003 L2003 **PD** *100 †55
BERNICK, Steven John. USNH-GTMO BAY, CUBA, BOX 27 09589 #023-12-2004 L2005 **IM** *100 †20
BIRMINGHAM, Sean Daniel. ■ 09636 #023-12-1998 L2000 **AN** *020 †05
BLEYER, Susanna Butler. ■ 09609 #036-05-1997 L1999 **FM** *020 †18
BODE, Amy Virginia. ■ 09835 #016-11-1984 L1985 **IM** *020 †20,70
BOYNTON, Bruce Ryland. ■ 09636 #008-01-1977 L1978 **NPM PD** *030 †55
BRITO, Jorge Luis. PSC 819 BOX 1834 09645 #005-11-2000 L2004 **ORS** *020
BROWSKE, Kristin Mary. ■ 09834 #036-01-2004 L2006 **FM** *020
BUCHANAN, Bryan Scott. ■ 09645 #001-02-1993 L1995 **U** *020
BUFF, Ann Margaret. PSC 812 BOX 3540, NEPMU-7 09627 #017-20-1997 L1998 **GPM** *062 †70
BURGESS, Lloyd Geo. ■ 09636 #016-42-1992 L1992 **FM** *020 †18
CARDONA, Jing-Jing M. PCS 836, BOX 131 09636 #011-02-2002 L2004 **FM** *020 †18
CARLSON, Frank Jos. PSC 810 BOX 19, US NAVAL HOSP NAPLES 09619 #026-04-1989 L1991 **IM** *020 †20
CHO, Aaron Anthony. ■ 09636 #017-20-1995 L1996 **FM** *020 †18,80
CHOI, Chul Ja. FOSIF ROTA PSC818 1675 09644 #583-03-1953 L1982 **P** *075
CLAGETT, Christopher D. ■ 09623 #023-12-1992 L1994 **GPM** *020 †70
CRAIG, Thomas Allen, Jr. ■ 09645 #023-12-1993 L1994 **EM GS** *020 †16
DALITSCH, Walter Wm, III. ■ 09622 #016-11-1993 L1994 **GPM** *020 †70
DAVILA, Pedro V. PO BOX 18, US NAVAL HOSP 09645 #847-10-1970 L1972 **IM** *020
DAVIS, Thomas Preston. ■ 09619 #045-01-1990 L1992 **GS** *020 †85
DEEDS, Scott Montgomery. PSC 819 BOX 18 09645 #038-43-1994 L1995 **AN** *020 †05
DELIMA, Maria Lisa. ■ 09728 #030-06-2002 L2004 **FM** *030 †18
DENSERT, Ruchira Desai. ■ 09645 #023-12-1997 L1998 **P** *020 †75
DICTADO, Florencio Abalos. PSC 1003 BOX 8 09728 #051-04-1994 L1997 **FM** *020 †18
DIGAN, Amalia Stokes. ■ 09645 #023-12-1992 L1993 **PTH** *020 †50
DINELLI, Darin Lance. USS ENTERPRISE, FPO AE 09543 #023-12-1998 L1999 **FM** *020 †18
EARHART, Kenneth Clark. PSC 452 BOX 5000, US NAVAL MED RESEARCH 09835 #025-07-1988 L1990 **ID** *020 †20
ELLINGSON, Christopher I. ■ 09636 #028-02-1998 L1998 **ORS** *020
EMERSON, Lynn A Chase. ■ 09645 #007-02-1996 L1996 **EM** *020
FARRELL, Maureen Erin. ■ 09645 #028-02-1999 L2001 **OBG** *020 †30
FLYNN, Mark Joseph. PSC 810 BOX 19, USN HOSP 09619 #035-09-1993 L1995 **FM** *020 †18
FRASER, Michael Robson, Jr. USS EMORY S LAND 39, MEDICAL DEPT 09545 #056-06-2002 **ORS** *012
FRIEDRICH, Thomas George. ■ 09645 #026-04-1995 L1997 **EM** *020 †16
GREENHALGH, Walter Mark. ■ 09645 #041-02-1992 L1993 **FM** *020 †18
GROBE, Macy John. PSC 824 BOX 129 09623 #561-11-1964 L1967 **PTH** *071
HOWARD, John Philip, II. ■ 09636 #024-07-1993 L1995 **PD** *020 †55
JACOBS, Michael Bradley. ■ 09636 #041-13-1998 L1999 **OM UM** *030 †70
JOHNSON, Dennis William. ■ 09622 #005-12-1999 L2001 **FM** *020 †18
JOHNSON, John Wm. NAVEMEDCOM EURREG BOX 22 09499 #016-11-1953 L1954 **P** *020
KERNEN, Lisa Marie Martz. ■ 09636 #041-07-1998 L2000 **PD** *020 †55
KOPMANN, Karen Jean. ■ 09645 #016-01-1992 L1994 **GS** *020 †85
LANGENFELD, Robert James. US NAVAL HOSPITAL GTMO, BOX 23 09589 #030-06-2000 L2003 **P** *020
LEYNES, Maryann Ramos. PSC 836 BOX 326 09636 #031-01-2002 L2003 **P** *100
LOUP, Davonne Sheryl. ■ 09645 #020-12-1978 L1980 **OBG ATP** *020 †50,30
MAANO, Rio Rita M. ■ 09645 #748-01-1962 L1976 **PD GP** *020 †55
MAHER, John Michael. ■ 09728 #035-19-1981 L1983 **DR NM** *020 †28,80
MAHONEY, Francis J. ■ 09835 #048-14-1983 L1983 **FM** *030 †18
MALEY, Elizabeth Anne. ■ 09636 #028-34-1993 L1994 **OM** *020 †70
MARFIN, Anthony Andrew. ■ 09835 #005-19-1983 L1984 **ID** *050 †20
MASTAW, Gerald Anthony, Jr. ■ 09645 #025-01-2000 L2002 **AN** *020 †05
MILLER, Deana Jane. ■ 09645 #023-12-1994 L1996 **FM** *020 †18
MITCHELL, Jeanne Poitras. ■ 09730 #011-02-1995 L1996 **RHU** *020 †20
MITCHELL, Lashawne M. ■ 09636 #038-41-1998 L1999 **PD** *020 †55
MOORE, Jerome A. ■ 09645 #020-02-1941 L1941 **GPM** *020
MOORE, Thomas Weller, Jr. ■ 09609 #045-01-1996 L1996 **FM** *020 †18
MOTT, Timothy Francis. ■ 09636 #045-04-1995 L1996 **FM** *020 †18
NIEMANN, Sandor Shawn. ■ 09612 #023-12-1992 L1993 **FM** *020 †18
OLIVERAS-PEREZ, Odette. ■ 09636 #042-01-1998 L2000 **IM** *020 †20
PECHINSKY, Geoffrey Alan. ■ 09645 #024-05-1997 L1999 **FM** *020 †18
PUDER, Robert David. ■ 09645 #048-02-1975 L1975 **P EM** *020 †75
PUMAREJO, Raymond M. ■ 09645 #023-12-1987 L1988 **CCM PUD** *020 †20
QUARLES, Christopher S. PSC 819 BOX 18-308, USNH ROTA 09645 #028-46-1992 L1993 **FM** *020 †18
QUE, Leon Tan, Jr. ■ 09834 #016-02-2002 L2002 **DR** *020
REES, Brian Michael. UNIT 60534, 310 MP BN 09501 #021-01-1979 L1982 **FM OS** *020 †18
REINA, Bryn Joi. PSC 836 BOX 374, BRYN REINA MD 09636 #023-12-1996 L1997 **P** *020 †75
SANDERS, John W, III. PSC 452 BOX 117 09835 #021-01-1992 L1993 **ID** *020 †20
SCHUMACHER, Bryan Paul. PSC 819 BOX 18, US NAVAL HOSPITAL ROTA 09645 #028-34-1992 L1994 **FM** *020 †18
SHALES, Paul Douglas. PSC 819, BOX 50 09645 #016-11-1972 L1976 **PD** *020 †55
SINOPOLE, Patrick L. ■ 09728 #023-12-1997 L1999 **AN** *020 †05
SMITH, Clifford Lawrence. ■ 09636 #038-41-1994 L1996 **GS** *100 †85
SMITH, David Jay. ■ 09645 #016-06-1981 L1983 **OM GPM** *020 †70
SMITH, Loren James. ■ 09645 #012-01-1993 L1995 **U** *020 †95
STOMBAUGH, Dana D. ■ 09645 #028-34-1975 L1978 **FM** *020 †18
SULLIVAN, Michael Andrew. USS NASHVILLE LPD-13, MEDICAL OFFICER 09579 #023-12-2004 L2004 **GS** *020
TATRO, Christopher Robert. PSC 836 BOX 2670, NAVAL HOSPITAL SIGONELLA 09636 #035-45-2001 L2004 **OBG** *020
TAYLOR, Harry A, III. ■ 09636 #040-02-1986 L1988 **FM GP** *020 †18
TEAGUE, Gilbert Randy. ■ 09420 #039-01-1987 L1988 **OBG** *020 †30
THIBODEAU, Kristopher P. ■ 09636 #023-12-2000 L2003 **FM** *020 †18
THIER, Gregory Todd. ■ 09645 #023-12-1996 L1997 **FM** *020 †18
TUASON, Olivia Alcantara. PSC 810 BOX 18 09619 #748-08-1962 L1974 **OBG** *020
TUTKO, Eugene George, Jr. ■ 09645 #051-04-1995 L1998 **FM** *020 †18
VANDERPAS, Shannon M. PO BOX 36, US NAVAL HOSP GTMO 09589 #051-01-2003 L2004 *100
WALKER, Errika Maire. PSC 836 BOX 166 09636 #005-06-2000 L2001 **EM** *020 †16
WALSH, Michael J. PSC 1005 BOX 36, NAVY HOSP 09593 #048-14-1988 *100
WIEDEL, Lisa Marie. ■ 09645 #016-06-1998 L1998 **OBG** *020 †30
YAO, Flora. ■ 09622 #005-12-2002 L2004 **FM** *020 †18
YUE, David Noel. ■ 09622 #010-01-1999 L2000 **EM** *012
YUND, Alan Jeffrey. ■ 09627 #041-01-1982 L1983 **GPM** *020 †70
YUND, Lowell Conrad. PSC 812 BOX 3540 09627 #041-01-1947 L1948 **ORS** *071 †40
ZIEBER, Robert Thomas. ■ 09645 #010-02-1994 L1995 **FM** *020 †18
ZIEBER, Tara J. ■ 09645 #010-02-1994 L1995 **EM** *020 †16

FPO – AP

ADEOGBA, Saint Mayoke. ■ 96306 #041-14-2005 L2005 **GS** *100
ALLARD, Jay Edmond. PSC 475 BOX 1600, USNH YOKOSUKA JAPAN 96350 #050-02-2000 L2002 **OBG** *020
ALTAMAR, Hernan O. PSC 490 BOX 9127, USNH GUAM UROLOGY SVC 96538 #023-12-1997 L1998 **U** *100 †95
ALTHOFF, Juliann Marie. ■ 96377 #038-45-1995 **GPM AM** *020 †70
ARFAA, Kaivon. ■ 96362 #010-01-2002 L2004 **EM** *020 †30
ARTHUR, Joshua Daniel. ■ 96349 #036-07-2005 L2005 **PD** *100
BABCOCK, Megan Manicke. PSC 558 BOX 4179, PH: 011816117394184 96375 #034-01-1997 L1997 **IM** *020 †20
BAILEY, Lynn Ann. PSC 475 BOX A 96350 #023-12-1989 L1991 **PD** *020 †55
BALAGTAS, Jaymichael S. ■ 96538 #035-09-1998 L2000 **PHO** *012 †55
BAXTER, Charles Frank, Jr. PSC 475 96350 #047-07-1986 L1988 **GS** *020
BEANE, Richard Alan. PSC 557 BOX 1295 96379 #035-15-1984 L1988 **AM GP** *020 †70
BELTRA, Linda Jo. ■ 96634 #023-12-1989 L1990 **GS** *020 †85
BENDER, Sandra Marie. ■ 96350 #041-15-1999 L2002 **FM** *020 †18
BEVERLY, David Temple, IV. PSC 475 BOX 1656 96350 #023-12-1998 L1999 **OPH** *020 †35
BOGARD, John Fitzgerald. ■ 96350 #023-12-1995 L1997 **OS** *020 †35
BROOKS, Daren Richard. ■ 96310 #004-01-2004 L2005 **GS** *020
BROWN, Jill Elizabeth. ■ 96350 #024-07-2001 L2002 **OBG** *020
BROWN, Ryan Patrick. ■ 96362 #017-20-2005 L2006 *100
BUCCOLO, Larissa Sarah. PSC 490 BOX 156, COMNAVMAR BRANCH MED CLC 96538 #012-05-2002 L2004 **FM** *020 †18
BUCKLEY, Kevin Donald. PSC 490 96538 #024-07-1993 L2005 **EM** *020 †16
BURATTO, James Theodore. ■ 96362 #030-06-1998 L1999 **DR** *100 †80
BURCH, David Marshall. ■ 96350 #030-05-1984 L1988 **PTH** *020 †50
BURGESS, Timothy Hampton. ■ 96520 #017-20-1994 L1996 **ID IM** *050 †20
BUTLER, Robert Francis. PSC 475 BOX 1645, NAVY HOSP YOKOSUKA 96350 #028-34-1987 L1989 **D** *020 †15
CAPP, Joseph Aresenio. ■ 96362 #035-09-2005 L2006 *100
CARDINALE, Nicholas M. ■ 96350 #019-02-1992 L1995 **FM** *020 †18
CARMICHAEL, Jacob Jonas. ■ 96377 #019-02-2004 L2005 *100
CARUSO, James Louis. ■ 96362 #016-11-1988 L1990 **FOP PTH** *030 †50
CASON, Sheila A. PSC 490 BOX 7686, DEPT OF OPHTHAMOLOGY 96538 #010-01-2000 L2000 **PD** *020 †55
CECE, Jennifer Ann. ■ 96350 #023-12-1989 L1991 **PD** *020 †55
CHEN, Chun Wen. ■ 96362 #021-01-1999 L2000 **GS** *100 †80
CHENG, Jacky Pozen. ■ 96350 #039-01-1997 L1999 **OBG** *020
CHRISTIE, Pearl Elizabeth. ■ 96350 #024-05-2001 L2003 **FM** *020 †18
CHRISTOPHER, Merlene V. ■ 96310 #011-04-2002 L2004 **FM** *020 †18
CLARK, Susan Christine. USS KITTY HAWK CV63, MEDICAL DEPT/ H-DIVISION 96634 #041-15-1999 L2002 **GS** *020 †85
CLIFFORD, Daniel Peter. ■ 96362 #051-07-1995 L1995 *020
CLINTON, Tony Shuowen. ■ 96362 #023-12-1996 L1998 **D** *020 †15
COPENHAVER, Catherine S. PSC 475 BOX A 96350 #023-12-1992 L1994 **OBG** *020 †30
COURINGTON, Cleo C. NAVAL REG MED CTR GUAM 96540 #011-03-1972 L1974 **CHP PD** *020
COURTNEY, Richard Gilman. ■ 96362 #041-13-1996 L1999 **GS** *020 †80
COVEY, Dana Curtis. ■ 96362 #054-04-1984 L1989 **ORS OSM** *020 †40
CRAVEN, Charles Edward, II. ■ 96362 #035-03-1998 L2000 **ORS** *020
CRAWFORD, Glen Collier. PSC 482 BOX 214, US NAVAL HOSPITAL 96362 #023-12-1992 L1994 **P CHP** *020 †75
CREGAN, Meghan Joy. PSC 561 BOX 398 96310 #038-40-2001 L2003 **FM** *100 †18
CRUZ, Audrey Ann. ■ 96362 #056-06-1999 L2001 **IM** *020
CUSICK, Howard Thomas. UNIT 25454 96601 #020-12-2005 L2006 **GP AM** *020
DAVIS, Leslie Ann. ■ 96538 #010-02-2004 L2005 **FM** *020 †18
DELGADO, Anthony Edward. PSC 482 96362 #023-12-1996 L1997 **PD** *020 †55
DEMITRACK, James Gus. UNIT 35970, HQ CO 4TH MAR RAS 96602 #023-12-2004 L2004 **GP** *020
DODGE, William Randolph. ■ 96350 #023-12-1997 L1999 **EM** *020 †16 ‡
DRUMMOND, Brian Scott. PSC 490, BOX 9011 96538 #016-06-2001 L2003 **EM** *020
ECKER, Lissa M Diaz. ■ 96362 #051-04-1996 L1996 **OBG** *020 †30
ECKER, Robert Doniger. PSC 482 BOX 2695, USNH OKINAWA 96362 #051-04-1999 L1999 **NS** *100
EDWARDS, Richard C. ■ 96350 #040-02-1982 L1986 **OTO GP** *020 †45
ENDRES, Jonathan Michael. ■ 96362 #038-06-2003 L2005 **FM** *100
EPHRON, Paul H. PSC 466 BOX 3 96595 #005-14-1982 L1983 **FM OM** *020 †18
EPPERLY, Michael Eugene. ■ 96362 #051-01-1997 L1998 *020 †55
EPSTEIN, David Kalman. ■ 96362 #041-14-2000 L2002 *020 †75
ERVIN, Michelle Kanney. ■ 96362 #023-12-1999 L2001 **DBP** *020 †55
ESCOBAR, Steven John. PSC 490 BOX 9085 96538 #023-12-1996 L1997 **IM** *020 †20
FISHER, Dan Eugene. PSC 475 BOX 1523, US NAVAL HOSPITAL 96350 #023-12-1994 L1995 **IM** *020 †20
FOWLER, Ryan Curt. ■ 96269 #055-02-2003 L2005 **FM** *020 †18
GABALL, Curtis Wesley. ■ 96538 #025-07-2000 L2001 **OTO** *020 †45
GILBERT, Lara Diane. ■ 96306 #011-04-2002 L2003 *020
GILSTAD, John Reed-Hill. ■ 96350 #023-12-1993 L1995 **IMG** *020 †20
GINDLER, Jacqueline Jacob. ■ 96521 #041-12-1986 L1989 **PD** *020 †55
GOMEZ, Jose Enrique. PSC 475 BOX 1351 96350 #026-04-2002 L2002 **MPD** *100 †20
GOODWIN, Robert Hewitt. PSC 475 BOX 1724 96350 #010-02-1999 L2000 **EM AM** *020 †16
HAINES, Joe D, Jr. PSC 482 BOX 2770 96362 #039-01-1981 L1982 **FM OS** *020 †18
HAMMER, Noa Christopher. ■ 96362 #024-07-2003 L2004 **FM** *020 †18
HAMMER, Peter Michael. PSC 490 BOX 9125 96538 #025-07-2001 L2005 **GS** *020 †85
HANSEN, Danae Aplas. PSC 477 BOX 730 96306 #005-06-1994 L1995 **GPM AN** *020 †05,70

■ = Address Information Privacy Protected

HARRIS, Ryan Jed. ■ 96669 #023-12-2001 L2003 *020
HERZER, Christopher M. PSC 490 BOX 156, COMNAVMAR BRANCH MED CLNC 96538 #023-12-1998 L1999 **FM** *020 †18
HOANG, Tuan Q. PSC 490 BOX 9006, US NAVAL HOSP GUAM 96538 #023-12-1999 L2001 **AN** *100 †05
HOFF, Elise Regine. ■ 96362 #038-40-1998 L1999 **PTH** *100
HOFFMAN, Roy Allen. UNIT 25117 96601 #005-12-2002 L2003 *020
HOFFMANN, Michael Anthony. ■ 96362 #041-02-2000 L2002 **OTO** *020 †45
HOLLENSBE, Jason Wilford. ■ 96362 #007-02-1997 L1997 **GS** *100 †85
HOOKER, Stephen Glenn. PSC 559 BOX 5515 96377 #027-01-1983 L1986 **UM FM** *020 †18,70
HUI, Kim. ■ 96362 #001-02-2002 L2004 **OBG**
JACOBS, Michael Matthew. PSC 561 BOX 20 96310 #023-12-1989 L1990 **FM** *020 †18
JACOBY, Geoffrey Samuel. ■ 96322 #041-01-1998 L1999 *020 †18
JOHNSON, Michael Garth. ■ 96350 #041-02-1994 L2003 **OSS** *100
JOHNSON, Nathan Carl. ■ 96362 #023-12-2000 L2001 **FM** *020 †18
JONES, Carla Lanette. ■ 96362 #051-07-2001 L2003 **FM** *020
KASOWSKI, Eric John. ■ 96350 #023-12-1998 L1999 **GPM** *020 †70
KELLEY, Steven Dale. PSC 475 BOX 1785 96350 #036-01-1996 L1997 **EM** *020 †16
KIM, Janeth Francis. ■ 96362 #023-12-1996 L1998 **ORS** *020 †40
KING, John Cameron. ■ 96362 #005-06-1989 L1991 **PD** *020 †55
KUHN, Laurence John. ■ 96310 #051-07-1996 L1997 **FM** *020 †18
KURZYNSKE, Nicole Georgan. ■ 96350 #005-12-2002 L2003 *020
LABRADOR, Augusto N. PFC 459 BOX 204 96452 #748-01-1960 L1977 **P** *020
LANDES, Christopher B. ■ 96362 #023-12-2000 L2002 **DR** *020 †80
LANE, David Allen. ■ 96604 #023-12-1991 L1993 **FM EP** *062 †18
LECHER, Michelle Nicole. ■ 96362 #056-06-2003 L2004 **PD** *020
LEE, Christopher Sien. ■ 96362 #035-19-1998 L1999 **GE** *020 †20 ‡
LEONARD, Sean Patrick. ■ 96362 #023-12-2003 L2004 **FM** *020
LINNAN, Michael James. PSC 461 BOX 400 96521 #001-02-1981 L1983 **PHP IM** *020 †20
LINZ, Nelle Alexandria. UNIT 38404 96604 #051-01-2002 L2003 *020 †20
LOPATA, Adrienne Marie. ■ 96310 #041-15-2006 L2007 *012
LOVAN, Wendell David. USS CARL VINSON # 70 96629 #020-12-1974 L1975 **AM FM** *020 †18,70
LOVELACE, Kimberley Rae. ■ 96350 #004-01-2003 L2007 **OPH** *020
LOVERN, Robert Edward. ■ 96349 #048-13-2005 L2006 **P** *100
LYSZCZARZ, Heidi. ■ 96362 #023-12-1993 L1995 **CHP** *020 †75
LYSZCZARZ, John Lawrence. PSC 482 96362 #023-12-1993 L1995 **P** *020 †75
MALLARI, Jesus Velasquez. PSC 490, BOX 7606 96538 #748-08-1976 L1982 **PDC PD** *020 †55
MARESSO, Cynthia Jean. ■ 96350 #010-02-2003 L2005 **FM** *020 †18
MARGRAF, Scott Nelson. ■ 96322 #040-02-2004 L2007 *020 †75
MARIETTA, Robert. ■ 96377 #028-34-2000 L2001 *020 †75
MARSHALL, Robert Carter. UNIT 35801, HQ BN DIV SURGEON 96602 #011-04-1985 L1989 **FM PHP** *020 †18
MARSHALL, Robin Ac. ■ 96362 #033-05-1996 L1997 *020 †16
MC ADAMS, Paul Doey. PSC 482, USNH OKINAWA-UROLOGY 96362 #041-12-1993 L1995 **U AM** *020 †95 ‡
MC ADAMS, Ryan Michael. ■ 96362 #056-06-1998 L2000 **NPM** *100 †55
MC CARTNEY, Stephen F. US NAVY, CAPT. SF MC CARTNEY MD 96606 #039-01-1978 L1979 **VS GS** *020 †85
MCCORD, Michael Lee. ■ 96362 #023-12-2002 L2004 **FM** *020
MC DONALD, Elizabeth G. PSC 482 BOX 103 96362 #025-12-1990 L1991 **FM OBG** *020 †18
MC LAUGHLIN, Donna Ann. ■ 96322 #039-01-2002 L2003 **FM** *020 †18
MERCADO, Gemma Miranda. PSC 490 BOX 9024, NAVAL HOSP GUAM 96538 #005-12-2004 L2006 **FM** *100 †18
MERCADO, Michael Gasmen. ■ 96538 #005-12-2004 L2005 **FM** *100 †18
MESSMER, Caroline Tierney. USS KITTY HAWK CV-63 96634 #023-12-2006 L2007 **OTO** *020
MILLER, Jessica M. ■ 96377 #056-06-2002 L2004 **FM** *020 †18
MILLER, Robert Neils, Jr. ■ 96538 #021-01-1999 L1999 **FM** *020 †18
MINARCIK, Allison Marie. ■ 96322 #023-12-2000 L2003 **FM** *020 †18
MITCHELL, Robert Ryan. ■ 96362 #045-04-2004 L2006 **FM** *100 †18
MORENO, Fernando. PSC 482 BOX 2490, NAVAL HOSPITAL OKINAWA 96362 #035-09-1979 L1981 **OBG** *020 †30
MULLENS, Frank Edward. ■ 96350 #047-05-2000 L2002 **DR** *020 †80
MURPHY, David Patrick. ■ 96362 #023-12-1994 L1995 **PCC** *020 †20
MURPHY, Enchanta Lachelle. ■ 96350 #045-01-1999 L2001 **OBG** *020 †30
NEDEROSTEK, James C. PSC 561 BOX 7181 96310 #038-43-2002 L2003 **U** *012
NELSON, Tiffany Sammt. ■ 96362 #041-12-1995 L1996 **FM** *020 †50
NGUYEN, Tuan Ngoc. PSC 476 BOX 4, BLDG 1603 96322 #025-12-1996 L1998 **FM** *020 †18
NIPPER, Thomas William. ■ 96350 #047-06-2003 L2004 *100
NORRIS, Craig Dewayne. PSC 490, P.O.BOX 9085 96538 #041-09-1998 L2001 **IM** *020 †20
NORWOOD, Brian Gilbert. ■ 96350 #024-05-2003 L2003 **PD** *100 †55

OBERMAN, James Phillip. ■ 96362 #024-07-1996 L1997 **OTO** *020 †45
OBERMAN, Margaret Perusse. ■ 96362 #024-07-1996 L1997 **IM** *020 †20
O'CONNOR, Cormac John. ■ 96350 #021-01-2002 L2003 **FM** *100 †18
OHTAKE, Chikara. PSC 473 BOX 893 96349 #572-35-1961 L1969 **GS TS** *071 †85
O'MALLEY, Kevin Chas. ■ 96362 #010-02-1989 L1991 **FM** *020 †16
O MEARA, Kevin Michael. ■ 96350 #023-12-1999 L1999 **PD** *020 †55
ONIFER, Dana John. ■ 96377 #023-12-2005 L2005 *100
OSHIRAK, Kimberly Tyler. UNIT 4280, BOX 20 96507 #051-04-1998 L1999 **PD** *071
PADGET, Larry G, Jr. PSC 461 BOX 50 96521 #048-12-1991 L1992 **FM** *020 †18 ‡
PALMA, James Keith. PSC 475 BOX 1750 96350 #023-12-2000 L2000 **EM** *020 †16
PARISIEN, Karen Marie. ■ 96362 #025-07-2002 L2003 *020 †75
PARK, Chan Woo. ■ 96538 #035-46-1999 L2001 **EM** *020 †16
PARK, Peter Joonsun. ■ 96362 #026-04-1994 L1996 **EM** *020 †16
PAULSON, Jeffery Wayne. US NAMRU 2, US EMBASSY JAKARTA 96520 #023-12-1986 L1988 **FM ADL** *030 †18
PENHOLLOW, Tammy J. ■ 96362 #028-79-1998, ▲ L2000 **AN** *020
PERKINS, Shelley Kathleen. ■ 96362 #021-01-1994 L1995 **GS** *020 †85
PICKEN, David Joseph. ■ 96350 #048-14-1995 L1995 **FP** *012
POTHULA, Viswanadham. PSC 475 BOX 1752 96350 #495-11-1981 L1991 **CRS** *020 †85
PRATT, Randall Nicoll, Jr. PSC 475 BOX A, NAVAL HOSP YOKOSVKA 96350 #035-09-1975 L1977 **CHP P** *020 †75
PRINCE, Ethan Andrew. PSC 561, BOX651 96310 #038-06-2000 L2001 **DR** *012
PUMAREJO, Ramon Albert. PSC 490 96538 #847-02-1957 L1960 **GS OS** *020
QUINER, Timothy Robt. PSC 475 BOX 1, NAVAL HOSP YOKOSUKA 96350 #023-12-1992 L1994 **FM** *020 †18
RIM, Peter Chun. ■ 96362 #051-04-2002 L2003 **IM** *020 †20
ROBINSON, Michael Aaron. ■ 96362 #028-46-1999 L2001 **ORS** *020
ROSSI, Mario Adrian. ■ 96362 #032-01-2000 L2003 **U** *020 †95
ROSSI, Vy Bui. PSC 482 BOX 3041 96362 #035-45-2001 L2004 **OBG** *020 †30
SANGIORGI, Michelle. ■ 96538 #030-06-2006 L2007 *012
SCHOFER, Joel Martin. ■ 96362 #041-15-2001 L2002 **EM** *020 †16
SCHOFER, Wendy Elizabeth. ■ 96362 #041-15-2001 L2002 **PD** *020 †55
SELF, Amanda Rose. ■ 96606 #021-05-2005 *100
SHERCK, Eric Scott. PSC 561 BOX 681 96310 #017-20-1993 **FM** *020 †18
SHOEMAKER, Michael Todd. ■ 96362 #023-12-2001 L2003 **PD** *020 †55
SINGLEY, Jeffrey Wayne. ■ 96362 #051-04-2001 L2002 **FM** *100 †18
SLINGLUFF, Marguerite I. PSC 475 BOX 1486, USNH YOKOSUKA JAPAN 96350 #051-07-1999 L1999 **AI** *012 †55
SNYDER, Kurt Matthew. ■ 96306 #035-46-2000 L2001 **RO** *012
SOHN, Hong. PSC 479 BOX 87, COM FLE ACTS CHINHAE 96269 #583-06-1960 L1975 **GP** *020
SONG, Sung Wook. PSC 475 BOX 1574, USNH YOKOSUKA 96350 #041-09-1995 L1996 **FM** *020 †18
SORTOR, Brett Vandyke. USS ESSEX LHD-2 96643 #045-01-1997 L1999 **FM UM** *020 †18
SULLIVAN, Michele E. ■ 96310 #028-34-2002 L2004 **FM** *020 †18
SWANSON, Rozales Antonio. ■ 96350 #010-03-1999 L1999 **GS** *020
TABOR, Camille Ann. USS BOXER LHD4 96661 #023-12-2002 L2003 **D** *012
TEMPLE, Richard Wilson. PSC 490 BOX 7638 96538 #038-45-1999 L2007 **FM** *020 †18
TOONE, Kimberly Pearcy. ■ 96362 #011-03-1997 L1999 **FM** *100 †18
TRAINOR, Timothy James. ■ 96362 #016-06-1997 L1997 **ORS** *020 †40
VALADE, Michael Steele. ■ 96362 #032-01-1997 L1998 **DR** *020 †80
VELASQUEZ, A Lenny. ■ 96306 #007-02-2001 L2003 **FM** *020 †18
VERBRUGGE, Joel Kenneth. ■ 96322 #056-06-2003 L2004 *100
VOLK, Bradford Scott. PSC 473, BOX 50 96349 #010-02-2000 L2001 **FM** *020 †18
WALKER, Linda K. PSC 475 BOX 1680, USNH-YOKOSUKA 96350 #051-01-1998 L1999 **OBG** *020 †30
WALTERS, John Robert. ■ 96350 #041-15-2000 L2002 **FM** *020 †18 ‡
WARREN, Dirk Adam. ■ 96306 #023-12-2002 L2003 **FM** *020
WAXMAN, Erna Anita. ■ 96362 #035-09-1989 L1991 **OBG** *020 †30
WEIS, David Alden. ■ 96362 #028-03-2002 L2003 **FM** *020
WELLS, Kenneth. ■ 96322 #035-09-1994 L1996 **FM** *020 †18
WIKE, William Mickey. ■ 96310 #023-12-1996 L1998 **FM** *020 †18
WILKES, Cynthia Ann. ■ 96538 #023-12-1994 L1998 **OBG** *020
WILKS, Timothy Marc. ■ 96362 #048-15-1999 L2001 **PD** *020 †55
WILLOCK, Roland Oswald. ■ 96538 #056-06-1998 L1999 **AN** *100 †18
WOLFE, Mitchell Ian. ■ 96521 #050-02-1995 L1997 **FM** *020 †70
WOODWORTH, James Martin. ■ 96350 #025-07-1984 L1986 **PD** *020 †55
WYATT, Kimberly S. ■ 96350 #041-13-1993 L1995 **IM** *020 †20
YARDE, William Leon. ■ 96362 #012-21-1985 L1986 **NS GS** *020
YIP, Ray. ■ 96521 #026-04-1976 L1977 **GPM PHO** *020 †55
YOO, Ji Hyung. ■ 96350 #005-18-1998 L2000 **P** *020 †75
ZHOU, Wiegong. ■ 96515 #243-47-1984 L1997 **FM** *020 †18